UK Rail Timetable

Sunday 9 December 2007 to Saturday 17 I

Britain's national railway network and stations are owned by Network Rail. Passenge included in this timetable, who work together closely to provide a co-ordinated N opportunities. Details and identification codes are shown on the Train Operator pages over the National Rail network, together with rail and shipping connections with Irel Channel Islands. Network Rail operate 17 major stations but the remainder are op Companies. Details are shown in the station index.

Contents

Bank Holiday Services

Altered services may apply over the relevant Bank Holiday periods and Public Holidays in Scotland. Details of services are available from National Rail Enquiries (08457 484950).

Engineering Works

Services may be changed, particularly at weekends, to cater for **Engineering Works**.

Passengers should check their service with their local station or by calling National Rail Enquiries (08457 484950) prior to travel.

National Rail Conditions of Carriage

A booklet containing the conditions on which tickets, including Season Tickets are issued and the Regulations and Conditions which apply to passengers' luggage can be obtained free from principal station ticket offices.

What's New

Welcome to the UK Rail Timetable valid from 9 December 2007 to 17 May 2008.

Franchise Changes

From 11 November 2007 East Midlands Trains will operate the East Midlands franchise, with services between London, the East Midlands and South Yorkshire, as well as services in central England and between Liverpool and Norwich. This new franchise combines services previously operated by Midland Mainline and some of the services previously operated by Central Trains.

From 11 November 2007 London Midland will operate the West Midlands franchise with services spanning from London in the south, to Liverpool in the North and covering the local and regional services throughout the West Midlands. This new franchise combines services previously operated by Silverlink County and some of the services previously operated by Central Trains.

From 11 November 2007 CrossCountry will operate the Cross Country franchise, with services extending across Great Britain from Penzance to Aberdeen, from Cardiff to Stansted Airport and from Manchester to Bournemouth. This new franchise combines most of the services previously operated by Virgin Trains CrossCountry and some services previously operated by Central Trains. Virgin Trains CrossCountry services that previously operated between Birmingham and Glasgow via Preston will be transferred and operated by Virgin Trains West Coast.

From 11 November 2007 London Overground will operate services on the North London Railway under the management of Transport for London. These services were previously operated by Silverlink Metro.

From 9 December 2007 First TransPennine Express will be operating services between Manchester Airport and Glasgow Central/Edinburgh. These services were previously operated by Virgin Trains CrossCountry.

From 9 December 2007 National Express East Coast will operate the InterCity East Coast franchise, with services between London, Northern England and Scotland via Peterborough, Leeds, Doncaster, York, Newcastle, Edinburgh, Aberdeen and Inverness. These services were previously operated by GNER.

Other updates

From 9 December 2007 Thameslink services will serve St Pancras International station and Kings Cross Thameslink station will close.

High Speed Trains replace Adelantes (class 180) on the North Cotswold route from London Paddington to Worcester and Hereford.

On 27 March 2008 Heathrow Terminal 5 will open. From this date Heathrow Express trains will be diverted to Heathrow Terminal 5 and will cease to serve Heathrow Terminal 4. Heathrow Connect trains will be extended to serve Heathrow Terminal 4. Both services will continue to serve Heathrow Terminals 1, 2, 3. Customers travelling on Heathrow Express requiring Terminal 4 and customers travelling on Heathrow Connect requiring Terminal 5 can change trains at Heathrow Terminals 1, 2, 3.

An additional hourly service will operate between Leeds and Hebden Bridge via Brighouse on Mondays to Saturdays

A new peak time direct service will operate from Burnley to Manchester Victoria.

Services west of Southampton will be revised on Mondays to Saturdays to provide two trains per hour between Waterloo and Weymouth, and one train per hour Waterloo to Poole. The existing Brockenhurst to Wareham service will be withdrawn. On Sundays the existing Waterloo to Bournemouth service will be extended Poole.

The existing Romsey to Totton service will be replaced by a new daily Romsey – Eastleigh – Southampton Airport Parkway – Southampton Central – Romsey – Salisbury service providing additional services between Southampton Central and Salisbury and providing new links between Eastleigh, Southampton Airport Parkway and Salisbury.

Additional evening services will be provided on Mondays to Saturdays between Waterloo and Epsom, Reading, Surbiton and Windsor. Additional Sunday services *will be provided* between Waterloo and Reading, Waterloo and Kingston and services will be *extended* beyond Epsom to Dorking and Guildford via Bookham.

What's New – continued

The existing Reading, Basingstoke to Brighton through services will be withdrawn although there will be some additional services operated over parts of the route.

For the first time there will be four trains per hour during Monday to Friday off-peak and Saturday between London Victoria and Orpington via Beckenham Junction.

The flow of morning peak time services into Blackfriars and Victoria have been reorganised and offer a modest improvement to some journey times, with some trains now able to use the route via Herne Hill, instead of going via Catford.

The Charing Cross to Orpington/Sevenoaks service will operate via Lewisham off-peak Monday to Friday and all day Saturday.

During the evening peak period, there is an additional train from Charing Cross to Tunbridge Wells and a later service from Cannon Street to Faversham with connection at Chatham for stations along the Thanet coast.

Changes have been made to standardise Southeastern services via London Bridge, particularly the early morning and evening main line via Tonbridge.

On the Chichester to London Victoria route there are additional faster peak services and regular half hourly faster off peak services.

Frequency of the off-peak services from Bognor Regis to London Victoria and Littlehampton to London Victoria will double.

Services from Chichester to Southampton will double in frequency.

The frequency of services from Chichester to Portsmouth will be increased by 50%.

There will be services from Brighton to West Coastway approximately every 10 minutes, including:

- Two trains per hour to Hove where passengers can change for stations to Worthing and Littlehampton
- Two trains per hour all stations to West Worthing
- Two trains per hour semi-fast to Chichester, which then alternately serve Portsmouth and Southampton
- Faster services from Littlehampton to Brighton with a change at Hove
- New regular through train from Littlehampton – Chichester – Portsmouth

The 1629 Watford Junction to Brighton train will terminate at Clapham Junction so that it can form an extra stopping train at 1725 between Kensington Olympia and East Croydon.

Extra train at 1702 from London Victoria and Brighton.

Following completion of the Edinburgh Waverley Station upgrade, there will be the following service changes:

- services temporarily terminating at Haymarket will now run through to Waverley
- North Berwick peak-hour trains will again run through to Haymarket
- Edinburgh Crossrail service will resume providing through services between Newcraighall and Edinburgh Park
- New Glasgow - Stirling and Partick - Larkhall services will be introduced on Sundays, enabling Bishopbriggs, Chatelherault, Merryton and Larkhall to be opened on Sundays for the first time.

From Spring 2008, regular services from Wrexham and Shropshire to London will be operated by a new open *access operator* Wrexham & Shropshire.

How to use this Timetable

Some tables are self-contained (such as Table 1 London–Shoeburyness) showing every train running between any two stations on the route. Train journey-lengths vary from the under-three-quarters-of-a-mile Stourbridge Town – Stourbridge Junction shuttle to the 703 mile Penzance–Dundee service. To show details of longer-distance services in a single table, short-distance services are omitted, these appearing in separate 'composite' tables.

WHICH TABLE?

General Layout of the Timetable

There are several ways of finding the correct table(s) for a journey. Tables start with the north bank of the Thames and radiate anti-clockwise around London as far as the south bank (Table 212, London-Faversham-Margate) with non-London tables (like the Cardiff Valleys) placed close to the appropriate London route. Internal Scottish routes follow from Table 216. Tables numbered 400-406 cover domestic Sleeper services. Once used to this geographic layout, required tables can usually be found with relative ease, but there are more precise methods:

Using the Index

Look up your destination. If it appears in up to five tables, those tables are listed (for example Hilsea appears in Tables 156, 157, 158, 165 and 188). If it appears in six or more then there may be sub-divisions. If your destination is sub-divided in this way and your origin is NOT shown (for example Shipley is not shown under Lancaster) then look up the origin instead as it probably has fewer tables. Alongside the station name is shown a two character code indicating which operator is responsible for operating the facilities at that station (see also Train Operator pages).

Using Route/Network Diagrams

For many tables a Route or Network Diagram is also provided. Route Diagrams are generally used for longer distance tables (for example Table 26) and show the route and stations served in diagrammatic form as well as the principal connecting links. Network Diagrams (for example Tables 152–154) are generally used where there is a dense network of shorter distance routes and show *all* stations and routes in the area concerned in diagrammatic form.

Using the Table

Having found the table you require make sure you look at the correct set of pages: Mondays to Fridays, Mondays to Saturdays, Saturdays, Sundays plus any relevant dates. Look for the station from which you will leave, read across until you find a suitable train, then read down to see when you will arrive at your destination.

↪ indicates the train is continued in a later column.

↩ indicates the train is continued from an earlier column.

When services in a table follow a particular pattern throughout a day or part of a day, the pattern is identified by thick downward lines at the start and end of the pattern and by a note within the lines stating "and at the same minutes past each hour until".

Bold times denote through trains whilst light, *italic*, times are connections (PLEASE READ CAREFULLY THE SECTION ON THE CONNECTIONS PAGE). Check if there is a column-heading and if there is, refer to the foot of the table for an explanation.

Because of the large number of services that 'cross' midnight, a railway timetable needs to be precise in the meaning of 'a day'. Trains starting their journeys before midnight are shown towards the end of a table – but if you are looking for the 'last' train don't stop there, as there may be later ones at the start of the table!

A train crossing midnight will be shown in full at the END of a table and any column heading denoting the day of the week applies to the day the train STARTS. For example a 2350 train headed 'SO' (see the general notes on inside front cover) commences 2350 Saturday and runs into Sunday. The train will also be shown at the front of the Sunday table with the times prior to midnight shown with note 'p', e.g. 23p50, to indicate that they refer to the previous night. Don't worry about the ambiguity as to which day midnight itself belongs, for, to avoid this problem, all times skip from 2359 to 0001 and neither 0000 nor 2400 is ever used!

A two character code is shown at the head of each train column indicating which operator is providing the train service (see also Train Operator pages).

How to use this Timetable

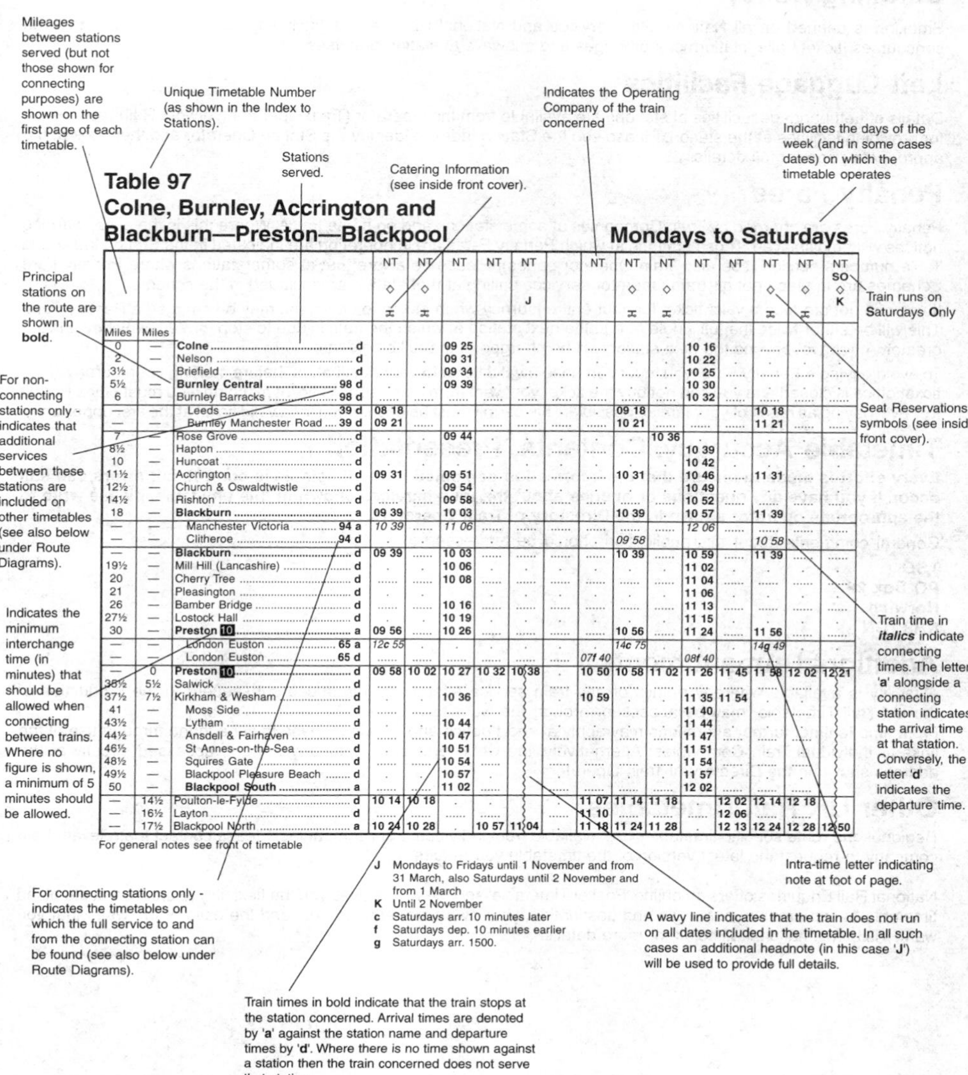

Mileages between stations served (but not those shown for connecting purposes) are shown on the first page of each timetable.
Unique Timetable Number (as shown in the Index to Stations).
Stations served.
Catering Information (see inside front cover).
Indicates the Operating Company of the train concerned
Indicates the days of the week (and in some cases dates) on which the timetable operates
Principal stations on the route are shown in **bold**.
Train runs on **S**aturdays **O**nly
For non-connecting stations only - indicates that additional services between these stations are included on other timetables (see also below under Route Diagrams).
Seat Reservations symbols (see inside front cover).
Indicates the minimum interchange time (in minutes) that should be allowed when connecting between trains. Where no figure is shown, a minimum of 5 minutes should be allowed.
Train time in ***italics*** indicate connecting times. The letter '**a**' alongside a connecting station indicates the arrival time at that station. Conversely, the letter '**d**' indicates the departure time.
Intra-time letter indicating note at foot of page.
For connecting stations only - indicates the timetables on which the full service to and from the connecting station can be found (see also below under Route Diagrams).
A wavy line indicates that the train does not run on all dates included in the timetable. In all such cases an additional headnote (in this case '**J**') will be used to provide full details.
Train times in bold indicate that the train stops at the station concerned. Arrival times are denoted by '**a**' against the station name and departure times by '**d**'. Where there is no time shown against a station then the train concerned does not serve that station.

Table 97
Colne, Burnley, Accrington and Blackburn—Preston—Blackpool

Mondays to Saturdays

				NT	NT	NT	NT	NT		NT	NT	NT	NT	NT	NT	NT	NT
																	SO
				◇	◇						◇	◇			◇	◇	◇
								J									K
				H	H						H	H			H	H	
Miles	Miles																
0	—	**Colne**	d			09 25							10 16				
2	—	Nelson	d			09 31							10 22				
3½	—	Briefield	d			09 34							10 25				
5½	—	**Burnley Central**	98 d			09 39							10 30				
6	—	Burnley Barracks	98 d										10 32				
—	—	Leeds	39 d	*08 18*							*09 18*				*10 18*		
—	—	Burnley Manchester Road	39 d	*09 21*							*10 21*				*11 21*		
7	—	Rose Grove	d			09 44						10 36					
8½	—	Hapton	d										10 39				
10	—	Huncoat	d										10 42				
11½	—	Accrington	d	09 31		09 51					10 31		10 46		11 31		
12½	—	Church & Oswaldtwistle	d			09 54							10 49				
14½	—	Rishton	d			09 58							10 52				
18	—	**Blackburn**	a	09 39		10 03					10 39		10 57		11 39		
—	—	Manchester Victoria	94 a	*10 39*		*11 06*							*12 06*				
—	—	Clitheroe	94 d								*09 58*				*10 58*		
—	—	**Blackburn**	d	09 39		10 03					10 39		10 59		11 39		
19½	—	Mill Hill (Lancashire)	d			10 06							11 02				
20	—	Cherry Tree	d			10 08							11 04				
21	—	Pleasington	d										11 06				
26	—	Bamber Bridge	d			10 16							11 13				
27½	—	Lostock Hall	d			10 19							11 15				
30	—	**Preston** [10]	a	09 56		10 26					10 56		11 24		11 56		
—	—	London Euston	65 a	*12c 55*							*14c 75*				*14g 49*		
—	—	London Euston	65 d							*07f 40*			*08f 40*				
—	0	**Preston** [10]	d	09 58	10 02	10 27	10 32	10 38		10 50	10 58	11 02	11 26	11 45	11 58	12 02	12 21
35½	5½	Salwick	d														
37½	7½	Kirkham & Wesham	d			10 36				10 59			11 35	11 54			
41	—	Moss Side	d										11 40				
43½	—	Lytham	d			10 44							11 44				
44½	—	Ansdell & Fairhaven	d			10 47							11 47				
46½	—	St Annes-on-the-Sea	d			10 51							11 51				
48½	—	Squires Gate	d			10 54							11 54				
49½	—	Blackpool Pleasure Beach	d			10 57							11 57				
50	—	**Blackpool South**	a			11 02							12 02				
—	14½	Poulton-le-Fylde	d	10 14	10 18					11 07	11 14	11 18		12 02	12 14	12 18	
—	16½	Layton	d							11 10				12 06			
—	17½	Blackpool North	a	10 24	10 28		10 57	11 04		11 18	11 24	11 28		12 13	12 24	12 28	12 50

For general notes see front of timetable

J Mondays to Fridays until 1 November and from 31 March, also Saturdays until 2 November and from 1 March
K Until 2 November
c Saturdays arr. 10 minutes later
f Saturdays dep. 10 minutes earlier
g Saturdays arr. 1500.

Route/Network Diagrams (see previous page): For many tables a Route/Network Diagram is also provided to show the routes and stations served in diagrammatic form. Where this is the case, a reference to the Route/Network Diagram will be provided at the top of each page of the timetable concerned. Timetable numbers for connecting or alternative services will not be included within the Table itself but will instead be indicated on the accompanying Route/Network Diagram.

General Information

Smoking Policy

Smoking is banned on all National Rail services and National Rail stations, including all covered and uncovered concourses, ticket halls, platforms, footbridges and subways at station premises.

Left Luggage Facilities

Details of Left Luggage facilities at stations are available from the Operator (Train Operator/Network Rail) responsible for providing facilities at the station. Please see the Station Index to identify the Station Operator and then look at the appropriate page for full details.

Penalty Fares

Penalty Fares are charged by Train Companies at some stations and on some trains. Where this is the case, warning notices will be displayed. Those stations at which Penalty Fares are in operation are indicated in the Station Index and Table numbers section (see also Train Operator pages). Please be aware that at some stations where Penalty Fare Schemes are in place not all Train Operator services calling at that station are included in the scheme.

If you can not produce a valid ticket for your entire journey when asked to do so you may be charged a Penalty Fare. This will be either twice the full single fare to the next station at which the train is due to stop, or £20, whichever is the greater. Any travel beyond the next station will be charged at the full single fare.

To avoid paying a Penalty Fare, you must purchase a valid ticket to your destination, before starting your journey. If the ticket office is closed and you can not buy the ticket you want from a self service ticket machine, you must buy a Permit to Travel paying as much of your fare as possible. This permit must be exchanged for a valid ticket at the first opportunity.

Timetable Accuracy, Contents, Presentation

Every effort is made to ensure that the information contained in the timetable is correct, but errors can still occur. If you have any questions or queries about the train services shown in this timetable, please write to the appropriate operator shown in the Directory of Train Operators.

General comments about this publication should be addressed to:–

TSO
PO Box 29
Norwich
NR3 1GN

Additional Amendments

A facility is available whereby details of any train service alterations introduced subsequent to the production of the UK Rail Timetable, may be accessed through the website.

From time to time, further alterations may apply at short notice and details of these may be found through use of the links to individual Train Companies. Alternatively, the website of each company may be accessed directly at the address shown in the Directory of Train Operators.

Other UK Rail Timetables

Regional and route specific timetables are available from individual train companies. Please contact the relevant train company to request the latest version of the timetable you require.

National Rail Enquiries offers an online 'Pocket Timetable' service which gives you the flexibility to create a customised timetable based around your origin and destination, your own time requirements and the days of the week that you want. Visit www.nationalrail.co.uk for more details.

Connections

Bold type times in vertical columns in the timetable show direct trains. In a few cases, where one train overtakes another, the times appear in more than one column and arrow symbols indicate where the train continues in the timetable.

Many more journey opportunities are possible by changing trains. To help plan such journeys, times in light italic type are shown in many of the timetables for departures (if the time is earlier than the bold type times for the station below in the column at which you should change trains) or arrivals (if they are later than the bold type times for the station above in the column at which you should change trains).

Where light type italic times are not shown you may have to refer to other tables in the book to work out your connecting services. In order to find the right table to reference, first look at the Route/Network Diagram that covers the table you are working from. This will show the principal connecting links and their table references, which may include the destination you are searching for. If your journey is not covered, follow the advice given on page 3 'How to use this Timetable' under the heading 'Using the Index'.

Connections between trains cannot be guaranteed. The nature of the integrated operation of railway passenger services means that to delay one train to await customers from a late running train arriving at a station may cause significant disruption to many other customers when they make connections at other stations along the route. Every endeavour is made to minimise the total disruption and particular attention is given to services operating infrequently and the last train services each day.

The aim of all Train Operating Companies is to run punctually, but inevitably some disruption occurs from time to time. When planning a journey you may wish to consider the effects which any disruption could have and to allow some contingency margin when planning connections.

Minimum Interchange Times at Stations

Unless a connection is shown by times printed in light type, you should generally allow a minimum of five minutes between arrival and departure.

The exceptions to this rule are indicated by minimum interchange times (e.g. **15**) alongside the station name in the tables. In certain cases the minimum interchange time is different according to the Train Operators involved.

These are detailed below:-

STATION AND 'STANDARD' MINIMUM CONNECTIONAL ALLOWANCE (Minutes)		EXCEPTIONS *Showing the Train Operator(s) and minimum connectional allowance applicable*	
Barnham	5	*SN*	2
Bournemouth	5	*SW*	3
Brighton	10	*SN*	4
Cardiff Central	7	*AW*	3*
Clapham Junction	10	*SN*	5
Gatwick Airport	10	*SE, SN*	5
Guildford	5	*GW*	4
Leatherhead	5	*SN*	4
London Blackfriars	3	SE	5
London Victoria	15	*SE, SN*	10
Luton	10	*FC*	4
Luton Airport Parkway	7	*FC*	4
Redhill	5	*SN*	3
St. Denys	5	*SW*	3
Southampton Central	5	*SN, SW*	4
Tulse Hill	3	FC	4
Wimbledon	6	*SN, FC*	5

Example

At Barnham a different minimum connectional allowance applies for Train Operator SN. This means that if your journey involves changing between two trains *both of which* are operated by SN, you need only allow 2 minutes. If, however, one or both trains are provided by any other Operator then the minimum of 5 minutes (as shown after the station name) applies.

* Applicable to Valley Lines services only (table 130).

Train Information

 National Rail Enquiries

Timetable and fares available at: www.nationalrail.co.uk

National Rail Enquiries provides up-to-the-minute advice on all aspects of journey planning, fares and buying tickets, live train running updates and other useful information. 0845 telephone numbers are charged at local-rate from anywhere in the UK.

For information on reservations and purchasing tickets please refer to individual train company listings in the Directory of Train Operators.

08457 48 49 50 24 Hours Daily

(calls to this number may be recorded)

0845 60 40 500 Welsh Language

0845 60 50 600 Textphone – 06.00 - 21.00 Daily

Train company numbers for disabled passengers requiring assistance:–

Company	Telephone	Textphone
ARRIVA Trains Wales	08453 003 005	0870 410 0355
c2c	01702 357 640	08457 125 988
Chiltern Railways	08456 005 165	08457 078 051
East Midlands Trains	08457 125 678	08457 078 051
First Capital Connect	0800 058 2844	0800 975 1052
First Great Western	08001 971 329	08002 949 209
First ScotRail	0800 912 2901	0800 912 2899
First TransPennine Express	0800 172 2149	0800 107 2061
Gatwick Express	08458 501 530	
Hull Trains	08450 710 222	08456 786 967
Island Line	0800 528 2100	0800 692 0792
London Midland	0870 609 6060	08457 078 051
London Overground	0845 601 4867	
Merseyrail	0151 702 2071	0870 055 2681
National Express East Coast	08457 225 444	08451 202 067
Northern Rail	08456 008 008	08456 045 608
one	08000 282 878	0845 606 7245
Southeastern	08007 834 524	08007 834 548
South West Trains	0800 528 2100	0800 692 0792
Southern	0800 138 1016	0800 138 1018
Virgin Trains	08457 443 366	08457 443 367

London Travel Information

020 7222 1234 — 24 hours (Daily) — www.tfl.gov.uk

Services to Europe on Eurostar via the Channel Tunnel

08705 186 186 — 0800-2100 (Daily) — www.eurostar.com

Ireland

NI Railways 028 90 66 6630 — 0700-2000 (Daily) — www.translink.co.uk.

Iarnrod Eireann (IE) (Irish Rail) 1850 366 222 — www.irishrail.ie

Train Information

Transport Direct

Plan journeys by car, bus, train, tube, coach, plane at www.transportdirect.info. Transport Direct is the first door-to-door on-line journey planner for Great Britain.

It's free to use; simply enter your departure point, destination and time of travel and Transport Direct will offer a number of options by different modes of transport - both public and private. Journey plans are presented as step-by-step instructions supported by detailed maps including bus stops and other points of interest to travellers. Tickets for rail and coach journeys can be booked via retail web sites without the need to re-enter journey details. Transport Direct includes live travel news for rail and car users. The car journey planner gives route information that takes account of historical traffic level data, offering the user the choice to travel at a different time, or choose public transport. When travelling by public transport, users can adjust their expected walking speed to plan rail, coach and bus connections more efficiently. You can also access Transport Direct via mobile phone and PDA to find out when your next train is due or to check road conditions.

Bus Information in Great Britain

For details of buses within Greater London ring the Transport for London line: 020 7222 1234 (24-hours).

Bus information for the rest of Great Britain is available nationally from 'Traveline' which is run by local authorities and bus operators. There are regional call centres all of which share the same telephone number and any centre will switch calls pertaining to another part of the country through to the relevant centre. Alternatively codes for reaching the appropriate centre direct can be obtained from www.traveline.org.uk/powercodes.htm.
The number is 0871 200 22 33 (calls from landlines cost 10p per minute) and centres are open at least between the hours of 0800 and 2000 daily (except Christmas Day and Boxing Day). Website: www.traveline.org.uk.

PlusBus

PlusBus provides you with a simple, easy-to-use add-on to your train ticket and gives unlimited bus travel on most bus services in the town or city. ***PlusBus*** is available to over 200 towns and cities across Great Britain with season tickets also available for many ***PlusBus*** locations. For more information visit www.plusbus.info.

Traintaxi

Taxi symbols on the Station index pages

Where 🚕 appears against any station that has sub-entries, there will be a taxi rank outside the station from which taxis should usually be available. This also applies to Basingstoke, Bournemouth, Chelmsford, Cheltenham, Colchester, Lincoln, Middlesbrough, Milton Keynes, Northampton, Sunderland and Swindon.

Where 🚕 appears against any other station, there will be a taxi rank or a cab office within 100 metres of the station. However, you are advised to check availability before travelling, and to pre-book if necessary. Indication of a rank or office is no guarantee of cabs being available.

Visit **www.traintaxi.co.uk** for information on cab firms serving **all** train, tram, metro and underground stations in Great Britain, and all bus and ferry destinations listed in this *UK Rail Timetable*.

RailPlanner for home and office (network) PC-based timetables

For details of this computerised timetable, contact Travel InfoSystems Sales, Suite 1, Grand Union House, 20 Kentish Town Road, London NW1 9NR

Tel: 020 7428 1288
Fax: 020 7267 2745
E-mail: sales@travelinfosystems.com
Website: www.travelinfosystems.com

Rail Travel for Disabled Passengers

All train operators are able to carry disabled passengers and can provide additional assistance for boarding and alighting rail services and during train journeys.

If using a wheelchair, it is recommended that passengers book assistance in advance as space on trains for wheelchair users is limited.

National Rail produce a booklet called 'Rail Travel Made Easy' which details the provisions Train Companies make for disabled people. The booklet is available from major stations or can be obtained by writing to: Disability & Inclusion Section, ATOC, 3rd Floor, 40 Bernard Street, London WC1N 1BY.

Further information is available on the **www.nationalrail.co.uk**

Seat Reservations, Luggage, Cycles and Pets

Seat Reservations

You can reserve seats on any train marked [R], [R], ◇ or ✗ at the top of the column in the timetable pages. Further detailed information is shown in the Directory of Train Operators. Reservations can normally be made from about 2 months in advance of the day of travel, up to about 2 hours before the train departs from its start point, or, for early morning trains, up to 1600 hours the previous evening.

Where and How to reserve

You can reserve either by visiting a station identified in the Index pages by ◇, or a rail appointed travel agent or by calling one of the telephone booking facilities listed on each Train Operator's page. Telephone reservations are only available when made in conjunction with purchasing a ticket. When reserving you will need to tell your station or agent:

1. Starting and finishing point of your journey.
2. Date of travel (Take care if your departure is soon after midnight – see How to use this Timetable).
3. Departure time of train.
4. Number of seats required.
5. You may be able to specify other preferences such as facing or back to direction of travel*, window seat, seat in Restaurant Car where available, seats round a table or airline style with fold down table where available.
   *Customers should note that some trains reverse their direction of travel during the journey.
6. First Class or Standard accommodation (if you do not specify class of travel it will be assumed that you require Standard accommodation).

Names on seats

Your name can be included in your seat reservation label or on the electronic display above your seat, if you wish, when travelling First Class on some East Midlands Trains, National Express East Coast and 'one' services or First and Standard Class on CrossCountry, First Great Western, First ScotRail, First TransPennine Express, South West Trains, and Virgin Trains services.

Connecting reservations

If your journey involves changing between trains on which seats are reservable (including journeys crossing London or other major cities), through reservations on both services are available.

Children

Seats may be reserved for children, but for a child under 5 years of age a seat may be reserved only if an appropriate child rail ticket is held.

Reservations Recommended

Trains shown [R] at the head of a column in the timetable pages are expected to be very busy. Seat reservations are therefore recommended for a comfortable journey and will consequently be provided free of charge to holders of valid travel tickets.

Seat Reservations, Luggage, Cycles and Pets

Reservations Compulsory
On trains shown Ⓡ at the head of a column, seat reservations are compulsory and are available free of charge. Passengers may not be able to board the train if they do not have a reservation.

Trains For Weekends Away
Most long distance services after 1400 on Fridays and on Saturday mornings, also trains arriving in London on Sunday evenings and Monday mornings can be extremely busy.

Customers are advised to reserve seats in advance if planning to travel at these times.

Travelling at Peak Holiday Periods
Trains are usually extremely busy immediately before and after Bank Holidays and in some cases access to trains is only by reservation and/or boarding pass. Customers are advised to reserve seats as early as possible.

Cycles by Train
You can take your cycle on many National Rail services, however reservations may be required and restrictions may apply for peak services. Folded cycles can be carried on most train services. More information is shown in the Directory of Train Operators, the National Rail 'Cycling by Train' leaflet and online at www.nationalrail.co.uk. Cycle storage is also available at many stations.

Weekend First

Weekend First is available on many CrossCountry, East Midlands Trains, First Great Western, First ScotRail*, First TransPennine Express*, National Express East Coast, 'one', South West Trains* and Virgin Trains (Virgin Weekend Upgrade on Virgin Trains services) services on Saturdays, Sundays and Bank Holidays. You can enjoy the luxury of special First Class accommodation on payment of a supplement. Weekend First is available to holders of most types of ticket valid in Standard accommodation, although there are certain exceptions – for full details please ring National Rail Enquiries on 08457 48 49 50.

If Weekend First is purchased at least a day in advance, you receive the additional benefit of a free reserved seat. Alternatively, if seats are still available, Weekend First may be purchased from a member of the on train staff.

Weekend First tickets may only be used in coaches which have Weekend First window labels. However, please note First ScotRail do not use window labels.

*may only be purchased on trains at time of travel

Customers' Luggage and Pets

Customers may take luggage provided there is space for it on the train and it is properly packed so as not to cause inconvenience or damage. Please bear in mind many trains have limited luggage space and large suitcases may not be able to be accommodated.

Excess luggage and certain more bulky items (such as skis) may be carried, subject to available space, at an extra charge.

On Gatwick Express services bulky items such as skis are conveyed free in the luggage van. There is plenty of space on board for other luggage; for further information call 0845 850 15 30.

Dogs and other pets may be taken, in most circumstances, free of charge. Animals may not be conveyed on Heathrow Express services. On First ScotRail Caledonian Sleepers dogs (except guide dogs) are not conveyed free of charge. Dogs are only permitted in the Sleeper berth providing the owner has exclusive use of the cabin and pays the relevant charge. Special arrangements are made for guide dogs.

Directory of Train Operators

The following pages contain details of the Train Operating Companies who operate trains included in this timetable and indicate the services they provide.

Each operator is identified by a two character code listed below. The codes are displayed in the index alongside the station name indicating which operator is responsible for operating the facilities at that station. The code is also shown at the head of each train column in the timetable pages indicating which operator is providing the train service.

17 stations are the operating responsibility of Network Rail and are shown in the index by the code NR and information about Network Rail is shown at the end of the Train Operating Company pages.

ARRIVA Trains Wales

AW

ADDRESS

St Marys House, 47 Penarth Road, Cardiff CF10 5DJ
Telephone: 08456 061 660
Website: www.arrivatrainswales.co.uk
Email: customer.relations@arrivatrainswales.co.uk

MANAGING DIRECTOR

Bob Holland

RESERVATIONS AND TICKETS BY TELEPHONE

Tickets may be booked in advance and seats reserved, by telephone, from the following numbers (0800–2000 daily):
0870 9000 773 for Great Britain, tickets and reservations. 0870 9000 767 for Group and 0845 300 3005 for Disabled travel arrangements. Textphone 0845 300 6105
Please allow 5 days for delivery.

RESERVATION DETAILS

All seat reservations are free to ticket holders.

CATERING ON TRAINS

At-seat catering service of cold snacks, sandwiches and hot and cold drinks on all services marked ⚲, for all or part of the journey.

Train catering on ARRIVA Trains Wales services is provided by:

At Seat Catering (2003) Ltd,
ARRIVA Trains Wales
3rd Floor
St Davids House
Wood Street
Cardiff
CF10 1ES

CYCLES

See Cycling by Train, a guide to ARRIVA Trains Wales services leaflet for full details.

LOST PROPERTY

Contact your nearest staffed station or contact ARRIVA Trains Wales Customer Relations on 0845 6061 660.

TRAIN SERVICE UPDATE

Please consult our website at www.arrivatrainswales.co.uk for real time service updates.

PENALTY FARES

Penalty Fares are not in force on ARRIVA Trains Wales services. Customers are reminded that they must have a valid ticket when boarding at a staffed station, if not it will be necessary to charge you the full single/return fare for the journey.

DISABLED PERSON'S PROTECTION POLICY

Address as above.

CODE OF PRACTICE FOR COMMENTS, COMPLAINTS AND SUGGESTIONS

Address as above.

c2c

A member of the National Express Group plc

ADDRESS	207 Old Street, London EC1V 9NR Telephone: 0845 601 4873 Fax: 01603 214517 Website: www.c2c-online.co.uk
MANAGING DIRECTOR	Mark Hopwood
RESERVATIONS AND TICKETS BY TELEPHONE	Tickets may be booked in advance by telephoning 08457 44 44 22.
RESERVATION DETAILS	Reservations are not available.
CATERING ON TRAINS	Not available.
CYCLES	Cycles can be taken on off-peak trains free-of-charge when accompanied by a fare-paying passenger, subject to space availability. Bicycles are not permitted, Mondays to Fridays on services that arrive in London between 0720 and 1010, or those which leave London between 1630 and 1840. To comply with safety regulations, all cycles, with the exception of folding cycles which are completely enclosed in a container or case throughout the journey, must be conveyed in the designated area on trains. During engineering work, cycles cannot be accommodated on replacement bus services.
LOST PROPERTY	Telephone: 01702 357 699
TRAIN SERVICE UPDATE	Up to date train running information is available on the c2c website www.c2c-online.co.uk, by calling 08457 48 49 50 or on ceefax page 433.
PENALTY FARES	If you travel without a valid ticket you may be charged a penalty fare of £20 or twice the full single fare, whichever is the greater.
DISABLED PERSON'S PROTECTION POLICY	Available from:- Customer Relations, c2c, FREEPOST ADM3968, Southend SS1 1ZS Telephone: 0845 601 4873
CODE OF PRACTICE FOR COMMENTS, COMPLAINTS AND SUGGESTIONS	Available from Customer Relations at above address or telephone 0845 601 4873.

CrossCountry

ADDRESS	CrossCountry 85 Smallbrook Queensway Birmingham B5 4HA Telephone: To be advised Website: www.crosscountrytrains.co.uk Email: customer.relations@crosscountrytrains.co.uk
MANAGING DIRECTOR	To be advised
RESERVATIONS AND TICKETS BY TELEPHONE	Sunday – Saturday 0800-2200 Group Travel reservations: Monday to Friday 0800-1800 Details of telephone number to be advised - check our website
RESERVATION DETAILS	You are strongly advised to make a seat reservation in advance. Seat reservations are free of charge.
CATERING ON TRAINS	Catering is available on a number of trains. In First Class, on weekdays between 0600-2000, customers can enjoy complimentary light refreshments including hot and soft drinks, served either at the customer's seat or available for collection from the on-board shop (where in operation). In Standard Class, between 0600-2000, we offer a range of quality snacks, sandwiches, hot drinks, plus soft and alcoholic beverages.
CYCLES	All customers travelling with bikes must have a reservation to travel for which there may be a charge.
LOST PROPERTY	Monday – Friday 0830-2015 Saturday 0900-1600 Details of telephone number to be advised - check our website
TRAIN SERVICE UPDATE	Details of any disruption to services or weekend engineering work are summarised on BBC Ceefax and BBCi on digital TV. Details of engineering work can also be found on www.crosscountrytrains.co.uk.
PENALTY FARES	Details to be advised - check our website.
DISABLED PERSON'S PROTECTION POLICY	Copies of the CrossCountry Disabled Person's Protection Policy are available free of charge from www.crosscountrytrains.co.uk
CODE OF PRACTICE FOR COMMENTS, COMPLAINTS AND SUGGESTIONS	Copies of our Complaints Handling Procedure are available from www.crosscountrytrains.co.uk.

Chiltern Railway Co.

CH

ADDRESS	Customer Services, Western House, 14 Rickfords Hill, Aylesbury HP20 2RX Telephone: 08456 005 165 (Mondays to Fridays 0830-1730) Fax: 01296 332126 Website: www.chilternrailways.co.uk
MANAGING DIRECTOR	Adrian Shooter (Acting)
RESERVATIONS AND TICKETS BY TELEPHONE	Telephone 08456 005 165 (0700-2000, 7 days a week)
RESERVATION DETAILS	Reservations are not required on Chiltern Railways services.
CATERING ON TRAINS	A trolley catering service is available on Monday to Friday peak services between Birmingham Snow Hill and London Marylebone.
CYCLES	Passengers with bicycles are welcome on Chiltern Railways. Cycles are carried off-peak free of charge but cannot be accommodated at busy times, i.e. throughout the journey on trains arriving at London Marylebone and Birmingham Snow Hill between 0745 and 1000, or throughout the journey on trains departing London Marylebone or Birmingham Snow Hill between 1630 and 1930 on Mondays to Fridays. There are no restrictions on folding bicycles. Tandems are not carried at any time.
LOST PROPERTY	Telephone 08456 005 165 (1000-1500 Mondays to Fridays).
TRAIN SERVICE UPDATE	For a recorded summary of engineering work call: 08456 005 165.
PENALTY FARES	If you do not have a valid rail ticket for the journey you are making, you will have to pay a Penalty Fare of £20 or twice the single fare, whichever is the greater, for the journey you are making on Chiltern Railways services. For full details write to the above address, or see our website.
DISABLED PERSON'S PROTECTION POLICY	Copies of the Disabled Person's Protection Policy can be obtained from the above address, or from our website.
CODE OF PRACTICE FOR COMMENTS, COMPLAINTS AND SUGGESTIONS	If you have any comments, complaints or suggestions regarding Chiltern Railways services, please write to the address shown above or telephone 08456 005 165 (0830-1730 Mondays to Fridays), Fax 01296 332126. Alternatively you can use the 'Contact Us' option on our website.

East Midlands Trains

EM

ADDRESS

Midland House
Nelson Street
Derby DE1 2SA
Telephone: 08457 125 678
Website: www.eastmidlandstrains.co.uk
Email: getintouch@eastmidlandstrains.co.uk

MANAGING DIRECTOR

Tim Shoveller

RESERVATIONS AND TICKETS BY TELEPHONE

Buy your tickets online at eastmidlandstrains.co.uk. You can buy tickets for all rail journeys (within Great Britain) with us. Alternatively call 08457 125 678 between 0800-2000 (7 days a week).

RESERVATION DETAILS

Seat reservations on East Midlands Trains services are free. Just book in advance when you buy your ticket. We advise that you always make a reservation, as seats cannot be guaranteed without one. On our Connect services reservations are available on the Liverpool to Norwich services.

CATERING ON TRAINS

On our East Midlands Mainline services (to/from St Pancras International), our buffet provides a range of delicious healthy food options, plus snacks and Fairtrade drinks. A trolley service is available on selected East Midlands Connect services (denoted by a symbol within the timetable).

CYCLES

Bicycles are accepted for free on most East Midlands Trains services; however reservations must be made in advance.

LOST PROPERTY

For all journeys, you can make enquiries at your local station, or by calling 08457 125 678. Left Luggage and Lost Property services are also available at: Sheffield, Derby, Leicester and London St Pancras stations. Call 08457 125 678 for opening hours.

TRAIN SERVICE UPDATE

Details of services and real time running information, including travel alerts by email are available through our website. Visit eastmidlandstrains.co.uk. Alternatively, call National Rail Enquiries on 08457 48 49 50.

PENALTY FARES

You should always buy a ticket in advance of boarding your train. Penalty fares may be in operation on your service.

DISABLED PERSON'S PROTECTION POLICY

We aim to make travelling with us accessible to all our customers. If you require assistance in travelling, have special needs or mobility problems please call our team on 08457 125 678 to arrange help for your journey. A textphone service is also available on 08457 078 051.

CODE OF PRACTICE FOR COMMENTS, COMPLAINTS AND SUGGESTIONS

Our Customer Relations team is available to receive your comments, complaints or suggestions. Please write to Customer Relations at the above address, or email getintouch@eastmidlandstrains.co.uk

FC First Capital Connect FC

A member of the First Rail Division

ADDRESS

Freepost, RRBR-REEJ-KTKY, First Capital Connect, Customer Relations Department, PO Box 443, Plymouth PL4 6WP
Telephone: 0845 026 4700 (open 7 days a week 0700-2200 with the exception of Christmas Day)
Fax: 0845 676 9904
Website: www.firstcapitalconnect.co.uk
Email: customer.relations.fcc@firstgroup.com

CHIEF EXECUTIVE

Moir Lockhead

MANAGING DIRECTOR

Elaine Holt

RESERVATIONS AND TICKETS BY TELEPHONE

It is not necessary to pre-book on First Capital Connect services. There is no telesales.

RESERVATION DETAILS

First Capital Connect does not operate a reservation system.

CATERING ON TRAINS

None.

CYCLES

We welcome passengers with bicycles on services where they can be safely accommodated, however restrictions apply, bicycles cannot be carried on:

- trains that are scheduled to arrive at a London terminal between 07:00 and 10:00;
- trains that are scheduled to depart from a London terminal between 16:00 and 19:00;
- trains running between Drayton Park and Moorgate;
- services between Royston and Ely that depart or arrive at Cambridge between 07:45 and 08:45, with the exception of the 07:15 and 07:45 departures from King's Cross;
- replacement bus services unless stated otherwise in any associated publicity; and
- any train where a member of our staff asks you to remove your bicycle.
- Bicycles cannot be conveyed within Travelcard zone 1 in any direction between the hours of 0700-1000 and 1600-1900 Monday to Friday

Fold up bicycles can be carried on any service at any time.

LOST PROPERTY

In order to trace lost property please contact our Customer Relations department on 0845 026 4700, between 07:00 - 22:00 Monday to Sunday.

TRAIN SERVICE UPDATE

For current train information call First Capital Connect Travel Check on 0845 330 3660, National Rail enquiries on 08457 48 49 50 or check our website at: www.firstcapitalconnect.co.uk/live-info

PENALTY FARES

First Capital Connect operates a Penalty Fares System. If you do not have a valid ticket or permit to travel, you will be liable to pay a penalty fare. This is £20 or twice the appropriate single fare to the next station stop, whichever is greater. This does not apply for travel from Crews Hill.

If you do not buy a ticket, you could also be prosecuted and this can lead to a criminal conviction.

DISABLED PERSON'S PROTECTION POLICY

Our Disabled Person's Protection Policy is available from Customer Relations, and is also available on our website and available at all staffed sations. First Capital Connect operates a dedicated telephone and textphone service for disabled or mobility impaired customers, the contact details are:

Telephone: 0800 058 2844

Textphone: 0800 975 1052

These are available 07:00 - 22:00, Monday to Sunday, with the exception of Christmas Day.

CODE OF PRACTICE FOR COMMENTS, COMPLAINTS AND SUGGESTIONS

Our Passenger's Charter details our code of practice and is available from all staffed stations and from our Customer Relations department. The Customer Relations department will be happy to assist with any comments, complaints or suggestions and can be contacted using the contact details above.

GW First Great Western GW

A member of the First Rail Division

ADDRESS	Milford House, 1 Milford Street, Swindon SN1 1HL Telephone: 01793 499400 Fax: 01793 499460 Website: www.firstgreatwestern.co.uk where customers can buy tickets, check train times, obtain current information on train services, download timetables, check latest alterations to services, view promotions and offers and contact us with your comments.
MANAGING DIRECTOR	Andrew Haines
RESERVATIONS AND TICKETS BY TELEPHONE	Tickets may be booked in advance using credit and debit cards and seats reserved by ringing **08457 000 125** (open 0700-2200 Mondays to Fridays and 0700-2100 Saturdays and Sundays). Allow at least 3 working days for postal delivery. A next day delivery can be arranged at £5 per transaction. Arrangements can be made for tickets to be collected from Fast Ticket machines (the credit or debit card used for purchase will be needed at many stations). For Group Travel call **08457 000 125**.
RESERVATION DETAILS	One complimentary seat reservation per single journey when purchasing a ticket, additional reservations will be subject to a £5 fee.
CATERING ON TRAINS	Most First Great Western high speed services offer a buffet or trolley service with a selection of hot and cold snacks, sandwiches, beverages, crisps and confectionery. First Class customers also enjoy additional complimentary services: • An at seat trolley service offering light refreshments available on Monday to Friday services between 0700 and 1900, including tea, freshly made coffee, soft drinks, mineral water, morning goods, biscuits, peanuts and fresh fruit. • A complimentary daily newspaper (available up to 09.00) and evening paper (after 15.00) on services out of London. • At the weekend and on weekdays after 1900 complimentary refreshments are available from the buffet on production of valid travel tickets. • Friday night wine offers first class customers a complimentary glass of wine between 1500 and 1900. Some weekday high speed services offer Pullman Restaurant or Travelling Chef/ Brasserie providing food freshly prepared on board by one of our own chefs. These services are available on over 200 services per week.
CYCLES	First Great Western welcomes customers with bicycles on services where they can be safely accommodated. However it is not possible to carry bicycles on some services particularly during peak periods. For full details of when bicycles cannot be carried or when reservations are required, please visit our website or pick up a leaflet at any of our staffed stations.
LOST PROPERTY	Customers who have left property on First Great Western services should contact our Customer Services team on **08457 000 125**.
TRAIN SERVICE UPDATE	For current train information including details of engineering work please visit our website: www.firstgreatwestern.co.uk
PENALTY FARES	These operate on most of our services. A penalty fare of £20 or twice the appropriate single fare to the next station stop (whichever is the greater) will be charged to anybody who is unable to produce a valid ticket or other authority when required to do so. For further information, pick up a leaflet about penalty fares from any staffed station.
DISABLED PERSON'S PROTECTION POLICY	Available from Customer Services Team First Great Western PO Box 313 Plymouth PL4 6YD Tel: 08457 000 125 Email: fgwfeedback@firstgroup.com Opening hours 0700-2200, daily. Customers requiring assistance should contact 0800 197 1329 (0800 294 9209 textphone service) giving 24 hours notice of travel plans, if possible.
CODE OF PRACTICE FOR COMMENTS, COMPLAINTS AND SUGGESTIONS	Your views leaflets and copies of the Passenger's Charter are available to download from our website www.firstgreatwestern.co.uk, at all staffed First Great Western stations or alternatively from the Customer Services Team at the address above.

First ScotRail

SR

A member of the First Rail Division

ADDRESS

1st Floor, Atrium Court, 50 Waterloo Street, Glasgow G2 6HQ
Telephone: 08700 00 51 51
Fax: 0141 335 4592
Website: www.firstscotrail.com
Email: enquiries@firstscotrail.com

MANAGING DIRECTOR

Mary Dickson

RESERVATIONS AND TICKETS BY TELEPHONE

Tickets may be purchased in advance and Sleepers or seats reserved, by telephone, using a debit/credit card from the following number:

08457 550033 (opening hours 0700-2200)

Please allow 3 days for tickets by post, tickets on departure arrangements available at selected stations. Tickets can also be purchased through the website - www.firstscotrail.com

First ScotRail customers can buy selected Caledonian Sleeper tickets online - and have the ticket confirmation sent to their mobile phone. Passengers simply turn up for their train, show the text message to train staff and hop on board. A confirmatory email is sent as a back-up. This free SMS service is available for 'Bargain Berth' tickets on the Caledonian Sleeper, which connects Scottish cities to Central London. Tickets can be booked up to 12 weeks in advance of travel - and right up until midday on the day of travel, subject to availability. The berths start from just £19.

RESERVATION DETAILS

Seat Reservations are free and can be made from 12 weeks in advance up to 1800 hours one day prior to the date of departure. Caledonian Sleeper reservations can be made up to 12 weeks in advance.

CATERING ON TRAINS

A Lounge Car is provided on all Caledonian Sleeper services offering a wide range of drinks, snacks and hot meals. A trolley service is available on many longer distance services as indicated in the timetable. Any comments about our daytime catering services should be made to Martin O'Rourke, Head of Hospitality tel: 0141 335 2066.

CYCLES

Cycles are carried free on all First ScotRail services subject to availability. Reservations are required on Caledonian Sleeper services and on longer distance routes. Tandems, tricycles, cycle trailers, motorcycles, mopeds or any mechanically driven vehicle (except mechanically driven vehicle wheelchairs) cannot be carried on any First ScotRail service.

LOST PROPERTY

Please phone 0141 335 3276 (0700-1900 Mon-Sat)

TRAIN SERVICE UPDATE

Register with JourneyCheck/JourneyAlert on our website: www.firstscotrail.com

PENALTY FARES

Penalty Fares are not in force on any First ScotRail services.

DISABLED PERSON'S PROTECTION POLICY

Available from the Customer Relations Manager, First ScotRail, Disabled Assistance, PO Box 7034, Fort William PH33 6WS. Tel: 0800 912 2 901 or minicom 0800 912 2 899
Fax: 0141 335 4611

Travel arrangements may be made for disabled people by calling 08 00 912 2 901*. One lightweight travel scooter, length 104cm, width 56cm with a turning radius of 99cm and combined weight of 30kg can be conveyed per train. Details of station facilities for disabled customers are also available on our website www.firstscotrail.com

*For assisted travel at least 24 hours notice is required.

CODE OF PRACTICE FOR COMMENTS, COMPLAINTS AND SUGGESTIONS

First ScotRail welcomes comments on the services we provide. A leaflet is available at all staffed First ScotRail stations explaining the procedures and is also available from the Customer Relations Manager at the address above. Tel: 0845 601 5929

First TransPennine Express

TP

A joint venture between First and Keolis

ADDRESS	7th Floor, Bridgewater House, 60 Whitworth Street, Manchester M1 6LT Telephone: 08700 005151 Website: www.tpexpress.co.uk
MANAGING DIRECTOR	Vernon Barker
RESERVATIONS AND TICKETS BY TELEPHONE	Reservations and tickets are available from all local staffed stations.
RESERVATION DETAILS	Seat reservations are available at staffed stations. Seat reservations for travel on First TransPennine Express services can be booked up until the day before travel. There is no charge for making a seat reservation if you have a rail ticket, or buy one at the same time.
CATERING ON TRAINS	Catering trolley services are available between 0700 and 1900 Monday to Friday on First TransPennine Express trains between Manchester Piccadilly and York, Manchester Piccadilly and Doncaster and Manchester Piccadilly and Preston.
CYCLES	Customers may take their bicycle with them on First TransPennine Express trains at no extra cost. As space is limited reservations for cycle space should be made at least 24 hours before the journey.
LOST PROPERTY	Customers who have left their property on First TransPennine Express trains or stations should contact 0845 600 1672.
TRAIN SERVICE UPDATE	Call TrainTracker on 0871 200 4950 for updated information on train departures and arrivals.
PENALTY FARES	Penalty Fares are not applicable on First TransPennine Express services. Customers are reminded that they must have a valid ticket when they travel. If not it will be necessary to charge the full Open Single or Return fare for the journey.
DISABLED PERSON'S PROTECTION POLICY	Available from: Customer Relations, First TransPennine Express, ADMAIL 3878, Freepost, Manchester M1 9YB Customers who have special needs and require customer assistance should contact us on 0800 107 2149. A textphone service is available on 0800 107 2061.
CODE OF PRACTICE FOR COMMENTS, COMPLAINTS AND SUGGESTIONS	Feedback leaflets and copies of the Passenger's Charter are available from all stations served by First TransPennine Express services or alternatively contact: Customer Relations, First TransPennine Express, ADMAIL 3878, Freepost, Manchester M1 9YB. Telephone: 0845 600 1671 Email: tpecustomer.relations@firstgroup.com

GX Gatwick Express GX

A member of the National Express Group plc

ADDRESS	207 Old Street, London EC1V 9NR Telephone: 0845 601 4873 Fax: 01603 214567 Website: www.gatwickexpress.com
MANAGING DIRECTOR	Mark Hopwood
RESERVATIONS AND TICKETS BY TELEPHONE	Reservations are not necessary on Gatwick Express services. For information and telesales please call 0845 850 1530. Tickets can also be purchased through the website - www.gatwickexpress.com
RESERVATION DETAILS	Gatwick Express is a high frequency service, so reservations are not required.
CATERING ON TRAINS	An at-seat trolley service of drinks and light refreshments is available throughout the day.
CYCLES	Cycles and other bulky items such as skis are conveyed free in the luggage van. There is plenty of space on board for other luggage – for further information call 0845 850 15 30.
LOST PROPERTY	Please call our Lost Property Office on 0845 850 15 30, select option 3.
TRAIN SERVICE UPDATE	Journey time is 30 minutes (35 minutes on Sundays). First Class and Express Class accommodation is available. From London Victoria at 0330, 0430, 0500 then every 15 minutes (xx15, xx30, xx45, xx00) until 0001, 0030. From Gatwick Airport at 0435, 0520, 0550 then every 15 minutes (xx05, xx20, xx35, xx50) until 0050, 0135. For current train information call 0845 850 15 30.
PENALTY FARES	Penalty fares are not charged on Gatwick Express services. Tickets may be bought on the train, or from our ticket offices.
DISABLED PERSON'S PROTECTION POLICY	Customers requiring assistance can book this prior to travel. Arrangements can be made by calling 0845 850 15 30, textphone available. It is advisable to give 24 hours notice of travel plans, although customers will be given assistance if they arrive at the stations without notice but please allow a little extra time.
CODE OF PRACTICE FOR COMMENTS, COMPLAINTS AND SUGGESTIONS	Initially comments or issues requiring immediate attention should be addressed to any member of Gatwick Express staff on the train or platforms. Additionally Customer Comments forms and our Passenger's Charter are available at Gatwick Express ticket offices. Alternatively you may write to the Gatwick Express Customer Relations, 52 Grosvenor Gardens, London SW1W 0AU.

Grand Central

GC

ADDRESS	Grand Central Railway Co. Ltd, 5 The Crescent, York YO24 1AW Telephone: 01904 633307 Fax: 01904 466066 Website: www.grandcentralrail.com Email: info@grandcentralrail.com
MANAGING DIRECTOR	Ian Yeowart
RESERVATIONS AND TICKETS BY TELEPHONE	Minimum transaction value: £10. Full details on the website.
RESERVATION DETAILS	All seats are reservable. No charge for reservations.
CATERING ON TRAINS	Full catering services are available. Full details on the website.
CYCLES	Normal cycles conveyed at no charge.
LOST PROPERTY	Contact the above address.
TRAIN SERVICE UPDATE	Please phone: 01904 633307 or check our website: www.grandcentralrail.com
PENALTY FARES	No penalty fares are applicable.
DISABLED PERSON'S PROTECTION POLICY	Available from the above address.
CODE OF PRACTICE FOR COMMENTS, COMPLAINTS AND SUGGESTIONS	Available from the above address.

HC Heathrow Connect HC

A joint venture between First Rail Division and BAA (Heathrow Express)

ADDRESS	Full postal address for customer correspondence Freepost RLRZ-TZXE-BYKY Heathrow Connect 3rd Floor 30 Eastbourne Terrace London W2 6LE Telephone: 0845 678 6975 Fax: 020 8745 6615 Website: www.heathrowconnect.com Email: queries@heathrowconnect.com
MANAGING DIRECTORS	*Heathrow Connect is a joint venture between First Great Western and BAA (Heathrow Express).* Andrew Haines (First Great Western) Brian Raven (Heathrow Express)
RESERVATIONS AND TICKETS BY TELEPHONE	Reservations are not neccessary. Tickets can be booked by telephone by ringing 0845 700 0125. Open 0700-2200 (0800-1900 Saturdays and Sundays). Allow 3 working days for delivery. A next day delivery can be arranged at £5 per transaction.
RESERVATION DETAILS	Heathrow Connect services are not reservable.
CATERING ON TRAINS	Catering on trains is not available.
CYCLES	Cycles are carried free of charge, but are not allowed on trains timed to arrive at London Paddington between 0745-0945, or depart London Paddington between 1630-1830 Mondays to Fridays. In the interest of safety and customer comfort, we reserve the right to limit the number of cycles at other times.
LOST PROPERTY	For property lost on a Heathrow Connect train or at London Paddington, call the Lost Property Office at Paddington on 0207 313 1514. For property left at Heathrow call the BAA Lost Property Office at Heathrow Central Station on 0208 745 7727. For property left at one of the intermediate stations contact the FGW Lost Property helpline on 0845 602 4304.
TRAIN SERVICE UPDATE	For current train information call 0845 678 6975. Website: www.heathrowconnect.com
PENALTY FARES	Penalty Fares apply at stations between Hayes & Harlington and Paddington (incl). Customers are liable to a Penalty Fare of £20 to the next station stop.
DISABLED PERSON'S PROTECTION POLICY	This is available from Customer Relations at the above address and telephone number.
CODE OF PRACTICE FOR COMMENTS, COMPLAINTS AND SUGGESTIONS	This is available from Customer Relations at the above address and telephone number.

HX Heathrow Express HX

ADDRESS

Customer contact:
Freepost RLXY-ETJG-XKZS
London W2 6LG
Telephone: 0845 600 1515
(call centre)

Corporate contact:
3rd Floor, 30 Eastbourne Terrace,
London W2 6LE or
FREEPOST LON 16331, Hounslow TW6 2BR
Telephone: 020 8750 6600
Fax: 020 8750 6615
Website: www.heathrowexpress.com

MANAGING DIRECTOR

Brian Raven

RESERVATIONS AND TICKETS BY TELEPHONE

Reservations are not necessary on Heathrow Express services. Tickets may be purchased in advance from Heathrow Express sales desks, ticket machines and from a range of other appointed outlets. For details call the Customer Care Line on 0845 600 15 15. (24-hour service – local rate call)

RESERVATION DETAILS

Heathrow Express operates a 'turn up and go' service and reservations are not necessary.

CATERING ON TRAINS

As the overall journey time is only 15 minutes, or 23 minutes to Terminal 4 (23 minutes to Terminal 5 from 27 March 2008), there is currently no catering on Heathrow Express services. (From 27 March 2008, Terminal 4 is served by a connecting 'shuttle' service at Heathrow Terminals 1, 2 & 3, taking a minimum 8 minutes extra).

CYCLES

Limited accommodation is available for cycles on Heathrow Express services, for passengers flying with their cycles from the airport. Heathrow Express reserve the right to limit the number of cycles conveyed on each train to no more than three at busy times. Cyclists not travelling onwards by air may use the service to and from Heathrow Terminals, subject to space being available for airline passengers. (Terminal 5 from 27 March 2008).

LOST PROPERTY

Property lost at Paddington station is collected by Network Rail, who can be contacted on 020 7313 1514. For items lost at Heathrow Airport call 020 8745 7727. For items lost on Heathrow Express trains, please ask our Customer Service Representatives, or alternatively write to: Lost Property, Heathrow Express Atrium, Heathrow Airport UB3 5AP.

TRAIN SERVICE UPDATE

For current information on train services please contact our customer care line on 0845 600 15 15.

PENALTY FARES

Penalty Fares do not apply on Heathrow Express services, therefore customers may join the train without having first purchased a ticket or authority to travel. Customer Service Representatives on every train will accept cash, debit and credit cards, for ticket purchase. Please note however for tickets purchased on board there is a £2.00 premium to pay. Only full fare tickets are available to purchase on board the train. (Disabled Railcard is accepted on board however).

DISABLED PERSON'S PROTECTION POLICY

Heathrow Express trains have been specially designed with the needs of the disabled in mind. Platforms at all our stations give level access into the trains and there is space for wheelchairs on all trains.

For further information on facilities for the disabled, call the Customer Care Line on 0845 600 15 15, or write to the Managing Director at the address at the top of this page.

CODE OF PRACTICE FOR COMMENTS, COMPLAINTS AND SUGGESTIONS

It is our aim to try and resolve any problems or grievances on the spot. All our Customer Service Representatives have a supply of comment forms and our Customer Care Line on 0845 600 15 15 can deal with problems over the telephone. If you wish to write with a suggestion or complaint, please write to the Managing Director at the address at the top of this page.

Please note that Heathrow Terminal 5 station opens on 27 March 2008.
Certain information is only applicable from this date, as stated

HT Hull Trains HT

A joint venture between First Rail Division and Renaissance Railways Ltd.

ADDRESS	Hull Trains Customer Services, Freepost RLYY-XSTG-YXCK, Premier House, Ferensway, Kingston Upon Hull, HU1 3UF. Telephone: 08456 76 99 05 Website: www.hulltrains.co.uk Email: customer.services@hulltrains.co.uk
MANAGING DIRECTOR	Mark Leving
RESERVATIONS AND TICKETS BY TELEPHONE	Hull Trains tickets can be booked in advance and seats reserved by ringing 08450 710 222 (0800-2200 weekdays, 0800-1830 weekends and Bank Holidays). Please allow five working days for delivery. Tickets on departure are available.
RESERVATION DETAILS	Seat reservations are free for First and Standard Class ticket holders. Season Ticket holders may reserve seats at a cost of £2 for First class and £1 for Standard class.
CATERING ON TRAINS	Hull Trains provides a buffet on all services, and a comprehensive catering package for First Class passengers. Catering is subject to availability and may be limited when services are disrupted by engineering works or Bank Holidays.
CYCLES	Cycles and tandems are carried free of charge, however, a reservation is compulsory. Please telephone 08450 710 222
LOST PROPERTY	Please contact Customer Services.
TRAIN SERVICE UPDATE	Available at www.hulltrains.co.uk, or by telephone on 08450 710222.
PENALTY FARES	Penalty fares are not in force on any Hull Trains Service
DISABLED PERSON'S PROTECTION POLICY	Available at: www.hulltrains.co.uk. Alternatively, a copy can be requested from Customer Services.
CODE OF PRACTICE FOR COMMENTS, COMPLAINTS AND SUGGESTIONS	Hull Trains' Passenger's Charter is available at www.hulltrains.co.uk. Alternatively, any comments, complaints or suggestions can be sent to Customer Services

Island Line

ADDRESS	Friars Bridge Court, 41–45 Blackfriars Road, London SE1 8NZ Telephone: 08700 005151 Fax: 020 7620 5177 Website: www.southwesttrains.co.uk Email: customerrelations@swtrains.co.uk
MANAGING DIRECTOR	Stewart Palmer
RESERVATIONS AND TICKETS BY TELEPHONE	Reservations are not required on Island Line services. Group travel information can be obtained by calling 01983 812591.
RESERVATION DETAILS	Reservations are not required.
CATERING ON TRAINS	There are no catering facilities on trains.
CYCLES	A maximum of 4 cycles may be carried in the Shanklin end of all trains at no extra charge. Island Line reserves the right to restrict the carriage of bicycles on any train when the safety and comfort of passengers or the punctuality of the train may be jeopardised. Implementation of this restriction is at the conductor's discretion.
LOST PROPERTY	All items of lost property are retained at Ryde Esplanade Ticket Office. If you have lost an item please telephone the Ticket Office on 01983 562492 (0900-1700 Daily). A charge may be applicable on collection.
TRAIN SERVICE UPDATE	For current train information, please call our helpline on 0845 6000 650 or visit www.island-line.com or www.southwesttrains.co.uk For details of Bank Holiday services see also the boxed note on the page immediately preceding Table 149.
PENALTY FARES	Penalty Fares are not in force on any Island Line services.
DISABLED PERSON'S PROTECTION POLICY	Island Line is committed to making travel easier for customers with disabilities including wheelchair users. For travel on the mainland/Island Line the telephone for special arrangements is 0845 6050440 (textphone 0845 6050441), giving 24 hours notice before travelling. For journeys wholly within Island Line, please telephone 01983 562492 giving 24 hours notice if assistance is required.
CODE OF PRACTICE FOR COMMENTS, COMPLAINTS AND SUGGESTIONS	Feedback leaflets are available at Ryde Esplanade or Shanklin Ticket Offices. Copies of South West Trains' Passenger's Charter are available from any staffed station or by writing to: Customer Service Centre, South West Trains, Overline House, Blechynden Terrace, Southampton SO15 1GW Telephone 0845 6000 650. Fax 023 8072 8187 Email: customerrelations@swtrains.co.uk The Passenger's Charter is also featured on the website www.southwesttrains.co.uk

London Midland

LM

A member of the Go-Ahead Group

ADDRESS

PO Box 4323
Birmingham B2 4JB
Telephone: 0121 634 2040
Website: www.londonmidland.com
Email: londonmidland@go-ahead-rail.com

MANAGING DIRECTOR

TBA

RESERVATIONS AND TICKETS BY TELEPHONE

Tickets can be booked in advance on-line at www.londonmidland.com or by ringing 0870 609 6060, 0800-2000 Monday to Sunday. £5 minimum transaction, please allow 5 days for delivery.

RESERVATION DETAILS

Group travel enquiries and bookings can also be made on 0870 609 6060. Seat reservations are only available on our Birmingham–Liverpool route but are all free of charge with a valid rail ticket.

CATERING ON TRAINS

A trolley service of hot drinks and light refreshments is available for all or part of the journey on our Birmingham–Liverpool services and are indicated by a trolley symbol in the timtable pages.

CYCLES

Cycles are carried free of charge on most off-peak services, however, advance reservations are required for our Birmingham–Liverpool services. Cycles cannot be conveyed on trains arriving in London Euston between 0700 and 0959 and departing London Euston between 1600 and 1859 on Mondays to Fridays (excluding Bank Holidays). Folding cycles, completely folded down, are regarded as accompanied luggage and carried free.

LOST PROPERTY

Enquiries can be made at your nearest staffed station or by ringing Customer Relations on 0121 634 2040.

TRAIN SERVICE UPDATE

Available from National Rail Enquiries on 08457 484950.

PENALTY FARES

A Penalty Fares system is in operation across the London Midland network. If you board a service from a staffed station without a valid ticket or permit to travel, you will be liable to a £20 penalty fare or twice the standard single fare to the next station whichever is the greater. On-train purchase arrangements are in place on our Watford Junction–St Albans Abbey and Bedford–Bletchley branch lines. Details of the scheme can be obtained by writing to Customer Relations at the address below.

DISABLED PERSON'S PROTECTION POLICY

Available from Customer Relations,
London Midland
PO Box 4323
Birmingham B2 4JB
Telephone: 0121 634 2040

CODE OF PRACTICE FOR COMMENTS, COMPLAINTS AND SUGGESTIONS

Available from Customer Relations at the above address.

LO London Overground LO

Operated by London Overground Rail Operations Ltd. (LOROL)
on behalf of Rail for London Ltd., a subsidiary of TfL

ADDRESS
125 Finchley Road
London NW3 6HY
Telephone: 0845 601 4867
Website: www.tfl.gov/overground
Email: info@lorol.co.uk

MANAGING DIRECTOR
Steve Murphy

RESERVATIONS AND TICKETS BY TELEPHONE
Tickets may be booked in advance and seats reserved on many long distance national rail services from most London Overground ticket offices. Oyster tickets may be purchased online from https://oyster.tfl.gov.uk

RESERVATION DETAILS
Seat reservations cannot be made for journeys on London Overground services.

CATERING ON TRAINS
Catering is not provided on London Overground services.

CYCLES
London Overground allows cycles on its trains and conveys them free of charge provided it is safe to do so. Due to space constraints, cycles are not permitted on services between Willesden Junction High Level and Gospel Oak and Blackhorse Road in either direction between 0800–1000 and 1630–1830. On the Euston to Watford Line cycles are not permitted on London Overground services timed to arrive at London Euston between 0700–1000 or depart London Euston between 1630 and 1900. These restrictions apply on Mondays to Fridays only. There are no restrictions on Saturdays, Sundays and Bank Holidays. Folding bicycles can be carried on any of our services at any time. Only one cycle is allowed per customer and this must be folded and within a limit of one cycle per vestibule area. Tandems and three-wheeled vehicles cannot be accommodated on any London Overground service. Cycles are not carried on buses that replace trains due to engineering work.

LOST PROPERTY
Please contact the TfL Lost Property Office at Baker Street on 0845 330 9882 or our Customer Services Team on 0845 601 4867.

TRAIN SERVICE UPDATE
Information about London Overground services and fares can be obtained by telephoning either:

- London Travel Information on 020 7222 1234 (Textphone 020 7918 3015)
- National Rail Enquiries 08457 48 49 50 (Textphone 08456 050 600, 0800-2000 daily)

A wide range of information about London Overground is also available from our website: www.tlf.gov/overground

PENALTY FARES
London Overground operates a Penalty Fares scheme. If you cannot produce, on request, a valid ticket for your entire journey or, when using Oyster to Pay as You Go, your Oyster card containing a record of the start of your Pay as You Go journey, you will be liable to pay a Penalty Fare of £20.00.

DISABLED PERSON'S PROTECTION POLICY
This can be obtained from our Customer Services Team at the above address.

CODE OF PRACTICE FOR COMMENTS, COMPLAINTS AND SUGGESTIONS
For a copy of the London Overground Passengers Charter please contact our Customer Services Team at the above address or ask for a copy at any London Overground station.

Merseyrail

A Serco/NedRailways company

ADDRESS	Rail House, Lord Nelson Street, Liverpool L1 1JF Telephone: 0151 702 2534 Fax: 0151 702 3074
MANAGING DIRECTOR	Patrick Verwer
RESERVATIONS AND TICKETS BY TELEPHONE	Tickets may be booked in advance and seats reserved from most Merseyrail stations for National Rail Services.
RESERVATION DETAILS	Not available.
CATERING ON TRAINS	Not available.
CYCLES	Cycles carried free of charge at any time, subject to sufficient space being available.
LOST PROPERTY	Please contact:- Station Supervisor Merseyrail Liverpool Central Station Ranelagh Street Liverpool L1 1JT Phone: 0151 702 2951
TRAIN SERVICE UPDATE	For current train information please call 08457 48 49 50. ***For details of Bank Holiday services see also the boxed note immediately preceding Table 103.***
PENALTY FARES	Please refer to notices displayed at stations for details of the penalty fare scheme in operation.
DISABLED PERSON'S PROTECTION POLICY	Available from:– Customer Relations Merseyrail Rail House, Lord Nelson Street, Liverpool L1 1JF Phone : 0151 702 2071 (Textphone 0870 0552 681) Fax : 0151 702 2413
CODE OF PRACTICE FOR COMMENTS, COMPLAINTS AND SUGGESTIONS	Available from above address

National Express East Coast (NXEC)

GR

ADDRESS

Freepost YO352, York YO1 6ZZ
Telephone: 08457 225 225
Fax: 01904 524 532
Website: www.youreastcoast.co.uk
Email: info@youreastcoast.co.uk

CHIEF EXECUTIVE OFFICER

To be advised

RESERVATIONS AND TICKETS BY TELEPHONE

Internet – purchase tickets via the internet 24 hours a day at www.youreastcoast.co.uk.
Self service ticket machines – at all NXEC stations. Purchase tickets for today or collect pre-booked tickets.
Telesales – call 08457 225 225 – open Sunday-Thursday 0800 – 2200, Friday and Saturday 0800 – 2000. The minimum transaction is £10. Please allow 7 days from the time of booking for tickets to reach you through the post.
Business Travel – corporate credit card and account holder bookings – call 08457 225 225 – open Monday–Friday 0800 – 1800.
Group Travel – discounts are available for groups of 10 or more people – call 08457 225 225 – open Monday–Friday 0900 – 1800.
Seat reservations can only be made in conjunction with ticket purchases.

RESERVATION DETAILS

Complimentary seat reservations can usually be made on any NXEC train up to ten weeks in advance. They are available to any ticket holder upon request, and are compulsory with some ticket types. Only one reservation can be made per single journey.

CATERING ON TRAINS

Catering is available on all NXEC trains. There is a Buffet available on every service. The Restaurant is available on selected services from Monday–Friday, which are highlighted in the timetable. Website: www.youreastcoast.co.uk/restaurant

CYCLES

Bicycles are welcome on NXEC at no extra cost. A reservation must be made and bookings are subject to space being available. Telephone 08457 225 225 or book at an NXEC ticket office. Folding cycles are welcome and no reservation is required for these.

LOST PROPERTY

If you lose something on an NXEC train or at a station please speak to a member of staff or contact us on 08457 225 225. Please note that charges are normally made for returning items of lost property. Please note that we are unable to forward items of lost property on train services.

TRAIN SERVICE UPDATE

Visit www.youreastcoast.co.uk or call National Rail Enquiries on 08457 48 49 50.

PENALTY FARES

NXEC does not operate a Penalty Fares scheme. However, you should always purchase a ticket valid for travel before you board an NXEC service as only full fare tickets are sold on our trains. The only exception being Disabled Railcard holders who will be sold appropriate discounted tickets on board.

DISABLED PERSON'S PROTECTION POLICY

A copy of our DPPP can be obtained free of charge from the address at the top of this page.

Our Assisted Travel Team can help you plan your journey and organise tickets, assistance and seat reservations. To ensure the best possible levels of assistance we recommend contacting us at least 24 hours before you intend to travel. Telephone 08457 225 444 or textphone 08457 202 067 (open 7 days a week 0800-2000).

CODE OF PRACTICE FOR COMMENTS, COMPLAINTS AND SUGGESTIONS

Our Passenger's Charter is available free from all NXEC stations or from our website www.youreastcoast.co.uk. All correspondence should be sent using the address at the top of this page.

NY North Yorkshire Moors Railway NY

(Operators of the 'Whitby Endeavour' steam service, and heritage services between Pickering and Grosmont)

ADDRESS	Pickering Station, Pickering, North Yorkshire, YO18 7AJ Telephone: 01751-472508 (Customer Services and Information) Fax: 01751-476048 Website: www.nymr.com Email: info@nymr.co.uk
GENERAL MANAGER	Philip Benham
RESERVATIONS AND TICKETS BY TELEPHONE	Telephone: 01751-472508 Hours of operation: 17 March to 28 October and other operating dates: 09:30-16:30 (Monday - Friday), 10:00-14:00 (Saturday and Sunday); All other times: 10:00-14:30 (Monday - Friday). At least 7 days should be allowed for receipt of tickets purchased by telephone.
RESERVATION DETAILS	Reservations are not required on normal services. They can be made for groups of 20 or more passengers and are required on North Yorkshire Moors Railways dining train services (between Pickering and Grosmont).
CATERING ON TRAINS	An at seat trolley service of drinks and snacks is provided on most trains.
CYCLES	Cycles and dogs are carried for a charge of £2 (subject to space being available).
LOST PROPERTY	Enquiries about lost property should be made to Pickering Station at the above, or by telephone (01751-472508).
TRAIN SERVICE UPDATE	Updated train service information on all North Yorkshire Moors Railway is available on the website (see address above). A 'talking timetable' is also available giving current details of all North Yorkshire Moors Railway services by telephoning 01751-473535.
PENALTY FARES	Penalty fares are not in force on any North Yorkshire Moors Railway service.
DISABLED PERSON'S PROTECTION POLICY	Available from the address above, or Pickering and Grosmont Stations.
CODE OF PRACTICE FOR COMMENTS, COMPLAINTS AND SUGGESTIONS	North Yorkshire Moors Railway welcomes comments from passengers. Comments/suggestion cards are available from stations and on-board staff, or alternatively please write to the General Manager. Details of the company's policy are available from the above address, or Pickering and Grosmont Stations.

Northern

A Serco-NedRailways company

ADDRESS

Northern Rail Ltd.,
Northern House
9 Rougier Street
York
YO1 6HZ
Telephone: 08700 005151
Website: www.northernrail.org

MANAGING DIRECTOR

Heidi Mottram

RESERVATIONS AND TICKETS BY TELEPHONE

Reservations and tickets are available from all local staffed stations.

RESERVATION DETAILS

Reservations are not required on Northern services.

For groups of 10 or more travelling on the Leeds-Settle-Carlisle line, blocks of seats will be reserved wherever possible. Telephone 0800 9800 766, between 0900 and 1700 on Mondays to Fridays to make a booking.

All accommodation on Northern trains is standard class.

CATERING ON TRAINS

On most Leeds-Settle-Carlisle services, food and drink can be purchased from the trolley which will pass through the train.

CYCLES

Up to two cycles can be carried on each service. This is subject to space being available, however, and cannot be booked in advance. For further details telephone 0845 000 0125.

LOST PROPERTY

Call 0870 602 3322, contact your nearest staffed station or write to Northern at the address below.

TRAIN SERVICE UPDATE

Information about Northern services and fares can be obtained by telephoning: **08457 48 49 50** or access the website on www.nationalrail.co.uk.

For more information on our services, please visit our website on www.northernrail.org

The latest information on train running is available by phoning TrainTracker™ from National Rail Enquiries on 0871 200 4950 or by texting TrainTracker™. Text to 484950.

PENALTY FARES

Penalty fares are not in force on any Northern service.

DISABLED PERSON'S PROTECTION POLICY

If you would like a copy of Northern's Policy or wish to arrange assistance for your journey, please phone: 0845 600 8008. (Textphone 0845 604 5608) or by writing to Customer Relations, Northern, PO Box 208, Leeds LS1 2BU, or email: assistance@northernrail.org.

CODE OF PRACTICE FOR COMMENTS, COMPLAINTS AND SUGGESTIONS

Please contact our Customer Helpline on 0845 000 0125, a textphone is available on 0845 604 5608. Alternatively you can write to us at: Customer Relations, Northern, PO Box 208, Leeds LS1 2BU.

If you would like a copy of the Northern Passenger's Charter, or Northern's Guide for Customers with Disabilities please contact our Customer Relations team.

'one'

A member of the National Express Group plc

ADDRESS	'one', Customer Services Centre, Grosvenor House, 112-114 Prince of Wales Road, Norwich, NR1 1NS Telephone: 0845 600 7245 Fax: 01603 214567 Website: www.onerailway.com Email: customer.relations@onerailway.com
MANAGING DIRECTOR	Andrew Chivers
RESERVATIONS AND TICKETS BY TELEPHONE	Tickets may be booked in advance by telephoning 0845 600 7245 between 0800 and 2200 Monday to Friday, from 0900 to 1800 at weekends and Bank Holidays.
RESERVATION DETAILS	'one' offers seat reservations free of charge (except for season ticket holders) on intercity services between London Liverpool Street and Norwich, and on direct services between London Liverpool Street and Lowestoft/Peterborough. On other 'one' routes as service frequency is high and seats are generally available off peak we do not operate a seat reservation service.
CATERING ON TRAINS	The Stansted Express services between Stansted Airport and London Liverpool Street and our intercity services from London to Norwich offer refreshments on most trains, providing hot and cold drinks, sandwiches and light snacks. In addition, full restaurant services are provided on some intercity services between London and Norwich.
CYCLES	We welcome passengers with bicycles on services where they can be safely accommodated. However, it is not possible to carry bicycles on some services, particularly during peak periods. For full details of when cycles cannot be carried or when reservations are required, please visit www.onerailway.com or call our Customer Services on 0845 600 7245.
LOST PROPERTY	In order to trace lost property, please contact 0845 600 7245 or email us at onelost.property@onerailway.com
TRAIN SERVICE UPDATE	For current train information check on line at www.onerailway.com, call our Customer Services on 0845 600 7245 or call our recorded information line on 020 7247 5488.
PENALTY FARES	'one' operates a Penalty Fares system for all journeys, except from certain specified stations and on designated 'paytrain' routes. Stations within the Penalty Fare area are identified by warning notices at each entrance. At these stations you must buy the ticket you require from the station ticket office or from self service ticket machines. If you cannot present a valid ticket for the journey you are making, you may be liable to pay a Penalty Fare of £20 or twice the single fare to the next station at which the train stops, whichever is the greater.
DISABLED PERSON'S PROTECTION POLICY	Available from: 'one', Customer Services Centre, Grosvenor House, 112-114 Prince of Wales Road, Norwich NR1 1NS or from www.onerailway.com. Customers who require assistance are recommended to book at least 24 hours in advance through our Customer Services Centre on 0800 028 2878 or Textphone 0845 606 7245.
CODE OF PRACTICE FOR COMMENTS, COMPLAINTS AND SUGGESTIONS	Available from: 'one', Customer Services Centre, Grosvenor House, 112-114 Prince of Wales Road, Norwich NR1 1NS or from www.onerailway.com. The 'one' Passenger's Charter is also available from the Customer Services Centre, from our staffed stations or on our website www.onerailway.com.

South West Trains

SW

ADDRESS

Friars Bridge Court, 41–45 Blackfriars Road, London SE1 8NZ
Telephone: 08700 005151 Fax: 020 7620 5177
Website: www.southwesttrains.co.uk
Email: customerrelations@swtrains.co.uk

CHAIRMAN

Ian Dobbs

MANAGING DIRECTOR

Stewart Palmer

RESERVATIONS AND TICKETS BY TELEPHONE

Tickets may be booked in advance and seats reserved by telephone, on the following number:
0845 6000 650.

Tickets may also be purchased via the South West Trains' website (see above). When ordering, please allow 5 working days for ticket delivery.

RESERVATION DETAILS

On many South West Trains' main line services (excluding peak time commuter services) seats can be reserved free of charge in First and Standard Class.

CATERING ON TRAINS

Catering on South West Trains is provided on those services marked with the symbol ☕ for all or part of the journey. Catering may be provided from a buffet area, at seat trolley service or a combination of both according to the route and time of day. All catering on South West Trains' services is provided in partnership with our contractors, Rail Gourmet (UK) Ltd. Comments on the service should be sent to the Customer Relations Department at the above address.

CYCLES

A limited number of cycles can be carried on most of our services except during the Monday to Friday peak periods. Restrictions apply on certain routes into and out of London Waterloo between 0715 and 1000 and between 1645 and 1900. At all times some services require advance reservations, as space is limited.

To obtain full details of South West Trains Cycling Policy and full details of routes and times when cycles are not carried visit www.southwesttrains.co.uk, pick up a leaflet from stations served by South West Trains or contact our Customer Service Centre at the address shown.

Cycles that can be folded to a size which allows them to be carried safely in the luggage racks on our services may be carried folded at all times.

For reasons of safety and comfort of our passengers, if the available identified cycle spaces on the train are already taken, the guard has the right to refuse to carry any further cycles on that train.

LOST PROPERTY

A lost property helpline is available between 0730-1900 Mondays to Fridays by calling 020 7401 7861

TRAIN SERVICE UPDATE

For current train information, please call our helpline on 0845 6000 650 or visit www.southwesttrains.co.uk

For details of Bank Holiday services see also the boxed note on the page immediately preceding Table 149.

PENALTY FARES

South West Trains has a duty to its fare paying passengers to ensure no-one travels for free. To this end South West Trains operates a penalty fares scheme across its network, with the only exceptions being stations west of Salisbury and at intermediate stations between Salisbury and Eastleigh via Chandlers Ford/Romsey.

Passengers travelling to and from stations within the penalty fares area without a valid ticket may be liable to a penalty of £20 or twice the single fare to the next station at which their train stops (whichever is the greater).

DISABLED PERSON'S PROTECTION POLICY

For a copy of this publication, please contact the Customer Service Centre at the address below.

Assistance for mobility impaired passengers can be arranged by telephoning 0800 5282 100 between 0800 - 2000 daily. Please give at least 24 hours notice.

A textphone facility is available on 0800 6920 792 (calls are charged at local rates).

CODE OF PRACTICE FOR COMMENTS, COMPLAINTS AND SUGGESTIONS

Copies of South West Trains' Passenger's Charter are available from any staffed station or by writing to:
Customer Service Centre, South West Trains, Overline House, Blechynden Terrace, Southampton SO15 1GW
Telephone 0845 6000 650. Fax 023 8072 8187
Email: customerrelations@swtrains.co.uk

The Passenger's Charter is also featured on the website www.southwesttrains.co.uk

SE Southeastern SE

ADDRESS

Southeastern Customer Services, PO Box 286, Plymouth PL4 6WU
Telephone: 0845 000 2222
Assisted Travel: 0800 783 4524
Fax: 0845 678 6976
Textphone: 0800 783 4548

Website: www.southeasternrailway.co.uk

This customer service centre is staffed 24 hours a day, seven days a week (closed Christmas Day). Comments and complaints are dealt with here by post, fax, and web as well as on the telephone.

MANAGING DIRECTOR

Charles Horton

RESERVATIONS AND TICKETS BY TELEPHONE

Group travel (parties of 10 persons or more) on Southeastern services must be booked at least seven days in advance so that space can be allocated. To order, go to www.southeasternrailway.co.uk, select tickets, then group tickets then complete the online form.

Customers can renew six monthly and annual season tickets online at www.southeasternrailway.co.uk or at local stations. Payment may be made by debit card and by most major credit and charge cards (NB customers must hold a rail photocard).

For new monthly season ticket purchases, please complete an application form available at local stations or online at www.southeasternrailway.co.uk.

A business and continental travel and reservations account service is available from Network Business Travel Service at First Floor Offices, Cannon Street Station, London EC4N 6AP.

To open an account telephone 020 7904 0500 or visit www.nbts.co.uk

RESERVATIONS

Reservations are only needed on Southeastern services for Group Travel and mobility impaired customers who require assistance.

CATERING ON TRAINS

A light refreshment trolley is available on trains marked with .

CYCLES

Cycles are not permitted on peak time services, which are those timed to arrive in London terminals between 0700 and 0959, and those timed to leave between 1600 and 1859. Folding cycles are permitted provided they are folded.

LOST PROPERTY

Customers who have lost property on a train or at a station should contact Southeastern Customer Services on 0845 000 2222.

TRAIN SERVICE UPDATE

For current train running information contact Southeastern Customer Services on 0845 000 2222

Information is also available from national and local radio station travel updates on Ceefax page 433, and from our website: www.southeasternrailway.co.uk, select plan my journey.

PENALTY FARES

Please check notices displayed at stations for details of any penalty fares or other revenue protection systems in operation on Southeastern services.

DISABLED PERSON'S PROTECTION POLICY

Copies of the Disabled Person's Protection Policy are available from Southeastern Customer Services.

If you have any special needs and would like help with planning your journey anywhere in Great Britain please call 0800 783 4524 or use the Textphone 0800 783 4548 - open 24 hours a day.

The Southeastern Assisted Travel team will offer advice and make any special arrangements you need. If at least 24 hours' notice can be given, this will be very much appreciated.

CODE OF PRACTICE FOR COMMENTS, COMPLAINTS AND SUGGESTIONS

Southeastern Passengers' Charter leaflets are available at any Southeastern sales point or Southeastern Customer Services at the address shown above.

Southern

SN

ADDRESS	Southern Customer Services, PO Box 277, Tonbridge TN9 2ZP Telephone: 08451 27 29 20 (Customer Services) Fax: 08451 27 29 30 (Customer Services) Website: www.southernrailway.com
MANAGING DIRECTOR	Chris Burchell
RESERVATIONS AND TICKETS BY TELEPHONE	It is not necessary to pre-book on Southern services.
RESERVATION DETAILS	Reservations are not required, as Southern offer a high frequency train service.
CATERING ON TRAINS	A light refreshment of food and drinks is available on trains marked with ⚲.
CYCLES	A limited number of cycles are carried on all services except on trains due to arrive into London and Brighton on Mondays to Fridays between 0700 and 1000, or due to depart from London Stations and Brighton between 1600 and 1900 Mondays to Fridays.
LOST PROPERTY	Please call Southern Customer Services on 08451 27 29 20.
TRAIN SERVICE UPDATE	For current train information call Customer Services on 08451 27 29 20 or check our website at www.southernrailway.com
PENALTY FARES	Southern operate a Penalty Fares Scheme on all routes. You must buy a valid ticket (or permit to travel) for your journey before boarding a train. If you do not have a valid ticket or permit to travel, you may have to pay a Penalty Fare of £20.00 or twice the single fare, whichever is the greater. Please pick up a Penalty Fare leaflet from a staffed station for your information.
DISABLED PERSON'S PROTECTION POLICY	Available from Southern Customer Services at P.O. Box 277, Tonbridge TN9 2ZP. Disabled and Special needs assistance on 0800 138 1016; minicom/ textphone - 0800 138 1018; Fax - 0800 138 1017.
CODE OF PRACTICE FOR COMMENTS, COMPLAINTS AND SUGGESTIONS	Write to Southern Customer Services at the above address. Copies of Southern Passenger's charter are available from any staffed stations. You can also obtain a copy by contacting Customer Services or from Southern's website.

VT Virgin Trains VT

The trading name of West Coast Trains Ltd

ADDRESS	Virgin Trains, 85 Smallbrook Queensway, Birmingham B5 4HA Telephone: 0845 000 8000 Textphone: 0121 654 7528 Website: www.virgintrains.com Email: customer.relations@virgintrains.co.uk
CHIEF EXECUTIVE	Tony Collins
MANAGING DIRECTOR	Chris Gibb
RESERVATIONS AND TICKETS BY TELEPHONE	Buy tickets for Virgin Trains and any other train company in Great Britain on the internet at www.virgintrains.com or by calling 08457 222 333 - between 0800 and 2200 7 days a week. If you have a disability or have specific needs and wish to arrange assistance on your journey call the Virgin Trains JourneyCare service on 08457 44 33 66 (Textphone 08457 44 33 67) between 0800 and 2200 every day except Christmas Day or Boxing Day.
RESERVATION DETAILS	You are strongly advised to make a seat reservation in advance. Reservations can be made for the Quiet Zone carriage, where customers should refrain from using mobile phones or creating unnecessary noise. On routes to and from London, Standard Class Quiet Zone is in coach A and in coach H for First Class. On other routes, Quiet Zone is located in Standard Class, coach F. Seat reservations are free of charge.
CATERING ON TRAINS	In First Class on a Pendolino from Monday to Friday customers can enjoy a selection of hot or cold snacks throughout the day, including a cooked breakfast on many morning peak services. In addition, Fairtrade tea, Fairtrade coffee, soft drinks and alcoholic drinks (alcohol not served with breakfast services) and a newspaper are served at seat throughout the day. In First Class on Voyager from Monday to Friday customers can enjoy complimentary light refreshments on all trains including Fairtrade tea, Fairtrade coffee, soft drinks and a newspaper with an at-seat service available. In Standard Class, we have a wide range of snacks and sandwiches, Fairtrade teas, fresh ground Fairtrade coffee, soft and alcoholic drinks and a selection of non-food items available at our onboard shop. The shop is generally open throughout. Pendolinos offer an at-seat trolley service to standard class customers on Mondays to Fridays. For more information about our onboard service pick up a copy of Travelling with Virgin Trains.
CYCLES	Subject to availability of space cycles can be carried on all trains. Most trains can carry 3 cycles, and on journeys to and from London Euston, Pendolinos can carry tandems (however, tandems are not carried on Voyager services). An advance reservation is required for all journeys.
LOST PROPERTY	Call Customer Relations on 0845 000 8000 – 0830 to 2015 Mondays to Fridays, 0900 to 1600 Saturdays, answerphone available at all other times.
TRAIN SERVICE UPDATE	Details of any disruption to services or weekend engineering work are summarised on BBC Ceefax and on BBCi on digital TV. Details of Engineering work can also be found at www.virgintrains.com.
PENALTY FARES	Penalty Fares are not applicable on any Virgin Trains service.
DISABLED PERSON'S PROTECTION POLICY	Our Customer Relations Manager (at the address above) will be pleased to supply a free copy of the Disabled Person's Protection Policy. It can also be downloaded at www.virgintrains.com. For information on station accessibility and to arrange special help please contact Virgin Trains JourneyCare (details above).
CODE OF PRACTICE FOR COMMENTS, COMPLAINTS AND SUGGESTIONS	We want you to tell us what you think of our service, good or bad. A copy of our Code of Practice for handling comments, complaints and suggestions together with Virgin Trains Passenger's Charter is available free on request from our Customer Relations Manager at the above address.

West Coast Railway Company

WR

(Operators of the Fort William - Mallaig "Jacobite" Steam Service)

ADDRESS	Jesson Way, Carnforth, Lancashire LA5 9UR Telephone: 01524 737751/737753 Fax: 01524 735518 Website: www.steamtrain.info or www.wcrc.co.uk Email: jacobite@wcrc.co.uk
GENERAL MANAGER	Mrs Pat Marshall
COMMERCIAL MANAGER	James Shuttleworth
RESERVATIONS AND TICKETS BY TELEPHONE	Advance bookings can be made, by post (enclose SAE) to the Carnforth Office (address above) or by telephone on 01524 737751/737753, during normal office hours. Credit cards accepted. 'Jacobite' bookings can also be made in person at the Booking Office, Fort William Station.
RESERVATION DETAILS	Phone 01524 737751/737753
CATERING ON TRAINS	A buffet service, serving hot and cold drinks and cold snacks is available on all trains.
CYCLES	Cycles carried free-of-charge subject to space.
LOST PROPERTY	Telephone: 01524 737751/737753
PENALTY FARES	Penalty fares are not in force on any West Coast Railway Co. service.
TRAIN SERVICE UPDATE	For current train information please phone 08457 48 49 50.
DISABLED PERSON'S PROTECTION POLICY	Available from the above address.
CODE OF PRACTICE FOR COMMENTS, COMPLAINTS AND SUGGESTIONS	West Coast Railway Co. welcomes comments on services provided. Write to Carnforth office (address above).

WS Wrexham & Shropshire

ADDRESS	Great Central House, Marylebone Station, Melcombe Place, London NW1 6JJ Telephone: 0845 260 5233 Website: www.wrexhamandshropshire.co.uk Email: info@wrexhamandshropshire.co.uk
MANAGING DIRECTOR	Andy Hamilton
RESERVATIONS AND TICKETS BY TELEPHONE	Wrexham & Shropshire tickets can be bought in advance and seats reserved. Full details will be available on the Wrexham & Shropshire website www.wrexhamandshropshire.co.uk in advance of the launch of train services.
RESERVATION DETAILS	All First and Standard Class seats are reservable at no charge.
CATERING ON TRAINS	Wrexham & Shropshire provides a comprehensive range of catering on all services. Full details will be available on the website www.wrexhamandshropshire.co.uk in advance of the launch of train services.
CYCLES	Cycles are carried free of charge.
LOST PROPERTY	Please contact the above address.
TRAIN SERVICE UPDATE	Available at www.wrexhamandshropshire.co.uk
PENALTY FARES	Wrexham & Shropshire does not operate a penalty fares policy.
DISABLED PERSON'S PROTECTION POLICY	Please contact the above address.
CODE OF PRACTICE FOR COMMENTS, COMPLAINTS AND SUGGESTIONS	Please contact the above address.

Wrexham & Shropshire services are expected to start operating in Spring 2008.
Please visit the Wrexham & Shropshire website www.wrexhamandshropshire.co.uk for updated information, or call National Rail Enquiries on 08457 48 49 50.

Network Rail

NR

ADDRESS	40 Melton Street, London NW1 2EE Telephone: 020 7557 8000 Fax: 020 7557 9000 Website: www.networkrail.co.uk
CHIEF EXECUTIVE	Iain Coucher

Network Rail is responsible for operating 17 major stations, indicated in the index by the code **NR**. Details of facilities provided, including the Disabled Peoples Protection Policy, are obtainable from the Network Rail Station Manager at the following station addresses:–

London Bridge	Network Rail Offices, Platform 14, London Bridge Station, Station Approach, London SE1 9SP.
London Cannon Street	Cannon Street Station, Cannon Street, London EC4N 6AP.
London Charing Cross	Network Rail Offices, Charing Cross Station, The Strand, London WC2 5HS.
London Euston	Room 430, Stephenson Room, East Colonnade, Euston, London NW1 2RT.
London Fenchurch Street	Network Rail Office, Fenchurch Place, London EC3M 4AJ.
London Kings Cross	Room 101, West Side Offices, Kings Cross Station, London N1 9AP.
London Liverpool Street	Ashbee House, Platform 10, Liverpool Street Station, London EC2M 7QH.
London Paddington	Room B115, Tournament House, Paddington Station, London W2 1FT.
London Victoria	3rd Floor, Kent Side Offices, Victoria Station, London SW1V 1JU.
London Waterloo	CP3-1-J General Offices, Waterloo Station, London SE1 8SW.
Birmingham New Street	Reception, Network Rail Offices, Station Forecourt, Birmingham New Street Station, Birmingham B2 4ND.
Edinburgh Waverley	Room 255, North Block, Waverley Station, Edinburgh EH1 1BB.
Gatwick Airport	Gatwick Station Manager, Gatwick Airport Station, Gatwick Airport, Sussex RH6 0RD.
Glasgow Central	Glasgow Central Station, Gordon Street, Glasgow G1 3SL.
Leeds City	Room 405, Administration Block, Leeds City Station, Leeds LS1 4DY.
Manchester Piccadilly	Room 622, Tower Block, Piccadilly Station, Manchester M60 7RA.
Liverpool Lime Street	Station Manager, The Barrier Line Building, Liverpool Lime Street Station, Liverpool L1 1JF.

Staffed Left Luggage facilities, offering maximum security, are available at all Network Rail Stations.

If you wish to raise any issue concerning the rail infrastructure or the 17 Major Stations operated by Network Rail (excluding matters concerning the running of trains or ticket purchase) please call the national 24 hour Helpline:- **08457 11 41 41**

Other Addresses

Department for Transport

Great Minster House, 76 Marsham Street, London SW1P 4DR

Telephone: 020 7944 8300

Email: rail@dft.gsi.gov.uk

Office of Rail Regulation

One Kemble Street, London WC2B 4AN
Telephone: 020 7282 2000 Fax: 020 7282 2040

Chairman: Chris Bolt

The main areas of the Regulator's statutory functions are:

- the issue, modification and enforcement of licences to operate trains, networks, stations and light maintenance depots;
- the approval of agreements for access by operators of railway assets to track, stations and light maintenance depots;
- the enforcement of domestic competition law; and consumer protection including a duty under the Railways Act 1993 in relation to the protection of the interests of users of railway services, including the disabled.

Publications are available from:

Sue MacSwan, The Library, ORR, 1 Waterhouse Square, 138–142 Holborn, London EC1N 2TQ (Telephone: 020 7282 2001). Email: rail.library@orr.gsi.gov.uk

Association of Train Operating Companies (ATOC)

3rd Floor, 40 Bernard Street, London WC1N 1BY. Telephone: 020 7841 8000

Director General: George Muir

ATOC represents the interests of most of the national and international passenger Train Operating Companies whose services are shown in this timetable. It manages a range of network services, products and responsibilities on behalf of these train operators including:

- the National Rail Conditions of Carriage (the passenger's contract with the train operators)
- the National Rail Enquiry Service
- the licensing of rail appointed travel agents
- national Railcards, the London Travelcard and Network Railcard.

London Underground Limited

55 Broadway, London SW1H 0BD Telephone: 020 7222 5600

Responsible for the operation of stations indicated in the index by the code **LT**

How to Cross London

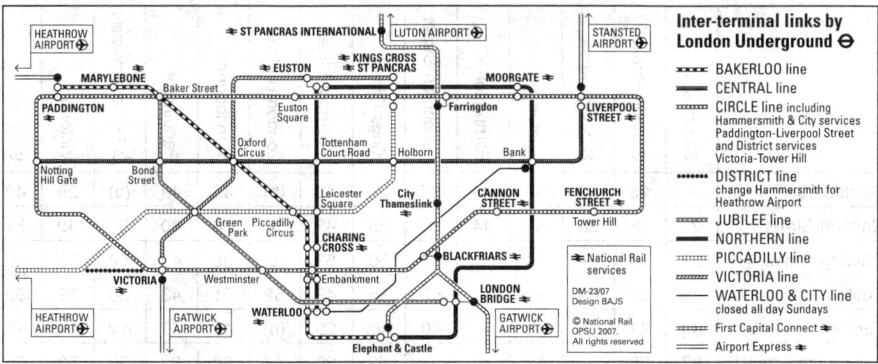

Introduction

The time taken to travel between London's stations will vary from journey to journey dependent on distance, mode of transport, time of day and the need to change en route. The quickest way to cross London is usually by the Underground network with frequent services operating between the following hours*:

- 0530 to 0015 on Monday to Friday
- 0630 to 0115 on Saturday
- 0700 to 0001 on Sunday

(* Times shown are approximate)

Buses also link many of London's main terminal stations including an extensive network of Night Bus services.

Ticket & Fares

Rail tickets for journeys routed via London are valid for transfer by London Underground or First Capital Connect services between London terminal stations, and other designated interchange stations* appropriate to the route of the through journey being made, at no extra cost. For example a Brighton to Leeds ticket is valid on London Underground services from Victoria to Kings Cross (Victoria Line), or alternatively on First Capital Connect services to St Pancras International. A Chelmsford to Southampton ticket is valid on London Underground services to Waterloo via either Liverpool Street (Circle Line) or Stratford (Jubilee Line).

(*NB. check before you travel which cross London routes your ticket is valid for before you travel. A break of journey is permitted at an intermediate Underground station, but a further ticket must be purchased in order to continue the journey)

London's Fare Zones – National Rail, Underground and Docklands Light Railway (DLR) stations within the Greater London area are in one of six Fare Zones. Single and return tickets are available for through journeys to and from all Underground and DLR stations with prices determined by the number of zones crossed or travelled through.

A range of day and longer period Travelcards are also available and provide unlimited travel on National Rail, London Underground, Docklands Light Railway and Croydon Tramlink services within the Fare Zones for which they are valid. All Travelcards, irrespective of the zones for which they are issued, can also be used on any London bus displaying this sign ⊖.

For information on ticket prices and availability contact your local staffed station, call National Rail Enquiries anytime on **08457 48 49 50** (Textphone **0845 60 50 600**), or visit www.nationalrail.co.uk.

More detailed information about London's Underground and Bus services, also Docklands Light Railway and Croydon Tramlink is available anytime from London Travel Information on **020 7222 1234** (textphone **020 7918 3015**) or visit **www.tfl.gov.uk**.

First Capital Connect

First Capital Connect operates fast, direct services from Bedford, Luton and St Albans via Central London to East Croydon, Gatwick Airport and Brighton and stopping trains between Luton, St Albans, North London, the City, Streatham, Wimbledon and Sutton. There are nine Central London First Capital Connect stations with Underground connections. First Capital Connect connects with East Midlands Trains at Luton, Luton Airport Parkway and Bedford – see Tables 52 and 53.

London Overground

Trains run daily between Willesden Junction, Kensington Olympia, West Brompton and Clapham Junction on Mondays to Sundays – see Table 186.

Southern Services

Direct services are provided from Brighton, Gatwick Airport and South London to Watford Junction. These services also call at West Brompton and Kensington Olympia. Connections for Birmingham and the West Midlands, also for North West destinations (including Manchester, Liverpool and Preston) and Glasgow are available from Watford Junction. Full details are shown on tables 66 and 186. Frequent connections from Clapham Junction or East Croydon for the rest of the Southern Network are available.

Cross London Transfer Times (in minutes)

	Blackfriars	Cannon Street	Charing Cross	Euston	Farringdon	Fenchurch Street*	Kings Cross	Liverpool Street	London Bridge	Marylebone	Paddington	St. Pancras International †	Victoria	Waterloo
Blackfriars	–	23	23	49	(b)	27	(b)	40	(b)	45	49	(b)	29	40
Cannon Street	23	–	34	60	44	30	55	43	(a)	56	60	58	40	51
Charing Cross	23	34	–	44	n/a	38	50	51	(a)	38	43	52	32	(a)
Euston	49	60	44	–	n/a	57	35	43	52	51	43	38	39	53
Farringdon	(b)	44	n/a	n/a	–	40	n/a	29	(b)	45	39	n/a	n/a	n/a
Fenchurch Street*	27	30	38	57	40	–	52	26	47	68	60	52	53	56
Kings Cross	(b)	55	50	35	n/a	52	–	41	50	50	45	30	41	55
Liverpool Street	40	43	51	43	29	26	41	–	49	56	55	41	57	62
London Bridge	(b)	(a)	(a)	52	(b)	47	50	49	–	58	62	60	n/a	(a)
Marylebone	45	56	38	51	45	68	50	56	58	–	32	53	43	47
Paddington	49	60	43	43	39	60	45	55	62	32	–	45	47	51
St. Pancras International †	(b)	58	52	38	n/a	52	30	41	60	53	45	–	41	61
Victoria	29	40	32	39	n/a	53	41	57	n/a	43	47	41	–	47
Waterloo	40	51	(a)	53	n/a	56	55	62	(a)	47	51	61	47	–

All times are based on use of London Underground services and are shown as a guide only – extra time should be allowed during the early morning/late evening and on Sundays.

* Tower Hill Underground station
† An additional 35 minutes should be allowed for Eurostar Connections
(a) Direct train services available (operated by Southeastern)
(b) Direct train services available (operated by First Capital Connect)
n/a Transfer not likely to be required as part of a through rail journey.

Some other useful transfers

If your journey requires a transfer between any of the following pairs of stations, you should allow a margin of at least the number of minutes shown when planning connections. All transfers are assumed to be by foot unless otherwise stated.

Abercynon North – South	10
Ash Vale – North Camp	19
Bicester North – Town	30
Burnley Central – Manchester Rd	25
Burscough Bridge – Junction	20
Canterbury East – West	25
Catford – Bridge	10
Clock House – Kent House	15
Dorchester South – West	15
Dorking – Deepdene	9
Edenbridge – Town	20
Enfield Chase – Town	29
Falkirk High – Grahamston	44
Farnborough Main – North	24
Forest Gate – Wanstead Park	13
Gainsborough Central – Lea Rd	33
Hackney Central – Downs	14
Harringay – Green Lanes	14
Heath High Level – Low Level	10
Hertford North – East	34
Maidstone Barracks – East	16
New Mills Central – Newtown	25
Penge East – West	19
Seven Sisters – South Tottenham	14
Southend Central – Victoria	17
Upper Warlingham – Whyteleafe	10
Walthamstow Central – Queens Rd	14
West Hampstead – Thameslink	11
Windsor & Eton Central – Riverside	14
Yeovil Junction – Pen Mill	30*

* Connection between Yeovil Junction and Yeovil Pen Mill is assumed by taxi (at passengers own expense)

Tyne and Wear Metro

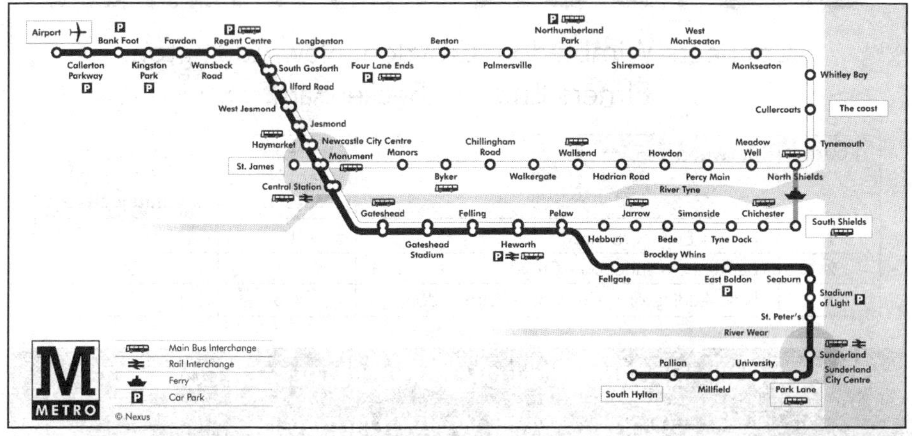

Summary Timetable

Route	Service Frequencies				
	Mon-Fri Peak	Mon-Fri Daytime	Saturday Daytime	Sunday Daytime	Evenings Daily
Airport - Monument - Pelaw - Sunderland - South Hylton	12 mins	12 mins	12 mins	15 mins	15 mins
St.James - Whitley Bay - Monument - Pelaw - South Shields	12 mins	12 mins	12 mins	15 mins	15 mins

First and last Metro trains to and from Newcastle Central Station

From Central Station to:	First Train Mon-Fri	First Train Saturday	First Train Sunday	Last Train Daily
South Hylton	0523	0524	0620	2305
Sunderland	0519	0519	0620	2320
Pelaw	0519	0519	0617	2343
South Shields	0521	0522	0635	2328
Tynemouth (via Benton)	0548	0557	0656	2337
Whitley Bay (via North Shields)	0548 ❑	0557 ❑	0656 ❑	2322 ❑
Airport	0551	0619	0641	2329

❑ Change at Monument

To Central Station from:	First Train Mon-Fri	First Train Saturday	First Train Sunday	Last Train Daily
South Hylton	0604	0605	0704	2346
Sunderland	0549	0552	0714	2356
Pelaw	0540	0547	0633	0015
South Shields	0549	0552	0703	2356
Tynemouth (via Benton)	0533	0538	0633	2311
Whitley Bay (via North Shields)	0542 ❑	0552 ❑	0639 ❑	2304 ❑
Airport	0544	0543	0627	2312

❑ Change at Monument

Ticketing

- Interchangeable tickets for both Rail and Metro are available between Sunderland and Newcastle Central Station.
- Tyne and Wear operates a Penalty Fare policy.

Information

For all travel information call

traveline
public transport info
0870 608 2 608
north east

For timetable information visit **www.nexus.org.uk**

CROYDON TRAMLINK

Connects Wimbledon, Croydon, New Addington, Elmers End and Beckenham.

Route	Between	Monday – Saturday daytime	Evenings 1900 - 2400 & Sunday all day
1	Elmers End - Croydon	10	30
2	Beckenham Junction - Croydon	10	30
3	New Addington – Croydon – Wimbledon	7-8	15

FOR FULL INFORMATION ON SERVICES, PLEASE CONTACT:

On the web: **www.tfl.gov.uk**

London Travel Information: **020 7222 1234**

Tramlink enquiries: **020 8681 8300**

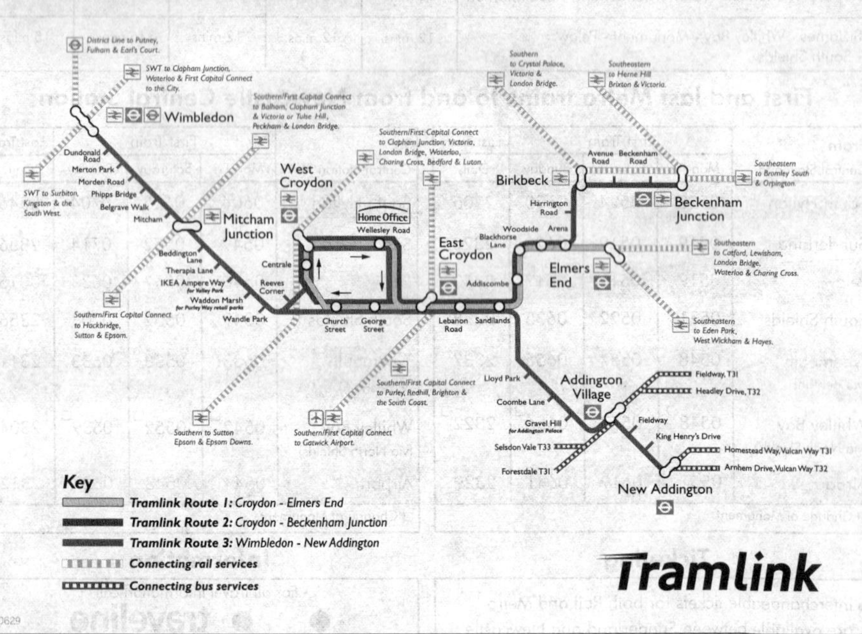

Airport Links

Aberdeen Airport

Dyce station is situated close to Aberdeen Airport and is served by services between Aberdeen and Inverness. Taxis are available - journey time approx. 5 minutes. In addition there are several through trains daily to and from Glasgow and Edinburgh (see Table 229). Journey time by taxi is 20 minutes approx. from Aberdeen Station.

Birmingham International Airport

Birmingham Airport is alongside Birmingham International station. The free Air-Rail Link transit system operates to the passenger terminals about every 2 minutes with a journey time of less than 2 minutes. Birmingham International station is served by direct trains from London Euston, Derby, Edinburgh, Glasgow, Manchester, Newcastle, Oxford, Sheffield, Southampton, York and other principal towns and cities. In addition a frequent service operates between Birmingham New Street and Birmingham International providing connections at Birmingham New Street to and from all parts of the country. (See Tables 65, 66, 68, 71, 74 and 116). Regular buses operated by Travel West Midlands (966) also run from Solihull station (see Tables 71 and 115). The journey time is approximately 20 minutes and through ticketing is available. Solihull is served by Chiltern Railways services from London Marylebone, Gerrards Cross, Beaconsfield, High Wycombe, Princes Risborough, Haddenham & Thame Parkway, Bicester North, Banbury, Leamington Spa and Warwick and by London Midland local services.

Bristol International Airport

First runs a frequent coach service from directly outside Bristol Temple Meads station. It departs daily at 0525 then every 15 minutes to 1955, then every 30 minutes to 2255. Return services start at 0615, then every 15 minutes until 2000, then every 30 minutes until 2345. Journey time is 25 minutes depending on traffic. Further information from Traveline on **0871 200 22 33** or visit **www.traveline.org.uk.**

Cardiff International Airport

The airport is served by bus service X45 and is operated by Shamrock on Mon-Sat and First on Sundays. This operates on an hourly daytime frequency to/from Barry station, Monday to Saturday. Journey time is 7 minutes. Cardiff bus service (X91) provides an hourly daytime service from Cardiff Central Bus Station (stop E1) direct to Cardiff International Airport. Services run every hour Monday to Saturday daytimes and every 2 hours on Sundays. Journey time is 30 minutes and through ticketing is available from any rail station.

The airport is served by a free bus link from Rhoose Cardiff International Airport Station to/from the airport operated by Arriva Trains Wales. Full details of the timetable and further information can be obtained from Traveline on **0871 200 22 33** or visit **www.traveline.org.uk.**

Coventry Airport

Coventry Airport is accessible from Coventry rail station by a scheduled bus service (No. 737). A combined discounted bus and rail ticket can be purchased for travel to the airport.

For bus times call **0871 200 22 33** or visit **www.traveline.org.uk.**

Durham Tees Valley Airport

Darlington Railway station is situated just 5 miles away. Sky Express Tees Valley is a frequent dedicated shuttle bus which operates between Darlington Railway station and the airport terminal building, between 0700 and 2000. The service is free to airline passengers. Visit **www.durhamteesvalleyairport.com**.

East Midlands Airport

Bus services operate from Derby, Loughborough and Nottingham stations to East Midlands Airport. Journey times are approx 35 mins from Derby, 30 mins from Loughborough and Nottingham. A combined discounted bus and rail ticket is available from any station for travel to East Midlands Airport.

Derby is served by CrossCountry and East Midlands Trains direct services from Central and Southern England, South Wales, South Yorkshire and North Eastern England.

Loughborough is served by East Midlands Trains services from Leicester, London and the Home Counties.

Nottingham is served by East Midlands Trains services from London, North Western England, Lincolnshire, East Anglia and the West Midlands.

Combined rail and discounted bus tickets are available when travelling from Nottingham, Loughborough and Derby Stations.

For details of bus times call **01509 815637** or visit **www.kinchbus.co.uk** for Derby and Loughborough services, call **0115 950 6070** or visit **www.skylink.co.uk** for Nottingham services.

Edinburgh Airport

A frequent bus service (No. 100) links Edinburgh Waverley and Haymarket stations with Edinburgh Airport. Journey time is approx. 25 minutes. Stagecoach operate a 747 service half hourly during the day, hourly evenings and Sundays between Inverkeithing and Edinburgh Airport. Through ticketing is available. For further information telephone **0131 555 6363**.

Exeter International Airport

Stagecoach operates an hourly daytime service (56 Monday - Saturday, 379 Sundays) from Exeter St. Davids station forecourt direct to Exeter Airport. For more information call Traveline on **0871 200 22 33** or visit **www.traveline.org.uk.**

Airport Links

Glasgow Airport

Regular direct bus services are available to and from Glasgow Airport from the city centre (Central/Queen Street), Paisley Gilmour Street and Partick stations from early morning to late evening daily. Through bus/rail tickets are available between any station and Glasgow Airport via the Paisley Gilmour Street bus link, city centre bus link and First Glasgow bus service via Partick.

For further information on these services please contact the Strathclyde Passenger Transport Travel Centre at Glasgow Airport, on **0141 887 1111** or **0141 848 4330.**

Leeds Bradford International Airport

Leeds Bradford International Airport is located to the north of the cities of Bradford and Leeds, to the south of the spa town of Harrogate and to the west of the historic city of York. For more information on Leeds Bradford International Airport visit **www.lbia.co.uk**

From Leeds a direct bus service, MetroConnect 757, operates half hourly throughout the day Mondays to Saturdays (hourly early mornings, evenings and Sundays) every day from Stand S8 from outside Leeds Rail Station (Leeds Station Interchange). The journey time is approximately 40 minutes. Through ticketing is available.

From Bradford a half hourly direct bus service, MetroConnect 747, operates throughout the day Mondays to Saturdays (hourly evenings and Sundays) from Bradford Interchange and Forster Square rail stations. The journey time from Bradford is approximately 40 minutes. Through ticketing is available with a PlusBus ticket.

From Harrogate a direct bus service, Bus2Jet 767, operates daily from Harrogate, from Stand 11 in the Bus Station, to the airport. The journey time from Harrogate is approximately 35 minutes. Through ticketing is available with a PlusBus ticket.

From York an hourly direct express coach service operates daily from outside York Rail Station to the airport. The journey time from York is approximately 55 minutes. For more information telephone **01904 883 000** or visit **www.yorkaircoach.com**

For further information on the above services please telephone MetroLine **0113 245 7676** or visit **www.wymetro.com**.

Liverpool John Lennon Airport

The airport is located to the south of the city centre. A direct bus service operates between Lime Street, Moorfields and James Street stations to the airport seven days a week. Buses run every 30 minutes between 0600 & 0100 hours from the Liverpool City Centre Stations to the Airport, and between 0515 and 0015 from the Airport to the Liverpool City Centre Stations. Journey time is approximately 45 minutes. In addition regular bus services operate between Liverpool John Lennon Airport and the new Liverpool South Parkway station; journey time is 15 minutes. Liverpool South Parkway is served by direct services from North, South and East Liverpool, Manchester, Warrington, Southport, Crewe, Stafford, Wolverhampton and Birmingham. For further information please contact **0871 200 22 33,** or visit **www.traveline.org.uk**.

London City Airport

London City Airport is located in London's Docklands. There are no National Rail services direct to the airport. However the Docklands Light Railway (DLR) airport link operates from Canning Town station on the Jubilee Line of London Underground. It takes you directly to the terminal building. Journey time is just 6 minutes from Canning Town to the airport, and the DLR trains run every 7-10 minutes.

If you are travelling to or from Central London the Jubilee Line has direct connections with National Rail at London Waterloo, London Bridge, West Ham and Stratford (east London). DLR operates from Bank and Tower Gateway stations.

For further information on London City Airport telephone **020 7646 0088** or visit **www.londoncityairport.com**.

London Gatwick Airport

Gatwick has its own railway station underneath the South Terminal. Access to the North Terminal is via a free transit. Direct train services also serve many parts of the country.

Airport to/from London

Gatwick Express operate a dedicated non-stop service every 15 minutes throughout the day to/from London (Victoria) and Gatwick Airport (See Table 186).

Southern provides frequent trains throughout the day and hourly throughout the night between London Victoria and Gatwick Airport (See Table 186). Frequent train services also run between Gatwick Airport and stations throughout Sussex, Surrey and parts of Hampshire and Kent.

First Capital Connect operate direct services throughout the day between St Pancras International, Farringdon, City Thameslink, London Blackfriars, London Bridge and Gatwick Airport (generally every 15 mins, See Table 52). A reduced frequency between London and Gatwick operates through the night.

Airport to/from Reading

First Great Western operate a direct rail service between Reading and Gatwick – (See Table 148). Customers using this route should allow at least 7 minutes at Reading to make a connection.

Other direct services to/from Airport

Southern offers direct services between Gatwick Airport and Watford Junction. Connections for Birmingham and the West Midlands, also for North West destinations (including Manchester, Liverpool and Preston) and Glasgow are available from Watford Junction.

Southern also operates direct services to/from Hastings, Southampton, Portsmouth and intermediate stations on the South Coast (See Tables 186, 187, 188, 189) Clapham Jn and East Croydon (SeeTable 186).

Southeastern operates direct services from Tonbridge (See Table 209).

First Great Western operate services from Wokingham, North Camp and Guildford (See Table 148).

First Capital Connect operate direct services to Brighton and through St Pancras International to St Albans, Luton and Bedford. Connections with East Midlands Trans services to the East Midlands and South Yorkshire and Eurostar services to Continental Europe are available at St Pancras International.

Airport Links

London Gatwick Airport continued

First Capital Connect provide regular direct services from Gatwick Airport to St. Albans, Luton, Bedford, East Croydon, Haywards Heath and Brighton (See Table 52). At Luton Airport Parkway, Luton and Bedford, they also offer convenient connections with East Midlands Trains to Leicester, Derby, Nottingham and Sheffield (See Table 53).

London Heathrow Airport

Please note that Heathrow Terminal 5 station opens on 27 March 2008. Certain information is only applicable from the date.

Express dedicated coaches link Reading, Watford Junction and Woking with all four terminals at Heathrow Airport. Other services link Watford, Luton, Stevenage, Feltham and Central London with the airport. For full details see the individual route information below.

Airport to/from Central London

Heathrow Express operates a direct rail service from the airport to London Paddington. Stations are located at Terminal 4 and in the Central Terminal Area, serving Terminals 1, 2 and 3 (Terminal 5 from 27 March 2008). Minimum journey time is 15 minutes between Paddington and Terminals 1, 2 and 3, 23 minutes to Terminal 4. Trains run every 15 minutes. (From 27 March 2008, terminal 4 is served by a connecting 'shuttle' service to/from Heathrow Terminals 1, 2 and 3, taking a minimum of 8 minutes extra. Heathrow Express trains will operate to/from Terminal 5 from this date, and journey time to/from London Paddington will be 23 minutes.)

- 0510 to 2325 from Paddington
- 0507 to 2340 from Heathrow Terminal 4 (0503 to 2342 on Sundays)
- 0512 to 2348 from Heathrow Terminal 1, 2 and 3 (0508 to 2337 on Sundays)

From 27 March 2008

- 0510 to 2325 from Paddington
- 0507 to 2342 from Heathrow Terminal 5 (0503 to 2348 on Sundays)
- 0512 to 2348 from Heathrow Terminal 1, 2 and 3 (0508 to 2353 on Sundays)

For further details see Table 118.

Through tickets can be purchased from any National Rail or London Underground Station to the airport via Heathrow Express. For further information visit **www.heathrowexpress.com**.

Heathrow Connect operates a local rail service every 30 minutes between Heathrow Terminals 1,2,3 and London Paddington, calling at Hayes & Harlington, Southall, Hanwell, West Ealing and Ealing Broadway. For details see Table 117. Through tickets are available from most stations.

The London Underground Piccadilly Line connects central London with all four terminals (Terminal 1/2/3 and Terminal 4). Through single and return tickets can be issued to customers travelling via a Rail terminus in Zone 1.

Sample journey time from Piccadilly Circus to the Airport is approximately one hour.

Airport to/from Reading

RailAir coaches leave from Reading railway station every 20 minutes during the daytime on Mondays to Fridays (every 30 minutes early weekday mornings and evenings, on weekends and public holidays). The luxury, air-conditioned coaches run non-stop to Terminals 1, 2 and 3 in 40-50 minutes. On the return journey from Heathrow Airport they only pick up passengers at Heathrow Central Bus Station (stands one and two) and not the terminals. Customers travelling to/from Terminal 4 should use Heathrow Express from Terminal 1.

Follow the RailAir signs from your platform at Reading station. You can buy your ticket in the RailAir lounge, or combined rail and coach tickets are also available from many stations. You should allow 15 minutes at Reading to transfer between train and coach.

For further information telephone **0118 957 9425** or visit **www.RailAir.com.**

Airport to/from Watford Junction

Coaches leave at regular intervals throughout the day to/from terminals 1, 3, 4 and Central Bus Station (for terminal 2) (see Table 65D).

Customers travelling to Heathrow should proceed from the platform to the station exit using the underpass. The coach leaves from the bus departure area immediately left of the station front.

Customers travelling from Heathrow can purchase combined coach and rail tickets from the dedicated ticket office in the central bus station.

Customers should allow at least 10 minutes to transfer between train and coach or vice versa at Watford.

For further information telephone **08457 48 49 50**

Airport to/from Woking

Coaches leave at half-hourly intervals throughout most of the day to/from Terminal 4 and Heathrow Central Bus Station (for Terminals 1, 2 and 3) (see Table 158A).

Customers travelling to Heathrow should exit on platform 5 and the coach leaves from outside the station. Tickets must be purchased before boarding.

Customers travelling from Heathrow can purchase combined coach and rail tickets from the Railair outlets at the airport. On arrival at Woking customers should allow at least 10 minutes to transfer to your train after the arrival of the coach at the station. There will be changes to this service when Terminal 5 opens on 27 March. Please check with the operator. Tickets may also be booked at **www.nationalexpress.com** or by calling **08705 757 747**. For further information telephone **08457 48 49 50.**

Airport to/from Feltham

A frequent bus service operates to Heathrow Airport throughout the day linking Feltham with Heathrow Central Bus station (for Terminals 1,2 and 3). For Terminal 4 customers should change at Hatton Cross. Buses operate every 10 minutes for much of the day reducing to every 20 minutes in the early morning and late evening. Buses operate every 30 minutes throughout the night. Customers should allow 10 minutes at Feltham to transfer between train and bus. Through tickets to Heathrow via Feltham can be purchased from many stations.

Airport Links

London Heathrow Airport continued

Other direct services to/from Airport

A coach service, Green Line 724, runs throughout the day between Heathrow, West Drayton, Uxbridge, Rickmansworth, Watford, St. Albans, Hatfield, Welwyn Garden City, Hertford and Harlow. Tickets can only be purchased on the coach. A frequent bus service (route 140) runs 24 hours between Hayes & Harlington and Heathrow Airport (Central Bus Station).

For further information telephone **0870 608 7261** (Green Line Travel Information)

London Luton Airport

A frequent dedicated shuttle bus links Luton Airport with Luton Airport Parkway station – journey time 5 minutes. Luton Airport Parkway is served by frequent First Capital Connect services direct to Bedford, Central London, South London, Gatwick Airport and Brighton – see Table 52 for details. East Midlands Trains services link Luton Airport Parkway with St Pancras International and Leicester, Derby, Nottingham and Sheffield – see Table 53 for details.

In addition Virgin Trains provides an hourly dedicated coach link between the Airport, Luton railway station and town centre and Milton Keynes Central railway station and town centre (see Table 65B for details).

London Stansted Airport

Stansted Airport has its own railway station right in the heart of the airport terminal building.

The Stansted Express is a dedicated rail service operating between London Liverpool Street and Stansted Airport station (See Table 22). Trains run every 15 minutes throughout the day, seven days per week.

Typical journey time is 46 minutes including an intermediate stop at Tottenham Hale to enable transfer onto the Victoria Line (London Underground) for the West End. Occasionally services may be diverted via Seven Sisters at weekends.

CrossCountry operates an hourly express service seven days a week between Birmingham and Stansted Airport calling at Leicester, Peterborough and Cambridge – see Table 49 – offering connections with services to Yorkshire and the North East. Customers should be advised to arrive at the airport 1 hour 45 minutes prior to their latest check-in time.

For further information telephone **08457 48 49 50**.

The airport is also served by the Stansted Coachlink (Service X22) – an hourly service from Colchester station – which also calls intermediately at Braintree station. Coaches run hourly throughout the day, seven days per week.

For further information telephone **0871 200 22 33** or visit **www.traveline.org.uk**

Manchester Airport

The airport station is right in the heart of the airport complex, linked by a covered escalator. The station is served by up to 6 trains per hour from Manchester Piccadilly and direct services operate between Middlesbrough, Newcastle, York, Leeds, Huddersfield, Cleethorpes, Doncaster, Meadowhall, Sheffield, Barrow-in-Furness, Windermere, Lancaster, Preston, Liverpool, Edinburgh and Glasgow and the Airport. Additional regular services operate during the day, to/from many stations which can be found under the entry for Manchester Airport in the index to this timetable.

Newcastle Airport

A frequent Tyne and Wear Metro service runs between Newcastle Central Station and Newcastle Airport providing links with Northern, National Express East Coast, First TransPennine Express and CrossCountry services. Inclusive 'Train and Metro' tickets are available at discount prices.

Metro journey time approximately 20 minutes.

Metro frequency up to 6 trains each way each hour. Service operates between approx. 0600 and 2300.

Prestwick International Airport

Prestwick International Airport Station is situated directly opposite the main airport terminal buildings. A covered walkway links the station with the airport terminal. The station is served by direct trains from Glasgow Central and Ayr, with a half hourly frequency operating between the hours of 0600 and 0015 approximately. (See Table 221). Journey time is approx. 45 minutes. Discounts are available for airline users. For further information telephone **01292 678000**.

Robin Hood Airport

Robin Hood Airport, the UK's newest purpose built international airport, is built on the site of the former RAF Finningley airbase. It is situated 7 miles south of Doncaster. For more information on Robin Hood Airport visit **www.robinhoodairport.com**

From Doncaster a dedicated bus service, The Airport Arrow 707, operates hourly throughout the day from the Frenchgate Interchange (Stand A1) adjacent to Doncaster Rail Station from 0535 to 2235. The journey takes under 25 minutes.

The Airport Arrow 707 service runs alongside other local bus services which link to Robin Hood Airport, including service X19 from Barnsley.

For further information on the above services please telephone Travel South Yorkshire **01709 515151** or visit **www.travelsouthyorkshire.com**

Southampton Airport

Southampton Airport (Parkway) station is adjacent to Southampton Airport.

South West Trains operate up to 3 trains per hour between London Waterloo, Winchester and Southampton Airport with up to 2 direct services to Bournemouth, Poole, Wareham and Weymouth and most intermediate stations (See Table 158).

CrossCountry services link Southampton Airport (Parkway) with Reading, Oxford, the Midlands, North West and North East England and Scotland. (See Table 51).

Station index and table numbers

10 Connection time
Ⓟ Station Car Park
🚲 Bicycle storage facility
◇ Seat reservations can be made at this station
⚠ Penalty Fare Schemes in operation on some or all services from this station
🚕 Taxi rank or cab office at station, or signposted and within 100 metres
Ⓤ Unstaffed station
[ ] Station Operator Code

A

Abbey Wood [SE] Ⓟ 🚲 ⚠ 200
Aber [AW] Ⓟ 130
Abercynon North [AW] Ⓟ Ⓤ 130
Abercynon South [AW] Ⓤ 130
Aberdare [AW] **3** Ⓟ ◇ 130
Aberdeen [SR] Ⓟ 🚲 ◇ 🚕
  Birmingham 51, 65
  Blackpool 65
  Bournemouth 51
  Bristol 51
  Cambridge 26
  Cardiff 51
  Carlisle 65
  Crewe 65, *Sleepers* 402
  Darlington 26
  Derby 51
  Doncaster 26
  Dundee 229
  Dyce 240
  Edinburgh 229
  Elgin 240
  Exeter 51
  Glasgow 229
  Grantham 26
  Inverkeithing 229
  Inverness 240
  Kirkcaldy 229
  Kyle of Lochalsh 239
  Leeds 26
  Liverpool 65
  London 26, *Sleepers* 402
  Manchester 65
  Newcastle 26
  Newport (South Wales) 51
  Norwich 26
  Oxenholme Lake District 65
  Oxford 51
  Paignton 51
  Penzance 51
  Perth 229
  Peterborough 26
  Plymouth 51
  Preston 65, *Sleepers* 402
  Reading 51
  Sheffield 26
  Southampton 51
  Stirling 229
  Thurso 239
  Torquay 51
  Watford 65
  Wick 239
  York 26
Aberdour [SR] Ⓟ 🚲 242
Aberdovey [AW] 🚲 Ⓤ 75
Abererch [AW] Ⓤ 75
Abergavenny [AW] Ⓟ 🚲 ◇ 🚕 131
Abergele & Pensarn [AW] Ⓟ Ⓤ 81
Aberystwyth [AW] Ⓟ ◇ 🚕 75
Abingdon High Street *Bus* 116B
Accrington [NT] Ⓟ ◇ 🚕 41, 97
Achanalt [SR] Ⓟ 🚲 Ⓤ 239
Achnasheen [SR] Ⓟ 🚲 Ⓤ 239
Achnashellach [SR] Ⓟ 🚲 Ⓤ 239
Acklington [NT] Ⓟ 🚲 Ⓤ 48
Acle [LE] Ⓟ 🚲 Ⓤ 15
Acocks Green [LM] Ⓟ ⚠ 71
Acton Bridge [LM] Ⓟ Ⓤ 91
Acton Central [LO] 59
Acton Main Line [GW] ⚠ 117
Acton, South [LO] (see South Acton)
Adderley Park [LM] ◇ ⚠ 68
Addiewell [SR] Ⓟ 🚲 Ⓤ 225
Addlestone [SW] ⚠ 🚕 149
Adisham [SE] Ⓟ Ⓤ 212
Adlington (Cheshire) [NT] Ⓟ Ⓤ 84
Adlington (Lancashire) [NT] Ⓟ 82
Adwick [NT] Ⓟ 🚲 Ⓤ 29, 31
Agbrigg [NT] (See Sandal & Agbrigg)
Aigburth [ME] Ⓟ 103
Ainsdale [ME] Ⓟ 103
Aintree [ME] Ⓟ 103
Airbles [SR] Ⓟ 🚲 Ⓤ 226
Airdrie [SR] Ⓟ 🚲 🚕 226
Albany Park [SE] ⚠ 200
Albrighton [LM] Ⓟ Ⓤ 74
Alderley Edge [NT] Ⓟ 84
Aldermaston [GW] Ⓟ Ⓤ 116
Aldershot [SW] Ⓟ 🚲 ◇ ⚠ 🚕 149, 155
Aldrington [SN] ⚠ Ⓤ 188
Alexandra Palace [FC] 🚲 ⚠ 24
Alexandra Parade [SR] 🚲 Ⓤ 226
Alexandria [SR] Ⓟ 🚲 226
Alfreton [EM] Ⓟ ◇ 🚕 49, 53
Allens West [NT] 🚲 Ⓤ 44
Alness [SR] Ⓟ 🚲 Ⓤ 239
Alnmouth [NT] Ⓟ 🚲 ◇ 26, 48, 51
Alresford [LE] 🚲 ⚠ 11
Alsager [EM] Ⓤ 50
Althorne [LE] Ⓟ 🚲 Ⓤ 5
Althorpe [NT] Ⓤ 29
Altnabreac [SR] 🚲 Ⓤ 239
Alton [SW] Ⓟ 🚲 ◇ ⚠ 🚕 155
Altrincham [NT] Ⓟ 🚲 ◇ 🚕 88
Alvechurch [LM] Ⓟ ⚠ Ⓤ 69
Ambergate [EM] Ⓟ Ⓤ 56
Amberley [SN] 🚲 ⚠ Ⓤ 188
Amersham [LT] Ⓟ 🚲 ⚠ 🚕 114
Ammanford [AW] Ⓤ 129
Ancaster [EM] Ⓟ Ⓤ 19
Anderston [SR] 🚲 226
Andover [SW] Ⓟ 🚲 ⚠ ◇ 🚕 160
Anerley [SN] 🚲 ⚠ 178
Angel Road [LE] ⚠ Ⓤ 22
Angmering [SN] **3** Ⓟ 🚲 ⚠ 🚕 188
Annan [SR] Ⓟ 🚲 Ⓤ 216
Anniesland [SR] 🚲 🚕 226, 232
Ansdell & Fairhaven [NT] Ⓤ 97
Appleby [NT] Ⓟ ◇ 36
Appledore (Kent) [SN] Ⓤ 189
Appleford [GW] Ⓤ 116
Appley Bridge [NT] Ⓟ Ⓤ 82
Apsley [LM] Ⓟ 66
Arbroath [SR] Ⓟ 🚲 ◇ 🚕 26, 51, 229, *Sleepers* 402
Ardgay [SR] Ⓟ 🚲 Ⓤ 239
Ardlui [SR] 🚲 Ⓤ 227, *Sleepers* 404
Ardrossan Harbour [SR] Ⓟ 🚲 Ⓤ 221, *Ship* 221A
Ardrossan South Beach [SR] Ⓟ 🚲 221
Ardrossan Town [SR] 🚲 Ⓤ 221
Ardwick [NT] Ⓤ 78, 79
Argyle Street [SR] 226
Arisaig [SR] Ⓟ 🚲 Ⓤ 227
Arlesey [FC] Ⓟ 🚲 ⚠ 25
Armadale *Ship* 227A
Armathwaite [NT] Ⓟ Ⓤ 36
Arnside [TP] Ⓤ 82
Arram [NT] Ⓤ 43
Arrochar & Tarbet [SR] Ⓟ 🚲 Ⓤ 227, *Sleepers* 404
Arundel [SN] Ⓟ 🚲 ⚠ 🚕 188
Ascot [SW] **3** Ⓟ 🚲 ◇ ⚠ 🚕 149
Ascott-under-Wychwood [GW] Ⓤ 126
Ash [SW] **3** Ⓟ 🚲 148, 149
Ash Vale [SW] 🚲 ⚠ 149, 155
Ashburys [NT] Ⓤ 78, 79
Ashchurch for Tewkesbury [GW] Ⓟ 🚲 Ⓤ 57
Ashfield [SR] 🚲 Ⓤ 232
Ashford International [SE] Ⓟ 🚲 ◇ ⚠ 🚕 189, 196, 207
Ashford (Surrey) [SW] Ⓟ 🚲 ⚠ 149
Ashley [NT] Ⓤ 88
Ashtead [SN] Ⓟ 🚲 ◇ ⚠ 152, 182
Ashton-under-Lyne [NT] Ⓟ 🚲 39
Ashurst [SN] Ⓟ Ⓤ 184
Ashurst New Forest [SW] Ⓟ 🚲 ⚠ Ⓤ 158
Ashwell & Morden [FC] Ⓟ 🚲 ⚠ 25
Askam [NT] Ⓟ Ⓤ 100
Aslockton [EM] Ⓟ Ⓤ 19
Aspatria [NT] Ⓟ Ⓤ 100
Aspley Guise [LM] Ⓤ 64
Aston [LM] ⚠ 69, 70
Atherstone [LM] Ⓟ Ⓤ 67
Atherton [NT] Ⓟ 🚲 82
Attadale [SR] 🚲 Ⓤ 239
Attenborough [EM] Ⓤ 57
Attleborough [LE] Ⓟ Ⓤ 17
Auchinleck [SR] Ⓟ 🚲 Ⓤ 216
Audley End [LE] Ⓟ 🚲 ⚠ 🚕 22, 49

10 Connection time
Ⓟ Station Car Park
🚲 Bicycle storage facility
◇ Seat reservations can be made at this station
⚠ Penalty Fare Schemes in operation on some or all services from this station
🚕 Taxi rank or cab office at station, or signposted and within 100 metres
Ⓤ Unstaffed station
[ ] Station Operator Code

Station index and table numbers

Aughton Park [ME] 103
Aviemore [SR] Ⓟ 🚲 ◇ 🚕 229, *Sleepers* 403
Avoncliff [GW] Ⓤ 123
Avonmouth [GW] **2** Ⓟ 🚲 Ⓤ 133
Axminster [SW] Ⓟ 🚲 ◇ 🚕 160
Aylesbury [CH] Ⓟ 🚲 ◇ ⚠ 🚕 114, 115
Aylesford [SE] Ⓤ 208
Aylesham [SE] Ⓟ 212
Ayr [SR] Ⓟ 🚲 ◇ 🚕 216, 218, 221

B

Bache [ME] Ⓤ 106
Backwell [GW] (see Nailsea)
Baglan [AW] Ⓟ 🚲 Ⓤ 128
Bagshot [SW] Ⓟ 🚲 ⚠ 149
Baildon [NT] Ⓟ Ⓤ 38
Baillieston [SR] 🚲 Ⓤ 220
Bakewell (Square) *Bus* 65H
Balcombe [SN] ◇ ⚠ 52, 186
Baldock [FC] Ⓟ ⚠ 25
Balham [SN] **4** ◇ ⚠ 🚕 177, 178, 182
Balloch [SR] 🚲 🚕 226
Balmossie [SR] 🚲 Ⓤ 229
Bamber Bridge [NT] Ⓟ Ⓤ 97
Bamford [NT] Ⓟ Ⓤ 78
Banavie [SR] Ⓟ 🚲 Ⓤ 227
Banbury [CH] Ⓟ 🚲 ◇ ⚠ 🚕 51, 71, 75, 115, 116
Bangor (Gwynedd) [AW] Ⓟ ◇ 🚕 65, 81, 102, 131
Bank Hall [ME] 103
Banstead [SN] ⚠ Ⓤ 182
Barassie [SR] Ⓟ 🚲 Ⓤ 221
Barbican [LT] (see London)
Bardon Mill [NT] Ⓟ Ⓤ 48
Bare Lane [NT] Ⓟ Ⓤ 36, 98
Bargeddie [SR] Ⓟ 🚲 Ⓤ 220
Bargoed [AW] 🚕 130
Barking [CC] ◇ ⚠ 🚕 1, 62
Barlaston Orchard Place *Bus* 68A
Barming [SE] Ⓟ ⚠ 196
Barmouth [AW] 🚲 75
Barnehurst [SE] **4** Ⓟ ⚠ 200
Barnes [SW] 🚲 ⚠ 149
Barnes Bridge [SW] 🚲 Ⓤ 149
Barnetby [TP] Ⓟ Ⓤ 27, 29, 30
Barnham [SN] Ⓟ 🚲 ⚠ 🚕 123, 188
Barnhill [SR] 🚲 Ⓤ 226
Barnsbury [LO] (see Caledonian Road)
Barnsley [NT] Ⓟ 🚲 ◇ 🚕 30, 34, 53
Barnsley West Bus Station *Bus* 26E
Barnstaple [GW] Ⓟ 🚲 ◇ 🚕 135, 136
Barnt Green [LM] Ⓟ ⚠ Ⓤ 69, 71
Barrhead [SR] Ⓟ 🚲 🚕 222
Barrhill [SR] Ⓟ 🚲 218
Barrow Haven [NT] Ⓤ 29
Barrow-in-Furness [TP] Ⓟ ◇ 🚕 65, 82, 100
Barrow Upon Soar [EM] Ⓤ 53
Barry [AW] **3** Ⓟ ◇ 🚕 130
Barry Docks [AW] Ⓤ 130
Barry Island [AW] Ⓤ 130
Barry Links [SR] 🚲 Ⓤ 229
Barton-on-Humber [NT] Ⓟ Ⓤ 29
Basildon [CC] 🚲 ◇ ⚠ 🚕 1
Basingstoke [SW] Ⓟ 🚲 ◇ ⚠ 🚕
Aberdeen 51
Bath 160
Birmingham 51
Bournemouth 158
Bristol 160
Brockenhurst 158
Clapham Junction 155
Coventry 51
Crewe 51
Derby 51
Dorchester 158
Dundee 51
Eastleigh 158
Edinburgh 51
Exeter 160
Fareham 158
Farnborough 158
Glasgow 51
Leeds 51
London 155
Lymington 158
Manchester 51
Newcastle 51
Oxford 51
Plymouth 160
Poole 158
Portsmouth 158
Preston 51
Reading 122
Salisbury 160
Sheffield 51
Southampton 158
Southampton Airport 158
Stoke-on-Trent 51
Surbiton 155
Torquay 160
Weymouth 158
Weybridge 155
Wimbledon 155
Winchester 158
Woking 155
Wolverhampton 51
Yeovil 160
York 51
Bat & Ball [SE] Ⓟ ⚠ Ⓤ 195
Bath Spa [GW] **7** Ⓟ 🚲 ◇ ⚠ 🚕
Bournemouth 123
Brighton 123
Bristol 132
Cardiff 132
Crewe 131
Gatwick Airport 125
Heathrow Airport 125
London 125, 160
Manchester 131
Newport 132
Oxford 125
Portsmouth 123
Reading 125
Salisbury 123
Shrewsbury 131
Slough 125
Southampton Central 123
Swindon 125
Taunton 134
Westbury 123
Weston-super-Mare 134
Weymouth 123
Yeovil 123
Bathgate [SR] Ⓟ 🚲 🚕 Ⓤ 230
Batley [NT] Ⓟ 🚲 Ⓤ 39
Battersby [NT] Ⓟ Ⓤ 45
Battersea Park [SN] **4** ◇ ⚠ 177, 178
Battle [SE] Ⓟ ◇ 🚕 206
Battlesbridge [LE] Ⓟ 🚲 Ⓤ 5
Bayford [FC] Ⓟ ⚠ Ⓤ 24
Beaconsfield [CH] Ⓟ 🚲 ◇ ⚠ 🚕 115
Bearley [LM] Ⓟ ⚠ Ⓤ 115
Bearsden [SR] Ⓟ 🚲 🚕 226
Bearsted [SE] Ⓟ 🚲 ◇ ⚠ 196
Beasdale [SR] 🚲 Ⓤ 227
Beaulieu Road [SW] 🚲 ⚠ Ⓤ 158
Beauly [SR] Ⓟ 🚲 Ⓤ 239
Bebington [ME] Ⓟ 106
Beccles [LE] Ⓟ 🚲 Ⓤ 13
Beckenham Hill [SE] 🚲 ⚠ 195
Beckenham Junction [SE] **4** Ⓟ 🚲 ◇ ⚠ 🚕 177, 195, 196
Bedford [FC] **7** Ⓟ 🚲 ◇ ⚠ 🚕
Barnsley 53
Bletchley 64
Brighton 52, 186
Chesterfield 53
Derby 53
Doncaster 53
East Croydon 52
Gatwick Airport 52, 186
Haywards Heath 52, 186
Herne Hill 52
Hove 186
Kettering 53
Leeds 53
Leicester 53
London 52
Luton 52
Luton Airport Parkway 52
Meadowhall 53
Milton Keynes Central 64
Nottingham 53
Redhill 52, 186

Station index and table numbers

10 Connection time
Ⓟ Station Car Park
🚲 Bicycle storage facility
◇ Seat reservations can be made at this station
⚠ Penalty Fare Schemes in operation on some or all services from this station
🚕 Taxi rank or cab office at station, or signposted and within 100 metres
🚶 Unstaffed station
[ ] Station Operator Code

Station index and table numbers

- **10** Connection time
- Ⓟ Station Car Park
- 🚲 Bicycle storage facility
- ◇ Seat reservations can be made at this station
- ⚠ Penalty Fare Schemes in operation on some or all services from this station
- 🚕 Taxi rank or cab office at station, or signposted and within 100 metres
- Ⓤ Unstaffed station
- [ ] Station Operator Code

Peterborough 49
Plymouth 135
Preston 65
Reading 116
Redditch 69
Rugby 66
Rugeley 70
Sheffield 51
Shrewsbury 74
Solihull 71
Southampton 51
Stafford 68, 70
Stansted Airport 49
Stockport 65
Stoke-on-Trent 65
Stourbridge 71
Stratford-upon-Avon 71
Swindon 125
Telford 74
Torquay 135
Walsall 70
Warrington 65
Warwick 71
Watford 66
Wigan 65
Wolverhampton 68
Worcester 71
Wrexham 75
York 51
Birnam [SR] (see Dunkeld)
Bishop Auckland [NT] Ⓟ 🚕 Ⓤ 44
Bishopbriggs [SR] 🚲 228, 230
Bishops Stortford [LE] Ⓟ 🚲 ◇ ⚠ 🚕 22
Bishopstone [SN] Ⓤ 189
Bishopton [SR] Ⓟ 🚲 219
Bitterne [SW] Ⓟ 🚲 Ⓤ 165
Blackburn [NT] Ⓟ ◇ 🚕 41, 94, 97
Blackfriars [FC] (see London)
Blackheath [SE] **4** ⚠ 200
Blackhorse Road [LT] ⚠ 62
Blackpool
North [NT] Ⓟ ◇ 🚕
Pleasure Beach [NT] Ⓤ
South [NT] 🚕 Ⓤ
Aberdeen 65
Birmingham 65
Birmingham International 65
Blackburn 97
Bolton 82
Bradford 41
Burnley 97
Carlisle 36, 65
Colne 97
Coventry 65
Crewe 65
Dundee 65
Edinburgh 65
Glasgow 65
Inverness 65
Lancaster 65
Leeds 41
Liverpool 65, 90
London 65
Manchester 82
Manchester Airport 82
Milton Keynes Central 65
Oxenholme Lake District 65
Preston 97
Rugby 65
St Helens 90
Stafford 65
Stockport 82
Warrington 65
Watford 65
Wigan 65
Windermere 65
Wolverhampton 65
York 41
Blackrod [NT] Ⓤ 82
Blackwater [GW] Ⓟ Ⓤ 148
Blaenau Ffestiniog [AW] Ⓤ 102
Blair Atholl [SR] Ⓟ 🚲 229, *Sleepers* 403
Blairhill [SR] Ⓟ 🚲 🚕 226
Blake Street [LM] Ⓟ ⚠ 69
Blakedown [LM] Ⓟ ⚠ Ⓤ 71
Blantyre [SR] Ⓟ 🚲 226
Blaydon [NT] Ⓟ Ⓤ 48
Bleasby [EM] Ⓤ 27
Bledlow, Village Hall *Bus* 115A
Bletchley [LM] Ⓟ 🚲 ◇ 🚕 64, 66
Bloxwich [LM] ⚠ Ⓤ 70
Bloxwich North [LM] ⚠ Ⓤ 70
Bluewater [SE] (see Greenhithe for Bluewater)
Blundellsands & Crosby [ME] Ⓟ 103
Blythe Bridge [EM] Ⓟ Ⓤ 50
Bodmin Mount Folly *Bus* 135C
Bodmin Parkway [GW] Ⓟ 🚲 ◇ 🚕 51, 135, *Bus* 135C, *Sleepers* 406
Bodorgan [AW] Ⓟ Ⓤ 81
Bognor Regis [SN] **4** Ⓟ 🚲 ◇ ⚠ 🚕 188
Bogston [SR] 🚲 Ⓤ 219
Bolton [NT] ◇ 🚕 51, 65, 82, 94, 95
Bolton-on-Dearne [NT] Ⓟ Ⓤ 31
Bookham [SW] Ⓟ 🚲 ⚠ 🚕 152, 182
Bootle [NT] Ⓟ Ⓤ 100
Bootle New Strand [ME] 🚕 103
Bootle Oriel Road [ME] Ⓟ 103
Bordesley [LM] ⚠ Ⓤ 71
Bordon Camp (Fire Station) *Bus* 156A
Borehamwood [FC] (see Elstree)
Borough Green & Wrotham [SE] Ⓟ ⚠ 🚕 196
Borth [AW] Ⓟ Ⓤ 75
Bosham [SN] 🚲 ⚠ 188
Boston [EM] Ⓟ 🚲 ◇ 🚕 19
Botley [SW] Ⓟ 🚲 ⚠ Ⓤ 158
Bottesford [EM] Ⓟ Ⓤ 19
Bourne End [GW] **3** Ⓟ 🚲 ⚠ 120
Bournemouth [SW] Ⓟ 🚲 ◇ ⚠ 🚕 51, 123, 158
Bournville [LM] ⚠ 69
Bow Brickhill [LM] Ⓤ 64
Bowes Park [FC] ⚠ 24
Bowling [SR] Ⓟ 🚲 Ⓤ 226
Boxhill & Westhumble [SN] Ⓟ ⚠ Ⓤ 152, 182
Bracknell [SW] Ⓟ 🚲 ◇ ⚠ 🚕 149
Bradford
Forster Square [NT] Ⓟ 🚲 ◇ 🚕
Interchange [NT] Ⓟ 🚲 ◇ 🚕
Blackpool 41
Blackburn 41
Brighouse 41
Cambridge 26
Carlisle 36
Grantham 26
Halifax 41
Huddersfield 41
Ilkley 38
Lancaster 36
Leeds 37
Liverpool 41
London 26
Manchester 41
Morecambe 36
Newark 26
Norwich 26
Peterborough 26
Preston 41
Retford 26
Rochdale 41
Selby 41
Settle 36
Shipley 37
Skipton 36
York 41
Bradford-on-Avon [GW] Ⓟ 🚲 ◇ 🚕 123, 160
Brading [IL] Ⓟ Ⓤ 167
Braintree [LE] Ⓟ 🚲 ⚠ 🚕 11
Braintree Freeport [LE] 🚲 ⚠ Ⓤ 11
Bramhall [NT] 84
Bramley (Hants) [GW] ⚠ 122
Bramley [NT] Ⓟ Ⓤ 37, 41
Brampton (Cumbria) [NT] Ⓟ Ⓤ 48
Brampton (Suffolk) [LE] Ⓤ 13
Branchton [SR] Ⓟ 🚲 Ⓤ 219
Brandon [LE] Ⓟ Ⓤ 17
Branksome [SW] Ⓟ 🚲 ⚠ 158
Braystones [NT] Ⓤ 100
Bredbury [NT] Ⓟ 78
Breich [SR] 🚲 Ⓤ 225
Brentford [SW] Ⓟ 🚲 Ⓤ 149
Brentwood [LE] Ⓟ 🚲 ⚠ 🚕 5
Bricket Wood [LM] Ⓤ 61
Bridge of Allan [SR] Ⓟ 🚲 Ⓤ 230

Station index and table numbers

[10] Connection time
Ⓟ Station Car Park
🚲 Bicycle storage facility
◇ Seat reservations can be made at this station
⚠ Penalty Fare Schemes in operation on some or all services from this station
🚕 Taxi rank or cab office at station, or signposted and within 100 metres
Ⓤ Unstaffed station
[ ] Station Operator Code

■10 Connection time
℗ Station Car Park
🚲 Bicycle storage facility
◇ Seat reservations can be made at this station
⚠ Penalty Fare Schemes in operation on some or all services from this station
🚕 Taxi rank or cab office at station, or signposted and within 100 metres
Ⓤ Unstaffed station
[ ] Station Operator Code

Station index and table numbers

Buxted [SN] ℗ 184
Buxton [NT] ℗ ◇ 82, 86
Buxton (Market Place) *Bus* 65H
Byfleet & New Haw [SW] 🚲 🚕 155
Bynea [AW] Ⓤ 129

C

Cadoxton [AW] ℗ ◇ 130
Caerau Park *Bus* 128A
Caerau (Square) *Bus* 128A
Caergwrle [AW] Ⓤ 101
Caerphilly [AW] ■3 ℗ 🚲 ◇ 🚕 130
Caersws [AW] ℗ Ⓤ 75
Caldicot [AW] Ⓤ 132
Caledonian Rd & Barnsbury [LO] 59
Calstock [GW] ℗ 🚲 Ⓤ 139
Cam & Dursley [GW] ℗ 🚲 Ⓤ 134
Camberley [SW] ℗ 🚲 ⚠ 🚕 149
Camborne [GW] ℗ 🚲 ◇ 🚕 51, 135, *Sleepers* 406
Cambridge [LE] ℗ 🚲 ◇ ⚠ 🚕
- Birmingham 49
- Bishops Stortford 22
- Broxbourne 22
- Doncaster 26
- Edinburgh 26
- Ely 17
- Finsbury Park 25
- Grantham 26
- Harlow 22
- Harwich International 14
- Hitchin 25
- Ipswich 14
- Kings Lynn 17
- Leeds 26
- Leicester 49
- Liverpool 49
- London
  - Kings Cross 17, 25
  - Liverpool St. 17, 22
- Manchester 49
- Newark 26
- Newcastle 26
- Norwich 17
- Nottingham 49
- Peterborough 17
- Retford 26
- Royston 25
- Sheffield 49
- Stansted Airport 22
- Stevenage 25
- Stockport 49
- Tottenham Hale 22
- Welwyn Garden City 25
- York 26

Cambridge Bus Station 🚕 *Bus* 65C
Cambridge Heath [LE] ⚠ Ⓤ 21
Cambuslang [SR] 🚲 🚕 225, 226
Camden Road [LO] 59
Camelon [SR] ℗ 🚲 Ⓤ 224, 230
Canley [LM] ℗ 🚲 ⚠ 68
Canna *Ship* 227A
Cannock [LM] ℗ ⚠ Ⓤ 70
Cannon Street [NR] (see London)
Canonbury [LO] 59
Canterbury East [SE] ■4 ℗ 🚲 ◇ 🚕 212
Canterbury West [SE] ■4 ℗ 🚲 ◇ 🚕 207
Cantley [LE] ℗ 🚲 Ⓤ 15
Capenhurst [ME] ℗ Ⓤ 106
Carbis Bay [GW] ℗ Ⓤ 144
Cardenden [SR] ℗ 🚲 Ⓤ 242
Cardiff
- **Bay [AW]** Ⓤ
- **Central [AW]** ■7 ℗ 🚲 ◇ 🚕
- **Queen Street [AW]** ■3 ◇
- Aberdeen 51
- Aberystwyth 75
- Bangor (Gwynedd) 81, 131
- Barry Island 130
- Bath Spa 132
- Birmingham 57
- Bournemouth 123
- Bridgend 128, 130
- Brighton 123
- Bristol 132
- Cardiff International Airport *Bus* 125C (also see Rhoose)
- Cheltenham Spa 57
- Chester 75, 81, 131
- Coryton 130
- Crewe 131
- Darlington 51
- Derby 57
- Dundee 51
- Durham 51
- Ebbw Vale Parkway 127
- Edinburgh 51
- Exeter 135
- Fishguard Harbour 128
- Gatwick Airport 125
- Gloucester 132
- Heathrow Airport 125
- Hereford 131
- Holyhead 81, 131
- Leeds 51
- Liverpool 131
- Llandudno Junction 81, 131
- London 125
- Maesteg 128
- Manchester 131
- Merthyr Tydfil 130
- Milford Haven 128
- Newcastle 51
- Newport (South Wales) 132
- Nottingham 57
- Oxford 125
- Paignton 135
- Penzance 135
- Plymouth 135
- Pontypridd 130
- Portsmouth 123
- Reading 125
- Rhoose 130
- Rhymney 130
- Rosslare Harbour 128
- Sheffield 51
- Shrewsbury 131
- Slough 125
- Southampton Central 123
- Swansea 128
- Swindon 125
- Taunton 132, 134
- Torquay 135
- Treherbert 130
- Weymouth 123
- Worcester 57
- Wrexham 75
- York 51

Cardiff International Airport *Bus* 🚕 125C
Cardiff International Airport [AW] (see Rhoose)
Cardonald [SR] 🚲 219
Cardross [SR] ℗ 🚲 226
Carfin [SR] ℗ 🚲 Ⓤ 225
Cark [NT] ℗ Ⓤ 82
Carlisle [VT] ■8 ℗ 🚲 ◇ 🚕
- Aberdeen 65
- Ayr 218
- Barrow-in-Furness 100
- Belfast *Catamaran/Ship* 218
- Birmingham 65
- Blackpool 36, 65
- Bolton 65
- Bournemouth 51
- Bradford 36
- Bristol 51
- Coventry 65
- Crewe 65
- Dumfries 216
- Dundee 65
- Exeter 51
- Edinburgh 65
- Galashiels *Bus* 65G
- Gatwick Airport 65
- Glasgow 65, 216
- Hawick *Bus* 65G
- Haymarket 65
- Hexham 48
- Inverness 65
- Kilmarnock 216
- Lancaster 65
- Langholm *Bus* 65G
- Leeds 36
- Liverpool 65
- London 65, *Sleepers* 400, 401
- Manchester 65
- Manchester Airport 65
- Milton Keynes Central 65
- Motherwell 65
- Newcastle 48

Station index and table numbers

10 Connection time
Ⓟ Station Car Park
🚲 Bicycle storage facility
◇ Seat reservations can be made at this station
⚠ Penalty Fare Schemes in operation on some or all services from this station
🚕 Taxi rank or cab office at station, or signposted and within 100 metres
Ⓤ Unstaffed station
[ ] Station Operator Code

Station index and table numbers

10 Connection time
Ⓟ Station Car Park
🚲 Bicycle storage facility
◇ Seat reservations can be made at this station
⚠ Penalty Fare Schemes in operation on some or all services from this station
🚕 Taxi rank or cab office at station, or signposted and within 100 metres
Ⓤ Unstaffed station
[ ] Station Operator Code

Epsom 152, 182
Epsom Downs 182
Exeter 160
Gatwick Airport 186
Guildford 152, 156
Hampton Court 152
Hastings 189
Haywards Heath 186
Horsham 186
Hounslow 149
Hove 186
Kensington Olympia 66, 186
Kingston 149, 152
Lewes 189
London
Victoria 175, 177
Waterloo 149, 152
Milton Keynes Central 66
Northampton 66
Oxted 184
Portsmouth 156, 158, 188
Purley 175
Reading 149
Redhill 186
Rugby 66
Salisbury 160
Shepperton 152
Southampton 158, 188
Staines 149
Surbiton 152
Sutton (Surrey) 182
Tattenham Corner 181
Twickenham 149
Uckfield 184
Watford Junction 66, 186
West Croydon 177
Weybridge 155
Willesden Junction 186
Wimbledon 152
Windsor 149
Woking 155
Worthing 188
Yeovil Junction 160
Clapham (Nth Yorkshire) [NT] Ⓟ Ⓤ 36
Clapton [LE] ⚠ 20, 22
Clarbeston Road [AW] Ⓤ 128
Clarkston [SR] 🚲 222
Claverdon [LM] ⚠ Ⓤ 115
Claygate [SW] Ⓟ 🚲 ⚠ 🚕 152
Cleethorpes [TP] Ⓟ 🚲 ◇ 🚕 27, 29, 30
Cleland [SR] Ⓟ 🚲 Ⓤ 225
Clifton [NT] Ⓤ 82
Clifton Down [GW] Ⓟ Ⓤ 133
Clitheroe [NT] Ⓟ 94, 97
Clock House [SE] 🚲 ⚠ 203
Clunderwen [AW] Ⓟ Ⓤ 128
Clydebank [SR] 🚲 🚕 226
Coatbridge Central [SR] Ⓟ 🚲 🚕 Ⓤ 224, 226
Coatbridge Sunnyside [SR] Ⓟ 🚲 226
Coatdyke [SR] Ⓟ 🚲 Ⓤ 226
Cobham & Stoke d'Abernon [SW] Ⓟ 🚲 🚕 152
Cockermouth (Main Street) *Bus* 65F
Codsall [LM] Ⓟ Ⓤ 74
Cogan [AW] Ⓟ Ⓤ 130
Colchester [LE] **4** Ⓟ 🚲 ◇ ⚠ 🚕 10, 11, 13, 14
Colchester Town [LE] Ⓟ 🚲 ⚠ 11
Coleshill Parkway [LM] Ⓟ 🚲 ◇ 🚕 57
Coll *Ship* 227B
Collingham [EM] Ⓤ 27
Collington [SN] Ⓤ 189
Colne [NT] Ⓟ Ⓤ 97
Colonsay *Ship* 227B
Colwall [LM] Ⓟ ⚠ Ⓤ 71, 126
Colwyn Bay [AW] Ⓟ ◇ 🚕 81
Combe [GW] Ⓤ 126
Commondale [NT] Ⓤ 45
Congleton [NT] Ⓟ ◇ 51, 65, 84
Conisbrough [NT] Ⓟ Ⓤ 29
Connel Ferry [SR] Ⓟ 🚲 Ⓤ 227
Cononley [NT] Ⓟ Ⓤ 36
Conway Park [ME] 106
Conwy [AW] Ⓤ 81
Cooden Beach [SN] Ⓟ 🚲 ⚠ 189
Cookham [GW] Ⓟ 120
Cooksbridge [SN] Ⓟ Ⓤ 189
Coombe [GW] Ⓤ 140
Copplestone [GW] Ⓟ Ⓤ 136
Corbridge [NT] Ⓟ Ⓤ 48
Corby George Street *Bus* 26B
Corby Town Centre *Bus* 53A
Corkerhill [SR] 🚲 Ⓤ 217
Corkickle [NT] Ⓤ 100
Corpach [SR] Ⓟ 🚲 Ⓤ 227
Corrour [SR] 🚲 Ⓤ 227, *Sleepers* 404
Coryton [AW] Ⓤ 130
Coseley [LM] Ⓟ ⚠ 65, 68, 74
Cosford [LM] Ⓟ Ⓤ 74, 75
Cosham [SW] Ⓟ 🚲 ◇ ⚠ 🚕 123, 158, 165, 188
Cottingham [NT] Ⓟ 🚲 🚕 Ⓤ 43
Cottingley [NT] Ⓤ 39
Coulsdon South [SN] Ⓟ ⚠ 186
Coventry [VT] Ⓟ 🚲 ◇ ⚠ 🚕
Aberdeen 65
Barrow-in-Furness 65
Banbury 71
Basingstoke 51
Birmingham 68
Birmingham International 68
Blackpool 65
Bournemouth 51
Brighton 66
Carlisle 65
Clapham Junction 66
Crewe 65
Derby 51
Dundee 65
East Croydon 66
Edinburgh 51, 65
Gatwick Airport 66
Glasgow 51, 65
Holyhead 65
Inverness 65
Leamington Spa 71
Leeds 51
Liverpool 65
London 66
Manchester 65
Manchester Airport 65
Milton Keynes Central 66
Newcastle 51
Northampton 66
Nuneaton 67
Oxenholme Lake District 65
Oxford 51
Preston 65
Reading 51
Rugby 66
Sheffield 51
Southampton 51
Stafford 67, 68
Stoke-on-Trent 65
Watford 66
Wolverhampton 68
York 51
Cowden [SN] Ⓟ Ⓤ 184
Cowdenbeath [SR] 🚲 ◇ 242
Cradley Heath [LM] Ⓟ 🚲 ◇ ⚠ 71, 115
Craigendoran [SR] Ⓟ 🚲 Ⓤ 226
Craignure *Ship* 227B
Cramlington [NT] Ⓟ 🚲 Ⓤ 48
Craven Arms [AW] Ⓟ Ⓤ 129, 131
Crawley [SN] Ⓟ 🚲 ◇ ⚠ 🚕 186, 188, 209
Crayford [SE] Ⓟ ⚠ 200
Crediton [GW] Ⓟ 🚲 Ⓤ 136
Cressing [LE] 🚲 ⚠ Ⓤ 11
Cressington [ME] Ⓟ 103
Creswell [EM] Ⓤ 55
Crewe [VT] **10** Ⓟ 🚲 ◇ 🚕
Aberdeen 65, *Sleepers* 402
Aberystwyth 75
Bangor (Gwynedd) 81
Barrow-in-Furness 65
Birmingham 65
Birmingham International 65
Blackpool 65
Blaenau Ffestiniog 102
Bournemouth 51
Bristol 51, 131
Cardiff 131
Carlisle 65
Cheltenham Spa 51
Chester 81
Coventry 65
Derby 50
Douglas (IOM) 98A
Dundee 65, *Sleepers* 402
East Croydon 51
Edinburgh 65
Exeter 51
Fort William *Sleepers* 404
Gatwick Airport 65

Station index and table numbers

[10] Connection time
Ⓟ Station Car Park
🚲 Bicycle storage facility
◇ Seat reservations can be made at this station
⚠ Penalty Fare Schemes in operation on some or all services from this station
🚕 Taxi rank or cab office at station, or signposted and within 100 metres
Ⓤ Unstaffed station
[ ] Station Operator Code

Glasgow 65
Hartford 91
Hereford 131
Holyhead 81
Inverkeithing *Sleepers* 402
Inverness 65, *Sleepers* 403
Kirkcaldy *Sleepers* 402
Lancaster 65
Liverpool 91
Liverpool South Parkway 91
Llandudno 81
London 65
Manchester 84
Manchester Airport 84
Milton Keynes Central 65
Newport (South Wales) 131
Nottingham 50
Oxenholme Lake District 65
Oxford 51
Paignton 51
Penzance 51
Perth 65, *Sleepers* 403
Plymouth 51
Preston 65
Reading 51
Rugby 65
Runcorn 91
Shrewsbury 131
Southampton 51
Stafford 65
Stirling *Sleepers* 403
Stockport 84
Stoke-on-Trent 50
Torquay 51
Watford 65
Wilmslow 84
Wolverhampton 65
Crewkerne [SW] Ⓟ 🚲 ◇ 160
Crews Hill [FC] ⚠ Ⓤ 24
Crianlarich [SR] Ⓟ 🚲 Ⓤ 227, *Sleepers* 404
Criccieth [AW] Ⓟ 🚲 Ⓤ 75
Cricklewood [FC] 🚲 ◇ ⚠ 52
Croftfoot [SR] 🚲 223
Crofton Park [SE] ⚠ 195
Cromer [LE] Ⓟ 🚲 Ⓤ 16
Cromford [EM] Ⓟ Ⓤ 54, 56
Crompton [NT] (see Shaw)
Crookston [SR] 🚲 Ⓤ 217
Crosby [ME] (see Blundellsands)
Crossflatts [NT] Ⓟ 🚲 Ⓤ 36
Cross Gates [NT] Ⓟ 41
Crosshill [SR] 223
Crosskeys [AW] Ⓤ 127
Crossmyloof [SR] 🚲 Ⓤ 222
Croston [NT] Ⓟ Ⓤ 99
Crouch Hill [LO] Ⓤ 62
Crowborough [SN] Ⓟ 184
Crowhurst [SE] Ⓟ 206
Crowle [NT] Ⓤ 29
Crowthorne [GW] Ⓟ 🚲 148
Croy [SR] [3] Ⓟ 🚲 228, 230
Croydon
see East Croydon
see South Croydon
see West Croydon
Crystal Palace [SN] [4] Ⓟ ⚠ 177, 178
Cuddington [NT] Ⓟ Ⓤ 88
Cuffley [FC] Ⓟ 🚲 ⚠ 🚕 24
Culdrose (R.N.A.S.) *Bus* 135A
Culham [GW] Ⓟ 🚲 Ⓤ 116
Culrain [SR] 🚲 Ⓤ 239
Cumbernauld [SR] Ⓟ 🚲 🚕 224
Cupar [SR] Ⓟ 🚲 ◇ 51, 229
Curriehill [SR] Ⓟ 🚲 Ⓤ 225
Cuxton [SE] Ⓟ Ⓤ 208
Cwmbach [AW] Ⓟ Ⓤ 130
Cwmbran [AW] Ⓟ 🚲 ◇ 🚕 131
Cynghordy [AW] Ⓤ 129

D

Dagenham Dock [CC] Ⓟ ◇ ⚠ 1
Daisy Hill [NT] Ⓟ 🚲 82
Dalgety Bay [SR] Ⓟ 🚲 🚕 Ⓤ 242
Dalmally [SR] Ⓟ 🚲 Ⓤ 227
Dalmarnock [SR] 226
Dalmeny [SR] Ⓟ 🚲 242
Dalmuir [SR] Ⓟ 🚲 226, 227, *Sleepers* 404
Dalreoch [SR] Ⓟ 🚲 226
Dalry [SR] Ⓟ 🚲 Ⓤ 221
Dalston [NT] Ⓟ Ⓤ 100
Dalston Kingsland [LO] 59
Dalton [NT] Ⓟ Ⓤ 82
Dalwhinnie [SR] Ⓟ 🚲 Ⓤ 229, *Sleepers* 403
Danby [NT] Ⓟ Ⓤ 45
Danescourt [AW] Ⓤ 130
Danzey [LM] Ⓟ ⚠ Ⓤ 71
Darfield Saltersbrook Road *Bus* 26D
Darlington [GR] [7] Ⓟ 🚲 ◇ 🚕
Aberdeen 26
Birmingham 51
Bishop Auckland 44
Bournemouth 51
Brighton 51
Bristol 51
Cambridge 26
Cardiff 51
Catterick Garrison *Bus* 26H
Derby 51
Doncaster 26
Durham 26
Durham Tees Valley Airport *Bus* 26J
Dundee 26
Edinburgh 26
Exeter 51
Glasgow 26
Grantham 26
Huddersfield 39
Leeds 26
Liverpool 39
London 26
Manchester 39
Manchester Airport 39
Middlesbrough 44
Newark 26
Newcastle 26
Newport (South Wales) 51
Norwich 26
Northallerton 26
Oxford 51
Paignton 51
Penzance 51
Peterborough 26
Plymouth 51
Reading 51
Redcar 44
Retford 26
Richmond *Bus* 26H
Saltburn 44
Sheffield 26
Southampton 51
Stansted Airport 26
Sunderland 26, 44
Torquay 51
Whitby 45
York 26
Darnall [NT] Ⓤ 30
Darnley [SR] (see Priesthill)
Darsham [LE] Ⓟ 🚲 Ⓤ 13
Dartford [SE] [4] Ⓟ ◇ ⚠ 🚕 200, 212
Darton [NT] Ⓟ Ⓤ 34
Darwen [NT] Ⓤ 94
Datchet [SW] 🚲 ⚠ 149
Davenport [NT] Ⓟ 86
Dawlish [GW] Ⓟ ◇ 🚕 51, 135, 160
Dawlish Warren [GW] Ⓟ 🚲 Ⓤ 135, 160
Deal [SE] Ⓟ 🚲 ◇ 🚕 207
Dean [GW] 🚲 Ⓤ 123, 158
Dean Lane [NT] Ⓤ 95
Deansgate [NT] 82, 84, 85, 86, 89
Deganwy [AW] Ⓤ 81, 102
Deighton [NT] Ⓤ 39
Delamere [NT] Ⓟ Ⓤ 88
Denby Dale [NT] Ⓟ Ⓤ 34
Denham [CH] Ⓟ 🚲 ◇ ⚠ 🚕 115
Denham Golf Club [CH] ⚠ Ⓤ 115
Denmark Hill [SE] [4] ⚠ 178, 195, 200
Dent [NT] Ⓤ 36
Denton [NT] Ⓤ 78
Deptford [SE] ⚠ 200
Derby [EM] [10] Ⓟ 🚲 ◇ 🚕
Barnsley 53
Bedford 53
Belper 53, 56
Birmingham 57
Birmingham International 51
Bournemouth 51
Brighton 51
Bristol 57
Burton-on-Trent 57

[10] Connection time
Ⓟ Station Car Park
🚲 Bicycle storage facility
◇ Seat reservations can be made at this station
⚠ Penalty Fare Schemes in operation on some or all services from this station
🚕 Taxi rank or cab office at station, or signposted and within 100 metres
Ⓤ Unstaffed station
[ ] Station Operator Code

Station index and table numbers

- Cardiff 57
- Chesterfield 53
- Coventry 51
- Crewe 50
- Doncaster 53
- East Croydon 51
- Edinburgh 51
- Exeter 51
- Gatwick Airport 53
- Gloucester 57
- Kettering 53
- Leeds 53
- Leicester 53
- London 53
- Long Eaton 56
- Loughborough 53
- Luton 53
- Market Harborough 53
- Matlock 56
- Meadowhall 53
- Newcastle 51
- Newport (South Wales) 57
- Nottingham 57
- Oxford 51
- Paignton 51
- Penzance 51
- Plymouth 51
- Reading 51
- Sheffield 53
- Southampton 51
- Stoke-on-Trent 50
- Swansea 57
- Wakefield 53
- Wellingborough 53
- York 53

Derby Road [LE] 🚲 Ⓤ 13
Dereham 🚕 *Bus* 26A
Derker [NT] Ⓤ 95
Devonport [GW] Ⓟ 🚲 Ⓤ 135, 139
Dewsbury [TP] Ⓟ 🚲 ◇ 🚕 39
Didcot Parkway [GW] Ⓟ 🚲 ◇ ⚠ 🚕 116, 125
Digby & Sowton [GW] Ⓟ Ⓤ 136
Dilton Marsh [GW] Ⓤ 123
Dinas Powys [AW] Ⓤ 130
Dinas Rhondda [AW] Ⓟ Ⓤ 130
Dingle Road [AW] Ⓤ 130
Dingwall [SR] Ⓟ 🚲 ◇ 🚕 239
Dinsdale [NT] Ⓤ 44
Dinting [NT] **[3]** Ⓟ 🚲 79
Disley [NT] Ⓟ 86
Diss [LE] Ⓟ 🚲 ◇ 🚕 11
Dockyard [GW] Ⓤ 135, 139
Dodworth [NT] Ⓟ Ⓤ 34
Dolau [AW] 🚲 Ⓤ 129
Doleham [SN] Ⓤ 189
Dolgarrog [AW] Ⓤ 102
Dolwyddelan [AW] Ⓟ Ⓤ 102
Doncaster [GR] **[7]** Ⓟ 🚲 ◇ 🚕

- Aberdeen 26
- Bedford 53
- Birmingham 51
- Bournemouth 51
- Brighton 51
- Bristol 51
- Cambridge 26
- Cleethorpes 29
- Darlington 26
- Derby 53
- Dundee 26
- Durham 26
- Edinburgh 26
- Exeter 51
- Gainsborough 18
- Glasgow 26
- Goole 29
- Grantham 26
- Grimsby 29
- Hull 29
- Leeds 31
- Leicester 53
- Lincoln 18
- London 26
- Luton 53
- Manchester 29
- Manchester Airport 29
- Middlesbrough 26
- Newark 26
- Newcastle 26
- Norwich 26
- Nottingham 53
- Oxford 51
- Paignton 51
- Penzance 51
- Peterborough 18, 26
- Plymouth 51
- Reading 51
- Retford 26
- Robin Hood Airport *Bus* 26F
- Rotherham 29
- Scunthorpe 29
- Selby 29
- Sheffield 29
- Sleaford 18
- Southampton 51
- Spalding 18
- Stansted Airport 26
- Stevenage 26
- Stockport 29
- Sunderland 26
- Torquay 51
- Wakefield 31
- York 26

Doncaster Interchange *Bus* 26E, 26F
Dorchester South [SW] Ⓟ 🚲 ◇ ⚠ 🚕 158
Dorchester West [GW] Ⓤ 123, 158
Dore [NT] Ⓟ Ⓤ 78
Dorking [SN] **[4]** Ⓟ 🚲 ◇ ⚠ 🚕 152, 182
Dorking Deepdene [GW] Ⓤ 148
Dorking West [GW] Ⓤ 148
Dormans [SN] ⚠ 184
Dorridge [LM] Ⓟ 🚲 ◇ ⚠ 71, 115
Douglas (IOM) *Ship* 98A
Dove Holes [NT] Ⓟ Ⓤ 86
Dovercourt [LE] Ⓟ 🚲 11
Dover Priory [SE] **[4]** Ⓟ 🚲 ◇ 🚕 207, 212
Dovey Junction [AW] **[4]** Ⓤ 75
Downham Market [FC] Ⓟ 🚲 ⚠ 🚕 17
Drayton Green [GW] Ⓤ 117
Drayton Park [FC] 🚲 ⚠ 24
Drem [SR] Ⓟ 🚲 Ⓤ 238
Driffield [NT] Ⓟ 🚲 🚕 43
Drigg [NT] Ⓟ Ⓤ 100
Droitwich Spa [LM] Ⓟ ◇ ⚠ 71
Dronfield [NT] Ⓟ Ⓤ 53
Drumchapel [SR] Ⓟ 🚲 🚕 226
Drumfrochar [SR] 🚲 Ⓤ 219
Drumgelloch [SR] 🚲 Ⓤ 226
Drumry [SR] Ⓟ 🚲 226
Dublin Ferryport *Ship* 81A
Duddeston [LM] ⚠ 69, 70
Dudley Port [LM] Ⓟ ⚠ 68
Duffield [EM] Ⓟ Ⓤ 56
Duirinish [SR] Ⓟ 🚲 Ⓤ 239
Duke Street [SR] 🚲 Ⓤ 226
Dullingham [LE] Ⓟ 🚲 Ⓤ 14
Dumbarton Central [SR] 🚲 ◇ 🚕 226, 227
Dumbarton East [SR] 🚲 Ⓤ 226
Dumbreck [SR] 🚲 Ⓤ 217
Dumfries [SR] Ⓟ 🚲 ◇ 🚕 216, 218
Dumpton Park [SE] Ⓤ 207, 212
Dun Laoghaire *Ship* 81A
Dunbar [GR] Ⓟ 🚲 ◇ 26, 51
Dunblane [SR] Ⓟ 🚲 ◇ 229, 230, *Sleepers* 403
Duncraig [SR] 🚲 Ⓤ 239
Dundee [SR] Ⓟ 🚲 ◇ 🚕 26, 51, 65, 229, *Sleepers* 402
Dunfermline Queen Margaret [SR] Ⓟ 🚲 Ⓤ 242
Dunfermline Town [SR] Ⓟ 🚲 ◇ 🚕 242
Dunkeld & Birnam [SR] Ⓟ 🚲 Ⓤ 229, *Sleepers* 403
Dunlop [SR] 🚲 Ⓤ 222
Dunoon *Ship* 219A
Dunrobin Castle [SR] Ⓤ *Summer only* 239
Duns *Bus* 26K
Dunstable *Bus* 52A
Dunster Steep *Bus* 135E
Dunston [NT] Ⓤ 48
Dunton Green [SE] Ⓟ ⚠ Ⓤ 204
Durham [GR] Ⓟ 🚲 ◇ 🚕 26, 39, 44, 51
Durham Tees Valley Airport *Bus* 🚕 26J
Durrington-on-Sea [SN] 🚲 ⚠ 188
Dursley [GW] (see Cam & Dursley)
Dyce [SR] Ⓟ 🚲 🚕 Ⓤ 229, 240
Dyffryn Ardudwy [AW] Ⓤ 75

Station index and table numbers

⟦10⟧ Connection time
Ⓟ Station Car Park
🚲 Bicycle storage facility
◇ Seat reservations can be made at this station
⚠ Penalty Fare Schemes in operation on some or all services from this station
🚕 Taxi rank or cab office at station, or signposted and within 100 metres
Ⓤ Unstaffed station
[ ] Station Operator Code

E

Eaglescliffe [NT] Ⓟ 🚲 🚕 Ⓤ 26, 44
Ealing Broadway [GW] ⟦3⟧ ◇ ⚠ 🚕 116, 117
Earlestown [NT] ⟦8⟧ 81, 90
Earley [SW] Ⓟ 🚲 ⚠ 149
Earlsfield [SW] 🚲 ⚠ 152, 155
Earlston *Bus* 26K
Earlswood (Surrey) [SN] 🚲 ◇ ⚠ 186
Earlswood (West Midlands) [LM] Ⓟ ⚠ Ⓤ 71
East Croydon [SN] 🚲 ◇ ⚠ 🚕
- Aberdeen 51
- Bedford 52
- Bexhill 189
- Birmingham 66
- Birmingham International 66
- Bognor Regis 188
- Brighton 186
- Carlisle 51
- Caterham 181
- Chichester 188
- Clapham Junction 175
- Coventry 66
- Crewe 51
- Eastbourne 189
- East Grinstead 184
- Edinburgh 51
- Gatwick Airport 186
- Glasgow 51
- Hastings 189
- Haywards Heath 186
- Horsham 186
- Hove 186
- Kensington Olympia 66, 186
- Lewes 189
- Littlehampton 188
- London 175
- Luton 52
- Luton Airport Parkway 52
- Manchester 51
- Milton Keynes Central 66
- Northampton 66
- Norwood Junction 177, 178
- Oxford 51
- Oxted 184
- Portsmouth 188
- Preston 51
- Purley 175
- Redhill 186
- Rugby 66
- St Albans 52
- St Pancras International 52
- Seaford 189
- Southampton Central 188
- Tattenham Corner 181
- Tonbridge 186, 209
- Uckfield 184
- Watford Junction 66, 186
- West Hampstead Thameslink 52
- Wolverhampton 66
- Worthing 188

East Didsbury [NT] Ⓟ 85
East Dulwich [SN] ⚠ 177, 179
East Farleigh [SE] Ⓟ Ⓤ 208
East Garforth [NT] Ⓤ 41
East Grinstead [SN] Ⓟ 🚲 ◇ ⚠ 🚕 184
East Kilbride [SR] Ⓟ 🚲 ◇ 🚕 222
East Malling [SE] ⚠ Ⓤ 196
East Tilbury [CC] ◇ ⚠ 1
East Worthing [SN] ⚠ Ⓤ 188
Eastbourne [SN] ⟦4⟧ Ⓟ 🚲 ◇ ⚠ 🚕 189
Eastbrook [AW] Ⓟ Ⓤ 130
Easterhouse [SR] Ⓟ 🚲 226
Eastfield [SN] 52, 179, 182
Eastham Rake [ME] Ⓟ 🚲 106
Eastleigh [SW] ⟦3⟧ Ⓟ 🚲 ◇ ⚠ 🚕 158
Eastrington [NT] Ⓟ Ⓤ 29
Ebbw Vale Parkway [AW] Ⓟ Ⓤ 127
Eccles [NT] 90
Eccles Road [LE] Ⓟ Ⓤ 17
Eccleston Park [NT] Ⓟ 90
Edale [NT] Ⓟ Ⓤ 78
Eden Camp *Bus* 26G
Eden Park [SE] ⚠ 203
Eden Project *Bus* 135B
Edenbridge [SE] Ⓟ Ⓤ 209
Edenbridge Town [SN] 🚕 184
Edge Hill [NT] Ⓟ 89, 90, 91
Edinburgh [NR] ⟦10⟧ Ⓟ 🚲 ◇ 🚕
- Aberdeen 229
- Bathgate 230
- Birmingham New Street 51, 65
- Birmingham International 51, 65
- Blackpool 65
- Bournemouth 51
- Brighton 51
- Bristol 51
- Cambridge 26
- Cardiff 51
- Carlisle 65
- Carstairs 225
- Cowdenbeath 242
- Crewe 65
- Croy 228
- Cumbernauld 224
- Darlington 26
- Derby 51
- Doncaster 26
- Dunblane 230
- Dundee 229
- Dunfermline 242
- Dyce 229
- Edinburgh Park 230
- Exeter 51
- Falkirk 228, 230
- Fort William 227
- Gatwick Airport 51, 65
- Glasgow 225, 228
- Glenrothes with Thornton 242
- Grantham 26
- Inverkeithing 242
- Inverness 229
- Kirkcaldy 242
- Kyle of Lochalsh 239
- Lancaster 65
- Larbert 230
- Leeds 26
- Linlithgow 230
- Liverpool 65
- Livingston 225, 230
- London 26, *Sleepers* 400
- Mallaig 227
- Manchester 65
- Manchester Airport 65
- Markinch 242
- Motherwell 225
- Newcastle 26
- Newcraighall 230
- Newport (South Wales) 51
- North Berwick 238
- Oban 227
- Oxenholme Lake District 65
- Oxford 51
- Paignton 51
- Penzance 51
- Perth 229
- Peterborough 26
- Plymouth 51
- Polmont 230
- Preston 65
- Reading 51
- Sheffield 26
- Shotts 225
- Southampton 51
- Springburn 224
- Stafford 65
- Stirling 230
- Thurso 239
- Torquay 51
- Warrington 65
- Watford 65, *Sleepers* 400
- West Calder 225
- Western Isles *Ship* 239B
- Wick 239
- Wigan 65
- York 26

Edinburgh Park [SR] 🚲 Ⓤ 230
Edmonton Green [LE] ⚠ 21
Effingham Junction [SW] ⟦6⟧ Ⓟ 🚲 ⚠ 152, 182
Eggesford [GW] Ⓟ Ⓤ 136
Egham [SW] Ⓟ 🚲 🚕 149
Egton [NT] Ⓟ Ⓤ 45
Eigg *Ship* 227A
Elephant & Castle [FC] 🚲 ◇ ⚠
- Ashford 196
- Bromley South 195
- Canterbury 212
- Catford 195
- Chatham 212
- Dover 212
- East Croydon 177
- Faversham 212
- London 52, 177

Station index and table numbers

[10] Connection time
Ⓟ Station Car Park
🚲 Bicycle storage facility
◇ Seat reservations can be made at this station
⚠ Penalty Fare Schemes in operation on some or all services from this station
🚕 Taxi rank or cab office at station, or signposted and within 100 metres
Ⓤ Unstaffed station
[ ] Station Operator Code

F

Station index and table numbers

[10] Connection time
Ⓟ Station Car Park
🚲 Bicycle storage facility
◇ Seat reservations can be made at this station
⚠ Penalty Fare Schemes in operation on some or all services from this station
🚕 Taxi rank or cab office at station, or signposted and within 100 metres
Ⓤ Unstaffed station
[ ] Station Operator Code

G

■10 Connection time
Ⓟ Station Car Park
🚲 Bicycle storage facility
◇ Seat reservations can be made at this station
⚠ Penalty Fare Schemes in operation on some or all services from this station
🚕 Taxi rank or cab office at station, or signposted and within 100 metres
ⓤ Unstaffed station
[ ] Station Operator Code

Station index and table numbers

Newcastle 26, 216
Newton 223, 226
Norwich 26
Oban 227
Oxenholme Lake District 65
Oxford 51
Paignton 51
Paisley 217, 219, 221
Penzance 51
Perth 229
Peterborough 26
Plymouth 51
Preston 65
Prestwick International Airport 221
Reading 51
Sheffield 26
Shotts 225
Southampton 51
Springburn 224, 226
Stafford 65
Stirling 230
Stranraer 218
Thurso 239
Torquay 51
Warrington 51
Watford 65, *Sleepers* 401
Wemyss Bay 219
Western Isles *Ship*
via Inverness 239B
via Mallaig 227A
via Oban 227B, 227C
Whifflet 220
Wick 239
Wigan 65
York 26

Glasshoughton [NT] Ⓟ 🚲 ⓤ 32
Glazebrook [NT] Ⓟ 89
Gleneagles [SR] Ⓟ 🚲 ⓤ 229, *Sleepers* 403
Glenfinnan [SR] Ⓟ 🚲 ⓤ 227
Glengarnock [SR] Ⓟ 🚲 221
Glenrothes With Thornton [SR] Ⓟ 🚲 ⓤ 242
Glossop [NT] Ⓟ 🚲 79
Gloucester [GW] ■7 Ⓟ 🚲 ◇ 🚕
Birmingham 57
Bristol 134
Cardiff 132
Carmarthen 128
Cheltenham 57
Chepstow 132
Derby 57
Didcot 125
Gatwick Airport 125
Heathrow Airport 125
Kemble 125
London 125
Lydney 132
Maesteg 128
Newcastle 51
Newport (South Wales) 132
Nottingham 57
Reading 125
Sheffield 51
Stroud 125
Swansea 128
Swindon 125
Taunton 134
Weston-super-Mare 134
Worcester 57
York 51

Glynde [SN] Ⓟ ⓤ 189
Goathland [NY] 45
Gobowen [AW] Ⓟ 75
Godalming [SW] Ⓟ 🚲 ⚠ 🚕 156
Godley [NT] ⓤ 79
Godstone [SE] ⓤ 209
Goldthorpe [NT] Ⓟ ⓤ 31
Goldthorpe Police Station *Bus* 26E
Golf Street [SR] ⓤ 229
Golspie [SR] Ⓟ 🚲 ⓤ 239
Gomshall [GW] Ⓟ ⓤ 148
Goodmayes [LE] 🚲 ⚠ 5
Goole [NT] Ⓟ 🚲 ◇ 🚕 29, 32
Goostrey [NT] Ⓟ ⓤ 84
Gordon Hill [FC] Ⓟ 🚲 ⚠ 24
Goring & Streatley [GW] Ⓟ 🚲 116
Goring-by-Sea [SN] Ⓟ 🚲 ⚠ 188
Gorton [NT] 78, 79
Gospel Oak [LO] 59, 62
Gourock [SR] Ⓟ 🚲 ◇ 🚕 219, *Ship* 219A
Gowerton [AW] Ⓟ ⓤ 128, 129
Goxhill [NT] ⓤ 29
Grange Park [FC] Ⓟ ⚠ 24
Grange-over-Sands [TP] ◇ 82
Grangetown [AW] ⓤ 130
Grantham [GR] ■7 Ⓟ 🚲 ◇ 🚕 19, 26, 49
Grateley [SW] Ⓟ 🚲 ⚠ ⓤ 160
Gravelly Hill [LM] ⚠ 69
Gravesend [SE] ■4 Ⓟ ◇ ⚠ 🚕 200, 209, 212
Grays [CC] Ⓟ 🚲 ◇ ⚠ 🚕 1
Great Ayton [NT] Ⓟ 🚲 ⓤ 45
Great Bentley [LE] 🚲 ⚠ 11
Great Chesterford [LE] ⚠ 22
Great Coates [NT] ⓤ 29
Great Malvern [LM] Ⓟ ◇ ⚠ 71, 126
Great Missenden [CH] Ⓟ 🚲 ◇ ⚠ 🚕 114
Great Yarmouth [LE] Ⓟ 🚲 ◇ 🚕 15
Green Lane [ME] 106
Green Road [NT] Ⓟ ⓤ 100
Greenbank [NT] Ⓟ ⓤ 88
Greenfaulds [SR] Ⓟ 🚲 ⓤ 224
Greenfield [NT] 🚲 39
Greenford [LT] Ⓟ ⚠ 117
Greenhithe for Bluewater [SE] ⚠ 200, 209, 212
Greenock Central [SR] Ⓟ 🚲 219
Greenock West [SR] 🚕 219
Greenwich [SE] ■4 ⚠ 200
Gretna Green [SR] Ⓟ 🚲 ⓤ 216
Grimsby Docks [NT] ⓤ 29
Grimsby Town [TP] Ⓟ 🚲 ◇ 🚕 26, 27, 29, 30
Grindleford [NT] ⓤ 78
Grosmont [NT] Ⓟ ⓤ 45
Grove Park [SE] ■4 ⚠ 204
Guide Bridge [NT] Ⓟ 78, 79
Guildford [SW] Ⓟ 🚲 ◇ ⚠ 🚕
Ascot 149
Birmingham 51
Clapham Junction 152, 155, 156
Gatwick Airport 148
London 152, 155, 156
Portsmouth 156
Reading 148
Surbiton 152
West Croydon 182

Guiseley [NT] Ⓟ 🚲 ◇ 38
Gunnersbury [LT] 59
Gunnislake [GW] Ⓟ 🚲 ⓤ 139
Gunton [LE] Ⓟ 🚲 ⓤ 16
Gwersyllt [AW] Ⓟ ⓤ 101
Gypsy Lane [NT] 🚲 ⓤ 45

H

Habrough [NT] Ⓟ ⓤ 27, 29, 30
Hackbridge [SN] Ⓟ ◇ ⚠ 52, 179, 182
Hackney Central [LO] 🚕 59
Hackney Downs [LE] 🚲 ⚠ 20, 21, 22
Hackney Wick [LO] 59
Haddenham & Thame Parkway [CH] Ⓟ 🚲 ◇ ⚠ 🚕 115
Haddiscoe [LE] Ⓟ 🚲 ⓤ 15
Hadfield [NT] Ⓟ 🚲 79
Hadley Wood [FC] ⚠ 24
Hag Fold [NT] 82
Hagley [LM] Ⓟ ⚠ 71
Hairmyres [SR] Ⓟ 🚲 ⓤ 222
Hale [NT] 88
Halesworth [LE] Ⓟ 🚲 ⓤ 13
Halewood [NT] 89
Halifax [NT] Ⓟ 🚲 ◇ 🚕 41
Hall Green [LM] Ⓟ ⚠ 71
Hall I' Th' Wood [NT] ⓤ 94
Hall Road [ME] 🚲 103
Halling [SE] ⓤ 208
Haltwhistle [NT] Ⓟ 🚲 ⓤ 48
Ham Street [SN] Ⓟ 189
Hamble [SW] 🚲 ⚠ ⓤ 165
Hamilton Central [SR] Ⓟ 🚲 ◇ 🚕 226
Hamilton Square [ME] ◇ 🚕 106
Hamilton West [SR] Ⓟ 🚲 🚕 226
Hammerton [NT] Ⓟ ⓤ 35
Hampden Park [SN] ■4 ⚠ 189
Hampstead Heath [LO] 59
Hampstead (South) [LO] (see South Hampstead)

Station index and table numbers

10 Connection time
Ⓟ Station Car Park
🚲 Bicycle storage facility
◇ Seat reservations can be made at this station
⚠ Penalty Fare Schemes in operation on some or all services from this station
🚕 Taxi rank or cab office at station, or signposted and within 100 metres
Ⓤ Unstaffed station
[ ] Station Operator Code

10 Connection time
Ⓟ Station Car Park
🚲 Bicycle storage facility
◇ Seat reservations can be made at this station
⚠ Penalty Fare Schemes in operation on some or all services from this station
🚕 Taxi rank or cab office at station, or signposted and within 100 metres
ⓤ Unstaffed station
[ ] Station Operator Code

Station index and table numbers

I

Station index and table numbers

〔10〕 Connection time
Ⓟ Station Car Park
🚲 Bicycle storage facility
◇ Seat reservations can be made at this station
⚠ Penalty Fare Schemes in operation on some or all services from this station
🚕 Taxi rank or cab office at station, or signposted and within 100 metres
Ⓤ Unstaffed station
[ ] Station Operator Code

Station index and table numbers

10 Connection time
Ⓟ Station Car Park
🚲 Bicycle storage facility
◇ Seat reservations can be made at this station
⚠ Penalty Fare Schemes in operation on some or all services from this station
🚕 Taxi rank or cab office at station, or signposted and within 100 metres
🚹 Unstaffed station
[ ] Station Operator Code

Dundee 229
Edinburgh 242
Inverness 229
London 26, *Sleepers* 402
Newcastle 26
Oxford 51
Penzance 51
Perth 229
Plymouth 51
Preston 51, *Sleepers* 402
Reading 51
Sheffield 51
Southampton 51
York 26

Kirkconnel [SR] Ⓟ 🚲 🚹 216
Kirkdale [ME] 103
Kirkham & Wesham [NT] Ⓟ ◇ 82, 97
Kirk Sandall [NT] Ⓟ 🚹 29
Kirkhill [SR] Ⓟ 🚹 223
Kirknewton [SR] Ⓟ 🚲 🚹 225
Kirkoswald [NT] (see Lazonby)
Kirkwood [SR] 🚹 220
Kirton Lindsey [NT] Ⓟ 🚹 30
Kiveton Bridge [NT] 🚹 30
Kiveton Park [NT] Ⓟ 🚹 30
Knaresborough [NT] Ⓟ 🚹 35
Knebworth [FC] Ⓟ 🚲 ⚠ 24, 25
Knighton [AW] 🚹 129
Knockholt [SE] Ⓟ ⚠ 204
Knottingley [NT] Ⓟ 🚹 32
Knucklas [AW] 🚹 129
Knutsford [NT] Ⓟ 88
Kyle of Lochalsh [SR] Ⓟ 🚲 ◇ 239, *Ship* 239B

L

Ladybank [SR] Ⓟ 🚲 229
Ladywell [SE] 🚲 ⚠ 203
Laindon [CC] Ⓟ 🚲 ◇ ⚠ 🚕 1
Lairg [SR] Ⓟ 🚲 🚹 239
Lake [IL] (IOW) 🚹 167
Lake District [VT] (see Oxenholme)
Lakenheath [LE] 🚹 17
Lamphey [AW] 🚹 128
Lanark [SR] Ⓟ 🚲 🚕 226
Lancaster [VT] **6** Ⓟ 🚲 ◇ 🚕
Aberdeen 65
Barrow-in-Furness 82
Birmingham 65
Blackpool 65
Bolton 82
Bournemouth 51
Bradford 36
Brighton 51
Bristol 51
Carlisle 65
Chorley 82
Crewe 65
Douglas (IOM) 98A
Edinburgh 65
Exeter 51
Glasgow 65
Heysham Port 98
Leeds 36
Liverpool 65
London 65
Manchester 82
Manchester Airport 82
Millom 100
Milton Keynes Central 65
Morecambe 98
Oxenholme Lake District 65
Oxford 51
Paignton 51
Penzance 51
Plymouth 51
Preston 65
Reading 51
Skipton 36
Southampton 51
Stafford 65
Torquay 51
Warrington 65
Whitehaven 100
Wigan 65
Windermere 65
Workington 100

Lancing [SN] Ⓟ 🚲 ⚠ 🚕 188
Landywood [LM] Ⓟ ⚠ 🚹 70
Langbank [SR] Ⓟ 🚲 🚹 219
Langho [NT] Ⓟ 🚹 94
Langholm *Bus* 65G
Langley [GW] Ⓟ 🚲 ⚠ 🚕 117
Langley Green [LM] Ⓟ ⚠ 71
Langley Mill [EM] 🚹 49, 53
Langside [SR] 🚲 🚹 223
Langwathby [NT] Ⓟ 🚹 36
Langwith - Whaley Thorns [EM] 🚹 55
Lapford [GW] 🚹 136
Lapworth [CH] Ⓟ ⚠ 🚹 71, 115
Larbert [SR] Ⓟ 🚲 ◇ 229, 230
Largs [SR] Ⓟ 🚲 🚕 221
Larkhall [SR] 🚲 🚹 226
Latimer [LT] (see Chalfont & Latimer)
Lawrence Hill [GW] 🚹 133, 134
Layton [NT] Ⓟ 🚹 82, 97
Lazonby & Kirkoswald [NT] Ⓟ 🚹 36
Lea Green [NT] Ⓟ 🚲 90
Lea Hall [LM] Ⓟ ⚠ 68
Leagrave [FC] Ⓟ 🚲 ◇ ⚠ 🚕 52
Lealholm [NT] 🚹 45
Leamington Spa [CH] **8** Ⓟ 🚲 ◇ ⚠ 🚕 51, 71, 115, 116
Leasowe [ME] Ⓟ 106
Leatherhead [SN] Ⓟ 🚲 ◇ ⚠ 🚕 152, 182
Ledbury [LM] Ⓟ ⚠ 🚹 71, 126
Lee [SE] Ⓟ ⚠ 200
Leeds [NR] **10** Ⓟ 🚲 ◇ 🚕
Barnsley 34
Bedford 53
Birmingham 51
Birmingham International 51
Blackburn 41
Blackpool 41
Bournemouth 51
Bradford 37
Brighouse 41
Bristol 51
Burnley 41
Cambridge 26
Cardiff 51
Carlisle 36
Carnforth 36
Chesterfield 53
Darlington 26
Derby 53
Dewsbury 39
Doncaster 31
Edinburgh 26
Exeter 51
Gatwick Airport 53
Glasgow 26, 36
Goole 32
Grantham 26
Halifax 41
Harrogate 35
Huddersfield 39
Hull 39
Ilkley 38
Keighley 36
Knaresborough 35
Lancaster 36
Leicester 53
Liverpool 39, 41
London 26, 53
Luton 53
Manchester 39, 41
Manchester Airport 39
Meadowhall 31
Morecambe 36
Newark 26
Newcastle 26
Newport (South Wales) 51
Norwich 26
Nottingham 53
Oxford 51
Paignton 51
Penzance 51
Peterborough 26
Plymouth 51
Preston 41
Reading 51
Retford 26
Rochdale 41
Scarborough 39
Selby 41
Settle 36
Sheffield 31
Shipley 37
Skipton 36
Stansted Airport 26
Southampton 51
Torquay 51
Wakefield 31
Warrington 39

Station index and table numbers

10 Connection time
Ⓟ Station Car Park
🚲 Bicycle storage facility
◇ Seat reservations can be made at this station
⚠ Penalty Fare Schemes in operation on some or all services from this station
🚕 Taxi rank or cab office at station, or signposted and within 100 metres
Ⓤ Unstaffed station
[ ] Station Operator Code

York 35, 41
Leicester [EM] Ⓟ 🚲 ◇ 🚕 49, 53, 57
Leigh (Kent) [SE] Ⓤ 209
Leigh-on-Sea [CC] Ⓟ 🚲 ◇ ⚠ 🚕 1
Leighton Buzzard [LM] Ⓟ 🚲 ◇ 🚕 66
Lelant [GW] Ⓟ Ⓤ 144
Lelant Saltings [GW] Ⓟ Ⓤ 144
Lenham [SE] Ⓟ ⚠ 196
Lenzie [SR] **3** Ⓟ 🚲 🚕 228, 230
Leominster [AW] Ⓟ 131
Letchworth Garden City [FC] 🚲 ⚠ 🚕 24, 25
Leuchars (for St. Andrews) **[SR]** **3** Ⓟ 🚲 ◇ 🚕 26, 51, 229, *Sleepers* 402
Levenshulme [NT] 84, 86
Lewes [SN] **4** Ⓟ 🚲 ◇ ⚠ 🚕 186, 189
Lewisham [SE] **4** Ⓟ 🚲 ⚠ 🚕
Bexleyheath 200
Dartford 200
Gillingham (Kent) 200
Gravesend 200
Hayes (Kent) 203
London 195, 199
Orpington 199, 204
Sidcup 200
Woolwich Arsenal 200
Leyland [NT] Ⓟ ◇ 🚕 82, 90
Leyton Midland Road [LO] Ⓤ 62
Leytonstone High Road [LO] Ⓤ 62
Lichfield City [LM] Ⓟ ◇ ⚠ 69
Lichfield Trent Valley [LM] Ⓟ ◇ ⚠ 65, 67, 69
Lidlington [LM] Ⓤ 64
Limehouse [CC] ⚠ 1
Lincoln [EM] Ⓟ 🚲 ◇ 🚕 18, 26, 27, 30
Lincoln Bus Station *Bus* 26D
Lindford (Liphook Road) *Bus* 156A
Lingfield [SN] Ⓟ 🚲 ⚠ 🚕 184
Lingwood [LE] Ⓟ 🚲 Ⓤ 15
Linlithgow [SR] Ⓟ 🚲 ◇ 228, 230
Liphook [SW] Ⓟ 🚲 ⚠ 🚕 156, *Bus* 156A
Liskeard [GW] **3** Ⓟ 🚲 ◇ 51, 135, 140, *Sleepers* 406
Lismore *Ship* 227B
Liss [SW] Ⓟ 🚲 ⚠ 156
Lisvane & Thornhill [AW] Ⓟ Ⓤ 130
Litherland [ME] (see Seaforth & Litherland)
Little Kimble [CH] ⚠ Ⓤ 115
Little Sutton [ME] Ⓤ 106
Littleborough [NT] Ⓟ 41
Littlehampton [SN] **4** Ⓟ 🚲 ⚠ 🚕 186, 188
Littlehaven [SN] ◇ ⚠ 187
Littleport [FC] 🚲 ⚠ Ⓤ 17
Liverpool
Central [ME] **10** 🚕
James Street [ME] ◇
Lime Street (Main Line) **[NR]** **10** Ⓟ 🚲 ◇ 🚕
Lime Street (Low Level) **[ME]** **10** ◇ 🚕
Moorfields [ME] **10**
Aberdeen 65
Bangor (Gwynedd) 81
Barrow-in-Furness 65
Birkenhead 106
Birmingham 65
Birmingham International 65
Blackpool 65, 90
Bolton 82
Bradford 41
Cambridge 49
Cardiff 131
Carlisle 65
Chester 106
Coventry 65
Crewe 91
Darlington 39
Douglas (IOM) 98A
Dundee 65
Durham 39
Edinburgh 65
Ellesmere Port 106
Ely 49
Gatwick Airport 65
Glasgow 65
Hartford 91
Holyhead 81
Hooton 106
Huddersfield 39
Hull 39
Hunts Cross 89, 103
Inverness 65
Ipswich 49
Kirkby 103
Lancaster 65
Leeds 39, 41
Liverpool South Parkway 91
Llandudno 81
London 65
Manchester 89, 90
Manchester Airport 89
Middlesbrough 39
Milton Keynes Central 65
Mossley Hill 91
Motherwell 65
New Brighton 106
Newcastle 39
Newport (South Wales) 131
Norwich 49
Nottingham 49
Nuneaton 65
Ormskirk 103
Oxenholme Lake District 65
Peterborough 49
Preston 90, 99
Rhyl 81
Rochdale 95
Rock Ferry 106
Rugby 65
Runcorn 91
St Helens 90
Scarborough 39
Sheffield 89
Shrewsbury 131
Southport 103
Stafford 65
Stansted Airport 49
Stockport 89
Wakefield 39
Warrington 89, 90
Watford 65
West Kirby 106
Wigan 82, 90
Windermere 65
Wolverhampton 65
Wrexham 101
York 39
Liverpool Landing Stage *Ship* 98A
Liverpool South Parkway [ME] **7** Ⓟ 🚲 ⚠ 🚕 65, 89, 91, 103
Liverpool Street [NR] (see London)
Livingston North [SR] Ⓟ 🚲 Ⓤ 230
Livingston South [SR] Ⓟ 🚲 Ⓤ 225
Llanaber [AW] Ⓤ 75
Llanbedr [AW] Ⓤ 75
Llanbister Road [AW] Ⓤ 129
Llanbradach [AW] Ⓟ Ⓤ 130
Llandaf [AW] Ⓟ 130
Llandanwg [AW] Ⓤ 75
Llandecwyn [AW] Ⓤ 75
Llandeilo [AW] Ⓟ Ⓤ 129
Llandovery [AW] Ⓟ Ⓤ 129
Llandrindod [AW] Ⓟ ◇ 129
Llandudno [AW] ◇ 🚕 65, 81, 102
Llandudno Junction [AW] Ⓟ ◇ 🚕 65, 81, 102, 131
Llandybie [AW] Ⓟ Ⓤ 129
Llanelli [AW] ◇ 128, 129
Llanfairfechan [AW] Ⓟ Ⓤ 81
Llanfairpwll [AW] Ⓟ Ⓤ 81
Llangadog [AW] Ⓤ 129
Llangammarch [AW] Ⓤ 129
Llangennech [AW] Ⓤ 129
Llangynllo [AW] Ⓤ 129
Llanharan [AW] Ⓟ Ⓤ 128
Llanhilleth [AW] Ⓟ Ⓤ 127
Llanishen [AW] Ⓟ Ⓤ 130
Llanrwst [AW] Ⓤ 102
Llansamlet [AW] Ⓟ Ⓤ 128
Llantwit Major [AW] Ⓟ 🚲 Ⓤ 130
Llanwrda [AW] Ⓤ 129
Llanwrtyd [AW] Ⓟ Ⓤ 129
Llwyngwril [AW] Ⓤ 75
Llwynypia [AW] Ⓟ Ⓤ 130
Loch Awe [SR] Ⓟ 🚲 Ⓤ 227
Loch Eil Outward Bound [SR] 🚲 Ⓤ 227
Lochailort [SR] Ⓟ 🚲 Ⓤ 227

Station index and table numbers

- ■10 Connection time
- Ⓟ Station Car Park
- 🚲 Bicycle storage facility
- ◇ Seat reservations can be made at this station
- ⚠ Penalty Fare Schemes in operation on some or all services from this station
- 🚕 Taxi rank or cab office at station, or signposted and within 100 metres
- Ⓤ Unstaffed station
- [ ] Station Operator Code

Station index and table numbers

10 Connection time
Ⓟ Station Car Park
🚲 Bicycle storage facility
◇ Seat reservations can be made at this station
⚠ Penalty Fare Schemes in operation on some or all services from this station
🚕 Taxi rank or cab office at station, or signposted and within 100 metres
Ⓤ Unstaffed station
[ ] Station Operator Code

Station index and table numbers

[10] Connection time
Ⓟ Station Car Park
🚲 Bicycle storage facility
◇ Seat reservations can be made at this station
⚠ Penalty Fare Schemes in operation on some or all services from this station
🚕 Taxi rank or cab office at station, or signposted and within 100 metres
⊛ Unstaffed station
[ ] Station Operator Code

Lostwithiel [GW] Ⓟ ⊛ 135, *Sleepers* 406
Loughborough [EM] Ⓟ 🚲 ◇ 🚕 53
Loughborough Junction [FC] 🚲 ◇ ⚠ 52, 177, 179, 195
Lowdham [EM] Ⓟ ⊛ 27
Lower Sydenham [SE] 🚲 ⚠ 203
Lowestoft [LE] Ⓟ 🚲 ◇ 🚕 11, 13, 15
Ludlow [AW] Ⓟ ◇ 131
Luton [FC] [10] Ⓟ 🚲 ◇ ⚠ 🚕 52, *Bus* 52A, 53, *Bus*65B
Luton Airport (see London Luton Airport)
Luton Airport Parkway [FC] [7] Ⓟ 🚲 ◇ ⚠ 🚕 52, 53, 177, 179, 186
Luxulyan [GW] Ⓟ ⊛ 142
Lydney [AW] Ⓟ ⊛ 132
Lye [LM] Ⓟ ⚠ 71
Lymington Pier [SW] 🚲 ⚠ ⊛ 158
Lymington Town [SW] Ⓟ 🚲 ◇ ⚠ 158
Lympstone Commando [GW] ⊛ 136
Lympstone Village [GW] Ⓟ 🚲 ⊛ 136
Lytham [NT] ⊛ 97

M

Macclesfield [VT] Ⓟ 🚲 ◇ 🚕 51, 65, *Bus* 65H, 84
Machynlleth [AW] [4] Ⓟ ◇ 75
Maesteg [AW] Ⓟ ⊛ 128, *Bus* 128A
Maesteg (Ewenny Road) [AW] ⊛ 128
Maghull [ME] Ⓟ 🚲 🚕 103
Maidenhead [GW] [3] Ⓟ 🚲 ◇ ⚠ 🚕 116, 117, 120
Maiden Newton [GW] Ⓟ ⊛ 123
Maidstone Barracks [SE] ⊛ 208
Maidstone East [SE] [4] Ⓟ ◇ ⚠ 🚕 196, 207
Maidstone West [SE] [4] Ⓟ 🚕 200, 207, 208
Malden Manor [SW] Ⓟ 🚲 ⚠ 152
Mallaig [SR] 🚲 ◇ 227, *Ship* 227A
Malton [TP] Ⓟ 🚲 ◇ 🚕 39
Malvern Link [LM] Ⓟ ◇ ⚠ 71, 126
Manchester
Oxford Road [NT] Ⓟ ◇ 🚕
Piccadilly [NR] [10] Ⓟ 🚲 ◇ 🚕
Victoria [NT] ◇ 🚕
Aberdeen 65
Aberystwyth 75
Altrincham 88
Bangor (Gwynedd) 81
Barrow-in-Furness 82
Birmingham 65
Birmingham International 65
Blackburn 94
Blackpool 82
Bolton 82
Bournemouth 51
Bradford 41
Brighton 51
Bristol 51, 131
Burnley 97
Buxton 86
Cambridge 49
Cardiff 131
Carlisle 65
Carmarthen 128
Cheadle Hulme 84
Chester 81, 88
Chinley 78
Cleethorpes 29
Clitheroe 94
Coventry 65
Crewe 84
Darlington 39
Doncaster 29
Douglas (IOM) 98A
Dundee 65
Durham 39
East Croydon 51
Edinburgh 65
Exeter 51
Gatwick Airport 51, 65
Glasgow 65
Glossop 79
Grimsby 29
Guide Bridge 78
Hadfield 79
Haywards Heath 51
Heysham Port 98A
Holyhead 81
Huddersfield 39
Hull 29, 39
Inverness 65
Ipswich 49
Kensington Olympia 51
Kirkby 82
Lancaster 82
Leeds 39, 41
Liverpool 89, 90
Liverpool South Parkway 89
Llandudno 81
London 65
Macclesfield 84
Manchester Airport 85
Marple 78
Middlesbrough 39
Milford Haven 128
Milton Keynes Central 65
Motherwell 65
Newcastle 39
New Mills 78, 86
Newport (South Wales) 131
Northwich 88
Nottingham 49
Oldham 95
Oxenholme Lake District 65
Oxford 51
Paignton 51
Penzance 51
Peterborough 49
Plymouth 51
Preston 82
Reading 51
Rhyl 81
Rochdale 95
Rose Hill Marple 78
Rugby 65
St Helens 90
Salford 82
Scarborough 39
Sheffield 78
Shrewsbury 131
Southampton 51
Southport 82
Stafford 84
Stalybridge 39
Stansted Airport 49
Stockport 84
Stoke-on-Trent 84
Swansea 131
Tenby 128
Torquay 51
Wakefield 39
Warrington 89, 90
Watford 65
Wigan 82
Wilmslow 84
Windermere 82
Wolverhampton 65
York 39
Manchester Airport [TP] ◇
Bangor (Gwynedd) 81
Barrow-in-Furness 82
Birmingham 65
Birmingham International 65
Blackburn 94
Blackpool 82
Bolton 82
Carlisle 65
Coventry 65
Crewe 84
Darlington 39
Doncaster 29
Durham 39
Edinburgh 65
Glasgow 65
Huddersfield 39
Hull 29, 39
Holyhead 81
Lancaster 82
Leeds 39
Liverpool 89
London 65
Manchester 85
Middlesbrough 39
Motherwell 65
Newcastle 39
Oxenholme Lake District 82

Station index and table numbers

[10] Connection time
Ⓟ Station Car Park
🚲 Bicycle storage facility
◇ Seat reservations can be made at this station
⚠ Penalty Fare Schemes in operation on some or all services from this station
🚕 Taxi rank or cab office at station, or signposted and within 100 metres
ⓤ Unstaffed station
[ ] Station Operator Code

Penrith North Lakes 65
Preston 82
St Helens 90
Salford 82
Scarborough 39
Sheffield 78
Southport 82
Stafford 65, 84
Wakefield 39
Warrington 89
Watford 65
Wigan 82
Wilmslow 84
Windermere 82
Wolverhampton 65
York 39
Manea [LE] ⓤ 17
Manningtree [LE] [2] Ⓟ 🚲 ⚠ 🚕 11, 13, 14
Manor Park [LE] 🚲 ⚠ 5
Manor Road [ME] 🚲 106
Manorbier [AW] ⓤ 128
Manors [NT] ⓤ 48
Mansfield [EM] Ⓟ 🚲 🚕 55
Mansfield Woodhouse [EM] Ⓟ ⓤ 55
March [LE] Ⓟ ◇ 🚕 14, 17, 49
Marden [SE] Ⓟ ⚠ 207
Margate [SE] [4] Ⓟ 🚲 ◇ 🚕 207, 212
Market Harborough [EM] Ⓟ 🚲 ◇ 🚕 53
Market Rasen [EM] Ⓟ 🚲 ⓤ 27
Markinch [SR] Ⓟ 🚲 🚕 51, 229, 242
Marks Tey [LE] [2] Ⓟ 🚲 ⚠ 10, 11, 13, 14
Marlow [GW] 🚲 ⓤ 120
Marple [NT] Ⓟ 78
Marsden [NT] Ⓟ ⓤ 39
Marske [NT] 🚲 ⓤ 44
Marston Green [LM] Ⓟ ◇ ⚠ 68
Martin Mill [SE] Ⓟ 207
Martins Heron [SW] Ⓟ 🚲 ⚠ 149
Marton [NT] Ⓟ 🚲 ⓤ 45
Maryhill [SR] 🚲 ⓤ 232
Maryland [LE] 🚲 ⚠ 5
Marylebone [CH] (see London)
Maryport [NT] Ⓟ ⓤ 100
Matlock [EM] Ⓟ ⓤ 53, 56
Matlock Bath [EM] Ⓟ ⓤ 56
Mauldeth Road [NT] 85
Maxwell Park [SR] 🚲 ⓤ 223
Maybole [SR] Ⓟ 🚲 ⓤ 218
Maze Hill [SE] ⚠ 200
Meadowhall [NT] Ⓟ 🚲 ◇
Barnsley 34
Castleford 34
Chesterfield 53
Cleethorpes 29
Derby 53
Doncaster 29
Gainsborough 30
Grimsby 29
Huddersfield 34
Hull 29
Leeds 31
Leicester 53
Lincoln 30
Manchester 29
Manchester Airport 29
Penistone 34
Pontefract 33
Retford 30
Rotherham 29
Scunthorpe 29
Sheffield 29
Wakefield 31
Worksop 30
York 29, 33
Meldreth [FC] Ⓟ 🚲 ⚠ 25
Melksham [GW] Ⓟ ⓤ 123
Melrose *Bus* 26K
Melton [LE] Ⓟ 🚲 🚕 ⓤ 13
Melton Mowbray [EM] Ⓟ 🚲 ◇ 🚕 49
Menheniot [GW] Ⓟ ⓤ 135
Menston [NT] Ⓟ 🚲 ◇ 38
Meols [ME] Ⓟ 🚲 🚕 106
Meols Cop [NT] ⓤ 82
Meopham [SE] Ⓟ ⚠ 🚕 212
Merryton [SR] 🚲 ⓤ 226
Merstham [SN] Ⓟ 🚲 ⚠ 🚕 186
Merthyr Tydfil [AW] Ⓟ ◇ 130
Merthyr Vale [AW] ⓤ 130
Metheringham [EM] Ⓟ 🚲 ⓤ 18
MetroCentre [NT] Ⓟ ⓤ 44, 48
Mexborough [NT] Ⓟ 🚲 ◇ 29
Micheldever [SW] Ⓟ ⚠ 158
Micklefield [NT] Ⓟ 🚲 ⓤ 41
Middlesbrough [TP] Ⓟ 🚲 ◇ 🚕 26, 39, 44, 45
Middlewood [NT] ⓤ 86
Midgham [GW] Ⓟ ⓤ 116
Milford Haven [AW] Ⓟ 🚕 ⓤ 128
Milford (Surrey) [SW] Ⓟ 🚲 ⚠ 156
Millbrook (Bedfordshire) [LM] ⓤ 64
Millbrook (Hants.) [SW] 🚲 ⚠ ⓤ 158
Mill Hill Broadway [FC] Ⓟ 🚲 ◇ ⚠ 52
Mill Hill (Lancashire) [NT] ⓤ 97
Milliken Park [SR] 🚲 ⓤ 221
Millom [NT] Ⓟ ⓤ 100
Mills Hill [NT] ⓤ 41, 95
Milngavie [SR] Ⓟ 🚲 226
Milnrow [NT] Ⓟ ⓤ 95
Milton Keynes Central [LM] Ⓟ 🚲 ◇ 🚕
Bedford 64, *Bus* 65C
Bicester *Bus* 65A
Birmingham International 66
Birmingham New Street 66
Blackpool 65
Bletchley 66
Brighton 66
Buckingham *Bus* 65A
Cambridge *Bus* 65C
Coventry 66
Crewe 65
Edinburgh 65
Fenny Stratford 64
Gatwick Airport 66
Glasgow 65
Lancaster 65
Liverpool 65
London 66
Luton *Bus* 65B
Luton Airport *Bus* 65B
Manchester 65
Northampton 66
Oxenholme Lake District 65
Preston 65
Rugby 66
St Neots *Bus* 65C
Stafford 65
Stockport 65
Stoke-on-Trent 65
Tring 66
Warrington 65
Watford 66
Wembley 66
Wigan 65
Wolverhampton 66
Milton Keynes City Centre *Bus* 65B
Minehead Parade *Bus* 135E
Minffordd [AW] ⓤ 75
Minster [SE] [4] Ⓟ ⓤ 207
Mirfield [NT] Ⓟ ⓤ 39
Mistley [LE] 🚲 ⓤ 11
Mitcham Junction [SN] Ⓟ 🚲 ◇ ⚠ 52, 179, 182
Mobberley [NT] ⓤ 88
Monifieth [SR] 🚲 ⓤ 229
Monks Risborough [CH] ⚠ ⓤ 115
Montpelier [GW] 🚲 ⓤ 133
Montrose [SR] Ⓟ 🚲 ◇ 🚕 26, 51, 229, *Sleepers* 402
Moorfields [ME] (see Liverpool)
Moorgate [LT] ⚠ 24, 52
Moorside [NT] 82
Moorthorpe [NT] Ⓟ ⓤ 31, 33
Morar [SR] Ⓟ 🚲 ⓤ 227
Morchard Road [GW] Ⓟ ⓤ 136
Morden (Herts) **[FC]** (see Ashwell & Morden)
Morden South [FC] ⚠ ⓤ 52, 179
Morecambe [NT] Ⓟ 🚲 ◇ 36, 98, 98A
Moreton (Dorset) [SW] Ⓟ 🚲 ⓤ 158
Moreton (Merseyside) [ME] 🚲 🚕 106
Moreton-in-Marsh [GW] Ⓟ 🚲 ◇ 126
Morfa Mawddach [AW] ⓤ 75
Morley [NT] Ⓟ ⓤ 39
Morpeth [NT] Ⓟ 🚲 ◇ 🚕 26, 48
Mortimer [GW] Ⓟ 122
Mortlake [SW] Ⓟ 🚲 ◇ ⚠ 149
Moses Gate [NT] ⓤ 82

Station index and table numbers

❿ Connection time
Ⓟ Station Car Park
🚲 Bicycle storage facility
◇ Seat reservations can be made at this station
⚠ Penalty Fare Schemes in operation on some or all services from this station
🚕 Taxi rank or cab office at station, or signposted and within 100 metres
Ⓤ Unstaffed station
[ ] Station Operator Code

Moss Side [NT] Ⓤ 97
Mossley [NT] Ⓟ 🚲 39
Mossley Hill [NT] Ⓟ 89, 91
Mosspark [SR] 🚲 Ⓤ 217
Moston [NT] Ⓤ 41, 95
Motherwell [SR] Ⓟ 🚲 ◇ 🚕
Birmingham 51, 65
Bournemouth 51
Brighton 51
Bristol 51
Crewe 65
Cumbernauld 224
Darlington 26
Doncaster 26
Edinburgh 225
Exeter 51
Glasgow 225, 226
Liverpool 65
London 26, 65, *Sleepers* 401
Manchester 65
Manchester Airport 65
Newcastle 26
Oxenholme Lake District 65
Oxford 51
Paignton 51
Penzance 51
Peterborough 26
Plymouth 51
Reading 51
Southampton 51
Torquay 51
Watford 65, *Sleepers* 401
York 26
Motspur Park [SW] ⚠ 152
Mottingham [SE] Ⓟ ⚠ 200
Mottisfont & Dunbridge [GW] Ⓤ 123, 158
Mouldsworth [NT] Ⓟ Ⓤ 88
Moulsecoomb [SN] ⚠ 189
Mount Florida [SR] 🚲 223
Mount Vernon [SR] 🚲 Ⓤ 220
Mountain Ash [AW] Ⓟ Ⓤ 130
Muck *Ship* 227A
Muir of Ord [SR] Ⓟ 🚲 Ⓤ 239
Muirend [SR] 🚲 223
Mullion Holiday Park *Bus* 135A
Musselburgh [SR] Ⓟ 🚲 Ⓤ 238
Mytholmroyd [NT] Ⓟ Ⓤ 41

N

Nafferton [NT] Ⓤ 43
Nailsea & Backwell [GW] Ⓟ 🚲 134
Nairn [SR] Ⓟ 🚲 ◇ 🚕 240
Nantwich [AW] Ⓤ 131
Narberth [AW] Ⓤ 128
Narborough [EM] Ⓟ 57
National Exhibition Centre [VT] (see Birmingham International)
Navigation Road [NT] Ⓤ 88
Neath [AW] Ⓟ 🚲 ◇ 🚕 125, 128
Needham Market [LE] Ⓤ 11, 14
Neilston [SR] Ⓟ 🚲 🚕 223
Nelson [NT] Ⓟ Ⓤ 97
Neston [AW] Ⓟ Ⓤ 101
Netherfield [EM] Ⓤ 19
Nethertown [NT] Ⓟ Ⓤ 100
Netley [SW] Ⓟ 🚲 165
New Barnet [FC] Ⓟ 🚲 ⚠ 24
New Beckenham [SE] ❹ Ⓟ 🚲 ⚠ 203
New Brighton [ME] 106
New Clee [NT] Ⓤ 29
New Cross [SE] ❹ 🚲 ⚠ 199, 200, 203, 204
New Cross Gate [SN] ❹ ⚠ 178, 181, 182
New Cumnock [SR] Ⓟ 🚲 Ⓤ 216
New Eltham [SE] Ⓟ ⚠ 200
New Haw [SW] (see Byfleet & New Haw)
New Hey [NT] Ⓤ 95
New Holland [NT] 🚲 Ⓤ 29
New Hythe [SE] Ⓤ 208
New Inn [AW] (see Pontypool and New Inn)
New Lane [NT] Ⓤ 82
New Malden [SW] ❻ Ⓟ 🚲 ⚠ 152
New Mills Central [NT] 78
New Mills Newtown [NT] Ⓟ 🚲 86
New Milton [SW] Ⓟ 🚲 ◇ ⚠ 🚕 158
New Pudsey [NT] Ⓟ 🚲 ◇ 37, 41
New Southgate [FC] Ⓟ ⚠ 24
Newark Castle [EM] Ⓟ 🚲 Ⓤ 27
Newark North Gate [GR] ❼ Ⓟ 🚲 ◇ 🚕 26, *Bus* 26D, 27
Newbridge [AW] Ⓟ Ⓤ 127
Newbury [GW] Ⓟ 🚲 ◇ 🚕 116, 135
Newbury Racecourse [GW] Ⓤ 116
Newcastle [GR] ❽ Ⓟ 🚲 ◇ 🚕
Aberdeen 26
Alnmouth 26
Arbroath 26
Belfast *Catamaran/Ship* 218
Berwick-upon-Tweed 26
Birmingham 51
Birmingham International 51
Bournemouth 51
Bradford 39
Bristol 51
Cambridge 26
Cardiff 51
Carlisle 48
Chathill 48
Darlington 26
Derby 51
Doncaster 26
Dundee 26
Edinburgh 26
Exeter 51
Glasgow 26, 216
Grantham 26
Haltwhistle 48
Hartlepool 44
Hexham 48
Huddersfield 39
Hull 26
Leeds 26
Liverpool 39
London 26
Manchester 39
Manchester Airport 39
MetroCentre 48
Middlesbrough 44
Morpeth 48
Newark 26
Newport (South Wales) 51
Northallerton 26
Norwich 26
Oxford 51
Paignton 51
Penzance 51
Peterborough 26
Plymouth 51
Preston 39
Reading 51
Retford 26
Sheffield 26
Southampton 51
Stansted Airport 26
Stockton 44
Stranraer 218
Sunderland 44
Torquay 51
Whitby 45
York 26
Newcraighall [SR] Ⓟ 🚲 Ⓤ 230
Newhaven Harbour [SN] Ⓤ 189
Newhaven Town [SN] 🚲 ⚠ 189
Newington [SE] Ⓟ ⚠ 212
Newmarket [LE] Ⓟ 🚲 Ⓤ 14
Newport (Essex) [LE] Ⓟ 🚲 ⚠ 22
Newport (S. Wales) [AW] Ⓟ 🚲 ◇ 🚕
Aberdeen 51
Bangor (Gwynedd) 131
Bath Spa 132
Birmingham 57
Bournemouth 123
Bristol 132
Cardiff 132
Cheltenham Spa 57
Chester 131
Crewe 131
Darlington 51
Derby 57
Dundee 51
Durham 51
Edinburgh 51
Exeter 135
Gatwick Airport 125
Gloucester 132
Heathrow Airport 125
Hereford 131
Holyhead 131

Station index and table numbers

[10] Connection time
Ⓟ Station Car Park
🚲 Bicycle storage facility
◇ Seat reservations can be made at this station
⚠ Penalty Fare Schemes in operation on some or all services from this station
🚕 Taxi rank or cab office at station, or signposted and within 100 metres
🚶 Unstaffed station
[ ] Station Operator Code

Station index and table numbers

■10 Connection time
Ⓟ Station Car Park
🚲 Bicycle storage facility
◇ Seat reservations can be made at this station
⚠ Penalty Fare Schemes in operation on some or all services from this station
🚕 Taxi rank or cab office at station, or signposted and within 100 metres
ⓤ Unstaffed station
[ ] Station Operator Code

Station index and table numbers

■10 Connection time
Ⓟ Station Car Park
🚲 Bicycle storage facility
◇ Seat reservations can be made at this station
⚠ Penalty Fare Schemes in operation on some or all services from this station
🚕 Taxi rank or cab office at station, or signposted and within 100 metres
ⓤ Unstaffed station
[ ] Station Operator Code

Petts Wood [SE] ■4 Ⓟ ⚠ 195, 199, 204
Pevensey & Westham [SN] Ⓟ 🚲 ⚠ 189
Pevensey Bay [SN] ⓤ 189
Pewsey [GW] Ⓟ 🚲 ◇ ⚠ 135
Pickering [NY] 45
Pickering Eastgate *Bus* 26G
Pilning [GW] Ⓟ ⓤ 132
Pinhoe [SW] ⓤ 160
Pitlochry [SR] Ⓟ 🚲 🚕 229, *Sleepers* 403
Pitsea [CC] Ⓟ 🚲 ◇ ⚠ 🚕 1
Pleasington [NT] Ⓟ ⓤ 97
Pleasure Beach [NT] (see Blackpool)
Plockton [SR] Ⓟ 🚲 ⓤ 239
Pluckley [SE] Ⓟ 🚲 ⚠ 207
Plumley [NT] Ⓟ ⓤ 88
Plumpton [SN] Ⓟ ⚠ 189
Plumstead [SE] ⚠ 200
Plymouth [GW] Ⓟ 🚲 ◇ ⚠ 🚕
- Aberdeen 51
- Basingstoke 160
- Birmingham 51, 135
- Bristol 135
- Cardiff 135
- Carlisle 51
- Crewe 51
- Derby 51
- Dundee 51
- Edinburgh 51
- Exeter 135
- Gatwick Airport 135
- Glasgow 51
- Gunnislake 139
- Heathrow Airport 135
- Leeds 51
- London 135, 160, *Sleepers* 406
- Manchester 51
- Newcastle 51
- Newton Abbot 135
- Paignton 135
- Penzance 135
- Preston 51
- Reading 135, *Sleepers* 406
- Salisbury 160
- Sheffield 51
- Taunton 135
- Torquay 135
- Wolverhampton 51
- York 51

Pokesdown [SW] 🚲 ⚠ 158
Polegate [SN] Ⓟ 🚲 ⚠ 🚕 189
Polesworth [LM] Ⓟ ⓤ 67
Pollokshaws East [SR] 🚲 ⓤ 223
Pollokshaws West [SR] 🚲 ⓤ 222
Pollokshields East [SR] 🚲 223
Pollokshields West [SR] 🚲 ⓤ 223
Polmont [SR] ■3 Ⓟ 🚲 ◇ 🚕 228, 230
Polsloe Bridge [GW] ⓤ 136
Ponders End [LE] ⚠ 22
Pontarddulais [AW] Ⓟ ⓤ 129
Pontefract Baghill [NT] Ⓟ ⓤ 33
Pontefract Monkhill [NT] Ⓟ ⓤ 32
Pontefract Tanshelf [NT] Ⓟ ⓤ 32
Pontlottyn [AW] Ⓟ ⓤ 130
Pont-y-Pant [AW] ⓤ 102
Pontyclun [AW] Ⓟ ⓤ 128
Pontypool & New Inn [AW] Ⓟ ⓤ 131
Pontypridd [AW] ■3 🚲 ◇ 🚕 130
Poole [SW] ■4 Ⓟ 🚲 ◇ 🚕 158
Poppleton [NT] Ⓟ 🚲 ⓤ 35
Portchester [SW] Ⓟ 🚲 158, 165, 188
Port Glasgow [SR] 🚲 🚕 219
Porth [AW] Ⓟ ◇ 130
Porthmadog [AW] ⓤ 75
Portlethen [SR] Ⓟ 🚲 ⓤ 229
Portslade [SN] Ⓟ 🚲 ⚠ 188
Portsmouth Arms [GW] Ⓟ ⓤ 136
Portsmouth
- **Harbour [SW]** 🚲 ◇ ⚠ 🚕
- **& Southsea [SW]** Ⓟ 🚲 ◇ ⚠ 🚕
- Bognor Regis 188
- Brighton 188
- Bristol 123
- Cardiff 123
- Chichester 188
- Exeter 160
- Fareham 165
- Gatwick Airport 188
- Guildford 156
- Haslemere 156
- Havant 157
- Littlehampton 188
- London 156, 158, 188
- Reading
  - via Eastleigh 158
  - via Guildford 156
- Ryde 167
- Salisbury 123
- Sandown 167
- Shanklin 167
- Southampton Central 165
- Winchester 158
- Worthing 188

Port Sunlight [ME] 🚲 106
Port Talbot Parkway [AW] Ⓟ 🚲 ◇ 🚕 125, 128
Possilpark & Parkhouse [SR] 🚲 ⓤ 232
Potters Bar [FC] Ⓟ ◇ ⚠ 🚕 24, 25
Poulton-le-Fylde [NT] Ⓟ ◇ 🚕 41, 82, 97
Poynton [NT] Ⓟ 84
Prees [AW] ⓤ 131
Prescot [NT] Ⓟ 90
Prestatyn [AW] ◇ 🚕 ⓤ 81
Prestbury [NT] Ⓟ ⓤ 84
Preston [VT] ■8 Ⓟ 🚲 ◇ 🚕
- Aberdeen 65, *Sleepers* 402
- Barrow-in-Furness 82
- Birmingham 65
- Birmingham International 65
- Blackburn 97
- Blackpool 97
- Bolton 82
- Bournemouth 51
- Bradford 41
- Brighton 51
- Bristol 51
- Burnley 97
- Carlisle 65
- Chorley 82
- Clitheroe 94, 97
- Colne 97
- Coventry 65
- Crewe 65
- Douglas (IOM) 98A
- Dundee 65, *Sleepers* 402
- Edinburgh 65
- Exeter 51
- Fort William *Sleepers* 404
- Gatwick Airport 65
- Glasgow 65
- Inverkeithing *Sleepers* 402
- Inverness 65, *Sleepers* 403
- Kirkcaldy *Sleepers* 402
- Lancaster 65
- Leeds 41
- Liverpool 90, 99
- London 65
- Manchester 82
- Manchester Airport 82
- Milton Keynes Central 65
- Ormskirk 99
- Oxenholme Lake District 652
- Oxford 51
- Paignton 51
- Penzance 51
- Perth 65, *Sleepers* 403
- Plymouth 51
- Reading 51
- Rugby 65
- Southampton 51
- Stafford 65
- Stirling *Sleepers* 403
- Stockport 82
- Torquay 51
- Warrington 65
- Watford 65
- Wigan 65
- Windermere 653
- Wolverhampton 65
- York 41

Preston Park [SN] ⚠ 52, 186
Preston (Fishergate) *Bus* 65E
Prestonpans [SR] Ⓟ 🚲 ⓤ 238
Prestwick International Airport ⓤ 218, 221
Prestwick Town [SR] Ⓟ 🚲 🚕 218, 221
Priesthill & Darnley [SR] 🚲 ⓤ 222
Princes Risborough [CH] ■2 Ⓟ 🚲 ◇ ⚠ 🚕 115, 115A

[10] Connection time
Ⓟ Station Car Park
🚲 Bicycle storage facility
◇ Seat reservations can be made at this station
⚠ Penalty Fare Schemes in operation on some or all services from this station
🚕 Taxi rank or cab office at station, or signposted and within 100 metres
🚶 Unstaffed station
[ ] Station Operator Code

Station index and table numbers

Prittlewell [LE] Ⓟ 🚲 ⚠ 5
Prudhoe [NT] Ⓟ 🚲 🚶 48
Pulborough [SN] Ⓟ 🚲 ⚠ 🚕 188
Purfleet [CC] Ⓟ ◇ ⚠ 1
Purley [SN] [4] Ⓟ ⚠ 🚕 175, 181, 186
Purley Oaks [SN] Ⓟ ⚠ 175, 181
Putney [SW] 🚲 ◇ ⚠ 149
Pwllheli [AW] 🚲 🚕 75
Pyle [AW] Ⓟ 🚲 🚶 128

Q

Quakers Yard [AW] 🚶 130
Queenborough [SE] Ⓟ 212
Queens Park (Glasgow) **[SR]** 🚲 223
Queens Park (London) **[LT]** 60
Queens Road, Peckham [SN] 🚲 ◇ ⚠ 177, 178, 179
Queens Road, Walthamstow [LO] (see Walthamstow Queens Road)
Queenstown Road (Battersea) [SW] ⚠ 🚶 149
Quintrell Downs [GW] 🚶 142

R

Radcliffe (Notts.) **[EM]** Ⓟ 🚶 19
Radlett [FC] Ⓟ 🚲 ◇ ⚠ 🚕 52
Radley [GW] Ⓟ 🚶 116
Radyr [AW] [3] Ⓟ 🚲 ◇ 130
Rainford [NT] Ⓟ 🚶 82
Rainham (Essex) **[CC]** Ⓟ 🚲 ◇ ⚠ 1
Rainham (Kent) [SE] Ⓟ ⚠ 🚕 212
Rainhill [NT] 90
Ramsgate [SE] [4] Ⓟ 🚲 ◇ 🚕 207, 212
Ramsgreave & Wilpshire [NT] 🚶 94
Rannoch [SR] Ⓟ 🚲 🚶 227, *Sleepers* 404
Rauceby [EM] 🚶 19
Ravenglass for Eskdale [NT] 🚶 100
Ravensbourne [SE] ⚠ 195
Ravensthorpe [NT] Ⓟ 🚶 39
Rawcliffe [NT] 🚶 32
Rayleigh [LE] Ⓟ 🚲 ⚠ 🚕 5
Raynes Park [SW] [6] 🚲 ⚠ 152
Reading [GW] [7] Ⓟ 🚲 ◇ ⚠ 🚕
Aberdeen 51
Ascot 149
Banbury 116
Basingstoke 122
Bath Spa 125
Birmingham 116
Bodmin Parkway 135, *Sleepers* 406
Bournemouth 158
Brighton 148
Bristol 125
Camborne 135, *Sleepers* 406
Cardiff 125
Carlisle 51
Cheltenham Spa 125
Clapham Junction 149
Coventry 51
Crewe 51
Derby 51
Didcot 116
Dundee 51
Edinburgh 51
Exeter 135, *Sleepers* 406
Gatwick Airport 148
Glasgow 51
Gloucester 125
Guildford 148
Hayle 135, *Sleepers* 406
Heathrow Airport *Bus* 125A
Henley-on-Thames 121
Hereford 126
Leamington Spa 116
Leeds 51
Liskeard 135, *Sleepers* 406
London 116, 117, 149
Lostwithiel 135, *Sleepers* 406
Manchester 51
Marlow 120
Milford Haven 128
Moreton-in-Marsh 126
Newbury 116
Newcastle 51
Newport (South Wales) 125
Newton Abbot 135, *Sleepers* 406
Oxford 116
Paignton 135
Par 135, *Sleepers* 406
Penzance 135, *Sleepers* 406
Plymouth 135, *Sleepers* 406
Poole 158
Portsmouth
via Basingstoke 158
via Guildford 156
Preston 51
Redhill 148
Redruth 135, *Sleepers* 406
Rosslare Harbour 128
Salisbury 160
Sheffield 51
Slough 117
Southampton 158
St Austell 135, *Sleepers* 406
St Erth 135, *Sleepers* 406
Staines 149
Stratford-upon-Avon 116
Swansea 125
Swindon 125
Taunton 135
Torquay 135
Truro 135, *Sleepers* 406
Wallingford *Bus* 116A
Weston-super-Mare 125
Weymouth 158
Winchester 158
Windsor & Eton Central 117
Wolverhampton 51
Worcester 126
York 51
Reading West [GW] [3] 116, 122
Rectory Road [LE] ⚠ 21
Redbridge [SW] Ⓟ ⚠ 🚶 158
Redcar British Steel [NT] 🚶 44
Redcar Central [NT] Ⓟ 🚲 ◇ 🚕 44
Redcar East [NT] 🚲 🚶 44
Reddish North [NT] Ⓟ 78
Reddish South [NT] 🚶 78
Redditch [LM] Ⓟ ◇ ⚠ 69
Redhill [SN] Ⓟ 🚲 ◇ ⚠ 🚕
Birmingham 51
Brighton 186
Clapham Junction 186
Dorking 148
East Croydon 186
Edenbridge 209
Gatwick Airport 186
Guildford 148
Haywards Heath 186
Horsham 186
Hove 186
Lewes 186
London 186
Manchester 51
Reading 148
Stoke-on-Trent 51
Three Bridges 186
Tonbridge 209
Tunbridge Wells 209
Wokingham 148
Wolverhampton 51
Redland [GW] 🚲 🚶 133
Redruth [GW] Ⓟ 🚲 ◇ 🚕 51, 135, *Sleepers* 406
Reedham (Norfolk) [LE] Ⓟ 🚲 🚶 15
Reedham (Surrey) **[SN]** ⚠ 181
Reigate [SN] Ⓟ 🚲 ◇ ⚠ 148, 186, 209
Renton [SR] 🚲 🚶 226
Retford [GR] [10] Ⓟ 🚲 ◇ 🚕 26, 30
Rhiwbina [AW] 🚶 130
Rhoose Cardiff Int. Airport [AW] Ⓟ 🚲 🚶 130
Rhosneigr [AW] 🚶 81
Rhyl [AW] ◇ 🚕 81, 102
Rhymney [AW] [3] Ⓟ 🚕 🚶 130
Ribblehead [NT] Ⓟ 🚶 36
Rice Lane [ME] 103
Richmond (Greater London) **[SW]** Ⓟ 🚲 ◇ ⚠ 🚕 59, 149
Richmond (Market) 🚕 *Bus* 26H
Rickmansworth [LT] Ⓟ 🚲 ⚠ 114

Station index and table numbers

◼10 Connection time
Ⓟ Station Car Park
🚲 Bicycle storage facility
◇ Seat reservations can be made at this station
⚠ Penalty Fare Schemes in operation on some or all services from this station
🚕 Taxi rank or cab office at station, or signposted and within 100 metres
🚶 Unstaffed station
[ ] Station Operator Code

Riddlesdown [SN] ⚠ 184
Ridgmont [LM] 🚶 64
Riding Mill [NT] Ⓟ 🚲 🚶 48
Risca & Pontymister [AW] Ⓟ 🚶 127
Rishton [NT] 🚶 97
Robin Hood Airport 🚕 *Bus* 26F
Robertsbridge [SE] Ⓟ 206
Roby [NT] 90
Rochdale [NT] ◇ 🚕 41, 82, 95
Roche [GW] 🚶 142
Rochester [SE] ◼4 Ⓟ ⚠ 🚕 200, 212
Rochford [LE] Ⓟ 🚲 ⚠ 🚕 5
Rock Ferry [ME] Ⓟ 🚲 ◇ 🚕 106
Rogart [SR] Ⓟ 🚲 🚶 239
Rogerstone [AW] Ⓟ 🚶 127
Rolleston [EM] 🚶 27
Roman Bridge [AW] 🚶 102
Romford [LE] 🚲 ◇ ⚠ 🚕 4, 5, 11
Romiley [NT] 🚲 78
Romsey [GW] Ⓟ 🚲 123, 158, 160
Roose [NT] Ⓟ 🚶 82
Rose Grove [NT] 🚶 97
Rose Hill Marple [NT] Ⓟ 🚲 78
Rosslare Harbour *Ship* 128
Rosyth [SR] Ⓟ 🚶 242
Rotherham Central [NT] Ⓟ ◇ 🚕 29, 31, 33
Rothesay *Ship* 219B
Roughton Road [LE] 🚲 🚶 16
Rowlands Castle [SW] Ⓟ ⚠ 156
Rowley Regis [LM] Ⓟ ◇ ⚠ 71, 115
Roy Bridge [SR] 🚲 🚶 227, *Sleepers* 404
Roydon [LE] Ⓟ ⚠ 22
Royston [FC] Ⓟ 🚲 ◇ ⚠ 🚕 25
Ruabon [AW] Ⓟ 🚶 75
Rufford [NT] Ⓟ 🚶 99
Rugby [VT] Ⓟ 🚲 ◇ 🚕 65, 66, 67, 68
Rugeley Town [LM] Ⓟ 🚶 70
Rugeley Trent Valley [LM] 🚶 67, 70
Ruislip [CH] (see South and West Ruislip)
Rum *Ship* 227A
Runcorn [VT] Ⓟ 🚲 ◇ 🚕 65, 91, 131
Runcorn East [AW] Ⓟ 81
Ruskington [EM] Ⓟ 🚲 🚶 18
Ruswarp [NT] 🚶 45
Rutherglen [SR] 🚲 226
Ryde Esplanade [IL] ◇ 🚕 167
Ryde Pier Head [IL] Ⓟ 🚲 ◇ 167
Ryde St. Johns Road [IL] Ⓟ 🚲 🚶 167
Ryder Brow [NT] 🚶 78
Rye [SN] Ⓟ ⚠ 🚕 189, 207
Rye House [LE] ⚠ 22

S

St Albans [FC] Ⓟ 🚲 ◇ ⚠ 🚕 52, 186
St Albans Abbey [LM] Ⓟ 🚶 61
St Andrews (see Leuchars)
St Andrews Road [GW] Ⓟ 🚲 🚶 133
St Annes-on-the-Sea [NT] Ⓟ ◇ 🚕 97
St Austell [GW] Ⓟ 🚲 ◇ 🚕 51, 135, *Bus* 135B, *Sleepers* 406
St Bees [NT] Ⓟ 🚶 100
St Budeaux Ferry Road [GW] 🚶 135, 139
St Budeaux Victoria Road [GW] 🚶 139
St Columb Road [GW] Ⓟ 🚶 142
St Denys [SW] Ⓟ 🚲 ⚠ 158, 165
St Erth [GW] ◼2 Ⓟ ◇ 51, 135, 144, *Sleepers* 406
St Germans [GW] 🚶 135
St Helens Central [NT] Ⓟ ◇ 🚕 90
St Helens Junction [NT] Ⓟ 90
St Helier (Surrey) **[FC]** 🚲 ⚠ 🚶 52, 179
St Ives [GW] Ⓟ 🚶 135, 144
St James' Park [GW] 🚶 136
St James Street [LE] 🚲 ⚠ 20
St Johns [SE] ⚠ 199, 200, 203, 204
St Keyne [GW] 🚶 140
St Leonards Warrior Square [SE] ◼4 Ⓟ ⚠ 🚕 189, 206
St Margarets (Herts.) [LE] Ⓟ ⚠ 🚕 22
St Margarets (Greater London) **[SW]** 🚲 ◇ ⚠ 149
St Mary Cray [SE] Ⓟ ⚠ 195, 196, 212
St Michaels [ME] Ⓟ 103
St Neots [FC] Ⓟ 🚲 ⚠ 🚕 25
St Neots Cross Keys Mall *Bus* 65C
St Neots Square *Bus* 65C
St Pancras International (see London)
Salford Central [NT] 82, 94, 95
Salford Crescent [NT] 82, 94, 95
Salfords [SN] ◇ ⚠ 186
Salhouse [LE] Ⓟ 🚲 🚶 16
Salisbury [SW] Ⓟ 🚲 ◇ 🚕 123, 158, 160
Saltaire [NT] 🚶 36
Saltash [GW] Ⓟ 🚲 🚶 135
Saltburn [NT] 🚶 44
Saltcoats [SR] Ⓟ 🚲 🚕 221
Saltmarshe [NT] Ⓟ 🚶 29
Salwick [NT] 🚶 97
Sampford Courtenay 🚶 136
Sandal & Agbrigg [NT] Ⓟ 🚲 🚶 31
Sandbach [NT] Ⓟ 84
Sanderstead [SN] Ⓟ ⚠ 184
Sandhills [ME] 103
Sandhurst [GW] 🚶 148
Sandling [SE] Ⓟ 207
Sandown [IL] Ⓟ 🚲 🚶 167
Sandplace [GW] 🚶 140
Sandringham Norwich Gates *Bus* 17A
Sandringham Visitor Centre *Bus* 17A
Sandwell & Dudley [LM] Ⓟ 🚲 ◇ ⚠ 🚕 65, 66, 68
Sandwich [SE] Ⓟ 207
Sandy [FC] Ⓟ 🚲 ⚠ 25
Sankey for Penketh [NT] Ⓟ 89
Sanquhar [SR] Ⓟ 🚲 🚶 216
Sarn [AW] Ⓟ 🚶 128
Saundersfoot [AW] 🚶 128
Saunderton [CH] Ⓟ 🚲 ⚠ 🚶 115
Sawbridgeworth [LE] Ⓟ ⚠ 22
Saxilby [EM] Ⓟ 🚲 🚶 18, 30
Saxmundham [LE] Ⓟ 🚲 🚶 13
Scarborough [TP] Ⓟ 🚲 ◇ 🚕 26, 39, 43
Scotscalder [SR] Ⓟ 🚲 🚶 239
Scotstounhill [SR] Ⓟ 🚲 226
Scrabster *Ship* 239A
Scunthorpe [TP] Ⓟ ◇ 🚕 29
Sea Mills [GW] 🚲 🚶 133
Seaford [SN] Ⓟ 🚲 ⚠ 🚕 189
Seaforth & Litherland [ME] 🚕 103
Seaham [NT] Ⓟ 🚶 44
Seamer [TP] Ⓟ 🚶 39, 43
Seascale [NT] Ⓟ 🚶 100
Seaton Carew [NT] Ⓟ 🚲 🚶 44
Seer Green [CH] Ⓟ 🚲 ⚠ 115
Selby [TP] Ⓟ 🚲 ◇ 🚕 26, 29, 39, 41
Selhurst [SN] ◼4 🚲 ◇ ⚠ 177
Selkirk *Bus* 65G
Sellafield [NT] Ⓟ 🚶 100
Selling [SE] Ⓟ 🚶 212
Selly Oak [LM] Ⓟ 🚲 ◇ ⚠ 69
Settle [NT] Ⓟ ◇ 36
Seven Kings [LE] 🚲 ⚠ 5
Seven Sisters [LE] ⚠ 21, 22
Sevenoaks [SE] ◼4 Ⓟ ◇ ⚠ 🚕
  Ashford International 207
  Bromley South 195
  Dover 207
  Folkestone 207
  Hastings 206
  London 195, 204
  Orpington 204
  Ramsgate 207
  Tunbridge Wells 206
Severn Beach [GW] 🚲 🚶 133
Severn Tunnel Junction [AW] Ⓟ 🚲 ◇ 123, 132
Shalford [GW] Ⓟ 🚶 148
Shanklin [IL] Ⓟ 🚲 ◇ 🚕 167
Shaw & Crompton [NT] Ⓟ 🚲 95
Shawford [SW] Ⓟ 🚲 🚶 158
Shawlands [SR] 🚲 🚶 223

Station index and table numbers

■10 Connection time
Ⓟ Station Car Park
🚲 Bicycle storage facility
◇ Seat reservations can be made at this station
⚠ Penalty Fare Schemes in operation on some or all services from this station
🚕 Taxi rank or cab office at station, or signposted and within 100 metres
Ⓤ Unstaffed station
[ ] Station Operator Code

Station index and table numbers

[10] Connection time
Ⓟ Station Car Park
🚲 Bicycle storage facility
◇ Seat reservations can be made at this station
⚠ Penalty Fare Schemes in operation on some or all services from this station
🚕 Taxi rank or cab office at station, or signposted and within 100 metres
ⓤ Unstaffed station
[ ] Station Operator Code

■10 Connection time
℗ Station Car Park
🚲 Bicycle storage facility
◇ Seat reservations can be made at this station
⚠ Penalty Fare Schemes in operation on some or all services from this station
🚕 Taxi rank or cab office at station, or signposted and within 100 metres
Ⓤ Unstaffed station
[ ] Station Operator Code

Station index and table numbers

Station index and table numbers

■10 Connection time
Ⓟ Station Car Park
🚲 Bicycle storage facility
◇ Seat reservations can be made at this station
⚠ Penalty Fare Schemes in operation on some or all services from this station
🚕 Taxi rank or cab office at station, or signposted and within 100 metres
Ⓤ Unstaffed station
[ ] Station Operator Code

Thornton (Fife) **[SR]** (see Glenrothes With Thornton)
Thornton Abbey [NT] Ⓤ 29
Thorntonhall [SR] 🚲 Ⓤ 222
Thornton Heath [SN] 🚲 ◇ ⚠ 177
Thorpe Bay [CC] Ⓟ 🚲 ◇ ⚠ 🚕 1
Thorpe Culvert [EM] Ⓟ Ⓤ 19
Thorpe-le-Soken [LE] ■1 Ⓟ 🚲 ⚠ 11
Three Bridges [SN] ■4 Ⓟ 🚲 ◇ ⚠ 🚕 52, 186, 188, 209
Three Oaks [SN] Ⓤ 189
Thurgarton [EM] Ⓤ 27
Thurnscoe [NT] Ⓤ 31
Thurso [SR] Ⓟ 🚲 ◇ 🚕 239, *Ship* 239A
Thurston [LE] Ⓟ 🚲 Ⓤ 14
Tilbury Riverside ⚠ *Bus* 1A
Tilbury Town [CC] ■4 ◇ ⚠ 1, *Bus* 1A
Tile Hill [LM] Ⓟ ⚠ 68
Tilehurst [GW] Ⓟ 🚲 116
Tipton [LM] Ⓟ ⚠ 68
Tiree *Ship* 227B
Tir-phil [AW] Ⓟ Ⓤ 130
Tisbury [SW] Ⓟ 160
Tiverton Parkway [GW] Ⓟ 🚲 ◇ ⚠ 🚕 51, 135
Todmorden [NT] Ⓟ 🚲 🚕 41
Tolworth [SW] Ⓟ 🚲 ⚠ 152
Tonbridge [SE] ■4 Ⓟ 🚲 ◇ ⚠ 🚕 204, 206, 207, 208, 209
Ton Pentre [AW] Ⓤ 130
Tondu [AW] Ⓟ Ⓤ 128
Tonfanau [AW] Ⓤ 75
Tonypandy [AW] Ⓤ 130
Tooting [FC] ◇ ⚠ 52, 179
Topsham [GW] Ⓟ 🚲 Ⓤ 136
Torquay [GW] Ⓟ 🚲 ◇ 🚕 51, 135, 160
Torre [GW] Ⓟ Ⓤ 135
Totnes [GW] Ⓟ 🚲 ◇ ⚠ 🚕 51, 135, 160, *Sleepers* 406
Tottenham Hale [LE] ⚠ 🚕 22
Tottenham South [LO] (see South Tottenham)
Totton [SW] Ⓟ 🚲 ⚠ 158
Town Green [ME] Ⓟ 103
Trafford Park [NT] Ⓤ 89
Treforest [AW] Ⓟ ◇ 130
Treforest Estate [AW] Ⓤ 130
Trehafod [AW] Ⓟ Ⓤ 130
Treherbert [AW] Ⓤ 130
Treorchy [AW] Ⓟ Ⓤ 130
Trimley [LE] Ⓟ 🚲 Ⓤ 13
Tring [LM] Ⓟ 🚲 🚕 66
Troed-y-rhiw [AW] Ⓤ 130
Troon [SR] Ⓟ 🚲 🚕 218, 221
Trowbridge [GW] Ⓟ 🚲 ◇ 🚕 123, 160
Truro [GW] Ⓟ 🚲 ◇ 🚕 51, 135, 143, *Sleepers* 406
Tulloch [SR] Ⓟ 🚲 Ⓤ 227, *Sleepers* 404
Tulse Hill [SN] ■3 ◇ ⚠ 52, 177, 179, 182
Tunbridge Wells [SE] ■4 Ⓟ 🚲 ◇ ⚠ 🚕 206
Turkey Street [LE] ⚠ 21
Tutbury & Hatton [EM] Ⓤ 50
Twickenham [SW] Ⓟ 🚲 ◇ ⚠ 149
Twyford [GW] ■3 Ⓟ 🚲 ⚠ 🚕 116, 117, 121
Ty Croes [AW] Ⓤ 81
Ty Glas [AW] Ⓤ 130
Tygwyn [AW] Ⓟ Ⓤ 75
Tyndrum Lower [SR] Ⓟ 🚲 Ⓤ 227
Tyndrum Upper [SR] (see Upper Tyndrum)
Tyseley [LM] ⚠ 71
Tywyn [AW] 🚲 Ⓤ 75

U

Uckfield [SN] Ⓟ 184
Uddingston [SR] Ⓟ 🚲 🚕 225, 226
Uig *Ship* 239B
Ulceby [NT] Ⓤ 29
Ullapool *Ship* 239B
Ulleskelf [NT] Ⓤ 33, 41
Ulverston [TP] ◇ 82
Umberleigh [GW] Ⓟ Ⓤ 136
University [LM] ◇ ⚠ 69, 71
Uphall [SR] Ⓟ 🚲 Ⓤ 230
Upholland [NT] Ⓤ 82
Upminster [CC] Ⓟ 🚲 ◇ ⚠ 🚕 1, 4
Upper Halliford [SW] ⚠ 152
Upper Holloway [LO] Ⓤ 62
Upper Tyndrum [SR] Ⓟ 🚲 Ⓤ 227, *Sleepers* 404
Upper Warlingham [SN] Ⓟ 🚲 ⚠ 184
Upton [AW] Ⓤ 101
Upwey [SW] Ⓟ 🚲 ⚠ Ⓤ 123, 158
Urmston [NT] Ⓟ 🚲 89
Uttoxeter [EM] Ⓟ Ⓤ 50

V

Valley [AW] Ⓟ Ⓤ 81
Vauxhall (London) **[SW]** ⚠ 149, 152, 155
Victoria [NR] (see London)
Virginia Water [SW] Ⓟ 🚲 ⚠ 🚕 149

W

Waddon [SN] ◇ ⚠ 182
Wadebridge Bus Station *Bus* 135C
Wadhurst [SE] Ⓟ 206
Wainfleet [EM] Ⓟ 🚲 Ⓤ 19
Wakefield
Kirkgate [NT] ■4 Ⓟ 🚲 Ⓤ
Westgate [GR] ■7 Ⓟ 🚲 ◇ 🚕
Barnsley 34
Bedford 53
Birmingham 51
Bournemouth 51
Bristol 51
Cambridge 26
Derby 53
Doncaster 31
Exeter 51
Huddersfield 39
Knottingley 32
Leeds 31
Leicester 53
Liverpool 39
London 26, 53
Luton 53
Manchester 39
Manchester Airport 39
Meadowhall 31
Newquay 51
Norwich 26
Nottingham 53
Paignton 51
Penzance 51
Plymouth 51
Pontefract 32
Sheffield 31
Southampton 51
Torquay 51
Wakes Colne [LE] (see Chappel & Wakes Colne)
Walkden [NT] 82
Wallasey Grove Road [ME] Ⓟ 106
Wallasey Village [ME] 106
Wallingford Market Place *Bus* 116A
Wallington [SN] Ⓟ ◇ ⚠ 182
Wallyford [SR] Ⓟ 🚲 Ⓤ 238
Walmer [SE] Ⓟ 🚕 207
Walsall [LM] ◇ ⚠ 70
Walsden [NT] Ⓤ 41
Waltham Cross [LE] Ⓟ ⚠ 🚕 22
Walthamstow Central [LE] Ⓟ 🚲 ⚠ 🚕 20
Walthamstow Queens Road [LO] Ⓤ 62
Walton (Merseyside) [ME] 103
Walton-on-the-Naze [LE] 🚲 ⚠ 11
Walton-on-Thames [SW] Ⓟ 🚲 ◇ 🚕 155

Station index and table numbers

[10] Connection time
Ⓟ Station Car Park
🚲 Bicycle storage facility
◇ Seat reservations can be made at this station
⚠ Penalty Fare Schemes in operation on some or all services from this station
🚕 Taxi rank or cab office at station, or signposted and within 100 metres
Ⓤ Unstaffed station
[ ] Station Operator Code

Station index and table numbers

■10 Connection time
Ⓟ Station Car Park
🚲 Bicycle storage facility
◇ Seat reservations can be made at this station
⚠ Penalty Fare Schemes in operation on some or all services from this station
🚕 Taxi rank or cab office at station, or signposted and within 100 metres
Ⓤ Unstaffed station
[ ] Station Operator Code

▮10 Connection time
Ⓟ Station Car Park
🚲 Bicycle storage facility
◇ Seat reservations can be made at this station
⚠ Penalty Fare Schemes in operation on some or all services from this station
🚕 Taxi rank or cab office at station, or signposted and within 100 metres
Ⓤ Unstaffed station
[ ] Station Operator Code

Station index and table numbers

Network Diagram for Tables 1, 4

DM-1/06
Design BAJS

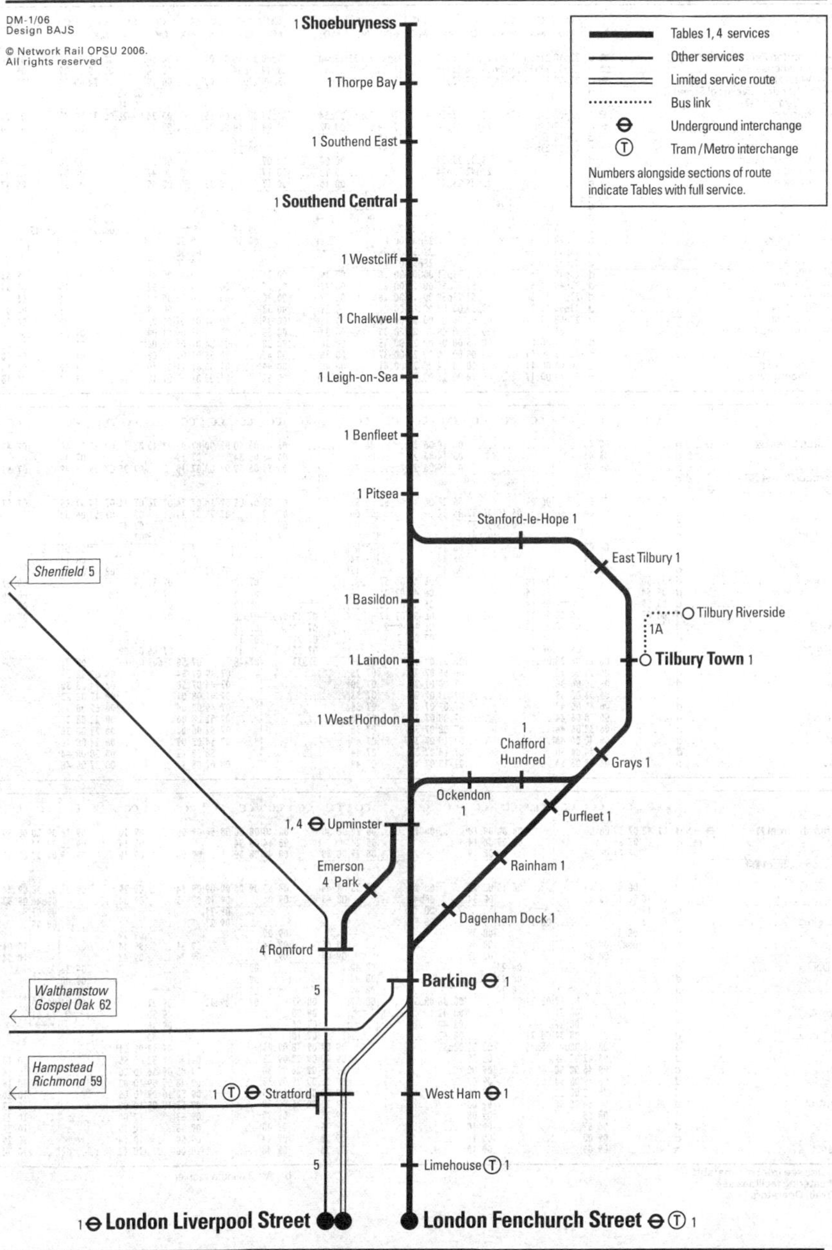
1 Shoeburyness
1 Thorpe Bay
1 Southend East
1 Southend Central
1 Westcliff
1 Chalkwell
1 Leigh-on-Sea
1 Benfleet
1 Pitsea
Stanford-le-Hope 1
East Tilbury 1
Tilbury Riverside
1A
Tilbury Town 1
1 Basildon
1 Laindon
1 West Horndon
1 Chafford Hundred
Grays 1
Ockendon 1
Purfleet 1
1, 4 Upminster
Rainham 1
Emerson Park 4
Dagenham Dock 1
4 Romford
Shenfield 5
Barking 1
5
Walthamstow Gospel Oak 62
Hampstead Richmond 59
1 Stratford
West Ham 1
5
Limehouse 1
1 London Liverpool Street
London Fenchurch Street 1
Tables 1, 4 services
Other services
Limited service route
Bus link
Underground interchange
Tram / Metro interchange
Numbers alongside sections of route indicate Tables with full service.

London → Southend Central and Shoeburyness

Network diagram - see first page of Table I

Miles	Miles	Miles	Station		CC MO	CC MX	CC MX	CC MO	CC MX	CC MX	CC MX	CC MX	CC MO		CC MX	CC MX	CC MX	CC MX	CC MO	CC MX	CC MX	CC MX	CC	CC
0	0	—	**London Fenchurch Street 7**	⊖ ⛴ d	22p50	22p50	23p05	23p10	23p10		23p20	23p35	23p40		23p40	23p50	00 01		00 10		00 15	00 25		05 10
1¾	1¾	—	Limehouse	⛴ d	22p54	22p54	23p09	23p14	23p14		23p24	23p39	23p44		23p44	23p54			00 14		00 19	00 29		05 14
4¾	4¾	—	West Ham	⊖ d	22p59	22p59	23p14	23p19	23p19		23p29	23p44	23p49		23p49	23p59	00 09		00 19		00 24	00 34		05 19
—	—	—	**London Liverpool Street 15**	⊖ d																00 12				
—	—	—	Stratford 7	⊖ ⛴ d																00 19				
7½	7½	—	Barking	⊖ d	23p04	23p05	23p20	23p24	23p25		23p35	23p51	23p54		23p55	00 05	00 15		00 24	00a28	00 31	00 40		05 25
15¼	—	0	Upminster	⊖ d	23p12	23p14		23p32	23p34		23p44		00 02		00 04	00 14	00 24		00 32			00 49	05 32	05 34
—	—	3	Ockendon	d	23p18	23p19					23p49					00 19							05 37	
—	—	5	Chafford Hundred	d	23p21	23p23					23p53					00 23							05 41	
19¼	—	—	West Horndon	d				23p37	23p39				00 07		00 09				00 37			00 54		05 39
22¾	—	—	Laindon	d				23p42	23p44				00 12		00 14		00 32		00 42			00 59		05 44
24½	—	—	Basildon	d				23p45	23p47				00 15		00 17		00 35		00 45			01 02		05 47
—	10½	—	Dagenham Dock	d			23p25					23p56									00 36			
—	12¾	—	Rainham	d			23p29					23p59									00 40			
—	16	—	Purfleet	d			23p34			←		00 05									00 45			
—	19¾	7½	Grays	d	23p25	23p27	23p42			23p42	23p57	00a11				00 27		←			00a51		05a45	
—	21⅓	—	**Tilbury Town 4**	d	23p28	23p30	→			23p45	00 01					00 30		00 30						
—	25¼	—	East Tilbury	d	23p34	23p36				23p51	00 06					→		00 36						
—	27¼	—	Stanford-le-Hope	d	23p37	23p40				23p55	00 10							00 40						
26½	32¼	—	Pitsea	d	23p45	23p48		23p49	23p51	00b06	00 18		00 19		00 21			00 48	00 49			01 06		05 51
29¼	35	—	Benfleet	d	23p49	23p52		23p52	23p55	00 10	00 22		00 22		00 25		00 41	00 52	00 52			01 10		05 55
32½	38¼	—	Leigh-on-Sea	d	23p53	23p56		23p57	23p59	00 15	00 26		00 27		00 30		00 46	00 56	00 57			01 14		06 00
34	39¾	—	Chalkwell	d	23p56	23p59		23p59	00 03	00 18	00 29		00 29		00 33		00 49	00 59	00 59			01 17		06 03
34¾	40½	—	Westcliff	d	23p58	00 02		00 02	00 05	00 20	00 32		00 32		00 35		00 51	01 02	01 02			01 20		06 05
35¾	41½	—	**Southend Central**	a	00 01	00 05		00 05	00 08	00 23	00 35		00 34		00 38		00 54	01 05	01 04			01 23		06 08
—	—	—		d	00 01	00 05		00 06	00 08	00 23	00 35		00 36		00 38		00 54	01 05	01 06			01 23		06 08
36½	42¼	—	Southend East	d	00 03	00 07		00 08	00 10	00 25	00 37		00 38		00 40		00 56	01 07	01 08			01 25		06 10
38	43¾	—	Thorpe Bay	d	00 06	00 11		00 10	00 14	00 29	00 41		00 40		00 44		01 00	01 11	01 10			01 29		06 14
39½	45¼	—	**Shoeburyness**	a	00 13	00 17		00 18	00 26	00 34	00 48		00 48		00 52		01 08	01 17	01 18			01 33		06 18

Station		CC		CC	CC	CC	CC	CC	CC	CC	CC	CC		CC	CC	CC	CC	CC	CC	CC	CC	CC		CC
London Fenchurch Street 7	⊖ ⛴ d			05 40					06 10	06 20		06 40		06 44	06 50	07 00	07 09	07 13	07 17	07 30	07 40			07 42
Limehouse	⛴ d			05 44					06 14	06 24		06 44		06 48	06 54		07 13				07 44			
West Ham	⊖ d			05 49					06 19	06 29		06 49		06 53	06 59	07 08	07 18		07 25	07 38	07 49			07 52
London Liverpool Street 15	⊖ d																							
Stratford 7	⊖ ⛴ d																							
Barking	⊖ d	05 45		05 55		06 05			06 25	06 35	06 52	06 55		07 00	07 05	07 14	07 24	07 26	07 31	07 44	07 55			07 57
Upminster	⊖ d			06 04			06 10	06 32	06 34			07 04		07b12		07 23	07 33		07 41	07 53	08 04			
Ockendon	d						06a15	06 37						07 17					07 47					
Chafford Hundred	d							06 41						07 21					07 51					
West Horndon	d			06 09					06 39			07 09					07 38				08 09			
Laindon	d			06 14					06 44			07 14					07 43				08 14			
Basildon	d			06 17					06 47			07 17				07 33	07 46			08 03	08 17			
Dagenham Dock	d	05 50				06 10				06 40	06 57				07 10			07 31						08 02
Rainham	d	05 54				06 14				06 44	07 01				07 14			07 35						08 06
Purfleet	d	05 59			←	06 19				06 49	07 06		←		07 19			07 40						08 12
Grays	d	06 05			06 05	06 25		06a46		06 55	07 12		07 12	07a25	07b28			07 46	07 55					08 17
Tilbury Town 4	d	→			06 08	06 28				06 58	→		07 15		07 31				07 59					→
East Tilbury	d				06 14	06 34				07 04			07 21		07 37				08 05					
Stanford-le-Hope	d				06 18	06 38				07 08			07 25		07 41			07 56	08 09					
Pitsea	d			06 21	06 28	06a46			06 51	07 16		07 21	07a33		07a48		07 50	08a03	08a16		08 21			
Benfleet	d			06 25	06 32				06 55	07 20		07 25				07 39	07 54			08 09	08 25			
Leigh-on-Sea	d			06 30	06 36				07 00	07 24		07 30				07 44	07 58			08 14	08 30			
Chalkwell	d			06 33	06 39				07 03	07 27		07 33				07 47	08 01			08 17	08 33			
Westcliff	d			06 35	06 42				07 05	07 30		07 35				07 49	08 04			08 19	08 35			
Southend Central	a			06 38	06 44				07 08	07 32		07 38				07 52	08 06			08 22	08 38			
	d			06 38	06 44				07 08	07 33		07 38				07 52	08 07			08 22	08 38			
Southend East	d			06 40	06 46				07 10	07 35		07 40				07 54	08 09			08 24	08 40			
Thorpe Bay	d			06 44	06 50				07 14	07 38		07 44				07 58	08 12			08 28	08 44			
Shoeburyness	a			06 48	06 54				07 18	07 43		07 48				08 02	08 17			08 32	08 48			

Station		CC	CC	CC	CC	CC	CC	CC	CC	CC		CC	CC	CC	CC	CC	CC	CC	CC	CC		CC	CC	CC
London Fenchurch Street 7	⊖ ⛴ d	07 48	07 52	08 00			08 05	08 10		08 15		08 20	08 30		08 40	08 50	08 54	09 00		09 10		09 16	09 20	09 30
Limehouse	⛴ d		07 56				08 09	08 14				08 24			08 44	08 54				09 14		09 20	09 24	
West Ham	⊖ d		08 01	08 08				08 19				08 29	08 38		08 49	08 59		09 08		09 19		09 25	09 29	09 38
London Liverpool Street 15	⊖ d																							
Stratford 7	⊖ ⛴ d																							
Barking	⊖ d		08 07	08 14			08 18	08 25		08 29		08 35	08 44		08 55	09 06	09 09	09 14		09 25		09 31	09 35	09 44
Upminster	⊖ d	08b10	08 16	08 23				08 34		08b41			08 53		09 04		09 18	09 23		09 34			09b46	09 53
Ockendon	d	08 19				←				08 46							09 23						09 51	
Chafford Hundred	d	08 23				08 23				08 50							09 27						09 55	
West Horndon	d	→	08 21					08 39							09 09					09 39				
Laindon	d		08a27	08 31				08 44					09 01		09 14			09 31		09 44				10 01
Basildon	d			08 34				08 47					09 04		09 17			09 34		09 47				10 04
Dagenham Dock	d						08 23					08 40				09 11						09 36		
Rainham	d						08 27					08 44				09 15						09 40		
Purfleet	d				←		08 32		←			08 49		←		09 20			←			09 45		
Grays	d				08 17	08 27	08 38		08 38	08a54		08 57		08 57		09 27	09a33		09 27			09 51	09 59	
Tilbury Town 4	d				08 21		→		08 42			→		09 00		→			09 30			→	10 01	
East Tilbury	d				08 27				08 48					09 06					09 36				→	
Stanford-le-Hope	d				08 31	08 37			08 52					09 10					09 40					
Pitsea	d			08 38	08b41	08a45		08 51	08a59				09 07	09 18	09 21				09 48	09 51				
Benfleet	d			08 42	08 45			08 55					09 10	09 22	09 25			09 40	09 52	09 55				10 10
Leigh-on-Sea	d			08 46	08 50			09 00					09 15	09 26	09 30			09 45	09 56	10 00				10 15
Chalkwell	d			08 49	08 53			09 03					09 18	09 29	09 33			09 48	09 59	10 03				10 18
Westcliff	d			08 52	08 55			09 05					09 20	09 32	09 35			09 50	10 02	10 05				10 20
Southend Central	a			08 54	08 58			09 08					09 23	09 35	09 38			09 53	10 05	10 08				10 23
	d			08 55				09 08					09 23		09 38			09 53		10 08				10 23
Southend East	d			08 57				09 10					09 25		09 40			09 55		10 10				10 25
Thorpe Bay	d			09 00				09 14					09 29		09 44			09 59		10 14				10 29
Shoeburyness	a			09 05				09 18					09 36		09 48			10 06		10 18				10 34

For general notes see front of timetable
For details of catering facilities see Directory of Train Operators

b Arr. 3 minutes earlier

London → Southend Central and Shoeburyness

Network diagram - see first page of Table 1

Station		CC	CC	CC	CC	CC	CC	CC	CC		CC	CC	CC	CC	CC		CC	CC	CC	CC	CC	CC	CC	CC
London Fenchurch Street 7 ⊖	d		09 35	09 40		09 50	10 00	10 05	10 10			10 20	10 30		10 35		10 40	10 50	11 00		11 05	11 10	11 20	11 30
Limehouse	d		09 39	09 44		09 54		10 09	10 14			10 24			10 39		10 44	10 54			11 09	11 14	11 24	
West Ham ⊖	d		09 44	09 49		09 59	10 08	10 14	10 19			10 29	10 38		10 44		10 49	10 59	11 08		11 14	11 19	11 29	11 38
London Liverpool Street 15 ⊖	d																							
Stratford 7 ⊖	d																							
Barking ⊖	d		09 50	09 55		10 05	10 14	10 20	10 25			10 35	10 44		10 50		10 55	11 05	11 14		11 20	11 25	11 35	11 44
Upminster ⊖	d			10 04		10 15	10 23		10 34			10 44	10 53				11 04	11 14	11 23			11 34	11 44	11 53
Ockendon	d					10 20						10 49						11 19					11 49	
Chafford Hundred	d					10 24						10 53						11 23					11 53	
West Horndon	d			10 09					10 39								11 09					11 39		
Laindon	d			10 14			10 31		10 44				11 01				11 14		11 31			11 44		12 01
Basildon	d			10 17			10 34		10 47				11 04				11 17		11 34			11 47		12 04
Dagenham Dock	d		09 55					10 25							10 55						11 25			
Rainham	d		09 59					10 29							10 59						11 29			
Purfleet	d	←	10 04					10 34							11 04						11 34			
Grays	d	09 51	10a10		←	10 28		10a40			←	10 57		←	11a10			11 27		←	11a40		11 57	
Tilbury Town 4	d	09 54			10 01	10 32 →					10 32	11 00 →		11 00				11 30 →		11 30			12 00 →	
East Tilbury	d	10 00			10 07						10 38			11 06						11 36				
Stanford-le-Hope	d	10 04			10 11						10 42			11 10						11 40				
Pitsea	d	10 12		10 21	10b25				10 51		10c54			11 18			11 21			11 48		11 51		
Benfleet	d	10 16		10 25	10 29		10 40		10 55		10 58		11 10	11 22			11 25		11 40	11 52		11 55		12 10
Leigh-on-Sea	d	10 20		10 30	10 34		10 45		10 59		11 03		11 15	11 26			11 30		11 45	11 56		12 00		12 15
Chalkwell	d	10 23		10 33	10 37		10 48		11 02		11 06		11 18	11 29			11 33		11 48	11 59		12 03		12 18
Westcliff	d	10 26		10 35	10 39		10 50		11 05		11 08		11 20	11 32			11 35		11 50	12 02		12 05		12 20
Southend Central	a	10 29		10 38	10 42		10 53		11 08		11 11		11 23	11 35			11 38		11 53	12 05		12 08		12 23
	d			10 38			10 53		11 08				11 23				11 38		11 53			12 08		12 23
Southend East	d			10 40			10 55		11 10				11 25				11 40		11 55			12 10		12 25
Thorpe Bay	d			10 44			10 59		11 14				11 29				11 44		11 59			12 14		12 29
Shoeburyness	a			10 48			11 04		11 18				11 34				11 48		12 04			12 18		12 34

Station		CC	CC			CC	CC	CC	CC	CC	CC	CC	CC	CC		CC	CC	CC	CC	CC	CC	CC	CC
London Fenchurch Street 7 ⊖	d		11 35			14 40	14 50	15 00		15 05	15 10	15 20	15 30	15 35		15 40		15 50	15 55	16 00	16 10	16 13	16 20
Limehouse	d		11 39			14 44	14 54			15 09	15 14	15 24		15 39		15 44		15 54	15 59		16 14	16 17	16 24
West Ham ⊖	d		11 44			14 49	14 59	15 08		15 14	15 19	15 29	15 38	15 44		15 49		15 59	16 04	16 08	16 19	16 22	16 29
London Liverpool Street 15 ⊖	d																						
Stratford 7 ⊖	d																						
Barking ⊖	d		11 50			14 55	15 05	15 14		15 20	15 25	15 35	15 44	15 50		15 54		16 05	16 10	16 14	16 25	16 28	16 35
Upminster ⊖	d					15 04	15 14	15 23			15 34	15 44	15 53			16 02		16 14		16 23	16 34		16 45
Ockendon	d			and at			15 19					15 49						16 19					16 50
Chafford Hundred	d						15 23					15 53						16 23					16 54
West Horndon	d			the same		15 09					15 39					16 07					16 39		
Laindon	d					15 14		15 31			15 44		16 01			16 12					16 44		
Basildon	d					15 17		15 34			15 47		16 04			16 15				16 33	16 47		
Dagenham Dock	d		11 55	minutes						15 25				15 55					16 15			16 33	
Rainham	d		11 59							15 29				15 59					16 19			16 37	
Purfleet	d		12 04	past						15 34				16 04					16 24			16 42	
Grays	d	←	12a10				15 27		←	15a40		15 57		16a10			←	16 27	16a33			16 48	16 59
Tilbury Town 4	d	12 00		each			15 30 →		15 30			16 00 →					16 00	16 31				16 52	17 02
East Tilbury	d	12 06							15 36								16 06	16 37				16 58	17 08
Stanford-le-Hope	d	12 10		hour until					15 40								16 10	16 41				17 02	17a15
Pitsea	d	12 18				15 21			15 48		15 51					16 19	16b22	16a48			16 51	17a12	
Benfleet	d	12 22				15 25		15 40	15 52		15 55		16 10			16 22	16 26			16 40	16 55		
Leigh-on-Sea	d	12 26				15 30		15 45	15 56		16 00		16 15			16 27	16 30			16 45	17 00		
Chalkwell	d	12 29				15 33		15 48	15 59		16 03		16 18			16 29	16 33			16 48	17 03		
Westcliff	d	12 32				15 35		15 50	16 02		16 05		16 20			16 32	16 36			16 50	17 05		
Southend Central	a	12 35				15 38		15 53	16 05		16 08		16 23			16 34	16 40			16 53	17 08		
	d					15 38		15 53			16 08		16 23			16 35				16 53	17 08		
Southend East	d					15 40		15 55			16 10		16 25			16 37				16 55	17 10		
Thorpe Bay	d					15 44		15 59			16 14		16 29			16 39				16 59	17 14		
Shoeburyness	a					15 48		16 04			16 18		16 34			16 44				17 05	17 20		

Station		CC	CC	CC		CC	CC	CC	CC	CC	CC	CC	CC	CC		CC	CC	CC	CC	CC	CC	CC	CC	CC
London Fenchurch Street 7 ⊖	d	16 28	16 30	16 33		16 37	16 45	16 48	16 54	17 00		17 02	17 05	17 07		17 11	17 15	17 18		17 20	17 22		17 26	17 30
Limehouse	d		16 34	16 37		16 41	16 49	16 52	16 58				17 09	17 12		17 16	17 19			17 24	17 27		17 30	
West Ham ⊖	d	16 36	16 39	16 42		16 46		16 57	17 03					17 17							17 32			
London Liverpool Street 15 ⊖	d																							
Stratford 7 ⊖	d																							
Barking ⊖	d		16 45	16 48		16 52	16 59	17 03	17 09			17 15	17 19	17 22		17 25				17 34	17 37		17 40	
Upminster ⊖	d		16 55			17 02	17 08	17 13				17 24		17 31				17 39			17 46			
Ockendon	d					17 08						17 29												
Chafford Hundred	d					17 12						17 33												
West Horndon	d		17 00					17 18						17 36							17 51			
Laindon	d	16 56	17a08				17 17	17a26					17 35	17a43						17 50	17a58			
Basildon	d	16 59					17 20						17 38					17 50		17 54				
Dagenham Dock	d			16 53					17 14							17 30							17 45	
Rainham	d			16 57					17 18							17 34						←	17 49	
Purfleet	d			17 03					17 24		←					17 39 →			←			17 39	17 54	
Grays	d			17 09 →		17a18			17 30 →		17 09	17a40							17 30			17 48	18 00 →	
Tilbury Town 4	d										17 12								17 33			17 51		
East Tilbury	d										17 18								17 39			17 57		
Stanford-le-Hope	d										17 22								17 43			18 01		
Pitsea	d						17 24				17a32		17 42					17 53	17a53	17 57		18a11		
Benfleet	d	17 06					17 28			17 33			17 46				17 52	17 58		18 02				18 07
Leigh-on-Sea	d	17 11					17 33			17 37			17 51				17 56	18 02		18 06				18 11
Chalkwell	d	17 14					17 36			17 40			17 54				17 59	18 05		18 09				18 14
Westcliff	d	17 16					17 38			17 43			17 56				18 02	18 08		18 12				18 17
Southend Central	a	17 19					17 41			17 45			17 59				18 04	18 13		18 14				18 19
	d	17 19					17 41			17 45			17 59				18 04			18 15				18 19
Southend East	d	17 21					17 43			17 47			18 01				18 06			18 17				18 21
Thorpe Bay	d	17 24					17 46			17 51			18 04				18 10			18 20				18 25
Shoeburyness	a	17 31					17 53			17 59			18 11				18 16			18 28				18 31

For general notes see front of timetable
For details of catering facilities see Directory of Train Operators

b Arr. 4 minutes earlier
c Arr. 5 minutes earlier

London → Southend Central and Shoeburyness

Network diagram - see first page of Table I

	CC	CC		CC	CC	CC	CC	CC	CC	CC	CC	CC		CC	CC	CC	CC	CC	CC	CC	CC	CC	CC
London Fenchurch Street 7 ⊖ d	17 32	17 35		17 37	17 41	17 45		17 47	17 50	17 53	17 56	18 00			18 02	18 05	18 08	18 12	18 20			18 22	18 25
Limehouse d		17 39		17 42	17 45	17 49		17 52		17 57	18 00				18 06	18 09	18 12	18 16				18 26	18 29
West Ham ⊖ d				17 47					17 58			18 08					18 17	18 21					18 34
London Liverpool Street 15 ⊖ d																							
Stratford 7 ⊖ d																							
Barking ⊖ d	17 45	17 49		17 52	17 55					18 07	18 10				18 16	18 19	18 23	18 28					18 40
Upminster ⊖ d	17 54			18 01				18 09	18 11						18 26		18 33					18 43	18 50
Ockendon d	18 00							18 14							18 32							18 48	
Chafford Hundred d	18 04							18 18							18 36							18 52	
West Horndon d				18 06						18 19							18 38						18 55
Laindon d		18 05		18a13						18 25						18 36	18 42		18 46				19 00
Basildon d		18 08							18 23	18 28		18 33				18 40	18 46		18 50				19 04
Dagenham Dock d					18 00						18 15							18 33					
Rainham d					18 04						18 19			←				18 37		←			
Purfleet d					18 09		←				18 24			18 09				18 42		18 24	←		
Grays d	18a10				→		18 00	18a24			→			18 18	18 41			18 48		18 31	18 41	18 57	
Tilbury Town 4 d							18 04							18 21	→			→		18 35	18 44	→	
East Tilbury d							18 10							18 27						18 41	18 50		
Stanford-le-Hope d							18 14							18 31						18 45	18 54		
Pitsea d		18 12					18a23		18 26	18 32		18 37		18a41		18 43	18 49			18b56	19a04		19 08
Benfleet d		18 16				18 22			18 31	18 36		18 40				18 48	18 53		18 57	19 01			19 12
Leigh-on-Sea d		18 21				18 26			18 35	18 41		18 46				18 52	18 58		19 02	19 05			19 16
Chalkwell d		18 24				18 29			18 38	18 44		18 49				18 55	19 00		19 05	19 08			19 19
Westcliff d		18 26				18 32			18 41	18 47		18 51				18 58	19 03		19 07	19 11			19 22
Southend Central a		18 29				18 34			18 43	18 49		18 54				19 00	19 05		19 10	19 16			19 24
d		18 29				18 34			18 43	18 49		18 54				19 00	19 06		19 10				19 24
Southend East d		18 31				18 36			18 45	18 51		18 56				19 02	19 08		19 12				19 26
Thorpe Bay d		18 34				18 40			18 49	18 55		18 59				19 06	19 10		19 15				19 30
Shoeburyness a		18 41				18 49			18 55	19 01		19 06				19 12	19 17		19 24				19 36

	CC		CC	CC	CC	CC	CC	CC	CC	CC	CC		CC	CC	CC	CC	CC	CC	CC	CC	CC		CC
London Fenchurch Street 7 ⊖ d				18 30	18 33	18 40	18 45		18 51	19 00	19 02		19 05		19 08	19 10		19 20	19 30		19 32		19 35
Limehouse d				18 34	18 37		18 50		18 54				19 09		19 12	19 14		19 24					19 39
West Ham ⊖ d						18 48	18 55		18 59		19 10				19 17	19 19		19 29			19 40		19 44
London Liverpool Street 15 ⊖ d																							
Stratford 7 ⊖ d																							
Barking ⊖ d				18 45	18 47		19 00		19 05		19 16		19 19		19 23	19 25		19 35			19 46		19 50
Upminster ⊖ d					18 56		19 09				19 26		19 30			19 34		19 44	19 50		19 55		
Ockendon d					19 03						19 33							19 49					
Chafford Hundred d					19 08						19 38							19 53					
West Horndon d							19 14									19 39					20 00		
Laindon d							19 19			19 26						19 44					20a06		
Basildon d						19 12	19 22						19 40			19 47			20 00				
Dagenham Dock d				18 50					19 10						19 28								19 55
Rainham d				18 54					19 14					←	19 32								19 59
Purfleet d	←		←	18 59				←	19 20					19 20	19 37		←						20 04
Grays d	18 48		18 57	19 05	19a14			19 05	→		19 46			19 27	19a43		19 46	19 57		←			20a10
Tilbury Town 4 d	18 52		19 00	→				19 09			→			19 30			19 50	20 00		20 00			
East Tilbury d	18 58		19 06					19 15						19 36			19 56	→		20 06			
Stanford-le-Hope d	19 02		19 10					19 19						19 40			20 00			20 10			
Pitsea d	19a11		19a22				19 26	19a28					19 44	19 48		19 51	20a07			20 18			
Benfleet d						19 19	19 30			19 32			19 48	19 52		19 55			20 06	20 22			
Leigh-on-Sea d						19 24	19 34			19 36			19 52	19 56		20 00			20 11	20 27			
Chalkwell d						19 27	19 37			19 39			19 55	19 59		20 03			20 14	20 30			
Westcliff d						19 29	19 39			19 42			19 58	20 02		20 05			20 16	20 32			
Southend Central a						19 32	19 42			19 44			20 00	20 07		20 08			20 19	20 35			
d						19 32	19 42			19 44			20 00			20 08			20 19				
Southend East d						19 34	19 44			19 47			20 02			20 10			20 21				
Thorpe Bay d						19 37	19 46			19 51			20a06			20 14			20 25				
Shoeburyness a						19 44	19 53			19 58						20 18			20 29				

	CC	CC	CC	CC	CC	CC	CC	CC	CC		CC	CC	CC	CC	CC	CC	CC	CC	CC		CC	CC	CC
London Fenchurch Street 7 ⊖ d	19 40	19 50	20 00		20 05	20 10	20 20	20 30	20 35			20 40	20 50	21 00		21 05	21 10	21 20	21 30		21 35		
Limehouse d	19 44	19 54			20 09	20 14	20 24		20 39			20 44	20 54			21 09	21 14	21 24			21 39		
West Ham ⊖ d	19 49	19 59	20 08		20 14	20 19	20 29	20 38	20 44			20 49	20 59	21 08		21 14	21 19	21 29	21 38		21 44		
London Liverpool Street 15 ⊖ d																						21 38	
Stratford 7 ⊖ d																						21 45	
Barking ⊖ d	19 55	20 05	20 14		20 20	20 25	20 35	20 44	20 50			20 55	21 05	21 14		21 20	21 25	21 35	21 44		21 50	21a54	
Upminster ⊖ d	20 04	20 14	20 23			20 34	20 44	20 53				21 04	21 14	21 23			21 34	21 44	21 53				
Ockendon d		20 19					20 49						21 19					21 49					
Chafford Hundred d		20 23					20 53						21 23					21 53					
West Horndon d	20 09					20 39						21 09					21 39						
Laindon d	20 14		20 31			20 44		21 01				21 14		21 31			21 44		22 01				
Basildon d	20 17		20 34			20 47		21 04				21 17		21 34			21 47		22 04				
Dagenham Dock d					20 25				20 55							21 25					21 55		
Rainham d					20 29				20 59							21 29					21 59		
Purfleet d					20 34				21 04							21 34					22 04		
Grays d		20 27		←	20a40		20 57		21a10		←		21 27		←	21a40		21 57			22a10		←
Tilbury Town 4 d		20 30		20 30			21 00				21 00		21 30		21 30			22 00					22 00
East Tilbury d		→		20 36			→				21 06		→		21 36			→					22 06
Stanford-le-Hope d				20 40							21 10				21 40								22 10
Pitsea d	20 21			20 48		20 51					21 18	21 21			21 48		21 51						22 18
Benfleet d	20 26		20 40	20 52		20 55		21 10			21 22	21 25		21 40	21 52		21 55		22 10				22 22
Leigh-on-Sea d	20 30		20 45	20 56		21 00		21 15			21 26	21 30		21 45	21 56		22 00		22 15				22 26
Chalkwell d	20 33		20 48	20 59		21 03		21 18			21 29	21 33		21 48	21 59		22 03		22 18				22 29
Westcliff d	20 36		20 50	21 02		21 05		21 20			21 32	21 35		21 50	22 02		22 05		22 20				22 32
Southend Central a	20 38		20 53	21 05		21 08		21 23			21 35	21 38		21 53	22 05		22 08		22 23				22 35
d	20 38		20 53			21 08		21 23				21 38		21 53			22 08		22 23				
Southend East d	20 40		20 55			21 10		21 25				21 40		21 56			22 10		22 25				
Thorpe Bay d	20 44		20 59			21 14		21 29				21 44		21 58			22 14		22 29				
Shoeburyness a	20 48		21 04			21 18		21 34				21 48		22 04			22 18		22 34				

For general notes see front of timetable
For details of catering facilities see Directory of Train Operators

b Arr. 3 minutes earlier

London → Southend Central and Shoeburyness

Network diagram - see first page of Table I

Mondays to Fridays

		CC	CC	CC	CC	CC	CC	CC	CC		CC	CC	CC	CC	CC	CC	CC	CC	CC		CC	CC		
London Fenchurch Street 7	⊖ d	21 40	21 50	22 00		22 05	22 10	22 20	22 35		22 40	22 50	23 00		23 05	23 10		23 20	23 35		23 40	23 50		
Limehouse	d	21 44	21 54			22 09	22 14	22 24	22 39		22 44	22 54			23 09	23 14		23 24	23 39		23 44	23 54		
West Ham	⊖ d	21 49	21 59	22 08		22 14	22 19	22 29	22 44		22 49	22 59	23 08		23 14	23 19		23 29	23 44		23 49	23 59		
London Liverpool Street 15	⊖ d																							
Stratford 7	⊖ d																							
Barking	⊖ d	21 55	22 05	22 14		22 20	22 25	22 35	22 50		22 55	23 05	23 14		23 20	23 25		23 35	23 51		23 55	00 05		
Upminster	⊖ d	22 04	22 14	22 23			22 34	22 44			23 04	23 14	23 23			23 34		23 44			00 04	00 14		
Ockendon	d		22 19					22 49				23 19						23 49				00 19		
Chafford Hundred	d		22 23					22 53				23 23						23 53				00 23		
West Horndon	d	22 09					22 39				23 09					23 39					00 09			
Laindon	d	22 14		22 31			22 44				23 14		23 31			23 44					00 14			
Basildon	d	22 17		22 34			22 47				23 17		23 34			23 47					00 17			
Dagenham Dock	d					22 25			22 55						23 25				23 56					
Rainham	d					22 29			22 59						23 29				23 59					
Purfleet	d					22 33			23 04						23 34		←		00 05					
Grays	d		22 27		←	22a40		22 57	23a10			23 27		←	23 42 →		23 42	23 57	00a11			00 27		
Tilbury Town 4	d		22 30 →		22 30			23 00				23 30 →		23 30			23 45	00 01				00 30		
East Tilbury	d				22 36			23 06						23 36			23 51	00 06				00 36		
Stanford-le-Hope	d				22 40			23 10						23 40			23 55	00 10				00 40		
Pitsea	d	22 21			22 48		22 51	23 18			23 21			23 48		23 51	00b06	00 18			00 21	00 48		
Benfleet	d	22 25		22 40	22 52		22 55	23 22			23 25		23 40	23 52		23 55	00 10	00 22			00 25	00 52		
Leigh-on-Sea	d	22 30		22 45	22 56		23 00	23 27			23 30		23 45	23 56		23 59	00 15	00 26			00 30	00 56		
Chalkwell	d	22 33		22 48	22 59		23 03	23 30			23 33		23 48	23 59		00 03	00 18	00 29			00 33	00 59		
Westcliff	d	22 35		22 50	23 02		23 05	23 32			23 36		23 50	00 02		00 05	00 20	00 32			00 35	01 02		
Southend Central	a	22 38		22 52	23 05		23 08	23 35			23 39		23 53	00 05		00 08	00 23	00 35			00 38	01 05		
	d	22 38		22 53	23 05		23 08	23 36			23 39		23 53	00 05		00 08	00 23	00 35			00 38	01 05		
Southend East	d	22 40		22 55	23 07		23 10	23 38			23 40		23 55	00 07		00 10	00 25	00 37			00 40	01 07		
Thorpe Bay	d	22 44		22 59	23 10		23 14	23 42			23 45		23 59	00 11		00 14	00 29	00 41			00 44	01 11		
Shoeburyness	a	22 48		23 04	23 15		23 18	23 48			23 50		00 07	00 17		00 26	00 34	00 48			00 52	01 17		

Saturdays

		CC	CC	CC	CC	CC	CC	CC		CC	CC	CC	CC	CC	CC	CC		CC	CC	CC	CC	CC	CC	CC
London Fenchurch Street 7	⊖ d	22p50	23p05	23p10		23p20	23p35	23p40		23p50	00 01			00 15	00 25				05 10	05 35	05 50	06 05	06 10	06 20
Limehouse	d	22p54	23p09	23p14		23p24	23p39	23p44		23p54				00 19	00 29				05 14	05 39	05 54	06 09	06 14	06 24
West Ham	⊖ d	22p59	23p14	23p19		23p29	23p44	23p49		23p59	00 09			00 24	00 34				05 19	05 44	05 59	06 14	06 19	06 29
London Liverpool Street 15	⊖ d											00 12												
Stratford 7	⊖ d											00 19												
Barking	⊖ d	23p05	23p20	23p25		23p35	23p51	23p55		00 05	00 15	00a28		00 31	00 40				05 24	05 49	06 04	06 19	06 24	06 34
Upminster	⊖ d	23p14		23p34		23p44		00 04		00 14	00 24				00 49	05 05		05 27	05 32		06 12		06 32	06 42
Ockendon	d	23p19				23p49				00 19						05a12		05 32			06 18			06 48
Chafford Hundred	d	23p23				23p53				00 23								05 36			06 21			06 51
West Horndon	d			23p39				00 09							00 54				05 37				06 37	
Laindon	d			23p44				00 14			00 32				00 59				05 42				06 42	
Basildon	d			23p47				00 17			00 35				01 02				05 45				06 45	
Dagenham Dock	d		23p25				23p56							00 36						05 54		06 24		
Rainham	d		23p29				23p59							00 40						05 57		06 27		
Purfleet	d		23p34		←		00 05							00 45						06 03		06 33		
Grays	d	23p27	23p42 →		23p42	23p57	00a11			00 27			←	00a51				05a42		06a12	06 25	06a42		06 55
Tilbury Town 4	d	23p30			23p45	00 01				00 30 →			00 30								06 28			06 58
East Tilbury	d	23p36			23p51	00 06							00 36								06 34			07 04
Stanford-le-Hope	d	23p40			23p55	00 10							00 40								06 37			07 07
Pitsea	d	23p48		23p51	00b06	00 18		00 21					00 48		01 06				05 50		06 45		06 49	07 15
Benfleet	d	23p52		23p55	00 10	00 22		00 25			00 41		00 52		01 10				05 54		06 49		06 52	07 19
Leigh-on-Sea	d	23p56		23p59	00 15	00 26		00 30			00 46		00 56		01 14				05 58		06 53		06 57	07 23
Chalkwell	d	23p59		00 03	00 18	00 29		00 33			00 49		00 59		01 17				06 01		06 56		06 59	07 26
Westcliff	d	00 02		00 05	00 20	00 32		00 35			00 51		01 02		01 20				06 03		06 58		07 02	07 28
Southend Central	a	00 05		00 08	00 23	00 35		00 38			00 54		01 05		01 23				06 06		07 04		07 05	07 34
	d	00 05		00 08	00 23	00 35		00 38			00 54		01 05		01 23				06 07				07 06	
Southend East	d	00 07		00 10	00 25	00 37		00 40			00 56		01 07		01 25				06 09				07 08	
Thorpe Bay	d	00 11		00 14	00 29	00 41		00 44			01 00		01 11		01 29				06 12				07 10	
Shoeburyness	a	00 17		00 26	00 34	00 48		00 52			01 08		01 17		01 33				06 19				07 18	

		CC	CC		CC	CC	CC	CC	CC	CC	CC		CC	CC	CC	CC	CC	CC	CC		CC		CC	CC
London Fenchurch Street 7	⊖ d	06 35	06 40		06 50	07 05	07 10	07 20	07 35	07 40	07 50		08 05	08 10	08 20	08 35	08 40	08 50	09 00				09 05	09 10
Limehouse	d	06 39	06 44		06 54	07 09	07 14	07 24	07 39	07 44	07 54		08 09	08 14	08 24	08 39	08 44	08 54					09 09	09 14
West Ham	⊖ d	06 44	06 49		06 59	07 14	07 19	07 29	07 44	07 49	07 59		08 14	08 19	08 29	08 44	08 49	08 59	09 08				09 14	09 19
London Liverpool Street 15	⊖ d																							
Stratford 7	⊖ d																							
Barking	⊖ d	06 49	06 54		07 04	07 19	07 24	07 34	07 49	07 54	08 04		08 19	08 24	08 34	08 49	08 54	09 04	09 13				09 19	09 24
Upminster	⊖ d		07 02		07 12		07 32	07 42		08 02	08 12			08 32	08 42		09 02	09 12	09 21					09 32
Ockendon	d				07 18			07 48			08 18				08 48			09 18						
Chafford Hundred	d				07 21			07 51			08 21				08 51			09 21						
West Horndon	d		07 07				07 37			08 07				08 37			09 07							09 37
Laindon	d		07 12				07 42			08 12				08 42			09 12		09 29					09 42
Basildon	d		07 15				07 45			08 15				08 45			09 15		09 32					09 45
Dagenham Dock	d	06 54				07 24			07 54				08 24			08 54							09 24	
Rainham	d	06 57				07 27			07 57				08 27			08 57							09 27	
Purfleet	d	07 03				07 33			08 03				08 33			09 03							09 33	
Grays	d	07a12			07 25	07a42		07 55	08a12		08 25		08a42		08 55	09a12		09 25			←		09a42	
Tilbury Town 4	d				07 28			07 58			08 28				08 58			09 28 →			09 28			
East Tilbury	d				07 34			08 04			08 34				09 04						09 34			
Stanford-le-Hope	d				07 37			08 07			08 37				09 07						09 37			
Pitsea	d		07 19		07 45		07 49	08 15		08 19	08 45			08 49	09 15		09 19				09 45			09 49
Benfleet	d		07 22		07 49		07 52	08 19		08 22	08 49			08 52	09 19		09 22		09 38		09 49			09 52
Leigh-on-Sea	d		07 27		07 53		07 57	08 23		08 27	08 53			08 57	09 23		09 27		09 42		09 53			09 57
Chalkwell	d		07 29		07 56		07 59	08 26		08 29	08 56			08 59	09 26		09 29		09 45		09 56			09 59
Westcliff	d		07 32		07 58		08 02	08 28		08 32	08 58			09 02	09 28		09 32		09 47		09 58			10 02
Southend Central	a		07 35		08 04		08 05	08 34		08 35	09 04			09 05	09 34		09 35		09 50		10 04			10 05
	d		07 36				08 06			08 36				09 06			09 36		09 50					10 06
Southend East	d		07 38				08 08			08 38				09 08			09 38		09 52					10 08
Thorpe Bay	d		07 40				08 10			08 40				09 10			09 40		09 55					10 10
Shoeburyness	a		07 48				08 18			08 48				09 18			09 48		10 02					10 18

For general notes see front of timetable
For details of catering facilities see
Directory of Train Operators

b Arr. 3 minutes earlier

Table 1

Saturdays

London → Southend Central and Shoeburyness

Network diagram - see first page of Table 1

		CC	CC	CC	CC	CC	CC	CC	CC			CC	CC	CC	CC	CC	CC	CC		CC	CC	CC	CC
London Fenchurch Street 7 ⊖	d	09 20	09 30		09 35	09 40	09 50	10 00		and at the same minutes past each hour until		20 05	20 10	20 20	20 35	20 40	20 50	21 00			21 05	21 10	21 20
Limehouse	d	09 24			09 39	09 44	09 54					20 09	20 14	20 24	20 39	20 44	20 54				21 09	21 14	21 24
West Ham ⊖	d	09 29	09 38		09 44	09 49	09 59	10 08				20 14	20 19	20 29	20 44	20 49	20 59	21 08			21 14	21 19	21 29
London Liverpool Street 15 ⊖	d																						
Stratford 7 ⊖	d																						
Barking ⊖	d	09 34	09 43		09 49	09 54	10 04	10 13				20 19	20 24	20 34	20 49	20 54	21 04	21 13			21 19	21 24	21 34
Upminster ⊖	d	09 42	09 51			10 02	10 12	10 21					20 32	20 42		21 02	21 12	21 21				21 32	21 42
Ockendon	d	09 48					10 18							20 48			21 18						21 48
Chafford Hundred	d	09 51					10 21							20 51			21 21						21 51
West Horndon	d					10 07							20 37			21 07						21 37	
Laindon	d		09 59			10 12		10 29					20 42			21 12		21 29				21 42	
Basildon	d		10 02			10 15		10 32					20 45			21 15		21 32				21 45	
Dagenham Dock	d				09 54							20 24			20 54						21 24		
Rainham	d				09 57							20 27			20 57						21 27		
Purfleet	d				10 03							20 33			21 03						21 33		
Grays	d	09 55		←	10a12		10 25		←			20a42		20 55	21a12		21 25			←	21a42		21 55
Tilbury Town 4	d	09 58		09 58			10 28		10 28					20 58			21 28			21 28			21 58
East Tilbury	d	→		10 04			→		10 34					21 04			→			21 34			22 04
Stanford-le-Hope	d			10 07					10 37					21 07						21 37			22 07
Pitsea	d			10 15		10 19			10 45				20 49	21 15		21 19				21 45		21 49	22 15
Benfleet	d		10 08	10 19		10 22		10 38	10 49				20 52	21 19		21 22		21 38		21 49		21 52	22 19
Leigh-on-Sea	d		10 12	10 23		10 27		10 42	10 53				20 57	21 23		21 27		21 42		21 53		21 57	22 23
Chalkwell	d		10 15	10 26		10 29		10 45	10 56				20 59	21 26		21 29		21 45		21 56		21 59	22 26
Westcliff	d		10 17	10 28		10 32		10 47	10 58				21 02	21 28		21 32		21 47		21 58		22 02	22 28
Southend Central	a		10 20	10 34		10 35		10 50	11 04				21 05	21 34		21 35		21 50		22 04		22 05	22 34
	d		10 20			10 36		10 50					21 06			21 36		21 50				22 06	
Southend East	d		10 22			10 38		10 52					21 08			21 38		21 52				22 08	
Thorpe Bay	d		10 25			10 40		10 55					21 10			21 40		21 55				22 10	
Shoeburyness	a		10 32			10 48		11 02					21 18			21 48		22 02				22 18	

		CC	CC	CC	CC	CC		CC	CC	CC	CC	CC	CC	CC		CC	CC	CC	CC	CC	CC	CC		
London Fenchurch Street 7 ⊖	d	21 35	21 40	21 50	22 00			22 05	22 10	22 20	22 35	22 40	22 50	23 05		23 10		23 20	23 35	23 40		23 50		
Limehouse	d	21 39	21 44	21 54				22 09	22 14	22 24	22 39	22 44	22 54	23 09		23 14		23 24	23 39	23 44		23 54		
West Ham ⊖	d	21 44	21 49	21 59	22 08			22 14	22 19	22 29	22 44	22 49	22 59	23 14		23 19		23 29	23 44	23 49		23 59		
London Liverpool Street 15 ⊖	d																							
Stratford 7 ⊖	d																							
Barking ⊖	d	21 49	21 54	22 04	22 13			22 19	22 24	22 34	22 49	22 54	23 04	23 19		23 24		23 34	23 49	23 54		00 04		
Upminster ⊖	d		22 02	22 12	22 21				22 32	22 42		23 02	23 12			23 32		23 42		00 02		00 12		
Ockendon	d			22 18						22 48			23 18					23 48				00 18		
Chafford Hundred	d			22 21						22 51			23 21					23 51				00 21		
West Horndon	d		22 07						22 37			23 07				23 37				00 07				
Laindon	d		22 12		22 29				22 42			23 12				23 42				00 12				
Basildon	d		22 15		22 32				22 45			23 15				23 45				00 15				
Dagenham Dock	d	21 54						22 24			22 54			23 24					23 54					
Rainham	d	21 57						22 27			22 57			23 27					23 57					
Purfleet	d	22 03						22 33			23 03			23 33			←		00 03		←			
Grays	d	22a12		22 25		←		22a42		22 55	23a12		23 25	23 38			23 38	23 55	00 08		00 08	00 25		
Tilbury Town 4	d			22 28		22 28				22 58			23 28	→			23 41	23 58	→		00 11	00 28		
East Tilbury	d			→		22 34				23 04			23 34				23 47	00 04			00 17	00 34		
Stanford-le-Hope	d					22 37				23 07			23 37				23 50	00 07			00 20	00 37		
Pitsea	d		22 19			22 45			22 49	23 15		23 19	23 45			23 49	23 58	00 15		00 19	00 28	00 45		
Benfleet	d		22 22		22 38	22 49			22 52	23 19		23 22	23 49			23 52	00 01	00 19		00 22	00 31	00 49		
Leigh-on-Sea	d		22 27		22 42	22 53			22 57	23 23		23 27	23 53			23 57	00 06	00 23		00 27	00 36	00 53		
Chalkwell	d		22 29		22 45	22 56			22 59	23 26		23 29	23 56			23 59	00 08	00 26		00 29	00 38	00 56		
Westcliff	d		22 32		22 47	22 58			23 02	23 28		23 32	23 58			00 02	00 11	00 28		00 32	00 41	00 58		
Southend Central	a		22 35		22 50	23 04			23 05	23 31		23 35	00 01			00 05	00 13	00 31		00 35	00 43	01 01		
	d		22 36		22 50				23 06	23 31		23 36	00 01			00 06	00 14	00 31		00 36	00 44	01 01		
Southend East	d		22 38		22 52				23 08	23 33		23 38	00 03			00 08	00 16	00 33		00 38	00 46	01 03		
Thorpe Bay	d		22 40		22 55				23 10	23 36		23 40	00 06			00 10	00 18	00 36		00 40	00 48	01 06		
Shoeburyness	a		22 48		23 02				23 18	23 43		23 48	00 13			00 18	00 25	00 43		00 48	00 55	01 13		

Sundays

		CC	CC	CC	CC	CC	CC	CC	CC	CC	CC	CC	CC	CC	CC	CC	CC	CC	CC	CC	CC	CC	CC	CC
London Fenchurch Street 7 ⊖	d	22p50	23p05	23p10		23p20	23p35	23p40		23p50	00 10	00 40	06 40		07 10	07 40	07 50	08 10			08 40	08 50	09 10	
Limehouse	d	22p54	23p09	23p14		23p24	23p39	23p44		23p54	00 14	00 44	06 44		07 14	07 44	07 54	08 14			08 44	08 54	09 14	
West Ham ⊖	d	22p59	23p14	23p19		23p29	23p44	23p49		23p59	00 19	00 49	06 49		07 19	07 49	07 59	08 19			08 49	08 59	09 19	
London Liverpool Street 15 ⊖	d																							
Stratford 7 ⊖	d																							
Barking ⊖	d	23p04	23p19	23p24		23p34	23p49	23p54		00 04	00 24	00 54	06 54	07 04	07 24	07 54	08 04	08 24	08 29	08 34	08 54	09 04	09 24	09 29
Upminster ⊖	d	23p12		23p32		23p42		00 02		00 12	00 32	01 02	07 02	07 12	07 32	08 02	08 12	08 32		08 42	09 02	09 12	09 32	
Ockendon	d	23p18				23p48				00 18				07 18			08 18			08 48		09 18		
Chafford Hundred	d	23p21				23p51				00 21				07 21			08 21			08 51		09 21		
West Horndon	d			23p37				00 07			00 37	01 07	07 07		07 37	08 07		08 37			09 07		09 37	
Laindon	d			23p42				00 12			00 42	01 12	07 12		07 42	08 12		08 42			09 12		09 42	
Basildon	d			23p45				00 15			00 45	01 15	07 15		07 45	08 15		08 45			09 15		09 45	
Dagenham Dock	d		23p24				23p54												08 33					09 33
Rainham	d		23p27				23p57												08 37					09 37
Purfleet	d		23p33		←		00 03		←										08 42					09 42
Grays	d	23p25	23p38		23p38	23p55	00 08		00 08	00 25				07 25			08 25		08a50	08 55		09 25		09a50
Tilbury Town 4	d	23p28	→		23p41	23p58	→		00 11	00 28				07 28			08 28			08 58		09 28		
East Tilbury	d	23p34			23p47	00 04			00 17	00 34				07 34			08 34			09 04		09 34		
Stanford-le-Hope	d	23p37			23p50	00 07			00 20	00 37				07 37			08 37			09 07		09 37		
Pitsea	d	23p45		23p49	23p58	00 15		00 19	00 28	00 45	00 49	01 19	07 19	07 45	07 49	08 19	08 45	08 49		09 15	09 19	09 45	09 49	
Benfleet	d	23p49		23p52	00 01	00 19		00 22	00 31	00 49	00 52	01 22	07 22	07 49	07 52	08 22	08 49	08 52		09 19	09 22	09 49	09 52	
Leigh-on-Sea	d	23p53		23p57	00 06	00 23		00 27	00 36	00 53	00 57	01 27	07 27	07 53	07 57	08 27	08 53	08 57		09 23	09 27	09 53	09 57	
Chalkwell	d	23p56		23p59	00 08	00 26		00 29	00 38	00 56	00 59	01 29	07 29	07 56	07 59	08 29	08 56	08 59		09 26	09 29	09 56	09 59	
Westcliff	d	23p58		00 02	00 11	00 28		00 32	00 41	00 58	01 02	01 32	07 32	07 58	08 02	08 32	08 58	09 02		09 28	09 32	09 58	10 02	
Southend Central	a	00 01		00 05	00 13	00 31		00 35	00 43	01 01	01 05	01 35	07 34	08 04	08 05	08 34	09 04	09 05		09 34	09 35	10 04	10 05	
	d	00 01		00 06	00 14	00 31		00 36	00 44	01 01	01 06	01 36	07 36		08 06	08 36		09 06			09 36		10 06	
Southend East	d	00 03		00 08	00 16	00 33		00 38	00 46	01 03	01 08	01 38	07 38		08 08	08 38		09 08			09 38		10 08	
Thorpe Bay	d	00 06		00 10	00 18	00 36		00 40	00 48	01 06	01 10	01 40	07 40		08 10	08 40		09 10			09 40		10 10	
Shoeburyness	a	00 13		00 18	00 25	00 43		00 48	00 55	01 13	01 18	01 48	07 48		08 18	08 48		09 18			09 48		10 18	

For general notes see front of timetable
For details of catering facilities see
Directory of Train Operators

Table 1

Sundays

London → Southend Central and Shoeburyness

Network diagram - see first page of Table 1

		CC	CC	CC		CC	CC	CC	CC	CC		CC	CC	CC	CC	CC	CC	CC	CC	CC	CC		
London Fenchurch Street 7	⊖ ⛴ d		09 40	09 50		10 10		10 20	10 40	10 50	and at the same minutes past each hour until	21 10		21 20	21 40	21 50	22 10	22 40	22 50	23 10	23 40		
Limehouse	⛴ d		09 44	09 54		10 14		10 24	10 44	10 54		21 14		21 24	21 44	21 54	22 14	22 44	22 54	23 14	23 44		
West Ham	⊖ d		09 49	09 59		10 19		10 29	10 49	10 59		21 19		21 29	21 49	21 59	22 19	22 49	22 59	23 19	23 49		
London Liverpool Street 15	⊖ d																						
Stratford 7	⊖ ⛴ d																						
Barking	⊖ d	09 34	09 54	10 04		10 24	10 29	10 34	10 54	11 04		21 24	21 29	21 34	21 54	22 04	22 24	22 54	23 04	23 24	23 54		
Upminster	⊖ d	09 42	10 02	10 12		10 32		10 42	11 02	11 12		21 32		21 42	22 02	22 12	22 32	23 02	23 12	23 32	00 02		
Ockendon	d	09 48		10 18				10 48		11 18				21 48		22 18			23 18				
Chafford Hundred	d	09 51		10 21				10 51		11 21				21 51		22 21			23 21				
West Horndon	d		10 07			10 37			11 07			21 37			22 07		22 37	23 07		23 37	00 07		
Laindon	d		10 12			10 42			11 12			21 42			22 12		22 42	23 12		23 42	00 12		
Basildon	d		10 15			10 45			11 15			21 45			22 15		22 45	23 15		23 45	00 15		
Dagenham Dock	d						10 33						21 33										
Rainham	d						10 37						21 37										
Purfleet	d						10 42						21 42										
Grays	d	09 55		10 25			10a50	10 55		11 25			21a51	21 55		22 25			23 25				
Tilbury Town 4	d	09 58		10 28				10 58		11 28				21 58		22 28			23 28				
East Tilbury	d	10 04		10 34				11 04		11 34				22 04		22 34			23 34				
Stanford-le-Hope	d	10 07		10 37				11 07		11 37				22 07		22 37			23 37				
Pitsea	d	10 15	10 19	10 45		10 49		11 15	11 19	11 45		21 49		22 15	22 19	22 45	22 49	23 19	23 45	23 49	00 19		
Benfleet	d	10 19	10 22	10 49		10 52		11 19	11 22	11 49		21 52		22 19	22 22	22 49	22 52	23 22	23 49	23 52	00 22		
Leigh-on-Sea	d	10 23	10 27	10 53		10 57		11 23	11 27	11 53		21 57		22 23	22 27	22 53	22 57	23 27	23 53	23 57	00 27		
Chalkwell	d	10 26	10 29	10 56		10 59		11 26	11 29	11 56		21 59		22 26	22 29	22 56	22 59	23 29	23 56	23 59	00 29		
Westcliff	d	10 28	10 32	10 58		11 02		11 28	11 32	11 58		22 02		22 28	22 32	22 58	23 02	23 32	23 58	00 02	00 32		
Southend Central	a	10 34	10 35	11 04		11 05		11 34	11 35	12 04		22 05		22 34	22 35	23 01	23 05	23 35	00 01	00 05	00 34		
	d		10 36			11 06			11 36			22 06			22 36	23 01	23 06	23 36	00 01	00 06	00 36		
Southend East	d		10 38			11 08			11 38			22 08			22 38	23 03	23 08	23 38	00 03	00 08	00 38		
Thorpe Bay	d		10 40			11 10			11 40			22 10			22 40	23 06	23 10	23 40	00 06	00 10	00 40		
Shoeburyness	a		10 48			11 18			11 48			22 18			22 48	23 13	23 18	23 48	00 13	00 18	00 48		

For general notes see front of timetable
For details of catering facilities see Directory of Train Operators

Shoeburyness and Southend Central → London

Network diagram - see first page of Table I

Miles	Miles	Miles			CC MX	CC MX	CC	CC	CC	CC	CC	CC	CC	CC	CC	CC	CC	CC	CC	CC	CC	CC	CC	CC
0	0	—	**Shoeburyness**	d		23p05		04 20		04 40	04 59		05 13	05 24			05 28		05 45		05 58			06 04
1½	1½	—	Thorpe Bay	d		23p09		04 24		04 44	05 03		05 17	05 28			05 32		05 49	05 58	06 02			06 08
3	3	—	Southend East	d		23p12		04 27		04 47	05 06		05 20	05 31			05 35		05 52	06 01	06 05			06 11
3¾	3¾	—	**Southend Central**	a		23p14		04 29		04 49	05 08		05 22	05 33			05 37		05 54	06 03	06 07			06 13
—	—	—		d		23p15		04 29		04 50	05 09		05 23	05 34			05 38	05 47	05 55	06 04	06 08			06 14
4¾	4¾	—	Westcliff	d		23p17		04 31		04 52	05 11		05 25	05 36			05 40	05 49	05 57	06 06	06 10			06 16
5½	5½	—	Chalkwell	d		23p19		04 34		04 54	05 13		05 27	05 38			05 42	05 51	05 59	06 08	06 12			06 18
7	7	—	Leigh-on-Sea	d		23p22		04 37		04 57	05 16		05 30	05 41			05 45	05 54	06 02	06 11	06 15			06 21
10¼	10¼	—	Benfleet	d		23p27		04 41		05 02	05 21		05 35	05 46			05 50	05 59	06 07	06 16	06 20			06 26
13	13	—	Pitsea	d		23p32		04 45		05 06	05 25		05 39	05 50			05 54	06 04	06 11	06b24				06 30
—	18	—	Stanford-le-Hope	d			04 29			05 14			05 46				06 01	06 11		06 31				
—	20	—	East Tilbury	d			04 33			05 18			05 50				06 05	06 15		06 35			←	
—	23¾	—	**Tilbury Town** 4	d			04 39			05 24			05 56		←		06 11	06 21		06 41			06 21	
—	25½	0	Grays	d	23p34		04 42		05 12	05 27		05 50	06 00		06 00		06 15	→		06 45		06 28	06 25	
—	29¼	—	Purfleet	d	23p39					05 33			→		06 05		06 20			→		06 33		
—	32½	—	Rainham	d	23p44					05 38					06 10		06 25					06 39		
—	34¾	—	Dagenham Dock	d	23p48					05 41					06 14		06 29					06 42		
15	—	—	Basildon	d		23p36		04 50			05 29			05 54					06 16		06 27			06 35
16¾	—	—	Laindon	d		23p39		04 53			05 32			05 57					06 19		06 31			06 38
20¼	—	—	West Horndon	d		23p44		04 58			05 37			06 02					06 24					06 43
—	—	2½	Chafford Hundred	d			04 46		05 16			05 54											06 30	
—	—	4½	Ockendon	d			04 50		05 20			05 58				06 20							06c37	
24¼	—	7½	Upminster	⊖ d		23p50	04 57	05 04	05a25		05 42	06 03		06 08		06a25			06 30				06 43	06 49
32	37¾	—	Barking	⊖ d	23p53	23p58	05 06	05 13		05 47	05 51	06 12		06 16	06 20		06 35		06 38			06 49		06 58
—	—	—	Stratford 7	⊖ ⛴ a			05 13																	
—	—	—	**London Liverpool Street** 15	⊖ a			05 23																	
35	40¾	—	West Ham	⊖ d	23p59	00 04		05 18		05 53	05 57	06 17		06 22	06 26		06 41		06 43			06 54	06 57	07 03
37¾	43½	—	Limehouse	⛴ d	00 04	00 09		05 23		05 58	06 02	06 22		06 27	06 31		06 46		06 48		06 54	06 59	07 02	
39½	45¼	—	**London Fenchurch Street** 7	⊖ ⛴ a	00 09	00 14		05 30		06 04	06 08	06 29		06 31	06 37		06 52		06 53		07 01	07 06	07 08	07 14

		CC		CC	CC	CC	CC	CC	CC	CC	CC	CC	CC	CC	CC	CC	CC	CC	CC	CC	CC	CC		CC
Shoeburyness	d			06 13		06 17		06 28			06 32	06 46					06 53			07 05				
Thorpe Bay	d	06 13		06 17		06 21		06 32			06 36	06 50					06 57			07 09				07 14
Southend East	d	06 16		06 20		06 24		06 35			06 39	06 53					07 00			07 12				07 17
Southend Central	a	06 18		06 22		06 26		06 37			06 41	06 55					07 02			07 14				07 19
	d	06 19		06 23		06 27		06 38			06 42	06 56					07 03		07 10	07 15				07 20
Westcliff	d	06 21		06 25		06 29		06 40			06 44	06 58					07 05		07 12	07 17				07 22
Chalkwell	d	06 23		06 27		06 31		06 42			06 46	07 00					07 07		07 14	07 19				07 24
Leigh-on-Sea	d	06 26		06 30		06 34		06 45			06 49	07 03					07 10		07 18	07 22				07 27
Benfleet	d	06 31		06 35		06 39		06 50			06 54	07 08					07 15		07 22	07 27				07 32
Pitsea	d	06b39				06 43				06 55	06 58				07 02	07 15	07 19		07 27					07 36
Stanford-le-Hope	d	06 46								07 02					07 09	07 22			07 34					
East Tilbury	d	06 50							←	07 06					07 13	07 26			07 38					
Tilbury Town 4	d	06 56			←				06 56	07 12			←		07 20	07 32		←	07 44					
Grays	d	→			06 45		06 51		07 00	07 16			07 16		07 24	07 36		07 24	07 48		07 32			
Purfleet	d				06 51				07 05	→			07 21		→	→			→		07 37			
Rainham	d				06 56				07 11				07 27								07 43			
Dagenham Dock	d				07 00				07 14				07 30								07 46			
Basildon	d			06 42		06 48		06 57			07 03	07 15					07 24							07 41
Laindon	d					06 51					07 06			07 22			07 27					07 37		07 44
West Horndon	d					06 56					07 11			07 27								07 42		
Chafford Hundred	d						06 55											07 28						
Ockendon	d						07 00											07 32						
Upminster	⊖ d					07 02	07 06	07 10			07 17			07 32				07 39				07 48		
Barking	⊖ d			07 00	07 06	07 11	07 15		07 21		07 27		07 37	07 41			07 45	07 48			07 54	07 56		08 01
Stratford 7	⊖ ⛴ a																							
London Liverpool Street 15	⊖ a																							
West Ham	⊖ d			07 07	07 12		07 20	07 23	07 26					07 46								08 02		
Limehouse	⛴ d				07 17	07 20	07 25		07 32		07 36		07 46	07 51			07 54			08 00	08 03	08 08		08 10
London Fenchurch Street 7	⊖ ⛴ a			07 17	07 23	07 26	07 32	07 34	07 38		07 42	07 46	07 52	07 58			08 00	08 03		08 07	08 10	08 14		08 17

		CC	CC	CC	CC	CC	CC	CC	CC	CC	CC	CC	CC	CC	CC	CC	CC	CC	CC	CC		CC	CC	CC
Shoeburyness	d		07 20					07 24		07 35							07 50			07 54			08 05	
Thorpe Bay	d		07 24					07 28		07 39				07 43			07 54			07 58			08 09	
Southend East	d		07 27					07 31		07 42				07 46			07 57			08 01			08 12	
Southend Central	a		07 29					07 33		07 44				07 48			07 59			08 03			08 14	
	d		07 30					07 34		07 45				07 49			08 00			08 04			08 15	
Westcliff	d		07 32					07 36		07 47				07 51			08 02			08 06			08 17	
Chalkwell	d		07 34					07 38		07 49				07 53			08 04			08 08			08 19	
Leigh-on-Sea	d		07 37					07 41		07 52				07 56			08 07			08 11			08 22	
Benfleet	d		07 42					07 46		07 57				08 01			08 12			08 16			08 27	
Pitsea	d					07 42	07 49	07 50					07 54	08 05					08 13	08 20				
Stanford-le-Hope	d					07 49	07 56		07 44				08 02						08 20			08 12		
East Tilbury	d					07 53							08 06						08 24			08 16		
Tilbury Town 4	d	←		←		07 59					←		08 12			←			08 30			08 22		←
Grays	d	07 36		07 48		08 03	08 07		07 54		08 03		08 16			08 16			08 34			08 26		08 34
Purfleet	d			07 53		→					08 08		→			08 21			→					08 40
Rainham	d			07 59							08 14					08 27								08 45
Dagenham Dock	d			08 02							08 17					08 30								08 49
Basildon	d							07 55						08 10						08 25				
Laindon	d				07 52			07 58				08 08		08 13				08 23		08 28				
West Horndon	d				07 57							08 13			←			08 28						
Chafford Hundred	d	07 40					08 11		07 59						08 11							08 30		
Ockendon	d	07b48					→		08 03						08 18							08 34		
Upminster	⊖ d	07 54			08 03				08 10	08 14		08 18			08 25		08 29	08 33				08 41		
Barking	⊖ d			08 09	08 12			08 15	08 19		08 24	08 27		08 30		08 37		08 43		08 46		08 51		08 55
Stratford 7	⊖ ⛴ a																							
London Liverpool Street 15	⊖ a																							
West Ham	⊖ d				08 17							08 32						08 48						09 01
Limehouse	⛴ d		08 16	08 19	08 22			08 25		08 31	08 34	08 37		08 39		08 46	08 48	08 53		08 56				09 06
London Fenchurch Street 7	⊖ ⛴ a	08 19	08 22	08 25	08 28			08 32	08 34	08 37	08 40	08 43		08 45	08 48	08 52	08 55	08 59		09 02		09 06	09 08	09 12

For general notes see front of timetable
For details of catering facilities see
Directory of Train Operators

b Arr. 4 minutes earlier
c Arr. 3 minutes earlier

Table I

Shoeburyness and Southend Central → London

Network diagram - see first page of Table I

	CC	CC	CC	CC	CC	CC	CC	CC	CC	CC	CC	CC	CC	CC	CC		CC	CC	CC	CC	CC	CC	CC
Shoeburyness d			08 10		08 25					08 40							09 05			09 20		09 35	
Thorpe Bay d			08 14		08 29					08 44							09 09			09 24		09 39	
Southend East d			08 17		08 32					08 47							09 12			09 27		09 42	
Southend Central a			08 19		08 34					08 49							09 14			09 29		09 44	
d			08 20		08 34					08 50			09 06				09 15		09 20	09 30		09 45	
Westcliff d			08 22		08 36					08 52			09 08				09 17		09 23	09 32		09 47	
Chalkwell d			08 24		08 39					08 54			09 11				09 19		09 25	09 34		09 49	
Leigh-on-Sea d			08 27		08 42					08 57			09 14				09 22		09 28	09 37		09 52	
Benfleet d			08 32		08 47					09 02			09 19				09 27		09 33	09 42		09 57	
Pitsea d		08 34	08 36		08 51				08 54	09 06					09 08		09 32		09 37			10 02	
Stanford-le-Hope d		08 41		08 32					09 01						09 16				09 44				
East Tilbury d		08 45		08 36		←			09 05						09 20				09 48		←		
Tilbury Town [4] d		08 51		08 42		08 51			09 11		←				09 26				09 54		09 54		
Grays d		→		08 46		08 56	09 03		09 15		09 15				09 29			09 46	→		09 57		10 16
Purfleet d				08 51			09 08		→		09 20							09 51					10 21
Rainham d				08 57			09 13				09 26							09 56					10 26
Dagenham Dock d				09 00			09 17				09 29							10 00					10 30
Basildon d			08 41		08 55					09 11			09 26				09 36			09 49		10 06	
Laindon d	08 38		08 44					09 04		09 14		09 17		09 31			09 39			09 52		10 09	
West Horndon d	08 43							09 10				09 22					09 44					10 14	
Chafford Hundred d						09 01									09 34						10 01		
Ockendon d						09 05									09 38						10 05		
Upminster ⊖ d	08 49		08 54		09 06	09 11		09 16				09 28		09 41	09 45		09 50			10 00	10 10	10 20	
Barking ⊖ d	08 58		09 03	09 07		09 20	09 23	09 25		09 30	09 35	09 37		09 50	09 54		09 58	10 06		10 08	10 18	10 28	10 36
Stratford [7] ⊖ ⛴ a																							
London Liverpool Street [15] ⊖ a																							
West Ham ⊖ d	09 04		09 08			09 25	09 29	09 31				09 43		09 56	09 59		10 04	10 11		10 16	10 26	10 34	10 41
Limehouse ⛴ d	09 09		09 14	09 17	09 23	09 30	09 34	09 36			09 44		09 51	10 01	10 04		10 09	10 16			10 31	10 39	10 46
London Fenchurch Street [7] ⊖ ⛴ a	09 15		09 20	09 24	09 29	09 38	09 40	09 43		09 45	09 51	09 53	09 57	10 07	10 09		10 13	10 21		10 24	10 35	10 43	10 51

	CC	CC	CC			CC	CC	CC	CC	CC	CC	CC	CC	CC	CC	CC	CC	CC	CC	CC	CC	CC
Shoeburyness d		09 50				15 05			15 20		15 35			15 50		16 05			16 15			16 28
Thorpe Bay d		09 54				15 09			15 24		15 39			15 54		16 09			16 19			16 32
Southend East d		09 57				15 12			15 27		15 42			15 57		16 12			16 22			16 35
Southend Central a		09 59				15 14			15 29		15 44			15 59		16 14			16 24			16 37
d	09 50	10 00				15 15		15 20	15 30		15 45		15 48	16 00		16 15		16 19	16 25	16 33		16 38
Westcliff d	09 53	10 02				15 17		15 23	15 32		15 47		15 50	16 02		16 17		16 21	16 27	16 35		16 40
Chalkwell d	09 55	10 04				15 19		15 25	15 34		15 49		15 53	16 04		16 19		16 23	16 29	16 37		16 42
Leigh-on-Sea d	09 58	10 07		and at		15 22		15 28	15 37		15 52		15 56	16 07		16 22		16 26	16 32	16 40		16 45
Benfleet d	10 03	10 12				15 27		15 33	15 42		15 57		16 00	16 12		16 27		16 31	16 37	16 45		16 50
Pitsea d	10 07			the same		15 32		15 37			16 02		16 04			16 31		16 35		16 49		16 54
Stanford-le-Hope d	10 14							15 44					16 11					16 42				
East Tilbury d	10 18		←					15 48		←			16 15		←			16 46				
Tilbury Town [4] d	10 24		10 24	minutes				15 54		15 54			16 21		16 21			16 52				
Grays d	→		10 27	past			15 46	→		15 57		16 16	→		16 26		16 39	→			16 52	
Purfleet d							15 51					16 21					16 44				16 57	
Rainham d				each			15 56					16 26					16 49				17 02	
Dagenham Dock d							16 00					16 30					16 53				17 06	
Basildon d		10 19		hour until		15 36			15 49		16 06			16 19		16 35			16 43	16 53		16 58
Laindon d		10 22				15 39			15 52		16 09					16 38						17 01
West Horndon d						15 44					16 14					16 43						17 06
Chafford Hundred d			10 31							16 01					16 30							
Ockendon d			10 35							16 05					16 34							
Upminster ⊖ d		10 30	10 40			15 50			16 00	16 10	16 20			16 30	16 41	16 48			16 54			17 11
Barking ⊖ d		10 38	10 48			15 58	16 06		16 08	16 18	16 28	16 36		16 38	16 49	16 57	17 00		17 03		17b16	17 20
Stratford [7] ⊖ ⛴ a																						
London Liverpool Street [15] ⊖ a																						
West Ham ⊖ d		10 46	10 56			16 04	16 11		16 16	16 26	16 34			16 44		17 02			17 09		17 22	
Limehouse ⛴ d			11 01			16 09	16 16			16 31	16 39					17 08	17 10		17 14			17 29
London Fenchurch Street [7] ⊖ ⛴ a		10 54	11 05			16 13	16 21		16 26	16 36	16 43	16 48		16 52	17 03	17 12	17 15		17 18	17 24	17 30	17 33

	CC	CC	CC	CC		CC	CC	CC	CC	CC	CC	CC	CC	CC	CC	CC	CC	CC	CC	CC	CC	CC	CC
Shoeburyness d				16 49						17 12					17 30			17 45				18 05	
Thorpe Bay d				16 53						17 16					17 34			17 49				18 09	
Southend East d				16 56						17 19					17 37			17 52				18 12	
Southend Central a				16 58						17 21					17 39			17 54				18 14	
d			16 54	16 59						17 21					17 40			17 55				18 15	18 20
Westcliff d			16 56	17 01						17 23					17 42			17 57				18 17	18 23
Chalkwell d			16 59	17 03						17 26					17 44			17 59				18 19	18 25
Leigh-on-Sea d			17 02	17 06						17 29					17 47			18 02				18 22	18 28
Benfleet d			17 06	17 11						17 33					17 52			18 07				18 27	18 33
Pitsea d		16 56	17 10	17 15					17 24	17 37				17 43	17 56		17 59	18 11			18 31	18 32	18 37
Stanford-le-Hope d		17 03						17 19	17 32					17 50			18 06				18 38		18 44
East Tilbury d	←	17 07					←	17 23	17 36					17 54			18 10		←		18 42		18 48
Tilbury Town [4] d	16 52	17 13					17 13	17 29	17 42				←	18 00		←	18 16		18 16		18 48		18 54
Grays d	16 57	→				17 22	17 19	17 32	17 49		17 44		17 49	18 04		18 04	→		18 20	18 28	→		→
Purfleet d						17 27		17 38	→		17 49			→		18 09				18 33			
Rainham d						17 32		17 43			17 54					18 14				18 38			
Dagenham Dock d						17 36		17 46			17 58					18 18				18 42			
Basildon d			17 14	17 19						17 41					18 00			18 15				18 36	
Laindon d			17 17							17 44		17 47			18 05			18 18				18 39	
West Horndon d			17 22									17 52			18 10			18 23				18 44	
Chafford Hundred d	17 01						17 23						17 53						18 25				
Ockendon d	17 07						17c30						17 59						18 31				
Upminster ⊖ d	17 15		17 28	17 31			17 38					17 58	18 06		18 15			18 30	18 38			18 50	
Barking ⊖ d	17 25		17 36	17 40		17 42	17 47	17 52			18 04	18 06	18 14		18 24	18 26		18 38		18 48		18 58	
Stratford [7] ⊖ ⛴ a																							
London Liverpool Street [15] ⊖ a																							
West Ham ⊖ d	17 31							17 58			18 09	18 12			18 29	18 32		18 44		18 53		19 04	
Limehouse ⛴ d								18 03				18 17				18 37		18 49		18 58		19 09	
London Fenchurch Street [7] ⊖ ⛴ a	17 39		17 49	17 52		17 54	18 00	18 08		18 12	18 18	18 21	18 27		18 38	18 41		18 53	19 00	19 03		19 13	

For general notes see front of timetable
For details of catering facilities see
Directory of Train Operators

b Arr. 4 minutes earlier
c Arr. 3 minutes earlier

Shoeburyness and Southend Central → London

Network diagram - see first page of Table I

		CC	CC	CC		CC	CC	CC	CC	CC	CC	CC	CC	CC	CC	CC	CC	CC	CC	CC	CC	CC	CC	CC
Shoeburyness	d	18 20				18 35			18 50		19 05			19 20		19 35			19 50		20 05			
Thorpe Bay	d	18 24				18 39			18 54		19 09			19 24		19 39			19 54		20 09			
Southend East	d	18 27				18 42			18 57		19 12			19 27		19 42			19 57		20 12			
Southend Central	a	18 29				18 44			18 59		19 15			19 29		19 44			19 59		20 14			
	d	18 30				18 45		18 49	19 00		19 15	19 20		19 30		19 45		19 50	20 00		20 15	20 20		
Westcliff	d	18 32				18 47		18 51	19 02		19 17	19 23		19 32		19 47		19 53	20 02		20 17	20 23		
Chalkwell	d	18 34				18 49		18 53	19 04		19 19	19 25		19 34		19 49		19 55	20 04		20 19	20 25		
Leigh-on-Sea	d	18 37				18 52		18 56	19 07		19 22	19 28		19 37		19 52		19 58	20 07		20 22	20 28		
Benfleet	d	18 42				18 57		19 01	19 12		19 27	19 33		19 42		19 57		20 03	20 12		20 27	20 33		
Pitsea	d					19 02		19 05			19 32	19 37				20 02		20 07			20 32	20 37		
Stanford-le-Hope	d							19 12				19 44						20 14				20 44		
East Tilbury	d		←	←				19 16		←		19 48			←			20 18		←		20 48		
Tilbury Town 4	d		18 54	18 48				19 22		19 22		19 54			19 54			20 24		20 24		20 54		
Grays	d		18 57	18b54			19 18	→		19 25		→	19 48		19 57		20 16	→		20 27		→		20 46
Purfleet	d		19 04				19 23						19 53				20 21							20 51
Rainham	d		19 09				19 28						19 58				20 26							20 56
Dagenham Dock	d		19 12				19 32						20 02				20 30							21 00
Basildon	d	18 49				19 06			19 19		19 36			19 49		20 06			20 19		20 36			
Laindon	d	18 52				19 09			19 22		19 39			19 52		20 09			20 22		20 39			
West Horndon	d					19 14					19 44					20 14					20 44			
Chafford Hundred	d			18 59						19 29					20 01					20 31				
Ockendon	d			19 04						19 34					20 05					20 35				
Upminster ⊖	d	19 00		19 10		19 20			19 30	19 40	19 50			20 00	20 10	20 20			20 30	20 40	20 50			
Barking ⊖	d	19 08	19 18	19 18		19 28	19 37		19 38	19 48	19 58		20 08	20 08	20 18	20 28	20 36		20 38	20 48	20 58		21 03	21 06
Stratford 7 ⊖ ⛴	a																						21 09	
London Liverpool Street 15 ⊖	a																						21 19	
West Ham ⊖	d	19 16		19 26		19 34	19 43		19 46	19 56	20 04		20 13	20 16	20 26	20 34	20 41		20 46	20 56	21 04			21 11
Limehouse ⛴	d		19 27			19 39	19 48			20 01	20 09		20 18		20 31	20 39	20 46			21 01	21 09			21 16
London Fenchurch Street 7 ⊖ ⛴	a	19 24	19 32	19 38		19 43	19 53		19 55	20 05	20 13		20 23	20 25	20 35	20 43	20 51		20 54	21 05	21 13			21 21

		CC	CC		CC	CC	CC	CC	CC	CC	CC	CC	CC	CC	CC	CC	CC	CC	CC	CC	CC	CC		
Shoeburyness	d	20 20			20 35			21 05			21 20		21 35			22 05			22 35			23 05		
Thorpe Bay	d	20 24			20 39			21 09			21 24		21 40			22 09			22 39			23 09		
Southend East	d	20 27			20 42			21 12			21 27		21 43			22 12			22 42			23 12		
Southend Central	a	20 29			20 44			21 14			21 29		21 45			22 14			22 44			23 14		
	d	20 30			20 45		20 50	21 15		21 20	21 30		21 46		21 50	22 15		22 20	22 45	22 50		23 15		
Westcliff	d	20 32			20 47		20 53	21 17		21 23	21 32		21 48		21 53	22 17		22 23	22 47	22 53		23 17		
Chalkwell	d	20 34			20 49		20 55	21 19		21 25	21 34		21 50		21 55	22 19		22 25	22 49	22 55		23 19		
Leigh-on-Sea	d	20 37			20 52		20 58	21 22		21 28	21 37		21 53		21 58	22 22		22 28	22 52	22 58		23 22		
Benfleet	d	20 42			20 57		21 03	21 27		21 33	21 42		21 58		22 03	22 27		22 33	22 57	23 03		23 27		
Pitsea	d				21 02		21 07	21 32		21 37			22 02		22 07	22 32		22 37	23 02	23 07		23 32		
Stanford-le-Hope	d						21 14			21 44					22 14			22 44		23 14				
East Tilbury	d		←				21 18			21 48		←			22 18			22 48		23 18				
Tilbury Town 4	d		20 54				21 24			21 54		21 54			22 24			22 54		23 24				
Grays	d		20 57			21 16	21 27		21 46	→		21 57		22 16	22 27		22 46	22 57		23 27	23 31			
Purfleet	d					21 21			21 51					22 21			22 51				23 36			
Rainham	d					21 26			21 56					22 26			22 56				23 41			
Dagenham Dock	d					21 30			22 00					22 30			23 00				23 45			
Basildon	d	20 49			21 06			21 36			21 49		22 06			22 36			23 06			23 36		
Laindon	d	20 52			21 09			21 39			21 52		22 09			22 39			23 09			23 39		
West Horndon	d				21 14			21 44					22 14			22 44			23 14			23 44		
Chafford Hundred	d		21 01				21 31					22 01			22 31			23 01		23 31				
Ockendon	d		21 05				21 35					22 05			22 35			23 05		23 35				
Upminster ⊖	d	21 00	21 10		21 20		21 40	21 50			22 00	22 10	22 20		22 42	22 50		23 12	23 20	23 42		23 50		
Barking ⊖	d	21 08	21 18		21 28	21 36	21 48	21 58	22 06		22 08	22 18	22 28	22 36	22 50	22 58	23 05	23 20	23 28	23a50	23 50	23 58		
Stratford 7 ⊖ ⛴	a																				23 57			
London Liverpool Street 15 ⊖	a																				00 05			
West Ham ⊖	d	21 16	21 26		21 34	21 41	21 56	22 04	22 11		22 16	22 26	22 34	22 41	22 56	23 04	23 11	23 26	23 34			00 04		
Limehouse ⛴	d		21 31		21 39	21 46	22 01	22 09	22 16			22 31	22 39	22 46	23 01	23 09	23 16	23 31	23 39			00 09		
London Fenchurch Street 7 ⊖ ⛴	a	21 24	21 35		21 43	21 51	22 05	22 13	22 21		22 24	22 35	22 43	22 51	23 05	23 13	23 21	23 35	23 43			00 14		

Saturdays

		CC	CC	CC	CC	CC	CC	CC		CC	CC	CC	CC	CC	CC	CC		CC	CC	CC	CC	CC	CC	CC
Shoeburyness	d		23p05		04 20		05 05				05 35			06 05				06 35			07 05			07 35
Thorpe Bay	d		23p09		04 23		05 08				05 38			06 08				06 38			07 08			07 38
Southend East	d		23p12		04 26		05 11				05 41			06 11				06 41			07 11			07 41
Southend Central	a		23p14		04 28		05 13				05 43			06 13				06 43			07 13			07 43
	d		23p15		04 29		05 14			05 20	05 44		05 50	06 14		06 20		06 44		06 50	07 14		07 20	07 44
Westcliff	d		23p17		04 31		05 16			05 23	05 46		05 53	06 16		06 23		06 46		06 53	07 16		07 23	07 46
Chalkwell	d		23p19		04 33		05 18			05 25	05 48		05 55	06 18		06 25		06 48		06 55	07 18		07 25	07 48
Leigh-on-Sea	d		23p22		04 36		05 21			05 28	05 51		05 58	06 21		06 28		06 51		06 58	07 21		07 28	07 51
Benfleet	d		23p27		04 40		05 25			05 32	05 55		06 02	06 25		06 32		06 55		07 02	07 25		07 32	07 55
Pitsea	d		23p32		04 44		05 29			05 36	05 59		06 06	06 29		06 36		06 59		07 06	07 29		07 36	07 59
Stanford-le-Hope	d			04 30						05 42			06 12			06 42				07 12			07 42	
East Tilbury	d			04 33						05 45			06 15			06 45				07 15			07 45	
Tilbury Town 4	d			04 39						05 51			06 21			06 51				07 21			07 51	
Grays	d	23p34		04 42				05 48		05 54		06 18	06 24		06 48	06 54			07 18	07 24		07 48	07 54	
Purfleet	d	23p39						05 53				06 23			06 53				07 23			07 53		
Rainham	d	23p44						05 58				06 28			06 58				07 28			07 58		
Dagenham Dock	d	23p48						06 02				06 32			07 02				07 32			08 02		
Basildon	d		23p36		04 47		05 32				06 02			06 32				07 02			07 32			08 02
Laindon	d		23p39		04 50		05 35				06 05			06 35				07 05			07 35			08 05
West Horndon	d		23p44		04 55		05 40				06 10			06 40				07 10			07 40			08 10
Chafford Hundred	d			04 46						05 59			06 29			06 59				07 29			07 59	
Ockendon	d			04 50		05 16				06 02			06 32			07 02				07 32			08 02	
Upminster ⊖	d		23p50	04a58	05 01	05a23	05 46			06 09	06 16		06 39	06 46		07 09		07 16		07 39	07 46		08 09	08 16
Barking ⊖	d	23p53	23p58		05 09		05 54	06 08		06 17	06 24	06 38	06 47	06 54	07 08	07 17		07 24	07 38	07 47	07 54	08 08	08 17	08 24
Stratford 7 ⊖ ⛴	a																							
London Liverpool Street 15 ⊖	a																							
West Ham ⊖	d	23p59	00 04		05 15		06 00	06 14		06 23	06 30	06 44	06 53	07 00	07 14	07 23		07 30	07 44	07 53	08 00	08 14	08 23	08 30
Limehouse ⛴	d	00 04	00 09		05 20		06 05	06 19		06 28	06 35	06 49	06 58	07 05	07 19	07 28		07 35	07 49	07 58	08 05	08 19	08 28	08 35
London Fenchurch Street 7 ⊖ ⛴	a	00 09	00 14		05 27		06 12	06 26		06 34	06 42	06 56	07 04	07 12	07 26	07 34		07 42	07 56	08 04	08 12	08 26	08 34	08 42

For general notes see front of timetable
For details of catering facilities see Directory of Train Operators

b Arr. 3 minutes earlier

Table I

Shoeburyness and Southend Central → London

Saturdays

Network diagram - see first page of Table I

Station		cc	cc		cc	cc		cc	cc	cc	cc	cc	cc	cc	cc	cc	cc	and at the same minutes past each hour until		cc	cc	cc	cc
Shoeburyness	d		07 50					08 05		08 20			08 35		08 50					20 05			20 35
Thorpe Bay	d		07 53					08 08		08 23			08 38		08 53					20 08			20 38
Southend East	d		07 56					08 11		08 26			08 41		08 56					20 11			20 41
Southend Central	a		07 58					08 13		08 28			08 43		08 58					20 13			20 43
	d	07 50	07 59					08 14	08 20	08 29			08 44	08 50	08 59					20 14		20 20	20 44
Westcliff	d	07 53	08 01					08 16	08 23	08 31			08 46	08 53	09 01					20 16		20 23	20 46
Chalkwell	d	07 55	08 03					08 18	08 25	08 33			08 48	08 55	09 03					20 18		20 25	20 48
Leigh-on-Sea	d	07 58	08 06					08 21	08 28	08 36			08 51	08 58	09 06					20 21		20 28	20 51
Benfleet	d	08 02	08 10					08 25	08 32	08 40			08 55	09 02	09 10					20 25		20 32	20 55
Pitsea	d	08 06						08 29	08 36				08 59	09 06						20 29		20 36	20 59
Stanford-le-Hope	d	08 12							08 42					09 12								20 42	
East Tilbury	d	08 15				←			08 45			←		09 15			←					20 45	
Tilbury Town 4	d	08 21				08 21			08 51			08 51		09 21			09 21					20 51	
Grays	d	→			08 18	08 24			→		08 48	08 54		→		09 18	09 24				20 48	20 54	
Purfleet	d				08 23						08 53					09 23					20 53		
Rainham	d				08 28						08 58					09 28					20 58		
Dagenham Dock	d				08 32						09 02					09 32					21 02		
Basildon	d		08 16					08 32		08 46			09 02		09 16					20 32			21 02
Laindon	d		08 19					08 35		08 49			09 05		09 19					20 35			21 05
West Horndon	d							08 40					09 10							20 40			21 10
Chafford Hundred	d					08 29						08 59					09 29					20 59	
Ockendon	d					08 32						09 02					09 32					21 02	
Upminster ⊖	d		08 28			08 39		08 46		08 58		09 09	09 16		09 28		09 39			20 46		21 09	21 16
Barking ⊖	d		08 36		08 38	08 47		08 54		09 06	09 08	09 17	09 24		09 36	09 38	09 47			20 54	21 08	21 17	21 24
Stratford 7 ⊖ ⛴	a																						
London Liverpool Street 15 ⊖	a																						
West Ham ⊖	d		08 42		08 44	08 53		09 00		09 12	09 14	09 23	09 30		09 42	09 44	09 53			21 00	21 14	21 23	21 30
Limehouse ⛴	d				08 49	08 58		09 05			09 19	09 28	09 35			09 49	09 58			21 05	21 19	21 28	21 35
London Fenchurch Street 7 ⊖ ⛴	a		08 53		08 56	09 04		09 12		09 23	09 26	09 34	09 42		09 53	09 56	10 04			21 12	21 26	21 34	21 42

Station		cc	cc	cc	cc	cc		cc	cc	cc	cc	cc	cc	cc		cc	cc	cc	cc	cc	cc			
Shoeburyness	d		20 50			21 05				21 35			22 05				22 35			23 05				
Thorpe Bay	d		20 53			21 08				21 38			22 08				22 38			23 08				
Southend East	d		20 56			21 11				21 41			22 11				22 41			23 11				
Southend Central	a		20 58			21 13				21 43			22 13				22 43			23 13				
	d	20 50	20 59			21 14			21 20	21 44		21 50	22 14			22 20	22 44		22 50	23 14	23 20			
Westcliff	d	20 53	21 01			21 16			21 23	21 46		21 53	22 16			22 23	22 46		22 53	23 16	23 23			
Chalkwell	d	20 55	21 03			21 18			21 25	21 48		21 55	22 18			22 25	22 48		22 55	23 18	23 25			
Leigh-on-Sea	d	20 58	21 06			21 21			21 28	21 51		21 58	22 21			22 28	22 51		22 58	23 21	23 28			
Benfleet	d	21 02	21 10			21 25			21 32	21 55		22 02	22 25			22 32	22 55		23 02	23 25	23 32			
Pitsea	d	21 06				21 29			21 36	21 59		22 06	22 29			22 36	22 59		23 06	23 29	23 36			
Stanford-le-Hope	d	21 12							21 42			22 12				22 42			23 12		23 42			
East Tilbury	d	21 15			←				21 45			22 15				22 45			23 15		23 45			
Tilbury Town 4	d	21 21			21 21				21 51			22 21				22 51			23 21		23 51			
Grays	d	→		21 18	21 24			21 48	21 54		22 18	22 24		22 48		22 54		23 18	23 24		23 54			
Purfleet	d			21 23				21 53			22 23			22 53				23 23						
Rainham	d			21 28				21 58			22 28			22 58				23 28						
Dagenham Dock	d			21 32				22 02			22 32			23 02				23 32						
Basildon	d		21 16			21 32				22 02			22 32				23 02			23 32				
Laindon	d		21 19			21 35				22 05			22 35				23 05			23 35				
West Horndon	d					21 40				22 10			22 40				23 10			23 40				
Chafford Hundred	d				21 29				21 59			22 29				22 59			23 29		23 59			
Ockendon	d				21 32				22 02			22 32				23 02			23 32		00 02			
Upminster ⊖	d		21 28		21 39	21 46			22 09	22 16		22 39	22 46			23 09	23 16		23 39	23 46	00 08			
Barking ⊖	d		21 36	21 38	21 47	21 54		22 08	22 17	22 24	22 38	22 47	22 54	23 08		23 17	23 24	23a39	23 47	23 54	00a18			
Stratford 7 ⊖ ⛴	a																							
London Liverpool Street 15 ⊖	a																							
West Ham ⊖	d		21 42	21 44	21 53	22 00		22 14	22 23	22 30	22 44	22 53	23 00	23 14		23 23	23 30		23 53	00 01				
Limehouse ⛴	d			21 49	21 58	22 05		22 19	22 28	22 35	22 49	22 58	23 05	23 19		23 28	23 35		23 58	00 05				
London Fenchurch Street 7 ⊖ ⛴	a		21 53	21 56	22 04	22 12		22 26	22 34	22 42	22 56	23 04	23 12	23 24		23 34	23 42		00 04	00 12				

Sundays

Station		cc		cc		cc		cc		cc		cc		cc		cc		cc			cc	cc	cc	cc
Shoeburyness	d	23p05				05 35		06 05		06 10		06 35		07 05		07 10		07 35			08 05			08 35
Thorpe Bay	d	23p08				05 38		06 08		06 14		06 38		07 08		07 14		07 38			08 08			08 38
Southend East	d	23p11				05 41		06 11		06 16		06 41		07 11		07 16		07 41			08 11			08 41
Southend Central	a	23p13				05 43		06 13		06 19		06 43		07 13		07 19		07 43			08 13			08 43
	d	23p14		23p20		05 44		06 14		06 20		06 44		07 14		07 20		07 44			08 14	08 20		08 44
Westcliff	d	23p16		23p23		05 46		06 16		06 23		06 46		07 16		07 23		07 46			08 16	08 23		08 46
Chalkwell	d	23p18		23p25		05 48		06 18		06 25		06 48		07 18		07 25		07 48			08 18	08 25		08 48
Leigh-on-Sea	d	23p21		23p28		05 51		06 21		06 28		06 51		07 21		07 28		07 51			08 21	08 28		08 51
Benfleet	d	23p25		23p32		05 55		06 25		06 32		06 55		07 25		07 32		07 55			08 25	08 32		08 55
Pitsea	d	23p29		23p36		05 59		06 29		06 36		06 59		07 29		07 36		07 59			08 29	08 36		08 59
Stanford-le-Hope	d			23p42						06 42						07 42						08 42		
East Tilbury	d			23p45						06 45						07 45						08 45		
Tilbury Town 4	d			23p51						06 51						07 51						08 51		
Grays	d			23p54						06 54						07 54						08 54	08 59	
Purfleet	d																						09 04	
Rainham	d																						09 09	
Dagenham Dock	d																						09 13	
Basildon	d	23p32				06 02		06 32				07 02		07 32				08 02			08 32			09 02
Laindon	d	23p35				06 05		06 35				07 05		07 35				08 05			08 35			09 05
West Horndon	d	23p40				06 10		06 40				07 10		07 40				08 10			08 40			09 10
Chafford Hundred	d			23p59						06 59						07 59						08 59		
Ockendon	d			00 02						07 02						08 02						09 02		
Upminster ⊖	d	23p46		00 08		06 16		06 46		07 09		07 16		07 46		08 09		08 16			08 46	09 09		09 16
Barking ⊖	d	23p54		00a18		06 25		06 55		07 17		07 25		07 55		08 17		08 25			08 55	09 17	09a20	09 25
Stratford 7 ⊖ ⛴	a																							
London Liverpool Street 15 ⊖	a																							
West Ham ⊖	d	00 01				06 31		07 01		07 23		07 31		08 01		08 23		08 31			09 01	09 23		09 31
Limehouse ⛴	d	00 05				06 36		07 06		07 28		07 36		08 06		08 28		08 36			09 06	09 28		09 36
London Fenchurch Street 7 ⊖ ⛴	a	00 12				06 42		07 12		07 34		07 42		08 12		08 34		08 42			09 12	09 34		09 42

For general notes see front of timetable
For details of catering facilities see Directory of Train Operators

Table I

Shoeburyness and Southend Central → London

Network diagram - see first page of Table I

		CC		CC	CC	CC	CC	CC	CC	CC
Shoeburyness	d		and at the same minutes past each hour until	21 05			21 35	22 05		22 35
Thorpe Bay	d			21 08			21 38	22 08		22 38
Southend East	d			21 11			21 41	22 11		22 41
Southend Central	a			21 13			21 43	22 13		22 43
	d	08 50		21 14	21 20		21 44	22 14	22 20	22 44
Westcliff	d	08 53		21 16	21 23		21 46	22 16	22 23	22 46
Chalkwell	d	08 55		21 18	21 25		21 48	22 18	22 25	22 48
Leigh-on-Sea	d	08 58		21 21	21 28		21 51	22 21	22 28	22 51
Benfleet	d	09 02		21 25	21 32		21 55	22 25	22 32	22 55
Pitsea	d	09 06		21 29	21 36		21 59	22 29	22 36	22 59
Stanford-le-Hope	d	09 12			21 42				22 42	
East Tilbury	d	09 15			21 45				22 45	
Tilbury Town [4]	d	09 21			21 51				22 51	
Grays	d	09 24			21 54	21 59			22 54	
Purfleet	d					22 04				
Rainham	d					22 09				
Dagenham Dock	d					22 13				
Basildon	d			21 32			22 02	22 32		23 02
Laindon	d			21 35			22 05	22 35		23 05
West Horndon	d			21 40			22 10	22 40		23 10
Chafford Hundred	d	09 29			21 59				22 59	
Ockendon	d	09 32			22 02				23 02	
Upminster	⊖ d	09 39		21 46	22 09		22 16	22 46	23 09	23 16
Barking	⊖ d	09 47		21 55	22 17	22a20	22 25	22 55	23 17	23 25
Stratford [7]	⊖ ⛴ a									
London Liverpool Street [15]	⊖ a									
West Ham	⊖ d	09 53		22 01	22 23		22 31	23 01	23 23	23 31
Limehouse	⛴ d	09 58		22 06	22 28		22 36	23 06	23 28	23 36
London Fenchurch Street [7]	⊖ ⛴ a	10 04		22 12	22 34		22 42	23 12	23 34	23 42

For general notes see front of timetable
For details of catering facilities see Directory of Train Operators

Table 1A

Mondays to Fridays

Tilbury Town — Tilbury Riverside

Bus Service

Network diagram - see first page of Table 1

	CC	CC	CC	CC	CC	CC	CC		CC	CC		CC	CC		CC	CC	CC	CC	CC	CC	CC		
London Fenchurch Street 7 ⊖ d	.....	05b10	05b40	06 20	06 50	07 21	07 42	.....	08 20	08 50	.....	09 20	09 50	and every 30 minutes until	15 20	15 50	16 13	16 33	17 11	17 41	18 12	.....	.....
Tilbury Town 4 d	05 40	06 18	06 50	07 18	07 45	08 13	08 38	.	09 03	09 33	.	10 03	10 33		16 03	16 33	17 03	17 33	18 00	18 30	19 00	.	.
Tilbury Riverside a	05 47	06 25	06 57	07 25	07 52	08 20	08 45	.....	09 10	09 40	.....	10 10	10 40		16 10	16 40	17 11	17 41	18 08	18 38	19 08	.....	.....

Saturdays

	CC		CC		CC			CC	CC			CC		CC									
London Fenchurch Street 7 ⊖ d	.....	.....	.....	.....	06 20	.....	.....	06 50	07 20	and every 30 minutes until	.....	17 50	.....	18 20	.....	.....	.....	.....	.....	.....	.....	.....	.....
Tilbury Town 4 d	05 40	.	06 15	.	07 01	.	.	07 31	08 01		.	18 31	.	19 01	.	.	.	.	.	.	.	.	.
Tilbury Riverside a	05 47	.....	06 22	.....	07 08	.....	.....	07 38	08 08		.....	18 38	.....	19 08	.....	.....	.....	.....	.....	.....	.....	.....	.....

Mondays to Fridays

	CC	CC	CC	CC	CC	CC	CC	CC	CC		CC	CC		CC	CC	CC	CC	CC	CC	CC	CC	CC	
Tilbury Riverside d	05 50	06 30	07 00	07 30	07 55	08 23	08 50	09 12	09 42	.....	10 12	10 42	and every 30 minutes until	15 12	15 42	16 12	16 40	17 15	17 45	18 15	18 40	19 10	.....
Tilbury Town 4 a	05 57	06 37	07 07	07 37	08 02	08 30	08 57	09 19	09 49	.	10 19	10 49		15 19	15 49	16 19	16 47	17 22	17 52	18 22	18 47	19 17	.
London Fenchurch Street 7 ⊖ a	06 52	07 23	07 52	08 25	08 52	09 17	09 51	10 09	10 35	.....	11 05	11 35		16 05	16 36	17 03	17 39	18 08	18 41	.....	19 32	20 05	.....

Saturdays

	CC		CC		CC		CC		CC			CC	CC			CC		CC					
Tilbury Riverside d	05 50	.....	06 30	.....	07 10	.....	07 50	.....	08 09	.....	.....	08 39	09 09	and every 30 minutes until	.....	18 39	.....	19 09	.....	.....	.....	.....	.....
Tilbury Town 4 a	05 57	.	06 37	.	07 17	.	07 57	.	08 16	.	.	08 46	09 16		.	18 46	.	19 16	.	.	.	.	.
London Fenchurch Street 7 ⊖ a	07 04	.....	07 34	.....	08 04	.....	.....	.....	09 04	.....	.....	09 34	10 04		.....	19 34	.....	20 04	.....	.....	.....	.....	.....

For general notes see front of timetable
For details of catering facilities see Directory of Train Operators

For full services between Tilbury Town and London Fenchurch Street refer to Table 1

b Change at Barking and Tilbury Town

No Sunday Service

Table 4

Mondays to Fridays

Romford — Upminster

Network diagram - see first page of Table I

Miles		LE		LE		LE		LE		LE		LE		LE			LE	LE			LE		LE		
0	**Romford** d	06 12		06 42		07 06		07 30		07 54		08 18		08 42			09 12	09 42	and every 30 minutes until		19 12		19 42		
2	Emerson Park d	06 16		06 46		07 10		07 34		07 58		08 22		08 46			09 16	09 46			19 16		19 46		
3½	**Upminster** ⊖ a	06 20		06 50		07 14		07 38		08 02		08 26		08 50			09 20	09 50			19 20		19 50		

Saturdays

	LE		LE		LE		LE		LE		LE			LE	LE			LE		LE					
Romford d	06 12		06 42		07 12		07 42		08 12		08 42			09 12	09 42	and every 30 minutes until		19 12		19 42					
Emerson Park d	06 16		06 46		07 16		07 46		08 16		08 46			09 16	09 46			19 16		19 46					
Upminster ⊖ a	06 20		06 50		07 20		07 50		08 20		08 50			09 20	09 50			19 20		19 50					

Mondays to Fridays

Miles		LE		LE		LE		LE		LE		LE		LE			LE	LE			LE		LE		
0	**Upminster** ⊖ d	06 24		06 54		07 18		07 42		08 06		08 30		08 54			09 24	09 54	and every 30 minutes until		19 24		19 54		
1½	Emerson Park d	06 28		06 58		07 22		07 46		08 10		08 34		08 58			09 28	09 58			19 28		19 58		
3½	**Romford** a	06 32		07 02		07 26		07 50		08 14		08 38		09 02			09 32	10 02			19 32		20 02		

Saturdays

	LE		LE		LE		LE		LE		LE			LE	LE			LE		LE					
Upminster ⊖ d	06 24		06 54		07 24		07 54		08 24		08 54			09 24	09 54	and every 30 minutes until		19 24		19 54					
Emerson Park d	06 28		06 58		07 28		07 58		08 28		08 58			09 28	09 58			19 28		19 58					
Romford a	06 32		07 02		07 32		08 02		08 32		09 02			09 32	10 02			19 32		20 02					

For general notes see front of timetable
For details of catering facilities see Directory of Train Operators

No Sunday Service

Network Diagram for Tables 5, 10, 11

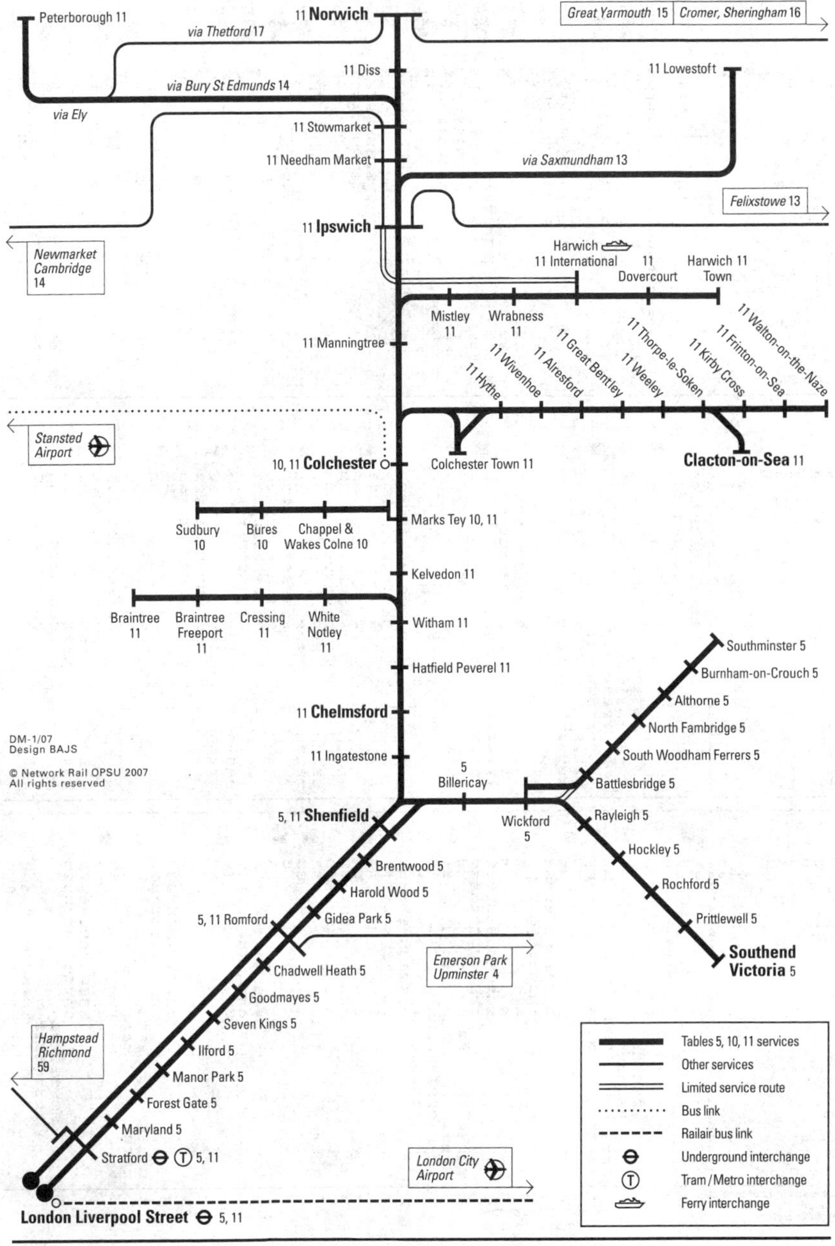
Peterborough 11
via Thetford 17
11 Norwich
Great Yarmouth 15
Cromer, Sheringham 16
11 Diss
11 Lowestoft
via Bury St Edmunds 14
via Ely
11 Stowmarket
11 Needham Market
via Saxmundham 13
Felixstowe 13
11 Ipswich
Newmarket
Cambridge
14
Harwich
11 International
11
Dovercourt
Harwich 11
Town
Mistley
11
Wrabness
11
11 Manningtree
11 Hythe
11 Wivenhoe
11 Alresford
11 Great Bentley
11 Weeley
11 Thorpe-le-Soken
11 Kirby Cross
11 Frinton-on-Sea
11 Walton-on-the-Naze
Stansted
Airport
10, 11 Colchester
Colchester Town 11
Clacton-on-Sea 11
Sudbury
10
Bures
10
Chappel &
Wakes Colne 10
Marks Tey 10, 11
Kelvedon 11
Braintree
11
Braintree
Freeport
11
Cressing
11
White
Notley
11
Witham 11
Hatfield Peverel 11
Southminster 5
Burnham-on-Crouch 5
Althorne 5
11 Chelmsford
North Fambridge 5
South Woodham Ferrers 5
11 Ingatestone
5
Billericay
Battlesbridge 5
5, 11 Shenfield
Wickford
5
Rayleigh 5
Hockley 5
Brentwood 5
Rochford 5
Harold Wood 5
5, 11 Romford
Gidea Park 5
Prittlewell 5
Southend
Victoria 5
Chadwell Heath 5
Emerson Park
Upminster 4
Goodmayes 5
Seven Kings 5
Hampstead
Richmond
59
Ilford 5
Manor Park 5
Forest Gate 5
Maryland 5
Stratford 5, 11
London City
Airport
London Liverpool Street 5, 11
Tables 5, 10, 11 services
Other services
Limited service route
Bus link
Railair bus link
Underground interchange
Tram / Metro interchange
Ferry interchange

DM-1/07
Design BAJS

London → Shenfield, Southminster and Southend Victoria

Network diagram - see first page of Table 5

Miles	Miles			LE	LE	LE	LE	LE	LE	LE	LE	LE	LE	CC	LE	LE	LE	LE	LE	LE	LE	LE		LE	LE
				MX	MO	MO	MX	MX	MO	MX	MO	MX	MO	MX	MX	MO	MX	MX	MX	MO	MO	MX		MX	MX
				1	1			1	1		1				1	1	1				1	1		1	
																						A			
0	—	**London Liverpool Street** 15 ⊖	d	23p15	23p15	23p35	23p37	23p45	23p45	23p52	00 02	00 02	00 05	00 12	00 15	00 15	00 18	00 22	00 32	00 35	00 45	00 48		00 50	00 55
4	—	Stratford 7 ⊖	d	23p22	23p22	23p42	23p44	23p52	23p52	23p58	00 09	00 09	00 12	00a19	00 22	00 22	00 25	00 29	00 39	00 42	00 52	00 55		00 57	01 02
4½	—	Maryland	d			23p43	23p45			23p59		00 10	00 13					00 30	00 40	00 43					01 03
5¼	—	Forest Gate	d			23p45	23p47			00 02		00 12	00 15					00 32	00 42	00 45					01 05
6¼	—	Manor Park	d			23p47	23p49			00 04		00 14	00 17					00 34	00 44	00 47					01 07
7¼	—	Ilford 2	d			23p50	23p52			00 07		00 17	00 20					00 37	00 47	00 50					01 10
8½	—	Seven Kings	d			23p53	23p55			00 10		00 20	00 23					00 40	00 50	00 53					01 13
9¼	—	Goodmayes	d			23p55	23p57			00 12		00 22	00 25					00 42	00 52	00 55					01 15
10	—	Chadwell Heath	d			23p57	23p59			00 14		00 24	00 27					00 44	00 54	00 57					01 17
12½	—	Romford	d		23p33	23p59	00 02		00 03	00 17		00 27	00 30		00 32	00 33		00 47	00 57	01 00	01 03			01 08	01 20
13½	—	Gidea Park 2	d		23p37	00 04	00 06		00 07	00 21		00a31	00a36			00 37		00 51	01a01	01a06	01 07	01 07			01 24
15	—	Harold Wood	d		23p40	00 07	00 09		00 10	00 24						00 40		00 54			01 10				01 27
18¼	—	Brentwood	d		23p44	00 11	00 13		00 14	00 28						00 44		00 58			01 14				01 31
20¼	—	**Shenfield** 3	a	23p39	23p50	00 16	00 18	00 09	00 20	00 33	00 30				00 44	00 50	00 47	01 03			01 20	01 17		01 20	01 36
—	—		d	23p40	23p50			00 10	00 20						00 45	00 50					01 20			01 20	
24¼	—	Billericay	d	23p46	23p56			00 16	00 26						00 51	00 56					01 26			01 26	
29	0	**Wickford** 2	d	23p51	00 01			00 21	00 31						00 56	01 01					01 31			01 31	
—	2½	Battlesbridge	d																						
—	5	South Woodham Ferrers	d																						
—	8¼	North Fambridge	d																						
—	11¼	Althorne	d																						
—	14¼	Burnham-on-Crouch	d																						
—	16½	**Southminster**	a																						
33	—	Rayleigh	d	23p56	00 06			00 26	00 36						01 01	01 06					01 36			01 36	
36	—	Hockley	d	00 01	00 11			00 31	00 41						01 06	01 11					01 41			01 41	
38¾	—	Rochford	d	00 04	00 14			00 34	00 44						01 09	01 14					01 44			01 44	
41	—	Prittlewell	d	00 08				00 38							01 13									01 48	
41½	—	**Southend Victoria**	a	00 15	00 24			00 45	00 54						01 20	01 24					01 54			01 55	

		LE	LE	LE	LE	LE	LE	LE	LE	LE	LE	LE	LE	LE	LE	LE	LE	LE	LE	LE		LE	LE	LE	LE
		MO																							
			1	1	1				1	1	1		1		1			1		1			1		1
London Liverpool Street 15 ⊖	d	00 55	05 25			05 26	05 37	05 39	05 55	06 02		06 02	06 12	06 12	06 15	06 22	06 32	06 34	06 42	06 48		06 52	06 55	07 02	07 04
Stratford 7 ⊖	d	01 02	05 32			05 33	05a48	05 46	06 02	06 09		06 09	06 19	06 19	06 22	06 29	06 39	06 41	06 49	06 55		06 59	07 02	07 09	07 11
Maryland	d	01 03						05 47				06 10		06 20		06 30	06 40		06 50			07 00		07 10	
Forest Gate	d	01 05						05 49				06 12		06 22		06 32	06 42		06 52			07 02		07 12	
Manor Park	d	01 07						05 51				06 14		06 24		06 34	06 44		06 54			07 04		07 14	
Ilford 2	d	01 10				05 38		05 54				06 17		06 27		06 37	06 47		06 57			07 07		07 17	
Seven Kings	d	01 13				05 40		05 57				06 20		06 30		06 40	06 50		07 00			07 10		07 20	
Goodmayes	d	01 15						05 59				06 22		06 32		06 42	06 52		07 02			07 12		07 22	
Chadwell Heath	d	01 17						06 01				06 24		06 34		06 44	06 54		07 04			07 14		07 24	
Romford	d	01 20	05 40			05 46		06 04		06 17		06 27		06 37		06 47	06 57	06 49	07 07			07 17		07 27	
Gidea Park 2	d	01 24				05 49		06 08				06 31		06 41		06 51	07 01		07 11			07 21		07 31	
Harold Wood	d	01 27				05 52		06 11				06 34		06 44		06 54	07 04		07 14			07 24		07 34	
Brentwood	d	01 31				05 57		06 15				06 38		06 48		06 58	07 08		07 18			07 28		07 38	
Shenfield 3	a	01 38	05 50			06 02		06 20	06 19	06 27		06 43	06 36	06 53	06 40	07 03	07 13	07 00	07 23	07 12		07 33	07 20	07 43	07 28
	d				05 58	06 02			06 20		06 35				06 40			07 00					07 20		
Billericay	d				06 04	06 08			06 26		06 41				06 46			07 06					07 26		
Wickford 2	d			05 20	06 10	06 13			06 31		06 47				06 51			07 11					07 31		
Battlesbridge	d			05 24	06 14						06 51														
South Woodham Ferrers	d			05 28	06 18						06 55														
North Fambridge	d			05b45	06 25						07c07														
Althorne	d			05 50	06 30						07 12														
Burnham-on-Crouch	d			05 55	06 35						07 17														
Southminster	a			06 00	06 40						07 22														
Rayleigh	d					06 19			06 36						06 56			07 16					07 36		
Hockley	d					06 23			06 41						07 01			07 21					07 41		
Rochford	d					06 27			06 44						07 04			07 24					07 44		
Prittlewell	d					06 30			06 48						07 08			07 28					07 48		
Southend Victoria	a					06 34			06 51						07 11			07 31					07 51		

		LE	LE	LE	LE	LE	LE	LE	LE	LE	LE	LE	LE	LE	LE	LE	LE	LE		LE	LE	LE	LE	LE	LE
		1		1	1	1		1		1	1		1		1	1		1			1	1		1	
London Liverpool Street 15 ⊖	d	07 08	07 12		07 15	07 18	07 22	07 27	07 32	07 34	07 40	07 42	07 48	07 52	07 55	08 02	08 02	08 08		08 12	08 14	08 18	08 22		08 32
Stratford 7 ⊖	d	07 15	07 19		07 22	07 25	07 29		07 39	07 41	07 47	07 49	07 55	07 59	08 02		08 09	08 15		08 19	08 21	08 25	08 29		08 39
Maryland	d		07 20				07 30		07 40			07 50		08 00			08 10			08 20			08 30		08 40
Forest Gate	d		07 22				07 32		07 42			07 52		08 02			08 12			08 22			08 32		08 42
Manor Park	d		07 24				07 34		07 44			07 54		08 04			08 14			08 24			08 34		08 44
Ilford 2	d		07 27				07 37		07 47			07 57		08 07			08 17			08 27			08 37		08 47
Seven Kings	d		07 30				07 40		07 50			08 00		08 10			08 20			08 30			08 40		08 50
Goodmayes	d		07 32				07 42		07 52			08 02		08 12			08 22			08 32			08 42		08 52
Chadwell Heath	d		07 34				07 44		07 54			08 04		08 14			08 24			08 34			08 44		08 54
Romford	d	07 23	07 37				07 47		07 57	07 49		08 07		08 17		08 16	08 27			08 37	08 29		08 47		08 57
Gidea Park 2	d		07 41				07 51		08 01			08 11		08 21			08 31			08 41			08 51		09 01
Harold Wood	d		07 44				07 54		08 04			08 14		08 24			08 34			08 44			08 54		09 04
Brentwood	d		07 48				07 58		08 08			08 18		08 28			08 38			08 48			08 58		09 08
Shenfield 3	a	07 33	07 53		07 40	07 41	08 03	07 50	08 13	08 00	08 06	08 23	08 12	08 33	08 19	08 26	08 43	08 31		08 53	08 40	08 41	09 03		09 13
	d				07 41					08 00	08 08				08 20						08 40			09 08	
Billericay	d				07 47					08 06	08 14				08 26						08 46			09 14	
Wickford 2	d			07 35	07 52					08 11	08 20				08 31						08 51			09 20	
Battlesbridge	d			07 39							08 24													09 24	
South Woodham Ferrers	d			07 43							08 28													09 28	
North Fambridge	d			07 51							08 34													09 34	
Althorne	d			07 56							08 39													09 39	
Burnham-on-Crouch	d			08 01							08 44													09 44	
Southminster	a			08 06							08 49													09 49	
Rayleigh	d				07 57					08 16					08 36						08 56				
Hockley	d				08 02					08 21					08 41						09 01				
Rochford	d				08 05					08 24					08 44						09 04				
Prittlewell	d				08 09					08 28					08 48						09 08				
Southend Victoria	a				08 14					08 31					08 51						09 11				

For general notes see front of timetable
For details of catering facilities see Directory of Train Operators

A To Colchester (Table 11)
b Arr. 11 minutes earlier
c Arr. 6 minutes earlier

London → Shenfield, Southminster and Southend Victoria

Network diagram - see first page of Table 5

		LE 1	LE 1	LE	LE 1	LE	LE 1	LE	LE 1	LE	LE 1	LE 1	LE	LE	LE 1	LE 1		LE	LE 1	LE	LE 1		LE	LE 1	LE
London Liverpool Street 15	⊖ d	08 35	08 38	08 42	08 48	08 52	08 55	09 02	09 08	09 12	09 15	09 18	09 22	09 32	09 34	09 40		09 42	09 48	09 52	09 55		10 02	10 08	10 12
Stratford 7	⊖ d	08 42		08 49	08 55	08 59	09 02	09 09	09 15	09 19	09 22	09 25	09 29	09 39	09 41	09 47		09 49	09 55	09 59	10 02		10 09	10 15	10 19
Maryland	d			08 50		09 00		09 10		09 20			09 30	09 40				09 50		10 00			10 10		10 20
Forest Gate	d			08 52		09 02		09 12		09 22			09 32	09 42				09 52		10 02			10 12		10 22
Manor Park	d			08 54		09 04		09 14		09 24			09 34	09 44				09 54		10 04			10 14		10 24
Ilford 2	d			08 57		09 07		09 17		09 27			09 37	09 47				09 57		10 07			10 17		10 27
Seven Kings	d			09 00		09 10		09 20		09 30			09 40	09 50				10 00		10 10			10 20		10 30
Goodmayes	d			09 02		09 12		09 22		09 32			09 42	09 52				10 02		10 12			10 22		10 32
Chadwell Heath	d			09 04		09 14		09 24		09 34			09 44	09 54				10 04		10 14			10 24		10 34
Romford	d			09 07		09 17		09 27	09 23	09 37			09 47	09 57		09 49		10 07		10 17			10 27	10 23	10 37
Gidea Park 2	d			09 11		09 21		09 31		09 41			09 51	10 01				10 11		10 21			10 31		10 41
Harold Wood	d			09 14		09 24		09 34		09 44			09 54	10 04				10 14		10 24			10 34		10 44
Brentwood	d			09 18		09 28		09 38		09 48			09 58	10 08				10 18		10 28			10 38		10 48
Shenfield 3	a	08 59	09 02	09 23	09 12	09 33	09 19	09 43	09 33	09 53	09 39	09 41	10 03	10 13	10 00	10 07		10 23	10 12	10 33	10 19		10 43	10 33	10 53
	d	09 00					09 20				09 40				10 00	10 08					10 20				
Billericay	d	09 06					09 26				09 46				10 06	10 14					10 26				
Wickford 2	d	09 11					09 31				09 51				10 11	10 20					10 31				
Battlesbridge	d															10 24									
South Woodham Ferrers	d															10 28									
North Fambridge	d															10 34									
Althorne	d															10 39									
Burnham-on-Crouch	d															10 44									
Southminster	a															10 49									
Rayleigh	d	09 16					09 36				09 56				10 16						10 36				
Hockley	d	09 21					09 41				10 01				10 21						10 41				
Rochford	d	09 24					09 44				10 04				10 24						10 44				
Prittlewell	d	09 28					09 48				10 08				10 28						10 48				
Southend Victoria	a	09 31					09 51				10 11				10 31						10 51				

		LE 1	LE 1	LE	LE 1	LE	LE 1	LE	LE 1	LE	LE 1	and at the same minutes past each hour until	LE	LE 1	LE	LE 1		LE 1	LE	LE 1	LE 1	LE	LE 1	LE
London Liverpool Street 15	⊖ d	10 15	10 18	10 22		10 32	10 34	10 42	10 48	10 52	10 55		15 02	15 08	15 12	15 15		15 18	15 22	15 32		15 32	15 34	15 42
Stratford 7	⊖ d	10 22	10 25	10 29		10 39	10 41	10 49	10 55	10 59	11 02		15 09	15 15	15 19	15 22		15 25	15 29			15 39	15 41	15 49
Maryland	d			10 30		10 40		10 50		11 00			15 10		15 20				15 30			15 40		15 50
Forest Gate	d			10 32		10 42		10 52		11 02			15 12		15 22				15 32			15 42		15 52
Manor Park	d			10 34		10 44		10 54		11 04			15 14		15 24				15 34			15 44		15 54
Ilford 2	d			10 37		10 47		10 57		11 07			15 17		15 27				15 37			15 47		15 57
Seven Kings	d			10 40		10 50		11 00		11 10			15 20		15 30				15 40			15 50		16 00
Goodmayes	d			10 42		10 52		11 02		11 12			15 22		15 32				15 42			15 52		16 02
Chadwell Heath	d			10 44		10 54		11 04		11 14			15 24		15 34				15 44			15 54		16 04
Romford	d			10 47		10 57	10 49	11 07		11 17			15 27	15 23	15 37				15 47			15 57	15 49	16 07
Gidea Park 2	d			10 51		11 01		11 11		11 21			15 31		15 41				15 51			16 01		16 11
Harold Wood	d			10 54		11 04		11 14		11 24			15 34		15 44				15 54			16 04		16 14
Brentwood	d			10 58		11 08		11 18		11 28			15 38		15 48				15 58			16 08		16 18
Shenfield 3	a	10 39	10 41	11 03		11 13	11 00	11 23	11 12	11 33	11 19		15 43	15 33	15 53	15 39		15 41	16 03	15 54		16 13	16 00	16 23
	d	10 40			11 08		11 00				11 20					15 40					16 08		16 00	
Billericay	d	10 46			11 14		11 06				11 26					15 46					16 14		16 06	
Wickford 2	d	10 51			11 20		11 11				11 31					15 51					16 20		16 11	
Battlesbridge	d				11 24																16 24			
South Woodham Ferrers	d				11 28																16 28			
North Fambridge	d				11 34																16 34			
Althorne	d				11 39																16 39			
Burnham-on-Crouch	d				11 44																16 44			
Southminster	a				11 49																16 49			
Rayleigh	d	10 56					11 16				11 36					15 56							16 16	
Hockley	d	11 01					11 21				11 41					16 01							16 21	
Rochford	d	11 04					11 24				11 44					16 04							16 24	
Prittlewell	d	11 08					11 28				11 48					16 08							16 28	
Southend Victoria	a	11 11					11 31				11 51					16 11							16 31	

		LE 1	LE	LE 1	LE	LE 1	LE 1	LE	LE 1	LE	LE 1	LE	LE 1	LE 1	LE 1		LE	LE	LE 1	LE	LE 1	LE	LE 1	LE	LE 1
London Liverpool Street 15	⊖ d	15 48	15 52	15 55	16 02	16 02	16 10	16 12	16 17	16 22	16 25	16 32	16 36		16 40		16 42	16 46	16 47	16 52	16 55	16 56	17 02	17 02	17 04
Stratford 7	⊖ d	15 55	15 59	16 02	16 09	16 10	16 18	16 19	16 25	16 29	16 33	16 39			16 48		16 49	16 53	16 55	16 59	17 03	17 03		17 09	17 12
Maryland	d		16 00		16 10			16 20		16 30		16 40						16 55				17 05			
Forest Gate	d		16 02		16 12			16 22		16 32		16 42						16 57				17 07			
Manor Park	d		16 04		16 14			16 24		16 34		16 44						16 59				17 09			
Ilford 2	d		16 07		16 17			16 27		16 37		16 47					16 55	17 02		17 05		17 12		17 15	
Seven Kings	d		16 10		16 20			16 30		16 40		16 50					16 58			17 08				17 18	
Goodmayes	d		16 12		16 22			16 32		16 42		16 52					17 00			17 10				17 20	
Chadwell Heath	d		16 14		16 24			16 34		16 44		16 54					17 02	17 06		17 12		17 16		17 22	
Romford	d		16 17		16 27			16 37		16 47		16 57					17 06	17 10		17 16		17 20		17 26	
Gidea Park 2	d		16 21		16 31			16 41		16 51		17 01					17a11	17 14		17a21		17 24		17a31	
Harold Wood	d		16 24		16 34			16 44		16 54		17 04						17 17				17 27			
Brentwood	d		16 28		16 38			16 48		16 58		17 08						17 21				17 31			
Shenfield 3	a	16 12	16 33	16 19	16 45	16 25	16 34	16 55	16 40	17 05	16 50	17 15	16 57		17 04			17 29	17 10		17 20	17 39	17 24		17 29
	d			16 20			16 35				16 50				17 05						17 20				17 30
Billericay	d			16 26			16 41				16 56				17 11						17 26				17 36
Wickford 2	d			16 31			16 46				17 01			17 07	17 16						17 31				17 42
Battlesbridge	d													17 11											
South Woodham Ferrers	d													17 15											
North Fambridge	d													17 21											
Althorne	d													17 26											
Burnham-on-Crouch	d													17 31											
Southminster	a													17 36											
Rayleigh	d			16 36			16 51				17 06				17 21						17 36				17 47
Hockley	d			16 41			16 56				17 11				17 26						17 41				17 52
Rochford	d			16 44			16 59				17 14				17 29						17 44				17 55
Prittlewell	d			16 48			17 03				17 18				17 33						17 48				17 59
Southend Victoria	a			16 51			17 09				17 23				17 39						17 53				18 04

For general notes see front of timetable
For details of catering facilities see Directory of Train Operators

London → Shenfield, Southminster and Southend Victoria

Network diagram - see first page of Table 5

Station		LE	LE 1	LE	LE 1	LE 1	LE	LE 1	LE 1	LE	LE 1	LE	LE 1		LE	LE 1	LE	LE 1	LE	LE	LE 1	LE 1	LE	LE	LE 1
London Liverpool Street 15 ⊖	d	17 06	17 08	17 12	17 12	17 15	17 16	17 17	17 22	17 22	17 25	17 26	17 32		17 32	17 34	17 36	17 38	17 39	17 42	17 42	17 45	17 46	17 49	17 52
Stratford 7 ⊖	d	17 13	17a16	17 19	17a20		17 23			17 29	17 33	17 33			17 39	17 42	17 43	17a46	17 46	17 49	17a50	17 53	17 53	17 56	
Maryland	d	17 15					17 25					17 35					17 45						17 55		
Forest Gate	d	17 17					17 27					17 37			17 42					17 52					
Manor Park	d	17 19					17 29					17 39							17 50					18 00	
Ilford 2	d	17 22		17 25			17 32			17 35		17 42			17 46		17 50		17 53	17 56			18 00	18 03	
Seven Kings	d			17 28						17 38					17 49		17 52		17 56	17 59			18 02	18 06	
Goodmayes	d			17 30						17 40					17 51		17 54		17 58	18 01			18 04	18 08	
Chadwell Heath	d	17 26		17 32			17 36			17 42		17 46			17 53		17 56		18 00	18 03			18 06	18 10	
Romford	d	17 30		17 36			17 40			17 46		17 50			17 57		18 00		18 04	18 07			18 10	18 14	
Gidea Park 2	d	17 34		17a41			17 44			17a51		17 54			18a02		18 04		18a09	18 11			18 14	18a19	
Harold Wood	d	17 37					17 47					17 57					18 07			18 14			18 17		
Brentwood	d	17 41					17 51					18 01					18 11			18 18			18 21		
Shenfield 3	a	17 49					17 59	17 41	17 44		17 51	18 09	17 54			17 59	18 19			18 24		18 10	18 29		18 14
	d							17 42			17 52					18 00				18 25		18 11			
Billericay	d							17 48			17 58					18 06				18 32		18 17			
Wickford 2	d					17 47		17 54			18 04					18 12				18 38		18 23			
Battlesbridge	d																								
South Woodham Ferrers	d					17 54																			
North Fambridge	d					18b03																			
Althorne	d					18 08																			
Burnham-on-Crouch	d					18 13																			
Southminster	a					18 20																			
Rayleigh	d							17 59			18 09					18 17				18 44		18 28			
Hockley	d							18 04			18 14					18 22				18 48		18 33			
Rochford	d							18 07			18 17					18 25				18 52		18 36			
Prittlewell	d							18 11			18 21					18 29				18 55		18 40			
Southend Victoria	a							18 16			18 26					18 34				19 01		18 45			

Station		LE	LE 1	LE 1	LE	LE	LE 1	LE 1	LE	LE 1	LE		LE 1	LE 1	LE	LE 1	LE	LE 1	LE	LE	LE 1	LE 1	LE	LE 1	LE
London Liverpool Street 15 ⊖	d	17 52	17 54	17 56	17 56	18 02	18 02	18 04	18 06	18 08	18 12		18 12	18 15	18 16	18 22	18 22	18 25	18 26	18 32	18 32	18 35	18 38	18 38	18 42
Stratford 7 ⊖	d	17 59			18 03	18 09	18a10	18 13	18 13	18a16	18 19		18a20	18 23	18 23		18 29	18 33	18 33	18 39	18a40	18 43	18 45	18 46	18 49
Maryland	d				18 05				18 15						18 25				18 35	18 40			18 46		18 50
Forest Gate	d	18 02			18 07				18 17						18 27				18 37	18 42			18 48		18 52
Manor Park	d				18 09				18 19						18 29				18 39	18 44			18 50		18 54
Ilford 2	d	18 06			18 12	18 15			18 22		18 25				18 32		18 35		18 42	18 47			18 53		18 57
Seven Kings	d	18 09				18 18					18 28						18 38			18 50			18 56		19 00
Goodmayes	d	18 11				18 20					18 30						18 40			18 52			18 58		19 02
Chadwell Heath	d	18 13			18 16	18 22			18 26		18 32				18 36		18 42		18 46	18 54			19 00		19 04
Romford	d	18 17			18 20	18 26			18 30		18 36				18 40		18 46		18 50	18 57			19 03		19 07
Gidea Park 2	d	18 21			18 24	18a31			18 34		18a41				18 44		18a51		18 54	19 01			19a09		19 11
Harold Wood	d	18 24			18 27				18 37						18 47				18 57	19 04					19 14
Brentwood	d	18 28			18 31				18 41						18 51				19 01	19 08					19 18
Shenfield 3	a	18 34		18 21	18 39			18 29	18 49					18 40	18 59	18 44		18 50	19 09	19 15		19 00		19 01	19 25
	d	18 35		18 22				18 29						18 41				18 51				19 01			
Billericay	d	18 41		18 28				18 36						18 47				18 57				19 07			
Wickford 2	d	18 47	18 29	18 34				18 42						18 53				19 03				19 13			
Battlesbridge	d		18 33																						
South Woodham Ferrers	d		18 37																						
North Fambridge	d		18 43																						
Althorne	d		18 48																						
Burnham-on-Crouch	d		18 53																						
Southminster	a		19 00																						
Rayleigh	d	18 53		18 39				18 47						18 58				19 08				19 18			
Hockley	d	18 57		18 44				18 52						19 03				19 13				19 23			
Rochford	d	19 01		18 47				18 55						19 06				19 16				19 26			
Prittlewell	d	19 04		18 51				18 59						19 10				19 20				19 30			
Southend Victoria	a	19 10		18 56				19 04						19 15				19 25				19 35			

Station		LE 1	LE 1	LE 1	LE	LE 1	LE 1	LE	LE 1		LE	LE 1	LE 1	LE	LE	LE 1	LE 1	LE	LE 1	LE	LE 1	LE 1	LE	LE 1	LE
London Liverpool Street 15 ⊖	d	18 42	18 45	18 48	18 52	18 55	19 02	19 02	19 08		19 12	19 15	19 18	19 22	19 32	19 34	19 38	19 42	19 48	19 52		19 55	20 02	20 08	20 12
Stratford 7 ⊖	d	18 50	18 53		18 59	19 03	19 09	19 09	19a15		19 19	19 22	19 25	19 29	19 39	19 41	19 45	19 49	19 55	19 59		20 03	20 09	20 15	20 19
Maryland	d				19 00			19 10			19 20			19 30	19 40			19 50		20 00			20 10		20 20
Forest Gate	d				19 02			19 12			19 22			19 32	19 42			19 52		20 02			20 12		20 22
Manor Park	d				19 04			19 14			19 24			19 34	19 44			19 54		20 04			20 14		20 24
Ilford 2	d				19 07			19 17			19 27			19 37	19 47			19 57		20 07			20 17		20 27
Seven Kings	d				19 10			19 20			19 30			19 40	19 50			20 00		20 10			20 20		20 30
Goodmayes	d				19 12			19 22			19 32			19 42	19 52			20 02		20 12			20 22		20 32
Chadwell Heath	d				19 14			19 24			19 34			19 44	19 54			20 04		20 14			20 24		20 34
Romford	d				19 17			19 27			19 37			19 47	19 57	19 49		20 07		20 17			20 27		20 37
Gidea Park 2	d				19 21			19 31			19 41			19 51	20 01			20 11		20 21			20 31		20 41
Harold Wood	d				19 24			19 34			19 44			19 54	20 04			20 14		20 24			20 34		20 44
Brentwood	d				19 28			19 38			19 48			19 58	20 08			20 18		20 28			20 38		20 48
Shenfield 3	a		19 10	19 11	19 35	19 20	19 25	19 43			19 53	19 39	19 41	20 03	20 13	20 00	20 01	20 23	20 12	20 33		20 20	20 43	20 31	20 53
	d		19 11			19 21						19 40				20 00						20 20			
Billericay	d		19 17			19 27						19 46				20 06						20 26			
Wickford 2	d	19 17	19 23			19 33						19 51				20 11					20 20	20 31			
Battlesbridge	d	19 22																			20 24				
South Woodham Ferrers	d	19 26																			20 28				
North Fambridge	d	19 32																			20 34				
Althorne	d	19 37																			20 39				
Burnham-on-Crouch	d	19 42																			20 44				
Southminster	a	19 49																			20 49				
Rayleigh	d		19 28			19 38						19 56				20 16						20 36			
Hockley	d		19 33			19 43						20 01				20 21						20 41			
Rochford	d		19 36			19 46						20 04				20 24						20 44			
Prittlewell	d		19 40			19 50						20 08				20 28						20 48			
Southend Victoria	a		19 45			19 55						20 11				20 31						20 51			

For general notes see front of timetable
For details of catering facilities see Directory of Train Operators

b Arr. 3 minutes earlier

London → Shenfield, Southminster and Southend Victoria

Network diagram - see first page of Table 5

Station		LE 1	LE 1	LE	LE 1	LE	LE 1		LE 1	LE	LE 1	LE	LE 1	LE	LE 1	LE	LE 1	LE 1	LE	LE 1	LE	LE 1	CC	LE	LE 1
London Liverpool Street 15 ⊖	d	20 15	20 18	20 22		20 32	20 34		20 38	20 42	20 48	20 52	20 55	21 02	21 08	21 12	21 15	21 18	21 22		21 32	21 34	21 38	21 42	21 48
Stratford 7 ⊖	d	20 22	20 25	20 29		20 39	20 41		20 45	20 49	20 55	20 59	21 02	21 09	21 15	21 19	21 22	21 25	21 29		21 39	21 41	21a45	21 49	21 55
Maryland	d			20 30		20 40				20 50		21 00		21 10		21 20			21 30		21 40			21 50	
Forest Gate	d			20 32		20 42				20 52		21 02		21 12		21 22			21 32		21 42			21 52	
Manor Park	d			20 34		20 44				20 54		21 04		21 14		21 24			21 34		21 44			21 54	
Ilford 2	d			20 37		20 47				20 57		21 07		21 17		21 27			21 37		21 47			21 57	
Seven Kings	d			20 40		20 50				21 00		21 10		21 20		21 30			21 40		21 50			22 00	
Goodmayes	d			20 42		20 52				21 02		21 12		21 22		21 32			21 42		21 52			22 02	
Chadwell Heath	d			20 44		20 54				21 04		21 14		21 24		21 34			21 44		21 54			22 04	
Romford	d			20 47		20 57	20 49			21 07		21 17		21 27	21 23	21 37			21 47		21 57	21 49		22 07	
Gidea Park 2	d			20 51		21 01				21 11		21 21		21 31		21 41			21 51		22 01			22 11	
Harold Wood	d			20 54		21 04				21 14		21 24		21 34		21 44			21 54		22 04			22 14	
Brentwood	d			20 58		21 08				21 18		21 28		21 38		21 48			21 58		22 08			22 18	
Shenfield 3	a	20 39	20 41	21 03		21 13	21 00		21 01	21 23	21 12	21 33	21 19	21 43	21 33	21 53	21 39	21 41	22 03		22 13	22 00		22 23	22 12
	d	20 40			21 08		21 00						21 20				21 40			22 08		22 00			
Billericay	d	20 46			21 14		21 06						21 26				21 46			22 14		22 06			
Wickford 2	d	20 51			21 20		21 11						21 31				21 51			22 20		22 11			
Battlesbridge	d				21 24															22 24					
South Woodham Ferrers	d				21 28															22 28					
North Fambridge	d				21 34															22 34					
Althorne	d				21 39															22 39					
Burnham-on-Crouch	d				21 44															22 44					
Southminster	a				21 49															22 49					
Rayleigh	d	20 56					21 16						21 36				21 56					22 16			
Hockley	d	21 01					21 21						21 41				22 01					22 21			
Rochford	d	21 04					21 24						21 44				22 04					22 24			
Prittlewell	d	21 08					21 28						21 48				22 08					22 28			
Southend Victoria	a	21 11					21 31						21 51				22 11					22 31			

Station		LE	LE 1	LE 1	LE		LE 1	LE 1	LE	LE	LE 1	LE 1	LE 1	LE	LE 1	LE	LE 1	LE 1	LE	LE	LE 1	LE 1	LE		
London Liverpool Street 15 ⊖	d	21 52	21 55	22 00	22 07		22 15	22 18	22 22	22 37		22 45	22 48	22 52	23 00	23 07	23 15	23 18	23 22	23 37	23 45	23 48	23 52		
Stratford 7 ⊖	d	21 59	22 02		22 14		22 22	22 25	22 29	22 44		22 52	22 55	22 59	23 07	23 14	23 22	23 25	23 29	23 44	23 52	23 55	23 58		
Maryland	d	22 00			22 15				22 30	22 45				23 00		23 15			23 30	23 45			23 59		
Forest Gate	d	22 02			22 17				22 32	22 47				23 02		23 17			23 32	23 47			00 02		
Manor Park	d	22 04			22 19				22 34	22 49				23 04		23 19			23 34	23 49			00 04		
Ilford 2	d	22 07			22 22				22 37	22 52				23 07		23 22			23 37	23 52			00 07		
Seven Kings	d	22 10			22 25				22 40	22 55				23 10		23 25			23 40	23 55			00 10		
Goodmayes	d	22 12			22 27				22 42	22 57				23 12		23 27			23 42	23 57			00 12		
Chadwell Heath	d	22 14			22 29				22 44	22 59				23 14		23 29			23 44	23 59			00 14		
Romford	d	22 17			22 32				22 47	23 02				23 17		23 32			23 47	00 02			00 17		
Gidea Park 2	d	22 21			22 36				22 51	23 06				23 21		23 36			23 51	00 06			00 21		
Harold Wood	d	22 24			22 39				22 54	23 09				23 24		23 39			23 54	00 09			00 24		
Brentwood	d	22 28			22 43				22 58	23 13				23 28		23 43			23 58	00 13			00 28		
Shenfield 3	a	22 33	22 19	22 22	22 48		22 39	22 41	23 03	23 18		23 09	23 12	23 33	23 23	23 48	23 39	23 41	00 03	00 18	00 09	00 12	00 33		
	d		22 20				22 40					23 10					23 40				00 10				
Billericay	d		22 26				22 46					23 16					23 46				00 16				
Wickford 2	d		22 31				22 51				22 58	23 21					23 51				00 21				
Battlesbridge	d										23 02														
South Woodham Ferrers	d										23 06														
North Fambridge	d										23 12														
Althorne	d										23 17														
Burnham-on-Crouch	d										23 22														
Southminster	a										23 27														
Rayleigh	d		22 36				22 56					23 26					23 56				00 26				
Hockley	d		22 41				23 01					23 31					00 01				00 31				
Rochford	d		22 44				23 04					23 34					00 04				00 34				
Prittlewell	d		22 48				23 08					23 38					00 08				00 38				
Southend Victoria	a		22 51				23 11					23 45					00 15				00 45				

For general notes see front of timetable
For details of catering facilities see Directory of Train Operators

London → Shenfield, Southminster and Southend Victoria

Network diagram - see first page of Table 5

		LE 1	LE	LE 1	LE	LE		CC 1	LE 1	LE 1	LE	LE		LE 1 A	LE 1	LE	LE	LE 1		LE	LE	LE 1	LE 1	LE	LE 1
London Liverpool Street 15 ⊖	d	23p15	23p37	23p45	23p52	00 02		00 12	00 15	00 18	00 22	00 32		00 48	00 50	00 55	05 23			05 26	05 28	05 30		05 42	06 00
Stratford 7 ⊖	d	23p22	23p44	23p52	23p58	00 09		00a19	00 22	00 25	00 29	00 39		00 55	00 57	01 02	05a31			05 33	05a36	05 37		05 49	06 07
Maryland	d		23p45		23p59	00 10					00 30	00 40				01 03								05 50	
Forest Gate	d		23p47		00 02	00 12					00 32	00 42				01 05								05 52	
Manor Park	d		23p49		00 04	00 14					00 34	00 44				01 07								05 54	
Ilford 2	d		23p52		00 07	00 17					00 37	00 47				01 10				05 38				05 57	
Seven Kings	d		23p55		00 10	00 20					00 40	00 50				01 13				05 40				06 00	
Goodmayes	d		23p57		00 12	00 22					00 42	00 52				01 15								06 02	
Chadwell Heath	d		23p59		00 14	00 24					00 44	00 54				01 17								06 04	
Romford	d		00 02		00 17	00 27			00 32		00 47	00 57			01 08	01 20				05 46		05 45		06 07	06 15
Gidea Park 2	d		00 06		00 21	00a31					00 51	01a01		01 07		01 24				05 49				06 11	
Harold Wood	d		00 09		00 24						00 54					01 27				05 52				06 14	
Brentwood	d		00 13		00 28						00 58					01 31				05 57				06 18	
Shenfield 3	a	23p39	00 18	00 09	00 33				00 44	00 47	01 03			01 17	01 20	01 36				06 02		05 55		06 23	06 25
	d	23p40		00 10					00 45						01 20					06 02			06 08		
Billericay	d	23p46		00 16					00 51						01 26					06 08			06 14		
Wickford 2	d	23p51		00 21					00 56						01 31			05 39		06 13			06 20		
Battlesbridge	d																	05 43					06 24		
South Woodham Ferrers	d																	05 47					06 28		
North Fambridge	d																	05 53					06 34		
Althorne	d																	05 58					06 39		
Burnham-on-Crouch	d																	06 03					06 44		
Southminster	a																	06 08					06 49		
Rayleigh	d	23p56		00 26					01 01						01 36					06 19					
Hockley	d	00 01		00 31					01 06						01 41					06 23					
Rochford	d	00 04		00 34					01 09						01 44					06 27					
Prittlewell	d	00 08		00 38					01 13						01 48					06 30					
Southend Victoria	a	00 15		00 45					01 20						01 55					06 34					

		LE		LE	LE 1	LE	LE 1	LE 1		LE	LE 1	LE 1	LE	LE 1		LE	LE 1	LE 1	LE	LE 1		LE	LE 1	LE	LE 1
London Liverpool Street 15 ⊖	d	06 04		06 12	06 18	06 23	06 34			06 42	06 48	06 55	07 02	07 08		07 12	07 15	07 18	07 22			07 32	07 34	07 42	07 48
Stratford 7 ⊖	d	06 11		06 19	06 25	06a31	06 41			06 49	06 55	07 02	07 09	07 15		07 19	07 22	07 25	07 29			07 39	07 41	07 49	07 55
Maryland	d			06 20						06 50			07 10			07 20			07 30			07 40		07 50	
Forest Gate	d			06 22						06 52			07 12			07 22			07 32			07 42		07 52	
Manor Park	d			06 24						06 54			07 14			07 24			07 34			07 44		07 54	
Ilford 2	d			06 27						06 57			07 17			07 27			07 37			07 47		07 57	
Seven Kings	d			06 30						07 00			07 20			07 30			07 40			07 50		08 00	
Goodmayes	d			06 32						07 02			07 22			07 32			07 42			07 52		08 02	
Chadwell Heath	d			06 34						07 04			07 24			07 34			07 44			07 54		08 04	
Romford	d			06 37			06 49			07 07			07 27	07 23		07 37			07 47			07 57	07 49	08 07	
Gidea Park 2	d			06 41						07 11			07 31			07 41			07 51			08 01		08 11	
Harold Wood	d			06 44						07 14			07 34			07 44			07 54			08 04		08 14	
Brentwood	d			06 48						07 18			07 38			07 48			07 58			08 08		08 18	
Shenfield 3	a	06 30		06 53	06 41		07 00			07 23	07 12	07 19	07 43	07 33		07 53	07 39	07 41	08 03			08 13	08 00	08 23	08 12
	d	06 30					07 00	07 08				07 20					07 40			08 08			08 00		
Billericay	d	06 36					07 06	07 14				07 26					07 46			08 14			08 06		
Wickford 2	d	06 41					07 11	07 20				07 31					07 51			08 20			08 11		
Battlesbridge	d							07 24												08 24					
South Woodham Ferrers	d							07 28												08 28					
North Fambridge	d							07 34												08 34					
Althorne	d							07 39												08 39					
Burnham-on-Crouch	d							07 44												08 44					
Southminster	a							07 49												08 49					
Rayleigh	d	06 46					07 16					07 36					07 56						08 16		
Hockley	d	06 51					07 21					07 41					08 01						08 21		
Rochford	d	06 54					07 24					07 44					08 04						08 24		
Prittlewell	d	06 58					07 28					07 48					08 08						08 28		
Southend Victoria	a	07 02					07 31					07 51					08 11						08 31		

		LE	LE 1		LE	LE 1	LE	LE 1	LE 1	LE	LE 1	LE	LE 1	LE	LE 1	LE	LE 1			LE	LE 1	LE	LE 1	LE 1
London Liverpool Street 15 ⊖	d	07 52	07 55		08 02	08 08	08 12	08 15	08 18	08 22		08 32	08 34	08 42	08 48	08 52	08 55			20 02	20 08	20 12	20 15	20 18
Stratford 7 ⊖	d	07 59	08 02		08 09	08 15	08 19	08 22	08 25	08 29		08 39	08 41	08 49	08 55	08 59	09 02			20 09	20 15	20 19	20 22	20 25
Maryland	d	08 00			08 10		08 20			08 30		08 40		08 50		09 00				20 10		20 20		
Forest Gate	d	08 02			08 12		08 22			08 32		08 42		08 52		09 02				20 12		20 22		
Manor Park	d	08 04			08 14		08 24			08 34		08 44		08 54		09 04				20 14		20 24		
Ilford 2	d	08 07			08 17		08 27			08 37		08 47		08 57		09 07				20 17		20 27		
Seven Kings	d	08 10			08 20		08 30			08 40		08 50		09 00		09 10		and at		20 20		20 30		
Goodmayes	d	08 12			08 22		08 32			08 42		08 52		09 02		09 12				20 22		20 32		
Chadwell Heath	d	08 14			08 24		08 34			08 44		08 54		09 04		09 14		the same		20 24		20 34		
Romford	d	08 17			08 27	08 23	08 37			08 47		08 57	08 49	09 07		09 17				20 27	20 23	20 37		
Gidea Park 2	d	08 21			08 31		08 41			08 51		09 01		09 11		09 21		minutes		20 31		20 41		
Harold Wood	d	08 24			08 34		08 44			08 54		09 04		09 14		09 24				20 34		20 44		
Brentwood	d	08 28			08 38		08 48			08 58		09 08		09 18		09 28				20 38		20 48		
Shenfield 3	a	08 33	08 19		08 43	08 33	08 53	08 39	08 41	09 03		09 13	09 00	09 23	09 12	09 33	09 19	past		20 43	20 33	20 53	20 39	20 41
	d		08 20					08 40			09 08		09 00				09 20						20 40	
Billericay	d		08 26					08 46			09 14		09 06				09 26	each					20 46	
Wickford 2	d		08 31					08 51			09 20		09 11				09 31	hour until					20 51	
Battlesbridge	d										09 24													
South Woodham Ferrers	d										09 28													
North Fambridge	d										09 34													
Althorne	d										09 39													
Burnham-on-Crouch	d										09 44													
Southminster	a										09 49													
Rayleigh	d		08 36					08 56					09 16				09 36						20 56	
Hockley	d		08 41					09 01					09 21				09 41						21 01	
Rochford	d		08 44					09 04					09 24				09 44						21 04	
Prittlewell	d		08 48					09 08					09 28				09 48						21 08	
Southend Victoria	a		08 51					09 11					09 31				09 51						21 11	

For general notes see front of timetable
For details of catering facilities see
Directory of Train Operators

A To Colchester (Table 11)

London → Shenfield, Southminster and Southend Victoria

Network diagram - see first page of Table 5

	LE	LE 1		LE	LE 1	LE 1	LE	LE 1		LE	LE 1	LE 1	LE	LE 1		LE 1	LE	LE	LE 1	LE 1		LE 1	LE	LE 1
London Liverpool Street 15 ⊖ d	20 22			20 32	20 34	20 38	20 42	20 48		20 52	20 55	21 04	21 07	21 15		21 18	21 22	21 37	21 45	21 48			21 52	22 00
Stratford 7 ⊖ ⛴ d	20 29			20 39	20 41	20 45	20 49	20 55		20 59	21 02	21 11	21 14	21 22		21 25	21 29	21 44	21 52	21 55			21 59	22 07
Maryland d	20 30			20 40			20 50			21 00			21 15				21 30	21 45					22 00	
Forest Gate d	20 32			20 42			20 52			21 02			21 17				21 32	21 47					22 02	
Manor Park d	20 34			20 44			20 54			21 04			21 19				21 34	21 49					22 04	
Ilford 2 d	20 37			20 47			20 57			21 07			21 22				21 37	21 52					22 07	
Seven Kings d	20 40			20 50			21 00			21 10			21 25				21 40	21 55					22 10	
Goodmayes d	20 42			20 52			21 02			21 12			21 27				21 42	21 57					22 12	
Chadwell Heath d	20 44			20 54			21 04			21 14			21 29				21 44	21 59					22 14	
Romford d	20 47			20 57	20 49		21 07			21 17		21 19	21 32				21 47	22 02					22 17	
Gidea Park 2 d	20 51			21 01			21 11			21 21			21 36				21 51	22 06					22 21	
Harold Wood d	20 54			21 04			21 14			21 24			21 39				21 54	22 09					22 24	
Brentwood d	20 58			21 08			21 18			21 28			21 43				21 58	22 13					22 28	
Shenfield 3 a	21 03			21 13	20 59	21 02	21 23	21 12		21 33	21 19	21 33	21 48	21 43		21 45	22 03	22 18	22 13	22 15			22 33	22 27
d		21 08			21 00						21 20			21 43					22 13			22 22		
Billericay d		21 14			21 06						21 26			21 49					22 19			22 28		
Wickford 2 d		21 20			21 11						21 31			21 54					22 24			22 34		
Battlesbridge d		21 24																				22 38		
South Woodham Ferrers d		21 28																				22 42		
North Fambridge d		21 34																				22 48		
Althorne d		21 39																				22 53		
Burnham-on-Crouch d		21 44																				22 58		
Southminster a		21 49																				23 03		
Rayleigh d					21 16						21 36			21 59					22 29					
Hockley d					21 21						21 41			22 04					22 34					
Rochford d					21 24						21 44			22 07					22 37					
Prittlewell d					21 28						21 48			22 11					22 41					
Southend Victoria a					21 31						21 51			22 14					22 44					

	LE	LE 1	LE 1	LE		LE	LE 1	LE 1	LE	LE 1		LE	LE 1	LE 1	LE	LE		LE 1	LE 1	LE				
London Liverpool Street 15 ⊖ d	22 07	22 15	22 18	22 22		22 37	22 45	22 48	22 52	23 00		23 07	23 15	23 18	23 22	23 37		23 45	23 48	23 52				
Stratford 7 ⊖ ⛴ d	22 14	22 22	22 25	22 29		22 44	22 52	22 55	22 59	23 07		23 14	23 22	23 25	23 29	23 44		23 52	23 55	23 58				
Maryland d	22 15			22 30		22 45			23 00			23 15			23 30	23 45				23 59				
Forest Gate d	22 17			22 32		22 47			23 02			23 17			23 32	23 47				00 02				
Manor Park d	22 19			22 34		22 49			23 04			23 19			23 34	23 49				00 04				
Ilford 2 d	22 22			22 37		22 52			23 07			23 22			23 37	23 52				00 07				
Seven Kings d	22 25			22 40		22 55			23 10			23 25			23 40	23 55				00 10				
Goodmayes d	22 27			22 42		22 57			23 12			23 27			23 42	23 57				00 12				
Chadwell Heath d	22 29			22 44		22 59			23 14			23 29			23 44	23 59				00 14				
Romford d	22 32			22 47		23 02			23 17			23 32			23 47	00 02				00 17				
Gidea Park 2 d	22 36			22 51		23 06			23 21			23 36			23 51	00 06				00 21				
Harold Wood d	22 39			22 54		23 09			23 24			23 39			23 54	00 09				00 24				
Brentwood d	22 43			22 58		23 13			23 28			23 43			23 58	00 13				00 28				
Shenfield 3 a	22 48	22 43	22 45	23 03		23 18	23 13	23 15	23 33	23 27		23 48	23 43	23 45	00 03	00 18		00 13	00 15	00 33				
d		22 43					23 13						23 43					00 13						
Billericay d		22 49					23 19						23 49					00 19						
Wickford 2 d		22 54					23 24						23 54					00 24						
Battlesbridge d																								
South Woodham Ferrers d																								
North Fambridge d																								
Althorne d																								
Burnham-on-Crouch d																								
Southminster a																								
Rayleigh d		22 59					23 29						23 59					00 29						
Hockley d		23 04					23 34						00 04					00 34						
Rochford d		23 07					23 37						00 07					00 37						
Prittlewell d		23 11					23 41						00 11					00 41						
Southend Victoria a		23 14					23 48						00 18					00 48						

For general notes see front of timetable
For details of catering facilities see Directory of Train Operators

London → Shenfield, Southminster and Southend Victoria

Network diagram - see first page of Table 5

		LE 1	LE	LE 1	LE	LE		LE 1	LE 1	LE	LE	LE 1		LE	LE	LE	LE 1	LE 1		LE	LE 1	LE 1	LE 1	LE	LE 1
London Liverpool Street 15 ⊖	d	23p15	23p37	23p45	23p52	00 02		00 15	00 18	00 22	00 32	00 50		00 55	06 35	07 05		07 15		07 35		07 45	08 02	08 05	08 15
Stratford 7 ⊖	d	23p22	23p44	23p52	23p58	00 09		00 22	00 25	00 29	00 39	00 57		01 02	06 42	07 12		07 22		07 42		07 52	08 09	08 12	08 22
Maryland	d		23p45		23p59	00 10				00 30	00 40			01 03	06 43	07 13				07 43				08 13	
Forest Gate	d		23p47		00 02	00 12				00 32	00 42			01 05	06 45	07 15				07 45				08 15	
Manor Park	d		23p49		00 04	00 14				00 34	00 44			01 07	06 47	07 17				07 47				08 17	
Ilford 2	d		23p52		00 07	00 17				00 37	00 47			01 10	06 50	07 20				07 50				08 20	
Seven Kings	d		23p55		00 10	00 20				00 40	00 50			01 13	06 53	07 23				07 53				08 23	
Goodmayes	d		23p57		00 12	00 22				00 42	00 52			01 15	06 55	07 25				07 55				08 25	
Chadwell Heath	d		23p59		00 14	00 24				00 44	00 54			01 17	06 57	07 27				07 57				08 27	
Romford	d		00 02		00 17	00 27		00 32		00 47	00 57	01 08		01 20	07 00	07 30		07 33		08 00		08 03		08 30	08 33
Gidea Park 2	d		00 06		00 21	00a31				00 51	01a01			01 24	07 04	07 34		07 37		08 04		08 07		08 34	08 37
Harold Wood	d		00 09		00 24					00 54				01 27	07 07	07 37		07 40		08 07		08 10		08 37	08 40
Brentwood	d		00 13		00 28					00 58				01 31	07 11	07 41		07 44		08 11		08 14		08 41	08 44
Shenfield 3	a	23p43	00 18	00 13	00 33			00 44	00 47	01 03		01 20		01 36	07 16	07 46		07 50		08 16		08 20	08 30	08 46	08 50
	d	23p43		00 13				00 45				01 20						07 50				08 20			08 50
Billericay	d	23p49		00 19				00 51				01 26						07 56				08 26			08 56
Wickford 2	d	23p54		00 24				00 56				01 31					07 30	08 01			08 05	08 31			09 01
Battlesbridge	d																07 34				08 09				
South Woodham Ferrers	d																07 38				08 13				
North Fambridge	d																07 44				08 20				
Althorne	d																07 49				08 25				
Burnham-on-Crouch	d																07 54				08 30				
Southminster	a																07 59				08 35				
Rayleigh	d	23p59		00 29				01 01				01 36						08 06				08 36			09 06
Hockley	d	00 04		00 34				01 06				01 41						08 11				08 41			09 11
Rochford	d	00 07		00 37				01 09				01 44						08 14				08 44			09 14
Prittlewell	d	00 11		00 41				01 13				01 48													
Southend Victoria	a	00 18		00 48				01 20				01 55						08 22				08 52			09 22

		LE 1		LE	LE 1	LE 1	LE		LE 1	LE	LE 1	LE	LE 1	LE	LE 1	LE 1	LE	and at the same minutes past each hour until		LE 1	LE	LE 1	LE	LE 1
London Liverpool Street 15 ⊖	d	08 32		08 35		08 45	08 47		09 02	09 05	09 15	09 17	09 32	09 35		09 45	09 47			19 02	19 05	19 15	19 17	19 32
Stratford 7 ⊖	d	08 39		08 42		08 52	08 54		09 09	09 12	09 22	09 24	09 39	09 42		09 52	09 54			19 09	19 12	19 22	19 24	19 39
Maryland	d			08 43						09 13				09 43							19 13			
Forest Gate	d			08 45			08 57			09 15		09 27		09 45			09 57				19 15		19 27	
Manor Park	d			08 47			08 59			09 17		09 29		09 47			09 59				19 17		19 29	
Ilford 2	d			08 50			09 02			09 20		09 32		09 50			10 02				19 20		19 32	
Seven Kings	d			08 53			09 04			09 23		09 34		09 53			10 04				19 23		19 34	
Goodmayes	d			08 55			09 06			09 25		09 36		09 55			10 06				19 25		19 36	
Chadwell Heath	d			08 57			09 08			09 27		09 38		09 57			10 08				19 27		19 38	
Romford	d			09 00		09 03	09 12			09 30	09 33	09 42		10 00		10 03	10 12				19 30	19 33	19 42	
Gidea Park 2	d			09 04		09 07	09a17			09 34	09 37	09a47		10 04		10 07	10a17				19 34	19 37	19a47	
Harold Wood	d			09 07		09 10				09 37	09 40			10 07		10 10					19 37	19 40		
Brentwood	d			09 11		09 14				09 41	09 44			10 11		10 14					19 41	19 44		
Shenfield 3	a	09 00		09 16		09 20			09 30	09 46	09 50		10 00	10 16		10 20				19 30	19 46	19 50		20 00
	d					09 20					09 50					10 20						19 50		
Billericay	d					09 26					09 56					10 26						19 56		
Wickford 2	d				09 05	09 31					10 01				10 05	10 31						20 01		
Battlesbridge	d				09 09										10 09									
South Woodham Ferrers	d				09 13										10 13									
North Fambridge	d				09 20										10 20									
Althorne	d				09 25										10 25									
Burnham-on-Crouch	d				09 30										10 30									
Southminster	a				09 35										10 35									
Rayleigh	d					09 36					10 06					10 36						20 06		
Hockley	d					09 41					10 11					10 41						20 11		
Rochford	d					09 44					10 14					10 44						20 14		
Prittlewell	d																							
Southend Victoria	a					09 52					10 22					10 52						20 22		

		LE	LE 1		LE 1	LE	LE 1	LE 1	LE		LE 1	LE	LE 1	LE	LE 1		LE 1	LE	LE 1	LE	LE 1		LE	LE 1	LE
London Liverpool Street 15 ⊖	d	19 35			19 45	19 47	20 00	20 02	20 05		20 15	20 17	20 32	20 35			20 45	20 47	21 02	21 05	21 15		21 17	21 32	21 35
Stratford 7 ⊖	d	19 42			19 52	19 54		20 09	20 12		20 22	20 24	20 39	20 42			20 52	20 54	21 09	21 12	21 22		21 24	21 39	21 42
Maryland	d	19 43							20 13					20 43						21 13					21 43
Forest Gate	d	19 45				19 57			20 15			20 27		20 45				20 57		21 15			21 27		21 45
Manor Park	d	19 47				19 59			20 17			20 29		20 47				20 59		21 17			21 29		21 47
Ilford 2	d	19 50				20 02			20 20			20 32		20 50				21 02		21 20			21 32		21 50
Seven Kings	d	19 53				20 04			20 23			20 34		20 53				21 04		21 23			21 34		21 53
Goodmayes	d	19 55				20 06			20 25			20 36		20 55				21 06		21 25			21 36		21 55
Chadwell Heath	d	19 57				20 08			20 27			20 38		20 57				21 08		21 27			21 38		21 57
Romford	d	20 00			20 03	20 12			20 30		20 33	20 42		21 00			21 03	21 12		21 30	21 33		21 42		22 00
Gidea Park 2	d	20 04			20 07	20a17			20 34		20 37	20a47		21 04			21 07	21a17		21 34	21 37		21a47		22 04
Harold Wood	d	20 07			20 10				20 37		20 40			21 07			21 10			21 37	21 40				22 07
Brentwood	d	20 11			20 14				20 41		20 44			21 11			21 14			21 41	21 44				22 11
Shenfield 3	a	20 16			20 20		20 27	20 30	20 46		20 50		21 00	21 16			21 20		21 30	21 46	21 50			22 00	22 16
	d				20 20						20 50						21 20				21 50				
Billericay	d				20 26						20 56						21 26				21 56				
Wickford 2	d		20 05		20 31						21 01				21 05		21 31				22 01				
Battlesbridge	d		20 09												21 09										
South Woodham Ferrers	d		20 13												21 13										
North Fambridge	d		20 20												21 20										
Althorne	d		20 25												21 25										
Burnham-on-Crouch	d		20 30												21 30										
Southminster	a		20 35												21 35										
Rayleigh	d				20 36						21 06						21 36				22 06				
Hockley	d				20 41						21 11						21 41				22 11				
Rochford	d				20 44						21 14						21 44				22 14				
Prittlewell	d																								
Southend Victoria	a				20 52						21 22						21 52				22 22				

For general notes see front of timetable
For details of catering facilities see Directory of Train Operators

Table 5

Sundays

London → Shenfield, Southminster and Southend Victoria

Network diagram - see first page of Table 5

		LE 1	LE 1	LE	LE 1		LE	LE 1	LE	LE 1	LE		LE 1	LE 1	LE	LE 1	LE 1		LE	LE 1					
London Liverpool Street 15 ⊖	d		21 45	21 47	22 02		22 05	22 15	22 17	22 32	22 35		22 45	23 02	23 05	23 15	23 32		23 35	23 45					
Stratford 7 ⊖	d		21 52	21 54	22 09		22 12	22 22	22 24	22 39	22 42		22 52	23 09	23 12	23 22	23 39		23 42	23 52					
Maryland	d						22 13				22 43				23 13				23 43						
Forest Gate	d			21 57			22 15		22 27		22 45				23 15				23 45						
Manor Park	d			21 59			22 17		22 29		22 47				23 17				23 47						
Ilford 2	d			22 02			22 20		22 32		22 50				23 20				23 50						
Seven Kings	d			22 04			22 23		22 34		22 53				23 23				23 53						
Goodmayes	d			22 06			22 25		22 36		22 55				23 25				23 55						
Chadwell Heath	d			22 08			22 27		22 38		22 57				23 27				23 57						
Romford	d		22 03	22 12			22 30	22 33	22 42		23 00		23 03		23 30	23 33			23 59	00 03					
Gidea Park 2	d		22 07	22a17			22 34	22 37	22a47		23 04		23 07		23 34	23 37			00 04	00 07					
Harold Wood	d		22 10				22 37	22 40			23 07		23 10		23 37	23 40			00 07	00 10					
Brentwood	d		22 14				22 41	22 44			23 11		23 14		23 41	23 44			00 11	00 14					
Shenfield 3	a		22 20		22 30		22 46	22 50		23 00	23 16		23 20	23 30	23 46	23 50	00 01		00 16	00 20					
	d		22 20					22 50					23 20			23 50				00 20					
Billericay	d		22 26					22 56					23 26			23 56				00 26					
Wickford 2	d	22 05	22 31					23 01					23 31			00 01				00 31					
Battlesbridge	d	22 09																							
South Woodham Ferrers	d	22 13																							
North Fambridge	d	22 20																							
Althorne	d	22 25																							
Burnham-on-Crouch	d	22 30																							
Southminster	a	22 35																							
Rayleigh	d		22 36					23 06					23 36			00 06				00 36					
Hockley	d		22 41					23 11					23 41			00 11				00 41					
Rochford	d		22 44					23 14					23 44			00 14				00 44					
Prittlewell	d																								
Southend Victoria	a		22 52					23 24					23 54			00 24				00 54					

For general notes see front of timetable
For details of catering facilities see
Directory of Train Operators

Southend Victoria, Southminster and Shenfield → London

Network diagram - see first page of Table 5

Miles	Miles	Station		LE MX	LE MO	LE MX	LE	CC	LE	LE	LE	LE	LE	LE	LE	LE	LE	LE	LE	LE	LE	LE	LE	LE	LE
												1 A		1		1	1				1	1		1	1
0	—	**Southend Victoria**	d				04 02			04 32				05 06		05 26						05 46			06 01
½	—	Prittlewell	d				04 04			04 34				05 08		05 28						05 48			06 03
2¾	—	Rochford	d				04 08			04 38				05 12		05 32						05 52			06 07
5½	—	Hockley	d				04 12			04 42				05 16		05 36						05 56			06 11
8¼	—	Rayleigh	d				04 16			04 46				05 20		05 40						06 00			06 15
—	0	**Southminster**	d																		05 30				
—	2¼	Burnham-on-Crouch	d																		05 34				
—	5¼	Althorne	d																		05 39				
—	8¼	North Fambridge	d																		05 45				
—	11½	South Woodham Ferrers	d																		05 50				
—	14	Battlesbridge	d																		05 54				
12½	16½	**Wickford** 2	d				04 21			04 51				05 25		05 45					06a00	06 05			06 20
17¼	—	Billericay	d				04 28			04 58				05 31		05 51						06 11			06 26
21¼	—	**Shenfield** 3	a				04 39			05 09				05 38		05 58						06 18			06 33
—	—		d	23p29	23p43	23p44	04 39			05 09		05 26	05 29	05 38	05 44	05 58	06 02		06 04	06 14		06 18	06 24	06 26	06 33
23¼	—	Brentwood	d	23p32	23p46	23p47	04 42			05 12			05 32		05 47				06 07	06 17			06 27		
26½	—	Harold Wood	d	23p37	23p51	23p52	04 47			05 17			05 37		05 52				06 12	06 22			06 32		
28	—	Gidea Park 2	d	23p41	23p55	23p56	04 51			05 21		05 33	05 41		05 56			06 06	06 16	06 26			06 36		
29	—	Romford	d	23p43	23p57	23p58	04 53			05 23			05 43		05 58			06 08	06 18	06 28			06 38		
31½	—	Chadwell Heath	d	23p47	00 01	00 02	04 57			05 27			05 47		06 02			06 12	06 22	06 32			06 42		
32¼	—	Goodmayes	d	23p49	00 03	00 04	04 59			05 29			05 49		06 04			06 14	06 24	06 34			06 44		
33	—	Seven Kings	d	23p51	00 05	00 06	05 01			05 31		05 38	05 51		06 06			06 16	06 26	06 36			06 46		
34¼	—	Ilford 2	d	23p54	00 08	00 09	05 04		05 09	05 34	05 39		05 54		06 09			06 19	06 29	06 39			06 49		
35¼	—	Manor Park	d	23p56	00 10	00 11			05 11		05 41		05 56		06 11			06 21	06 31	06 41			06 51		
36¼	—	Forest Gate	d	23p58	00 12	00 13			05 13		05 43		05 58		06 13			06 23	06 33	06 43			06 53		
37	—	Maryland	d	23p59	00 14	00 15			05 15		05 45		06 00		06 15			06 25	06 35	06 45			06 55		
37½	—	Stratford 7 ⊖	d	00 02	00 16	00 17	05 09	05 13	05 17	05 39	05 47	05s44	06 02	05s53	06 17	06s15	06s18	06 27	06 37	06 47		06s32	06 57	06s41	06s47
41½	—	**London Liverpool Street** 15 ⊖	a	00 10	00 25	00 25	05 17	05 23	05 25	05 47	05 55	05 57	06 10	06 01	06 25	06 24	06 27	06 35	06 45	06 55		06 41	07 07	06 49	06 56

Station		LE	LE	LE	LE	LE	LE	LE	LE	LE	LE	LE	LE	LE	LE	LE	LE	LE	LE	LE	LE	LE	LE	LE	LE
			1			1	1						1	1			1	1	1	1			1	1	
Southend Victoria	d					06 16				06 29				06 40					06 56					07 17	
Prittlewell	d					06 18				06 31				06 42					06 58					07 19	
Rochford	d					06 22				06 35				06 46					07 02					07 23	
Hockley	d					06 26				06 39				06 50					07 06					07 27	
Rayleigh	d					06 30				06 43				06 54					07 10					07 31	
Southminster	d						06 10													06 52					
Burnham-on-Crouch	d						06 14													06 56					
Althorne	d						06 19													07 01					
North Fambridge	d						06 26													07 08					
South Woodham Ferrers	d						06 32													07 14					
Battlesbridge	d						06 36													07 18					
Wickford 2	d					06 35	06 41			06 48				06 59					07 15	07 23				07 36	
Billericay	d					06 42	06 48			06 55				07 05					07 22	07 30				07 43	
Shenfield 3	a					06 48	06 54			07 01				07 12					07 28						
	d	06 34	06 39		06 44	06 48	06 54		06 54	07 01		07 04	07 06	07 12		07 15	07 16	07 20	07 28			07 28	07 32		07 34
Brentwood	d	06 37			06 47				06 57			07 07				07 18						07 31			07 37
Harold Wood	d	06 42			06 52				07 02			07 12				07 23						07 36			07 42
Gidea Park 2	d	06 46		06 49	06 56			06 59	07 06		07 09	07 16			07 22	07 27					07 34	07 40			07 46
Romford	d	06 48		06 51	06 58			07 01	07 08		07 11	07 18			07 24	07 29					07 36	07 42			07 48
Chadwell Heath	d	06 52		06 55	07 02			07 05	07 12		07 15	07 22			07 28	07 33					07 40	07 46			07 52
Goodmayes	d			06 57				07 07			07 17	07 24			07 30	07 35					07 42	07 48			07 54
Seven Kings	d			06 59				07 09			07 19	07 26			07 32	07 37					07 44	07 50			07 56
Ilford 2	d	06 57		07 02	07 07			07 12	07 17		07 22	07 29			07 35	07 40					07 47	07 53			07 59
Manor Park	d			07 05				07 15			07 25				07 38						07 50				
Forest Gate	d			07 07				07 17			07 27				07 40						07 52				
Maryland	d			07 09				07 19			07 29				07 42						07 54				
Stratford 7 ⊖	d	07 03	06s56	07 11	07 14	07s05	07s11	07 21	07 24	07s18	07 31	07 35		07s29	07 44	07 46	07s33	07s37	07s45		07 56	07 59			08 05
London Liverpool Street 15 ⊖	a	07 13	07 07	07 21	07 24	07 16	07 23	07 31	07 34	07 29	07 41	07 45	07 33	07 40	07 54	07 56	07 44	07 48	07 57	08 01	08 06	08 09	07 59	08 14	08 15

Station		LE	LE	LE	LE	LE	LE	LE	LE	LE	LE	LE	LE	LE	LE	LE	LE	LE	LE	LE	LE	LE	LE	LE	LE
		1	1			1					1		1	1	1	1				1	1				1
Southend Victoria	d		07 09							07 21	07 25			07 33						07 40					07 53
Prittlewell	d		07 11							07 23	07 27			07 35						07 42					07 55
Rochford	d		07 15							07 27	07 31			07 39						07 46					07 59
Hockley	d		07 19							07 31	07 35			07 43						07 50					08 03
Rayleigh	d		07 23							07 35	07 39			07 47						07 54					08 07
Southminster	d															07 35									
Burnham-on-Crouch	d															07 39									
Althorne	d															07 44									
North Fambridge	d															07 50									
South Woodham Ferrers	d															07b58									
Battlesbridge	d																								
Wickford 2	d		07 28							07 40	07 44			07 52		08 06				07 59					08 12
Billericay	d		07 35							07 47	07 51			07 59		08 13				08 06					08 19
Shenfield 3	a		07 42							07 55	07 58			08 06						08 13					08 26
	d	07 38	07 42		07 44	07 50		07 50		07 56	07 58	08 00	08 02	08 06	08 08				08 10	08 13	08 20			08 20	08 26
Brentwood	d				07 47			07 53		07 59		08 03							08 13					08 23	
Harold Wood	d				07 52			07 58		08 04		08 08							08 18					08 28	
Gidea Park 2	d			07 49	07 56		07 59	08 02	08 05	08 09		08 12					08 15	08 19	08 22				08 29	08 32	
Romford	d			07 51	07 58		08 01	08 04	08 07	08 11		08 14					08 17	08 21	08 24				08 31	08 34	
Chadwell Heath	d			07 55	08 02		08 05	08 08	08 11	08 15		08 18					08 21	08 25	08 28				08 35	08 38	
Goodmayes	d			07 57	08 04		08 07	08 10	08 13	08 17		08 20					08 23	08 27	08 30				08 37	08 40	
Seven Kings	d			07 59	08 06		08 09	08 12	08 15	08 19		08 22					08 25	08 29	08 32				08 39	08 42	
Ilford 2	d			08 02	08 09		08 12	08 15	08 18	08 22		08 25					08 28	08 32	08 35			08 38	08 42	08 45	
Manor Park	d			08 05					08 21								08 31					08 41			
Forest Gate	d			08 07					08 23								08 33					08 43			
Maryland	d			08 09					08 25								08 35					08 45			
Stratford 7 ⊖	d	07s55	08s00	08 11	08 15		08 18	08 21	08 27	08 30	08s15	08 33			08s25		08 37	08 40	08 43	08s30		08 47	08 50	08 53	08s44
London Liverpool Street 15 ⊖	a	08 06	08 12	08 21	08 25	08 16	08 28	08 31	08 37	08 40	08 26	08 43	08 28	08 32	08 36	08 46	08 47	08 50	08 53	08 44	08 48	08 57	09 00	09 03	08 56

For general notes see front of timetable
For details of catering facilities see Directory of Train Operators

A From Colchester (Table 11)
b Arr. 3 minutes earlier

Southend Victoria, Southminster and Shenfield → London

Network diagram - see first page of Table 5

Station		LE [1]	LE	LE	LE	LE [1]	LE [1]	LE [1]	LE	LE	LE [1]	LE	LE [1]	LE [1]	LE [1]	LE	LE	LE [1]	LE [1]	LE	LE [1]	LE	LE [1]	LE [1]	LE
Southend Victoria	d					08 03		08 11						08 26				08 46					09 06		
Prittlewell	d					08 05		08 13						08 28				08 48					09 08		
Rochford	d					08 09		08 17						08 32				08 52					09 12		
Hockley	d					08 13		08 21						08 36				08 56					09 16		
Rayleigh	d					08 17		08 25						08 40				09 00					09 20		
Southminster	d														08 17										
Burnham-on-Crouch	d														08 21										
Althorne	d														08 26										
North Fambridge	d														08 34										
South Woodham Ferrers	d														08 40										
Battlesbridge	d														08 44										
Wickford [2]	d					08 22		08 30						08 45	08 49			09 05					09 25		
Billericay	d					08 29		08 37						08 52	08 56			09 12					09 31		
Shenfield [3]	a					08 36		08 44						08 59	09 03			09 19					09 38		
	d	08 32			08 34	08 36	08 40	08 44		08 44	08 52	08 54	08 55	08 59	09 03	09 04	09 14	09 19	09 22	09 24	09 25	09 34	09 38	09 40	09 44
Brentwood	d				08 37					08 47		08 57				09 07	09 17			09 27		09 37			09 47
Harold Wood	d				08 42					08 52		09 02				09 12	09 22			09 32		09 42			09 52
Gidea Park [2]	d			08 39	08 46					08 56		09 06				09 16	09 26			09 36		09 46			09 56
Romford	d			08 41	08 48			08 52		08 58		09 08				09 18	09 28			09 38		09 48		09 48	09 58
Chadwell Heath	d			08 45	08 52					09 02		09 12				09 22	09 32			09 42		09 52			10 02
Goodmayes	d			08 47	08 54					09 04		09 14				09 24	09 34			09 44		09 54			10 04
Seven Kings	d			08 49	08 56					09 06		09 16				09 26	09 36			09 46		09 56			10 06
Ilford [2]	d		08 48	08 52	08 59				09 02	09 09		09 19				09 29	09 39			09 49		09 59			10 09
Manor Park	d		08 51						09 05			09 21				09 31	09 41			09 51		10 01			10 11
Forest Gate	d		08 53						09 07			09 23				09 33	09 43			09 53		10 03			10 13
Maryland	d		08 55						09 09			09 25				09 35	09 45			09 55		10 05			10 15
Stratford [7] ⊖ ⛴	d	08s49	08 57	09 00	09 05	08s53		09s03	09 11	09 15	09s09	09 27		09s16	09s20	09 37	09 47	09s36	09s39	09 57		10 07	09s52	09s57	10 17
London Liverpool Street [15] ⊖	a	09 01	09 07	09 10	09 15	09 04	09 06	09 14	09 21	09 25	09 20	09 37	09 22	09 28	09 31	09 47	09 57	09 47	09 50	10 07	09 52	10 15	10 04	10 05	10 25

Station		LE [1]	LE	LE [1]	LE [1]	LE	LE [1]	LE	LE [1]	LE	LE		LE [1]	LE [1]	LE	LE [1]	LE	LE [1]	LE [1]	LE	LE [1]	LE	LE [1]	LE	
Southend Victoria	d			09 26					09 46				10 06					10 26					10 46		
Prittlewell	d			09 28					09 48				10 08					10 28					10 48		
Rochford	d			09 32					09 52				10 12					10 32					10 52		
Hockley	d			09 36					09 56				10 16					10 36					10 56		
Rayleigh	d			09 40					10 00				10 20					10 40					11 00		
Southminster	d				09 17														10 17						
Burnham-on-Crouch	d				09 21														10 21						
Althorne	d				09 26														10 26						
North Fambridge	d				09 34														10 34						
South Woodham Ferrers	d				09 39														10 39						
Battlesbridge	d				09 43														10 43						
Wickford [2]	d			09 45	09 49				10 05				10 25					10 45	10 49				11 05		
Billericay	d			09 51	09 55				10 11				10 31					10 51	10 55				11 11		
Shenfield [3]	a			09 58	10 02				10 18				10 38					10 58	11 02				11 18		
	d	09 54	09 54	09 58	10 02	10 04	10 10	10 14	10 18	10 24	10 34		10 38	10 40	10 44	10 51	10 54	10 58		11 04	11 10	11 14	11 18	11 24	
Brentwood	d		09 57			10 07		10 17		10 27	10 37				10 47		10 57			11 07		11 17		11 27	
Harold Wood	d		10 02			10 12		10 22		10 32	10 42				10 52		11 02			11 12		11 22		11 32	
Gidea Park [2]	d		10 06			10 16		10 26		10 36	10 46				10 56		11 06			11 16		11 26		11 36	
Romford	d		10 08			10 18		10 28	10 26	10 38	10 48				10 58	10 59	11 08			11 18		11 28	11 26	11 38	
Chadwell Heath	d		10 12			10 22		10 32		10 42	10 52				11 02		11 12			11 22		11 32		11 42	
Goodmayes	d		10 14			10 24		10 34		10 44	10 54				11 04		11 14			11 24		11 34		11 44	
Seven Kings	d		10 16			10 26		10 36		10 46	10 56				11 06		11 16			11 26		11 36		11 46	
Ilford [2]	d		10 19			10 29		10 39		10 49	10 59				11 09		11 19			11 29		11 39		11 49	
Manor Park	d		10 21			10 31		10 41		10 51	11 01				11 11		11 21			11 31		11 41		11 51	
Forest Gate	d		10 23			10 33		10 43		10 53	11 03				11 13		11 23			11 33		11 43		11 53	
Maryland	d		10 25			10 35		10 45		10 55	11 05				11 15		11 25			11 35		11 45		11 55	
Stratford [7] ⊖ ⛴	d	10s08	10 27	10s13	10s16	10 37	10s24	10 47	10s34	10 57	11 07		10s52	10s55	11 17	11s07	11 27	11s12		11 37	11s24	11 47	11s34	11 57	
London Liverpool Street [15] ⊖	a	10 17	10 35	10 22	10 25	10 45	10 33	10 55	10 44	11 05	11 15		11 01	11 03	11 25	11 18	11 35	11 24		11 45	11 33	11 55	11 43	12 05	

Station		LE	and at the same minutes past each hour until	LE [1]	LE [1]	LE	LE [1]	LE	LE [1]	LE [1]	LE	LE [1]	LE	LE [1]	LE	LE [1]	LE	LE [1]	LE [1]	LE	LE [1]	LE [1]	LE	LE
Southend Victoria	d			15 06					15 26					15 46				16 06				16 21		
Prittlewell	d			15 08					15 28					15 48				16 08				16 23		
Rochford	d			15 12					15 32					15 52				16 12				16 27		
Hockley	d			15 16					15 36					15 56				16 16				16 31		
Rayleigh	d			15 20					15 40					16 00				16 20				16 35		
Southminster	d									15 17														
Burnham-on-Crouch	d									15 21														
Althorne	d									15 26														
North Fambridge	d									15 34														
South Woodham Ferrers	d									15 39														
Battlesbridge	d									15 43														
Wickford [2]	d			15 25					15 45	15 49				16 05				16 25				16 40		
Billericay	d			15 31					15 51	15 55				16 11				16 31				16 46		
Shenfield [3]	a			15 38					15 58	16 02				16 18				16 38				16 53		
	d	11 34		15 38	15 40	15 44	15 51	15 54	15 58		16 04	16 12	16 14	16 18	16 24	16 25	16 34	16 38	16 40	16 44	16 51	16 53	16 54	17 04
Brentwood	d	11 37				15 47		15 57			16 07		16 17		16 27		16 37			16 47			16 57	17 07
Harold Wood	d	11 42				15 52		16 02			16 12		16 22		16 32		16 42			16 52			17 02	17 12
Gidea Park [2]	d	11 46				15 56		16 06			16 16		16 26		16 36		16 46			16 56			17 06	17 16
Romford	d	11 48				15 58	15 59	16 08			16 18		16 28	16 26	16 38		16 48		16 48	16 58			17 08	17 18
Chadwell Heath	d	11 52				16 02		16 12			16 22		16 32		16 42		16 52			17 02			17 12	17 22
Goodmayes	d	11 54				16 04		16 14			16 24		16 34		16 44		16 54			17 04			17 14	17 24
Seven Kings	d	11 56				16 06		16 16			16 26		16 36		16 46		16 56			17 06			17 16	17 26
Ilford [2]	d	11 59				16 09		16 19			16 29		16 39		16 49		16 59			17 09			17 19	17 29
Manor Park	d	12 01				16 11		16 21			16 31		16 41		16 51		17 01			17 11			17 21	
Forest Gate	d	12 03				16 13		16 23			16 33		16 43		16 53		17 03			17 13			17 23	
Maryland	d	12 05				16 15		16 25			16 35		16 45		16 55		17 05			17 15			17 25	
Stratford [7] ⊖ ⛴	d	12 07		15s52	15s55	16 17	16s07	16 27	16s12		16 37	16s26	16 47	16s34	16 57	16s39	17 07	16s52	16s56	17 17	17s05	17s08	17 27	17 34
London Liverpool Street [15] ⊖	a	12 15		16 01	16 03	16 25	16 18	16 35	16 21		16 45	16 35	16 55	16 43	17 05	16 48	17 15	17 03	17 05	17 25	17 15	17 18	17 35	17 42

For general notes see front of timetable
For details of catering facilities see Directory of Train Operators

Southend Victoria, Southminster and Shenfield → London

Network diagram - see first page of Table 5

Station		LE 1	LE 1	LE 1	LE	LE	LE 1	LE	LE	LE 1	LE	LE	LE 1	LE 1	LE	LE	LE 1	LE 1	LE 1	LE 1	LE	LE	LE	LE	LE 1
Southend Victoria	d		16 35				16 51							17 06						17 21					17 36
Prittlewell	d		16 37				16 53							17 08						17 23					17 38
Rochford	d		16 41				16 57							17 12						17 27					17 42
Hockley	d		16 45				17 01							17 16						17 31					17 46
Rayleigh	d		16 49				17 05							17 20						17 35					17 50
Southminster	d	16 17																17 05							
Burnham-on-Crouch	d	16 21																17 09							
Althorne	d	16 26																17 14							
North Fambridge	d	16 34																17 21							
South Woodham Ferrers	d	16 39																17 26							
Battlesbridge	d	16 43																17 30							
Wickford 2	d	16a50	16 54				17 10							17 25				17 36		17 40					17 55
Billericay	d		17 00				17 16							17 31				17 42		17 46					18 01
Shenfield 3	a		17 07				17 23							17 38				17 49		17 53					18 08
	d		17 07	17 12		17 14	17 23		17 24	17 27		17 34	17 36	17 38		17 44	17 46	17 49	17 51	17 53		17 54		18 04	18 08
Brentwood	d					17 17			17 27			17 37				17 47						17 57		18 07	
Harold Wood	d					17 22			17 32			17 42				17 52						18 02		18 12	
Gidea Park 2	d				17 22	17 26		17 32	17 36		17 42	17 46			17 52	17 56					18 02	18 06	18 12	18 16	
Romford	d				17 24	17 28		17 34	17 38		17 44	17 48			17 54	17 58			17 59		18 04	18 08	18 14	18 18	
Chadwell Heath	d					17 32			17 42			17 52				18 02						18 12		18 22	
Goodmayes	d					17 34			17 44			17 54				18 04						18 14		18 24	
Seven Kings	d					17 36			17 46			17 56				18 06						18 16		18 26	
Ilford 2	d				17 31	17 39		17 41	17 49		17 51	17 59			18 01	18 09					18 11	18 19	18 21	18 29	
Manor Park	d				17 34			17 44			17 54				18 04						18 14		18 24	18 31	
Forest Gate	d				17 36			17 46			17 56				18 06						18 16		18 26	18 33	
Maryland	d				17 38			17 48			17 58				18 08						18 18		18 28	18 35	
Stratford 7 ⊖	d			17s26	17 40	17 44	17s37	17 50	17 54		18 00	18 05	17s50	17s53	18 10	18 15	18s02	18s03	18s07	18s12	18 20	18 24	18 30	18 37	18s22
London Liverpool Street 15 ⊖	a		17 29	17 38	17 48	17 52	17 46	17 58	18 02	17 49	18 09	18 13	18 00	18 02	18 18	18 23	18 11	18 14	18 20	18 21	18 28	18 32	18 41	18 45	18 31

Station		LE 1	LE	LE 1	LE	LE 1	LE	LE 1	LE 1	LE	LE 1	LE	LE 1	LE	LE 1	LE 1	LE	LE 1	LE 1	LE	LE	LE 1	LE 1	CC 1	LE
Southend Victoria	d			17 51				18 06					18 26						18 46			19 06			
Prittlewell	d			17 53				18 08					18 28						18 48			19 08			
Rochford	d			17 57				18 12					18 32						18 52			19 12			
Hockley	d			18 01				18 16					18 36						18 56			19 16			
Rayleigh	d			18 05				18 20					18 40						19 00			19 20			
Southminster	d					17 47										18 27									
Burnham-on-Crouch	d					17 51										18 31									
Althorne	d					17 56										18 36									
North Fambridge	d					18 03										18 43									
South Woodham Ferrers	d					18 08										18 48									
Battlesbridge	d					18 12										18 52									
Wickford 2	d			18 10		18 18		18 25					18 45			18 58			19 05			19 25			
Billericay	d			18 16		18 24		18 31					18 51			19 04			19 11			19 31			
Shenfield 3	a			18 23		18 31		18 38					18 58			19 11			19 18			19 38			
	d	18 12	18 14	18 23	18 24	18 31	18 34	18 38	18 40	18 44	18 51	18 54	18 58	19 04	19 10		19 14	19 16	19 18	19 24	19 34	19 38	19 40		19 44
Brentwood	d		18 17		18 27		18 37			18 47		18 57		19 07			19 17			19 27	19 37				19 47
Harold Wood	d		18 22		18 32		18 42			18 52		19 02		19 12			19 22			19 32	19 42				19 52
Gidea Park 2	d		18 26		18 36		18 46			18 56		19 06		19 16			19 26			19 36	19 46				19 56
Romford	d		18 28		18 38		18 48			18 58	18 59	19 08		19 18			19 28		19 26	19 38	19 48				19 58
Chadwell Heath	d		18 32		18 42		18 52			19 02		19 12		19 22			19 32			19 42	19 52				20 02
Goodmayes	d		18 34		18 44		18 54			19 04		19 14		19 24			19 34			19 44	19 54				20 04
Seven Kings	d		18 36		18 46		18 56			19 06		19 16		19 26			19 36			19 46	19 56				20 06
Ilford 2	d		18 39		18 49		18 59			19 09		19 19		19 29			19 39			19 49	19 59				20 09
Manor Park	d		18 41		18 51		19 01			19 11		19 21		19 31			19 41			19 51	20 01				20 11
Forest Gate	d		18 43		18 53		19 03			19 13		19 23		19 33			19 43			19 53	20 03				20 13
Maryland	d		18 45		18 55		19 05			19 15		19 25		19 35			19 45			19 55	20 05				20 15
Stratford 7 ⊖	d	18s26	18 47	18s37	18 57	18s46	19 07	18s52	18s55	19 17	19s07	19 27	19s12	19 37	19s24		19 47		19s35	19 57	20 07	19s52	19s55	20 10	20 17
London Liverpool Street 15 ⊖	a	18 35	18 55	18 46	19 05	18 55	19 15	19 01	19 05	19 25	19 16	19 35	19 21	19 45	19 33		19 55	19 39	19 44	20 05	20 15	20 01	20 04	20 20	20 25

Station		LE 1	LE	LE 1	LE 1	LE	LE 1	LE	LE 1	LE	LE	LE 1	LE 1	CC 1	LE	LE 1	LE	LE 1	LE 1	LE	LE 1	LE	LE 1	LE	LE
Southend Victoria	d			19 26					19 46			20 06						20 26					20 46		
Prittlewell	d			19 28					19 48			20 08						20 28					20 48		
Rochford	d			19 32					19 52			20 12						20 32					20 52		
Hockley	d			19 36					19 56			20 16						20 36					20 56		
Rayleigh	d			19 40					20 00			20 20						20 40					21 00		
Southminster	d				19 17														20 17						
Burnham-on-Crouch	d				19 21														20 21						
Althorne	d				19 26														20 26						
North Fambridge	d				19 34														20 34						
South Woodham Ferrers	d				19 39														20 39						
Battlesbridge	d				19 43														20 43						
Wickford 2	d			19 45	19 49				20 05			20 25						20 45	20 49				21 05		
Billericay	d			19 51	19 55				20 11			20 31						20 51	20 55				21 11		
Shenfield 3	a			19 58	20 03				20 18			20 38						20 58	21 02				21 18		
	d	19 51	19 54	19 58		20 04	20 10	20 14	20 18	20 24	20 34	20 38	20 40		20 44	20 51	20 54	20 58		21 04	21 10	21 14	21 18	21 24	21 34
Brentwood	d		19 57			20 07		20 17		20 27	20 37				20 47		20 57			21 07		21 17		21 27	21 37
Harold Wood	d		20 02			20 12		20 22		20 32	20 42				20 52		21 02			21 12		21 22		21 32	21 42
Gidea Park 2	d		20 06			20 16		20 26		20 36	20 46				20 56		21 06			21 16		21 26		21 36	21 46
Romford	d	19 59	20 08			20 18		20 28	20 26	20 38	20 48				20 58	20 59	21 08			21 18		21 28	21 26	21 38	21 48
Chadwell Heath	d		20 12			20 22		20 32		20 42	20 52				21 02		21 12			21 22		21 32		21 42	21 52
Goodmayes	d		20 14			20 24		20 34		20 44	20 54				21 04		21 14			21 24		21 34		21 44	21 54
Seven Kings	d		20 16			20 26		20 36		20 46	20 56				21 06		21 16			21 26		21 36		21 46	21 56
Ilford 2	d		20 19			20 29		20 39		20 49	20 59				21 09		21 19			21 29		21 39		21 49	21 59
Manor Park	d		20 21			20 31		20 41		20 51	21 01				21 11		21 21			21 31		21 41		21 51	22 01
Forest Gate	d		20 23			20 33		20 43		20 53	21 03				21 13		21 23			21 33		21 43		21 53	22 03
Maryland	d		20 25			20 35		20 45		20 55	21 05				21 15		21 25			21 35		21 45		21 55	22 05
Stratford 7 ⊖	d	20s07	20 27	20s12		20 37	20s24	20 47	20s34	20 57	21 07	20s52	20s55	21 09	21 17	21s07	21 27	21s12		21 37	21s24	21 47	21s34	21 57	22 07
London Liverpool Street 15 ⊖	a	20 16	20 35	20 21		20 45	20 33	20 55	20 43	21 05	21 15	21 01	21 04	21 19	21 25	21 17	21 35	21 21		21 45	21 33	21 55	21 43	22 05	22 15

For general notes see front of timetable
For details of catering facilities see
Directory of Train Operators

Southend Victoria, Southminster and Shenfield → London

Network diagram - see first page of Table 5

	LE 1	LE 1	LE	LE 1	LE 1	LE	LE 1	LE 1	LE 1	LE	LE	LE 1	LE 1	LE	LE 1	LE	LE 1	LE 1	LE 1	LE	LE	LE 1	LE 1	LE
Southend Victoria d	21 06							21 36				22 06						22 36				23 06		
Prittlewell d	21 08							21 38				22 08						22 38				23 08		
Rochford d	21 12							21 42				22 12						22 42				23 12		
Hockley d	21 16							21 46				22 16						22 46				23 16		
Rayleigh d	21 20							21 50				22 20						22 50				23 20		
Southminster d							21 17										22 17						22 56	
Burnham-on-Crouch d							21 21										22 21						23 00	
Althorne d							21 26										22 26						23 05	
North Fambridge d							21 34										22 34						23 12	
South Woodham Ferrers d							21 39										22 39						23 17	
Battlesbridge d							21 43										22 43						23 21	
Wickford 2 d	21 25						21 49	21 55				22 25					22a49	22 55				23 25	23 29	
Billericay d	21 31						21 55	22 01				22 31						23 01				23 31	23 35	
Shenfield 3 a	21 38						22 02	22 08				22 38						23 08				23 38	23 42	
d	21 38	21 40	21 44	21 51	21 58	21 59		22 08	22 11	22 14	22 29	22 38	22 40	22 44	22 51	22 59		23 08	23 10	23 14	23 29	23 38	23 42	23 44
Brentwood d			21 47			22 02				22 17	22 32			22 47		23 02				23 17	23 32			23 47
Harold Wood d			21 52			22 07				22 22	22 37			22 52		23 07				23 22	23 37			23 52
Gidea Park 2 d			21 56			22 11				22 26	22 41			22 56		23 11				23 26	23 41			23 56
Romford d			21 58	21 59		22 13				22 28	22 43			22 58	22 59	23 13				23 28	23 43		23 50	23 58
Chadwell Heath d			22 02			22 17				22 32	22 47			23 02		23 17				23 32	23 47			00 02
Goodmayes d			22 04			22 19				22 34	22 49			23 04		23 19				23 34	23 49			00 04
Seven Kings d			22 06			22 21				22 36	22 51			23 06		23 21				23 36	23 51			00 06
Ilford 2 d			22 09			22 24				22 39	22 54			23 09		23 24				23 39	23 54			00 09
Manor Park d			22 11			22 26				22 41	22 56			23 11		23 26				23 41	23 56			00 11
Forest Gate d			22 13			22 28				22 43	22 58			23 13		23 28				23 43	23 58			00 13
Maryland d			22 15			22 30				22 45	23 00			23 15		23 30				23 45	23 59			00 15
Stratford 7 ⊖ d	21s52	21s55	22 17	22s10	22s12	22 32		22s22	22s27	22 47	23 02	22s52	22s55	23 17	23s07	23 32		23s22	23s25	23 47	00 02	23s54	23s58	00 17
London Liverpool Street 15 ⊖ a	22 01	22 03	22 25	22 19	22 23	22 40		22 31	22 36	22 55	23 10	23 01	23 03	23 25	23 16	23 40		23 31	23 34	23 55	00 10	00 03	00 07	00 25

Saturdays

	LE	LE	LE	LE	LE	LE	LE 1 A	LE 1		LE	LE	LE 1	LE	LE 1	LE	LE 1	LE		LE	LE	LE 1	LE 1	LE 1	LE 1
Southend Victoria d			04 02		04 32			05 06				05 36				06 06							06 26	
Prittlewell d			04 04		04 34			05 08				05 38				06 08							06 28	
Rochford d			04 08		04 38			05 12				05 42				06 12							06 32	
Hockley d			04 12		04 42			05 16				05 46				06 16							06 36	
Rayleigh d			04 16		04 46			05 20				05 50				06 20							06 40	
Southminster d																								06 17
Burnham-on-Crouch d																								06 21
Althorne d																								06 26
North Fambridge d																								06 34
South Woodham Ferrers d																								06 39
Battlesbridge d																								06 43
Wickford 2 d			04 21		04 51			05 25				05 55				06 25							06 45	06 49
Billericay d			04 28		04 58			05 31				06 01				06 31							06 51	06 55
Shenfield 3 a			04 39		05 09			05 38				06 08				06 38							06 58	07 02
d	23p29	23p44	04 39		05 09		05 26	05 38			05 44	06 08		06 11	06 14	06 38				06 44	06 47	06 51	06 58	
Brentwood d	23p32	23p47	04 42		05 12						05 47				06 17					06 47				
Harold Wood d	23p37	23p52	04 47		05 17						05 52				06 22					06 52				
Gidea Park 2 d	23p41	23p56	04 51		05 21		05 33				05 56		06 16		06 26		06 36		06 46	06 56				
Romford d	23p43	23p58	04 53		05 23			05 46			05 58	06 16	06 18	06 19	06 28		06 38		06 48	06 58		06 59		
Chadwell Heath d	23p47	00 02	04 57		05 27						06 02		06 22		06 32		06 42		06 52	07 02				
Goodmayes d	23p49	00 04	04 59		05 29						06 04		06 24		06 34		06 44		06 54	07 04				
Seven Kings d	23p51	00 06	05 01		05 31		05 38				06 06		06 26		06 36		06 46		06 56	07 06				
Ilford 2 d	23p54	00 09	05 04	05 09	05 34	05 39					06 09		06 29		06 39		06 49		06 59	07 09				
Manor Park d	23p56	00 11		05 11		05 41					06 11		06 31		06 41		06 51		07 01	07 11				
Forest Gate d	23p58	00 13		05 13		05 43					06 13		06 33		06 43		06 53		07 03	07 13				
Maryland d	23p59	00 15		05 15		05 45					06 15		06 35		06 45		06 55		07 05	07 15				
Stratford 7 ⊖ d	00 02	00 17	05 09	05 17	05 39	05 47	05s44	05s54		06 05	06 17	06s24	06 37	06s27	06 47	06s52	06 57		07 07	07 17	07s01	07s07	07s12	
London Liverpool Street 15 ⊖ a	00 10	00 25	05 17	05 25	05 47	05 55	05 57	06 03		06 18	06 25	06 33	06 45	06 36	06 55	07 01	07 05		07 15	07 25	07 10	07 16	07 21	

For general notes see front of timetable
For details of catering facilities see Directory of Train Operators

A From Colchester (Table 11)

Table 5

Southend Victoria, Southminster and Shenfield → London

Network diagram - see first page of Table 5

		LE	LE	LE 1	LE 1		LE	LE	LE	LE 1	LE 1	LE	LE 1	LE		LE 1	LE 1	LE	LE 1	LE 1	LE	LE 1	LE		LE
Southend Victoria	d				06 46					07 06						07 26						07 46			
Prittlewell	d				06 48					07 08						07 28						07 48			
Rochford	d				06 52					07 12						07 32						07 52			
Hockley	d				06 56					07 16						07 36						07 56			
Rayleigh	d				07 00					07 20						07 40						08 00			
Southminster	d																07 17								
Burnham-on-Crouch	d																07 21								
Althorne	d																07 26								
North Fambridge	d																07 34								
South Woodham Ferrers	d																07 39								
Battlesbridge	d																07 43								
Wickford 2	d				07 05					07 25						07 45	07 49					08 05			
Billericay	d				07 11					07 31						07 51	07 55					08 11			
Shenfield 3	a				07 18					07 38						07 58	08 02					08 18			
	d		07 04	07 10	07 18			07 24	07 34	07 38	07 40	07 44	07 51	07 54		07 58		08 04	08 10	08 14	08 14	08 18	08 24		08 34
Brentwood	d		07 07					07 27	07 37			07 47		07 57				08 07			08 17		08 27		08 37
Harold Wood	d		07 12					07 32	07 42			07 52		08 02				08 12			08 22		08 32		08 42
Gidea Park 2	d	07 06	07 16				07 26	07 36	07 46			07 56		08 06				08 16			08 26		08 36		08 46
Romford	d	07 08	07 18		07 26		07 28	07 38	07 48			07 58	07 59	08 08				08 18			08 28	08 26	08 38		08 48
Chadwell Heath	d	07 12	07 22				07 32	07 42	07 52			08 02		08 12				08 22			08 32		08 42		08 52
Goodmayes	d	07 14	07 24				07 34	07 44	07 54			08 04		08 14				08 24			08 34		08 44		08 54
Seven Kings	d	07 16	07 26				07 36	07 46	07 56			08 06		08 16				08 26			08 36		08 46		08 56
Ilford 2	d	07 19	07 29				07 39	07 49	07 59			08 09		08 19				08 29			08 39		08 49		08 59
Manor Park	d	07 21	07 31				07 41	07 51	08 01			08 11		08 21				08 31			08 41		08 51		09 01
Forest Gate	d	07 23	07 33				07 43	07 53	08 03			08 13		08 23				08 33			08 43		08 53		09 03
Maryland	d	07 25	07 35				07 45	07 55	08 05			08 15		08 25				08 35			08 45		08 55		09 05
Stratford 7 ⊖	d	07 27	07 37	07s24	07s34		07 47	07 57	08 07	07s52	07s55	08 17	08s07	08 27		08s12		08 37	08s24	08s30	08 47	08s34	08 57		09 07
London Liverpool Street 15 ⊖	a	07 35	07 45	07 33	07 43		07 55	08 05	08 15	08 01	08 03	08 25	08 16	08 35		08 21		08 45	08 33	08 39	08 55	08 43	09 05		09 15

		LE 1	LE 1	LE	LE 1	LE		LE 1	LE 1	LE	LE 1	LE	LE 1	LE	LE	LE 1	LE 1	LE	LE 1	LE	and at the same minutes past each hour until		LE 1	LE 1
Southend Victoria	d	08 06						08 26					08 46			09 06							19 26	
Prittlewell	d	08 08						08 28					08 48			09 08							19 28	
Rochford	d	08 12						08 32					08 52			09 12							19 32	
Hockley	d	08 16						08 36					08 56			09 16							19 36	
Rayleigh	d	08 20						08 40					09 00			09 20							19 40	
Southminster	d								08 17															19 17
Burnham-on-Crouch	d								08 21															19 21
Althorne	d								08 26															19 26
North Fambridge	d								08 34															19 34
South Woodham Ferrers	d								08 39															19 39
Battlesbridge	d								08 43															19 43
Wickford 2	d	08 25						08 45	08 49				09 05			09 25							19 45	19 49
Billericay	d	08 31						08 51	08 55				09 11			09 31							19 51	19 55
Shenfield 3	a	08 38						08 58	09 02				09 18			09 38							19 58	20 02
	d	08 38	08 40	08 44	08 51	08 54		08 58		09 04	09 10	09 14	09 18	09 24	09 34	09 38	09 40	09 44	09 51	09 54			19 58	
Brentwood	d			08 47		08 57				09 07		09 17		09 27	09 37			09 47		09 57				
Harold Wood	d			08 52		09 02				09 12		09 22		09 32	09 42			09 52		10 02				
Gidea Park 2	d			08 56		09 06				09 16		09 26		09 36	09 46			09 56		10 06				
Romford	d			08 58	08 59	09 08				09 18		09 28	09 26	09 38	09 48			09 58	09 59	10 08				
Chadwell Heath	d			09 02		09 12				09 22		09 32		09 42	09 52			10 02		10 12				
Goodmayes	d			09 04		09 14				09 24		09 34		09 44	09 54			10 04		10 14				
Seven Kings	d			09 06		09 16				09 26		09 36		09 46	09 56			10 06		10 16				
Ilford 2	d			09 09		09 19				09 29		09 39		09 49	09 59			10 09		10 19				
Manor Park	d			09 11		09 21				09 31		09 41		09 51	10 01			10 11		10 21				
Forest Gate	d			09 13		09 23				09 33		09 43		09 53	10 03			10 13		10 23				
Maryland	d			09 15		09 25				09 35		09 45		09 55	10 05			10 15		10 25				
Stratford 7 ⊖	d	08s52	08s55	09 17	09s07	09 27		09s12		09 37	09s24	09 47	09s34	09 57	10 07	09s52	09s55	10 17	10s07	10 27			20s12	
London Liverpool Street 15 ⊖	a	09 01	09 03	09 25	09 16	09 35		09 21		09 45	09 33	09 55	09 43	10 05	10 15	10 01	10 03	10 25	10 16	10 35			20 21	

		LE	LE 1	LE	LE 1	LE	LE	LE 1	LE 1		LE	LE 1	LE	LE 1	LE 1	LE 1	LE	LE		LE 1	LE 1	LE	LE 1	LE 1	LE
Southend Victoria	d				19 46			20 06							20 36					21 06					
Prittlewell	d				19 48			20 08							20 38					21 08					
Rochford	d				19 52			20 12							20 42					21 12					
Hockley	d				19 56			20 16							20 46					21 16					
Rayleigh	d				20 00			20 20							20 50					21 20					
Southminster	d													20 17											
Burnham-on-Crouch	d													20 21											
Althorne	d													20 26											
North Fambridge	d													20 34											
South Woodham Ferrers	d													20 39											
Battlesbridge	d													20 43											
Wickford 2	d				20 05			20 25						20 49	20 55					21 25					
Billericay	d				20 11			20 31						20 55	21 01					21 31					
Shenfield 3	a				20 18			20 38						21 02	21 08					21 38					
	d	20 04	20 10	20 14	20 18	20 24	20 34	20 38	20 40		20 44	20 51	20 59		21 08	21 11	21 14	21 29		21 38	21 40	21 44	21 51	21 58	21 59
Brentwood	d	20 07		20 17		20 27	20 37				20 47		21 02				21 17	21 32				21 47			22 02
Harold Wood	d	20 12		20 22		20 32	20 42				20 52		21 07				21 22	21 37				21 52			22 07
Gidea Park 2	d	20 16		20 26		20 36	20 46				20 56		21 11				21 26	21 41				21 56			22 11
Romford	d	20 18		20 28	20 26	20 38	20 48				20 58	20 59	21 13				21 28	21 43				21 58	21 59		22 13
Chadwell Heath	d	20 22		20 32		20 42	20 52				21 02		21 17				21 32	21 47				22 02			22 17
Goodmayes	d	20 24		20 34		20 44	20 54				21 04		21 19				21 34	21 49				22 04			22 19
Seven Kings	d	20 26		20 36		20 46	20 56				21 06		21 21				21 36	21 51				22 06			22 21
Ilford 2	d	20 29		20 39		20 49	20 59				21 09		21 24				21 39	21 54				22 09			22 24
Manor Park	d	20 31		20 41		20 51	21 01				21 11		21 26				21 41	21 56				22 11			22 26
Forest Gate	d	20 33		20 43		20 53	21 03				21 13		21 28				21 43	21 58				22 13			22 28
Maryland	d	20 35		20 45		20 55	21 05				21 15		21 30				21 45	22 00				22 15			22 30
Stratford 7 ⊖	d	20 37	20s24	20 47	20s34	20 57	21 07	20s52	20s55		21 17	21s07	21 32		21s22	21s25	21 47	22 02		21s52	21s54	22 17	22s07	22s12	22 32
London Liverpool Street 15 ⊖	a	20 45	20 33	20 55	20 43	21 05	21 15	21 01	21 03		21 29	21 16	21 44		21 35	21 38	21 59	22 14		22 05	22 07	22 29	22 20	22 25	22 44

For general notes see front of timetable
For details of catering facilities see Directory of Train Operators

Southend Victoria, Southminster and Shenfield → London

Network diagram - see first page of Table 5

Saturdays

		LE 1	LE 1	LE 1	LE	LE	LE 1	LE 1	LE 1	LE	LE 1	LE	LE 1	LE 1	LE	LE	LE 1	LE	LE 1
Southend Victoria	d		21 36				22 06						22 36				23 06		
Prittlewell	d		21 38				22 08						22 38				23 08		
Rochford	d		21 42				22 12						22 42				23 12		
Hockley	d		21 46				22 16						22 46				23 16		
Rayleigh	d		21 50				22 20						22 50				23 20		
Southminster	d	21 17							21 59										23 07
Burnham-on-Crouch	d	21 21							22 03										23 11
Althorne	d	21 26							22 08										23 16
North Fambridge	d	21 34							22 14										23 22
South Woodham Ferrers	d	21 39							22 19										23 27
Battlesbridge	d	21 43							22 23										23 31
Wickford 2	d	21 49	21 55				22 25		22 29				22 55				23 25		23a37
Billericay	d	21 55	22 01				22 31		22 35				23 01				23 31		
Shenfield 3	a	22 02	22 08				22 38		22 42				23 08				23 38		
	d		22 08	22 11	22 14	22 29	22 38	22 40		22 44	22 51	22 59	23 08	23 10	23 14	23 29	23 38	23 44	
Brentwood	d				22 17	22 32				22 47		23 02			23 17	23 32		23 47	
Harold Wood	d				22 22	22 37				22 52		23 07			23 22	23 37		23 52	
Gidea Park 2	d				22 26	22 41				22 56		23 11			23 26	23 41		23 56	
Romford	d				22 28	22 43				22 58	22 59	23 13			23 28	23 43		23 58	
Chadwell Heath	d				22 32	22 47				23 02		23 17			23 32	23 47		00 02	
Goodmayes	d				22 34	22 49				23 04		23 19			23 34	23 49		00 04	
Seven Kings	d				22 36	22 51				23 06		23 21			23 36	23 51		00 06	
Ilford 2	d				22 39	22 54				23 09		23 24			23 39	23 54		00 09	
Manor Park	d				22 41	22 56				23 11		23 26			23 41	23 56		00 11	
Forest Gate	d				22 43	22 58				23 13		23 28			23 43	23 58		00 13	
Maryland	d				22 45	23 00				23 15		23 30			23 45	23 59		00 15	
Stratford 7 ⊖	d		22s22	22s25	22 47	23 02	22s52	22s55		23 17	23s07	23 32	23s22	23s25	23 47	00 02	23s54	00 17	
London Liverpool Street 15 ⊖	a		22 35	22 38	22 59	23 14	23 05	23 07		23 29	23 20	23 44	23 35	23 38	23 59	00 14	00 07	00 29	

Sundays

		LE	LE	LE	LE	LE	LE	LE 1	LE	LE 1	LE	LE 1	LE	LE 1	LE	LE 1	LE	LE 1	LE	LE 1	LE 1
Southend Victoria	d							06 18				06 48				07 18					07 52
Prittlewell	d																				
Rochford	d							06 22				06 52				07 22					07 56
Hockley	d							06 26				06 56				07 26					08 00
Rayleigh	d							06 30				07 00				07 30					08 04
Southminster	d																				
Burnham-on-Crouch	d																				
Althorne	d																				
North Fambridge	d																				
South Woodham Ferrers	d																				
Battlesbridge	d																				
Wickford 2	d							06 35				07 05				07 35					08 09
Billericay	d							06 41				07 11				07 41					08 15
Shenfield 3	a							06 52				07 22				07 52					08 22
	d	23p29		23p44			06 43	06 53		07 07	07 13	07 23		07 37	07 43	07 53		08 07	08 13	08 18	08 23
Brentwood	d	23p32		23p47			06 46	06 56			07 16	07 26			07 46	07 56			08 16		08 26
Harold Wood	d	23p37		23p52			06 51	07 01			07 21	07 31			07 51	08 01			08 21		08 31
Gidea Park 2	d	23p41		23p56	05 55	06 25	06 55	07 05	07 11		07 25	07 35	07 41		07 55	08 05	08 11		08 25		08 35
Romford	d	23p43		23p58	05 57	06 27	06 57	07 07	07 13		07 27	07 37	07 43		07 57	08 07	08 13		08 27		08 37
Chadwell Heath	d	23p47		00 02	06 01	06 31	07 01		07 17		07 31		07 47		08 01		08 17		08 31		
Goodmayes	d	23p49		00 04	06 03	06 33	07 03		07 19		07 33		07 49		08 03		08 19		08 33		
Seven Kings	d	23p51		00 06	06 05	06 35	07 05		07 21		07 35		07 51		08 05		08 21		08 35		
Ilford 2	d	23p54		00 09	06 08	06 38	07 08		07 24		07 38		07 54		08 08		08 24		08 38		
Manor Park	d	23p56		00 11	06 10	06 40	07 10		07 26		07 40		07 56		08 10		08 26		08 40		
Forest Gate	d	23p58		00 13	06 12	06 42	07 12		07 28		07 42		07 58		08 12		08 28		08 42		
Maryland	d	23p59		00 15	06 14	06 44	07 14				07 44				08 14				08 44		
Stratford 7 ⊖	d	00 02	00 05	00 17	06 16	06 46	07 16	07 19	07 31	07s34	07 46	07 49	08 01	08s04	08 16	08 19	08 31	08s34	08 46	08s49	08 49
London Liverpool Street 15 ⊖	a	00 14	00 17	00 29	06 26	06 56	07 24	07 27	07 41	07 42	07 54	07 57	08 11	08 12	08 24	08 27	08 41	08 42	08 54	08 59	08 59

		LE	LE 1	LE	LE 1	LE 1	LE	LE 1	LE	LE 1	LE	LE 1	LE	LE 1	LE 1	LE	LE 1	LE		LE 1
Southend Victoria	d					08 22				08 52					09 22				and at the same minutes past each hour until	20 52
Prittlewell	d																			
Rochford	d					08 26				08 56					09 26					20 56
Hockley	d					08 30				09 00					09 30					21 00
Rayleigh	d					08 34				09 04					09 34					21 04
Southminster	d				08 05									09 05						
Burnham-on-Crouch	d				08 09									09 09						
Althorne	d				08 14									09 14						
North Fambridge	d				08 20									09 20						
South Woodham Ferrers	d				08 25									09 25						
Battlesbridge	d				08 29									09 29						
Wickford 2	d				08a35	08 39				09 09				09a35	09 39					21 09
Billericay	d					08 45				09 15					09 45					21 15
Shenfield 3	a					08 52				09 22					09 52					21 22
	d		08 41	08 43		08 53		09 11	09 13	09 23		09 41	09 43		09 53		10 11	10 13		21 23
Brentwood	d			08 46		08 56			09 16	09 26			09 46		09 56			10 16		21 26
Harold Wood	d			08 51		09 01			09 21	09 31			09 51		10 01			10 21		21 31
Gidea Park 2	d	08 41		08 55		09 05	09 11		09 25	09 35	09 41		09 55		10 05	10 11		10 25		21 35
Romford	d	08 43		08 57		09 07	09 13		09 27	09 37	09 43		09 57		10 07	10 13		10 27		21 37
Chadwell Heath	d	08 47		09 01			09 17		09 31		09 47		10 01			10 17		10 31		
Goodmayes	d	08 49		09 03			09 19		09 33		09 49		10 03			10 19		10 33		
Seven Kings	d	08 51		09 05			09 21		09 35		09 51		10 05			10 21		10 35		
Ilford 2	d	08 54		09 08			09 24		09 38		09 54		10 08			10 24		10 38		
Manor Park	d	08 56		09 10			09 26		09 40		09 56		10 10			10 26		10 40		
Forest Gate	d	08 58		09 12			09 28		09 42		09 58		10 12			10 28		10 42		
Maryland	d			09 14					09 44				10 14					10 44		
Stratford 7 ⊖	d	09 01	09s04	09 16		09 19	09 31	09s34	09 46	09 49	10 01	10s04	10 16		10 19	10 31	10s34	10 46		21 49
London Liverpool Street 15 ⊖	a	09 11	09 12	09 24		09 29	09 41	09 42	09 54	09 59	10 11	10 12	10 24		10 29	10 41	10 42	10 54		21 59

For general notes see front of timetable
For details of catering facilities see Directory of Train Operators

Table 5

Sundays

Southend Victoria, Southminster and Shenfield → London

Network diagram - see first page of Table 5

		LE 1	LE	LE 1	LE 1		LE 1	LE	LE 1	LE 1		LE	LE 1	LE 1	LE 1		LE 1	LE	LE 1	LE 1		LE			
Southend Victoria	d				21 22				21 52					22 22					22 52						
Prittlewell	d																								
Rochford	d				21 26				21 56					22 26					22 56						
Hockley	d				21 30				22 00					22 30					23 00						
Rayleigh	d				21 34				22 04					22 34					23 04						
Southminster	d			21 05									22 05							22 45					
Burnham-on-Crouch	d			21 09									22 09							22 49					
Althorne	d			21 14									22 14							22 54					
North Fambridge	d			21 20									22 20							23 00					
South Woodham Ferrers	d			21 25									22 25							23 05					
Battlesbridge	d			21 29									22 29							23 09					
Wickford 2	d			21a35	21 39				22 09				22a35	22 39					23 09	23 15					
Billericay	d				21 45				22 15					22 45					23 15						
Shenfield 3	a				21 52				22 22					22 52					23 22	23 26					
	d	21 41	21 43		21 53		22 11	22 13	22 23	22 41		22 43		22 53			23 11	23 13	23 23			23 43			
Brentwood	d		21 46		21 56			22 16	22 26			22 46		22 56				23 16	23 26			23 46			
Harold Wood	d		21 51		22 01			22 21	22 31			22 51		23 01				23 21	23 31			23 51			
Gidea Park 2	d		21 55		22 05			22 25	22 35			22 55		23 05				23 25	23 35			23 55			
Romford	d		21 57		22 07			22 27	22 37			22 57		23 07				23 27	23 37			23 57			
Chadwell Heath	d		22 01					22 31				23 01						23 31				00 01			
Goodmayes	d		22 03					22 33				23 03						23 33				00 03			
Seven Kings	d		22 05					22 35				23 05						23 35				00 05			
Ilford 2	d		22 08					22 38				23 08						23 38				00 08			
Manor Park	d		22 10					22 40				23 10						23 40				00 10			
Forest Gate	d		22 12					22 42				23 12						23 42				00 12			
Maryland	d		22 14					22 44				23 14						23 44				00 14			
Stratford 7 ⊖	d	22s04	22 16		22 19		22s34	22 46	22 49	23s04		23 16		23 19	23 23		23s34	23 46	23 49			00 16			
London Liverpool Street 15 ⊖	a	22 12	22 24		22 29		22 42	22 54	22 59	23 12		23 24		23 31	23 38		23 42	23 54	23 59			00 25			

For general notes see front of timetable
For details of catering facilities see
Directory of Train Operators

Table 10

Marks Tey — Sudbury

Mondays to Fridays

Network diagram - see first page of Table 5

Miles			LE	LE	LE	LE		LE	LE	LE	LE		LE	LE	LE	LE		LE	LE	LE	LE	LE	LE		
0	**Colchester** 4	d	05 48	06 29	07 18	08 18		09 17	10 17	11 17	12 17		13 17	14 17	15 17	15 48		16 53	17 49	18 49	19 33	20 15	21 17		
—	London Liverpool Street 15	⊖d		05 25	06 38	07 38		08 38	09 38	10 38	11 38		12 38	13 38	14 38	15 18		16 15	17 08	18 02	18 38	19 38	20 38		
5	Marks Tey 2	d	05 57	06 53	07 40	08 33		09 33	10 33	11 33	12 33		13 33	14 33	15 31	16 17		17 07	18 05	18 59	19 45	20 33	21 33		
8½	Chappel & Wakes Colne	d	06 03	06 59		08 39		09 39	10 39	11 39	12 39		13 39	14 39	15 37	16 23		17 13	18 11	19 05	19 51	20 39	21 39		
11¾	Bures	d	06 09	07 05		08 45		09 45	10 45	11 45	12 45		13 45	14 45	15 43	16 29		17 19	18 17	19 11	19 57	20 45	21 45		
16¾	**Sudbury**	a	06 16	07 12	07 56	08 52		09 52	10 52	11 52	12 52		13 52	14 52	15 52	16 36		17 26	18 24	19 20	20 06	20 52	21 52		

Saturdays

		LE	LE		LE	LE		LE	LE		LE	LE		LE	LE		LE	LE		LE	LE	LE	LE		
Colchester 4	d	06 17	07 17		08 17	09 17		10 17	11 17		12 17	13 17		14 17	15 17		16 17	17 17		18 17	19 17	20 17	21 17		
London Liverpool Street 15	⊖d	05 30	06 38		07 38	08 38		09 38	10 38		11 38	12 38		13 38	14 38		15 38	16 38		17 38	18 38	19 38	20 38		
Marks Tey 2	d	06 33	07 33		08 33	09 33		10 33	11 33		12 33	13 33		14 33	15 33		16 33	17 33		18 33	19 33	20 33	21 33		
Chappel & Wakes Colne	d	06 39	07 39		08 39	09 39		10 39	11 39		12 39	13 39		14 39	15 39		16 39	17 39		18 39	19 39	20 39	21 39		
Bures	d	06 45	07 45		08 45	09 45		10 45	11 45		12 45	13 45		14 45	15 45		16 45	17 45		18 45	19 45	20 45	21 45		
Sudbury	a	06 52	07 52		08 52	09 52		10 52	11 52		12 52	13 52		14 52	15 52		16 52	17 52		18 52	19 52	20 52	21 52		

Sundays

		LE	LE		LE	LE		LE	LE		LE	LE		LE	LE		LE	LE		LE	LE		LE		
Colchester 4	d	07 07	08 06		09 06	10 06		11 06	12 06		13 06	14 06		15 06	16 06		17 06	18 06		19 06	20 06		21 06		
London Liverpool Street 15	⊖d				08 02	09 02		10 02	11 02		12 02	13 02		14 02	15 02		16 02	17 02		18 02	19 02		20 02		
Marks Tey 2	d	07 15	08 15		09 15	10 15		11 15	12 15		13 15	14 15		15 15	16 15		17 15	18 15		19 15	20 15		21 15		
Chappel & Wakes Colne	d	07 21	08 21		09 21	10 21		11 21	12 21		13 21	14 21		15 21	16 21		17 21	18 21		19 21	20 21		21 21		
Bures	d	07 27	08 27		09 27	10 27		11 27	12 27		13 27	14 27		15 27	16 27		17 27	18 27		19 27	20 27		21 27		
Sudbury	a	07 34	08 34		09 34	10 34		11 34	12 34		13 34	14 34		15 34	16 34		17 34	18 34		19 34	20 34		21 34		

Mondays to Fridays

Miles			LE	LE	LE	LE	LE		LE	LE	LE	LE	LE		LE	LE	LE	LE	LE	LE	LE	LE	LE		
0	**Sudbury**	d	05 30	06 30	07 17	08 00	09 00		10 00	11 00	12 00	13 00	14 00		15 00	15 54	16 40	17 31	18 31	19 22	20 08	21 00	22 00		
5	Bures	d	05 37	06 37	07 24	08 07	09 07		10 07	11 07	12 07	13 07	14 07		15 07	16 01		17 38	18 38	19 29	20 15	21 07	22 07		
8¼	Chappel & Wakes Colne	d	05 43	06 43	07 30	08 13	09 13		10 13	11 13	12 13	13 13	14 13		15 13	16 07		17 44	18 44	19 35	20 21	21 13	22 13		
11¾	Marks Tey 2	a	05 49	06 49	07 36	08 19	09 19		10 19	11 19	12 19	13 19	14 19		15 19	16 13	16 56	17 50	18 50	19 41	20 27	21 19	22 19		
—	London Liverpool Street 15	⊖a	06 49	07 51	08 48	09 22	10 17		11 18	12 16	13 16	14 16	15 16		16 18	17 15	17 49	18 49	19 47	20 46	21 33	22 19	23 16		
16¾	**Colchester** 4	a	06 32	07 04	07 56	08 38	09 37		10 37	11 37	12 37	13 37	14 37		15 37	16 41	17 09	18 03	19 03	20 08	20 38	21 38	22 30		

Saturdays

		LE	LE		LE	LE		LE	LE		LE	LE		LE	LE		LE	LE		LE	LE	LE	LE		
Sudbury	d	07 00	08 00		09 00	10 00		11 00	12 00		13 00	14 00		15 00	16 00		17 00	18 00		19 00	20 00	21 00	22 00		
Bures	d	07 07	08 07		09 07	10 07		11 07	12 07		13 07	14 07		15 07	16 07		17 07	18 07		19 07	20 07	21 07	22 07		
Chappel & Wakes Colne	d	07 13	08 13		09 13	10 13		11 13	12 13		13 13	14 13		15 13	16 13		17 13	18 13		19 13	20 13	21 13	22 13		
Marks Tey 2	a	07 19	08 19		09 19	10 19		11 19	12 19		13 19	14 19		15 19	16 19		17 19	18 19		19 19	20 19	21 19	22 19		
London Liverpool Street 15	⊖a	08 16	09 16		10 16	11 16		12 16	13 16		14 16	15 16		16 16	17 16		18 16	19 16		20 16	21 16	22 20	23 20		
Colchester 4	a	07 37	08 37		09 37	10 37		11 37	12 37		13 37	14 37		15 37	16 37		17 37	18 36		19 36	20 37	21 37	22 30		

Sundays

		LE	LE		LE	LE		LE	LE		LE	LE		LE	LE		LE	LE		LE	LE		LE		
Sudbury	d	07 40	08 40		09 40	10 40		11 40	12 40		13 40	14 40		15 40	16 40		17 40	18 40		19 40	20 40		21 40		
Bures	d	07 47	08 47		09 47	10 47		11 47	12 47		13 47	14 47		15 47	16 47		17 47	18 47		19 47	20 47		21 47		
Chappel & Wakes Colne	d	07 53	08 53		09 53	10 53		11 53	12 53		13 53	14 53		15 53	16 53		17 53	18 53		19 53	20 53		21 53		
Marks Tey 2	a	07 59	08 59		09 59	10 59		11 59	12 59		13 59	14 59		15 59	16 59		17 59	18 59		19 59	20 59		21 59		
London Liverpool Street 15	⊖a	09 12	10 12		11 12	12 12		13 12	14 12		15 12	16 12		17 12	18 12		19 12	20 12		21 12	22 12		23 12		
Colchester 4	a		09 12		10 12	11 12		12 12	13 12		14 12	15 12		16 12	17 12		18 12	19 12		20 12	21 12		22 09		

For general notes see front of timetable
For details of catering facilities see Directory of Train Operators

London → Chelmsford, Colchester, Walton-on-Naze, Clacton, Harwich, Ipswich and Norwich

Network diagram - see first page of Table 5

Miles	Miles	Miles	Miles	Miles			LE MX 1 ◇	LE MO 1 ◇	LE MX 1	LE MO 1	LE FO 1	LE MFX 1	LE MX 1 ◇	LE MO 1 ◇	LE MO 1	LE MX 1	LE MO 1	LE MX 1	LE MX 1	LE A	LE 1		LE 1	LE A	LE 1
0	—	—	—	—	**London Liverpool Street 15**	⊖ d	22p30	22p30	23p00	23p02	23p18	23p18	23p30	23p30	23p32	23p48	00 02	00 18	00 48						
4	—	—	—	—	Stratford 7	⊖ ⛴ d	22b38		23p07	23p09	23p25	23p25	23b38		23p39	23p55	00 09	00 25	00 55						
12¼	—	—	—	—	Romford	d																			
20¼	—	—	—	—	Shenfield 3	d		22b57	23p24	23p31	23p42	23p42		23b57	00 01	00 12	00 31	00 47	01 17						
23½	—	—	—	—	Ingatestone	d				23p35	23p46	23p46				00 16	00 35	00 51	01 21						
29¾	—	—	—	—	**Chelmsford 3**	d	23p03		23p33	23p42	23p53	23p53	00 03		00 10	00 23	00 42	00 58	01 28						
36	—	—	—	—	Hatfield Peverel	d				23p49						00 30	00 49	01 05							
38½	0	—	—	—	**Witham 2**	d			23p42	23p54	00 03	00 03			00 19	00 35	00 54	01 10	01 38				05 21		
—	3	—	—	—	White Notley	d																	05 28		
—	4¼	—	—	—	Cressing	d																	05 30		
—	5½	—	—	—	Braintree Freeport	d																	05 33		
—	6¼	—	—	—	**Braintree**	a																	05 37		
42¼	—	—	—	—	Kelvedon	d				23p59						00 40	00 59	01 15							
46¾	—	—	—	—	Marks Tey 2	d				00 04					00 27	00 45	01 04	01 20							
51¾	—	—	—	—	**Colchester 4**	a	23p22	23p23	23p56	00 12	00 17	00 21	00 25	00 27	00 40	00 57	01 18	01 32	02 03						
—	0	0	—	—		d	23p23	23p24	23p57	00 12	00 17		00 27	00 28							05 35				05 43
—	—	2¼	—	—	Colchester Town	a																			
—	—	—	—	—		d																			
—	2¾	3¼	—	—	Hythe	d																			
—	—	5¾	—	—	Wivenhoe 3	d					00 25														
—	—	7½	—	—	Alresford (Essex)	d					00 28														
—	—	9¾	—	—	Great Bentley	d					00 32														
—	—	12½	—	—	Weeley	d																			
—	—	14¾	—	—	Thorpe-le-Soken 1	a					00 37														
—	—	—	0	—		d					00 37														
—	—	—	4¾	—	**Clacton-on-Sea**	a					00 51														
—	—	17¼	—	—	Kirby Cross	d																			
—	—	18½	—	—	Frinton-on-Sea	d																			
—	—	19¾	—	—	**Walton-on-the-Naze**	a																			
59½	—	—	—	0	Manningtree 2	d	23p32	23p33	00 04	00 20			00 36	00 37							05 44				05 51
—	—	—	—	1¾	Mistley	d																			05 55
—	—	—	—	5¾	Wrabness	d																			06 00
—	—	—	—	9½	Harwich International	d																			06 09
—	—	—	—	10¾	Dovercourt	d																			06 12
—	—	—	—	11¼	**Harwich Town**	a																			06 14
68¾	—	—	—	—	**Ipswich**	a	23p42	23p42	00 20	00 36			00 46	00 46							05 55				
—	—	—	—	—		d	23p43	23p44					00 48	00 48						05 10	06 01			06 13	
—	—	—	—	—	**Lowestoft**	a																			
77	—	—	—	—	Needham Market	d														05 20				06 23	
80¾	—	—	—	—	Stowmarket	d	23p54	23p55					00 59	00 59						05a25	06 12			06a28	
—	—	—	—	—	**Peterborough 8**	a															07 37				
95	—	—	—	—	Diss	d	00 07	00 07					01 12	01 11											
115	—	—	—	—	**Norwich**	a	00 39	00 39					01 44	01 43											

For general notes see front of timetable
For details of catering facilities see Directory of Train Operators

A To Cambridge (Table 14)
b Previous night. Stops to pick up only

Due to major track repair work in the Bury St Edmunds area, trains between Ipswich and Peterborough are subject to disruption, resulting in bus replacements and extended journey times for part or all of this timetable. See local publicity or contact National Rail Enquiries 08457 48 49 50 for further details.

London → Chelmsford, Colchester, Walton-on-Naze, Clacton, Harwich, Ipswich and Norwich

Network diagram - see first page of Table 5

		LE	LE	LE	LE	LE	LE	LE	LE	LE	LE	LE	LE	LE	LE		LE	LE	LE	LE	LE	LE	LE	LE	LE
		1	1	1		1	1	1	1	1	1 ◇	1	1	1	1		1 ◇	1	1 ◇	1	1	1 ◇		1	1
					A																		A		
London Liverpool Street 15 ⊖	d							05 25			06 00		06 02	06 12			06 25		06 38	06 48		07 00			
Stratford 7 ⊖	d							05 32					06 09	06 19			06u33			06 55					
Romford	d							05 40					06 17												
Shenfield 3	d							05 51			06u23		06 28	06 37					07u02	07 12		07u23			
Ingatestone	d							05 55						06 41						07 16					
Chelmsford 3	d							06 02					06 37	06 49			06 57		07 12	07 23					←
Hatfield Peverel	d							06 09						06 55						07 30					07 30
Witham 2	d							06 14	06 16				06 46	07 03			07 07		07 21	→					07 36
White Notley	d								06 23					07 10											
Cressing	d								06 25					07 12											
Braintree Freeport	d								06 28					07 15											
Braintree	a								06 32					07 20											
Kelvedon	d							06 19					06 51						07 27						
Marks Tey 2	d							06 24					06 56						07 33						07 47
Colchester 4	a							06 32			06 48		07 04				07 20		07 41			07 49			07 56
	d	05 55	06 22					06 33		06 45	06 50		07 04		07 18		07 22	07 26	07 41		07 48	07 50			
Colchester Town	a									06 52								07 33			07 55				
	d																	07 37							
Hythe	d												07 09					07 41							
Wivenhoe 3	d							06 40					07 13		07 25			07 45							
Alresford (Essex)	d												07 16		07 29			07 48							
Great Bentley	d												07 20		07 33			07 52							
Weeley	d												07 23					07 56							
Thorpe-le-Soken 1	a							06 50					07 27		07 39			08 00							
	d			06 26			06 41	06 50				07 20	07 27		07 39			08 00							
Clacton-on-Sea	a							07 00					07 36					08 09							
Kirby Cross	d			06 30			06b49					07 24			07c46										
Frinton-on-Sea	d			06 33			06 52					07 27			07 49										
Walton-on-the-Naze	a			06 38			06 57					07 32			07 55										
Manningtree 2	d	06 03	06 31			06 36					06 59						07 32		07 50			07 59		07 35	
Mistley	d					06 40																		07 39	
Wrabness	d					06 45																		07 44	
Harwich International	d					06 52																	07 47	07 51	
Dovercourt	d					06 55																		07 54	
Harwich Town	a					06 57																		07 56	
Ipswich	a	06 17	06 41								07 08						07 41		07 59			08 08	08 15		
	d		06 42		06 52						07 09						07 42		08 03			08 09	08 16		
Lowestoft	a																								
Needham Market	d				07 02																		08 26		
Stowmarket	d		06 53		07a07						07 20						07 53		08 14			08 20	08a31		
Peterborough 8	a																		09 41						
Diss	d		07 05								07 32						08 05					08 32			
Norwich	a		07 27								07 54						08 27					08 54			

For general notes see front of timetable
For details of catering facilities see Directory of Train Operators

A To Cambridge (Table 14)
b Arr. 0645
c Arr. 0743

Due to major track repair work in the Bury St Edmunds area, trains between Ipswich and Peterborough are subject to disruption, resulting in bus replacements and extended journey times for part or all of this timetable. See local publicity or contact National Rail Enquiries 08457 48 49 50 for further details.

London → Chelmsford, Colchester, Walton-on-Naze, Clacton, Harwich, Ipswich and Norwich

Network diagram - see first page of Table 5

		LE 1	LE 1	LE 1	LE 1	LE 1 ◇	LE 1	LE 1	LE 1 ◇	LE 1	LE 1	LE 1 ◇	LE	LE 1		LE 1	LE 1	LE 1	LE 1 ◇	LE 1	LE 1	LE 1	LE 1	LE 1
						☕						☕	A						✕					
London Liverpool Street 15 ⊖	d	07 04	07 08	07 18	07 27	07 30			07 38	07 48		08 00		08 02		08 08		08 18	08 30			08 38	08 48	
Stratford 7 ⊖	d	07 11	07 15	07 25		07u38				07 55						08 15		08 25	08u38				08 55	
Romford	d		07 23											08 16										
Shenfield 3	d	07 28	07 34	07 42	07 51				08u02	08 12		08u23		08 26		08 32		08 42				09 02	09 12	
Ingatestone	d			07 46						08 16						08 36		08 46					09 16	
Chelmsford 3	d	07 37	07 43	07 53	08 00	08 04			08 12	08 23				08 35		08 43		08 53	09 02			09 12	09 23	
Hatfield Peverel	d							⟵		08 30													09 30	
Witham 2	d	07 47	07 52	08 03	08b12			08 12	08 22	08c38				08 44		08 52		09 03				09 21	09 37	
White Notley	d	07 54			⟶					08 44													09 43	
Cressing	d	07 56								08 47													09 46	
Braintree Freeport	d	07 59								08 49													09 48	
Braintree	a	08 04								08 54													09 53	
Kelvedon	d			08 07				08 19										09 07						
Marks Tey 2	d			08 13					08 30									09 13				09 29		
Colchester 4	a		08 06	08 20		08 23		08 30	08 38			08 49		08 58		09 06		09 20	09 23			09 37		
	d		08 06	08 21		08 24		08 31	08 38		08 46	08 50		09 02	09 04	09 07	09 14		09 24		09 30	09 38		
Colchester Town	a							08 38			08 53			09 09							09 37			
	d										08 57													
Hythe	d		08 11								09 00													
Wivenhoe 3	d		08 15								09 04					09 14								
Alresford (Essex)	d		08 18								09 08													
Great Bentley	d		08 22								09 12													
Weeley	d										09 16													
Thorpe-le-Soken 1	a		08 27								09 19					09 24				⟵				
	d		08 27				08 29				09 26					09 24				09 26				
Clacton-on-Sea	a		08 37								⟶					09 34								
Kirby Cross	d						08 33													09 30				
Frinton-on-Sea	d						08 36													09 33				
Walton-on-the-Naze	a						08 41													09 39				
Manningtree 2	d			08 29		08 34						08 59			09 12		09 22		09 34			09 46		
Mistley	d			08 33													09 26							
Wrabness	d			08 38													09 31							
Harwich International	d			08 46													09 39							
Dovercourt	d			08 49													09 42							
Harwich Town	a			08 51													09 44							
Ipswich	a					08 43			08 56			09 08			09 23				09 43			09 58		
	d					08 44			09 02			09 09	09 16						09 44					10 03
Lowestoft	a								10 32															
Needham Market	d												09 26											
Stowmarket	d					08 55							09a31						09 55					10 14
Peterborough 8	a																							11 38
Diss	d					09 07						09 30							10 07					
Norwich	a					09 27						09 52							10 27					

For general notes see front of timetable
For details of catering facilities see Directory of Train Operators

A To Cambridge (Table 14)
b Arr. 0809
c Arr. 0835

Due to major track repair work in the Bury St Edmunds area, trains between Ipswich and Peterborough are subject to disruption, resulting in bus replacements and extended journey times for part or all of this timetable. See local publicity or contact National Rail Enquiries 08457 48 49 50 for further details.

Table 11

Mondays to Fridays

London → Chelmsford, Colchester, Walton-on-Naze, Clacton, Harwich, Ipswich and Norwich

Network diagram - see first page of Table 5

		LE	LE		LE	LE	LE	LE	LE	LE	LE	LE	LE	LE	LE	LE	LE	LE	LE		LE	LE	LE	LE	LE
		1	1 ◇		1		1	1	1 ◇	1	1	1 ◇	1	1	1 ◇	1		1	1		1 ◇	1	1	1 ◇	1
						A											A								
			✕						✕						✕						✕				
London Liverpool Street 15 ⊖	d		09 00				09 08	09 18	09 30			09 38	09 48		10 00			10 08	10 18		10 30			10 38	10 48
Stratford 7 ⊖	d						09 15	09 25	09u38				09 55					10 15	10 25		10u38				10 55
Romford	d						09 23											10 23							
Shenfield 3	d		09u23				09 34	09 42				10u02	10 12		10u23			10 34	10 42					11u02	11 12
Ingatestone	d												10 16												11 16
Chelmsford 3	d						09 43	09 51	10 02			10 12	10 23					10 43	10 51		11 02			11 12	11 23
Hatfield Peverel	d												10 30												11 30
Witham 2	d						09 52	10 00				10 21	10 36					10 52	11 00					11 21	11 36
White Notley	d												10 43												11 43
Cressing	d												10 45												11 45
Braintree Freeport	d												10 48												11 48
Braintree	a												10 53												11 53
Kelvedon	d							10 05											11 05						
Marks Tey 2	d							10 10				10 29							11 10					11 29	
Colchester 4	a		09 49				10 06	10 18	10 21			10 37			10 49			11 06	11 18		11 21			11 37	
	d	09 46	09 50		10 00		10 07	10 21	10 24		10 30	10 38		10 46	10 50	11 00		11 07	11 18		11 22		11 30	11 38	
Colchester Town	a	09 53			10 07						10 37			10 53		11 07							11 37		
	d	09 57												10 57											
Hythe	d	10 00												11 00											
Wivenhoe 3	d	10 04					10 14							11 04				11 14							
Alresford (Essex)	d	10 08												11 08											
Great Bentley	d	10 12												11 12											
Weeley	d	10 16												11 16											
Thorpe-le-Soken 1	a	10 19					10 24			←				11 19				11 24				←			
	d	10 26					10 24			10 26				11 26				11 24				11 26			
Clacton-on-Sea	a	→					10 34							→				11 34							
Kirby Cross	d									10 30												11 30			
Frinton-on-Sea	d									10 33												11 33			
Walton-on-the-Naze	a									10 39												11 39			
Manningtree 2	d		09 59					10 29	10 34						10 59				11 26		11 31				
Mistley	d							10 33											11 30						
Wrabness	d							10 38											11 35						
Harwich International	d							10 47											11 44						
Dovercourt	d							10 50											11 47						
Harwich Town	a							10 52											11 49						
Ipswich	a		10 08						10 43			10 56			11 08						11 41			11 56	
	d		10 09			10 16			10 44			11 02			11 09		11 16				11 42			12 03	
Lowestoft	a											12 32													
Needham Market	d					10 26											11 26								
Stowmarket	d					10a31			10 55								11a31				11 53			12 14	
Peterborough 8	a																							13 38	
Diss	d		10 30						11 07						11 30						12 05				
Norwich	a		10 52						11 27						11 52						12 27				

For general notes see front of timetable
For details of catering facilities see Directory of Train Operators

A To Cambridge (Table 14)

Due to major track repair work in the Bury St Edmunds area, trains between Ipswich and Peterborough are subject to disruption, resulting in bus replacements and extended journey times for part or all of this timetable. See local publicity or contact National Rail Enquiries 08457 48 49 50 for further details.

London → Chelmsford, Colchester, Walton-on-Naze, Clacton, Harwich, Ipswich and Norwich

Network diagram - see first page of Table 5

		LE [1]	LE [1] ◇ ☕	LE [1]	LE A	LE [1]	LE [1]	LE [1] ◇ ☕	LE [1]	LE [1]	LE [1] ◇	LE [1]	LE [1]		LE [1] ◇ ☕	LE [1]	LE A	LE [1]	LE [1]	LE [1] ◇ ☕	LE [1]	LE [1]	LE [1] ◇	LE [1]	LE [1]
London Liverpool Street [15] ⊖	d		11 00			11 08	11 18	11 30			11 38	11 48			12 00			12 08	12 18	12 30			12 38	12 48	
Stratford [7] ⊖	d					11 15	11 25	11u38				11 55						12 15	12 25	12u38				12 55	
Romford	d					11 23												12 23							
Shenfield [3]	d		11u23			11 34	11 42				12u02	12 12			12u23			12 34	12 42				13u02	13 12	
Ingatestone	d											12 16												13 16	
Chelmsford [3]	d					11 43	11 51	12 02			12 12	12 23						12 43	12 51	13 02			13 12	13 23	
Hatfield Peverel	d											12 30												13 30	
Witham [2]	d					11 52	12 00				12 21	12 36						12 52	13 00				13 21	13 36	
White Notley	d											12 43												13 43	
Cressing	d											12 45												13 45	
Braintree Freeport	d											12 48												13 48	
Braintree	a											12 53												13 53	
Kelvedon	d						12 05												13 05						
Marks Tey [2]	d						12 10				12 29								13 10				13 29		
Colchester [4]	a		11 49			12 06	12 18	12 21			12 37				12 49			13 06	13 18	13 21			13 37		
	d	11 46	11 50	12 00		12 07	12 18	12 22		12 30	12 38		12 46		12 50	13 00		13 07	13 18	13 22		13 30	13 38		13 46
Colchester Town	a	11 53		12 07						12 37			12 53			13 07						13 37			13 53
	d	11 57											12 57												13 57
Hythe	d	12 00											13 00												14 00
Wivenhoe [3]	d	12 04				12 14							13 04					13 14							14 04
Alresford (Essex)	d	12 08											13 08												14 08
Great Bentley	d	12 12											13 12												14 12
Weeley	d	12 16											13 16												14 16
Thorpe-le-Soken [1]	a	12 19				12 24				←			13 19					13 24			←				14 19
	d	12 26 →				12 24				12 26			13 26 →					13 24			13 26				14 26 →
Clacton-on-Sea	a					12 34												13 34							
Kirby Cross	d									12 30											13 30				
Frinton-on-Sea	d									12 33											13 33				
Walton-on-the-Naze	a									12 39											13 39				
Manningtree [2]	d		11 59				12 26	12 31							12 59				13 26	13 31					
Mistley	d						12 30												13 30						
Wrabness	d						12 35												13 35						
Harwich International	d						12 44												13 44						
Dovercourt	d						12 47												13 47						
Harwich Town	a						12 49												13 49						
Ipswich	a		12 08					12 41			12 56				13 08					13 41			13 56		
	d		12 09		12 16			12 42			13 02				13 09		13 16			13 42			14 03		
Lowestoft	a										14 32														
Needham Market	d				12 26												13 26								
Stowmarket	d				12a31			12 53									13a31			13 53			14 14		
Peterborough [8]	a																						15 39		
Diss	d		12 30					13 05							13 30					14 05					
Norwich	a		12 52					13 27							13 52					14 27					

For general notes see front of timetable
For details of catering facilities see Directory of Train Operators

A To Cambridge (Table 14)

Due to major track repair work in the Bury St Edmunds area, trains between Ipswich and Peterborough are subject to disruption, resulting in bus replacements and extended journey times for part or all of this timetable. See local publicity or contact National Rail Enquiries 08457 48 49 50 for further details.

London → Chelmsford, Colchester, Walton-on-Naze, Clacton, Harwich, Ipswich and Norwich

Network diagram - see first page of Table 5

		LE 1 ◇	LE 1	LE	LE 1	LE 1	LE 1 ◇		LE 1	LE 1	LE 1 ◇	LE 1	LE 1	LE 1 ◇	LE 1	LE	LE 1	LE 1	LE 1 ◇	LE 1	LE 1	LE 1 ◇	LE 1		LE 1
				A												A									
		☕					✕							☕					✕						
London Liverpool Street 15 ⊖	d	13 00			13 08	13 18	13 30				13 38	13 48		14 00			14 08	14 18	14 30			14 38	14 48		
Stratford 7 ⊖	d				13 15	13 25	13u38					13 55					14 15	14 25	14u38				14 55		
Romford	d				13 23												14 23								
Shenfield 3	d	13u23			13 34	13 42					14u02	14 12		14u23			14 34	14 42				15u02	15 12		
Ingatestone	d											14 16											15 16		
Chelmsford 3	d				13 43	13 51	14 02				14 12	14 23					14 43	14 51	15 02			15 12	15 23		
Hatfield Peverel	d											14 30											15 30		
Witham 2	d				13 52	14 00					14 21	14 36					14 52	15 00				15 21	15 36		
White Notley	d											14 43											15 43		
Cressing	d											14 45											15 45		
Braintree Freeport	d											14 48											15 48		
Braintree	a											14 53											15 53		
Kelvedon	d					14 05												15 05							
Marks Tey 2	d					14 10					14 29							15 10				15 29			
Colchester 4	a	13 49			14 06	14 18	14 21				14 37			14 49			15 06	15 18	15 21			15 37			
	d	13 50	14 00		14 07	14 18	14 22			14 30	14 38		14 46	14 50	15 00		15 07	15 18	15 22		15 30	15 38			15 46
Colchester Town	a		14 07							14 37			14 53		15 07						15 37				15 53
	d												14 57												15 57
Hythe	d												15 00												16 00
Wivenhoe 3	d				14 14								15 04				15 14								16 04
Alresford (Essex)	d												15 08												16 08
Great Bentley	d												15 12												16 12
Weeley	d												15 16												16 16
Thorpe-le-Soken 1	a				14 24				←				15 19				15 24			←					16 19
	d				14 24				14 26				15 26 →				15 24			15 26					16 26 →
Clacton-on-Sea	a				14 34												15 34								
Kirby Cross	d								14 30											15 30					
Frinton-on-Sea	d								14 33											15 33					
Walton-on-the-Naze	a								14 39											15 39					
Manningtree 2	d	13 59				14 26	14 31							14 59				15 26	15 31						
Mistley	d					14 30												15 30							
Wrabness	d					14 35												15 35							
Harwich International	d					14 44												15 44							
Dovercourt	d					14 47												15 47							
Harwich Town	a					14 49												15 49							
Ipswich	a	14 08					14 41				14 56			15 08					15 41			15 56			
	d	14 09		14 16			14 42				15 02			15 09		15 16			15 42			16 03			
Lowestoft	a										16 32														
Needham Market	d			14 26												15 26									
Stowmarket	d			14a31			14 53									15a31			15 53			16 14			
Peterborough 8	a																					17 38			
Diss	d	14 30					15 05							15 30					16 05						
Norwich	a	14 52					15 27							15 52					16 27						

For general notes see front of timetable
For details of catering facilities see Directory of Train Operators

A To Cambridge (Table 14)

Due to major track repair work in the Bury St Edmunds area, trains between Ipswich and Peterborough are subject to disruption, resulting in bus replacements and extended journey times for part or all of this timetable. See local publicity or contact National Rail Enquiries 08457 48 49 50 for further details.

London → Chelmsford, Colchester, Walton-on-Naze, Clacton, Harwich, Ipswich and Norwich

Network diagram - see first page of Table 5

		LE	LE	LE	LE	LE	LE	LE	LE	LE	LE	LE	LE	LE	LE	LE		LE	LE	LE	LE	LE	LE	LE	
							R				R		R							R			R		
		1 ◇	1		1	1	1	1	1	1	1	1	1	1	1	1		1		1	1	1	1	1	
				A															A						
		☕					✕						☕							☕					
London Liverpool Street 15 ⊖	d	15 00			15 08	15 18	15 30		15 32		15 38	15 48	16 00		16 02	16 15		16 17		16 30			16 32	16 36	
Stratford 7 ⊖	d				15 15	15 25						15 55			16 10			16 25							
Romford	d				15 23																				
Shenfield 3	d	15u23			15 34	15 42			15 55		16u02	16 12			16 25			16 40					16u54	16 57	
Ingatestone	d								15 59			16 16						16 44							
Chelmsford 3	d				15 43	15 51	15 59		16 06		16u12	16 23	16 30		16 36	16 45		16 53						17 08	
Hatfield Peverel	d								16 13			16 30												17 15	
Witham 2	d				15 52	16 00			16 19		16 23	16 36			16 45			17a06					17 13	17 21	
White Notley	d											16 43												17 28	
Cressing	d											16 45												17 30	
Braintree Freeport	d											16 48												17 33	
Braintree	a											16 53												17 40	
Kelvedon	d					16 05			16 24						16 50	16 56									
Marks Tey 2	d					16 10					16 32					17 01									
Colchester 4	a	15 49			16 06	16 18	16 21		16 37		16 41		16 49		17 01	17 09				17 17			17 26		
	d	15 50	16 00		16 07	16 18	16 22			16 41	16 41		16 50	16 54	17 02	17 13				17 18		17 24	17 26		
Colchester Town	a		16 07							16 48				17 01								17 31			
	d									16 52												17 35			
Hythe	d									16 55												17 38			
Wivenhoe 3	d				16 14					16 59					17 09							17 42			
Alresford (Essex)	d									17 03												17 46			
Great Bentley	d									17 07												17 50			
Weeley	d									17 11												17 54			
Thorpe-le-Soken 1	a				16 24			←		17 14					17 19						←	17 57			
	d				16 24			16 26		17 21 →					17 19						17 21	18 03 →			
Clacton-on-Sea	a				16 34										17 31										
Kirby Cross	d							16 30													17 25				
Frinton-on-Sea	d							16 33													17 28				
Walton-on-the-Naze	a							16 39													17 34				
Manningtree 2	d	15 59				16 26	16 31						16 59			17 21							17 35		
Mistley	d					16 30										17 25									
Wrabness	d					16 35										17 30									
Harwich International	d					16 44										17 38									
Dovercourt	d					16 47										17 41									
Harwich Town	a					16 49										17 45									
Ipswich	a	16 08					16 41				16 58		17 08							17 33			17 47		
	d	16 09		16 16			16 42				17 02		17 09						17 16	17 34			17 49		
Lowestoft	a										18 33														
Needham Market	d			16 26															17 26				17 58		
Stowmarket	d			16a31			16 53						17 20						17a31	17 45			18 03		
Peterborough 6	a																						19 44		
Diss	d	16 30					17 05						17 32							17 57					
Norwich	a	16 52					17 27						17 55							18 20					

For general notes see front of timetable
For details of catering facilities see Directory of Train Operators

A To Cambridge (Table 14)

Due to major track repair work in the Bury St Edmunds area, trains between Ipswich and Peterborough are subject to disruption, resulting in bus replacements and extended journey times for part or all of this timetable. See local publicity or contact National Rail Enquiries 08457 48 49 50 for further details.

London → Chelmsford, Colchester, Walton-on-Naze, Clacton, Harwich, Ipswich and Norwich

Network diagram - see first page of Table 5

Station		LE		LE	LE	LE	LE	LE	LE	LE	LE	LE	LE	LE	LE	LE	LE	LE	LE	LE	LE	LE	LE	LE
					R											R						R		
		1		1	1	1	1	1	1		1	1	1	1	1	1	1	1	1	1	1	1	1	1
										A														
					☕											☕						☕		
London Liverpool Street 15 ⊖	d	16 45		16 47	17 00				17 02		17 08	17 12	17 20	17 22		17 30	17 32		17 38	17 42		17 50		
Stratford 7 ⊖	d			16 55							17 16	17 20							17 46	17 50				
Romford	d																							
Shenfield 3	d			17 10					17 24					17 44			17 54							
Ingatestone	d			17 14										17 48										
Chelmsford 3	d	17 15		17 23					17 35			17 44	17 51	17 58			18 05			18 14				
Hatfield Peverel	d											17 51								18 21				
Witham 2	d			17a36					17 45		17 50	17a59		18 09			18 15		18 20	→				
White Notley	d													18 16										
Cressing	d													18 18										
Braintree Freeport	d													18 21										
Braintree	a													18 28										
Kelvedon	d	17 26							17 50		17 54						18 20		18 24					
Marks Tey 2	d	17 31							17 55		18 00								18 30					
Colchester 4	a	17 39							18 03		18 08		18 11				18 31		18 38			18 42		
	d	17 43	17 47				17 49	17 51	18 03		18 08		18 11				18 34		18 38		18 42	18 43		
Colchester Town	a						17 56										18 42							←
	d						18 00										18 48							18 48
Hythe	d						18 03										→							18 51
Wivenhoe 3	d	17 50					18 07				18 16								18 46		18 50			18 55
Alresford (Essex)	d						18 11				18 19										18 53			18 59
Great Bentley	d						18 15				18 23										18 57			19 03
Weeley	d						18 19																	19 07
Thorpe-le-Soken 1	a	18 01				←	18 22				18 28							←	18 56		19 02			19 11
	d	18 01				18 03	18 30				18 28							18 30	18 56		19 03			19 11
Clacton-on-Sea	a	18 12					→				18 40								19 07					19 22
Kirby Cross	d					18 07												18 34			19 07			
Frinton-on-Sea	d					18 10												18 37			19 10			
Walton-on-the-Naze	a					18 16												18 43			19 15			
Manningtree 2	d		17 55					17 59	18 11				18 19		18 23	18 27						18 52	18 57	
Mistley	d		17 59												18 27								19 01	
Wrabness	d		18 04												18 32								19 06	
Harwich International	d		18 12						18a29						18 39								19 13	
Dovercourt	d		18 15												18 42								19 16	
Harwich Town	a		18 19												18 44								19 18	
Ipswich	a				17 58			18 10					18 33			18 36						19 01		
	d				17 59					18 16						18 37						19 03		
Lowestoft	a																							
Needham Market	d									18 26														
Stowmarket	d									18a31						18 48								
Peterborough 8	a																							
Diss	d															19 00								
Norwich	a				18 39											19 23						19 44		

For general notes see front of timetable
For details of catering facilities see Directory of Train Operators

A To Cambridge (Table 14)

Due to major track repair work in the Bury St Edmunds area, trains between Ipswich and Peterborough are subject to disruption, resulting in bus replacements and extended journey times for part or all of this timetable. See local publicity or contact National Rail Enquiries 08457 48 49 50 for further details.

London → Chelmsford, Colchester, Walton-on-Naze, Clacton, Harwich, Ipswich and Norwich

Network diagram - see first page of Table 5

		LE	LE	LE	LE	LE	LE	LE	LE	LE	LE	LE	LE	LE	LE	LE	LE	LE	LE	LE	LE	LE	LE
				R						R		R									R		
		1	1	1	1	1	1	1	1	1	1	1	1	1	1	1	1	1	1	1	1	1	1
						A																	
				☕						✕		☕									☕		
London Liverpool Street 15 ⊖	d		17 52	18 00			18 02	18 08	18 12	18 20	18 22	18 30				18 32	18 38			18 48	19 00	19 02	
Stratford 7 ⊖	d						18 10	18 16	18 20							18 40	18 46					19 09	
Romford	d																						
Shenfield 3	d		18 14								18 44						19 01			19 11		19 26	
Ingatestone	d		18 18								18 48									19 15			
Chelmsford 3	d	←	18 28				18 35	18 40	18 44		18 58					19 05	19 13			19 24		19 35	
Hatfield Peverel	d	18 21							18 51						←	19 12						19 41	
Witham 2	d	18b30	18a41				18 45	18 50	18 57		19c11				19 11	19 18	19 23			19 34		19 47	
White Notley	d								19 04		→											19 54	
Cressing	d								19 06													19 56	
Braintree Freeport	d								19 09													19 59	
Braintree	a								19 16													20 04	
Kelvedon	d	18 36					18 50	18 54							19 17	19 23	19 27						
Marks Tey 2	d						18 55	19 00							19 23		19 33						
Colchester 4	a	18 48		18 51			19 03	19 08		19 11		19 22			19 31	19 34	19 41			19 50	19 51		
	d	18 52		18 53	18 56		19 03	19 08		19 12		19 23			19 31	19 34	19 41		19 46		19 53		
Colchester Town	a				19 03														19 53				
	d																		19 57				
Hythe	d														19 36				20 00				
Wivenhoe 3	d	18 59						19 16							19 40		19 49		20 04				
Alresford (Essex)	d	19 03													19 43				20 08				
Great Bentley	d	19 07													19 47				20 12				
Weeley	d														19 50				20 16				
Thorpe-le-Soken 1	a	19 15						19 26							19 54		19 59		20 19				
	d	19 15						19 26						19 28	19 54		19 59	20 03	20 28				
Clacton-on-Sea	a	19 26						19 37							20 05		20 10		→				
Kirby Cross	d													19 32				20 07					
Frinton-on-Sea	d													19 35				20 10					
Walton-on-the-Naze	a													19 40				20 15					
Manningtree 2	d			19 02			19 11			19 21			19 27			19 42					20 02		
Mistley	d												19 31										
Wrabness	d												19 36										
Harwich International	d												19 43										
Dovercourt	d												19 46										
Harwich Town	a												19 48										
Ipswich	a			19 11			19 24			19 30		19 39				19 56					20 11		
	d			19 12		19 16				19 32		19 40									20 12		20 16
Lowestoft	a																						
Needham Market	d					19 26																	20 25
Stowmarket	d			19 23		19a31						19 51									20 23		20 30
Peterborough 8	a																						21 58
Diss	d			19 35								20 03									20 35		
Norwich	a			19 58						20 14		20 26									20 57		

For general notes see front of timetable
For details of catering facilities see Directory of Train Operators

A To Cambridge (Table 14)
b Arr. 1826
c Arr. 1907

Due to major track repair work in the Bury St Edmunds area, trains between Ipswich and Peterborough are subject to disruption, resulting in bus replacements and extended journey times for part or all of this timetable. See local publicity or contact National Rail Enquiries 08457 48 49 50 for further details.

London → Chelmsford, Colchester, Walton-on-Naze, Clacton, Harwich, Ipswich and Norwich

Network diagram - see first page of Table 5

Station																									
		LE	LE	LE	LE	LE	LE	LE	LE	LE	LE	LE	LE	LE		LE	LE	LE	LE	LE	LE	LE	LE	LE	LE
					R	R																			
		1	1	1	1	1	1	1	1	1	1 ◇		1	1			1	1 ◇	1	1		1	1 ◇		1
					✕						☕	A						✕						B	
London Liverpool Street 15 ⊖	d		19 08	19 18	19 30	19 32		19 38	19 48		20 00		20 08				20 18	20 30	20 38	20 48			21 00		21 08
Stratford 7 ⊖ ⛴	d		19 15	19 25				19 45	19 55				20 15				20 25	20u38	20 45	20 55					21 15
Romford	d																								21 23
Shenfield 3	d			19 42		19u55		20 02	20 12				20 32				20 42		21 02	21 12			21u23		21 34
Ingatestone	d			19 46					20 16								20 46			21 16					
Chelmsford 3	d		19 39	19 53	20 00			20 11	20 23				20 41				20 53	21 03	21 11	21 23					21 43
Hatfield Peverel	d								20 30											21 30					
Witham 2	d		19 50	20 03		20 12		20 20	20 36				20 50				21 03		21 20	21 36					21 52
White Notley	d								20 43											21 43					
Cressing	d								20 45											21 45					
Braintree Freeport	d								20 48											21 48					
Braintree	a								20 53											21 53					
Kelvedon	d		19 54					20 25					20 55						21 25						
Marks Tey 2	d		20 00					20 30					21 00						21 30						
Colchester 4	a		20 08	20 16	20 20	20 25		20 38			20 49		21 08				21 16	21 22	21 38				21 49		22 06
	d		20 08	20 17	20 21	20 26		20 38		20 46	20 50		21 09				21 17	21 23	21 38			21 46	21 50		22 07
Colchester Town	a									20 53												21 53			
	d									20 57												21 57			
Hythe	d									21 00												22 00			
Wivenhoe 3	d		20 16							21 04			21 16									22 04			22 14
Alresford (Essex)	d									21 08												22 08			
Great Bentley	d									21 12												22 12			
Weeley	d									21 16												22 16			
Thorpe-le-Soken 1	a		20 26				←			21 19			21 26	←								22 19			22 24
	d		20 26				20 28			21 28			21 26	21 28								22 26			22 24
Clacton-on-Sea	a		20 35							→			21 36									→			22 34
Kirby Cross	d						20 32							21 32											
Frinton-on-Sea	d						20 35							21 35											
Walton-on-the-Naze	a						20 41							21 41											
Manningtree 2	d	20 07		20 25	20 30						20 59						21 25	21 32	21 46				21 58		
Mistley	d	20 11		20 29													21 29								
Wrabness	d	20 16		20 34													21 34				←				
Harwich International	d	20 23		20 42												21 34	21 42		22a02		21 34				
Dovercourt	d	20 26		20 45												→	21 45								
Harwich Town	a	20 28		20 47													21 47								
Ipswich	a				20 40	20 44		20 57			21 08							21 42			22 00		22 07		
	d				20 41	20 52					21 09	21 16						21 43					22 15	22 16	
Lowestoft	a					22 22																	23 45		
Needham Market	d											21 26												22 26	
Stowmarket	d				20 52						21 20	21a31						21 54						22a31	
Peterborough 8	a																								
Diss	d				21 04						21 32							22 06							
Norwich	a				21 26						21 54							22 28							

For general notes see front of timetable
For details of catering facilities see Directory of Train Operators

A To Cambridge (Table 14)
B To Bury St Edmunds (Table 14)

Due to major track repair work in the Bury St Edmunds area, trains between Ipswich and Peterborough are subject to disruption, resulting in bus replacements and extended journey times for part or all of this timetable. See local publicity or contact National Rail Enquiries 08457 48 49 50 for further details.

London → Chelmsford, Colchester, Walton-on-Naze, Clacton, Harwich, Ipswich and Norwich

Network diagram - see first page of Table 5

		LE	LE	LE	LE	LE	LE	LE	LE	LE	LE	LE	LE	LE	LE	LE	LE	LE	LE	LE	LE	LE
																		ThFO	ThFX		
		1	1 ◇	1	1	1		1	1	1	1	1	1 ◇	1	1	1	1	1	1	1	1 ◇	1
							A															
			☕										☕								☕	
London Liverpool Street 15 ⊖	d	21 18	21 30					21 38	21 48	22 00		22 18	22 30		22 48	23 00			23 18	23 18	23 30	23 48
Stratford 7 ⊖	d	21 25	21u38						21 55			22 25	22u38		22 55	23 07			23 25	23 25	23u38	23 55
Romford	d																					
Shenfield 3	d	21 42						22u02	22 12	22 22		22 42			23 12	23 24			23 42	23 42		00 12
Ingatestone	d								22 16						23 16				23 46	23 46		00 16
Chelmsford 3	d	21 51	22 03					22u12	22 23	22 31		22 51	23 03		23 23	23 33			23 53	23 53	00 03	00 23
Hatfield Peverel	d								22 30						23 30							00 30
Witham 2	d	22 00						22 21	22 36	22 40		23 00			23 35	23 42		23 44	00 03	00 03		00 35
White Notley	d								22 43									23 50				
Cressing	d								22 45									23 53				
Braintree Freeport	d								22 48									23 55				
Braintree	a								22 53								←	23 59				
Kelvedon	d	22 05										23 05			23 40		23 40					00 40
Marks Tey 2	d	22 10					22 21	22 29				23 10			→		23 45					00 45
Colchester 4	a	22 18	22 22			←	22 30	22 37		22 54		23 18	23 22			23 56	23 57		00 17	00 21	00 25	00 57
	d	22 26	22 23			22 26		22 38		22 54	22 58	23 19	23 23			23 57			00 17		00 27	
Colchester Town	a	→									23 05											
	d										23 09											
Hythe	d										23 12											
Wivenhoe 3	d					22 33					23 16	23 26							00 25			
Alresford (Essex)	d					22 36					23 20	23 29							00 28			
Great Bentley	d					22 40					23 24	23 33							00 32			
Weeley	d										23 28											
Thorpe-le-Soken 1	a				←	22 46					23 31	23 39							00 37			
	d				22 26	22 46					23 31	23 39							00 37			
Clacton-on-Sea	a										23 41	23 48							00 51			
Kirby Cross	d				22 30	22 51																
Frinton-on-Sea	d				22 33	22 54																
Walton-on-the-Naze	a				22 39	23 00																
Manningtree 2	d		22 32	22 38						23 02			23 32	23 38		00 04					00 36	
Mistley	d			22 42										23 42								
Wrabness	d			22 47										23 47								
Harwich International	d			22 54										23 54								
Dovercourt	d			22 57										23 57								
Harwich Town	a			22 59										23 59								
Ipswich	a		22 42					22 56		23 14			23 42			00 20					00 46	
	d		22 43										23 43								00 48	
Lowestoft	a																					
Needham Market	d																					
Stowmarket	d		22 54										23 54								00 59	
Peterborough 8	a																					
Diss	d		23 06										00 07								01 12	
Norwich	a		23 28										00 39								01 44	

For general notes see front of timetable
For details of catering facilities see Directory of Train Operators

A From Sudbury (Table 10)

Due to major track repair work in the Bury St Edmunds area, trains between Ipswich and Peterborough are subject to disruption, resulting in bus replacements and extended journey times for part or all of this timetable. See local publicity or contact National Rail Enquiries 08457 48 49 50 for further details.

Table 11

London → Chelmsford, Colchester, Walton-on-Naze, Clacton, Harwich, Ipswich and Norwich

Network diagram - see first page of Table 5

Station		LE 1 ◇	LE 1	LE 1	LE 1 ◇	LE 1	LE 1	LE 1	LE	LE 1	LE 1	LE 1	LE	LE 1		LE 1	LE 1	LE 1	LE 1	LE	LE 1	LE 1	LE 1	LE 1 ◇	LE 1
		☕			☕				A				A							A					
London Liverpool Street 15	⊖ d	22p30	23p00	23p18	23p30	23p48	00 18	00 48									05 30					06 00	06 18	06 30	
Stratford 7	⊖ d	22b38	23p07	23p25	23b38	23p55	00 25	00 55									05 37					06 07	06 25	06u38	
Romford	d																05 45					06 15			
Shenfield 3	d		23p24	23p42		00 12	00 47	01 17									05 56					06 26	06 42		
Ingatestone	d			23p46		00 16	00 51	01 21									06 00					06 30			
Chelmsford 3	d	23p03	23p33	23p53	00 03	00 23	00 58	01 28									06 07					06 37	06 51	07 02	
Hatfield Peverel	d					00 30	01 05										06 14					06 44			
Witham 2	d		23p42	00 03		00 35	01 10	01 38				05 36					06 19	06 25				06 49	07 00		
White Notley	d											05 43						06 32							
Cressing	d											05 45						06 34							
Braintree Freeport	d											05 48						06 37							
Braintree	a											05 52						06 41							
Kelvedon	d					00 40	01 15										06 24						07 05		
Marks Tey 2	d					00 45	01 20										06 29						07 10		
Colchester 4	a	23p22	23p56	00 17	00 25	00 57	01 32	02 03									06 37					07 03	07 18	07 21	
	d	23p23	23p57	00 17	00 27					05 18	05 38			06 18			06 37				06 46	07 07	07 18	07 22	
Colchester Town	a																				06 53				
	d																				06 57				
Hythe	d																				07 00				
Wivenhoe 3	d			00 25																	07 04	07 14			
Alresford (Essex)	d			00 28																	07 08				
Great Bentley	d			00 32																	07 12				
Weeley	d																				07 16				
Thorpe-le-Soken 1	a			00 37																	07 19	07 24			⟵
	d			00 37												06 26					07 26	07 24			07 26
Clacton-on-Sea	a			00 51																	⟶	07 34			
Kirby Cross	d															06 30									07 30
Frinton-on-Sea	d															06 33									07 33
Walton-on-the-Naze	a															06 38									07 39
Manningtree 2	d	23p32	00 04		00 36					05 26	05 46			06 26			06 45						07 26	07 31	
Mistley	d									05 30				06 30									07 30		
Wrabness	d									05 35				06 35									07 35		
Harwich International	d									05 44				06 44									07 44		
Dovercourt	d									05 47				06 47									07 47		
Harwich Town	a									05 49				06 49									07 49		
Ipswich	a	23p42	00 20		00 46						05 58						06 56							07 41	
	d	23p43			00 48				05 10		06 00		06 14						07 09	07 16				07 42	
Lowestoft	a																								
Needham Market	d								05 20				06 24							07 26					
Stowmarket	d	23p54			00 59				05a25		06 11		06a29						07 20	07a31				07 53	
Peterborough 8	a										07 37														
Diss	d	00 07			01 12														07 32					08 05	
Norwich	a	00 39			01 44														07 52					08 27	

For general notes see front of timetable
For details of catering facilities see Directory of Train Operators

A To Cambridge (Table 14)
b Previous night.
u Stops to pick up only

Due to major track repair work in the Bury St Edmunds area, trains between Ipswich and Peterborough are subject to disruption, resulting in bus replacements and extended journey times for part or all of this timetable. See local publicity or contact National Rail Enquiries 08457 48 49 50 for further details.

Table 11

Saturdays

London → Chelmsford, Colchester, Walton-on-Naze, Clacton, Harwich, Ipswich and Norwich

Network diagram - see first page of Table 5

Station		LE 1◇	LE 1	LE 1	LE 1◇	LE A		LE 1	LE 1	LE 1	LE 1◇ ☕	LE 1	LE 1	LE 1◇	LE 1	LE 1	LE 1◇ ☕	LE 1	LE A	LE 1		LE 1	LE 1◇ ☕	LE 1	LE 1
London Liverpool Street 15 ⊖	d	06 38		06 48	07 00				07 08	07 18	07 30			07 38	07 48		08 00			08 08		08 18	08 30		
Stratford 7 ⊖	d			06 55					07 15	07 25	07u38				07 55					08 15		08 25	08u38		
Romford	d								07 23											08 23					
Shenfield 3	d	07u02		07 12	07u23				07 34	07 42				08u02	08 12		08u23			08 34		08 42			
Ingatestone	d			07 16											08 16										
Chelmsford 3	d	07 12		07 23					07 43	07 51	08 02			08 12	08 23					08 43		08 51	09 02		
Hatfield Peverel	d			07 30											08 30										
Witham 2	d	07 21		07 36					07 52	08 00				08 21	08 36					08 52		09 00			
White Notley	d			07 43											08 43										
Cressing	d			07 45											08 45										
Braintree Freeport	d			07 48											08 48										
Braintree	a			07 53											08 53										
Kelvedon	d									08 05												09 05			
Marks Tey 2	d	07 29								08 10				08 29								09 10			
Colchester 4	a	07 37			07 49				08 06	08 18	08 21			08 37			08 49			09 06		09 18	09 21		
	d	07 38	07 46		07 50			08 00	08 07	08 18	08 22		08 30	08 38		08 46	08 50	09 00		09 07		09 18	09 22		09 30
Colchester Town	a		07 53					08 07					08 37			08 53		09 07							09 37
	d		07 57													08 57									
Hythe	d		08 00													09 00									
Wivenhoe 3	d		08 04						08 14							09 04				09 14					
Alresford (Essex)	d		08 08													09 08									
Great Bentley	d		08 12													09 12									
Weeley	d		08 16													09 16									
Thorpe-le-Soken 1	a		08 19						08 24			←				09 19				09 24				←	
	d		08 26						08 24			08 26				09 26				09 24				09 26	
Clacton-on-Sea	a		→						08 34							→				09 34					
Kirby Cross	d											08 30												09 30	
Frinton-on-Sea	d											08 33												09 33	
Walton-on-the-Naze	a											08 39												09 39	
Manningtree 2	d	07 46			07 59					08 26	08 31						08 59					09 26	09 31		
Mistley	d									08 30												09 30			
Wrabness	d									08 35												09 35			
Harwich International	d					07 47				08 44												09 44			
Dovercourt	d									08 47												09 47			
Harwich Town	a									08 49												09 49			
Ipswich	a	07 58			08 08	08 15					08 41			08 56			09 08						09 41		
	d	08 03			08 09	08 16					08 42			09 02			09 09		09 16				09 42		
Lowestoft	a													10 32											
Needham Market	d					08 26													09 26						
Stowmarket	d	08 14				08a31					08 53								09a31				09 53		
Peterborough 8	a	09 38																							
Diss	d				08 30						09 05						09 30						10 05		
Norwich	a				08 52						09 27						09 52						10 27		

Station		LE 1◇	LE 1	LE 1	LE 1◇ ☕	LE 1	LE A	LE 1	LE 1	LE 1◇ ☕	LE 1	LE 1		LE R 1	LE 1	LE 1	LE 1◇ ☕	LE 1	LE A	LE 1	LE 1	LE 1◇ ☕	LE 1	LE 1	LE R 1
London Liverpool Street 15 ⊖	d	08 38	08 48		09 00			09 08	09 18	09 30				09 38	09 48		10 00			10 08	10 18	10 30			10 38
Stratford 7 ⊖	d		08 55					09 15	09 25	09u38					09 55					10 15	10 25	10u38			
Romford	d							09 23												10 23					
Shenfield 3	d	09u02	09 12		09u23			09 34	09 42					10u02	10 12		10u23			10 34	10 42				11u02
Ingatestone	d		09 16												10 16										
Chelmsford 3	d	09 12	09 23					09 43	09 51	10 02				10 12	10 23					10 43	10 51	11 02			11 12
Hatfield Peverel	d		09 30												10 30										
Witham 2	d	09 21	09 36					09 52	10 00					10 21	10 36					10 52	11 00				11 21
White Notley	d		09 43												10 43										
Cressing	d		09 45												10 45										
Braintree Freeport	d		09 48												10 48										
Braintree	a		09 53												10 53										
Kelvedon	d								10 05												11 05				
Marks Tey 2	d	09 29							10 10					10 29							11 10				11 29
Colchester 4	a	09 37			09 49			10 06	10 18	10 21				10 37			10 49			11 06	11 18	11 21			11 37
	d	09 38		09 46	09 50	10 00		10 07	10 18	10 22		10 30		10 38		10 46	10 50	11 00		11 07	11 18	11 22		11 30	11 38
Colchester Town	a			09 53		10 07						10 37				10 53		11 07						11 37	
	d			09 57												10 57									
Hythe	d			10 00												11 00									
Wivenhoe 3	d			10 04				10 14								11 04				11 14					
Alresford (Essex)	d			10 08												11 08									
Great Bentley	d			10 12												11 12									
Weeley	d			10 16												11 16									
Thorpe-le-Soken 1	a			10 19				10 24			←					11 19				11 24			←		
	d			10 26				10 24			10 26					11 26				11 24			11 26		
Clacton-on-Sea	a			→				10 34								→				11 34					
Kirby Cross	d										10 30												11 30		
Frinton-on-Sea	d										10 33												11 33		
Walton-on-the-Naze	a										10 39												11 39		
Manningtree 2	d	09 46			09 59				10 26	10 31							10 59				11 26	11 31			
Mistley	d								10 30												11 30				
Wrabness	d								10 35												11 35				
Harwich International	d								10 44												11 44				
Dovercourt	d								10 47												11 47				
Harwich Town	a								10 49												11 49				
Ipswich	a	09 58			10 08					10 41				10 56			11 08					11 41			11 56
	d	10 03			10 09		10 16			10 42				11 02			11 09		11 16			11 42			12 03
Lowestoft	a													12 32											
Needham Market	d						10 26												11 26						
Stowmarket	d	10 14					10a31			10 53									11a31			11 53			12 14
Peterborough 8	a	11 38																							13 38
Diss	d				10 30					11 05							11 30					12 05			
Norwich	a				10 52					11 27							11 52					12 27			

For general notes see front of timetable
For details of catering facilities see
Directory of Train Operators

A To Cambridge (Table 14)

Due to major track repair work in the Bury St Edmunds area, trains between Ipswich and Peterborough are subject to disruption, resulting in bus replacements and extended journey times for part or all of this timetable. See local publicity or contact National Rail Enquiries 08457 48 49 50 for further details.

London → Chelmsford, Colchester, Walton-on-Naze, Clacton, Harwich, Ipswich and Norwich

Network diagram - see first page of Table 5

Station		LE 1	LE 1	LE 1 ◇ ☕		LE 1	LE A	LE 1	LE 1	LE 1 ◇ ☕	LE 1	LE 1	LE R 1	LE 1	LE 1	LE 1 ◇ ☕	LE 1	LE A		LE 1	LE 1	LE 1 ◇ ☕	LE 1	LE 1	LE R 1
London Liverpool Street 15 ⊖	d	10 48		11 00				11 08	11 18	11 30			11 38	11 48		12 00				12 08	12 18	12 30			12 38
Stratford 7 ⊖	d	10 55						11 15	11 25	11u38				11 55						12 15	12 25	12u38			
Romford	d							11 23												12 23					
Shenfield 3	d	11 12		11u23				11 34	11 42				12u02	12 12		12u23				12 34	12 42				13u02
Ingatestone	d	11 16												12 16											
Chelmsford 3	d	11 23						11 43	11 51	12 02			12 12	12 23						12 43	12 51	13 02			13 12
Hatfield Peverel	d	11 30												12 30											
Witham 2	d	11 36						11 52	12 00				12 21	12 36						12 52	13 00				13 21
White Notley	d	11 43												12 43											
Cressing	d	11 45												12 45											
Braintree Freeport	d	11 48												12 48											
Braintree	a	11 53												12 53											
Kelvedon	d								12 05												13 05				
Marks Tey 2	d								12 10				12 29								13 10				13 29
Colchester 4	a			11 49				12 06	12 18	12 21			12 37			12 49				13 06	13 18	13 21			13 37
	d		11 46	11 50		12 00		12 07	12 18	12 22		12 30	12 38		12 46	12 50	13 00			13 07	13 18	13 22		13 30	13 38
Colchester Town	a		11 53			12 07						12 37			12 53		13 07							13 37	
	d		11 57												12 57										
Hythe	d		12 00												13 00										
Wivenhoe 3	d		12 04					12 14							13 04					13 14					
Alresford (Essex)	d		12 08												13 08										
Great Bentley	d		12 12												13 12										
Weeley	d		12 16												13 16										
Thorpe-le-Soken 1	a		12 19					12 24			←				13 19					13 24			←		
	d		12 26					12 24			12 26				13 26					13 24			13 26		
Clacton-on-Sea	a		→					12 34							→					13 34					
Kirby Cross	d										12 30												13 30		
Frinton-on-Sea	d										12 33												13 33		
Walton-on-the-Naze	a										12 39												13 39		
Manningtree 2	d			11 59					12 26	12 31						12 59					13 26	13 31			
Mistley	d								12 30												13 30				
Wrabness	d								12 35												13 35				
Harwich International	d								12 44												13 44				
Dovercourt	d								12 47												13 47				
Harwich Town	a								12 49												13 49				
Ipswich	a			12 08						12 41			12 56			13 08						13 41			13 56
	d			12 09			12 16			12 42			13 02			13 09		13 16				13 42			14 03
Lowestoft	a												14 32												
Needham Market	d						12 26											13 26							
Stowmarket	d						12a31			12 53								13a31				13 53			14 14
Peterborough 8	a																								15 38
Diss	d			12 30						13 05						13 30						14 05			
Norwich	a			12 52						13 27						13 52						14 27			

Station		LE 1	LE 1	LE 1 ◇ ☕	LE 1	LE A	LE 1	LE 1	LE 1 ◇ ☕	LE 1		LE 1	LE R 1	LE 1	LE 1	LE 1 ◇ ☕	LE 1	LE A	LE 1	LE 1	LE 1 ◇ ☕	LE 1	LE 1	LE 1 ◇	LE 1
London Liverpool Street 15 ⊖	d	12 48		13 00			13 08	13 18	13 30				13 38	13 48		14 00			14 08	14 18	14 30			14 38	14 48
Stratford 7 ⊖	d	12 55					13 15	13 25	13u38					13 55					14 15	14 25	14u38				14 55
Romford	d						13 23												14 23						
Shenfield 3	d	13 12		13u23			13 34	13 42					14u02	14 12		14u23			14 34	14 42				15u02	15 12
Ingatestone	d	13 16												14 16											15 16
Chelmsford 3	d	13 23					13 43	13 51	14 02				14 12	14 23					14 43	14 51	15 02			15 12	15 23
Hatfield Peverel	d	13 30												14 30											15 30
Witham 2	d	13 36					13 52	14 00					14 21	14 36					14 52	15 00				15 21	15 36
White Notley	d	13 43												14 43											15 43
Cressing	d	13 45												14 45											15 45
Braintree Freeport	d	13 48												14 48											15 48
Braintree	a	13 53												14 53											15 53
Kelvedon	d							14 05												15 05					
Marks Tey 2	d							14 10					14 29							15 10				15 29	
Colchester 4	a			13 49			14 06	14 18	14 21				14 37			14 49			15 06	15 18	15 21			15 37	
	d		13 46	13 50	14 00		14 07	14 18	14 22			14 30	14 38		14 46	14 50	15 00		15 07	15 18	15 22		15 30	15 38	
Colchester Town	a		13 53		14 07							14 37			14 53		15 07						15 37		
	d		13 57												14 57										
Hythe	d		14 00												15 00										
Wivenhoe 3	d		14 04				14 14								15 04				15 14						
Alresford (Essex)	d		14 08												15 08										
Great Bentley	d		14 12												15 12										
Weeley	d		14 16												15 16										
Thorpe-le-Soken 1	a		14 19				14 24			←					15 19				15 24			←			
	d		14 26				14 24			14 26					15 26				15 24			15 26			
Clacton-on-Sea	a		→				14 34								→				15 34						
Kirby Cross	d									14 30												15 30			
Frinton-on-Sea	d									14 33												15 33			
Walton-on-the-Naze	a									14 39												15 39			
Manningtree 2	d			13 59				14 26	14 31							14 59				15 26	15 31				
Mistley	d							14 30												15 30					
Wrabness	d							14 35												15 35					
Harwich International	d							14 44												15 44					
Dovercourt	d							14 47												15 47					
Harwich Town	a							14 49												15 49					
Ipswich	a			14 08					14 41				14 56			15 08					15 41			15 56	
	d			14 09		14 16			14 42				15 02			15 09		15 16			15 42			16 03	
Lowestoft	a												16 32												
Needham Market	d					14 26												15 26							
Stowmarket	d					14a31			14 53									15a31			15 53			16 14	
Peterborough 8	a																							17 38	
Diss	d			14 30					15 05							15 30					16 05				
Norwich	a			14 52					15 27							15 52					16 27				

For general notes see front of timetable
For details of catering facilities see Directory of Train Operators

A To Cambridge (Table 14)

Due to major track repair work in the Bury St Edmunds area, trains between Ipswich and Peterborough are subject to disruption, resulting in bus replacements and extended journey times for part or all of this timetable. See local publicity or contact National Rail Enquiries 08457 48 49 50 for further details.

London → Chelmsford, Colchester, Walton-on-Naze, Clacton, Harwich, Ipswich and Norwich

Network diagram - see first page of Table 5

		LE		LE	LE	LE	LE	LE	LE	LE	LE	LE	LE	LE	LE	LE		LE	LE	LE	LE	LE	LE	LE	LE
		1		1◇	1		1	1	1◇	1	1	R 1	1	1	1◇	1			1	1	1◇	1	1	R 1	1
						A												A							
				☕					☕						☕						☕				
London Liverpool Street 15 ⊖	d			15 00			15 08	15 18	15 30			15 38	15 48		16 00				16 08	16 18	16 30			16 38	16 48
Stratford 7 ⊖	d						15 15	15 25	15u38				15 55						16 15	16 25	16u38				16 55
Romford	d						15 23												16 23						
Shenfield 3	d			15u23			15 34	15 42				16u02	16 12		16u23				16 34	16 42				17u02	17 12
Ingatestone	d												16 16												17 16
Chelmsford 3	d						15 43	15 51	16 02			16 12	16 23						16 43	16 51	17 02			17 12	17 23
Hatfield Peverel	d												16 30												17 30
Witham 2	d						15 52	16 00				16 21	16 36						16 52	17 00				17 21	17 36
White Notley	d												16 43												17 43
Cressing	d												16 45												17 45
Braintree Freeport	d												16 48												17 48
Braintree	a												16 53												17 53
Kelvedon	d							16 05												17 05					
Marks Tey 2	d							16 10				16 29								17 10				17 29	
Colchester 4	a			15 49			16 06	16 18	16 21			16 37			16 49				17 06	17 18	17 21			17 37	
	d	15 46		15 50	16 00		16 07	16 18	16 22		16 30	16 38		16 46	16 50	17 00			17 07	17 18	17 22		17 30	17 38	
Colchester Town	a	15 53			16 07						16 37			16 53		17 07							17 37		
	d	15 57												16 57											
Hythe	d	16 00												17 00											
Wivenhoe 3	d	16 04					16 14							17 04					17 14						
Alresford (Essex)	d	16 08												17 08											
Great Bentley	d	16 12												17 12											
Weeley	d	16 16												17 16											
Thorpe-le-Soken 1	a	16 19					16 24			←				17 19					17 24			←			
	d	16 26					16 24			16 26				17 26					17 24			17 26			
Clacton-on-Sea	a	→					16 34							→					17 34						
Kirby Cross	d									16 30												17 30			
Frinton-on-Sea	d									16 33												17 33			
Walton-on-the-Naze	a									16 39												17 39			
Manningtree 2	d			15 59				16 26	16 31						16 59					17 26	17 31				
Mistley	d							16 30												17 30					
Wrabness	d							16 35												17 35					
Harwich International	d							16 44												17 44					
Dovercourt	d							16 47												17 47					
Harwich Town	a							16 49												17 49					
Ipswich	a			16 08					16 41			16 56			17 08						17 41			17 56	
	d			16 09		16 16			16 42			17 02			17 09			17 16			17 42			18 03	
Lowestoft	a											18 32													
Needham Market	d					16 26												17 26							
Stowmarket	d					16a31			16 53						17 20			17a31			17 53			18 14	
Peterborough 8	a																							19 38	
Diss	d			16 30					17 05						17 32						18 05				
Norwich	a			16 52					17 27						17 52						18 27				

		LE	LE	LE	LE	LE	LE	LE		LE	LE	LE	LE	LE	LE	LE	LE	LE	LE	LE	LE	LE		LE	LE
		1	1◇	1		1	1	1◇		1	1	1	R 1	1	1	1◇	1		1	1	1◇	1		1	1
					A													A							
			☕					☕								☕					☕				
London Liverpool Street 15 ⊖	d		17 00			17 08	17 18	17 30				17 38	17 46	17 48		18 00			18 08	18 18	18 30				18 38
Stratford 7 ⊖	d					17 15	17 25	17u38						17 55					18 15	18 25	18u38				
Romford	d					17 23													18 23						
Shenfield 3	d		17u23			17 34	17 42					18u02		18 12		18u23			18 34	18 42					19u02
Ingatestone	d													18 16											
Chelmsford 3	d					17 43	17 51	18 02				18 11	18u16	18 23					18 43	18 51	19 02				19 11
Hatfield Peverel	d													18 30											
Witham 2	d					17 52	18 00					18 21		18 36					18 52	19 00					19 21
White Notley	d													18 43											
Cressing	d													18 45											
Braintree Freeport	d													18 48											
Braintree	a													18 53											
Kelvedon	d						18 05													19 05					
Marks Tey 2	d						18 10					18 28								19 10					19 28
Colchester 4	a		17 49			18 06	18 18	18 21				18 36	18 39			18 49			19 06	19 18	19 21				19 36
	d	17 46	17 50	18 00		18 07	18 18	18 22			18 30		18 40		18 46	18 50	19 00		19 07	19 18	19 22			19 30	
Colchester Town	a	17 53		18 07							18 37				18 53		19 07							19 37	
	d	17 57													18 57										
Hythe	d	18 00													19 00										
Wivenhoe 3	d	18 04				18 14									19 04				19 14						
Alresford (Essex)	d	18 08													19 08										
Great Bentley	d	18 12													19 12										
Weeley	d	18 16													19 16										
Thorpe-le-Soken 1	a	18 19				18 24				←					19 19				19 24			←			
	d	18 26				18 24				18 26					19 26				19 24			19 26			
Clacton-on-Sea	a	→				18 34									→				19 34						
Kirby Cross	d									18 30												19 30			
Frinton-on-Sea	d									18 33												19 33			
Walton-on-the-Naze	a									18 39												19 39			
Manningtree 2	d		17 59				18 26	18 31								18 59				19 26	19 31				
Mistley	d						18 30													19 30					
Wrabness	d						18 35													19 35					
Harwich International	d						18 44													19 44					
Dovercourt	d						18 47													19 47					
Harwich Town	a						18 49													19 49					
Ipswich	a		18 08					18 41					18 56			19 08					19 41				
	d		18 09		18 16			18 42					19 02			19 09		19 16			19 42				
Lowestoft	a												20 32												
Needham Market	d				18 26													19 26							
Stowmarket	d				18a31			18 53										19a32			19 53				
Peterborough 8	a																								
Diss	d		18 30					19 05								19 30					20 05				
Norwich	a		18 52					19 27								19 52					20 27				

For general notes see front of timetable
For details of catering facilities see Directory of Train Operators

A To Cambridge (Table 14)

Due to major track repair work in the Bury St Edmunds area, trains between Ipswich and Peterborough are subject to disruption, resulting in bus replacements and extended journey times for part or all of this timetable. See local publicity or contact National Rail Enquiries 08457 48 49 50 for further details.

London → Chelmsford, Colchester, Walton-on-Naze, Clacton, Harwich, Ipswich and Norwich

Network diagram - see first page of Table 5

		LE R 1	LE 1	LE 1	LE 1 ◇ ☕	LE A	LE 1	LE 1	LE 1 ◇ ☕	LE 1	LE R 1	LE 1	LE 1	LE 1 ◇ ☕		LE 1	LE 1	LE	LE 1	LE 1 ◇ ☕	LE 1	LE 1	LE	LE 1	LE 1 ◇
London Liverpool Street 15 ⊖	d	18 46	18 48		19 00		19 08	19 18	19 30		19 38		19 48	20 00		20 08			20 18	20 30	20 38	20 48			21 00
Stratford 7 ⊖	d		18 55				19 15	19 25	19u38				19 55			20 15			20 25	20u38	20 45	20 55			
Romford	d						19 23									20 23									
Shenfield 3	d		19 12		19u23		19 34	19 42			20u02		20 12	20u23		20 34			20 42		21 02	21 12			21u23
Ingatestone	d		19 16										20 16									21 16			
Chelmsford 3	d	19u16	19 23				19 43	19 51	20 03		20 12		20 23			20 43			20 51	21 03	21 12	21 23			
Hatfield Peverel	d		19 30										20 30									21 30			
Witham 2	d		19 36				19 52	20 00			20 21		20 36			20 52			21 00		21 21	21 36			
White Notley	d		19 43										20 43									21 43			
Cressing	d		19 45										20 45									21 45			
Braintree Freeport	d		19 48										20 48									21 48			
Braintree	a		19 53										20 53									21 53			
Kelvedon	d							20 05											21 05						
Marks Tey 2	d							20 10			20 29								21 10		21 29				
Colchester 4	a	19 39			19 49		20 06	20 18	20 22		20 37			20 49		21 06			21 18	21 22	21 37				21 49
	d	19 40		19 46	19 50		20 07	20 18	20 23		20 38	20 46		20 50		21 07			21 18	21 23	21 38			21 46	21 50
Colchester Town	a			19 53								20 53												21 53	
	d			19 57								20 57												21 57	
Hythe	d			20 00								21 00												22 00	
Wivenhoe 3	d			20 04			20 14					21 04				21 14								22 04	
Alresford (Essex)	d			20 08								21 08												22 08	
Great Bentley	d			20 12								21 12												22 12	
Weeley	d			20 16								21 16												22 16	
Thorpe-le-Soken 1	a			20 19			20 24			←		21 19				21 24	←							22 19	
	d			20 26 →			20 24			20 26		21 26 →				21 24	21 26							22 26 →	
Clacton-on-Sea	a						20 34									21 34									
Kirby Cross	d									20 30							21 30								
Frinton-on-Sea	d									20 33							21 33								
Walton-on-the-Naze	a									20 39							21 39								
Manningtree 2	d				19 59			20 26	20 32					20 59					21 26	21 32	21 46				21 58
Mistley	d							20 30											21 30						
Wrabness	d							20 35											21 35				←		
Harwich International	d							20 44										21 34 →	21 44		22a02		21 34		
Dovercourt	d							20 47											21 47						
Harwich Town	a							20 49											21 49						
Ipswich	a	19 56			20 08				20 42		20 56			21 08						21 42			22 00		22 09
	d	20 03			20 09	20 16			20 43		21 02			21 09						21 43					22 15
Lowestoft	a										22 32														23 45
Needham Market	d					20 26																			
Stowmarket	d	20 14				20a31			20 54											21 54					
Peterborough 8	a	21 38																							
Diss	d				20 30				21 06					21 30						22 06					
Norwich	a				20 52				21 28					21 52						22 28					

		LE B	LE 1	LE 1	LE 1 ◇ ☕	LE C		LE 1	LE 1	LE 1	LE 1	LE 1	LE 1	LE 1	LE 1 ◇ ☕	LE 1	LE 1	LE 1	LE 1	LE 1		LE 1 ◇ ☕	LE 1		
London Liverpool Street 15 ⊖	d		21 04	21 18	21 30					21 34		21 48	22 00	22 18	22 30		22 48	23 00		23 18		23 30	23 48		
Stratford 7 ⊖	d		21 11	21 25								21 55	22 07	22 25			22 55	23 07		23 25			23 55		
Romford	d		21 19																						
Shenfield 3	d		21 34	21 46						22u02		22 16	22 28	22 46			23 16	23 28		23 46			00 16		
Ingatestone	d											22 20					23 20			23 50			00 20		
Chelmsford 3	d		21 43	21 55	22 04					22 12		22 27	22 37	22 55	23 04		23 27	23 37		23 57		00 04	00 27		
Hatfield Peverel	d											22 34					23 34						00 34		
Witham 2	d		21 52	22 04						22 21		22 40	22 46	23 04			23 39	23 46	23 48	00 07			00 39		
White Notley	d											22 47							23 54						
Cressing	d											22 49							23 57						
Braintree Freeport	d											22 52							23 59						
Braintree	a											22 57							00 03						
Kelvedon	d			22 09										23 09			23 44						00 44		
Marks Tey 2	d			22 14		22 21				22 29				23 14			23 49						00 49		
Colchester 4	a		22 06	22 22	22 25	22 30				22 37			23 00	23 22	23 25		00 01	00 01		00 25		00 28	01 01		
	d		22 07		22 26					22 38	22 46		23 00	23 23	23 26			00 01				00 29			
Colchester Town	a										22 53														
	d										22 57														
Hythe	d										23 00														
Wivenhoe 3	d		22 14								23 04			23 30											
Alresford (Essex)	d										23 08			23 33											
Great Bentley	d										23 12			23 37											
Weeley	d										23 16														
Thorpe-le-Soken 1	a		22 24						←		23 19			23 43											
	d		22 24						22 26		23 19			23 43											
Clacton-on-Sea	a		22 34								23 29			23 52											
Kirby Cross	d								22 30																
Frinton-on-Sea	d								22 33																
Walton-on-the-Naze	a								22 39																
Manningtree 2	d				22 35			22 38					23 08		23 35	23 38		00 08				00 38			
Mistley	d							22 42								23 42									
Wrabness	d							22 47								23 47									
Harwich International	d							22 54								23 54									
Dovercourt	d							22 57								23 57									
Harwich Town	a							22 59								23 59									
Ipswich	a				22 45					22 56			23 20		23 45			00 24				00 48			
	d	22 17			22 46										23 46							00 50			
Lowestoft	a																								
Needham Market	d	22 27																							
Stowmarket	d	22a32			22 57										23 57							01 01			
Peterborough 8	a																								
Diss	d				23 10										00 10							01 14			
Norwich	a				23 32										00 32							01 36			

For general notes see front of timetable
For details of catering facilities see Directory of Train Operators

A To Cambridge (Table 14)
B To Bury St Edmunds (Table 14)
C From Sudbury (Table 10)

Due to major track repair work in the Bury St Edmunds area, trains between Ipswich and Peterborough are subject to disruption, resulting in bus replacements and extended journey times for part or all of this timetable. See local publicity or contact National Rail Enquiries 08457 48 49 50 for further details.

Table 11

Sundays

London → Chelmsford, Colchester, Walton-on-Naze, Clacton, Harwich, Ipswich and Norwich

Network diagram - see first page of Table 5

		LE	LE	LE	LE	LE	LE		LE	LE	LE	LE	LE	LE		LE	LE	LE	LE	LE	LE		LE	LE	LE
		1 ◇	1	1	1 ◇	1	1		1	1	1			1		1	1	1	1	1	1 ◇		1	1	1
												A	B												
London Liverpool Street 15 ⊖	d	22p30	23p00	23p18	23p30	23p48	00 18												08 02		08 30		08 32		
Stratford 7 ⊖	d		23p07	23p25		23p55	00 25												08 09				08 39		
Romford	d																								
Shenfield 3	d		23p28	23p46		00 16	00 47												08 31		08u57		09 01		
Ingatestone	d			23p50		00 20	00 51												08 35						
Chelmsford 3	d	23p04	23p37	23p57	00 04	00 27	00 58												08 42				09 10		
Hatfield Peverel	d					00 34	01 05												08 49						
Witham 2	d		23p46	00 07		00 39	01 10			07 33							08 23		08 54				09 19	09 23	
White Notley	d									07 39							08 29							09 29	
Cressing	d									07 42							08 32							09 32	
Braintree Freeport	d									07 44							08 34							09 34	
Braintree	a									07 48							08 38							09 38	
Kelvedon	d					00 44	01 15												08 59						
Marks Tey 2	d					00 49	01 20												09 04				09 27		
Colchester 4	a	23p25	00 01	00 25	00 28	01 01	01 32												09 12		09 23		09 35		
	d	23p26	00 01		00 29				07 40		08 12			08 18		08 35			09 12		09 24		09 35		
Colchester Town	a																								
	d																								
Hythe	d																								
Wivenhoe 3	d															08 43							09 43		
Alresford (Essex)	d															08 46							09 46		
Great Bentley	d															08 50							09 50		
Weeley	d																								
Thorpe-le-Soken 1	a															08 55							09 55		
	d															08 55		08 57					09 55		
Clacton-on-Sea	a															09 07							10 05		
Kirby Cross	d																	09 01							
Frinton-on-Sea	d																	09 04							
Walton-on-the-Naze	a																	09 09							
Manningtree 2	d	23p35	00 08		00 38				07 48		08 20			08 26					09 20	09 26	09 33				
Mistley	d													08 30						09 30					
Wrabness	d													08 35						09 35					
Harwich International	d												08 30	08 42						09 42					
Dovercourt	d													08 45						09 45					
Harwich Town	a													08 47						09 47					
Ipswich	a	23p45	00 24		00 48				08 00		08 32		08 55						09 32		09 42				
	d	23p46			00 50							08 45	09 02								09 44				09 55
Lowestoft	a																								
Needham Market	d												09 12												10 07
Stowmarket	d	23p57			01 01							08a58	09a17								09 55				
Peterborough 8	a																								11 41
Diss	d	00 10			01 14																10 07				
Norwich	a	00 32			01 36																10 29				

For general notes see front of timetable
For details of catering facilities see Directory of Train Operators

A To Bury St Edmunds (Table 14)
B To Cambridge (Table 14)

Due to major track repair work in the Bury St Edmunds area, trains between Ipswich and Peterborough are subject to disruption, resulting in bus replacements and extended journey times for part or all of this timetable. See local publicity or contact National Rail Enquiries 08457 48 49 50 for further details.

Sundays

London → Chelmsford, Colchester, Walton-on-Naze, Clacton, Harwich, Ipswich and Norwich

Network diagram - see first page of Table 5

		LE 1	LE 1	LE 1	LE 1 ◇ 🍴	LE 1	LE 1	LE A	LE 1	LE 1	LE 1	LE 1 ◇ 🍴	LE 1	LE 1	LE 1	LE 1	LE 1	LE 1	LE 1 ◇ 🍴	LE 1	LE 1	LE A
London Liverpool Street 15 ⊖	d		09 02		09 30	09 32				10 02		10 30	10 32				11 02		11 30	11 32		
Stratford 7 ⊖	d		09 09			09 39				10 09			10 39				11 09			11 39		
Romford	d																					
Shenfield 3	d		09 31		09u57	10 01				10 31		10u57	11 01				11 31		11u57	12 01		
Ingatestone	d		09 35							10 35							11 35					
Chelmsford 3	d		09 42			10 10				10 42			11 10				11 42			12 10		
Hatfield Peverel	d		09 49							10 49							11 49					
Witham 2	d		09 54			10 19	10 23			10 54			11 19	11 23			11 54			12 19	12 23	
White Notley	d						10 29							11 29							12 29	
Cressing	d						10 32							11 32							12 32	
Braintree Freeport	d						10 34							11 34							12 34	
Braintree	a						10 38							11 38							12 38	
Kelvedon	d		09 59							10 59							11 59					
Marks Tey 2	d		10 04			10 27				11 04			11 27				12 04			12 27		
Colchester 4	a		10 12		10 23	10 35				11 12		11 23	11 35				12 12		12 23	12 35		
	d		10 12		10 24	10 35				11 12		11 24	11 35				12 12		12 24	12 35		
Colchester Town	a																					
	d																					
Hythe	d																					
Wivenhoe 3	d					10 43							11 43							12 43		
Alresford (Essex)	d					10 46							11 46							12 46		
Great Bentley	d					10 50							11 50							12 50		
Weeley	d																					
Thorpe-le-Soken 1	a					10 55							11 55							12 55		
	d	09 57				10 55			10 57				11 55			11 57				12 55		
Clacton-on-Sea	a					11 05							12 05							13 05		
Kirby Cross	d	10 01							11 01							12 01						
Frinton-on-Sea	d	10 04							11 04							12 04						
Walton-on-the-Naze	a	10 09							11 09							12 09						
Manningtree 2	d		10 20	10 26	10 33					11 20	11 26	11 33					12 20	12 26	12 33			
Mistley	d			10 30							11 30							12 30				
Wrabness	d			10 35							11 35							12 35				
Harwich International	d			10 42							11 42							12 42				
Dovercourt	d			10 45							11 45							12 45				
Harwich Town	a			10 47							11 47							12 47				
Ipswich	a		10 32		10 42					11 32		11 42					12 32		12 42			
	d				10 44			11 02				11 44			11 55				12 44			13 02
Lowestoft	a																					
Needham Market	d							11 12														13 12
Stowmarket	d				10 55			11a17				11 55			12 07				12 55			13a17
Peterborough 8	a														13 42							
Diss	d				11 07							12 07							13 07			
Norwich	a				11 29							12 29							13 29			

		LE 1	LE 1	LE 1	LE 1 ◇ 🍴	LE 1	LE 1	LE 1	LE 1	LE 1	LE 1	LE 1 ◇ 🍴	LE 1	LE 1	LE A	LE 1	LE 1	LE 1	LE 1 ◇ 🍴	LE 1	LE 1	LE 1
London Liverpool Street 15 ⊖	d		12 02		12 30	12 32				13 02		13 30	13 32				14 02		14 30	14 32		
Stratford 7 ⊖	d		12 09			12 39				13 09			13 39				14 09			14 39		
Romford	d																					
Shenfield 3	d		12 31		12u57	13 01				13 31		13u57	14 01				14 31		14u57	15 01		
Ingatestone	d		12 35							13 35							14 35					
Chelmsford 3	d		12 42			13 10				13 42			14 10				14 42			15 10		
Hatfield Peverel	d		12 49							13 49							14 49					
Witham 2	d		12 54			13 19	13 23			13 54			14 19	14 23			14 54			15 19	15 23	
White Notley	d						13 29							14 29							15 29	
Cressing	d						13 32							14 32							15 32	
Braintree Freeport	d						13 34							14 34							15 34	
Braintree	a						13 38							14 38							15 38	
Kelvedon	d		12 59							13 59							14 59					
Marks Tey 2	d		13 04			13 27				14 04			14 27				15 04			15 27		
Colchester 4	a		13 12		13 23	13 35				14 12		14 23	14 35				15 12		15 23	15 35		
	d		13 12		13 24	13 35				14 12		14 24	14 35				15 12		15 24	15 35		
Colchester Town	a																					
	d																					
Hythe	d																					
Wivenhoe 3	d					13 43							14 43							15 43		
Alresford (Essex)	d					13 46							14 46							15 46		
Great Bentley	d					13 50							14 50							15 50		
Weeley	d																					
Thorpe-le-Soken 1	a					13 55							14 55							15 55		
	d	12 57				13 55			13 57				14 55			14 57				15 55		
Clacton-on-Sea	a					14 05							15 05							16 05		
Kirby Cross	d	13 01							14 01							15 01						
Frinton-on-Sea	d	13 04							14 04							15 04						
Walton-on-the-Naze	a	13 09							14 09							15 09						
Manningtree 2	d		13 20	13 26	13 33					14 20	14 26	14 33					15 20	15 26	15 33			
Mistley	d			13 30							14 30							15 30				
Wrabness	d			13 35							14 35							15 35				
Harwich International	d			13 42							14 42							15 42				
Dovercourt	d			13 45							14 45							15 45				
Harwich Town	a			13 47							14 47							15 47				
Ipswich	a		13 32		13 42					14 32		14 42					15 32		15 42			
	d				13 44			13 55				14 44			15 02				15 44			15 55
Lowestoft	a																					
Needham Market	d														15 12							
Stowmarket	d				13 55			14 07				14 55			15a17				15 55			16 07
Peterborough 8	a							15 42														17 36
Diss	d				14 07							15 07							16 07			
Norwich	a				14 29							15 29							16 29			

For general notes see front of timetable
For details of catering facilities see Directory of Train Operators

A To Cambridge (Table 14)

Due to major track repair work in the Bury St Edmunds area, trains between Ipswich and Peterborough are subject to disruption, resulting in bus replacements and extended journey times for part or all of this timetable. See local publicity or contact National Rail Enquiries 08457 48 49 50 for further details.

Table 11

Sundays

London → Chelmsford, Colchester, Walton-on-Naze, Clacton, Harwich, Ipswich and Norwich

Network diagram - see first page of Table 5

		LE 1	LE 1	LE 1	LE 1 ◇ ☕	LE 1	LE 1	LE A	LE 1	LE 1	LE 1	LE 1 ◇ ☕	LE 1	LE 1	LE 1	LE 1	LE 1	LE 1	LE 1 ◇ ☕	LE 1	LE 1	LE A
London Liverpool Street 15 ⊖	d		15 02		15 30	15 32				16 02		16 30	16 32				17 02		17 30	17 32		
Stratford 7 ⊖	d		15 09			15 39				16 09			16 39				17 09			17 39		
Romford	d																					
Shenfield 3	d		15 31		15u57	16 01				16 31		16u57	17 01				17 31		17u57	18 01		
Ingatestone	d		15 35							16 35							17 35					
Chelmsford 3	d		15 42			16 10				16 42			17 10				17 42			18 10		
Hatfield Peverel	d		15 49							16 49							17 49					
Witham 2	d		15 54			16 19	16 23			16 54			17 19	17 23			17 54			18 19	18 23	
White Notley	d						16 29							17 29							18 29	
Cressing	d						16 32							17 32							18 32	
Braintree Freeport	d						16 34							17 34							18 34	
Braintree	a						16 38							17 38							18 38	
Kelvedon	d		15 59							16 59							17 59					
Marks Tey 2	d		16 04			16 27				17 04			17 27				18 04			18 27		
Colchester 4	a		16 12		16 23	16 35				17 12		17 23	17 35				18 12		18 23	18 35		
	d		16 12		16 24	16 35				17 12		17 24	17 35				18 12		18 24	18 35		
Colchester Town	a																					
	d																					
Hythe	d																					
Wivenhoe 3	d					16 43							17 43							18 43		
Alresford (Essex)	d					16 46							17 46							18 46		
Great Bentley	d					16 50							17 50							18 50		
Weeley	d																					
Thorpe-le-Soken 1	a					16 55							17 55							18 55		
	d	15 57				16 55			16 57				17 55			17 57				18 55		
Clacton-on-Sea	a					17 05							18 05							19 05		
Kirby Cross	d	16 01							17 01							18 01						
Frinton-on-Sea	d	16 04							17 04							18 04						
Walton-on-the-Naze	a	16 09							17 09							18 09						
Manningtree 2	d		16 20	16 26	16 33					17 20	17 26	17 33					18 20	18 26	18 33			
Mistley	d			16 30							17 30							18 30				
Wrabness	d			16 35							17 35							18 35				
Harwich International	d			16 42							17 42							18 42				
Dovercourt	d			16 45							17 45							18 45				
Harwich Town	a			16 47							17 47							18 47				
Ipswich	a		16 32		16 42					17 32		17 42					18 32		18 42			
	d				16 44			17 02				17 44			17 55				18 44			19 02
Lowestoft	a																					
Needham Market	d							17 12														19 12
Stowmarket	d				16 55			17a17				17 55			18 07				18 55			19a17
Peterborough 8	a														19 36							
Diss	d				17 07							18 07							19 07			
Norwich	a				17 29							18 29							19 29			

		LE 1	LE 1	LE 1	LE 1 ◇ ☕	LE 1	LE 1 ◇ ☕	LE 1	LE 1	LE 1	LE 1	LE 1 ◇ ☕	LE 1	LE 1	LE A	LE 1	LE	LE 1	LE 1	LE	LE 1	LE 1 ◇ ☕
London Liverpool Street 15 ⊖	d		18 02		18 30	18 32	19 00			19 02		19 30	19 32					20 00	20 02			20 30
Stratford 7 ⊖	d		18 09			18 39				19 09			19 39						20 09			
Romford	d																					
Shenfield 3	d		18 31		18u57	19 01				19 31		19u57	20 01					20 27	20 31			20u57
Ingatestone	d		18 35							19 35									20 35			
Chelmsford 3	d		18 42			19 10				19 42			20 10					20 37	20 42			
Hatfield Peverel	d		18 49							19 49									20 49			
Witham 2	d		18 54			19 19		19 23		19 54			20 19	20 23					20 54			
White Notley	d							19 29						20 29								
Cressing	d							19 32						20 32								
Braintree Freeport	d							19 34						20 34								
Braintree	a							19 38						20 38								
Kelvedon	d		18 59							19 59									20 59			
Marks Tey 2	d		19 04			19 27				20 04			20 27						21 04			
Colchester 4	a		19 12		19 23	19 35				20 12		20 23	20 35					20 55	21 12			21 23
	d		19 12		19 24	19 35				20 12		20 24	20 35					20 56	21 12			21 24
Colchester Town	a																					
	d																					
Hythe	d																					
Wivenhoe 3	d					19 43							20 43									
Alresford (Essex)	d					19 46							20 46									
Great Bentley	d					19 50							20 50									
Weeley	d																					
Thorpe-le-Soken 1	a					19 55							20 55									
	d	18 57				19 55			19 57				20 55			20 57						
Clacton-on-Sea	a					20 05							21 05									
Kirby Cross	d	19 01							20 01							21 01						
Frinton-on-Sea	d	19 04							20 04							21 04						
Walton-on-the-Naze	a	19 09							20 09							21 09						
Manningtree 2	d		19 20	19 26	19 33					20 20	20 26	20 33						21 04	21 20		21 26	21 33
Mistley	d			19 30							20 30										21 30	
Wrabness	d			19 35							20 35									←	21 35	
Harwich International	d			19 42							20 42						21 10 →	21a22		21 10	21 42	
Dovercourt	d			19 45							20 45										21 45	
Harwich Town	a			19 47							20 47										21 47	
Ipswich	a		19 32		19 42		20 04			20 32		20 42							21 32	21 37		21 42
	d				19 44		20 06					20 44			21 02							21 44
Lowestoft	a																					
Needham Market	d														21 12							
Stowmarket	d				19 55		20 17					20 55			21a17							21 55
Peterborough 8	a																					
Diss	d				20 07		20 29					21 07										22 07
Norwich	a				20 29		20 51					21 29										22 29

For general notes see front of timetable
For details of catering facilities see Directory of Train Operators

A To Cambridge (Table 14)

Due to major track repair work in the Bury St Edmunds area, trains between Ipswich and Peterborough are subject to disruption, resulting in bus replacements and extended journey times for part or all of this timetable. See local publicity or contact National Rail Enquiries 08457 48 49 50 for further details.

Table 11

Sundays

London → Chelmsford, Colchester, Walton-on-Naze, Clacton, Harwich, Ipswich and Norwich

Network diagram - see first page of Table 5

Station		LE 1	LE 1	LE 1	LE A	LE 1	LE 1	LE 1 ◇ ☕	LE 1	LE 1	LE 1	LE 1	LE 1 ◇ ☕	LE 1	LE 1	LE 1	LE 1 ◇	LE 1
London Liverpool Street 15 ⊖	d	20 32				21 02		21 30	21 32			22 02	22 30	22 32		23 02	23 30	23 32
Stratford 7 ⊖	d	20 39				21 09			21 39			22 09		22 39		23 09		23 39
Romford	d																	
Shenfield 3	d	21 01				21 31		21u57	22 01			22 31	22u57	23 01		23 31	23u57	00 01
Ingatestone	d					21 35						22 35				23 35		
Chelmsford 3	d	21 10				21 42			22 10			22 42		23 10		23 42		00 10
Hatfield Peverel	d					21 49						22 49				23 49		
Witham 2	d	21 19	21 23			21 54			22 19	22 23		22 54		23 19	23 23	23 54		00 19
White Notley	d		21 29							22 29					23 29			
Cressing	d		21 32							22 32					23 32			
Braintree Freeport	d		21 34							22 34					23 34			
Braintree	a		21 38							22 38					23 38			
Kelvedon	d					21 59						22 59				23 59		
Marks Tey 2	d	21 27			22 00	22 04			22 27			23 04		23 27		00 04		00 27
Colchester 4	a	21 35			22 09	22 12		22 23	22 35			23 12	23 23	23 35		00 12	00 27	00 40
	d	21 35				22 12		22 24	22 35			23 12	23 24	23 35		00 12	00 28	
Colchester Town	a																	
	d																	
Hythe	d																	
Wivenhoe 3	d	21 43							22 43					23 43				
Alresford (Essex)	d	21 46							22 46					23 46				
Great Bentley	d	21 50							22 50					23 50				
Weeley	d																	
Thorpe-le-Soken 1	a	21 55							22 55					23 55				
	d	21 55		21 57					22 55		22 57			23 55				
Clacton-on-Sea	a	22 05							23 05					00 05				
Kirby Cross	d			22 01							23 01							
Frinton-on-Sea	d			22 04							23 04							
Walton-on-the-Naze	a			22 09							23 09							
Manningtree 2	d					22 20	22 26	22 33				23 20	23 33			00 20	00 37	
Mistley	d						22 30											
Wrabness	d						22 35											
Harwich International	d						22 42											
Dovercourt	d						22 45											
Harwich Town	a						22 47											
Ipswich	a					22 32		22 42				23 32	23 42			00 36	00 46	
	d							22 44					23 44				00 48	
Lowestoft	a																	
Needham Market	d																	
Stowmarket	d							22 55					23 55				00 59	
Peterborough 8	a																	
Diss	d							23 07					00 07				01 11	
Norwich	a							23 29					00 39				01 43	

For general notes see front of timetable
For details of catering facilities see Directory of Train Operators

A From Sudbury (Table 10)

Due to major track repair work in the Bury St Edmunds area, trains between Ipswich and Peterborough are subject to disruption, resulting in bus replacements and extended journey times for part or all of this timetable. See local publicity or contact National Rail Enquiries 08457 48 49 50 for further details.

Norwich, Ipswich, Harwich, Clacton, Walton-on-Naze, Colchester and Chelmsford → London

Network diagram - see first page of Table 5

Miles	Miles	Miles	Miles	Miles	Station		LE	LE	LE	LE	LE	LE	LE	LE	LE	LE	LE	LE	LE	LE	LE	LE	LE	LE	LE
							MX	MO																	
							1		1	1	1 ◇	1	1	1	1	1	R 1	1		1	1	R 1	1	1	1
								A											B						
																	☕					☕			
0	—	—	—	—	**Norwich**	d											05 10					05 40			
20	—	—	—	—	Diss	d											05 28					05 58			
—	—	—	—	—	**Peterborough 8**	d																			
34¼	—	—	—	—	Stowmarket	d		00 04									05 40		05 57			06 10			
38	—	—	—	—	Needham Market	d		00 09											06 03						
—	—	—	—	—	**Lowestoft**	d																			
46¼	—	—	—	—	**Ipswich**	a		00 21									05 51		06 14			06 21			
—	—	—	—	—		d					05 23						05 53					06 23			
—	0	—	—	—	**Harwich Town**	d									05 37										
—	½	—	—	—	Dovercourt	d									05 39										
—	1¾	—	—	—	Harwich International	d									05 42										
—	5½	—	—	—	Wrabness	d									05 48										
—	9½	—	—	—	Mistley	d									05 53										
55½	11¼	—	—	—	Manningtree 2	d					05 33				05a58		06 03					06 33			
—	—	0	—	—	**Walton-on-the-Naze**	d								05 38							06 10				
—	—	1¼	—	—	Frinton-on-Sea	d								05 41							06 13				
—	—	2½	—	—	Kirby Cross	d								05 44							06 16				
—	—	—	0	—	**Clacton-on-Sea**	d							05 20					05 44							06 19
—	—	5	4¾	—	Thorpe-le-Soken 1	a							05 27	05 50				05 51			06 22				06 27
—	—	—	—	—		d							05 27					05 51							06 27
—	—	7¼	—	—	Weeley	d												05 55							
—	—	10	—	—	Great Bentley	d												05 59							
—	—	12¼	—	—	Alresford (Essex)	d												06 03							
—	—	14	—	—	Wivenhoe 3	d							05 38					06 06							06 38
—	—	16½	—	—	Hythe	d												06 10							
—	—	18	—	—	Colchester Town	a																			
—	—	—	—	—		d														06 21					
63¼	0	19¾	—	—	**Colchester 4**	a					05 43		05 47				06 13	06 17		06 28		06 43			06 47
—	—	—	—	—		d			04 45	05 21	05 43		05 48				06 15	06 18		06 29		06 45			06 48
68¼	—	—	—	—	Marks Tey 2	d			04 51	05 27			05 54							06 35					06 54
72¾	—	—	—	—	Kelvedon	d			04 56	05 32			06 00					06 28		06 41					07 00
—	—	—	—	0	**Braintree**	d	00 03					05 45												06 42	
—	—	—	—	¾	Braintree Freeport	d	00 05					05 47												06 44	
—	—	—	—	2	Cressing	d	00 08					05 50												06 47	
—	—	—	—	3¼	White Notley	d	00 11					05 53												06 50	
76½	—	—	—	6¼	**Witham 2**	d	00a18		05 01	05 37	05 56	06a01	06 05			06 15	06 27	06 33		06 46				06 58	07 05
79	—	—	—	—	Hatfield Peverel	d			05 05	05 41						06 19								07 02	
85¼	—	—	—	—	**Chelmsford 3**	d			05 12	05 48	06 05		06 14			06 26		06 42		06 55			07 03	07 09	07 14
91½	—	—	—	—	Ingatestone	d			05 19	05 55						06 33		06 48					07 10		
94¾	—	—	—	—	Shenfield 3	a			05 25	06 01			06 25			06 39				07 06			07 16	07 20	
102¾	—	—	—	—	Romford	a																			
111¼	—	—	—	—	Stratford 7 ⊖	a			05s44	06s18	06s29		06s41			06s56	06s59	07s08				07s26	07s33	07s37	07s40
115	—	—	—	—	**London Liverpool Street 15** ⊖	a			05 57	06 27	06 41		06 49			07 07	07 10	07 20		07 33		07 37	07 44	07 48	07 51

For general notes see front of timetable
For details of catering facilities see Directory of Train Operators

A From Cambridge (Table 14)
B From Bury St Edmunds (Table 14)

Due to major track repair work in the Bury St Edmunds area, trains between Ipswich and Peterborough are subject to disruption, resulting in bus replacements and extended journey times for part or all of this timetable. See local publicity or contact National Rail Enquiries 08457 48 49 50 for further details.

Norwich, Ipswich, Harwich, Clacton, Walton-on-Naze, Colchester and Chelmsford → London

Network diagram - see first page of Table 5

		LE	LE	LE	LE	LE	LE	LE	LE	LE	LE	LE	LE	LE	LE	LE	LE	LE	LE	LE	LE	LE	LE		LE
								R								R							R		
		1	1	1	1	1	1	1	1	1	1	1	1	1		1	1	1	1	1	1	1	1		1
															A										
								✕								🛒							✕		
Norwich	d							06 10								06 25							06 40		
Diss	d							06 28								06 43							06 58		
Peterborough 8	d																								
Stowmarket	d							06 40							06 44	06 55							07 10		
Needham Market	d																								
Lowestoft	d																								
Ipswich	a							06 51							07 00	07 06							07 21		
	d		06 38					06 53							07 00	07 08							07 23		
Harwich Town	d	06 22												07 08											
Dovercourt	d	06 24												07 10											
Harwich International	d	06 27											07 10	07 13	07a25										
Wrabness	d	06 33												07 19											
Mistley	d	06 38												07 24							←				
Manningtree 2	d	06 43	06 48					07 03					07b25	07a29		07 18					07 25		07 33		
Walton-on-the-Naze	d					06 43							↪							07 04					
Frinton-on-Sea	d					06 46														07 07					
Kirby Cross	d					06 49														07 10					
Clacton-on-Sea	d			06 34	06 38					06 49									07 04						
Thorpe-le-Soken 1	a			06 42	06 46	06 54				06 57		←							07 12	07 16					
	d			06 42	06 46	07 01 ↪				06 57		07 01							07 12						
Weeley	d				06 50							07 05													
Great Bentley	d				06 53							07 08													
Alresford (Essex)	d				06 58							07 13													
Wivenhoe 3	d			06 53	07 01					07 08	←	07 16							07 23			←			
Hythe	d				07 05						07 05	07 20										07 20			
Colchester Town	a				↪						07 09	↪										07 24			
	d						06 59				07 13											07 28			
Colchester 4	a	06 53	06 58	07 02			07 06	07 13		07 17	07 22					07 28			07 32		07 37	07 38	07 43		
	d		06 59	07 03			07 07	07 15		07 18						07 30			07 33		07 37		07 45		
Marks Tey 2	d						07 13			07 24											07 43				
Kelvedon	d			07 13						07 30									07 43						
Braintree	d																	07 27							
Braintree Freeport	d																	07 29							
Cressing	d																	07 32							
White Notley	d								←									07 35							←
Witham 2	d		07 11	07 18			07b28		07 28	07 35								07 43	07 48		07c58				07 58
Hatfield Peverel	d						↪		07 32												↪				08 02
Chelmsford 3	d		07 20	07 27					07 39								07 49	07 53	07 57						08 09
Ingatestone	d		07 26														07 56								
Shenfield 3	a		07 32	07 38					07 50								08 02		08 08						08 20
Romford	a																								
Stratford 7 ⊖ ⛴	a			07s55						08s09									08s25						
London Liverpool Street 15 ⊖	a		07 59	08 06				08 09	08 16	08 20						08 23	08 28	08 30	08 36				08 39		08 48

For general notes see front of timetable
For details of catering facilities see Directory of Train Operators

A From Bury St Edmunds (Table 14)
b Arr. 0722
c Arr. 0752

Due to major track repair work in the Bury St Edmunds area, trains between Ipswich and Peterborough are subject to disruption, resulting in bus replacements and extended journey times for part or all of this timetable. See local publicity or contact National Rail Enquiries 08457 48 49 50 for further details.

Norwich, Ipswich, Harwich, Clacton, Walton-on-Naze, Colchester and Chelmsford → London

Network diagram - see first page of Table 5

		LE	LE	LE	LE	LE	LE	LE	LE	LE	LE	LE	LE	LE	LE	LE	LE	LE	LE	LE	LE	LE	LE	LE	LE
		1	1	R 1		1	1	1	R 1	1	1	1	1		1	R 1	1	1 ◇	1	1	1	1	1 ◇	1	1
					A									B		C									
				✕					☕									✕					✕		
Norwich	d			06 55					07 10							07 30		07 40					08 00		
Diss	d			07 13					07 28									07 58					08 17		
Peterborough 8	d																								
Stowmarket	d			07 25					07 40					07 45				08 10					08 29		
Needham Market	d													07 50											
Lowestoft	d																								
Ipswich	a			07 36					07 51					08 02		08 07		08 22					08 40		
	d			07 38					07 53							08 18		08 23					08 42		
Harwich Town	d																08 00								
Dovercourt	d																08 02								
Harwich International	d				07 47												08 06								
Wrabness	d				07 53												08 12								
Mistley	d				07a59												08 17								
Manningtree 2	d			07 48					08 03								08 22	08 33					08 52		
Walton-on-the-Naze	d		07 40												08 09							08 45			
Frinton-on-Sea	d		07 43												08 12							08 48			
Kirby Cross	d		07 46												08 15							08 51			
Clacton-on-Sea	d	07 10									07 45									08 15					08 50
Thorpe-le-Soken 1	a	07 17	07 51								07 52		←		08 21					08 22		08 56			08 57
	d	07 17	07 56								07 52		07 56							08 22		09 01			08 57
Weeley	d	07 21	→										08 00									→			
Great Bentley	d	07 25											08 03							08 28					
Alresford (Essex)	d	07 29											08 08							08 32					
Wivenhoe 3	d	07 33									08 03		08 11							08 35					09 07
Hythe	d	07 37											08 15												
Colchester Town	a												08 19												
	d							08 02				←	08 23								08 45				
Colchester 4	a	07 44		07 58				08 09	08 13		08 16	08 09	08 32				08 32	08 43		08 44	08 52		09 01		09 17
	d	07 49		08 00			08 03	→	08 15		08 18						08 37	08 45		08 48			09 03		09 17
Marks Tey 2	d						08 09				08 24									08 54					09 23
Kelvedon	d	07 59					08 15				08 30									09 00					09 29
Braintree	d									08 12														09 00	
Braintree Freeport	d									08 14														09 02	
Cressing	d									08 17														09 05	
White Notley	d									08 20														09 08	
Witham 2	d	08 04					08 20			08 28	08 35						08 49		08 58	09 05				09 15	09 34
Hatfield Peverel	d									08 32									09 02					09 20	
Chelmsford 3	d	08 13				08 19	08 29			08 39	08 44						08 58	09 02	09 09	09 14				09 27	09 43
Ingatestone	d					08 26				08 46									09 16					09 33	
Shenfield 3	a					08 32	08 40			08 52	08 55								09 22	09 25			09s29	09 40	09 54
Romford	a																							09 48	
Stratford 7 ⊖	a	08s39				08s49			08s59	09s09								09s28	09s39					09s57	10s08
London Liverpool Street 15 ⊖	a	08 50		08 55		09 01	09 06		09 10	09 20	09 22					09 25	09 33	09 40	09 50	09 52			09 56	10 05	10 17

For general notes see front of timetable
For details of catering facilities see Directory of Train Operators

A To Cambridge (Table 14)
B From Cambridge (Table 14)
C From Great Yarmouth (Table 15)

Due to major track repair work in the Bury St Edmunds area, trains between Ipswich and Peterborough are subject to disruption, resulting in bus replacements and extended journey times for part or all of this timetable. See local publicity or contact National Rail Enquiries 08457 48 49 50 for further details.

Norwich, Ipswich, Harwich, Clacton, Walton-on-Naze, Colchester and Chelmsford → London

Network diagram - see first page of Table 5

		LE	LE	LE	LE	LE	LE	LE	LE	LE	LE	LE	LE	LE	LE	LE	LE	LE		LE	LE	LE	LE	LE	LE
		1		R 1	1	1	1	R 1	1	1	R 1	1	1	1		1 ◇	1	1		R 1	1	1	1 ◇	1	1
			A												A										
				☕							☕					☕							☕		
Norwich	d			08 30							09 00					09 30							10 00		
Diss	d			08 47							09 17					09 47							10 17		
Peterborough 8	d							07 52																	
Stowmarket	d		08 45					09 12			09 29				09 45								10 29		
Needham Market	d		08 51												09 50										
Lowestoft	d																			08 58					
Ipswich	a		09 03	09 07				09 26			09 40				10 02	10 07				10 26			10 40		
	d			09 08				09 30			09 42					10 08				10 30			10 42		
Harwich Town	d				09 00												10 00								
Dovercourt	d				09 02												10 02								
Harwich International	d				09 06												10 06								
Wrabness	d				09 12												10 12								
Mistley	d				09 17												10 17								
Manningtree 2	d			09 18	09 22						09 52					10 18	10 22						10 52		
Walton-on-the-Naze	d									09 45												10 45			
Frinton-on-Sea	d									09 48												10 48			
Kirby Cross	d									09 51												10 51			
Clacton-on-Sea	d												09 50												10 50
Thorpe-le-Soken 1	a					←				09 56			09 57					←				10 56			10 57
	d					09 01				10 01 →			09 57					10 01				11 01 →			10 57
Weeley	d					09 05												10 05							
Great Bentley	d					09 08												10 08							
Alresford (Essex)	d					09 13												10 13							
Wivenhoe 3	d					09 16							10 07					10 16							11 07
Hythe	d					09 20												10 20							
Colchester Town	a					09 24												10 24							
	d	09 15				09 28			09 45					10 15				10 28			10 45				
Colchester 4	a	09 22		09 27	09 32	09 37		09 48	09 52		10 01		10 17	10 22		10 27	10 32	10 37		10 48	10 52		11 01		11 17
	d			09 29	09 33		09 44	09 49			10 03		10 17			10 29	10 33			10 49			11 03		11 17
Marks Tey 2	d				09 39								10 23				10 39								11 23
Kelvedon	d				09 44												10 44								
Braintree	d											10 00												11 00	
Braintree Freeport	d											10 02												11 02	
Cressing	d											10 05												11 05	
White Notley	d											10 08												11 08	
Witham 2	d				09 49		09 56	10 02				10 15	10 31				10 49			11 02				11 15	11 31
Hatfield Peverel	d											10 20												11 20	
Chelmsford 3	d			09 47	09 58		10 05	10s10				10 27	10 40			10 46	10 58			11 11				11 27	11 40
Ingatestone	d						10 12					10 33												11 33	
Shenfield 3	a				10 09			10s22			10s29	10 40	10 51				11 09			11s22			11s29	11 40	11 51
Romford	a												10 59												11 59
Stratford 7 ⊖	a			10s11	10s24		10s32					10s55	11s07			11s10	11s24							11s55	12s07
London Liverpool Street 15 ⊖	a			10 24	10 33		10 41	10 46			10 54	11 03	11 18			11 24	11 33			11 45			11 54	12 03	12 16

For general notes see front of timetable
For details of catering facilities see Directory of Train Operators

A From Cambridge (Table 14)

Due to major track repair work in the Bury St Edmunds area, trains between Ipswich and Peterborough are subject to disruption, resulting in bus replacements and extended journey times for part or all of this timetable. See local publicity or contact National Rail Enquiries 08457 48 49 50 for further details.

Norwich, Ipswich, Harwich, Clacton, Walton-on-Naze, Colchester and Chelmsford → London

Network diagram - see first page of Table 5

		LE	LE	LE	LE	LE	LE	LE	LE	LE	LE	LE	LE	LE	LE	LE	LE	LE	LE	LE	LE	LE	LE	LE	LE
		1	A	1 ◇	1	1	1 ◇	1	1	1 ◇	1	1	1	A	1 ◇	1	1	1 ◇	1	1	1 ◇	1	1	1	A
				☕						✕					☕						✕				
Norwich	d			10 30						11 00					11 30						12 00				
Diss	d			10 47						11 17					11 47						12 17				
Peterborough 8	d						09 47																		
Stowmarket	d		10 45				11 12			11 29				11 45							12 29				12 45
Needham Market	d		10 50											11 50											12 50
Lowestoft	d																	10 58							
Ipswich	a		11 02	11 07			11 25			11 40				12 02	12 07			12 26			12 40				13 02
	d			11 08			11 30			11 42					12 08			12 30			12 42				
Harwich Town	d				11 00											12 00									
Dovercourt	d				11 02											12 02									
Harwich International	d				11 06											12 06									
Wrabness	d				11 12											12 12									
Mistley	d				11 17											12 17									
Manningtree 2	d			11 18	11 22					11 52					12 18	12 22					12 52				
Walton-on-the-Naze	d								11 45											12 45					
Frinton-on-Sea	d								11 48											12 48					
Kirby Cross	d								11 51											12 51					
Clacton-on-Sea	d											11 50											12 50		
Thorpe-le-Soken 1	a					←			11 56			11 57					←			12 56			12 57		
	d					11 01			12 01 →			11 57					12 01			13 01 →			12 57		
Weeley	d					11 05											12 05								
Great Bentley	d					11 08											12 08								
Alresford (Essex)	d					11 13											12 13								
Wivenhoe 3	d					11 16						12 07					12 16						13 07		
Hythe	d					11 20											12 20								
Colchester Town	a					11 24											12 24								
	d	11 15				11 28		11 45					12 15				12 28		12 45					13 15	
Colchester 4	a	11 22		11 27	11 32	11 37	11 48	11 52		12 01		12 17	12 22		12 27	12 32	12 37	12 48	12 52		13 01		13 17	13 22	
	d			11 29	11 33		11 49			12 03		12 17			12 29	12 33		12 49			13 03		13 17		
Marks Tey 2	d				11 39							12 23				12 39							13 23		
Kelvedon	d				11 44											12 44									
Braintree	d										12 00											13 00			
Braintree Freeport	d										12 02											13 02			
Cressing	d										12 05											13 05			
White Notley	d										12 08											13 08			
Witham 2	d				11 49		12 02				12 15	12 31				12 49		13 02				13 15	13 31		
Hatfield Peverel	d										12 20											13 20			
Chelmsford 3	d			11 46	11 58		12 11				12 27	12 40			12 46	12 58		13 11				13 27	13 40		
Ingatestone	d										12 33											13 33			
Shenfield 3	a				12 09		12s22			12s29	12 40	12 51				13 09		13s22			13s29	13 40	13 51		
Romford	a											12 59											13 59		
Stratford 7 ⊖	a			12s10	12s24						12s55	13s07			13s10	13s24						13s55	14s07		
London Liverpool Street 15 ⊖	a			12 24	12 33		12 45			12 54	13 03	13 16			13 24	13 33		13 45			13 54	14 03	14 16		

For general notes see front of timetable
For details of catering facilities see Directory of Train Operators

A From Cambridge (Table 14)

Due to major track repair work in the Bury St Edmunds area, trains between Ipswich and Peterborough are subject to disruption, resulting in bus replacements and extended journey times for part or all of this timetable. See local publicity or contact National Rail Enquiries 08457 48 49 50 for further details.

Norwich, Ipswich, Harwich, Clacton, Walton-on-Naze, Colchester and Chelmsford → London

Network diagram - see first page of Table 5

Station		LE	LE	LE	LE	LE	LE	LE	LE	LE	LE	LE	LE	LE		LE	LE	LE	LE	LE	LE	LE	LE	LE	LE
		1◇	1	1	1◇	1	1	1◇	1	1	1	A	1◇	1		1	1◇	1	1	1◇	1	1	1	A	1◇
		☕						✕					☕							☕					☕
Norwich	d	12 30						13 00					13 30							14 00					14 30
Diss	d	12 47						13 17					13 47							14 17					14 47
Peterborough 8	d				11 48																				
Stowmarket	d				13 12			13 29				13 45								14 29				14 45	
Needham Market	d											13 50												14 50	
Lowestoft	d																12 58								
Ipswich	a	13 07			13 25			13 40				14 02	14 07				14 26			14 40				15 02	15 07
	d	13 08			13 30			13 42					14 08				14 30			14 42					15 08
Harwich Town	d		13 00											14 00											
Dovercourt	d		13 02											14 02											
Harwich International	d		13 06											14 06											
Wrabness	d		13 12											14 12											
Mistley	d		13 17											14 17											
Manningtree 2	d	13 18	13 22					13 52					14 18	14 22						14 52					15 18
Walton-on-the-Naze	d						13 45												14 45						
Frinton-on-Sea	d						13 48												14 48						
Kirby Cross	d						13 51												14 51						
Clacton-on-Sea	d									13 50												14 50			
Thorpe-le-Soken 1	a			⟵			13 56			13 57						⟵			14 56			14 57			
	d			13 01			14 01 ⟶			13 57						14 01			15 01 ⟶			14 57			
Weeley	d			13 05												14 05									
Great Bentley	d			13 08												14 08									
Alresford (Essex)	d			13 13												14 13									
Wivenhoe 3	d			13 16						14 07						14 16						15 07			
Hythe	d			13 20												14 20									
Colchester Town	a			13 24												14 24									
	d			13 28		13 45					14 15					14 28		14 45					15 15		
Colchester 4	a	13 27	13 32	13 37	13 48	13 52		14 01		14 17	14 22		14 27	14 32		14 37	14 48	14 52		15 01		15 17	15 22		15 27
	d	13 29	13 33		13 49			14 03		14 17			14 29	14 33			14 49			15 03		15 17			15 29
Marks Tey 2	d		13 39							14 23				14 39								15 23			
Kelvedon	d		13 44											14 44											
Braintree	d								14 00												15 00				
Braintree Freeport	d								14 02												15 02				
Cressing	d								14 05												15 05				
White Notley	d								14 08												15 08				
Witham 2	d		13 49		14 02				14 15	14 31				14 49			15 02				15 15	15 31			
Hatfield Peverel	d								14 20												15 20				
Chelmsford 3	d	13 46	13 58		14 11				14 27	14 40			14 46	14 58			15 11				15 27	15 40			15 46
Ingatestone	d								14 33												15 33				
Shenfield 3	a		14 09		14s22			14s29	14 40	14 51				15 09			15s22			15s29	15 40	15 51			
Romford	a									14 59												15 59			
Stratford 7 ⊖ ⛴	a	14s10	14s24						14s55	15s07			15s10	15s24							15s55	16s07			16s10
London Liverpool Street 15 ⊖	a	14 24	14 33		14 45			14 54	15 03	15 16			15 24	15 34			15 45			15 54	16 03	16 18			16 24

For general notes see front of timetable
For details of catering facilities see
Directory of Train Operators

A From Cambridge (Table 14)

Due to major track repair work in the Bury St Edmunds area, trains between Ipswich and Peterborough are subject to disruption, resulting in bus replacements and extended journey times for part or all of this timetable. See local publicity or contact National Rail Enquiries 08457 48 49 50 for further details.

Norwich, Ipswich, Harwich, Clacton, Walton-on-Naze, Colchester and Chelmsford → London

Network diagram - see first page of Table 5

		LE 1	LE 1	LE 1	LE 1	LE 1	LE 1	LE 1 ◇ ☕	LE 1	LE 1	LE A	LE 1	LE 1 ◇ ☕
Norwich	d							15 00					15 30
Diss	d							15 17					15 47
Peterborough 8	d			13 47									
Stowmarket	d			15 12				15 29			15 45		
Needham Market	d										15 50		
Lowestoft	d												
Ipswich	a			15 25				15 40			16 02		16 07
	d			15 26				15 42					16 08
Harwich Town	d	15 00											
Dovercourt	d	15 02											
Harwich International	d	15 06											
Wrabness	d	15 12											
Mistley	d	15 17											
Manningtree 2	d	15 22						15 52					16 18
Walton-on-the-Naze	d						15 45						
Frinton-on-Sea	d						15 48						
Kirby Cross	d						15 51						
Clacton-on-Sea	d									15 50			
Thorpe-le-Soken 1	a		←				15 56			15 57			
	d		15 01				16 01 →			15 57			
Weeley	d		15 05										
Great Bentley	d		15 08										
Alresford (Essex)	d		15 13										
Wivenhoe 3	d		15 16							16 07			
Hythe	d		15 20										
Colchester Town	a		15 24										
	d		15 28			15 45						16 15	
Colchester 4	a	15 32	15 37	15 43		15 52		16 01		16 17		16 22	16 27
	d	15 36			15 48			16 03		16 17			16 29
Marks Tey 2	d				15 54					16 23			
Kelvedon	d	15 45			15 59								
Braintree	d								16 00				
Braintree Freeport	d								16 02				
Cressing	d								16 05				
White Notley	d								16 08				
Witham 2	d	15 49			16 04				16 15	16 31			
Hatfield Peverel	d								16 20				
Chelmsford 3	d	15 58			16 13				16 27	16 40			16 46
Ingatestone	d	16 05							16 33				
Shenfield 3	a	16 11			16 24			16s29	16 40	16 51			
Romford	a								16 48				
Stratford 7 ⊖	a	16s26			16s39				16s56	17s05			17s10
London Liverpool Street 15 ⊖	a	16 35			16 48			16 54	17 05	17 15			17 24

		LE 1	LE 1	LE 1	LE 1	LE 1	LE 1 ◇ ✕	LE 1	LE 1	LE 1	LE 1	LE A	LE 1 ◇ ☕
Norwich	d						16 00						16 30
Diss	d						16 17						16 47
Peterborough 8	d												
Stowmarket	d						16 29					16 45	
Needham Market	d											16 50	
Lowestoft	d												
Ipswich	a						16 40					17 02	17 07
	d				16 30		16 42						17 08
Harwich Town	d			16 05									
Dovercourt	d			16 07									
Harwich International	d			16 11									
Wrabness	d			16 17									
Mistley	d			16 22									
Manningtree 2	d			16 27			16 52						17 18
Walton-on-the-Naze	d					16 43							
Frinton-on-Sea	d					16 46							
Kirby Cross	d					16 49							
Clacton-on-Sea	d										16 48		
Thorpe-le-Soken 1	a		←			16 54					16 55		
	d		16 01			17 01 →					16 55		
Weeley	d		16 05										
Great Bentley	d		16 08										
Alresford (Essex)	d		16 13										
Wivenhoe 3	d		16 16								17 05		
Hythe	d		16 20								17 09		
Colchester Town	a		16 24										
	d		16 28						17 05				
Colchester 4	a		16 37	16 40	16 48		17 01		17 12		17 17		17 27
	d	16 33		16 53			17 03				17 17		17 29
Marks Tey 2	d	16 39		16 59							17 23		
Kelvedon	d	16 44											
Braintree	d							17 00					
Braintree Freeport	d							17 02					
Cressing	d							17 05					
White Notley	d							17 08					
Witham 2	d	16 49		17 07				17 15		17 21	17 31		
Hatfield Peverel	d									17 25			
Chelmsford 3	d	16 58		17 16				17 25		17 32	17 40		17 46
Ingatestone	d	17 05								17 39			
Shenfield 3	a	17 11		17 27			17s30	17 36		17 45	17 51		
Romford	a										17 59		
Stratford 7 ⊖	a	17s26						17s50		18s02	18s07		18s12
London Liverpool Street 15 ⊖	a	17 38		17 49			17 54	18 00		18 11	18 20		18 24

For general notes see front of timetable
For details of catering facilities see Directory of Train Operators

A From Cambridge (Table 14)

Due to major track repair work in the Bury St Edmunds area, trains between Ipswich and Peterborough are subject to disruption, resulting in bus replacements and extended journey times for part or all of this timetable. See local publicity or contact National Rail Enquiries 08457 48 49 50 for further details.

Norwich, Ipswich, Harwich, Clacton, Walton-on-Naze, Colchester and Chelmsford → London

Network diagram - see first page of Table 5

		LE 1	LE 1	LE 1	LE 1◇	LE 1	LE 1◇ ✕	LE 1	LE 1	LE 1	LE A	LE 1◇ ☕	LE 1	LE 1	LE 1	LE 1◇	LE 1	LE 1◇ ✕	LE 1	LE 1	LE 1	LE 1	LE A	LE 1
Norwich	d						17 00					17 30						18 00						
Diss	d						17 17					17 47						18 17						
Peterborough 8	d				15 47																			
Stowmarket	d				17 12		17 29				17 46	17 59						18 29					18 46	
Needham Market	d										17 52												18 52	
Lowestoft	d															16 58								
Ipswich	a				17 27		17 40				18 03	18 10				18 26		18 40					19 03	
	d				17 30		17 42					18 11				18 30		18 42			18 56			
Harwich Town	d	17 00						17 53									18 25					18 53		
Dovercourt	d	17 02						17 55									18 27					18 55		
Harwich International	d	17 06						17 58									18 30					18 58		
Wrabness	d	17 12						18 04									18 36					19 04		
Mistley	d	17 17						18 09									18 41					19 09		
Manningtree 2	d	17 22					17 52	18a14				18 21					18a46	18 52			19 06	19a14		
Walton-on-the-Naze	d					17 38									18 26									
Frinton-on-Sea	d					17 41									18 29									
Kirby Cross	d					17 44									18b35									
Clacton-on-Sea	d									17 45										18 45				
Thorpe-le-Soken 1	a		←			17 49				17 52			←		18 41					18 52				
	d		17 01			17 56 →				17 52			17 56							18 52				
Weeley	d		17 05										18 00											
Great Bentley	d		17 08							17 58			18 03							18 58				
Alresford (Essex)	d		17 13							18 02			18 08							19 02				
Wivenhoe 3	d		17 16							18 05			18 11							19 05				
Hythe	d		17 20										18 15											
Colchester Town	a		17 24										18 19											
	d		17 28										18 23											19 15
Colchester 4	a	17 32	17 37		17 48		18 01			18 14		18 30	18 32			18 48		19 01		19 14	19 17			19 22
	d	17 33			17 49		18 03			18 15		18 32	18 35			18 49		19 03		19 15				19 33 →
Marks Tey 2	d	17 39			17 55					18 21						18 55				19 21				
Kelvedon	d	17 44								18 26			18 44							19 26				
Braintree	d			17 44										18 36										
Braintree Freeport	d			17 46										18 38										
Cressing	d			17 49										18 41										
White Notley	d			17 52										18 44										
Witham 2	d	17 49		18 00	18 04				18 15	18 31			18 49	18 52		19 04			19 15	19 31				
Hatfield Peverel	d								18 20										19 20					
Chelmsford 3	d	17 58		18 09	18 13				18 27	18 40		18 49	18 58	19 02		19 13			19 27	19 40				
Ingatestone	d	18 05							18 33					19 09					19 33					
Shenfield 3	a	18 11			18s25		18s29		18 40	18 51			19 09	19 15		19s24		19s29	19 40	19 51				
Romford	a									18 59										19 59				
Stratford 7 ⊖ ⛴	a	18s26							18s55	19s07		19s15	19s24						19s55	20s07				
London Liverpool Street 15 ⊖	a	18 35		18 41	18 49		18 54		19 05	19 16		19 27	19 33	19 39		19 47		19 54	20 04	20 16				

For general notes see front of timetable
For details of catering facilities see Directory of Train Operators

A From Cambridge (Table 14)
b Arr. 1832

Due to major track repair work in the Bury St Edmunds area, trains between Ipswich and Peterborough are subject to disruption, resulting in bus replacements and extended journey times for part or all of this timetable. See local publicity or contact National Rail Enquiries 08457 48 49 50 for further details.

Norwich, Ipswich, Harwich, Clacton, Walton-on-Naze, Colchester and Chelmsford → London

Network diagram - see first page of Table 5

		LE 1	LE 1 ◊	LE 1	LE 1	LE 1	LE 1 ◊	LE 1	LE 1	LE 1 ◊	LE 1	LE 1	LE 1	LE	LE 1	LE 1	LE 1	LE 1	LE 1 ◊	LE 1	LE 1 ◊	LE 1	LE 1	LE 1	LE 1
														A											
			☕							☕											☕				
Norwich	d		18 30							19 00											20 00				
Diss	d		18 47							19 17											20 17				
Peterborough 8	d						17 47																		
Stowmarket	d						19 12			19 29				19 45							20 29				
Needham Market	d													19 50											
Lowestoft	d																		18 43						
Ipswich	a		19 07				19 25			19 40				20 02					20 16		20 40				
	d		19 08				19 27	19 35		19 42					20 08				20 30		20 42				
Harwich Town	d								19 28							20 00							20 33		21 00
Dovercourt	d								19 30							20 02							20 35		21 02
Harwich International	d								19 33							20 06							20 38		21 06
Wrabness	d								19 39							20 12							20 44		21 12
Mistley	d								19 44							20 17							20 49		21 17
Manningtree 2	d		19 18				19 37	19 46	19a49	19 52					20 18	20 22					20 52		20 56		21 22
Walton-on-the-Naze	d				18 48	19 24											19 51	20 24		20 45					→
Frinton-on-Sea	d				18 51	19 27											19 54	20 27		20 48					
Kirby Cross	d				18 54	19b33											19 57	20c33		20 51					
Clacton-on-Sea	d												19 45											20 50	
Thorpe-le-Soken 1	a				18 59	19 39							19 52				20 02	20 39		20 56				20 57	
	d				19 01								19 52				20 03			21 01				20 57	
Weeley	d				19 05												20 07			→					
Great Bentley	d				19 08								19 58				20 10								
Alresford (Essex)	d				19 13								20 02				20 15								
Wivenhoe 3	d				19 16								20 05				20 18							21 07	
Hythe	d				19 20												20 22								
Colchester Town	a				19 24												20 26								
	d				19 28												20 30								
Colchester 4	a		19 27	←	19 37		19 47	19 57		20 01			20 14		20 28	20 32	20 39		20 48		21 01		21 06	21 17	
	d		19 29	19 33			19 48			20 03			20 15		20 29	20 33			20 49		21 03			21 17	
Marks Tey 2	d			19 39			19 54						20 21			20 39								21 23	
Kelvedon	d			19 44									20 26			20 44									
Braintree	d	19 25										20 10										21 00			
Braintree Freeport	d	19 27										20 12										21 02			
Cressing	d	19 30										20 15										21 05			
White Notley	d	19 33										20 18										21 08			
Witham 2	d	19 41		19 49			20 02				20 15	20a25	20 31			20 49			21 02			21 15		21 31	
Hatfield Peverel	d										20 20											21 20			
Chelmsford 3	d	19 50	19 46	19 58			20 11				20 27		20 40		20 46	20 58			21 11			21 27		21 40	
Ingatestone	d										20 33											21 33			
Shenfield 3	a			20 09			20s23			20s29	20 40		20 51			21 09			21s22		21s29	21 40		21 51	
Romford	a												20 59											21 59	
Stratford 7 ⊖ ⛴	a		20s10	20s24							20s55		21s07		21s10	21s24						21s55		22s10	
London Liverpool Street 15 ⊖	a	20 23	20 24	20 33			20 46			20 54	21 04		21 17		21 21	21 33			21 45		21 54	22 03		22 19	

For general notes see front of timetable
For details of catering facilities see Directory of Train Operators

A From Cambridge (Table 14)
b Arr. 1930
c Arr. 2030

Due to major track repair work in the Bury St Edmunds area, trains between Ipswich and Peterborough are subject to disruption, resulting in bus replacements and extended journey times for part or all of this timetable. See local publicity or contact National Rail Enquiries 08457 48 49 50 for further details.

Norwich, Ipswich, Harwich, Clacton, Walton-on-Naze, Colchester and Chelmsford → London

Network diagram - see first page of Table 5

		LE	LE 1	LE 1	LE 1	LE 1 ◇	LE 1	LE 1 ◇	LE 1	LE 1	LE 1	LE	LE 1	LE 1	LE 1	LE 1	LE 1	LE 1 ◇	LE 1	LE 1	LE 1	LE 1	LE
		A										A											A
Norwich	d							21 00										22 00				23 05	
Diss	d							21 17										22 17				23 22	
Peterborough [8]	d					19 49															22 05		
Stowmarket	d	20 45				21 08		21 29				21 46						22 29			23 24	23 34	23 46
Needham Market	d	20 50										21 52											23 52
Lowestoft	d																						
Ipswich	a	21 02				21 25		21 40				22 03						22 40			23 37	23 48	00 03
	d	21 04	21 08			21 27		21 42					22 08					22 42		23 20	23 38		
Harwich Town	d										21 54								23 05				
Dovercourt	d										21 56								23 07				
Harwich International	d	21a28									21 59								23 10				
Wrabness	d										22 05								23 16				
Mistley	d			←							22 10								23 21				
Manningtree [2]	d		21 18	21 22		21 37		21 52			22a15		22 18					22 52	23a26	23 29	23 48		
Walton-on-the-Naze	d						21 45										22 43						
Frinton-on-Sea	d						21 48										22 46						
Kirby Cross	d						21 51										22b52						
Clacton-on-Sea	d									21 50						22 24							
Thorpe-le-Soken [1]	a				←		21 56			21 57					←	22 31	22 58						
	d				21 01		22 01 →			21 57					22 01	22 31							
Weeley	d				21 05										22 05	22 35							
Great Bentley	d				21 08										22 08	22 39							
Alresford (Essex)	d				21 13										22 13	22 43							
Wivenhoe [3]	d				21 16					22 07					22 16	22 46							
Hythe	d				21 20										22 20	22 50							
Colchester Town	a				21 24										22 24								
	d				21 28										22 28								
Colchester [4]	a		21 28	21 32	21 37	21 48		22 01		22 17			22 28	22 37		22 57		23 01		23 39	23 58		
	d		21 29	21 33		21 49		22 03		22 17			22 29					23 03					
Marks Tey [2]	d			21 39						22 23			22 35										
Kelvedon	d			21 44									22 40										
Braintree	d								22 00						22 57								
Braintree Freeport	d								22 02						22 59								
Cressing	d								22 05						23 02								
White Notley	d								22 08						23 05								
Witham [2]	d			21 49		22 02			22 15	22 31			22 45		23a12			23 15					
Hatfield Peverel	d								22 20				22 49										
Chelmsford [3]	d		21 46	21 58		22 11			22 27	22 40			22 56					23 24					
Ingatestone	d								22 33				23 03										
Shenfield [3]	a		21 58	22 11		22s22		22s29	22 40	22 51			23 09					23s36					
Romford	a									22 59													
Stratford [7] ⊖	a		22s12	22s27					22s55	23s07			23s25					23s52					
London Liverpool Street [15] ⊖	a		22 23	22 36		22 45		22 54	23 03	23 16			23 34					00 03					

For general notes see front of timetable
For details of catering facilities see Directory of Train Operators

A From Cambridge (Table 14)
b Arr. 2249

Due to major track repair work in the Bury St Edmunds area, trains between Ipswich and Peterborough are subject to disruption, resulting in bus replacements and extended journey times for part or all of this timetable. See local publicity or contact National Rail Enquiries 08457 48 49 50 for further details.

Table 11

Norwich, Ipswich, Harwich, Clacton, Walton-on-Naze, Colchester and Chelmsford → London

Network diagram - see first page of Table 5

		LE	LE	LE	LE	LE	LE	LE	LE	LE	LE		LE	LE	LE	LE	LE	LE	LE	LE	LE	LE		LE	LE
		1	1	1	1	1	1 ◇	1	1	1 ◇	1		1	1	1	1 ◇	1	1	1	1				1 ◇	1
																						A			
							☕			☕						☕								☕	
Norwich	d						05 00			05 30						06 00								06 30	
Diss	d						05 17			05 47						06 17								06 47	
Peterborough 8	d																								
Stowmarket	d						05 29									06 29						06 45			
Needham Market	d																					06 50			
Lowestoft	d																								
Ipswich	a						05 40			06 07						06 40						07 02		07 07	
	d						05 42			06 08				06 30		06 42					07 00			07 08	
Harwich Town	d										06 00								07 00						
Dovercourt	d										06 02								07 02						
Harwich International	d										06 06								07 06	07 15	07a25				
Wrabness	d										06 12								07 12						
Mistley	d										06 17								07 17						←
Manningtree 2	d						05 52			06 18	06 22					06 52			07 22	07 28				07 18	07 22
Walton-on-the-Naze	d				05 45										06 45				→	→					
Frinton-on-Sea	d				05 48										06 48										
Kirby Cross	d				05 51										06 51										
Clacton-on-Sea	d								05 50									06 50							
Thorpe-le-Soken 1	a				05 56				05 57				←		06 56			06 57							
	d				06 01 →				05 57				06 01		07 01 →			06 57							
Weeley	d												06 05												
Great Bentley	d												06 08												
Alresford (Essex)	d												06 13												
Wivenhoe 3	d								06 07				06 16					07 07							
Hythe	d												06 20												
Colchester Town	a												06 24												
	d												06 28												
Colchester 4	a						06 01		06 17	06 27	06 32		06 37	06 48		07 01		07 17						07 27	07 32
	d		04 45	05 30			06 03	06 06	06 17	06 29	06 33			06 49		07 03		07 17						07 29	07 33
Marks Tey 2	d		04 51	05 36				06 12	06 23		06 39							07 23							07 39
Kelvedon	d		04 56	05 41				06 17			06 44														07 44
Braintree	d	00 03				06 00											07 00								
Braintree Freeport	d	00 05				06 02											07 02								
Cressing	d	00 08				06 05											07 05								
White Notley	d	00 11				06 08											07 08								
Witham 2	d	00a18	05 01	05 46		06a15		06 22	06 31		06 49			07 02			07 15	07 31							07 49
Hatfield Peverel	d		05 05	05 50				06 26									07 20								
Chelmsford 3	d		05 12	05 57				06 33	06 40	06 46	06 58			07 11			07 27	07 40						07 46	07 58
Ingatestone	d		05 19	06 04				06 40									07 33								
Shenfield 3	a		05 25	06 10			06s29	06 46	06 51		07 09			07s22		07s29	07 40	07 51							08 09
Romford	a			06 19					06 59									07 59							
Stratford 7 ⊖	a		05s44	06s27				07s01	07s07	07s10	07s24						07s55	08s07						08s10	08s24
London Liverpool Street 15 ⊖	a		05 57	06 36			06 54	07 10	07 16	07 24	07 33			07 45		07 54	08 03	08 16						08 24	08 33

For general notes see front of timetable
For details of catering facilities see Directory of Train Operators

A From Bury St Edmunds (Table 14)

Due to major track repair work in the Bury St Edmunds area, trains between Ipswich and Peterborough are subject to disruption, resulting in bus replacements and extended journey times for part or all of this timetable. See local publicity or contact National Rail Enquiries 08457 48 49 50 for further details.

Norwich, Ipswich, Harwich, Clacton, Walton-on-Naze, Colchester and Chelmsford → London

Network diagram - see first page of Table 5

		LE	LE	LE	LE	LE	LE	LE	LE	LE	LE	LE	LE	LE	LE	LE	LE	LE	LE	LE	LE	LE	LE
		1	1	R 1	1	1 ◇		1	1	1		1 ◇	1	1	R 1	1	1	1	1 ◇	1	1	1	
							A				B												B
						☕						☕							☕				
Norwich	d					07 00						07 30							08 00				
Diss	d					07 17						07 47							08 17				
Peterborough 8	d																						
Stowmarket	d					07 29					07 45								08 29				08 45
Needham Market	d										07 50												08 50
Lowestoft	d			05 58											06 58								
Ipswich	a			07 26		07 40					08 02	08 07			08 26				08 40				09 02
	d			07 30		07 42						08 08			08 30				08 42				
Harwich Town	d												08 00										
Dovercourt	d												08 02										
Harwich International	d						07 47						08 06										
Wrabness	d						07 53						08 12										
Mistley	d		←				07a59						08 17										
Manningtree 2	d		07 28			07 52						08 18	08 22						08 52				
Walton-on-the-Naze	d				07 45													08 45					
Frinton-on-Sea	d				07 48													08 48					
Kirby Cross	d				07 51													08 51					
Clacton-on-Sea	d								07 50												08 50		
Thorpe-le-Soken 1	a	←			07 56				07 57					←				08 56			08 57		
	d	07 01			08 01 →				07 57					08 01				09 01 →			08 57		
Weeley	d	07 05												08 05									
Great Bentley	d	07 08												08 08									
Alresford (Essex)	d	07 13												08 13									
Wivenhoe 3	d	07 16							08 07					08 16							09 07		
Hythe	d	07 20												08 20									
Colchester Town	a	07 24												08 24									
	d	07 28								08 15				08 28			08 45					09 15	
Colchester 4	a	07 37	07 38	07 48		08 01			08 17	08 22		08 27	08 32	08 37	08 48		08 52		09 01		09 17	09 22	
	d		07 41	07 49		08 03			08 17			08 29	08 33		08 49	08 52			09 03		09 17		
Marks Tey 2	d								08 23				08 39								09 23		
Kelvedon	d												08 44										
Braintree	d							08 00												09 00			
Braintree Freeport	d							08 02												09 02			
Cressing	d							08 05												09 05			
White Notley	d							08 08												09 08			
Witham 2	d			08 02				08 15	08 31				08 49			09 04				09 15	09 31		
Hatfield Peverel	d							08 20												09 20			
Chelmsford 3	d		08 02	08 11				08 27	08 40			08 46	08 58		09s06	09 13				09 27	09 40		
Ingatestone	d							08 33												09 33			
Shenfield 3	a		08 13	08s22		08s29		08 40	08 51				09 09			09s24			09s29	09 40	09 51		
Romford	a								08 59												09 59		
Stratford 7 ⊖	a		08s30					08s55	09s07			09s10	09s24							09s55	10s07		
London Liverpool Street 15 ⊖	a		08 39	08 45		08 54		09 03	09 16			09 24	09 33		09 38	09 47			09 54	10 03	10 16		

		LE	LE	LE	LE	LE	LE	LE	LE	LE	LE	LE	LE	LE	LE	LE	LE	LE	LE	LE	LE	LE	LE
		1 ◇	1	1	R 1	1	1	1	1 ◇	1	1	1		1 ◇	1	1	R 1	1	1	1	1 ◇	1	1
													B										
		☕							☕					☕							☕		
Norwich	d	08 30							09 00					09 30							10 00		
Diss	d	08 47							09 17					09 47							10 17		
Peterborough 8	d				07 52																		
Stowmarket	d				09 12				09 29				09 45								10 29		
Needham Market	d												09 50										
Lowestoft	d																08 58						
Ipswich	a	09 07			09 25				09 40				10 02	10 07			10 26				10 40		
	d	09 08			09 30				09 42					10 08			10 30				10 42		
Harwich Town	d		09 00												10 00								
Dovercourt	d		09 02												10 02								
Harwich International	d		09 06												10 06								
Wrabness	d		09 12												10 12								
Mistley	d		09 17												10 17								
Manningtree 2	d	09 18	09 22						09 52					10 18	10 22						10 52		
Walton-on-the-Naze	d							09 45												10 45			
Frinton-on-Sea	d							09 48												10 48			
Kirby Cross	d							09 51												10 51			
Clacton-on-Sea	d										09 50												10 50
Thorpe-le-Soken 1	a			←				09 56			09 57					←				10 56			10 57
	d			09 01				10 01 →			09 57					10 01				11 01 →			10 57
Weeley	d			09 05												10 05							
Great Bentley	d			09 08												10 08							
Alresford (Essex)	d			09 13												10 13							
Wivenhoe 3	d			09 16							10 07					10 16							11 07
Hythe	d			09 20												10 20							
Colchester Town	a			09 24												10 24							
	d			09 28			09 45					10 15				10 28			10 45				
Colchester 4	a	09 27	09 32	09 37	09 48		09 52		10 01		10 17	10 22		10 27	10 32	10 37	10 48		10 52		11 01		11 17
	d	09 29	09 33		09 49	09 52			10 03		10 17			10 29	10 33		10 49	10 52			11 03		11 17
Marks Tey 2	d		09 39								10 23				10 39								11 23
Kelvedon	d		09 44												10 44								
Braintree	d									10 00												11 00	
Braintree Freeport	d									10 02												11 02	
Cressing	d									10 05												11 05	
White Notley	d									10 08												11 08	
Witham 2	d		09 49			10 04				10 15	10 31				10 49			11 04				11 15	11 31
Hatfield Peverel	d									10 20												11 20	
Chelmsford 3	d	09 46	09 58		10s06	10 13				10 27	10 40			10 46	10 58		11s06	11 13				11 27	11 40
Ingatestone	d									10 33												11 33	
Shenfield 3	a		10 09			10s24			10s29	10 40	10 51				11 09			11s24			11s29	11 40	11 51
Romford	a										10 59												11 59
Stratford 7 ⊖	a	10s10	10s24							10s55	11s07			11s10	11s24							11s55	12s07
London Liverpool Street 15 ⊖	a	10 24	10 33		10 38	10 47			10 54	11 03	11 16			11 24	11 33		11 42	11 47			11 54	12 03	12 16

For general notes see front of timetable
For details of catering facilities see Directory of Train Operators

A To Cambridge (Table 14)
B From Cambridge (Table 14)

Due to major track repair work in the Bury St Edmunds area, trains between Ipswich and Peterborough are subject to disruption, resulting in bus replacements and extended journey times for part or all of this timetable. See local publicity or contact National Rail Enquiries 08457 48 49 50 for further details.

Table 11

Norwich, Ipswich, Harwich, Clacton, Walton-on-Naze, Colchester and Chelmsford → London

Network diagram - see first page of Table 5

		LE	LE	LE	LE	LE	LE	LE	LE	LE	LE	LE	LE	LE	LE	LE	LE	LE	LE	LE	LE	LE	LE
		1		1 ◇	1	1	R 1	1	1	1 ◇	1	1	1		1 ◇	1	1	R 1	1	1	1 ◇	1	1
			A											A									
				☕						☕					☕						☕		
Norwich	d			10 30						11 00					11 30						12 00		
Diss	d			10 47						11 17					11 47						12 17		
Peterborough 8	d						09 55																
Stowmarket	d		10 45				11 14			11 29				11 45							12 29		
Needham Market	d		10 50											11 50									
Lowestoft	d																	10 58					
Ipswich	a		11 02	11 07			11 27			11 40				12 02	12 07			12 26			12 40		
	d			11 08			11 30			11 42					12 08			12 30			12 42		
Harwich Town	d				11 00											12 00							
Dovercourt	d				11 02											12 02							
Harwich International	d				11 06											12 06							
Wrabness	d				11 12											12 12							
Mistley	d				11 17											12 17							
Manningtree 2	d			11 18	11 22					11 52					12 18	12 22					12 52		
Walton-on-the-Naze	d								11 45											12 45			
Frinton-on-Sea	d								11 48											12 48			
Kirby Cross	d								11 51											12 51			
Clacton-on-Sea	d											11 50											12 50
Thorpe-le-Soken 1	a					←			11 56			11 57					←			12 56			12 57
	d					11 01			12 01 →			11 57					12 01			13 01 →			12 57
Weeley	d					11 05											12 05						
Great Bentley	d					11 08											12 08						
Alresford (Essex)	d					11 13											12 13						
Wivenhoe 3	d					11 16						12 07					12 16						13 07
Hythe	d					11 20											12 20						
Colchester Town	a					11 24											12 24						
	d	11 15				11 28		11 45					12 15				12 28		12 45				
Colchester 4	a	11 22		11 27	11 32	11 37	11 48	11 52		12 01		12 17	12 22		12 27	12 32	12 37	12 48	12 52		13 01		13 17
	d			11 29	11 33		11 49			12 03		12 17			12 29	12 33		12 49			13 03		13 17
Marks Tey 2	d				11 39							12 23				12 39							13 23
Kelvedon	d				11 44											12 44							
Braintree	d										12 00											13 00	
Braintree Freeport	d										12 02											13 02	
Cressing	d										12 05											13 05	
White Notley	d										12 08											13 08	
Witham 2	d				11 49		12 02				12 15	12 31				12 49		13 02				13 15	13 31
Hatfield Peverel	d										12 20											13 20	
Chelmsford 3	d			11 46	11 58		12 11				12 27	12 40			12 46	12 58		13 11				13 27	13 40
Ingatestone	d										12 33											13 33	
Shenfield 3	a				12 09		12s22			12s29	12 40	12 51				13 09		13s22			13s29	13 40	13 51
Romford	a											12 59											13 59
Stratford 7 ⊖ ⛴	a			12s10	12s24						12s55	13s07			13s10	13s24						13s55	14s07
London Liverpool Street 15 ⊖	a			12 24	12 33		12 45			12 54	13 03	13 16			13 24	13 33		13 45			13 54	14 03	14 16

		LE	LE	LE	LE	LE	LE	LE	LE	LE	LE	LE	LE	LE	LE	LE	LE	LE	LE	LE	LE	LE	LE
		1		1 ◇	1	1	1 ◇	1	1	1 ◇	1	1	1		1 ◇	1	1	1 ◇	1	1	1 ◇	1	1
			A											A									
				☕						☕					☕						☕		
Norwich	d			12 30						13 00					13 30						14 00		
Diss	d			12 47						13 17					13 47						14 17		
Peterborough 8	d						11 48																
Stowmarket	d		12 45				13 12			13 29				13 45							14 29		
Needham Market	d		12 50											13 50									
Lowestoft	d																	12 58					
Ipswich	a		13 02	13 07			13 27			13 40				14 02	14 07			14 26			14 40		
	d			13 08			13 30			13 42					14 08			14 30			14 42		
Harwich Town	d				13 00											14 00							
Dovercourt	d				13 02											14 02							
Harwich International	d				13 06											14 06							
Wrabness	d				13 12											14 12							
Mistley	d				13 17											14 17							
Manningtree 2	d			13 18	13 22					13 52					14 18	14 22					14 52		
Walton-on-the-Naze	d								13 45											14 45			
Frinton-on-Sea	d								13 48											14 48			
Kirby Cross	d								13 51											14 51			
Clacton-on-Sea	d											13 50											14 50
Thorpe-le-Soken 1	a					←			13 56			13 57					←			14 56			14 57
	d					13 01			14 01 →			13 57					14 01			15 01 →			14 57
Weeley	d					13 05											14 05						
Great Bentley	d					13 08											14 08						
Alresford (Essex)	d					13 13											14 13						
Wivenhoe 3	d					13 16						14 07					14 16						15 07
Hythe	d					13 20											14 20						
Colchester Town	a					13 24											14 24						
	d	13 15				13 28		13 45					14 15				14 28		14 45				
Colchester 4	a	13 22		13 27	13 32	13 37	13 48	13 52		14 01		14 17	14 22		14 27	14 32	14 37	14 48	14 52		15 01		15 17
	d			13 29	13 33		13 49			14 03		14 17			14 29	14 33		14 49			15 03		15 17
Marks Tey 2	d				13 39							14 23				14 39							15 23
Kelvedon	d				13 44											14 44							
Braintree	d										14 00											15 00	
Braintree Freeport	d										14 02											15 02	
Cressing	d										14 05											15 05	
White Notley	d										14 08											15 08	
Witham 2	d				13 49		14 02				14 15	14 31				14 49		15 02				15 15	15 31
Hatfield Peverel	d										14 20											15 20	
Chelmsford 3	d			13 46	13 58		14 11				14 27	14 40			14 46	14 58		15 11				15 27	15 40
Ingatestone	d										14 33											15 33	
Shenfield 3	a				14 09		14s22			14s29	14 40	14 51				15 09		15s22			15s29	15 40	15 51
Romford	a											14 59											15 59
Stratford 7 ⊖ ⛴	a			14s10	14s24						14s55	15s07			15s10	15s24						15s55	16s07
London Liverpool Street 15 ⊖	a			14 24	14 33		14 45			14 54	15 03	15 16			15 24	15 33		15 45			15 54	16 03	16 16

For general notes see front of timetable
For details of catering facilities see Directory of Train Operators

A From Cambridge (Table 14)

Due to major track repair work in the Bury St Edmunds area, trains between Ipswich and Peterborough are subject to disruption, resulting in bus replacements and extended journey times for part or all of this timetable. See local publicity or contact National Rail Enquiries 08457 48 49 50 for further details.

Norwich, Ipswich, Harwich, Clacton, Walton-on-Naze, Colchester and Chelmsford → London

Network diagram - see first page of Table 5

		LE 1	LE A	LE 1 ◇ ☕	LE 1	LE 1	LE 1 ◇	LE 1	LE 1	LE 1 ◇ ☕	LE 1		LE 1	LE 1	LE A	LE 1 ◇ ☕	LE 1	LE 1	LE 1 ◇	LE 1	LE 1	LE 1 ◇ ☕		LE 1	LE 1
Norwich	d			14 30						15 00						15 30						16 00			
Diss	d			14 47						15 17						15 47						16 17			
Peterborough 8	d						13 47																		
Stowmarket	d		14 45				15 12			15 29					15 45							16 29			
Needham Market	d		14 50												15 50										
Lowestoft	d																		14 58						
Ipswich	a		15 02	15 07			15 25			15 40					16 02	16 07			16 26			16 40			
	d			15 08			15 30			15 42						16 08			16 30			16 42			
Harwich Town	d				15 00												16 00								
Dovercourt	d				15 02												16 02								
Harwich International	d				15 06												16 06								
Wrabness	d				15 12												16 12								
Mistley	d				15 17												16 17								
Manningtree 2	d			15 18	15 22					15 52						16 18	16 22					16 52			
Walton-on-the-Naze	d								15 45												16 45				
Frinton-on-Sea	d								15 48												16 48				
Kirby Cross	d								15 51												16 51				
Clacton-on-Sea	d												15 50												16 50
Thorpe-le-Soken 1	a					←			15 56				15 57					←			16 56				16 57
	d					15 01			16 01 →				15 57					16 01			17 01 →				16 57
Weeley	d					15 05												16 05							
Great Bentley	d					15 08												16 08							
Alresford (Essex)	d					15 13												16 13							
Wivenhoe 3	d					15 16							16 07					16 16							17 07
Hythe	d					15 20												16 20							
Colchester Town	a					15 24												16 24							
	d	15 15				15 28		15 45						16 15				16 28		16 45					
Colchester 4	a	15 22		15 27	15 32	15 37	15 48	15 52		16 01			16 17	16 22		16 27	16 32	16 37	16 48	16 52		17 01			17 17
	d			15 29	15 33		15 49			16 03			16 17			16 29	16 33		16 49			17 03			17 17
Marks Tey 2	d				15 39								16 23				16 39								17 23
Kelvedon	d				15 44												16 44								
Braintree	d										16 00													17 00	
Braintree Freeport	d										16 02													17 02	
Cressing	d										16 05													17 05	
White Notley	d										16 08													17 08	
Witham 2	d				15 49		16 02				16 15		16 31				16 49		17 02					17 15	17 31
Hatfield Peverel	d										16 20													17 20	
Chelmsford 3	d			15 46	15 58		16 11				16 27		16 40			16 46	16 58		17 11					17 27	17 40
Ingatestone	d										16 33													17 33	
Shenfield 3	a				16 09		16s22			16s29	16 40		16 51				17 09		17s22			17s29		17 40	17 51
Romford	a												16 59												17 59
Stratford 7 ⊖	a			16s10	16s24						16s55		17s07			17s10	17s24							17s55	18s07
London Liverpool Street 15 ⊖	a			16 24	16 33		16 45			16 54	17 03		17 16			17 24	17 33		17 45			17 54		18 03	18 16

		LE 1	LE A	LE 1 ◇ ☕	LE 1	LE 1	LE 1 ◇	LE 1	LE 1	LE 1 ◇ ☕	LE 1		LE 1	LE 1	LE A	LE 1 ◇ ☕	LE 1	LE 1	LE 1 ◇	LE 1	LE 1	LE 1 ◇ ☕		LE 1	LE 1
Norwich	d			16 30						17 00						17 30						18 00			
Diss	d			16 47						17 17						17 47						18 17			
Peterborough 8	d						15 47																		
Stowmarket	d		16 45				17 12			17 29					17 46							18 29			
Needham Market	d		16 50												17 52										
Lowestoft	d																		16 58						
Ipswich	a		17 02	17 07			17 27			17 40					18 03	18 07			18 26			18 40			
	d			17 08			17 30			17 42						18 08			18 30			18 42			
Harwich Town	d				17 00												18 00								
Dovercourt	d				17 02												18 02								
Harwich International	d				17 06												18 06								
Wrabness	d				17 12												18 12								
Mistley	d				17 17												18 17								
Manningtree 2	d			17 18	17 22					17 52						18 18	18 22					18 52			
Walton-on-the-Naze	d								17 45												18 45				
Frinton-on-Sea	d								17 48												18 48				
Kirby Cross	d								17 51												18 51				
Clacton-on-Sea	d												17 50												18 50
Thorpe-le-Soken 1	a					←			17 56				17 57					←			18 56				18 57
	d					17 01			18 01 →				17 57					18 01			19 01 →				18 57
Weeley	d					17 05												18 05							
Great Bentley	d					17 08												18 08							
Alresford (Essex)	d					17 13												18 13							
Wivenhoe 3	d					17 16							18 07					18 16							19 07
Hythe	d					17 20												18 20							
Colchester Town	a					17 24												18 24							
	d	17 15				17 28		17 45						18 15				18 28		18 45					
Colchester 4	a	17 22		17 27	17 32	17 37	17 48	17 52		18 01			18 17	18 22		18 27	18 32	18 37	18 48	18 52		19 01			19 17
	d			17 29	17 33		17 49			18 03			18 17			18 29	18 33		18 49			19 03			19 17
Marks Tey 2	d				17 39								18 23				18 39								19 23
Kelvedon	d				17 44												18 44								
Braintree	d										18 00													19 00	
Braintree Freeport	d										18 02													19 02	
Cressing	d										18 05													19 05	
White Notley	d										18 08													19 08	
Witham 2	d				17 49		18 02				18 15		18 31				18 49		19 02					19 15	19 31
Hatfield Peverel	d										18 20													19 20	
Chelmsford 3	d			17 46	17 58		18 11				18 27		18 40			18 46	18 58		19 11					19 27	19 40
Ingatestone	d										18 33													19 33	
Shenfield 3	a				18 09		18s22			18s29	18 40		18 51				19 09		19s22			19s29		19 40	19 51
Romford	a												18 59												19 59
Stratford 7 ⊖	a			18s10	18s24						18s55		19s07			19s10	19s24							19s55	20s07
London Liverpool Street 15 ⊖	a			18 24	18 33		18 45			18 54	19 03		19 16			19 24	19 33		19 45			19 54		20 03	20 16

For general notes see front of timetable
For details of catering facilities see Directory of Train Operators

A From Cambridge (Table 14)

Due to major track repair work in the Bury St Edmunds area, trains between Ipswich and Peterborough are subject to disruption, resulting in bus replacements and extended journey times for part or all of this timetable. See local publicity or contact National Rail Enquiries 08457 48 49 50 for further details.

Norwich, Ipswich, Harwich, Clacton, Walton-on-Naze, Colchester and Chelmsford → London

Network diagram - see first page of Table 5

Station		LE 1	LE A	LE 1 ◇ ☕	LE 1	LE 1	LE 1 ◇	LE 1	LE 1	LE 1 ◇ ☕	LE 1		LE 1	LE A	LE 1	LE 1	LE 1	LE 1 ◇	LE 1	LE 1 ◇ ☕	LE 1	LE 1		LE 1	LE A
Norwich	d			18 30						19 00										20 00					
Diss	d			18 47						19 17										20 17					
Peterborough [8]	d						17 47																		
Stowmarket	d		18 46				19 12			19 29				19 45						20 29					20 45
Needham Market	d		18 52											19 50											20 50
Lowestoft	d																	18 58							
Ipswich	a		19 03	19 07			19 25			19 40				20 02				20 26		20 40					21 02
	d			19 08			19 27			19 42					20 08			20 30		20 42					21 04
Harwich Town	d				19 00											20 00								21 00	
Dovercourt	d				19 02											20 02								21 02	
Harwich International	d				19 06											20 06								21 06	21a28
Wrabness	d				19 12											20 12								21 12	
Mistley	d				19 17											20 17								21 17	
Manningtree [2]	d			19 18	19 22		19 37			19 52					20 18	20 22				20 52				21 22	
Walton-on-the-Naze	d								19 45										20 45					→	
Frinton-on-Sea	d								19 48										20 48						
Kirby Cross	d								19 51										20 51						
Clacton-on-Sea	d												19 50									20 50			
Thorpe-le-Soken [1]	a					←			19 56				19 57				←		20 56			20 57			
	d					19 01			20 01 →				19 57				20 01		21 01 →			20 57			
Weeley	d					19 05											20 05								
Great Bentley	d					19 08											20 08								
Alresford (Essex)	d					19 13											20 13								
Wivenhoe [3]	d					19 16							20 07				20 16					21 07			
Hythe	d					19 20											20 20								
Colchester Town	a					19 24											20 24								
	d	19 15				19 28		19 45									20 28								
Colchester [4]	a	19 22		19 27	19 32	19 37	19 48	19 52		20 01			20 17		20 28	20 32	20 37	20 48		21 01		21 17			
	d			19 29	19 33		19 49			20 03			20 17		20 29	20 33		20 49		21 03		21 17			
Marks Tey [2]	d				19 39								20 23			20 39						21 23			
Kelvedon	d				19 44											20 44									
Braintree	d										20 00										21 00				
Braintree Freeport	d										20 02										21 02				
Cressing	d										20 05										21 05				
White Notley	d										20 08										21 08				
Witham [2]	d				19 49		20 02				20 15		20 31			20 49		21 02			21 15	21 31			
Hatfield Peverel	d										20 20										21 20				
Chelmsford [3]	d			19 46	19 58		20 11				20 27		20 40		20 46	20 58		21 11			21 27	21 40			
Ingatestone	d										20 33										21 33				
Shenfield [3]	a				20 09		20s22			20s29	20 40		20 51			21 10		21s22		21s29	21 40	21 51			
Romford	a												20 59									21 59			
Stratford [7] ⊖	a			20s10	20s24						20s55		21s07		21s10	21s25					21s54	22s07			
London Liverpool Street [15] ⊖	a			20 24	20 33		20 45			20 54	21 03		21 16		21 19	21 38		21 49		21 58	22 07	22 20			

Station		LE 1	LE 1	LE 1	LE 1 ◇	LE 1	LE 1 ◇ ☕	LE 1	LE 1	LE 1	LE A		LE 1	LE 1	LE 1	LE 1	LE 1 ◇	LE A	LE 1	LE 1	LE 1	LE 1	LE 1		
Norwich	d						21 00										22 00						23 05		
Diss	d						21 17										22 17						23 22		
Peterborough [8]	d				19 46																	21 49			
Stowmarket	d				21 12		21 29				21 45						22 29	22 46				23 17	23 34		
Needham Market	d										21 50							22 52				23 22			
Lowestoft	d																								
Ipswich	a				21 27		21 40				22 02						22 40	23 03				23 32	23 50		
	d	21 08			21 27		21 42						22 08				22 42				23 26	23 35			
Harwich Town	d									21 54										23 10					
Dovercourt	d									21 56										23 12					
Harwich International	d									21 59										23 15					
Wrabness	d									22 05										23 21					
Mistley	d		←							22 10										23 26					
Manningtree [2]	d	21 18	21 22		21 37		21 52			22a15			22 18				22 52			23a31	23 35	23 45			
Walton-on-the-Naze	d					21 45										22 45									
Frinton-on-Sea	d					21 48										22 48									
Kirby Cross	d					21 51										22 51									
Clacton-on-Sea	d								21 50						22 25										
Thorpe-le-Soken [1]	a			←		21 56			21 57					←	22 32	22 57									
	d			21 01		22 01 →			21 57					22 01	22 32										
Weeley	d			21 05										22 05	22 36										
Great Bentley	d			21 08										22 08	22 40										
Alresford (Essex)	d			21 13										22 13	22 44										
Wivenhoe [3]	d			21 16					22 07					22 16	22 47										
Hythe	d			21 20										22 20	22 51										
Colchester Town	a			21 24										22 24											
	d			21 28										22 28											
Colchester [4]	a	21 28	21 32	21 37	21 48		22 01		22 17				22 28	22 37	22 58		23 01				23 45	23 56			
	d	21 29	21 33		21 49		22 03		22 17				22 29				23 03								
Marks Tey [2]	d		21 39						22 23				22 35												
Kelvedon	d		21 44										22 40												
Braintree	d							22 00											23 07						
Braintree Freeport	d							22 02											23 09						
Cressing	d							22 05											23 12						
White Notley	d							22 08											23 15						
Witham [2]	d		21 49		22 02			22 15	22 31				22 45				23 15		23a22						
Hatfield Peverel	d							22 20					22 49												
Chelmsford [3]	d	21 46	21 58		22 11			22 27	22 40				22 56				23 24								
Ingatestone	d							22 33					23 03												
Shenfield [3]	a	21 58	22 10		22s22		22s29	22 40	22 51				23 09				23s36								
Romford	a								22 59																
Stratford [7] ⊖	a	22s12	22s25					22s55	23s07				23s25				23s52								
London Liverpool Street [15] ⊖	a	22 25	22 38		22 49		22 58	23 07	23 20				23 38				00 07								

For general notes see front of timetable
For details of catering facilities see
Directory of Train Operators

A From Cambridge (Table 14)

Due to major track repair work in the Bury St Edmunds area, trains between Ipswich and Peterborough are subject to disruption, resulting in bus replacements and extended journey times for part or all of this timetable. See local publicity or contact National Rail Enquiries 08457 48 49 50 for further details.

Table 11

Sundays

Norwich, Ipswich, Harwich, Clacton, Walton-on-Naze, Colchester and Chelmsford → London

Network diagram - see first page of Table 5

		LE 1	LE 1	LE 1	LE	LE 1	LE 1	LE 1	LE 1 ◇	LE 1	LE	LE 1	LE 1	LE 1	LE 1 ◇	LE 1	LE 1	LE 1	LE 1	LE 1		LE 1 ◇	LE 1	LE 1	LE 1
					A				☕						☕							☕			
Norwich	d								07 00						08 00							09 00			
Diss	d								07 17						08 17							09 17			
Peterborough 8	d																								
Stowmarket	d								07 29						08 29							09 29			
Needham Market	d																								
Lowestoft	d																								
Ipswich	a								07 40						08 40							09 40			
	d								07 42		07 45	08 08			08 42			09 08				09 42			10 08
Harwich Town	d																08 53							09 53	
Dovercourt	d																08 55							09 55	
Harwich International	d						07 25				08a10						08 58							09 58	
Wrabness	d																09 04							10 04	
Mistley	d																09 09							10 09	
Manningtree 2	d						07 38		07 52			08 18			08 52		09a14	09 18				09 52		10a14	10 18
Walton-on-the-Naze	d												08 30						09 30						
Frinton-on-Sea	d												08 33						09 33						
Kirby Cross	d												08 36						09 36						
Clacton-on-Sea	d									07 36						08 36							09 36		
Thorpe-le-Soken 1	a									07 43			08 42			08 43			09 42				09 43		
	d									07 43						08 43							09 43		
Weeley	d																								
Great Bentley	d									07 49						08 49							09 49		
Alresford (Essex)	d									07 53						08 53							09 53		
Wivenhoe 3	d									07 56						08 56							09 56		
Hythe	d																								
Colchester Town	a																								
	d																								
Colchester 4	a						07 48		08 01	08 06		08 29			09 01	09 06		09 29				10 01	10 06		10 29
	d			06 56	07 07	07 26	07 49		08 03	08 06		08 30			09 03	09 06		09 30				10 03	10 06		10 30
Marks Tey 2	d			07 02	07a14	07 32				08 12		08 36				09 12		09 36					10 12		10 36
Kelvedon	d			07 07		07 37						08 41						09 41							10 41
Braintree	d	00 07						08 00						09 00						10 00					
Braintree Freeport	d	00 09						08 02						09 02						10 02					
Cressing	d	00 12						08 05						09 05						10 05					
White Notley	d	00 15						08 08						09 08						10 08					
Witham 2	d	00a22		07 12		07 42		08a16		08 20		08 46		09a16		09 20		09 46		10a16			10 20		10 46
Hatfield Peverel	d			07 16		07 46						08 50						09 50							10 50
Chelmsford 3	d		06 53	07 23		07 53	08 07			08 29		08 57				09 29		09 57					10 29		10 57
Ingatestone	d		07 00	07 30		08 00						09 04						10 04							11 04
Shenfield 3	a		07 06	07 36		08 06	08 18		08s29	08 40		09 10			09s29	09 40		10 10				10s29	10 40		11 10
Romford	a																								
Stratford 7 ⊖	a		07s34	08s04		08s34	08s49			09s04		09s34				10s04		10s34					11s04		11s34
London Liverpool Street 15 ⊖	a		07 42	08 12		08 42	08 59		09 03	09 12		09 42			10 01	10 12		10 42				11 03	11 12		11 42

For general notes see front of timetable
For details of catering facilities see Directory of Train Operators

A To Sudbury (Table 10)

Due to major track repair work in the Bury St Edmunds area, trains between Ipswich and Peterborough are subject to disruption, resulting in bus replacements and extended journey times for part or all of this timetable. See local publicity or contact National Rail Enquiries 08457 48 49 50 for further details.

Norwich, Ipswich, Harwich, Clacton, Walton-on-Naze, Colchester and Chelmsford → London

Network diagram - see first page of Table 5

		LE 1	LE	LE 1	LE 1◇	LE 1	LE 1	LE 1	LE 1	LE 1	LE 1◇	LE 1	LE 1	LE 1	LE 1	LE	LE 1	LE 1◇		LE 1	LE 1	LE 1	LE 1	LE 1	LE 1
			A													B									
					☕						☕							☕							
Norwich	d				10 00						11 00							12 00							
Diss	d				10 17						11 17							12 17							
Peterborough 8	d																						11 46		
Stowmarket	d		10 17		10 29						11 29					12 17		12 29					13 12		
Needham Market	d		10 22													12 22									
Lowestoft	d																								
Ipswich	a		10 34		10 40						11 40					12 34		12 40					13 25		
	d				10 42			11 08			11 42			12 08				12 42				13 08			
Harwich Town	d						10 53						11 53								12 53				
Dovercourt	d						10 55						11 55								12 55				
Harwich International	d						10 58						11 58								12 58				
Wrabness	d						11 04						12 04								13 04				
Mistley	d						11 09						12 09								13 09				
Manningtree 2	d				10 52		11a14	11 18			11 52		12a14	12 18				12 52			13a14	13 18			
Walton-on-the-Naze	d	10 30							11 30						12 30									13 30	
Frinton-on-Sea	d	10 33							11 33						12 33									13 33	
Kirby Cross	d	10 36							11 36						12 36									13 36	
Clacton-on-Sea	d					10 36						11 36								12 36					
Thorpe-le-Soken 1	a	10 42				10 43			11 42			11 43			12 42					12 43				13 42	
	d					10 43						11 43								12 43					
Weeley	d																								
Great Bentley	d					10 49						11 49								12 49					
Alresford (Essex)	d					10 53						11 53								12 53					
Wivenhoe 3	d					10 56						11 56								12 56					
Hythe	d																								
Colchester Town	a																								
	d																								
Colchester 4	a				11 01	11 06		11 29			12 01	12 06		12 29				13 01		13 06		13 29			
	d				11 03	11 06		11 30			12 03	12 06		12 30				13 03		13 06		13 30			
Marks Tey 2	d					11 12		11 36				12 12		12 36						13 12		13 36			
Kelvedon	d							11 41						12 41								13 41			
Braintree	d			11 00						12 00							13 00								14 00
Braintree Freeport	d			11 02						12 02							13 02								14 02
Cressing	d			11 05						12 05							13 05								14 05
White Notley	d			11 08						12 08							13 08								14 08
Witham 2	d			11a16		11 20		11 46		12a16		12 20		12 46			13a16			13 20		13 46			14a16
Hatfield Peverel	d							11 50						12 50								13 50			
Chelmsford 3	d					11 29		11 57				12 29		12 57						13 29		13 57			
Ingatestone	d							12 04						13 04								14 04			
Shenfield 3	a				11s29	11 40		12 10			12s29	12 40		13 10				13s29		13 40		14 10			
Romford	a																								
Stratford 7 ⊖ ⛴	a					12s04		12s34				13s04		13s34						14s04		14s34			
London Liverpool Street 15 ⊖	a				12 01	12 12		12 42			13 01	13 12		13 42				14 01		14 12		14 42			

		LE 1◇	LE 1	LE 1	LE 1	LE 1	LE	LE 1	LE 1◇	LE 1	LE 1	LE 1	LE 1	LE 1	LE 1	LE 1◇		LE 1	LE 1	LE 1	LE 1	LE	LE 1	LE R 1	LE 1
							B															B			
		☕							☕							☕								☕	
Norwich	d	13 00							14 00							15 00								16 00	
Diss	d	13 17							14 17							15 17								16 17	
Peterborough 8	d												13 48												
Stowmarket	d	13 29					14 17		14 29				15 12			15 29						16 17		16 29	
Needham Market	d						14 22															16 22			
Lowestoft	d																								
Ipswich	a	13 40					14 34		14 40				15 27			15 40						16 34		16 40	
	d	13 42			14 08				14 42			15 08				15 42				16 08				16 42	
Harwich Town	d			13 53							14 53								15 53						
Dovercourt	d			13 55							14 55								15 55						
Harwich International	d			13 58							14 58								15 58						
Wrabness	d			14 04							15 04								16 04						
Mistley	d			14 09							15 09								16 09						
Manningtree 2	d	13 52		14a14	14 18				14 52		15a14	15 18				15 52			16a14	16 18				16 52	
Walton-on-the-Naze	d					14 30								15 30							16 30				
Frinton-on-Sea	d					14 33								15 33							16 33				
Kirby Cross	d					14 36								15 36							16 36				
Clacton-on-Sea	d		13 36							14 36								15 36							16 36
Thorpe-le-Soken 1	a		13 43			14 42				14 43				15 42				15 43			16 42				16 43
	d		13 43							14 43								15 43							16 43
Weeley	d																								
Great Bentley	d		13 49							14 49								15 49							16 49
Alresford (Essex)	d		13 53							14 53								15 53							16 53
Wivenhoe 3	d		13 56							14 56								15 56							16 56
Hythe	d																								
Colchester Town	a																								
	d																								
Colchester 4	a	14 01	14 06		14 29				15 01	15 06		15 29				16 01		16 06		16 29				17 01	17 06
	d	14 03	14 06		14 30				15 03	15 06		15 30				16 03		16 06		16 30				17 03	17 06
Marks Tey 2	d		14 12		14 36					15 12		15 36						16 12		16 36					17 12
Kelvedon	d				14 41							15 41								16 41					
Braintree	d							15 00							16 00								17 00		
Braintree Freeport	d							15 02							16 02								17 02		
Cressing	d							15 05							16 05								17 05		
White Notley	d							15 08							16 08								17 08		
Witham 2	d		14 20		14 46			15a16		15 20		15 46			16a16			16 20		16 46			17a16		17 20
Hatfield Peverel	d				14 50							15 50								16 50					
Chelmsford 3	d		14 29		14 57					15 29		15 57						16 29		16 57					17 29
Ingatestone	d				15 04							16 04								17 04					
Shenfield 3	a	14s29	14 40		15 10				15s29	15 40		16 10				16s29		16 40		17 10				17s29	17 40
Romford	a																								
Stratford 7 ⊖ ⛴	a		15s04		15s34					16s04		16s34						17s04		17s34					18s04
London Liverpool Street 15 ⊖	a	15 01	15 12		15 42				16 01	16 12		16 42				17 01		17 12		17 42				18 01	18 12

For general notes see front of timetable
For details of catering facilities see Directory of Train Operators

A From Bury St Edmunds (Table 14)
B From Cambridge (Table 14)

Due to major track repair work in the Bury St Edmunds area, trains between Ipswich and Peterborough are subject to disruption, resulting in bus replacements and extended journey times for part or all of this timetable. See local publicity or contact National Rail Enquiries 08457 48 49 50 for further details.

Table 11

Sundays

Norwich, Ipswich, Harwich, Clacton, Walton-on-Naze, Colchester and Chelmsford → London

Network diagram - see first page of Table 5

		LE 1	LE 1 ◇ ☕	LE 1	LE 1	LE 1	LE 1	LE 1 ◇ ☕	LE 1	LE 1	LE 1	LE 1	LE A	LE 1		LE 1 ◇ ☕	LE 1	LE 1	LE 1	LE 1	LE 1	LE 1	LE 1 ◇ ☕	LE 1	LE 1
Norwich	d		16 20					17 00								18 00							19 00		
Diss	d		16 37					17 17								18 17							19 17		
Peterborough 8	d				15 47															17 47					
Stowmarket	d		16 49		17 12			17 29					18 17			18 29				19 12			19 29		
Needham Market	d												18 22												
Lowestoft	d																								
Ipswich	a		17 00		17 25			17 40					18 34			18 40				19 27			19 40		
	d		17 03	17 08				17 42			18 08					18 42			19 08				19 42		
Harwich Town	d	16 53								17 53								18 53							19 53
Dovercourt	d	16 55								17 55								18 55							19 55
Harwich International	d	16 58								17 58								18 58							19 58
Wrabness	d	17 04								18 04								19 04							20 04
Mistley	d	17 09								18 09								19 09							20 09
Manningtree 2	d	17a14		17 18				17 52		18a14	18 18					18 52		19a14	19 18				19 52		20a14
Walton-on-the-Naze	d					17 30						18 30									19 30				
Frinton-on-Sea	d					17 33						18 33									19 33				
Kirby Cross	d					17 36						18 36									19 36				
Clacton-on-Sea	d								17 36								18 36							19 36	
Thorpe-le-Soken 1	a					17 42			17 43			18 42					18 43				19 42			19 43	
	d								17 43								18 43							19 43	
Weeley	d																								
Great Bentley	d								17 49								18 49							19 49	
Alresford (Essex)	d								17 53								18 53							19 53	
Wivenhoe 3	d								17 56								18 56							19 56	
Hythe	d																								
Colchester Town	a																								
	d																								
Colchester 4	a		17 19	17 29				18 01	18 06		18 29					19 01	19 06		19 29				20 01	20 06	
	d		17 21	17 30				18 03	18 06		18 30					19 03	19 06		19 30				20 03	20 06	
Marks Tey 2	d			17 36					18 12		18 36						19 12		19 36					20 12	
Kelvedon	d			17 41							18 41								19 41						
Braintree	d						18 00							19 00								20 00			
Braintree Freeport	d						18 02							19 02								20 02			
Cressing	d						18 05							19 05								20 05			
White Notley	d						18 08							19 08								20 08			
Witham 2	d			17 46			18a16		18 20		18 46			19a16			19 20		19 46			20a16		20 20	
Hatfield Peverel	d			17 50							18 50								19 50						
Chelmsford 3	d			17 57					18 29		18 57						19 29		19 57					20 29	
Ingatestone	d			18 04							19 04								20 04						
Shenfield 3	a			18 10				18s29	18 40		19 10					19s29	19 40		20 10				20s29	20 40	
Romford	a																								
Stratford 7 ⊖	a			18s34					19s04		19s34						20s04		20s34					21s04	
London Liverpool Street 15 ⊖	a		18 28	18 42				19 01	19 12		19 42					20 01	20 12		20 42				21 01	21 12	

		LE 1	LE 1	LE 1	LE 1	LE A	LE 1 ◇ ☕	LE 1	LE 1	LE 1	LE 1	LE 1	LE 1 ◇	LE 1	LE 1	LE 1	LE 1	LE 1	LE A	LE 1	LE 1 ◇	LE 1	LE 1
Norwich	d						20 00						21 00								22 00		23 05
Diss	d						20 17						21 17								22 17		23 22
Peterborough 8	d									19 44													
Stowmarket	d					20 17	20 29			21 05			21 29						22 17		22 29		23 34
Needham Market	d					20 22													22 22				
Lowestoft	d																						
Ipswich	a					20 34	20 40			21 18			21 40						22 34		22 40		23 48
	d	20 08				20 35	20 42		21 08	21 19			21 42				22 08				22 42		
Harwich Town	d				20 53											21 53						22 53	
Dovercourt	d				20 55											21 55						22 55	
Harwich International	d				20 58	21a02										21 58						22 58	
Wrabness	d				21 04											22 04						23 04	
Mistley	d				21 09											22 09						23 09	
Manningtree 2	d	20 18			21a14		20 52		21 18	21 29			21 52			22a14	22 18				22 52	23 14	
Walton-on-the-Naze	d		20 30								21 30				22 13								
Frinton-on-Sea	d		20 33								21 33				22 16								
Kirby Cross	d		20 36								21 36				22 19								
Clacton-on-Sea	d							20 36						21 36				22 20					
Thorpe-le-Soken 1	a		20 42					20 43			21 42			21 43	22 25			22 27					
	d							20 43						21 43				22 27					
Weeley	d																						
Great Bentley	d							20 49						21 49									
Alresford (Essex)	d							20 53						21 53									
Wivenhoe 3	d							20 56						21 56				22 37					
Hythe	d																						
Colchester Town	a																						
	d																						
Colchester 4	a	20 29					21 01	21 06	21 29	21 40			22 01	22 06			22 29	22 47			23 01	23 24	
	d	20 30					21 03	21 06	21 30				22 03	22 06			22 30				23 03		
Marks Tey 2	d	20 36						21 12	21 36					22 12			22 36						
Kelvedon	d	20 41							21 41								22 41						
Braintree	d			21 00								22 00								22 56			
Braintree Freeport	d			21 02								22 02								22 58			
Cressing	d			21 05								22 05								23 01			
White Notley	d			21 08								22 08								23 04			
Witham 2	d	20 46		21a16				21 20	21 46			22a16		22 20			22 46			23a12	23 15		
Hatfield Peverel	d	20 50							21 50								22 50						
Chelmsford 3	d	20 57						21 29	21 57					22 29			22 57				23 24		
Ingatestone	d	21 04							22 04								23 04						
Shenfield 3	a	21 10					21s29	21 40	22 10				22s29	22 40			23 10				23s36		
Romford	a																						
Stratford 7 ⊖	a	21s34						22s04	22s34					23s04			23s34				23s57		
London Liverpool Street 15 ⊖	a	21 42					22 01	22 12	22 42				23 01	23 12			23 42				00 07		

For general notes see front of timetable
For details of catering facilities see Directory of Train Operators

A From Cambridge (Table 14)

Due to major track repair work in the Bury St Edmunds area, trains between Ipswich and Peterborough are subject to disruption, resulting in bus replacements and extended journey times for part or all of this timetable. See local publicity or contact National Rail Enquiries 08457 48 49 50 for further details.

Network Diagram for Tables 13, 14, 15, 16, 17

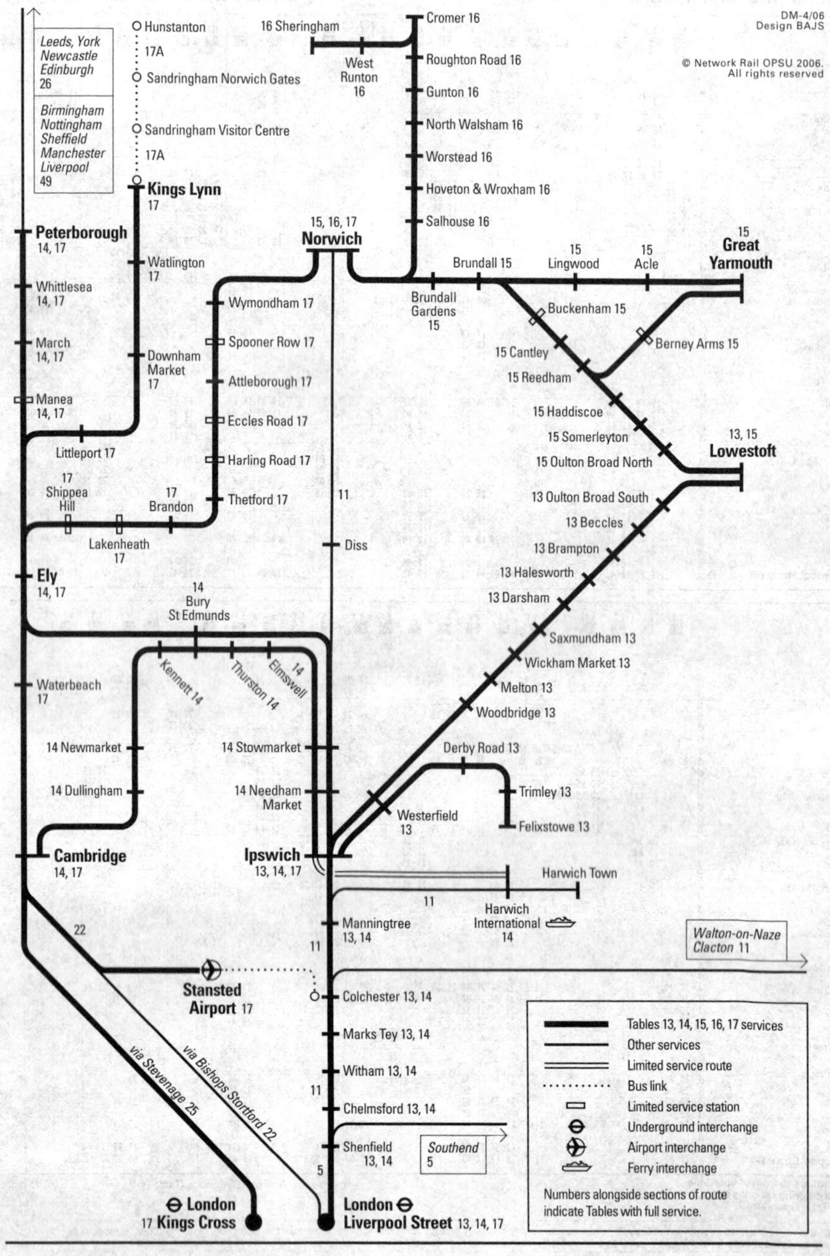

DM-4/06
Design BAJS
Leeds, York Newcastle Edinburgh 26
Birmingham Nottingham Sheffield Manchester Liverpool 49
Hunstanton
17A
Sandringham Norwich Gates
Sandringham Visitor Centre
17A
Kings Lynn 17
Peterborough 14, 17
Watlington 17
Whittlesea 14, 17
March 14, 17
Downham Market 17
Manea 14, 17
Littleport 17
17 Shippea Hill
17 Brandon
Lakenheath 17
Ely 14, 17
14 Bury St Edmunds
Kennett 14
Thurston 14
14 Elmswell
Waterbeach 17
14 Newmarket
14 Dullingham
Cambridge 14, 17
22
Stansted Airport 17
via Stevenage 25
via Bishops Stortford 22
London Kings Cross 17
16 Sheringham
West Runton 16
Cromer 16
Roughton Road 16
Gunton 16
North Walsham 16
Worstead 16
Hoveton & Wroxham 16
Salhouse 16
15, 16, 17 Norwich
Wymondham 17
Spooner Row 17
Attleborough 17
Eccles Road 17
Harling Road 17
Thetford 17
11
Diss
Brundall 15
Brundall Gardens 15
15 Lingwood
15 Acle
15 Great Yarmouth
Buckenham 15
Berney Arms 15
15 Cantley
15 Reedham
15 Haddiscoe
15 Somerleyton
15 Oulton Broad North
13, 15 Lowestoft
13 Oulton Broad South
13 Beccles
13 Brampton
13 Halesworth
13 Darsham
Saxmundham 13
Wickham Market 13
Melton 13
Woodbridge 13
Derby Road 13
Trimley 13
Westerfield 13
Felixstowe 13
14 Stowmarket
14 Needham Market
Ipswich 13, 14, 17
Harwich Town
11
Harwich International 14
Manningtree 13, 14
11
Walton-on-Naze Clacton 11
Colchester 13, 14
Marks Tey 13, 14
Witham 13, 14
11
Chelmsford 13, 14
Shenfield 13, 14
Southend 5
5
London Liverpool Street 13, 14, 17
Tables 13, 14, 15, 16, 17 services
Other services
Limited service route
Bus link
Limited service station
Underground interchange
Airport interchange
Ferry interchange
Numbers alongside sections of route indicate Tables with full service.

Ipswich → Felixstowe and Lowestoft

Network diagram - see first page of Table 13

Miles	Miles			LE	LE	LE 1	LE	LE	LE	LE 1 ◇	LE	LE	LE 1 ◇	LE	LE	LE 1 ◇	LE	LE
—	—	London Liverpool Street 15	⊖ d				06 00		07 00	07 38	08 02	09 00	09 38	10 00	11 00	11 38	12 00	13 00
—	—	Shenfield 3	d				06 23		07 23	08u02	08 26	09 23	10u02	10 23	11 23	12u02	12 23	13 23
—	—	Chelmsford 3	d				06b02		07 12	08 12	08 35	09 12	10 12		11 12	12 12		13 12
—	—	Witham 2	d				06b14		07 21	08 22	08 44	09 21	10 21		11 21	12 21		13 21
—	—	Marks Tey 2	d				06b24		07 33	08 30		09 29	10 29		11 29	12 29		13 29
—	—	Colchester 4	d		05 35	06 22	06 50		07 50	08 38	09 04	09 50	10 38	10 50	11 50	12 38	12 50	13 50
—	—	Manningtree 2	d		05 44	06 31	06 59		07 59	08 34	09 12	09 59	10 34	10 59	11 59	12 31	12 59	13 59
0	—	**Ipswich**	d	05 04	06 04	06 48	07 13	07 35	08 27	09 02	09 27	10 27	11 02	11 27	12 27	13 02	13 27	14 27
3½	0	Westerfield	d	05 10	06 10	06 55	07 19	07 42	08 33	09 09	09 33	10 33	11 09	11 33	12 33	13 09	13 33	14 33
—	2½	Derby Road	d	05 15	06 15		07 24		08 38		09 38	10 38		11 38	12 38		13 38	14 38
—	10½	Trimley	d	05 24	06 24		07 33		08 47		09 47	10 47		11 47	12 47		13 47	14 47
—	12¼	**Felixstowe**	a	05 29	06 29		07 38		08 52		09 52	10 52		11 52	12 52		13 52	14 52
10¼	—	Woodbridge	d			07 07		07 54		09 21			11 21			13 21		
11½	—	Melton	d			07 11		07 58		09 25			11 25			13 25		
15¾	—	Wickham Market	d			07 17		08 04		09 31			11 31			13 31		
22½	—	Saxmundham	d			07 28		08a16		09 42			11 42			13 42		
26¾	—	Darsham	d			07 34				09 48			11 48			13 48		
32	—	Halesworth	d			07 44				09 58			11 58			13 58		
36	—	Brampton (Suffolk)	d			07 51				10 05			12 05			14 05		
40¼	—	Beccles	d			07 59				10 13			12 13			14 13		
46¾	—	Oulton Broad South	d			08 09				10 23			12 23			14 23		
49	—	**Lowestoft**	a			08 18				10 32			12 32			14 32		
—	—	Norwich	a			09 25				11 25			13 25			15 25		

		LE 1 ◇	LE	LE	LE R 1	LE	LE	LE	LE	LE	LE	LE R 1	LE 1 ◇	LE
London Liverpool Street 15	⊖ d	13 38	14 00	15 00	15 38	16 00	17 00		17 30	18 00	19 00	19 32	21 00	
Shenfield 3	d	14u02	14 23	15 23	16u02	16 02	16 54		17b24	17b54	19b01	19u55	21u23	
Chelmsford 3	d	14 12		15 12	16u12	16 30	16b45	17b15	17 51	18b14	19b13	20c00	21 11	21b11
Witham 2	d	14 21		15 21	16 23	16 23	17 13		17b45	18b30	19b23	20 12	21 20	21b20
Marks Tey 2	d	14 29		15 29	16 32	16 32	17b01	17b31	17b55	18b30	19b33	20 00	21 30	21b30
Colchester 4	d	14 38	14 50	15 50	16 41	16 50	17 26	17 51	18 11	18 53	19 53	20 26	21 50	
Manningtree 2	d	14 31	14 59	15 59	16 31	16 59	17 35	17 59	18 27	19 02	20 02	20 30	21 58	
Ipswich	d	15 02	15 27	16 27	17 02	17 27	18 13	18 27	18 55	19 27	20 27	20 52	22 15	22 27
Westerfield	d	15 09	15 33	16 33	17 09	17 33	18 20	18 33	19 02	19 33	20 33	20 59	22 22	22 33
Derby Road	d		15 38	16 38		17 38		18 38		19 38	20 38			22 38
Trimley	d		15 47	16 47		17 47		18 47		19 47	20 47			22 47
Felixstowe	a		15 52	16 52		17 52		18 52		19 52	20 52			22 52
Woodbridge	d	15 21			17 22		18 32		19 14			21 11	22 34	
Melton	d	15 25			17 26		18 36		19 18			21 15	22 38	
Wickham Market	d	15 31			17 32		18 42		19 24			21 21	22 44	
Saxmundham	d	15 42			17 43		18 53		19 35			21 32	22 55	
Darsham	d	15 48			17 49		18 59		19 41			21 38	23 01	
Halesworth	d	15 58			17 59		19e16		19 51			21 48	23 11	
Brampton (Suffolk)	d	16 05			18 06		19 23		19 58			21 55	23 18	
Beccles	d	16 13			18 14		19 31		20 06			22 03	23 26	
Oulton Broad South	d	16 23			18 24		19 41		20 16			22 13	23 36	
Lowestoft	a	16 32			18 33		19 50		20 25			22 22	23 45	
Norwich	a	17 30			19 30				21 25			23 28		

Saturdays

		LE	LE 1	LE	LE	LE 1 ◇	LE	LE	LE R 1	LE	LE	LE R 1	LE	LE
London Liverpool Street 15	⊖ d			05 30	07 00	07 38	08 00	09 00	09 38	10 00	11 00	11 38	12 00	13 00
Shenfield 3	d			05 56	07 23	08u02	08 23	09 23	10u02	10 23	11 23	12u02	12 23	13 23
Chelmsford 3	d			06 07	07 12	08 12		09 12	10 12	10 12	11 12	12 12	12 12	13 12
Witham 2	d			06 19	07 21	08 21		09 21	10 21	10 21	11 21	12 21	12 21	13 21
Marks Tey 2	d			06 29	07 29	08 29		09 29	10 29	10 29	11 29	12 29	12 29	13 29
Colchester 4	d	05 38	05 38	06 37	07 50	08 38	08 50	09 50	10 38	10 50	11 50	12 38	12 50	13 50
Manningtree 2	d	05 46	05 46	06 45	07 59	08 31	08 59	09 59	10 31	10 59	11 59	12 31	12 59	13 59
Ipswich	d	06 27	06 50	07 27	08 27	09 02	09 27	10 27	11 02	11 27	12 27	13 02	13 27	14 27
Westerfield	d	06 33	06 57	07 33	08 33	09 09	09 33	10 33	11 09	11 33	12 33	13 09	13 33	14 33
Derby Road	d	06 38		07 38	08 38		09 38	10 38		11 38	12 38		13 38	14 38
Trimley	d	06 47		07 47	08 47		09 47	10 47		11 47	12 47		13 47	14 47
Felixstowe	a	06 52		07 52	08 52		09 52	10 52		11 52	12 52		13 52	14 52
Woodbridge	d		07 09			09 21			11 21			13 21		
Melton	d		07 13			09 25			11 25			13 25		
Wickham Market	d		07 19			09 31			11 31			13 31		
Saxmundham	d		07 30			09 42			11 42			13 42		
Darsham	d		07 36			09 48			11 48			13 48		
Halesworth	d		07 46			09 58			11 58			13 58		
Brampton (Suffolk)	d		07 53			10 05			12 05			14 05		
Beccles	d		08 01			10 13			12 13			14 13		
Oulton Broad South	d		08 11			10 23			12 23			14 23		
Lowestoft	a		08 20			10 32			12 32			14 32		
Norwich	a		09 25			11 25			13 25			15 25		

For general notes see front of timetable
For details of catering facilities see Directory of Train Operators

b Change at Colchester and Ipswich
c Change at Colchester
e Arr. 1908

Table 13

Ipswich → Felixstowe and Lowestoft

Network diagram - see first page of Table 13

Saturdays

		LE [R] [1]	LE	LE	LE [R] [1]	LE	LE	LE [R] [1]	LE	LE	LE [R] [1]	LE [1] ◇	LE
London Liverpool Street [15]	⊖ d	13 38	14 00	15 00	15 38	16 00	17 00	17 46	18 00	19 00	19 38	21 00	
Shenfield [3]	d	14u02	14 23	15 23	16u02	16 23	17 23	18b02	18 23	19 23	20u02	21u23	
Chelmsford [3]	d	14 12	14 12	15 12	16 12	16 12	17 12	18u16	18 16	19 16	20 12	21 12	21c12
Witham [2]	d	14 21	14 21	15 21	16 21	16 21	17 21	18 21	18c21	19c21	20 21	21 21	21c21
Marks Tey [2]	d	14 29	14 29	15 29	16 29	16 29	17 29	18 28	18c28	19c28	20 29	21 29	21c29
Colchester [4]	d	14 38	14 50	15 50	16 38	16 50	17 50	18 40	18 50	19 50	20 38	21 50	
Manningtree [2]	d	14 31	14 59	15 59	16 31	16 59	17 59	18 31	18 59	19 59	20 32	21 58	
Ipswich	d	15 02	15 27	16 27	17 02	17 27	18 27	19 02	19 27	20 27	21 02	22 15	22 27
Westerfield	d	15 09	15 33	16 33	17 09	17 33	18 33	19 09	19 33	20 33	21 09	22 22	22 33
Derby Road	d		15 38	16 38		17 38	18 38		19 38	20 38			22 38
Trimley	d		15 47	16 47		17 47	18 47		19 47	20 47			22 47
Felixstowe	a		15 52	16 52		17 52	18 52		19 52	20 52			22 52
Woodbridge	d	15 21			17 21			19 21			21 21	22 34	
Melton	d	15 25			17 25			19 25			21 25	22 38	
Wickham Market	d	15 31			17 31			19 31			21 31	22 44	
Saxmundham	d	15 42			17 42			19 42			21 42	22 55	
Darsham	d	15 48			17 48			19 48			21 48	23 01	
Halesworth	d	15 58			17 58			19 58			21 58	23 11	
Brampton (Suffolk)	d	16 05			18 05			20 05			22 05	23 18	
Beccles	d	16 13			18 13			20 13			22 13	23 26	
Oulton Broad South	d	16 23			18 23			20 23			22 23	23 36	
Lowestoft	a	16 32			18 32			20 32			22 32	23 45	
Norwich	a	17 30			19 30			21 25			23 28		

Sundays

		LE [1]	LE	LE	LE	LE [1]	LE	LE	LE	LE	LE	LE	LE	LE	LE [1]	LE	LE
London Liverpool Street [15]	⊖ d	08 30	10 30		11 30	12 30		13 30	14 30		15 30	16 30		17 30	18 30		20 30
Shenfield [3]	d	08 57	10 57		11 57	12 57		13 57	14 57		15 57	16 57		17 57	18 57		20 57
Chelmsford [3]	d	08 42	10 42		11 42	12 42		13 42	14 42		15 42	16 42		17 42	18 42		20 42
Witham [2]	d	08 54	10 54		11 54	12 54		13 54	14 54		15 54	16 54		17 54	18 54		20 54
Marks Tey [2]	d	09 04	11 04		12 04	13 04		14 04	15 04		16 04	17 04		18 04	19 04		21 04
Colchester [4]	d	09 24	11 24		12 24	13 24		14 24	15 24		16 24	17 24		18 24	19 24		21 24
Manningtree [2]	d	09 33	11 33		12 33	13 33		14 33	15 33		16 33	17 33		18 33	19 33		21 33
Ipswich	d	09 50	11 50	12 02	13 02	13 50	14 02	15 02	15 50	16 02	17 02	17 50	18 02	19 02	19 50	20 02	21 50
Westerfield	d	09 57	11 57	12 08	13 08	13 57	14 08	15 08	15 57	16 08	17 08	17 57	18 08	19 08	19 57	20 08	21 57
Derby Road	d			12 13	13 13		14 13	15 13		16 13	17 13		18 13	19 13		20 13	
Trimley	d			12 22	13 22		14 22	15 22		16 22	17 22		18 22	19 22		20 22	
Felixstowe	a			12 27	13 27		14 27	15 27		16 27	17 27		18 27	19 27		20 27	
Woodbridge	d	10 09	12 09			14 09			16 09			18 09			20 09		22 09
Melton	d	10 13	12 13			14 13			16 13			18 13			20 13		22 13
Wickham Market	d	10 19	12 19			14 19			16 19			18 19			20 19		22 19
Saxmundham	d	10 30	12 30			14 30			16 30			18 30			20 30		22 30
Darsham	d	10 36	12 36			14 36			16 36			18 36			20 36		22 36
Halesworth	d	10 46	12 46			14 46			16 46			18 46			20 46		22 46
Brampton (Suffolk)	d	10 53	12 53			14 53			16 53			18 53			20 53		22 53
Beccles	d	11 01	13 01			15 01			17 01			19 01			21 01		23 01
Oulton Broad South	d	11 11	13 11			15 11			17 11			19 11			21 11		23 11
Lowestoft	a	11 20	13 20			15 20			17 20			19 20			21 20		23 20
Norwich	a	12 33	14 33			16 33			18 33			20 33			22 33		00 03

For general notes see front of timetable
For details of catering facilities see Directory of Train Operators

b Change at Colchester
c Change at Colchester and Ipswich

Table 13

Mondays to Fridays

Lowestoft and Felixstowe → Ipswich

Network diagram - see first page of Table 13

Miles	Miles			LE	LE	LE	LE R 1	LE	LE	LE	LE	LE R 1	LE	LE	LE 1 ◇	LE	LE	LE 1 ◇
—	—	Norwich	d				05 45					07 54			09 57			11 57
0	—	**Lowestoft**	d		05 31		06 44					08 58			10 58			12 58
2¼	—	Oulton Broad South	d		05 38		06 51					09 05			11 05			13 05
8½	—	Beccles	d		05 47		07 00					09 14			11 14			13 14
13	—	Brampton (Suffolk)	d		05 55		07 08					09 22			11 22			13 22
17	—	Halesworth	d		06 03		07 16					09 30			11 30			13 30
22¼	—	Darsham	d		06 11		07 24					09 38			11 38			13 38
26½	—	Saxmundham	d		06 19		07 32		08 21			09 46			11 46			13 46
33¼	—	Wickham Market	d		06 28		07 41		08 30			09 55			11 55			13 55
37¼	—	Melton	d		06 35		07 48		08 37			10 02			12 02			14 02
38¾	—	Woodbridge	d		06 40		07 53		08 42			10 07			12 07			14 07
—	0	**Felixstowe**	d	05 34		06 38		07 50		08 56	09 56		10 56	11 56		12 56	13 56	
—	1¾	Trimley	d	05 37		06 41		07 53		08 59	09 59		10 59	11 59		12 59	13 59	
—	9¾	Derby Road	d	05 47		06 51		08 03		09 09	10 09		11 09	12 09		13 09	14 09	
45½	12¼	Westerfield	d	05 52	06 51	06 56	08 04	08 08	08 53	09 14	10 14	10 18	11 14	12 14	12 18	13 14	14 14	14 18
49	—	**Ipswich**	a	06 00	06 59	07 03	08 12	08 16	09 01	09 21	10 21	10 26	11 21	12 21	12 26	13 21	14 21	14 26
—	—	Manningtree 2	a	06 32		07 17	08 32		09 17	09 51	10 51	10 51	11 51		12 51	13 51		14 51
—	—	Colchester 4	a	06 24		07 28	08 43		09 27	09 48	10 48	10 48	11 48		12 48	13 48		14 48
—	—	Marks Tey 2	a	06b35		07b43	08b54		09b39	10b23	11b23	11 23	12b23	13b23	13 23	14b23	15b23	15 23
—	—	Witham 2	a	06 38		07b47	09b05		09b49	10 02	11 02	11 02	12 02		13 02	14 02		15 02
—	—	Chelmsford 3	a	06 48		07b56	09 02		09 46	10 10	11 10	11 10	12 10		13 10	14 10		15 10
—	—	Shenfield 3	a	07b06		08b08	09b25		10b09	10 22	11 22	11s22	12 22		13s22	14 22		15s22
—	—	London Liverpool Street 15	⊖ a	07 26		08 23	09 25		10 24	10 46	11 45	11 45	12 45		13 45	14 45		15 45

		LE	LE	LE	LE	LE	LE 1 ◇	LE	LE 1 ◇	LE	LE	LE	LE
Norwich	d			13 57			15 57		16 57			19 57	
Lowestoft	d			14 58			16 58		18 43			20 58	
Oulton Broad South	d			15 05			17 05		18 50			21 05	
Beccles	d			15 14			17 14		18 59			21 14	
Brampton (Suffolk)	d			15 22			17 22		19 07			21 22	
Halesworth	d			15 30			17 30		19 15			21 30	
Darsham	d			15 38			17 38		19 23			21 38	
Saxmundham	d			15 46			17 46		19c36			21 46	
Wickham Market	d			15 55			17 55		19 45			21 55	
Melton	d			16 02			18 02		19 52			22 02	
Woodbridge	d			16 07			18 07		19 57			22 07	
Felixstowe	d	14 56	15 56		16 56	17 56		18 56		19 56	20 56		22 56
Trimley	d	14 59	15 59		16 59	17 59		18 59		19 59	20 59		22 59
Derby Road	d	15 09	16 09		17 09	18 09		19 09		20 09	21 09		23 09
Westerfield	d	15 14	16 14	16 18	17 14	18 14	18 18	19 14	20 08	20 14	21 14	22 18	23 14
Ipswich	a	15 21	16 21	16 26	17 21	18 21	18 26	19 21	20 16	20 21	21 21	22 26	23 21
Manningtree 2	a	15 51		16 51	17 51		18 51	19 36	20 51	20 51	21 36	22 51	23 47
Colchester 4	a	15 43		16 48	17 48		18 48	19 47	20 48	20 48	21 48	23 01	23 58
Marks Tey 2	a	15b54		16 59	17 55		18 55	19 54	21 23	21b23	22b23		
Witham 2	a	16b04		17 06	18 03		19 03	20 02	21 02	21 02	22 02	23 15	
Chelmsford 3	a	16b13		17 15	18 13		19 12	20 11	21 10	21 10	22 10	23 24	
Shenfield 3	a	16b24		17 27	18 25		19s24	20 23	21s22	21 22	22 22	23 36	
London Liverpool Street 15	⊖ a	16b48		17 49	18 49		19 47	20 46	21 45	21 45	22 45	00 03	

Saturdays

		LE	LE R 1	LE	LE R 1	LE	LE	LE R 1	LE	LE	LE R 1	LE	LE	LE 1 ◇
Norwich	d				05 49			07 54			09 57			11 57
Lowestoft	d		05 58		06 58			08 58			10 58			12 58
Oulton Broad South	d		06 05		07 05			09 05			11 05			13 05
Beccles	d		06 14		07 14			09 14			11 14			13 14
Brampton (Suffolk)	d		06 22		07 22			09 22			11 22			13 22
Halesworth	d		06 30		07 30			09 30			11 30			13 30
Darsham	d		06 38		07 38			09 38			11 38			13 38
Saxmundham	d		06 46		07 46			09 46			11 46			13 46
Wickham Market	d		06 55		07 55			09 55			11 55			13 55
Melton	d		07 02		08 02			10 02			12 02			14 02
Woodbridge	d		07 07		08 07			10 07			12 07			14 07
Felixstowe	d	06 56		07 56		08 56	09 56		10 56	11 56		12 56	13 56	
Trimley	d	06 59		07 59		08 59	09 59		10 59	11 59		12 59	13 59	
Derby Road	d	07 09		08 09		09 09	10 09		11 09	12 09		13 09	14 09	
Westerfield	d	07 14	07 18	08 14	08 18	09 14	10 14	10 18	11 14	12 14	12 18	13 14	14 14	14 18
Ipswich	a	07 21	07 26	08 21	08 26	09 21	10 21	10 26	11 21	12 21	12 26	13 21	14 21	14 26
Manningtree 2	a	07 51	07 51	08 51	08 51	09 51	10 51	10 51	11 51	12 51	12 51	13 51		14 51
Colchester 4	a	07 48	07 48	08 48	08 48	09 48	10 48	10 48	11 48	12 48	12 48	13 48		14 48
Marks Tey 2	a	08b23	08 23	09b23	09 23	10b23	11b23	11 23	12b23	13b23	13 23	14b23	15b23	15 23
Witham 2	a	08 02	08 02	09b04	09 04	10b04	11b04	11 04	12 02	13 02	13 02	14 02		15 02
Chelmsford 3	a	08 10	08 10	09 06	09s06	10 06	11 06	11s06	12 10	13 10	13 10	14 10		15 10
Shenfield 3	a	08 22	08s22	09b24	09e24	10b24	11b24	11e24	12 22	13 22	13s22	14 22		15s22
London Liverpool Street 15	⊖ a	08 45	08 45	09 38	09 38	10 38	11 42	11 42	12 45	13 45	13 45	14 45		15 45

For general notes see front of timetable
For details of catering facilities see Directory of Train Operators

b Change at Ipswich and Colchester
c Arr. 1930
e Change at Colchester

Table 13

Saturdays

Lowestoft and Felixstowe → Ipswich

Network diagram - see first page of Table 13

		LE	LE	LE 1 ◇	LE	LE	LE 1 ◇	LE	LE	LE 1 ◇	LE	LE	LE
Norwich	d			13 57			15 57			17 57		19 57	
Lowestoft	d			14 58			16 58			18 58		20 58	
Oulton Broad South	d			15 05			17 05			19 05		21 05	
Beccles	d			15 14			17 14			19 14		21 14	
Brampton (Suffolk)	d			15 22			17 22			19 22		21 22	
Halesworth	d			15 30			17 30			19 30		21 30	
Darsham	d			15 38			17 38			19 38		21 38	
Saxmundham	d			15 46			17 46			19 46		21 46	
Wickham Market	d			15 55			17 55			19 55		21 55	
Melton	d			16 02			18 02			20 02		22 02	
Woodbridge	d			16 07			18 07			20 07		22 07	
Felixstowe	d	14 56	15 56		16 56	17 56		18 56	19 56		20 56		22 56
Trimley	d	14 59	15 59		16 59	17 59		18 59	19 59		20 59		22 59
Derby Road	d	15 09	16 09		17 09	18 09		19 09	20 09		21 09		23 09
Westerfield	d	15 14	16 14	16 18	17 14	18 14	18 18	19 14	20 14	20 18	21 14	22 18	23 14
Ipswich	a	15 21	16 21	16 26	17 21	18 21	18 26	19 21	20 21	20 26	21 21	22 26	23 21
Manningtree 2	a	15 51		16 51	17 51		18 51	19 36		20 51	21 37	22 51	23 35
Colchester 4	a	15 48		16 48	17 48		18 48	19 48		20 48	21 48	23 01	23 45
Marks Tey 2	a	16b23	17b23	17 23	18b23	19b23	19 23	20b23	21b23	21 23	22b23		
Witham 2	a	16 02		17 02	18 02		19 02	20 02		21 02	22 02	23 15	
Chelmsford 3	a	16 10		17 10	18 10		19 10	20 10		21 10	22 10	23 24	
Shenfield 3	a	16 22		17s22	18 22		19s22	20 22		21s22	22 22	23 36	
London Liverpool Street 15	⊖ a	16 45		17 45	18 45		19 45	20 45		21 49	22 49	00 07	

Sundays

		LE 1	LE	LE	LE 1	LE	LE	LE	LE	LE	LE	LE	LE	LE 1	LE	LE	LE
Norwich	d	07 25	08 57		10 57			12 57			14 57			16 57			18 57
Lowestoft	d	08 05	10 05		12 05			14 05			16 05			18 05			20 05
Oulton Broad South	d	08 12	10 12		12 12			14 12			16 12			18 12			20 12
Beccles	d	08 21	10 21		12 21			14 21			16 21			18 21			20 21
Brampton (Suffolk)	d	08 29	10 29		12 29			14 29			16 29			18 29			20 29
Halesworth	d	08 37	10 37		12 37			14 37			16 37			18 37			20 37
Darsham	d	08 45	10 45		12 45			14 45			16 45			18 45			20 45
Saxmundham	d	08 53	10 53		12 53			14 53			16 53			18 53			20 53
Wickham Market	d	09 02	11 02		13 02			15 02			17 02			19 02			21 02
Melton	d	09 09	11 09		13 09			15 09			17 09			19 09			21 09
Woodbridge	d	09 14	11 14		13 14			15 14			17 14			19 14			21 14
Felixstowe	d			12 32		13 32	14 32		15 32	16 32		17 32	18 32		19 32	20 32	
Trimley	d			12 35		13 35	14 35		15 35	16 35		17 35	18 35		19 35	20 35	
Derby Road	d			12 45		13 45	14 45		15 45	16 45		17 45	18 45		19 45	20 45	
Westerfield	d	09 25	11 25	12 50	13 25	13 50	14 50	15 25	15 50	16 50	17 25	17 50	18 50	19 25	19 50	20 50	21 25
Ipswich	a	09 33	11 33	12 57	13 33	13 57	14 57	15 33	15 57	16 57	17 33	17 57	18 57	19 33	19 57	20 57	21 33
Manningtree 2	a	09 51	11 51	13 18	13 51	14 18	15 18	15 51	16 18	17 18	17 51	18 18	19 18	19 51	20 18	21 18	21 51
Colchester 4	a	10 01	12 01	13 29	14 01	14 29	15 29	16 01	16 29	17 19	18 01	18 29	19 29	20 01	20 29	21 29	22 01
Marks Tey 2	a	10b12	12b12	13 36	14b12	14 36	15 36	16b12	16 36	17 36	18b12	18 36	19 36	20b12	20 36	21 36	22b12
Witham 2	a	10b20	12b20	13 46	14b20	14 46	15 46	16b20	16 46	17 46	18b20	18 46	19 46	20b20	20 46	21 46	22b20
Chelmsford 3	a	10b29	12b29	13 57	14b29	14 57	15 57	16b29	16 57	17 57	18b29	18 57	19 57	20b29	20 57	21 57	22b29
Shenfield 3	a	10 29	12 29	14 10	14 29	15 10	16 10	16 29	17 10	18 10	18 29	19 10	20 10	20 29	21 10	22 10	22 29
London Liverpool Street 15	⊖ a	11 03	13 01	14 42	15 01	15 42	16 42	17 01	17 42	18 28	19 01	19 42	20 42	21 01	21 42	22 42	23 01

For general notes see front of timetable
For details of catering facilities see
Directory of Train Operators

b Change at Ipswich and Colchester

Ipswich → Bury St Edmunds, Cambridge, Ely and Peterborough

Network diagram - see first page of Table 13

Mondays to Fridays

Miles	Miles	Miles			LE	LE 1	LE	LE	LE 1 ◇	LE	LE	LE 1	LE	LE	LE 1 ◇
—	—	—	London Liverpool Street 15 ⊖	d					06 38		08 00	08 38	09 00	10 00	10 38
—	—	—	Shenfield	d					07u02		08 23	09 02	09 23	10 23	11u02
—	—	—	Chelmsford	d					07 12		08 12	09 12		10 12	11 12
—	—	—	Witham	d					07 21		08 22	09 21		10 21	11 21
—	—	—	Marks Tey	d					07 33		08 30	09 29		10 29	11 29
—	—	—	Colchester	d		05 35		06 22	07 41		08 50	09 38	09 50	10 50	11 38
—	—	—	Manningtree	d		05 44		06 31	07 50		08 59	09 46	09 59	10 59	
—	—	0	Harwich International	d						07 47					
0	—	18	**Ipswich**	d	05 10	06 01	06 13	06 52	08 03	08 16	09 16	10 03	10 16	11 16	12 03
8¼	—	—	Needham Market	d	05 20		06 23	07 02		08 26	09 26		10 26	11 26	
12	—	—	Stowmarket	d	05 26	06 12	06 29	07 08	08 14	08 32	09 32	10 14	10 32	11 32	12 14
17¾	—	—	Elmswell	d	05 35		06 38	07 18		08 41	09 41		10 41	11 41	
22¼	—	—	Thurston	d	05 41		06 44	07 24		08 47	09 47		10 47	11 47	
26¼	—	—	Bury St Edmunds	a	05 47	06 28	06 50	07 30	08 30	08 53	09 53	10 30	10 53	11 53	12 30
—	—	—		d	05 49	06 28	06 51	07 30	08 30	08 55	09 55	10 30	10 55	11 55	12 30
36	0	—	Kennett	d	06 00		07 02	07 42			10 06			12 06	
41	—	—	Newmarket	d	06 10		07 13	07 51		09 15	10 17		11 15	12 17	
44¼	—	—	Dullingham	d	06 15		07 18	08b00		09 20			11 20		
55¼	—	—	**Cambridge**	a	06 32		07 37	08 19		09 39	10 39		11 39	12 39	
70	14¾	—	**Ely 6**	d		06 57			08 59			10 59			12 59
79¾	—	—	Manea	d											
85¼	—	—	March	d		07 14			09 16			11 16			13 16
93¼	—	—	Whittlesea	d		07 25			09 27			11 27			13 27
99¼	—	—	**Peterborough 8**	a		07 37			09 41			11 38			13 38

		LE	LE	LE 1 ◇	LE	LE	LE 1 ◇	LE	LE	LE R 1	LE	LE	LE 1	LE	LE
London Liverpool Street 15 ⊖	d	11 00	12 00	12 38	13 00	14 00	14 38	15 00	16 00	16 32	17 00	18 00	19 00		21 00
Shenfield	d	11 23	12 23	13u02	13 23	14 23	15u02	15 23	16 02	16u54	16 54	17c54	19c01	20 02	21 23
Chelmsford	d		12 12	13 12		14 12	15 12		16 30	16e45	17c15	18c14	19c13	20 11	21c11
Witham	d		12 21	13 21		14 21	15 21		16 23	17 13	17 13	18c30	19c23	20 20	21c20
Marks Tey	d		12 29	13 29		14 29	15 29		16 32	17 01	17c31	18c30	19c33	20 30	21c30
Colchester	d	11 50	12 50	13 38	13 50	14 50	15 38	15 50	16 50	17 26	17 51	18 53	19 53		21 50
Manningtree	d	11 59	12 59		13 59	14 59		15 59	16 59	17 35	17 59	19 02	20 02		21 58
Harwich International	d														21 34
Ipswich	d	12 16	13 16	14 03	14 16	15 16	16 03	16 16	17 16	17 49	18 16	19 16	20 16	21 16	22 16
Needham Market	d	12 26	13 26		14 26	15 26		16 26	17 26	17 58	18 26	19 26	20 25	21 26	22 26
Stowmarket	d	12 32	13 32	14 14	14 32	15 32	16 14	16 32	17 32	18 03	18 32	19 32	20 30	21 32	22 32
Elmswell	d	12 41	13 41		14 41	15 41		16 41	17 41	18 12	18 41	19 41	20 39	21 41	22 41
Thurston	d	12 47	13 47		14 47	15 47		16 47	17 47	18 17	18 47	19 47	20 44	21 47	22 47
Bury St Edmunds	a	12 53	13 53	14 30	14 53	15 53	16 30	16 53	17 53	18 23	18 53	19 53	20 50	21 53	22 54
	d	12 55	13 55	14 30	14 55	15 55	16 30	16 55	17 55	18 23	18 55	19 55	20 50	21 55	
Kennett	d		14 06			16 06			18 06			20 06		22 06	
Newmarket	d	13 15	14 17		15 15	16 17		17 17	18 17		19 15	20 17		22 15	
Dullingham	d	13 20			15 20						19 20			22 20	
Cambridge	a	13 39	14 39		15 39	16 39		17 39	18 39		19 39	20 39		22 39	
Ely 6	d			14 59			16 59			18f59			21 19		
Manea	d														
March	d			15 16			17 16			19 16			21 36		
Whittlesea	d			15 27			17 27			19 27			21 47		
Peterborough 8	a			15 39			17 38			19 44			21 58		

Saturdays

		LE	LE 1	LE	LE	LE 1 ◇	LE	LE	LE 1 ◇	LE	LE	LE R 1	LE	LE
London Liverpool Street 15 ⊖	d				05 30	06 38	07g00	08 00	08 38	09 00	10 00	10 38	11 00	12 00
Shenfield	d				05 56	07u02	07g23	08 23	09u02	09 23	10 23	11u02	11 23	12 23
Chelmsford	d				06 07	07 12		08 12	09 12		10 12	11 12	11 12	12 12
Witham	d				06 19	07 21		08 21	09 21		10 21	11 21	11 21	12 21
Marks Tey	d				06 29	07 29		08 29	09 29		10 29	11 29	11 29	12 29
Colchester	d		05 38		06 37	07 38	07g50	08 50	09 38	09 50	10 50	11 38	11 50	12 50
Manningtree	d		05 46		06 45	07 46	07g59	08 59	09 46	09 59	10 59		11 59	12 59
Harwich International	d						07 47							
Ipswich	d	05 10	06 00	06 14	07 16	08 03	08 16	09 16	10 03	10 16	11 16	12 03	12 16	13 16
Needham Market	d	05 20		06 24	07 26		08 26	09 26		10 26	11 26		12 26	13 26
Stowmarket	d	05 26	06 11	06 30	07 32	08 14	08 32	09 32	10 14	10 32	11 32	12 14	12 32	13 32
Elmswell	d	05 35		06 39	07 41		08 41	09 41		10 41	11 41		12 41	13 41
Thurston	d	05 41		06 45	07 47		08 47	09 47		10 47	11 47		12 47	13 47
Bury St Edmunds	a	05 47	06 27	06 51	07 53	08 30	08 53	09 53	10 30	10 53	11 53	12 30	12 53	13 53
	d	05 49	06 27	06 53	07 55	08 30	08 55	09 55	10 30	10 55	11 55	12 30	12 55	13 55
Kennett	d	06 00		07 04	08 06			10 06			12 06			14 06
Newmarket	d	06 10		07 15	08 17		09 15	10 17		11 15	12 17		13 15	14 17
Dullingham	d	06 15		07 20	08 22		09 20			11 20			13 20	
Cambridge	a	06 36		07 39	08 39		09 39	10 39		11 39	12 39		13 39	14 39
Ely 6	d		06 57			08 59			10 59			12 59		
Manea	d													
March	d		07 14			09 16			11 16			13 16		
Whittlesea	d		07 25			09 27			11 27			13 27		
Peterborough 8	a		07 37			09 38			11 38			13 38		

For general notes see front of timetable
For details of catering facilities see Directory of Train Operators

b Arr. 0757
c Change at Colchester and Ipswich
e Change at Colchester
f Arr. 1852
g Change at Ipswich

Due to major track repair work in the Bury St Edmunds area, trains between Ipswich and Peterborough are subject to disruption, resulting in bus replacements and extended journey times for part or all of this timetable. See local publicity or contact National Rail Enquiries 08457 48 49 50 for further details.

Table 14

Saturdays

Ipswich → Bury St Edmunds, Cambridge, Ely and Peterborough

Network diagram - see first page of Table 13

		LE R 1	LE	LE	LE 1 ◇	LE	LE	LE R 1	LE	LE	LE R 1	LE	LE
London Liverpool Street 15 ⊖	d	12 38	13 00	14 00	14 38	15 00		16 38	17 00	18 00	18 46	19 00	21 00
Shenfield	d	13u02	13 23	14 23	15u02	15 23		17u02	17 23	18 23	19b02	19 23	21 23
Chelmsford	d	13 12	13 12	14 12	15 12		16 12	17 12	17 12	18 16	19u16	19 16	21c12
Witham	d	13 21	13 21	14 21	15 21		16 21	17 21	17 21	18c21	19 21	19c21	21c21
Marks Tey	d	13 29	13 29	14 29	15 29		16 29	17 29	17 29	18c28	19 28	19c28	21c29
Colchester	d	13 38	13 50	14 50	15 38	15 50		17 38	17 50	18 50	19 40	19 50	21 50
Manningtree	d		13 59	14 59		15 59			17 59	18 59		19 59	21 58
Harwich International	d												21 34
Ipswich	d	14 03	14 16	15 16	16 03	16 16	17 16	18 03	18 16	19 16	20 03	20 16	22 17
Needham Market	d		14 26	15 26		16 26	17 26		18 26	19 26		20 26	22 27
Stowmarket	d	14 14	14 32	15 32	16 14	16 32	17 32	18 14	18 32	19 32	20 14	20 32	22 33
Elmswell	d		14 41	15 41		16 41	17 41		18 41	19 42		20 41	22 42
Thurston	d		14 47	15 47		16 47	17 47		18 47	19 48		20 47	22 48
Bury St Edmunds	a	14 30	14 53	15 53	16 30	16 53	17 53	18 30	18 53	19 53	20 30	20 53	22 55
	d	14 30	14 55	15 55	16 30	16 55	17 55	18 30	18 55	19 55	20 30	20 55	
Kennett	d			16 06			18 06			20 06		21 06	
Newmarket	d		15 15	16 17		17 17	18 17		19 15	20 17		21 15	
Dullingham	d		15 20						19 20			21 20	
Cambridge	a		15 39	16 39		17 39	18 39		19 39	20 39		21 39	
Ely 6	d	14 59			16 59			18 59			20 59		
Manea	d												
March	d	15 16			17 16			19 16			21 16		
Whittlesea	d	15 27			17 27			19 27			21 27		
Peterborough 8	a	15 38			17 38			19 38			21 38		

Sundays

		LE	LE	LE 1	LE	LE 1	LE	LE 1	LE	LE 1	LE	LE 1	LE	LE
London Liverpool Street 15 ⊖	d													
Shenfield	d													
Chelmsford	d			08 42	09 42	10 42	11 42	12 42	13 42	14 42	15 42	16 42	17 42	19 42
Witham	d			08 54	09 54	10 54	11 54	12 54	13 54	14 54	15 54	16 54	17 54	19 54
Marks Tey	d			09 04	10 04	11 04	12 04	13 04	14 04	15 04	16 04	17 04	18 04	20 04
Colchester	d	08 12												
Manningtree	d	08 20												
Harwich International	d		08 30											
Ipswich	d	08 45	09 02	09 55	11 02	11 55	13 02	13 55	15 02	15 55	17 02	17 55	19 02	21 02
Needham Market	d		09 12		11 12		13 12		15 12		17 12		19 12	21 12
Stowmarket	d	08 59	09 18	10 07	11 18	12 07	13 18	14 07	15 18	16 07	17 18	18 07	19 18	21 18
Elmswell	d		09 27		11 27		13 27		15 27		17 27		19 27	21 27
Thurston	d		09 33		11 33		13 33		15 33		17 33		19 33	21 33
Bury St Edmunds	a	09 17	09 39	10 22	11 39	12 22	13 39	14 22	15 39	16 22	17 39	18 22	19 39	21 39
	d		09 40	10 23	11 40	12 23	13 40	14 23	15 40	16 23	17 40	18 23	19 40	21 40
Kennett	d		09 51		11 51		13 51		15 51		17 51		19 51	21 51
Newmarket	d		10 00		12 00		14 00		16 00		18 00		20 00	22 00
Dullingham	d		10 05		12 05		14 05		16 05		18 05		20 05	22 05
Cambridge	a		10 24		12 24		14 24		16 27		18 24		20 24	22 24
Ely 6	d			10e57		12f57		14g57		16h57		18j57		
Manea	d													
March	d			11 14		13 15		15 15		17 14		19 14		
Whittlesea	d			11 25		13 26		15 26		17 25		19 25		
Peterborough 8	a			11 41		13 42		15 42		17 36		19 36		

For general notes see front of timetable
For details of catering facilities see Directory of Train Operators

b Change at Colchester
c Change at Colchester and Ipswich
e Arr. 1051
f Arr. 1251
g Arr. 1451
h Arr. 1651
j Arr. 1852

Due to major track repair work in the Bury St Edmunds area, trains between Ipswich and Peterborough are subject to disruption, resulting in bus replacements and extended journey times for part or all of this timetable. See local publicity or contact National Rail Enquiries 08457 48 49 50 for further details.

Peterborough, Ely, Cambridge and Bury St Edmunds → Ipswich

Network diagram - see first page of Table 13

Miles	Miles	Miles			LE	LE	LE	LE	LE	LE	LE	LE	LE	LE	LE	LE	LE	LE	LE
					MO					R 1			1 ◊			1 ◊			1
0	—	—	**Peterborough** [8]	d						07 52			09 47			11 48			13 47
6	—	—	Whittlesea	d						08 00			09 55			11 56			13 55
13¼	—	—	March	d						08 11			10 06			12 07			14 06
19¼	—	—	Manea	d															
29¼	0	—	**Ely** [6]	d						08 30			10 30			12 30			14 30
45	—	—	**Cambridge**	d	23p00			06 41	07 43		08 43	09 43		10 43	11 43		12 43	13 43	
56	—	—	Dullingham	d	23p16				08 00			09 59			11 59			13 59	
58¼	—	—	Newmarket	d	23p21			07 01	08 04		09 03	10 04		11 03	12 04		13 03	14 04	
63¼	14¾	—	Kennett	d	23p29			07 09			09 11			11 11			13 11		
73¼	—	—	Bury St Edmunds	a	23p41			07 21	08 23	08 55	09 23	10 23	10 55	11 23	12 23	12 55	13 23	14 23	14 55
—	—	—		d	23p42	05 36	06 22	07 23	08 24	08 56	09 23	10 23	10 56	11 23	12 23	12 56	13 23	14 23	14 56
77¼	—	—	Thurston	d	23p48	05 42	06 28	07 30	08 30		09 30	10 30		11 30	12 30		13 30	14 30	
81¼	—	—	Elmswell	d	23p55	05 49	06 35	07 36	08 37		09 36	10 36		11 36	12 36		13 36	14 36	
87¼	—	—	Stowmarket	d	00 04	05 57	06 44	07 45	08 45	09 12	09 45	10 45	11 12	11 45	12 45	13 12	13 45	14 45	15 12
90¾	—	—	Needham Market	d	00 09	06 03		07 50	08 51		09 50	10 50		11 50	12 50		13 50	14 50	
99¼	—	0	**Ipswich**	a	00 21	06 14	07 00	08 02	09 03	09 26	10 02	11 02	11 25	12 02	13 02	13 25	14 02	15 02	15 25
—	—	18	Harwich International	a			07 25												
—	—	—	Manningtree	a		06 32	07b17		09 17	09 51	10 17	11 17	11 51	12 17	13 17	13 51	14 17	15 17	15 51
—	—	—	Colchester	a		06 43	07b28		09 27	09 48	10 27	11 27	11 48	12 27	13 27	13 48	14 27	15 27	15 43
—	—	—	Marks Tey	a		06c54	07c43	08c54	09c39	10 23	10c39	11c39	12 23	12c39	13c39	14 23	14c39	15c54	15 54
—	—	—	Witham	a		07c05	07c47	09c05	09c49	10 02	10c49	11c49	12 02	12c49	13c49	14 02	14c49	15c49	16 04
—	—	—	Chelmsford	a		07c14	07c56		09 46	10s10	10 45	11 45	12 10	12 45	13 45	14 10	14 45	15 45	16 13
—	—	—	Shenfield	a		07 32	08c08	09c25	10c09	10s22	11c09	12c09	12s22	13c09	14c09	14s22	15c09	16c11	16 24
—	—	—	London Liverpool Street [15] ⊖	a		07 37	08b23	09 25	10 24	10 46	11 24	12 24	12 45	13 24	14 24	14 45	15 24	16 24	16 48

		LE	LE	LE	LE	LE	LE	LE	LE	LE	LE	LE	LE
				1 ◊			1 ◊			1 ◊		1	
Peterborough [8]	d			15 47			17 47			19 49		22 05	
Whittlesea	d			15 55			17 55			19 57		22 13	
March	d			16 06			18 06			20 08		22 24	
Manea	d												
Ely [6]	d			16 30			18 30			20 27		22 42	
Cambridge	d	14 43	15 43		16 43	17 43		18 43	19 43		20 43		22 43
Dullingham	d		15 59		16 59	17 59			19 59		20 59		22 59
Newmarket	d	15 03	16 04		17 04	18 04		19 03	20 04		21 04		23 04
Kennett	d	15 11			17 12	18 12		19 11			21 12		23 12
Bury St Edmunds	a	15 23	16 23	16 55	17 24	18 24	18 55	19 23	20 23	20 52	21 24	23 07	23 24
	d	15 23	16 23	16 56	17 25	18 25	18 56	19 23	20 23	20 52	21 25	23 08	23 25
Thurston	d	15 30	16 30		17 31	18 31		19 30	20 30		21 31		23 31
Elmswell	d	15 36	16 36		17 38	18 38		19 36	20 36		21 38		23 38
Stowmarket	d	15 45	16 45	17 12	17 46	18 46	19 12	19 45	20 45	21 08	21 46	23 24	23 46
Needham Market	d	15 50	16 50		17 52	18 52		19 50	20 50		21 52		23 52
Ipswich	a	16 02	17 02	17 27	18 03	19 03	19 25	20 02	21 02	21 25	22 03	23 37	00 03
Harwich International	a								21 28				
Manningtree	a	16 17	17 17	17 51		19 17	19 36	20 18	21b18	21 36	22 18	23 47	
Colchester	a	16 27	17 27	17 48		19 27	19 47	20 28	21b28	21 48	22 28	23 58	
Marks Tey	a	16c39	17c39	17 55	18 55	19c39	19 54	20c39	21c39	22 23	22 35		
Witham	a	16c49	17c49	18 03	18c49	19c49	20 02	20c49	21c49	22 02	22 45		
Chelmsford	a	16 45	17 45	18 13		19 45	20 11	20 46	21b46	22 10	22 56		
Shenfield	a	17c11	18c11	18s25	19c09	20c09	20s23	21c09	21b58	22s22	23 09		
London Liverpool Street [15] ⊖	a	17 24	18 24	18 49		20 24	20 46	21 21	22b23	22 45	23 34		

For general notes see front of timetable
For details of catering facilities see Directory of Train Operators

b Change at Ipswich
c Change at Ipswich and Colchester

Due to major track repair work in the Bury St Edmunds area, trains between Ipswich and Peterborough are subject to disruption, resulting in bus replacements and extended journey times for part or all of this timetable. See local publicity or contact National Rail Enquiries 08457 48 49 50 for further details.

Table 14

Peterborough, Ely, Cambridge and Bury St Edmunds → Ipswich

Network diagram - see first page of Table 13

		LE	LE	LE	LE R 1	LE	LE	LE R 1	LE	LE	LE 1 ◇	LE	LE	LE 1 ◇
Peterborough 8	d				07 52			09 55			11 48			13 47
Whittlesea	d				08 00			10 03			11 56			13 55
March	d				08 11			10 14			12 07			14 06
Manea	d													
Ely 6	d				08 30			10 32			12 30			14 30
Cambridge	d		06 43	07 43		08 43	09 43		10 43	11 43		12 43	13 43	
Dullingham	d			07 59			09 59			11 59			13 59	
Newmarket	d		07 03	08 04		09 03	10 04		11 03	12 04		13 03	14 04	
Kennett	d		07 11			09 11			11 11			13 11		
Bury St Edmunds	a		07 23	08 23	08 55	09 23	10 23	10 57	11 23	12 23	12 55	13 23	14 23	14 55
	d	06 23	07 23	08 23	08 56	09 23	10 23	10 58	11 23	12 23	12 56	13 23	14 23	14 56
Thurston	d	06 30	07 30	08 30		09 30	10 30		11 30	12 30		13 30	14 30	
Elmswell	d	06 36	07 36	08 36		09 36	10 36		11 36	12 36		13 36	14 36	
Stowmarket	d	06 45	07 45	08 45	09 12	09 45	10 45	11 14	11 45	12 45	13 12	13 45	14 45	15 12
Needham Market	d	06 50	07 50	08 50		09 50	10 50		11 50	12 50		13 50	14 50	
Ipswich	a	07 02	08 02	09 02	09 25	10 02	11 02	11 27	12 02	13 02	13 27	14 02	15 02	15 25
Harwich International	a													
Manningtree	a	07 17	08 17	09 17	09 51	10 17	11 17	11 51	12 17	13 17	13 51	14 17	15 17	15 51
Colchester	a	07 27	08 27	09 27	09 48	10 27	11 27	11 48	12 27	13 27	13 48	14 27	15 27	15 48
Marks Tey	a	07b39	08b39	09b39	10 23	10b39	11b39	12 23	12b39	13b39	14 23	14b39	15b39	16 23
Witham	a	07b49	08b49	09b49	10 04	10b49	11b49	12 02	12b49	13b49	14 02	14b49	15b49	16 02
Chelmsford	a	07 45	08 45	09 45	10s06	10 45	11 45	12 10	12 45	13 45	14 10	14 45	15 45	16 10
Shenfield	a	08b09	09b09	10b09	10c24	11b09	12b09	12s22	13b09	14b09	14s22	15b09	16b09	16s22
London Liverpool Street 15 ⊖	a	08 24	09 24	10 24	10 38	11 24	12 24	12 45	13 24	14 24	14 45	15 24	16 24	16 45

		LE	LE	LE 1 ◇	LE	LE	LE 1 ◇	LE	LE	LE 1 ◇	LE	LE	LE 1
Peterborough 8	d			15 47			17 47			19 46			21 49
Whittlesea	d			15 55			17 55			19 54			21 57
March	d			16 06			18 06			20 05			22 08
Manea	d												
Ely 6	d			16 30			18 30			20 30			22 30
Cambridge	d	14 43	15 43		16 43	17 43		18 43	19 43		20 43	21 43	
Dullingham	d		15 59		16 59	17 59			19 59			21 59	
Newmarket	d	15 03	16 04		17 04	18 04		19 03	20 04		21 03	22 04	
Kennett	d	15 11			17 12	18 12		19 11			21 11	22 12	22 47
Bury St Edmunds	a	15 23	16 23	16 55	17 24	18 24	18 55	19 23	20 23	20 55	21 23	22 24	22 57
	d	15 23	16 23	16 56	17 25	18 25	18 56	19 23	20 23	20 56	21 23	22 25	22 58
Thurston	d	15 30	16 30		17 31	18 31		19 30	20 30		21 30	22 31	23 03
Elmswell	d	15 36	16 36		17 38	18 38		19 36	20 36		21 36	22 38	23 09
Stowmarket	d	15 45	16 45	17 12	17 46	18 46	19 12	19 45	20 45	21 12	21 45	22 46	23 17
Needham Market	d	15 50	16 50		17 52	18 52		19 50	20 50		21 50	22 52	23 22
Ipswich	a	16 02	17 02	17 27	18 03	19 03	19 25	20 02	21 02	21 27	22 02	23 03	23 32
Harwich International	a								21 28				
Manningtree	a	16 17	17 17	17 51	18 17	19 17	19 36	20 17	21e18	21 37	22 18	23 35	23 44
Colchester	a	16 27	17 27	17 48	18 27	19 27	19 48	20 28	21e28	21 48	22 28	23 45	23 56
Marks Tey	a	16b39	17b39	18 23	18b39	19b39	20 23	20b39	21b39	22 23	22 35		
Witham	a	16b49	17b49	18 02	18b49	19b49	20 02	20b49	21b49	22 02	22 45		
Chelmsford	a	16 45	17 45	18 10	18 45	19 45	20 10	20 46	21e46	22 10	22 56		
Shenfield	a	17b09	18b09	18s22	19b09	20b09	20s22	21b10	21e58	22s22	23 09		
London Liverpool Street 15 ⊖	a	17 24	18 24	18 45	19 24	20 24	20 45	21 19	22e25	22 49	23 38		

For general notes see front of timetable
For details of catering facilities see Directory of Train Operators

b Change at Ipswich and Colchester
c Change at Colchester
e Change at Ipswich

Due to major track repair work in the Bury St Edmunds area, trains between Ipswich and Peterborough are subject to disruption, resulting in bus replacements and extended journey times for part or all of this timetable. See local publicity or contact National Rail Enquiries 08457 48 49 50 for further details.

Table 14

Sundays

Peterborough, Ely, Cambridge and Bury St Edmunds → Ipswich

Network diagram - see first page of Table 13

		LE	LE	LE 1	LE	LE 1	LE	LE 1	LE	LE 1	LE	LE 1	LE	LE
Peterborough 8	d			11 46		13 48		15 47		17 47		19 44		
Whittlesea	d			11 54		13 56		15 55		17 55		19 52		
March	d			12 05		14 07		16 06		18 06		20 03		
Manea	d													
Ely 6	d			12 30		14 30		16 30		18b30		20 22		
Cambridge	d		11 12		13 12		15 12		17 12		19 12		21 12	23 00
Dullingham	d		11 28		13 28		15 28		17 28		19 28		21 28	23 16
Newmarket	d		11 33		13 33		15 33		17 33		19 33		21 33	23 21
Kennett	d		11 41		13 41		15 41		17 41		19 41		21 41	23 29
Bury St Edmunds	a		11 53	12 55	13 53	14 55	15 53	16 55	17 53	18 55	19 53	20 47	21 53	23 41
	d	09 55	11 55	12 56	13 55	14 56	15 55	16 56	17 55	18 56	19 55	20 47	21 55	23 42
Thurston	d	10 01	12 01		14 01		16 01		18 01		20 01		22 01	23 48
Elmswell	d	10 08	12 08		14 08		16 08		18 08		20 08		22 08	23 55
Stowmarket	d	10 17	12 17	13 12	14 17	15 12	16 17	17 12	18 17	19 12	20 17	21 05	22 17	00 04
Needham Market	d	10 22	12 22		14 22		16 22		18 22		20 22		22 22	00 09
Ipswich	a	10 34	12 34	13 25	14 34	15 27	16 34	17 25	18 34	19 27	20 34	21 18	22 34	00 21
Harwich International	a										21 02			
Manningtree	a	10 51	12 51	13 51	14 51	15 51	16 51	17 51	18 51	19 51	20c51	21 28		
Colchester	a	11 01	13 01	14 01	15 01	16 01	17 01	18 01	19 01	20 01	21c01	21 40		
Marks Tey	a	11e12	13e12	14e12	15e12	16e12	17e12	18e12	19e12	20e12	21e12	22 12		
Witham	a	11e20	13e20	14e20	15e20	16e20	17e20	18e20	19e20	20e20	21e20	22 20		
Chelmsford	a	11e29	13e29	14e29	15e29	16e29	17e29	18e29	19e29	20e29	21e29	22 29		
Shenfield	a	11 29	13 29	14 29	15 29	16 29	17 29	18 29	19 29	20 29	21c29	22 29		
London Liverpool Street 15 ⊖	a	12 01	14 01	15 01	16 01	17 01	18 01	19 01	20 01	21 01	22c01	23 01		

For general notes see front of timetable
For details of catering facilities see Directory of Train Operators

b Arr. 1827
c Change at Ipswich
e Change at Ipswich and Colchester

Due to major track repair work in the Bury St Edmunds area, trains between Ipswich and Peterborough are subject to disruption, resulting in bus replacements and extended journey times for part or all of this timetable. See local publicity or contact National Rail Enquiries 08457 48 49 50 for further details.

Norwich → Great Yarmouth and Lowestoft

Network diagram - see first page of Table 13

Miles	Miles	Miles			LE 1	LE 1	LE 1	LE	LE 1		LE	LE	LE	LE	LE		LE	LE	LE	LE	LE		LE	LE	LE	LE
—	—	—	London Liverpool Street 15	⊖ d										06 25			07 30	08 00	08 30	09 00	09 30		10 00	10 30	11 00	11 30
0	0	0	**Norwich**	d	05 15	05 45	06 24	06 36	06 55		07 05	07 36	07 54	08 36	08 57		09 36	09 57	10 36	10 57	11 36		11 57	12 36	12 57	13 36
4¾	4¾	4¾	Brundall Gardens	d		05 52		06 43			07 12		08 01	08 43			09 43		10 43		11 43			12 43		13 43
5¾	5¾	5¾	Brundall	d	05 23	05 55	06 32	06 46	07 03		07 15	07 44	08 04	08 46			09 46	10 05	10 46		11 46		12 05	12 46		13 46
8	—	—	Lingwood	d				06 51			07 20			08 51			09 51				11 51			12 51		13 51
10½	—	—	Acle	d				06 55			07b27			08 55			09 55				11 55			12 55		13 55
—	7¾	7¾	Buckenham	d																						
—	10	10	Cantley	d		06 01			07 09			07 50	08 10					10 11	10 52				12 11			
—	12¼	12¼	Reedham (Norfolk)	d		06 06	06 41		07 14			07 55	08 15					10 16	10 57				12 16			
—	16	—	Berney Arms	d								08x01							11x03							
18¼	20½	—	**Great Yarmouth**	a	05 45			07 07			07 39	08 11		09 07			10 07		11 13		12 07			13 07		14 07
—	—	16¼	Haddiscoe	d		06 14			07 22				08 23					10 24					12 24			
—	—	18	Somerleyton	d		06 18			07 26				08 27					10 28					12 28			
—	—	22	Oulton Broad North	d		06 24	06 56		07 32				08 33		09 26			10 34		11 26			12 34		13 26	
—	—	23½	**Lowestoft**	a		06 30	07 02		07 37				08 38		09 32			10 40		11 32			12 40		13 32	

		LE	LE	LE		LE 1	LE	LE	LE 1	LE		LE	LE	LE 1	LE 1	LE		LE	LE 1	LE	LE 1	LE 1	LE 1	LE 1		
London Liverpool Street 15	⊖ d	12 00	12 30	13 00		13 30	14 00	14 30	15 00			15 30		16 30	17 00	17 30		17 50	18 30		19 30		20 30			
Norwich	d	13 57	14 36	14 57		15 36	15 57	16 40	16 57	17 05		17 36	17 57	18 40	18 57	19 36		19 57	20 40	20 57	21 40	21 57	22 40	23 00		
Brundall Gardens	d		14 43			15 43		16 47		17 12		17 43		18 47		19 43			20 47		21 47					
Brundall	d	14 05	14 46			15 46	16 05	16 50	17 05	17 15		17 46	18 05	18 50	19 05	19 46		20 05	20 50	21 05	21 50	22 05	22 48	23 08		
Lingwood	d		14 51			15 51		16 55		17 20		17 51		18 55		19 51			20 55		21 55			23 13		
Acle	d		14 55			15 55		16 59		17c27		17 55		18 59		19 55			20 59		21 59			23 17		
Buckenham	d																									
Cantley	d	14 11					16 11		17 11				18 11		19 11			20 11		21 11		22 11	22 54			
Reedham (Norfolk)	d	14 16					16 16		17 16				18 16		19 16			20 16		21 16		22 16	22 59			
Berney Arms	d																									
Great Yarmouth	a		15 07			16 07		17 11		17 39		18 07		19 11		20 07			21 11		22 11			23 29		
Haddiscoe	d	14 24					16 24		17 24				18 24		19 24			20 24				22 24	23 07			
Somerleyton	d	14 28					16 28		17 28				18 28		19 28			20 28				22 28	23 11			
Oulton Broad North	d	14 34		15 26			16 34		17 34				18 34		19 34			20 34		21 31		22 34	23 17			
Lowestoft	a	14 40		15 32			16 40		17 40				18 40		19 40			20 40		21 37		22 40	23 23			

Saturdays

		LE	LE 1	LE		LE	LE	LE		LE	LE	LE		LE	LE	LE		LE	LE	LE		LE	LE	LE		LE
London Liverpool Street 15	⊖ d										06 30	07 00		07 30	08 00	08 30		09 00	09 30	10 00		10 30	11 00	11 30		12 00
Norwich	d	05 36	05 49	06 36		06 55	07 05	07 36		07 54	08 36	08 57		09 36	09 57	10 36		10 57	11 36	11 57		12 36	12 57	13 36		13 57
Brundall Gardens	d		05 56	06 43			07 12			08 01	08 43			09 43		10 43			11 43			12 43		13 43		
Brundall	d	05 44	05 59	06 46		07 03	07 15	07 44		08 04	08 46			09 46	10 05	10 46			11 46	12 05		12 46		13 46		14 05
Lingwood	d			06 51			07 20				08 51			09 51					11 51			12 51		13 51		
Acle	d			06 55			07b27				08 55			09 55					11 55			12 55		13 55		
Buckenham	d														10x09											
Cantley	d		06 05			07 09		07 50		08 10					10 13	10 52				12 11						14 11
Reedham (Norfolk)	d	05 52	06 10			07 14		07 55		08 15					10 17	10 57				12 16						14 16
Berney Arms	d							08x01								11x03										
Great Yarmouth	a	06 07		07 07			07 39	08 11			09 07			10 07		11 13			12 07			13 07		14 07		
Haddiscoe	d		06 18			07 22				08 23					10 26					12 24						14 24
Somerleyton	d		06 22			07 26				08 27					10 29					12 28						14 28
Oulton Broad North	d		06 28			07 32				08 33		09 26			10 35			11 26		12 34			13 26			14 34
Lowestoft	a		06 34			07 37				08 38		09 32			10 41			11 32		12 40			13 32			14 40

		LE	LE	LE		LE	LE	LE		LE	LE	LE		LE	LE	LE		LE	LE	LE	LE 1	LE	LE 1	LE 1		
London Liverpool Street 15	⊖ d	12 30	13 00	13 30		14 00	14 30	15 00			15 30	16 00		16 30	17 00	17 30		18 00	18 30	19 00	19 30	20 00	20 30			
Norwich	d	14 36	14 57	15 36		15 57	16 40	16 57		17 05	17 36	17 57		18 40	18 57	19 36		19 57	20 40	20 57	21 40	21 57	22 40	23 00		
Brundall Gardens	d	14 43		15 43			16 47			17 12	17 43			18 47		19 43			20 47		21 47					
Brundall	d	14 46		15 46		16 05	16 50	17 05		17 15	17 46	18 05		18 50	19 05	19 46		20 05	20 50	21 05	21 50	22 05	22 48	23 08		
Lingwood	d	14 51		15 51			16 55			17 20	17 51			18 55		19 51			20 55		21 55			23 13		
Acle	d	14 55		15 55			16 59			17c27	17 55			18 59		19 55			20 59		21 59			23 17		
Buckenham	d																									
Cantley	d					16 11		17 11				18 11			19 11			20 11		21 11		22 11	22 54			
Reedham (Norfolk)	d					16 16		17 16				18 16			19 16			20 16		21 16		22 16	22 59			
Berney Arms	d																									
Great Yarmouth	a	15 07		16 07			17 11			17 39	18 07			19 11		20 07			21 11		22 11			23 29		
Haddiscoe	d					16 24		17 24				18 24			19 24			20 24				22 24	23 07			
Somerleyton	d					16 28		17 28				18 28			19 28			20 28				22 28	23 11			
Oulton Broad North	d		15 26			16 34		17 34				18 34			19 34			20 34		21 31		22 34	23 17			
Lowestoft	a		15 32			16 40		17 40				18 40			19 40			20 40		21 37		22 40	23 23			

For general notes see front of timetable
For details of catering facilities see
Directory of Train Operators

b Arr. 0724
c Arr. 1724

Table 15

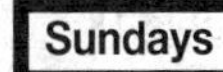

Sundays

Norwich → Great Yarmouth and Lowestoft

Network diagram - see first page of Table 13

	LE 1	LE	LE	LE 1	LE	LE	LE 1	LE	LE	LE	LE	LE
London Liverpool Street 15 ⊖ d						*08 30*	*08 30*	*09 30*	*10 30*		*11 30*	*12 30*
Norwich d	07 25	07 36	08 45	08 57	09 36	10 45	10 57	11 36	12 45	12 57	13 36	14 45
Brundall Gardens d			08 52			10 52			12 52			14 52
Brundall d		07 44	08 55	09 05	09 44	10 55	11 05	11 44	12 55	13 05	13 44	14 55
Lingwood d			09 00			11 00			13 00			15 00
Acle d			09 04			11 04			13 04			15 04
Buckenham d					09x48			11x48				
Cantley d		07 50		09 11	09 52		11 11	11 52		13 11	13 50	
Reedham (Norfolk) d		07 55		09 16	09 56		11 16	11 56		13 16	13 55	
Berney Arms d		08x01			10x03			12x03			14x01	
Great Yarmouth a		08 11	09 16		10 13	11 16		12 13	13 16		14 11	15 16
Haddiscoe d				09 24			11 24			13 24		
Somerleyton d				09 28			11 28			13 28		
Oulton Broad North d	07 53			09 34			11 34			13 34		
Lowestoft a	07 59			09 40			11 40			13 40		

	LE	LE	LE	LE 1	LE	LE	LE	LE	LE	LE	LE	LE
London Liverpool Street 15 ⊖ d		*13 30*	*14 30*	*14 30*	*15 30*	*16 30*		*17 30*	*18 30*	*19 00*	*19 30*	*20 30*
Norwich d	14 57	15 36	16 45	16 57	17 36	18 45	18 57	19 36	20 45	20 57	21 36	22 36
Brundall Gardens d			16 52			18 52			20 52			22 43
Brundall d	15 05	15 44	16 55	17 05	17 44	18 55	19 05	19 44	20 55	21 05	21 44	22 46
Lingwood d			17 00			19 00			21 00			22 51
Acle d			17 04			19 04			21 04			22 55
Buckenham d		15x48		17x09								
Cantley d	15 11	15 52		17 13	17 50		19 11	19 50		21 11	21 50	
Reedham (Norfolk) d	15 16	15 56		17 17	17 55		19 16	19 55		21 16	21 55	
Berney Arms d												
Great Yarmouth a		16 11	17 16		18 09	19 16		20 09	21 16		22 09	23 07
Haddiscoe d	15 24			17 26			19 24			21 24		
Somerleyton d	15 28			17 29			19 28			21 28		
Oulton Broad North d	15 34			17 35			19 34			21 34		
Lowestoft a	15 40			17 41			19 40			21 40		

For general notes see front of timetable
For details of catering facilities see
Directory of Train Operators

Lowestoft and Great Yarmouth → Norwich

Network diagram - see first page of Table 13

Mondays to Fridays

Miles	Miles	Miles			LE MX 1	LE	LE 1	LE R 1	LE 1	LE	LE	LE 1	LE 1	LE	LE	LE	LE	LE	LE	LE	LE	LE	LE	LE	LE
0	—	—	**Lowestoft**	d	23p30	05 36			06 40			07 40	07 52		08 42		09 42		10 50		11 42		12 50		13 42
1½	—	—	Oulton Broad North	d	23p34	05 40			06 44			07 44	07 56		08 46		09 46		10 54		11 46		12 54		13 46
5¼	—	—	Somerleyton	d		05 46			06 50			07 50			08 52		09 52				11 52				13 52
7¾	—	—	Haddiscoe	d		05 49			06 53			07 53			08 55		09 55				11 55				13 55
—	0	0	**Great Yarmouth**	d			05 55	06 42		07 17	07 44			08 17		09 17		10 17		11 17		12 17		13 17	
—	—	4½	Berney Arms	d																					
11¾	—	8¼	Reedham (Norfolk)	d	23p51	05 58			07 02			08 02	08 11		09 04		10 04				12 04				14 04
13½	—	10½	Cantley	d	23p55	06 02			07 06			08 06	08 15		09 08		10 08				12 08				14 08
15¾	—	12¾	Buckenham	d																					
—	8	—	Acle	d			06 06	06b55		07 27	07 54			08 27		09 27		10 27		11 27		12 27		13 27	
—	10½	—	Lingwood	d			06 11	07 00		07 32	07 59			08 32		09 32		10 32		11 32		12 32		13 32	
17¾	12¾	14¾	Brundall	d	00 01	06 08	06 15	07 04	07 12	07 36	08 03	08 12		08 36	09 14	09 36	10 14	10 36		11 36	12 14	12 36		13 36	14 14
18¾	13¾	15¾	Brundall Gardens	d			06 18		07 15	07 39	08 06			08 39		09 39		10 39		11 39		12 39		13 39	
23½	18½	20½	**Norwich**	a	00 12	06 19	06 28	07 14	07 25	07 49	08 18	08 25	08 30	08 49	09 25	09 49	10 25	10 49	11 25	11 49	12 25	12 49	13 25	13 49	14 25
—	—	—	London Liverpool Street 15 ⊖	a		08 23	08 39	09 25	09 25	09 56		10 24	10 54	10 54	11 24	11 54	12 24	12 54	13 24	13 54	14 24	14 54	15 24	15 54	16 24

		LE	LE 1	LE	LE	LE 1	LE	LE	LE A	LE B	LE 1	LE	LE	LE 1	LE 1	LE	LE	LE 1	LE	LE 1	LE 1	LE 1	LE 1
Lowestoft	d		14 50		15 42		16 47				17 47		18 47		19 47		20 50		21 42		22 45		23 30
Oulton Broad North	d		14 54		15 46		16 51				17 51		18 51		19 51		20 54		21 46		22 49		23 34
Somerleyton	d				15 52		16 57				17 57		18 57		19 57				21 52		22 55		
Haddiscoe	d				15 55		17 00				18 00		19 00		20 00				21 55		22 58		
Great Yarmouth	d	14 12		15 17		16 17		17 17	17 47	17 47		18 17		19 17		20 17		21 17		22 17		23 33	
Berney Arms	d	14x19								17x54													
Reedham (Norfolk)	d	14 26			16 04		17 09		18 01	18 01	18 09		19 09		20 09				22 04		23 07	23 46	23 51
Cantley	d	14 30			16 08		17 13		18 05	18 05	18 13		19 13		20 13				22 08		23 11		23 55
Buckenham	d																						
Acle	d			15 27		16 27		17 27				18 27		19 27		20 27		21 27		22 27			
Lingwood	d			15 32		16 32		17 32				18 32		19 32		20 32		21 32		22 32			
Brundall	d	14 36		15 36	16 14	16 36	17 19	17 36	18 12	18 12	18 19	18 36	19 19	19 36	20 19	20 36		21 36	22 14	22 36	23 17	23 54	00 01
Brundall Gardens	d	14 39		15 39		16 39		17 39				18 39		19 39		20 39		21 39		22 39			
Norwich	a	14 49	15 25	15 49	16 25	16 49	17 30	17 49	18 22	18 22	18 30	18 49	19 30	19 49	20 30	20 49	21 25	21 49	22 25	22 49	23 28	00 04	00 12
London Liverpool Street 15 ⊖	a	16 54	17 24	17 54	18 24	18 54		19 54	20 24	20 24	20 54	20 54		21 54	22 54	22 54		00 03					

Saturdays

		LE 1	LE	LE 1	LE	LE	LE	LE	LE	LE	LE	LE	LE	LE	LE	LE	LE	LE	LE	LE	LE	LE
Lowestoft	d	23p30		06 40			07 42		08 42		09 42		10 50		11 42		12 50		13 42		14 50	
Oulton Broad North	d	23p34		06 44			07 46		08 46		09 46		10 54		11 46		12 54		13 46		14 54	
Somerleyton	d			06 50			07 52		08 52		09 52				11 52				13 52			
Haddiscoe	d			06 53			07 55		08 55		09 55				11 55				13 55			
Great Yarmouth	d		06 17		07 17	07 44		08 17		09 17		10 17		11 17		12 17		13 17		14 12		15 17
Berney Arms	d																			14x19		
Reedham (Norfolk)	d	23p51		07 02			08 04		09 04		10 04				12 04				14 04	14 26		
Cantley	d	23p55		07 06			08 08		09 08		10 08				12 08				14 08	14 30		
Buckenham	d																					
Acle	d		06 27		07 27	07 54		08 27		09 27		10 27		11 27		12 27		13 27				15 27
Lingwood	d		06 32		07 32	07 59		08 32		09 32		10 32		11 32		12 32		13 32				15 32
Brundall	d	00 01	06 36	07 12	07 36	08 03	08 14	08 36	09 14	09 36	10 14	10 36		11 36	12 14	12 36		13 36	14 14	14 36		15 36
Brundall Gardens	d		06 39	07 15	07 39	08 06		08 39		09 39		10 39		11 39		12 39		13 39		14 39		15 39
Norwich	a	00 12	06 49	07 25	07 49	08 18	08 25	08 49	09 25	09 49	10 25	10 49	11 25	11 49	12 25	12 49	13 25	13 49	14 25	14 49	15 25	15 49
London Liverpool Street 15 ⊖	a		08 54	09 24	09 54		10 24	10 54	11 24	11 54	12 24	12 54	13 24	13 54	14 24	14 54	15 24	15 54	16 24	16 54	17 24	17 54

		LE	LE	LE	LE	LE C	LE D	LE	LE	LE	LE	LE	LE	LE 1	LE	LE	LE 1	LE	LE 1	LE 1
Lowestoft	d	15 42		16 47				17 47		18 47		19 47		20 50		21 42		22 45		23 30
Oulton Broad North	d	15 46		16 51				17 51		18 51		19 51		20 54		21 46		22 49		23 34
Somerleyton	d	15 52		16 57				17 57		18 57		19 57				21 52		22 55		
Haddiscoe	d	15 55		17 00				18 00		19 00		20 00				21 55		22 58		
Great Yarmouth	d		16 17		17 17	17 47	17 47		18 17		19 17		20 17		21 17		22 17		23 33	
Berney Arms	d						17x54													
Reedham (Norfolk)	d	16 04		17 09		18 01	18 01	18 09		19 09		20 09				22 04		23 07	23 46	23 51
Cantley	d	16 08		17 13		18 05	18 05	18 13		19 13		20 13				22 08		23 11		23 55
Buckenham	d	16x11																		
Acle	d		16 27		17 27				18 27		19 27		20 27		21 27		22 27			
Lingwood	d		16 32		17 32				18 32		19 32		20 32		21 32		22 32			
Brundall	d	16 14	16 36	17 19	17 36	18 12	18 12	18 19	18 36	19 19	19 36	20 19	20 36		21 36	22 14	22 36	23 17	23 54	00 01
Brundall Gardens	d		16 39		17 39				18 39		19 39		20 39		21 39		22 39			
Norwich	a	16 25	16 49	17 30	17 49	18 22	18 22	18 30	18 49	19 30	19 49	20 30	20 49	21 25	21 49	22 25	22 49	23 28	00 04	00 12
London Liverpool Street 15 ⊖	a	18 24	18 54		19 54	20 24	20 24		20 54		21 58		22 58	00 07	00 07					

For general notes see front of timetable
For details of catering facilities see Directory of Train Operators

- **A** Until 28 March
- **B** From 31 March
- **C** Until 29 March
- **D** From 5 April
- **b** Arr. 0652

Lowestoft and Great Yarmouth → Norwich

Network diagram - see first page of Table 13

		LE 1	LE	LE	LE 1	LE	LE	LE 1	LE	LE	LE	LE	LE	LE 1	LE	LE	LE	LE	LE	LE	LE	LE	LE	LE	LE	LE
Lowestoft	d	23p30			09 50			11 50			13 50			15 50			17 50			19 50			21 50			23 25
Oulton Broad North	d	23p34			09 54			11 54			13 54			15 54			17 54			19 54			21 54			23 29
Somerleyton	d				10 00			12 00			14 00			16 00			18 00			20 00			22 00			
Haddiscoe	d				10 03			12 03			14 03			16 03			18 03			20 03			22 03			
Great Yarmouth	d		08 20	09 22		10 18	11 22		12 18	13 22		14 20	15 22		16 20	17 22		18 22	19 22		20 22	21 22		22 22	23 20	
Berney Arms	d		08x27			10x25			12x25			14x27														
Reedham (Norfolk)	d	23p51	08 34		10 12	10 32		12 12	12 32		14 12	14 34		16 12	16 32		18 12	18 34		20 12	20 34		22 12	22 34	23 32	23 44
Cantley	d	23p55	08 38		10 16	10 36		12 16	12 36		14 16	14 38		16 16	16 36		18 16	18 38		20 16	20 38		22 16	22 38	23 36	
Buckenham	d				10x20	10x40			12x40						16x40											
Acle	d			09 32			11 32			13 32			15 32			17 32			19 32			21 32				
Lingwood	d			09 37			11 37			13 37			15 37			17 37			19 37			21 37				
Brundall	d	00 01	08 45	09 41	10 24	10 44	11 41	12 22	12 44	13 41	14 22	14 45	15 41	16 22	16 44	17 41	18 22	18 45	19 41	20 22	20 45	21 41	22 22	22 45	23 43	23 53
Brundall Gardens	d			09 44			11 44			13 44			15 44			17 44			19 44			21 44			23 45	
Norwich	a	00 12	08 55	09 54	10 34	10 55	11 54	12 33	12 55	13 54	14 33	14 55	15 54	16 33	16 55	17 54	18 33	18 55	19 54	20 33	20 55	21 54	22 33	22 55	23 55	00 03
London Liverpool Street 15 ⊖	a		*11 03*	*12 01*	*13 01*	*13 01*	*14 01*	*15 01*	*15 01*	*16 01*		*17 01*	*18 01*	*19 01*	*19 01*	*20 01*		*21 01*	*22 01*		*23 01*	*00 07*				

For general notes see front of timetable
For details of catering facilities see Directory of Train Operators

Norwich—Cromer and Sheringham

Mondays to Saturdays

Network diagram - see first page of Table 13

Miles			LE SX	LE SO	LE SO	LE SX	LE	LE	LE	LE	LE	LE	LE	LE	LE	LE	LE	LE	LE	LE	LE
—	London Liverpool Street 15 ⊖	d						06b00	07 30	08 30	09 30	10 30	11 30	12 30	13 30	14 30	15 30	17c00	17 30	19 00	20 30
0	**Norwich**	d	05 20	05 20	05 45	05 50	07 15	08 23	09 45	10 45	11 45	12 45	13 45	14 45	15 45	16 45	17 45	18 45	19 45	21 15	22 45
6	Salhouse	d		05 30	05 55	06 00	07 25	08 33	09 55		11 55		13 55		15 55	16 55	17 55	18 55	19 55	21 25	22 55
8¾	Hoveton & Wroxham	d	05 34	05 35	06 00	06 05	07 30	08 38	10 00	10 59	12 00	12 59	14 00	14 59	16 00	17 00	18 00	19 00	20 00	21 30	23 00
13	Worstead	d		05 42	06 07	06 12	07 37	08 45		11 06		13 06		15 06	16 07	17 07	18 07	19 07	20 07	21 37	23 07
16	North Walsham	a	05 44	05 48	06 13	06 18	07 43	08 51	10 10	11 11	12 10	13 11	14 10	15 11	16 13	17 13	18 13	19 13	20 13	21 43	23 13
—		d	05 44	05 48	06 13	06 21	07 46	08 53	10 13	11 14	12 13	13 14	14 13	15 14	16 15	17 15	18 16	19 15	20 16	21 43	23 13
19¾	Gunton	d		05 54	06 19	06 27	07 52	08 59	10 19		12 19		14 19		16 21	17 21	18 22	19 21	20 22	21 49	23 19
23½	Roughton Road	d		06 01	06 26	06 34	07 59	09 06		11 25		13 25		15 25	16 28	17 28	18 29	19 28	20 29	21 56	23 26
26½	**Cromer**	a	05 59	06 06	06 31	06 39	08 04	09 11	10 29	11 30	12 29	13 30	14 29	15 30	16 33	17 33	18 34	19 33	20 34	22 01	23 31
—		d	06 06	06 10	06 36	06 46	08 08	09 15	10 33	11 33	12 33	13 33	14 33	15 33	16 36	17 36	18 37	19 36	20 37	22 04	23 34
28¾	West Runton	d	06 10	06 14	06 40	06 50	08 12	09 19	10 37	11 37	12 37	13 37	14 37	15 37	16 40	17 40	18 41	19 40	20 41	22 08	23 38
30½	**Sheringham**	a	06 14	06 18	06 44	06 54	08 16	09 23	10 41	11 41	12 41	13 41	14 41	15 41	16 44	17 44	18 45	19 44	20 45	22 12	23 42

Sundays

		LE	LE	LE	LE	LE	LE	LE
London Liverpool Street 15 ⊖	d		08 30	10 30	12 30	14 30	16 30	18 30
Norwich	d	08 36	10 36	12 36	14 36	16 36	18 36	20 36
Salhouse	d	08 46	10 46	12 46	14 46	16 46	18 46	20 46
Hoveton & Wroxham	d	08 51	10 51	12 51	14 51	16 51	18 51	20 51
Worstead	d	08 58	10 58	12 58	14 58	16 58	18 58	20 58
North Walsham	a	09 04	11 04	13 04	15 04	17 04	19 04	21 04
	d	09 04	11 04	13 04	15 04	17 04	19 04	21 04
Gunton	d	09 10	11 10	13 10	15 10	17 10	19 10	21 10
Roughton Road	d	09 17	11 17	13 17	15 17	17 17	19 17	21 17
Cromer	a	09 22	11 22	13 22	15 22	17 22	19 22	21 22
	d	09 26	11 26	13 26	15 26	17 26	19 26	21 26
West Runton	d	09 30	11 30	13 30	15 30	17 30	19 30	21 30
Sheringham	a	09 35	11 35	13 35	15 35	17 35	19 35	21 35

Mondays to Saturdays

Miles			LE MX	LE SX	LE SO	LE SX	LE	LE	LE	LE	LE	LE	LE	LE	LE	LE	LE	LE	LE	LE	LE	LE
0	**Sheringham**	d	23p46		06 22	06 32	07 17	08 25	09 46	10 46	11 46	12 46	13 46	14 46	15 46	16 49	17 48	18 49	19 48	20 49	22 16	23 46
1¾	West Runton	d	23p50		06 26	06 36	07 21	08 29	09 50	10 50	11 50	12 50	13 50	14 50	15 50	16 53	17 52	18 53	19 52	20 53	22 20	23 50
4	**Cromer**	a	23p54		06 30	06 40	07 25	08 33	09 54	10 54	11 54	12 54	13 54	14 54	15 54	16 57	17 56	18 57	19 56	20 57	22 24	23 54
—		d	23p57	06 03	06 33	06 43	07 28	08 36	09 57	10 57	11 57	12 57	13 57	14 57	15 57	17 00	17 59	19 00	19 59	21 00	22 27	23 57
7	Roughton Road	d		06 08	06 38	06 48	07 33	08 41	10 02		12 02		14 02	15 02	16 02		18 04		20 04	21 05	22 32	
10¾	Gunton	d		06 15	06 45	06 55	07 40	08 48		11 08		13 08			16 09		18 11		20 11	21 12	22 39	
14½	North Walsham	a	00 12	06 20	06 50	07 00	07 45	08 53	10 12	11 13	12 12	13 13	14 12	15 13	16 15	17 15	18 16	19 15	20 16	21 17	22 44	00 12
—		d	00 12	06 21	06 51	07 01	07 46	08 54	10 13	11 14	12 13	13 14	14 13	15 14	16 15	17 15	18 17	19 15	20 17	21 18	22 45	00 12
17½	Worstead	d		06 25	06 55	07 05	07 50	08 58	10 17		12 17		14 17		16 20		18 21		20 21	21 22	22 49	
21¾	Hoveton & Wroxham	d	00 22	06 33	07 03	07 13	07 58	09 06	10 25	11 24	12 25	13 24	14 25	15 24	16 27	17 26	18 29	19 26	20 29	21 30	22 57	00 22
24½	Salhouse	d		06 38	07 08	07 18	08 03	09 11		11 29		13 29		15 29	16 32		18 34		20 34	21 35	23 02	
30½	**Norwich**	a	00 36	06 49	07 19	07 29	08 14	09 21	10 40	11 40	12 40	13 40	14 40	15 40	16 44	17 40	18 44	19 40	20 44	21 45	23 12	00 36
—	London Liverpool Street 15 ⊖	a		08 55	09 24	09 40	10 24	11 24	12 54	13 54	14 54	15 54	16 54	17 54	18 54	19 54	20 54	21e54	22e54	00e03		

Sundays

		LE	LE	LE	LE	LE	LE	LE	LE
Sheringham	d	23p46	09 43	11 43	13 43	15 43	17 43	19 43	21 43
West Runton	d	23p50	09 47	11 47	13 47	15 47	17 47	19 47	21 47
Cromer	a	23p54	09 51	11 51	13 51	15 51	17 51	19 51	21 51
	d	23p57	09 54	11 54	13 54	15 54	17 54	19 54	21 54
Roughton Road	d		09 59	11 59	13 59	15 59	17 59	19 59	21 59
Gunton	d		10 06	12 06	14 06	16 06	18 06	20 06	22 06
North Walsham	a	00 12	10 11	12 11	14 11	16 11	18 11	20 11	22 11
	d	00 12	10 12	12 12	14 12	16 12	18 12	20 12	22 12
Worstead	d		10 16	12 16	14 16	16 16	18 16	20 16	22 16
Hoveton & Wroxham	d	00 22	10 24	12 24	14 24	16 24	18 24	20 24	22 24
Salhouse	d		10 29	12 29	14 29	16 29	18 29	20 29	22 29
Norwich	a	00 36	10 40	12 40	14 40	16 40	18 40	20 40	22 40
London Liverpool Street 15 ⊖	a		13 01	15 01	17 01	19 01	21 01	23 01	

For general notes see front of timetable
For details of catering facilities see Directory of Train Operators

b Mondays to Fridays only
c Saturdays dep. 1630
e Saturdays arr. 4 minutes later

London, Norwich and Cambridge → Ely, Kings Lynn and Peterborough

Network Diagram - see first page of Table 13

Miles	Miles			FC	FC	XC	XC	LE	EM	FC	EM	LE	XC	FC	LE	LE	EM	FC	XC	FC	LE	LE	EM
				MX 1	MO 1	◇ A	◇ A	1		1	◇ B ⊤	1	◇ A	1	1	1	◇ B ⊤	1	◇	1	1	1	◇
—	—	**London Liverpool Street**	d																				
—	0	**London Kings Cross**	d	23p15	23p15									05 45				06 45		07 15			
—	—	Ipswich	d									06 01											
—	—	Stansted Airport	d				05 21												07 25				
—	—	**Norwich**	d					05 33			05 52					06 33						07 37	07 57
10¾	—	Wymondham	d					05 45			06 04					06 45						07 49	
12¾	—	Spooner Row	d																				
16	—	Attleborough	d					05 52			06 11					06 52						07 56	
19¾	—	Eccles Road	d																				
22¾	—	Harling Road	d																				
30½	—	Thetford	d					06 05			06 25					07 05						08 09	08 24
37¾	—	Brandon	d					06 13								07 13						08 17	
41½	—	Lakenheath	d																				
47	—	Shippea Hill	d																				
—	58	**Cambridge**	d	00 13	00 19	05 07	05 58		06 17	06 23			06 50	06 56	07 05		07 27	07 35	07 59	08 04	08 12		
—	63¼	Waterbeach	d	00 19	00 25					06 29				07 02				07 41		08 10			
53	72¾	**Ely 6**	a	00 29	00 38	05 23	06 13	06 30	06 33	06 38	06 46	06 57	07 04	07 11	07 19	07 30	07 43	07 51	08 13	08 20	08 26	08 37	08 47
—	—	**Cambridge**	a					06 50								07 51						08 55	
—	—	**Ely 6**	d			05 24	06 13			06 38	06 51	06 57	07 05	07 11			07 44	07 51	08 16	08 21			08 51
—	78¼	Littleport	d							06 45				07 18				07 58		08 28			
—	88½	Downham Market	d							06 54				07 27				08 07		08 37			
—	93¼	Watlington	d							07 01				07 33				08 13		08 43			
—	99¼	**Kings Lynn**	a							07 10				07 43				08 22		08 52			
62¾	—	Manea	d				06x24																
68¼	—	March	d			05 40	06 32				07 07	07 14	07 21				08 01		08 33				09 07
76¼	—	Whittlesea	d			05 52	06 43					07 25	07 33				08 12						
82¼	—	**Peterborough 8**	a			06 02	06 54				07 25	07 37	07 43				08 23		08 50				09 25

		FC	LE	XC	LE	LE	FC	EM	XC	LE	LE	FC	EM	LE	XC	LE	LE	FC	EM	XC	LE	LE	FC
		1	1 ◇	◇ ⊤	1	1	1	◇	◇ ⊤	1	1	1	◇	1	◇ ⊤	1	1	1	◇	◇ ⊤	1	1	1
London Liverpool Street	d		06 38																				
London Kings Cross	d	07 45					08 45					09 45						10 45					11 45
Ipswich	d		08 03											10 03									
Stansted Airport	d			08 21					09 25						10 20					11 25			
Norwich	d					08 40		08 57			09 40		09 57				10 40		10 57			11 40	
Wymondham	d					08 52					09 52						10 52					11 52	
Spooner Row	d																						
Attleborough	d					08 59					09 59						10 59					11 59	
Eccles Road	d																						
Harling Road	d																						
Thetford	d					09 12		09 24			10 12		10 24				11 12		11 24			12 12	
Brandon	d					09 20					10 20						11 20					12 20	
Lakenheath	d																						
Shippea Hill	d																						
Cambridge	d	08 38		09 04	09 12		09 33		10 04	10 12		10 33			11 04	11 12		11 33		12 04	12 12		12 33
Waterbeach	d	08 44					09 39					10 39						11 39					12 39
Ely 6	a	08 53	08 59	09 18	09 26	09 37	09 50	09 45	10 18	10 26	10 37	10 48	10 46	10 59	11 18	11 26	11 37	11 48	11 46	12 18	12 26	12 37	12 48
Cambridge	a					09 55					10 55						11 55					12 55	
Ely 6	d	08 54	08 59	09 19			09 50	09 51	10 19			10 48	10 52	10 59	11 19			11 48	11 52	12 19			12 48
Littleport	d	09 01					09 57					10 55						11 55					12 55
Downham Market	d	09 10					10 06					11 04						12 04					13 04
Watlington	d	09 16					10 12					11 10						12 10					13 10
Kings Lynn	a	09 25					10 26					11 20						12 20					13 20
Manea	d																						
March	d		09 16	09 35					10 35					11 16	11 35					12 35			
Whittlesea	d		09 27											11 27									
Peterborough 8	a		09 41	09 53				10 25	10 53				11 24	11 38	11 53				12 24	12 53			

For general notes see front of timetable
For details of catering facilities see Directory of Train Operators

A To Birmingham New Street (Table 49)
B To Liverpool Lime Street (Table 49). ⊤ from Nottingham

Due to major track repair work in the Bury St Edmunds area, trains between Ipswich and Peterborough are subject to disruption, resulting in bus replacements and extended journey times for part or all of this timetable. See local publicity or contact National Rail Enquiries 08457 48 49 50 for further details.

London, Norwich and Cambridge → Ely, Kings Lynn and Peterborough

Network Diagram - see first page of Table 13

	EM	LE	XC	LE	LE	FC	EM	XC	LE	LE	FC	EM	LE	XC	LE	LE	FC	EM	XC	LE	LE	FC
	◇	[1] ◇	◇ (trolley)	[1]	[1]	[1]	◇	◇ (trolley)	[1]	[1]	[1]	◇	[1] ◇	◇ (trolley)	[1]	[1]	[1]	◇	◇ (trolley)	[1]	[1]	[1]
London Liverpool Street d		10 38											12 38									
London Kings Cross d						12 45					13 45						14 45					
Ipswich d		12 03											14 03									
Stansted Airport d			12 25					13 25						14 25					15 25			
Norwich d	11 57				12 40		12 57			13 40		13 57				14 40		14 57			15 40	
Wymondham d					12 52					13 52						14 52					15 52	
Spooner Row d																						
Attleborough d					12 59					13 59						14 59					15 59	
Eccles Road d																						
Harling Road d																						
Thetford d	12 24				13 12		13 24			14 12		14 24				15 12		15 24			16 12	
Brandon d					13 20					14 20						15 20					16 20	
Lakenheath d																						
Shippea Hill d																						
Cambridge d			13 04	13 12		13 33		14 04	14 12		14 33			15 04	15 12		15 33		16 04	16 12		16 24
Waterbeach d						13 39					14 39						15 39					16 30
Ely [6] a	12 45	12 59	13 18	13 26	13 37	13 48	13 46	14 18	14 26	14 40	14 48	14 45	14 59	15 18	15 26	15 37	15 48	15 44	16 18	16 26	16 37	16 40
Cambridge a					13 55					14 57						15 55					16 55	
Ely [6] d	12 51	12 59	13 19			13 48	13 52	14 19			14 50	14 52	14 59	15 19			15 48	15 52	16 19			
Littleport d						13 55					14 57						15 55					
Downham Market d						14 04					15 06						16 04					
Watlington d						14 10					15 12						16 10					
Kings Lynn a						14 20					15 21						16 20					
Manea d																						
March d		13 16	13 35					14 35					15 16	15 35					16 35			
Whittlesea d		13 27											15 27									
Peterborough [8] a	13 24	13 38	13 53				14 25	14 53				15 25	15 39	15 53				16 25	16 53			

	FC	EM	LE	XC	LE	LE	LE	EM	FC	XC	LE	LE	LE	LE	EM	FC	LE	XC	FC	LE	LE
	[1]	◇ A	[1] ◇	◇ (trolley)	[1]	[1]	[1]	◇	[1]	◇ B (trolley)	[1]	[1]	[1]	[1]	◇ C	[1]	[R] [1]	◇ (trolley)	[1]	[1]	[1]
London Liverpool Street d			14 38				15 58					16 58					16 32			17 58	
London Kings Cross d	15 45								16 45							17 45			18 15		
Ipswich d			16 03														17 49				
Stansted Airport d				16 20						17 17								18 20			
Norwich d		15 52				16 38		16 57						17 35	17 54						18 40
Wymondham d						16 50								17 47	18 06						18 52
Spooner Row d						16x54															
Attleborough d		16 09				16 59								17 54							18 59
Eccles Road d		16 14												17 59							
Harling Road d		16 18												18 03							
Thetford d		16 27				17 12		17 24						18 12	18 24						19 12
Brandon d						17 20								18 20							19 20
Lakenheath d																					
Shippea Hill d																					
Cambridge d	16 35			17 04	17 12		17 22		17 40	17 49	18 05	18 14	18 25			18 40		19 04	19 12	19 19	
Waterbeach d	16 41						17 28		17 46			18 20				18 46				19 25	
Ely [6] a	16 50	16 48	16 59	17 18	17 26	17 37	17 40	17 45	17 55	18 04	18 19	18 29	18 39	18 40	18 45	18 55	18 52	19 18	19 27	19 34	19 37
Cambridge a						17 55								18 57							19 55
Ely [6] d	16 50	16 52	16 59	17 19				17 50	17 55	18 06		18 30			18 52	18 56	18 59	19 19		19 34	
Littleport d	16 57								18 02			18 38				19 03				19 41	
Downham Market d	17 06								18 11			18 48				19 12				19 51	
Watlington d	17 12								18 17			18 54				19 18				19 57	
Kings Lynn a	17 21								18 26			19 05				19 29				20 08	
Manea d										18x16											
March d			17 16	17 35				18 07		18 24							19 16	19 35			
Whittlesea d			17 27														19 27				
Peterborough [8] a		17 26	17 38	17 53				18 24		18 43					19 31		19 44	19 53			

For general notes see front of timetable
For details of catering facilities see Directory of Train Operators

A To Liverpool Lime Street (Table 49)
B To Birmingham New Street (Table 49)
C To Nottingham (Table 49)

Due to major track repair work in the Bury St Edmunds area, trains between Ipswich and Peterborough are subject to disruption, resulting in bus replacements and extended journey times for part or all of this timetable. See local publicity or contact National Rail Enquiries 08457 48 49 50 for further details.

London, Norwich and Cambridge → Ely, Kings Lynn and Peterborough

Network Diagram - see first page of Table 13

		LE	EM	FC	XC	LE	LE		LE	FC	XC	LE	FC	LE		LE	FC	LE	EM	FC	FC FO		FC FX			
		1	◇	1	◇	1	1		1	1	◇	1	1	1		1	1	1		1	1		1			
London Liverpool Street	d					18 58																				
London Kings Cross	d			18 45						19 45			20 15				21 15			22 15	23 15		23 15			
Ipswich	d											20 16														
Stansted Airport	d				19 18						20 20															
Norwich	d		18 57						19 45							20 48			22 10							
Wymondham	d								19 57							21 00			22 22							
Spooner Row	d																									
Attleborough	d								20 04							21 07			22 29							
Eccles Road	d																									
Harling Road	d																									
Thetford	d		19 24						20 17							21 20			22 43							
Brandon	d								20 25							21 28			22 51							
Lakenheath	d																									
Shippea Hill	d																									
Cambridge	d	19 25		19 46	19 50	20 15	20 20			20 40	20 57		21 10	21 13			22 10	22 55		23 11	00 13		00 13			
Waterbeach	d			19 52		20 21				20 46			21 16				22 16			23 17	00 19		00 19			
Ely 6	a	19 39	19 49	20 01	20 05	20 31	20 34		20 43	20 55	21 13	21 19	21 25	21 29		21 45	22 25	23 09	23 10	23 26	00 28		00 29			
Cambridge	a								21 01							22 02			23 28							
Ely 6	d		19 52	20 01	20 05	20 31				20 55	21 14	21 19	21 25				22 25			23 26	00 29					
Littleport	d			20 08		20 38				21 02			21 32				22 32			23 33	00 36					
Downham Market	d			20 18		20 47				21 11			21 41				22 41			23 42	00 45					
Watlington	d			20 23		20 53				21 17			21 47				22 47			23 48	00 50					
Kings Lynn	a			20 33		21 05				21 26			21 56				22 56			23 57	01 00					
Manea	d																									
March	d				20 22						21 30	21 36														
Whittlesea	d											21 47														
Peterborough 8	a		20 25		20 39						21 52	21 58														

Saturdays

		FC	XC	XC	LE	EM	FC	EM	LE	XC	LE	LE	EM		FC	XC	LE	LE	LE	FC	EM	LE	XC	LE	LE	FC
		1	◇ A	◇ A	1		1	◇ B	1	◇	1	1	◇		1	◇	1	1	1	1	◇	1 ◇	◇	1	1	1
London Liverpool Street	d																	06 58				06 38				
London Kings Cross	d	23p15													06 45					07 45						08 45
Ipswich	d								06 00													08 03				
Stansted Airport	d			05 21												07 27							08 25			
Norwich	d				05 38			05 52				06 40							07 40		07 57				08 40	
Wymondham	d				05 50			06 04				06 52							07 52						08 52	
Spooner Row	d																									
Attleborough	d				05 57			06 11				06 59							07 59						08 59	
Eccles Road	d																									
Harling Road	d																									
Thetford	d				06 10			06 25				07 12							08 12		08 24				09 12	
Brandon	d				06 18							07 20							08 20						09 20	
Lakenheath	d																									
Shippea Hill	d																									
Cambridge	d	00 13	05 11	05 51		06 20	06 32			06 55	06 59		07 25		07 33	08 04	08 12	08 20		08 33			09 04	09 12		09 33
Waterbeach	d	00 19					06 38								07 39			08 26		08 39						09 39
Ely 6	a	00 28	05 27	06 07	06 35	06 36	06 47	06 46	06 56	07 09	07 13	07 37	07 43		07 48	08 18	08 26	08 37	08 37	08 48	08 45	08 59	09 18	09 26	09 37	09 48
Cambridge	a				06 52							07 55							08 55						09 55	
Ely 6	d	00 29	05 28	06 08			06 47	06 51	06 57	07 10			07 44		07 48	08 19				08 48	08 52	08 59	09 19			09 48
Littleport	d	00 36					06 54								07 55					08 55						09 55
Downham Market	d	00 45					07 03								08 04					09 04						10 04
Watlington	d	00 50					07 09								08 10					09 10						10 10
Kings Lynn	a	01 00					07 20								08 20					09 21						10 21
Manea	d			06x19																						
March	d		05 44	06 27				07 07	07 14	07 26			08 01			08 35					09 09	09 16	09 35			
Whittlesea	d		05 56	06 38					07 25													09 27				
Peterborough 8	a		06 06	06 48				07 25	07 37	07 52			08 24			08 54					09 27	09 38	09 53			

For general notes see front of timetable
For details of catering facilities see Directory of Train Operators

A Until 22 March to Birmingham New Street (Table 49). From 29 March to Leicester (Table 49)

B To Liverpool Lime Street (Table 49)

Due to major track repair work in the Bury St Edmunds area, trains between Ipswich and Peterborough are subject to disruption, resulting in bus replacements and extended journey times for part or all of this timetable. See local publicity or contact National Rail Enquiries 08457 48 49 50 for further details.

London, Norwich and Cambridge → Ely, Kings Lynn and Peterborough

Network Diagram - see first page of Table 13

		EM	XC		LE	LE	FC	EM	LE	XC	LE	LE	FC	EM	XC	LE		LE	FC	EM	LE	XC	LE	LE	FC	EM
		◇	◇		1	1	1	◇	1 ◇	◇	1	1	1	◇	◇	1		1	1	◇	R 1	◇	1	1	1	◇
London Liverpool Street	d								08 38												10 38					
London Kings Cross	d						09 45						10 45						11 45						12 45	
Ipswich	d								10 03												12 03					
Stansted Airport	d		09 25							10 25					11 25							12 25				
Norwich	d	08 57				09 40		09 57				10 40		10 57				11 40		11 57				12 40		12 57
Wymondham	d					09 52						10 52						11 52						12 52		
Spooner Row	d																									
Attleborough	d					09 59						10 59						11 59						12 59		
Eccles Road	d																									
Harling Road	d																									
Thetford	d	09 24				10 12		10 24				11 12		11 24				12 12		12 24				13 12		13 24
Brandon	d					10 20						11 20						12 20						13 20		
Lakenheath	d					10x25																				
Shippea Hill	d																									
Cambridge	d		10 04		10 12		10 33			11 04	11 12		11 33		12 04	12 12			12 33			13 04	13 12		13 33	
Waterbeach	d						10 39						11 39						12 39						13 39	
Ely 6	a	09 46	10 18		10 26	10 38	10 48	10 45	10 59	11 18	11 26	11 37	11 48	11 45	12 18	12 26		12 37	12 48	12 45	12 59	13 18	13 26	13 37	13 48	13 45
Cambridge	a					10 55						11 55						12 55						13 55		
Ely 6	d	09 53	10 19				10 48	10 53	10 59	11 19			11 48	11 52	12 19				12 48	12 53	12 59	13 19			13 48	13 52
Littleport	d						10 55						11 55						12 55						13 55	
Downham Market	d						11 04						12 04						13 04						14 04	
Watlington	d						11 10						12 10						13 10						14 12	
Kings Lynn	a						11 21						12 21						13 21						14 21	
Manea	d																									
March	d		10 35						11 16	11 35					12 35						13 16	13 35				
Whittlesea	d								11 27												13 27					
Peterborough 8	a	10 25	10 53					11 25	11 38	11 53				12 25	12 53					13 25	13 38	13 53				14 23

		XC	LE	LE	FC	EM		LE	XC	LE	LE	FC	EM	XC	LE	LE	FC	EM	LE		XC	LE	LE	FC	EM	XC
		◇	1	1	1	◇		R 1	◇	1	1	1	◇	◇	1	1	1	◇	1 ◇		◇	1	1	1	◇	◇ A
London Liverpool Street	d							12 38											14 38							
London Kings Cross	d				13 45							14 45					15 45							16 45		
Ipswich	d							14 03											16 03							
Stansted Airport	d	13 25							14 25					15 25							16 25					17 25
Norwich	d			13 40		13 57					14 40		14 57			15 35		15 52					16 38		16 57	
Wymondham	d			13 52							14 52					15 47							16 50			
Spooner Row	d																						16x54			
Attleborough	d			13 59							14 59					15 54							16 59			
Eccles Road	d															15 59										
Harling Road	d															16 03										
Thetford	d			14 12		14 24					15 12		15 24			16 12		16 22					17 12		17 24	
Brandon	d			14 20							15 20					16 20							17 20			
Lakenheath	d																									
Shippea Hill	d																									
Cambridge	d	14 04	14 12		14 33				15 04	15 12		15 33		16 04	16 12		16 33				17 04	17 12		17 33		18 02
Waterbeach	d				14 39							15 39					16 39							17 39		
Ely 6	a	14 18	14 26	14 37	14 48	14 45		14 59	15 18	15 26	15 37	15 48	15 45	16 18	16 26	16 37	16 48	16 43	16 59		17 18	17 26	17 37	17 48	17 45	18 16
Cambridge	a			14 55							15 55					16 55							17 55			
Ely 6	d	14 19			14 48	14 52		14 59	15 19			15 48	15 55	16 19			16 48	16 51	16 59		17 19			17 48	17 51	18 17
Littleport	d				14 55							15 55					16 55							17 55		
Downham Market	d				15 04							16 04					17 04							18 04		
Watlington	d				15 10							16 10					17 10							18 10		
Kings Lynn	a				15 21							16 21					17 21							18 21		
Manea	d																									18x27
March	d	14 35						15 16	15 35					16 35					17 16		17 35					18 35
Whittlesea	d							15 27											17 27							
Peterborough 8	a	14 53				15 25		15 38	15 53				16 27	16 53				17 24	17 38		17 53				18 24	18 53

		LE	LE	FC	EM	LE	XC	LE	LE		FC	EM	XC	LE	LE	FC	LE	LE	LE	FC	LE	EM	FC	FC		
		1	1	1	◇	R 1	◇	1	1		1	◇	◇	1	1	1	R 1	1	1	1	1		1	1		
London Liverpool Street	d					16 38											18 46									
London Kings Cross	d			17 45							18 45					19 45				20 52			21 52	23 08		
Ipswich	d					18 03											20 03									
Stansted Airport	d						18 25						19 18													
Norwich	d		17 35		17 57				18 40			18 57			19 40				20 40			22 10				
Wymondham	d		17 47						18 52						19 52				20 52			22 22				
Spooner Row	d																									
Attleborough	d		17 54						18 59						19 59				20 59			22 29				
Eccles Road	d		17 59																							
Harling Road	d		18 03																							
Thetford	d		18 12		18 24				19 12			19 24			20 12				21 12			22 43				
Brandon	d		18 20						19 20						20 20				21 20			22 51				
Lakenheath	d																									
Shippea Hill	d								19x28																	
Cambridge	d	18 12		18 33			19 04	19 12			19 33		19 50	20 12		20 33		21 12		21 56	22 30		22 56	00 16		
Waterbeach	d			18 39							19 39					20 39				22 02			23 02	00 22		
Ely 6	a	18 26	18 37	18 48	18 45	18 59	19 18	19 26	19 37		19 48	19 46	20 04	20 26	20 37	20 48	20 59	21 26	21 37	22 11	22 44	23 07	23 11	00 31		
Cambridge	a		18 55						19 55						20 55				21 55			23 25				
Ely 6	d			18 48	18 52	18 59	19 19				19 48	19 52	20 05			20 48	20 59			22 11			23 11	00 31		
Littleport	d			18 55							19 55					20 55				22 18			23 18	00 38		
Downham Market	d			19 04							20 04					21 04				22 27			23 27	00 47		
Watlington	d			19 10							20 10					21 10				22 32			23 32	00 53		
Kings Lynn	a			19 21							20 21					21 21				22 43			23 43	01 04		
Manea	d																									
March	d				19 09	19 16	19 35						20 21				21 16									
Whittlesea	d					19 27											21 27									
Peterborough 8	a				19 26	19 38	19 53					20 25	20 39				21 38									

For general notes see front of timetable
For details of catering facilities see Directory of Train Operators

A From 29 March to Leicester (Table 49). Until 22 March to Birmingham New Street (Table 49)

Due to major track repair work in the Bury St Edmunds area, trains between Ipswich and Peterborough are subject to disruption, resulting in bus replacements and extended journey times for part or all of this timetable. See local publicity or contact National Rail Enquiries 08457 48 49 50 for further details.

Table 17

Sundays

London, Norwich and Cambridge → Ely, Kings Lynn and Peterborough

Network Diagram - see first page of Table 13

		FC 1	FC 1 A	FC 1 B	LE 1	LE 1	LE 1	XC ◇	FC 1	EM ◇	LE 1	XC ◇	LE 1	LE 1	FC 1	LE 1	XC	LE 1	XC ◇	LE 1
London Liverpool Street	d																			
London Kings Cross	d	23p08		07 52					10 15						12 15					
Ipswich	d					09 55							11 55							
Stansted Airport	d											12 05								
Norwich	d				09 15					10 47	11 15					12 15				13 15
Wymondham	d				09 27						11 27					12 27				13 27
Spooner Row	d																			
Attleborough	d				09 34						11 34					12 34				13 34
Eccles Road	d																			
Harling Road	d																			
Thetford	d				09 47					11 14	11 47					12 47				13 47
Brandon	d				09 55						11 55					12 55				13 55
Lakenheath	d				10x00						12x00									
Shippea Hill	d																			
Cambridge	d	00 16	09 07	09 07			10 44	10 48	11 02			12 36		12 46	13 02		13 09	13 38	13 43	
Waterbeach	d	00 22	09 13	09 13					11 08						13 08					
Ely 6	a	00 31	09 22	09 22	10 20	10 51	11 01	11 06	11 17	11 35	12 18	12 53	12 51	13 01	13 17	13 17	13 25	13 52	13 59	14 17
Cambridge	a				10 38						12 34					13 34				14 34
Ely 6	d	00 31	09 22	09 22		10 57		11 09	11 17	11 39		12 54	12 57		13 17		13 27		14 00	
Littleport	d	00 38	09 29	09 29					11 24						13 24					
Downham Market	d	00 47	09 38	09 38					11 33						13 33					
Watlington	d	00 53	09 43	09 43					11 38						13 38					
Kings Lynn	a	01 04	09 54	09 54					11 50						13 50					
Manea	d																			
March	d					11 14		11 25				13 10	13 15				13 44		14 16	
Whittlesea	d					11 25							13 26							
Peterborough 8	a					11 41		11 50		12 16		13 31	13 42				14 06		14 39	

		EM ◇	XC ◇	LE 1	LE 1	FC 1	LE 1	LE 1	XC ◇	LE 1	FC 1	LE 1	EM ◇	LE 1	XC ◇	FC 1	LE 1	EM ◇	LE 1	LE 1
London Liverpool Street	d																			
London Kings Cross	d					14 15					15 15					16 15				
Ipswich	d			13 55										15 55						
Stansted Airport	d		14 05						15 18						16 12					
Norwich	d	13 49					14 15			15 15			15 53				16 15	16 57		17 15
Wymondham	d						14 27			15 27							16 27			17 27
Spooner Row	d																			
Attleborough	d						14 34			15 34							16 34			17 34
Eccles Road	d																			
Harling Road	d																			
Thetford	d	14 16					14 47			15 47			16 20				16 47	17 24		17 47
Brandon	d						14 55			15 55							16 55			17 55
Lakenheath	d									16x00										
Shippea Hill	d																			
Cambridge	d		14 36		14 46	15 02		15 38	15 47		16 02	16 38			16 47	17 02			17 44	
Waterbeach	d					15 08					16 08					17 08				
Ely 6	a	14 42	14 53	14 51	15 01	15 17	15 17	15 52	16 04	16 14	16 17	16 52		16 51	17 03	17 17	17 17	17 48	17 58	18 12
Cambridge	a						15 34			16 31							17 34			18 29
Ely 6	d	14 45	14 53	14 57		15 17			16 04		16 17			16 57	17 04	17 17		17 51		
Littleport	d					15 24					16 24					17 24				
Downham Market	d					15 33					16 33					17 33				
Watlington	d					15 38					16 38					17 38				
Kings Lynn	a					15 50					16 50					17 50				
Manea	d																			
March	d		15 10	15 15					16 21					17 14	17 20					
Whittlesea	d			15 26										17 25						
Peterborough 8	a	15 24	15 31	15 42					16 38				17 10	17 36	17 40			18 23		

For general notes see front of timetable
For details of catering facilities see Directory of Train Operators

A Until 23 March. From Hitchin (Table 25)
B From 30 March

Due to major track repair work in the Bury St Edmunds area, trains between Ipswich and Peterborough are subject to disruption, resulting in bus replacements and extended journey times for part or all of this timetable. See local publicity or contact National Rail Enquiries 08457 48 49 50 for further details.

Table 17

Sundays

London, Norwich and Cambridge → Ely, Kings Lynn and Peterborough

Network Diagram - see first page of Table 13

		FC 1	XC ◇	EM ◇		LE 1	LE 1	LE 1		FC 1	XC ◇	LE 1		EM ◇	FC 1	EM ◇		LE 1	FC 1	EM ◇	LE 1	FC 1	FC 1	FC 1		
London Liverpool Street	d																									
London Kings Cross	d	17 15								18 15					19 15				20 15			21 15	22 15	23 15		
Ipswich	d						17 55																			
Stansted Airport	d		17 35								18 35															
Norwich	d			17 54				18 15						18 57		19 44		20 15		20 52						
Wymondham	d							18 27										20 27								
Spooner Row	d																									
Attleborough	d							18 34										20 34								
Eccles Road	d																									
Harling Road	d																									
Thetford	d			18 21				18 47						19 24		20 11		20 47		21 19						
Brandon	d							18 55										20 55								
Lakenheath	d																									
Shippea Hill	d																									
Cambridge	d	18 02	18 09			18 38				19 02	19 08	19 38			20 02				21 02		21 38	22 02	23 11	00 19		
Waterbeach	d	18 08								19 08					20 08				21 08			22 08	23 17	00 25		
Ely 6	a	18 17	18 25	18 42		18 52	18 52	19 12		19 17	19 28	19 52		19 45	20 17	20 32		21 12	21 17	21 40	21 52	22 17	23 26	00 38		
Cambridge	a							19 30										21 29								
Ely 6	d	18 17	18 26	18 48			18 57			19 17	19 28			19 56	20 17	20 35			21 17	21 44		22 17	23 26			
Littleport	d	18 24								19 24					20 24				21 24			22 24	23 33			
Downham Market	d	18 33								19 33					20 33				21 33			22 33	23 42			
Watlington	d	18 38								19 38					20 38				21 38			22 38	23 47			
Kings Lynn	a	18 50								19 50					20 50				21 50			22 50	23 59			
Manea	d																									
March	d		18 42				19 14				19 44															
Whittlesea	d						19 25																			
Peterborough 8	a		19 00	19 20			19 36				20 02			20 29		21 08				22 20						

For general notes see front of timetable
For details of catering facilities see Directory of Train Operators

Due to major track repair work in the Bury St Edmunds area, trains between Ipswich and Peterborough are subject to disruption, resulting in bus replacements and extended journey times for part or all of this timetable. See local publicity or contact National Rail Enquiries 08457 48 49 50 for further details.

Peterborough, Kings Lynn and Ely → Cambridge, Norwich and London

Network Diagram - see first page of Table 13

Miles	Miles			FC 1	LE 1	FC 1	LE 1		EM	LE 1	FC 1	EM ◇ A		LE 1	FC 1	LE 1	LE 1		XC ◇ B	FC 1	LE 1	EM ◇ A		FC 1	LE 1	LE R 1
0	—	**Peterborough** 8	d									06 27							07 10			07 35				07 52
6	—	Whittlesea	d																07 19							08 00
14	—	March	d									06 43							07 30			07 51				08 11
19¼	—	Manea	d																07x37							
—	0	**Kings Lynn**	d		05 21	05 53				06 18					06 53					07 23				07 55		
—	6	Watlington	d		05 28	06 00				06 25					07 00					07 30				08 02		
—	10¾	Downham Market	d		05 35	06 06				06 32					07 06					07 36				08 08		
—	21	Littleport	d		05 44	06 15				06 41					07 15					07 45				08 17		
29¼	26½	**Ely** 3	a		05 52	06 23				06 50		07 01			07 23				07 51	07 54		08 13		08 25		08 30
—	—	**Cambridge**	d						06 17					07 05											08 12	
—	—	**Ely** 3	d	05 26	05 53	06 23	06 30		06 34	06 50	06 58	07 05		07 20	07 23	07 30	07 33		07 51	07 54	08 05	08 16		08 25	08 28	08 30
—	36	Waterbeach	d	05 35	06 02	06 33				07 00					07 33					08 04	08 14			08 35		
—	41¼	**Cambridge**	a	05 44	06 09	06 43	06 50			07 09	07 13				07 44	07 46	07 51		08 07	08 14	08 21			08 44		
35¼	—	Shippea Hill	d											07x29												
40¾	—	Lakenheath	d																							
44½	—	Brandon	d						06 49			07 20		07 39											08 44	
51¾	—	Thetford	d						06 58			07 29		07 48								08 37			08 53	
59½	—	Harling Road	d						07 07					07 56												
62½	—	Eccles Road	d						07 12					08 00												
66¼	—	Attleborough	d						07 17			07 43		08 06								08 51			09 07	
69½	—	Spooner Row	d											08x11												
72	—	Wymondham	d						07 24			07 50		08 15								08 58			09 14	
82¼	—	**Norwich**	a						07 44			08 10		08 29								09 16			09 30	
—	—	Stansted Airport	a																08 43							
—	—	Ipswich	a																							09 26
—	99¼	**London Kings Cross**	a	06 35		07 40					08 15				08 45					09 12				09 42		
—	—	London Liverpool Street	a		07 33					08 33						09 03					09 48					10 46

		LE 1	FC 1	XC ◇		LE 1	FC 1	LE 1	EM ◇ C		XC ◇	EM ◇	FC 1	LE 1		LE 1 ◇	LE 1	XC ◇	EM ◇		FC 1	LE 1	LE 1	XC ◇		EM ◇
Peterborough 8	d			08 31					08 59		09 18	09 41				09 47		10 18	10 43					11 18		11 36
Whittlesea	d															09 55										
March	d			08 47							09 34					10 06		10 34						11 34		
Manea	d																									
Kings Lynn	d		08 27				08 59						09 56								10 56					
Watlington	d		08 34				09 06						10 03								11 03					
Downham Market	d		08 40				09 12						10 09								11 09					
Littleport	d		08 49				09 21						10 18								11 18					
Ely 6	a		08 57	09 05			09 29		09 35		09 52	10 14	10 26			10 30		10 52	11 16		11 26			11 52		12 14
Cambridge	d					09 12								10 12								11 12				
Ely 6	d	08 38	08 57	09 05		09 27	09 29	09 38	09 44		09 53	10 18	10 26	10 27		10 30	10 38	10 53	11 20		11 26	11 27	11 38	11 53		12 17
Waterbeach	d		09 07				09 38						10 35								11 35					
Cambridge	a	08 55	09 15	09 21			09 45	09 55			10 08		10 44				10 55	11 08			11 44		11 55	12 08		
Shippea Hill	d																									
Lakenheath	d																									
Brandon	d					09 43								10 43								11 43				
Thetford	d					09 52			10 05			10 39		10 52					11 41			11 52				12 38
Harling Road	d																									
Eccles Road	d																									
Attleborough	d					10 06								11 06								12 06				
Spooner Row	d					10x11																				
Wymondham	d					10 15								11 13								12 13				
Norwich	a					10 30			10 43			11 14		11 30					12 15			12 30				13 13
Stansted Airport	a			09 58							10 49							11 49						12 49		
Ipswich	a															11 25										
London Kings Cross	a		10 11				10 38						11 35								12 33					
London Liverpool Street	a															12 45										

For general notes see front of timetable
For details of catering facilities see Directory of Train Operators

A From Nottingham (Table 49)
B From Birmingham New Street (Table 49)
C From Mansfield Woodhouse (Table 55)

Due to major track repair work in the Bury St Edmunds area, trains between Ipswich and Peterborough are subject to disruption, resulting in bus replacements and extended journey times for part or all of this timetable. See local publicity or contact National Rail Enquiries 08457 48 49 50 for further details.

Peterborough, Kings Lynn and Ely → Cambridge, Norwich and London

Network Diagram - see first page of Table 13

		FC 1	LE 1	LE 1 ◇	LE 1		XC ◇	EM ◇	FC 1	LE 1		LE 1	XC ◇	EM ◇	FC 1		LE 1	LE 1	LE 1	XC ◇		EM ◇	FC 1	LE 1	LE 1	XC ◇
Peterborough 8	d			11 48			12 18	12 43					13 18	13 40				13 47		14 18		14 40				15 18
Whittlesea	d			11 56														13 55								
March	d			12 07			12 34						13 34					14 06		14 34						15 34
Manea	d																									
Kings Lynn	d	11 56							12 56						13 56								14 56			
Watlington	d	12 03							13 03						14 03								15 03			
Downham Market	d	12 09							13 09						14 09								15 09			
Littleport	d	12 18							13 18						14 18								15 18			
Ely 6	a	12 26		12 30			12 52	13 16	13 26				13 52	14 13	14 26			14 30		14 52		15 13	15 26			15 52
Cambridge	d		12 12							13 12							14 12							15 12		
Ely 6	d	12 26	12 27	12 30	12 38		12 53	13 20	13 26	13 29		13 38	13 53	14 16	14 26		14 27	14 30	14 40	14 53		15 16	15 26	15 27	15 38	15 53
Waterbeach	d	12 35							13 35						14 35								15 35			
Cambridge	a	12 44			12 55		13 08		13 44			13 55	14 08		14 44				14 57	15 08			15 44		15 55	16 08
Shippea Hill	d																									
Lakenheath	d																									
Brandon	d		12 43							13 45							14 43							15 43		
Thetford	d		12 52					13 41		13 54				14 37			14 52					15 37		15 52		
Harling Road	d																									
Eccles Road	d																									
Attleborough	d		13 06							14 08							15 06							16 06		
Spooner Row	d																									
Wymondham	d		13 13							14 15							15 13							16 13		
Norwich	a		13 30					14 14		14 30				15 13			15 30					16 13		16 30		
Stansted Airport	a						13 49						14 49							15 49						16 49
Ipswich	a			13 25														15 25								
London Kings Cross	a	13 33							14 33						15 33								16 33			
London Liverpool Street	a			14 45																						

		FC 1		EM ◇	FC 1	LE 1	LE 1 ◇		LE 1	XC ◇	EM ◇	FC 1		LE 1	LE 1	XC ◇ A	FC 1		LE 1	LE 1 ◇	XC ◇	LE 1		FC 1	XC ◇	EM ◇
Peterborough 8	d			15 35			15 47			16 18	16 36					17 18				17 47	18 00				18 33	18 50
Whittlesea	d						15 55									17 26				17 55						
March	d						16 06			16 34						17 37				18 06	18 16				18 51	19 07
Manea	d															17x44										
Kings Lynn	d				15 56							16 54					17 36							18 36		
Watlington	d				16 03							17 01					17 43							18 43		
Downham Market	d				16 09							17 07					17 49							18 49		
Littleport	d				16 18							17 16					17 58							18 58		
Ely 6	a			16 08	16 26		16 30			16 52	17 09	17 24				17 58	18 06			18 28	18 34			19 06	19 09	19 25
Cambridge	d					16 12								17 12					18 05							
Ely 6	d	16 02		16 12	16 26	16 27	16 30		16 38	16 53	17 13	17 24		17 27	17 38	17 58	18 06		18 20	18 30	18 34	18 40		19 06	19 10	19 28
Waterbeach	d	16 11			16 35							17 33					18 15							19 15		
Cambridge	a	16 19			16 44				16 55	17 08		17 43			17 55	18 16	18 22				18 51	18 57		19 22	19 29	
Shippea Hill	d																									
Lakenheath	d																									
Brandon	d					16 43								17 43					18 36							
Thetford	d			16 33		16 52					17 34			17 52					18 44							19 49
Harling Road	d																									
Eccles Road	d																									
Attleborough	d					17 06								18 06					18 58							
Spooner Row	d																									
Wymondham	d					17 13								18 13					19 05							
Norwich	a			17 13		17 30					18 13			18 28					19 25							20 22
Stansted Airport	a									17 43						18 47									20 05	
Ipswich	a						17 27													19 25						
London Kings Cross	a				17 36							18 38					19 33							20 33		
London Liverpool Street	a						18 49													20 46						

For general notes see front of timetable
For details of catering facilities see
Directory of Train Operators

A From Birmingham New Street (Table 49)

Due to major track repair work in the Bury St Edmunds area, trains between Ipswich and Peterborough are subject to disruption, resulting in bus replacements and extended journey times for part or all of this timetable. See local publicity or contact National Rail Enquiries 08457 48 49 50 for further details.

Peterborough, Kings Lynn and Ely → Cambridge, Norwich and London

Network Diagram - see first page of Table 13

		LE 1	LE 1	XC ◇		FC 1	EM ◇	LE 1 ◇	LE 1		LE 1	XC ◇	FC 1	LE 1		LE 1	XC ◇	FC 1	EM ◇ A ⚲	LE 1	XC ◇ B	FC 1	LE 1	EM		
Peterborough 8	d			19 19			19 37	19 49				20 24					21 18		21 37	22 05	22 17					
Whittlesea	d							19 57												22 13	22 26					
March	d			19 37				20 08				20 40					21 34			22 24	22 37					
Manea	d																									
Kings Lynn	d					19 39							20 39					21 36				22 32				
Watlington	d					19 46							20 46					21 43				22 39				
Downham Market	d					19 52							20 52					21 49				22 45				
Littleport	d					20 01							21 01					21 58				22 54				
Ely 6	a			19 56		20 09	20 13	20 26				20 58	21 09				21 52	22 06	22 10	22 42	22 55	23 02				
Cambridge	d		19 25						20 20					21 13									22 55			
Ely 6	d	19 38	19 40	19 56		20 09	20 16	20 27	20 35		20 44	20 58	21 09	21 29		21 45	21 52	22 06	22 13	22 42	22 55	23 02	23 10	23 11		
Waterbeach	d					20 18							21 18					22 15				23 11				
Cambridge	a	19 55		20 11		20 27					21 01	21 16	21 27			22 02	22 08	22 23	22 29		23 14	23 19		23 28		
Shippea Hill	d																									
Lakenheath	d																									
Brandon	d		19 56						20 51					21 45									23 26			
Thetford	d		20 04				20 37		20 59					21 54									23 34			
Harling Road	d																									
Eccles Road	d																									
Attleborough	d		20 18						21 13					22 08									23 48			
Spooner Row	d																									
Wymondham	d		20 25						21 20					22 15									23 55			
Norwich	a		20 40				21 13		21 35					22 30									00 10			
Stansted Airport	a																									
Ipswich	a							21 25												23 37						
London Kings Cross	a					21 30							22 30					23 35				00 42				
London Liverpool Street	a							22 45																		

Saturdays

		FC 1	LE 1	EM	LE 1	FC 1	LE 1	XC ◇ C	EM ◇	FC 1	LE 1		LE R 1	LE 1	XC ◇	LE 1	EM ◇	FC 1	LE 1	LE 1	XC ◇	EM ◇		FC 1	LE 1	LE R 1
Peterborough 8	d							07 10	07 39				07 52		08 32		08 46				09 18	09 46				09 55
Whittlesea	d							07 19					08 00													10 03
March	d							07 30	07 55				08 11		08 48						09 34					10 14
Manea	d							07x37																		
Kings Lynn	d	05 56				06 56				07 56								08 56						09 56		
Watlington	d	06 03				07 03				08 03								09 03						10 03		
Downham Market	d	06 09				07 09				08 09								09 09						10 09		
Littleport	d	06 18				07 18				08 18								09 18						10 18		
Ely 6	a	06 26				07 26		07 50	08 17	08 26			08 30		09 06		09 19	09 26			09 52	10 19		10 26		10 32
Cambridge	d			06 20	06 59						08 12								09 12						10 12	
Ely 6	d	06 26	06 35	06 37	07 14	07 26	07 38	07 51	08 18	08 26	08 27		08 30	08 38	09 07	09 12	09 22	09 26	09 29	09 38	09 53	10 22		10 26	10 29	10 32
Waterbeach	d	06 35				07 35				08 35						09 21		09 35						10 35		
Cambridge	a	06 44	06 52			07 44	07 55	08 06		08 44				08 55	09 22	09 28		09 44		09 55	10 08			10 44		
Shippea Hill	d				07x22																					
Lakenheath	d																									
Brandon	d			06 52	07 32						08 43								09 45						10 45	
Thetford	d			07 01	07 41				08 39		08 52						09 44		09 54			10 44			10 54	
Harling Road	d			07 09	07 49																					
Eccles Road	d			07 14	07 53																					
Attleborough	d			07 19	07 59						09 06								10 08						11 08	
Spooner Row	d				08x04																					
Wymondham	d			07 26	08 08						09 13								10 15						11 15	
Norwich	a			07 44	08 23				09 12		09 30						10 17		10 30			11 17			11 30	
Stansted Airport	a							08 49							09 58						10 49					
Ipswich	a												09 25													11 27
London Kings Cross	a	07 34				08 33				09 33								10 34						11 35		
London Liverpool Street	a												10 38			10 43										12 45

For general notes see front of timetable
For details of catering facilities see Directory of Train Operators

A From Liverpool Lime Street (Table 49). ⚲ to Nottingham
B From Birmingham New Street (Table 49)
C Until 22 March from Birmingham New Street (Table 49). From 29 March from Leicester (Table 49)

Due to major track repair work in the Bury St Edmunds area, trains between Ipswich and Peterborough are subject to disruption, resulting in bus replacements and extended journey times for part or all of this timetable. See local publicity or contact National Rail Enquiries 08457 48 49 50 for further details.

Table 17

Peterborough, Kings Lynn and Ely → Cambridge, Norwich and London

Network Diagram - see first page of Table 13

		LE 1	XC ◇	EM ◇	FC 1	LE 1	LE 1	XC ◇	EM ◇	FC 1		LE 1	LE 1 ◇	LE 1	XC ◇	EM ◇	FC 1	LE 1	LE 1	XC ◇	EM ◇		FC 1	LE 1	LE 1 ◇	LE 1
Peterborough 8	d		10 18	10 46				11 18	11 38				11 48		12 18	12 39				13 18	13 37				13 47	
Whittlesea	d												11 56												13 55	
March	d		10 34					11 34					12 07		12 34					13 34					14 06	
Manea	d																									
Kings Lynn	d				10 56					11 56							12 56						13 56			
Watlington	d				11 03					12 03							13 03						14 03			
Downham Market	d				11 09					12 09							13 09						14 09			
Littleport	d				11 18					12 18							13 18						14 18			
Ely 6	a		10 52	11 19	11 26			11 52	12 11	12 26			12 30		12 52	13 12	13 26			13 52	14 10		14 26		14 30	
Cambridge	d					11 12						12 12						13 12						14 12		
Ely 6	d	10 38	10 53	11 23	11 26	11 29	11 38	11 53	12 16	12 26		12 27	12 30	12 38	12 53	13 15	13 26	13 27	13 38	13 53	14 16		14 26	14 27	14 30	14 38
Waterbeach	d				11 35					12 35							13 35						14 35			
Cambridge	a	10 55	11 08		11 44		11 55	12 08		12 44				12 55	13 08		13 44		13 55	14 08			14 44			14 55
Shippea Hill	d																									
Lakenheath	d																									
Brandon	d					11 45						12 43						13 43						14 43		
Thetford	d			11 44		11 54			12 37			12 52				13 36		13 52			14 37			14 52		
Harling Road	d																									
Eccles Road	d																									
Attleborough	d					12 08						13 06						14 06						15 06		
Spooner Row	d																									
Wymondham	d					12 15						13 13						14 13						15 13		
Norwich	a			12 17		12 30			13 13			13 30				14 13		14 30			15 13			15 30		
Stansted Airport	a		11 49					12 49							13 49					14 49						
Ipswich	a												13 27												15 25	
London Kings Cross	a				12 33					13 35							14 34						15 33			
London Liverpool Street	a												14 45												16 45	

		XC ◇	EM ◇	FC 1	LE 1	LE 1	XC ◇	EM ◇	FC 1		LE 1	LE 1 ◇	LE 1	XC ◇	EM ◇	FC 1	LE 1	LE 1	XC ◇ A	FC 1		LE 1	LE 1 ◇	LE 1	XC ◇	FC 1
Peterborough 8	d	14 18	14 40				15 18	15 36				15 47		16 18	16 38				17 18				17 47		18 18	
Whittlesea	d											15 55							17 26				17 55			
March	d	14 34					15 34					16 06		16 34					17 37				18 06		18 34	
Manea	d																		17x44							
Kings Lynn	d			14 56					15 56							16 56				17 56						18 34
Watlington	d			15 03					16 03							17 03				18 03						18 41
Downham Market	d			15 09					16 09							17 09				18 09						18 47
Littleport	d			15 18					16 18							17 18				18 18						18 56
Ely 6	a	14 52	15 12	15 26			15 52	16 09	16 26			16 30		16 52	17 11	17 26			17 58	18 26			18 30		18 52	19 04
Cambridge	d				15 12						16 12						17 12					18 12				
Ely 6	d	14 53	15 16	15 26	15 27	15 38	15 53	16 14	16 26		16 27	16 30	16 38	16 53	17 17	17 26	17 27	17 38	17 58	18 26		18 27	18 30	18 38	18 53	19 05
Waterbeach	d			15 35					16 35							17 35				18 35						19 15
Cambridge	a	15 08		15 44		15 55	16 08		16 44				16 55	17 08		17 44		17 55	18 15	18 44				18 55	19 08	19 21
Shippea Hill	d																									
Lakenheath	d				15x40																					
Brandon	d				15 45						16 43						17 43					18 43				
Thetford	d		15 38		15 54			16 35			16 52				17 38		17 52					18 52				
Harling Road	d																									
Eccles Road	d																									
Attleborough	d				16 08						17 06						18 06					19 06				
Spooner Row	d																									
Wymondham	d				16 15						17 13						18 13					19 13				
Norwich	a		16 13		16 30			17 13			17 30				18 13		18 30					19 30				
Stansted Airport	a	15 49					16 49							17 49					18 58							
Ipswich	a											17 27											19 25			
London Kings Cross	a			16 36					17 35							18 34				19 33						20 32
London Liverpool Street	a											18 45											20 45			

		EM ◇	LE 1	LE 1	XC ◇	FC 1	EM ◇	LE 1		LE 1 ◇	LE 1	XC ◇	FC 1	EM ◇	LE 1	LE 1	XC ◇	FC 1	EM ◇ B	LE 1	LE 1	XC ◇ A	EM	FC 1		
Peterborough 8	d	18 42			19 18		19 35			19 46		20 18		20 39			21 21		21 39	21 49		22 17				
Whittlesea	d									19 54										21 57		22 25				
March	d	18 58			19 34					20 05		20 34		20 55			21 37		21 55	22 08		22 36				
Manea	d																									
Kings Lynn	d					19 34							20 34					21 34						23 15		
Watlington	d					19 41							20 41					21 41						23 22		
Downham Market	d					19 47							20 47					21 47						23b31		
Littleport	d					19 56							20 56					21 56						23 40		
Ely 6	a	19 16			19 52	20 04	20 08			20 30		20 52	21 04	21 13			21 55	22 04	22 13	22 30		22 54		23 47		
Cambridge	d		19 12					20 12							21 12						22 30					
Ely 6	d	19 19	19 27	19 38	19 53	20 05	20 15	20 27		20 30	20 38	20 53	21 05	21 15	21 27	21 38	21 56	22 05	22 14	22 30	22 45	22 55	23 08	23 47		
Waterbeach	d					20 15							21 15					22 15						23 57		
Cambridge	a			19 55	20 08	20 21					20 55	21 11	21 21	21 31		21 55	22 16	22 21	22 33			23 11	23 25	00 06		
Shippea Hill	d																									
Lakenheath	d																									
Brandon	d		19 43					20 43							21 43						23 01					
Thetford	d	19 40	19 52				20 36	20 52							21 52						23 09					
Harling Road	d																									
Eccles Road	d																									
Attleborough	d		20 06					21 06							22 06						23 23					
Spooner Row	d																									
Wymondham	d		20 13					21 13							22 13						23 30					
Norwich	a	20 13	20 30				21 13	21 30							22 30						23 45					
Stansted Airport	a				20 49																					
Ipswich	a									21 27										23 32						
London Kings Cross	a					21 32							22 32					23 47								
London Liverpool Street	a									22 49																

For general notes see front of timetable
For details of catering facilities see Directory of Train Operators

A Until 22 March from Birmingham New Street (Table 49). From 29 March from Leicester (Table 49)

B From Liverpool Lime Street (Table 49)

b Arr. 2328

Due to major track repair work in the Bury St Edmunds area, trains between Ipswich and Peterborough are subject to disruption, resulting in bus replacements and extended journey times for part or all of this timetable. See local publicity or contact National Rail Enquiries 08457 48 49 50 for further details.

Table 17

Sundays

Peterborough, Kings Lynn and Ely → Cambridge, Norwich and London

Network Diagram - see first page of Table 13

		FC 1	LE 1	FC 1	LE 1	LE 1	LE 1	FC 1	LE 1	LE 1	LE 1	FC 1	XC ◇	LE 1	EM ◇ A	LE 1	XC	FC 1	LE 1	LE 1
Peterborough 8	d						11 46						13 21		13 43	13 48	14 12			
Whittlesea	d						11 54									13 56				
March	d						12 05						13 37			14 07	14 28			
Manea	d																			
Kings Lynn	d	08 26		10 26				12 26				13 26						14 26		
Watlington	d	08 33		10 33				12 33				13 33						14 33		
Downham Market	d	08 39		10 39				12 39				13 39						14 39		
Littleport	d	08 48		10 48				12 48				13 48						14 48		
Ely 6	a	08 56		10 56			12 28	12 56				13 56	14 02		14 21	14 30	14 52	14 56		
Cambridge	d				10 44				12 46		13 38								14 46	
Ely 6	d	08 56	10 21	10 56	11 01	12 18	12 30	12 56	13 01	13 17	13 53	13 56	14 02	14 17	14 28	14 30	14 53	14 56	15 01	15 17
Waterbeach	d	09 05		11 05				13 05				14 05						15 05		
Cambridge	a	09 14	10 38	11 14		12 34		13 14		13 34		14 14	14 19	14 34			15 09	15 14		15 34
Shippea Hill	d																			
Lakenheath	d				11x15				13x14											
Brandon	d				11 20				13 20		14 09								15 17	
Thetford	d				11 29				13 28		14 18				14 49				15 26	
Harling Road	d																			
Eccles Road	d																			
Attleborough	d				11 43				13 42		14 32								15 40	
Spooner Row	d																			
Wymondham	d				11 50				13 49		14 39								15 47	
Norwich	a				12 09				14 09		14 58				15 28				16 09	
Stansted Airport	a												14 58				15 43			
Ipswich	a						13 25									15 27				
London Kings Cross	a	10 03		12 04				14 05				15 05						16 06		
London Liverpool Street	a																			

		EM ◇	LE 1	FC 1	XC ◇	LE 1	LE 1	EM ◇	LE 1	FC 1	XC ◇	LE 1	EM ◇	FC 1	LE 1	XC ◇	LE 1	LE 1	EM ◇	LE 1
Peterborough 8	d	14 56			15 28		15 47	16 05			16 28		17 00			17 28		17 47	17 53	
Whittlesea	d						15 55											17 55		
March	d				15 44		16 06				16 44					17 44		18 06		
Manea	d																			
Kings Lynn	d			15 26						16 26				17 26						
Watlington	d			15 33						16 33				17 33						
Downham Market	d			15 39						16 39				17 39						
Littleport	d			15 48						16 48				17 48						
Ely 6	a	15 34		15 56	16 06		16 29	16 38		16 56	17 06		17 33	17 56		18 02		18 27	18 31	
Cambridge	d		15 38						16 38						17 44					18 38
Ely 6	d	15 38	15 53	15 56	16 08	16 14	16 30	16 41	16 53	16 56	17 06	17 17	17 39	17 56	17 59	18 02	18 12	18 30	18 35	18 53
Waterbeach	d			16 05						17 05				18 05						
Cambridge	a			16 14	16 22	16 31				17 14	17 23	17 34		18 14		18 21	18 29			
Shippea Hill	d																			
Lakenheath	d		16x06																	
Brandon	d		16 12						17 09						18 15					19 09
Thetford	d	15 59	16 20					17 02	17 18				18 00		18 24				18 56	19 18
Harling Road	d																			
Eccles Road	d																			
Attleborough	d		16 34						17 32						18 38					19 32
Spooner Row	d																			
Wymondham	d		16 41						17 39						18 45					19 39
Norwich	a	16 37	16 55					17 35	17 53				18 35		18 59				19 29	19 53
Stansted Airport	a				16 59						17 58									
Ipswich	a						17 25											19 27		
London Kings Cross	a			17 03						18 03				19 07						
London Liverpool Street	a																			

For general notes see front of timetable
For details of catering facilities see
Directory of Train Operators

A From Nottingham (Table 19)

Due to major track repair work in the Bury St Edmunds area, trains between Ipswich and Peterborough are subject to disruption, resulting in bus replacements and extended journey times for part or all of this timetable. See local publicity or contact National Rail Enquiries 08457 48 49 50 for further details.

Peterborough, Kings Lynn and Ely → Cambridge, Norwich and London

Network Diagram - see first page of Table 13

		FC 1	XC ◇	LE 1		EM ◇	LE 1	FC 1		XC ◇	LE 1	EM ◇		FC 1	XC ◇	LE 1		LE 1	FC 1	EM ◇ A		FC 1	XC ◇			
Peterborough 8	d		18 29			18 55				19 29	19 44	19 55			20 25					21 55			22 24			
Whittlesea	d										19 52															
March	d		18 45							19 45	20 03				20 46								22 40			
Manea	d																									
Kings Lynn	d	18 26						19 26						20 26					21 26			22 26				
Watlington	d	18 33						19 33						20 33					21 33			22 33				
Downham Market	d	18 39						19 39						20 39					21 39			22 39				
Littleport	d	18 48						19 48						20 48					21 48			22 48				
Ely 6	a	18 56	19 03			19 28		19 56		20 04	20 21	20 28		20 56	21 04				21 56	22 28		22 56	22 59			
Cambridge	d						19 38											21 38								
Ely 6	d	18 56	19 03	19 12		19 32	19 53	19 56		20 05	20 22	20 31		20 56	21 04	21 12		21 53	21 56	22 31		22 56	23 00			
Waterbeach	d	19 05						20 05						21 05					22 05			23 05				
Cambridge	a	19 14	19 20	19 30				20 14		20 21				21 14	21 19	21 29			22 14			23 13	23 17			
Shippea Hill	d																									
Lakenheath	d																									
Brandon	d						20 09											22 09								
Thetford	d					19 55	20 18					20 52						22 18		22 52						
Harling Road	d																									
Eccles Road	d																									
Attleborough	d						20 32											22 32		23 06						
Spooner Row	d																									
Wymondham	d						20 39											22 39		23 13						
Norwich	a					20 28	20 53					21 25						22 53		23 35						
Stansted Airport	a		19 58							20 58					21 53											
Ipswich	a										21 18															
London Kings Cross	a	20 03						21 05						22 03					23 15			00 32				
London Liverpool Street	a																									

For general notes see front of timetable
For details of catering facilities see Directory of Train Operators

A Until 27 January from Sheffield (Table 49). From 3 February from Liverpool Lime Street (Table 49)

Due to major track repair work in the Bury St Edmunds area, trains between Ipswich and Peterborough are subject to disruption, resulting in bus replacements and extended journey times for part or all of this timetable. See local publicity or contact National Rail Enquiries 08457 48 49 50 for further details.

Kings Lynn → Sandringham and Hunstanton
Bus Service

This service is operated by First Eastern Counties.
Telephone Lo-call 08456-020-121

		FC	FC	FC	FC	FC	FC	FC	FC	FC	FC	FC	FC	FC	FC	FC	FC	FC
London Kings Cross	⊖ 17 d				06 45		07 15		07 45				08 45				09 45	
London Liverpool Street	⊖ 17 d						05b58		06b28				07b28				08b58	
Cambridge	17 d			06 23	07 35		08 04		08 38				09 33				10 33	
Kings Lynn	d	06 25	06 55	07 28	08 35	08 50	09 05	09 20	09 35	09 50	10 05	10 20	10 35	10 50	11 05	11 20	11 35	11 50
Sandringham Visitor Centre	a					09 12		09 42		10 12		10 42		11 12		11 42		12 12
Sandringham Norwich Gates	a			07 51		09 14		09 44		10 14		10 44		11 14		11 44		12 14
Hunstanton Bus Station	a	07 14	07 44	08 21	09 25	09 44	09 55	10 14	10 25	10 44	10 55	11 14	11 25	11 44	11 55	12 14	12 25	12 44

		FC		FC	FC	FC	FC	FC	FC	FC	FC	FC	FC	FC	FC	FC	FC	FC	FC	FC
London Kings Cross	⊖ 17 d		and at the same minutes past each hour until		12 45		13 45				14 45				15 45			16 45	17 45	18 45
London Liverpool Street	⊖ 17 d				11b58		12b58				13b58				14b28			15b58	16 58	18 58
Cambridge	17 d				13 33		14 33				15 33				16 35			17 40	18 40	20 15
Kings Lynn	d	12 05		14 20	14 30	15 05	15 35	15 50	16 05	16 20	16 35	16 50	17 05	17 20	17 35	17 50	18 20	19 00	20 00	21 30
Sandringham Visitor Centre	a			14 42		15 27		16 12		16 42		17 12		17 42		18 12				
Sandringham Norwich Gates	a			14 44		15 29		16 14		16 44		17 14		17 44		18 14				
Hunstanton Bus Station	a	12 55		15 14	15 20	15 59	16 25	16 44	16 55	17 14	17 25	17 44	17 55	18 14	18 25	18 41	19 03	19 40	20 40	22 10

		FC
London Kings Cross	⊖ 17 d	20 15
London Liverpool Street	⊖ 17 d	19b28
Cambridge	17 d	21 10
Kings Lynn	d	23 00
Sandringham Visitor Centre	a	
Sandringham Norwich Gates	a	
Hunstanton Bus Station	a	23 40

Saturdays

This service is operated by First Eastern Counties.
Telephone Lo-call 08456-020-121

		FC	FC	FC	FC	FC	FC	FC	FC	FC	FC	FC		FC	FC	FC	FC	FC
London Kings Cross	⊖ 17 d			06 45				07 45				08 45	and at the same minutes past each hour until				13 45	
London Liverpool Street	⊖ 17 d			05b58				06b58				07b58					12b58	
Cambridge	17 d		06 32	07 33				08 33				09 33					14 33	
Kings Lynn	d	06 35	07 35	08 35	08 50	09 05	09 20	09 35	09 50	10 05	10 20	10 35		14 50	15 05	15 20	15 35	15 50
Sandringham Visitor Centre	a				09 12		09 42		10 12		10 42			15 12	15 27	15 42		16 12
Sandringham Norwich Gates	a				09 14		09 44		10 14		10 44			15 14	15 29	15 44		16 14
Hunstanton Bus Station	a	07 25	08 25	09 25	09 44	09 55	10 14	10 25	10 44	10 55	11 14	11 25		15 44	15 59	16 14	16 25	16 44

		FC	FC	FC	FC	FC	FC	FC	FC	FC	FC	FC	FC	FC
London Kings Cross	⊖ 17 d			14 45				15 45			16 45	17 45	19 45	20 52
London Liverpool Street	⊖ 17 d			13b58				14b58			15b58	16b58	18b58	20b28
Cambridge	17 d			15 33				16 33			17 33	18 33	20 33	21 56
Kings Lynn	d	16 05	16 20	16 35	16 50	17 05	17 20	17 35	17 50	18 20	19 00	20 00	21 30	23 00
Sandringham Visitor Centre	a		16 42		17 12		17 42		18 12					
Sandringham Norwich Gates	a		16 44		17 14		17 44		18 14					
Hunstanton Bus Station	a	16 55	17 14	17 25	17 44	17 55	18 14	18 25	18 41	19 03	19 40	20 40	22 10	23 40

Sundays

This service is operated by First Eastern Counties.
Telephone Lo-call 08456-020-121

		FC	FC	FC	FC	FC	FC	FC	FC	FC	FC	FC	FC	FC
London Kings Cross	⊖ 17 d			07c52		10 15		12 15		14 15	15 15	18 15	19 15	21 15
London Liverpool Street	⊖ 17 d					09b28		11b28		13b28	14b28	17b28	18b28	20b28
Cambridge	17 d			09 07		11 07		13 02		15 02	16 02	19 02	20 02	22 02
Kings Lynn	d	08 50	09 50	10 50	11 50	12 50	13 50	14 50	15 50	16 50	17 50	20 00	21 30	23 00
Sandringham Visitor Centre	a	09 12	10 12	11 12	12 12	13 12	14 12	15 12	16 12	17 12	18 12			
Sandringham Norwich Gates	a	09 14	10 14	11 14	12 14	13 14	14 14	15 14	16 14	17 14	18 14			
Hunstanton Bus Station	a	09 42	10 42	11 42	12 42	13 42	14 42	15 42	16 42	17 42	18 42	20 40	22 10	23 40

For general notes see front of timetable
For details of catering facilities see Directory of Train Operators

b Change at Cambridge and Kings Lynn
c From 30 March only

Hunstanton and Sandringham → Kings Lynn

Bus Service

This service is operated by First Eastern Counties.
Telephone Lo-call 08456-020-121

		FC	FC	FC	FC	FC	FC	FC	FC	FC		FC	FC	FC	FC	FC	FC	FC
Hunstanton Bus Station	d	06 30	07 16	07 48	08 33	08 48	09 03	09 18	09 33	09 48	and at the same minutes past each hour until	14 03	14 18	14 33	14 48	15 18	15 25	16 03
Sandringham Norwich Gates	d	06 55	07 43			09 15		09 45		10 15			14 45		15 15	15 45	15 56	
Sandringham Visitor Centre	d					09 17		09 47		10 17			14 47		15 17	15 47	15 58	
Kings Lynn	a	07 20	08 10	08 40	09 25	09 44	09 55	10 14	10 25	10 44		14 55	15 14	15 25	15 44	16 14	16 25	16 55
Cambridge	17 a	08 44	09 15	09 45		10 44				11 44					16 44		17 43	
London Liverpool Street	⊖ 17 a		10b43	11b43		12b43				13b45					18b49		19b18	
London Kings Cross	⊖ 17 a	09 42	10 11	10 38		11 35				12 33					17 36		18 38	

		FC	FC	FC	FC	FC	FC	FC	FC	FC	FC	FC	FC	FC	FC
Hunstanton Bus Station	d	16 18	16 33	16 48	17 08	17 18	17 33	17 48	18 03	18 44	19 14	19 44	20 44	22 14	23 44
Sandringham Norwich Gates	d	16 45		17 15		17 45		18 15							
Sandringham Visitor Centre	d	16 47		17 17		17 47		18 17							
Kings Lynn	a	17 14	17 25	17 44	18 00	18 14	18 25	18 44	18 55	19 22	19 52	20 22	21 22	22 52	00 22
Cambridge	17 a		18 22				19 22			20 27		21 27	22 23		
London Liverpool Street	⊖ 17 a		20b17				21b15			22b15		23b15	23b43		
London Kings Cross	⊖ 17 a		19 33				20 33			21 30		22 30	23 35		

Saturdays

This service is operated by First Eastern Counties.
Telephone Lo-call 08456-020-121

		FC	FC	FC	FC	FC	FC	FC	FC		FC	FC	FC	FC	FC
Hunstanton Bus Station	d	06 30	07 30	08 33	08 48	09 03	09 18	09 33	09 48	and at the same minutes past each hour until	16 03	16 18	16 33	16 48	17 03
Sandringham Norwich Gates	d	06 55	07 55		09 15		09 45		10 15			16 45		17 15	
Sandringham Visitor Centre	d				09 17		09 47		10 17			16 47		17 17	
Kings Lynn	a	07 20	08 20	09 25	09 44	09 55	10 14	10 25	10 44		16 55	17 14	17 25	17 44	17 55
Cambridge	17 a	08 44	09 44		10 44				11 44					18 44	
London Liverpool Street	⊖ 17 a	10b43	11b43		12b43				13b43						
London Kings Cross	⊖ 17 a	09 33	10 34		11 35				12 33					19 33	

		FC	FC	FC	FC	FC	FC	FC	FC	FC	FC
Hunstanton Bus Station	d	17 18	17 33	17 48	18 03	18 44	19 14	19 44	20 44	22 14	23 44
Sandringham Norwich Gates	d	17 45		18 15							
Sandringham Visitor Centre	d	17 47		18 17							
Kings Lynn	a	18 14	18 25	18 44	18 55	19 22	19 52	20 22	21 22	22 52	00 22
Cambridge	17 a		19 21					21 21	22 21	00 06	
London Liverpool Street	⊖ 17 a		20b43					22b43	23b43		
London Kings Cross	⊖ 17 a		20 32					22 32	23 47		

Sundays

This service is operated by First Eastern Counties.
Telephone Lo-call 08456-020-121

		FC	FC	FC	FC	FC	FC	FC	FC	FC	FC	FC	FC	FC
Hunstanton Bus Station	d	09 47	10 47	11 47	12 47	13 47	14 47	15 47	16 47	17 47	18 47	20 44	22 14	23 44
Sandringham Norwich Gates	d	10 14	11 14	12 14	13 14	14 14	15 14	16 14	17 14	18 14	19 14			
Sandringham Visitor Centre	d	10 16	11 16	12 16	13 16	14 16	15 16	16 16	17 16	18 16				
Kings Lynn	a	10 40	11 40	12 40	13 40	14 40	15 40	16 40	17 40	18 40	19 38	21 22	22 52	00 22
Cambridge	17 a		13 14	14 14	15 14	16 14	17 14	18 14	19 14	20 14	21 14	23 13		
London Liverpool Street	⊖ 17 a		14b45	15b45	16b45	17b45	18b45	19b45	20b45	21b45	22b45			
London Kings Cross	⊖ 17 a		14 05	15 05	16 06	17 03	18 03	19 07	20 03	21 05	22 03	00 32		

For general notes see front of timetable
For details of catering facilities see Directory of Train Operators

b Change at Kings Lynn and Cambridge

Network Diagram for Tables 18, 19, 27, 29, 30

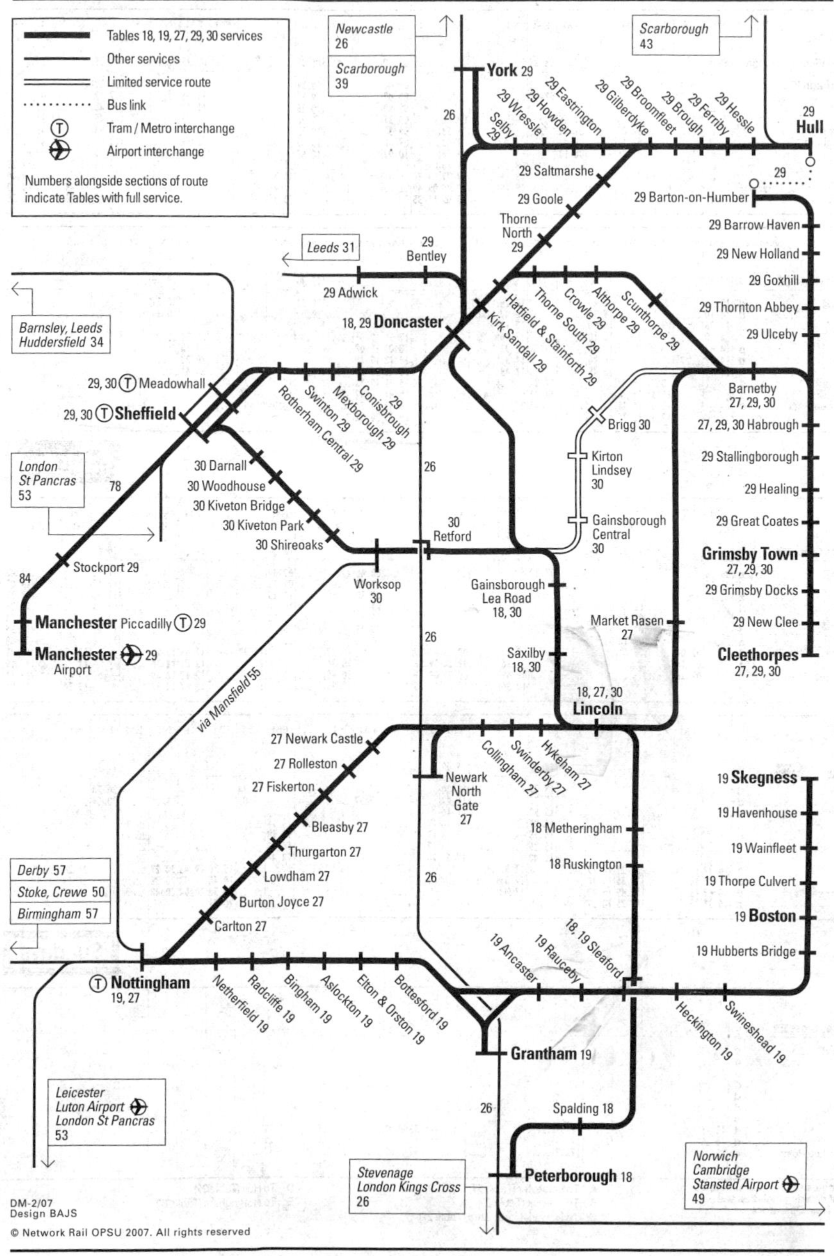

Tables 18, 19, 27, 29, 30 services
Other services
Limited service route
Bus link
Tram / Metro interchange
Airport interchange
Numbers alongside sections of route indicate Tables with full service.
Newcastle 26
Scarborough 39
Scarborough 43
York 29
29 Hull
Leeds 31
Barnsley, Leeds Huddersfield 34
18, 29 Doncaster
29, 30 Meadowhall
29, 30 Sheffield
London St Pancras 53
Stockport 29
Manchester Piccadilly 29
Manchester Airport 29
Worksop 30
30 Retford
Gainsborough Lea Road 18, 30
Saxilby 18, 30
18, 27, 30 Lincoln
Brigg 30
Kirton Lindsey 30
Gainsborough Central 30
Market Rasen 27
Barnetby 27, 29, 30
27, 29, 30 Habrough
Grimsby Town 27, 29, 30
Cleethorpes 27, 29, 30
19 Skegness
19 Boston
Nottingham 19, 27
Grantham 19
Peterborough 18
Spalding 18
Derby 57
Stoke, Crewe 50
Birmingham 57
Leicester Luton Airport London St Pancras 53
Stevenage London Kings Cross 26
Norwich Cambridge Stansted Airport 49
via Mansfield 55

DM-2/07
Design BAJS

Table 18

Mondays to Fridays

Peterborough → Sleaford, Lincoln and Doncaster

Network Diagram - see first page of Table 18

Miles			EM	NT	EM		EM	EM	NT		EM	NT	EM		NT	EM	NT		EM	EM	NT		EM	NT	EM	NT
					A				B			B			B		B				B			B	C	B
—	London Kings Cross 15	⊖ d						06 35					07 30			08 35				09 35			10 35		11 35	
0	**Peterborough 8**	d	06 30					07 32					08 40			09 34				10 43			11 50		12 41	
16½	Spalding	d	06a57					07a58					09 02			09 57				11 05			12 12		13 03	
35½	Sleaford	a											09 30			10 25				11 33			12 40		13 31	
—		d			06 55		07 45				08 46		09 31			10 26				11 33			12 45		13 32	
40	Ruskington	d			07 02		07 52				08 53		09 38			10 33				11 41			12 53		13 39	
47¼	Metheringham	d			07 12		08 02				09 03		09 48			10 43				11 51			13 02		13 49	
56¾	**Lincoln**	a			07 26		08 17				09 16		10 02			10 57				12 06			13 16		14 02	
—		d		07 04					08 27		09 18	09 27			10 27		11 27		11 55		12 27		13 18	13 27		14 27
62¾	Saxilby	d		07 14					08 36		09 27	09 36			10 36		11 36		12 04		12 36		13 28	13 36		14 36
72¼	Gainsborough Lea Road	d		07a26					08 49		09 40	09 49			10 49		11 49		12 17		12 49		13 40	13 49		14 49
93½	**Doncaster 7**	a							10 36		10 09	11 35			12 35		13 35		12 47		14 35		14 17	15 36		16 35

		EM		NT	NT	EM		NT	EM	EM		NT	EM	EM		EM	NT	NT		EM	EM	NT				
				B	D															E						
London Kings Cross 15	⊖ d	12 30				14 10			15 30	16 35						17 30					19 30					
Peterborough 8	d	13 48				15 09			16 25	17 32						18 35					20 27					
Spalding	d	14 10				15 32			16 47	18a01						19a02					20a54					
Sleaford	a	14 38				16 00			17 15																	
	d	14 40				16 10			17 16				17 55	19 01						20 11						
Ruskington	d	14 47				16 18			17 23				18 03	19 08						20 18						
Metheringham	d	14 57				16 28			17 33				18 13	19 18						20 28						
Lincoln	a	15 11				16 45			17 48				18 26	19 31						20 41						
	d			15 27	16 27			17 22				18 24	18 29	19 33			19 43	20 27				21 27				
Saxilby	d			15 36	16 36			17 31				18 33	18 41	19 42			19 52	20 36				21 36				
Gainsborough Lea Road	d			15 49	16 49			17a43				18a45	18 57	19 54			20a04	20a48				21a48				
Doncaster 7	a			17 35	18 35								19 25	20 22												

Saturdays

		EM	NT		EM	EM		EM	NT		EM	NT		EM	NT		EM	NT		EM	NT		EM	NT		EM
					A				B			B			B			B			B			B		
London Kings Cross 15	⊖ d							06 15						07 10			08 30						10 40			11 30
Peterborough 8	d	06 28						07 30						08 40			09 34						11 50			12 43
Spalding	d	06a55						07a56						09 02			09 57						12 12			13 05
Sleaford	a													09 30			10 25						12 40			13 37
	d				06 56	07 45								09 31			10 26						12 44			13 37
Ruskington	d				07 03	07 52								09 38			10 33						12 51			13 45
Metheringham	d				07 13	08 02								09 48			10 43						13 01			13 54
Lincoln	a				07 26	08 17								10 04			10 58						13 16			14 08
	d		07 04						08 27		09 15	09 27			10 27			11 27		11 55	12 27			13 27		14 09
Saxilby	d		07 14						08 36		09 24	09 36			10 36			11 36		12 05	12 36			13 36		14 19
Gainsborough Lea Road	d		07a26						08 49		09 37	09 49			10 49			11 49		12 17	12 49			13 49		14 31
Doncaster 7	a								10 36		10 06	11 35			12 35			13 35		12 47	14 35			15 36		15 01

		NT	EM		NT	NT		EM	NT		EM	EM		EM	NT		EM	EM	EM	NT	NT	EM	EM	NT		
		B			B																					
London Kings Cross 15	⊖ d							14 00			15 00			16 30				17 40					19 30			
Peterborough 8	d							15 09			16 24			17 31				18 34					20 28			
Spalding	d							15 31			16 47			17a57				19a05					20a54			
Sleaford	a							15 59			17 16															
	d							16 07			17 16	17 33					18 11					20 20				
Ruskington	d							16 15			17 24	17 40					18 19					20 27				
Metheringham	d							16 25			17 33	17 50					18 28					20 37				
Lincoln	a							16 40			17 50	18 03					18 44					20 52				
	d	14 27	15 10		15 27	16 27			17 22						18 24				19 30	19 43	20 27			21 24		
Saxilby	d	14 36	15 20		15 36	16 36			17 31						18 33				19 40	19 52	20 36			21 33		
Gainsborough Lea Road	d	14 49	15 32		15 49	16 49			17a43						18a45				19 52	20a04	20a48			21a45		
Doncaster 7	a	16 35	16 01		17 35	18 37													20 21							

Sundays

		NT	NT	NT	NT
London Kings Cross 15	⊖ d				
Peterborough 8	d				
Spalding	d				
Sleaford	a				
	d				
Ruskington	d				
Metheringham	d				
Lincoln	a				
	d	15 15	17 35	19 35	21 15
Saxilby	d	15 25	17 45	19 45	21 25
Gainsborough Lea Road	d	15a37	17a57	19a57	21a37
Doncaster 7	a				

For general notes see front of timetable
For details of catering facilities see Directory of Train Operators

A To Leicester (Table 53)
B To Adwick (Table 29)
C To Newark North Gate (Table 27)
D To Hull (Table 29)
E To Nottingham (Table 27)

Doncaster, Lincoln and Sleaford → Peterborough

Network Diagram - see first page of Table 18

Miles			NT	EM	EM	EM		EM	NT	NT	EM		NT	EM	NT A	EM		EM	NT A	EM	NT A		EM B	EM	NT A	EM
0	**Doncaster 7**	d													09 01			10 22	10 02		11 02			13 04	11 58	
21¼	Gainsborough Lea Road	d	06 25						07 38	08 24			09 38		10 38			10 52	11 38		12 38			13 30	13 39	
30¾	Saxilby	d	06 37						07 51	08 37			09 51		10 51			11 05	11 51		12 51			13 43	13 52	
36¾	**Lincoln**	a	06 53						08 06	08 52			10 06		11 06			11 18	12 05		13 05			13 56	14 06	
—		d			07 09			08 04			09 11			10 17		11 12				12 14			13 31			14 50
46¼	Metheringham	d			07 21			08 16			09 23			10 29		11 23				12 26			13 44			15 02
53½	Ruskington	d			07 31			08 26			09 33			10 39		11 33				12 36			13 53			15 11
58	Sleaford	a			07 40			08 35			09 42			10 54		11 44				12 45			14 02			15 21
—		d						08 38			09 43			10 55		11 44				12 46			14 03			15 22
77	Spalding	d		07 01		08 03		09 03			10 08			11 20		12 09				13 11			14 28			15 46
93½	**Peterborough 8**	a		07 26		08 28		09 28			10 37			11 45		12 36				13 38			14 53			16 12
—	London Kings Cross 15	⊖ a		*08 34*		*09 45*		*10 40*			*11 50*			*13 10*		*13 43*				*14 57*			*15 58*			*17 41*

		NT A	EM		EM	EM B	NT A	NT A		EM C	EM	NT A	EM		NT A	EM	EM	NT		EM	EM D	EM	NT	EM		
Doncaster 7	d	13 02	14 25				14 01	15 02				16 02			17 00					19 34				20 33		
Gainsborough Lea Road	d	14 38	14 54				15 38	16 38				17 38			18 38			19 39		20 00			20 42	21 00		
Saxilby	d	14 51	15 07				15 51	16 51				17 51			18 51			19 52		20 13			20 55	21 14		
Lincoln	a	15 06	15 18				16 05	17 06				18 06			19 07			20 06		20 25			21 10	21 24		
	d				15 23	16 02				17 13			18 15				19 30					20 40				
Metheringham	d				15 35	16 15				17 26			18 27				19 42					20 53				
Ruskington	d				15 45	16 24				17 36			18 37				19 52					21 03				
Sleaford	a				15 56	16 33				17 47			18 48				20 08					21 14				
	d					16 34																				
Spalding	d					16 58					18 02					19 53					21 00					
Peterborough 8	a					17 24					18 28					20 21					21 26					
London Kings Cross 15	⊖ a					*18 45*					*19 59*					*21 33*					*23 32*					

Saturdays

		NT	EM		EM	EM		EM	NT		NT	NT		EM	NT A		EM	EM		NT A	NT A		EM	EM		NT A
Doncaster 7	d														09 02			10 19		10 02	11 02			13 04		12 02
Gainsborough Lea Road	d	06 25							07 38		08 24	09 38			10 38			10 52		11 38	12 38			13 30		13 40
Saxilby	d	06 37							07 51		08 37	09 51			10 51			11 05		11 51	12 51			13 43		13 53
Lincoln	a	06 53							08 06		08 52	10 06			11 06			11 17		12 05	13 05			13 56		14 06
	d				07 09			08 04						10 15			11 12						13 28			
Metheringham	d				07 21			08 16						10 27			11 23						13 40			
Ruskington	d				07 31			08 26						10 37			11 33						13 50			
Sleaford	a				07 40			08 35						10 46			11 43						13 59			
	d							08 38						10 51			11 43						13 59			
Spalding	d		07 01			08 03		09 03						11 16			12 08						14 24			
Peterborough 8	a		07 26			08 28		09 29						11 41			12 34						14 53			
London Kings Cross 15	⊖ a		*08 40*			*09 51*		*10 41*						*13 10*			*13 44*						*15 58*			

		EM	NT A		EM	NT A		EM	NT A		EM	EM		NT A	NT A		EM	EM C		NT A	EM E		NT	EM		
Doncaster 7	d		13 01		15 07	14 02			15 02		16 27			16 02	17 02					18 02				20 33		
Gainsborough Lea Road	d		14 40		15 33	15 45			16 38		16 56			17 38	18 38					19 39			20 42	21 00		
Saxilby	d		14 53		15 46	15 58			16 51		17 09			17 51	18 51					19 52			20 55	21 14		
Lincoln	a		15 06		15 57	16 09			17 06		17 20			18 06	19 07					20 06			21 10	21 26		
	d	14 51			15 59			16 55			17 22							19 31								
Metheringham	d	15 03			16 11			17 07			17 34							19 44								
Ruskington	d	15 13			16 21			17 17			17 44							19 54								
Sleaford	a	15 22			16 30			17 28			17 55							20 05								
	d	15 23			16 31																					
Spalding	d	15 47			16 56							18 04					19 53				20 58					
Peterborough 8	a	16 13			17 21							18 29					20 21				21 23					
London Kings Cross 15	⊖ a	*17 28*			*18 28*							*19 40*					*21 48*				*22 47*					

Sundays

		NT	NT	NT	NT
Doncaster 7	d				
Gainsborough Lea Road	d	14 32	16 53	18 53	20 16
Saxilby	d	14 45	17 06	19 06	20 29
Lincoln	a	15 00	17 20	19 21	20 44
	d				
Metheringham	d				
Ruskington	d				
Sleaford	a				
	d				
Spalding	d				
Peterborough 8	a				
London Kings Cross 15	⊖ a				

For general notes see front of timetable
For details of catering facilities see Directory of Train Operators

A From Scunthorpe (Table 29)
B From Newark North Gate (Table 27)
C From Leicester (Table 53)
D To Nottingham (Table 49)
E To Nottingham (Table 19)

Skegness → Grantham and Nottingham

Network Diagram - see first page of Table 18

Mondays to Fridays

Miles	Miles	Station		EM	EM	EM ◇ A	EM	EM ◇	EM	EM ◇	EM	EM ◇	EM	EM ◇	EM	EM ◇	EM	EM ◇
0	—	**Skegness**	d				07 15		08 11		09 38		10 03		11 32		12 06	
3¼	—	Havenhouse	d														12 11	
5	—	Wainfleet	d				07 23		08 19		09 46		10 11		11 40		12 15	
7	—	Thorpe Culvert	d				07 27										12 19	
23¾	—	**Boston**	d		06 16		07 50		08 45		10 14		10 40		12 06		12 42	
27½	—	Hubberts Bridge	d				07 56								12 12			
30¾	—	Swineshead	d				08 01											
35¾	—	Heckington	d		06 30		08 07		08 59		10 28		10 54		12 21		12 56	
40¼	—	**Sleaford**	d		06 37		08 15		09 07		10 37		11 02		12 29		13 04	
42½	—	Rauceby	d		06 41								11 06				13 08	
46¼	0	Ancaster	d		06 47								11 12				13 14	
57¾	—	**Grantham** 7	a		07 07		08 42		09 33				11 33				13 35	
—	—	London Kings Cross 15	⊖ a		*08 34*		*10 10*		*10 51*				*12 44*				*15 20*	
—	—	**Grantham** 7	d	06 09	07 10	07 59	08 46	09 00	09 40	09 59		11 12	11 40	11 57		12 59	13 40	13 57
65¼	12¾	Bottesford	d	06 19	07 20	08 10			09 50				11 50				13 50	
67¾	—	Elton & Orston	d	06 24														
69½	—	Aslockton	d	06 27	07 27	08 17			09 56				11 56				13 56	
71¾	—	Bingham	d	06 32	07 31	08 21	09 03		10 01				12 01				14 01	
75¼	—	Radcliffe (Notts)	d	06 37	07 37	08 27			10 06				12 06				14 06	
77	—	Netherfield	d		07 41	08 31			10 11									
80¼	—	**Nottingham** 8	a	06 48	07 52	08 39	09 22	09 39	10 22	10 28	11 29	11 41	12 22	12 34	13 20	13 28	14 22	14 33

Station		EM	EM ◇	EM	EM ◇	EM	EM ◇	EM	EM ◇	EM	EM ◇	EM	EM ◇	EM	EM ◇	EM	EM
Skegness	d	13 32		14 02		15 32		16 10		17 32		18 22		19 18		20 25	21 10
Havenhouse	d							16 15									
Wainfleet	d	13 40		14 10		15 40		16 19		17 40		18 30		19 26		20 33	21 18
Thorpe Culvert	d							16 24									21 22
Boston	d	14 06		14 39		16 06		16 46		18 06		18 56		19 52		20 58	21 45
Hubberts Bridge	d											19 02					
Swineshead	d											19 07					
Heckington	d	14 20		14 53		16 20		17 00		18 20		19 14		20 10		21 12	
Sleaford	d	14 29		15 03		16 29		17 08		18 29		19 21		20 17		21 20	22 06
Rauceby	d			15 07								19 25					
Ancaster	d			15 13								19 31		20 26			
Grantham 7	a			15 33				17 34				19 50		20 45		21 46	
London Kings Cross 15	⊖ a			*17 04*				*19 11*				*21 33*				*23 32*	
Grantham 7	d		14 58	15 40	15 56		17 02	17 40	18 00		18 56	19 54	20 04	20 49	20 56	21 52	
Bottesford	d			15 50				17 50				20 04		20 59		22 02	
Elton & Orston	d															22 06	
Aslockton	d			15 56				17 56				20 10				22 10	
Bingham	d			16 01				18 01				20 15		21 07		22 14	
Radcliffe (Notts)	d			16 06				18 06				20 20				22 21	
Netherfield	d			16 11								20 25				22 25	
Nottingham 8	a	15 20	15 27	16 22	16 26	17 21	17 38	18 22	18 30	19 20	19 25	20 37	20 44	21 25	21 35	22 37	22 56

Saturdays

Station		EM	EM	EM ◇ B	EM	EM ◇	EM	EM ◇	EM	EM ◇	EM	EM ◇	EM	EM ◇	EM	EM ◇	EM	EM ◇
Skegness	d				07 15		08 11		09 32		10 00		11 32		12 06		13 32	
Havenhouse	d														12 11			
Wainfleet	d				07 23		08 19		09 40		10 08		11 40		12 15		13 40	
Thorpe Culvert	d				07 27										12 19			
Boston	d		06 15		07 50		08 45		10 06		10 40		12 06		12 42		14 06	
Hubberts Bridge	d				07 56								12 12					
Swineshead	d				08 01													
Heckington	d		06 29		08 07		08 59		10 20		10 54		12 21		12 56		14 20	
Sleaford	d		06 37		08 15		09 07		10 29		11 02		12 29		13 04		14 29	
Rauceby	d		06 41								11 06				13 08			
Ancaster	d		06 47								11 12				13 14			
Grantham 7	a		07 06		08 42		09 34				11 42				13 36			
London Kings Cross 15	⊖ a		*08 40*		*10 20*		*10 49*				*13 10*				*15 41*			
Grantham 7	d	06 17	07 10	08 01	08 46	08 57	09 40	10 00		10 58	11 46	11 58		12 59	13 40	13 56		14 58
Bottesford	d	06 28		08 12			09 50				11 56				13 50			
Elton & Orston	d		07 23															
Aslockton	d	06 34	07 26				09 56				12 02				13 56			
Bingham	d	06 39	07 30	08 20	09 03		10 01				12 07				14 01			
Radcliffe (Notts)	d	06 44		08 26			10 06				12 12				14 06			
Netherfield	d	06 49		08 30			10 11				12 17							
Nottingham 8	a	06 56	07 50	08 37	09 22	09 27	10 22	10 37	11 20	11 28	12 29	12 38	13 20	13 28	14 22	14 26	15 20	15 28

For general notes see front of timetable
For details of catering facilities see Directory of Train Operators

A From Norwich (Table 17) to Liverpool Lime Street (Table 49).
⊼ from Nottingham

B From Norwich (Table 17) to Liverpool Lime Street (Table 49)

Table 19

Skegness → Grantham and Nottingham

Network Diagram - see first page of Table 18

Saturdays

		EM	EM ◇	EM	EM ◇	EM	EM ◇	EM	EM ◇	EM	EM ◇	EM	EM ◇	EM	EM A	EM
Skegness	d	14 05		15 32		16 11		17 32		18 21		19 18		20 20		20 59
Havenhouse	d					16 16										
Wainfleet	d	14 13		15 40		16 20		17 40		18 29		19 26		20 28		21 07
Thorpe Culvert	d					16 24								20 32		21 11
Boston	d	14 39		16 06		16 46		18 06		18 55		19 52		20 55		21 33
Hubberts Bridge	d									19 01						
Swineshead	d									19 06						
Heckington	d	14 53		16 20		17 00		18 20		19 13		20 07		21 09		
Sleaford	d	15 03		16 29		17 08		18 29		19 20		20 14		21 17		21 54
Rauceby	d	15 07								19 24						
Ancaster	d	15 13								19 30		20 23				
Grantham 7	a	15 33				17 34				19 49		20 42				22 20
London Kings Cross 15	⊖ a	*17 28*				*20 12*				*21 15*		*22 47*				
Grantham 7	d	15 40	15 56		17 02	17 40	17 55		18 57	19 53	20 02	20 46	21 00		22 02	22 24
Bottesford	d	15 50				17 50				20 03		20 56				22 34
Elton & Orston	d															22 38
Aslockton	d	15 56				17 56				20 09						22 42
Bingham	d	16 01				18 01				20 14		21 04				22 46
Radcliffe (Notts)	d	16 06				18 06				20 19						22 51
Netherfield	d					18 11										22 56
Nottingham 8	🚋 a	16 22	16 25	17 20	17 38	18 22	18 28	19 20	19 26	20 35	20 44	21 22	21 30	22 08	22 33	23 08

Sundays

		EM ◇ B	EM	EM	EM ◇ B	EM	EM ◇ C	EM ◇ C	EM	EM ◇	EM	EM ◇	EM	EM ◇
Skegness	d			14 10		16 12			18 06		19 13			
Havenhouse	d													
Wainfleet	d			14 18		16 20			18 14		19 21			
Thorpe Culvert	d													
Boston	d		12 19	14 43		16 45			18 39		19 48			
Hubberts Bridge	d													
Swineshead	d													
Heckington	d		12 33	14 57		16 59			18 55		20 04			
Sleaford	d		12 40	15 04		17 07			19 02		20 12		21 32	
Rauceby	d													
Ancaster	d													
Grantham 7	a		13 09	15 32		17 33			19 29		20 39		22 00	
London Kings Cross 15	⊖ a		*14 42*	*16 50*		*18 55*			*20 59*		*22 16*		*23 50*	
Grantham 7	d	12 51		15 39	15 59	17 37	17 49	19 00	19 36	19 57	20 42	21 03	22 04	22 51
Bottesford	d	13 01		15 49			17 59		19 46		20 52		22 14	
Elton & Orston	d													
Aslockton	d	13 08		15 55			18 06		19 52		20 59		22 21	
Bingham	d	13 12		16 00			18 10		19 57		21 03		22 25	
Radcliffe (Notts)	d	13 18		16 05			18 16		20 02		21 09		22 31	
Netherfield	d	13 22		16 10			18 20		20 11		21 13		22 35	
Nottingham 8	🚋 a	13 29		16 22	16 29	18 07	18 27	19 30	20 22	20 31	21 26	21 32	22 43	23 29

For general notes see front of timetable
For details of catering facilities see Directory of Train Operators

A From Spalding (Table 18)

B Until 27 January from Norwich to Sheffield (Table 49). From 3 February from Norwich to Liverpool Lime Street (Table 49)

C Until 27 January from Norwich to Sheffield (Table 49). From 3 February from Norwich to Manchester Piccadilly (Table 49)

Table 19

Nottingham and Grantham → Skegness

Network Diagram - see first page of Table 18

Miles	Miles	Station		EM A	EM		EM	EM		EM ◇	EM		EM ◇	EM		EM ◇	EM		EM ◇	EM		EM ◇	EM		EM ◇
0	—	**Nottingham 8**	d	05 09			05 50	06 50		07 52	07 59		08 31	08 50		09 35	09 50		10 31	10 50		11 32	11 50		12 34
4½	—	Netherfield	d				05 56													10 56					
5	—	Radcliffe (Notts)	d				06 01							09 00						11 01					
8½	—	Bingham	d	05 23			06 07	07 04						09 06						11 07					
10¾	—	Aslockton	d	05 27			06 11							09 10						11 11					
14½	—	Elton & Orston	d																						
15	0	Bottesford	d	05 34			06 17	07 14						09 16						11 17					
22½	—	**Grantham 7**	a	05 48			06 30	07 27		08 24			09 07	09 29		10 06			11 03	11 30		12 05			13 08
—	—	London Kings Cross 15	⊖ d					*06 00*						*07 30*						*10 10*					
—	—	**Grantham 7**	d				06 37	07 31						09 35						11 36					
34	12¾	Ancaster	d					07 48						09 52											
37¾	—	Rauceby	d					07 54						09 58											
40	—	**Sleaford**	d				07 03	07 59			08 44			10 05			10 35			12 01			12 41		
44½	—	Heckington	d				07 10	08 05			08 51			10 12			10 42			12 08			12 47		
49½	—	Swineshead	d					08 12																	
52¾	—	Hubberts Bridge	d					08 17																	
56½	—	**Boston**	d		06 33		07 26	08 24			09 06			10b37			10 58			12 23			13 03		
73¼	—	Thorpe Culvert	d				07 47													12 44					
75¼	—	Wainfleet	d		06 56		07 52	08 48			09 30			11 01			11 22			12 49			13 27		
77	—	Havenhouse	d				07 55													12 52					
80¼	—	**Skegness**	a		07 12		08 09	09 04			09 46			11 17			11 38			13 06			13 43		

Station		EM	EM ◇		EM	EM ◇		EM	EM ◇		EM	EM		EM ◇ B	EM		EM ◇	EM		EM ◇	EM				
Nottingham 8	d	12 50	13 31		13 50	14 31		14 50	15 31		15 50	16 50		17 39	17 50		18 31	18 50		20 36	20 51				
Netherfield	d	12 56									15 56	16 56			17 56						20 57				
Radcliffe (Notts)	d	13 00						15 00			16 01	17 01		17 49	18 01			18 59			21 02				
Bingham	d	13 06						15 06			16 07	17 07		17 55	18 07			19 05			21 08				
Aslockton	d	13 10						15 10			16 11	17 11			18 11			19 09			21 12				
Elton & Orston	d	13 14													18 14										
Bottesford	d	13 18						15 16			16 17	17 17			18 19			19 16			21 18				
Grantham 7	a	13 31	14 05			15 05		15 29	16 04		16 30	17 30		18 14	18 32		19 05	19 29		21 07	21 31				
London Kings Cross 15	⊖ d	*12 10*						*14 10*			*15 10*	*16 10*			*17 03*			*18 03*			*20 30*				
Grantham 7	d	13 37						15 35			16 34	17 36			18 35			19 32			21 48				
Ancaster	d	13 54						15 52				17 53						19 50			22 05				
Rauceby	d							15 58				17 59						19 56			22 11				
Sleaford	d	14 09			14 39			16 03			17c08	18 04			19 01			20 00			22 16				
Heckington	d	14 16			14 45			16 09			17 14	18 11			19 08			20 07			22 22				
Swineshead	d							16 16																	
Hubberts Bridge	d							16 21				18 20													
Boston	d	14 36			15 01			16 28			17 31	18 28			19 24			20 22			22a39				
Thorpe Culvert	d							16 49							19 45										
Wainfleet	d	15 00			15 25			16 54			17 55	18 52			19 50			20 46							
Havenhouse	d														19 53										
Skegness	a	15 16			15 41			17 10			18 11	19 08			20 07			21 02							

Saturdays

Station		EM A	EM		EM	EM		EM ◇	EM		EM ◇	EM		EM ◇	EM		EM ◇	EM		EM ◇	EM		EM ◇	EM	EM ◇
Nottingham 8	d	05 09			05 50	06 50		07 39	07 55		08 33	08 50		09 32	09 50		10 31	10 50		11 32	11 50		12 31	12 50	13 31
Netherfield	d				05 56																			12 56	
Radcliffe (Notts)	d				06 01							09 00						11 00						13 00	
Bingham	d	05 22			06 07	07 04						09 06						11 06						13 06	
Aslockton	d	05 27			06 11							09 10						11 10						13 10	
Elton & Orston	d																							13 14	
Bottesford	d	05 35			06 17	07 13						09 16						11 16						13 18	
Grantham 7	a	05 48			06 30	07 26		08 13			09 09	09 29		10 09			11 05	11 29		12 06			13 07	13 31	14 06
London Kings Cross 15	⊖ d											*08 10*						*10 10*						*12 10*	
Grantham 7	d				06 37	07 30						09 35						11 35						13 36	
Ancaster	d					07 47						09 52												13 54	
Rauceby	d					07 53						09 58													
Sleaford	d				07 03	07 58			08 45			10 05			10 35			12 01			12 35			14 09	
Heckington	d				07 10	08 04			08 52			10 12			10 42			12 07			12 42			14 16	
Swineshead	d					08 11																			
Hubberts Bridge	d					08 16																			
Boston	d		06 33		07 26	08 23			09 08			10e34			10 58			12 23			12 58			14f39	
Thorpe Culvert	d				07 47													12 44							
Wainfleet	d		06 56		07 52	08 47			09 32			10 58			11 22			12 49			13 22			15 03	
Havenhouse	d				07 55													12 52							
Skegness	a		07 12		08 09	09 03			09 48			11 14			11 38			13 06			13 40			15 19	

For general notes see front of timetable
For details of catering facilities see Directory of Train Operators

A To Peterborough (Table 26)
B From Liverpool Lime Street to Norwich (Table 49)
b Arr. 1029
c Arr. 1659
e Arr. 1027
f Arr. 1431

Table 19

Saturdays

Nottingham and Grantham → Skegness

Network Diagram - see first page of Table 18

Station		EM	EM ◇	EM	EM ◇	EM	EM	EM ◇ A	EM	EM ◇ A	EM	EM ◇ A	EM
Nottingham 8	d	13 50	14 32	14 50	15 32	15 50	16 50	17 36	17 50	18 31	18 42	20 32	20 59
Netherfield	d					15 56	16 56		17 56				21 05
Radcliffe (Notts)	d			15 00		16 01	17 01	17 46	18 01		18 51		21 10
Bingham	d			15 06		16 07	17 07	17 52	18 07		18 57		21 16
Aslockton	d			15 10		16 11	17 11		18 11		19 01		21 20
Elton & Orston	d								18 14				21 23
Bottesford	d			15 16		16 17	17 17		18 19		19 08		21 28
Grantham 7	a		15 05	15 29	16 05	16 30	17 30	18 12	18 32	19 05	19 21	21 09	21 41
London Kings Cross 15	⊖ d			*13 38*		*14 30*	*15 30*		*17 05*		*17 40*		*20 30*
Grantham 7	d			15 35		16 34	17 36		18 35		19 24		21 45
Ancaster	d			15 52			17 53				19 42		22 02
Rauceby	d			15 58			17 59				19 48		22 08
Sleaford	d	14 39		16 03		17b08	18 04		19 01		19 52		22 13
Heckington	d	14 45		16 09		17 14	18 11		19 08		19 59		22 19
Swineshead	d			16 16									
Hubberts Bridge	d			16 21			18 20						
Boston	d	15 01		16 28		17 31	18 28		19 24		20 14		22a34
Thorpe Culvert	d			16 49					19 45				
Wainfleet	d	15 25		16 54		17 55	18 52		19 50		20 38		
Havenhouse	d								19 53				
Skegness	a	15 41		17 10		18 11	19 08		20 07		20 54		

Sundays

Station		EM	EM ◇ B	EM	EM ◇	EM	EM ◇	EM	EM ◇	EM ◇	EM	EM ◇	EM	EM ◇ C
Nottingham 8	d	12 00	12 32		13 44	14 44	15 48	16 22	16 40	17 38	18 23	18 46	19 41	20 35
Netherfield	d		12 38			14 50		16 28			18 30		19 47	20 42
Radcliffe (Notts)	d		12 43			14 55		16 33			18 35		19 52	20 46
Bingham	d		12 49			15 01		16 39			18 41		19 58	20 52
Aslockton	d		12 53			15 05		16 43			18 45		20 02	20 56
Elton & Orston	d													
Bottesford	d		13 00			15 12		16 49			18 52		20 08	21 03
Grantham 7	a	12 34	13 13		14 17	15 27	16 23	17 03	17 15	18 13	19 07	19 20	20 21	21 18
London Kings Cross 15	⊖ d	*10 42*		*12 10*		*14 10*		*15 30*			*18 00*		*19 10*	
Grantham 7	d	12 38		13 29		15 34		17 06			19 13		20 27	
Ancaster	d													
Rauceby	d													
Sleaford	d	13 04		13 55		16 04		17 35			19 40		20a52	
Heckington	d	13 10		14 01		16 10		17 41			19 47			
Swineshead	d													
Hubberts Bridge	d													
Boston	d	13 26		14 17		16 26		17 58			20a05			
Thorpe Culvert	d													
Wainfleet	d	13 50		14 41		16 49		18 21						
Havenhouse	d													
Skegness	a	14 06		14 57		17 05		18 37						

For general notes see front of timetable
For details of catering facilities see Directory of Train Operators

A From Liverpool Lime Street to Norwich (Table 49)
B To Norwich (Table 49)
C Until 27 January from Sheffield (Table 49) to Norwich (Table 17). From 3 February from Liverpool Lime Street (Table 49) to Norwich (Table 17)
b Arr. 1659

Network Diagram for Tables 20, 21, 22

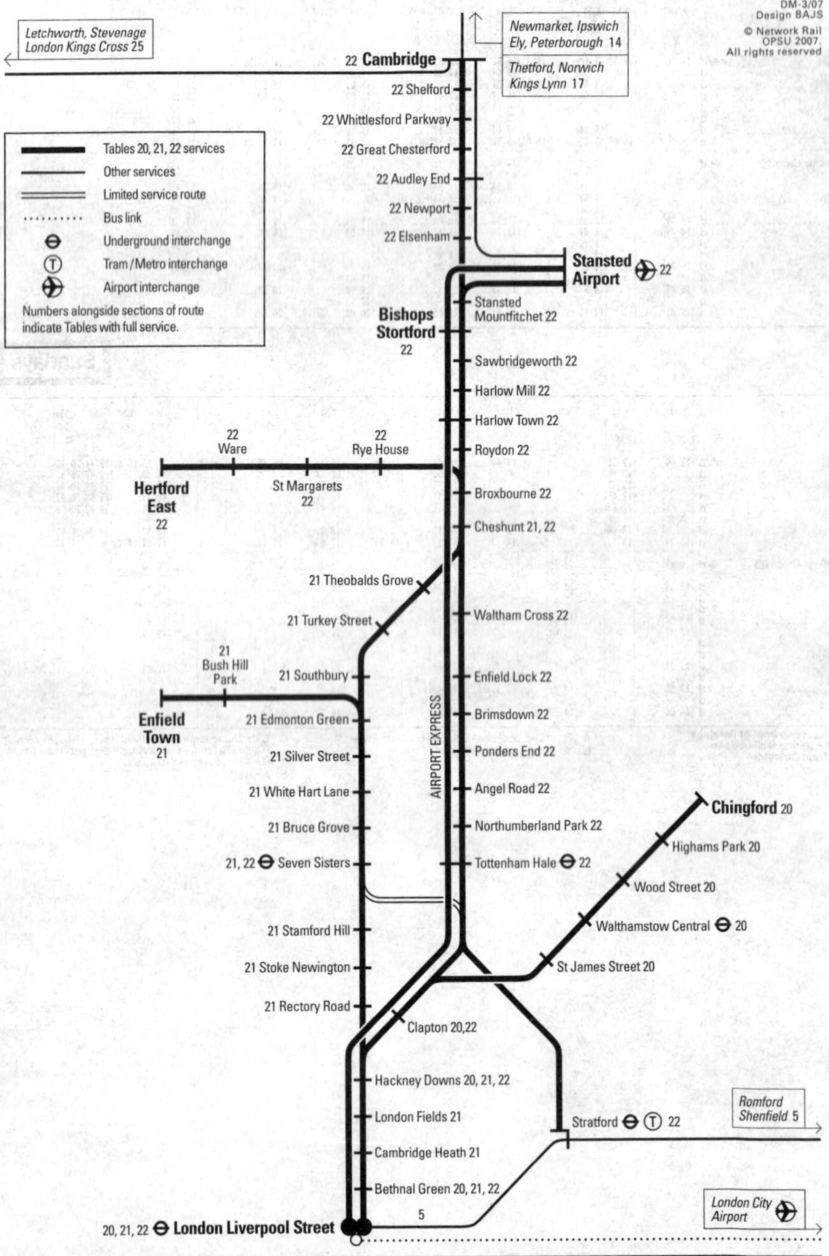

DM-3/07
Design BAJS
© Network Rail
OPSU 2007.
All rights reserved
Letchworth, Stevenage
London Kings Cross 25
Newmarket, Ipswich
Ely, Peterborough 14
Thetford, Norwich
Kings Lynn 17
22 Cambridge
22 Shelford
22 Whittlesford Parkway
22 Great Chesterford
22 Audley End
22 Newport
22 Elsenham
Stansted Airport 22
Stansted Mountfitchet 22
Bishops Stortford 22
Sawbridgeworth 22
Harlow Mill 22
Harlow Town 22
Roydon 22
22 Ware
22 Rye House
Hertford East 22
St Margarets 22
Broxbourne 22
Cheshunt 21, 22
21 Theobalds Grove
21 Turkey Street
Waltham Cross 22
21 Bush Hill Park
21 Southbury
Enfield Town 21
21 Edmonton Green
Enfield Lock 22
Brimsdown 22
Ponders End 22
Angel Road 22
AIRPORT EXPRESS
21 Silver Street
21 White Hart Lane
21 Bruce Grove
21, 22 Seven Sisters
Northumberland Park 22
Tottenham Hale 22
Chingford 20
Highams Park 20
Wood Street 20
Walthamstow Central 20
St James Street 20
21 Stamford Hill
21 Stoke Newington
21 Rectory Road
Clapton 20,22
Hackney Downs 20, 21, 22
London Fields 21
Cambridge Heath 21
Bethnal Green 20, 21, 22
Stratford 22
Romford
Shenfield 5
5
20, 21, 22 London Liverpool Street
London City Airport
Tables 20, 21, 22 services
Other services
Limited service route
Bus link
Underground interchange
Tram / Metro interchange
Airport interchange
Numbers alongside sections of route indicate Tables with full service.

London → Chingford

Network diagram - see first page of Table 20

Mondays to Fridays

Miles	Station		LE	LE MX	LE MO	LE MX	LE MX	LE	LE	LE	LE	LE	LE	LE	LE		LE	LE
0	**London Liverpool Street** [15] ⊖	d	00 01	00 15	00 30	00 30	00 45	01 00	06 00	06 30	07 00	07 30	07 45	08 00	08 15	and	15 30	15 45
1¼	Bethnal Green	d	00 04	00 18	00 33	00 33			06 03	06 33	07 03	07 33	07 48	08 03	08 18	every 15	15 33	15 48
3	Hackney Downs	d	00 08	00 22	00 37	00 37	00 52	01 07	06 07	06 37	07 07	07 37	07 52	08 07	08 22		15 37	15 52
4	Clapton	d	00 11	00 25	00 40	00 40	00 55	01 10	06 10	06 40	07 10	07 40	07 55	08 10	08 25	minutes	15 40	15 55
5¾	St James Street	d	00 14	00 28	00 43	00 43	00 58	01 13	06 13	06 43	07 13	07 43	07 58	08 13	08 28		15 43	15 58
6¼	Walthamstow Central ⊖	d	00 16	00 30	00 45	00 45	01 00	01 15	06 15	06 45	07 15	07 45	08 00	08 15	08 30	until	15 45	16 00
7	Wood Street	d	00 18	00 32	00 47	00 47	01 02	01 17	06 17	06 47	07 17	07 47	08 02	08 17	08 32		15 47	16 02
8½	Highams Park	d	00 21	00 35	00 50	00 50	01 05	01 20	06 20	06 50	07 20	07 50	08 05	08 20	08 35		15 50	16 05
10½	**Chingford**	a	00 28	00 42	00 57	00 58	01 12	01 27	06 27	06 57	07 27	07 57	08 12	08 27	08 42		15 57	16 12

Station		LE	LE	LE	LE	LE	LE	LE	LE	LE	LE	LE	LE	LE	LE	LE	LE	LE
London Liverpool Street [15] ⊖	d	16 00	16 20	16 35	16 50	17 05	17 20	17 35	17 50	18 05	18 20	18 35	18 50	19 05	19 20	19 30	19 45	20 00
Bethnal Green	d	16 03	16 23		16 53		17 23		17 53		18 23		18 53		19 23	19 33	19 48	20 03
Hackney Downs	d	16 07	16 27	16 42	16 57	17 12	17 27	17 42	17 57	18 12	18 27	18 42	18 57	19 12	19 27	19 37	19 52	20 07
Clapton	d	16 10	16 30	16 45	17 00	17 15	17 30	17 45	18 00	18 15	18 30	18 45	19 00	19 15	19 30	19 40	19 55	20 10
St James Street	d	16 13	16 33	16 48	17 03	17 18	17 33	17 48	18 03	18 18	18 33	18 48	19 03	19 18	19 33	19 43	19 58	20 13
Walthamstow Central ⊖	d	16 16	16 36	16 51	17 06	17 21	17 36	17 51	18 06	18 21	18 36	18 51	19 06	19 21	19 35	19 45	20 00	20 15
Wood Street	d	16 18	16 38	16 53	17 08	17 23	17 38	17 53	18 08	18 23	18 38	18 53	19 08	19 23	19 37	19 47	20 02	20 17
Highams Park	d	16 21	16 41	16 56	17 11	17 26	17 41	17 56	18 11	18 26	18 41	18 56	19 11	19 26	19 40	19 50	20 05	20 20
Chingford	a	16 27	16 47	17 02	17 17	17 32	17 47	18 03	18 17	18 33	18 47	19 03	19 17	19 32	19 47	19 57	20 12	20 27

Station		LE	LE	LE	LE	LE	LE	LE	LE	LE	LE	LE	LE	LE	LE
London Liverpool Street [15] ⊖	d	20 15	20 30	20 45	21 00	21 15	21 30	21 45	22 00	22 15	22 30	22 45	23 00	23 15	23 30
Bethnal Green	d	20 18	20 33	20 48	21 03	21 18	21 33	21 48	22 03	22 18	22 33	22 48	23 03	23 18	
Hackney Downs	d	20 22	20 37	20 52	21 07	21 22	21 37	21 52	22 07	22 22	22 37	22 52	23 07	23 22	
Clapton	d	20 25	20 40	20 55	21 10	21 25	21 40	21 55	22 10	22 25	22 40	22 55	23 10	23 25	
St James Street	d	20 28	20 43	20 58	21 13	21 28	21 43	21 58	22 13	22 28	22 43	22 58	23 13	23 28	23 41
Walthamstow Central ⊖	d	20 30	20 45	21 00	21 15	21 30	21 45	22 00	22 15	22 30	22 45	23 00	23 15	23 30	23 43
Wood Street	d	20 32	20 47	21 02	21 17	21 32	21 47	22 02	22 17	22 32	22 47	23 02	23 17	23 32	23 45
Highams Park	d	20 35	20 50	21 05	21 20	21 35	21 50	22 05	22 20	22 35	22 50	23 05	23 20	23 35	23 48
Chingford	a	20 42	20 57	21 12	21 27	21 42	21 57	22 12	22 27	22 42	22 57	23 12	23 27	23 42	23 55

Saturdays

Station		LE	LE	LE	LE	LE	LE	LE	LE	LE	LE		LE	LE	LE	LE	LE
London Liverpool Street [15] ⊖	d	00 01	00 15	00 30	00 45	01 00	06 00	06 30	06 45	07 00	07 15	and	22 30	22 45	23 00	23 15	23 30
Bethnal Green	d	00 04	00 18	00 33			06 03	06 33	06 48	07 03	07 18	every 15	22 33	22 48	23 03	23 18	
Hackney Downs	d	00 08	00 22	00 37	00 52	01 07	06 07	06 37	06 52	07 07	07 22		22 37	22 52	23 07	23 22	
Clapton	d	00 11	00 25	00 40	00 55	01 10	06 10	06 40	06 55	07 10	07 25	minutes	22 40	22 55	23 10	23 25	
St James Street	d	00 14	00 28	00 43	00 58	01 13	06 13	06 43	06 58	07 13	07 28		22 43	22 58	23 13	23 28	23 41
Walthamstow Central ⊖	d	00 16	00 30	00 45	01 00	01 15	06 15	06 45	07 00	07 15	07 30	until	22 45	23 00	23 15	23 30	23 43
Wood Street	d	00 18	00 32	00 47	01 02	01 17	06 17	06 47	07 02	07 17	07 32		22 47	23 02	23 17	23 32	23 45
Highams Park	d	00 21	00 35	00 50	01 05	01 20	06 20	06 50	07 05	07 20	07 35		22 50	23 05	23 20	23 35	23 48
Chingford	a	00 28	00 42	00 58	01 12	01 27	06 27	06 57	07 12	07 27	07 42		22 57	23 12	23 27	23 42	23 55

Sundays

Station		LE	LE	LE	LE	LE	LE	LE	LE	LE	LE	LE	LE	LE		LE	LE	LE
London Liverpool Street [15] ⊖	d	00 01	00 15	00 30	01 00	07 30	08 00	08 30	08 45	09 00	09 15	09 30	09 45	10 00	and	18 15	18 30	18 45
Bethnal Green	d	00 04	00 18	00 33							09 18	09 33	09 48	10 03	every 15	18 18	18 33	18 48
Hackney Downs	d	00 08	00 22	00 37	01 07	07 37	08 07	08 37	08 52	09 07	09 22	09 37	09 52	10 07		18 22	18 37	18 52
Clapton	d	00 11	00 25	00 40	01 10	07 40	08 10	08 40	08 55	09 10	09 25	09 40	09 55	10 10	minutes	18 25	18 40	18 55
St James Street	d	00 14	00 28	00 43	01 13	07 43	08 13	08 43	08 58	09 13	09 28	09 43	09 58	10 13		18 28	18 43	18 58
Walthamstow Central ⊖	d	00 16	00 30	00 45	01 15	07 45	08 15	08 45	09 00	09 15	09 30	09 45	10 00	10 15	until	18 30	18 45	19 00
Wood Street	d	00 18	00 32	00 47	01 17	07 47	08 17	08 47	09 02	09 17	09 32	09 47	10 02	10 17		18 32	18 47	19 02
Highams Park	d	00 21	00 35	00 50	01 20	07 50	08 20	08 50	09 05	09 20	09 35	09 50	10 05	10 20		18 35	18 50	19 05
Chingford	a	00 28	00 42	00 57	01 27	07 57	08 27	08 59	09 12	09 27	09 42	09 57	10 12	10 27		18 42	18 57	19 12

Station		LE	LE	LE	LE	LE	LE	LE	LE	LE	LE
London Liverpool Street [15] ⊖	d	19 00	19 30	20 00	20 30	21 00	21 30	22 00	22 30	23 00	23 30
Bethnal Green	d	19 03	19 33	20 03	20 33	21 03	21 33	22 03	22 33	23 03	23 33
Hackney Downs	d	19 07	19 37	20 07	20 37	21 07	21 37	22 07	22 37	23 07	23 37
Clapton	d	19 10	19 40	20 10	20 40	21 10	21 40	22 10	22 40	23 10	23 40
St James Street	d	19 13	19 43	20 13	20 43	21 13	21 43	22 13	22 43	23 13	23 43
Walthamstow Central ⊖	d	19 15	19 45	20 15	20 45	21 15	21 45	22 15	22 45	23 15	23 45
Wood Street	d	19 17	19 47	20 17	20 47	21 17	21 47	22 17	22 47	23 17	23 47
Highams Park	d	19 20	19 50	20 20	20 50	21 20	21 50	22 20	22 50	23 20	23 50
Chingford	a	19 27	19 57	20 27	20 57	21 27	21 57	22 27	22 57	23 27	23 57

For general notes see front of timetable
For details of catering facilities see Directory of Train Operators

Chingford → London

Network diagram - see first page of Table 20

Miles	Station		LE	LE	LE	LE		LE	LE	LE	LE		LE	LE	LE	LE		LE	LE	LE	LE		LE	LE	
0	**Chingford**	d	05 12	05 27	05 42	05 57		06 12	06 27	06 42	06 57		07 12	07 24	07 42	07 54		08 12	08 27	08 42	08 57		09 12	09 27	
2	Highams Park	d	05 15	05 30	05 45	06 00		06 15	06 31	06 46	07 01		07 16	07 28	07 46	07 58		08 16	08 31	08 46	09 01		09 16	09 31	
3½	Wood Street	d	05 18	05 33	05 48	06 03		06 18	06 34	06 49	07 04		07 19	07 31	07 49	08 01		08 19	08 34	08 49	09 04		09 19	09 34	
4¼	Walthamstow Central ⊖	d	05 20	05 35	05 50	06 05		06 20	06 37	06 52	07 07		07 22	07 34	07 52	08 04		08 22	08 37	08 52	09 07		09 22	09 37	
4¾	St James Street	d	05 22	05 37	05 52	06 07		06 22	06 39	06 54	07 09		07 24	07 36	07 54	08 06		08 24	08 39	08 54	09 09		09 24	09 39	
6¼	Clapton	d	05 26	05 41	05 56	06 11		06 26	06 44	06 59	07 14		07 29	07 41	07 59	08 11		08 29	08 44	08 59	09 14		09 29	09 44	
7½	Hackney Downs	d	05 28	05 43	05 58	06 13		06 28	06 46	07 01	07 16		07 31	07 43	08 01	08 13		08 31	08 46	09 01	09 16		09 31	09 46	
9¼	Bethnal Green	d	05 32	05 47	06 02	06 17		06 32	06 50		07 20			07 48		08 17			08 50		09 20			09 50	
10½	**London Liverpool Street** 15 ⊖	a	05 39	05 53	06 08	06 23		06 38	06 56	07 10	07 26		07 40	07 54	08 10	08 23		08 40	08 56	09 10	09 26		09 40	09 56	

Station			LE	LE	LE	LE			LE	LE	LE	LE		LE	LE	LE	LE		LE	LE	LE	LE		LE
Chingford	d		09 42	09 57	10 12	10 27	and every 15 minutes until		15 42	15 57	16 12	16 27		16 42	16 57	17 12	17 27		17 42	17 57	18 12	18 27		18 42
Highams Park	d		09 45	10 00	10 15	10 30			15 45	16 00	16 15	16 30		16 45	17 00	17 15	17 30		17 45	18 00	18 15	18 30		18 45
Wood Street	d		09 48	10 03	10 18	10 33			15 48	16 03	16 18	16 33		16 48	17 03	17 18	17 33		17 48	18 03	18 18	18 33		18 48
Walthamstow Central ⊖	d		09 50	10 05	10 20	10 35			15 50	16 05	16 20	16 35		16 50	17 05	17 20	17 35		17 50	18 05	18 20	18 35		18 50
St James Street	d		09 52	10 07	10 22	10 37			15 52	16 07	16 22	16 37		16 52	17 07	17 22	17 37		17 52	18 07	18 22	18 37		18 52
Clapton	d		09 56	10 11	10 26	10 41			15 56	16 11	16 26	16 41		16 56	17 11	17 26	17 41		17 56	18 11	18 26	18 41		18 56
Hackney Downs	d		09 58	10 13	10 28	10 43			15 58	16 13	16 28	16 43		16 58	17 13	17 28	17 43		17 58	18 13	18 28	18 43		18 58
Bethnal Green	d		10 02	10 17	10 32	10 47			16 02	16 17	16 32	16 49			17 19	17 32	17 49		18 02	18 19	18 32	18 49		19 02
London Liverpool Street 15 ⊖	a		10 08	10 24	10 38	10 53			16 08	16 23	16 38	16 55		17 08	17 25	17 38	17 55		18 08	18 25	18 38	18 55		19 08

Station		LE	LE	LE	LE		LE	LE	LE	LE		LE	LE	LE	LE		LE	LE	LE	LE		LE	LE	LE	
Chingford	d	18 57	19 12	19 27	19 42		19 57	20 12	20 27	20 42		20 57	21 12	21 27	21 42		21 57	22 12	22 27	22 42		22 57	23 12	23 27	
Highams Park	d	19 00	19 15	19 30	19 45		20 00	20 15	20 30	20 45		21 00	21 15	21 30	21 45		22 00	22 15	22 30	22 45		23 00	23 15	23 30	
Wood Street	d	19 03	19 18	19 33	19 48		20 03	20 18	20 33	20 48		21 03	21 18	21 33	21 48		22 03	22 18	22 33	22 48		23 03	23 18	23 33	
Walthamstow Central ⊖	d	19 05	19 20	19 35	19 50		20 05	20 20	20 35	20 50		21 05	21 20	21 35	21 50		22 05	22 20	22 35	22 50		23 05	23 20	23 35	
St James Street	d	19 07	19 22	19 37	19 52		20 07	20 22	20 37	20 52		21 07	21 22	21 37	21 52		22 07	22 22	22 37	22 52		23 07	23 22	23 37	
Clapton	d	19 11	19 26	19 41	19 56		20 11	20 26	20 41	20 56		21 11	21 26	21 41	21 56		22 11	22 26	22 41	22 56		23 11	23 26	23 41	
Hackney Downs	d	19 13	19 28	19 43	19 58		20 13	20 28	20 43	20 58		21 13	21 28	21 43	21 58		22 13	22 28	22 43	22 58		23 13	23 28	23 43	
Bethnal Green	d	19 17	19 32	19 47	20 02		20 17	20 32	20 47	21 02		21 17	21 32	21 47	22 02		22 17	22 32	22 47	23 02		23 17	23 32	23 47	
London Liverpool Street 15 ⊖	a	19 23	19 38	19 53	20 08		20 24	20 38	20 53	21 08		21 23	21 38	21 53	22 08		22 23	22 38	22 53	23 08		23 23	23 38	23 53	

Saturdays

Station		LE		LE			LE	LE	LE	LE			LE		LE		LE		LE		LE			
Chingford	d	05 12		05 42			06 12	06 27	06 42	06 57	and every 15 minutes until		22 12		22 27		22 57		23 12		23 27			
Highams Park	d	05 15		05 45			06 15	06 30	06 45	07 00			22 15		22 30		23 00		23 15		23 30			
Wood Street	d	05 18		05 48			06 18	06 33	06 48	07 03			22 18		22 33		23 03		23 18		23 33			
Walthamstow Central ⊖	d	05 20		05 50			06 20	06 35	06 50	07 05			22 20		22 35		23 05		23 20		23 35			
St James Street	d	05 22		05 52			06 22	06 37	06 52	07 07			22 22		22 37		23 07		23 22		23 37			
Clapton	d	05 26		05 56			06 26	06 41	06 56	07 11			22 26		22 41		23 11		23 26		23 41			
Hackney Downs	d	05 28		05 58			06 28	06 43	06 58	07 13			22 28		22 43		23 13		23 28		23 43			
Bethnal Green	d	05 32		06 02			06 32	06 47	07 02	07 17			22 32		22 47		23 17		23 32		23 47			
London Liverpool Street 15 ⊖	a	05 38		06 08			06 38	06 53	07 08	07 23			22 38		22 53		23 23		23 38		23 53			

Sundays

Station		LE	LE		LE	LE		LE	LE		LE	LE		LE		LE	LE	LE	LE			LE	LE	LE
Chingford	d	06 42	06 57		07 12	07 27		07 42	07 57		08 12	08 27		08 42		08 57	09 12	09 27	09 42	and every 15 minutes until		17 57	18 12	18 27
Highams Park	d	06 45	07 00		07 15	07 30		07 45	08 00		08 15	08 30		08 45		09 00	09 15	09 30	09 45			18 00	18 15	18 30
Wood Street	d	06 48	07 03		07 18	07 33		07 48	08 03		08 18	08 33		08 48		09 03	09 18	09 33	09 48			18 03	18 18	18 33
Walthamstow Central ⊖	d	06 50	07 05		07 20	07 35		07 50	08 05		08 20	08 35		08 50		09 05	09 20	09 35	09 50			18 05	18 20	18 35
St James Street	d	06 52	07 07		07 22	07 37		07 52	08 07		08 22	08 37		08 52		09 07	09 22	09 37	09 52			18 07	18 22	18 37
Clapton	d	06 56	07 11		07 26	07 41		07 56	08 11		08 26	08 41		08 56		09 11	09 26	09 41	09 56			18 11	18 26	18 41
Hackney Downs	d	06 58	07 13		07 28	07 43		07 58	08 13		08 28	08 43		08 58		09 13	09 28	09 43	09 58			18 13	18 28	18 43
Bethnal Green	d															09 17	09 32	09 47	10 02			18 17	18 32	18 47
London Liverpool Street 15 ⊖	a	07 08	07 23		07 38	07 53		08 09	08 23		08 40	08 53		09 09		09 23	09 38	09 53	10 08			18 23	18 38	18 53

Station		LE		LE	LE		LE	LE		LE	LE		LE	LE		LE
Chingford	d	18 42		19 12	19 42		20 12	20 42		21 12	21 42		22 12	22 42		23 12
Highams Park	d	18 45		19 15	19 45		20 15	20 45		21 15	21 45		22 15	22 45		23 15
Wood Street	d	18 48		19 18	19 48		20 18	20 48		21 18	21 48		22 18	22 48		23 18
Walthamstow Central ⊖	d	18 50		19 20	19 50		20 20	20 50		21 20	21 50		22 20	22 50		23 20
St James Street	d	18 52		19 22	19 52		20 22	20 52		21 22	21 52		22 22	22 52		23 22
Clapton	d	18 56		19 26	19 56		20 26	20 56		21 26	21 56		22 26	22 56		23 26
Hackney Downs	d	18 58		19 28	19 58		20 28	20 58		21 28	21 58		22 28	22 58		23 28
Bethnal Green	d	19 02		19 32	20 02		20 32	21 02		21 32	22 02		22 32	23 02		23 32
London Liverpool Street 15 ⊖	a	19 08		19 38	20 08		20 38	21 08		21 38	22 08		22 38	23 08		23 38

For general notes see front of timetable
For details of catering facilities see
Directory of Train Operators

London → Cheshunt (via Seven Sisters) and Enfield Town

Network diagram - see first page of Table 20

Miles	Miles			LE MO	LE MX	LE MX A	LE MX	LE	LE	LE	LE	LE	LE	LE	LE	LE	LE	LE	LE	LE
0	0	**London Liverpool Street** 15	⊖ d	23p33	23p33	23p48	00 03	05 48	06 03	06 14	06 18	06 33	06 44	06 48	07 04	07 14	07 18	07 33	07 44	07 49
1¼	1¼	Bethnal Green	d	23p36	23p36	23p51	00 07	05 51	06 06		06 21	06 36		06 52	07 07		07 22	07 36		07 52
1¾	1¾	Cambridge Heath	d	23p38	23p38	23p53	00 09	05 53	06 08		06 23	06 38		06 54	07 09		07 24	07 38		07 54
2½	2½	London Fields	d	23p40	23p40	23p55	00 11	05 55	06 10		06 25	06 40		06 56	07 11		07 26	07 40		07 56
3	3	Hackney Downs	d	23p42	23p42	23p57	00 13	05 57	06 12	06 21	06 27	06 42	06 51	06 58	07 13	07 21	07 28	07 42	07 51	07 58
3¾	3¾	Rectory Road	d	23p45	23p45	23p59	00 16	06 00	06 15		06 30	06 45		07 00	07 16		07 30	07 45		08 01
4¼	4¼	Stoke Newington	d	23p46	23p46	00 01	00 17	06 01	06 16	06 24	06 31	06 46	06 54	07 02	07 17	07 24	07 32	07 46	07 54	08 02
5	5	Stamford Hill	d	23p48	23p48	00 03	00 19	06 03	06 18		06 33	06 48		07 04	07 19		07 34	07 48		08 04
5½	5½	Seven Sisters	⊖ d	23p50	23p50	00 05	00 21	06 05	06 20	06 27	06 35	06 50	06 57	07 06	07 21	07 27	07 36	07 50	07 57	08 06
6¼	6¼	Bruce Grove	d	23p52	23p52	00 07	00 23	06 07	06 22	06 29	06 37	06 52	06 59	07 08	07 23	07 29	07 38	07 52	07 59	08 08
7¼	7¼	White Hart Lane	d	23p54	23p54	00 09	00 25	06 09	06 24	06 31	06 39	06 54	07 01	07 10	07 25	07 31	07 40	07 54	08 01	08 10
8	8	Silver Street	d	23p56	23p56	00 11	00 27	06 11	06 26	06 33	06 41	06 56	07 03	07 12	07 27	07 33	07 42	07 56	08 03	08 12
8½	8½	Edmonton Green	d	23p58	23p58	00 13	00 29	06 13	06 28	06 35	06 43	06 58	07 05	07 14	07 29	07 35	07 44	07 58	08 05	08 14
—	9¾	Bush Hill Park	d	00 01	00 01		00 32		06 31		06 46	07 01		07 16	07 32		07 46	08 01		08 17
—	10¾	**Enfield Town**	a	00 05	00 06		00 35		06 36		06 51	07 06		07 21	07 37		07 51	08 06		08 22
10½	—	Southbury	d			00 16		06 16		06 38			07 08			07 38			08 08	
12¼	—	Turkey Street	d			00 19		06 19		06 41			07 11			07 41			08 11	
13½	—	Theobalds Grove	d			00 22		06 22		06 43			07 13			07 43			08 13	
14½	—	**Cheshunt**	a			00 25		06 26		06 49			07 20			07 50			08 20	

		LE	LE	LE	LE	LE	LE	LE	LE	LE	LE	LE		LE	LE	LE	LE	LE	LE
London Liverpool Street 15	⊖ d	08 03	08 14	08 18	08 33	08 44	08 48	09 03	09 18	09 33	09 48	10 03	and at	15 18	15 33	15 48	16 03	16 14	16 23
Bethnal Green	d	08 06		08 22	08 36		08 52	09 06	09 21	09 36	09 51	10 06	the same	15 21	15 36	15 51	16 06	16 17	16 26
Cambridge Heath	d	08 08		08 24	08 38		08 54	09 08	09 23	09 38	09 53	10 08	minutes	15 23	15 38	15 53	16 08	16 19	16 28
London Fields	d	08 10		08 26	08 40		08 56	09 10	09 25	09 40	09 55	10 10	past	15 25	15 40	15 55	16 10	16 21	16 30
Hackney Downs	d	08 12	08 21	08 28	08 42	08 51	08 58	09 12	09 27	09 42	09 57	10 12	each	15 27	15 42	15 57	16 12	16 23	16 32
Rectory Road	d	08 15		08 30	08 45		09 00	09 15	09 30	09 45	10 00	10 15	hour until	15 30	15 45	16 00	16 15	16 26	16 35
Stoke Newington	d	08 16	08 24	08 32	08 46	08 54	09 02	09 16	09 31	09 46	10 01	10 16		15 31	15 46	16 01	16 16	16 27	16 36
Stamford Hill	d	08 18		08 34	08 48		09 04	09 18	09 33	09 48	10 03	10 18		15 33	15 48	16 03	16 18	16 29	16 38
Seven Sisters	⊖ d	08 20	08 27	08 36	08 50	08 57	09 06	09 20	09 35	09 50	10 05	10 20		15 35	15 50	16 05	16 20	16 32	16 41
Bruce Grove	d	08 22	08 29	08 38	08 52	08 59	09 08	09 22	09 37	09 52	10 07	10 22		15 37	15 52	16 07	16 22	16 34	16 43
White Hart Lane	d	08 24	08 31	08 40	08 54	09 01	09 10	09 24	09 39	09 54	10 09	10 24		15 39	15 54	16 09	16 24	16 36	16 45
Silver Street	d	08 26	08 33	08 42	08 56	09 03	09 12	09 26	09 41	09 56	10 11	10 26		15 41	15 56	16 11	16 26	16 38	16 47
Edmonton Green	d	08 28	08 35	08 44	08 58	09 05	09 14	09 28	09 43	09 58	10 13	10 28		15 43	15 58	16 13	16 28	16 40	16 49
Bush Hill Park	d	08 31		08 46	09 01		09 16	09 31		10 01		10 31			16 01		16 31		16 52
Enfield Town	a	08 36		08 51	09 06		09 22	09 36		10 06		10 36			16 06		16 36		16 56
Southbury	d		08 38			09 08			09 46		10 16			15 46		16 16		16 43	
Turkey Street	d		08 41			09 11			09 49		10 19			15 49		16 19		16 46	
Theobalds Grove	d		08 43			09 13			09 52		10 22			15 52		16 22		16 49	
Cheshunt	a		08 49			09 20			09 56		10 26			15 56		16 26		16 52	

		LE	LE	LE	LE	LE	LE	LE	LE	LE	LE	LE	LE	LE	LE	LE	LE	LE	LE
London Liverpool Street 15	⊖ d	16 33	16 44	16 53	17 03	17 14	17 23	17 33	17 44	17 53	18 03	18 14	18 23	18 33	18 44	18 53	19 03	19 18	19 33
Bethnal Green	d	16 36		16 56	17 06		17 26	17 36		17 56	18 06		18 26	18 36		18 56	19 06	19 21	19 36
Cambridge Heath	d	16 38	16 49	16 58	17 08	17 19	17 28	17 38	17 49	17 58	18 08	18 19	18 28	18 38	18 49	18 58	19 08	19 23	19 38
London Fields	d	16 40	16 51	17 00	17 10	17 21	17 30	17 40	17 51	18 00	18 10	18 21	18 30	18 40	18 51	19 00	19 10	19 25	19 40
Hackney Downs	d	16 42	16 53	17 02	17 12	17 23	17 32	17 42	17 53	18 02	18 12	18 23	18 32	18 42	18 53	19 02	19 12	19 27	19 42
Rectory Road	d	16 45	16 55	17 05	17 15	17 25	17 35	17 45	17 55	18 05	18 15	18 25	18 35	18 45	18 55	19 05	19 15	19 30	19 45
Stoke Newington	d	16 46	16 57	17 06	17 16	17 27	17 36	17 46	17 57	18 06	18 16	18 27	18 36	18 46	18 57	19 06	19 16	19 31	19 46
Stamford Hill	d	16 48	16 59	17 08	17 18	17 29	17 38	17 48	17 59	18 08	18 18	18 29	18 38	18 48	18 59	19 08	19 18	19 33	19 48
Seven Sisters	⊖ d	16 51	17 02	17 11	17 21	17 32	17 41	17 51	18 02	18 11	18 21	18 32	18 41	18 51	19 02	19 11	19 20	19 35	19 50
Bruce Grove	d	16 53	17 04	17 13	17 23	17 34	17 43	17 53	18 04	18 13	18 23	18 34	18 43	18 53	19 04	19 13	19 22	19 37	19 52
White Hart Lane	d	16 55	17 06	17 15	17 25	17 36	17 45	17 55	18 06	18 15	18 25	18 36	18 45	18 55	19 06	19 15	19 24	19 39	19 54
Silver Street	d	16 57	17 08	17 17	17 27	17 38	17 47	17 57	18 08	18 17	18 27	18 38	18 47	18 57	19 08	19 17	19 26	19 41	19 56
Edmonton Green	d	16 59	17 10	17 19	17 29	17 40	17 49	17 59	18 10	18 19	18 29	18 40	18 49	18 59	19 10	19 19	19 28	19 43	19 58
Bush Hill Park	d	17 02		17 22	17 32		17 52	18 02		18 22	18 32		18 52	19 02		19 22	19 31		20 01
Enfield Town	a	17 06		17 26	17 36		17 56	18 06		18 26	18 36		18 56	19 06		19 26	19 36		20 06
Southbury	d		17 13			17 43			18 13			18 43			19 13			19 46	
Turkey Street	d		17 16			17 46			18 16			18 46			19 16			19 49	
Theobalds Grove	d		17 19			17 49			18 19			18 49			19 19			19 52	
Cheshunt	a		17 22			17 52			18 22			18 52			19 22			19 56	

		LE	LE	LE	LE	LE	LE	LE	LE	LE	LE	LE	LE	LE	LE	LE	LE	LE A
London Liverpool Street 15	⊖ d	19 48	20 03	20 18	20 33	20 48	21 03	21 18	21 33	21 48	22 03	22 18	22 33	22 48	23 03	23 18	23 33	23 48
Bethnal Green	d	19 51	20 06	20 21	20 36	20 51	21 06	21 21	21 36	21 51	22 06	22 21	22 36	22 51	23 06	23 21	23 36	23 51
Cambridge Heath	d	19 53	20 08	20 23	20 38	20 53	21 08	21 23	21 38	21 53	22 08	22 23	22 38	22 53	23 08	23 23	23 38	23 53
London Fields	d	19 55	20 10	20 25	20 40	20 55	21 10	21 25	21 40	21 55	22 10	22 25	22 40	22 55	23 10	23 25	23 40	23 55
Hackney Downs	d	19 57	20 12	20 27	20 42	20 57	21 12	21 27	21 42	21 57	22 12	22 27	22 42	22 57	23 12	23 27	23 42	23 57
Rectory Road	d	20 00	20 15	20 30	20 45	21 00	21 15	21 30	21 45	22 00	22 15	22 30	22 45	23 00	23 15	23 30	23 45	23 59
Stoke Newington	d	20 01	20 16	20 31	20 46	21 01	21 16	21 31	21 46	22 01	22 16	22 31	22 46	23 01	23 16	23 31	23 46	00 01
Stamford Hill	d	20 03	20 18	20 33	20 48	21 03	21 18	21 33	21 48	22 03	22 18	22 33	22 48	23 03	23 18	23 33	23 48	00 03
Seven Sisters	⊖ d	20 05	20 20	20 35	20 50	21 05	21 20	21 35	21 50	22 05	22 20	22 35	22 50	23 05	23 20	23 35	23 50	00 05
Bruce Grove	d	20 07	20 22	20 37	20 52	21 07	21 22	21 37	21 52	22 07	22 22	22 37	22 52	23 07	23 22	23 37	23 52	00 07
White Hart Lane	d	20 09	20 24	20 39	20 54	21 09	21 24	21 39	21 54	22 09	22 24	22 39	22 54	23 09	23 24	23 39	23 54	00 09
Silver Street	d	20 11	20 26	20 41	20 56	21 11	21 26	21 41	21 56	22 11	22 26	22 41	22 56	23 11	23 26	23 41	23 56	00 11
Edmonton Green	d	20 13	20 28	20 43	20 58	21 13	21 28	21 43	21 58	22 13	22 28	22 43	22 58	23 13	23 28	23 43	23 58	00 13
Bush Hill Park	d		20 31		21 01		21 31		22 01		22 31		23 01		23 31		00 01	
Enfield Town	a		20 36		21 06		21 36		22 06		22 36		23 04		23 34		00 06	
Southbury	d	20 16		20 46		21 16		21 46		22 16		22 46		23 16		23 46		00 16
Turkey Street	d	20 19		20 49		21 19		21 49		22 19		22 49		23 19		23 49		00 19
Theobalds Grove	d	20 22		20 52		21 22		21 52		22 22		22 52		23 22		23 52		00 22
Cheshunt	a	20 26		20 56		21 26		21 56		22 26		22 56		23 25		23 56		00 25

For general notes see front of timetable
For details of catering facilities see
Directory of Train Operators

A To Bishops Stortford (Table 22)

Table 21

Saturdays

London → Cheshunt (via Seven Sisters) and Enfield Town

Network diagram - see first page of Table 20

		LE	LE A	LE	LE	LE	LE	LE	LE	LE	LE		LE	LE	LE
London Liverpool Street 15	⊖ d	23p33	23p48	00 03	05 18	05 28	05 48	06 03	06 18	06 33	06 48		23 03	23 33	23 48
Bethnal Green	d	23p36	23p51	00 07	05 21		05 51	06 06	06 21	06 36	06 51		23 06	23 36	23 51
Cambridge Heath	d	23p38	23p53	00 09	05 23		05 53	06 08	06 23	06 38	06 53		23 08	23 38	23 53
London Fields	d	23p40	23p55	00 11	05 25		05 55	06 10	06 25	06 40	06 55		23 10	23 40	23 55
Hackney Downs	d	23p42	23p57	00 13	05 27		05 57	06 12	06 27	06 42	06 57	and at	23 12	23 42	23 57
Rectory Road	d	23p45	23p59	00 16	05 30		06 00	06 15	06 30	06 45	07 00	the same	23 15	23 45	23 59
Stoke Newington	d	23p46	00 01	00 17	05 31		06 01	06 16	06 31	06 46	07 01		23 16	23 46	00 01
Stamford Hill	d	23p48	00 03	00 19	05 33		06 03	06 18	06 33	06 48	07 03	minutes	23 18	23 48	00 03
Seven Sisters	⊖ d	23p50	00 05	00 21	05 35	05 50	06 05	06 20	06 35	06 50	07 05		23 20	23 50	00 05
Bruce Grove	d	23p52	00 07	00 23	05 37	05 52	06 07	06 22	06 37	06 52	07 07	past	23 22	23 52	00 07
White Hart Lane	d	23p54	00 09	00 25	05 39	05 54	06 09	06 24	06 39	06 54	07 09	each	23 24	23 54	00 09
Silver Street	d	23p56	00 11	00 27	05 41	05 56	06 11	06 26	06 41	06 56	07 11		23 26	23 56	00 11
Edmonton Green	d	23p58	00 13	00 29	05 43	05 58	06 13	06 28	06 43	06 58	07 13	hour until	23 28	23 58	00 13
Bush Hill Park	d	00 01		00 32		06 01		06 31		07 01			23 31	00 01	
Enfield Town	a	00 06		00 35		06 04		06 35		07 05			23 35	00 05	
Southbury	d		00 16		05 46		06 16		06 46		07 16				00 16
Turkey Street	d		00 19		05 49		06 19		06 49		07 19				00 19
Theobalds Grove	d		00 22		05 52		06 22		06 52		07 22				00 22
Cheshunt	a		00 25		05 55		06 25		06 55		07 25				00 25

Sundays

		LE	LE	LE	LE	LE B	LE	LE B	LE	LE B	LE	LE B	LE	LE B	LE	LE B		LE
London Liverpool Street 15	⊖ d	23p33	23p48	00 03	07 33	07 53	08 03	08 23	08 33	08 53	09 03	09 23	09 33	09 53	10 03	10 23		18 33
Bethnal Green	d	23p36	23p51	00 07									09 36		10 06			18 36
Cambridge Heath	d	23p38	23p53	00 09									09 38		10 08			18 38
London Fields	d	23p40	23p55	00 11									09 40		10 10			18 40
Hackney Downs	d	23p42	23p57	00 13	07 42	08 00	08 12	08 30	08 42	09 00	09 12	09 30	09 42	10 00	10 12	10 30	and at	18 42
Rectory Road	d	23p45	23p59	00 16	07 45		08 15		08 45		09 15		09 45		10 15		the same	18 45
Stoke Newington	d	23p46	00 01	00 17	07 46		08 16		08 46		09 16		09 46		10 16			18 46
Stamford Hill	d	23p48	00 03	00 19	07 48		08 18		08 48		09 18		09 48		10 18		minutes	18 48
Seven Sisters	⊖ d	23p50	00 05	00 21	07 50	08 05	08 20	08 35	08 50	09 05	09 20	09 35	09 50	10 05	10 20	10 35		18 50
Bruce Grove	d	23p52	00 07	00 23	07 52		08 22		08 52		09 22		09 52		10 22		past	18 52
White Hart Lane	d	23p54	00 09	00 25	07 54		08 24		08 54		09 24		09 54		10 24		each	18 54
Silver Street	d	23p56	00 11	00 27	07 56		08 26		08 56		09 26		09 56		10 26			18 56
Edmonton Green	d	23p58	00 13	00 29	07 58	08 09	08 28	08 39	08 58	09 09	09 28	09 39	09 58	10 09	10 28	10 39	hour until	18 58
Bush Hill Park	d	00 01		00 32	08 01		08 31		09 01		09 31		10 01		10 31			19 01
Enfield Town	a	00 05		00 35	08 05		08 35		09 06		09 35		10 05		10 35			19 05
Southbury	d		00 16			08 12		08 42		09 12		09 42		10 12		10 42		
Turkey Street	d		00 19			08 15		08 45		09 15		09 45		10 15		10 45		
Theobalds Grove	d		00 22			08 18		08 48		09 18		09 48		10 18		10 48		
Cheshunt	a		00 25			08 21		08 53		09 21		09 53		10 21		10 53		

		LE B	LE	LE B	LE	LE B	LE	LE B	LE	LE B	LE
London Liverpool Street 15	⊖ d	19 03	19 33	20 03	20 33	21 03	21 33	22 03	22 33	23 03	23 33
Bethnal Green	d	19 06	19 36	20 06	20 36	21 06	21 36	22 06	22 36	23 06	23 36
Cambridge Heath	d	19 08	19 38	20 08	20 38	21 08	21 38	22 08	22 38	23 08	23 38
London Fields	d	19 10	19 40	20 10	20 40	21 10	21 40	22 10	22 40	23 10	23 40
Hackney Downs	d	19 12	19 42	20 12	20 42	21 12	21 42	22 12	22 42	23 12	23 42
Rectory Road	d	19 15	19 45	20 15	20 45	21 15	21 45	22 15	22 45	23 15	23 45
Stoke Newington	d	19 16	19 46	20 16	20 46	21 16	21 46	22 16	22 46	23 16	23 46
Stamford Hill	d	19 18	19 48	20 18	20 48	21 18	21 48	22 18	22 48	23 18	23 48
Seven Sisters	⊖ d	19 20	19 50	20 20	20 50	21 20	21 50	22 20	22 50	23 20	23 50
Bruce Grove	d	19 22	19 52	20 22	20 52	21 22	21 52	22 22	22 52	23 22	23 52
White Hart Lane	d	19 24	19 54	20 24	20 54	21 24	21 54	22 24	22 54	23 24	23 54
Silver Street	d	19 26	19 56	20 26	20 56	21 26	21 56	22 26	22 56	23 26	23 56
Edmonton Green	d	19 28	19 58	20 28	20 58	21 28	21 58	22 28	22 58	23 28	23 58
Bush Hill Park	d		20 01		21 01		22 01		23 01		00 01
Enfield Town	a		20 05		21 05		22 05		23 05		00 05
Southbury	d	19 31		20 31		21 31		22 31		23 31	
Turkey Street	d	19 34		20 34		21 34		22 34		23 34	
Theobalds Grove	d	19 37		20 37		21 37		22 37		23 37	
Cheshunt	a	19 40		20 40		21 40		22 40		23 40	

For general notes see front of timetable
For details of catering facilities see
Directory of Train Operators

A To Bishops Stortford (Table 22)
B To Hertford East (Table 22)

Cheshunt (via Seven Sisters) and Enfield Town → London

Network diagram - see first page of Table 20

Miles	Miles			LE MX	LE MO A	LE MX 1	LE 1	LE MX	LE 1	LE	LE	LE	LE	LE	LE	LE	LE	LE	LE	LE	LE
0	—	**Cheshunt**	d	23p31	23p31	23p51		23p58		05 16		06 01			06 32			07 02			07 32
1	—	Theobalds Grove	d	23p34	23p34					05 19		06 04			06 35			07 05			07 35
2¼	—	Turkey Street	d	23p36	23p36					05 21		06 06			06 37			07 07			07 37
4	—	Southbury	d	23p39	23p39					05 24		06 09			06 40			07 10			07 40
—	0	**Enfield Town**	d								05 53		06 18	06 28		06 48	06 58		07 17	07 28	
—	1	Bush Hill Park	d								05 55		06 20	06 30		06 50	07 00		07 19	07 30	
6	2¼	Edmonton Green	d	23p43	23p43					05 28	05 58	06 13	06 23	06 33	06 44	06 53	07 03	07 14	07 22	07 33	07 44
6½	2¾	Silver Street	d	23p45	23p45					05 30	06 00	06 15	06 25	06 35	06 46	06 55	07 05	07 16	07 24	07 35	07 46
7¼	3½	White Hart Lane	d	23p47	23p47					05 32	06 02	06 17	06 27	06 37	06 48	06 57	07 07	07 18	07 26	07 37	07 48
8¼	4½	Bruce Grove	d	23p49	23p49					05 34	06 04	06 19	06 29	06 39	06 50	06 59	07 09	07 20	07 28	07 39	07 50
9	5¼	Seven Sisters	⊖ d	23p51	23p51	00 02	00 06	00 10	00 19	05 36	06 06	06 21	06 32	06b44	06 53	07 02	07c14	07 23	07 31	07e44	07 53
9½	5¾	Stamford Hill	d	23p53	23p53					05 38	06 08	06 23	06 34	06 46	06 55	07 04	07 16	07 25	07 33	07 46	07 55
10¼	6½	Stoke Newington	d	23p55	23p55					05 40	06 10	06 25	06 36	06 48	06 57	07 06	07 18	07 27	07 35	07 48	07 57
10¾	7	Rectory Road	d	23p56	23p56					05 41	06 11	06 26	06 37	06 49	06 58	07 07	07 19	07 28	07 36	07 49	07 58
11½	7¾	Hackney Downs	d	23p59	23p59			00 15		05 44	06 14	06 29	06 41	06 54	07 02	07 11	07 24	07 32	07 40	07 54	08 02
12	8¼	London Fields	d	00 01	00 02					05 46	06 16	06 31	06 43	06 56	07 04	07 13	07 26	07 34	07 42	07 56	08 04
12¾	9	Cambridge Heath	d	00 03	00 04					05 48	06 18	06 33	06 45	06 58	07 06	07 15	07 28	07 36	07 44	07 58	08 06
13¼	9½	Bethnal Green	d	00 05	00 06					05 50	06 20	06 35	06 47		07 08	07 17		07 38	07 46		08 08
14½	10¾	**London Liverpool Street 15**	⊖ a	00 10	00 11	00 17	00 21	00 24	00 34	05 55	06 27	06 40	06 53	07 06	07 13	07 23	07 35	07 43	07 51	08 05	08 13

		LE	LE	LE	LE	LE	LE	LE	LE	LE	LE	LE	LE	LE	LE	LE	and at the same minutes past each hour until	LE	LE	LE
Cheshunt	d			08 02			08 32			09 02			09 31		10 01			15 31		16 01
Theobalds Grove	d			08 05			08 35			09 05			09 34		10 04			15 34		16 04
Turkey Street	d			08 07			08 37			09 07			09 36		10 06			15 36		16 06
Southbury	d			08 10			08 40			09 10			09 39		10 09			15 39		16 09
Enfield Town	d	07 46	07 58		08 18	08 28		08 48	08 58		09 18	09 28		09 53		10 23			15 53	
Bush Hill Park	d	07 48	08 00		08 20	08 30		08 50	09 00		09 20	09 30		09 55		10 25			15 55	
Edmonton Green	d	07 51	08 03	08 14	08 23	08 33	08 44	08 53	09 03	09 14	09 23	09 33	09 43	09 58	10 13	10 28		15 43	15 58	16 13
Silver Street	d	07 53	08 05	08 16	08 25	08 35	08 46	08 55	09 05	09 16	09 25	09 35	09 45	10 00	10 15	10 30		15 45	16 00	16 15
White Hart Lane	d	07 55	08 07	08 18	08 27	08 37	08 48	08 57	09 07	09 18	09 27	09 37	09 47	10 02	10 17	10 32		15 47	16 02	16 17
Bruce Grove	d	07 57	08 09	08 20	08 29	08 39	08 50	08 59	09 09	09 20	09 29	09 39	09 49	10 04	10 19	10 34		15 49	16 04	16 19
Seven Sisters	⊖ d	08 00	08f14	08 24	08 32	08g44	08 53	09 02	09h14	09 23	09 32	09 42	09 51	10 06	10 21	10 36		15 51	16 06	16 21
Stamford Hill	d	08 02	08 16	08 26	08 34	08 46	08 55	09 04	09 16	09 25	09 34	09 44	09 53	10 08	10 23	10 38		15 53	16 08	16 23
Stoke Newington	d	08 04	08 18	08 28	08 36	08 48	08 57	09 06	09 18	09 27	09 36	09 46	09 55	10 10	10 25	10 40		15 55	16 10	16 25
Rectory Road	d	08 05	08 19	08 29	08 37	08 49	08 58	09 07	09 19	09 28	09 37	09 47	09 56	10 11	10 26	10 41		15 56	16 11	16 26
Hackney Downs	d	08 09	08 24	08 33	08 41	08 54	09 02	09 11	09 24	09 32	09 41	09 50	09 59	10 14	10 29	10 44		15 59	16 14	16 29
London Fields	d	08 11	08 26	08 35	08 43	08 56	09 04	09 13	09 26	09 34	09 43	09 52	10 01	10 16	10 31	10 46		16 01	16 16	16 31
Cambridge Heath	d	08 13	08 28	08 37	08 45	08 58	09 06	09 15	09 28	09 36	09 45	09 54	10 03	10 18	10 33	10 48		16 03	16 18	16 33
Bethnal Green	d	08 15		08 39	08 47		09 08	09 17		09 38	09 48		10 05	10 20	10 35	10 50		16 05	16 20	16 35
London Liverpool Street 15	⊖ a	08 20	08 35	08 45	08 53	09 05	09 13	09 23	09 36	09 45	09 54	10 02	10 10	10 25	10 40	10 55		16 10	16 25	16 40

		LE	LE	LE	LE	LE	LE	LE	LE	LE	LE	LE	LE	LE	LE	LE	LE	LE	LE	LE	LE
Cheshunt	d		16 31			17 07			17 37			18 07			18 37			19 07			19 37
Theobalds Grove	d		16 34			17 10			17 40			18 10			18 40			19 10			19 40
Turkey Street	d		16 36			17 12			17 42			18 12			18 42			19 12			19 42
Southbury	d		16 39			17 15			17 45			18 15			18 45			19 15			19 45
Enfield Town	d	16 20		16 50	17 05		17 20	17 35		17 50	18 05		18 20	18 35		18 53	19 05		19 23	19 35	
Bush Hill Park	d	16 22		16 52	17 07		17 22	17 37		17 52	18 07		18 22	18 37		18 55	19 07		19 25	19 37	
Edmonton Green	d	16 25	16 43	16 55	17 13	17 19	17 25	17 43	17 49	17 55	18 13	18 19	18 25	18 43	18 49	18 58	19 13	19 19	19 28	19 43	19 49
Silver Street	d	16 27	16 45	16 57	17 15	17 21	17 27	17 45	17 51	17 57	18 15	18 21	18 27	18 45	18 51	19 00	19 15	19 21	19 30	19 45	19 51
White Hart Lane	d	16 29	16 47	16 59	17 17	17 23	17 29	17 47	17 53	17 59	18 17	18 23	18 29	18 47	18 53	19 02	19 17	19 23	19 32	19 47	19 53
Bruce Grove	d	16 31	16 49	17 01	17 19	17 25	17 31	17 49	17 55	18 01	18 19	18 25	18 31	18 49	18 55	19 04	19 19	19 25	19 34	19 49	19 55
Seven Sisters	⊖ d	16 33	16 51	17 03	17 21	17 27	17 33	17 51	17 57	18 03	18 21	18 27	18 33	18 51	18 57	19 06	19 21	19 27	19 36	19 51	19 57
Stamford Hill	d	16 35	16 53	17 05	17 23		17 35	17 53		18 05	18 23		18 35	18 53		19 08	19 23		19 38	19 53	
Stoke Newington	d	16 37	16 55	17 07	17 25	17 30	17 37	17 55	18 00	18 07	18 25	18 30	18 37	18 55	19 00	19 10	19 25	19 30	19 40	19 55	20 00
Rectory Road	d	16 38	16 56	17 08	17 26		17 38	17 56		18 08	18 26		18 38	18 56		19 11	19 26		19 41	19 56	
Hackney Downs	d	16 41	16 59	17 11	17 29	17 33	17 41	17 59	18 03	18 11	18 29	18 33	18 41	18 59	19 03	19 14	19 29	19 33	19 44	19 59	20 03
London Fields	d	16 43	17 01	17 13	17 31		17 43	18 01		18 13	18 31		18 43	19 01		19 16	19 31		19 46	20 01	
Cambridge Heath	d	16 45	17 03	17 15	17 33		17 45	18 03		18 15	18 33		18 45	19 03		19 18	19 33		19 48	20 03	
Bethnal Green	d	16 47	17 05	17 17	17 35		17 47	18 05		18 17	18 35		18 47	19 05		19 20	19 35		19 50	20 05	
London Liverpool Street 15	⊖ a	16 52	17 10	17 23	17 41	17 45	17 53	18 11	18 13	18 23	18 42	18 46	18 52	19 10	19 12	19 26	19 42	19 45	19 55	20 10	20 12

For general notes see front of timetable
For details of catering facilities see Directory of Train Operators

A From Hertford East (Table 22)
b Arr. 0641
c Arr. 0711
e Arr. 0741
f Arr. 0811
g Arr. 0841
h Arr. 0911

Cheshunt (via Seven Sisters) and Enfield Town → London

Network diagram - see first page of Table 20

Mondays to Fridays

		LE		LE	LE	LE	LE		LE	LE	LE	LE		LE	LE	LE	LE		LE	LE	LE 1	LE			
Cheshunt	d			20 03		20 31			21 01		21 31			22 01		22 31				23 31	23 51	23 58			
Theobalds Grove	d			20 06		20 34			21 04		21 34			22 04		22 34				23 34					
Turkey Street	d			20 08		20 36			21 06		21 36			22 06		22 36				23 36					
Southbury	d			20 11		20 39			21 09		21 39			22 09		22 39				23 39					
Enfield Town	d	19 53			20 23		20 53			21 23		21 53			22 23		22 53		23 23						
Bush Hill Park	d	19 55			20 25		20 55			21 25		21 55			22 25		22 55		23 25						
Edmonton Green	d	19 58		20 15	20 28	20 43	20 58		21 13	21 28	21 43	21 58		22 13	22 28	22 43	22 58		23 28	23 43					
Silver Street	d	20 00		20 17	20 30	20 45	21 00		21 15	21 30	21 45	22 00		22 15	22 30	22 45	23 00		23 30	23 45					
White Hart Lane	d	20 02		20 19	20 32	20 47	21 02		21 17	21 32	21 47	22 02		22 17	22 32	22 47	23 02		23 32	23 47					
Bruce Grove	d	20 04		20 21	20 34	20 49	21 04		21 19	21 34	21 49	22 04		22 19	22 34	22 49	23 04		23 34	23 49					
Seven Sisters	⊖ d	20 06		20 23	20 36	20 51	21 06		21 21	21 36	21 51	22 06		22 21	22 36	22 51	23 06		23 36	23 51	00 02	00 10			
Stamford Hill	d	20 08		20 25	20 38	20 53	21 08		21 23	21 38	21 53	22 08		22 23	22 38	22 53	23 08		23 38	23 53					
Stoke Newington	d	20 10		20 27	20 40	20 55	21 10		21 25	21 40	21 55	22 10		22 25	22 40	22 55	23 10		23 40	23 55					
Rectory Road	d	20 11		20 28	20 41	20 56	21 11		21 26	21 41	21 56	22 11		22 26	22 41	22 56	23 11		23 41	23 56					
Hackney Downs	d	20 14		20 31	20 44	20 59	21 14		21 29	21 44	21 59	22 14		22 29	22 44	22 59	23 14		23 44	23 59		00 15			
London Fields	d	20 16		20 33	20 46	21 01	21 16		21 31	21 46	22 01	22 16		22 31	22 46	23 01	23 16		23 46	00 01					
Cambridge Heath	d	20 18		20 35	20 48	21 03	21 18		21 33	21 48	22 03	22 18		22 33	22 48	23 03	23 18		23 48	00 03					
Bethnal Green	d	20 20		20 37	20 50	21 05	21 20		21 35	21 50	22 05	22 20		22 35	22 50	23 05	23 20		23 50	00 05					
London Liverpool Street 15	⊖ a	20 27		20 42	20 55	21 10	21 26		21 40	21 55	22 10	22 25		22 40	22 55	23 10	23 25		23 55	00 10	00 17	00 24			

Saturdays

		LE	LE 1	LE 1	LE	LE 1		LE A	LE	LE		LE	LE	LE	LE			LE	LE	LE	LE	LE		
Cheshunt	d	23p31	23p51		23p58			05 16	06 01			06 31		07 01				22 31			23 31			
Theobalds Grove	d	23p34						05 18	06 04			06 34		07 04				22 34			23 34			
Turkey Street	d	23p36						05 21	06 06			06 36		07 06				22 36			23 36			
Southbury	d	23p39						05 24	06 09			06 39		07 09		and at		22 39			23 39			
Enfield Town	d									06 23			06 53		07 23	the same			22 53	23 23		23 53		
Bush Hill Park	d									06 25			06 55		07 25	minutes			22 55	23 25		23 55		
Edmonton Green	d	23p43						05 27	06 13	06 28		06 43	06 58	07 13	07 28			22 43	22 58	23 28	23 43	23 58		
Silver Street	d	23p45						05 29	06 15	06 30		06 45	07 00	07 15	07 30	past		22 45	23 00	23 30	23 45	23 59		
White Hart Lane	d	23p47						05 31	06 17	06 32		06 47	07 02	07 17	07 32			22 47	23 02	23 32	23 47	00 02		
Bruce Grove	d	23p49						05 33	06 19	06 34		06 49	07 04	07 19	07 34	each		22 49	23 04	23 34	23 49	00 04		
Seven Sisters	⊖ d	23p51	00 02	00 06	00 10	00 19		05 35	06 21	06 36		06 51	07 06	07 21	07 36	hour until		22 51	23 06	23 36	23 51	00 06		
Stamford Hill	d	23p53						05 37	06 23	06 38		06 53	07 08	07 23	07 38			22 53	23 08	23 38	23 53	00 08		
Stoke Newington	d	23p55						05 39	06 25	06 40		06 55	07 10	07 25	07 40			22 55	23 10	23 40	23 55	00 10		
Rectory Road	d	23p56						05 41	06 26	06 41		06 56	07 11	07 26	07 41			22 56	23 11	23 41	23 56	00 11		
Hackney Downs	d	23p59			00 15			05 46	06 29	06 44		06 59	07 14	07 29	07 44			22 59	23 14	23 44	23 59	00 14		
London Fields	d	00 01							06 31	06 46		07 01	07 16	07 31	07 46			23 01	23 16	23 46	00 01	00 16		
Cambridge Heath	d	00 03							06 33	06 48		07 03	07 18	07 33	07 48			23 03	23 18	23 48	00 03	00 18		
Bethnal Green	d	00 05						05 50	06 35	06 50		07 05	07 20	07 35	07 50			23 05	23 20	23 50	00 05	00 20		
London Liverpool Street 15	⊖ a	00 10	00 17	00 21	00 24	00 34		05 55	06 40	06 55		07 10	07 25	07 40	07 55			23 10	23 25	23 55	00 10	00 25		

Sundays

		LE		LE		LE		LE B		LE		LE B			LE	LE B	LE	LE B			LE		LE B	LE
Cheshunt	d	23p31						08 16				08 46				09 16		09 46					18 16	
Theobalds Grove	d	23p34						08 19				08 49				09 19		09 49					18 19	
Turkey Street	d	23p36						08 21				08 51				09 21		09 51					18 21	
Southbury	d	23p39						08 24				08 54				09 24		09 54	and at				18 24	
Enfield Town	d			23p53		07 59				08 29					08 59		09 29		the same		17 59			18 29
Bush Hill Park	d			23p55		08 01				08 31					09 01		09 31				18 01			18 31
Edmonton Green	d	23p43		23p58		08 04		08 28		08 34		08 58			09 04	09 28	09 34	09 58	minutes		18 04		18 28	18 34
Silver Street	d	23p45		23p59		08 06				08 36					09 06		09 36				18 06			18 36
White Hart Lane	d	23p47		00 02		08 08				08 38					09 08		09 38		past		18 08			18 38
Bruce Grove	d	23p49		00 04		08 10				08 40					09 10		09 40				18 10			18 40
Seven Sisters	⊖ d	23p51		00 06		08 12		08 33		08 42		09 03			09 12	09 33	09 42	10 03	each		18 12		18 33	18 42
Stamford Hill	d	23p53		00 08		08 14				08 44					09 14		09 44		hour until		18 14			18 44
Stoke Newington	d	23p55		00 10		08 16				08 46					09 16		09 46				18 16			18 46
Rectory Road	d	23p56		00 11		08 17				08 47					09 17		09 47				18 17			18 47
Hackney Downs	d	23p59		00 14		08 20		08 40		08 50		09 10			09 20	09 40	09 50	10 10			18 20		18 40	18 50
London Fields	d	00 01		00 16											09 22		09 52				18 22			18 52
Cambridge Heath	d	00 03		00 18											09 24		09 54				18 24			18 54
Bethnal Green	d	00 05		00 20											09 26		09 56				18 26			18 56
London Liverpool Street 15	⊖ a	00 10		00 25		08 29		08 51		09 05		09 20			09 31	09 49	10 01	10 19			18 31		18 49	19 01

For general notes see front of timetable
For details of catering facilities see Directory of Train Operators

A From Cambridge (Table 22)
B From Hertford East (Table 22)

Table 21

Sundays

Cheshunt (via Seven Sisters) and Enfield Town → London

Network diagram - see first page of Table 20

		LE A	LE	LE A	LE	LE A	LE	LE A	LE	LE A	LE	LE A
Cheshunt	d	18 46		19 31		20 31		21 31		22 31		23 31
Theobalds Grove	d	18 49		19 34		20 34		21 34		22 34		23 34
Turkey Street	d	18 51		19 36		20 36		21 36		22 36		23 36
Southbury	d	18 54		19 39		20 39		21 39		22 39		23 39
Enfield Town	d		19 09		20 09		21 09		22 09		23 09	
Bush Hill Park	d		19 11		20 11		21 11		22 11		23 11	
Edmonton Green	d	18 58	19 14	19 43	20 14	20 43	21 14	21 43	22 14	22 43	23 14	23 43
Silver Street	d		19 16	19 45	20 16	20 45	21 16	21 45	22 16	22 45	23 16	23 45
White Hart Lane	d		19 18	19 47	20 18	20 47	21 18	21 47	22 18	22 47	23 18	23 47
Bruce Grove	d		19 20	19 49	20 20	20 49	21 20	21 49	22 20	22 49	23 20	23 49
Seven Sisters ⊖	d	19 03	19 22	19 51	20 22	20 51	21 22	21 51	22 22	22 51	23 22	23 51
Stamford Hill	d		19 24	19 53	20 24	20 53	21 24	21 53	22 24	22 53	23 24	23 53
Stoke Newington	d		19 26	19 55	20 26	20 55	21 26	21 55	22 26	22 55	23 26	23 55
Rectory Road	d		19 27	19 56	20 27	20 56	21 27	21 56	22 27	22 56	23 27	23 56
Hackney Downs	d	19 10	19 30	20 00	20 30	21 00	21 30	22 00	22 30	23 00	23 30	23 59
London Fields	d		19 32	20 02	20 32	21 02	21 32	22 02	22 32	23 02	23 32	00 02
Cambridge Heath	d		19 34	20 04	20 34	21 04	21 34	22 04	22 34	23 04	23 34	00 04
Bethnal Green	d		19 36	20 06	20 36	21 06	21 36	22 06	22 36	23 06	23 36	00 06
London Liverpool Street 15 ⊖	a	19 19	19 41	20 11	20 41	21 11	21 41	22 11	22 41	23 11	23 41	00 11

For general notes see front of timetable
For details of catering facilities see Directory of Train Operators

A From Hertford East (Table 22)

London → Broxbourne, Hertford East, Bishops Stortford, Stansted Airport and Cambridge

Network diagram - see first page of Table 20

Miles	Miles			LE MO [1]	LE MX [1]	LE MO	LE MO [1] ⌶	LE MX [1] ⌶	LE MX [1]	LE MO [1]	LE MO	LE MX	LE MX	LE MO [1]		LE MX [1]	LE MX	LE MO [1] ⌶	LE MFO [1] ⌶	XC ◇	LE [1] ⌶	LE [1] ⌶	LE [1]	LE [1] ⌶	LE
0	—	**London Liverpool Street [15]** ⊖	d		22p58	23p03	23p25	23p25	23p28	23p28		23p42	23p48	23p58		23p58		03 40	04 10		04 40	05 10		05 25	
1¼	—	Bethnal Green	d			23p06							23p51				←								
3	—	Hackney Downs	d			23p12						23p48	23p57 →				23p57								
—	0	Stratford [7] ⊖ ⛴	d	22p45																					
4	—	Clapton	d									23p51													
—	6¾	Seven Sisters ⊖	d			23p20											00 05								
6	—	Tottenham Hale ⊖	d	22p55	23p10		23p37	23b37	23p40	23p40		23p55		00 09		00 10					04u52	05u22		05u37	
7	—	Northumberland Park	d									23p57													
7¾	—	Angel Road	d																						
10	—	Ponders End	d	23p00						23p45		00 01													
10¾	—	Brimsdown	d	23p03						23p48		00 03													
11¾	—	Enfield Lock	d	23p05						23p50		00 06													
12¾	—	Waltham Cross	d	23p08						23p53		00 08													
14	—	Cheshunt	d	23p10	23p18	23p40			23p48	23p55		00 11		00 17		00 18	00 25								
17¼	—	Broxbourne [3]	a	23p15	23p22	23p44			23p52	23p59	←	00 15		00 22		00 22	00 29								
—	0		d	23p20	23p22	00 03			23p52	23p59	00 03	00 15		00 22		00 22	00 29								05 42
—	1¾	Rye House	d			→					00 06	00 19													05 46
—	3	St Margarets (Herts)	d								00 09	00 22													05 49
—	5	Ware	d								00 12	00 26													05 53
—	7	**Hertford East**	a								00 18	00 31													06 00
20	—	Roydon	d	23p25	23p27									00 26		00 27									
22¾	—	Harlow Town	d	23p29	23p31		23p52	23p54	23p59	00 06				00 30		00 31	00 36				05 11	05 37		05 56	
24½	—	Harlow Mill	d	23p32	23p34									00 33		00 34									
26¾	—	Sawbridgeworth	d	23p35	23p37				00 04	00 12				00 37		00 37						05 43			
30¼	—	**Bishops Stortford**	a	23p42	23p44		00 02	00 04	00 11	00 19				00 46		00 46	00 48				05 21	05 50		06 06	
—	—		d	23p42	23p44		00 03	00 05	00 12												05 21	05 50	05 55	06 06	
33¾	0	Stansted Mountfitchet	d	23p47	23p49				00 16												05 25		05 59		
—	3¾	**Stansted Airport** ✈	a				00 11	00 15										04 26	04 56		05 30	05 58		06 14	
—	—	✈	d																	05 21					
35½	8¼	Elsenham	d	23p50	23p52				00 20														06 03		
40	—	Newport (Essex)	d	23p56	23p58				00 25														06 08		
41¾	—	Audley End	d	23p59	00 01				00 28											05 33			06 11		
45¾	—	Great Chesterford	d	00 04	00 06				00 33														06 16		
49	—	Whittlesford Parkway	d	00 08	00 10				00 38														06 21		
52½	—	Shelford	d	00 13	00 15				00 42														06 25		
55¾	—	**Cambridge**	a	00 21	00 22				00 49											05 55			06 34		

		LE	LE [1] ⌶	LE		LE	LE [1] ⌶	LE [1]	LE [1] ⌶	LE [1]	LE	LE [1] ⌶	LE [1]	XC ◇	LE [1] ⌶	LE [1]		LE	LE	LE [1] ⌶	LE [1]	LE [1] ⌶	LE [1]	LE	LE
London Liverpool Street [15] ⊖	d	05 37	05 40	05 42			05 55	05 58	06 10		06 12	06 25	06 28		06 40			06 42		06 55	06 58	07 10		07 12	
Bethnal Green	d																								
Hackney Downs	d			05 48		←					06 18							06 48						07 18	
Stratford [7] ⊖ ⛴	d	05 50 →				05 50													06 50						07 20
Clapton	d																								
Seven Sisters ⊖	d																								
Tottenham Hale ⊖	d		05u52	05 55		06 00	06u07	06 10	06u22		06 25	06u37	06 40		06u52			06 55	07 00	07u07	07 10	07u22		07 25	07 30
Northumberland Park	d					06 02													07 02						07 32
Angel Road	d					06 04													07 04						07 34
Ponders End	d			06 00							06 30							07 00						07 30	
Brimsdown	d			06 02							06 32							07 02						07 32	
Enfield Lock	d			06 05		06 09					06 35							07 05	07 09					07 35	07 39
Waltham Cross	d			06 07							06 37							07 07						07 37	
Cheshunt	d			06 10		06 13		06 19			06 40		06 49					07 10	07 13		07 19			07 40	07 43
Broxbourne [3]	a			06 14		06 17		06 25			06 44		06 53					07 14	07 17		07 27			07 44	07 47
	d			06 14		06 22		06 25			06 44		06 54					07 14	07 17		07 27			07 44	07 47
Rye House	d					06 26					06 48							07 18	07 22					07 48	
St Margarets (Herts)	d					06 29					06 51							07 21	07 25					07 51	
Ware	d					06 33					06 55							07 25	07 29					07 55	
Hertford East	a			06 29		06 38					07 01							07 31	07 36					08 01	
Roydon	d							06 29		←			06 59			←					07 33		←		
Harlow Town	d		06 07					06c41 →	06 37	06 41			07e11 →		07 07	07 11					07f44 →	07 41	07 44		
Harlow Mill	d									06 44						07 14							07 47		
Sawbridgeworth	d									06 47						07 17							07 50		
Bishops Stortford	a						06 32			06 54		07 02				07 24				07 36			07 57		08 04
	d						06 32			06 58		07 02				07 25				07 37			07 58		
Stansted Mountfitchet	d						06 37			07 02						07 29				07 41			08 02		
Stansted Airport ✈	a		06 25				06 45		06 55			07 12			07 25					07 51		08 08			
✈	d													07 25											
Elsenham	d									07 06						07 34							08 06		
Newport (Essex)	d									07 11						07 39							08 11		
Audley End	d									07 15				07 38		07 42							08 14		
Great Chesterford	d									07 20						07 47							08 19		
Whittlesford Parkway	d									07 25						07 52							08 24		
Shelford	d									07 29						07 56							08 28		
Cambridge	a									07 37				07 57		08 05							08 37		

For general notes see front of timetable
For details of catering facilities see Directory of Train Operators

b Previous night.
Stops to pick up only
c Arr. 0634
e Arr. 0703
f Arr. 0737

London → Broxbourne, Hertford East, Bishops Stortford, Stansted Airport and Cambridge

Network diagram - see first page of Table 20

		LE 1 ⚲	LE 1	XC ◇ ⚲	LE 1 ⚲	LE 1		LE	LE 1 ⚲	LE 1	LE 1 ⚲	LE	LE	LE	LE 1 ⚲	LE 1	XC ◇ ⚲	LE 1 ⚲		LE	LE 1 ⚲	LE 1	LE 1 ⚲	LE	LE
London Liverpool Street 15	⊖ d	07 25	07 28		07 40			07 42	07 55	07 58	08 10		08 12		08 25	08 28		08 40		08 42	08 55	08 58	09 10		09 12
Bethnal Green	d																								
Hackney Downs	d							07 48					08 18							08 48					09 18
Stratford 7	⊖ d											08 00		08 20										09 00	
Clapton	d																								
Seven Sisters	⊖ d																								
Tottenham Hale	⊖ d	07u37	07 40		07u52			07 55	08u07	08 10	08u22	08 13	08 25	08 30	08u37	08 40		08u52		08 55	09u07	09 10	09u22	09 14	09 25
Northumberland Park	d											08 15		08 32										09 16	
Angel Road	d											08 17		08 34										09 18	
Ponders End	d							08 00					08 30							09 00					09 30
Brimsdown	d							08 02					08 32							09 02					09 32
Enfield Lock	d							08 05				08 23	08 35	08 39						09 05				09 23	09 35
Waltham Cross	d							08 07					08 37							09 07					09 37
Cheshunt	d		07 49					08 10		08 19		08 26	08 40	08 43		08 48				09 10		09 17		09 27	09 40
Broxbourne 3	a		07 57					08 14		08 23		08 31	08 44	08 50		08 52				09 14		09 21		09 31	09 44
	d		07 57					08 14		08 24		08 36	08 44			08 52				09 14		09 21		09 37	09 44
Rye House	d							08 18					08 48							09 18					09 48
St Margarets (Herts)	d							08 21					08 51							09 21					09 51
Ware	d							08 25					08 55							09 25					09 55
Hertford East	a							08 30					09 01							09 31					10 01
Roydon	d		08 03			←				08 29												09 26			
Harlow Town	d		08b14 →		08 11	08 14				08 33	08 37	08 43				08 59		09 05				09 30	09 38	09 44	
Harlow Mill	d					08 17				08 36												09 33			
Sawbridgeworth	d					08 20				08 40						09 04						09 36			
Bishops Stortford	a	08 07				08 27			08 32	08 47		08 55			09 02	09 11					09 32	09 43		09 58	
	d	08 07				08 28			08 32	08 47					09 02	09 12					09 32	09 43			
Stansted Mountfitchet	d					08 32			08 37	08 51											09 37	09 48			
Stansted Airport	✈ a	08 15			08 30				08 44		09 01				09 15			09 27			09 44		09 58		
	✈ d			08 21													09 25								
Elsenham	d					08 36				08 55												09 51			
Newport (Essex)	d					08 41				09 00												09 57			
Audley End	d			08 36		08 44				09 04						09 24	09 38					10 00			
Great Chesterford	d					08 49				09 09												10 05			
Whittlesford Parkway	d					08 54				09 14						09 31						10 09			
Shelford	d					08 58				09 18						09 36									
Cambridge	a			08 57		09 05				09 33						09 44	09 57					10 21			

		LE 1 ⚲	LE 1	XC ◇ ⚲	LE 1 ⚲	LE	LE	LE 1 ⚲		LE 1	LE 1 ⚲	LE	LE	LE 1 ⚲	LE 1	XC ◇ ⚲	LE 1 ⚲	LE	LE	LE 1 ⚲		LE 1	LE 1 ⚲	LE	LE 1 ⚲
London Liverpool Street 15	⊖ d	09 25	09 28		09 40		09 42	09 55		09 58	10 10		10 12	10 25	10 28		10 40		10 42	10 55		10 58	11 10	11 12	11 25
Bethnal Green	d																								
Hackney Downs	d						09 48						10 18						10 48					11 18	
Stratford 7	⊖ d					09 30						10 00						10 33							
Clapton	d																								
Seven Sisters	⊖ d																								
Tottenham Hale	⊖ d	09u37	09 40		09u52	09 44	09 55	10u07		10 10	10u22	10 13	10 25	10u37	10 40		10u52	10 43	10 55	11u07		11 10	11u22	11 25	11u37
Northumberland Park	d					09 46						10 15						10 45							
Angel Road	d					09 48																			
Ponders End	d						10 00						10 30						11 00					11 30	
Brimsdown	d						10 02						10 32						11 02					11 32	
Enfield Lock	d					09 53	10 05					10 20	10 35					10 50	11 05					11 35	
Waltham Cross	d						10 07						10 37						11 07					11 37	
Cheshunt	d		09 48			09 57	10 10			10 18		10 24	10 40		10 48			10 54	11 10			11 18		11 40	
Broxbourne 3	a		09 52			10 01	10 14			10 22		10 28	10 44		10 52			10 58	11 14			11 22		11 44	
	d		09 52			10 07	10 14			10 22		10 35	10 44		10 52			11 05	11 14			11 22		11 44	
Rye House	d						10 18						10 48						11 18					11 48	
St Margarets (Herts)	d						10 21						10 51						11 21					11 51	
Ware	d						10 25						10 55						11 25					11 55	
Hertford East	a						10 32						11 01						11 31					12 01	
Roydon	d					10 10				10 27								11 09				11 27			
Harlow Town	d		09 59		10 08	10 15				10 31	10 37	10 42			10 59		11 07	11 14				11 31	11 37		
Harlow Mill	d					10 18				10 34								11 17				11 34			
Sawbridgeworth	d		10 04			10 22				10 37					11 04			11 20				11 37			
Bishops Stortford	a	10 02	10 11			10 29		10 32		10 44		10 54		11 02	11 11			11 27		11 32		11 44			12 02
	d	10 02	10 12			10 29		10 32		10 44				11 02	11 12			11 28		11 32		11 44			12 02
Stansted Mountfitchet	d					10 33				10 49								11 32				11 49			
Stansted Airport	✈ a	10 12			10 30	10 40		10 43			10 58			11 13			11 25	11 40		11 43			11 58		12 13
	✈ d			10 20												11 25									
Elsenham	d									10 52												11 52			
Newport (Essex)	d									10 58												11 58			
Audley End	d		10 24	10 38						11 01					11 24	11 38						12 01			
Great Chesterford	d									11 06												12 06			
Whittlesford Parkway	d		10 31							11 10					11 31							12 10			
Shelford	d		10 36												11 36										
Cambridge	a		10 43	10 57						11 21					11 43	11 57						12 21			

For general notes see front of timetable
For details of catering facilities see Directory of Train Operators

b Arr. 0807

London → Broxbourne, Hertford East, Bishops Stortford, Stansted Airport and Cambridge

Network diagram - see first page of Table 20

Station		LE 1	XC ◇ 🚲	LE 1 🚲	LE	LE	LE 1 🚲	LE 1	LE 1 🚲	LE		LE 1 🚲	LE 1	XC ◇ 🚲	LE 1 🚲	LE	LE	LE 1 🚲	LE 1	LE 1 🚲	LE	LE 1 🚲		LE 1	XC ◇ 🚲
London Liverpool Street 15	⊖ d	11 28		11 40		11 42	11 55	11 58	12 10	12 12		12 25	12 28		12 40		12 42	12 55	12 58	13 10	13 12	13 25		13 28	
Bethnal Green	d																								
Hackney Downs	d					11 48				12 18							12 48				13 18				
Stratford 7	⊖ ⛴ d				11 33											12 33									
Clapton	d																								
Seven Sisters	⊖ d																								
Tottenham Hale	⊖ d	11 40		11u52	11 43	11 55	12u07	12 10	12u22	12 25		12u37	12 40		12u52	12 43	12 55	13u07	13 10	13u22	13 25	13u37		13 40	
Northumberland Park	d				11 45											12 45									
Angel Road	d																								
Ponders End	d					12 00				12 30							13 00				13 30				
Brimsdown	d					12 02				12 32							13 02				13 32				
Enfield Lock	d				11 50	12 05				12 35						12 50	13 05				13 35				
Waltham Cross	d					12 07				12 37							13 07				13 37				
Cheshunt	d	11 48			11 54	12 10		12 18		12 40			12 48			12 54	13 10		13 18		13 40			13 48	
Broxbourne 3	a	11 52			11 58	12 14		12 22		12 44			12 52			12 58	13 14		13 22		13 44			13 52	
	d	11 52			12 05	12 14		12 22		12 44			12 52			13 05	13 14		13 22		13 44			13 52	
Rye House	d					12 18				12 48							13 18				13 48				
St Margarets (Herts)	d					12 21				12 51							13 21				13 51				
Ware	d					12 25				12 55							13 25				13 55				
Hertford East	a					12 31				13 01							13 31				14 01				
Roydon	d				12 09			12 27								13 09			13 27						
Harlow Town	d	11 59		12 07	12 14			12 31	12 37				12 59		13 07	13 14			13 31	13 37				13 59	
Harlow Mill	d				12 17			12 34								13 17			13 34						
Sawbridgeworth	d	12 04			12 20			12 37					13 04			13 20			13 37					14 04	
Bishops Stortford	a	12 11			12 27		12 32	12 44				13 02	13 11			13 27		13 32	13 44			14 02		14 11	
	d	12 12			12 28		12 32	12 44				13 02	13 12			13 28		13 32	13 44			14 02		14 12	
Stansted Mountfitchet	d				12 32			12 49								13 32			13 49						
Stansted Airport	✈ a			12 25	12 40		12 43		12 58			13 13			13 25	13 40		13 43		13 58		14 13			
	✈ d		12 25											13 25											14 25
Elsenham	d							12 52											13 52						
Newport (Essex)	d							12 58											13 58						
Audley End	d	12 24	12 38					13 01					13 24	13 38					14 01					14 24	14 38
Great Chesterford	d							13 06											14 06						
Whittlesford Parkway	d	12 31						13 10					13 31						14 10					14 31	
Shelford	d	12 36											13 36											14 36	
Cambridge	a	12 43	12 57					13 21					13 43	13 57					14 21					14 43	14 57

Station		LE 1 🚲	LE	LE	LE 1 🚲	LE 1	LE 1 🚲	LE	LE 1 🚲	LE 1	XC ◇ 🚲	LE 1 🚲		LE	LE	LE 1 🚲	LE 1	LE 1 🚲	LE	LE 1 🚲	LE 1	XC ◇ 🚲	LE 1 🚲	LE	LE
London Liverpool Street 15	⊖ d	13 40		13 42	13 55	13 58	14 10	14 12	14 25	14 28		14 40			14 42	14 55	14 58	15 10	15 12	15 25	15 28		15 40		15 42
Bethnal Green	d																								
Hackney Downs	d			13 48				14 18							14 48				15 18						15 48
Stratford 7	⊖ ⛴ d		13 33											14 33										15 33	
Clapton	d																								
Seven Sisters	⊖ d																								
Tottenham Hale	⊖ d	13u52	13 43	13 55	14u07	14 10	14u22	14 25	14u37	14 40		14u52		14 43	14 55	15u07	15 10	15u22	15 25	15u37	15 40		15u52	15 43	15 55
Northumberland Park	d		13 45											14 45										15 45	
Angel Road	d																							15 47	
Ponders End	d			14 00				14 30							15 00				15 30						16 00
Brimsdown	d			14 02				14 32							15 02				15 32						16 02
Enfield Lock	d		13 50	14 05				14 35						14 50	15 05				15 35					15 52	16 05
Waltham Cross	d			14 07				14 37							15 07				15 37						16 07
Cheshunt	d		13 54	14 10		14 18		14 40		14 48				14 54	15 10		15 18		15 40		15 48			15 56	16 10
Broxbourne 3	a		13 58	14 14		14 22		14 44		14 52				14 58	15 14		15 22		15 44		15 52			16 00	16 14
	d		14 05	14 14		14 22		14 44		14 52				15 05	15 14		15 22		15 44		15 52			16 06	16 14
Rye House	d			14 18				14 48							15 18				15 48						16 18
St Margarets (Herts)	d			14 21				14 51							15 21				15 51						16 21
Ware	d			14 25				14 55							15 25				15 55						16 25
Hertford East	a			14 31				15 01							15 31				16 01						16 31
Roydon	d		14 09			14 27								15 09			15 27							16 10	
Harlow Town	d	14 07	14 14			14 31	14 37			14 59		15 07		15 14			15 31	15 37			15 59		16 07	16 15	
Harlow Mill	d		14 17			14 34								15 17			15 34							16 18	
Sawbridgeworth	d		14 20			14 37				15 04				15 20			15 37				16 04			16 21	
Bishops Stortford	a		14 27		14 32	14 44			15 02	15 11				15 27		15 32	15 44			16 02	16 11			16 28	
	d		14 28		14 32	14 44			15 02	15 12				15 28		15 32	15 44			16 02	16 11			16 29	
Stansted Mountfitchet	d		14 32			14 49								15 32			15 49				16 16			16 33	
Stansted Airport	✈ a	14 25	14 40		14 43		14 58		15 13			15 25		15 40		15 43		16 00		16 13			16 30	16 40	
	✈ d										15 25											16 20			
Elsenham	d					14 52											15 52				16 19				
Newport (Essex)	d					14 58											15 59				16 25				
Audley End	d					15 01				15 24	15 38						16 03				16 28	16 33			
Great Chesterford	d					15 06											16 08				16 33				
Whittlesford Parkway	d					15 10				15 31							16 12				16 37				
Shelford	d									15 36							16 17				16 42				
Cambridge	a					15 21				15 43	15 57						16 28				16 51	16 58			

For general notes see front of timetable
For details of catering facilities see
Directory of Train Operators

Table 22

Mondays to Fridays

London → Broxbourne, Hertford East, Bishops Stortford, Stansted Airport and Cambridge

Network diagram - see first page of Table 20

		LE ■1 🛒		LE ■1 A	LE ■1 🛒	LE	LE ■1 🛒	LE ■1	LE	XC ◇ 🛒	LE ■1 🛒	LE ■1	LE	LE ■1 🛒		LE ■1 B	LE	LE ■1 🛒	LE ■1	LE	LE ■1 🛒	LE ■1	LE	XC ◇ 🛒	LE ■1 🛒
London Liverpool Street ■15 ⊖	d	15 55		15 58	16 10	16 12	16 25	16 28			16 40	16 42	16 46	16 55		16 58		17 10	17 12	17 16	17 25	17 28			17 40
Bethnal Green	d																								
Hackney Downs	d					16 19							16 52							17 22					
Stratford ■7 ⊖	d								16 30								17 00						17 30		
Clapton	d																								
Seven Sisters ⊖	d																								
Tottenham Hale ⊖	d	16u07		16 10	16u22	16 25	16u37	16 40	16 43		16u52	16 55	16 58	17u07		17 10	17 13	17u22	17 25	17 28	17u37	17 40	17 43		17u52
Northumberland Park	d								16 45								17 15						17 45		
Angel Road	d								16 47								17 17						17 47		
Ponders End	d					16 30							17 03							17 33					
Brimsdown	d					16 32							17 06							17 36					
Enfield Lock	d					16 35			16 53				17 08				17 23			17 38			17 53		
Waltham Cross	d					16 37			16 55				17 11				17 25			17 41			17 55		
Cheshunt	d			16 18		16 40			16 58			17 04	17 13				17 28		17 34	17 43			17 58		
Broxbourne ■3	a			16 22		16 44		16 51	17 04			17 08	17 18			17 25	17 32		17 40	17 48		17 55	18 04		
	d			16 22		16 45		16 52				17 09	17 18			17 25	17 32		17 41	17 48		17 55			
Rye House	d					16 48							17 22				17 36			17 52					
St Margarets (Herts)	d					16 51							17 25				17 39			17 55					
Ware	d					16 55							17 29				17 43			17 59					
Hertford East	a					17 01							17 36				17 50			18 05					
Roydon	d			16 27								17 13							17 45						
Harlow Town	d			16 31	16 37			16 59			17 11	17 18				17 32		17 42	17 50		17 59				18 11
Harlow Mill	d			16 34								17 21							17 53						
Sawbridgeworth	d			16 37				17 04				17 24							17 56			18 07			
Bishops Stortford	a	16 32		16 44			17 02	17 11				17 31		17 36		17 42			18 03		18 09	18 14			18 21
	d	16 32		16 44			17 02	17 12				17 32		17 37		17 43			18 04		18 09	18 14			18 21
Stansted Mountfitchet	d			16 49				17 16				17 36		17 41					18 08						
Stansted Airport ✈	a	16 43			17 00		17 13				17 30			17 46				18 01			18 17				18 31
✈	d									17 17														18 20	
Elsenham	d			16 52								17 40							18 12						
Newport (Essex)	d			16 58								17 45							18 17						
Audley End	d			17 01				17 26		17 32		17 49				17 55			18 21			18 27		18 32	
Great Chesterford	d			17 06								17 54							18 26						
Whittlesford Parkway	d			17 10				17 33				17 58				18 03			18 30			18 35			
Shelford	d			17 15								18 03							18 35						
Cambridge	a			17 21				17 43		17 48		18 12				18 13			18 42			18 45		18 48	

		LE ■1	LE	LE ■1 🛒		LE ■1 B	LE	LE ■1 🛒	LE ■1	LE	LE ■1 🛒	LE ■1	XC ◇ 🛒	LE ■1 🛒	LE	LE ■1		LE	LE ■1 🛒	LE ■1 B	LE ■1 🛒	LE	LE ■1	LE	LE ■1 🛒
London Liverpool Street ■15 ⊖	d	17 42	17 46	17 55		17 58		18 10	18 12	18 16	18 25	18 28		18 40		18 42		18 46	18 55	18 58	19 10		19 12	19 15	19 25
Bethnal Green	d																								
Hackney Downs	d		17 52							18 22								18 52						19 21	
Stratford ■7 ⊖	d						18 00								18 30							19 00			
Clapton	d																								
Seven Sisters ⊖	d																								
Tottenham Hale ⊖	d	17 55	17 58	18u07		18 10	18 13	18u22	18 25	18 28	18u37	18 40		18u52	18 43	18 55		18 58	19u07	19 10	19u22	19 13	19 25	19 28	19u37
Northumberland Park	d						18 15								18 45							19 15			
Angel Road	d						18 17								18 47							19 17			
Ponders End	d		18 03							18 33								19 03						19 33	
Brimsdown	d		18 06							18 36								19 06						19 35	
Enfield Lock	d		18 08				18 23			18 38					18 53			19 08				19 23		19 38	
Waltham Cross	d		18 11				18 25			18 41					18 55			19 11				19 25		19 40	
Cheshunt	d	18 04	18 13				18 28		18 34	18 43					18 58	19 04		19 13				19 28	19 34	19 43	
Broxbourne ■3	a	18 08	18 18			18 25	18 32		18 40	18 48		18 55			19 02	19 10		19 18		19 25		19 32	19 40	19 47	
	d	18 09	18 18			18 25	18 32		18 41	18 48		18 55			19 08	19 11		19 18		19 25		19 38	19 41	19 48	
Rye House	d		18 22				18 36			18 52								19 22						19 51	
St Margarets (Herts)	d		18 25				18 39			18 55								19 25						19 54	
Ware	d		18 29				18 43			18 59								19 29						19 58	
Hertford East	a		18 35				18 50			19 05								19 35						20 04	
Roydon	d	18 13							18 45						19 12	19 15							19 45		
Harlow Town	d	18 18		18 29				18 42	18 50			19 04		19 11	19 17	19 20				19 32	19 41	19 45	19 50		
Harlow Mill	d	18 21							18 53						19 20	19 23							19 53		
Sawbridgeworth	d	18 24				18 36			18 56			19 09			19 23	19 26						19 50	19 56		
Bishops Stortford	a	18 31		18 39		18 43			19 03		19 07	19 16			19 30	19 33			19 36	19 42		20 00	20 03		20 07
	d	18 32		18 40		18 44			19 04		19 08	19 17			19 31	19 34			19 37	19 43			20 03		20 07
Stansted Mountfitchet	d	18 36		18 44					19 08		19 12				19 35	19 38							20 08		
Stansted Airport ✈	a			18 53				19 00			19 17			19 31	19 41				19 47		19 59				20 15
✈	d												19 18												
Elsenham	d	18 40							19 12							19 42							20 11		
Newport (Essex)	d	18 45							19 17							19 47							20 17		
Audley End	d	18 49				18 56			19 21			19 29	19 32			19 51				19 55			20 20		
Great Chesterford	d	18 54							19 26							19 56							20 25		
Whittlesford Parkway	d	18 58				19 04			19 30			19 37				20 00				20 04			20 30		
Shelford	d	19 03							19 35							20 05							20 34		
Cambridge	a	19 12				19 15			19 42			19 48	19 49			20 12				20 14			20 42		

For general notes see front of timetable
For details of catering facilities see Directory of Train Operators

A To Ely (Table 17)
B To Kings Lynn (Table 17)

London → Broxbourne, Hertford East, Bishops Stortford, Stansted Airport and Cambridge

Network diagram - see first page of Table 20

		XC	LE	LE	LE	LE		LE	LE	LE	LE	LE	LE	LE	LE	LE	LE	LE		LE	LE	LE	LE	LE	LE
		◇	1	1				1	1	1		1	1	1			1	1		1		1	1	1	
		🍴		🍴				🍴		🍴		🍴		🍴			🍴			🍴		🍴		🍴	
London Liverpool Street 15	⊖ d		19 28	19 40		19 42		19 55	19 58	20 10	20 12	20 25	20 28	20 40		20 42	20 55	20 58		21 10	21 12	21 25	21 28	21 40	
Bethnal Green	d																								
Hackney Downs	d					19 48					20 18					20 48					21 18				
Stratford 7	⊖ ⛴ d				19 33										20 33										21 33
Clapton	d																								
Seven Sisters	⊖ d																								
Tottenham Hale	⊖ d		19 40	19u52	19 43	19 55		20u07	20 10	20u22	20 25	20u37	20 40	20u52	20 43	20 55	21u07	21 10		21u22	21 25	21u37	21 40	21u52	21 43
Northumberland Park	d				19 45										20 45										21 45
Angel Road	d																								
Ponders End	d					20 00					20 30					21 00					21 30				
Brimsdown	d					20 02					20 32					21 02					21 32				
Enfield Lock	d				19 50	20 05					20 35				20 50	21 05					21 35				21 50
Waltham Cross	d					20 07					20 37					21 07					21 37				
Cheshunt	d		19 50		19 54	20 10			20 18		20 40		20 48		20 54	21 10		21 18			21 40		21 48		21 54
Broxbourne 3	a		19 55		19 58	20 14			20 22		20 44		20 52		20 58	21 14		21 22			21 44		21 52		21 58
	d		19 55		20 05	20 14			20 22		20 44		20 52		21 05	21 14		21 22			21 44		21 52		22 05
Rye House	d					20 18					20 48					21 18					21 48				
St Margarets (Herts)	d					20 21					20 51					21 21					21 51				
Ware	d					20 25					20 55					21 25					21 55				
Hertford East	a					20 31					21 01					21 31					22 01				
Roydon	d		19 59		20 09				20 27						21 09			21 27							22 09
Harlow Town	d		20 03	20 07	20 14				20 31	20 37			20 59	21 07	21 14			21 31		21 37			21 59	22 07	22 14
Harlow Mill	d		20 06		20 17				20 34						21 17			21 34							22 17
Sawbridgeworth	d		20 10		20 20				20 37				21 04		21 20			21 37					22 04		22 20
Bishops Stortford	a		20 17		20 27			20 32	20 44			21 02	21 11		21 27		21 32	21 44				22 02	22 11		22 27
	d		20 17		20 28			20 32	20 44			21 02	21 12		21 28		21 32	21 44				22 02	22 12		22 28
Stansted Mountfitchet	d		20 21		20 32				20 49			21 07			21 32			21 49				22 07			22 32
Stansted Airport	✈ a			20 30	20 40			20 43		20 58		21 14		21 28	21 40		21 43			21 58		22 14		22 25	22 40
	✈ d	20 20																							
Elsenham	d		20 29						20 52									21 52							
Newport (Essex)	d		20 34						20 58									21 58							
Audley End	d	20 32	20 37						21 01				21 24					22 01					22 24		
Great Chesterford	d		20 42						21 06									22 07							
Whittlesford Parkway	d		20 47						21 10				21 31					22 11					22 31		
Shelford	d		20 51						21 15									22 16							
Cambridge	a	20 50	20 58						21 21				21 42					22 22					22 42		

		LE	LE	LE	LE	LE	LE	LE		LE	LE	LE	LE	LE	LE	LE	LE	LE	LE	LE		LE	LE		
																				FO		FX			
			1	1	1		1	1		1			1	1		1	1			1		1			
			🍴		🍴		🍴			🍴			🍴			🍴									
London Liverpool Street 15	⊖ d	21 42	21 55	21 58	22 10	22 12	22 25	22 28		22 40		22 42	22 55	22 58	23 12	23 25	23 28	23 42	23 48	23 58		23 58	←		
Bethnal Green	d																		23 51						
Hackney Downs	d	21 48				22 18						22 48			23 18			23 48	23 57 →				23 57		
Stratford 7	⊖ ⛴ d										22 33														
Clapton	d																	23 51							
Seven Sisters	⊖ d																						00 05		
Tottenham Hale	⊖ d	21 55	22u07	22 10	22u22	22 25	22u37	22 40		22u52	22 43	22 55	23u07	23 10	23 25	23u37	23 40	23 55		00 10		00 10			
Northumberland Park	d										22 45							23 57							
Angel Road	d																								
Ponders End	d	22 00				22 30						23 00			23 30			00 01							
Brimsdown	d	22 02				22 32						23 02			23 32			00 03							
Enfield Lock	d	22 05				22 35					22 50	23 05			23 35			00 06							
Waltham Cross	d	22 07				22 37						23 07			23 37			00 08							
Cheshunt	d	22 10		22 18		22 40		22 48			22 54	23 10		23 18	23 40		23 48	00 11		00 18		00 18	00 25		
Broxbourne 3	a	22 14		22 22		22 44		22 52			22 58	23 14		23 22	23 44		23 52	00 15		00 22		00 22	00 29		
	d	22 14		22 22		22 44		22 52			23 05	23 14		23 22	23 44		23 52	00 15		00 22		00 22	00 29		
Rye House	d	22 18				22 48						23 18			23 48			00 19							
St Margarets (Herts)	d	22 21				22 51						23 21			23 51			00 22							
Ware	d	22 25				22 55						23 25			23 55			00 26							
Hertford East	a	22 31				23 01						23 31			00 01			00 31							
Roydon	d			22 27							23 09			23 27						00 27		00 27			
Harlow Town	d			22 31	22 37			22 59		23 07	23 14			23 31		23 54	23 59			00 31		00 31	00 36		
Harlow Mill	d			22 34							23 17			23 34						00 34		00 34			
Sawbridgeworth	d			22 37				23 04			23 20			23 37			00 04			00 37		00 37			
Bishops Stortford	a		22 32	22 44			23 02	23 11			23 29		23 32	23 44		00 04	00 11			00 44		00 46	00 48		
	d		22 32	22 44			23 02	23 12					23 32	23 44		00 05	00 12			00 44					
Stansted Mountfitchet	d			22 49			23 07						23 37	23 49			00 16			00 49					
Stansted Airport	✈ a		22 43		22 58		23 14			23 24			23 42			00 15									
	✈ d																								
Elsenham	d			22 52										23 52			00 20			00 52					
Newport (Essex)	d			22 58										23 58			00 25			00 58					
Audley End	d			23 01				23 24						00 01			00 28			01 01					
Great Chesterford	d			23 06										00 06			00 33			01 06					
Whittlesford Parkway	d			23 10				23 31						00 10			00 38			01 10					
Shelford	d			23 15										00 15			00 42								
Cambridge	a			23 21				23 42						00 22			00 49			01 21					

For general notes see front of timetable
For details of catering facilities see Directory of Train Operators

Table 22

Saturdays

London → Broxbourne, Hertford East, Bishops Stortford, Stansted Airport and Cambridge

Network diagram - see first page of Table 20

		LE 1	LE 1 trolley	LE 1	LE	LE	LE 1	LE	LE 1 trolley		XC ◇	LE 1 trolley	LE	LE 1 trolley	LE	LE 1 trolley	LE A	LE 1 trolley		LE	LE	LE 1 trolley	LE 1	LE 1 trolley	LE
London Liverpool Street 15 ⊖	d	22p58	23p25	23p28	23p42	23p48	23p58		04 10			04 40		05 10	05 23	05 25	05 28	05 40			05 42	05 55	05 58	06 10	06 12
Bethnal Green	d					23p51		←																	
Hackney Downs	d				23p48	23p57		23p57												←	05 48				06 18
Stratford 7 ⊖	d					→									05 33 →		05 37			05 33					
Clapton	d				23p51																				
Seven Sisters ⊖	d							00 05									05a50								
Tottenham Hale ⊖	d	23p10	23b37	23p40	23p55		00 10					04u52		05u22		05u37		05u52		05 43	05 55	06u07	06 10	06u22	06 25
Northumberland Park	d				23p57															05 45					
Angel Road	d																								
Ponders End	d				00 01																06 00				06 30
Brimsdown	d				00 03																06 02				06 32
Enfield Lock	d				00 06															05 50	06 05				06 35
Waltham Cross	d				00 08																06 07				06 37
Cheshunt	d	23p18		23p48	00 11		00 18	00 25												05 54	06 10		06 18		06 40
Broxbourne 3	a	23p22		23p52	00 15		00 22	00 29												05 59	06 14		06 22		06 44
	d	23p22		23p52	00 15		00 22	00 29												06 05	06 14		06 22		06 44
Rye House	d				00 19																06 18				06 48
St Margarets (Herts)	d				00 22																06 21				06 51
Ware	d				00 26																06 25				06 55
Hertford East	a				00 31																06 30				07 00
Roydon	d	23p27					00 27													06 09			06 27		
Harlow Town	d	23p31	23p54	23p59			00 31	00 36				05 11		05 37		05 56		06 07		06 14			06 31	06 37	
Harlow Mill	d	23p34					00 34													06 17			06 34		
Sawbridgeworth	d	23p37		00 04			00 37							05 43						06 20			06 37		
Bishops Stortford	a	23p44	00 04	00 11			00 44	00 48				05 21		05 50		06 06				06 27		06 32	06 44		
	d	23p44	00 05	00 12			00 44					05 21	05 43	05 50		06 06				06 28		06 32	06 44		
Stansted Mountfitchet	d	23p49		00 16			00 49					05 25	05 47							06 32			06 49		
Stansted Airport ✈	a		00 15						04 56			05 30	05 54	05 58		06 14		06 25		06 38		06 41		06 56	
✈	d										05 21														
Elsenham	d	23p52		00 20			00 52																06 52		
Newport (Essex)	d	23p58		00 25			00 58																06 58		
Audley End	d	00 01		00 28			01 01				05 33												07 01		
Great Chesterford	d	00 06		00 33			01 06																07 06		
Whittlesford Parkway	d	00 10		00 38			01 10																07 10		
Shelford	d	00 15		00 42																			07 15		
Cambridge	a	00 22		00 49			01 21				05 50												07 21		

		LE	LE 1 trolley	LE 1	LE 1 trolley		XC ◇	LE	LE	LE 1 trolley	LE 1 B	LE 1 trolley	LE	LE 1 trolley		LE 1	XC ◇	LE 1 trolley	LE	LE	LE 1 trolley	LE 1	LE 1 trolley		LE
London Liverpool Street 15 ⊖	d	06 23	06 25	06 28	06 40				06 42	06 55	06 58	07 10	07 12	07 25		07 28		07 40		07 42	07 55	07 58	08 10		08 12
Bethnal Green	d																								
Hackney Downs	d							←	06 48				07 18							07 48					08 18
Stratford 7 ⊖	d	06 33 →						06 33											07 33						
Clapton	d																								
Seven Sisters ⊖	d																								
Tottenham Hale ⊖	d		06u37	06 40	06u52			06 43	06 55	07u07	07 10	07u22	07 25	07u37		07 40		07u52	07 43	07 55	08u07	08 10	08u22		08 25
Northumberland Park	d							06 45											07 45						
Angel Road	d																								
Ponders End	d								07 00				07 30							08 00					08 30
Brimsdown	d								07 02				07 32							08 02					08 32
Enfield Lock	d							06 50	07 05				07 35						07 50	08 05					08 35
Waltham Cross	d								07 07				07 37							08 07					08 37
Cheshunt	d			06 48				06 54	07 10		07 18		07 40			07 48			07 54	08 10		08 18			08 40
Broxbourne 3	a			06 52				06 59	07 14		07 22		07 44			07 52			07 59	08 14		08 22			08 44
	d			06 52				07 05	07 14		07 22		07 44			07 52			08 05	08 14		08 22			08 44
Rye House	d								07 18				07 48							08 18					08 48
St Margarets (Herts)	d								07 21				07 51							08 21					08 51
Ware	d								07 25				07 55							08 25					08 55
Hertford East	a								07 30				08 00							08 32					09 00
Roydon	d							07 09											08 09			08 27			
Harlow Town	d			06 59	07 07			07 14			07 29	07 37				07 59		08 07	08 14			08 31	08 37		
Harlow Mill	d							07 17											08 17			08 34			
Sawbridgeworth	d			07 04				07 20			07 34					08 04			08 20			08 37			
Bishops Stortford	a		07 02	07 11				07 27		07 32	07 41			08 02		08 11			08 27		08 32	08 44			
	d		07 02	07 12				07 28		07 32	07 41			08 02		08 12			08 28		08 32	08 44			
Stansted Mountfitchet	d		07 06					07 32			07 46			08 06					08 32			08 49			
Stansted Airport ✈	a		07 11		07 25			07 38		07 41		07 56		08 11				08 25	08 38		08 41		08 56		
✈	d						07 27										08 25								
Elsenham	d										07 49											08 52			
Newport (Essex)	d										07 55											08 58			
Audley End	d			07 24			07 40				07 58					08 24	08 38					09 01			
Great Chesterford	d										08 03											09 06			
Whittlesford Parkway	d			07 31							08 07					08 31						09 10			
Shelford	d										08 12					08 36									
Cambridge	a			07 42			07 55				08 18					08 42	08 57					09 19			

For general notes see front of timetable
For details of catering facilities see Directory of Train Operators

A To Enfield Town (Table 21)
B To Ely (Table 17)

b Previous night.
Stops to pick up only

Table 22

Saturdays

London → Broxbourne, Hertford East, Bishops Stortford, Stansted Airport and Cambridge

Network diagram - see first page of Table 20

Station	LE ■1 ⚲	LE ■1	XC ◇	LE ■1 ⚲	LE	LE	LE ■1 ⚲	LE ■1		LE ■1 ⚲	LE	LE ■1 ⚲	LE ■1	XC ◇	LE ■1 ⚲	LE	LE		LE ■1 ⚲	LE ■1	LE ■1 ⚲	LE	LE ■1 ⚲	LE ■1
London Liverpool Street 15 ⊖ d	08 25	08 28		08 40		08 42	08 55	08 58		09 10	09 12	09 25	09 28		09 40		09 42		09 55	09 58	10 10	10 12	10 25	10 28
Bethnal Green d																								
Hackney Downs d						08 48					09 18						09 48					10 18		
Stratford 7 ⊖ ⛴ d					08 33											09 33								
Clapton d																								
Seven Sisters ⊖ d																								
Tottenham Hale ⊖ d	08u37	08 40		08u52	08 43	08 55	09u07	09 10		09u22	09 25	09u37	09 40		09u52	09 43	09 55		10u07	10 10	10u22	10 25	10u37	10 40
Northumberland Park d					08 45											09 45								
Angel Road d																								
Ponders End d						09 00					09 30						10 00					10 30		
Brimsdown d						09 02					09 32						10 02					10 32		
Enfield Lock d					08 50	09 05					09 35					09 50	10 05					10 35		
Waltham Cross d						09 07					09 37						10 07					10 37		
Cheshunt d		08 48			08 54	09 10		09 18			09 40		09 48			09 54	10 10			10 18		10 40		10 48
Broxbourne 3 a		08 52			08 59	09 14		09 22			09 44		09 52			09 59	10 14			10 22		10 44		10 52
d		08 52			09 05	09 14		09 22			09 44		09 52			10 05	10 14			10 22		10 44		10 52
Rye House d						09 18					09 48						10 18					10 48		
St Margarets (Herts) d						09 21					09 51						10 21					10 51		
Ware d						09 25					09 55						10 25					10 55		
Hertford East a						09 30					10 00						10 32					11 00		
Roydon d					09 09			09 27								10 09				10 27				
Harlow Town d		08 59		09 07	09 14			09 31		09 37			09 59		10 07	10 14				10 31	10 37			10 59
Harlow Mill d					09 17			09 34								10 17				10 34				
Sawbridgeworth d		09 04			09 20			09 37					10 04			10 20				10 37				11 04
Bishops Stortford a	09 02	09 11			09 27		09 32	09 44				10 02	10 11			10 27			10 32	10 44			11 02	11 11
d	09 02	09 12			09 28		09 32	09 44				10 02	10 12			10 28			10 32	10 44			11 02	11 12
Stansted Mountfitchet d	09 06				09 32			09 49				10 06				10 32				10 49			11 06	
Stansted Airport ✈ a	09 11			09 25	09 38		09 41			09 56		10 11			10 25	10 38			10 41		10 56		11 11	
✈ d			09 25											10 25										
Elsenham d								09 52												10 52				
Newport (Essex) d								09 58												10 58				
Audley End d		09 24	09 38					10 01					10 24	10 38						11 01				11 24
Great Chesterford d								10 06												11 06				
Whittlesford Parkway d		09 31						10 10					10 31							11 10				11 31
Shelford d		09 36											10 36											11 36
Cambridge a		09 42	09 57					10 19					10 42	10 57						11 19				11 42

Station	XC ◇	LE ■1 ⚲	LE	LE		LE ■1 ⚲	LE ■1	LE ■1 ⚲	LE	LE ■1 ⚲	LE ■1	XC ◇	LE ■1 ⚲		LE	LE	LE ■1 ⚲	LE ■1	LE ■1 ⚲	LE	LE ■1 ⚲	LE ■1		XC ◇
London Liverpool Street 15 ⊖ d		10 40		10 42		10 55	10 58	11 10	11 12	11 25	11 28		11 40			11 42	11 55	11 58	12 10	12 12	12 25	12 28		
Bethnal Green d																								
Hackney Downs d				10 48					11 18							11 48				12 18				
Stratford 7 ⊖ ⛴ d			10 33												11 33									
Clapton d																								
Seven Sisters ⊖ d																								
Tottenham Hale ⊖ d		10u52	10 43	10 55		11u07	11 10	11u22	11 25	11u37	11 40		11u52		11 43	11 55	12u07	12 10	12u22	12 25	12u37	12 40		
Northumberland Park d			10 45												11 45									
Angel Road d																								
Ponders End d				11 00					11 30							12 00				12 30				
Brimsdown d				11 02					11 32							12 02				12 32				
Enfield Lock d			10 50	11 05					11 35						11 50	12 05				12 35				
Waltham Cross d				11 07					11 37							12 07				12 37				
Cheshunt d			10 54	11 10			11 18		11 40		11 48				11 54	12 10		12 18		12 40		12 48		
Broxbourne 3 a			10 59	11 14			11 22		11 44		11 52				11 59	12 14		12 22		12 44		12 52		
d			11 05	11 14			11 22		11 44		11 52				12 05	12 14		12 22		12 44		12 52		
Rye House d				11 18					11 48							12 18				12 48				
St Margarets (Herts) d				11 21					11 51							12 21				12 51				
Ware d				11 25					11 55							12 25				12 55				
Hertford East a				11 30					12 00							12 30				13 00				
Roydon d			11 09				11 27								12 09			12 27						
Harlow Town d		11 07	11 14				11 31	11 37			11 59		12 07		12 14			12 31	12 37			12 59		
Harlow Mill d			11 17				11 34								12 17			12 34						
Sawbridgeworth d			11 20				11 37				12 04				12 20			12 37				13 04		
Bishops Stortford a			11 27			11 32	11 44			12 02	12 11				12 27		12 32	12 44			13 02	13 11		
d			11 28			11 32	11 44			12 02	12 12				12 28		12 32	12 44			13 02	13 12		
Stansted Mountfitchet d			11 32				11 49			12 06					12 32			12 49			13 06			
Stansted Airport ✈ a		11 25	11 38			11 41		11 56		12 11			12 25		12 38		12 41		12 56		13 11			
✈ d	11 25											12 25												13 25
Elsenham d							11 52											12 52						
Newport (Essex) d							11 58											12 58						
Audley End d	11 38						12 01				12 24	12 38						13 01				13 24		13 38
Great Chesterford d							12 06											13 06						
Whittlesford Parkway d							12 10				12 31							13 10				13 31		
Shelford d											12 36											13 36		
Cambridge a	11 57						12 19				12 42	12 57						13 19				13 42		13 57

For general notes see front of timetable
For details of catering facilities see
Directory of Train Operators

Table 22

London → Broxbourne, Hertford East, Bishops Stortford, Stansted Airport and Cambridge

Network diagram - see first page of Table 20

		LE 1 ⚒	LE	LE	LE 1 ⚒	LE 1	LE 1 ⚒	LE	LE 1 ⚒		LE 1	XC ◇	LE 1 ⚒	LE	LE	LE 1 ⚒	LE 1	LE 1 ⚒		LE	LE 1 ⚒	LE 1	XC ◇	LE 1 ⚒	LE
London Liverpool Street 15 ⊖	d	12 40		12 42	12 55	12 58	13 10	13 12	13 25		13 28		13 40		13 42	13 55	13 58	14 10		14 12	14 25	14 28		14 40	
Bethnal Green	d																								
Hackney Downs	d			12 48				13 18							13 48					14 18					
Stratford 7 ⊖ ⛴	d		12 33											13 33											14 33
Clapton	d																								
Seven Sisters ⊖	d																								
Tottenham Hale ⊖	d	12u52	12 43	12 55	13u07	13 10	13u22	13 25	13u37		13 40		13u52	13 43	13 55	14u07	14 10	14u22		14 25	14u37	14 40		14u52	14 43
Northumberland Park	d		12 45											13 45											14 45
Angel Road	d																								
Ponders End	d			13 00				13 30							14 00					14 30					
Brimsdown	d			13 02				13 32							14 02					14 32					
Enfield Lock	d		12 50	13 05				13 35						13 50	14 05					14 35					14 50
Waltham Cross	d			13 07				13 37							14 07					14 37					
Cheshunt	d		12 54	13 10		13 18		13 40			13 48			13 54	14 10		14 18			14 40		14 48			14 54
Broxbourne 3	a		12 59	13 14		13 22		13 44			13 52			13 59	14 14		14 22			14 44		14 52			14 59
	d		13 05	13 14		13 22		13 44			13 52			14 05	14 14		14 22			14 44		14 52			15 05
Rye House	d			13 18				13 48							14 18					14 48					
St Margarets (Herts)	d			13 21				13 51							14 21					14 51					
Ware	d			13 25				13 55							14 25					14 55					
Hertford East	a			13 30				14 00							14 30					15 00					
Roydon	d		13 09			13 27								14 09			14 27								15 09
Harlow Town	d	13 07	13 14			13 31	13 37				13 59		14 07	14 14			14 31	14 37				14 59		15 07	15 14
Harlow Mill	d		13 17			13 34								14 17			14 34								15 17
Sawbridgeworth	d		13 20			13 37					14 04			14 20			14 37					15 04			15 20
Bishops Stortford	a		13 27		13 32	13 44			14 02		14 11			14 27		14 32	14 44				15 02	15 11			15 27
	d		13 28		13 32	13 44			14 02		14 12			14 28		14 32	14 44				15 02	15 12			15 28
Stansted Mountfitchet	d		13 32			13 49			14 06					14 32			14 49				15 06				15 32
Stansted Airport ✈	a	13 25	13 38		13 41		13 56		14 11				14 25	14 38		14 41		14 56			15 11			15 25	15 38
✈	d											14 25											15 25		
Elsenham	d					13 52											14 52								
Newport (Essex)	d					13 58											14 58								
Audley End	d					14 01					14 24	14 38					15 01					15 24	15 38		
Great Chesterford	d					14 06											15 06								
Whittlesford Parkway	d					14 10					14 31						15 10					15 31			
Shelford	d										14 36											15 36			
Cambridge	a					14 19					14 42	14 57					15 19					15 42	15 57		

		LE	LE 1 ⚒	LE 1	LE 1 ⚒		LE	LE 1 ⚒	LE 1	XC ◇	LE 1 ⚒	LE	LE	LE 1 ⚒		LE 1	LE 1 ⚒	LE	LE 1 ⚒	LE 1	XC ◇	LE 1 ⚒	LE		LE
London Liverpool Street 15 ⊖	d	14 42	14 55	14 58	15 10		15 12	15 25	15 28		15 40		15 42	15 55		15 58	16 10	16 12	16 25	16 28		16 40			16 42
Bethnal Green	d																								
Hackney Downs	d	14 48					15 18						15 48					16 18							16 48
Stratford 7 ⊖ ⛴	d											15 33											16 33		
Clapton	d																								
Seven Sisters ⊖	d																								
Tottenham Hale ⊖	d	14 55	15u07	15 10	15u22		15 25	15u37	15 40		15u52	15 43	15 55	16u07		16 10	16u22	16 25	16u37	16 40		16u52	16 43		16 55
Northumberland Park	d											15 45											16 45		
Angel Road	d																								
Ponders End	d	15 00					15 30						16 00					16 30							17 00
Brimsdown	d	15 02					15 32						16 02					16 32							17 02
Enfield Lock	d	15 05					15 35					15 50	16 05					16 35					16 50		17 05
Waltham Cross	d	15 07					15 37						16 07					16 37							17 07
Cheshunt	d	15 10		15 18			15 40		15 48			15 54	16 10			16 18		16 40		16 48			16 54		17 10
Broxbourne 3	a	15 14		15 22			15 44		15 52			15 59	16 14			16 22		16 44		16 52			16 59		17 14
	d	15 14		15 22			15 44		15 52			16 05	16 14			16 22		16 44		16 52			17 05		17 14
Rye House	d	15 18					15 48						16 18					16 48							17 18
St Margarets (Herts)	d	15 21					15 51						16 21					16 51							17 21
Ware	d	15 25					15 55						16 25					16 55							17 25
Hertford East	a	15 30					16 00						16 30					17 00							17 30
Roydon	d			15 27								16 09				16 27							17 09		
Harlow Town	d			15 31	15 37				15 59		16 07	16 14				16 31	16 37			16 59		17 07	17 14		
Harlow Mill	d			15 34								16 17				16 34							17 17		
Sawbridgeworth	d			15 37					16 04			16 20				16 37				17 04			17 20		
Bishops Stortford	a		15 32	15 44				16 02	16 11			16 27		16 32		16 44			17 02	17 11			17 27		
	d		15 32	15 44				16 02	16 12			16 28		16 32		16 44			17 02	17 12			17 28		
Stansted Mountfitchet	d			15 49				16 06				16 32				16 49			17 06				17 32		
Stansted Airport ✈	a		15 41		15 56			16 11			16 25	16 38		16 41			16 56		17 11			17 25	17 38		
✈	d									16 25											17 25				
Elsenham	d			15 52												16 52									
Newport (Essex)	d			15 58												16 58									
Audley End	d			16 01					16 24	16 38						17 01				17 24	17 38				
Great Chesterford	d			16 06												17 06									
Whittlesford Parkway	d			16 10					16 31							17 10				17 31					
Shelford	d								16 36											17 36					
Cambridge	a			16 19					16 42	16 57						17 19				17 42	17 57				

For general notes see front of timetable
For details of catering facilities see Directory of Train Operators

London → Broxbourne, Hertford East, Bishops Stortford, Stansted Airport and Cambridge

Network diagram - see first page of Table 20

		LE 1 🚲	LE 1	LE 1 🚲	LE	LE 1 🚲	LE 1	XC ◇	LE 1 🚲		LE	LE	LE 1 🚲	LE 1	LE 1 🚲	LE	LE 1 🚲	LE 1		XC ◇	LE 1 🚲	LE	LE	LE 1 🚲	LE 1
London Liverpool Street 15 ⊖	d	16 55	16 58	17 10	17 12	17 25	17 28		17 40			17 42	17 55	17 58	18 10	18 12	18 25	18 28			18 40		18 42	18 55	18 58
Bethnal Green	d																								
Hackney Downs	d				17 18							17 48				18 18							18 48		
Stratford 7 ⊖	d										17 33											18 33			
Clapton	d																								
Seven Sisters ⊖	d																								
Tottenham Hale ⊖	d	17u07	17 10	17u22	17 25	17u37	17 40		17u52		17 43	17 55	18u07	18 10	18u22	18 25	18u37	18 40			18u52	18 43	18 55	19u07	19 10
Northumberland Park	d										17 45											18 45			
Angel Road	d																								
Ponders End	d				17 30							18 00				18 30							19 00		
Brimsdown	d				17 32							18 02				18 32							19 02		
Enfield Lock	d				17 35						17 50	18 05				18 35						18 50	19 05		
Waltham Cross	d				17 37							18 07				18 37							19 07		
Cheshunt	d		17 18		17 40		17 48				17 54	18 10		18 18		18 40		18 48				18 54	19 10		19 18
Broxbourne 3	a		17 22		17 44		17 52				17 59	18 14		18 22		18 44		18 52				18 59	19 14		19 22
	d		17 22		17 44		17 52				18 05	18 14		18 22		18 44		18 52				19 05	19 14		19 22
Rye House	d				17 48							18 18				18 48							19 18		
St Margarets (Herts)	d				17 51							18 21				18 51							19 21		
Ware	d				17 55							18 25				18 55							19 25		
Hertford East	a				18 00							18 30				19 00							19 30		
Roydon	d		17 27								18 09			18 27								19 09			19 27
Harlow Town	d		17 31	17 37			17 59		18 07		18 14			18 31	18 37			18 59			19 07	19 14			19 31
Harlow Mill	d		17 34								18 17			18 34								19 17			19 34
Sawbridgeworth	d		17 37				18 04				18 20			18 37				19 04				19 20			19 37
Bishops Stortford	a	17 32	17 44			18 02	18 11				18 27		18 32	18 44			19 02	19 11				19 27		19 32	19 44
	d	17 32	17 44			18 02	18 12				18 28		18 32	18 44			19 02	19 12				19 28		19 32	19 44
Stansted Mountfitchet	d		17 49			18 06					18 32			18 49			19 06					19 32			19 49
Stansted Airport ✈	a	17 41		17 56		18 11			18 25		18 38		18 41		18 56		19 11				19 26	19 38		19 41	
✈	d							18 25												19 18					
Elsenham	d		17 52											18 52											19 52
Newport (Essex)	d		17 58											18 58											19 58
Audley End	d		18 01				18 24	18 38						19 01				19 24		19 32					20 01
Great Chesterford	d		18 06											19 06											20 06
Whittlesford Parkway	d		18 10				18 31							19 10				19 31							20 10
Shelford	d						18 36											19 36							20 15
Cambridge	a		18 19				18 42	18 57						19 19				19 42		19 49					20 21

		LE 1 🚲	LE	LE 1 🚲	LE 1		LE 1 🚲	LE	LE	LE 1 🚲	LE 1	LE 1 🚲	XC	LE		LE 1 🚲	LE 1	LE 1 🚲	LE	LE	LE 1 🚲	LE 1	LE 1 🚲		LE
London Liverpool Street 15 ⊖	d	19 10	19 12	19 25	19 28		19 40		19 42	19 55	19 58	20 10		20 12		20 25	20 28	20 40		20 42	20 55	20 58	21 10		21 12
Bethnal Green	d																								
Hackney Downs	d		19 18						19 48					20 18						20 48					21 18
Stratford 7 ⊖	d							19 33											20 33						
Clapton	d																								
Seven Sisters ⊖	d																								
Tottenham Hale ⊖	d	19u22	19 25	19u37	19 40		19u52	19 43	19 55	20u07	20 10	20u22		20 25		20u37	20 40	20u52	20 43	20 55	21u07	21 10	21u22		21 25
Northumberland Park	d							19 45											20 45						
Angel Road	d																								
Ponders End	d		19 30						20 00					20 30						21 00					21 30
Brimsdown	d		19 32						20 02					20 32						21 02					21 32
Enfield Lock	d		19 35					19 50	20 05					20 35					20 50	21 05					21 35
Waltham Cross	d		19 37						20 07					20 37						21 07					21 37
Cheshunt	d		19 40		19 48			19 54	20 10		20 18			20 40			20 48		20 54	21 10		21 18			21 40
Broxbourne 3	a		19 44		19 52			19 59	20 14		20 22			20 44			20 52		20 59	21 14		21 22			21 44
	d		19 44		19 52			20 05	20 14		20 22			20 44			20 52		21 05	21 14		21 22			21 44
Rye House	d		19 48						20 18					20 48						21 18					21 48
St Margarets (Herts)	d		19 51						20 21					20 51						21 21					21 51
Ware	d		19 55						20 25					20 55						21 25					21 55
Hertford East	a		20 00						20 30					21 00						21 30					22 00
Roydon	d							20 09			20 27								21 09			21 27			
Harlow Town	d	19 37			19 59		20 07	20 14			20 31	20 37					20 59	21 07	21 14			21 31	21 37		
Harlow Mill	d							20 17			20 34								21 17			21 34			
Sawbridgeworth	d				20 04			20 20			20 37						21 04		21 20			21 37			
Bishops Stortford	a			20 02	20 11			20 27		20 32	20 44					21 02	21 11		21 27		21 32	21 44			
	d			20 02	20 12			20 28		20 32	20 44					21 02	21 12		21 28		21 32	21 44			
Stansted Mountfitchet	d			20 06				20 32			20 49					21 06			21 32			21 49			
Stansted Airport ✈	a	19 56		20 11			20 25	20 38		20 41		20 56				21 11		21 25	21 38		21 41		21 56		
✈	d												20 57												
Elsenham	d										20 52											21 52			
Newport (Essex)	d										20 58											21 58			
Audley End	d				20 24						21 01		21 10				21 24					22 01			
Great Chesterford	d										21 06											22 06			
Whittlesford Parkway	d				20 31						21 10						21 31					22 10			
Shelford	d										21 15											22 15			
Cambridge	a				20 42						21 21		21 31				21 42					22 21			

For general notes see front of timetable
For details of catering facilities see Directory of Train Operators

Table 22

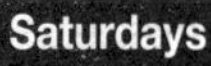

London → Broxbourne, Hertford East, Bishops Stortford, Stansted Airport and Cambridge

Network diagram - see first page of Table 20

Saturdays

Station		LE 1 🚲	LE 1	LE 1 🚲	LE	LE	LE 1 🚲	LE 1	LE 1 🚲	LE	LE 1 🚲	LE 1	LE 1 🚲	LE	LE	LE 1 🚲	LE 1	LE	LE 1 🚲	LE 1	LE	LE 1
London Liverpool Street 15 ⊖	d	21 25	21 28	21 40		21 42	21 55	21 58	22 10	22 12	22 25	22 28	22 40		22 42	22 55	22 58	23 12	23 25	23 28	23 42	23 58
Bethnal Green	d																					
Hackney Downs	d					21 48				22 18					22 48			23 18			23 48	
Stratford 7 ⊖ ⛴	d				21 33									22 33								
Clapton	d																				23 51	
Seven Sisters ⊖	d																					
Tottenham Hale ⊖	d	21u37	21 40	21u52	21 43	21 55	22u07	22 10	22u22	22 25	22u37	22 40	22u52	22 43	22 55	23u07	23 10	23 25	23u37	23 40	23 55	00 10
Northumberland Park	d				21 45									22 45				23 27			23 57	
Angel Road	d																					
Ponders End	d					22 00				22 30					23 00			23 31			00 01	
Brimsdown	d					22 02				22 32					23 02			23 33			00 03	
Enfield Lock	d				21 50	22 05				22 35				22 50	23 05			23 36			00 06	
Waltham Cross	d					22 07				22 37					23 07			23 38			00 08	
Cheshunt	d		21 48		21 54	22 10		22 18		22 40		22 48		22 54	23 10		23 18	23 41		23 48	00 11	00 18
Broxbourne 3	a		21 52		21 59	22 14		22 22		22 44		22 52		22 59	23 14		23 22	23 45		23 52	00 15	00 22
	d		21 52		22 05	22 14		22 22		22 44		22 52		23 05	23 14		23 22	23 45		23 52	00 15	00 22
Rye House	d					22 18				22 48					23 18			23 49			00 19	
St Margarets (Herts)	d					22 21				22 51					23 21			23 52			00 22	
Ware	d					22 25				22 55					23 25			23 56			00 26	
Hertford East	a					22 30				23 00					23 30			00 01			00 31	
Roydon	d				22 09			22 27						23 09			23 27					00 27
Harlow Town	d		21 59	22 07	22 14			22 31	22 37			22 59	23 07	23 14			23 31		23 55	23 59		00 31
Harlow Mill	d				22 17			22 34						23 17			23 34					00 34
Sawbridgeworth	d		22 04		22 20			22 37				23 04		23 20			23 37			00 05		00 37
Bishops Stortford	a	22 02	22 11		22 27		22 32	22 44			23 02	23 11		23 30		23 32	23 44		00 05	00 12		00 44
	d	22 02	22 12		22 28		22 32	22 44			23 02	23 12				23 32	23 44		00 05	00 13		00 44
Stansted Mountfitchet	d	22 06			22 32			22 49			23 06						23 49					00 49
Stansted Airport ✈	a	22 11		22 25	22 38		22 41		22 56		23 11		23 25			23 41			00 13			
✈	d																					
Elsenham	d							22 52									23 52					00 52
Newport (Essex)	d							22 58									23 58					00 58
Audley End	d		22 24					23 01				23 24					00 01			00 25		01 01
Great Chesterford	d							23 06									00 06					01 06
Whittlesford Parkway	d		22 31					23 10				23 31					00 10			00 32		01 10
Shelford	d							23 15									00 15					
Cambridge	a		22 42					23 21				23 42					00 21			00 42		01 19

Sundays

Station		LE 1	LE 1 🚲	LE 1	LE	LE 1	LE 1 🚲	LE 1 🚲	LE 1 🚲	LE 1 🚲	LE 1 🚲	LE 1 🚲	LE 1 🚲	LE 1 🚲	LE 1 🚲	LE 1 🚲	LE 1 🚲	LE	LE 1	LE 1	LE	LE 1 🚲	LE 1	LE 1 🚲
London Liverpool Street 15 ⊖	d	22p58	23p25	23p28	23p42	23p58	04 10	04 40	05 10	05 40	06 10	06 25	06 40	06 55	07 10	07 25	07 40		07 43		07 53	07 55		08 10
Bethnal Green	d																							
Hackney Downs	d				23p48																08 00			
Stratford 7 ⊖ ⛴	d																							
Clapton	d				23p51																			
Seven Sisters ⊖	d																				08 05			
Tottenham Hale ⊖	d	23p10	23b37	23p40	23p55	00 10		04u52	05u22	05u52	06u22	06u37	06u52	07 07	07 22	07 37	07 52		07 55			08 07		08 22
Northumberland Park	d				23p57																			
Angel Road	d																							
Ponders End	d				00 01														08 00					
Brimsdown	d				00 03														08 03					
Enfield Lock	d				00 06														08 05	←				
Waltham Cross	d				00 08														08 08	08 08				
Cheshunt	d	23p18		23p48	00 11	00 18													→	08 10	08 21			
Broxbourne 3	a	23p22		23p52	00 15	00 22														08 15	08 25			
	d	23p22		23p52	00 15	00 22												07 57		08 20	08 25			
Rye House	d				00 19													08 01			08 29			
St Margarets (Herts)	d				00 22													08 03			08 31			
Ware	d				00 26													08 07			08 35			
Hertford East	a				00 31													08 15			08 43		←	
Roydon	d	23p27				00 27														08 25 →			08 25	
Harlow Town	d	23p31	23p55	23p59		00 31		05 07	05 37	06 11		06 52		07 22		07 52						08 22	08 29	08 37
Harlow Mill	d	23p34				00 34																	08 32	
Sawbridgeworth	d	23p37		00 05		00 37																	08 35	
Bishops Stortford	a	23p44	00 05	00 12		00 44		05 17	05 47	06 21		07 02		07 32		08 02						08 32	08 42	
	d	23p44	00 05	00 13		00 44		05 17	05 48	06 21		07 02		07 32		08 02						08 32	08 42	
Stansted Mountfitchet	d	23p49				00 49		05 22				07 07				08 07							08 47	
Stansted Airport ✈	a		00 13				04 58	05 27	05 56	06 29	06 54	07 12	07 25	07 41	07 55	08 13	08 25					08 41		08 56
✈	d																							
Elsenham	d	23p52				00 52																	08 50	
Newport (Essex)	d	23p58				00 58																	08 56	
Audley End	d	00 01		00 25		01 01																	08 59	
Great Chesterford	d	00 06				01 06																	09 04	
Whittlesford Parkway	d	00 10		00 32		01 10																	09 08	
Shelford	d	00 15																					09 13	
Cambridge	a	00 21		00 42		01 19																	09 19	

For general notes see front of timetable
For details of catering facilities see Directory of Train Operators

b Previous night.
Stops to pick up only

Table 22

Sundays

London → Broxbourne, Hertford East, Bishops Stortford, Stansted Airport and Cambridge

Network diagram - see first page of Table 20

		LE		LE 1 ⊼	LE 1	LE	LE 1 ⊼	LE 1	LE	LE 1 ⊼	LE 1 ⊼	LE	LE 1	LE 1 ⊼		LE 1	LE	LE 1 ⊼	LE 1	LE	LE 1 ⊼	LE 1 ⊼	LE	LE 1	LE 1 ⊼
London Liverpool Street 15 ⊖	d	08 23		08 25	08 28		08 40		08 53	08 55	09 10	09 23		09 25		09 28		09 40		09 53	09 55	10 10	10 23		10 25
Bethnal Green	d					←											←								
Hackney Downs	d	08 30				08 30			09 00			09 30					09 30			10 00			10 30		
Stratford 7 ⊖	d	→						08 45				→							09 45				→		
Clapton	d																								
Seven Sisters ⊖	d					08 35			09 05								09 35			10 05					
Tottenham Hale ⊖	d			08 37	08 40		08 52	08 55		09 07	09 22			09 37		09 40		09 52	09 55		10 07	10 22			10 37
Northumberland Park	d																								
Angel Road	d																								
Ponders End	d							09 00											10 00						
Brimsdown	d							09 03											10 03						
Enfield Lock	d							09 05											10 05						
Waltham Cross	d							09 08											10 08						
Cheshunt	d				08 48	08 53		09 10	09 21							09 48	09 53		10 10	10 21					
Broxbourne 3	a				08 53	08 57		09 15	09 25							09 53	09 57		10 15	10 25					
	d				08 53	08 57		09 20	09 25							09 53	09 57		10 20	10 25					
Rye House	d					09 01			09 29								10 01			10 29					
St Margarets (Herts)	d					09 03			09 31								10 03			10 31					
Ware	d					09 07			09 35								10 07			10 35					
Hertford East	a					09 13			09 43								10 13			10 43					
Roydon	d							09 25											10 25						
Harlow Town	d				08 59		09 07	09 29			09 37					09 59		10 07	10 29			10 37			
Harlow Mill	d							09 32					←						10 32					←	
Sawbridgeworth	d				09 05			09 35					09 35			10 05			10 35					10 35	
Bishops Stortford	a			09 00	09 12			→		09 31			09 42	10 00		10 12			→		10 31			10 42	11 00
	d			09 01	09 12					09 31			09 42	10 01		10 12					10 31			10 42	11 01
Stansted Mountfitchet	d			09 05									09 47	10 05										10 47	11 05
Stansted Airport ✈	a			09 11			09 25			09 41	09 56			10 11				10 26			10 41	10 56			11 11
✈	d																								
Elsenham	d												09 50											10 50	
Newport (Essex)	d												09 56											10 56	
Audley End	d				09 24								09 59			10 24								10 59	
Great Chesterford	d												10 04											11 04	
Whittlesford Parkway	d				09 31								10 08			10 31								11 08	
Shelford	d												10 13											11 13	
Cambridge	a				09 43								10 21			10 43								11 21	

		LE 1	LE	LE 1 ⊼		LE 1	LE	LE 1 ⊼	LE 1 ⊼	LE	LE 1	XC ◇	LE 1 ⊼	LE 1	LE	LE 1 ⊼		LE 1	LE	LE 1 ⊼	LE 1 ⊼	LE	LE 1	LE 1 ⊼	LE 1
London Liverpool Street 15 ⊖	d	10 28		10 40			10 53	10 55	11 10	11 23			11 25	11 28		11 40			11 53	11 55	12 10	12 23		12 25	12 28
Bethnal Green	d		←												←										
Hackney Downs	d		10 30				11 00			11 30					11 30				12 00			12 30			
Stratford 7 ⊖	d					10 45				→								11 45				→			
Clapton	d																								
Seven Sisters ⊖	d		10 35				11 05								11 35				12 05						
Tottenham Hale ⊖	d	10 40		10 52		10 55		11 07	11 22				11 37	11 40		11 52		11 55		12 07	12 22			12 37	12 40
Northumberland Park	d																								
Angel Road	d																								
Ponders End	d					11 00												12 00							
Brimsdown	d					11 03												12 03							
Enfield Lock	d					11 05												12 05							
Waltham Cross	d					11 08												12 08							
Cheshunt	d	10 48	10 53			11 10	11 21							11 48	11 53			12 10	12 21						12 48
Broxbourne 3	a	10 53	10 57			11 15	11 25							11 53	11 57			12 15	12 25						12 53
	d	10 53	10 57			11 20	11 25							11 53	11 57			12 20	12 25						12 53
Rye House	d		11 01				11 29								12 01				12 29						
St Margarets (Herts)	d		11 03				11 31								12 03				12 31						
Ware	d		11 07				11 35								12 07				12 35						
Hertford East	a		11 13				11 43								12 13				12 43						
Roydon	d					11 25												12 25							
Harlow Town	d	10 59		11 07		11 29			11 37					11 59		12 07		12 29			12 37				12 59
Harlow Mill	d					11 32					←							12 32					←		
Sawbridgeworth	d	11 05				11 35					11 35			12 05				12 35					12 35		13 05
Bishops Stortford	a	11 12				→		11 31			11 42		12 00	12 12				→		12 31			12 42	13 00	13 12
	d	11 12						11 31			11 42		12 01	12 12						12 31			12 42	13 01	13 12
Stansted Mountfitchet	d										11 47		12 05										12 47	13 05	
Stansted Airport ✈	a			11 25				11 41	11 56				12 14			12 26				12 41	12 56			13 11	
✈	d											12 05													
Elsenham	d										11 50												12 50		
Newport (Essex)	d										11 56												12 56		
Audley End	d	11 24									11 59	12 18		12 24									12 59		13 24
Great Chesterford	d										12 04												13 04		
Whittlesford Parkway	d	11 31									12 08			12 31									13 08		13 31
Shelford	d										12 13												13 13		
Cambridge	a	11 43									12 21	12 35		12 43									13 21		13 43

For general notes see front of timetable
For details of catering facilities see
Directory of Train Operators

Table 22

Sundays

London → Broxbourne, Hertford East, Bishops Stortford, Stansted Airport and Cambridge

Network diagram - see first page of Table 20

		LE	LE 1 🛒	LE 1	LE	LE 1 🛒		LE 1 🛒	LE	LE 1	XC ◇	LE 1 🛒	LE 1	LE	LE 1 🛒	LE 1	LE	LE 1 🛒		LE 1 🛒	LE	LE 1	LE 1 🛒	LE 1	LE
London Liverpool Street 15 ⊖	d		12 40		12 53	12 55		13 10	13 23			13 25	13 28		13 40		13 53	13 55		14 10	14 23		14 25	14 28	
Bethnal Green	d	←												←											←
Hackney Downs	d	12 30			13 00				13 30					13 30			14 00				14 30				14 30
Stratford 7 ⊖ ⛴	d			12 45					→							13 45					→				
Clapton	d																								
Seven Sisters ⊖	d	12 35			13 05									13 35			14 05								14 35
Tottenham Hale ⊖	d		12 52	12 55		13 07		13 22				13 37	13 40		13 52	13 55		14 07		14 22			14 37	14 40	
Northumberland Park	d																								
Angel Road	d																								
Ponders End	d			13 00												14 00									
Brimsdown	d			13 03												14 03									
Enfield Lock	d			13 05												14 05									
Waltham Cross	d			13 08												14 08									
Cheshunt	d	12 53		13 10	13 21								13 48	13 53		14 10	14 21							14 48	14 53
Broxbourne 3	a	12 57		13 15	13 25								13 53	13 57		14 15	14 25							14 53	14 57
	d	12 57		13 20	13 25								13 53	13 57		14 20	14 25							14 53	14 57
Rye House	d	13 01			13 29									14 01			14 29								15 01
St Margarets (Herts)	d	13 03			13 31									14 03			14 31								15 03
Ware	d	13 07			13 35									14 07			14 35								15 07
Hertford East	a	13 13			13 43									14 13			14 43								15 13
Roydon	d			13 25												14 25									
Harlow Town	d		13 07	13 29				13 37					13 59		14 07	14 29				14 37				14 59	
Harlow Mill	d			13 32						←						14 32						←			
Sawbridgeworth	d			13 35						13 35			14 05			14 35						14 35		15 05	
Bishops Stortford	a			→		13 31				13 42		14 00	14 12			→		14 31				14 42	15 00	15 12	
	d					13 31				13 42		14 01	14 12					14 31				14 42	15 01	15 12	
Stansted Mountfitchet	d									13 47		14 05										14 47	15 05		
Stansted Airport ✈	a		13 26			13 41		13 56				14 14			14 26			14 41		14 56			15 11		
✈	d										14 05														
Elsenham	d									13 50												14 50			
Newport (Essex)	d									13 56												14 56			
Audley End	d									13 59	14 18		14 24									14 59		15 24	
Great Chesterford	d									14 04												15 04			
Whittlesford Parkway	d									14 08			14 31									15 08		15 31	
Shelford	d									14 13												15 13			
Cambridge	a									14 21	14 35		14 43									15 21		15 43	

		XC ◇	LE 1 🛒	LE 1	LE	LE 1 🛒	LE 1 🛒	LE		LE 1	XC ◇	LE 1 🛒	LE 1	LE	LE 1 🛒	LE 1	LE	LE 1 🛒	LE 1 🛒	LE		LE 1	LE 1 🛒	LE 1	LE
London Liverpool Street 15 ⊖	d		14 40		14 53	14 55	15 10	15 23				15 25	15 28		15 40		15 53	15 55	16 10	16 23			16 25	16 28	
Bethnal Green	d													←											←
Hackney Downs	d				15 00			15 30						15 30			16 00			16 30					16 30
Stratford 7 ⊖ ⛴	d			14 45				→								15 45				→					
Clapton	d																								
Seven Sisters ⊖	d				15 05									15 35			16 05								16 35
Tottenham Hale ⊖	d		14 52	14 55		15 07	15 22					15 37	15 40		15 52	15 55		16 07	16 22				16 37	16 40	
Northumberland Park	d																								
Angel Road	d																								
Ponders End	d			15 00												16 00									
Brimsdown	d			15 03												16 03									
Enfield Lock	d			15 05												16 05									
Waltham Cross	d			15 08												16 08									
Cheshunt	d			15 10	15 21								15 48	15 53		16 10	16 21							16 48	16 53
Broxbourne 3	a			15 15	15 25								15 53	15 57		16 15	16 25							16 53	16 57
	d			15 20	15 25								15 53	15 57		16 20	16 25							16 53	16 57
Rye House	d				15 29									16 01			16 29								17 01
St Margarets (Herts)	d				15 31									16 03			16 31								17 03
Ware	d				15 35									16 07			16 35								17 07
Hertford East	a				15 43									16 13			16 43								17 13
Roydon	d			15 25												16 25									
Harlow Town	d		15 07	15 29			15 37						15 59		16 07	16 29			16 37					16 59	
Harlow Mill	d			15 32						←						16 32						←			
Sawbridgeworth	d			15 35						15 35			16 05			16 35						16 35		17 05	
Bishops Stortford	a			→		15 31				15 42		16 00	16 12			→		16 31				16 42	17 00	17 12	
	d					15 31				15 42		16 01	16 12					16 31				16 42	17 01	17 12	
Stansted Mountfitchet	d									15 47		16 05										16 47	17 05		
Stansted Airport ✈	a		15 29			15 41	15 56					16 13			16 29			16 41	16 56				17 11		
✈	d	15 18									16 12														
Elsenham	d									15 50												16 50			
Newport (Essex)	d									15 56												16 56			
Audley End	d	15 31								15 59	16 24		16 24									16 59		17 24	
Great Chesterford	d									16 04												17 04			
Whittlesford Parkway	d									16 08			16 31									17 08		17 31	
Shelford	d									16 13												17 13			
Cambridge	a	15 46								16 21	16 40		16 46									17 21		17 43	

For general notes see front of timetable
For details of catering facilities see Directory of Train Operators

Table 22

Sundays

London → Broxbourne, Hertford East, Bishops Stortford, Stansted Airport and Cambridge

Network diagram - see first page of Table 20

		LE	XC	LE	LE	LE	LE	LE	LE	LE		LE	LE	LE	XC	LE	LE	LE	LE	LE	LE	LE		LE	LE
		[1] ✠	◇	[1]		[1] ✠	[1] ✠		[1]	[1] ✠		[1]		[1] ✠	◇	[1]		[1] ✠	[1] ✠		[1]	[1] ✠		[1]	
London Liverpool Street 15 ⊖	d	16 40			16 53	16 55	17 10	17 23		17 25		17 28	←	17 40			17 53	17 55	18 10	18 23		18 25		18 28	←
Bethnal Green	d																								
Hackney Downs	d				17 00			17 30					17 30				18 00			18 30					18 30
Stratford 7 ⊖	d			16 45				→								17 45				→					
Clapton	d																								
Seven Sisters ⊖	d				17 05								17 35				18 05								18 35
Tottenham Hale ⊖	d	16 52		16 55		17 07	17 22			17 37		17 40		17 52		17 55		18 07	18 22			18 37		18 40	
Northumberland Park	d																								
Angel Road	d																								
Ponders End	d			17 00												18 00									
Brimsdown	d			17 03												18 03									
Enfield Lock	d			17 05												18 05									
Waltham Cross	d			17 08												18 08									
Cheshunt	d			17 10	17 21							17 48	17 53			18 10	18 21							18 48	18 53
Broxbourne 3	a			17 15	17 25							17 53	17 57			18 15	18 25							18 53	18 57
	d			17 20	17 25							17 53	17 57			18 20	18 25							18 53	18 57
Rye House	d				17 29								18 01				18 29								19 01
St Margarets (Herts)	d				17 31								18 03				18 31								19 03
Ware	d				17 35								18 07				18 35								19 07
Hertford East	a				17 43								18 13				18 43								19 13
Roydon	d			17 25												18 25									
Harlow Town	d	17 07		17 29			17 37					17 59		18 07		18 29			18 37					18 59	
Harlow Mill	d			17 32					←							18 32					←				
Sawbridgeworth	d			17 35					17 35			18 05				18 35					18 35			19 05	
Bishops Stortford	a			→		17 31			17 42	18 00		18 12				→		18 31			18 42	19 00		19 12	
	d					17 31			17 42	18 01		18 12						18 31			18 42	19 01		19 12	
Stansted Mountfitchet	d								17 47	18 05											18 47	19 05			
Stansted Airport ✈	a	17 26				17 45	17 56			18 11				18 26				18 44	18 54			19 11			
✈	d		17 35												18 35										
Elsenham	d								17 50												18 50				
Newport (Essex)	d								17 56												18 56				
Audley End	d		17 48						17 59			18 24			18 48						18 59			19 24	
Great Chesterford	d								18 04												19 04				
Whittlesford Parkway	d								18 08			18 31									19 08			19 31	
Shelford	d								18 13												19 13				
Cambridge	a		18 08						18 21			18 43			19 06						19 21			19 43	

		LE	LE	LE	LE	LE	LE	LE	XC	LE	LE	LE		LE	LE	LE	LE	LE	XC	LE	LE	LE	LE	LE	LE
		[1] ✠	[1] ✠	[1]		[1] ✠	[1] ✠	[1]		[1] ✠		[1] ✠		[1]		[1] ✠	[1] ✠	[1]		[1] ✠		[1] ✠	[1]		[1] ✠
London Liverpool Street 15 ⊖	d	18 40	18 55		19 03	19 10	19 25	19 28		19 40		19 55			20 03	20 10	20 25	20 28		20 40		20 55		21 03	21 10
Bethnal Green	d				19 06										20 06									21 06	
Hackney Downs	d				19 12										20 12									21 12	
Stratford 7 ⊖	d			18 45										19 45									20 45		
Clapton	d																								
Seven Sisters ⊖	d				19 20										20 20									21 20	
Tottenham Hale ⊖	d	18 52	19 07	18 55		19 22	19 37	19 40		19 52		20 07		19 55		20 22	20 37	20 40		20 52		21 07	20 55		21 22
Northumberland Park	d																								
Angel Road	d																								
Ponders End	d			19 00										20 00									21 00		
Brimsdown	d			19 03										20 03									21 03		
Enfield Lock	d			19 05										20 05									21 05		
Waltham Cross	d			19 08										20 08									21 08		
Cheshunt	d			19 10	19 40			19 48						20 10	20 40			20 48					21 10	21 40	
Broxbourne 3	a			19 15	19 44			19 53			←			20 15	20 44			20 53			←		21 15	21 44	
	d			19 20	19 56			19 53			19 56			20 20	20 56			20 53			20 56		21 20	21 56	
Rye House	d				→						19 59				→						20 59			→	
St Margarets (Herts)	d										20 02										21 02				
Ware	d										20 05										21 05				
Hertford East	a										20 11										21 11				
Roydon	d			19 25										20 25									21 25		
Harlow Town	d	19 07		19 29		19 37		19 59		20 07				20 29		20 37		20 59		21 07			21 29		21 37
Harlow Mill	d			19 32										20 32									21 32		
Sawbridgeworth	d			19 35				20 05						20 35				21 05					21 35		
Bishops Stortford	a		19 31	19 42			20 00	20 12				20 31		20 42			21 00	21 12				21 31	21 42		
	d		19 31	19 42			20 01	20 12				20 31		20 42			21 01	21 12				21 31	21 42		
Stansted Mountfitchet	d			19 47			20 05							20 47			21 05						21 47		
Stansted Airport ✈	a	19 26	19 41			19 56	20 11			20 29		20 41				20 56	21 11			21 29		21 41			21 56
✈	d								20 19										21 19						
Elsenham	d			19 50										20 50									21 50		
Newport (Essex)	d			19 56										20 56									21 56		
Audley End	d			19 59				20 24	20 33					20 59				21 24	21 33				21 59		
Great Chesterford	d			20 04										21 04									22 04		
Whittlesford Parkway	d			20 08				20 31						21 08				21 31					22 08		
Shelford	d			20 13										21 13									22 13		
Cambridge	a			20 21				20 42	20 48					21 21				21 42	21 48				22 21		

For general notes see front of timetable
For details of catering facilities see Directory of Train Operators

Table 22

Sundays

London → Broxbourne, Hertford East, Bishops Stortford, Stansted Airport and Cambridge

Network diagram - see first page of Table 20

		LE		LE	XC	LE	LE	LE	LE	LE	LE	LE	LE	LE		LE	LE	LE	LE	LE	LE	LE	LE		
		1		1		1		1	1		1	1	1	1			1	1		1	1		1		
		🛒				🛒		🛒			🛒	🛒		🛒			🛒			🛒					
London Liverpool Street 15 ⊖	d	21 25		21 28		21 40		21 55		22 03	22 10	22 25	22 28	22 40			22 55		23 03	23 25	23 28		23 58		
Bethnal Green	d									22 06									23 06						
Hackney Downs	d									22 12									23 12						
Stratford 7 ⊖	d								21 45									22 45							
Clapton	d																								
Seven Sisters ⊖	d									22 20									23 20						
Tottenham Hale ⊖	d	21 37		21 40		21 52		22 07	21 55		22 22	22 37	22 40	22 52			23 07	22 55		23 37	23 40		00 09		
Northumberland Park	d																								
Angel Road	d																								
Ponders End	d								22 00									23 00			23 45				
Brimsdown	d								22 03									23 03			23 48				
Enfield Lock	d								22 05									23 05			23 50				
Waltham Cross	d								22 08									23 08			23 53				
Cheshunt	d			21 48					22 10	22 40			22 48					23 10	23 40		23 55		00 17		
Broxbourne 3	a			21 53			←		22 15	22 44			22 53			←		23 15	23 44		23 59	←	00 22		
	d			21 53			21 56		22 20	22 56			22 53			22 56		23 20	00 03		23 59	00 03	00 22		
Rye House	d						21 59			→						22 59			→			00 06			
St Margarets (Herts)	d						22 02									23 02						00 09			
Ware	d						22 05									23 05						00 12			
Hertford East	a						22 11									23 11						00 18			
Roydon	d								22 25									23 25					00 26		
Harlow Town	d			21 59		22 07			22 29		22 37		22 59	23 07				23 29		23 52	00 06		00 30		
Harlow Mill	d								22 32									23 32					00 33		
Sawbridgeworth	d			22 05					22 35				23 05					23 35			00 12		00 37		
Bishops Stortford	a	22 00		22 12				22 31	22 42			23 00	23 12				23 31	23 42		00 02	00 19		00 46		
	d	22 01		22 12				22 31	22 42			23 01	23 12				23 31	23 42		00 03					
Stansted Mountfitchet	d	22 05							22 47			23 05						23 47							
Stansted Airport ✈	a	22 11				22 29		22 41			22 56	23 11		23 25			23 41			00 11					
✈	d				22 19																				
Elsenham	d								22 50									23 50							
Newport (Essex)	d								22 56									23 56							
Audley End	d			22 24					22 59				23 24					23 59							
Great Chesterford	d								23 04									00 04							
Whittlesford Parkway	d			22 31					23 08				23 31					00 08							
Shelford	d								23 13									00 13							
Cambridge	a			22 42	22 47				23 21				23 42					00 21							

For general notes see front of timetable
For details of catering facilities see
Directory of Train Operators

Table 22

Cambridge, Stansted Airport, Bishops Stortford, Hertford East and Broxbourne → London

Network diagram - see first page of Table 20

Miles	Miles			LE MO	LE MX [1]	LE MX [1] ⚒	LE MO [1] ⚒	LE MX	LE [1] ⚒	LE [1] ⚒	LE [1] ⚒	LE MFO [1] ⚒	LE MFO [1] ⚒	XC	LE [1]	LE	LE MFO [1] ⚒		LE MFX [1] ⚒	LE	LE [1]	LE [1] ⚒	LE	LE	LE [1]
0	—	**Cambridge**	d		22p51									04 39	04 48						05 21				05 42
3¼	—	Shelford	d		22p55																05 25				05 46
6¾	—	Whittlesford Parkway	d		23p00										04 55						05 30				05 51
10	—	Great Chesterford	d		23p04																05 34				05 55
14	—	Audley End	d		23p10									04 53	05 02						05 40				06 01
15¾	—	Newport (Essex)	d		23p13																05 43				06 04
20¼	0	Elsenham	d		23p19																05 49				06 09
—	4½	**Stansted Airport** ✈	a											05 12											
—	—	✈	d			23p30	23p30		23p45	23p59	00 30	01 00	01 30				05 30					06 00			
22½	8¼	Stansted Mountfitchet	d		23p22																05 52	06 05			06 13
25½	—	**Bishops Stortford**	a		23p28		23p38		23p53	00 08	00 38				05 17		05 38				05 58	06 09			06 19
—	—		d		23p28		23p38		23p53	00 08	00 38				05 18		05 38		05 38	05 43	05 58	06 10		06 14	06 19
29	—	Sawbridgeworth	d		23p32										05 22					05 47	06 03			06 18	
31¼	—	Harlow Mill	d		23p36										05 26					05 51	06 06				
33	—	Harlow Town	d		23p39	23p45	23p47			00 17	00 46				05 29		05 46		05 46	05 54	06 10	06 18		06 23	06 27
35¾	—	Roydon	d		23p43										05 33					05 58	06 14				
—	0	**Hertford East**	d	22p56				23p38								05 25							06 05		
—	2	Ware	d	23p00				23p42								05 29							06 09		
—	4	St Margarets (Herts)	d	23p04				23p46								05 33							06 13		
—	5¼	Rye House	d	23p07				23p49								05 36							06 16		
38½	7	Broxbourne [3]	a	23p12	23p47			23p54							05 37	05 40	05 52		05 52	06 02	06 18		06 24	06 30	06 33
—	—		d	23p26	23p47			23p54							05 37	05 40	05 52		05 52	06 02	06 18		06 24	06 39	06 34
41¾	—	Cheshunt	d	23p31	23p51			23p58							05 41	05 44	05 56		05 56	06 06	06 23		06 29	→	
43	—	Waltham Cross	d													05 47				06 08			06 31		
44	—	Enfield Lock	d													05 49				06 11			06 34		
45	—	Brimsdown	d													05 52				06 13			06 36		
45¾	—	Ponders End	d													05 54				06 15			06 38		
48	—	Angel Road	d													05 57				06 19					
48¾	—	Northumberland Park	d													05 59				06 21					
49¾	—	Tottenham Hale ⊖	d												05 49	06 01	06 04		06 04	06 23	06 31	06 35	06 44		06 47
—	0	Seven Sisters ⊖	d	23p51	00 02	00 06	00 06	00 10	00 19																
51¼	—	Clapton	d																						
—	6¾	Stratford [7] ⊖	a																	06 37					
52¾	—	Hackney Downs	d	23p59				00 15								06 08							06 50		
54¼	—	Bethnal Green	d	00 06												06 12									
55¾	—	**London Liverpool Street** [15] ⊖	a	00 11	00 17	00 21	00 21	00 24	00 34	00 50	01 20	01 50	02 20		06 05	06 18	06 20		06 20		06 47	06 51	07 00		07 04

		LE [1] ⚒	LE	LE [1]	LE [1] ⚒	LE	LE	LE [1] A	LE [1] ⚒	LE		LE [1]	LE [1] ⚒	XC	LE	LE	LE [1]	LE [1] ⚒	LE	LE [1]	LE [1] ⚒	LE	LE	LE [1] A	LE [1] ⚒
Cambridge	d			05 51				06 18				06 21		06 32			06 48			06 51				07 18	
Shelford	d			05 55								06 26								06 55					
Whittlesford Parkway	d			06 00				06 25				06 30					06 55			07 00				07 25	
Great Chesterford	d			06 04								06 35								07 04					
Audley End	d			06 10				06 34				06 40		06 46			07 04			07 10				07 34	
Newport (Essex)	d			06 13								06 43								07 13					
Elsenham	d			06 19								06 49								07 19					
Stansted Airport ✈	a													07 05											
✈	d	06 15			06 30				06 43				07 00					07 15			07 30				07 43
Stansted Mountfitchet	d			06 22					06 48			06 52								07 22					07 48
Bishops Stortford	a	06 23		06 28	06 38			06 48	06 53			06 58	07 08				07 17	07 23		07 28	07 38			07 48	07 53
	d	06 23		06 28	06 38		06 41	06 49	06 53			06 58	07 08				07 18	07 23		07 28	07 38			07 49	07 53
Sawbridgeworth	d			06 33			06 45					07 03					07 22			07 33					
Harlow Mill	d			06 36			06 49					07 06								07 36					
Harlow Town	d			06 40	06 47		06 52	06 57	07 02			07 10					07 27	07 32		07 40				07 57	08 02
Roydon	d			06 44			06 56					07 14								07 44					
Hertford East	d					06 35									07 07	07 15						07 37	07 45		
Ware	d					06 39									07 11	07 19						07 41	07 49		
St Margarets (Herts)	d					06 43									07 15	07 23						07 45	07 53		
Rye House	d					06 46									07 18	07 26						07 48	07 56		
Broxbourne [3]	a		←	06 48		06 54	07 00	07 03		←		07 18	07 21		07 24	07 30	07 33		←	07 48	07 51	07 54	08 00	08 03	
	d		06 39	06 48		06 54	07 09	07 04		07 09		07 18	07 21		07 24	07 39	07 34		07 39	07 48	07 51	07 54	08 09	08 04	
Cheshunt	d		06 43	06 53		06 59	→			07 13			07 26		07 29	→			07 43	07 53		07 59	→		
Waltham Cross	d		06 46			07 01				07 16					07 31				07 46		07 58	08 01			
Enfield Lock	d		06 48			07 04				07 18					07 34				07 48			08 04			
Brimsdown	d					07 06							07 30		07 36				07 51		08 02	08 06			
Ponders End	d					07 08							07 32		07 38						08 04	08 08			
Angel Road	d		06 53							07 23															
Northumberland Park	d		06 55							07 25									07 56						
Tottenham Hale ⊖	d	06 51	06 58	07 01	07 04	07 14		07 17	07 20	07 28		07 31	07 37		07 44		07 47	07 50	07 58	08 01	08 09	08 14		08 17	08 20
Seven Sisters ⊖	d																								
Clapton	d																								
Stratford [7] ⊖	a		07 11							07 41									08 11						
Hackney Downs	d					07 20									07 50							08 20			
Bethnal Green	d																								
London Liverpool Street [15] ⊖	a	07 08		07 17	07 20	07 30		07 33	07 37			07 47	07 56		08 00		08 03	08 07		08 17	08 26	08 30		08 33	08 37

For general notes see front of timetable
For details of catering facilities see Directory of Train Operators

A From Kings Lynn (Table 17)

Cambridge, Stansted Airport, Bishops Stortford, Hertford East and Broxbourne → London

Network diagram - see first page of Table 20

Station		LE	LE 1		LE 1 🛒	XC	LE	LE	LE 1 A	LE 1 🛒	LE	LE 1	LE 1 🛒	LE	XC ◇	LE 1	LE 1 🛒	LE		LE 1 A	LE 1 🛒	LE	LE	LE 1 🛒	LE
Cambridge	d		07 21			07 32			07 48			07 51			08 09	08 18				08 21					
Shelford	d		07 25									07 55								08 25					
Whittlesford Parkway	d		07 30						07 55			08 00				08 25				08 30					
Great Chesterford	d		07 34									08 04								08 34					
Audley End	d		07 40			07 46			08 04			08 10			08 24	08 34				08 40					
Newport (Essex)	d		07 43									08 13								08 43					
Elsenham	d		07 49									08 19								08 49					
Stansted Airport ✈	a					08 05									08 43										
	d				08 00					08 15			08 30				08 45				09 00			09 15	
Stansted Mountfitchet	d		07 52									08 22					08 50			08 53					
Bishops Stortford	a		07 58						08 18	08 23		08 28				08 48	08 54			08 59				09 23	
	d		07 58					08 11	08 18	08 23		08 28				08 49	08 55			08 59			09 13	09 23	
Sawbridgeworth	d		08 03					08 15	08 23			08 33								09 04			09 17		
Harlow Mill	d		08 06					08 19				08 36								09 07			09 21		
Harlow Town	d		08 10		08 15			08 22	08 28			08 40	08 45			08 57				09 11	09 15		09 24		
Roydon	d		08 14					08 26				08 44								09 15			09 28		
Hertford East	d						08 08							08 38								09 08			
Ware	d						08 12							08 42								09 12			
St Margarets (Herts)	d						08 16							08 46								09 16			
Rye House	d						08 19							08 49								09 19			
Broxbourne 3	a	←	08 18				08 24	08 30	08 34		←	08 48		08 54		09 03				09 19		09 24	09 32		←
	d	08 09	08 18				08 24	08 40	08 34		08 40	08 48		08 54		09 04		09 09		09 19		09 24	09 38		09 38
Cheshunt	d	08 13	08 23				08 29	→			08 44	08 53		08 59				09 13		09 24		09 28	→		09 42
Waltham Cross	d	08 16					08 31				08 46			09 01				09 16				09 30			
Enfield Lock	d	08 18					08 34				08 49			09 04				09 18				09 33			09 46
Brimsdown	d						08 36							09 06								09 35			
Ponders End	d						08 38							09 08								09 37			
Angel Road	d	08 23									08 54							09 23							09 51
Northumberland Park	d	08 25									08 56							09 25							09 53
Tottenham Hale ⊖	d	08 28	08 31		08 34		08 44		08 47	08 50	08 58	09 01	09 04	09 14		09 18	09 21	09 28		09 32	09 36	09 42		09 48	09 55
Seven Sisters ⊖	d																								
Clapton	d																								
Stratford 7 ⊖	a	08 40									09 12							09 40							10 09
Hackney Downs	d						08 50							09 20								09 49			
Bethnal Green	d																								
London Liverpool Street 15 ⊖	a		08 47		08 50		09 00		09 03	09 07		09 17	09 20	09 30		09 34	09 38			09 48	09 58	10 00		10 04	

Station		LE 1	LE 1 🛒	LE	LE 1 🛒	XC ◇	LE 1	LE 1 🛒	LE	LE	LE 1 🛒		LE	LE 1	LE 1 🛒	LE	LE 1 🛒	XC ◇	LE 1	LE 1 🛒	LE	LE	LE 1 🛒	LE	LE 1
Cambridge	d	08 51				09 23	09 32							09 51				10 09	10 32						10 51
Shelford	d	08 55												09 55											10 55
Whittlesford Parkway	d	09 00					09 39							10 00					10 39						11 00
Great Chesterford	d	09 04												10 04											11 04
Audley End	d	09 10				09 37	09 46							10 10				10 23	10 46						11 10
Newport (Essex)	d	09 13												10 13											11 13
Elsenham	d	09 19												10 19											11 19
Stansted Airport ✈	a					09 58												10 49							
	d		09 30		09 45			10 00			10 15				10 30		10 45			11 00		11 03	11 15		
Stansted Mountfitchet	d	09 22			09 50									10 22								11 08			11 22
Bishops Stortford	a	09 28			09 53		10 00				10 23			10 28			10 53		11 00			11 12	11 23		11 28
	d	09 28			09 53		10 00			10 13	10 23			10 28			10 53		11 00			11 13	11 23		11 28
Sawbridgeworth	d	09 32					10 04			10 17				10 32					11 04			11 17			11 32
Harlow Mill	d	09 36								10 21				10 36								11 21			11 36
Harlow Town	d	09 39	09 45				10 09	10 15		10 24			←	10 39	10 45				11 09	11 15		11 24		←	11 39
Roydon	d	09 43								10 28			10 28	10 43								11 28		11 28	11 43
Hertford East	d			09 38					10 08	→						10 38					11 08	→			
Ware	d			09 42					10 12							10 42					11 12				
St Margarets (Herts)	d			09 46					10 16							10 46					11 16				
Rye House	d			09 49					10 19							10 49					11 19				
Broxbourne 3	a	09 47		09 54			10 15		10 24				10 32	10 47		10 54			11 15		11 24			11 32	11 47
	d	09 47		09 54			10 15		10 24				10 38	10 47		10 54			11 15		11 24			11 38	11 47
Cheshunt	d	09 51		09 58			10 19		10 28				10 42	10 51		10 58			11 19		11 28			11 42	11 51
Waltham Cross	d			10 00					10 30							11 00					11 30				
Enfield Lock	d			10 03					10 33				10 46			11 03					11 33			11 46	
Brimsdown	d			10 05					10 35							11 05					11 35				
Ponders End	d			10 07					10 37							11 07					11 37				
Angel Road	d																								
Northumberland Park	d												10 51											11 51	
Tottenham Hale ⊖	d	10 01	10 04	10 12	10 16		10 27	10 30	10 42		10 46		10 53	10 59	11 02	11 12	11 16		11 27	11 30	11 42		11 46	11 53	11 59
Seven Sisters ⊖	d																								
Clapton	d																								
Stratford 7 ⊖	a												11 07											12 07	
Hackney Downs	d			10 19					10 49							11 19					11 49				
Bethnal Green	d																								
London Liverpool Street 15 ⊖	a	10 17	10 20	10 30	10 33		10 43	10 47	11 00		11 02			11 15	11 18	11 30	11 32		11 43	11 46	12 00		12 02		12 15

For general notes see front of timetable
For details of catering facilities see
Directory of Train Operators

A From Ely (Table 17)

Cambridge, Stansted Airport, Bishops Stortford, Hertford East and Broxbourne → London

Network diagram - see first page of Table 20

		LE 1 🛒	LE	LE 1 🛒		XC ◇	LE 1	LE 1 🛒	LE	LE	LE 1 🛒	LE	LE 1	LE 1 🛒	LE	LE 1 🛒	XC ◇	LE 1	LE 1 🛒		LE	LE	LE 1 🛒	LE	LE 1
Cambridge	d					11 09	11 32						11 51				12 09	12 32							12 51
Shelford	d												11 55												12 55
Whittlesford Parkway	d						11 39						12 00					12 39							13 00
Great Chesterford	d												12 04												13 04
Audley End	d					11 23	11 46						12 10				12 23	12 46							13 10
Newport (Essex)	d												12 13												13 13
Elsenham	d												12 19												13 19
Stansted Airport ✈	a					11 49											12 49								
	d	11 30		11 45				12 00		12 03	12 15			12 30		12 45			13 00			13 03	13 15		
Stansted Mountfitchet	d									12 08			12 22									13 08			13 22
Bishops Stortford	a			11 53			12 00			12 12	12 23		12 28			12 53		13 00				13 12	13 23		13 28
	d			11 53			12 00			12 13	12 23		12 28			12 53		13 00				13 13	13 23		13 28
Sawbridgeworth	d						12 04			12 17			12 32					13 04				13 17			13 32
Harlow Mill	d									12 21			12 36									13 21			13 36
Harlow Town	d	11 45					12 09	12 15		12 24		←	12 39	12 45				13 09	13 15			13 24		←	13 39
Roydon	d									12 28		12 28	12 43									13 28		13 28	13 43
Hertford East	d		11 38						12 08	→					12 38						13 08	→			
Ware	d		11 42						12 12						12 42						13 12				
St Margarets (Herts)	d		11 46						12 16						12 46						13 16				
Rye House	d		11 49						12 19						12 49						13 19				
Broxbourne 3	a		11 54				12 15		12 24			12 32	12 47		12 54			13 15			13 24			13 32	13 47
	d		11 54				12 15		12 24			12 38	12 47		12 54			13 15			13 24			13 38	13 47
Cheshunt	d		11 58				12 19		12 28			12 42	12 51		12 58			13 19			13 28			13 42	13 51
Waltham Cross	d		12 00						12 30						13 00						13 30				
Enfield Lock	d		12 03						12 33			12 46			13 03						13 33			13 46	
Brimsdown	d		12 05						12 35						13 05						13 35				
Ponders End	d		12 07						12 37						13 07						13 37				
Angel Road	d																								
Northumberland Park	d											12 51												13 51	
Tottenham Hale ⊖	d	12 02	12 12	12 16			12 27	12 30	12 42		12 46	12 53	12 59	13 02	13 12	13 16		13 27	13 30		13 42		13 46	13 53	13 59
Seven Sisters ⊖	d																								
Clapton	d																								
Stratford 7 ⊖	a											13 07												14 07	
Hackney Downs	d		12 19						12 49						13 19						13 49				
Bethnal Green	d																								
London Liverpool Street 15 ⊖	a	12 18	12 30	12 32			12 43	12 46	13 00		13 02		13 15	13 18	13 30	13 32		13 45	13 47		14 00		14 02		14 15

		LE 1 🛒	LE	LE 1 🛒	XC ◇	LE 1	LE 1 🛒	LE	LE	LE 1 🛒	LE	LE 1		LE 1 🛒	LE	LE 1 🛒	XC ◇	LE 1	LE 1 🛒	LE	LE	LE 1 🛒	LE	LE 1	LE 1 🛒
Cambridge	d				13 09	13 32						13 51					14 09	14 32						14 51	
Shelford	d											13 55												14 55	
Whittlesford Parkway	d					13 39						14 00						14 39						15 00	
Great Chesterford	d											14 04												15 04	
Audley End	d				13 23	13 46						14 10					14 23	14 46						15 10	
Newport (Essex)	d											14 13												15 13	
Elsenham	d											14 19												15 19	
Stansted Airport ✈	a				13 49												14 49								
	d	13 30		13 45			14 00		14 03	14 15				14 30		14 45			15 00		15 03	15 15			15 30
Stansted Mountfitchet	d								14 08			14 22									15 08			15 22	
Bishops Stortford	a			13 53		14 00			14 12	14 23		14 28				14 53		15 00			15 12	15 23		15 28	
	d			13 53		14 00			14 13	14 23		14 28				14 53		15 00			15 13	15 23		15 28	
Sawbridgeworth	d					14 04			14 17			14 32						15 04			15 17			15 32	
Harlow Mill	d								14 21			14 36									15 21			15 36	
Harlow Town	d	13 45				14 09	14 15		14 24		←	14 39		14 45				15 09	15 15		15 24			15 39	15 45
Roydon	d								14 28		14 28	14 43									15 28			15 43	
Hertford East	d		13 38					14 08	→						14 38					15 08					
Ware	d		13 42					14 12							14 42					15 12					
St Margarets (Herts)	d		13 46					14 16							14 46					15 16					
Rye House	d		13 49					14 19							14 49					15 19					
Broxbourne 3	a		13 54			14 15		14 24			14 32	14 47			14 54			15 15		15 24	15 32		←	15 47	
	d		13 54			14 15		14 24			14 38	14 47			14 54			15 15		15 24	15 38		15 38	15 47	
Cheshunt	d		13 58			14 19		14 28			14 42	14 51			14 58			15 19		15 28	→		15 42	15 51	
Waltham Cross	d		14 00					14 30							15 00					15 30					
Enfield Lock	d		14 03					14 33			14 46				15 03					15 33			15 46		
Brimsdown	d		14 05					14 35							15 05					15 35					
Ponders End	d		14 07					14 37							15 07					15 37					
Angel Road	d																						15 51		
Northumberland Park	d										14 51												15 53		
Tottenham Hale ⊖	d	14 02	14 12	14 16		14 27	14 30	14 42		14 46	14 53	14 59		15 02	15 12	15 16		15 27	15 30	15 42		15 46	15 55	15 59	16 02
Seven Sisters ⊖	d																								
Clapton	d																								
Stratford 7 ⊖	a										15 07												16 09		
Hackney Downs	d		14 19					14 49							15 19					15 49					
Bethnal Green	d																								
London Liverpool Street 15 ⊖	a	14 18	14 30	14 32		14 43	14 46	15 00		15 02		15 15		15 18	15 30	15 33		15 43	15 46	16 00		16 02		16 15	16 19

For general notes see front of timetable
For details of catering facilities see Directory of Train Operators

Cambridge, Stansted Airport, Bishops Stortford, Hertford East and Broxbourne → London

Network diagram - see first page of Table 20

		LE	LE	LE 1 🚲	XC ◇		LE	LE 1	LE 1 🚲	LE	LE	LE 1 🚲	LE	LE 1	LE 1 🚲	LE	LE 1 🚲	XC ◇	LE	LE 1		LE 1 🚲	LE	LE	LE 1 🚲
Cambridge	d				15 09			15 21						15 51				16 09		16 21					
Shelford	d							15 25						15 55						16 25					
Whittlesford Parkway	d							15 30						16 00						16 30					
Great Chesterford	d							15 34						16 04						16 34					
Audley End	d				15 23			15 40						16 10				16 23		16 40					
Newport (Essex)	d							15 43						16 13						16 43					
Elsenham	d							15 49						16 19						16 49					
Stansted Airport ✈	a				15 49													16 49							
	d			15 45					16 00		16 03	16 15			16 30		16 45					17 00		17 03	17 15
Stansted Mountfitchet	d							15 52			16 08			16 22						16 52				17 08	
Bishops Stortford	a			15 53				15 58			16 12	16 23		16 28			16 53			16 58				17 12	17 23
	d		15 48	15 53				15 58			16 13	16 23		16 28			16 53			16 58				17 13	17 23
Sawbridgeworth	d							16 02			16 17			16 32						17 02				17 17	
Harlow Mill	d							16 06			16 21			16 36						17 06				17 21	
Harlow Town	d		15 56					16 09	16 15		16 24			16 39	16 45					17 09		17 15		17 24	
Roydon	d							16 13			16 28			16 43						17 13				17 28	
Hertford East	d	15 38								16 08						16 38							17 08		
Ware	d	15 42								16 12						16 42							17 12		
St Margarets (Herts)	d	15 46								16 16						16 46							17 16		
Rye House	d	15 49								16 19						16 49							17 19		
Broxbourne 3	a	15 54	16 02					16 17		16 24	16 32		←	16 47		16 54				17 17			17 24	17 32	
	d	15 54	16 08				←	16 17		16 24	16 38		16 38	16 47		16 54			17 09	17 17			17 24	17 38	
Cheshunt	d	15 58	16 12				16 12	16 21		16 28	→		16 42	16 51		16 58			17 13	17 21			17 28	→	
Waltham Cross	d	16 00	→							16 30						17 00							17 30		
Enfield Lock	d	16 03					16 16			16 33			16 46			17 03			17 17				17 33		
Brimsdown	d	16 05								16 35						17 05							17 35		
Ponders End	d	16 07								16 37						17 07							17 37		
Angel Road	d						16 21						16 51						17 22						
Northumberland Park	d						16 23						16 53						17 24						
Tottenham Hale ⊖	d	16 12		16 16			16 25	16 29	16 32	16 42		16 46	16 55	16 59	17 02	17 12	17 17		17 27	17 30		17 33	17 42		17 46
Seven Sisters ⊖	d																								
Clapton	d																								
Stratford 7 ⊖ ⛴	a						16 39						17 09						17 39						
Hackney Downs	d	16 19								16 49						17 19							17 49		
Bethnal Green	d																								
London Liverpool Street 15 ⊖	a	16 30		16 32				16 45	16 48	17 00		17 02		17 13	17 18	17 30	17 33			17 47		17 51	18 00		18 03

		LE	LE 1	LE 1 🚲	LE	XC ◇	LE 1 🚲	LE	LE 1	LE 1 🚲	LE	LE 1 🚲	LE		LE 1	LE 1 🚲	LE	LE 1 🚲	XC ◇	LE 1	LE 1 🚲	LE	LE 1 🚲	LE	LE 1
Cambridge	d		16 51			17 09			17 21						17 51				18 18	18 21					18 51
Shelford	d		16 55						17 25						17 55					18 26					18 55
Whittlesford Parkway	d		17 00						17 30						18 00					18 31					19 00
Great Chesterford	d		17 04						17 34						18 04					18 35					19 04
Audley End	d		17 10			17 23			17 40						18 10					18 41					19 10
Newport (Essex)	d		17 13						17 43						18 13					18 44					19 13
Elsenham	d		17 19						17 49						18 19					18 50					19 19
Stansted Airport ✈	a					17 43													18 47						
	d			17 30			17 45			18 00		18 15				18 30		18 45			19 00		19 15		
Stansted Mountfitchet	d		17 22				17 50		17 54						18 24			18 50		18 53					19 24
Bishops Stortford	a		17 28				17 53		18 00			18 23			18 30			18 54		18 59			19 23		19 30
	d		17 28				17 53		18 00			18 23			18 30			18 55		18 59			19 23		19 30
Sawbridgeworth	d		17 32						18 04						18 34					19 03					19 34
Harlow Mill	d		17 36						18 08						18 38										19 38
Harlow Town	d		17 39	17 45					18 11	18 15					18 41	18 45				19 08	19 15				19 41
Roydon	d		17 43						18 15						18 45										19 45
Hertford East	d				17 43						18 10		18 18				18 43					19 10		19 18	
Ware	d				17 47								18 22				18 47							19 22	
St Margarets (Herts)	d				17 51								18 26				18 51							19 26	
Rye House	d				17 54								18 29				18 54							19 29	
Broxbourne 3	a	←	17 47		17 58				18 19		18 24		18 33		18 49		18 58			19 14		19 23		19 33	19 49
	d	17 38	17 47		17 58			18 10	18 19		18 24		18 40		18 49		18 58			19 14		19 24		19 39	19 49
Cheshunt	d	17 42	17 51		18 02			18 14	18 23		18 28		18 44		18 53		19 02			19 18		19 28		19 43	19 53
Waltham Cross	d				18 05						18 30						19 05					19 30			
Enfield Lock	d	17 46			18 07			18 18			18 33		18 48				19 07					19 33		19 47	
Brimsdown	d				18 10						18 35						19 10					19 35			
Ponders End	d				18 12						18 37						19 12					19 37			
Angel Road	d	17 51						18 23					18 53											19 52	
Northumberland Park	d	17 53						18 25					18 55											19 54	
Tottenham Hale ⊖	d	17 55	17 59	18 03	18 17		18 21	18 27	18 31	18 34	18 42	18 48	18 57		19 01	19 04	19 17	19 21		19 26	19 32	19 42	19 47	19 57	20 01
Seven Sisters ⊖	d																								
Clapton	d																								
Stratford 7 ⊖ ⛴	a	18 09						18 40					19 10											20 09	
Hackney Downs	d				18 23						18 49						19 23					19 49			
Bethnal Green	d																								
London Liverpool Street 15 ⊖	a		18 17	18 21	18 33		18 40		18 49	18 57	19 00	19 05			19 18	19 25	19 35	19 40		19 47	19 50	20 00	20 03		20 17

For general notes see front of timetable
For details of catering facilities see Directory of Train Operators

Cambridge, Stansted Airport, Bishops Stortford, Hertford East and Broxbourne → London

Network diagram - see first page of Table 20

		LE 1 🍴	LE	LE 1 🍴	LE 1	LE 1 🍴		LE	XC ◇	LE	LE 1 🍴	LE	LE 1	LE 1 🍴	LE	LE 1 🍴	LE 1	LE 1 🍴	LE	LE	LE 1 🍴		LE	LE 1	LE 1 🍴
Cambridge	d				19 21				19 30				19 51				20 32							20 51	
Shelford	d				19 25								19 55											20 55	
Whittlesford Parkway	d				19 30								20 00				20 39							21 00	
Great Chesterford	d				19 34								20 04											21 04	
Audley End	d				19 40				19 44				20 10				20 46							21 10	
Newport (Essex)	d				19 43								20 13											21 13	
Elsenham	d				19 49								20 19											21 19	
Stansted Airport ✈	a								20 05																
✈	d	19 30		19 45		20 00		20 03			20 15			20 30		20 45		21 00		21 03	21 15				21 30
Stansted Mountfitchet	d				19 56			20 08					20 22							21 08				21 22	
Bishops Stortford	a			19 53	20 02			20 12			20 23		20 28			20 53	21 00			21 12	21 23			21 28	
	d			19 53	20 02			20 13			20 23		20 28			20 53	21 00			21 13	21 23			21 28	
Sawbridgeworth	d				20 06			20 17					20 32				21 04			21 17				21 32	
Harlow Mill	d							20 21					20 36							21 21				21 36	
Harlow Town	d	19 45			20 11	20 15		20 24				←	20 39	20 45			21 09	21 15		21 24			←	21 39	21 45
Roydon	d							20 28				20 28	20 43							21 28			21 28	21 43	
Hertford East	d		19 42					↪		20 10					20 38				21 08	↪					
Ware	d		19 46							20 14					20 42				21 12						
St Margarets (Herts)	d		19 50							20 18					20 46				21 16						
Rye House	d		19 53							20 21					20 49				21 19						
Broxbourne [3]	a		19 57		20 17					20 25		20 32	20 47		20 54		21 15		21 24				21 32	21 47	
	d		19 57		20 17					20 25		20 38	20 47		20 54		21 15		21 24				21 38	21 47	
Cheshunt	d		20 01		20 21					20 29		20 42	20 51		20 58		21 19		21 28				21 42	21 51	
Waltham Cross	d		20 04							20 32					21 00				21 30						
Enfield Lock	d		20 06							20 34		20 46			21 03				21 33				21 46		
Brimsdown	d		20 09							20 37					21 05				21 35						
Ponders End	d		20 11							20 39					21 07				21 37						
Angel Road	d																								
Northumberland Park	d											20 51											21 51		
Tottenham Hale	⊖ d	20 04	20 16	20 20	20 29	20 32				20 44	20 48	20 53	20 59	21 03	21 12	21 16	21 27	21 30	21 42		21 46		21 53	21 59	22 02
Seven Sisters	⊖ d																								
Clapton	d																								
Stratford [7]	⊖ 🚆 a											21 07											22 07		
Hackney Downs	d		20 22							20 50					21 19				21 49						
Bethnal Green	d																								
London Liverpool Street [15]	⊖ a	20 20	20 31	20 40	20 45	20 50				21 00	21 04		21 15	21 20	21 30	21 33	21 43	21 46	22 00		22 02			22 15	22 18

		LE	LE 1 🍴	LE 1	LE 1 🍴	LE	LE	LE 1 🍴	LE 1	LE 1 🍴	LE	LE 1 🍴	LE 1	LE 1 🍴		LE	LE	LE 1 🍴	LE 1	LE 1 🍴	LE	LE 1 🍴	LE 1 🍴		
Cambridge	d			21 32					21 51				22 32						22 51						
Shelford	d								21 55										22 55						
Whittlesford Parkway	d			21 39					22 00				22 39						23 00						
Great Chesterford	d								22 04										23 04						
Audley End	d			21 46					22 10				22 46						23 10						
Newport (Essex)	d								22 13										23 13						
Elsenham	d								22 19										23 19						
Stansted Airport ✈	a																								
✈	d		21 45		22 00		22 03	22 15		22 30		22 45		23 00			23 03	23 15		23 30		23 45	23 59		
Stansted Mountfitchet	d						22 08		22 22								23 08		23 22						
Bishops Stortford	a		21 53	22 00			22 14	22 23	22 28			22 53	23 00				23 14	23 23	23 28			23 53	00 08		
	d		21 53	22 00				22 23	22 28			22 53	23 00					23 23	23 28			23 53	00 08		
Sawbridgeworth	d			22 04					22 32				23 04						23 32						
Harlow Mill	d								22 36										23 36						
Harlow Town	d			22 09	22 15				22 39	22 45			23 09	23 15					23 39	23 45			00 17		
Roydon	d								22 43										23 43						
Hertford East	d	21 38				22 08					22 38					23 08					23 38				
Ware	d	21 42				22 12					22 42					23 12					23 42				
St Margarets (Herts)	d	21 46				22 16					22 46					23 16					23 46				
Rye House	d	21 49				22 19					22 49					23 19					23 49				
Broxbourne [3]	a	21 54		22 15		22 24			22 47		22 54		23 15			23 24			23 47		23 54				
	d	21 54		22 15		22 24			22 47		22 54		23 15			23 24			23 47		23 54				
Cheshunt	d	21 58		22 19		22 28			22 51		22 58		23 19			23 28			23 51		23 58				
Waltham Cross	d	22 00				22 30					23 00					23 30									
Enfield Lock	d	22 03				22 33					23 03					23 33									
Brimsdown	d	22 05				22 35					23 05					23 35									
Ponders End	d	22 07				22 37					23 07					23 37									
Angel Road	d																								
Northumberland Park	d										23 11														
Tottenham Hale	⊖ d	22 12	22 16	22 27	22 30	22 42		22 46	22 59	23 02	23 13	23 17	23 27	23 30		23 42		23 46							
Seven Sisters	⊖ d																		00 02	00 06	00 10	00 18			
Clapton	d																								
Stratford [7]	⊖ 🚆 a																								
Hackney Downs	d	22 19				22 49					23 19					23 49					00 15				
Bethnal Green	d																								
London Liverpool Street [15]	⊖ a	22 30	22 32	22 43	22 46	23 00		23 02	23 15	23 18	23 30	23 33	23 43	23 46		00 01		00 01	00 17	00 21	00 24	00 33	00 50		

For general notes see front of timetable
For details of catering facilities see Directory of Train Operators

Table 22

Saturdays

Cambridge, Stansted Airport, Bishops Stortford, Hertford East and Broxbourne → London

Network diagram - see first page of Table 20

Station		LE 1	LE 1 🛒	LE	LE 1 🛒	LE 1 🛒	LE 1 🛒	LE 1 🛒	LE 1 🛒	LE	XC	LE	LE 1 🛒	LE 1	LE 1 🛒	LE	LE	LE 1 🛒	LE	LE 1	LE 1 🛒	LE	LE 1 🛒	XC	LE 1
Cambridge	d	22p51								04 25	04 39			05 21						05 51				06 25	06 32
Shelford	d	22p55												05 25						05 55					
Whittlesford Parkway	d	23p00								04 32				05 30						06 00					06 39
Great Chesterford	d	23p04												05 34						06 04					
Audley End	d	23p10								04 39	04 53			05 40						06 10				06 39	06 46
Newport (Essex)	d	23p13												05 43						06 13					
Elsenham	d	23p19												05 49						06 19					
Stansted Airport ✈	a										05 13													06 58	
✈	d		23p30		23p45	23p59	00 30	01 00	01 30				05 30		06 00		06 03	06 15			06 30		06 45		
Stansted Mountfitchet	d	23p22												05 52			06 08			06 22			06 50		
Bishops Stortford	a	23p28			23p53	00 08	00 38			04 52			05 38	05 58			06 12	06 23		06 28			06 54		07 00
	d	23p28			23p53	00 08	00 38			04 53		05 15	05 38	05 58			06 13	06 23		06 28			06 54		07 00
Sawbridgeworth	d	23p32								04 57		05 19		06 02			06 17			06 32					07 04
Harlow Mill	d	23p36								05 01		05 23		06 06			06 21			06 36					
Harlow Town	d	23p39	23p45			00 17	00 46			05 04		05 26	05 46	06 09	06 15		06 24		←	06 39	06 45				07 09
Roydon	d	23p43								05 08		05 30		06 13			06 28		06 28	06 43					
Hertford East	d			23p38												06 08	→					06 38			
Ware	d			23p42												06 12						06 42			
St Margarets (Herts)	d			23p46												06 16						06 46			
Rye House	d			23p49												06 19						06 49			
Broxbourne 3	a	23p47		23p54						05 12		05 34	05 52	06 17		06 24			06 32	06 47		06 54			07 15
	d	23p47		23p54						05 12		05 34	05 52	06 17		06 24			06 38	06 47		06 54			07 15
Cheshunt	d	23p51		23p58						05 16		05 38	05 56	06 21		06 28			06 42	06 51		06 58			07 19
Waltham Cross	d											05 41				06 30						07 00			
Enfield Lock	d											05 43				06 33			06 46			07 03			
Brimsdown	d											05 46				06 35						07 05			
Ponders End	d											05 48				06 37						07 07			
Angel Road	d																								
Northumberland Park	d											05 52							06 51						
Tottenham Hale	⊖ d											05 54	06 04	06 29	06 32	06 42		06 46	06 53	06 59	07 02	07 12	07 16		07 27
Seven Sisters	⊖ d	00 02	00 06	00 10	00 19					05 35															
Clapton	d																								
Stratford 7	⊖ a											06 05							07 07						
Hackney Downs	d			00 15						05 46						06 49						07 19			
Bethnal Green	d									05 50															
London Liverpool Street 15	⊖ a	00 17	00 21	00 24	00 34	00 50	01 20	01 50	02 20	05 55		06 18	06 20	06 45	06 48	07 00		07 02		07 15	07 18	07 30	07 32		07 43

Station		LE 1 🛒		LE	LE	LE 1 🛒	LE	LE 1	LE 1 🛒	LE	LE 1 🛒	XC	LE 1	LE 1 🛒	LE	LE	LE 1 🛒	LE	LE 1	LE 1 🛒	LE	LE 1 🛒	XC ◇	LE 1	LE 1 🛒
Cambridge	d							06 51				07 24	07 32						07 51				08 09	08 32	
Shelford	d							06 55											07 55						
Whittlesford Parkway	d							07 00					07 39						08 00					08 39	
Great Chesterford	d							07 04											08 04						
Audley End	d							07 10				07 38	07 46						08 10				08 23	08 46	
Newport (Essex)	d							07 13											08 13						
Elsenham	d							07 19											08 19						
Stansted Airport ✈	a											07 58											08 49		
✈	d	07 00			07 03	07 15			07 30		07 45			08 00		08 03	08 15			08 30		08 45			09 00
Stansted Mountfitchet	d				07 08			07 22			07 50					08 08			08 22			08 50			
Bishops Stortford	a				07 12	07 23		07 28			07 54		08 00			08 12	08 23		08 28			08 54		09 00	
	d				07 13	07 23		07 28			07 54		08 00			08 13	08 23		08 28			08 54		09 00	
Sawbridgeworth	d				07 17			07 32					08 04			08 17			08 32					09 04	
Harlow Mill	d				07 21			07 36								08 21			08 36						
Harlow Town	d	07 15			07 24		←	07 39	07 45				08 09	08 15		08 24		←	08 39	08 45				09 09	09 15
Roydon	d				07 28		07 28	07 43								08 28		08 28	08 43						
Hertford East	d			07 08	→					07 38					08 08	→					08 38				
Ware	d			07 12						07 42					08 12						08 42				
St Margarets (Herts)	d			07 16						07 46					08 16						08 46				
Rye House	d			07 19						07 49					08 19						08 49				
Broxbourne 3	a			07 24			07 32	07 47		07 54			08 15		08 24			08 32	08 47		08 54			09 15	
	d			07 24			07 38	07 47		07 54			08 15		08 24			08 38	08 47		08 54			09 15	
Cheshunt	d			07 28			07 42	07 51		07 58			08 19		08 28			08 42	08 51		08 58			09 19	
Waltham Cross	d			07 30						08 00					08 30						09 00				
Enfield Lock	d			07 33			07 46			08 03					08 33			08 46			09 03				
Brimsdown	d			07 35						08 05					08 35						09 05				
Ponders End	d			07 37						08 07					08 37						09 07				
Angel Road	d																								
Northumberland Park	d						07 51											08 51							
Tottenham Hale	⊖ d	07 30		07 42		07 46	07 53	07 59	08 02	08 12	08 16		08 27	08 30	08 42		08 46	08 53	08 59	09 02	09 12	09 16		09 27	09 30
Seven Sisters	⊖ d																								
Clapton	d																								
Stratford 7	⊖ a						08 07											09 07							
Hackney Downs	d			07 49						08 19					08 49						09 19				
Bethnal Green	d																								
London Liverpool Street 15	⊖ a	07 46		08 00		08 02		08 15	08 18	08 30	08 32		08 43	08 46	09 00		09 02		09 15	09 18	09 30	09 32		09 43	09 46

For general notes see front of timetable
For details of catering facilities see Directory of Train Operators

Cambridge, Stansted Airport, Bishops Stortford, Hertford East and Broxbourne → London

Network diagram - see first page of Table 20

		LE	LE	LE [1] ✠		LE	LE [1]	LE [1] ✠	LE	LE [1] ✠	XC ◇	LE [1] A	LE [1] ✠	LE	LE	LE [1] ✠	LE	LE [1]	LE [1] ✠	LE	LE [1] ✠	XC ◇	LE [1]	LE [1] ✠	LE
Cambridge	d						08 51				09 24	09 32						09 51				10 09	10 32		
Shelford	d						08 55											09 55							
Whittlesford Parkway	d						09 00					09 39						10 00					10 39		
Great Chesterford	d						09 04											10 04							
Audley End	d						09 10				09 38	09 46						10 10				10 23	10 46		
Newport (Essex)	d						09 13											10 13							
Elsenham	d						09 19											10 19							
Stansted Airport ✈	a										09 58											10 49			
	d		09 03	09 15				09 30		09 45			10 00		10 03	10 15			10 30		10 45			11 00	
Stansted Mountfitchet	d		09 08				09 22			09 50					10 08			10 22			10 50				
Bishops Stortford	a		09 12	09 23			09 28			09 54		10 00			10 12	10 23		10 28			10 54		11 00		
	d		09 13	09 23			09 28			09 54		10 00			10 13	10 23		10 28			10 54		11 00		
Sawbridgeworth	d		09 17				09 32					10 04			10 17			10 32					11 04		
Harlow Mill	d		09 21				09 36								10 21			10 36							
Harlow Town	d		09 24			←	09 39	09 45				10 09	10 15		10 24		←	10 39	10 45				11 09	11 15	
Roydon	d		09 28			09 28	09 43								10 28		10 28	10 43							
Hertford East	d	09 08	→						09 38					10 08	→					10 38					11 08
Ware	d	09 12							09 42					10 12						10 42					11 12
St Margarets (Herts)	d	09 16							09 46					10 16						10 46					11 16
Rye House	d	09 19							09 49					10 19						10 49					11 19
Broxbourne [3]	a	09 24				09 32	09 47		09 54			10 15		10 24			10 32	10 47		10 54			11 15		11 24
	d	09 24				09 38	09 47		09 54			10 15		10 24			10 38	10 47		10 54			11 15		11 24
Cheshunt	d	09 28				09 42	09 51		09 58			10 19		10 28			10 42	10 51		10 58			11 19		11 28
Waltham Cross	d	09 30							10 00					10 30						11 00					11 30
Enfield Lock	d	09 33				09 46			10 03					10 33			10 46			11 03					11 33
Brimsdown	d	09 35							10 05					10 35						11 05					11 35
Ponders End	d	09 37							10 07					10 37						11 07					11 37
Angel Road	d																								
Northumberland Park	d					09 51											10 51								
Tottenham Hale ⊖	d	09 42		09 46		09 53	09 59	10 02	10 12	10 16		10 27	10 30	10 42		10 46	10 53	10 59	11 02	11 12	11 16		11 27	11 30	11 42
Seven Sisters ⊖	d																								
Clapton	d																								
Stratford [7] ⊖	a					10 07											11 07								
Hackney Downs	d	09 49							10 19					10 49						11 19					11 49
Bethnal Green	d																								
London Liverpool Street [15] ⊖	a	10 00		10 02			10 15	10 18	10 30	10 32		10 43	10 46	11 00		11 02		11 15	11 18	11 30	11 32		11 43	11 46	12 00

		LE	LE [1] ✠	LE	LE [1]	LE [1] ✠		LE	LE [1] ✠	XC ◇	LE [1]	LE [1] ✠	LE	LE	LE [1] ✠	LE	LE [1]	LE [1] ✠	LE	LE [1] ✠	XC ◇	LE [1]	LE [1] ✠	LE	LE
Cambridge	d				10 51					11 09	11 32						11 51				12 09	12 32			
Shelford	d				10 55												11 55								
Whittlesford Parkway	d				11 00						11 39						12 00					12 39			
Great Chesterford	d				11 04												12 04								
Audley End	d				11 10					11 23	11 46						12 10				12 23	12 46			
Newport (Essex)	d				11 13												12 13								
Elsenham	d				11 19												12 19								
Stansted Airport ✈	a									11 49											12 49				
	d	11 03	11 15			11 30			11 45			12 00		12 03	12 15			12 30		12 45			13 00		13 03
Stansted Mountfitchet	d	11 08			11 22				11 50					12 08			12 22			12 50					13 08
Bishops Stortford	a	11 12	11 23		11 28				11 54		12 00			12 12	12 23		12 28			12 54		13 00			13 12
	d	11 13	11 23		11 28				11 54		12 00			12 13	12 23		12 28			12 54		13 00			13 13
Sawbridgeworth	d	11 17			11 32						12 04			12 17			12 32					13 04			13 17
Harlow Mill	d	11 21			11 36									12 21			12 36								13 21
Harlow Town	d	11 24		←	11 39	11 45					12 09	12 15		12 24		←	12 39	12 45				13 09	13 15		13 24
Roydon	d	11 28		11 28	11 43									12 28		12 28	12 43								13 28
Hertford East	d	→						11 38					12 08	→					12 38					13 08	→
Ware	d							11 42					12 12						12 42					13 12	
St Margarets (Herts)	d							11 46					12 16						12 46					13 16	
Rye House	d							11 49					12 19						12 49					13 19	
Broxbourne [3]	a			11 32	11 47			11 54			12 15		12 24			12 32	12 47		12 54			13 15		13 24	
	d			11 38	11 47			11 54			12 15		12 24			12 38	12 47		12 54			13 15		13 24	
Cheshunt	d			11 42	11 51			11 58			12 19		12 28			12 42	12 51		12 58			13 19		13 28	
Waltham Cross	d							12 00					12 30						13 00					13 30	
Enfield Lock	d			11 46				12 03					12 33			12 46			13 03					13 33	
Brimsdown	d							12 05					12 35						13 05					13 35	
Ponders End	d							12 07					12 37						13 07					13 37	
Angel Road	d																								
Northumberland Park	d			11 51												12 51									
Tottenham Hale ⊖	d		11 46	11 53	11 59	12 02		12 12	12 16		12 27	12 30	12 42		12 46	12 53	12 59	13 02	13 12	13 16		13 27	13 30	13 42	
Seven Sisters ⊖	d																								
Clapton	d																								
Stratford [7] ⊖	a			12 07												13 07									
Hackney Downs	d							12 19					12 49						13 19					13 49	
Bethnal Green	d																								
London Liverpool Street [15] ⊖	a		12 02		12 15	12 18		12 30	12 32		12 43	12 46	13 00		13 02		13 15	13 18	13 30	13 32		13 43	13 46	14 00	

For general notes see front of timetable
For details of catering facilities see Directory of Train Operators

A From Ely (Table 17)

Table 22

Saturdays

Cambridge, Stansted Airport, Bishops Stortford, Hertford East and Broxbourne → London

Network diagram - see first page of Table 20

		LE 1 ⚲	LE	LE 1	LE 1 ⚲	LE	LE 1 ⚲	XC ◇		LE 1	LE 1 ⚲	LE	LE	LE 1 ⚲	LE	LE 1	LE 1 ⚲	LE	LE 1 ⚲	XC ◇	LE 1	LE 1 ⚲	LE	LE	LE 1 ⚲
Cambridge	d			12 51				13 09		13 32						13 51				14 09	14 32				
Shelford	d			12 55												13 55									
Whittlesford Parkway	d			13 00						13 39						14 00					14 39				
Great Chesterford	d			13 04												14 04									
Audley End	d			13 10				13 23		13 46						14 10				14 23	14 46				
Newport (Essex)	d			13 13												14 13									
Elsenham	d			13 19												14 19									
Stansted Airport ✈	a							13 49												14 49					
✈	d	13 15			13 30		13 45				14 00		14 03	14 15			14 30		14 45			15 00		15 03	15 15
Stansted Mountfitchet	d			13 22			13 50						14 08			14 22			14 50					15 08	
Bishops Stortford	a	13 23		13 28			13 54			14 00			14 12	14 23		14 28			14 54		15 00			15 12	15 23
	d	13 23		13 28			13 54			14 00			14 13	14 23		14 28			14 54		15 00			15 13	15 23
Sawbridgeworth	d			13 32						14 04			14 17			14 32					15 04			15 17	
Harlow Mill	d			13 36									14 21			14 36								15 21	
Harlow Town	d		←	13 39	13 45					14 09	14 15		14 24		←	14 39	14 45				15 09	15 15		15 24	
Roydon	d		13 28	13 43									14 28		14 28	14 43								15 28	
Hertford East	d					13 38						14 08	→					14 38					15 08	→	
Ware	d					13 42						14 12						14 42					15 12		
St Margarets (Herts)	d					13 46						14 16						14 46					15 16		
Rye House	d					13 49						14 19						14 49					15 19		
Broxbourne 3	a		13 32	13 47		13 54				14 15		14 24			14 32	14 47		14 54			15 15		15 24		
	d		13 38	13 47		13 54				14 15		14 24			14 38	14 47		14 54			15 15		15 24		
Cheshunt	d		13 42	13 51		13 58				14 19		14 28			14 42	14 51		14 58			15 19		15 28		
Waltham Cross	d					14 00						14 30						15 00					15 30		
Enfield Lock	d		13 46			14 03						14 33			14 46			15 03					15 33		
Brimsdown	d					14 05						14 35						15 05					15 35		
Ponders End	d					14 07						14 37						15 07					15 37		
Angel Road	d																								
Northumberland Park	d		13 51												14 51										
Tottenham Hale ⊖	d	13 46	13 53	13 59	14 02	14 12	14 16			14 27	14 30	14 42		14 46	14 53	14 59	15 02	15 12	15 16		15 27	15 30	15 42		15 46
Seven Sisters ⊖	d																								
Clapton	d																								
Stratford 7 ⊖	a		14 07												15 07										
Hackney Downs	d					14 19						14 49						15 19					15 49		
Bethnal Green	d																								
London Liverpool Street 15 ⊖	a	14 02		14 15	14 18	14 30	14 32			14 43	14 46	15 00		15 02		15 15	15 18	15 30	15 32		15 43	15 46	16 00		16 02

		LE	LE 1	LE 1 ⚲	LE	LE 1 ⚲	XC ◇	LE 1	LE 1 ⚲	LE		LE	LE 1 ⚲	LE	LE 1	LE 1 ⚲	LE	LE 1 ⚲	XC ◇	LE 1	LE 1 ⚲	LE	LE	LE 1 ⚲	LE
Cambridge	d		14 51				15 09	15 32							15 51				16 09	16 32					
Shelford	d		14 55												15 55										
Whittlesford Parkway	d		15 00					15 39							16 00					16 39					
Great Chesterford	d		15 04												16 04										
Audley End	d		15 10				15 23	15 46							16 10				16 23	16 46					
Newport (Essex)	d		15 13												16 13										
Elsenham	d		15 19												16 19										
Stansted Airport ✈	a						15 49												16 49						
✈	d			15 30		15 45			16 00			16 03	16 15			16 30		16 45			17 00		17 03	17 15	
Stansted Mountfitchet	d		15 22			15 50						16 08			16 22			16 50					17 08		
Bishops Stortford	a		15 28			15 54		16 00				16 12	16 23		16 28			16 54		17 00			17 12	17 23	
	d		15 28			15 54		16 00				16 13	16 23		16 28			16 54		17 00			17 13	17 23	
Sawbridgeworth	d		15 32					16 04				16 17			16 32					17 04			17 17		
Harlow Mill	d		15 36									16 21			16 36								17 21		
Harlow Town	d	←	15 39	15 45				16 09	16 15			16 24		←	16 39	16 45				17 09	17 15		17 24		←
Roydon	d	15 28	15 43									16 28		16 28	16 43								17 28		17 28
Hertford East	d				15 38					16 08		→					16 38					17 08	→		
Ware	d				15 42					16 12							16 42					17 12			
St Margarets (Herts)	d				15 46					16 16							16 46					17 16			
Rye House	d				15 49					16 19							16 49					17 19			
Broxbourne 3	a	15 32	15 47		15 54			16 15		16 24				16 32	16 47		16 54			17 15		17 24			17 32
	d	15 38	15 47		15 54			16 15		16 24				16 38	16 47		16 54			17 15		17 24			17 38
Cheshunt	d	15 42	15 51		15 58			16 19		16 28				16 42	16 51		16 58			17 19		17 28			17 42
Waltham Cross	d				16 00					16 30							17 00					17 30			
Enfield Lock	d	15 46			16 03					16 33				16 46			17 03					17 33			17 46
Brimsdown	d				16 05					16 35							17 05					17 35			
Ponders End	d				16 07					16 37							17 07					17 37			
Angel Road	d																								
Northumberland Park	d	15 51												16 51											17 51
Tottenham Hale ⊖	d	15 53	15 59	16 02	16 12	16 16		16 27	16 30	16 42			16 46	16 53	16 59	17 02	17 12	17 16		17 27	17 30	17 42		17 46	17 53
Seven Sisters ⊖	d																								
Clapton	d																								
Stratford 7 ⊖	a	16 07												17 07											18 07
Hackney Downs	d				16 19					16 49							17 19					17 49			
Bethnal Green	d																								
London Liverpool Street 15 ⊖	a		16 15	16 18	16 30	16 32		16 43	16 46	17 00			17 02		17 15	17 18	17 30	17 32		17 43	17 46	18 00		18 02	

For general notes see front of timetable
For details of catering facilities see Directory of Train Operators

Cambridge, Stansted Airport, Bishops Stortford, Hertford East and Broxbourne → London

Network diagram - see first page of Table 20

		LE 1	LE 1 🚲	LE	LE 1 🚲	XC ◇	LE 1	LE 1 🚲	LE	LE	LE 1 🚲	LE		LE 1	LE 1 🚲	LE	LE 1 🚲	XC ◇	LE 1	LE 1 🚲	LE	LE	LE 1 🚲	LE	LE 1
Cambridge	d	16 51				17 09	17 32							17 51				18 18	18 32						18 51
Shelford	d	16 55												17 55											18 55
Whittlesford Parkway	d	17 00					17 39							18 00					18 39						19 00
Great Chesterford	d	17 04												18 04											19 04
Audley End	d	17 10				17 23	17 46							18 10				18 32	18 46						19 10
Newport (Essex)	d	17 13												18 13											19 13
Elsenham	d	17 19												18 19											19 19
Stansted Airport	a					17 49												18 58							
	d		17 30		17 45			18 00		18 03	18 15				18 30		18 45			19 00		19 03	19 15		
Stansted Mountfitchet	d	17 22			17 50					18 08				18 22			18 50					19 08			19 22
Bishops Stortford	a	17 28			17 54		18 00			18 12	18 23			18 28			18 54		19 00			19 12	19 23		19 28
	d	17 28			17 54		18 00			18 13	18 23			18 28			18 54		19 00			19 13	19 23		19 28
Sawbridgeworth	d	17 32					18 04			18 17				18 32					19 04			19 17			19 32
Harlow Mill	d	17 36								18 21				18 36								19 21			19 36
Harlow Town	d	17 39	17 45				18 09	18 15		18 24		←		18 39	18 45				19 09	19 15		19 24		←	19 39
Roydon	d	17 43								18 28		18 28		18 43								19 28		19 28	19 43
Hertford East	d			17 38					18 08	→						18 38					19 08	→			
Ware	d			17 42					18 12							18 42					19 12				
St Margarets (Herts)	d			17 46					18 16							18 46					19 16				
Rye House	d			17 49					18 19							18 49					19 19				
Broxbourne [3]	a	17 47		17 54			18 15		18 24			18 32		18 47		18 54			19 15		19 24			19 32	19 47
	d	17 47		17 54			18 15		18 24			18 38		18 47		18 54			19 15		19 24			19 38	19 47
Cheshunt	d	17 51		17 58			18 19		18 28			18 42		18 51		18 58			19 19		19 28			19 42	19 51
Waltham Cross	d			18 00					18 30							19 00					19 30				
Enfield Lock	d			18 03					18 33			18 46				19 03					19 33			19 46	
Brimsdown	d			18 05					18 35							19 05					19 35				
Ponders End	d			18 07					18 37							19 07					19 37				
Angel Road	d																								
Northumberland Park	d											18 51												19 51	
Tottenham Hale	d	17 59	18 02	18 12	18 16		18 27	18 30	18 42		18 46	18 53		18 59	19 02	19 12	19 16		19 27	19 30	19 42		19 46	19 53	19 59
Seven Sisters	d																								
Clapton	d																								
Stratford [7]	a											19 07												20 07	
Hackney Downs	d			18 19					18 49							19 19					19 49				
Bethnal Green	d																								
London Liverpool Street [15]	a	18 15	18 18	18 30	18 32		18 43	18 46	19 00		19 02			19 15	19 18	19 30	19 32		19 43	19 46	20 00		20 02		20 15

		LE 1 🚲	LE	LE 1 🚲	LE 1	LE 1 🚲	LE	LE	LE 1 🚲	LE	LE 1	LE 1 🚲	LE	LE 1 🚲		XC ◇	LE 1	LE 1 🚲	LE	LE	LE 1 🚲	LE	LE 1	LE 1 🚲	LE
Cambridge	d				19 32						19 51					20 13	20 32						20 51		
Shelford	d										19 55												20 55		
Whittlesford Parkway	d				19 39						20 00						20 39						21 00		
Great Chesterford	d										20 04												21 04		
Audley End	d				19 46						20 10					20 27	20 46						21 10		
Newport (Essex)	d										20 13												21 13		
Elsenham	d										20 19												21 19		
Stansted Airport	a															20 49									
	d	19 30		19 45		20 00		20 03	20 15			20 30		20 45				21 00		21 03	21 15			21 30	
Stansted Mountfitchet	d			19 50				20 08			20 22			20 50						21 08			21 22		
Bishops Stortford	a			19 54	20 00			20 12	20 23		20 28			20 54			21 00			21 12	21 23		21 28		
	d			19 54	20 00			20 13	20 23		20 28			20 54			21 00			21 13	21 23		21 28		
Sawbridgeworth	d				20 04			20 17			20 32						21 04			21 17			21 32		
Harlow Mill	d							20 21			20 36									21 21			21 36		
Harlow Town	d	19 45			20 09	20 15		20 24		←	20 39	20 45					21 09	21 15		21 24		←	21 39	21 45	
Roydon	d							20 28		20 28	20 43									21 28		21 28	21 43		
Hertford East	d		19 38				20 08	→					20 38						21 08	→					21 38
Ware	d		19 42				20 12						20 42						21 12						21 42
St Margarets (Herts)	d		19 46				20 16						20 46						21 16						21 46
Rye House	d		19 49				20 19						20 49						21 19						21 49
Broxbourne [3]	a		19 54		20 15		20 24			20 32	20 47		20 54				21 15		21 24			21 32	21 47		21 54
	d		19 54		20 15		20 24			20 38	20 47		20 54				21 15		21 24			21 38	21 47		21 54
Cheshunt	d		19 58		20 19		20 28			20 42	20 51		20 58				21 19		21 28			21 42	21 51		21 58
Waltham Cross	d		20 00				20 30						21 00						21 30						22 00
Enfield Lock	d		20 03				20 33			20 46			21 03						21 33			21 46			22 03
Brimsdown	d		20 05				20 35						21 05						21 35						22 05
Ponders End	d		20 07				20 37						21 07						21 37						22 07
Angel Road	d																								
Northumberland Park	d									20 51												21 51			
Tottenham Hale	d	20 02	20 12	20 16	20 27	20 30	20 42		20 46	20 53	20 59	21 02	21 12	21 16			21 27	21 30	21 42		21 46	21 53	21 59	22 02	22 12
Seven Sisters	d																								
Clapton	d																								
Stratford [7]	a									21 07												22 07			
Hackney Downs	d		20 19				20 49						21 19						21 49						22 19
Bethnal Green	d																								
London Liverpool Street [15]	a	20 18	20 30	20 32	20 43	20 46	21 00		21 02		21 15	21 18	21 30	21 32			21 43	21 46	22 00		22 02		22 15	22 18	22 30

For general notes see front of timetable
For details of catering facilities see Directory of Train Operators

Table 22

Saturdays

Cambridge, Stansted Airport, Bishops Stortford, Hertford East and Broxbourne → London

Network diagram - see first page of Table 20

		LE 1 ⊼	LE 1	LE 1 ⊼	LE	LE	LE 1 ⊼	LE 1	LE 1 ⊼	LE	LE 1 ⊼	LE 1	LE 1 ⊼	LE	LE	LE 1 ⊼	LE	LE 1	LE	LE 1 ⊼	LE	LE 1 ⊼	LE 1 ⊼
Cambridge	d		21 32					21 51				22 32						22 51					
Shelford	d							21 55										22 55					
Whittlesford Parkway	d		21 39					22 00				22 39						23 00					
Great Chesterford	d							22 04										23 04					
Audley End	d		21 46					22 10				22 46						23 10					
Newport (Essex)	d							22 13										23 13					
Elsenham	d							22 19										23 19					
Stansted Airport ✈	a																						
✈	d	21 45		22 00		22 03	22 15		22 30		22 45		23 00		23 03	23 15				23 30		23 45	23 59
Stansted Mountfitchet	d	21 50				22 08		22 22			22 50				23 08			23 22					
Bishops Stortford	a	21 54	22 00			22 14	22 23	22 28			22 54	23 00			23 12	23 23		23 28				23 53	00 08
	d	21 54	22 00				22 23	22 28			22 54	23 00			23 13	23 23		23 28				23 53	00 08
Sawbridgeworth	d		22 04					22 32				23 04			23 17			23 32					
Harlow Mill	d							22 36							23 21			23 36					
Harlow Town	d		22 09	22 15				22 39	22 45			23 09	23 15		23 24		←	23 39		23 45			00 17
Roydon	d							22 43							23 28		23 28	23 43					
Hertford East	d				22 08					22 38				23 08	→						23 38		
Ware	d				22 12					22 42				23 12							23 42		
St Margarets (Herts)	d				22 16					22 46				23 16							23 46		
Rye House	d				22 19					22 49				23 19							23 49		
Broxbourne 3	a		22 15		22 24			22 47		22 54		23 15		23 24			23 32	23 47			23 54		
	d		22 15		22 24			22 47		22 54		23 15		23 24			23 38	23 47			23 54		
Cheshunt	d		22 19		22 28			22 51		22 58		23 19		23 28			23 42	23 51			23 58		
Waltham Cross	d				22 30					23 00				23 30							00 01		
Enfield Lock	d				22 33					23 03				23 33			23 46				00 03		
Brimsdown	d				22 35					23 05				23 35							00 05		
Ponders End	d				22 37					23 07				23 37							00 07		
Angel Road	d																						
Northumberland Park	d									23 11							23 51		←				
Tottenham Hale ⊖	d	22 16	22 27	22 30	22 42		22 46	22 59	23 02	23 13	23 17	23 27	23 30	23 42		23 46	23 53	23 59	23 53	00 02	00 12	00 16	
Seven Sisters ⊖	d																→						
Clapton	d																						
Stratford 7 ⊖ ⛴	a																		00 05				
Hackney Downs	d				22 49					23 19				23 49							00 19		
Bethnal Green	d																						
London Liverpool Street 15 ⊖	a	22 32	22 43	22 46	23 00		23 02	23 15	23 18	23 30	23 33	23 43	23 46	00 01		00 03		00 15	00 17	00 20	00 30	00 32	00 50

Sundays

		LE	LE 1 ⊼	LE	LE 1 ⊼	LE 1 ⊼	LE 1 ⊼	LE 1 ⊼	LE 1 ⊼		LE 1 ⊼	LE 1	LE 1 ⊼	LE 1 ⊼	LE 1	LE 1 ⊼	LE 1	LE		LE 1 ⊼	LE 1	LE 1 ⊼	LE	LE 1 ⊼	LE
Cambridge	d																				07 32				
Shelford	d																								
Whittlesford Parkway	d																				07 39				
Great Chesterford	d																								
Audley End	d																				07 46				
Newport (Essex)	d																								
Elsenham	d																								
Stansted Airport ✈	a																								
✈	d	23p03	23p30		23p45	23p59	00 30	05 30	06 00		06 30		07 00	07 15		07 30				07 45		08 00		08 15	
Stansted Mountfitchet	d	23p08																		07 50					
Bishops Stortford	a	23p12			23p53	00 08	00 38	05 38	06 08		06 38		07 08	07 23						07 54	07 59			08 23	
	d	23p13			23p53	00 08	00 38	05 38	06 08		06 38	06 42	07 08	07 23	07 28					07 54	08 00			08 23	
Sawbridgeworth	d	23p17										06 46			07 32						08 04				
Harlow Mill	d	23p21													07 36										
Harlow Town	d	23p24	23p45			00 17	00 46	05 46	06 16		06 46	06 51	07 16		07 39	07 45					08 09	08 15			
Roydon	d	23p28													07 43										
Hertford East	d			23p38														07 54							08 24
Ware	d			23p42														07 58							08 28
St Margarets (Herts)	d			23p46														08 02							08 32
Rye House	d			23p49														08 05							08 35
Broxbourne 3	a	23p32		23p54								06 57			07 47			08 10			08 15				08 40
	d	23p38		23p54								06 57			07 53			08 11			08 15				08 41
Cheshunt	d	23p42		23p58								07 01			07 57		←	08 16			08 19				08 46
Waltham Cross	d			00 01								07 03			07 59		07 59								
Enfield Lock	d	23p46		00 03								07 06			→		08 02								
Brimsdown	d			00 05								07 08					08 04								
Ponders End	d			00 07								07 10					08 06								
Angel Road	d																								
Northumberland Park	d	23p51																							
Tottenham Hale ⊖	d	23p53	00 02	00 12	00 16			06 02	06 31		07 01	07 15	07 31	07 44		07 59	08 11			08 15	08 27	08 30	←	08 44	
Seven Sisters ⊖	d																	08 33					08 33		09 03
Clapton	d																	→							
Stratford 7 ⊖ ⛴	a	00 05															08 25								
Hackney Downs	d			00 19																			08 40		09 10
Bethnal Green	d																								→
London Liverpool Street 15 ⊖	a	00 17	00 20	00 30	00 32	00 50	01 20	06 18	06 47		07 17	07 31	07 47	08 01		08 16				08 31	08 44	08 46	08 51	09 01	

For general notes see front of timetable
For details of catering facilities see Directory of Train Operators

Table 22

Sundays

Cambridge, Stansted Airport, Bishops Stortford, Hertford East and Broxbourne → London

Network diagram - see first page of Table 20

Station		LE 1	LE 1 🛒	LE	LE 1		LE	LE 1 🛒	LE 1	LE 1 🛒	LE	LE 1 🛒	LE	LE 1		LE 1 🛒	LE	LE 1	LE	LE 1 🛒	LE 1	LE 1 🛒	LE		LE 1 🛒
Cambridge	d	07 51							08 32					08 51							09 32				
Shelford	d	07 55												08 55											
Whittlesford Parkway	d	08 00							08 39					09 00							09 39				
Great Chesterford	d	08 04												09 04											
Audley End	d	08 10							08 46					09 10							09 46				
Newport (Essex)	d	08 13												09 13											
Elsenham	d	08 19												09 19											
Stansted Airport ⇄	a																								
	d		08 30					08 45		09 00		09 15				09 30				09 45		10 00			10 15
Stansted Mountfitchet	d	08 22						08 50						09 22						09 50					
Bishops Stortford	a	08 28						08 54	08 59			09 23		09 28						09 54	09 59				10 23
	d	08 28						08 54	09 00			09 23		09 28						09 54	10 00				10 23
Sawbridgeworth	d	08 32							09 04					09 32							10 04				
Harlow Mill	d	08 36												09 36											
Harlow Town	d	08 39	08 45						09 09	09 15				09 39		09 45					10 09	10 15			
Roydon	d	08 43												09 43											
Hertford East	d						08 54						09 24						09 54						
Ware	d						08 58						09 28						09 58						
St Margarets (Herts)	d						09 02						09 32						10 02						
Rye House	d						09 05						09 35						10 05						
Broxbourne 3	a	08 47					09 10		09 15				09 40	09 47					10 10		10 15				
	d	08 53					09 11		09 15				09 41	09 53					10 11		10 15				
Cheshunt	d	08 57			←		09 16		09 19				09 46	09 57				←	10 16		10 19				
Waltham Cross	d	08 59 →			08 59									09 59 →				09 59							
Enfield Lock	d				09 02													10 02							
Brimsdown	d				09 04													10 04							
Ponders End	d				09 06													10 06							
Angel Road	d																								
Northumberland Park	d																								
Tottenham Hale ⊖	d		08 59		09 11			09 15	09 27	09 30	←	09 44				09 59		10 11		10 15	10 27	10 30	←		10 44
Seven Sisters ⊖	d						09 33 →				09 33		10 03						10 33 →				10 33		
Clapton	d																								
Stratford 7 ⊖ ⛴	a			←	09 25												←	10 25							
Hackney Downs	d			09 10							09 40		10 10 →				10 10						10 40		
Bethnal Green	d																								
London Liverpool Street 15 ⊖	a		09 16	09 20				09 33	09 45	09 47	09 49	10 03				10 15	10 19			10 33	10 45	10 47	10 49		11 03

Station		LE	LE 1	LE 1 🛒	LE	LE 1	LE	LE 1 🛒	LE 1		LE 1 🛒	LE	LE 1 🛒	LE	LE 1	LE 1 🛒	LE	LE		LE 1	LE 1 🛒	XC	LE 1	LE 1 🛒	LE
Cambridge	d		09 51						10 32						10 51							11 23	11 32		
Shelford	d		09 55												10 55										
Whittlesford Parkway	d		10 00						10 39						11 00								11 39		
Great Chesterford	d		10 04												11 04										
Audley End	d		10 10						10 46						11 10							11 39	11 46		
Newport (Essex)	d		10 13												11 13										
Elsenham	d		10 19												11 19										
Stansted Airport ⇄	a																					11 58			
	d			10 30				10 45			11 00		11 15			11 30					11 45			12 00	
Stansted Mountfitchet	d		10 22					10 50							11 22						11 50				
Bishops Stortford	a		10 28					10 54	10 59				11 23		11 28						11 54		11 59		
	d		10 28					10 54	11 00				11 23		11 28						11 54		12 00		
Sawbridgeworth	d		10 32						11 04						11 32								12 04		
Harlow Mill	d		10 36												11 36										
Harlow Town	d		10 39	10 45					11 09		11 15				11 39	11 45							12 09	12 15	
Roydon	d		10 43												11 43										
Hertford East	d	10 24					10 54							11 24				11 54							
Ware	d	10 28					10 58							11 28				11 58							
St Margarets (Herts)	d	10 32					11 02							11 32				12 02							
Rye House	d	10 35					11 05							11 35				12 05							
Broxbourne 3	a	10 40	10 47				11 10		11 15					11 40	11 47			12 10					12 15		
	d	10 41	10 53				11 11		11 15					11 41	11 53			12 11					12 15		
Cheshunt	d	10 46	10 57			←	11 16		11 19					11 46	11 57			12 16		←			12 19		
Waltham Cross	d		10 59 →			10 59									11 59 →					11 59					
Enfield Lock	d					11 02														12 02					
Brimsdown	d					11 04														12 04					
Ponders End	d					11 06														12 06					
Angel Road	d																								
Northumberland Park	d																								
Tottenham Hale ⊖	d			10 59		11 11		11 15	11 27		11 31	←	11 44			11 59				12 11	12 15		12 27	12 31	←
Seven Sisters ⊖	d	11 03					11 33 →					11 33		12 03				12 33 →							12 33
Clapton	d																								
Stratford 7 ⊖ ⛴	a				←	11 25											←			12 25					
Hackney Downs	d	11 10 →			11 10							11 40		12 10 →			12 10								12 40
Bethnal Green	d																								
London Liverpool Street 15 ⊖	a			11 15	11 19			11 33	11 45		11 47	11 49	12 03			12 15	12 19				12 33		12 45	12 47	12 49

For general notes see front of timetable
For details of catering facilities see Directory of Train Operators

Table 22

Sundays

Cambridge, Stansted Airport, Bishops Stortford, Hertford East and Broxbourne → London

Network diagram - see first page of Table 20

	LE	LE	LE	LE		LE	LE	LE	LE	LE	LE	LE	LE		LE	LE	LE	LE	LE	LE	LE	XC		LE
	1		1	1			1		1	1	1		1			1	1			1	1			1
	🍴			🍴					🍴		🍴		🍴				🍴				🍴			
Cambridge d			11 51							12 32						12 51						13 24		13 32
Shelford d			11 55													12 55								
Whittlesford Parkway d			12 00							12 39						13 00								13 39
Great Chesterford d			12 04													13 04								
Audley End d			12 10							12 46						13 10						13 39		13 46
Newport (Essex) d			12 13													13 13								
Elsenham d			12 19													13 19								
Stansted Airport ✈ a																						13 58		
Stansted Airport ✈ d	12 15			12 30					12 45		13 00		13 15				13 30				13 45			
Stansted Mountfitchet d			12 22						12 50							13 22					13 50			
Bishops Stortford a	12 23		12 28						12 54	12 59			13 23			13 28					13 54			13 59
d	12 23		12 28						12 54	13 00			13 23			13 28					13 54			14 00
Sawbridgeworth d			12 32							13 04						13 32								14 04
Harlow Mill d			12 36													13 36								
Harlow Town d			12 39	12 45						13 09	13 15					13 39	13 45							14 09
Roydon d			12 43													13 43								
Hertford East d		12 24						12 54							13 24				13 54					
Ware d		12 28						12 58							13 28				13 58					
St Margarets (Herts) d		12 32						13 02							13 32				14 02					
Rye House d		12 35						13 05							13 35				14 05					
Broxbourne 3 a		12 40	12 47					13 10		13 15					13 40	13 47			14 10					14 15
d		12 41	12 53					13 11		13 15					13 41	13 53			14 11					14 15
Cheshunt d		12 46	12 57				←	13 16		13 19					13 46	13 57			14 16	←				14 19
Waltham Cross d			12 59 →				12 59									13 59 →				13 59				
Enfield Lock d							13 02													14 02				
Brimsdown d							13 04													14 04				
Ponders End d							13 06													14 06				
Angel Road d																								
Northumberland Park d																								
Tottenham Hale ⊖ d	12 44			12 59			13 11		13 15	13 27	13 31	←	13 44				13 59			14 11	14 15			14 27
Seven Sisters ⊖ d		13 03						13 33 →				13 33			14 03				14 33 →					
Clapton d																								
Stratford 7 ⊖ a						←	13 25											←		14 25				
Hackney Downs d		13 10 →				13 10						13 40			14 10 →			14 10						
Bethnal Green d																								
London Liverpool Street 15 ⊖ a	13 03			13 15		13 19			13 33	13 45	13 47	13 49	14 03				14 15	14 19			14 33			14 45

	LE	LE	LE	LE	LE	LE	LE	LE		LE	LE	XC	LE	LE	LE	LE	LE		LE	LE	XC	LE	LE	LE
	1		1		1	1				1	1	◇	1	1		1			1	1	A		1	
	🍴		🍴			🍴					🍴			🍴		🍴				🍴				
Cambridge d					13 51							14 20	14 32						14 51		15 09			
Shelford d					13 55														14 55					
Whittlesford Parkway d					14 00								14 39						15 00					
Great Chesterford d					14 04														15 04					
Audley End d					14 10							14 35	14 46						15 10		15 24			
Newport (Essex) d					14 13														15 13					
Elsenham d					14 19														15 19					
Stansted Airport ✈ a												14 58									15 43			
Stansted Airport ✈ d	14 00		14 15			14 30					14 45			15 00		15 15				15 30				
Stansted Mountfitchet d					14 22						14 50								15 22					
Bishops Stortford a			14 23		14 28						14 54		14 59			15 23			15 28					
d			14 23		14 28						14 54		15 00			15 23			15 28					
Sawbridgeworth d					14 32								15 04						15 32					
Harlow Mill d					14 36														15 36					
Harlow Town d	14 15				14 39	14 45							15 09	15 15					15 39	15 45				
Roydon d					14 43														15 43					
Hertford East d				14 24				14 54									15 24							15 54
Ware d				14 28				14 58									15 28							15 58
St Margarets (Herts) d				14 32				15 02									15 32							16 02
Rye House d				14 35				15 05									15 35							16 05
Broxbourne 3 a				14 40	14 47			15 10					15 15				15 40		15 47					16 10
d				14 41	14 53			15 11					15 15				15 41		15 53					16 11
Cheshunt d				14 46	14 57			15 16		←			15 19				15 46		15 57				←	16 16
Waltham Cross d					14 59 →					14 59									15 59 →				15 59	
Enfield Lock d										15 02													16 02	
Brimsdown d										15 04													16 04	
Ponders End d										15 06													16 06	
Angel Road d																								
Northumberland Park d																								
Tottenham Hale ⊖ d	14 31	←	14 44			14 59				15 11	15 15		15 27	15 31	←	15 44				15 59			16 11	
Seven Sisters ⊖ d		14 33		15 03				15 33 →							15 33		16 03							16 33 →
Clapton d																								
Stratford 7 ⊖ a							←			15 25												←	16 25	
Hackney Downs d		14 40		15 10 →			15 10								15 40		16 10 →					16 10		
Bethnal Green d																								
London Liverpool Street 15 ⊖ a	14 47	14 49	15 03			15 15	15 19				15 33		15 45	15 47	15 49	16 03				16 15		16 19		

For general notes see front of timetable
For details of catering facilities see Directory of Train Operators

A From Peterborough (Table 17)

Table 22

Sundays

Cambridge, Stansted Airport, Bishops Stortford, Hertford East and Broxbourne → London

Network diagram - see first page of Table 20

Station		LE 1 🚲	LE 1	LE 1 🚲	LE		LE 1 🚲	LE	LE 1	LE 1 🚲	LE	LE	LE 1	LE 1 🚲		XC ◇	LE 1	LE 1 🚲	LE	LE 1 🚲	LE	LE 1	LE 1 🚲		LE
Cambridge	d		15 32						15 51							16 24	16 32					16 51			
Shelford	d								15 55													16 55			
Whittlesford Parkway	d		15 39						16 00								16 39					17 00			
Great Chesterford	d								16 04													17 04			
Audley End	d		15 46						16 10							16 39	16 46					17 10			
Newport (Essex)	d								16 13													17 13			
Elsenham	d								16 19													17 19			
Stansted Airport ✈	a															16 59									
	d	15 45		16 00			16 15			16 30				16 45				17 00		17 15			17 30		
Stansted Mountfitchet	d	15 50							16 22					16 50								17 22			
Bishops Stortford	a	15 54	15 59				16 23		16 28					16 54			16 59			17 23		17 28			
	d	15 54	16 00				16 23		16 28					16 54			17 00			17 23		17 28			
Sawbridgeworth	d		16 04						16 32								17 04					17 32			
Harlow Mill	d								16 36													17 36			
Harlow Town	d		16 09	16 15					16 39	16 45							17 09	17 15				17 39	17 45		
Roydon	d								16 43													17 43			
Hertford East	d							16 24				16 54									17 24				
Ware	d							16 28				16 58									17 28				
St Margarets (Herts)	d							16 32				17 02									17 32				
Rye House	d							16 35				17 05									17 35				
Broxbourne 3	a		16 15					16 40	16 47			17 10					17 15				17 40	17 47			
	d		16 15					16 41	16 53			17 11					17 15				17 41	17 53			
Cheshunt	d		16 19					16 46	16 57			17 16	←				17 19				17 46	17 57			
Waltham Cross	d								16 59 →				16 59									17 59 →			
Enfield Lock	d												17 02												
Brimsdown	d												17 04												
Ponders End	d												17 06												
Angel Road	d																								
Northumberland Park	d																								
Tottenham Hale ⊖	d	16 15	16 27	16 31	←		16 44			16 59			17 11	17 15			17 27	17 31	←	17 44			17 59		
Seven Sisters ⊖	d				16 33			17 03				17 33 →							17 33		18 03				
Clapton	d																								
Stratford 7 ⊖	a										←		17 25												←
Hackney Downs	d				16 40			17 10 →			17 10								17 40		18 10 →				18 10
Bethnal Green	d																								
London Liverpool Street 15 ⊖	a	16 33	16 45	16 47	16 49		17 03			17 15	17 19			17 33			17 45	17 47	17 49	18 03			18 15		18 19

Station		LE	LE 1	LE 1 🚲	XC ◇	LE 1	LE 1 🚲	LE	LE 1 🚲		LE	LE 1	LE 1 🚲	LE 1	LE	LE	LE 1 🚲	LE 1		LE 1 🚲	LE 1 🚲	LE	LE 1	LE 1 🚲	LE 1
Cambridge	d				17 24	17 32						17 51						18 32					18 51		
Shelford	d											17 55											18 55		
Whittlesford Parkway	d					17 39						18 00						18 39					19 00		
Great Chesterford	d											18 04											19 04		
Audley End	d				17 39	17 46						18 10						18 46					19 10		
Newport (Essex)	d											18 13											19 13		
Elsenham	d											18 19											19 19		
Stansted Airport ✈	a				17 58																				
	d			17 45			18 00		18 15				18 30				18 45			19 00	19 15			19 30	
Stansted Mountfitchet	d			17 50								18 22					18 50						19 22		
Bishops Stortford	a			17 54		17 59			18 23			18 28					18 54	18 59			19 23		19 28		
	d			17 54		18 00			18 23			18 28					18 54	19 00			19 23		19 28		
Sawbridgeworth	d					18 04						18 32						19 04					19 32		
Harlow Mill	d											18 36											19 36		
Harlow Town	d					18 09	18 15					18 39	18 45					19 09		19 15			19 39	19 45	
Roydon	d											18 43											19 43		
Hertford East	d	17 54									18 24				18 56										
Ware	d	17 58									18 28				19 00										
St Margarets (Herts)	d	18 02									18 32				19 04										
Rye House	d	18 05									18 35				19 07										
Broxbourne 3	a	18 10				18 15					18 40	18 47			19 12			19 15				←	19 47		
	d	18 11				18 15					18 41	18 53			19 26			19 15				19 26	19 53		
Cheshunt	d	18 16	←			18 19					18 46	18 57		←	→			19 19				19 31	19 57		←
Waltham Cross	d		17 59									18 59 →		18 59									19 59 →		19 59
Enfield Lock	d		18 02											19 02											20 02
Brimsdown	d		18 04											19 04											20 04
Ponders End	d		18 06											19 06											20 06
Angel Road	d																								
Northumberland Park	d																								
Tottenham Hale ⊖	d		18 11	18 15		18 27	18 31	←	18 44				18 59	19 11			19 15	19 27		19 30	19 44			19 59	20 11
Seven Sisters ⊖	d	18 33 →						18 33			19 03											19 51			
Clapton	d																								
Stratford 7 ⊖	a		18 25											19 25		←									20 25
Hackney Downs	d							18 40			19 10 →					19 10						20 00			
Bethnal Green	d																					20 06			
London Liverpool Street 15 ⊖	a			18 33		18 45	18 47	18 49	19 03				19 15			19 19	19 31	19 45		19 47	20 00	20 11		20 15	

For general notes see front of timetable
For details of catering facilities see
Directory of Train Operators

Table 22

Sundays

Cambridge, Stansted Airport, Bishops Stortford, Hertford East and Broxbourne → London

Network diagram - see first page of Table 20

		LE 1 ⏚	LE	XC ◇	LE 1	LE 1 ⏚	LE 1 ⏚	LE	LE 1	LE 1 ⏚	LE 1	LE 1 ⏚	LE	XC ◇	LE 1	LE 1 ⏚	LE 1 ⏚	LE	LE 1	LE 1 ⏚	LE 1	LE 1 ⏚
Cambridge	d			19 24	19 32				19 51					20 24	20 32				20 51			
Shelford	d								19 55										20 55			
Whittlesford Parkway	d				19 39				20 00						20 39				21 00			
Great Chesterford	d								20 04										21 04			
Audley End	d			19 39	19 46				20 10					20 39	20 46				21 10			
Newport (Essex)	d								20 13										21 13			
Elsenham	d								20 19										21 19			
Stansted Airport ✈	a			19 58										20 58								
	d	19 45				20 00	20 15			20 30		20 45				21 00	21 15			21 30		21 45
Stansted Mountfitchet	d	19 50							20 22			20 50							21 22			21 50
Bishops Stortford	a	19 54			19 59		20 23		20 28			20 54			20 59		21 23		21 28			21 54
	d	19 54			20 00		20 23		20 28			20 54			21 00		21 23		21 28			21 54
Sawbridgeworth	d				20 04				20 32						21 04				21 32			
Harlow Mill	d								20 36										21 36			
Harlow Town	d				20 09	20 15			20 39	20 45					21 09	21 15			21 39	21 45		
Roydon	d								20 43										21 43			
Hertford East	d		19 56										20 56									
Ware	d		20 00										21 00									
St Margarets (Herts)	d		20 04										21 04									
Rye House	d		20 07										21 07									
Broxbourne 3	a		20 12		20 15			←	20 47				21 12		21 15			←	21 47			
	d		20 26		20 15			20 26	20 53				21 26		21 15			21 26	21 53			
Cheshunt	d		→		20 19			20 31	20 57		←		→		21 19			21 31	21 57		←	
Waltham Cross	d								20 59		20 59								21 59		21 59	
Enfield Lock	d								→		21 02								→		22 02	
Brimsdown	d										21 04										22 04	
Ponders End	d										21 06										22 06	
Angel Road	d																					
Northumberland Park	d																					
Tottenham Hale ⊖	d	20 15			20 27	20 30	20 44			20 59	21 11	21 15			21 27	21 30	21 44			21 59	22 11	22 15
Seven Sisters ⊖	d							20 51										21 51				
Clapton	d																					
Stratford 7 ⊖ ⛴	a										21 25										22 25	
Hackney Downs	d							21 00										22 00				
Bethnal Green	d							21 06										22 06				
London Liverpool Street 15 ⊖	a	20 31			20 45	20 47	21 00	21 11		21 15		21 31			21 45	21 47	22 00	22 11		22 15		22 31

		XC ◇	LE	LE 1	LE 1 ⏚	LE 1 ⏚	LE	LE 1	LE 1 ⏚	LE 1	LE 1 ⏚	LE	LE 1	LE 1	LE 1 ⏚	LE 1 ⏚	LE	LE 1	LE 1 ⏚	LE 1 ⏚	LE 1 ⏚
Cambridge	d	21 19		21 32				21 51						22 32				22 51			
Shelford	d							21 55										22 55			
Whittlesford Parkway	d			21 39				22 00						22 39				23 00			
Great Chesterford	d							22 04										23 04			
Audley End	d	21 34		21 46				22 10						22 46				23 10			
Newport (Essex)	d							22 13										23 13			
Elsenham	d							22 19										23 19			
Stansted Airport ✈	a	21 53																			
	d				22 00	22 15			22 30		22 45				23 00	23 15			23 30	23 45	23 59
Stansted Mountfitchet	d							22 22			22 50							23 22			
Bishops Stortford	a			21 59		22 23		22 28			22 54			22 59		23 23		23 30	23 38	23 53	00 08
	d			22 00		22 23		22 28			22 54			23 00		23 23			23 38	23 53	00 08
Sawbridgeworth	d			22 04				22 32						23 04							
Harlow Mill	d							22 36													
Harlow Town	d			22 09	22 15			22 39	22 45					23 09	23 15				23 47		00 17
Roydon	d							22 43													
Hertford East	d		21 56									22 56									
Ware	d		22 00									23 00									
St Margarets (Herts)	d		22 04									23 04									
Rye House	d		22 07									23 07									
Broxbourne 3	a		22 12	22 15			←	22 47				23 12		23 15			←				
	d		22 26	22 15			22 26	22 53				23 26		23 15			23 26				
Cheshunt	d		→	22 19			22 31	22 57		←		→		23 19			23 31				
Waltham Cross	d							22 59		22 59											
Enfield Lock	d							→		23 02											
Brimsdown	d									23 04											
Ponders End	d									23 06											
Angel Road	d																				
Northumberland Park	d												←								
Tottenham Hale ⊖	d			22 27	22 30	22 44			22 59	23 11	23 15		23 11	23 27	23 30	23 44					
Seven Sisters ⊖	d						22 51			→							23 51		00 06	00 19	
Clapton	d																				
Stratford 7 ⊖ ⛴	a												23 23								
Hackney Downs	d						23 00										23 59				
Bethnal Green	d						23 06										00 06				
London Liverpool Street 15 ⊖	a			22 45	22 47	23 00	23 11		23 15		23 31		23 38	23 45	23 47	00 01	00 11		00 21	00 34	00 50

For general notes see front of timetable
For details of catering facilities see Directory of Train Operators

Network Diagram for Tables 24, 25

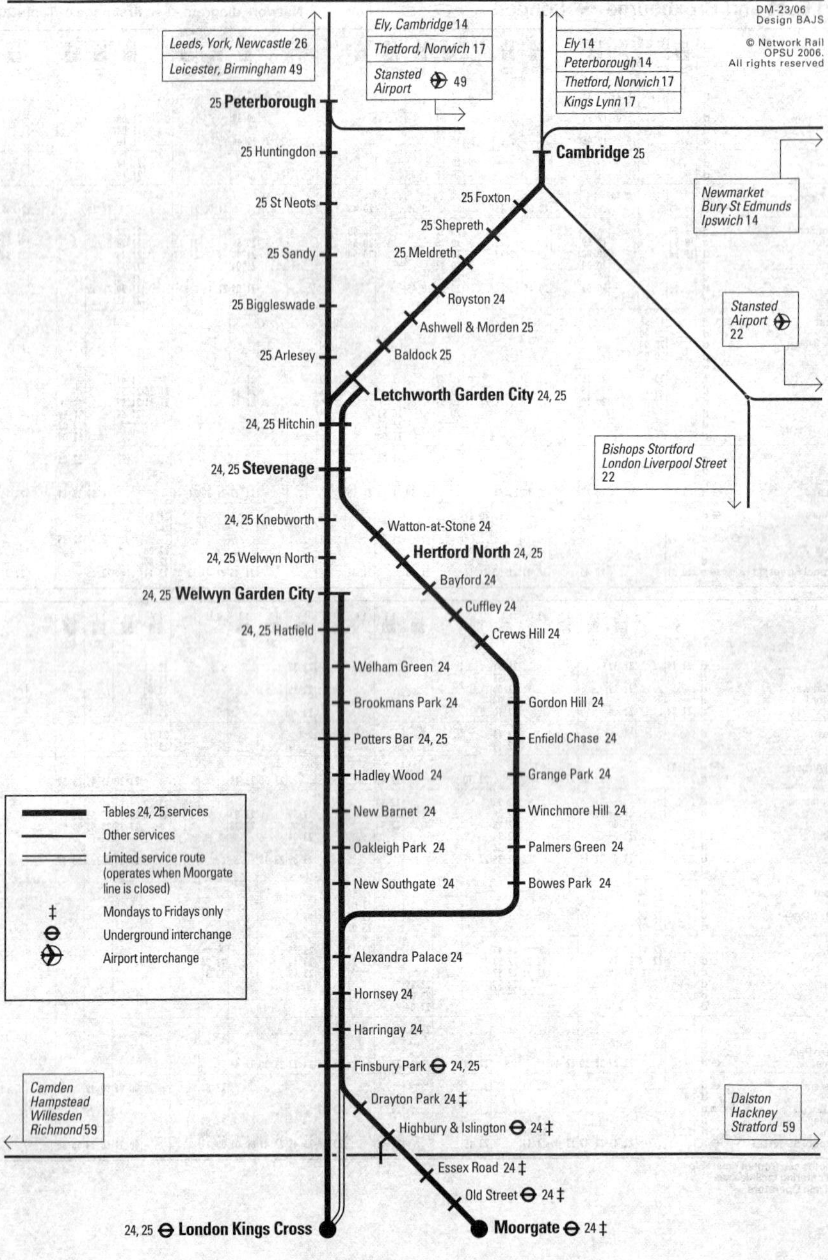

DM-23/06
Design BAJS
© Network Rail OPSU 2006. All rights reserved
Leeds, York, Newcastle 26
Leicester, Birmingham 49
Ely, Cambridge 14
Thetford, Norwich 17
Stansted Airport 49
Ely 14
Peterborough 14
Thetford, Norwich 17
Kings Lynn 17
25 Peterborough
25 Huntingdon
25 St Neots
25 Sandy
25 Biggleswade
25 Arlesey
Cambridge 25
25 Foxton
25 Shepreth
25 Meldreth
Royston 24
Ashwell & Morden 25
Baldock 25
Letchworth Garden City 24, 25
Newmarket
Bury St Edmunds
Ipswich 14
Stansted Airport 22
Bishops Stortford
London Liverpool Street
22
24, 25 Hitchin
24, 25 Stevenage
24, 25 Knebworth
24, 25 Welwyn North
24, 25 Welwyn Garden City
24, 25 Hatfield
Watton-at-Stone 24
Hertford North 24, 25
Bayford 24
Cuffley 24
Crews Hill 24
Welham Green 24
Brookmans Park 24
Potters Bar 24, 25
Hadley Wood 24
New Barnet 24
Oakleigh Park 24
New Southgate 24
Gordon Hill 24
Enfield Chase 24
Grange Park 24
Winchmore Hill 24
Palmers Green 24
Bowes Park 24
Tables 24, 25 services
Other services
Limited service route (operates when Moorgate line is closed)
‡ Mondays to Fridays only
Underground interchange
Airport interchange
Alexandra Palace 24
Hornsey 24
Harringay 24
Finsbury Park 24, 25
Drayton Park 24 ‡
Highbury & Islington 24 ‡
Essex Road 24 ‡
Old Street 24 ‡
Camden
Hampstead
Willesden
Richmond 59
Dalston
Hackney
Stratford 59
24, 25 London Kings Cross
Moorgate 24 ‡

London → Welwyn Garden City, Hertford North and Letchworth Garden City

Saturday service operates on Bank Holiday Mondays

Network Diagram - see first page of Table 24

Miles	Miles		FC MX	FC MO	FC MX 1	FC MO	FC MX	FC 1 A	FC MX 1 B	FC MO 1 B	FC MO	FC MX 1	FC MX 1 B	FC MO 1 B	FC 1	FC	FC		FC 1	FC	FC	FC 1	FC	FC	FC 1
0	—	London Kings Cross 15 ⊖ d	23p26	23p28	23p36	23p41	23p41	00 07	00 36	00 36	01 06	01 06	01 36	01 36	05 21	05 26	05 56		06 06	06 11	06 26	06 36			07 06
—	0	**Moorgate** ⊖ d																					06 35	06 50	
—	½	Old Street ⊖ d																					06 37	06 52	
—	1¾	Essex Road d																					06 40	06 55	
—	2¼	Highbury & Islington ⊖ d																					06 42	06 57	
—	2¾	Drayton Park d																					06 44	06 59	
2½	3½	Finsbury Park ⊖ d	23p32	23p33	23p41	23p47	23p47	00 12	00 41	00 41	01 11	01 11	01 41	01 41	05 26	05 32	06 02		06 11	06 17	06 32	06 41	06 47	07 02	07 11
3½	4½	Harringay d	23p34	23p36		23p49	23p49									05 34	06 04			06 19	06 34		06 49	07 04	
4	5	Hornsey d	23p36	23p38		23p51	23p51									05 36	06 06			06 21	06 36		06 51	07 06	
5	6	Alexandra Palace d	23p38	23p39		23p53	23p53	00 17	00 45	00 45	01 15	01 15	01 45	01 45		05 38	06 08			06 23	06 38		06 53	07 08	
6½	—	New Southgate d				23p56	23p56													06 26			06 56		
8½	—	Oakleigh Park d				23p59	23p59		00 50	00 50			01 50	01 50						06 29			06 59		
9¼	—	New Barnet d				00 01	00 01		00 52	00 52			01 52	01 52						06 31			07 01		
10½	—	Hadley Wood d				00 04	00 04		00 54	00 54			01 54	01 54						06 34			07 04		
12¾	—	Potters Bar d			23p51	00 08	00 08		00 58	00 58			01 58	01 58	05 36				06 21	06 38		06 51	07 08		07 21
14½	—	Brookmans Park d				00 11	00 11													06 41			07 11		
15½	—	Welham Green d				00 13	00 13													06 43			07 13		
17¾	—	Hatfield d			23p57	00 16	00 16		01 04	01 04			02 04	02 04	05 42				06 27	06 46		06 57	07 16		07 27
20¼	—	**Welwyn Garden City 4** d			00 01	00 20	00a24		01 08	01 08			02 08	02 08	05 46				06 31	06a53		07 01	07a21		07 31
22	—	Welwyn North d			00 04	00 23			01s11	01s16			02s11	02s16	05 49				06 34			07 04			07 34
25	—	Knebworth d			00 08	00 28			01s15	01s20			02s15	02s20	05 53				06 38			07 08			07 38
—	6¾	Bowes Park d	23p40	23p42												05 40	06 10				06 40			07 10	
—	7¾	Palmers Green d	23p42	23p44				00 20				01 18				05 42	06 12				06 42			07 12	
—	8¾	Winchmore Hill d	23p45	23p46				00 22				01 21				05 45	06 15				06 45			07 15	
—	9½	Grange Park d	23p47	23p48												05 47	06 17				06 47			07 17	
—	10¼	Enfield Chase d	23p49	23p50				00 25				01 23				05 49	06 19				06 49			07 19	
—	11	Gordon Hill d	23p51	23p52				00 27				01 25				05 51	06 21				06 51			07 21	
—	12½	Crews Hill d	23p54	23p55												05 54	06 24				06 54			07 24	
—	14¼	Cuffley d	23p57	23p58				00 31				01 30				05 57	06 27				06 57			07 27	
—	17¾	Bayford d	00 02	00 03												06 02	06 32				07 02			07 32	
—	20¾	**Hertford North** d	00 07	00 08				00 39				01 37				06a10	06a40				07 07			07a37	
—	25	Watton-at-Stone d	00 12	00 14																	07 12				
27½	30	**Stevenage 4** d	00a20	00a24	00 12	00 31		00 48	01 18	01 23	01 47	01 47	02 18	02 23	05 57				06 42		07a22	07 12			07 42
31¾	34¼	Hitchin 4 d			00 20	00a47		00 56	01a23	01a28	01 52	01 52	02a23	02a28	06a05				06 47			07a17			07 47
34¾	37¼	**Letchworth Garden City** a			00 29			01 00			02 06	02 06							06 51						07 51

	FC	FC	FC 1	FC	FC	FC 1	FC	FC	FC	FC 1		FC	FC	FC	FC 1	FC	FC	FC	FC 1	FC	FC	FC	FC 1	FC	FC
London Kings Cross 15 ⊖ d			07 36			08 06				08 36					09 06				09 36				10 06		
Moorgate ⊖ d	07 05	07 20		07 35	07 50		08 05	08 12	08 22			08 32	08 42	08 52		09 02	09 12	09 22		09 32	09 42	09 52		10 02	10 12
Old Street ⊖ d	07 07	07 22		07 37	07 52		08 07	08 14	08 24			08 34	08 44	08 54		09 04	09 14	09 24		09 34	09 44	09 54		10 04	10 14
Essex Road d	07 10	07 25		07 40	07 55		08 10	08 17	08 27			08 37	08 47	08 57		09 07	09 17	09 27		09 37	09 47	09 57		10 07	10 17
Highbury & Islington ⊖ d	07 12	07 27		07 42	07 57		08 12	08 19	08 29			08 39	08 49	08 59		09 09	09 19	09 29		09 39	09 49	09 59		10 09	10 19
Drayton Park d	07 14	07 29		07 44	07 59		08 14	08 21	08 31			08 41	08 51	09 01		09 11	09 21	09 31		09 41	09 51	10 01		10 11	10 21
Finsbury Park ⊖ d	07 17	07 32	07 41	07 47	08 02	08 11	08 17	08 24	08 34	08 41		08 44	08 54	09 04	09 11	09 14	09 24	09 34	09 41	09 44	09 54	10 04	10 11	10 14	10 24
Harringay d	07 19	07 34		07 49	08 04		08 19	08 26	08 36			08 46	08 56	09 06		09 16	09 26	09 36		09 46	09 56	10 06		10 16	10 26
Hornsey d	07 21	07 36		07 51	08 06		08 21	08 28	08 38			08 48	08 58	09 08		09 18	09 28	09 38		09 48	09 58	10 08		10 18	10 28
Alexandra Palace d	07 23	07 38		07 53	08 08		08 23	08 30	08 40			08 50	09 00	09 10		09 20	09 30	09 40		09 50	10 00	10 10		10 20	10 30
New Southgate d	07 26			07 56			08 26		08 43				09 03			09 23		09 43			10 03			10 23	
Oakleigh Park d	07 29			07 59			08 29		08 46				09 06			09 26		09 46			10 06			10 26	
New Barnet d	07 31			08 01			08 31		08 48				09 08			09 28		09 48			10 08			10 28	
Hadley Wood d	07 34			08 04			08 34		08 51				09 11			09 31		09 51			10 11			10 31	
Potters Bar d	07 38		07 51	08 08		08 21	08 38		08 55	08 51			09 15		09 21	09 35		09 55	09 51		10 15		10 21	10 35	
Brookmans Park d	07 41			08 11			08 41		08 58				09 18			09 38		09 58			10 18			10 38	
Welham Green d	07 43			08 13			08 43		09 00				09 20			09 40		10 00			10 20			10 40	
Hatfield d	07 46		07 57	08 16		08 27	08 46		09 03	08 57			09 23		09 27	09 43		10 03	09 57		10 23		10 27	10 43	
Welwyn Garden City 4 d	07a51		08 01	08a21		08 31	08a51		09a09	09 01			09a29		09 31	09a49		10a09	10 01		10a29		10 31	10a49	
Welwyn North d			08 04			08 34				09 04					09 34				10 04				10 34		
Knebworth d			08 08			08 38				09 08					09 38				10 08				10 38		
Bowes Park d		07 40			08 10			08 32				08 52		09 12			09 32			09 52		10 12			10 32
Palmers Green d		07 42			08 12			08 34				08 54		09 14			09 34			09 54		10 14			10 34
Winchmore Hill d		07 45			08 15			08 37				08 57		09 17			09 37			09 57		10 17			10 37
Grange Park d		07 47			08 17			08 39				08 59		09 19			09 39			09 59		10 19			10 39
Enfield Chase d		07 49			08 19			08 41				09 01		09 21			09 41			10 01		10 21			10 41
Gordon Hill d		07 51			08 21			08 43				09 03		09 23			09 43			10 03		10 23			10 43
Crews Hill d		07 54			08 24			08 46				09 06		09 26			09 46			10 06		10 26			10 46
Cuffley d		07 57			08 27			08 49				09 09		09 29			09 49			10 09		10 29			10 49
Bayford d		08 02			08 32			08 54				09 14		09 34			09 54			10 14		10 34			10 54
Hertford North d		08 07			08 37			09b07				09a20		09 39			10a00			10a20		10 39			10a59
Watton-at-Stone d		08 12			08 42			09 12						09 44								10 44			
Stevenage 4 d		08a22	08 12		08a52	08 42		09 20		09 12				09 51	09 42				10 12			10 51	10 42		
Hitchin 4 d			08a17			08 47		09 26		09a17				09 56	09 47				10a17			10 56	10 47		
Letchworth Garden City a						08 51		09 34						10 04	09 51							11 04	10 51		

For general notes see front of timetable
For details of catering facilities see
Directory of Train Operators

A To Cambridge (Table 25)
B To Peterborough (Table 25)
b Arr. 0859

London → Welwyn Garden City, Hertford North and Letchworth Garden City

Saturday service operates on Bank Holiday Mondays

Network Diagram - see first page of Table 24

		FC	FC 1	FC		FC	FC	FC 1	FC	FC	FC	FC 1	FC	FC	FC	FC 1	FC	FC	FC	FC 1		FC	FC	FC	FC 1	FC
London Kings Cross 15	⊖ d		10 36					11 06				11 36				12 06				12 36					13 06	
Moorgate	⊖ d	10 22		10 32		10 42	10 52		11 02	11 12	11 22		11 32	11 42	11 52		12 02	12 12	12 22			12 32	12 42	12 52		13 02
Old Street	⊖ d	10 24		10 34		10 44	10 54		11 04	11 14	11 24		11 34	11 44	11 54		12 04	12 14	12 24			12 34	12 44	12 54		13 04
Essex Road	d	10 27		10 37		10 47	10 57		11 07	11 17	11 27		11 37	11 47	11 57		12 07	12 17	12 27			12 37	12 47	12 57		13 07
Highbury & Islington	⊖ d	10 29		10 39		10 49	10 59		11 09	11 19	11 29		11 39	11 49	11 59		12 09	12 19	12 29			12 39	12 49	12 59		13 09
Drayton Park	d	10 31		10 41		10 51	11 01		11 11	11 21	11 31		11 41	11 51	12 01		12 11	12 21	12 31			12 41	12 51	13 01		13 11
Finsbury Park	⊖ d	10 34	10 41	10 44		10 54	11 04	11 11	11 14	11 24	11 34	11 41	11 44	11 54	12 04	12 11	12 14	12 24	12 34	12 41		12 44	12 54	13 04	13 11	13 14
Harringay	d	10 36		10 46		10 56	11 06		11 16	11 26	11 36		11 46	11 56	12 06		12 16	12 26	12 36			12 46	12 56	13 06		13 16
Hornsey	d	10 38		10 48		10 58	11 08		11 18	11 28	11 38		11 48	11 58	12 08		12 18	12 28	12 38			12 48	12 58	13 08		13 18
Alexandra Palace	d	10 40		10 50		11 00	11 10		11 20	11 30	11 40		11 50	12 00	12 10		12 20	12 30	12 40			12 50	13 00	13 10		13 20
New Southgate	d	10 43				11 03			11 23		11 43			12 03			12 23		12 43				13 03			13 23
Oakleigh Park	d	10 46				11 06			11 26		11 46			12 06			12 26		12 46				13 06			13 26
New Barnet	d	10 48				11 08			11 28		11 48			12 08			12 28		12 48				13 08			13 28
Hadley Wood	d	10 51				11 11			11 31		11 51			12 11			12 31		12 51				13 11			13 31
Potters Bar	d	10 55	10 51			11 15		11 21	11 35		11 55	11 51		12 15		12 21	12 35		12 55	12 51			13 15		13 21	13 35
Brookmans Park	d	10 58				11 18			11 38		11 58			12 18			12 38		12 58				13 18			13 38
Welham Green	d	11 00				11 20			11 40		12 00			12 20			12 40		13 00				13 20			13 40
Hatfield	d	11 03	10 57			11 23		11 27	11 43		12 03	11 57		12 23		12 27	12 43		13 03	12 57			13 23		13 27	13 43
Welwyn Garden City 4	d	11a09	11 01			11a29		11 31	11a49		12a09	12 01		12a29		12 31	12a49		13a09	13 01			13a29		13 31	13a49
Welwyn North	d		11 04					11 34				12 04				12 34				13 04					13 34	
Knebworth	d		11 08					11 38				12 08				12 38				13 08					13 38	
Bowes Park	d			10 52			11 12			11 32			11 52		12 12			12 32				12 52		13 12		
Palmers Green	d			10 54			11 14			11 34			11 54		12 14			12 34				12 54		13 14		
Winchmore Hill	d			10 57			11 17			11 37			11 57		12 17			12 37				12 57		13 17		
Grange Park	d			10 59			11 19			11 39			11 59		12 19			12 39				12 59		13 19		
Enfield Chase	d			11 01			11 21			11 41			12 01		12 21			12 41				13 01		13 21		
Gordon Hill	d			11 03			11 23			11 43			12 03		12 23			12 43				13 03		13 23		
Crews Hill	d			11 06			11 26			11 46			12 06		12 26			12 46				13 06		13 26		
Cuffley	d			11 09			11 29			11 49			12 09		12 29			12 49				13 09		13 29		
Bayford	d			11 14			11 34			11 54			12 14		12 34			12 54				13 14		13 34		
Hertford North	d			11a19			11 39			11a59			12a19		12 39			12a59				13a19		13 39		
Watton-at-Stone	d						11 44								12 44									13 44		
Stevenage 4	d		11 12				11 51	11 42				12 12			12 51	12 42				13 12				13 51	13 42	
Hitchin 4	d		11a17				11 56	11 47				12a17			12 56	12 47				13a17				13 56	13 47	
Letchworth Garden City	a						12 04	11 51							13 04	12 51								14 04	13 51	

		FC	FC	FC 1	FC	FC	FC	FC 1	FC	FC	FC	FC 1	FC		FC	FC	FC 1	FC	FC	FC	FC 1	FC	FC	FC	FC 1	FC
London Kings Cross 15	⊖ d			13 36				14 06				14 36					15 06				15 36				16 06	
Moorgate	⊖ d	13 12	13 22		13 32	13 42	13 52		14 02	14 12	14 22		14 32		14 42	14 52		15 02	15 12	15 22		15 32	15 42	15 52		16 05
Old Street	⊖ d	13 14	13 24		13 34	13 44	13 54		14 04	14 14	14 24		14 34		14 44	14 54		15 04	15 14	15 24		15 34	15 44	15 54		16 07
Essex Road	d	13 17	13 27		13 37	13 47	13 57		14 07	14 17	14 27		14 37		14 47	14 57		15 07	15 17	15 27		15 37	15 47	15 57		16 10
Highbury & Islington	⊖ d	13 19	13 29		13 39	13 49	13 59		14 09	14 19	14 29		14 39		14 49	14 59		15 09	15 19	15 29		15 39	15 49	15 59		16 12
Drayton Park	d	13 21	13 31		13 41	13 51	14 01		14 11	14 21	14 31		14 41		14 51	15 01		15 11	15 21	15 31		15 41	15 51	16 01		16 14
Finsbury Park	⊖ d	13 24	13 34	13 41	13 44	13 54	14 04	14 11	14 14	14 24	14 34	14 41	14 44		14 54	15 04	15 11	15 14	15 24	15 34	15 41	15 44	15 54	16 04	16 11	16 17
Harringay	d	13 26	13 36		13 46	13 56	14 06		14 16	14 26	14 36		14 46		14 56	15 06		15 16	15 26	15 36		15 46	15 56	16 06		16 19
Hornsey	d	13 28	13 38		13 48	13 58	14 08		14 18	14 28	14 38		14 48		14 58	15 08		15 18	15 28	15 38		15 48	15 58	16 08		16 21
Alexandra Palace	d	13 30	13 40		13 50	14 00	14 10		14 20	14 30	14 40		14 50		15 00	15 10		15 20	15 30	15 40		15 50	16 00	16 10		16 23
New Southgate	d		13 43			14 03			14 23		14 43				15 03			15 23		15 43			16 03			16 26
Oakleigh Park	d		13 46			14 06			14 26		14 46				15 06			15 26		15 46			16 06			16 29
New Barnet	d		13 48			14 08			14 28		14 48				15 08			15 28		15 48			16 08			16 31
Hadley Wood	d		13 51			14 11			14 31		14 51				15 11			15 31		15 51			16 11			16 34
Potters Bar	d		13 55	13 51		14 15		14 21	14 35		14 55	14 51			15 15		15 21	15 35		15 55	15 51		16 15		16 21	16 38
Brookmans Park	d		13 58			14 18			14 38		14 58				15 18			15 38		15 58			16 18			16 41
Welham Green	d		14 00			14 20			14 40		15 00				15 20			15 40		16 00			16 20			16 43
Hatfield	d		14 03	13 57		14 23		14 27	14 43		15 03	14 57			15 23		15 27	15 43		16 03	15 57		16 23		16 27	16 46
Welwyn Garden City 4	d		14a10	14 01		14a29		14 31	14a49		15a09	15 01			15a29		15 31	15a49		16a09	16 01		16a29		16 31	16a53
Welwyn North	d			14 04				14 34				15 04					15 34				16 04				16 34	
Knebworth	d			14 08				14 38				15 08					15 38				16 08				16 38	
Bowes Park	d	13 32			13 52		14 12			14 32			14 52			15 12			15 32			15 52		16 12		
Palmers Green	d	13 34			13 54		14 14			14 34			14 54			15 14			15 34			15 54		16 14		
Winchmore Hill	d	13 37			13 57		14 17			14 37			14 57			15 17			15 37			15 57		16 17		
Grange Park	d	13 39			13 59		14 19			14 39			14 59			15 19			15 39			15 59		16 19		
Enfield Chase	d	13 41			14 01		14 21			14 41			15 01			15 21			15 41			16 01		16 21		
Gordon Hill	d	13 43			14 03		14 23			14 43			15 03			15 23			15 43			16 03		16 23		
Crews Hill	d	13 46			14 06		14 26			14 46			15 06			15 26			15 46			16 06		16 26		
Cuffley	d	13 49			14 09		14 29			14 49			15 09			15 29			15 49			16 09		16 29		
Bayford	d	13 54			14 14		14 34			14 54			15 14			15 34			15 54			16 14		16 34		
Hertford North	d	13a59			14a19		14 39			14a59			15a19			15 39			16b09			16a19		16 39		
Watton-at-Stone	d						14 44									15 44			16 14					16 44		
Stevenage 4	d			14 12			14 51	14 42				15 12				15 51	15 42		16a22		16 12			16a52	16 42	
Hitchin 4	d			14a17			14 56	14 47				15a17				15 56	15 47				16a17				16 47	
Letchworth Garden City	a						15 04	14 51								16 04	15 51								16 51	

For general notes see front of timetable
For details of catering facilities see Directory of Train Operators

b Arr. 1559

Saturday service operates on Bank Holiday Mondays

London → Welwyn Garden City, Hertford North and Letchworth Garden City

Network Diagram - see first page of Table 24

	FC	FC	FC 1	FC	FC		FC	FC	FC	FC	FC 1	FC	FC	FC	FC	FC	FC	FC 1	FC	FC	FC		FC	FC	FC
															A								A		
London Kings Cross 15 ⊖ d			16 36					16 52			17 06				17 22			17 36					17 52		
Moorgate ⊖ d	16 10	16 20		16 30	16 35		16 40		16 50	16 55		17 00	17 05	17 10		17 20	17 25		17 30	17 35	17 40			17 50	17 55
Old Street ⊖ d	16 12	16 22		16 32	16 37		16 42		16 52	16 57		17 02	17 07	17 12		17 22	17 27		17 32	17 37	17 42			17 52	17 57
Essex Road d	16 15	16 25		16 35	16 40		16 45		16 55	17 00		17 05	17 10	17 15		17 25	17 30		17 35	17 40	17 45			17 55	18 00
Highbury & Islington ⊖ d	16 17	16 27		16 37	16 42		16 47		16 57	17 02		17 07	17 12	17 17		17 27	17 32		17 37	17 42	17 47			17 57	18 02
Drayton Park d	16 19	16 29		16 39	16 44		16 49		16 59	17 04		17 09	17 14	17 19		17 29	17 34		17 39	17 44	17 49			17 59	18 04
Finsbury Park ⊖ d	16 22	16 32	16 41	16 42	16 47		16 52	16 57	17 02	17 07	17 11	17 12	17 17	17 22	17 27	17 32	17 37	17 41	17 42	17 47	17 52		17 57	18 02	18 07
Harringay d	16 24	16 34			16 49		16 54		17 04	17 09				17 24		17 34	17 39			17 49				18 04	18 09
Hornsey d	16 26	16 36			16 51		16 56		17 06	17 11				17 26		17 36	17 41			17 51				18 06	18 11
Alexandra Palace d	16 28	16 38			16 53		16 58		17 08	17 13				17 28		17 38	17 43				17 57			18 08	18 13
New Southgate d					16 56			17 02		17 16			17 22		17 32		17 46			17 54			18 02		18 16
Oakleigh Park d					16 59			17 06		17 19			17 25		17 36		17 49			17 58			18 06		18 19
New Barnet d					17 01			17 08		17 21			17 27		17 38		17 51			18 00			18 08		18 21
Hadley Wood d					17 04					17 24			17 30				17 54			18 02					18 24
Potters Bar d			16 51		17 08			17 13		17 28			17 34		17 43		17 58			18 06			18 13		18 28
Brookmans Park d					17 11					17 31			17 37				18 01			18 09					18 31
Welham Green d					17 13					17 33			17 39				18 03			18 11					18 33
Hatfield d			16 57		17 16			17 19		17 36	17 29		17 42		17 49		18 06			18 15			18 19		18 36
Welwyn Garden City 4 d			17 01		17a23			17 24		17a43	17 33		17a49		17 53		18a13	17 59		18a22			18 23		18a43
Welwyn North d			17 04					17 27			17 38				17 56			18 02					18 26		
Knebworth d			17 08					17 32			17 42				18 01			18 06					18 31		
Bowes Park d	16 30	16 40					17 00		17 10					17 30		17 40					18 00			18 10	
Palmers Green d	16 32	16 42		16 49			17 02		17 12			17 19		17 32		17 42			17 49		18 02			18 12	
Winchmore Hill d	16 35	16 45		16 51			17 05		17 15			17 21		17 35		17 45			17 51		18 04			18 15	
Grange Park d	16 37	16 47					17 07		17 17					17 37		17 47					18 06			18 17	
Enfield Chase d	16 39	16 49		16 54			17 09		17 19			17 24		17 39		17 49			17 54		18 08			18 19	
Gordon Hill d	16 41	16a52		16 56			17 11		17a22			17 26		17 41		17 51			17 56		18 11			18 22	
Crews Hill d	16 44						17 14							17 44							18 14				
Cuffley d	16 47			17 01			17 17					17 31		17 47		17 55			18 01		18 17			18 26	
Bayford d	16 52						17 22							17 52							18 22				
Hertford North d	16a59			17 10			17a29					17 40		17a59		18a06			18 10		18a29			18a37	
Watton-at-Stone d				17 15								17 45							18 15						
Stevenage 4 d			17 12	17a25				17 37			17 46	17a55			18 06			18 11	18a25				18 36		
Hitchin 4 d			17 17					17 42			17 51				18 12			18 17					18 42		
Letchworth Garden City a			17 21					17 50			17 56				18 16			18 23					18 46		

	FC 1	FC	FC	FC	FC	FC	FC	FC 1	FC	FC	FC	FC	FC	FC		FC 1	FC	FC	FC	FC 1	FC	FC	FC	FC	FC 1
					A																				
London Kings Cross 15 ⊖ d	18 06				18 22			18 36				18 52				19 06				19 36					20 06
Moorgate ⊖ d		18 00	18 05	18 10		18 20	18 25		18 30	18 35	18 40		18 50	18 55			19 05	19 10	19 20		19 30	19 35	19 40	19 50	
Old Street ⊖ d		18 02	18 07	18 12		18 22	18 27		18 32	18 37	18 42		18 52	18 57			19 07	19 12	19 22		19 32	19 37	19 42	19 52	
Essex Road d		18 05	18 10	18 15		18 25	18 30		18 35	18 40	18 45		18 55	19 00			19 10	19 15	19 25		19 35	19 40	19 45	19 55	
Highbury & Islington ⊖ d		18 07	18 12	18 17		18 27	18 32		18 37	18 42	18 47		18 57	19 02			19 12	19 17	19 27		19 37	19 42	19 47	19 57	
Drayton Park d		18 09	18 14	18 19		18 29	18 34		18 39	18 44	18 49		18 59	19 04			19 14	19 19	19 29		19 39	19 44	19 49	19 59	
Finsbury Park ⊖ d	18 11	18 12	18 17	18 22	18 27	18 32	18 37	18 41	18 42	18 47	18 52	18 57	19 02	19 07		19 11	19 17	19 22	19 32	19 41	19 42	19 47	19 52	20 02	20 11
Harringay d			18 19			18 34	18 39				18 54		19 04	19 09			19 19	19 24	19 34		19 44	19 49	19 54	20 04	
Hornsey d			18 21			18 36	18 41				18 56		19 06	19 11			19 21	19 26	19 36		19 46	19 51	19 56	20 06	
Alexandra Palace d				18 27		18 38	18 43				18 58		19 08	19 13			19 23	19 28	19 38		19 48	19 53	19 58	20 08	
New Southgate d			18 24		18 32		18 46			18 52		19 02		19 16			19 26					19 56			
Oakleigh Park d			18 28		18 36		18 49			18 55		19 06		19 19			19 29					19 59			
New Barnet d			18 30		18 38		18 51			18 57		19 08		19 21			19 31					20 01			
Hadley Wood d			18 32				18 54			19 00				19 24			19 34					20 04			
Potters Bar d			18 36		18 43		18 58			19 04		19 13		19 28		19 22	19 38			19 51		20 08			20 21
Brookmans Park d			18 39				19 01			19 07				19 31			19 41					20 11			
Welham Green d			18 41				19 03			19 09				19 33			19 43					20 13			
Hatfield d			18 45		18 49		19 06			19 12		19 19		19 36		19 28	19 46			19 57		20 16			20 27
Welwyn Garden City 4 d	18 29		18a52		18 53		19a13	18 59		19a19		19 23		19a43		19 32	19a53			20 01		20a23			20 31
Welwyn North d	18 32				18 56			19 02				19 26				19 35				20 04					20 34
Knebworth d	18 36				19 01			19 06				19 31				19 39				20 08					20 38
Bowes Park d				18 30		18 40					19 00		19 10					19 30	19 40		19 50		20 00	20 10	
Palmers Green d		18 19		18 32		18 42			18 49		19 02		19 12					19 32	19 42		19 52		20 02	20 12	
Winchmore Hill d		18 21		18 34		18 45			18 51		19 05		19 15					19 35	19 45		19 55		20 05	20 15	
Grange Park d				18 36		18 47					19 07		19 17					19 37	19 47		19 57		20 07	20 17	
Enfield Chase d		18 25		18 38		18 49			18 55		19 09		19 19					19 39	19 49		19 59		20 09	20 19	
Gordon Hill d		18 27		18 41		18 52			18 57		19 12		19 22					19 42	19 52		20 02		20 11	20 21	
Crews Hill d				18 44							19 15							19 45			20 05			20 24	
Cuffley d		18 32		18 47		18 56			19 02		19 18		19 26					19 48	19 56		20 08		20 15	20 27	
Bayford d				18 52							19 23							19 53			20 13			20 32	
Hertford North d		18 41		18a59		19a07			19 11		19a30		19 35					20a00	20 05		20a20		20a26	20a37	
Watton-at-Stone d		18 46							19 16				19 41						20 11						
Stevenage 4 d	18 41	18 53			19 06			19 11	19 23			19 36	19 50			19 43			20 20	20 12					20 42
Hitchin 4 d	18 47	18 59			19 12			19 17	19 29			19 42	19 57			19 48			20 27	20 17					20 47
Letchworth Garden City a	18 54	19 06			19 16			19 23	19 36			19 50	20 05			19 54			20 35	20 23					20 51

For general notes see front of timetable
For details of catering facilities see
Directory of Train Operators

A To Royston (Table 25)

London → Welwyn Garden City, Hertford North and Letchworth Garden City

Saturday service operates on Bank Holiday Mondays

Network Diagram - see first page of Table 24

Station		FC	FC	FC 1	FC	FC	FC 1	FC		FC	FC 1	FC	FC	FC 1	FC	FC	FC 1	FC	FC	FC 1	FC	FC	FC 1	FC		
London Kings Cross 15	⊖ d			20 36			21 06				21 36			22 06	22 11	22 26	22 36	22 41	22 56	23 06	23 11	23 26	23 36	23 41		
Moorgate	⊖ d	20 05	20 20		20 35	20 50		21 05		21 20		21 35	21 50													
Old Street	⊖ d	20 07	20 22		20 37	20 52		21 07		21 22		21 37	21 52													
Essex Road	d	20 10	20 25		20 40	20 55		21 10		21 25		21 40	21 55													
Highbury & Islington	⊖ d	20 12	20 27		20 42	20 57		21 12		21 27		21 42	21 57													
Drayton Park	d	20 14	20 29		20 44	20 59		21 14		21 29		21 44	21 59													
Finsbury Park	⊖ d	20 17	20 32	20 41	20 47	21 02	21 11	21 17		21 32	21 41	21 47	22 02	22 11	22 17	22 32	22 41	22 47	23 02	23 11	23 17	23 32	23 41	23 47		
Harringay	d	20 19	20 34		20 49	21 04		21 19		21 34		21 49	22 04		22 19	22 34		22 49	23 04		23 19	23 34		23 49		
Hornsey	d	20 21	20 36		20 51	21 06		21 21		21 36		21 51	22 06		22 21	22 36		22 51	23 06		23 21	23 36		23 51		
Alexandra Palace	d	20 23	20 38		20 53	21 08		21 23		21 38		21 53	22 08		22 23	22 38		22 53	23 08		23 23	23 38		23 53		
New Southgate	d	20 26			20 56			21 26				21 56			22 26			22 56			23 26			23 56		
Oakleigh Park	d	20 29			20 59			21 29				21 59			22 29			22 59			23 29			23 59		
New Barnet	d	20 31			21 01			21 31				22 01			22 31			23 01			23 31			00 01		
Hadley Wood	d	20 34			21 04			21 34				22 04			22 34			23 04			23 34			00 04		
Potters Bar	d	20 38		20 51	21 08		21 21	21 38			21 51	22 08		22 21	22 38		22 51	23 08		23 21	23 38		23 51	00 08		
Brookmans Park	d	20 41			21 11			21 41				22 11			22 41			23 11			23 41			00 11		
Welham Green	d	20 43			21 13			21 43				22 13			22 43			23 13			23 43			00 13		
Hatfield	d	20 46		20 57	21 16		21 27	21 46			21 57	22 16		22 27	22 46		22 57	23 16		23 27	23 46		23 57	00 16		
Welwyn Garden City 4	d	20a51		21 01	21a21		21 31	21a51			22 01	22a21		22 31	22a51		23 01	23a24		23 31	23a54		00 01	00a24		
Welwyn North	d			21 04			21 34				22 04			22 34			23 04			23 34			00 04			
Knebworth	d			21 08			21 38				22 08			22 38			23 08			23 38			00 08			
Bowes Park	d		20 40			21 10				21 40			22 10			22 40			23 10			23 40				
Palmers Green	d		20 42			21 12				21 42			22 12			22 42			23 12			23 42				
Winchmore Hill	d		20 45			21 15				21 45			22 15			22 45			23 15			23 45				
Grange Park	d		20 47			21 17				21 47			22 17			22 47			23 17			23 47				
Enfield Chase	d		20 49			21 19				21 49			22 19			22 49			23 19			23 49				
Gordon Hill	d		20 51			21 21				21 51			22 21			22 51			23 21			23 51				
Crews Hill	d		20 54			21 24				21 54			22 24			22 54			23 24			23 54				
Cuffley	d		20 57			21 27				21 57			22 27			22 57			23 27			23 57				
Bayford	d		21 02			21 32				22 02			22 32			23 02			23 32			00 02				
Hertford North	d		21 07			21a37				22 07			22a37			23 07			23a37			00 07				
Watton-at-Stone	d		21 12							22 12						23 12						00 12				
Stevenage 4	d		21 20	21 12			21 42			22 20	22 12			22 42		23 20	23 12			23 42		00a20	00 12			
Hitchin 4	d		21 28	21 17			21 47			22 25	22 17			22 50		23 28	23 20			23 50			00 20			
Letchworth Garden City	a		21 35	21 23			21 51			22 33	22 23			22 54		23 36	23 26			23 54			00 29			

Saturdays

Station		FC	FC 1	FC	FC 1 A	FC	FC	FC 1	FC	FC 1	FC 1 B	FC 1	FC	FC	FC 1	FC	FC	FC 1	FC	FC	FC 1	FC	FC	FC 1	FC	FC
London Kings Cross 15	⊖ d	23p26	23p36	23p41	00 07	00 11	00 26	00 36	00 41	01 06	01 36	05 21	05 26	05 56	06 06	06 11	06 26	06 36	06 41	06 56	07 06	07 11	07 26	07 36	07 41	07 56
Finsbury Park	⊖ d	23p32	23p41	23p47	00 12	00 17	00 32	00 41	00 47	01 11	01 41	05 26	05 32	06 02	06 11	06 17	06 32	06 41	06 47	07 02	07 11	07 17	07 32	07 41	07 47	08 02
Harringay	d	23p34		23p49		00 19	00 34						05 34	06 04		06 19	06 34		06 49	07 04		07 19	07 34		07 49	08 04
Hornsey	d	23p36		23p51		00 21	00 36						05 36	06 06		06 21	06 36		06 51	07 06		07 21	07 36		07 51	08 06
Alexandra Palace	d	23p38		23p53	00 17	00 23	00 38		00 51	01 15	01 45		05 38	06 08		06 23	06 38		06 53	07 08		07 23	07 38		07 53	08 08
New Southgate	d			23p56		00 26			00 54							06 26			06 56			07 26			07 56	
Oakleigh Park	d			23p59		00 29			00 57		01 50					06 29			06 59			07 29			07 59	
New Barnet	d			00 01		00 31			00 59		01 52					06 31			07 01			07 31			08 01	
Hadley Wood	d			00 04		00 34			01 02		01 54					06 34			07 04			07 34			08 04	
Potters Bar	d		23p51	00 08		00 38		00 51	01 06		01 58	05 36			06 21	06 38		06 51	07 08		07 21	07 38		07 51	08 08	
Brookmans Park	d			00 11		00 41			01 09							06 41			07 11			07 41			08 11	
Welham Green	d			00 13		00 43										06 43			07 13			07 43			08 13	
Hatfield	d		23p57	00 16		00 46		00 57	01 13		02 04	05 42			06 27	06 46		06 57	07 16		07 27	07 46		07 57	08 16	
Welwyn Garden City 4	d		00 01	00a24		00a54		01 01	01a21		02 08	05 46			06 31	06a51		07 01	07a21		07 31	07a51		08 01	08a21	
Welwyn North	d		00 04					01s04			02s11	05 49			06 34			07 04			07 34			08 04		
Knebworth	d		00 08					01s08			02s15	05 53			06 38			07 08			07 38			08 08		
Bowes Park	d	23p40					00 40						05 40	06 10			06 40			07 10			07 40			08 10
Palmers Green	d	23p42			00 20		00 42			01 18			05 42	06 12			06 42			07 12			07 42			08 12
Winchmore Hill	d	23p45			00 22		00 45			01 21			05 45	06 15			06 45			07 15			07 45			08 15
Grange Park	d	23p47					00 47						05 47	06 17			06 47			07 17			07 47			08 17
Enfield Chase	d	23p49			00 25		00 49			01 23			05 49	06 19			06 49			07 19			07 49			08 19
Gordon Hill	d	23p51			00 27		00 51			01 25			05 51	06 21			06 51			07 21			07 51			08 21
Crews Hill	d	23p54					00 54						05 54	06 24			06 54			07 24			07 54			08 24
Cuffley	d	23p57			00 31		00 57			01 30			05 57	06 27			06 57			07 27			07 57			08 27
Bayford	d	00 02					01 02						06 02	06 32			07 02			07 32			08 02			08 32
Hertford North	d	00 07			00 39		01a07			01 37			06a07	06a37			07 07			07a37			08 07			08a37
Watton-at-Stone	d	00 12															07 12						08 12			
Stevenage 4	d	00a20	00 12		00 48			01 12		01 47	02 18	05 57			06 42		07a20	07 12			07 42		08a20	08 12		
Hitchin 4	d		00 20		00 56			01a17		01 52	02a23	06a05			06 47			07a17			07 47			08a17		
Letchworth Garden City	a		00 29		01 00					02 06					06 51						07 51					

For general notes see front of timetable
For details of catering facilities see
Directory of Train Operators

A To Cambridge (Table 25)
B To Peterborough (Table 25)

There is no service between Moorgate and Finsbury Park on Saturdays

London → Welwyn Garden City, Hertford North and Letchworth Garden City

Network Diagram - see first page of Table 24

	FC 1		FC	FC	FC 1	FC	FC	FC 1	FC	FC	FC 1	FC	FC	FC 1	FC	FC	FC 1	FC	FC	FC 1	FC	FC	FC 1	FC	FC
London Kings Cross 15 ⊖ d	08 06		08 11	08 26	08 36	08 41	08 56	09 06	09 11	09 26	09 36	09 41	09 56	10 06	10 11	10 26	10 36	10 41	10 56	11 06	11 11	11 26	11 36	11 41	11 56
Finsbury Park ⊖ d	08 11		08 17	08 32	08 41	08 47	09 02	09 11	09 17	09 32	09 41	09 47	10 02	10 11	10 17	10 32	10 41	10 47	11 02	11 11	11 17	11 32	11 41	11 47	12 02
Harringay d			08 19	08 34		08 49	09 04		09 19	09 34		09 49	10 04		10 19	10 34		10 49	11 04		11 19	11 34		11 49	12 04
Hornsey d			08 21	08 36		08 51	09 06		09 21	09 36		09 51	10 06		10 21	10 36		10 51	11 06		11 21	11 36		11 51	12 06
Alexandra Palace d			08 23	08 38		08 53	09 08		09 23	09 38		09 53	10 08		10 23	10 38		10 53	11 08		11 23	11 38		11 53	12 08
New Southgate d			08 26			08 56			09 26			09 56			10 26			10 56			11 26			11 56	
Oakleigh Park d			08 29			08 59			09 29			09 59			10 29			10 59			11 29			11 59	
New Barnet d			08 31			09 01			09 31			10 01			10 31			11 01			11 31			12 01	
Hadley Wood d			08 34			09 04			09 34			10 04			10 34			11 04			11 34			12 04	
Potters Bar d	08 21		08 38		08 51	09 08		09 21	09 38		09 51	10 08		10 21	10 38		10 51	11 08		11 21	11 38		11 51	12 08	
Brookmans Park d			08 41			09 11			09 41			10 11			10 41			11 11			11 41			12 11	
Welham Green d			08 43			09 13			09 43			10 13			10 43			11 13			11 43			12 13	
Hatfield d	08 27		08 46		08 57	09 16		09 27	09 46		09 57	10 16		10 27	10 46		10 57	11 16		11 27	11 46		11 57	12 16	
Welwyn Garden City 4 d	08 31		08a51		09 01	09a21		09 31	09a51		10 01	10a21		10 31	10a51		11 01	11a21		11 31	11a51		12 01	12a21	
Welwyn North d	08 34				09 04			09 34			10 04			10 34			11 04			11 34			12 04		
Knebworth d	08 38				09 08			09 38			10 08			10 38			11 08			11 38			12 08		
Bowes Park d				08 40			09 10			09 40			10 10			10 40			11 10			11 40			12 10
Palmers Green d				08 42			09 12			09 42			10 12			10 42			11 12			11 42			12 12
Winchmore Hill d				08 45			09 15			09 45			10 15			10 45			11 15			11 45			12 15
Grange Park d				08 47			09 17			09 47			10 17			10 47			11 17			11 47			12 17
Enfield Chase d				08 49			09 19			09 49			10 19			10 49			11 19			11 49			12 19
Gordon Hill d				08 51			09 21			09 51			10 21			10 51			11 21			11 51			12 21
Crews Hill d				08 54			09 24			09 54			10 24			10 54			11 24			11 54			12 24
Cuffley d				08 57			09 27			09 57			10 27			10 57			11 27			11 57			12 27
Bayford d				09 02			09 32			10 02			10 32			11 02			11 32			12 02			12 32
Hertford North d				09 07			09a37			10 07			10a37			11 07			11a37			12 07			12a37
Watton-at-Stone d				09 12						10 12						11 12						12 12			
Stevenage 4 d	08 42			09a20	09 12			09 42		10a20	10 12			10 42		11a20	11 12			11 42		12a20	12 12		
Hitchin 4 d	08 47				09a17			09 47			10a17			10 47			11a17			11 47			12a17		
Letchworth Garden City a	08 51							09 51						10 51						11 51					

	FC 1	FC	FC		FC 1	FC	FC	FC 1	FC	FC	FC 1	FC	FC	FC 1	FC	FC	FC 1	FC	FC	FC 1	FC	FC	FC 1	FC	FC
London Kings Cross 15 ⊖ d	12 06	12 11	12 26		12 36	12 41	12 56	13 06	13 11	13 26	13 36	13 41	13 56	14 06	14 11	14 26	14 36	14 41	14 56	15 06	15 11	15 26	15 36	15 41	15 56
Finsbury Park ⊖ d	12 11	12 17	12 32		12 41	12 47	13 02	13 11	13 17	13 32	13 41	13 47	14 02	14 11	14 17	14 32	14 41	14 47	15 02	15 11	15 17	15 32	15 41	15 47	16 02
Harringay d		12 19	12 34			12 49	13 04		13 19	13 34		13 49	14 04		14 19	14 34		14 49	15 04		15 19	15 34		15 49	16 04
Hornsey d		12 21	12 36			12 51	13 06		13 21	13 36		13 51	14 06		14 21	14 36		14 51	15 06		15 21	15 36		15 51	16 06
Alexandra Palace d		12 23	12 38			12 53	13 08		13 23	13 38		13 53	14 08		14 23	14 38		14 53	15 08		15 23	15 38		15 53	16 08
New Southgate d		12 26				12 56			13 26			13 56			14 26			14 56			15 26			15 56	
Oakleigh Park d		12 29				12 59			13 29			13 59			14 29			14 59			15 29			15 59	
New Barnet d		12 31				13 01			13 31			14 01			14 31			15 01			15 31			16 01	
Hadley Wood d		12 34				13 04			13 34			14 04			14 34			15 04			15 34			16 04	
Potters Bar d	12 21	12 38			12 51	13 08		13 21	13 38		13 51	14 08		14 21	14 38		14 51	15 08		15 21	15 38		15 51	16 08	
Brookmans Park d		12 41				13 11			13 41			14 11			14 41			15 11			15 41			16 11	
Welham Green d		12 43				13 13			13 43			14 13			14 43			15 13			15 43			16 13	
Hatfield d	12 27	12 46			12 57	13 16		13 27	13 46		13 57	14 16		14 27	14 46		14 57	15 16		15 27	15 46		15 57	16 16	
Welwyn Garden City 4 d	12 31	12a51			13 01	13a21		13 31	13a51		14 01	14a21		14 31	14a51		15 01	15a21		15 31	15a51		16 01	16a21	
Welwyn North d	12 34				13 04			13 34			14 04			14 34			15 04			15 34			16 04		
Knebworth d	12 38				13 08			13 38			14 08			14 38			15 08			15 38			16 08		
Bowes Park d			12 40				13 10			13 40			14 10			14 40			15 10			15 40			16 10
Palmers Green d			12 42				13 12			13 42			14 12			14 42			15 12			15 42			16 12
Winchmore Hill d			12 45				13 15			13 45			14 15			14 45			15 15			15 45			16 15
Grange Park d			12 47				13 17			13 47			14 17			14 47			15 17			15 47			16 17
Enfield Chase d			12 49				13 19			13 49			14 19			14 49			15 19			15 49			16 19
Gordon Hill d			12 51				13 21			13 51			14 21			14 51			15 21			15 51			16 21
Crews Hill d			12 54				13 24			13 54			14 24			14 54			15 24			15 54			16 24
Cuffley d			12 57				13 27			13 57			14 27			14 57			15 27			15 57			16 27
Bayford d			13 02				13 32			14 02			14 32			15 02			15 32			16 02			16 32
Hertford North d			13 07				13a37			14 07			14a37			15 07			15a37			16 07			16a37
Watton-at-Stone d			13 12							14 12						15 12						16 12			
Stevenage 4 d	12 42		13a20		13 12			13 42		14a20	14 12			14 42		15a20	15 12			15 42		16a20	16 12		
Hitchin 4 d	12 47				13a17			13 47			14a17			14 47			15a17			15 47			16a17		
Letchworth Garden City a	12 51							13 51						14 51						15 51					

For general notes see front of timetable
For details of catering facilities see Directory of Train Operators

There is no service between Moorgate and Finsbury Park on Saturdays

Table 24

Saturdays

London → Welwyn Garden City, Hertford North and Letchworth Garden City

Network Diagram - see first page of Table 24

		FC 1	FC	FC	FC 1	FC		FC	FC 1	FC	FC	FC 1	FC	FC	FC 1	FC	FC	FC 1	FC	FC	FC 1	FC	FC	FC 1	FC	FC
London Kings Cross 15 ⊖	d	16 06	16 11	16 26	16 36	16 41		16 56	17 06	17 11	17 26	17 36	17 41	17 56	18 06	18 11	18 26	18 36	18 41	18 56	19 06	19 11	19 26	19 36	19 41	19 56
Finsbury Park ⊖	d	16 11	16 17	16 32	16 41	16 47		17 02	17 11	17 17	17 32	17 41	17 47	18 02	18 11	18 17	18 32	18 41	18 47	19 02	19 11	19 17	19 32	19 41	19 47	20 02
Harringay	d		16 19	16 34		16 49		17 04		17 19	17 34		17 49	18 04		18 19	18 34		18 49	19 04		19 19	19 34		19 49	20 04
Hornsey	d		16 21	16 36		16 51		17 06		17 21	17 36		17 51	18 06		18 21	18 36		18 51	19 06		19 21	19 36		19 51	20 06
Alexandra Palace	d		16 23	16 38		16 53		17 08		17 23	17 38		17 53	18 08		18 23	18 38		18 53	19 08		19 23	19 38		19 53	20 08
New Southgate	d		16 26			16 56				17 26			17 56			18 26			18 56			19 26			19 56	
Oakleigh Park	d		16 29			16 59				17 29			17 59			18 29			18 59			19 29			19 59	
New Barnet	d		16 31			17 01				17 31			18 01			18 31			19 01			19 31			20 01	
Hadley Wood	d		16 34			17 04				17 34			18 04			18 34			19 04			19 34			20 04	
Potters Bar	d	16 21	16 38		16 51	17 08			17 21	17 38		17 51	18 08		18 21	18 38		18 51	19 08		19 21	19 38		19 51	20 08	
Brookmans Park	d		16 41			17 11				17 41			18 11			18 41			19 11			19 41			20 11	
Welham Green	d		16 43			17 13				17 43			18 13			18 43			19 13			19 43			20 13	
Hatfield	d	16 27	16 46		16 57	17 16			17 27	17 46		17 57	18 16		18 27	18 46		18 57	19 16		19 27	19 46		19 57	20 16	
Welwyn Garden City 4	d	16 31	16a51		17 01	17a21			17 31	17a51		18 01	18a21		18 31	18a51		19 01	19a21		19 31	19a51		20 01	20a21	
Welwyn North	d	16 34			17 04				17 34			18 04			18 34			19 04			19 34			20 04		
Knebworth	d	16 38			17 08				17 38			18 08			18 38			19 08			19 38			20 08		
Bowes Park	d			16 40				17 10			17 40			18 10			18 40			19 10			19 40			20 10
Palmers Green	d			16 42				17 12			17 42			18 12			18 42			19 12			19 42			20 12
Winchmore Hill	d			16 45				17 15			17 45			18 15			18 45			19 15			19 45			20 15
Grange Park	d			16 47				17 17			17 47			18 17			18 47			19 17			19 47			20 17
Enfield Chase	d			16 49				17 19			17 49			18 19			18 49			19 19			19 49			20 19
Gordon Hill	d			16 51				17 21			17 51			18 21			18 51			19 21			19 51			20 21
Crews Hill	d			16 54				17 24			17 54			18 24			18 54			19 24			19 54			20 24
Cuffley	d			16 57				17 27			17 57			18 27			18 57			19 27			19 57			20 27
Bayford	d			17 02				17 32			18 02			18 32			19 02			19 32			20 02			20 32
Hertford North	d			17 07				17a37			18 07			18a37			19 07			19a37			20 07			20a37
Watton-at-Stone	d			17 12							18 12						19 12						20 12			
Stevenage 4	d	16 42		17a20	17 12				17 42		18a20	18 12			18 42		19a20	19 12			19 42		20a20	20 12		
Hitchin 4	d	16 47			17a17				17 47			18a17			18 47			19a17			19 47			20a17		
Letchworth Garden City	a	16 51							17 51						18 51						19 51					

		FC 1	FC	FC	FC 1	FC	FC	FC 1	FC	FC	FC 1	FC	FC	FC 1	FC	FC	FC 1	FC	FC	FC 1	FC	FC	FC A	FC B		
London Kings Cross 15 ⊖	d	20 06	20 11	20 26	20 36	20 41	20 56	21 06	21 11	21 26	21 36	21 41	21 56	22 06	22 11	22 26	22 36	22 41	22 56	23 15	23 19	23 26	23 35	23 35		
Finsbury Park ⊖	d	20 11	20 17	20 32	20 41	20 47	21 02	21 11	21 17	21 32	21 41	21 47	22 02	22 11	22 17	22 32	22 41	22 47	23 02	23 20	23 24	23 32	23 40	23 41		
Harringay	d		20 19	20 34		20 49	21 04		21 19	21 34		21 49	22 04		22 19	22 34		22 49	23 04		23 26	23 34	23 42	23 43		
Hornsey	d		20 21	20 36		20 51	21 06		21 21	21 36		21 51	22 06		22 21	22 36		22 51	23 06		23 28	23 36	23 44	23 45		
Alexandra Palace	d		20 23	20 38		20 53	21 08		21 23	21 38		21 53	22 08		22 23	22 38		22 53	23 08		23 30	23 38	23 46	23 47		
New Southgate	d		20 26			20 56			21 26			21 56			22 26			22 56			23 33		23 49	23 50		
Oakleigh Park	d		20 29			20 59			21 29			21 59			22 29			22 59			23 37		23 52	23 52		
New Barnet	d		20 31			21 01			21 31			22 01			22 31			23 01			23 39		23 54	23 54		
Hadley Wood	d		20 34			21 04			21 34			22 04			22 34			23 04			23 41		23 57	23 58		
Potters Bar	d	20 21	20 38		20 51	21 08		21 21	21 38		21 51	22 08		22 21	22 38		22 51	23 08		23 30	23 45		00 01	00 01		
Brookmans Park	d		20 41			21 11			21 41			22 11			22 41			23 11			23 48		00 04	00 04		
Welham Green	d		20 43			21 13			21 43			22 13			22 43			23 13			23 50		00 06	00 07		
Hatfield	d	20 27	20 46		20 57	21 16		21 27	21 46		21 57	22 16		22 27	22 46		22 57	23 16		23 36	23 54		00 09	00 09		
Welwyn Garden City 4	d	20 31	20a51		21 01	21a21		21 31	21a51		22 01	22a21		22 31	22a53		23 01	23a23		23 40	00a05		00b28	00b30		
Welwyn North	d	20 34			21 04			21 34			22 04			22 34			23 04			23 45			00 31	00 33		
Knebworth	d	20 38			21 08			21 38			22 08			22 38			23 08			23 49			00 35	00 37		
Bowes Park	d			20 40			21 10			21 40			22 10			22 40			23 10			23 40				
Palmers Green	d			20 42			21 12			21 42			22 12			22 42			23 12			23 42				
Winchmore Hill	d			20 45			21 15			21 45			22 15			22 45			23 15			23 45				
Grange Park	d			20 47			21 17			21 47			22 17			22 47			23 17			23 47				
Enfield Chase	d			20 49			21 19			21 49			22 19			22 49			23 19			23 49				
Gordon Hill	d			20 51			21 21			21 51			22 21			22 51			23 21			23 51				
Crews Hill	d			20 54			21 24			21 54			22 24			22 54			23 24			23 54				
Cuffley	d			20 57			21 27			21 57			22 27			22 57			23 27			23 57				
Bayford	d			21 02			21 32			22 02			22 32			23 02			23 32			00 02				
Hertford North	d			21 07			21a37			22 07			22a37			23 07			23a37			00 07				
Watton-at-Stone	d			21 12						22 12						23 12						00 12				
Stevenage 4	d	20 42		21a20	21 12			21 42		22a20	22 12			22 42		23a21	23 12			23 55		00a23	00 41	00 42		
Hitchin 4	d	20 47			21a17			21 47			22a17			22 47			23a17			00 02			00 49	00c56		
Letchworth Garden City	a	20 51						21 51						22 51						00 06			00 57	01 00		

For general notes see front of timetable
For details of catering facilities see Directory of Train Operators

A From 29 March
B Until 22 March. To Cambridge (Table 25)

b Arr. 0015
c Arr. 0049

There is no service between Moorgate and Finsbury Park on Saturdays

Table 24

Sundays

London → Welwyn Garden City, Hertford North and Letchworth Garden City

Network Diagram - see first page of Table 24

Station		FC 1	FC	FC A	FC B	FC C bus	FC 1	FC	FC C bus	FC A	FC C bus	FC 1 A	FC 1 C	FC bus	FC C bus	FC	FC C bus	FC bus	FC 1 C	FC	FC bus		FC 1 C	FC C bus	FC	FC 1 C
London Kings Cross 15	⊖ d	23p15	23p26	23p35	23p35	....	00 07	00 11	....	00 26	00 26	00 36	00 36	....	....	00 41	....	05 26	06 01	06 11	....	....	06 31	....	06 41	07 01
Finsbury Park	⊖ d	23p20	23p32	23p40	23p41	.	00 12	00 17	00 22	00 32	00 41	00 41	00 42	.	.	00 47	.	05 41	06 06	06 17	.	.	06 36	.	06 47	07 06
Harringay	d	....	23p34	23p42	23p43	....		00 19		00 34				....	....	00 49	....	....		06 19	....	....		....	06 49	
Hornsey	d	.	23p36	23p44	23p45	.		00 21		00 36				.	.	00 51	.	.		06 21	.	.		.	06 51	
Alexandra Palace	d	....	23p38	23p46	23p47	00 01	00 17	00 23	00 52	00 38	01 01			....	....	00 53	....	06 01		06 23	06 31	....		....	06 53	
New Southgate	d	.	.	23p49	23p50			00 26						.	.	00 56	.	.		06 26	.	.		.	06 56	
Oakleigh Park	d	....	....	23p52	23p52			00 29						....	....	00 59	....	....		06 29	....	....		....	06 59	
New Barnet	d	.	.	23p54	23p54			00 31						.	.	01 01	.	.		06 31	.	.		.	07 01	
Hadley Wood	d	....	....	23p57	23p58			00 34						....	....	01 04	....	....		06 34	....	....		....	07 04	
Potters Bar	d	23p30	.	00 01	00 01			00 38				00 51	00 54	.	.	01 08	.	.		06 38	.	.	06 46	.	07 08	07 16
Brookmans Park	d	....	....	00 04	00 04			00 41						....	....	01 11	....	....		06 41	....	....		....	07 11	
Welham Green	d	.	.	00 06	00 07			00 43						.	.	01 13	.	.		06 43	.	.		.	07 13	
Hatfield	d	23p36	....	00 09	00 09			00 46				00 57	01 00	....	....	01 16	....	....		06 46	....	....	06 52	....	07 16	07 22
Welwyn Garden City 4	d	23p40	.	00b28	00b30			00a57				01 03	01a06	01 11	01 12	01a26	.	.		06a55	.	.	06 57	.	07a25	07 28
Welwyn North	d	23p45	....	00 31	00 33			....				01s08	....		01s22	....	....	....		....	....	....	07 00	....	....	07 31
Knebworth	d	23p49	.	00 35	00 37			.				01s12	.		01s33	.	06 44	.	06a32	.	.	.	07a08	07 14	.	07a37
Bowes Park	d	....	23p40			00 06		....		00 40	01 06		....			....		06 06	....	....	06 36	....	....		....	....
Palmers Green	d	.	23p42			00 16	00 20	.	01 03	00 42	01s16		.			.		06 16	.	.	06 46	.	.		.	.
Winchmore Hill	d	....	23p45			00 24	00 22	....	01 11	00 45	01s24		....			....		06 24	....	....	06 54	....	....		....	....
Grange Park	d	.	23p47			00 30		.		00 47	01s30		.			.		06 30	.	.	07 00	.	.		.	.
Enfield Chase	d	....	23p49			00 35	00 25	....	01 21	00 49	01s35		....			....		06 35	....	....	07 05	....	....		....	....
Gordon Hill	d	.	23p51			00 41	00 27	.	01 27	00 51	01s41		.			.		06 41	.	.	07 11	.	.		.	.
Crews Hill	d	....	23p54			00 51		....		00 54	01s51		....			....		06 51	....	....	07 21	....	....		....	....
Cuffley	d	.	23p57			00 59	00 31	.	01s42	00 57	01s59		.			.		06 59	.	.	07 29	.	.		.	.
Bayford	d	....	00 02			01 14		....		01 02	02s14		....			....		07 14	....	....	07 44	....	....		....	....
Hertford North	d	.	00 07			01a29	00 39	.	02s07	01a09	02a29		.			.		07 29	.	.	07a59	.	.		.	.
Watton-at-Stone	d	....	00 12			....		....		....	....		....			....		07 43	....	....	....	....	....		....	....
Stevenage 4	d	23p55	00a23	00 41	00 42	.	00 48	.	02a29	.	.	01 14	.	01 14	01a40	.	06 51	08a00	.	.	.	.	.	07 21	.	.
Hitchin 4	d	00 02	....	00 49	00c56	....	00 56	....	....	....	....	01a19	....	01 19	....	....	07a11	....	....	....	....	....	....	07a41	....	....
Letchworth Garden City	a	00 06	.	00 57	01 00	.	01 00	.	.	.	.	.	.	.	.	.	.	.	.	.	.	.	.	.	.	.

Station		FC C	FC 1 A	FC C bus	FC 1 C	FC C bus	FC C bus	FC A bus	FC	FC A	FC 1 C	FC 1 A	FC C bus	FC bus	FC C bus	FC	FC A	FC C bus	FC		FC A	FC 1	FC C bus	FC	FC A	FC C bus
London Kings Cross 15	⊖ d	07 04	07 06	....	07 26	....	....	....	07 41	07 56	08 01	08 06	....	....	....	08 11	08 26	....	08 41	....	08 56	09 06	....	09 11	09 26	....
Finsbury Park	⊖ d	07 10	07 11	.	07 31	.	.	.	07 47	08 02	08 06	08 11	.	.	.	08 17	08 32	.	08 47	.	09 02	09 11	.	09 17	09 32	.
Harringay	d	07 12		....		....	....	....	07 49	08 04			....	....	....	08 19	08 34	....	08 49	....	09 04	....	....	09 19	09 34	....
Hornsey	d	07 14		.		.	.	.	07 51	08 06			.	.	.	08 21	08 36	.	08 51	.	09 06	.	.	09 21	09 36	.
Alexandra Palace	d	07 16		....		....	07 31	07 31	07 53	08 08			....	07 01	08 01	08 23	08 38	08 31	08 53	....	09 08	....	09 01	09 23	09 38	09 31
New Southgate	d	07 19		.		.			07 56				.	.		08 26			08 56	.		.		09 26		
Oakleigh Park	d	07 22		....		....			07 59				....	....		08 29			08 59	....		....		09 29		
New Barnet	d	07 24		.		.			08 01				.	.		08 31			09 01	.		.		09 31		
Hadley Wood	d	07 27		....		....			08 04				....	....		08 34			09 04	....		....		09 34		
Potters Bar	d	07 31	07 21	.		.			08 08		08 16	08 21	.	.		08 38			09 08	.		09 21		09 38		
Brookmans Park	d	07 34		....		....			08 11				....	....		08 41			09 11	....		....		09 41		
Welham Green	d	07 36		.		.			08 13				.	.		08 43			09 13	.		.		09 43		
Hatfield	d	07 39	07 27	....		....			08 16		08 22	08 27	....	....		08 46			09 16	....		09 27		09 46		
Welwyn Garden City 4	d	07a48	07 33	.		.			08a25		08 28	08 31	.	.		08a55			09a21	.		09 31		09a51		
Welwyn North	d	....	07 36	....		....			....		08 33	08 36	....	....		....			....	....		09 34		....		
Knebworth	d	.	07 40	07 42	07a57	08 02			.		08a39	08 38	08 44	.		.			.	.		09 38		.		
Bowes Park	d	....			....		07 36	07 36	....	08 10	....			07 06	08 06	....	08 40	08 36	....	....	09 10	....	09 06	....	09 40	09 36
Palmers Green	d	.			.		07 46	07 46	.	08 12	.			07 16	08 16	.	08 42	08 46	.	.	09 12	.	09 16	.	09 42	09 46
Winchmore Hill	d	....			....		07 54	07 54	....	08 15	....			07 24	08 24	....	08 45	08 54	....	....	09 15	....	09 24	....	09 45	09 54
Grange Park	d	.			.		08 00	08 00	.	08 17	.			07 30	08 30	.	08 47	09 00	.	.	09 17	.	09 30	.	09 47	10 00
Enfield Chase	d	....			....		08 05	08 05	....	08 19	....			07 35	08 35	....	08 49	09 05	....	....	09 19	....	09 35	....	09 49	10 05
Gordon Hill	d	.			.		08 11	08a11	.	08 21	.			07 41	08 41	.	08 51	09 11	.	.	09 21	.	09 41	.	09 51	10a11
Crews Hill	d	....			....		08 21	....	....	08 24	....			07 51	08 51	....	08 54	09 21	....	....	09 24	....	09 51	....	09 54	....
Cuffley	d	.			.		08 29	.	.	08 27	.			07 59	08 59	.	08 57	09 29	.	.	09 27	.	09 59	.	09 57	.
Bayford	d	....			....		08 44	....	....	08 32	....			08 14	09 14	....	09 02	09 44	....	....	09 32	....	10 14	....	10 02	....
Hertford North	d	.			.		08a59	.	.	08a39	.			08 29	09 29	.	09 07	09a59	.	.	09a37	.	10 29	.	10 07	.
Watton-at-Stone	d	....			....		....	....	....	....	....			08 43	09 43	....	09 12	....	....	....	....	....	10 43	....	10 12	....
Stevenage 4	d	.	07 45	07 49	.	08 09	.	.	.	.	.	08 42	08 51	09a00	10a00	.	09a20	.	.	.	.	09 42	11a00	.	10a20	.
Hitchin 4	d	....	07 52	08a09	....	08a26	....	....	....	....	....	08 47	09a11	....	....	....	....	....	....	....	....	09 47	....	....	....	....
Letchworth Garden City	a	.	07 56	.	.	.	.	.	.	.	.	08 54	.	.	.	.	.	.	.	.	.	09 51	.	.	.	.

For general notes see front of timetable
For details of catering facilities see Directory of Train Operators

A From 30 March
B Until 23 March. To Cambridge (Table 25)
C Until 23 March
b Arr. 0015
c Arr. 0049

There is no service between Moorgate and Finsbury Park on Sundays

Sundays

London → Welwyn Garden City, Hertford North and Letchworth Garden City

Network Diagram - see first page of Table 24

		FC	FC	FC 1	FC	FC	FC	FC	FC 1	FC	FC	FC	FC	FC 1	FC	FC	FC		FC	FC 1	FC	FC	FC	FC	FC 1	FC
London Kings Cross 15 ⊖	d	09 41	09 56	10 06	10 11	10 26	10 41	10 56	11 06	11 11	11 26	11 41	11 56	12 06	12 11	12 26	12 41		12 56	13 06	13 11	13 26	13 41	13 56	14 06	14 11
Finsbury Park ⊖	d	09 47	10 02	10 11	10 17	10 32	10 47	11 02	11 11	11 17	11 32	11 47	12 02	12 11	12 17	12 32	12 47		13 02	13 11	13 17	13 32	13 47	14 02	14 11	14 17
Harringay	d	09 49	10 04		10 19	10 34	10 49	11 04		11 19	11 34	11 49	12 04		12 19	12 34	12 49		13 04		13 19	13 34	13 49	14 04		14 19
Hornsey	d	09 51	10 06		10 21	10 36	10 51	11 06		11 21	11 36	11 51	12 06		12 21	12 36	12 51		13 06		13 21	13 36	13 51	14 06		14 21
Alexandra Palace	d	09 53	10 08		10 23	10 38	10 53	11 08		11 23	11 38	11 53	12 08		12 23	12 38	12 53		13 08		13 23	13 38	13 53	14 08		14 23
New Southgate	d	09 56			10 26		10 56			11 26		11 56			12 26		12 56				13 26		13 56			14 26
Oakleigh Park	d	09 59			10 29		10 59			11 29		11 59			12 29		12 59				13 29		13 59			14 29
New Barnet	d	10 01			10 31		11 01			11 31		12 01			12 31		13 01				13 31		14 01			14 31
Hadley Wood	d	10 04			10 34		11 04			11 34		12 04			12 34		13 04				13 34		14 04			14 34
Potters Bar	d	10 08		10 21	10 38		11 08		11 21	11 38		12 08		12 21	12 38		13 08			13 21	13 38		14 08		14 21	14 38
Brookmans Park	d	10 11			10 41		11 11			11 41		12 11			12 41		13 11				13 41		14 11			14 41
Welham Green	d	10 13			10 43		11 13			11 43		12 13			12 43		13 13				13 43		14 13			14 43
Hatfield	d	10 16		10 27	10 46		11 16		11 27	11 46		12 16		12 27	12 46		13 16			13 27	13 46		14 16		14 27	14 46
Welwyn Garden City 4	d	10a21		10 31	10a51		11a21		11 31	11a51		12a21		12 31	12a51		13a21			13 31	13a51		14a21		14 31	14a51
Welwyn North	d			10 34					11 34					12 34						13 34					14 34	
Knebworth	d			10 38					11 38					12 38						13 38					14 38	
Bowes Park	d		10 10			10 40		11 10			11 40		12 10			12 40			13 10			13 40		14 10		
Palmers Green	d		10 12			10 42		11 12			11 42		12 12			12 42			13 12			13 42		14 12		
Winchmore Hill	d		10 15			10 45		11 15			11 45		12 15			12 45			13 15			13 45		14 15		
Grange Park	d		10 17			10 47		11 17			11 47		12 17			12 47			13 17			13 47		14 17		
Enfield Chase	d		10 19			10 49		11 19			11 49		12 19			12 49			13 19			13 49		14 19		
Gordon Hill	d		10 21			10 51		11 21			11 51		12 21			12 51			13 21			13 51		14 21		
Crews Hill	d		10 24			10 54		11 24			11 54		12 24			12 54			13 24			13 54		14 24		
Cuffley	d		10 27			10 57		11 27			11 57		12 27			12 57			13 27			13 57		14 27		
Bayford	d		10 32			11 02		11 32			12 02		12 32			13 02			13 32			14 02		14 32		
Hertford North	d		10a37			11 07		11a37			12 07		12a37			13 07			13a37			14 07		14a37		
Watton-at-Stone	d					11 12					12 12					13 12						14 12				
Stevenage 4	d			10 42		11a20			11 42		12a20			12 42		13a20				13 42		14a20			14 42	
Hitchin 4	d			10 47					11 47					12 47						13 47					14 47	
Letchworth Garden City	a			10 51					11 51					12 51						13 51					14 51	

		FC	FC	FC	FC 1	FC	FC	FC	FC	FC 1	FC	FC	FC	FC	FC 1		FC	FC	FC	FC	FC 1	FC	FC	FC	FC	FC 1
London Kings Cross 15 ⊖	d	14 26	14 41	14 56	15 06	15 11	15 26	15 41	15 56	16 06	16 11	16 26	16 41	16 56	17 06		17 11	17 26	17 41	17 56	18 06	18 11	18 26	18 41	18 56	19 06
Finsbury Park ⊖	d	14 32	14 47	15 02	15 11	15 17	15 32	15 47	16 02	16 11	16 17	16 32	16 47	17 02	17 11		17 17	17 32	17 47	18 02	18 11	18 17	18 32	18 47	19 02	19 11
Harringay	d	14 34	14 49	15 04		15 19	15 34	15 49	16 04		16 19	16 34	16 49	17 04			17 19	17 34	17 49	18 04		18 19	18 34	18 49	19 04	
Hornsey	d	14 36	14 51	15 06		15 21	15 36	15 51	16 06		16 21	16 36	16 51	17 06			17 21	17 36	17 51	18 06		18 21	18 36	18 51	19 06	
Alexandra Palace	d	14 38	14 53	15 08		15 23	15 38	15 53	16 08		16 23	16 38	16 53	17 08			17 23	17 38	17 53	18 08		18 23	18 38	18 53	19 08	
New Southgate	d		14 56			15 26		15 56			16 26		16 56				17 26		17 56			18 26		18 56		
Oakleigh Park	d		14 59			15 29		15 59			16 29		16 59				17 29		17 59			18 29		18 59		
New Barnet	d		15 01			15 31		16 01			16 31		17 01				17 31		18 01			18 31		19 01		
Hadley Wood	d		15 04			15 34		16 04			16 34		17 04				17 34		18 04			18 34		19 04		
Potters Bar	d		15 08		15 21	15 38		16 08		16 21	16 38		17 08		17 21		17 38		18 08		18 21	18 38		19 08		19 21
Brookmans Park	d		15 11			15 41		16 11			16 41		17 11				17 41		18 11			18 41		19 11		
Welham Green	d		15 13			15 43		16 13			16 43		17 13				17 43		18 13			18 43		19 13		
Hatfield	d		15 16		15 27	15 46		16 16		16 27	16 46		17 16		17 27		17 46		18 16		18 27	18 46		19 16		19 27
Welwyn Garden City 4	d		15a21		15 31	15a51		16a21		16 31	16a51		17a21		17 31		17a51		18a21		18 31	18a51		19a21		19 31
Welwyn North	d				15 34					16 34					17 34						18 34					19 34
Knebworth	d				15 38					16 38					17 38						18 38					19 38
Bowes Park	d	14 40		15 10			15 40		16 10			16 40		17 10				17 40		18 10			18 40		19 10	
Palmers Green	d	14 42		15 12			15 42		16 12			16 42		17 12				17 42		18 12			18 42		19 12	
Winchmore Hill	d	14 45		15 15			15 45		16 15			16 45		17 15				17 45		18 15			18 45		19 15	
Grange Park	d	14 47		15 17			15 47		16 17			16 47		17 17				17 47		18 17			18 47		19 17	
Enfield Chase	d	14 49		15 19			15 49		16 19			16 49		17 19				17 49		18 19			18 49		19 19	
Gordon Hill	d	14 51		15 21			15 51		16 21			16 51		17 21				17 51		18 21			18 51		19 21	
Crews Hill	d	14 54		15 24			15 54		16 24			16 54		17 24				17 54		18 24			18 54		19 24	
Cuffley	d	14 57		15 27			15 57		16 27			16 57		17 27				17 57		18 27			18 57		19 27	
Bayford	d	15 02		15 32			16 02		16 32			17 02		17 32				18 02		18 32			19 02		19 32	
Hertford North	d	15 07		15a37			16 07		16a37			17 07		17a37				18 07		18a37			19 07		19a37	
Watton-at-Stone	d	15 12					16 12					17 12						18 12					19 12			
Stevenage 4	d	15a20			15 42		16a20			16 42		17a20			17 42			18a20			18 42		19a20			19 42
Hitchin 4	d				15 47					16 47					17 47						18 47					19 47
Letchworth Garden City	a				15 51					16 51					17 51						18 51					19 51

For general notes see front of timetable
For details of catering facilities see
Directory of Train Operators

There is no service between Moorgate and Finsbury Park on Sundays

Table 24

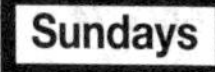

London → Welwyn Garden City, Hertford North and Letchworth Garden City

Network Diagram - see first page of Table 24

		FC	FC	FC	FC	FC 1	FC	FC	FC	FC	FC 1	FC	FC	FC	FC	FC 1	FC	FC	FC	FC	FC 1	FC	FC	FC
London Kings Cross 15	⊖ d	19 11	19 26	19 41	19 56	20 06	20 11	20 26	20 41	20 56	21 06	21 11	21 26	21 41	21 56	22 06	22 11	22 26	22 41	22 56	23 06	23 19	23 28	23 41
Finsbury Park	⊖ d	19 17	19 32	19 47	20 02	20 11	20 17	20 32	20 47	21 02	21 11	21 17	21 32	21 47	22 02	22 11	22 17	22 32	22 47	23 02	23 11	23 25	23 33	23 47
Harringay	d	19 19	19 34	19 49	20 04		20 19	20 34	20 49	21 04		21 19	21 34	21 49	22 04		22 19	22 34	22 49	23 04		23 27	23 36	23 49
Hornsey	d	19 21	19 36	19 51	20 06		20 21	20 36	20 51	21 06		21 21	21 36	21 51	22 06		22 21	22 36	22 51	23 06		23 29	23 38	23 51
Alexandra Palace	d	19 23	19 38	19 53	20 08		20 23	20 38	20 53	21 08		21 23	21 38	21 53	22 08		22 23	22 38	22 53	23 08		23 31	23 39	23 53
New Southgate	d	19 26		19 56			20 26		20 56			21 26		21 56			22 26		22 56			23 34		23 56
Oakleigh Park	d	19 29		19 59			20 29		20 59			21 29		21 59			22 29		22 59			23 37		23 59
New Barnet	d	19 31		20 01			20 31		21 01			21 31		22 01			22 31		23 01			23 39		00 01
Hadley Wood	d	19 34		20 04			20 34		21 04			21 34		22 04			22 34		23 04			23 42		00 04
Potters Bar	d	19 38		20 08		20 21	20 38		21 08		21 21	21 38		22 08		22 21	22 38		23 08		23 21	23 46		00 08
Brookmans Park	d	19 41		20 11			20 41		21 11			21 41		22 11			22 41		23 11			23 49		00 11
Welham Green	d	19 43		20 13			20 43		21 13			21 43		22 13			22 43		23 13			23 51		00 13
Hatfield	d	19 46		20 16		20 27	20 46		21 16		21 27	21 46		22 16		22 27	22 46		23 16		23 27	23 54		00 16
Welwyn Garden City 4	d	19a51		20a21		20 31	20a51		21a21		21 31	21a51		22a21		22 31	22a54		23a24		23 31	00a04		00 20
Welwyn North	d					20 34					21 34					22 34					23 36			00 23
Knebworth	d					20 38					21 38					22 38					23 40			00 28
Bowes Park	d		19 40		20 10			20 40		21 10			21 40		22 10			22 40		23 10			23 42	
Palmers Green	d		19 42		20 12			20 42		21 12			21 42		22 12			22 42		23 12			23 44	
Winchmore Hill	d		19 45		20 15			20 45		21 15			21 45		22 15			22 45		23 15			23 46	
Grange Park	d		19 47		20 17			20 47		21 17			21 47		22 17			22 47		23 17			23 48	
Enfield Chase	d		19 49		20 19			20 49		21 19			21 49		22 19			22 49		23 19			23 50	
Gordon Hill	d		19 51		20 21			20 51		21 21			21 51		22 21			22 51		23 21			23 52	
Crews Hill	d		19 54		20 24			20 54		21 24			21 54		22 24			22 54		23 24			23 55	
Cuffley	d		19 57		20 27			20 57		21 27			21 57		22 27			22 57		23 27			23 58	
Bayford	d		20 02		20 32			21 02		21 32			22 02		22 32			23 02		23 32			00 03	
Hertford North	d		20 07		20a37			21 07		21a37			22 07		22a37			23 07		23a37			00 08	
Watton-at-Stone	d		20 12					21 12					22 12					23 12					00 14	
Stevenage 4	d		20a20			20 42		21a20			21 42		22a20			22 42		23a20			23 43		00a24	00 31
Hitchin 4	d					20 47					21 47					22 47					23 53			00a47
Letchworth Garden City	a					20 51					21 51					22 51					23 57			

For general notes see front of timetable
For details of catering facilities see
Directory of Train Operators

There is no service between Moorgate and Finsbury Park on Sundays

Letchworth Garden City, Hertford North and Welwyn Garden City → London

Saturday service operates on Bank Holiday Mondays

Network Diagram - see first page of Table 24

Miles	Miles			FC MX	FC MO	FC MX	FC MO 1	FC MX 1	FC 1 A	FC	FC 1	FC	FC	FC 1	FC		FC 1	FC	FC	FC	FC 1	FC	FC	FC	FC	FC
0	0	**Letchworth Garden City**	d	23p20			23p36	23p50		04 50	05 30	05 20		05 59	05 50		06 19					06 27			06 46	
3	3	Hitchin [4]	d	23p24			23p40	23p54	04 48	04 54	05 34	05 24		06 03	05 54		06 24				06 46	06 31			06 50	
7¼	7¼	**Stevenage [4]**	d	23p29	23p29		23p45	23p59	04 53	04 59	05 39	05 29		06 09	05 59		06 30				06 52	06 36			06 56	
—	12¼	Watton-at-Stone	d	23p36	23p36					05 06		05 36			06 06							06 42				
—	16½	**Hertford North**	d	23p42	23p42					05 12		05 42			06 12					06 34		06 50				07 04
—	19½	Bayford	d	23p46	23p46					05 16		05 46			06 16					06 38						07 08
—	23	Cuffley	d	23p51	23p51					05 21		05 51			06 21					06 43		06 57				07 13
—	24¾	Crews Hill	d	23p54	23p54					05 24		05 54			06 24					06 46						07 16
—	26¼	Gordon Hill	d	23p57	23p57					05 27		05 57			06 27					06 49		07 02		07 09		07 19
—	27	Enfield Chase	d	23p59	23p59					05 29		05 59			06 29					06 52		07 04		07 12		07 22
—	27¾	Grange Park	d	00 01	00 01					05 31		06 01			06 31					06 54				07 14		07 24
—	28½	Winchmore Hill	d	00 03	00 03					05 33		06 03			06 33					06 56		07 06		07 16		07 26
—	29½	Palmers Green	d	00 05	00 05					05 35		06 05			06 35					06 58		07 09		07 18		07 28
—	30½	Bowes Park	d	00 08	00 08					05 38		06 08			06 38					07 01				07 21		07 31
9¾	—	Knebworth	d				23p48	00 02			05 43			06 13			06 33								07 00	
12¾	—	Welwyn North	d				23p52	00 06			05 47			06 17			06 37								07 04	
14½	—	**Welwyn Garden City [4]**	d				23p55	00 09	05 01		05 50		05 58	06 20			06 40	06 25	06 35		07 00		06 50		07 08	
17	—	Hatfield	d				23p58	00 12	05 05		05 53		06 02	06 23			06 44	06 29	06 39				06 54		07 12	
19¼	—	Welham Green	d										06 06					06 33					06 58			
20¼	—	Brookmans Park	d										06 08					06 35					07 00			
22	—	Potters Bar	d				00 04	00 18	05 11		05 59		06 11	06 29			06 49	06 38	06 46				07 03		07 18	
24¼	—	Hadley Wood	d										06 15					06 42	06 49				07 07			
25½	—	New Barnet	d						05 15				06 17					06 44	06 52				07 09		07 23	
26¼	—	Oakleigh Park	d						05 17				06 19					06 46	06 54				07 11		07 25	
28¼	—	New Southgate	d						05 20				06 22					06 49	06 57				07 14		07 28	
29¾	31½	Alexandra Palace	d	00 10	00 10				05 23	05 40		06 10	06 25		06 40			06 52		07 03			07 17	07 23		07 33
30¾	32¼	Hornsey	d	00 12	00 12				05 25	05 42		06 12	06 27		06 42			06 54		07 05			07 19	07 25		07 35
31¼	32¾	Harringay	d	00 14	00 14	⟵				05 44		06 14	06 29		06 44			06 56		07 07			07 21	07 27		07 37
32¼	33¾	Finsbury Park	⊖ d	00 17	00 17	00 17	00 20	00 29	05 29	05 47	06 08	06 17	06 32	06 41	06 47		06 58	06 59	07 03	07 10	07 14	07 16	07 24	07 30	07 34	07 40
—	34½	Drayton Park	d	↪								06 19	06 34		06 49			07 01		07 12		07 18	07 26	07 32		07 42
—	35	Highbury & Islington	⊖ d									06 20	06 35		06 51			07 03		07 14		07 20	07 28	07 34		07 44
—	35½	Essex Road	d									06 22	06 37		06 53			07 05		07 16		07 22	07 30	07 36		07 46
—	36¾	Old Street	⊖ d									06 25	06 40		06 56			07 08		07 19		07 25	07 33	07 39		07 49
—	37¼	**Moorgate**	⊖ a									06 30	06 45		07 01			07 13		07 24		07 30	07 39	07 44		07 54
34¾	—	London Kings Cross [15]	⊖ a		00 27	00 28	00 32	00 42	05 45	05 58	06 19			06 49			07 07		07 10		07 23				07 41	

		FC	FC 1	FC	FC			FC 1	FC	FC	FC	FC	FC 1	FC	FC	FC	FC	FC		FC	FC	FC 1	FC	FC	FC	FC
Letchworth Garden City	d	06 54	07 05					07 28			07 19		07 35									08 05	07 54			
Hitchin [4]	d	06 58	07 09					07 32			07 23		07 39									08 09	07 58			
Stevenage [4]	d	07 04	07 15					07 38			07 29		07 45	07 35								08 15	08 05			
Watton-at-Stone	d	07 10												07 42									08 12			
Hertford North	d	07 18			07 25					07 33		07 39		07 50		07 55				08 05			08 20		08 25	
Bayford	d											07 43								08 09						
Cuffley	d	07 25			07 32					07 40		07 48		07 57		08 02				08 14			08 27		08 32	
Crews Hill	d											07 51								08 17						
Gordon Hill	d	07 30			07 37					07 45		07 54		08 02		08 07		08 15		08 20			08 32		08 37	
Enfield Chase	d	07 32			07 39					07 47		07 56		08 04		08 09		08 17		08 22			08 34		08 39	
Grange Park	d				07 41					07 49		07 58				08 11		08 19		08 24					08 41	
Winchmore Hill	d	07 34			07 43					07 51		08 00				08 13		08 21		08 26					08 43	
Palmers Green	d	07 37			07 45					07 53		08 02				08 15		08 23		08 28					08 45	
Bowes Park	d				07 48					07 56		08 05		08 08		08 18		08 26		08 31			08 38		08 48	
Knebworth	d		07 18				07 41	07 41			07 33		07 48									08 18				
Welwyn North	d		07 22								07 37		07 52									08 22				
Welwyn Garden City [4]	d		07 26	07 17					07 30		07 42		07 56		07 47		07 59				08 14	08 26		08 18		08 29
Hatfield	d		07 30	07 21					07 34		07 46				07 51		08 03				08 18			08 22		08 33
Welham Green	d			07 25					07 38						07 55		08 07							08 26		08 37
Brookmans Park	d			07 27					07 40						07 57		08 09							08 28		08 39
Potters Bar	d			07 30					07 43		07 52				08 00		08 12				08 25			08 31		08 43
Hadley Wood	d			07 34					07 47						08 04		08 16							08 35		08 46
New Barnet	d			07 36					07 49		07 57				08 06		08 18				08 29			08 37		08 49
Oakleigh Park	d			07 38					07 51		07 59				08 08		08 20				08 31			08 39		08 51
New Southgate	d			07 41					07 54		08 02				08 11		08 23				08 34			08 42		08 54
Alexandra Palace	d			07 44	07 50					07 58		08 07		08 11	08 14	08 20		08 28		08 33	08 37		08 41	08 45	08 50	08 57
Hornsey	d			07 46	07 52					08 00				08 13	08 16	08 22	08 27	08 30					08 43	08 47	08 52	08 59
Harringay	d			07 48	07 54					08 02				08 15	08 18	08 24	08 29	08 32					08 45	08 49	08 54	09 01
Finsbury Park	⊖ d	07 44	07 46	07 51	07 57		07 59	07 59	08 01	08 06	08 09	08 12	08 16	08 18	08 22	08 27	08 31	08 35		08 39	08 42	08 43	08 48	08 52	08 57	09 03
Drayton Park	d	07 46		07 53	07 59				08 03	08 08		08 14		08 20	08 24	08 29	08 33	08 37		08 41			08 50	08 54	08 59	09 05
Highbury & Islington	⊖ d	07 48		07 55	08 01				08 05	08 10		08 16		08 22	08 26	08 31	08 35	08 39		08 43			08 52	08 56	09 01	09 07
Essex Road	d	07 50		07 57	08 03				08 07	08 12		08 18		08 24	08 28	08 33	08 37	08 41		08 45			08 54	08 58	09 03	09 09
Old Street	⊖ d	07 53		08 00	08 06				08 10	08 15		08 21		08 27	08 31	08 36	08 40	08 44		08 48			08 57	09 01	09 06	09 12
Moorgate	⊖ a	07 59		08 05	08 11				08 16	08 20		08 27		08 32	08 36	08 41	08 46	08 50		08 55			09 02	09 06	09 11	09 18
London Kings Cross [15]	⊖ a		07 56					08b11			08 17		08 25								08 50	08 53				

For general notes see front of timetable
For details of catering facilities see Directory of Train Operators

A From Peterborough (Table 25)

b Arrives0807 Mondays until 28 January and from 31 March

Saturday service operates on Bank Holiday Mondays

Letchworth Garden City, Hertford North and Welwyn Garden City → London

Network Diagram - see first page of Table 24

	FC	FC 1	FC	FC	FC	FC	FC 1		FC	FC	FC	FC	FC 1	FC	FC	FC	FC 1	FC	FC	FC		FC 1	FC	FC	FC
Letchworth Garden City d		08 30					09 00						09 29				09 59	09 50				10 29			
Hitchin 4 d		08 34					09 04						09 33				10 03	09 54				10 33			
Stevenage 4 d		08 40		08 32			09 10		09 02				09 39				10 09	09 59				10 39			
Watton-at-Stone d				08 39					09 09									10 06							
Hertford North d				08 47					09 15			09 32			09 52			10 12		10 32				10 52	
Bayford d				08 51					09 19			09 36			09 56			10 16		10 36				10 56	
Cuffley d				08 56					09 24			09 41			10 01			10 21		10 41				11 01	
Crews Hill d				08 59					09 27			09 44			10 04			10 24		10 44				11 04	
Gordon Hill d			08 55	09 02	09 12				09 30			09 47			10 07			10 27		10 47				11 07	
Enfield Chase d			08 57	09 04	09 14				09 32			09 49			10 09			10 29		10 49				11 09	
Grange Park d			08 59	09 06	09 16				09 34			09 51			10 11			10 31		10 51				11 11	
Winchmore Hill d			09 01	09 08	09 18				09 36			09 53			10 13			10 33		10 53				11 13	
Palmers Green d			09 03	09 11	09 21				09 38			09 55			10 15			10 35		10 55				11 15	
Bowes Park d			09 06	09 13	09 23				09 41			09 58			10 18			10 38		10 58				11 18	
Knebworth d		08 44					09 13						09 43				10 13					10 43			
Welwyn North d		08 48					09 17						09 47				10 17					10 47			
Welwyn Garden City 4 d	08 40	08 52				09 03	09 20			09 23	09 40		09 50	09 43		10 03	10 20		10 23			10 50	10 43		11 03
Hatfield d	08 44					09 07	09 24			09 27	09 43		09 53	09 47		10 07	10 23		10 27			10 53	10 47		11 07
Welham Green d						09 11				09 31				09 51		10 11			10 31				10 51		11 11
Brookmans Park d						09 13				09 33				09 53		10 13			10 33				10 53		11 13
Potters Bar d	08 51					09 16	09 30			09 36	09 49		09 59	09 56		10 16	10 29		10 36			10 59	10 56		11 16
Hadley Wood d						09 20				09 40				10 00		10 20			10 40				11 00		11 20
New Barnet d	08 55					09 22				09 42				10 02		10 22			10 42				11 02		11 22
Oakleigh Park d	08 57					09 24				09 44				10 04		10 24			10 44				11 04		11 24
New Southgate d	09 00					09 27				09 47				10 07		10 27			10 47				11 07		11 27
Alexandra Palace d			09 09	09 16	09 26	09 30			09 43	09 50		10 00		10 10	10 20	10 30		10 40	10 50	11 00			11 10	11 20	11 30
Hornsey d			09 11	09 18	09 28	09 32			09 45	09 52		10 02		10 12	10 22	10 32		10 42	10 52	11 02			11 12	11 22	11 32
Harringay d			09 13	09 20	09 30	09 34			09 47	09 54		10 04		10 14	10 24	10 34		10 44	10 54	11 04			11 14	11 24	11 34
Finsbury Park ⊖ d	09 07	09 11	09 16	09 22	09 32	09 37	09 41		09 50	09 57	10 01	10 07	10 08	10 17	10 27	10 37	10 41	10 47	10 57	11 07		11 08	11 17	11 27	11 37
Drayton Park d			09 18	09 24	09 34	09 39			09 52	09 59		10 09		10 19	10 29	10 39		10 49	10 59	11 09			11 19	11 29	11 39
Highbury & Islington ⊖ d			09 19	09 26	09 36	09 40			09 53	10 00		10 10		10 20	10 30	10 40		10 50	11 00	11 10			11 20	11 30	11 40
Essex Road d			09 21	09 28	09 38	09 42			09 55	10 02		10 12		10 22	10 32	10 42		10 52	11 02	11 12			11 22	11 32	11 42
Old Street ⊖ d			09 24	09 31	09 41	09 45			09 58	10 05		10 15		10 25	10 35	10 45		10 55	11 05	11 15			11 25	11 35	11 45
Moorgate ⊖ a			09 29	09 36	09 46	09 50			10 04	10 10		10 20		10 30	10 40	10 50		11 00	11 10	11 20			11 30	11 40	11 50
London Kings Cross 15 ⊖ a	09 14	09 19					09 50				10 10		10 19				10 49					11 19			

	FC 1	FC	FC	FC	FC 1	FC	FC	FC	FC 1	FC		FC	FC	FC 1	FC	FC	FC	FC 1	FC	FC	FC	FC 1	FC		FC
Letchworth Garden City d		10 50			11 29					11 50				12 29					12 50			13 29			
Hitchin 4 d	11 03	10 54			11 33				12 03	11 54				12 33				13 03	12 54			13 33			
Stevenage 4 d	11 09	10 59			11 39				12 09	11 59				12 39				13 09	12 59			13 39			
Watton-at-Stone d		11 06								12 06									13 06						
Hertford North d		11 12		11 32			11 52			12 12			12 32			12 52			13 12		13 32				13 52
Bayford d		11 16		11 36			11 56			12 16			12 36			12 56			13 16		13 36				13 56
Cuffley d		11 21		11 41			12 01			12 21			12 41			13 01			13 21		13 41				14 01
Crews Hill d		11 24		11 44			12 04			12 24			12 44			13 04			13 24		13 44				14 04
Gordon Hill d		11 27		11 47			12 07			12 27			12 47			13 07			13 27		13 47				14 07
Enfield Chase d		11 29		11 49			12 09			12 29			12 49			13 09			13 29		13 49				14 09
Grange Park d		11 31		11 51			12 11			12 31			12 51			13 11			13 31		13 51				14 11
Winchmore Hill d		11 33		11 53			12 13			12 33			12 53			13 13			13 33		13 53				14 13
Palmers Green d		11 35		11 55			12 15			12 35			12 55			13 15			13 35		13 55				14 15
Bowes Park d		11 38		11 58			12 18			12 38			12 58			13 18			13 38		13 58				14 18
Knebworth d	11 13				11 43				12 13					12 43				13 13				13 43			
Welwyn North d	11 17				11 47				12 17					12 47				13 17				13 47			
Welwyn Garden City 4 d	11 20		11 23		11 50	11 43		12 03	12 20			12 23		12 50	12 43		13 03	13 20		13 23		13 50	13 43		
Hatfield d	11 23		11 27		11 53	11 47		12 07	12 23			12 27		12 53	12 47		13 07	13 23		13 27		13 53	13 47		
Welham Green d			11 31			11 51		12 11				12 31			12 51		13 11			13 31			13 51		
Brookmans Park d			11 33			11 53		12 13				12 33			12 53		13 13			13 33			13 53		
Potters Bar d	11 29		11 36		11 59	11 56		12 16	12 29			12 36		12 59	12 56		13 16	13 29		13 36		13 59	13 56		
Hadley Wood d			11 40			12 00		12 20				12 40			13 00		13 20			13 40			14 00		
New Barnet d			11 42			12 02		12 22				12 42			13 02		13 22			13 42			14 02		
Oakleigh Park d			11 44			12 04		12 24				12 44			13 04		13 24			13 44			14 04		
New Southgate d			11 47			12 07		12 27				12 47			13 07		13 27			13 47			14 07		
Alexandra Palace d		11 40	11 50	12 00		12 10	12 20	12 30		12 40		12 50	13 00		13 10	13 20	13 30		13 40	13 50	14 00		14 10		14 20
Hornsey d		11 42	11 52	12 02		12 12	12 22	12 32		12 42		12 52	13 02		13 12	13 22	13 32		13 42	13 52	14 02		14 12		14 22
Harringay d		11 44	11 54	12 04		12 14	12 24	12 34		12 44		12 54	13 04		13 14	13 24	13 34		13 44	13 54	14 04		14 14		14 24
Finsbury Park ⊖ d	11 41	11 47	11 57	12 07	12 11	12 17	12 27	12 37	12 41	12 47		12 57	13 07	13 08	13 17	13 27	13 37	13 41	13 47	13 57	14 07	14 08	14 17		14 27
Drayton Park d		11 49	11 59	12 09		12 19	12 29	12 39		12 49		12 59	13 09		13 19	13 29	13 39		13 49	13 59	14 09		14 19		14 29
Highbury & Islington ⊖ d		11 50	12 00	12 10		12 20	12 30	12 40		12 50		13 00	13 10		13 20	13 30	13 40		13 50	14 00	14 10		14 20		14 30
Essex Road d		11 52	12 02	12 12		12 22	12 32	12 42		12 52		13 02	13 12		13 22	13 32	13 42		13 52	14 02	14 12		14 22		14 32
Old Street ⊖ d		11 55	12 05	12 15		12 25	12 35	12 45		12 55		13 05	13 15		13 25	13 35	13 45		13 55	14 05	14 15		14 25		14 35
Moorgate ⊖ a		12 00	12 10	12 20		12 30	12 40	12 50		13 00		13 10	13 20		13 30	13 40	13 50		14 00	14 10	14 20		14 30		14 40
London Kings Cross 15 ⊖ a	11 49				12 19				12 49					13 19				13 48				14 19			

For general notes see front of timetable
For details of catering facilities see Directory of Train Operators

Letchworth Garden City, Hertford North and Welwyn Garden City → London

Saturday service operates on Bank Holiday Mondays

Network Diagram - see first page of Table 24

		FC	FC 1	FC	FC	FC	FC 1	FC	FC	FC	FC 1	FC	FC		FC	FC 1	FC	FC	FC	FC 1	FC	FC	FC	FC	FC	FC 1
Letchworth Garden City	d			13 50			14 29					14 50				15 29					15 50				16 20	16 29
Hitchin 4	d		14 03	13 54			14 33				15 03	14 54				15 33				16 03	15 54				16 24	16 33
Stevenage 4	d		14 09	13 59			14 39				15 09	14 59				15 39				16 09	15 59				16 29	16 39
Watton-at-Stone	d			14 06								15 06									16 06				16 36	
Hertford North	d			14 12		14 32			14 52			15 12			15 32			15 52			16 12			16 32	16 42	
Bayford	d			14 16		14 36			14 56			15 16			15 36			15 56			16 16			16 36	16 46	
Cuffley	d			14 21		14 41			15 01			15 21			15 41			16 01			16 21			16 41	16 51	
Crews Hill	d			14 24		14 44			15 04			15 24			15 44			16 04			16 24			16 44	16 54	
Gordon Hill	d			14 27		14 47			15 07			15 27			15 47			16 07			16 27			16 47	16 57	
Enfield Chase	d			14 29		14 49			15 09			15 29			15 49			16 09			16 29			16 49	16 59	
Grange Park	d			14 31		14 51			15 11			15 31			15 51			16 11			16 31			16 51		
Winchmore Hill	d			14 33		14 53			15 13			15 33			15 53			16 13			16 33			16 53	17 01	
Palmers Green	d			14 35		14 55			15 15			15 35			15 55			16 15			16 35			16 55	17 04	
Bowes Park	d			14 38		14 58			15 18			15 38			15 58			16 18			16 38			16 58		
Knebworth	d		14 13				14 43				15 13					15 43				16 13						16 43
Welwyn North	d		14 17				14 47				15 17					15 47				16 17						16 47
Welwyn Garden City 4	d	14 03	14 20		14 23		14 50	14 43		15 03	15 20		15 23			15 50	15 43		16 03	16 20		16 23	16 40			16 50
Hatfield	d	14 07	14 23		14 27		14 53	14 47		15 07	15 23		15 27			15 53	15 47		16 07	16 23		16 27	16 43			16 53
Welham Green	d	14 11			14 31			14 51		15 11			15 31				15 51		16 11			16 31				
Brookmans Park	d	14 13			14 33			14 53		15 13			15 33				15 53		16 13			16 33				
Potters Bar	d	14 16	14 29		14 36		14 59	14 56		15 16	15 29		15 36			15 59	15 56		16 16	16 29		16 36	16 49			16 59
Hadley Wood	d	14 20			14 40			15 00		15 20			15 40				16 00		16 20			16 40				
New Barnet	d	14 22			14 42			15 02		15 22			15 42				16 02		16 22			16 42				
Oakleigh Park	d	14 24			14 44			15 04		15 24			15 44				16 04		16 24			16 44				
New Southgate	d	14 27			14 47			15 07		15 27			15 47				16 07		16 27			16 47				
Alexandra Palace	d	14 30		14 40	14 50	15 00		15 10	15 20	15 30		15 40	15 50		16 00		16 10	16 20	16 30		16 40	16 50		17 00		
Hornsey	d	14 32		14 42	14 52	15 02		15 12	15 22	15 32		15 42	15 52		16 02		16 12	16 22	16 32		16 42	16 52		17 02		
Harringay	d	14 34		14 44	14 54	15 04		15 14	15 24	15 34		15 44	15 54		16 04		16 14	16 24	16 34		16 44	16 54		17 04		
Finsbury Park	⊖ d	14 37	14 41	14 47	14 57	15 07	15 11	15 17	15 27	15 37	15 41	15 47	15 57		16 07	16 11	16 17	16 27	16 37	16 38	16 47	16 57	17 01	17 07	17 11	17 11
Drayton Park	d	14 39		14 49	14 59	15 09		15 19	15 29	15 39		15 49	15 59		16 09		16 19	16 29	16 39		16 49	16 59		17 09	17 13	
Highbury & Islington	⊖ d	14 40		14 50	15 00	15 10		15 20	15 30	15 40		15 50	16 00		16 10		16 20	16 30	16 40		16 50	17 00		17 10	17 14	
Essex Road	d	14 42		14 52	15 02	15 12		15 22	15 32	15 42		15 52	16 02		16 12		16 22	16 32	16 42		16 52	17 02		17 12	17 16	
Old Street	⊖ d	14 45		14 55	15 05	15 15		15 25	15 35	15 45		15 55	16 05		16 15		16 25	16 35	16 45		16 55	17 05		17 15	17 19	
Moorgate	⊖ a	14 50		15 00	15 10	15 20		15 30	15 40	15 50		16 00	16 10		16 20		16 30	16 40	16 50		17 00	17 10		17 20	17 24	
London Kings Cross 15	⊖ a		14 49				15 20				15 49					16 19				16 48			17 10			17 19

		FC	FC		FC	FC 1	FC	FC	FC 1	FC	FC	FC 1	FC	FC	FC 1	FC		FC	FC 1	FC	FC	FC 1	FC	FC	FC 1	FC
Letchworth Garden City	d								17 29						18 29							19 29				
Hitchin 4	d					17 03			17 33			18 03			18 33				19 03			19 33			20 03	
Stevenage 4	d					17 09	16 59		17 39	17 29		18 09	17 59		18 39	18 29			19 09			19 39	19 29		20 09	
Watton-at-Stone	d						17 06			17 36			18 06			18 36							19 36			
Hertford North	d		16 52				17 12			17 42			18 12			18 42				19 12			19 42			20 12
Bayford	d		16 56				17 16			17 46			18 16			18 46				19 16			19 46			20 16
Cuffley	d		17 01				17 21			17 51			18 21			18 51				19 21			19 51			20 21
Crews Hill	d		17 04				17 24			17 54			18 24			18 54				19 24			19 54			20 24
Gordon Hill	d		17 07				17 27			17 57			18 27			18 57				19 27			19 57			20 27
Enfield Chase	d		17 09				17 29			17 59			18 29			18 59				19 29			19 59			20 29
Grange Park	d		17 11				17 31			18 01			18 31			19 01				19 31			20 01			20 31
Winchmore Hill	d		17 13				17 33			18 03			18 33			19 03				19 33			20 03			20 33
Palmers Green	d		17 15				17 35			18 05			18 35			19 05				19 35			20 05			20 35
Bowes Park	d		17 18				17 38			18 08			18 38			19 08				19 38			20 08			20 38
Knebworth	d					17 13			17 43			18 13			18 43				19 13			19 43			20 13	
Welwyn North	d					17 17			17 47			18 17			18 47				19 17			19 47			20 17	
Welwyn Garden City 4	d	16 43			17 03	17 20		17 28	17 50		17 58	18 20		18 28	18 50			18 58	19 20		19 28	19 50		19 58	20 20	
Hatfield	d	16 47			17 07	17 23		17 32	17 53		18 02	18 23		18 32	18 53			19 02	19 23		19 32	19 53		20 02	20 23	
Welham Green	d	16 51			17 11			17 36			18 06			18 36				19 06			19 36			20 06		
Brookmans Park	d	16 53			17 13			17 38			18 08			18 38				19 08			19 38			20 08		
Potters Bar	d	16 56			17 16	17 29		17 41	17 59		18 11	18 29		18 41	18 59			19 11	19 29		19 41	19 59		20 11	20 29	
Hadley Wood	d	17 00			17 20			17 45			18 15			18 45				19 15			19 45			20 15		
New Barnet	d	17 02			17 22			17 47			18 17			18 47				19 17			19 47			20 17		
Oakleigh Park	d	17 04			17 24			17 49			18 19			18 49				19 19			19 49			20 19		
New Southgate	d	17 07			17 27			17 52			18 22			18 52				19 22			19 52			20 22		
Alexandra Palace	d	17 10	17 20		17 30		17 40	17 55		18 10	18 25		18 40	18 55		19 10		19 25		19 40	19 55		20 10	20 25		20 40
Hornsey	d	17 12	17 22		17 32		17 42	17 57		18 12	18 27		18 42	18 57		19 12		19 27		19 42	19 57		20 12	20 27		20 42
Harringay	d	17 14	17 24		17 34		17 44	17 59		18 14	18 29		18 44	18 59		19 14		19 29		19 44	19 59		20 14	20 29		20 44
Finsbury Park	⊖ d	17 17	17 27		17 37	17 38	17 47	18 02	18 08	18 17	18 32	18 41	18 47	19 02	19 11	19 17		19 32	19 41	19 47	20 02	20 11	20 17	20 32	20 38	20 47
Drayton Park	d	17 19	17 29		17 39		17 49	18 04		18 19	18 34		18 49	19 04		19 19		19 34		19 49	20 04		20 19	20 34		20 49
Highbury & Islington	⊖ d	17 20	17 30		17 40		17 50	18 05		18 20	18 35		18 50	19 05		19 20		19 35		19 50	20 05		20 20	20 35		20 50
Essex Road	d	17 22	17 32		17 42		17 52	18 07		18 22	18 37		18 52	19 07		19 22		19 37		19 52	20 07		20 22	20 37		20 52
Old Street	⊖ d	17 25	17 35		17 45		17 55	18 10		18 25	18 40		18 55	19 10		19 25		19 40		19 55	20 10		20 25	20 40		20 55
Moorgate	⊖ a	17 30	17 40		17 50		18 00	18 15		18 30	18 45		19 00	19 15		19 30		19 45		20 00	20 15		20 30	20 45		21 00
London Kings Cross 15	⊖ a					17 48			18 18			18 52			19 20				19 48			20 19			20 49	

For general notes see front of timetable
For details of catering facilities see Directory of Train Operators

Letchworth Garden City, Hertford North and Welwyn Garden City → London

Saturday service operates on Bank Holiday Mondays

Network Diagram - see first page of Table 24

		FC	FC 1	FC	FC	FC 1		FC	FC	FC 1	FC	FC	FC 1	FC	FC 1	FC	FC 1	FC	FC		FC	FC 1	FC	FC 1		
Letchworth Garden City	d		20 29	20 20						21 29	21 20						22 29	22 20					23 20	23 50		
Hitchin 4	d		20 33	20 24		21 03				21 33	21 24		22 11				22 33	22 24				23 11	23 24	23 54		
Stevenage 4	d		20 39	20 29		21 09				21 39	21 29		22 17				22 39	22 29				23 17	23 29	23 59		
Watton-at-Stone	d			20 36							21 36							22 36					23 36			
Hertford North	d			20 42				21 12			21 42			22 12				22 42			23 12		23 42			
Bayford	d			20 46				21 16			21 46			22 16				22 46			23 16		23 46			
Cuffley	d			20 51				21 21			21 51			22 21				22 51			23 21		23 51			
Crews Hill	d			20 54				21 24			21 54			22 24				22 54			23 24		23 54			
Gordon Hill	d			20 57				21 27			21 57			22 27				22 57			23 27		23 57			
Enfield Chase	d			20 59				21 29			21 59			22 29				22 59			23 29		23 59			
Grange Park	d			21 01				21 31			22 01			22 31				23 01			23 31		00 01			
Winchmore Hill	d			21 03				21 33			22 03			22 33				23 03			23 33		00 03			
Palmers Green	d			21 05				21 35			22 05			22 35				23 05			23 35		00 05			
Bowes Park	d			21 08				21 38			22 08			22 38				23 08			23 38		00 08			
Knebworth	d		20 43			21 13				21 43			22 20				22 43					23 20		00 02		
Welwyn North	d		20 47			21 17				21 47			22 24				22 47					23 24		00 06		
Welwyn Garden City 4	d	20 28	20 50		20 58	21 20			21 28	21 50		21 58	22 27			22 30	22 50		23 00			23 27		00 09		
Hatfield	d	20 32	20 53		21 02	21 23			21 32	21 53		22 02	22 30			22 34	22 53		23 04			23 30		00 12		
Welham Green	d	20 36			21 06				21 36			22 06				22 38			23 08							
Brookmans Park	d	20 38			21 08				21 38			22 08				22 40			23 10							
Potters Bar	d	20 41	20 59		21 11	21 29			21 41	21 59		22 11	22 36			22 43	22 59		23 13			23 36		00 18		
Hadley Wood	d	20 45			21 15				21 45			22 15				22 47			23 17							
New Barnet	d	20 47			21 17				21 47			22 17				22 49			23 19							
Oakleigh Park	d	20 49			21 19				21 49			22 19				22 51			23 21							
New Southgate	d	20 52			21 22				21 52			22 22				22 54			23 24							
Alexandra Palace	d	20 55		21 10	21 25			21 40	21 55		22 10	22 25		22 40		22 57		23 10	23 27		23 40		00 10			
Hornsey	d	20 57		21 12	21 27			21 42	21 57		22 12	22 27		22 42		22 59		23 12	23 29		23 42		00 12			
Harringay	d	20 59		21 14	21 29			21 44	21 59		22 14	22 29		22 44	←	23 01		23 14	23 31		23 44		00 14			
Finsbury Park	⊖ d	21 02	21 11	21 17	21 32	21 38		21 47	22 02	22 11	22 17	22 32	22 44	22 47	22 44	23 04	23 11	23 17	23 34		23 47	23s50	00 17	00 29		
Drayton Park	d	21 04		21 19	21 34			21 49					→													
Highbury & Islington	⊖ d	21 05		21 20	21 35			21 50																		
Essex Road	d	21 07		21 22	21 37			21 52																		
Old Street	⊖ d	21 10		21 25	21 40			21 55																		
Moorgate	⊖ a	21 15		21 30	21 45			22 00																		
London Kings Cross 15	⊖ a		21 19			21 48			22 10	22 19	22 26	22 40		22 55	22 56	23 12	23 21	23 25	23 42		23 55	00 01	00 28	00 42		

Saturdays

		FC	FC 1	FC 1 A	FC	FC 1	FC	FC	FC 1	FC		FC	FC 1	FC	FC	FC 1	FC	FC	FC 1	FC		FC	FC 1	FC	FC	FC 1
Letchworth Garden City	d	23p20	23p50		04 50	05 30							06 29						07 29							08 29
Hitchin 4	d	23p24	23p54	04 48	04 54	05 33			06 03				06 33			07 03			07 33				08 03			08 33
Stevenage 4	d	23p29	23p59	04 53	04 59	05 39			06 09				06 39	06 29		07 09			07 39	07 29			08 09			08 39
Watton-at-Stone	d	23p36			05 06									06 36						07 36						
Hertford North	d	23p42			05 12		05 42			06 12				06 42			07 12			07 42				08 12		
Bayford	d	23p46			05 16		05 46			06 16				06 46			07 16			07 46				08 16		
Cuffley	d	23p51			05 21		05 51			06 21				06 51			07 21			07 51				08 21		
Crews Hill	d	23p54			05 24		05 54			06 24				06 54			07 24			07 54				08 24		
Gordon Hill	d	23p57			05 27		05 57			06 27				06 57			07 27			07 57				08 27		
Enfield Chase	d	23p59			05 29		05 59			06 29				06 59			07 29			07 59				08 29		
Grange Park	d	00 01			05 31		06 01			06 31				07 01			07 31			08 01				08 31		
Winchmore Hill	d	00 03			05 33		06 03			06 33				07 03			07 33			08 03				08 33		
Palmers Green	d	00 05			05 35		06 05			06 35				07 05			07 35			08 05				08 35		
Bowes Park	d	00 08			05 38		06 08			06 38				07 08			07 38			08 08				08 38		
Knebworth	d		00 02			05 43			06 13				06 43			07 13			07 43				08 13			08 43
Welwyn North	d		00 06			05 47			06 17				06 47			07 17			07 47				08 17			08 47
Welwyn Garden City 4	d		00 09	05 01		05 50		05 58	06 20			06 28	06 50		06 58	07 20		07 28	07 50			07 58	08 20		08 28	08 50
Hatfield	d		00 12	05 05		05 53		06 02	06 23			06 32	06 53		07 02	07 23		07 32	07 53			08 02	08 23		08 32	08 53
Welham Green	d							06 06				06 36			07 06			07 36				08 06			08 36	
Brookmans Park	d							06 08				06 38			07 08			07 38				08 08			08 38	
Potters Bar	d		00 18	05 11		05 59		06 11	06 29			06 41	06 59		07 11	07 29		07 41	07 59			08 11	08 29		08 41	08 59
Hadley Wood	d							06 15				06 45			07 15			07 45				08 15			08 45	
New Barnet	d			05 15				06 17				06 47			07 17			07 47				08 17			08 47	
Oakleigh Park	d			05 17				06 19				06 49			07 19			07 49				08 19			08 49	
New Southgate	d			05 20				06 22				06 52			07 22			07 52				08 22			08 52	
Alexandra Palace	d	00 10		05 23	05 40		06 10	06 25		06 40		06 55		07 10	07 25		07 40	07 55		08 10		08 25		08 40	08 55	
Hornsey	d	00 12		05 25	05 42		06 12	06 27		06 42		06 57		07 12	07 27		07 42	07 57		08 12		08 27		08 42	08 57	
Harringay	d	00 14			05 44		06 14	06 29		06 44		06 59		07 14	07 29		07 44	07 59		08 14		08 29		08 44	08 59	
Finsbury Park	⊖ d	00 17	00 29	05 29	05 47	06 11	06 17	06 32	06 41	06 47		07 02	07 08	07 17	07 32	07b41	07 47	08 02	08 08	08 17		08 32	08 41	08 47	09 02	09 08
London Kings Cross 15	⊖ a	00 28	00 42	05 45	05 55	06 21	06 25	06 40	06 49	06 55		07 10	07 19	07 25	07 40	07 49	07 55	08 10	08 19	08 25		08 40	08 49	08 55	09 10	09 19

For general notes see front of timetable
For details of catering facilities see Directory of Train Operators

A From Peterborough (Table 25)
b Arr. 0738

There is no service between Finsbury Park and Moorgate on Saturdays

Table 24

Saturdays

Letchworth Garden City, Hertford North and Welwyn Garden City → London

Network Diagram - see first page of Table 24

	FC	FC	FC 1	FC	FC	FC 1		FC	FC	FC 1	FC	FC	FC 1	FC	FC	FC 1		FC	FC	FC 1	FC	FC	FC 1	FC	FC
Letchworth Garden City d						09 29							10 29							11 29					
Hitchin 4 d			09 03			09 33				10 03			10 33			11 03				11 33			12 03		
Stevenage 4 d	08 29		09 09			09 39		09 29		10 09			10 39	10 29		11 09				11 39	11 29		12 09		
Watton-at-Stone d	08 36							09 36						10 36							11 36				
Hertford North d	08 42			09 12				09 42			10 12			10 42				11 12			11 42			12 12	
Bayford d	08 46			09 16				09 46			10 16			10 46				11 16			11 46			12 16	
Cuffley d	08 51			09 21				09 51			10 21			10 51				11 21			11 51			12 21	
Crews Hill d	08 54			09 24				09 54			10 24			10 54				11 24			11 54			12 24	
Gordon Hill d	08 57			09 27				09 57			10 27			10 57				11 27			11 57			12 27	
Enfield Chase d	08 59			09 29				09 59			10 29			10 59				11 29			11 59			12 29	
Grange Park d	09 01			09 31				10 01			10 31			11 01				11 31			12 01			12 31	
Winchmore Hill d	09 03			09 33				10 03			10 33			11 03				11 33			12 03			12 33	
Palmers Green d	09 05			09 35				10 05			10 35			11 05				11 35			12 05			12 35	
Bowes Park d	09 08			09 38				10 08			10 38			11 08				11 38			12 08			12 38	
Knebworth d			09 13			09 43				10 13			10 43			11 13				11 43			12 13		
Welwyn North d			09 17			09 47				10 17			10 47			11 17				11 47			12 17		
Welwyn Garden City 4 d		08 58	09 20		09 28	09 50			09 58	10 20		10 28	10 50		10 58	11 20			11 28	11 50		11 58	12 20		12 28
Hatfield d		09 02	09 23		09 32	09 53			10 02	10 23		10 32	10 53		11 02	11 23			11 32	11 53		12 02	12 23		12 32
Welham Green d		09 06			09 36				10 06			10 36			11 06				11 36			12 06			12 36
Brookmans Park d		09 08			09 38				10 08			10 38			11 08				11 38			12 08			12 38
Potters Bar d		09 11	09 29		09 41	09 59			10 11	10 29		10 41	10 59		11 11	11 29			11 41	11 59		12 11	12 29		12 41
Hadley Wood d		09 15			09 45				10 15			10 45			11 15				11 45			12 15			12 45
New Barnet d		09 17			09 47				10 17			10 47			11 17				11 47			12 17			12 47
Oakleigh Park d		09 19			09 49				10 19			10 49			11 19				11 49			12 19			12 49
New Southgate d		09 22			09 52				10 22			10 52			11 22				11 52			12 22			12 52
Alexandra Palace d	09 10	09 25		09 40	09 55			10 10	10 25		10 40	10 55		11 10	11 25			11 40	11 55		12 10	12 25		12 40	12 55
Hornsey d	09 12	09 27		09 42	09 57			10 12	10 27		10 42	10 57		11 12	11 27			11 42	11 57		12 12	12 27		12 42	12 57
Harringay d	09 14	09 29		09 44	09 59			10 14	10 29		10 44	10 59		11 14	11 29			11 44	11 59		12 14	12 29		12 44	12 59
Finsbury Park ⊖ d	09 17	09 32	09 41	09 47	10 02	10 08		10 17	10 32	10 41	10 47	11 02	11 08	11 17	11 32	11 41		11 47	12 02	12 08	12 17	12 32	12 41	12 47	13 02
London Kings Cross 15 ⊖ a	09 25	09 40	09 49	09 55	10 10	10 19		10 25	10 40	10 49	10 55	11 10	11 19	11 25	11 40	11 49		11 55	12 10	12 19	12 25	12 40	12 49	12 55	13 10

	FC 1	FC	FC		FC 1	FC	FC	FC 1	FC	FC	FC 1	FC	FC		FC 1	FC	FC	FC 1	FC	FC	FC 1	FC	FC		FC 1
Letchworth Garden City d	12 29							13 29							14 29						15 29				
Hitchin 4 d	12 33				13 03			13 33			14 03				14 33			15 03			15 33				16 03
Stevenage 4 d	12 39	12 29			13 09			13 39	13 29		14 09				14 39	14 29		15 09			15 39	15 29			16 09
Watton-at-Stone d		12 36							13 36							14 36						15 36			
Hertford North d		12 42				13 12			13 42			14 12				14 42			15 12			15 42			
Bayford d		12 46				13 16			13 46			14 16				14 46			15 16			15 46			
Cuffley d		12 51				13 21			13 51			14 21				14 51			15 21			15 51			
Crews Hill d		12 54				13 24			13 54			14 24				14 54			15 24			15 54			
Gordon Hill d		12 57				13 27			13 57			14 27				14 57			15 27			15 57			
Enfield Chase d		12 59				13 29			13 59			14 29				14 59			15 29			15 59			
Grange Park d		13 01				13 31			14 01			14 31				15 01			15 31			16 01			
Winchmore Hill d		13 03				13 33			14 03			14 33				15 03			15 33			16 03			
Palmers Green d		13 05				13 35			14 05			14 35				15 05			15 35			16 05			
Bowes Park d		13 08				13 38			14 08			14 38				15 08			15 38			16 08			
Knebworth d	12 43				13 13			13 43			14 13				14 43			15 13			15 43				16 13
Welwyn North d	12 47				13 17			13 47			14 17				14 47			15 17			15 47				16 17
Welwyn Garden City 4 d	12 50		12 58		13 20		13 28	13 50		13 58	14 20		14 28		14 50		14 58	15 20		15 28	15 50		15 58		16 20
Hatfield d	12 53		13 02		13 23		13 32	13 53		14 02	14 23		14 32		14 53		15 02	15 23		15 32	15 53		16 02		16 23
Welham Green d			13 06				13 36			14 06			14 36				15 06			15 36			16 06		
Brookmans Park d			13 08				13 38			14 08			14 38				15 08			15 38			16 08		
Potters Bar d	12 59		13 11		13 29		13 41	13 59		14 11	14 29		14 41		14 59		15 11	15 29		15 41	15 59		16 11		16 29
Hadley Wood d			13 15				13 45			14 15			14 45				15 15			15 45			16 15		
New Barnet d			13 17				13 47			14 17			14 47				15 17			15 47			16 17		
Oakleigh Park d			13 19				13 49			14 19			14 49				15 19			15 49			16 19		
New Southgate d			13 22				13 52			14 22			14 52				15 22			15 52			16 22		
Alexandra Palace d		13 10	13 25			13 40	13 55		14 10	14 25		14 40	14 55			15 10	15 25		15 40	15 55		16 10	16 25		
Hornsey d		13 12	13 27			13 42	13 57		14 12	14 27		14 42	14 57			15 12	15 27		15 42	15 57		16 12	16 27		
Harringay d		13 14	13 29			13 44	13 59		14 14	14 29		14 44	14 59			15 14	15 29		15 44	15 59		16 14	16 29		
Finsbury Park ⊖ d	13 08	13 17	13 32		13 41	13 47	14 02	14 08	14 17	14 32	14 41	14 47	15 02		15 08	15 17	15 32	15 41	15 47	16 02	16 08	16 17	16 32		16 41
London Kings Cross 15 ⊖ a	13 19	13 25	13 40		13 49	13 55	14 10	14 19	14 25	14 40	14 49	14 55	15 10		15 19	15 25	15 40	15 49	15 55	16 10	16 19	16 25	16 40		16 49

For general notes see front of timetable
For details of catering facilities see Directory of Train Operators

There is no service between Finsbury Park and Moorgate on Saturdays

Table 24

Saturdays

Letchworth Garden City, Hertford North and Welwyn Garden City → London

Network Diagram - see first page of Table 24

		FC	FC	FC 1	FC	FC	FC 1	FC	FC	FC 1		FC	FC	FC 1	FC	FC	FC 1	FC	FC	FC 1		FC	FC	FC 1	FC	FC
Letchworth Garden City	d			16 29						17 29							18 29							19 29		
Hitchin 4	d			16 33			17 03			17 33				18 03			18 33			19 03				19 33		
Stevenage 4	d			16 39	16 29		17 09			17 39		17 29		18 09			18 39	18 29		19 09				19 39	19 29	
Watton-at-Stone	d				16 36							17 36						18 36							19 36	
Hertford North	d	16 12			16 42			17 12				17 42			18 12			18 42				19 12			19 42	
Bayford	d	16 16			16 46			17 16				17 46			18 16			18 46				19 16			19 46	
Cuffley	d	16 21			16 51			17 21				17 51			18 21			18 51				19 21			19 51	
Crews Hill	d	16 24			16 54			17 24				17 54			18 24			18 54				19 24			19 54	
Gordon Hill	d	16 27			16 57			17 27				17 57			18 27			18 57				19 27			19 57	
Enfield Chase	d	16 29			16 59			17 29				17 59			18 29			18 59				19 29			19 59	
Grange Park	d	16 31			17 01			17 31				18 01			18 31			19 01				19 31			20 01	
Winchmore Hill	d	16 33			17 03			17 33				18 03			18 33			19 03				19 33			20 03	
Palmers Green	d	16 35			17 05			17 35				18 05			18 35			19 05				19 35			20 05	
Bowes Park	d	16 38			17 08			17 38				18 08			18 38			19 08				19 38			20 08	
Knebworth	d			16 43			17 13			17 43				18 13			18 43			19 13				19 43		
Welwyn North	d			16 47			17 17			17 47				18 17			18 47			19 17				19 47		
Welwyn Garden City 4	d		16 28	16 50		16 58	17 20		17 28	17 50			17 58	18 20		18 28	18 50		18 58	19 20			19 28	19 50		19 58
Hatfield	d		16 32	16 53		17 02	17 23		17 32	17 53			18 02	18 23		18 32	18 53		19 02	19 23			19 32	19 53		20 02
Welham Green	d		16 36			17 06			17 36				18 06			18 36			19 06				19 36			20 06
Brookmans Park	d		16 38			17 08			17 38				18 08			18 38			19 08				19 38			20 08
Potters Bar	d		16 41	16 59		17 11	17 29		17 41	17 59			18 11	18 29		18 41	18 59		19 11	19 29			19 41	19 59		20 11
Hadley Wood	d		16 45			17 15			17 45				18 15			18 45			19 15				19 45			20 15
New Barnet	d		16 47			17 17			17 47				18 17			18 47			19 17				19 47			20 17
Oakleigh Park	d		16 49			17 19			17 49				18 19			18 49			19 19				19 49			20 19
New Southgate	d		16 52			17 22			17 52				18 22			18 52			19 22				19 52			20 22
Alexandra Palace	d	16 39	16 55		17 10	17 25		17 40	17 55			18 10	18 25		18 40	18 55		19 10	19 25			19 40	19 55		20 10	20 25
Hornsey	d	16 41	16 57		17 12	17 27		17 42	17 57			18 12	18 27		18 42	18 57		19 12	19 27			19 42	19 57		20 12	20 27
Harringay	d	16 43	16 59		17 14	17 29		17 44	17 59			18 14	18 29		18 44	18 59		19 14	19 29			19 44	19 59		20 14	20 29
Finsbury Park ⊖	d	16 47	17 02	17 08	17 17	17 32	17 41	17 47	18 02	18 08		18 17	18 32	18 41	18 47	19 02	19 08	19 17	19 32	19 41		19 47	20 02	20 08	20 17	20 32
London Kings Cross 15 ⊖	a	16 55	17 10	17 19	17 25	17 40	17 49	17 55	18 10	18 19		18 25	18 40	18 49	18 55	19 10	19 19	19 25	19 40	19 49		19 55	20 10	20 19	20 25	20 40

		FC 1	FC	FC	FC 1	FC	FC		FC 1	FC	FC	FC 1	FC	FC	FC 1	FC	FC	FC	FC 1	FC	FC 1	FC	FC	FC 1		
Letchworth Garden City	d				20 29							21 29							22 29					23 37		
Hitchin 4	d	20 03			20 33				21 03			21 33			22 03				22 33		23 03			23 41		
Stevenage 4	d	20 09			20 39	20 29			21 09			21 39	21 29		22 09			22 29	22 39		23 09		23 29	23 46		
Watton-at-Stone	d					20 36							21 36					22 36					23 36			
Hertford North	d		20 12			20 42				21 12			21 42			22 12		22 42				23 12	23 42			
Bayford	d		20 16			20 46				21 16			21 46			22 16		22 46				23 16	23 46			
Cuffley	d		20 21			20 51				21 21			21 51			22 21		22 51				23 21	23 51			
Crews Hill	d		20 24			20 54				21 24			21 54			22 24		22 54				23 24	23 54			
Gordon Hill	d		20 27			20 57				21 27			21 57			22 27		22 57				23 27	23 57			
Enfield Chase	d		20 29			20 59				21 29			21 59			22 29		22 59				23 29	23 59			
Grange Park	d		20 31			21 01				21 31			22 01			22 31		23 01				23 31	00 01			
Winchmore Hill	d		20 33			21 03				21 33			22 03			22 33		23 03				23 33	00 03			
Palmers Green	d		20 35			21 05				21 35			22 05			22 35		23 05				23 35	00 05			
Bowes Park	d		20 38			21 08				21 38			22 08			22 38		23 08				23 38	00 08			
Knebworth	d	20 13			20 43				21 13			21 43			22 13				22 43		23 13			23 49		
Welwyn North	d	20 17			20 47				21 17			21 47			22 17				22 47		23 17			23 53		
Welwyn Garden City 4	d	20 20		20 28	20 50		20 58		21 20		21 28	21 50		21 58	22 20		22 28		22 50	22 58	23 20			23 56		
Hatfield	d	20 23		20 32	20 53		21 02		21 23		21 32	21 53		22 02	22 23		22 32		22 53	23 02	23 23			23 59		
Welham Green	d			20 36			21 06				21 36			22 06			22 36			23 06						
Brookmans Park	d			20 38			21 08				21 38			22 08			22 38			23 08						
Potters Bar	d	20 29		20 41	20 59		21 11		21 29		21 41	21 59		22 11	22 29		22 41		22 59	23 11	23 29			00 05		
Hadley Wood	d			20 45			21 15				21 45			22 15			22 45			23 15						
New Barnet	d			20 47			21 17				21 47			22 17			22 47			23 17						
Oakleigh Park	d			20 49			21 19				21 49			22 19			22 49			23 19						
New Southgate	d			20 52			21 22				21 52			22 22			22 52			23 22						
Alexandra Palace	d		20 40	20 55		21 10	21 25			21 40	21 55		22 10	22 25		22 40	22 55	23 10		23 25		23 40	00 10			
Hornsey	d		20 42	20 57		21 12	21 27			21 42	21 57		22 12	22 27		22 42	22 57	23 12		23 27		23 42	00 12			
Harringay	d		20 44	20 59		21 14	21 29			21 44	21 59		22 14	22 29		22 44	22 59	23 14		23 29		23 44	00 14			
Finsbury Park ⊖	d	20 41	20 47	21 02	21 08	21 17	21 32		21 41	21 47	22 02	22 08	22 17	22 32	22 41	22 47	23 02	23 17	23 16	23 32	23 44	23 47	00 17	00s23		
London Kings Cross 15 ⊖	a	20 49	20 55	21 10	21 19	21 25	21 40		21 49	21 54	22 10	22 19	22 25	22 40	22 49	22 55	23 10	23 25	23 30	23 42	23 53	23 58	00 25	00 34		

For general notes see front of timetable
For details of catering facilities see
Directory of Train Operators

There is no service between Finsbury Park and Moorgate on Saturdays

Table 24

Sundays

Letchworth Garden City, Hertford North and Welwyn Garden City → London

Network Diagram - see first page of Table 24

		FC	FC 1	FC 🚌	FC	FC 🚌	FC 1 A		FC	FC 🚌	FC A 🚌	FC A 🚌	FC 1 A	FC		FC 🚌	FC B 🚌	FC A 🚌	FC A 🚌	FC 1 B	FC 1 A		FC	FC 1 A	FC B	FC
Letchworth Garden City	d		23p37																							
Hitchin 4	d		23p41								06 10	06 40							07 10	07 28						
Stevenage 4	d	23p29	23p46			05 21					06 30	07 00				06 21			07 30	07 33						
Watton-at-Stone	d	23p36				05 38										06 38										
Hertford North	d	23p42		05 22		05 52				06 22						06 52	07 22	07 22								
Bayford	d	23p46		05 37		06 07				06 37						07 07	07 37	07 37								
Cuffley	d	23p51		05 52		06 22				06 52						07 22	07 52	07 52								
Crews Hill	d	23p54		06 00		06 30				07 00						07 30	08 00	08 00								
Gordon Hill	d	23p57		06 10		06 40				07 10						07 40	08a10	08 10							08 27	
Enfield Chase	d	23p59		06 16		06 46				07 16						07 46		08 16							08 29	
Grange Park	d	00 01		06 21		06 51				07 21						07 51		08 21							08 31	
Winchmore Hill	d	00 03		06 27		06 57				07 27						07 57		08 27							08 33	
Palmers Green	d	00 05		06 35		07 05				07 35						08 05		08 35							08 35	
Bowes Park	d	00 08		06 45		07 15				07 45						08 15		08 45							08 38	
Knebworth	d		23p49				06 44				06a37	07a07	07 14						07a37	07 37	07 44			08 14		
Welwyn North	d		23p53										07 19							07 40				08 19		
Welwyn Garden City 4	d		23p56		06 28				06 58				07 22	07 28						07 43			07 58	08 22		08 28
Hatfield	d		23p59		06 32				07 02				07 26	07 32									08 02	08 26		08 32
Welham Green	d				06 36				07 06					07 36									08 06			08 36
Brookmans Park	d				06 38				07 08					07 38									08 08			08 38
Potters Bar	d		00 05		06 41				07 11				07 31	07 41									08 11	08 31		08 41
Hadley Wood	d				06 45				07 15					07 45									08 15			08 45
New Barnet	d				06 47				07 17					07 47									08 17			08 47
Oakleigh Park	d				06 49				07 19					07 49									08 19			08 49
New Southgate	d				06 52				07 22					07 52									08 22			08 52
Alexandra Palace	d	00 10		06a50	06 55	07a20			07 25	07a50				07 55		08a20		08a50					08 25		08 40	08 55
Hornsey	d	00 12			06 57				07 27					07 57									08 27		08 42	08 57
Harringay	d	00 14			06 59				07 29					07 59									08 29		08 44	08 59
Finsbury Park	⊖ d	00 17	00s23		07 02		07 10		07 32				07 44	08 02						08 02	08 10		08 32	08 44	08 47	09 02
London Kings Cross 15	⊖ a	00 25	00 34		07 13		07 19		07 43				07 54	08 13						08 13	08 19		08 40	08 54	08 56	09 10

		FC A 🚌	FC B 🚌	FC A 🚌	FC A 🚌		FC 1 B	FC 1 A	FC B	FC	FC A 🚌	FC B		FC	FC A 🚌	FC A 🚌	FC 1	FC B	FC		FC A	FC B	FC	FC A 🚌	FC 1	FC
Letchworth Garden City	d						08 29										09 29								10 29	
Hitchin 4	d			07 40	08 10		08 33										09 33								10 33	
Stevenage 4	d	07 21	07 29	08 00	08 30		08 39		08 29						08 21		09 39	09 29						09 22	10 39	10 29
Watton-at-Stone	d	07 38	07 46						08 36						08 38			09 36						09 38		10 36
Hertford North	d	07 52	08 00						08 42		08 22	09 12			08 52	09 22		09 42				10 12		09 52		10 42
Bayford	d	08 07	08 15						08 46		08 37	09 16			09 07	09 37		09 46				10 16		10 07		10 46
Cuffley	d	08 22	08 30						08 51		08 52	09 21			09 22	09 52		09 51				10 21		10 22		10 51
Crews Hill	d	08 30	08 38						08 54		09 00	09 24			09 30	10 00		09 54				10 24		10 30		10 54
Gordon Hill	d	08 40	08a48						08 57		09 10	09 27			09 40	10a10		09 57			10 27	10 27		10 40		10 57
Enfield Chase	d	08 46							08 59		09 16	09 29			09 46			09 59			10 29	10 29		10a46		10 59
Grange Park	d	08 51							09 01		09 21	09 31			09 51			10 01			10 31	10 31				11 01
Winchmore Hill	d	08 57							09 03		09 27	09 33			09 57			10 03			10 33	10 33				11 03
Palmers Green	d	09 05							09 05		09 35	09 35			10 05			10 05			10 35	10 35				11 05
Bowes Park	d	09 15							09 08		09 45	09 38			10 15			10 08			10 38	10 38				11 08
Knebworth	d			08a07	08a37		08 43	08 44									09 43								10 43	
Welwyn North	d						08 47	08 49									09 47								10 47	
Welwyn Garden City 4	d						08 50	08 52		08 58				09 28			09 50		09 58				10 28		10 50	
Hatfield	d						08 53	08 56		09 02				09 32			09 53		10 02				10 32		10 53	
Welham Green	d									09 06				09 36					10 06				10 36			
Brookmans Park	d									09 08				09 38					10 08				10 38			
Potters Bar	d						08 59	09 01		09 11				09 41			09 59		10 11				10 41		10 59	
Hadley Wood	d									09 15				09 45					10 15				10 45			
New Barnet	d									09 17				09 47					10 17				10 47			
Oakleigh Park	d									09 19				09 49					10 19				10 49			
New Southgate	d									09 22				09 52					10 22				10 52			
Alexandra Palace	d	09a20							09 10	09 25	09a50	09 40		09 55	10a20			10 10	10 25		10 40	10 40	10 55			11 10
Hornsey	d								09 12	09 27		09 42		09 57				10 12	10 27		10 42	10 42	10 57			11 12
Harringay	d								09 14	09 29		09 44		09 59				10 14	10 29		10 44	10 44	10 59			11 14
Finsbury Park	⊖ d						09 11	09 14	09 17	09 32		09 47		10 02			10 11	10 17	10 32		10 47	10 47	11 02		11 11	11 17
London Kings Cross 15	⊖ a						09 18	09 21	09 26	09 40		09 55		10 10			10 19	10 25	10 40		10 55	10 55	11 10		11 19	11 25

For general notes see front of timetable
For details of catering facilities see Directory of Train Operators

A Until 23 March
B From 30 March

There is no service between Finsbury Park and Moorgate on Sundays

Table 24

Sundays

Letchworth Garden City, Hertford North and Welwyn Garden City → London

Network Diagram - see first page of Table 24

	FC	FC		FC	FC 1	FC	FC	FC	FC		FC 1	FC	FC	FC	FC	FC 1		FC	FC	FC	FC	FC 1	FC		FC
Letchworth Garden City d					11 29						12 29					13 29						14 29			
Hitchin 4 d					11 33						12 33					13 33						14 33			
Stevenage 4 d					11 39	11 29					12 39	12 29				13 39		13 29				14 39	14 29		
Watton-at-Stone d						11 36						12 36						13 36					14 36		
Hertford North d		11 12				11 42		12 12				12 42		13 12				13 42		14 12			14 42		
Bayford d		11 16				11 46		12 16				12 46		13 16				13 46		14 16			14 46		
Cuffley d		11 21				11 51		12 21				12 51		13 21				13 51		14 21			14 51		
Crews Hill d		11 24				11 54		12 24				12 54		13 24				13 54		14 24			14 54		
Gordon Hill d		11 27				11 57		12 27				12 57		13 27				13 57		14 27			14 57		
Enfield Chase d		11 29				11 59		12 29				12 59		13 29				13 59		14 29			14 59		
Grange Park d		11 31				12 01		12 31				13 01		13 31				14 01		14 31			15 01		
Winchmore Hill d		11 33				12 03		12 33				13 03		13 33				14 03		14 33			15 03		
Palmers Green d		11 35				12 05		12 35				13 05		13 35				14 05		14 35			15 05		
Bowes Park d		11 38				12 08		12 38				13 08		13 38				14 08		14 38			15 08		
Knebworth d					11 43						12 43					13 43						14 43			
Welwyn North d					11 47						12 47					13 47						14 47			
Welwyn Garden City 4 d	10 58			11 28	11 50		11 58		12 28		12 50		12 58		13 28	13 50			13 58		14 28	14 50			14 58
Hatfield d	11 02			11 32	11 53		12 02		12 32		12 53		13 02		13 32	13 53			14 02		14 32	14 53			15 02
Welham Green d	11 06			11 36			12 06		12 36				13 06		13 36				14 06		14 36				15 06
Brookmans Park d	11 08			11 38			12 08		12 38				13 08		13 38				14 08		14 38				15 08
Potters Bar d	11 11			11 41	11 59		12 11		12 41		12 59		13 11		13 41	13 59			14 11		14 41	14 59			15 11
Hadley Wood d	11 15			11 45			12 15		12 45				13 15		13 45				14 15		14 45				15 15
New Barnet d	11 17			11 47			12 17		12 47				13 17		13 47				14 17		14 47				15 17
Oakleigh Park d	11 19			11 49			12 19		12 49				13 19		13 49				14 19		14 49				15 19
New Southgate d	11 22			11 52			12 22		12 52				13 22		13 52				14 22		14 52				15 22
Alexandra Palace d	11 25	11 40		11 55		12 10	12 25	12 40	12 55			13 10	13 25	13 40	13 55			14 10	14 25	14 40	14 55		15 10		15 25
Hornsey d	11 27	11 42		11 57		12 12	12 27	12 42	12 57			13 12	13 27	13 42	13 57			14 12	14 27	14 42	14 57		15 12		15 27
Harringay d	11 29	11 44		11 59		12 14	12 29	12 44	12 59			13 14	13 29	13 44	13 59			14 14	14 29	14 44	14 59		15 14		15 29
Finsbury Park ⊖ d	11 32	11 47		12 02	12 11	12 17	12 32	12 47	13 02		13 11	13 17	13 32	13 47	14 02	14 11		14 17	14 32	14 47	15 02	15 11	15 17		15 32
London Kings Cross 15 ⊖ a	11 40	11 55		12 10	12 19	12 25	12 40	12 55	13 10		13 19	13 25	13 40	13 55	14 10	14 19		14 25	14 40	14 55	15 10	15 19	15 25		15 40

	FC	FC	FC 1	FC	FC	FC		FC	FC 1	FC	FC	FC	FC		FC 1	FC	FC	FC	FC	FC 1		FC	FC	FC	FC
Letchworth Garden City d			15 29						16 29						17 29					18 29					
Hitchin 4 d			15 33						16 33						17 33					18 33					
Stevenage 4 d			15 39	15 29					16 39	16 29					17 39	17 29				18 39		18 29			
Watton-at-Stone d				15 36						16 36						17 36						18 36			
Hertford North d	15 12			15 42		16 12				16 42		17 12				17 42		18 12				18 42		19 12	
Bayford d	15 16			15 46		16 16				16 46		17 16				17 46		18 16				18 46		19 16	
Cuffley d	15 21			15 51		16 21				16 51		17 21				17 51		18 21				18 51		19 21	
Crews Hill d	15 24			15 54		16 24				16 54		17 24				17 54		18 24				18 54		19 24	
Gordon Hill d	15 27			15 57		16 27				16 57		17 27				17 57		18 27				18 57		19 27	
Enfield Chase d	15 29			15 59		16 29				16 59		17 29				17 59		18 29				18 59		19 29	
Grange Park d	15 31			16 01		16 31				17 01		17 31				18 01		18 31				19 01		19 31	
Winchmore Hill d	15 33			16 03		16 33				17 03		17 33				18 03		18 33				19 03		19 33	
Palmers Green d	15 35			16 05		16 35				17 05		17 35				18 05		18 35				19 05		19 35	
Bowes Park d	15 38			16 08		16 38				17 08		17 38				18 08		18 38				19 08		19 38	
Knebworth d			15 43						16 43						17 43					18 43					
Welwyn North d			15 47						16 47						17 47					18 47					
Welwyn Garden City 4 d		15 28	15 50		15 58			16 28	16 50		16 58		17 28		17 50		17 58		18 28	18 50			18 58		19 28
Hatfield d		15 32	15 53		16 02			16 32	16 53		17 02		17 32		17 53		18 02		18 32	18 53			19 02		19 32
Welham Green d		15 36			16 06			16 36			17 06		17 36				18 06		18 36				19 06		19 36
Brookmans Park d		15 38			16 08			16 38			17 08		17 38				18 08		18 38				19 08		19 38
Potters Bar d		15 41	15 59		16 11			16 41	16 59		17 11		17 41		17 59		18 11		18 41	18 59			19 11		19 41
Hadley Wood d		15 45			16 15			16 45			17 15		17 45				18 15		18 45				19 15		19 45
New Barnet d		15 47			16 17			16 47			17 17		17 47				18 17		18 47				19 17		19 47
Oakleigh Park d		15 49			16 19			16 49			17 19		17 49				18 19		18 49				19 19		19 49
New Southgate d		15 52			16 22			16 52			17 22		17 52				18 22		18 52				19 22		19 52
Alexandra Palace d	15 40	15 55		16 10	16 25	16 40		16 55		17 10	17 25	17 40	17 55			18 10	18 25	18 40	18 55			19 10	19 25	19 40	19 55
Hornsey d	15 42	15 57		16 12	16 27	16 42		16 57		17 12	17 27	17 42	17 57			18 12	18 27	18 42	18 57			19 12	19 27	19 42	19 57
Harringay d	15 44	15 59		16 14	16 29	16 44		16 59		17 14	17 29	17 44	17 59			18 14	18 29	18 44	18 59			19 14	19 29	19 44	19 59
Finsbury Park ⊖ d	15 47	16 02	16 11	16 17	16 32	16 47		17 02	17 11	17 17	17 32	17 47	18 02		18 11	18 17	18 32	18 47	19 02	19 11		19 17	19 32	19 47	20 02
London Kings Cross 15 ⊖ a	15 55	16 10	16 19	16 25	16 40	16 55		17 10	17 19	17 25	17 40	17 55	18 10		18 19	18 25	18 40	18 55	19 10	19 19		19 25	19 40	19 55	20 10

For general notes see front of timetable
For details of catering facilities see
Directory of Train Operators

There is no service between Finsbury Park and Moorgate on Sundays

Table 24

Sundays

Letchworth Garden City, Hertford North and Welwyn Garden City → London

Network Diagram - see first page of Table 24

		FC 1	FC	FC	FC		FC	FC 1	FC	FC	FC	FC		FC 1	FC	FC	FC	FC	FC 1	FC	FC	FC	FC	FC 1		
Letchworth Garden City	d	19 29						20 29						21 29					22 29					23 36		
Hitchin 4	d	19 33						20 33						21 33					22 33					23 40		
Stevenage 4	d	19 39	19 29					20 39	20 29					21 39	21 29				22 39	22 29			23 29	23 45		
Watton-at-Stone	d		19 36						20 36						21 36					22 36			23 36			
Hertford North	d		19 42		20 12				20 42		21 12				21 42		22 12			22 42		23 12	23 42			
Bayford	d		19 46		20 16				20 46		21 16				21 46		22 16			22 46		23 16	23 46			
Cuffley	d		19 51		20 21				20 51		21 21				21 51		22 21			22 51		23 21	23 51			
Crews Hill	d		19 54		20 24				20 54		21 24				21 54		22 24			22 54		23 24	23 54			
Gordon Hill	d		19 57		20 27				20 57		21 27				21 57		22 27			22 57		23 27	23 57			
Enfield Chase	d		19 59		20 29				20 59		21 29				21 59		22 29			22 59		23 29	23 59			
Grange Park	d		20 01		20 31				21 01		21 31				22 01		22 31			23 01		23 31	00 01			
Winchmore Hill	d		20 03		20 33				21 03		21 33				22 03		22 33			23 03		23 33	00 03			
Palmers Green	d		20 05		20 35				21 05		21 35				22 05		22 35			23 05		23 35	00 05			
Bowes Park	d		20 08		20 38				21 08		21 38				22 08		22 38			23 08		23 38	00 08			
Knebworth	d	19 43						20 43						21 43					22 43					23 48		
Welwyn North	d	19 47						20 47						21 47					22 47					23 52		
Welwyn Garden City 4	d	19 50		19 58			20 28	20 50		20 58		21 28		21 50		21 58		22 28	22 50		22 58			23 55		
Hatfield	d	19 53		20 02			20 32	20 53		21 02		21 32		21 53		22 02		22 32	22 53		23 02			23 58		
Welham Green	d			20 06			20 36			21 06		21 36				22 06		22 36			23 06					
Brookmans Park	d			20 08			20 38			21 08		21 38				22 08		22 38			23 08					
Potters Bar	d	19 59		20 11			20 41	20 59		21 11		21 41		21 59		22 11		22 41	22 59		23 11			00 04		
Hadley Wood	d			20 15			20 45			21 15		21 45				22 15		22 45			23 15					
New Barnet	d			20 17			20 47			21 17		21 47				22 17		22 47			23 17					
Oakleigh Park	d			20 19			20 49			21 19		21 49				22 19		22 49			23 19					
New Southgate	d			20 22			20 52			21 22		21 52				22 22		22 52			23 22					
Alexandra Palace	d		20 10	20 25	20 40		20 55		21 10	21 25	21 40	21 55			22 10	22 25	22 40	22 55		23 11	23 25	23 40	00 10			
Hornsey	d		20 12	20 27	20 42		20 57		21 12	21 27	21 42	21 57			22 12	22 27	22 42	22 57		23 13	23 27	23 42	00 12			
Harringay	d		20 14	20 29	20 44		20 59		21 14	21 29	21 44	21 59			22 14	22 29	22 44	22 59		23 15	23 29	23 44	00 14			
Finsbury Park	⊖ d	20 11	20 17	20 32	20 47		21 02	21 11	21 17	21 32	21 47	22 02		22 11	22 17	22 32	22 47	23 02	23 11	23 18	23 32	23 47	00 17	00 20		
London Kings Cross 15	⊖ a	20 19	20 25	20 40	20 55		21 10	21 19	21 25	21 40	21 55	22 10		22 19	22 25	22 40	22 58	23 12	23 24	23 27	23 44	23 57	00 27	00 32		

For general notes see front of timetable
For details of catering facilities see
Directory of Train Operators

There is no service between Finsbury Park and Moorgate on Sundays

First Capital Connect will run a Saturday service on Bank Holiday Mondays

London → Stevenage, Cambridge and Peterborough

Network Diagram - see first page of Table 24

Miles	Miles			FC	FC	FC	FC	FC	FC	FC	FC	FC	FC	FC	FC	FC	FC	FC	FC	FC	FC	GR	FC		FC	GR
				MO	MX	MO	MX	MO	MX	MO	MX	MO		MX	MO	MO	MX	MX	MO							
				1	1	1	1	1	1	1	1		1	1	1		1	1	1	1	1	R 1	1		1	R 1
						A															B	☕ trolley				✕ trolley
0	0	**London Kings Cross 15** ⊖	d	23p06	23p06	23p15			23p22	23p25	23p36	23p41	00 07	00 36	00 36	01 06	01 06	01 36	01 36	05 21	05 45	06 00			06 06	06 15
2½	2½	Finsbury Park ⊖	d	23p11	23p11				23p27	23p30	23p41	23p47	00 12	00 41	00 41	01 11	01 11	01 41	01 41	05 26	05 50				06 11	
12¾	12¾	Potters Bar	d	23p21	23p21						23p51	00 08		00 58	00 58			01 58	01 58	05 36					06 21	
17¾	17¾	Hatfield	d	23p27	23p27		←	←			23p57	00 16		01 04	01 04			02 04	02 04	05 42					06 27	
20¼	20¼	Welwyn Garden City 4	d	23p31	23p31		23p31	23p31			00 01	00 20		01 08	01 08			02 08	02 08	05 46					→	
22	22	Welwyn North	d	→	→		23p34	23p36			00 04	00 23		01s11	01s16			02s11	02s16	05 49						
25	25	Knebworth	d				23p38	23p40			00 08	00 28		01s15	01s20			02s15	02s20	05 53						
—	—	Hertford North	d										00 39				01 37									
27½	27½	**Stevenage 4**	d				23p42	23p43	23p46	23p49	00 12	00 31	00 48	01 18	01 23	01 47	01 47	02 18	02 23	05 57	06 08	06 19				06 34
31¾	31¾	Hitchin 4	d				23p50	23p53	23p54	00 04	00 20	00a47	00 56	01 23	01 28	01 52	01 52	02 23	02 28	06 05	06 13					
34¾	—	Letchworth Garden City	d			23p52	23p54	23p57			00a29		01 00			02a06	02a06				06 16					
36¾	—	Baldock	d				23p58	23p59					01 04								06 19					
41	—	Ashwell & Morden	d				00 03	00 05					01 09								06 24					
45	—	Royston	d			00 01	00 07	00 10					01 13								06 29					
48	—	Meldreth	d				00 11	00 13					01 17								06 32					
50	—	Shepreth	d				00 14	00 16					01 20								06 35					
51	—	Foxton	d				00 17	00 18					01 23								06 38					
58	—	**Cambridge**	a			00 19	00 29	00 35					01 39								06 53					
—	37	Arlesey	d						23p59	00 10				01s35	01s37					06 10			←			
—	41	Biggleswade	d						00 04	00 15				01s40	01s42			02s38	02s40	06 15			06 15			
—	44	Sandy	d						00 08	00 18				01s44	01s46					→			06 19			
—	51½	St Neots	d						00 15	00 26				01s51	01s53			02s48	02s50				06 27			
—	58¾	Huntingdon	a						00 26	00 33				02s02	02s04			02s59	03s01				06 34			
—	—		d						00 26	00 33													06 34			
—	76¼	**Peterborough 8**	a						00 42	00 55				02 24	02 26			03 21	03 23			06 50	06 54			07 05

		FC	FC	GR	FC	FC	FC	FC	GR	FC	GR	FC	FC	FC	FC	GR	FC	FC	FC	FC	FC		GR	FC	GR	FC
		1	1	R 1	1	1	1	1	R 1	1	R 1	1	1	1	1	R 1	1	1	1	1	1		R 1	1	R 1	1
				☕ trolley					✕ trolley		✕ trolley					✕ trolley							✕ trolley		✕ trolley	
London Kings Cross 15 ⊖	d		06 22	06 35		06 36	06 45	06 52	07 00	07 06	07 10		07 15		07 22	07 30		07 36	07 45		07 52		08 00	08 06	08 10	08 15
Finsbury Park ⊖	d		06 27			06 41		06 57		07 11					07 27			07 41			07 57			08 11		
Potters Bar	d	←				06 51				07 21				←				07 51						08 21		
Hatfield	d	06 27				06 57				07 27				07 27				07 57						08 27		
Welwyn Garden City 4	d	06 31				07 01				→				07 31				08 01						08 31		
Welwyn North	d	06 34				07 04								07 34				08 04						08 34		
Knebworth	d	06 38				07 08								07 38				08 08						08 38		
Hertford North	d																			←						
Stevenage 4	d	06 42	06 46			07 12		07 16	07 19		07 29			07 42	07 46	07 50		08 12		08 12	08 16			08 42		
Hitchin 4	d	06 47	06 51			07 17		07 21						07 47	07 51			→		08 17	08 21			08 47		
Letchworth Garden City	d	06 51						07 25						07 51							08 25			→		
Baldock	d	06 55						07 28						07 55							08 28					
Ashwell & Morden	d	07 00						07 33						08 00							08 33					
Royston	d	07 06						07 37						08 04							08 37					
Meldreth	d	07 10						07 41						08 08							08 41					
Shepreth	d	07 13						07 44						08 11							08 44					
Foxton	d	07 16						07 46						08 14							08 46					
Cambridge	a	07 29			←		07 31	08 01					08 02	08 28					08 35		09 01					09 02
Arlesey	d		06 56		06 56	07 23						←			07 56		←			08 23						
Biggleswade	d		→		07 01	07 28						07 28			08 01		08 01			08 28						
Sandy	d				07 05	→						07 32			→		08 05			08 32						
St Neots	d				07 12							07 39					08 12			08 39						
Huntingdon	a				07 20							07 47					08 20			08 47						
	d				07 20							07 47					08 20			08 47						
Peterborough 8	a			07 21	07 38				07 50		08 00	08 09				08 21	08 38			09 13			08 46		08 59	

		FC	GR	GR	FC	FC	FC	FC	FC	FC	FC	GR	FC	GR	FC	FC	GR	FC	FC		GR	FC	FC	FC	FC	FC
		1	R 1	R 1	1	1	1	1	1	1		R 1	1	R 1	1	1	R 1	1			R 1	1	1	1	1	1
			✕ trolley	☕ trolley								✕ trolley		✕ trolley			✕ trolley				✕ trolley					
London Kings Cross 15 ⊖	d	08 22	08 30	08 35		08 36		08 45		08 52		09 00	09 06	09 10	09 15	09 22	09 30				09 35		09 36	09 45		09 52
Finsbury Park ⊖	d	08 27				08 41				08 57	08 24		09 11			09 27			09 04				09 41			09 57
Potters Bar	d					08 51							09 21										09 51			
Hatfield	d					08 57							09 27										09 57			
Welwyn Garden City 4	d					09 01							09 31										10 01			
Welwyn North	d					09 04							09 34										10 04			
Knebworth	d					09 08							09 38										10 08			
Hertford North	d								←		09 07								09 39						←	
Stevenage 4	d	08 46	08 49	08 55		09 12	←		09 12	09 16	09 20		09 42			09 46	09 49	←	09 51		09 54		10 12		10 12	10 16
Hitchin 4	d	08 51				→	08 47		09 17	09 21	09 26		09 47			09 51		09 47	09 56				→		10 17	10 21
Letchworth Garden City	d						08 54			09 25	09a34		→					09 51	10a04							10 25
Baldock	d						08 57			09 28								09 55								10 28
Ashwell & Morden	d						09 02											10 00								
Royston	d						09 07			09 36								10 04								10 36
Meldreth	d						09 11											10 08								
Shepreth	d						09 14											10 11								
Foxton	d						09 16											10 14								
Cambridge	a						09 31	09 31		09 54					10 02			10 27						10 31		10 54
Arlesey	d	08 56			←				09 23																10 23	
Biggleswade	d	09 01			09 01				09 28							09 59						←			10 28	
Sandy	d	→			09 05				09 32							10 03						10 03			10 32	
St Neots	d				09 12				09 39							→						10 10			10 39	
Huntingdon	a				09 20				09 47													10 18			10 47	
	d				09 20				09 47													10 18			10 47	
Peterborough 8	a		09 20	09 26	09 38				10 05			09 46		09 56			10 20				10 26	10 34			11 05	

For general notes see front of timetable
For details of catering facilities see
Directory of Train Operators

A To Ely (Table 17)
B To Kings Lynn (Table 17)

First Capital Connect will run a Saturday service on Bank Holiday Mondays

London → Stevenage, Cambridge and Peterborough

Network Diagram - see first page of Table 24

		GR	FC	GR	FC	FC	GR	GR	FC	FC	FC	FC	FC	FC	FC	GR	FC		GR	FC	FC	GR	FC	FC	GR	FC
		R 1	1	R 1	1	1	R 1	R 1	1	1		1	1	1	1	R 1	1		R 1	1	1	R 1	1		R 1	1
		A ✕		✕			B ✕	trolley								✕			trolley			✕			trolley	
London Kings Cross 15 ⊖	d	10 00	10 06	10 10	10 15	10 22	10 30	10 35				10 36	10 45		10 52	11 00	11 06		11 10	11 15	11 22	11 30			11 35	
Finsbury Park ⊖	d		10 11			10 27					10 04	10 41			10 57		11 11				11 27			11 04		
Potters Bar	d		10 21									10 51					11 21									
Hatfield	d		10 27									10 57					11 27									
Welwyn Garden City 4	d		10 31									11 01					11 31									
Welwyn North	d		10 34									11 04					11 34									
Knebworth	d		10 38									11 08					11 38									
Hertford North	d										10 39			←										11 39		
Stevenage 4	d		10 42			10 46				←	10 51	11 12 →		11 12	11 16		11 42				11 46	11 50	←	11 51	11 54	
Hitchin 4	d		10 47 →			10 51				10 47	10 56			11 17	11 21		11 47 →				11 51		11 47	11 56		
Letchworth Garden City	d									10 51	11a04				11 25								11 51	12a04		
Baldock	d									10 55					11 28								11 55			
Ashwell & Morden	d									11 00													12 00			
Royston	d									11 04					11 36								12 04			
Meldreth	d									11 08													12 08			
Shepreth	d									11 11													12 11			
Foxton	d									11 14													12 14			
Cambridge	a				11 02					11 27			11 31		11 54					12 01			12 27			
Arlesey	d								←					11 23												
Biggleswade	d					10 59 →			10 59					11 28							11 59					←
Sandy	d								11 03					11 32							12 03 →					12 03
St Neots	d								11 10					11 39												12 10
Huntingdon	a								11 18					11 47												12 18
	d								11 18					11 47												12 18
Peterborough 8	a	10 45		10 56			11 16	11 22	11 34					12 04		11 46			11 56			12 21			12 27	12 34

		FC	FC	FC	FC	GR	FC	GR	FC	FC	FC	FC	GR	FC	FC		FC	FC	FC	GR	FC	GR	FC	FC	GR	FC
		1	1	1	1	R 1	1	R 1	1	1	1		R 1	1	1		1	1	1	R 1	1	R 1	1	1	R 1	1
						C ✕		✕					✕							✕		✕			trolley	
London Kings Cross 15 ⊖	d	11 36	11 45		11 52	12 00	12 06	12 10	12 15		12 22		12 30		12 36		12 45		12 52	13 00	13 06	13 10	13 15	13 22	13 35	
Finsbury Park ⊖	d	11 41			11 57		12 11				12 27	12 04			12 41				12 57		13 11			13 27		
Potters Bar	d	11 51					12 21			←					12 51						13 21					
Hatfield	d	11 57					12 27 →			12 27					12 57						13 27					
Welwyn Garden City 4	d	12 01								12 31					13 01						13 31					
Welwyn North	d	12 04								12 34					13 04						13 34					
Knebworth	d	12 08								12 38					13 08						13 38					
Hertford North	d			←								12 39						←								
Stevenage 4	d	12 12 →		12 12	12 16			12 29		12 42	12 46	12 51			13 12 →			13 12	13 16		13 42			13 46		
Hitchin 4	d			12 17	12 21					12 47	12 51	12 56						13 17	13 21		13 47 →			13 51		
Letchworth Garden City	d				12 25					12 51		13a04							13 25							
Baldock	d				12 28					12 55									13 28							
Ashwell & Morden	d									13 00																
Royston	d				12 36					13 04									13 36							
Meldreth	d									13 08																
Shepreth	d									13 11																
Foxton	d									13 14																
Cambridge	a		12 31		12 54				13 02	13 27				←			13 31		13 54				14 02			←
Arlesey	d			12 23							12 56 →			12 56				13 23						13 56 →		13 56
Biggleswade	d			12 28										13 01				13 28								14 01
Sandy	d			12 32										13 05				13 32								14 05
St Neots	d			12 39										13 12				13 39								14 12
Huntingdon	a			12 47										13 20				13 47								14 20
	d			12 47										13 20				13 47								14 20
Peterborough 8	a			13 07		12 46		13 00					13 16	13 36				14 05		13 46		13 57			14 24	14 36

		FC	FC	FC	FC	FC	FC	FC	GR	FC	FC	GR	FC		FC	FC	FC	FC	FC	FC	FC	GR	FC	FC	GR	FC
		1		1	1	1	1	1	R 1	1	1	R 1	1		1		1	1	1	1	1	R 1	1	1	R 1	1
									✕			trolley										✕			✕	
London Kings Cross 15 ⊖	d			13 36	13 45		13 52	14 06	14 10	14 15	14 22	14 30					14 36	14 45		14 52	15 06	15 10	15 15	15 22	15 30	
Finsbury Park ⊖	d		13 04	13 41			13 57	14 11			14 27					14 04	14 41			14 57	15 11			15 27		
Potters Bar	d			13 51				14 21									14 51				15 21					
Hatfield	d			13 57				14 27									14 57				15 27					
Welwyn Garden City 4	d			14 01				14 31									15 01				15 31					
Welwyn North	d			14 04				14 34									15 04				15 34					
Knebworth	d			14 08				14 38									15 08				15 38					
Hertford North	d		13 39			←										14 39			←							
Stevenage 4	d	←	13 51	14 12 →		14 12	14 16	14 42			14 46				←	14 51	15 12 →		15 12	15 16	15 42			15 46		←
Hitchin 4	d	13 47	13 56			14 17	14 21	14 47 →			14 51				14 47	14 56			15 17	15 21	15 47 →			15 51		15 47
Letchworth Garden City	d	13 51	14a04				14 25								14 51	15a04				15 25						15 51
Baldock	d	13 55					14 28								14 55					15 28						15 55
Ashwell & Morden	d	14 00													15 00											16 00
Royston	d	14 04					14 36								15 04					15 36						16 04
Meldreth	d	14 08													15 08											16 08
Shepreth	d	14 11													15 11											16 11
Foxton	d	14 14													15 14											16 14
Cambridge	a	14 27			14 31		14 54			15 04			←		15 27			15 31		15 54			16 03			16 30
Arlesey	d					14 23					14 56 →		14 56						15 23					15 56 →		
Biggleswade	d					14 28							15 01						15 28							
Sandy	d					14 32							15 05						15 32							
St Neots	d					14 39							15 12						15 39							
Huntingdon	a					14 47							15 20						15 47							
	d					14 47							15 20						15 47							
Peterborough 8	a					15 05			14 56			15 16	15 36						16 04			15 56			16 16	

For general notes see front of timetable
For details of catering facilities see
Directory of Train Operators

A The Flying Scotsman
B The Northern Lights
C The Highland Chieftain

First Capital Connect will run a Saturday service on Bank Holiday Mondays

London → Stevenage, Cambridge and Peterborough

Network Diagram - see first page of Table 24

		FC	GR	FC	FC	FC	FC	FC	FC	GR	FC		FC	GR	FC	FC	FC	FC	FC	FC	FC	GR	FC	FC	FC	FC
			R 1 ☕ 🚲	1	1	1	1	1	1	R 1 ☕ 🚲	1		1	R 1 🍴 🚲	1	1	1	1 A		1	1	R 1 🍴 🚲	1	1	1	1
London Kings Cross 15 ⊖	d		15 35		15 36	15 45		15 52	16 06	16 10	16 15		16 23	16 35	16 36	16 40		16 45	16 52		16 53	17 03		17 06	17 07	17 15
Finsbury Park ⊖	d	15 04			15 41			15 57	16 11				16 28		16 41				16 57		16u58			17 11		
Potters Bar	d				15 51				16 21						16 51				17 13							
Hatfield	d				15 57				16 27						16 57				17 19	←				17 29		
Welwyn Garden City 4	d				16 01				16 31						17 01				17 24	17 01				17 33		
Welwyn North	d				16 04				16 34						→				→	17 04				17 38		
Knebworth	d				16 08				16 38											17 08				→		
Hertford North	d	15 39					←																			
Stevenage 4	d	15 51	15 54		16 12		16 12	16 16	16 42				16 47				←			17 12	17 19					
Hitchin 4	d	15 56			→		16 17	16 21	16 47				16 53				16 47			17 17	17 25					
Letchworth Garden City	d	16a04						16 25	→								16 51	17 10		17 24						17 40
Baldock	d							16 28									16 55			17 27						
Ashwell & Morden	d							16 33									17 00			17 32						
Royston	d							16 37									17 06	17 19		17 37						17 49
Meldreth	d																17 10			17 41						
Shepreth	d																17 13			17 44						
Foxton	d																17 16			17 46						
Cambridge	a			←		16 33		16 54			17 04						17 32	17 36		18 02			←			18 07
Arlesey	d			15 56			16 23						16 58								17 30		16 58			
Biggleswade	d			16 01			16 28						→								17 35		17 03			
Sandy	d			16 05			16 32														→		17 07			
St Neots	d			16 12			16 39									17 15							17 14		17 42	
Huntingdon	a			16 20			16 47									17 22							17 27		→	
	d			16 20			16 47									17 23							17 27			
Peterborough 8	a		16 25	16 37			17 04			16 56				17 24		17 41						17 51	17 55			

		GR	FC	FC	FC	FC	FC	GR	FC		FC	FC	FC	GR	FC	FC	FC	FC	GR	FC	FC	FC	FC	FC	FC	GR
		R 1 B 🍴 🚲	1			1	1	R 1 🍴 🚲	1		1	1	1 A	R 1 ☕ 🚲			1	1	R 1 🍴 🚲	1	1	1	1	1 C		R 1 🍴 🚲
London Kings Cross 15 ⊖	d	17 20			17 22		17 23	17 30			17 36	17 37	17 45	17 50		17 52		17 53	18 03			18 06	18 07	18 15		18 20
Finsbury Park ⊖	d				17 27		17u28				17 41					17 57		17u58				18 11				
Potters Bar	d				17 43											18 13										
Hatfield	d			←	17 49										←	18 19	←								←	
Welwyn Garden City 4	d			17 24	17 53	←					17 59				17 53	18 23	17 59					18 29			18 23	
Welwyn North	d			17 27	→	17 38					→				17 56	→	18 02					18 32			18 26	
Knebworth	d			17 32		17 42									18 01		18 06					→			18 31	
Hertford North	d																									
Stevenage 4	d			17 37		17 46	17 50					18 00			18 06		18 11	18 17			←				18 36	18 41
Hitchin 4	d			17 42		17 51	17 56					18 05			18 12		18 17	18 23			18 05				18 42	
Letchworth Garden City	d			17a50		17 56						→	18 10		18 16		18 24							18 40	18 46	
Baldock	d					17 59											18 28							18 43		
Ashwell & Morden	d					18 04											18 33							18 48		
Royston	d					18 09							18 19		18a33		18 37							18 53	19a03	
Meldreth	d					18 13											18 41									
Shepreth	d					18 16											18 44									
Foxton	d					18 18											18 47									
Cambridge	a					18 32							18 36				19 02							19 09		
Arlesey	d						18 01		←									18 28		←						
Biggleswade	d						18 06		17 35									18 33		18 06						
Sandy	d		←				→		17 39									→		18 10						
St Neots	d		17 42						17 47											18 18	18 23		18 42			
Huntingdon	a		17 50						17 55											18 25	18 30		18 49			
	d		17 50						17 56											18 26	18 31		18 50			
Peterborough 8	a	18 06	18 10					18 16	18 22					18 38					18 53	18 55	18 58		19 06			19 12

		FC	FC	FC	FC	GR	FC		FC	FC	FC	FC	FC	FC	FC	FC	GR	GR	FC	FC	FC	FC	FC	FC	FC	FC
		1		1		R 1 🍴 🚲	1		1	1	1 A		1		1		R 1 🍴 🚲	R 1 🍴 🚲	1	1	1	1	1		1	1
London Kings Cross 15 ⊖	d		18 22	18 23		18 33			18 36	18 37	18 45			18 52	18 53		19 00	19 03		19 06	19 07		19 15			19 23
Finsbury Park ⊖	d		18 27	18u28	18 12				18 41					18 57	18u58	18 42				19 11						19 28
Potters Bar	d		18 43											19 13						19 22						
Hatfield	d		18 49									←		19 19						19 28				←	←	
Welwyn Garden City 4	d	←	18 53						18 59			18 53	←	19 23						19 32				19 23	19 32	
Welwyn North	d	18 32	→						19 02			18 56	19 02	→						→				19 26	19 35	
Knebworth	d	18 36							→			19 01	19 06											19 31	19 39	
Hertford North	d				18 41											19 11										
Stevenage 4	d	18 41		18 47	18 53							19 06	19 11		19 17	19 23								19 36	19 43	19 47
Hitchin 4	d	18 47		18 53	18 59							19 12	19 17		19 23	19 29								19 42	19 48	19 53
Letchworth Garden City	d	18 54			19a06						19 10	19 16	19 24			19a36							19 40	19a50	19 54	
Baldock	d	18 58									19 13		19 28												19 58	
Ashwell & Morden	d	19 03									19 18		19 33												20 03	
Royston	d	19 07									19 23	19a33	19 37										19 49		20 07	
Meldreth	d	19 11											19 41												20 11	
Shepreth	d	19 14											19 44												20 14	
Foxton	d	19 17											19 47												20 17	
Cambridge	a	19 32									19 38		20 02										20 08		20 32	
Arlesey	d			18 58			←								19 28				←			←				19 58
Biggleswade	d			19 03			18 33			19 05					19 33				19 03			19 33				→
Sandy	d			→			18 37								→				19 07			19 37				
St Neots	d						18 47			19 14									19 19		19 41	19 45				
Huntingdon	a						18 55			19 22									19 27		19 49	19 53				
	d						18 56			19 22									19 27		19 49	19 53				
Peterborough 8	a					19 22	19 25			19 41							19 46	19 52	19 55		20 05	20 10				

For general notes see front of timetable
For details of catering facilities see Directory of Train Operators

A To Kings Lynn (Table 17)
B The Hull Executive
C To Ely (Table 17)

First Capital Connect will run a Saturday service on Bank Holiday Mondays

London → Stevenage, Cambridge and Peterborough

Network Diagram - see first page of Table 24

		FC	GR	FC	FC		FC	FC	FC	GR	GR	FC	FC	FC	FC	FC	GR	FC	FC	FC	FC	GR	FC	FC	FC	FC
			R 1	1	1		1	1		R 1	R 1	1	1	1	1	1	R 1	1	1	1		R 1	1	1	1	1
							A							A											A	
			✕							✕	✕						☕					☕				
London Kings Cross 15 ⊖	d		19 30		19 36		19 45	19 52		20 00	20 03	20 06	20 07	20 15		20 22	20 30		20 36	20 52		21 00	21 06	21 07	21 15	
Finsbury Park ⊖	d	19 02			19 41			19 57	19 32			20 11				20 27			20 41	20 57	20 32		21 11			
Potters Bar	d				19 51							20 21							20 51				21 21			
Hatfield	d				19 57							20 27			←				20 57				21 27			←
Welwyn Garden City 4	d				20 01							20 31 →			20 31				21 01				21 31 →			21 31
Welwyn North	d				20 04										20 34				21 04							21 34
Knebworth	d				20 08										20 38				21 08							21 38
Hertford North	d	19 35							20 05												21 07					
Stevenage 4	d	19 50			20 12			20 16	20 20						20 42	20 46			21 12	21 16	21 20	21 21				21 42
Hitchin 4	d	19 57			20 17			20 21	20 27						20 47	20 51			21 17	21 21	21 28					21 47
Letchworth Garden City	d	20a05			20a23		20 10	20 28	20a35					20 40	20 51				21a23	21 28	21a35				21 40	21 51
Baldock	d							20 31							20 55					21 31						21 55
Ashwell & Morden	d							20 36							21 00					21 36						22 00
Royston	d						20 19	20 40						20 49	21 04					21 40					21 49	22 04
Meldreth	d							20 44							21 08					21 44						22 08
Shepreth	d							20 47							21 11					21 47						22 11
Foxton	d							20 49							21 14					21 49						22 14
Cambridge	a			←			20 36	21 03						21 06	21 27			←		22 03					22 06	22 27
Arlesey	d			19 58												20 56 →		20 56								
Biggleswade	d			20 03														21 01						21 34		
Sandy	d			20 07														21 05								
St Neots	d			20 14									20 41					21 12						21 42		
Huntingdon	a			20 22									20 49					21 20						21 50		
	d			20 22									20 49					21 20						21 50		
Peterborough 8	a		20 16	20 39						20 46	20 52		21 05				21 20	21 36				21 53		22 07		

		FC	GR		FC	FC	FC	FC	GR	FC	FC	FC	FC	FC	FC	FC	FC	FC	FC	FC	FC	GR	FC	FC		
		1	R 1		1	1	1		R 1	1	1	1	1		1	1		1	1	1	1	R 1	1	1		
											A								B							
			☕						☕													☕				
London Kings Cross 15 ⊖	d	21 22	21 30			21 36	21 52		22 00	22 06	22 15		22 22	22 26	22 36	22 52	←	23 06	23 15		23 22	23 30		23 36		
Finsbury Park ⊖	d	21 27				21 41	21 57	21 32		22 11			22 27	22 32 →	22 41	22 57	22 32	23 11			23 27			23 41		
Potters Bar	d					21 51				22 21					22 51			23 21						23 51		
Hatfield	d					21 57				22 27		←			22 57			23 27		←				23 57		
Welwyn Garden City 4	d					22 01				22 31 →		22 31			23 01			23 31 →		23 31				00 01		
Welwyn North	d					22 04						22 34			23 04					23 34				00 04		
Knebworth	d					22 08						22 38			23 08					23 38				00 08		
Hertford North	d							22 07									23 07									
Stevenage 4	d	21 46				22 12	22 16	22 20				22 42	22 46		23 12	23 16	23 20			23 42	23 46			00 12		
Hitchin 4	d	21 51				22 17	22 21	22 25				22 50	22 54		23 20	23 24	23 28			23 50	23 54			00 20		
Letchworth Garden City	d					22a23	22 28	22a33			22 45	22 54			23a26	23 31	23a36		23 45	23 54				00a29		
Baldock	d						22 31					22 58				23 34				23 58						
Ashwell & Morden	d						22 36					23 03				23 39				00 03						
Royston	d						22 40				22 54	23 07				23 44			23 54	00 07						
Meldreth	d											23 11								00 11						
Shepreth	d											23 14								00 14						
Foxton	d											23 17								00 17						
Cambridge	a				←		22 57				23 10	23 29				00 01			00 10	00 29			←			
Arlesey	d	21 56 →			21 56								22 59								23 59 →		23 59			
Biggleswade	d				22 01								23 04										00 04			
Sandy	d				22 05								23 08										00 08			
St Neots	d				22 12								23 15										00 15			
Huntingdon	a				22 20								23 26										00 26			
	d				22 20								23 26										00 26			
Peterborough 8	a		22 16		22 36				22 46				23 42									00s23	00 42			

For general notes see front of timetable
For details of catering facilities see
Directory of Train Operators

A To Kings Lynn (Table 17)
B Fridays to Kings Lynn (Table 17). Mondays to Thursdays to Ely (Table 17)

Table 25

London → Stevenage, Cambridge and Peterborough

Network Diagram - see first page of Table 24

		FC	FC	FC	FC	FC	FC	FC	FC	FC	FC	FC	FC	GR	FC	FC	FC	FC	FC	FC	GR	FC		GR	FC	FC
		1	1	1	1	1	1	1	1	1	1	1	1	R 1	1	1	1	1	1	1	R 1	1		R 1	1	1
London Kings Cross 15 ⊖	d	23p06	23p22	23p36	00 01	00 04	00 07	00 36	01 06	01 36	05 21	05 45	06 06	06 15		06 22	06 36	06 45		06 52	07 00	07 06		07 10	07 22	07 36
Finsbury Park ⊖	d	23p11	23p27	23p41			00 12	00 41	01 11	01 41	05 26	05 50	06 11			06 27	06 41			06 57		07 11			07 27	07 41
Potters Bar	d	23p21		23p51				00 51		01 58	05 36		06 21		←		06 51					07 21				07 51
Hatfield	d	23p27		23p57				00 57		02 04	05 42		06 27 →		06 27		06 57					07 27				07 57
Welwyn Garden City 4	d	23p31		00 01				01 01		02 08	05 46				06 31		07 01					07 31				08 01
Welwyn North	d	23p34		00 04				01s04		02s11	05 49				06 34		07 04					07 34				08 04
Knebworth	d	23p38		00 08				01s08		02s15	05 53				06 38		07 08					07 38				08 08
Hertford North	d						00 39		01 37										←							
Stevenage 4	d	23p42	23p46	00 12		00s23	00 48	01 12	01 47	02 18	05 57	06 08		06 34	06 42	06 46	07 12 →		07 12	07 16		07 42			07 46	08 12
Hitchin 4	d	23p50	23p54	00 20		00s38	00 56	01 17	01 52	02 23	06 05	06 13			06 47	06 51			07 17	07 21		07 47			07 51	08 17
Letchworth Garden City	d	23p54		00a29		00s41	01 00		02a06			06 16			06 51					07 25		07 51				
Baldock	d	23p58					01 04					06 19			06 55					07 28		07 55				
Ashwell & Morden	d	00 03					01 09					06 24			07 00					07 33		08 00				
Royston	d	00 07				00s50	01 13					06 29			07 04					07 36		08 04				
Meldreth	d	00 11					01 17					06 32			07 08					07 41		08 08				
Shepreth	d	00 14					01 20					06 35			07 11					07 44		08 11				
Foxton	d	00 17					01 23					06 38			07 14					07 46		08 14				
Cambridge	a	00 29				01 07	01 39					06 50			07 27			07 31		07 59		08 27				
Arlesey	d		23p59					01s28			06 10					06 56			07 23						07 56	08 23
Biggleswade	d		00 04		00s40			01s33		02s38	06 15					07 01			07 28						08 01	08 28 →
Sandy	d		00 08					01s37			06 19					07 05			07 32						08 05	
St Neots	d		00 15		00s49			01s45		02s48	06 27					07 12			07 39						08 12	
Huntingdon	a		00 26		01s00			01s55		02s59	06 34					07 20			07 47						08 20	
	d		00 26								06 34					07 20			07 47						08 20	
Peterborough 8	a		00 42		01 20			02 20		03 21	06 55			07 05		07 36			08 05		07 46			07 56	08 36	

		FC	FC	GR	FC	GR	FC	FC	FC	GR	FC	FC	FC	FC	FC	FC	GR	FC	FC	FC	GR		FC	FC	FC	FC
		1	1	R 1	1	R 1	1	1	1	R 1	1	1	1	1	1	1	R 1	1	1	1	R 1		1	1	1	1
London Kings Cross 15 ⊖	d	07 45	07 52	08 00	08 06	08 10		08 15	08 22	08 30			08 36	08 45		08 52	09 00	09 06	09 15	09 22	09 30				09 36	09 45
Finsbury Park ⊖	d		07 57		08 11				08 27				08 41			08 57		09 11		09 27					09 41	
Potters Bar	d				08 21								08 51					09 21							09 51	
Hatfield	d				08 27								08 57					09 27							09 57	
Welwyn Garden City 4	d				08 31								09 01					09 31							10 01	
Welwyn North	d				08 34								09 04					09 34							10 04	
Knebworth	d				08 38								09 08					09 38							10 08	
Hertford North	d														←											
Stevenage 4	d		08 16	08 20	08 42				08 46	08 49		←	09 12 →		09 12	09 16		09 42		09 46	09 49			←	10 12 →	
Hitchin 4	d		08 21		08 47 →				08 51			08 47			09 17	09 21		09 47 →		09 51				09 47		
Letchworth Garden City	d		08 25									08 51				09 25								09 51		
Baldock	d		08 28									08 55				09 28								09 55		
Ashwell & Morden	d											09 00												10 00		
Royston	d		08 36									09 04				09 36								10 04		
Meldreth	d											09 08												10 08		
Shepreth	d											09 11												10 11		
Foxton	d											09 14												10 14		
Cambridge	a	08 31	08 54					09 02				09 27		09 29		09 54			10 01					10 27		10 31
Arlesey	d						←		08 56		←				09 23					09 56			←			
Biggleswade	d						08 28		09 01 →		09 01				09 28					10 01 →			10 01			
Sandy	d						08 32				09 05				09 32								10 05			
St Neots	d						08 39				09 12				09 39								10 12			
Huntingdon	a						08 47				09 20				09 47								10 20			
	d						08 47				09 20				09 47								10 20			
Peterborough 8	a			08 51		08 56	09 05			09 20	09 37				10 05		09 46				10 20		10 37			

		FC	FC	GR	FC	GR	FC	FC	GR	FC	GR	FC	FC	FC	FC	FC	GR	FC	GR	FC		FC	GR	FC	FC	FC
		1	1	R 1	1	R 1	1	1	R 1	1	R 1	1	1	1	1	1	R 1	1	R 1	1		1	R 1	1	1	1
				A					B																	
London Kings Cross 15 ⊖	d		09 52	10 00	10 06	10 10	10 15	10 22	10 30	10 36	10 40			10 45		10 52	11 00	11 06	11 10	11 15		11 22	11 30			11 36
Finsbury Park ⊖	d		09 57		10 11			10 27		10 41						10 57		11 11				11 27				11 41
Potters Bar	d				10 21					10 51								11 21								11 51
Hatfield	d				10 27					10 57								11 27								11 57
Welwyn Garden City 4	d				10 31					11 01								11 31								12 01
Welwyn North	d				10 34					11 04								11 34								12 04
Knebworth	d				10 38					11 08								11 38								12 08
Hertford North	d	←													←											
Stevenage 4	d	10 12	10 16		10 42			10 46		11 12 →			←		11 12	11 16		11 42				11 46	11 50		←	12 12 →
Hitchin 4	d	10 17	10 21		10 47 →			10 51					10 47		11 17	11 21		11 47 →				11 51			11 47	
Letchworth Garden City	d		10 25										10 51			11 25									11 51	
Baldock	d		10 28										10 55			11 28									11 55	
Ashwell & Morden	d												11 00												12 00	
Royston	d		10 36										11 04			11 36									12 04	
Meldreth	d												11 08												12 08	
Shepreth	d												11 11												12 11	
Foxton	d												11 14												12 14	
Cambridge	a		10 54				11 01					←	11 27	11 31		11 54				12 02					12 27	
Arlesey	d	10 23						10 56 →				10 56			11 23							11 56		←		
Biggleswade	d	10 28										11 01			11 28							12 01 →		12 01		
Sandy	d	10 32										11 05			11 32									12 05		
St Neots	d	10 39										11 12			11 39									12 12		
Huntingdon	a	10 47										11 20			11 47									12 20		
	d	10 47										11 20			11 47									12 20		
Peterborough 8	a	11 05		10 46		10 56			11 16		11 26	11 38			12 05		11 46		11 56				12 21	12 39		

For general notes see front of timetable
For details of catering facilities see Directory of Train Operators

A The Flying Scotsman
B The Northern Lights

Table 25

Saturdays

London → Stevenage, Cambridge and Peterborough

Network Diagram - see first page of Table 24

		FC	FC	FC	GR	FC	GR	FC	FC	GR	FC	FC	FC	FC	FC	FC	GR	FC	GR	FC	FC	FC	GR	FC	FC
					R		R			R							R		R				R		
		1	1	1	1	1	1	1	1	1	1	1	1	1	1	1	1	1	1	1	1	1	1	1	1
					A																				
London Kings Cross 15 ⊖	d	11 45		11 52	12 00	12 06	12 10	12 15	12 22	12 30			12 36	12 45		12 52	13 00	13 06	13 10	13 15	13 22		13 30		
Finsbury Park ⊖	d			11 57		12 11			12 27				12 41			12 57		13 11			13 27				
Potters Bar	d					12 21							12 51					13 21							
Hatfield	d					12 27							12 57					13 27							
Welwyn Garden City 4	d					12 31							13 01					13 31							
Welwyn North	d					12 34							13 04					13 34							
Knebworth	d					12 38							13 08					13 38							
Hertford North	d		←												←										
Stevenage 4	d		12 12	12 16		12 42			12 46			←	13 12		13 12	13 16		13 42			13 46		13 49		←
Hitchin 4	d		12 17	12 21		12 47			12 51			12 47	→		13 17	13 21		13 47			13 51				13 47
Letchworth Garden City	d			12 25		→						12 51				13 25		→							13 51
Baldock	d			12 28								12 55				13 28									13 55
Ashwell & Morden	d											13 00													14 00
Royston	d			12 36								13 04				13 36									14 04
Meldreth	d											13 08													14 08
Shepreth	d											13 11													14 11
Foxton	d											13 14													14 14
Cambridge	a	12 31		12 54				13 01			←	13 27		13 29		13 54				14 01					14 27
Arlesey	d		12 23						12 56		12 56				13 23						13 56			←	
Biggleswade	d		12 28						→		13 01				13 28						14 01			14 01	
Sandy	d		12 32								13 05				13 32						→			14 05	
St Neots	d		12 39								13 12				13 39									14 12	
Huntingdon	a		12 47								13 20				13 47							←		14 20	
	d		12 47								13 20				13 47							13 47		14 20	
Peterborough 8	a		13 05		12 46		12 56			13 16	13 36				→		13 46		13 56			14 05	14 19	14 36	

		FC	FC	FC	FC	GR	FC	FC	FC	GR	FC	FC	FC	FC	FC	FC	GR	FC	FC	FC	GR	FC	FC	FC	FC
						R				R							R				R				
		1	1	1	1	1	1	1	1	1	1	1	1	1	1	1	1	1	1	1	1	1	1	1	1
London Kings Cross 15 ⊖	d	13 36	13 45		13 52	14 00	14 06	14 15	14 22	14 30			14 36	14 45		14 52	15 00	15 06	15 15	15 22	15 30			15 36	15 45
Finsbury Park ⊖	d	13 41			13 57		14 11		14 27				14 41			14 57		15 11		15 27				15 41	
Potters Bar	d	13 51					14 21						14 51					15 21						15 51	
Hatfield	d	13 57					14 27						14 57					15 27						15 57	
Welwyn Garden City 4	d	14 01					14 31						15 01					15 31						16 01	
Welwyn North	d	14 04					14 34						15 04					15 34						16 04	
Knebworth	d	14 08					14 38						15 08					15 38						16 08	
Hertford North	d			←											←										
Stevenage 4	d	14 12		14 12	14 16		14 42		14 46			←	15 12		15 12	15 16		15 42		15 46	15 49		←	16 12	
Hitchin 4	d	→		14 17	14 21		14 47		14 51			14 47	→		15 17	15 21		15 47		15 51			15 47	→	
Letchworth Garden City	d				14 25		→					14 51				15 25		→					15 51		
Baldock	d				14 28							14 55				15 28							15 55		
Ashwell & Morden	d											15 00											16 00		
Royston	d				14 36							15 04				15 36							16 04		
Meldreth	d											15 08											16 08		
Shepreth	d											15 11											16 11		
Foxton	d											15 14											16 14		
Cambridge	a		14 29		14 54			15 01			←	15 27		15 31		15 54			16 02				16 27		16 31
Arlesey	d			14 23					14 56		14 56				15 23					15 56		←			
Biggleswade	d			14 28					→		15 01				15 28					16 01		16 01			
Sandy	d			14 32							15 05				15 32					→		16 05			
St Neots	d			14 39							15 12				15 39							16 12			
Huntingdon	a			14 47							15 20				15 47							16 20			
	d			14 47							15 20				15 47							16 20			
Peterborough 8	a			15 05		14 46				15 16	15 36				16 05		15 46				16 20	16 37			

		FC	FC	GR	FC	FC	FC	GR	FC	FC	FC	FC	FC	FC	GR	FC	FC	FC	GR	FC	GR	FC	FC	FC	FC
				R				R							R				R		R				
		1	1	1	1	1	1	1	1	1	1	1	1	1	1	1	1	1	1	1	1	1	1	1	1
London Kings Cross 15 ⊖	d		15 52	16 00	16 06	16 15	16 22	16 30			16 36	16 45		16 52	17 00	17 06	17 15	17 22	17 30	17 36	17 40			17 45	
Finsbury Park ⊖	d		15 57		16 11		16 27				16 41			16 57		17 11		17 27		17 41					
Potters Bar	d				16 21						16 51					17 21				17 51					
Hatfield	d				16 27						16 57					17 27				17 57					
Welwyn Garden City 4	d				16 31						17 01					17 31				18 01					
Welwyn North	d				16 34						17 04					17 34				18 04					
Knebworth	d				16 38						17 08					17 38				18 08					
Hertford North	d	←											←												←
Stevenage 4	d	16 12	16 16		16 42		16 46			←	17 12		17 12	17 16		17 42		17 46	17 50	18 12			←		18 12
Hitchin 4	d	16 17	16 21		16 47		16 51			16 47	→		17 17	17 21		17 47		17 51		→			17 47		18 17
Letchworth Garden City	d		16 25		→					16 51				17 25		→							17 51		
Baldock	d		16 28							16 55				17 28									17 55		
Ashwell & Morden	d									17 00													18 00		
Royston	d		16 36							17 04				17 36									18 04		
Meldreth	d									17 08													18 08		
Shepreth	d									17 11													18 11		
Foxton	d									17 14													18 14		
Cambridge	a		16 54			17 01			←	17 27		17 31		17 54			18 01						18 27	18 31	
Arlesey	d	16 23					16 56		16 56				17 23					17 56				←			18 23
Biggleswade	d	16 28					→		17 01				17 28					18 01				18 01			18 28
Sandy	d	16 32							17 05				17 32					→				18 05			18 32
St Neots	d	16 39							17 12				17 39									18 12			18 39
Huntingdon	a	16 47							17 20				17 47									18 20			18 47
	d	16 47							17 20				17 47									18 20			18 47
Peterborough 8	a	17 05		16 46				17 16	17 36				18 05		17 46				18 21		18 26	18 36			19 05

For general notes see front of timetable
For details of catering facilities see Directory of Train Operators

A The Highland Chieftain

Table 25

Saturdays

London → Stevenage, Cambridge and Peterborough

Network Diagram - see first page of Table 24

		FC	GR	FC	FC	FC	FC	FC	GR	FC	GR	FC	FC	FC	FC	GR		FC	FC	FC	GR	FC	FC	FC	FC	FC
			R						R		R					R					R					
		1	1	1	1	1	1	1	1	1	1	1	1	1	1	1		1	1	1	1	1	1	1	1	1
London Kings Cross 15 ⊖	d	17 52	18 00	18 06	18 08	18 15		18 22	18 35	18 36	18 40		18 45		18 52	19 00		19 06	19 15	19 22	19 30			19 36	19 45	
Finsbury Park ⊖	d	17 57		18 11				18 27		18 41					18 57			19 11		19 27				19 41		
Potters Bar	d			18 21			←			18 51								19 21						19 51		
Hatfield	d			18 27 →			18 27			18 57								19 27						19 57		
Welwyn Garden City 4	d						18 31			19 01								19 31						20 01		
Welwyn North	d						18 34			19 04								19 34						20 04		
Knebworth	d						18 38			19 08								19 38						20 08		
Hertford North	d													←												←
Stevenage 4	d	18 16			18 27		18 42	18 46		19 12				19 12	19 16	19 19		19 42		19 46			←	20 12		20 12
Hitchin 4	d	18 21			18 32		18 47	18 51		→				19 17	19 21			19 47		19 51			19 47	→		20 17
Letchworth Garden City	d	18 25					18 51								19 25			→					19 51			
Baldock	d	18 28					18 55								19 28								19 55			
Ashwell & Morden	d						19 00																20 00			
Royston	d	18 36					19 04								19 36								20 04			
Meldreth	d						19 08																20 08			
Shepreth	d						19 11																20 11			
Foxton	d						19 14																20 14			
Cambridge	a	18 54				19 01	19 27					←	19 29		19 54				20 01			←	20 27		20 29	
Arlesey	d							18 56 →				18 56		19 23						19 56 →		19 56				20 23
Biggleswade	d											19 01		19 28								20 01				20 28
Sandy	d											19 05		19 32								20 05				20 32
St Neots	d				18 46							19 12		19 39								20 12				20 39
Huntingdon	a				18 53							19 20		19 47								20 20				20 47
	d				18 53							19 20		19 47								20 20				20 47
Peterborough 8	a		18 46		19 09				19 21		19 26	19 36		20 05		19 50					20 16	20 36				21 05

		FC	GR	FC	FC	GR	FC	FC	FC	FC	FC	FC	FC	FC	FC	FC	FC	FC	FC	FC	FC	FC	FC	FC		
			R			R																				
		1	1	1	1	1	1	1	1	1	1	1	1	1	1	1	1	1	1			1				
									A				A				A			B	C		B	C		
London Kings Cross 15 ⊖	d	19 52	20 00	20 06	20 22	20 30		20 36	20 52	21 06	21 22	21 36	21 52	22 06	22 22	22 36	23 08	23 12	23 15	23 35	23 35	23 50				
Finsbury Park ⊖	d	19 57		20 11	20 27			20 41	20 57	21 11	21 27	21 41	21 57	22 11	22 27	22 41	23 13	23 17	23 20	23 40	23 41	23 55				
Potters Bar	d			20 21				20 51		21 21		21 51		22 21		22 51			23 30	00 01	00 01					
Hatfield	d			20 27				20 57		21 27		21 57		22 27		22 57			23 36	00 09	00 09		←	←		
Welwyn Garden City 4	d			20 31				21 01		21 31		22 01		22 31		23 01			23 40	00b28	00b30		00 28	00 30		
Welwyn North	d			20 34				21 04		21 34		22 04		22 34		23 04			23 45	→	→		00 31	00 33		
Knebworth	d			20 38				21 08		21 38		22 08		22 38		23 08			23 49				00 35	00 37		
Hertford North	d																									
Stevenage 4	d	20 16		20 42	20 46			21 12	21 16	21 42	21 46	22 12	22 16	22 42	22 46	23 12		23 46	23 55				00 41	00 42		
Hitchin 4	d	20 21		20 47	20 51			21 17	21 21	21 47	21 51	22 17	22 21	22 47	22 51	23 17		23 51	00 02			00s34	00 49	00c56		
Letchworth Garden City	d	20 25		20 51					21 25	21 51			22 25	22 51			23 48		00 06				00a57	01 00		
Baldock	d	20 28		20 55					21 28	21 55			22 28	22 55					00 09					01 04		
Ashwell & Morden	d			21 00						22 00				23 00					00 14					01 09		
Royston	d	20 36		21 04					21 36	22 04			22 36	23 04			23 55		00 19					01 16		
Meldreth	d			21 08						22 08				23 08					00 22					01 20		
Shepreth	d			21 11						22 11				23 11					00 25					01 23		
Foxton	d			21 14						22 14				23 14					00 28					01 25		
Cambridge	a	20 54		21 27			←		21 54	22 27			22 54	23 28			00 15		00 45					01 38		
Arlesey	d				20 56 →		20 56	21 23			21 56	22 23			22 56	23 23		23 56								
Biggleswade	d						21 01	21 28			22 01	22 28			23 01	23 28		00 01				00s43				
Sandy	d						21 05	21 32			22 05	22 32			23 05	23 32		00 05								
St Neots	d						21 12	21 39			22 12	22 39			23 12	23 39		00 12				00s52				
Huntingdon	a						21 20	21 47			22 20	22 47			23 20	23 47		00 20				01s00				
	d						21 20	21 47			22 20	22 47			23 20	23 47		00 20								
Peterborough 8	a		20 46			21 16	21 36	22 05			22 36	23 05			23 43	00 14		00 42				01 19				

For general notes see front of timetable
For details of catering facilities see Directory of Train Operators

A To Kings Lynn (Table 17)
B From 29 March
C Until 22 March

b Arr. 0015
c Arr. 0049

Table 25

Sundays

London → Stevenage, Cambridge and Peterborough

Network Diagram - see first page of Table 24

		FC	FC	FC	FC	FC	FC	FC	FC	FC	FC	FC	FC	FC	FC		FC	FC	FC	FC	FC	FC	FC	FC	FC	FC
		1	1			1	1			1		1	1				1		1	1	1		1	1		1
				A	B			A	B	A	C	C	A	B	B		B	B	B	B	A	B	B	A	B	A
											Bus			Bus	Bus			Bus				Bus			Bus	
London Kings Cross 15 ⊖	d	23p12	23p15	23p35	23p35	23p50	00 04			00 07			00 36				06 01		06 31		06 52		07 01	07 06		07 22
Finsbury Park ⊖	d	23p17	23p20	23p40	23p41	23p55	00 10			00 12			00 41				06 06		06 36		06 57		07 06	07 11		07 27
Potters Bar	d		23p30	00 01	00 01								00 51						06 46				07 16	07 21		
Hatfield	d		23p36	00 09	00 09			←	←				00 57						06 52				07 22	07 27		
Welwyn Garden City 4	d		23p40	00b28	00b30			00b28	00b30				01 03	01 11	01 12				06 57				07 28	07 33		
Welwyn North	d		23p45	→	→			00 31	00 33				01s08		01s22				07 00				07 31	07 36		
Knebworth	d		23p49					00 35	00 37				01s12		01s33		06a32	06 44	07a08			07 14	07a37	07 40	07 42	
Hertford North	d									00 48																
Stevenage 4	d	23p46	23p55				00 36	00 41	00 42	00 56	00 54		01 14	01 31	01a40			06 51			07 16	07 21		07 45	07 49	07 50
Hitchin 4	d	23p51	00 02			00s35	00 44	00 49	00 56	01 00	01a14	01 19	01 19	01 51				07a11		07 26	07 26	07a41		07 52	08a09	08 00
Letchworth Garden City	d		00 06				00s50	00a57	01 00	01 04										07 33	07 33			07 56		
Baldock	d		00 09						01 04	01 09										07 36	07 36			07 59		
Ashwell & Morden	d		00 14						01 09	01 13														08 04		
Royston	d		00 19				01s00		01 16	01 17										07 44	07 44			08 09		
Meldreth	d		00 22						01 20	01 28														08 13		
Shepreth	d		00 25						01 23	01 33														08 16		
Foxton	d		00 28						01 25	01 39														08 18		
Cambridge	a		00 45				01 16		01 38											08 03	08 03			08 34		
Arlesey	d	23p56										01s26	01s26	02s09												08 05
Biggleswade	d	00 01				00s43						01s31	01s31	02s29												08 10
Sandy	d	00 05										01s35	01s35	02s39												08 14
St Neots	d	00 12				00s53						01s43	01s43	02s59												08 21
Huntingdon	a	00 20				01s00						01s50	01s50	03s29												08 29
	d	00 20																								08 29
Peterborough 8	a	00 42				01 19						02 12	02 12	04 04												08 48

		FC	FC	FC	FC	FC	FC		FC	FC	FC	FC	FC	FC	GR	FC	GR	FC	FC	GR	FC	FC		FC	GR	FC
															R		R			R					R	
		1	1		1	1	1		1	1	1		1	1	1	1	1	1	1	1	1	1		1	1	1
		B	B	B	D	E	B		D	A	A	B	B												G	
				Bus								Bus														
London Kings Cross 15 ⊖	d	07 26				07 52	08 01			08 06	08 22			08 52	09 00	09 06	09 10	09 15	09 22	09 30				09 52	10 00	10 06
Finsbury Park ⊖	d	07 31				07 58	08 06			08 11	08 27			08 57		09 11			09 27					09 57		10 11
Potters Bar	d						08 16			08 21						09 21										10 21
Hatfield	d						08 22			08 27						09 27										10 27
Welwyn Garden City 4	d						08 28			08 31						09 31										10 31
Welwyn North	d						08 33			08 36						09 34										10 34
Knebworth	d	07a57		08 02			08a39			08 38		08 44				09 38										10 38
Hertford North	d																									
Stevenage 4	d			08 09		08 16				08 42	08 46	08 51		09 16	09 20	09 42			09 46			←		10 16		10 42
Hitchin 4	d		08 14	08a26	08 28	08 30				08 47	08 51	09a11	09 16	09 21		09 47			09 51			09 47		10 21		10 47
Letchworth Garden City	d				08 31	08 33				08 54				09 25		→						09 51		10 25		→
Baldock	d				08 34	08 36				08 57				09 28								09 54		10 28		
Ashwell & Morden	d				08 42					09 02												09 59				
Royston	d				08 44	08 44			←	09 07				09 36								10 04		10 36		
Meldreth	d				08 50 →				08 50	09 13												10 08				
Shepreth	d								08 53	09 16												10 11				
Foxton	d								08 56	09 18												10 13				
Cambridge	a					09 03			09 07	09 31				09 54				10 01			←	10 26		10 54		
Arlesey	d		08 16								08 56		09 21						09 56 →		09 56					
Biggleswade	d		08 21								09 01		09 26								10 01					
Sandy	d		08 25								09 05		09 30								10 05					
St Neots	d		08 32								09 12		09 37								10 12					
Huntingdon	a		08 40								09 20		09 45								10 20					
	d		08 40								09 20		09 45								10 20					
Peterborough 8	a		09 02								09 39		10 02		09 49		09 54			10 14	10 36				10 45	

For general notes see front of timetable
For details of catering facilities see Directory of Train Operators

- **A** From 30 March
- **B** Until 23 March
- **C** Until 27 January
- **D** Until 23 March. To Kings Lynn (Table 17)
- **E** From 30 March. To Kings Lynn (Table 17)
- **G** **The Flying Scotsman**
- **b** Arr. 0015

Table 25

Sundays

London → Stevenage, Cambridge and Peterborough

Network Diagram - see first page of Table 24

		GR	FC	FC	GR	FC	FC	FC	GR	FC	FC	FC	FC	FC		GR	FC	GR	FC	FC	FC	GR	FC	FC	GR	FC
		R			R				R							R		R				R			R	
		1	1	1	1	1	1	1	1	1	1	1	1	1		1	1	1	1	1	1	1	1	1	1	1
									A													B				
		☕ 🛒			☕ 🛒				☕ 🛒							☕ 🛒		☕ 🛒				☕ 🛒			☕ 🛒	
London Kings Cross 15 ⊖	d	10 10	10 15	10 22	10 30			10 52	11 00	11 06	11 15		11 22	11 52		12 00	12 06	12 10	12 15		12 22	12 30		12 52	13 00	13 06
Finsbury Park ⊖	d			10 27				10 57		11 11			11 27	11 57			12 11				12 27			12 57		13 11
Potters Bar	d									11 21							12 21			←						13 21
Hatfield	d									11 27							12 27 →			12 27						13 27
Welwyn Garden City 4	d									11 31										12 31						13 31
Welwyn North	d									11 34										12 34						13 34
Knebworth	d									11 38										12 38						13 38
Hertford North	d																									
Stevenage 4	d			10 46	10 49		←	11 16		11 42		←	11 46	12 16				12 29		12 42	12 46			13 16	13 19	13 42
Hitchin 4	d			10 51			10 47	11 21		11 47 →		11 47	11 51	12 21						12 47	12 51			13 21		13 47 →
Letchworth Garden City	d						10 51	11 25				11 51		12 25						12 51				13 25		
Baldock	d						10 54	11 28				11 54		12 28						12 54				13 28		
Ashwell & Morden	d						10 59					11 59								12 59						
Royston	d						11 04	11 36				12 04		12 36						13 04				13 36		
Meldreth	d						11 08					12 08								13 08						
Shepreth	d						11 11					12 11								13 11						
Foxton	d						11 13					12 13								13 14						
Cambridge	a		11 06				11 27	11 54			12 01	12 26		12 54					13 02	13 27			←	13 54		
Arlesey	d			10 56		←							11 56								12 56 →		12 56			
Biggleswade	d			11 01 →		11 01							12 01										13 01			
Sandy	d					11 05							12 05										13 05			
St Neots	d					11 12							12 12										13 12			
Huntingdon	a					11 20							12 20										13 20			
	d					11 20							12 20										13 20			
Peterborough 8	a	10 59			11 18	11 36			11 44				12 36			12 44		12 58				13 14	13 36		13 48	

		GR	FC	FC	GR	FC		FC	FC	GR	FC	GR	FC	FC	GR	FC	FC	FC	GR	FC	GR		FC	FC	GR	FC
		R			R					R		R			R				R		R				R	
		1	1	1	1	1		1	1	1	1	1	1	1	1	1	1	1	1	1	1		1	1	1	1
		☕ 🛒			☕ 🛒					☕ 🛒		☕ 🛒			☕ 🛒				☕ 🛒		☕ 🛒				☕ 🛒	
London Kings Cross 15 ⊖	d	13 10	13 15	13 22	13 30				13 52	14 00	14 06	14 10	14 15	14 22	14 30			14 52	15 00	15 06	15 10		15 15	15 22	15 30	
Finsbury Park ⊖	d			13 27					13 57		14 11			14 27				14 57		15 11				15 27		
Potters Bar	d										14 21									15 21						
Hatfield	d										14 27									15 27						
Welwyn Garden City 4	d										14 31									15 31						
Welwyn North	d										14 34									15 34						
Knebworth	d										14 38									15 38						
Hertford North	d																									
Stevenage 4	d			13 46	13 49			←	14 16		14 42			14 46			←	15 16	15 19	15 42				15 46		
Hitchin 4	d			13 51				13 47	14 21		14 47 →			14 51			14 47	15 21		15 47 →				15 51		
Letchworth Garden City	d							13 51	14 25								14 51	15 25								
Baldock	d							13 54	14 28								14 55	15 28								
Ashwell & Morden	d							13 59									15 00									
Royston	d							14 04	14 36								15 04	15 36								
Meldreth	d							14 08									15 08									
Shepreth	d							14 11									15 11									
Foxton	d							14 14									15 14									
Cambridge	a		14 01					14 27	14 54				15 01			←	15 27	15 54					16 01			←
Arlesey	d			13 56		←								14 56 →		14 56								15 56 →		15 56
Biggleswade	d			14 01 →		14 01										15 01										16 01
Sandy	d					14 05										15 05										16 05
St Neots	d					14 12										15 12										16 12
Huntingdon	a					14 20										15 20										16 20
	d					14 20										15 20										16 20
Peterborough 8	a	13 56			14 18	14 37				14 44		14 54			15 14	15 36			15 48		15 54				16 14	16 36

		FC	FC	GR	FC	GR	FC	FC	FC	GR	FC	FC	GR		FC	GR	FC	FC	GR	FC	FC	FC	GR	FC	GR	GR
				R		R				R			R			R			R				R		R	R
		1	1	1	1	1	1	1	1	1	1	1	1		1	1	1	1	1	1	1	1	1	1	1	1
				☕ 🛒		☕ 🛒				☕ 🛒			☕ 🛒			☕ 🛒			☕ 🛒				☕ 🛒		☕ 🛒	☕ 🛒
London Kings Cross 15 ⊖	d		15 52	16 00	16 06	16 10	16 15		16 22	16 30		16 52	17 00		17 06	17 10	17 15	17 22	17 30			17 52	18 00	18 06	18 10	18 14
Finsbury Park ⊖	d		15 57		16 11				16 27			16 57			17 11			17 27				17 57		18 11		
Potters Bar	d				16 21			←							17 21									18 21		
Hatfield	d				16 27 →			16 27							17 27									18 27		
Welwyn Garden City 4	d							16 31							17 31									18 31		
Welwyn North	d							16 34							17 34									18 34		
Knebworth	d							16 38							17 38									18 38		
Hertford North	d																									
Stevenage 4	d	←	16 16			16 29		16 42	16 46	16 49		17 16			17 42			17 46	17 49		←	18 16		18 42		18 42
Hitchin 4	d	15 47	16 21					16 47	16 51			17 21			17 47 →			17 51			17 47	18 21		18 47 →		
Letchworth Garden City	d	15 51	16 25					16 51				17 25									17 51	18 25				
Baldock	d	15 54	16 28					16 55				17 28									17 55	18 28				
Ashwell & Morden	d	15 59						17 00													18 00					
Royston	d	16 04	16 36					17 04				17 36									18 04	18 36				
Meldreth	d	16 08						17 08													18 08					
Shepreth	d	16 11						17 11													18 11					
Foxton	d	16 14						17 14													18 14					
Cambridge	a	16 27	16 54				17 02	17 27				17 54					18 01				18 27	18 54				
Arlesey	d								16 56		←							17 56		←						
Biggleswade	d								17 01 →		17 01							18 01 →		18 01						
Sandy	d										17 05									18 05						
St Neots	d										17 12									18 12						
Huntingdon	a										17 20									18 20						
	d										17 20									18 20						
Peterborough 8	a			16 44		16 58				17 18	17 37		17 44			17 54			18 18	18 38			18 44		18 54	19 12

For general notes see front of timetable
For details of catering facilities see
Directory of Train Operators

A The Northern Lights
B The Highland Chieftain

London → Stevenage, Cambridge and Peterborough

Network Diagram - see first page of Table 24

		FC	FC	GR	GR		FC	FC	FC	GR	FC	GR	FC	FC	GR	GR	FC	FC	FC	GR		FC	FC	FC	GR	FC
		1	1	R 1	R 1		1	1	1	R 1	1	R 1	1	1	R 1	R 1	1	1	1	R 1		1	1	1	R 1	1
London Kings Cross 15 ⊖	d	18 15	18 22	18 30	18 40				18 52	19 00	19 06	19 10	19 15	19 22	19 30	19 35			19 52	20 00		20 06	20 15	20 22	20 30	
Finsbury Park ⊖	d		18 27						18 57		19 11			19 27					19 57			20 11		20 27		
Potters Bar	d										19 21											20 21				
Hatfield	d										19 27											20 27				
Welwyn Garden City 4	d										19 31											20 31				
Welwyn North	d										19 34											20 34				
Knebworth	d										19 38											20 38				
Hertford North	d																									
Stevenage 4	d		18 46	18 50				←	19 16		19 42			19 46	19 49	19 54		←	20 16			20 42		20 46		
Hitchin 4	d		18 51					18 47	19 21		19 47			19 51				19 47	20 21			20 47		20 51		
Letchworth Garden City	d							18 51	19 25		→							19 51	20 25			→				
Baldock	d							18 55	19 28									19 54	20 28							
Ashwell & Morden	d							19 00										19 59								
Royston	d							19 04	19 36									20 04	20 36							
Meldreth	d							19 08										20 08								
Shepreth	d							19 11										20 11								
Foxton	d							19 14										20 13								
Cambridge	a	19 01						19 27	19 54				20 01					20 27	20 54				21 01			←
Arlesey	d		18 56				←							19 56			←							20 56		20 56
Biggleswade	d		19 01 →				19 01							20 01 →			20 01							→		21 01
Sandy	d						19 05										20 05									21 05
St Neots	d						19 12										20 12									21 12
Huntingdon	a						19 20										20 20									21 20
	d						19 20										20 20									21 20
Peterborough 8	a			19 19	19 25		19 36			19 44		19 54			20 18	20 24	20 36			20 44					21 14	21 36

		FC	FC	GR	FC	FC	FC	GR	FC	FC	FC	GR		FC	GR	FC	FC	FC	FC	FC	FC	FC	FC	FC		
		1	1	R 1	1	1	1	R 1	1	1	1	R 1		1	R 1	1	1	1	1	1	1 A	1	1			
London Kings Cross 15 ⊖	d		20 52	21 00	21 06	21 15	21 22	21 30			21 52	22 00		22 06	22 10	22 15		22 22	22 52	23 06	23 15		23 25	23 41		
Finsbury Park ⊖	d		20 57		21 11		21 27				21 57			22 11				22 27	22 57	23 11			23 30	23 47		
Potters Bar	d				21 21									22 21						23 21				00 08		
Hatfield	d				21 27									22 27						23 27		←		00 16		
Welwyn Garden City 4	d				21 31									22 31						23 31 →		23 31		00 20		
Welwyn North	d				21 34									22 34								23 36		00 23		
Knebworth	d				21 38									22 38								23 40		00 28		
Hertford North	d																									
Stevenage 4	d	←	21 16		21 42		21 46			←	22 16			22 42			←	22 46	23 17			23 43	23 49	00 31		
Hitchin 4	d	20 47	21 21		21 47		21 51			21 47	22 21			22 47			22 47	22 51	23 26			23 53	00 04	00a47		
Letchworth Garden City	d	20 51	21 25		→					21 51	22 25			→			22 51		23 30		23 52	23 57				
Baldock	d	20 54	21 28							21 55	22 28						22 55		23 33			23 59				
Ashwell & Morden	d	20 59								22 00							23 00					00 05				
Royston	d	21 04	21 36							22 04	22 36						23 04		23 41		00 01	00 10				
Meldreth	d	21 08								22 08							23 08					00 13				
Shepreth	d	21 11								22 11							23 11					00 16				
Foxton	d	21 14								22 14							23 14					00 18				
Cambridge	a	21 27	21 55			22 01			←	22 27	22 54					23 10	23 29		00 01		00 19	00 35				
Arlesey	d						21 56		21 56									22 56					00 10			
Biggleswade	d						→		22 01									23 01					00 15			
Sandy	d								22 05									23 05					00 18			
St Neots	d								22 12									23 12					00 26			
Huntingdon	a								22 20									23 27					00 33			
	d								22 20									23 27					00 33			
Peterborough 8	a			21 44				22 14	22 36			22 44			22s59			23 49					00 55			

For general notes see front of timetable
For details of catering facilities see
Directory of Train Operators

A To Ely (Table 17)

First Capital Connect will run a Saturday service on Bank Holiday Mondays

Peterborough, Cambridge and Stevenage → London

Network Diagram - see first page of Table 24

Miles	Miles			FC	FC	FC	FC	FC	FC	FC	FC	FC	FC	FC	FC	FC	FC	FC	FC	FC	GR	FC	FC	FC	GR	FC
				MX	MO	MX																				
					1	1	1			1		1	1	1	1	1	1		1	1	R 1		1	1	R 1	1
					A	A							B													
																					✕				✕	
0	—	**Peterborough 8**	d				03 58					05 12								06 00	06 10		06 20	06 32	06 40	06 54
17½	—	Huntingdon	a				04 12					05 26								06 14			06 34	06 46		07 09
—	—		d				04 12					05 26								06 15			06 35	06 47		07 13 →
24¾	—	St Neots	d				04 20					05 34								06 23			06 43	06 55		
32¼	—	Sandy	d				04 27					05 41								06 31				07 03		
35¼	—	Biggleswade	d				04 31					05 45								06 35			06 52	07 07 →		
39¼	—	Arlesey	d				04 36					05 50								06 40						
—	0	**Cambridge**	d		23p13	23p19							05 45				05 48		06 15							
—	7	Foxton	d			23p28											05 57									
—	8	Shepreth	d			23p31											05 59									
—	10	Meldreth	d			23p34											06 02									
—	13	Royston	d		23p26	23p38				05 16					06 00		06 06		06 28							
—	17	Ashwell & Morden	d			23p42				05 21							06 11									
—	21¼	Baldock	d			23p47				05 26							06 16									
—	23¼	Letchworth Garden City	d	23p20	23p36	23p50		04 50	05 20	05 30	05 50			05 59	06 10		06 19	06 27	06 38			06 46				
44½	26	Hitchin 4	d	23p24	23p40	23p54	04 48	04 54	05 24	05 34	05 54	05 58		06 03	06 14		06 24	06 31	06 42	06 46		06 50				
48¾	30¼	**Stevenage 4**	d	23p29	23p45	23p59	04 53	04 59	05 29	05 39	05 59	06 03		06 09	06 19		06 30	06 36	06 47	06 52		06 56				
—	—	Hertford North	a	23p42				05 12	05 42		06 12							06 49								
51¼	33	Knebworth	d		23p48	00 02				05 43				06 13			06 33					07 00				
54¼	36	Welwyn North	d		23p52	00 06				05 47				06 17		←	06 37					07 04				
56	37¾	Welwyn Garden City 4	d		23p55	00 09	05 01			05 50				06 20 →		06 20	06 40			07 00		07 08 →				
58½	40¼	Hatfield	d		23p58	00 12	05 05			05 53						06 23	06 44									
63½	45¼	Potters Bar	d		00 04	00 18	05 11			05 59						06 29	06 49									
73¾	55½	Finsbury Park	⊖ d	00 17	00 20	00 29	05 29	05 47	06a16	06 08	06a46	06 21	06 27		06 38	06 41	06 58	07a15	07 06	07 14						
76¼	58	**London Kings Cross 15**	⊖ a	00 28	00 32	00 42	05 45	05 58		06 19		06 30	06 35		06 46	06 49	07 07		07 15	07 23	07 00		07 27		07 30	

		FC	FC	FC	FC	FC	FC	GR	FC	FC	FC	FC	FC	FC	FC	FC	GR	FC	FC	FC	FC	FC	FC	FC	GR	FC
													MO													
			1	1	1		1	R 1	1		1	1	1	1	1	1	R 1	1		1	1	1	1	1	R 1	
					A							C	D					B								
								✕									✕								✕	
Peterborough 8	d							07 00							07 05	07 14	07 20						07 26	07 34	07 40	
Huntingdon	a										←				07 19	07 28				←			07 40	07 48		
	d										07 13				07 20	07 32 →				07 32			07 40	07 50		
St Neots	d										07 21				07 28					07 40			07 47	07 58		
Sandy	d						←								07 36									08 06		
Biggleswade	d						07 07								07 40							←	07 55	08 10 →		
Arlesey	d						07 12								07 45 →							07 45				
Cambridge	d			06 28	06 45									06 58				07 15								
Foxton	d			06 38										07 08												
Shepreth	d			06 40										07 10												
Meldreth	d			06 43										07 13												
Royston	d		06 44	06 51	06 58							07 14	07 14	07 21				07 28								
Ashwell & Morden	d		06 49	06 56								07 19	07 19	07 26												
Baldock	d		06 54	07 01								07 24	07 24	07 31												
Letchworth Garden City	d	06 54	06 58	07 05	07 09					07 19		07 28	07 28	07 35				07 39								07 54
Hitchin 4	d	06 58	07 02	07 09			07 18			07 23		07 32	07 32	07 39				07 43				07 51				07 58
Stevenage 4	d	07 04	07 08	07 15			07 23			07 29		07 38	07 38	07 45				07 49				07 57				08 05
Hertford North	a	07 16																								08 19
Knebworth	d			07 18					←	07 33		07 41	07 41	07 48							←					
Welwyn North	d			07 22 →		←			07 22	07 37				07 52 →					←		07 52					
Welwyn Garden City 4	d					07 08			07 26	07 42 →									07 42		07 56					
Hatfield	d					07 12			07 30										07 46							
Potters Bar	d					07 18													07 52							
Finsbury Park	⊖ d	07a44	07 28			07 34	07 41		07 46			07 59	07 59						08 09		08 16	08 19				08a47
London Kings Cross 15	⊖ a		07 36		07 40	07 41	07 50	07 53	07 56		08 00	08 07	08 11				08 12	08 15	08 17	08 19	08 25	08 30	08 31		08 34	

		FC	FC	GR	FC	FC	FC	FC	FC	GR	FC	FC	FC	FC	FC	GR	FC	FC	FC	FC	GR	FC	FC	FC	FC	FC
		1	1	R 1	1	1	1	1	1	R 1	1	1	1	1	1	R 1	1	1	1	1	R 1	1	1	1	1	1
					A							A							A		E					
				✕						✕						✕					✕					
Peterborough 8	d			07 46		07 59				08 04					08 16	08 33				08 45	08 51					
Huntingdon	a					08 13					←				08 31					08 59						
	d					08 13 →					08 13				08 31					09 00						
St Neots	d										08 21				08 38					09 07						
Sandy	d							←							08 46		←			09 15			←			
Biggleswade	d							08 10							08 49 →		08 49			09 18 →			09 18			
Arlesey	d							08 15									08 54						09 23			
Cambridge	d		07 26		07 45				07 54			08 15						08 24	08 45					08 54	09 20	
Foxton	d		07 36						08 04									08 34						09 04		
Shepreth	d		07 38						08 06									08 36						09 06		
Meldreth	d		07 43						08 09									08 39						09 09		
Royston	d	07 44	07 51		07 58				08 16			08 28						08 46	08 58					09 15		
Ashwell & Morden	d	07 49	07 56		08 03				08 21									08 51						09 20		
Baldock	d	07 54	08 01		08 07				08 26									08 56						09 25		
Letchworth Garden City	d	07 58	08 05		08 11				08 30			08 38		08 44				09 00	09 08					09 29		←
Hitchin 4	d	08 02	08 09					08 21	08 34					08 48			09 00	09 04					09 29	09 33 →		09 33
Stevenage 4	d	08 08	08 15					08 27	08 40					08 53			09 05	09 10					09 35			09 39
Hertford North	a						←						←													
Knebworth	d		08 18 →				08 18		08 44 →				08 44					09 13				←				09 43
Welwyn North	d						08 22						08 48					09 17 →				09 17				09 47
Welwyn Garden City 4	d						08 26						08 52									09 20				09 50
Hatfield	d																					09 24				09 53
Potters Bar	d																					09 30				09 59
Finsbury Park	⊖ d						08 43	08 47					09 11	09 12			09 23					09 41	09 53			10 08
London Kings Cross 15	⊖ a	08 36		08 42	08 45		08 53	08 58		08 59	09 01	09 12	09 19	09 21		09 26	09 32		09 42		09 45	09 50	10 02		10 11	10 19

For general notes see front of timetable
For details of catering facilities see Directory of Train Operators

A From Kings Lynn (Table 17)
B From Ely (Table 17)
C All Tuesdays to Fridays, also Mondays until 28 January and from 31 March
D 4 February to 24 March
E **The Hull Executive**

First Capital Connect will run a Saturday service on Bank Holiday Mondays

Peterborough, Cambridge and Stevenage → London

Network Diagram - see first page of Table 24

		FC	FC	GR	FC	FC	FC	FC	FC	GR	FC	FC	FC	FC	FC	GR	FC	FC	FC	GR	FC	GR	FC	FC	FC	GR
		1	1	R 1		1	1	1	1	R 1	1	1	1	1	1	R 1		1	1	R 1	1	R 1	1	1	1	R 1
				✖						✖						☕				✖		✖				✖
Peterborough 8	d	09 15	09 23	09 26					09 44	09 48						10 08			10 15	10 18		10 34			10 46	10 57
Huntingdon	a	09 29	09 37						09 58										10 29						11 00	
	d	09 30	09 43						09 59										10 33						11 00	
St Neots	d	09 37	09 51						10 06		←								10 41						11 07	
Sandy	d		09 58						10 14		09 58		←						10 48						11 15	
Biggleswade	d	09 45	→						10 17		10 02		10 17						10 52						11 18	
Arlesey	d								→		10 07		10 22						10 57						→	
Cambridge	d					09 28	09 45							09 55	10 15			10 28					10 45			
Foxton	d													10 05												
Shepreth	d													10 07												
Meldreth	d													10 10												
Royston	d					09 43								10 15				10 43								
Ashwell & Morden	d													10 20												
Baldock	d					09 51								10 25				10 51								
Letchworth Garden City	d				09 50	09 54		09 59						10 29			10 50	10 54						←		
Hitchin 4	d				09 54	09 58		10 03			10 13		10 28	10 33			10 54	10 58	11 03							
Stevenage 4	d	09 56		09 57	09 59	10 03		10 09			10 18		10 33	10 39		10 42	10 59	11 03	11 09					11 09		
Hertford North	a				10 12												11 12		→							
Knebworth	d							10 13						10 43										11 13		
Welwyn North	d							10 17				←		10 47							←			11 17		
Welwyn Garden City 4	d							10 20				10 20		10 50							10 50			11 20		
Hatfield	d							→				10 23		→							10 53			11 23		
Potters Bar	d											10 29									10 59			11 29		
Finsbury Park	⊖ d				10a47	10 21					10 36	10 41	10 51				11a46	11 21			11 08			11 41		
London Kings Cross 15	⊖ a	10 22		10 25		10 30	10 38			10 40	10 46	10 49	11 00		11 04	11 10		11 31		11 13	11 19	11 27	11 35	11 49		11 50

		FC	FC	GR	FC	FC	FC	GR	FC	GR	FC	FC	FC	FC	GR	FC	FC	FC	FC	GR	FC	FC	FC	FC	GR	FC
		1	1	R 1	1	1	1	R 1	1	R 1		1	1	1	R 1	1	1	1	1	R 1	1		1	1	R 1	1
				☕				✖		✖					✖					☕					☕	
Peterborough 8	d			11 06			11 14	11 17		11 31				11 44	11 49					12 14				12 18	12 29	
Huntingdon	a						11 28							11 58										12 33		
	d						11 33							12 00										12 33		
St Neots	d						11 41							12 07		←								12 41		
Sandy	d	←					11 48							12 15		11 48	←							12 48		
Biggleswade	d	11 18					→							12 18		11 52	12 18							12 52		
Arlesey	d													→		11 57								12 57		
Cambridge	d		10 55		11 15							11 28	11 45					11 55	12 15				12 28			12 45
Foxton	d		11 05															12 05								
Shepreth	d		11 07															12 07								
Meldreth	d		11 10															12 10								
Royston	d		11 15									11 43						12 15					12 43			
Ashwell & Morden	d		11 20															12 20								
Baldock	d		11 25									11 51						12 25					12 51			
Letchworth Garden City	d		11 29			←					11 50	11 54						12 29				12 50	12 54			
Hitchin 4	d	11 28	11 33			11 33					11 54	11 58				12 03	12 28	12 33				12 54	12 58	13 03		
Stevenage 4	d	11 33	→			11 39		11 47			11 59	12 03				12 09	12 33	12 39		12 43		12 59	13 03	13 09		
Hertford North	a										12 12											13 12		→		
Knebworth	d					11 43										12 13		12 43								
Welwyn North	d					11 47			←							12 17		12 47			←					
Welwyn Garden City 4	d					11 50			11 50							12 20		12 50			12 50					
Hatfield	d					→			11 53							12 23		→			12 53					
Potters Bar	d								11 59							12 29					12 59					
Finsbury Park	⊖ d	11 51							12 11		12a46	12 21				12 41	12 51				13 08	13a46	13 21			
London Kings Cross 15	⊖ a	12 00		12 03	12 04			12 17	12 19	12 25		12 30	12 33		12 42	12 49	13 00		13 03	13 10	13 19		13 30		13 22	13 33

		FC	GR	FC	FC	FC	GR	FC	GR	FC	FC	FC	FC	FC	FC	GR	FC	GR	FC	FC	GR	FC	FC	FC	FC	FC
		1	R 1	1	1	1	R 1	1	R 1	1		1	1	1	1	R 1	1	R 1	1	1	R 1	1	1		1	1
			✖				☕		✖							✖		✖			☕					
Peterborough 8	d	12 43	12 47				13 06		13 12					13 18	13 43	13 45		14 03			14 10					
Huntingdon	a	12 57												13 32	13 57											
	d	13 00												13 33	13 59											
St Neots	d	13 07			←									13 41	14 06				←							
Sandy	d	13 15			13 15									13 48	14 14				14 14							
Biggleswade	d	→			13 18									13 52	→				14 17							
Arlesey	d													13 57					14 22							
Cambridge	d					12 55		13 15				13 28	13 45							13 55		14 15			14 28	14 45
Foxton	d					13 05														14 05						
Shepreth	d					13 07														14 07						
Meldreth	d					13 10														14 10						
Royston	d					13 15						13 43								14 15					14 43	
Ashwell & Morden	d					13 20														14 20						
Baldock	d					13 25						13 51								14 25					14 51	
Letchworth Garden City	d					13 29				←	13 50	13 54								14 29			←	14 50	14 54	
Hitchin 4	d			←	13 28	13 33				13 33	13 54	13 58		14 03					14 28	14 33			14 33	14 54	14 58	
Stevenage 4	d		13 16	13 09	13 33	→				13 39	13 59	14 03		14 09		14 16			14 33	→			14 39	14 59	15 03	
Hertford North	a										14 12													15 12		
Knebworth	d			13 13						13 43				14 13									14 43			
Welwyn North	d			13 17						13 47				14 17			←						14 47			
Welwyn Garden City 4	d			13 20						13 50				14 20			14 20						14 50			
Hatfield	d			13 23						13 53				→			14 23						14 53			
Potters Bar	d			13 29						13 59							14 29						14 59			
Finsbury Park	⊖ d			13 41	13 51					14 08	14a46	14 21					14 41		14 51				15 11	15a46	15 21	
London Kings Cross 15	⊖ a		13 43	13 48	14 00		14 02	14 05	14 10	14 19		14 30	14 33			14 44	14 49	14 57	15 00		15 05	15 07	15 20		15 30	15 33

For general notes see front of timetable
For details of catering facilities see Directory of Train Operators

First Capital Connect will run a Saturday service on Bank Holiday Mondays

Peterborough, Cambridge and Stevenage → London

Network Diagram - see first page of Table 24

		FC	GR	FC	GR	FC	GR	FC	FC	FC	FC	FC	GR	FC	FC	FC	FC	FC	GR	FC	GR	FC	FC	FC	FC	FC
		1	R 1	1	R 1	1	R 1	1	1	1	1	1	R 1	1		1	1	1	R 1	1	R 1		1	1	1	1
			✕		✕		⊡						✕						✕		A ✕					
Peterborough 8	d	14 18	14 43	14 47	14 50		15 06					15 18	15 23	15 44					15 47		16 02					
Huntingdon	a	14 32		15 01								15 32		15 58												
	d	14 33		15 01								15 33		15 59												
St Neots	d	14 41		15 08								15 41		16 06				←					←			
Sandy	d	14 48		15 16				←				15 48		16 14				15 48					16 14			
Biggleswade	d	14 52		15 19				15 19				→		→				15 52					16 17			
Arlesey	d	14 57		→				15 24										15 57					16 22			
Cambridge	d								14 55	15 15						15 28	15 45							15 55	16 15	
Foxton	d								15 05															16 05		
Shepreth	d								15 07															16 07		
Meldreth	d								15 10															16 10		
Royston	d								15 15							15 43								16 15		
Ashwell & Morden	d								15 20															16 20		
Baldock	d								15 25							15 51								16 25		
Letchworth Garden City	d								15 29		←				15 50	15 54						16 20		16 29		←
Hitchin 4	d	15 03						15 30	15 33		15 33				15 54	15 58		16 03				16 24	16 28	16 33		16 33
Stevenage 4	d	15 09	15 12					15 35	→		15 39		15 52		15 59	16 03		16 09	16 17			16 29	16 33	→		16 39
Hertford North	a														16 12							16 42				
Knebworth	d	15 13									15 43							16 13								16 43
Welwyn North	d	15 17				←					15 47							16 17		←						16 47
Welwyn Garden City 4	d	15 20				15 20					15 50							16 20		16 20						16 50
Hatfield	d	→				15 23					15 53							→		16 23						→
Potters Bar	d					15 29					15 59									16 29						
Finsbury Park ⊖	d					15 41		15 53			16 11				16a46	16 21				16 38		17a10	16 51			
London Kings Cross 15 ⊖	a		15 40		15 44	15 49	15 58	16 02		16 08	16 19		16 22			16 30	16 33		16 46	16 48	16 57		17 01		17 06	

		FC	GR	FC	FC	FC	FC	GR	FC	GR	FC	FC	GR	FC	FC	FC	FC	GR	FC	FC	GR	FC	FC	FC	FC	FC
		1	R 1	1	1	1	1	R 1	1	R 1	1	1	R 1	1	1	1	1	R 1	1	1	R 1	1	1	1	1	1
			✕					B ✕		✕			✕					✕			✕					
Peterborough 8	d	16 14	16 17				16 45	16 48		16 56			17 04				17 18	17 27		17 47	17 49					
Huntingdon	a	16 28					16 59										17 33			18 01						
	d	16 33					16 59										17 33			18 01						
St Neots	d	16 41					17 06		←								17 41			18 08						
Sandy	d	16 48					17 14		16 48		←						17 48			18 16			←			
Biggleswade	d	→					17 17		16 52		17 17						17 52			18 19			18 19			
Arlesey	d						→		16 57		17 22						17 57			→			18 24			
Cambridge	d				16 24	16 45						16 55		17 15		17 24			17 45					17 55	18 15	
Foxton	d				16 33							17 05				17 33								18 05		
Shepreth	d				16 35							17 07				17 35								18 07		
Meldreth	d				16 38							17 10				17 38								18 10		
Royston	d				16 43							17 15				17 43								18 15		
Ashwell & Morden	d				16 47							17 20				17 47								18 20		
Baldock	d				16 52							17 25				17 52								18 25		
Letchworth Garden City	d				16 55							17 29			←	17 55								18 29		←
Hitchin 4	d				17 00				17 03		17 28	17 33			17 33	18 00	18 03					←	18 30	18 33		18 33
Stevenage 4	d		16 48		17 05				17 09		17 33	→	17 34		17 39	18 05	18 09					18 09	18 35	→		18 39
Hertford North	a																→									
Knebworth	d								17 13						17 43							18 13				18 43
Welwyn North	d			←					17 17						17 47							18 17				18 47
Welwyn Garden City 4	d			16 50					17 20						17 50							18 20				18 50
Hatfield	d			16 53					17 23						17 53							18 23				18 53
Potters Bar	d			16 59					17 29						17 59							18 29				18 59
Finsbury Park ⊖	d			17 11	17 23				17 38		17 51				18 08	18 23						18 41	18 53			19 11
London Kings Cross 15 ⊖	a		17 15	17 19	17 33	17 36		17 41	17 48	17 50	18 01		18 04	18 08	18 18	18 33		18 23	18 38		18 45	18 52	19 02		19 05	19 20

		FC	FC	GR	FC	FC	FC	GR	FC	FC	FC	FC	FC	GR	FC	GR	FC	FC	FC	FC	GR	FC	FC	FC	FC	FC
		1	1	R 1	1	1	1	R 1	1	1	1	1	1	R 1	1	R 1	1	1	1	1	R 1	1		1	1	1
		C		✕				✕						✕		✕	C				✕					C
Peterborough 8	d		18 18	18 26			18 45	19 07					19 15	19 20		19 26				19 41	19 46					
Huntingdon	a		18 32				18 59						19 29							19 56						
	d		18 33				18 59						19 33							19 59						
St Neots	d		18 41				19 06						19 41						←	20 06				←		
Sandy	d		18 48				19 14		←				19 48						19 48	20 14				20 14		
Biggleswade	d		18 52				19 17		19 17				→						19 52	→				20 17		
Arlesey	d		18 57				→		19 22										19 57					20 22		
Cambridge	d	18 24			18 45					18 55	19 15						19 24	19 45							19 55	20 28
Foxton	d	18 33								19 05							19 33								20 05	
Shepreth	d	18 35								19 07							19 35								20 07	
Meldreth	d	18 38								19 10							19 38								20 10	
Royston	d	18 43								19 15							19 43								20 15	20 43
Ashwell & Morden	d	18 47								19 20							19 47								20 20	
Baldock	d	18 52								19 25							19 52								20 25	20 51
Letchworth Garden City	d	18 55								19 29		←					19 55						20 20		20 29	20 54
Hitchin 4	d	19 00	19 03			←			19 28	19 33		19 33					20 00		20 03				20 24	20 28	20 33	20 58
Stevenage 4	d	19 05	19 09			19 09			19 33	→		19 39		19 50			20 05		20 09		20 15		20 29	20 33	20 39	21 03
Hertford North	a		→																				20 42			
Knebworth	d					19 13						19 43							20 13						20 43	
Welwyn North	d					19 17						19 47			←				20 17			←			20 47	
Welwyn Garden City 4	d					19 20						19 50			19 50				20 20			20 20			20 50	
Hatfield	d					19 23						→			19 53				→			20 23			20 53	
Potters Bar	d					19 29									19 59							20 29			20 59	
Finsbury Park ⊖	d	19 23				19 41			19 52						20 11		20 23					20 38	21a17	20 51	21 11	21 21
London Kings Cross 15 ⊖	a	19 33		19 18	19 36	19 48		19 59	20 03		20 10			20 18	20 19	20 21	20 33	20 36			20 42	20 49		21 00	21 19	21 30

For general notes see front of timetable
For details of catering facilities see Directory of Train Operators

A The Northern Lights
B The Flying Scotsman
C From Kings Lynn (Table 17)

First Capital Connect will run a Saturday service on Bank Holiday Mondays

Peterborough, Cambridge and Stevenage → London

Network Diagram - see first page of Table 24

		FC	GR	GR	FC	GR	FC	GR	FC	FC	GR	FC	FC	FC	FC	FC	FC	GR	FC	FC	FC	GR	FC	FC		
			R	R		R		R			R							R				R				
		1	1	1	1	1	1	1		1	1		1	1		1		1	1	1		1		1		
													A						A					A		
			☕	☕		X		☕			X							☕				☕				
Peterborough 8	d	20 18	20 25	20 38		20 46		21 12			21 21			21 28				22 15		22 25		22 59				
Huntingdon	a	20 32												21 42						22 39						
	d	20 33												21 42						22 39						
St Neots	d	20 41												21 49						22 46						
Sandy	d	20 48												21 57						22 54						
Biggleswade	d	20 52												22 00						22 57						
Arlesey	d	20 57												22 05						23 02						
Cambridge	d				20 45					20 55			21 28			21 55			22 28					23 19		
Foxton	d									21 05						22 05								23 28		
Shepreth	d									21 07						22 07								23 31		
Meldreth	d									21 10						22 10								23 34		
Royston	d									21 15			21 43			22 15			22 43					23 38		
Ashwell & Morden	d									21 20						22 20								23 42		
Baldock	d									21 25			21 51			22 25			22 51					23 47		
Letchworth Garden City	d								21 20	21 29			21 54		22 20	22 29			22 54		23 20			23 50		
Hitchin 4	d	21 03					←		21 24	21 33		←	21 58	22 11	22 24	22 33	←		22 58	23 11	23 24			23 54		
Stevenage 4	d	21 09				21 17	21 09		21 29	21 39	21 51	21 29	22 03	22 17	22 29	22 39	22 29	22s51	23 03	23 17	23 29	23s35	←	23 59		
Hertford North	a	→							→			21 42			→		22 42				23 42		23 42			
Knebworth	d						21 13			21 43				22 20		22 43				23 20	→			00 02		
Welwyn North	d						21 17			21 47				22 24		22 47				23 24				00 06		
Welwyn Garden City 4	d						21 20			21 50				22 27		22 50				23 27				00 09		
Hatfield	d						21 23			21 53				22 30		22 53				23 30				00 12		
Potters Bar	d						21 29			21 59				22 36		22 59				23 36				00 18		
Finsbury Park	⊖ d						21 38			22 11		22 17	22 21	22 44		23 11	23 17		23 21	23s50			00 17	00 29		
London Kings Cross 15	⊖ a		21 17	21 33	21 36	21 44	21 48	22 04		22 19	22 19	22 26	22 30	22 56		23 21	23 25	23 32	23 35	00 01		00 15	00 28	00 42		

Saturdays

		FC	FC	FC	FC	FC	FC	FC	FC	FC	FC	GR	FC	FC	FC	GR	FC	FC	FC	FC	FC	GR		FC	FC	FC
												R				R						R				
			1	1		1	1	1	1	1	1	1	1	1	1	1	1	1	1	1	1	1		1	1	1
			A																							
												☕				☕						☕				
Peterborough 8	d			03 58			05 14	05 45			06 18	06 37			06 45	07 09				07 18	07 44	07 48				
Huntingdon	a			04 12			05 28	05 59			06 32				06 59					07 32	07 58					
	d			04 12			05 28	05 59			06 33				06 59					07 33	07 59					
St Neots	d			04 20			05 36	06 06			06 41				07 06					07 41	08 06					
Sandy	d			04 27			05 43	06 14			06 48				07 14					07 48	08 14				←	
Biggleswade	d			04 31			05 47	06 17			06 52				07 17					07 52	08 17				08 17	
Arlesey	d			04 36			05 52	06 22			06 57				07 22					07 57	→				08 22	
Cambridge	d		23p19						05 55	06 28			06 45				06 55	07 28	07 45							07 55
Foxton	d		23p28						06 05								07 05									08 05
Shepreth	d		23p31						06 07								07 07									08 07
Meldreth	d		23p34						06 10								07 10									08 10
Royston	d		23p38			05 16			06 15	06 43							07 15	07 43								08 15
Ashwell & Morden	d		23p42			05 21			06 20								07 20									08 20
Baldock	d		23p47			05 26			06 25	06 51							07 25	07 51								08 25
Letchworth Garden City	d	23p20	23p50		04 50	05 30			06 29	06 54							07 29	07 54								08 29
Hitchin 4	d	23p24	23p54	04 48	04 54	05 33	06 03	06 28	06 33	06 58	07 03			←	07 28		07 33	07 58		08 03				←	08 28	08 33
Stevenage 4	d	23p29	23p59	04 53	04 59	05 39	06 09	06 33	06 39	07 03	07 09			07 09	07 33		07 39	08 03		08 09				08 09	08 33	→
Hertford North	a	23p42			05 12						→									→						
Knebworth	d		00 02			05 43	06 13		06 43					07 13			07 43							08 13		
Welwyn North	d		00 06			05 47	06 17		06 47					07 17			07 47							08 17		
Welwyn Garden City 4	d		00 09	05 01		05 50	06 20		06 50					07 20			07 50							08 20		
Hatfield	d		00 12	05 05		05 53	06 23		06 53					07 23			07 53							08 23		
Potters Bar	d		00 18	05 11		05 59	06 29		06 59					07 29			07 59							08 29		
Finsbury Park	⊖ d	00 17	00 29	05 29	05 47	06 11	06 41	06 51	07 08	07 21				07 41	07 51		08 08	08 21						08 41	08 51	
London Kings Cross 15	⊖ a	00 28	00 42	05 45	05 55	06 21	06 49	07 02	07 19	07 32		07 29	07 34	07 49	07 59	08 04	08 19	08 32	08 33			08 40		08 49	09 02	

For general notes see front of timetable
For details of catering facilities see
Directory of Train Operators

A From Kings Lynn (Table 17)

Table 25

Peterborough, Cambridge and Stevenage → London

Network Diagram - see first page of Table 24

		GR	FC	FC	FC	FC	GR	GR	FC	FC	FC	GR	GR	FC	FC	FC	FC	FC	GR	FC	FC		GR	GR	FC	FC
		R					R	R				R	R						R				R	R		
		1	1	1	1	1	1	1	1	1	1	1	1	1	1	1	1	1	1	1	1		1	1	1	1
		🍴 🛒					🍴 🛒	🍴 🛒				🍴 🛒	🍴 🛒						🍴 🛒				🍴 🛒	🍴 🛒		
Peterborough 8	d	08 09				08 18	08 26	08 32			08 45	08 57	09 07				09 12		09 15				09 26	09 33		
Huntingdon	a					08 32					08 59						09 26			←						
	d					08 33					08 59						09 26			09 26						
St Neots	d					08 41					09 06						→			09 34						
Sandy	d					08 48					09 14			←												
Biggleswade	d					08 52					09 17			09 17												
Arlesey	d					08 57					→			09 22												
Cambridge	d		08 15		08 28				08 45						08 55	09 15									09 28	09 45
Foxton	d														09 05											
Shepreth	d														09 07											
Meldreth	d														09 10											
Royston	d				08 43										09 15										09 43	
Ashwell & Morden	d														09 20											
Baldock	d				08 51										09 25										09 51	
Letchworth Garden City	d			←	08 54										09 29			←							09 54	
Hitchin 4	d			08 33	08 58	09 03				←				09 28	09 33			09 33							09 58	
Stevenage 4	d			08 39	09 03	09 09				09 09				09 33	→			09 39	09 45						10 03	
Hertford North	a					→																				
Knebworth	d			08 43						09 13								09 43								
Welwyn North	d			08 47						09 17								09 47			←					
Welwyn Garden City 4	d			08 50						09 20								09 50			09 50					
Hatfield	d			08 53						09 23								→			09 53					
Potters Bar	d			08 59						09 29											09 59					
Finsbury Park	⊖ d			09 08	09 21					09 41				09 51							10 08				10 21	
London Kings Cross 15	⊖ a	09 03	09 06	09 19	09 32		09 18	09 26	09 33	09 49		09 51	10 00	10 02		10 05			10 13	10 15	10 19		10 20	10 27	10 32	10 34

		FC	FC	FC	GR	GR	FC	FC	FC	FC	FC	GR	FC	FC	FC	GR	FC	FC	FC	FC		FC	GR	FC	GR	FC
					R	R						R				R							R		R	
		1	1	1	1	1	1	1	1	1	1	1	1	1	1	1	1	1	1	1		1	1	1	1	1
					🍴 🛒	🍴 🛒						🍴 🛒				🍴 🛒							🍴 🛒		🍴 🛒	
Peterborough 8	d			09 45	09 48	10 06					10 18	10 33			10 45	10 54						11 11	11 16		11 32	
Huntingdon	a			09 59							10 32				10 59							11 27				
	d		09 33	09 59							10 33				10 59							11 33				
St Neots	d		09 41	10 06							10 41			←	11 06							11 41				
Sandy	d		09 48	10 14			←				10 48			10 48	11 14		←					11 48				
Biggleswade	d		09 52	10 17			10 17				→			10 52	11 17		11 17					→				
Arlesey	d		09 57	→			10 22							10 57	→		11 22									
Cambridge	d	09 55						10 15		10 28			10 45					10 55	11 15							11 28
Foxton	d	10 05																11 05								
Shepreth	d	10 07																11 07								
Meldreth	d	10 10																11 10								
Royston	d	10 15								10 43								11 15								11 43
Ashwell & Morden	d	10 20																11 20								
Baldock	d	10 25								10 51								11 25								11 51
Letchworth Garden City	d	10 29							←	10 54								11 29		←						11 54
Hitchin 4	d	10 33	10 03				10 28		10 33	10 58				11 03			11 28	11 33		11 33						11 58
Stevenage 4	d	→	10 09				10 33		10 39	11 03		11 03		11 09			11 33	→		11 39			11 47			12 03
Hertford North	a																									
Knebworth	d		10 13						10 43					11 13						11 43						
Welwyn North	d		10 17						10 47					11 17						11 47				←		
Welwyn Garden City 4	d		10 20						10 50					11 20						11 50				11 50		
Hatfield	d		10 23						10 53					11 23						→				11 53		
Potters Bar	d		10 29						10 59					11 29										11 59		
Finsbury Park	⊖ d		10 41				10 51		11 08	11 21				11 41			11 51							12 08		12 21
London Kings Cross 15	⊖ a		10 49		10 41	10 58	11 02	11 05	11 19	11 32		11 32	11 35	11 49		11 50	12 02		12 03				12 14	12 19	12 24	12 32

		FC	FC	GR	FC	FC	FC	FC	GR	FC	FC	FC	GR	FC	FC	GR	FC	GR	FC		FC	FC	FC	FC	FC	FC
				R					R				R			R		R								
		1	1	1	1	1	1	1	1	1	1	1	1	1	1	1	1	1	1		1	1	1	1	1	1
				🍴 🛒					🍴 🛒				🍴 🛒			🍴 🛒		🍴 🛒								
Peterborough 8	d		11 45	11 48					12 15			12 18	12 34		12 45	12 50		13 07								13 18
Huntingdon	a		11 59									12 33			12 59											13 32
	d		11 59									12 33			12 59											13 33
St Neots	d		12 06		←							12 41			13 06		←									13 41
Sandy	d		12 14		11 48	←						12 48			13 14		12 48		←							13 48
Biggleswade	d		12 17		11 52	12 17						→			13 17		12 52		13 17							13 52
Arlesey	d		→		11 57	12 22									→		12 57		13 22							13 57
Cambridge	d	11 45					11 55	12 15			12 28			12 45							12 55	13 15		13 28	13 45	
Foxton	d						12 05														13 05					
Shepreth	d						12 07														13 07					
Meldreth	d						12 10														13 10					
Royston	d						12 15				12 43										13 15			13 43		
Ashwell & Morden	d						12 20														13 20					
Baldock	d						12 25				12 51										13 25			13 51		
Letchworth Garden City	d						12 29			←	12 54										13 29		←	13 54		
Hitchin 4	d				12 03	12 28	12 33			12 33	12 58						13 03		13 28		13 33		13 33	13 58		14 03
Stevenage 4	d				12 09	12 33	→			12 39	13 03		13 03				13 09		13 33		→		13 39	14 03		14 09
Hertford North	a																									
Knebworth	d				12 13					12 43							13 13						13 43			14 13
Welwyn North	d				12 17					12 47							13 17						13 47			14 17
Welwyn Garden City 4	d				12 20					12 50							13 20						13 50			14 20
Hatfield	d				12 23					12 53							13 23						13 53			→
Potters Bar	d				12 29					12 59							13 29						13 59			
Finsbury Park	⊖ d				12 41	12 51				13 08	13 21						13 41		13 51				14 08	14 21		
London Kings Cross 15	⊖ a	12 33		12 41	12 49	13 02		13 03	13 10	13 19	13 32		13 33	13 35		13 44	13 49	13 59	14 02			14 05	14 19	14 32	14 34	

For general notes see front of timetable
For details of catering facilities see
Directory of Train Operators

Peterborough, Cambridge and Stevenage → London

Network Diagram - see first page of Table 24

		FC	GR	FC	FC	FC	FC	GR	FC	FC	FC	GR	FC	FC	GR	FC	GR	FC		FC	FC	FC	FC	FC	GR	FC
		1	R 1	1	1	1	1	R 1	1	1	1	R 1	1	1	R 1	1	R 1	1		1	1	1	1	1	R 1	1
																	A									
Peterborough 8	d	13 42	13 48					14 13			14 18	14 29		14 44	14 49		15 04							15 18	15 38	
Huntingdon	a	13 56									14 32			14 58										15 32		
	d	13 59									14 33			14 59										15 33		
St Neots	d	14 06			←						14 41			15 06										15 41		
Sandy	d	14 14			14 14						14 48			15 14				←						15 48		
Biggleswade	d	→			14 17						14 52			15 17				15 17						15 52		
Arlesey	d				14 22						14 57			→				15 22						15 57		
Cambridge	d					13 55	14 15			14 28			14 45							14 55	15 15		15 28			15 45
Foxton	d					14 05														15 05						
Shepreth	d					14 07														15 07						
Meldreth	d					14 10														15 10						
Royston	d					14 15				14 43										15 15			15 43			
Ashwell & Morden	d					14 20														15 20						
Baldock	d					14 25				14 51										15 25			15 51			
Letchworth Garden City	d					14 29			←	14 54										15 29		←	15 54			
Hitchin 4	d				14 28	14 33			14 33	14 58	15 03					←		15 28		15 33		15 33	15 58	16 03		
Stevenage 4	d		14 17		14 33	→			14 39	15 03	15 09					15 09		15 33		→		15 39	16 03	16 09		
Hertford North	a										→													→		
Knebworth	d								14 43							15 13						15 43				
Welwyn North	d			←					14 47							15 17						15 47				
Welwyn Garden City 4	d			14 20					14 50							15 20						15 50				
Hatfield	d			14 23					14 53							15 23						15 53				
Potters Bar	d			14 29					14 59							15 29						15 59				
Finsbury Park ⊖	d			14 41	14 51				15 08	15 21						15 41		15 51				16 08	16 21			
London Kings Cross 15 ⊖	a		14 44	14 49	15 02		15 03	15 10	15 19	15 32		15 21	15 33		15 41	15 49	15 58	16 02			16 05	16 19	16 32		16 30	16 36

		FC	GR	FC	FC	FC	FC	FC	FC	GR	FC	FC	FC	FC	GR	FC	FC		FC	FC	GR	FC	FC	FC	GR	FC
		1	R 1	1	1	1	1	1	1	R 1	1	1	1	1	R 1	1	1		1	1	R 1	1	1	1	R 1	1
															B											
Peterborough 8	d	15 45	15 50						16 18	16 31				16 43	16 46						17 12			17 18	17 36	
Huntingdon	a	15 59							16 32					16 57										17 32		
	d	15 59							16 33					16 59										17 33		
St Neots	d	16 06			←				16 41				←	17 06			←							17 41		
Sandy	d	16 14			16 14				16 48				16 48	17 14			17 14							17 48		
Biggleswade	d	→			16 17				→				16 52	→			17 17							17 52		
Arlesey	d				16 22								16 57				17 22							17 57		
Cambridge	d					15 55	16 15				16 28	16 45							16 55	17 15			17 28			17 45
Foxton	d					16 05													17 05							
Shepreth	d					16 07													17 07							
Meldreth	d					16 10													17 10							
Royston	d					16 15					16 43								17 15				17 43			
Ashwell & Morden	d					16 20													17 20							
Baldock	d					16 25					16 51								17 25				17 51			
Letchworth Garden City	d					16 29		←			16 54								17 29			←	17 54			
Hitchin 4	d			←	16 28	16 33		16 33			16 58		17 03				17 28		17 33			17 33	17 58	18 03		
Stevenage 4	d		16 19	16 09	16 33	→		16 39		17 00	17 03		17 09		17 16		17 33		→			17 39	18 03	18 09		
Hertford North	a																							→		
Knebworth	d			16 13				16 43					17 13									17 43				
Welwyn North	d			16 17				16 47					17 17			←						17 47				
Welwyn Garden City 4	d			16 20				16 50					17 20			17 20						17 50				
Hatfield	d			16 23				16 53					→			17 23						17 53				
Potters Bar	d			16 29				16 59								17 29						17 59				
Finsbury Park ⊖	d			16 41	16 51			17 08			17 21					17 41	17 51					18 08	18 21			
London Kings Cross 15 ⊖	a		16 47	16 49	17 02		17 02	17 19		17 28	17 32	17 35			17 43	17 49	18 02			18 05	18 10	18 19	18 32		18 28	18 34

		FC	GR	FC	FC	FC	FC	FC	FC	FC	FC	FC	GR	FC	FC	FC		GR	FC	FC	FC	GR	FC	FC	FC	FC
		1	R 1	1	1	1	1	1	1	1	1	1	R 1	1	1	1		R 1	1	1	1	R 1	1	1	1	1
																					C					
Peterborough 8	d	17 44	17 50								18 18	18 43	18 48					19 12	19 18			19 38		19 45		
Huntingdon	a	17 58									18 32	18 57							19 32					19 59		
	d	17 59									18 33	18 59							19 33					19 59		
St Neots	d	18 06			←						18 41	19 06							19 41				←	20 06		
Sandy	d	18 14			18 14						18 48	19 14			←				19 48				19 48	20 14		
Biggleswade	d	→			18 17						18 52	19 17			19 17				→				19 52	20 17		
Arlesey	d				18 22						18 57	→			19 22								19 57	20 22		
Cambridge	d					17 55	18 15		18 28	18 45						18 55					19 28				19 55	20 28
Foxton	d					18 05										19 05									20 05	
Shepreth	d					18 07										19 07									20 07	
Meldreth	d					18 10										19 10									20 10	
Royston	d					18 15			18 43							19 15					19 43				20 15	20 43
Ashwell & Morden	d					18 20										19 20									20 20	
Baldock	d					18 25			18 51							19 25					19 51				20 25	20 51
Letchworth Garden City	d					18 29		←	18 54							19 29					19 54				20 29	20 54
Hitchin 4	d			←	18 28	18 33		18 33	18 58		19 03			←	19 28	19 33					19 58		20 03	20 28	20 33	20 58
Stevenage 4	d		18 19	18 09	18 33	→		18 39	19 03		19 09			19 09	19 33	19 39		19 43			20 03	20 07	20 09	20 33	20 39	21 03
Hertford North	a										→															
Knebworth	d			18 13				18 43						19 13		19 43							20 13		20 43	
Welwyn North	d			18 17				18 47						19 17		19 47				←			20 17		20 47	
Welwyn Garden City 4	d			18 20				18 50						19 20		19 50				19 50			20 20		20 50	
Hatfield	d			18 23				18 53						19 23		→				19 53			20 23		→	
Potters Bar	d			18 29				18 59						19 29						19 59			20 29			
Finsbury Park ⊖	d			18 41	18 51			19 08	19 21					19 41	19 51					20 08	20 21		20 41	20 51		21 21
London Kings Cross 15 ⊖	a		18 46	18 49	19 02		19 03	19 19	19 32	19 33			19 40	19 49	20 02			20 12		20 19	20 32	20 35	20 49	21 02		21 32

For general notes see front of timetable
For details of catering facilities see
Directory of Train Operators

A The Highland Chieftain
B The Flying Scotsman
C From Kings Lynn (Table 17)

Table 25

Saturdays

Peterborough, Cambridge and Stevenage → London

Network Diagram - see first page of Table 24

		FC	GR	FC	FC	FC	GR	FC	FC	FC	FC	GR	FC	FC	FC	FC	GR	FC	FC	FC	FC	FC	FC	FC
		1	R 1	1	1	1	R 1	1	1	1	1	R 1	1	1	1	1	R 1	1	1	1	1	1	1	1
														A							A			
			🍴				🍴					🍴					🍴							
Peterborough 8	d	20 14	20 17			20 45	20 51				21 15	21 19				21 45	21 51					22 18	22 42	
Huntingdon	a	20 28				20 59					21 29					21 59						22 32	22 56	
	d	20 33				20 59					21 33					21 59						22 33	22 56	
St Neots	d	20 41			←	21 06			←		21 41				←	22 06			←			22 41	23 03	
Sandy	d	20 48			20 48	21 14			21 14		21 48				21 48	22 14			22 14			22 48	23 11	
Biggleswade	d	→			20 52	→			21 17		→				21 52	→			22 17			22 52	23 14	
Arlesey	d				20 57				21 22						21 57				22 22			22 57	23 19	
Cambridge	d									20 55				21 28						21 55	22 28			23 06
Foxton	d									21 05										22 05				23 15
Shepreth	d									21 07										22 07				23 18
Meldreth	d									21 10										22 10				23 21
Royston	d									21 15				21 43						22 15	22 43			23 25
Ashwell & Morden	d									21 20										22 20				23 29
Baldock	d									21 25				21 51						22 25	22 51			23 34
Letchworth Garden City	d									21 29				21 54						22 29	22 54			23 37
Hitchin 4	d				21 03				21 28	21 33				21 58	22 03				22 28	22 33	22 58	23 03	23 25	23 41
Stevenage 4	d		20 48		21 09		21 20		21 33	21 39		21 51		22 03	22 09		22 20		22 33	22 39	23 03	23 09	23 30	23 46
Hertford North	a																							
Knebworth	d				21 13					21 43					22 13					22 43		23 13		23 49
Welwyn North	d			←	21 17			←		21 47			←		22 17			←		22 47		23 17		23 53
Welwyn Garden City 4	d			20 50	21 20 →			21 20		21 50 →			21 50		22 20 →			22 20		22 50		23 20		23 56
Hatfield	d			20 53				21 23					21 53					22 23		22 53		23 23		23 59
Potters Bar	d			20 59				21 29					21 59					22 29		22 59		23 29		00 05
Finsbury Park	⊖ d			21 08				21 41	21 51				22 08	22 21				22 41	23 06	23 16	23 34	23 44	23 55	00s23
London Kings Cross 15	⊖ a		21 15	21 19			21 48	21 49	22 02			22 17	22 19	22 32			22 47	22 49	23 16	23 30	23 47	23 53	00 07	00 34

Sundays

		FC	FC	FC	FC	FC	FC	FC	FC	FC	FC	FC	FC	FC	FC	FC	FC	FC	FC	FC	FC	FC	FC	FC	FC	FC
		1		1			1		1	1	1		1	1	1			1	1	1			1	1		1
			B	B	C	C	D	E	B	G	B	B	E	G	B	E	C	G	B	B	B	C	H	G	C	B
			🚌		🚌	🚌		🚌				🚌				🚌	🚌				🚌	🚌			🚌	
Peterborough 8	d				04 27	05 27	05 50						06 45	06 45								06 45	07 45		07 45	
Huntingdon	a				05 02	06 02	06 04						06 59	06 59								07 20	07 59		08 20	
	d				05 02	06 02	06 04						06 59	06 59								07 20	07 59			
St Neots	d				05 32	06 32	06 11						07 06	07 06			←					07 50	08 06			
Sandy	d				05 52	06 52	06 19						07 14	07 14								08 10	08 14			
Biggleswade	d				06 02	07 02	06 22						07 17	07 17								08 20	08 17			
Arlesey	d				06 22	07 22	06 27						07 22	07 22			07 22					08 40	08 22			
Cambridge	d	23p06				→			06 28	06 28								07 28	07 28					07 55		
Foxton	d	23p15																	07 37					08 05		
Shepreth	d	23p18																	07 40					08 07		
Meldreth	d	23p21																	07 43					08 10		
Royston	d	23p25							06 43	06 43								07 43	07 47					08 15		
Ashwell & Morden	d	23p29																	07 51					08 20		
Baldock	d	23p34							06 51	06 51								07 52	07 56					08 25		
Letchworth Garden City	d	23p37							06 54	06 54								07 55	07 59					08 29		
Hitchin 4	d	23p41	06 10		06 40		06a33	06 40	06a58	06 58		07 10	07a28	07 28		07 40	07 40	07 59	08a03		08 10	08a58	08 28	08 33		
Stevenage 4	d	23p46	06 30		07 00			07 00		07 03		07 30		07 33		08 00	08 00	08 05			08 30		08 33	08 39		
Hertford North	a																									
Knebworth	d	23p49	06a37	06 44	07a07			07a07			07 14	07a37		07 37	07 44	08a07	08a07			08 14	08a37			08 43		08 44
Welwyn North	d	23p53									07 19			07 40						08 19				08 47		08 49
Welwyn Garden City 4	d	23p56									07 22			07 43						08 22				08 50		08 52
Hatfield	d	23p59									07 26									08 26				08 53		08 56
Potters Bar	d	00 05									07 31									08 31				08 59		09 01
Finsbury Park	⊖ d	00s23		07 10						07 31	07 44			08 02	08 10			08 32		08 44			08 50	09 11		09 14
London Kings Cross 15	⊖ a	00 34		07 19						07 39	07 54			08 13	08 19			08 42		08 54			09 00	09 18		09 21

For general notes see front of timetable
For details of catering facilities see Directory of Train Operators

- **A** From Kings Lynn (Table 17)
- **B** Until 23 March
- **C** 3 February to 23 March
- **D** Until 27 January and from 30 March
- **E** Until 27 January
- **G** From 30 March
- **H** From 6 April

Table 25

Peterborough, Cambridge and Stevenage → London

Network Diagram - see first page of Table 24

		FC		FC	FC	FC	FC	FC	FC	FC	FC	FC	FC	GR	FC	FC	FC	FC	GR	FC	FC	FC	FC	GR	FC	FC
				1	1	1	1	1	1	1	1	1	1	R 1	1	1	1	1	R 1	1	1	1	1	R 1	1	1
		A 🚌		A	B	A	A																			
														☕🍴					☕🍴					☕🍴		
Peterborough [8]	d			08 15						08 58			09 45	09 53					10 27		10 45			11 26		
Huntingdon	a			08 29						09 12			09 59								10 59					
	d			08 29						09 12			09 59								10 59					
St Neots	d			08 36						09 20			10 06								11 06					
Sandy	d			08 44						09 27			10 14		←						11 14					
Biggleswade	d			08 47						09 31			10 17		10 17						11 17					
Arlesey	d			08 52						09 36			→		10 22						11 22					
Cambridge	d				08 28	08 40		08 55	09 15			09 28				09 55	10 15			10 28		10 55	11 15			11 28
Foxton	d							09 05								10 05						11 05				
Shepreth	d							09 07								10 07						11 07				
Meldreth	d							09 10								10 10						11 10				
Royston	d				08 43	08 54		09 15				09 43				10 15				10 43		11 15				11 43
Ashwell & Morden	d							09 20								10 20						11 20				
Baldock	d				08 51	09 02		09 25				09 51				10 25				10 51		11 25				11 51
Letchworth Garden City	d				08 54	09 05		09 29				09 54				10 29		←		10 54		11 29			←	11 54
Hitchin [4]	d	08 40		08a58	08 58	09 11	09 28	09 33		09 42		09 58			10 28	10 33		10 33		10 58	11 28	11 33			11 33	11 58
Stevenage [4]	d	09 00			09 03	09 16	09 33	09 39		09 47		10 03			10 33	→		10 39	11 00	11 03	11 33	→			11 39	12 03
Hertford North	a																									
Knebworth	d							09 43										10 43							11 43	
Welwyn North	d							09 47			←							10 47							11 47	
Welwyn Garden City [4]	d	09a22						09 50			09 50							10 50							11 50	
Hatfield	d							→			09 53							10 53							11 53	
Potters Bar	d										09 59							10 59							11 59	
Finsbury Park ⊖	d				09 21	09 34	09 51			10 06	10 11	10 21			10 51			11 11		11 21	11 51				12 11	12 21
London Kings Cross [15] ⊖	a				09 30	09 44	09 58		10 03	10 16	10 19	10 29		10 47	11 02		11 09	11 19	11 28	11 30	12 02		12 04	12 19	12 19	12 30

		GR	FC	FC		FC	GR	FC	FC	GR	FC	FC	GR	FC	FC	FC	FC	FC	FC	GR	GR	FC	FC	GR	FC	FC
		R 1	1	1		1	R 1	1	1	R 1	1	1	R 1	1	1	1	1	1	1	R 1	R 1	1	1	R 1	1	1
		☕🍴					☕🍴			☕🍴			☕🍴							☕🍴	☕🍴			☕🍴		
Peterborough [8]	d	11 38	11 45				12 16			12 41	12 46		13 04				13 48			14 10	14 22			14 43	14 49	
Huntingdon	a		11 59								12 59						13 59								14 59	
	d		11 59								12 59						13 59								14 59	
St Neots	d		12 06								13 06						14 06								15 06	
Sandy	d		12 14								13 14						14 14								15 14	
Biggleswade	d		12 17								13 17						14 17								15 17	
Arlesey	d		12 22								13 22						14 22								15 22	
Cambridge	d			11 55		12 15			12 28			12 55		13 15		13 28		13 55	14 15				14 28			14 55
Foxton	d			12 05								13 05						14 05								15 05
Shepreth	d			12 07								13 07						14 07								15 07
Meldreth	d			12 10								13 10						14 10								15 10
Royston	d			12 15					12 43			13 15				13 43		14 15					14 43			15 15
Ashwell & Morden	d			12 20								13 20						14 20								15 20
Baldock	d			12 25					12 51			13 25				13 51		14 25					14 51			15 25
Letchworth Garden City	d			12 29				←	12 54			13 29			←	13 54		14 29				←	14 54			15 29
Hitchin [4]	d		12 28	12 33				12 33	12 58		13 28	13 33			13 33	13 58	14 28	14 33				14 33	14 58		15 28	15 33
Stevenage [4]	d	12 09	12 33	→				12 39	13 03		13 33	→	13 34		13 39	14 03	14 33	→				14 39	15 03		15 33	→
Hertford North	a																									
Knebworth	d							12 43							13 43							14 43				
Welwyn North	d							12 47							13 47							14 47				
Welwyn Garden City [4]	d							12 50							13 50							14 50				
Hatfield	d							12 53							13 53							14 53				
Potters Bar	d							12 59							13 59							14 59				
Finsbury Park ⊖	d		12 51					13 11	13 21		13 51				14 11	14 21	14 51					15 11	15 21		15 51	
London Kings Cross [15] ⊖	a	12 37	13 02			13 03	13 13	13 19	13 30	13 36	14 02		14 04	14 05	14 19	14 30	15 02		15 05	15 11	15 15	15 19	15 30	15 38	16 03	

		FC	FC	GR	FC	FC		GR	FC	FC	FC	FC	GR	FC	FC	FC	GR	GR	FC	FC	FC	GR	FC	FC	GR	GR
		1	1	R 1	1	1		R 1	1	1	1	1	R 1	1	1	1	R 1	R 1	1	1	1	R 1	1	1	R 1	R 1
																	C					D				
				☕🍴				☕🍴					☕🍴				☕🍴	☕🍴				☕🍴			☕🍴	☕🍴
Peterborough [8]	d			15 36		15 43		15 47					16 19			16 45	16 51	17 02				17 18			17 23	17 41
Huntingdon	a					15 59										16 59										
	d					15 59										16 59										
St Neots	d					16 06			←							17 06			←							
Sandy	d					16 14			16 14							17 14			17 14							
Biggleswade	d					→			16 17							→			17 17							
Arlesey	d								16 22										17 22							
Cambridge	d	15 15			15 28					15 55	16 15				16 28					16 55	17 15			17 28		
Foxton	d									16 05										17 05						
Shepreth	d									16 07										17 07						
Meldreth	d									16 10										17 10						
Royston	d				15 43					16 15					16 43					17 15				17 43		
Ashwell & Morden	d									16 20										17 20						
Baldock	d				15 51					16 25					16 51					17 25				17 51		
Letchworth Garden City	d		←		15 54					16 29		←			16 54					17 29			←	17 54		
Hitchin [4]	d		15 33		15 58				16 28	16 33		16 33			16 58				17 28	17 33			17 33	17 58		
Stevenage [4]	d		15 39		16 03			16 17	16 33	→		16 39	16 49		17 03		17 22		17 33	→			17 39	18 03	18 24	18 11
Hertford North	a																									
Knebworth	d		15 43									16 43											17 43			
Welwyn North	d		15 47									16 47		←									17 47			
Welwyn Garden City [4]	d		15 50									16 50		16 50									17 50			
Hatfield	d		15 53									→		16 53									17 53			
Potters Bar	d		15 59											16 59									17 59			
Finsbury Park ⊖	d		16 11		16 21				16 51					17 11	17 21				17 51				18 11	18 21		
London Kings Cross [15] ⊖	a	16 06	16 19	16 29	16 33			16 45	17 02		17 03		17 17	17 19	17 30		17 49	17 55	18 02		18 03	18 15	18 19	18 30	18 49	18 40

For general notes see front of timetable
For details of catering facilities see
Directory of Train Operators

A Until 23 March
B From 30 March
C The Flying Scotsman
D The Highland Chieftain

Table 25

Sundays

Peterborough, Cambridge and Stevenage → London

Network Diagram - see first page of Table 24

Station		FC	GR	FC	FC	FC	GR	FC		FC	FC	GR	GR	FC	FC	FC	GR	FC	GR	FC	GR	GR	FC	GR	FC	FC
		1	R 1 ✕	1	1	1	R 1 ✕	1		1	1	R 1 ✕	R 1 ✕	1	1	1	R 1 ✕	1	R 1 ✕	1	R 1 ✕	R 1 ✕	1	R 1 ✕	1	1
Peterborough 8	d	17 45	18 02				18 21				18 45	18 49	18 57				19 19		19 29		19 36	19 42	19 47	20 02		
Huntingdon	a	17 59									18 59												19 59			
	d	17 59									18 59												19 59			
St Neots	d	18 06									19 06			←									20 06		←	
Sandy	d	18 14		←							19 14 →			19 14									20 14 →		20 14	
Biggleswade	d	18 17 →		18 17										19 17											20 17	
Arlesey	d			18 22										19 22											20 22	
Cambridge	d				17 55	18 15				18 28					18 55	19 15				19 28						19 55
Foxton	d				18 05										19 05											20 05
Shepreth	d				18 07										19 07											20 07
Meldreth	d				18 10										19 10											20 10
Royston	d				18 15					18 43					19 15					19 43						20 15
Ashwell & Morden	d				18 20										19 20											20 20
Baldock	d				18 25					18 51					19 25					19 51						20 25
Letchworth Garden City	d				18 29			←		18 54					19 29			←		19 54						20 29
Hitchin 4	d			18 28	18 33 →			18 33		18 58				19 28	19 33 →			19 33		19 58					20 28	20 33 →
Stevenage 4	d			18 33				18 39		19 03		19 20		19 33				19 39		20 03	20 08	20 12		20 32	20 33	
Hertford North	a																									
Knebworth	d							18 43										19 43								
Welwyn North	d							18 47										19 47								
Welwyn Garden City 4	d							18 50										19 50								
Hatfield	d							18 53										19 53								
Potters Bar	d							18 59										19 59								
Finsbury Park ⊖	d			18 51				19 11		19 21				19 51				20 11		20 21					20 51	
London Kings Cross 15 ⊖	a		18 55	19 02		19 07	19 16	19 19		19 29		19 47	19 51	20 02		20 03	20 12	20 19	20 23	20 30	20 36	20 42		20 59	21 04	

Station		FC	FC	GR	FC	FC	GR	FC	FC	FC	FC	GR	FC	FC	GR	FC	FC	GR	FC	FC	GR	FC	FC	FC		
		1	1	R 1 ✕	1	1	R 1 ✕	1	1	1	1	R 1 ✕	1	1	R 1 ✕	1	1	R 1 ✕	1	1	R 1 ✕	1	1	1 A		
Peterborough 8	d			20 26		20 45	20 48					21 18			21 36	21 45		22 04			22 44		22 48			
Huntingdon	a					20 59										21 59							22 59			
	d					20 59										21 59							22 59			
St Neots	d					21 06		←								22 06							23 06			
Sandy	d					21 14 →		21 14								22 14							23 14			
Biggleswade	d							21 17								22 17							23 17			
Arlesey	d							21 22								22 22							23 22			
Cambridge	d	20 15			20 28				20 55	21 15				21 28			21 55		22 15			22 41		23 13		
Foxton	d								21 05								22 05									
Shepreth	d								21 07								22 07									
Meldreth	d								21 10								22 10									
Royston	d				20 43				21 15					21 43			22 15					22 55		23 26		
Ashwell & Morden	d								21 20								22 20									
Baldock	d				20 51				21 25					21 51			22 25					23 03				
Letchworth Garden City	d		←		20 54				21 29		←			21 54			22 29			←		23 06		23 36		
Hitchin 4	d		20 33		20 58			21 28	21 33 →		21 33			21 58		22 28	22 33 →			22 33		23 10	23 28	23 40		
Stevenage 4	d		20 39	20 57	21 03		21 20	21 33			21 39	21 48		22 03	22 09	22 33		22 34		22 39		23 15	23 33	23 45		
Hertford North	a																									
Knebworth	d		20 43								21 43									22 43				23 48		
Welwyn North	d		20 47								21 47		←							22 47				23 52		
Welwyn Garden City 4	d		20 50								21 50 →		21 50							22 50				23 55		
Hatfield	d		20 53										21 53							22 53				23 58		
Potters Bar	d		20 59										21 59							22 59				00 04		
Finsbury Park ⊖	d		21 11		21 21			21 51					22 11	22 21		22 56				23 11		23 38	23 58	00 20		
London Kings Cross 15 ⊖	a	21 05	21 19	21 25	21 30		21 47	22 02		22 03		22 16	22 19	22 32	22 37	23 09		23 14	23 15	23 24	23 50	23 54	00 13	00 32		

For general notes see front of timetable
For details of catering facilities see
Directory of Train Operators

A From Kings Lynn (Table 17)

Route Diagram for Table 26

DM-1/07
Design BAJS

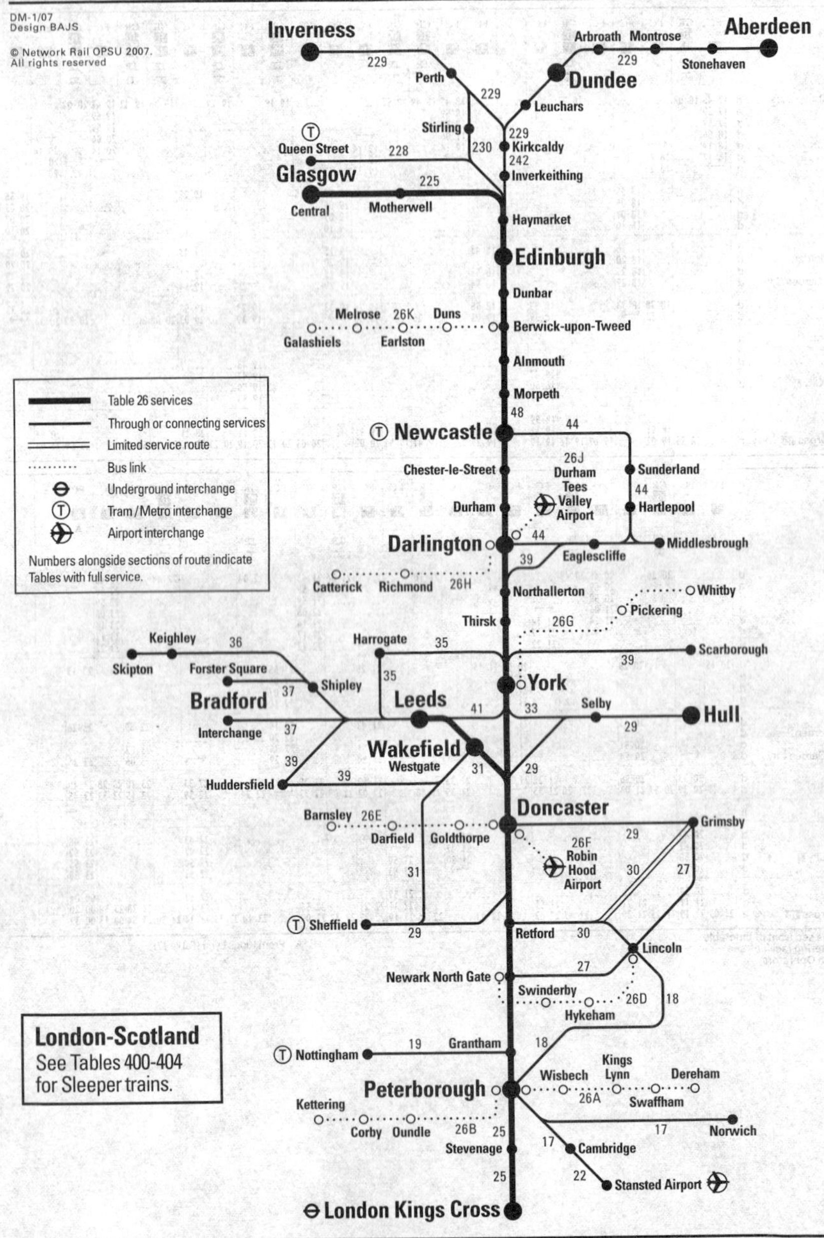

Table 26

London → Humberside, Yorkshire, North East England and Scotland

Route Diagram - see first page of Table 26

Miles	Miles	Miles		XC	NT	GR	NT	TP	GR	NT	TP	TP	GR	NT	XC	TP	XC	GR	GR	TP	GR	XC	EM	GR	TP
				1◇		R 1		1◇	R 1		1◇	1◇	R 1		1◇	1◇	1◇	R 1	R 1	1◇	R 1	1◇	◇	R 1	1◇
					A		B	C		D	E			D		C	G			H		G	J		C
0	—	—	**London Kings Cross 15** ⊖ d															06 00	06 15		06 35			07 00	
27½	—	—	**Stevenage 4** d															06 19	06 34					07 19	
76¼	—	—	**Peterborough 8** a															06 50	07 05		07 21			07 50	
—	—	—	Norwich d																				05 52		
—	—	—	Stansted Airport d																05 21						
—	—	—	Cambridge d															05 11	05 58					06 50	
—	—	—	**Peterborough 8** d															06 51	07 06		07 21		07 27	07 51	
105½	—	—	**Grantham 7** a															07 10	07 25		07 40		07 58		
—	—	—	d															07 10	07 25		07 40				
120	—	—	**Newark North Gate 7** a															07 22	07 37						
—	—	—	Lincoln a																08 13						
—	—	—	Grimsby Town a																09 15		09b42				
—	—	—	**Newark North Gate 7** d															07 22	07 37						
138½	—	—	**Retford 10** d															07 37	07 52						
156	0	—	**Doncaster 7** a															07 51	08 07		08 12				
—	—	—	Selby a																						
—	—	—	Hull a																		09 13				
—	19¾	—	**Wakefield Westgate 7** a															08 10			08 36				
—	—	—	Huddersfield a															09 04			09c27				
—	29¾	—	**Leeds 10** a															08 32			08 52				
—	—	—	Shipley a															09 01			09 21				
—	—	—	Bradford Forster Square a															09e09			09e28				
—	—	—	Keighley a															09 11			09 50				
—	—	—	Skipton a															09 24			10 07				
—	—	—	Sheffield 7 d						05 29				05 50		06 55		07 12					07 54			
—	—	—	**Doncaster 7** d						06 15						07 49				08 08			08 26			
188½	—	—	**York 8** a						06 35						08 10				08 31			08 48		08 55	
—	—	—	Scarborough a																					10 30	
—	—	—	Harrogate a																09 18					09 43	
—	—	—	Leeds 10 d					04g50			06 35	06 55	07 10			07 50	07 57			08 12					08 27
—	—	—	Hull d									06h00							07 07						
—	—	—	**York 8** d					05 40	06 37		07 06	07 32	07 37		08 12	08 22	08 27		08 33	08 42		08 50		08 57	09 03
210¾	—	—	Thirsk d					06 01			07 22	07 54				08 38									
218½	—	—	Northallerton d					06 17			07 30	08 02				08 49				09 03					09 24
232½	—	—	**Darlington 7** a					06 28	07 05		07 41		08 05		08 38		08 53		09 02	09 14		09 20		09 30	09 36
—	—	—	Eaglescliffe a																						
—	—	—	Middlesbrough a					07 01	07 50		08 12	08 32				09 20	09 27					09 57			10 23
—	—	—	**Darlington 7** d				06 14		07 06	07 20	07 43		08 05	08 15	08 39		08 53		09 03	09 15		09 22		09 31	09 38
254½	—	—	**Durham** d				06 35		07 23	07 41	07 59		08 23	08 36	08 57		09 09		09 20	09 32		09 38			09 54
260¼	—	—	Chester-le-Street d				06 42			07 48	08 05			08 43	09 03							09 45			
268½	—	—	**Newcastle 8** a				06 55		07 39	08 01	08 20		08 39	08 59	09 22		09 26		09 38	09 49		10 01		10 02	10 12
—	—	—	Hartlepool a																						
—	—	—	Sunderland a				07 49				08 49				09 49										10 49
—	—	—	**Newcastle 8** d		06 00	06 25			07 41				08 41				09 29		09 39					10 04	
285	—	—	Morpeth d		06 20	06 38			08a21				08 55				09 42							10a35	
303¼	—	—	Alnmouth d		06a37	06 52			08 07								09 56								
335½	—	—	**Berwick-upon-Tweed** d			07 14			08 29				09 28						10 22					10 47	
363¾	—	—	Dunbar d	06 40		07 38			08 52				09 55												
393	—	—	**Edinburgh 10** a	07 13		08 05			09 19				10 20				11 02		11 14					11 30	
—	—	0	**Edinburgh** d	07 25		08 08			09 21				10 26											11 39	
394¼	—	1¼	Haymarket d	07 29		08 14			09 26				10 31											11 44	
437½	—	—	Motherwell a	08 05		09 03			10 05															12 24	
450¼	—	—	**Glasgow Central 15** a	08 28		09 25			10 24				11j21				12k06		12k21					12 45	
—	—	—	Stirling a	08m23		09m23			10m23				11m23						12 23					12m53	
—	—	—	Perth a	09n37		09m54			10m56				12n37						12 56					13n37	
—	—	—	**Inverness** a	11m59		11m59			13q35										15 18						
—	—	13¼	Inverkeithing a	08m04		08m55			09m56				10 47				11 36							12m05	
—	—	26	Kirkcaldy a	08m26		09m11			10m12				11 04				11 58							12m27	
—	—	51	Leuchars 3 a	09m12		10m09			11m12				11 29											13m12	
—	—	59¼	**Dundee** a	09m25		10m21			11m24				11 44											13m24	
—	—	76¼	Arbroath a	09m45		10m38			11m41				12 01											13m41	
—	—	90	Montrose a	10r32		10m52			12m17				12 17											14r32	
—	—	114¼	Stonehaven a	10m18		11m14			12m15				12 40											14m16	
—	—	130½	**Aberdeen** a	10m38		11m34			12m35				13 04											14m36	

For general notes see front of timetable
For details of catering facilities see Directory of Train Operators

A To Chathill (Table 48)
B From Middlesbrough (Table 44)
C From Manchester Airport (Table 39)
D From Saltburn (Table 44)
E From Manchester Piccadilly (Table 39)
G From Birmingham New Street (Table 51)
H From Liverpool Lime Street (Table 39)
J To Liverpool Lime Street (Table 49)
b Change at Doncaster
c Change at Leeds
e Bradford Interchange
f Change at York
g Mondays dep. 0452
h Change at Selby and York
j Glasgow Queen Street. Change at Edinburgh
k Glasgow Queen Street
m Change at Edinburgh
n Change at Edinburgh and Stirling
q Change at Edinburgh and Perth
r Change at Edinburgh and Arbroath

London → Humberside, Yorkshire, North East England and Scotland

Route Diagram - see first page of Table 26

		TP	XC	GR	HT	GR	XC	EM	GR	GR	XC	TP	GC	TP	XC	GR	GR	XC	TP	EM	GR	GR	TP	XC	GR
			R	R		R			R	R			R		R	R	R				R	R			R
		1 ◇	1	1	1 ◇	1	1 ◇	◇	1	1	1 ◇	1 ◇	1	1 ◇	1	1	1	1 ◇	1 ◇	◇	1	1	1 ◇	1 ◇	1
		A	B				B	C			B	A		A	D			D	A	C			A	E	
London Kings Cross [15] ⊖	d			07 10	07 20	07 30			07 35	08 00			08 04			08 10	08 30				08 35	09 00			09 10
Stevenage [4]	d			07 29	07u44	07 50			07 56								08 49				08 55				
Peterborough [8]	a			08 00		08 21				08 46						08 59	09 20				09 26	09 46			09 56
Norwich	d									06b33										07 57					
Stansted Airport	d															07 25									
Cambridge	d							07 27								07 59						08b12			08b38
Peterborough [8]	d			08 01		08 21		08 30		08 46						08 59	09 21			09 27	09 27	09 46			09 56
Grantham [7]	a				08 30	08 45		08 58												09 57	09 48				
	d				08 31	08 45															09 48				
Newark North Gate [7]	a			08 28													09 48								
Lincoln	a			09 00		10c02											10 21				10c57				
Grimsby Town	a					10e47											11 20					11e42			
Newark North Gate [7]	d			08 28													09 48								
Retford [10]	d				08 52																10 11				
Doncaster [7]	a			08 58	09 04	09 16															10 26	10 33			
Selby	a				09 21																				
Hull	a				10 04	10 49																11 53			
Wakefield Westgate [7]	a			09 16					09 25							10 01					10 51				10 56
Huddersfield	a			10 04					10f27							10f58					11f45				11f58
Leeds [10]	a			09 35					09 46							10 21					11 09				11 18
Shipley	a			10 01					10 07							10 51					11 37				11 51
Bradford Forster Square	a			10g11					10g28							10g57					11g42				11g57
Keighley	a			10 11					10 20							11 11					11 50				12 20
Skipton	a			10 24					10 37							11 24					12 07				12 37
Sheffield [7]	d		08 21			08 41	08 54								09 21			09 54						10 21	
Doncaster [7]	d					09 17	09 22											10 17				10 35			
York [8]	a					09 39	09 48			09 51			10 07				10 33	10 40				11 01			
Scarborough	a												11 30									12 30			
Harrogate	a								10 33	10 43						11 33						11 43			12 03
Leeds [10]	d	08 57	09 05				09 12					09 27		09 57	10 05				10 27				10 57	11 05	
Hull	d											08h37		09 02										10h12	
York [8]	d	09 26	09 36			09 42	09 51			09 54		10 00	10 14	10 26	10 31		10 35	10 43	10 54			11 03	11 26	11 32	
Thirsk	d	09 46											10 30	10 46									11 43		
Northallerton	d	09 55										10 21	10 39	10 55					11 15				11 55		
Darlington [7]	a		10 01			10 10	10 16			10 22		10 32			10 59		11 05	11 12	11 26			11 33		11 58	
Eaglescliffe	a												10 57												
Middlesbrough	a	10 30								10 54		11 22		11 30					12 00				12 30	12 31	
Darlington [7]	d		10 03			10 10	10 18			10 23		10 33			11 01		11 06	11 14	11 28			11 33		12 00	
Durham	d		10 19				10 34			10 40	←	10 51			11 18		11 23	11 30	11 44					12 23	
Chester-le-Street	d						10 41 →				10 41	10 57													
Newcastle [8]	a		10 35			10 44				10 58	10 59	11 11			11 33		11 41	11 54	12 02			12 03		12 37	
Hartlepool	a												11 20												
Sunderland	a											11 49	11 50									12 49			
Newcastle [8]	d		10 39							10 59					11 36							12 04		12 40	
Morpeth	d										11a35				11 49							12a36			
Alnmouth	d														12 03							12 30			
Berwick-upon-Tweed	d		11 21							11 42												12 52		13 22	
Dunbar	d		11 44																					13 45	
Edinburgh [10]	a		12 13							12 30					13 16							13 38		14 16	
Edinburgh	d																					13 41			
Haymarket	d																								
Motherwell	a																					14 25			
Glasgow Central [15]	a		13j21							13j36					14j21							14 45		15j21	
Stirling	a		13 23							13 53					14 23							14k53		15 23	
Perth	a									14m37					14 54							15m36			
Inverness	a														17 07										
Inverkeithing	a									13 04					14 05							14k11			
Kirkcaldy	a									13 26					14 27							14k42			
Leuchars [3]	a									14 11												15k12			
Dundee	a									14 23												15k24			
Arbroath	a									14 40												15k43			
Montrose	a									14 55												16n30			
Stonehaven	a									15 16												16k17			
Aberdeen	a									15 36												16k37			

For general notes see front of timetable
For details of catering facilities see Directory of Train Operators

A From Manchester Airport (Table 39)
B From Birmingham New Street (Table 51)
C To Liverpool Lime Street (Table 49)
D From Bristol Temple Meads (Table 51)
E From Southampton Central (Table 51)
b Change at Ely and Peterborough
c Change at Peterborough
e Change at Doncaster
f Change at Leeds
g Bradford Interchange
h Change at Selby and York
j Glasgow Queen Street
k Change at Edinburgh
m Change at Edinburgh and Stirling
n Change at Edinburgh and Arbroath

London → Humberside, Yorkshire, North East England and Scotland

Route Diagram - see first page of Table 26

		GR	GR	HT	EM	XC	GR	XC	TP	TP	GR	GR	XC	XC	GR	EM	GR	TP	GR	GC	TP	XC	GR	XC	EM	GR
		R 1	R 1	1 ◇	◇	1 ◇	R 1	1 ◇	1 ◇	1 ◇	R 1	R 1	1 ◇	1 ◇	R 1	◇	R 1	1 ◇	R 1	R 1	1 ◇	1 ◇	R 1	1 ◇	◇	R 1
					A	B	C	B	D	D		E	G	G		A		D			D	H		J	A	
London Kings Cross 15 ⊖	d	09 30	09 35	09 48			10 00				10 10	10 30			10 35		11 00		11 10	11 27			11 30			11 35
Stevenage 4	d	09 49	09 54	10u09								10 12					10 46						11 50			11 54
Peterborough 8	a	10 20	10 26				10 45				10 56	11 16			11 22		11 46		11 56				12 21			12 27
Norwich	d				08 57											09 57									10 57	
Stansted Airport	d	08 21										09 25											10 20			
Cambridge	d	09 04					09b12					10 04					10b38						11 04			
Peterborough 8	d	10 21	10 27		10 30		10 45				10 56	11 17			11 23	11 25	11 46		11 56				12 21		12 25	12 27
Grantham 7	a		10 46	10 53	11 10						11 15				11 42	11 56			12 15						12 58	12 46
	d		10 46	10 54							11 15				11 42				12 15							12 46
Newark North Gate 7	a	10 48									11 27				11 55				12 27				12 50			12 58
Lincoln	a		12c06												12 30											13 28
Grimsby Town	a			12e44											13 35											
Newark North Gate 7	d	10 48									11 27				11 55				12 27				12 50			12 58
Retford 10	d			11 17							11 42															
Doncaster 7	a	11 12	11 17	11 32							11 57				12 18				12 59				13 14			
Selby	a			11 51																						
Hull	a			12 32							13 06				13 52				14 08							
Wakefield Westgate 7	a		11 36								12 15				12 36				13 17							13 37
Huddersfield	a		12f27								13 04				13f27				14 04							14f27
Leeds 10	a		11 55								12 35				12 54				13 41							13 55
Shipley	a		12 21								13 01				13 21				14 07							14 21
Bradford Forster Square	a		12g28								13g11				13g28				14g11							14g28
Keighley	a		12 50								13 11				13 52				14 20							14 50
Skipton	a		13 07								13 24				14 08				14 37							15 07
Sheffield 7 🚌	d	10 25				10 54							11 21	11 54								12 21	12 25	12 54		
Doncaster 7	d	11 12				11 17								12 17									13 15	13 24		
York 8	a	11 37				11 41	11 53					12 26		12 43			12 51			13 19			13 39	13 46		
Scarborough	a											13 30								14 30						
Harrogate	a						12 43				13 33						13 43		14 33							
Leeds 10	d					11 12			11 27	11 57		11 41	12 05	12 12				12 27			12 57	13 05		13 12		
Hull	d									11 05											11h37					
York 8	d	11 41				11 46	11 54		12 01	12 26		12 29	12 34	12 46			12 52	12 59		13 22	13 26	13 32	13 42	13 50		
Thirsk	d									12 46										13 38	13 46					
Northallerton	d	12 00							12 22	12 55								13 20		13 47	13 55					
Darlington 7	a	12 14				12 20	12 25		12 33				13 00	13 11			13 20	13 31				14 00	14 10	14 16		
Eaglescliffe	a																			14 04						
Middlesbrough	a					12 53			13 17	13 30							13 56				14 30	14 32		14 55		
Darlington 7	d	12 14				12 21	12 26	←	12 34				13 02	13 13			13 20	13 32				14 02	14 11	14 18		
Durham	d	12 32				12j45 →		12 45	12 51				13 19	13 29				13 49				14 19	14 28	14 35		
Chester-le-Street	d							12 51										13 55						14 42		
Newcastle 8 🚌	a	12 50					12 55	13 07	13 09			13 22	13 34	13 50			13 50	14 10				14 37	14 47	14 57		
Hartlepool	a																			14 23						
Sunderland	a											13 49						14 49		14 50						
Newcastle 8 🚌	d						12 57					13 24	13 37				13 51					14 40				
Morpeth	d						13a23										14a35									
Alnmouth	d												14 01													
Berwick-upon-Tweed	d																14 34					15 22				
Dunbar	d																					15 45				
Edinburgh 10	a						14 24					14 51	15 16				15 20					16 16				
Edinburgh	d											15 00					15 22					16 30				
Haymarket	d											15 04										16 35				
Motherwell	a																16 06									
Glasgow Central 15	a						15k36					16k08	16k21				16 25					17m21				
Stirling	a											15n53					16n23									
Perth	a											16q37					17q20									
Inverness	a																19q34									
Inverkeithing	a						15 04					15 19					16n04					16 47				
Kirkcaldy	a						15 26					15 36					16n26					17 02				
Leuchars 3	a											16 01					17n12					17 31				
Dundee	a											16 17					17n26					17 44				
Arbroath	a											16 35					17n50					18 03				
Montrose	a											16 50					18n04					18 17				
Stonehaven	a											17 13					18n26					18 37				
Aberdeen	a											17 38					18n46					19 02				

For general notes see front of timetable
For details of catering facilities see Directory of Train Operators

- **A** To Liverpool Lime Street (Table 49)
- **B** From Cardiff Central (Table 51)
- **C** **The Flying Scotsman**
- **D** From Manchester Airport (Table 39)
- **E** **The Northern Lights**
- **G** From Plymouth (Table 51)
- **H** From Bournemouth (Table 51)
- **J** From Bristol Temple Meads (Table 51)
- **b** Change at Ely and Peterborough
- **c** Change at Peterborough
- **e** Change at Doncaster
- **f** Change at Leeds
- **g** Bradford Interchange
- **h** Change at Selby and York
- **j** Arr. 1238
- **k** Glasgow Queen Street
- **m** Glasgow Queen Street. Change at Edinburgh
- **n** Change at Edinburgh
- **q** Change at Edinburgh and Stirling

London → Humberside, Yorkshire, North East England and Scotland

Route Diagram - see first page of Table 26

		HT	TP	GR	TP	TP	XC	GR	GR	GR	EM	XC	TP	GR	XC	TP	TP	GR	GR	XC	HT	XC	GR	EM	GR
			A	B	A	A	C				D	E	A		E	A	A			G		H		D	
London Kings Cross 15 ⊖	d	11 48		12 00				12 10	12 30	12 35				13 00				13 10	13 30		13 33		13 35		14 00
Stevenage 4	d							12 29		12 58				12 46									13 12		
Peterborough 8	a			12 46				13 00	13 16					13 46				13 57					14 24		
Norwich	d										11 57													12 57	
Stansted Airport	d							11 25															12 25		
Cambridge	d			11b12				12 04						12b33									13 04		
Peterborough 8	d			12 47				13 01	13 17		13 25			13 46				13 58					14 25	14 26	
Grantham 7	a	12 53						13 20		13 44	13 56							14 17			14 34		14 44	14 56	
	d	12 54						13 20		13 44								14 17			14 35		14 44		
Newark North Gate 7	a									13 56								14 29					15 00		
Lincoln	a									14 56															
Grimsby Town	a	14c44												15c42											16c44
Newark North Gate 7	d									13 56								14 29					15 01		
Retford 10	d	13 16						13 42											14 48		14 56				
Doncaster 7	a	13 29						13 57	14 06	14 20				14 33				14 53	15 02		15 11		15 25		15 29
Selby	a	13 44																			15 27				
Hull	a	14 25							15 07					15 51					16 04		16 10				16 49
Wakefield Westgate 7	a							14 14		14 39								15 14	15 42				15 51		
Huddersfield	a							15 04		15e45								16 04					16e45		
Leeds 10	a							14 35		15 01								15 35	16 02				16 09		
Shipley	a							15 01		15 37								16 07					16 37		
Bradford Forster Square	a							15f11		15f42								16f11					16f42		
Keighley	a							15 11		15 50								16 20					16 51		
Skipton	a							15 24		16 07								16 37					17 07		
Sheffield 7 ⛴	d						13 21		13 11			13 54							14 11	14 21		14 54			
Doncaster 7	d								14 07			14 20		14 34					15 03			15 17			15 30
York 8	a			14 00					14 34			14 45		14 58					15 26			15 40			15 53
Scarborough	a			15 30																					
Harrogate	a			14 43				15 33						15 43				16 33							16 43
Leeds 10	d		13 27			13 57	14 05					14 12	14 27			←	14 57		14 41	15 05		15 12			
Hull	d								13 12																
York 8	d		13 54	14 02		14 26	14 33		14 36			14 46	14 54 →	15 00		14 54	15 26		15 28	15 34		15 44			15 55
Thirsk	d				←	14 43											15 46								
Northallerton	d		14 16 →		14 16	14 54			14 58							15 23	15 55								
Darlington 7	a				14 27		14 58		15 11			15 16		15 27		15 34			16 01	16 06		16 11			16 23
Eaglescliffe	a																								
Middlesbrough	a				15 22	15 30						15 55				16 23	16 30								16 54
Darlington 7	d				14 34		15 00		15 11			15 18		15 28	←	15 35			16 01	16 07		16 13			16 23
Durham	d				14 50		15 16		15 29			15 35 →			15 35	15 52				16 25		16 30			
Chester-le-Street	d															15 58						16 37			
Newcastle 8 ⛴	a			14 58	15 06		15 32		15 47					15 57	16 00	16 14			16 31	16 39		16 52			16 53
Hartlepool	a																								
Sunderland	a				15 49											16 49				17 13					17 49
Newcastle 8 ⛴	d			15 00			15 35							15 59					16 32	16 41					16 54
Morpeth	d				15a35		15 48								16a36										
Alnmouth	d						16 02												16 58						
Berwick-upon-Tweed	d													16 42						17 25					17 38
Dunbar	d																			17 48					
Edinburgh 10	a			16 26			17 16							17 34					18 04	18 16					18 23
Edinburgh	d			16 34										17 39											18 32
Haymarket	d			16 39										17 44											18 37
Motherwell	a													18 23					19 25						
Glasgow Central 15	a			17g36			18g21							18 41					19g06	19g21					19g36
Stirling	a			17 19			18 07							18h53											19h23
Perth	a			17 55			18j48							19j42											20j37
Inverness	a			20 08			20 58																		
Inverkeithing	a			17h04			17 51							18h12					18 50						18 54
Kirkcaldy	a			17h26										18h34											19 10
Leuchars 3	a			18h05										19h15											19 34
Dundee	a			18h22										19h27											19 49
Arbroath	a			18h40										19h45											20 07
Montrose	a			18h55																					20 22
Stonehaven	a			19h16										20h21											20 46
Aberdeen	a			19h38										20h44											21 10

For general notes see front of timetable
For details of catering facilities see Directory of Train Operators

- A From Manchester Airport (Table 39)
- **B The Highland Chieftain**
- C From Plymouth (Table 51)
- D To Liverpool Lime Street (Table 49)
- E From Bristol Temple Meads (Table 51)
- G From Bournemouth (Table 51)
- H From Paignton (Table 51)
- b Change at Ely and Peterborough
- c Change at Doncaster
- e Change at Leeds
- f Bradford Interchange
- g Glasgow Queen Street
- h Change at Edinburgh
- j Change at Edinburgh and Stirling

London → Humberside, Yorkshire, North East England and Scotland

Route Diagram - see first page of Table 26

		NT	GR	GR	TP	XC	EM	GR	XC	GR	XC	TP	XC	GR	GR	TP	XC	GR	EM	GR	TP	XC	HT	GR	GR
			R 1	R 1	1◇	R 1	◇	R 1	1◇	R 1	1◇	1◇	R 1	R 1	R 1	1◇	1◇	R 1	◇	R 1	1◇	R 1	1◇	R 1	FX R 1
		A			B	C	D		E		E	B	G			H	J		D		B	K			
			✕ ⌶	⊐P ⌶	⌶	⊐P		⊐P ⌶	⊐P	✕ ⌶	⊐P	⌶	⊐P	✕ ⌶	✕ ⌶	⌶	⊐P	⊐P ⌶		✕ ⌶	⌶	⊐P	⊠ ⊐P	⊐P ⌶	✕ ⌶
London Kings Cross 15 ⊖	d		14 10	14 30				14 35		15 00				15 10	15 30			15 35		16 00			16 05	16 10	16 30
Stevenage 4	d		*13 46*	*14 12*				14 54						*14 46*	*15 12*			15 54							16 49
Peterborough 8	a		14 56	15 16										15 56	16 16			16 25						16 56	
Norwich	d						13 57												14 57						
Stansted Airport	d			*13 25*											*14 25*										
Cambridge	d		*13b12*	*14 04*											*15 04*									*15b12*	
Peterborough 8	d		14 56	15 16			15 26							15 57	16 17			16 26	16 27					16 56	
Grantham 7	a		15 15				15 55							16 18				16 45	16 58				17 06	17 15	17 34
	d		15 15											16 18				16 45					17 07	17 15	17 34
Newark North Gate 7	a		15 27											16 29										17 27	17 46
Lincoln	a		*16 00*												*17 48*									*17 57*	
Grimsby Town	a							*17c42*												*18c46*					
Newark North Gate 7	d		15 27											16 29										17 27	17 46
Retford 10	d													16 45									17 28		
Doncaster 7	a		15 55					16 09						17 00	17 08			17 19		17 29			17 41		18 09
Selby	a																						17 59		
Hull	a							*17 08*						*18 06*									18 40		*19 09*
Wakefield Westgate 7	a		16 13					16 30						17 18				17 36						18 04	
Huddersfield	a		*17 05*					*17e27*						*18 05*				*18e27*						*19 04*	
Leeds 10	a		16 35					16 48						17 36				17 56						18 23	
Shipley	a		*16 56*					*17 21*						*18 02*				*18 21*						*18 52*	
Bradford Forster Square	a		*17f11*					*17f28*						*18f11*				*18f28*						*18f57*	
Keighley	a		*17 10*					*17 45*						*18 16*				*18 50*						*19 15*	
Skipton	a		*17 26*					*18 01*						*18 33*				*19 06*						*19 33*	
Sheffield 7 ⛴	d					15 21			15 54				16 21		*16 11*		16 54					17 21			
Doncaster 7	d								16 17						17 09		17 17			17 31					18 10
York 8	a			16 21					16 40	16 45					17 34		17 40			17 54					18 34
Scarborough	a			*17 30*						*18 17*					*18 51*										*19 30*
Harrogate	a									*17 26*				*18 33*						*18 43*				*19 33*	
Leeds 10	d			*15 27*	15 57	16 05			*16 12*			16 27	17 05		*16 57*	17 12					17 57	18 05			
Hull	d			*15 06*									*16 10*												
York 8	d			16 22	16 26	16 32			16 43	16 46		16 58	17 33		17 36	17 43	17 46			17 56	18 26	18 32			18 39
Thirsk	d				16 46							17 14				18 00					18 44				
Northallerton	d				16 55							17 22			17 56	18 10					18 55				19 00
Darlington 7	a			16 50		16 57			17 08			17 36	18 02		18 09		18 15			18 26		18 58			19 13
Eaglescliffe	a																								
Middlesbrough	a			*17 23*	17 30				*17 41*		⟵	*18 28*				18 42				*18 56*	19 30				
Darlington 7	d			16 51		16 59			17 15 ⟶		17 15	17 38	18 05		18 10		18 17			18 27		18 59			19 13
Durham	d			17 08							17 32	17 55	18 21		18 27		18 34					19 16			19 31
Chester-le-Street	d											18 01					18 41								
Newcastle 8 ⛴	a			17 26		17 28				17 38	17 54	18 16	18 37		18 45		18 56			18 57		19 35			19 49
Hartlepool	a																								
Sunderland	a											*18 49*								*19 49*					
Newcastle 8 ⛴	d	17 15				17 31				17 40			18 40		18 46					18 59		19 40			
Morpeth	d	17 36				*18a07*						*18a49*													
Alnmouth	d	18a18				17 55									19 13							20 04			
Berwick-upon-Tweed	d									18 26			19 23							19 43		20 25			
Dunbar	d												19 46												
Edinburgh 10	a					18 57				19 12			20 11		20 19					20 27		21 08			
Edinburgh	d					19 01				19 14			20 15							20 30		21 15			
Haymarket	d					19 06							20 19							20 35		21 19			
Motherwell	a									19 53												21s59			
Glasgow Central 15	a									20 15			21 28		*21g22*					*21g51*		22 42			
Stirling	a									*20h23*					*21 23*										
Perth	a									*20h51*					*22j36*										
Inverness	a									*23h10*															
Inverkeithing	a					19 18				*19h53*										20 50		*21h47*			
Kirkcaldy	a					19 34				*20h09*										21 07		*22h09*			
Leuchars 3	a					20 04				*21h28*										21 38		*22h41*			
Dundee	a					20 25				*21h41*										21 53		*22h55*			
Arbroath	a					*20k43*														22 10					
Montrose	a					*20k57*														22 26					
Stonehaven	a					*21k19*														22 49					
Aberdeen	a					*21k39*														23 13					

For general notes see front of timetable
For details of catering facilities see Directory of Train Operators

- **A** From MetroCentre to Chathill (Table 48)
- **B** From Manchester Airport (Table 39)
- **C** From Penzance (Table 135)
- **D** To Liverpool Lime Street (Table 49)
- **E** From Bristol Temple Meads (Table 51)
- **G** From Bournemouth (Table 51). ⊐P to Edinburgh
- **H** From Liverpool Lime Street (Table 39)
- **J** From Plymouth (Table 51)
- **K** From Plymouth (Table 51). ⊐P to Edinburgh
- **b** Change at Ely and Peterborough
- **c** Change at Doncaster
- **e** Change at Leeds
- **f** Bradford Interchange
- **g** Glasgow Queen Street
- **h** Change at Edinburgh
- **j** Change at Edinburgh and Stirling
- **k** Change at Leuchars

London → Humberside, Yorkshire, North East England and Scotland

Route Diagram - see first page of Table 26

	GR	GR	EM	XC	GC	GR	XC	TP	GR	GR	GR	TP	GR	EM	XC	XC	GR	GR	XC	XC	GR	GR	GR	TP	XC
	FO R 1	R 1	◇ A	R 1 B	R 1 C	R 1	R 1 B	1 ◇ D	R 1	R 1 E	R 1	1 ◇ D	R 1	◇ G	R 1 H	R 1 J	R 1	R 1	R 1 J	R 1 K	R 1	R 1	R 1	1 ◇ D	R 1 L
	✕ 🛒	✕ 🛒		☕	✕	✕ 🛒	☕	🛒	✕ 🛒	✕ 🛒	✕ 🛒	🛒	✕ 🛒		☕	☕	☕ 🛒	✕ 🛒			☕ 🛒	✕ 🛒	✕ 🛒		☕
London Kings Cross 15 ⊖ d	16 30	16 35			16 50	17 00			17 03	17 20	17 30		17 33				17 50	18 00				18 03	18 20		
Stevenage 4 d	16 49	16 12								16 47			17 52				17 19						18 41		
Peterborough 8 a		17 24							17 51	18 06	18 16						18 38					18 53	19 12		
Norwich d			15 52											16 57											
Stansted Airport d		15 25								16 20												17 17			
Cambridge d		16 04							16b35	17 04							17b22					17 49			
Peterborough 8 d		17 25	17 27						17 52	18 07	18 16			18 26			18 39					18 53	19 13		
Grantham 7 a	17 34		17 58						18 11				18 39	18 54			19 04				←	19 14			
d	17 34								18 11				18 39				19 05 →				19 05	19 14			
Newark North Gate 7 a	17 46									18 35											19 17		19 40		
Lincoln a		19c07																			19 49				
Grimsby Town a									19e58									20e43			20 52				
Newark North Gate 7 d	17 46									18 35											19 17		19 40		
Retford 10 d		18 04											19 01												
Doncaster 7 a	18 09	18 19							18 41	19 04			19 16					19 27			19 41	19 47			
Selby a										19 20															
Hull a	19 09	19 47								20 00											20 55	21 06			
Wakefield Westgate 7 a		18 36							19 01				19 34								20 01	20 06			
Huddersfield a		19f27							19f59				20f27									20f59			
Leeds 10 a		18 55							19 21				19 53								20 21	20 25			
Shipley a		19 21							20 07				20s11									21 07			
Bradford Forster Square a		19g28							19g57				20 22									20g57			
Keighley a		19 41							20 20				20h29									20s57			
Skipton a		19 54							20 35				20h46									21 13			
Sheffield 7 🚌 d				17 54											18 21	18 54									19 26
Doncaster 7 d	18 10			18 18												19 19		19 28							
York 8 a	18 34			18 41	18 44	18 51					19 23					19 44		19 51					20 22		
Scarborough a	19 30										20 30												21 30		
Harrogate a						19 43												20 43							
Leeds 10 d					18 12			18 27				18 57			19 05	19 12							19 27	19 57	20 09
Hull d				17 18																			19 10		
York 8 d	18 39			18 44	18 47	18 53		18 59			19 25	19 31			19 38	19 47		19 53					20 23	20 26	20 37
Thirsk d					19 05							19 47												20 42	
Northallerton d	19 00				19 16			19 21				19 59												20 50	
Darlington 7 a	19 13			19 17		19 22		19 33			19 52				20 03	20 12		20 22					20 51		21 07
Eaglescliffe a					19 33																				
Middlesbrough a						19 55						20 31						20 55						21 25	
Darlington 7 d	19 13			19 19		19 23	←	19 34			19 53				20 05	20 14		20 23	←				20 51		21 09
Durham d	19 31			19j42 →			19 42	19 51			20 10				20 21	20 31 →			20 31				21 09		21 26
Chester-le-Street d								19 57											20 38						
Newcastle 8 🚌 a	19 49					19 52	20 04	20 12			20 26				20 37			20 52	20 54				21 27		21 42
Hartlepool a					20 00																				
Sunderland a					20 35			20 49																	
Newcastle 8 🚌 d	19 49					19 55					20 29				20 40			20 54							21 48
Morpeth d											20 44								21a26						22 01
Alnmouth d											21 00				21 08					←					22 15
Berwick-upon-Tweed d											21 22				21 30 →			21 37		21 30					22 36
Dunbar d											21 46														22 59
Edinburgh 10 a	21 20					21 23					22 14							22 22		22 24					23 28
Edinburgh d																		22 25							
Haymarket d																		22 30							
Motherwell a																		23 13							
Glasgow Central 15 a	22k22					22k51					23k25							23 33							
Stirling a						22 24												23m23							
Perth a						23 02												00n15							
Inverness a																									
Inverkeithing a						22 14												22m58							
Kirkcaldy a																		23m20							
Leuchars 3 a																		23m52							
Dundee a																		00m07							
Arbroath a																									
Montrose a																									
Stonehaven a																									
Aberdeen a																									

For general notes see front of timetable
For details of catering facilities see Directory of Train Operators

- **A** To Liverpool Lime Street (Table 49)
- **B** From Bristol Temple Meads (Table 51)
- **C** **The 21st Century Limited**
- **D** From Manchester Airport (Table 39)
- **E** **The Hull Executive**
- **G** To Manchester Piccadilly (Table 49)
- **H** From Bournemouth (Table 51). ☕ to Newcastle
- **J** From Paignton (Table 51)
- **K** From Bournemouth (Table 51)
- **L** From Plymouth (Table 51). ☕ to Leeds
- **b** Change at Ely and Peterborough
- **c** Change at Retford
- **e** Change at Doncaster
- **f** Change at Leeds
- **g** Bradford Interchange
- **h** Change at Shipley
- **j** Arr. 1935
- **k** Glasgow Queen Street
- **m** Change at Edinburgh
- **n** Change at Edinburgh and Stirling

Table 26

Mondays to Fridays

London → Humberside, Yorkshire, North East England and Scotland

Route Diagram - see first page of Table 26

		GR	GR	GR	XC	HT	EM	GR	GR	TP	XC	XC	GR	GR	EM	GR	GR	HT	GR	GR	TP	GR	GR	GR
		FX	FO					FX	FO									BHX						
		R 1	R 1	R 1	R 1	1 ◇	◇	R 1	R 1	1 ◇	R 1	1 ◇	R 1	R 1	◇	R 1	R 1	1 ◇	R 1	R 1	1 ◇	R 1	R 1	R 1
					A		B			C	D	E			B						C			
London Kings Cross 15 ⊖	d	18 30	18 30	18 33		18 50		19 00	19 00				19 03	19 30		20 00	20 03	20 27	20 30	21 00		21 30	22 00	23 30
Stevenage 4	d													18 47		19 17	19 47			21 21			21 46	
Peterborough 8	a			19 22				19 46	19 46				19 52	20 16		20 46	20 52		21 20	21 53		22 16	22 46	00s23
Norwich	d						17 54								18 57							19b45		
Stansted Airport	d													18 20			19 18					20 20		
Cambridge	d							18b25	18b25					19 04		19b25	19 50					20 57		
Peterborough 8	d			19 23			19 31	19 46	19 46				19 52	20 17	20 26	20 46	20 52		21 20	21 53		22 17	22 47	
Grantham 7	a	19 36	19 36			19 55	20 01	20 05	20 05					20 35	20 54		21 14	21 30	21 39			22 38	23 08	00s44
	d	19 36	19 36			19 56		20 05	20 05					20 35			21 14	21 32	21 39			22 38	23 08	
Newark North Gate 7	a			19 52									20 21	20 47			21 26		21 51	22 22		22 49	23 19	00s56
Lincoln	a			20 28		21c10								21 44								23 33		
Grimsby Town	a					21e44								22e42					23e57					
Newark North Gate 7	d			19 52									20 21	20 47			21 26		21 51	22 22		22 49	23 19	
Retford 10	d	19 58	19 58			20 17								21 02				21 53				23 05		
Doncaster 7	a	20 14	20 14	20 18		20 30		20 37	20 37				20 49	21 16		21 36	21 52	22 11	22 17	22 47		23 24	23 49	01s24
Selby	a					20 46		21 01	21 01									22 29						
Hull	a					21 28		21 45	21 45							22 57		23 13						
Wakefield Westgate 7	a			20 38		21e10							21 14	21 35			22 13		22 35			23 42		
Huddersfield	a			21f27		21g59							22 04	22f27					23 15					03f56
Leeds 10	a			20 54		21e27							21 34	21 53			22 33		22 53			23 59		02 35
Shipley	a			21 37									22 07	22 37			23 07		23 30					
Bradford Forster Square	a			21h28		21j57								22h28					23h29					
Keighley	a			21 50									22 20	22 50			23 21		23 43					
Skipton	a			22 06									22 36	23 06			23 39		23 58					
Sheffield 7 ⛴	d	19 30	19 30		19 54						20 21	20 54				21 00				21 51			22 21	
Doncaster 7	d	20 15	20 15		20 22			20 38	20 38							21 36				22 47			23 49	
York 8	a	20 40	20 40		20 46			21 01	21 01							21 59				23 12			00 39	
Scarborough	a															23 02								
Harrogate	a							21 43	21 43							22 45			00 06					
Leeds 10	d	20 12	20 12							20 45	21 10	21 12								22 12	22 42			
Hull	d									19k55														
York 8	d	20 44	20 44		20 51			21 03	21 03	21 12	21 38	21 50				22 00				23 14	23 22			
Thirsk	d									21 28											23 39			
Northallerton	d	21 03	21 03							21 36						22 21					23 55			
Darlington 7	a	21 16	21 16		21 20			21 30	21 30	21 47	22 03	22 18				22 34				23 49	00 06		01m26	
Eaglescliffe	a																							
Middlesbrough	a							22 09	22 09							23 10								
Darlington 7	d	21 16	21 16		21 22			21 31	21 31	21 49	22 05	22 20				22 34				23 49	00 08			
Durham	d	21 34	21 34		21 39			21 49	21 49	22 05	22 21	22 36				22 54				00 07	00 24		01n44	
Chester-le-Street	d				21 46							22 46												
Newcastle 8 ⛴	a	21 52	21 52		22 01			22 07	22 07	22 24	22 42	23 00				23 13				00 42	00 57		02m23	
Hartlepool	a																							
Sunderland	a																							
Newcastle 8 ⛴	d		21 53						22 08															
Morpeth	d								22 22															
Alnmouth	d								22 38															
Berwick-upon-Tweed	d		22 41						23 00															
Dunbar	d																							
Edinburgh 10	a		23 29						23 54															
Edinburgh	d																							
Haymarket	d																							
Motherwell	a																							
Glasgow Central 15	a																							
Stirling	a																							
Perth	a																							
Inverness	a																							
Inverkeithing	a																							
Kirkcaldy	a																							
Leuchars 3	a																							
Dundee	a																							
Arbroath	a																							
Montrose	a																							
Stonehaven	a																							
Aberdeen	a																							

For general notes see front of timetable
For details of catering facilities see Directory of Train Operators

A From Bristol Temple Meads (Table 51)
B To Nottingham (Table 19)
C From Manchester Airport (Table 39)
D From Bournemouth (Table 51)
E From Paignton (Table 51)
b Change at Ely and Peterborough
c Change at Retford
e Change at Doncaster
f Change at Leeds
g Change at Doncaster and Leeds
h Bradford Interchange
j Bradford Interchange. Change at Doncaster and Leeds
k Change at Selby and York
m Tuesday to Saturday mornings
n Arrival time. Tuesday to Saturday mornings

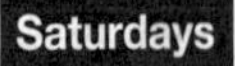

London → Humberside, Yorkshire, North East England and Scotland

Route Diagram - see first page of Table 26

		NT	GR	GR	TP	GR	GR	NT	TP	TP	GR	TP	NT	XC	GR	TP	XC	EM	TP	GR	GR	TP	XC	GR	EM
			R 1	R 1	1 ◇	R 1	R 1		1 ◇	1 ◇	R 1	1 ◇		1 ◇	R 1	1 ◇	1 ◇	◇	1 ◇	R 1	R 1	1 ◇	1 ◇	R 1	◇
		A	B	C	D	B	C	E	G			D	E	H			H	J	D	B	C	D	H		J
London Kings Cross 15 ⊖	d														06 15					07 00	07 00			07 10	
Stevenage 4	d														06 34					06 46	06 46				
Peterborough 8	a														07 05					07 46	07 46			07 56	
Norwich	d																	05 52							
Stansted Airport	d														05 21										
Cambridge	d														05 51					06b32	06b32				07 25
Peterborough 8	d														07 06			07 28		07 46	07 46			07 56	08 25
Grantham 7	a														07 25			07 59		08 05	08 05			08 15	08 53
	d														07 25					08 05	08 05			08 15	
Newark North Gate 7	a														07 37					08 17	08 17			08 27	
Lincoln	a																			08 54	08 54			10c04	
Grimsby Town	a														09e42									10e46	
Newark North Gate 7	d														07 37					08 17	08 17			08 27	
Retford 10	d														07 52									08 42	
Doncaster 7	a														08 07					08 41	08 41			08 57	
Selby	a																								
Hull	a														09 13					09 55	09 55			10 10	
Wakefield Westgate 7	a																							09 15	
Huddersfield	a																							10 04	
Leeds 10	a																							09 35	
Shipley	a																							10 01	
Bradford Forster Square	a																							10f11	
Keighley	a																							10 11	
Skipton	a																							10 24	
Sheffield 7	d					05 29	05 29					06 14		07 12			07 54						08 21		
Doncaster 7	d					06 20	06 20								08 08		08 25			08 42	08 42				
York 8	a					06 40	06 40								08 31		08 49			09 04	09 04				
Scarborough	a																								
Harrogate	a														09 17									10 33	
Leeds 10	d				04 49				06 35	06 55	07 10	07 50		07 57		08 12			08 27			08 57	09 05		
Hull	d									06g00		06 57													
York 8	d				05 40	06 42	06 42		07 06	07 32	07 37	08 22		08 27	08 33	08 42	08 53		08 57	09 06	09 06	09 26	09 35		
Thirsk	d				06 01				07 22	07 54		08 44										09 46			
Northallerton	d				06 17	07 01	07 01		07 30	08 02		08 55				09 03			09 18			09 55			
Darlington 7	a				06 28	07 15	07 15		07 41		08 08			08 52	09 00	09 14	09 19		09 29	09 35	09 35		10 00		
Eaglescliffe	a																								
Middlesbrough	a				07 01	08 02	08 02		08 36	08 32		09 32		09 25		09 52				10 16	10 16	10 30	10 52		
Darlington 7	d					07 15	07 15	07 20	07 43		08 09		08 16	08 54	09 01	09 15	09 21		09 30	09 36	09 36		10 02		
Durham	d					07 33	07 33	07 41	07 59		08 26		08 37	09 10	09 18	09 32	09 38		09 47				10 18		
Chester-le-Street	d							07 48	08 05				08 44				09 45								
Newcastle 8	a					07 50	07 50	08 01	08 19		08 43		08 56	09 26	09 34	09 49	09 59		10 04	10 05	10 05		10 34		
Hartlepool	a																								
Sunderland	a								08 49				09 49							10 49	10 49				
Newcastle 8	d	06 05	06 30	06 30		07 52	07 52				08 45			09 29	09 36					10 07	10 07		10 39		
Morpeth	d	06 25	06 43	06 43		08 06	08 06	08a44						09 42						10a35	10a35				
Alnmouth	d	06a43	06 57	06 57		08 20	08 20							09 56											
Berwick-upon-Tweed	d		07 19	07 19		08 42	08 42				09 29				10 22					10 50	10 50		11 21		
Dunbar	d		07 43	07 43		09 06	09 06				09 54												11 44		
Edinburgh 10	a		08 09	08 09		09 35	09 35				10 20			11 02	11 12					11 37	11 37		12 13		
Edinburgh	d		08 12			09 39					10 26									11 38					
Haymarket	d					09 43					10 31									11 44					
Motherwell	a		08 56	09h24		10 27	10h50													12 29	12h52				
Glasgow Central 15	a		09 16	09j21		10 48	10j36				11k21			12j06	12j21					12 49	12j51		13j21		
Stirling	a		09m23	09 23		10m53	10 53				11m23			12 23	12 23					12m53	12 53		13 23		
Perth	a		09m54	09 54		11n37	11n37				12n37			12 56	12 56					13n37	13n37		14n37		
Inverness	a		11m59	11 59										15 18	15 18										
Inverkeithing	a		08m52	08 52		10m12	10 12				10 47			11 36	12 05					12m11	12 11		13 04		
Kirkcaldy	a		09m08	09 08		10m42	10 42				11 04			11 58	12 27					12m42	12 42		13 26		
Leuchars 3	a		10m09	10 09		11m12	11 12				11 29									13m12	13 12				
Dundee	a		10m21	10 21		11m24	11 24				11 44									13m24	13 24				
Arbroath	a		10m38	10 38		11m41	11 41				12 01									13m41	13 41				
Montrose	a		10m52	10 52		12m17	12 17				12 17									14q32	14q32				
Stonehaven	a		11m14	11 14		12m15	12 15				12 40									14m16	14 16				
Aberdeen	a		11m34	11 34		12m35	12 35				13 04									14m36	14 36				

For general notes see front of timetable
For details of catering facilities see Directory of Train Operators

- **A** To Chathill (Table 48)
- **B** Until 22 March
- **C** From 29 March
- **D** From Manchester Airport (Table 39)
- **E** From Saltburn (Table 44)
- **G** From Manchester Piccadilly (Table 39)
- **H** From Birmingham New Street (Table 51)
- **J** To Liverpool Lime Street (Table 49)
- **b** Change at Ely and Peterborough
- **c** Change at Peterborough
- **e** Change at Doncaster
- **f** Bradford Interchange
- **g** Change at Selby and York
- **h** By bus
- **j** Glasgow Queen Street
- **k** Glasgow Queen Street. Change at Edinburgh
- **m** Change at Edinburgh
- **n** Change at Edinburgh and Stirling
- **q** Change at Edinburgh and Arbroath

London → Humberside, Yorkshire, North East England and Scotland

Route Diagram - see first page of Table 26

	XC	TP	GC	GR	TP	EM	TP	XC	GR	GR	XC	EM	TP	GR	GR	TP	XC	GR	GR	XC	TP	HT	EM	GR
	1◇	1◇	R 1	R 1	1◇	1◇	1◇	1◇	R 1	R 1	1◇	◇	1◇	R 1	R 1	1◇	1◇	R 1	R 1	1◇	1◇	1◇	◇	R 1
	A	B			B	C	B	D			A	E	B	G	H	B	J			D	B		E	K
London Kings Cross 15 ⊖ d			07 57	08 00					08 10	08 30				09 00	09 00			09 05	09 30			09 34		10 00
Stevenage 4 d				08 20					07 46	08 49								09 24	09 49					
Peterborough 8 a				08 51					08 56	09 20				09 46	09 46				10 20					10 46
Norwich d										06b40		07 57											08 57	
Stansted Airport d										07 27									08 25					
Cambridge d				06b59						08 04				08b33	08b33				09 04					09b12
Peterborough 8 d				08 51					08 57	09 21		09 29		09 46	09 46				10 21				10 26	10 46
Grantham 7 a									09 16	09 40		09 59							10 40			10 44	10 56	
d									09 16	09 40									10 40			10 44		
Newark North Gate 7 a									09 28									10 18						
Lincoln a									10 19	10c58														
Grimsby Town a									11 17	11e42														12e48
Newark North Gate 7 d									09 28									10 18						
Retford 10 d														10 24	10 24							11 06		
Doncaster 7 a				09 37					09 56	10 13				10 38	10 38			10 47	11 13			11 24		11 32
Selby a																						11 39		
Hull a				10 50						11 12				11 53	11 53			12 08				12 20		12 50
Wakefield Westgate 7 a									10 14									11 11						
Huddersfield a									11 04									12 04						
Leeds 10 a									10 35									11 35						
Shipley a									11 01									12 07						
Bradford Forster Square a									11f11									12f11						
Keighley a									11 11									12 20						
Skipton a									11 24									12 37						
Sheffield 7 d	08 54					09 21		09 21		09 25	09 54						10 21		10 25	10 54				
Doncaster 7 d	09 23			09 37		09 54				10 14	10 20			10 39	10 39				11 14	11 20				11 32
York 8 a	09 48		09 57	10 01		10 16				10 39	10 44			11 02	11 02				11 39	11 45				11 56
Scarborough a				11 30										12 30	12 30									
Harrogate a				10 43					11 33					11 43	11 43			12 33						12 43
Leeds 10 d		09 27					09 57	10 05			10 12		10 27			10 57	11 05			11 12	11 27			
Hull d	08g37						09 02									10g05								
York 8 d	09 51	09 56	10 00	10 03			10 26	10 35		10 42	10 46		10 54	11 03	11 03	11 26	11 35		11 41	11 47	11 54			11 57
Thirsk d			10 21		←		10 46									11 43								
Northallerton d		10 25	10 32		10 25		10 55						11 15			11 55					12 15			12 20
Darlington 7 a	10 16	→		10 30	10 36			11 01		11 11	11 16		11 26	11 32	11 32		12 01		12 09	12 15	12 26			12 32
Eaglescliffe a			10 48																					
Middlesbrough a					11 08		11 30				11 55			12 32	12 32	12 30					12 58			13 23
Darlington 7 d	10 18			10 31	10 38			11 03		11 11	11 17		11 28	11 32	11 32		12 03		12 10	12 17	12 28			12 33
Durham d	10 34			10 48	10 54			11 21			11 34		11 44				12 19		12 27	12 34	12 45			
Chester-le-Street d	10 41				11 00															12 41				
Newcastle 8 a	10 59			11 04	11 15			11 36		11 43	11 57		12 02	12 02	12 02		12 35		12 44	12 57	13 01			13 02
Hartlepool a			11 20																					
Sunderland a			11 50		11 49									12 49	12 49									13 49
Newcastle 8 d				11 08				11 39		11 45				12 03	12 03		12 39		12 46					13 04
Morpeth d				11a35				11 52						12a35	12a35									13a36
Alnmouth d				11 34				12 06																
Berwick-upon-Tweed d										12 31							13 21		13 29					
Dunbar d																	13 44							
Edinburgh 10 a				12 45				13 13		13 19				13 32	13 32		14 13		14 16					14 31
Edinburgh d														13 39										
Haymarket d														13 44										
Motherwell a														14 27	14h47									
Glasgow Central 15 a				13j51						14j21				14 47	14j36				15j21					15j36
Stirling a				13 53						14 23				14k53	14 53				15 23					15 53
Perth a				14m37						14 54				15m36	15m36									16m37
Inverness a										17 07														
Inverkeithing a				13 27										14k05	14 05									15 04
Kirkcaldy a				13 43										14k27	14 27									15 26
Leuchars 3 a				14 11										15k12	15 12									
Dundee a				14 23										15k24	15 24									
Arbroath a				14 40										15k43	15 43									
Montrose a				14 55										16n30	16n30									
Stonehaven a				15 16										16k17	16 17									
Aberdeen a				15 36										16k37	16 37									

For general notes see front of timetable
For details of catering facilities see Directory of Train Operators

- A From Birmingham New Street (Table 51)
- B From Manchester Airport (Table 39)
- C From St Pancras International (Table 53)
- D From Bristol Temple Meads (Table 51)
- E To Liverpool Lime Street (Table 49)
- G Until 22 March
- H From 29 March
- J From Southampton Central (Table 51)
- K **The Flying Scotsman**
- b Change at Ely and Peterborough
- c Change at Peterborough
- e Change at Doncaster
- f Bradford Interchange
- g Change at Selby and York
- h By bus
- j Glasgow Queen Street
- k Change at Edinburgh
- m Change at Edinburgh and Stirling
- n Change at Edinburgh and Arbroath

Table 26

London → Humberside, Yorkshire, North East England and Scotland

Route Diagram - see first page of Table 26

	TP	GR	GR	XC	XC	GR	EM	TP	GR	GR	TP	TP	GR	GC	XC	GR		XC	TP	HT	EM	GR	TP	TP	XC
	1 ◇	R 1	R 1	1 ◇	1 ◇	R 1	◇	1 ◇	R 1	R 1	1 ◇	1 ◇	R 1	R 1	1 ◇	R 1		1 ◇	1 ◇	1 ◇	◇	R 1	1 ◇	1 ◇	1 ◇
	A		B	C	D		E	A	G	H	A	A			J			K	A		E	L	A	A	C
London Kings Cross 15 ⊖ d		10 10	10 30			10 40			11 00	11 00			11 10	11 27		11 30				11 48		12 00			
Stevenage 4 d			*10 12*						*10 46*	*10 46*						11 50									
Peterborough 8 a		10 56	11 16			11 26			11 46	11 46			11 56			12 21						12 46			
Norwich d							09 57														10 57				
Stansted Airport d			*09 25*													*10 25*									
Cambridge d			*10 04*						*10b33*	*10b33*						*11 04*						*11b12*			
Peterborough 8 d		10 56	11 18			11 27	11 27		11 46	11 46			11 56			12 21					12 27	12 47			
Grantham 7 a		11 15				11 48	11 57						12 15			12 42				12 48	12 57				
d		11 15				11 48							12 16			12 43				12 48					
Newark North Gate 7 a		11 27											12 28												
Lincoln a		*11 57*				*13c16*																			
Grimsby Town a		*12 55*							*13e42*	*13e42*										*14e47*					
Newark North Gate 7 d		11 27											12 28												
Retford 10 d													12 43							13 14					
Doncaster 7 a		11 53				12 19			12 33	12 33			12 58			13 14				13 26					
Selby a																				13 42					
Hull a		*13 07*							*13 50*	*13 50*			*14 10*							14 22					
Wakefield Westgate 7 a		12 13											13 16												
Huddersfield a		*13 04*											*14 04*												
Leeds 10 a		12 35											13 35												
Shipley a		*13 01*											*14 03*												
Bradford Forster Square a		*13f11*											*14f11*												
Keighley a		*13 11*											*14 13*												
Skipton a		*13 24*											*14 26*												
Sheffield 7 ⇌ d				11 21	11 54	*11 41*									12 21	*12 25*		12 54							13 21
Doncaster 7 d					12 17	12 20			12 34	12 34						13 15		13 21							
York 8 a			12 27		12 43	12 46			12 56	12 56				13 25		13 39		13 44				13 56			
Scarborough a			*13 30*											*14 30*											
Harrogate a		*13 33*							*13 43*	*13 43*			*14 33*									*14 43*			
Leeds 10 d	11 57		*11 41*	12 05	*12 12*			12 27				12 57		*12 41*	13 05			*13 12*	13 27				13 57		14 05
Hull d	*11 08*										⟵				*11g37*										*13 12*
York 8 d	12 26		12 29	12 35	12 46	12 49		12 54 ⟶	12 58	12 58	12 54	13 26		13 30	13 35	13 42		13 49	13 54			13 57	14 26 ⟶		14 34
Thirsk d	12 46											13 43		13 51											
Northallerton d	12 55										13 23	13 55		14 09					14 23						
Darlington 7 a				13 01	13 11	13 17			13 25	13 25	13 34				14 01	14 12		14 17	14 34						14 59
Eaglescliffe a														14 26											
Middlesbrough a	13 30					*13 57*					*14 18*	14 30						*14 58*	*15 27*					⟵	
Darlington 7 d				13 03	13 13	13 17			13 26	13 26	13 36				14 03	14 12		14 19	14 35 ⟶					14 35	15 02
Durham d				13 19	13 29	13 35					13 52				14 19	14 30		14 36						14 52	15 18
Chester-le-Street d											13 58														
Newcastle 8 ⇌ a			13 24	13 35	13 50	13 53			13 59	13 59	14 13				14 35	14 46		14 54				14 57		15 12	15 34
Hartlepool a														14 45											
Sunderland a											*14 49*			15 11										*15 50*	
Newcastle 8 ⇌ d			13 26	13 39					14 01	14 01					14 39	14 48						14 58			15 39
Morpeth d									*14a36*	*14a36*												*15a35*			15 52
Alnmouth d				14 03																					16 06
Berwick-upon-Tweed d									14 44	14 44					15 21							15 42			
Dunbar d															15 44										
Edinburgh 10 a			14 54	15 13					15 35	15 35					16 19	16 19						16 30			17 14
Edinburgh d			15 00						15 37						16 30							16 34			
Haymarket d			15 04						15 41						16 35							16 39			
Motherwell a									16 28	*16h50*															
Glasgow Central 15 a			*16j08*	*16j21*					16 48	*16j36*						*17j21*						*17j36*			
Stirling a				*16 23*					*16k53*	*16 53*												17 19			
Perth a				*17m20*					*17m36*	*17m36*												17 55			
Inverness a				*19m34*																		20 08			
Inverkeithing a			15 19	*16 04*					*16k12*	*16 12*					16 47	*16 47*						*17k04*			
Kirkcaldy a			15 36	*16 26*					*16k40*	*16 40*					17 02	*17 02*						*17k26*			
Leuchars 3 a			16 01						*17k10*	*17 10*					17 31	*17 31*						*18k05*			
Dundee a			16 17						*17k26*	*17 26*					17 44	*17 44*						*18k22*			
Arbroath a			16 35						*17k48*	*17 48*					18 03	*18 03*						*18k40*			
Montrose a			16 50						*18k03*	*18 03*					18 17	*18 17*						*18k55*			
Stonehaven a			17 13						*18k24*	*18 24*					18 37	*18 37*						*19k16*			
Aberdeen a			17 38						*18k44*	*18 44*					19 02	*19 02*						*19k38*			

For general notes see front of timetable
For details of catering facilities see Directory of Train Operators

- **A** From Manchester Airport (Table 39)
- **B** **The Northern Lights**
- **C** From Plymouth (Table 51)
- **D** From Bristol Temple Meads (Table 51)
- **E** To Liverpool Lime Street (Table 49)
- **G** Until 22 March
- **H** From 29 March
- **J** From Bournemouth (Table 51)
- **K** From Cardiff Central (from 29 March from Bristol Temple Meads) (Table 51)
- **L** **The Highland Chieftain**
- **b** Change at Ely and Peterborough
- **c** Change at Peterborough
- **e** Change at Doncaster
- **f** Bradford Interchange
- **g** Change at Selby and York
- **h** By bus
- **j** Glasgow Queen Street
- **k** Change at Edinburgh
- **m** Change at Edinburgh and Stirling

London → Humberside, Yorkshire, North East England and Scotland

Route Diagram - see first page of Table 26

	GR	GR	EM	TP	XC	TP	GR	GR	TP	TP	XC	GR	GR	XC	HT	EM	GR	TP	NT	XC	XC	GR	EM	GR
	R 1	R 1	◇	1 ◇	1 ◇	1 ◇	R 1	R 1	1 ◇	1 ◇	1 ◇	R 1	R 1	1 ◇	1 ◇	◇	R 1	1 ◇		1 ◇	1 ◇	R 1	◇	R 1
			A	B	C	B	D	E	B	B	G			H		A		B	J	K	C		A	D
	☕ 🍴	☕ 🍴		🍴	☕	🍴	☕ 🍴	☕ 🍴	🍴	🍴	☕	☕ 🍴	☕ 🍴	☕	⊠ ☕		☕ 🍴			☕	☕	☕ 🍴		☕ 🍴
London Kings Cross 15 ⊖ d	12 10	12 30					13 00	13 00				13 10	13 30		13 38		14 00					14 30		15 00
Stevenage 4 d		12 12					12 46	12 46					13 49									14 12		14 46
Peterborough 8 a	12 56	13 16					13 46	13 46				13 56	14 19				14 46					15 16		15 46
Norwich d			11 57													12 57							13 57	
Stansted Airport d		11 25											12 25									13 25		
Cambridge d		12 04					12b33	12b33					13 04				13b12					14 04		14b12
Peterborough 8 d	12 56	13 16	13 26				13 46	13 46				13 56	14 20			14 24	14 47					15 16	15 26	15 46
Grantham 7 a	13 15	13 35	13 55									14 15	14 39		14 43	14 57						15 35	15 54	
d	13 15	13 35										14 15	14 39		14 43							15 35		
Newark North Gate 7 a	13 27											14 27	14 51									15 47		
Lincoln a	13 58												15 26		16c09		16 40							17 50
Grimsby Town a	15 01						15e42	15e42									16e48							17e42
Newark North Gate 7 d	13 27											14 27	14 51									15 47		
Retford 10 d												14 42			15 10							16 02		
Doncaster 7 a	13 52	14 07					14 33	14 33				14 57			15 24		15 35					16 20		16 32
Selby a															15 40									
Hull a		15 12					15 51	15 51				16 07			16 20		16 50							17 53
Wakefield Westgate 7 a	14 13	14 42										15 15										16 38		
Huddersfield a	15 04	15f45										16 04										17g45		
Leeds 10 a	14 35	15 02										15 35										17 01		
Shipley a	15 01	15f37										16 07										17 37		
Bradford Forster Square a	15h11	15j42										16h11										17h42		
Keighley a	15 11	15f50										16 20										17 51		
Skipton a	15 24	16f07										16 37										18 07		
Sheffield 7 d		13 11			13 54						14 21			14 54						15 21	15 54			
Doncaster 7 d		14 07			14 17		14 34	14 34						15 18			15 36				16 17			16 32
York 8 a		14 30			14 43		14 58	14 58					15 35	15 43			15 59				16 45			16 56
Scarborough a		15 30					16 30	16 30									17 30							18 17
Harrogate a	15 33						15 43	15 43				16 33					16 43					17 47		17 49
Leeds 10 d		13 57			14 12	14 27	14 27	14 27		14 57	15 05			15 12			15 27	15 57		16 05	16 12			
Hull d				←					←									14 51						
York 8 d		14 36		14 26	14 49	14 54 →	15 00	15 00	14 54	15 26	15 35		15 40	15 45			16 01	16 26		16 35	16 51			16 57
Thirsk d				14 46						15 46								16 46						
Northallerton d		14 56		15 01					15 23	15 55								16 55						
Darlington 7 a		15 09			15 15		15 27	15 27	15 34		16 00		16 07	16 12			16 29			17 00	17 16			17 26
Eaglescliffe a																								
Middlesbrough a				15 34	15 57				16 22	16 30				16 52			17 26	17 34			17 54			
Darlington 7 d		15 09			15 17		15 28	15 28	15 35		16 02		16 08	16 14			16 29			17 02	17 18			17 26
Durham d		15 27			15 34		15 45	15 45	15 52		16 18		16 25	16 30						17 18	17 34			17 44
Chester-le-Street d									15 58												17 44			
Newcastle 8 a		15 43			15 55		16 01	16 01	16 14		16 34		16 41	16 51			16 59			17 34	17 58			18 00
Hartlepool a																								
Sunderland a									16 49				17 13				17 50							
Newcastle 8 d		15 44					16 03	16 03			16 39		16 43				17 01		17 10	17 39				18 01
Morpeth d							16a36	16a36											17 32	18a06				
Alnmouth d							16 29	16 29											18a09	18 03				
Berwick-upon-Tweed d							16 52	16 52			17 21													18 48
Dunbar d											17 44													
Edinburgh 10 a		17 15					17 39	17 39			18 16		18 16				18 28			19 12				19 33
Edinburgh d							17 41										18 32			19 12				19 36
Haymarket d																	18 37			19 17				19 41
Motherwell a							18 29	18k54																20 20
Glasgow Central 15 a		18m21					18 50	18m50					19m21				19m36			20m24				20 44
Stirling a		18 23					18n53	18 53					19 23				19n53			20n23				20n53
Perth a		18 54					19q42	19q42									20q37			20n51				21q42
Inverness a		20 58																		23n13				
Inverkeithing a		17 51					18n12	18 12					18 50				18 54			19 32				20n14
Kirkcaldy a		18 14					18n34	18 34									19 10			19 49				20n56
Leuchars 3 a							19n15	19 15									19 34			20 27				21n28
Dundee a							19n27	19 27									19 49			20 50				21n41
Arbroath a							19n45	19 45									20 07			21 18				22r25
Montrose a																	20 22			21 33				22r39
Stonehaven a							20n18	20 18									20 46			21 53				23r01
Aberdeen a							20n41	20 41									21 10			22 15				

For general notes see front of timetable
For details of catering facilities see Directory of Train Operators

- **A** To Liverpool Lime Street (Table 49)
- **B** From Manchester Airport (Table 39)
- **C** From Bristol Temple Meads (Table 51)
- **D** Until 22 March
- **E** From 29 March
- **G** From Bournemouth (Table 51)
- **H** From Paignton (Table 51)
- **J** From MetroCentre to Chathill (Table 48)
- **K** From Penzance (Table 135)
- **b** Change at Ely and Peterborough
- **c** Change at Retford
- **e** Change at Doncaster
- **f** Change at Doncaster and Leeds
- **g** Change at Leeds
- **h** Bradford Interchange
- **j** Bradford Interchange. Change at Doncaster and Leeds
- **k** By bus
- **m** Glasgow Queen Street
- **n** Change at Edinburgh
- **q** Change at Edinburgh and Stirling
- **r** Change at Edinburgh and Dundee

London → Humberside, Yorkshire, North East England and Scotland

Route Diagram - see first page of Table 26

	GR	TP	XC	XC	TP	GR	XC	EM	GR	TP	XC	XC	GR	EM	XC	GC	TP	GR	GR	TP	GC	TP	HT	XC
	R 1	1 ◇	1 ◇	1 ◇	1 ◇	R 1	1 ◇	◇	R 1	1 ◇	1 ◇	1 ◇	R 1	◇	1 ◇	R 1	1 ◇	R 1	R 1	1 ◇	R 1	1 ◇	1 ◇	1 ◇
	A	B	C	D	E		G	H		B	J	K		L	G	N	B	Q	A	B	N	B		U
London Kings Cross 15 ⊖ d	15 00					15 30			16 00				16 30			16 50		17 00	17 00				17 05	
Stevenage 4 d	14 46					15 49							16 12					16 46	16 46					
Peterborough 8 a	15 46					16 20			16 46				17 16					17 46	17 46					
Norwich d								14 57						15 52										
Stansted Airport d						14 25							15 25											
Cambridge d	14b12					15 04			15b12				16 04					16b33	16b33					
Peterborough 8 d	15 46					16 21		16 30	16 46				17 16	17 25				17 46	17 46					
Grantham 7 a						16 40		16 58					17 35	17 53									18 10	
Grantham d						16 40							17 35										18 10	
Newark North Gate 7 a						16 52							17 47											
Lincoln a	17 50					18 14							19 19										20c06	
Grimsby Town a	17e42								18e49														19e58	
Newark North Gate 7 d						16 52							17 47											
Retford 10 d													18 02										18 31	
Doncaster 7 a	16 32					17 16			17 35				18 17					18 33	18 33				18 46	
Selby a																							19 07	
Hull a	17 53								18 57				19 15										19 47	
Wakefield Westgate 7 a						17 33							18 35											
Huddersfield a						18f27							19f27											
Leeds 10 a						17 53							18 53											
Shipley a						18 21							19 21											
Bradford Forster Square a						18g28							19g28											
Keighley a						18 50							19 41											
Skipton a						19 06							19 54											
Sheffield 7 d			16 21	16 21			16 54				17 21	17 21			17 54									18 21
Doncaster 7 d	16 32						17 21		17 35						18 23			18 33	18 33					
York 8 a	16 56						17 45		18 01						18 46	18 50		18 56	18 56					
Scarborough a	18 17								19 30									20 30	20 30					
Harrogate a	17 49								18 43									19 43	19 43					
Leeds 10 d		16 27	17 05	17 05	17 12					17 57	18 05	18 05			18 12		18 27			←		18 57		19 05
Hull d			16 10	16 10											17 18									
York 8 d	16 57	17 02	17 35	17 35	17 43		17 48		18 03	18 26	18 33	18 33			18 49	18 52	18 56 →	18 58	18 58	18 56	←	19 26		19 35
Thirsk d		17 20			18 00					18 44						19 21 →					19 21	19 42		
Northallerton d		17 28			18 10				18 22	18 55										19 21	19 30	19 50		
Darlington 7 a	17 26	17 39	18 00	18 00			18 15		18 35		19 00	19 00			19 14			19 26	19 26	19 33				20 02
Eaglescliffe a																					19 49			
Middlesbrough a		18 25			18 42		19 00			19 30					19 52							20 23		
Darlington 7 d	17 26	17 41	18 02	18 02			18 17		18 35		19 02	19 02			19 16			19 27	19 27	19 34				20 04
Durham d	17 44	17 57	18 18	18 18			18 33				19 18	19 18			19 32			19 44	19 44	19 51				20 23
Chester-le-Street d		18 03					18 40													19 57				
Newcastle 8 a	18 00	18 18	18 34	18 34			18 56		19 05		19 34	19 34			19 53			20 00	20 00	20 12				20 36
Hartlepool a																					20 08			
Sunderland a		18 49							19 50												20 35			
Newcastle 8 d	18 01		18 39	18 39					19 06		19 39	19 39						20 02	20 02					20 39
Morpeth d		18a49																		20a45				
Alnmouth d											20 03	20 03												21 03
Berwick-upon-Tweed d	18 48		19 21	19 21					19 49		20 24	20 24												21 24
Dunbar d			19 44	19 44														21 05	21 05					
Edinburgh 10 a	19 33		20 13	20 13					20 37		21 13	21 13						21 34	21 34					22 13
Edinburgh d			20 14								21 15							21 39						
Haymarket d			20 18								21 19							21 44						
Motherwell a	20h48		21s00								22s04							22 26	22h49					
Glasgow Central 15 a	20j51		21 27	21j22					21j51		22 43	22j22						22 46	22j51					23j25
Stirling a	20 53		21k23	21 23							22k26	22 26												23 24
Perth a	21m42		22m36	22m36							23k05	23 05												00m15
Inverness a																								
Inverkeithing a	20 14								21 12		21k47	21 47						22k14	22 14					22 58
Kirkcaldy a	20 56								21 43		22k09	22 09												23 20
Leuchars 3 a	21 28								22 13		22k41	22 41												23 52
Dundee a	21 41								22 26		22k55	22 55												00 07
Arbroath a	22n25								22 44															
Montrose a	22n39								22 58															
Stonehaven a	23n01								23 20															
Aberdeen a									23 40															

For general notes see front of timetable
For details of catering facilities see Directory of Train Operators

- A From 29 March
- B From Manchester Airport (Table 39)
- C Until 22 March. From Bournemouth (Table 51). ⊡ to Edinburgh
- D From 29 March. From Bournemouth (Table 51)
- E From Liverpool Lime Street (Table 39)
- G From Bristol Temple Meads (Table 51)
- H To Manchester Piccadilly (Table 49)
- J Until 22 March. From Plymouth (Table 51). ⊡ to Edinburgh
- K From 29 March. From Plymouth (Table 51)
- L To Manchester Oxford Road (Table 49)
- N **The 21st Century Limited**
- Q Until 22 March
- U From Bournemouth (Table 51)
- b Change at Ely and Peterborough
- c Change at Retford
- e Change at Doncaster
- f Change at Leeds
- g Bradford Interchange
- h By bus
- j Glasgow Queen Street
- k Change at Edinburgh
- m Change at Edinburgh and Stirling
- n Change at Edinburgh and Dundee

London → Humberside, Yorkshire, North East England and Scotland

Route Diagram - see first page of Table 26

	GR	XC	EM	GR	GR	TP	XC	GR	GR	XC	GR	EM	GR	TP	XC	XC	GR	XC	HT	EM	GR	GR	EM
	R 1	1 ◇	◇	R 1	R 1	1 ◇	1 ◇	R 1	R 1	1 ◇	R 1	◇	R 1	1 ◇	1 ◇	1 ◇	R 1	1 ◇	1 ◇	◇	R 1	R 1	
		A	B			C	D			E		G		C	E	H		H		G			J
London Kings Cross 15 ⊖ d	17 30			17 40	18 00			18 30	18 35		18 40		19 00				19 30		19 41		20 00	20 30	
Stevenage 4 d	17 50			17 12					18 27				19 19								19 46	20 12	
Peterborough 8 a	18 21			18 26	18 46				19 21		19 26		19 50				20 16				20 46	21 16	
Norwich d			16 57									17 57								18 57			
Stansted Airport d	16 25								17 25								18 25					19 18	
Cambridge d	17 04				17b12				18 02				18b33				19 04				19b12	19 50	
Peterborough 8 d	18 21		18 25	18 26	18 46				19 21		19 27	19 28	19 51				20 16			20 27	20 46	21 17	21 27
Grantham 7 a	18 42		18 56	18 47				19 30				20 00					20 35		20 41	20 58	21 05	21 38	22 00
Grantham d	18 42			18 47				19 30									20 35		20 43		21 05	21 38	
Newark North Gate 7 a	18 54			18 59							19 56						20 47				21 17	21 49	
Lincoln a											20 38											22 36	
Grimsby Town a					20c47						21c46								22c46			23c49	
Newark North Gate 7 d	18 54			18 59							19 56						20 47				21 17	21 49	
Retford 10 d											20 11								21 05		21 32		
Doncaster 7 a	19 17			19 23	19 33			20 01	20 08		20 27		20 39				21 11		21 19		21 47	22 14	
Selby a											20 43								21 35				
Hull a					20 52			21 04			21 27		21 45						22 15		22 58		
Wakefield Westgate 7 a	19 35			19 59				20 19			20c53		21 34						21c57		22 05	22 38	
Huddersfield a	20e27			20f59				21 05			21f59		22f27								23e00	23g49	
Leeds 10 a	19 52			20 22				20 36			21c15		21 54						22c18		22 24	23 00	
Shipley a	20 18							20s56			21f38		22f37								23 07	23f30	
Bradford Forster Square a	20h28			20j57				21 06			21j57		22j28								22h57		
Keighley a	20s17							21k20			21f51		22f50								23 20	23f43	
Skipton a	20 32							21k36			22f07		23f06								23 39	23f58	
Sheffield 7 d		18 54					19 21			19 54						20 21	20 15					21 14	
Doncaster 7 d		19 21		19 25	19 34				20 08	20 18			20 40				21 12					22 14	
York 8 a		19 49		19 54	19 58				20 34	20 42			21 03				21 38					22 38	
Scarborough a					21 30												23 02						
Harrogate a					20 43			21e54									22 29		23f06			23f58	
Leeds 10 d		19 12			19 15	19 57	20 05			20 12				20 45		21 10	20 48	←				21 45	
Hull d					18 46									19m55									
York 8 d		19 52		19 56	20 01	20 26	20 36		20 41	20 46			21 06	21 12		21 37 →	21 41	21 37				22 39	
Thirsk d						20 43								21 28									
Northallerton d						20 51							21 26	21 36									
Darlington 7 a		20 17		20 23	20 29		21 03		21 08	21 14			21 38	21 47			22 09					23 07	
Eaglescliffe a																							
Middlesbrough a				20 55		21 25				22 09					←		22 57						
Darlington 7 d		20 19		20 24	20 30		21 04		21 09	21 25 →			21 39	21 49	21 25		22 10					23 08	
Durham d		20 35		20 41			21 22		21 26	→			21 56	22 05	22 11		22 27	22 49				23 25	
Chester-le-Street d		20 42													22 18								
Newcastle 8 a		20 54		21 00	21 02		21 41		21 44				22 14	22 24	22 34		22 45	23 11				23 46	
Hartlepool a																							
Sunderland a																							
Newcastle 8 d		20 57			21 03																		
Morpeth d					21 19																		
Alnmouth d					21 35																		
Berwick-upon-Tweed d		21 39			21 57																		
Dunbar d		22 02																					
Edinburgh 10 a		22 31			22 48																		
Edinburgh d																							
Haymarket d																							
Motherwell a																							
Glasgow Central 15 a					00n03																		
Stirling a																							
Perth a																							
Inverness a																							
Inverkeithing a					23 29																		
Kirkcaldy a					23 51																		
Leuchars 3 a					00 21																		
Dundee a					00 36																		
Arbroath a																							
Montrose a																							
Stonehaven a																							
Aberdeen a																							

For general notes see front of timetable
For details of catering facilities see Directory of Train Operators

- **A** From Paignton (Table 51)
- **B** To Manchester Piccadilly (Table 49)
- **C** From Manchester Airport (Table 39)
- **D** From Plymouth (Table 51). to Leeds
- **E** From Bristol Temple Meads (Table 51)
- **G** To Nottingham (Table 19)
- **H** From Bournemouth (Table 51). to Leeds
- **J** From Spalding (Table 18) to Nottingham (Table 19)
- **b** Change at Ely and Peterborough
- **c** Change at Doncaster
- **e** Change at Leeds
- **f** Change at Doncaster and Leeds
- **g** Until 26 January and from 29 March change at Doncaster and Leeds. 2 February to 22 March change at Doncaster and Leeds, by bus from Leeds arr. 0030 Sunday mornings
- **h** Bradford Interchange
- **j** Bradford Interchange. Change at Doncaster and Leeds
- **k** Change at Shipley
- **m** Change at Selby and York
- **n** Glasgow Queen Street

Table 26

Sundays

London → Humberside, Yorkshire, North East England and Scotland

until 27 January and from 30 March

Route Diagram - see first page of Table 26

		GR	TP	GR	TP	GR	TP	TP	GC	GR	TP	GR	GR	XC	XC	EM	GR	TP	EM	XC	GR	GR	XC	XC	HT	GR
		R 1	1 ◇	R 1	1 ◇	R 1	1 ◇	1 ◇	R 1	R 1	1 ◇	R 1	R 1	1 ◇	1 ◇	1 ◇	R 1	1 ◇	1 ◇	1 ◇	R 1	R 1	1 ◇	1 ◇	1 ◇	R 1
			A		A	B	A	C			A			D	D	E	G	A	H	D			D	D		J
London Kings Cross 15 ⊖	d								08 55	09 00		09 10	09 30				10 00				10 10	10 30			10 42	11 00
Stevenage 4	d									09 20		08b46									09 46	10 49				
Peterborough 8	a									09 49		09 54	10 14				10 45				10 59	11 18				11 44
Norwich	d																									
Stansted Airport	d																									
Cambridge	d																									
Peterborough 8	d									09 49		09 55	10 14				10 46				10 59	11 19				11 45
Grantham 7	a									10 11											11 21				11 45	
	d									10 11											11 21				11 46	
Newark North Gate 7	a											10 27					11 16									
Lincoln	a																11 56									
Grimsby Town	a																								13c38	
Newark North Gate 7	d											10 27					11 16									
Retford 10	d											10 43									11 43				12 07	
Doncaster 7	a									10 44		11 00	11 05				11 41				11 59	12 09			12 23	12 37
Selby	a																								12 41	
Hull	a									11e45															13 21	13 48
Wakefield Westgate 7	a											11 19									12 17					13 38
Huddersfield	a											12f20									13f27					14g27
Leeds 10	a											11 38									12 36					13 58
Shipley	a											12 19									13 19					14g19
Bradford Forster Square	a											12h25									13h23					14g54
Keighley	a											12 32									13 32					14g32
Skipton	a											12 48									13 48					14g48
Sheffield 7	d					08 45				09 58			10 26	10 21	10 54	11 12			11 26	11 21				11 54		
Doncaster 7	d					09 42				10 44			11 06		11 17	11 35	11 41		11 55			12 10		12 17		12 38
York 8	a					10 06			10 51	11 07			11 29		11 44	11 57	12 05		12 19			12 38		12 45		13 05
Scarborough	a												12 30													14 29
Harrogate	a																12 50				13 28					
Leeds 10	d		07 43		08 40	09 10	09 40	10 06			10 42			11 08	11 10			11 40		12 08						
Hull	d					08 54																				11 54
York 8	d		08 10	09 00	09 10	10 06	10 10	10 32	10 54	11 09	11 10		11 30	11 36	11 47		12 06	12 10		12 36		12 40		12 48		13 07
Thirsk	d		08 27				10 27		11 10									12 27								
Northallerton	d		08 35	09 20	09 31		10 35		11 21		11 33							12 36								
Darlington 7	a			09 32	09 42	10 35		11 02		11 36	11 44		11 58	12 03	12 13		12 34			13 02		13 11		13 15		13 35
Eaglescliffe	a								11 39																	
Middlesbrough	a		09 10		10 18	11 29	11 10				12 24							13 10		13 35						
Darlington 7	d			09 33	09 43	10 36		11 04		11 37	11 45		11 58	12 05	12 15		12 34			13 04		13 12		13 17		13 35
Durham	d			09 50	10 00	10 53		11 20		11 54	12 02			12 21	12 32		12 52			13 20				13 34		13 53
Chester-le-Street	d							11 26																		
Newcastle 8	a			10 06	10 18	11 09		11 41		12 10	12 20		12 28	12 37	12 51		13 08			13 36		13 41		13 53		14 09
Hartlepool	a								12 06																	
Sunderland	a				11 22			12 21	12 52						13 22							14 21	←			
Newcastle 8	d			10 10		11 11				12 15			12 33	12 40			13 09			13 48 →		13 43	13 48			14 13
Morpeth	d			10 24																						
Alnmouth	d			10 41																			14 15			
Berwick-upon-Tweed	d			11 03		11 54				12 58				13 22								14 26				
Dunbar	d			11 27										13 45												
Edinburgh 10	a			11 56		12 39				13 46			14 00	14 14			14 36					15 10	15 21			15 42
Edinburgh	d	09 10		12 03		12 42								14 15								15 13				16 00
Haymarket	d	09 14		12 08										14 19								15 18				16 04
Motherwell	a			12 46		13 24								14s53								15 55				
Glasgow Central 15	a			13 05		13 44				14j52				15 17			15j52					16 14				16k51
Stirling	a			13m24		14m28								15m24									16 24			
Perth	a			14n46		15m12								16n46												
Inverness	a					17m38																				
Inverkeithing	a	09 31		12m41		13m40				14 30			14 40				15 40						16 17			16q24
Kirkcaldy	a	09 48		13m03		14m02							15 02				16 02									16 41
Leuchars 3	a	10 13		13m39		14m33											16 33									17 09
Dundee	a	10 27		13m52		14m48											16 48									17 24
Arbroath	a	10 45		14m09		15r27											17r27									17 41
Montrose	a	11 01		14m24		15r41											17r41									17 59
Stonehaven	a	11 24		14m45		16r03											18r03									18 22
Aberdeen	a	11 47		15m05		16r23											18r23									18 44

For general notes see front of timetable
For details of catering facilities see Directory of Train Operators

- **A** From Manchester Airport (Table 39)
- **B** From Leeds (Table 31)
- **C** From Liverpool Lime Street (Table 39)
- **D** From Birmingham New Street (Table 51)
- **E** Until 27 January. From Leicester (Table 53)
- **G** **The Flying Scotsman**
- **H** From 30 March. From Leicester (Table 53)
- **J** **The Northern Lights**
- **b** Until 27 January dep. 0749, by bus to Hitchin
- **c** Change at Doncaster
- **e** From 30 March arr. 1146
- **f** Change at Leeds
- **g** Change at Doncaster and Leeds
- **h** Bradford Interchange
- **j** Glasgow Queen Street
- **k** Glasgow Queen Street. Change at Edinburgh
- **m** Change at Edinburgh
- **n** Change at Edinburgh and Stirling
- **q** By changing at Edinburgh, passengers may arrive at 1617
- **r** Change at Edinburgh and Dundee

Table 26

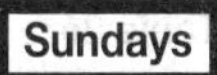

Sundays

until 27 January and from 30 March

London → Humberside, Yorkshire, North East England and Scotland

Route Diagram - see first page of Table 26

		TP	XC	EM	XC	GR	TP	GR	GR	XC	XC	GR	TP	XC	GR	GR	XC	GC	GR	TP	TP	XC	GR	GR	XC	XC
		1 ◇	1 ◇	◇	1 ◇	R 1	1 ◇	R 1	R 1	1 ◇	1 ◇	R 1	1 ◇	1 ◇	R 1	R 1	1 ◇	R 1	R 1	1 ◇	1 ◇	R 1	R 1	R 1	R 1	1 ◇
		A	B	C	B		A		D	E	E		A	G			H			A	J	K			K	L
London Kings Cross 15 ⊖	d					12 00		12 10	12 30			13 00			13 10	13 30		13 45	14 00				14 10	14 30		
Stevenage 4	d							12 29				13 19				13 49										
Peterborough 8	a					12 44		12 58	13 14			13 48			13 56	14 18			14 44				14 54	15 14		
Norwich	d			10 47								11b15				12b15										
Stansted Airport	d											12 05														
Cambridge	d					11b07						12 36				13b02			13 09				13 43			
Peterborough 8	d			12 18		12 44		12 59	13 15			13 49			13 56	14 19			14 45				14 54	15 14		
Grantham 7	a			12 50				13 21							14 19								15 16			
	d							13 21							14 19								15 16			
Newark North Gate 7	a					13 14									14 31								15 28			
Lincoln	a					13 56		15c00																		
Grimsby Town	a								15e36							16e38										
Newark North Gate 7	d					13 14									14 31								15 28			
Retford 10	d							13 43															15 43			
Doncaster 7	a					13 39		13 59	14 07			14 39			14 56	15 09			15 38				15 59	16 08		
Selby	a																									
Hull	a					14 59						15 57							16 50							
Wakefield Westgate 7	a							14 16							15 14								16 17			
Huddersfield	a							15f27							16f14								17f27			
Leeds 10	a							14 36							15 33								16 37			
Shipley	a							15 12							16 19								17 19			
Bradford Forster Square	a							15g23							16g23								17g10			
Keighley	a							15 23							16 32								17 32			
Skipton	a							15 36							16 48								17 48			
Sheffield 7	d		12 21		12 54				13 24	13 21	13 54	14 08		14 21		14 28	14 54					15 21		15 28		15 54
Doncaster 7	d				13 17	13 40			14 08		14 17	14 41				15 10	15 17		15 39					16 09		16 17
York 8	a				13 44	14 04			14 33		14 41	15 05				15 36	15 43	15 51	16 04					16 34		16 44
Scarborough	a															16 33										
Harrogate	a					14 51		15 28							16 28				16 50				17 28			
Leeds 10	d	12 40	13 08		13 10		13 40			14 08			14 40	15 08			15 08	15 10		15 40	15 55	16 08				16 08
Hull	d															14 28										
York 8	d	13 10	13 36		13 46	14 06	14 11		14 35	14 40	14 46	15 07	15 12	15 36		15 39	15 46	15 53	16 06	16 10	16 23	16 36		16 40		16 47
Thirsk	d						14 28											16 10			16 39					
Northallerton	d	13 33				14 25	14 36						15 33					16 20			16 49					
Darlington 7	a	13 44	14 04		14 13	14 38			15 03	15 08	15 13	15 34	15 44	16 02		16 07	16 13		16 34	16 41		17 01		17 07		17 12
Eaglescliffe	a																	16 39								
Middlesbrough	a	14 32					15 09			15 41		16 04				16 41					17 24					17 49
Darlington 7	d	13 45	14 06		14 15	14 38			15 03	15 09	15 15	15 35	15 45	16 03		16 08	16 15		16 34	16 42		17 03		17 08	←	17 14
Durham	d	14 02	14 22		14 31	14 56				15 26	15 31	15 53	16 02	16 19		16 25	16 32			16 59		17h26			17 26	17 30
Chester-le-Street	d	14 08																				→				
Newcastle 8	a	14 23	14 37		14 51	15 12			15 33	15 42	15 51	16 10	16 20	16 35		16 42	16 52		17 04	17 17				17 37	17 41	17 52
Hartlepool	a																	16 58								
Sunderland	a				15 22						16 21						17 22	17 36								18 21
Newcastle 8	d		14 42			15 14			15 34	15 45		16 11		16 40		16 44			17 05					17 39	17 45	
Morpeth	d									15 58						16 59										
Alnmouth	d									16 12						17 15									18 10	
Berwick-upon-Tweed	d		15 24			15 57								17 22		17 37								18 22		
Dunbar	d		15 55											17 45												
Edinburgh 10	a		16 24			16 46			17 01	17 18		17 36		18 14		18 24			18 32					19 08	19 11	
Edinburgh	d		16 35						17 12			17 41							18 43						19 25	
Haymarket	d		16 40						17 16			17 46							18 47						19 30	
Motherwell	a											18 24														
Glasgow Central 15	a					17j52				18j22		18 44		19 22					19j51						20k22	
Stirling	a		17m24						17 51	18 24						19 27									20m23	
Perth	a		18m27						18 27	19n15						20n47										
Inverness	a		20m44						20 44	21n34																
Inverkeithing	a		16 52			17 22			17m37			18m07							19 05						19 42	
Kirkcaldy	a		17 08			17 38			17m59			18m23							19 22						20 05	
Leuchars 3	a		17 36			18 01			18m30										19 46						20 45	
Dundee	a		17 49			18 14			18m46										20 01						21 05	
Arbroath	a		18 06			18 31			19q27										20 18						21 27	
Montrose	a		18 20			18 46			19q41										20 34						21 43	
Stonehaven	a		18 40			19 07			20q03										20 57						22 04	
Aberdeen	a		19 05			19 30			20q26										21 21						22 24	

For general notes see front of timetable
For details of catering facilities see Directory of Train Operators

- **A** From Manchester Airport (Table 39)
- **B** From Birmingham New Street (Table 51)
- **C** To Sheffield (from 30 March to Liverpool Lime Street) (Table 49)
- **D** The Highland Chieftain
- **E** From Bristol Temple Meads (Table 51)
- **G** From Bournemouth (from 30 March from Oxford) (Table 51)
- **H** From Exeter St Davids (Table 51)
- **J** From Manchester Piccadilly (Table 39)
- **K** From Plymouth (Table 51)
- **L** From Cardiff Central (from 30 March from Bristol Temple Meads) (Table 51)
- **b** Change at Ely and Peterborough
- **c** Change at Retford
- **e** Change at Doncaster
- **f** Change at Leeds
- **g** Bradford Interchange
- **h** Arr. 1719
- **j** Glasgow Queen Street
- **k** Glasgow Queen Street. Change at Edinburgh
- **m** Change at Edinburgh
- **n** Change at Edinburgh and Stirling
- **q** Change at Edinburgh and Dundee

London → Humberside, Yorkshire, North East England and Scotland

until 27 January and from 30 March

Route Diagram - see first page of Table 26

		HT	EM	GR	TP	XC	GR	XC	GR	GR	TP	XC	GR	EM	GR	XC	GR	TP	XC	GR	XC	GR	HT	EM	GR	TP
				R		R	R		R	R		R	R		R		R		R	R	R	R			R	
		1 ◇	◇	1	1 ◇	1	1	1 ◇	1	1	1 ◇	1	1	◇	1	1 ◇	1	1 ◇	1	1	1	1	1 ◇	◇	1	1 ◇
			A		B	C		D			B	E		G		D		B	H		J			G		B
		⊠ 🛒		🛒 🍴		🛒	🛒 🍴	🛒	🛒 🍴	🛒 🍴		🛒	🛒 🍴		🛒 🍴	🛒	🛒 🍴		🛒	🛒 🍴	🛒	🛒 🍴	⊠ 🛒		🛒 🍴	
London Kings Cross 15 ⊖	d	14 44		15 00			15 10		15 30	16 00			16 10		16 30		17 00			17 10		17 30	17 40		18 00	
Stevenage 4	d			15 19			*14 46*						16 29		16 49							17 49				
Peterborough 8	a			15 48			15 54		16 14	16 44			16 58		17 18		17 44			17 54		18 18			18 44	
Norwich	d		13 49										*14b15*	15 53										16 57		
Stansted Airport	d			*14 05*									*15 18*							*16c12*						
Cambridge	d			*14 36*									*15 47*				*16b02*			*16 47*					*17 02*	
Peterborough 8	d		15 26	15 49			15 55		16 15	16 45			16 59	17 15	17 19		17 44			17 54		18 19		18 30	18 44	
Grantham 7	a	15 44	15 56				16 17		16 39					17 47						18 16			18 47	18 58	19 06	
	d	15 45					16 18		16 39											18 16			18 51		19 06	
Newark North Gate 7	a						16 30		16 50								18 14					18 49				
Lincoln	a	*17e20*							*17 51*				*19e21*									*19 50*				
Grimsby Town	a	*17f36*							*18f38*						*19f36*								*20f36*			
Newark North Gate 7	d						16 31		16 50								18 14					18 49				
Retford 10	d	16 06											17 39										19 11			
Doncaster 7	a	16 20					16 57		17 16	17 39			17 55		18 09		18 39			18 49		19 14	19 26		19 42	
Selby	a	16 41																					19 40			
Hull	a	17 21											*18 57*				*19 54*						20 22			
Wakefield Westgate 7	a						17 14						18 12							19 06		*19 57*				
Huddersfield	a						*18g15*						*19g19*							*20g00*		*21h19*				
Leeds 10	a						17 34						18 32							19 28		*20 19*				
Shipley	a						*18 19*						*19 19*							*20 19*		*20h45*				
Bradford Forster Square	a						*18j23*						*19j23*							*20j23*		*20h54*				
Keighley	a						*18 32*						*19 32*							*20 32*						
Skipton	a						*18 48*						*19 48*							*20 48*						
Sheffield 7 🚌	d					16 21		16 54	*16 28*			17 21			*17 28*	17 54	*18 08*		18 21		18 54	*18 28*			*19 08*	
Doncaster 7	d							17 14	17 20	17 40					18 10	18 17	18 40				19 17	19 20			19 42	
York 8	a			17 02				17 40	17 45	18 05					18 34	18 41	19 03				19 43	19 46			20 07	
Scarborough	a			*18 29*													*20 30*								*21 29*	
Harrogate	a			*17 50*			*18 28*			*18 50*			*19 28*				*19 50*			*20 28*					*20 50*	
Leeds 10	d				16 40	17 08			*17 10*		17 40	18 08				*18 10*		18 40	19 08		*19 10*				*19 25*	19 40
Hull	d											*17 23*														
York 8	d			17 03	17 10	17 36		17 43	17 46	18 07	18 10	18 36			18 38	18 46	19 05	19 10	19 36		19 46	19 48			20 08	20 10
Thirsk	d										18 27															20 27
Northallerton	d				17 33						18 35				18 58			19 31				20 08				20 35
Darlington 7	a			17 31	17 44	18 01		18 08	18 14	18 35		19 01			19 10	19 15	19 33	19 42	20 02		20 13	20 22			20 36	
Eaglescliffe	a																									
Middlesbrough	a								*18 53*		19 10					*20 01*						*20 55*				21 10
Darlington 7	d			17 31	17 45	18 03		18 10	18 15	18 35		19 03			19 11	19 17	19 34	19 43	20 03		20 15	20 22			20 36	
Durham	d				18 02	18 19		18 26	18 32			19 19			19 28	19 33	19 51	20 00	20 19		20 32	20 40				
Chester-le-Street	d				18 08													20 06								
Newcastle 8 🚌	a			18 01	18 23	18 35		18 47	18 51	19 05		19 35			19 46	19 54	20 07	20 21	20 36		20 51	20 58			21 06	
Hartlepool	a																									
Sunderland	a								*19 22*						*20 21*											
Newcastle 8 🚌	d			18 05		18 39				19 06		19 43					20 09		20 45						21 07	
Morpeth	d																									
Alnmouth	d											20 08							21 09						21 34	
Berwick-upon-Tweed	d			18 48		19 21						20 28					20 52		21 30						21 57	
Dunbar	d					19 44													21 53							
Edinburgh 10	a			19 34		20 13				20 35		21 14					21 36		22 22						22 44	
Edinburgh	d			19 37		20 14						21 14					21 39									
Haymarket	d					20 18						21 17														
Motherwell	a			20 16		20s53						21s59					22 18									
Glasgow Central 15	a			20 35		21 19				*21k55*		22 23					22 37								*23k55*	
Stirling	a					*21m24*						*22m24*							*23 26*							
Perth	a					*22n47*													*00 06*							
Inverness	a																									
Inverkeithing	a			*20m17*						*21 17*							*22m17*									
Kirkcaldy	a			*20m59*						*21 33*							*23m05*									
Leuchars 3	a									*22 04*							*23m40*									
Dundee	a									*22 17*							*23m56*									
Arbroath	a									*22 34*																
Montrose	a									*22 49*																
Stonehaven	a									*23 10*																
Aberdeen	a									*23 33*																

For general notes see front of timetable
For details of catering facilities see Directory of Train Operators

- **A** To Sheffield (from 30 March to Liverpool Lime Street) (Table 49)
- **B** From Manchester Airport (Table 39)
- **C** From Bournemouth (from 30 March from Oxford) (Table 51). 🛒 to Edinburgh
- **D** From Bristol Temple Meads (Table 51)
- **E** From Penzance (Table 135). 🛒 to Edinburgh
- **G** To Sheffield (from 30 March to Manchester Piccadilly) (Table 49)
- **H** From Bournemouth (from 30 March from Oxford) (Table 51). 🛒 to Newcastle
- **J** From Paignton (Table 51)
- **b** Change at Ely and Peterborough
- **c** From 30 March dep. 1518
- **e** Change at Retford
- **f** Change at Doncaster
- **g** Change at Leeds
- **h** Change at Doncaster and Leeds
- **j** Bradford Interchange
- **k** Glasgow Queen Street
- **m** Change at Edinburgh
- **n** Change at Edinburgh and Stirling

Table 26

Sundays

London → Humberside, Yorkshire, North East England and Scotland

until 27 January and from 30 March

Route Diagram - see first page of Table 26

		XC	GR	GR	XC	EM	GR	GR	TP	XC	GR	GR	XC	GR	EM	GR	TP	HT	GR	GR	GR	EM	GR	GR
		R 1	R 1	R 1	1 ◇	◇	R 1	R 1	1 ◇	R 1	R 1	R 1	1 ◇	R 1	◇	R 1	1 ◇	1 ◇	R 1	R 1	R 1	◇	R 1	R 1
		A			B	C			D	E			B		C		G					C		
London Kings Cross 15 ⊖	d		18 10	18 30			18 40	19 00			19 10	19 30		19 35		20 00		20 05	20 30	21 00	21 30		22 00	22 10
Stevenage 4	d			18 50								19 49		19 54							20 46			
Peterborough 8	a		18 54	19 19			19 25	19 44			19 54	20 18		20 24		20 44			21 14	21 44	22 14		22 44	22s59
Norwich	d			17b15		17 54						18b15			18 57					19 44		20 52		
Stansted Airport	d			17 35								18 35												
Cambridge	d			18 09								19 08								20b02			21b02	
Peterborough 8	d		18 55	19 19		19 22	19 25	19 44			19 55	20 19		20 25	20 32	20 44			21 14	21 45	22 15	22 22	22 45	
Grantham 7	a					19 56	19 47				20 19				21 00			21 17	21 36		22 39	22 50		23s31
	d						19 47				20 19							21 18	21 36		22 39			
Newark North Gate 7	a		19 25								20 30								21 48		22 50			23s42
Lincoln	a		20c44								21 49										23 52			
Grimsby Town	a							21e44						22e44						23e58				
Newark North Gate 7	d		19 26								20 30								21 48		22 50			
Retford 10	d		19 42															21 39	22 03		23 06			
Doncaster 7	a		19 58	20 12			20 20	20 35			20 56	21 09		21 16		21 36		21 53	22 19	22 42	23 27		23 42	00s12
Selby	a										21 15							22 08						
Hull	a						21 23				21 56							22 50		00 02				
Wakefield Westgate 7	a		20 16				20 38					21 27				22f01			22 40					
Huddersfield	a						21g30					22g27				23h20			23g27					03g03
Leeds 10	a		20 41				20 59					21 47				22f22			23 00		00 22			01 17
Shipley	a		21 19				21 45					22 19				22h45			23 21					
Bradford Forster Square	a		21j23				21 54					22j23				22h54			23j43					
Keighley	a		21 32									22 32							23 34					
Skipton	a		21 48									22 48							23 50					
Sheffield 7	d	19 21		19 27	19 54					20 21			20 54	20 27						21 24				
Doncaster 7	d			20 12	20 17			20 35					21 17	21 20		21 36				22 43			23 45	
York 8	a			20 38	20 42			21 00					21 41	21 47		22 00				23 11			00 39	
Scarborough	a															23 01								
Harrogate	a						21 51	21 58				23 00							23 59					
Leeds 10	d	20 08			20 08			20 10	20 45	21 08				21 10			22 10							
Hull	d									20 22														
York 8	d	20 36		20 39	20 44			21 02	21 10	21 36			21 43	21 48		22 02	22 40			23 13				
Thirsk	d								21 28								23 06							
Northallerton	d			20 59					21 38								23 16			23 47				
Darlington 7	a	21 02		21 12	21 18			21 30	21 49	22 03			22 11	22 16		22 43	23 31			00 01			01k32	
Eaglescliffe	a																							
Middlesbrough	a							22 07						23 10										
Darlington 7	d	21 04		21 12	21 19			21 30	21 50	22 05			22 12	22 16		22 43	23 32			00 01				
Durham	d	21 20		21 30	21 36				22 07	22 21			22 29	22 34		23 01	23 49			00 19			01m50	
Chester-le-Street	d																							
Newcastle 8	a	21 37		21 46	21 57			22 02	22 25	22n42			22 50	22 52		23 34	00 21			00 52			02k25	
Hartlepool	a																							
Sunderland	a																							
Newcastle 8	d	21 45		21 53																				
Morpeth	d																							
Alnmouth	d	22 09																						
Berwick-upon-Tweed	d	22 30		22 37																				
Dunbar	d			23 00																				
Edinburgh 10	a	23 18		23 29																				
Edinburgh	d																							
Haymarket	d																							
Motherwell	a																							
Glasgow Central 15	a	00q25																						
Stirling	a																							
Perth	a																							
Inverness	a																							
Inverkeithing	a	23 58																						
Kirkcaldy	a																							
Leuchars 3	a																							
Dundee	a																							
Arbroath	a																							
Montrose	a																							
Stonehaven	a																							
Aberdeen	a																							

For general notes see front of timetable
For details of catering facilities see Directory of Train Operators

A From Plymouth (Table 51)
B From Bristol Temple Meads (Table 51)
C To Nottingham (Table 19)
D From Manchester Airport (Table 39)
E From Bournemouth (from 30 March from Oxford) (Table 51)
G From Liverpool Lime Street (Table 39)
b Change at Ely and Peterborough
c Change at Retford
e Change at Doncaster
f From 30 March arr. Wakefield Westgate 2219, Leeds 2239
g Change at Leeds
h Until 27 January only. Change at Doncaster and Leeds
j Bradford Interchange
k Monday mornings
m Arrival time. Monday mornings
n From 30 March arr. 2245
q Glasgow Queen Street

Sundays

London → Humberside, Yorkshire, North East England and Scotland

3 February to 23 March

Route Diagram - see first page of Table 26

		GR	TP	GR	TP	GR	TP	TP	GC	GR	TP	GR	GR	XC	EM	GR	TP	XC	GR	GR		XC	HT	XC	GR	TP
		R 1	1 ◇	R 1	1 ◇	R 1	1 ◇	1 ◇	R 1	R 1	1 ◇	R 1	R 1	1 ◇	1 ◇	R 1	1 ◇	1 ◇	R 1	R 1		1 ◇	1 ◇	1 ◇	R 1	1 ◇
						A	B	C			B			D	E	G	B	D				D		D	H	B
London Kings Cross 15 ⊖	d								08 55	09 00		09 10	09 30			10 00			10 10	10 30			10 42		11 00	
Stevenage 4	d									09 20		*07b49*							*09 46*	10 49						
Peterborough 8	a									09 49		09 54	10 14			10 45			10 59	11 18					11 44	
Norwich	d																									
Stansted Airport	d																									
Cambridge	d																									
Peterborough 8	d									09 49		09 55	10 14			10 46			10 59	11 19					11 45	
Grantham 7	a									10 11									11 21				11 45			
	d									10 11									11 21				11 46			
Newark North Gate 7	a											10 27				11 16										
Lincoln	a															*11 56*										
Grimsby Town	a																						*13c38*			
Newark North Gate 7	d											10 27				11 16										
Retford 10	d											10 43							11 43				12 07			
Doncaster 7	a									10 44		11 00	11 05			11 41			11 59	12 09			12 23		12 37	
Selby	a																						12 41			
Hull	a									*11e45*													13 21		*13 48*	
Wakefield Westgate 7	a											11 19							12 17	*12 44*					*13 38*	
Huddersfield	a											*12f20*							*13f27*	*14g00*					*14g27*	
Leeds 10	a											11 38							12 36	*13 01*					*13 58*	
Shipley	a											*12 19*							*13 19*	*13g28*					*14g19*	
Bradford Forster Square	a											*12h25*							*13h23*	*13j53*					*14g54*	
Keighley	a											*12 32*							*13 32*	*13g39*					*14g32*	
Skipton	a											*12 48*							*13 48*	*13g53*					*14g48*	
Sheffield 7	d					*08 45*				*09 58*			*10 26*	10 21	11 12			11 21						12 04		
Doncaster 7	d					09 42				10 44			11 06		11 35	11 41				12 10				12 28	12 38	
York 8	a					10 06			10 51	11 07			11 29		11 57	12 05				12 38					13 05	
Scarborough	a												*12 30*												*14 29*	
Harrogate	a															*12 50*			*13 28*							
Leeds 10	d		07 42		08 40	*09 10*	09 42	10 06			10 42			11 08		*11 10*	11 40	12 08						13 08 →		12 40
Hull	d					*08 54*																			*11 54*	
York 8	d		08 35	09 00	09 10	10 06	10 10	10 32	10 54	11 09	11 10		11 30	11 36		12 06	12 10	12 36		12 40					13 07	13 10
Thirsk	d		08 51				10 27		11 10								12 27									
Northallerton	d		08 59	09 20	09 31		10 35		11 21		11 33						12 36									13 33
Darlington 7	a			09 32	09 42	10 35		11 02		11 36	11 44		11 58	12 03		12 34		13 02		13 11					13 35	13 44
Eaglescliffe	a								11 39																	
Middlesbrough	a		09 32		*10 18*		11 10				*12 24*						13 10	*13 35*								
Darlington 7	d			09 33	09 43	10 36		11 04		11 37	11 45		11 58	12 05		12 34		13 04		13 12					13 35	13 45
Durham	d			09 50	10 00	10 53		11 20		11 54	12 02			12 21		12 52		13 20							13 53	14 02
Chester-le-Street	d							11 26																		14 08
Newcastle 8	a			10 06	10 18	11 09		11 41		12 10	12 20		12 28	12 37		13 08		13 36		13 41					14 09	14 23
Hartlepool	a								12 06																	
Sunderland	a				*11 22*			*12 21*	12 52					*13 22*						*14 21*		←				
Newcastle 8	d			10 10		11 11				12 15			12 33	12 40		13 09		13 48 →		13 43		13 48			14 13	
Morpeth	d			10 24																						
Alnmouth	d			10 41																		14 15				
Berwick-upon-Tweed	d			11 03		11 54				12 58				13 22						14 26						
Dunbar	d			11 27										13 45												
Edinburgh 10	a			11 56		12 39				13 46			14 00	14 14		14 36				15 10		15 21			15 42	
Edinburgh	d	09 10		12 03		12 42								14 15						15 13					16 00	
Haymarket	d	09 14		12 08										14 19						15 18					16 04	
Motherwell	a			12 46		13 24								14s53						15 55						
Glasgow Central 15	a			13 05		13 44				*14k52*				15 17		*15k52*				16 14					*16m51*	
Stirling	a			*13n24*		*14n28*								*15n24*								*16 24*				
Perth	a			*14q46*		*15n12*								*16q46*												
Inverness	a					*17n38*																				
Inverkeithing	a	09 31		*12n41*		*13n40*				*14 30*			*14 40*			*15 40*						*16 17*			*16r24*	
Kirkcaldy	a	09 48		*13n03*		*14n02*							*15 02*			*16 02*									16 41	
Leuchars 3	a	10 13		*13n39*		*14n33*										*16 33*									17 09	
Dundee	a	10 27		*13n52*		*14n48*										*16 48*									17 24	
Arbroath	a	10 45		*14n09*		*15t27*										*17t27*									17 41	
Montrose	a	11 01		*14n24*		*15t41*										*17t41*									17 59	
Stonehaven	a	11 24		*14n45*		*16t03*										*18t03*									18 22	
Aberdeen	a	11 47		*15n05*		*16t23*										*18t23*									18 44	

For general notes see front of timetable
For details of catering facilities see Directory of Train Operators

- **A** From Leeds (Table 31)
- **B** From Manchester Airport (Table 39)
- **C** From Liverpool Lime Street (Table 39)
- **D** From Birmingham New Street (Table 51)
- **E** From Leicester (Table 53)
- **G** **The Flying Scotsman**
- **H** **The Northern Lights**
- **b** Change at Hitchin and Peterborough. By bus to Hitchin
- **c** Change at Doncaster
- **e** 23 March arr. 1146
- **f** Change at Leeds
- **g** Change at Doncaster and Leeds
- **h** Bradford Interchange
- **j** Bradford Interchange. Change at Doncaster and Leeds
- **k** Glasgow Queen Street
- **m** Glasgow Queen Street. Change at Edinburgh
- **n** Change at Edinburgh
- **q** Change at Edinburgh and Stirling
- **r** By changing at Edinburgh, passengers may arrive at 1617
- **t** Change at Edinburgh and Dundee

Table 26

Sundays

London → Humberside, Yorkshire, North East England and Scotland

3 February to 23 March

Route Diagram - see first page of Table 26

	XC	EM	XC	GR	TP	GR	GR	XC	XC	GR	TP	XC	GR	GR	GC	XC		GR	TP	TP	XC	GR	GR	HT	EM
				R		R	R			R			R	R	R			R				R	R		
	1 ◇	◇	1 ◇	1	1 ◇	1	1	1 ◇	1 ◇	1	1 ◇	1 ◇	1	1	1	1 ◇		1	1 ◇	1 ◇	1 ◇	1	1	1 ◇	◇
	A	B	A		C		D	A	E		C	E				G			C	H	G				B
	☕		☕	☕		☕	☕	☕	☕	☕		☕	☕	☕	☕	☕		☕			☕	☕	☕	⊠	
				🍴		🍴	🍴			🍴			🍴	🍴				🍴				🍴	🍴		
London Kings Cross 15 ⊖ d				12 00		12 10	12 30			13 00			13 10	13 30	13 45			14 00				14 10	14 30	14 44	
Stevenage 4 d						12 29				13 19				13 49											
Peterborough 8 a				12 44		12 58	13 14			13 48			13 56	14 18				14 44				14 54	15 14		
Norwich d		10 47								11b15				12b15											13 49
Stansted Airport d										12 05															
Cambridge d				11b07						12 36				13b02				13 09				13 43			
Peterborough 8 d		12 18		12 44		12 59	13 15			13 49			13 56	14 19				14 45				14 54	15 14		15 26
Grantham 7 a		12 50				13 21							14 19									15 16		15 44	15 56
d						13 21							14 19									15 16		15 45	
Newark North Gate 7 a				13 14									14 31									15 28			
Lincoln a				13 56		15c00																		17c20	
Grimsby Town a							15e36							16e38										17e36	
Newark North Gate 7 d				13 14									14 31									15 28			
Retford 10 d						13 43																15 43		16 06	
Doncaster 7 a				13 39		13 59	14 07			14 39			14 56	15 09				15 38				15 59	16 08	16 20	
Selby a																								16 41	
Hull a				14 59						15 57								16 50						17 21	
Wakefield Westgate 7 a						14 16	14 44						15 14	15 44								16 17		16e44	
Huddersfield a						15f27	16g01						16f14	17g00								17f27		17g59	
Leeds 10 a						14 36	15 01						15 33	16 01								16 37		17e01	
Shipley a						15 12	15g45						16 19	16g46								17 19		17g35	
Bradford Forster Square a						15h23	15j53						16h23	16j53								17h10		17j53	
Keighley a						15 23							16 32									17 32		17g46	
Skipton a						15 36							16 48									17 48		17g59	
Sheffield 7 🚌 d			13 04				13 24		14 04	14 08				14 28		15 04							15 28		
Doncaster 7 d			13 28	13 40			14 08		14 28	14 41				15 10		15 28		15 39					16 09		
York 8 a				14 04			14 33			15 05				15 36	15 51			16 04					16 34		
Scarborough a														16 33											
Harrogate a	←			14 51		15 28		←				←	16 28					16 50			←	17 28			
Leeds 10 d	13 08		14 08 →	13 10	13 40			14 08	15 08 →		14 40	15 08			15 10	16 08 →			15 40	15 55	16 08				
Hull d														14 28					14 28						
York 8 d	13 36			14 06	14 11		14 35	14 40		15 07	15 12	15 36		15 39	15 53			16 06	16 10	16 23	16 36		16 40		
Thirsk d					14 28										16 10					16 39					
Northallerton d				14 25	14 36						15 33				16 20					16 49					
Darlington 7 a	14 04			14 38			15 03	15 08		15 34	15 44	16 02		16 07				16 34	16 41		17 03		17 07		
Eaglescliffe a															16 39										
Middlesbrough a	14 32				15 09			15 41		16 04				16 41						17 24			17 49		
Darlington 7 d	14 06			14 38			15 03	15 09		15 35	15 45	16 03		16 08				16 34	16 42		17 03		17 08		
Durham d	14 22			14 56				15 26		15 53	16 02	16 20		16 25					16 59		17 19				
Chester-le-Street d																									
Newcastle 8 🚌 a	14 37			15 12			15 33	15 42		16 10	16 20	16 36		16 42				17 04	17 17		17 35		17 37		
Hartlepool a															16 58										
Sunderland a	15 22							16 21						17 22	17 36								18 21		
Newcastle 8 🚌 d	14 42			15 14			15 34	15 45		16 11		16 40		16 44				17 05			17 45 →		17 39		
Morpeth d								15 58						16 59											
Alnmouth d								16 12						17 15											
Berwick-upon-Tweed d	15 24			15 57								17 22		17 37									18 22		
Dunbar d	15 55											17 45													
Edinburgh 10 a	16 24			16 46			17 01	17 18		17 36		18 14		18 24				18 32					19 08		
Edinburgh d	16 35						17 12			17 41								18 43							
Haymarket d	16 40						17 16			17 46								18 47							
Motherwell a										18 24															
Glasgow Central 15 a				17k52				18k22		18 44		19k22						19k51							
Stirling a	17m24						17 51	18 24						19 27											
Perth a							18 27	19n15						20n47											
Inverness a							20 44	21n34																	
Inverkeithing a	16 52			17 22			17m37			18m07								19 05							
Kirkcaldy a	17 08			17 38			17m59			18m23								19 22							
Leuchars 3 a	17 36			18 01			18m30											19 46							
Dundee a	17 49			18 14			18m46											20 01							
Arbroath a	18 06			18 31			19q27											20 18							
Montrose a	18 20			18 46			19q41											20 34							
Stonehaven a	18 40			19 07			20q03											20 57							
Aberdeen a	19 05			19 30			20q26											21 21							

For general notes see front of timetable
For details of catering facilities see Directory of Train Operators

A From Birmingham New Street (Table 51)
B To Liverpool Lime Street (Table 49)
C From Manchester Airport (Table 39)
D **The Highland Chieftain**
E From Bristol Temple Meads (Table 51)
G From Bournemouth (Table 51)
H From Manchester Piccadilly (Table 39)
b Change at Ely and Peterborough
c Change at Retford
e Change at Doncaster
f Change at Leeds
g Change at Doncaster and Leeds
h Bradford Interchange
j Bradford Interchange. Change at Doncaster and Leeds
k Glasgow Queen Street
m Change at Edinburgh
n Change at Edinburgh and Stirling
q Change at Edinburgh and Dundee

Table 26

Sundays

London → Humberside, Yorkshire, North East England and Scotland

3 February to 23 March

Route Diagram - see first page of Table 26

		XC	GR	TP	XC	GR	GR	XC	GR	TP	XC	GR	EM	GR		XC	GR	TP	XC	GR	GR	HT	EM	XC	GR	TP
		R 1	R 1	1 ◇	R 1	R 1	R 1	R 1	R 1	1 ◇	R 1	R 1	◇	R 1		R 1	R 1	1 ◇	R 1	R 1	R 1	1 ◇	◇	R 1	R 1	1 ◇
		A		B	C			D		B	D		E			H		B	H				E	A		B
London Kings Cross 15 ⊖	d		15 00			15 10	15 30		16 00			16 10		16 30			17 00			17 10	17 30	17 40			18 00	
Stevenage 4	d		15 19			14 46						16 29		16 49							17 49					
Peterborough 8	a		15 48			15 54	16 14		16 44			16 58		17 18			17 44			17 54	18 18				18 44	
Norwich	d											14b15	15 53										16 57			
Stansted Airport	d		14 05									15 18								16 12						
Cambridge	d		14 36									15 47					16b02			16 47					17b02	
Peterborough 8	d		15 49			15 55	16 15		16 45			16 59	17 15	17 19			17 44			17 54	18 19		18 30		18 44	
Grantham 7	a					16 17	16 39						17 47							18 16		18 47	18 58		19 06	
	d					16 18	16 39													18 16		18 51			19 06	
Newark North Gate 7	a					16 30	16 50										18 14				18 49					
Lincoln	a						17 51					19c21									19 50					
Grimsby Town	a						18e38							19e36								20e36				
Newark North Gate 7	d					16 31	16 50										18 14				18 49					
Retford 10	d											17 39										19 11				
Doncaster 7	a					16 57	17 16		17 39			17 55		18 09			18 39			18 49	19 14	19 26			19 42	
Selby	a																					19 40				
Hull	a											18 57					19 54					20 22				
Wakefield Westgate 7	a					17 14	17 44					18 12		18 44						19 06	19 44					
Huddersfield	a					18f15	19g00					19f19		19g33						20f00	21g19					
Leeds 10	a					17 34	18 01					18 32		19 01						19 28	20 01					
Shipley	a					18 19	18g45					19 19		19g45						20 19	20g45					
Bradford Forster Square	a					18h23	18g54					19h23		19j53						20h23	20g54					
Keighley	a					18 32						19 32								20 32						
Skipton	a					18 48						19 48								20 48						
Sheffield 7 ⛴	d			15k46	16 04		16 28	17 04	17 08					17 28		18 04					18 28			19 04	19 08	
Doncaster 7	d				16 28		17 20	17 28	17 40					18 10		18 28	18 40				19 20			19 28	19 42	
York 8	a		17 02				17 45		18 05					18 34			19 03				19 46				20 07	
Scarborough	a		18 29														20 30								21 29	
Harrogate	a		17 50			18 28			18 50		←	19 28					19 50		←	20 28					20 50	
Leeds 10	d			16 40	17 08		17 10	18 08 →		17 40	18 08					19 08 →	18 10	18 40	19 08		19 10			20 08 →	19 25	19 40
Hull	d										17 23															
York 8	d		17 03	17 10	17 36		17 46		18 07	18 10	18 36			18 38			19 05	19 10	19 36		19 48				20 08	20 10
Thirsk	d									18 27																20 27
Northallerton	d			17 33						18 35				18 58				19 31			20 08					20 35
Darlington 7	a		17 31	17 44	18 01		18 14		18 35		19 01			19 10			19 33	19 42	20 01		20 22				20 36	
Eaglescliffe	a																									
Middlesbrough	a						18 53			19 10				20 01							20 55					21 10
Darlington 7	d		17 31	17 45	18 03		18 15		18 35		19 03			19 11			19 34	19 43	20 03		20 22				20 36	
Durham	d			18 02	18 19		18 32				19 19			19 28			19 51	20 00	20 19		20 40					
Chester-le-Street	d			18 08														20 06								
Newcastle 8 ⛴	a		18 01	18 23	18 35		18 51		19 05		19 35			19 46			20 07	20 21	20 35		20 58				21 06	
Hartlepool	a																									
Sunderland	a	←					19 22							20 21												
Newcastle 8 ⛴	d	17 45	18 05		18 42				19 06		19 43						20 09		20 45						21 07	
Morpeth	d																									
Alnmouth	d	18 10									20 08								21 09						21 34	
Berwick-upon-Tweed	d		18 48		19 24						20 28						20 52		21 30						21 57	
Dunbar	d				19 47														21 53							
Edinburgh 10	a	19 11	19 34		20 14				20 35		21 14						21 36		22 22						22 44	
Edinburgh	d	19 25	19 37		20 14						21 14						21 39									
Haymarket	d	19 30			20 18						21 17															
Motherwell	a		20 16		20s53						21s59						22 18									
Glasgow Central 15	a	20m22	20 35		21 19				21n55		22 23						22 37								23n55	
Stirling	a	20q23			21q24						22q24								23 26							
Perth	a				22r47														00 06							
Inverness	a																									
Inverkeithing	a	19 42	20q17						21 17								22q17									
Kirkcaldy	a	20 05	20q59						21 33								23q05									
Leuchars 3	a	20 45							22 04								23q40									
Dundee	a	21 05							22 17								23q56									
Arbroath	a	21 27							22 34																	
Montrose	a	21 43							22 49																	
Stonehaven	a	22 04							23 10																	
Aberdeen	a	22 24							23 33																	

For general notes see front of timetable
For details of catering facilities see Directory of Train Operators

A From Bournemouth (Table 51)
B From Manchester Airport (Table 39)
C From Plymouth (Table 51). to Edinburgh
D From Bournemouth (Table 51). to Edinburgh
E To Manchester Piccadilly (Table 49)
H From Penzance (Table 135)
b Change at Ely and Peterborough
c Change at Retford
e Change at Doncaster
f Change at Leeds
g Change at Doncaster and Leeds
h Bradford Interchange
j Bradford Interchange. Change at Doncaster and Leeds
k Change at York
m Glasgow Queen Street. Change at Edinburgh
n Glasgow Queen Street
q Change at Edinburgh
r Change at Edinburgh and Stirling

Table 26

Sundays

London → Humberside, Yorkshire, North East England and Scotland

3 February to 23 March

Route Diagram - see first page of Table 26

		XC	GR	GR	EM	GR	XC	GR	TP	GR	XC	GR	GR	EM	GR	XC	TP	HT	GR	GR	GR	EM	GR	GR
		A			B		E		D		E			B		A	G					B		
London Kings Cross 15 ⊖	d		18 10	18 30		18 40		19 00		19 10		19 30	19 35		20 00			20 05	20 30	21 00	21 30		22 00	22 10
Stevenage 4	d			18 50								19 49	19 54								*20 46*			
Peterborough 8	a		18 54	19 19		19 25		19 44		19 54		20 18	20 24		20 44				21 14	21 44	22 14		22 44	22s59
Norwich	d			*17b15*	17 54							*18b15*		18 57						*19 44*		20 52		
Stansted Airport	d			*17 35*								*18 35*												
Cambridge	d			*18 09*								*19 08*								*20b02*			*21b02*	
Peterborough 8	d		18 55	19 19	19 22	19 25		19 44		19 55		20 19	20 25	20 32	20 44				21 14	21 45	22 15	22 22	22 45	
Grantham 7	a				19 56	19 47				20 19				21 00				21 17	21 36		22 39	22 50		23s31
	d					19 47				20 19								21 18	21 36		22 39			
Newark North Gate 7	a		19 25							20 30									21 48		22 50			23s42
Lincoln	a		*20c44*							*21 49*											*23 52*			
Grimsby Town	a							*21e44*					*22e44*							*23e58*				
Newark North Gate 7	d		19 26							20 30									21 48		22 50			
Retford 10	d		19 42															21 39	22 03		23 06			
Doncaster 7	a		19 58	20 12		20 20		20 35		20 56		21 09	21 16		21 36			21 53	22 19	22 42	23 27		23 42	00s12
Selby	a									21 15								22 08						
Hull	a					*21 23*				21 56								22 50		*00 02*				
Wakefield Westgate 7	a		20 16			20 38						21 27	*21 44*		*22 01*				22 40	*23 34*				
Huddersfield	a					*21f30*						*22f27*			*23g20*				*23f27*					*03f03*
Leeds 10	a		20 41			20 59						21 47	*22 01*		*22 22*				23 00	*00 16*	00 22			01 17
Shipley	a		*21 19*			*21 45*						*22 19*			*22g45*				*23 21*					
Bradford Forster Square	a		*21h23*			*21 54*						*22h23*			*22g54*				*23h43*					
Keighley	a		*21 32*									*22 32*							*23 34*					
Skipton	a		*21 48*									*22 48*							*23 50*					
Sheffield 7 ⛴	d			*19 27*			20 08						*20 27*			21 04				*22 04*			*22 54*	
Doncaster 7	d			20 12			20 34	20 35					21 20		21 36	21 28				22 43			23 45	
York 8	a			20 38				21 00					21 47		22 00	22 36				23 11			00 39	
Scarborough	a														*23 01*									
Harrogate	a	←				*21 51*		*21 58*			←		*23g00*						*23 59*					
Leeds 10	d	20 08					21 08 →	*20 10*	20 45		21 08		*21 10*				22 10							
Hull	d										*20 22*						*20 22*							
York 8	d	20 36		20 39				21 02	21 10		21 45		21 48		22 02		22 40			23 13				
Thirsk	d								21 28								23 06							
Northallerton	d			20 59					21 38								23 16			23 47				
Darlington 7	a	21 02		21 12				21 30	21 49		22 10		22 16		22 43		23 31			00 01			*01j32*	
Eaglescliffe	a																							
Middlesbrough	a							*22 07*					*23 10*											
Darlington 7	d	21 04		21 12				21 30	21 50		22 12		22 16		22 43		23 32			00 01				
Durham	d	21 20		21 30					22 07		22 30		22 34		23 01		23 49			00 19			*01k50*	
Chester-le-Street	d																							
Newcastle 8 ⛴	a	21 37		21 46				22 02	22 25		22 51		22 52		23 34		00 21			00 52			*02j25*	
Hartlepool	a																							
Sunderland	a																							
Newcastle 8 ⛴	d	21 45		21 53																				
Morpeth	d																							
Alnmouth	d	22 09																						
Berwick-upon-Tweed	d	22 30		22 37																				
Dunbar	d			23 00																				
Edinburgh 10	a	23 18		23 29																				
Edinburgh	d																							
Haymarket	d																							
Motherwell	a																							
Glasgow Central 15	a	*00m25*																						
Stirling	a																							
Perth	a																							
Inverness	a																							
Inverkeithing	a	*23 58*																						
Kirkcaldy	a																							
Leuchars 3	a																							
Dundee	a																							
Arbroath	a																							
Montrose	a																							
Stonehaven	a																							
Aberdeen	a																							

For general notes see front of timetable
For details of catering facilities see Directory of Train Operators

- **A** From Bournemouth (Table 51)
- **B** To Nottingham (Table 19)
- **D** From Manchester Airport (Table 39)
- **E** From Penzance (Table 135)
- **G** From Liverpool Lime Street (Table 39)
- **b** Change at Ely and Peterborough
- **c** Change at Retford
- **e** Change at Doncaster
- **f** Change at Leeds
- **g** Change at Doncaster and Leeds
- **h** Bradford Interchange
- **j** Monday mornings
- **k** Arrival time. Monday mornings
- **m** Glasgow Queen Street

Scotland, North East England, Yorkshire and Humberside → London

Route Diagram - see first page of Table 26

Miles	Miles	Miles			GR	EM	GR	GR	GR	GR	GR	GR	GR	HT	TP	GR	GR	HT	TP	GR	XC		TP	GR	GR	GR
									MX	MO																
					R 1		R 1	R 1	R 1	R 1	R 1	R 1	R 1	BHX 1 ◇	1 ◇	R 1	R 1	BHX 1 ◇	1 ◇	R 1	R 1		1 ◇	R 1	R 1	R 1
						A									B				C		D		C		E	
					✕		✕	✕	✕	✕	✕	✕	✕	⊠		✕	✕	⊠		✕				✕	✕	✕
—	—	0	**Aberdeen**	d																						
—	—	16¼	Stonehaven	d																						
—	—	40½	Montrose	d																						
—	—	54¼	Arbroath	d																						
—	—	71¼	**Dundee**	d																						
—	—	79½	Leuchars 3	d																						
—	—	104½	Kirkcaldy	d																						
—	—	117¼	Inverkeithing	d																						
—	—	—	**Inverness**	d																						
—	—	—	Perth	d																						
—	—	—	Stirling	d																						
0	—	—	**Glasgow Central 15**	d																						
12¾	—	—	Motherwell	d																						
56	—	129¼	Haymarket	d																						
57¼	—	130½	**Edinburgh 10**	a																						
—	—	—	**Edinburgh**	d																						
86½	—	—	Dunbar	d																						
114¾	—	—	**Berwick-upon-Tweed**	d																						
147	—	—	Alnmouth	d																						
165¼	—	—	Morpeth	d																						
181¾	—	—	**Newcastle 8** ⛴	a																						
—	—	—	Sunderland	d																						
—	—	—	Hartlepool	d																						
—	—	—	**Newcastle 8** ⛴	d					04 31	04 22		05 26				06 00			06 13		06 19			06 30		
190	—	—	Chester-le-Street	d																	06 31					
195¾	—	—	**Durham**	d					04 45	04 37		05 38				06 12			06 29		06 38			06 42		
217¾	—	—	**Darlington 7**	a					05 02	04 54		05 55				06 29			06 45		06 53			07 00		
—	—	—	Middlesbrough	d											05 58											
—	—	—	Eaglescliffe	d																						
—	—	—	**Darlington 7**	d					05 03	04 55		05 56				06 30			06 47		06 55		⟵	07 01		
231¾	—	—	Northallerton	d					05 30	05 22		06 08			06 26				06 58 ⟶				06 58	07 12		
239½	—	—	Thirsk	d											06 33								07 07			
261¾	—	—	**York 8**	a					05 56	05 57		06 28			06 52	06 57					07 22		07 32	07 34		
—	—	—	Hull	a					08b21	08b21											08 45					
—	—	—	Leeds 10	a					06 49	06 49					07 23	07 49							08 04			
—	—	—	Harrogate	d													06c06			06 30				06 45		
—	—	—	Scarborough	d																				06 30		
—	—	—	**York 8**	d					06 00	06 00		06 30				07 00					07 27			07 36		
294¼	—	—	**Doncaster 7**	a					06 22	06 22		06 53									07 49					
—	—	—	Sheffield 7 ⛴	a					07 07	07 07		07 40									08 20					
—	—	—	Skipton	d									05 48				06e02			06 18						06 55
—	—	—	Keighley	d									06 01				06e15			06 31						07u05
—	—	—	Bradford Forster Square	d									06 01				06 30			06f48						07g05
—	—	—	Shipley	d									06 13				06u36			06 44						07u15
—	0	—	**Leeds 10**	d			05 05	05 30			06 05	06 14	06 40				07 00			07 20						07 40
—	—	—	Huddersfield	d			04h26				05 32						06c11			06 41						06c54
—	10	—	**Wakefield Westgate 7**	d			05 17	05 42			06 18	06 26	06 52				07 12			07 32						07 52
—	—	—	Hull	d					05 20	05 20				06 25											07 00	
—	—	—	Selby	d								06 15		07 00											07 32	
—	29¾	—	**Doncaster 7**	d			05 35	06 00	06 23	06 23		06 54		07 19			07 30	⟵							07 55	
311¾	—	—	**Retford 10**	d			05 50				06 48			07 32				07 32								08 19
330¼	—	—	**Newark North Gate 7**	a			06 05	06 24	06 46	06 46	07 03		07 29	⟶												08 34
—	—	—	Grimsby Town	d								05j26	05 58												06j26	07 03
—	—	—	Lincoln	d			05 23						06 54													07 59
—	—	—	**Newark North Gate 7**	d			06 05	06 24	06 46	06 46	07 04		07 29													08 34
344¾	—	—	**Grantham 7**	a			06 18	06 37	06 59	06 59	07 16	07 25						07 56							08 29	
—	—	—		d		05 51	06 18	06 37	06 59	06 59	07 17	07 25						07 57							08 29	
374	—	—	**Peterborough 8**	a		06 27	06 37	06 58	07 18	07 18	07 37	07 45				08 03				08 32					08 50	
—	—	—	Cambridge	a				08 07	08k44	08k44	08k55					09 21									10 08	
—	—	—	Stansted Airport	a				08 43								09 58									10 49	
—	—	—	Norwich	a					09 16	09 16						10k30										
—	—	—	**Peterborough 8**	d	06 10		06 40	07 00	07 20	07 20	07 40	07 46				08 04				08 33					08 51	
422¾	—	—	**Stevenage 4**	a			07 57		08 26	08 26						09 05				09 35				09 06	09 56	
450¼	—	—	**London Kings Cross 15** ⊖	a	06 58		07 30	07 53	08 12	08 12	08 34	08 42	08 48			08 59	09 06	09 18		09 26				09 35	09 45	09 51

For general notes see front of timetable
For details of catering facilities see Directory of Train Operators

- **A** From Nottingham (Table 19)
- **B** To Manchester Airport (Table 39)
- **C** To Liverpool Lime Street (Table 39)
- **D** To Paignton (Table 51)
- **E** **The Hull Executive**
- **b** Change at York and Selby
- **c** Change at Leeds
- **e** Change at Shipley
- **f** Bradford Interchange
- **g** Bradford Interchange. Change at Leeds
- **h** Change at Leeds. Mondays dep. 0411
- **j** Change at Doncaster
- **k** Change at Peterborough and Ely

Scotland, North East England, Yorkshire and Humberside → London

Route Diagram - see first page of Table 26

Station		EM ◇ A	XC R 1 B	GR R 1	GR R 1	GR R 1	GC R 1 C	EM ◇ D	TP 1 ◇ E	XC 1 ◇ G	TP 1 ◇ E	GR R 1	HT 1 ◇	GR R 1	XC 1 ◇ H	GR R 1		GR R 1	TP 1 ◇ E	XC 1 ◇ J	NT K	EM ◇ L	GR R 1	GR R 1	XC R 1 B	TP 1 ◇ E
Aberdeen	d																									
Stonehaven	d																									
Montrose	d																									
Arbroath	d																									
Dundee	d																									
Leuchars 3	d																									
Kirkcaldy	d																						*05 55*			
Inverkeithing	d																						*06 21*			
Inverness	d																									
Perth	d																									
Stirling	d																						*05 30*			
Glasgow Central 15	d																						*06b00*		06 00	
Motherwell	d																									
Haymarket	d																								06 52	
Edinburgh 10	a																								06 56	
Edinburgh	d				05 50							06 00			06 05								07 00		07 05	
Dunbar	d											06 20													07 25	
Berwick-upon-Tweed	d				06 29							06 43			06 49								07 40		07 49	
Alnmouth	d											07 03			07 11						07 34				08 08	
Morpeth	d											07 19									08 00				*08 00*	
Newcastle 8	a				07 16							07 38			07 41						08 25		08 29		08 39	
Sunderland	d						06 46													*07 55*						
Hartlepool	d						07 10																			
Newcastle 8	d		06 44	07 00	07 20					07 23	07 26	07 40			07 44	07 49				08 24			08 30		08 40	
Chester-le-Street	d										07 37									08 33						
Durham	d		06 56	07 12						07 37	07 43				07 56	08 01				08 40			08 44		08 52	
Darlington 7	a		07 12	07 29						07 52	07 59				08 13	08 19				08 55			09 04		09 10	
Middlesbrough	d			*06 49*					07 23							*07 42*			←	*08 02*			*08 26*			09 00
Eaglescliffe	d						07 29																			
Darlington 7	d		07 14	07 30						07 54	08 01 →				08 14	08 19			08 01	08 57			09 05		09 10	
Northallerton	d						07 46		07 54										08 12							09 28
Thirsk	d						07 57		08 02										08 20							09 36
York 8	a		07 41	07 58	08 09		08 18		08 19	08 24		08 35			08 41	08 47			08 54	09 24			09 34		09 41	09 55
Hull	a											*10c04*													*10 56*	
Leeds 10	a		08 08				*09 02*		08 50	*09 04*					09 08				09 23	*10 04*					10 08	10 23
Harrogate	d			*07 05*		07 28								*07 51*				*08 14*					*08 16*	*08 30*		
Scarborough	d			*07 00*												*07 47*										
York 8	d			08 00	08 10		08 22			08 27		08 37				08 49				09 27			09 35			
Doncaster 7	a									08 50						09 16				09 54			10 03			
Sheffield 7	a		08 51							09 20					09 51	*10 04*				10 20					10 51	
Skipton	d					*07 08*								*07 47*				*07 56*						*08 43*		
Keighley	d					*07 21*								*08 00*				*08 09*						*08 56*		
Bradford Forster Square	d					*07e18*								*08e05*				*08 26*						*09e06*		
Shipley	d					*07 35*								*08 13*				*08 33*						*09 09*		
Leeds 10	d					08 05								08 40				09 05						09 40		
Huddersfield	d					*07f25*								*07f57*				*08 37*						*08f57*		
Wakefield Westgate 7	d					08 17								08 52				09 19						09 52		
Hull	d												08 12										*08 56*			
Selby	d												08 45													
Doncaster 7	d					08 36							09 05			09 17		09 36					10 04	10 15		
Retford 10	d												09 19					09 51								
Newark North Gate 7	a													09 39		09 45		10 06						10 38		
Grimsby Town	d												*07g26*										*08g36*			
Lincoln	d											*08h04*	*08j27*	*09 10*									*09h11*			
Newark North Gate 7	d													09 40		09 45		10 06						10 38		
Grantham 7	a				09 00							09 27	09 43			09 57							10 36			
	d	08 26			09 00			09 11				09 28	09 43			09 57						10 08	10 36			
Peterborough 8	a	08 57				09 26		09 38				09 47		10 08		10 17		10 33				10 42	10 56	11 06		
Cambridge	a					*10k44*								*11 08*				*11k44*						*12 08*		
Stansted Airport	a													*11 49*										*12 49*		
Norwich	a	10 43						11 14														12 15				
Peterborough 8	d					09 26						09 48		10 08		10 18		10 34					10 57	11 06		
Stevenage 4	a					09 57								10 42				*11 33*								
London Kings Cross 15 ⊖	a			09 54	10 10	10 25	10 32					10 40	10 51	11 10		11 13		11 27					11 50	12 03		

For general notes see front of timetable
For details of catering facilities see Directory of Train Operators

A From Mansfield Woodhouse (Table 55)
B To Bournemouth (Table 51)
C **The Zephyr**
D From Sheffield (Table 49)
E To Manchester Airport (Table 39)
G To Bristol Temple Meads (Table 51)
H To Plymouth (Table 51)
J To Paignton (Table 51)
K From Chathill (Table 48)
L From Liverpool Lime Street (Table 49)
b Glasgow Queen Street
c Change at York and Selby
e Bradford Interchange
f Change at Leeds
g Change at Doncaster
h Change at Peterborough
j Change at Retford
k Change at Peterborough and Ely

Scotland, North East England, Yorkshire and Humberside → London

Route Diagram - see first page of Table 26

		GR	GR	EM	TP	GR	XC	HT	XC	GR	GR		TP	EM	TP	XC	GR	GR	XC	TP	GR	EM	GR	TP	XC	GR
		R 1	R 1	◇	1 ◇	R 1	1 ◇	1 ◇	1 ◇	R 1	R 1		1 ◇	◇	1 ◇	R 1	R 1	R 1	R 1	1 ◇	R 1	◇	R 1	1 ◇	1 ◇	R 1
				A	B		C		D				B	A	B	D			E	B		A		B	C	
Aberdeen	d																06b00				06c34					
Stonehaven	d																06b16				06c53					
Montrose	d																06b38				07c15					
Arbroath	d																06b52				07c29					
Dundee	d								06 38								07b11		07 33		07 59					
Leuchars 3	d								06 51								07b23		07 46		08 11					
Kirkcaldy	d								07 25								07b57		08 18		08 43					
Inverkeithing	d					07b14			07 43								08b19		08 37		08 59					
Inverness	d																									
Perth	d					05e15			06b14								07b03				07e14					
Stirling	d					06b36											07b48				08 06					
Glasgow Central 15	d					06 50			07f00								07 50		08f00		08g30					
Motherwell	d					07 04											08 07		07b28							
Haymarket	d					07 50			08 00								08 50		08 58							
Edinburgh 10	a					07 55			08 06								08 56		09 03							
Edinburgh	d					08 00			08 13								09 00		09 05		09 30					
Dunbar	d																		09 25							
Berwick-upon-Tweed	d								08 52								09 42		09 49		10 10					
Alnmouth	d					08 56			09 12																	
Morpeth	d				08 32										09 32										10 50	
Newcastle 8	a					09 29			09 40								10 31		10 37		10 59					
Sunderland	d	08 30													09 30						10 30					
Hartlepool	d																									
Newcastle 8	d	09 00			09 12	09 30	09 35		09 40						10 15	10 25	10 34		10 40		11 00			11 15	11 25	11 30
Chester-le-Street	d				09 21											10 34										
Durham	d	09 12			09 28		09 47		09 52						10 27	10 41	10 47		10 52					11 27	11 37	11 43
Darlington 7	a	09 29			09 44	09 58	10 04		10 10						10 43	10 56	11 05		11 10		11 28			11 43	11 54	12 01
Middlesbrough	d												09 59				10 24			11 00	10 54					11 24
Eaglescliffe	d																									
Darlington 7	d	09 30			09 45	09 58	10 04		10 10						10 45	10 58	11 06		11 10		11 28			11 45	11 56	12 02
Northallerton	d	09 43			09 56								10 27		10 56					11 28				11 56		
Thirsk	d												10 35							11 36						
York 8	a	10 05			10 22	10 27	10 31		10 41				10 54		11 22	11 24	11 33		11 41	11 55	11 57			12 21	12 22	12 29
Hull	a	11h34																	13 02		13h34					
Leeds 10	a				10 53		11 04		11 08				11 23		11 53	12 05			12 08	12 23	12 49			12 51	13 04	13 04
Harrogate	d	09 05								09 44	10 14						10j14	10 44			11 05		11 14			
Scarborough	d	08 47																			10 45					
York 8	d	10 06				10 29	10 34									11 27	11 35				12 00				12 25	12 31
Doncaster 7	a	10 30				10 53	10 57									11 51	12 00								12 50	12 54
Sheffield 7	a	11 07				11 41	11 20		11 51							12 20			12 51						13 20	13 41
Skipton	d									09 48								10 48					10 59			
Keighley	d									10 01								11 01					11 09			
Bradford Forster Square	d		09 31							10k05	10 31							11k05					11 31			
Shipley	d		09 39							10 14	10 39							11 14					11 39			
Leeds 10	d		10 05							10 40	11 05							11 40					12 05			
Huddersfield	d		09 35							09m57	10 35							10m57					11 35			
Wakefield Westgate 7	d		10 18							10 52	11 17							11 54					12 17			
Hull	d		09 25			09 56		10 12			10 22						10 57						11 22			11 55
Selby	d							10 47																		
Doncaster 7	d	10 30	10 35			10 53		11 05		11 13	11 37						12 00	12 12					12 36			12 55
Retford 10	d					11 08		11 20															12 51			
Newark North Gate 7	a		10 59							11 41								12 37								
Grimsby Town	d		09 28			09n36											10n36									11n36
Lincoln	d		10 23					10q27									11 12						11q27			
Newark North Gate 7	d		10 59							11 41								12 37								
Grantham 7	a		11 11					11 40		11 54	12 09												13 14			
	d		11 11	11 04				11 40		11 54	12 09			12 07								13 08	13 14			
Peterborough 8	a	11 16	11 31	11 34		11 48				12 13	12 28			12 42			12 46	13 05			13 11	13 38				13 42
Cambridge	a	12r44	12r55			13 08					13r44							14 08			14r44					
Stansted Airport	a					13 49												14 49								
Norwich	a			13 13										14 14								15 13				
Peterborough 8	d	11 17	11 31			11 49				12 14	12 29						12 47	13 06			13 12					13 45
Stevenage 4	a	11 47	12 33							12 43							13 16	14 08								14 16
London Kings Cross 15 ⊖	a	12 17	12 25			12 42		12 44		13 10	13 22						13 43	14 02			14 10		14 20			14 44

For general notes see front of timetable
For details of catering facilities see Directory of Train Operators

A From Liverpool Lime Street (Table 49)
B To Manchester Airport (Table 39)
C To Bristol Temple Meads (Table 51)
D To Plymouth (Table 51)
E To Bournemouth (Table 51)
b Change at Edinburgh
c Change at Dundee and Edinburgh
e Change at Stirling and Edinburgh
f Glasgow Queen Street. Change at Edinburgh
g Glasgow Queen Street
h Change at York and Selby
j Change at Leeds and Doncaster
k Bradford Interchange
m Change at Leeds
n Change at Doncaster
q Change at Retford
r Change at Peterborough and Ely

Scotland, North East England, Yorkshire and Humberside → London

Route Diagram - see first page of Table 26

		XC	GR	GR	EM	HT		GR	TP	TP	XC	XC	GR	XC	TP	GR	GR	GC	GR	EM	TP	GR	XC	XC		TP
		R 1	R 1	R 1	◇	1 ◇		R 1	1 ◇	1 ◇	1 ◇	R 1	R 1	R 1	1 ◇	R 1	R 1	R 1	R 1	◇	1 ◇	R 1	1 ◇	R 1		1 ◇
		A			B				C	C	D	E		E	C	G				B	C		H	D		C
Aberdeen	d	07b20	07 53									08 20				08b50										
Stonehaven	d	07b36	08 10									08 37				09b06										
Montrose	d	07b58	08 33									08 59				09c14										
Arbroath	d	08b12	08 48									09 15				09b42										
Dundee	d	08b31	09 06									09 33				09b59										
Leuchars 3	d	08b43	09 20									09 46				10b11										
Kirkcaldy	d	09b15	09 44									10 13	09b59			10b43						10 58				
Inverkeithing	d	09b24	10 00									10 28	10b20			10b59						11 20				
Inverness	d	05b00	06b45													07 55										
Perth	d		08b48													09 56										
Stirling	d	08b36	09b06										09b36			10 30						10 36				
Glasgow Central 15	d	09 00	09e15										09 50			10e30						11f00				
Motherwell	d	09u14											10 04													
Haymarket	d	09 55	10 19									10 47	10 50			11 10										
Edinburgh 10	a	10 01	10 25									10 51	10 56	←		11 20										
Edinburgh	d	10 05	10 30									11 05 →	11 00	11 05		11 30						12 00		12 05		
Dunbar	d													11 25												
Berwick-upon-Tweed	d												11 41	11 49								12 39				
Alnmouth	d	11 04											12 01											13 04		
Morpeth	d	11 18											11 50									12 50		13 19		
Newcastle 8	a	11 35	11 57										12 34	12 38		12 58						13 27		13 37		
Sunderland	d									11 30						12 30		12 30								
Hartlepool	d																	12 54								
Newcastle 8	d	11 40	11 59							12 15	12 19		12 35	12 40		13 01					13 15	13 29	13 33	13 40		
Chester-le-Street	d										12 32															
Durham	d	11 52								12 28	12 40		12 48	12 53							13 27		13 46	13 52		
Darlington 7	a	12 09								12 44	12 59		13 06	13 10							13 43	13 55	14 02	14 10		
Middlesbrough	d								12 00		12 24				12 51						12 57		13 25			13 50
Eaglescliffe	d																	13 16								
Darlington 7	d	12 10								12 46	13 00		13 06	13 10							13 45	13 56	14 03	14 10		
Northallerton	d								12 28	12 56					13 21			13 38			13 56					14 18
Thirsk	d								12 36						13 29			13 47								14 26
York 8	a	12 41	12 50						12 55	13 24	13 27		13 35	13 41	13 49	13 52		14 07			14 22	14 24	14 29	14 41		14 48
Hull	a												14 48													
Leeds 10	a	13 08							13 23	13 53	14 04			14 08	14 23	14 49					14 53		15 04	15 08		15 23
Harrogate	d		12 05					12 14								13 05			13 14							
Scarborough	d		11 45													12 47										
York 8	d		12 53								13 29		13 36			13 54		14 10				14 26	14 32			
Doncaster 7	a										13 53		14 03									14 49	14 55			
Sheffield 7	a	13 51									14 20			14 51									15 20	15 51		
Skipton	d			11 48				12 12									12 48									
Keighley	d			12 01				12 22									13 01									
Bradford Forster Square	d			12g05				12 31									13g05		13 31							
Shipley	d			12 14				12 39									13 14		13 39							
Leeds 10	d			12 40				13 05									13 40		14 05							
Huddersfield	d			11h57				12 35									12h57		13 35							
Wakefield Westgate 7	d			12 52				13 18									13 53		14 18							
Hull	d					12 45		12 22					12 57									13 25				
Selby	d					13 20																				
Doncaster 7	d			13 14		13 37		13 38					14 03				14 15					14 50				
Retford 10	d							13 55																		
Newark North Gate 7	a			13 42				14 10														15 13				
Grimsby Town	d												12j36									13j37				
Lincoln	d		12 14	12 23				12k27									13 31					14 04				
Newark North Gate 7	d			13 42				14 10														15 13				
Grantham 7	a					14 08		14 23											15 03			15 26				
	d				14 06	14 09		14 23											15 03	15 07		15 26				
Peterborough 8	a		14 03	14 09	14 38			14 42					14 49				15 05		15 22	15 34		15 45				
Cambridge	a			15 08													16 08		16m44							
Stansted Airport	a			15 49													16 49									
Norwich	a				16 13															17 13						
Peterborough 8	d		14 03	14 10				14 43					14 50				15 06		15 23			15 47				
Stevenage 4	a			15 08				15 12											15 52			16 17				
London Kings Cross 15 ⊖	a		14 57	15 05		15 20		15 40					15 44			15 51	15 58	16 05	16 22			16 46				

For general notes see front of timetable
For details of catering facilities see Directory of Train Operators

A To Penzance (Table 135)
B From Liverpool Lime Street (Table 49)
C To Manchester Airport (Table 39)
D To Plymouth (Table 51)
E To Bournemouth (Table 51)
G **The Highland Chieftain**
H To Bristol Temple Meads (Table 51)
b Change at Edinburgh
c Change at Arbroath and Edinburgh
e Glasgow Queen Street. Change at Edinburgh
f Glasgow Queen Street
g Bradford Interchange
h Change at Leeds
j Change at Doncaster
k Change at Retford
m Change at Peterborough and Ely

Scotland, North East England, Yorkshire and Humberside → London

Route Diagram - see first page of Table 26

		GR	GR	GR	EM	GR	TP	XC	GR	GR	XC	TP	GR	HT	GR	TP	XC	GR		GR	XC	TP	GR	TP	XC	GR
		R 1	R 1	R 1	◇	R 1	1 ◇	R 1	R 1	R 1	R 1	1 ◇	R 1	1 ◇	R 1	1 ◇	R 1	R 1		R 1	1 ◇	1 ◇	R 1	1 ◇	R 1	R 1
		A			B		C	D	E		G	H				C	J				K	C		C	L	
Aberdeen	d	09 52							10b22									11 22								12b24
Stonehaven	d	10 09							10b38									11 38								12b43
Montrose	d	10 32							11b00									12 00								12c15
Arbroath	d	10 47							11b14									12 14								13b17
Dundee	d	11 05							11b30									12 30								13b33
Leuchars 3	d	11 19							11b42									12 42								13b45
Kirkcaldy	d	11 43							12b12									13 14								14b15
Inverkeithing	d	11 59							12b20									13 30								14b19
Inverness	d																	09e19								10b53
Perth	d	10e12							11b08									11e39								13b04
Stirling	d	11b06							11b36									12 36								13b36
Glasgow Central 15	d	11f30							11 50									13g00								13 50
Motherwell	d								12 04																	14 04
Haymarket	d	12 17							12 50																	14 50
Edinburgh 10	a	12 22							12 58																	14 58
Edinburgh	d	12 30							13 00		13 05							14 00			14 05					15 00
Dunbar	d										13 25															
Berwick-upon-Tweed	d								13 41		13 49							14 40								
Alnmouth	d																				15 05					
Morpeth	d							13 50									14 50				15 21				15 50	
Newcastle 8	a	13 58							14 30		14 37							15 28			15 38					16 26
Sunderland	d	13 30														14 30								15 30		
Hartlepool	d																									
Newcastle 8	d	14 00				14 05	14 12	14 22	14 34		14 40		14 56			15 12	15 22	15 30			15 40		15 55	16 06	16 27	16 28
Chester-le-Street	d							14 33								15 21								16 15	16 42	
Durham	d					14 17	14 24	14 40			14 52		15 08			15 27	15 34				15 52		16 08	16 22	16 49	
Darlington 7	a					14 36	14 39	14 55	15 03		15 10		15 25			15 44	15 50	16 01			16 09		16 26	16 38	⟶	
Middlesbrough	d					13 55			14 24			14 50				14 55					15 27	15 50				
Eaglescliffe	d																									
Darlington 7	d					14 37	14 45	14 57	15 04		15 10		15 26			15 45	15 51	16 02			16 10		16 26	16 39 ⟶		
Northallerton	d					14 49	14 56					15 18				15 56						16 18				
Thirsk	d											15 26										16 26				
York 8	a	14 51				15 09	15 25	15 26	15 33		15 41	15 51	15 53			16 21	16 23	16 30			16 41	16 47	16 54			17 20
Hull	a	15 58											17 27										18 29			
Leeds 10	a	15 49					15 53	16 04			16 08	16 23	16 49			16 53		17 04			17 08	17 23	17 50			
Harrogate	d	14 05		14 14						14 44			15 05		15 14					15 44			16 05			
Scarborough	d	13 47											14 47										15 47			
York 8	d	14 53				15 11		15 29	15 35				15 55				16 25	16 32					16 56			17 21
Doncaster 7	a					15 35		15 54	16 00								16 50	16 56					17 20			
Sheffield 7	a					16 07		16 20			16 51						17 18				17 51		18 07			
Skipton	d		13 48	13 59						14 48										15 48						
Keighley	d		14 01	14 09						15 01										16 01						
Bradford Forster Square	d		14h05	14 31						15h05					15 31					16h05						
Shipley	d		14 14	14 39						15 14					15 39					16 14						
Leeds 10	d		14 40	15 05						15 40					16 05					16 40						
Huddersfield	d		13j57	14 35						14j57					15 35					15j57						
Wakefield Westgate 7	d		14 52	15 17						15 52					16 17					16 52						
Hull	d		13 57			14 25			14 57					15 18	15 21			15 57								
Selby	d													15 57												
Doncaster 7	d		15 15			15 36			16 01					16 15	16 36			16 57		17 10			17 20			
Retford 10	d					15 51								16 34												
Newark North Gate 7	a		15 41			16 06												17 20		17 33			17 44			
Grimsby Town	d		13 52						14k36									15k36		16 03						13m52
Lincoln	d		14 47						14 50					15n27				16q02		16 56						
Newark North Gate 7	d		15 41			16 06												17 20		17 33			17 44			
Grantham 7	a		15 54			16 19							16 44	16 55									17 57			
	d		15 54		16 07	16 19							16 44	16 55									17 57			
Peterborough 8	a	16 01		16 17	16 34				16 47	16 55			17 04		17 27			17 48								18 26
Cambridge	a	17 08		17r43									18 16					18 51								19r55
Stansted Airport	a	17 43											18 47					20 05								
Norwich	a				18 13								19r25													
Peterborough 8	d	16 02		16 17					16 48	16 56			17 04		17 27			17 49								18 26
Stevenage 4	a			16 48									17 34	17s46	18 35			19 09					18 42			19 33
London Kings Cross 15 ⊖	a	16 57	17 04	17 15		17 30			17 41	17 50			18 04	18 12	18 23			18 45		18 48			19 11			19 18

For general notes see front of timetable
For details of catering facilities see Directory of Train Operators

- **A** **The Northern Lights**
- **B** From Liverpool Lime Street (Table 49)
- **C** To Manchester Airport (Table 39)
- **D** To Cardiff Central (Table 51)
- **E** **The Flying Scotsman**
- **G** To Bournemouth (Table 51)
- **H** To Manchester Piccadilly (Table 39)
- **J** To Weston-super-Mare (Table 51)
- **K** To Plymouth (Table 51)
- **L** To Bristol Temple Meads (Table 51)
- **b** Change at Edinburgh
- **c** Change at Arbroath and Edinburgh
- **e** Change at Stirling and Edinburgh
- **f** Glasgow Queen Street. Change at Edinburgh
- **g** Glasgow Queen Street
- **h** Bradford Interchange
- **j** Change at Leeds
- **k** Change at Doncaster
- **m** Change at Lincoln and Peterborough
- **n** Change at Retford
- **q** Change at Peterborough
- **r** Change at Peterborough and Ely

Scotland, North East England, Yorkshire and Humberside → London

Route Diagram - see first page of Table 26

Station		GR	EM	TP	XC	HT	GR	XC	TP	GR	TP	GR	XC	EM	TP	GR	GR	XC	TP	GC	GR	GR	XC	GR	GR
			A	B	C			D	E		B		G	A	B			C	B				G		
Aberdeen	d															13 21									14b25
Stonehaven	d															13 37									14b41
Montrose	d															13 59									14c15
Arbroath	d															14 13									15b15
Dundee	d															14 30									15b32
Leuchars 3	d															14 42									15b44
Kirkcaldy	d															15 14									16b14
Inverkeithing	d															15 30									16b30
Inverness	d																								12b40
Perth	d															13e12									14b49
Stirling	d															14 36									15b36
Glasgow Central 15	d															15f00									15 50
Motherwell	d																								16 04
Haymarket	d																								16 50
Edinburgh 10	a																								16 57
Edinburgh	d							15 05								16 00		16 05							17 00
Dunbar	d							15 25								16 20									
Berwick-upon-Tweed	d							15 49								16 43									
Alnmouth	d																	17 08							17 59
Morpeth	d															16 50		17 23							
Newcastle 8	a							16 37								17 30		17 38							18 32
Sunderland	d										16 30									17 30					
Hartlepool	d																			17 56					
Newcastle 8	d							16 40		16 55	17 10		17 17			17 32		17 40				18 10	18 20		18 35
Chester-le-Street	d				←								17 26										18 29		
Durham	d				16 49			16 52		17 07	17 22		17 33					17 54				18 22	18 36		
Darlington 7	a			←	17 04					17 25	17 38		17 48			17 58		18 11				18 39	18 54		19 03
Middlesbrough	d			15 55	16 24				16 50		16 57							17 24	17 50			17 55	18 24		
Eaglescliffe	d																			18 15					
Darlington 7	d			16 39	17 06					17 25	17 40		17 50		←	17 59		18 11				18 40	18 56		19 04
Northallerton	d			16 51					17 18		17 51 →				17 51				18 18	18 36		18 51			
Thirsk	d			16 59					17 26						17 59				18 26	18 45					
York 8	a			17 25	17 32			17 41	17 50	17 53			18 18		18 24	18 28		18 41	18 51	19 04		19 11	19 25		19 33
Hull	a									19 32												20g37			
Leeds 10	a			17 53	18 04			18 08	18 23	18 47					18 52	19 04		19 08	19 35				20 04		
Harrogate	d	16 14					16 44					17 14					17 50			18 05					18h18
Scarborough	d									16 47															
York 8	d				17 34					17 55			18 24			18 30				19 06		19 13	19 29		19 35
Doncaster 7	a				17 56					18 20			18 49			18 53						19 37	19 55		19 59
Sheffield 7	a				18 20			18 51		19 07			19 20					19 51				20 18	20 20		
Skipton	d	16 12					16 49					16 58					17 49								
Keighley	d	16 22					17 02					17 08					18 02								
Bradford Forster Square	d	16 31					17j05					17 31					18j05				18 27				18h27
Shipley	d	16 39					17 15					17 39					18 14				18 34				18h34
Leeds 10	d	17 05					17 40					18 05					18 40				19 05				19 05
Huddersfield	d	16 35					16k57					17 33					17k57				18 34				18m34
Wakefield Westgate 7	d	17 17					17 52					18 17					18 52				19 17				
Hull	d					17 06										17 56					18 22				18 53
Selby	d					17 43										18 27									
Doncaster 7	d	17 37				18 02	18 11			18 21		18 35				18 54	19 12				19 36	19 37			20 00
Retford 10	d	17 57				18 16				18 36														←	
Newark North Gate 7	a						18 34			18 51						19 17	19 34				20 05				
Grimsby Town	d					16n36										17n36								18 30	18n36
Lincoln	d					17q22				18 17														19 26	
Newark North Gate 7	d						18 34			18 51						19 17	19 34				20 05 →			20 05	
Grantham 7	a					18 36	18 47										19 49							20 17	
	d		18 16			18 36	18 47							19 09			19 49							20 17	
Peterborough 8	a		18 49				19 06			19 19		19 25		19 36		19 45						20 24		20 37	20 46
Cambridge	a						20 11					21r01				21 16									22 08
Stansted Airport	a																								
Norwich	a		20 22											21 13		22r30									
Peterborough 8	d						19 07			19 20		19 26				19 46						20 25		20 38	20 46
Stevenage 4	a	19 00				19s24				19 50						20 15	20 35								21 17
London Kings Cross 15 ⊖	a	19 29				19 49	19 59			20 18		20 21				20 42	21 03			21 08		21 17		21 33	21 44

For general notes see front of timetable
For details of catering facilities see Directory of Train Operators

A From Liverpool Lime Street (Table 49)
B To Manchester Airport (Table 39)
C To Bristol Temple Meads (Table 51)
D To Southampton Central (Table 51)
E To Manchester Piccadilly (Table 39)
G To Birmingham New Street (Table 51)
b Change at Edinburgh
c Change at Arbroath and Edinburgh
e Change at Stirling and Edinburgh
f Glasgow Queen Street
g Change at York and Selby
h Change at Leeds and Doncaster
j Bradford Interchange
k Change at Leeds
m Change at Wakefield Westgate and Doncaster
n Change at Doncaster
q Change at Retford
r Change at Peterborough and Ely

Scotland, North East England, Yorkshire and Humberside → London

Route Diagram - see first page of Table 26

		HT	GR	XC	TP	TP	GR	XC		EM	GR	XC	NT	TP	GR	XC	GR	TP	TP	TP	NT	GR	GR	XC FO		
		1 ◇	R 1	1 ◇	1 ◇	1 ◇	R 1	1 ◇		◇	R 1	1 ◇		1 ◇	R 1	1 ◇	R 1	1 ◇	1 ◇	1 ◇		R 1	R 1	1 ◇		
				A		B				C		D	E	B		G	H	J		B	K					
Aberdeen	d						14 50					15 20					16b21					18 20		19c41		
Stonehaven	d						15 07					15 36					16b37					18 37		20c00		
Montrose	d						15 30					16 00					16e13					19 00		20c24		
Arbroath	d						15 45					16 14					17b11					19 15		20c38		
Dundee	d						16 03					16 31					17b31					19 33		21b28		
Leuchars 3	d						16 17					16 43					17b43					19 47		21b40		
Kirkcaldy	d						16 41					17 17			17 31		18b15					20 11		22b13		
Inverkeithing	d						16 57					17 33			17 47		18b12					20 27		22b36		
Inverness	d														14 41								16f56	18b27		
Perth	d						15g12								16 48								19b13	21g18		
Stirling	d						16b06					16 36			17 06		17b36						19b36	22b06		
Glasgow Central 15	d			16h00			16j15					17h00			17h15		17 50						19 50	21 55		
Motherwell	d			15 38													18 04						20 04	22 25		
Haymarket	d						17 15										18 50					20 46	20 50	23 10		
Edinburgh 10	a						17 23										18 57					20 50	20 55	23 19		
Edinburgh	d			17 05			17 30					18 05			18 35		19 00						21 00	23 23		
Dunbar	d			17 25			17 53					18 25			18 55		19 23						21 22	23a50		
Berwick-upon-Tweed	d			17 49			18 16								19 18		19 46						21 45			
Alnmouth	d											19 05	19 20		19 40								22 07			
Morpeth	d						18 32					19 01	19 45		19 57						21 34		22 24			
Newcastle 8	a			18 39			19 07					19 35	20 06		20 18		20 35				21 56		22 45			
Sunderland	d						18 30									19 27				20 27	21 27					
Hartlepool	d																									
Newcastle 8	d			18 40		18 58	19 08	19 25				19 40				20 26	20 37			21 47	22 00		22 46			
Chester-le-Street	d							19 36													22 09					
Durham	d			18 52		19 10		19 44				19 52				20 38	20 50			22 00	22 18		23 01			
Darlington 7	a			19 10		19 26	19 38	20 01				20 10				20 54	21 07			22 16	22 38		23 19			
Middlesbrough	d				19 00							19 25		20 10				20 50	21 40				21 55			
Eaglescliffe	d																									
Darlington 7	d			19 10		19 28	19 38	20 02				20 10				20 55	21 08		22 07	22 18			23 19			
Northallerton	d				19 28	19 39								20 38				21 21	22 18	22 29						
Thirsk	d				19 36									20 47					22 26							
York 8	a			19 41	19 59	20 03	20 06	20 28				20 41		21 05		21 21	21 36	21 42	22 52	23 04			00 16			
Hull	a																	23 08								
Leeds 10	a			20 08		20 35		21 04				21 08		21 33		22 00		22 08		23 33						
Harrogate	d		18 44				19 05				19 44						20 05									
Scarborough	d			18 46								19 45					20 37									
York 8	d						20 08	20 31								21 24	21 38									
Doncaster 7	a						20 31	20 54									22 02									
Sheffield 7	a			20 51			21 18	21 30				21 51				22 21	22 54	23 57								
Skipton	d		18 48								19 48															
Keighley	d		19 01								20 01															
Bradford Forster Square	d		19k05								20k04															
Shipley	d		19 14								20 14															
Leeds 10	d		19 40								20 40															
Huddersfield	d		18m57								19m45															
Wakefield Westgate 7	d		19 54								20 55															
Hull	d	19 18									20 03						20 56									
Selby	d	19 53																								
Doncaster 7	d	20 10	20 15				20 32				21 12						22 03									
Retford 10	d										21 27															
Newark North Gate 7	a		20 39								21 42						22 26									
Grimsby Town	d										19n36						20n36									
Lincoln	d										20q40															
Newark North Gate 7	d		20 39								21 42						22 26									
Grantham 7	a	20 42	20 51								21 55						22 39									
	d	20 42	20 51							21 08	21 55						22 39									
Peterborough 8	a		21 11				21 20			21 36	22 14						22 58									
Cambridge	a						23 14			22 29																
Stansted Airport	a																									
Norwich	a									23r45																
Peterborough 8	d		21 12				21 21				22 15						22 59									
Stevenage 4	a	21s31					21 51				22s51						23s35									
London Kings Cross 15 ⊖	a	21 59	22 04				22 19				23 32						00 15									

For general notes see front of timetable
For details of catering facilities see Directory of Train Operators

A To Bristol Temple Meads (Table 51). to Leeds
B To Manchester Airport (Table 39)
C From Liverpool Lime Street (Table 49)
D To Birmingham New Street (Table 51). to Leeds
E From Chathill to Hexham (Table 48)
G To Birmingham New Street (Table 51)
H GNER cannot guarantee connections with London Underground services
J To Manchester Piccadilly (Table 39)
K To Middlesbrough (Table 44)
b Change at Edinburgh
c Change at Dundee and Edinburgh
e Change at Arbroath and Edinburgh
f Change at Perth and Edinburgh
g Change at Stirling and Edinburgh
h Glasgow Queen Street
j Glasgow Queen Street. Change at Edinburgh
k Bradford Interchange
m Change at Leeds
n Change at Doncaster
q Change at Sleaford and Grantham
r Change at Ely

Scotland, North East England, Yorkshire and Humberside → London

Route Diagram - see first page of Table 26

	EM	GR	GR	GR	TP	GR	GR	GR	EM	XC	XC	TP		GR	XC	GR	XC	GR	XC	GR	GR	TP	EM	GR	GC
		R 1	R 1	R 1	1 ◇	R 1	R 1	R 1	◇	1 ◇	1 ◇	1 ◇		R 1	1 ◇	R 1	1 ◇	R 1	1 ◇	R 1	R 1	1 ◇	◇	R 1	R 1
	A				B				A	C	D	E			D		G		G			B	A		H
Aberdeen d																									
Stonehaven d																									
Montrose d																									
Arbroath d																									
Dundee d																									
Leuchars 3 d																									
Kirkcaldy d																									
Inverkeithing d																									
Inverness d																									
Perth d																									
Stirling d																									
Glasgow Central 15 d																									
Motherwell d																									
Haymarket d																									
Edinburgh 10 a																									
Edinburgh d																									
Dunbar d																									
Berwick-upon-Tweed d																									
Alnmouth d																									
Morpeth d																									
Newcastle 8 a																									
Sunderland d																									06 53
Hartlepool d																									07 17
Newcastle 8 d			04 31			06 00					06 08	06 13		06 35			06 50	07 00						07 30	
Chester-le-Street d															←				←						
Durham d			04 45			06 12					06 23	06 29		06 48	06 23		07 02	07 12	07 02					07 42	
Darlington 7 a			05 02			06 29					→	06 45		07 05	07 10		→	07 29						07 59	
Middlesbrough d					05 58													*06 49*				07 21			
Eaglescliffe d																									07 45
Darlington 7 d			05 03			06 30						06 47		07 06	07 12			07 30						08 00	
Northallerton d			05 30		06 26							06 58						07 41				07 49			08 06
Thirsk d					06 33							07 07										07 57			08 15
York 8 a			05 57		06 52	06 57						07 32		07 34	07 41			08 01	08 16			08 19		08 28	
Hull a			*08b21*			*08 45*																*09b31*			
Leeds 10 a			*06 49*		07 23	*07 49*						08 04			08 08							08 50		*09 04*	
Harrogate d							*06 06*							*06 45*				*07 14*			07 44				*07 49*
Scarborough d														*06 34*				*07 05*							*07 47*
York 8 d			06 00			07 00				07 27				07 36				08 03						08 30	08 47
Doncaster 7 a			06 22			07 22				07 49				07 59										08 54	
Sheffield 7 a			*07 07*			*08 00*				08 20					08 51				09 20					*09 41*	
Skipton d							*05 48*									06 42				*07c01*					
Keighley d							*06 01*									06u52				*07c15*					
Bradford Forster Square d							*06e23*									*07f05*				07 36					
Shipley d							*06 13*									07u00				07u41					
Leeds 10 d		05 05		06 10		*06 19*	07 00									07 40				08 05	08 15				
Huddersfield d		*04g26*					*06g11*									*06g54*				*07 32*					
Wakefield Westgate 7 d		05 17		06 22		*06 32*	07 12									07 52				08 18	*07 39*				
Hull d			*05 20*			*06 07*		06 50																*07 36*	
Selby d						*06 15*		07 23																	
Doncaster 7 d		05 35	06 23	06 40		07 23	07 30	07 40						08 00							08 45			08 55	
Retford 10 d		05 50		06 55												08 20								09 10	
Newark North Gate 7 a		06 05		07 10			07 54							08 24		08 34				08 54					
Grimsby Town d						*05h26*		*06h26*						*06 59*							*07h26*				
Lincoln d							*06 55*							*07 54*										*08 04*	
Newark North Gate 7 d		06 05		07 10			07 54							08 24		08 34				08 54					
Grantham 7 a		06 17		07 23			08 06							08 37		08 46				09 06					
Grantham 7 d	05 53	06 17		07 23			08 06		08 17					08 37		08 46				09 06			09 10		
Peterborough 8 a	06 25	06 37	07 09	07 42		08 09	08 26	08 32	08 44					08 57		09 06		09 12		09 26	09 32		09 44	09 48	
Cambridge a		*08 06*	*08j44*	*08j55*		*09 22*		*09j44*								*10 08*					*10j44*				
Stansted Airport a		*08 49*				*09 58*										*10 49*									
Norwich a			*09 12*						10 17														11 17		
Peterborough 8 d		06 37	07 09	07 48		08 09	08 26	08 32						08 57		09 07		09 15		09 26	09 33			09 48	
Stevenage 4 a		*07 33*	*08 08*			*09 08*		*09 33*										09 45			*10 33*				
London Kings Cross 15 ⊖ a		07 29	08 04	08 40		09 03	09 18	09 26						09 51		10 00		10 13		10 20	10 27			10 41	10 45

For general notes see front of timetable
For details of catering facilities see Directory of Train Operators

- **A** From Nottingham (Table 19)
- **B** To Manchester Airport (Table 39)
- **C** To Paignton (Table 51)
- **D** To Bournemouth (Table 51)
- **E** To Liverpool Lime Street (Table 39)
- **G** To Bristol Temple Meads (Table 51)
- **H** **The Zephyr**
- **b** Change at York and Selby
- **c** Change at Shipley
- **e** Bradford Interchange
- **f** Bradford Interchange. Change at Leeds
- **g** Change at Leeds
- **h** Change at Doncaster
- **j** Change at Peterborough and Ely

Scotland, North East England, Yorkshire and Humberside → London

Route Diagram - see first page of Table 26

	TP	XC	HT	GR	GR	TP	XC	NT	EM	GR	XC	TP	GR	GR	TP	XC	EM	GR	GR	HT	XC	TP	GR
	1 ◇	1 ◇	1 ◇	R 1	R 1	1 ◇	1 ◇		◇	R 1	1 ◇	1 ◇	R 1	R 1	1 ◇	1 ◇	◇	R 1	R 1	1 ◇	1 ◇	1 ◇	R 1
	A	B				A	C	D	E		G	A			A	C	E	H	J		B	A	
Aberdeen d																							
Stonehaven d																							
Montrose d																							
Arbroath d																							
Dundee d																			06 16				
Leuchars 3 d																			06 28				
Kirkcaldy d													06 15						07 02				07 44
Inverkeithing d													06 39					07b13	07 26				08 00
Inverness d																							
Perth d																		05c15	05c15				07 03
Stirling d										05 30								06b36	06 36				07 16
Glasgow Central 15 d										06e00	05 50							06 50	06e30		07e00		07e30
Motherwell d											06u10							07 06	06f45				
Haymarket d											06 51							07 49					
Edinburgh 10 a											06 57							07 53					
Edinburgh d		06 05		06 15						07 00	07 05		07 30					08 00	08 00		08 05		08 35
Dunbar d				06 35							07 25												
Berwick-upon-Tweed d		06 47		06 59						07 40	07 51		08 11								08 46		09 14
Alnmouth d		07 07		07 19				07 34			08 11							08 58	08 58		09 06		
Morpeth d				07 35				08 00															09 32
Newcastle 8 a		07 33		07 53				08 25		08 31	08 37		08 58					09 31	09 31		09 35		10 02
Sunderland d							07 30			07 55					08 30								09 30
Hartlepool d																							
Newcastle 8 d	07 33	07 40		07 54			08 24			08 33	08 40		09 00		09 12	09 25		09 32	09 32		09 40		10 03
Chester-le-Street d	07 42						08 33								09 21								
Durham d	07 49	07 54					08 40			08 46	08 52		09 13		09 27	09 37					09 52		
Darlington 7 a	08 05	08 11		08 21			08 55			09 04	09 10		09 30		09 44	09 55		10 00	10 00		10 09		10 31
Middlesbrough d				07 42			08 05			08 25		09 00										10 00	09 39
Eaglescliffe d																							
Darlington 7 d	08 06	08 12		08 21		←	08 57			09 05	09 11		09 31		09 45	09 56		10 01	10 01		10 11		10 31
Northallerton d	08 18					08 18						09 28	09 42		09 56							10 28	
Thirsk d	→					08 26						09 36										10 36	
York 8 a		08 41		08 50		08 53	09 24			09 34	09 41	09 56	10 03		10 22	10 23		10 29	10 29		10 41	10 54	10 59
Hull a											10 56		11g34										
Leeds 10 a		09 08				09 23	10 04				10 08	10 23	10 49		10 53			11 04	11 04		11 08	11 23	11 49
Harrogate d					08 00					08 16			09 05	09 18									10 05
Scarborough d													08 47										09 47
York 8 d				08 51			09 27			09 36			10 05			10 25		10 31	10 31				11 00
Doncaster 7 a				09 15			09 49			10 02			10 28			10 48		10 54	10 54				11 24
Sheffield 7 a		09 51		10 04			10 20				10 51		11 07			11 20		11 41	11 41		11 51		12 07
Skipton d					07 56								08h18	08 48									09h28
Keighley d					08 09								08h31	09 01									09h38
Bradford Forster Square d					08 31								08j35	09 31									09j35
Shipley d					08 38								08h44	09 39									09h49
Leeds 10 d				08 19	09 05								09 19	10 05									10 19
Huddersfield d					08 37								08h45	09 35									09h45
Wakefield Westgate 7 d				08 34	09 17								09 33	10 18									10 32
Hull d			08 02	08 08						08 56				09 25				09 56	09 56	10 05			
Selby d			08 37																	10 41			
Doncaster 7 d			09 01	09 15	09 35					10 03			10 29	10 36				10 55	10 55	11 01			11 24
Retford 10 d			09k21															11 10	11 10	11 17			
Newark North Gate 7 a					09 59									11 00									
Grimsby Town d			07m26							08m36				09 28				09m36	09m36				
Lincoln d			08n27		09 10									10 23				10n27	10n27				
Newark North Gate 7 d					09 59									11 00									
Grantham 7 a			09 42		10 12									11 12						11 38			11 55
Grantham 7 d			09 42		10 12				10 16					11 12			11 07			11 38			11 55
Peterborough 8 a				10 06	10 32				10 43	10 54			11 15	11 32			11 36	11 48	11 48				12 14
Cambridge a				11 08	11q44					12 08			12q44	12q55				13 08	13 08				13q44
Stansted Airport a				11 49						12 49								13 49	13 49				
Norwich a									12 17								13 13						
Peterborough 8 d				10 06	10 33					10 54			11 16	11 32				11 48	11 48				12 15
Stevenage 4 a					11 03								11 47	12 33									
London Kings Cross 15 ⊖ a			10 49	10 58	11 32					11 50			12 14	12 24				12 41	12 41	12 46			13 10

For general notes see front of timetable
For details of catering facilities see Directory of Train Operators

- **A** To Manchester Airport (Table 39)
- **B** To Plymouth (Table 51)
- **C** To Bristol Temple Meads (Table 51)
- **D** From Chathill (Table 48)
- **E** From Liverpool Lime Street (Table 49)
- **G** To Bournemouth (Table 51). ⊏P from Edinburgh
- **H** Until 22 March
- **J** From 29 March
- **b** Change at Edinburgh
- **c** Change at Stirling and Edinburgh
- **e** Glasgow Queen Street
- **f** By bus
- **g** Change at York and Selby
- **h** Change at Leeds and Doncaster
- **j** Bradford Interchange. Change at Leeds and Doncaster
- **k** Arr. 0916
- **m** Change at Doncaster
- **n** Change at Retford
- **q** Change at Peterborough and Ely

Table 26

Saturdays

Scotland, North East England, Yorkshire and Humberside → London

Route Diagram - see first page of Table 26

		GR	TP	XC	EM	GR	GR	XC	TP	GR	EM	GR	TP	XC	GR	GR	XC	XC	TP	GR	GR	TP	XC	EM
		R 1	1 ◇	1 ◇	◇	R 1	R 1	1 ◇	1 ◇	R 1	◇	R 1	1 ◇	1 ◇	R 1	R 1	1 ◇	1 ◇	1 ◇	R 1	R 1	1 ◇	1 ◇	◇
			A	B	C	D	E	G	A		C		A	H	D	E	J	K	A			A	H	C
Aberdeen	d					06b00	06 00			06c34					07b20	07 20				07 53				
Stonehaven	d					06b16	06 16			06c53					07b36	07 36				08 10				
Montrose	d					06b38	06 38			07c15					07b58	07 58				08 33				
Arbroath	d					06b52	06 52			07c29					08b12	08 12				08 48				
Dundee	d					07b11	07 11	07 35		07 59					08b31	08 31				09 06				
Leuchars 3	d					07b23	07 23	07 48		08 11					08b43	08 43				09 20				
Kirkcaldy	d					07b50	07 50	08 20		08 43					09b15	09 15				09 44				
Inverkeithing	d					08b15	08 15	08 36		08 59					09b24	09 24				10 00				
Inverness	d														05b00	05 00				06b45				
Perth	d									07e14										08b48				
Stirling	d									08 06					08b36	08 36				09b06				
Glasgow Central 15	d					07 50	08f00			08f30					08 50	08f45	09 00	09f00		09g15				
Motherwell	d					08 04	07h45								09 04	08h45	09u14							
Haymarket	d					08 49		08 57									09 55			10 19				
Edinburgh 10	a					08 57		09 02							09 54		09 59			10 25				
Edinburgh	d					09 00	09 00	09 05		09 30					10 00	10 00	10 05	10 05		10 30				
Dunbar	d							09 25																
Berwick-upon-Tweed	d					09 41	09 41	09 49		10 11														
Alnmouth	d																11 04	11 04						
Morpeth	d													10 50			11 18	11 18						
Newcastle 8	a					10 31	10 31	10 37		10 58					11 27	11 27	11 36	11 36		11 58				
Sunderland	d									10 30										11 30		11 30		
Hartlepool	d																							
Newcastle 8	d		10 15	10 25		10 32	10 32	10 40		11 00			11 15	11 25	11 29	11 29	11 40	11 40		12 00		12 15	12 17	
Chester-le-Street	d			10 34																			12 29	
Durham	d		10 27	10 41		10 45	10 45	10 52					11 27	11 38	11 42	11 42	11 52	11 52		12 13		12 27	12 36	
Darlington 7	a		10 43	10 56		11 03	11 03	11 11		11 26			11 43	11 55	12 00	12 00	12 10	12 10		12 31		12 43	12 51	
Middlesbrough	d					10 24	10 24		11 00	10 55					11 24	11 24			12 00	11 55				
Eaglescliffe	d																							
Darlington 7	d		10 45	10 58		11 03	11 03	11 11		11 27			11 45	11 57	12 01	12 01	12 11	12 11		12 31		12 45	12 53	
Northallerton	d		10 56						11 28				11 56						12 28			12 56		
Thirsk	d								11 36										12 36					
York 8	a		11 22	11 24		11 32	11 32	11 41	11 54	11 57			12 20	12 23	12 30	12 30	12 41	12 41	12 55	13 00		13 20	13 24	
Hull	a							12 54		13j34													14 45	
Leeds 10	a		11 53			12 04	12 04	12 08	12 23	12 49			12 53		13 04	13 04	13 08	13 08	13 23	13 49		13 53		
Harrogate	d	10 14								11 05		11 14								12 05	12 14			
Scarborough	d									10 45										11 47				
York 8	d			11 27		11 33	11 33			11 59				12 25	12 31	12 31				13 02			13 28	
Doncaster 7	a			11 51		11 57	11 57			12 20				12 50	12 55	12 55							13 52	
Sheffield 7	a			12 20				12 51		13 07				13 20			13 51	13 51					14 20	
Skipton	d	09 58								10k18		10 48									12 12			
Keighley	d	10 08								10k31		11 01									12 22			
Bradford Forster Square	d	10 31								10m35		11 31									12 31			
Shipley	d	10 39								10k44		11 39									12 39			
Leeds 10	d	11 05								11 19		12 05									13 05			
Huddersfield	d	10 35								10k45		11 35									12 35			
Wakefield Westgate 7	d	11 17								11 32		12 17									13 17			
Hull	d	10 25				10 57	10 57					11 22			11 57	11 57					12 22			
Selby	d																							
Doncaster 7	d	11 39				11 57	11 57			12 21		12 35			12 57	12 57					13 38			
Retford 10	d											12 50												
Newark North Gate 7	a	12 01										13 05									14 01			
Grimsby Town	d					10n36	10n36					11 30			11n36	11n36								
Lincoln	d					11q12	11q12					12 23												
Newark North Gate 7	d	12 01										13 05									14 01			
Grantham 7	a	12 14				12 28	12 28					13 17												
	d	12 14			12 06	12 28	12 28				13 08	13 17												14 08
Peterborough 8	a	12 33			12 37	12 49	12 49			13 07	13 35				13 46	13 46				14 12	14 29			14 39
Cambridge	a									14 08					15 08	15 08					15r44			
Stansted Airport	a									14 49					15 49	15 49								
Norwich	a				14 13						15 13													16 13
Peterborough 8	d	12 34				12 50	12 50			13 07					13 48	13 48				14 13	14 29			
Stevenage 4	a	13 03								14 08					14 17	14 17					15 33			
London Kings Cross 15 ⊖	a	13 33				13 44	13 44			13 59		14 27			14 44	14 44				15 10	15 21			

For general notes see front of timetable
For details of catering facilities see Directory of Train Operators

- **A** To Manchester Airport (Table 39)
- **B** To Plymouth (Table 51)
- **C** From Liverpool Lime Street (Table 49)
- **D** Until 22 March
- **E** From 29 March
- **G** To Bournemouth (Table 51)
- **H** To Bristol Temple Meads (Table 51)
- **J** Until 22 March. To Penzance (Table 135)
- **K** From 29 March. To Penzance (Table 135)
- **b** Change at Edinburgh
- **c** Change at Dundee and Edinburgh
- **e** Change at Stirling and Edinburgh
- **f** Glasgow Queen Street
- **g** Glasgow Queen Street. Change at Edinburgh
- **h** By bus
- **j** Change at York and Selby
- **k** Change at Leeds and Doncaster
- **m** Bradford Interchange. Change at Leeds and Doncaster
- **n** Change at Doncaster
- **q** Change at Peterborough
- **r** Change at Peterborough and Ely

Table 26

Scotland, North East England, Yorkshire and Humberside → London

Route Diagram - see first page of Table 26

		XC	GR	GR	HT	XC	TP	GR	GC	EM	GR	TP	XC	GR	XC	TP	GR	GR	EM	TP	XC	GR	GR	HT
			R	R				R	R		R			R			R	R				R	R	
		1◇	1	1	1◇	1◇	1◇	1	1	◇	1	1◇	1◇	1	1◇	1◇	1	1	◇	1◇	1◇	1	1	1◇
		A	B	C		A	D	E		G		D	H		J	D	K		G	D	L	N	P	
		⊡	⊡ ✠	⊡ ✠	⊠ ⊡	⊡	✠	⊡ ✠	⊡		⊡ ✠	✠	⊡	⊡ ✠	⊡	✠	⊡ ✠	⊡ ✠		✠	⊡	⊡ ✠	⊡ ✠	⊠ ⊡
Aberdeen	d	08 20						08b50									09 52					10b22	10 22	
Stonehaven	d	08 37						09b06									10 09					10b38	10 38	
Montrose	d	08 58						09c14									10 32					11b00	11 00	
Arbroath	d	09 15						09b42									10 47					11b14	11 14	
Dundee	d	09 32						09b59									11 05					11b30	11 30	
Leuchars 3	d	09 45						10b11									11 19					11b42	11 42	
Kirkcaldy	d	10 12	09b59	09 59				10b43						10 59			11 43					12b12	12 12	
Inverkeithing	d	10 27	10b20	10 20				10b59						11 20			11 59					12b20	12 20	
Inverness	d							07 55																
Perth	d							09 56									10e12					11b08	11 08	
Stirling	d		09b36	09 36				10 30						10 39			11b06					11b36	11 36	
Glasgow Central 15	d		09 50	10f00				10g15						10f45	11f00		11g15					11 50	11f45	
Motherwell	d		10 04	09h45																		12 04	11h45	
Haymarket	d	10 46	10 50					11 10									12 17					12 50		
Edinburgh 10	a	10 55	10 57			←		11 20									12 22					12 57		
Edinburgh	d	11 05 →	11 00	11 00		11 05		11 30						12 00	12 05		12 30					13 00	13 00	
Dunbar	d					11 25																		
Berwick-upon-Tweed	d		11 41	11 41		11 49								12 39										
Alnmouth	d							12 29							13 03									
Morpeth	d		11 50	11 50									12 50		13 18						13 50			
Newcastle 8	a		12 31	12 31		12 36		13 02						13 27	13 36		13 57					14 27	14 27	
Sunderland	d							12 30	12 30											13 30				
Hartlepool	d								12 54															
Newcastle 8	d		12 33	12 33		12 40		13 04				13 15	13 27	13 31	13 40		13 59			14 15	14 22	14 29	14 29	
Chester-le-Street	d																				14 31			
Durham	d		12 46	12 46		12 52						13 27	13 39	13 44	13 52		14 12			14 27	14 38	14 42	14 42	
Darlington 7	a		13 03	13 03		13 08						13 43	13 56	14 02	14 08		14 30			14 43	14 53	14 59	14 59	
Middlesbrough	d		12 20	12 20			12 51					12 55		13 24		14 00	13 55			13 55		14 23	14 23	
Eaglescliffe	d								13 13															
Darlington 7	d		13 04	13 04		13 09						13 45	13 58	14 03	14 09		14 30			14 45	14 55	15 00	15 00	
Northallerton	d						13 21		13 31			13 56		14 14		14 28				14 56				
Thirsk	d						13 29		13 42							14 36								
York 8	a		13 32	13 32		13 42	13 49	13 55	14 03			14 20	14 24	14 37	14 41	14 54	14 59			15 22	15 24	15 28	15 28	
Hull	a															16 03								
Leeds 10	a		14 04	14 04		14 08	14 23		14 49			14 53	15 04		15 08	15 23	15 49			15 53		16 04	16 04	
Harrogate	d							13 05			13 14						14 05	14 14						
Scarborough	d							12 47									13 45							
York 8	d		13 34	13 34		13 44		13 57	14 05				14 30	14 40			15 01				15 27	15 30	15 30	
Doncaster 7	a		13 58	13 58									14 53	15 03							15 52	15 55	15 55	
Sheffield 7	a					14 51							15 20	16 04	15 51		16 20				16 20	16 41	16 41	
Skipton	d										12 48							13 59						
Keighley	d										13 01							14 09						
Bradford Forster Square	d										13 31							14 31						
Shipley	d										13 39							14 39						
Leeds 10	d										14 05							15 05						
Huddersfield	d										13 35							14 35						
Wakefield Westgate 7	d										14 17							15 17						
Hull	d			12 57	13 05						13 25			13 57				14 25				14 57	14 57	15 06
Selby	d				13 40																			15 42
Doncaster 7	d		13 58	13 58	14 04						14 35			15 04				15 35				15 55	15 55	16 02
Retford 10	d				14 19						14 50													16 17
Newark North Gate 7	a										15 05							15 59						
Grimsby Town	d		12j36	12j36							13 25			13j36								14j36	14j36	
Lincoln	d				13k27			13 28			14 19							14m51						15k27
Newark North Gate 7	d										15 05							15 59						
Grantham 7	a		14 29	14 29	14 39						15 18							16 11						16 37
	d		14 29	14 29	14 39					15 06	15 18							16 11	16 06					16 37
Peterborough 8	a		14 49	14 49				15 04		15 33	15 37			15 50				16 31	16 37			16 42	16 42	
Cambridge	a							16 08			16n55			17 08								18 15	18 15	
Stansted Airport	a							16 49						17 49								18 58	18 58	
Norwich	a									17 13									18 13			19n30	19n30	
Peterborough 8	d		14 49	14 49				15 04			15 38			15 50				16 31				16 46	16 46	
Stevenage 4	a							16 08						16 19				17 00				17 16	17 16	
London Kings Cross 15 ⊖	a		15 41	15 41	15 49			15 58	16 02		16 30			16 47			16 57	17 28				17 43	17 43	17 45

For general notes see front of timetable
For details of catering facilities see Directory of Train Operators

- **A** To Bournemouth (Table 51)
- **B** Until 22 March
- **C** From 29 March
- **D** To Manchester Airport (Table 39)
- **E** **The Highland Chieftain**
- **G** From Liverpool Lime Street (Table 49)
- **H** To Bristol Temple Meads (Table 51)
- **J** To Plymouth (Table 51)
- **K** **The Northern Lights**
- **L** To Cardiff Central (from 29 March to Bristol Temple Meads) (Table 51)
- **N** **The Flying Scotsman.** until 22 March
- **P** **The Flying Scotsman.** from 29 March
- **b** Change at Edinburgh
- **c** Change at Arbroath and Edinburgh
- **e** Change at Stirling and Edinburgh
- **f** Glasgow Queen Street
- **g** Glasgow Queen Street. Change at Edinburgh
- **h** By bus
- **j** Change at Doncaster
- **k** Change at Retford
- **m** Change at Peterborough
- **n** Change at Peterborough and Ely

Table 26

Scotland, North East England, Yorkshire and Humberside → London

Route Diagram - see first page of Table 26

		XC	TP	GR	GR	TP	XC	GR	XC	TP	EM	TP	XC	GR	GR	GR	XC	EM	TP	TP	XC	EM	TP	GR	HT
		1◇	1◇	R 1	R 1	1◇	1◇	R 1	1◇	1◇	◇	1◇	1◇	R 1	R 1	R 1	1◇	1◇	1◇	1◇	1◇	◇	1◇	R 1	1◇
		A	B			C	D		E	C	G	C	D	H	J		K	L	B	C	N	G	C		
Aberdeen	d							11 22						12b24	12 24									13 21	
Stonehaven	d							11 38						12b43	12 43									13 37	
Montrose	d							12 00						12c15	12c15									13 59	
Arbroath	d							12 14						13b17	13 17									14 13	
Dundee	d							12 30						13b33	13 33									14 30	
Leuchars 3	d							12 42						13b45	13 45									14 42	
Kirkcaldy	d			12 29				13 14						14b15	14 15									15 14	
Inverkeithing	d			12 50				13 30						14b19	14 19									15 30	
Inverness	d							09e19						10b53	10 53										
Perth	d			11e12				11e39						13b04	13 04									13e12	
Stirling	d			12 06				12 36						13b36	13 36									14 36	
Glasgow Central 15	d	12f00		12f15				12f45	13f00					13 50	14f00									15f00	
Motherwell	d													14 04	13g45										
Haymarket	d													14 50											
Edinburgh 10	a													14 57											
Edinburgh	d	13 05		13 30				14 00	14 05					15 00	15 00		15 05							16 00	
Dunbar	d	13 25															15 25								
Berwick-upon-Tweed	d	13 49		14 10				14 39									15 49							16 39	
Alnmouth	d								15 04																
Morpeth	d						14 50		15 18					15 50	15 50									16 50	
Newcastle 8	a	14 36		14 57				15 26	15 37					16 27	16 27		16 36							17 27	
Sunderland	d					14 31						15 30								16 30					
Hartlepool	d																								
Newcastle 8	d	14 40		14 59		15 09	15 22	15 28	15 40			16 06	16 20	16 29	16 29		16 40			17 10	17 19			17 29	
Chester-le-Street	d					15 18						16 15	16 29								17 28				
Durham	d	14 52				15 25	15 34	15 41	15 52			16 22	16 36	16 42	16 42		16 52			17 22	17 35				
Darlington 7	a	15 08		15 25		15 41	15 50	16 03	16 08			16 39	16 52	16 59	16 59		17 08			17 38	17 51			17 55	
Middlesbrough	d		14 50			14 55		15 27		15 50		15 55		16 24	16 24				17 00						
Eaglescliffe	d																								
Darlington 7	d	15 09		15 26		15 42	15 52	16 04	16 09			16 39	16 54	17 00	17 00		17 09			17 40	17 52		←	17 56	
Northallerton	d		15 18			15 54				16 18		16 51							17 28	17 51			17 51		
Thirsk	d		15 26							16 26		16 59							17 36	→			17 59		
York 8	a	15 41	15 52	15 55		16 21	16 23	16 32	16 41	16 49		17 19	17 22	17 29	17 29		17 41		17 55		18 22		18 24	18 26	
Hull	a			17 27						18 21									19 28						
Leeds 10	a	16 08	16 23	16 49		16 53		17 04	17 08	17 23		17 53		18 04	18 04		18 08		18 23		19 04		18 52	19 04	
Harrogate	d			15 05	15 14									16 05	16 05	16 44								17 08	
Scarborough	d			14 45										15 47	15 47									16 47	
York 8	d			15 57			16 25	16 34					17 25	17 31	17 31			17 49			18 25			18 28	
Doncaster 7	a			16 20			16 50	16 57					17 50	17 54	17 54			18 13			18 48			18 51	
Sheffield 7	a	16 51		17 07			17 18		17 51				18 20	18 41	18 41		18h51	18 45			19 20			19 42	
Skipton	d			14j28	14 48									15j18	15j18	16 49									
Keighley	d			14j39	15 01									15j31	15j31	17 02									
Bradford Forster Square	d			14k35	15 31									15k35	15k35	17m05									
Shipley	d			14j49	15 39									15j44	15j44	17 15									
Leeds 10	d			15 19	16 05									16 19	16 19	17 40									
Huddersfield	d			14j45	15 35									15j45	15j45	16n57									
Wakefield Westgate 7	d			15 32	16 17									16 32	16 32	17 52									
Hull	d				15 25			15 57						16 54	16 54									17 55	18 12
Selby	d																							18 26	18 47
Doncaster 7	d			16 21	16 38			16 58						17 55	17 55	18 10								18 52	19 05
Retford 10	d				16 53											18 25									19 20
Newark North Gate 7	a				17 08									18 18	18 18	18 40									
Grimsby Town	d				15 28			15q36						16q36	16q36									17q36	
Lincoln	d				16 22											18 09									
Newark North Gate 7	d				17 08									18 18	18 18	18 40									
Grantham 7	a			16 52				17 29								18 52									19 40
	d			16 52				17 29			18 13					18 52						19 06			19 40
Peterborough 8	a			17 11	17 36			17 48			18 40			18 46	18 46	19 12						19 33		19 38	
Cambridge	a				18r55			19 08						20 08	20 08									20r55	
Stansted Airport	a													20 49	20 49										
Norwich	a										20 13											21 13		22r30	
Peterborough 8	d			17 12	17 36			17 50						18 48	18 48	19 12								19 38	
Stevenage 4	a							18 19								19 43								20 07	
London Kings Cross 15 ⊖	a			18 10	18 28			18 46						19 40	19 40	20 12								20 35	20 46

For general notes see front of timetable
For details of catering facilities see Directory of Train Operators

- **A** To Bournemouth (Table 51)
- **B** To Manchester Piccadilly (Table 39)
- **C** To Manchester Airport (Table 39)
- **D** To Bristol Temple Meads (Table 51)
- **E** To Plymouth (Table 51)
- **G** From Liverpool Lime Street (Table 49)
- **H** Until 22 March
- **J** From 29 March
- **K** To Southampton Central (Table 51)
- **L** To St Pancras International (Table 53)
- **N** To Birmingham New Street (Table 51)
- **b** Change at Edinburgh
- **c** Change at Arbroath and Edinburgh
- **e** Change at Stirling and Edinburgh
- **f** Glasgow Queen Street
- **g** By bus
- **h** By changing at York, passengers may arrive at 1845
- **j** Change at Leeds and Doncaster
- **k** Bradford Interchange. Change at Leeds and Doncaster
- **m** Bradford Interchange
- **n** Change at Leeds
- **q** Change at Doncaster
- **r** Change at Peterborough and Ely

Table 26

Saturdays

Scotland, North East England, Yorkshire and Humberside → London

Route Diagram - see first page of Table 26

		GR	XC	EM	TP	GC	GR	GR	XC	TP	TP	GR	EM	GR	XC	TP	NT	TP	GR	GR	TP	NT
		R 1	1 ◇	◇	1 ◇	R 1	R 1	R 1	1 ◇	1 ◇	1 ◇	R 1	◇	R 1	1 ◇	1 ◇		1 ◇	R 1	R 1	1 ◇	
			A	B	C		D	E	G		C		B		H	C	J	K	L	N	C	U
		🍴	🍴			🍴	🍴	🍴	🍴			🍴		🍴	🍴				🍴	🍴		
Aberdeen	d						14b25	14 25				14 50			15 20				16b21	16 21		
Stonehaven	d						14b41	14 41				15 07			15 36				16b37	16 37		
Montrose	d						14c15	14c15				15 30			16 00				16c13	16c13		
Arbroath	d						15b15	15 15				15 45			16 14				17b11	17 11		
Dundee	d						15b32	15 32				16 03			16 31				17b31	17 31		
Leuchars 3	d						15b44	15 44				16 17			16 43				17b43	17 43		
Kirkcaldy	d						16b14	16 14				16 41			17 17				18b15	18 15		
Inverkeithing	d						16b30	16 30				16 57			17 33				18b12	18 12		
Inverness	d						12b40	12 40											14b41	14 41		
Perth	d						14b49	14 49				15e12			15e12				16b48	16 48		
Stirling	d						15b36	15 36				16b06			16 36				17b36	17 36		
Glasgow Central 15	d						15 50	15f45				16g15			17f00				17 50	18f00		
Motherwell	d						16 04	15h45											18 04	17h45		
Haymarket	d						16 50					17 15							18 50			
Edinburgh 10	a						16 57					17 23							18 57			
Edinburgh	d		16 05				17 00	17 00				17 30			18 05				19 00	19 00		
Dunbar	d											17 51			18 25				19 23	19 23		
Berwick-upon-Tweed	d											18 14			18 51				19 46	19 46		
Alnmouth	d		17 09				17 59	17 59							19 11		19 24		20 08	20 08		
Morpeth	d		17 23									18 32			19 04		19 49		20 25	20 25		21 15
Newcastle 8	a		17 37				18 32	18 32				19 05			19 37		20 12		20 45	20 45		21 40
Sunderland	d					17 30						18 30							19 27	19 27		20 27
Hartlepool	d					17 56																
Newcastle 8	d		17 40				18 34	18 34	18 40		18 52	19 06			19 45				20 46	20 46		21 50
Chester-le-Street	d								18 49													21 59
Durham	d		17 54				18 47	18 47	18 56		19 04				19 57				20 59	20 59		22 08
Darlington 7	a		18 10				19 04	19 04	19 11		19 20	19 34			20 13				21 17	21 17		22 28
Middlesbrough	d		17 25		18 07		18 24	18 24		19 00		18 53			19 25	20 10		20 50	19 59	19 59	21 50	
Eaglescliffe	d					18 28																
Darlington 7	d		18 11				19 05	19 05	19 13		19 22	19 34			20 14				21 17	21 17	22 19	
Northallerton	d				18 35	18 45				19 28	19 36					20 38		21 17	21 29	21 29	22 30	
Thirsk	d				18 43	18 54				19 36						20 46		21 25			22 38	
York 8	a		18 42		19 04	19 13	19 34	19 34	19 41	19 59	20 02	20 03			20 41	21 07		21 42	21 50	21 50	22 57	
Hull	a					20j37						21 22				23j21						
Leeds 10	a		19 08		19 35	20 04			20 08		20 32	20 53			21 08	21 33		22 08	22k49	22k49	23 33	
Harrogate	d	17 50				18 05						19 05		18 44	19 05							
Scarborough	d					17 45						18 45										
York 8	d					19 16	19 40	19 40				20 05			20 44				21 51	21 51		
Doncaster 7	a						20 03	20 03				20 29							22 16	22 16		
Sheffield 7	a		19 51						20 51			21 18			21 51	23 02			23 05	23 05		
Skipton	d	17 49										18m28		19 18								
Keighley	d	18 02										18m38		19 31								
Bradford Forster Square	d	18n05										18q48		19n35								
Shipley	d	18 14										18m48		19 44								
Leeds 10	d	18 40										19 22		20 15								
Huddersfield	d	17r58										18m47		19 35								
Wakefield Westgate 7	d	18 54										19 32		20 31								
Hull	d						18 53	18 53						19 24								
Selby	d																					
Doncaster 7	d	19 14					20 04	20 04				20 30		20 48								
Retford 10	d	19 29												21 03								
Newark North Gate 7	a	19 44												21 18								
Grimsby Town	d	18 06					18t36	18t36						19t36								
Lincoln	d	19 10												20 41								
Newark North Gate 7	d	19 44												21 18								
Grantham 7	a	19 56												21 31								
	d	19 56		20 11									21 10	21 31								
Peterborough 8	a	20 16		20 38			20 51	20 51				21 18	21 37	21 50								
Cambridge	a			21 31			22 16	22 16					22 33	23 11								
Stansted Airport	a																					
Norwich	a			22v30									23v45									
Peterborough 8	d	20 17					20 51	20 51				21 19		21 51								
Stevenage 4	a	20 48					21 20	21 20				21 51		22 20								
London Kings Cross 15 ⊖	a	21 15				21 18	21 48	21 48				22 17		22 47								

For general notes see front of timetable
For details of catering facilities see Directory of Train Operators

- **A** To Bristol Temple Meads (Table 51)
- **B** From Liverpool Lime Street (Table 49)
- **C** To Manchester Airport (Table 39)
- **D** Until 22 March
- **E** From 29 March
- **G** To Birmingham New Street (Table 51). 🍴 to Leeds
- **H** To Birmingham New Street (Table 51)
- **J** From Chathill to Hexham (Table 48)
- **K** To Manchester Piccadilly (Table 39)
- **L** Until 22 March. To Leeds (Table 31)
- **N** From 29 March. To Leeds (Table 31)
- **U** To Middlesbrough (Table 44)
- **b** Change at Edinburgh
- **c** Change at Arbroath and Edinburgh
- **e** Change at Stirling and Edinburgh
- **f** Glasgow Queen Street
- **g** Glasgow Queen Street. Change at Edinburgh
- **h** By bus
- **j** Change at York and Selby
- **k** Change at York
- **m** Change at Leeds and Doncaster
- **n** Bradford Interchange
- **q** Bradford Interchange. Change at Leeds and Doncaster
- **r** Change at Leeds
- **t** Change at Doncaster
- **v** Change at Ely

Table 26

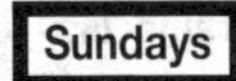

until 27 January and from 30 March

Scotland, North East England, Yorkshire and Humberside → London

Route Diagram - see first page of Table 26

		GR	GR	XC	GR	XC	GC	GR	HT	XC	TP	GC	GR	TP	XC	XC	GR	GR	EM	TP	XC	XC
		R 1	R 1	1 ◇	R 1	1 ◇	R 1	R 1	1 ◇	1 ◇	1 ◇	R 1	R 1	1 ◇	1 ◇	R 1	R 1	R 1	◇	1 ◇	1 ◇	R 1
				A		A				B	C			D	B	E			G	D	A	H
Aberdeen	d																					
Stonehaven	d																					
Montrose	d																					
Arbroath	d																					
Dundee	d																	07 25				
Leuchars 3	d																	07 37				
Kirkcaldy	d																	08 09				
Inverkeithing	d																	08 30				
Inverness	d																					
Perth	d																					
Stirling	d																					
Glasgow Central 15	d																07b50					08b30
Motherwell	d																					
Haymarket	d																					
Edinburgh 10	a																					
Edinburgh	d															08 50	09 00	09 30				09 50
Dunbar	d																					
Berwick-upon-Tweed	d															09 31	09 41					
Alnmouth	d																					10 48
Morpeth	d																					
Newcastle 8	a															10 17	10 28	10 55				11 17
Sunderland	d						09 10								09 28			10 28				
Hartlepool	d						09 34															
Newcastle 8	d		07 58		08 55			09 25		09 28	09 33				10 16	10 25	10 30	10 57		11 03	11 16	11 25
Chester-le-Street	d										09 42											
Durham	d		08 10		09 07					09 41	09 49				10 28	10 37		11 10		11 16	11 28	11 37
Darlington 7	a		08 28		09 25			09 51		09 57	10 04				10 44	10 53	10 59			11 32	11 44	11 53
Middlesbrough	d				*08 45*					*09 15*				10 15	*10 00*					*10 53*		
Eaglescliffe	d						09 55															
Darlington 7	d		08 28		09 25			09 52		09 58	10 05				10 45	10 54	10 59			11 34	11 45	11 54
Northallerton	d				09 39		10 13				10 17	←		10 42						11 45		
Thirsk	d						10 26					10 26		10 50								
York 8	a		08 58		10 00		→	10 20		10 27	10 44	10 45		11 09	11 13	11 22	11 28	11 51		12 12	12 16	12 22
Hull	a									*11 38*												
Leeds 10	a		*09 38*		*10 38*					10 51	11 08	*11 32*		11 38		11 51	*12 07*			12 38		12 51
Harrogate	d												*09 53*								*11 30*	
Scarborough	d							*09 20*										*10 45*				
York 8	d		09 00	09 20	10 02	10 20		10 23				10 47			11 20		11 29	11 53			12 20	
Doncaster 7	a		09 25	09 47	10 25	10 46		10 47							11 47		11 53				12 45	
Sheffield 7	a		*10 09*	10 20	*11 09*	11 20		*11 25*		11 40					12 20	12 40	*12 55*				13 20	13 40
Skipton	d								*09c15*													
Keighley	d								*09c28*													
Bradford Forster Square	d				*08e31*				*09e21*				*10 02*									
Shipley	d								*09c40*				*10 08*									
Leeds 10	d	08 24	*08f35*		*09g05*				*10h09*				10 40									
Huddersfield	d	*07j12*			*08c12*				*09c12*				*10j02*									
Wakefield Westgate 7	d	08 36	*08k47*		*09g17*				*10h22*				10 52									
Hull	d				*08 42*			*09 41*	10 12								*10 41*					
Selby	d								10 47													
Doncaster 7	d	08 54	09 26		10 29			10 48	11 04				11 13				11 53					
Retford 10	d		09 41						11 19				11 28									
Newark North Gate 7	a	09 18			10 52								11 42					12 34				
Grimsby Town	d								*09h49*								*10h36*					
Lincoln	d												*11 05*									
Newark North Gate 7	d	09 18			10 52								11 42					12 34				
Grantham 7	a	09 30	10 03		11 04				11 38				11 54									
	d	09 30	10 03		11 04				11 39				11 54						13 14			
Peterborough 8	a	09 52	10 25		11 26			11 37					12 16				12 40	13 03	13 41			
Cambridge	a							*13m14*										*14 19*				
Stansted Airport	a																	*14 58*				
Norwich	a							*14m09*											15 28			
Peterborough 8	d	09 53	10 27		11 26			11 38					12 16				12 41	13 04				
Stevenage 4	a		11 00					12 09					*13 33*					13 34				
London Kings Cross 15 ⊖	a	10 47	11 28		12 19			12 37	12 48			12 51	13 13				13 36	14 04				

For general notes see front of timetable
For details of catering facilities see Directory of Train Operators

- **A** To Bristol Temple Meads (Table 51)
- **B** To Plymouth (Table 51)
- **C** To Liverpool Lime Street (Table 39)
- **D** To Manchester Airport (Table 39)
- **E** To Bournemouth (from 30 March to Oxford) (Table 51)
- **G** From Nottingham (Table 19)
- **H** To Penzance (Table 135)
- **b** Glasgow Queen Street
- **c** Change at Leeds and Doncaster
- **e** Bradford Interchange. Change at Leeds and Doncaster
- **f** From 30 March dep. 0824
- **g** From 30 March dep. Leeds 0918, Wakefield Westgate 0929
- **h** Change at Doncaster
- **j** Change at Leeds
- **k** From 30 March dep. 0836
- **m** Change at Peterborough and Ely

Table 26

Sundays

Scotland, North East England, Yorkshire and Humberside → London

until 27 January and from 30 March

Route Diagram - see first page of Table 26

		GR		GR	GR	TP	GR		XC	XC	GR	EM		GR	TP	GR	TP		GR	XC	XC	GR		HT	TP	GR
		R 1		R 1	R 1	1 ◇	R 1		1 ◇	R 1	R 1	◇		R 1	1 ◇	R 1	1 ◇		R 1	1 ◇	R 1	R 1		1 ◇	1 ◇	R 1
						A			B	C		D			A		A			B	E				G	H
Aberdeen	d																									09 50
Stonehaven	d																									10 07
Montrose	d																									10 30
Arbroath	d																									10 45
Dundee	d															09 25										11 03
Leuchars 3	d															09 37										11 17
Kirkcaldy	d															10 09										11 41
Inverkeithing	d															10 32										11 57
Inverness	d																									
Perth	d															09 27										
Stirling	d				09 05											10 02										11b06
Glasgow Central 15	d									09c30											10 30	10 50				
Motherwell	d																				10u53	11 05				
Haymarket	d																				11 37	11 49				12 18
Edinburgh 10	a																				11 42	11 54				12 24
Edinburgh	d	10 00			10 30					10 50	11 00					11 30					11 50	12 00				12 30
Dunbar	d									11 11																
Berwick-upon-Tweed	d	10 41			11 11					11 35												12 41				
Alnmouth	d																				12 48					13 30
Morpeth	d															12 42										
Newcastle 8	a	11 30			11 58					12 21	12 28					13 01					13 17	13 29				14 01
Sunderland	d				11 28											12 28										13 28
Hartlepool	d																									
Newcastle 8	d	11 32			12 00				12 16	12 25	12 32				12 49	13 03			13 20	13 23	13 25	13 32				14 03
Chester-le-Street	d														12 58											
Durham	d								12 28	12 37	12 45				13 05					13 36	13 37	13 45				
Darlington 7	a				12 26				12 44	12 54	13 02				13 22	13 29			13 45	13 52	13 53	14 03				14 30
Middlesbrough	d				11 24	12 15					12 25											13 25			13 45	
Eaglescliffe	d																									
Darlington 7	d				12 27				12 45	12 54	13 03				13 23	13 30	←		13 46	13 53	13 54	14 04				14 31
Northallerton	d					12 42									13 35	13 42	13 35								14 12	
Thirsk	d					12 50									→										14 19	
York 8	a	12 28			12 55	13 12			13 17	13 22	13 31					14 03	14 11		14 17	14 21	14 22	14 34			14 40	15 00
Hull	a					14 21																				
Leeds 10	a	13 08				13 38			13 51	13 51	14 07						14 38				14 51				15 08	
Harrogate	d	11 30		11 53										12 53					13 30							
Scarborough	d															12 45										
York 8	d	12 29			12 57				13 20		13 33					14 05			14 19	14 24		14 36				15 01
Doncaster 7	a	12 54			13 20				13 45		13 56					14 28			14 43	14 49		14 59				
Sheffield 7	a	13 55			14 03				14 20	14 40	14 52					15e12				15 20	15 45					
Skipton	d			11 30										12 15										13f15		
Keighley	d			11 40										12 28										13f28		
Bradford Forster Square	d			12 02										13 02										13g31		
Shipley	d			12 08										13 08										13f40		
Leeds 10	d			12 40										13 40										14h09		
Huddersfield	d			11j44										12j44										13f12		
Wakefield Westgate 7	d			12 52										13 52										14h22		
Hull	d	11 41									12 41								13 41					14 10		
Selby	d																							14 45		
Doncaster 7	d	12 54		13 10	13 21		←				13 57			14 10		14 29			14 48			15 00		15 05		
Retford 10	d			13k34			13 34																	15 20		
Newark North Gate 7	a			→			13 48							14 33												
Grimsby Town	d										12h36								13h36							
Lincoln	d						13 05																			
Newark North Gate 7	d						13 48							14 33												
Grantham 7	a	13 26					14 00									14 59								15 40		
	d	13 26					14 00					14 20				14 59								15 40		
Peterborough 8	a				14 09		14 22				14 43	14 53							15 35			15 47				
Cambridge	a										16m14											17m14				
Stansted Airport	a										16 59															
Norwich	a											16 37										17 35				
Peterborough 8	d				14 10		14 22				14 43								15 36			15 47				
Stevenage 4	a	14 14					15 33							15 28								16 17				
London Kings Cross 15 ⊖	a	14 42			15 11		15 15				15 38			15 55		16 11			16 29			16 45		16 50		17 11

For general notes see front of timetable
For details of catering facilities see Directory of Train Operators

- **A** To Manchester Airport (Table 39)
- **B** To Bristol Temple Meads (Table 51)
- **C** To Bournemouth (Table 51)
- **D** From Sheffield (Table 49)
- **E** To Plymouth (Table 51)
- **G** To Liverpool Lime Street (Table 39)
- **H** **The Northern Lights**
- **b** Change at Edinburgh
- **c** Glasgow Queen Street
- **e** From 30 March arr. 1509
- **f** Change at Leeds and Doncaster
- **g** Bradford Interchange. Change at Leeds and Doncaster
- **h** Change at Doncaster
- **j** Change at Leeds
- **k** Arr. 1325
- **m** Change at Peterborough and Ely

Table 26

Scotland, North East England, Yorkshire and Humberside → London

until 27 January and from 30 March

Route Diagram - see first page of Table 26

	GR	TP	XC		XC	GC	GR	EM		GR	TP	GR	TP		XC	XC	GR	EM		EM	GR	HT	TP		GR
	R 1	1 ◇	R 1		R 1	R 1	R 1	◇		R 1	1 ◇	R 1	1 ◇		1 ◇	R 1	R 1	1 ◇		◇	R 1	1 ◇	1 ◇		R 1
		A	B		C		D	E			A	G	A		H	J		K		E			L		
	☕ 🍴		☕		☕	☕	☕ 🍴			☕ 🍴		☕ 🍴			☕	☕	☕ 🍴	☕			☕ 🍴	⊠ ☕			☕ 🍴
Aberdeen d																									
Stonehaven d																									
Montrose d																									
Arbroath d																									
Dundee d												11b25													
Leuchars 3 d												11b37													
Kirkcaldy d												12b09													
Inverkeithing d												12b32													
Inverness d												09 38													
Perth d												11 55													
Stirling d												12 32													
Glasgow Central 15 d					11 30											12c30	12 50								
Motherwell d					11u56												13 04								
Haymarket d					12 37							13 12					13 50								
Edinburgh 10 a					12 42							13 18					13 56								
Edinburgh d					12 50		13 00					13 30				13 50	14 00								
Dunbar d					13 12																				
Berwick-upon-Tweed d					13 35		13 40					14 11													
Alnmouth d																14 48									
Morpeth d																									
Newcastle 8 a					14 21		14 30					15 00				15 17	15 25								
Sunderland d						13 42					14 28														
Hartlepool d						14 06																			
Newcastle 8 d		14 10	14 16		14 25		14 32				14 57	15 01			15 16	15 25	15 30								15 50
Chester-le-Street d																									
Durham d		14 22	14 28		14 38						15 09	15 15			15 28	15 37									
Darlington 7 a		14 38	14 44		14 53		14 59				15 25	15 32			15 44	15 53	15 59								16 18
Middlesbrough d											14 38												15 45		
Eaglescliffe d						14 32																			
Darlington 7 d		14 40	14 45		14 54		15 00				15 27	15 33	←		15 45	15 54	15 59								16 20
Northallerton d						14 57	15 11				15 38 →		15 38										16 14		16 32
Thirsk d						15 06																	16 22		
York 8 a		15 14	15 20		15 22	15 28	15 32					16 02	16 12		16 18	16 22	16 28						16 41		16 52
Hull a							16 41																		
Leeds 10 a		15 39			15 51	16 07	16 32						16 38			16 51							17 08		
Harrogate d										14 53							15 30								
Scarborough d												14 45													
York 8 d			15 21			15 31	15 34					16 03			16 20		16 29	16 40							16 53
Doncaster 7 a			15 46				15 57					16 28			16 48		16 53	17 02							17 19
Sheffield 7 a			16 20		16e43		16 52					17f12			17 20	17g40		17 28							
Skipton d										14 15											15 15				
Keighley d										14 28											15 28				
Bradford Forster Square d	14 02									15 02											16 02				
Shipley d	14 08									15 08											16 08				
Leeds 10 d	14 40									15 40											16 40				
Huddersfield d	13h44									14h44											15h44				
Wakefield Westgate 7 d	14 52									15 52											16 52				
Hull d							14 41										15 41					16 21			
Selby d																						16 56			
Doncaster 7 d	15 10						15 58			16 10		16 28					16 53				17 10	17 15			17 19
Retford 10 d	15 25																					17 30			
Newark North Gate 7 a	15 39						16 20																		17 46
Grimsby Town d							14j36																		
Lincoln d	14 59																					15k15			
Newark North Gate 7 d	15 39						16 20																		17 46
Grantham 7 a	15 52									16 40											17 40	17 49			
d	15 52							16 24		16 40										17 24	17 40	17 49			
Peterborough 8 a	16 13						16 50	16 55		17 01		17 18					17 40			17 51	18 02				
Cambridge a	17 23						18m14					18 21					19m14								
Stansted Airport a	17 58																								
Norwich a								18 35												19 29					
Peterborough 8 d	16 19						16 51			17 02		17 18					17 41				18 02				
Stevenage 4 a	16 49						17 22										18 11								18 42
London Kings Cross 15 ⊖ a	17 17					17 31	17 49			17 55		18 15					18 40				18 55	19 06			19 12

For general notes see front of timetable
For details of catering facilities see Directory of Train Operators

- **A** To Manchester Airport (Table 39)
- **B** To Cardiff Central (from 30 March to Bristol Temple Meads) (Table 51)
- **C** To Bournemouth (from 30 March to Oxford) (Table 51)
- **D** **The Flying Scotsman**
- **E** From Sheffield (from 30 March from Liverpool Lime Street) (Table 49)
- **G** **The Highland Chieftain**
- **H** To Bristol Temple Meads (Table 51)
- **J** To Plymouth (Table 51)
- **K** Until 27 January. To St Pancras International (Table 53)
- **L** To Liverpool Lime Street (Table 39)
- **b** Change at Edinburgh
- **c** Glasgow Queen Street
- **e** From 30 March arr. 1640
- **f** From 30 March arr. 1711
- **g** By changing at York, until 27 January passengers may arrive at 1728
- **h** Change at Leeds
- **j** Change at Doncaster
- **k** Change at Retford
- **m** Change at Peterborough and Ely

Sundays

Scotland, North East England, Yorkshire and Humberside → London

until 27 January and from 30 March

Route Diagram - see first page of Table 26

		GR	GR	TP	XC	EM	XC	GR	EM	GR	TP	GR	GR	GR	GR	XC	XC	GR	EM	GR	HT	TP
		R	R				R	R		R		R	R	R	R			R		R		
		1	1	1 ◇	1 ◇	1 ◇	1	1	◇	1	1 ◇	1	1	1	1	1 ◇	1 ◇	1	◇	1	1 ◇	1 ◇
				A	B	C	D		E		A					G	B		E			H
		☕ 🍴	☕ 🍴		☕	☕	☕	☕ 🍴		☕ 🍴		☕ 🍴	☕ 🍴	☕ 🍴	☕ 🍴	☕	☕	☕ 🍴		☕ 🍴	⊠ ☕	
Aberdeen	d	11 42					11 58															
Stonehaven	d	11 59					12 16															
Montrose	d	12 22					12 39															
Arbroath	d	12 37					12 56															
Dundee	d	12 58					13 14						13 25									
Leuchars [3]	d	13 12					13 27						13 39									
Kirkcaldy	d	13 36					13 58						14 11									
Inverkeithing	d	13 54					14 14						14 32									
Inverness	d																					
Perth	d												13b05									
Stirling	d	13c07											14 07									
Glasgow Central [15]	d	13e00					13e30						14f00				14f30	14 50				
Motherwell	d																	15 04				
Haymarket	d	14 19					14 29											15 48				
Edinburgh [10]	a	14 24					14 33											15 53				
Edinburgh	d	14 30					14 50	15 00					15 30				15 50	16 00				
Dunbar	d						15 10															
Berwick-upon-Tweed	d						15 35	15 41					16 11									
Alnmouth	d																16 48					
Morpeth	d												16 46				17 03					
Newcastle [8]	a	15 57					16 21	16 31					17 05				17 20	17 25				
Sunderland	d	15 28											16 28									
Hartlepool	d																					
Newcastle [8]	d	15 59		16 08	16 16		16 25	16 33			16 48		17 06		17 12	17 16	17 25	17 30				
Chester-le-Street	d										16 57											
Durham	d	16 12		16 20	16 29		16 37	16 46			17 04				17 24	17 31	17 37					
Darlington [7]	a	16 30		16 36	16 47		16 53	17 03			17 20		17 33		17 42	17 47	17 53	17 59				
Middlesbrough	d	15 50											16 45				17 14					17 45
Eaglescliffe	d																					
Darlington [7]	d	16 30		16 38	16 48		16 54	17 04			17 21		17 33		17 42	17 48	17 54	17 59				
Northallerton	d										17 33		17 45									18 12
Thirsk	d																					18 20
York [8]	a	16 59		17 12	17 16		17 22	17 32			17 59		18 06		18 10	18 16	18 22	18 28				18 39
Hull	a																					
Leeds [10]	a			17 37			17 51	18 07			18 38		18 38				18 51					19 08
Harrogate	d							16 30		16 53								17 30		17 53		
Scarborough	d												16 45									
York [8]	d	17 01			17 20	17⌇25		17 35					18 07		18 12	18 20		18 29				
Doncaster [7]	a	17 25			17 47	17⌇54		18 02					18 31		18 37	18 45		18 53				
Sheffield [7]	a	18 02			18 20	18⌇28	18 40	18 51					19g12			19 20	19 40	19 53				
Skipton	d		16 15																	17 15		
Keighley	d		16 28																	17 28		
Bradford Forster Square	d		16h31							17 02										18 02		
Shipley	d		16 40							17 09										18 08		
Leeds [10]	d		17 05							17 40										18 40		
Huddersfield	d		16j30							16j44										17j44		
Wakefield Westgate [7]	d		17 18							17 52										18 52		
Hull	d							16 41				17 30						17 41			18 30	
Selby	d											18 05									19 05	
Doncaster [7]	d	17 26	17 36					18 02				18 23	18 31	←	18 37			18 53		19 10	19 22	
Retford [10]	d		17 51									18k44 →		18 44							19 37	
Newark North Gate [7]	a		18 05												19 05							
Grimsby Town	d							16m36										17m36				
Lincoln	d													17n35	18 00							
Newark North Gate [7]	d		18 05												19 05							
Grantham [7]	a									18 35				19 06						19 40	19 56	
	d								18 18	18 35				19 06					19 22	19 40	19 57	
Peterborough [8]	a	18 21						18 48	18 52	18 57			19 18	19 28	19 35			19 41	19 51	20 01		
Cambridge	a	19 20											20 21					21q14		21 19		
Stansted Airport	a	19 58											20 58							21 53		
Norwich	a								20 28										21 25	22q53		
Peterborough [8]	d	18 21						18 49		18 57			19 19	19 29	19 36			19 42		20 02		
Stevenage [4]	a		19 01					19 20							20 08			20 12		20 32		
London Kings Cross [15] ⊖	a	19 16	19 33					19 47		19 51			20 12	20 23	20 36			20 42		20 59	21 12	

For general notes see front of timetable
For details of catering facilities see Directory of Train Operators

- **A** To Manchester Airport (Table 39)
- **B** To Bristol Temple Meads (Table 51)
- **C** From 30 March. To St Pancras International (Table 53)
- **D** To Southampton Central (from 30 March to Oxford) (Table 51)
- **E** From Sheffield (from 30 March from Liverpool Lime Street) (Table 49)
- **G** To Birmingham New Street (Table 51)
- **H** To Liverpool Lime Street (Table 39)
- **b** Change at Stirling and Edinburgh
- **c** Change at Edinburgh
- **e** Glasgow Queen Street. Change at Edinburgh
- **f** Glasgow Queen Street
- **g** From 30 March arr. 1909
- **h** Bradford Interchange
- **j** Change at Leeds
- **k** Arr. 1838
- **m** Change at Doncaster
- **n** Change at Retford
- **q** Change at Peterborough and Ely

Scotland, North East England, Yorkshire and Humberside → London

until 27 January and from 30 March

Route Diagram - see first page of Table 26

		TP	GR	XC	XC	GR	GR	GC	TP	GR	XC	EM	TP	GR	TP	XC	GR	NT	TP	GR	GR
		1◇	R 1	1◇	1◇	R 1	R 1	R 1	1◇	R 1	1◇	◇	1◇	R 1	1◇	1◇	R 1		1◇	R 1	R 1
		A		B	C				D		E	G	D		A	H		J	A		
			☕ 🍴	☕	☕	☕ 🍴	☕ 🍴	☕		☕ 🍴	☕			☕ 🍴		☕	☕ 🍴			☕ 🍴	☕ 🍴
Aberdeen	d		13 50											15 10						17 10	
Stonehaven	d		14 07											15 29						17 26	
Montrose	d		14 30											15 51						17 48	
Arbroath	d		14 45											16 05						18 02	
Dundee	d		15 03				15 25							16 25						18 19	
Leuchars 3	d		15 17				15 37							16 37						18 31	
Kirkcaldy	d		15 41			16b02	16 11							17 03						18 56	19b07
Inverkeithing	d		16 02			16b18	16 32							17 19						19 12	19b47
Inverness	d					13b25															16c15
Perth	d					15b25														17c05	18c27
Stirling	d		15b07				16 07									17 07				18 07	19b11
Glasgow Central 15	d		15e00		15 45	15 50	16f00				16f30					17f30	17 50			18f30	19 50
Motherwell	d				15u59	16 05											18 05				20 04
Haymarket	d		16 20		16 39	16 46											18 46				20 45
Edinburgh 10	a		16 26		16 44	16 52											18 53				20 51
Edinburgh	d		16 30		16 50	17 00	17 30				17 50			18 00		18 50	19 00			20 00	21 00
Dunbar	d				17 10						18 10						19 20			20 20	21 21
Berwick-upon-Tweed	d		17 11		17 33									18 41						20 45	21 44
Alnmouth	d		17 34								18 52			19 03							22 05
Morpeth	d																			21 19	
Newcastle 8	a		18 05		18 19	18 26	18 55				19 21			19 33		20 13	20 29			21 38	22 41
Sunderland	d	17 28					18 28	18 42								19 28				20 28	
Hartlepool	d							19 06													
Newcastle 8	d	17 57	18 10	18 16	18 25	18 29	18 57		19 20		19 25			19 35		20 25	20 31	21 06		21 40	
Chester-le-Street	d																	21 15			
Durham	d	18 09		18 28	18 37	18 42	19 10		19 32		19 37			19 48		20 37		21 24		21 53	
Darlington 7	a	18 25		18 44	18 53	18 59	19 27		19 48		19 54			20 05		20 53	20 57	21 44		22 10	
Middlesbrough	d	17 49							18 53						20 15				22 07	20 55	
Eaglescliffe	d							19 25													
Darlington 7	d	18 27		18 45	18 54	19 00	19 28		19 50		19 54		←	20 06		20 54	20 58			22 11	
Northallerton	d						19 39	19 48	20 01				20 01		20 42				22 34	22 41	
Thirsk	d							19 57	→						20 50				22 42		
York 8	a	19 00	19 04	19 13	19 22	19 28	20 00	20 13			20 22		20 32	20 38	21 09	21 21	21 26		23 09	23 19	
Hull	a	20 08															22 39				
Leeds 10	a	19 38	19 38		19 51	20 07					20 51		21 08	21 33	21 38		22 04		23 38		
Harrogate	d					19 30											20 30				
Scarborough	d						18 45														
York 8	d		19 05	19 20		19 30	20 02	20 15						20 40		21 26	21 28				
Doncaster 7	a		19 30	19 48		19 53	20 25							21 05		21 49	21 51				
Sheffield 7	a		20 07	20 20	20 40	20 53	21 17				21 43			21 56		22 20	22 59				
Skipton	d									19 23											
Keighley	d									19 36											
Bradford Forster Square	d									19g31											
Shipley	d									19 48											
Leeds 10	d									20 15							20 20				
Huddersfield	d									19h44											
Wakefield Westgate 7	d									20 27							20 33				
Hull	d					18 38											20 30				
Selby	d																				
Doncaster 7	d		19 30			19 54	20 26			20 47				21 05			21 52				
Retford 10	d													21 20							
Newark North Gate 7	a					20 16								21 34							
Grimsby Town	d					18j36								19j36			20j36				
Lincoln	d													20 59							
Newark North Gate 7	d					20 16								21 34							
Grantham 7	a						20 56										22 22				
	d						20 56					21 19					22 22				
Peterborough 8	a		20 25			20 46	21 17			21 35		21 51		22 04			22 43				
Cambridge	a									23k13				23 17							
Stansted Airport	a																				
Norwich	a											23 35									
Peterborough 8	d		20 26			20 48	21 18			21 36				22 04			22 44				
Stevenage 4	a		20 57			21 20	21 48			22 09				22 34							
London Kings Cross 15 ⊖	a		21 25			21 47	22 16	22 20		22 37				23 14			23 50				

For general notes see front of timetable
For details of catering facilities see Directory of Train Operators

- **A** To Manchester Airport (Table 39)
- **B** To Birmingham New Street (Table 51)
- **C** To Bristol Temple Meads (Table 51) ☕ To Leeds
- **D** To Liverpool Lime Street (Table 39)
- **E** To Birmingham New Street (Table 51). ☕ to Leeds
- **G** From Sheffield (from 30 March from Liverpool Lime Street) (Table 49)
- **H** To Birmingham New Street (Table 51). ☕ to Newcastle
- **J** To Saltburn (Table 44)

- **b** Change at Edinburgh
- **c** Change at Stirling and Edinburgh
- **e** Glasgow Queen Street. Change at Edinburgh
- **f** Glasgow Queen Street
- **g** Bradford Interchange
- **h** Change at Leeds
- **j** Change at Doncaster
- **k** Change at Peterborough and Ely

Table 26

Sundays

Scotland, North East England, Yorkshire and Humberside → London

3 February to 23 March

Route Diagram - see first page of Table 26

		GR	GR	GR	GR	HT	XC	GC	TP	GC	TP	XC	GR	GR	GR	XC	TP	EM	XC	GR	GR	GR
		R	R	R	R		R	R		R		R	R	R	R	R			R	R	R	R
		1	1	1	1	1 ◇	1	1	1 ◇	1	1 ◇	1	1	1	1	1	1 ◇	◇	1	1	1	1
							A		B		C	D				D	C	E	A			
Aberdeen	d																					
Stonehaven	d																					
Montrose	d																					
Arbroath	d																					
Dundee	d														07 25							
Leuchars 3	d														07 37							
Kirkcaldy	d														08 09							
Inverkeithing	d														08 30							
Inverness	d																					
Perth	d																					
Stirling	d																					09 05
Glasgow Central 15	d													07b50					08b30			
Motherwell	d																					
Haymarket	d																					
Edinburgh 10	a																					
Edinburgh	d											08 50		09 00	09 30				09 50	10 00		10 30
Dunbar	d																					
Berwick-upon-Tweed	d											09 31		09 41						10 41		11 11
Alnmouth	d																		10 48			
Morpeth	d																					
Newcastle 8	a											10 17		10 28	10 55				11 17	11 30		11 58
Sunderland	d							09 10				09 28			10 28							11 28
Hartlepool	d							09 34														
Newcastle 8	d		07 58	08 55	09 25		09 28		09 33			10 25		10 30	10 57		11 03		11 25	11 32		12 00
Chester-le-Street	d								09 42													
Durham	d		08 10	09 07			09 42		09 49			10 37			11 10		11 16		11 37			
Darlington 7	a		08 28	09 25	09 51		09 57		10 04			10 53		10 59			11 32		11 53			12 26
Middlesbrough	d			08 45			09 15				10 15						10 53					11 24
Eaglescliffe	d							09 55														
Darlington 7	d		08 28	09 25	09 52		09 59		10 05	←		10 54		10 59			11 34		11 54			12 27
Northallerton	d			09 38				10 13	10 17		10 42						11 45					
Thirsk	d							10 26		10 26	10 50											
York 8	a		08 56	10 00	10 20		10 27	→	10 44	10 45	11 09	11 22		11 28	11 51		12 12		12 22	12 28		12 55
Hull	a						11 38															
Leeds 10	a		09 38	10 38			10 51		11 08	11 32	11 38	11 51 →		12 07		← 11 51	12 38		12 51 →	13 08		
Harrogate	d													09c53						11 30		11c53
Scarborough	d				09 20										10 45							
York 8	d		08 58	10 02	10 23					10 47				11 29	11 53					12 29		12 57
Doncaster 7	a		09 25	10 25	10 47		11 28							11 53		12 29				12 54		13 20
Sheffield 7	a		09 58	10 58	11 25		11 57							12 55		12 59				13 55		
Skipton	d				08c35	09c15														10c15		11c30
Keighley	d				08c48	09c28														10c28		11c40
Bradford Forster Square	d			08e31	09e21								10 02							11c02		12c02
Shipley	d				09c10	09c40							10 08							11c10		12c08
Leeds 10	d	08 24	08 35	09 05	10 00	10f09							10 40	11 00						12 00	12 40	
Huddersfield	d			07g47	09c18								10 02	10c14						11c12	11h44	
Wakefield Westgate 7	d	08 36	08 47	09 17	10 12	10f22							10 52	11 12						12 12	12 52	
Hull	d			08 42	09 41	10 12								10 41						11 41		
Selby	d					10 47																
Doncaster 7	d	08 54	09 26	10 29	10 48	11 04							11 13	11 53						12 54	13 10	13 21
Retford 10	d		09 41			11 19							11 28								13j34 →	
Newark North Gate 7	a	09 18		10 52									11 42		12 34							
Grimsby Town	d					09f49								10f36								
Lincoln	d												11 05									
Newark North Gate 7	d	09 18		10 52									11 42		12 34							
Grantham 7	a	09 30	10 03	11 04		11 38							11 54							13 26		
	d	09 30	10 03	11 04		11 39							11 54					13 14		13 26		
Peterborough 8	a	09 52	10 25	11 26	11 37								12 16	12 40	13 03			13 41				14 09
Cambridge	a				13k14										14 19							
Stansted Airport	a														14 58							
Norwich	a				14k09													15 28				
Peterborough 8	d	09 53	10 27	11 26	11 38								12 16	12 41	13 04							14 10
Stevenage 4	a		11 00		12 09										13 34					14 14		
London Kings Cross 15 ⊖	a	10 47	11 28	12 19	12 37	12 48				12 51			13 13	13 36	14 04					14 42		15 11

For general notes see front of timetable
For details of catering facilities see Directory of Train Operators

- **A** To Bournemouth (Table 51)
- **B** To Liverpool Lime Street (Table 39)
- **C** To Manchester Airport (Table 39)
- **D** To Penzance (Table 135)
- **E** From Nottingham (Table 19)
- **b** Glasgow Queen Street
- **c** Change at Leeds and Doncaster
- **e** Bradford Interchange. Change at Leeds and Doncaster
- **f** Change at Doncaster
- **g** Change at Leeds and Doncaster. By bus to Leeds
- **h** Change at Leeds
- **j** Arr. 1325
- **k** Change at Peterborough and Ely

Sundays

Scotland, North East England, Yorkshire and Humberside → London

3 February to 23 March

Route Diagram - see first page of Table 26

		XC R 1 A	TP 1 ◇ B	GR R 1	XC R 1 C	GR R 1	XC R 1 C	TP 1 ◇ B	EM ◇ D	GR R 1	GR R 1	TP 1 ◇ B	GR R 1	XC R 1 A	GR R 1	HT 1 ◇	TP 1 ◇ E	XC R 1 A	GR R 1 G	GR R 1	TP 1 ◇ B
Aberdeen	d																		09 50		
Stonehaven	d																		10 07		
Montrose	d																		10 30		
Arbroath	d																		10 45		
Dundee	d										09 25								11 03		
Leuchars 3	d										09 37								11 17		
Kirkcaldy	d										10 09								11 41		
Inverkeithing	d										10 32								11 57		
Inverness	d																				
Perth	d										09 27										
Stirling	d										10 02								11b06		
Glasgow Central 15	d				09c30									10 30	10 50						
Motherwell	d													10u56	11 05						
Haymarket	d													11 37	11 49				12 18		
Edinburgh 10	a													11 42	11 54				12 24		
Edinburgh	d				10 50	11 00					11 30			11 50	12 00				12 30		
Dunbar	d				11 11																
Berwick-upon-Tweed	d				11 35										12 41						
Alnmouth	d													12 48					13 30		
Morpeth	d										12 42										
Newcastle 8	a				12 21	12 30					13 01			13 17	13 29				14 01		
Sunderland	d										12 28								13 28		
Hartlepool	d																				
Newcastle 8	d				12 25	12 32		12 49			13 03		13 20	13 25	13 32				14 03		14 10
Chester-le-Street	d							12 58													
Durham	d				12 37	12 45		13 05						13 37	13 45						14 22
Darlington 7	a				12 53	13 02		13 22			13 29		13 45	13 53	14 03				14 30		14 38
Middlesbrough	d		12 15			12 25									13 25		13 45				
Eaglescliffe	d																				
Darlington 7	d				12 54	13 03		13 23			13 30	←	13 46	13 55	14 04				14 31		14 40
Northallerton	d		12 42					13 35 →			13 42	13 35					14 12				
Thirsk	d		12 50														14 19				
York 8	a		13 12		13 22	13 31					14 03	14 11	14 17	14 22	14 34		14 40		15 00		15 14
Hull	a	←	14 21				←											←			
Leeds 10	a	12 51	13 38		13 52 →	14 07	13 52					14 38		14 51 →			15 08	14 51			15 39
Harrogate	d									12 53			13 30								
Scarborough	d										12 45										
York 8	d					13 33					14 05		14 19		14 36				15 01		
Doncaster 7	a	13 28				13 56	14 28				14 28		14 43		14 59			15 28			
Sheffield 7	a	13 58	14 58			14 52	14 58				15 12					15 51		15 58			
Skipton	d									12 15						13e15					
Keighley	d									12 28						13e28					
Bradford Forster Square	d									13 02						13f31				14 02	
Shipley	d									13 08						13e40				14 08	
Leeds 10	d					13 00				13 40			14 00			14g09				14 40	
Huddersfield	d					12e12				12h44			13e12							13h44	
Wakefield Westgate 7	d					13 12				13 52			14 12							14 52	
Hull	d					12 41							13 41			14 10					
Selby	d															14 45					
Doncaster 7	d			←		13 57				14 10	14 29		14 48		15 00	15 05				15 10	
Retford 10	d			13 34												15 20				15 25	
Newark North Gate 7	a			13 48						14 33										15 39	
Grimsby Town	d					12g36							13g36			13g36					
Lincoln	d			13 05																14 59	
Newark North Gate 7	d			13 48						14 33										15 39	
Grantham 7	a			14 00							14 59					15 40				15 52	
	d			14 00					14 20		14 59					15 40				15 52	
Peterborough 8	a			14 22		14 43			14 53				15 35		15 47					16 13	
Cambridge	a					16j14									17j14					17 23	
Stansted Airport	a					16 59														17 58	
Norwich	a								16 37						17 35						
Peterborough 8	d			14 22		14 43							15 36		15 47					16 19	
Stevenage 4	a			15 33						15 28					16 17					16 49	
London Kings Cross 15 ⊖	a			15 15		15 38				15 55	16 11		16 29		16 45	16 50			17 11	17 17	

For general notes see front of timetable
For details of catering facilities see Directory of Train Operators

- **A** To Bournemouth (Table 51)
- **B** To Manchester Airport (Table 39)
- **C** To Plymouth (Table 51)
- **D** From Sheffield (Table 49)
- **E** To Liverpool Lime Street (Table 39)
- **G** **The Northern Lights**
- **b** Change at Edinburgh
- **c** Glasgow Queen Street
- **e** Change at Leeds and Doncaster
- **f** Bradford Interchange. Change at Leeds and Doncaster
- **g** Change at Doncaster
- **h** Change at Leeds
- **j** Change at Peterborough and Ely

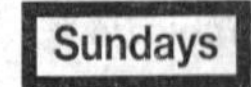

Scotland, North East England, Yorkshire and Humberside → London

3 February to 23 March

Route Diagram - see first page of Table 26

		XC	GC	GR	XC	TP	EM	GR	GR	TP	XC	GR	EM	EM	GR	HT	TP	GR	GR	XC	GR
		R 1	R 1	R 1	R 1	1 ◇	◇	R 1	R 1	1 ◇	R 1	R 1	1 ◇	◇	R 1	1 ◇	1 ◇	R 1	R 1	R 1	R 1
		A		B	A	C	D		E	C	G		H	D			J			G	
Aberdeen	d																		11 42		
Stonehaven	d																		11 59		
Montrose	d																		12 22		
Arbroath	d																		12 37		
Dundee	d								11b25										12 58		
Leuchars 3	d								11b37										13 12		
Kirkcaldy	d								12b09										13 36		
Inverkeithing	d								12b32										13 54		
Inverness	d								09 38												
Perth	d								11 55												
Stirling	d								12 32										13b07		
Glasgow Central 15	d	11 30									12c30	12 50							13e00		
Motherwell	d	11u56										13 04									
Haymarket	d	12 37							13 12			13 50							14 19		
Edinburgh 10	a	12 42							13 18			13 56							14 24		
Edinburgh	d	12 50		13 00					13 30		13 50	14 00							14 30		
Dunbar	d	13 12																			
Berwick-upon-Tweed	d	13 35		13 40					14 11												
Alnmouth	d										14 48										
Morpeth	d																				
Newcastle 8	a	14 21		14 30					15 00		15 17	15 25							15 57		
Sunderland	d		13 42			14 28													15 28		
Hartlepool	d		14 06																		
Newcastle 8	d	14 25		14 32		14 57			15 01		15 25	15 30						15 50	15 59		
Chester-le-Street	d																				
Durham	d	14 38				15 09			15 15		15 37								16 12		
Darlington 7	a	14 53		14 59		15 25			15 32		15 53	15 59						16 18	16 30		
Middlesbrough	d					14 38											15 45		15 50		
Eaglescliffe	d		14 32																		
Darlington 7	d	14 54		15 00		15 27			15 33	←	15 54	15 59						16 21	16 30		
Northallerton	d		14 57	15 11		15 38 →				15 38							16 14	16 33			
Thirsk	d		15 06														16 22				
York 8	a	15 22	15 28	15 32					16 02	16 12	16 22	16 28					16 41	16 52	16 59		
Hull	a			16 41	←															←	
Leeds 10	a	15 51 →	16 07	16 32	15 51					16 38	16 51 →						17 08			16 51	
Harrogate	d							14 53				15 30									
Scarborough	d								14 45												
York 8	d		15 31	15 34					16 03			16 29	16 40					16 53	17 01		
Doncaster 7	a			15 57	16 28				16 28			16 53	17 02					17 19	17 25	17 28	
Sheffield 7	a			16 52	16 58				17 11				17 28						18 04	17 58	
Skipton	d							14 15							15 15						16 15
Keighley	d							14 28							15 28						16 28
Bradford Forster Square	d							15 02							16 02						16g31
Shipley	d							15 08							16 08						16 40
Leeds 10	d			15 00				15 40				16 00			16 40						17 05
Huddersfield	d			14f12				14h44				15f12			15h44						16h30
Wakefield Westgate 7	d			15 12				15 52				16 12			16 52						17 18
Hull	d			14 41								15 41				16 21					
Selby	d															16 56					
Doncaster 7	d			15 58				16 10	16 28			16 53			17 10	17 15		17 19	17 26		17 36
Retford 10	d															17 30					17 51
Newark North Gate 7	a			16 20														17 46			18 05
Grimsby Town	d			14j36								15j36									
Lincoln	d															15k15					
Newark North Gate 7	d			16 20														17 46			18 05
Grantham 7	a							16 40							17 40	17 49					
	d						16 24	16 40						17 24	17 40	17 49					
Peterborough 8	a			16 50			16 55	17 01	17 18			17 40		17 51	18 02				18 21		
Cambridge	a			18m14					18 21			19m14							19 20		
Stansted Airport	a																		19 58		
Norwich	a						18 35							19 29							
Peterborough 8	d			16 51				17 02	17 18			17 41			18 02				18 21		
Stevenage 4	a			17 22								18 11						18 42			19 01
London Kings Cross 15 ⊖	a		17 31	17 49				17 55	18 15			18 40			18 55	19 06		19 12	19 16		19 33

For general notes see front of timetable
For details of catering facilities see Directory of Train Operators

- **A** To Plymouth (Table 51)
- **B** **The Flying Scotsman**
- **C** To Manchester Airport (Table 39)
- **D** From Liverpool Lime Street (Table 49)
- **E** **The Highland Chieftain**
- **G** To Southampton Central (Table 51)
- **H** To St Pancras International (Table 53)
- **J** To Liverpool Lime Street (Table 39)
- **b** Change at Edinburgh
- **c** Glasgow Queen Street
- **e** Glasgow Queen Street. Change at Edinburgh
- **f** Change at Leeds and Doncaster
- **g** Bradford Interchange
- **h** Change at Leeds
- **j** Change at Doncaster
- **k** Change at Retford
- **m** Change at Peterborough and Ely

Table 26

Sundays

3 February to 23 March

Scotland, North East England, Yorkshire and Humberside → London

Route Diagram - see first page of Table 26

		TP	XC	GR	EM	GR	GR	XC	TP	GR	GR	GR	XC	GR	XC	EM	GR	HT	TP	TP	GR
			R	R		R	R	R		R	R	R		R			R				R
		1◇	1	1	◇	1	1	1	1◇	1	1	1	1◇	1	1◇	◇	1	1◇	1◇	1◇	1
		A	B		C			B	A				B		B	C			D	A	
Aberdeen	d		11 58																		13 50
Stonehaven	d		12 16																		14 07
Montrose	d		12 39																		14 30
Arbroath	d		12 56																		14 45
Dundee	d		13 14							13 25											15 03
Leuchars 3	d		13 27							13 39											15 17
Kirkcaldy	d		13 58							14 11											15 41
Inverkeithing	d		14 14							14 32											16 02
Inverness	d																				
Perth	d									13b05											
Stirling	d									14 07											15c07
Glasgow Central 15	d		13e30							14f00			14f30	14 50							15e00
Motherwell	d													15 04							
Haymarket	d		14 29											15 48							16 20
Edinburgh 10	a		14 33											15 53							16 26
Edinburgh	d		14 50	15 00						15 30			15 50	16 00							16 30
Dunbar	d		15 10																		
Berwick-upon-Tweed	d		15 35	15 41						16 11											17 11
Alnmouth	d												16 48								17 34
Morpeth	d									16 46			17 03								
Newcastle 8	a		16 21	16 31						17 05			17 20	17 25							18 05
Sunderland	d									16 28										17 28	
Hartlepool	d																				
Newcastle 8	d	16 08	16 25	16 33					16 48	17 06		17 12	17 25	17 30						17 57	18 10
Chester-le-Street	d								16 57												
Durham	d	16 20	16 37	16 46					17 04			17 24	17 37							18 09	
Darlington 7	a	16 36	16 53	17 03					17 20	17 33		17 42	17 53	17 59						18 25	
Middlesbrough	d									16 45			17 14						17 45	17 49	
Eaglescliffe	d																				
Darlington 7	d	16 38	16 54	17 04					17 21	17 33		17 42	17 54	17 59						18 27	
Northallerton	d								17 33	17 45									18 12		
Thirsk	d																		18 20		
York 8	a	17 12	17 22	17 32					17 59	18 06		18 10	18 22	18 28					18 39	19 00	19 04
Hull	a																			20 08	
Leeds 10	a	17 37	17 51 →	18 07				17 51	18 38	18 38			18 51 →		← 18 51				19 08	19 38	19 38
Harrogate	d			16 30			16 53							17 30			17 53				
Scarborough	d									16 45											
York 8	d			17 35						18 07		18 12		18 29							19 05
Doncaster 7	a			18 02				18 28		18 31		18 37		18 53	19 29						19 30
Sheffield 7	a			18 51				18 58		19 09				19 53	19 59						20 07
Skipton	d																17 15				
Keighley	d																17 28				
Bradford Forster Square	d						17 02										18 02				
Shipley	d						17 09										18 08				
Leeds 10	d						17 40					18 00					18 40				
Huddersfield	d						16g44					17h12					17g44				
Wakefield Westgate 7	d						17 52					18 12					18 52				
Hull	d			16 41		17 30								17 41				18 30			
Selby	d					18 05												19 05			
Doncaster 7	d			18 02		18 23				18 31	←	18 37		18 53			19 10	19 22			19 30
Retford 10	d					18j44 →					18 44							19 37			
Newark North Gate 7	a											19 05									
Grimsby Town	d			16k36										17k36							
Lincoln	d										17m35	18 00									
Newark North Gate 7	d											19 05									
Grantham 7	a						18 35				19 06						19 40	19 56			
	d				18 18		18 35				19 06					19 22	19 40	19 57			
Peterborough 8	a			18 48	18 52		18 57			19 18	19 28	19 35		19 41		19 51	20 01				20 25
Cambridge	a									20 21				21n14			21 19				
Stansted Airport	a									20 58							21 53				
Norwich	a				20 28											21 25	22n53				
Peterborough 8	d			18 49			18 57			19 19	19 29	19 36		19 42			20 02				20 26
Stevenage 4	a			19 20								20 08		20 12			20 32				20 57
London Kings Cross 15 ⊖	a			19 47			19 51			20 12	20 23	20 36		20 42			20 59	21 12			21 25

For general notes see front of timetable
For details of catering facilities see Directory of Train Operators

- **A** To Manchester Airport (Table 39)
- **B** To Bristol Temple Meads (Table 51)
- **C** From Liverpool Lime Street (Table 49)
- **D** To Liverpool Lime Street (Table 39)
- **b** Change at Stirling and Edinburgh
- **c** Change at Edinburgh
- **e** Glasgow Queen Street. Change at Edinburgh
- **f** Glasgow Queen Street
- **g** Change at Leeds
- **h** Change at Leeds and Doncaster
- **j** Arr. 1838
- **k** Change at Doncaster
- **m** Change at Retford
- **n** Change at Peterborough and Ely

Table 26

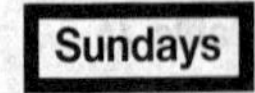

Sundays

Scotland, North East England, Yorkshire and Humberside → London

3 February to 23 March

Route Diagram - see first page of Table 26

		XC		GR	GR	XC	GC		TP	GR	XC	EM		TP	GR	XC	TP		XC	GR	NT	TP	GR	GR		
		1 ◇		R 1	R 1	1 ◇	R 1		1 ◇	R 1	1 ◇	◇		1 ◇	R 1	1 ◇	1 ◇		1 ◇	R 1		1 ◇	R 1	R 1		
		A				A			B		A	C		B		A	D				E	D				
		☕		☕ ✂	☕ ✂	☕	☕			☕ ✂	☕				☕ ✂	☕			☕	☕ ✂			☕ ✂	☕ ✂		
Aberdeen	d														15 10								17 10			
Stonehaven	d														15 29								17 26			
Montrose	d														15 51								17 48			
Arbroath	d														16 05								18 02			
Dundee	d				15 25										16 25								18 19			
Leuchars 3	d				15 37										16 37								18 31			
Kirkcaldy	d			16b02	16 11										17 03				17 07				18 56	19b07		
Inverkeithing	d			16b18	16 32										17 19				17 47				19 12	19b47		
Inverness	d			13b25																				16c15		
Perth	d			15b25															15c05				17c05	18c27		
Stirling	d				16 07														17 07				18 07	19b11		
Glasgow Central 15	d	15 45		15 50	16e00						16e30								17e30	17 50			18e30	19 50		
Motherwell	d	15u59		16 05																18 05				20 04		
Haymarket	d	16 39		16 46																18 46				20 46		
Edinburgh 10	a	16 44		16 52																18 53				20 51		
Edinburgh	d	16 50		17 00	17 30						17 50				18 00				18 50	19 00			20 00	21 00		
Dunbar	d	17 10									18 10								19 12	19 20			20 20	21 21		
Berwick-upon-Tweed	d	17 33													18 41								20 45	21 44		
Alnmouth	d										18 52				19 03				19 52					22 05		
Morpeth	d																						21 19			
Newcastle 8	⛴ a	18 19		18 26	18 55						19 21				19 33				20 19	20 29			21 38	22 41		
Sunderland	d				18 28		18 42												19 28		20 28					
Hartlepool	d						19 06																			
Newcastle 8	⛴ d	18 25		18 29	18 57				19 20		19 25				19 35				20 25	20 31	21 06		21 40			
Chester-le-Street	d																				21 15					
Durham	d	18 37		18 42	19 10				19 32		19 37				19 48				20 37		21 24		21 53			
Darlington 7	a	18 53		18 59	19 27				19 48		19 54				20 05				20 53	20 57	21 44		22 10			
Middlesbrough	d								18 53								20 15					22 07	20 55			
Eaglescliffe	d						19 25																			
Darlington 7	d	18 54		19 00	19 28				19 50		19 54			←	20 06				20 54	20 58			22 11			
Northallerton	d				19 39		19 48		20 01					20 01			20 42					22 34	22 41			
Thirsk	d						19 57		→								20 50					22 42				
York 8	a	19 22		19 28	20 00		20 13				20 22			20 32	20 38		21 09		21 19	21 26		23 09	23 19			
Hull	a					←										←				22 39						
Leeds 10	a	19 51		20 07		19 51					20 51			21 08	21 33	20 51	21 38		21 56	22 04		23 38				
Harrogate	d	→		18 30						18 53	→				19 30					20 30						
Scarborough	d				18 45																					
York 8	d			19 30	20 02		20 15								20 40					21 28						
Doncaster 7	a			19 53	20 25	20 29									21 05	21 29				21 51						
Sheffield 7	⛴ a			20 53	21 17	20 59									21 56	21 57				22 59						
Skipton	d									19 23																
Keighley	d									19 36																
Bradford Forster Square	d									19f31										20g14						
Shipley	d									19 48										20h08						
Leeds 10	d			19 00						20 15										21 00						
Huddersfield	d			18h12						19j44										20h12						
Wakefield Westgate 7	d			19 12						20 27										21 12						
Hull	d			18 38																20 30						
Selby	d																									
Doncaster 7	d			19 54	20 26					20 47					21 05					21 52						
Retford 10	d														21 20											
Newark North Gate 7	a			20 16											21 34											
Grimsby Town	d			18k36											19k36					20k36						
Lincoln	d														20 59											
Newark North Gate 7	d			20 16											21 34											
Grantham 7	a				20 56															22 22						
	d				20 56							21 19								22 22						
Peterborough 8	a			20 46	21 17					21 35		21 51			22 04					22 43						
Cambridge	a									23m13					23 17											
Stansted Airport	a																									
Norwich	a											23 35														
Peterborough 8	d			20 48	21 18					21 36					22 04					22 44						
Stevenage 4	a			21 20	21 48					22 09					22 34											
London Kings Cross 15	⊖ a			21 47	22 16		22 20			22 37					23 14					23 50						

For general notes see front of timetable
For details of catering facilities see Directory of Train Operators

A To Birmingham New Street (Table 51). ☕ to Leeds
B To Liverpool Lime Street (Table 39)
C From Liverpool Lime Street (Table 49)
D To Manchester Airport (Table 39)
E To Saltburn (Table 44)
b Change at Edinburgh
c Change at Stirling and Edinburgh
e Glasgow Queen Street
f Bradford Interchange
g Bradford Interchange. Change at Leeds and Doncaster
h Change at Leeds and Doncaster
j Change at Leeds
k Change at Doncaster
m Change at Peterborough and Ely

Table 26A

Mondays to Saturdays

Peterborough — Wisbech, Kings Lynn, Swaffham and Dereham

Bus Service

		GR	GR	GR	GR	GR	GR	GR	GR	GR	GR	GR	GR	GR	GR
Peterborough	d	07 48	08 18	08 48	09 18	09 48	10 48	11 18	11 48	12 18	12 48	13 18	13 48	14 18	
Wisbech Bus Station	d	08 35	09 05	09 35	10 05	10 35	11 35	12 05	12 35	13 05	13 35	14 05	14 35	15 05	
Kings Lynn Bus Station	d	09 07	09 37	10 07	10 37	11 07	12 07	12 37	13 07	13 37	14 07	14 37	15 07	15 37	
Swaffham Market Place	d	09 42	10 12	10 42	11 12	11 42	12 42	13 12	13 42	14 12	14 42	15 12	15 42	16 12	
Dereham Market Place	a	10 13	10 43	11 13	11 43	12 13	13 13	13 43	14 13	14 43	15 13	15 43	16 13	16 43	

		GR	GR	GR	GR	GR	GR	GR	GR	GR	GR	GR	GR	GR	GR
Peterborough	d	14 48	15 18	15 48	16 18	16 48	17 18	17 48	18 18	18 48	19 18	20 18	21 18	22 18	23 18
Wisbech Bus Station	d	15 35	16 05	16 35	17 05	17 35	18 05	18 35	19 05	19 35	20 05	21 05	22 05	23 05	00 05
Kings Lynn Bus Station	d	16 07	16 37	17 07	17 37	18 07	18 37	19a07	19 37	20a07	20 37	21 37	22a37	23a37	00a37
Swaffham Market Place	d	16 42	17 12	17 42	18 12	18 42	19 12		20 12		21 12	22 12			
Dereham Market Place	a	17 13	17 43	18 13	18 43	19 13	19 43		20 43		21 43	22 43			

Sundays

		GR	GR	GR	GR	GR	GR	GR	GR	GR	GR	GR	GR	GR	GR	GR	GR
Peterborough	d	08 18	09 18	10 18	11 18	12 18	13 18	14 18	15 18	16 18	17 18	18 18	19 18	20 18	21 18	22 18	23 18
Wisbech Bus Station	d	09 05	10 05	11 05	12 05	13 05	14 05	15 05	16 05	17 05	18 05	19 05	20 05	21 05	22 05	23 05	00 05
Kings Lynn Bus Station	d	09 37	10 37	11 37	12 37	13 37	14 37	15 37	16 37	17 37	18 37	19 37	20 37	21 37	22a37	23a37	00a37
Swaffham Market Place	d	10 12	11 12	12 12	13 12	14 12	15 12	16 12	17 12	18 12	19 12	20 12	21 12	22 12			
Dereham Market Place	a	10 43	11 43	12 43	13 43	14 43	15 43	16 43	17 43	18 43	19 43	20 43	21 43	22 43			

Mondays to Saturdays

		GR	GR	GR	GR	GR	GR	GR	GR	GR	GR	GR	GR	GR	GR	GR	GR	GR
Dereham Market Place	d				07 19	07 24	07 27	07 49	07 54	08 24	08 54	09 24	09 54	10 24	10 54	11 24	11 54	12 24
Swaffham Market Place	d				07 49	07 54	07 50	08 19	08 24	08 54	09 24	09 54	10 24	10 54	11 24	11 54	12 24	12 54
Kings Lynn Bus Station	d	06 29	06 59	07 29	08 29	08 29	08 30	08 59	08 59	09 29	09 59	10 29	10 59	11 29	11 59	12 29	12 59	13 29
Wisbech Bus Station	d	07 01	07 31	08 01	09 01	09 01	09 03	09 31	09 31	10 01	10 31	11 01	11 31	12 01	12 31	13 01	13 31	14 01
Peterborough	a	07 43	08 13	08 43	09 43	09 43	09 45	10 13	10 13	10 43	11 13	11 43	12 13	12 43	13 13	13 43	14 13	14 43

		GR	GR	GR	GR	GR	GR	GR	GR	GR	GR	GR	GR	GR	GR
Dereham Market Place	d	12 54	13 24	13 54	14 24	14 27	14 54	15 24	15 54	16 24	16 54	17 54	18 54	19 54	20 54
Swaffham Market Place	d	13 24	13 54	14 24	14 54	14 50	15 24	15 54	16 24	16 54	17 24	18 24	19 24	20 24	21 24
Kings Lynn Bus Station	d	13 59	14 29	14 59	15 29	15 30	15 59	16 29	16 59	17 29	17 59	18 59	19 59	20 59	21 59
Wisbech Bus Station	d	14 31	15 01	15 31	16 01	16 03	16 31	17 01	17 31	18 01	18 31	19 31	20 31	21 31	22 31
Peterborough	a	15 13	15 43	16 13	17 43	16 45	17 13	17 43	18 13	18 43	19 13	20 13	21 13	22 13	23 13

Sundays

		GR	GR	GR	GR	GR	GR	GR	GR	GR	GR	GR	GR	GR	GR	GR	GR
Dereham Market Place	d				08 54	09 54	10 54	11 54	12 54	13 54	14 54	15 54	16 54	17 54	18 54	19 54	20 54
Swaffham Market Place	d				09 24	10 24	11 24	12 24	13 24	14 24	15 24	16 24	17 24	18 24	19 24	20 24	21 24
Kings Lynn Bus Station	d	06 59	07 59	08 59	09 59	10 59	11 59	12 59	13 59	14 59	15 59	16 59	17 59	18 59	19 59	20 59	21 59
Wisbech Bus Station	d	07 31	08 31	09 31	10 31	11 31	12 31	13 31	14 31	15 31	16 31	17 31	18 31	19 31	20 31	21 31	22 31
Peterborough	a	08 13	09 13	10 13	11 13	12 13	13 13	14 13	15 13	16 13	17 13	18 13	19 13	20 13	21 13	22 13	23 13

For general notes see front of timetable
For details of catering facilities see Directory of Train Operators

Sunday service operates on Bank Holiday Monday

Table 26B

Mondays to Saturdays

Peterborough — Oundle, Corby and Kettering

Bus Service

		GR	GR	GR	GR	GR	GR	GR	GR	GR	GR	GR	GR	GR	GR
Peterborough §	d	07 10	07 40	09 10	10 10	11 10	12 10	13 10	14 10	15 10	16 10	17 10	18 10	19 10	20 10
Oundle Market Place	a	07 32	08 27	09 32	10 32	11 32	12 32	13 32	14 32	15 32	16 32	17 32	18 32	19 32	20 37
Corby George Street	a	08 05	09 05	10 05	11 05	12 05	13 05	14 05	15 05	16 05	17 05	18 05	19 05	20 05	21 05
Kettering Library	a	08 35	09 35	10 35	11 35	12 35	13 35	14 35	15 35	16 35	17 35	18 35	19 35	20 35	21 35

Sundays

		GR	GR	GR	GR	GR	GR
Peterborough §	d	10 10	12 10	14 10	16 10	18 10	20 10
Oundle Market Place	a	10 37	12 37	14 37	16 37	18 37	20 37
Corby George Street	a	11 05	13 05	15 05	17 05	19 05	21 05
Kettering Library	a	11 35	13 35	15 35	17 35	19 35	21 33

Mondays to Saturdays

		GR	GR	GR	GR	GR	GR	GR	GR	GR	GR	GR	GR	GR	GR	GR
Kettering Library	d	05 30	06 00	07 00	08 15	09 15	10 15	11 15	12 15	13 15	14 15	15 15	16 15	17 20	18 20	19 20
Corby George Street	d	05 55	06 25	07 25	08 40	09 40	10 40	11 40	12 40	13 40	14 40	15 40	16 40	17 45	18 45	19a45
Oundle Market Place	d	06 23	06 53	07 53	09 08	10 08	11 08	12 08	13 08	14 08	15 08	16 08	17 08	18 13	19 13	20 13
Peterborough §	a	06 40	07 25	08 25	09 30	10 30	11 30	12 30	13 30	14 30	15 30	16 30	17 30	18 35	19 40	20 45

Sundays

		GR	GR	GR	GR	GR	GR
Kettering Library	d	08 15	10 15	12 15	14 15	16 15	18 15
Corby George Street	d	08 40	10 40	12 40	14 40	16 40	18 40
Oundle Market Place	d	09 08	11 08	13 08	15 00	17 08	19 08
Peterborough §	a	09 40	11 40	13 40	15 40	17 40	19 40

For general notes see front of timetable
For details of catering facilities see Directory of Train Operators

§ Peterborough Queensgate Bus Station

Table 26D

Mondays to Fridays

Newark — Lincoln
Bus Service

		GR	GR	GR	GR	GR	GR	GR
Newark North Gate	d	14 37	16 36	17 36	18 45	19 45	22 55	23 27
Witham St Hughes	a	14 50	16 50	17 50	19 00	20 00	23 10	23 40
Hykeham Crossroads	a	14 58	16 58	17 58	19 05	20 05	23 18	23 48
Lincoln Bus Station	a	15 15	17 15	18 15	19 23	20 23	23 35	00 05

Mondays to Fridays

		GR	GR	GR	GR	GR	GR	GR
Lincoln Bus Station	d	05 20	05 45	06 20	07 20	11 45	14 15	16 35
Hykeham Crossroads	d	05 37	06 02	06 37	07 37	12 02	14 32	16 47
Witham St Hughes	d	05 43	06 07	06 43	07 45	12 10	14 40	16 55
Newark North Gate	a	05 55	06 15	06 55	08 00	12 25	14 55	17 10

For general notes see front of timetable
For details of catering facilities see Directory of Train Operators

Table 26E

Mondays to Fridays

Doncaster — Barnsley

Bus Service

		GR	GR	GR	GR	GR	GR	GR	GR	GR	GR	GR	GR	GR	GR	GR	GR
Doncaster Interchange	d	07 05	07 25	08 00	09 10	10 10	11 10	12 10	13 10	14 10	15 10	16 10	17 10	18 10	19 10	20 10	21 10
Goldthorpe Police Station	a	07 31	07 45	08 26	09 36	10 36	11 36	12 36	13 36	14 36	15 36	16 36	17 36	18 36	19 36	20 36	21 36
Darfield Roundabout	a	07 38	07 51	08 33	09 43	10 43	11 43	12 43	13 43	14 43	15 43	16 43	17 43	18 43	19 43	20 43	21 43
Barnsley West Bus Station	a	07 45	08 15	08 50	09 57	10 57	11 57	12 57	13 57	14 57	15 57	16 57	17 57	18 57	19 57	20 57	21 57

Saturdays

		GR	GR	GR	GR	GR	GR	GR	GR	GR	GR	GR	GR	GR	GR	GR
Doncaster Interchange	d	07 05	07 25	09 10	10 10	11 10	12 10	13 10	14 10	15 10	16 10	17 10	18 10	19 10	20 10	21 10
Goldthorpe Police Station	a	07 31	07 45	09 36	10 36	11 36	12 36	13 36	14 36	15 36	16 36	17 36	18 36	19 36	20 36	21 36
Darfield Roundabout	a	07 38	07 51	09 43	10 43	11 43	12 43	13 43	14 43	15 43	16 43	17 43	18 43	19 43	20 43	21 43
Barnsley West Bus Station	a	07 45	08 15	09 57	10 57	11 57	12 57	13 57	14 57	15 57	16 57	17 57	18 57	19 57	20 57	21 57

Mondays to Fridays

		GR	GR	GR	GR	GR	GR	GR	GR	GR	GR	GR	GR	GR	GR	GR
Barnsley West Bus Station	d	06 05	07 05	07 50	09 15	10 15	11 15	12 15	13 15	14 15	15 15	16 15	17 15	18 15	19 15	20 15
Darfield Roundabout	d	06 19	07 19	08 04	09 29	10 29	11 29	12 29	13 29	14 29	15 29	16 29	17 29	18 29	19 29	20 29
Goldthorpe Police Station	d	06 26	07 26	08 11	09 36	10 36	11 36	12 36	13 36	14 36	15 36	16 36	17 36	18 36	19 36	20 36
Doncaster Interchange	a	06 52	07 52	08 47	10 02	11 02	12 02	13 02	14 02	15 02	16 02	17 02	18 02	19 02	20 02	21 02

Saturdays

		GR	GR	GR	GR	GR	GR	GR	GR	GR	GR	GR	GR	GR	GR
Barnsley West Bus Station	d	06 05	08 15	09 15	10 15	11 15	12 15	13 15	14 15	15 15	16 15	17 15	18 15	19 15	20 15
Darfield Roundabout	d	06 19	08 29	09 29	10 29	11 29	12 29	13 29	14 29	15 29	16 29	17 29	18 29	19 29	20 29
Goldthorpe Police Station	d	06 26	08 36	09 36	10 36	11 36	12 36	13 36	14 36	15 36	16 36	17 36	18 36	19 36	20 36
Doncaster Interchange	a	06 52	09 02	10 02	11 02	12 02	13 02	14 02	15 02	16 02	17 02	18 02	19 02	20 02	21 02

For general notes see front of timetable
For details of catering facilities see
Directory of Train Operators

No Sunday Service

Table 26F

Mondays to Fridays

Doncaster — Robin Hood Airport
Bus Service

		GR	GR	GR	GR	GR	GR	GR	GR	GR	GR	GR	GR	GR	GR	GR	GR	GR	GR
Doncaster Interchange	d	05 35	06 35	07 35	08 35	09 35	10 35	11 35	12 35	13 35	14 35	15 35	16 35	17 35	18 35	19 35	20 35	21 35	22 35
Robin Hood Airport	a	06 00	07 00	08 00	09 00	10 00	11 00	12 00	13 00	14 00	15 00	16 00	17 00	18 00	19 00	20 00	21 00	22 00	23 00

Saturdays

		GR	GR	GR	GR	GR	GR	GR	GR	GR	GR	GR	GR	GR	GR	GR	GR	GR	GR
Doncaster Interchange	d	05 35	06 35	07 35	08 35	09 35	10 35	11 35	12 35	13 35	14 35	15 35	16 35	17 35	18 35	19 35	20 35	21 35	22 35
Robin Hood Airport	a	06 00	07 00	08 00	09 00	10 00	11 00	12 00	13 00	14 00	15 00	16 00	17 00	18 00	19 00	20 00	21 00	22 00	23 00

Sundays

		GR	GR	GR	GR	GR	GR	GR	GR	GR	GR
Doncaster Interchange	d	08 35	09 35	10 35	11 35	12 35	13 35	14 35	15 35	16 35	17 35
Robin Hood Airport	a	09 00	10 00	11 00	12 00	13 00	14 00	15 00	16 00	17 00	18 00

Mondays to Fridays

		GR	GR	GR	GR	GR	GR	GR	GR	GR	GR	GR	GR	GR	GR	GR	GR	GR	GR
Robin Hood Airport	d	06 05	07 05	08 05	09 05	10 05	11 05	12 05	13 05	14 05	15 05	16 05	17 05	18 05	19 05	20 05	21 05	22 05	23 05
Doncaster Interchange	a	06 30	07 30	08 30	09 30	10 30	11 30	12 30	13 30	14 30	15 30	16 30	17 30	18 30	19 30	20 30	21 30	22 30	23 30

Saturdays

		GR	GR	GR	GR	GR	GR	GR	GR	GR	GR	GR	GR	GR	GR	GR	GR	GR	GR
Robin Hood Airport	d	06 05	07 05	08 05	09 05	10 05	11 05	12 05	13 05	14 05	15 05	16 05	17 05	18 05	19 05	20 05	21 05	22 05	23 05
Doncaster Interchange	a	06 30	07 30	08 30	09 30	10 30	11 30	12 30	13 30	14 30	15 30	16 30	17 30	18 30	19 30	20 30	21 30	22 30	23 30

Sundays

		GR	GR	GR	GR	GR	GR	GR	GR	GR	GR
Robin Hood Airport	d	09 05	10 05	11 05	12 05	13 05	14 05	15 05	16 05	17 05	18 05
Doncaster Interchange	a	09 30	10 30	11 30	12 30	13 30	14 30	15 30	16 30	17 30	18 30

For general notes see front of timetable
For details of catering facilities see
Directory of Train Operators

Mondays to Fridays

York — Pickering and Whitby

Bus Service

		GR	GR	GR	GR	GR	GR	GR	GR	GR	GR
York	d	08 15	09 15	10 22	11 20	12 22	13 20	15 22	16 24	17 29	18 29
Eden Camp	a	09 15	10 20	11 17	12 15	13 17	14 15	16 17	17 20	18 25	19 25
Flamingo Land	a		10 33								
Pickering Eastgate	a	09 31	10 43	11 31	12 31	13 31	14 25	16 31	17 36	18 41	19 35
Whitby Bus Station	a	10 29		12 29		14 29		17 29		19 39	

Saturdays

		GR	GR	GR	GR	GR	GR	GR	GR	GR	GR
York	d	08 20	09 20	10 22	11 20	12 22	13 20	15 22	16 20	17 25	18 25
Eden Camp	a	09 15	10 20	11 17	12 15	13 17	14 15	16 17	17 15	18 20	19 20
Flamingo Land	a		10 33								
Pickering Eastgate	a	09 31	10 43	11 31	12 31	13 31	14 25	16 31	17 31	18 36	19 30
Whitby Bus Station	a	10 29		12 29		14 29		17 29		19 34	

Sundays

		GR A	GR	GR
York	d	09 10	09 20	10 20
Eden Camp	a	10 15	10 15	11 15
Flamingo Land	a		10 28	11 28
Pickering Eastgate	a	10 30	10 40	11 40
Whitby Bus Station	a	11 28		12 38

Mondays to Fridays

		GR	GR	GR B	GR	GR	GR C	GR	GR	GR	GR
Whitby Bus Station	d				10 45	12 45		14 45		17 00	
Pickering Eastgate	d	07 10	08 42	09 32	11 42	13 42	14 40	15 42		17 42	18 02
Flamingo Land	d								16 45		18 20
Eden Camp	d	07 20	08 58	09 48	11 58	13 58	14 50	15 58	16 58	17 52	18 33
York	a	08 13	09 53	10 53	12 53	14 53	15 53	16 53	17 53	18 53	19 28

Saturdays

		GR	GR	GR B	GR	GR	GR C	GR	GR	GR	GR
Whitby Bus Station	d				10 45	12 45		14 45		17 00	
Pickering Eastgate	d	07 15	08 42	09 32	11 42	13 42	14 40	15 42		17 42	18 02
Flamingo Land	d								16 45		18 20
Eden Camp	d	07 25	08 58	09 48	11 58	13 58	14 50	15 58	16 58	17 52	18 33
York	a	08 18	09 53	10 53	12 53	14 53	15 53	16 53	17 53	18 53	19 28

Sundays

		GR D	GR	GR
Whitby Bus Station	d	13 10		18 10
Pickering Eastgate	d	14 07		19 07
Flamingo Land	d		18 20	
Eden Camp	d	14 23	18 31	19 23
York	a	15 33	19 23	20 23

For general notes see front of timetable
For details of catering facilities see Directory of Train Operators

A Also stops at Castle Howard 0948
B Also stops at Castle Howard 1015
C Also stops at Castle Howard 1515
D Also stops at Castle Howard 1455

Darlington → Richmond and Catterick

Bus Service

		GR	GR	GR		GR	GR	GR		GR	GR	GR		GR	GR	GR		GR	GR	GR		GR	GR	GR	GR
Darlington	d	06 50	07 28	08 00		08 36	09 00	09 20		09 40	10 00	10 20		10 40	11 00	11 20		11 40	12 00	12 20		12 40	13 00	13 20	13 40
Richmond (Market)	a	07 26	08 00	08 36		09 12	09 36	09 52		10 12	10 36	10 52		11 12	11 36	11 52		12 12	12 36	12 52		13 12	13 36	13 52	14 12
Catterick Garrison Tesco	a							10 08				11 08				12 08				13 08				14 08	
Catterick Camp Centre	a	07 43	08 15	08 53		09 27	09 53			10 27	10 53			11 27	11 53			12 27	12 53			13 27	13 53		14 27
Catterick Garrison Kemmel	a	07 50	08 22	09 00		09 34	10 00			10 34	11 00			11 34	12 00			12 34	13 00			13 34	14 00		14 34

		GR		GR	GR	GR		GR	GR	GR		GR	GR	GR		GR	GR	GR	GR	GR	GR	GR	GR		
Darlington	d	14 00		14 20	14 40	15 00		15 20	15 40	16 00		16 20	16 40	17 00		17 20	17 40	18 00	18 30	19 00	20 00	21 00	22 00		
Richmond (Market)	a	14 36		14 52	15 12	15 36		15 52	16 12	16 36		16 52	17 12	17 36		17 52	18 12	18 36	19 04	19 36	20 36	21 36	22 36		
Catterick Garrison Tesco	a			15 08				16 08				17 08				18 08		18 51		19 51	20 51	21 51	22 51		
Catterick Camp Centre	a	14 53			15 27	15 53			16 27	16 53			17 27	17 53			18 27	18 53		19 53	20 53	21 53	22 53		
Catterick Garrison Kemmel	a	15 00			15 34	16 00			16 34	17 00			17 34	18 00			18 34	19 00		20 00	21 00	22 00	23 00		

Saturdays

		GR	GR		GR	GR		GR	GR		GR	GR		GR	GR		GR	GR		GR	GR		GR	GR	GR
Darlington	d	08 00	08 36		09 00	09 40		10 00	10 20		10 40	11 00		11 20	11 40		12 00	12 20		12 40	13 00		13 20	13 40	14 00
Richmond (Market)	a	08 36	09 12		09 36	10 12		10 36	10 52		11 12	11 36		11 52	12 12		12 36	12 52		13 12	13 36		13 52	14 12	14 36
Catterick Garrison Tesco	a								11 08					12 08				13 08					14 08		
Catterick Camp Centre	a	08 53	09 27		09 53	10 27		10 53			11 27	11 53			12 27		12 53			13 27	13 53			14 27	14 53
Catterick Garrison Kemmel	a	09 00	09 34		10 00	10 34		11 00			11 34	12 00			12 34		13 00			13 34	14 00			14 34	15 00

		GR		GR	GR		GR	GR		GR	GR		GR	GR		GR	GR	GR	GR	GR	GR	GR	GR		
Darlington	d	14 20		14 40	15 00		15 20	15 40		16 00	16 20		16 40	17 00		17 20	17 40	18 00	18 30	19 00	20 00	21 00	22 00		
Richmond (Market)	a	14 52		15 12	15 36		15 52	16 12		16 36	16 52		17 12	17 36		17 52	18 12	18 36	19 04	19 36	20 36	21 36	22 36		
Catterick Garrison Tesco	a	15 08					16 08				17 08					18 08		18 51		19 51	20 51	21 51	22 51		
Catterick Camp Centre	a			15 27	15 53			16 27		16 53			17 27	17 53			18 27	18 53		19 53	20 53	21 53	22 53		
Catterick Garrison Kemmel	a			15 34	16 00			16 34		17 00			17 34	18 00			18 34	19 00		20 00	21 00	22 00	23 00		

Sundays

		GR	GR	GR	GR	GR	GR	GR		GR	GR	GR	GR	GR	GR	GR	GR	GR	GR	GR	GR	GR	GR		
Darlington	d	10 00	10 30	11 00	11 30	12 00	12 30	13 00		13 30	14 00	14 30	15 00	15 30	16 00	16 30	17 00	17 30	18 00	19 00	20 00	21 00	22 00		
Richmond (Market)	a	10 36	11 00	11 36	12 00	12 36	13 00	13 36		14 00	14 36	15 00	15 36	16 00	16 36	17 00	17 36	18 00	18 36	19 36	20 36	21 36	22 36		
Catterick Garrison Tesco	a	10 51	11 13	11 51	12 13	12 51	13 13	13 51		14 13	14 51	15 13	15 51	16 13	16 51	17 13		18 13							
Catterick Camp Centre	a	10 53		11 53		12 53		13 53			14 53		15 53		16 53		17 53		18 53	19 53	20 53	21 53	22 53		
Catterick Garrison Kemmel	a	11 00		12 00		13 00		14 00			15 00		16 00		17 00		18 00		19 00	20 00	21 00	22 00	23 00		

For general notes see front of timetable
For details of catering facilities see Directory of Train Operators

Table 26H

Mondays to Fridays

Catterick and Richmond → Darlington

Bus Service

		GR	GR	GR	GR		GR	GR	GR	GR		GR	GR	GR	GR		GR	GR	GR	GR		GR	GR	GR	GR
Catterick Garrison Kemmel	d		06 27	06 58	07 22		07 50		08 22	09 00			09 35	10 00			10 35	11 00		11 35		12 00		12 35	13 00
Catterick Camp Centre	d		06 34	07 04	07 29		07 56		08 29	09 06			09 42	10 06			10 42	11 06		11 42		12 06		12 42	13 06
Catterick Garrison Tesco	d							08 17				09 29			10 29				11 29				12 29		
Richmond (Market)	d	06 16	06 53	07 20	07 47		08 12	08 37	08 52	09 25		09 44	10 00	10 25	10 44		11 00	11 25	11 44	12 00		12 25	12 44	13 00	13 25
Darlington	a	06 49	07 26	07 55	08 27		08 52	09 12	09 27	09 55		10 14	10 35	10 55	11 14		11 35	11 55	12 14	12 35		12 55	13 14	13 35	13 55

		GR	GR		GR	GR	GR	GR		GR	GR	GR	GR		GR	GR	GR	GR		GR	GR	GR	GR		
Catterick Garrison Kemmel	d		13 35		14 00		14 35	15 00			15 35	16 00			16 35	17 00		18 00		19 00	20 00	21 00	22 00		
Catterick Camp Centre	d		13 42		14 06		14 42	15 06			15 42	16 06			16 42	17 06		18 06		19 06	20 06	21 06	22 06		
Catterick Garrison Tesco	d	13 29				14 29				15 29			16 29				17 42			19 08	20 08	21 08	22 08		
Richmond (Market)	d	13 44	14 00		14 25	14 44	15 00	15 25		15 44	16 00	16 25	16 44		17 00	17 25	17 59	18 25		19 25	20 25	21 25	22 25		
Darlington	a	14 14	14 35		14 55	15 14	15 35	15 55		16 14	16 35	16 55	17 14		17 35	18 00	18 29	19 00		20 00	21 00	22 00	23 00		

Saturdays

		GR	GR	GR		GR	GR	GR		GR	GR	GR		GR	GR	GR		GR	GR	GR		GR	GR	GR	GR
Catterick Garrison Kemmel	d			07 55			08 22	09 00			09 35	10 00			10 35	11 00			11 35	12 00			12 35	13 00	
Catterick Camp Centre	d			08 01			08 29	09 06			09 42	10 06			10 42	11 06			11 42	12 06			12 42	13 06	
Catterick Garrison Tesco	d					08 17				09 29				10 29				11 29				12 29			13 29
Richmond (Market)	d	07 21	07 54	08 17		08 37	08 52	09 25		09 44	10 00	10 25		10 44	11 00	11 25		11 44	12 00	12 25		12 44	13 00	13 25	13 44
Darlington	a	07 54	08 27	08 52		09 12	09 27	09 55		10 14	10 35	10 55		11 14	11 35	11 55		12 14	12 35	12 55		13 14	13 35	13 55	14 14

		GR		GR	GR	GR		GR	GR	GR		GR	GR	GR		GR	GR	GR		GR	GR	GR	GR		
Catterick Garrison Kemmel	d	13 35		14 00		14 35		15 00		15 35		16 00		16 35		17 00		18 00		19 00	20 00	21 00	22 00		
Catterick Camp Centre	d	13 42		14 06		14 42		15 06		15 42		16 06		16 42		17 06		18 06		19 06	20 06	21 06	22 06		
Catterick Garrison Tesco	d				14 29				15 29				16 29				17 42			19 08	20 08	21 08	22 08		
Richmond (Market)	d	14 00		14 25	14 44	15 00		15 25	15 44	16 00		16 25	16 44	17 00		17 25	17 57	18 25		19 25	20 25	21 25	22 25		
Darlington	a	14 35		14 55	15 14	15 35		15 55	16 14	16 35		16 55	17 14	17 35		18 00	18 27	19 00		20 00	21 00	22 00	23 00		

Sundays

		GR	GR	GR	GR	GR	GR	GR	GR	GR	GR	GR	GR	GR	GR	GR	GR	GR	GR	GR	GR	GR	GR		
Catterick Garrison Kemmel	d	09 00		10 00		11 00		12 00		13 00		14 00		15 00		16 00		17 00	18 00	19 00	20 00	21 00	22 00		
Catterick Camp Centre	d	09 06		10 06		11 06		12 06		13 06		14 06		15 06		16 06		17 06	18 06	19 06	20 06	21 06	22 06		
Catterick Garrison Tesco	d	09 08	09 43	10 08	10 43	11 08	11 43	12 08	12 43	13 08	13 43	14 08	14 43	15 08	15 43	16 08	16 43	17 08							
Richmond (Market)	d	09 25	10 00	10 25	11 00	11 25	12 00	12 25	13 00	13 25	14 00	14 25	15 00	15 25	16 00	16 25	17 00	17 25	18 25	19 25	20 25	21 25	22 25		
Darlington	a	10 00	10 30	11 00	11 30	12 00	12 30	13 00	13 30	14 00	14 30	15 00	15 30	16 00	16 30	17 00	17 30	18 00	19 00	20 00	21 00	22 00	23 00		

For general notes see front of timetable
For details of catering facilities see Directory of Train Operators

Table 26J

Mondays to Fridays

Darlington — Durham Tees Valley Airport

Bus Service

	GR	GR	GR	GR	GR	GR	GR	GR	GR	GR	GR	GR	GR	GR	GR	GR	GR	GR	GR	GR	GR	GR	GR	GR	GR	GR
Darlington .... d	07 00	08 00	09 00	10 00	10 30	11 00	11 30	12 00	12 30	13 00	13 30	14 00	14 30	15 00	15 30	16 00	16 30	17 00	17 30	18 00	18 30	19 00	19 30	20 00	21 00	22 00
Tees Valley Airport a	07 25	08 25	09 25	10 25	10 55	11 25	11 55	12 25	12 55	13 25	13 55	14 25	14 55	15 25	15 55	16 25	16 55	17 25	17 55	18 25	18 55	19 25	19 55	20 25	21 25	22 25

Saturdays

	GR	GR	GR	GR	GR	GR	GR	GR	GR	GR	GR	GR	GR	GR	GR	GR	GR	GR	GR	GR	GR	GR	GR	GR	GR	GR
Darlington .... d	07 00	08 00	09 00	10 00	10 30	11 00	11 30	12 00	12 30	13 00	13 30	14 00	14 30	15 00	15 30	16 00	16 30	17 00	17 30	18 00	18 30	19 00	19 30	20 00	21 00	22 00
Tees Valley Airport a	07 25	08 25	09 25	10 25	10 55	11 25	11 55	12 25	12 55	13 25	13 55	14 25	14 55	15 25	15 55	16 25	16 55	17 25	17 55	18 25	18 55	19 25	19 55	20 25	21 25	22 25

Sundays

	GR	GR	GR		GR	GR	GR		GR	GR	GR		GR	GR	GR		GR	GR	GR	GR	GR	GR	GR	GR		
Darlington .... d	09 00	10 00	11 00	.....	12 00	12 30	13 00	.....	13 30	14 00	14 30	.....	15 00	15 30	16 00	.....	16 30	17 00	17 30	18 00	19 00	20 00	21 00	22 00	.....	.....
Tees Valley Airport a	09 25	10 25	11 25	.	12 25	12 55	13 25	.	13 55	14 25	14 55	.	15 25	15 55	16 25	.	16 55	17 25	17 55	18 25	19 25	20 25	21 25	22 25	.	.

Mondays to Fridays

	GR	GR	GR	GR	GR	GR	GR	GR	GR	GR	GR	GR	GR	GR	GR	GR	GR	GR	GR	GR	GR	GR	GR	GR	GR	GR
Tees Valley Airport ... d	07 35	08 35	09 35	10 35	11 05	11 35	12 05	12 35	13 05	13 35	14 05	14 35	15 05	15 35	16 05	16 35	17 05	17 35	18 05	18 35	19 05	19 35	20 05	20 35	21 35	22 35
Darlington . . . a	07 55	08 55	09 55	10 55	11 25	11 55	12 25	12 55	13 25	13 55	14 25	14 55	15 25	15 55	16 25	16 55	17 25	17 55	18 25	18 55	19 25	19 55	20 25	20 55	21 55	22 55

Saturdays

	GR	GR	GR	GR	GR	GR	GR	GR	GR	GR	GR	GR	GR	GR	GR	GR	GR	GR	GR	GR	GR	GR	GR	GR	GR	GR
Tees Valley Airport ... d	07 35	08 35	09 35	10 35	11 05	11 35	12 05	12 35	13 05	13 35	14 05	14 35	15 05	15 35	16 05	16 35	17 05	17 35	18 05	18 35	19 05	19 35	20 05	20 35	21 35	22 35
Darlington . . . a	07 55	08 55	09 55	10 55	11 25	11 55	12 25	12 55	13 25	13 55	14 25	14 55	15 25	15 55	16 25	16 55	17 25	17 55	18 25	18 55	19 25	19 55	20 25	20 55	21 55	22 55

Sundays

	GR	GR	GR		GR	GR	GR		GR	GR	GR		GR	GR	GR		GR	GR	GR	GR	GR	GR	GR	GR		
Tees Valley Airport ... d	09 35	10 35	11 35	.....	12 35	13 05	13 35	.....	14 05	14 35	15 05	.....	15 35	16 05	16 35	.....	17 05	17 35	18 05	18 35	19 35	20 35	21 35	22 35	.....	.....
Darlington . . . a	09 55	10 55	11 55	.	12 55	13 25	13 55	.	14 25	14 55	15 25	.	15 55	16 25	16 55	.	17 25	17 55	18 25	18 55	19 55	20 55	21 55	22 55	.	.

For general notes see front of timetable
For details of catering facilities see
Directory of Train Operators

Mondays to Fridays

Berwick-upon-Tweed — Scottish Border Towns
Bus Service

This service is operated by First Lowland under contract to Scottish Borders Council. Telephone: 01835 824000

		VT	VT	VT	VT	VT	VT	VT	VT	VT
Berwick-upon-Tweed	d	06 57	08 17	09 47	10 47	12 52	15 07	17 47	18 37	20 22
Duns	a	07 30	08 50	10 20	11 20	13 25	15 40	18 20	19 10	20 55
Earlston	a	08 08	09 38	10 58	12 01	14 03	16 29	18 58	19 48	21 33
Melrose	a	08 20	09 50	11 10	12 13	14 15	16 40	19 10	20 00	21 45
Galashiels Bus Station	a	08 37	10 05	11 25	12 28	14 30	16 55	19 25	20 15	22 00

Saturdays

This service is operated by First Lowland under contract to Scottish Borders Council. Telephone: 01835 824000

		VT	VT	VT	VT	VT	VT
Berwick-upon-Tweed	d	08 27	10 47	12 52	15 17	17 17	19 17
Duns	a	09 00	11 20	13 25	15 50	17 50	19 50
Earlston	a	09 38	11 58	14 03	16 28	18 28	20 28
Melrose	a	09 50	12 10	14 15	16 40	18 40	20 40
Galashiels Bus Station	a	10 05	12 25	14 30	16 55	18 55	20 55

Sundays

This service is operated by First Lowland under contract to Scottish Borders Council. Telephone: 01835 824000

		VT	VT	VT	VT	VT	VT
Berwick-upon-Tweed	d	10 47	12 52	15 17	17 42	19 07	20 32
Duns	a	11 20	13 25	15 50	18 30	19 55	21 05
Earlston	a	11 58	14 03	16 28	19 08	20 33	21 43
Melrose	a	12 10	14 15	16 40	19 20	20 45	21 55
Galashiels Bus Station	a	12 25	14 30	16 55	19 35	21 00	22 10

Mondays to Fridays

This service is operated by First Lowland under contract to Scottish Borders Council. Telephone: 01835 824000

		VT	VT	VT	VT	VT	VT	VT	VT
Galashiels Bus Station	d	06 30	07 40	08 15	10 50	12 50	14 35	16 32	17 25
Melrose	d	06 45	07 55	08 30	11 05	13 05	14 50	16 47	17 40
Earlston	d	06 57	08 07	08 42	11 16	13 16	15 07	16 59	17 52
Duns	d	07 35	08 55	09 25	11 55	13 55	15 55	17 37	18 30
Berwick-upon-Tweed	a	08 06	09 26	10 03	12 26	14 28	16 26	18 10	19 01

Saturdays

This service is operated by First Lowland under contract to Scottish Borders Council. Telephone: 01835 824000

		VT	VT	VT	VT	VT	VT
Galashiels Bus Station	d	06 40	08 20	10 50	12 50	14 50	17 25
Melrose	d	06 55	08 35	11 05	13 05	15 05	17 40
Earlston	d	07 07	08 47	11 16	13 16	15 16	17 52
Duns	d	07 45	09 30	11 55	13 55	15 55	18 30
Berwick-upon-Tweed	a	08 20	10 03	12 26	14 28	16 26	19 01

Sundays

This service is operated by First Lowland under contract to Scottish Borders Council. Telephone: 01835 824000

		VT	VT	VT	VT	VT	VT
Galashiels Bus Station	d	08 50	10 50	12 35	14 50	16 35	18 30
Melrose	d	09 05	11 05	12 50	15 05	16 50	18 45
Earlston	d	09 16	11 16	13 02	15 17	17 02	18 57
Duns	d	09 55	11 55	13 40	15 55	17 40	19 35
Berwick-upon-Tweed	a	10 28	12 28	14 28	16 28	18 28	20 23

For general notes see front of timetable
For details of catering facilities see Directory of Train Operators

Table 27

Mondays to Fridays

Cleethorpes → Lincoln → Newark → Nottingham

Network Diagram - see first page of Table 18

Miles	Miles			EM	EM	EM	EM A	EM	EM B	EM	EM B	EM	EM B	EM B	EM	EM B	EM B	EM C
0	—	**Cleethorpes**	d		05 51													
3¼	—	**Grimsby Town**	d		05 58			07 03				09 28			11 28			
11¼	—	Habrough	d		06 08			07 13				09 38			11 38			
17¾	—	Barnetby	d		06 17			07 22				09 47			11 47			
32¼	—	Market Rasen	d		06 34			07 39				10 03			12 03			
47	—	**Lincoln**	a		06 52			07 57				10 22			12 22			
—	—		d	05 23	06 54	07 10	07 29	07 59	08 34	09 10	09 31	10 23	10 36	11 43	12 23	12 31	13 35	14 04
51	—	Hykeham	d	05 31			07 37		08 42		09 39		10 44			12 39	13 43	
55¾	—	Swinderby	d	05 37			07 43		08 48		09 45		10 50			12 45	13 49	
58½	0	Collingham	d	05 41			07 48		08 53		09 50		10 54			12 49	13 53	
—	5	**Newark North Gate** 7	a	05 51	07 17			08 22		09 33		10 49			12 49			14 28
—	—	London Kings Cross 15	⊖ a	*07 30*	*08 48*			*09 51*		*11 10*		*12 25*			*15 05*			*16 46*
—	—	**Newark North Gate** 7	d	06 00														
63½	—	**Newark Castle**	d	06 08		07 33	07 57		09 05		09 58		11 03	12 05		12 58	14 03	
67	—	Rolleston	d	06 15		07 40	08 04				10 05		11 10			13 05		
68	—	Fiskerton	d	06 17		07 42	08 06				10 07					13 07		
69¾	—	Bleasby	d	06 21		07 45	08 10				10 11					13 10		
70¾	—	Thurgarton	d	06 24		07 48	08 13				10 14					13 13		
71½	—	Lowdham	d	06 28		07 52	08 17				10 18		11 17			13 17		
75¾	—	Burton Joyce	d	06 32		07 56	08 21				10 22		11 21			13 21		
77¾	—	Carlton	d	06 35		08 00	08 24				10 25					13 25		
80¾	—	**Nottingham** 8	a	06 48		08 12	08 32		09 30		10 33		11 31	12 28		13 32	14 28	

		EM B	EM	EM B	EM B	EM	EM	EM	EM B	EM	EM D	EM	EM
Cleethorpes	d											21 14	
Grimsby Town	d		13 52			16 03				18 30		21 21	
Habrough	d		14 02			16 12				18 40		21 30	
Barnetby	d		14 11			16 21				18 49		21 39	
Market Rasen	d		14 27			16 36				19 06		21 54	
Lincoln	a		14 46			16 54				19 24		22 15	
	d	14 38	14 47	15 32	16 40	16 56	17 29	18 17	18 33	19 26	20 43		22 31
Hykeham	d			15 40			17 37				20 51		22 39
Swinderby	d						17 44				20 57		22 45
Collingham	d			15 49		17 11	17 49	18 32			21 01		22 49
Newark North Gate 7	a		15 11			17 22		18 42		19 50			
London Kings Cross 15	⊖ a		*17 04*			*18 48*		*20 18*		*21 33*			
Newark North Gate 7	d												
Newark Castle	d	15 01		15 58	17 05		17 59		18 55		21 10		22 58
Rolleston	d	15 08		16 05			18 06		19 02		21 17		23 05
Fiskerton	d	15 10					18 08		19 04		21 19		23 07
Bleasby	d	15 13					18 12		19 08		21 22		23 10
Thurgarton	d	15 16					18 15		19 11				
Lowdham	d	15 20		16 13			18 19		19 15		21 27		23 15
Burton Joyce	d	15 24		16 17			18 23		19 19		21 31		23 19
Carlton	d	15 28		16 20			18 27		19 23		21 35		23 23
Nottingham 8	a	15 35		16 30	17 28		18 40		19 30		21 47		23 35

Saturdays

		EM	EM	EM A	EM	EM B	EM	EM B	EM	EM B	EM B	EM	EM B	EM B
Cleethorpes	d													
Grimsby Town	d				06 59				09 28			11 30		
Habrough	d				07 09				09 37			11 39		
Barnetby	d				07 18				09 46			11 48		
Market Rasen	d				07 33				10 01			12 03		
Lincoln	a				07 52				10 21			12 21		
	d	05 50	06 55	07 30	07 54	08 34	09 10	09 23	10 23	10 36	11 41	12 23	12 31	13 35
Hykeham	d	05 58	07 03	07 38		08 42		09 31		10 44			12 39	13 43
Swinderby	d	06 04	07 09	07 44		08 48		09 37		10 50			12 45	13 49
Collingham	d	06 08	07 13	07 48		08 53		09 42		10 54			12 49	13 53
Newark North Gate 7	a		07 23		08 15		09 33		10 45			12 45		
London Kings Cross 15	⊖ a		*09 18*		*09 51*		*11 32*		*12 24*			*14 27*		
Newark North Gate 7	d		07 27											
Newark Castle	d	06 17	07 35	07 57		09 05		09 54		11 04	12 07		12 58	14 04
Rolleston	d	06 24	07 42	08 04		09 12		10 01		11 10			13 05	
Fiskerton	d	06 26	07 44	08 06				10 03					13 07	
Bleasby	d	06 29	07 47	08 09				10 07					13 10	
Thurgarton	d	06 32	07 50	08 12				10 10					13 13	
Lowdham	d	06 36	07 54	08 16				10 14		11 18			13 17	
Burton Joyce	d	06 40	07 58	08 20				10 18		11 22			13 21	
Carlton	d	06 44	08 02	08 24				10 21		11 25			13 25	
Nottingham 8	a	06 56	08 15	08 31		09 32		10 29		11 33	12 33		13 32	14 31

For general notes see front of timetable
For details of catering facilities see Directory of Train Operators

A From Sleaford (Table 18) to Leicester (Table 53)
B To Leicester (Table 53)
C From Peterborough (Table 18)
D From Sleaford (Table 18)

Table 27

Saturdays

Cleethorpes → Lincoln → Newark → Nottingham

Network Diagram - see first page of Table 18

		EM	EM A	EM A	EM	EM A	EM A	EM	EM	EM	EM	EM	EM
Cleethorpes	d												
Grimsby Town	d	13 25			15 28					18 06		19 28	
Habrough	d	13 35			15 37					18 16		19 38	
Barnetby	d	13 44			15 46					18 26		19 47	
Market Rasen	d	13 59			16 01					18 42		20 02	
Lincoln	a	14 17			16 19					19 01		20 20	
	d	14 19	14 32	15 35	16 22	16 40	17 35	18 09	18 43	19 10	19 40		20 41
Hykeham	d			15 43			17 43				19 48		20 49
Swinderby	d						17 49				19 54		20 55
Collingham	d			15 53			17 53				19 58		20 59
Newark North Gate 7	a	14 44			16 52			18 32		19 34			21 09
London Kings Cross 15 ⊖	a	*16 30*			*18 28*			*20 12*		*21 15*			*22 47*
Newark North Gate 7	d												21 13
Newark Castle	d		14 58	16 01		17 06	18 02		19 07		20 08		21 25
Rolleston	d		15 05	16 08			18 09				20 15		21 31
Fiskerton	d		15 07				18 11				20 17		21 33
Bleasby	d		15 11				18 15				20 21		21 36
Thurgarton	d		15 14				18 18				20 24		21 39
Lowdham	d		15 18	16 16			18 22				20 28		21 43
Burton Joyce	d		15 22	16 20			18 26				20 32		21 47
Carlton	d		15 25	16 23			18 29				20 35		21 51
Nottingham 8	a		15 33	16 31		17 30	18 36		19 33		20 51		22 03

Sundays

		EM	EM	EM	EM	EM	EM	EM	EM
Cleethorpes	d								
Grimsby Town	d								
Habrough	d								
Barnetby	d								
Market Rasen	d								
Lincoln	a								
	d	11 05	13 05	14 59	18 00	19 10	20 12	20 59	22 12
Hykeham	d			15 07	18 08	19 18	20 20	21 07	22 20
Swinderby	d			15 13	18 14	19 24	20 26	21 13	22 26
Collingham	d			15 17	18 18	19 28	20 30	21 17	22 30
Newark North Gate 7	a	11 28	13 28	15 27	18 29			21 27	
London Kings Cross 15 ⊖	a	*13 13*	*15 15*	*17 17*	*20 36*			*23 14*	
Newark North Gate 7	d			15 30	18 33			21 31	
Newark Castle	d			15 42	18 44	19 39	20 39	21 40	22 40
Rolleston	d			15 49	18 51	19 46	20 46		22 47
Fiskerton	d			15 51	18 53	19 48	20 48		22 49
Bleasby	d			15 54	18 56	19 51	20 51		22 53
Thurgarton	d			15 57	18 59	19 54	20 54		22 56
Lowdham	d			16 01	19 03	19 58	20 58		23 00
Burton Joyce	d			16 05	19 07	20 02	21 02		23 04
Carlton	d			16 09	19 11	20 06	21 06		23 07
Nottingham 8	a			16 22	19 22	20 18	21 18	22 08	23 20

For general notes see front of timetable
For details of catering facilities see
Directory of Train Operators

A To Leicester (Table 53)

Table 27

Mondays to Fridays

Nottingham → Newark → Lincoln → Cleethorpes

Network Diagram - see first page of Table 18

Miles	Miles			EM	EM	EM	EM	EM	EM A	EM B	EM	EM B	EM B	EM	EM B	EM C	EM B	EM
0	—	**Nottingham** 8	d		06 03	06 58			08 09	09 26		10 26	11 26		12 26		13 26	
3	—	Carlton	d		06 09	07 04			08 15			10 32	11 32				13 32	
5	—	Burton Joyce	d		06 12	07 08			08 18			10 35	11 35		12 34		13 35	
9¼	—	Lowdham	d		06 16	07 12			08 22			10 39			12 38		13 39	
10	—	Thurgarton	d		06 20				08 26			10 43					13 43	
11	—	Bleasby	d		06 23	07 17			08 29			10 46					13 46	
12¾	—	Fiskerton	d		06 27	07 20			08 33			10 50					13 50	
13¾	—	Rolleston	d		06 29	07 22			08 35			10 52	11 45		12 46		13 52	
17¼	—	**Newark Castle**	d		06 35	07 29			08 41	09 49		10 58	11 51		12 52		13 58	
—	—	**Newark North Gate** 7	a															
—	—	London Kings Cross 15 ⊖	d				*06 15*	*07 10*			*08 30*			*10 35*		*11 35*		*12 35*
—	0	**Newark North Gate** 7	d				07 46	08 35			09 57			12 07		13 05		14 33
22¼	5	Collingham	d		06 45	07 38	07 55					11 07			13 01			
25	—	Swinderby	d		06 49	07 43						11 12			13 06			
29¾	—	Hykeham	d		06 55	07 49	08 04					11 18			13 12			
33¾	—	**Lincoln**	a		07 11	08 03	08 13	09 00	09 10	10 18	10 21	11 32	12 19	12 30	13 26	13 28	14 28	14 56
—	—		d	05 57			08 17				10 22			12 38				14 57
48½	—	Market Rasen	d	06 13			08 34				10 39			12 55				15 14
63½	—	Barnetby	a	06 30			08 51				10 55			13 11				15 32
69½	—	Habrough	a	06 41			09 01				11 05			13 21				15 41
77½	—	**Grimsby Town**	a	06 57			09 15				11 20			13 35				15 56
80¾	—	**Cleethorpes**	a															

		EM B	EM C	EM B	EM D	EM	EM	EM B	EM	EM B	EM	EM	EM B	EM
Nottingham 8	d	14 26		15 25	16 25			17 21	17 46	18 25			20 24	22 22
Carlton	d			15 31				17 27	17 52	18 31			20 30	
Burton Joyce	d			15 34				17 30	17 56	18 34			20 33	
Lowdham	d	14 38		15 38				17 34	18 00	18 38			20 37	
Thurgarton	d			15 42				17 38		18 42			20 41	
Bleasby	d	14 43		15 45				17 41		18 45			20 44	
Fiskerton	d	14 46		15 49				17 45		18 49			20 48	
Rolleston	d			15 51				17 47	18 07	18 51			20 50	
Newark Castle	d	14 52		15 57	16 46			17 53	18 14	18 58			20 56	22 43
Newark North Gate 7	a												21 06	22 54
London Kings Cross 15 ⊖	d		*14 10*				*16 10*				*17 50*	*18 33*	*19 30*	*21 30*
Newark North Gate 7	d		15 37				17 34				19 24	20 00	21 11	22 58
Collingham	d			16 07				18 03	18 24	19 07			21 20	23 07
Swinderby	d			16 11					18 28	19 12			21 24	23 12
Hykeham	d			16 17				18 12	18 34	19 18			21 30	23 18
Lincoln	a	15 27	16 00	16 34	17 13		17 57	18 25	18 48	19 32	19 49	20 28	21 44	23 33
	d					17 18					19 52			
Market Rasen	d					17 35					20 09			
Barnetby	a					17 51					20 30			
Habrough	a					18 01					20 40			
Grimsby Town	a					18 14					20 52			
Cleethorpes	a										21 01			

Saturdays

		EM	EM	EM	EM	EM	EM	EM B	EM	EM B	EM	EM B	EM B	EM
Nottingham 8	d		06 03	07 00			08 06	09 27		10 25		11 24	12 26	
Carlton	d		06 09	07 06			08 12			10 31			12 32	
Burton Joyce	d		06 12	07 09			08 15			10 34			12 35	
Lowdham	d		06 16	07 13			08 19			10 38			12 39	
Thurgarton	d		06 20				08 23			10 42				
Bleasby	d		06 23	07 18			08 26			10 45				
Fiskerton	d		06 27	07 22			08 30			10 49				
Rolleston	d		06 29	07 24			08 32			10 51		11 41	12 47	
Newark Castle	d		06 35	07 30			08 38	09 49		10 57		11 51	12 53	
Newark North Gate 7	a													
London Kings Cross 15 ⊖	d					*07 00*			*08 10*		*10 10*			*12 10*
Newark North Gate 7	d					08 31			09 56		11 34			13 35
Collingham	d		06 45	07 41			08 47						13 02	
Swinderby	d		06 49	07 45			08 52						13 06	
Hykeham	d		06 55	07 51			08 58						13 12	
Lincoln	a		07 11	08 05		08 54	09 12	10 18	10 19	11 27	11 57	12 21	13 27	13 58
	d	05 57			08 29				10 21		11 59			14 06
Market Rasen	d	06 13			08 45				10 37		12 15			14 22
Barnetby	a	06 29			09 00				10 54		12 31			14 38
Habrough	a	06 39			09 09				11 03		12 41			14 47
Grimsby Town	a	06 53			09 23				11 17		12 55			15 01
Cleethorpes	a													

For general notes see front of timetable
For details of catering facilities see Directory of Train Operators

A From Worksop (Table 55)
B From Leicester (Table 53)
C To Peterborough (Table 18)
D From Leicester (Table 53) to Sleaford (Table 18)

Table 27

Nottingham → Newark → Lincoln → Cleethorpes

Network Diagram - see first page of Table 18

		EM A	EM A	EM	EM A	EM	EM A	EM	EM A	EM	EM B	EM A	EM	EM A	EM
Nottingham [8]	d	13 26	14 24		15 24		16 26		17 24		18 26	19 26		20 26	21 27
Carlton	d	13 32			15 31		16 32		17 30		18 32	19 32			
Burton Joyce	d	13 35			15 34		16 35		17 33		18 35	19 35			
Lowdham	d	13 39			15 38		16 39		17 37		18 39	19 39			
Thurgarton	d	13 43			15 42		16 43		17 41		18 43	19 43			
Bleasby	d	13 46			15 45		16 46		17 44		18 46	19 46			
Fiskerton	d	13 50			15 49		16 50		17 48		18 50	19 50			
Rolleston	d	13 52			15 51		16 52		17 50		18 52	19 52			
Newark Castle	d	13 58	14 49		15 57		16 59		17 56		18 59	19 59		20 48	21 51
Newark North Gate [7]	a														22 03
London Kings Cross [15]	⊖ d			*13 30*				*15 30*		*16 30*			*18 40*		*20 30*
Newark North Gate [7]	d			15 03				17 51		18 51			20 15		22 05
Collingham	d				16 06				18 06	19 00	19 10	20 09		21 01	22 15
Swinderby	d				16 11				18 10	19 04	19 15	20 14		21 05	
Hykeham	d				16 17				18 16	19 10	19 21	20 20		21 11	
Lincoln	a	14 27	15 25	15 26	16 31		17 30	18 14	18 30	19 19	19 30	20 34	20 38	21 25	22 36
	d					16 50		18 16					20 40		
Market Rasen	d					17 07		18 33					20a56		
Barnetby	a					17 31		18 49							
Habrough	a					17 40		18 58							
Grimsby Town	a					17 54		19 14							
Cleethorpes	a														

Sundays

		EM	EM	EM	EM	EM	EM	EM	EM
Nottingham [8]	d			16 30	17 30	18 30	19 30	20 30	22 30
Carlton	d			16 36	17 36	18 36	19 36	20 36	22 36
Burton Joyce	d			16 39	17 39	18 39	19 39	20 39	22 39
Lowdham	d			16 43	17 43	18 43	19 43	20 43	22 43
Thurgarton	d			16 47	17 47	18 47	19 47	20 47	22 47
Bleasby	d			16 50	17 50	18 50	19 50	20 50	22 50
Fiskerton	d			16 54	17 54	18 54	19 54	20 54	22 54
Rolleston	d			16 56	17 56	18 56	19 56	20 56	22 56
Newark Castle	d			17 02	18 03	19 02	20 02	21 02	23 02
Newark North Gate [7]	a			17 12		19 13		21 12	23 13
London Kings Cross [15]	⊖ d	*10 00*	*12 00*	*15 30*		*17 30*		*19 10*	*21 30*
Newark North Gate [7]	d	11 34	13 34	17 17		19 17		21 15	23 18
Collingham	d			17 26	18 13	19 26	20 11	21 24	23 27
Swinderby	d			17 30	18 17	19 30	20 16	21 29	23 32
Hykeham	d			17 36	18 23	19 36	20 22	21 35	23 38
Lincoln	a	11 56	13 56	17 51	18 37	19 50	20 37	21 49	23 52
	d								
Market Rasen	d								
Barnetby	a								
Habrough	a								
Grimsby Town	a								
Cleethorpes	a								

For general notes see front of timetable
For details of catering facilities see Directory of Train Operators

A From Leicester (Table 53)
B From Leicester (Table 53) to Sleaford (Table 18)

Hull and Cleethorpes → Doncaster → Meadowhall, Sheffield, Manchester and Manchester Airport Cleethorpes → Barton-on-Humber

Network Diagram - see first page of Table 18

Miles	Miles	Miles	Miles	Miles			NT	TP	NT	NT	NT	NT	NT	NT	TP	TP	EM	EM	NT	XC		NT	NT	NT
								1 ◇							1 ◇	1 ◇		1 ◇		1 ◇				
							A		B		C	D			E		G	H	J	K				L
0	0	—	—	—	**Hull**	d							05 20		06 00									
4¾	4¾	—	—	—	Hessle	d																		
7½	7½	—	—	—	Ferriby	d																		
10½	10½	—	—	—	Brough	d							05 32		06 12									
14½	14½	—	—	—	Broomfleet	d																		
17	17	—	—	—	Gilberdyke	d									06 20									
—	19¼	—	—	—	Eastrington	d																		
—	22¼	—	—	—	Howden	d									06 27									
—	25	—	—	—	Wressle	d																		
—	31	—	—	—	**Selby**	a									06 36									
—	—	—	—	—		d								06 15	06 38									
—	—	—	—	—	York 8	33 a									*07 20*									
20¾	—	—	—	—	Saltmarshe	d																		
23¾	—	—	—	—	Goole	d							05 47											
31	—	—	—	—	Thorne North	d							05 56											
—	—	0	0	—	**Cleethorpes**	d										05 18	05 51					06 00		
—	—	1½	1½	—	New Clee	d																		
—	—	2¼	2¼	—	Grimsby Docks	d																		
—	—	3¼	3¼	—	**Grimsby Town**	a										05 25	05 57					06 08		
—	—	—	—	—		d										05 26	05 58					06 08		
—	—	5¼	5¼	—	Great Coates	d																		
—	—	6¼	6¼	—	Healing	d																06 15		
—	—	7½	7½	—	Stallingborough	d																06 18		
—	—	11¼	11¼	—	Habrough	d										05 36	06 08					06 24		
—	—	—	13	—	Ulceby	d																06 28		
—	—	—	15¾	—	Thornton Abbey	d																		
—	—	—	17¼	—	Goxhill	d																06 36		
—	—	—	19¼	—	New Holland	d																06 41		
—	—	—	20¾	—	Barrow Haven	d																06 44		
—	—	—	22¾	—	**Barton-on-Humber**	a																06 49		
—	—	—	—	—	Barton-on-Humber	d																	06 53	
—	—	—	—	—	Hull Bus Station	a																	07 18	
—	—	17¾	—	—	Barnetby	d										05 45	06a17							
—	—	29	—	—	**Scunthorpe**	a										06 00								
—	—	—	—	—		d										06 00								
—	—	32½	—	—	Althorpe	d										06 06								
—	—	36¼	—	—	Crowle	d										06 12								
—	—	42¼	—	—	Thorne South	d										06 20								
34¼	—	45¼	—	—	Hatfield & Stainforth	d							06 03			06 25								
37	—	48	—	—	Kirk Sandall	d							06 10											
—	—	—	—	0	Adwick	31 d																		
—	—	—	—	2¼	Bentley (S.Yorks)	31 d																		
41	49¼	52	—	4	**Doncaster 7**	31 a							06 16	06 36		06 38								
—	—	—	—	—	London Kings Cross 15	⊖ 26 a							*08 12*			*08 42*								
—	—	—	—	—	York 8	26 d										*06 00*				06 16				
—	—	—	—	—	**Doncaster 7**	d		05 42		06 00			06 25			06 40		06 45						
45¾	—	—	—	—	Conisbrough	d				06 07			06 32											
48	—	—	—	—	Mexborough	d				06 11			06 36											
49¼	—	—	—	—	Swinton (S.Yorks)	d				06 14	06 22		06 39											
53¾	—	—	—	—	Rotherham Central	d				06 22	06 31		06 46											
56½	—	—	—	—	**Meadowhall**	d	05 39	06 00	06 13	06 27	06 37	06 49	06 52			06 59			07 04					07 19
60	—	—	—	—	**Sheffield 7**	a	05 49	06 08	06 25	06 38	06 47	06 57	07 03			07 07		07 09	07 12	07 20				07 29
—	—	—	—	—		d		06 11								07 10								
96¾	—	—	—	—	Stockport	78 a		06 53							*08b24*	07 55								*08 26*
102¾	—	—	—	—	**Manchester Piccadilly 10**	78 a		07 05							08 05	08 08								*08 36*
112½	—	—	—	—	**Manchester Airport**	85 a		07 35							*08 42*	08 33								

For general notes see front of timetable
For details of catering facilities see Directory of Train Operators

A From Barnsley (Table 34) to Retford (Table 30)
B From Barnsley (Table 34)
C From Leeds (Table 31)
D From Wakefield Kirkgate (Table 34)
E To Liverpool Lime Street (Table 39)
G To Newark North Gate (Table 27)
H From Leeds to St Pancras International (Table 53)
J From Leeds (Table 34)
K To Bristol Temple Meads (Table 51)
L From Huddersfield (Table 34)
b Change at Manchester Piccadilly

Hull and Cleethorpes → Doncaster → Meadowhall, Sheffield, Manchester and Manchester Airport
Cleethorpes → Barton-on-Humber

Network Diagram - see first page of Table 18

		NT	NT	NT	NT	HT	TP	TP	EM	NT	NT	NT	XC	GR		EM	NT	NT	NT	EM	NT	XC	NT	NT
						BHX 1 ◇	1 ◇	1 ◇					R 1	R 1		1 ◇				1 ◇		R 1		
		A		B	C				D	C			E	G		H	J	K		L	C	N		
						⊠ 🍽	⊼	⊼					🍽	✕ ⊼		🍽				🍽		🍽		
Hull	d		06 07			06 25	06 35					06 40		07 00										
Hessle	d		06 14									06 47												
Ferriby	d		06 19									06 52												
Brough	d		06 24			06 37	06 47					06 57		07 12										
Broomfleet	d																							
Gilberdyke	d		06 32									07 04												
Eastrington	d																							
Howden	d					06 49																		
Wressle	d																							
Selby	a					06 59	07 07							07 32										
	d					07 00	07 08							07 32										
York 8	33 a																							
Saltmarshe	d		06 38									07 10												
Goole	d		06 43									07 15												
Thorne North	d		06 51									07 24												
Cleethorpes	d							06 18																07 00
New Clee	d																							
Grimsby Docks	d																							07 05
Grimsby Town	a							06 25																07 07
	d							06 26	07 03															07 08
Great Coates	d																							07 12
Healing	d																							07 15
Stallingborough	d																							07 18
Habrough	d							06 36	07 13															07 24
Ulceby	d																							07 28
Thornton Abbey	d																							07 32
Goxhill	d																							07 35
New Holland	d																							07 40
Barrow Haven	d																							07 43
Barton-on-Humber	a																							07 48
Barton-on-Humber	🚌 d																							
Hull Bus Station	🚌 a																							
Barnetby	d							06 45	07a22															
Scunthorpe	a							07 00																
	d							07 00									07 34							
Althorpe	d																07 39							
Crowle	d																07 45							
Thorne South	d																07 53							
Hatfield & Stainforth	d		06 57									07 30					07 59							
Kirk Sandall	d		07 02									07 34					08 03							
Adwick	31 d							*06 53*			07 29												08 07	
Bentley (S.Yorks)	31 d							*06 57*			07 33												08 11	
Doncaster 7	31 a		07 12			07 16		07 33			07 37	07 45		07 53			08 13						08 15	
London Kings Cross 15	⊖ 26 a		*09 06*			09b18								09 45									*10 25*	
York 8	26 d	*06 30*											07 27									07 44		
Doncaster 7	d	07 02						07 35			07 39	07 46	07 52			07 59							08 17	
Conisbrough	d	07 09									07 46	07 53											08 24	
Mexborough	d	07 13									07 50	07 57							←				08 28	
Swinton (S.Yorks)	d	07 16		07 29							07 53	08 00							08 00				08 31	
Rotherham Central	d	07 27		07 41							08 01	→							08c15				08 41	
Meadowhall	🚊 d	07 33		07 47	07 48			07 53		08 03	08 07							08 17	08 22	08 24	08 34		08 49	
Sheffield 7	🚊 a	07 40		07 57	07 59			08 00		08 15	08 16		08 20			08 22		08 28	08 30	08 33	08 45	08 51	08 56	
	d							08 05																
Stockport	78 a						*09e01*	08 51												*09 24*				
Manchester Piccadilly 10	78 🚊 a						08 37	09 01												*09 36*				
Manchester Airport	85 ✈ a						*09 06*	09 33																

For general notes see front of timetable
For details of catering facilities see Directory of Train Operators

A To Worksop (Table 30)
B From Leeds (Table 31)
C From Leeds (Table 34)
D To Newark North Gate (Table 27)
E From Newcastle to Paignton (Table 51)
G **The Hull Executive**
H From Leeds to St Pancras International (Table 53)
J To Adwick (Table 31)
K From Huddersfield (Table 34)
L From Barnsley to St Pancras International (Table 53)
N From Newcastle to Bournemouth (Table 51)
b By changing at Doncaster, passengers may arrive at 0906
c Arr. 0811
e Change at Manchester Piccadilly

Hull and Cleethorpes → Doncaster → Meadowhall, Sheffield, Manchester and Manchester Airport
Cleethorpes → Barton-on-Humber

Network Diagram - see first page of Table 18

	NT BHX	NT	TP	NT	TP	NT	NT		NT	XC	NT	NT	NT	XC	NT	NT	HT	NT	NT	TP	TP	NT	NT
			1 ◇		**1** ◇					**1** ◇				**1** ◇			**1** ◇			**1** ◇	**1** ◇		
		A		B		C	D		E	G	C	H	D	J	E	B			K			E	C
	🚌		🚲		🚲					☕				☕			☒ ☕			🚲	🚲		
Hull d		07 07	07 33			07 36					08 04						08 12		08 29	08 37			08 56
Hessle d						07 43													08 36				
Ferriby d						07 48													08 41				
Brough d		07 19	07 45			07 53					08 16						08 24		08 46	08 49			09 08
Broomfleet d						07 58																	
Gilberdyke d		07 26				08 03													08 53				
Eastrington d		07 31																					
Howden d		07 35	07 57														08 36						
Wressle d		07 40																					
Selby a		07 48	08 07														08 45			09 07			
d		07 48	08 08														08 45			09 08			
York 8 33 a		08 22																		*09 48*			
Saltmarshe d						08 08																	
Goole d						08 13					08 30								09 02				09 22
Thorne North d						08 22													09 10				
Cleethorpes d					07 18																08 28		
New Clee d																							
Grimsby Docks d																							
Grimsby Town a					07 25																08 35		
d					07 26																08 36		
Great Coates d																							
Healing d																							
Stallingborough d																							
Habrough d					07 36																08 46		
Ulceby d																							
Thornton Abbey d																							
Goxhill d																							
New Holland d																							
Barrow Haven d																							
Barton-on-Humber a																							
Barton-on-Humber 🚌 d	07 53																						
Hull Bus Station 🚌 a	08 18																						
Barnetby d					07 45																08 54		
Scunthorpe a					07 59																09 10		
d					08 00		08 10														09 10		
Althorpe d							08 15																
Crowle d							08 21																
Thorne South d							08 30																
Hatfield & Stainforth d						08 28	08 35												09 17				
Kirk Sandall d						08 33	08 39												09 21				
Adwick 31 d					*08 10*					*08b35*								09 13					
Bentley (S.Yorks) 31 d					*08 14*					*08b39*								09 17					
Doncaster 7 31 a					08 30	08 43	08 50				08 56						09 03	09 22	09 31		09 40		09 47
London Kings Cross 15 ⊖ 26 a																	10 51	*11 27*					
York 8 26 d										08 27			←	08 44				*08 49*					
Doncaster 7 d					08 42		09 01 ↳			08 51	08 57		09 01					09 24			09 42		09 49
Conisbrough d													09 08					09 31					
Mexborough d													09 12					09 35					
Swinton (S.Yorks) d				08 34									09 15			09 35		09 42					
Rotherham Central d				08 47									09 27			09 44		09 50					
Meadowhall 🚊 d				08 53	09 00				09 03		09 15	09 21	09 33		09 49	09 51		09 56			10 00	10 03	10 07
Sheffield 7 🚊 a				09 02	09 07				09 15	09 20	09 27	09 30	09 41	09 51	09 57	10 02		10 04			10 07	10 15	10 18
d					09 11																10 11		
Stockport 78 a			*10c03*		09 53							*10 24*								*11c02*	10 53		
Manchester Piccadilly 10 78 🚊 a			09 37		10 03							*10 36*								10 35	11 03		
Manchester Airport 85 ✈ a			*10 01*		10 33															*11 01*	11 33		

For general notes see front of timetable
For details of catering facilities see Directory of Train Operators

A From Beverley (Table 43)
B From Leeds (Table 31)
C From Bridlington (Table 43)
D To Lincoln (Table 30)
E From Leeds (Table 34)
G From Newcastle to Bristol Temple Meads (Table 51)
H From Huddersfield (Table 34)
J From Edinburgh to Plymouth (Table 51)
K From Scarborough (Table 43)
b Change at Doncaster
c Change at Manchester Piccadilly

Hull and Cleethorpes → Doncaster → Meadowhall, Sheffield, Manchester and Manchester Airport
Cleethorpes → Barton-on-Humber

Network Diagram - see first page of Table 18

		XC		NT	NT	NT	XC	NT	NT	EM	NT	NT	NT	NT	TP	TP	NT		NT	XC	NT	NT	XC	NT
		1 ◇					R 1								1 ◇	1 ◇				1 ◇			1 ◇	
		A			B	C	D		(bus)	E	G	H		J			G		K	L	B	C	N	G
		(trolley)					(trolley)								(trolley)	(trolley)				(trolley)			(trolley)	
Hull	d			09 02										09 25	09 37				09 56					
Hessle	d													09 32										
Ferriby	d													09 37										
Brough	d			09 14										09 42	09 49				10 08					
Broomfleet	d																							
Gilberdyke	d			09 21										09 49										
Eastrington	d																							
Howden	d			09 28																				
Wressle	d																							
Selby	a			09 38											10 07									
	d			09 38											10 08									
York 8	33 a			10 07																				
Saltmarshe	d																							
Goole	d													09 58					10 22					
Thorne North	d													10 06										
Cleethorpes	d							09 00								09 28								
New Clee	d							09x03																
Grimsby Docks	d							09 05																
Grimsby Town	a							09 08								09 35								
	d							09 08		09 28						09 36								
Great Coates	d							09 12																
Healing	d							09 15																
Stallingborough	d							09 18																
Habrough	d							09 24		09 38														
Ulceby	d							09 28																
Thornton Abbey	d							09 32																
Goxhill	d							09 35																
New Holland	d							09 40																
Barrow Haven	d							09 43																
Barton-on-Humber	a							09 48																
Barton-on-Humber	(bus) d								09 53															
Hull Bus Station	(bus) a								10 18															
Barnetby	d									09a47						09 54								
Scunthorpe	a															10 10								
	d					09 17										10 10						10 18		
Althorpe	d					09 22																10 23		
Crowle	d					09 29																10 29		
Thorne South	d					09 37																10 38		
Hatfield & Stainforth	d					09 42								10 12								10 43		
Kirk Sandall	d					09 47								10 17								10 47		
Adwick	31 d												10 13											
Bentley (S.Yorks)	31 d												10 17											
Doncaster 7	31 a					09 57							10 22	10 27		10 40			10 45			10 58		
London Kings Cross 15	⊖ 26 a					*11 50*							*12 17*	*12 25*					*12 42*					
York 8	26 d	09 27					09 44						*09 35*			*10 06*				10 34		*10 29*	10 44	
Doncaster 7	d	09 56				10 02							10 24			10 42			10 48	10 58		11 02		
Conisbrough	d					10 09							10 31									11 09		
Mexborough	d					10 13							10 35									11 13		
Swinton (S.Yorks)	d					10 16						10 34	10b41									11 16		
Rotherham Central	d					10 27						10 44	10 49									11 27		
Meadowhall	(tram) d				10 19	10 33					10 49	10 51	10 55			11 00	11 04		11 07		11 19	11 33		11 49
Sheffield 7	(tram) a	10 20			10 30	10 41	10 51				10 57	11 02	11 05			11 07	11 15		11 17	11 20	11 30	11 41	11 51	11 57
	d															11 11								
Stockport	78 a				*11 24*										*12c02*	11 53					*12 24*			
Manchester Piccadilly 10	78 (tram) a				*11 36*										*11 35*	12 03					*12 36*			
Manchester Airport	85 (plane) a														*12 01*	12 33								

For general notes see front of timetable
For details of catering facilities see
Directory of Train Operators

A From Newcastle to Paignton (Table 51)
B From Huddersfield (Table 34)
C To Lincoln (Table 30)
D From Glasgow Central to Bournemouth (Table 51)
E To Newark North Gate (Table 27)
G From Leeds (Table 34)
H From Leeds (Table 31)
J From Beverley (Table 43)
K From Bridlington (Table 43)
L From Newcastle to Bristol Temple Meads (Table 51)
N From Dundee (Table 229) to Plymouth (Table 51)
b Arr. 1038
c Change at Manchester Piccadilly

Table 29 **Mondays to Fridays**

Hull and Cleethorpes → Doncaster → Meadowhall, Sheffield, Manchester and Manchester Airport
Cleethorpes → Barton-on-Humber

Network Diagram - see first page of Table 18

	NT	HT	NT	NT	TP	TP	NT	NT	NT	EM		NT	XC	NT	NT	NT	NT	XC	NT	NT	NT	NT	TP
		1 ◇			1 ◇	1 ◇							R 1					R 1					1 ◇
	A								B	C		D	E	G		H	J	K	B	A			
		⊠ ☕			trolley	trolley		bus					☕					☕					trolley
Hull d		10 12		10 22	10 37							10 57			11 05							11 22	11 37
Hessle d				10 32																		11 29	
Ferriby d				10 37																		11 34	
Brough d		10 24		10 42	10 49							11 09			11 18							11 39	11 49
Broomfleet d																							
Gilberdyke d				10 49																		11 46	
Eastrington d																							
Howden d		10 36																					
Wressle d																							
Selby a		10 46			11 07										11 38								12 07
d		10 47			11 08										11 39								12 08
York 8 33 a		*11 20*													12 10								*13 15*
Saltmarshe d																						11 52	
Goole d				10 58								11 23										11 58	
Thorne North d				11 06																		12 06	
Cleethorpes d						10 28	11 00																
New Clee d							11x03																
Grimsby Docks d							11 05																
Grimsby Town a						10 35	11 08																
d						10 36	11 08			11 28													
Great Coates d							11 12																
Healing d							11 15																
Stallingborough d							11 18																
Habrough d						10 46	11 24			11 38													
Ulceby d							11 28																
Thornton Abbey d							11 32																
Goxhill d							11 35																
New Holland d							11 40																
Barrow Haven d							11 43																
Barton-on-Humber a							11 48																
Barton-on-Humber bus d								11 53															
Hull Bus Station bus a								12 18															
Barnetby d						10 54				11a47													
Scunthorpe a						11 10																	
d						11 10											11 17						
Althorpe d																	11 22						
Crowle d																	11 28						
Thorne South d																	11 37						
Hatfield & Stainforth d				11 12													11 42					12 12	
Kirk Sandall d				11 17													11 46					12 17	
Adwick 31 d			11 16																		12 15		
Bentley (S.Yorks) 31 d			11 20																		12 19		
Doncaster 7 31 a		11 04	11 25	11 27		11 40						11 46					11 58				12 24	12 27	
London Kings Cross 15 ⊖ 26 a		12 44		*13 22*								*13 43*					*14 02*					*14 20*	
York 8 26 d													11 27	11 03				11 44			*11 35*		
Doncaster 7 d			11 27			11 42						11 48	11 54				11 58				12 26		
Conisbrough d			11 34														12 06				12 33		
Mexborough d			11 38														12 10				12 37		
Swinton (S.Yorks) d	11 34		11 41											12 02			12 16			12 34	12 42		
Rotherham Central d	11 45		11 50											12 11			12 27			12 45	12 50		
Meadowhall tram d	11 51		11 56			12 00			12 03			12 06		12 16		12 19	12 33		12 49	12 51	12 56		
Sheffield 7 tram a	12 02		12 05			12 07			12 15			12 18	12 20	12 26		12 30	12 41	12 51	12 57	13 02	13 06		
d						12 11																	
Stockport 78 a					13b01	12 53										13 24							14b02
Manchester Piccadilly 10 78 tram a			*13 31*		12 35	13 03										13 36							13 35
Manchester Airport 85 ✈ a					*13 01*	13 33																	*14 01*

For general notes see front of timetable
For details of catering facilities see Directory of Train Operators

A From Leeds (Table 31)
B From Leeds (Table 34)
C To Newark North Gate (Table 27)
D From Bridlington (Table 43)
E From Newcastle to Plymouth (Table 51)
G Via Pontefract Baghill (Table 33)
H From Huddersfield (Table 34)
J To Lincoln (Table 30)
K From Dundee (Table 229) to Bournemouth (Table 51)
b Change at Manchester Piccadilly

Hull and Cleethorpes → Doncaster → Meadowhall, Sheffield, Manchester and Manchester Airport
Cleethorpes → Barton-on-Humber

Network Diagram - see first page of Table 18

		TP	NT	NT	XC		NT	NT	XC	NT	NT	NT	NT	TP	HT	TP	NT	NT	XC	NT		NT	XC	NT
		1 ◇			1 ◇				R 1					1 ◇	1 ◇	1 ◇			1 ◇				R 1	
			A	B	C		D	E	G	A	H						A	J	K	D		E	L	
Hull	d			11 55									12 22	12 37	12 45			12 57						
Hessle	d												12 29											
Ferriby	d												12 34											
Brough	d			12 07									12 39	12 49	12 57			13 09						
Broomfleet	d												12 44											
Gilberdyke	d												12 49											
Eastrington	d																							
Howden	d														13 09									
Wressle	d																							
Selby	a													13 07	13 19									
	d													13 08	13 20									
York 8	33 a																							
Saltmarshe	d																							
Goole	d			12 22									12 58					13 23						
Thorne North	d												13 06											
Cleethorpes	d	11 28														12 28								13 00
New Clee	d																							13x03
Grimsby Docks	d																							13 05
Grimsby Town	a	11 35														12 35								13 08
	d	11 36														12 36								13 08
Great Coates	d																							13 12
Healing	d																							13 15
Stallingborough	d																							13 18
Habrough	d																							13 24
Ulceby	d																							13 28
Thornton Abbey	d																							13 32
Goxhill	d																							13 35
New Holland	d																							13 40
Barrow Haven	d																							13 43
Barton-on-Humber	a																							13 48
Barton-on-Humber	🚌 d																							
Hull Bus Station	🚌 a																							
Barnetby	d	11 54														12 54								
Scunthorpe	a	12 09														13 10								
	d	12 10						12 17								13 10						13 18		
Althorpe	d							12 22														13 23		
Crowle	d							12 28														13 29		
Thorne South	d							12 37														13 38		
Hatfield & Stainforth	d							12 42					13 14									13 43		
Kirk Sandall	d							12 46					13 19									13 47		
Adwick	31 d											13 11												
Bentley (S.Yorks)	31 d											13 15												
Doncaster 7	31 a	12 40		12 46				12 57				13 20	13 29		13 37	13 40		13 46				13 58		
London Kings Cross 15	⊖ 26 a			14 44				15 05							15 20			15 44				15 58		
York 8	26 d				12 25			12 31	12 44										13 29				13 44	
Doncaster 7	d	12 42		12 48	12 55			13 02				13 24				13 42		13 48	13 54			14 01		
Conisbrough	d							13 09				13 31										14 08		
Mexborough	d							13 13				13 35										14 12		
Swinton (S.Yorks)	d							13 16			13 34	13 42										14 16		
Rotherham Central	d							13 27			13 45	13 50										14 27		
Meadowhall	🚋 d	13 00	13 04	13 07			13 21	13 33		13 49	13 51	13 56				14 00	14 03	14 06		14 19		14 33		
Sheffield 7	🚋 a	13 07	13 15	13 17	13 20		13 31	13 41	13 51	13 57	14 02	14 04				14 07	14 15	14 17	14 20	14 30		14 41	14 51	
	d	13 11														14 11								
Stockport	78 a	13 53					14 24							15b01		14 53				15 24				
Manchester Piccadilly 10	78 🚋 a	14 03					14 36							14 35		15 03				15 36				
Manchester Airport	85 ✈ a	14 33												15 01		15 33								

For general notes see front of timetable
For details of catering facilities see Directory of Train Operators

A From Leeds (Table 34)
B From Bridlington (Table 43)
C From Newcastle to Bristol Temple Meads (Table 51)
D From Huddersfield (Table 34)
E To Lincoln (Table 30)
G From Glasgow Central (Table 51) to Penzance (Table 135)
H From Leeds (Table 31)
J From Scarborough (Table 43)
K From Newcastle to Plymouth (Table 51)
L From Aberdeen (Table 229) to Bournemouth (Table 51)
b Change at Manchester Piccadilly

Hull and Cleethorpes → Doncaster → Meadowhall, Sheffield, Manchester and Manchester Airport
Cleethorpes → Barton-on-Humber

Network Diagram - see first page of Table 18

	NT BHX	NT	NT	NT	NT	NT	TP	TP	EM	NT	NT	XC	NT		NT	XC	NT	NT	NT	NT	TP	TP	NT
							1 ◇	1 ◇				1 ◇				R 1					1 ◇	1 ◇	
			A	B					C	A	D	E	G		H	J	A	B					A
	🚌						trolley	trolley				buffet				buffet					trolley	trolley	
Hull d		13 12				13 25	13 37				13 57									14 25	14 37		
Hessle d						13 32														14 32			
Ferriby d						13 37														14 37			
Brough d		13 24				13 42	13 49				14 09									14 42	14 49		
Broomfleet d																							
Gilberdyke d		13 31				13 49														14 49			
Eastrington d		13 36																					
Howden d		13 40																					
Wressle d		13 45																					
Selby a		13 55					14 07														15 07		
d		13 56					14 08														15 08		
York 8 33 a		14 27																					
Saltmarshe d																							
Goole d						13 58					14 23									14 58			
Thorne North d						14 06														15 06			
Cleethorpes d								13 28														14 28	
New Clee d																							
Grimsby Docks d																							
Grimsby Town a								13 35														14 35	
d								13 36	13 52													14 36	
Great Coates d																							
Healing d																							
Stallingborough d																							
Habrough d									14 02													14 46	
Ulceby d																							
Thornton Abbey d																							
Goxhill d																							
New Holland d																							
Barrow Haven d																							
Barton-on-Humber a																							
Barton-on-Humber 🚌 d	13 53																						
Hull Bus Station 🚌 a	14 18																						
Barnetby d								13 54	14a11													14 54	
Scunthorpe a								14 10														15 10	
d								14 10							14 18							15 10	
Althorpe d															14 23								
Crowle d															14 29								
Thorne South d															14 38								
Hatfield & Stainforth d						14 14									14 43					15 12			
Kirk Sandall d						14 18									14 47					15 17			
Adwick 31 d					14 18														15 13				
Bentley (S.Yorks) 31 d					14 22														15 17				
Doncaster 7 31 a					14 26	14 29		14 40			14 46				14 58				15 22	15 27		15 40	
London Kings Cross 15 ⊖ 26 a								*16 46*							*17 04*					*17 30*			
York 8 26 d					*13 36*							14 32				14 44						*15 11*	
Doncaster 7 d					14 28			14 42			14 48	14 57			15 02				15 25			15 42	
Conisbrough d					14 35										15 09				15 32				
Mexborough d					14 39										15 13				15 36				
Swinton (S.Yorks) d				14 34	14 42										15 16			15 34	15 42				
Rotherham Central d				14 45	14 50										15 27			15 43	15 50				
Meadowhall 🚋 d			14 49	14 51	14 56			15 00		15 03	15 06		15 19		15 33		15 49	15 51	15 56			16 00	16 06
Sheffield 7 🚋 a			14 57	15 02	15 06			15 07		15 15	15 18	15 20	15 30		15 41	15 51	15 57	16 02	16 04			16 07	16 15
d								15 11														16 11	
Stockport 78 a							*16b02*	15 53					*16 24*								*17b00*	16 53	
Manchester Piccadilly 10 78 🚋 a							15 35	16 03													16 35	17 03	
Manchester Airport 85 ✈ a							*16 01*	16 33													*17 14*	17 39	

For general notes see front of timetable
For details of catering facilities see Directory of Train Operators

- **A** From Leeds (Table 34)
- **B** From Leeds (Table 31)
- **C** To Newark North Gate (Table 27)
- **D** From Bridlington (Table 43)
- **E** From Newcastle to Bristol Temple Meads (Table 51)
- **G** From Huddersfield (Table 34)
- **H** To Lincoln (Table 30)
- **J** From Edinburgh to Plymouth (Table 51)
- **b** Change at Manchester Piccadilly

Hull and Cleethorpes → Doncaster → Meadowhall, Sheffield, Manchester and Manchester Airport
Cleethorpes → Barton-on-Humber

Network Diagram - see first page of Table 18

		NT	XC	NT	NT	NT	XC	NT		NT	NT	NT	NT	HT	NT	NT	TP	TP	EM	NT	NT	XC	NT	NT
			R 1				R 1				BHX			1 ◇			1 ◇	1 ◇				R 1		
		A	B	C	D	E	G				Bus	H	J						K	H	L	N	D	E
Hull	d	14 57						15 06						15 18		15 21	15 37				15 57			
Hessle	d															15 28								
Ferriby	d															15 33								
Brough	d	15 09						15 18						15 30		15 38	15 49				16 09			
Broomfleet	d																							
Gilberdyke	d															15 45								
Eastrington	d																							
Howden	d													15 42										
Wressle	d																							
Selby	a							15 37						15 56			16 07							
	d							15 38						15 57			16 08							
York 8	33 a							16 06																
Saltmarshe	d																							
Goole	d	15 23														15 58					16 23			
Thorne North	d															16 06								
Cleethorpes	d									15 00								15 28						
New Clee	d									15x03														
Grimsby Docks	d									15 05														
Grimsby Town	a									15 08								15 35						
	d									15 09								15 36	16 03					
Great Coates	d									15 13														
Healing	d									15 16														
Stallingborough	d									15 19														
Habrough	d									15 25									16 12					
Ulceby	d									15 28														
Thornton Abbey	d									15 33														
Goxhill	d									15 36														
New Holland	d									15 40														
Barrow Haven	d									15 43														
Barton-on-Humber	a									15 49														
Barton-on-Humber	Bus d										15 56													
Hull Bus Station	Bus a										16 21													
Barnetby	d																	15 54	16a21					
Scunthorpe	a																	16 10						
	d					15 18												16 10						16 18
Althorpe	d					15 23																		16 23
Crowle	d					15 29																		16 29
Thorne South	d					15 38																		16 38
Hatfield & Stainforth	d					15 43										16 12								16 43
Kirk Sandall	d					15 47										16 17								16 47
Adwick	31 d														16 14									
Bentley (S.Yorks)	31 d														16 18									
Doncaster 7	31 a	15 46				15 58								16 15	16 22	16 27		16 40			16 46			16 58
London Kings Cross 15	⊖ 26 a	*17 41*												18 12		*18 23*					*18 45*			*18 48*
York 8	26 d		15 29	15 02			15 44								*15 35*							16 25		
Doncaster 7	d	15 48	15 55			16 02									16 24			16 42			16 47	16 53		17 00
Conisbrough	d					16 09									16 31									17 09
Mexborough	d					16 13									16 35									17 13
Swinton (S.Yorks)	d			16 01		16 16							16 34		16 42									17 16
Rotherham Central	d			16 10		16 27							16 43		16 50									17 27
Meadowhall	d	16 09		16 18	16 19	16 33						16 49	16 51		16 56			17 00		17 03	17 07		17 19	17 33
Sheffield 7	a	16 17	16 20	16 25	16 30	16 41	16 51					16 57	17 02		17 04			17 07		17 15	17 17	17 18	17 30	17 41
	d																	17 11						
Stockport	78 a				*17 25*												*17b59*	17 53					*18 26*	
Manchester Piccadilly 10	78 a				*17 36*												17 35	18 03						
Manchester Airport	85 ✈ a																*18 05*	18 38						

For general notes see front of timetable
For details of catering facilities see Directory of Train Operators

A From Scarborough (Table 43)
B From Newcastle to Cardiff Central (Table 51)
C Via Pontefract Baghill (Table 33)
D From Huddersfield (Table 34)
E To Lincoln (Table 30)
G From Edinburgh to Bournemouth (Table 51)
H From Leeds (Table 34)
J From Leeds (Table 31)
K To Newark North Gate (Table 27)
L From Bridlington (Table 43)
N From Newcastle to Weston-super-Mare (Table 51)
b Change at Manchester Piccadilly

Hull and Cleethorpes → Doncaster → Meadowhall, Sheffield, Manchester and Manchester Airport Cleethorpes → Barton-on-Humber

Network Diagram - see first page of Table 18

	XC		NT	NT	NT	NT	NT	TP	TP	NT	NT	XC	NT	NT	TP	XC		NT	NT	NT	NT	HT	NT
	1 ◇							1 ◇	1 ◇			R 1			1 ◇	R 1						1 ◇	
	A			B	C		D			B	E	G	H		J	K			🚌	B	C		
	☕							🛒	🛒			☕				☕						⊠ ☕	
Hull d			16 10				16 27	16 37			16 54				17 00							17 06	
Hessle d							16 34																
Ferriby d							16 39																
Brough d			16 22				16 44	16 49			17 06				17 12							17 18	
Broomfleet d							16 49																
Gilberdyke d			16 29				16 54				17 13												
Eastrington d																							
Howden d			16 36																			17 32	
Wressle d																							
Selby a			16 46					17 07							17 30							17 42	
d			16 47					17 08														17 43	
York 8 33 a			17 13																				
Saltmarshe d							16 59																
Goole d							17 04				17 22												
Thorne North d							17 13																
Cleethorpes d									16 28									17 00					
New Clee d																							
Grimsby Docks d																		17 05					
Grimsby Town a									16 35									17 07					
d									16 36									17 08					
Great Coates d																		17 12					
Healing d																		17 15					
Stallingborough d																		17 18					
Habrough d																		17 24					
Ulceby d																		17 28					
Thornton Abbey d																		17 32					
Goxhill d																		17 35					
New Holland d																		17 40					
Barrow Haven d																		17 43					
Barton-on-Humber a																		17 48					
Barton-on-Humber 🚌 d																			17 57				
Hull Bus Station 🚌 a																			18 23				
Barnetby d									16 54														
Scunthorpe a									17 10														
d									17 10					17 18									
Althorpe d														17 23									
Crowle d														17 29									
Thorne South d														17 38									
Hatfield & Stainforth d							17 19							17 43									
Kirk Sandall d							17 23							17 47									
Adwick 31 d						*16 54*			*17 09*														*17 53*
Bentley (S.Yorks) 31 d						*16 58*			*17 14*														*17 57*
Doncaster 7 31 a							17 34		17 41		17 47			17 58								18 00	
London Kings Cross 15 ⊖ 26 a														*19 59*								19 49	
York 8 26 d	16 44					*16 32*			*16 56*			17 34				17 44							
Doncaster 7 d						17 24			17 42		17 49	17 58		18 02									18 26
Conisbrough d						17 31								18 09									18 33
Mexborough d						17 35								18 13									18 37
Swinton (S.Yorks) d					17 34	17 42								18 16							18 34		18 42
Rotherham Central d					17 45	17 50								18 27							18b45		18 49
Meadowhall 🚋 d				17 49	17 51	17 55			18 00	18 04	18 07		18 19	18 33						18 48	18 51		18 56
Sheffield 7 🚋 a	17 51			17 57	18 02	18 04			18 07	18 15	18 18	18 20	18 30	18 41		18 51				18 57	19 02		19 05
d									18 11														
Stockport 78 a								*19c02*	18 53				*19 24*										
Manchester Piccadilly 10 78 🚋 a								*18 36*	19 03				*19 36*										*20 31*
Manchester Airport 85 ✈ a								*19 09*	19 34				*20e05*										*21e06*

For general notes see front of timetable
For details of catering facilities see Directory of Train Operators

A From Edinburgh to Plymouth (Table 51)
B From Leeds (Table 34)
C From Leeds (Table 31)
D From Scarborough (Table 43)
E From Beverley (Table 43)
G From Newcastle to Bristol Temple Meads (Table 51)
H From Huddersfield (Table 34)
J To Huddersfield (Table 39)
K From Edinburgh to Southampton Central (Table 51)
b Arr. 1841
c Change at Manchester Piccadilly
e Change at Sheffield and Manchester Piccadilly

Hull and Cleethorpes → Doncaster → Meadowhall, Sheffield, Manchester and Manchester Airport
Cleethorpes → Barton-on-Humber

Network Diagram - see first page of Table 18

	TP 1◇	EM	NT	NT	NT	NT	XC 1◇	TP 1◇	NT	NT		NT	NT	NT	XC 1◇	NT	NT	NT	TP 1◇	NT	NT	NT	XC 1◇
		A	B	C	C	D	E		G	C				B	H	B	J			B			E
Hull d				17 18	17 42	17 56		18 02					18 22								18 53		
Hessle d				17 25	17 49								18 29										
Ferriby d				17 30	17 54								18 34										
Brough d				17 35	17 59	18 08		18 14					18 39								19 05		
Broomfleet d				17 40																			
Gilberdyke d				17 45	18 06								18 46										
Eastrington d				17 49																			
Howden d				17 54																			
Wressle d				17 58																			
Selby a				18 06		18 26		18 32															
d				18 06		18 27		18 33															
York 8 33 a				18 35																			
Saltmarshe d					18 12					←													
Goole d					18b20 →					18 20			18 55								19 19		
Thorne North d										18 28			19 03										
Cleethorpes d	17 28																		18 28				
New Clee d																							
Grimsby Docks d																							
Grimsby Town a	17 35																		18 35				
d	17 36	18 30																	18 36				
Great Coates d																							
Healing d																							
Stallingborough d																							
Habrough d	17 46	18 40																	18 46				
Ulceby d																							
Thornton Abbey d																							
Goxhill d																							
New Holland d																							
Barrow Haven d																							
Barton-on-Humber a																							
Barton-on-Humber (bus) d																							
Hull Bus Station (bus) a																							
Barnetby d	17 54	18a48																	18 54				
Scunthorpe a	18 10																		19 10				
d	18 10											18 18							19 10			19 15	
Althorpe d												18 23										19 20	
Crowle d												18 29										19 26	
Thorne South d												18 38										19 34	
Hatfield & Stainforth d										18 34		18 46	19 12									19 40	
Kirk Sandall d										18 39		18 50	19 16									19 44	
Adwick 31 d	*18 16*																	*18 53*					
Bentley (S.Yorks) 31 d	*18 20*																	*18 57*					
Doncaster 7 31 a	18 40					18 45				18 50		19 01	19 27						19 40		19 45	19 56	
London Kings Cross 15 ⊖ 26 a						*20 42*						*21 03*	*21 17*								*21 44*		
York 8 26 d	*17 55*						*18 24*								*18 44*			*18 30*			*19 14*		*19 29*
Doncaster 7 d	18 42					18 47	18 52			18 55								19 28	19 42		19 49		19 57
Conisbrough d										19 02								19 35					
Mexborough d										19 06								19 39					
Swinton (S.Yorks) d										19 09							19 34	19 43					
Rotherham Central d										19 19							19 45	19 50					
Meadowhall (tram) d	19 00		19 04			19 07			19 16	19 25				19 34		19 50	19 51	19 57	20 00	20 04	20 08		
Sheffield 7 (tram) a	19 07		19 15			19 19	19 20		19 30	19 34				19 44	19 51	19 57	20 02	20 06	20 07	20 15	20 18		20 20
d	19 11																		20 11				
Stockport 78 a	19 53									*20 26*									20 53				*21 17*
Manchester Piccadilly 10 78 (tram) a	20 03							*19 59*		*20 36*									21 03				*21 30*
Manchester Airport 85 (rail-air) a	20 34							*20 58*		*21c09*									21 34				*22c15*

For general notes see front of timetable
For details of catering facilities see Directory of Train Operators

A To Newark North Gate (Table 27)
B From Leeds (Table 34)
C From Beverley (Table 43)
D From Scarborough (Table 43)
E From Newcastle to Birmingham New Street (Table 51)
G From Huddersfield (Table 34)
H From Edinburgh to Bristol Temple Meads (Table 51)
J From Leeds (Table 31)
b Arr. 1817
c Change at Sheffield and Manchester Piccadilly

Hull and Cleethorpes → Doncaster → Meadowhall, Sheffield, Manchester and Manchester Airport
Cleethorpes → Barton-on-Humber

Network Diagram - see first page of Table 18

Station		TP	NT	NT	XC		NT	NT	NT BHX	NT	NT	NT	HT	NT	TP	TP	XC	NT	NT	NT		XC	NT	NT
		1 ◇ A	B	C	1 ◇ D				🚌	E	G	E	1 ◇ ⊠ ☕	H	1 ◇	1 ◇ A	1 ◇ J		B	K		1 ◇ L		E
Hull	d	18 59					19 10						19 18	19 24		19 55				20 03				
Hessle	d													19 31						20 10				
Ferriby	d													19 36						20 15				
Brough	d	19 11					19 22						19 30	19 41		20 07				20 20				
Broomfleet	d																							
Gilberdyke	d						19 29							19 48						20 27				
Eastrington	d																							
Howden	d						19 36						19 43											
Wressle	d																							
Selby	a	19 29					19 46						19 52			20 25								
	d						19 47						19 53											
York 8	33 a						20 15									*21 00*								
Saltmarshe	d																							
Goole	d													19 58						20 36				
Thorne North	d													20 06						20 44				
Cleethorpes	d							19 00							19 28									
New Clee	d																							
Grimsby Docks	d							19 05																
Grimsby Town	a							19 07							19 35									
	d							19 08							19 36									
Great Coates	d							19 12																
Healing	d							19 15																
Stallingborough	d							19 18																
Habrough	d							19 24							19 46									
Ulceby	d							19 28																
Thornton Abbey	d							19 32																
Goxhill	d							19 35																
New Holland	d							19 40																
Barrow Haven	d							19 43																
Barton-on-Humber	a							19 48																
Barton-on-Humber 🚌	d								19 55															
Hull Bus Station 🚌	a								20 20															
Barnetby	d														19 54									
Scunthorpe	a														20 10									
	d														20 10									
Althorpe	d																	20 18						
Crowle	d																	20 23						
Thorne South	d																	20 29						
																		20 38						
Hatfield & Stainforth	d													20 14				20 43		20 50				
Kirk Sandall	d													20 19				20 47		20 55				
Adwick	31 d														*19 53*								*20 55*	
Bentley (S.Yorks)	31 d														*19 57*								*20 59*	
Doncaster 7	31 a												20 10	20 29	20 40			20 59		21 05				
London Kings Cross 15	⊖ 26 a												21 59							*23 32*				
York 8	26 d				19 44										*20 08*		20 31					20 44		
Doncaster 7	d			20 03											20 42		20 56			21 07			21 30	
Conisbrough	d			20 10											20 48					21 14			21 37	
Mexborough	d			20 14											20 52					21 18			21 41	
Swinton (S.Yorks)	d			20 17							20 34				20 55					21 21			→	
Rotherham Central	d			20 28							20 43				21 01					21 28				
Meadowhall	🚋 d		20 24	20 33						20 48	20 51	21 04			21 07				21 24	21 34				21 49
Sheffield 7	🚋 a		20 35	20 41	20 51					20 57	21 02	21 15			21 18		21 30		21 35	21 45		21 51		21 57
	d																							
Stockport	78 a																							
Manchester Piccadilly 10	78 🚋 a																							
Manchester Airport	85 ✈ a																							

For general notes see front of timetable
For details of catering facilities see Directory of Train Operators

A To Leeds (Table 39)
B From Huddersfield (Table 34)
C To Worksop (Table 30)
D From Edinburgh to Bristol Temple Meads (Table 51)
E From Leeds (Table 34)
G From Leeds (Table 31)
H From Scarborough (Table 43)
J From Newcastle (Table 26)
K From Bridlington (Table 43)
L From Edinburgh to Birmingham New Street (Table 51)

Hull and Cleethorpes → Doncaster → Meadowhall, Sheffield, Manchester and Manchester Airport
Cleethorpes → Barton-on-Humber

Network Diagram - see first page of Table 18

		NT	TP	NT	NT	XC	NT	NT	NT	EM	TP	NT	NT	NT		NT	NT	NT	NT	NT	NT	NT		
									ThFO BHX											FX	FO			
			1 ◇			1 ◇					1 ◇													
		A				B				C		D		E		A		D	E			A		
									🚌															
Hull	d				20 56						21 33									22 20	22 25			
Hessle	d																			22 27				
Ferriby	d																			22 32				
Brough	d				21 08						21 45									22 37	22 37			
Broomfleet	d																							
Gilberdyke	d										21 53													
Eastrington	d																							
Howden	d																							
Wressle	d																							
Selby	a										22 06													
	d										22 07													
York 8	33 a																							
Saltmarshe	d																							
Goole	d				21 22								21 42							22 51	22 51			
Thorne North	d												21 51							23 00	23 00			
Cleethorpes	d		20 28					21 00		21 14														
New Clee	d																							
Grimsby Docks	d							21 05																
Grimsby Town	a		20 35					21 07		21 20														
	d		20 36					21 08		21 21														
Great Coates	d							21 12																
Healing	d							21 15																
Stallingborough	d							21 18																
Habrough	d							21 24		21 30														
Ulceby	d							21 27																
Thornton Abbey	d							21 32																
Goxhill	d							21 35																
New Holland	d							21 39																
Barrow Haven	d							21 42																
Barton-on-Humber	a							21 48																
Barton-on-Humber	🚌 d								21 55															
Hull Bus Station	🚌 a								22 20															
Barnetby	d		20 54							21a39														
Scunthorpe	a		21 09																					
	d		21 10				21 26										22 21							
Althorpe	d						21 31										22 26							
Crowle	d						21 37										22 32							
Thorne South	d						21 45										22 41							
Hatfield & Stainforth	d						21 51						21 56				22 46			23 06	23 06			
Kirk Sandall	d						21 55						22 01				22 50			23 10	23 10			
Adwick	31 d																			*22 02*	*22 02*			
Bentley (S.Yorks)	31 d																			*22 06*	*22 06*			
Doncaster 7	31 a		21 40		21 45		22 06						22 11				23 02			23 21	23 21			
London Kings Cross 15	⊖ 26 a				*00 15*																			
York 8	26 d					*21 24*							*21 38*											
Doncaster 7	d		21 42		21 48								22 13							23 21	23 22			
Conisbrough	d			⟵									22 20							23 29	23 29			
Mexborough	d			21 41									22 24							23 33	23 33			
Swinton (S.Yorks)	d	21 35		21 44									22 29			22 34				23 36	23 36	23 55		
Rotherham Central	d	21 44		21b55									22 38			22 43				23 45	23 45	00 03		
Meadowhall	🚊 d	21 51	22 00	22 04	22 10							22 25	22 44	22 49		22 51		23 26	23 49	23 52	23 52	00 08		
Sheffield 7	🚊 a	22 02	22 07	22 12	22 18	22 21						22 35	22 54	22 57		23 02		23 35	23 57	00 01	00 01	00 23		
	d		22 11																					
Stockport	78 a		22 53									23 46												
Manchester Piccadilly 10	78 🚊 a		23 03								23 37	23 59										*02c42*		
Manchester Airport	85 ✈ a		23 28									00e45										*03 06*		

For general notes see front of timetable
For details of catering facilities see Directory of Train Operators

A From Leeds (Table 31)
B From Newcastle to Birmingham New Street (Table 51)
C To Lincoln (Table 27)
D From Huddersfield (Table 34)
E From Leeds (Table 34)
b Arr. 2151
c Fridays arr. 0243
e Change at Sheffield and Manchester Piccadilly

Table 29

Hull and Cleethorpes → Doncaster → Meadowhall, Sheffield, Manchester and Manchester Airport
Cleethorpes → Barton-on-Humber

Network Diagram - see first page of Table 18

		NT	TP	NT	NT	NT	NT	NT	TP	TP	NT	NT	NT	NT	TP	XC	NT	NT	TP	EM	NT	NT	NT	GR
			1 ◊						1 ◊	1 ◊					1 ◊	1 ◊			1 ◊					R 1
		A		B		B			C			D				E	G	H		J			H	
Hull	d						05 20		06 00					06 07	06 35						06 40			06 50
Hessle	d													06 14							06 47			
Ferriby	d													06 19							06 52			
Brough	d						05 32		06 12					06 24	06 47						06 57			07 02
Broomfleet	d																							
Gilberdyke	d								06 20					06 31							07 04			
Eastrington	d																							
Howden	d								06 27															
Wressle	d																							
Selby	a								06 36						07 05									07 23
	d							06 15	06 38						07 06									07 23
York 8	33 a								07 20															
Saltmarshe	d													06 37							07 10			
Goole	d						05 47							06 42							07 15 →			
Thorne North	d						05 56							06 51										
Cleethorpes	d									05 18	06 00								06 18					
New Clee	d																							
Grimsby Docks	d																							
Grimsby Town	a									05 25	06 08								06 25					
	d									05 26	06 08								06 26	06 59				
Great Coates	d																							
Healing	d										06 15													
Stallingborough	d										06 18													
Habrough	d									05 36	06 24								06 36	07 09				
Ulceby	d										06 28													
Thornton Abbey	d																							
Goxhill	d										06 36													
New Holland	d										06 41													
Barrow Haven	d										06 44													
Barton-on-Humber	a										06 49													
Barton-on-Humber	bus d																							
Hull Bus Station	bus a																							
Barnetby	d									05 45									06 45	07a18				
Scunthorpe	a									06 00									07 00					
	d									06 00									07 00					
Althorpe	d									06 06														
Crowle	d									06 12														
Thorne South	d									06 20														
Hatfield & Stainforth	d						06 03			06 25				06 57										
Kirk Sandall	d						06 10							07 01										
Adwick	31 d															06 53						07 29		
Bentley (S.Yorks)	31 d															06 57						07 33		
Doncaster 7	31 a						06 16	06 36		06 38				07 14					07 33			07 37		07 40
London Kings Cross 15	⊖ 26 a						08 04							09 03										09 26
York 8	26 d									06 00									07 00					
Doncaster 7	d		05 42		06 00		06 27			06 40			07 02			07 26			07 35			07 39		
Conisbrough	d				06 07		06 34						07 09									07 46		
Mexborough	d				06 11		06 38						07 13									07 50		
Swinton (S.Yorks)	d				06 14		06 41						07 16				07 29					07 53		
Rotherham Central	d				06 22		06 49						07b27				07 41					08 00		
Meadowhall	d	05 39	06 00	06 13	06 27	06 49	06 55			07 00		07 19	07 33				07 47	07 48	07 53			08 06	08 03	
Sheffield 7	a	05 49	06 08	06 25	06 38	06 57	07 06			07 07		07 29	07 45			07 51	07 57	07 59	08 00			08 14	08 15	
	d		06 11							07 10									08 05					
Stockport	78 a		06 53							07 55		08 25			09c02				08 51					
Manchester Piccadilly 10	78 a		07 05				08 31		08 05	08 08					08 36			09 31	09 01					
Manchester Airport	85 a		07 35						08 42	08 33					09 06				09 33					

For general notes see front of timetable
For details of catering facilities see Directory of Train Operators

A From Barnsley (Table 34) to Retford (Table 30)
B From Barnsley (Table 34)
C To Liverpool Lime Street (Table 39)
D From Huddersfield (Table 34)
E From Leeds to Plymouth (Table 51)
G From Leeds (Table 31)
H From Leeds (Table 34)
J To Newark North Gate (Table 27)
b Arr. 0723
c Change at Manchester Piccadilly

Table 29

Hull and Cleethorpes → Doncaster → Meadowhall, Sheffield, Manchester and Manchester Airport
Cleethorpes → Barton-on-Humber

Network Diagram - see first page of Table 18

	NT	XC	EM	NT	NT	NT	NT	NT	NT	XC	NT	TP	EM	NT	NT	TP	NT	NT	HT	NT	XC	NT	NT
		1 ◇	1 ◇							1 ◇		1 ◇	1 ◇			1 ◇			1 ◇		1 ◇		
		A	B	C	D				E	G	H		J		K		L	N		E	Q	L	D
		☕	☕					🚌		☕			☕			🛒			⊠ ☕		☕		
Hull d											06 57	07 33					07 36		08 02			08 08	
Hessle d																	07 43						
Ferriby d																	07 48						
Brough d											07 09	07 45					07 53		08 14			08 20	
Broomfleet d																	07 58						
Gilberdyke d											07 17						08 03						
Eastrington d											07 21												
Howden d											07 26	07 57							08 26 →				
Wressle d											07 31												
Selby a											07 40	08 07											
Selby d											07 40	08 08											
York [8] 33 a											08 14												
Saltmarshe d	←																08 08						
Goole d	07 15																08 13					08 34	
Thorne North d	07 24																08 22						
Cleethorpes d							07 00									07 18							
New Clee d																							
Grimsby Docks d							07 05																
Grimsby Town a							07 07									07 25							
Grimsby Town d							07 08									07 26							
Great Coates d							07 12																
Healing d							07 15																
Stallingborough d							07 18																
Habrough d							07 24									07 36							
Ulceby d							07 28																
Thornton Abbey d							07 32																
Goxhill d							07 35																
New Holland d							07 40																
Barrow Haven d							07 43																
Barton-on-Humber a							07 48																
Barton-on-Humber 🚌 d								07 53															
Hull Bus Station 🚌 a								08 18															
Barnetby d																07 45							
Scunthorpe a																07 59							
Scunthorpe d				07 34												08 00		08 10					
Althorpe d				07 39														08 15					
Crowle d				07 45														08 21					
Thorne South d				07 53														08 30					
Hatfield & Stainforth d	07 30			07 59													08 28	08 35					
Kirk Sandall d	07 34			08 03													08 32	08 39					
Adwick 31 d														08 07		*08 12*						*08 35*	
Bentley (S.Yorks) 31 d														08 11		*08 16*						*08 39*	
Doncaster [7] 31 a	07 45			08 13										08 15		08 30	08 43	08 52				08 57	
London Kings Cross [15] ⊖ 26 a	*09 51*															*10 27*	*10 41*					*10 58*	
York [8] 26 d		07 27								07 44				*07 36*				*08 30*			08 19		
Doncaster [7] d	07 46	07 52	07 59											08 17		08 42		09 02 →				08 59	
Conisbrough d	07 53													08 24									
Mexborough d	07 57					←								08 28									
Swinton (S.Yorks) d	08 00 →					08 00								08 31	08 34								
Rotherham Central d						08b12								08 41	08 47								
Meadowhall 🚋 d					08 17	08c22			08 37				08 47	08 49	08 53	09 00				09 03		09 19	09 22
Sheffield [7] 🚋 a		08 20	08 21		08 28	08 31			08 47	08 51			08 54	08 57	09 01	09 07				09 15	09 20	09 27	09 30
Sheffield d																09 11							
Stockport 78 a						*09 25*						*10e01*				09 53							*10 24*
Manchester Piccadilly [10] 78 🚋 a						*09 36*						09 37				10 03							*10 36*
Manchester Airport 85 ✈ a												*10 02*				10 33							

For general notes see front of timetable
For details of catering facilities see Directory of Train Operators

A To Paignton (Table 51)
B From Leeds to St Pancras International (Table 53)
C To Adwick (Table 31)
D From Huddersfield (Table 34)
E From Leeds (Table 34)
G From Newcastle to Bournemouth (Table 51)
H From Beverley (Table 43)
J From Barnsley to St Pancras International (Table 53)
K From Leeds (Table 31)
L From Bridlington (Table 43)
N To Lincoln (Table 30)
Q From Newcastle to Bristol Temple Meads (Table 51)
b Arr. 0809
c Arr. 0819
e Change at Manchester Piccadilly

Hull and Cleethorpes → Doncaster → Meadowhall, Sheffield, Manchester and Manchester Airport
Cleethorpes → Barton-on-Humber

Network Diagram - see first page of Table 18

		HT	NT	XC	NT	NT	NT	NT	TP		TP	NT	NT	XC	NT	NT	XC	NT	NT	NT	EM	NT	NT	NT
		1 ◇		1 ◇					1 ◇		1 ◇			1 ◇			1 ◇							
			A	B	C	D		E				C	G	H	J	A	K			[bus]	L	C	D	
		[1st class restaurant] [buffet]		[buffet]							[trolley]			[buffet]			[buffet]							
Hull	d							08 29	08 37				08 56					09 02						
Hessle	d							08 36																
Ferriby	d							08 41																
Brough	d							08 46	08 49				09 08					09 14						
Broomfleet	d																							
Gilberdyke	d							08 53										09 21						
Eastrington	d	←																						
Howden	d	08 26																09 28						
Wressle	d																							
Selby	a	08 36							09 07									09 38						
	d	08 37							09 08									09 38						
York 8	33 a								*09 41*									10 10						
Saltmarshe	d																							
Goole	d							09 02					09 22											
Thorne North	d							09 10																
Cleethorpes	d										08 28								09 00					
New Clee	d																		09x03					
Grimsby Docks	d																		09 05					
Grimsby Town	a										08 35								09 08					
	d										08 36								09 08		09 28			
Great Coates	d																		09 12					
Healing	d																		09 15					
Stallingborough	d																		09 18					
Habrough	d										08 46								09 24		09 37			
Ulceby	d																		09 28					
Thornton Abbey	d																		09 32					
Goxhill	d																		09 35					
New Holland	d																		09 40					
Barrow Haven	d																		09 43					
Barton-on-Humber	a																		09 48					
Barton-on-Humber	[bus] d																			09 53				
Hull Bus Station	[bus] a																			10 18				
Barnetby	d										08 54										09a46			
Scunthorpe	a										09 10													
	d										09 10					09 17								
Althorpe	d															09 22								
Crowle	d															09 29								
Thorne South	d															09 37								
Hatfield & Stainforth	d							09 16								09 42								
Kirk Sandall	d							09 21								09 47								
Adwick	31 d						09 13																	10 10
Bentley (S.Yorks)	31 d						09 17																	10 14
Doncaster 7	31 a	09 00					09 22	09 31			09 40		09 46			09 57								10 19
London Kings Cross 15	⊖ 26 a	10 49	←				*11 32*						*11 50*											*12 14*
York 8	26 d		*08 30*	08 44			*08 51*							09 27			09 44							*09 36*
Doncaster 7	d		09 02				09 24				09 42		09 48	09 51		10 02								10 24
Conisbrough	d		09 09				09 31									10 09								10 31
Mexborough	d		09 13				09 35									10 13								10 35
Swinton (S.Yorks)	d		09 16			09 35	09 42									10 16							10 34	10b41
Rotherham Central	d		09 27			09 44	09 50									10 27							10 45	10 50
Meadowhall	[tram] d		09 33		09 49	09 51	09 56				10 00	10 03	10 07		10 19	10 33						10 49	10 51	10 56
Sheffield 7	[tram] a		09 41	09 51	09 57	10 02	10 04				10 07	10 15	10 18	10 20	10 30	10 41	10 51					10 57	11 02	11 05
	d										10 11													
Stockport	78 a								*11c03*		10 53				*11 24*									
Manchester Piccadilly 10	78 [tram] a								10 35		11 03				*11 36*									*12 31*
Manchester Airport	85 [air] a								*11 01*		11 33													

For general notes see front of timetable
For details of catering facilities see Directory of Train Operators

- **A** To Lincoln (Table 30)
- **B** From Edinburgh to Plymouth (Table 51)
- **C** From Leeds (Table 34)
- **D** From Leeds (Table 31)
- **E** From Scarborough (Table 43)
- **G** From Bridlington (Table 43)
- **H** From Newcastle to Bristol Temple Meads (Table 51)
- **J** From Huddersfield (Table 34)
- **K** From Glasgow Central to Bournemouth (Table 51)
- **L** To Newark North Gate (Table 27)
- **b** Arr. 1038
- **c** Change at Manchester Piccadilly

Table 29

Saturdays

Hull and Cleethorpes → Doncaster → Meadowhall, Sheffield, Manchester and Manchester Airport
Cleethorpes → Barton-on-Humber

Network Diagram - see first page of Table 18

		NT	TP	TP	NT	NT	XC	NT	NT	NT	XC	HT	NT	NT	NT	NT	TP	TP	NT	NT	NT	NT	EM	NT
			1 ◇	1 ◇			1 ◇				1 ◇	1 ◇					1 ◇	1 ◇						
		A			B	C	D	E	G	H	J		B	K							L	B	N	C
Hull	d	09 25	09 37			09 56						10 05				10 25	10 37							10 57
Hessle	d	09 32														10 32								
Ferriby	d	09 37														10 37								
Brough	d	09 42	09 49			10 08						10 17				10 42	10 49							11 09
Broomfleet	d																							
Gilberdyke	d	09 49														10 49								
Eastrington	d																							
Howden	d											10 30												
Wressle	d																							
Selby	a		10 07									10 40					11 07							
	d		10 08									10 41					11 08							
York 8	33 a											*11 16*												
Saltmarshe	d																							
Goole	d	09 58				10 22										10 58								11 23
Thorne North	d	10 06														11 06								
Cleethorpes	d			09 28				10 20										10 28	11 00		11 13			
New Clee	d																		11x03					
Grimsby Docks	d																		11 05					
Grimsby Town	a			09 35				10 35										10 35	11 08		11 19			
	d			09 36				10 35										10 36	11 08		11 20		11 30	
Great Coates	d																		11 12					
Healing	d																		11 15					
Stallingborough	d																		11 18					
Habrough	d							10 55										10 46	11 24		11 30		11 39	
Ulceby	d																		11 28					
Thornton Abbey	d																		11 32					
Goxhill	d																		11 35					
New Holland	d																		11 40					
Barrow Haven	d																		11 43					
Barton-on-Humber	a																		11 48					
Barton-on-Humber (bus)	d																			11 53				
Hull Bus Station (bus)	a																			12 18				
Barnetby	d			09 54				11a15										10 54			11a40		11a48	
Scunthorpe	a			10 10														11 10						
	d			10 10						10 18								11 10						
Althorpe	d									10 23														
Crowle	d									10 29														
Thorne South	d									10 38														
Hatfield & Stainforth	d	10 12								10 43						11 11								
Kirk Sandall	d	10 17								10 47						11 17								
Adwick	31 d														11 08									
Bentley (S.Yorks)	31 d														11 12									
Doncaster 7	31 a	10 27		10 40		10 46				10 58		11 01			11 20	11 28		11 40						11 46
London Kings Cross 15	⊖ 26 a	*12 24*				*12 41*				*13 10*		12 46				*13 33*								*13 44*
York 8	26 d			*10 05*			10 25			*10 31*	10 44							*11 00*						
Doncaster 7	d			10 42		10 48	10 53			11 02					11 24			11 42						11 48
Conisbrough	d									11 09					11 31									
Mexborough	d									11 13					11 35									
Swinton (S.Yorks)	d									11 16				11 34	11 41									
Rotherham Central	d									11 27				11 45	11 50									
Meadowhall	d			11 00	11 04	11 06			11 19	11 33			11 49	11 51	11 56			12 00				12 03		12 06
Sheffield 7	a			11 07	11 15	11 17	11 20		11 30	11 41	11 51		11 57	12 02	12 05			12 07				12 15		12 17
	d			11 11														12 11						
Stockport	78 a		*12b03*	11 53					*12 24*								*13b03*	12 53						
Manchester Piccadilly 10	78 a		11 35	12 03					*12 36*						*13 31*		12 35	13 03						
Manchester Airport	85 a		*12 01*	12 33													*13 01*	13 33						

For general notes see front of timetable
For details of catering facilities see Directory of Train Operators

- **A** From Beverley (Table 43)
- **B** From Leeds (Table 34)
- **C** From Bridlington (Table 43)
- **D** From Newcastle to Bristol Temple Meads (Table 51)
- **E** From 2 February. To Gainsborough Central (Table 30)
- **G** From Huddersfield (Table 34)
- **H** To Lincoln (Table 30)
- **J** From Edinburgh to Plymouth (Table 51)
- **K** From Leeds (Table 31)
- **L** Until 26 January. To Sheffield via Retford (Table 30)
- **N** To Newark North Gate (Table 27)
- **b** Change at Manchester Piccadilly

Table 29

Hull and Cleethorpes → Doncaster → Meadowhall, Sheffield, Manchester and Manchester Airport Cleethorpes → Barton-on-Humber

Network Diagram - see first page of Table 18

	XC 1◇ A	NT B	NT C	NT D	XC 1◇ E	NT	NT G	NT H	NT	NT	TP 1◇	TP 1◇	NT G	NT J	XC 1◇ K	NT C	NT D		XC 1◇ L	NT G	NT H	NT	NT
Hull d						11 08				11 22	11 37			11 57									12 22
Hessle d										11 29													12 29
Ferriby d										11 34													12 34
Brough d						11 20				11 39	11 49			12 09									12 39
Broomfleet d																							12 44
Gilberdyke d										11 46													12 49
Eastrington d																							
Howden d																							
Wressle d																							
Selby a						11 39					12 07												
d						11 40					12 08												
York 8 33 a						12 10					*13 23*												
Saltmarshe d										11 52													
Goole d										11 58				12 23									12 58
Thorne North d										12 06													13 06
Cleethorpes d												11 28											
New Clee d																							
Grimsby Docks d																							
Grimsby Town a												11 35											
d												11 36											
Great Coates d																							
Healing d																							
Stallingborough d																							
Habrough d																							
Ulceby d																							
Thornton Abbey d																							
Goxhill d																							
New Holland d																							
Barrow Haven d																							
Barton-on-Humber a																							
Barton-on-Humber (bus) d																							
Hull Bus Station (bus) a																							
Barnetby d												11 54											
Scunthorpe a												12 10											
d				11 17								12 10					12 18						
Althorpe d				11 22													12 23						
Crowle d				11 29													12 29						
Thorne South d				11 37													12 38						
Hatfield & Stainforth d				11 42						12 12							12 43						13 12
Kirk Sandall d				11 47						12 17							12 47						13 17
Adwick 31 d									12 13													13 12	
Bentley (S.Yorks) 31 d									12 17													13 16	
Doncaster 7 31 a				11 58					12 22	12 27		12 40		12 45			12 59					13 23	13 27
London Kings Cross 15 ⊖ 26 a				*13 59*						*14 27*				*14 44*									*15 21*
York 8 26 d	11 27	11 01			11 44				*11 33*			*11 59*			12 25				12 44			*12 31*	
Doncaster 7 d	11 55			12 02					12 24			12 42		12 48	12 52		13 01					13 25	
Conisbrough d				12 09					12 31								13 09					13 32	
Mexborough d				12 13					12 35								13 13					13 36	
Swinton (S.Yorks) d		12 01		12 16				12 34	12 42								13 16				13 34	13 42	
Rotherham Central d		12 11		12 27				12 45	12 50								13 27				13 45	13 50	
Meadowhall (tram) d		12 16	12 19	12 33			12 49	12 51	12 56			13 00	13 03	13 06		13 21	13 33			13 49	13 51	13 56	
Sheffield 7 (tram) a	12 20	12 25	12 30	12 41	12 51		12 57	13 02	13 04			13 07	13 15	13 17	13 20	13 31	13 41		13 51	13 57	14 02	14 04	
d												13 11											
Stockport 78 a			*13 24*								*14b03*	13 53				*14 25*							
Manchester Piccadilly 10 78 (tram) a			*13 36*								13 35	14 03				*14 36*							
Manchester Airport 85 ✈ a											*14 01*	14 33							*15 33*				

For general notes see front of timetable
For details of catering facilities see Directory of Train Operators

A From Newcastle to Plymouth (Table 51)
B Via Pontefract Baghill (Table 33)
C From Huddersfield (Table 34)
D To Lincoln (Table 30)
E From Dundee (Table 229) to Bournemouth (Table 51)
G From Leeds (Table 34)
H From Leeds (Table 31)
J From Bridlington (Table 43)
K From Newcastle to Bristol Temple Meads (Table 51)
L From Glasgow Central (from 29 March from Edinburgh) (Table 51) to Penzance (Table 135)
b Change at Manchester Piccadilly

Table 29 — Saturdays

Hull and Cleethorpes → Doncaster → Meadowhall, Sheffield, Manchester and Manchester Airport
Cleethorpes → Barton-on-Humber

Network Diagram - see first page of Table 18

		TP	TP	NT	NT	XC	NT	NT	XC	NT	NT	EM	NT	NT	HT	NT	NT	NT	TP	TP	NT	NT	NT	XC
		1◇	1◇			1◇			1◇						1◇				1◇	1◇				1◇
				A	B	C	D	E	G		🚌	H	A	J							K 🚌	A	L	C
			🛒			☕			☕						⊠ ☕					🛒				☕
Hull	d	12 37			12 57										13 05		13 12	13 25	13 37				13 57	
Hessle	d																	13 32						
Ferriby	d																	13 37						
Brough	d	12 49			13 09										13 17		13 24	13 42	13 49				14 09	
Broomfleet	d																							
Gilberdyke	d																13 31	13 49						
Eastrington	d																13 36							
Howden	d														13 29		13 40							
Wressle	d																13 45							
Selby	a	13 07													13 39		13 53		14 07					
	d	13 08													13 40		13 54		14 08					
York 8	33 a																14 25							
Saltmarshe	d																							
Goole	d				13 23													13 58					14 23	
Thorne North	d																	14 06						
Cleethorpes	d		12 28							13 00										13 28	13 30			
New Clee	d									13x03														
Grimsby Docks	d									13 05														
Grimsby Town	a		12 35							13 08										13 35	13 45			
	d		12 36							13 08		13 25								13 36	13 45			
Great Coates	d									13 12														
Healing	d									13 15														
Stallingborough	d									13 18														
Habrough	d									13 24		13 35									14 05			
Ulceby	d									13 28														
Thornton Abbey	d									13 32														
Goxhill	d									13 35														
New Holland	d									13 40														
Barrow Haven	d									13 43														
Barton-on-Humber	a									13 48														
Barton-on-Humber	🚌 d										13 53													
Hull Bus Station	🚌 a										14 18													
Barnetby	d		12 54									13a43								13 54	14a25			
Scunthorpe	a		13 10																	14 10				
	d		13 10					13 17												14 10				
Althorpe	d							13 22																
Crowle	d							13 29																
Thorne South	d							13 37																
Hatfield & Stainforth	d							13 42										14 12						
Kirk Sandall	d							13 47										14 17						
Adwick	31 d															14 14								
Bentley (S.Yorks)	31 d															14 18								
Doncaster 7	31 a		13 40		13 46			13 58							14 03	14 22		14 27		14 40			14 46	
London Kings Cross 15	⊖ 26 a				*15 41*										15 49			*16 30*					*16 47*	
York 8	26 d					13 28			13 44							*13 34*								14 30
Doncaster 7	d		13 42		13 48	13 54		14 02								14 24				14 42			14 48	14 55
Conisbrough	d							14 09								14 31								
Mexborough	d							14 13								14 35								
Swinton (S.Yorks)	d							14 16						14 34		14 42								
Rotherham Central	d							14 27						14 45		14 50								
Meadowhall	🚊 d		14 00	14 03	14 07		14 19	14 33					14 49	14 51		14 56				15 00		15 03	15 06	
Sheffield 7	🚊 a		14 07	14 15	14 17	14 20	14 30	14 41	14 51				14 57	15 02		15 04				15 07		15 15	15 17	15 20
	d		14 11																	15 11				
Stockport	78 a	*15b03*	14 53				*15 24*												*16b03*	15 53				
Manchester Piccadilly 10	78 🚊 a	14 37	15 03				*15 36*												15 35	16 03				
Manchester Airport	85 ✈ a	*15 01*	15 33																*16 01*	16 33				

For general notes see front of timetable
For details of catering facilities see Directory of Train Operators

A From Leeds (Table 34)
B From Scarborough (Table 43)
C From Newcastle to Bristol Temple Meads (Table 51)
D From Huddersfield (Table 34)
E To Lincoln (Table 30)
G From Aberdeen (Table 229) to Bournemouth (Table 51)
H To Newark North Gate (Table 27)
J From Leeds (Table 31)
K From 2 February. To Gainsborough Central (Table 30)
L From Bridlington (Table 43)
b Change at Manchester Piccadilly

Hull and Cleethorpes → Doncaster → Meadowhall, Sheffield, Manchester and Manchester Airport
Cleethorpes → Barton-on-Humber

Network Diagram - see first page of Table 18

		NT	NT	XC	NT	NT	NT	NT	TP	TP	NT	NT	NT
				1◇					1◇	1◇			
		A	B	C	D	E					D		G
Hull	d							14 25	14 37			14 51	14 57
Hessle	d							14 32					
Ferriby	d							14 37					
Brough	d							14 42	14 49			15 03	15 09
Broomfleet	d												
Gilberdyke	d							14 49					
Eastrington	d												
Howden	d												
Wressle	d												
Selby	a								15 07			15 22	
	d								15 08			15 22	
York 8	33 a											15 55	
Saltmarshe	d												
Goole	d							14 58					15 23
Thorne North	d							15 06					
Cleethorpes	d									14 28			
New Clee	d												
Grimsby Docks	d												
Grimsby Town	a									14 35			
	d									14 36			
Great Coates	d												
Healing	d												
Stallingborough	d												
Habrough	d									14 46			
Ulceby	d												
Thornton Abbey	d												
Goxhill	d												
New Holland	d												
Barrow Haven	d												
Barton-on-Humber	a												
Barton-on-Humber	bus d												
Hull Bus Station	bus a												
Barnetby	d									14 54			
Scunthorpe	a									15 10			
	d		14 18							15 10			
Althorpe	d		14 23										
Crowle	d		14 29										
Thorne South	d		14 38										
Hatfield & Stainforth	d		14 43					15 12					
Kirk Sandall	d		14 47					15 17					
Adwick	31 d						15 13						
Bentley (S.Yorks)	31 d						15 17						
Doncaster 7	31 a		14 58				15 22	15 27		15 40			15 47
London Kings Cross 15	⊖ 26 a							*17 28*					*17 43*
York 8	26 d			14 44			*14 40*						
Doncaster 7	d		15 02				15 24			15 42			15 48
Conisbrough	d		15 09				15 31						
Mexborough	d		15 13				15 35						
Swinton (S.Yorks)	d		15 16			15 34	15 42						
Rotherham Central	d		15 27			15 43	15 50						
Meadowhall	d	15 19	15 33		15 49	15 51	15 56			16 00	16 06		16 09
Sheffield 7	a	15 30	15 41	15 51	15 57	16 02	16 04			16 07	16 15		16 17
	d									16 11			
Stockport	78 a	*16 24*							17b01	16 53			
Manchester Piccadilly 10	78 a	*16 37*							16 35	17 03			
Manchester Airport	85 a								*17 11*	17 39			

		XC	NT	NT	NT	XC	NT	NT	HT	NT	NT	NT
		1◇				1◇			1◇			
		H	A	J	B	K	D	E			L	
Hull	d								15 06			
Hessle	d											
Ferriby	d											
Brough	d								15 18			
Broomfleet	d											
Gilberdyke	d											
Eastrington	d											
Howden	d								15 31			
Wressle	d											
Selby	a								15 41			
	d								15 42			
York 8	33 a											
Saltmarshe	d											
Goole	d											
Thorne North	d											
Cleethorpes	d										14 56	15 00
New Clee	d											15x03
Grimsby Docks	d											15 05
Grimsby Town	a										15 02	15 09
	d										15 04	15 10
Great Coates	d											15 14
Healing	d											15 17
Stallingborough	d											15 20
Habrough	d										15 14	15 26
Ulceby	d											15 29
Thornton Abbey	d											15 34
Goxhill	d											15 37
New Holland	d											15 41
Barrow Haven	d											15 44
Barton-on-Humber	a											15 50
Barton-on-Humber	bus d											
Hull Bus Station	bus a											
Barnetby	d										15a23	
Scunthorpe	a											
	d				15 17							
Althorpe	d				15 22							
Crowle	d				15 29							
Thorne South	d				15 37							
Hatfield & Stainforth	d				15 42							
Kirk Sandall	d				15 47							
Adwick	31 d									16 13		
Bentley (S.Yorks)	31 d									16 17		
Doncaster 7	31 a				15 58				16 01	16 22		
London Kings Cross 15	⊖ 26 a				*18 10*				17 45			
York 8	26 d	15 27		15 12	*15 30*	15 44						
Doncaster 7	d	15 55			16 02					16 24		
Conisbrough	d				16 09					16 31		
Mexborough	d				16 13					16 35		
Swinton (S.Yorks)	d			16 10	16 16			16 34		16 42		
Rotherham Central	d			16 18	16 27			16 43		16 50		
Meadowhall	d		16 19	16 24	16 33		16 49	16 51		16 56		
Sheffield 7	a	16 20	16 30	16 35	16 41	16 51	16 57	17 02		17 04		
	d											
Stockport	78 a			*17 24*								
Manchester Piccadilly 10	78 a											
Manchester Airport	85 a											

For general notes see front of timetable
For details of catering facilities see Directory of Train Operators

- **A** From Huddersfield (Table 34)
- **B** To Lincoln (Table 30)
- **C** From Edinburgh to Plymouth (Table 51)
- **D** From Leeds (Table 34)
- **E** From Leeds (Table 31)
- **G** From Scarborough (Table 43)
- **H** From Newcastle to Cardiff Central (from 29 March to Bristol Temple Meads) (Table 51)
- **J** Via Pontefract Baghill (Table 33)
- **K** From Edinburgh to Bournemouth (Table 51)
- **L** Until 26 January. To Sheffield via Retford (Table 30)
- **b** Change at Manchester Piccadilly

Table 29

Saturdays

Hull and Cleethorpes → Doncaster → Meadowhall, Sheffield, Manchester and Manchester Airport
Cleethorpes → Barton-on-Humber

Network Diagram - see first page of Table 18

	NT	EM	NT	TP	TP		NT	NT	XC	NT	NT	XC	NT	NT	NT	NT	NT	TP	TP	NT	NT	NT	XC
				1 ◇	1 ◇				1 ◇			1 ◇						1 ◇	1 ◇				1 ◇
		A					B	C	D	E	G	H		B	J		K					L	D
Hull d			15 25	15 37				15 57					16 10				16 27	16 37				16 54	
Hessle d			15 32														16 34						
Ferriby d			15 37														16 39						
Brough d			15 42	15 49				16 09					16 22				16 44	16 49				17 06	
Broomfleet d																	16 49						
Gilberdyke d			15 49										16 29				16 54					17 13	
Eastrington d																							
Howden d													16 36										
Wressle d																							
Selby a				16 07									16 46					17 07					
d				16 08									16 47					17 08					
York 8 33 a													17 13										
Saltmarshe d																	16 59						
Goole d			15 58					16 24									17 04					17 22	
Thorne North d			16 06														17 13						
Cleethorpes d					15 28														16 28	17 00			
New Clee d																							
Grimsby Docks d																				17 05			
Grimsby Town a					15 35														16 35	17 07			
d		15 28			15 36														16 36	17 08			
Great Coates d																				17 12			
Healing d																				17 15			
Stallingborough d																				17 18			
Habrough d		15 37																		17 24			
Ulceby d																				17 28			
Thornton Abbey d																				17 32			
Goxhill d																				17 35			
New Holland d																				17 40			
Barrow Haven d																				17 43			
Barton-on-Humber a																				17 48			
Barton-on-Humber (bus) d	15 56																				17 57		
Hull Bus Station (bus) a	16 21																				18 23		
Barnetby d		15a46			15 54														16 54				
Scunthorpe a					16 10														17 09				
d					16 10						16 18								17 10				
Althorpe d											16 23												
Crowle d											16 29												
Thorne South d											16 38												
Hatfield & Stainforth d			16 12								16 43						17 19						
Kirk Sandall d			16 17								16 47						17 23						
Adwick 31 d																*17 05*							
Bentley (S.Yorks) 31 d																*17 09*							
Doncaster 7 31 a			16 28		16 41			16 46			16 58						17 34		17 40			17 45	
London Kings Cross 15 ⊖ 26 a			*18 28*					*18 46*														*19 40*	
York 8 26 d					*15 57*				16 25			16 44				*16 34*							17 25
Doncaster 7 d					16 42			16 48	16 53		17 02					17 24			17 42			17 48	17 55
Conisbrough d											17 09					17 31							
Mexborough d											17 13					17 35							
Swinton (S.Yorks) d											17 16				17 34	17 42							
Rotherham Central d											17 27				17 45	17 50							
Meadowhall d					17 00		17 03	17 06		17 19	17 33			17 49	17 51	17 56			18 00			18 06	
Sheffield 7 a					17 07		17 15	17 17	17 18	17 30	17 41	17 51		17 57	18 02	18 05			18 07			18 18	18 20
d					17 11														18 11				
Stockport 78 a				*18b01*	17 53					*18 26*								*19b01*	18 53				
Manchester Piccadilly 10 78 a				17 35	18 03											*19 33*		18 35	19 03				
Manchester Airport 85 a				*18 05*	18 38													*19 08*	19 34				

For general notes see front of timetable
For details of catering facilities see Directory of Train Operators

A To Newark North Gate (Table 27)
B From Leeds (Table 34)
C From Bridlington (Table 43)
D From Newcastle to Bristol Temple Meads (Table 51)
E From Huddersfield (Table 34)
G To Lincoln (Table 30)
H From Edinburgh to Plymouth (Table 51)
J From Leeds (Table 31)
K From Scarborough (Table 43)
L From Beverley (Table 43)
b Change at Manchester Piccadilly

Table 29

Hull and Cleethorpes → Doncaster → Meadowhall, Sheffield, Manchester and Manchester Airport
Cleethorpes → Barton-on-Humber

Network Diagram - see first page of Table 18

		NT	NT	TP	EM	XC	NT	NT	NT	NT	NT	TP	EM	NT	NT	NT	NT	NT	XC	NT	TP	NT	NT	XC
				1 ◇	1 ◇	1 ◇						1 ◇							1 ◇		1 ◇			1 ◇
		A	B	C	D	E	G	H	G	J			K	L	G	N	N	Q	U	N		A		V
Hull	d			17 00												17 18	17 42	17 55			18 02			
Hessle	d															17 25	17 49							
Ferriby	d															17 30	17 54							
Brough	d			17 12												17 35	17 59	18 07			18 14			
Broomfleet	d															17 40								
Gilberdyke	d															17 45	18 06							
Eastrington	d															17 49								
Howden	d															17 54								
Wressle	d															17 58								
Selby	a			17 30												18 06		18 25			18 32			
	d															18 06		18 26			18 33			
York 8	33 a															18 36								
Saltmarshe	d																18 12			←				
Goole	d																18 19 →			18 19				
Thorne North	d																			18 28				
Cleethorpes	d							17 15				17 28		18 06										
New Clee	d																							
Grimsby Docks	d																							
Grimsby Town	a							17 30				17 35		18 12										
	d							17 30				17 36	18 06	18 13										
Great Coates	d																							
Healing	d																							
Stallingborough	d																							
Habrough	d							17 50				17 46	18 16	18 23										
Ulceby	d																							
Thornton Abbey	d																							
Goxhill	d																							
New Holland	d																							
Barrow Haven	d																							
Barton-on-Humber	a																							
Barton-on-Humber	d																							
Hull Bus Station	a																							
Barnetby	d							18a10				17 54	18a25	18a34										
Scunthorpe	a											18 10												
	d		17 18									18 10											18 17	
Althorpe	d		17 23																				18 22	
Crowle	d		17 29																				18 29	
Thorne South	d		17 38																				18 37	
Hatfield & Stainforth	d		17 43																	18 34			18 45	
Kirk Sandall	d		17 47																	18 39			18 50	
Adwick	31 d				17b54							18 14												
Bentley (S.Yorks)	31 d				17b58							18 18												
Doncaster 7	31 a		17 58									18 40						18 45		18 51			19 01	
London Kings Cross 15	⊖ 26 a		20 12															20 35					21 15	
York 8	26 d		17 31		17 49	17 44													18 25				18 28	18 44
Doncaster 7	d		18 02		18 15						18 24	18 42						18 47	18 51				19 03	
Conisbrough	d		18 09								18 31												19 10	
Mexborough	d		18 13								18 35												19 14	
Swinton (S.Yorks)	d		18 16							18 34	18 41												19 17	
Rotherham Central	d		18 27							18 43	18 48												19 27	
Meadowhall	d	18 19	18 33		18 38		18 04		18 48	18 51	18 54	19 00			19 04			19 06				19 19	19 33	
Sheffield 7	a	18 30	18 41		18 45	18 51	18 15		18 57	19 02	19 04	19 07			19 15			19 15	19 20			19 30	19 42	19 51
	d											19 11												
Stockport	78 a	19 24										19 53									20c24	20 25		
Manchester Piccadilly 10	78 a	19 35										20 03									19 59	20 36		
Manchester Airport	85 a	20e05										20 34									20 58	21e09		

For general notes see front of timetable
For details of catering facilities see Directory of Train Operators

- **A** From Huddersfield (Table 34)
- **B** To Lincoln (Table 30)
- **C** To Huddersfield (Table 39)
- **D** To St Pancras International (Table 53)
- **E** From Edinburgh to Southampton Central (Table 51)
- **G** From Leeds (Table 34)
- **H** From 2 February. To Gainsborough Central (Table 30)
- **J** From Leeds (Table 31)
- **K** To Newark North Gate (Table 27)
- **L** Until 26 January. To Sheffield via Retford (Table 30)
- **N** From Beverley (Table 43)
- **Q** From Scarborough (Table 43)
- **U** From Newcastle to Birmingham New Street (Table 51)
- **V** From Edinburgh to Bristol Temple Meads (Table 51)
- **b** Change at Doncaster
- **c** Change at Manchester Piccadilly
- **e** Change at Sheffield and Manchester Piccadilly

Table 29

Saturdays

Hull and Cleethorpes → Doncaster → Meadowhall, Sheffield, Manchester and Manchester Airport
Cleethorpes → Barton-on-Humber

Network Diagram - see first page of Table 18

		NT	NT	HT	NT	NT	TP	NT	NT	NT	EM	NT	NT	NT	TP	NT	NT	XC	NT	NT	NT	TP	NT	TP
				1 ◇			1 ◇								1 ◇			1 ◇				1 ◇		1 ◇
		A	B					A			C				D	E	G	H	J	A	B	D	A	
				⊠ ☕			🍴			🚌														
Hull	d			18 12		18 24						18 46	18 53		18 59				19 24			19 55		
Hessle	d					18 31													19 31					
Ferriby	d					18 36													19 36					
Brough	d			18 25		18 41						18 58	19 05		19 11				19 41			20 07		
Broomfleet	d																							
Gilberdyke	d					18 48						19 05							19 48					
Eastrington	d																							
Howden	d			18 37								19 12												
Wressle	d																							
Selby	a			18 46								19 22			19 29							20 25		
	d			18 47								19 22												
York 8 33	a											19 50										*21 00*		
Saltmarshe	d																							
Goole	d					18 57							19 19						19 58					
Thorne North	d					19 05													20 06					
Cleethorpes	d						18 28		19 00															19 28
New Clee	d																							
Grimsby Docks	d								19 05															
Grimsby Town	a						18 35		19 07															19 35
	d						18 36		19 08		19 28													19 36
Great Coates	d								19 12															
Healing	d								19 15															
Stallingborough	d								19 18															
Habrough	d						18 46		19 24		19 38													19 46
Ulceby	d								19 28															
Thornton Abbey	d								19 32															
Goxhill	d								19 35															
New Holland	d								19 40															
Barrow Haven	d								19 43															
Barton-on-Humber	a								19 48															
Barton-on-Humber 🚌	d									19 55														
Hull Bus Station 🚌	a									20 20														
Barnetby	d						18 54				19a46													19 54
Scunthorpe	a						19 10																	20 10
	d						19 10							19 15										20 10
Althorpe	d													19 20										
Crowle	d													19 26										
Thorne South	d													19 35										
Hatfield & Stainforth	d					19 12								19 40					20 13					
Kirk Sandall	d					19 17								19 44					20 17					
Adwick 31	d				*18 53*																			*19 53*
Bentley (S.Yorks) 31	d				*18 57*																			*19 57*
Doncaster 7 31	a			19 04		19 26	19 40						19 45	19 56					20 30					20 40
London Kings Cross 15 ⊖ 26	a			20 46										*21 48*										*22 47*
York 8 26	d																	19 44						*20 05*
Doncaster 7	d				19 25		19 42						19 49				20 03							20 42
Conisbrough	d				19 32												20 10							20 48
Mexborough	d				19 36												20 14							20 52
Swinton (S.Yorks)	d		19 34		19 43												20 17				20 34			20 55
Rotherham Central	d		19 43		19 51												20 29				20 43			21 01
Meadowhall 🚊	d	19 49	19 52		19 56		20 00	20 04					20 07			20 24	20 35			20 48	20 51		21 03	21 07
Sheffield 7 🚊	a	19 57	20 02		20 05		20 07	20 15					20 18			20 35	20 42	20 51		20 57	21 02		21 15	21 18
	d						20 11																	
Stockport 78	a						20 53						*21 11*											
Manchester Piccadilly 10 78 🚊	a						21 03						*21 25*											
Manchester Airport 85 ✈	a						21 34						*21b58*											

For general notes see front of timetable
For details of catering facilities see Directory of Train Operators

- **A** From Leeds (Table 34)
- **B** From Leeds (Table 31)
- **C** To Lincoln (Table 27)
- **D** To Leeds (Table 39)
- **E** From Huddersfield (Table 34)
- **G** To Worksop (Table 30)
- **H** From Newcastle to Birmingham New Street (Table 51)
- **J** From Scarborough (Table 43)
- **b** Change at Sheffield and Manchester Piccadilly

Table 29

Saturdays

Hull and Cleethorpes → Doncaster → Meadowhall, Sheffield, Manchester and Manchester Airport
Cleethorpes → Barton-on-Humber

Network Diagram - see first page of Table 18

		NT	NT	NT	XC	NT	NT	TP	NT	NT	NT	NT	NT	TP	NT	NT	NT	NT	NT	NT	NT	NT
					1 ◇			1 ◇						1 ◇								
			A	B	C	D	E						🚌		A	D	E			A	E	B
Hull	d			20 03					20 51					21 33								22 22
Hessle	d			20 10																		
Ferriby	d			20 15																		
Brough	d			20 20					21 03					21 45								22 34
Broomfleet	d																					
Gilberdyke	d			20 27										21 53								
Eastrington	d																					
Howden	d																					
Wressle	d																					
Selby	a													22 06								
	d													22 07								
York 8	33 a													*22 53*								
Saltmarshe	d																					
Goole	d			20 36					21 17													22 48
Thorne North	d			20 44					21 26													22 57
Cleethorpes	d							20 28				21 00										
New Clee	d																					
Grimsby Docks	d											21 05										
Grimsby Town	a							20 35				21 07										
	d							20 36				21 08										
Great Coates	d											21 12										
Healing	d											21 15										
Stallingborough	d											21 18										
Habrough	d											21 24										
Ulceby	d											21 27										
Thornton Abbey	d											21 32										
Goxhill	d											21 35										
New Holland	d											21 39										
Barrow Haven	d											21 42										
Barton-on-Humber	a											21 48										
Barton-on-Humber	🚌 d												21 55									
Hull Bus Station	🚌 a												22 20									
Barnetby	d							20 54														
Scunthorpe	a							21 09														
	d	20 18						21 10			21 21								22 21			
Althorpe	d	20 23									21 26								22 26			
Crowle	d	20 30									21 32								22 32			
Thorne South	d	20 38									21 40								22 41			
Hatfield & Stainforth	d	20 43		20 51					21 31		21 46								22 46			23 03
Kirk Sandall	d	20 48		20 56					21 36		21 50								22 50			23 07
Adwick	31 d							*20 57*														*22 50*
Bentley (S.Yorks)	31 d							*21 01*														*22 54*
Doncaster 7	31 a	20 59		21 05				21 40	21 46		22 02								23 02			23 18
London Kings Cross 15	⊖ 26 a																					
York 8	26 d				20 44													*21 51*				
Doncaster 7	d			21 07				21 42	21 49	21 54								22 24				23 19
Conisbrough	d			21 14						22 01								22 31				23 26
Mexborough	d			21 18						22 05								22 35				23 30
Swinton (S.Yorks)	d			21 21			21 35			22 08							22 34	22 38			23 30	23 33
Rotherham Central	d			21 28			21 44			22 16							22 43	22 48			23 38	23 43
Meadowhall	🚋 d		21 24	21 35		21 49	21 53	22 00	22 09	22 22					22 25	22 49	22 51	22 56		23 26	23 43	23 48
Sheffield 7	🚋 a		21 35	21 45	21 51	21 57	22 07	22 07	22 18	22 32					22 35	22 57	23 02	23 05		23 35	23 58	23 58
	d																					
Stockport	78 a							*23 21*														
Manchester Piccadilly 10	78 🚋 a							*23 36*						23 38								
Manchester Airport	85 ✈ a													*00 45*								

For general notes see front of timetable
For details of catering facilities see Directory of Train Operators

- **A** From Huddersfield (Table 34)
- **B** From Bridlington (Table 43)
- **C** From Edinburgh to Birmingham New Street (Table 51)
- **D** From Leeds (Table 34)
- **E** From Leeds (Table 31)

Table 29

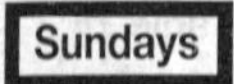

Sundays

until 27 January

Hull and Cleethorpes → Doncaster → Meadowhall, Sheffield, Manchester and Manchester Airport Cleethorpes → Barton-on-Humber

Network Diagram - see first page of Table 18

		NT	TP	EM	NT	NT	NT	NT	XC	NT	TP	NT	NT	NT	TP	NT	XC	TP	XC	NT	HT	NT	NT	TP
			1 ◇	1 ◇					1 ◇		1 ◇				1 ◇		1 ◇	1 ◇	1 ◇		1 ◇			1 ◇
				A		B	C		D			E				B	D		G	B				
				⊡					⊡								⊡		⊡		⊠ ⊡			
Hull	d							08 42		08 54	09 05			09 41							10 12		10 41	
Hessle	d							08 49																
Ferriby	d							08 54																
Brough	d							08 59		09 06	09 17			09 53							10 24		10 53	
Broomfleet	d																							
Gilberdyke	d							09 06						10 00									11 00	
Eastrington	d																							
Howden	d																				10 36			
Wressle	d																							
Selby	a									09 25	09 36										10 46			
	d									09 25	09 36										10 47			
York 8	33 a									09 54														
Saltmarshe	d																							
Goole	d							09 15					09 43	10 09									11 09	
Thorne North	d												09 51											
Cleethorpes	d																	09 41						10 28
New Clee	d																							
Grimsby Docks	d																							
Grimsby Town	a																	09 49						10 35
	d																	09 49						10 36
Great Coates	d																							
Healing	d																							
Stallingborough	d																							
Habrough	d																	09 59						10 46
Ulceby	d																							
Thornton Abbey	d																							
Goxhill	d																							
New Holland	d																							
Barrow Haven	d																							
Barton-on-Humber	a																							
Barton-on-Humber	🚌 d																							
Hull Bus Station	🚌 a																							
Barnetby	d																	10 08						10 54
Scunthorpe	a																	10 23						11 10
	d																	10 23						11 10
Althorpe	d																							
Crowle	d																							
Thorne South	d																							
Hatfield & Stainforth	d												09 57	10 21										
Kirk Sandall	d												10 02	10 26										
Adwick	31 d																					*10 43*		
Bentley (S.Yorks)	31 d																					*10 47*		
Doncaster 7	31 a							09 38					10 11	10 36				10 53			11 03		11 32	11 41
London Kings Cross 15	⊖ 26 a												*12 19*	*12 37*							12 48			*13 36*
York 8	26 d							*09 00*	09 20						*10 02*		10 20	*10 23*	10 28					
Doncaster 7	d	08 03		09 07	09 13			09 39	09 50				10 13		10 42		10 50	10 55				11 13	11 33	11 42
Conisbrough	d	08 10			09 20								10 20									11 20		
Mexborough	d	08 14			09 24								10 24									11 24		
Swinton (S.Yorks)	d	08 17			09 28		09 36						10 27									11 29		
Rotherham Central	d	08 25			09 35		09b48						10 36									11 38		
Meadowhall	🚊 d	08 30	09 00		09 41	09 41	09 54	10 00				10 33	10 42		11 00	11 05		11 13		11 33		11 44	11 51	12 00
Sheffield 7	🚊 a	08 41	09 07	09 31	09 51	09 51	10 04	10 09	10 20			10 43	10 52		11 09	11 15	11 20	11 25	11 40	11 43		11 52	12 03	12 12
	d																							
Stockport	78 a		*11c00*					*12c00*	*12e10*		*11f31*				*13c01*			*13e10*						*13e40*
Manchester Piccadilly 10	78 🚊 a		*10e40*					*11e40*			11 05				*12e40*									
Manchester Airport	85 ✈ a		*11e05*					*12e05*			*11 33*				*13e05*									*14e00*

For general notes see front of timetable
For details of catering facilities see Directory of Train Operators

A From Leeds to St Pancras International (Table 53)
B From Leeds (Table 34)
C From Leeds (Table 31)
D To Bristol Temple Meads (Table 51)
E From Huddersfield (Table 34)
G From Newcastle to Plymouth (Table 51)
b Arr. 0945
c Change at Sheffield and Manchester Piccadilly. By bus to Manchester Piccadilly
e By bus
f Change at Manchester Piccadilly

Table 29

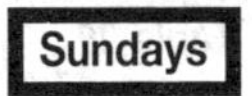

until 27 January

Hull and Cleethorpes → Doncaster → Meadowhall, Sheffield, Manchester and Manchester Airport
Cleethorpes → Barton-on-Humber

Network Diagram - see first page of Table 18

	NT A		XC 1◇ B ☕	TP 1◇	NT C	XC R 1 D ☕	NT E	NT	NT	TP 1◇	XC 1◇ G ☕	XC R 1 H ☕	NT	NT J	NT	NT K	TP 1◇	TP 1◇	NT A	XC 1◇ G ☕	NT C	XC R 1 D ☕	NT E
Hull d				11 00					11 41				11 54			12 41		12 50					
Hessle d																							
Ferriby d																							
Brough d				11 12					11 53				12 06			12 53		13 02					
Broomfleet d																							
Gilberdyke d									12 00							13 00							
Eastrington d																							
Howden d																							
Wressle d																							
Selby a				11 30									12 25					13 21					
d				11 31									12 25					13 21					
York [8] 33 a													12 56										
Saltmarshe d																							
Goole d								11 43	12 09							13 09							
Thorne North d								11 51															
Cleethorpes d																	12 28						
New Clee d																							
Grimsby Docks d																							
Grimsby Town a																	12 35						
d																	12 36						
Great Coates d																							
Healing d																							
Stallingborough d																							
Habrough d																							
Ulceby d																							
Thornton Abbey d																							
Goxhill d																							
New Holland d																							
Barrow Haven d																							
Barton-on-Humber a																							
Barton-on-Humber 🚌 d																							
Hull Bus Station 🚌 a																							
Barnetby d																	12 54						
Scunthorpe a																	13 10						
d																	13 10						
Althorpe d																							
Crowle d																							
Thorne South d																							
Hatfield & Stainforth d								11 57															
Kirk Sandall d								12 02															
Adwick 31 d															12 43								
Bentley (S.Yorks) 31 d															12 47								
Doncaster [7] 31 a								12 11	12 32							13 32	13 41						
London Kings Cross [15] ⊖ 26 a									*14 42*								*15 38*						
York [8] 26 d			11 20			11 28		*11 29*			12 20	12 28			*12 29*	*12 57*				13 20		13 28	
Doncaster [7] d			11 50					12 16		12 42	12 50				13 13	13 33	13 42			13 50			
Conisbrough d								12 23							13 20								
Mexborough d								12 27							13 24								
Swinton (S.Yorks) d					11 55			12 30							13 29						14 01		
Rotherham Central d					12 06			12 38							13 37						14 08		
Meadowhall 🚋 d	12 05				12 11		12 33	12 43		13 00				13 33	13 43	13 51	14 00		14 05		14 14		14 33
Sheffield [7] 🚋 a	12 15		12 20		12 21	12 40	12 43	12 55		13 08	13 20	13 40		13 43	13 55	14 03	14 12		14 15	14 20	14 23	14 40	14 43
d																							
Stockport 78 a				*13b31*			*14c15*			*14c40*	*15c10*						*15c40*	*15b32*			*16c10*		
Manchester Piccadilly [10] 78 🚋 a				12 57														14 52					
Manchester Airport 85 ✈ a				*13 24*						*15c00*							*16c00*	*15 21*					

For general notes see front of timetable
For details of catering facilities see Directory of Train Operators

- **A** From Leeds (Table 34)
- **B** From Newcastle to Plymouth (Table 51)
- **C** From Leeds (Table 31)
- **D** From Edinburgh to Bournemouth (Table 51)
- **E** From Huddersfield (Table 34)
- **G** From Newcastle to Bristol Temple Meads (Table 51)
- **H** From Edinburgh (Table 51) to Penzance (Table 135)
- **J** From Leeds (Table 34) to Lincoln (Table 30)
- **K** From Beverley (Table 43)
- **b** Change at Manchester Piccadilly
- **c** By bus

Table 29

until 27 January

Hull and Cleethorpes → Doncaster → Meadowhall, Sheffield, Manchester and Manchester Airport
Cleethorpes → Barton-on-Humber

Network Diagram - see first page of Table 18

		NT	NT	TP		XC	XC	NT	HT	NT	NT	NT	TP	XC	TP	NT	XC	NT	NT	NT	TP	XC	EM	XC
				1 ◇		1 ◇	R 1		1 ◇				1 ◇	R 1	1 ◇		R 1				1 ◇	1 ◇	1 ◇	R 1
			A			B	C	D						E		G	H	J		A		B	K	L
						🍴	🍴		⊠ 🍴					🍴			🍴					🍴	🍴	🍴
Hull	d		13 41						14 10		14 28	14 41			14 50					15 41				
Hessle	d										14 35													
Ferriby	d										14 40													
Brough	d		13 53						14 22		14 45	14 53			15 02					15 53				
Broomfleet	d																							
Gilberdyke	d		14 00									15 00								16 00				
Eastrington	d																							
Howden	d								14 34															
Wressle	d																							
Selby	a								14 44		15 04				15 21									
	d								14 45		15 04				15 21									
York 8	33 a										15 30													
Saltmarshe	d																							
Goole	d	13 43	14 09									15 09							15 43	16 09				
Thorne North	d	13 51																	15 51					
Cleethorpes	d			13 28									14 28								15 28			
New Clee	d																							
Grimsby Docks	d																							
Grimsby Town	a			13 35									14 35								15 35			
	d			13 36									14 36								15 36			
Great Coates	d																							
Healing	d																							
Stallingborough	d																							
Habrough	d												14 46											
Ulceby	d																							
Thornton Abbey	d																							
Goxhill	d																							
New Holland	d																							
Barrow Haven	d																							
Barton-on-Humber	a																							
Barton-on-Humber	🚌 d																							
Hull Bus Station	🚌 a																							
Barnetby	d			13 54									14 54								15 54			
Scunthorpe	a			14 10									15 10								16 10			
	d			14 10									15 10								16 10			
Althorpe	d																							
Crowle	d																							
Thorne South	d																							
Hatfield & Stainforth	d	13 57																	15 57					
Kirk Sandall	d	14 02																	16 02					
Adwick	31 d									*14 43*													*16b43*	
Bentley (S.Yorks)	31 d									*14 47*													*16b47*	
Doncaster 7	31 a	14 11	14 32	14 41					15 05			15 32	15 41						16 11	16 32	16 41			
London Kings Cross 15	⊖ 26 a	*16 11*		*16 29*					16 50				*17 49*						*18 15*		*18 38*			
York 8	26 d	*13 33*		*14 05*		14 24	14 28			*14 36*				15 21			15 28		*15 34*		*16 03*	16 20	16 40	16 28
Doncaster 7	d	14 13	14 33	14 42		14 50				15 13		15 33	15 42	15 50					16 13	16 33	16 42	16 50	17 06	
Conisbrough	d	14 20								15 20									16 20					
Mexborough	d	14 24								15 24									16 24					
Swinton (S.Yorks)	d	14 29								15 29						15 55			16 29					
Rotherham Central	d	14 37								15 37						16 05			16 37					
Meadowhall	🚊 d	14 42	14 52	15 00				15 33		15 42		15 52	16 00			16 11		16 33	16 42	16 52	17 00			
Sheffield 7	🚊 a	14 52	15 04	15 12		15 20	15 40	15 43		15 51		16 03	16 12	16 20		16 26	16 43	16 43	16 52	17 03	17 12	17 20	17 28	17 40
	d																							
Stockport	78 a			*16c40*		*17c10*							*17c40*		*17e31*	*18c10*					*18c40*			
Manchester Piccadilly 10	78 🚊 a														16 50									
Manchester Airport	85 ✈ a			*17c00*									*18c00*		17 18						*19c00*			

For general notes see front of timetable
For details of catering facilities see Directory of Train Operators

- **A** From Bridlington (Table 43)
- **B** From Newcastle to Bristol Temple Meads (Table 51)
- **C** From Glasgow Central to Plymouth (Table 51)
- **D** From Leeds (Table 34)
- **E** From Newcastle to Cardiff Central (Table 51)
- **G** From Leeds (Table 31)
- **H** From Glasgow Central to Bournemouth (Table 51)
- **J** From Huddersfield (Table 34)
- **K** To St Pancras International (Table 53)
- **L** From Edinburgh to Plymouth (Table 51)
- **b** Change at Doncaster
- **c** By bus
- **e** Change at Manchester Piccadilly

Table 29

Sundays
until 27 January

Hull and Cleethorpes → Doncaster → Meadowhall, Sheffield, Manchester and Manchester Airport Cleethorpes → Barton-on-Humber

Network Diagram - see first page of Table 18

	NT	NT	HT	NT	TP		XC	TP	NT	NT	XC	NT	NT	NT	GR	NT	TP	XC	XC	TP	NT	NT	HT
			1 ◇		1 ◇		1 ◇	1 ◇			R 1				R 1		1 ◇	1 ◇	1 ◇	1 ◇			1 ◇
	A						B		C	D	E	G						H	J		A		
			⊠ ☕				☕				☕				☕			☕	☕				⊠ ☕
Hull d			16 21	16 41				16 50						17 23	17 30	17 41				18 10			18 30
Hessle d																							
Ferriby d																							
Brough d			16 33	16 53				17 02						17 35	17 42	17 53				18 22			18 42
Broomfleet d																							
Gilberdyke d				17 00												18 00							
Eastrington d																							
Howden d			16 45																				18 54
Wressle d																							
Selby a			16 55					17 20						17 54	18 05					18 41			19 04
d			16 56					17 21						17 54	18 05					18 41			19 05
York 8 33 a														18 23									
Saltmarshe d																							
Goole d				17 09									17 43			18 09							
Thorne North d													17 51										
Cleethorpes d					16 28												17 28						
New Clee d																							
Grimsby Docks d																							
Grimsby Town a					16 35												17 35						
d					16 36												17 36						
Great Coates d																							
Healing d																							
Stallingborough d																							
Habrough d																	17 46						
Ulceby d																							
Thornton Abbey d																							
Goxhill d																							
New Holland d																							
Barrow Haven d																							
Barton-on-Humber a																							
Barton-on-Humber 🚌 d																							
Hull Bus Station 🚌 a																							
Barnetby d					16 54												17 54						
Scunthorpe a					17 10												18 10						
d					17 10												18 10						
Althorpe d																							
Crowle d																							
Thorne South d																							
Hatfield & Stainforth d													17 57										
Kirk Sandall d													18 02										
Adwick 31 d																						*18 43*	
Bentley (S.Yorks) 31 d																						*18 47*	
Doncaster 7 31 a			17 14	17 31	17 41								18 11		18 23	18 33	18 41						19 21
London Kings Cross 15 ⊖ 26 a			19 06		*19 47*								*20 12*		20b23		*20 42*						21 12
York 8 26 d				*17 01*			17 20			17 17	17 28		*17 35*				*18 07*	18 20	18 28			*18 29*	
Doncaster 7 d		17 13		17 32	17 42		17 50						18 13			18 34	18 42	18 50				19 15	
Conisbrough d		17 21											18 20									19 22	
Mexborough d		17 25											18 24									19 26	
Swinton (S.Yorks) d		17 29							17 55	18 11			18 29									19 29	
Rotherham Central d		17 37							18 05	18 20			18 37									19 39	
Meadowhall 🚊 d	17 33	17 42		17 52	18 00				18 11	18 26		18 33	18 42			18 52	19 00				19 33	19 44	
Sheffield 7 🚊 a	17 43	17 53		18 02	18 12		18 20		18 23	18 35	18 44	18 47	18 51			19 03	19 12	19 20	19 40		19 43	19 53	
d																							
Stockport 78 a	*19c15*				*19c40*			*19e32*		*20c10*							*20c40*	*21c10*		*20e31*			
Manchester Piccadilly 10 78 🚊 a								18 52		*20c35*								*21c35*		20 11			
Manchester Airport 85 ✈ a					*20c00*			*19 18*									*21c00*			20 52			

For general notes see front of timetable
For details of catering facilities see Directory of Train Operators

A From Leeds (Table 34)
B From Newcastle to Bristol Temple Meads (Table 51)
C From Leeds (Table 31)
D Via Pontefract Baghill (Table 33)
E From Aberdeen (Table 229) to Southampton Central (Table 51)
G From Huddersfield (Table 34)
H From Newcastle to Birmingham New Street (Table 51)
J From Edinburgh to Bristol Temple Meads (Table 51)
b By changing at Doncaster, passengers may arrive at 2012
c By bus
e Change at Manchester Piccadilly

Table 29

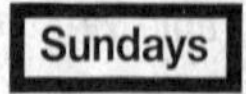

until 27 January

Hull and Cleethorpes → Doncaster → Meadowhall, Sheffield, Manchester and Manchester Airport Cleethorpes → Barton-on-Humber

Network Diagram - see first page of Table 18

		NT	TP 1◇	XC 1◇	NT	XC 1◇	TP 1◇	NT	NT	TP 1◇	XC 1◇	NT	NT	NT	NT	TP 1◇	XC 1◇	TP 1◇	NT	NT	NT	NT
		A		B	C	D	E	G			H	J			K		H	E	L	C	A	J
Hull	d	18 38					19 04						20 22	20 30				21 00			21 15	
Hessle	d																				21 22	
Ferriby	d																				21 27	
Brough	d	18 50					19 16						20 34	20 42				21 12			21 32	
Broomfleet	d																					
Gilberdyke	d	18 57												20 49							21 39	
Eastrington	d																					
Howden	d																					
Wressle	d																					
Selby	a						19 35						20 53					21 31				
	d												20 53									
York 8	33 a												21 18									
Saltmarshe	d																					
Goole	d	19 06												20 58							21 48	
Thorne North	d	19 14																			21 56	
Cleethorpes	d		18 28							19 28						20 28						
New Clee	d																					
Grimsby Docks	d																					
Grimsby Town	a		18 35							19 35						20 35						
	d		18 36							19 36						20 36						
Great Coates	d																					
Healing	d																					
Stallingborough	d																					
Habrough	d									19 46						20 46						
Ulceby	d																					
Thornton Abbey	d																					
Goxhill	d																					
New Holland	d																					
Barrow Haven	d																					
Barton-on-Humber	a																					
Barton-on-Humber	bus d																					
Hull Bus Station	bus a																					
Barnetby	d		18 54							19 54						20 54						
Scunthorpe	a		19 09							20 10						21 10						
	d		19 10							20 10						21 10						
Althorpe	d																					
Crowle	d																					
Thorne South	d																					
Hatfield & Stainforth	d	19 20																			22 02	
Kirk Sandall	d	19 25																			22 07	
Adwick	31 d													20 54							21 43	
Bentley (S.Yorks)	31 d													20 58							21 47	
Doncaster 7	31 a	19 35	19 41							20 41				21 21		21 41					22 17	
London Kings Cross 15	⊖ 26 a		21 47							23 14						23 50						
York 8	26 d	19 05		19 20		19 28			19 30	20 02	20 28			20 40	20 44		21 26				21 28	
Doncaster 7	d	19 37	19 42	19 50					20 14	20 42				21 23		21 42	21 50				22 20	
Conisbrough	d								20 21	20 49											22 27	
Mexborough	d								20 25	20 53											22 31	
Swinton (S.Yorks)	d				19 55				20 32	20 56					21 38					22 32	22 35	
Rotherham Central	d				20 06				20 39	21 02				21 39	21 49					22 40	22 44	
Meadowhall	tram d	19 56	20 00		20 11			20 38	20 45	21 08		21 32		21 45	21 54	22 00			22 41	22 45	22 50	23 33
Sheffield 7	tram a	20 07	20 12	20 20	20 23	20 40		20 46	20 53	21 17	21 43	21 43		21 56	22 05	22 11	22 20		22 51	22 54	22 59	23 43
	d																					
Stockport	78 a		21b40			22b15				23c38		23b59										
Manchester Piccadilly 10	78 tram a					22b40				22b50		00b20										
Manchester Airport	85 ✈ a		22b00							23b15		00c54										

For general notes see front of timetable
For details of catering facilities see Directory of Train Operators

- **A** From Bridlington (Table 43)
- **B** From Newcastle to Birmingham New Street (Table 51)
- **C** From Leeds (Table 31)
- **D** From Glasgow Central to Bristol Temple Meads (Table 51)
- **E** To Leeds (Table 39)
- **G** From Huddersfield (Table 34)
- **H** From Edinburgh to Birmingham New Street (Table 51)
- **J** From Leeds (Table 34)
- **K** Via Pontefract Baghill (Table 33)
- **L** From Barnsley (Table 34)
- **b** By bus
- **c** Change at Sheffield and Manchester Piccadilly. By bus to Manchester Piccadilly

3 February to 23 March

Hull and Cleethorpes → Doncaster → Meadowhall, Sheffield, Manchester and Manchester Airport
Cleethorpes → Barton-on-Humber

Network Diagram - see first page of Table 18

	NT	TP	EM	NT	NT	XC	NT	NT	NT	TP	NT	NT	XC	NT	TP	NT	TP	NT	HT	NT	XC
		1 ◇	1 ◇			1 ◇				1 ◇			1 ◇		1 ◇		1 ◇		1 ◇		R 1
			A		B	C	D				E		G			B		B			H
			☕			☕							☕						⊠ ☕		☕
Hull d								08 42	08 54	09 05				09 41					10 12		
Hessle d								08 49													
Ferriby d								08 54													
Brough d								08 59	09 06	09 17				09 53					10 24		
Broomfleet d																					
Gilberdyke d								09 06						10 00							
Eastrington d																					
Howden d																			10 36		
Wressle d																					
Selby a									09 25	09 36									10 46		
d									09 25	09 36									10 47		
York 8 33 a									09 54												
Saltmarshe d																					
Goole d								09 15				09 43		10 09							
Thorne North d												09 51									
Cleethorpes d																	09 41				
New Clee d																					
Grimsby Docks d																					
Grimsby Town a																	09 49				
d																	09 49				
Great Coates d																					
Healing d																					
Stallingborough d																					
Habrough d																	09 59				
Ulceby d																					
Thornton Abbey d																					
Goxhill d																					
New Holland d																					
Barrow Haven d																					
Barton-on-Humber a																					
Barton-on-Humber 🚌 d																					
Hull Bus Station 🚌 a																					
Barnetby d																	10 08				
Scunthorpe a																	10 23				
d																	10 23				
Althorpe d																					
Crowle d																					
Thorne South d																					
Hatfield & Stainforth d												09 57		10 21							
Kirk Sandall d												10 02		10 26							
Adwick 31 d																				*10 43*	
Bentley (S.Yorks) 31 d																				*10 47*	
Doncaster 7 31 a								09 38				10 11		10 36			10 53		11 03		
London Kings Cross 15 ⊖ 26 a												*12 19*		*12 37*					12 48		
York 8 26 d						*08 58*							*10 02*				*10 23*				*10 28*
Doncaster 7 d	08 03		09 07	09 13		09 34		09 39				10 13	10 35		10 42		10 55			11 13	11 30
Conisbrough d	08 10			09 20								10 20								11 20	
Mexborough d	08 14			09 24								10 24								11 24	
Swinton (S.Yorks) d	08 17			09 28			09 36					10 27								11 29	
Rotherham Central d	08 25			09 35			09b48					10 36								11 38	
Meadowhall 🚋 d	08 30	09 00		09 41	09 41		09 54	10 00			10 33	10 42			11 00	11 05	11 13	11 33		11 44	
Sheffield 7 🚋 a	08 41	09 07	09 31	09 51	09 51	09 58	10 04	10 09			10 43	10 52	10 58		11 09	11 15	11 25	11 43		11 52	11 57
d		09 13													11 13						
Stockport 78 a		09 58						*11 18*		*11c31*					11 58		*12 23*				
Manchester Piccadilly 10 78 🚋 a		10 08						*11 33*		11 05					12 08		*12 36*				
Manchester Airport 85 ✈ a	*10e33*	10f36						*12e11*		*11 33*					12 30		*13e12*				

For general notes see front of timetable
For details of catering facilities see Directory of Train Operators

A From Leeds to St Pancras International (Table 53)
B From Leeds (Table 34)
C From Leeds to Bournemouth (Table 51)
D From Leeds (Table 31)
E From Huddersfield (Table 34)
G From Leeds to Plymouth (Table 51)
H From Newcastle to Bournemouth (Table 51)
b Arr. 0945
c Change at Manchester Piccadilly
e Change at Sheffield and Manchester Piccadilly
f By changing at Manchester Piccadilly, passengers may arrive at 1033

Table 29

Sundays

Hull and Cleethorpes → Doncaster → Meadowhall, Sheffield, Manchester and Manchester Airport
Cleethorpes → Barton-on-Humber

3 February to 23 March

Network Diagram - see first page of Table 18

	NT	TP	TP	NT	NT	NT	NT	NT	XC	TP	NT	NT	XC	NT	NT	TP	TP	NT	NT	NT
		1 ◇	1 ◇						R 1	1 ◇			R 1			1 ◇	1 ◇			
	A			B	C	D			E 🍴		G		H 🍴		J			B	C	D
Hull d	10 41	11 00						11 41						11 54	12 41	12 50				
Hessle d																				
Ferriby d																				
Brough d	10 53	11 12						11 53						12 06	12 53	13 02				
Broomfleet d																				
Gilberdyke d	11 00							12 00							13 00					
Eastrington d																				
Howden d																				
Wressle d																				
Selby a		11 30												12 25		13 21				
d		11 31												12 25		13 21				
York 8 33 a														12 56						
Saltmarshe d																				
Goole d	11 09						11 43	12 09							13 09					
Thorne North d							11 51													
Cleethorpes d			10 28														12 28			
New Clee d																				
Grimsby Docks d																				
Grimsby Town a			10 35														12 35			
d			10 36														12 36			
Great Coates d																				
Healing d																				
Stallingborough d																				
Habrough d			10 46																	
Ulceby d																				
Thornton Abbey d																				
Goxhill d																				
New Holland d																				
Barrow Haven d																				
Barton-on-Humber a																				
Barton-on-Humber 🚌 d																				
Hull Bus Station 🚌 a																				
Barnetby d			10 54														12 54			
Scunthorpe a			11 10														13 10			
d			11 10														13 10			
Althorpe d																				
Crowle d																				
Thorne South d																				
Hatfield & Stainforth d							11 57													
Kirk Sandall d							12 02													
Adwick 31 d												*12 43*								
Bentley (S.Yorks) 31 d												*12 47*								
Doncaster 7 31 a	11 32		11 41				12 11	12 32							13 32		13 41			
London Kings Cross 15 ⊖ 26 a			*13 36*					*14 42*									*15 38*			
York 8 26 d							*11 29*		11b28			*12 29*	12 28		*12 57*					
Doncaster 7 d	11 33		11 42				12 16		12 33	12 42		13 13	13 30		13 33		13 42			
Conisbrough d							12 23					13 20								
Mexborough d							12 27					13 24								
Swinton (S.Yorks) d					11 55		12 30					13 29							14 01	
Rotherham Central d					12 06		12 38					13 37							14 08	
Meadowhall d	11 51		12 00	12 05	12 11	12 33	12 43			13 00	13 33	13 43			13 51		14 00	14 05	14 14	14 33
Sheffield 7 a	12 03		12 08	12 15	12 21	12 43	12 55		12 59	13 08	13 43	13 55	13 58		14 03		14 09	14 15	14 23	14 43
d			12 13							13 13							14 12			
Stockport 78 a		*13c21*	12 56		*13 24*					14 02							15 01		*15 22*	
Manchester Piccadilly 10 78 a		12 57	13 10		*13 36*					14 12						14 52	15 13		*15 33*	
Manchester Airport 85 a		*13 24*	13 36		*14e14*					14 36						*15 18*	15 36		*16e11*	

For general notes see front of timetable
For details of catering facilities see Directory of Train Operators

A 23 March from Bridlington (Table 43)
B From Leeds (Table 34)
C From Leeds (Table 31)
D From Huddersfield (Table 34)
E From Edinburgh (Table 51) to Penzance (Table 135)
G From Leeds (Table 34) to Lincoln (Table 30)
H From Edinburgh to Bournemouth (Table 51)
J From Beverley (23 March from Scarborough) (Table 43)
b By changing at Doncaster, passengers may depart at 1129
c Change at Manchester Piccadilly
e Change at Sheffield and Manchester Piccadilly

Table 29

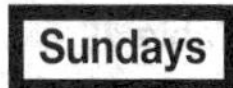

3 February to 23 March

Hull and Cleethorpes → Doncaster → Meadowhall, Sheffield, Manchester and Manchester Airport
Cleethorpes → Barton-on-Humber

Network Diagram - see first page of Table 18

	NT	XC	NT	TP	NT		HT	NT	XC	NT	NT	TP	TP		NT	NT	NT	XC	NT	TP	EM		NT
		R 1		1 ◇			1 ◇		R 1			1 ◇	1 ◇					R 1		1 ◇	1 ◇		
		A	B		C				D		E				G	H		J	B		K		C
		☕					⊠ ☕		☕									☕			☕		
Hull d			13 41				14 10			14 28	14 41	14 50							15 41				
Hessle d										14 35													
Ferriby d										14 40													
Brough d			13 53				14 22			14 45	14 53	15 02							15 53				
Broomfleet d																							
Gilberdyke d			14 00								15 00								16 00				
Eastrington d																							
Howden d							14 34																
Wressle d																							
Selby a							14 44			15 04		15 21											
d							14 45			15 04		15 21											
York 8 33 a										15 30													
Saltmarshe d																							
Goole d	13 43		14 09								15 09						15 43		16 09				
Thorne North d	13 51																15 51						
Cleethorpes d				13 28									14 28							15 28			
New Clee d																							
Grimsby Docks d																							
Grimsby Town a				13 35									14 35							15 35			
d				13 36									14 36							15 36			
Great Coates d																							
Healing d																							
Stallingborough d																							
Habrough d													14 46										
Ulceby d																							
Thornton Abbey d																							
Goxhill d																							
New Holland d																							
Barrow Haven d																							
Barton-on-Humber a																							
Barton-on-Humber 🚌 d																							
Hull Bus Station 🚌 a																							
Barnetby d				13 54									14 54							15 54			
Scunthorpe a				14 10									15 10							16 10			
d				14 10									15 10							16 10			
Althorpe d																							
Crowle d																							
Thorne South d																							
Hatfield & Stainforth d	13 57																15 57						
Kirk Sandall d	14 02																16 02						
Adwick 31 d								14 43													16b43		
Bentley (S.Yorks) 31 d								14 47													16b47		
Doncaster 7 31 a	14 11		14 32	14 41			15 05				15 32		15 41				16 11		16 32	16 41			
London Kings Cross 15 ⊖ 26 a	16 11			16 29			16 50						17 49				18 15			18 38			
York 8 26 d	13 33	13 28		14 05				14 36	14c28								15 34	15e28		16 03	16 40		
Doncaster 7 d	14 13	14 30	14 33	14 42				15 13	15 30		15 33		15 42				16 13	16 30	16 33	16 42	17 06		
Conisbrough d	14 20							15 20									16 20						
Mexborough d	14 24							15 24									16 24						
Swinton (S.Yorks) d	14 29							15 29							15 55		16 29						
Rotherham Central d	14 37							15 37							16 05		16 37						
Meadowhall 🚊 d	14 42		14 51	15 00	15 33			15 42			15 51		16 00		16 11	16 33	16 42		16 51	17 00			17 33
Sheffield 7 🚊 a	14 52	14 58	15 02	15 12	15 43			15 51	15 58		16 02		16 09		16 20	16 43	16 52	16 58	17 02	17 11	17 28		17 43
d				15 13									16 13							17 13			
Stockport 78 a				16 03									16 56		17 22					17 55	18 24		
Manchester Piccadilly 10 78 🚊 a				16 13								16 50	17 11		17 36					18 12	18 36		
Manchester Airport 85 ✈ a				16 36								17 18	17 36		18f11					18 36	19f12		

For general notes see front of timetable
For details of catering facilities see Directory of Train Operators

- **A** From Edinburgh to Plymouth (Table 51)
- **B** From Bridlington (23 March from Scarborough) (Table 43)
- **C** From Leeds (Table 34)
- **D** From Glasgow Central to Bournemouth (Table 51)
- **E** 23 March from Bridlington (Table 43)
- **G** From Leeds (Table 31)
- **H** From Huddersfield (Table 34)
- **J** From Glasgow Central to Plymouth (Table 51)
- **K** To St Pancras International (Table 53)
- **b** Change at Doncaster
- **c** By changing at Doncaster, passengers may depart at 1436
- **e** By changing at Doncaster, passengers may depart at 1534
- **f** Change at Sheffield and Manchester Piccadilly

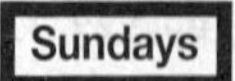

Sundays

3 February to 23 March

Hull and Cleethorpes → Doncaster → Meadowhall, Sheffield, Manchester and Manchester Airport
Cleethorpes → Barton-on-Humber

Network Diagram - see first page of Table 18

	NT	HT	XC	NT	TP	TP	NT		NT	NT	NT	NT	GR	XC	NT		TP	TP	NT	NT	HT	XC	NT
		1 ◇	R 1		1 ◇	1 ◇							R 1	R 1			1 ◇	1 ◇			1 ◇	1 ◇	
			A	B			C		D	E				G	H				J			K	L
		⊠ 🍽	🍽										🍽 ✕	🍽							⊠ 🍽	🍽	
Hull d		16 21		16 41	16 50							17 23	17 30		17 41		18 10				18 30		18 38
Hessle d																							
Ferriby d																							
Brough d		16 33		16 53	17 02							17 35	17 42		17 53		18 22				18 42		18 50
Broomfleet d																							
Gilberdyke d				17 00											18 00								18 57
Eastrington d																							
Howden d		16 45																			18 54		
Wressle d																							
Selby a		16 55			17 20							17 54	18 05				18 41				19 04		
d		16 56			17 21							17 54	18 05				18 41				19 05		
York 8 33 a												18 23											
Saltmarshe d																							
Goole d				17 09							17 43				18 09								19 06
Thorne North d											17 51												19 14
Cleethorpes d						16 28												17 28					
New Clee d																							
Grimsby Docks d																							
Grimsby Town a						16 35												17 35					
d						16 36												17 36					
Great Coates d																							
Healing d																							
Stallingborough d																							
Habrough d																		17 46					
Ulceby d																							
Thornton Abbey d																							
Goxhill d																							
New Holland d																							
Barrow Haven d																							
Barton-on-Humber a																							
Barton-on-Humber (bus) d																							
Hull Bus Station (bus) a																							
Barnetby d						16 54												17 54					
Scunthorpe a						17 10												18 10					
d						17 10												18 10					
Althorpe d																							
Crowle d																							
Thorne South d																							
Hatfield & Stainforth d											17 57												19 20
Kirk Sandall d											18 02												19 25
Adwick 31 d																				18 43			
Bentley (S.Yorks) 31 d																				18 47			
Doncaster 7 31 a		17 14		17 31		17 41					18 11		18 23		18 33			18 41			19 21		19 35
London Kings Cross 15 ⊖ 26 a		19 06				19 47					20 12		20b23					20 42			21 12		
York 8 26 d			16c28	17 01					17 17		17 35			17e28				18 07		18 29		18 28	19 05
Doncaster 7 d	17 13		17 30	17 32		17 42					18 13			18 30	18 34			18 42		19 15		19 30	19 37
Conisbrough d	17 21										18 20									19 22			
Mexborough d	17 25										18 24									19 26			
Swinton (S.Yorks) d	17 29						17 55		18 11		18 29									19 29			
Rotherham Central d	17 37						18 05		18 20		18 37									19 39			
Meadowhall (tram) d	17 42			17 51		18 00	18 11		18 26	18 33	18 42				18 52			19 00	19 33	19 44			19 56
Sheffield 7 (tram) a	17 53		17 58	18 04		18 08	18 23		18 35	18 47	18 51			18 58	19 03			19 09	19 43	19 53		19 59	20 07
d						18 13												19 13					
Stockport 78 a					19f22	19 00	19 21										20f31	20 00					
Manchester Piccadilly 10 78 (tram) a					18 52	19 10	19 33										20 11	20 12					
Manchester Airport 85 (plane) a					19 18	19 36	20g12										20 52	20 36				21g33	

For general notes see front of timetable
For details of catering facilities see Directory of Train Operators

- **A** From Edinburgh to Southampton Central (Table 51)
- **B** 23 March from Bridlington (Table 43)
- **C** From Leeds (Table 31)
- **D** Via Pontefract Baghill (Table 33)
- **E** From Huddersfield (Table 34)
- **G** From Aberdeen (Table 229) to Bristol Temple Meads (Table 51)
- **H** 23 March from Scarborough (Table 43)
- **J** From Leeds (Table 34)
- **K** From Edinburgh to Bristol Temple Meads (Table 51)
- **L** From Bridlington (Table 43)
- **b** By changing at Doncaster, passengers may arrive at 2012
- **c** By changing at Doncaster, passengers may depart at 1653
- **e** By changing at Doncaster, passengers may depart at 1735
- **f** Change at Manchester Piccadilly
- **g** Change at Sheffield and Manchester Piccadilly

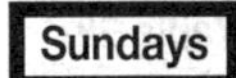

Hull and Cleethorpes → Doncaster → Meadowhall, Sheffield, Manchester and Manchester Airport
Cleethorpes → Barton-on-Humber

Sundays

3 February to 23 March

Network Diagram - see first page of Table 18

	TP 1◇	NT		NT	NT	XC 1◇	TP 1◇	TP 1◇	NT	NT		NT	XC 1◇	NT	TP 1◇	TP 1◇	NT	NT		NT	NT		
		A		B		C		D	E				G	H		D	J	A		K	E		
Hull d								19 04		20 22		20 30				21 00				21 15			
Hessle d																				21 22			
Ferriby d																				21 27			
Brough d								19 16		20 34		20 42				21 12				21 32			
Broomfleet d																							
Gilberdyke d												20 49								21 39			
Eastrington d																							
Howden d																							
Wressle d																							
Selby a								19 35		20 53						21 31							
d										20 53													
York 8 33 a										21 18													
Saltmarshe d																							
Goole d												20 58								21 48			
Thorne North d																				21 56			
Cleethorpes d	18 28						19 28								20 28								
New Clee d																							
Grimsby Docks d																							
Grimsby Town a	18 35						19 35								20 35								
d	18 36						19 36								20 36								
Great Coates d																							
Healing d																							
Stallingborough d																							
Habrough d							19 46								20 46								
Ulceby d																							
Thornton Abbey d																							
Goxhill d																							
New Holland d																							
Barrow Haven d																							
Barton-on-Humber a																							
Barton-on-Humber 🚌 d																							
Hull Bus Station 🚌 a																							
Barnetby d	18 54						19 54								20 54								
Scunthorpe a	19 09						20 10								21 10								
d	19 10						20 10								21 10								
Althorpe d																							
Crowle d																							
Thorne South d																							
Hatfield & Stainforth d																				22 02			
Kirk Sandall d																				22 07			
Adwick 31 d												*20 54*								*21 43*			
Bentley (S.Yorks) 31 d												*20 58*								*21 47*			
Doncaster 7 31 a	19 41						20 41					21 21			21 41					22 17			
London Kings Cross 15 ⊖ 26 a	*21 47*						*23 14*								*23 50*								
York 8 26 d					*19 30*	19 28	*20 02*					*20 40*	20b28	20 44						*21 28*			
Doncaster 7 d	19 42				20 14	20 31	20 42					21 23	21 30		21 42					22 20			
Conisbrough d					20 21		20 49													22 27			
Mexborough d					20 25		20 53													22 31			
Swinton (S.Yorks) d		19 55			20 32		20 56							21 38				22 32		22 35			
Rotherham Central d		20 06			20 39		21 02					21 39		21 49				22 40		22 44			
Meadowhall 🚋 d	20 00	20 11		20 38	20 45		21 08		21 32			21 45		21 54	22 00		22 41	22 45		22 50	23 33		
Sheffield 7 🚋 a	20 10	20 23		20 46	20 53	20 59	21 17		21 43			21 56	21 57	22 05	22 11		22 51	22 54		22 59	23 43		
d	20 13						21 19																
Stockport 78 a	20 55	*21 18*					22 00		*23 00*														
Manchester Piccadilly 10 78 🚋 a	21 06	*21 33*					22 13		*23 12*														
Manchester Airport 85 ✈ a	21c36	*22e11*					22 36		*23e49*														

For general notes see front of timetable
For details of catering facilities see Directory of Train Operators

- **A** From Leeds (Table 31)
- **B** From Huddersfield (Table 34)
- **C** From Glasgow Central to Birmingham New Street (Table 51)
- **D** To Leeds (Table 39)
- **E** From Leeds (Table 34)
- **G** From Edinburgh to Birmingham New Street (Table 51)
- **H** Via Pontefract Baghill (Table 33)
- **J** From Barnsley (Table 34)
- **K** From Bridlington (23 March from Scarborough) (Table 43)
- **b** By changing at Doncaster, passengers may depart at 2040
- **c** By changing at Manchester Piccadilly, passengers may arrive at 2133
- **e** Change at Sheffield and Manchester Piccadilly

Sundays

from 30 March

Hull and Cleethorpes → Doncaster → Meadowhall, Sheffield, Manchester and Manchester Airport
Cleethorpes → Barton-on-Humber

Network Diagram - see first page of Table 18

	NT	TP	NT	NT	NT	NT	EM	XC	NT	TP	NT	NT	NT	TP	NT	XC	TP	XC	NT	HT	NT	NT	TP
		1 ◇					1 ◇	1 ◇		1 ◇				1 ◇		1 ◇	1 ◇	1 ◇		1 ◇			1 ◇
				A	B		C	D			E				A	D		G	A			H	
							☕	☕								☕		☕		☒ ☕			
Hull d						08 42			08 54	09 05			09 41							10 12		10 41	11 00
Hessle d						08 49																	
Ferriby d						08 54																	
Brough d						08 59			09 06	09 17			09 53							10 24		10 53	11 12
Broomfleet d																							
Gilberdyke d						09 06							10 00									11 00	
Eastrington d																							
Howden d																				10 36			
Wressle d																							
Selby a									09 25	09 36										10 46			11 30
Selby d									09 25	09 36										10 47			11 31
York 8 33 a									09 54														
Saltmarshe d																							
Goole d						09 15						09 43	10 09									11 09	
Thorne North d												09 51											
Cleethorpes d																	09 41						
New Clee d																							
Grimsby Docks d																							
Grimsby Town a																	09 49						
Grimsby Town d																	09 49						
Great Coates d																							
Healing d																							
Stallingborough d																							
Habrough d																	09 59						
Ulceby d																							
Thornton Abbey d																							
Goxhill d																							
New Holland d																							
Barrow Haven d																							
Barton-on-Humber a																							
Barton-on-Humber 🚌 d																							
Hull Bus Station 🚌 a																							
Barnetby d																	10 08						
Scunthorpe a																	10 23						
Scunthorpe d																	10 23						
Althorpe d																							
Crowle d																							
Thorne South d																							
Hatfield & Stainforth d												09 57	10 21										
Kirk Sandall d												10 02	10 26										
Adwick 31 d																					*10 43*		
Bentley (S.Yorks) 31 d																					*10 47*		
Doncaster 7 31 a						09 38						10 11	10 36				10 53			11 03		11 32	
London Kings Cross 15 ⊖ 26 a												*12 19*	*12 37*							12 48			
York 8 26 d						*09 00*		09 20						*10 02*		10 20	*10 23*	10 28					
Doncaster 7 d	08 03		09 13			09 39	09 48	09 50				10 13		10 42		10 50	10 55				11 13	11 33	
Conisbrough d	08 10		09 20									10 20									11 20		
Mexborough d	08 14		09 24									10 24									11 24		
Swinton (S.Yorks) d	08 17		09 28		09 36							10 27									11 29		
Rotherham Central d	08 25		09 35		09b48							10 36									11 38		
Meadowhall 🚋 d	08 30	09 00	09 41	09 41	09 54	10 00					10 33	10 42		11 00	11 05		11 13		11 33		11 44	11 51	
Sheffield 7 🚋 a	08 41	09 07	09 51	09 51	10 04	10 09	10 11	10 20			10 43	10 52		11 09	11 15	11 20	11 25	11 40	11 43		11 52	12 03	
Sheffield 7 d		09 13												11 13									
Stockport 78 a		09 58					*11 18*			*11c24*				11 58			*12 23*						*13c21*
Manchester Piccadilly 10 78 🚋 a		10 08					*11 33*			11 05				12 08			*12 36*						12 57
Manchester Airport 85 ✈ a	*10e33*	10f36					*12e11*			*11 33*				12 30			*13e12*						*13 24*

For general notes see front of timetable
For details of catering facilities see Directory of Train Operators

A From Leeds (Table 34)
B From Leeds (Table 31)
C From Leeds to St Pancras International (Table 53)
D To Bristol Temple Meads (Table 51)
E From Huddersfield (Table 34)
G From Newcastle to Plymouth (Table 51)
H From Bridlington (Table 43)

b Arr. 0945
c Change at Manchester Piccadilly
e Change at Sheffield and Manchester Piccadilly
f By changing at Manchester Piccadilly, passengers may arrive at 1033

Table 29

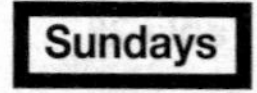

Sundays

from 30 March

Hull and Cleethorpes → Doncaster → Meadowhall, Sheffield, Manchester and Manchester Airport
Cleethorpes → Barton-on-Humber

Network Diagram - see first page of Table 18

		TP		NT	XC	NT	XC	NT	NT	NT	TP	XC	XC	NT	NT	NT	NT	TP	TP	NT	XC	NT	XC	NT
		1◇			1◇		R 1				1◇	1◇	R 1					1◇	1◇		1◇		R 1	
				A	B ☕	C	D ☕	E				G ☕	H ☕		J		K			A	G ☕	C	D ☕	E
Hull	d									11 41				11 54			12 41	12 50						
Hessle	d																							
Ferriby	d																							
Brough	d									11 53				12 06			12 53	13 02						
Broomfleet	d																							
Gilberdyke	d									12 00							13 00							
Eastrington	d																							
Howden	d																							
Wressle	d																							
Selby	a													12 25				13 21						
	d													12 25				13 21						
York 8	33 a													12 56										
Saltmarshe	d																							
Goole	d								11 43	12 09							13 09							
Thorne North	d								11 51															
Cleethorpes	d	10 28																	12 28					
New Clee	d																							
Grimsby Docks	d																							
Grimsby Town	a	10 35																	12 35					
	d	10 36																	12 36					
Great Coates	d																							
Healing	d																							
Stallingborough	d																							
Habrough	d	10 46																						
Ulceby	d																							
Thornton Abbey	d																							
Goxhill	d																							
New Holland	d																							
Barrow Haven	d																							
Barton-on-Humber	a																							
Barton-on-Humber	🚌 d																							
Hull Bus Station	🚌 a																							
Barnetby	d	10 54																	12 54					
Scunthorpe	a	11 10																	13 10					
	d	11 10																	13 10					
Althorpe	d																							
Crowle	d																							
Thorne South	d																							
Hatfield & Stainforth	d								11 57															
Kirk Sandall	d								12 02															
Adwick	31 d															12 43								
Bentley (S.Yorks)	31 d															12 47								
Doncaster 7	31 a	11 41							12 11	12 32							13 32		13 41					
London Kings Cross 15	⊖ 26 a	*13 36*								*14 42*									*15 38*					
York 8	26 d				11 20		11 28		*11 29*			12 20	12 28			*12 29*	*12 57*				13 20		13 28	
Doncaster 7	d	11 42			11 50				12 16		12 42	12 50				13 13	13 33		13 42		13 50			
Conisbrough	d								12 23							13 20								
Mexborough	d								12 27							13 24								
Swinton (S.Yorks)	d					11 55			12 30							13 29						14 01		
Rotherham Central	d					12 06			12 38							13 37						14 08		
Meadowhall	🚊 d	12 00		12 05		12 11		12 33	12 43		13 00				13 33	13 43	13 51		14 00	14 05		14 14		14 33
Sheffield 7	🚊 a	12 08		12 15	12 20	12 21	12 40	12 43	12 55		13 08	13 20	13 40		13 43	13 55	14 03		14 09	14 15	14 20	14 23	14 40	14 43
	d	12 13									13 13								14 12					
Stockport	78 a	12 56				*13 24*					14 02	*14 21*						*15b11*	15 01			*15 22*		
Manchester Piccadilly 10	78 🚊 a	13 10				*13 36*					14 12	*14 31*						14 52	15 13			*15 33*		
Manchester Airport	85 ✈ a	13 36				*14c14*					14 36	*15c11*					*15 36*	*15 21*	15 36			*16c11*		

For general notes see front of timetable
For details of catering facilities see Directory of Train Operators

- **A** From Leeds (Table 34)
- **B** From Newcastle to Plymouth (Table 51)
- **C** From Leeds (Table 31)
- **D** From Edinburgh to Oxford (Table 51)
- **E** From Huddersfield (Table 34)
- **G** From Newcastle to Bristol Temple Meads (Table 51)
- **H** From Edinburgh (Table 51) to Penzance (Table 135)
- **J** From Leeds (Table 34) to Lincoln (Table 30)
- **K** From Scarborough (Table 43)
- **b** Change at Manchester Piccadilly
- **c** Change at Sheffield and Manchester Piccadilly

Table 29

Sundays

from 30 March

Hull and Cleethorpes → Doncaster → Meadowhall, Sheffield, Manchester and Manchester Airport Cleethorpes → Barton-on-Humber

Network Diagram - see first page of Table 18

	NT	NT	TP		XC	NT	XC	HT	NT	NT	NT	TP	TP	XC	NT	XC	NT	NT	NT	TP	XC	XC	NT
			1 ◇		1 ◇		R 1	1 ◇				1 ◇	1 ◇	R 1		R 1				1 ◇	1 ◇	R 1	
		A			B	C	D				E			B	G	H	J		A		B	K	C
					⊡		⊡	⊠ ⊡						⊡		⊡					⊡	⊡	
Hull d		13 41						14 10		14 28	14 41	14 50							15 41				
Hessle d										14 35													
Ferriby d										14 40													
Brough d		13 53						14 22		14 45	14 53	15 02							15 53				
Broomfleet d																							
Gilberdyke d		14 00									15 00								16 00				
Eastrington d																							
Howden d								14 34															
Wressle d																							
Selby a								14 44		15 04		15 21											
d								14 45		15 04		15 21											
York 8 33 a										15 30													
Saltmarshe d																							
Goole d	13 43	14 09									15 09							15 43	16 09				
Thorne North d	13 51																	15 51					
Cleethorpes d			13 28										14 28							15 28			
New Clee d																							
Grimsby Docks d																							
Grimsby Town a			13 35										14 35							15 35			
d			13 36										14 36							15 36			
Great Coates d																							
Healing d																							
Stallingborough d																							
Habrough d													14 46										
Ulceby d																							
Thornton Abbey d																							
Goxhill d																							
New Holland d																							
Barrow Haven d																							
Barton-on-Humber a																							
Barton-on-Humber 🚌 d																							
Hull Bus Station 🚌 a																							
Barnetby d			13 54										14 54							15 54			
Scunthorpe a			14 10										15 10							16 10			
d			14 10										15 10							16 10			
Althorpe d																							
Crowle d																							
Thorne South d																							
Hatfield & Stainforth d	13 57																	15 57					
Kirk Sandall d	14 02																	16 02					
Adwick 31 d									14 43														
Bentley (S.Yorks) 31 d									14 47														
Doncaster 7 31 a	14 11	14 32	14 41					15 05			15 32		15 41					16 11	16 32	16 41			
London Kings Cross 15 ⊖ 26 a	16 11		16 29					16 50					17 49					18 15		18 38			
York 8 26 d	13 33		14 05		14 24		14 28		14 36					15 21		15 28		15 34		16 03	16 20	16 28	
Doncaster 7 d	14 13	14 33	14 42		14 50				15 13		15 33		15 42	15 50				16 13	16 33	16 42	16 50		
Conisbrough d	14 20								15 20									16 20					
Mexborough d	14 24								15 24									16 24					
Swinton (S.Yorks) d	14 29								15 29						15 55			16 29					
Rotherham Central d	14 37								15 37						16 05			16 37					
Meadowhall 🚊 d	14 42	14 52	15 00			15 33			15 42		15 52		16 00		16 11		16 33	16 42	16 52	17 00			17 33
Sheffield 7 🚊 a	14 52	15 04	15 09		15 20	15 43	15 45		15 51		16 03		16 09	16 20	16 20	16 40	16 43	16 52	17 03	17 11	17 20	17 40	17 43
d			15 13										16 13							17 13			
Stockport 78 a			16 03		16 19							17b11	16 56		17 22					17 55	18 24		
Manchester Piccadilly 10 78 🚊 a			16 13		16 32							16 50	17 11		17 36					18 12	18 36		
Manchester Airport 85 ✈ a			16 36		17c12							17 21	17 36		18c11					18 36	19c12		

For general notes see front of timetable
For details of catering facilities see
Directory of Train Operators

A From Scarborough (Table 43)
B From Newcastle to Bristol Temple Meads (Table 51)
C From Leeds (Table 34)
D From Glasgow Central to Plymouth (Table 51)
E From Bridlington (Table 43)
G From Leeds (Table 31)
H From Glasgow Central to Oxford (Table 51)
J From Huddersfield (Table 34)
K From Edinburgh to Plymouth (Table 51)
b Change at Manchester Piccadilly
c Change at Sheffield and Manchester Piccadilly

Table 29

Sundays

from 30 March

Hull and Cleethorpes → Doncaster → Meadowhall, Sheffield, Manchester and Manchester Airport
Cleethorpes → Barton-on-Humber

Network Diagram - see first page of Table 18

	NT	HT	NT	TP	TP		XC	NT	EM	NT	XC	NT	NT	NT	GR	NT	TP	TP	XC	XC	NT	NT	HT
		1 ◇		1 ◇	1 ◇		1 ◇		1 ◇		R 1				R 1		1 ◇	1 ◇	1 ◇	1 ◇			1 ◇
			A				B	C	D	E	G	H				J			K	L	N		
		⊠ ☕					☕		☕		☕				☕ ✂				☕	☕			⊠ ☕
Hull d		16 21	16 41	16 50										17 23	17 30	17 41	18 10						18 30
Hessle d																							
Ferriby d																							
Brough d		16 33	16 53	17 02										17 35	17 42	17 53	18 22						18 42
Broomfleet d																							
Gilberdyke d			17 00													18 00							
Eastrington d																							
Howden d		16 45																					18 54
Wressle d																							
Selby a		16 55		17 20										17 54	18 05		18 41						19 04
d		16 56		17 21										17 54	18 05		18 41						19 05
York 8 33 a														18 23									
Saltmarshe d																							
Goole d			17 09										17 43			18 09							
Thorne North d													17 51										
Cleethorpes d					16 28													17 28					
New Clee d																							
Grimsby Docks d																							
Grimsby Town a					16 35													17 35					
d					16 36													17 36					
Great Coates d																							
Healing d																							
Stallingborough d																							
Habrough d																		17 46					
Ulceby d																							
Thornton Abbey d																							
Goxhill d																							
New Holland d																							
Barrow Haven d																							
Barton-on-Humber a																							
Barton-on-Humber 🚌 d																							
Hull Bus Station 🚌 a																							
Barnetby d					16 54													17 54					
Scunthorpe a					17 10													18 10					
d					17 10													18 10					
Althorpe d																							
Crowle d																							
Thorne South d																							
Hatfield & Stainforth d													17 57										
Kirk Sandall d													18 02										
Adwick 31 d	*16 43*																					*18 43*	
Bentley (S.Yorks) 31 d	*16 47*																					*18 47*	
Doncaster 7 31 a		17 14	17 31		17 41								18 11		18 23	18 33		18 41					19 21
London Kings Cross 15 ⊖ 26 a		19 06			*19 47*								*20 12*		20b23			*20 42*					21 12
York 8 26 d	*16 29*		*17 01*				17 20		17 25	17 17	17 28		*17 35*					*18 07*	18 20	18 28		*18 29*	
Doncaster 7 d	17 13		17 32		17 42		17 50		18 00				18 13			18 34		18 42	18 50			19 15	
Conisbrough d	17 21												18 20									19 22	
Mexborough d	17 25												18 24									19 26	
Swinton (S.Yorks) d	17 29							17 55		18 11			18 29									19 29	
Rotherham Central d	17 37							18 05		18 20			18 37									19 39	
Meadowhall 🚋 d	17 42		17 52		18 00			18 11		18 26		18 33	18 42			18 52		19 00			19 33	19 44	
Sheffield 7 🚋 a	17 53		18 02		18 08		18 20	18 23	18 28	18 35	18 40	18 47	18 51			19 03		19 09	19 20	19 40	19 43	19 53	
d					18 13													19 13					
Stockport 78 a				*19c11*	19 00				*19 21*								*20c31*	20 00	*20 24*				
Manchester Piccadilly 10 78 🚋 a				*18 52*	19 10				*19 33*								20 11	20 12	*20 35*				
Manchester Airport 85 ✈ a				*19 21*	19 36				*20e12*								*20 52*	20 36	*21e12*			*21e33*	

For general notes see front of timetable
For details of catering facilities see Directory of Train Operators

- **A** From Bridlington (Table 43)
- **B** From Newcastle to Bristol Temple Meads (Table 51)
- **C** From Leeds (Table 31)
- **D** To St Pancras International (Table 53)
- **E** Via Pontefract Baghill (Table 33)
- **G** From Aberdeen (Table 229) to Oxford (Table 51)
- **H** From Huddersfield (Table 34)
- **J** From Scarborough (Table 43)
- **K** From Newcastle to Birmingham New Street (Table 51)
- **L** From Edinburgh to Bristol Temple Meads (Table 51)
- **N** From Leeds (Table 34)
- **b** By changing at Doncaster, passengers may arrive at 2012
- **c** Change at Manchester Piccadilly
- **e** Change at Sheffield and Manchester Piccadilly

Table 29

from 30 March

Hull and Cleethorpes → Doncaster → Meadowhall, Sheffield, Manchester and Manchester Airport
Cleethorpes → Barton-on-Humber

Network Diagram - see first page of Table 18

		NT	TP	XC	NT	XC	TP	NT	NT	TP	XC	NT	NT	NT	NT	TP	XC	TP	NT	NT	NT	NT
			1 ◇	1 ◇		1 ◇	1 ◇			1 ◇	1 ◇					1 ◇	1 ◇	1 ◇				
		A		B	C	D	E	G			H	J			K		H	E	L	C	N	J
Hull	d	18 38					19 04						20 22	20 30				21 00			21 15	
Hessle	d																				21 22	
Ferriby	d																				21 27	
Brough	d	18 50					19 16						20 34	20 42				21 12			21 32	
Broomfleet	d																					
Gilberdyke	d	18 57												20 49							21 39	
Eastrington	d																					
Howden	d																					
Wressle	d																					
Selby	a						19 35						20 53					21 31				
	d												20 53									
York 8	33 a						21 22						21 18									
Saltmarshe	d																					
Goole	d	19 06												20 58							21 48	
Thorne North	d	19 14																			21 56	
Cleethorpes	d		18 28							19 28						20 28						
New Clee	d																					
Grimsby Docks	d																					
Grimsby Town	a		18 35							19 35						20 35						
	d		18 36							19 36						20 36						
Great Coates	d																					
Healing	d																					
Stallingborough	d																					
Habrough	d									19 46						20 46						
Ulceby	d																					
Thornton Abbey	d																					
Goxhill	d																					
New Holland	d																					
Barrow Haven	d																					
Barton-on-Humber	a																					
Barton-on-Humber (bus)	d																					
Hull Bus Station (bus)	a																					
Barnetby	d		18 54							19 54						20 54						
Scunthorpe	a		19 09							20 10						21 10						
	d		19 10							20 10						21 10						
Althorpe	d																					
Crowle	d																					
Thorne South	d																					
Hatfield & Stainforth	d	19 20																			22 02	
Kirk Sandall	d	19 25																			22 07	
Adwick	31 d													20 54							21 43	
Bentley (S.Yorks)	31 d													20 58							21 47	
Doncaster 7	31 a	19 35	19 41							20 41				21 21		21 41					22 17	
London Kings Cross 15	⊖ 26 a		21 47							23 14						23 50						
York 8	26 d	19 05		19 20		19 28			19 30	20 02	20 28			20 40	20 44		21 26				21 28	
Doncaster 7	d	19 37	19 42	19 50					20 14	20 42				21 23		21 42	21 50				22 20	
Conisbrough	d								20 21	20 49											22 27	
Mexborough	d								20 25	20 53											22 31	
Swinton (S.Yorks)	d				19 55				20 32	20 56					21 38					22 32	22 35	
Rotherham Central	d				20 06				20 39	21 02				21 39	21 49					22 40	22 44	
Meadowhall	(tram) d	19 56	20 00		20 11			20 38	20 45	21 08		21 32		21 45	21 54	22 00			22 41	22 45	22 50	23 33
Sheffield 7	(tram) a	20 07	20 10	20 20	20 23	20 40		20 46	20 53	21 17	21 43	21 43		21 56	22 05	22 11	22 20		22 51	22 54	22 59	23 43
	d		20 13							21 19												
Stockport	78 a		20 55		21 18					22 00		23 00										
Manchester Piccadilly 10	78 (tram) a		21 06		21 33					22 13		23 12										
Manchester Airport	85 (air) a		21b36		22c11					22 36		23c54										

For general notes see front of timetable
For details of catering facilities see Directory of Train Operators

A From Bridlington (Table 43)
B From Newcastle to Birmingham New Street (Table 51)
C From Leeds (Table 31)
D From Glasgow Central to Bristol Temple Meads (Table 51)
E To Leeds (Table 39)
G From Huddersfield (Table 34)
H From Edinburgh to Birmingham New Street (Table 51)
J From Leeds (Table 34)
K Via Pontefract Baghill (Table 33)
L From Barnsley (Table 34)
N From Scarborough (Table 43)
b By changing at Manchester Piccadilly, passengers may arrive at 2133
c Change at Sheffield and Manchester Piccadilly

Manchester Airport, Manchester, Sheffield and Meadowhall → Doncaster → Cleethorpes and Hull
Barton-on-Humber → Cleethorpes

Network Diagram - see first page of Table 18

Miles	Miles	Miles	Miles	Miles	Station		TP MX 1 ◇	TP MO 1 ◇	NT A	NT B	NT	NT C	NT D	NT E	NT E	EM G	NT BHX (bus)	NT	NT	NT		NT A	NT D	NT E
0	—	—	—	—	**Manchester Airport**	85 d	03 21	03 18																
9¾	—	—	—	—	**Manchester Piccadilly 10**	78 d	03 40	03 37																
15¾	—	—	—	—	Stockport	78 d																		
52½	—	—	—	—	**Sheffield 7**	a	04 31	04 37																
—	—	—	—	—		d	04 40	04 40	05 10	05 16		05 29	05 36	05 50	06 14					06 18		06 28	06 36	06 49
56	—	—	—	—	**Meadowhall**	d			05 16	05a21		05 35	05a42	05a55	06a19					06 24		06 34	06a41	06a54
58¾	—	—	—	—	Rotherham Central	d			05 22			05 41								06 30		06 40		
63¼	—	—	—	—	Swinton (S.Yorks)	d			05a30			05 49								06 38		06a48		
64½	—	—	—	—	Mexborough	d						05 52								06 41				
66¾	—	—	—	—	Conisbrough	d						05 56								06 45				
71½	—	—	—	—	**Doncaster 7**	a	05 14	05 14				06 06								06 56				
—	—	—	—	—	York 8	26 a						*06 35*												
—	—	—	—	—	London Kings Cross 15	⊖ 26 d																		
—	0	0	—	0	**Doncaster**	31 d					05 52	06 14							06 47	06 59				
—	—	—	—	1¾	Bentley (S.Yorks)	31 a						*06 28*								07 02				
—	—	—	—	4	Adwick	31 a						*06 32*								07 08				
75½	—	4	—	—	Kirk Sandall	d						06 20							06 53					
78¼	—	6¾	—	—	Hatfield & Stainforth	d						06 25							06 58					
—	—	9¾	—	—	Thorne South	d													07 03					
—	—	15¾	—	—	Crowle	d													07 11					
—	—	19½	—	—	Althorpe	d													07 17					
—	—	23	—	—	**Scunthorpe**	a													07 26					
—	—	—	—	—		d																		
—	—	34¼	—	—	Barnetby	d										06 31								
—	—	—	—	—	Hull Bus Station	d											06 25							
—	—	—	—	—	Barton-on-Humber	a											06 50							
—	—	—	0	—	**Barton-on-Humber**	d												06 58						
—	—	—	2	—	Barrow Haven	d												07 03						
—	—	—	3½	—	New Holland	d												07 07						
—	—	—	5½	—	Goxhill	d												07 11						
—	—	—	7	—	Thornton Abbey	d																		
—	—	—	9¾	—	Ulceby	d												07 19						
—	—	40¾	11½	—	Habrough	d										06 41		07 23						
—	—	44½	15¼	—	Stallingborough	d												07 28						
—	—	45¼	16½	—	Healing	d												07 31						
—	—	45½	17¼	—	Great Coates	d																		
—	—	48¾	19½	—	**Grimsby Town**	a										06 57		07 37						
—	—	—	—	—		d												07 38						
—	—	49¾	20½	—	Grimsby Docks	d																		
—	—	50½	21¼	—	New Clee	d																		
—	—	52	22¾	—	**Cleethorpes**	a												07 50						
81½	—	—	—	—	Thorne North	d						06 30												
88¾	—	—	—	—	Goole	d						06 41												
92¼	—	—	—	—	Saltmarshe	d						06 46												
—	—	—	—	—	York 8	33 d																		
—	18¼	—	—	—	**Selby**	a					06 11													
—	—	—	—	—		d																		
—	24½	—	—	—	Wressle	d																		
—	27	—	—	—	Howden	d																		
—	30	—	—	—	Eastrington	d																		
95½	32¼	—	—	—	Gilberdyke	d						06 53												
98	34¾	—	—	—	Broomfleet	d						06 57												
102	38¾	—	—	—	Brough	d						07 03												
105	41¾	—	—	—	Ferriby	d						07 07												
107¾	44½	—	—	—	Hessle	d						07 12												
112	49¼	—	—	—	**Hull**	a						07 22												

For general notes see front of timetable
For details of catering facilities see Directory of Train Operators

A To Leeds (Table 31)
B To Barnsley (Table 34)
C To Beverley (Table 43)
D To Huddersfield (Table 34)
E To Leeds (Table 34)
G From Lincoln (Table 27)

Manchester Airport, Manchester, Sheffield and Meadowhall → Doncaster → Cleethorpes and Hull Barton-on-Humber → Cleethorpes

Network Diagram - see first page of Table 18

		NT	TP	NT	NT BHX	NT	NT	TP	NT	NT	NT	XC	NT	NT		EM	NT	NT	NT	EM	XC	NT	TP	TP
			1 ◇					1 ◇				1 ◇				1 ◇					1 ◇		1 ◇	1 ◇
				A			B		C			D	E			G	H	J	K	L	N	A		
					bus																			
								trolley				buffet				buffet					buffet		trolley	trolley
Manchester Airport	85 ✈ d		05 15					*05 47*															06 44	*07 02*
Manchester Piccadilly 10	78 ⇌ d		05 48					*06 21*				*05 52*											07 18	*07 35*
Stockport	78 d		05 56					*05b53*				*06 01*											07 26	*07b11*
Sheffield 7	⇌ a		06 48																				08 10	
	d	06 52	06 55	07 04								07 12	07 14	07 23		07 25	07 36	07 41	07 51		07 54	08 08	08 11	
Meadowhall	⇌ d	06 58	07 02	07a09									07 21	07 29		07a31	07a41	07 47	07a57			08a13	08 17	
Rotherham Central	d	07 05									←		07 27	07 35				07 55						
Swinton (S.Yorks)	d	07 15									07 15		07a35	07 45				08 03						
Mexborough	d	→									07 18			07 48				08 06						
Conisbrough	d										07 22			07 52				08 10						
Doncaster 7	a		07 22								07 30			08 02				08 20			08 24		08 40	
York 8	26 a										*08 10*	08 24									08 48			
London Kings Cross 15	⊖ 26 d													*06 00*				*06 35*						
Doncaster	31 d		07 24						07 28		07 32			08 04				08 22					08 42	
Bentley (S.Yorks)	31 a										07 35			*08 19*									*08 55*	
Adwick	31 a										07 41			*08 25*									*09 01*	
Kirk Sandall	d								07 34					08 10										
Hatfield & Stainforth	d								07 39					08 15										
Thorne South	d													08 20										
Crowle	d													08 29										
Althorpe	d													08 35										
Scunthorpe	a		07 49											08 43									09 08	
	d		07 50																				09 08	
Barnetby	d		08 04																	08 52			09 22	
Hull Bus Station	bus d				07 25																			
Barton-on-Humber	bus a				07 50																			
Barton-on-Humber	d					08 00																		
Barrow Haven	d					08 05																		
New Holland	d					08 08																		
Goxhill	d					08 13																		
Thornton Abbey	d					08 16																		
Ulceby	d					08 20																		
Habrough	d		08 13			08 25														09 01				
Stallingborough	d					08 30																		
Healing	d					08 33																		
Great Coates	d					08 36																		
Grimsby Town	a		08 26			08 41														09 15			09 42	
	d		08 35			08 41																	09 43	
Grimsby Docks	d					08 44																		
New Clee	d					08x46																		
Cleethorpes	a		08 46			08 51																	09 58	
Thorne North	d								07 44															
Goole	d								07 53									08 43						
Saltmarshe	d								07 58															
York 8	33 d							*06 09*		07 30														*07 30*
Selby	a							07 43		07 49														08 58
	d							07 43		07 49														08 59
Wressle	d									07 57														
Howden	d							07 52		08 02														
Eastrington	d									08 07														
Gilberdyke	d						07 39		08 04	08 11														
Broomfleet	d						07 43			08 15														
Brough	d						07 49	08 04	08 12	08 21								08 57						
Ferriby	d						07 53		08 16	08 26														
Hessle	d						07 58		08 21	08 30														
Hull	a						08 11	08 21	08 34	08 45								09 13						09 31

For general notes see front of timetable
For details of catering facilities see Directory of Train Operators

A To Leeds (Table 34)
B To Scarborough (Table 43)
C To Beverley (Table 43)
D From Birmingham New Street to Edinburgh (Table 51)
E To Leeds (Table 31)
G From Derby to Barnsley (Table 53)
H To Huddersfield (Table 34)
J To Bridlington (Table 43)
K From Retford (Table 30) to Leeds (Table 34)
L From Newark North Gate (Table 27)
N From Birmingham New Street to Newcastle (Table 51)
b Change at Manchester Piccadilly

Manchester Airport, Manchester, Sheffield and Meadowhall → Doncaster → Cleethorpes and Hull Barton-on-Humber → Cleethorpes

Network Diagram - see first page of Table 18

		NT	NT	HT	XC	NT	NT	NT		NT	NT	NT	XC	NT	NT	TP	TP	NT	NT	NT	NT	XC	NT	NT
				1 ◇	R 1	BHX 🚌							1 ◇			1 ◇	1 ◇					R 1		
		A			B					C	D	E	G	H	E			A			H	J		K
				⊠ ☕	☕								☕			🛒	🛒					☕		
Manchester Airport	85 ✈ d										*07b05*					07 52	*08 07*							
Manchester Piccadilly 10	78 🚆 d										*07 43*					08 17	*08 41*							
Stockport	78 d										*07 54*					08 26	*08c21*							
Sheffield 7	🚊 a															09 09								
	d	08 14			08 21			08 23		08 36	08 41	08 51	08 54	08 57	09 08	09 11		09 14				09 21	09 25	09 29
Meadowhall	🚊 d	08 23						08 31		08a41	08 47	08a56		09 03	09a13	09 17		09 21					09 31	09 35
Rotherham Central	d	08 29						08 37						09 10				09 27					09 37	09 42
Swinton (S.Yorks)	d	08a38						08 47						09 18				09a36					09 48	09 51
Mexborough	d							08 50						09 21									09 51	
Conisbrough	d							08 54						09 25									09 55	
Doncaster 7	a							09 05			09 10		09 19	09 35		09 40							10 04	
York 8	26 a				09 33						*09 40*		09 48								←	10 29		10 51
London Kings Cross 15	⊖ 26 d			07 20												*07 30*								
Doncaster	31 d		08 56	09 05				09 12			09 17			09 49 →		09 42			09 46		09 49		10 06	
Bentley (S.Yorks)	31 a							*09 17*													09 52		*10 17*	
Adwick	31 a							*09 21*													09 58		*10 21*	
Kirk Sandall	d		09 02					09 18											09 52				10 12	
Hatfield & Stainforth	d		09 07					09 23											09 57				10 17	
Thorne South	d							09 28															10 22	
Crowle	d							09 36															10 31	
Althorpe	d							09 42															10 37	
Scunthorpe	a							09 51								10 07							10 45	
	d															10 08								
Barnetby	d															10 22								
Hull Bus Station	🚌 d					09 25																		
Barton-on-Humber	🚌 a					09 50																		
Barton-on-Humber	d						09 58																	
Barrow Haven	d						10 03																	
New Holland	d						10 06																	
Goxhill	d						10 11																	
Thornton Abbey	d						10 14																	
Ulceby	d						10 18																	
Habrough	d						10 23									10 31								
Stallingborough	d						10 28																	
Healing	d						10 31																	
Great Coates	d						10 34																	
Grimsby Town	a						10 39									10 47								
	d						10 39									10 48								
Grimsby Docks	d						10 42																	
New Clee	d						10x44																	
Cleethorpes	a						10 49									10 59								
Thorne North	d		09 12																10 02					
Goole	d		09 21								09 39								10 11					
Saltmarshe	d																							
York 8	33 d			*08 43*																09 53				
Selby	a			09 21													09 58			10 12				
	d			09 22													09 59			10 12				
Wressle	d																							
Howden	d			09 32																10 22				
Eastrington	d																							
Gilberdyke	d		09 29																10 19	10 29				
Broomfleet	d																							
Brough	d		09 37	09 44							09 56						10 17		10 27	10 37				
Ferriby	d		09 42																10 32					
Hessle	d		09 46																10 36					
Hull	a		09 59	10 04							10 10						10 34		10 49	10 56				

For general notes see front of timetable
For details of catering facilities see Directory of Train Operators

- **A** To Leeds (Table 31)
- **B** From Birmingham New Street to Edinburgh (Table 51)
- **C** To Huddersfield (Table 34)
- **D** To Bridlington (Table 43)
- **E** To Leeds (Table 34)
- **G** From Birmingham New Street to Newcastle (Table 51)
- **H** From Worksop (Table 30)
- **J** From Bristol Temple Meads to Edinburgh (Table 51)
- **K** Via Pontefract Baghill (Table 33)
- **b** Change at Manchester Piccadilly and Sheffield
- **c** Change at Manchester Piccadilly

Manchester Airport, Manchester, Sheffield and Meadowhall → Doncaster → Cleethorpes and Hull Barton-on-Humber → Cleethorpes

Network Diagram - see first page of Table 18

Station		NT		NT	NT	XC	NT	NT	EM	TP	TP	NT	NT	NT	XC	NT	NT		NT	NT	XC	HT	NT	NT
						1 ◇				1 ◇	1 ◇				1 ◇						1 ◇	1 ◇		
		A		B	C	D	E	C	G			H	E		J		A		K	C	L		E	C
Manchester Airport 85 ✈	d									08 52	*09 07*													
Manchester Piccadilly 10 78	d				*08 42*					09 20	*09 42*	*08 44*								*09 42*				
Stockport 78	d				*08 53*					09 28	*09b20*									*09 55*				
Sheffield 7	a									10 08														
	d	09 36		09 41	09 51	09 54	09 57	10 08		10 11		10 14			10 21	10 25	10 36		10 41	10 51	10 54		10 57	11 08
Meadowhall	d	09a41		09 45	09a56		10 03	10a13		10 17		10 21				10 31	10a41		10 47	10a56			11 03	11a13
Rotherham Central	d						10 10					10 27				10 37							11 10	
Swinton (S.Yorks)	d						10 18					10a36				10 47							11 20	
Mexborough	d						10 21									10 50							11 23	
Conisbrough	d						10 25									10 54							11 27	
Doncaster 7	a			10 12		10 15	10 36			10 40						11 04			11 08		11 15		11 35	
York 8 26	a			*11 01*		10 40									11 29	*11 37*					11 41			
London Kings Cross 15 ⊖ 26	d									*09 00*			←									09 48	*09 35*	
Doncaster 31	d			10 16			10 44 →			10 42			10 44	10 47		11 07			11 17			11 35	11 38	
Bentley (S.Yorks) 31	a												10 47								*11c29*		11 41	
Adwick 31	a												10 53								*11c33*		11 47	
Kirk Sandall	d													10 53		11 13								
Hatfield & Stainforth	d													10 58		11 18								
Thorne South	d															11 23								
Crowle	d															11 31								
Althorpe	d															11 37								
Scunthorpe	a									11 07						11 45								
	d									11 08														
Barnetby	d								10 56	11 22														
Hull Bus Station 🚌	d																							
Barton-on-Humber 🚌	a																							
Barton-on-Humber	d																							
Barrow Haven	d																							
New Holland	d																							
Goxhill	d																							
Thornton Abbey	d																							
Ulceby	d																							
Habrough	d								11 05															
Stallingborough	d																							
Healing	d																							
Great Coates	d																							
Grimsby Town	a								11 20	11 42														
	d									11 43														
Grimsby Docks	d																							
New Clee	d																							
Cleethorpes	a									11 54														
Thorne North	d													11 03										
Goole	d			10 35										11 12					11 38					
Saltmarshe	d																							
York 8 33	d										*10 22*													
Selby	a										10 58											11 51		
	d										10 59											11 52		
Wressle	d																							
Howden	d																					12 02		
Eastrington	d																							
Gilberdyke	d													11 20										
Broomfleet	d													11 25										
Brough	d			10 49							11 17			11 31					11 52			12 15		
Ferriby	d													11 35										
Hessle	d													11 40										
Hull	a			11 06							11 34			11 53					12 09			12 32		

For general notes see front of timetable
For details of catering facilities see Directory of Train Operators

A To Huddersfield (Table 34)
B To Scarborough (Table 43)
C To Leeds (Table 34)
D From Bristol Temple Meads to Newcastle (Table 51)
E From Lincoln (Table 30)
G From Newark North Gate (Table 27)
H To Leeds (Table 31)
J From Southampton Central to Edinburgh (Table 51)
K To Bridlington (Table 43)
L From Cardiff Central to Newcastle (Table 51)
b Change at Manchester Piccadilly
c Change at Doncaster

Manchester Airport, Manchester, Sheffield and Meadowhall → Doncaster → Cleethorpes and Hull
Barton-on-Humber → Cleethorpes

Network Diagram - see first page of Table 18

	NT BHX	NT	TP	TP	NT	NT	NT	XC	NT	NT		NT	NT	XC	NT	NT	EM	TP	TP	NT	NT	XC	NT
			1 ◇	1 ◇				1 ◇						1 ◇				1 ◇	1 ◇			1 ◇	
					A			B		C		D	E	G	H	E	J			A		K	
Manchester Airport 85 d			09 52	*10 07*														10 52	*11 07*				
Manchester Piccadilly 10 78 d			10 20	10 42														11 20	11 42	*10 46*			
Stockport 78 d			10 28	*10b18*									*10 55*					11 27	*11b19*				
Sheffield 7 a			11 08															12 08					
d			11 11		11 14			11 21	11 25	11 36		11 41	11 51	11 54	11 57	12 08		12 11		12 14		12 21	12 25
Meadowhall d			11 17		11 21				11 31	11a41		11 47	11a56		12 03	12a13		12 17		12 21			12 31
Rotherham Central d					11 27				11 37						12 10					12 27			12 37
Swinton (S.Yorks) d					11a36				11 48						12 19					12a35			12 47
Mexborough d									11 51						12 22								12 50
Conisbrough d									11 55						12 26								12 54
Doncaster 7 a			11 40						12 04			12 11		12 15	12 35			12 38					13 04
York 8 26 a								12 29						12 43								13 29	*13 39*
London Kings Cross 15 26 d									*10 10*						*10 35*								*11 10*
Doncaster 31 d			11 42			11 49			12 07			12 14			12 36			12 42			12 49		13 06
Bentley (S.Yorks) 31 a														*12c28*	12 40								
Adwick 31 a														*12c32*	12 45								
Kirk Sandall d						11 55			12 14												12 55		13 12
Hatfield & Stainforth d						12 00			12 19												13 00		13 17
Thorne South d									12 24														13 22
Crowle d									12 32														13 31
Althorpe d									12 38														13 37
Scunthorpe a			12 07						12 46									13 07					13 45
d			12 08															13 08					
Barnetby d			12 22														13 12	13 22					
Hull Bus Station d	11 25																						
Barton-on-Humber a	11 50																						
Barton-on-Humber d		11 58																					
Barrow Haven d		12 03																					
New Holland d		12 06																					
Goxhill d		12 11																					
Thornton Abbey d		12 14																					
Ulceby d		12 18																					
Habrough d		12 23	12 31														13 21						
Stallingborough d		12 28																					
Healing d		12 31																					
Great Coates d		12 34																					
Grimsby Town a		12 39	12 44														13 35	13 42					
d		12 39	12 45															13 43					
Grimsby Docks d		12 42																					
New Clee d		12x44																					
Cleethorpes a		12 49	12 56															13 54					
Thorne North d						12 05															13 05		
Goole d						12 14						12 35									13 14		
Saltmarshe d																							
York 8 33 d							11 53												*12 18*				
Selby a				11 58			12 17												12 58				
d				11 59			12 18												12 59				
Wressle d																							
Howden d							12 27																
Eastrington d																							
Gilberdyke d						12 22	12 34														13 22		
Broomfleet d																							
Brough d				12 17		12 30	12 42					12 49							13 17		13 30		
Ferriby d						12 35															13 35		
Hessle d						12 39															13 39		
Hull a				12 36		12 52	13 02					13 06							13 34		13 52		

For general notes see front of timetable
For details of catering facilities see Directory of Train Operators

- **A** To Leeds (Table 31)
- **B** From Plymouth to Edinburgh (Table 51)
- **C** To Huddersfield (Table 34)
- **D** To Scarborough (Table 43)
- **E** To Leeds (Table 34)
- **G** From Plymouth to Newcastle (Table 51)
- **H** From Lincoln (Table 30)
- **J** From Newark North Gate (Table 27)
- **K** From Bournemouth (Table 51) to Aberdeen (Table 229)
- **b** Change at Manchester Piccadilly
- **c** Change at Doncaster

Manchester Airport, Manchester, Sheffield and Meadowhall → Doncaster → Cleethorpes and Hull Barton-on-Humber → Cleethorpes

Network Diagram - see first page of Table 18

	NT	NT	NT	NT	NT	XC	HT	NT	NT	TP	TP	NT	NT	XC	NT	NT	NT	NT	NT	NT	XC
				BHX		1◇	1◇			1◇	1◇			1◇							1◇
	A	B	C			D		E	C			G		H			J	A	B	C	D
Manchester Airport 85 d										11 52	*12 07*										
Manchester Piccadilly 10 78 d										12 20	12 42										
Stockport 78 d			*11 55*							12 28	*12b19*									*12 55*	
Sheffield 7 a										13 08											
d	12 36	12 41	12 51			12 54		12 57	13 08	13 11		13 14		13 21		13 25	13 28	13 36	13 41	13 51	13 54
Meadowhall d	12a41	12 47	12a56					13 03	13a13	13 17		13 21				13 31	13 35	13a41	13 46	13a57	
Rotherham Central d								13 10				13 27				13 37	13 42				
Swinton (S.Yorks) d								13 18				13a36				13 47	13 50				
Mexborough d								13 21								13 50					
Conisbrough d								13 25								13 54					
Doncaster 7 a		13 11				13 22		13 35		13 38						14 04			14 14		14 18
York 8 26 a						13 46				*14 34*				14 29			14 50		*14 58*		14 45
London Kings Cross 15 ⊖ 26 d							11 48									*12 10*			*12 30*		
Doncaster 31 d		13 17					13 29	13 38		13 42					13 46	14 06			14 17		
Bentley (S.Yorks) 31 a		*13 30*						13 41													*14c30*
Adwick 31 a		*13 34*						13 47													*14c34*
Kirk Sandall d															13 52	14 12					
Hatfield & Stainforth d															13 57	14 17					
Thorne South d																14 23					
Crowle d																14 32					
Althorpe d																14 38					
Scunthorpe a										14 07						14 45					
d										14 08											
Barnetby d										14 22											
Hull Bus Station d				13 25																	
Barton-on-Humber a				13 50																	
Barton-on-Humber d					13 58																
Barrow Haven d					14 03																
New Holland d					14 06																
Goxhill d					14 11																
Thornton Abbey d					14 14																
Ulceby d					14 18																
Habrough d					14 23					14 31											
Stallingborough d					14 28																
Healing d					14 31																
Great Coates d					14 34																
Grimsby Town a					14 39					14 44											
d					14 39					14 45											
Grimsby Docks d					14 42																
New Clee d					14x44																
Cleethorpes a					14 49					14 57											
Thorne North d															14 02						
Goole d		13 37													14 12				14 36		
Saltmarshe d															14 17						
York 8 33 d													13 45								
Selby a							13 44				13 58		14 09								
d							13 45				13 59		14 09								
Wressle d																					
Howden d							13 55														
Eastrington d																					
Gilberdyke d															14 28						
Broomfleet d																					
Brough d		13 50					14 08				14 17		14 29		14 36				14 52		
Ferriby d															14 40						
Hessle d															14 45						
Hull a		14 08					14 25				14 34		14 48		14 56				15 07		

For general notes see front of timetable
For details of catering facilities see Directory of Train Operators

A To Huddersfield (Table 34)
B To Bridlington (Table 43)
C To Leeds (Table 34)
D From Bristol Temple Meads to Newcastle (Table 51)
E From Lincoln (Table 30)
G To Leeds (Table 31)
H From Plymouth to Edinburgh (Table 51)
J Via Pontefract Baghill (Table 33)
b Change at Manchester Piccadilly
c Change at Doncaster

Manchester Airport, Manchester, Sheffield and Meadowhall → Doncaster → Cleethorpes and Hull Barton-on-Humber → Cleethorpes

Network Diagram - see first page of Table 18

		NT	NT	TP	TP	NT	NT	NT	XC	NT	HT	NT	NT	NT		HT	XC	NT	NT	EM	NT	NT	TP	TP
									R												BHX			
				1 ◇	1 ◇				1		1 ◇					1 ◇	1 ◇						1 ◇	1 ◇
		A	B			C	D		E			G		B			H	A	B	J				
																					bus			
				trolley	trolley				buffet		restaurant, buffet					restaurant, buffet	buffet						trolley	trolley
Manchester Airport	85 ✈ d			12 52	*13 07*																		13 52	*14 07*
Manchester Piccadilly 10	78 🚉 d			13 20	13 42	*12 46*																	14 20	14 42
Stockport	78 d			13 28	*13b19*									*13 55*									14 28	*14b19*
Sheffield 7	🚉 a			14 08																			15 08	
	d	13 57	14 08	14 11		14 14			14 21	14 25		14 36	14 41	14 51			14 54	14 57	15 08				15 11	
Meadowhall	🚉 d	14 03	14a13	14 17		14 21				14 31		14a41	14 47	14a56				15 03	15a13				15 17	
Rotherham Central	d	14 10				14 27				14 37								15 10						
Swinton (S.Yorks)	d	14 18				14a36				14 48								15 18						
Mexborough	d	14 21								14 51								15 21						
Conisbrough	d	14 25								14 55								15 25						
Doncaster 7	a	14 35		14 39						15 04			15 09				15 15	15 36					15 38	
York 8	26 a			*15 26*					15 29								15 40							
London Kings Cross 15	⊖ 26 d	*12 35*		*13 00*						*13 10*	13 33		*13 30*					*14 00*						
Doncaster	31 d	14 38		14 42			14 46			15 06	15 12		15 14					15 38					15 42	
Bentley (S.Yorks)	31 a	14 41								*15 17*								15 41						
Adwick	31 a	14 47								*15 21*								15 47						
Kirk Sandall	d						14 54			15 12														
Hatfield & Stainforth	d						14 59			15 17														
Thorne South	d									15 22														
Crowle	d									15 30														
Althorpe	d									15 36														
Scunthorpe	a			15 07						15 45													16 07	
	d			15 08																			16 08	
Barnetby	d			15 22																15 32			16 22	
Hull Bus Station	bus d																				15 25			
Barton-on-Humber	bus a																				15 50			
Barton-on-Humber	d																					15 58		
Barrow Haven	d																					16 03		
New Holland	d																					16 06		
Goxhill	d																					16 11		
Thornton Abbey	d																					16 14		
Ulceby	d																					16 18		
Habrough	d																			15 42		16 23	16 31	
Stallingborough	d																					16 28		
Healing	d																					16 31		
Great Coates	d																					16 34		
Grimsby Town	a			15 42																15 56		16 39	16 44	
	d			15 43																		16 39	16 45	
Grimsby Docks	d																					16 42		
New Clee	d																							
Cleethorpes	a			15 54																		16 48	16 56	
Thorne North	d						15 04																	
Goole	d						15 13						15 33											
Saltmarshe	d																							
York 8	33 d							14 59																
Selby	a				14 58			15 19			15 27					←								15 58
	d				14 59			15 19			15 28 →					15 28								15 59
Wressle	d																							
Howden	d															15 38								
Eastrington	d																							
Gilberdyke	d						15 21																	
Broomfleet	d																							
Brough	d				15 17		15 29	15 39					15 47			15 53								16 17
Ferriby	d						15 34																	
Hessle	d						15 38																	
Hull	a				15 34		15 51	15 58					16 04			16 10								16 34

For general notes see front of timetable
For details of catering facilities see Directory of Train Operators

A From Lincoln (Table 30)
B To Leeds (Table 34)
C To Leeds (Table 31)
D To Scarborough (Table 43)
E From Bournemouth to Edinburgh (Table 51)
G To Huddersfield (Table 34)
H From Paignton to Newcastle (Table 51)
J From Newark North Gate (Table 27)
b Change at Manchester Piccadilly

Manchester Airport, Manchester, Sheffield and Meadowhall → Doncaster → Cleethorpes and Hull
Barton-on-Humber → Cleethorpes

Network Diagram - see first page of Table 18

	NT	NT	XC	NT	NT	NT	NT		NT	XC	NT	NT	TP	TP	NT	NT	XC	NT	NT	NT	NT	NT	XC
			R 1							1 ◇			1 ◇	1 ◇			R 1						1 ◇
	A	B	C		D		E		G	H	J	E			A	B	K		D		E		L
			catering							catering			trolley	trolley			catering						catering
Manchester Airport 85 ✈ d													14 52	*15 07*									
Manchester Piccadilly 10 78 ferry d													15 20	15 42	*14 46*								
Stockport 78 d							*14 55*						15 28	*15b19*							*15 51*		
Sheffield 7 ferry a													16 08										
d	15 14		15 21	15 25	15 36	15 41	15 51			15 54	15 57	16 08	16 11		16 14		16 21	16 25	16 36	16 41	16 51		16 54
Meadowhall ferry d	15 21			15 31	15a41	15 47	15a56				16 03	16a13	16 17		16 21			16 31	16a41	16 47	16a56		
Rotherham Central d	15 27			15 37							16 10				16 27			16 37					
Swinton (S.Yorks) d	15a36			15 47							16 18				16a36			16 47					
Mexborough d				15 50							16 21							16 50					
Conisbrough d				15 54							16 25							16 54					
Doncaster 7 a				16 04		16 12				16 15	16 35		16 38					17 07		17 11			17 15
York 8 26 a			16 29							16 40			*17 34*				17 29			*17 54*			17 40
London Kings Cross 15 ⊖ 26 d				*14 10*		*14 35*														*15 10*			
Doncaster 31 d		15 46		16 09		16 18					16 38		16 42			16 46				17 14			
Bentley (S.Yorks) 31 a				*16 17*							16 41												*17c30*
Adwick 31 a				*16 21*							16 47												*17c34*
Kirk Sandall d		15 52		16 15												16 52							
Hatfield & Stainforth d		15 57		16 20												16 57							
Thorne South d				16 25																			
Crowle d				16 34																			
Althorpe d				16 40																			
Scunthorpe a				16 48									17 07										
d													17 08										
Barnetby d													17 22										
Hull Bus Station bus d																							
Barton-on-Humber bus a																							
Barton-on-Humber d																							
Barrow Haven d																							
New Holland d																							
Goxhill d																							
Thornton Abbey d																							
Ulceby d																							
Habrough d																							
Stallingborough d																							
Healing d																							
Great Coates d																							
Grimsby Town a													17 42										
d													17 43										
Grimsby Docks d																							
New Clee d																							
Cleethorpes a													17 54										
Thorne North d		16 02														17 02				17 26			
Goole d		16 11				16 37										17 11				17 35			
Saltmarshe d																17 16							
York 8 33 d									16 12													17 27	
Selby a									16 38					16 59								17 45	
d									16 39					16 59								17 46	
Wressle d									16 46														
Howden d									16 51													17 55	
Eastrington d																							
Gilberdyke d		16 20							16 58							17 23						18 01	
Broomfleet d																							
Brough d		16 28				16 51			17 06					17 17		17 31				17 49		18 09	
Ferriby d		16 32							17 10							17 36							
Hessle d		16 37														17 40							
Hull a		16 49				17 08			17 27					17 36		17 53				18 06		18 29	

For general notes see front of timetable
For details of catering facilities see Directory of Train Operators

A To Leeds (Table 31)
B To Bridlington (Table 43)
C From Penzance (Table 135) to Dundee (Table 229)
D To Huddersfield (Table 34)
E To Leeds (Table 34)
G To Scarborough (Table 43)
H From Bristol Temple Meads to Newcastle (Table 51)
J From Lincoln (Table 30)
K From Bournemouth to Glasgow Central (Table 51)
L From Plymouth to Newcastle (Table 51)
b Change at Manchester Piccadilly
c Change at Doncaster

Manchester Airport, Manchester, Sheffield and Meadowhall → Doncaster → Cleethorpes and Hull
Barton-on-Humber → Cleethorpes

Network Diagram - see first page of Table 18

Station		NT		NT	HT	NT	EM	NT BHX	NT	TP	TP	NT	NT	XC	NT	NT	NT		NT	NT	XC	NT	NT	NT
					1 ◇					1 ◇	1 ◇			R 1							R 1			
		A		B		C	D	(bus)				E	G	H			J		C		K	A	B	C
Manchester Airport	85 ✈ d									15 52	*16 07*													
Manchester Piccadilly 10	78 d									16 20	16 42	*15 46*												
Stockport	78 d									16 28	*16b19*								*16 53*					
Sheffield 7	a									17 08														
	d			16 57		17 08				17 11		17 14		17 21	17 25	17 36	17 41		17 51		17 54		17 57	18 08
Meadowhall	d			17 03		17a13				17 17		17 21			17 31	17a41	17 47		17a56				18 03	18a13
Rotherham Central	d			17 10								17 27			17 38								18 09	
Swinton (S.Yorks)	d			17 18								17a36			17 47								18 17	
Mexborough	d			17 21											17 50								18 20	
Conisbrough	d			17 25											17 54								18 24	
Doncaster 7	a			17 35						17 38					18 07		18 13				18 16		18 35	
York 8	26 a									*18 34*				18 29							18 41			
London Kings Cross 15	⊖ 26 d	*15 30*		*16 00*	16 05												*16 30*					*16 35*		
Doncaster	31 d	17 22		17 38	17 42					17 42			17 56				18 16					18 27	18 41	
Bentley (S.Yorks)	31 a			17 41																	*18c30*			
Adwick	31 a			17 47																	*18c34*			
Kirk Sandall	d	17 29											18 02									18 34	18 47	
Hatfield & Stainforth	d	17 34											18 07									18 39	18 52	
Thorne South	d	17 39																				18 44		
Crowle	d	17 47																				18 52		
Althorpe	d	17 53																				18 58		
Scunthorpe	a	18 01								18 08												19 06		
	d									18 08														
Barnetby	d						17 52			18 22														
Hull Bus Station	(bus) d							17 30																
Barton-on-Humber	(bus) a							17 55																
Barton-on-Humber	d								18 00															
Barrow Haven	d								18 05															
New Holland	d								18 08															
Goxhill	d								18 13															
Thornton Abbey	d								18 16															
Ulceby	d								18 20															
Habrough	d						18 01		18 25	18 31														
Stallingborough	d								18 30															
Healing	d								18 33															
Great Coates	d								18 36															
Grimsby Town	a						18 14		18 41	18 46														
	d								18 41	18 46														
Grimsby Docks	d								18 44															
New Clee	d																							
Cleethorpes	a								18 50	19 00														
Thorne North	d												18 12										18 57	
Goole	d												18 21				18 36						19 06	
Saltmarshe	d												18 26											
York 8	33 d																			18 14				
Selby	a				17 59						18 05									18 43				
	d				18 00						18 07									18 43				
Wressle	d																			18 51				
Howden	d				18 10						18 16									18 56				
Eastrington	d																			19 00				
Gilberdyke	d												18 37							19 05			19 15	
Broomfleet	d												18 41											
Brough	d				18 23						18 28		18 47				18 53			19 13			19 23	
Ferriby	d												18 51										19 27	
Hessle	d												18 56										19 32	
Hull	a				18 40						18 45		19 06				19 09			19 32			19 47	

For general notes see front of timetable
For details of catering facilities see Directory of Train Operators

A From Adwick (Table 31)
B From Lincoln (Table 30)
C To Leeds (Table 34)
D From Lincoln (Table 27)
E To Leeds (Table 31)
G To Scarborough (Table 43)
H From Plymouth to Glasgow Central (Table 51)
J To Huddersfield (Table 34)
K From Bristol Temple Meads to Newcastle (Table 51)
b Change at Manchester Piccadilly
c Change at Doncaster

Manchester Airport, Manchester, Sheffield and Meadowhall → Doncaster → Cleethorpes and Hull Barton-on-Humber → Cleethorpes

Network Diagram - see first page of Table 18

	NT	XC	TP	TP	GR	NT	NT	NT	NT	XC		NT	NT	NT	NT	NT	TP	TP	NT	NT	XC	NT	NT
		R 1	1 ◇	1 ◇	R 1					R 1					BHX		1 ◇	1 ◇			R 1		
	A	B			C		D	E	G	H			J	G					A		K		D
Manchester Airport 85 d			16 52	*17 04*													17 52	*18 10*					
Manchester Piccadilly 10 78 d			17 20	17 42													18 18	18 42					
Stockport 78 d			17 28	*17b18*					*17 53*								18 26	*18b19*					
Sheffield 7 a			18 15														19 08						
d	18 14	18 21	18 24			18 29	18 36	18 41	18 51	18 54			18 57	19 08			19 11		19 18		19 26	19 30	19 38
Meadowhall d	18 21		18 29			18 35	18a41	18 47	18a56				19 03	19a13			19 17		19 25			19 36	19a43
Rotherham Central d	18 27					18 42							19 10						19 31			19 42	
Swinton (S.Yorks) d	18a36					18 50							19 20						19a40			19 51	
Mexborough d						18 53							19 23									19 54	
Conisbrough d						18 57							19 27									19 58	
Doncaster 7 a			18 54			19 08		19 11		19 17			19 39				19 41					20 08	
York 8 26 a		19 29								19 44											20 33	*20 40*	
London Kings Cross 15 ⊖ 26 d			*17 03*		17 20			*17 20*									*18 00*						
Doncaster 31 d			18 55		19 05			19 14				19 20					19 42			19 51			
Bentley (S.Yorks) 31 a										*19c32*													
Adwick 31 a										*19c36*													
Kirk Sandall d												19 27								19 57			
Hatfield & Stainforth d												19 32								20 02			
Thorne South d												19 37											
Crowle d												19 46											
Althorpe d												19 52											
Scunthorpe a			19 22									19 59					20 07						
d			19 23														20 08						
Barnetby d			19 37														20 22						
Hull Bus Station d															19 25								
Barton-on-Humber a															19 50								
Barton-on-Humber d																19 58							
Barrow Haven d																20 03							
New Holland d																20 06							
Goxhill d																20 11							
Thornton Abbey d																20 14							
Ulceby d																20 18							
Habrough d																20 23							
Stallingborough d																20 28							
Healing d																20 31							
Great Coates d																20 34							
Grimsby Town a			19 58													20 39	20 43						
d			19 58													20 39	20 44						
Grimsby Docks d																20 42							
New Clee d																							
Cleethorpes a			20 09													20 48	20 57						
Thorne North d																				20 08			
Goole d								19 34												20 17			
Saltmarshe d																							
York 8 33 d																		*19 23*					
Selby a				19 01	19 20													20 01					
d				19 02	19 21													20 02					
Wressle d																							
Howden d																							
Eastrington d																							
Gilberdyke d																				20 25			
Broomfleet d																							
Brough d				19 20	19 42			19 49										20 20		20 33			
Ferriby d																				20 37			
Hessle d																				20 42			
Hull a				19 37	20 00			20 07										20 37		20 55			

For general notes see front of timetable
For details of catering facilities see Directory of Train Operators

- **A** To Leeds (Table 31)
- **B** From Bournemouth to Edinburgh (Table 51)
- **C** **The Hull Executive**
- **D** To Huddersfield (Table 34)
- **E** To Bridlington (Table 43)
- **G** To Leeds (Table 34)
- **H** From Paignton to Newcastle (Table 51)
- **J** From Retford (Table 30)
- **K** From Plymouth to Edinburgh (Table 51)
- **b** Change at Manchester Piccadilly
- **c** Change at Doncaster

Manchester Airport, Manchester, Sheffield and Meadowhall → Doncaster → Cleethorpes and Hull Barton-on-Humber → Cleethorpes

Network Diagram - see first page of Table 18

Station		NT	NT	XC	EM		NT	HT	NT	NT	TP	NT	NT	NT	XC	NT	NT	NT	XC	EM		NT	TP	NT
				R 1				1 ◇ ⊠ ☕			1 ◇				R 1				1 ◇	1 ◇ ☕			1 ◇	ThFO BHX 🚌
		A	B	C	D					B		E			G	H		J	K	L		B	N	
Manchester Airport	85 ✈ d										18 52								19b12					
Manchester Piccadilly 10	78 🚆 d	*18 44*									19 18								19 42					
Stockport	78 d	*18 55*									19 26								19 55					
Sheffield 7	🚆 a										20 08													
	d	19 44	19 51	19 54					19 57	20 08	20 11			20 15	20 21	20 27	20 39	20 41	20 54	21 00		21 08		
Meadowhall	🚆 d	19 50	19a56						20 03	20a13	20 17			20 21		20 35	20 45	20a47				21a13		
Rotherham Central	d								20 10					20 27		20 41	20 52							
Swinton (S.Yorks)	d								20 19					20 36		20a50	21 00							
Mexborough	d								20 22					20 39			21 03							
Conisbrough	d								20 26					20 43			21 07							
Doncaster 7	a	20 11		20 20					20 36		20 41			20 55			21 18			21 25				
York 8	26 a			20 46											21 34				21 48	*21 59*				
London Kings Cross 15	⊖ 26 d	*18 03*					*18 33*	18 50				*19 00*					*19 03*							
Doncaster	31 d	20 15					20 25	20 31			20 42	20 44	20 49				21 18							
Bentley (S.Yorks)	31 a			*20c41*																*21 41*				
Adwick	31 a			*20c45*																*21 45*				
Kirk Sandall	d						20 31						20 55				21 26							
Hatfield & Stainforth	d						20 36						21 00				21 31							
Thorne South	d						20 41										21 38							
Crowle	d						20 50										21 46							
Althorpe	d						20 56										21 52							
Scunthorpe	a						21 04				21 07						22 01							
	d										21 08													
Barnetby	d				20 31						21 22													
Hull Bus Station	🚌 d																							21 25
Barton-on-Humber	🚌 a																							21 50
Barton-on-Humber	d																							
Barrow Haven	d																							
New Holland	d																							
Goxhill	d																							
Thornton Abbey	d																							
Ulceby	d																							
Habrough	d				20 40						21 31													
Stallingborough	d																							
Healing	d																							
Great Coates	d																							
Grimsby Town	a				20 52						21 44													
	d				20 53						21 45													
Grimsby Docks	d																							
New Clee	d																							
Cleethorpes	a				21 01						21 59													
Thorne North	d												21 06											
Goole	d	20 36											21a17											
Saltmarshe	d																							
York 8	33 d																							
Selby	a							20 46				21 01												
	d							20 47				21 02											21 28	
Wressle	d																							
Howden	d							20 57																
Eastrington	d																							
Gilberdyke	d											21 15												
Broomfleet	d																							
Brough	d	20 49						21 09				21 23											21 47	
Ferriby	d											21 28												
Hessle	d											21 32												
Hull	a	21 06						21 28				21 45											22 04	

For general notes see front of timetable
For details of catering facilities see Directory of Train Operators

- **A** To Beverley (Table 43)
- **B** To Leeds (Table 34)
- **C** From Bristol Temple Meads to Newcastle (Table 51)
- **D** From Newark North Gate (Table 27)
- **E** To Bridlington (Table 43)
- **G** From Bournemouth to Newcastle (Table 51)
- **H** To Leeds (Table 31)
- **J** To Huddersfield (Table 34)
- **K** From Paignton to Newcastle (Table 51)
- **L** From St Pancras International to Leeds (Table 53)
- **N** From Leeds (Table 39)
- **b** Change at Manchester Piccadilly and Sheffield
- **c** Change at Doncaster

Manchester Airport, Manchester, Sheffield and Meadowhall → Doncaster → Cleethorpes and Hull
Barton-on-Humber → Cleethorpes

Network Diagram - see first page of Table 18

		NT	TP	NT	NT	HT	XC	NT	NT	EM	NT	TP	NT	TP		NT	NT	NT	NT	NT FX	NT
			1 ◇	A		BHX 1 ◇ ⊠	1 ◇ B	C	D	1 ◇ E	G	1 ◇	C	1 ◇ H			D		C	J	
Manchester Airport	85 d		19 52						20b15			20 52								21 52	21 52
Manchester Piccadilly 10	78 d		20 18						20 42			21 18	20 46							22 18	22 18
Stockport	78 d		20 26						20 55			21 26								22 26	22 26
Sheffield 7	a		21 08									22 09									
	d		21 11	21 15			21 21	21 31	21 41	21 51	22 08	22 11	22 15			22 21	22 41		23 15	23 24	23 27
Meadowhall	d		21 17	21 21				21 37	21a46		22a13	22 17	22 21			22 31	22a46		23 21	23a29	23 33
Rotherham Central	d			21 27				21 43					22 27			22 37			23 27		23 39
Swinton (S.Yorks)	d			21 36				21a51					22a36			22 48			23a36		23 47
Mexborough	d			21 39												22 51					23 50
Conisbrough	d			21 43												22 55					23 54
Doncaster 7	a		21 40	21 54						22 12		22 42				23 04					00 07
York 8	26 a						22 58			23 12						00 39					
London Kings Cross 15	⊖ 26 d		19 30	20 00		20 27						20 30						21 00			
Doncaster	31 d		21 42	21 56		22 12						22 43						23 25			
Bentley (S.Yorks)	31 a									22 33											
Adwick	31 a									22 37											
Kirk Sandall	d			22 02								22 49						23 31			
Hatfield & Stainforth	d			22 07								22 53						23 36			
Thorne South	d											22 58									
Crowle	d											23 07									
Althorpe	d											23 13									
Scunthorpe	a		22 07									23 18									
	d		22 08									23 18									
Barnetby	d		22 23									23 36									
Hull Bus Station	🚌 d																				
Barton-on-Humber	🚌 a																				
Barton-on-Humber	d	21 58																			
Barrow Haven	d	22 03																			
New Holland	d	22 06																			
Goxhill	d	22 11																			
Thornton Abbey	d	22 14																			
Ulceby	d	22 18																			
Habrough	d	22 23	22 31									23 44									
Stallingborough	d	22 28																			
Healing	d	22 31																			
Great Coates	d	22 34																			
Grimsby Town	a	22 39	22 42									23 57									
	d	22 39	22 42									23 58									
Grimsby Docks	d	22 42																			
New Clee	d																				
Cleethorpes	a	22 48	22 56									00 09									
Thorne North	d			22 13														23 42			
Goole	d			22 22														23a53			
Saltmarshe	d			22 26																	
York 8	33 d				22 03																
Selby	a				22 22	22 29															
	d				22 22	22 30								22 44							
Wressle	d																				
Howden	d					22 40															
Eastrington	d																				
Gilberdyke	d			22 31	22 38																
Broomfleet	d																				
Brough	d			22 39	22 46	22 54								23 04							
Ferriby	d				22 51																
Hessle	d				22 55																
Hull	a			22 57	23 08	23 13								23 21							

For general notes see front of timetable
For details of catering facilities see Directory of Train Operators

A To Beverley (Table 43)
B From Plymouth (Table 51)
C To Leeds (Table 31)
D To Huddersfield (Table 34)
E From St Pancras International to Leeds (Table 53)
G To Leeds (Fridays to Barnsley) (Table 34)
H From Leeds (Table 39)
J To Wakefield Westgate (Table 31)
b Change at Manchester Piccadilly and Sheffield

Table 29

Manchester Airport, Manchester, Sheffield and Meadowhall → Doncaster → Cleethorpes and Hull Barton-on-Humber → Cleethorpes

Network Diagram - see first page of Table 18

	TP 1 ◊	NT	NT	NT	NT	NT	EM	NT	NT	NT	NT	NT	NT	TP 1 ◊	NT	NT	TP 1 ◊	NT	NT	NT	NT	NT	XC 1 ◊
		A		B	A	C	D			E	G				C	H		🚌		B			J
Manchester Airport 85 d	03 21													05 15			*05 47*						
Manchester Piccadilly 10 78 d	03 40													05 48	*05 52*		06 21						
Stockport 78 d														05 56	*06 01*		05b53						
Sheffield 7 a	04 31													06 48									
d	04 40	05 16		05 29	05 48	06 14			06 18	06 28	06 36	06 52		06 55	07 08								07 12
Meadowhall d		05a21		05 35	05a53	06a19			06 24	06 34	06a41	06 58		07 02	07a13								
Rotherham Central d				05 41					06 30	06 40		07 04										←	
Swinton (S.Yorks) d				05 49					06 38	06a48		07 14										07 14	
Mexborough d				05 52					06 41			→										07 17	
Conisbrough d				05 56					06 45													07 21	
Doncaster 7 a	05 14			06 06					06 57					07 22								07 31	
York 8 26 a				*06 40*																		*08 31*	08 24
London Kings Cross 15 ⊖ 26 d																							
Doncaster 31 d			05 50	06 14				06 47	07 00					07 24						07 28		07 32	
Bentley (S.Yorks) 31 a				*06 28*					07 03													07 35	
Adwick 31 a				*06 32*					07 09													07 41	
Kirk Sandall d				06 20				06 53												07 34			
Hatfield & Stainforth d				06 25				06 58												07 39			
Thorne South d								07 03															
Crowle d								07 11															
Althorpe d								07 17															
Scunthorpe a								07 25						07 49									
d														07 50									
Barnetby d							06 30							08 04									
Hull Bus Station 🚌 d																		07 25					
Barton-on-Humber 🚌 a																		07 50					
Barton-on-Humber d													06 58						08 00				
Barrow Haven d													07 03						08 05				
New Holland d													07 07						08 08				
Goxhill d													07 11						08 13				
Thornton Abbey d																			08 16				
Ulceby d													07 19						08 20				
Habrough d							06 39						07 23	08 13					08 25				
Stallingborough d													07 28						08 30				
Healing d													07 31						08 33				
Great Coates d																			08 36				
Grimsby Town a							06 53						07 37	08 26					08 41				
d													07 38	08 35					08 43				
Grimsby Docks d																			08 45				
New Clee d																			08x48				
Cleethorpes a													07 50	08 46					08 52				
Thorne North d				06 30																07 44			
Goole d				06 39																07 53			
Saltmarshe d				06 44																07 58			
York 8 33 d																	*06 05*				07 30		
Selby a			06 10														07 43				07 49		
d																	07 43				07 49		
Wressle d																					07 57		
Howden d																	07 52				08 02		
Eastrington d																					08 07		
Gilberdyke d				06 50												07 39				08 04	08 11		
Broomfleet d				06 54												07 43					08 15		
Brough d				07 00												07 49	08 04			08 12	08 21		
Ferriby d				07 04												07 53				08 16	08 26		
Hessle d				07 09												07 58				08 21	08 30		
Hull a				07 22												08 11	08 21			08 34	08 45		

For general notes see front of timetable
For details of catering facilities see Directory of Train Operators

- **A** To Barnsley (Table 34)
- **B** To Beverley (Table 43)
- **C** To Leeds (Table 34)
- **D** From Lincoln (Table 27)
- **E** To Leeds (Table 31)
- **G** To Huddersfield (Table 34)
- **H** To Scarborough (Table 43)
- **J** From Birmingham New Street to Edinburgh (Table 51)
- **b** Change at Manchester Piccadilly

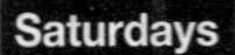

Manchester Airport, Manchester, Sheffield and Meadowhall → Doncaster → Cleethorpes and Hull Barton-on-Humber → Cleethorpes

Network Diagram - see first page of Table 18

		NT	EM	NT	NT	NT	NT	XC	NT	EM	TP	TP	NT	NT	XC	NT	NT	NT	NT	NT	NT	NT	XC	NT
			1 ◇					1 ◇			1 ◇	1 ◇			1 ◇								1 ◇	
		A	B		C	D	E	G	H	J			A		K		C	L	D	H	bus		G	
			catering					catering			catering	catering			catering								catering	
Manchester Airport	85 d										06 44	07 02								07b05				
Manchester Piccadilly 10	78 d								06 32		07 18	07 35								07 43				
Stockport	78 d										07 26	07c13								07 54				
Sheffield 7	a										08 10													
	d	07 14	07 17	07 23	07 36	07 41	07 51	07 54	08 08		08 11		08 14		08 21	08 23	08 36		08 41	08 51			08 54	08 57
Meadowhall	d	07 21	07a23	07 29	07a41	07 47	07a57		08a13		08 17		08 23			08 31	08a41		08 47	08a56				09 03
Rotherham Central	d	07 27		07 37		07 55							08 29			08 37								09 10
Swinton (S.Yorks)	d	07a37		07 46		08 03							08a38			08 47								09 19
Mexborough	d			07 49		08 06										08 50								09 22
Conisbrough	d			07 53		08 10										08 54								09 26
Doncaster 7	a			08 02		08 20		08 23			08 40					09 05			09 09				09 21	09 37
York 8	26 a					09 04		08 49							09 31								09 48	
London Kings Cross 15	⊖ 26 d					06 15								07 00		07 10								
Doncaster	31 d			08 04		08 22					08 42			08 48		09 10			09 16					09 38
Bentley (S.Yorks)	31 a			08 19							08 53					09 17								09 44
Adwick	31 a			08 25							08 59					09 21								09 50
Kirk Sandall	d			08 10										08 55		09 18								
Hatfield & Stainforth	d			08 15										09 00		09 23								
Thorne South	d			08 19												09 28								
Crowle	d			08 28												09 36								
Althorpe	d			08 34												09 42								
Scunthorpe	a			08 43							09 08					09 49								
	d										09 08													
Barnetby	d									09 00	09 22							09 40						
Hull Bus Station	bus d																				09 25			
Barton-on-Humber	bus a																				09 50			
Barton-on-Humber	d																					09 58		
Barrow Haven	d																					10 03		
New Holland	d																					10 06		
Goxhill	d																					10 11		
Thornton Abbey	d																					10 14		
Ulceby	d																					10 18		
Habrough	d									09 09								09 49				10 23		
Stallingborough	d																					10 28		
Healing	d																					10 31		
Great Coates	d																					10 34		
Grimsby Town	a									09 23	09 42							10 01				10 39		
	d										09 43							10 01				10 39		
Grimsby Docks	d																					10 42		
New Clee	d																					10x44		
Cleethorpes	a										09 58							10 14				10 49		
Thorne North	d													09 05										
Goole	d					08 42								09 14					09 39					
Saltmarshe	d																							
York 8	33 d											08 34												
Selby	a											08 58												
	d											08 59												
Wressle	d																							
Howden	d																							
Eastrington	d																							
Gilberdyke	d													09 22										
Broomfleet	d																							
Brough	d					08 56								09 30					09 53					
Ferriby	d													09 35										
Hessle	d													09 39										
Hull	a					09 13						09 31		09 55					10 10					

For general notes see front of timetable
For details of catering facilities see Directory of Train Operators

- **A** To Leeds (Table 31)
- **B** From Derby to Barnsley (Table 53)
- **C** To Huddersfield (Table 34)
- **D** To Bridlington (Table 43)
- **E** From Retford (Table 30) to Leeds (Table 34)
- **G** From Birmingham New Street to Newcastle (Table 51)
- **H** To Leeds (Table 34)
- **J** From Lincoln (Table 27)
- **K** From Birmingham New Street to Edinburgh (Table 51)
- **L** Until 26 January. From Sheffield via Retford (Table 30)
- **b** Change at Manchester Piccadilly and Sheffield
- **c** Change at Manchester Piccadilly

Table 29

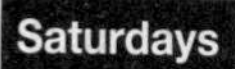

Manchester Airport, Manchester, Sheffield and Meadowhall → Doncaster → Cleethorpes and Hull Barton-on-Humber → Cleethorpes

Network Diagram - see first page of Table 18

		NT	TP	TP	NT	NT	NT	EM	NT	XC	NT	NT	NT	NT	NT	XC	NT	NT	EM	TP	TP	NT	NT	XC
			1◇	1◇				1◇		1◇						1◇				1◇	1◇			1◇
		A			B			C	D	E		G	H	J	A	K	L	A	N			B		Q
Manchester Airport	85 d		07 52	*08 07*																08 52	*09 07*			
Manchester Piccadilly 10	78 d		08 18	08 42	*07 46*															09 18	09 42	*08 46*		
Stockport	78 d		08 26	*08b20*											*08 55*					09 26	*09b21*			
Sheffield 7	a		09 09																	10 08				
	d	09 08	09 11		09 14			09 21		09 21	09 25	09 31	09 36	09 41	09 51	09 54	09 57	10 08		10 11		10 14		10 21
Meadowhall	d	09a13	09 17		09 21			09 29			09 32	09 37	09a41	09 47	09a56		10 03	10a13		10 17		10 21		
Rotherham Central	d				09 27						09 39	09 44					10 10					10 27		
Swinton (S.Yorks)	d				09a36						09 48	09 52					10 18					10a36		
Mexborough	d										09 51						10 21							
Conisbrough	d										09 55						10 25							
Doncaster 7	a		09 40					09 52			10 05			10 11		10 18	10 36			10 40				
York 8	26 a							10 16		10 31	*10 39*	10 53				10 44								11 29
London Kings Cross 15	⊖ 26 d					*08 00*					*08 10*			*08 30*									*09 00*	
Doncaster	31 d		09 42			09 46					10 07			10 21			10 38			10 42			10 46	
Bentley (S.Yorks)	31 a										*10 17*						10 41							
Adwick	31 a										*10 21*						10 47							
Kirk Sandall	d					09 53					10 14												10 52	
Hatfield & Stainforth	d					09 58					10 19												10 57	
Thorne South	d										10 24													
Crowle	d										10 33													
Althorpe	d										10 39													
Scunthorpe	a		10 07								10 46									11 07				
	d		10 08																	11 08				
Barnetby	d		10 22						10 10										10 55	11 22				
Hull Bus Station	d																							
Barton-on-Humber	a																							
Barton-on-Humber	d																							
Barrow Haven	d																							
New Holland	d																							
Goxhill	d																							
Thornton Abbey	d																							
Ulceby	d																							
Habrough	d		10 31						10 30										11 03					
Stallingborough	d																							
Healing	d																							
Great Coates	d																							
Grimsby Town	a		10 46						10 50										11 17	11 42				
	d		10 47						10 50											11 43				
Grimsby Docks	d																							
New Clee	d																							
Cleethorpes	a		10 56						11 10											11 54				
Thorne North	d					10 03																	11 02	
Goole	d					10 12								10 40									11 12	
Saltmarshe	d																							
York 8	33 d						09 52														*10 17*			
Selby	a			09 58			10 12														10 58			
	d			09 59			10 12														10 59			
Wressle	d																							
Howden	d						10 22																	
Eastrington	d																							
Gilberdyke	d					10 20	10 29																11 20	
Broomfleet	d																						11 25	
Brough	d			10 17		10 28	10 37							10 54							11 17		11 31	
Ferriby	d					10 33																	11 35	
Hessle	d					10 37																	11 40	
Hull	a			10 34		10 50	10 56							11 12							11 34		11 53	

For general notes see front of timetable
For details of catering facilities see Directory of Train Operators

- **A** To Leeds (Table 34)
- **B** To Leeds (Table 31)
- **C** From St Pancras International (Table 53)
- **D** From 2 February. From Gainsborough Central (Table 30)
- **E** From Bristol Temple Meads to Edinburgh (Table 51)
- **G** Via Pontefract Baghill (Table 33)
- **H** To Huddersfield (Table 34)
- **J** To Scarborough (Table 43)
- **K** From Birmingham New Street to Newcastle (Table 51)
- **L** From Lincoln (Table 30)
- **N** From Newark North Gate (Table 27)
- **Q** From Southampton Central to Edinburgh (Table 51)
- **b** Change at Manchester Piccadilly

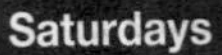

Manchester Airport, Manchester, Sheffield and Meadowhall → Doncaster → Cleethorpes and Hull
Barton-on-Humber → Cleethorpes

Network Diagram - see first page of Table 18

Station		NT	NT A	NT B	NT C	XC 1◇ D	HT 1◇	NT E	NT C	NT (bus)	NT	TP 1◇	TP 1◇	NT G	NT	NT	XC 1◇ H	NT	NT A	NT J	NT C	XC 1◇ D	NT E	NT C
Manchester Airport	85 ✈ d											09 52	*10 07*											
Manchester Piccadilly 10	78 ⇌ d											10 18	10 42	09 46										
Stockport	78 d				*09 55*							10 26	*10b21*								*10 55*			
Sheffield 7	⇌ a											11 08												
	d	10 25	10 36	10 41	10 51	10 54		10 57	11 08			11 11		11 14			11 21	11 25	11 36	11 41	11 51	11 54	11 57	12 08
Meadowhall	⇌ d	10 31	10a41	10 47	10a56			11 03	11a13			11 17		11 21				11 31	11a41	11 47	11a56		12 03	12a13
Rotherham Central	d	10 37						11 10						11 27				11 37					12 10	
Swinton (S.Yorks)	d	10 47						11 20						11a36				11 48					12 19	
Mexborough	d	10 50						11 23										11 51					12 22	
Conisbrough	d	10 54						11 27										11 55					12 26	
Doncaster 7	a	11 04		11 09		11 16		11 35				11 38						12 04		12 11		12 15	12 35	
York 8	26 a	*11 39*				11 45											12 29			*12 46*		12 43		
London Kings Cross 15	⊖ 26 d	*09 05*					09 34					*10 00*						*10 10*					*10 40*	
Doncaster	31 d	11 07		11 18			11 24	11 38				11 42			11 46			12 08		12 16			12 36	
Bentley (S.Yorks)	31 a	*11 17*						11 41										*12 17*					12 40	
Adwick	31 a	*11 21*						11 47										*12 21*					12 45	
Kirk Sandall	d	11 13													11 52			12 14						
Hatfield & Stainforth	d	11 18													11 57			12 19						
Thorne South	d	11 23																12 24						
Crowle	d	11 31																12 32						
Althorpe	d	11 37																12 38						
Scunthorpe	a	11 45										12 07						12 47						
	d											12 08												
Barnetby	d											12 22												
Hull Bus Station	🚌 d									11 25														
Barton-on-Humber	🚌 a									11 50														
Barton-on-Humber	d										11 58													
Barrow Haven	d										12 03													
New Holland	d										12 06													
Goxhill	d										12 11													
Thornton Abbey	d										12 14													
Ulceby	d										12 18													
Habrough	d										12 23	12 31												
Stallingborough	d										12 28													
Healing	d										12 31													
Great Coates	d										12 34													
Grimsby Town	a										12 39	12 48												
	d										12 39	12 49												
Grimsby Docks	d										12 42													
New Clee	d										12x44													
Cleethorpes	a										12 49	12 56												
Thorne North	d														12 02									
Goole	d			11 37											12 12					12 35				
Saltmarshe	d																							
York 8	33 d															11 49								
Selby	a						11 39						11 58			12 09								
	d						11 40						11 59			12 09								
Wressle	d																							
Howden	d						11 50									12 19								
Eastrington	d																							
Gilberdyke	d														12 20	12 27								
Broomfleet	d																							
Brough	d			11 51			12 03						12 17		12 28	12 35				12 49				
Ferriby	d														12 33									
Hessle	d														12 37									
Hull	a			12 08			12 20						12 34		12 50	12 54				13 07				

For general notes see front of timetable
For details of catering facilities see Directory of Train Operators

A To Huddersfield (Table 34)
B To Bridlington (Table 43)
C To Leeds (Table 34)
D From Bristol Temple Meads to Newcastle (Table 51)
E From Lincoln (Table 30)
G To Leeds (Table 31)
H From Plymouth to Edinburgh (Table 51)
J To Scarborough (Table 43)
b Change at Manchester Piccadilly

Table 29

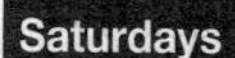

Manchester Airport, Manchester, Sheffield and Meadowhall → Doncaster → Cleethorpes and Hull Barton-on-Humber → Cleethorpes

Network Diagram - see first page of Table 18

	EM	TP	TP	NT	NT	XC	NT	NT	NT	NT	NT	NT	NT	XC	HT	NT	NT	TP	TP	NT	NT	NT	XC
		1◇	1◇			1◇								1◇	1◇			1◇	1◇				1◇
	A			B		C	D		E	G	H	🚌		J		K	H			B			L
Manchester Airport 85 d		10 52	*11 07*															11 52	*12 07*				
Manchester Piccadilly 10 78 d		11 18	11 42	*10 46*														12 18	12 42	*11 46*			
Stockport 78 d		11 26	*11b19*								*11 55*							12 26	*12b19*				
Sheffield 7 a		12 08																13 08					
d		12 11		12 14		12 21		12 25	12 36	12 41	12 51			12 54		12 57	13 08	13 11		13 14			13 21
Meadowhall d		12 17		12 21				12 31	12a41	12 47	12a56					13 03	13a13	13 17		13 21			
Rotherham Central d				12 27				12 37								13 10				13 27			
Swinton (S.Yorks) d				12a36				12 47								13 18				13a36			
Mexborough d								12 50								13 21							
Conisbrough d								12 54								13 25							
Doncaster 7 a		12 38						13 04		13 11				13 19		13 35		13 39					
York 8 26 a						13 29		*13 39*						13 44				*14 30*					14 29
London Kings Cross 15 ⊖ 26 d		*11 00*						*11 10*							11 48								
Doncaster 31 d		12 42			12 46			13 06		13 20					13 27	13 38		13 42				13 46	
Bentley (S.Yorks) 31 a								*13 17*								13 41							
Adwick 31 a								*13 21*								13 47							
Kirk Sandall d					12 52			13 12														13 52	
Hatfield & Stainforth d					12 57			13 17														13 57	
Thorne South d								13 22															
Crowle d								13 31															
Althorpe d								13 37															
Scunthorpe a		13 07						13 45										14 07					
d		13 08																14 08					
Barnetby d	12 32	13 22					13 43											14 22					
Hull Bus Station 🚌 d												13 25											
Barton-on-Humber 🚌 a												13 50											
Barton-on-Humber d													13 58										
Barrow Haven d													14 03										
New Holland d													14 06										
Goxhill d													14 11										
Thornton Abbey d													14 14										
Ulceby d													14 18										
Habrough d	12 41						13 52						14 23					14 31					
Stallingborough d													14 28										
Healing d													14 31										
Great Coates d													14 34										
Grimsby Town a	12 55	13 42					14 05						14 39					14 47					
d		13 43					14 05						14 39					14 48					
Grimsby Docks d													14 42										
New Clee d													14x44										
Cleethorpes a		13 54					14 16						14 49					14 57					
Thorne North d					13 02																	14 02	
Goole d					13 11					13 39												14 12	
Saltmarshe d																						14 17	
York 8 33 d			*12 18*																		13 38		
Selby a			12 58												13 42				13 58		14 03		
d			12 59												13 43				13 59		14 04		
Wressle d																							
Howden d															13 53						14 13		
Eastrington d																							
Gilberdyke d					13 20																	14 26	
Broomfleet d																							
Brough d			13 17		13 28					13 53					14 05				14 17		14 25	14 34	
Ferriby d					13 32																	14 39	
Hessle d					13 37																	14 43	
Hull a			13 34		13 50					14 10					14 22				14 34		14 45	14 56	

For general notes see front of timetable
For details of catering facilities see Directory of Train Operators

A From Newark North Gate (Table 27)
B To Leeds (Table 31)
C From Bournemouth (Table 51) to Aberdeen (Table 229)
D Until 26 January. From Sheffield via Retford (Table 30)
E To Huddersfield (Table 34)
G To Bridlington (Table 43)
H To Leeds (Table 34)
J From Cardiff Central (from 29 March from Bristol Temple Meads) to Newcastle (Table 51)
K From Lincoln (Table 30)
L From Plymouth to Edinburgh (Table 51)
b Change at Manchester Piccadilly

Table 29

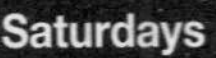

Manchester Airport, Manchester, Sheffield and Meadowhall → Doncaster → Cleethorpes and Hull Barton-on-Humber → Cleethorpes

Network Diagram - see first page of Table 18

		NT	NT	NT	NT	NT	NT	XC	NT	NT	EM	TP	TP	NT	NT	NT	XC	NT	NT	NT	NT	XC	HT	NT
								1 ◇				1 ◇	1 ◇				1 ◇					1 ◇	1 ◇	
			A	B	C	D	E	G	H	D	J			K	L		N		B		D	Q		H
							🚌																⊠	
Manchester Airport	85 ✈ d											12 52	*13 07*											
Manchester Piccadilly 10	78 🚢 d											13 18	13 42	*12 46*										
Stockport	78 d					*12 55*						13 26	*13b19*								*13 55*			
Sheffield 7	🚢 a											14 08												
	d	13 25	13 28	13 36	13 41	13 51		13 54	13 57	14 08		14 11		14 14			14 21	14 25	14 36	14 41	14 51	14 54		14 57
Meadowhall	🚢 d	13 31	13 35	13a41	13 47	13a57			14 03	14a13		14 17		14 21				14 31	14a41	14 47	14a56			15 03
Rotherham Central	d	13 37	13 42						14 10					14 27				14 37						15 10
Swinton (S.Yorks)	d	13 47	13 50						14 18					14a36				14 47						15 18
Mexborough	d	13 50							14 21									14 50						15 21
Conisbrough	d	13 54							14 25									14 54						15 25
Doncaster 7	a	14 04			14 11			14 15	14 35			14 38						15 04		15 11		15 15		15 36
York 8	26 a		14 50		*14 58*			14 43									15 29					15 43		
London Kings Cross 15	⊖ 26 d	*12 10*			*12 30*							*13 00*						*13 10*					13 38	
Doncaster	31 d	14 06			14 18				14 38			14 42			14 46			15 07		15 16			15 25	15 38
Bentley (S.Yorks)	31 a	*14 17*							14 41									*15 17*						15 41
Adwick	31 a	*14 21*							14 47									*15 21*						15 47
Kirk Sandall	d	14 12													14 52			15 13						
Hatfield & Stainforth	d	14 17													14 57			15 18						
Thorne South	d	14 22																15 23						
Crowle	d	14 31																15 31						
Althorpe	d	14 37																15 37						
Scunthorpe	a	14 45										15 07						15 46						
	d											15 08												
Barnetby	d						14 10				14 39	15 22												
Hull Bus Station	🚌 d																							
Barton-on-Humber	🚌 a																							
Barton-on-Humber	d																							
Barrow Haven	d																							
New Holland	d																							
Goxhill	d																							
Thornton Abbey	d																							
Ulceby	d																							
Habrough	d						14 30				14 47													
Stallingborough	d																							
Healing	d																							
Great Coates	d																							
Grimsby Town	a						14 50				15 01	15 42												
	d						14 50					15 43												
Grimsby Docks	d																							
New Clee	d																							
Cleethorpes	a						15 10					15 54												
Thorne North	d														15 02									
Goole	d				14 37										15 13					15 37				
Saltmarshe	d																							
York 8	33 d															15 05								
Selby	a												14 58			15 24							15 40	
	d												14 59			15 24							15 41	
Wressle	d																							
Howden	d																						15 51	
Eastrington	d																							
Gilberdyke	d														15 21									
Broomfleet	d																							
Brough	d				14 54								15 17		15 29	15 44				15 51			16 03	
Ferriby	d														15 34									
Hessle	d														15 38									
Hull	a				15 12								15 34		15 51	16 03				16 07			16 20	

For general notes see front of timetable
For details of catering facilities see Directory of Train Operators

A Via Pontefract Baghill (Table 33)
B To Huddersfield (Table 34)
C To Bridlington (Table 43)
D To Leeds (Table 34)
E From 2 February. From Gainsborough Central (Table 30)
G From Bristol Temple Meads to Newcastle (Table 51)
H From Lincoln (Table 30)
J From Newark North Gate (Table 27)
K To Leeds (Table 31)
L To Scarborough (Table 43)
N From Bournemouth to Edinburgh (Table 51)
Q From Paignton to Newcastle (Table 51)
b Change at Manchester Piccadilly

Table 29

Saturdays

Manchester Airport, Manchester, Sheffield and Meadowhall → Doncaster → Cleethorpes and Hull Barton-on-Humber → Cleethorpes

Network Diagram - see first page of Table 18

		NT	NT	NT	TP	TP	NT	NT	XC	NT	NT	NT	NT	NT	NT	XC	NT	NT	TP	TP	NT	NT	EM	NT
					1 ◇	1 ◇			1 ◇							1 ◇			1 ◇	1 ◇				
		A					B	C	D		E	G		A	H	J	K	A			B	C	L	N
			bus		trolley				café							café			trolley					bus
Manchester Airport	85 ✈ d				13 52	*14 07*													14 52	*15 07*				
Manchester Piccadilly 10	78 🚌 d				14 18	14 42	*13 46*												15 18	15 42	*14 46*			
Stockport	78 d				14 26	*14b19*								*14 55*					15 26	*15b19*				
Sheffield 7	🚌 a				15 08														16 08					
	d	15 08			15 11		15 14		15 21	15 25		15 36	15 40	15 51		15 54	15 57	16 08	16 11		16 14			
Meadowhall	🚌 d	15a13			15 17		15 21			15 31		15a41	15 46	15a56			16 03	16a13	16 17		16 21			
Rotherham Central	d						15 27			15 37							16 10				16 27			
Swinton (S.Yorks)	d						15a36			15 47							16 18				16a36			
Mexborough	d									15 50							16 21							
Conisbrough	d									15 54							16 25							
Doncaster 7	a				15 41					16 04			16 11			16 15	16 35		16 38					
York 8	26 a								16 29				*16 56*			16 45								
London Kings Cross 15	⊖ 26 d				*14 00*												*14 30*		*15 00*					
Doncaster	31 d				15 42			15 46		16 06			16 14				16 38		16 42			16 47		
Bentley (S.Yorks)	31 a															*16c31*	16 41							
Adwick	31 a															*16c35*	16 47							
Kirk Sandall	d							15 52		16 13												16 53		
Hatfield & Stainforth	d							15 57		16 18												16 58		
Thorne South	d									16 24														
Crowle	d									16 33														
Althorpe	d									16 39														
Scunthorpe	a				16 07					16 46									17 07					
	d				16 08														17 08					
Barnetby	d				16 22						17 07								17 22				17 31	17 35
Hull Bus Station	bus d		15 25																					
Barton-on-Humber	bus a		15 50																					
Barton-on-Humber	d			15 58																				
Barrow Haven	d			16 03																				
New Holland	d			16 06																				
Goxhill	d			16 11																				
Thornton Abbey	d			16 14																				
Ulceby	d			16 18																				
Habrough	d			16 23	16 31						17 19												17 40	17 55
Stallingborough	d			16 28																				
Healing	d			16 31																				
Great Coates	d			16 34																				
Grimsby Town	a			16 39	16 48						17 37								17 42				17 54	18 15
	d			16 39	16 49						17 38								17 43					18 15
Grimsby Docks	d			16 42																				
New Clee	d																							
Cleethorpes	a			16 48	16 56						17 46								17 54					18 35
Thorne North	d							16 02														17 03		
Goole	d							16 12					16 36									17 12		
Saltmarshe	d																					17 17		
York 8	33 d														16 12									
Selby	a					15 58									16 38					16 59				
	d					15 59									16 39					16 59				
Wressle	d														16 46									
Howden	d														16 51									
Eastrington	d																							
Gilberdyke	d							16 20							16 58							17 23		
Broomfleet	d																							
Brough	d					16 17		16 28					16 50		17 06					17 17		17 31		
Ferriby	d							16 33							17 10							17 36		
Hessle	d							16 37														17 40		
Hull	a					16 34		16 50					17 07		17 27					17 36		17 53		

For general notes see front of timetable
For details of catering facilities see Directory of Train Operators

- **A** To Leeds (Table 34)
- **B** To Leeds (Table 31)
- **C** To Bridlington (Table 43)
- **D** From Penzance (Table 135) to Dundee (Table 229)
- **E** Until 26 January. From Sheffield via Retford (Table 30)
- **G** To Huddersfield (Table 34)
- **H** To Scarborough (Table 43)
- **J** From Bristol Temple Meads to Newcastle (Table 51)
- **K** From Lincoln (Table 30)
- **L** From Lincoln (Table 27)
- **N** From 2 February. From Gainsborough Central (Table 30)
- **b** Change at Manchester Piccadilly
- **c** Change at Doncaster

Table 29

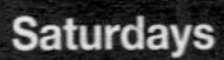

Manchester Airport, Manchester, Sheffield and Meadowhall → Doncaster → Cleethorpes and Hull Barton-on-Humber → Cleethorpes

Network Diagram - see first page of Table 18

		NT	NT	XC	NT	NT	NT	NT	NT	XC	NT	NT	NT	TP	TP	NT	NT	EM	XC	NT	NT	NT	NT	NT
				1 ◇						1 ◇				1 ◇	1 ◇				1 ◇					
				A		B		C		D	E	G	C			H		J	K		B			C
		🚌		☕						☕				🍴					☕					
Manchester Airport	85 ✈ d													15 52	16 07									
Manchester Piccadilly 10	78 🚆 d													16 18	16 42	15 46								
Stockport	78 d							15 55						16 26	16b19									16 53
Sheffield 7	🚆 a													17 08										
	d			16 21	16 25	16 36	16 41	16 51		16 54		16 57	17 08	17 11		17 14			17 21	17 25	17 36	17 41		17 51
Meadowhall	🚆 d				16 31	16a41	16 47	16a56				17 03	17a13	17 17		17 21				17 31	17a41	17 47		17a56
Rotherham Central	d				16 37							17 10				17 27				17 38				
Swinton (S.Yorks)	d				16 47							17 18				17a36				17 47				
Mexborough	d				16 50							17 21								17 50				
Conisbrough	d				16 54							17 25								17 54				
Doncaster 7	a				17 08		17 11			17 19		17 35		17 38						18 07		18 10		
York 8	26 a			17 30						17 45									18 29					
London Kings Cross 15	⊖ 26 d											15 30		16 00								16 30		
Doncaster	31 d						17 14				17 22	17 38		17 42			17 48					18 24		
Bentley (S.Yorks)	31 a									17c30		17 41												
Adwick	31 a									17c34		17 47												
Kirk Sandall	d										17 28						17 54							
Hatfield & Stainforth	d										17 33						17 59							
Thorne South	d										17 38													
Crowle	d										17 47													
Althorpe	d										17 53													
Scunthorpe	a										18 01			18 08										
	d													18 08										
Barnetby	d													18 22				18 49						
Hull Bus Station	🚌 d	17 30																						
Barton-on-Humber	🚌 a	17 55																						
Barton-on-Humber	d		18 00																					
Barrow Haven	d		18 05																					
New Holland	d		18 08																					
Goxhill	d		18 13																					
Thornton Abbey	d		18 16																					
Ulceby	d		18 20																					
Habrough	d		18 25											18 31				18 58						
Stallingborough	d		18 30																					
Healing	d		18 33																					
Great Coates	d		18 36																					
Grimsby Town	a		18 41											18 49				19 14						
	d		18 41											18 49										
Grimsby Docks	d		18 44																					
New Clee	d																							
Cleethorpes	a		18 50											18 59										
Thorne North	d						17 28										18 04							
Goole	d						17 37										18 13					18 44		
Saltmarshe	d																18 18							
York 8	33 d								17 18														18 13	
Selby	a								17 37						17 59								18 41	
	d								17 37						18 00								18 42	
Wressle	d																							
Howden	d								17 47						18 09								18 51	
Eastrington	d																						18 56	
Gilberdyke	d								17 57								18 22						19 00	
Broomfleet	d																18 26							
Brough	d						17 56		18 05						18 20		18 32					18 58	19 08	
Ferriby	d																18 37							
Hessle	d																18 42							
Hull	a						18 10		18 21						18 37		18 57					19 15	19 28	

For general notes see front of timetable
For details of catering facilities see Directory of Train Operators

A From Bournemouth to Glasgow Central (from 29 March to Edinburgh) (Table 51)
B To Huddersfield (Table 34)
C To Leeds (Table 34)
D From Bristol Temple Meads to Newcastle (Table 51)
E From Adwick (Table 31)
G From Lincoln (Table 30)
H To Leeds (Table 31)
J From Newark North Gate (Table 27)
K From Plymouth to Glasgow Central (from 29 March to Edinburgh) (Table 51)
b Change at Manchester Piccadilly
c Change at Doncaster

Table 29

Saturdays

Manchester Airport, Manchester, Sheffield and Meadowhall → Doncaster → Cleethorpes and Hull Barton-on-Humber → Cleethorpes

Network Diagram - see first page of Table 18

		XC	NT	NT	NT	NT	TP	HT	XC	TP	NT	NT	NT	NT	NT	XC	NT	EM	NT	NT	NT	NT	TP	TP
		1◇					1◇	1◇	1◇	1◇						1◇		1◇					1◇	1◇
		A	B	C	D	E			G				H	J	D	K	L	N	D	L				
		☕						⊠ ☕	☕	trolley						☕		☕			🚌		trolley	
Manchester Airport	85 ✈ d						17 04		16 52	16 52													17 52	18 10
Manchester Piccadilly 10	78 d					16 46	17 42		17 18	17 18													18 18	18 41
Stockport	78 d						17b18		17 26	17 26					17 55								18 26	18b19
Sheffield 7	a									18 12													19 08	
	d	17 54		17 57	18 08	18 14			18 21	18 24		18 29	18 36	18 41	18 51	18 54	19 00	19 04	19 08				19 11	
Meadowhall	d			18 03	18a13	18 21				18 29		18 35	18a41	18 47	18a56		19 06		19a13				19 17	
Rotherham Central	d			18 10		18 27						18 42					19 13			←				
Swinton (S.Yorks)	d			18 18		18a36						18 50					19 22			19 22				
Mexborough	d			18 21								18 53					→			19 25				
Conisbrough	d			18 25								18 57								19 29				
Doncaster 7	a	18 21		18 37						18 53		19 08		19 10		19 18		19 29		19 40			19 41	
York 8	26 a	18 46							19 32							19 49							20 34	
London Kings Cross 15	⊖ 26 d							17 05															18 00	
Doncaster	31 d		18 28					18 48		18 53	18 58	19 13		19 13									19 42	
Bentley (S.Yorks)	31 a	18c32														19c30								
Adwick	31 a	18c36														19c34								
Kirk Sandall	d		18 35								19 06	19 20												
Hatfield & Stainforth	d		18 40								19 11	19 25												
Thorne South	d		18 45									19 30												
Crowle	d		18 53									19 39												
Althorpe	d		18 59									19 45												
Scunthorpe	a		19 07							19 22		19 52											20 08	
	d									19 23													20 08	
Barnetby	d									19 37													20 22	
Hull Bus Station	🚌 d																				19 25			
Barton-on-Humber	🚌 a																				19 50			
Barton-on-Humber	d																					19 58		
Barrow Haven	d																					20 03		
New Holland	d																					20 06		
Goxhill	d																					20 11		
Thornton Abbey	d																					20 14		
Ulceby	d																					20 18		
Habrough	d																					20 23		
Stallingborough	d																					20 28		
Healing	d																					20 31		
Great Coates	d																					20 34		
Grimsby Town	a									19 58												20 39	20 47	
	d									19 58												20 39	20 48	
Grimsby Docks	d																					20 42		
New Clee	d																							
Cleethorpes	a									20 09												20 48	20 55	
Thorne North	d										19 16													
Goole	d										19 25													
Saltmarshe	d																							
York 8	33 d																							19 23
Selby	a						19 01	19 07						19 34										20 01
	d						19 02	19 08						19 34										20 02
Wressle	d																							
Howden	d							19 18																
Eastrington	d																							
Gilberdyke	d										19 33													
Broomfleet	d																							
Brough	d						19 20	19 30			19 41			19 54										20 20
Ferriby	d										19 46													
Hessle	d										19 50													
Hull	a						19 37	19 47			20 03			20 11										20 37

For general notes see front of timetable
For details of catering facilities see Directory of Train Operators

- **A** From Bristol Temple Meads to Newcastle (Table 51)
- **B** From Adwick (Table 31)
- **C** From Lincoln (Table 30)
- **D** To Leeds (Table 34)
- **E** To Leeds (Table 31)
- **G** From Bournemouth to Edinburgh (Table 51)
- **H** To Huddersfield (Table 34)
- **J** To Bridlington (Table 43)
- **K** From Paignton to Edinburgh (Table 51)
- **L** From Retford (Table 30)
- **N** From St Pancras International (Table 53)
- **b** Change at Manchester Piccadilly
- **c** Change at Doncaster

Table 29

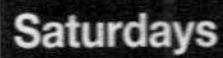

Saturdays

Manchester Airport, Manchester, Sheffield and Meadowhall → Doncaster → Cleethorpes and Hull Barton-on-Humber → Cleethorpes

Network Diagram - see first page of Table 18

	NT	NT	XC	NT	NT	NT	NT	NT	XC	NT	GR	NT	NT	EM	TP	NT	NT	XC	NT	NT	NT	EM	NT
	A		1◇ B		C	D	E		1◇ G		R 1		E	1◇ H	1◇	J		1◇ K	A		C	1◇ L	
Manchester Airport 85 d															18 52						19b12		
Manchester Piccadilly 10 78 d	17 46					18 44								18 46	19 18						19 42		
Stockport 78 d						18 55									19 26						19 55		
Sheffield 7 a															20 08								
d	19 14		19 21	19 30	19 38	19 44	19 51		19 54			19 57	20 08	20 11	20 11		20 15	20 21	20 31	20 38	20 41	20 48	
Meadowhall d	19 21			19 36	19a43	19 50	19a56					20 03	20a13		20 17		20 20		20 37	20 44	20a47	20a53	
Rotherham Central d	19 27			19 42								20 09					20 26		20 43	20 53			
Swinton (S.Yorks) d	19a40			19 51								20 17					20 36		20a51	21 05			
Mexborough d				19 54								20 20					20 39						
Conisbrough d				19 58								20 24					20 43						
Doncaster 7 a				20 09		20 11			20 16			20 36		20 36	20 41		20 56						
York 8 26 a			20 29						20 42								21 38	21 35					
London Kings Cross 15 ⊖ 26 d						18 30				18 35	18 40					19 00							
Doncaster 31 d		19 47				20 14				20 25	20 28				20 42	20 46							21 07
Bentley (S.Yorks) 31 a														20 48									
Adwick 31 a														20 52									
Kirk Sandall d		19 53								20 31						20 52							21 13
Hatfield & Stainforth d		19 58								20 36						20 57							21 18
Thorne South d										20 41													21 23
Crowle d										20 50													21 31
Althorpe d										20 56													21 37
Scunthorpe a										21 04					21 08								21 46
d															21 08								
Barnetby d															21 22								
Hull Bus Station d																							
Barton-on-Humber a																							
Barton-on-Humber d																							
Barrow Haven d																							
New Holland d																							
Goxhill d																							
Thornton Abbey d																							
Ulceby d																							
Habrough d															21 29								
Stallingborough d																							
Healing d																							
Great Coates d																							
Grimsby Town a															21 46								
d															21 46								
Grimsby Docks d																							
New Clee d																							
Cleethorpes a															22 00								
Thorne North d		20 03														21 02							
Goole d		20 12				20 33										21 11							
Saltmarshe d																							
York 8 33 d								20 17															
Selby a								20 36			20 43												
d								20 36			20 45												
Wressle d																							
Howden d																							
Eastrington d																							
Gilberdyke d		20 22						20 50								21 19							
Broomfleet d																							
Brough d		20 30				20 47		20 58			21 07					21 27							
Ferriby d		20 35						21 02															
Hessle d		20 39						21 07															
Hull a		20 52				21 04		21 22			21 27					21 45							

For general notes see front of timetable
For details of catering facilities see Directory of Train Operators

A To Leeds (Table 31)
B From Plymouth to Newcastle (Table 51)
C To Huddersfield (Table 34)
D To Beverley (Table 43)
E To Leeds (Table 34)
G From Bristol Temple Meads to Newcastle (Table 51)
H From St Pancras International to Leeds (Table 53)
J To Bridlington (Table 43)
K From Bournemouth to Newcastle (Table 51)
L From St Pancras International to Barnsley (Table 53)
b Change at Manchester Piccadilly and Sheffield

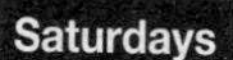

Manchester Airport, Manchester, Sheffield and Meadowhall → Doncaster → Cleethorpes and Hull Barton-on-Humber → Cleethorpes

Network Diagram - see first page of Table 18

Station		EM	TP	HT	NT	XC	NT	NT	NT	TP	NT	XC	NT	NT	EM	NT	TP	TP	NT	NT	NT	NT
		1 ◇	1 ◇	1 ◇		1 ◇				1 ◇		1 ◇			1 ◇		1 ◇	1 ◇				
		A	B			C	D				E	G	H	J	A	K	L			H	J	
Manchester Airport	85 d									19 52				20b15				20 52			21b04	21 52
Manchester Piccadilly 10	78 d									20 18				20 42				21 18			21 42	22 18
Stockport	78 d									20 26				20 55				21 26			21 52	22 26
Sheffield 7	a									21 08								22 09				
	d	20 51				20 54	21 08			21 11	21 14	21 21	21 26	21 41	21 57	22 08		22 11	22 26	22 31	22 41	23 24
Meadowhall	d						21a13			21 17	21 22		21 32	21a46		22a13		22 17	22 32	22 37	22a46	23 31
Rotherham Central	d				←						21 28		21 38						22 39	22 43		23 37
Swinton (S.Yorks)	d				21 05						21 40		21a48						22 47	22a50		23 45
Mexborough	d				21 08						21 43								22 50			23 48
Conisbrough	d				21 12						21 47								22 54			23 52
Doncaster 7	a	21 13			21 23					21 40	21 55				22 21			22 36	23 04			00 03
York 8	26 a					21 54						22 38										
London Kings Cross 15	⊖ 26 d			19 41							20 00							20 30				
Doncaster	31 d			21 20						21 42	21 57							22 38	23 05			
Bentley (S.Yorks)	31 a	21 31																22 52				
Adwick	31 a	21 35																22 56				
Kirk Sandall	d										22 03							22 44	23 12			
Hatfield & Stainforth	d										22 08							22 48	23 17			
Thorne South	d																	22 53				
Crowle	d																	23 02				
Althorpe	d																	23 08				
Scunthorpe	a									22 10								23 13				
	d									22 11								23 13				
Barnetby	d									22 25								23 28				
Hull Bus Station	🚌 d							21 25														
Barton-on-Humber	🚌 a							21 50														
Barton-on-Humber	d								21 58													
Barrow Haven	d								22 03													
New Holland	d								22 06													
Goxhill	d								22 11													
Thornton Abbey	d								22 14													
Ulceby	d								22 18													
Habrough	d								22 23	22 34								23 36				
Stallingborough	d								22 28													
Healing	d								22 31													
Great Coates	d								22 34													
Grimsby Town	a								22 39	22 46								23 49				
	d								22 39	22 47								23 50				
Grimsby Docks	d								22 42													
New Clee	d																					
Cleethorpes	a								22 48	22 59								00 01				
Thorne North	d										22 13											
Goole	d										22 22								23 22			
Saltmarshe	d										22 27								23a33			
York 8	33 d																21 45					
Selby	a			21 35																		
	d		21 28	21 36													22 45					
Wressle	d																					
Howden	d			21 46																		
Eastrington	d																					
Gilberdyke	d										22 33											
Broomfleet	d																					
Brough	d		21 47	21 58							22 41						23 05					
Ferriby	d																					
Hessle	d																					
Hull	a		22 04	22 15							22 58						23 21					

For general notes see front of timetable
For details of catering facilities see Directory of Train Operators

A From St Pancras International to Leeds (Table 53)
B From Leeds (Table 41)
C From Bristol Temple Meads (Table 51)
D To Leeds (Table 34)
E To Beverley (Table 43)
G From Plymouth (Table 51)
H To Leeds (Table 31)
J To Huddersfield (Table 34)
K To Barnsley (Table 34)
L From Leeds (Table 39)
b Change at Manchester Piccadilly and Sheffield

Table 29

Sundays

until 27 January

Manchester Airport, Manchester, Sheffield and Meadowhall → Doncaster → Cleethorpes and Hull Barton-on-Humber → Cleethorpes

Network Diagram - see first page of Table 18

		NT	NT A	NT	NT	NT B	NT C		TP 1 ◇	NT	TP 1 ◇	NT	TP 1 ◇	XC 1 ◇ D		NT E	NT A	NT	XC 1 ◇ G	NT	EM 1 ◇ H		TP 1 ◇	XC 1 ◇ J
Manchester Airport	85 ✈ d										08 51		07b36										10 47	
Manchester Piccadilly 10	78 ⇌ d										09 30		08c00										11 12	
Stockport	78 d												08c25										10e43	
Sheffield 7	⇌ a																							
	d	08 00	08 39		08 45	09 36	09 39		09 42				09 58	10 21		10 26	10 39		10 54	11 05	11 12			11 21
Meadowhall	⇌ d	08 06	08a44		08 51	09 42	09a44		09 48				10 03			10 32	10a44			11 12				
Rotherham Central	d	08 12			08 57	09 48			09 57											11 18				
Swinton (S.Yorks)	d	08 20			09 05	09a58			10 05											11 28 →				
Mexborough	d	08 23			09 08				10 08															
Conisbrough	d	08 27			09 12				10 12															
Doncaster 7	a	08 38			09 22				10 20				10 26			10 51			11 16		11 34			
York 8	26 a				10 06								11 07	11 33		11 29			11 44		11 57			12 33
London Kings Cross 15	⊖ 26 d															09 00		09 10						
Doncaster	31 d			09 07	09 26					10 21			10 27			10 53		11 07						
Bentley (S.Yorks)	31 a	09 13														11 13								
Adwick	31 a	09 17														11 17								
Kirk Sandall	d			09 13														11 13						
Hatfield & Stainforth	d			09 18														11 18						
Thorne South	d																							
Crowle	d																							
Althorpe	d																							
Scunthorpe	a												10 53											
	d												10 53											
Barnetby	d												11 08											
Hull Bus Station	🚌 d																							
Barton-on-Humber	🚌 a																							
Barton-on-Humber	d																							
Barrow Haven	d																							
New Holland	d																							
Goxhill	d																							
Thornton Abbey	d																							
Ulceby	d																							
Habrough	d																							
Stallingborough	d																							
Healing	d																							
Great Coates	d																							
Grimsby Town	a												11 27											
	d												11 28											
Grimsby Docks	d																							
New Clee	d																							
Cleethorpes	a												11 39											
Thorne North	d			09 24	09 38													11 25						
Goole	d			09a35	09 47					10 40						11 12		11a36						
Saltmarshe	d																							
York 8	33 d											10 40												
Selby	a										10 47	10 59											12 32	
	d										10 48	10 59											12 32	
Wressle	d																							
Howden	d																							
Eastrington	d																							
Gilberdyke	d				09 58					10 48						11 23								
Broomfleet	d																							
Brough	d				10 06					10 56	11 07	11 19				11 31							12 54	
Ferriby	d																							
Hessle	d																							
Hull	a				10 21					11 14	11 24	11 38				11 45							13 11	

For general notes see front of timetable
For details of catering facilities see Directory of Train Operators

- **A** To Leeds (Table 34)
- **B** To Leeds (Table 31)
- **C** To Huddersfield (Table 34)
- **D** From Birmingham New Street to Glasgow Central (Table 51)
- **E** To Bridlington (Table 43)
- **G** From Birmingham New Street to Newcastle (Table 51)
- **H** From Leicester (Table 53)
- **J** From Birmingham New Street to Edinburgh (Table 51)
- **b** Change at Manchester Piccadilly and Sheffield. By bus from Manchester Piccadilly
- **c** By bus
- **e** Change at Manchester Piccadilly

Table 29

Sundays
until 27 January

Manchester Airport, Manchester, Sheffield and Meadowhall → Doncaster → Cleethorpes and Hull Barton-on-Humber → Cleethorpes

Network Diagram - see first page of Table 18

Station		NT	NT	NT	NT	XC	HT		TP	XC	NT	NT	NT	NT		NT	XC	XC	NT	TP	NT		NT	NT
			A	B	C	1 ◇ D	1 ◇		1 ◇	1 ◇ E		G	A				1 ◇ D	1 ◇ H		1 ◇	A		B	C
Manchester Airport	85 ✈ d								09b47											12 46	11b05			
Manchester Piccadilly 10	78 d								10c15									11c15		13 12	11c35			
Stockport	78 d								10c40									11c40		12e43	12c00			
Sheffield 7	a																							
	d		11 32	11 36	11 39	11 54			12 08	12 21	12 24	12 28	12 39				12 54	13 21	13 24		13 32		13 36	13 39
Meadowhall	d		11a37	11 42	11a44				12 14		12 30	12 34	12a44						13 30		13a37		13 42	13a44
Rotherham Central	d	←		11 48							12 36			←					13 36				13 48	
Swinton (S.Yorks)	d	11 28		11a57							12 46 →			12 46					13 44				13a56	
Mexborough	d	11 31												12 49					13 47					
Conisbrough	d	11 35												12 53					13 51					
Doncaster 7	a	11 47				12 16			12 33			12 54		13 03			13 15		14 01					
York 8	26 a	*12 38*				12 45				13 33							13 44	14 32	*14 33*					
London Kings Cross 15	⊖ 26 d						10 42					*11 00*							*12 00*					
Doncaster	31 d						12 24		12 36			12 55		13 05					14 03					
Bentley (S.Yorks)	31 a													*13 13*										
Adwick	31 a													*13 17*										
Kirk Sandall	d													13 11										
Hatfield & Stainforth	d													13 16										
Thorne South	d																							
Crowle	d																							
Althorpe	d																							
Scunthorpe	a								13 01															
	d								13 02															
Barnetby	d								13 16															
Hull Bus Station	🚌 d																							
Barton-on-Humber	🚌 a																							
Barton-on-Humber	d																							
Barrow Haven	d																							
New Holland	d																							
Goxhill	d																							
Thornton Abbey	d																							
Ulceby	d																							
Habrough	d								13 25															
Stallingborough	d																							
Healing	d																							
Great Coates	d																							
Grimsby Town	a								13 38															
	d								13 39															
Grimsby Docks	d																							
New Clee	d																							
Cleethorpes	a								13 51															
Thorne North	d													13 25										
Goole	d											13 15		13a35					14 25					
Saltmarshe	d																							
York 8	33 d															13 23								
Selby	a						12 41									13 42				14 33				
	d						12 42									13 42				14 33				
Wressle	d																							
Howden	d						12 52																	
Eastrington	d																							
Gilberdyke	d											13 26							14 33					
Broomfleet	d																							
Brough	d						13 04					13 34				14 02			14 41	14 55				
Ferriby	d																							
Hessle	d																							
Hull	a						13 21					13 48				14 21			14 59	15 12				

For general notes see front of timetable
For details of catering facilities see Directory of Train Operators

A To Leeds (Table 34)
B To Leeds (Table 31)
C To Huddersfield (Table 34)
D From Birmingham New Street to Newcastle (Table 51)
E From Birmingham New Street (Table 51) to Aberdeen (Table 229)
G To Bridlington (Table 43)
H From Bristol Temple Meads to Edinburgh (Table 51)
b Change at Manchester Piccadilly and Sheffield. By bus from Manchester Piccadilly
c By bus
e Change at Manchester Piccadilly

Table 29

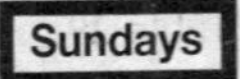

until 27 January

Manchester Airport, Manchester, Sheffield and Meadowhall → Doncaster → Cleethorpes and Hull Barton-on-Humber → Cleethorpes

Network Diagram - see first page of Table 18

		XC	TP	XC	NT	NT	NT		NT	NT	XC	TP	XC	NT		NT	TP	NT	NT	NT	NT		NT	XC
		1◇ A	1◇	1◇ B		C	D				1◇ E	1◇	R 1 G			H	1◇ J	D		K	L		N	1◇ Q
Manchester Airport	85 d		12b15									13b15					14 47							
Manchester Piccadilly 10	78 d						12b35										15 12							
Stockport	78 d		12b35				13b00					13b35					14c43	14b00						
Sheffield 7	a																							
	d	13 54	14 08	14 21	14 24	14 28	14 39				14 54	15 08	15 21	15 24		15 28		15 32		15 36	15 39		15 46	15 54
Meadowhall	d		14 14		14 30	14 34	14a44					15 14		15 30		15 34		15a37		15 42	15a44		15 52	
Rotherham Central	d				14 36				←					15 36					←	15 48			15 58	
Swinton (S.Yorks)	d				14 46 →				14 46					15 46 →					15 46	15a56			16 08	
Mexborough	d								14 49										15 49					
Conisbrough	d								14 53										15 53					
Doncaster 7	a	14 16	14 33			14 56			15 03		15 16	15 33				15 54			16 04					16 16
York 8	26 a	14 41	15 05	15 33					15 36		15 43		16 33			16 34							17 01	16 44
London Kings Cross 15	26 d		12 30			13 00			13 10			13 30				14 00								
Doncaster	31 d		14 36			14 59			15 05			15 36				15 56								
Bentley (S.Yorks)	31 a								15 13															
Adwick	31 a								15 17															
Kirk Sandall	d								15 13															
Hatfield & Stainforth	d								15 18															
Thorne South	d																							
Crowle	d																							
Althorpe	d																							
Scunthorpe	a		15 02									16 02												
	d		15 02									16 02												
Barnetby	d		15 16									16 16												
Hull Bus Station	d																							
Barton-on-Humber	a																							
Barton-on-Humber	d																							
Barrow Haven	d																							
New Holland	d																							
Goxhill	d																							
Thornton Abbey	d																							
Ulceby	d																							
Habrough	d											16 25												
Stallingborough	d																							
Healing	d																							
Great Coates	d																							
Grimsby Town	a		15 36									16 38												
	d		15 37									16 39												
Grimsby Docks	d																							
New Clee	d																							
Cleethorpes	a		15 48									16 50												
Thorne North	d								15 25															
Goole	d					15 19			15a33							16 17								
Saltmarshe	d																							
York 8	33 d									15 43														
Selby	a									16 01							16 34							
	d									16 02							16 34							
Wressle	d																							
Howden	d																							
Eastrington	d																							
Gilberdyke	d					15 27										16 25								
Broomfleet	d																							
Brough	d					15 35				16 21						16 33	16 54							
Ferriby	d					15 40																		
Hessle	d					15 44																		
Hull	a					15 57				16 41						16 50	17 11							

For general notes see front of timetable
For details of catering facilities see Directory of Train Operators

- **A** From Bristol Temple Meads to Newcastle (Table 51)
- **B** From Bournemouth to Edinburgh (Table 51)
- **C** To Beverley (Table 43)
- **D** To Leeds (Table 34)
- **E** From Exeter St Davids to Newcastle (Table 51)
- **G** From Plymouth (Table 51) to Dundee (Table 229)
- **H** To Bridlington (Table 43)
- **J** From Liverpool Lime Street (Table 39)
- **K** To Leeds (Table 31)
- **L** From Retford (Table 30) to Huddersfield (Table 34)
- **N** Via Pontefract Baghill (Table 33)
- **Q** From Cardiff Central to Newcastle (Table 51)
- **b** By bus
- **c** Change at Manchester Piccadilly

Table 29

Sundays
until 27 January

Manchester Airport, Manchester, Sheffield and Meadowhall → Doncaster → Cleethorpes and Hull
Barton-on-Humber → Cleethorpes

Network Diagram - see first page of Table 18

	HT	TP	XC	NT	NT	TP		NT	NT	XC	TP	TP	XC		NT	NT	NT	NT	NT	XC		TP	XC
	1 ◇ ⊠ ☕	1 ◇	R 1 A ☕			1 ◇		B		1 ◇ C ☕	1 ◇	1 ◇	R 1 D ☕			E		G	H	1 ◇ C ☕		1 ◇	R 1 J ☕
Manchester Airport 85 ✈ d		14b15				15 27					16 27	15b15										16b15	
Manchester Piccadilly 10 78 d						16 00					17 00												
Stockport 78 d		14b35				15c28		15b00			16c29	15b35				16b00						16b35	
Sheffield 7 a																							
d		16 08	16 21	16 24	16 28			16 39		16 54		17 08	17 21		17 24	17 28		17 36	17 39	17 54		18 08	18 21
Meadowhall d		16 14		16 30	16 34			16a44				17 14			17 30	17 34		17 42	17a44			18 14	
Rotherham Central d				16 36					←						17 36		←	17 48					
Swinton (S.Yorks) d				16 46					16 46						17 46		17 46	17a56					
Mexborough d				→					16 49						→		17 49						
Conisbrough d									16 53								17 53						
Doncaster 7 a		16 33			16 54				17 03	17 14		17 33				17 57	18 06			18 16		18 33	
York 8 26 a			17 33							17 40		18 05	18 33			18 34				18 41		19 03	19 33
London Kings Cross 15 ⊖ 26 d	14 44								15 10			15 30				16 10						16 30	
Doncaster 31 d	16 21	16 36			16 55				17 04			17 36				18 03						18 36	
Bentley (S.Yorks) 31 a									17 13														
Adwick 31 a									17 17														
Kirk Sandall d									17 13														
Hatfield & Stainforth d									17 18														
Thorne South d																							
Crowle d																							
Althorpe d																							
Scunthorpe a		17 01										18 01										19 02	
d		17 02										18 02										19 02	
Barnetby d		17 16										18 16										19 16	
Hull Bus Station 🚌 d																							
Barton-on-Humber 🚌 a																							
Barton-on-Humber d																							
Barrow Haven d																							
New Holland d																							
Goxhill d																							
Thornton Abbey d																							
Ulceby d																							
Habrough d												18 25											
Stallingborough d																							
Healing d																							
Great Coates d																							
Grimsby Town a		17 36										18 38										19 36	
d		17 37										18 39										19 37	
Grimsby Docks d																							
New Clee d																							
Cleethorpes a		17 48										18 50										19 50	
Thorne North d									17 25														
Goole d					17 15				17a34							18 22							
Saltmarshe d																							
York 8 33 d																							
Selby a	16 41					17 13					18 16												
d	16 42					17 14					18 16												
Wressle d																							
Howden d	16 52																						
Eastrington d																							
Gilberdyke d					17 23											18 35							
Broomfleet d																							
Brough d	17 04				17 31	17 37					18 36					18 43							
Ferriby d																							
Hessle d																							
Hull a	17 21				17 48	17 53					18 53					18 57							

For general notes see front of timetable
For details of catering facilities see Directory of Train Operators

A From Bournemouth to Glasgow Central (Table 51)
B From Lincoln (Table 30) to Leeds (Table 34)
C From Bristol Temple Meads to Newcastle (Table 51)
D From Penzance (Table 135) to Glasgow Central (Table 51)
E To Bridlington (Table 43)
G To Leeds (Table 31)
H To Huddersfield (Table 34)
J From Bournemouth to Edinburgh (Table 51)
b By bus
c Change at Manchester Piccadilly

Table 29

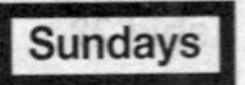

Sundays

until 27 January

Manchester Airport, Manchester, Sheffield and Meadowhall → Doncaster → Cleethorpes and Hull Barton-on-Humber → Cleethorpes

Network Diagram - see first page of Table 18

Station		NT	NT A	NT B	NT	NT	XC [R] [1] C ☕		HT [1] ◇ ⊠ ☕	NT D	TP [1] ◇	TP [1] ◇	XC [R] [1] E	NT		NT G	NT H	XC [1] ◇ J	NT	TP [1] ◇	GR [R] [1] ☕ ✕		XC [R] [1] K	NT
Manchester Airport	85 ✈ d										18 27	17b15							18b15					
Manchester Piccadilly [10]	78 🚇 d										19 00													
Stockport	78 d			17b00							18c29	17b35							18b35					
Sheffield [7]	🚇 a																							
	d	18 24	18 28	18 39			18 54			18 58		19 08	19 21	19 27		19 36	19 39	19 54	20 03	20 08			20 21	20 27
Meadowhall	🚇 d	18 30	18 34	18a44	←					19 04		19 14		19 33		19 42	19a44		20 09	20 14				20 33
Rotherham Central	d	18 36								19 10				19 39		19 48								20 39
Swinton (S.Yorks)	d	18 46			18 46					19 18				19 47		19a56								20 47
Mexborough	d	→			18 49									19 50										20 50
Conisbrough	d				18 53									19 54										20 54
Doncaster [7]	a		18 54		19 04		19 16					19 33		20 05				20 16	20 30	20 34				21 04
York [8]	26 a						19 43			20 16		20 07	20 33	20 38				20 42					21 32	
London Kings Cross [15]	⊖ 26 d		17 00						17 40										18 40	19 00	19 10			
Doncaster	31 d		18 55						19 26			19 36							20 30	20 42	20 58			21 06
Bentley (S.Yorks)	31 a						19e32																	
Adwick	31 a						19e36																	
Kirk Sandall	d		19 01																					21 12
Hatfield & Stainforth	d		19 06																					21 17
Thorne South	d																							
Crowle	d																							
Althorpe	d																							
Scunthorpe	a											20 02								21 07				
	d											20 02								21 08				
Barnetby	d											20 16								21 22				
Hull Bus Station	🚌 d																							
Barton-on-Humber	🚌 a																							
Barton-on-Humber	d																							
Barrow Haven	d																							
New Holland	d																							
Goxhill	d																							
Thornton Abbey	d																							
Ulceby	d																							
Habrough	d																			21 31				
Stallingborough	d																							
Healing	d																							
Great Coates	d																							
Grimsby Town	a											20 36								21 44				
	d											20 37								21 45				
Grimsby Docks	d																							
New Clee	d																							
Cleethorpes	a											20 49								21 56				
Thorne North	d		19 12																					21 23
Goole	d		19 21																20 49					21a34
Saltmarshe	d																							
York [8]	33 d					19 10																		
Selby	a					19 29			19 40		20 19										21 15			
	d					19 29			19 40		20 19										21 15			
Wressle	d																							
Howden	d								19 52															
Eastrington	d																							
Gilberdyke	d		19 29																20 57					
Broomfleet	d																							
Brough	d		19 37			19 49			20 03		20 39								21 05		21 36			
Ferriby	d																							
Hessle	d																							
Hull	a		19 54			20 08			20 22		20 56								21 23		21 56			

For general notes see front of timetable
For details of catering facilities see Directory of Train Operators

A To Beverley (Table 43)
B To Leeds (Table 34)
C From Paignton to Newcastle (Table 51)
D Via Pontefract Baghill (Table 33)
E From Plymouth to Edinburgh (Table 51)
G To Leeds (Table 31)
H To Huddersfield (Table 34)
J From Bristol Temple Meads to Newcastle (Table 51)
K From Bournemouth to Newcastle (Table 51)
b By bus
c Change at Manchester Piccadilly
e Change at Doncaster

Table 29

Sundays

until 27 January

Manchester Airport, Manchester, Sheffield and Meadowhall → Doncaster → Cleethorpes and Hull
Barton-on-Humber → Cleethorpes

Network Diagram - see first page of Table 18

Station			NT	NT	XC	TP	EM	HT		XC	NT	NT	NT	EM	TP		NT	TP	NT	NT	NT
					■1 ◇	■1 ◇	■1 ◇	■1 ◇		R ■1				■1 ◇	■1 ◇			■1 ◇			
			A		B		C			D		E	G	C	H				J		
							☕	⊠ ☕						☕							
Manchester Airport	85 ✈	d				19b15											19c47				20c47
Manchester Piccadilly 10	78 🚆	d															20b25				21b25
Stockport	78	d	19b00			19b35						20b00					20b50		21b00		21b50
Sheffield 7	🚆	a																			
		d	20 39		20 54	21 08	21 12			21 21	21 24	21 36	21 43	22 16			22 26	22 30	22 39		23 20
Meadowhall	🚆	d	20a44			21 14					21 30	21 42	21a48				22 32	22 36	22a44		23 26
Rotherham Central		d									21 37	21 48					22 38			←	23 32
Swinton (S.Yorks)		d									21 46	21a56					22 48			22 48	23 43
Mexborough		d									21 49						→			22 51	23 46
Conisbrough		d									21 53									22 55	23 50
Doncaster 7		a			21 16	21 34	21 38				22 02			22 38				22 55		23 03	23 58
York 8	26	a			21 41					22 36	*23 11*									*00 39*	
London Kings Cross 15	⊖ 26	d				*19 35*		20 05										*21 00*			
Doncaster	31	d				21 42		21 54			22 04							22 58		23 07	
Bentley (S.Yorks)	31	a					*21 52*														
Adwick	31	a					*21 56*														
Kirk Sandall		d																			
Hatfield & Stainforth		d																			
Thorne South		d																			
Crowle		d																			
Althorpe		d																			
Scunthorpe		a				22 08												23 23			
		d				22 08												23 24			
Barnetby		d				22 22												23 38			
Hull Bus Station	🚌	d																			
Barton-on-Humber	🚌	a																			
Barton-on-Humber		d																			
Barrow Haven		d																			
New Holland		d																			
Goxhill		d																			
Thornton Abbey		d																			
Ulceby		d																			
Habrough		d				22 31															
Stallingborough		d																			
Healing		d																			
Great Coates		d																			
Grimsby Town		a				22 44												23 58			
		d				22 45												23 59			
Grimsby Docks		d																			
New Clee		d																			
Cleethorpes		a				22 56												00 10			
Thorne North		d																		23 19	
Goole		d									22 23									23 28	
Saltmarshe		d																			
York 8	33	d		21 41																	
Selby		a		22 00				22 08													
		d		22 00				22 08							22 39						
Wressle		d																			
Howden		d						22 20													
Eastrington		d																			
Gilberdyke		d									22 31									23 36	
Broomfleet		d																			
Brough		d		22 20				22 31			22 39				22 59					23 44	
Ferriby		d																			
Hessle		d																			
Hull		a		22 39				22 50			22 56				23 16					00 02	

For general notes see front of timetable
For details of catering facilities see Directory of Train Operators

- **A** To Leeds (Table 34)
- **B** From Bristol Temple Meads to Newcastle (Table 51)
- **C** From St Pancras International to Leeds (Table 53)
- **D** From Plymouth (Table 51)
- **E** To Leeds (Table 31)
- **G** To Barnsley (Table 34)
- **H** From Leeds (Table 39)
- **J** From Lincoln (Table 30) to Leeds (Table 34)
- **b** By bus
- **c** Change at Manchester Piccadilly and Sheffield. By bus from Manchester Piccadilly

Table 29

Sundays

3 February to 23 March

Manchester Airport, Manchester, Sheffield and Meadowhall → Doncaster → Cleethorpes and Hull Barton-on-Humber → Cleethorpes

Network Diagram - see first page of Table 18

		NT	NT	NT	NT	NT	NT	TP	NT	TP	TP	NT	XC	NT	NT	NT		NT	EM	TP	XC	NT	HT	NT
								1◇		1◇	1◇		1◇						1◇	1◇	1◇		1◇	
			A		B	C	D		E				G	H	A				J		K			A
Manchester Airport	85 d					07b10				08 40	08 51									10 47				
Manchester Piccadilly 10	78 d					07 45				09 05	09 30							09 35		11 12				
Stockport	78 d									09 13	08c38									10c43				
Sheffield 7	a									09 54														
	d	08 00	08 39		08 45	09 36	09 39	09 42		09 58			10 21	10 26	10 39			11 05	11 12		11 21			11 32
Meadowhall	d	08 06	08a44		08 51	09 42	09a44	09 48		10 03				10 32	10a44			11 12						11a37
Rotherham Central	d	08 12			08 57	09 48		09 57										11 18				←		
Swinton (S.Yorks)	d	08 20			09 05	09a58		10 05										11 28				11 28		
Mexborough	d	08 23			09 08			10 08										→				11 31		
Conisbrough	d	08 27			09 12			10 12														11 35		
Doncaster 7	a	08 38			09 22			10 20		10 26				10 51					11 34			11 47		
York 8	26 a				10 06					11 07			11 33	11 29					11 57		12 33	12 38		
London Kings Cross 15	⊖ 26 d													09 00		09 10							10 42	
Doncaster	31 d			09 07	09 26				10 21	10 27				10 53		11 07							12 24	
Bentley (S.Yorks)	31 a	09 13												11 13										
Adwick	31 a	09 17												11 17										
Kirk Sandall	d			09 13												11 13								
Hatfield & Stainforth	d			09 18												11 18								
Thorne South	d																							
Crowle	d																							
Althorpe	d																							
Scunthorpe	a									10 53														
	d									10 53														
Barnetby	d									11 08														
Hull Bus Station	d																							
Barton-on-Humber	a																							
Barton-on-Humber	d																							
Barrow Haven	d																							
New Holland	d																							
Goxhill	d																							
Thornton Abbey	d																							
Ulceby	d																							
Habrough	d																							
Stallingborough	d																							
Healing	d																							
Great Coates	d																							
Grimsby Town	a									11 27														
	d									11 28														
Grimsby Docks	d																							
New Clee	d																							
Cleethorpes	a									11 39														
Thorne North	d			09 24	09 38											11 25								
Goole	d			09a35	09 47				10 40					11 12		11a36								
Saltmarshe	d																							
York 8	33 d											10 40												
Selby	a										10 47	10 59								12 32			12 41	
	d										10 48	10 59								12 32			12 42	
Wressle	d																							
Howden	d																						12 52	
Eastrington	d																							
Gilberdyke	d				09 58				10 48					11 23										
Broomfleet	d																							
Brough	d				10 06				10 56		11 07	11 19		11 31						12 54			13 04	
Ferriby	d																							
Hessle	d																							
Hull	a				10 21				11 14		11 24	11 38		11e45						13 11			13 21	

For general notes see front of timetable
For details of catering facilities see Directory of Train Operators

- **A** To Leeds (Table 34)
- **B** 23 March to Scarborough (Table 43)
- **C** To Leeds (Table 31)
- **D** To Huddersfield (Table 34)
- **E** 23 March to Bridlington (Table 43)
- **G** From Birmingham New Street to Glasgow Central (Table 51)
- **H** To Bridlington (23 March to Scarborough) (Table 43)
- **J** From Leicester (Table 53)
- **K** From Birmingham New Street to Edinburgh (Table 51)
- **b** Change at Manchester Piccadilly and Sheffield
- **c** Change at Manchester Piccadilly
- **e** From 23 March arr. 1146

Table 29

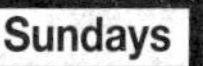

3 February to 23 March

Manchester Airport, Manchester, Sheffield and Meadowhall → Doncaster → Cleethorpes and Hull Barton-on-Humber → Cleethorpes

Network Diagram - see first page of Table 18

		NT	NT	XC	TP	NT	NT	NT	NT	NT	XC		NT	TP	NT	NT	NT	XC	TP	NT	NT	NT	NT	NT
				1 ◇	1 ◇						1 ◇			1 ◇				1 ◇	1 ◇					
		A	B	C			D	E			G		H		E	A	B	J			K	E		
				☕							☕							☕						
Manchester Airport	85 ✈ d				10 52									12 46	11b27			12b13	12 52					
Manchester Piccadilly 10	78 🚢 d				11 12									13 12	12 01			12 44	13 12					
Stockport	78 d	09b11			11 21									12c43	11b29			12 54	13 21					
Sheffield 7	🚢 a				12 03														14 06					
	d	11 36	11 39	12 04	12 08	12 24	12 28	12 39			13 04		13 24		13 32	13 36	13 39	14 04	14 08	14 24	14 28	14 39		
Meadowhall	🚢 d	11 42	11a44		12 14	12 30	12 34	12a44	←				13 30		13a37	13 42	13a44		14 14	14 30	14 34	14a44	←	
Rotherham Central	d	11 48				12 36							13 36			13 48				14 36				
Swinton (S.Yorks)	d	11a57				12 46 →			12 46				13 44			13a56				14 46 →			14 46	
Mexborough	d								12 49				13 47										14 49	
Conisbrough	d								12 53				13 51										14 53	
Doncaster 7	a			12 27	12 33		12 54		13 03		13 26		14 01					14 27	14 33		14 56		15 03	
York 8	26 a			13e33					*14 04*		14f32		*14 33*					15g32	*15 05*				*15 36*	
London Kings Cross 15	⊖ 26 d						*11 00*						*12 00*						*12 30*		*13 00*		*13 10*	
Doncaster	31 d				12 36		12 55		13 05				14 03						14 36		14 59		15 05	
Bentley (S.Yorks)	31 a								*13 13*														*15 13*	
Adwick	31 a								*13 17*														*15 17*	
Kirk Sandall	d								13 11														15 13	
Hatfield & Stainforth	d								13 16														15 18	
Thorne South	d																							
Crowle	d																							
Althorpe	d																							
Scunthorpe	a				13 01														15 02					
	d				13 02														15 02					
Barnetby	d				13 16														15 16					
Hull Bus Station	🚌 d																							
Barton-on-Humber	🚌 a																							
Barton-on-Humber	d																							
Barrow Haven	d																							
New Holland	d																							
Goxhill	d																							
Thornton Abbey	d																							
Ulceby	d																							
Habrough	d				13 25																			
Stallingborough	d																							
Healing	d																							
Great Coates	d																							
Grimsby Town	a				13 38														15 36					
	d				13 39														15 37					
Grimsby Docks	d																							
New Clee	d																							
Cleethorpes	a				13 51														15 48					
Thorne North	d								13 25														15 25	
Goole	d						13 15		13a35				14 25								15 19		15a33	
Saltmarshe	d																							
York 8	33 d									13 23														15 43
Selby	a									13 42				14 33										16 01
	d									13 42				14 33										16 02
Wressle	d																							
Howden	d																							
Eastrington	d																							
Gilberdyke	d						13 23						14 33								15 27			
Broomfleet	d																							
Brough	d						13 31			14 02			14 41	14 55							15 35			16 21
Ferriby	d																				15 40			
Hessle	d																				15 44			
Hull	a						13 48			14 21			14 59	15 12							15 57			16 41

For general notes see front of timetable
For details of catering facilities see Directory of Train Operators

A To Leeds (Table 31)
B To Huddersfield (Table 34)
C From Birmingham New Street (Table 51) to Aberdeen (Table 229)
D To Bridlington (23 March to Scarborough) (Table 43)
E To Leeds (Table 34)
G From Birmingham New Street to Edinburgh (Table 51)
H 23 March to Bridlington (Table 43)
J From Bristol Temple Meads to Edinburgh (Table 51)
K To Beverley (23 March to Scarborough) (Table 43)
b Change at Manchester Piccadilly and Sheffield
c Change at Manchester Piccadilly
e By changing at Doncaster, passengers may arrive at 1305
f By changing at Doncaster, passengers may arrive at 1404
g By changing at Doncaster, passengers may arrive at 1505

Table 29

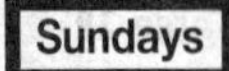

Manchester Airport, Manchester, Sheffield and Meadowhall → Doncaster → Cleethorpes and Hull Barton-on-Humber → Cleethorpes

3 February to 23 March

Network Diagram - see first page of Table 18

		XC	TP	NT	NT	TP		NT	NT	HT	NT	NT	NT	XC	TP	NT	NT	TP	NT	NT	XC	TP		TP
		1 ◇	1 ◇			1 ◇				1 ◇				R 1	1 ◇			1 ◇			R 1	1 ◇		1 ◇
		A			B	C		D			E	G	H	J			K		L		N			
		⊡								⊠ ⊡				⊡							⊡			
Manchester Airport	85 ✈ d	13b22	13 52			14 47							14b00		14 52			15 27			15b08	15 52		16 27
Manchester Piccadilly [10]	78 🚇 d	13 49	14 15			15 12							14 43		15 15			16 00			15 43	16 15		17 00
Stockport	78 d	13 58	14 22			14c43							14 54		15 22			15c28			15 54	16 22		16c29
Sheffield [7]	🚇 a		15 03												16 03							17 03		
	d	15 04	15 08	15 24	15 28			15 32			15 36	15 39	15 46	16 04	16 08	16 24	16 28		16 39		17 04	17 08		
Meadowhall	🚇 d		15 14	15 30	15 34			15a37	←		15 42	15a44	15 52		16 14	16 30	16 34		16a44	←		17 14		
Rotherham Central	d			15 36							15 48		15 58			16 36								
Swinton (S.Yorks)	d			15 46					15 46		15a56		16 08			16 46				16 46				
Mexborough	d			→					15 49							→				16 49				
Conisbrough	d								15 53											16 53				
Doncaster [7]	a	15 26	15 33		15 54				16 04					16 26	16 33		16 54			17 03	17 26	17 33		
York [8]	26 a	16e33			*16 34*				*17 33*				17 01	17 33						*17 45*	18f33	*18 05*		
London Kings Cross [15]	⊖ 26 d		*13 30*		*14 00*					14 44										*15 10*		*15 30*		
Doncaster	31 d		15 36		15 56					16 21					16 36		16 55			17 04		17 36		
Bentley (S.Yorks)	31 a																			*17 13*				
Adwick	31 a																			*17 17*				
Kirk Sandall	d																			17 13				
Hatfield & Stainforth	d																			17 18				
Thorne South	d																							
Crowle	d																							
Althorpe	d																							
Scunthorpe	a		16 02												17 01							18 01		
	d		16 02												17 02							18 02		
Barnetby	d		16 16												17 16							18 16		
Hull Bus Station	🚌 d																							
Barton-on-Humber	🚌 a																							
Barton-on-Humber	d																							
Barrow Haven	d																							
New Holland	d																							
Goxhill	d																							
Thornton Abbey	d																							
Ulceby	d																							
Habrough	d		16 25																			18 25		
Stallingborough	d																							
Healing	d																							
Great Coates	d																							
Grimsby Town	a		16 38												17 36							18 38		
	d		16 39												17 37							18 39		
Grimsby Docks	d																							
New Clee	d																							
Cleethorpes	a		16 50												17 48							18 50		
Thorne North	d																			17 25				
Goole	d				16 17												17 15			17a34				
Saltmarshe	d																							
York [8]	33 d																							
Selby	a					16 34				16 41								17 13						18 16
	d					16 34				16 42								17 14						18 16
Wressle	d																							
Howden	d									16 52														
Eastrington	d																							
Gilberdyke	d				16 25												17 23							
Broomfleet	d																							
Brough	d				16 33	16 54				17 04							17 31	17 37						18 36
Ferriby	d																							
Hessle	d																							
Hull	a				16 50	17 11				17 21							17 48	17 53						18 53

For general notes see front of timetable
For details of catering facilities see Directory of Train Operators

- **A** From Bournemouth (Table 51) to Dundee (Table 229)
- **B** To Bridlington (Table 43)
- **C** From Liverpool Lime Street (Table 39)
- **D** To Leeds (Table 34)
- **E** To Leeds (Table 31)
- **G** From Retford (Table 30) to Huddersfield (Table 34)
- **H** Via Pontefract Baghill (Table 33)
- **J** From Plymouth to Glasgow Central (Table 51)
- **K** 23 March to Scarborough (Table 43)
- **L** From Lincoln (Table 30) to Leeds (Table 34)
- **N** From Bournemouth to Glasgow Central (Table 51)
- **b** Change at Manchester Piccadilly and Sheffield
- **c** Change at Manchester Piccadilly
- **e** By changing at Doncaster, passengers may arrive at 1604
- **f** By changing at Doncaster, passengers may arrive at 1805

Table 29

3 February to 23 March

Manchester Airport, Manchester, Sheffield and Meadowhall → Doncaster → Cleethorpes and Hull Barton-on-Humber → Cleethorpes

Network Diagram - see first page of Table 18

Station		NT	NT	NT	NT	NT	XC	TP	NT	NT	NT	NT	NT	HT	NT	XC		TP	TP	NT	NT	NT	NT	XC
							R 1	1 ◇						1 ◇		R 1		1 ◇	1 ◇					R 1
			A		B	C	D			E	G				H	J					B	C		K
							🍽							⊠ 🍽										
Manchester Airport	85 ✈ d						16b01	16 52							17b05			17 52	18 27				18b01	
Manchester Piccadilly 10	78 d						16 43	17 15							17 43			18 15	19 00				18 42	
Stockport	78 d						16 55	17 22							17 54			18 22	18c29				18 56	
Sheffield 7	a							18 06										19 03						
	d	17 24	17 28		17 36	17 39	18 04	18 08	18 24	18 28	18 39				18 58	19 04		19 08		19 27	19 36	19 39	20 03	20 08
Meadowhall	d	17 30	17 34		17 42	17a44		18 14	18 30	18 34	18a44				19 04			19 14		19 33	19 42	19a44	20 09	
Rotherham Central	d	17 36		←	17 48				18 36			←			19 10					19 39	19 48			
Swinton (S.Yorks)	d	17 46		17 46	17a56				18 46			18 46			19 18					19 47	19a56			
Mexborough	d	→		17 49					→			18 49								19 50				
Conisbrough	d			17 53								18 53								19 54				
Doncaster 7	a		17 57	18 06			18 26	18 33		18 54		19 04				19 27		19 33		20 05			20 30	20 32
York 8	26 a		18 34				19e33	19 03				19 46			20 16	20f33		20 07		20 38				21 33
London Kings Cross 15	⊖ 26 d		16 10					16 30		17 00				17 40									18 40	
Doncaster	31 d		18 03					18 36		18 55				19 26				19 36					20 30	
Bentley (S.Yorks)	31 a											19 32												
Adwick	31 a											19 36												
Kirk Sandall	d									19 01														
Hatfield & Stainforth	d									19 06														
Thorne South	d																							
Crowle	d																							
Althorpe	d																							
Scunthorpe	a							19 02										20 02						
	d							19 02										20 02						
Barnetby	d							19 16										20 16						
Hull Bus Station	🚌 d																							
Barton-on-Humber	🚌 a																							
Barton-on-Humber	d																							
Barrow Haven	d																							
New Holland	d																							
Goxhill	d																							
Thornton Abbey	d																							
Ulceby	d																							
Habrough	d																							
Stallingborough	d																							
Healing	d																							
Great Coates	d																							
Grimsby Town	a							19 36										20 36						
	d							19 37										20 37						
Grimsby Docks	d																							
New Clee	d																							
Cleethorpes	a							19 50										20 49						
Thorne North	d									19 12														
Goole	d		18 22							19 21													20 49	
Saltmarshe	d																							
York 8	33 d												19 10											
Selby	a												19 29	19 40					20 19					
	d												19 29	19 40					20 19					
Wressle	d																							
Howden	d													19 52										
Eastrington	d																							
Gilberdyke	d		18 35							19 29													20 57	
Broomfleet	d																							
Brough	d		18 43							19 37			19 49	20 03					20 39				21 05	
Ferriby	d																							
Hessle	d																							
Hull	a		18 57							19 54			20 08	20 22					20 56				21 23	

For general notes see front of timetable
For details of catering facilities see Directory of Train Operators

A To Bridlington (Table 43)
B To Leeds (Table 31)
C To Huddersfield (Table 34)
D From Penzance (Table 135) to Edinburgh (Table 51)
E To Beverley (Table 43)
G To Leeds (Table 34)
H Via Pontefract Baghill (Table 33)
J From Bournemouth to Edinburgh (Table 51)
K From Penzance (Table 135) to Newcastle (Table 51)

b Change at Manchester Piccadilly and Sheffield
c Change at Manchester Piccadilly
e By changing at Doncaster, passengers may arrive at 1903
f By changing at Doncaster, passengers may arrive at 2007

Table 29

3 February to 23 March

Manchester Airport, Manchester, Sheffield and Meadowhall → Doncaster → Cleethorpes and Hull
Barton-on-Humber → Cleethorpes

Network Diagram - see first page of Table 18

		TP	GR	NT	NT	NT	XC	TP	EM	HT	NT	NT	NT	XC	EM	TP	NT	TP	NT	NT	XC	NT
		1 ◇	R 1				R 1	1 ◇	1 ◇	1 ◇				R 1	1 ◇	1 ◇		1 ◇			1 ◇	
					A		B		C			D	E	G	C	H			J		K	
			🍴 ✈						🍴	⊠ 🍴					🍴							
Manchester Airport	85 ✈ d	18 52					19b05	19 52						20b01	20 52							21 52
Manchester Piccadilly 10	78 🚆 d	19 15					19 42	20 15						20 43	21 15							22 15
Stockport	78 d	19 22					19 54	20 22						20 53	21 22							22 22
Sheffield 7	🚆 a	20 04						21 06														
	d	20 08		20 27	20 39		21 04	21 08	21 12		21 24	21 36	21 43	22 04	22 16		22 26	22 30	22 39		22 54	23 20
Meadowhall	🚆 d	20 14		20 33	20a44			21 14			21 30	21 42	21a48				22 32	22 36	22a44	←		23 26
Rotherham Central	d			20 39							21 37	21 48					22 38					23 32
Swinton (S.Yorks)	d			20 47							21 46	21a56					22 48			22 48		23 43
Mexborough	d			20 50							21 49						→			22 51		23 46
Conisbrough	d			20 54							21 53									22 55		23 50
Doncaster 7	a	20 37		21 04			21 26	21 34	21 42		22 02			22 26	22 38			22 55		23 03	23 16	23 58
York 8	26 a			21 47			22c36							23 11							00 39	
London Kings Cross 15	⊖ 26 d	19 00	19 10					19 35		20 05								21 00				
Doncaster	31 d	20 42	20 58	21 06				21 42		21 54	22 04							22 58		23 07		
Bentley (S.Yorks)	31 a								21 52													
Adwick	31 a								21 56													
Kirk Sandall	d			21 12																		
Hatfield & Stainforth	d			21 17																		
Thorne South	d																					
Crowle	d																					
Althorpe	d																					
Scunthorpe	a	21 07						22 08										23 23				
	d	21 08						22 08										23 24				
Barnetby	d	21 22						22 22										23 38				
Hull Bus Station	🚌 d																					
Barton-on-Humber	🚌 a																					
Barton-on-Humber	d																					
Barrow Haven	d																					
New Holland	d																					
Goxhill	d																					
Thornton Abbey	d																					
Ulceby	d																					
Habrough	d	21 31						22 31														
Stallingborough	d																					
Healing	d																					
Great Coates	d																					
Grimsby Town	a	21 44						22 44										23 58				
	d	21 45						22 45										23 59				
Grimsby Docks	d																					
New Clee	d																					
Cleethorpes	a	21 56						22 56										00 10				
Thorne North	d			21 23																23 19		
Goole	d			21a34							22 23									23 28		
Saltmarshe	d																					
York 8	33 d					21 41																
Selby	a		21 15			22 00				22 08												
	d		21 15			22 00				22 08						22 39						
Wressle	d																					
Howden	d									22 20												
Eastrington	d																					
Gilberdyke	d										22 31									23 36		
Broomfleet	d																					
Brough	d		21 36			22 20				22 31	22 39					22 59				23 44		
Ferriby	d																					
Hessle	d																					
Hull	a		21 56			22 39				22 50	22 56					23 16				00 02		

For general notes see front of timetable
For details of catering facilities see Directory of Train Operators

- **A** To Leeds (Table 34)
- **B** From Bournemouth (Table 51)
- **C** From St Pancras International to Leeds (Table 53)
- **D** To Leeds (Table 31)
- **E** To Barnsley (Table 34)
- **G** From Plymouth to Leeds (Table 51)
- **H** From Leeds (Table 39)
- **J** From Lincoln (Table 30) to Leeds (Table 34)
- **K** From Bournemouth to Leeds (Table 51)
- **b** Change at Manchester Piccadilly and Sheffield
- **c** By changing at Doncaster, passengers may arrive at 2200

Table 29

Sundays

from 30 March

Manchester Airport, Manchester, Sheffield and Meadowhall → Doncaster → Cleethorpes and Hull Barton-on-Humber → Cleethorpes

Network Diagram - see first page of Table 18

	NT	NT	NT	NT	NT		NT	TP	NT	TP	TP		NT	XC	NT	NT	NT		XC	NT	TP	XC	EM
								1 ◇		1 ◇	1 ◇			1 ◇					1 ◇		1 ◇	1 ◇	1 ◇
		A		B	C		D		E					G	B	A			H			J	K
														☕					☕			☕	☕
Manchester Airport 85 ✈ d					07b10					08 40	08 51										10 47		
Manchester Piccadilly 10 78 🚉 d					07 45					09 05	09 30									09 35	11 12		
Stockport 78 d										09 13	08c38										10c43		
Sheffield 7 🚉 a										09 54													
d	08 00	08 39		08 45	09 36		09 39	09 42		09 58				10 21	10 26	10 39			10 54	11 05		11 21	11 26
Meadowhall 🚉 d	08 06	08a44		08 51	09 42		09a44	09 48		10 03					10 32	10a44				11 12			
Rotherham Central d	08 12			08 57	09 48			09 57												11 18			
Swinton (S.Yorks) d	08 20			09 05	09a58			10 05												11 28			
Mexborough d	08 23			09 08				10 08												11 31			
Conisbrough d	08 27			09 12				10 12												11 35			
Doncaster 7 a	08 38			09 22				10 20		10 26					10 51				11 16	11 47			11 54
York 8 26 a				10 06						11 07				11 33	11 29				11 44			12 33	12 19
London Kings Cross 15 ⊖ 26 d															09 00		09 10						
Doncaster 31 d			09 07	09 26					10 21	10 27					10 53		11 07						
Bentley (S.Yorks) 31 a	09 13														11 13								
Adwick 31 a	09 17														11 17								
Kirk Sandall d			09 13														11 13						
Hatfield & Stainforth d			09 18														11 18						
Thorne South d																							
Crowle d																							
Althorpe d																							
Scunthorpe a										10 53													
d										10 53													
Barnetby d										11 08													
Hull Bus Station 🚌 d																							
Barton-on-Humber 🚌 a																							
Barton-on-Humber d																							
Barrow Haven d																							
New Holland d																							
Goxhill d																							
Thornton Abbey d																							
Ulceby d																							
Habrough d																							
Stallingborough d																							
Healing d																							
Great Coates d																							
Grimsby Town a										11 27													
d										11 28													
Grimsby Docks d																							
New Clee d																							
Cleethorpes a										11 39													
Thorne North d			09 24	09 38													11 25						
Goole d			09a35	09 47					10 40						11 12		11a36						
Saltmarshe d																							
York 8 33 d													10 40										
Selby a											10 47		10 59								12 32		
d											10 48		10 59								12 32		
Wressle d																							
Howden d																							
Eastrington d																							
Gilberdyke d				09 58					10 48						11 23								
Broomfleet d																							
Brough d				10 06					10 56		11 07		11 19		11 31						12 54		
Ferriby d																							
Hessle d																							
Hull a				10 21					11 14		11 24		11 38		11 46						13 11		

For general notes see front of timetable
For details of catering facilities see Directory of Train Operators

A To Leeds (Table 34)
B To Scarborough (Table 43)
C To Leeds (Table 31)
D To Huddersfield (Table 34)
E To Bridlington (Table 43)
G From Birmingham New Street to Glasgow Central (Table 51)
H From Birmingham New Street to Newcastle (Table 51)
J From Birmingham New Street to Edinburgh (Table 51)
K From Leicester (Table 53)
b Change at Manchester Piccadilly and Sheffield
c Change at Manchester Piccadilly

Sundays from 30 March

Manchester Airport, Manchester, Sheffield and Meadowhall → Doncaster → Cleethorpes and Hull Barton-on-Humber → Cleethorpes

Network Diagram - see first page of Table 18

	NT	NT		NT	XC	HT	TP	XC		NT	NT	NT	NT	NT		XC	XC	NT	TP	NT		NT	NT
					1 ◇	1 ◇	1 ◇	1 ◇								1 ◇	1 ◇		1 ◇				
	A	B		C	D			E			G	A				D	H	J		A		B	C
Manchester Airport 85 d							10 52												12 46	11b22			
Manchester Piccadilly 10 78 d							11 12												13 12	*12 01*			
Stockport 78 d		09b11					11 21												12c43	11b31			
Sheffield 7 a							12 03																
d	11 32	11 36		11 39	11 54		12 08	12 21		12 24	12 28	12 39				12 54	13 21	13 24		13 32		13 36	13 39
Meadowhall d	11a37	11 42		11a44			12 14			12 30	12 34	12a44	←					13 30		13a37		13 42	13a44
Rotherham Central d		11 48								12 36								13 36				13 48	
Swinton (S.Yorks) d		11a57								12 46 →			12 46					13 44				13a56	
Mexborough d													12 49					13 47					
Conisbrough d													12 53					13 51					
Doncaster 7 a					12 16		12 33				12 54		13 03			13 15		14 01					
York 8 26 a					12 45			13 33								13 44	14 32	*14 33*					
London Kings Cross 15 ⊖ 26 d						10 42					*11 00*							*12 00*					
Doncaster 31 d						12 24	12 36				12 55		13 05					14 03					
Bentley (S.Yorks) 31 a													*13 13*										
Adwick 31 a													*13 17*										
Kirk Sandall d													13 11										
Hatfield & Stainforth d													13 16										
Thorne South d																							
Crowle d																							
Althorpe d																							
Scunthorpe a							13 01																
d							13 02																
Barnetby d							13 16																
Hull Bus Station d																							
Barton-on-Humber a																							
Barton-on-Humber d																							
Barrow Haven d																							
New Holland d																							
Goxhill d																							
Thornton Abbey d																							
Ulceby d																							
Habrough d							13 25																
Stallingborough d																							
Healing d																							
Great Coates d																							
Grimsby Town a							13 38																
d							13 39																
Grimsby Docks d																							
New Clee d																							
Cleethorpes a							13 51																
Thorne North d													13 25										
Goole d											13 15		13a35					14 25					
Saltmarshe d																							
York 8 33 d														13 23									
Selby a						12 41								13 42					14 33				
d						12 42								13 42					14 33				
Wressle d																							
Howden d						12 52																	
Eastrington d																							
Gilberdyke d											13 23							14 33					
Broomfleet d																							
Brough d						13 04					13 31			14 02				14 41	14 55				
Ferriby d																							
Hessle d																							
Hull a						13 21					13 48			14 21				14 59	15 12				

For general notes see front of timetable
For details of catering facilities see Directory of Train Operators

A To Leeds (Table 34)
B To Leeds (Table 31)
C To Huddersfield (Table 34)
D From Birmingham New Street to Newcastle (Table 51)
E From Birmingham New Street (Table 51) to Aberdeen (Table 229)
G To Scarborough (Table 43)
H From Bristol Temple Meads to Edinburgh (Table 51)
J To Bridlington (Table 43)
b Change at Manchester Piccadilly and Sheffield
c Change at Manchester Piccadilly

Table 29

Sundays
from 30 March

Manchester Airport, Manchester, Sheffield and Meadowhall → Doncaster → Cleethorpes and Hull
Barton-on-Humber → Cleethorpes

Network Diagram - see first page of Table 18

	XC	TP	XC	NT	NT	NT	NT	NT	XC	TP	XC	NT	NT	TP	NT	NT	NT	NT	NT	XC
											R									
	1 ◇	1 ◇	1 ◇						1 ◇	1 ◇	1			1 ◇						1 ◇
	A		B		C	D			E		G		H	J	D		K	L	N	A
	☕		☕						☕		☕									☕
Manchester Airport 85 ✈ d	12b13	12 52							13b22	13 52				14 47					14b00	
Manchester Piccadilly 10 78 d	12 44	13 12							13 49	14 15				15 12					14 43	
Stockport 78 d	12 54	13 21							13 58	14 22				14c43					14 54	
Sheffield 7 a		14 06								15 03										
d	13 54	14 08	14 21	14 24	14 28	14 39			14 54	15 08	15 21	15 24	15 28		15 32		15 36	15 39	15 46	15 54
Meadowhall d		14 14		14 30	14 34	14a44				15 14		15 30	15 34		15a37		15 42	15a44	15 52	
Rotherham Central d				14 36			←					15 36				←	15 48		15 58	
Swinton (S.Yorks) d				14 46 →			14 46					15 46 →				15 46	15a56		16 08	
Mexborough d							14 49									15 49				
Conisbrough d							14 53									15 53				
Doncaster 7 a	14 16	14 33			14 56		15 03		15 16	15 33			15 54			16 04				16 16
York 8 26 a	14 41	*15 05*	15 33				*15 36*		15 43		16 33		*16 34*						17 01	16 44
London Kings Cross 15 ⊖ 26 d		*12 30*			*13 00*		*13 10*			*13 30*			*14 00*							
Doncaster 31 d		14 36			14 59		15 05			15 36			15 56							
Bentley (S.Yorks) 31 a							*15 13*													
Adwick 31 a							*15 17*													
Kirk Sandall d							15 13													
Hatfield & Stainforth d							15 18													
Thorne South d																				
Crowle d																				
Althorpe d																				
Scunthorpe a		15 02								16 02										
d		15 02								16 02										
Barnetby d		15 16								16 16										
Hull Bus Station 🚌 d																				
Barton-on-Humber 🚌 a																				
Barton-on-Humber d																				
Barrow Haven d																				
New Holland d																				
Goxhill d																				
Thornton Abbey d																				
Ulceby d																				
Habrough d										16 25										
Stallingborough d																				
Healing d																				
Great Coates d																				
Grimsby Town a		15 36								16 38										
d		15 37								16 39										
Grimsby Docks d																				
New Clee d																				
Cleethorpes a		15 48								16 50										
Thorne North d							15 25													
Goole d					15 19		15a33						16 17							
Saltmarshe d																				
York 8 33 d								15 43												
Selby a								16 01						16 34						
d								16 02						16 34						
Wressle d																				
Howden d																				
Eastrington d																				
Gilberdyke d					15 27								16 25							
Broomfleet d																				
Brough d					15 35			16 21					16 33	16 54						
Ferriby d					15 40															
Hessle d					15 44															
Hull a					15 57			16 41					16 50	17 11						

For general notes see front of timetable
For details of catering facilities see Directory of Train Operators

- **A** From Bristol Temple Meads to Newcastle (Table 51)
- **B** From Oxford to Edinburgh (Table 51)
- **C** To Scarborough (Table 43)
- **D** To Leeds (Table 34)
- **E** From Exeter St Davids to Newcastle (Table 51)
- **G** From Plymouth (Table 51) to Dundee (Table 229)
- **H** To Bridlington (Table 43)
- **J** From Liverpool Lime Street (Table 39)
- **K** To Leeds (Table 31)
- **L** From Retford (Table 30) to Huddersfield (Table 34)
- **N** Via Pontefract Baghill (Table 33)
- **b** Change at Manchester Piccadilly and Sheffield
- **c** Change at Manchester Piccadilly

Table 29

Sundays
from 30 March

Manchester Airport, Manchester, Sheffield and Meadowhall → Doncaster → Cleethorpes and Hull
Barton-on-Humber → Cleethorpes

Network Diagram - see first page of Table 18

	HT	TP	XC	NT	NT	TP	NT	NT	XC	TP	TP	XC	NT	NT	NT	NT	NT	XC	TP
	1 ◇	1 ◇	R 1			1 ◇			1 ◇	1 ◇	1 ◇	R 1						1 ◇	1 ◇
			A		B		C		D			E		G		H	J	D	
	⊠ ☕		☕						☕			☕						☕	
Manchester Airport 85 ✈ d		14 52				15 22			15b08	15 52	16 22							16b01	16 52
Manchester Piccadilly 10 78 🚋 d		15 15				16 00			15 43	16 15	17 00							16 43	17 15
Stockport 78 d		15 22				15c28	15 27		15 54	16 22	16c29							16 55	17 22
Sheffield 7 🚋 a		16 03								17 03									18 06
d		16 08	16 21	16 24	16 28		16 39		16 54	17 08		17 21	17 24	17 28		17 36	17 39	17 54	18 08
Meadowhall 🚋 d		16 14		16 30	16 34		16a44			17 14			17 30	17 34		17 42	17a44		18 14
Rotherham Central d				16 36				←					17 36		←	17 48			
Swinton (S.Yorks) d				16 46				16 46					17 46		17 46	17a56			
Mexborough d				→				16 49					→		17 49				
Conisbrough d								16 53							17 53				
Doncaster 7 a		16 33			16 54			17 03	17 14	17 33				17 57	18 06			18 16	18 33
York 8 26 a			17 33						17 40	18 05		18 33		18 34				18 41	19 03
London Kings Cross 15 ⊖ 26 d	14 44							15 10		15 30				16 10					16 30
Doncaster 31 d	16 21	16 36			16 55			17 04		17 36				18 03					18 36
Bentley (S.Yorks) 31 a								17 13											
Adwick 31 a								17 17											
Kirk Sandall d								17 13											
Hatfield & Stainforth d								17 18											
Thorne South d																			
Crowle d																			
Althorpe d																			
Scunthorpe a		17 01								18 01									19 02
d		17 02								18 02									19 02
Barnetby d		17 16								18 16									19 16
Hull Bus Station 🚌 d																			
Barton-on-Humber 🚌 a																			
Barton-on-Humber d																			
Barrow Haven d																			
New Holland d																			
Goxhill d																			
Thornton Abbey d																			
Ulceby d																			
Habrough d										18 25									
Stallingborough d																			
Healing d																			
Great Coates d																			
Grimsby Town a		17 36								18 38									19 36
d		17 37								18 39									19 37
Grimsby Docks d																			
New Clee d																			
Cleethorpes a		17 48								18 50									19 50
Thorne North d								17 25											
Goole d					17 15			17a34						18 22					
Saltmarshe d																			
York 8 33 d																			
Selby a	16 41					17 13					18 16								
d	16 42					17 14					18 16								
Wressle d																			
Howden d	16 52																		
Eastrington d																			
Gilberdyke d					17 23									18 35					
Broomfleet d																			
Brough d	17 04				17 31	17 37					18 36			18 43					
Ferriby d																			
Hessle d																			
Hull a	17 21				17 48	17 53					18 53			18 57					

For general notes see front of timetable
For details of catering facilities see Directory of Train Operators

A From Oxford to Glasgow Central (Table 51)
B To Scarborough (Table 43)
C From Lincoln (Table 30) to Leeds (Table 34)
D From Bristol Temple Meads to Newcastle (Table 51)
E From Penzance (Table 135) to Glasgow Central (Table 51)
G To Bridlington (Table 43)
H To Leeds (Table 31)
J To Huddersfield (Table 34)
b Change at Manchester Piccadilly and Sheffield
c Change at Manchester Piccadilly

Table 29

Sundays

from 30 March

Manchester Airport, Manchester, Sheffield and Meadowhall → Doncaster → Cleethorpes and Hull Barton-on-Humber → Cleethorpes

Network Diagram - see first page of Table 18

		XC	NT	NT	NT	NT		NT	XC	HT	NT	TP		TP	XC	NT	NT	NT		XC	EM	NT	TP	GR
		R 1							R 1	1 ◇		1 ◇		1 ◇	R 1					1 ◇	1 ◇		1 ◇	R 1
		A		B	C				D		E				G		H	J		K	L			
		☕							☕	☒ ☕											☕			☕ 🍴
Manchester Airport 85 ✈	d								*17b05*			17 52		*18 22*						*18b01*			18 52	
Manchester Piccadilly 10 78 🚢	d								*17 43*			18 15		19 00						*18 42*			19 15	
Stockport 78	d								*17 54*			18 22		*18c29*						*18 56*			19 22	
Sheffield 7 🚢	a											19 03											20 04	
	d	18 21	18 24	18 28	18 39				18 54		18 58	19 08			19 21	19 27	19 36	19 39		19 54	19 59	20 03	20 08	
Meadowhall 🚢	d		18 30	18 34	18a44	←					19 04	19 14				19 33	19 42	19a44				20 09	20 14	
Rotherham Central	d		18 36								19 10					19 39	19 48							
Swinton (S.Yorks)	d		18 46			18 46					19 18					19 47	19a56							
Mexborough	d		→			18 49										19 50								
Conisbrough	d					18 53										19 54								
Doncaster 7	a			18 54		19 04			19 16			19 33				20 05				20 16	20 22	20 30	20 34	
York 8 26	a	19 33							19 43		20 16	*20 07*			20 33	*20 38*				20 42	*21 00*			
London Kings Cross 15 ⊖ 26	d			*17 00*						17 40												*18 40*	*19 00*	19 10
Doncaster 31	d			18 55						19 26		19 36										20 30	20 42	20 58
Bentley (S.Yorks) 31	a								*19e32*															
Adwick 31	a								*19e36*															
Kirk Sandall	d			19 01																				
Hatfield & Stainforth	d			19 06																				
Thorne South	d																							
Crowle	d																							
Althorpe	d																							
Scunthorpe	a											20 02											21 07	
	d											20 02											21 08	
Barnetby	d											20 16											21 22	
Hull Bus Station 🚌	d																							
Barton-on-Humber 🚌	a																							
Barton-on-Humber	d																							
Barrow Haven	d																							
New Holland	d																							
Goxhill	d																							
Thornton Abbey	d																							
Ulceby	d																							
Habrough	d																						21 31	
Stallingborough	d																							
Healing	d																							
Great Coates	d																							
Grimsby Town	a											20 36											21 44	
	d											20 37											21 45	
Grimsby Docks	d																							
New Clee	d																							
Cleethorpes	a											20 49											21 56	
Thorne North	d			19 12																				
Goole	d			19 21																		20 49		
Saltmarshe	d																							
York 8 33	d							19 10																
Selby	a							19 29		19 40				20 19										21 15
	d							19 29		19 40				20 19										21 15
Wressle	d																							
Howden	d									19 52														
Eastrington	d																							
Gilberdyke	d			19 29																		20 57		
Broomfleet	d																							
Brough	d			19 37				19 49		20 03				20 39								21 05		21 36
Ferriby	d																							
Hessle	d																							
Hull	a			19 54				20 08		20 22				20 56								21 23		21 56

For general notes see front of timetable
For details of catering facilities see Directory of Train Operators

A From Oxford to Edinburgh (Table 51)
B To Beverley (Table 43)
C To Leeds (Table 34)
D From Paignton to Newcastle (Table 51)
E Via Pontefract Baghill (Table 33)
G From Plymouth to Edinburgh (Table 51)
H To Leeds (Table 31)
J To Huddersfield (Table 34)
K From Bristol Temple Meads to Newcastle (Table 51)
L From St Pancras International to Leeds (Table 53)
b Change at Manchester Piccadilly and Sheffield
c Change at Manchester Piccadilly
e Change at Doncaster

Table 29

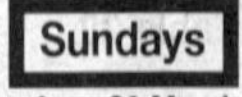

from 30 March

Manchester Airport, Manchester, Sheffield and Meadowhall → Doncaster → Cleethorpes and Hull Barton-on-Humber → Cleethorpes

Network Diagram - see first page of Table 18

		XC	NT	NT	NT	XC	EM	TP	HT	XC	NT	NT	NT	TP	NT	TP	NT	NT	NT
		R 1				1 ◇	1 ◇	1 ◇	1 ◇ ⊠ ☕	R 1				1 ◇		1 ◇			
		A		B		C	D ☕			E		G	H	J			K		
Manchester Airport	85 d					19b05		19 52							20 52				21 52
Manchester Piccadilly 10	78 d					19 42		20 15							21 15				22 15
Stockport	78 d					19 54		20 22							21 22				22 22
Sheffield 7	a							21 06											
	d	20 21	20 27	20 39		20 54	20 57	21 08		21 21	21 24	21 36	21 43		22 26	22 30	22 39		23 20
Meadowhall	d		20 33	20a44				21 14			21 30	21 42	21a48		22 32	22 36	22a44		23 26
Rotherham Central	d		20 39								21 37	21 48			22 38			⟵	23 32
Swinton (S.Yorks)	d		20 47								21 46	21a56			22 48			22 48	23 43
Mexborough	d		20 50								21 49				⟶			22 51	23 46
Conisbrough	d		20 54								21 53							22 55	23 50
Doncaster 7	a		21 04			21 16	21 20	21 34			22 02					22 55		23 03	23 58
York 8	26 a	21 32				21 41	22 00			22 36	23 11							00 39	
London Kings Cross 15	⊖ 26 d							19 35	20 05							21 00			
Doncaster	31 d		21 06					21 42	21 54		22 04					22 58		23 07	
Bentley (S.Yorks)	31 a							21 52											
Adwick	31 a							21 56											
Kirk Sandall	d		21 12																
Hatfield & Stainforth	d		21 17																
Thorne South	d																		
Crowle	d																		
Althorpe	d																		
Scunthorpe	a							22 08								23 23			
	d							22 08								23 24			
Barnetby	d							22 22								23 38			
Hull Bus Station	🚌 d																		
Barton-on-Humber	🚌 a																		
Barton-on-Humber	d																		
Barrow Haven	d																		
New Holland	d																		
Goxhill	d																		
Thornton Abbey	d																		
Ulceby	d																		
Habrough	d							22 31											
Stallingborough	d																		
Healing	d																		
Great Coates	d																		
Grimsby Town	a							22 44								23 58			
	d							22 45								23 59			
Grimsby Docks	d																		
New Clee	d																		
Cleethorpes	a							22 56								00 10			
Thorne North	d		21 23															23 19	
Goole	d		21a34								22 23							23 28	
Saltmarshe	d																		
York 8	33 d				21 41														
Selby	a				22 00				22 08										
	d				22 00				22 08					22 39					
Wressle	d																		
Howden	d								22 20										
Eastrington	d																		
Gilberdyke	d										22 31							23 36	
Broomfleet	d																		
Brough	d				22 20				22 31		22 39			22 59				23 44	
Ferriby	d																		
Hessle	d																		
Hull	a				22 39				22 50		22 56			23 16				00 02	

For general notes see front of timetable
For details of catering facilities see Directory of Train Operators

A From Oxford to Newcastle (Table 51)
B To Leeds (Table 34)
C From Bristol Temple Meads to Newcastle (Table 51)
D From St Pancras International to Leeds (Table 53)
E From Plymouth (Table 51)
G To Leeds (Table 31)
H To Barnsley (Table 34)
J From Leeds (Table 39)
K From Lincoln (Table 30) to Leeds (Table 34)
b Change at Manchester Piccadilly and Sheffield

Sheffield → Retford and Lincoln

Network Diagram - see first page of Table 18

Mondays to Fridays

Miles			NT	NT	NT	NT	NT A	NT	NT B	NT B	NT B	NT B	NT B	NT B	NT B	NT B	NT	NT B	NT	NT	NT A	NT	NT
—	Huddersfield	34 d					06 10	07 10	08 10	09 13	10 13	11 13	12 13	13 13	14 13	15 13		16 13	17 13	17 56	19 18	20 18	21 18
—	Barnsley	34 d		05 18	05 53	06 46	06 58	08 06	08 58	10 01	11 01	12 01	13 01	14 01	15 01	16 01	16 26	17 01	18 01	18 58	20 06	21 06	22 06
—	Meadowhall	29 🚋 d		05 39	06 13	07 04	07 33	08 24	09 33	10 33	11 33	12 33	13 33	14 33	15 33	16 33	17 00	17 33	18 19	19 25	20 33	21 24	22 25
0	**Sheffield** 7	🚋 d	05 39	05 53	06 44	07 30	07 44	08 44	09 44	10 44	11 44	12 44	13 44	14 44	15 44	16 44	17 18	17 44	18 44	19 48	20 44	21 44	22 44
2¼	Darnall	d		05 58	06 49	07 35		08 49	09 49	10 49	11 49	12 49	13 49	14 49	15 49	16 49	17 23	17 49	18 50	19 53	20 49	21 49	22 49
5¼	Woodhouse	d		06 03	06 54	07 40		08 54	09 54	10 54	11 54	12 54	13 54	14 54	15 54	16 54	17 28	17 54	18 55	19 58	20 54	21 54	22 54
9½	Kiveton Bridge	d		06 10	07 01	07 47		09 01	10 01	11 01	12 01	13 01	14 01	15 01	16 01	17 01	17 35	18 01	19 02	20 05	21 01	22 01	23 01
10¾	Kiveton Park	d	05 54	06 13	07 04	07 50	07 59	09 04	10 04	11 04	12 04	13 04	14 04	15 04	16 04	17 04	17 38	18 04	19 05	20 08	21 04	22 04	23 04
13¾	Shireoaks	d		06 18	07 09	07 55		09 09	10 09	11 09	12 09	13 09	14 09	15 09	16 09	17 09	17 43	18 09	19 10	20 13	21 09	22 09	23 09
15¾	Worksop	d	06 01	06 24	07 14	07 59	08a10	09 13	10 13	11 13	12 13	13 13	14 13	15 13	16 13	17 13	17 47	18 13	19 14	20 17	21a21	22 15	23a18
23½	**Retford Low Level** 10	a	06 10	06b38	07 23	08 09		09 23	10 23	11 23	12 23	13 23	14 23	15 23	16 23	17 23	18 01	18 23	19 24	20 27		22b30	
—	London Kings Cross 15	⊖ 26 a		08 34		09 51		11 27	12 42		14 20	15 40		17 30	18 12	19 29	19 49	20 18		23 32			
—	**Retford Low Level** 10	d	06 10		07 24	08 09		09 23	10 23	11 24	12 23	13 23	14 23	15 23	16 23	17 23		18 23	19 24	20 27			
33	Gainsborough Lea Road	18 d	06 25		07 38	08 24		09 38	10 38	11 38	12 38	13 39	14 38	15 38	16 38	17 38		18 38	19 39	20 42			
42½	Saxilby	18 d	06 37		07 51	08 37		09 51	10 51	11 51	12 51	13 52	14 51	15 51	16 51	17 51		18 51	19 52	20 55			
48½	**Lincoln**	18 a	06 53		08 06	08 52		10 06	11 06	12 05	13 05	14 06	15 06	16 05	17 06	18 06		19 07	20 06	21 10			

Saturdays

		NT	NT	NT	NT	NT C	NT D	NT D 🚌	NT	NT B	NT B	NT B	NT C	NT D	NT D 🚌	NT B	NT B	NT B
Huddersfield	34 d					06 10	06 10		07 10	08 10	09 13	10 13				11 13	12 13	13 13
Barnsley	34 d		05 18	05 53	06 27	06 58	06 58		07 58	08 58	10 01	11 01				12 01	13 01	14 01
Meadowhall	29 🚋 d		05 39	06 13	07 00	07 33	07 33		08 22	09 33	10 33	11 33				12 33	13 33	14 33
Sheffield 7	🚋 d	05 39	05 51	06 44	07 30	08 02	08 02		08 44	09 44	10 44	11 44	12 01	12 01		12 44	13 44	14 44
Darnall	d		05 57	06 49	07 35	08 08	08 08		08 49	09 49	10 49	11 49	12 07	12 07		12 49	13 49	14 49
Woodhouse	d		06 02	06 54	07 40	08 13	08 13		08 54	09 54	10 54	11 54	12 12	12 12		12 54	13 54	14 54
Kiveton Bridge	d		06 09	07 01	07 47	08 20	08 20		09 01	10 01	11 01	12 01	12 19	12 19		13 01	14 01	15 01
Kiveton Park	d	05 54	06 12	07 04	07 50	08 23	08 23		09 04	10 04	11 04	12 04	12 22	12 22		13 04	14 04	15 04
Shireoaks	d		06 16	07 09	07 55	08 28	08 28		09 09	10 09	11 09	12 09	12 27	12 27		13 09	14 09	15 09
Worksop	d	06 01	06 23	07 14	07 59	08 32	08 32		09 13	10 13	11 13	12 13	12 35	12 35		13 13	14 13	15 13
Retford Low Level 10	a	06 10	06b38	07 23	08 09	08 42	08 42		09 23	10 23	11 23	12 23	12 44	12 44		13 23	14 23	15 23
London Kings Cross 15	⊖ 26 a		08 40		10 00	10 41	10 41			12 41		14 27				15 49	16 30	17 45
Retford Low Level 10	d	06 10		07 24	08 09	08 42	08 42		09 24	10 23	11 24	12 23	12 45	12 45		13 23	14 23	15 23
Gainsborough Lea Road	18 d	06 25		07 38	08 24				09 38	10 38	11 38	12 38				13 40	14 40	15 45
Saxilby	18 d	06 37		07 51	08 37				09 51	10 51	11 51	12 51				13 53	14 53	15 58
Lincoln	18 a	06 53		08 06	08 52				10 06	11 06	12 05	13 05				14 06	15 06	16 09
Gainsborough Central	d					08 57	08a57	09 05					13 00	13a00	13 05			
Kirton Lindsey	d					09 16		09 35					13 18		13 35			
Brigg	d					09 29		09 55					13 32		13 55			
Barnetby	29 a					09 40		10 10					13 42		14 10			
Habrough	29 a					09 49		10 30					13 52		14 30			
Grimsby Town	29 a					10 01		10 50					14 05		14 50			
Cleethorpes	29 a					10 14		11 10					14 16		15 10			

		NT C	NT D	NT D 🚌	NT B	NT B	NT	NT B	NT B	NT	NT A	NT	NT
Huddersfield	34 d				14 13	15 13		16 13	17 13	18 13	19 18	20 18	21 18
Barnsley	34 d	14 48	14 48		15 01	16 01	16 26	17 01	18 01	19 01	20 06	21 06	22 06
Meadowhall	29 🚋 d	15 06	15 06		15 33	16 33	17 00	17 33	18 33	19 19	20 35	21 24	22 25
Sheffield 7	🚋 d	15 30	15 30		15 44	16 44	17 18	17 44	18 44	19 48	20 44	21 44	22 44
Darnall	d	15 35	15 35		15 49	16 49	17 23	17 49	18 50	19 53	20 49	21 49	22 49
Woodhouse	d	15 40	15 40		15 54	16 54	17 28	17 54	18 55	19 58	20 54	21 54	22 54
Kiveton Bridge	d	15 47	15 47		16 01	17 01	17 35	18 01	19 02	20 05	21 01	22 01	23 01
Kiveton Park	d	15 50	15 50		16 04	17 04	17 38	18 04	19 05	20 08	21 04	22 04	23 04
Shireoaks	d	15 55	15 55		16 09	17 09	17 43	18 09	19 10	20 13	21 09	22 09	23 09
Worksop	d	15 59	15 59		16 13	17 13	17 47	18 13	19 14	20 17	21a21	22 15	23a18
Retford Low Level 10	a	16 09	16 09		16 23	17 23	18 01	18 23	19 24	20 27		22b30	
London Kings Cross 15	⊖ 26 a				18 28		20 12	20 46		22 47			
Retford Low Level 10	d	16 09	16 09		16 23	17 23		18 23	19 24	20 27			
Gainsborough Lea Road	18 d				16 38	17 38		18 38	19 39	20 42			
Saxilby	18 d				16 51	17 51		18 51	19 52	20 55			
Lincoln	18 a				17 06	18 06		19 07	20 06	21 10			
Gainsborough Central	d	16 24	16a24	16 30									
Kirton Lindsey	d	16 43		17 00									
Brigg	d	16 56		17 20									
Barnetby	29 a	17 07		17 35									
Habrough	29 a	17 19		17 55									
Grimsby Town	29 a	17 37		18 15									
Cleethorpes	29 a	17 46		18 35									

For general notes see front of timetable
For details of catering facilities see Directory of Train Operators

A From Doncaster (Table 29)
B From Scunthorpe (Table 29)
C Until 26 January
D From 2 February
b Retford High Level

Sheffield → Retford and Lincoln

Network Diagram - see first page of Table 18

		NT A	NT	NT	NT	NT	NT
Huddersfield	34 d	11 19		13 19	15 19	17 19	19 19
Barnsley	34 d	13 12		15 12	17 12	18 12	20 12
Meadowhall	29 d	13 33		15 42	17 42	19 00	20 45
Sheffield 7	d	13 48	14 01	16 00	18 01	19 24	21 06
Darnall	d		14 06	16 05	18 06	19 29	21 11
Woodhouse	d		14 11	16 10	18 11	19 34	21 16
Kiveton Bridge	d		14 18	16 17	18 18	19 41	21 23
Kiveton Park	d		14 21	16 20	18 21	19 44	21 26
Shireoaks	d		14 25	16 24	18 25	19 48	21 30
Worksop	d	14 08	14 29	16 29	18 29	19 52	21 34
Retford Low Level 10	a	14 17	14 44	16 38	18 38	20 01	21 49
London Kings Cross 15	⊖ 26 a		16 50	19 06	21 12	23 14	
Retford Low Level 10	d	14 18		16 39	18 39	20 02	
Gainsborough Lea Road	18 d	14 32		16 53	18 53	20 16	
Saxilby	18 d	14 45		17 06	19 06	20 29	
Lincoln	18 a	15 00		17 20	19 21	20 44	

For general notes see front of timetable
For details of catering facilities see Directory of Train Operators

A From Leeds (Table 34)

Lincoln and Retford → Sheffield

Network Diagram - see first page of Table 18

Mondays to Fridays

Miles	Station	NT	NT A	NT	NT B	NT B	NT B	NT B	NT B	NT B	NT B	NT B	NT B	NT C	NT	NT D	NT	NT	NT	NT	NT	NT	NT
0	**Lincoln** 18 d			07 04		08 27	09 27	10 27	11 27	12 27	13 27	14 27	15 27	16 27	17 22		18 24	19 43	20 27		21 27		
6	Saxilby 18 d			07 14		08 36	09 36	10 36	11 36	12 36	13 36	14 36	15 36	16 36	17 31		18 33	19 52	20 36		21 36		
15½	Gainsborough Lea Road 18 d			07 26		08 49	09 49	10 49	11 49	12 49	13 49	14 49	15 49	16 49	17 44		18 46	20 05	20 49		21 49		
25	**Retford Low Level** 10 a			07 40		09 03	10 03	11 03	12 03	13 03	14 03	15 03	16 03	17 02	17 58		19 04	20 19	21 03		22 03		
—	London Kings Cross 15 ⊖ 26 d					07 20		08 35	10 10		12 10	13 33		15 10	16 05		16 35	18 30	18 50		20 27		
—	**Retford Low Level** 10 d		07b03	07 40		09 03	10 03	11 03	12 03	13 03	14 03	15 03	16 03	17 03	17 58	18 10	19 04	20 19	21 03		22 03	22b45	
32¾	Worksop d	06 30	07 16	07 52	08 14	09 15	10 15	11 15	12 15	13 15	14 15	15 15	16 15	17 15	18 10	18 21	19 16	20 31	21 15	21 26	22 15	22 58	23 28
34¾	Shireoaks d	06 33	07 20	07 55	08 19	09 19	10 19	11 19	12 19	13 19	14 19	15 19	16 19	17 19		18 25	19 20	20 35		21 31	22 19	23 02	23 32
37¾	Kiveton Park d	06 39	07 25	08 01	08 25	09 25	10 25	11 25	12 25	13 25	14 25	15 25	16 25	17 25		18 31	19 26	20 41	21 23	21 37	22 25	23 08	23 38
39	Kiveton Bridge d	06 42	07 28	08 04	08 28	09 28	10 28	11 28	12 28	13 28	14 28	15 28	16 28	17 28		18 34	19 29	20 44		21 40	22 28	23 11	23 41
43¼	Woodhouse d	06 48	07 34	08 10	08 34	09 34	10 34	11 34	12 34	13 34	14 34	15 34	16 34	17 34		18 41	19 35	20 50		21 46	22 34	23 17	23 52
46¼	Darnall d	06 53	07 39	08 15	08 39	09 39	10 39	11 39	12 39	13 39	14 39	15 39	16 39	17 39		18 46	19 40	20 55		21 51	22 39	23 22	23 57
48½	**Sheffield** 7 a	07 02	07 47	08 26	08 48	09 48	10 48	11 48	12 48	13 48	14 48	15 48	16 48	17 47	18 35	18 54	19 54	21 05	21 43	22 00	22 50	23 31	00 03
—	Meadowhall 29 a	07 20	07 57	08 41	09 03	10 03	11 03	12 03	13 03	14 03	15 03	16 03	17 03	18 03	18 56	19 03	20 13	21 21		22 13	23 20		
—	Barnsley 34 a	07 48	08 11	09 00	09 34	10 34	11 34	12 34	13 34	14 34	15 34	16 34	17 34	18 34	19 15	19 34	20 34	22 05		22 34	23c50		
—	Huddersfield 34 a	08 49		09 49	10 49	11 49	12 49	13 49	14 49	15 49	16 49	17 50	18 57	19 57		20 54	21 54	22 54		23 55			

Saturdays

Station	NT	NT A	NT	NT B	NT B	NT B	NT B	NT E (bus)	NT E	NT G	NT B	NT B	NT B	NT E (bus)	NT E	NT B	NT G
Cleethorpes 29 d								10 20		11 13				13 30			14 56
Grimsby Town 29 d								10 35		11 20				13 45			15 04
Habrough 29 d								10 55		11 30				14 05			15 14
Barnetby 29 d								11 15		11 40				14 25			15 23
Brigg d								11 25		11 50				14 35			15 34
Kirton Lindsey d								11 45		12 04				14 55			15 48
Gainsborough Central d								12a15	12 22	12 22				15a25	15 33		16 06
Lincoln 18 d			07 04	08 27	09 27	10 27	11 27				12 27	13 27	14 27			15 27	
Saxilby 18 d			07 14	08 36	09 36	10 36	11 36				12 36	13 36	14 36			15 36	
Gainsborough Lea Road 18 d			07 26	08 49	09 49	10 49	11 49				12 49	13 49	14 49			15 49	
Retford Low Level 10 a			07 40	09 03	10 03	11 03	12 03		12 37	12 37	13 03	14 03	15 03		15 47	16 03	16 20
London Kings Cross 15 ⊖ 26 d				07 10		09 00	09 34				11 10	11 48	13 10		13 38	13 38	14 30
Retford Low Level 10 d		07b03	07 40	09 03	10 03	11 03	12 03		12 37	12 37	13 03	14 03	15 03		15 48	16 03	16 21
Worksop d	06 30	07 16	07 52	09 15	10 15	11 15	12 15		12 49	12 49	13 15	14 15	15 15		15 59	16 15	16 32
Shireoaks d	06 33	07 20	07 55	09 19	10 19	11 19	12 19		12 53	12 53	13 19	14 19	15 19		16 03	16 19	16 36
Kiveton Park d	06 39	07 25	08 01	09 25	10 25	11 25	12 25		12 59	12 59	13 25	14 25	15 25		16 09	16 25	16 42
Kiveton Bridge d	06 42	07 28	08 04	09 28	10 28	11 28	12 28		13 02	13 02	13 28	14 28	15 28		16 12	16 28	16 45
Woodhouse d	06 48	07 34	08 10	09 34	10 34	11 34	12 34		13 08	13 08	13 34	14 34	15 34		16 19	16 34	16 52
Darnall d	06 53	07 39	08 15	09 39	10 39	11 39	12 39		13 13	13 13	13 39	14 39	15 39		16 24	16 39	16 57
Sheffield 7 a	07 02	07 47	08 26	09 48	10 48	11 48	12 48		13 26	13 26	13 48	14 48	15 48		16 35	16 48	17 06
Meadowhall 29 a	07 20	07 57	08 41	10 03	11 03	12 03	13 03		13 41	13 41	14 03	15 03	16 03		16 56	17 03	17 20
Barnsley 34 a	07 43	08 11	09 00	10 34	11 34	12 34	13 34		14 00	14 00	14 34	15 34	16 34		17 11	17 34	18 02
Huddersfield 34 a	08 49		09 49	11 49	12 49	13 49			14 49	14 49	15 49	16 49	17 50			18 50	18 50

Station	NT D	NT	NT D	NT	NT E (bus)	NT E	NT G	NT	NT	NT	NT	NT	NT
Cleethorpes 29 d					17 15		18 06						
Grimsby Town 29 d					17 30		18 13						
Habrough 29 d					17 50		18 23						
Barnetby 29 d					18 10		18 34						
Brigg d					18 20		18 46						
Kirton Lindsey d					18 40		19 00						
Gainsborough Central d					19a10	19 18	19 18						
Lincoln 18 d	16 27	17 22		18 24				19 43	20 27		21 24		
Saxilby 18 d	16 36	17 31		18 33				19 52	20 36		21 33		
Gainsborough Lea Road 18 d	16 49	17 44		18 46				20 05	20 49		21 46		
Retford Low Level 10 a	17 03	17 58		19 04		19 32	19 32	20 19	21 03		22 00		
London Kings Cross 15 ⊖ 26 d	14 30			17 05					18 40		20 00		
Retford Low Level 10 d	17 03	17 58	18 10	19 04		19 33	19 33	20 19	21 03		22 00	22b45	
Worksop d	17 15	18 10	18 21	19 16		19 44	19 44	20 31	21 15	21 26	22 12	22 58	23 28
Shireoaks d	17 19		18 25	19 20		19 48	19 48	20 35		21 31	22 16	23 02	23 32
Kiveton Park d	17 25		18 31	19 26		19 54	19 54	20 41	21 23	21 37	22 22	23 08	23 38
Kiveton Bridge d	17 28		18 34	19 29		19 57	19 57	20 44		21 40	22 25	23 11	23 41
Woodhouse d	17 34		18 41	19 35		20 04	20 04	20 50		21 46	22 31	23 17	23 47
Darnall d	17 39		18 46	19 40		20 09	20 09	20 55		21 51	22 36	23 22	23 52
Sheffield 7 a	17 48	18 35	18 54	19 54		20 21	20 21	21 05	21 43	22 02	22 46	23 31	00 01
Meadowhall 29 a	18 03	18 56	19 06	20 13		20 36	20 36	21 21	22 13	22 17	23 30		
Barnsley 34 a	18 34	19 15	19 34	20 34		21 06	21 06	22 05	22 34	23 06			
Huddersfield 34 a	19 51		20 54			21 54	21 54	22 54		23 55			

For general notes see front of timetable
For details of catering facilities see Directory of Train Operators

- **A** To Leeds (Table 31)
- **B** To Adwick (Table 29)
- **C** To Hull (Table 29)
- **D** To Doncaster (Table 29)
- **E** From 2 February
- **G** Until 26 January
- **b** Retford High Level
- **c** Mondays to Thursdays only

Lincoln and Retford → Sheffield

Network Diagram - see first page of Table 18

		NT	NT A	NT	NT	NT A	NT
Lincoln	18 d		15 15	17 35	19 35	21 15	
Saxilby	18 d		15 25	17 45	19 45	21 25	
Gainsborough Lea Road	18 d		15 37	17 57	19 57	21 37	
Retford Low Level 10	a		15 51	18 11	20 11	21 51	
London Kings Cross 15	⊖ 26 d	*12 10*		*16 10*	*18 10*	*20 05*	*20 30*
Retford Low Level 10	d	14 50	15 51	18 11	20 11	21 51	22 24
Worksop	d	15 01	16 03	18 23	20 23	22 03	22 35
Shireoaks	d	15 05	16 06	18 26	20 26	22 06	22 39
Kiveton Park	d	15 10	16 12	18 32	20 32	22 12	22 44
Kiveton Bridge	d	15 13	16 15	18 35	20 35	22 15	22 47
Woodhouse	d	15 19	16 21	18 41	20 41	22 21	22 53
Darnall	d	15 24	16 26	18 46	20 46	22 26	22 58
Sheffield 7	🚌 a	15 33	16 35	18 55	20 56	22 34	23 07
Meadowhall	29 🚌 a	15 44	16 44	*19 13*	*21 14*	22 44	*23 25*
Barnsley	34 a	16 06	17 05	*20 05*	*22 09*	23 05	
Huddersfield	34 a	16 55	*18 54*	*20 53*			

For general notes see front of timetable
For details of catering facilities see Directory of Train Operators

A To Leeds (Table 34)

Network Diagram for Tables 31, 32, 33, 34

DM-4/06(2)
Design BAJS

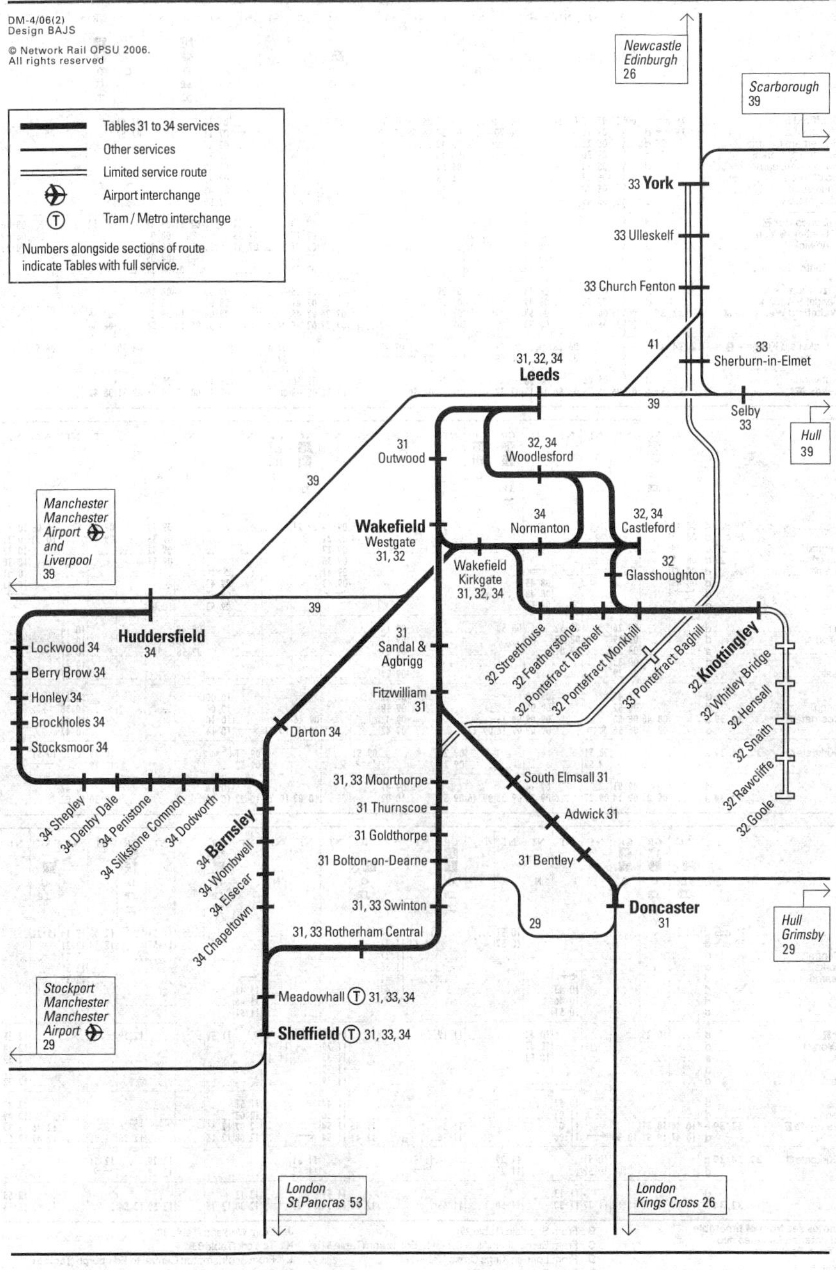

Sheffield, Doncaster and Wakefield → Leeds

Network Diagram - see first page of Table 31

Miles	Miles			EM MO	NT	NT	NT	NT	NT	NT	NT	NT		XC	NT	NT	NT	NT	GR	NT	NT	GR		NT	NT
				1 ◊ A					B					1 ◊ C			B		R 1 D		E	R 1 D			G
—	0	**Sheffield** [7]	29 d	00 01	05 10	05 50		06 14		06 28	06 49	07 04		07 12				07 14			07 51			08 08	
—	3½	Meadowhall	29 d		05 16	05 56		06 20		06 34	06 55	07 10						07 21			07 57			08 14	
—	6¾	Rotherham Central	29 d		05 22					06 40								07 27							
—	10¾	Swinton (S.Yorks)	29 d		05 30					06 48								07 35							
—	13	Bolton-on-Dearne	d		05 34					06 53								07 39							
—	14¼	Goldthorpe	d		05 37					06 55								07 42							
—	15	Thurnscoe	d		05 40					06 58								07 45							
—	18½	Moorthorpe	d		05 45					07 03								07 50							
0	—	**Doncaster** [7]	d				06 25		06 59						07 14		07 32		07 51	07 58		08 12			08 16
1¾	—	Bentley (S.Yorks)	d				06 28		07 02						07 17		07 35			08 01					08 19
4	—	Adwick	a				06 32		07 08						07 21		07 41			08 05					08 25
—	—		d				06 32								07 21					08 05					
8¾	—	South Elmsall	d				06 38								07 27					08 11					
13¼	22¼	Fitzwilliam	d		05 50		06 43			07 09					07 35			07 56		08 16					
18	27	Sandal & Agbrigg	d		05 56		06 49			07 15					07 41			08 02		08 22					
19¾	28¾	**Wakefield Westgate** [7]	32, 39 a	00 29	06 01		06 53			07 19				07 36	07 45			08 06	08 10	08 26		08 36			
—	—		d	00 29	06 01		06 53			07 20				07 37	07 45	←		08 07	08 10	08 26		08 36			
—	—	Wakefield Kirkgate [4]	32, 34, 39 a			06 28		06 57			07 29	07 47				07 47					08 28			08 51	
—	—		d			06 29		06 58			07 29	→				07 47					08 29			→	
22¼	31¼	Outwood	d		06 06		06 58			07 25					07 50			08 12		08 31					
29¾	38¾	**Leeds** [10]	32, 34 a	01 06	06 26	06 50	07 13	07 33		07 44	07 50			07 52	08 03	08 23		08 30	08 32	08 46	08 51	08 52			

		NT	XC	NT	NT	NT	NT	GR	GR	NT		NT	NT	NT	XC	GR	NT	NT	NT	NT		NT	NT	NT	NT
			R 1 C					R 1 D	R 1 D						R 1 H	R 1 D			J	K					
Sheffield [7]	29 d	08 14	08 21							08 51			09 08	09 14	09 21					09 29		09 51		10 08	10 14
Meadowhall	29 d	08 23								08 57			09 14	09 21						09 35		09 57		10 14	10 21
Rotherham Central	29 d	08 29												09 27						09 42					10 27
Swinton (S.Yorks)	29 d	08 38												09 36						09 51					10 36
Bolton-on-Dearne	d	08 42					←							09 41				←							10 41
Goldthorpe	d	08 45					08 45							09 43				09 43							10 43
Thurnscoe	d	→					08 48							→				09 46							→
Moorthorpe	d						08 53											09 53		10a01					
Doncaster [7]	d			08 26		08 52		08 58				09 14							09 49				10 14		
Bentley (S.Yorks)	d			08 29		08 55						09 17							09 52				10 17		
Adwick	a			08 33		09 01						09 21							09 58				10 21		
	d			08 33								09 21											10 21		
South Elmsall	d			08 39								09 27											10 27		
Fitzwilliam	d			08 46			08 59					09 32						10 00					10 32		
Sandal & Agbrigg	d			08 52			09 05					09 38						10 06					10 38		
Wakefield Westgate [7]	32, 39 a		08 46	08 56			09 09	09 16				09 42			09 46			10 10					10 42		
	d		08 47	08 56	←		09 09	09 16	09 27			09 42			09 47	10 01	←	10 11					10 42		
Wakefield Kirkgate [4]	32, 34, 39 a				08 51					09 29			09 51				09 51					10 29		10 51	
	d				08 52					09 29			→				09 52					10 29		→	
Outwood	d			09 01			09 14					09 47						10 16					10 47		
Leeds [10]	32, 34 a		09 02	09 14	09 27		09 30	09 35	09 46	09 50		10 02			10 02	10 21	10 27	10 30				10 50	11 02		

		XC	GR	GR	NT	NT	NT	NT		GR	NT	NT	XC	NT	NT	NT	NT	GR		NT	GR	NT	NT	XC	NT
		1 ◊ L	R 1 D	R 1 D			N			R 1 D			1 ◊ Q			N		R 1 D			R 1 D			1 ◊ U	
Sheffield [7]	29 d	10 21						10 51			11 08	11 14	11 21							11 51		12 08	12 14	12 21	
Meadowhall	29 d							10 57			11 14	11 21								11 57		12 14	12 21		
Rotherham Central	29 d											11 27											12 27		
Swinton (S.Yorks)	29 d											11 36											12 35		
Bolton-on-Dearne	d					←						11 41					←						12 39		
Goldthorpe	d					10 43						11 43					11 43						12 42		
Thurnscoe	d					10 46						→					11 46						→		
Moorthorpe	d					10 51											11 51								
Doncaster [7]	d		10 28				10 44			11 19				11 26		11 38		11 58			12 19				12 25
Bentley (S.Yorks)	d						10 47							11 29		11 41									12 28
Adwick	a						10 53							11 33		11 47									12 32
	d													11 33											12 32
South Elmsall	d													11 39											12 38
Fitzwilliam	d					10 57								11 44			11 57								12 43
Sandal & Agbrigg	d					11 03								11 50			12 03								12 49
Wakefield Westgate [7]	32, 39 a	10 46	10 51			11 07				11 36			11 46	11 54			12 07	12 15			12 36			12 46	12 53
	d	10 47	10 51	10 56	←	11 08				11 36			11 47	11 54	←		12 08	12 15			12 36			12 47	12 53
Wakefield Kirkgate [4]	32, 34, 39 a				10 51			11 29			11 51				11 51					12 29		12 51			
	d				10 52			11 29			→				11 52					12 29		→			
Outwood	d					11 13								11 59			12 13								12 58
Leeds [10]	32, 34 a	11 02	11 09	11 18	11 27	11 30		11 50		11 55			12 02	12 14	12 27		12 30	12 35		12 50	12 54			13 02	13 13

For general notes see front of timetable
For details of catering facilities see Directory of Train Operators

- **A** Until 24 March. From St Pancras International (Table 53)
- **B** From Sheffield (Table 29)
- **C** From Birmingham New Street to Edinburgh (Table 51)
- **D** From London Kings Cross (Table 26)
- **E** From Retford (Table 30)
- **G** From Scunthorpe (Table 29)
- **H** From Bristol Temple Meads to Edinburgh (Table 51)
- **J** From Worksop (Table 30)
- **K** To York (Table 33)
- **L** From Southampton Central to Edinburgh (Table 51)
- **N** From Lincoln (Table 30)
- **Q** From Plymouth to Edinburgh (Table 51)
- **U** From Bournemouth (Table 51) to Aberdeen (Table 229)

Sheffield, Doncaster and Wakefield → Leeds

Network Diagram - see first page of Table 31

Station																									
		NT	NT A	NT	GR R 1 B ☕ 🛒	NT		GR R 1 B	NT	NT	XC 1 ◇ C ☕	NT	NT	NT A	NT	GR R 1 B ☕ 🛒		NT D	NT	GR R 1 B ☕ 🛒	NT	NT	XC R 1 E ☕	NT	NT
Sheffield 7	29 🚊 d					12 51			13 08	13 14	13 21							13 28	13 51		14 08	14 14	14 21		
Meadowhall	29 🚊 d					12 57			13 14	13 21								13 35	13 57		14 14	14 21			
Rotherham Central	29 d									13 27								13 42				14 27			
Swinton (S.Yorks)	29 d									13 36								13 50				14 36			
Bolton-on-Dearne	d			←						13 41					←							14 41			
Goldthorpe	d			12 42						13 43					13 43							14 43			
Thurnscoe	d			12 45						→					13 46							→			
Moorthorpe	d			12 50											13 51			14a01							
Doncaster 7	d		12 36		13 00							13 27		13 38		13 57				14 21				14 27	
Bentley (S.Yorks)	d		12 40									13 30		13 41										14 30	
Adwick	a		12 45									13 34		13 47										14 34	
	d											13 34												14 34	
South Elmsall	d											13 40												14 40	
Fitzwilliam	d			12 57								13 45			13 57									14 45	
Sandal & Agbrigg	d			13 03								13 51			14 03									14 51	
Wakefield Westgate 7	32, 39 a			13 07	13 17						13 46	13 55			14 07	14 14				14 39			14 46	14 55	
	d	←		13 08	13 17			13 37			13 47	13 55	←		14 08	14 14				14 39			14 47	14 55	←
Wakefield Kirkgate 4	32, 34, 39 a	12 51				13 29			13 51				13 51						14 28		14 51				14 51
	d	12 52				13 29			→				13 52						14 29		→				14 52
Outwood	d			13 13								14 00			14 13									15 00	
Leeds 10	32, 34 a	13 27		13 33	13 41	13 50		13 55			14 02	14 15	14 27		14 30	14 35			14 50	15 01			15 02	15 15	15 27

Station																									
		NT A	NT	GR R 1 B ☕ 🛒		NT	NT	NT	NT	XC R 1 G ☕	GR R 1 B ☕ 🛒	NT	NT A	NT		GR R 1 B ☕ 🛒	GR R 1 B ☕ 🛒	NT	NT	NT	NT	XC R 1 H ☕	NT	NT A	NT
Sheffield 7	29 🚊 d					14 51		15 08	15 14	15 21								15 51		16 08	16 14	16 21			
Meadowhall	29 🚊 d					14 57		15 14	15 21									15 57		16 14	16 21				
Rotherham Central	29 d								15 27												16 27				
Swinton (S.Yorks)	29 d								15 36												16 36				
Bolton-on-Dearne	d		←						15 38					←							16 41				←
Goldthorpe	d		14 43						15 43					15 43							16 43				16 43
Thurnscoe	d		14 46						→					15 46							→				16 46
Moorthorpe	d		14 51											15 51											16 51
Doncaster 7	d	14 38		14 53			15 14				15 30		15 38			15 55	16 10		16 14					16 38	
Bentley (S.Yorks)	d	14 41					15 17						15 41						16 17					16 41	
Adwick	a	14 47					15 21						15 47						16 21					16 47	
	d						15 21												16 21						
South Elmsall	d						15 27												16 27						
Fitzwilliam	d		14 57				15 32							15 57					16 32						16 57
Sandal & Agbrigg	d		15 03				15 38							16 03					16 38						17 03
Wakefield Westgate 7	32, 39 a		15 08	15 14			15 42			15 46	15 51			16 08		16 13	16 30		16 42			16 46			17 07
	d		15 08	15 14			15 42			15 47	15 51	←		16 08		16 14	16 30		16 43			16 47	←		17 08
Wakefield Kirkgate 4	32, 34, 39 a					15 29		15 51				15 51						16 27		16 51			16 51		
	d					15 29		→				15 52						16 27		→			16 52		
Outwood	d		15 13				15 47							16 13					16 50						17 13
Leeds 10	32, 34 a		15 30	15 35		15 50	16 02			16 02	16 09	16 27		16 30		16 35	16 48	16 50	17 02			17 02	17 27		17 30

Station																									
		GR R 1 B ☕ 🛒		NT	GR R 1 B ☕ 🛒	NT	NT	XC R 1 J ☕	NT	GR R 1 B	NT	NT A		NT	NT	GR R 1 B ☕	NT	NT	XC R 1 E ☕	NT	GR R 1 B ☕ 🛒	NT		NT	GR R 1 K ☕ 🛒
Sheffield 7	29 🚊 d			16 51		17 08	17 14	17 21							17 51		18 08	18 14	18 21						
Meadowhall	29 🚊 d			16 57		17 14	17 21								17 57		18 14	18 21							
Rotherham Central	29 d						17 27											18 27							
Swinton (S.Yorks)	29 d						17 36											18 36							
Bolton-on-Dearne	d						17 41							←				18 41						←	
Goldthorpe	d						17 43							17 43				18 43						18 43	
Thurnscoe	d						→							17 46				→						18 46	
Moorthorpe	d													17 51										18 51	
Doncaster 7	d	17 01			17 19				17 27			17 38				18 19				18 27	18 43				19 17
Bentley (S.Yorks)	d								17 30			17 41								18 30					
Adwick	a								17 34			17 47								18 34					
	d								17 34											18 34					
South Elmsall	d								17 40											18 40					
Fitzwilliam	d								17 45					18 02						18 46				19 01	
Sandal & Agbrigg	d								17 51					18 08						18 51				19 07	
Wakefield Westgate 7	32, 39 a	17 18			17 36			17 46	17 55					18 12		18 36			18 46	18 55	19 01			19 12	19 34
	d	17 18			17 36			17 47	17 55	18 04	←			18 13		18 36			18 47	18 56	19 01	←		19 12	19 34
Wakefield Kirkgate 4	32, 34, 39 a			17 29		17 51					17 51				18 36		18 51					18 51			
	d			17 29		→					17 52				18 36		→					18 52			
Outwood	d								18 00					18 18						19 00				19 17	
Leeds 10	32, 34 a	17 36		17 50	17 56			18 02	18 15	18 23	18 27			18 33	18 55	18 55			19 02	19 15	19 21	19 27		19 33	19 53

For general notes see front of timetable
For details of catering facilities see Directory of Train Operators

A From Lincoln (Table 30)
B From London Kings Cross (Table 26)
C From Plymouth to Edinburgh (Table 51)
D To York (Table 33)
E From Bournemouth to Edinburgh (Table 51)
G From Penzance (Table 135) to Dundee (Table 229)
H From Bournemouth to Glasgow Central (Table 51)
J From Plymouth to Glasgow Central (Table 51)
K From London Kings Cross to Bradford Forster Square (Table 26)

Sheffield, Doncaster and Wakefield → Leeds

Network Diagram - see first page of Table 31

		NT	NT	EM	NT	XC	NT	GR	GR	NT		NT	NT	GR	NT	XC	NT	EM	NT	NT		GR	NT	GR	EM
				1 ◊ A ☕		R 1 B ☕		R 1 C ☕ 🍴	R 1 D ☕ 🍴					R 1 C ☕ 🍴		R 1 E		1 ◊ A ☕				R 1 C ☕ 🍴		R 1 C ☕ 🍴	1 ◊ A ☕
Sheffield 7	29 🚊 d	18 51	19 08	19 15	19 18	19 26							19 51		20 08	20 21	20 27	20 35							21 00
Meadowhall	29 🚊 d	18 57	19 14		19 25								19 57		20 14		20 35								
Rotherham Central	29 d				19 31												20 41								
Swinton (S.Yorks)	29 d				19 40												20 50								
Bolton-on-Dearne	d				19 44							←					20 55						←		
Goldthorpe	d				19 47							19 47					20 57						20 57		
Thurnscoe	d				→							19 50					→						21 00		
Moorthorpe	d											19 55											21 05		
Doncaster 7	d						19 29	19 42	19 47					20 19					20 38			20 50		21 17	21 26
Bentley (S.Yorks)	d						19 32												20 41						
Adwick	a						19 36												20 45						
	d						19 36												20 45						
South Elmsall	d						19 42												20 51						
Fitzwilliam	d						19 48					20 04							21 01				21 11		
Sandal & Agbrigg	d						19 53					20 10							21 06				21 17		
Wakefield Westgate 7	32, 39 a			19 44		19 49	19 57	20 01	20 06			20 14		20 38		20 53		21 01	21 10			21 14	21 21	21 35	21 44
	d			19 44		19 50	19 58	20 01	20 06	←		20 15		20 38		20 54		21 01	21 11	←		21 14	21 22	21 35	21 44
Wakefield Kirkgate 4	32, 34, 39 a	19 36	19 51							19 51			20 28		20 51					20 51					
	d	19 36	→							19 52			20 29		→					20 52					
Outwood	d						20 02					20 20							21 15				21 27		
Leeds 10	32, 34 a	19 56		20 06		20 06	20 17	20 21	20 25	20 27		20 37	20 50	20 54		21 09		21 21	21 27	21 27		21 34	21 46	21 53	22 05

		NT	XC	NT	NT	GR	NT	EM		GR	NT FX	NT	XC	NT	NT FX	NT FO	NT	GR		NT FX	NT FO	NT FX			
			1 ◊ G			R 1 C ☕ 🍴		1 ◊ A ☕		R 1 C ☕ 🍴			1 ◊ H					R 1 C ☕ 🍴							
Sheffield 7	29 🚊 d	21 08	21 21				21 31	21 51			22 08	22 15	22 21							23 15	23 15	23 24			
Meadowhall	29 🚊 d	21 14					21 37				22 14	22 21								23 21	23 21	23 30			
Rotherham Central	29 d						21 43					22 27								23 27	23 27				
Swinton (S.Yorks)	29 d						21 51					22 36								23 36	23 36				
Bolton-on-Dearne	d						21 55					22 41					←			23 41	23 41				
Goldthorpe	d						21 58					22 43					22 43			23 44	23 44				
Thurnscoe	d						22 01					→					22 46			23 47	23 47				
Moorthorpe	d						22 06										22 51			23 52	23 52				
Doncaster 7	d				21 38	21 53		22 13		22 18				22 30				23 24							
Bentley (S.Yorks)	d				21 41									22 33											
Adwick	a				21 45									22 37											
	d				21 45									22 37											
South Elmsall	d				21 51									22 43											
Fitzwilliam	d				21 58		22 12							22 48			22 57								
Sandal & Agbrigg	d				22 04		22 18							22 54			23 03								
Wakefield Westgate 7	32, 39 a		21 49		22 08	22 13	22 22	22 30		22 35			22s46	22 58			23 07	23 42		00 09		00 17			
	d		21 50	←	22 09	22 13	22 23	22 30		22 35				22 58	←		23 08	23 42		00 10					
Wakefield Kirkgate 4	32, 34, 39 a	21 51		21 51							22 51				22 51							00s10			
	d	→		21 52							→				22 52	22 52									
Outwood	d				22 14		22 28							23 03			23 13								
Leeds 10	32, 34 a		22 05	22 27	22 28	22 33	22 46	22 50		22 53			23 05	23 18	23 27	23 27	23 30	23 59		00 30	00 30				

Saturdays

		NT	NT	NT	NT	NT	XC	NT	NT	NT	NT	NT	NT	NT	NT	XC	NT	NT	NT	GR	NT	NT	NT	NT	XC
				J			1 ◊ K ☕			J		L		N		1 ◊ K ☕				R 1 C ☕ 🍴					1 ◊ Q ☕
Sheffield 7	29 🚊 d		06 14		06 28	07 08	07 12				07 14	07 51	08 08		08 14	08 21					08 51		09 08	09 14	09 21
Meadowhall	29 🚊 d		06 20		06 34	07 14					07 21	07 57	08 14		08 23						08 57		09 14	09 21	
Rotherham Central	29 d				06 40						07 27				08 29									09 27	
Swinton (S.Yorks)	29 d				06 48						07 37				08 38									09 36	
Bolton-on-Dearne	d				06 52						07 42				08 42				←					09 41	
Goldthorpe	d				06 55						07 44				08 45				08 45					09 43	
Thurnscoe	d				06 58						07 47				→				08 48					→	
Moorthorpe	d				07 03						07 52								08 53						
Doncaster 7	d	06 25		07 00				07 14		07 32				08 16				08 50		08 58		09 14			
Bentley (S.Yorks)	d	06 28		07 03				07 17		07 35				08 19				08 53				09 17			
Adwick	a	06 32		07 09				07 21		07 41				08 25				08 59				09 21			
	d	06 32						07 21														09 21			
South Elmsall	d	06 38						07 27														09 27			
Fitzwilliam	d	06 43			07 09			07 35			07 58								08 59			09 32			
Sandal & Agbrigg	d	06 49			07 15			07 41			08 04								09 05			09 38			
Wakefield Westgate 7	32, 39 a	06 53			07 19		07 36	07 45			08 08					08 46			09 09	09 15		09 42			09 46
	d	06 53			07 19		07 37	07 45	←		08 09					08 47	←		09 09	09 15		09 42			09 47
Wakefield Kirkgate 4	32, 34, 39 a		06 57			07 51			07 51			08 28	08 51				08 51				09 29		09 51		
	d		06 58			→			07 51			08 29	→				08 52				09 29		→		
Outwood	d	06 58			07 24			07 50			08 14								09 14			09 47			
Leeds 10	32, 34 a	07 15	07 33		07 44		07 52	08 04	08 27		08 30	08 51				09 04	09 27		09 30	09 35	09 50	10 02			10 02

For general notes see front of timetable
For details of catering facilities see Directory of Train Operators

A From St Pancras International (Table 53)
B From Plymouth to Edinburgh (Table 51)
C From London Kings Cross (Table 26)
D From London Kings Cross to Skipton (Table 26)
E From Bournemouth to Newcastle (Table 51)
G From Plymouth to York (Table 51)
H From Bournemouth (Table 51)
J From Sheffield (Table 29)
K From Birmingham New Street to Edinburgh (Table 51)
L From Retford (Table 30)
N From Scunthorpe (Table 29)
Q From Bristol Temple Meads to Edinburgh (Table 51)

Table 31

Saturdays

Sheffield, Doncaster and Wakefield → Leeds

Network Diagram - see first page of Table 31

	NT	NT	NT	GR	NT	NT	NT	NT	NT	XC	NT	NT	NT	GR	NT	NT	NT	NT	XC	NT	NT	NT	GR	NT
				R 1						1 ◇				R 1					1 ◇				R 1	
		A		B	C					D		E		B					G		E		B	
Sheffield 7 29 d					09 31	09 51		10 08	10 14	10 21					10 51		11 08	11 14	11 21					11 51
Meadowhall 29 d					09 37	09 57		10 14	10 21						10 57		11 14	11 21						11 57
Rotherham Central 29 d					09 44				10 27									11 27						
Swinton (S.Yorks) 29 d					09 52				10 36									11 36						
Bolton-on-Dearne d			←						10 41				←					11 41				←		
Goldthorpe d			09 43						10 43				10 43					11 43				11 43		
Thurnscoe d			09 46						→				10 46					→				11 46		
Moorthorpe d			09 51		10a01								10 51									11 51		
Doncaster 7 d		09 38		09 57			10 14					10 38		10 48		11 14					11 38		11 54	
Bentley (S.Yorks) d		09 44					10 17					10 41				11 17					11 41			
Adwick a		09 50					10 21					10 47				11 21					11 47			
Adwick d							10 21									11 21								
South Elmsall d							10 27									11 27								
Fitzwilliam d			09 57				10 32						10 57			11 32						11 57		
Sandal & Agbrigg d			10 03				10 38						11 03			11 38						12 03		
Wakefield Westgate 7 32, 39 a			10 07	10 14			10 42			10 46			11 07	11 11		11 42			11 46			12 07	12 13	
Wakefield Westgate d	←		10 08	10 16			10 42			10 47	←		11 08	11 13		11 42			11 47	←		12 08	12 13	
Wakefield Kirkgate 4 32, 34, 39 a	09 51					10 29		10 51			10 51				11 29		11 51			11 51				12 29
Wakefield Kirkgate d	09 52					10 29		→			10 52				11 29		→			11 52				12 29
Outwood d			10 13				10 47						11 13			11 47						12 13		
Leeds 10 32, 34 a	10 27		10 30	10 35		10 50	11 02			11 02	11 27		11 30	11 35	11 50	12 02			12 02	12 27		12 30	12 35	12 50

	NT	NT	NT		XC	NT	NT	NT	GR	NT	NT	NT	NT	XC	NT	NT	NT	GR	NT	NT	NT	NT	NT	XC
					1 ◇				R 1					1 ◇				R 1						1 ◇
					H		E		B					G		E		B	C					J
Sheffield 7 29 d		12 08	12 14		12 21					12 51		13 08	13 14	13 21					13 28	13 51		14 08	14 14	14 21
Meadowhall 29 d		12 14	12 21							12 57		13 14	13 21						13 35	13 57		14 14	14 21	
Rotherham Central 29 d			12 27										13 27						13 42				14 27	
Swinton (S.Yorks) 29 d			12 36										13 36						13 50				14 36	
Bolton-on-Dearne d			12 41					←					13 41				←						14 41	
Goldthorpe d			12 43					12 43					13 43				13 43						14 43	
Thurnscoe d			→					12 46					→				13 46						→	
Moorthorpe d								12 51									13 51		14a00					
Doncaster 7 d	12 14						12 36		12 59		13 14					13 38		13 53			14 14			
Bentley (S.Yorks) d	12 17						12 40				13 17					13 41					14 17			
Adwick a	12 21						12 45				13 21					13 47					14 21			
Adwick d	12 21										13 21										14 21			
South Elmsall d	12 27										13 27										14 27			
Fitzwilliam d	12 32							12 57			13 32						13 57				14 32			
Sandal & Agbrigg d	12 38							13 03			13 38						14 03				14 38			
Wakefield Westgate 7 32, 39 a	12 42				12 46			13 07	13 16		13 42			13 46			14 07	14 13			14 42			14 46
Wakefield Westgate d	12 42				12 47	←		13 08	13 16		13 42			13 47	←		14 08	14 13			14 42			14 47
Wakefield Kirkgate 4 32, 34, 39 a		12 51				12 51				13 29		13 51			13 51					14 28		14 51		
Wakefield Kirkgate d		→				12 52				13 29		→			13 52					14 29		→		
Outwood d	12 47							13 13			13 47						14 13				14 47			
Leeds 10 32, 34 a	13 02				13 02	13 27		13 30	13 35	13 50	14 02			14 02	14 27		14 30	14 35		14 50	15 02			15 02

	NT	NT	NT	GR	NT	NT	NT	NT	XC	NT	NT	NT	NT	GR	NT	NT	XC	NT	NT	NT	NT	NT	GR	NT
				R 1					1 ◇					R 1			1 ◇						R 1	
		E		B					K		E			B			L			E			B	
Sheffield 7 29 d					14 51		15 08	15 14	15 21				15 51		16 08	16 14	16 21					16 51		17 08
Meadowhall 29 d					14 57		15 14	15 21					15 57		16 14	16 21						16 57		17 14
Rotherham Central 29 d								15 27								16 27								
Swinton (S.Yorks) 29 d								15 36								16 36								
Bolton-on-Dearne d			←					15 41				←				16 41					←			
Goldthorpe d			14 43					15 43				15 43				16 43					16 43			
Thurnscoe d			14 46					→				15 46				→					16 46			
Moorthorpe d			14 51									15 51									16 51			
Doncaster 7 d		14 38		14 58		15 14					15 38			16 21				16 28		16 38			17 16	
Bentley (S.Yorks) d		14 41				15 17					15 41							16 31		16 41				
Adwick a		14 47				15 21					15 47							16 35		16 47				
Adwick d						15 21												16 35						
South Elmsall d						15 27												16 41						
Fitzwilliam d			14 57			15 32						15 57						16 47			16 57			
Sandal & Agbrigg d			15 03			15 38						16 03						16 53			17 03			
Wakefield Westgate 7 32, 39 a			15 07	15 15		15 42			15 46			16 07		16 38			16 46	16 57			17 07		17 33	
Wakefield Westgate d	←		15 08	15 15		15 42			15 47	←		16 08		16 38			16 47	16 57	←		17 08		17 33	
Wakefield Kirkgate 4 32, 34, 39 a	14 51				15 29		15 51			15 51			16 27		16 51				16 51			17 29		17 51
Wakefield Kirkgate d	14 52				15 29		→			15 52			16 27		→				16 52			17 29		→
Outwood d			15 13			15 47						16 13						17 02			17 13			
Leeds 10 32, 34 a	15 27		15 30	15 35	15 50	16 02			16 02	16 27		16 30	16 50	17 01			17 04	17 16	17 27		17 30	17 50	17 53	

For general notes see front of timetable
For details of catering facilities see Directory of Train Operators

A From Sheffield (Table 29)

B From London Kings Cross (Table 26)

C To York (Table 33)

D From Southampton Central to Edinburgh (Table 51)

E From Lincoln (Table 30)

G From Plymouth to Edinburgh (Table 51)

H From Bournemouth (Table 51) to Aberdeen (Table 229)

J From Bournemouth to Edinburgh (Table 51)

K From Penzance (Table 135) to Dundee (Table 229)

L From Bournemouth to Glasgow Central (from 29 March to Edinburgh) (Table 51)

Table 31

Saturdays

Sheffield, Doncaster and Wakefield → Leeds

Network Diagram - see first page of Table 31

		NT	XC	NT	NT	NT	NT	GR	NT	NT	NT	XC	NT	NT	NT	GR	NT	EM	NT	NT	XC	NT	EM	NT	NT
			1 ◇					R 1				1 ◇				R 1		1 ◇			1 ◇		1 ◇		
			A			B		C				D				E		G			H		G		
			☕					☕ 🍴				☕				☕ 🍴		☕			☕		☕		
Sheffield 7	29 🚊 d	17 14	17 21						17 51	18 08	18 14	18 21					18 51	19 04	19 08	19 14	19 21				
Meadowhall	29 🚊 d	17 21							17 57	18 14	18 21						18 57		19 14	19 21					
Rotherham Central	29 d	17 27									18 27									19 27					
Swinton (S.Yorks)	29 d	17 36									18 36									19 40					
Bolton-on-Dearne	d	17 41					←				18 41				←					19 44					←
Goldthorpe	d	17 43					17 43				18 43				18 43					19 47					19 47
Thurnscoe	d	→					17 46				→				18 46					→					19 50
Moorthorpe	d						17 51								18 51								←		19 55
Doncaster 7	d			17 27		17 38		18 18					18 29			19 18		19 31				19 27	19 31		
Bentley (S.Yorks)	d			17 30		17 41							18 32					→				19 30			
Adwick	a			17 34		17 47							18 36									19 34			
	d			17 34									18 36									19 34			
South Elmsall	d			17 40									18 42									19 40			
Fitzwilliam	d			17 45			17 57						18 47		18 57							19 45			20 01
Sandal & Agbrigg	d			17 51			18 03						18 53		19 03							19 51			20 07
Wakefield Westgate 7	32, 39 a		17 46	17 55			18 07	18 35				18 46	18 57		19 07	19 35					19 46	19 55	19 59		20 11
	d		17 47	17 55	←		18 08	18 35				18 47	18 57	←	19 08	19 35					19 47	19 55	19 59	←	20 11
Wakefield Kirkgate 4	32, 34, 39 a				17 51				18 36	18 51				18 51			19 36		19 51					19 51	
	d				17 52				18 36	→				18 52			19 36		→					19 52	
Outwood	d			18 00			18 13						19 02		19 13							20 00			20 16
Leeds 10	32, 34 a		18 02	18 15	18 27		18 30	18 53	18 55			19 02	19 17	19 27	19 31	19 52	19 57				20 02	20 15	20 22	20 27	20 32

		GR	NT	NT	EM	XC	EM	NT	NT	NT	EM	NT	XC	NT	GR	NT	NT	EM	GR	XC	NT	NT	NT
		R 1			1 ◇	1 ◇	1 ◇				1 ◇		1 ◇		R 1			1 ◇	R 1	1 ◇			
		J			G	K	G				G		L		C			G	N	Q			
		☕ 🍴			☕		☕				☕				☕ 🍴			☕	☕ 🍴				
Sheffield 7	29 🚊 d		19 51	20 08	20 11	20 21				20 31	20 51	21 08	21 21				21 26	21 57		22 21			22 31
Meadowhall	29 🚊 d		19 57	20 14						20 37		21 14					21 32						22 37
Rotherham Central	29 d									20 43							21 38						22 43
Swinton (S.Yorks)	29 d									20 51							21 48						22 51
Bolton-on-Dearne	d									20 55							21 52						22 55
Goldthorpe	d									20 58							21 55						22 58
Thurnscoe	d									21 01							21 58						23 01
Moorthorpe	d						←			21 06							22 03						23 06
Doncaster 7	d	20 02			20 36		20 36		20 45		21 15			21 28	21 48			22 21	22 25			22 49	
Bentley (S.Yorks)	d				→				20 48					21 31								22 52	
Adwick	a								20 52					21 35								22 56	
	d								20 52					21 35								22 56	
South Elmsall	d								20 58					21 41								23 02	
Fitzwilliam	d								21 03	21 12				21 48			22 09					23 07	23 12
Sandal & Agbrigg	d								21 09	21 18				21 53			22 15					23 13	23 18
Wakefield Westgate 7	32, 39 a	20 19				20 48	20 53		21 13	21 22	21 34		21 46	21 57	22 05		22 19	22 38	22 43	22s46		23 17	23 22
	d	20 19				20 49	20 53	←	21 13	21 22	21 34		21 47	21 58	22 05	←	22 19	22 38	22 43			23 17	23 23
Wakefield Kirkgate 4	32, 34, 39 a		20 28	20 51				20 51				21 51				21 51							
	d		20 29	→				20 52				→				21 52					22 52		
Outwood	d								21 18	21 27				22 02			22 26					23 22	23 28
Leeds 10	32, 34 a	20 36	20 50			21 05	21 15	21 27	21 33	21 47	21 54		22 01	22 18	22 24	22 27	22 42	23 00	23 03	23 09	23 29	23 37	23 47

Sundays

until 27 January and from 30 March

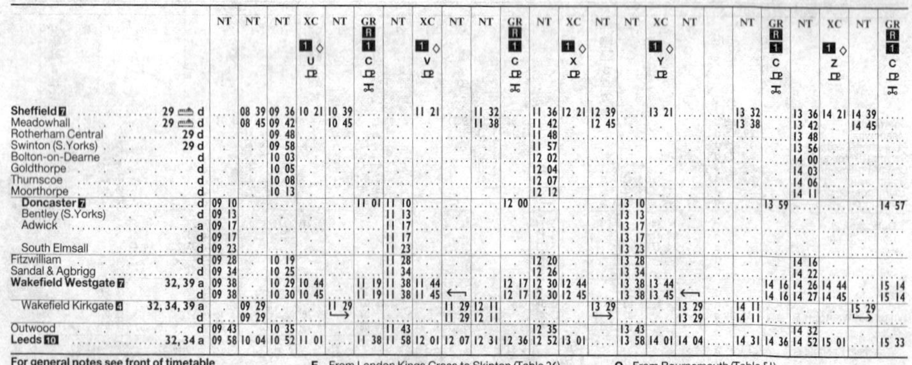

		NT	NT	NT	XC	NT	GR	NT	XC	NT	NT	GR	NT	XC	NT	NT	XC	NT		NT	GR	NT	XC	NT	GR
					1 ◇		R 1		1 ◇			R 1		1 ◇			1 ◇				R 1		1 ◇		R 1
					U		C		V			C		X			Y				C		Z		C
					☕		☕ 🍴		☕			☕ 🍴		☕			☕				☕ 🍴		☕		☕ 🍴
Sheffield 7	29 🚊 d		08 39	09 36	10 21	10 39			11 21		11 32		11 36	12 21	12 39		13 21			13 32		13 36	14 21	14 39	
Meadowhall	29 🚊 d		08 45	09 42		10 45					11 38		11 42		12 45					13 38		13 42		14 45	
Rotherham Central	29 d			09 48									11 48									13 48			
Swinton (S.Yorks)	29 d			09 58									11 57									13 56			
Bolton-on-Dearne	d			10 03									12 02									14 00			
Goldthorpe	d			10 05									12 04									14 03			
Thurnscoe	d			10 08									12 07									14 06			
Moorthorpe	d			10 13									12 12									14 11			
Doncaster 7	d	09 10					11 01	11 10				12 00				13 10					13 59				14 57
Bentley (S.Yorks)	d	09 13						11 13								13 13									
Adwick	a	09 17						11 17								13 17									
	d	09 17						11 17								13 17									
South Elmsall	d	09 23						11 23								13 23									
Fitzwilliam	d	09 28		10 19				11 28					12 20			13 28						14 16			
Sandal & Agbrigg	d	09 34		10 25				11 34					12 26			13 34						14 22			
Wakefield Westgate 7	32, 39 a	09 38		10 29	10 44		11 19	11 38	11 44			12 17	12 30	12 44		13 38	13 44				14 16	14 26	14 44		15 14
	d	09 38		10 30	10 45		11 19	11 38	11 45	←		12 17	12 30	12 45		13 38	13 45	←			14 16	14 27	14 45		15 14
Wakefield Kirkgate 4	32, 34, 39 a		09 29			11 29				11 29	12 11				13 29			13 29		14 11				15 29	
	d		09 29			→				11 29	12 11				→			13 29		14 11				→	
Outwood	d	09 43		10 35				11 43					12 35			13 43						14 32			
Leeds 10	32, 34 a	09 58	10 04	10 52	11 01		11 38	11 58	12 01	12 07	12 31	12 36	12 52	13 01		13 58	14 01	14 04		14 31	14 36	14 52	15 01		15 33

For general notes see front of timetable
For details of catering facilities see Directory of Train Operators

- **A** From Plymouth to Glasgow Central (from 29 March to Edinburgh) (Table 51)
- **B** From Lincoln (Table 30)
- **C** From London Kings Cross (Table 26)
- **D** From Bournemouth to Edinburgh (Table 51)
- **E** From London Kings Cross to Skipton (Table 26)
- **G** From St Pancras International (Table 53)
- **H** From Plymouth to Newcastle (Table 51)
- **J** From London Kings Cross to Bradford Forster Square (Table 26)
- **K** From Bournemouth to Newcastle (Table 51)
- **L** From Plymouth to York (Table 51)
- **N** From Glasgow Central (from 29 March from Edinburgh) (Table 26)
- **Q** From Bournemouth (Table 51)
- **U** From Birmingham New Street to Glasgow Central (Table 51)
- **V** From Birmingham New Street to Edinburgh (Table 51)
- **X** From Birmingham New Street (Table 51) to Aberdeen (Table 229)
- **Y** From Bristol Temple Meads to Edinburgh (Table 51)
- **Z** From Bournemouth (from 30 March from Oxford) to Edinburgh (Table 51)

Table 31

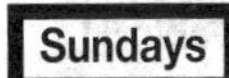

Sundays

until 27 January and from 30 March

Sheffield, Doncaster and Wakefield → Leeds

Network Diagram - see first page of Table 31

	NT	XC	NT	NT	GR	NT	NT	XC	NT	GR	NT	XC	NT		GR	NT	XC	GR	NT	NT	XC	NT	NT	GR
		R 1			R 1			R 1		R 1		R 1			R 1		R 1	R 1			R 1			R 1
		A			B		C	D	E	B		G	E		B		H	B		C	J			B
		☕			☕ 🛒			☕		☕ 🛒		☕			☕ 🛒		☕	☕ 🛒			☕			☕ 🛒
Sheffield 7 29 🚌 d		15 21		15 32		15 36	15 46	16 21	16 39			17 21				17 36	18 21		18 39	18 58	19 21			
Meadowhall 29 🚌 d				15 38		15 42	15 52		16 45							17 42			18 45	19 04				
Rotherham Central 29 d						15 48	15 58									17 48				19 10				
Swinton (S.Yorks) 29 d						15 56	16 08									17 56				19 18				
Bolton-on-Dearne d						16 00										18 00								
Goldthorpe d						16 03										18 03								
Thurnscoe d						16 06										18 06								
Moorthorpe d						16 11	16a17									18 11				19a28				
Doncaster 7 d	15 10				16 00					16 57	17 10				17 55			18 49					19 29	19 59
Bentley (S.Yorks) d	15 13										17 13												19 32	
Adwick a	15 17										17 17												19 36	
d	15 17										17 17												19 36	
South Elmsall d	15 23										17 23												19 42	
Fitzwilliam d	15 28					16 17					17 28					18 17							19 47	
Sandal & Agbrigg d	15 34					16 23					17 34					18 23							19 53	
Wakefield Westgate 7 32, 39 a	15 38	15 44			16 17	16 27		16 44		17 14	17 38	17 44			18 12	18 27	18 44	19 06			19 44		19 57	20 16
d	15 38	15 45	←		16 17	16 27		16 45		17 14	17 38	17 45	←		18 12	18 27	18 45	19 06			19 45	←	19 57	20 16
Wakefield Kirkgate 4 32, 34, 39 a			15 29	16 11					17 29				17 29						19 29			19 29		
d			15 29	16 11					→				17 29						→			19 29		
Outwood d	15 43					16 32					17 43					18 32							20 02	
Leeds 10 32, 34 a	15 58	16 01	16 04	16 31	16 37	16 52		17 01		17 34	17 58	18 01	18 04		18 32	18 52	19 01	19 28			20 01	20 04	20 19	20 41

	NT	GR	EM	XC	EM	NT	GR	EM	EM	XC	NT	EM	NT	NT	GR	EM	XC	EM	NT	EM	GR	XC		
		R 1	1 ◇	R 1	1 ◇		R 1	1 ◇	1 ◇	R 1		1 ◇			R 1	1 ◇	1 ◇	1 ◇		1 ◇	R 1	1 ◇		
		B	K	L	K		B	K	N	Q		N			B	N	U	N	E	K	B	V		
		☕ 🛒	☕		☕		☕ 🛒	☕	☕			☕			☕ 🛒	☕		☕		☕	☕ 🛒			
Sheffield 7 29 🚌 d	19 36		19 59	20 21		20 39		20 57	21 12	21 21				21 36		22 16	22 21		22 39	23 14		23 29		
Meadowhall 29 🚌 d	19 42					20 45								21 42					22 45					
Rotherham Central 29 d	19 48													21 48										
Swinton (S.Yorks) 29 d	19 56													21 56										
Bolton-on-Dearne d	20 00													22 00										
Goldthorpe d	20 03													22 03										
Thurnscoe d	20 06													22 06										
Moorthorpe d	20 11				←							←		22 11				←						
Doncaster 7 d		20 20	20 27		20 27		21 10	21 21	21 44			21 44	21 49		22 20	22 39		22 39			23 27			
Bentley (S.Yorks) d			→						→				21 52			→								
Adwick a													21 56											
d													21 56											
South Elmsall d													22 02											
Fitzwilliam d	20 16												22 09	22 16										
Sandal & Agbrigg d	20 22												22 15	22 22										
Wakefield Westgate 7 32, 39 a	20 26	20 38		20 44	20 49		21 27	21 39		21 44		22 01	22 19	22 26	22 40		22s45	22 56		23 39		23s52		
d	20 27	20 38		20 45	20 49		21 27	21 39		21 45	←	22 01	22 20	22 27	22 40			22 56		23 39				
Wakefield Kirkgate 4 32, 34, 39 a						21 29					21 29								23 28					
d						→					21 29								23 29					
Outwood d	20 32												22 25	22 32										
Leeds 10 32, 34 a	20 52	20 59		21 01	21 10		21 47	22 02		22 01	22 04	22 22	22 39	22 52	23 00		23 09	23 17	00 04	00 16	00 22	00 34		

Sundays

3 February to 23 March

	NT	NT	NT	XC	NT	GR		NT	XC	NT	NT	GR	NT		XC	NT	NT	XC	NT	NT		GR	NT	XC
				1 ◇		R 1			1 ◇			R 1			1 ◇			1 ◇				R 1		1 ◇
				X		B			Y			B			Z			Y				B		AA
				☕		☕ 🛒			☕			☕ 🛒			☕			☕				☕ 🛒		☕
Sheffield 7 29 🚌 d		08 39	09 36	10 21	10 39				11 21		11 32		11 36		12 04	12 39		13 04		13 32			13 36	14 04
Meadowhall 29 🚌 d		08 45	09 42		10 45						11 38		11 42			12 45				13 38			13 42	
Rotherham Central 29 d			09 48										11 48										13 48	
Swinton (S.Yorks) 29 d			09 58										11 57										13 56	
Bolton-on-Dearne d			10 03										12 02										14 00	
Goldthorpe d			10 05										12 04										14 03	
Thurnscoe d			10 08										12 07										14 06	
Moorthorpe d			10 13										12 12										14 11	
Doncaster 7 d	09 10					11 01		11 10				12 00			12 28		13 10	13 28				13 59		14 28
Bentley (S.Yorks) d	09 13							11 13									13 13							
Adwick a	09 17							11 17									13 17							
d	09 17							11 17									13 17							
South Elmsall d	09 23							11 23									13 23							
Fitzwilliam d	09 28		10 19					11 28					12 20				13 28						14 16	
Sandal & Agbrigg d	09 34		10 25					11 34					12 26				13 34						14 22	
Wakefield Westgate 7 32, 39 a	09 38		10 29	10 44		11 19		11 38	11 44			12 17	12 30		12 44		13 38	13 44				14 16	14 26	14 44
d	09 38		10 30	10 45		11 19		11 38	11 45	←		12 17	12 30		12 45		13 38	13 45	←			14 16	14 27	14 45
Wakefield Kirkgate 4 32, 34, 39 a		09 29			11 29					11 29	12 11					13 29			13 29	14 11				
d		09 29			→					11 29	12 11					→			13 29	14 11				
Outwood d	09 43		10 35					11 43					12 35				13 43						14 32	
Leeds 10 32, 34 a	09 58	10 04	10 52	11 01		11 38		11 58	12 01	12 07	12 31	12 36	12 52		13 01		13 58	14 01	14 04	14 31		14 36	14 52	15 01

For general notes see front of timetable
For details of catering facilities see Directory of Train Operators

- **A** From Plymouth (Table 51) to Dundee (Table 229)
- **B** From London Kings Cross (Table 26)
- **C** To York (Table 33)
- **D** From Bournemouth (from 30 March from Oxford) to Glasgow Central (Table 51)
- **E** From Lincoln (Table 30)
- **G** From Penzance (Table 135) to Glasgow Central (Table 51)
- **H** From Bournemouth (from 30 March from Oxford) to Edinburgh (Table 51)
- **J** From Plymouth to Edinburgh (Table 51)
- **K** From 30 March. From St Pancras International (Table 53)
- **L** From Bournemouth (from 30 March from Oxford) to Newcastle (Table 51)
- **N** Until 27 January. From St Pancras International (Table 53)
- **Q** From Plymouth to York (Table 51)
- **U** From Bournemouth (from 30 March from Oxford) (Table 51)
- **V** From Plymouth (Table 51)
- **X** From Birmingham New Street to Glasgow Central (Table 51)
- **Y** From Birmingham New Street to Edinburgh (Table 51)
- **Z** From Birmingham New Street (Table 51) to Aberdeen (Table 229)
- **AA** From Bristol Temple Meads to Edinburgh (Table 51)

3 February to 23 March

Sheffield, Doncaster and Wakefield → Leeds

Network Diagram - see first page of Table 31

Station		NT	GR R 1 A	NT	XC 1◇ B	NT		NT	GR R 1 A	NT	NT C	XC R 1 D	NT E		GR R 1 A	NT	XC R 1 G	NT E	GR R 1 A	NT		XC R 1 H	GR R 1 A	NT	NT C
Sheffield 7	29 ⇌ d	14 39			15 04			15 32		15 36	15 46	16 04	16 39				17 04			17 36		18 04		18 39	18 58
Meadowhall	29 ⇌ d	14 45						15 38		15 42	15 52		16 45							17 42				18 45	19 04
Rotherham Central	29 d									15 48	15 58									17 48					19 10
Swinton (S.Yorks)	29 d									15 56	16 08									17 56					19 18
Bolton-on-Dearne	d									16 00										18 00					
Goldthorpe	d									16 03										18 03					
Thurnscoe	d									16 06										18 06					
Moorthorpe	d									16 11	16a17									18 11					19a28
Doncaster 7	d		14 57	15 10	15 28				16 00			16 28			16 57	17 10	17 28		17 55			18 28	18 49		
Bentley (S.Yorks)	d			15 13												17 13									
Adwick	a			15 17												17 17									
	d			15 17												17 17									
South Elmsall	d			15 23												17 23									
Fitzwilliam	d			15 28						16 17						17 28				18 17					
Sandal & Agbrigg	d			15 34						16 23						17 34				18 23					
Wakefield Westgate 7	32, 39 a		15 14	15 38	15 44				16 17	16 27		16 44			17 14	17 38	17 44		18 12	18 27		18 44	19 06		
	d		15 14	15 38	15 45	←			16 17	16 27		16 45			17 14	17 38	17 45	←	18 12	18 27		18 45	19 06		
Wakefield Kirkgate 4	32, 34, 39 a	15 29				15 29		16 11					17 29					17 29						19 29	
	d	→				15 29		16 11					→					17 29						→	
Outwood	d			15 43						16 32						17 43				18 32					
Leeds 10	32, 34 a		15 33	15 58	16 01	16 04		16 31	16 37	16 52		17 01			17 34	17 58	18 01	18 04	18 32	18 52		19 01	19 28		

Station		XC R 1 J	NT	NT	GR R 1 A		NT	GR R 1 A	XC R 1 K	NT	GR R 1 A	XC R 1 L		NT	EM 1◇ N	NT	NT	GR R 1 A	XC R 1 Q	EM 1◇ N	NT E	XC 1◇ U	GR R 1 A		
Sheffield 7	29 ⇌ d	19 04					19 36		20 08	20 39		21 04			21 12		21 36		22 04	22 16	22 39	22 54			
Meadowhall	29 ⇌ d						19 42			20 45							21 42				22 45				
Rotherham Central	29 d						19 48										21 48								
Swinton (S.Yorks)	29 d						19 56										21 56								
Bolton-on-Dearne	d						20 00										22 00								
Goldthorpe	d						20 03										22 03								
Thurnscoe	d						20 06										22 06								
Moorthorpe	d						20 11										22 11								
Doncaster 7	d	19 28		19 29	19 59			20 20	20 34		21 10	21 28			21 44	21 49		22 20	22 28	22 39		23 18	23 27		
Bentley (S.Yorks)	d			19 32												21 52									
Adwick	a			19 36												21 56									
	d			19 36												21 56									
South Elmsall	d			19 42												22 02									
Fitzwilliam	d			19 47			20 16									22 09	22 16								
Sandal & Agbrigg	d			19 53			20 22									22 15	22 22								
Wakefield Westgate 7	32, 39 a	19 44		19 57	20 16		20 26	20 38	20 50		21 27	21 44			22 01	22 19	22 26	22 40	22s45	22 56		23s34			
	d	19 45	←	19 57	20 16		20 27	20 38	20 51		21 27	21 45		←	22 01	22 20	22 27	22 40		22 56					
Wakefield Kirkgate 4	32, 34, 39 a		19 29							21 29				21 29							23 28				
	d		19 29							→				21 29							23 29				
Outwood	d			20 02			20 32									22 25	22 32								
Leeds 10	32, 34 a	20 01	20 04	20 19	20 41		20 52	20 59	21 06		21 47	22 01		22 04	22 22	22 39	22 52	23 00	23 09	23 17	00 04	00 16	00 22		

For general notes see front of timetable
For details of catering facilities see Directory of Train Operators

- A From London Kings Cross (Table 26)
- B From Bournemouth (Table 51) to Dundee (Table 229)
- C To York (Table 33)
- D From Plymouth to Glasgow Central (Table 51)
- E From Lincoln (Table 30)
- G From Bournemouth to Glasgow Central (Table 51)
- H From Penzance (Table 135) to Edinburgh (Table 51)
- J From Bournemouth to Edinburgh (Table 51)
- K From Penzance (Table 135) to Newcastle (Table 51)
- L From Bournemouth to York (Table 51)
- N From St Pancras International (Table 53)
- Q From Plymouth (Table 51)
- U From Bournemouth (Table 51)

Leeds → Wakefield, Doncaster and Sheffield

Network Diagram - see first page of Table 31

Miles	Miles	Station		GR	GR	NT	XC	NT	GR	NT		NT	EM	NT	NT	NT	GR	NT		GR	XC	NT	NT	NT	NT
				R 1 A ☕ 🍴	R 1 A ☕ 🍴		1◇ B ☕		R 1 A				1◇ C ☕ 🍴				R 1 A			R 1 D ☕ 🍴	R 1 E ☕				G
0	0	**Leeds** 10	32, 34 d	05 05	05 30	05 33	06 00		06 05			06 05	06 14		06 19	06 38	06 40	06 43		07 00	07 05			07 16	
7½	7½	Outwood	d			05 44									06 28			06 54							
—	—	Wakefield Kirkgate 4	32, 34, 39 a									06 22		←		07 09							←	07 32	
—	—		d							06 10		06 22		06 22		07 10							07 10	07 32	
10	10	**Wakefield Westgate** 7	32, 39 a	05 17	05 42	05 49	06 11		06 18			→	06 26		06 32	→	06 52	06 58		07 12	07 18				
—	—		d	05 17	05 42	05 49	06 12						06 26		06 33			06 58		07 12	07 19				
11¾	11¾	Sandal & Agbrigg	d			05 53									06 36			07 02							
16½	16½	Fitzwilliam	d			06 00									06 42			07 09							
21	—	South Elmsall	d												06 47										
25¾	—	Adwick	a												06 53										
—	—		d												06 53										07 29
28	—	Bentley (S.Yorks)	d												06 57										07 33
29¾	—	**Doncaster** 7	a	05 35	05 59								06 44		07 07					07 29					07 37
—	20½	Moorthorpe	d			06 06												07 14							
—	23¾	Thurnscoe	d			06 12		←										07 20				←			
—	24½	Goldthorpe	d			06 14 →		06 14										07 22 →				07 22			
—	25¾	Bolton-on-Dearne	d					06 17														07 25			
—	28	Swinton (S.Yorks)	29 a					06 22														07 29			
—	32½	Rotherham Central	29 a					06 30														07 39			
—	35¼	Meadowhall	29 🚋 a					06 37		06 48				07 03								07 46	07 48	08 03	
—	38¾	**Sheffield** 7	29 🚋 a				06 40	06 47		06 57			07 09	07 12							07 51	07 57	07 59	08 15	

Station		GR	NT	EM		NT	NT	NT	GR	NT	GR	XC		NT	NT	NT	NT	EM	NT	GR		NT	NT	GR	XC
		R 1 A		1◇ C ☕			G		R 1 H		R 1 J ☕ 🍴	R 1 K ☕						1◇ C ☕		R 1 A			G	R 1 A ☕ 🍴	1◇ L ☕
Leeds 10	32, 34 d	07 20	07 23	07 26				07 27	07 40	07 47	08 05	08 10				08 16	08 19	08 28	08 34	08 40		08 48		09 05	09 10
Outwood	d							07 36		07 59							08 28					08 59			
Wakefield Kirkgate 4	32, 34, 39 a		07 54			←										08 32			09 02						
	d		07 55			07 55										08 32			09 03						
Wakefield Westgate 7	32, 39 a	07 32	→	07 38				07 42	07 52	08 03	08 17	08 23					08 33	08 39	→	08 52		09 03		09 18	09 23
	d			07 38				07 42		08 03	08 17	08 23					08 34	08 39				09 03		09 19	09 23
Sandal & Agbrigg	d							07 45		08 07							08 37					09 07			
Fitzwilliam	d							07 51		08 14							08 43					09 12			
South Elmsall	d							08 06									08 48								
Adwick	a							08 10									08 54								
	d						08 07	08 10						08 35			08 54						09 13		
Bentley (S.Yorks)	d						08 11	08 14						08 39			08 58						09 17		
Doncaster 7	a			07 58			08 15	08 24			08 36			08 44			09 07						09 22	09 35	
Moorthorpe	d									08 19												09 20			
Thurnscoe	d									08 25					←							09 26			
Goldthorpe	d									08 27 →					08 27							09 28 →			
Bolton-on-Dearne	d														08 30										
Swinton (S.Yorks)	29 a														08 34										
Rotherham Central	29 a														08 46										
Meadowhall	29 🚋 a					08 33									08 52	09 03									
Sheffield 7	29 🚋 a			08 22		08 45						08 51			09 02	09 15		09 15							09 51

Station		NT	NT	NT	NT	NT		GR	NT	NT	GR	XC	NT	NT		NT	NT	NT	GR	NT	NT	GR		XC	NT
								R 1 A ☕ 🍴		G	R 1 A ☕ 🍴	R 1 N ☕							R 1 A ☕ 🍴		G	R 1 A ☕ 🍴		1◇ Q ☕	
Leeds 10	32, 34 d			09 16	09 19	09 34		09 40	09 48		10 05	10 10				10 16	10 19	10 34	10 40	10 48		11 05		11 10	
Outwood	d				09 28				09 59								10 28			10 59					
Wakefield Kirkgate 4	32, 34, 39 a	←		09 32		10 03							←			10 32		11 03							←
	d	09 03		09 32		10 03							10 03			10 32		11 03							11 03
Wakefield Westgate 7	32, 39 a				09 32	→		09 52	10 03		10 18	10 23					10 32	→	10 52	11 03		11 17		11 23	
	d				09 33			09 52	10 03		10 18	10 23					10 32		10 52	11 03		11 17		11 23	
Sandal & Agbrigg	d				09 36				10 07								10 35			11 07					
Fitzwilliam	d				09 42				10 14								10 42			11 14					
South Elmsall	d				09 49												10 47								
Adwick	a				09 54												10 52								
	d				09 55					10 13							10 53				11 16				
Bentley (S.Yorks)	d				09 59					10 17							10 57				11 20				
Doncaster 7	a				10 08			10 14		10 22	10 35						11 07		11 12		11 25	11 37			
Moorthorpe	d								10 19											11 19					
Thurnscoe	d		←						10 25					←						11 25					
Goldthorpe	d		09 28						10 27 →					10 27						11 27 →					
Bolton-on-Dearne	d		09 31											10 30											
Swinton (S.Yorks)	29 a		09 35											10 34											
Rotherham Central	29 a		09 44											10 42											
Meadowhall	29 🚋 a	09 48	09 51	10 03									10 48	10 51		11 03									11 48
Sheffield 7	29 🚋 a	09 57	10 02	10 15								10 51	10 57	11 02		11 15								11 51	11 57

For general notes see front of timetable
For details of catering facilities see Directory of Train Operators

- **A** To London Kings Cross (Table 26)
- **B** To Bournemouth (Table 51)
- **C** To St Pancras International (Table 53)
- **D** From Bradford Forster Square to London Kings Cross (Table 26)
- **E** To Plymouth (Table 51)
- **G** To Sheffield (Table 29)
- **H** From Skipton to London Kings Cross (Table 26)
- **J** From Harrogate to London Kings Cross (Table 26)
- **K** From Newcastle to Bournemouth (Table 51)
- **L** From Edinburgh to Plymouth (Table 51)
- **N** From Glasgow Central to Bournemouth (Table 51)
- **Q** From Dundee (Table 229) to Plymouth (Table 51)

Leeds → Wakefield, Doncaster and Sheffield

Network Diagram - see first page of Table 31

Station			NT	NT	NT	NT	NT	GR	NT		NT	GR	XC	NT	NT	NT	NT		NT	GR	NT	NT	GR	XC	NT	NT
								R 1				R 1	R 1							R 1			R 1	R 1		
					A			B			C	B	D							B		C	B	E		
Leeds 10	32, 34	d		11 16		11 19	11 34	11 40	11 48			12 05	12 10			12 16	12 19		12 34	12 40	12 48		13 05	13 10		
Outwood		d				11 28			11 59								12 28				12 59					
Wakefield Kirkgate 4	32, 34, 39	a		11 32			12 04							←		12 32			13 03						←	
		d		11 32			12 05							12 05		12 32			13 03						13 03	
Wakefield Westgate 7	32, 39	a				11 32	→	11 54	12 03			12 17	12 23				12 32		→	12 52	13 03		13 18	13 23		
		d				11 32		11 54	12 03			12 17	12 23				12 32			12 52	13 03		13 18	13 23		
Sandal & Agbrigg		d				11 35			12 07								12 35				13 07					
Fitzwilliam		d				11 42			12 14								12 42				13 14					
South Elmsall		d				11 47											12 47									
Adwick		a				11 52											12 52									
		d				11 53					12 15						12 53					13 11				
Bentley (S.Yorks)		d				11 57					12 19						12 57					13 15				
Doncaster 7		a				12 07		12 12			12 24	12 36					13 07			13 11		13 20	13 37			
Moorthorpe		d			11 51				12 19												13 19					
Thurnscoe		d	←						12 25						←						13 25					←
Goldthorpe		d	11 27						12 27 →						12 27						13 27 →					13 27
Bolton-on-Dearne		d	11 30												12 30											13 30
Swinton (S.Yorks)	29	a	11 34		12 01										12 34											13 34
Rotherham Central	29	a	11 44		12 10										12 44											13 44
Meadowhall	29	a	11 51	12 03	12 16									12 48	12 51	13 03									13 48	13 51
Sheffield 7	29	a	12 02	12 15	12 26								12 51	12 57	13 02	13 15								13 51	13 57	14 02

Station			NT		NT	NT	GR	NT	GR	XC	NT		NT	NT	NT	NT	NT	GR	NT		GR	XC	NT	NT	NT	NT
							R 1		R 1	R 1								R 1			R 1	R 1				
							B		B	G				C				B			B	H			C	
Leeds 10	32, 34	d	13 16		13 19	13 34	13 40	13 48	14 05	14 10					14 16	14 19	14 34	14 40	14 48		15 05	15 10				15 16
Outwood		d			13 28			13 59								14 28			14 59							
Wakefield Kirkgate 4	32, 34, 39	a	13 32			14 03					←				14 32		15 03						←			15 32
		d	13 32			14 03					14 03				14 32		15 03						15 03			15 32
Wakefield Westgate 7	32, 39	a			13 32	→	13 53	14 03	14 18	14 23						14 32	→	14 52	15 03		15 17	15 23				
		d			13 32		13 53	14 03		14 23						14 32		14 52	15 03			15 23				
Sandal & Agbrigg		d			13 35			14 07								14 35			15 07							
Fitzwilliam		d			13 42			14 14								14 42			15 14							
South Elmsall		d			13 47											14 47										
Adwick		a			13 52											14 52										
		d			13 53									14 18		14 53									15 13	
Bentley (S.Yorks)		d			13 57									14 22		14 57									15 17	
Doncaster 7		a			14 07		14 15							14 26		15 07		15 13							15 22	
Moorthorpe		d						14 19											15 19							
Thurnscoe		d						14 25					←						15 25					←		
Goldthorpe		d						14 27 →					14 27						15 27 →					15 27		
Bolton-on-Dearne		d											14 30											15 30		
Swinton (S.Yorks)	29	a											14 34											15 34		
Rotherham Central	29	a											14 44											15 42		
Meadowhall	29	a	14 03								14 48		14 51		15 03								15 48	15 51		16 05
Sheffield 7	29	a	14 15							14 51	14 57		15 02		15 15							15 51	15 57	16 02		16 15

Station			NT	NT	NT		GR	NT	NT	GR	XC	NT	NT		NT	NT	NT	GR	NT	NT	GR		XC	NT	NT	NT
							R 1			R 1	R 1							R 1			R 1		1 ◊			
			A				B		C	B	J							B	K		B		H			
Leeds 10	32, 34	d		15 19	15 34		15 40	15 48		16 05	16 10				16 16	16 19	16 34	16 40		16 48	17 05		17 10			17 16
Outwood		d		15 28				15 59								16 28				16 59						
Wakefield Kirkgate 4	32, 34, 39	a			16 03							←			16 32		17 03							←		17 32
		d			16 03							16 03			16 32		17 03							17 03		17 32
Wakefield Westgate 7	32, 39	a		15 32	→		15 52	16 03		16 17	16 23					16 33	→	16 52		17 03	17 17		17 23			
		d		15 32				16 03		16 17	16 23					16 33		16 52		17 03	17 17		17 23			
Sandal & Agbrigg		d		15 35				16 07								16 36				17 07						
Fitzwilliam		d		15 42				16 14								16 43				17 14						
South Elmsall		d		15 47												16 48										
Adwick		a		15 52												16 53										
		d		15 53					16 14							16 54			17 09							
Bentley (S.Yorks)		d		15 57					16 18							16 58			17 14							
Doncaster 7		a		16 07					16 22	16 36						17 07		17 10	17 19		17 36					
Moorthorpe		d	15 50					16 19												17 19						
Thurnscoe		d						16 25					←							17 25					←	
Goldthorpe		d						16 27 →					16 27							17 27 →					17 27	
Bolton-on-Dearne		d											16 30												17 30	
Swinton (S.Yorks)	29	a	16 01										16 34												17 34	
Rotherham Central	29	a	16 10										16 43												17 44	
Meadowhall	29	a	16 18									16 48	16 51		17 03									17 48	17 51	18 03
Sheffield 7	29	a	16 25								16 51	16 57	17 02		17 15								17 51	17 57	18 02	18 15

For general notes see front of timetable
For details of catering facilities see Directory of Train Operators

- **A** From York (Table 33)
- **B** To London Kings Cross (Table 26)
- **C** To Sheffield (Table 29)
- **D** From Dundee (Table 229) to Bournemouth (Table 51)
- **E** From Glasgow Central (Table 51) to Penzance (Table 135)
- **G** From Aberdeen (Table 229) to Bournemouth (Table 51)
- **H** From Edinburgh to Plymouth (Table 51)
- **J** From Edinburgh to Bournemouth (Table 51)
- **K** To Scunthorpe (Table 29)

Leeds → Wakefield, Doncaster and Sheffield

Network Diagram - see first page of Table 31

	NT	NT	GR R 1 A	NT	NT B		GR R 1 A	XC R 1 C	NT	NT	NT	NT	NT		GR R 1 A	NT	GR R 1 A	XC 1 ◇ D	NT	NT	NT		NT	NT
Leeds 10 32, 34 d	17 19	17 34	17 40	17 48			18 05	18 10			18 16	18 19	18 34		18 40	18 48	19 05	19 10			19 16		19 19	19 34
Outwood d	17 28			17 59								18 28				18 59							19 28	
Wakefield Kirkgate 4 32, 34, 39 a		18 03							←		18 32		19 03						←		19 32			20 03
d		18 03							18 03		18 32		19 03						19 03		19 32			20 03
Wakefield Westgate 7 32, 39 a	17 32	→	17 52	18 03			18 17	18 23				18 32	→		18 52	19 03	19 17	19 23					19 32	→
d	17 32		17 52	18 03			18 17	18 23				18 32			18 52	19 03	19 17	19 23					19 32	
Sandal & Agbrigg d	17 35			18 07								18 35				19 07							19 35	
Fitzwilliam d	17 42			18 14								18 42				19 14							19 42	
South Elmsall d	17 47											18 47											19 47	
Adwick a	17 52											18 52											19 52	
d	17 53				18 16							18 53											19 53	
Bentley (S.Yorks) d	17 57				18 20							18 57											19 57	
Doncaster 7 a	18 07		18 09		18 25		18 34					19 07			19 10		19 34						20 07	
Moorthorpe d				18 19												19 19								
Thurnscoe d				18 25						←						19 25				←				
Goldthorpe d				18 27						18 27						19 27				19 27				
Bolton-on-Dearne d				→						18 30						→				19 30				
Swinton (S.Yorks) 29 a										18 34										19 34				
Rotherham Central 29 a										18 41										19 44				
Meadowhall 29 a									18 47	18 51	19 03								19 48	19 51	20 03			
Sheffield 7 29 a								18 51	18 57	19 02	19 15							19 51	19 57	20 02	20 15			

	GR R 1 A	NT	XC 1 ◇ D	NT	NT	NT	NT		NT	GR R 1 A	NT	XC 1 ◇ E	NT	NT	NT		NT	NT	NT	NT	NT			
Leeds 10 32, 34 d	19 40	19 48	20 10			20 16	20 21		20 34	20 40	20 48	21 10			21 28		21 34	21 48	22 34	22 39	23 09			
Outwood d		19 59					20 30				20 59				21 37			21 59		22 48	23 20			
Wakefield Kirkgate 4 32, 34, 39 a				←		20 32			21 03				←				22 03		23 03					
d				20 03		20 32			21 03				21 03				22 03		23 03					
Wakefield Westgate 7 32, 39 a	19 54	20 03	20 23				20 34		→	20 55	21 03	21 23			21 41			22 03		22 53	23 24			
d	19 54	20 03	20 23				20 34			20 55	21 03	21 23			21 42			22 03		22 54	23 24			
Sandal & Agbrigg d		20 07					20 37				21 07				21 45			22 07		22 57	23 28			
Fitzwilliam d		20 14					20 44				21 13				21 51			22 14		23 03	23 35			
South Elmsall d							20 49								21 56					23 08				
Adwick a							20 54								22 02					23 14				
d							20 55								22 02					23 14				
Bentley (S.Yorks) d							20 59								22 06					23 18				
Doncaster 7 a	20 14						21 09			21 12					22 16					23 27				
Moorthorpe d		20 19									21 20							22 19			23 40			
Thurnscoe d		20 25			←						21 26			←				22 25			23 46			
Goldthorpe d		20 27			20 27						21 28			21 28				22 27			23 48			
Bolton-on-Dearne d		→			20 30						→			21 31				22 30			23 51			
Swinton (S.Yorks) 29 a					20 34									21 35				22 34			23 55			
Rotherham Central 29 a					20 42									21 44				22 43			00 02			
Meadowhall 29 a				20 47	20 50	21 03							21 48	21 50			22 48	22 51	23 48		00 08			
Sheffield 7 29 a			20 51	20 57	21 02	21 15						21 51	21 57	22 02			22 57	23 02	23 57		00 23			

Saturdays

	GR R 1 A	XC 1 ◇ G	GR R 1 A	NT	NT	NT	GR R 1 A	NT	NT H	NT	EM 1 ◇ J	NT	NT H	NT	GR R 1 K	NT	GR R 1 L	XC 1 ◇ N	NT	GR R 1 Q	NT	NT	NT	NT
Leeds 10 32, 34 d	05 05	06 00	06 10	06 19	06 38	06 43	07 00			07 16	07 19	07 23		07 26	07 40	07 47	08 05	08 10		08 15		08 16	08 19	08 34
Outwood d				06 28		06 54								07 35		07 59							08 28	
Wakefield Kirkgate 4 32, 34, 39 a					07 09			←		07 32		07 54										08 32		09 03
d					07 10			07 10		07 32		07 55										08 32		09 03
Wakefield Westgate 7 32, 39 a	05 17	06 11	06 22	06 32	→	06 58	07 12				07 32			07 39	07 52	08 03	08 18	08 23					08 33	→
d	05 17	06 12	06 22	06 32		06 58	07 12				07 32			07 39		08 03		08 23					08 34	
Sandal & Agbrigg d				06 35		07 02								07 42		08 07							08 37	
Fitzwilliam d				06 42		07 09								07 49		08 14							08 43	
South Elmsall d				06 47										08 06									08 48	
Adwick a				06 52										08 12									08 54	
d				06 53					07 29				08 07	08 12					08 35				08 54	
Bentley (S.Yorks) d				06 57					07 33				08 11	08 16					08 39				08 58	
Doncaster 7 a	05 34		06 40	07 07			07 30		07 37		07 58		08 15	08 22					08 43	08 45			09 07	
Moorthorpe d						07 14										08 19								
Thurnscoe d						07 20										08 25					←			
Goldthorpe d						07 22										08 27					08 27			
Bolton-on-Dearne d						07 25										→					08 30			
Swinton (S.Yorks) 29 a						07 29															08 34			
Rotherham Central 29 a						07 39															08 46			
Meadowhall 29 a						07 46		07 48		08 03		08 36									08 52	09 03		
Sheffield 7 29 a		06 41				07 57		07 59		08 15	08 21	08 47						08 51			09 01	09 15		

For general notes see front of timetable
For details of catering facilities see Directory of Train Operators

A To London Kings Cross (Table 26)
B To Scunthorpe (Table 29)
C From Edinburgh to Southampton Central (Table 51)
D From Edinburgh to Bristol Temple Meads (Table 51)
E From Edinburgh to Birmingham New Street (Table 51)
G To Bristol Temple Meads (Table 51)
H To Sheffield (Table 29)
J To St Pancras International (Table 53)
K From Skipton to London Kings Cross (Table 26)
L From Bradford Forster Square to London Kings Cross (Table 26)
N From Newcastle to Bournemouth (Table 51)
Q From Harrogate to Kings Cross (Table 26)

Table 31

Leeds → Wakefield, Doncaster and Sheffield

Network Diagram - see first page of Table 31

	EM	NT	NT	GR	XC	NT	NT	NT	NT	NT	NT	NT	GR	XC	NT	NT	NT	NT	NT	NT	NT	GR	XC	NT
	1 ◇ A ☕		B	R 1 C ☕ ✕	1 ◇ D ☕							B	R 1 C ☕ ✕	1 ◇ E ☕							B	R 1 C ☕ ✕	1 ◇ D ☕	
Leeds 10 32, 34 d	08 40	08 48		09 05	09 10			09 16	09 19	09 34	09 48		10 05	10 10			10 16	10 19	10 34	10 48		11 05	11 10	
Outwood d		08 59							09 28		09 59							10 28		10 59				
Wakefield Kirkgate 4 32, 34, 39 a						←		09 32		10 03					←		10 32		11 03					←
d						09 03		09 32		10 03					10 03		10 32		11 03					11 03
Wakefield Westgate 7 32, 39 a	08 51	09 03		09 17	09 23				09 33	→	10 03		10 18	10 23				10 32	→	11 03		11 17	11 23	
d	08 52	09 03		09 17	09 23				09 33		10 03		10 18	10 23				10 32		11 03		11 17	11 23	
Sandal & Agbrigg d		09 07							09 36		10 07							10 35		11 07				
Fitzwilliam d		09 14							09 43		10 14							10 42		11 14				
South Elmsall d									09 48									10 47						
Adwick a									09 53									10 52						
d			09 13						09 54			10 10						10 53			11 08			
Bentley (S.Yorks) d			09 17						09 58			10 14						10 57			11 12			
Doncaster 7 a			09 22	09 35					10 06			10 19	10 36					11 07			11 20	11 38		
Moorthorpe d		09 20									10 19					←				11 19				
Thurnscoe d		09 26					←				10 25					10 25				11 25				
Goldthorpe d		09 28					09 28				10 27					10 27				11 27				
Bolton-on-Dearne d		→					09 31				→					10 30				→				
Swinton (S.Yorks) 29 a							09 35									10 34								
Rotherham Central 29 a							09 44									10 44								
Meadowhall 29 🚊 a						09 48	09 51	10 03							10 48	10 51	11 03							11 48
Sheffield 7 29 🚊 a	09 21				09 51	09 57	10 02	10 15						10 51	10 57	11 02	11 15						11 51	11 57

	NT	NT	NT	NT	NT	NT	NT	GR	XC	NT	NT	NT	NT	NT	NT	NT	GR	XC	NT	NT	NT	NT	NT	NT
			G				B	R 1 C ☕ ✕	1 ◇ H ☕							B	R 1 C ☕ ✕	1 ◇ J ☕						
Leeds 10 32, 34 d		11 16		11 19	11 34	11 48		12 05	12 10			12 16	12 19	12 34	12 48		13 05	13 10			13 16	13 19	13 34	13 48
Outwood d				11 28		11 59							12 28		12 59							13 28		13 59
Wakefield Kirkgate 4 32, 34, 39 a		11 32			12 04					←		12 32		13 03					←		13 32		14 03	
d		11 32			12 05					12 05		12 32		13 03					13 03		13 32		14 03	
Wakefield Westgate 7 32, 39 a				11 32	→	12 03		12 17	12 23				12 32	→	13 03		13 17	13 23				13 32	→	14 03
d				11 32		12 03		12 17	12 23				12 32		13 03		13 17	13 23				13 32		14 03
Sandal & Agbrigg d				11 35		12 07							12 35		13 07							13 35		14 07
Fitzwilliam d				11 42		12 14							12 42		13 14							13 42		14 14
South Elmsall d				11 47									12 47									13 47		
Adwick a				11 52									12 52									13 52		
d				11 53			12 13						12 53			13 12						13 53		
Bentley (S.Yorks) d				11 57			12 17						12 57			13 16						13 57		
Doncaster 7 a				12 07			12 22	12 34					13 07			13 23	13 37					14 07		
Moorthorpe d			11 49			12 19									13 19									14 19
Thurnscoe d	←					12 25					←				13 25					←				14 25
Goldthorpe d	11 27					12 27					12 27				13 27					13 27				14 27
Bolton-on-Dearne d	11 30					→					12 30				→					13 30				→
Swinton (S.Yorks) 29 a	11 34		11 59								12 34									13 34				
Rotherham Central 29 a	11 44		12 10								12 44									13 44				
Meadowhall 29 🚊 a	11 51	12 03	12 16							12 48	12 51	13 03							13 48	13 51	14 03			
Sheffield 7 29 🚊 a	12 02	12 15	12 25						12 51	12 57	13 02	13 15						13 51	13 57	14 02	14 15			

	NT	GR	XC	NT	NT	NT	NT	NT	NT	NT	GR	XC	NT	NT	NT	NT	NT	NT	NT	NT	GR	XC	NT	NT
	B	R 1 C ☕ ✕	1 ◇ K ☕							B	R 1 C ☕ ✕	1 ◇ D ☕				G				B	R 1 C ☕ ✕	1 ◇ L ☕		
Leeds 10 32, 34 d		14 05	14 10			14 16	14 19	14 34	14 48		15 05	15 10			15 16		15 19	15 34	15 48		16 05	16 10		
Outwood d							14 28		14 59								15 28		15 59					
Wakefield Kirkgate 4 32, 34, 39 a				←		14 32		15 03					←		15 32			16 03					←	
d				14 03		14 32		15 03					15 03		15 32			16 03					16 03	
Wakefield Westgate 7 32, 39 a		14 17	14 22				14 32	→	15 03		15 17	15 23					15 32	→	16 03		16 17	16 23		
d		14 17	14 22				14 32		15 03		15 17	15 23					15 32		16 03		16 17	16 23		
Sandal & Agbrigg d							14 35		15 07								15 35		16 07					
Fitzwilliam d							14 42		15 14								15 42		16 14					
South Elmsall d							14 47										15 47							
Adwick a							14 52										15 52							
d	14 14						14 53			15 13							15 53			16 13				
Bentley (S.Yorks) d	14 18						14 57			15 17							15 57			16 17				
Doncaster 7 a	14 22	14 34					15 07			15 22	15 35						16 07			16 22	16 38			
Moorthorpe d									15 19							16 01			16 19					
Thurnscoe d					←				15 25					←					16 25					←
Goldthorpe d					14 27				15 27					15 27					16 27					16 27
Bolton-on-Dearne d					14 30				→					15 30					→					16 30
Swinton (S.Yorks) 29 a					14 34									15 34		16 10								16 34
Rotherham Central 29 a					14 44									15 42		16 17								16 43
Meadowhall 29 🚊 a				14 48	14 51	15 03							15 48	15 51	16 05	16 23							16 48	16 51
Sheffield 7 29 🚊 a			14 51	14 57	15 02	15 15						15 51	15 57	16 02	16 15	16 35						16 51	16 57	17 02

For general notes see front of timetable
For details of catering facilities see Directory of Train Operators

- **A** To St Pancras International (Table 53)
- **B** To Sheffield (Table 29)
- **C** To London Kings Cross (Table 26)
- **D** From Edinburgh to Plymouth (Table 51)
- **E** From Glasgow Central to Bournemouth (Table 51)
- **G** From York (Table 33)
- **H** From Dundee (Table 229) to Bournemouth (Table 51)
- **J** From Glasgow Central (from 29 March from Edinburgh) (Table 51) to Penzance (Table 135)
- **K** From Aberdeen (Table 229) to Bournemouth (Table 51)
- **L** From Edinburgh to Bournemouth (Table 51)

Table 31

Saturdays

Leeds → Wakefield, Doncaster and Sheffield

Network Diagram - see first page of Table 31

		NT	NT	NT	NT	NT	XC	NT	NT	NT	NT	NT	GR	NT	NT	XC	NT	NT	NT	NT	NT	GR	NT	XC	NT
					A		1 ◇ B ⊡						R 1 C ⊡ ✕		A	1 ◇ D ⊡						R 1 C ⊡ ✕		1 ◇ E ⊡	
Leeds 10	32, 34 d	16 16	16 19	16 34		16 48	17 10			17 16	17 19	17 34	17 40	17 46		18 10			18 16	18 19	18 34	18 40	18 48	19 10	
Outwood	d		16 28			16 59					17 28			17 57						18 28			18 59		
Wakefield Kirkgate 4	32, 34, 39 a	16 32		17 03				←		17 32		18 03					←		18 32		19 03				←
	d	16 32		17 03				17 03		17 32		18 03					18 03		18 32		19 03				19 03
Wakefield Westgate 7	32, 39 a		16 32	→		17 03	17 23				17 33	→	17 52	18 01		18 23				18 32	→	18 54	19 03	19 23	
	d		16 32			17 03	17 23				17 33		17 52	18 01		18 23				18 33		18 54	19 03	19 23	
Sandal & Agbrigg	d		16 35			17 07					17 36			18 05						18 36			19 07		
Fitzwilliam	d		16 42			17 14					17 43			18 12						18 42			19 14		
South Elmsall	d		16 47								17 48									18 47					
Adwick	a		16 52								17 53									18 53					
	d		16 53		17 05						17 54				18 14					18 53					
Bentley (S.Yorks)	d		16 57		17 09						17 58				18 18					18 57					
Doncaster 7	a		17 07		17 14						18 07		18 09		18 23					19 07		19 11			
Moorthorpe	d					17 19								18 17									19 19		
Thurnscoe	d					17 25			←					18 23				←					19 25		
Goldthorpe	d					17 27			17 27					18 25				18 25					19 27		
Bolton-on-Dearne	d					→			17 30					→				18 28					→		
Swinton (S.Yorks)	29 a								17 34									18 34							
Rotherham Central	29 a								17 44									18 43							
Meadowhall	29 🚋 a	17 03						17 48	17 51	18 03							18 47	18 50	19 03						19 48
Sheffield 7	29 🚋 a	17 15					17 51	17 57	18 02	18 15						18 51	18 57	19 02	19 15					19 51	19 57

		NT	NT	NT	NT	NT	XC	NT	NT	GR	NT	NT	NT	NT	XC	NT	NT	NT	NT	NT	NT	NT	NT
							1 ◇ G			R 1 C ⊡ ✕					1 ◇ H								
Leeds 10	32, 34 d		19 16	19 22	19 34	19 48	20 10			20 15	20 16	20 21	20 34	20 48	21 10			21 34	21 34	21 48	22 16	22 34	22 44
Outwood	d			19 28		19 59						20 30		20 59				21 43		21 59	22 25		22 55
Wakefield Kirkgate 4	32, 34, 39 a		19 32		20 03			←			20 32		21 03			←			22 03			23 03	
	d		19 32		20 03			20 03			20 32		21 03			21 03			22 03				
Wakefield Westgate 7	32, 39 a			19 32	→	20 03	20 23			20 31		20 36	→	21 03	21 22			21 47		22 03	22 29		22 59
	d			19 32		20 03	20 23			20 31		20 36		21 03	21 23			21 47		22 03	22 30		22 59
Sandal & Agbrigg	d			19 35		20 07						20 39		21 07				21 50		22 07	22 33		23 03
Fitzwilliam	d			19 42		20 14						20 46		21 13				21 57		22 14	22 39		23 10
South Elmsall	d			19 47								20 51						22 02			22 44		
Adwick	a			19 53								20 56						22 07			22 50		
	d			19 53								20 57						22 08			22 50		
Bentley (S.Yorks)	d			19 57								21 01						22 12			22 54		
Doncaster 7	a			20 10						20 48		21 09						22 22			23 04		
Moorthorpe	d					20 19			←					21 20						22 19			23 15
Thurnscoe	d	←				20 25			20 25					21 26			←			22 25			23 21
Goldthorpe	d	19 27				20 27			20 27					21 28			21 28			22 27			23 23
Bolton-on-Dearne	d	19 30				→			20 30					→			21 31			22 30			23 26
Swinton (S.Yorks)	29 a	19 34							20 34								21 35			22 34			23 30
Rotherham Central	29 a	19 43							20 42								21 42			22 43			23 37
Meadowhall	29 🚋 a	19 50	20 03					20 47	20 50		21 03					21 48	21 53		22 48	22 51			23 43
Sheffield 7	29 🚋 a	20 02	20 15				20 51	20 57	21 02		21 15				21 51	21 57	22 07		22 57	23 02			23 58

Sundays

until 27 January and from 30 March

		GR	NT	EM	XC	EM	NT	NT	GR	EM	XC	NT		NT	NT	EM	NT	GR	XC	NT	EM	NT	NT	NT	XC
		R 1 C ⊡ ✕		1 ◇ J ⊡	1 ◇ K ⊡	1 ◇ J ⊡			R 1 L ⊡ ✕	1 ◇ N ⊡	1 ◇ Q ⊡					1 ◇ J ⊡		R 1 C ⊡ ✕	1 ◇ U ⊡		1 ◇ N ⊡				R 1 V ⊡
Leeds 10	32, 34 d	08 24	08 30	08 35	08 45			08 50	09 05	09 18	10 00	10 09		10 14	10 17	10 25		10 40	11 00		11 06	11 09	11 14		12 00
Outwood	d							09 01				10 18										11 20			
Wakefield Kirkgate 4	32, 34, 39 a		08 59				←							10 30	10 46					←			11 30		
	d		09 00				09 00							10 30	10 46					10 46			11 30		
Wakefield Westgate 7	32, 39 a	08 36	→	08 46	08 56			09 05	09 17	09 29	10 11	10 22			→	10 36		10 52	11 11		11 17	11 24			12 11
	d	08 36		08 47	08 57			09 05	09 17	09 29	10 12	10 22				10 36		10 52	11 12		11 17	11 24			12 12
Sandal & Agbrigg	d							09 09				10 25										11 28			
Fitzwilliam	d							09 16				10 32										11 35			
South Elmsall	d											10 37													
Adwick	a											10 42													
	d											10 43													
Bentley (S.Yorks)	d					←						10 47													
Doncaster 7	a	08 54		09 04		09 04			09 37	09 46		10 57						11 12							
Moorthorpe	d			→				09 21														11 40			
Thurnscoe	d							09 27														11 46		←	
Goldthorpe	d							09 29														11 48		11 48	
Bolton-on-Dearne	d							09 32														→		11 51	
Swinton (S.Yorks)	29 a							09 36																11 55	
Rotherham Central	29 a							09 45									←							12 05	
Meadowhall	29 🚋 a						09 41	09 53						11 04			11 04			11 32			12 04	12 11	
Sheffield 7	29 🚋 a				09 25	09 31	09 51	10 04		10 11	10 45			→		11 12	11 15		11 40	11 43	11 47		12 15	12 21	12 40

For general notes see front of timetable
For details of catering facilities see Directory of Train Operators

- **A** To Scunthorpe (Table 29)
- **B** From Edinburgh to Plymouth (Table 51)
- **C** To London Kings Cross (Table 26)
- **D** From Edinburgh to Southampton Central (Table 51)
- **E** From Edinburgh to Bristol Temple Meads (Table 51)
- **G** From Newcastle to Birmingham New Street (Table 51)
- **H** From Edinburgh to Birmingham New Street (Table 51)
- **J** Until 27 January. To St Pancras International (Table 53)
- **K** To Plymouth (Table 51)
- **L** To Glasgow Central (Table 26)
- **N** From 30 March. To St Pancras International (Table 53)
- **Q** To Bournemouth (from 30 March to Oxford) (Table 51)
- **U** From Newcastle to Plymouth (Table 51)
- **V** From Edinburgh to Bournemouth (from 30 March to Oxford) (Table 51)

Table 31

Sundays

until 27 January and from 30 March

Leeds → Wakefield, Doncaster and Sheffield

Network Diagram - see first page of Table 31

	NT		NT	GR	XC	NT	NT	NT	NT	GR	XC	NT	NT		GR	NT	XC	NT	GR	XC	NT	NT	GR	XC
				R 1	R 1					R 1	R 1				R 1		R 1		R 1	R 1			R 1	R 1
			A	B	C	A				B	D				B		E		B	G			B	H
Leeds 10 32, 34 d	12 09		12 17	12 40	13 00		13 09	13 14		13 40	14 00	14 09	14 17		14 40		15 00	15 09	15 40	16 00	16 09	16 17	16 40	17 00
Outwood d	12 18						13 20					14 18						15 20			16 18			
Wakefield Kirkgate 4 32, 34, 39 a			12 46			←		13 30					14 46			←						16 46		
d			12 46			12 46		13 30					14 46			14 46						16 46		
Wakefield Westgate 7 32, 39 a	12 22		→	12 52	13 11		13 24			13 52	14 11	14 22	→		14 52		15 11	15 24	15 52	16 11	16 22	→	16 52	17 11
d	12 22			12 52	13 12		13 24			13 52	14 12	14 22			14 52		15 12	15 24	15 52	16 12	16 22		16 52	17 12
Sandal & Agbrigg d	12 25						13 28					14 25						15 28			16 25			
Fitzwilliam d	12 32						13 35					14 32						15 35			16 32			
South Elmsall d	12 37											14 37									16 37			
Adwick a	12 42											14 42									16 42			
d	12 43											14 43									16 43			
Bentley (S.Yorks) d	12 47											14 47									16 47			
Doncaster 7 a	12 57			13 10					←	14 09		14 57			15 10				16 09		16 57		17 10	
Moorthorpe d							13 40 →		13 40									15 40						
Thurnscoe d									13 46									15 46						
Goldthorpe d									13 48									15 48						
Bolton-on-Dearne d									13 51									15 51						
Swinton (S.Yorks) 29 a									13 58									15 55						
Rotherham Central 29 a									14 08									16 05						
Meadowhall 29 a						13 32		14 04	14 13							15 32		16 10						
Sheffield 7 29 a					13 40	13 43		14 15	14 23		14 40					15 43	15b45	16c26		16e43				17 40

	NT	GR	NT		GR	NT	XC	NT	NT	GR	XC	NT	NT	XC	GR	NT	NT	XC	NT	NT	NT	NT		
		R 1			R 1		R 1			R 1	1 ◊			1 ◊	R 1			1 ◊						
		B			B	J	K			B	L			N	B			Q	J					
Leeds 10 32, 34 d		17 05	17 09		17 40		18 00	18 09	18 17	18 40	19 00		19 09	20 00	20 15	20 17	20 20	21 00		21 09	21 40	22 17		
Outwood d			17 20					18 18					19 20				20 29			21 18	21 51			
Wakefield Kirkgate 4 32, 34, 39 a	←								18 46			←				20 46						22 46		
d	16 46								18 46			18 46				20 46						22 46		
Wakefield Westgate 7 32, 39 a		17 18	17 24		17 52		18 11	18 22	→	18 52	19 11		19 24	20 11	20 27		20 33	21 11		21 22	21 55			
d		17 18	17 24				18 12	18 22		18 52	19 12		19 24	20 12	20 27		20 33	21 12		21 22	21 55			
Sandal & Agbrigg d			17 28					18 25					19 28				20 36			21 25	21 59			
Fitzwilliam d			17 35					18 32					19 35				20 43			21 32	22 06			
South Elmsall d								18 37									20 48			21 37				
Adwick a								18 42									20 53			21 42				
d								18 43									20 54			21 43				
Bentley (S.Yorks) d								18 47									20 58			21 47				
Doncaster 7 a		17 35						18 57		19 09					20 47		21 08			21 57				
Moorthorpe d			17 40			18 02							19 40						21 29		22 11			
Thurnscoe d			17 46										19 46								22 17			
Goldthorpe d			17 48										19 48								22 19			
Bolton-on-Dearne d			17 51										19 51								22 22			
Swinton (S.Yorks) 29 a			17 55			18 11							19 55						21 38		22 32			
Rotherham Central 29 a			18 05			18 20							20 04						21 48		22 39			
Meadowhall 29 a	17 32		18 10			18 25						19 32	20 11			21 32			21 54		22 45	23 32		
Sheffield 7 29 a	17 43		18 23			18 35	18f44				19 40	19 43	20 23	20 40		21 43		21 43	22 05		22 54	23 43		

Sundays

3 February to 23 March

	GR	NT	EM	NT	NT		XC	NT	GR	XC	NT		NT	NT	EM	NT	GR		NT	XC	NT	NT	NT	XC
	R 1		1 ◊				1 ◊		R 1	1 ◊					1 ◊		R 1			R 1				R 1
	B		U				V		X	Y					U		B			Z				C
Leeds 10 32, 34 d	08 24	08 30	08 35		08 50		09 00		09 05	10 00	10 09		10 14	10 17	10 25		10 40			11 00	11 09	11 14		12 00
Outwood d					09 01						10 18										11 20			
Wakefield Kirkgate 4 32, 34, 39 a		08 59		←									10 30	10 46					←			11 30		
d		09 00		09 00									10 30	10 46					10 46			11 30		
Wakefield Westgate 7 32, 39 a	08 36	→	08 46		09 05		09 11		09 17	10 11	10 22			→	10 36		10 52			11 11	11 24			12 11
d	08 36		08 47		09 05		09 12		09 17	10 12	10 22				10 36		10 52			11 12	11 24			12 12
Sandal & Agbrigg d					09 09						10 25										11 28			
Fitzwilliam d					09 16						10 32										11 35			
South Elmsall d											10 37													
Adwick a											10 42													
d											10 43													
Bentley (S.Yorks) d											10 47													
Doncaster 7 a	08 54		09 04				09 33		09 37	10 29	10 57						11 12			11 28				12 29
Moorthorpe d					09 21																11 40			
Thurnscoe d					09 27			←													11 46		←	
Goldthorpe d					09 29 →			09 29													11 48 →		11 48	
Bolton-on-Dearne d								09 32															11 51	
Swinton (S.Yorks) 29 a								09 36															11 55	
Rotherham Central 29 a								09 45								←							12 05	
Meadowhall 29 a				09 41				09 54					11 04 →			11 04			11 32			12 04	12 11	
Sheffield 7 29 a			09 31	09 51			09 58	10 04		10 58					11 12	11 15			11 43	11 57		12 15	12 21	12 59

For general notes see front of timetable
For details of catering facilities see Directory of Train Operators

- **A** To Lincoln (Table 30)
- **B** To London Kings Cross (Table 26)
- **C** From Edinburgh (Table 51) to Penzance (Table 135)
- **D** From Edinburgh to Bournemouth (from 30 March to Oxford) (Table 51)
- **E** From Glasgow Central to Plymouth (Table 51)
- **G** From Glasgow Central to Bournemouth (from 30 March to Oxford) (Table 51)
- **H** From Edinburgh to Plymouth (Table 51)
- **J** From York (Table 33)
- **K** From Aberdeen (Table 229) to Southampton Central (from 30 March to Oxford) (Table 51)
- **L** From Edinburgh to Bristol Temple Meads (Table 51)
- **N** From Glasgow Central to Bristol Temple Meads (Table 51)
- **Q** From Edinburgh to Birmingham New Street (Table 51)
- **U** To St Pancras International (Table 53)
- **V** To Bournemouth (Table 51)
- **X** To Glasgow Central (Table 26)
- **Y** To Plymouth (Table 51)
- **Z** From Newcastle to Bournemouth (Table 51)
- **b** Until 27 January arr. 1540
- **c** From 30 March arr. 1620
- **e** From 30 March arr. 1640
- **f** From 30 March arr. 1840

Table 31

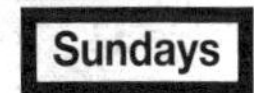

3 February to 23 March

Leeds → Wakefield, Doncaster and Sheffield

Network Diagram - see first page of Table 31

	NT		NT	GR	XC	NT	NT		NT	GR	XC	NT	NT		GR	XC	NT	GR	XC		NT	NT	GR	XC
				R 1	R 1					R 1	R 1				R 1	R 1		R 1	R 1				R 1	R 1
			A	B	C					B	D				B	E		B	G				B	H
				☕ 🛒	☕					☕ 🛒	☕				☕ 🛒	☕		☕ 🛒	☕				☕ 🛒	☕
Leeds [10] 32, 34 d	12 09		12 17	12 40	13 00	13 09	13 14			13 40	14 00	14 09	14 17		14 40	15 00	15 09	15 40	16 00		16 09	16 17	16 40	17 00
Outwood d	12 18					13 20						14 18					15 20				16 18			
Wakefield Kirkgate [4] 32, 34, 39 a			12 46				13 30						14 46									16 46		
d			12 46				13 30						14 46									16 46		
Wakefield Westgate [7] 32, 39 a	12 22			12 52	13 11	13 24				13 52	14 11	14 22			14 52	15 11	15 24	15 52	16 11		16 22		16 52	17 11
d	12 22			12 52	13 12	13 24				13 52	14 12	14 22			14 52	15 12	15 24	15 52	16 12		16 22		16 52	17 12
Sandal & Agbrigg d	12 25					13 28						14 25					15 28				16 25			
Fitzwilliam d	12 32					13 35						14 32					15 35				16 32			
South Elmsall d	12 37											14 37									16 37			
Adwick a	12 42											14 42									16 42			
d	12 43											14 43									16 43			
Bentley (S.Yorks) d	12 47											14 47									16 47			
Doncaster [7] a	12 57			13 10	13 28					14 09	14 28	14 57			15 10	15 28		16 09	16 28		16 57		17 10	17 28
Moorthorpe d						13 40											15 40							
Thurnscoe d						13 46			←								15 46							
Goldthorpe d						13 48 →			13 48								15 48							
Bolton-on-Dearne d									13 51								15 51							
Swinton (S.Yorks) 29 a									13 58								15 55							
Rotherham Central 29 a									14 08								16 05							
Meadowhall 29 🚋 a			13 32				14 04		14 13				15 32				16 10					17 32		
Sheffield [7] 29 🚋 a			13 43		13 58		14 15		14 23		14 58		15 43			15 58	16 20		16 58			17 43		17 58

	GR	NT	GR		NT	XC	NT	NT	GR		XC	NT	XC	GR	NT		NT	XC	NT	NT	NT	NT		
	R 1		R 1			R 1			R 1		1 ◊		1 ◊	R 1				1 ◊						
	B		B		J	K			B		L		N	B				Q	J					
	☕ 🛒		☕ 🛒			☕			☕ 🛒		☕			☕ 🛒										
Leeds [10] 32, 34 d	17 05	17 09	17 40			18 00	18 09	18 17	18 40		19 00	19 09	20 00	20 15	20 17		20 20	21 00		21 09	21 40	22 17		
Outwood d		17 20					18 18					19 20					20 29			21 18	21 51			
Wakefield Kirkgate [4] 32, 34, 39 a								18 46							20 46							22 46		
d								18 46							20 46							22 46		
Wakefield Westgate [7] 32, 39 a	17 18	17 24	17 52			18 11	18 22		18 52		19 11	19 24	20 11	20 27			20 33	21 11		21 22	21 55			
d	17 18	17 24				18 12	18 22		18 52		19 12	19 24	20 12	20 27			20 33	21 12		21 22	21 55			
Sandal & Agbrigg d		17 28					18 25					19 28					20 36			21 25	21 59			
Fitzwilliam d		17 35					18 32					19 35					20 43			21 32	22 06			
South Elmsall d							18 37										20 48			21 37				
Adwick a							18 42										20 53			21 42				
d							18 43										20 54			21 43				
Bentley (S.Yorks) d							18 47										20 58			21 47				
Doncaster [7] a	17 35					18 28	18 57		19 09		19 29		20 29	20 47			21 08	21 29		21 57				
Moorthorpe d		17 40			18 02							19 40							21 29		22 11			
Thurnscoe d		17 46										19 46									22 17			
Goldthorpe d		17 48										19 48									22 19			
Bolton-on-Dearne d		17 51										19 51									22 22			
Swinton (S.Yorks) 29 a		17 55			18 11							19 55							21 38		22 32			
Rotherham Central 29 a		18 05			18 20							20 04							21 48		22 39			
Meadowhall 29 🚋 a		18 10			18 25			19 32				20 11			21 32				21 54		22 45	23 32		
Sheffield [7] 29 🚋 a		18 23			18 35	18 58		19 43			19 59	20 23	20 59		21 43			21 57	22 05		22 54	23 43		

For general notes see front of timetable
For details of catering facilities see Directory of Train Operators

- **A** To Lincoln (Table 30)
- **B** To London Kings Cross (Table 26)
- **C** From Edinburgh to Bournemouth (Table 51)
- **D** From Edinburgh to Plymouth (Table 51)
- **E** From Glasgow Central to Bournemouth (Table 51)
- **G** From Glasgow Central to Plymouth (Table 51)
- **H** From Edinburgh to Southampton Central (Table 51)
- **J** From York (Table 33)
- **K** From Aberdeen (Table 229) to Bristol Temple Meads (Table 51)
- **L** From Edinburgh to Bristol Temple Meads (Table 51)
- **N** From Glasgow Central to Birmingham New Street (Table 51)
- **Q** From Edinburgh to Birmingham New Street (Table 51)

Leeds and Wakefield → Pontefract, Knottingley and Goole

Network Diagram - see first page of Table 31

Miles	Miles	Station		NT SX	NT	NT	NT	NT		NT	NT	NT	NT	NT	NT
0	—	**Leeds** 10	31, 34 d	05 46		07 04		08 04	and at the same minutes past each hour until	16 04		17 19		18 04	
6	—	Woodlesford	34 d	05 54		07 12		08 12		16 12		17 28		18 12	
10¾	—	Castleford	a	06 03		07 23		08 21		16 21		17 37		18 21	
—	—		34 d	06 05		07 26		08 23		16 23		17 40		18 23	
12¼	—	Glasshoughton	d	06 10		07 30		08 28		16 28		17 44		18 28	
—	0	**Wakefield Westgate** 7	31, 39 d		06 25										
—	1	Wakefield Kirkgate 4	31, 34, 39 a		06 29										
—	—		d		06 29		07 38				16 38		17 38		18 38
—	5¼	Streethouse	d		06 36		07 46				16 46		17 46		18 46
—	7	Featherstone	d		06 40		07 50				16 50		17 50		18 50
—	9	Pontefract Tanshelf	d		06 44		07 53				16 53		17 53		18 53
14	9¾	Pontefract Monkhill	a	06 14	06 47	07 35	07 56	08 32		16 32	16 56	17 49	17 56	18 32	18 56
—	—		d	06 14	06 47	07 35	07 56	08 32		16 32	16 56	17 49	17 56	18 32	18 56
16	—	**Knottingley**	a	06 21	06 54	07 42	08 03	08 39		16 39	17 03	17 55	18 03	18 39	19 03
—	—		d									17 55			
20¼	—	Whitley Bridge	d									18 01			
22	—	Hensall	d									18 06			
25¾	—	Snaith	d									18 12			
28½	—	Rawcliffe	d									18 17			
32½	—	**Goole**	a									18 29			

Station		NT	NT	NT	NT	NT	NT	NT	NT SX	NT SO
Leeds 10	31, 34 d	19 04		20 04		21 04		22 04		
Woodlesford	34 d	19 12		20 12		21 12		22 12		
Castleford	a	19 21		20 21		21 21		22 21		
	34 d	19 23		20 23		21 23		22 23		
Glasshoughton	d	19 28		20 28		21 28		22 28		
Wakefield Westgate 7	31, 39 d						21 57		23 04	23 04
Wakefield Kirkgate 4	31, 34, 39 a						22 00		23 07	23 07
	d		19 38		20 38		22 00		23 07	23 07
Streethouse	d		19 46		20 46		22 08		23 15	23 15
Featherstone	d		19 50		20 50		22 12		23 19	23 19
Pontefract Tanshelf	d		19 53		20 53		22 16		23 23	23 23
Pontefract Monkhill	a	19 32	19 56	20 32	20 56	21 32	22 18	22 32	23 29	23 29
	d	19 32	19 56	20 32	20 56	21 32	22 19	22 32	23 29	
Knottingley	a	19 39	20 03	20 39	21 03	21 39	22 25	22 39	23 33	
	d									
Whitley Bridge	d									
Hensall	d									
Snaith	d									
Rawcliffe	d									
Goole	a									

Sundays

Station		NT	NT	NT	NT	NT	NT	NT
Leeds 10	34 d	09 30	11 17	13 17	15 17	17 17	19 17	21 17
Woodlesford	34 d	09 38	11 25	13 25	15 25	17 25	19 25	21 25
Castleford	34 a	09 46	11 33	13 33	15 33	17 33	19 35	21 33
	d	09 49	11 36	13 36	15 36	17 36	19 36	21 36
Glasshoughton	d	09 53	11 40	13 40	15 40	17 40	19 40	21 40
Pontefract Monkhill	d	09 58	11 45	13 45	15 45	17 45	19 45	21 45
Knottingley	a	10 04	11 52	13 52	15 52	17 52	19 52	21 52

For general notes see front of timetable
For details of catering facilities see Directory of Train Operators

Goole, Knottingley and Pontefract → Wakefield and Leeds

Network Diagram - see first page of Table 31

Miles	Miles			NT SX	NT	NT SO	NT SX	NT	NT	NT	NT		NT	NT	NT
0	—	**Goole**	d	.	.	07 04	07 11	.	.	.	.	and at the same minutes past each hour until	.	.	.
4	—	Rawcliffe	d	.	.	07 11	07 18	.	.	.	.		.	.	.
6¾	—	Snaith	d	.	.	07 16	07 23	.	.	.	.		.	.	.
10½	—	Hensall	d	.	.	07 23	07 30	.	.	.	.		.	.	.
12¼	—	Whitley Bridge	d	.	.	07 27	07 34	.	.	.	.		.	.	.
16½	—	**Knottingley**	a	.	.	07 35	07 42	.	.	.	.		.	.	.
—	—		d	06 25	06 56	07 35	07 46	07 56	08 18	08 56	09 18		17 18	18 05	18 43
18½	0	Pontefract Monkhill	a	06 29	07 00	07 39	07 50	08 00	08 22	09 00	09 22		17 22	18 09	18 47
—	—		d	06 29	07 00	07 39	07 50	08 00	08 22	09 00	09 22		17 22	18 09	18 47
—	¾	Pontefract Tanshelf	d	.	07 03	.	.	08 03	.	09 03	.		.	18 12	.
—	2¾	Featherstone	d	.	07 06	.	.	08 06	.	09 06	.		.	18 15	.
—	4½	Streethouse	d	.	07 10	.	.	08 10	.	09 10	.		.	18 19	.
—	8¾	Wakefield Kirkgate 4 31, 34, 39	a	.	07 22	.	.	08 21	.	09 21	.		.	18 32	.
—	—		d	.	.	.	.	.	.	.	.		.	.	.
—	9¾	**Wakefield Westgate 7** 31, 39	a	.	.	.	.	.	.	.	.		.	.	.
20	—	Glasshoughton	d	06 34	.	07 44	07 55	.	08 27	.	09 27		17 27	.	18 52
21½	—	Castleford	a	06 38	.	07 49	08 04	.	08 31	.	09 31		17 31	.	18 56
—	—	34	d	06 41	.	07 51	08 06	.	08 34	.	09 34		17 34	.	18 59
26½	—	Woodlesford 34	d	06 50	.	08 00	08 15	.	08 43	.	09 43		17 43	.	19 08
32½	—	**Leeds 10** 31, 34	a	07 03	.	08 13	08 27	.	09 00	.	09 55		17 55	.	19 21

		NT	NT	NT	NT	NT	NT	NT	NT	NT
Goole	d	.	18 49	.	.	.	.	.	.	.
Rawcliffe	d	.	18 56	.	.	.	.	.	.	.
Snaith	d	.	19 01	.	.	.	.	.	.	.
Hensall	d	.	19 08	.	.	.	.	.	.	.
Whitley Bridge	d	.	19 12	.	.	.	.	.	.	.
Knottingley	a	.	19 20	.	.	.	.	.	.	.
	d	19 05	19 27	19 56	20 18	21 18	21 23	22 18	22 30	23 18
Pontefract Monkhill	a	19 09	19 31	20 00	20 22	21 22	21 27	22 25	22 34	23 22
	d	19 09	19 31	20 00	20 22	21 22	21 27	22 25	22 34	23 22
Pontefract Tanshelf	d	19 12	.	20 03	.	.	21 30	.	22 37	.
Featherstone	d	19 15	.	20 06	.	.	21 33	.	22 40	.
Streethouse	d	19 19	.	20 10	.	.	21 37	.	22 44	.
Wakefield Kirkgate 4 31, 34, 39	a	19 31	.	20 22	.	.	21 47	.	22 55	.
	d	.	.	.	.	.	21 47	.	22 55	.
Wakefield Westgate 7 31, 39	a	.	.	.	.	.	21 52	.	23 00	.
Glasshoughton	d	.	19 36	.	20 27	21 27	.	22 30	.	23 27
Castleford	a	.	19 40	.	20 31	21 31	.	22 34	.	23 31
34	d	.	19 43	.	20 34	21 34	.	22 37	.	23 34
Woodlesford 34	d	.	19 52	.	20 43	21 43	.	22 46	.	23 43
Leeds 10 31, 34	a	.	20 04	.	20 55	21 55	.	23 01	.	23 55

Sundays

		NT	NT	NT	NT	NT	NT	NT
Knottingley	d	10 26	12 26	14 26	16 26	18 26	20 26	22 26
Pontefract Monkhill	d	10 30	12 30	14 30	16 30	18 30	20 30	22 30
Glasshoughton	d	10 35	12 35	14 35	16 35	18 35	20 35	22 35
Castleford	a	10 39	12 39	14 39	16 39	18 39	20 39	22 39
34	d	10 42	12 42	14 42	16 42	18 42	20 42	22 42
Woodlesford 34	d	10 51	12 51	14 51	16 51	18 51	20 51	22 51
Leeds 10 34	a	11 04	13 04	15 04	17 04	19 04	21 04	23 04

For general notes see front of timetable
For details of catering facilities see Directory of Train Operators

Sheffield and Selby → York

Local services only

Network Diagram - see first page of Table 31

Miles	Miles			NT	NT A	NT B	NT A	NT	NT	NT A	NT	NT	NT	NT A	NT
0	—	**Sheffield 7**	29, 31 d								09 29				
3½	—	Meadowhall	29, 31 d								09 35				
6¼	—	Rotherham Central	29, 31 d								09 42				
10¾	—	Swinton (S.Yorks)	29, 31 d								09 51				
18½	—	Moorthorpe	31 d								10 01				
25½	—	Pontefract Baghill	d								10 10				
—	—	Hull	29 d	*06 00*		07 07		*08 37*	09 02			*10 12*	11 05		*11 37*
—	0	**Selby**	d	06 48		07 48		09 16	09 38			10 54	11 39		12 51
33¾	8¼	Sherburn-in-Elmet	d	07 00		08 02		09 28			10 27				
36	10½	Church Fenton	d	07 04	08 04		09 09			10 05	10 31			12 05	
38	12½	Ulleskelf	d			08 08					10 35				
46¾	21	**York 8**	29 a	07 20	08 19	08 22	09 23	09 48	10 07	10 20	10 51	11 20	12 10	12 20	13 15

		NT A	NT	NT	NT	NT A	NT	NT A	NT B	NT A	NT	NT	NT A	NT A
Sheffield 7	29, 31 d			13 28										
Meadowhall	29, 31 d			13 35										
Rotherham Central	29, 31 d			13 42										
Swinton (S.Yorks)	29, 31 d			13 50										
Moorthorpe	31 d			14 01										
Pontefract Baghill	d			14 10										
Hull	29 d		13 12		15 06		16 10		17 18		19 10	*19 55*		
Selby	d		13 56		15 38		16 47		18 06		19 47	20 37		
Sherburn-in-Elmet	d		14 10	14 27										
Church Fenton	d	14 05		14 31		16 05		18 06		19 05			21 12	23 16
Ulleskelf	d			14 35				18 10					21 16	
York 8	29 a	14 20	14 27	14 50	16 06	16 22	17 13	18 24	18 35	19 20	20 15	21 00	21 29	23 33

Saturdays

		NT	NT B	NT A	NT A	NT	NT	NT A	NT	NT	NT	NT A	NT	NT A
Sheffield 7	29, 31 d								09 31					
Meadowhall	29, 31 d								09 37					
Rotherham Central	29, 31 d								09 44					
Swinton (S.Yorks)	29, 31 d								09 52					
Moorthorpe	31 d								10 02					
Pontefract Baghill	d								10 11					
Hull	29 d	*06 00*	06 57			*08 37*	09 02			*10 05*	11 08		*11 37*	
Selby	d	06 48	07 40			09 14	09 38			10 54	11 40		12 51	
Sherburn-in-Elmet	d	07 00	07 54			09 26			10 27				13 03	
Church Fenton	d	07 04		08 04	09 05			10 05	10 32			12 05		14 05
Ulleskelf	d		08 00						10 36					
York 8	29 a	07 20	08 14	08 19	09 20	09 41	10 10	10 20	10 53	11 16	12 10	12 20	13 23	14 20

		NT	NT	NT	NT A	NT	NT A	NT B	NT A	NT	NT	NT A	NT	NT A
Sheffield 7	29, 31 d		13 28											
Meadowhall	29, 31 d		13 35											
Rotherham Central	29, 31 d		13 42											
Swinton (S.Yorks)	29, 31 d		13 50											
Moorthorpe	31 d		14 00											
Pontefract Baghill	d		14 09											
Hull	29 d	13 12		14 51		16 10		17 18		18 46	*19 55*		*21 33*	
Selby	d	13 54		15 22		16 47		18 06		19 22	20 35		22 28	
Sherburn-in-Elmet	d		14 26											
Church Fenton	d		14 30		16 05		18 06		19 05			21 13		23 19
Ulleskelf	d		14 34				18 10					21 18		
York 8	29 a	14 25	14 50	15 55	16 22	17 13	18 24	18 36	19 19	19 50	21 00	21 30	22 53	23 36

Sundays

		NT C	NT	NT D	NT	NT D	NT D	NT	NT	NT D	NT	NT D	NT	NT E	NT	NT G
Sheffield 7	29, 31 d								15 46				18 58			
Meadowhall	29, 31 d								15 52				19 04			
Rotherham Central	29, 31 d								15 58				19 10			
Swinton (S.Yorks)	29, 31 d								16 08				19 18			
Moorthorpe	31 d								16 18				19 28			
Pontefract Baghill	d								16 26				19 37			
Hull	29 d		08 54		11 54			14 28			17 23				20 22	
Selby	d		09 25		12 25			15 04			17 54				20 53	
Sherburn-in-Elmet	d								16 42				19 54			
Church Fenton	d	09 19		10 53		12 49	14 49		16 46	16 49		18 49	19 58	20 49		22 59
Ulleskelf	d															
York 8	29 a	09 33	09 54	11 07	12 56	13 03	15 03	15 30	17 01	17 04	18 23	19 03	20 16	21 02	21 18	23 17

For general notes see front of timetable
For details of catering facilities see Directory of Train Operators

A From Blackpool North (Table 41)
B From Beverley (Table 43)
C From Bradford Interchange (Table 41)
D From Huddersfield (Table 41)
E Until 27 January from Hebden Bridge, 3 February to 23 March from Preston and from 30 March from Blackpool North (Table 41)
G From Leeds (Table 41)

York → Selby and Sheffield

Local services only

Network Diagram - see first page of Table 31

Mondays to Fridays

Miles	Miles	Station		NT	NT A	NT	NT B	NT	NT A	NT	NT	NT	NT A	NT	NT
0	0	**York 8**	29 d	06 09	07 06	07 30	07 48	08 43	09 09	09 53	10 22	11 03	11 09	11 53	12 18
8¾	8¾	Ulleskelf	d		07 15							11 13			
10¾	10¾	Church Fenton	d		07a20		08a00		09a20			11 17	11a20		
12¾	12¾	Sherburn-in-Elmet	d									11 21			
—	21	**Selby**	a	06 30		07 49		09 08		10 12	10 42			12 17	12 38
—	—	Hull	29 a	*08 21*		08 45		*10 04*		10 56	*11 34*			13 02	*13 34*
21¼	—	Pontefract Baghill	d									11 39			
28¼	—	Moorthorpe	31 a									11 51			
36	—	Swinton (S.Yorks)	29, 31 a									12 01			
40½	—	Rotherham Central	29, 31 a									12 10			
43¼	—	Meadowhall	29, 31 a									12 16			
46¾	—	**Sheffield 7**	29, 31 a									12 26			

Station		NT A	NT	NT	NT	NT A	NT C	NT A	NT	NT	NT A	NT	NT B	NT B	NT	NT B
York 8	29 d	13 09	13 45	14 59	15 02	15 09	16 12	17 07	17 27	18 14	19 04	19 23	20 13	21 13	22 03	23 13
Ulleskelf	d				15 12					18 23				21 22		
Church Fenton	d	13a20			15 16	15a20	16 23	17a19		18 28	19a15		20a24	21a28		23a28
Sherburn-in-Elmet	d		13 57		15 20		16 27			18 31						
Selby	a		14 09	15 19			16 38		17 45	18 43		19 44			22 22	
Hull	29 a		14 48	15 58			17 27		18 29	19 32		*20 37*			23 08	
Pontefract Baghill	d				15 38											
Moorthorpe	31 a				15 50											
Swinton (S.Yorks)	29, 31 a				16 01											
Rotherham Central	29, 31 a				16 10											
Meadowhall	29, 31 a				16 18											
Sheffield 7	29, 31 a				16 25											

Saturdays

Station		NT	NT A	NT	NT A	NT	NT A	NT	NT	NT	NT A	NT	NT	NT A
York 8	29 d	06 05	07 06	07 30	08 07	08 34	09 09	09 52	10 17	11 01	11 09	11 49	12 18	13 09
Ulleskelf	d		07 15							11 11				
Church Fenton	d		07a20		08a19		09a20			11 15	11a20			13a20
Sherburn-in-Elmet	d									11 19				
Selby	a	06 26		07 49		08 54		10 12	10 37			12 09	12 38	
Hull	29 a	*08 21*		08 45		*09 31*		10 56	*11 34*			12 54	*13 34*	
Pontefract Baghill	d									11 37				
Moorthorpe	31 a									11 49				
Swinton (S.Yorks)	29, 31 a									11 59				
Rotherham Central	29, 31 a									12 10				
Meadowhall	29, 31 a									12 16				
Sheffield 7	29, 31 a									12 25				

Station		NT	NT	NT A	NT	NT C	NT A	NT	NT	NT A	NT	NT B	NT	NT B	NT	NT B
York 8	29 d	13 38	15 05	15 09	15 12	16 12	17 09	17 18	18 13	19 04	19 23	20 13	20 17	21 13	21 45	23 13
Ulleskelf	d				15 23				18 22					21 22		
Church Fenton	d			15a20	15 27	16 23	17a20		18 27	19a15		20a24		21a28		23a27
Sherburn-in-Elmet	d	13 52			15 31	16 27			18 30							
Selby	a	14 03	15 24			16 38		17 37	18 41		19 44		20 36		22 05	
Hull	29 a	14 45	16 03			17 27		18 21	19 28		*20 37*		21 22		*23 21*	
Pontefract Baghill	d				15 49											
Moorthorpe	31 a				16 01											
Swinton (S.Yorks)	29, 31 a				16 10											
Rotherham Central	29, 31 a				16 17											
Meadowhall	29, 31 a				16 23											
Sheffield 7	29, 31 a				16 35											

Sundays

Station		NT D	NT E	NT	NT E	NT	NT E	NT	NT D	NT	NT E	NT	NT E	NT	NT	NT B
York 8	29 d	08 48	09 52	10 40	11 52	13 23	13 52	15 43	15 52	17 17	17 52	19 10	19 52	20 44	21 41	21 52
Ulleskelf	d															
Church Fenton	d	09a00	10a04		12a04		14a04		16a03	17 28	18a04		20a04	20 55		22a04
Sherburn-in-Elmet	d									17 32				20 59		
Selby	a			10 59		13 42		16 01				19 29			22 00	
Hull	29 a			11 38		14 21		16 41				20 08			22 39	
Pontefract Baghill	d									17 49				21 17		
Moorthorpe	31 a									18 01				21 29		
Swinton (S.Yorks)	29, 31 a									18 11				21 38		
Rotherham Central	29, 31 a									18 20				21 48		
Meadowhall	29, 31 a									18 25				21 54		
Sheffield 7	29, 31 a									18 35				22 05		

For general notes see front of timetable
For details of catering facilities see Directory of Train Operators

A To Blackpool North (Table 41)
B To Leeds (Table 41)
C To Scarborough (Table 43)
D Until 27 January to Hebden Bridge, 3 February to 23 March to Preston and from 30 March to Blackpool North (Table 41)
E To Huddersfield (Table 41)

Sheffield → Barnsley → Huddersfield and Leeds

Network Diagram - see first page of Table 31

Miles	Miles			NT	NT SX	NT SO	NT SX	NT SX A	NT	NT		NT SX	NT SX	NT SO B	NT SX	NT SO	EM SO 1 ◊ C ☕	EM SX 1 ◊ C ☕		NT SX B	NT	NT D	NT A	NT	NT
—	—	St Pancras International	⊖ 53 d																						
0	0	**Sheffield 7**	29, 31 🚌 d	05 16	05 36	05 48	05 50		06 14	06 36		06 49			07 04	07 08	07 17	07 25			07 36	07 51		08 08	08 36
3½	3½	Meadowhall	29, 31 🚌 d	05 22	05 42	05 54	05 56		06 20	06 42		06 55			07 10	07 14	07 23	07 31			07 42	07 57		08 14	08 42
7¼	7¼	Chapeltown	d	05 28	05 48	06 00			06 26	06 48					07 16	07 20					07 48			08 20	08 48
10½	10½	Elsecar	d	05 33		06 05			06 31						07 21	07 25								08 25	
12	12	Wombwell	d	05 37	05 55	06 09			06 35	06 55					07 25	07 29					07 55			08 29	08 55
16	16	**Barnsley**	a	05 42	06 01	06 14	06 10		06 40	07 00		07 09			07 30	07 34	07 43	07 48			08 00	08 11		08 34	09 00
—	—		d		06 01		06 11		06 41	07 01		07 10			07 31	07 35					08 01	08 12		08 35	09 01
—	19	Dodworth	d		06 07					07 07											08 07				09 07
—	20¼	Silkstone Common	d		06 11					07 11											08 11				09 11
—	23¼	Penistone	d		06 18					07 18											08 18				09 18
—	27¼	Denby Dale	d		06 25					07 24											08 24				09 24
—	29¾	Shepley	d		06 30					07 29											08 29				09 29
—	30¾	Stocksmoor	d		06 32					07 32											08 32				09 32
—	32¾	Brockholes	d		06 36					07 36											08 36				09 36
—	33¾	Honley	d		06 39					07 38											08 38				09 38
—	34¾	Berry Brow	d		06 42					07 41											08 41				09 41
—	35¾	Lockwood	d		06 44					07 44											08 44				09 44
—	37	**Huddersfield**	a		06 50					07 49											08 49				09 49
19½	—	Darton	d						06 46						07 36	07 40								08 40	
27	—	Wakefield Kirkgate 4	31 d				06 29		06 58			07 29			07 47	07 51						08 29		08 52	
30	—	Normanton	d				06 33		07 02			07 33			07 52	07 56								08 56	
33½	—	Castleford	a						07 08						07 58	08 02								09 02	
—	—		d					06 41	07 10				07 38	07 51	08 00	08 04				08 06			08 34	09 04	
38¼	—	Woodlesford	d					06 50	07 19				07 47	08 00	08 09	08 13				08 15			08 43	09 13	
44¼	—	**Leeds 10**	31 a				06 50	07 03	07 33			07 50	08 01	08 13	08 23	08 27				08 27		08 51	09 00	09 27	

		NT	NT A	NT		NT	NT	NT A	NT	NT	NT	NT A		NT	NT	NT	NT A	NT	NT	NT		NT A	NT	NT	NT
St Pancras International	⊖ 53 d					*06b10*			*07 25*					*08 25*				*09 25*					*10 25*		
Sheffield 7	29, 31 🚌 d	08 51		09 08		09 36	09 51		10 08	10 36	10 51			11 08	11 36	11 51		12 08	12 36	12 51			13 08	13 36	13 51
Meadowhall	29, 31 🚌 d	08 57		09 14		09 42	09 57		10 14	10 42	10 57			11 14	11 42	11 57		12 14	12 42	12 57			13 14	13 42	13 57
Chapeltown	d			09 20		09 48			10 20	10 48				11 20	11 48			12 20	12 48				13 20	13 48	
Elsecar	d			09 25					10 25					11 25				12 25					13 25		
Wombwell	d			09 29		09 55			10 29	10 55				11 29	11 55			12 29	12 55				13 29	13 55	
Barnsley	a	09 11		09 34		10 00	10 11		10 34	11 00	11 11			11 34	12 00	12 11		12 34	13 00	13 11			13 34	14 00	14 12
	d	09 12		09 35		10 01	10 12		10 35	11 01	11 12			11 35	12 01	12 12		12 35	13 01	13 12			13 35	14 01	14 12
Dodworth	d					10 07				11 07					12 07				13 07					14 07	
Silkstone Common	d					10 11				11 11					12 11				13 11					14 11	
Penistone	d					10 18				11 18					12 18				13 18					14 18	
Denby Dale	d					10 24				11 24					12 24				13 24					14 24	
Shepley	d					10 29				11 29					12 29				13 29					14 29	
Stocksmoor	d					10 32				11 32					12 32				13 32					14 32	
Brockholes	d					10 36				11 36					12 36				13 36					14 36	
Honley	d					10 38				11 38					12 38				13 38					14 38	
Berry Brow	d					10 41				11 41					12 41				13 41					14 41	
Lockwood	d					10 44				11 44					12 44				13 44					14 44	
Huddersfield	a					10 49				11 49					12 49				13 49					14 49	
Darton	d			09 40					10 40					11 40				12 40					13 40		
Wakefield Kirkgate 4	31 d	09 29		09 52			10 29		10 52		11 29			11 52		12 29		12 52		13 29			13 52		14 29
Normanton	d			09 56					10 56					11 56				12 56					13 56		
Castleford	a			10 02					11 02					12 02				13 02					14 02		
	d		09 34	10 04				10 34	11 04			11 34		12 04			12 34	13 04				13 34	14 04		
Woodlesford	d		09 43	10 13				10 43	11 13			11 43		12 13			12 43	13 13				13 43	14 13		
Leeds 10	31 a	09 50	09 55	10 27			10 50	10 55	11 27		11 50	11 55		12 27		12 50	12 55	13 27		13 50		13 55	14 27		14 50

		NT A	NT	NT	NT	NT A		NT SX	NT	NT	NT A	NT	NT	NT		NT A	NT	NT SO	NT SX	NT	NT A	NT		NT SO	NT SX
St Pancras International	⊖ 53 d		*11 25*					*12 25*				*13 25*					*14 25*			*14 25*		*15c25*			
Sheffield 7	29, 31 🚌 d		14 08	14 36	14 51			15 08	15 36	15 51		16 08	16 36	16 51			17 08	17 36	17 36	17 51		18 08		18 36	18 36
Meadowhall	29, 31 🚌 d		14 14	14 42	14 57			15 14	15 42	15 57		16 14	16 42	16 57			17 14	17 42	17 42	17 57		18 14		18 42	18 42
Chapeltown	d		14 20	14 48				15 20	15 48			16 20	16 48				17 20	17 48	17 48			18 20		18 48	18 48
Elsecar	d		14 25					15 25				16 25	16 53				17 25	17 53	17 53			18 25		18 53	18 53
Wombwell	d		14 29	14 55				15 29	15 55			16 29	16 57				17 29	17 57	17 57			18 29		18 57	18 57
Barnsley	a		14 34	15 00	15 11			15 34	16 00	16 11		16 34	17 02	17 11			17 34	18 02	18 02	18 11		18 34		19 02	19 02
	d		14 35	15 01	15 12			15 35	16 01	16 12		16 35	17 03	17 12			17 35	18 03	18 03	18 18		18 35		19 03	19 09
Dodworth	d			15 07					16 07				17 09					18 09	18 09					19 09	19 15
Silkstone Common	d			15 11					16 11				17 13					18 13	18 13					19 13	19 19
Penistone	d			15 18					16 18				17 20					18 20	18e27					19 20	19 26
Denby Dale	d			15 24					16 24				17 26					18 26	18 33					19 26	19 33
Shepley	d			15 29					16 29				17 31					18 31	18 38					19 31	19 38
Stocksmoor	d			15 32					16 32				17 34					18 34	18 41					19 34	19 40
Brockholes	d			15 36					16 36				17 38					18 38	18 45					19 38	19 44
Honley	d			15 38					16 38				17 40					18 40	18 47					19 41	19 47
Berry Brow	d			15 41					16 41				17 43					18 43	18 50					19 44	19 50
Lockwood	d			15 44					16 44				17 46					18 46	18 53					19 46	19 52
Huddersfield	a			15 49					16 49				17 50					18 50	18 57					19 51	19 57
Darton	d		14 40					15 40				16 40					17 40					18 40			
Wakefield Kirkgate 4	31 d		14 52		15 29			15 52		16 27		16 52		17 29			17 52			18 36		18 52			
Normanton	d		14 56					15 56				16 56					17 56					18 56			
Castleford	a		15 02					16 02				17 02					18 02					19 02			
	d	14 34	15 04			15 34		16 04			16 34	17 04				17 34	18 04				18 59	19 04			
Woodlesford	d	14 43	15 13			15 43		16 13			16 43	17 13				17 43	18 13				19 08	19 13			
Leeds 10	31 a	14 55	15 27		15 50	15 55		16 27		16 50	16 55	17 27		17 50		17 55	18 27			18 55	19 21	19 27			

For general notes see front of timetable
For details of catering facilities see Directory of Train Operators

A From Knottingley (Table 32)
B From Goole (Table 32)
C From Derby (Table 53)
D From Retford (Table 30)
b Saturdays dep. 0620
c Mondays to Fridays only
e Arr. 1819

Sheffield → Barnsley → Huddersfield and Leeds

Network Diagram - see first page of Table 31

		NT	NT	NT	NT	NT	NT	NT	NT	NT	EM	NT	NT	NT	NT	NT	NT	NT	NT	NT	NT
		SX	SO								SO 1 ◇					FSX	FSO	FSO			FSX
				A				B			☕	B		B					B		C
St Pancras International	⊖ 53 d				16 25	16b55				17c45	18 00		18 25			19 25	19 25				20 25
Sheffield 7	29, 31 ⛴ d	18 51	18 51		19 08	19 38	19 51		20 08	20 41	20 48		21 08		21 41	22 08	22 08			22 41	23 24
Meadowhall	29, 31 ⛴ d	18 57	18 57		19 14	19 44	19 57		20 14	20 47	20 54		21 14		21 47	22 14	22 14			22 47	23 30
Chapeltown	d				19 20	19 50			20 20	20 53			21 20		21 53	22 20	22 20			22 53	23 36
Elsecar	d				19 25	19 55			20 25				21 25			22 25	22 25			22 58	23 41
Wombwell	d				19 29	19 59			20 29	21 00			21 29		22 00	22 29	22 29			23 00	23 45
Barnsley	a	19 15	19 15		19 34	20 04	20 12		20 34	21 06	21 14		21 34		22 05	22 34	22 34			23 06	23 50
	d	19 18	19 18		19 35	20 07	20 12		20 35	21 06			21 35		22 06	22 35				23 06	23 51
Dodworth	d					20 13				21 12					22 12					23 12	
Silkstone Common	d					20 17				21 16					22 16					23 16	
Penistone	d					20 24				21 23					22 23					23 23	
Denby Dale	d					20 30				21 29					22 29					23 29	
Shepley	d					20 35				21 34					22 34					23 34	
Stocksmoor	d					20 38				21 37					22 37					23 37	
Brockholes	d					20 42				21 41					22 41					23 41	
Honley	d					20 44				21 43					22 43					23 43	
Berry Brow	d					20 47				21 46					22 46					23 46	
Lockwood	d					20 50				21 49					22 49					23 49	
Huddersfield	a					20 54				21 54					22 54					23 55	
Darton	d				19 40				20 40				21 40			22 40					23 56
Wakefield Kirkgate 4	31 d	19 36	19 36		19 52		20 29		20 52				21 52			22 52		22 52			00s10
Normanton	d				19 56				20 56				21 56			22 56		22 56			
Castleford	a				20 02				21 02				22 02			23 02		23 02			
	d			19 43	20 04			20 34	21 04			21 34	22 04	22 37		23 04		23 04	23 34		
Woodlesford	d			19 52	20 13			20 43	21 13			21 43	22 13	22 46		23 13		23 13	23 43		
Leeds 10	31 a	19 56	19 57	20 04	20 27		20 50	20 55	21 27			21 55	22 27	23 01		23 27		23 27	23 55		

Sundays

		NT	NT	NT	NT	NT	NT	NT	NT	NT	NT	NT	NT	NT
			B				B				B			
St Pancras International	⊖ 53 d								09e30	09f30			10 30	11 30
Sheffield 7	29, 31 ⛴ d	08 39		09 39	10 39	11 32		11 39	12 39	13 32		13 39	14 39	15 32
Meadowhall	29, 31 ⛴ d	08 45		09 45	10 45	11 38		11 45	12 45	13 38		13 45	14 45	15 38
Chapeltown	d	08 51		09 51	10 51			11 51	12 51			13 51	14 51	
Elsecar	d	08 56		09 56	10 56			11 56	12 56			13 56	14 56	
Wombwell	d	09 00		10 00	11 00			12 00	13 00			14 00	15 00	
Barnsley	a	09 05		10 05	11 05	11 52		12 06	13 05	13 52		14 05	15 05	15 52
	d	09 09		10 06	11 09	11 53		12 06	13 09	13 53		14 06	15 09	15 53
Dodworth	d			10 12				12 12				14 12		
Silkstone Common	d			10 16				12 16				14 16		
Penistone	d			10 23				12 23				14 23		
Denby Dale	d			10 29				12 29				14 29		
Shepley	d			10 34				12 34				14 34		
Stocksmoor	d			10 37				12 37				14 37		
Brockholes	d			10 41				12 41				14 41		
Honley	d			10 43				12 43				14 43		
Berry Brow	d			10 46				12 46				14 46		
Lockwood	d			10 49				12 49				14 49		
Huddersfield	a			10 53				12 54				14 53		
Darton	d	09 14			11 14				13 14				15 14	
Wakefield Kirkgate 4	31 d	09 29			11 29	12 11			13 29	14 11			15 29	16 11
Normanton	d	09 34			11 34				13 34				15 34	
Castleford	a	09 39			11 39				13 39				15 39	
	d	09 42	10 42		11 42		12 42		13 42		14 42		15 42	
Woodlesford	d	09 51	10 51		11 51		12 51		13 51		14 51		15 51	
Leeds 10	31 a	10 04	11 04		12 07	12 31	13 04		14 04	14 31	15 04		16 04	16 31

		NT	NT	NT	NT	NT	NT	NT	NT	NT	NT	NT	NT
		B	D	E	B			B				B	E
St Pancras International	⊖ 53 d			12 30		13g30	14g30		15g30	16h30	17j30		18g30
Sheffield 7	29, 31 ⛴ d		15 39	16 39		17 39	18 39		19 39	20 39	21 43		22 39
Meadowhall	29, 31 ⛴ d		15 45	16 45		17 45	18 45		19 45	20 45	21 49		22 45
Chapeltown	d		15 51	16 51		17 51	18 51		19 51	20 51	21 55		22 51
Elsecar	d		15 56	16 56		17 56	18 56		19 56	20 56	22 00		22 56
Wombwell	d		16 00	17 00		18 00	19 00		20 00	21 00	22 04		23 00
Barnsley	a		16 06	17 05		18 05	19 05		20 05	21 05	22 09		23 05
	d		16 06	17 09		18 07	19 09		20 06	21 09			23 09
Dodworth	d		16 12			18 13			20 12				
Silkstone Common	d		16 16			18 17			20 16				
Penistone	d		16 23			18 24			20 23				
Denby Dale	d		16 29			18 30			20 29				
Shepley	d		16 34			18 35			20 34				
Stocksmoor	d		16 37			18 38			20 37				
Brockholes	d		16 41			18 42			20 41				
Honley	d		16 43			18 44			20 43				
Berry Brow	d		16 46			18 47			20 46				
Lockwood	d		16 49			18 50			20 49				
Huddersfield	a		16 55			18 54			20 53				
Darton	d			17 14			19 14			21 14			23 14
Wakefield Kirkgate 4	31 d			17 29			19 29			21 29			23 29
Normanton	d			17 34			19 34			21 34			23 34
Castleford	a			17 39			19 41			21 39			23 39
	d	16 42		17 42	18 42		19 42	20 42		21 42		22 42	23 42
Woodlesford	d	16 51		17 51	18 51		19 51	20 51		21 51		22 51	23 51
Leeds 10	31 a	17 04		18 04	19 04		20 04	21 04		22 04		23 04	00 04

For general notes see front of timetable
For details of catering facilities see Directory of Train Operators

A From Goole (Table 32)
B From Knottingley (Table 32)
C To Wakefield Westgate (Table 31)
D From Retford (Table 30)
E From Lincoln (Table 30)
b Mondays to Fridays only
c Saturdays dep. 1740
e From 30 March only
f Until 23 March only
g From 30 March dep. 1 hour later
h From 30 March dep. 1725
j From 30 March dep. 1825

Table 34

Mondays to Saturdays

Leeds and Huddersfield → Barnsley → Sheffield

Network Diagram - see first page of Table 31

Miles	Miles		NT A	NT	NT SX B	NT SO	NT SX	NT SX	NT	NT	NT B	NT	NT	EM SX 1 ◇ ☕	NT SX	NT SO	NT B	EM SO 1 ◇ ☕	NT	NT	NT
0	—	**Leeds** 10 31 d			05 46			06 05		06 38	07 04	07 16			07 23	07 23	08 04		08 16		08 34
6	—	Woodlesford d			05 54					06 46	07 12				07 31	07 31	08 12				08 42
10¾	—	Castleford a			06 03					06 57	07 23				07 42	07 42	08 21				08 50
—	—	d								06 59					07 44	07 44					08 53
14½	—	Normanton d								07 05					07 50	07 50					08 58
17¼	—	Wakefield Kirkgate 4 31 d					06 10	06 22		07 10		07 32			07 55	07 55			08 32		09 03
24¾	—	Darton d					06 21			07 21					08 06	08 06					09 14
—	0	**Huddersfield** d							06 10				07 10							08 10	
—	1¼	Lockwood d							06 13				07 13							08 13	
—	2¼	Berry Brow d							06 16				07 16							08 16	
—	3¼	Honley d							06 19				07 19							08 19	
—	4¼	Brockholes d							06 22				07 22							08 22	
—	6¼	Stocksmoor d							06 26				07 26							08 26	
—	7¼	Shepley d							06 28				07 28							08 28	
—	9¼	Denby Dale d							06 34				07 33							08 34	
—	13¼	Penistone d							06 42				07 42							08 42	
—	16¾	Silkstone Common d							06 47				07 47							08 47	
—	18	Dodworth d							06 51				07 51							08 51	
28¼	21	**Barnsley** a					06 27	06 44	06 57	07 27		07 48	07 57		08 13	08 16			08 48	08 57	09 22
—	—	d	05 18	05 53		06 27	06 27	06 46	06 58	07 28		07 48	07 58	08 06	08 14	08 17		08 30	08 48	08 58	09 26
32¼	25	Wombwell d	05 23	05 58		06 32	06 32		07 03	07 33			08 03		08 19	08 22				09 03	09 31
33¾	26½	Elsecar d	05 27	06 02		06 36	06 36		07 07	07 37			08 07		08 23	08 26				09 07	09 35
37	29¾	Chapeltown d	05 33	06 07		06 41	06 41		07 12	07 42			08 12		08 28	08 31				09 12	09 40
40¾	33½	Meadowhall 29, 31 🚋 a	05 38	06 13		06 48	06 48	07 03	07 19	07 48		08 03	08 17	08 24	08 33	08 36		08 45	09 03	09 19	09 48
44¼	37	**Sheffield** 7 29, 31 🚋 a	05 49	06 25		06 57	06 57	07 12	07 29	07 59		08 15	08 28	08 33	08 45	08 47		08 54	09 15	09 30	09 57
—	—	St Pancras International ⊖ 53 a	08b42	09c17		09 49	09 29	09 33				10e48		11 34				11 34	11f51		

	NT B	NT	NT	NT	NT B	NT	NT	NT	NT B	NT	NT	NT	NT B	NT	NT	NT	NT B	NT	NT	NT
Leeds 10 31 d	09 04	09 16		09 34	10 04	10 16		10 34	11 04	11 16		11 34	12 04	12 16		12 34	13 04	13 16		13 34
Woodlesford d	09 12			09 42	10 12			10 42	11 12			11 42	12 12			12 42	13 12			13 42
Castleford a	09 21			09 50	10 21			10 50	11 21			11 50	12 21			12 50	13 21			13 50
d				09 53				10 53				11 53				12 53				13 53
Normanton d				09 58				10 58				11 58				12 58				13 58
Wakefield Kirkgate 4 31 d		09 32		10 03		10 32		11 03		11 32		12 05		12 32		13 03		13 32		14 03
Darton d				10 14				11 14				12 16				13 14				14 14
Huddersfield d			09 13				10 13				11 13				12 13				13 13	
Lockwood d			09 16				10 16				11 16				12 16				13 16	
Berry Brow d			09 19				10 19				11 19				12 19				13 19	
Honley d			09 22				10 22				11 22				12 22				13 22	
Brockholes d			09 25				10 25				11 25				12 25				13 25	
Stocksmoor d			09 29				10 29				11 29				12 29				13 29	
Shepley d			09 31				10 31				11 31				12 31				13 31	
Denby Dale d			09 36				10 36				11 36				12 36				13 36	
Penistone d			09 44				10 44				11 44				12 44				13 44	
Silkstone Common d			09 49				10 49				11 49				12 49				13 49	
Dodworth d			09 53				10 53				11 53				12 53				13 53	
Barnsley a		09 48	10 00	10 21		10 48	11 00	11 21		11 48	12 00	12 22		12 48	13 00	13 21		13 48	14 00	14 21
d		09 48	10 01	10 26		10 48	11 01	11 26		11 48	12 01	12 26		12 48	13 01	13 26		13 48	14 01	14 26
Wombwell d			10 06	10 31			11 06	11 31			12 06	12 31			13 06	13 31			14 06	14 31
Elsecar d				10 35				11 35				12 35				13 35				14 35
Chapeltown d			10 13	10 40			11 13	11 40			12 13	12 40			13 13	13 40			14 13	14 40
Meadowhall 29, 31 🚋 a		10 03	10 19	10 48		11 03	11 19	11 48		12 03	12 19	12 48		13 03	13 20	13 48		14 03	14 19	14 48
Sheffield 7 29, 31 🚋 a		10 15	10 30	10 57		11 15	11 30	11 57		12 15	12 30	12 57		13 15	13 31	13 57		14 15	14 30	14 57
St Pancras International ⊖ 53 a		12 51				13g45				14h44				15h50				16 45		

	NT B	NT	NT	NT	NT B	NT	NT	NT	NT B	NT	NT	NT	NT	NT	NT C	NT	NT SX	NT B	NT	NT SX	NT SO
Leeds 10 31 d	14 04	14 16		14 34	15 04	15 16		15 34	16 04	16 16		16 34	17 16		17 19	17 34	17j43	18 04	18 16		
Woodlesford d	14 12			14 42	15 12			15 42	16 12			16 42			17 28	17 42		18 12			
Castleford a	14 21			14 50	15 21			15 50	16 21			16 50			17 37	17 50		18 21			
d				14 53				15 53				16 53				17 53					
Normanton d				14 58				15 58				16 58	17 28			17 58					
Wakefield Kirkgate 4 31 d		14 32		15 03		15 32		16 03		16 32		17 03	17 32			18 03			18 32		
Darton d				15 14				16 14				17 14				18 14					
Huddersfield d			14 13				15 13				16 13			17 13			18 22 →			17 56	18 13
Lockwood d			14 16				15 16				16 16			17 16						17 59	18 16
Berry Brow d			14 19				15 19				16 19			17 19						18 02	18 19
Honley d			14 22				15 22				16 22			17 22						18 05	18 22
Brockholes d			14 25				15 25				16 25			17 25						18 08	18 25
Stocksmoor d			14 29				15 29				16 29			17 29						18 12	18 29
Shepley d			14 31				15 31				16 31			17 31						18 14	18 31
Denby Dale d			14 36				15 36				16 36			17 36						18 19	18 36
Penistone d			14 44				15 44				16 44			17 44						18k36	18 44
Silkstone Common d			14 49				15 49				16 49			17 49						18 41	18 49
Dodworth d			14 53				15 53				16 53			17 53						18 45	18 53
Barnsley a		14 48	15 00	15 21		15 48	16 00	16 21		16 48	17 00	17 21	17 48	18 00		18 22			18 48	18 52	19 00
d		14 48	15 01	15 26		15 48	16 01	16 26		16 48	17 01	17 26	17 48	18 01		18 26			18 48	18 58	19 01
Wombwell d			15 06	15 31			16 06	16 31			17 06	17 31		18 06		18 31				19 03	19 06
Elsecar d				15 35				16 35				17 35				18 35				19 07	
Chapeltown d			15 13	15 40			16 13	16 40			17 13	17 40		18 13		18 40				19 12	19 13
Meadowhall 29, 31 🚋 a		15 03	15 19	15 48		16 05	16 19	16 48		17 03	17 19	17 48	18 03	18 19		18 47			19 03	19 16	19 19
Sheffield 7 29, 31 🚋 a		15 15	15 30	15 57		16 15	16 30	16 57		17 15	17 30	17 57	18 15	18 30		18 57			19 15	19 30	19 30
St Pancras International ⊖ 53 a		17e53				18 51				19m52			20n41			21c52			21q53		

For general notes see front of timetable
For details of catering facilities see Directory of Train Operators

A To Retford (Table 30)
B To Knottingley (Table 32)
C To Goole (Table 32)
b Saturdays arr. 0845
c Saturdays only
e Saturdays arr. 2 minutes earlier
f Saturdays arr. 1159
g Saturdays arr. 1344
h Saturdays arr. 1 minute later
j Via Dewsbury (Table 39)
k Arr. 1826
m Saturdays arr. 1945
n Saturdays arr. 2048
q Mondays to Fridays only

Leeds and Huddersfield → Barnsley → Sheffield

Network Diagram - see first page of Table 31

Station		NT SX	NT	NT A	NT	NT	NT	NT A	NT	NT	NT	NT	NT A	NT	NT	NT A	NT SX	NT SO
Leeds 10	31 d		18 34	19 04	19 16		19 34	20 04	20 16		20 34		21 04	21 34		22 04	22 34	22 34
Woodlesford	d		18 42	19 12			19 42	20 12			20 42		21 12	21 42		22 12	22 42	22 42
Castleford	a		18 50	19 21			19 50	20 21			20 51		21 21	21 50		22 21	22 50	22 50
	d		18 53				19 53				20 53			21 53			22 53	22 53
Normanton	d		18 58				19 58				20 58			21 58			22 58	22 58
Wakefield Kirkgate 4	31 d		19 03		19 32		20 03		20 32		21 03			22 03			23 03	23a03
Darton	d	⟵	19 14				20 14				21 14			22 14			23 14	
Huddersfield	d	18 22				19 18				20 18		21 18			22 18			
Lockwood	d	18 25				19 21				20 21		21 21			22 21			
Berry Brow	d	18 28				19 24				20 24		21 24			22 24			
Honley	d	18 31				19 27				20 27		21 27			22 27			
Brockholes	d	18 34				19 30				20 30		21 30			22 30			
Stocksmoor	d	18 38				19 34				20 34		21 34			22 34			
Shepley	d	18 40				19 36				20 36		21 36			22 36			
Denby Dale	d	18 45				19 41				20 41		21 41			22 41			
Penistone	d	18 53				19 49				20 49		21 49			22 49			
Silkstone Common	d	18 58				19 54				20 54		21 54			22 54			
Dodworth	d	19 02				19 58				20 58		21 58			22 58			
Barnsley	a	19 09	19 21		19 48	20 05	20 22		20 48	21 05	21 22	22 05		22 25	23 05		23 24	
	d	19 16	19 26		19 48	20 06	20 26		20 48	21 06	21 26	22 06		22 26	23 06		23 26	
Wombwell	d	19 21	19 31			20 11	20 31			21 11	21 31	22 11		22 31	23 11		23 31	
Elsecar	d		19 35				20 35				21 35			22 35	23 15		23 35	
Chapeltown	d	19 28	19 40			20 18	20 40			21 18	21 41	22 18		22 40	23 20		23 40	
Meadowhall	29, 31 a	19 34	19 48		20 03	20 23	20 47		21 03	21 24	21 48	22 23		22 48	23 25		23 48	
Sheffield 7	29, 31 a	19 44	19 57		20 15	20 35	20 57		21 15	21 35	21 57	22 35		22 57	23 35		23 57	
St Pancras International	⊖ 53 a				23b04													

Sundays

Station		NT	NT	NT A	NT	NT	NT	NT	NT A	NT B	NT	NT	NT A	NT
Leeds 10	31 d	08 30		09 30	10 14	10 17	11 14		11 17	12 17	13 14		13 17	14 17
Woodlesford	d	08 38		09 38		10 25			11 25	12 25			13 25	14 25
Castleford	a	08 47		09 46		10 33			11 33	12 33			13 33	14 33
	d	08 49				10 36				12 36				14 36
Normanton	d	08 55				10 41				12 41				14 41
Wakefield Kirkgate 4	31 d	09 00			10 30	10 46	11 30			12 46	13 30			14 46
Darton	d	09 14				11 00				13 00				15 00
Huddersfield	d		09 19					11 19				13 19		
Lockwood	d		09 22					11 22				13 22		
Berry Brow	d		09 25					11 25				13 25		
Honley	d		09 28					11 28				13 28		
Brockholes	d		09 31					11 31				13 31		
Stocksmoor	d		09 35					11 35				13 35		
Shepley	d		09 37					11 37				13 37		
Denby Dale	d		09 42					11 42				13 42		
Penistone	d		09 50					11 50				13 50		
Silkstone Common	d		09 55					11 55				13 55		
Dodworth	d		09 59					11 59				13 59		
Barnsley	a	09 20	10 06		10 49	11 07	11 49	12 06		13 07	13 49	14 06		15 07
	d	09 21	10 12		10 49	11 12	11 49	12 12		13 12	13 49	14 12		15 12
Wombwell	d	09 26	10 17			11 17		12 17		13 17		14 17		15 17
Elsecar	d	09 30	10 21			11 21		12 21		13 21		14 21		15 21
Chapeltown	d	09 35	10 26			11 26		12 26		13 26		14 26		15 26
Meadowhall	29, 31 a	09 41	10 32		11 04	11 32	12 04	12 32		13 32	14 04	14 32		15 32
Sheffield 7	29, 31 a	09 51	10 43		11 15	11 43	12 15	12 43		13 43	14 15	14 43		15 43
St Pancras International	⊖ 53 a	14c18	14e18		15f11	14e55	16f06	17g06			17h55	18j57		19k56

Station		NT	NT A	NT	NT	NT A	NT	NT	NT A	NT	NT A	NT	NT
Leeds 10	31 d		15 17	16 17		17 17	18 17		19 17	20 17	21 17		22 17
Woodlesford	d		15 25	16 25		17 25	18 25		19 25	20 25	21 25		22 25
Castleford	a		15 33	16 33		17 33	18 33		19 35	20 33	21 33		22 33
	d			16 36			18 36			20 36			22 36
Normanton	d			16 41			18 41			20 41			22 41
Wakefield Kirkgate 4	31 d			16 46			18 46			20 46			22 46
Darton	d			17 00			19 00			21 00			23 00
Huddersfield	d	15 19			17 19			19 19					
Lockwood	d	15 22			17 22			19 22					
Berry Brow	d	15 25			17 25			19 25					
Honley	d	15 28			17 28			19 28					
Brockholes	d	15 31			17 31			19 31					
Stocksmoor	d	15 35			17 35			19 35					
Shepley	d	15 37			17 37			19 37					
Denby Dale	d	15 42			17 42			19 42					
Penistone	d	15 50			17 50			19 50					
Silkstone Common	d	15 55			17 55			19 55					
Dodworth	d	15 59			17 59			19 59					
Barnsley	a	16 06		17 07	18 06		19 07	20 06		21 07			23 07
	d	16 12		17 12	18 12		19 12	20 12		21 12		22 21	23 12
Wombwell	d	16 17		17 17	18 17		19 17	20 17		21 17		22 26	23 17
Elsecar	d	16 21		17 21	18 21		19 21	20 21		21 21		22 30	23 21
Chapeltown	d	16 26		17 26	18 26		19 26	20 26		21 26		22 35	23 26
Meadowhall	29, 31 a	16 32		17 32	18 32		19 32	20 32		21 32		22 40	23 32
Sheffield 7	29, 31 a	16 43		17 43	18 47		19 43	20 46		21 43		22 51	23 43
St Pancras International	⊖ 53 a	20m49		22n19	22e18								

For general notes see front of timetable
For details of catering facilities see Directory of Train Operators

- **A** To Knottingley (Table 32)
- **B** To Lincoln (Table 30)
- **b** Mondays to Fridays only
- **c** From 30 March arr. 1318
- **e** From 30 March only
- **f** Until 23 March only
- **g** From 30 March arr. 1606
- **h** From 30 March arr. 1706
- **j** From 30 March arr. 1724
- **k** From 30 March arr. 1857
- **m** From 30 March arr. 1956
- **n** From 30 March arr. 2049

Network Diagram for Tables 35, 36, 37, 38

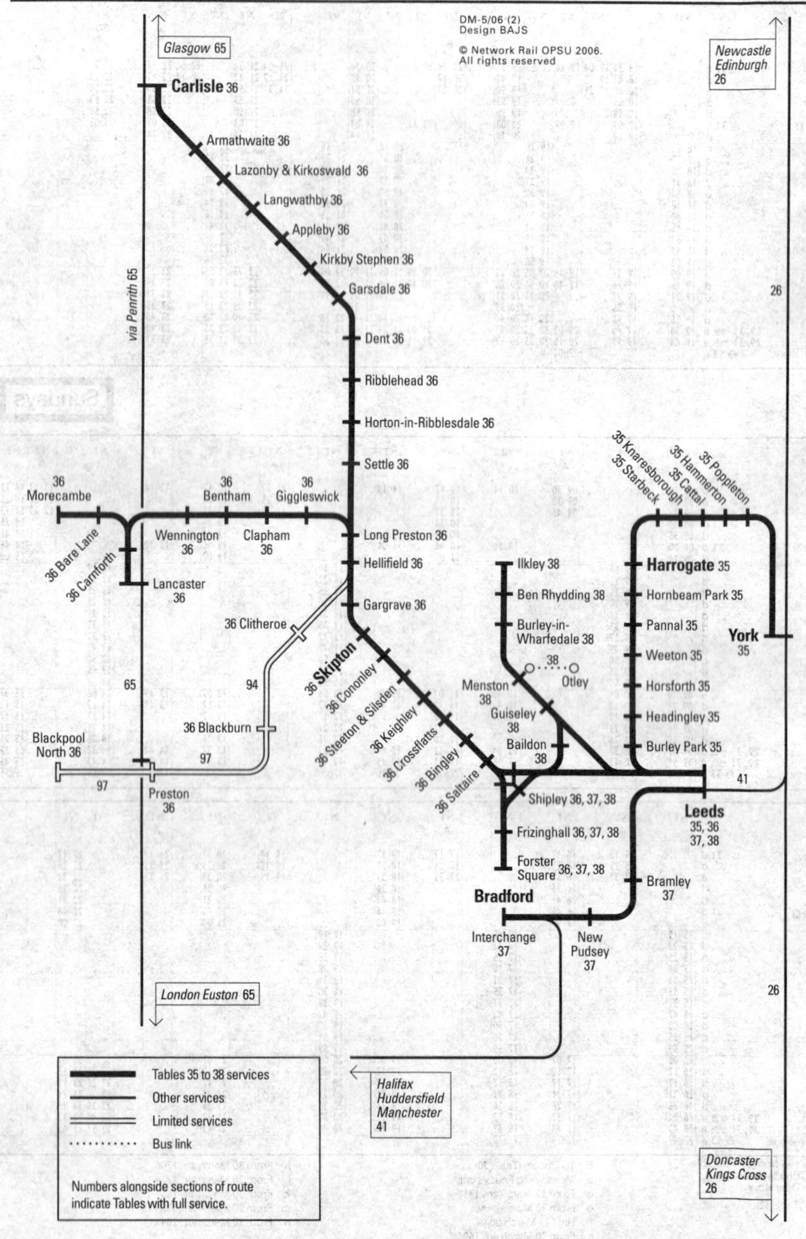

DM-5/06 (2)
Design BAJS
© Network Rail OPSU 2006.
All rights reserved
Glasgow 65
Carlisle 36
Armathwaite 36
Lazonby & Kirkoswald 36
Langwathby 36
Appleby 36
Kirkby Stephen 36
Garsdale 36
Dent 36
Ribblehead 36
Horton-in-Ribblesdale 36
Settle 36
via Penrith 65
Newcastle
Edinburgh
26
26
36 Morecambe
36 Bentham
36 Giggleswick
Wennington 36
Clapham 36
Long Preston 36
Hellifield 36
36 Bare Lane
36 Carnforth
Lancaster 36
Gargrave 36
36 Clitheroe
36 Skipton
36 Cononley
36 Steeton & Silsden
36 Keighley
36 Crossflatts
36 Bingley
36 Saltaire
65
94
36 Blackburn
Blackpool North 36
97
97
Preston 36
35 Knaresborough
35 Starbeck
35 Hammerton
35 Cattal
35 Poppleton
Harrogate 35
Hornbeam Park 35
Pannal 35
Weeton 35
Horsforth 35
Headingley 35
Burley Park 35
York 35
Ilkley 38
Ben Rhydding 38
Burley-in-Wharfedale 38
38
Otley
Menston 38
Guiseley 38
Baildon 38
Shipley 36, 37, 38
Frizinghall 36, 37, 38
Forster Square 36, 37, 38
41
Leeds 35, 36 37, 38
Bramley 37
Bradford
Interchange 37
New Pudsey 37
26
London Euston 65
Halifax
Huddersfield
Manchester
41
Doncaster
Kings Cross
26
Tables 35 to 38 services
Other services
Limited services
Bus link
Numbers alongside sections of route indicate Tables with full service.

York → Harrogate → Leeds

Network Diagram - see first page of Table 35

Mondays to Fridays

Miles	Station		NT	NT	NT	GR R 1 A ✕	NT	NT	NT	NT	NT	NT	NT	NT	NT	NT	NT	NT	NT	NT
0	**York** 8	41 d					06 52				07 57		08 45	09 10		10 11		11 11		12 11
3	Poppleton	d					06 56				08 01		08 50	09 14		10 15		11 15		12 15
8¾	Hammerton	d					07 04				08 09		08 58	09 22		10 23		11 23		12 23
10¼	Cattal	d					07 07				08 12		09 01	09 26		10 26		11 26		12 26
16¾	**Knaresborough**	a									08 21		09 09	09 34		10 34		11 34		12 34
—		d			07 00			07 42	07 56		08 21	08 56	09 10	09 35	10 05	10 35	11 05	11 35	12 05	12 35
18¼	Starbeck	d			07 03		07 27	07 45	07 59		08 24	08 59	09 13	09 38	10 08	10 38	11 08	11 38	12 08	12 38
20½	**Harrogate**	a			07 08		07 32	07 50	08 04		08 29	09 04	09 18	09 43	10 13	10 43	11 13	11 43	12 13	12 43
—		d	06 06	06 30	07 11	07 28	07 40	07 51	08 06	08 14	08 30	09 05	09 19	09 44	10 14	10 44	11 14	11 44	12 14	12 44
21½	Hornbeam Park	d	06 08	06 32	07 14		07 42	07 54		08 17	08 33		09 22	09 47	10 17	10 47	11 17	11 47	12 17	12 47
23¾	Pannal	d	06 13	06 37	07 19		07 47	07 59		08 22	08 38		09 27	09 52	10 22	10 52	11 22	11 52	12 22	12 52
27	Weeton	d	06 18	06 42	07 23		07 51	08 03		08 26	08 42		09 31	09 56	10 26	10 56	11 26	11 56	12 26	12 56
33	Horsforth	d	06 28	06 50	07 32	07u46	08 00	08 12	08 22	08 35	08 51	09 21	09 40	10 05	10 35	11 05	11 35	12 05	12 35	13 05
35¾	Headingley	d	06 32	06 54	07 36		08 04	08 16	08 26	08 39	08 55	09 25	09 44	10 09	10 39	11 09	11 39	12 09	12 39	13 09
36½	Burley Park	d	06 34	06 56	07 38		08 06	08 18	08 29	08 41	08 57	09 27	09 47	10 11	10 41	11 11	11 41	12 11	12 41	13 11
38¾	**Leeds** 10	41 a	06 44	07 08	07 48	07 58	08 17	08 29	08 40	08 52	09 08	09 37	09 56	10 22	10 52	11 22	11 52	12 22	12 52	13 22

Station		NT	NT	NT	NT	NT	NT	NT	NT	NT	NT	NT	NT	NT	NT	NT	NT	NT	NT
York 8	41 d		13 11		14 11		15 11		16 11		16 54	17 17		18 11		19 11	20 11	21 11	22 11
Poppleton	d		13 15		14 15		15 15		16 15		16 58	17 21		18 15		19 15	20 15	21 16	22 15
Hammerton	d		13 23		14 23		15 23		16 23		17 06	17 29		18 23		19 23	20 23	21 23	22 23
Cattal	d		13 26		14 26		15 26		16 26		17 09	17 32		18 26		19 26	20 26	21 27	22 27
Knaresborough	a		13 34		14 34		15 34		16 34		17 17	17 40		18 34		19 34	20 34	21 34	22 35
	d	13 05	13 35	14 05	14 35	15 05	15 35	16 05	16 35	17 05	17 18	17 41	18 05	18 35	19 05	19 35	20 35	21 35	22 36
Starbeck	d	13 08	13 38	14 08	14 38	15 08	15 38	16 08	16 38	17 08	17 21	17 44	18 12	18 38	19 08	19 38	20 38	21 39	22 40
Harrogate	a	13 13	13 43	14 13	14 43	15 13	15 43	16 13	16 43	17 14	17 26	17 49	18 17	18 43	19 13	19 43	20 43	21 43	22 45
	d	13 14	13 44	14 14	14 44	15 14	15 44	16 14	16 44	17 14	17 30	17 50	18 18	18 44	19 14	19 44	20 44	21 45	22 47
Hornbeam Park	d	13 17	13 47	14 17	14 47	15 17	15 47	16 17	16 47	17 17	17 32	17 53	18 21	18 47	19 17	19 47	20 47	21 48	22 49
Pannal	d	13 22	13 52	14 22	14 52	15 22	15 52	16 22	16 52	17 22	17 37	17 58	18 26	18 52	19 22	19 52	20 52	21 53	22 54
Weeton	d	13 26	13 56	14 26	14 56	15 26	15 56	16 26	16 56	17 26	17 42	18 02	18 30	18 56	19 26	19 56	20 56	21 58	22 59
Horsforth	d	13 35	14 05	14 35	15 05	15 35	16 05	16 35	17 05	17 38	17 50	18 11	18 39	19 05	19 35	20 05	21 05	22 06	23 08
Headingley	d	13 39	14 09	14 39	15 09	15 39	16 09	16 39	17 09	17 42	17 54	18 15	18 43	19 09	19 39	20 09	21 09	22 10	23 12
Burley Park	d	13 41	14 11	14 41	15 11	15 41	16 11	16 41	17 11	17 44	17 57	18 17	18 45	19 11	19 41	20 11	21 11	22 13	23 15
Leeds 10	41 a	13 52	14 22	14 52	15 22	15 52	16 22	16 52	17 22	17 55	18 07	18 28	18 55	19 22	19 52	20 22	21 22	22 23	23 25

Saturdays

Station		NT	NT	NT	GR R 1 A	NT	NT	NT	NT	NT	NT	NT	NT	NT	NT
York 8	41 d			06 52			07 57		08 45	09 10		10 11		11 11	
Poppleton	d			06 56			08 01		08 49	09 14		10 15		11 15	
Hammerton	d			07 04			08 09		08 57	09 22		10 23		11 23	
Cattal	d			07 07			08 12		09 00	09 26		10 26		11 26	
Knaresborough	a			07 15			08 21		09 08	09 34		10 34		11 34	
	d		06 47	07 21		07 51	08 21	08 51	09 09	09 35	10 05	10 35	11 05	11 35	12 05
Starbeck	d		06 50	07 24		07 54	08 24	08 54	09 12	09 38	10 08	10 38	11 08	11 38	12 08
Harrogate	a		06 55	07 29		07 59	08 29	08 59	09 17	09 43	10 13	10 43	11 13	11 43	12 13
	d	06 06	06 56	07 31	07 44	08 00	08 30	09 00	09 18	09 44	10 14	10 44	11 14	11 44	12 14
Hornbeam Park	d	06 08	06 59	07 33		08 03	08 33	09 03	09 21	09 47	10 17	10 47	11 17	11 47	12 17
Pannal	d	06 13	07 04	07 38		08 08	08 38	09 08	09 26	09 52	10 22	10 52	11 22	11 52	12 22
Weeton	d	06 18	07 08	07 42		08 12	08 42	09 12	09 30	09 56	10 26	10 56	11 26	11 56	12 26
Horsforth	d	06 28	07 17	07 51		08 21	08 51	09 21	09 39	10 05	10 35	11 05	11 35	12 05	12 35
Headingley	d	06 32	07 21	07 55		08 25	08 55	09 25	09 43	10 09	10 39	11 09	11 39	12 09	12 39
Burley Park	d	06 34	07 23	07 57		08 27	08 57	09 27	09 47	10 11	10 41	11 11	11 41	12 11	12 41
Leeds 10	41 a	06 44	07 34	08 08	08 12	08 38	09 08	09 37	09 55	10 22	10 52	11 22	11 52	12 22	12 52

Station		NT	NT	NT	NT	NT	NT	NT	NT	NT	NT	NT	NT	NT	NT	NT	NT	NT
York 8	41 d	12 11		13 11		14 11		15 11		16 11		16 54	17 17		18 11	19 11	20 11	21 57
Poppleton	d	12 15		13 15		14 15		15 15		16 15		16 58	17 21		18 15	19 15	20 15	22 01
Hammerton	d	12 23		13 23		14 23		15 23		16 23		17 06	17 29		18 23	19 23	20 23	22 09
Cattal	d	12 26		13 26		14 26		15 26		16 26		17 09	17 32		18 26	19 26	20 26	22 12
Knaresborough	a	12 34		13 34		14 34		15 34		16 34		17 17	17 40		18 34	19 34	20 34	22 20
	d	12 35	13 05	13 35	14 05	14 35	15 05	15 35	16 05	16 35	17 05	17 18	17 41	18 05	18 35	19 35	20 35	22 21
Starbeck	d	12 38	13 08	13 38	14 08	14 38	15 08	15 38	16 08	16 38	17 08	17 21	17 44	18 12	18 38	19 38	20 38	22 24
Harrogate	a	12 43	13 13	13 43	14 13	14 43	15 13	15 43	16 13	16 43	17 14	17 26	17 49	18 17	18 43	19 43	20 43	22 29
	d	12 44	13 14	13 44	14 14	14 44	15 14	15 44	16 14	16 44	17 14	17 30	17 50	18 18	18 44	19 44	20 44	22 37
Hornbeam Park	d	12 47	13 17	13 47	14 17	14 47	15 17	15 47	16 17	16 47	17 17	17 32	17 53	18 21	18 47	19 47	20 47	22 39
Pannal	d	12 52	13 22	13 52	14 22	14 52	15 22	15 52	16 22	16 52	17 22	17 37	17 58	18 26	18 52	19 52	20 52	22 44
Weeton	d	12 56	13 26	13 56	14 26	14 56	15 26	15 56	16 26	16 56	17 26	17 42	18 02	18 30	18 56	19 56	20 56	22 49
Horsforth	d	13 05	13 35	14 05	14 35	15 05	15 35	16 05	16 35	17 05	17 38	17 50	18 11	18 39	19 05	20 05	21 05	22 57
Headingley	d	13 09	13 39	14 09	14 39	15 09	15 39	16 09	16 39	17 09	17 42	17 54	18 15	18 43	19 09	20 09	21 09	23 01
Burley Park	d	13 11	13 41	14 11	14 41	15 11	15 41	16 11	16 41	17 11	17 44	17 57	18 17	18 45	19 11	20 11	21 11	23 04
Leeds 10	41 a	13 22	13 52	14 22	14 52	15 22	15 52	16 22	16 52	17 22	17 55	18 07	18 28	18 55	19 22	20 22	21 22	23 14

For general notes see front of timetable
For details of catering facilities see
Directory of Train Operators

A To London Kings Cross (Table 26)

Sundays

York → Harrogate → Leeds

Network Diagram - see first page of Table 35

		NT	NT	NT	NT	NT	NT	NT	NT	NT	NT	NT	NT
York 8 41	d				12 18	14 19	16 18	17 17	18 17	19 17	20 18	21 26	
Poppleton	d				12 22	14 23	16 22	17 21	18 21	19 21	20 22	21 30	
Hammerton	d				12 30	14 31	16 30	17 29	18 29	19 29	20 30	21 38	
Cattal	d				12 33	14 34	16 33	17 32	18 32	19 32	20 33	21 41	
Knaresborough	a				12 41	14 42	16 41	17 40	18 40	19 40	20 41	21 49	
	d			11 42	12 42	14 43	16 42	17 42	18 42	19 42	20 42	21 50	
Starbeck	d			11 45	12 45	14 46	16 45	17 45	18 45	19 45	20 45	21 53	
Harrogate	a			11 50	12 50	14 51	16 50	17 50	18 50	19 50	20 50	21 58	
	d	09 53	10 53	11 53	12 53	14 53	16 53	17 53	18 53	19 53	20 53	22 02	23 05
Hornbeam Park	d	09 56	10 56	11 56	12 56	14 56	16 56	17 56	18 56	19 56	20 56	22 04	23 08
Pannal	d	10 01	11 01	12 01	13 01	15 01	17 01	18 01	19 01	20 01	21 01	22 09	23 13
Weeton	d	10 05	11 05	12 05	13 05	15 05	17 05	18 05	19 05	20 05	21 05	22 14	23 17
Horsforth	d	10 14	11 14	12 14	13 14	15 14	17 14	18 14	19 14	20 14	21 14	22 22	23 26
Headingley	d	10 18	11 18	12 18	13 18	15 18	17 18	18 18	19 18	20 18	21 18	22 26	23 30
Burley Park	d	10 20	11 20	12 20	13 20	15 20	17 20	18 20	19 20	20 20	21 20	22 29	23 32
Leeds 10 41	a	10 30	11 28	12 30	13 30	15 30	17 30	18 30	19 30	20 30	21 30	22 40	23 43

For general notes see front of timetable
For details of catering facilities see
Directory of Train Operators

Leeds → Harrogate → York

Network Diagram - see first page of Table 35

Mondays to Fridays

Miles	Station		NT	NT	NT	NT	NT	NT	NT	NT	NT	NT	NT	NT	NT	NT	NT	NT	NT	NT
0	Leeds 10	41 d	06 06	06 29	07 13	07 43	07 59	08 29	08 59	09 29	09 59	10 29	10 59	11 29	11 59	12 29	12 59	13 29	13 59	14 29
2¼	Burley Park	d	06 10	06 33	07 17	07 47	08 03	08 33	09 03	09 33	10 03	10 33	11 03	11 33	12 03	12 33	13 03	13 33	14 03	14 33
3	Headingley	d	06 13	06 36	07 20	07 50	08 06	08 36	09 06	09 36	10 06	10 36	11 06	11 36	12 06	12 36	13 06	13 36	14 06	14 36
5¾	Horsforth	d	06 18	06 41	07 25	07 55	08 11	08 41	09 11	09 41	10 11	10 41	11 11	11 41	12 11	12 41	13 11	13 41	14 11	14 41
11¾	Weeton	d	06 26	06 49	07 33		08 19	08 49	09 19	09 49	10 19	10 49	11 19	11 49	12 19	12 49	13 19	13 49	14 19	14 49
15	Pannal	d	06 32	06 55	07 39		08 25	08 55	09 25	09 55	10 25	10 55	11 25	11 55	12 25	12 55	13 25	13 55	14 25	14 55
17¼	Hornbeam Park	d	06 37	07 00	07 44	08 10	08 30	09 00	09 30	10 00	10 30	11 00	11 30	12 00	12 30	13 00	13 30	14 00	14 30	15 00
18¼	**Harrogate**	a	06 40	07 04	07 49	08 13	08 33	09 03	09 33	10 03	10 33	11 03	11 33	12 03	12 33	13 03	13 33	14 03	14 33	15 03
—		d	06 45	07 05	07 49	08 16	08 34	09 05	09 35	10 05	10 35	11 05	11 35	12 05	12 35	13 05	13 35	14 05	14 35	15 05
20½	Starbeck	d	06 49	07 08	07 52	08 19	08 38	09 08	09 38	10 08	10 38	11 08	11 38	12 08	12 38	13 08	13 38	14 08	14 38	15 08
22	**Knaresborough**	a	06 54	07 15	07 59	08 25	08 45	09 14	09 45	10 14	10 45	11 14	11 45	12 14	12 45	13 14	13 45	14 14	14 45	15 14
—		d	06 55	07 18	07 59	08 28		09 15		10 14		11 14		12 14		13 14		14 14		15 14
28½	Cattal	d	07 03	07 26	08 07	08 36		09 23		10 22		11 22		12 22		13 22		14 22		15 22
30	Hammerton	d	07 06	07 30	08 11	08 39		09 27		10 26		11 26		12 26		13 26		14 26		15 26
35¾	Poppleton	d	07 13	07 37	08 18	08 46		09 34		10 33		11 33		12 33		13 33		14 33		15 33
38¾	**York 3**	41 a	07 21	07 49	08 30	08 58		09 45		10 45		11 45		12 45		13 45		14 44		15 47

Station		NT	NT	NT	NT	NT	NT	NT	NT	NT	NT	NT	NT	NT	NT	NT	NT	NT
Leeds 10	41 d	14 59	15 29	15 59	16 29	16 42	16 59	17 13	17 29	17 44	17 59	18 29	18 59	19 29	20 29	21 29	22 29	23 29
Burley Park	d	15 03	15 33	16 03	16 33	16 46	17 03	17 17	17 33	17 48	18 03	18 33	19 03	19 33	20 33	21 33	22 33	23 33
Headingley	d	15 06	15 36	16 06	16 36	16 49	17 06	17 20	17 36	17 51	18 06	18 36	19 06	19 36	20 36	21 36	22 36	23 36
Horsforth	d	15 11	15 41	16 11	16 41	16a54	17 11	17 25	17 41	17 56	18 11	18 41	19 11	19 41	20 41	21 41	22 41	23 41
Weeton	d	15 19	15 49	16 19	16 49		17 19	17 33	17 49		18 19	18 49	19 19	19 49	20 49	21 49	22 49	23 49
Pannal	d	15 25	15 55	16 25	16 55		17 25	17 39	17 55		18 25	18 55	19 25	19 55	20 55	21 55	22 55	23 55
Hornbeam Park	d	15 30	16 00	16 30	17 00		17 30	17 44	18 00		18 30	19 00	19 30	20 00	21 00	22 00	23 01	23 59
Harrogate	a	15 33	16 03	16 33	17 03		17 33	17 47	18 03	18 15	18 33	19 03	19 33	20 03	21 03	22 03	23 08	00 06
	d	15 35	16 05	16 35	17 08		17 35	17 49	18 05	18 16	18 35	19 05	19 35	20 05	21 05	22 05		
Starbeck	d	15 38	16 08	16 38	17 11		17 38	17 52	18 08	18 20	18 38	19 08	19 38	20 08	21 08	22 08		
Knaresborough	a	15 45	16 14	16 45	17 17		17 45	17 59	18 14	18 26	18 45	19 14	19 45	20 14	21 14	22 15		
	d		16 14		17 21				18 14			19 14		20 14	21 14			
Cattal	d		16 22		17 29				18 22			19 22		20 22	21 22			
Hammerton	d		16 26		17 32				18 26			19 26		20 26	21 26			
Poppleton	d		16 33		17 39				18 33			19 33		20 33	21 33			
York 8	41 a		16 45		17 48				18 45			19 45		20 44	21 46			

Saturdays

Station		NT	NT	NT	NT	NT	NT	NT	NT	NT	NT	NT	NT	NT	NT
Leeds 10	41 d	06 08	06 37	07 13	07 39	07 54	08 29	08 59	09 29	09 59	10 29	10 59	11 29	11 59	12 29
Burley Park	d	06 12	06 41	07 17	07 43	07 58	08 33	09 03	09 33	10 03	10 33	11 03	11 33	12 03	12 33
Headingley	d	06 15	06 44	07 20	07 46	08 01	08 36	09 06	09 36	10 06	10 36	11 06	11 36	12 06	12 36
Horsforth	d	06 20	06 49	07 25	07 51	08 06	08 41	09 11	09 41	10 11	10 41	11 11	11 41	12 11	12 41
Weeton	d	06 28	06 57	07 33	07 59	08 14	08 49	09 19	09 49	10 19	10 49	11 19	11 49	12 19	12 49
Pannal	d	06 34	07 03	07 39	08 05	08 20	08 55	09 25	09 55	10 25	10 55	11 25	11 55	12 25	12 55
Hornbeam Park	d	06 39	07 08	07 44	08 10	08 25	09 00	09 30	10 00	10 30	11 00	11 30	12 00	12 30	13 00
Harrogate	a	06 42	07 11	07 49	08 13	08 28	09 03	09 33	10 03	10 33	11 03	11 33	12 03	12 33	13 03
	d	06 45	07 14	07 49	08 16	08 29	09 05	09 35	10 05	10 35	11 05	11 35	12 05	12 35	13 05
Starbeck	d	06 49	07 17	07 52	08 19	08 33	09 08	09 38	10 08	10 38	11 08	11 38	12 08	12 38	13 08
Knaresborough	a	06 54	07 23	07 59	08 25	08 40	09 14	09 45	10 14	10 45	11 14	11 45	12 14	12 45	13 14
	d	06 55	07 23	07 59	08 28		09 15		10 14		11 14		12 14		13 14
Cattal	d	07 03	07 31	08 07	08 36		09 23		10 22		11 22		12 22		13 22
Hammerton	d	07 06	07 35	08 11	08 39		09 27		10 26		11 26		12 26		13 26
Poppleton	d	07 13	07 42	08 19	08 46		09 34		10 33		11 33		12 33		13 33
York 8	41 a	07 21	07 49	08 26	08 58		09 45		10 42		11 45		12 45		13 42

Station		NT	NT	NT	NT	NT	NT	NT	NT	NT	NT	NT	NT	NT	NT	NT	NT	NT	NT
Leeds 10	41 d	12 59	13 29	13 59	14 29	14 59	15 29	15 59	16 29	16 59	17 13	17 29	17 59	18 29	19 29	20 29	21 20	22 29	23 21
Burley Park	d	13 03	13 33	14 03	14 33	15 03	15 33	16 03	16 33	17 03	17 17	17 33	18 03	18 33	19 33	20 33	21 24	22 33	23 25
Headingley	d	13 06	13 36	14 06	14 36	15 06	15 36	16 06	16 36	17 06	17 20	17 36	18 06	18 36	19 36	20 36	21 27	22 36	23 28
Horsforth	d	13 11	13 41	14 11	14 41	15 11	15 41	16 11	16 41	17 11	17 25	17 41	18 11	18 41	19 41	20 41	21 32	22 41	23 33
Weeton	d	13 19	13 49	14 19	14 49	15 19	15 49	16 19	16 49	17 19	17 33	17 49	18 19	18 49	19 49	20 49	21 40	22 49	23 41
Pannal	d	13 25	13 55	14 25	14 55	15 25	15 55	16 25	16 55	17 25	17 39	17 55	18 25	18 55	19 55	20 55	21 46	22 55	23 47
Hornbeam Park	d	13 30	14 00	14 30	15 00	15 30	16 00	16 30	17 00	17 30	17 44	18 00	18 30	19 00	20 00	21 00	21 51	23 00	23 52
Harrogate	a	13 33	14 03	14 33	15 03	15 33	16 03	16 33	17 03	17 33	17 47	18 03	18 33	19 03	20 03	21 03	21 54	23 06	23 58
	d	13 35	14 05	14 35	15 05	15 35	16 05	16 35	17 08	17 35	17 49	18 05	18 35	19 05	20 05	21 05	21 56		
Starbeck	d	13 38	14 08	14 38	15 08	15 38	16 08	16 38	17 11	17 38	17 52	18 08	18 38	19 08	20 08	21 08	21 59		
Knaresborough	a	13 45	14 14	14 45	15 14	15 45	16 14	16 45	17 17	17 45	17 59	18 14	18 45	19 14	20 14	21 14	22 06		
	d		14 14		15 14		16 14		17 21			18 14		19 14	20 14	21 14			
Cattal	d		14 22		15 22		16 22		17 29			18 22		19 22	20 22	21 22			
Hammerton	d		14 26		15 26		16 26		17 33			18 26		19 26	20 26	21 26			
Poppleton	d		14 33		15 33		16 33		17 40			18 33		19 33	20 33	21 33			
York 8	41 a		14 46		15 45		16 45		17 47			18 46		19 45	20 42	21 47			

For general notes see front of timetable
For details of catering facilities see
Directory of Train Operators

Table 35

Sundays

Leeds → Harrogate → York

Network Diagram - see first page of Table 35

		NT	NT	NT	NT	NT	NT	NT	NT	NT	NT	NT	NT
Leeds 10	41 d	09 54	10 54	12 54	14 54	15 54	16 54	17 54	18 54	19 54	21 16	22 23	23 22
Burley Park	d	09 59	10 59	12 59	14 59	15 59	16 59	17 59	18 59	19 59	21 21	22 28	23 27
Headingley	d	10 01	11 01	13 01	15 01	16 01	17 01	18 01	19 01	20 01	21 23	22 30	23 29
Horsforth	d	10 07	11 07	13 07	15 07	16 07	17 07	18 07	19 07	20 07	21 29	22 36	23 35
Weeton	d	10 14	11 14	13 14	15 14	16 14	17 14	18 14	19 14	20 14	21 37	22 43	23 42
Pannal	d	10 20	11 20	13 20	15 20	16 20	17 20	18 20	19 20	20 20	21 43	22 49	23 48
Hornbeam Park	d	10 25	11 25	13 25	15 25	16 25	17 25	18 25	19 25	20 25	21 48	22 54	23 53
Harrogate	a	10 31	11 28	13 28	15 28	16 28	17 28	18 28	19 28	20 28	21 51	23 00	23 59
	d		11 30	13 30	15 30	16 30	17 30	18 30	19 30	20 30	21 53		
Starbeck	d		11 34	13 34	15 34	16 34	17 34	18 34	19 34	20 34	21 57		
Knaresborough	a		11 39	13 39	15 39	16 39	17 39	18 39	19 39	20 39	22 03		
	d		11 40	13 40	15 40	16 45	17 44	18 44	19 44	20 45			
Cattal	d		11 48	13 48	15 48	16 53	17 52	18 52	19 52	20 53			
Hammerton	d		11 51	13 51	15 51	16 56	17 55	18 55	19 55	20 56			
Poppleton	d		11 58	13 58	15 58	17 03	18 02	19 02	20 02	21 03			
York 8	41 a		12 08	14 08	16 08	17 10	18 11	19 12	20 10	21 13			

For general notes see front of timetable
For details of catering facilities see Directory of Train Operators

Leeds and Bradford → Skipton, Lancaster, Morecambe and Carlisle

Network Diagram - see first page of Table 35

Miles	Miles	Miles		NT	NT	NT	NT	NT	NT	NT	NT		NT	NT	NT	NT	NT	NT	NT	NT		NT	NT	NT
—	—	—	London Kings Cross 15 ⊖ 26 d																	*06 00*				*06 35*
0	0	—	**Leeds 10** 37 d		05 55		06 21			06 56			07 25		07 51		08 19	08 25		08 49		08 56		09 26
—	—	0	**Bradford Forster Square** 37 d			06 10	*06 15*	06 40		*06 55*	07 15			07 42	*07 46*	08 11	*08 16*		08 41	*08 46*			09 11	*09 16*
—	—	1¾	Frizinghall 37 d			06 13	*06 18*	06 43		*06 58*	07 18			07 45	*07 49*	08 14	*08 19*		08 44	*08 49*			09 14	*09 19*
10¾	10¾	2¾	Shipley 37 a		06 07	06 17	06 32	06 47		07 09	07 22		07 36	07 49	08 02	08 18	08 31	08 37	08 48	09 01		09 07	09 18	09 37
—	—	—	d		06 08	06 19	06 33	06 48		07 10	07 23		07 37	07 50	08 03	08 19	08 32	08 37	08 49	09 02		09 09	09 19	09 38
11½	11½	—	Saltaire d		06 10	06 21	06 35	06 50		07 12	07 25		07 39	07 52	08 05	08 21		08 39	08 51			09 11	09 21	09 40
13¾	13¾	—	Bingley d		06 14	06 25	06 39	06 54		07 16	07 29		07 43	07 56	08 09	08 25	08 37	08 43	08 55	09 06		09 15	09 25	09 44
14½	14½	—	Crossflatts d		06 16	06 27	06 41	06 56		07 18	07 31		07 45	07 58	08 11	08 27		08 45	08 57			09 17	09 27	09 46
17	17	—	Keighley d		06 21	06 32	06 45	07 01		07 22	07 36		07 49	08 03	08 15	08 32	08 42	08 49	09 02	09 12		09 21	09 32	09 50
20	20	—	Steeton & Silsden d		06 26	06 36	06 49	07 05		07 26	07 40		07 53	08 07	08 19	08 36		08 53	09 06			09 25	09 36	09 54
23¼	23¼	—	Cononley d		06 30	06 40	06 53	07 09		07 30	07 44		07 57	08 11	08 23	08 40		08 57	09 10			09 29	09 40	09 58
26¼	26¼	—	**Skipton** a		06 38	06 48	07 00	07 17		07 37	07 51		08 05	08 19	08 32	08 47	08 55	09 07	09 18	09 24		09 37	09 47	10 07
—	—	—	d	05 43													08 56			09 26				
30	30	—	Gargrave d	05 48													09 02			09 32				
36¼	36¼	—	Hellifield d	05 57													09 10			09 40				
37½	37½	—	Long Preston d	06 00													09 13			09 43				
—	41¼	—	Giggleswick d	06 09													09 20							
—	48	—	Clapham (Nth Yorkshire) d	06 16													09 28							
—	51¼	—	Bentham d	06 22													09 33							
—	54½	—	Wennington d	06 27													09 39							
—	64	—	Carnforth 83 a	06 43													09 54							
—	70¼	—	**Lancaster 6** 65, 83, 98 a	06 53													10 04							
—	72¾	—	Bare Lane 98 a	*07 16*													10 16							
—	75½	—	**Morecambe** 98 a	*07 20*													10 22							
41¼	—	—	Settle d																	09 50				
47½	—	—	Horton In Ribblesdale d																	09 58				
52¼	—	—	Ribblehead d																	10 06				
58¼	—	—	Dent d																	10 16				
61¾	—	—	Garsdale d																	10 21				
71½	—	—	Kirkby Stephen d						07 28											10 34				
82¼	—	—	Appleby d						07 40											10 47				
93¼	—	—	Langwathby d						07 54											11 01				
97½	—	—	Lazonby & Kirkoswald d						08 00											11 07				
103	—	—	Armathwaite d						08 08											11 15				
113	—	—	**Carlisle 8** 65 a						08 24											11 34				
—	—	—	Glasgow Central 15 65 a	*10 18*					*10 18*								*13b16*			*13 16*				

	NT	NT	NT	NT	NT	NT	NT		NT	NT	NT	NT	NT	NT	NT	NT		NT	NT	NT	NT	NT	NT	NT
London Kings Cross 15 ⊖ 26 d		*07 10*			*07c20*							*08 35*				*09 35*			*10 10*			*10 35*		
Leeds 10 37 d		09 47	09 56		10 19	10 26			10 49	10 56		11 26		11 56		12 26			12 49	12 56		13 26		13 49
Bradford Forster Square 37 d	09 41	*09 46*		10 11	*10 16*		10 41		*10 46*		11 11	*11 16*	11 41	*11 46*	12 11	*12 16*		12 41	*12 46*		13 11	*13 16*	13 41	*13 46*
Frizinghall 37 d	09 44	*09 49*		10 14	*10 19*		10 44		*10 49*		11 14	*11 19*	11 44	*11 49*	12 14	*12 19*		12 44	*12 49*		13 14	*13 19*	13 44	*13 49*
Shipley 37 a	09 48	10 01	10 07	10 18	10 31	10 37	10 48		11 01	11 07	11 18	11 37	11 48	12 07	12 18	12 37		12 48	13 01	13 07	13 18	13 37	13 48	14 03
d	09 49	10 02	10 08	10 19	10 32	10 38	10 49		11 02	11 08	11 19	11 38	11 49	12 08	12 19	12 38		12 49	13 02	13 08	13 19	13 38	13 49	14 03
Saltaire d	09 51		10 10	10 21		10 40	10 51			11 10	11 21	11 40	11 51	12 10	12 21	12 40		12 51		13 10	13 21	13 41	13 51	
Bingley d	09 55	10 06	10 14	10 25		10 44	10 55		11 06	11 14	11 25	11 44	11 55	12 14	12 25	12 44		12 55	13 06	13 14	13 25	13 45	13 55	14 08
Crossflatts d	09 57		10 16	10 27		10 46	10 57			11 16	11 27	11 46	11 57	12 16	12 27	12 46		12 57		13 16	13 27	13 47	13 57	
Keighley d	10 02	10 12	10 20	10 32	10 40	10 50	11 02		11 12	11 20	11 32	11 50	12 02	12 20	12 32	12 50		13 02	13 12	13 20	13 32	13 52	14 02	14 13
Steeton & Silsden d	10 06		10 24	10 36		10 54	11 06			11 24	11 36	11 54	12 06	12 24	12 36	12 54		13 06		13 24	13 36	13 56	14 06	
Cononley d	10 10		10 28	10 40		10 58	11 10			11 28	11 40	11 58	12 10	12 28	12 40	12 58		13 10		13 28	13 40	14 00	14 10	
Skipton a	10 17	10 24	10 37	10 47	10 52	11 07	11 17		11 24	11 37	11 47	12 07	12 17	12 37	12 47	13 07		13 17	13 24	13 37	13 47	14 08	14 17	14 26
d		10 26			10 54				11 26										13 26					14 27
Gargrave d					10 59														13 31					14 33
Hellifield d					11 08				11 37										13 40					14 41
Long Preston d					11 11														13 42					14 44
Giggleswick d					11 18																			14 51
Clapham (Nth Yorkshire) d					11 25																			14 59
Bentham d					11 31																			15 04
Wennington d					11 36																			15 10
Carnforth 83 a					11 52																			15 25
Lancaster 6 65, 83, 98 a					12 01																			15 38
Bare Lane 98 a					12 16																			16 08
Morecambe 98 a					12 21																			16 13
Settle d		10 44							11 46										13 48					
Horton In Ribblesdale d									11 54										13 57					
Ribblehead d									12 02										14 05					
Dent d									12 12										14 14					
Garsdale d									12 17										14 20					
Kirkby Stephen d		11 22							12 30										14 32					
Appleby d		11 36							12 43										14 45					
Langwathby d									12 57										14 59					
Lazonby & Kirkoswald d									13 03										15 04					
Armathwaite d									13 11										15 12					
Carlisle 8 65 a		12 17							13 29										15 32					
Glasgow Central 15 65 a		*13 46*			*15b25*				*14 54*										*17 21*					*18b46*

For general notes see front of timetable
For details of catering facilities see Directory of Train Operators

b Change at Lancaster
c Change at Doncaster and Leeds

Leeds and Bradford → Skipton, Lancaster, Morecambe and Carlisle

Network Diagram - see first page of Table 35

Station		NT	NT	NT		NT	NT	NT	NT	NT	NT	NT	NT		NT	NT	NT	NT	NT	NT	NT	NT		NT	NT
London Kings Cross 15	⊖ 26 d	11 10		11b30			12 10			12 35		13 10			13 35		14 10			14 35		15 10			
Leeds 10	37 d	13 56		14 26			14 49	14 56		15 26		15 56			16 26		16 45	16 52		17 20		17 51		17 56	
Bradford Forster Square	37 d		14 11	14 16		14 41	14 46		15 11	15 16	15 41	15 46	16 11		16 16	16 40	16 44		17 11	17 16	17 38	17 46			18 11
Frizinghall	37 d		14 14	14 19		14 44	14 49		15 14	15 19	15 44	15 49	16 14		16 19	16 43	16 48		17 14	17 19	17 41	17 49			18 14
Shipley	37 a	14 07	14 18	14 37		14 48	15 01	15 07	15 18	15 37	15 48	16 07	16 18		16 37	16 48	16 56	17 04	17 18	17 31	17 45	18 02		18 08	18 18
	d	14 08	14 19	14 38		14 49	15 02	15 08	15 19	15 38	15 49	16 08	16 19		16 38	16 49	16 57	17 05	17 19	17 32	17 46	18 03		18 09	18 19
Saltaire	d	14 10	14 21	14 40		14 51		15 10	15 21	15 40	15 51	16 10	16 22		16 40	16 52	16 59		17 22	17 34	17 49	18 05			18 21
Bingley	d	14 14	14 25	14 44		14 55	15 06	15 14	15 25	15 44	15 55	16 14	16 26		16 44	16 56	17 03	17 10	17 26	17 38	17 53	18 09		18 16	18 25
Crossflatts	d	14 16	14 27	14 46		14 57		15 16	15 27	15 46	15 57	16 16	16 28		16 47	16 58	17 06		17 28	17 41	17 55	18 12			18 27
Keighley	d	14 20	14 32	14 50		15 02	15 12	15 20	15 32	15 50	16 02	16 20	16 33		16 51	17 03	17 10	17 15	17 33	17 45	18 00	18 16		18 23	18 32
Steeton & Silsden	d	14 24	14 36	14 54		15 06		15 24	15 36	15 54	16 06	16 24	16 37		16 56	17 07	17 15	17 20	17 37	17 50	18 04	18 21		18 29	18 36
Cononley	d	14 28	14 40	14 58		15 10		15 28	15 40	15 58	16 10	16 28	16 41		17 00	17 11	17 19		17 41	17 54	18 08	18 25			18 40
Skipton	a	14 37	14 47	15 07		15 17	15 24	15 37	15 47	16 07	16 17	16 37	16 49		17 07	17 19	17 26	17 31	17 49	18 01	18 16	18 33		18 39	18 47
	d						15 26											17 32						18 40	
Gargrave	d																	17 38						18 46	
Hellifield	d						15 37											17 46						18 54	
Long Preston	d																	17 49						18 57	
Giggleswick	d																	17 56							
Clapham (Nth Yorkshire)	d																	18 04							
Bentham	d																	18 09							
Wennington	d																	18 15							
Carnforth	83 a																	18 30							
Lancaster 6	65, 83, 98 a																	18 43							
Bare Lane	98 a																	18 51							
Morecambe	98 a																	18 57							
Settle	d						15 45																	19 03	
Horton In Ribblesdale	d						15 53																	19 11	
Ribblehead	d						16 01																	19 19	
Dent	d						16 11																	19 29	
Garsdale	d						16 16																	19 34	
Kirkby Stephen	d						16 29																	19 47	
Appleby	d						16 41																	19 59	
Langwathby	d						16 55																	20 13	
Lazonby & Kirkoswald	d						17 01																	20 19	
Armathwaite	d						17 09																	20 27	
Carlisle 8	65 a						17 28																	20 47	
Glasgow Central 15	65 a						19 37											21c11						22 31	

Station		NT	NT	NT	NT	NT	NT	NT	NT		NT	NT	GR R 1 ✕	NT	NT	NT	NT	NT		NT	NT	NT	NT		
London Kings Cross 15	⊖ 26 d	15 35				16 35			17 03		17e33		18 03			18 33	19 03			19 30	20 03		20 30		
Leeds 10	37 d	18 26		18 50		19 19	19 25		19 56		19e59	20 26	20 33	20 55		21 26	21 56			22 26	22 56		23 18		
Bradford Forster Square	37 d	18 16	18 41	18 46	19 08			19 36	19 41		20 06	20 25		20 38	21 05	21 25	21 38	22 05		22 25	22 38	23 09			
Frizinghall	37 d	18 19	18 44	18 49	19 11			19 39	19 44		20 09	20 28		20 41	21 08	21 28	21 41	22 08		22 28	22 41	23 12			
Shipley	37 a	18 37	18 48	19 03	19 15	19 31	19 37	19 43	20 07		20 16	20 37		21 07	21 12	21 37	22 07	22 12		22 37	23 07	23 16	23 30		
	d	18 38	18 49	19 03	19 16	19 32	19 38	19 44	20 08		20 16	20 38		21 08	21 14	21 38	22 08	22 14		22 38	23 08	23 17	23 31		
Saltaire	d	18 40	18 51	19 05	19 18		19 40	19 46	20 10		20 19	20 40		21 10	21 16	21 40	22 10	22 16		22 40	23 10	23 19	23 33		
Bingley	d	18 44	18 55	19 09	19 22	19 36	19 44	19 50	20 14		20 23	20 44		21 14	21 20	21 44	22 14	22 20		22 44	23 14	23 23	23 37		
Crossflatts	d	18 46	18 57	19 11	19 24		19 46	19 52	20 16		20 25	20 46		21 16	21 22	21 46	22 16	22 22		22 46	23 16	23 25	23 39		
Keighley	d	18 50	19 02	19 15	19 29	19 42	19 50	19 57	20 20		20 29	20 50	20s57	21 20	21 27	21 50	22 20	22 27		22 50	23 21	23 30	23 43		
Steeton & Silsden	d	18 54	19 06	19 19	19 33		19 54	20 01	20 24		20 33	20 54		21 24	21 31	21 54	22 24	22 31		22 54	23 26	23 34	23 47		
Cononley	d	18 58	19 10	19 23	19 37		19 58	20 05	20 28		20 37	20 58		21 28	21 35	21 58	22 28	22 35		22 58	23 31	23 38	23 51		
Skipton	a	19 06	19 17	19 33	19 44	19 54	20 06	20 12	20 35		20 46	21 06	21 13	21 36	21 42	22 06	22 36	22 42		23 06	23 39	23 45	23 58		
	d					19 59																			
Gargrave	d					20 05																			
Hellifield	d					20 14																			
Long Preston	d					20 16																			
Giggleswick	d																								
Clapham (Nth Yorkshire)	d																								
Bentham	d																								
Wennington	d																								
Carnforth	83 a																								
Lancaster 6	65, 83, 98 a																								
Bare Lane	98 a																								
Morecambe	98 a																								
Settle	d					20 22																			
Horton In Ribblesdale	d					20 31																			
Ribblehead	d					20a41																			
Dent	d																								
Garsdale	d																								
Kirkby Stephen	d																								
Appleby	d																								
Langwathby	d																								
Lazonby & Kirkoswald	d																								
Armathwaite	d																								
Carlisle 8	65 a																								
Glasgow Central 15	65 a																								

For general notes see front of timetable
For details of catering facilities see Directory of Train Operators

b Change at Doncaster and Leeds
c Change at Lancaster
e Change at Shipley

Table 36

Leeds and Bradford → Skipton, Lancaster, Morecambe and Carlisle

Network Diagram - see first page of Table 35

		NT	NT	NT	NT	NT	NT	NT	NT A	NT	NT	NT	NT	NT	NT	NT	NT	NT	NT	NT	NT
London Kings Cross 15	⊖ 26 d																*07 10*				
Leeds 10	37 d	05 55		06 19	06 56		07 56		08 19	08 25		08 49	08 56		09 26		09 47	09 56		10 19	10 26
Bradford Forster Square	37 d		06 10	*06 15*		07 11	*07 16*	08 11	*08 16*		08 41	*08 46*		09 11	*09 16*	09 41	*09 46*		10 11	*10 16*	
Frizinghall	37 d		06 13	*06 18*		07 14	*07 19*	08 14	*08 19*		08 44	*08 49*		09 14	*09 19*	09 44	*09 49*		10 14	*10 19*	
Shipley	37 a	06 07	06 17	06 31	07 07	07 18	08 08	08 18	08 31	08 37	08 48	09 01	09 07	09 18	09 37	09 48	10 01	10 07	10 18	10 31	10 37
	d	06 08	06 19	06 32	07 08	07 19	08 08	08 19	08 32	08 37	08 49	09 02	09 09	09 19	09 38	09 49	10 02	10 08	10 19	10 32	10 38
Saltaire	d	06 10	06 21		07 10	07 21	08 10	08 21		08 39	08 51		09 11	09 21	09 40	09 51		10 10	10 21		10 40
Bingley	d	06 14	06 25	06 36	07 14	07 25	08 14	08 25	08 37	08 43	08 55	09 06	09 15	09 25	09 44	09 55	10 06	10 14	10 25		10 44
Crossflatts	d	06 16	06 27		07 16	07 27	08 16	08 27		08 45	08 57		09 17	09 27	09 46	09 57		10 16	10 27		10 46
Keighley	d	06 21	06 32	06 42	07 20	07 32	08 20	08 32	08 42	08 49	09 02	09 12	09 21	09 32	09 50	10 02	10 12	10 20	10 32	10 40	10 50
Steeton & Silsden	d	06 26	06 36		07 24	07 36	08 24	08 36		08 53	09 06		09 25	09 36	09 54	10 06		10 24	10 36		10 54
Cononley	d	06 30	06 40		07 28	07 40	08 28	08 40		08 57	09 10		09 29	09 40	09 58	10 10		10 28	10 40		10 58
Skipton	a	06 37	06 48	06 55	07 37	07 47	08 37	08 47	08 55	09 07	09 18	09 24	09 37	09 47	10 07	10 17	10 24	10 37	10 47	10 52	11 07
	d	06 40		06 56					08 56			09 26					10 26			10 54	
Gargrave	d	06 45							09 02			09 32								10 59	
Hellifield	d	06 54		07 08					09 10			09 40								11b11	
Long Preston	d	06 57							09 13			09 43								11 14	
Giggleswick	d	07 05							09 20											11 21	
Clapham (Nth Yorkshire)	d	07 13							09 28											11 28	
Bentham	d	07 18							09 33											11 34	
Wennington	d	07 24							09 39											11 39	
Carnforth	83 a	07 39							09 53											11 55	
Lancaster 6	65, 83, 98 a	07 53							10 04											12 04	
Bare Lane	98 a	*08 25*							10c19											12 20	
Morecambe	98 a	*08 29*							10c25											12 25	
Settle	d			07 15								09 51					10 44				
Horton In Ribblesdale	d			07 24								10 00									
Ribblehead	d			07 32								10 08									
Dent	d			07 41								10 17									
Garsdale	d			07 47								10 23									
Kirkby Stephen	d			07 59								10 35									
Appleby	d			08 12								10 49					11 22				
Langwathby	d			08 26								11 03					11 36				
Lazonby & Kirkoswald	d			08 31								11 08									
Armathwaite	d			08 39								11 16									
Carlisle 8	65 a			08 58								11 36					12 17				
Glasgow Central 15	65 a																				

		NT	NT	NT	NT	NT	NT	NT	NT	NT	NT	NT	NT	NT	NT	NT	NT	NT	NT	NT
London Kings Cross 15	⊖ 26 d		*08 10*					*09 05*				*10 10*					*11 10*			
Leeds 10	37 d		10 49	10 56		11 26		11 56		12 26		12 49	12 56		13 26		13 49	13 56		14 26
Bradford Forster Square	37 d	10 41	*10 46*		11 11	*11 16*	11 41	*11 46*	12 11	*12 16*	12 41	*12 46*		13 11	*13 16*	13 41	*13 46*		14 11	*14 16*
Frizinghall	37 d	10 44	*10 49*		11 14	*11 19*	11 44	*11 49*	12 14	*12 19*	12 44	*12 49*		13 14	*13 19*	13 44	*13 49*		14 14	*14 19*
Shipley	37 a	10 48	11 01	11 07	11 18	11 37	11 48	12 07	12 18	12 37	12 48	13 01	13 07	13 18	13 38	13 48	14 03	14 07	14 18	14 37
	d	10 49	11 02	11 08	11 19	11 38	11 49	12 08	12 19	12 38	12 49	13 02	13 08	13 19	13 39	13 49	14 03	14 08	14 19	14 38
Saltaire	d	10 51		11 10	11 21	11 40	11 51	12 10	12 21	12 40	12 51		13 10	13 21	13 41	13 51		14 10	14 21	14 40
Bingley	d	10 55	11 06	11 14	11 25	11 44	11 55	12 14	12 25	12 44	12 55	13 06	13 14	13 25	13 45	13 55	14 08	14 14	14 25	14 44
Crossflatts	d	10 57		11 16	11 27	11 46	11 57	12 16	12 27	12 46	12 57		13 16	13 27	13 47	13 57		14 16	14 27	14 46
Keighley	d	11 02	11 12	11 20	11 32	11 50	12 02	12 20	12 32	12 50	13 02	13 12	13 20	13 32	13 52	14 02	14 13	14 20	14 32	14 50
Steeton & Silsden	d	11 06		11 24	11 36	11 54	12 06	12 24	12 36	12 54	13 06		13 24	13 36	13 57	14 06		14 24	14 36	14 54
Cononley	d	11 10		11 28	11 40	11 58	12 10	12 28	12 40	12 58	13 10		13 28	13 40	14 01	14 10		14 28	14 40	14 58
Skipton	a	11 17	11 24	11 37	11 47	12 07	12 17	12 37	12 47	13 07	13 17	13 24	13 37	13 47	14 09	14 17	14 26	14 37	14 47	15 07
	d		11 26									13 26					14 27			
Gargrave	d											13 31					14 33			
Hellifield	d		11 37									13 41					14 41			
Long Preston	d											13 43					14 44			
Giggleswick	d																14 51			
Clapham (Nth Yorkshire)	d																14 59			
Bentham	d																15 04			
Wennington	d																15 10			
Carnforth	83 a																15 25			
Lancaster 6	65, 83, 98 a																15 38			
Bare Lane	98 a																16 08			
Morecambe	98 a																16 13			
Settle	d		11 46									13 49								
Horton In Ribblesdale	d		11 54									13 58								
Ribblehead	d		12 02									14 06								
Dent	d		12 12									14 15								
Garsdale	d		12 17									14 21								
Kirkby Stephen	d		12 30									14 33								
Appleby	d		12 43									14 46								
Langwathby	d		12 57									15 00								
Lazonby & Kirkoswald	d		13 03									15 05								
Armathwaite	d		13 11									15 13								
Carlisle 8	65 a		13 29									15 32								
Glasgow Central 15	65 a																			

For general notes see front of timetable
For details of catering facilities see Directory of Train Operators

A From 29 March
b Arr. 1107
c Until 22 March arr. 3 minutes earlier

Leeds and Bradford → Skipton, Lancaster, Morecambe and Carlisle

Network Diagram - see first page of Table 35

		NT	NT	NT	NT	NT	NT	NT	NT	NT	NT	NT	NT	NT	NT	NT	NT	NT	NT	NT	NT
London Kings Cross 15	⊖ 26 d		12 10			12b30		13 10							14 30					15 30	
Leeds 10	37 d		14 49	14 56		15 26		15 56		16 26		16 49	16 56		17 26		17 49	17 56		18 26	
Bradford Forster Square	37 d	14 41	14 46		15 11	15 16	15 41	15 46	16 11	16 16	16 40	16 44		17 11	17 16	17 41	17 46		18 11	18 16	18 41
Frizinghall	37 d	14 44	14 49		15 14	15 19	15 44	15 49	16 14	16 19	16 43	16 48		17 14	17 19	17 44	17 49		18 14	18 19	18 44
Shipley	37 a	14 48	15 01	15 07	15 18	15 37	15 48	16 07	16 18	16 37	16 48	17 01	17 07	17 18	17 37	17 48	18 02	18 07	18 18	18 37	18 48
	d	14 49	15 02	15 08	15 19	15 38	15 49	16 08	16 19	16 38	16 49	17 02	17 08	17 19	17 38	17 49	18 02	18 08	18 19	18 38	18 49
Saltaire	d	14 51		15 10	15 21	15 40	15 51	16 10	16 22	16 40	16 52		17 10	17 22	17 40	17 51		18 10	18 21	18 40	18 51
Bingley	d	14 55	15 06	15 14	15 25	15 44	15 55	16 14	16 26	16 44	16 56	17 07	17 14	17 26	17 44	17 55	18 07	18 14	18 25	18 44	18 55
Crossflatts	d	14 57		15 16	15 27	15 46	15 57	16 16	16 28	16 47	16 58		17 17	17 28	17 47	17 57		18 17	18 27	18 46	18 57
Keighley	d	15 02	15 12	15 20	15 32	15 50	16 02	16 20	16 33	16 51	17 03	17 12	17 21	17 33	17 51	18 02	18 13	18 21	18 32	18 50	19 02
Steeton & Silsden	d	15 06		15 24	15 36	15 54	16 06	16 24	16 37	16 56	17 07	17 17	17 26	17 37	17 56	18 06	18 18	18 26	18 36	18 54	19 06
Cononley	d	15 10		15 28	15 40	15 58	16 10	16 28	16 41	17 00	17 11		17 30	17 41	18 00	18 10		18 30	18 40	18 58	19 10
Skipton	a	15 17	15 24	15 37	15 47	16 07	16 17	16 37	16 49	17 07	17 19	17 27	17 37	17 49	18 07	18 17	18 28	18 37	18 47	19 06	19 17
	d		15 26									17 31					18 30				
Gargrave	d											17 37					18 37				
Hellifield	d		15 37									17 45					18 46				
Long Preston	d											17 48					18 48				
Giggleswick	d											17 55									
Clapham (Nth Yorkshire)	d											18 03									
Bentham	d											18 08									
Wennington	d											18 14									
Carnforth	83 a											18 29									
Lancaster 6	65, 83, 98 a											18 42									
Bare Lane	98 a											18 51									
Morecambe	98 a											18 57									
Settle	d		15 45														18 54				
Horton In Ribblesdale	d		15 53														19 03				
Ribblehead	d		16 01														19 11				
Dent	d		16 11														19 20				
Garsdale	d		16 16														19 26				
Kirkby Stephen	d		16 29														19 38				
Appleby	d		16 41														19 51				
Langwathby	d		16 55														20 05				
Lazonby & Kirkoswald	d		17 01														20 10				
Armathwaite	d		17 09														20 18				
Carlisle 8	65 a		17 28														20 37				
Glasgow Central 15	65 a																				

		NT	NT	NT	NT	NT	GR R 1	NT	NT	NT	NT	NT	NT	NT	NT	NT	NT	NT	NT
London Kings Cross 15	⊖ 26 d			16 30			17 30				18c30		18b40			19b00	20 00		20b30
Leeds 10	37 d	18 56		19 19	19 25		19 57		20 06	20 26	20 55		21 26	21 56		22 26	22 56		23 18
Bradford Forster Square	37 d	18 46	19 07			19 36		20 07		20 25	20 38	21 05	21 25	21 38	22 05	22 25	22 38	23 05	
Frizinghall	37 d	18 49	19 10			19 39		20 10		20 28	20 41	21 08	21 28	21 41	22 08	22 28	22 41	23 08	
Shipley	37 a	19 07	19 14	19 31	19 37	19 43		20 12	20 18	20 37	21 07	21 12	21 38	22 07	22 12	22 37	23 07	23 12	23 30
	d	19 08	19 15	19 32	19 38	19 44		20 12	20 20	20 38	21 08	21 14	21 39	22 08	22 14	22 38	23 08	23 14	23 31
Saltaire	d	19 10	19 17		19 40	19 46		20 14	20 22	20 40	21 10	21 16	21 41	22 10	22 16	22 40	23 10	23 16	23 33
Bingley	d	19 14	19 21	19 36	19 44	19 50		20 18	20 26	20 44	21 14	21 20	21 45	22 14	22 20	22 44	23 14	23 20	23 37
Crossflatts	d	19 16	19 23		19 46	19 52		20 20	20 28	20 46	21 16	21 22	21 47	22 16	22 22	22 46	23 16	23 22	23 39
Keighley	d	19 20	19 28	19 42	19 50	19 57	20s17	20 25	20 33	20 50	21 20	21 27	21 51	22 20	22 27	22 50	23 20	23 27	23 43
Steeton & Silsden	d	19 24	19 32		19 54	20 01		20 29	20 37	20 54	21 24	21 31	21 55	22 24	22 31	22 54	23 24	23 31	23 47
Cononley	d	19 28	19 36		19 58	20 05		20 33	20 41	20 58	21 28	21 35	21 59	22 28	22 35	22 58	23 28	23 35	23 51
Skipton	a	19 37	19 43	19 54	20 06	20 12	20 32	20 43	20 49	21 06	21 36	21 42	22 07	22 36	22 42	23 06	23 39	23 41	23 58
	d			19 59															
Gargrave	d			20 05															
Hellifield	d			20 14															
Long Preston	d			20 16															
Giggleswick	d																		
Clapham (Nth Yorkshire)	d																		
Bentham	d																		
Wennington	d																		
Carnforth	83 a																		
Lancaster 6	65, 83, 98 a																		
Bare Lane	98 a																		
Morecambe	98 a																		
Settle	d			20 22															
Horton In Ribblesdale	d			20 31															
Ribblehead	d			20a40															
Dent	d																		
Garsdale	d																		
Kirkby Stephen	d																		
Appleby	d																		
Langwathby	d																		
Lazonby & Kirkoswald	d																		
Armathwaite	d																		
Carlisle 8	65 a																		
Glasgow Central 15	65 a																		

For general notes see front of timetable
For details of catering facilities see Directory of Train Operators

b Change at Doncaster and Leeds
c Change at Shipley

Table 36

Sundays

Leeds and Bradford → Skipton, Lancaster, Morecambe and Carlisle

Network Diagram - see first page of Table 35

		NT A	NT	NT B ⚲	NT	NT	NT A	NT	NT	NT	NT	NT	NT	NT	NT	NT	NT	NT
London Kings Cross 15	⊖ 26 d								09 10		10 10	10b30	11c00		12 10		13 10	
Leeds 10	37 d	08 40	09 00		10 08	10e34	10 54	11 08	12 08	12e34	13 08	13 15	14 08	14e34	15 00	15 08	16 08	16e35
Bradford Forster Square	37 d		09 02		10 02	10 48		11 02	12 02	12 48	13 02		14 02	14 48	15 02		16 02	16 48
Frizinghall	37 d		09 05		10 05	10 51		11 05	12 05	12 51	13 05		14 05	14 51	15 05		16 05	16 51
Shipley	37 a	08 52	09 13		10 19	10 54	11 06	11 19	12 19	12 54	13 19	13 28	14 19	14 54	15 12	15 19	16 19	16 54
	d	08 53	09 14		10 20	10 55	11 07	11 20	12 20	12 55	13 20	13 29	14 20	14 55	15 13	15 20	16 20	16 55
Saltaire	d	08 55	09 16		10 22	10 57		11 22	12 22	12 57	13 22		14 22	14 57		15 22	16 22	16 57
Bingley	d	08 59	09 20		10 26	11 01	11 12	11 26	12 26	13 01	13 26	13 34	14 26	15 01	15 18	15 26	16 26	17 01
Crossflatts	d	09 01	09 22		10 28	11 03		11 28	12 28	13 03	13 28		14 28	15 03		15 28	16 28	17 03
Keighley	d	09 06	09 28		10 32	11 08	11 17	11 32	12 32	13 08	13 32	13 39	14 32	15 08	15 23	15 32	16 32	17 08
Steeton & Silsden	d	09 11	09 32		10 36	11 12		11 36	12 36	13 12	13 36		14 36	15 12		15 36	16 36	17 12
Cononley	d	09 16	09 37		10 40	11 16		11 40	12 40	13 16	13 40		14 40	15 16		15 40	16 40	17 16
Skipton	a	09 23	09 44		10 48	11 23	11 30	11 48	12 48	13 23	13 48	13 53	14 48	15 23	15 36	15 48	16 48	17 23
	d	09 30	09 46				11 34					13 54			15 37			
Gargrave	d	09 35					11 40					14 00			15 43			
Blackpool North	97 d			08 42														
Preston 8	94, 97 d			09 10														
Blackburn	94 d			09 30														
Clitheroe	94 d			09 53														
Hellifield	d	09 44	09 57	10 16			11 48					14 08			15 51			
Long Preston	d	09 46					11 51					14 11			15 55			
Giggleswick	d	09 55					11 58								16 02			
Clapham (Nth Yorkshire)	d	10 03					12 06								16 09			
Bentham	d	10 09					12 12								16 15			
Wennington	d	10 14					12 17								16 20			
Carnforth	83 a	10 30					12 33								16 36			
Lancaster 6	65, 83, 98 a	10 39					12 42								16 47			
Bare Lane	98 a	10 51					12 54								16 56			
Morecambe	98 a	10 55					12 59								17 00			
Settle	d		10 06	10 36								14 17						
Horton In Ribblesdale	d		10 15	10 45								14 26						
Ribblehead	d		10 23	10 53								14 34						
Dent	d		10 33	11 03								14 44						
Garsdale	d		10 39	11 08								14 50						
Kirkby Stephen	d		10 52	11 21								15 03						
Appleby	d		11 05	11 35								15 15						
Langwathby	d		11 19	11 49								15 29						
Lazonby & Kirkoswald	d		11 25	11 55								15 35						
Armathwaite	d		11 33	12 03								15 43						
Carlisle 8	65 a		11 49	12 18								16 00						
Glasgow Central 15	65 a		15 14	15 00								17 37						

		NT	NT	NT	NT	NT	NT	NT	NT	NT	NT	NT	NT
London Kings Cross 15	⊖ 26 d	14 10	14b44		15 10		16 10	17 10		18 10	19 30		20 30
Leeds 10	37 d	17 08	17 23	17 33	18 08	18e34	19 08	20 08	20e34	21 08	22 08	22e34	23 10
Bradford Forster Square	37 d	17 02			18 02	18 48	19 02	20 02	20 48	21 02	22 02	22 48	23 02
Frizinghall	37 d	17 05			18 05	18 51	19 05	20 05	20 51	21 05	22 05	22 51	23 05
Shipley	37 a	17 19	17 35	17 45	18 19	18 54	19 19	20 19	20 54	21 19	22 19	22 54	23 21
	d	17 20	17 36	17 46	18 20	18 55	19 20	20 20	20 55	21 20	22 20	22 55	23 22
Saltaire	d	17 22			18 22	18 57	19 22	20 22	20 57	21 22	22 22	22 57	23 24
Bingley	d	17 26	17 40	17 50	18 26	19 01	19 26	20 26	21 01	21 26	22 26	23 01	23 28
Crossflatts	d	17 28			18 28	19 03	19 28	20 28	21 03	21 28	22 28	23 03	23 30
Keighley	d	17 32	17 46	17 56	18 32	19 08	19 32	20 32	21 08	21 32	22 32	23 08	23 34
Steeton & Silsden	d	17 36			18 36	19 12	19 36	20 36	21 12	21 36	22 36	23 12	23 38
Cononley	d	17 40			18 40	19 16	19 40	20 40	21 16	21 40	22 40	23 16	23 42
Skipton	a	17 48	17 59	18 08	18 48	19 23	19 48	20 48	21 23	21 48	22 48	23 23	23 50
	d		18 00	18 11									
Gargrave	d		18 06										
Blackpool North	97 d												
Preston 8	94, 97 d												
Blackburn	94 d												
Clitheroe	94 d												
Hellifield	d		18 14	18 22									
Long Preston	d		18 18										
Giggleswick	d		18 25										
Clapham (Nth Yorkshire)	d		18 32										
Bentham	d		18 38										
Wennington	d		18 43										
Carnforth	83 a		18 57										
Lancaster 6	65, 83, 98 a		19 11										
Bare Lane	98 a		19 20										
Morecambe	98 a		19 24										
Settle	d			18 30									
Horton In Ribblesdale	d			18 39									
Ribblehead	d			18 47									
Dent	d			18 57									
Garsdale	d			19 02									
Kirkby Stephen	d			19 15									
Appleby	d			19 28									
Langwathby	d			19 42									
Lazonby & Kirkoswald	d			19 48									
Armathwaite	d			19 56									
Carlisle 8	65 a			20 13									
Glasgow Central 15	65 a			22 09									

For general notes see front of timetable
For details of catering facilities see Directory of Train Operators

A From 23 March
B 23 March and 4 May
b 3 February to 23 March only; change at Doncaster and Leeds
c Change at Doncaster and Leeds
e Change at Shipley

Carlisle, Morecambe, Lancaster and Skipton → Bradford and Leeds

Network Diagram - see first page of Table 35

Miles	Miles	Miles			NT	NT	NT	NT	NT	GR R 1 ✕	NT	NT	NT	NT	NT	NT	NT	NT	NT	NT	NT	NT	NT
—	—	—	Glasgow Central 15	65 d																			
0	—	—	**Carlisle 8**	65 d													06 20						
10	—	—	Armathwaite	d													06 34						
15¾	—	—	Lazonby & Kirkoswald	d													06 41						
19¾	—	—	Langwathby	d													06 47						
30¾	—	—	Appleby	d													07 03						
41¼	—	—	Kirkby Stephen	d													07a17						
51¼	—	—	Garsdale	d																			
54¾	—	—	Dent	d																			
60¾	—	—	Ribblehead	d												07 14							
65¼	—	—	Horton In Ribblesdale	d												07 21							
71¾	—	—	Settle	d												07 29							
—	0	—	**Morecambe**	98 d																06 55			
—	1¾	—	Bare Lane	98 d																06 59			
—	4¼	—	**Lancaster 6**	65, 83, 98 d																07 15			
—	11½	—	Carnforth	83 d																07 24			
—	21	—	Wennington	d																07 38			
—	24½	—	Bentham	d																07 43			
—	27½	—	Clapham (Nth Yorkshire)	d																07 49			
—	34¼	—	Giggleswick	d																07 57			
75½	38	—	Long Preston	d												07 34				08 05			
76¾	39¼	—	Hellifield	d												07 37				08 08			
83	45½	—	Gargrave	d												07 46				08 16			
86¾	49¼	—	**Skipton**	a												07 54				08 25			
—	—	—		d	05 48	06 02	06 18	06 27	06 42	06 55	07 01	07 08	07 24	07 32	07 47	07 56		08 01	08 15	08 27	08 32	08 43	09 02
89¾	52¼	—	Cononley	d	05 52	06 06	06 22	06 31	06 46		07 05	07 12	07 28	07 36	07 51			08 05	08 19		08 36	08 47	09 06
93	55½	—	Steeton & Silsden	d	05 56	06 10	06 26	06 35	06 51		07 10	07 17	07 33	07 41	07 56	08 04		08 10	08 24		08 40	08 51	09 10
96	58½	—	Keighley	d	06 01	06 15	06 31	06 40	06 56	07u05	07 15	07 21	07 37	07 45	08 00	08 09		08 14	08 28	08 37	08 45	08 56	09 15
98½	61	—	Crossflatts	d	06 04	06 18	06 34	06 43	07 00		07 19	07 26	07 41	07 49	08 04			08 18	08 32		08 48	08 59	09 18
99¼	61¾	—	Bingley	d	06 07	06 21	06 37	06 46	07 02		07 22	07 28	07 44	07 52	08 07	08 14		08 21	08 35	08 42	08 51	09 02	09 21
101½	64	—	Saltaire	d	06 10	06 24	06 40	06 49	07 06		07 25	07 32	07 48	07 56	08 11			08 25	08 39		08 54	09 05	09 24
102¼	64¾	0	Shipley	a	06 12	06 27	06 42	06 53	07 08		07 28	07 34	07 50	07 58	08 13	08 18		08 27	08 41	08 47	08 58	09 07	09 27
—	—	—		37 d	06 13	06 28	06 44	06 53	07 09	07u15	07 28	07 35	07 50	08 00	08 13	08 19		08 28	08 41	08 47	08 58	09 08	09 28
—	—	1	Frizinghall	37 a		06 32		06 57	07 17		07 32	07 49		08 03		08 25		08 31	08 50	08 54	09 02	09 21	09 32
—	—	2¾	**Bradford Forster Square**	37 a		06 38		07 03	07 22		07 39	07 56		08 09		08 31		08 37	08 56	09 00	09 09	09 27	09 38
113	75½	—	**Leeds 10**	37 a	06 27	06b53	06 58	07b16	07 23	07 29		07 49	08 05	08b24	08 27	08 37		08b49	08 56	09 04		09 23	09b53
—	—	—	London Kings Cross 15	⊖ 26 a		09b06				09 51		10 25	11c13			11 27						12 03	

		NT	NT	NT	NT	NT	NT	NT	NT	NT	NT	NT	NT	NT	NT	NT	NT	NT	NT	NT	NT	NT
Glasgow Central 15	65 d								07 10						08e10							
Carlisle 8	65 d								08 53													
Armathwaite	d								09 07													
Lazonby & Kirkoswald	d								09 14													
Langwathby	d								09 20													
Appleby	d								09 35													
Kirkby Stephen	d								09 48													
Garsdale	d								10 01													
Dent	d								10 06													
Ribblehead	d								10 17													
Horton In Ribblesdale	d								10 23													
Settle	d								10 31													
Morecambe	98 d														10 45							
Bare Lane	98 d														10 49							
Lancaster 6	65, 83, 98 d														11 02							
Carnforth	83 d														11 11							
Wennington	d														11 25							
Bentham	d														11 30							
Clapham (Nth Yorkshire)	d														11 37							
Giggleswick	d														11 44							
Long Preston	d														11 52							
Hellifield	d								10 39						11 55							
Gargrave	d														12 03							
Skipton	a								10 54						12 11							
	d	09 18	09 32	09 48	10 02	10 18	10 32	10 48	10 59	11 02	11 18	11 33	11 48	12 02	12 12	12 18	12 32	12 48	13 02	13 18	13 32	13 48
Cononley	d	09 22	09 36	09 52	10 06	10 22	10 36	10 52		11 06	11 22	11 37	11 52	12 06		12 22	12 36	12 52	13 06	13 22	13 36	13 52
Steeton & Silsden	d	09 26	09 40	09 56	10 10	10 26	10 40	10 56		11 10	11 26	11 41	11 56	12 10		12 26	12 40	12 56	13 10	13 26	13 40	13 56
Keighley	d	09 31	09 45	10 01	10 15	10 31	10 45	11 01	11 09	11 15	11 31	11 46	12 01	12 15	12 22	12 31	12 45	13 01	13 15	13 31	13 45	14 01
Crossflatts	d	09 34	09 48	10 04	10 18	10 34	10 48	11 04		11 18	11 34	11 49	12 04	12 18		12 34	12 48	13 04	13 18	13 34	13 48	14 04
Bingley	d	09 37	09 51	10 07	10 21	10 37	10 51	11 07	11 13	11 21	11 37	11 52	12 07	12 21	12 27	12 37	12 51	13 07	13 21	13 37	13 51	14 07
Saltaire	d	09 40	09 54	10 10	10 24	10 40	10 54	11 10		11 24	11 40	11 55	12 10	12 24		12 40	12 54	13 10	13 24	13 40	13 54	14 10
Shipley	a	09 42	09 57	10 12	10 27	10 42	10 57	11 12	11 18	11 28	11 42	11 58	12 12	12 27	12 32	12 42	12 57	13 12	13 27	13 42	13 57	14 12
	37 d	09 44	09 58	10 14	10 28	10 44	10 58	11 14	11 18	11 28	11 44	11 58	12 14	12 28	12 32	12 44	12 58	13 14	13 28	13 44	13 58	14 14
Frizinghall	37 a	09 54	10 02	10 24	10 32	10 54	11 02	11 24		11 32	11 54	12 02	12 24	12 32	12 47	12 54	13 02	13 24	13 32	13 54	14 02	14 24
Bradford Forster Square	37 a	10 00	10 08	10 30	10 38	11 00	11 08	11 30		11 38	12 00	12 10	12 30	12 38	12 53	13 00	13 08	13 30	13 38	14 00	14 08	14 30
Leeds 10	37 a	09 59	10b24	10 28	10b53	10 58	11b24	11 28	11 36	11b55	11 58	12b23	12 28		12 54	12 58	13b24	13 28	13b54	13 58	14b24	14 28
London Kings Cross 15	⊖ 26 a			13 10				14 02	14 20				15 05		15 40			15 58				17 04

For general notes see front of timetable
For details of catering facilities see Directory of Train Operators

b Change at Shipley
c Change at Leeds and Doncaster
e Change at Lancaster

Carlisle, Morecambe, Lancaster and Skipton → Bradford and Leeds

Network Diagram - see first page of Table 35

		NT	NT	NT	NT	NT	NT	NT	NT	NT	NT	NT	NT	NT	NT	NT	NT	NT	NT	NT	NT	NT
Glasgow Central 15	65 d	10 10			10b10								12 10				12 49					
Carlisle 8	65 d	11 51											14 00				15 03					
Armathwaite	d	12 05											14 14									
Lazonby & Kirkoswald	d	12 12											14 21									
Langwathby	d	12 18											14 27									
Appleby	d	12 33											14 43				15 40					
Kirkby Stephen	d	12 45											14 55				15 53					
Garsdale	d	12 59											15 09									
Dent	d	13 04											15 14									
Ribblehead	d	13 13											15 23									
Horton In Ribblesdale	d	13 20											15 29									
Settle	d	13 28											15 38				16 35					
Morecambe	98 d				12 44																	
Bare Lane	98 d				12 48																	
Lancaster 6	65, 83, 98 d				13 15																	
Carnforth	83 d				13 25																	
Wennington	d				13 38																	
Bentham	d				13 44																	
Clapham (Nth Yorkshire)	d				13 50																	
Giggleswick	d				13 58																	
Long Preston	d	13 33			14 07																	
Hellifield	d	13 36			14 10								15 46									
Gargrave	d	13 44			14 18																	
Skipton	a	13 53			14 26								16 05				16 55					
	d	13 59	14 02	14 18	14 27	14 32	14 48	15 02	15 18	15 32	15 48	16 02	16 12	16 18	16 36	16 49	16 58	17 02	17 19	17 30	17 49	18 02
Cononley	d		14 06	14 22		14 36	14 52	15 06	15 22	15 36	15 52	16 06		16 22	16 40	16 53		17 06	17 23	17 34	17 53	18 06
Steeton & Silsden	d		14 10	14 27		14 40	14 56	15 10	15 26	15 40	15 56	16 10		16 26	16 44	16 57		17 10	17 27	17 38	17 57	18 10
Keighley	d	14 09	14 15	14 31	14 39	14 45	15 01	15 15	15 31	15 45	16 01	16 15	16 22	16 31	16 49	17 02	17 08	17 15	17 32	17 43	18 02	18 15
Crossflatts	d		14 18	14 35		14 48	15 04	15 18	15 34	15 48	16 04	16 18		16 34	16 52	17 05		17 18	17 35	17 46	18 05	18 18
Bingley	d	14 13	14 21	14 38	14 43	14 51	15 07	15 21	15 37	15 51	16 07	16 21	16 26	16 37	16 55	17 08	17 15	17 21	17 38	17 49	18 08	18 21
Saltaire	d		14 24	14 42		14 54	15 10	15 24	15 40	15 54	16 10	16 24		16 40	16 58	17 11		17 24	17 41	17 52	18 11	18 24
Shipley	a	14 18	14 28	14 44	14 48	14 57	15 12	15 27	15 42	15 57	16 12	16 27	16 31	16 42	17 02	17 13	17 20	17 28	17 43	17 55	18 13	18 28
	37 d	14 18	14 28	14 45	14 51	14 58	15 14	15 28	15 44	15 58	16 14	16 28	16 31	16 44	17 02	17 15	17 20	17 28	17 45	17 56	18 14	18 28
Frizinghall	37 a		14 32	14 54		15 02	15 24	15 32	15 55	16 02	16 24	16 32	16 47	16 53	17 06	17 24		17 32	17 52	18 00	18 24	18 32
Bradford Forster Square	37 a		14 38	15 00		15 08	15 30	15 38	16 01	16 08	16 30	16 38	16 53	16 59	17 12	17 30		17 38	17 58	18 08	18 31	18 38
Leeds 10	37 a	14 37	14c53	14 59	15 07	15c24	15 28	15c53	15 58	16c24	16 28	16c53	16 51	16 58	17c24	17 29	17 40	17c55	18 00	18c24	18 29	18c48
London Kings Cross 15	⊖ 26 a				18e12		18 23				18 48		19 29			19 59	20 21				21 03	

		NT	NT	NT	NT	NT	NT	NT	NT	NT	NT	NT	NT	NT	NT	NT	NT	NT	NT	NT	NT
Glasgow Central 15	65 d	14b10		14 10								16 10		16b46							
Carlisle 8	65 d			16 18								17 55									
Armathwaite	d			16 32								18 09									
Lazonby & Kirkoswald	d			16 39								18 16									
Langwathby	d			16 45								18 22									
Appleby	d			17 01								18 37									
Kirkby Stephen	d			17 14								18 49									
Garsdale	d			17 28								19 03									
Dent	d			17 33								19 08									
Ribblehead	d			17 42								19 17						21 00			
Horton In Ribblesdale	d			17 49								19 24						21 06			
Settle	d			17 58								19 32						21 14			
Morecambe	98 d	16 38												19 05							
Bare Lane	98 d	16 42												19 09							
Lancaster 6	65, 83, 98 d	16 53												19 24							
Carnforth	83 d	17 03												19 33							
Wennington	d	17 16												19 47							
Bentham	d	17 22												19 52							
Clapham (Nth Yorkshire)	d	17 28												19 59							
Giggleswick	d	17 36												20 06							
Long Preston	d	17 44		18 03										20 14				21 20			
Hellifield	d	17 47		18 06								19 39		20 17				21 23			
Gargrave	d	17 55		18 15										20 25				21 31			
Skipton	a	18 03		18 23								19 54		20 34				21 40			
	d		18 16	18 28	18 32	18 48	19 00	19 18	19 32	19 48	19 54	20 06	20 18	20 37	20 48	20 54	21 18		21 48	21 54	22 18
Cononley	d		18 20		18 36	18 52	19 04	19 22	19 36	19 52	19 58		20 22		20 52	20 58	21 22		21 52	21 58	22 22
Steeton & Silsden	d		18 25		18 40	18 56	19 08	19 26	19 40	19 56	20 02		20 26		20 56	21 02	21 26		21 56	22 02	22 26
Keighley	d		18 29	18 38	18 45	19 01	19 13	19 31	19 45	20 01	20 07	20 16	20 31	20 47	21 01	21 07	21 31		22 01	22 07	22 31
Crossflatts	d		18 33		18 48	19 04	19 16	19 34	19 48	20 04	20 10		20 34		21 04	21 10	21 34		22 05	22 10	22 34
Bingley	d		18 35	18 42	18 51	19 07	19 19	19 37	19 51	20 07	20 13	20 21	20 37	20 52	21 07	21 13	21 37		22 07	22 13	22 37
Saltaire	d		18 39		18 54	19 10	19 22	19 40	19 54	20 10	20 16		20 40		21 10	21 16	21 40		22 11	22 16	22 40
Shipley	a		18 42	18 48	18 58	19 12	19 25	19 42	19 57	20 12	20 19	20 27	20 42	20 57	21 12	21 19	21 42		22 13	22 19	22 42
	37 d		18 44	18 48	18 58	19 14	19 26	19 44	19 58	20 14	20 20	20 28	20 43	20 57	21 14	21 19	21 43		22 14	22 19	22 43
Frizinghall	37 a		18 54		19 02	19 24	19 29		20 01		20 24		20 51	21 05		21 23	21 51			22 23	22 51
Bradford Forster Square	37 a		19 01		19 08	19 30	19 35		20 08		20 32		20 57	21 12		21 29	21 57			22 31	22 57
Leeds 10	37 a		18 59	19 07	19c25	19 29	19c55	19 59		20 28		20 44	21 00	21 15	21 30		21 57		22 32		23 01
London Kings Cross 15	⊖ 26 a					22 04				23 32											

For general notes see front of timetable
For details of catering facilities see Directory of Train Operators

b Change at Lancaster
c Change at Shipley
e Change at Leeds and Doncaster

Table 36

Carlisle, Morecambe, Lancaster and Skipton → Bradford and Leeds

Network Diagram - see first page of Table 35

Station		NT	NT	GR	NT	NT	NT	NT	NT	NT	NT	NT	NT	NT	NT	NT	NT	NT	NT	NT	NT	NT
				R 1												A	B					
Glasgow Central 15	65 d																					
Carlisle 8	65 d																			07 52		
Armathwaite	d																			08 06		
Lazonby & Kirkoswald	d																			08 13		
Langwathby	d																			08 19		
Appleby	d																			08 34		
Kirkby Stephen	d																			08 46		
Garsdale	d																			09 00		
Dent	d																			09 05		
Ribblehead	d								07 14											09 14		
Horton In Ribblesdale	d								07 21											09 21		
Settle	d								07 29											09 29		
Morecambe	98 d															07 34	07 32					
Bare Lane	98 d															07 38	07 36					
Lancaster 6	65, 83, 98 d															08 11	08 14					
Carnforth	83 d															08 20	08 23					
Wennington	d															08 34	08 37					
Bentham	d															08 39	08 42					
Clapham (Nth Yorkshire)	d															08 45	08 48					
Giggleswick	d															08 53	08 56					
Long Preston	d								07 34							09 01	09 04					
Hellifield	d								07 37							09 04	09 07			09 36		
Gargrave	d								07 46							09 12	09 15					
Skipton	a								07 54							09 23	09 23			09 53		
	d	05 48	06 02	06 42	06 48	07 01	07 32	07 47	07 56	08 01	08 18	08 32	08 48	09 02	09 18	09 28	09 28	09 32	09 48	09 58	10 02	10 18
Cononley	d	05 52	06 06		06 52	07 05	07 36	07 51		08 05	08 22	08 36	08 52	09 06	09 22			09 36	09 52		10 06	10 22
Steeton & Silsden	d	05 56	06 10		06 56	07 10	07 41	07 56	08 04	08 10	08 27	08 40	08 56	09 10	09 26			09 40	09 56		10 10	10 26
Keighley	d	06 01	06 15	06u52	07 01	07 15	07 45	08 00	08 09	08 14	08 31	08 45	09 01	09 15	09 31	09 38	09 38	09 45	10 01	10 08	10 15	10 31
Crossflatts	d	06 04	06 18		07 04	07 19	07 49	08 04		08 18	08 35	08 48	09 04	09 18	09 34			09 48	10 04		10 18	10 34
Bingley	d	06 07	06 21		07 07	07 22	07 52	08 07	08 14	08 21	08 38	08 51	09 07	09 21	09 37			09 51	10 07	10 12	10 21	10 37
Saltaire	d	06 10	06 24		07 10	07 25	07 56	08 11		08 25	08 42	08 54	09 10	09 24	09 40			09 54	10 10		10 24	10 40
Shipley	a	06 12	06 27		07 14	07 28	07 58	08 13	08 18	08 27	08 44	08 57	09 12	09 27	09 42	09 49	09 49	09 57	10 12	10 18	10 27	10 42
	37 d	06 13	06 28	07u00	07 14	07 28	08 00	08 13	08 19	08 28	08 44	08 58	09 14	09 28	09 44	09 49	09 49	09 58	10 14	10 19	10 28	10 44
Frizinghall	37 a		06 32		07 24	07 32	08 03		08 25	08 31	08 54	09 02	09 24	09 32	09 54			10 02	10 24		10 32	10 54
Bradford Forster Square	37 a		06 38		07 30	07 39	08 09		08 31	08 37	09 00	09 09	09 31	09 38	10 00			10 08	10 30		10 38	11 00
Leeds 10	37 a	06 27	07b15	07 15	07 28	07b58	08b23	08 27	08 37	08b53	08 58	09b26	09 28	09b53	09 59	10 08	10 08	10b24	10 28	10 37	10b53	10 58
London Kings Cross 15	⊖ 26 a	09 18		10 00		10b20			11 32		12c14		12 24			13c10	13c10			13 33		13c59

Station		NT	NT	NT	NT	NT	NT	NT	NT	NT	NT	NT	NT	NT	NT	NT	NT	NT	NT	NT	NT
Glasgow Central 15	65 d																				10 20
Carlisle 8	65 d					09 28												11 51			
Armathwaite	d					09 42												12 05			
Lazonby & Kirkoswald	d					09 49												12 12			
Langwathby	d					09 55												12 18			
Appleby	d					10 10												12 33			
Kirkby Stephen	d					10 22												12 45			
Garsdale	d					10 36												13 02			
Dent	d					10 41												13 07			
Ribblehead	d					10 50												13 16			
Horton In Ribblesdale	d					10 57												13 23			
Settle	d					11 05												13 31			
Morecambe	98 d									10e36											12 47
Bare Lane	98 d									10e40											12 51
Lancaster 6	65, 83, 98 d									10 56											13f09
Carnforth	83 d									11 05											13 23
Wennington	d									11 19											13 36
Bentham	d									11 24											13 42
Clapham (Nth Yorkshire)	d									11 31											13 48
Giggleswick	d									11 38											13 56
Long Preston	d									11 51								13 36			14 07
Hellifield	d					11 12				11 54								13 39			14 10
Gargrave	d									12 02								13 47			14 18
Skipton	a					11 29				12 12								13 56			14 26
	d	10 32	10 48	11 02	11 18	11 30	11 33	11 48	12 02	12 12	12 18	12 32	12 48	13 02	13 18	13 32	13 48	13 59	14 02	14 18	14 28
Cononley	d	10 36	10 52	11 06	11 22		11 37	11 52	12 06		12 22	12 36	12 52	13 06	13 22	13 36	13 52		14 06	14 22	
Steeton & Silsden	d	10 40	10 56	11 10	11 26		11 41	11 56	12 10		12 26	12 40	12 56	13 10	13 26	13 40	13 56		14 10	14 27	
Keighley	d	10 45	11 01	11 15	11 31	11 40	11 46	12 01	12 15	12 22	12 31	12 45	13 01	13 15	13 31	13 45	14 01	14 09	14 15	14 31	14 39
Crossflatts	d	10 48	11 04	11 18	11 34		11 49	12 04	12 18		12 34	12 48	13 04	13 18	13 34	13 48	14 04		14 18	14 35	
Bingley	d	10 51	11 07	11 21	11 37	11 44	11 52	12 07	12 21	12 27	12 37	12 51	13 07	13 21	13 37	13 51	14 07	14 13	14 21	14 38	14 43
Saltaire	d	10 54	11 10	11 24	11 40		11 55	12 10	12 24		12 40	12 54	13 10	13 24	13 40	13 54	14 10		14 24	14 42	
Shipley	a	10 57	11 12	11 27	11 42	11 49	11 58	12 12	12 27	12 32	12 42	12 57	13 12	13 27	13 42	13 57	14 12	14 18	14 28	14 44	14 49
	37 d	10 58	11 14	11 28	11 44	11 49	11 58	12 14	12 28	12 32	12 44	12 58	13 14	13 28	13 44	13 58	14 14	14 18	14 28	14 45	14 49
Frizinghall	37 a	11 02	11 24	11 32	11 54		12 02	12 24	12 32	12 47	12 54	13 02	13 24	13 32	13 54	14 02	14 24		14 32	14 54	
Bradford Forster Square	37 a	11 08	11 30	11 38	12 00		12 09	12 30	12 38	12 53	13 00	13 08	13 30	13 38	14 00	14 08	14 30		14 38	15 00	
Leeds 10	37 a	11b24	11 28	11b55	11 58	12 06	12b23	12 28		12 49	12 58	13b24	13 28	13b54	13 58	14b24	14 28	14 37	14b53	14 59	15 07
London Kings Cross 15	⊖ 26 a		14 27							15 21			16 30					17 28			18c10

For general notes see front of timetable
For details of catering facilities see Directory of Train Operators

A Until 22 March
B From 29 March
b Change at Shipley
c Change at Leeds and Doncaster
e From 29 March dep. 4 minutes later
f From 29 March dep. 1313

Table 36

Carlisle, Morecambe, Lancaster and Skipton → Bradford and Leeds

Network Diagram - see first page of Table 35

		NT	NT	NT	NT	NT	NT	NT	NT	NT	NT	NT	NT	NT	NT	NT	NT	NT	NT	NT	NT
Glasgow Central 15	65 d																				
Carlisle 8	65 d										14 26						15 48				
Armathwaite	d										14 40										
Lazonby & Kirkoswald	d										14 47										
Langwathby	d										14 53										
Appleby	d										15 09						16 25				
Kirkby Stephen	d										15 21						16 38				
Garsdale	d										15 35										
Dent	d										15 40										
Ribblehead	d										15 49										
Horton In Ribblesdale	d										15 56										
Settle	d										16 05						17 15				
Morecambe	98 d	12 47																		16 38	
Bare Lane	98 d	12 51																		16 42	
Lancaster 6	65, 83, 98 d	13 13																		16 53	
Carnforth	83 d	13 23																		17 02	
Wennington	d	13 36																		17 16	
Bentham	d	13 42																		17 21	
Clapham (Nth Yorkshire)	d	13 48																		17 28	
Giggleswick	d	13 56																		17 35	
Long Preston	d	14 07																		17 43	
Hellifield	d	14 10									16 12									17 46	
Gargrave	d	14 18																		17 54	
Skipton	a	14 26									16 27						17 36			18 03	
	d	14 28	14 32	14 48	15 02	15 18	15 32	15 48	16 02	16 18	16 29	16 32	16 49	17 02	17 19	17 30	17 41	17 49	18 02		18 16
Cononley	d		14 36	14 52	15 06	15 22	15 36	15 52	16 06	16 22		16 36	16 53	17 06	17 23	17 34		17 53	18 06		18 20
Steeton & Silsden	d		14 40	14 56	15 10	15 26	15 40	15 56	16 10	16 26		16 40	16 57	17 10	17 27	17 38		17 57	18 10		18 25
Keighley	d	14 39	14 45	15 01	15 15	15 31	15 45	16 01	16 15	16 31	16 39	16 45	17 02	17 15	17 32	17 43	17 51	18 02	18 15		18 29
Crossflatts	d		14 48	15 04	15 18	15 34	15 48	16 04	16 18	16 34		16 48	17 05	17 18	17 35	17 46		18 05	18 18		18 33
Bingley	d	14 43	14 51	15 07	15 21	15 37	15 51	16 07	16 21	16 37	16 44	16 51	17 08	17 21	17 38	17 49	17 55	18 08	18 21		18 35
Saltaire	d		14 54	15 10	15 24	15 40	15 54	16 10	16 24	16 40		16 54	17 11	17 24	17 41	17 52		18 11	18 24		18 39
Shipley	a	14 49	14 58	15 12	15 27	15 42	15 57	16 12	16 27	16 42	16 48	16 58	17 13	17 27	17 43	17 55	18 00	18 13	18 28		18 42
	37 d	14 49	14 58	15 14	15 28	15 44	15 58	16 14	16 28	16 44	16 49	16 58	17 15	17 28	17 45	17 56	18 00	18 14	18 28		18 44
Frizinghall	37 a		15 02	15 24	15 32	15 55	16 02	16 24	16 32	16 53		17 02	17 24	17 32	17 54	18 00	18 17	18 24	18 32		18 54
Bradford Forster Square	37 a		15 08	15 30	15 38	16 01	16 08	16 30	16 38	16 59		17 08	17 30	17 38	18 00	18 07	18 23	18 31	18 38		19 01
Leeds 10	37 a	15 07	15b24	15 28	15b53	15 58	16b24	16 28	16b53	16 58	17 07	17b24	17 29	17b55	18 00		18 17	18 29	18b52		18 59
London Kings Cross 15	⊖ 26 a	18 10		18 28		19c40							20 12					21 15			

		NT	NT	NT	NT	NT	NT	NT	NT	NT	NT	NT	NT	NT	NT	NT	NT	NT	NT
Glasgow Central 15	65 d																		
Carlisle 8	65 d	16 14								18 00									
Armathwaite	d	16 28								18 14									
Lazonby & Kirkoswald	d	16 35								18 21									
Langwathby	d	16 41								18 27									
Appleby	d	16 57								18 42									
Kirkby Stephen	d	17 09								18 54									
Garsdale	d	17 23								19 08									
Dent	d	17 28								19 13									
Ribblehead	d	17 37								19 23						21 00			
Horton In Ribblesdale	d	17 44								19 29						21 06			
Settle	d	17 53								19 37						21 14			
Morecambe	98 d											19 00							
Bare Lane	98 d											19 05							
Lancaster 6	65, 83, 98 d											19 19							
Carnforth	83 d											19 31							
Wennington	d											19 45							
Bentham	d											19 50							
Clapham (Nth Yorkshire)	d											19 57							
Giggleswick	d											20 04							
Long Preston	d	17 58										20 15				21 20			
Hellifield	d	18 06								19 46		20 18				21 23			
Gargrave	d	18 15										20 26				21 31			
Skipton	a	18 23								20 05		20 35				21 40			
	d	18 28	18 32	18 48	19 00	19 18	19 32	19 48	19 54	20 06	20 18	20 37	20 48	20 54	21 18		21 48	21 54	22 18
Cononley	d		18 36	18 52	19 04	19 22	19 36	19 52	19 58		20 22		20 52	20 58	21 22		21 52	21 58	22 22
Steeton & Silsden	d		18 40	18 56	19 08	19 26	19 40	19 56	20 02		20 26		20 56	21 02	21 26		21 56	22 02	22 26
Keighley	d	18 38	18 45	19 01	19 13	19 31	19 45	20 01	20 07	20 16	20 31	20 47	21 01	21 07	21 31		22 01	22 07	22 31
Crossflatts	d		18 48	19 04	19 16	19 34	19 48	20 04	20 10		20 34		21 04	21 10	21 34		22 04	22 10	22 34
Bingley	d	18 42	18 51	19 07	19 19	19 37	19 51	20 07	20 13	20 21	20 37	20 52	21 07	21 13	21 37		22 07	22 13	22 37
Saltaire	d		18 54	19 10	19 22	19 40	19 54	20 10	20 16		20 40		21 10	21 16	21 40		22 10	22 16	22 40
Shipley	a	18 48	18 58	19 12	19 25	19 42	19 57	20 12	20 20	20 27	20 42	20 57	21 12	21 19	21 42		22 12	22 19	22 42
	37 d	18 48	18 58	19 14	19 26	19 44	19 58	20 14	20 20	20 28	20 43	20 57	21 14	21 19	21 43		22 14	22 19	22 43
Frizinghall	37 a		19 02	19 24	19 29		20 01		20 24		20 51	21 05		21 23	21 51			22 23	22 51
Bradford Forster Square	37 a		19 08	19 30	19 35		20 08		20 32		20 57	21 12		21 29	21 57			22 31	22 57
Leeds 10	37 a	19 07	19b26	19 29	19b55	19 59		20 28		20 44	21 00	21 15	21 30		22 01		22 28		23 01
London Kings Cross 15	⊖ 26 a	22c17				22 47													

For general notes see front of timetable
For details of catering facilities see Directory of Train Operators

b Change at Shipley
c Change at Leeds and Doncaster

Carlisle, Morecambe, Lancaster and Skipton → Bradford and Leeds

Network Diagram - see first page of Table 35

Station		NT	NT	NT	NT	NT	NT	NT	NT	NT	NT	NT A	NT	NT	NT	NT A	NT B	NT A
Glasgow Central 15	65 d																	
Carlisle 8	65 d						09 24									13 51	13 51	
Armathwaite	d						09 38									14 05	14 05	
Lazonby & Kirkoswald	d						09 45									14 12	14 12	
Langwathby	d						09 52									14 19	14 19	
Appleby	d						10 06									14 33	14 33	
Kirkby Stephen	d						10 19									14 46	14 46	
Garsdale	d						10 33									15 00	15 00	
Dent	d						10 38									15 05	15 05	
Ribblehead	d						10 48									15 15	15 15	
Horton In Ribblesdale	d						10 55									15 22	15 22	
Settle	d						11 03									15 30	15 30	
Morecambe	98 d											12 26						14 28
Bare Lane	98 d											12 30						14 32
Lancaster 6	65, 83, 98 d											12 45						14 47
Carnforth	83 d											12 54						14 56
Wennington	d											13 07						15 09
Bentham	d											13 13						15 15
Clapham (Nth Yorkshire)	d											13 19						15 21
Giggleswick	d											13 27						15 29
Long Preston	d						11 09					13 35					15 35	15 45
Hellifield	d						11 12					13 38				15 37	15 38	15 48
Clitheroe	94 a																	
Blackburn	94, 97 a																	
Preston 8	97 a																	
Blackpool North	97 a																	
Gargrave	d						11 20					13 46					15 46	15 56
Skipton	a						11 28					13 56				15 52	15 55	16 04
	d	08 35	09 15	09 36	10 15	11 15	11 30	11 37	12 15	13 15	13 37	13 58	14 15	15 15	15 37	15 57	15 57	16 06
Cononley	d	08 39	09 19	09 40	10 19	11 19		11 41	12 19	13 19	13 41		14 19	15 19	15 41			
Steeton & Silsden	d	08 44	09 23	09 44	10 23	11 23		11 45	12 23	13 23	13 45		14 23	15 23	15 45			
Keighley	d	08 48	09 28	09 49	10 28	11 28	11 40	11 50	12 28	13 28	13 50	14 08	14 28	15 28	15 50	16 07	16 07	16 16
Crossflatts	d	08 52	09 31	09 52	10 31	11 31		11 53	12 31	13 31	13 53		14 31	15 31	15 53			
Bingley	d	08 54	09 34	09 55	10 34	11 34	11 44	11 56	12 34	13 34	13 56	14 13	14 34	15 34	15 56	16 11	16 11	16 21
Saltaire	d	08 58	09 37	09 58	10 37	11 37		11 59	12 37	13 37	13 59		14 37	15 37	15 59			
Shipley	a	09 00	09 39	10 01	10 39	11 39	11 49	12 02	12 39	13 39	14 02	14 17	14 39	15 39	16 02	16 16	16 16	16 25
	37 d	09 00	09 40	10 01	10 40	11 40	11 49	12 02	12 40	13 40	14 02	14 18	14 40	15 40	16 02	16 16	16 16	16 27
Frizinghall	37 a		09 48	10 05	10 48	11 48		12 06	12 48	13 48	14 06		14 48	15 48	16 06			
Bradford Forster Square	37 a		09 54	10 12	10 54	11 54		12 12	12 54	13 54	14 12		14 54	15 54	16 12			
Leeds 10	37 a	09 14	09 54	10b22	10 54	11 54	12 06	12b22	12 54	13 54	14b22	14 39	14 54	15 54	16b22	16 34	16 34	16 45
London Kings Cross 15	⊖ 26 a	12c37	12e48		14c42		15e11		15 55	16e50			17 55	18 55				

Station		NT	NT	NT	NT	NT	NT	NT	NT	NT	NT C 🚌	NT	NT	NT	NT	NT
Glasgow Central 15	65 d															
Carlisle 8	65 d					16 37					17 30					
Armathwaite	d					16 51					17 44					
Lazonby & Kirkoswald	d					16 58					17 52					
Langwathby	d					17 05					17 58					
Appleby	d					17 20					18 14					
Kirkby Stephen	d					17 33					18 27					
Garsdale	d					17 47					18 40					
Dent	d					17 52					18 46					
Ribblehead	d					18 02					18 55					
Horton In Ribblesdale	d					18 09					19 02					
Settle	d					18 18					19 10					
Morecambe	98 d						17 45						20 00			
Bare Lane	98 d						17 49						20 04			
Lancaster 6	65, 83, 98 d						18 04						20 15			
Carnforth	83 d						18 12						20 24			
Wennington	d						18 25						20 37			
Bentham	d						18 31						20 43			
Clapham (Nth Yorkshire)	d						18 39						20 50			
Giggleswick	d						18 47						20 58			
Long Preston	d						18 59						21 06			
Hellifield	d					18 25	19 02				19 20		21 09			
Clitheroe	94 a										19 47					
Blackburn	94, 97 a										20 14					
Preston 8	97 a										20 34					
Blackpool North	97 a										21 03					
Gargrave	d						19 10						21 17			
Skipton	a					18 40	19 18						21 25			
	d	16 15	17 15	17 37	18 15	18 42	19 18	19 23	19 37	20 15		21 15	21 26	21 37	22 15	23 15
Cononley	d	16 19	17 19	17 41	18 19			19 27	19 41	20 19		21 19		21 41	22 19	23 19
Steeton & Silsden	d	16 23	17 23	17 45	18 23			19 31	19 45	20 23		21 23		21 45	22 23	23 23
Keighley	d	16 28	17 28	17 50	18 28	18 52	19 28	19 36	19 50	20 28		21 28	21 36	21 50	22 28	23 28
Crossflatts	d	16 31	17 31	17 53	18 31			19 39	19 53	20 31		21 31		21 53	22 31	23 31
Bingley	d	16 34	17 34	17 56	18 34	18 56	19 32	19 42	19 56	20 34		21 34	21 41	21 56	22 34	23 34
Saltaire	d	16 37	17 37	17 59	18 37			19 45	19 59	20 37		21 37		21 59	22 37	23 37
Shipley	a	16 39	17 39	18 02	18 39	19 01	19 37	19 47	20 02	20 39		21 39	21 46	22 02	22 39	23 40
	37 d	16 40	17 40	18 02	18 40	19 02	19 38	19 48	20 02	20 40		21 40	21 47	22 02	22 40	23 40
Frizinghall	37 a	16 48	17 51	18 06	18 48		19 48		20 06	20 48		21 48		22 06	22 48	
Bradford Forster Square	37 a	16 55	17 58	18 12	18 54		19 54		20 12	20 54		21 54		22 12	22 54	
Leeds 10	37 a	16 54	17 54	18b23	18 54	19 19	19 56	20 02	20b22	20 54		21 54	22 03	22b22	22 54	23 58
London Kings Cross 15	⊖ 26 a	19 33	20 59					22 35								

For general notes see front of timetable
For details of catering facilities see Directory of Train Operators

- **A** From 23 March
- **B** Until 16 March
- **C** 23 March and 4 May
- **b** Change at Shipley
- **c** Change at Leeds and Doncaster 3 February to 23 March only
- **e** Change at Leeds and Doncaster

Leeds → Shipley and Bradford

Network Diagram - see first page of Table 35

Miles	Miles			NT	NT	NT	NT	NT	NT	NT	NT	NT	NT		NT	NT	NT	NT	NT	NT	NT	NT	NT	NT		NT
0	0	**Leeds** 10	d	05 08	05 51	05 55	06 03		06 21	06 22		06 37			06 49	06 51	06 56	07 09		07 23		07 25	07 37			07 39
10¾	—	**Shipley**	a			06 07			06 32						07 01		07 09					07 36				07 50
—	—		d					06 28			06 41		06 53		07 02				07 15		07 28			07 47		07 51
11¾	—	Frizinghall	d					06 32			06 44		06 57		07 04				07 17		07 32			07 49		07 53
—	4	Bramley	d	05 15	05 58					06 29		06 44						07 16		07 30			07 44			
—	5¾	New Pudsey	d	05 20	06 03		06 12			06 34		06 49				07 01		07 21		07 35			07 49			
—	9½	**Bradford Interchange**	a	05 28	06 11		06 23			06 42		06 57				07 11		07 29		07 43			07 57			
13½	—	**Bradford Forster Square**	a					06 38			06 50		07 03		07 10				07 22		07 39			07 56		07 59

		NT	NT	NT	NT	NT	NT	NT	NT	NT	NT		NT	NT	NT	NT	NT	NT	NT	NT	NT	NT		NT	NT	NT
Leeds 10	d	07 51		07 51	08 08		08 10		08 19	08 22	08 25		08 37		08 40		08 49	08 51	08 56	09 08		09 10		09 22		09 26
Shipley	a			08 02			08 22		08 31		08 37				08 51		09 01		09 07			09 21				09 37
	d		08 00			08 13	08 23	08 28						08 48	08 52	08 58					09 18	09 22			09 28	
Frizinghall	d		08 03			08 16	08 25	08 31						08 50	08 54	09 02					09 21	09 25			09 32	
Bramley	d				08 15					08 29			08 44							09 15				09 29		
New Pudsey	d	08 01			08 20					08 34			08 49					09 00		09 20				09 34		
Bradford Interchange	a	08 11			08 28					08 42			08 57					09 09		09 28				09 42		
Bradford Forster Square	a		08 09			08 22	08 31	08 37						08 56	09 00	09 09					09 27	09 30			09 38	

		NT	NT	NT	NT	NT	NT	NT	NT	NT		NT	NT	NT	NT	NT	NT	NT	NT	NT	NT		NT	NT	NT	NT
Leeds 10	d	09 37		09 40		09 47	09 51	09 56	10 08			10 10		10 19	10 22	10 26	10 37		10 40		10 49		10 51	10 56	11 08	
Shipley	a			09 51		10 01		10 07				10 21		10 31		10 37			10 51		11 01			11 07		
	d		09 44	09 52	09 58					10 14		10 22	10 28					10 44	10 52	10 58						11 14
Frizinghall	d		09 47	09 54	10 02					10 17		10 24	10 32					10 47	10 54	11 02						11 17
Bramley	d	09 44							10 15						10 29		10 44								11 15	
New Pudsey	d	09 49					10 01		10 20						10 34		10 49						11 01		11 20	
Bradford Interchange	a	09 57					10 11		10 28						10 42		10 57						11 11		11 28	
Bradford Forster Square	a		09 53	10 00	10 08					10 23		10 30	10 38					10 53	11 00	11 08						11 23

		NT	NT	NT	NT	NT	NT	NT	NT		NT	NT	NT	NT	NT	NT	NT	NT	NT	NT		NT	NT	NT	NT	NT
Leeds 10	d	11 10	11 22		11 26	11 37		11 40	11 51			11 56	12 08		12 10	12 22		12 26	12 37			12 40		12 49	12 51	12 56
Shipley	a	11 21			11 37			11 51				12 07			12 21			12 37				12 51		13 01		13 07
	d	11 22		11 28			11 44	11 52			11 58			12 14	12 22		12 28			12 44		12 52	12 58			
Frizinghall	d	11 24		11 32			11 47	11 54			12 02			12 17	12 24		12 32			12 47		12 54	13 02			
Bramley	d		11 29			11 44							12 15			12 29			12 44							
New Pudsey	d		11 34			11 49			12 01				12 20			12 34			12 49						13 01	
Bradford Interchange	a		11 42			11 57			12 11				12 28			12 42			12 57						13 11	
Bradford Forster Square	a	11 30		11 38			11 53	12 00			12 10			12 23	12 30		12 38			12 53		13 00	13 08			

		NT	NT	NT	NT	NT	NT	NT		NT	NT	NT	NT	NT	NT	NT	NT	NT	NT		NT	NT	NT	NT	NT	NT
Leeds 10	d	13 08		13 10	13 22		13 26	13 37			13 40		13 49	13 51	13 56	14 08		14 10	14 22			14 26	14 37		14 40	
Shipley	a			13 21			13 37				13 51		14 03		14 07			14 21				14 37			14 51	
	d		13 14	13 22		13 28				13 44	13 52	13 58					14 14	14 22			14 28			14 44	14 52	14 58
Frizinghall	d		13 17	13 24		13 32				13 47	13 54	14 02					14 17	14 24			14 32			14 47	14 54	15 02
Bramley	d	13 15			13 29			13 44								14 15			14 29				14 44			
New Pudsey	d	13 20			13 34			13 49						14 01		14 20			14 34				14 49			
Bradford Interchange	a	13 28			13 42			13 57						14 11		14 28			14 42				14 57			
Bradford Forster Square	a		13 23	13 30		13 38				13 53	14 00	14 08					14 23	14 30			14 38			14 53	15 00	15 08

		NT	NT	NT	NT	NT	NT		NT	NT	NT	NT	NT	NT	NT	NT	NT	NT		NT	NT	NT	NT	NT	NT	NT
Leeds 10	d	14 49	14 51	14 56	15 08		15 10		15 22		15 26	15 37		15 40	15 51		15 56	16 08			16 10	16 22		16 26	16 37	
Shipley	a	15 01		15 07			15 21				15 37			15 52			16 07				16 21			16 37		
	d					15 14	15 22			15 28			15 44	15 52		15 58				16 14	16 22		16 28			16 44
Frizinghall	d					15 17	15 24			15 32			15 47	15 55		16 02				16 17	16 24		16 32			16 47
Bramley	d				15 15				15 29			15 44						16 15				16 29			16 44	
New Pudsey	d		15 01		15 20				15 34			15 49			16 01			16 20				16 34			16 49	
Bradford Interchange	a		15 11		15 28				15 42			15 57			16 11			16 28				16 42			16 57	
Bradford Forster Square	a					15 23	15 30			15 38			15 53	16 01		16 08				16 23	16 30		16 38			16 53

		NT	NT	NT	NT	NT		NT	NT	NT	NT	NT	NT	NT	NT	NT	NT		NT	NT	NT	NT	NT	NT	NT	NT
Leeds 10	d	16 39	16 45	16 51		16 52		17 08		17 10		17 20	17 22		17 36	17 37			17 51	17 51	17 56	18 08		18 10	18 22	
Shipley	a	16 50	16 56			17 04				17 21		17 31			17 49					18 02	18 08			18 21		
	d	16 51			17 02				17 15	17 22	17 28			17 45	17 50		17 56						18 14	18 22		18 28
Frizinghall	d	16 53			17 06				17 17	17 24	17 32			17 47	17 52		18 00						18 17	18 24		18 32
Bramley	d							17 15					17 29			17 44						18 15			18 30	
New Pudsey	d			17 01				17 20					17 34			17 49			18 02			18 20			18 35	
Bradford Interchange	a			17 11				17 28					17 42			17 57			18 11			18 28			18 43	
Bradford Forster Square	a	16 59			17 12				17 23	17 30	17 38			17 53	17 58		18 08						18 23	18 31		18 38

For general notes see front of timetable
For details of catering facilities see
Directory of Train Operators

Leeds → Shipley and Bradford

Network Diagram - see first page of Table 35

Mondays to Fridays

		NT	NT	NT	NT		NT	NT	NT	NT	NT	NT	NT	NT	NT	NT		NT	NT	NT	NT	NT	GR R 1 A	NT	NT	NT
Leeds 10	d	18 26	18 37		18 40			18 50	18 51	19 08		19 10		19 19	19 22	19 25		19 37			19 51	19 56	19 59	20 08		
Shipley	a	18 37			18 52			19 03				19 21		19 31		19 37						20 07	20s11			
	d			18 44	18 52		18 58				19 14	19 22	19 26						19 44	19 58					20 20	20 28
Frizinghall	d			18 46	18 55		19 02				19 17	19 24	19 29						19 47	20 01					20 24	20 30
Bramley	d		18 44							19 15					19 29			19 44						20 15		
New Pudsey	d		18 49						19 01	19 20					19 34			19 49			20 01			20 20		
Bradford Interchange	a		18 57						19 11	19 28					19 45			19 57			20 11			20 28		
Bradford Forster Square	a			18 52	19 01		19 08				19 23	19 30	19 35						19 53	20 08			20 22		20 32	20 36

		NT	NT	NT		NT	NT	NT	NT	NT	NT	NT	NT	NT	NT		NT	NT	NT	NT	NT	NT	NT	NT		
Leeds 10	d	20 26	20 37				20 55	21 08		21 26	21 37			21 56	22 08			22 26	22 37			22 56	23 08	23 18		
Shipley	a	20 37					21 07			21 37				22 07				22 37				23 07		23 30		
	d			20 48		21 03			21 19			21 48	22 03				22 19			22 48	23 03					
Frizinghall	d			20 51		21 05			21 23			21 51	22 05				22 23			22 51	23 05					
Bramley	d		20 44					21 15			21 44				22 15				22 44				23 15			
New Pudsey	d		20 49					21 20			21 49				22 20				22 49				23 20			
Bradford Interchange	a		20 57					21 28			21 57				22 28				22 57				23 29			
Bradford Forster Square	a			20 57		21 12			21 29			21 57	22 11				22 31			22 57	23 13					

Saturdays

		NT	NT	NT	NT	NT	NT	NT	NT	NT	NT	NT	NT	NT	NT	NT	NT	NT	NT	NT	NT	NT	NT	NT	NT	NT
Leeds 10	d	05 51	05 55	06 03		06 19	06 22	06 37		06 51	06 56	07 09	07 10	07 23		07 37		07 51		07 56	08 08	08 10		08 19	08 22	08 25
Shipley	a		06 07			06 31					07 07		07 21							08 08		08 22		08 31		08 37
	d				06 28				06 44				07 22		07 28		07 47		08 00			08 23	08 28			
Frizinghall	d				06 32				06 47				07 24		07 32		07 49		08 03			08 25	08 31			
Bramley	d	05 58					06 29	06 44				07 16		07 30		07 44					08 15				08 29	
New Pudsey	d	06 03		06 12			06 34	06 49		07 01		07 21		07 35		07 49		08 01			08 20				08 34	
Bradford Interchange	a	06 11		06 23			06 42	06 57		07 11		07 29		07 43		07 57		08 11			08 28				08 42	
Bradford Forster Square	a				06 38				06 55				07 30		07 39		07 56		08 09			08 31	08 37			

		NT	NT	NT	NT	NT	NT	NT	NT	NT	NT	NT	NT	NT	NT	NT	NT	NT	NT	NT	NT	NT	NT	NT	NT	NT
Leeds 10	d	08 37		08 40		08 49	08 51	08 56	09 08		09 10	09 22		09 26	09 37		09 40		09 47	09 51	09 56	10 08		10 10		10 19
Shipley	a			08 51		09 01		09 07			09 21			09 37			09 51		10 01		10 07			10 21		10 31
	d		08 44	08 52	08 58					09 14	09 22		09 28			09 44	09 52	09 58					10 14	10 22	10 28	
Frizinghall	d		08 46	08 54	09 02					09 17	09 24		09 32			09 47	09 54	10 02					10 17	10 24	10 32	
Bramley	d	08 44							09 15			09 29			09 44							10 15				
New Pudsey	d	08 49					09 02		09 20			09 34			09 49					10 01		10 20				
Bradford Interchange	a	08 57					09 11		09 28			09 42			09 57					10 11		10 28				
Bradford Forster Square	a		08 53	09 00	09 09					09 24	09 31		09 38			09 53	10 00	10 08					10 23	10 30	10 38	

		NT	NT	NT	NT	NT	NT	NT	NT	NT	NT	NT	NT	NT	NT	NT	NT	NT	NT	NT	NT	NT	NT	NT	NT	NT
Leeds 10	d	10 22	10 26	10 37		10 40		10 49	10 51	10 56	11 08		11 10	11 22		11 26	11 37		11 40	11 51		11 56	12 08		12 10	12 22
Shipley	a		10 37			10 51		11 01		11 07			11 21			11 37			11 51			12 07			12 21	
	d				10 44	10 52	10 58					11 14	11 22		11 28			11 44	11 52		11 58			12 14	12 22	
Frizinghall	d				10 47	10 54	11 02					11 17	11 24		11 32			11 47	11 54		12 02			12 17	12 24	
Bramley	d	10 29		10 44							11 15			11 29			11 44						12 15			12 29
New Pudsey	d	10 34		10 49					11 01		11 20			11 34			11 49			12 01			12 20			12 34
Bradford Interchange	a	10 42		10 57					11 11		11 28			11 42			11 57			12 11			12 28			12 42
Bradford Forster Square	a				10 53	11 00	11 08					11 23	11 30		11 38			11 53	12 00		12 09			12 23	12 30	

		NT	NT	NT	NT	NT	NT	NT	NT	NT	NT	NT	NT	NT	NT	NT	NT	NT	NT	NT	NT	NT	NT	NT	NT	NT
Leeds 10	d		12 26	12 37		12 40		12 49	12 51	12 56	13 08		13 10	13 22		13 26	13 37		13 40		13 49	13 51	13 56	14 08		14 10
Shipley	a		12 37			12 51		13 01		13 07			13 21			13 38			13 51		14 03		14 07			14 21
	d	12 28			12 44	12 52	12 58					13 14	13 22		13 28			13 44	13 52	13 58					14 14	14 22
Frizinghall	d	12 32			12 47	12 54	13 02					13 17	13 24		13 32			13 47	13 54	14 02					14 17	14 24
Bramley	d			12 44							13 15			13 29			13 44							14 15		
New Pudsey	d			12 49					13 01		13 20			13 34			13 49					14 01		14 20		
Bradford Interchange	a			12 57					13 11		13 28			13 42			13 57					14 11		14 28		
Bradford Forster Square	a	12 38			12 53	13 00	13 08					13 23	13 30		13 38			13 53	14 00	14 08					14 23	14 30

For general notes see front of timetable
For details of catering facilities see
Directory of Train Operators

A From London Kings Cross (Table 26)

Table 37

Saturdays

Leeds → Shipley and Bradford

Network Diagram - see first page of Table 35

		NT	NT	NT	NT	NT	NT	NT	NT	NT	NT	NT	NT	NT	NT	NT	NT	NT	NT	NT	NT	NT	NT	NT	NT	NT
Leeds 10	d	14 22		14 26	14 37		14 40		14 49	14 51	14 56	15 08		15 10	15 22		15 26	15 37		15 40	15 51		15 56	16 08		16 10
Shipley	a			14 37			14 51		15 01		15 07			15 21			15 37			15 52			16 07			16 21
	d		14 28			14 44	14 52	14 58					15 14	15 22		15 28			15 44	15 52		15 58			16 14	16 22
Frizinghall	d		14 32			14 47	14 54	15 02					15 17	15 24		15 32			15 47	15 55		16 02			16 17	16 24
Bramley	d	14 29			14 44							15 15			15 29			15 44						16 15		
New Pudsey	d	14 34			14 49					15 01		15 20			15 34			15 49			16 01			16 20		
Bradford Interchange	a	14 42			14 57					15 11		15 28			15 42			15 57			16 11			16 28		
Bradford Forster Square	a		14 38			14 53	15 00	15 08					15 23	15 30		15 38			15 53	16 01		16 08			16 23	16 30

		NT	NT	NT	NT	NT	NT	NT	NT	NT	NT	NT	NT	NT	NT	NT	NT	NT	NT	NT	NT	NT	NT	NT	NT	NT
Leeds 10	d	16 22		16 26	16 37		16 39		16 49	16 51	16 56	17 08		17 10	17 22		17 26	17 37		17 40		17 49	17 51	17 56	18 08	
Shipley	a			16 37			16 50		17 01		17 07			17 21			17 37			17 51		18 02		18 07		
	d		16 28			16 44	16 51	16 58					17 15	17 22		17 28			17 45	17 52	17 56					18 14
Frizinghall	d		16 32			16 47	16 53	17 02					17 17	17 24		17 32			17 47	17 54	18 00					18 17
Bramley	d	16 29			16 44							17 15			17 29			17 44							18 15	
New Pudsey	d	16 34			16 49					17 01		17 20			17 34			17 49					18 01		18 20	
Bradford Interchange	a	16 42			16 57					17 11		17 28			17 42			17 57					18 11		18 28	
Bradford Forster Square	a		16 38			16 53	16 59	17 08					17 23	17 30		17 38			17 53	18 00	18 07					18 23

		NT	NT	NT	NT	NT	NT	NT	NT	NT	NT	NT	NT	NT	NT	NT	NT	NT	NT	NT	NT	NT	NT	NT	NT	NT
Leeds 10	d	18 10	18 22		18 26	18 37		18 40	18 51		18 56	19 08		19 10		19 19	19 22	19 25	19 37			19 51	20 06	20 08		
Shipley	a	18 21			18 37			18 52			19 07			19 21		19 31		19 37					20 18			
	d	18 22		18 28			18 44	18 52		18 58			19 14	19 22	19 26					19 44	19 58				20 20	20 28
Frizinghall	d	18 24		18 32			18 46	18 55		19 02			19 17	19 24	19 29					19 47	20 01				20 24	20 30
Bramley	d		18 30			18 44						19 15					19 29		19 44					20 15		
New Pudsey	d		18 35			18 49			19 01			19 20					19 34		19 49			20 01		20 20		
Bradford Interchange	a		18 43			18 57			19 11			19 28					19 45		19 57			20 11		20 28		
Bradford Forster Square	a	18 31		18 38			18 52	19 01		19 08			19 23	19 30	19 35					19 53	20 08				20 32	20 36

		NT	NT	NT	GR R 1 A	NT	NT	NT	NT	NT	NT	NT	NT	NT	NT	NT	NT	NT	NT	NT	NT	NT B	NT C	NT		
Leeds 10	d	20 26	20 37		20 43		20 55	21 08		21 26	21 37			21 56	22 08		22 26	22 37			22 56	23 00	23 08	23 18		
Shipley	a	20 37			20s56		21 07			21 38				22 07			22 37				23 07			23 30		
	d			20 48		21 03			21 19			21 48	22 03			22 19			22 48	23 03						
Frizinghall	d			20 51		21 05			21 23			21 51	22 05			22 23			22 51	23 05						
Bramley	d		20 44					21 15			21 44				22 15			22 44				23 07	23 15			
New Pudsey	d		20 49					21 20			21 49				22 20			22 49				23 12	23 20			
Bradford Interchange	a		20 57					21 28			21 57				22 28			22 57				23 20	23 28			
Bradford Forster Square	a			20 57	21 06	21 12			21 29			21 57	22 11			22 31			22 57	23 13						

Sundays

		NT	NT	NT	NT D	NT		NT	NT	NT	NT	NT		NT	NT	NT	NT	NT		NT D	NT	NT	NT	NT		NT
Leeds 10	d	08 02	08 21	08 34	08 40	09 00		09 02	09 25	09 34	09 35			10 02		10 08	10 34	10 34		10 54	11 02	11 08	11 34	11 35		
Shipley	a			08 46	08 52	09 13				09 45						10 19	10 45			11 06		11 19	11 45			
	d			08 47						09 46		10 01			10 15		10 46						11 46			12 02
Frizinghall	d			08 49						09 48		10 05			10 18		10 48						11 48			12 06
Bramley	d	08 10	08 28					09 10	09 32					10 10				10 42			11 10					
New Pudsey	d	08 15	08 33					09 15	09 37		09 45			10 15				10 47			11 15			11 44		
Bradford Interchange	a	08 23	08 41					09 23	09 45		09 54			10 23				10 55			11 23			11 53		
Bradford Forster Square	a			08 55						09 54		10 12			10 24		10 54						11 54			12 12

		NT	NT	NT	NT	NT		NT	NT	NT	NT	NT		NT	NT	NT	NT	NT		NT	NT	NT	NT	NT		NT
Leeds 10	d	12 04		12 08	12 34	12 35		13 02	13 08	13 15	13 34	13 35			14 02		14 08	14 34		14 35	15 00	15 02	15 08	15 34		15 35
Shipley	a			12 19	12 45				13 19	13 28	13 45						14 19	14 45			15 12		15 19	15 45		
	d		12 15		12 46						13 46			14 02		14 15		14 46						15 46		
Frizinghall	d		12 18		12 48						13 48			14 06		14 18		14 48						15 48		
Bramley	d	12 12				12 42		13 10							14 10					14 42		15 10				
New Pudsey	d	12 17				12 47		13 15				13 44			14 15					14 47		15 15				15 44
Bradford Interchange	a	12 25				12 55		13 23				13 53			14 23					14 55		15 23				15 53
Bradford Forster Square	a		12 24		12 54						13 54			14 12		14 24		14 54						15 54		

		NT	NT	NT	NT	NT		NT	NT	NT	NT	NT		NT	NT	NT	NT	NT		NT	NT	NT	NT	NT		NT
Leeds 10	d		16 02		16 08	16 35		16 35	16 50	17 02	17 08	17 23		17 33	17 35	17 37		18 02			18 08	18 34	18 35	19 02		19 08
Shipley	a				16 19			16 46			17 19	17 35		17 45		17 49					18 19	18 45				19 19
	d	16 02		16 15				16 46								17 49	18 02			18 15		18 46				
Frizinghall	d	16 06		16 18				16 48								17 51	18 06			18 18		18 48				
Bramley	d		16 10						16 57	17 10								18 10					18 42	19 10		
New Pudsey	d		16 15			16 44			17 02	17 15					17 44			18 15					18 47	19 15		
Bradford Interchange	a		16 23			16 53			17 10	17 23					17 53			18 23					18 55	19 23		
Bradford Forster Square	a	16 12		16 24				16 55								17 58	18 12			18 24		18 54				

For general notes see front of timetable
For details of catering facilities see Directory of Train Operators

A From London Kings Cross (Table 26)
B 2 February to 22 March
C Until 26 January and from 29 March
D From 23 March

Table 37

Sundays

Leeds → Shipley and Bradford

Network Diagram - see first page of Table 35

		NT	NT	NT	NT	NT		NT	NT	NT	NT	NT		NT	NT	NT	NT	NT		NT	NT	NT	NT	NT		
Leeds 10	d	19 34	19 35		20 02			20 08	20 34	20 35	21 02	21 08		21 34	21 35		22 02			22 08	22 34	22 35	23 10	23 22		
Shipley	a	19 45						20 19	20 45			21 19		21 45						22 19	22 45		23 21			
	d	19 46		20 02		20 15			20 46					21 46		22 02		22 15			22 46					
Frizinghall	d	19 48		20 06		20 18			20 48					21 48		22 06		22 18			22 48					
Bramley	d				20 10					20 42	21 10				21 43		22 10					22 42		23 29		
New Pudsey	d		19 44		20 15					20 47	21 14				21 47		22 15					22 47		23 34		
Bradford Interchange	a		19 53		20 23					20 55	21 23				21 56		22 23					22 55		23 43		
Bradford Forster Square	a	19 54		20 12		20 24			20 54					21 54		22 12		22 24			22 54					

For general notes see front of timetable
For details of catering facilities see
Directory of Train Operators

Bradford and Shipley → Leeds

Network Diagram - see first page of Table 35

Miles	Miles			NT MX	NT	NT	NT	NT	NT	GR [R] [1] A ✕	NT	NT	NT	NT		NT	NT	NT	GR [R] [1] B ✕	NT	NT	NT	NT	NT	NT	NT
0	—	Bradford Forster Square	d		06 01		06 10	06 15		06 30		06 40	06 44			06 55				07 11	07 15				07 42	
—	0	Bradford Interchange	d	00 35					06 18					06 48				07 05				07 18		07 35		
—	3½	New Pudsey	d						06 26					06 57				07 14				07 27		07 44		
—	5½	Bramley	d						06 30					07 01				07 18						07 48		
1¾	—	Frizinghall	d		06 04		06 13	06 18				06 43	06 47			06 58				07 14	07 18				07 45	
2¾	—	Shipley	a		06 08		06 17	06 22				06 47	06 51			07 02				07 18	07 22				07 49	
—	—		d		06 08	06 13				06u36	06 44					07 02	07 09		07u15				07 35			07 50
13½	9½	Leeds [10]	a	00 54	06 22	06 27			06 37	06 53	06 58			07 09		07 16	07 23	07 27	07 29			07 37	07 49	07 57		08 05

		NT	NT		NT	NT	NT	NT	NT	NT	NT	NT	NT	NT	NT		NT	NT	NT	NT	NT	NT	NT	NT	NT	NT
Bradford Forster Square	d	07 46			07 59			08 11		08 16		08 26					08 41	08 46			09 02		09 11	09 16		09 31
Bradford Interchange	d		07 49				08 05				08 19			08 35					08 47			09 06			09 18	
New Pudsey	d		07 58				08 14				08 28			08 44					08 57			09 15			09 27	
Bramley	d		08 02				08 18							08 48					09 01			09 19				
Frizinghall	d	07 49			08 02			08 14		08 19		08 29					08 44	08 49			09 05		09 14	09 19		09 34
Shipley	a	07 53			08 06			08 18		08 23		08 33					08 48	08 53			09 08		09 18	09 23		09 38
	d				08 07	08 13			08 19			08 33	08 41		08 47					09 08	09 09					09 39
Leeds [10]	a		08 11		08 24	08 27	08 28		08 37		08 39	08 49	08 56	08 57	09 04				09 12	09 23	09 26	09 28			09 39	09 53

		NT	NT	NT		NT	NT	NT	NT	NT	NT	NT	NT	NT	NT	NT		NT	NT	NT	NT	NT	NT	NT	NT	NT
Bradford Forster Square	d			09 41		09 46		10 01			10 11	10 16		10 31				10 41	10 46		11 01				11 11	11 16
Bradford Interchange	d	09 35					09 48		10 05				10 18		10 35					10 48		11 05				
New Pudsey	d	09 44					09 57		10 14				10 27		10 44					10 57		11 14				
Bramley	d	09 48					10 01		10 18						10 48					11 01		11 18				
Frizinghall	d			09 44		09 49		10 04			10 14	10 19		10 34				10 44	10 49		11 04				11 14	11 19
Shipley	a			09 48		09 53		10 08			10 18	10 23		10 38				10 48	10 53		11 08				11 18	11 23
	d		09 44					10 09		10 14				10 39		10 44					11 09		11 14	11 18		
Leeds [10]	a	09 58	09 59				10 10	10 24	10 27	10 28			10 37	10 53	10 58	10 58				11 10	11 24	11 28	11 28	11 36		

		NT	NT	NT	NT		NT	NT	NT	NT	NT	NT	NT	NT	NT	NT	NT		NT	NT	NT	NT	NT	NT	NT	NT
Bradford Forster Square	d		11 31				11 41	11 46		12 01			12 11	12 16			12 31				12 41	12 46		13 01		
Bradford Interchange	d	11 18		11 35					11 48		12 05				12 18				12 35				12 48		13 05	
New Pudsey	d	11 27		11 44					11 57		12 14				12 27				12 44				12 57		13 14	
Bramley	d			11 48					12 01		12 18								12 48				13 01		13 18	
Frizinghall	d		11 34				11 44	11 49		12 04			12 14	12 19			12 34				12 44	12 49		13 04		
Shipley	a		11 38				11 48	11 53		12 08			12 18	12 23			12 38				12 48	12 53		13 08		
	d		11 39		11 44					12 09		12 14				12 32	12 39			12 44				13 09		13 14
Leeds [10]	a	11 39	11 55	11 58	11 58				12 10	12 23	12 28	12 28			12 39	12 54	12 55		12 58	12 58			13 10	13 24	13 28	13 28

		NT	NT	NT	NT	NT		NT	NT	NT	NT	NT	NT	NT	NT	NT	NT	NT		NT	NT	NT	NT	NT	NT	NT
Bradford Forster Square	d	13 11	13 16		13 31				13 41	13 46		14 01				14 11	14 16			14 31			14 41		14 46	
Bradford Interchange	d			13 18		13 35					13 48		14 05					14 18			14 35					14 48
New Pudsey	d			13 27		13 44					13 57		14 14					14 27			14 44					14 57
Bramley	d					13 48					14 01		14 18								14 48					15 01
Frizinghall	d	13 14	13 19		13 34				13 44	13 49		14 04				14 14	14 19			14 34			14 44		14 49	
Shipley	a	13 18	13 23		13 38				13 48	13 53		14 08				14 18	14 23			14 38			14 48		14 53	
	d				13 39			13 44				14 09		14 14	14 18					14 39		14 45		14 51		
Leeds [10]	a			13 37	13 54	13 58		13 58			14 10	14 24	14 28	14 28	14 37			14 39		14 53	14 58	14 59		15 07		15 12

		NT	NT	NT	NT	NT	NT		NT	NT	NT	NT	NT	NT	NT	NT	NT	NT	NT		NT	NT	NT	NT	NT	NT
Bradford Forster Square	d	15 01			15 11	15 16			15 31			15 41	15 46		16 01			16 11	16 16				16 31			16 40
Bradford Interchange	d		15 05				15 18			15 35				15 48		16 05					16 18			16 35		
New Pudsey	d		15 14				15 27			15 44				15 57		16 14					16 27			16 44		
Bramley	d		15 18							15 48				16 01		16 18								16 48		
Frizinghall	d	15 04			15 14	15 19			15 34			15 44	15 49		16 04			16 14	16 19				16 34			16 43
Shipley	a	15 08			15 18	15 23			15 38			15 48	15 53		16 08			16 18	16 23				16 38			16 48
	d	15 09		15 14					15 39		15 44				16 09		16 14					16 31	16 39		16 44	
Leeds [10]	a	15 24	15 28	15 28			15 37		15 53	15 58	15 58			16 10	16 24	16 28	16 28				16 37	16 51	16 53	16 58	16 58	

For general notes see front of timetable
For details of catering facilities see
Directory of Train Operators

A To London Kings Cross (Table 26)
B From Skipton to London Kings Cross (Table 26)

Bradford and Shipley → Leeds

Network Diagram - see first page of Table 35

		NT	NT	NT	NT	NT	NT	NT		NT	NT	NT	NT	NT	NT	NT	NT	NT	NT	NT		NT	NT	NT	NT	NT
Bradford Forster Square	d	16 44		17 01			17 11				17 16	17 31			17 38	17 46		18 01				18 11	18 16		18 27	
Bradford Interchange	d		16 48		17 05			17 18					17 35				17 48		18 05					18 18		18 35
New Pudsey	d		16 57		17 14			17 27					17 44				17 57		18 14					18 27		18 44
Bramley	d		17 01		17 18								17 48				18 01		18 18							18 48
Frizinghall	d	16 48		17 04			17 14				17 19	17 34			17 41	17 49		18 04				18 14	18 19		18 30	
Shipley	a	16 51		17 08			17 18				17 23	17 38			17 45	17 53		18 08				18 18	18 23		18 34	
	d			17 09		17 15				17 20		17 39		17 45				18 09		18 14					18 34	
Leeds 10	a		17 10	17 24	17 28	17 29		17 37		17 40		17 55	17 58	18 00			18 10	18 24	18 28	18 29				18 37	18 48	18 59

		NT	NT	NT	NT	NT	NT	NT	NT		NT	NT	NT	NT	NT	NT	NT	NT	NT	NT	NT		NT	NT	NT	NT
Bradford Forster Square	d			18 41	18 46		19 01				19 08		19 31		19 36		19 41			20 06				20 25		
Bradford Interchange	d					18 48		19 05				19 18		19 35				20 04			20 18				20 35	
New Pudsey	d					18 57		19 14				19 27		19 44				20 13			20 27				20 44	
Bramley	d					19 01		19 18						19 48				20 17							20 48	
Frizinghall	d			18 44	18 49		19 04				19 11		19 34		19 39		19 44			20 09				20 28		
Shipley	a			18 48	18 53		19 08				19 15		19 38		19 43		19 48			20 16				20 32		
	d	18 44	18 48				19 09		19 14				19 39			19 44			20 14				20 28			20 43
Leeds 10	a	18 59	19 07			19 10	19 25	19 28	19 29			19 37	19 55	19 58		19 59		20 26	20 28		20 37		20 44		20 57	21 00

		NT	NT	NT	NT	NT	NT	NT	NT	NT		NT	NT	NT	NT	NT	NT	NT	NT	NT	NT	NT		NT		
Bradford Forster Square	d	20 38			21 05		21 25			21 38			22 05			22 25			22 38		23 09	23 20				
Bradford Interchange	d			21 04					21 35			22 04			22 18		22 35			23 04				23 35		
New Pudsey	d			21 13					21 44			22 13			22 27		22 44			23 13				23 44		
Bramley	d			21 17					21 48			22 17					22 48			23 17				23 48		
Frizinghall	d	20 41			21 08		21 28			21 41			22 08			22 28			22 41		23 12	23 23				
Shipley	a	20 45			21 12		21 32			21 45			22 12			22 32			22 45		23 16	23 27				
	d		20 57			21 14		21 43						22 14				22 43								
Leeds 10	a		21 15	21 25		21 30		21 57	21 58			22 25		22 32	22 38		22 58	23 01		23 25				23 58		

Saturdays

		NT	NT	NT	NT	NT	NT	GR R 1 A	NT	NT	NT	NT	NT	NT	GR R 1 B	NT	NT	NT	NT	NT	NT	NT	NT	NT	NT	NT
Bradford Forster Square	d		06 01		06 10	06 15			07 01			07 11	07 16		07 36			07 59			08 11			08 16	08 31	
Bradford Interchange	d	00 35					06 23			07 05				07 18		07 35	07 49			08 05		08 18				08 35
New Pudsey	d						06 32			07 14				07 27		07 44	07 57			08 14		08 27				08 44
Bramley	d						06 36			07 18						07 48	08 01			08 18						08 48
Frizinghall	d		06 04		06 13	06 18			07 04			07 14	07 19					08 02			08 14			08 19	08 34	
Shipley	a		06 08		06 17	06 22			07 08			07 18	07 23					08 05			08 18			08 23	08 38	
	d		06 08	06 13				07u00	07 09		07 14				07u41			08 07	08 13				08 19		08 38	
Leeds 10	a	00 54	06 22	06 27			06 44	07 15	07 23	07 27	07 28			07 37	07 58	07 59	08 13	08 23	08 27	08 28		08 37	08 37		08 53	08 57

		NT	NT	NT	NT	NT	NT	NT	NT	NT	NT	NT	NT	NT	NT	NT	NT	NT	NT	NT	NT	NT	NT	NT	NT	NT
Bradford Forster Square	d		08 41	08 46		09 01			09 11	09 16		09 31			09 41		09 46		10 01			10 11			10 16	10 31
Bradford Interchange	d				08 47		09 06				09 18		09 35					09 48		10 05			10 18			
New Pudsey	d				08 57		09 15				09 27		09 44					09 57		10 14			10 27			
Bramley	d				09 01		09 19						09 48					10 01		10 18						
Frizinghall	d		08 44	08 49		09 04			09 14	09 19		09 34			09 44		09 49		10 04			10 14			10 19	10 34
Shipley	a		08 48	08 53		09 08			09 18	09 23		09 38			09 48		09 53		10 08			10 18			10 23	10 38
	d	08 44				09 09		09 14				09 39		09 44		09 49			10 09		10 14			10 19		10 39
Leeds 10	a	08 58			09 12	09 26	09 28	09 28			09 39	09 53	09 58	09 59		10 08		10 10	10 24	10 28	10 28		10 37	10 37		10 53

		NT	NT	NT		NT	NT	NT	NT	NT	NT	NT	NT	NT	NT	NT	NT	NT	NT	NT	NT	NT	NT	NT	NT	NT
Bradford Forster Square	d			10 41		10 46		11 01			11 11	11 16		11 31			11 41		11 46		12 01			12 11	12 16	
Bradford Interchange	d	10 35					10 48		11 05				11 18		11 35					11 48		12 05				12 18
New Pudsey	d	10 44					10 57		11 14				11 27		11 44					11 57		12 14				12 27
Bramley	d	10 48					11 01		11 18						11 48					12 01		12 18				
Frizinghall	d			10 44		10 49		11 04			11 14	11 19		11 34			11 44		11 49		12 04			12 14	12 19	
Shipley	a			10 48		10 53		11 08			11 18	11 23		11 38			11 48		11 53		12 08			12 18	12 23	
	d		10 44					11 09		11 14				11 39		11 44		11 49			12 09		12 14			
Leeds 10	a	10 58	10 58				11 10	11 24	11 28	11 28			11 39	11 55	11 58	11 58		12 06		12 10	12 23	12 28	12 28			12 38

For general notes see front of timetable
For details of catering facilities see
Directory of Train Operators

A From Skipton to London Kings Cross (Table 26)
B To London Kings Cross (Table 26)

Table 37

Bradford and Shipley → Leeds

Network Diagram - see first page of Table 35

Saturdays

		NT	NT	NT	NT	NT	NT	NT	NT	NT	NT	NT	NT	NT	NT	NT	NT	NT	NT	NT	NT	NT	NT	NT	NT	NT
Bradford Forster Square	d		12 31			12 41	12 46		13 01			13 11	13 16		13 31			13 41	13 46		14 01				14 11	14 16
Bradford Interchange	d			12 35				12 48		13 05				13 18		13 35				13 48		14 05				
New Pudsey	d			12 44				12 57		13 14				13 27		13 44				13 57		14 14				
Bramley	d			12 48				13 01		13 18						13 48				14 01		14 18				
Frizinghall	d		12 34			12 44	12 49		13 04			13 14	13 19		13 34			13 44	13 49		14 04				14 14	14 19
Shipley	a		12 38			12 48	12 53		13 08			13 18	13 23		13 38			13 48	13 53		14 08				14 18	14 23
	d	12 32	12 39		12 44				13 09		13 14				13 39		13 44				14 09		14 14	14 18		
Leeds 10	a	12 49	12 55	12 58	12 58			13 10	13 24	13 28	13 28			13 37	13 54	13 58	13 58			14 10	14 24	14 28	14 28	14 37		

		NT	NT	NT	NT	NT	NT	NT		NT	NT	NT	NT	NT	NT	NT	NT	NT	NT	NT	NT	NT	NT	NT	NT	NT
Bradford Forster Square	d		14 31			14 41		14 46			15 01			15 11	15 16		15 31			15 41	15 46		16 01			16 11
Bradford Interchange	d	14 18		14 35						14 48		15 05				15 18		15 35				15 48		16 05		
New Pudsey	d	14 27		14 44						14 57		15 14				15 27		15 44				15 57		16 14		
Bramley	d			14 48						15 01		15 18						15 48				16 01		16 18		
Frizinghall	d		14 34			14 44		14 49			15 04			15 14	15 19		15 34			15 44	15 49		16 04			16 14
Shipley	a		14 38			14 48		14 53			15 08			15 18	15 23		15 38			15 48	15 53		16 08			16 18
	d		14 39		14 45		14 49				15 09		15 14				15 39		15 44				16 09		16 14	
Leeds 10	a	14 39	14 53	14 58	14 59		15 07			15 12	15 24	15 28	15 28			15 37	15 53	15 58	15 58			16 10	16 24	16 28	16 28	

		NT	NT	NT	NT	NT	NT	NT	NT	NT	NT	NT	NT	NT	NT	NT	NT	NT	NT	NT	NT	NT	NT	NT	NT	NT
Bradford Forster Square	d	16 16		16 31			16 40		16 44		17 01			17 11	17 16		17 31			17 41	17 46			18 01		
Bradford Interchange	d		16 18		16 35					16 48		17 05				17 18		17 35				17 48			18 05	
New Pudsey	d		16 27		16 44					16 57		17 14				17 27		17 44				17 57			18 14	
Bramley	d				16 48					17 01		17 18						17 48				18 01			18 18	
Frizinghall	d	16 19		16 34			16 43		16 48		17 04			17 14	17 19		17 34			17 44	17 49			18 04		
Shipley	a	16 23		16 38			16 48		16 51		17 08			17 18	17 23		17 38			17 48	17 53			18 08		
	d			16 39		16 44		16 49			17 09		17 15				17 39		17 45				18 00	18 09		18 14
Leeds 10	a		16 37	16 53	16 58	16 58		17 07		17 10	17 24	17 28	17 29			17 37	17 55	17 58	18 00			18 10	18 17	18 24	18 28	18 29

		NT	NT	NT	NT	NT	NT	NT	NT	NT	NT	NT	NT	NT	NT	NT	NT	NT	NT	NT	NT	NT	NT	NT	NT	NT
Bradford Forster Square	d	18 11	18 16		18 31				18 41	18 46		19 01			19 07		19 31		19 36		19 41	20 07				
Bradford Interchange	d			18 18		18 35					18 48		19 05			19 18		19 35						20 04	20 21	
New Pudsey	d			18 27		18 44					18 57		19 14			19 27		19 44						20 13	20 30	
Bramley	d					18 48					19 01		19 18					19 48						20 17		
Frizinghall	d	18 14	18 19		18 34				18 44	18 49		19 04			19 10		19 34		19 39		19 44	20 10				
Shipley	a	18 18	18 23		18 38				18 48	18 53		19 08			19 14		19 38		19 43		19 48	20 12				
	d				18 38		18 44	18 48				19 09		19 14			19 39			19 44			20 14			20 28
Leeds 10	a			18 37	18 52	18 59	18 59	19 07			19 10	19 26	19 28	19 29		19 37	19 55	19 58		19 59			20 28	20 29	20 40	20 44

		NT	NT	NT	NT	NT	NT	NT	NT	NT	NT	NT	NT	NT	NT	NT	NT	NT	NT	NT	NT	NT	NT	NT		
Bradford Forster Square	d	20 25		20 38				21 05		21 25			21 38		22 05			22 25			22 38		23 05	23 20		
Bradford Interchange	d				20 43		21 04				21 35			22 04			22 18		22 35			23 04				
New Pudsey	d				20 52		21 13				21 44			22 13			22 27		22 44			23 13				
Bramley	d				20 56		21 17				21 48			22 17					22 48			23 17				
Frizinghall	d	20 28		20 41				21 08		21 28			21 41		22 08			22 28			22 41		23 08	23 23		
Shipley	a	20 32		20 45				21 12		21 32			21 45		22 12			22 32			22 45		23 12	23 27		
	d		20 43			20 57			21 14			21 43				22 14				22 43						
Leeds 10	a		21 00		21 07	21 15	21 25		21 30		21 58	22 01		22 25		22 28	22 37		22 58	23 01		23 25				

Sundays

		NT	NT	NT	NT	NT		NT	NT	NT	NT	NT		NT	NT	NT	NT	NT		NT	NT	NT	NT	NT		NT
Bradford Forster Square	d				09 02				10 02					10 38	10 48		11 02						12 02			
Bradford Interchange	d	00 05	08 31			09 21				10 02	10 31					11 02		11 31				12 01		12 31		
New Pudsey	d	00 14	08 39			09 30				10 10	10 39					11 10		11 39				12 09		12 39		
Bramley	d	00 18	08 43			09 34				10 14	10 43							11 43				12 13		12 43		
Frizinghall	d				09 05				10 05					10 41	10 51		11 05						12 05			
Shipley	a				09 08				10 08					10 44	10 54		11 09						12 08			
	d			09 00	09 10			09 40	10 08			10 40					11 10			11 40	11 49		12 08			12 40
Leeds 10	a	00 28	08 52	09 14	09 24	09 42		09 54	10 22	10 24	10 52	10 54				11 21	11 24	11 54		11 54	12 06	12 21	12 22	12 52		12 54

For general notes see front of timetable
For details of catering facilities see
Directory of Train Operators

Table 37

Sundays

Bradford and Shipley → Leeds

Network Diagram - see first page of Table 35

		NT	NT	NT	NT	NT	NT	NT	NT	NT A	NT	NT	NT	NT	NT	NT	NT	NT	NT	NT	NT	NT A
Bradford Forster Square	d	12 38	12 48		13 02			14 02					14 38	14 48		15 02				16 02		
Bradford Interchange	d			13 02		13 31			14 02		14 31				15 02		15 31		16 01			
New Pudsey	d			13 10		13 39			14 10		14 39				15 10		15 39		16 09			
Bramley	d					13 43			14 14		14 43						15 43		16 13			
Frizinghall	d	12 41	12 51		13 05			14 05					14 41	14 51		15 05				16 05		
Shipley	a	12 44	12 54		13 08			14 08					14 44	14 54		15 08				16 08		
	d				13 08		13 40	14 08		14 18		14 40				15 08		15 40		16 08	16 16	16 27
Leeds 10	a			13 21	13 22	13 52	13 54	14 22	14 22	14 39	14 53	14 54			15 21	15 22	15 52	15 54	16 21	16 22	16 34	16 45

		NT	NT	NT	NT	NT	NT	NT	NT	NT	NT	NT	NT	NT	NT	NT	NT	NT	NT	NT	NT	NT
Bradford Forster Square	d			16 38	16 48		17 02				18 02			18 38	18 48			19 02				
Bradford Interchange	d	16 31				17 02		17 31		18 02		18 31					19 02		19 31			20 02
New Pudsey	d	16 39				17 10		17 39		18 10		18 39					19 10		19 39			20 10
Bramley	d	16 43						17 43		18 14		18 43							19 43			
Frizinghall	d			16 41	16 51		17 05				18 05			18 41	18 51			19 05				
Shipley	a			16 44	16 54		17 08				18 08			18 44	18 54			19 08				
	d		16 40				17 09		17 40		18 08		18 40			19 02		19 08		19 38	19 48	
Leeds 10	a	16 54	16 54			17 21	17 23	17 52	17 54	18 22	18 23	18 54	18 54			19 19	19 21	19 22	19 53	19 56	20 02	20 22

		NT	NT	NT	NT	NT	NT	NT	NT	NT	NT	NT	NT	NT	NT	NT	NT	NT	NT	NT	NT	NT
Bradford Forster Square	d	20 02				20 38	20 48		21 02				22 02				22 38	22 48		23 02		
Bradford Interchange	d		20 14	20 31				21 02		21 31				22 02	22 31				23 02		23 31	
New Pudsey	d		20 22	20 39				21 10		21 39				22 10	22 39				23 10		23 39	
Bramley	d		20 26	20 43						21 43				22 14	22 43						23 43	
Frizinghall	d	20 05				20 41	20 51		21 05				22 05				22 41	22 51		23 05		
Shipley	a	20 08				20 44	20 54		21 08				22 08				22 44	22 54		23 08		
	d	20 08			20 40				21 08		21 40	21 47	22 08			22 40				23 08		23 40
Leeds 10	a	20 22	20 34	20 54	20 54			21 21	21 24	21 54	21 54	22 03	22 22	22 22	22 53	22 54			23 21	23 22	23 52	23 58

For general notes see front of timetable
For details of catering facilities see
Directory of Train Operators

A From 23 March

Table 38

Mondays to Saturdays

Leeds and Bradford → Ilkley

Network Diagram - see first page of Table 35

Miles	Miles			NT	NT	NT SX	NT SX	NT	NT SX	NT SO	NT SX	NT SX	NT SX	NT	NT	NT SO	NT SX	NT	NT	NT	NT	NT	NT	NT	NT
0	—	**Leeds** 10	d	06 02		06 27		07 02			07 29	07 35		08 02		08 32	08 35		09 02		09 32		10 02		10 32
—	0	**Bradford Forster Square**	37 d		06 15		06 44		07 11	07 16			07 46		08 16			08 46		09 16		09 46		10 16	
—	1¾	Frizinghall	37 d		06 18		06 47		07 14	07 19			07 49		08 19			08 49		09 19		09 49		10 19	
—	2¾	Shipley	37 d		06 22		06 51		07 18	07 23			07 53		08 23			08 53		09 23		09 53		10 23	
—	4¼	Baildon	d		06 25		06 54		07 21	07 26			07 56		08 26			08 56		09 26		09 56		10 26	
10¼	7½	Guiseley	d	06 14	06 31	06b41	07 00	07 14	07 27	07 32	07 41	07 48	08 02	08 14	08 32	08 44	08 47	09 02	09 14	09 32	09 45	10 02	10 14	10 32	10 44
11½	8¾	Menston	d	06 17	06 34	06 44	07 03	07 17	07 30	07 35	07 44	07 51	08 05	08 17	08 35	08 47	08 50	09 05	09 17	09 35	09 48	10 05	10 17	10 35	10 47
13	10¼	Burley-in-Wharfedale	d	06 20	06 37	06 47	07 06	07 20	07 33	07 38	07 47	07 56	08 09	08 20	08 38	08 50	08 53	09 08	09 20	09 38	09 52	10 08	10 20	10 38	10 50
15¼	12½	Ben Rhydding	d	06 23	06 40	06 51	07 09	07 24	07 36	07 41	07 51	07 59	08 12	08 23	08 41	08 53	08 56	09 11	09 24	09 41	09 55	10 11	10 23	10 41	10 53
16¼	13½	**Ilkley**	a	06 29	06 46	06 56	07 15	07 29	07 42	07 47	07 56	08 05	08 18	08 29	08 49	08 59	09 02	09 17	09 33	09 47	10 01	10 17	10 29	10 47	10 59

		NT	NT	NT	NT	NT	NT	NT	NT	NT	NT	NT	NT	NT	NT	NT	NT	NT	NT	NT	NT	NT	NT	NT	NT
Leeds 10	d		11 02		11 32		12 02		12 32		13 02		13 32		14 02		14 32		15 02		15 32		16 02		16 32
Bradford Forster Square	37 d	10 46		11 16		11 46		12 16		12 46		13 16		13 46		14 16		14 46		15 16		15 46		16 16	
Frizinghall	37 d	10 49		11 19		11 49		12 19		12 49		13 19		13 49		14 19		14 49		15 19		15 49		16 19	
Shipley	37 d	10 53		11 23		11 53		12 23		12 53		13 23		13 53		14 23		14 53		15 23		15 53		16 23	
Baildon	d	10 56		11 26		11 56		12 26		12 56		13 26		13 56		14 26		14 56		15 26		15 56		16 26	
Guiseley	d	11 02	11 14	11 32	11 44	12 02	12 14	12 32	12 44	13 02	13 14	13 32	13 44	14 02	14 14	14 32	14 44	15 02	15 14	15 32	15 44	16 02	16 14	16 32	16 44
Menston	d	11 05	11 17	11 35	11 47	12 05	12 17	12 35	12 47	13 05	13 17	13 35	13 47	14 05	14 17	14 35	14 47	15 05	15 17	15 35	15 47	16 05	16 17	16 35	16 47
Burley-in-Wharfedale	d	11 08	11 20	11 38	11 50	12 08	12 20	12 38	12 50	13 08	13 20	13 38	13 50	14 08	14 20	14 38	14 50	15 08	15 20	15 38	15 50	16 08	16 20	16 38	16 50
Ben Rhydding	d	11 11	11 23	11 41	11 53	12 11	12 23	12 41	12 53	13 11	13 23	13 41	13 53	14 11	14 23	14 41	14 53	15 11	15 23	15 41	15 53	16 11	16 23	16 41	16 53
Ilkley	a	11 17	11 29	11 47	11 59	12 17	12 29	12 47	13 00	13 17	13 29	13 47	13 59	14 17	14 29	14 47	15 01	15 17	15 29	15 47	15 59	16 17	16 29	16 47	16 59

		NT	NT	NT SX	NT SO	NT SX	NT	NT	NT	NT	NT	NT	NT	NT	NT	NT	NT	NT SO	NT SX	NT	NT	NT	NT	NT
Leeds 10	d		17 02	17 15			17 32		18 02		18 32		19 02	19 32		20 02		21 02	21 06		22 02		23 15	
Bradford Forster Square	37 d	16 44			17 16	17 16		17 46		18 16		18 46			19 41		20 38			21 38		22 38		23 20
Frizinghall	37 d	16 48			17 19	17 19		17 49		18 19		18 49			19 44		20 41			21 41		22 41		23 23
Shipley	37 d	16 52			17 23	17 25		17 53		18 23		18 53			19 48		20 45			21 45		22 45		23 27
Baildon	d	16 55			17 26	17 28		17 57		18 26		18 56			19 51		20 48			21 48		22 48		23 30
Guiseley	d	17 01	17 14	17 28	17 32	17 35	17 44	18 02	18 14	18 32	18 44	19 02	19 14	19 44	19 56	20 14	20 54	21 14	21 18	21 54	22 14	22 54	23 27	23 36
Menston	d	17 04	17 17	17 31	17 35	17 38	17 47	18 05	18 17	18 35	18 47	19 05	19 17	19 47	19 59	20 17	20 57	21 17	21 21	21 57	22 17	22 57	23 30	23 39
Burley-in-Wharfedale	d	17 07	17 20	17 34	17 38	17 42	17 51	18 08	18 20	18 38	18 50	19 08	19 20	19 50	20 02	20 20	21 00	21 20	21 24	22 00	22 20	23 00	23 33	23 42
Ben Rhydding	d	17 10	17 23	17 37	17 41	17 46	17 54	18 12	18 23	18 41	18 53	19 11	19 24	19 53	20 06	20 23	21 03	21 23	21 27	22 03	22 23	23 03	23 36	23 45
Ilkley	a	17 17	17 29	17 43	17 47	17 51	18 00	18 17	18 29	18 47	19 00	19 17	19 29	20 00	20 12	20 30	21 09	21 29	21 33	22 09	22 29	23 09	23 42	23 51

Sundays

		NT	NT	NT	NT	NT	NT	NT	NT	NT	NT	NT	NT	NT	NT	NT	NT	NT	NT	NT	NT	NT	NT
Leeds 10	d	09 12	10 12		11 12	12 12		13 12	14 12		15 12	16 12		17 12	18 12		19 12	20 12		21 12	22 12		23 14
Bradford Forster Square	37 d			10 38			12 38			14 38			16 38			18 38			20 38			22 38	
Frizinghall	37 d			10 41			12 41			14 41			16 41			18 41			20 41			22 41	
Shipley	37 d			10 44			12 44			14 44			16 44			18 44			20 44			22 44	
Baildon	d			10 47			12 47			14 47			16 47			18 47			20 47			22 47	
Guiseley	d	09 23	10 23	10 52	11 23	12 23	12 52	13 23	14 23	14 52	15 23	16 23	16 52	17 23	18 23	18 52	19 23	20 23	20 52	21 23	22 23	22 52	23 25
Menston	d	09 26	10 26	10 55	11 26	12 26	12 55	13 26	14 26	14 55	15 26	16 26	16 55	17 26	18 26	18 55	19 26	20 26	20 55	21 26	22 26	22 55	23 28
Burley-in-Wharfedale	d	09 29	10 29	10 58	11 29	12 29	12 58	13 29	14 29	14 58	15 29	16 29	16 58	17 29	18 29	18 58	19 29	20 29	20 58	21 29	22 29	22 58	23 31
Ben Rhydding	d	09 33	10 33	11 02	11 33	12 33	13 02	13 33	14 33	15 02	15 33	16 33	17 02	17 33	18 33	19 02	19 33	20 33	21 02	21 33	22 33	23 02	23 35
Ilkley	a	09 38	10 38	11 07	11 38	12 38	13 07	13 38	14 38	15 07	15 38	16 38	17 07	17 38	18 38	19 07	19 38	20 38	21 07	21 38	22 38	23 07	23 40

For general notes see front of timetable
For details of catering facilities see
Directory of Train Operators

b Arr. 0638

Table 38

Mondays to Saturdays

Ilkley → Bradford and Leeds

Network Diagram - see first page of Table 35

Miles	Miles			NT	NT SX	NT SO		NT SX	NT SX	NT		NT	NT SX	NT SX		NT SX	NT SO	NT SX		NT SO	NT SX	NT		NT SO	NT SX
0	0	**Ilkley**	d	06 09	06 17	06 19		06 40	06 50	07 10		07 22	07 40	07 50		08 05	08 10	08 17		08 21	08 24	08 40		08 51	08 54
1	1	Ben Rhydding	d	06 11	06 19	06 21		06 42	06 52	07 12		07 24	07 42	07 52		08 07	08 12	08 19		08 23	08 26	08 42		08 53	08 56
3¼	3¼	Burley-in-Wharfedale	d	06 17	06 25	06 27		06 48	06 58	07 18		07 30	07 48	07 58		08 13	08 18	08 25		08 29	08 32	08 48		08 59	09 02
4¾	4¾	Menston	d	06 20	06 28	06 30		06 51	07 01	07 21		07 33	07 51	08 01		08 16	08 21	08 28		08 32	08 35	08 51		09 02	09 05
6	6	Guiseley	d	06 23	06 31	06 34		06 54	07 04	07 24		07 36	07 54	08 04		08 19	08 24	08 31		08 35	08 39	08 54		09 05	09 08
—	9¼	Baildon	d		06 36	06 39			07 09			07 41		08 09						08 40	08 44			09 10	09 13
—	10¾	Shipley	37 a		06 41	06 44			07 14			07 47		08 12						08 43	08 47			09 14	09 18
—	11¾	Frizinghall	37 a		06 44	06 47			07 17			07 49		08 16						08 46	08 50			09 17	09 21
—	13½	**Bradford Forster Square**	37 a		06 50	06 55			07 22			07 56		08 22						08 53	08 56			09 24	09 27
16¼	—	**Leeds** 10	a	06 39				07 10		07 38			08 09			08 34	08 39	08 46				09 11			

		NT	NT	NT		NT	NT	NT		NT	NT	NT		NT	NT	NT		NT	NT	NT		NT	NT	NT	NT
Ilkley	d	09 10	09 21	09 40		09 51	10 10	10 21		10 40	10 51	11 10		11 21	11 40	11 51		12 10	12 21	12 40		12 51	13 10	13 21	13 40
Ben Rhydding	d	09 12	09 23	09 42		09 53	10 12	10 23		10 42	10 53	11 12		11 23	11 42	11 53		12 12	12 23	12 42		12 53	13 12	13 23	13 42
Burley-in-Wharfedale	d	09 18	09 29	09 48		09 59	10 18	10 29		10 48	10 59	11 18		11 29	11 48	11 59		12 18	12 29	12 48		12 59	13 18	13 29	13 48
Menston	d	09 21	09 32	09 51		10 02	10 21	10 32		10 51	11 02	11 21		11 32	11 51	12 02		12 21	12 32	12 51		13 02	13 21	13 32	13 51
Guiseley	d	09 24	09 35	09 54		10 05	10 25	10 35		10 54	11 05	11 24		11 35	11 54	12 05		12 24	12 35	12 54		13 05	13 24	13 35	13 54
Baildon	d		09 40			10 10		10 40			11 10			11 40		12 10			12 40			13 10		13 40	
Shipley	37 a		09 44			10 14		10 44			11 14			11 44		12 14			12 44			13 14		13 44	
Frizinghall	37 a		09 47			10 17		10 47			11 17			11 47		12 17			12 47			13 17		13 47	
Bradford Forster Square	37 a		09 53			10 23		10 53			11 23			11 53		12 23			12 53			13 23		13 53	
Leeds 10	a	09 39		10b08			10 41			11 08		11 39			12 08			12 39		13 08			13 38		14 09

		NT		NT	NT	NT		NT	NT	NT		NT	NT	NT		NT	NT	NT		NT SO	NT SX	NT		NT	NT
Ilkley	d	13 51		14 10	14 21	14 40		14 51	15 10	15 21		15 40	15 51	16 10		16 21	16 40	16 51		17 10	17 14	17 21		17 40	17 51
Ben Rhydding	d	13 53		14 12	14 23	14 42		14 53	15 12	15 23		15 42	15 53	16 12		16 23	16 42	16 53		17 12	17 16	17 23		17 42	17 53
Burley-in-Wharfedale	d	13 59		14 18	14 29	14 48		14 59	15 18	15 29		15 48	15 59	16 18		16 29	16 48	16 59		17 18	17 22	17 29		17 48	17 59
Menston	d	14 02		14 21	14 32	14 51		15 02	15 21	15 32		15 51	16 02	16 21		16 32	16 51	17 02		17 21	17 25	17 32		17 51	18 02
Guiseley	d	14 05		14 24	14 35	14 54		15 05	15 24	15 35		15 54	16 05	16 24		16 35	16 54	17 05		17 24	17 29	17 35		17 54	18 05
Baildon	d	14 10			14 40			15 10		15 40			16 10			16 40		17 10				17 40			18 10
Shipley	37 a	14 14			14 44			15 14		15 44			16 14			16 44		17 14				17 44			18 14
Frizinghall	37 a	14 17			14 47			15 17		15 47			16 17			16 47		17 17				17 47			18 17
Bradford Forster Square	37 a	14 23			14 53			15 23		15 53			16 23			16 53		17 23				17 53			18 23
Leeds 10	a			14 39		15 10			15 40			16 08		16 38			17 09			17 38	17 44			18 09	

		NT SX	NT	NT		NT	NT	NT		NT	NT	NT		NT	NT	NT		NT	NT	NT		NT			
Ilkley	d	18 04	18 10	18 21		18 40	18 51	19 10		19 21	19 40	20 05		20 21	20 40	21 21		21 40	22 21	22 40		23 21			
Ben Rhydding	d	18 06	18 12	18 23		18 42	18 53	19 12		19 23	19 42	20 07		20 23	20 42	21 23		21 42	22 23	22 42		23 23			
Burley-in-Wharfedale	d	18 12	18 18	18 29		18 48	18 59	19 18		19 29	19 48	20 13		20 29	20 48	21 29		21 48	22 29	22 48		23 29			
Menston	d	18 15	18 21	18 32		18 51	19 02	19 21		19 32	19 51	20 16		20 32	20 51	21 32		21 51	22 32	22 51		23 32			
Guiseley	d	18 18	18 24	18 35		18 54	19 05	19 24		19 35	19 54	20 19		20 35	20 54	21 35		21 54	22 35	22 54		23 35			
Baildon	d			18 40			19 10			19 40		20 24			20 59			21 59		22 59					
Shipley	37 a			18 43			19 14			19 44		20 27			21 03			22 02		23 02					
Frizinghall	37 a			18 46			19 17			19 47		20 30			21 05			22 05		23 05					
Bradford Forster Square	37 a			18 52			19 23			19 53		20 36			21 12			22 11		23 13					
Leeds 10	a	18 35	18 40			19 09		19 40			20 09			20 53		21 49			22 49			23 49			

Sundays

		NT	NT	NT	NT	NT	NT	NT	NT	NT	NT	NT	NT	NT	NT	NT	NT	NT	NT	NT	NT	NT	NT		
Ilkley	d	09 30	09 53	10 21	11 21	11 53	12 21	13 21	13 53	14 21	15 21	15 53	16 21	17 21	17 53	18 21	19 21	19 53	20 21	21 21	21 53	22 21	23 21		
Ben Rhydding	d	09 32	09 55	10 23	11 23	11 55	12 23	13 23	13 55	14 23	15 23	15 55	16 23	17 23	17 55	18 23	19 23	19 55	20 23	21 23	21 55	22 23	23 23		
Burley-in-Wharfedale	d	09 38	10 01	10 29	11 29	12 01	12 29	13 29	14 01	14 29	15 29	16 01	16 29	17 29	18 01	18 29	19 29	20 01	20 29	21 29	22 01	22 29	23 29		
Menston	d	09 41	10 04	10 32	11 32	12 04	12 32	13 32	14 04	14 32	15 32	16 04	16 32	17 32	18 04	18 32	19 32	20 04	20 32	21 32	22 04	22 32	23 32		
Guiseley	d	09 44	10 07	10 35	11 35	12 07	12 35	13 35	14 07	14 35	15 35	16 07	16 35	17 35	18 07	18 35	19 35	20 07	20 35	21 35	22 07	22 35	23 35		
Baildon	d		10 12			12 12			14 12			16 12			18 12			20 12			22 12				
Shipley	37 a		10 15			12 15			14 15			16 15			18 15			20 15			22 15				
Frizinghall	37 a		10 18			12 18			14 18			16 18			18 18			20 18			22 18				
Bradford Forster Square	37 a		10 24			12 24			14 24			16 24			18 24			20 24			22 24				
Leeds 10	a	09 58		10 49	11 49		12 49	13 49		14 49	15 49		16 49	17 49		18 49	19 49		20 49	21 49		22 49	23 49		

For general notes see front of timetable
For details of catering facilities see Directory of Train Operators

b Saturdays arr. 1015

Network Diagram for Tables 39, 41, 43

DM-2/07
Design BAJS

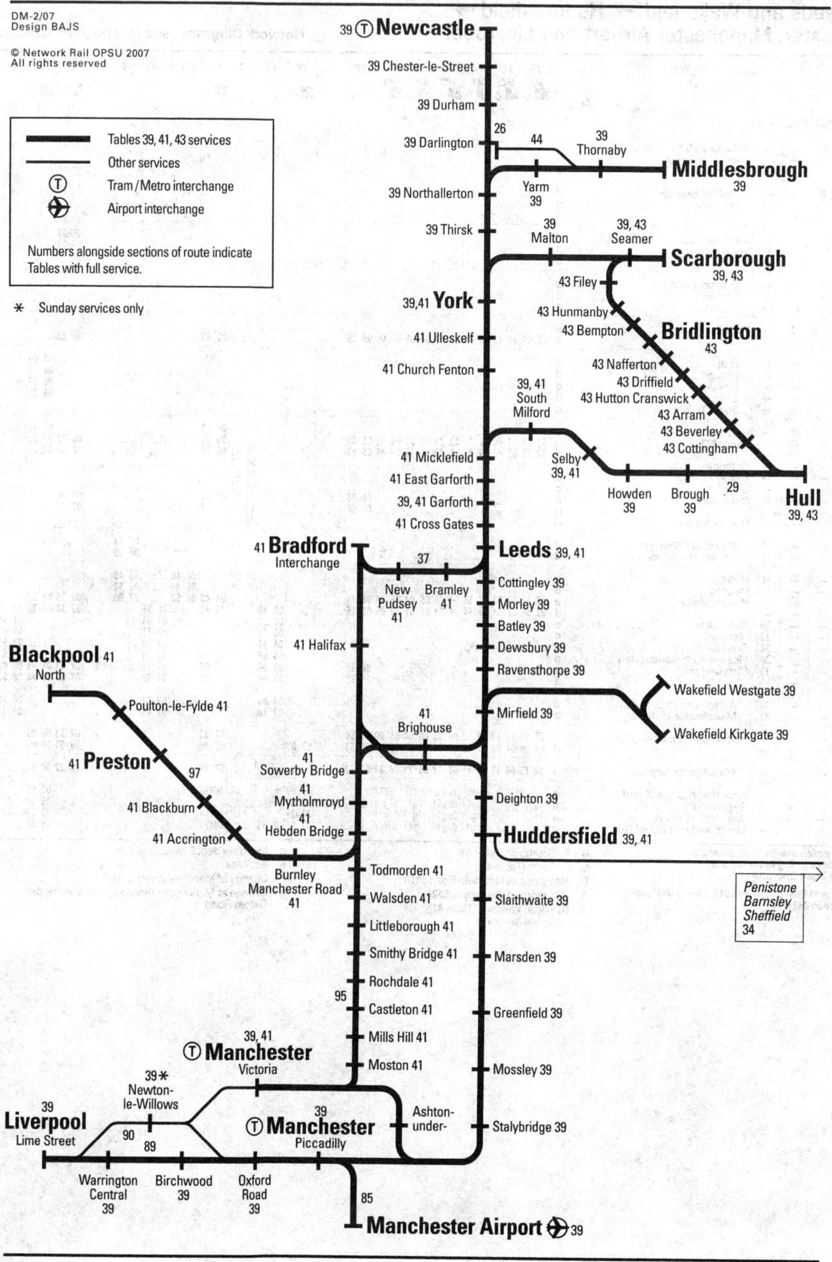
Tables 39, 41, 43 services
Other services
Tram / Metro interchange
Airport interchange
Numbers alongside sections of route indicate Tables with full service.
* Sunday services only
39 Newcastle
39 Chester-le-Street
39 Durham
39 Darlington
26
44
39 Thornaby
Middlesbrough 39
Yarm 39
39 Northallerton
39 Thirsk
39 Malton
39, 43 Seamer
Scarborough 39, 43
43 Filey
39,41 York
43 Hunmanby
43 Bempton
Bridlington 43
41 Ulleskelf
41 Church Fenton
43 Nafferton
43 Driffield
39, 41 South Milford
43 Hutton Cranswick
43 Arram
43 Beverley
43 Cottingham
41 Micklefield
Selby 39, 41
41 East Garforth
39, 41 Garforth
Howden 39
Brough 39
29
Hull 39, 43
41 Cross Gates
41 Bradford Interchange
37
Leeds 39, 41
New Pudsey 41
Bramley 41
Cottingley 39
Morley 39
Batley 39
41 Halifax
Dewsbury 39
Blackpool 41 North
Ravensthorpe 39
Wakefield Westgate 39
Poulton-le-Fylde 41
41 Brighouse
Mirfield 39
Wakefield Kirkgate 39
41 Preston
97
41 Sowerby Bridge
41 Blackburn
41 Mytholmroyd
Deighton 39
41 Hebden Bridge
41 Accrington
Huddersfield 39, 41
Burnley Manchester Road 41
Todmorden 41
Penistone
Barnsley
Sheffield
34
Walsden 41
Slaithwaite 39
Littleborough 41
Smithy Bridge 41
Marsden 39
Rochdale 41
95
Castleton 41
Greenfield 39
39, 41 Manchester Victoria
Mills Hill 41
Moston 41
Mossley 39
39* Newton-le-Willows
39 Liverpool Lime Street
90
89
39 Manchester Piccadilly
Ashton-under-
Stalybridge 39
Warrington Central 39
Birchwood 39
Oxford Road 39
85
Manchester Airport 39

Newcastle, Middlesbrough, Scarborough, York, Hull, Leeds and Wakefield → Huddersfield → Manchester, Manchester Airport and Liverpool

Network Diagram - see first page of Table 39

Miles	Miles	Miles	Miles	Miles			TP MX 1◇	TP MO 1◇	TP MX 1◇	TP MO 1◇	TP MO 1◇ A	TP MX 1◇ A	TP 1◇		TP 1◇	NT	NT	TP 1◇	NT	NT B	NT C		TP 1◇ D	TP 1◇ E	NT G
0	—	—	—	—	**Newcastle** 8	d																	04b31		
8¼	—	—	—	—	Chester-le-Street	d																			
14	—	—	—	—	Durham	d																	04c45		
—	—	0	—	—	**Middlesbrough**	d																			
—	—	3¼	—	—	Thornaby	d																			
—	—	8½	—	—	Yarm	d																			
36	—	—	—	—	**Darlington** 7	d																	05c03		
50	—	20¾	—	—	Northallerton	d																	05c30		
57¾	—	28½	—	—	Thirsk	d																			
—	—	—	0	—	**Scarborough**	d																			
—	—	—	2¾	—	Seamer	d																			
—	—	—	21	—	Malton	d																			
80	—	50¾	42	—	**York** 8	a																			
—	—	—	—	—		d	02 00	02 13	03 00	03 13	04 09	04 09	05 26					05 58					06 28		
—	0	—	—	—	**Hull**	d																		06 00	
—	10½	—	—	—	Brough	d																		06 12	
—	22¼	—	—	—	Howden	d																		06 27	
—	31	—	—	—	Selby	d																		06 38	
—	38¾	—	—	—	South Milford	d																			
98¼	44½	—	60¼	—	Garforth	d												06 13						*06 35*	
105½	51¾	—	67½	—	**Leeds** 10	a	02 33	02 40	03 33	03 39	04 37	04 42	05 52					06 23					06 53	07 05	
—	—	—	—	—		d	02 35	02 40	03 35	03 40	04 40	04 45	05 55				06 13	06 25					06 55	07 10	
108½	—	—	—	—	Cottingley	d											06 18								
110	—	—	—	—	Morley	d											06 22								
113¼	—	—	—	—	Batley	d											06 27								
114¾	—	—	—	—	**Dewsbury**	a							06 05				06 30	06 36					07 06		
—	—	—	—	—		d							06 06				06 31	06 37					07 07		
116	—	—	—	—	Ravensthorpe	d											06 34								
—	—	—	—	0	**Wakefield Westgate**	d															06 29				
—	—	—	—	1	Wakefield Kirkgate	d													⟵		06 35				
117¾	—	—	—	10½	Mirfield	d											06 38 ⟶		06 38		06 48				
120¾	—	—	—	13½	Deighton	d													06 44		06 52				
122¾	—	—	—	15½	**Huddersfield**	a	02 56	03 03	03 56	04 03	05 04	05 04	06 14					06 45	06 52		07 00		07 15	07 27	
—	—	—	—	—		d	02 59	03 04	03 59	04 04	05 05	05 05	06 15			06 30		06 46		06 56			07 16	07 28	07 32
127¼	—	—	—	20	Slaithwaite	d										06 37				07 03					07 39
129¾	—	—	—	22½	Marsden	d										06 43				07e11					07 45
135¾	—	—	—	28½	Greenfield	d										06 51				07 20					07 53
138	—	—	—	30¾	Mossley (Grtr Manchester)	d										06 55				07 24					07 57
140¾	—	—	—	33½	**Stalybridge**	a							06 33			07 00		07 05		07 29			07 34	07 45	08 02
—	—	—	—	—		d							06 33			07 00		07 05		07 30			07 35	07 46	08 03
—	—	—	—	34¾	Ashton-under-Lyne	d										07 04				07 34					08 07
—	—	—	—	41¼	**Manchester Victoria**	a										07 18				07 46					08 20
148¼	—	—	—	—	**Manchester Piccadilly** 10	a	03 59	03 59	04 58	04 58	06 00	06 00	06 50					07 22					07 53	08 05	
—	—	—	—	—		d	04 00	04 00	05 00	05 00	06 07	06 07	06 53		07 07			07 30					08 03	08 07	
—	—	—	—	—	**Manchester Airport**	a	04 15	04 15	05 19	05 19	06 29	06 29	07 12					07 49					08 22	*08 42*	
148¾	—	—	—	—	Manchester Oxford Road	a			*06f02*	*06f02*	*06f31*	*06f31*			07 09			*07f38*						08 09	
161¼	—	—	—	—	Birchwood	a			*06g51*	*06g51*	*07g11*	*07g11*			07 24									08 24	
164½	—	—	—	—	Warrington Central	a			*06g58*	*06g58*	*07g19*	*07g19*			07 29			*07f54*						08 29	
183	—	—	—	—	**Liverpool Lime Street** 10	a			*07g44*	*07g44*	*07f47*	*07f47*			07 57	08 35		*08f29*						08 57	

For general notes see front of timetable
For details of catering facilities see Directory of Train Operators

A Also stops at East Didsbury 0615, Gatley 0618, and Heald Green 0621

B To Southport (Table 82)
C To Selby (Table 41)
D Also stops at Mauldeth Road 0810
E Also stops at Gilberdyke 0620
G To Wigan Wallgate (Table 82)
b Mondays dep. 0422
c Mondays dep. 8 minutes earlier
e Arr. 0708
f Change at Manchester Piccadilly
g Change at Manchester Piccadilly and Manchester Oxford Road

Newcastle, Middlesbrough, Scarborough, York, Hull, Leeds and Wakefield → Huddersfield → Manchester, Manchester Airport and Liverpool

Network Diagram - see first page of Table 39

		NT	TP	TP	NT	NT	NT		NT	TP	NT	TP	NT	NT	TP		TP	NT	NT	TP	NT	NT	TP		NT
			1 ◇	1 ◇						1 ◇		1 ◇			1 ◇		1 ◇			1 ◇			1 ◇		
		A					B			C			A					B							D
Newcastle 8	d		05b26							06c00		06 13			06c44					07c20			07c23		
Chester-le-Street	d											06c31													
Durham	d		05b38							06c12		06 29			06c56					07c12			07c37		
Middlesbrough	d		05 58																	07 23					
Thornaby	d		06 03																	07 28					
Yarm	d		06 10																	07 39					
Darlington 7	d		05 56							06c30		06 47			07c14					07c30			07c54		
Northallerton	d		06 26									06 58			07c12					07 54					
Thirsk	d		06 33									07 07								08 02					
Scarborough	d									06 30					07 00								07 47		
Seamer	d									06 35					07 05								07 52		
Malton	d									06 53					07 23								08 10		
York 8	a		06 52							07 21		07 32			07 51					08 19			08 37		
	d		06 58							07 24		07 40			07 54					08 24			08 40		
Hull	d			06 35													07 33								
Brough	d			06 47													07 45								
Howden	d			06 49													07 57								
Selby	d			07 08									07 26				08 08						08 12		
South Milford	d			06e53									07 35				07 53						08 22		
Garforth	d		07 13	07 24								07 35	07 48		08u13					08 41					08 48
Leeds 10	a		07 23	07 35						07 52		08 04			08 23		08 37			08 50			09 04		
	d	07 13	07 25	07 38					07 43	07 55		08 10	08 13		08 25		08 40		08 43	08 55			09 10		09 13
Cottingley	d								07 48										08 48						
Morley	d	07 21							07 52				08 21						08 52						09 21
Batley	d	07 26							07 57				08 26						08 57						09 26
Dewsbury	a	07 29	07 36						08 00	08 06			08 29		08 36				09 00	09 06					09 29
	d	07 29	07 37						08 01	08 07			08 29		08 37				09 01	09 07					09 29
Ravensthorpe	d	07 32							08 04				08 32						09 04						
Wakefield Westgate	d						07 29											08 29							
Wakefield Kirkgate	d						07 35				←							08 35			←				
Mirfield	d	07a36					07 50		08 08 →		08 08		08a36					08 51	09 08 →		09 08				09a35
Deighton	d						07 56				08 14							08 57			09 16				
Huddersfield	a		07 45	07 56			08 03			08 15	08 21	08 27			08 42		08 58	09 04		09 15	09 21		09 27		
	d		07 46	07 57		08 02				08 16		08 28		08 32	08 42		08 59			09 16			09 28		
Slaithwaite	d					08 09								08 39											
Marsden	d					08 15								08 45											
Greenfield	d					08 23								08 53											
Mossley (Grtr Manchester)	d					08 27								08 57											
Stalybridge	a		08 08	08 17		08 32						08 45		09 02									09 45		
	d		08 08	08 18	08 22	08 33						08 46		09 03								09 42	09 46		
Ashton-under-Lyne	d				08 26	08 37								09 07								09 46			
Manchester Victoria	a				08 35	08 50								09 20								09 57			
Manchester Piccadilly 10	a		08 28	08 37						08 52		09 05			09 23		09 37			09 50			10 05		
	d		08 30							08 55		09 07			09 27					09 53			10 07		
Manchester Airport	a		08 51	09 06						09 18		09 40			09 44		10 01			10 14			10 40		
Manchester Oxford Road	a		08f47	08 52								09 09			09f36		09 51			10f05			10 09		
Birchwood	a											09 24			10g02								10 23		
Warrington Central	a											09 29			09f57								10 28		
Liverpool Lime Street 10	a				09 39	10 05						09 57			10f29		10 39					11 05	10 57		

For general notes see front of timetable
For details of catering facilities see Directory of Train Operators

- **A** To Brighouse (Table 41)
- **B** To Selby (Table 41)
- **C** Also stops at Cross Gates 0743
- **D** To Hebden Bridge via Brighouse (Table 41)
- **b** Change at Northallerton
- **c** Change at York
- **e** Change at Leeds
- **f** Change at Manchester Piccadilly
- **g** Change at Manchester Piccadilly and Manchester Oxford Road

Table 39

Mondays to Fridays

Newcastle, Middlesbrough, Scarborough, York, Hull, Leeds and Wakefield → Huddersfield → Manchester, Manchester Airport and Liverpool

Network Diagram - see first page of Table 39

Station		NT	TP	TP	NT	NT	TP	NT		NT	TP	NT	NT	TP	TP	NT		NT	TP	NT	NT	TP	NT	NT	TP
			1 ◇	1 ◇			1 ◇				1 ◇			1 ◇	1 ◇				1 ◇			1 ◇			1 ◇
					A							B				A							B		
			[trolley]	[trolley]			[trolley]				[trolley]			[trolley]	[trolley]				[trolley]			[trolley]			[trolley]
Newcastle 8	d		07 26				07 49				08b24			08b40					09 12			09b35			09b40
Chester-le-Street	d		07 37								08b33								09 21						
Durham	d		07 43				08 01				08b40			08b52					09 28			09b47			09b52
Middlesbrough	d													09 00											09 59
Thornaby	d													09 05											10 04
Yarm	d													09 13											10 12
Darlington 7	d		08 01				08 19				08b57			09b10					09 45			10b04			
Northallerton	d		08 12											09 28					09 56						10 27
Thirsk	d		08 20											09 36											10 35
Scarborough	d										08 47											09 47			
Seamer	d										08 52											09 52			
Malton	d										09 10											10 10			
York 8	a		08 54								09 37			09 55					10 22			10 37			10 54
	d		08 58				09 28				09 40			09 58					10 28			10 40			10 58
Hull	d			08 37											09 37										
Brough	d			08 49											09 49										
Howden	d			08 36											09 28										
Selby	d			09 08											10 08										
South Milford	d			08 52											09 53										
Garforth	d		09 13								09 35			10 13								10 35			11 13
Leeds 10	a		09 23	09 35			09 53				10 04			10 23	10 37				10 53			11 04			11 23
	d		09 25	09 40		09 43	09 55				10 10	10 13		10 25	10 40			10 43	10 55			11 10	11 13		11 25
Cottingley	d					09 48												10 48							
Morley	d					09 52						10 21						10 52					11 21		
Batley	d					09 57						10 26						10 57					11 26		
Dewsbury	a		09 36			10 00	10 06					10 29		10 36				11 00	11 06				11 29		11 36
	d		09 37			10 01	10 07					10 29		10 37				11 01	11 07				11 29		11 37
Ravensthorpe	d					10 04												11 04							
Wakefield Westgate	d				09 29											10 29									
Wakefield Kirkgate	d				09 35			←								10 35				←					
Mirfield	d				09 51	10 08 →		10 08				10a35				10 51		11 08 →		11 08			11a35		
Deighton	d				09 57			10 14								10 58				11 14					
Huddersfield	a		09 45	09 58	10 04		10 15	10 21			10 27			10 45	10 58	11 04			11 15	11 21		11 27			11 45
	d	09 32	09 46	09 59			10 16				10 28		10 32	10 46	10 59				11 16			11 28		11 32	11 46
Slaithwaite	d	09 39											10 39											11 39	
Marsden	d	09 45											10 45											11 45	
Greenfield	d	09 53											10 53											11 53	
Mossley (Grtr Manchester)	d	09 57											10 57											11 57	
Stalybridge	a	10 02									10 45		11 02									11 45		12 02	
	d	10 03								10 42	10 46		11 03								11 42	11 46		12 03	
Ashton-under-Lyne	d	10 07								10 46			11 07								11 46			12 07	
Manchester Victoria	a	10 20								10 57			11 20								11 57			12 20	
Manchester Piccadilly 10	a		10 22	10 35			10 50				11 05			11 22	11 35				11 50			12 05			12 22
	d		10 27				10 53				11 07			11 27					11 53			12 07			12 27
Manchester Airport	a		10 44	11 01			11 14				11 40			11 44	12 01				12 14			12 40			12 51
Manchester Oxford Road	a		10c40	10 47							11 09			11c40	11 47							12 09			12c40
Birchwood	a										11 23											12 23			
Warrington Central	a		10c57								11 28			11c57								12 28			12c57
Liverpool Lime Street 10	a		11c29	11 39						12 05	11 57			12c29	12 39						13 05	12 57			13c29

For general notes see front of timetable
For details of catering facilities see Directory of Train Operators

A To Selby (Table 41)
B To Hebden Bridge via Brighouse (Table 41)
b Change at York
c Change at Manchester Piccadilly

Newcastle, Middlesbrough, Scarborough, York, Hull, Leeds and Wakefield → Huddersfield → Manchester, Manchester Airport and Liverpool

Network Diagram - see first page of Table 39

Station		TP 1 ◇		NT A	NT	TP 1 ◇	NT	NT	TP 1 ◇	NT B		NT	TP 1 ◇	TP 1 ◇	NT A	NT	TP 1 ◇	NT		NT	TP 1 ◇	NT B	NT	TP 1 ◇	TP 1 ◇
Newcastle 8	d					10 15			*10b25*				*10b40*				11 15				*11b30*			*11b59*	
Chester-le-Street	d								*10b34*																
Durham	d					10 27			*10b41*				*10b52*				11 27				*11b43*			*11b52*	
Middlesbrough	d												11 00											12 00	
Thornaby	d												11 05											12 05	
Yarm	d												11 13											12 13	
Darlington 7	d					10 45			*10b58*				*11b10*				11 45				*12b02*			*12b10*	
Northallerton	d					10 56							11 28				11 56							12 28	
Thirsk	d												11 36											12 36	
Scarborough	d								10 45												11 45				
Seamer	d								10 50												11 50				
Malton	d								11 08												12 08				
York 8	a					11 22			11 37				11 55				12 21				12 35			12 55	
	d					11 28			11 39				11 58				12 28				12 38			12 58	
Hull	d	10 37												11 37											12 37
Brough	d	10 49												11 49											12 49
Howden	d	*10 36*																							
Selby	d	11 08												12 08											13 08
South Milford	d	*10 53*												*11 53*											*12 53*
Garforth	d								*11 35*				12 13								*12 35*			13 13	
Leeds 10	a	11 33				11 53			12 05				12 23	12 33			12 51				13 04			13 23	13 33
	d	11 40			11 43	11 55			12 10	12 13			12 25	12 40		12 43	12 55				13 10	13 13		13 25	13 40
Cottingley	d				11 48											12 48									
Morley	d				11 52					12 21						12 52						13 21			
Batley	d				11 57					12 26						12 57						13 26			
Dewsbury	a				12 00	12 06				12 29			12 36			13 00	13 06					13 29		13 36	
	d				12 01	12 07				12 29			12 37			13 01	13 07					13 29		13 37	
Ravensthorpe	d				12 04											13 04									
Wakefield Westgate	d			11 29											12 29										
Wakefield Kirkgate	d			11 34			←								12 35			←							
Mirfield	d			11 49	12 08 →		12 08			12a35					12 50	13 08 →		13 08				13a35			
Deighton	d			11 57			12 15								12 57			13 14							
Huddersfield	a	11 58		12 04		12 15	12 21		12 27				12 45	12 58	13 04		13 15	13 21			13 27			13 45	13 58
	d	11 59				12 16			12 28			12 32	12 46	12 59			13 16				13 28		13 32	13 46	13 59
Slaithwaite	d											12 39											13 39		
Marsden	d											12 45											13 45		
Greenfield	d											12 53											13 53		
Mossley (Grtr Manchester)	d											12 57											13 57		
Stalybridge	a								12 45			13 02									13 45		14 02		
	d							12 42	12 46			13 03								13 42	13 46		14 03		
Ashton-under-Lyne	d							12 46				13 07								13 46			14 07		
Manchester Victoria	a							12 57				13 20								13 57			14 20		
Manchester Piccadilly 10	a	12 35				12 50			13 05				13 22	13 35			13 50				14 05			14 22	14 35
	d					12 53			13 07				13 27				13 53				14 07			14 27	
Manchester Airport ✈	a	*13 01*				13 14			*13 40*				13 44	*14 01*			14 14				*14 40*			14 44	*15 01*
Manchester Oxford Road	a	*12 47*							13 09				*13c40*	*13 47*							14 09			*14c40*	*14 47*
Birchwood	a								13 23												14 23				
Warrington Central	a								13 28				*13c57*								14 28			*14c57*	
Liverpool Lime Street 10	a	*13 39*						14 05	13 57				*14c29*	*14 39*						15 05	14 57			*15c29*	*15 39*

For general notes see front of timetable
For details of catering facilities see Directory of Train Operators

A To Selby (Table 41)
B To Hebden Bridge via Brighouse (Table 41)
b Change at York
c Change at Manchester Piccadilly

Newcastle, Middlesbrough, Scarborough, York, Hull, Leeds and Wakefield → Huddersfield → Manchester, Manchester Airport and Liverpool

Network Diagram - see first page of Table 39

		NT	NT	TP		NT	NT	TP	NT	NT	TP	TP		NT	NT	TP	NT	NT	TP	NT		NT	TP	TP	NT
				1 ◇				1 ◇			1 ◇	1 ◇				1 ◇			1 ◇				1 ◇	1 ◇	
		A							B					A						B			C		A
Newcastle 8	d			12 15				12b19			12b40					13 15			13b33				13b40		
Chester-le-Street	d							12b32																	
Durham	d			12 28				12b40			12b53					13 27			13b46				13b52		
Middlesbrough	d										12 51												13 50		
Thornaby	d										12 56												13 55		
Yarm	d										13 04												14 03		
Darlington 7	d			12 46				13b00			13b10					13 45			14b03				14b10		
Northallerton	d			12 56							13 21					13 56							14 18		
Thirsk	d										13 29					13 47							14 26		
Scarborough	d							12 47											13 47						
Seamer	d							12 52											13 52						
Malton	d							13 10											14 10						
York 8	a			13 24				13 37			13 49					14 22			14 37				14 48		
	d			13 28				13 40			13 58					14 28			14 40				14 58		
Hull	d											13 37												14 37	
Brough	d											13 49												14 49	
Howden	d											13 40													
Selby	d											14 08												15 08	
South Milford	d											13 53												14 53	
Garforth	d							13 35			14 13								14 35				15 13		
Leeds 10	a			13 53				14 04			14 23	14 34				14 53			15 04				15 23	15 33	
	d		13 43	13 55				14 10	14 13		14 25	14 40			14 43	14 55			15 10	15 13			15 25	15 40	
Cottingley	d		13 48												14 48										
Morley	d		13 52						14 21						14 52					15 21					
Batley	d		13 57						14 26						14 57					15 26					
Dewsbury	a		14 00	14 06					14 29		14 36				15 00	15 06				15 29			15 36		
	d		14 01	14 07					14 29		14 37				15 01	15 07				15 29			15 37		
Ravensthorpe	d		14 04												15 04					15 32					
Wakefield Westgate	d	13 29												14 29											15 29
Wakefield Kirkgate	d	13 35				←								14 35			←								15 35
Mirfield	d	13 51	14 08			14 08			14a35					14 51	15 08		15 08			15a36					15 51
Deighton	d	13 57	→			14 14								14 57	→		15 15								15 57
Huddersfield	a	14 04		14 15		14 21		14 27			14 45	14 58		15 04		15 15	15 21		15 27				15 45	15 58	16 04
	d			14 16				14 28		14 32	14 46	14 59				15 16			15 28			15 32	15 46	15 59	
Slaithwaite	d									14 39												15 39			
Marsden	d									14 45												15 45			
Greenfield	d									14 53												15 53			
Mossley (Grtr Manchester)	d									14 57												15 57			
Stalybridge	a							14 45		15 02									15 45			16 02			
	d						14 42	14 46		15 03								15 42	15 46			16 03			
Ashton-under-Lyne	d						14 46			15 07								15 46				16 07			
Manchester Victoria	a						14 57			15 20								15 57				16 20			
Manchester Piccadilly 10	a			14 50				15 05			15 22	15 35				15 50			16 05				16 22	16 35	
	d			14 53				15 07			15 27					15 53			16 07				16 27		
Manchester Airport	a			15 14				15 40			15 44	16 01				16 14			16 40				16 51		
Manchester Oxford Road	a							15 09			15c40	15 47							16 09				16c39	16 50	
Birchwood	a							15 23											16 23						
Warrington Central	a							15 28			15c57								16 28				16c57		
Liverpool Lime Street 10	a						16 05	15 57			16c27	16 39						17 04	16 57				17c27	17 38	

For general notes see front of timetable
For details of catering facilities see Directory of Train Operators

A To Selby (Table 41)
B To Hebden Bridge via Brighouse (Table 41)
C Also stops at Heald Green 1638

b Change at York
c Change at Manchester Piccadilly

Newcastle, Middlesbrough, Scarborough, York, Hull, Leeds and Wakefield → Huddersfield → Manchester, Manchester Airport and Liverpool

Network Diagram - see first page of Table 39

		NT	TP	NT	NT	TP	NT	NT	TP	TP	NT	NT	TP	NT	TP	NT	NT	TP	TP	NT	NT	NT
					BHX																	
			1 ◇			1 ◇			1 ◇	1 ◇			1 ◇		1 ◇			1 ◇	1 ◇			
					A	B	C	D			E					C		G			H	J
			🛒			🛒			🛒	🛒			🛒		🛒			🛒	🛒			
Newcastle 8	d		14 12			14b22			14b40				15 12		15b30			15b40				
Chester-le-Street	d					14b33							15 21									
Durham	d		14 24			14b40			14b52				15 27		15b34			15b52				
Middlesbrough	d								14 50									15 50				
Thornaby	d								14 55									15 55				
Yarm	d								15 03									16 03				
Darlington 7	d		14 45			14b57			15b10				15 45		16b02							
Northallerton	d		14 56						15 18				15 56					16 18				
Thirsk	d								15 26									16 26				
Scarborough	d					14 47									15 47							
Seamer	d					14 52									15 52							
Malton	d					15 10									16 10							
York 8	a		15 25			15 37			15 51				16 21		16 37			16 47				
	d		15 28			15 40			15 58				16 28		16 40			16 58				
Hull	d									15 37									16 37			
Brough	d									15 49									16 49			
Howden	d									15 42									16 36			
Selby	d									16 08									17 08			
South Milford	d									15 53									16 53			
Garforth	d					15 35			16 13						16 35			17 13				
Leeds 10	a		15 53			16 04			16 23	16 36			16 53		17 04			17 23	17 35			
	d	15 43	15 55			16 10	16 13		16 25	16 40		16 43	16 55		17 10	17 13		17 25	17 40			17 43
Cottingley	d	15 48										16 48										17 48
Morley	d	15 52					16 21					16 52				17 21						17 52
Batley	d	15 57					16 26					16 57				17 26						17 57
Dewsbury	a	16 00	16 06				16 29		16 36			17 00	17 06			17 29		17 36	17 51			18 00
	d	16 01	16 07				16 29		16 37			17 01	17 07			17 29		17 37	17 51			18 01
Ravensthorpe	d	16 04					16 32					17 04				17 32						18 04
Wakefield Westgate	d										16 29										17 29	
Wakefield Kirkgate	d			←							16 35			←							17 35	
Mirfield	d	16 08 →		16 08			16a36				16 51	17 08 →		17 08		17a36					17 52	18 08 →
Deighton	d			16 15							16 57			17 14							17 57	
Huddersfield	a		16 15	16 21		16 27			16 45	16 58	17 05		17 15	17 21	17 27			17 45	18 00		18 05	
	d		16 16			16 28		16 32	16 46	16 59			17 16		17 28		17 32	17 46	18 01	18 05		
Slaithwaite	d							16 39									17 39			18 12		
Marsden	d							16 45									17 45			18 17		
Greenfield	d							16 53									17 53			18 25		
Mossley (Grtr Manchester)	d							16 57									17 57			18 29		
Stalybridge	a					16 46		17 02	17 06						17 45		18 02	18 06		18 34		
	d				16 42	16 47		17 03	17 07						17 46		18 03	18 07		18 34		
Ashton-under-Lyne	d				16 46			17 07									18 07			18 38		
Manchester Victoria	a				16 57			17 21									18 20			18 52		
Manchester Piccadilly 10	a		16 50			17 05			17 24	17 35			17 51		18 05			18 22	18 36			
	d		16 53			17 07							17 58		18 07			18 27				
Manchester Airport ✈	a		17 14			17 40				18 05			18 14		18 42			18 46	19 09			
Manchester Oxford Road	a					17 09			17 39	17 47					18 09			18c39	18 51			
Birchwood	a					17 23			17 56						18 23							
Warrington Central	a					17 28			18 02						18 28			18c57				
Liverpool Lime Street 10	a					18 00			18 32	18 40					18 57			19c29	19 38			

For general notes see front of timetable
For details of catering facilities see Directory of Train Operators

A To Blackpool North (Table 82)
B Also stops at Hunts Cross 1739
C To Hebden Bridge via Brighouse (Table 41)
D To Wigan North Western (Table 82)
E To Selby (Table 41)
G Also stops at Heald Green 1840
H To Leeds (Table 41)
J To Sheffield (Table 34)
b Change at York
c Change at Manchester Piccadilly

Newcastle, Middlesbrough, Scarborough, York, Hull, Leeds and Wakefield → Huddersfield → Manchester, Manchester Airport and Liverpool

Network Diagram - see first page of Table 39

		TP	NT	TP	TP	NT	NT	TP		NT	NT	TP	NT	TP	TP	NT		NT	TP	NT	TP	TP	TP	NT	NT
		■1 ◇		■1 ◇	■1 ◇			■1 ◇				■1 ◇		■1 ◇	■1 ◇				■1 ◇		■1 ◇	■1 ◇	■1 ◇		
		A	B			C																			
		🛒			🛒			🛒				🛒		🛒											
Newcastle ■8 ⛴	d	16 06			*16b28*			*16b40*				17 10			*17b32*				*17b40*			*18b20*			
Chester-le-Street	d	16 15			*16b42*										*17b26*							*18b29*			
Durham	d	16 22			*16b49*			*16b52*				17 22			*17b33*				*17b54*			*18b36*			
Middlesbrough	d							16 50											17 50				19 00		
Thornaby	d							16 55											17 55				19 05		
Yarm	d							17 03											18 03				19 13		
Darlington ■7	d	16 39			*17b06*							17 40			*17b59*							*18b56*	*18 40*		
Northallerton	d	16 51						17 18				17 51							18 18			*18b52*	19 28		
Thirsk	d	16 59						17 26				17 59							18 26			*18b45*	19 36		
Scarborough	d				16 47										17 45							18 46			
Seamer	d				16 52										17 50							18 51			
Malton	d				17 10										18 08							19 11			
York ■8	a	17 25			17 37			17 50				18 24			18 35				18 51			19 36	19 59		
	d	17 28			17 40			17 58				18 28			18 38				19 10			19 39			
Hull	d			17 00										18 02							18 59				
Brough	d			17 12										18 14							19 11				
Howden	d													*17 54*											
Selby	d			17 31								*17 43*		18 33					*18c43*		19 30				
South Milford	d											*17 53*							*18c53*						
Garforth	d			*17 35*				18 13						*18 31*					19 23			*19 35*			
Leeds ■10	a	17 53		17 59	18 04			18 23				18 52		18 58	19 04				19 35		19 56	20 04			
	d	17 55		18 02	18 10	18 13		18 25			18 40	18 52		19 02	19 10			19 13	19 40			20 10			20 13
Cottingley	d										18 45							19 18							20 18
Morley	d					18 21					18 49							19 22							20 22
Batley	d					18 26					18 54							19 27							20 27
Dewsbury	a	18 06		18 13		18 29		18 36			18 57			19 13				19 30	19 50						20 30
	d	18 07		18 13		18 29		18 37			18 58			19 13				19 31	19 51						20 31
Ravensthorpe	d					18 32					19 01							19 34							20 34
Wakefield Westgate	d									18 29										19 29					
Wakefield Kirkgate	d		←							18 35			←							19 35					
Mirfield	d		18 08			18a36				18 52	19 05		19 05					19 38		19 52					20 38
Deighton	d		18 13							18 57	→		19 10					19 45		20 01					20 44
Huddersfield	a	18 15	18 21	18 25	18 27			18 45		19 04		19 12	19 18	19 22	19 27			19 49	19 59	20 06		20 27			20 51
	d	18 16			18 28		18 32	18 46				19 13		19 23	19 28	19 32			20 00			20 28		20 32	
Slaithwaite	d						18 39									19 39								20 39	
Marsden	d						18 45									19 45								20 45	
Greenfield	d						18 53									19 53								20 53	
Mossley (Grtr Manchester)	d						18 57									19 57								20 57	
Stalybridge	a				18 45		19 02	19 06							19 46	20 02						20 45		21 02	
	d				18 46		19 03	19 07							19 46	20 03						20 46		21 03	
Ashton-under-Lyne	d						19 07									20 07								21 07	
Manchester Victoria ⛴	a						19 21									20 20								21 20	
Manchester Piccadilly ■10 ⛴	a	18 52			19 05			19 24				19 50		19 59	20 05				20 35			21 05			
	d	18 55			19 07							19 53			20 07				20 38			21 07			
Manchester Airport ✈	a	19 14			*19 40*			*20 05*				20 12							20 58			*21 37*			
Manchester Oxford Road	a				19 09			*19 40*							20 09				*20e54*			21 09			
Birchwood	a				19 23										20 23							21 23			
Warrington Central	a				19 28			*19 57*							20 28							21 28			
Liverpool Lime Street ■10	a				19 57			*20 29*							20 55							21 55			

For general notes see front of timetable
For details of catering facilities see Directory of Train Operators

A Also stops at Heald Green 1907
B To Sheffield (Table 34)
C To Hebden Bridge via Brighouse (Table 41)
b Change at York
c Change at Leeds
e Change at Manchester Piccadilly

Newcastle, Middlesbrough, Scarborough, York, Hull, Leeds and Wakefield → Huddersfield → Manchester, Manchester Airport and Liverpool

Network Diagram - see first page of Table 39

Station		TP 1◇	NT	TP 1◇	TP 1◇	NT	NT	TP 1◇	NT	TP 1◇	TP 1◇	NT	NT	TP 1◇ A	NT	TP 1◇	TP 1◇	NT	NT	TP 1◇
Newcastle 8	d	18 58			19b25			19b40		20b26	20b37									21 47
Chester-le-Street	d				19b36															
Durham	d	19 10			19b44			19b52		20b38	20b50									22 00
Middlesbrough	d							20 10			20 50					21 40				
Thornaby	d							20 15			20 55					21 45				
Yarm	d							20 23			21 03									
Darlington 7	d	19 28			20b02					20b55	21b08					22c07				22 18
Northallerton	d	19 39						20 38			21 21					22 18				22 29
Thirsk	d	19 36						20 47								22 26				22 26
Scarborough	d				19 45					20 37							22 07			
Seamer	d				19 50					20 42							22 12			
Malton	d				20 08					21 00							22 30			
York 8	a	20 03			20 35			21 05		21 28	21 42					22 52	22 57			23 04
	d	20 10			20 40			21 10		21 32	21 45									23 07
Hull	d			19 55										21 33						
Brough	d			20 07										21 45						
Howden	d			19 43																
Selby	d			20 26										22 07						
South Milford	d			20 36										22 17						
Garforth	d				20 39					21 47	21 47								22 35	22 35
Leeds 10	a	20 35		20 59	21 04			21 33		22 00	22 08			22 35						23 33
	d	20 40			21 10		21 13	21 40			22 10		22 13	22 40					23 13	23 35
Cottingley	d						21 18						22 18						23 18	
Morley	d						21 22						22 22						23 22	
Batley	d						21 27						22 27						23 27	
Dewsbury	a	20 50					21 30	21 50					22 30	22 51					23 30	23 46
	d	20 51					21 31	21 51					22 31	22 51					23 31	23 46
Ravensthorpe	d						21 34						22 34						23 34	
Wakefield Westgate	d		20 29						21 29						22 42					
Wakefield Kirkgate	d		20 35						21 35						22 47					
Mirfield	d		20 51				21 38		21 48				22 38		23 03				23 38	
Deighton	d		21 00				21 45		21 59				22 44		23 10				23 45	
Huddersfield	a	20 59	21 05		21 27		21 49	21 59	22 04		22 27		22 52	23 00	23 15				23 49	23 55
	d	21 00			21 28	21 32		22 00			22 28	22 32		23 00				23 22		23 56
Slaithwaite	d					21 39						22 39						23 29		
Marsden	d					21 45						22 45						23 35		
Greenfield	d					21 53						22 53						23 43		
Mossley (Grtr Manchester)	d					21 57						22 57						23 47		
Stalybridge	a				21 45	22 02					22 45	23 02						23 52		
	d				21 46	22 03					22 46	23 03						23 53		
Ashton-under-Lyne	d					22 07						23 07						23 57		
Manchester Victoria	a					22 20						23 20						00 11		
Manchester Piccadilly 10	a	21 35			22 05			22 35			23 05			23 37						00 50
	d	21 38			22 07			22 38												00 54
Manchester Airport	a	21 58			22 39			22 58			23 58			00 45						01 10
Manchester Oxford Road	a	21e49			22 09			22e51			23 22									
Birchwood	a				22 24						23f54									
Warrington Central	a				22 29						00f01									
Liverpool Lime Street 10	a	22e41			22 55						00f37									

For general notes see front of timetable
For details of catering facilities see Directory of Train Operators

A Also stops at Gilberdyke 2152
b Change at York
c Arr. 2202
e Change at Manchester Piccadilly
f Change at Manchester Piccadilly and Manchester Oxford Road

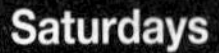

Newcastle, Middlesbrough, Scarborough, York, Hull, Leeds and Wakefield → Huddersfield → Manchester, Manchester Airport and Liverpool

Network Diagram - see first page of Table 39

		TP 1◇	TP 1◇	TP 1◇	TP 1◇	TP 1◇	TP 1◇	TP 1◇	TP 1◇	NT	NT	TP 1◇	TP 1◇	NT	NT	TP 1◇	TP 1◇		NT	NT	TP 1◇	TP 1◇	NT	NT	TP 1◇
				A				B	C	D	E				G				E				G		
									🚲								🚲								🚲
Newcastle 8	d							*04 31*								*06b00*	06 13				*06b35*				*07c00*
Chester-le-Street	d																								
Durham	d							*04 45*								*06b12*	06 29				*06b47*				*07c12*
Middlesbrough	d											05 58													07 21
Thornaby	d											06 03													07 26
Yarm	d											06 10													07 34
Darlington 7	d							*05 03*								*06b30*	06 47								*07 30*
Northallerton	d							*05 30*				06 26					06 58								07 49
Thirsk	d											06 33					07 07								07 57
Scarborough	d															06 34					07 05				
Seamer	d															06 39					07 10				
Malton	d															06 57					07 28				
York 8	a											06 52				07 24	07 32				07 55				08 19
	d	02 00	03 00	04 19	05 26		05 58	06 28				06 58				07 27	07 40				07 58				08 25
Hull	d								06 00				06 35									07 33			
Brough	d								06 12				06 47									07 45			
Howden	d								06 27													07 57			
Selby	d								06 38				07 06									08 08			
South Milford	d												*06 53*									*07 53*			
Garforth	d						06 13		*06 35*			07 13					*07 35*				08 13				
Leeds 10	a	02 33	03 33	04 44	05 52		06 23	06 53	07 05			07 23	07 35			07 52	08 04				08 23	08 37			08 50
	d	02 35	03 35	04 45	05 55		06 25	06 55	07 10		07 13	07 25	07 38			07 55	08 10		08 13		08 25	08 40		08 43	08 55
Cottingley	d																							08 48	
Morley	d										07 21								08 21					08 52	
Batley	d										07 26								08 26					08 57	
Dewsbury	a				06 05		06 36	07 06			07 29	07 36				08 06			08 29		08 36			09 00	09 06
	d				06 06		06 37	07 07			07 29	07 37				08 07			08 29		08 37			09 01	09 07
Ravensthorpe	d										07 32								08 32					09 04	
Wakefield Westgate	d														07 29								08 29		
Wakefield Kirkgate	d														07 35								08 35		
Mirfield	d										07a36				07 50				08a36				08 51	09 08	
Deighton	d														07 54								08 57	→	
Huddersfield	a	02 56	03 56	05 04	06 14		06 45	07 15	07 27			07 45	07 56		08 02	08 15	08 27				08 45	08 58	09 04		09 15
	d	02 59	03 59	05 05	06 15		06 46	07 16	07 28	07 32		07 46	07 57	08 02		08 16	08 28			08 32	08 46	08 59			09 16
Slaithwaite	d									07 39				08 09						08 39					
Marsden	d									07 45				08 15						08 45					
Greenfield	d									07 53				08 23						08 53					
Mossley (Grtr Manchester)	d									07 57				08 27						08 57					
Stalybridge	a				06 33		07 05	07 34	07 45	08 02		08 08	08 17	08 32			08 45			09 02					
	d				06 33		07 05	07 35	07 46	08 03		08 08	08 18	08 33			08 46			09 03					
Ashton-under-Lyne	d									08 07				08 37						09 07					
Manchester Victoria 🚋	a									08 20				08 50						09 20					
Manchester Piccadilly 10 🚋	a	03 59	04 58	06 00	06 50		07 22	07 53	08 05			08 28	08 36			08 52	09 05				09 23	09 37			09 50
	d	04 00	04 59	06 07	06 53	07 07	07 30	08 03	08 07			08 30				08 55	09 07				09 27				09 53
Manchester Airport ✈	a	04 15	05 19	06 29	07 12		07 49	08 22	*08 42*			08 51	*09 06*			09 18	*09 40*				09 44	*10 02*			10 14
Manchester Oxford Road	a		*06e02*	*06e31*		07 09	*07e38*		08 09			*08e47*	08 52				09 09				*09e36*	09 51			*10e05*
Birchwood	a		*06f56*			07 24			08 23								09 24				*10f02*				
Warrington Central	a		*07f03*			07 29	*07e54*		08 29								09 29				*09e57*				
Liverpool Lime Street 10	a		*07f47*	*07e48*		07 57	*08e29*		08 57				*09 42*	10 05			09 57				*10e27*	*10 39*			

For general notes see front of timetable
For details of catering facilities see Directory of Train Operators

A Also stops at East Didsbury 0617, Gatley 0619, and Heald Green 0621
B Also stops at Mauldeth Road 0810
C Also stops at Gilberdyke 0620
D To Wigan Wallgate (Table 82)
E To Hebden Bridge via Brighouse (Table 41)
G To Selby (Table 41)
b Change at York
c Change at Northallerton
e Change at Manchester Piccadilly
f Change at Manchester Piccadilly and Manchester Oxford Road

Newcastle, Middlesbrough, Scarborough, York, Hull, Leeds and Wakefield → Huddersfield → Manchester, Manchester Airport and Liverpool

Network Diagram - see first page of Table 39

		NT	NT	TP	NT	NT	TP	TP	NT	NT	TP	NT		NT	TP	NT	NT	TP	TP	NT	NT	TP	NT	NT	TP
				1 ◇			1 ◇	1 ◇			1 ◇				1 ◇			1 ◇	1 ◇			1 ◇			1 ◇
					A				B							A				B					
				🛒			🛒				🛒				🛒			🛒							🛒
Newcastle 8 ⛴	d			07b30			07 33				07 54				08b24			08b40				09 12			09b32
Chester-le-Street	d						07 42								08b33							09 21			
Durham	d			07b42			07 49				07 54				08b40			08b52				09 27			09b37
Middlesbrough	d																	09 00							
Thornaby	d																	09 05							
Yarm	d																	09 13							
Darlington 7	d			07b59			08 06				08 21				08b57							09 45			10b01
Northallerton	d						08 18				08 18							09 28				09 56			
Thirsk	d						08 26											09 36							
Scarborough	d			07 47											08 47										09 47
Seamer	d			07 52											08 52										09 52
Malton	d			08 10											09 10										10 10
York 8	a			08 37			08 53								09 37			09 56				10 22			10 37
	d			08 40			08 58				09 28				09 40			09 58				10 28			10 40
Hull	d							08 37											09 37						
Brough	d							08 49											09 49						
Howden	d							08 26											09 28						
Selby	d							09 08											10 08						
South Milford	d							08 53											09 53						
Garforth	d			08 35			09 13								09 35			10 13							10 35
Leeds 10	a			09 04			09 23	09 35			09 53				10 04			10 23	10 37			10 53			11 04
	d			09 10	09 13		09 25	09 40		09 43	09 55				10 10	10 13		10 25	10 40		10 43	10 55			11 10
Cottingley	d									09 48											10 48				
Morley	d				09 21					09 52						10 21					10 52				
Batley	d				09 26					09 57						10 26					10 57				
Dewsbury	a				09 29		09 36			10 00	10 06					10 29		10 36			11 00	11 06			
	d				09 29		09 37			10 01	10 07					10 29		10 37			11 01	11 07			
Ravensthorpe	d									10 04											11 04				
Wakefield Westgate	d								09 29											10 29					
Wakefield Kirkgate	d	←							09 35			←								10 35			←		
Mirfield	d	09 08			09a35				09 51	10 08		10 08				10a35				10 51	11 08		11 08		
Deighton	d	09 14							09 57	→		10 14								10 58	→		11 14		
Huddersfield	a	09 21		09 27			09 45	09 58	10 04		10 15	10 21			10 27			10 45	10 58	11 04		11 15	11 21		11 27
	d			09 28		09 32	09 46	09 59			10 16				10 28		10 32	10 46	10 59			11 16			11 28
Slaithwaite	d					09 39											10 39								
Marsden	d					09 45											10 45								
Greenfield	d					09 53											10 53								
Mossley (Grtr Manchester)	d					09 57											10 57								
Stalybridge	a			09 45		10 02									10 45		11 02								11 45
	d		09 42	09 46		10 03								10 42	10 46		11 03							11 42	11 46
Ashton-under-Lyne	d		09 46			10 07								10 46			11 07							11 46	
Manchester Victoria ⛴	a		09 57			10 20								10 57			11 20							11 57	
Manchester Piccadilly 10 ⛴	a			10 05			10 22	10 35			10 50				11 05			11 22	11 35			11 50			12 05
	d			10 07			10 27				10 53				11 07			11 27				11 53			12 07
Manchester Airport ✈	a			10 40			10 44	11 01			11 14				11 40			11 44	12 01			12 14			12 40
Manchester Oxford Road	a			10 09			10c40	10 47							11 09			11c40	11 47						12 09
Birchwood	a			10 23											11 23										12 23
Warrington Central	a			10 28			10c57								11 28			11c57							12 28
Liverpool Lime Street 10	a		11 05	10 57			11c29	11 39						12 05	11 57			12c29	12 39					13 05	12 57

For general notes see front of timetable
For details of catering facilities see Directory of Train Operators

A To Hebden Bridge via Brighouse (Table 41)
B To Selby (Table 41)
b Change at York
c Change at Manchester Piccadilly

Table 39

Saturdays

Newcastle, Middlesbrough, Scarborough, York, Hull, Leeds and Wakefield → Huddersfield → Manchester, Manchester Airport and Liverpool

Network Diagram - see first page of Table 39

		NT	NT	TP	TP	NT	NT		TP	NT	NT	TP	NT	NT	TP	TP	NT	NT	TP	NT	NT	TP	NT	NT	TP
				1 ◇	1 ◇				1 ◇			1 ◇			1 ◇	1 ◇			1 ◇			1 ◇			1 ◇
		A				B							A				B						A		
				🛒					🛒			🛒			🛒	🛒			🛒						🛒
Newcastle 8 ⛴	d			*09b40*					10 15			*10b32*			*10b40*				11 15			*11b29*			*11b40*
Chester-le-Street	d											*10b34*													
Durham	d			*09b52*					10 27			*10b45*			*10b52*				11 27			*11b42*			*11b52*
Middlesbrough	d			10 00											11 00										12 00
Thornaby	d			10 05											11 05										12 05
Yarm	d			10 13											11 13										12 13
Darlington 7	d								10 45			*11b03*							11 45			*12b01*			
Northallerton	d			10 28					10 56						11 28				11 56						12 28
Thirsk	d			10 36											11 36										12 36
Scarborough	d											10 45										11 47			
Seamer	d											10 50										11 52			
Malton	d											11 08										12 10			
York 8	a			10 54					11 22			11 35			11 54				12 20			12 37			12 55
	d			10 58					11 28			11 40			11 58				12 28			12 40			12 58
Hull	d				10 37											11 37									
Brough	d				10 49											11 49									
Howden	d				*10 30*																				
Selby	d				11 08											12 08									
South Milford	d				*10 53*											*11 53*									
Garforth	d			11 13								*11 35*			12 13							*12 35*			13 13
Leeds 10	a			11 23	11 33				11 53			12 04			12 23	12 33			12 53			13 04			13 23
	d	11 13		11 25	11 40		11 43		11 55			12 10	12 13		12 25	12 40		12 43	12 55			13 10	13 13		13 25
Cottingley	d						11 48											12 48							
Morley	d	11 21					11 52						12 21					12 52					13 21		
Batley	d	11 26					11 57						12 26					12 57					13 26		
Dewsbury	a	11 29		11 36			12 00		12 06				12 29		12 36			13 00	13 06				13 29		13 36
	d	11 29		11 37			12 01		12 07				12 29		12 37			13 01	13 07				13 29		13 37
Ravensthorpe	d						12 04											13 04							
Wakefield Westgate	d					11 29											12 29								
Wakefield Kirkgate	d					11 35				⟵							12 35			⟵					
Mirfield	d	11a35				11 51	12 08 →			12 08			12a35				12 51	13 08 →		13 08			13a35		
Deighton	d					11 57				12 14							12 57			13 14					
Huddersfield	a			11 45	11 58	12 04			12 15	12 21		12 27			12 45	12 58	13 04		13 15	13 21		13 27			13 45
	d		11 32	11 46	11 59				12 16			12 28		12 32	12 46	12 59			13 16			13 28		13 32	13 46
Slaithwaite	d		11 39											12 39										13 39	
Marsden	d		11 45											12 45										13 45	
Greenfield	d		11 53											12 53										13 53	
Mossley (Grtr Manchester)	d		11 57											12 57										13 57	
Stalybridge	a		12 02									12 45		13 02								13 45		14 02	
	d		12 03								12 42	12 46		13 03							13 42	13 46		14 03	
Ashton-under-Lyne	d		12 07								12 46			13 07							13 46			14 07	
Manchester Victoria ⛴	a		12 20								12 57			13 20							13 57			14 20	
Manchester Piccadilly 10 ⛴	a			12 22	12 35				12 50			13 05			13 22	13 35			13 50			14 05			14 22
	d			12 27					12 53			13 07			13 27				13 53			14 07			14 27
Manchester Airport ✈	a			12c51	*13 01*				13 14			*13 40*			13 44	*14 01*			14 14			*14 40*			14 44
Manchester Oxford Road	a			*12e40*	*12 47*							13 09			*13e40*	*13 47*						14 09			*14e40*
Birchwood	a											13 23										14 23			
Warrington Central	a			*12e57*								13 28			*13e57*							14 28			*14e57*
Liverpool Lime Street 10	a			*13e27*	*13 39*						14 05	13 57			*14e27*	*14 39*					15 05	14 57			*15e25*

For general notes see front of timetable
For details of catering facilities see Directory of Train Operators

A To Hebden Bridge via Brighouse (Table 41)
B To Selby (Table 41)
b Change at York
c From 2 February arr. 1244
e Change at Manchester Piccadilly

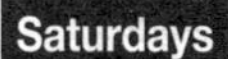

Newcastle, Middlesbrough, Scarborough, York, Hull, Leeds and Wakefield → Huddersfield → Manchester, Manchester Airport and Liverpool

Network Diagram - see first page of Table 39

		TP 1 ◇		NT	NT	TP 1 ◇	NT	NT	TP 1 ◇	NT	NT	TP 1 ◇	TP 1 ◇	NT	NT	TP 1 ◇	NT	NT	TP 1 ◇		NT	NT	TP 1 ◇	TP 1 ◇	NT
				A						B				A							B		C		A
						🍴						🍴				🍴			🍴				🍴		
Newcastle 8	d					12 15			12b33			12b40				13 15			13b27				13b40		
Chester-le-Street	d								12b29																
Durham	d					12 27			12b46			12b52				13 27			13b39				13b52		
Middlesbrough	d											12 51											14 00		
Thornaby	d											12 56											14 05		
Yarm	d											13 04											14 13		
Darlington 7	d					12 45			13b04							13 45			13b58						
Northallerton	d					12 56						13 21				13 56							14 28		
Thirsk	d											13 29				13 42							14 36		
Scarborough	d								12 47										13 45						
Seamer	d								12 52										13 50						
Malton	d								13 10										14 08						
York 8	a					13 20			13 37			13 49				14 20			14 35				14 54		
	d					13 28			13 40			13 58				14 28			14 38				14 58		
Hull	d	12 37											13 37											14 37	
Brough	d	12 49											13 49											14 49	
Howden	d												13 40												
Selby	d	13 08											14 08											15 08	
South Milford	d	12 53											13 53											14 53	
Garforth	d								13 35			14 13							14 35				15 13		
Leeds 10	a	13 33				13 53			14 04			14 23	14 33			14 53			15 04				15 23	15 33	
	d	13 40			13 43	13 55			14 10	14 13		14 25	14 40		14 43	14 55			15 10		15 13		15 25	15 40	
Cottingley	d				13 48										14 48										
Morley	d				13 52					14 21					14 52						15 21				
Batley	d				13 57					14 26					14 57						15 26				
Dewsbury	a				14 00	14 06				14 29		14 36			15 00	15 06					15 29		15 36		
	d				14 01	14 07				14 29		14 37			15 01	15 07					15 29		15 37		
Ravensthorpe	d				14 04										15 04						15 32				
Wakefield Westgate	d			13 29										14 29											15 29
Wakefield Kirkgate	d			13 35			←							14 35			←								15 35
Mirfield	d			13 51	14 08		14 08			14a35				14 51	15 08		15 08				15a36				15 51
Deighton	d			13 57	→		14 14							14 57	→		15 14								15 57
Huddersfield	a	13 58		14 04		14 15	14 21		14 27			14 45	14 58	15 04		15 15	15 21		15 27				15 45	15 58	16 04
	d	13 59				14 16			14 28		14 32	14 46	14 59			15 16			15 28			15 32	15 46	15 59	
Slaithwaite	d										14 39											15 39			
Marsden	d										14 45											15 45			
Greenfield	d										14 53											15 53			
Mossley (Grtr Manchester)	d										14 57											15 57			
Stalybridge	a								14 45		15 02								15 45			16 02			
	d							14 42	14 46		15 03							15 42	15 46			16 03			
Ashton-under-Lyne	d							14 46			15 07							15 46				16 07			
Manchester Victoria 🚢	a							14 57			15 20							15 57				16 20			
Manchester Piccadilly 10 🚢	a	14 37				14 50			15 05			15 22	15 35			15 50			16 05				16 22	16 35	
	d					14 53			15 07			15 27				15 53			16 07				16 27		
Manchester Airport ✈	a	15 01				15 14			15 40			15 44	16 01			16 14			16 40				16c51		
Manchester Oxford Road	a	14 51							15 09			15e40	15 47						16 09				16e40	16 50	
Birchwood	a								15 23										16 23						
Warrington Central	a								15 28			15e57							16 28				16e57		
Liverpool Lime Street 10	a	15 39						16 05	15 57			16e29	16 39					17 04	16 57				17e29	17 38	

For general notes see front of timetable
For details of catering facilities see Directory of Train Operators

A To Selby (Table 41)
B To Hebden Bridge via Brighouse (Table 41)
C Also stops at Heald Green 1638
b Change at York
c From 29 March arr. 1645
e Change at Manchester Piccadilly

Table 39

Saturdays

Newcastle, Middlesbrough, Scarborough, York, Hull, Leeds and Wakefield → Huddersfield → Manchester, Manchester Airport and Liverpool

Network Diagram - see first page of Table 39

		NT	TP	NT	NT	TP	NT	NT	TP	TP	NT	NT	NT	TP		NT	NT	TP	NT	NT	TP	TP	NT	NT	TP
			1 ◇			1 ◇			1 ◇	1 ◇				1 ◇				1 ◇			1 ◇	1 ◇			1 ◇
					A	B	C	D				E							C		G		H		J
			🛒			🛒			🛒	🛒				🛒				🛒			🛒				🛒
Newcastle 8	d		14 15			14b29			14b40					15 09				15b28			15b40				16 06
Chester-le-Street	d					14b31								15 18											16 15
Durham	d		14 27			14b42			14b52					15 25				15b41			15b52				16 22
Middlesbrough	d								14 50												15 50				
Thornaby	d								14 55												15 55				
Yarm	d								15 03												16 03				
Darlington 7	d		14 45			15b00								15 42				16b04							16 39
Northallerton	d		14 56						15 18					15 54							16 18				16 51
Thirsk	d								15 26												16 26				16 59
Scarborough	d					14 45												15 47							
Seamer	d					14 50												15 52							
Malton	d					15 08												16 10							
York 8	a		15 22			15 35			15 52					16 21				16 37			16 49				17 19
	d		15 28			15 38			15 58					16 28				16 40			16 58				17 28
Hull	d									15 37												16 37			
Brough	d									15 49												16 49			
Howden	d									15 31												16 36			
Selby	d									16 08												17 08			
South Milford	d									15 53												16 53			
Garforth	d					15 35			16 13									16 35			17 13				
Leeds 10	a		15 53			16 04			16 23	16 36				16 53				17 04			17 23	17 35			17 53
	d	15 43	15 55			16 10	16 13		16 25	16 40			16 43	16 55				17 10	17 13		17 25	17 40		17 43	17 55
Cottingley	d	15 48											16 48											17 48	
Morley	d	15 52					16 21						16 52						17 21					17 52	
Batley	d	15 57					16 26						16 57						17 26					17 57	
Dewsbury	a	16 00	16 06				16 29		16 36				17 00	17 06					17 29		17 36	17 51		18 00	18 06
	d	16 01	16 07				16 29		16 37				17 01	17 07					17 29		17 37	17 51		18 01	18 07
Ravensthorpe	d	16 04					16 32						17 04						17 32					18 04	
Wakefield Westgate	d											16 29											17 29		
Wakefield Kirkgate	d			←								16 35				←							17 35		
Mirfield	d	16 08 →		16 08			16a36					16 51	17 08 →			17 08			17a36				17 52	18 08 →	
Deighton	d			16 15								16 57				17 14							17 57		
Huddersfield	a		16 15	16 21		16 27			16 45	16 58		17 05		17 15		17 21		17 27			17 45	18 00	18 05		18 15
	d		16 16			16 28		16 32	16 46	16 59	17 04			17 16				17 28		17 32	17 46	18 01			18 16
Slaithwaite	d							16 39			17 11									17 39					
Marsden	d							16 45			17a17									17 45					
Greenfield	d							16 53												17 53					
Mossley (Grtr Manchester)	d							16 57												17 57					
Stalybridge	a					16 45		17 02	17 07									17 45		18 02	18 06				
	d				16 28	16 46		17 03	17 08								17 41	17 46		18 03	18 07				
Ashton-under-Lyne	d				16 32			17 07									17 45			18 07					
Manchester Victoria	a				16 42			17 21									17 59			18 20					
Manchester Piccadilly 10	a		16 50			17 05			17 24	17 35				17 52				18 05			18 22	18 35			18 52
	d		16 53			17 07								17 58				18 07			18 27				18 55
Manchester Airport	a		17 11			17 40				18 05				18 14				18 42			18 46	19 08			19 14
Manchester Oxford Road	a					17 09			17 39	17 47								18 09			18c39	18 47			
Birchwood	a					17 23			17 56									18 23							
Warrington Central	a					17 28			18 02									18 28			18c57				
Liverpool Lime Street 10	a					18 00			18 32	18 40							19 05	18 57			19c29	19 38			

For general notes see front of timetable
For details of catering facilities see Directory of Train Operators

A To Southport (Table 82)
B Also stops at Hunts Cross 1739
C To Hebden Bridge via Brighouse (Table 41)
D To Wigan Wallgate (Table 82)
E To Selby (Table 41)
G Also stops at Heald Green 1840
H To York (Table 41)
J Also stops at Heald Green 1907
b Change at York
c Change at Manchester Piccadilly

Table 39

Newcastle, Middlesbrough, Scarborough, York, Hull, Leeds and Wakefield → Huddersfield → Manchester, Manchester Airport and Liverpool

Network Diagram - see first page of Table 39

		NT	TP 1 ◇	NT	TP 1 ◇	NT	NT	TP 1 ◇	NT		NT	TP 1 ◇	NT	TP 1 ◇	TP 1 ◇	NT	NT	TP 1 ◇	NT	TP 1 ◇	TP 1 ◇	TP 1 ◇	NT	NT	TP 1 ◇
						A																			
Newcastle 8	d				16b29			16b40				17 10			17b29			17b40							18 52
Chester-le-Street	d				16b29										17b28										
Durham	d				16b42			16b52				17 22			17b35			17b54							19 04
Middlesbrough	d							17 00										18 07				19 00			
Thornaby	d							17 06										18 12				19 05			
Yarm	d							17 13										18 20				19 13			
Darlington 7	d				17b00							17 40			17b56										19 22
Northallerton	d							17 28				17 51						18 35			18b45	19 28			19 36
Thirsk	d							17 36				17 59						18 43			18b54	19 36			
Scarborough	d				16 47										17 45						18 45				
Seamer	d				16 52										17 50						18 51				
Malton	d				17 10										18 08						19 09				
York 8	a				17 37			17 55				18 24			18 36			19 04			19 36	19 59			20 02
	d				17 40			17 58				18 28			18 38			19 10			19 38				20 07
Hull	d		17 00											18 02						18 59					
Brough	d		17 12											18 14						19 11					
Howden	d													17 54						19 12					
Selby	d		17 31									17 43		18 33				18c43		19 30					
South Milford	d											17 53						18c53							
Garforth	d		17 35					18 13						18 31				19 23			19 35				
Leeds 10	a		17 59		18 04			18 23				18 52		18 58	19 04			19 35		19 56	20 04				20 32
	d		18 02		18 10	18 13		18 25			18 40	18 52		19 02	19 10		19 13	19 40			20 10			20 13	20 40
Cottingley	d										18 45						19 18							20 18	
Morley	d					18 21					18 49						19 22							20 22	
Batley	d					18 26					18 54						19 27							20 27	
Dewsbury	a		18 13			18 29		18 36			18 57			19 13			19 30	19 50						20 30	20 50
	d		18 13			18 29		18 37			18 58			19 13			19 31	19 51						20 31	20 51
Ravensthorpe	d					18 32					19 01						19 34							20 34	
Wakefield Westgate	d								18 29										19 29						
Wakefield Kirkgate	d	←							18 35				←						19 35						
Mirfield	d	18 08				18a36			18 52		19 05		19 05				19 38		19 52					20 38	
Deighton	d	18 13							18 57		→		19 10				19 45		20 01					20 44	
Huddersfield	a	18 21	18 25		18 27			18 45	19 04			19 12	19 18	19 22	19 27		19 49	19 59	20 06		20 27			20 48	20 59
	d				18 28		18 32	18 46				19 13		19 23	19 28	19 32		20 00			20 28		20 32	20 48	21 00
Slaithwaite	d						18 39									19 39							20 39	20 55	
Marsden	d						18 45									19 45							20 45	21a02	
Greenfield	d						18 53									19 53							20 53		
Mossley (Grtr Manchester)	d						18 57									19 57							20 57		
Stalybridge	a				18 45		19 02	19 06							19 46	20 02					20 45		21 02		
	d			18 41	18 46		19 03	19 07							19 46	20 03					20 46		21 03		
Ashton-under-Lyne	d			18 45			19 07									20 07							21 07		
Manchester Victoria	a			18 59			19 21									20 20							21 20		
Manchester Piccadilly 10	a				19 05			19 24				19 50		19 59	20 05			20 35			21 05				21 35
	d				19 07							19 53			20 07			20 38			21 07				21 38
Manchester Airport ✈	a				19 40			20 05				20 12						20 58			21 37				21 58
Manchester Oxford Road	a				19 09			19 46							20 09			20e54			21 09				21e52
Birchwood	a				19 23										20 23						21 23				
Warrington Central	a				19 28										20 28						21 28				
Liverpool Lime Street 10	a			20 05	19 57			20 38							20 55						21 55				22e41

For general notes see front of timetable
For details of catering facilities see Directory of Train Operators

A To Hebden Bridge via Brighouse (Table 41)
b Change at York
c Change at Leeds
e Change at Manchester Piccadilly

Table 39

Saturdays

Newcastle, Middlesbrough, Scarborough, York, Hull, Leeds and Wakefield → Huddersfield → Manchester, Manchester Airport and Liverpool

Network Diagram - see first page of Table 39

		NT	TP 1 ◇	TP 1 ◇		NT	NT	TP 1 ◇	TP 1 ◇	NT	TP 1 ◇	NT	NT	TP 1 ◇ A	NT	TP 1 ◇	NT	NT B	NT C	TP 1 ◇ B	TP 1 ◇ C	TP 1 ◇ B	TP B 🚌		
Newcastle 8	d			*19b06*				*19b45*													*20c46*	*20c46*			
Chester-le-Street	d			*18b49*																					
Durham	d							*19b57*													*20c59*	*20c59*			
Middlesbrough	d							20 10			20 50										21 50	21 50			
Thornaby	d							20 15			20 55										21 55	21 55			
Yarm	d							20 23			21 03														
Darlington 7	d			*19b34*																	22e19	22e19			
Northallerton	d							20 38			21 17										22 30	22 30			
Thirsk	d							20 46			21 25										22 38	22 38			
Scarborough	d			19 47					20 37							22 07									
Seamer	d			19 52					20 42							22 12									
Malton	d			20 10					21 00							22 30									
York 8	a			20 37				21 07	21 28		21 42					22 57					22 57	22 57			
	d			20 40				21 10			21 45										23 07	23 07			
Hull	d		19 55											21 33											
Brough	d		20 07											21 45											
Howden	d																								
Selby	d		20 26											22 07											
South Milford	d		20 36											22 17											
Garforth	d			*20 39*							*21 42*							*22 35*	*22 35*		*22 35*		*22 35*		
Leeds 10	a		20 59	21 04				21 33			22 08			22 35							23 33	23 33			
	d			21 10			21 13	21 40			22 10		22 13	22 40				23 05	23 13		23 35		23 45		
Cottingley	d						21 18						22 18					23 10	23 18						
Morley	d						21 22						22 22					23 14	23 22						
Batley	d						21 27						22 27					23 19	23 27						
Dewsbury	a						21 30	21 50					22 30	22 51				23 22	23 30		23 46		00 05		
	d						21 31	21 51					22 31	22 51				23 23	23 31		23 46		00 05		
Ravensthorpe	d						21 34						22 34					23 26	23 34						
Wakefield Westgate	d	20 29								21 29					22 42										
Wakefield Kirkgate	d	20 35								21 35					22 47										
Mirfield	d	20 51					21 38			21 48			22 38		23 00			23 30	23 38						
Deighton	d	21 01					21 45			22 01			22 44		23 08			23 37	23 45						
Huddersfield	a	21 05		21 27			21 49	21 59		22 05	22 27		22 52	23 00	23 12			23 41	23 49		23 55		00 30		
	d			21 28		21 32		22 00			22 28	22 32		23 00			23 22			23 53	23 56		00 30		
Slaithwaite	d					21 39						22 39					23 29								
Marsden	d					21 45						22 45					23 35								
Greenfield	d					21 53						22 53					23 43								
Mossley (Grtr Manchester)	d					21 57						22 57					23 47								
Stalybridge	a			21 45		22 02					22 45	23 02					23 52								
	d			21 46		22 03					22 46	23 03					23 53								
Ashton-under-Lyne	d					22 07						23 07					23 57								
Manchester Victoria 🚢	a					22 20						23 20					00 11			00 44					
Manchester Piccadilly 10 🚢	a			22 05				22 35			23 05			23 38						01 00	00 29				
	d			22 07				22 38												01 01	00 38				
Manchester Airport ✈	a			*22 39*				22 58			*23 55*			*00 45*						01 16	00 57		01 30		
Manchester Oxford Road	a			22 09				*22f51*			23 22														
Birchwood	a			22 23				*23g47*																	
Warrington Central	a			22 28				*23g54*																	
Liverpool Lime Street 10	a			22 55				*00g31*																	

For general notes see front of timetable
For details of catering facilities see Directory of Train Operators

A Also stops at Gilberdyke 2152
B 2 February to 22 March
C Until 26 January and from 29 March
b Change at York
c Change at Darlington
e Arr. 2215
f Change at Manchester Piccadilly
g Change at Manchester Piccadilly and Manchester Oxford Road

Table 39

Sundays

Newcastle, Middlesbrough, Scarborough, York, Hull and Leeds → Huddersield → Manchester, Manchester Airport and Liverpool

Network Diagram - see first page of Table 39

		TP	TP	TP	TP	TP	TP	TP	TP	TP	TP	TP	TP	TP	TP	NT	NT	NT		NT	NT	TP	NT	TP	TP
			1 ◇		1 ◇		1 ◇		1 ◇				1 ◇		1 ◇							1 ◇		1 ◇	1 ◇
		A	B	A	B	A	B	A	B	A	A	A	B	A	B	B	A	B		A	A		A		
		🚌		🚌		🚌		🚌		🚌	🚌	🚌		🚌							🚌		🚌		
Newcastle 8 ⛴	d																							07 58	
Chester-le-Street	d																								
Durham	d																							08 10	
Middlesbrough	d																								
Thornaby	d																								
Yarm	d																								
Darlington 7	d																							08 28	
Northallerton	d																								
Thirsk	d																								
Scarborough	d																								
Seamer	d																								
Malton	d																								
York 8	a																								
	d	02 00	02 40	03 00	03 55	04 30	05 10		06 10	06 00			07 22		08 10									09 15	
Hull	d																								09 05
Brough	d																								09 17
Howden	d																								
Selby	d																								09 36
South Milford	d																								09 46
Garforth	d																							09 16	
Leeds 10	a	02 45	03 08	03 45	04 23	05 15	05 38		06 38	06 45			07 50		08 38									09 38	10 03
	d	02 45	03 10	03 45	04 25	05 15	05 40	06 15	06 40	06 45			07 52	07 40	08 40			08 44			08 44	09 10		09 40	10 10
Cottingley	d																	08 49			08 59				
Morley	d																	08 53			09 07				
Batley	d																	08 58			09 17				
Dewsbury	a						05 51	06 40	06 51		←		08 03	08 05	08 51			09 01			09 25			09 51	
	d						05 51	06 40 →	06 51		06 40		08 03	08 05	08 51			09 02			09 25			09 51	
Ravensthorpe	d																	09 05			09 32		←		
Mirfield	d																	09 09			09 37		09 37		
Deighton	d																	09 15			→		09 47		
Huddersfield	a	03 20	03 27	04 20	04 42	05 50	06 00		07 00		07 05		08 12	08 30	09 00			09 19				09 27	09s54	10 00	10 27
	d	03 20	03 28	04 20	04 43	05 50	06 01		07 01		07 05		08 13	08 30	09 01	09 07		09 19		09 19		09 28		10 01	10 28
Slaithwaite	d															09 14		09 26		09 26			10s14		
Marsden	d															09 20		09a33		09a33			10 24		
Greenfield	d															09 28									
Mossley (Grtr Manchester)	d															09 32									
Stalybridge	a					06 35			07 18		07 50		08 30	09 15	09 18	09 37						09 46			10 46
	d					06 35			07 19		07 50	08 00	08 31	09 15	09 19	09 38	09 38					09 46			10 46
Ashton-under-Lyne	d															09 42	09 42								
Manchester Victoria ⛴	a											08 20				09 56	09 56								
	d																								
Manchester Piccadilly 10 ⛴	a		04 00	05 20	05 15	06 55	06 33		07 34		08 10		08 46	09 35	09 34							10 05		10 33	11 05
	d		04 05	05 20	05 20	06 55	06 37		07 41		08 10		08 50	09 35	09 39							10 07		10 39	
Manchester Airport ✈	a	04 20	04 21	05 45	05 36	07 20	06 53		07 58	08 05	08 35		09 05	10 00	09 58							10 33		11 04	11 33
Manchester Oxford Road	a																					10 09			
Birchwood	a					08b20			08b20		09b34		09b34									10 23		11b34	
Warrington Central	a					08b25			08b25		09b39		09b39									10 28		11b39	11c56
Liverpool Lime Street 10	a					09b20			09b20		10b20		10b20									10 58		12b20	12e21

For general notes see front of timetable
For details of catering facilities see Directory of Train Operators

- **A** 3 February to 23 March
- **B** Until 27 January and from 30 March
- **b** Change at Manchester Piccadilly and Manchester Oxford Road
- **c** From 3 February only
- **e** From 30 March arr. 1222

Table 39

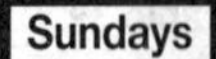

Sundays

Newcastle, Middlesbrough, Scarborough, York, Hull and Leeds → Huddersield → Manchester, Manchester Airport and Liverpool

Network Diagram - see first page of Table 39

		TP	NT	NT	TP	TP	TP	TP	TP	NT	NT	TP	TP	TP		TP	TP	NT	NT	TP	TP	TP	TP	TP	NT
		1 ◇			1 ◇	1 ◇	1 ◇	1 ◇	1 ◇			1 ◇	1 ◇	1 ◇		1 ◇	1 ◇			1 ◇	1 ◇	1 ◇	1 ◇	1 ◇	
Newcastle 8	d	08b55			09 33			10b30	11 03			11 32	12b00			12b32	12 49			13b32	14 10		14b25	14 57	
Chester-le-Street	d				09 42												12 58								
Durham	d	09b07			09 49			10b37	11 16			11 37				12b45	13 05			13b45	14 22		14c37	15 09	
Middlesbrough	d					10 15							12 15							13 45					
Thornaby	d					10 20							12 20							13 50					
Yarm	d					10 28							12 28							13 58					
Darlington 7	d	09b25			10 05			10b59	11 34			11 54	12b27			13b03	13 23			14b04	14 40		14c54	15 27	
Northallerton	d	09b38			10 17	10 42			11 45				12 42				13 35			14 12	14 12		14b57	15 38	
Thirsk	d					10 50							12 50							14 19			15b06		
Scarborough	d	09 20						10 45								12 45							14 45		
Seamer	d	09 25						10 50								12 50							14 50		
Malton	d	09 43						11 08								13 08							15 08		
York 8	a	10 10			10 44	11 09		11 35	12 12				13 12			13 35	14 11			14 40	15 14		15 35	16 12	
	d	10 15			10 45	11 15		11 40	12 15			12 45	13 15			13 42	14 15			14 45	15 15		15 39	16 15	
Hull	d						11 00							12 50								14 50			
Brough	d						11 12							13 02								15 02			
Howden	d						10 36															14 34			
Selby	d						11 31							13 21								15 21			
South Milford	d						11 41							13 31								15 31			
Garforth	d			10 19	10 19		11 18	11 57			12 19			13 18		13 57			14 19			15 18	15 57		
Leeds 10	a	10 38			11 08	11 38	12 01	12 07	12 38			13 08	13 38	13 49		14 07	14 38			15 08	15 39	15 49	16 07	16 38	
	d	10 40		10 44	11 10	11 40	12 02	12 10	12 40		12 44	13 10	13 40	13 58		14 10	14 40		14 44	15 10	15 40	15 57	16 10	16 40	
Cottingley	d			10 49							12 49								14 49						
Morley	d			10 53							12 53								14 53						
Batley	d			10 58							12 58								14 58						
Dewsbury	a	10 51		11 01		11 51			12 51		13 01		13 51				14 51		15 01		15 51			16 51	
	d	10 51		11 02		11 51			12 51		13 02		13 51				14 51		15 02		15 51			16 51	
Ravensthorpe	d			11 05							13 05								15 05						
Mirfield	d			11 09							13 09								15 09						
Deighton	d			11 15							13 15								15 15						
Huddersfield	a	11 00		11 19	11 27	12 00	12 20	12 27	13 00		13 19	13 27	14 00	14 15		14 27	15 00		15 19	15 27	16 01	16 14	16 27	17 00	
	d	11 01	11 09	11 19	11 28	12 01	12 21	12 28	13 01	13 09	13 19	13 28	14 01	14 16		14 28	15 01	15 09	15 19	15 28	16 01	16 15	16 28	17 01	17 09
Slaithwaite	d		11 16	11 26						13 16	13 26							15 16	15 26						17 16
Marsden	d		11 22	11a33						13 22	13a33							15 22	15a33						17 22
Greenfield	d		11 30							13 30								15 30							17 30
Mossley (Grtr Manchester)	d		11 34							13 34								15 34							17 34
Stalybridge	a		11 39		11 46			12 46		13 39		13 46				14 45		15 39		15 46			16 45		17 39
	d		11 40		11 46			12 46		13 40		13 46				14 46		15 40		15 46			16 46		17 40
Ashton-under-Lyne	d		11 44							13 44								15 44							17 44
Manchester Victoria	a		11 58							13 58								15 58							17 58
	d																								
Manchester Piccadilly 10	a	11 33			12 05	12 33	12 57	13 05	13 33			14 05	14 33	14 52		15 05	15 33			16 05	16 34	16 50	17 05	17 33	
	d	11 39			12 07	12 39		13 07	13 41			14 07	14 39			15 07	15 39			16 07	16 39		17 07	17 39	
Manchester Airport	a	11 58			12 33	12 58	13 24	13 33	13 58			14 33	14 58	15e21		15 33	15 58			16 33	16 58	17f18	17 33	17 58	
Manchester Oxford Road	a				12 09			13 09				14 09				15 09				16 09			17 09		
Birchwood	a				12 23			13 23				14 23				15 23				16 23			17 23		
Warrington Central	a				12 28			13 28				14 28				15 28				16 28			17 28		
Liverpool Lime Street 10	a				12 57			13 57				14 57				15 57				16 57			17 57		

For general notes see front of timetable
For details of catering facilities see Directory of Train Operators

b Change at York
c Change at York. Until 27 January dep. 1 minute later
e 3 February to 23 March arr. 1518
f From 30 March arr. 3 minutes later

Table 39

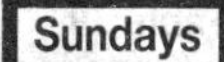

Sundays

Newcastle, Middlesbrough, Scarborough, York, Hull and Leeds → Huddersield → Manchester, Manchester Airport and Liverpool

Network Diagram - see first page of Table 39

		NT	TP	TP	TP	TP	TP	NT	NT	TP	TP	TP	TP	TP	NT	NT	TP	TP	TP	TP	NT	TP	TP		
			1 ◇	1 ◇	1 ◇	1 ◇	1 ◇			1 ◇	1 ◇	1 ◇	1 ◇	1 ◇			1 ◇	1 ◇	1 ◇	1 ◇		1 ◇	1 ◇		
Newcastle 8 ⛴	d		*15b30*	16 08		*16b33*	16 48			*17b30*		17 57		*18b29*			19 20	*19b35*		*20b31*					
Chester-le-Street	d						16 57																		
Durham	d		*15b37*	16 20		*16b46*	17 04			*17b37*		18 09		*18b42*			19 32	*19b48*		*20b37*					
Middlesbrough	d		15 45							17 45								20 15					22 07		
Thornaby	d		15 50							17 50								20 20					22 12		
Yarm	d		15 58							17 58								20 28					22 20		
Darlington 7	d		*15b59*	16 38		*17b04*	17 21			*17b59*		18 27		*19b00*			19 50	20b06		*20b58*					
Northallerton	d		16 14	*16 32*			17 33			18 12							20 01	20 42					22 34		
Thirsk	d		16 22							18 20								20 50					22 42		
Scarborough	d					16 45								18 45						20 45		21 45			
Seamer	d					16 50								18 50						20 50		21 50			
Malton	d					17 08								19 08						21 08		22 08			
York 8	a		16 41	17 12		17 35	17 59			18 39		19 00		19 35			20 32	21 09		21 35		22 35	23 09		
	d		16 45	17 14		17 40	18 15			18 45		19 15		19 42			20 45	21 15		21 38		22 42	23 12		
Hull	d				16 50						18 10		19 04						21 00						
Brough	d				17 02						18 22		19 16						21 12						
Howden	d				*16 45*								*18 54*												
Selby	d				17 21						18 41		19 35						21 31						
South Milford	d				17 31						18 53								21 41						
Garforth	d	*16 18*		*17 16*		17 57			*18 19*					19 57		*20 19*				21 54	*22 19*				
Leeds 10	a		17 08	17 37	17 49	18 07	18 38			19 08	19 12	19 38	19 59	20 07			21 08	21 38	21 59	22 04		23 08	23 38		
	d	16 44	17 10	17 40	17 57	18 10	18 40		18 44	19 10	19 16	19 40		20 10		20 44	21 10	21 40		22 10	22 44	23 10	23 40		
Cottingley	d	16 49							18 49							20 49					22 49				
Morley	d	16 53							18 53							20 53					22 53				
Batley	d	16 58							18 58							20 58					22 58				
Dewsbury	a	17 01		17 50			18 51		19 01			19 51		20 20		21 01	21 21	21 51			23 01		23 51		
	d	17 02		17 51			18 51		19 02			19 51		20 21		21 02	21 21	21 51			23 02		23 51		
Ravensthorpe	d	17 05							19 05							21 05					23 05				
Mirfield	d	17 09							19 09							21 09					23 09				
Deighton	d	17 15							19 15							21 15					23 15				
Huddersfield	a	17 19	17 27	17 59	18 15	18 27	19 00		19 19	19 27	19 33	20 00		20 29		21 19	21 30	22 00		22 27	23 20	23 27	23 59		
	d	17 19	17 28	18 01	18 16	18 28	19 01	19 09	19 19	19 28	19 34	20 01		20 30	21 09	21 19	21 30	22 01		22 28		23 28	00 01		
Slaithwaite	d	17 26						19 16	19 26						21 16	21 26									
Marsden	d	17a33						19 22	19a33						21 22	21a33									
Greenfield	d							19 30							21 30										
Mossley (Grtr Manchester)	d							19 34							21 34										
Stalybridge	a		17 46			18 45		19 39		19 45				20 48	21 39		21 48			22 45					
	d		17 46			18 46		19 40		19 46				20 48	21 40		21 48			22 46					
Ashton-under-Lyne	d							19 44							21 44										
Manchester Victoria ⛴	a							19 58							21 58										
	d																								
Manchester Piccadilly 10 ⛴	a		18 05	18 33	18 52	19 05	19 33			20 05	20 11	20 33		21 05			22 05	22 33		23 03		00 03	00 33		
	d		18 07	18 39		19 07	19 39			20 07		20 39		21 07			22 07	22 39					00 35		
Manchester Airport ✈	a		*18 33*	18 58	*19c18*	*19 33*	19 58			*20 33*	*20 52*	20 58		*21 33*			*22 33*	22 58		*23 33*		*00 33*	00 54		
Manchester Oxford Road	a		18 09			19 09				20 09				21 09			22 09								
Birchwood	a		18 23			19 24				20 23				21 23			22 23								
Warrington Central	a		18 28			19 29				20 28				21 28			22 28								
Liverpool Lime Street 10	a		18 57			19 57				20 57				21 57			23 00								

For general notes see front of timetable
For details of catering facilities see Directory of Train Operators

b Change at York
c From 30 March arr. 3 minutes later

Liverpool, Manchester Airport and Manchester → Huddersfield → Wakefield, Leeds, Hull, York, Scarborough, Middlesbrough and Newcastle

Network Diagram - see first page of Table 39

Miles	Miles	Miles	Miles	Miles			TP	TP	TP	TP	NT	TP	TP	TP	NT	NT	TP	NT	NT	TP	NT	TP	NT	NT
							MO	MX	MO	MX														
							1 ◇	1 ◇	1 ◇	1 ◇		1 ◇	1 ◇	1 ◇			1 ◇			1 ◇		1 ◇		
													⊼	⊼			⊼					⊼		
0	—	—	—	—	**Liverpool Lime Street** 10	d																		
18½	—	—	—	—	Warrington Central	d																		
21¾	—	—	—	—	Birchwood	d																		
34¼	—	—	—	—	Manchester Oxford Road	d																		
—	—	—	—	—	**Manchester Airport** ✈	d	01 22	01 22	03 22	03 17			*04 34*	05 34			*05 47*					06 23		
34¾	—	—	—	—	**Manchester Piccadilly** 10	a	01 36	01 36	03 36	03 31				05 48								06 39		
—	—	—	—	—		d	01 38	01 38	03 38	03 38			05 39	05 57			06 21					06 53		
—	—	—	—	0	**Manchester Victoria**	d																		06 57
—	—	—	—	6½	Ashton-under-Lyne	d																		07 07
42¼	—	—	—	7¾	**Stalybridge**	a							05 52									07 06		07 11
—	—	—	—	—		d							05 52						06 42			07 06		07 12
45	—	—	—	10½	Mossley (Grtr Manchester)	d													06 46					07 16
47½	—	—	—	12¾	Greenfield	d													06 50					07 20
53¼	—	—	—	18¾	Marsden	d												06 48	06 59					07 29
55¾	—	—	—	21¼	Slaithwaite	d												06 52	07 03					07 33
60¼	—	—	—	25¾	**Huddersfield**	a	02 12	02 23	04 10	04 23			06 10	06 26			06 52	07 00	07 11			07 24		07 41
—	—	—	—	—		d	02 13	02 27	04 11	04 27	05 32		06 11	06 27	06 31	06 41	06 54	07 00			07 16	07 25		
62¼	—	—	—	27¾	Deighton	d					05 36				06 34	06 45		07 03			07 19			
65¼	—	—	—	30¾	Mirfield	d					05 41				06 39	06 50		07 08			07 24			
—	—	—	—	40¼	Wakefield Kirkgate	a					05 57					07 03								
—	—	—	—	41¼	**Wakefield Westgate**	a					06 05					07 10								
66¾	—	—	—	—	Ravensthorpe	d									06 42			07 11			07 27			
68¼	—	—	—	—	**Dewsbury**	a								06 36	06 46		07 03	07 15			07 31		←	
—	—	—	—	—		d								06 37	06 46		07 03	07 15			07 35 →		07 35	
69¾	—	—	—	—	Batley	d									06 49			07 18					07 38	
73	—	—	—	—	Morley	d									06 55			07 24					07 44	
74½	—	—	—	—	Cottingley	d									06 59			07 28					07 47	
77½	0	—	0	—	**Leeds** 10	a	02 50	02 50	04 50	04 50			06 32	06 52	07 07		07 18	07 38				07 47	07 55	
—	—	—	—	—		d	02 50	02 50	04 50	04 50			06 35	06 55			07 23					07 50		
84¾	7¼	—	7½	—	Garforth	d											*07 41*					*08 09*		
—	12¾	—	—	—	South Milford	a											*07 52*					*08 20*		
—	20¾	—	—	—	Selby	a											07 43					*08 35*		
—	29½	—	—	—	Howden	a											07 52							
—	41½	—	—	—	Brough	a											08 03							
—	51¾	—	—	—	**Hull**	a											08 21							
103	—	0	25½	—	**York** 8	a	03 20	03 33	05 18	05 32			07 03	07 22								08 20		
—	—	—	—	—		d			05 40	05 40		06 38	07 06	07 25						07 32		08 22		
—	—	—	46½	—	Malton	d						07 02		07 49										
—	—	—	64¾	—	Seamer	a						07 19		08 06										
—	—	—	67½	—	**Scarborough**	a						07 30		08 14										
125¼	—	22¼	—	—	Thirsk	a			06 01	06 01			07 22							07 52		08 38		
133	—	30	—	—	Northallerton	a			06 17	06 17			07 30							08 01		08 49		
147	—	—	—	—	**Darlington** 7	a			06 28	06 28			07 41	*08b05*								*09b02*		
—	—	42¼	—	—	Yarm	d														08 16		09 03		
—	—	47½	—	—	Thornaby	a			06 52	06 52										08 25		09 11		
—	—	50¾	—	—	**Middlesbrough**	a			07 01	07 01										08 32		09 20		
169	—	—	—	—	Durham	a			*07c23*	*07c23*			07 58	*08b23*						*09e31*		*09b20*		
174¾	—	—	—	—	Chester-le-Street	a			*07c48*	*07c48*			08 04	*08f43*										
183	—	—	—	—	**Newcastle** 8	a			*07c39*	*07c39*			08 20	*08b39*								*09b38*		

For general notes see front of timetable
For details of catering facilities see Directory of Train Operators

b Change at York
c Change at Darlington
e Change at Northallerton
f Change at York and Durham

Liverpool, Manchester Airport and Manchester → Huddersfield → Wakefield, Leeds, Hull, York, Scarborough, Middlesbrough and Newcastle

Network Diagram - see first page of Table 39

Station		TP 1 ◇ ⊼		NT		NT A	TP 1 ◇ ⊼	TP 1 ◇ ⊼	NT	NT B	TP 1 ◇ ⊼	NT C	NT	NT D	TP 1 ◇ E ⊼	NT	TP 1 ◇ ⊼	NT	NT	TP 1 ◇ ⊼	NT B	TP 1 ◇ G ⊼	NT		NT D
Liverpool Lime Street 10	d	06 18							06 39		06b47				07 15			07 18	07 47						
Warrington Central	d	06 42									07b15				07 39							08b16			
Birchwood	d	06 47									07b20				07 44							08b21			
Manchester Oxford Road	d	07c07					07b13				07b43				08e07					08 20		08b45			
Manchester Airport ✈	d	06 44					07 02				07 34						08 04			08 07		08 33			
Manchester Piccadilly 10	a	07 10					07 19				07 48				08 10		08 19					08 49			
	d	07 12					07 25	07 35			07 55				08 12		08 25			08 41		08 57			
Manchester Victoria	d								07 39			07 57						08 27	08 57						
Ashton-under-Lyne	d								07 49			08 07						08 37	09 07						
Stalybridge	a	07 25					07 38		07 54		08 07	08 13			08 24			08 41	09 13						
	d	07 25					07 38		07 54		08 08				08 25			08 42							
Mossley (Grtr Manchester)	d								07 59									08 46							
Greenfield	d								08 03									08 50							
Marsden	d								08 11									08 59							
Slaithwaite	d								08 16									09 03							
Huddersfield	a	07 44					07 56	08 07	08 24		08 25				08 44		08 55	09 11		09 14		09 26			
	d	07 45		07 49			07 57	08 10			08 27		08 33	08 37	08 45		08 57			09 16		09 27	09 31		09 35
Deighton	d			07 53									08 36	08 40									09 34		09 38
Mirfield	d			07 59		07 54				08 19			08 41	08 45							09 13		09 39		09 43
Wakefield Kirkgate	a			08 13										09 00											09 58
Wakefield Westgate	a			08 22										09 08											10 10
Ravensthorpe	d									08 23			08 44								09 17		09 42		
Dewsbury	a	07 54				07 59	08 06	08 19		08 26	08 37		08 48			←	09 06				09 20	09 36	09 46		
	d	07 55				08 00	08 07	08 20		08 31	08 37		08 55 →			08 55	09 07				09 24	09 37	09 46		
Batley	d					08 03				08 34						08 58					09 27		09 49		
Morley	d					08 09				08 40						09 04					09 33		09 55		
Cottingley	d									08 43						09 08							09 59		
Leeds 10	a	08 10				08 18	08 23	08 35		08 51	08 54				09 06	09 18	09 22			09 36	09 44	09 52	10 07		
	d	08 12					08 27	08 38			08 57				09 12		09 27			09 38		09 57			
Garforth	d						08 35	08 56			09 05						09 53					10 05			
South Milford	a										09f38											10f38			
Selby	a							08 58			09f54									09 58		10f53			
Howden	a							09 31												10 22					
Brough	a																			10 17					
Hull	a							09 31												10 34					
York 8	a	08 35					08 55				09 25				09 36		09 54					10 23			
	d	08 38	08 42				09 03				09 26				09 38		10 00					10 26			
Malton	d	09 02													10 02										
Seamer	a	09 19													10 19										
Scarborough	a	09 30													10 30										
Thirsk	a										09 45						10 29					10 45			
Northallerton	a		09 02				09 23				09 54						10 20					10 54			
Darlington 7	a		09 14				09 36				10g01				10g16		10 32					10g59			
Yarm	d										10 10											11 10			
Thornaby	a										10 20											11 20			
Middlesbrough	a										10 30											11 30			
Durham	a		09 31				09 54				10g18				10g33		10 50					11g17			
Chester-le-Street	a		09 44												10g40		10 56								
Newcastle 8	a		09 49				10 12				10g35				10g58		11 11					11g33			

For general notes see front of timetable
For details of catering facilities see Directory of Train Operators

A From Hebden Bridge via Brighouse (Table 41)
B From Brighouse (Table 41)
C From Wigan Wallgate (Table 82)
D From Selby (Table 41)
E Also stops at Widnes 0732 amd Irlam 0749
G Also stops at Heald Green 0837
b Change at Manchester Piccadilly
c Arr. 0702
e Arr. 0804
f Change at Leeds
g Change at York

Liverpool, Manchester Airport and Manchester → Huddersfield → Wakefield, Leeds, Hull, York, Scarborough, Middlesbrough and Newcastle

Network Diagram - see first page of Table 39

		TP	TP	NT	NT	NT	TP	TP	NT	NT	TP	TP	NT	NT	NT	TP	TP	NT	NT		TP	TP	NT	NT	NT
		1 ◇	1 ◇				1 ◇	1 ◇			1 ◇	1 ◇				1 ◇	1 ◇				1 ◇	1 ◇			
				A						B			A						B				A		
		⊼	⊼				⊼	⊼			⊼	⊼				⊼	⊼				⊼	⊼			
Liverpool Lime Street 10	d	08 22				08 48		*08b52*			09 22				09 48		*09b52*				10 22				10 48
Warrington Central	d	08 44						*09b17*			09 44						*10b17*				10 44				
Birchwood	d	08 49						*09c03*			09 49						*10c03*				10 49				
Manchester Oxford Road	d	09 07					*09 27*	*09b43*			10 07					*10 27*	*10b43*				11 07				
Manchester Airport ✈	d		09 04				*09 07*	09 34				10 04				*10 07*	10 34					11 04			
Manchester Piccadilly 10 ⛴	a	09 10	09 19					09 48			10 10	10 19					10 48				11 10	11 19			
	d	09 12	09 25				09 42	09 57			10 12	10 27				10 42	10 57				11 12	11 27			
Manchester Victoria ⛴	d				09 27	09 57								10 27	10 57									11 27	11 57
Ashton-under-Lyne	d				09 37	10 07								10 37	11 07									11 37	12 07
Stalybridge	a	09 25			09 41	10 13					10 25			10 41	11 13						11 25			11 41	12 13
	d	09 25			09 42						10 25			10 42							11 25			11 42	
Mossley (Grtr Manchester)	d				09 46									10 47										11 47	
Greenfield	d				09 50									10 51										11 51	
Marsden	d				09 59									10 59										11 59	
Slaithwaite	d				10 04									11 04										12 04	
Huddersfield	a	09 44	09 56		10 12		10 15	10 26			10 44	10 56		11 12		11 15	11 26				11 44	11 56		12 12	
	d	09 45	09 57				10 17	10 27	10 31	10 35	10 45	10 57				11 17	11 27	11 31	11 35		11 45	11 57			
Deighton	d								10 34	10 38								11 34	11 38						
Mirfield	d			10 07					10 39	10 43			11 07					11 39	11 43				12 07		
Wakefield Kirkgate	a									10 56									11 56						
Wakefield Westgate	a									11 08									12 08						
Ravensthorpe	d								10 42									11 42							
Dewsbury	a		10 06	10 12				10 36	10 46			11 06	11 12				11 36	11 46				12 06	12 12		
	d		10 07	10 12				10 37	10 46			11 07	11 12				11 37	11 46				12 07	12 12		
Batley	d			10 15					10 49				11 15					11 49					12 15		
Morley	d			10 21					10 55				11 21					11 55					12 21		
Cottingley	d								10 59									11 59							
Leeds 10	a	10 09	10 22	10 31			10 36	10 52	11 07		11 09	11 22	11 33			11 36	11 52	12 07			12 09	12 22	12 32		
	d	10 12	10 27				10 38	10 57			11 12	11 27				11 38	11 57				12 12	12 27			
Garforth	d			*10 53*				11 05				*11 53*					12 05					*12 53*			
South Milford	a							*11e38*									*12e38*								
Selby	a						10 58	*11e55*								11 58	*12e53*								
Howden	a						*12 01*									*12 27*									
Brough	a						11 17									12 17									
Hull	a						11 34									12 36									
York 8	a	10 36	10 49					11 23			11 35	11 52					12 23				12 35	12 55			
	d	10 38	10 54					11 26			11 38	12 01					12 26				12 38	12 59			
Malton	d	11 02									12 02										13 02				
Seamer	a	11 19									12 19										13 19				
Scarborough	a	11 30									12 30										13 30				
Thirsk	a							11 42									12 46					*13 37*			
Northallerton	a		11 15					11 55				12 21					12 55					13 19			
Darlington 7	a		11 26					*11f58*			*12f20*	12 33					*13f00*				*13f11*	13 31			
Yarm	d							12 10									13 10								
Thornaby	a							12 18									13 20								
Middlesbrough	a							12 30									13 30								
Durham	a		11 44					*12f22*			*12f38*	12 50					*13f18*				*13f28*	13 48			
Chester-le-Street	a										*12f50*											13 54			
Newcastle 8 ⛴	a		12 02					*12f37*			*12f55*	13 09					*13f34*				*13f50*	14 10			

For general notes see front of timetable
For details of catering facilities see Directory of Train Operators

A From Hebden Bridge via Brighouse (Table 41)
B From Selby (Table 41)
b Change at Manchester Piccadilly
c Change at Manchester Oxford Road and Manchester Piccadilly
e Change at Leeds
f Change at York

Liverpool, Manchester Airport and Manchester → Huddersfield → Wakefield, Leeds, Hull, York, Scarborough, Middlesbrough and Newcastle

Network Diagram - see first page of Table 39

		TP 1 ◇	TP 1 ◇	NT	NT	TP 1 ◇	TP 1 ◇	NT	NT	NT	TP 1 ◇	TP 1 ◇	NT	NT	TP 1 ◇	TP 1 ◇		NT	NT	NT	TP 1 ◇	TP 1 ◇	NT	NT	TP 1 ◇
					A			B						C				B						A	
Liverpool Lime Street 10	d		10b52			11 22				11 48		11b52			12 22					12 48		12b52			13 22
Warrington Central	d		11b17			11 44						12b17			12 44							13b17			13 44
Birchwood	d		11c03			11 49						12c03			12 49							13c03			13 49
Manchester Oxford Road	d	11 27	11b43			12 07					12 27	12b43			13 07						13 27	13b43			14 07
Manchester Airport	d	11 07	11 34				12 04				12 07	12 34				13 04					13 07	13 34			
Manchester Piccadilly 10	a		11 48			12 10	12 19					12 48			13 10	13 19						13 48			14 10
	d	11 42	11 57			12 12	12 27				12 42	12 57			13 12	13 27					13 42	13 57			14 12
Manchester Victoria	d								12 27	12 57									13 27	13 57					
Ashton-under-Lyne	d								12 37	13 07									13 37	14 07					
Stalybridge	a					12 25			12 41	13 13					13 25				13 41	14 13					14 25
	d					12 25			12 42						13 25				13 42						14 25
Mossley (Grtr Manchester)	d								12 47										13 47						
Greenfield	d								12 51										13 51						
Marsden	d								12 59										13 59						
Slaithwaite	d								13 04										14 04						
Huddersfield	a	12 15	12 26			12 44	12 56		13 12		13 15	13 26			13 44	13 56			14 12		14 15	14 26			14 44
	d	12 17	12 27	12 31	12 35	12 45	12 57				13 17	13 27	13 31	13 35	13 45	13 57					14 17	14 27	14 31	14 35	14 45
Deighton	d			12 34	12 38								13 34	13 38									14 34	14 38	
Mirfield	d			12 39	12 43			13 07					13 39	13 43				14 07					14 39	14 43	
Wakefield Kirkgate	a				12 56									13 56										14 58	
Wakefield Westgate	a				13 08									14 08										15 08	
Ravensthorpe	d			12 42									13 42										14 42		
Dewsbury	a		12 36	12 46			13 06	13 12				13 36	13 46			14 06		14 12				14 36	14 46		
	d		12 37	12 46			13 07	13 12				13 37	13 46			14 07		14 12				14 37	14 46		
Batley	d			12 49				13 15					13 49					14 15					14 49		
Morley	d			12 55				13 21					13 55					14 21					14 55		
Cottingley	d			12 59									13 59										14 59		
Leeds 10	a	12 36	12 52	13 07		13 09	13 22	13 32			13 36	13 52	14 07		14 09	14 22		14 32			14 36	14 52	15 07		15 09
	d	12 38	12 57			13 12	13 27				13 38	13 57			14 12	14 27					14 38	14 57			15 12
Garforth	d		13 05				13 53					14 05				14 53						15 05			
South Milford	a		13e38									14e38										15e38			
Selby	a	12 58	13e53								13 58	14e52									14 58	15e53			
Howden	a	13 54																			15 37				
Brough	a	13 17									14 17										15 17				
Hull	a	13 34									14 34										15 34				
York 8	a		13 24			13 35	13 52					14 23			14 37	14 53						15 23			15 35
	d		13 26			13 38	13 54					14 26			14 38	14 54						15 26			15 38
Malton	d					14 02									15 02										16 02
Seamer	a					14 19									15 19										16 19
Scarborough	a					14 30									15 30										16 30
Thirsk	a		13 46									14 42										15 46			
Northallerton	a		13 55				14 15					14 53				15 22						15 55			
Darlington 7	a		14f00			14f16	14 27					14f58			15f16	15 34						16f06			16f11
Yarm	d		14 10									15 08										16 09			
Thornaby	a		14 18									15 18										16 19			
Middlesbrough	a		14 30									15 30										16 30			
Durham	a		14f18			14f34	14 50					15f15			15f34	15 51						16f24			16f29
Chester-le-Street	a					14f41										15 57									16f36
Newcastle 8	a		14f37			14f57	15 06					15f32			15f57	16 14						16f39			16f52

For general notes see front of timetable
For details of catering facilities see Directory of Train Operators

- **A** From Selby (Table 41)
- **B** From Hebden Bridge via Brighouse (Table 41)
- **C** From Leeds (Table 41)
- **b** Change at Manchester Piccadilly
- **c** Change at Manchester Oxford Road and Manchester Piccadilly
- **e** Change at Leeds
- **f** Change at York

Liverpool, Manchester Airport and Manchester → Huddersfield → Wakefield, Leeds, Hull, York, Scarborough, Middlesbrough and Newcastle

Network Diagram - see first page of Table 39

		TP	NT	NT	NT	TP	TP	NT	NT	TP	TP	NT	NT		NT	TP	TP	NT	NT	TP	NT	TP	NT	NT	TP
		1 ◇				1 ◇	1 ◇			1 ◇	1 ◇					1 ◇	1 ◇			1 ◇		1 ◇			1 ◇
			A						B			A							B	C			A		
Liverpool Lime Street 10	d				13 48		13b52			14 22					14 48		14b52			15 22					
Warrington Central	d						14b17			14 44							15b17			15 44					
Birchwood	d						14c03			14 49							15c03			15 49					
Manchester Oxford Road	d					14 27	14b43			15 07						15 27	15b43			16 07					16 27
Manchester Airport ✈	d	14 04				14 07	14 34				15 04					15 07	15 34					16 04			16 07
Manchester Piccadilly 10	a	14 19					14 48			15 10	15 19						15 48			16 10		16 19			
	d	14 27				14 42	14 57			15 12	15 27					15 42	15 57			16 12		16 27			16 42
Manchester Victoria	d			14 27	14 57								15 27		15 57						16 18			16 27	
Ashton-under-Lyne	d			14 37	15 07								15 37		16 07						16 28			16 37	
Stalybridge	a			14 41	15 13					15 25			15 41		16 13					16 25	16 34			16 41	
	d			14 42						15 25			15 42							16 25				16 42	
Mossley (Grtr Manchester)	d			14 47									15 47											16 47	
Greenfield	d			14 51									15 51											16 51	
Marsden	d			14 59									15 59											16 59	
Slaithwaite	d			15 04									16 04											17 04	
Huddersfield	a	14 56		15 12		15 15	15 26			15 44	15 56		16 12			16 15	16 26			16 44		16 56		17 12	17 15
	d	14 57				15 17	15 27	15 31	15 35	15 45	15 57					16 17	16 27	16 31	16 35	16 45		16 57			17 17
Deighton	d							15 34	15 38									16 34	16 38						
Mirfield	d		15 07					15 39	15 43			16 07						16 39	16 43				17 07		
Wakefield Kirkgate	a								15 58										16 58						
Wakefield Westgate	a								16 08										17 08						
Ravensthorpe	d							15 42										16 42							
Dewsbury	a	15 06	15 12				15 36	15 46			16 06	16 12					16 36	16 46				17 06	17 12		
	d	15 07	15 12				15 37	15 46			16 07	16 12					16 37	16 46				17 07	17 12		
Batley	d		15 15					15 49				16 15						16 49					17 15		
Morley	d		15 21					15 55				16 21						16 55					17 21		
Cottingley	d							15 59										16 59							
Leeds 10	a	15 22	15 31			15 36	15 52	16 07		16 10	16 22	16 32				16 36	16 52	17 07		17 09		17 22	17 31		17 37
	d	15 27				15 38	15 57			16 12	16 27					16 38	16 57			17 12		17 24			17 38
Garforth	d		*15 53*				16 05				*16 53*						17 05					17 34	*17 53*		*18 01*
South Milford	a						16e38										17e40								*18 12*
Selby	a					15 58	16e52									16 59	17e54						*18 25*		18 05
Howden	a					*16 51*										*17 54*									18 16
Brough	a					16 17										17 16									18 27
Hull	a					16 34										17 36									18 45
York 8	a	15 52					16 23			16 35	16 52						17 22			17 38		17 57			
	d						16 26			16 38	16 58						17 26			17 43		18 00			
Malton	d									17 02							17 50					18 24			
Seamer	a									17 19							18 07					18 41			
Scarborough	a									17 30							18 17					18 51			
Thirsk	a						16 46				17 14									17 59					
Northallerton	a						16 55				17 22						17f56			18 09					
Darlington 7	a	*16 50*					16f57			17f08	17 36						18f02			18f15		18f58			
Yarm	d						17 09													18 24					
Thornaby	a						17 19													18 32					
Middlesbrough	a						17 30													18 42					
Durham	a	*17 08*								17f31	17 55						18f20			18f33		19f15			
Chester-le-Street	a										18 01									18f40					
Newcastle 8	a	*17 26*					17f28			17f39	18 16						18f37			18f56		19f35			

For general notes see front of timetable
For details of catering facilities see Directory of Train Operators

- **A** From Hebden Bridge via Brighouse (Table 41)
- **B** From Selby (Table 41)
- **C** Also stops at Cross Gates 1718
- **b** Change at Manchester Piccadilly
- **c** Change at Manchester Oxford Road and Manchester Piccadilly
- **e** Change at Leeds
- **f** Change at York

Liverpool, Manchester Airport and Manchester → Huddersfield → Wakefield, Leeds, Hull, York, Scarborough, Middlesbrough and Newcastle

Network Diagram - see first page of Table 39

		TP	NT	NT	NT	TP	NT	NT	TP	NT		NT	TP	NT	TP	NT	NT	TP	NT	TP	NT	TP	TP	NT	NT
		1 ◇				1 ◇			1 ◇				1 ◇		1 ◇			1 ◇		1 ◇		1 ◇	1 ◇		
			A				B									A			C						A
		⊼				⊼			⊼				⊼		⊼			⊼		⊼		⊼			
Liverpool Lime Street 10	d	15b52			15 48	16 22						16 18			16b52		16 48	17 22					17b52		
Warrington Central	d	16b17				16 44									17b17			17 44					18b17		
Birchwood	d					16 49												17 49					18c08		
Manchester Oxford Road	d	16b38				17 07			17b13				17 27		17b38			18 07				18 18	18b40		
Manchester Airport ✈	d	16 34							17 04						17 34					17 52		18 10	18 34		
Manchester Piccadilly 10	a	16 48				17 10			17 19						17 49			18 10					18 49		
	d	16 55				17 12			17 25				17 42		17 55			18 12		18 25		18 42	18 57		
Manchester Victoria	d				16 57		17 14					17 27					17 57				18 27				
Ashton-under-Lyne	d				17 07		17 24					17 37					18 07				18 37				
Stalybridge	a	17 07			17 12	17 25	17 29		17 38			17 42			18 08		18 12	18 25			18 41				
	d	17 08			17 12	17 25	17 29		17 38			17 42			18 08		18 12	18 25			18 42				
Mossley (Grtr Manchester)	d				17 17		17 34					17 47					18 17				18 47				
Greenfield	d				17 21		17 38					17 51					18 21				18 51				
Marsden	d				17 29							17 59					18 29				18 59				
Slaithwaite	d				17 34							18 04					18 34				19 04				
Huddersfield	a	17 26			17 42	17 44	17 56		17 56			18 12	18 16		18 26		18 42	18 45		18 56	19 12	19 15	19 26		
	d	17 27	17 33	17 37		17 45			17 57	18 06			18 17		18 27	18 34		18 45		18 57		19 17	19 27	19 31	19 35
Deighton	d		17 36	17 40						18 09						18 37								19 34	19 38
Mirfield	d		17 41	17 45						18 14						18 42			18 47					19 39	19 43
Wakefield Kirkgate	a		17 58													18 58									19 58
Wakefield Westgate	a		18 08													19 08									20 08
Ravensthorpe	d			17 48						18 17									18 50					19 42	
Dewsbury	a	17 36		17 52				←	18 07	18 21				←	18 36				18 54	19 06			19 36	19 46	
	d	17 37		17 55 →				17 55	18 07	18 25 →				18 25	18 37				18 57	19 07			19 37	19 46	
Batley	d							17 58						18 28					19 00					19 49	
Morley	d							18 04						18 34					19 06					19 55	
Cottingley	d							18 08						18 37										19 59	
Leeds 10	a	17 52				18 09		18 18	18 22				18 36	18 45	18 53			19 09	19 17	19 23		19 36	19 52	20 07	
	d	17 57				18 12			18 27				18 38		18 57			19 12		19 27		19 38	19 57		
Garforth	d	18 05							*18 53*						19 05					*19 53*			20 05		
South Milford	a	18e38											18 51									19 51			
Selby	a	18e50											19 01									20 01			
Howden	a																					*20 56*			
Brough	a												19 20									20 20			
Hull	a												19 37									20 37			
York 8	a	18 25				18 37			18 52						19 22			19 35		19 55			20 23		
	d	18 26				18 42			18 59						19 31			19 38					20 26		
Malton	d					19 06												20 02							
Seamer	a					19 23												20 19							
Scarborough	a					19 30												20 30							
Thirsk	a	18 44				19f04									19 47								20 42		
Northallerton	a	18 55				19f15			19 20						19 58								20 50		
Darlington 7	a	19 13				19f22			19 33						20f03			20f12		20 51			21f07		
Yarm	d	19 09													20 13								21 04		
Thornaby	a	19 17													20 21								21 14		
Middlesbrough	a	19 30													20 31								21 25		
Durham	a	19g31							19 51						20f20			20f30		21 09			21f25		
Chester-le-Street	a								19 57									20f37							
Newcastle 8	a	19g49				19f52			20 12						20f37			20f52		21 27			21f42		

For general notes see front of timetable
For details of catering facilities see Directory of Train Operators

- **A** From Selby (Table 41)
- **B** From Wigan Wallgate (Table 82)
- **C** From Hebden Bridge via Brighouse (Table 41)
- **b** Change at Manchester Piccadilly
- **c** Change at Manchester Oxford Road and Manchester Piccadilly
- **e** Change at Leeds
- **f** Change at York
- **g** Change at Northallerton

Liverpool, Manchester Airport and Manchester → Huddersfield → Wakefield, Leeds, Hull, York, Scarborough, Middlesbrough and Newcastle

Network Diagram - see first page of Table 39

		TP 1 ◇	NT A	NT	TP 1 ◇	TP 1 ◇	NT		NT B	TP 1 ◇	NT	TP 1 ◇	NT	NT	TP 1 ◇	NT	TP 1 ◇	TP 1 ◇	NT	NT	TP 1 ◇	NT C	TP 1 ◇	TP 1 ◇	
Liverpool Lime Street 10	d	18 22								19 22					20 22						21b35		22 30		
Warrington Central	d	18 44								19 44					20 44						22b01		22 52		
Birchwood	d	18 49								19 49					20 49						21c39		22 57		
Manchester Oxford Road	d	19 07			19b17					20 07					21 07			21b28			22b23		23 15	23b26	
Manchester Airport ✈	d				19 22					*19 30*		20 22						21 22			22 22		*22 47*	23 22	
Manchester Piccadilly 10	a	19 10			19 38					20 10		20 38			21 10			21 38			22 38		23 17	23 38	
	d	19 12			19 42					20 12		20 42			21 12			21 42			22 42		23 19	23 42	
Manchester Victoria	d			19 27							20 27					21 27				22 27		23 00			
Ashton-under-Lyne	d			19 37							20 37					21 37				22 37		23 09			
Stalybridge	a	19 25		19 41						20 25	20 41				21 25	21 41		21 55		22 41		23 14	23 33		
	d	19 25		19 42						20 25	20 42				21 25	21 42		21 55		22 42		23 14	23 33		
Mossley (Grtr Manchester)	d			19 46							20 46					21 46				22 46		23 19			
Greenfield	d			19 50							20 50					21 50				22 50		23 23			
Marsden	d			19 59							20 59					21 59				22 59		23 31			
Slaithwaite	d			20 03							21 03					22 03				23 03		23 36			
Huddersfield	a	19 44		20 11	20 14					20 44	21 11	21 15			21 44	22 11		22 15		23 11	23 14	23 45	23 50	00 14	
	d	19 45			20 16		20 31		20 35	20 45		21 15	21 31	21 35	21 45			22 15	22 31		23 15		23 51	00 15	
Deighton	d						20 34		20 38				21 34	21 39					22 34						
Mirfield	d		20 07				20 39		20 43				21 39	21 44					22 39						
Wakefield Kirkgate	a								20 58					21 58											
Wakefield Westgate	a								21 08					22 10											
Ravensthorpe	d						20 42						21 42						22 42						
Dewsbury	a		20 12		20 25		20 46					21 25	21 46					22 25	22 46		23 25			00 24	
	d		20 12		20 25		20 46					21 25	21 46					22 25	22 46		23 25			00 24	
Batley	d		20 15				20 49						21 49						22 49						
Morley	d		20 21				20 55						21 55						22 55						
Cottingley	d						20 59						21 59						22 59						
Leeds 10	a	20 09	20 31		20 40		21 07			21 09		21 39	22 08		22 09			22 39	23 07		23 39		00 23	00 46	
	d	20 12			20 45	21 05				21 12		21 42			22 12		22 22	22 42			23 42		00 26	00 49	
Garforth	d		*20 59*									*22 03*						*23 03*							
South Milford	a					21 18											22 34								
Selby	a					21 28											22 44								
Howden	a					*22 39*																			
Brough	a					21 46											23 03								
Hull	a					22 04											23 21								
York 8	a	20 36			21 09					21 40		22 08			22 38			23 12			00 08		01 06	01 29	
	d	20 38			21 12							22 08						23 22							
Malton	d	21 02										22 32													
Seamer	a	21 19										22 49													
Scarborough	a	21 30										23 02													
Thirsk	a				21 28													23 38							
Northallerton	a	*21e03*			21 36					*22 20*					*23 55*			23 55							
Darlington 7	a	*21e16*			21 47					*22 18*					*23 49*			00 06			*01 26*				
Yarm	d																								
Thornaby	a																								
Middlesbrough	a																								
Durham	a	*21e34*			22 05					*22 35*					*00 07*			00 24			*01 44*				
Chester-le-Street	a	*21e45*								*22 45*															
Newcastle 8	a	*21e52*			22 24					*23 00*					*00 42*			00 57			*02 21*				

For general notes see front of timetable
For details of catering facilities see Directory of Train Operators

- **A** From Hebden Bridge via Brighouse (Table 41)
- **B** From Leeds (Table 41)
- **C** From Wigan Wallgate (Table 82)
- **b** Change at Manchester Piccadilly
- **c** Change at Manchester Oxford Road and Manchester Piccadilly
- **e** Change at York

Table 39

Saturdays

Liverpool, Manchester Airport and Manchester → Huddersfield → Wakefield, Leeds, Hull, York, Scarborough, Middlesbrough and Newcastle

Network Diagram - see first page of Table 39

		TP	TP	TP	TP	TP	NT	NT	TP		TP	TP	NT	NT	TP	NT	TP	TP		NT	NT	TP	NT	NT	TP
		1 ◇	1 ◇	1 ◇	1 ◇	1 ◇			1 ◇		1 ◇	1 ◇			1 ◇		1 ◇	1 ◇				1 ◇			1 ◇
																A								B	C
												🛒			🛒		🛒	🛒				🛒			🛒
Liverpool Lime Street 10	d														06 18						06 39	06b47			07 18
Warrington Central	d														06 42							07b15			07 43
Birchwood	d														06 47							07b20			07 48
Manchester Oxford Road	d														07 07		07b13					07b43			08 07
Manchester Airport ✈	d	01 22	03 17		04 35	05 34					05 47	06 23			06 28		07 02					07 34			
Manchester Piccadilly 10	a	01 36	03 31			05 48						06 40			07 10		07 19					07 48			08 10
	d	01 38	03 38		05 39	05 57					06 21	06 53			07 12		07 25	07 35				07 55			08 12
Manchester Victoria	d													06 57							07 39				
Ashton-under-Lyne	d													07 07							07 49				
Stalybridge	a				05 52							07 06		07 11	07 25		07 38				07 54	08 08			08 24
	d				05 52							07 06		07 12	07 25		07 38				07 54	08 08			08 25
Mossley (Grtr Manchester)	d													07 16							07 59				
Greenfield	d													07 20							08 03				
Marsden	d												07 20	07 29							08 11				
Slaithwaite	d												07 24	07 33							08 16				
Huddersfield	a	02 23	04 23		06 10	06 26					06 52	07 24	07 31	07 41	07 44		07 56	08 07			08 24	08 25			08 44
	d	02 27	04 27		06 11	06 27	06 31	06 41			06 54	07 25	07 32		07 45		07 57	08 10		08 14		08 27	08 33	08 37	08 45
Deighton	d						06 34	06 45					07 36							08 17			08 36	08 40	
Mirfield	d						06 39	06 50					07 41			07 54				08 22			08 41	08 45	
Wakefield Kirkgate	a							07 03					07 57											09 00	
Wakefield Westgate	a							07 10					08 08											09 08	
Ravensthorpe	d						06 42													08 25			08 44		
Dewsbury	a					06 36	06 46				07 03				07 54	07 59	08 06	08 19		08 28		08 37	08 48		
	d					06 37	06 46				07 03				07 55	08 00	08 07	08 20		08 28		08 37	08 53 ↪		
Batley	d						06 49									08 03				08 31					
Morley	d						06 55									08 09				08 37					
Cottingley	d						06 59													08 40					
Leeds 10	a	02 50	04 50		06 32	06 52	07 07				07 20	07 47			08 10	08 18	08 23	08 35		08 51		08 54			09 06
	d	02 50	04 50		06 35	06 55					07 23	07 50			08 12		08 27	08 38				08 57			09 12
Garforth	d										07 52	08 11				08 53	08 35					09 05			
South Milford	a											08 22										09c38			
Selby	a										07 43	08 35						08 58				09c54			
Howden	a										07 52														
Brough	a										08 03														
Hull	a										08 21							09 31							
York 8	a	03 35	05 28		07 02	07 22						08 20			08 34		08 53					09 25			
	d		05 40	06 38	07 06	07 25			07 32			08 22			08 38		08 57					09 26			
Malton	d			07 02		07 49									09 02										10 02
Seamer	a			07 19		08 06									09 19										10 19
Scarborough	a			07 30		08 14									09 30										10 30
Thirsk	a		06 01		07 22				07 54			08 44										09 45			
Northallerton	a		06 17		07 30				08 02			08 55			09e02		09 17					09 54			
Darlington 7	a		06 28		07 41	08e08			09 14			09e00			09e14		09 29					10e00			
Yarm	d								08 16			09 12										10 10			
Thornaby	a		06 52						08 24			09 22										10 20			
Middlesbrough	a		07 01						08 32			09 32										10 30			
Durham	a		07f33		07 59	08e26						09e18			09e31		09 46					10e17			
Chester-le-Street	a		07f48		08 05	08g44									09e44							10e40			
Newcastle 8	a		07f50		08 19	08e43						09e34			09e49		10 04					10e34			

For general notes see front of timetable
For details of catering facilities see Directory of Train Operators

- **A** From Hebden Bridge via Brighouse (Table 41)
- **B** From Selby (Table 41)
- **C** Also stops at Widnes 0736 and Irlam 0753
- **b** Change at Manchester Piccadilly
- **c** Change at Leeds
- **e** Change at York
- **f** Change at Darlington
- **g** Change at York and Durham

Table 39

Saturdays

Liverpool, Manchester Airport and Manchester → Huddersfield → Wakefield, Leeds, Hull, York, Scarborough, Middlesbrough and Newcastle

Network Diagram - see first page of Table 39

		NT	TP [1]◇ ⊥	NT A	NT	NT	TP [1]◇	TP [1]◇ B ⊥	NT	NT C	TP [1]◇ ⊥	TP [1]◇ ⊥	NT A	NT	NT	TP [1]◇	TP [1]◇ ⊥	NT	NT C	TP [1]◇ ⊥	TP [1]◇	NT A
Liverpool Lime Street [10]	d				07 18	07 47		*07b47*			08 21				08 48		*08b52*			09 22		
Warrington Central	d							*08b16*			08 44						*09b17*			09 44		
Birchwood	d							*08b21*			08 49						*09c03*			09 49		
Manchester Oxford Road	d						*08 21*	*08b45*			09 07					*09 27*	*09b43*			10 07		
Manchester Airport ✈	d		08 04				*08 07*	08 33				09 04				*09 07*	09 34				10 04	
Manchester Piccadilly [10] ⛴	a		08 19					08 49			09 10	09 21					09 48			10 10	10 19	
	d		08 25				08 42	08 57			09 12	09 27				09 42	09 57			10 12	10 27	
Manchester Victoria ⛴	d				08 27	08 57								09 27	09 57							
Ashton-under-Lyne	d				08 37	09 07								09 37	10 07							
Stalybridge	a				08 41	09 13					09 25			09 42	10 13					10 25		
	d				08 42						09 25			09 42						10 25		
Mossley (Grtr Manchester)	d				08 46									09 47								
Greenfield	d				08 50									09 51								
Marsden	d				08 59									09 59								
Slaithwaite	d				09 03									10 04								
Huddersfield	a		08 55		09 11		09 14	09 26			09 44	09 56		10 12		10 15	10 26			10 44	10 56	
	d		08 57				09 16	09 27	09 31	09 35	09 45	09 57				10 17	10 27	10 31	10 35	10 45	10 57	
Deighton	d								09 34	09 38								10 34	10 38			
Mirfield	d			09 07					09 39	09 43			10 07					10 39	10 43			11 07
Wakefield Kirkgate	a									09 58									10 56			
Wakefield Westgate	a									10 10									11 08			
Ravensthorpe	d								09 42									10 42				
Dewsbury	a	←	09 06	09 12				09 36	09 46			10 06	10 12				10 36	10 46			11 06	11 12
	d	08 53	09 07	09 12				09 37	09 46			10 07	10 12				10 37	10 46			11 07	11 12
Batley	d	08 56		09 15					09 49				10 15					10 49				11 15
Morley	d	09 02		09 21					09 55				10 21					10 55				11 21
Cottingley	d	09 06							09 59									10 59				
Leeds [10]	a	09 16	09 22	09 31			09 36	09 52	10 07		10 09	10 22	10 31			10 36	10 52	11 07		11 09	11 22	11 31
	d		09 27				09 38	09 57			10 12	10 27				10 38	10 57			11 12	11 27	
Garforth	d			*09 53*				10 05					*10 53*				11 05					*11 53*
South Milford	a							*10e38*									*11e38*					
Selby	a						09 58	*10e53*								10 58	*11e53*					
Howden	a						*10 22*									*11 49*						
Brough	a						10 17									11 17						
Hull	a						10 34									11 34						
York [8]	a		09 52					10 23			10 35	10 52					11 23			11 35	11 52	
	d		09 56					10 26			10 38	10 54					11 26			11 38	11 54	
Malton	d										11 02									12 02		
Seamer	a										11 19									12 19		
Scarborough	a										11 30									12 30		
Thirsk	a		*10 20*					10 45									11 42					
Northallerton	a		10 25					10 54				11 15					11 55				12 15	
Darlington [7]	a		10 36					*11f01*			*11f16*	11 26					*12f01*			*12f15*	12 26	
Yarm	d							11 10									12 10					
Thornaby	a							11 20									12 18					
Middlesbrough	a							11 30									12 30					
Durham	a		10 54					*11f20*			*11f33*	11 44					*12f18*			*12f33*	12 45	
Chester-le-Street	a		11 00																	*12f40*		
Newcastle [8] ⛴	a		11 15					*11f36*			*11f57*	12 02					*12f35*			*12f57*	13 01	

For general notes see front of timetable
For details of catering facilities see Directory of Train Operators

- **A** From Hebden Bridge via Brighouse (Table 41)
- **B** Also stops at Heald Green 0837
- **C** From Selby (Table 41)
- **b** Change at Manchester Piccadilly
- **c** Change at Manchester Oxford Road and Manchester Piccadilly
- **e** Change at Leeds
- **f** Change at York

Table 39

Saturdays

Liverpool, Manchester Airport and Manchester → Huddersfield → Wakefield, Leeds, Hull, York, Scarborough, Middlesbrough and Newcastle

Network Diagram - see first page of Table 39

		NT	NT	TP	TP	NT	NT	TP	TP		NT	NT	NT	TP	TP	NT	NT	TP		TP	NT	NT	NT	TP	TP
				1 ◇	1 ◇			1 ◇	1 ◇					1 ◇	1 ◇			1 ◇		1 ◇				1 ◇	1 ◇
							A				B						A				B				
				🛒	🛒			🛒	🛒						🛒			🛒		🛒					🛒
Liverpool Lime Street 10	d		09 48		09b52			10 22					10 48		10b52			11 22					11 48		11b52
Warrington Central	d				10b17			10 44							11b17			11 44							12b17
Birchwood	d				10c03			10 49							11c03			11 49							12c03
Manchester Oxford Road	d			10 27	10b43			11 07						11 27	11b43			12 07						12 27	12b43
Manchester Airport ✈	d			10 07	10 34				11 04					11 07	11 34					12 04				12 07	12 34
Manchester Piccadilly 10	a				10 48			11 10	11 19						11 48			12 10		12 19					12 48
	d			10 42	10 57			11 12	11 27					11 42	11 57			12 12		12 27				12 42	12 57
Manchester Victoria	d	10 27	10 57									11 27	11 57									12 27	12 57		
Ashton-under-Lyne	d	10 37	11 07									11 37	12 07									12 37	13 07		
Stalybridge	a	10 41	11 13					11 25				11 41	12 13					12 25				12 41	13 13		
	d	10 42						11 25				11 42						12 25				12 42			
Mossley (Grtr Manchester)	d	10 47										11 47										12 47			
Greenfield	d	10 51										11 51										12 51			
Marsden	d	10 59										11 59										12 59			
Slaithwaite	d	11 04										12 04										13 04			
Huddersfield	a	11 12		11 15	11 26			11 44	11 56			12 12		12 15	12 26			12 44		12 56		13 12		13 15	13 26
	d			11 17	11 27	11 31	11 35	11 45	11 57					12 17	12 27	12 31	12 35	12 45		12 57				13 17	13 27
Deighton	d					11 34	11 38									12 34	12 38								
Mirfield	d					11 39	11 43				12 07					12 39	12 43				13 07				
Wakefield Kirkgate	a						11 56										12 56								
Wakefield Westgate	a						12 08										13 08								
Ravensthorpe	d					11 42										12 42									
Dewsbury	a				11 36	11 46			12 06		12 12				12 36	12 46				13 06	13 12				13 36
	d				11 37	11 46			12 07		12 12				12 37	12 46				13 07	13 12				13 37
Batley	d					11 49					12 15					12 49					13 15				
Morley	d					11 55					12 21					12 55					13 21				
Cottingley	d					11 59										12 59									
Leeds 10	a			11 36	11 52	12 07		12 09	12 22		12 31			12 36	12 52	13 07		13 09		13 22	13 31			13 36	13 52
	d			11 38	11 57			12 12	12 27					12 38	12 57			13 12		13 27				13 38	13 57
Garforth	d				12 05						12 53				13 05						13 53				14 05
South Milford	a				12e38										13e38										14e38
Selby	a			11 58	12e53									12 58	13e53									13 58	14e52
Howden	a			12 19										13 52										14 13	
Brough	a			12 17										13 17										14 17	
Hull	a			12 34										13 34										14 34	
York 8	a				12 23			12 35	12 52						13 23			13 35		13 52					14 23
	d				12 26			12 38	12 54						13 26			13 38		13 54					14 26
Malton	d							13 02										14 02							
Seamer	a							13 19										14 19							
Scarborough	a							13 30										14 30							
Thirsk	a				12 46										13 43										14 45
Northallerton	a				12 55				13 23						13 55					14 22					15 00
Darlington 7	a				13f01			13f11	13 34						14f01			14f17		14 34					14f59
Yarm	d				13 10										14 10										15 15
Thornaby	a				13 20										14 18										15 27
Middlesbrough	a				13 30										14 30										15 34
Durham	a				13f18			13f28	13 52						14f18			14f35		14 51					15f17
Chester-le-Street	a								13 58																
Newcastle 8	a				13f35			13f50	14 13						14f35			14f54		15 12					15f34

For general notes see front of timetable
For details of catering facilities see Directory of Train Operators

- **A** From Selby (Table 41)
- **B** From Hebden Bridge via Brighouse (Table 41)
- **b** Change at Manchester Piccadilly
- **c** Change at Manchester Oxford Road and Manchester Piccadilly
- **e** Change at Leeds
- **f** Change at York

Liverpool, Manchester Airport and Manchester → Huddersfield → Wakefield, Leeds, Hull, York, Scarborough, Middlesbrough and Newcastle

Network Diagram - see first page of Table 39

		NT	NT	TP	TP		NT	NT	NT	TP	TP	NT	NT	TP		TP	NT	NT	NT	TP	TP	NT	NT		TP
				1 ◇	1 ◇					1 ◇	1 ◇			1 ◇		1 ◇				1 ◇	1 ◇				1 ◇
			A				B						A				B						A		
Liverpool Lime Street 10	d			12 22					12 48		*12b52*			13 22					13 48		*13b52*				14 22
Warrington Central	d			12 44							*13b17*			13 44							*14b17*				14 44
Birchwood	d			12 49							*13c03*			13 49							*14c03*				14 49
Manchester Oxford Road	d			13 07						*13 27*	*13b43*			14 07						*14 27*	*14b43*				15 07
Manchester Airport ✈	d				13 04					*13 07*	13 34					14 04				*14 07*	14 34				
Manchester Piccadilly 10	a			13 10	13 19						13 48			14 10		14 19					14 48				15 10
	d			13 12	13 27					13 42	13 57			14 12		14 27				14 42	14 57				15 12
Manchester Victoria	d							13 27	13 57									14 27	14 57						
Ashton-under-Lyne	d							13 37	14 07									14 37	15 07						
Stalybridge	a			13 25				13 41	14 13					14 25				14 41	15 13						15 25
	d			13 25				13 42						14 25				14 42							15 25
Mossley (Grtr Manchester)	d							13 47										14 47							
Greenfield	d							13 51										14 51							
Marsden	d							13 59										14 59							
Slaithwaite	d							14 04										15 04							
Huddersfield	a			13 44	13 56			14 12		14 15	14 26			14 44		14 56		15 12		15 15	15 26				15 44
	d	13 31	13 35	13 45	13 57					14 17	14 27	14 31	14 35	14 45		14 57				15 17	15 27	15 31	15 35		15 45
Deighton	d	13 34	13 38									14 34	14 38									15 34	15 38		
Mirfield	d	13 39	13 43				14 07					14 39	14 43				15 07					15 39	15 43		
Wakefield Kirkgate	a		13 56										14 58										15 58		
Wakefield Westgate	a		14 08										15 08										16 08		
Ravensthorpe	d	13 42										14 42										15 42			
Dewsbury	a	13 46			14 06		14 12				14 36	14 46				15 06	15 12				15 36	15 46			
	d	13 46			14 07		14 12				14 37	14 46				15 07	15 12				15 37	15 46			
Batley	d	13 49					14 15					14 49					15 15					15 49			
Morley	d	13 55					14 21					14 55					15 21					15 55			
Cottingley	d	13 59										14 59										15 59			
Leeds 10	a	14 07		14 09	14 22		14 31			14 36	14 52	15 07		15 09		15 22	15 31			15 36	15 52	16 07			16 09
	d			14 12	14 27					14 38	14 57			15 12		15 27				15 38	15 57				16 12
Garforth	d						*14 53*				15 05						*15 53*				16 05				
South Milford	a										*15e38*										*16e38*				
Selby	a									14 58	*15e53*									15 58	*16e54*				
Howden	a									*15 50*										*16 51*					
Brough	a									15 17										16 17					
Hull	a									15 34										16 34					
York 8	a			14 35	14 52						15 23			15 35		15 52					16 23				16 35
	d			14 38	14 54						15 26			15 38							16 26				16 38
Malton	d			15 02										16 02											17 02
Seamer	a			15 19										16 19											17 19
Scarborough	a			15 30										16 30											17 30
Thirsk	a										15 45										16 44				
Northallerton	a				15 22						15 55										16 55				
Darlington 7	a			*15f15*	15 34						*16f00*			*16f12*		16 29					*17f00*				*17f16*
Yarm	d										16 09										17 09				
Thornaby	a										16 20										17 23				
Middlesbrough	a										16 30										17 34				
Durham	a			*15f33*	15 51						*16f17*			*16f29*							*17f17*				*17f33*
Chester-le-Street	a				15 57																				*17f43*
Newcastle 8	a			*15f55*	16 14						*16f34*			*16f51*		16 59					*17f34*				*17f58*

For general notes see front of timetable
For details of catering facilities see Directory of Train Operators

A From Selby (Table 41)
B From Hebden Bridge via Brighouse (Table 41)
b Change at Manchester Piccadilly
c Change at Manchester Oxford Road and Manchester Piccadilly
e Change at Leeds
f Change at York

Liverpool, Manchester Airport and Manchester → Huddersfield → Wakefield, Leeds, Hull, York, Scarborough, Middlesbrough and Newcastle

Network Diagram - see first page of Table 39

		TP	NT	NT	NT	TP	TP	NT	NT		TP	TP	NT	NT	TP	TP	NT	NT		NT	NT	TP	NT	TP	NT
		1 ◇				1 ◇	1 ◇				1 ◇	1 ◇			1 ◇	1 ◇						1 ◇		1 ◇	
			A						B		C		A					B							
		🚲					🚲																		
Liverpool Lime Street 10	d				14 48		*14b52*				15 22					*15b52*	15 48					16 22			
Warrington Central	d						*15b17*				15 44					*16b17*						16 44			
Birchwood	d						*15c03*				15 49											16 49			
Manchester Oxford Road	d					*15 27*	*15b43*				16 07				*16 27*	*16b38*						17 07			
Manchester Airport ✈	d	15 04				*15 07*	15 34					16 04			*16 07*	16 34								17 04	
Manchester Piccadilly 10	a	15 19					15 48				16 10	16 19				16 48						17 10		17 19	
	d	15 27				15 42	15 57				16 12	16 27			16 42	16 55						17 12		17 25	
Manchester Victoria	d			15 27	15 57									16 27			16 57								
Ashton-under-Lyne	d			15 37	16 07									16 37			17 07								
Stalybridge	a			15 41	16 13						16 25			16 41		17 08	17 13					17 25		17 38	
	d			15 42							16 25			16 42		17 08						17 25		17 38	
Mossley (Grtr Manchester)	d			15 47										16 47											
Greenfield	d			15 51										16 51											
Marsden	d			15 59										16 59							17 29				
Slaithwaite	d			16 04										17 04							17 33				
Huddersfield	a	15 56		16 12		16 15	16 26				16 44	16 56		17 12	17 15	17 26					17 41	17 44		17 56	
	d	15 57				16 17	16 27	16 31	16 35		16 45	16 57			17 17	17 27		17 33		17 37		17 45		17 58	18 06
Deighton	d							16 34	16 38									17 36		17 40					18 09
Mirfield	d		16 07					16 39	16 43				17 07					17 41		17 45					18 14
Wakefield Kirkgate	a								16 58									17 58							
Wakefield Westgate	a								17 08									18 06							
Ravensthorpe	d							16 42												17 48					18 17
Dewsbury	a	16 06	16 12				16 36	16 46				17 06	17 12			17 36				17 52			←	18 07	18 21
	d	16 07	16 12				16 37	16 46				17 07	17 12			17 37				17 55 →			17 55	18 07	18 25 →
Batley	d		16 15					16 49					17 15										17 58		
Morley	d		16 21					16 55					17 21										18 04		
Cottingley	d							16 59															18 08		
Leeds 10	a	16 22	16 31			16 36	16 52	17 07			17 09	17 22	17 31		17 37	17 52						18 09	18 18	18 22	
	d	16 27				16 38	16 57				17 12	17 24			17 38	17 57						18 12		18 27	
Garforth	d		*16 53*				17 05					17 34	*17 53*			18 05								*18 53*	
South Milford	a						*17e40*									*18e38*									
Selby	a					16 59	*17e53*								17 59	*18e50*									
Howden	a					*17 47*									18 08										
Brough	a					17 16									18 20										
Hull	a					17 36									18 37										
York 8	a	16 52					17 22				17 38	17 57				18 25						18 35		18 52	
	d	17 02					17 26				17 43	18 00				18 26						18 38		18 56	
Malton	d						17 50					18 24										19 02			
Seamer	a						18 07					18 41										19 19			
Scarborough	a						18 17					18 51										19 30			
Thirsk	a	17 20									17 59					18 44						*19f20*			
Northallerton	a	17 28									18 09					18 55								19 20	
Darlington 7	a	17 39					*18f00*				*18f15*					*19f00*						*19f14*		19 33	
Yarm	d										18 24					19 09									
Thornaby	a										18 32					19 17									
Middlesbrough	a										18 42					19 30									
Durham	a	17 57					*18f17*				*18f32*					*19f17*						*19f31*		19 51	
Chester-le-Street	a	18 03									*18f39*													19 57	
Newcastle 8	a	18 18					*18f34*				*18f56*					*19f34*						*19f53*		20 12	

For general notes see front of timetable
For details of catering facilities see Directory of Train Operators

A From Hebden Bridge via Brighouse (Table 41)
B From Selby (Table 41)
C Also stops at Cross Gates 1718
b Change at Manchester Piccadilly
c Change at Manchester Oxford Road and Manchester Piccadilly
e Change at Leeds
f Change at York

Table 39

Saturdays

Liverpool, Manchester Airport and Manchester → Huddersfield → Wakefield, Leeds, Hull, York, Scarborough, Middlesbrough and Newcastle

Network Diagram - see first page of Table 39

		NT	TP	NT	TP		NT	NT	TP	NT	TP	NT	TP	TP		NT	NT	TP	NT	NT	TP	TP	NT		NT
			1 ◇		1 ◇				1 ◇		1 ◇		1 ◇	1 ◇				1 ◇			1 ◇	1 ◇			
								A		B							A		B						A
Liverpool Lime Street 10	d	16 18			16b52		16 48		17 22					17b52				18 22							
Warrington Central	d				17b17				17 44					18b17				18 44							
Birchwood	d								17 49					18c08				18 49							
Manchester Oxford Road	d		17 27		17b38				18 07				18 18	18b39				19 07			19b17				
Manchester Airport ✈	d				17 34						17 52		18 10	18 34							19 15				
Manchester Piccadilly 10	a				17 49				18 10					18 52				19 10			19 38				
	d		17 42		17 55				18 12		18 27		18 41	18 57				19 12			19 42				
Manchester Victoria	d	17 27					17 57					18 27								19 27					
Ashton-under-Lyne	d	17 37					18 07					18 37								19 37					
Stalybridge	a	17 41			18 08		18 13		18 25			18 41						19 25		19 41					
	d	17 42			18 08				18 25			18 42						19 25		19 42					
Mossley (Grtr Manchester)	d	17 47										18 47								19 46					
Greenfield	d	17 51										18 51								19 50					
Marsden	d	17 59										18 59								19 59					
Slaithwaite	d	18 04										19 04								20 03					
Huddersfield	a	18 12	18 16		18 26				18 45		18 56	19 12	19 15	19 26				19 44		20 11	20 14				
	d		18 17		18 27			18 34	18 45		18 57		19 17	19 27		19 31	19 35	19 45			20 16		20 31		20 35
Deighton	d							18 37								19 34	19 38						20 34		20 38
Mirfield	d							18 42		18 47						19 39	19 43		20 07				20 39		20 43
Wakefield Kirkgate	a							18 58									19 58								20 58
Wakefield Westgate	a							19 08									20 08								21 07
Ravensthorpe	d									18 50						19 42							20 42		
Dewsbury	a			←	18 36					18 54	19 06			19 36		19 46			20 12		20 25		20 46		
	d			18 25	18 37					18 57	19 07			19 37		19 46			20 12		20 25		20 46		
Batley	d			18 28						19 00						19 49			20 15				20 49		
Morley	d			18 34						19 06						19 55			20 21				20 55		
Cottingley	d			18 37												19 59							20 59		
Leeds 10	a		18 36	18 45	18 53				19 09	19 18	19 24		19 36	19 52		20 07		20 09	20 32		20 40		21 07		
	d		18 38		18 57				19 12		19 27		19 38	19 57				20 12			20 45	21 05			
Garforth	d				19 05						19 53			20 05					21 00						
South Milford	a		18 51										19 51									21 18			
Selby	a		19 01										20 01									21 28			
Howden	a		19 17																			21 45			
Brough	a		19 20										20 20									21 46			
Hull	a		19 37										20 37									22 04			
York 8	a				19 22				19 35		19 58			20 24				20 36			21 09				
	d				19 26				19 38					20 26				20 38			21 12				
Malton	d								20 02									21 02							
Seamer	a								20 19									21 19							
Scarborough	a								20 30									21 30							
Thirsk	a				19 42									20 43							21 28				
Northallerton	a				19 50									20 51				21e26			21 36				
Darlington 7	a				20e02				20e17					21e03				21e14			21 47				
Yarm	d				20 04									21 05											
Thornaby	a				20 12									21 14											
Middlesbrough	a				20 23									21 25											
Durham	a				20e22				20e34					21e21				21e56			22 05				
Chester-le-Street	a								20e41												22 17				
Newcastle 8	a				20e36				20e54					21e41				22e14			22 24				

For general notes see front of timetable
For details of catering facilities see Directory of Train Operators

- **A** From Selby (Table 41)
- **B** From Hebden Bridge via Brighouse (Table 41)
- **b** Change at Manchester Piccadilly
- **c** Change at Manchester Oxford Road and Manchester Piccadilly
- **e** Change at York

Table 39

Saturdays

Liverpool, Manchester Airport and Manchester → Huddersfield → Wakefield, Leeds, Hull, York, Scarborough, Middlesbrough and Newcastle

Network Diagram - see first page of Table 39

		TP 1◇	NT	TP 1◇	NT	NT	TP 1◇	NT	TP 1◇	TP 1◇	NT	NT	NT	TP 1◇	NT	NT	TP 1◇	TP 1◇	TP	TP 1◇	NT	TP
											A	B			C	D	B	A	A 🚌	B	A 🚌	A 🚌
Liverpool Lime Street 10	d	19 22					20 22										22 30	22 30				
Warrington Central	d	19 44					20 44										22 52	22 52				
Birchwood	d	19 49					20 49										22 57	22 57				
Manchester Oxford Road	d	20 07					21 07			21b28				22b16			23 15	23 15		23b26		23 33
Manchester Airport ✈	d	*19 30*		20 22						21 22				22 22			22 47	22 47		23 22		23 22
Manchester Piccadilly 10	a	20 10		20 38			21 10			21 37				22 38			23 17	23 17		23 38		
	d	20 12		20 42			21 12			21 42				22 42			23 19	23 19		23 42		23 50
Manchester Victoria	d		20 27					21 27					22 27		23 00	23 00						
Ashton-under-Lyne	d		20 37					21 37					22 37		23 09	23 09						
Stalybridge	a	20 25	20 41				21 25	21 41		21 55			22 41		23 14	23 14	23 33	23 33				00 10
	d	20 25	20 42				21 25	21 42		21 55			22 42		23 14	23 14	23 33	23 33				00 10
Mossley (Grtr Manchester)	d		20 46					21 46					22 46		23 19	23 19						
Greenfield	d		20 50					21 50					22 50		23 23	23a25					23 32	
Marsden	d		20 59		21 19			21 59					22 59		23 31						23 57	
Slaithwaite	d		21 03		21 23			22 03					23 03		23 36						00 04	
Huddersfield	a	20 44	21 11	21 15	21 30		21 44	22 11		22 14			23 11	23 14	23 44		23 51	23 51		00 14	00 22	00 55
	d	20 45		21 15	21 31	21 35	21 45			22 15	22 19	22 31		23 15			23 51		23 59	00 15		00 55
Deighton	d				21 34	21 39					22 22	22 34										
Mirfield	d				21 39	21 44					22 27	22 39										
Wakefield Kirkgate	a					21 58																
Wakefield Westgate	a					22 10																
Ravensthorpe	d				21 42						22 30	22 42										
Dewsbury	a			21 25	21 46					22 25	22 34	22 46		23 25					00 15	00 24		01 15
	d			21 25	21 46					22 25	22 34	22 46		23 25					00 15	00 24		01 15
Batley	d				21 49						22 37	22 49										
Morley	d				21 55						22 43	22 55										
Cottingley	d				21 59						22 47	22 59										
Leeds 10	a	21 09		21 39	22 07		22 09			22 39	22 55	23 07		23 39			00 13		00 35	00 39		01 40
	d	21 12		21 42			22 12		22 22	22 42				23 42			00 15			00 42		01 40
Garforth	d	*21 56*								*23 06*												
South Milford	a								22 35													
Selby	a								22 45													
Howden	a																					
Brough	a								23 04													
Hull	a								23 21													
York 8	a	21 40		22 05			22 38			23 09				00 08			00 41			01 08		02 25
	d			22 08																		
Malton	d			22 32																		
Seamer	a			22 49																		
Scarborough	a			23 02																		
Thirsk	a																					
Northallerton	a																					
Darlington 7	a			*23c07*																		
Yarm	d																					
Thornaby	a																					
Middlesbrough	a																					
Durham	a			*23c25*																		
Chester-le-Street	a																					
Newcastle 8	a			*23c46*																		

For general notes see front of timetable
For details of catering facilities see Directory of Train Operators

- **A** 2 February to 22 March
- **B** Until 26 January and from 29 March
- **C** Until 26 January and from 29 March. From Wigan Wallgate (Table 82)
- **D** 2 February to 22 March. From Wigan Wallgate (Table 82)
- **b** Change at Manchester Piccadilly
- **c** Change at York

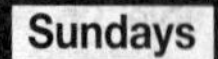

Liverpool, Manchester Airport and Manchester → Huddersfield → Leeds, Hull, York, Scarborough, Middlesbrough and Newcastle

Network Diagram - see first page of Table 39

		TP	TP	TP	TP	TP	TP	TP	NT	NT	TP	TP	NT	TP	NT	TP	TP	TP	TP	TP	NT	NT	TP	NT	TP
		1 ◇	1 ◇		1 ◇		1 ◇	1 ◇				1 ◇		1 ◇			1 ◇	1 ◇	1 ◇	1 ◇			1 ◇		1 ◇
		A	B	A	B	A	B	A	A	B	A	B	A	A	B	A		B	A		A				
				🚌		🚌			🚌		🚌		🚌			🚌									
Liverpool Lime Street 10	d																			08 22					
Warrington Central	d																			08 44					
Birchwood	d																			08 49					
Manchester Oxford Road	d																			09 07					
Manchester Airport ✈	d		01 22	01 35	04 42	04 45	06 22				06 22	07 22						08 22	07 41	*08 47*			*08 51*		09 25
Manchester Piccadilly 10	a		01 36	02 00	04 56	05 05	06 38				06 42	07 37						08 37	07 54	09 10					09 41
	d		01 42	02 00	05 02	05 05	06 42				06 42	07 42						08 42	07 57	09 12			09 30		09 42
Manchester Victoria	a																		08 11						
	d														08 18	08 25			08 30		09 18				
Ashton-under-Lyne	d														08 28						09 28				
Stalybridge	a						06 55				07 02	07 55			08 32	08 45		08 55			09 33		09 43		
	d						06 55				07 02	07 55			08 33			08 55					09 43		
Mossley (Grtr Manchester)	d														08 37										
Greenfield	d														08 41										
Marsden	d														08 50							09 40			
Slaithwaite	d														08 54							09 44			
Huddersfield	a		02 12	03 00	05 32	06 05	07 11				07 47	08 11			09 02			09 11	09 15	09 41		09 51	10 01		10 14
	d		02 13	03 00	05 33	06 05	07 12		07 30	07 48	07 47	08 12						09 12	09 18	09 42		09 51	10 02		10 14
Deighton	d								07 38	07 51												09 55			
Mirfield	d								07 48	07 56												10 00			
Ravensthorpe	d								07 53	07 59												10 03			
Dewsbury	a						07 22		07 59	08 03	08 07	08 22						09 22	09 27			10 06		←	10 25
	d						07 22		07 59	08 08	08 07	08 22						09 22	09 28			10 10 →		10 10	10 25
Batley	d								08 07	08 11			←											10 13	
Morley	d								08 17	08 17			08 17											10 19	
Cottingley	d								→	08 20			08 25											10 22	
Leeds 10	a		02 34	03 35	05 54	06 40	07 39			08 28	08 32	08 39	08 40					09 38	09 42	10 03			10 23	10 30	10 41
	d	00 45	02 38	03 35	05 58	06 40	07 43	07 42				08 40		08 40			09 10	09 40	09 42	10 06			10 25		10 42
Garforth	d										*09 07*	*09 07*					09 18	*09 59*		*10 41*					
South Milford	a																						10 38		
Selby	a																						10 47		
Howden	a																								
Brough	a																						11 07		
Hull	a																						11 24		
York 8	a	01 35	03 04	04 20	06 24	07 25	08 09	08 32				09 07		09 07			09 35	10 06	10 08	10 29					11 09
	d						08 10	08 35				09 10		09 10			09 38	10 10	10 10	10 32					11 10
Malton	d																10 02								
Seamer	a																10 19								
Scarborough	a																10 27								
Thirsk	a						08 27	08 51										10 26	10 27	*11 09*					
Northallerton	a						08 35	08 59				09 30		09 30				10 34	10 35	*11 20*					11 32
Darlington 7	a						*09 32*	*09 32*				09 42		09 42			*10b35*			11 02					11 44
Yarm	d						08 49	09 13										10 49	10 49						
Thornaby	a						08 57	09 21										10 57	10 57						
Middlesbrough	a						09 10	09 32										11 10	11 10						
Durham	a						*09c50*	*09c50*				09 59		09 59			*10b53*			11 20					12 01
Chester-le-Street	a																			11 26					
Newcastle 8	a						*10c06*	*10c06*				10 18		10 18			*11b09*			11 41					12 20

For general notes see front of timetable
For details of catering facilities see Directory of Train Operators

A 3 February to 23 March
B Until 27 January and from 30 March
b Change at York
c Change at Northallerton

Table 39

Sundays

Liverpool, Manchester Airport and Manchester → Huddersfield → Leeds, Hull, York, Scarborough, Middlesbrough and Newcastle

Network Diagram - see first page of Table 39

		TP 1 ◇		NT	TP 1 ◇	TP 1 ◇	NT	TP 1 ◇	TP 1 ◇	NT	TP 1 ◇	TP 1 ◇	NT	TP 1 ◇	TP 1 ◇	NT	TP 1 ◇	TP 1 ◇	TP 1 ◇	NT	TP 1 ◇	TP 1 ◇	TP 1 ◇	NT	TP 1 ◇
Liverpool Lime Street 10	d	09 22				09b30		09c57	11 22			11b30		12c00	13 22		13e30	13 52	14 22			14 52	15 22		
Warrington Central	d	09 45						10c32	11 44					12c35	13 44			14 18	14 44			15 18	15 44		
Birchwood	d	09 50						10c37	11 49					12c40	13 49				14 49				15 49		
Manchester Oxford Road	d	10 07							12 07						14 07				15 07				16 07		
Manchester Airport ✈	d	09 47			10 22	10 47		11 22	11 47		12 22	12 46		13 22	13 47		14 22	14f27	14 47		15g17	15f27	15 47		16 22
Manchester Piccadilly 10	a	10 10			10 38			11 38	12 10		12 37			13 38	14 10		14 38		15 10		15 39		16 10		16 38
	d	10 12			10 42	11 12		11 42	12 12		12 42	13 12		13 42	14 12		14 42	14 56	15 12		15 42	16 00	16 12		16 42
Manchester Victoria	a																								
	d			10 18						12 18						14 18								16 18	
Ashton-under-Lyne	d			10 28						12 28						14 28								16 28	
Stalybridge	a	10 25		10 32		11 25			12 25	12 32		13 24			14 25	14 32			15 25				16 25	16 32	
	d	10 25		10 33		11 25			12 25	12 33		13 25			14 25	14 33			15 25				16 25	16 33	
Mossley (Grtr Manchester)	d			10 37						12 37						14 37								16 37	
Greenfield	d			10 41						12 41						14 41								16 41	
Marsden	d			10 50			11 47			12 50			13 47			14 50				15 48				16 50	
Slaithwaite	d			10 54			11 51			12 54			13 51			14 54				15 52				16 54	
Huddersfield	a	10 43		11 02	11 11	11 43	11 58	12 11	12 43	13 02	13 11	13 43	13 58	14 11	14 43	15 02	15 11	15 29	15 43	15 59	16 11	16 29	16 43	17 02	17 11
	d	10 44			11 12	11 44	11 58	12 12	12 44		13 12	13 44	13 58	14 12	14 44		15 12	15 30	15 44	15 59	16 12	16 30	16 44		17 12
Deighton	d						12 02						14 02							16 03					
Mirfield	d						12 07						14 07							16 08					
Ravensthorpe	d						12 10						14 10							16 11					
Dewsbury	a				11 21		12 13	12 21			13 21		14 13	14 21			15 21			16 14	16 21				17 21
	d				11 22		12 14	12 22			13 22		14 14	14 22			15 22			16 15	16 22				17 22
Batley	d						12 17						14 17							16 18					
Morley	d						12 23						14 23							16 24					
Cottingley	d						12 26						14 26							16 27					
Leeds 10	a	11 05			11 38	12 05	12 34	12 37	13 07		13 37	14 08	14 34	14 37	15 06		15 37	15 52	16 06	16 35	16 37	16 51	17 06		17 37
	d	11 10			11 40	12 10		12 40	13 10		13 40	14 10		14 40	15 10		15 40	15 55	16 10		16 40	16 54	17 10		17 40
Garforth	d	11 18				12 36			13 18			14 36			15 18				16 36				17 18		
South Milford	a					12 22						14 23							16 24						
Selby	a					12 32						14 33							16 34			17 13			
Howden	a					12 51													16 51						
Brough	a					12 53						14 54							16 53			17 36			
Hull	a					13 11						15 12							17 11			17 53			
York 8	a	11 36			12 05			13 07	13 37		14 05			15 07	15 40		16 05	16 19			17 09		17 37		18 09
	d	11 38			12 10			13 10	13 38		14 11			15 12	15 44		16 10	16 23			17 10		17 38		18 10
Malton	d	12 02							14 02						16 08								18 02		
Seamer	a	12 19							14 19						16 25								18 19		
Scarborough	a	12 30							14 29						16 33								18 29		
Thirsk	a				12 27						14 27				16h09			16 39							18 27
Northallerton	a				12 35			13 32	14h25		14 35			15 32	16h19			16 47			17 32				18 35
Darlington 7	a	12j13			13k02			13 44	14m13		15h03			15 44	16h34		16 41	17n01			17 44		18h14		19h01
Yarm	d				12 50						14 50							17 03							18 49
Thornaby	a				12 58						14 58							17 13							18 58
Middlesbrough	a				13 10						15 09							17 24							19 10
Durham	a	12j31			13h19			14 01	14m30		15k25			16 01			16 58	17h19			18 01		18h32		19h18
Chester-le-Street	a							14 07													18 07				
Newcastle 8	a	12j51			13h36			14 23	14m51		15h33			16 20	17h04		17 17	17n37			18 23		18h51		19h35

For general notes see front of timetable
For details of catering facilities see Directory of Train Operators

b From 30 March dep. 13 minutes later
c Change at Manchester Oxford Road and Manchester Piccadilly
e Until 23 March only. Change at Manchester Piccadilly
f Until 23 March only
g From 3 February dep. 1522
h Change at York
j Change at York. 3 February to 23 March arr. Darlington 1234, Durham 1252, Newcastle 1308
k Change at York. 3 February to 23 March arr. 1 minute later
m Change at York. 3 February to 23 March arr. Darlington 1438, Durham 1456, Newcastle 1512
n Change at York. 3 February to 23 March arr. 2 minutes later

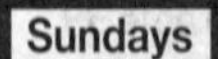

Liverpool, Manchester Airport and Manchester → Huddersfield → Leeds, Hull, York, Scarborough, Middlesbrough and Newcastle

Network Diagram - see first page of Table 39

		TP	TP	NT	TP	TP	NT	TP	TP	TP	NT	TP	TP	NT	TP	TP	TP	NT	NT	TP	NT	TP	TP
		1 ◇	1 ◇		1 ◇	1 ◇		1 ◇	1 ◇	1 ◇		1 ◇	1 ◇		1 ◇	1 ◇	1 ◇			1 ◇		1 ◇	1 ◇
Liverpool Lime Street 10	d	15 52	16 22			17 22			17 52	18 22			19 22			20 22						21 52	22b00
Warrington Central	d	16 18	16 44			17 44			18 18	18 44			19 44			20 44						22 15	22b35
Birchwood	d		16 49			17 49				18 49			19 49			20 49						22 20	22b40
Manchester Oxford Road	d		17 07			18 07				19 07			20 07			21 07						22 37	
Manchester Airport ✈	d	16c27	16 47		17 22	17 47		18 22	18c27	18 47		19 22	19 47		20 22	20 47				21 22		22 01	23 22
Manchester Piccadilly 10	a		17 10		17 38	18 10		18 39		19 10		19 38	20 10		20 38	21 10				21 38		22 40	23 36
	d	17 00	17 12		17 42	18 12		18 42	19 00	19 12		19 42	20 12		20 42	21 12				21 42		22 42	23 42
Manchester Victoria	a																						
	d						18 18							20 18							22 18		
Ashton-under-Lyne	d						18 28							20 28							22 28		
Stalybridge	a		17 25			18 25	18 32			19 25			20 25	20 32		21 25					22 33	22 55	
	d		17 25			18 25	18 33			19 25			20 25	20 33		21 25						22 55	
Mossley (Grtr Manchester)	d						18 37							20 37									
Greenfield	d						18 41							20 41									
Marsden	d			17 47			18 50				19 48			20 50					21 48				
Slaithwaite	d			17 51			18 54				19 52			20 54					21 52				
Huddersfield	a	17 29	17 43	17 58	18 11	18 43	19 02	19 11	19 31	19 43	19 59	20 11	20 43	21 02	21 11	21 43			21 59	22 11		23 11	00 11
	d	17 30	17 44	17 58	18 12	18 44		19 12	19 32	19 44	19 59	20 12	20 44		21 12	21 44			21 59	22 12		23 12	00 12
Deighton	d			18 02							20 03								22 03				
Mirfield	d			18 07							20 08								22 08				
Ravensthorpe	d			18 10							20 11								22 11				
Dewsbury	a			18 13	18 21			19 21			20 14	20 21			21 21				22 14	22 21		23 22	
	d			18 14	18 22			19 22			20 15	20 22			21 22				22 15	22 22		23 22	
Batley	d			18 17							20 18								22 18				
Morley	d			18 23							20 24								22 24				
Cottingley	d			18 26							20 27								22 27				
Leeds 10	a	17 51	18 05	18 34	18 37	19 06		19 37	19 53	20 05	20 35	20 39	21 07		21 37	22 05			22 35	22 37		23 38	00 33
	d	17 54	18 10		18 40	19 10		19 40	19 56	20 10		20 45	21 10		21 40	22 10	22 17	22 35		22 50		23 41	00 36
Garforth	d		18 36			19 18				20 36			21 18			22 46		22 47					
South Milford	a	18 06							20 09								22 29						
Selby	a	18 16							20 19								22 39						
Howden	a	19 51																					
Brough	a	18 35							20 38								22 58						
Hull	a	18 53							20 56								23 16						
York 8	a		18 37		19 07	19 38		20 05		20 37		21 09	21 38		22 06	22 38		23 17		23 21		00 08	01 02
	d				19 10	19 38		20 10		20 38		21 10			22 08	22 40							
Malton	d					20 02				21 02					22 32								
Seamer	a					20 19				21 19					22 49								
Scarborough	a					20 30				21 29					23 01								
Thirsk	a							20 27				21 27				23 05							
Northallerton	a				19 30	20e08		20 35				21 37				23 15							
Darlington 7	a		19f15		19 42	20g13		21h03		21e30		21 49	22 16			23 31						01 32	
Yarm	d							20 49															
Thornaby	a							20 57															
Middlesbrough	a							21 10															
Durham	a		19f32		19 59	20g31		21h20				22 06	22 34			23 48						01 50	
Chester-le-Street	a				20 05																		
Newcastle 8	a		19f54		20 21	20j51		21h37		22e02		22 25	22 52			00 21						02 25	

For general notes see front of timetable
For details of catering facilities see Directory of Train Operators

b Change at Manchester Oxford Road and Manchester Piccadilly
c Until 23 March only
e Change at York
f 3 February to 23 March arr. Darlington 1933, Durham 1951, Newcastle 2007
g Change at York. 3 February to 23 March arr. 9 minutes later
h Change at York. 3 February to 23 March arr. 1 minute earlier
j Change at York. 3 February to 23 March arr. 7 minutes later

York, Selby and Leeds → Huddersfield, Blackpool North and Manchester Victoria via Bradford Interchange and Halifax

Network Diagram - see first page of Table 39

Miles	Miles	Miles	Miles			TP	TP	TP	TP	TP	TP	NT	NT	TP	NT	NT	NT	TP	NT		NT	NT	TP	NT	NT
						MX	MO	MX	MO	MO	MX														
						1 ◇	1 ◇	1 ◇	1 ◇	1 ◇	1 ◇			1 ◇				1 ◇					1 ◇		
						A	A	A	A	A	A			A				A ⊼					A ⊼	B	
0	—	—	—	**York** 8	33 d	02 00	02 13	03 00	03 13	04 09	04 09			05 26		05 40		05 58				06 13	06 28		
8¾	—	—	—	Ulleskelf	33 d																				
10¾	—	—	—	Church Fenton	33 d																				
—	0	—	—	**Selby**	d																				
—	7¾	—	—	South Milford	d																				
15¾	11	—	—	Micklefield	d											05 58						06 28			
17½	12¾	—	—	East Garforth	d											06 02						06 32			
18¼	13½	—	—	Garforth	d											06 05		06 13				06 35			
21	16¼	—	—	Cross Gates	d											06 10						06 40			
25½	20¾	—	—	**Leeds** 10	a	02 33	02 40	03 33	03 39	04 37	04 42			05 52		06 18		06 23				06 49	06 53		
—	—	—	0		37, 39 d							05 08	05 51		06 03		06 22				06 37	06 51			07 09
29½	—	—	4	Bramley	37 d							05 15	05 58				06 29				06 44				07 16
31¼	—	—	5¾	New Pudsey	37 d							05 20	06 03		06 12		06 34				06 49	07 01			07 21
35	—	—	9½	**Bradford Interchange**	37 a							05 28	06 11		06 23		06 42				06 57	07 11			07 29
—	—	—	—		d							05 31	06 14		06 25		06 45				07 00	07 14			07 32
43	—	—	17½	**Halifax**	a							05 43	06 26		06 37		06 57				07 12	07 25			07 44
—	—	0	—		d							05 43	06 27		06 37		06 57				07 12	07 26			07 44
—	—	5¼	—	Brighouse	d																				
—	—	10½	—	**Huddersfield**	39 a																				
46½	—	—	21	Sowerby Bridge	d							05 50	06 33				07 04				07 19				07 51
50½	—	—	25	Mytholmroyd	d							05 56	06 39				07 10				07 25				07 57
51¾	—	—	26¼	Hebden Bridge	a							05 59	06 42		06 49		07 14				07 28	07 37			08 00
—	—	—	—		d							05 59	06 42		06 49						07 28	07 38			08 00
—	—	—	39	Burnley Manchester Road	97 a										07 08							07 57			
—	—	—	45¼	Accrington	97 a										07 17							08 06			
—	—	—	51½	Blackburn	97 a										07 25							08 14			
—	—	—	63½	**Preston** 8	97 a										07 46							08 33			
—	—	—	78	Poulton-le-Fylde	97 a										08 04							08 54			
—	—	—	81	**Blackpool North**	97 a										08 12							09 04			
56	—	—	—	Todmorden	d							06 06	06 50						07 18		07 35			07 48	08 07
57½	—	—	—	Walsden	d							06 09	06 53						07 21		07 38			07 51	08 10
61½	—	—	—	Littleborough	d							06 16	06 59						07 28		07 45			07 58	08 17
62½	—	—	—	Smithy Bridge	d							06 18	07 02						07 30		07 47			08 00	08 19
64¾	—	—	—	**Rochdale**	a							06 23	07 06						07 34		07 51			08 04	08 23
—	—	—	—		95 d							06 24	07 06						07 35		07 52			08 05	08 24
66½	—	—	—	Castleton	95 a							06 27	07 09						07 38		07 55			08 08	08 27
69¼	—	—	—	Mills Hill	95 a							06 31	07 14						07 41		07 59			08 12	08 31
71¼	—	—	—	Moston	95 a							06 35	07 17						07 45		08 03			08 15	08 35
75¼	—	—	—	**Manchester Victoria**	95 ⛴ a							06 46	07 29						07 57		08 16			08 25	08 46
—	—	—	—	Liverpool Lime Street 10	90 a							*08 13*							09 05					*09 39*	*10 05*

		TP	NT	NT	TP	NT	TP	NT	TP	NT	TP	XC		NT	NT	NT	NT	TP	NT	NT	TP	NT	TP	NT	NT
												R													
		1 ◇			1 ◇		1 ◇		1 ◇		1 ◇	1						1 ◇			1 ◇		1 ◇		
		C ⊼	D	E	G ⊼		H ⊼		J ⊼		K ⊼	L ⊡		D		E		J ⊼			H ⊼		G ⊼		
York 8	33 d				06 58			07 06	07 24		07 40	07 44					07 48	07 54					08 24	08 27	
Ulleskelf	33 d							07 15											⟵						
Church Fenton	33 d							07 21									08 05		08 05						
Selby	d	06 38		06 43			07 08			07 26						07 43	⟶				08 08	08 12			
South Milford	d			06 53						07 35						07 53						08 22			
Micklefield	d			06 58				07 28		07 41						07 58			08 13			08 28		08 42	
East Garforth	d			07 02				07 32		07 46						08 02			08 17			08 32		08 46	
Garforth	d			07 05	07 13		07 24	07 35		07 48						08 05		08u13	08 20			08 35	08 41	08 48	
Cross Gates	d			07 10				07 40	07 44	07 53						08 10			08 25			08 40		08 53	
Leeds 10	a	07 05		07 19	07 23		07 35	07 49	07 52	08 02	08 04	08 08				08 19		08 23	08 34		08 37	08 48	08 50	09 02	
	37, 39 d		07 13	07 23		07 37		07 51		08 08				08 13		08 22				08 37		08 51			09 08
Bramley	37 d			07 30		07 44				08 15						08 29				08 44					09 15
New Pudsey	37 d			07 35		07 49		08 01		08 20						08 34				08 49		09 00			09 20
Bradford Interchange	37 a			07 43		07 57		08 11		08 28						08 42				08 57		09 09			09 28
	d			07 46		08 00		08 14		08 31						08 45				09 00		09 11			09 31
Halifax	a			07 59		08 12		08 25		08 43						08 58				09 12		09 23			09 43
	d			08 07		08 12		08 26		08 43					09 03	09 07				09 12		09 25			09 43
Brighouse	d		07a49	08 17										08a49		09 17									
Huddersfield	39 a			08 30												09 30									
Sowerby Bridge	d					08 19				08 50					09 10					09 19					09 50
Mytholmroyd	d					08 25				08 56					09 16					09 25					09 56
Hebden Bridge	a					08 28		08 37		08 59					09 20					09 28		09 37			09 59
	d					08 28		08 38		08 59										09 28		09 37			09 59
Burnley Manchester Road	97 a							08 57														09 56			
Accrington	97 a							09 06														10 05			
Blackburn	97 a							09 14														10 13			
Preston 8	97 a							09 34														10 32			
Poulton-le-Fylde	97 a							09 53														10 52			
Blackpool North	97 a							10 02														11 02			
Todmorden	d					08 35				09 06										09 36					10 06
Walsden	d					08 38				09 09															10 09
Littleborough	d					08 45				09 16										09 46					10 16
Smithy Bridge	d					08 47				09 18										09 48					10 18
Rochdale	a					08 51				09 22										09 52					10 22
	95 d					08 52				09 23										09 53					10 23
Castleton	95 a																								
Mills Hill	95 a																								
Moston	95 a																								
Manchester Victoria	95 ⛴ a					09 09				09 40										10 10					10 40
Liverpool Lime Street 10	90 a									*11 05*															*12 05*

For general notes see front of timetable
For details of catering facilities see Directory of Train Operators

A To Manchester Airport (Table 39)
B To Kirkby (Table 82)
C From Hull to Liverpool Lime Street (Table 39)
D Via Dewsbury (Table 39)
E To Wakefield Westgate (Table 39)
G From Middlesbrough to Manchester Airport (Table 39)
H From Hull to Manchester Piccadilly (Table 39)
J From Scarborough to Manchester Airport (Table 39)
K From Newcastle to Liverpool Lime Street (Table 39)
L From Newcastle to Bournemouth (Table 51)

York, Selby and Leeds → Huddersfield, Blackpool North and Manchester Victoria via Bradford Interchange and Halifax

Network Diagram - see first page of Table 39

		TP 1◇ A	XC 1◇ B	NT C	NT D		TP 1◇ E	NT	TP 1◇ G	NT	TP 1◇ H	NT	TP 1◇ A	XC R 1 J	NT C	NT D	TP 1◇ K	NT	TP 1◇ G	NT		TP 1◇ E	NT	TP 1◇ A	XC 1◇ L
York 8	33 d	08 40	08 44				08 58			09 09	09 28		09 40	09 44			09 58			10 11		10 28		10 40	10 44
Ulleskelf	33 d																								
Church Fenton	33 d									09 21															
Selby	d				08 42				09 08							09 43			10 08						
South Milford	d				08 52											09 53									
Micklefield	d				08 58					09 28						09 58				10 28					
East Garforth	d				09 02					09 32						10 04				10 32					
Garforth	d				09 05		09 13			09 35						10 05	10 13			10 35					
Cross Gates	d				09 10					09 40						10 10				10 40					
Leeds 10	a	09 04	09 08		09 19		09 23		09 35	09 49	09 53		10 04	10 08		10 19	10 23		10 37	10 49		10 53		11 04	11 08
	37, 39 d			09 13	09 22			09 37		09 51		10 08			10 13	10 22		10 37		10 51			11 08		
Bramley	37 d				09 29			09 44				10 15				10 29		10 44					11 15		
New Pudsey	37 d				09 34			09 49		10 01		10 20				10 34		10 49		11 01			11 20		
Bradford Interchange	37 a				09 42			09 57		10 11		10 28				10 42		10 57		11 11			11 28		
	d				09 45			10 00		10 14		10 31				10 45		11 00		11 14			11 31		
Halifax	a				09 58			10 12		10 25		10 43				10 58		11 12		11 25			11 43		
	d				10 06			10 12		10 26		10 43				11 06		11 12		11 26			11 43		
Brighouse	d			09 49	10 16										10 49	11 16									
Huddersfield	39 a				10 30											11 30									
Sowerby Bridge	d			09 59				10 19				10 50			10 59			11 19					11 50		
Mytholmroyd	d			10 05				10 25				10 56			11 05			11 25					11 56		
Hebden Bridge	a			10 09				10 28		10 37		10 59			11 09			11 28		11 37			11 59		
	d							10 28		10 38		10 59						11 28		11 38			11 59		
Burnley Manchester Road	97 a									10 57										11 57					
Accrington	97 a									11 06										12 06					
Blackburn	97 a									11 14										12 14					
Preston 8	97 a									11 34										12 32					
Poulton-le-Fylde	97 a									11 52										12 52					
Blackpool North	97 a									12 01										13 00					
Todmorden	d							10 35				11 06						11 35					12 06		
Walsden	d											11 09											12 09		
Littleborough	d							10 43				11 16						11 43					12 16		
Smithy Bridge	d							10 45				11 18						11 45					12 18		
Rochdale	a							10 49				11 22						11 49					12 22		
	95 d							10 50				11 23						11 50					12 23		
Castleton	95 a																								
Mills Hill	95 a																								
Moston	95 a																								
Manchester Victoria	95 ⛴ a							11 10				11 40						12 09					12 40		
Liverpool Lime Street 10	90 a											*13 05*											*14 05*		

		NT C	NT D	TP 1◇ K	NT	TP 1◇ G	NT	TP 1◇ E	NT	TP 1◇ A	XC R 1 N	NT C	NT		NT D	TP 1◇ K	NT	TP 1◇ G	NT	TP 1◇ E	NT	TP 1◇ A	XC R 1 Q	NT C	NT D
York 8	33 d			10 58			11 09	11 28		11 39	11 44					11 58			12 13	12 28		12 38	12 44		
Ulleskelf	33 d																								
Church Fenton	33 d						11 21																		
Selby	d		10 43			11 08							11 43					12 08							12 43
South Milford	d		10 53										11 53												12 53
Micklefield	d		10 58				11 28						11 58						12 28						12 58
East Garforth	d		11 02				11 32						12 02						12 32						13 02
Garforth	d		11 05	11 13			11 35						12 05			12 13			12 35						13 05
Cross Gates	d		11 10				11 40						12 10						12 40						13 10
Leeds 10	a		11 19	11 23		11 33	11 49	11 53		12 05	12 08		12 19			12 23		12 33	12 49	12 51		13 04	13 08		13 19
	37, 39 d	11 13	11 22		11 37		11 51		12 08			12 13			12 22		12 37		12 51		13 08			13 13	13 22
Bramley	37 d		11 29		11 44				12 15						12 29		12 44				13 15				13 29
New Pudsey	37 d		11 34		11 49		12 01		12 20						12 34		12 49		13 01		13 20				13 34
Bradford Interchange	37 a		11 42		11 57		12 11		12 28						12 42		12 57		13 11		13 28				13 42
	d		11 45		12 00		12 14		12 31						12 45		13 00		13 14		13 31				13 45
Halifax	a		11 58		12 12		12 25		12 43						12 58		13 12		13 25		13 43				13 58
	d		12 06		12 12		12 26		12 43						13 06		13 12		13 26		13 43				14 06
Brighouse	d	11 49	12 16									12 49			13 16									13 49	14 16
Huddersfield	39 a		12 30												13 30										14 30
Sowerby Bridge	d	11 59			12 19				12 50			12 59					13 19				13 50			13 59	
Mytholmroyd	d	12 05			12 25				12 56			13 05					13 25				13 56			14 05	
Hebden Bridge	a	12 09			12 28		12 37		12 59			13 09					13 28		13 37		13 59			14 09	
	d				12 28		12 38		12 59								13 28		13 38		13 59				
Burnley Manchester Road	97 a						12 57												13 57						
Accrington	97 a						13 06												14 06						
Blackburn	97 a						13 14												14 14						
Preston 8	97 a						13 32												14 32						
Poulton-le-Fylde	97 a						13 52												14 52						
Blackpool North	97 a						13 59												15 00						
Todmorden	d				12 36				13 06								13 35				14 06				
Walsden	d								13 09												14 09				
Littleborough	d				12 44				13 16								13 43				14 16				
Smithy Bridge	d				12 46				13 18								13 45				14 18				
Rochdale	a				12 51				13 22								13 49				14 22				
	95 d				12 52				13 23								13 50				14 23				
Castleton	95 a																								
Mills Hill	95 a																								
Moston	95 a																								
Manchester Victoria	95 ⛴ a				13 09				13 40								14 09				14 40				
Liverpool Lime Street 10	90 a								*15 05*												*16 05*				

For general notes see front of timetable
For details of catering facilities see Directory of Train Operators

A From Scarborough to Liverpool Lime Street (Table 39)
B From Edinburgh to Plymouth (Table 51)
C Via Dewsbury (Table 39)
D To Wakefield Westgate (Table 39)
E From Newcastle to Manchester Airport (Table 39)
G From Hull to Manchester Piccadilly (Table 39)
H To Manchester Airport (Table 39)
J From Glasgow Central to Bournemouth (Table 51)
K From Middlesbrough to Manchester Airport (Table 39)
L From Dundee (Table 229) to Plymouth (Table 51)
N From Dundee (Table 229) to Bournemouth (Table 51)
Q From Glasgow Central (Table 51) to Penzance (Table 135)

York, Selby and Leeds → Huddersfield, Blackpool North and Manchester Victoria via Bradford Interchange and Halifax

Network Diagram - see first page of Table 39

		TP	NT	TP	NT	TP		NT	TP	XC	NT	NT	TP	NT	TP	NT	TP	NT	TP	XC	NT		NT	TP	NT
		1 ◇		1 ◇		1 ◇			1 ◇	R 1			1 ◇		1 ◇		1 ◇		1 ◇	R 1				1 ◇	
		A		B		C			D	E	G	H	A		B		C		D	J	G		H	A	
York 8	33 d	12 58			13 09	13 28			13 40	13 44			13 58			14 13	14 28		14 40	14 44				14 58	
Ulleskelf	33 d																								
Church Fenton	33 d				13 21																				
Selby	d			13 08								13 43			14 08								14 43		
South Milford	d											13 53											14 53		
Micklefield	d				13 28							13 58				14 28							14 58		
East Garforth	d				13 32							14 02				14 32							15 02		
Garforth	d	13 13			13 35							14 05	14 13			14 35							15 05	15 13	
Cross Gates	d				13 40							14 10				14 40							15 10		
Leeds 10	a	13 23		13 33	13 49	13 53			14 04	14 08		14 19	14 23		14 34	14 49	14 53		15 03	15 08			15 19	15 23	
	37, 39 d		13 37		13 51			14 08			14 13	14 22		14 37		14 51		15 08			15 13		15 22		15 37
Bramley	37 d		13 44					14 15				14 29		14 44				15 15					15 29		15 44
New Pudsey	37 d		13 49		14 01			14 20				14 34		14 49		15 01		15 20					15 34		15 49
Bradford Interchange	37 a		13 57		14 11			14 28				14 42		14 57		15 11		15 28					15 42		15 57
	d		14 00		14 14			14 31				14 45		15 00		15 14		15 31					15 45		16 00
Halifax	a		14 12		14 25			14 43				14 58		15 12		15 25		15 43					15 58		16 12
	d		14 12		14 26			14 43				15 06		15 12		15 26		15 43					16 06		16 12
Brighouse	d										14 49	15 16									15 49		16 16		
Huddersfield	39 a											15 30											16 30		
Sowerby Bridge	d		14 19					14 50			14 59			15 19				15 50			15 59				16 19
Mytholmroyd	d		14 25					14 56			15 05			15 25				15 56			16 05				16 25
Hebden Bridge	a		14 28		14 37			14 59			15 09			15 28		15 37		15 59			16 09				16 28
	d		14 28		14 38			14 59						15 28		15 38		15 59							16 28
Burnley Manchester Road	97 a				14 57											15 57									
Accrington	97 a				15 06											16 06									
Blackburn	97 a				15 14											16 14									
Preston 8	97 a				15 32											16 33									
Poulton-le-Fylde	97 a				15 52											16 52									
Blackpool North	97 a				16 00											17 00									
Todmorden	d		14 36					15 06						15 36				16 06							16 35
Walsden	d							15 09										16 09							16 38
Littleborough	d		14 44					15 16						15 46				16 16							16 45
Smithy Bridge	d		14 46					15 18						15 48				16 18							16 47
Rochdale	a		14 51					15 22						15 53				16 22							16 51
	95 d		14 52					15 23						15 54				16 23							16 52
Castleton	95 a																								
Mills Hill	95 a																								
Moston	95 a																								
Manchester Victoria	95 a		15 09					15 40						16 10				16 40							17 10
Liverpool Lime Street 10	90 a							*17 04*										*18 05*							

		TP	NT	TP	NT	TP	XC	NT	NT	TP	NT	TP	NT	TP		NT	TP	XC	NT	NT	TP	NT	TP	NT	TP
		1 ◇		1 ◇		1 ◇	R 1			1 ◇		1 ◇		1 ◇			1 ◇	1 ◇			1 ◇		1 ◇		1 ◇
		B		C		D	K	G	H	L		B		C			D	J	G	H	A		B		C
York 8	33 d		15 09	15 28		15 40	15 44			15 58			16 13	16 28			16 40	16 44			16 58			17 07	17 28
Ulleskelf	33 d																								
Church Fenton	33 d		15 21																					17 20	
Selby	d	15 08							15 43			16 08								16 43			17 08		
South Milford	d								15 53											16 53					
Micklefield	d		15 28						15 58				16 28							16 58				17 28	
East Garforth	d		15 32						16 02				16 32							17 02				17 32	
Garforth	d		15 35						16 05	16 13			16 35							17 05	17 13			17 35	
Cross Gates	d		15 40						16 10				16 40							17 10				17 40	
Leeds 10	a	15 33	15 49	15 53		16 04	16 08		16 19	16 23		16 36	16 49	16 53			17 04	17 08		17 19	17 23		17 35	17 50	17 53
	37, 39 d		15 51		16 08			16 13	16 22		16 37		16 51			17 08			17 13	17 22		17 37		17 51	
Bramley	37 d				16 15				16 29		16 44					17 15				17 29		17 44			
New Pudsey	37 d		16 01		16 20				16 34		16 49		17 01			17 20				17 34		17 49		18 02	
Bradford Interchange	37 a		16 11		16 28				16 42		16 57		17 11			17 28				17 42		17 57		18 11	
	d		16 14		16 31				16 45		17 00		17 14			17 31				17 45		18 00		18 14	
Halifax	a		16 25		16 43				16 58		17 12		17 25			17 43				17 58		18 12		18 26	
	d		16 26		16 43				17 06		17 12		17 26			17 43				18 06		18 12		18 26	
Brighouse	d							16 49	17 16										17 50	18 16					
Huddersfield	39 a								17 30											18 30					
Sowerby Bridge	d				16 50			16 59			17 19					17 50			17 59			18 19			
Mytholmroyd	d				16 56			17 05			17 25					17 56			18 05			18 25			
Hebden Bridge	a		16 37		16 59			17 09			17 28		17 37			17 59			18 09			18 28		18 38	
	d		16 38		16 59						17 28		17 38			17 59						18 28		18 38	
Burnley Manchester Road	97 a		16 57										17 57											18 58	
Accrington	97 a		17 06										18 06											19 07	
Blackburn	97 a		17 14										18 14											19 15	
Preston 8	97 a		17 34										18 34											19 36	
Poulton-le-Fylde	97 a		17 53										18 54											19 54	
Blackpool North	97 a		18 03										19 03											20 03	
Todmorden	d				17 06						17 35					18 06						18 35			
Walsden	d				17 09						17 38					18 09						18 38			
Littleborough	d				17 16						17 45					18 16						18 45			
Smithy Bridge	d				17 18						17 47					18 18						18 47			
Rochdale	a				17 22						17 51					18 22						18 51			
	95 d				17 23						17 52					18 23						18 52			
Castleton	95 a																					18 55			
Mills Hill	95 a																					18 59			
Moston	95 a																					19 03			
Manchester Victoria	95 a				17 40						18 10					18 41						19 14			
Liverpool Lime Street 10	90 a				*19 05*						*19 35*					*20 05*									

For general notes see front of timetable
For details of catering facilities see Directory of Train Operators

A From Middlesbrough to Manchester Airport (Table 39)
B From Hull to Manchester Piccadilly (Table 39)
C From Newcastle to Manchester Airport (Table 39)
D From Scarborough to Liverpool Lime Street (Table 39)
E From Aberdeen (Table 229) to Bournemouth (Table 51)
G Via Dewsbury (Table 39)
H To Wakefield Westgate (Table 39)
J From Edinburgh to Plymouth (Table 51)
K From Edinburgh to Bournemouth (Table 51)
L From Middlesbrough to Manchester Piccadilly (Table 39)

York, Selby and Leeds → Huddersfield, Blackpool North and Manchester Victoria via Bradford Interchange and Halifax

Network Diagram - see first page of Table 39

		TP	NT	TP	XC	NT	NT	TP	NT	NT	TP	TP	NT	TP	XC	NT	NT	NT	NT	TP	NT	TP	NT
		1 ◇		1 ◇	R 1			1 ◇			1 ◇	1 ◇		1 ◇	1 ◇					1 ◇		1 ◇	
		A		B	C	D	E	G			H	J		B	K		E			L		N	
York 8	33 d			17 40	17 44			17 58		18 10	18 28			18 38	18 44			19 04		19 10	←		
Ulleskelf	33 d																						
Church Fenton	33 d																	19 20			19 20		
Selby	d	17 31					17 43					18 33				18 43		→				19 30	
South Milford	d						17 53									18 53							
Micklefield	d						17 58			18 24						18 58					19 27		
East Garforth	d						18 02			18 28						19 02					19 31		
Garforth	d						18 05	18 13		18 31						19 05				19 23	19 35		
Cross Gates	d						18 10			18 36						19 10					19 40		
Leeds 10	a	17 59		18 04	18 08		18 20	18 23		18 47	18 52	18 58		19 04	19 08	19 21				19 35	19 49	19 56	
	37, 39 d		18 08			18 13	18 22		18 37	18 51			19 08				19 22		19 37		19 51		20 08
Bramley	37 d		18 15				18 30		18 44				19 15				19 29		19 44				20 15
New Pudsey	37 d		18 20				18 35		18 49	19 01			19 20				19 34		19 49		20 01		20 20
Bradford Interchange	37 a		18 28				18 43		18 57	19 11			19 28				19 45		19 57		20 11		20 28
	d		18 31				18 46		19 00	19 14			19 31				19 45		20 00		20 14		20 31
Halifax	a		18 43				18 59		19 12	19 25			19 43				20 01		20 12		20 25		20 44
	d		18 43				19 06		19 12	19 26			19 43				20 04		20 12		20 26		20 44
Brighouse	d					18 49	19 16										20 14						20 55
Huddersfield	39 a						19 30										20 30						21 08
Sowerby Bridge	d		18 50			18 59			19 19				19 50						20 19				
Mytholmroyd	d		18 56			19 05			19 25				19 56						20 25				
Hebden Bridge	a		18 59			19 09			19 28	19 37			19 59						20 28		20 37		
	d		18 59						19 28	19 38									20 28		20 38		
Burnley Manchester Road	97 a									19 57											20 57		
Accrington	97 a									20 06											21 06		
Blackburn	97 a									20 14											21 14		
Preston 8	97 a									20 31											21 31		
Poulton-le-Fylde	97 a									20 49											21 49		
Blackpool North	97 a									20 56											21 56		
Todmorden	d		19 06						19 35										20 35				
Walsden	d		19 09						19 38										20 38				
Littleborough	d		19 16						19 45										20 45				
Smithy Bridge	d		19 18						19 47										20 47				
Rochdale	a		19 22						19 51										20 51				
	95 d		19 23						19 52										20 52				
Castleton	95 a								19 55										20 55				
Mills Hill	95 a								19 59										20 59				
Moston	95 a								20 03										21 03				
Manchester Victoria	95 a		19 40						20 14										21 14				
Liverpool Lime Street 10	90 a		*21 05*						*22 05*										*23 05*				

		TP	XC	NT	TP	NT	TP	NT	TP	XC	NT	TP	NT	TP	NT	TP	NT	TP	NT	NT	TP	NT
		1 ◇	1 ◇		1 ◇		1 ◇		1 ◇	1 ◇		1 ◇		1 ◇		1 ◇		1 ◇			1 ◇	
		B	K		H		N		B	Q		L		U		G		J			H	
York 8	33 d	19 39	19 44		20 10	20 13			20 40	20 44		21 10	21 13	21 32		21 45			22 13		23 07	23 13
Ulleskelf	33 d												21 22									
Church Fenton	33 d					20 25							21 28									23 28
Selby	d						20 26											22 07				
South Milford	d						20 36											22 17				
Micklefield	d					20 32							21 36						22 28			23 36
East Garforth	d					20 36							21 40						22 33			23 40
Garforth	d					20 39							21 42	21 47					22 35			23 43
Cross Gates	d					20 44							21 47						22 40			23 47
Leeds 10	a	20 04	20 08		20 35	20 53	20 59		21 04	21 08		21 33	21 56	22 00		22 08		22 35	22 49		23 33	23 55
	37, 39 d			20 37				21 08			21 37				22 08		22 37			23 08		
Bramley	37 d			20 44				21 15			21 44				22 15		22 44			23 15		
New Pudsey	37 d			20 49				21 20			21 49				22 20		22 49			23 20		
Bradford Interchange	37 a			20 57				21 28			21 57				22 28		22 57			23 29		
	d			21 00				21 31			22 00				22 31		23 00			23 31		
Halifax	a			21 12				21 44			22 12				22 44		23 12			23 44		
	d			21 12				21 44			22 12				22 44		23 12			23 44		
Brighouse	d							21 55							22 55					23 55		
Huddersfield	39 a							22 07							23 07					00 09		
Sowerby Bridge	d			21 19							22 19						23 19					
Mytholmroyd	d			21 25							22 25						23 25					
Hebden Bridge	a			21 28							22 28						23 28					
	d			21 28							22 28						23 28					
Burnley Manchester Road	97 a																					
Accrington	97 a																					
Blackburn	97 a																					
Preston 8	97 a																					
Poulton-le-Fylde	97 a																					
Blackpool North	97 a																					
Todmorden	d			21 35							22 35						23 35					
Walsden	d			21 38							22 38						23 38					
Littleborough	d			21 45							22 45						23 45					
Smithy Bridge	d			21 47							22 47						23 47					
Rochdale	a			21 51							22 51						23 51					
	95 d			21 52							22 52						23 52					
Castleton	95 a			21 55							22 55											
Mills Hill	95 a			21 59							22 59											
Moston	95 a			22 03							23 03											
Manchester Victoria	95 a			22 14							23 14						00 08					
Liverpool Lime Street 10	90 a			*00 14*																		

For general notes see front of timetable
For details of catering facilities see Directory of Train Operators

- **A** From Hull to Huddersfield (Table 39)
- **B** From Scarborough to Liverpool Lime Street (Table 39)
- **C** From Edinburgh to Southampton Central (Table 51)
- **D** Via Dewsbury (Table 39)
- **E** To Wakefield Westgate (Table 39)
- **G** From Middlesbrough to Manchester Piccadilly (Table 39)
- **H** From Newcastle to Manchester Airport (Table 39)
- **J** From Hull to Manchester Piccadilly (Table 39)
- **K** From Edinburgh to Bristol Temple Meads (Table 51)
- **L** From Middlesbrough to Manchester Airport (Table 39)
- **N** From Hull (Table 39)
- **Q** From Edinburgh to Birmingham New Street (Table 51)
- **U** From Scarborough (Table 39)

Table 41

Saturdays

York, Selby and Leeds → Huddersfield, Blackpool North and Manchester Victoria via Bradford Interchange and Halifax

Network Diagram - see first page of Table 39

		TP	TP	TP	NT	TP	NT	NT	TP	NT	NT	NT	TP	NT	NT	TP	NT	NT	TP	NT	TP	NT	TP	NT	TP
		1 ◇	1 ◇	1 ◇		1 ◇			1 ◇				1 ◇			1 ◇			1 ◇		1 ◇		1 ◇		1 ◇
		A	A	A		A			A				A	B		C	D	E	G		H		J		K
																									🍴
York 8	33 d	02 00	03 00	04 19		05 26			05 58			06 13	06 28						06 58			07 06	07 27		07 40
Ulleskelf	33 d																					07 15			
Church Fenton	33 d																					07 21			
Selby	d															06 38		06 43			07 06				
South Milford	d																	06 53							
Micklefield	d											06 28						06 58				07 28			
East Garforth	d											06 32						07 02				07 32			
Garforth	d								06 13			06 35						07 05	07 13			07 35			
Cross Gates	d											06 40						07 10				07 40			
Leeds 10	a	02 33	03 33	04 44		05 52			06 23			06 49	06 53			07 05		07 17	07 23		07 35	07 49	07 52		08 04
	37, 39 d				05 51		06 03	06 22			06 37	06 51			07 09		07 13	07 23		07 37		07 51		08 08	
Bramley	37 d				05 58			06 29			06 44				07 16			07 30		07 44				08 15	
New Pudsey	37 d				06 03		06 12	06 34			06 49	07 01			07 21			07 35		07 49		08 01		08 20	
Bradford Interchange	37 a				06 11		06 23	06 42			06 57	07 11			07 29			07 43		07 57		08 11		08 28	
	d				06 14		06 25	06 45			07 00	07 14			07 32			07 46		08 00		08 14		08 31	
Halifax	a				06 26		06 37	06 57			07 12	07 25			07 44			07 59		08 12		08 25		08 43	
	d				06 27		06 37	06 57			07 12	07 26			07 44			08 07		08 12		08 26		08 43	
Brighouse	d																07 49	08 17							
Huddersfield	39 a																	08 30							
Sowerby Bridge	d				06 33			07 04			07 19				07 51		07 59			08 19				08 50	
Mytholmroyd	d				06 39			07 10			07 25				07 57		08 05			08 25				08 56	
Hebden Bridge	a				06 42		06 49	07 14			07 28	07 37			08 00		08 09			08 28		08 37		08 59	
	d				06 42		06 49				07 28	07 38			08 00					08 28		08 38		08 59	
Burnley Manchester Road	97 a						07 08					07 57										08 57			
Accrington	97 a						07 17					08 06										09 06			
Blackburn	97 a						07 25					08 14										09 14			
Preston 8	97 a						07 47					08 33										09 33			
Poulton-le-Fylde	97 a						08 04					08 54										09 54			
Blackpool North	97 a						08 12					09 03										10 02			
Todmorden	d				06 50					07 18	07 35			07 48	08 07					08 35				09 06	
Walsden	d				06 53					07 21	07 38			07 51	08 10					08 38				09 09	
Littleborough	d				06 59					07 28	07 45			07 58	08 17					08 45				09 16	
Smithy Bridge	d				07 02					07 30	07 47			08 00	08 19					08 47				09 18	
Rochdale	a				07 06					07 34	07 51			08 04	08 23					08 51				09 22	
	95 d				07 06					07 35	07 52			08 05	08 24					08 52				09 23	
Castleton	95 a				07 09					07 38	07 55			08 08	08 27										
Mills Hill	95 a				07 14					07 41	07 59			08 12	08 31										
Moston	95 a				07 17					07 45	08 03			08 15	08 35										
Manchester Victoria	95 🚋 a				07 29					07 57	08 16			08 25	08 46					09 09				09 40	
Liverpool Lime Street 10	90 a									09 05				*09 39*	*10 05*									*11 05*	

For general notes see front of timetable
For details of catering facilities see Directory of Train Operators

A To Manchester Airport (Table 39)
B To Kirkby (Table 82)
C From Hull to Liverpool Lime Street (Table 39)
D Via Dewsbury (Table 39)
E To Wakefield Westgate (Table 39)
G From Middlesbrough to Manchester Airport (Table 39)
H From Hull to Manchester Piccadilly (Table 39)
J From Scarborough to Manchester Airport (Table 39)
K From Newcastle to Liverpool Lime Street (Table 39)

Table 41

Saturdays

York, Selby and Leeds → Huddersfield, Blackpool North and Manchester Victoria via Bradford Interchange and Halifax

Network Diagram - see first page of Table 39

		XC	NT	NT	TP	NT	TP	NT	TP	NT	TP	XC	NT	NT	TP	NT	TP	NT	TP	NT		TP	XC	NT	NT
		1 ◇			1 ◇		1 ◇		1 ◇		1 ◇	1 ◇			1 ◇		1 ◇		1 ◇			1 ◇	1 ◇		
		A	B	C	D		E		G		H	J	B	C	K		E		L			H	N	B	C
		[buffet]							[trolley]		[trolley]	[buffet]			[trolley]				[trolley]			[trolley]	[buffet]		
York 8	33 d	07 44			07 58			08 07	08 25		08 40	08 44			08 58			09 09	09 28			09 40	09 44		
Ulleskelf	33 d																								
Church Fenton	33 d							08 20										09 21							
Selby	d			07 43			08 08							08 43			09 08								09 43
South Milford	d			07 53										08 53											09 53
Micklefield	d			07 58				08 27						08 58				09 28							09 58
East Garforth	d			08 02				08 32						09 02				09 32							10 02
Garforth	d			08 05	08 13			08 35						09 05	09 13			09 35							10 05
Cross Gates	d			08 10				08 40						09 10				09 40							10 10
Leeds 10	a	08 08		08 19	08 23		08 37	08 49	08 50		09 04	09 08		09 19	09 23		09 35	09 49	09 53			10 04	10 08		10 19
	37, 39 d		08 13	08 22		08 37		08 51		09 08			09 13	09 22		09 37		09 51		10 08				10 13	10 22
Bramley	37 d			08 29		08 44				09 15				09 29		09 44				10 15					10 29
New Pudsey	37 d			08 34		08 49		09 02		09 20				09 34		09 49		10 01		10 20					10 34
Bradford Interchange	37 a			08 42		08 57		09 11		09 28				09 42		09 57		10 11		10 28					10 42
	d			08 45		09 00		09 14		09 31				09 45		10 00		10 14		10 31					10 45
Halifax	a			08 58		09 12		09 26		09 43				09 58		10 12		10 25		10 43					10 58
	d			09 06		09 12		09 26		09 43				10 06		10 12		10 26		10 43					11 06
Brighouse	d		08 49	09 16									09 49	10 16										10 49	11 16
Huddersfield	39 a			09 30										10 30											11 30
Sowerby Bridge	d		08 59			09 19				09 50			09 59			10 19				10 50				10 59	
Mytholmroyd	d		09 05			09 25				09 56			10 05			10 25				10 56				11 05	
Hebden Bridge	a		09 09			09 28		09 38		09 59			10 09			10 28		10 37		10 59				11 09	
	d					09 28		09 38		10 00						10 28		10 38		10 59					
Burnley Manchester Road	97 a							09 58										10 57							
Accrington	97 a							10 07										11 06							
Blackburn	97 a							10 15										11 14							
Preston 8	97 a							10 32										11 34							
Poulton-le-Fylde	97 a							10 53										11 52							
Blackpool North	97 a							11 03										12 01							
Todmorden	d					09 35				10 07						10 35				11 06					
Walsden	d									10 10										11 09					
Littleborough	d					09 43				10 17						10 43				11 16					
Smithy Bridge	d					09 45				10 19						10 45				11 18					
Rochdale	a					09 49				10 23						10 49				11 22					
	95 d					09 50				10 24						10 50				11 23					
Castleton	95 a																								
Mills Hill	95 a																								
Moston	95 a																								
Manchester Victoria	95 ⛴ a					10 10				10 41						11 10				11 40					
Liverpool Lime Street 10	90 a									*12 05*										*13 05*					

		TP	NT	TP	NT	TP	NT	TP	XC	NT	NT	TP	NT	TP	NT	TP	NT	TP	XC	NT	NT	TP	NT	TP	NT
		1 ◇		1 ◇		1 ◇		1 ◇	1 ◇			1 ◇		1 ◇		1 ◇		1 ◇	1 ◇			1 ◇		1 ◇	
		G		E		K		H	J	B	C	G		E		K		H	Q	B	C	G		E	
		[trolley]				[trolley]		[trolley]	[buffet]			[trolley]				[trolley]		[trolley]	[buffet]			[trolley]		[trolley]	
York 8	33 d	09 58			10 11	10 28		10 40	10 44			10 58			11 09	11 28		11 40	11 44			11 58			12 13
Ulleskelf	33 d																								
Church Fenton	33 d														11 21										
Selby	d			10 08							10 43			11 08							11 43			12 08	
South Milford	d										10 53										11 53				
Micklefield	d				10 28						10 58				11 28						11 58				12 28
East Garforth	d				10 32						11 02				11 32						12 02				12 32
Garforth	d	10 13			10 35						11 05	11 13			11 35						12 05	12 13			12 35
Cross Gates	d				10 40						11 10				11 40						12 10				12 40
Leeds 10	a	10 23		10 37	10 49	10 53		11 04	11 08		11 19	11 23		11 33	11 49	11 53		12 04	12 08		12 19	12 23		12 33	12 49
	37, 39 d		10 37		10 51		11 08			11 13	11 22		11 37		11 51		12 08			12 13	12 22		12 37		12 51
Bramley	37 d		10 44				11 15				11 29		11 44				12 15				12 29		12 44		
New Pudsey	37 d		10 49		11 01		11 20				11 34		11 49		12 01		12 20				12 34		12 49		13 01
Bradford Interchange	37 a		10 57		11 11		11 28				11 42		11 57		12 11		12 28				12 42		12 57		13 11
	d		11 00		11 14		11 31				11 45		12 00		12 14		12 31				12 45		13 00		13 14
Halifax	a		11 12		11 25		11 43				11 58		12 12		12 25		12 43				12 58		13 12		13 25
	d		11 12		11 26		11 43				12 06		12 12		12 26		12 43				13 06		13 12		13 26
Brighouse	d									11 49	12 16									12 49	13 16				
Huddersfield	39 a										12 30										13 30				
Sowerby Bridge	d		11 19				11 50			11 59			12 19				12 50			12 59			13 19		
Mytholmroyd	d		11 25				11 56			12 05			12 25				12 56			13 05			13 25		
Hebden Bridge	a		11 28		11 37		11 59			12 09			12 28		12 37		12 59			13 09			13 28		13 37
	d		11 28		11 38		11 59						12 28		12 38		12 59						13 28		13 38
Burnley Manchester Road	97 a				11 57										12 57										13 57
Accrington	97 a				12 06										13 06										14 06
Blackburn	97 a				12 14										13 14										14 14
Preston 8	97 a				12 32										13 32										14 32
Poulton-le-Fylde	97 a				12 52										13 52										14 52
Blackpool North	97 a				13 01										14 00										15 01
Todmorden	d		11 35				12 06						12 36				13 06						13 35		
Walsden	d						12 09										13 09								
Littleborough	d		11 43				12 16						12 45				13 16						13 43		
Smithy Bridge	d		11 45				12 18						12 47				13 18						13 45		
Rochdale	a		11 49				12 22						12 51				13 22						13 49		
	95 d		11 50				12 23						12 52				13 23						13 50		
Castleton	95 a																								
Mills Hill	95 a																								
Moston	95 a																								
Manchester Victoria	95 ⛴ a		12 09				12 40						13 09				13 40						14 09		
Liverpool Lime Street 10	90 a						*14 05*										*15 05*								

For general notes see front of timetable
For details of catering facilities see Directory of Train Operators

A From Newcastle to Bournemouth (Table 51)
B Via Dewsbury (Table 39)
C To Wakefield Westgate (Table 39)
D From Scarborough to Manchester Airport (Table 39)
E From Hull to Manchester Piccadilly (Table 39)
G From Middlesbrough to Manchester Airport (Table 39)
H From Scarborough to Liverpool Lime Street (Table 39)
J From Edinburgh to Plymouth (Table 51)
K From Newcastle to Manchester Airport (Table 39)
L To Manchester Airport (Table 39)
N From Glasgow Central to Bournemouth (Table 51)
Q From Dundee (Table 229) to Bournemouth (Table 51)

Table 41

Saturdays

York, Selby and Leeds → Huddersfield, Blackpool North and Manchester Victoria via Bradford Interchange and Halifax

Network Diagram - see first page of Table 39

		TP 1◇ A 🛒	NT	TP 1◇ B	XC 1◇ C ☕	NT D	NT E	TP 1◇ G 🛒	NT	TP 1◇ H	NT	TP 1◇ A 🛒	NT	TP 1◇ B	XC 1◇ J ☕	NT D	NT E	TP 1◇ G 🛒		NT	TP 1◇ H	NT	TP 1◇ A 🛒	NT	TP 1◇ B 🛒
York 8	33 d	12 28		12 40	12 44			12 58			13 09	13 28		13 40	13 44			13 58				14 13	14 28		14 38
Ulleskelf	33 d																								
Church Fenton	33 d										13 21														
Selby	d						12 43			13 08							13 43				14 08				
South Milford	d						12 53										13 53								
Micklefield	d						12 58				13 28						13 58					14 28			
East Garforth	d						13 02				13 32						14 02					14 32			
Garforth	d						13 05	13 13			13 35						14 05	14 13				14 35			
Cross Gates	d						13 10				13 40						14 10					14 40			
Leeds 10	a	12 53		13 04	13 08		13 19	13 23		13 33	13 49	13 53		14 04	14 08		14 19	14 23			14 33	14 49	14 53		15 04
	37, 39 d		13 08			13 13	13 22		13 37		13 51		14 08			14 13	14 22			14 37		14 51		15 08	
Bramley	37 d		13 15				13 29		13 44				14 15				14 29			14 44				15 15	
New Pudsey	37 d		13 20				13 34		13 49		14 01		14 20				14 34			14 49		15 01		15 20	
Bradford Interchange	37 a		13 28				13 42		13 57		14 11		14 28				14 42			14 57		15 11		15 28	
	d		13 31				13 45		14 00		14 14		14 31				14 45			15 00		15 14		15 31	
Halifax	a		13 43				13 58		14 12		14 25		14 43				14 58			15 12		15 25		15 43	
	d		13 43				14 06		14 12		14 26		14 43				15 06			15 12		15 26		15 43	
Brighouse	d					13 49	14 16									14 49	15 16								
Huddersfield	39 a						14 30										15 30								
Sowerby Bridge	d		13 50			13 59			14 19				14 50			14 59				15 19				15 50	
Mytholmroyd	d		13 56			14 05			14 25				14 56			15 05				15 25				15 56	
Hebden Bridge	a		13 59			14 09			14 28		14 37		14 59			15 09				15 28		15 37		15 59	
	d		13 59						14 28		14 38		14 59							15 28		15 38		15 59	
Burnley Manchester Road	97 a										14 57											15 57			
Accrington	97 a										15 06											16 06			
Blackburn	97 a										15 14											16 14			
Preston 8	97 a										15 32											16 33			
Poulton-le-Fylde	97 a										15 52											16 52			
Blackpool North	97 a										16 01											17 01			
Todmorden	d		14 06						14 36				15 06							15 36				16 06	
Walsden	d		14 09										15 09											16 09	
Littleborough	d		14 16						14 44				15 16							15 46				16 16	
Smithy Bridge	d		14 18						14 46				15 18							15 48				16 18	
Rochdale	a		14 22						14 51				15 22							15 53				16 22	
	95 d		14 23						14 52				15 23							15 54				16 23	
Castleton	95 a																								
Mills Hill	95 a																								
Moston	95 a																								
Manchester Victoria	95 🚌 a		14 40						15 09				15 40							16 10				16 40	
Liverpool Lime Street 10	90 a		*16 05*										*17 04*											*18 05*	

		XC 1◇ K ☕	NT D	NT E	TP 1◇ G 🛒	NT	TP 1◇ H	NT	TP 1◇ A 🛒	NT	TP 1◇ B 🛒	XC 1◇ L ☕	NT D	NT E	TP 1◇ N 🛒	NT	TP 1◇ H 🛒	NT	TP 1◇ A 🛒	NT	TP 1◇ B 🛒	XC 1◇ K ☕	NT D	NT E	TP 1◇ G 🛒
York 8	33 d	14 44			14 58			15 09	15 28		15 38	15 44			15 58			16 13	16 28		16 40	16 44			16 58
Ulleskelf	33 d																								
Church Fenton	33 d							15 21																	
Selby	d			14 43			15 08							15 43			16 08							16 43	
South Milford	d			14 53										15 53										16 53	
Micklefield	d			14 58				15 28						15 58				16 28						16 58	
East Garforth	d			15 02				15 32						16 02				16 32						17 02	
Garforth	d			15 05	15 13			15 35						16 05	16 13			16 35						17 05	17 13
Cross Gates	d			15 10				15 40						16 10				16 40						17 10	
Leeds 10	a	15 08		15 19	15 23		15 33	15 49	15 53		16 04	16 08		16 19	16 23		16 36	16 49	16 53		17 04	17 08		17 19	17 23
	37, 39 d		15 13	15 22		15 37		15 51		16 08			16 13	16 22		16 37		16 51		17 08			17 13	17 22	
Bramley	37 d			15 29		15 44				16 15				16 29		16 44				17 15				17 29	
New Pudsey	37 d			15 34		15 49		16 01		16 20				16 34		16 49		17 01		17 20				17 34	
Bradford Interchange	37 a			15 42		15 57		16 11		16 28				16 42		16 57		17 11		17 28				17 42	
	d			15 45		16 00		16 14		16 31				16 45		17 00		17 14		17 31				17 45	
Halifax	a			15 58		16 12		16 25		16 43				16 58		17 12		17 25		17 43				17 58	
	d			16 06		16 12		16 26		16 43				17 06		17 12		17 26		17 43				18 06	
Brighouse	d		15 49	16 16									16 49	17 16									17 50	18 16	
Huddersfield	39 a			16 30										17 30										18 30	
Sowerby Bridge	d		15 59			16 19				16 50			16 59			17 19				17 50			17 59		
Mytholmroyd	d		16 05			16 25				16 56			17 05			17 25				17 56			18 05		
Hebden Bridge	a		16 09			16 28		16 37		16 59			17 09			17 28		17 37		17 59			18 10		
	d					16 28		16 38		16 59						17 28		17 38		17 59					
Burnley Manchester Road	97 a							16 57										17 57							
Accrington	97 a							17 06										18 06							
Blackburn	97 a							17 14										18 14							
Preston 8	97 a							17 34										18 34							
Poulton-le-Fylde	97 a							17 53										18 55							
Blackpool North	97 a							18 03										19 04							
Todmorden	d					16 35				17 06						17 35				18 06					
Walsden	d					16 38				17 09						17 38				18 09					
Littleborough	d					16 45				17 16						17 45				18 16					
Smithy Bridge	d					16 47				17 18						17 47				18 18					
Rochdale	a					16 51				17 22						17 51				18 22					
	95 d					16 52				17 23						17 52				18 23					
Castleton	95 a																								
Mills Hill	95 a																								
Moston	95 a																								
Manchester Victoria	95 🚌 a					17 10				17 40						18 10				18 41					
Liverpool Lime Street 10	90 a									*19 05*						*19 35*				*20 05*					

For general notes see front of timetable
For details of catering facilities see Directory of Train Operators

A From Newcastle to Manchester Airport (Table 39)
B From Scarborough to Liverpool Lime Street (Table 39)
C From Glasgow Central (from 29 March from Edinburgh) (Table 51) to Penzance (Table 135)
D Via Dewsbury (Table 39)
E To Wakefield Westgate (Table 39)
G From Middlesbrough to Manchester Airport (Table 39)
H From Hull to Manchester Piccadilly (Table 39)
J From Aberdeen (Table 229) to Bournemouth (Table 51)
K From Edinburgh to Plymouth (Table 51)
L From Edinburgh to Bournemouth (Table 51)
N From Middlesbrough to Manchester Piccadilly (Table 39)

York, Selby and Leeds → Huddersfield, Blackpool North and Manchester Victoria via Bradford Interchange and Halifax

Network Diagram - see first page of Table 39

	NT	TP	NT	TP	TP	NT	TP	XC	NT	NT	TP	NT	NT	TP	TP	NT	TP	XC	NT	NT	NT	TP	NT	TP
		1 ◇		1 ◇	1 ◇		1 ◇	1 ◇			1 ◇			1 ◇	1 ◇		1 ◇	1 ◇				1 ◇		1 ◇
		A		B	C		D	E	G	H	J			B	A		D	K	H			L		N
				⊼				☕										☕						
York [8] 33 d			17 09	17 28			17 40	17 44			17 58		18 10	18 28			18 38	18 44		19 04		19 10		
Ulleskelf 33 d																							←	
Church Fenton 33 d			17 21																	19 21 →			19 21	
Selby d		17 08			17 31					17 43					18 33				18 43					19 30
South Milford d										17 53									18 53					
Micklefield d			17 28							17 58			18 24						18 58				19 28	
East Garforth d			17 32							18 02			18 28						19 02				19 32	
Garforth d			17 35							18 05	18 13		18 31						19 05			19 23	19 35	
Cross Gates d			17 40							18 10			18 36						19 10				19 40	
Leeds [10] a		17 35	17 49	17 53	17 59		18 04	18 08		18 20	18 23		18 45	18 52	18 58		19 04	19 08	19 21			19 35	19 49	19 56
37, 39 d	17 37		17 51			18 08			18 13	18 22		18 37	18 51			19 08			19 22		19 37		19 51	
Bramley 37 d	17 44					18 15				18 30		18 44				19 15			19 29		19 44			
New Pudsey 37 d	17 49		18 01			18 20				18 35		18 49	19 01			19 20			19 34		19 49		20 01	
Bradford Interchange 37 a	17 57		18 11			18 28				18 43		18 57	19 11			19 28			19 45		19 57		20 11	
d	18 00		18 14			18 31				18 46		19 00	19 14			19 31			19 45		20 00		20 14	
Halifax a	18 12		18 26			18 43				18 59		19 12	19 25			19 43			20 01		20 12		20 25	
d	18 12		18 26			18 43				19 06		19 12	19 26			19 43			20 06		20 12		20 26	
Brighouse d									18 49	19 16									20 16					
Huddersfield 39 a										19 30									20 30					
Sowerby Bridge d	18 19					18 50			18 59			19 19				19 50					20 19			
Mytholmroyd d	18 25					18 56			19 05			19 25				19 56					20 25			
Hebden Bridge a	18 28		18 38			18 59			19 09			19 28	19 37			19 59					20 28		20 37	
d	18 28		18 38			18 59						19 28	19 38								20 28		20 38	
Burnley Manchester Road 97 a			18 57										19 57										20 57	
Accrington 97 a			19 06										20 06										21 06	
Blackburn 97 a			19 14										20 14										21 14	
Preston [8] 97 a			19 35										20 31										21 31	
Poulton-le-Fylde 97 a			19 58										20 49										21 49	
Blackpool North 97 a			20 07										20 56										21 56	
Todmorden d	18 35					19 06						19 35									20 35			
Walsden d	18 38					19 09						19 38									20 38			
Littleborough d	18 45					19 16						19 45									20 45			
Smithy Bridge d	18 47					19 18						19 47									20 47			
Rochdale a	18 53					19 22						19 51									20 51			
95 d	18 54					19 23						19 52									20 52			
Castleton 95 a	18 57											19 55									20 55			
Mills Hill 95 a	19 01											19 59									20 59			
Moston 95 a	19 05											20 03									21 03			
Manchester Victoria 95 ⛴ a	19 15					19 40						20 14									21 14			
Liverpool Lime Street [10] 90 a						*21 05*						*22 05*									*23 05*			

	NT	TP	XC	NT	TP	NT	TP	NT	TP	XC	NT	TP	NT	NT	TP	NT	TP	NT	NT	NT	TP	NT
		1 ◇	1 ◇		1 ◇		1 ◇		1 ◇	1 ◇		1 ◇			1 ◇		1 ◇				1 ◇	
		D	Q		B		N		D	U		L			J		A		V	X	Y	
			☕							☕												
York [8] 33 d		19 38	19 44		20 07	20 13			20 40	20 44		21 10	21 13		21 45			22 13			23 07	23 13
Ulleskelf 33 d													21 22									
Church Fenton 33 d						20 25							21 28									23 28
Selby d							20 26										22 07					
South Milford d							20 36										22 17					
Micklefield d						20 32							21 36					22 28				23 35
East Garforth d						20 36							21 40					22 32				23 39
Garforth d						20 39							21 42					22 35				23 42
Cross Gates d						20 44							21 47					22 40				23 47
Leeds [10] a		20 04	20 08		20 32	20 53	20 59		21 04	21 08		21 33	21 57		22 08		22 35	22 49			23 33	23 56
37, 39 d	20 08			20 37				21 08			21 37			22 08		22 37	22 40		23 00	23 08		
Bramley 37 d	20 15			20 44				21 15			21 44			22 15		22 44			23 07	23 15		
New Pudsey 37 d	20 20			20 49				21 20			21 49			22 20		22 49			23 12	23 20		
Bradford Interchange 37 a	20 28			20 57				21 28			21 57			22 28		22 57			23 20	23 28		
d	20 31			21 00				21 31			22 00			22 31		23 00			23 23	23 31		
Halifax a	20 44			21 12				21 44			22 12			22 44		23 12			23 36	23 44		
d	20 44			21 12				21 44			22 12			22 44		23 12			23 36	23 44		
Brighouse d	20 55							21 55						22 55					23 47	23 55		
Huddersfield 39 a	21 08							22 08						23 07			23 00		23 59	00 09		
Sowerby Bridge d				21 19							22 19					23 19						
Mytholmroyd d				21 25							22 25					23 25						
Hebden Bridge a				21 28							22 28					23 28						
d				21 28							22 28					23 28						
Burnley Manchester Road 97 a																						
Accrington 97 a																						
Blackburn 97 a																						
Preston [8] 97 a																						
Poulton-le-Fylde 97 a																						
Blackpool North 97 a																						
Todmorden d				21 35							22 35					23 35						
Walsden d				21 38							22 38					23 38						
Littleborough d				21 45							22 45					23 45						
Smithy Bridge d				21 47							22 47					23 47						
Rochdale a				21 51							22 51					23 51						
95 d				21 52							22 52					23 52						
Castleton 95 a				21 55							22 55											
Mills Hill 95 a				21 59							22 59											
Moston 95 a				22 03							23 03											
Manchester Victoria 95 ⛴ a				22 14							23 14					00 08						
Liverpool Lime Street [10] 90 a				*00 14*																		

For general notes see front of timetable
For details of catering facilities see Directory of Train Operators

A From Hull to Manchester Piccadilly (Table 39)
B From Newcastle to Manchester Airport (Table 39)
C From Hull to Huddersfield (Table 39)
D From Scarborough to Liverpool Lime Street (Table 39)
E From Edinburgh to Southampton Central (Table 51)
G Via Dewsbury (Table 39)
H To Wakefield Westgate (Table 39)
J From Middlesbrough to Manchester Piccadilly (Table 39)
K From Edinburgh to Bristol Temple Meads (Table 51)
L From Middlesbrough to Manchester Airport (Table 39)
N From Hull (Table 39)
Q From Newcastle to Birmingham New Street (Table 51)
U From Edinburgh to Birmingham New Street (Table 51)
V 2 February to 22 March
X Until 26 January and from 29 March
Y From Middlesbrough (Table 39). Until 26 January and from 29 March to Manchester Airport

Table 41

Sundays

until 27 January

York, Selby and Leeds → Huddersfield, Blackpool North and Manchester Victoria via Bradford Interchange and Halifax

Network Diagram - see first page of Table 39

		TP	TP	TP	TP	TP	NT	TP	NT	NT	NT	NT	NT	TP	NT	TP	NT	TP	XC	NT	TP
		1◇ A	1◇ A	1◇ A	1◇ A	1◇ A		1◇ A		🚌				1◇ A		1◇ B		1◇ C	1◇ D ☕		1◇ E
York 8	33 d	02 40	03 55	05 10	06 10	07 22		08 10					08 48	09 15			09 52	10 15	10 28		10 45
Ulleskelf	33 d																				
Church Fenton	33 d												09 01				10 04				
Selby	d															09 36					
South Milford	d															09 46					
Micklefield	d												09 09				10 12				
East Garforth	d												09 13				10 16				
Garforth	d												09 16				10 19				
Cross Gates	d												09 21				10 23				
Leeds 10	a	03 08	04 23	05 38	06 38	07 50		08 38					09 30	09 38		10 03	10 32	10 38	10 51		11 08
	37, 39 d						08 21		09 02			09 25	09 35		10 02		10 34			11 02	
Bramley	37 d						08 28		09 10			09 32			10 10		10 42			11 10	
New Pudsey	37 d						08 33		09 15			09 37	09 45		10 15		10 47			11 15	
Bradford Interchange	37 a						08 41		09 23			09 45	09 54		10 23		10 55			11 23	
	d						08 45		09 26			09 48	09 57		10 26		10 58			11 26	
Halifax	a						08 57		09 38			10 01	10 09		10 38		11 11			11 38	
	d						09 01		09 39			10 01	10 09		10 38		11 15			11 38	
Brighouse	d											10 11					11 25				
Huddersfield	39 a											10 24					11 39				
Sowerby Bridge	d						09 08		09 45						10 45					11 45	
Mytholmroyd	d						09 14		09 51						10 51					11 51	
Hebden Bridge	a						09 17		09 54				10 22		10 54					11 54	
	d						09 17		09 54	10 00					10 54					11 54	
Burnley Manchester Road	97 a																				
Burnley Central	97 a									10 30	10 37										
	d																				
Accrington	97 a										10 46										
Blackburn	97 a										10 55										
Preston 8	97 a										11 13										
Poulton-le-Fylde	97 a										11 31										
Blackpool North	97 a										11 38										
Todmorden	d						09 24		10 02						11 01					12 01	
Walsden	d						09 27		10 05						11 04					12 04	
Littleborough	d						09 34		10 11						11 11					12 11	
Smithy Bridge	d						09 36		10 14						11 13					12 13	
Rochdale	a						09 41		10 18						11 17					12 17	
	95 d						09 41		10 18						11 18					12 18	
Castleton	95 a						09 44		10 21						11 21					12 21	
Mills Hill	95 a						09 48		10 26						11 25					12 25	
Moston	95 a						09 52		10 29						11 29					12 29	
Manchester Victoria	95 ⛴ a						10 01		10 39						11 38					12 38	
Liverpool Lime Street 10	90 a																				

For general notes see front of timetable
For details of catering facilities see Directory of Train Operators

A To Manchester Airport (Table 39)
B From Hull to Manchester Piccadilly (Table 39)
C From Scarborough to Manchester Airport (Table 39)
D From Newcastle to Plymouth (Table 51)
E From Newcastle to Liverpool Lime Street (Table 39)

Table 41

Sundays

until 27 January

York, Selby and Leeds → Huddersfield, Blackpool North and Manchester Victoria via Bradford Interchange and Halifax

Network Diagram - see first page of Table 39

		NT (bus)	NT	NT	TP 1◇ A	XC R 1 B (catering)	TP 1◇ C	NT	TP 1◇ D	NT	TP 1◇ E	XC R 1 G (catering)	NT	TP 1◇ H	NT (bus)	NT	NT	TP 1◇ A	TP 1◇ C	XC R 1 B (catering)
York [8]	33 d			10 57	11 15	11 28			11 40	11 52	12 15	12 28		12 45			12 57	13 15		13 28
Ulleskelf	33 d																			
Church Fenton	33 d									12 04										
Selby	d						11 31												13 21	
South Milford	d						11 41												13 31	
Micklefield	d			11 12						12 12							13 12			
East Garforth	d			11 16						12 16							13 16			
Garforth	d			11 18					11 57	12 19							13 18			
Cross Gates	d			11 23						12 23							13 23			
Leeds [10]	a			11 32	11 38	11 51	12 01		12 07	12 32	12 38	12 51		13 08			13 32	13 38	13 49	13 51
	37, 39 d			11 35				12 04		12 35			13 02				13 35			
Bramley	37 d							12 12		12 42			13 10							
New Pudsey	37 d			11 44				12 17		12 47			13 15				13 44			
Bradford Interchange	37 a			11 53				12 25		12 55			13 23				13 53			
	d			11 55				12 28		12 58			13 26				13 55			
Halifax	a			12 07				12 40		13 11			13 38				14 07			
	d			12 07				12 40		13 15			13 38				14 07			
Brighouse	d									13 25										
Huddersfield	39 a									13 39										
Sowerby Bridge	d							12 47					13 45							
Mytholmroyd	d							12 53					13 51							
Hebden Bridge	a			12 20				12 56					13 54				14 20			
	d	12 00						12 56					13 54		14 00					
Burnley Manchester Road	97 a																			
Burnley Central	97 a	12 30	12 37												14 30	14 37				
	d																			
Accrington	97 a		12 46													14 46				
Blackburn	97 a		12 55													14 55				
Preston [8]	97 a		13 13													15 13				
Poulton-le-Fylde	97 a		13 31													15 31				
Blackpool North	97 a		13 38													15 38				
Todmorden	d							13 03					14 01							
Walsden	d							13 06					14 04							
Littleborough	d							13 13					14 11							
Smithy Bridge	d							13 15					14 13							
Rochdale	a							13 19					14 17							
	95 d							13 20					14 18							
Castleton	95 a							13 23					14 21							
Mills Hill	95 a							13 27					14 25							
Moston	95 a							13 31					14 29							
Manchester Victoria	95 (ship) a							13 40					14 38							
Liverpool Lime Street [10]	90 a																			

		NT	TP 1◇ D	NT	TP 1◇ E	XC R 1 J (catering)	NT	TP 1◇ K	NT (bus)	NT	NT	TP 1◇ E	TP 1◇ C	XC R 1 L (catering)	NT	TP 1◇ D	NT	NT (bus)	NT	TP 1◇	NT
York [8]	33 d		13 42	13 52	14 15	14 28		14 45			14 57	15 15		15 28		15 39	15 52			16 15	
Ulleskelf	33 d																				
Church Fenton	33 d			14 04													16 04				
Selby	d												15 21								
South Milford	d												15 31								
Micklefield	d			14 12							15 12						16 12				
East Garforth	d			14 16							15 16						16 16				
Garforth	d		13 57	14 19							15 18					15 57	16 18				
Cross Gates	d			14 23							15 23						16 23				
Leeds [10]	a		14 07	14 32	14 38	14 51		15 08			15 32	15 39	15 49	15 51		16 07	16 32			16 38	
	37, 39 d	14 02		14 35			15 02				15 35				16 02		16 35				16 50
Bramley	37 d	14 10		14 42			15 10								16 10						16 57
New Pudsey	37 d	14 15		14 47			15 15				15 44				16 15		16 44				17 02
Bradford Interchange	37 a	14 23		14 55			15 23				15 53				16 23		16 53				17 10
	d	14 26		14 58			15 26				15 55				16 26		16 55				17 13
Halifax	a	14 38		15 11			15 38				16 07				16 38		17 07				17 26
	d	14 38		15 14			15 38				16 07				16 38		17 07				17 26
Brighouse	d			15 26																	17 36
Huddersfield	39 a			15 39																	17 49
Sowerby Bridge	d	14 45					15 45								16 45						
Mytholmroyd	d	14 51					15 51								16 51						
Hebden Bridge	a	14 54					15 54				16 20				16 54		17 20				
	d	14 54					15 54		16 00						16 54			17 25			
Burnley Manchester Road	97 a																				
Burnley Central	97 a								16 30	16 37								17 55	18 00		
	d																				
Accrington	97 a									16 46									18 09		
Blackburn	97 a									16 55									18 18		
Preston [8]	97 a									17 13									18 37		
Poulton-le-Fylde	97 a									17 31									18 55		
Blackpool North	97 a									17 38									19 05		
Todmorden	d	15 01					16 01								17 01						
Walsden	d	15 04					16 04								17 04						
Littleborough	d	15 11					16 11								17 11						
Smithy Bridge	d	15 13					16 13								17 13						
Rochdale	a	15 17					16 17								17 17						
	95 d	15 18					16 18								17 18						
Castleton	95 a	15 21					16 21								17 21						
Mills Hill	95 a	15 25					16 25								17 25						
Moston	95 a	15 29					16 29								17 29						
Manchester Victoria	95 (ship) a	15 38					16 38								17 38						
Liverpool Lime Street [10]	90 a																				

For general notes see front of timetable
For details of catering facilities see Directory of Train Operators

A From Middlesbrough to Manchester Airport (Table 39)
B From Edinburgh to Bournemouth (Table 51)
C From Hull to Manchester Piccadilly (Table 39)
D From Scarborough to Liverpool Lime Street (Table 39)
E From Newcastle to Manchester Airport (Table 39)
G From Edinburgh (Table 51) to Penzance (Table 135)
H To Liverpool Lime Street (Table 39)
J From Glasgow Central to Plymouth (Table 51)
K From Middlesbrough to Liverpool Lime Street (Table 39)
L From Glasgow Central to Bournemouth (Table 51)

York, Selby and Leeds → Huddersfield, Blackpool North and Manchester Victoria via Bradford Interchange and Halifax

Sundays
until 27 January

Network Diagram - see first page of Table 39

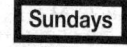

	XC	NT	TP	NT	NT	NT	TP	TP	XC	NT	TP	NT	TP	XC	NT	TP	TP	NT	NT
	R 1		1 ◇				1 ◇	1 ◇	R 1		1 ◇		1 ◇	1 ◇		1 ◇	1 ◇		
	A		B				C	D	E		G		C	H		B	D		
	⊡				bus				⊡					⊡				bus	
York 8 33 d	16 28		16 45	16 55			17 14		17 28		17 40	17 52	18 15	18 28		18 45			
Ulleskelf 33 d																			
Church Fenton 33 d												18 04							
Selby d								17 21									18 41		
South Milford d								17 31									18 53		
Micklefield d				17 10								18 12							
East Garforth d				17 14								18 16							
Garforth d				17 16							17 57	18 19							
Cross Gates d				17 21								18 23							
Leeds 10 a	16 51		17 08	17 30			17 37	17 49	17 51		18 07	18 32	18 38	18 51		19 08	19 12		
37, 39 d		17 02		17 35						18 02		18 35			19 02				
Bramley 37 d		17 10								18 10		18 42			19 10				
New Pudsey 37 d		17 15		17 44						18 15		18 47			19 15				
Bradford Interchange 37 a		17 23		17 53						18 23		18 55			19 23				
d		17 26		17 55						18 26		18 58			19 26				
Halifax a		17 38		18 07						18 38		19 11			19 38				
d		17 38		18 07						18 38		19 15			19 38				
Brighouse d												19 25							
Huddersfield 39 a												19 40							
Sowerby Bridge d		17 45								18 45					19 45				
Mytholmroyd d		17 51								18 51					19 51				
Hebden Bridge a		17 54		18 20						18 54					19 54				
d		17 54			18 25					18 54					19 54			20 00	
Burnley Manchester Road 97 a																			
Burnley Central 97 a					18 55	19 00												20 30	20 37
d																			
Accrington 97 a						19 11													20 46
Blackburn 97 a						19 20													20 55
Preston 8 97 a						19 38													21 13
Poulton-le-Fylde 97 a						19 56													21 31
Blackpool North 97 a						20 03													21 38
Todmorden d		18 01								19 01					20 01				
Walsden d		18 04								19 04					20 04				
Littleborough d		18 11								19 11					20 11				
Smithy Bridge d		18 13								19 13					20 13				
Rochdale a		18 17								19 17					20 17				
95 d		18 18								19 18					20 18				
Castleton 95 a		18 21								19 21					20 21				
Mills Hill 95 a		18 25								19 25					20 25				
Moston 95 a		18 29								19 29					20 29				
Manchester Victoria 95 ⇌ a		18 38								19 38					20 38				
Liverpool Lime Street 10 90 a																			

	NT	TP	XC	TP	NT	TP	NT	XC	NT	TP	NT	TP	TP	NT	TP	NT	NT	TP	TP
		1 ◇	1 ◇	1 ◇		1 ◇		1 ◇		1 ◇		1 ◇	1 ◇		1 ◇			1 ◇	1 ◇
		C	J	K		G		L		N		Q	K		U			U	Q
			⊡																
York 8 33 d	18 57	19 15	19 28			19 42	19 52	20 28		20 45	20 57	21 15			21 38	21 52		22 42	23 12
Ulleskelf 33 d																			
Church Fenton 33 d							20 04									22 04			
Selby d				19 35									21 31						
South Milford d													21 41						
Micklefield d	19 12						20 12				21 12					22 12			
East Garforth d	19 16						20 16				21 17					22 16			
Garforth d	19 18					19 57	20 19				21 19				21 54	22 19			
Cross Gates d	19 23						20 23				21 24					22 23			
Leeds 10 a	19 32	19 38	19 51	19 59		20 07	20 32	20 51		21 08	21 33	21 38	21 59		22 04	22 32		23 08	23 38
37, 39 d	19 35				20 02		20 35		21 02		21 35			22 02			22 35		
Bramley 37 d					20 10		20 42		21 10		21 43			22 10			22 42		
New Pudsey 37 d	19 44				20 15		20 47		21 14		21 47			22 15			22 47		
Bradford Interchange 37 a	19 53				20 23		20 55		21 23		21 56			22 23			22 55		
d	19 55				20 26		20 58		21 26		21 58			22 26			22 58		
Halifax a	20 07				20 38		21 11		21 38		22 10			22 39			23 11		
d	20 07				20 38		21 15		21 38		22 11			22 39			23 11		
Brighouse d							21 25							22 49			23a22		
Huddersfield 39 a							21 39							23 02					
Sowerby Bridge d					20 45				21 45		22 17								
Mytholmroyd d					20 51				21 51		22 23								
Hebden Bridge a	20 20				20 54				21 55		22 27								
d					20 54						22 27								
Burnley Manchester Road 97 a																			
Burnley Central 97 a																			
d																			
Accrington 97 a																			
Blackburn 97 a																			
Preston 8 97 a																			
Poulton-le-Fylde 97 a																			
Blackpool North 97 a																			
Todmorden d					21 01						22 34								
Walsden d					21 04						22 37								
Littleborough d					21 11						22 44								
Smithy Bridge d					21 13						22 46								
Rochdale a					21 17						22 50								
95 d					21 18						22 51								
Castleton 95 a					21 21						22 54								
Mills Hill 95 a					21 25						22 58								
Moston 95 a					21 29						23 02								
Manchester Victoria 95 ⇌ a					21 38						23 11								
Liverpool Lime Street 10 90 a																			

For general notes see front of timetable
For details of catering facilities see Directory of Train Operators

- **A** From Edinburgh to Plymouth (Table 51)
- **B** From Middlesbrough to Liverpool Lime Street (Table 39)
- **C** From Newcastle to Manchester Airport (Table 39)
- **D** From Hull to Manchester Piccadilly (Table 39)
- **E** From Aberdeen (Table 229) to Southampton Central (Table 51)
- **G** From Scarborough to Liverpool Lime Street (Table 39)
- **H** From Edinburgh to Bristol Temple Meads (Table 51)
- **J** From Glasgow Central to Bristol Temple Meads (Table 51)
- **K** From Hull (Table 39)
- **L** From Edinburgh to Birmingham New Street (Table 51)
- **N** From Newcastle to Liverpool Lime Street (Table 39)
- **Q** From Middlesbrough to Manchester Airport (Table 39)
- **U** From Scarborough to Manchester Piccadilly (Table 39)

Table 41

Sundays

3 February to 23 March

York, Selby and Leeds → Huddersfield, Blackpool North and Manchester Victoria via Bradford Interchange and Halifax

Network Diagram - see first page of Table 39

		TP	TP	TP	TP	TP	NT	TP		NT	NT	NT	TP	NT	TP	NT		TP	XC	NT	TP	NT	TP	XC	TP
						1 ◇		1 ◇					1 ◇		1 ◇			1 ◇	R 1		1 ◇		1 ◇	R 1	1 ◇
		A	A	A	A								A		B			C	D		E		G	H	B
		🚌	🚌	🚌	🚌														🍴					🍴	
York 8	33 d	02 00	03 00	04 30	06 00	06 42		07 33				08 48	09 15			09 52		10 15	10 28		10 45	10 57	11 15	11 28	
Ulleskelf	33 d																								
Church Fenton	33 d											09 01				10 04									
Selby	d														09 36										11 31
South Milford	d														09 46										11 41
Micklefield	d											09 09				10 12						11 12			
East Garforth	d											09 13				10 16						11 16			
Garforth	d											09 16				10 19						11 18			
Cross Gates	d											09 21				10 23						11 23			
Leeds 10	a	02 45	03 45	05 15	06 45	07 34		08 26				09 30	09 38		10 03	10 32		10 38	10 51		11 08	11 32	11 38	11 51	12 01
	37, 39 d						08 21			09 02	09 25	09 35		10 02		10 34				11 02		11 35			
Bramley	37 d						08 28			09 10	09 32			10 10		10 42				11 10					
New Pudsey	37 d						08 33			09 15	09 37	09 45		10 15		10 47				11 15		11 44			
Bradford Interchange	37 a						08 41			09 23	09 45	09 54		10 23		10 55				11 23		11 53			
	d						08 45			09 26	09 48	09 57		10 26		10 58				11 26		11 55			
Halifax	a						08 57			09 38	10 01	10 09		10 38		11 11				11 38		12 07			
	d						09 01			09 39	10 01	10 09		10 38		11 15				11 38		12 07			
Brighouse	d										10 11					11 25									
Huddersfield	39 a										10 24					11 39									
Sowerby Bridge	d						09 08			09 45				10 45						11 45					
Mytholmroyd	d						09 14			09 51				10 51						11 51					
Hebden Bridge	a						09 17			09 54		10 21		10 54						11 54		12 19			
	d						09 17			09 54		10 21		10 54						11 54		12 19			
Burnley Manchester Road	97 a											10 41										12 38			
Accrington	97 a											10 50										12 47			
Blackburn	97 a											10 58										12 55			
Preston 8	97 a											11 15										13 13			
Poulton-le-Fylde	97 a											12b05										14b05			
Blackpool North	97 a											12b20										14b20			
Todmorden	d						09 24			10 02				11 01						12 01					
Walsden	d						09 27			10 05				11 04						12 04					
Littleborough	d						09 34			10 11				11 11						12 11					
Smithy Bridge	d						09 36			10 14				11 13						12 13					
Rochdale	a						09 41			10 18				11 17						12 17					
	95 d						09 41			10 18				11 18						12 18					
Castleton	95 a						09 44			10 21				11 21						12 21					
Mills Hill	95 a						09 48			10 26				11 25						12 25					
Moston	95 a						09 52			10 29				11 29						12 29					
Manchester Victoria	95 🚊 a						10 01			10 39				11 38						12 38					
Liverpool Lime Street 10	90 a																								

For general notes see front of timetable
For details of catering facilities see Directory of Train Operators

A To Manchester Airport (Table 39)
B From Hull to Manchester Piccadilly (Table 39)
C From Scarborough to Manchester Airport (Table 39)
D From Newcastle to Bournemouth (Table 51)
E From Newcastle to Liverpool Lime Street (Table 39)
G From Middlesbrough to Manchester Airport (Table 39)
H From Edinburgh (Table 51) to Penzance (Table 135)
b By bus

Table 41

Sundays

York, Selby and Leeds → Huddersfield, Blackpool North and Manchester Victoria via Bradford Interchange and Halifax

3 February to 23 March

Network Diagram - see first page of Table 39

Station		NT	TP 1◊ A	NT	TP 1◊ B	XC R 1 C ☕	NT	TP 1◊ D	NT	TP 1◊ E	TP 1◊ G	XC R 1 H ☕	NT	TP 1◊ A	NT	TP 1◊ B	XC R 1 J ☕	NT	TP 1◊ K	NT	TP 1◊ B	TP 1◊ G
York 8	33 d		11 40	11 52	12 15	12 28		12 45	12 57	13 15		13 28		13 42	13 52	14 15	14 28		14 45	14 57	15 15	
Ulleskelf	33 d																					
Church Fenton	33 d			12 04											14 04							
Selby	d										13 21											15 21
South Milford	d										13 31											15 31
Micklefield	d			12 12					13 12						14 12					15 12		
East Garforth	d			12 16					13 16						14 16					15 16		
Garforth	d		11 57	12 19					13 18					13 57	14 19					15 18		
Cross Gates	d			12 23					13 23						14 23					15 23		
Leeds 10	a		12 07	12 32	12 38	12 51		13 08	13 32	13 38	13 49	13 52		14 07	14 32	14 38	14 51		15 08	15 32	15 39	15 49
	37, 39 d	12 04		12 35			13 02		13 35				14 02		14 35			15 02		15 35		
Bramley	37 d	12 12		12 42			13 10						14 10		14 42			15 10				
New Pudsey	37 d	12 17		12 47			13 15		13 44				14 15		14 47			15 15		15 44		
Bradford Interchange	37 a	12 25		12 55			13 23		13 53				14 23		14 55			15 23		15 53		
	d	12 28		12 58			13 26		13 55				14 26		14 58			15 26		15 55		
Halifax	a	12 40		13 11			13 38		14 07				14 38		15 11			15 38		16 07		
	d	12 40		13 15			13 38		14 07				14 38		15 14			15 38		16 07		
Brighouse	d			13 25											15 26							
Huddersfield	39 a			13 39											15 39							
Sowerby Bridge	d	12 47					13 45						14 45					15 45				
Mytholmroyd	d	12 53					13 51						14 51					15 51				
Hebden Bridge	a	12 56					13 54		14 19				14 54					15 54		16 19		
	d	12 56					13 54		14 19				14 54					15 54		16 19		
Burnley Manchester Road	97 a								14 38											16 38		
Accrington	97 a								14 47											16 47		
Blackburn	97 a								14 55											16 55		
Preston 8	97 a								15 13											17 13		
Poulton-le-Fylde	97 a								*16b05*											*18b05*		
Blackpool North	97 a								*16b20*											*18b20*		
Todmorden	d	13 03					14 01						15 01					16 01				
Walsden	d	13 06					14 04						15 04					16 04				
Littleborough	d	13 13					14 11						15 11					16 11				
Smithy Bridge	d	13 15					14 13						15 13					16 13				
Rochdale	a	13 19					14 17						15 17					16 17				
	95 d	13 20					14 18						15 18					16 18				
Castleton	95 a	13 23					14 21						15 21					16 21				
Mills Hill	95 a	13 27					14 25						15 25					16 25				
Moston	95 a	13 31					14 29						15 29					16 29				
Manchester Victoria	95 a	13 40					14 38						15 38					16 38				
Liverpool Lime Street 10	90 a																					

Station		XC R 1 L ☕	NT	TP 1◊ A	NT	TP 1◊ B	NT	XC R 1 N ☕	NT	TP 1◊ K	NT	TP 1◊ B	TP 1◊ G	XC R 1 Q ☕	NT	TP 1◊ A	NT	TP 1◊ B	XC 1◊ U ☕	NT	TP 1◊ K	TP 1◊ G
York 8	33 d	15 28		15 39	15 52	16 15		16 28		16 45	16 55	17 14		17 28		17 40	17 52	18 15	18 28		18 45	
Ulleskelf	33 d																					
Church Fenton	33 d				16 04												18 04					
Selby	d												17 21									18 41
South Milford	d												17 31									18 53
Micklefield	d				16 12						17 10						18 12					
East Garforth	d				16 16						17 14						18 16					
Garforth	d			15 57	16 18						17 16					17 57	18 19					
Cross Gates	d				16 23						17 21						18 23					
Leeds 10	a	15 51		16 07	16 32	16 38		16 51		17 08	17 30	17 37	17 49	17 51		18 07	18 32	18 38	18 51		19 08	19 12
	37, 39 d		16 02		16 35		16 50		17 02		17 35				18 02		18 35			19 02		
Bramley	37 d		16 10				16 57		17 10						18 10		18 42			19 10		
New Pudsey	37 d		16 15		16 44		17 02		17 15		17 44				18 15		18 47			19 15		
Bradford Interchange	37 a		16 23		16 53		17 10		17 23		17 53				18 23		18 55			19 23		
	d		16 26		16 55		17 13		17 26		17 55				18 26		18 58			19 26		
Halifax	a		16 38		17 07		17 26		17 38		18 07				18 38		19 11			19 38		
	d		16 38		17 07		17 26		17 38		18 07				18 38		19 15			19 38		
Brighouse	d						17 36										19 25					
Huddersfield	39 a						17 49										19 40					
Sowerby Bridge	d		16 45						17 45						18 45					19 45		
Mytholmroyd	d		16 51						17 51						18 51					19 51		
Hebden Bridge	a		16 54		17 19				17 54		18 19				18 54					19 54		
	d		16 54		17 19				17 54		18 19				18 54					19 54		
Burnley Manchester Road	97 a				17 38						18 38											
Accrington	97 a				17 47						18 47											
Blackburn	97 a				17 55						18 55											
Preston 8	97 a				18 13						19 13											
Poulton-le-Fylde	97 a				*19b05*						*20b05*											
Blackpool North	97 a				*19b20*						*20b20*											
Todmorden	d		17 01						18 01						19 01					20 01		
Walsden	d		17 04						18 04						19 04					20 04		
Littleborough	d		17 11						18 11						19 11					20 11		
Smithy Bridge	d		17 13						18 13						19 13					20 13		
Rochdale	a		17 17						18 17						19 17					20 17		
	95 d		17 18						18 18						19 18					20 18		
Castleton	95 a		17 21						18 21						19 21					20 21		
Mills Hill	95 a		17 25						18 25						19 25					20 25		
Moston	95 a		17 29						18 29						19 29					20 29		
Manchester Victoria	95 a		17 38						18 38						19 38					20 38		
Liverpool Lime Street 10	90 a																					

For general notes see front of timetable
For details of catering facilities see Directory of Train Operators

- **A** From Scarborough to Liverpool Lime Street (Table 39)
- **B** From Newcastle to Manchester Airport (Table 39)
- **C** From Edinburgh to Bournemouth (Table 51)
- **D** To Liverpool Lime Street (Table 39)
- **E** From Middlesbrough to Manchester Airport (Table 39)
- **G** From Hull to Manchester Piccadilly (Table 39)
- **H** From Edinburgh to Plymouth (Table 51)
- **J** From Glasgow Central to Bournemouth (Table 51)
- **K** From Middlesbrough to Liverpool Lime Street (Table 39)
- **L** From Glasgow Central to Plymouth (Table 51)
- **N** From Edinburgh to Southampton Central (Table 51)
- **Q** From Aberdeen (Table 229) to Bristol Temple Meads (Table 51)
- **U** From Edinburgh to Bristol Temple Meads (Table 51)
- **b** By bus

Table 41

Sundays

3 February to 23 March

York, Selby and Leeds → Huddersfield, Blackpool North and Manchester Victoria via Bradford Interchange and Halifax

Network Diagram - see first page of Table 39

		NT	TP 1◇ A	XC 1◇ B	TP 1◇ C	NT		TP 1◇ D	NT	XC 1◇ E	NT	TP 1◇ G	NT	TP 1◇ H		XC 1◇ J	TP 1◇ C	NT	TP 1◇ K	NT	NT	TP 1◇ K	TP 1◇ H	
York 8	33 d	18 57	19 15	19 28				19 42	19 52	20 28		20 45	20 57	21 15		21 28			21 38	21 52		22 42	23 12	
Ulleskelf	33 d																							
Church Fenton	33 d								20 04											22 04				
Selby	d				19 35												21 31							
South Milford	d																21 41							
Micklefield	d	19 12							20 12				21 12							22 12				
East Garforth	d	19 16							20 16				21 17							22 16				
Garforth	d	19 18						19 57	20 19				21 19						21 54	22 19				
Cross Gates	d	19 23							20 23				21 24							22 23				
Leeds 10	a	19 32	19 38	19 51	19 59			20 07	20 32	20 51		21 08	21 33	21 38		21 56	21 59		22 04	22 32		23 08	23 38	
	37, 39 d	19 35				20 02			20 35		21 02		21 35					22 02			22 35			
Bramley	37 d					20 10			20 42		21 10		21 43					22 10			22 42			
New Pudsey	37 d	19 44				20 15			20 47		21 14		21 47					22 15			22 47			
Bradford Interchange	37 a	19 53				20 23			20 55		21 23		21 56					22 23			22 55			
	d	19 55				20 26			20 58		21 26		21 58					22 26			22 58			
Halifax	a	20 07				20 38			21 11		21 38		22 10					22 39			23 11			
	d	20 07				20 38			21 15		21 38		22 11					22 39			23 11			
Brighouse	d								21 25									22 49			23a22			
Huddersfield	39 a								21 39									23 02						
Sowerby Bridge	d					20 45					21 45		22 17											
Mytholmroyd	d					20 51					21 51		22 23											
Hebden Bridge	a	20 19				20 54					21 55		22 27											
	d	20 19				20 54							22 27											
Burnley Manchester Road	97 a	20 38																						
Accrington	97 a	20 47																						
Blackburn	97 a	20 55																						
Preston 8	97 a	21 13																						
Poulton-le-Fylde	97 a	22b05																						
Blackpool North	97 a	22b20																						
Todmorden	d					21 01							22 34											
Walsden	d					21 04							22 37											
Littleborough	d					21 11							22 44											
Smithy Bridge	d					21 13							22 46											
Rochdale	a					21 17							22 50											
	95 d					21 18							22 51											
Castleton	95 a					21 21							22 54											
Mills Hill	95 a					21 25							22 58											
Moston	95 a					21 29							23 02											
Manchester Victoria	95 ⇌ a					21 38							23 11											
Liverpool Lime Street 10	90 a																							

For general notes see front of timetable
For details of catering facilities see Directory of Train Operators

A From Newcastle to Manchester Airport (Table 39)
B From Glasgow Central to Birmingham New Street (Table 51)
C From Hull (Table 39)
D From Scarborough to Liverpool Lime Street (Table 39)
E From Edinburgh to Birmingham New Street (Table 51)
G From Newcastle to Liverpool Lime Street (Table 39)
H From Middlesbrough to Manchester Airport (Table 39)
J From Edinburgh (Table 26)
K From Scarborough to Manchester Piccadilly (Table 39)
b By bus

Table 41

Sundays

from 30 March

York, Selby and Leeds → Huddersfield, Blackpool North and Manchester Victoria via Bradford Interchange and Halifax

Network Diagram - see first page of Table 39

	TP	TP	TP	TP	TP	NT		TP	NT	NT	NT	TP	NT		TP	NT	TP	XC	NT	TP		NT	TP	XC
	[1] ◇ A	[1] ◇ A	[1] ◇ A	[1] ◇ A	[1] ◇ A			[1] ◇ A				[1] ◇ A			[1] ◇ B		[1] ◇ C	[1] ◇ D (buffet)		[1] ◇ E			[1] ◇ G	[R] [1] H (buffet)
York [8] 33 d	02 40	03 55	05 10	06 10	07 22			08 10			08 48	09 15				09 52	10 15	10 28		10 45		10 57	11 15	11 28
Ulleskelf 33 d																								
Church Fenton 33 d											09 01					10 04								
Selby d															09 36									
South Milford d															09 46									
Micklefield d											09 09					10 12						11 12		
East Garforth d											09 13					10 16						11 16		
Garforth d											09 16					10 19						11 18		
Cross Gates d											09 21					10 23						11 23		
Leeds [10] a	03 08	04 23	05 38	06 38	07 50			08 38			09 30	09 38			10 03	10 32	10 38	10 51		11 08		11 32	11 38	11 51
37, 39 d						08 21			09 02	09 25	09 35		10 02			10 34			11 02			11 35		
Bramley 37 d						08 28			09 10	09 32			10 10			10 42			11 10					
New Pudsey 37 d						08 33			09 15	09 37	09 45		10 15			10 47			11 15			11 44		
Bradford Interchange 37 a						08 41			09 23	09 45	09 54		10 23			10 55			11 23			11 53		
d						08 45			09 26	09 48	09 57		10 26			10 58			11 26			11 55		
Halifax a						08 57			09 38	10 01	10 09		10 38			11 11			11 38			12 07		
d						09 01			09 39	10 01	10 09		10 38			11 15			11 38			12 07		
Brighouse d										10 11						11 25								
Huddersfield 39 a										10 24						11 39								
Sowerby Bridge d						09 08			09 45				10 45						11 45					
Mytholmroyd d						09 14			09 51				10 51						11 51					
Hebden Bridge a						09 17			09 54		10 21		10 54						11 54			12 19		
d						09 17			09 54		10 21		10 54						11 54			12 19		
Burnley Manchester Road 97 a											10 41											12 38		
Accrington 97 a											10 50											12 47		
Blackburn 97 a											10 58											12 55		
Preston [8] 97 a											11 15											13 13		
Poulton-le-Fylde 97 a											11 33											13 31		
Blackpool North 97 a											11 40											13 39		
Todmorden d						09 24			10 02				11 01						12 01					
Walsden d						09 27			10 05				11 04						12 04					
Littleborough d						09 34			10 11				11 11						12 11					
Smithy Bridge d						09 36			10 14				11 13						12 13					
Rochdale a						09 41			10 18				11 17						12 17					
95 d						09 41			10 18				11 18						12 18					
Castleton 95 a						09 44			10 21				11 21						12 21					
Mills Hill 95 a						09 48			10 26				11 25						12 25					
Moston 95 a						09 52			10 29				11 29						12 29					
Manchester Victoria 95 (bus) a						10 01			10 39				11 38						12 38					
Liverpool Lime Street [10] 90 a																								

For general notes see front of timetable
For details of catering facilities see Directory of Train Operators

A To Manchester Airport (Table 39)
B From Hull to Manchester Piccadilly (Table 39)
C From Scarborough to Manchester Airport (Table 39)
D From Newcastle to Plymouth (Table 51)
E From Newcastle to Liverpool Lime Street (Table 39)
G From Middlesbrough to Manchester Airport (Table 39)
H From Edinburgh to Oxford (Table 51)

Table 41

York, Selby and Leeds → Huddersfield, Blackpool North and Manchester Victoria via Bradford Interchange and Halifax

Sundays

from 30 March

Network Diagram - see first page of Table 39

Station	Table		TP	NT	TP	NT	TP		XC	NT	TP	NT	TP	TP		XC	NT	TP	NT	TP	XC		NT	TP	NT	TP
			1◇ A		1◇ B		1◇ C		R 1 D ☕		1◇ E		1◇ G	1◇ A		R 1 H ☕		1◇ B		1◇ C	R 1 J ☕			1◇ K		1◇ C
York 8	33	d			11 40	11 52	12 15		12 28		12 45	12 57	13 15			13 28		13 42	13 52	14 15	14 28			14 45	14 57	15 15
Ulleskelf	33	d																								
Church Fenton	33	d				12 04													14 04							
Selby		d	11 31											13 21												
South Milford		d	11 41											13 31												
Micklefield		d				12 12						13 12							14 12						15 12	
East Garforth		d				12 16						13 16							14 16						15 16	
Garforth		d			11 57	12 19						13 18						13 57	14 19						15 18	
Cross Gates		d				12 23						13 23							14 23						15 23	
Leeds 10		a	12 01		12 07	12 32	12 38		12 51		13 08	13 32	13 38	13 49		13 51		14 07	14 32	14 38	14 51			15 08	15 32	15 39
	37, 39	d		12 04		12 35				13 02		13 35					14 02		14 35				15 02		15 35	
Bramley	37	d		12 12		12 42				13 10							14 10		14 42				15 10			
New Pudsey	37	d		12 17		12 47				13 15		13 44					14 15		14 47				15 15		15 44	
Bradford Interchange	37	a		12 25		12 55				13 23		13 53					14 23		14 55				15 23		15 53	
		d		12 28		12 58				13 26		13 55					14 26		14 58				15 26		15 55	
Halifax		a		12 40		13 11				13 38		14 07					14 38		15 11				15 38		16 07	
		d		12 40		13 15				13 38		14 07					14 38		15 14				15 38		16 07	
Brighouse		d				13 25													15 26							
Huddersfield	39	a				13 39													15 39							
Sowerby Bridge		d		12 47						13 45							14 45						15 45			
Mytholmroyd		d		12 53						13 51							14 51						15 51			
Hebden Bridge		a		12 56						13 54		14 19					14 54						15 54		16 19	
		d		12 56						13 54		14 19					14 54						15 54		16 19	
Burnley Manchester Road	97	a										14 38													16 38	
Accrington	97	a										14 47													16 47	
Blackburn	97	a										14 55													16 55	
Preston 8	97	a										15 13													17 13	
Poulton-le-Fylde	97	a										15 32													17 31	
Blackpool North	97	a										15 40													17 38	
Todmorden		d		13 03						14 01							15 01						16 01			
Walsden		d		13 06						14 04							15 04						16 04			
Littleborough		d		13 13						14 11							15 11						16 11			
Smithy Bridge		d		13 15						14 13							15 13						16 13			
Rochdale		a		13 19						14 17							15 17						16 17			
	95	d		13 20						14 18							15 18						16 18			
Castleton	95	a		13 23						14 21							15 21						16 21			
Mills Hill	95	a		13 27						14 25							15 25						16 25			
Moston	95	a		13 31						14 29							15 29						16 29			
Manchester Victoria	95 🚋	a		13 40						14 38							15 38						16 38			
Liverpool Lime Street 10	90	a																								

Station	Table		TP	XC	NT	TP		NT	TP	NT	XC	NT	TP		NT	TP	TP	XC	NT	TP		NT	TP	XC	NT	TP
			1◇ A	R 1 L ☕		1◇ B			1◇ C		R 1 N ☕		1◇ K			1◇ C	1◇ A	R 1 Q ☕		1◇ B			1◇ C	1◇ U ☕		1◇ K
York 8	33	d		15 28		15 39		15 52	16 15		16 28		16 45		16 55	17 14		17 28		17 40		17 52	18 15	18 28		18 45
Ulleskelf	33	d																								
Church Fenton	33	d						16 04														18 04				
Selby		d	15 21														17 21									
South Milford		d	15 31														17 31									
Micklefield		d						16 12							17 10							18 12				
East Garforth		d						16 16							17 14							18 16				
Garforth		d				15 57		16 18							17 16					17 57		18 19				
Cross Gates		d						16 23							17 21							18 23				
Leeds 10		a	15 49	15 51		16 07		16 32	16 38		16 51		17 08		17 30	17 37	17 49	17 51		18 07		18 32	18 38	18 51		19 08
	37, 39	d			16 02			16 35		16 50		17 02			17 35				18 02			18 35			19 02	
Bramley	37	d			16 10					16 57		17 10							18 10			18 42			19 10	
New Pudsey	37	d			16 15			16 44		17 02		17 15			17 44				18 15			18 47			19 15	
Bradford Interchange	37	a			16 23			16 53		17 10		17 23			17 53				18 23			18 55			19 23	
		d			16 26			16 55		17 13		17 26			17 55				18 26			18 58			19 26	
Halifax		a			16 38			17 07		17 26		17 38			18 07				18 38			19 11			19 38	
		d			16 38			17 07		17 26		17 38			18 07				18 38			19 15			19 38	
Brighouse		d								17 36												19 25				
Huddersfield	39	a								17 49												19 40				
Sowerby Bridge		d			16 45							17 45							18 45						19 45	
Mytholmroyd		d			16 51							17 51							18 51						19 51	
Hebden Bridge		a			16 54			17 19				17 54			18 19				18 54						19 54	
		d			16 54			17 19				17 54			18 19				18 54						19 54	
Burnley Manchester Road	97	a						17 38							18 38											
Accrington	97	a						17 47							18 47											
Blackburn	97	a						17 55							18 55											
Preston 8	97	a						18 13							19 13											
Poulton-le-Fylde	97	a						18 31							19 31											
Blackpool North	97	a						18 38							19 38											
Todmorden		d			17 01							18 01							19 01						20 01	
Walsden		d			17 04							18 04							19 04						20 04	
Littleborough		d			17 11							18 11							19 11						20 11	
Smithy Bridge		d			17 13							18 13							19 13						20 13	
Rochdale		a			17 17							18 17							19 17						20 17	
	95	d			17 18							18 18							19 18						20 18	
Castleton	95	a			17 21							18 21							19 21						20 21	
Mills Hill	95	a			17 25							18 25							19 25						20 25	
Moston	95	a			17 29							18 29							19 29						20 29	
Manchester Victoria	95 🚋	a			17 38							18 38							19 38						20 38	
Liverpool Lime Street 10	90	a																								

For general notes see front of timetable
For details of catering facilities see Directory of Train Operators

- **A** From Hull to Manchester Piccadilly (Table 39)
- **B** From Scarborough to Liverpool Lime Street (Table 39)
- **C** From Newcastle to Manchester Airport (Table 39)
- **D** From Edinburgh (Table 51) to Penzance (Table 135)
- **E** To Liverpool Lime Street (Table 39)
- **G** From Middlesbrough to Manchester Airport (Table 39)
- **H** From Edinburgh to Oxford (Table 51)
- **J** From Glasgow Central to Plymouth (Table 51)
- **K** From Middlesbrough to Liverpool Lime Street (Table 39)
- **L** From Glasgow Central to Oxford (Table 51)
- **N** From Edinburgh to Plymouth (Table 51)
- **Q** From Aberdeen (Table 229) to Oxford (Table 51)
- **U** From Edinburgh to Bristol Temple Meads (Table 51)

Table 41

Sundays

from 30 March

York, Selby and Leeds → Huddersfield, Blackpool North and Manchester Victoria via Bradford Interchange and Halifax

Network Diagram - see first page of Table 39

		TP	NT	TP		XC	TP	NT	TP	NT	XC		NT	TP	NT	TP	TP	NT	TP	NT	NT	TP	TP		
		1 ◇		1 ◇		1 ◇	1 ◇		1 ◇		1 ◇			1 ◇		1 ◇	1 ◇		1 ◇			1 ◇	1 ◇		
		A		B		C	D		E		G			H		J	D		K			K	J		
						⊡																			
York 8	33 d		18 57	19 15		19 28			19 42	19 52	20 28			20 45	20 57	21 15			21 38	21 52		22 42	23 12		
Ulleskelf	33 d																								
Church Fenton	33 d									20 04										22 04					
Selby	d	18 41					19 35										21 31								
South Milford	d	18 53															21 41								
Micklefield	d		19 12							20 12					21 12					22 12					
East Garforth	d		19 16							20 16					21 17					22 16					
Garforth	d		19 18						19 57	20 19					21 19				21 54	22 19					
Cross Gates	d		19 23							20 23					21 24					22 23					
Leeds 10	a	19 12	19 32	19 38		19 51	19 59		20 07	20 32	20 51			21 08	21 33	21 38	21 59		22 04	22 32		23 08	23 38		
	37, 39 d		19 35					20 02		20 35			21 02		21 35			22 02			22 35				
Bramley	37 d							20 10		20 42			21 10		21 43			22 10			22 42				
New Pudsey	37 d		19 44					20 15		20 47			21 14		21 47			22 15			22 47				
Bradford Interchange	37 a		19 53					20 23		20 55			21 23		21 56			22 23			22 55				
	d		19 55					20 26		20 58			21 26		21 58			22 26			22 58				
Halifax	a		20 07					20 38		21 11			21 38		22 10			22 39			23 11				
	d		20 07					20 38		21 15			21 38		22 11			22 39			23 11				
Brighouse	d									21 25								22 49			23a22				
Huddersfield	39 a									21 39								23 02							
Sowerby Bridge	d							20 45					21 45		22 17										
Mytholmroyd	d							20 51					21 51		22 23										
Hebden Bridge	a		20 19					20 54					21 55		22 27										
	d		20 19					20 54							22 27										
Burnley Manchester Road	97 a		20 38																						
Accrington	97 a		20 47																						
Blackburn	97 a		20 55																						
Preston 8	97 a		21 13																						
Poulton-le-Fylde	97 a		21 31																						
Blackpool North	97 a		21 38																						
Todmorden	d							21 01							22 34										
Walsden	d							21 04							22 37										
Littleborough	d							21 11							22 44										
Smithy Bridge	d							21 13							22 46										
Rochdale	a							21 17							22 50										
	95 d							21 18							22 51										
Castleton	95 a							21 21							22 54										
Mills Hill	95 a							21 25							22 58										
Moston	95 a							21 29							23 02										
Manchester Victoria	95 ⇌ a							21 38							23 11										
Liverpool Lime Street 10	90 a																								

For general notes see front of timetable
For details of catering facilities see Directory of Train Operators

A From Hull to Manchester Piccadilly (Table 39)

B From Newcastle to Manchester Airport (Table 39)

C From Glasgow Central to Bristol Temple Meads (Table 51)

D From Hull (Table 39)

E From Scarborough to Liverpool Lime Street (Table 39)

G From Edinburgh to Birmingham New Street (Table 51)

H From Newcastle to Liverpool Lime Street (Table 39)

J From Middlesbrough to Manchester Airport (Table 39)

K From Scarborough to Manchester Piccadilly (Table 39)

Manchester Victoria, Blackpool North and Huddersfield → Leeds, Selby and York via Halifax and Bradford Interchange

Network Diagram - see first page of Table 39

Miles	Miles	Miles	Miles			TP	TP	TP	TP	TP	TP	TP	TP	NT	NT		TP	NT	GR	TP	NT	NT	TP	XC	NT
						MX	MO	MX	MO	MX	MO	MX													
						1 ◇	1 ◇	1 ◇	1 ◇	1 ◇	1 ◇	1 ◇	1 ◇				1 ◇		R 1	1 ◇			1 ◇	1 ◇	
						A	B	A	A	A	C	C	D				E		G	H			C	J	
—	—	—	—	Liverpool Lime Street 10	90 d																				
0	—	—	—	**Manchester Victoria**	95 d																05 54				06 18
4	—	—	—	Moston	95 d																				06 25
6	—	—	—	Mills Hill	95 d																				06 30
8¾	—	—	—	Castleton	95 d																				06 35
10½	—	—	—	**Rochdale**	95 a																06 08				06 38
—	—	—	—		d																06 09				06 39
12¾	—	—	—	Smithy Bridge	d																06 13				06 43
13¾	—	—	—	Littleborough	d																06 16				06 46
17¾	—	—	—	Walsden	d																06 22				06 52
19¼	—	—	—	Todmorden	d																06 26				06 56
—	—	—	0	**Blackpool North**	97 d																	05 30			
—	—	—	3	Poulton-le-Fylde	97 d																	05 36			
—	—	—	17½	**Preston** 8	97 d																	05 55			
—	—	—	29½	Blackburn	97 d																	06 11			
—	—	—	35¾	Accrington	97 d																	06 19			
—	—	—	42	Burnley Manchester Road	97 d																	06 28			
23½	—	—	54¾	Hebden Bridge	a																06 32	06 49			07 02
—	—	—	—		d													06 17			06 33	06 50			07 03
24¾	—	—	56	Mytholmroyd	d													06 20			06 36				07 06
28¾	—	—	60	Sowerby Bridge	d													06 26			06 42				07 12
—	—	0	—	**Huddersfield**	39 d																				
—	—	5¼	—	Brighouse	d									05 52											
32¼	—	10½	63½	**Halifax**	a									06 02				06 32			06 48	07 01			07 18
—	—	—	—		d									06 02				06 33			06 49	07 02			07 19
40¼	—	—	71½	**Bradford Interchange**	a									06 15				06 46			07 03	07 16			07 33
—	—	—	—		37 d									06 18				06 48			07 05	07 18			07 35
43¾	—	—	75	New Pudsey	37 d									06 26				06 57			07 14	07 27			07 44
45¾	—	—	77	Bramley	37 d									06 30				07 01			07 18				07 48
49¾	—	—	81	**Leeds** 10	37, 39 a									06 37				07 09			07 27	07 37			07 57
—	0	—	—		d	00 26	00 36	00 49	02 50	02 50	04 50	04 50	06 35		06 39		06 55		07 10	07 23	07 29	07 40	07 50	07 57	
54	4¼	—	—	Cross Gates	d										06 45						07 36	07 47			
57	7¼	—	—	Garforth	d										06 51						07 41	07 52			
57¾	8	—	—	East Garforth	d										06 53						07 43	07 55			
59½	9¾	—	—	Micklefield	d										06 57						07 47	07 58			
—	12¾	—	—	South Milford	d																07 52				
—	20¾	—	—	**Selby**	a															07 43	08 05				
64½	—	—	—	Church Fenton	33 a																	08 04			
66½	—	—	—	Ulleskelf	33 a																				
75¼	—	—	—	**York** 8	33 a	01 06	01 02	01 29	03 20	03 33	05 18	05 32	07 03		07 15		07 22		07 35			08 19	08 20	08 24	

		NT	TP	NT		NT	TP	NT	TP	NT	NT	TP	NT	XC	TP		NT	TP	NT	TP	NT	NT	TP	NT	XC
			1 ◇				1 ◇		1 ◇			1 ◇		R 1	1 ◇			1 ◇		1 ◇			1 ◇		R 1
			K	L		N	Q		H		N	C		J	U		L	Q		H		N	C		V
Liverpool Lime Street 10	90 d												05 47						06 39						
Manchester Victoria	95 d							06 49					07 18						07 47					08 19	
Moston	95 d							06 55					07 25						07 53					08 25	
Mills Hill	95 d							07 00					07 30						07 58					08 30	
Castleton	95 d							07 05					07 35						08 03					08 35	
Rochdale	95 a							07 08					07 38						08 06					08 38	
	d							07 09					07 39						08 07					08 39	
Smithy Bridge	d							07 13					07 43						08 11					08 43	
Littleborough	d							07 16					07 46						08 14					08 46	
Walsden	d							07 22					07 52						08 20					08 52	
Todmorden	d							07 26					07 56						08 24					08 56	
Blackpool North	97 d									06 28											07 30				
Poulton-le-Fylde	97 d									06 34											07 36				
Preston 8	97 d									06 54											07 55				
Blackburn	97 d									07 11											08 11				
Accrington	97 d									07 18											08 19				
Burnley Manchester Road	97 d									07 27											08 28				
Hebden Bridge	a							07 32		07 49			08 02						08 30		08 49			09 02	
	d					07 27		07 33		07 50			08 03						08 34		08 50			09 03	
Mytholmroyd	d					07 30		07 36					08 06						08 37					09 06	
Sowerby Bridge	d					07 36		07 42					08 12						08 43					09 12	
Huddersfield	39 d			07 11													08 06								
Brighouse	d			07 21		07 44					08 11						08b20					09 07			
Halifax	a			07 32				07 48		08 02			08 18				08 32		08 49		09 01			09 18	
	d			07 33				07 49		08 02			08 19				08 33		08 50		09 02			09 19	
Bradford Interchange	a			07 47				08 03		08 16			08 33				08 46		09 04		09 16			09 33	
	37 d			07 49				08 05		08 19			08 35				08 47		09 06		09 18			09 35	
New Pudsey	37 d			07 58				08 14		08 28			08 44				08 57		09 15		09 27			09 44	
Bramley	37 d			08 02				08 18					08 48				09 01		09 19					09 48	
Leeds 10	37, 39 a			08 11		08 18		08 28		08 39	08 51		08 57				09 12		09 28		09 39	09 44		09 58	
	d	07 58	08 12	08 15			08 27		08 38	08 45		08 57		09 05	09 12		09 15	09 27		09 38	09 41		09 57		10 05
Cross Gates	d	08 04		08 22						08 52							09 22				09 48				
Garforth	d	08 10		08 27			08 35			08 57		09 05					09 27				09 53		10 05		
East Garforth	d	08 12		08 29						08 59							09 29				09 56				
Micklefield	d	08 16		08 33						09 03							09 33				09 59				
South Milford	d	08 20		08 38													09 38								
Selby	a	08 35		08 53					08 58								09 54			09 58					
Church Fenton	33 a									09 08											10 05				
Ulleskelf	33 a																								
York 8	33 a		08 35				08 55			09 23		09 25		09 33	09 36			09 54			10 20		10 23		10 29

For general notes see front of timetable
For details of catering facilities see Directory of Train Operators

- **A** From Manchester Airport (Table 39)
- **B** From Liverpool Lime Street (Table 39)
- **C** From Manchester Airport to Middlesbrough (Table 39)
- **D** From Manchester Piccadilly to Newcastle (Table 39)
- **E** From Manchester Airport to Scarborough (Table 39)
- **G** To Aberdeen (Table 229)
- **H** From Manchester Piccadilly to Hull (Table 39)
- **J** From Birmingham New Street to Edinburgh (Table 51)
- **K** From Liverpool Lime Street to Newcastle and to Scarborough (Table 39)
- **L** From Wakefield Westgate (Table 39)
- **N** Via Dewsbury (Table 39)
- **Q** From Manchester Airport to Newcastle (Table 39)
- **U** From Liverpool Lime Street to Scarborough (Table 39)
- **V** From Bristol Temple Meads to Edinburgh (Table 51)
- **b** Arr. 0816

Manchester Victoria, Blackpool North and Huddersfield → Leeds, Selby and York via Halifax and Bradford Interchange

Network Diagram - see first page of Table 39

		TP 1◇ A	NT B	TP 1◇ C	NT	NT D	TP 1◇ E	NT	TP 1◇ G	NT	XC 1◇ H	TP 1◇ A	NT B	TP 1◇ C	NT	NT D	TP 1◇ E	NT	TP 1◇ G	NT	XC 1◇ J	TP 1◇ A	NT B
Liverpool Lime Street 10	90 d				07 47										08 48								
Manchester Victoria	95 d				08 54					09 24					09 54					10 24			
Moston	95 d																						
Mills Hill	95 d																						
Castleton	95 d																						
Rochdale	95 a				09 08					09 38					10 08					10 38			
	d				09 09					09 39					10 08					10 39			
Smithy Bridge	d				09 13					09 43					10 12					10 43			
Littleborough	d				09 16					09 46					10 16					10 46			
Walsden	d				09 22					09 52										10 52			
Todmorden	d				09 26					09 56					10 23					10 56			
Blackpool North	97 d							08 29										09 30					
Poulton-le-Fylde	97 d							08 35										09 36					
Preston 8	97 d							08 54										09 55					
Blackburn	97 d							09 11										10 11					
Accrington	97 d							09 19										10 19					
Burnley Manchester Road	97 d							09 28										10 28					
Hebden Bridge	a				09 32			09 49		10 02					10 32			10 49		11 02			
	d				09 33	09 40		09 50		10 03					10 33	10 40		10 50		11 03			
Mytholmroyd	d				09 36	09 43				10 06					10 36	10 43				11 06			
Sowerby Bridge	d				09 42	09 49				10 12					10 42	10 49				11 12			
Huddersfield	39 d		09 10										10 10										11 10
Brighouse	d		09 20			09 57							10 20			10 57							11 20
Halifax	a		09 32		09 48			10 01		10 18			10 32		10 48			11 01		11 18			11 32
	d		09 33		09 49			10 02		10 19			10 33		10 49			11 02		11 19			11 33
Bradford Interchange	a		09 46		10 03			10 16		10 33			10 46		11 03			11 16		11 33			11 46
	37 d		09 48		10 05			10 18		10 35			10 48		11 05			11 18		11 35			11 48
New Pudsey	37 d		09 57		10 14			10 27		10 44			10 57		11 14			11 27		11 44			11 57
Bramley	37 d		10 01		10 18					10 48			11 01		11 18					11 48			12 01
Leeds 10	37, 39 a		10 10		10 27	10 31		10 37		10 58			11 10		11 28	11 33		11 39		11 58			12 10
	d	10 12	10 15	10 27			10 38	10 41	10 57		11 05	11 12	11 15	11 27			11 38	11 41	11 57		12 05	12 12	12 15
Cross Gates	d		10 22					10 48					11 22					11 48					12 22
Garforth	d		10 27					10 53	11 05				11 27					11 53	12 05				12 27
East Garforth	d		10 29					10 56					11 29					11 56					12 29
Micklefield	d		10 33					10 59					11 33					11 59					12 33
South Milford	d		10 38										11 38										12 38
Selby	a		10 53				10 58						11 55				11 58						12 53
Church Fenton	33 a																	12 05					
Ulleskelf	33 a																						
York 8	33 a	10 36		10 49				11 17	11 23		11 29	11 35		11 52				12 20	12 23		12 29	12 35	

		TP 1◇ C	NT	NT D	TP 1◇ E	NT	TP 1◇ G	NT	XC 1◇ K	TP 1◇ A	NT B	TP 1◇ C	NT	NT D	TP 1◇ E	NT	TP 1◇ G	NT	XC 1◇ J	TP 1◇ A	NT B	TP 1◇ C	NT
Liverpool Lime Street 10	90 d		09 48										10 48										11 48
Manchester Victoria	95 d		10 54					11 24					11 54					12 24					12 54
Moston	95 d																						
Mills Hill	95 d																						
Castleton	95 d																						
Rochdale	95 a		11 08					11 38					12 08					12 38					13 08
	d		11 09					11 39					12 08					12 39					13 09
Smithy Bridge	d		11 13					11 43					12 12					12 43					13 13
Littleborough	d		11 16					11 46					12 16					12 46					13 16
Walsden	d							11 52										12 52					
Todmorden	d		11 26					11 56					12 25					12 56					13 26
Blackpool North	97 d					10 30										11 30							
Poulton-le-Fylde	97 d					10 36										11 36							
Preston 8	97 d					10 55										11 55							
Blackburn	97 d					11 11										12 11							
Accrington	97 d					11 19										12 19							
Burnley Manchester Road	97 d					11 28										12 28							
Hebden Bridge	a		11 32			11 49		12 02					12 32			12 49		13 02					13 32
	d		11 33	11 40		11 50		12 03					12 33	12 40		12 50		13 03					13 33
Mytholmroyd	d		11 36	11 43				12 06					12 36	12 43				13 06					13 36
Sowerby Bridge	d		11 42	11 49				12 12					12 42	12 49				13 12					13 42
Huddersfield	39 d										12 12										13 10		
Brighouse	d			11 57							12 22			12 57							13 20		
Halifax	a		11 48			12 01		12 18			12 32		12 48			13 01		13 18			13 32		13 48
	d		11 49			12 02		12 19			12 33		12 49			13 02		13 19			13 33		13 49
Bradford Interchange	a		12 03			12 16		12 33			12 46		13 03			13 16		13 33			13 46		14 03
	37 d		12 05			12 18		12 35			12 48		13 05			13 18		13 35			13 48		14 05
New Pudsey	37 d		12 14			12 27		12 44			12 57		13 14			13 27		13 44			13 57		14 14
Bramley	37 d		12 18					12 48			13 01		13 18					13 48			14 01		14 18
Leeds 10	37, 39 a		12 28	12 32		12 39		12 58			13 10		13 28	13 32		13 37		13 58			14 10		14 28
	d	12 27			12 38	12 41	12 57		13 05	13 12	13 15	13 27			13 38	13 41	13 57		14 05	14 12	14 15	14 27	
Cross Gates	d					12 48					13 22					13 48					14 22		
Garforth	d					12 53	13 05				13 27					13 53	14 05				14 27		
East Garforth	d					12 56					13 29					13 56					14 29		
Micklefield	d					12 59					13 33					13 59					14 33		
South Milford	d										13 38										14 38		
Selby	a				12 58						13 53				13 58						14 52		
Church Fenton	33 a															14 05							
Ulleskelf	33 a																						
York 8	33 a	12 55				13 17	13 24		13 29	13 35		13 52				14 20	14 23		14 29	14 37		14 53	

For general notes see front of timetable
For details of catering facilities see Directory of Train Operators

- **A** From Liverpool Lime Street to Scarborough (Table 39)
- **B** From Wakefield Westgate (Table 39)
- **C** From Manchester Airport to Newcastle (Table 39)
- **D** Via Dewsbury (Table 39)
- **E** From Manchester Piccadilly to Hull (Table 39)
- **G** From Manchester Airport to Middlesbrough (Table 39)
- **H** From Southampton Central to Edinburgh (Table 51)
- **J** From Plymouth to Edinburgh (Table 51)
- **K** From Bournemouth (Table 51) to Aberdeen (Table 229)

Manchester Victoria, Blackpool North and Huddersfield → Leeds, Selby and York via Halifax and Bradford Interchange

Network Diagram - see first page of Table 39

		NT	TP	NT	TP	NT	XC	TP	NT	TP	NT	NT	TP	NT	TP	NT	XC	TP	NT	TP	NT	NT	TP
							R										R						
			1 ◇		1 ◇		1	1 ◇		1 ◇			1 ◇		1 ◇		1	1 ◇		1 ◇			1 ◇
		A	B		C		D	E	G	H		A	B		C		J	E	G	K		A	B
Liverpool Lime Street [10]	90 d										12 48										13 48		
Manchester Victoria	95 d					13 24					13 54					14 24					14 54		
Moston	95 d																						
Mills Hill	95 d																						
Castleton	95 d																						
Rochdale	95 a					13 38					14 08					14 38					15 08		
	d					13 39					14 09					14 39					15 09		
Smithy Bridge	d					13 43					14 13					14 43					15 13		
Littleborough	d					13 46					14 16					14 46					15 16		
Walsden	d					13 52										14 52							
Todmorden	d					13 56					14 26					14 56					15 26		
Blackpool North	97 d			12 30										13 30									
Poulton-le-Fylde	97 d			12 36										13 36									
Preston [8]	97 d			12 55										13 55									
Blackburn	97 d			13 11										14 11									
Accrington	97 d			13 19										14 19									
Burnley Manchester Road	97 d			13 28										14 28									
Hebden Bridge	a			13 49		14 02					14 32			14 49		15 02					15 32		
	d	13 40		13 50		14 03					14 33	14 40		14 50		15 03					15 33	15 40	
Mytholmroyd	d	13 43				14 06					14 36	14 43				15 06					15 36	15 43	
Sowerby Bridge	d	13 49				14 12					14 42	14 49				15 12					15 42	15 49	
Huddersfield	39 d								14 10										15 10				
Brighouse	d	13 57							14 20			14 57							15 20			15 57	
Halifax	a			14 01		14 18			14 32		14 48			15 01		15 18			15 32		15 48		
	d			14 02		14 19			14 33		14 49			15 02		15 19			15 33		15 49		
Bradford Interchange	a			14 16		14 33			14 46		15 03			15 16		15 33			15 46		16 03		
	37 d			14 18		14 35			14 48		15 05			15 18		15 35			15 48		16 05		
New Pudsey	37 d			14 27		14 44			14 57		15 14			15 27		15 44			15 57		16 14		
Bramley	37 d					14 48			15 01		15 18					15 48			16 01		16 18		
Leeds [10]	37, 39 a	14 32		14 39		14 58			15 12		15 28	15 31		15 37		15 58			16 10		16 28	16 32	
	d		14 38	14 41	14 57		15 05	15 12	15 15	15 27			15 38	15 41	15 57		16 05	16 12	16 15	16 27			16 38
Cross Gates	d			14 48					15 22					15 48					16 22				
Garforth	d			14 53	15 05				15 27					15 53	16 05				16 28				
East Garforth	d			14 56					15 29					15 56					16 30				
Micklefield	d			14 59					15 33					15 59					16 34				
South Milford	d								15 38										16 39				
Selby	a		14 58						15 53				15 58						16 52				16 59
Church Fenton	33 a													16 05									
Ulleskelf	33 a																						
York [8]	33 a			15 17	15 23		15 29	15 35		15 52				16 22	16 23		16 29	16 35		16 52			

		NT	TP	NT	XC	TP	NT	TP	NT	NT	NT	TP	NT	NT	TP	NT	XC	TP	NT	TP	NT	TP	NT
					R												R						
			1 ◇		1	1 ◇		1 ◇				1 ◇			1 ◇		1	1 ◇		1 ◇		1 ◇	
			L		N	Q	G	L			A	B			C		U	E	G	K		B	
Liverpool Lime Street [10]	90 d									14 48											15 48		
Manchester Victoria	95 d			15 24						15 54						16 24					16 54		
Moston	95 d																						
Mills Hill	95 d																						
Castleton	95 d																						
Rochdale	95 a			15 38						16 08						16 38					17 08		
	d			15 39						16 09						16 39					17 09		
Smithy Bridge	d			15 43						16 13						16 43					17 13		
Littleborough	d			15 46						16 16						16 46					17 16		
Walsden	d			15 52						16 22						16 52					17 22		
Todmorden	d			15 56						16 26						16 56					17 26		
Blackpool North	97 d	14 30											15 30										16 30
Poulton-le-Fylde	97 d	14 36											15 36										16 36
Preston [8]	97 d	14 55											15 55										16 55
Blackburn	97 d	15 11											16 11										17 11
Accrington	97 d	15 19											16 19										17 19
Burnley Manchester Road	97 d	15 28											16 28										17 28
Hebden Bridge	a	15 49		16 02						16 32			16 49			17 02					17 32		17 49
	d	15 50		16 03						16 33	16 40		16 50			17 03					17 33		17 50
Mytholmroyd	d			16 06						16 36	16 43					17 06					17 36		
Sowerby Bridge	d			16 12						16 42	16 49					17 12					17 42		
Huddersfield	39 d						16 10												17 10				
Brighouse	d						16 20				16 57								17 20				
Halifax	a	16 01		16 18			16 32			16 48			17 01			17 18			17 32		17 48		18 01
	d	16 02		16 19			16 33			16 49			17 02			17 19			17 33		17 49		18 02
Bradford Interchange	a	16 16		16 33			16 46			17 03			17 16			17 33			17 46		18 03		18 16
	37 d	16 18		16 35			16 48			17 05			17 18			17 35			17 48		18 05		18 18
New Pudsey	37 d	16 27		16 44			16 57			17 14			17 27			17 44			17 57		18 14		18 27
Bramley	37 d			16 48			17 01			17 18						17 48			18 01		18 18		
Leeds [10]	37, 39 a	16 37		16 58			17 10			17 28	17 31		17 37			17 58			18 10		18 28		18 37
	d	16 41	16 57		17 05	17 12	17 15	17 24	17 28			17 38	17 41	17 49	17 57		18 05	18 12	18 15	18 27		18 38	18 41
Cross Gates	d	16 48				17 18	17 24		17 34				17 48	17 56					18 22				18 48
Garforth	d	16 53	17 05				17 29	17 34	17 40				17 53	18 01	18 05				18 27				18 53
East Garforth	d	16 56					17 31		17 42				17 56	18 04					18 29				18 56
Micklefield	d	16 59					17 35		17 46				17 59	18 08					18 33				18 59
South Milford	d						17 40							18 12					18 38			18 52	
Selby	a						17 54					18 05		18 25					18 50			19 01	
Church Fenton	33 a												18 05										19 05
Ulleskelf	33 a												18 10										
York [8]	33 a	17 18	17 22		17 29	17 38		17 57	18 06				18 24		18 25		18 29	18 37		18 52			19 20

For general notes see front of timetable
For details of catering facilities see Directory of Train Operators

A Via Dewsbury (Table 39)
B From Manchester Piccadilly to Hull (Table 39)
C From Manchester Airport to Middlesbrough (Table 39)
D From Bournemouth to Edinburgh (Table 51)
E From Liverpool Lime Street to Scarborough (Table 39)
G From Wakefield Westgate (Table 39)
H From Manchester Airport (Table 39)
J From Penzance (Table 135) to Dundee (Table 229)
K From Manchester Airport to Newcastle (Table 39)
L From Manchester Airport to Scarborough (Table 39)
N From Bournemouth to Glasgow Central (Table 51)
Q From Liverpool Lime Street to Middlesbrough (Table 39)
U From Plymouth to Glasgow Central (Table 51)

Manchester Victoria, Blackpool North and Huddersfield → Leeds, Selby and York via Halifax and Bradford Interchange

Network Diagram - see first page of Table 39

	TP 1◇ A	NT	XC R 1 B		TP 1◇ C	NT D	NT	NT E	TP 1◇ G	NT	TP 1◇ H	NT	TP 1◇ A	NT		XC R 1 J	NT	TP 1◇ C	NT	NT E	NT	TP 1◇ K	NT	NT
Liverpool Lime Street 10 90 d										16 18				17 12			17 35							17 50
Manchester Victoria 95 d		17 18								17 49				18 19			18 47							19 18
Moston 95 d		17 25								17 55				18 25			18 53							19 25
Mills Hill 95 d		17 30								18 00				18 30			18 57							19 30
Castleton 95 d		17 35								18 05				18 35			19 02							19 35
Rochdale 95 a		17 38								18 08				18 38			19 05							19 38
d		17 39								18 09				18 39			19 06							19 39
Smithy Bridge d		17 43								18 13				18 43			19 10							19 43
Littleborough d		17 46								18 16				18 46			19 13							19 46
Walsden d		17 52								18 22				18 52			19 19							19 52
Todmorden d		17 56								18 26				18 56			19a24							19 56
Blackpool North 97 d												17 19									18 30			
Poulton-le-Fylde 97 d												17 25									18 36			
Preston 8 97 d												17 44									18 55			
Blackburn 97 d												18 11									19 11			
Accrington 97 d												18 19									19 19			
Burnley Manchester Road 97 d												18 28									19 28			
Hebden Bridge a		18 02								18 32		18 49		19 02							19 49			20 02
d		18 03						18 23		18 33		18 50		19 03						19 40	19 50			20 03
Mytholmroyd d		18 06						18 26		18 36				19 06						19 43				20 06
Sowerby Bridge d		18 12						18 32		18 42				19 12						19 49				20 12
Huddersfield 39 d						18 10													19 23					
Brighouse d						18 20		18 40											19 33	19 57				
Halifax a		18 18				18 32				18 48		19 01		19 18					19 43		20 01			20 18
d		18 19				18 33				18 49		19 02		19 19					19 49		20 02			
Bradford Interchange a		18 33				18 46				19 03		19 16		19 33					20 02		20 16			20 33
37 d		18 35				18 48				19 05		19 18		19 35					20 04		20 18			20 35
New Pudsey 37 d		18 44				18 57				19 14		19 27		19 44					20 13		20 27			20 44
Bramley 37 d		18 48				19 01				19 18				19 48					20 17					20 48
Leeds 10 37, 39 a		18 59				19 10		19 17		19 28		19 37		19 58					20 26	20 31	20 37		←	20 57
d	18 57		19 05		19 12		19 15		19 27		19 38	19 41	19 57			20 09		20 12			20 48 →	20 45	20 48	
Cross Gates d							19 22					19 48											20 55	
Garforth d	19 05						19 27					19 53	20 05										21 00	
East Garforth d							19 29					19 56											21 02	
Micklefield d							19 33					19 59											21 06	
South Milford d											19 52													
Selby a											20 01													
Church Fenton 33 a																							21 11	
Ulleskelf 33 a																							21 16	
York 8 33 a	19 22		19 29		19 35		19 53		19 55			20 20	20 23			20 33		20 36				21 09	21 29	

	TP 1◇ L	XC R 1 N	TP 1◇ Q		NT	TP 1◇ U	NT	NT	XC 1◇ V	TP 1◇ Q	TP 1◇ L	NT	NT	TP 1◇ K		NT	NT	NT	TP 1◇ X	NT	NT			
Liverpool Lime Street 10 90 d								18 48									19 18			20 18	21 18			
Manchester Victoria 95 d								20 19									21 19			22 19	23 19			
Moston 95 d								20 25									21 25			22 25	23 25			
Mills Hill 95 d								20 30									21 30			22 30	23 30			
Castleton 95 d								20 35									21 35			22 35	23 35			
Rochdale 95 a								20 38									21 38			22 38	23 38			
d								20 39									21 39			22 39	23 39			
Smithy Bridge d								20 43									21 43			22 43	23 43			
Littleborough d								20 46									21 46			22 46	23 46			
Walsden d								20 52									21 52			22 52	23 52			
Todmorden d								20 56									21 56			22 56	23 56			
Blackpool North 97 d													20 28											
Poulton-le-Fylde 97 d													20 34											
Preston 8 97 d													20 54											
Blackburn 97 d													21 11											
Accrington 97 d													21 18											
Burnley Manchester Road 97 d													21 27											
Hebden Bridge a								21 02					21 49				22 02			23 02	00 02			
d								21 03					21 50				22 03			23 03	00 03			
Mytholmroyd d								21 06									22 06			23 06	00 06			
Sowerby Bridge d								21 12									22 12			23 12	00 12			
Huddersfield 39 d					20 25							21 27						22 25						
Brighouse d					20 35							21 37						22 35						
Halifax a					20 45			21 18				21 47	22 02				22 18	22 45		23 18	00 18			
d																								
Bradford Interchange a					21 02			21 33				22 02	22 16				22 33	23 02		23 33	00 33			
37 d					21 04			21 35				22 04	22 18				22 35	23 04		23 35	00 35			
New Pudsey 37 d					21 13			21 44				22 13	22 27				22 44	23 13		23 44				
Bramley 37 d					21 17			21 48				22 17					22 48	23 17		23 48				
Leeds 10 37, 39 a			21 09		21 25			21 58				22 25	22 38			←	22 58	23 25		23 58	00 54			
d	21 05	21 10	21 12			21 42	21 51		22 10	22 12	22 22		22 51 →	22 42		22 51			23 42					
Cross Gates d							21 58									22 58								
Garforth d							22 04									23 03								
East Garforth d							22 06									23 06								
Micklefield d							22 10									23 10								
South Milford d	21 18										22 35													
Selby a	21 28										22 44													
Church Fenton 33 a																23 16								
Ulleskelf 33 a																								
York 8 33 a		21 34	21 40			22 08	22 27		22 58	22 38				23 12		23 33			00 08					

For general notes see front of timetable
For details of catering facilities see Directory of Train Operators

- **A** From Manchester Airport to Middlesbrough (Table 39)
- **B** From Bournemouth to Edinburgh (Table 51)
- **C** From Liverpool Lime Street to Scarborough (Table 39)
- **D** From Wakefield Westgate (Table 39)
- **E** Via Dewsbury (Table 39)
- **G** From Manchester Piccadilly (Table 39)
- **H** From Manchester Piccadilly to Hull (Table 39)
- **J** From Plymouth to Edinburgh (Table 51)
- **K** From Manchester Airport to Newcastle (Table 39)
- **L** To Hull (Table 39)
- **N** From Bournemouth to Newcastle (Table 51)
- **Q** From Liverpool Lime Street (Table 39)
- **U** From Manchester Airport to Scarborough (Table 39)
- **V** From Plymouth (Table 51)
- **X** From Manchester Airport (Table 39)

Table 41

Saturdays

Manchester Victoria, Blackpool North and Huddersfield → Leeds, Selby and York via Halifax and Bradford Interchange

Network Diagram - see first page of Table 39

		TP	TP	TP	TP	TP	NT	NT	TP	GR	TP	NT	NT	TP	XC	NT	NT	TP	NT	NT	NT	TP	NT	TP	NT
		1◇	1◇	1◇	1◇	1◇			1◇	R 1	1◇			1◇	1◇			1◇				1◇		1◇	
		A	B	B	C	D			E	G	H			C	J			K			L	N		H	
Liverpool Lime Street 10	90 d																								
Manchester Victoria	95 d											05 54				06 24							06 49		
Moston	95 d																						06 55		
Mills Hill	95 d																						07 00		
Castleton	95 d																						07 05		
Rochdale	95 a											06 08				06 38							07 08		
	d											06 09				06 39							07 09		
Smithy Bridge	d											06 13				06 43							07 13		
Littleborough	d											06 16				06 46							07 16		
Walsden	d											06 22				06 52							07 22		
Todmorden	d											06 26				06 56							07 26		
Blackpool North	97 d												05 30												06 27
Poulton-le-Fylde	97 d												05 36												06 33
Preston 8	97 d												05 55												06 55
Blackburn	97 d												06 11												07 11
Accrington	97 d												06 19												07 19
Burnley Manchester Road	97 d												06 28												07 28
Hebden Bridge	a											06 32	06 49			07 02							07 32		07 49
	d											06 33	06 50			07 03					07 27		07 33		07 50
Mytholmroyd	d											06 36				07 06					07 30		07 36		
Sowerby Bridge	d											06 42				07 12					07 36		07 42		
Huddersfield	39 d																		07 10						
Brighouse	d							05 56											07 19		07 44				
Halifax	a							06 06				06 48	07 01			07 18			07 32				07 48		08 01
	d							06 06				06 49	07 02			07 19			07 33				07 49		08 02
Bradford Interchange	a							06 19				07 03	07 16			07 33			07 47				08 03		08 16
	37 d							06 23				07 05	07 18			07 35			07 49				08 05		08 18
New Pudsey	37 d							06 32				07 14	07 27			07 44			07 57				08 14		08 27
Bramley	37 d							06 36				07 18				07 48			08 01				08 18		
Leeds 10	37, 39 a							06 44				07 27	07 37			07 59			08 13		08 18		08 28		08 37
	d	00 26	00 49	02 50	04 50	06 35	06 38		06 55	07 10	07 23		07 40	07 50	07 57		08 00	08 12		08 15		08 27		08 38	08 41
Cross Gates	d						06 44						07 47				08 06			08 22					08 48
Garforth	d						06 50						07 52				08 12			08 27		08 35			08 53
East Garforth	d						06 52						07 55				08 14			08 29					08 56
Micklefield	d						06 56						07 58				08 18			08 34					08 59
South Milford	d																08 22			08 38					
Selby	a										07 43						08 35			08 53				08 58	
Church Fenton	33 a												08 04												09 05
Ulleskelf	33 a																								
York 8	33 a	01 06	01 29	03 35	05 28	07 02	07 14		07 22	07 35			08 19	08 20	08 24			08 34				08 53			09 20

For general notes see front of timetable
For details of catering facilities see Directory of Train Operators

A From Liverpool Lime Street (Table 39)
B From Manchester Airport (Table 39)
C From Manchester Airport to Middlesbrough (Table 39)
D From Manchester Piccadilly to Newcastle (Table 39)
E From Manchester Airport to Scarborough (Table 39)
G To Aberdeen (Table 229)
H From Manchester Piccadilly to Hull (Table 39)
J From Birmingham New Street to Edinburgh (Table 51)
K From Liverpool Lime Street to Scarborough (Table 39)
L Via Dewsbury (Table 39)
N From Manchester Airport to Newcastle (Table 39)

Manchester Victoria, Blackpool North and Huddersfield → Leeds, Selby and York via Halifax and Bradford Interchange

Network Diagram - see first page of Table 39

		TP 1◇ A		NT	XC 1◇ B	TP 1◇ C	NT D	TP 1◇ E	NT	NT G	TP 1◇ H	NT	TP 1◇ J	NT	XC 1◇ K	TP 1◇ L	NT D	TP 1◇ E	NT	NT G	TP 1◇ H	NT	TP 1◇ J	NT	XC 1◇ N
Liverpool Lime Street 10	90 d			*05 47*					*06 39*										*07 47*						
Manchester Victoria	95 d			07 18					07 47					08 19					08 54					09 24	
Moston	95 d			07 25					07 53					08 25											
Mills Hill	95 d			07 30					07 58					08 30											
Castleton	95 d			07 35					08 03					08 35											
Rochdale	95 a			07 38					08 06					08 38					09 08					09 38	
	d			07 39					08 07					08 39					09 09					09 39	
Smithy Bridge	d			07 43					08 11					08 43					09 13					09 43	
Littleborough	d			07 46					08 14					08 46					09 16					09 46	
Walsden	d			07 52					08 20					08 52					09 22					09 52	
Todmorden	d			07 56					08 24					08 56					09 26					09 56	
Blackpool North	97 d											07 30										08 27			
Poulton-le-Fylde	97 d											07 36										08 33			
Preston 8	97 d											07 55										08 52			
Blackburn	97 d											08 11										09 11			
Accrington	97 d											08 19										09 19			
Burnley Manchester Road	97 d											08 28										09 28			
Hebden Bridge	a			08 02					08 30			08 49		09 02					09 32			09 49		10 02	
	d			08 03					08 33	08 40		08 50		09 03					09 33	09 40		09 50		10 03	
Mytholmroyd	d			08 06					08 37	08 43				09 06					09 36	09 43				10 06	
Sowerby Bridge	d			08 12					08 43	08 49				09 12					09 42	09 49				10 12	
Huddersfield	39 d						08 06										09 10								
Brighouse	d						08b20			08 57							09 20			09 57					
Halifax	a			08 18			08 32		08 49			09 01		09 18			09 32		09 48			10 01		10 18	
	d			08 19			08 33		08 50			09 02		09 19			09 33		09 49			10 02		10 19	
Bradford Interchange	a			08 33			08 46		09 04			09 16		09 33			09 46		10 03			10 16		10 33	
	37 d			08 35			08 47		09 06			09 18		09 35			09 48		10 05			10 18		10 35	
New Pudsey	37 d			08 44			08 57		09 15			09 27		09 44			09 57		10 14			10 27		10 44	
Bramley	37 d			08 48			09 01		09 19					09 48			10 01		10 18					10 48	
Leeds 10	37, 39 a			08 57			09 12		09 28	09 31		09 39		09 58			10 10		10 28	10 31		10 37		10 58	
	d	08 57			09 05		09 15	09 27			09 38	09 41	09 57		10 05	10 12	10 15	10 27			10 38	10 41	10 57		11 05
Cross Gates	d						09 22					09 48					10 22					10 48			
Garforth	d	09 05					09 27					09 53	10 05				10 27					10 53	11 05		
East Garforth	d						09 29					09 56					10 29					10 56			
Micklefield	d						09 33					09 59					10 33					10 59			
South Milford	d						09 38										10 38								
Selby	a						09 54				09 58						10 53				10 58				
Church Fenton	33 a											10 05													
Ulleskelf	33 a																								
York 8	33 a	09 25			09 31			09 52				10 20	10 23		10 31	10 35		10 52				11 17	11 23		11 29

		TP 1◇ L	NT D	TP 1◇ E		NT	NT G	TP 1◇ H	NT	TP 1◇ J	NT	XC 1◇ Q	TP 1◇ L	NT D	TP 1◇ E	NT	NT G	TP 1◇ H	NT	TP 1◇ J	NT	XC 1◇ U	TP 1◇ L	NT D	TP 1◇ E
Liverpool Lime Street 10	90 d					*08 48*										*09 48*									
Manchester Victoria	95 d					09 54					10 24					10 54					11 24				
Moston	95 d																								
Mills Hill	95 d																								
Castleton	95 d																								
Rochdale	95 a					10 08					10 38					11 08					11 38				
	d					10 08					10 39					11 09					11 39				
Smithy Bridge	d					10 12					10 43					11 13					11 43				
Littleborough	d					10 16					10 46					11 16					11 46				
Walsden	d										10 52										11 52				
Todmorden	d					10 25					10 56					11 26					11 56				
Blackpool North	97 d								09 30										10 30						
Poulton-le-Fylde	97 d								09 36										10 36						
Preston 8	97 d								09 55										10 55						
Blackburn	97 d								10 11										11 11						
Accrington	97 d								10 19										11 19						
Burnley Manchester Road	97 d								10 28										11 28						
Hebden Bridge	a					10 32			10 49		11 02					11 32			11 49		12 02				
	d					10 33	10 40		10 50		11 03					11 33	11 40		11 50		12 03				
Mytholmroyd	d					10 36	10 43				11 06					11 36	11 43				12 06				
Sowerby Bridge	d					10 42	10 49				11 12					11 42	11 49				12 12				
Huddersfield	39 d		10 10											11 10										12 10	
Brighouse	d		10 20				10 57							11 20			11 57							12 20	
Halifax	a		10 32			10 48			11 01		11 18			11 32		11 48			12 01		12 18			12 32	
	d		10 33			10 49			11 02		11 19			11 33		11 49			12 02		12 19			12 33	
Bradford Interchange	a		10 46			11 03			11 16		11 33			11 46		12 03			12 16		12 33			12 46	
	37 d		10 48			11 05			11 18		11 35			11 48		12 05			12 18		12 35			12 48	
New Pudsey	37 d		10 57			11 14			11 27		11 44			11 57		12 14			12 27		12 44			12 57	
Bramley	37 d		11 01			11 18					11 48			12 01		12 18					12 48			13 01	
Leeds 10	37, 39 a		11 10			11 28	11 31		11 39		11 58			12 10		12 28	12 31		12 38		12 58			13 10	
	d	11 12	11 15	11 27				11 38	11 41	11 57		12 05	12 12	12 15	12 27			12 38	12 41	12 57		13 05	13 12	13 15	13 27
Cross Gates	d		11 22						11 48					12 22					12 48					13 22	
Garforth	d		11 27						11 53	12 05				12 27					12 53	13 05				13 27	
East Garforth	d		11 29						11 56					12 29					12 56					13 29	
Micklefield	d		11 33						11 59					12 33					12 59					13 33	
South Milford	d		11 38											12 38										13 38	
Selby	a		11 53					11 58						12 53				12 58						13 53	
Church Fenton	33 a								12 05																
Ulleskelf	33 a																								
York 8	33 a	11 35		11 52					12 20	12 23		12 29	12 35		12 52				13 17	13 23		13 29	13 35		13 52

For general notes see front of timetable
For details of catering facilities see Directory of Train Operators

A From Manchester Airport to Middlesbrough (Table 39)
B From Birmingham New Street to Edinburgh (Table 51)
C From Liverpool Lime Street to Scarborough (Table 39)
D From Wakefield Westgate (Table 39)
E From Manchester Airport to Newcastle (Table 39)
G Via Dewsbury (Table 39)
H From Manchester Piccadilly to Hull (Table 39)
J From Manchester Airport to Middlesbrough (Table 39)
K From Bristol Temple Meads to Edinburgh (Table 51)
L From Liverpool Lime Street to Scarborough (Table 39)
N From Southampton Central to Edinburgh (Table 51)
Q From Plymouth to Edinburgh (Table 51)
U From Bournemouth (Table 51) to Aberdeen (Table 229)
b Arr. 0816

Manchester Victoria, Blackpool North and Huddersfield → Leeds, Selby and York via Halifax and Bradford Interchange

Network Diagram - see first page of Table 39

		NT	NT	TP 1◇	NT	TP 1◇		NT	XC 1◇	TP 1◇	NT	TP 1◇	NT	NT	TP 1◇	NT	TP 1◇	NT	XC 1◇	TP 1◇	NT	TP 1◇	NT	NT	TP 1◇
			A	B		C			D	E	G	H		A	B		C		J	E	G	K		A	B
Liverpool Lime Street 10	90 d	10 48											11 48										12 48		
Manchester Victoria	95 d	11 54						12 24					12 54					13 24					13 54		
Moston	95 d																								
Mills Hill	95 d																								
Castleton	95 d																								
Rochdale	95 a	12 08						12 38					13 08					13 38					14 08		
	d	12 08						12 39					13 09					13 39					14 09		
Smithy Bridge	d	12 12						12 43					13 13					13 43					14 13		
Littleborough	d	12 16						12 46					13 16					13 46					14 16		
Walsden	d							12 52										13 52							
Todmorden	d	12 25						12 56					13 26					13 56					14 26		
Blackpool North	97 d				11 30											12 30									
Poulton-le-Fylde	97 d				11 36											12 36									
Preston 8	97 d				11 55											12 55									
Blackburn	97 d				12 11											13 11									
Accrington	97 d				12 19											13 19									
Burnley Manchester Road	97 d				12 28											13 28									
Hebden Bridge	a	12 32			12 49			13 02					13 32			13 49		14 02					14 32		
	d	12 33	12 40		12 50			13 03					13 33	13 40		13 50		14 03					14 33	14 40	
Mytholmroyd	d	12 36	12 43					13 06					13 36	13 43				14 06					14 36	14 43	
Sowerby Bridge	d	12 42	12 49					13 12					13 42	13 49				14 12					14 42	14 49	
Huddersfield	39 d										13 10										14 10				
Brighouse	d		12 57								13 20			13 57							14 20			14 57	
Halifax	a	12 48			13 01			13 18			13 32		13 48			14 01		14 18			14 32		14 48		
	d	12 49			13 02			13 19			13 33		13 49			14 02		14 19			14 33		14 49		
Bradford Interchange	a	13 03			13 16			13 33			13 46		14 03			14 16		14 33			14 46		15 03		
	37 d	13 05			13 18			13 35			13 48		14 05			14 18		14 35			14 48		15 05		
New Pudsey	37 d	13 14			13 27			13 44			13 57		14 14			14 27		14 44			14 57		15 14		
Bramley	37 d	13 18						13 48			14 01		14 18					14 48			15 01		15 18		
Leeds 10	37, 39 a	13 28	13 31		13 37			13 58			14 10		14 28	14 31		14 39		14 58			15 12		15 28	15 31	
	d			13 38	13 41	13 57			14 05	14 12	14 15	14 27			14 38	14 41	14 57		15 05	15 12	15 15	15 27			15 38
Cross Gates	d				13 48						14 22					14 48					15 22				
Garforth	d				13 53	14 05					14 27					14 53	15 05				15 27				
East Garforth	d				13 56						14 29					14 56					15 29				
Micklefield	d				13 59						14 33					14 59					15 33				
South Milford	d										14 38										15 38				
Selby	a			13 58							14 52				14 58						15 53				15 58
Church Fenton	33 a				14 05																				
Ulleskelf	33 a																								
York 8	33 a				14 20	14 23			14 29	14 35		14 52				15 19	15 23		15 29	15 35		15 52			

		NT	TP 1◇	NT	XC 1◇	TP 1◇	NT	TP 1◇		NT	NT	TP 1◇	NT	TP 1◇	NT	XC 1◇	TP 1◇	NT	TP 1◇	NT	NT	TP 1◇	NT	TP 1◇	NT
			C		L	E	G	H			A	B		N		Q	U	G	N		A	B		C	
Liverpool Lime Street 10	90 d									13 48										14 48					
Manchester Victoria	95 d			14 24						14 54					15 24					15 54					16 24
Moston	95 d																								
Mills Hill	95 d																								
Castleton	95 d																								
Rochdale	95 a			14 38						15 08					15 38					16 08					16 38
	d			14 39						15 09					15 39					16 09					16 39
Smithy Bridge	d			14 43						15 13					15 43					16 13					16 43
Littleborough	d			14 46						15 16					15 46					16 16					16 46
Walsden	d			14 52											15 52					16 22					16 52
Todmorden	d			14 56						15 26					15 56					16 26					16 56
Blackpool North	97 d	13 30											14 30										15 30		
Poulton-le-Fylde	97 d	13 36											14 36										15 36		
Preston 8	97 d	13 55											14 55										15 55		
Blackburn	97 d	14 11											15 11										16 11		
Accrington	97 d	14 19											15 19										16 19		
Burnley Manchester Road	97 d	14 28											15 28										16 28		
Hebden Bridge	a	14 49		15 02						15 32			15 49		16 02					16 32			16 49		17 02
	d	14 50		15 03						15 33	15 40		15 50		16 03					16 33	16 40		16 50		17 03
Mytholmroyd	d			15 06						15 36	15 43				16 06					16 36	16 43				17 06
Sowerby Bridge	d			15 12						15 42	15 49				16 12					16 42	16 49				17 12
Huddersfield	39 d						15 10							16 27				16 10							
Brighouse	d						15 20				15 57							16 20			16 57				
Halifax	a	15 01		15 18			15 32			15 48			16 01		16 18			16 32		16 48			17 01		17 18
	d	15 02		15 19			15 33			15 49			16 02		16 19			16 33		16 49			17 02		17 19
Bradford Interchange	a	15 16		15 33			15 46			16 03			16 16		16 33			16 46		17 03			17 16		17 33
	37 d	15 18		15 35			15 48			16 05			16 18		16 35			16 48		17 05			17 18		17 35
New Pudsey	37 d	15 27		15 44			15 57			16 14			16 27		16 44			16 57		17 14			17 27		17 44
Bramley	37 d			15 48			16 01			16 18					16 48			17 01		17 18					17 48
Leeds 10	37, 39 a	15 37		15 58			16 10			16 28	16 31		16 37	16 52	16 58			17 10		17 28	17 31		17 37		17 58
	d	15 41	15 57		16 05	16 12	16 15	16 27				16 38	16 41	16 57		17 05	17 12	17 15	17 24			17 38	17 41	17 57	
Cross Gates	d	15 48					16 22						16 48				17 18	17 24					17 48		
Garforth	d	15 53	16 05				16 28						16 53	17 05				17 29	17 34				17 53	18 05	
East Garforth	d	15 56					16 30						16 56					17 31					17 56		
Micklefield	d	15 59					16 34						16 59					17 35					17 59		
South Milford	d						16 39											17 40							
Selby	a						16 54					16 59						17 53				17 59			
Church Fenton	33 a	16 05																					18 06		
Ulleskelf	33 a																						18 10		
York 8	33 a	16 22	16 23		16 29	16 35		16 52					17 17	17 22		17 30	17 38		17 57				18 24	18 25	

For general notes see front of timetable
For details of catering facilities see Directory of Train Operators

- **A** Via Dewsbury (Table 39)
- **B** From Manchester Piccadilly to Hull (Table 39)
- **C** From Manchester Airport to Middlesbrough (Table 39)
- **D** From Plymouth to Edinburgh (Table 51)
- **E** From Liverpool Lime Street to Scarborough (Table 39)
- **G** From Wakefield Westgate (Table 39)
- **H** From Manchester Airport to Newcastle (Table 39)
- **J** From Bournemouth to Edinburgh (Table 51)
- **K** From Manchester Airport (Table 39)
- **L** From Penzance (Table 135) to Dundee (Table 229)
- **N** From Manchester Airport to Scarborough (Table 39)
- **Q** From Bournemouth to Glasgow Central (from 29 March to Edinburgh) (Table 51)
- **U** From Liverpool Lime Street to Middlesbrough (Table 39)

Table 41

Saturdays

Manchester Victoria, Blackpool North and Huddersfield → Leeds, Selby and York via Halifax and Bradford Interchange

Network Diagram - see first page of Table 39

		XC	TP	NT	TP	NT	TP	NT	TP	NT		XC	TP	NT	NT	TP	NT	TP	NT	TP	NT	XC	NT	TP	NT
		1 ◇ A	1 ◇ B	C	1 ◇ D		1 ◇ E		1 ◇ G			1 ◇ H	1 ◇ B	C	J	1 ◇ K		1 ◇ E		1 ◇ G		1 ◇ L		1 ◇ B	
Liverpool Lime Street 10	90 d					15 48											16 18				17 12		17 35		
Manchester Victoria	95 d					16 54				17 18							17 49				18 19		18 47		
Moston	95 d									17 25							17 55				18 25		18 53		
Mills Hill	95 d									17 30							18 00				18 30		18 57		
Castleton	95 d									17 35							18 05				18 35		19 02		
Rochdale	95 a					17 08				17 38							18 08				18 38		19 05		
	d					17 09				17 39							18 09				18 39		19 06		
Smithy Bridge	d					17 13				17 43							18 13				18 43		19 10		
Littleborough	d					17 16				17 46							18 16				18 46		19 13		
Walsden	d					17 22				17 52							18 22				18 52		19 19		
Todmorden	d					17 26				17 56							18 26				18 56		19a24		
Blackpool North	97 d							16 30											17 19						
Poulton-le-Fylde	97 d							16 36											17 25						
Preston 8	97 d							16 55											17 44						
Blackburn	97 d							17 11											18 11						
Accrington	97 d							17 19											18 19						
Burnley Manchester Road	97 d							17 28											18 28						
Hebden Bridge	a					17 32		17 49		18 02							18 32		18 49		19 02				
	d					17 33		17 50		18 03					18 23		18 33		18 50		19 03				
Mytholmroyd	d					17 36				18 06					18 26		18 36				19 06				
Sowerby Bridge	d					17 42				18 12					18 32		18 42				19 12				
Huddersfield	39 d			17 10										18 10											19 23
Brighouse	d			17 20										18 20	18 40										19 33
Halifax	a			17 32		17 48		18 01		18 18				18 32			18 48		19 01		19 18				19 43
	d			17 33		17 49		18 02		18 19				18 33			18 49		19 02		19 19				19 49
Bradford Interchange	a			17 46		18 03		18 16		18 33				18 46			19 03		19 16		19 33				20 02
	37 d			17 48		18 05		18 18		18 35				18 48			19 05		19 18		19 35				20 04
New Pudsey	37 d			17 57		18 14		18 27		18 44				18 57			19 14		19 27		19 44				20 13
Bramley	37 d			18 01		18 18				18 48				19 01			19 18				19 48				20 17
Leeds 10	37, 39 a			18 10		18 28		18 37		18 59				19 10	19 18		19 28		19 37		19 58				20 29
	d	18 05	18 12	18 15	18 27		18 38	18 41	18 57			19 05	19 12	19 15		19 27		19 38	19 41	19 57		20 05		20 12	
Cross Gates	d			18 22				18 48						19 22					19 48						
Garforth	d			18 27				18 53	19 05					19 27					19 53	20 05					
East Garforth	d			18 29				18 56						19 29					19 56						
Micklefield	d			18 33				18 59						19 33					19 59						
South Milford	d			18 38			18 52											19 52							
Selby	a			18 50			19 01											20 01							
Church Fenton	33 a							19 05																	
Ulleskelf	33 a																								
York 8	33 a	18 29	18 35		18 52			19 19	19 22			19 32	19 35	19 53		19 58			20 21	20 24		20 29		20 36	

		NT	TP	NT	TP	NT	XC	TP	NT	TP	NT	NT	XC	TP	TP	NT	NT	TP	NT	NT	NT	TP	NT		
		J	1 ◇ D		1 ◇ N		1 ◇ Q	1 ◇ U		1 ◇ V			1 ◇ X	1 ◇ U	1 ◇ N			1 ◇ Y				1 ◇ Y			
Liverpool Lime Street 10	90 d					17 48						18 48								19 18			21 18		
Manchester Victoria	95 d					19 26						20 19								21 19			22 49		
Moston	95 d					19 32						20 25								21 25			22 55		
Mills Hill	95 d					19 37						20 30								21 30			23 00		
Castleton	95 d					19 42						20 35								21 35			23 05		
Rochdale	95 a					19 45						20 38								21 38			23 08		
	d					19 47						20 39								21 39			23 09		
Smithy Bridge	d					19 51						20 43								21 43			23 13		
Littleborough	d					19 54						20 46								21 46			23 16		
Walsden	d					20 00						20 52								21 52			23 22		
Todmorden	d					20 04						20 56								21 56			23 26		
Blackpool North	97 d			18 30													20 30								
Poulton-le-Fylde	97 d			18 36													20 37								
Preston 8	97 d			18 56													20 55								
Blackburn	97 d			19 13													21 11								
Accrington	97 d			19 20													21 19								
Burnley Manchester Road	97 d			19 29													21 28								
Hebden Bridge	a			19 51		20 10						21 02					21 49			22 02			23 32		
	d	19 40		19 52		20 11						21 03					21 50			22 03			23 33		
Mytholmroyd	d	19 43				20 14						21 06								22 06			23 36		
Sowerby Bridge	d	19 49				20 20						21 12								22 12			23 42		
Huddersfield	39 d								20 25							21 25					22 25				
Brighouse	d	19 57							20 35							21 35					22 35				
Halifax	a			20 04		20 26			20 45			21 18				21 45	22 01			22 18	22 45		23 48		
	d			20 04		20 27			20 49			21 19				21 49	22 02			22 19	22 49		23 49		
Bradford Interchange	a			20 18		20 41			21 02			21 33				22 02	22 16			22 33	23 02		00 03		
	37 d			20 21		20 43			21 04			21 35				22 04	22 18			22 35	23 04		00 05		
New Pudsey	37 d			20 30		20 52			21 13			21 44				22 13	22 27			22 44	23 13		00 14		
Bramley	37 d					20 56			21 17			21 48				22 17				22 48	23 17		00 18		
Leeds 10	37, 39 a	20 32		20 40		21 07			21 25			21 58				22 25	22 37		←	22 58	23 25		00 28		
	d		20 45	20 48	21 05		21 10	21 12		21 42	21 45		22 05	22 12	22 22		22 54 →	22 42	22 54			23 42			
Cross Gates	d			20 55							21 52								23 01						
Garforth	d			21 00							21 57								23 06						
East Garforth	d			21 03							21 59								23 09						
Micklefield	d			21 07							22 03								23 13						
South Milford	d				21 18										22 36										
Selby	a				21 28										22 45										
Church Fenton	33 a			21 13															23 19						
Ulleskelf	33 a			21 18																					
York 8	33 a		21 09	21 30			21 35	21 40		22 05	22 19		22 38	22 38				23 09	23 36			00 08			

For general notes see front of timetable
For details of catering facilities see Directory of Train Operators

- **A** From Plymouth to Glasgow Central (from 29 March to Edinburgh) (Table 51)
- **B** From Liverpool Lime Street to Scarborough (Table 39)
- **C** From Wakefield Westgate (Table 39)
- **D** From Manchester Airport to Newcastle (Table 39)
- **E** From Manchester Piccadilly to Hull (Table 39)
- **G** From Manchester Airport to Middlesbrough (Table 39)
- **H** From Bournemouth to Edinburgh (Table 51)
- **J** Via Dewsbury (Table 39)
- **K** From Manchester Piccadilly (Table 39)
- **L** From Plymouth to Newcastle (Table 51)
- **N** To Hull (Table 39)
- **Q** From Bournemouth to Newcastle (Table 51)
- **U** From Liverpool Lime Street (Table 39)
- **V** From Manchester Airport to Scarborough (Table 39)
- **X** From Plymouth (Table 51)
- **Y** From Manchester Airport (Table 39)

Table 41

Sundays

until 27 January

Manchester Victoria, Blackpool North and Huddersfield → Leeds, Selby and York via Halifax and Bradford Interchange

Network Diagram - see first page of Table 39

		TP 1 ◇ A	TP 1 ◇ B	TP 1 ◇ B	TP 1 ◇ B	TP 1 ◇ C		TP 1 ◇ D	NT	TP 1 ◇ E	TP 1 ◇ C	NT		TP 1 ◇ G	TP 1 ◇ H	NT	TP 1 ◇ D	NT		XC 1 ◇ J 🍴	TP 1 ◇ K	NT	TP 1 ◇ C	NT	XC 1 ◇ L 🍴
Liverpool Lime Street 10	90 d																								
Manchester Victoria	95 ⇌ d																	09 14						10 15	
Moston	95 d																	09 21						10 21	
Mills Hill	95 d																	09 25						10 25	
Castleton	95 d																	09 30						10 30	
Rochdale	95 a																	09 34						10 34	
	d																	09 34						10 34	
Smithy Bridge	d																	09 38						10 38	
Littleborough	d																	09 42						10 42	
Walsden	d																	09 48						10 48	
Todmorden	d																	09 51						10 51	
Blackpool North	97 d																								
Poulton-le-Fylde	97 d																								
Preston 8	97 d																								
Blackburn	97 d																								
Accrington	97 d																								
Burnley Central	97 a																								
	d																								
Burnley Manchester Road	97 d																								
Hebden Bridge	a																	09 58						10 58	
	d																	09 58						10 58	
Mytholmroyd	d																	10 01						11 01	
Sowerby Bridge	d																	10 07						11 07	
Huddersfield	39 d															09 20									
Brighouse	d															09 30									
Halifax	a															09 42		10 14						11 14	
	d											09 06				09 47		10 14				10 45		11 14	
Bradford Interchange	a											09 19				09 59		10 28				10 59		11 28	
	37 d								08 31			09 21				10 02		10 31				11 02		11 31	
New Pudsey	37 d								08 39			09 30				10 10		10 39				11 10		11 39	
Bramley	37 d								08 43			09 34				10 14		10 43						11 43	
Leeds 10	37, 39 a								08 52			09 42				10 24		10 52				11 21		11 54	
	d	00 15	00 42	02 38	05 58	07 43		08 40	08 55	09 10	09 40	09 48		10 06	10 25	10 29	10 42			11 08	11 10	11 25	11 40		12 08
Cross Gates	d								09 02			09 54				10 36						11 32			
Garforth	d								09 07	09 18		10 00				10 41					11 18	11 37			
East Garforth	d								09 09			10 02				10 43						11 39			
Micklefield	d								09 13			10 06				10 47						11 43			
South Milford	d														10 38										
Selby	a														10 47										
Church Fenton	33 a								09 19							10 53									
Ulleskelf	33 a																								
York 8	33 a	00 41	01 08	03 04	06 24	08 09		09 07	09 33	09 35	10 06	10 23		10 29		11 07	11 09			11 33	11 36	11 59	12 05		12 33

For general notes see front of timetable
For details of catering facilities see Directory of Train Operators

A From Liverpool Lime Street (Table 39)
B From Manchester Airport (Table 39)
C From Manchester Airport to Middlesbrough (Table 39)
D From Manchester Airport to Newcastle (Table 39)
E To Scarborough (Table 39)
G From Liverpool Lime Street to Newcastle (Table 39)
H From Manchester Piccadilly to Hull (Table 39)
J From Birmingham New Street to Glasgow Central (Table 51)
K From Liverpool Lime Street to Scarborough (Table 39)
L From Birmingham New Street to Edinburgh (Table 51)

Manchester Victoria, Blackpool North and Huddersfield → Leeds, Selby and York via Halifax and Bradford Interchange

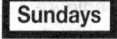

Network Diagram - see first page of Table 39

		TP [1] ◇ A	NT	TP [1] ◇ B	NT	XC [1] ◇ C ☕	TP [1] ◇ D	NT	NT	NT 🚌	TP [1] ◇ E	NT	XC [1] ◇ G ☕	TP [1] ◇ A	NT	TP [1] ◇ B	NT	XC [1] ◇ H ☕	TP [1] ◇ D	NT	NT
Liverpool Lime Street [10]	90 d																				
Manchester Victoria	95 🚊 d				11 15							12 15					13 15				
Moston	95 d				11 21							12 21					13 21				
Mills Hill	95 d				11 25							12 25					13 25				
Castleton	95 d				11 30							12 30					13 30				
Rochdale	95 a				11 34							12 34					13 34				
	d				11 34							12 34					13 34				
Smithy Bridge	d				11 38							12 38					13 38				
Littleborough	d				11 42							12 42					13 42				
Walsden	d				11 48							12 48					13 48				
Todmorden	d				11 51							12 51					13 51				
Blackpool North	97 d								11 12												13 12
Poulton-le-Fylde	97 d								11 18												13 18
Preston [8]	97 d								11 38												13 38
Blackburn	97 d								11 55												13 55
Accrington	97 d								12 02												14 02
Burnley Central	97 a								12 14												14 14
	d									12 20											
Burnley Manchester Road	97 d																				
Hebden Bridge	a				11 58					12 50		12 58					13 58				
	d				11 58			12 32				12 58					13 58			14 32	
Mytholmroyd	d				12 01							13 01					14 01				
Sowerby Bridge	d				12 07							13 07					14 07				
Huddersfield	39 d		11 20												13 20						
Brighouse	d		11 30												13 30						
Halifax	a		11 44		12 14			12 43				13 14			13 44		14 14			14 43	
	d		11 45		12 14			12 45				13 14			13 45		14 14			14 45	
Bradford Interchange	a		11 58		12 28			12 59				13 28			13 59		14 28			14 59	
	37 d		12 01		12 31			13 02				13 31			14 02		14 31			15 02	
New Pudsey	37 d		12 09		12 39			13 10				13 39			14 10		14 39			15 10	
Bramley	37 d		12 13		12 43							13 43			14 14		14 43				
Leeds [10]	37, 39 a		12 21		12 52			13 21				13 52			14 22		14 53			15 21	
	d	12 10	12 25	12 40		13 08	13 10	13 25			13 40		14 08	14 10	14 25	14 40		15 08	15 10	15 25	
Cross Gates	d		12 31					13 32							14 31					15 32	
Garforth	d		12 37				13 18	13 37							14 37				15 18	15 37	
East Garforth	d		12 39					13 39							14 39					15 39	
Micklefield	d		12 43					13 43							14 43					15 43	
South Milford	d	12 23												14 23							
Selby	a	12 32												14 33							
Church Fenton	33 a		12 49												14 49						
Ulleskelf	33 a																				
York [8]	33 a		13 03	13 07		13 33	13 37	13 59			14 05		14 32		15 03	15 07		15 33	15 40	15 59	

		NT 🚌	TP [1] ◇ B	NT	TP [1] ◇ J	XC [R] [1] K ☕	TP [1] ◇ L	NT	TP [1] ◇ B	TP [1] ◇ A	NT	XC [R] [1] N ☕	TP [1] ◇ D	NT	NT	NT 🚌	TP [1] ◇ E	TP [1] ◇ A	NT	XC [R] [1] Q ☕	TP [1] ◇ U
Liverpool Lime Street [10]	90 d																				
Manchester Victoria	95 🚊 d			14 15							15 15								16 15		
Moston	95 d			14 21							15 21								16 21		
Mills Hill	95 d			14 25							15 25								16 25		
Castleton	95 d			14 30							15 30								16 30		
Rochdale	95 a			14 34							15 34								16 34		
	d			14 34							15 34								16 34		
Smithy Bridge	d			14 38							15 38								16 38		
Littleborough	d			14 42							15 42								16 42		
Walsden	d			14 48							15 48								16 48		
Todmorden	d			14 51							15 51								16 51		
Blackpool North	97 d														15 12						
Poulton-le-Fylde	97 d														15 18						
Preston [8]	97 d														15 38						
Blackburn	97 d														15 55						
Accrington	97 d														16 02						
Burnley Central	97 a														16 14						
	d	14 20														16 20					
Burnley Manchester Road	97 d																				
Hebden Bridge	a	14 50		14 58							15 58					16 50			16 58		
	d			14 58							15 58			16 32					16 58		
Mytholmroyd	d			15 01							16 01								17 01		
Sowerby Bridge	d			15 07							16 07								17 07		
Huddersfield	39 d							15 20													
Brighouse	d							15 30													
Halifax	a			15 14				15 44			16 14			16 43					17 14		
	d			15 14				15 45			16 14			16 45					17 14		
Bradford Interchange	a			15 28				15 58			16 28			16 59					17 28		
	37 d			15 31				16 01			16 31			17 02					17 31		
New Pudsey	37 d			15 39				16 09			16 39			17 10					17 39		
Bramley	37 d			15 43				16 13			16 43								17 43		
Leeds [10]	37, 39 a			15 52				16 21			16 54			17 21					17 52		
	d		15 40		15 55	16 08	16 10	16 25	16 40	16 54		17 08	17 10	17 25			17 40	17 54		18 08	18 10
Cross Gates	d							16 31						17 32							
Garforth	d							16 37					17 18	17 37							
East Garforth	d							16 39						17 39							
Micklefield	d							16 43						17 43							
South Milford	d						16 25											18 07			
Selby	a						16 34			17 13								18 16			
Church Fenton	33 a							16 49													
Ulleskelf	33 a																				
York [8]	33 a		16 05		16 19	16 33		17 04	17 09			17 33	17 37	18 00			18 09			18 33	18 37

For general notes see front of timetable
For details of catering facilities see Directory of Train Operators

A From Manchester Piccadilly to Hull (Table 39)
B From Manchester Airport to Newcastle (Table 39)
C From Birmingham New Street (Table 51) to Aberdeen (Table 229)
D From Liverpool Lime Street to Scarborough (Table 39)
E From Manchester Airport to Middlesbrough (Table 39)
G From Bristol Temple Meads to Edinburgh (Table 51)
H From Bournemouth to Edinburgh (Table 51)
J From Manchester Piccadilly to Middlesbrough (Table 39)
K From Plymouth (Table 51) to Dundee (Table 229)
L From Liverpool Lime Street to Hull (Table 39)
N From Bournemouth to Glasgow Central (Table 51)
Q From Penzance (Table 135) to Glasgow Central (Table 51)
U From Liverpool Lime Street (Table 39)

Table 41

until 27 January

Manchester Victoria, Blackpool North and Huddersfield → Leeds, Selby and York via Halifax and Bradford Interchange

Network Diagram - see first page of Table 39

Station		NT	TP 1◇ A	NT	XC R 1 B	TP 1◇ C		NT	NT (bus)	NT	TP 1◇ D	NT		TP 1◇ E	XC R 1 G	TP 1◇ C	NT	NT (bus)		NT	NT	TP 1◇ A	NT	XC R 1 H	TP 1◇ J
Liverpool Lime Street 10	90 d																								
Manchester Victoria	95 ⛴ d			17 15								18 15											19 15		
Moston	95 d			17 21								18 21											19 21		
Mills Hill	95 d			17 25								18 25											19 25		
Castleton	95 d			17 30								18 30											19 30		
Rochdale	95 a			17 34								18 34											19 34		
	d			17 34								18 34											19 34		
Smithy Bridge	d			17 38								18 38											19 38		
Littleborough	d			17 42								18 42											19 42		
Walsden	d			17 48								18 48											19 48		
Todmorden	d			17 51								18 51											19 51		
Blackpool North	97 d							16 45									17 45								
Poulton-le-Fylde	97 d							16 51									17 51								
Preston 8	97 d							17 11									18 11								
Blackburn	97 d							17 28									18 28								
Accrington	97 d							17 38									18 35								
Burnley Central	97 a							17 52									18 47								
	d								17 52									18 56							
Burnley Manchester Road	97 d																								
Hebden Bridge	a			17 58					18 22			18 58						19 26					19 58		
	d			17 58						18 32		18 58								19 32			19 58		
Mytholmroyd	d			18 01								19 01											20 01		
Sowerby Bridge	d			18 07						18 39		19 07											20 07		
Huddersfield	39 d	17 20												19 32							19 36				
Brighouse	d	17 30																			19 46				
Halifax	a	17 44		18 14						18 45		19 14								19 43	19 55		20 14		
	d	17 45		18 14						18 45		19 14								19 45	19 55		20 14		
Bradford Interchange	a	17 59		18 28						18 59		19 28								19 59	20 11		20 28		
	37 d	18 02		18 31						19 02		19 31								20 02	20 14		20 31		
New Pudsey	37 d	18 10		18 39						19 10		19 39								20 10	20 22		20 39		
Bramley	37 d	18 14		18 43								19 43									20 26		20 43		
Leeds 10	37, 39 a	18 22		18 54						19 21		19 53		19 53						20 22	20 34		20 54		
	d	18 25	18 40		19 08	19 10				19 25	19 40			19 56	20 08	20 10				20 25		20 45		21 08	21 10
Cross Gates	d	18 31								19 32										20 32					
Garforth	d	18 37				19 18				19 37										20 37					21 18
East Garforth	d	18 39								19 39										20 39					
Micklefield	d	18 43								19 43										20 43					
South Milford	d													20 09											
Selby	a													20 19											
Church Fenton	33 a	18 49																		20 48					
Ulleskelf	33 a																								
York 8	33 a	19 03	19 07		19 33	19 38				19 59	20 05				20 33	20 37				21 02		21 09		21 32	21 38

Station		NT		NT	NT (bus)	TP 1◇ K	NT	XC R 1 L		TP 1◇ N	TP 1◇ Q	NT	NT	TP 1◇ U		NT	NT	TP 1◇ J	NT	NT (bus)		NT			
Liverpool Lime Street 10	90 d																								
Manchester Victoria	95 ⛴ d						20 15									21 15						22 15			
Moston	95 d						20 21									21 21						22 21			
Mills Hill	95 d						20 25									21 25						22 25			
Castleton	95 d						20 30									21 30						22 30			
Rochdale	95 a						20 34									21 34						22 34			
	d						20 34									21 34						22 34			
Smithy Bridge	d						20 38									21 38						22 38			
Littleborough	d						20 42									21 42						22 42			
Walsden	d						20 48									21 48						22 48			
Todmorden	d						20 51									21 51						22 51			
Blackpool North	97 d			19 12															21 12						
Poulton-le-Fylde	97 d			19 18															21 18						
Preston 8	97 d			19 38															21 38						
Blackburn	97 d			19 55															21 55						
Accrington	97 d			20 02															22 02						
Burnley Central	97 a			20 14															22 14						
	d				20 20															22 20					
Burnley Manchester Road	97 d																								
Hebden Bridge	a				20 50		20 58									21 58				22 50		22 58			
	d	20 32					20 58									21 58	22 32					22 58			
Mytholmroyd	d						21 01									22 01						23 01			
Sowerby Bridge	d						21 07									22 07						23 07			
Huddersfield	39 d											21 20													
Brighouse	d											21 30													
Halifax	a	20 43					21 14					21 45				22 14	22 43					23 14			
	d	20 45					21 14					21 45				22 14	22 45					23 14			
Bradford Interchange	a	20 59					21 28					21 59				22 28	22 59					23 28			
	37 d	21 02					21 31					22 02				22 31	23 02					23 31			
New Pudsey	37 d	21 10					21 39					22 10				22 39	23 10					23 39			
Bramley	37 d						21 43					22 14				22 43						23 43			
Leeds 10	37, 39 a	21 21					21 54					22 22				22 53	23 21					23 52			
	d	21 25				21 40		22 08		22 10	22 17		22 35	22 50				23 41							
Cross Gates	d	21 32											22 41												
Garforth	d	21 37											22 47												
East Garforth	d	21 39											22 49												
Micklefield	d	21 43											22 53												
South Milford	d										22 30														
Selby	a										22 39														
Church Fenton	33 a												22 59												
Ulleskelf	33 a																								
York 8	33 a	21 59				22 06		22 36		22 38			23 17	23 21				00 08							

For general notes see front of timetable
For details of catering facilities see Directory of Train Operators

A From Manchester Airport to Newcastle (Table 39)
B From Bournemouth to Edinburgh (Table 51)
C From Liverpool Lime Street to Scarborough (Table 39)
D From Manchester Airport to Middlesbrough (Table 39)
E From Manchester Piccadilly to Hull (Table 39)
G From Plymouth to Edinburgh (Table 51)
H From Bournemouth to Newcastle (Table 51)
J From Liverpool Lime Street (Table 39)
K From Manchester Airport to Scarborough (Table 39)
L From Plymouth (Table 51)
N From Liverpool Lime Street to Newcastle (Table 39)
Q To Hull (Table 39)
U From Manchester Airport (Table 39)

Table 41

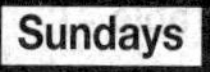

Sundays

3 February to 23 March

Manchester Victoria, Blackpool North and Huddersfield → Leeds, Selby and York via Halifax and Bradford Interchange

Network Diagram - see first page of Table 39

		TP	TP	TP	TP	TP		TP	NT	TP		TP	NT	TP	TP	NT	TP	NT	XC	TP		NT	TP	NT	XC
		1◇				1◇		1◇		1◇		1◇		1◇	1◇		1◇		1◇	1◇			1◇		1◇
			A	B	B	C		E		G		H		J	K		L		N	Q			H		U
			bus	bus	bus														catering						catering
Liverpool Lime Street 10	90 d																								
Manchester Victoria	95 d																	09 14						10 15	
Moston	95 d																	09 21						10 21	
Mills Hill	95 d																	09 25						10 25	
Castleton	95 d																	09 30						10 30	
Rochdale	95 a																	09 34						10 34	
	d																	09 34						10 34	
Smithy Bridge	d																	09 38						10 38	
Littleborough	d																	09 42						10 42	
Walsden	d																	09 48						10 48	
Todmorden	d																	09 51						10 51	
Blackpool North	97 d																								
Poulton-le-Fylde	97 d																								
Preston 8	97 d																								
Blackburn	97 d																								
Accrington	97 d																								
Burnley Manchester Road	97 d																								
Hebden Bridge	a																	09 58						10 58	
	d																	09 58						10 58	
Mytholmroyd	d																	10 01						11 01	
Sowerby Bridge	d																	10 07						11 07	
Huddersfield	39 d															09 20									
Brighouse	d															09 30									
Halifax	a															09 42		10 14						11 14	
	d												09 06			09 47		10 14				10 45		11 14	
Bradford Interchange	a												09 19			09 59		10 28				10 59		11 28	
	37 d								08 31				09 21			10 02		10 31				11 02		11 31	
New Pudsey	37 d								08 39				09 30			10 10		10 39				11 10		11 39	
Bramley	37 d								08 43				09 34			10 14		10 43						11 43	
Leeds 10	37, 39 a								08 52				09 42			10 24		10 52				11 21		11 54	
	d	00 45	01 40	03 35	06 40	07 42		08 40	08 55	09 10		09 42	09 48	10 06	10 25	10 29	10 42		11 08	11 10		11 25	11 40		12 08
Cross Gates	d								09 02				09 54			10 36						11 32			
Garforth	d								09 07	09 18			10 00			10 41				11 18		11 37			
East Garforth	d								09 09				10 02			10 43						11 39			
Micklefield	d								09 13				10 06			10 47						11 43			
South Milford	d														10 38										
Selby	a														10 47										
Church Fenton	33 a								09 19							10 53									
Ulleskelf	33 a																								
York 8	33 a	01 35	02 25	04 20	07 25	08 32		09 07	09 33	09 35		10 08	10 23	10 29		11 07	11 09		11 33	11 36		11 59	12 05		12 33

For general notes see front of timetable
For details of catering facilities see Directory of Train Operators

- **A** From Manchester Piccadilly (Table 39)
- **B** From Manchester Airport (Table 39)
- **C** To Middlesbrough (Table 39)
- **E** To Newcastle (Table 39)
- **G** To Scarborough (Table 39)
- **H** From Manchester Airport to Middlesbrough (Table 39)
- **J** From Liverpool Lime Street to Newcastle (Table 39)
- **K** From Manchester Piccadilly to Hull (Table 39)
- **L** From Manchester Airport to Newcastle (Table 39)
- **N** From Birmingham New Street to Glasgow Central (Table 51)
- **Q** From Liverpool Lime Street to Scarborough (Table 39)
- **U** From Birmingham New Street to Edinburgh (Table 51)

Table 41

3 February to 23 March

Manchester Victoria, Blackpool North and Huddersfield → Leeds, Selby and York via Halifax and Bradford Interchange

Network Diagram - see first page of Table 39

		TP 1◇ A	NT	TP 1◇ B	NT	XC 1◇ C ☕	TP 1◇ D	NT		TP 1◇ E	NT	XC 1◇ G ☕	TP 1◇ A	NT	TP 1◇ B	NT	XC 1◇ H ☕	TP 1◇ D		NT	TP 1◇ B	NT	TP 1◇ J	XC 1◇ K ☕	TP 1◇ L
Liverpool Lime Street 10	90 d																								
Manchester Victoria	95 d				11 15						12 15					13 15						14 15			
Moston	95 d				11 21						12 21					13 21						14 21			
Mills Hill	95 d				11 25						12 25					13 25						14 25			
Castleton	95 d				11 30						12 30					13 30						14 30			
Rochdale	95 a				11 34						12 34					13 34						14 34			
	d				11 34						12 34					13 34						14 34			
Smithy Bridge	d				11 38						12 38					13 38						14 38			
Littleborough	d				11 42						12 42					13 42						14 42			
Walsden	d				11 48						12 48					13 48						14 48			
Todmorden	d				11 51						12 51					13 51						14 51			
Blackpool North	97 d							10b30												12b30					
Poulton-le-Fylde	97 d							10b45												12b45					
Preston 8	97 d							11 37												13 37					
Blackburn	97 d							11 53												13 53					
Accrington	97 d							12 01												14 01					
Burnley Manchester Road	97 d							12 10												14 10					
Hebden Bridge	a				11 58			12 31			12 58					13 58				14 31		14 58			
	d				11 58			12 32			12 58					13 58				14 32		14 58			
Mytholmroyd	d				12 01						13 01					14 01						15 01			
Sowerby Bridge	d				12 07						13 07					14 07						15 07			
Huddersfield	39 d		11 20											13 20											
Brighouse	d		11 30											13 30											
Halifax	a		11 44		12 14			12 43			13 14			13 44		14 14				14 43		15 14			
	d		11 45		12 14			12 45			13 14			13 45		14 14				14 45		15 14			
Bradford Interchange	a		11 58		12 28			12 59			13 28			13 59		14 28				14 59		15 28			
	37 d		12 01		12 31			13 02			13 31			14 02		14 31				15 02		15 31			
New Pudsey	37 d		12 09		12 39			13 10			13 39			14 10		14 39				15 10		15 39			
Bramley	37 d		12 13		12 43						13 43			14 14		14 43						15 43			
Leeds 10	37, 39 a		12 21		12 52			13 21			13 52			14 22		14 53				15 21		15 52			
	d	12 10	12 25	12 40		13 08	13 10	13 25		13 40		14 08	14 10	14 25	14 40		15 08	15 10		15 25	15 40		15 55	16 08	16 10
Cross Gates	d		12 31					13 32						14 31						15 32					
Garforth	d		12 37				13 18	13 37						14 37				15 18		15 37					
East Garforth	d		12 39					13 39						14 39						15 39					
Micklefield	d		12 43					13 43						14 43						15 43					
South Milford	d	12 23											14 23												16 25
Selby	a	12 32											14 33												16 34
Church Fenton	33 a		12 49											14 49											
Ulleskelf	33 a																								
York 8	33 a		13 03	13 07		13 33	13 37	13 59		14 05		14 32		15 03	15 07		15 32	15 40		15 59	16 05		16 19	16 33	

		NT	TP 1◇ B	TP 1◇ A	NT	XC R 1 N ☕		TP 1◇ D	NT	TP 1◇ E	TP 1◇ A	NT	XC R 1 Q ☕	TP 1◇ U	NT	TP 1◇ B		NT	XC R 1 V ☕	TP 1◇ D	NT	TP 1◇ E	NT	TP 1◇ A	XC R 1 X
Liverpool Lime Street 10	90 d																								
Manchester Victoria	95 d				15 15							16 15						17 15					18 15		
Moston	95 d				15 21							16 21						17 21					18 21		
Mills Hill	95 d				15 25							16 25						17 25					18 25		
Castleton	95 d				15 30							16 30						17 30					18 30		
Rochdale	95 a				15 34							16 34						17 34					18 34		
	d				15 34							16 34						17 34					18 34		
Smithy Bridge	d				15 38							16 38						17 38					18 38		
Littleborough	d				15 42							16 42						17 42					18 42		
Walsden	d				15 48							16 48						17 48					18 48		
Todmorden	d				15 51							16 51						17 51					18 51		
Blackpool North	97 d								14b30												16b30				
Poulton-le-Fylde	97 d								14b45												16b45				
Preston 8	97 d								15 37												17 37				
Blackburn	97 d								15 53												17 53				
Accrington	97 d								16 01												18 01				
Burnley Manchester Road	97 d								16 10												18 10				
Hebden Bridge	a				15 58				16 31			16 58						17 58			18 31		18 58		
	d				15 58				16 32			16 58						17 58			18 32		18 58		
Mytholmroyd	d				16 01							17 01						18 01					19 01		
Sowerby Bridge	d				16 07							17 07						18 07			18 39		19 07		
Huddersfield	39 d	15 20													17 20										
Brighouse	d	15 30													17 30										
Halifax	a	15 44			16 14				16 43			17 14			17 44			18 14			18 45		19 14		
	d	15 45			16 14				16 45			17 14			17 45			18 14			18 45		19 14		
Bradford Interchange	a	15 58			16 28				16 59			17 28			17 59			18 28			18 59		19 28		
	37 d	16 01			16 31				17 02			17 31			18 02			18 31			19 02		19 31		
New Pudsey	37 d	16 09			16 39				17 10			17 39			18 10			18 39			19 10		19 39		
Bramley	37 d	16 13			16 43							17 43			18 14			18 43					19 43		
Leeds 10	37, 39 a	16 21			16 54				17 21			17 52			18 22			18 54			19 21		19 53		
	d	16 25	16 40	16 54		17 08		17 10	17 25	17 40	17 54		18 08	18 10	18 25	18 40			19 08	19 10	19 25	19 40		19 56	20 08
Cross Gates	d	16 31							17 32						18 31						19 32				
Garforth	d	16 37						17 18	17 37						18 37					19 18	19 37				
East Garforth	d	16 39							17 39						18 39						19 39				
Micklefield	d	16 43							17 43						18 43						19 43				
South Milford	d										18 07													20 09	
Selby	a			17 13							18 16													20 19	
Church Fenton	33 a	16 49													18 49										
Ulleskelf	33 a																								
York 8	33 a	17 04	17 09			17 33		17 37	18 00	18 09			18 33	18 37	19 03	19 07			19 33	19 38	19 59	20 05			20 33

For general notes see front of timetable
For details of catering facilities see Directory of Train Operators

- **A** From Manchester Piccadilly to Hull (Table 39)
- **B** From Manchester Airport to Newcastle (Table 39)
- **C** From Birmingham New Street (Table 51) to Aberdeen (Table 229)
- **D** From Liverpool Lime Street to Scarborough (Table 39)
- **E** From Manchester Airport to Middlesbrough (Table 39)
- **G** From Birmingham New Street to Edinburgh (Table 51)
- **H** From Bristol Temple Meads to Edinburgh (Table 51)
- **J** From Manchester Piccadilly to Middlesbrough (Table 39)
- **K** From Bournemouth (Table 51) to Dundee (Table 229)
- **L** From Liverpool Lime Street to Hull (Table 39)
- **N** From Plymouth to Glasgow Central (Table 51)
- **Q** From Bournemouth to Glasgow Central (Table 51)
- **U** From Liverpool Lime Street (Table 39)
- **V** From Penzance (Table 135) to Edinburgh (Table 51)
- **X** From Bournemouth to Edinburgh (Table 51)
- **b** By bus

Table 41

Sundays

3 February to 23 March

Manchester Victoria, Blackpool North and Huddersfield → Leeds, Selby and York via Halifax and Bradford Interchange

Network Diagram - see first page of Table 39

		TP	NT	NT		TP	NT	XC	TP	NT	TP	NT	XC	TP		TP	NT	NT	TP	NT	NT	TP	NT		
		1 ◇ A				1 ◇ B		R 1 C	1 ◇ D		1 ◇ E		R 1 G	1 ◇ H		1 ◇ J			1 ◇ K			1 ◇ D			
Liverpool Lime Street 10	90 d																								
Manchester Victoria	95 ⛴ d						19 15					20 15								21 15			22 15		
Moston	95 d						19 21					20 21								21 21			22 21		
Mills Hill	95 d						19 25					20 25								21 25			22 25		
Castleton	95 d						19 30					20 30								21 30			22 30		
Rochdale	95 a						19 34					20 34								21 34			22 34		
	d						19 34					20 34								21 34			22 34		
Smithy Bridge	d						19 38					20 38								21 38			22 38		
Littleborough	d						19 42					20 42								21 42			22 42		
Walsden	d						19 48					20 48								21 48			22 48		
Todmorden	d						19 51					20 51								21 51			22 51		
Blackpool North	97 d		17b30							18b30											20b30				
Poulton-le-Fylde	97 d		17b45							18b45											20b45				
Preston 8	97 d		18 37							19 37											21 37				
Blackburn	97 d		18 53							19 53											21 53				
Accrington	97 d		19 01							20 01											22 01				
Burnley Manchester Road	97 d		19 10							20 10											22 10				
Hebden Bridge	a		19 31				19 58			20 31		20 58								21 58	22 31		22 58		
	d		19 32				19 58			20 32		20 58								21 58	22 32		22 58		
Mytholmroyd	d						20 01					21 01								22 01			23 01		
Sowerby Bridge	d						20 07					21 07								22 07			23 07		
Huddersfield	39 d			19 36													21 20								
Brighouse	d			19 46													21 30								
Halifax	a		19 43	19 55			20 14			20 43		21 14					21 45			22 14	22 43		23 14		
	d		19 45	19 55			20 14			20 45		21 14					21 45			22 14	22 45		23 14		
Bradford Interchange	a		19 59	20 11			20 28			20 59		21 28					21 59			22 28	22 59		23 28		
	37 d		20 02	20 14			20 31			21 02		21 31					22 02			22 31	23 02		23 31		
New Pudsey	37 d		20 10	20 22			20 39			21 10		21 39					22 10			22 39	23 10		23 39		
Bramley	37 d			20 26			20 43					21 43					22 14			22 43			23 43		
Leeds 10	37, 39 a		20 22	20 34			20 54			21 21		21 54					22 22			22 53	23 21		23 52		
	d	20 10	20 25			20 45		21 08	21 10	21 25	21 40		22 08	22 10		22 17		22 35	22 50			23 41			
Cross Gates	d		20 32							21 32								22 41							
Garforth	d		20 37						21 18	21 37								22 47							
East Garforth	d		20 39							21 39								22 49							
Micklefield	d		20 43							21 43								22 53							
South Milford	d															22 30									
Selby	a															22 39									
Church Fenton	33 a		20 48															22 59							
Ulleskelf	33 a																								
York 8	33 a	20 37	21 02			21 09		21 33	21 38	21 59	22 06		22 36	22 38				23 17	23 21			00 08			

For general notes see front of timetable
For details of catering facilities see Directory of Train Operators

A From Liverpool Lime Street to Scarborough (Table 39)
B From Manchester Airport to Newcastle (Table 39)
C From Penzance (Table 135) to Newcastle (Table 51)
D From Liverpool Lime Street (Table 39)
E From Manchester Airport to Scarborough (Table 39)
G From Bournemouth (Table 51)
H From Liverpool Lime Street to Newcastle (Table 39)
J To Hull (Table 39)
K From Manchester Airport (Table 39)
b By bus

Table 41

Sundays

from 30 March

Manchester Victoria, Blackpool North and Huddersfield → Leeds, Selby and York via Halifax and Bradford Interchange

Network Diagram - see first page of Table 39

		TP	TP	TP	TP	TP	TP	NT	TP		TP	NT	TP	TP	NT	TP	NT	XC		TP	NT	TP	NT	XC	TP
		1 ◇	1 ◇	1 ◇	1 ◇	1 ◇	1 ◇		1 ◇		1 ◇		1 ◇	1 ◇		1 ◇		1 ◇		1 ◇		1 ◇		1 ◇	1 ◇
		L	A	A	A	B	C		D		B		E	G		C		H 🍴		J		B		K 🍴	G
Liverpool Lime Street 10	90 d																								
Manchester Victoria	95 ⛴ d																09 14						10 15		
Moston	95 d																09 21						10 21		
Mills Hill	95 d																09 25						10 25		
Castleton	95 d																09 30						10 30		
Rochdale	95 a																09 34						10 34		
	d																09 34						10 34		
Smithy Bridge	d																09 38						10 38		
Littleborough	d																09 42						10 42		
Walsden	d																09 48						10 48		
Todmorden	d																09 51						10 51		
Blackpool North	97 d																								
Poulton-le-Fylde	97 d																								
Preston 8	97 d																								
Blackburn	97 d																								
Accrington	97 d																								
Burnley Manchester Road	97 d																								
Hebden Bridge	a																09 58						10 58		
	d																09 58						10 58		
Mytholmroyd	d																10 01						11 01		
Sowerby Bridge	d																10 07						11 07		
Huddersfield	39 d														09 20										
Brighouse	d														09 30										
Halifax	a														09 42		10 14						11 14		
	d											09 06			09 47		10 14				10 45		11 14		
Bradford Interchange	a											09 19			09 59		10 28				10 59		11 28		
	37 d							08 31				09 21			10 02		10 31				11 02		11 31		
New Pudsey	37 d							08 39				09 30			10 10		10 39				11 10		11 39		
Bramley	37 d							08 43				09 34			10 14		10 43						11 43		
Leeds 10	37, 39 a							08 52				09 42			10 24		10 52				11 21		11 54		
	d	00 15	00 42	02 38	05 58	07 43	08 40	08 55	09 10		09 40	09 48	10 06	10 25	10 29	10 42		11 08		11 10	11 25	11 40		12 08	12 10
Cross Gates	d							09 02				09 54			10 36						11 32				
Garforth	d							09 07	09 18			10 00			10 41					11 18	11 37				
East Garforth	d							09 09				10 02			10 43						11 39				
Micklefield	d							09 13				10 06			10 47						11 43				
South Milford	d													10 38											12 23
Selby	a													10 47											12 32
Church Fenton	33 a							09 19							10 53										
Ulleskelf	33 a																								
York 8	33 a	00 41	01 08	03 04	06 24	08 09	09 07	09 33	09 35		10 06	10 23	10 29		11 07	11 09		11 33		11 36	11 59	12 05		12 33	

For general notes see front of timetable
For details of catering facilities see Directory of Train Operators

A From Manchester Airport (Table 39)
B From Manchester Airport to Middlesbrough (Table 39)
C From Manchester Airport to Newcastle (Table 39)
D To Scarborough (Table 39)
E From Liverpool Lime Street to Newcastle (Table 39)
G From Manchester Piccadilly to Hull (Table 39)
H From Birmingham New Street to Glasgow Central (Table 51)
J From Liverpool Lime Street to Scarborough (Table 39)
K From Birmingham New Street to Edinburgh (Table 51)
L From Liverpool Lime Street (Table 39)

Table 41

Sundays

from 30 March

Manchester Victoria, Blackpool North and Huddersfield → Leeds, Selby and York via Halifax and Bradford Interchange

Network Diagram - see first page of Table 39

		NT	TP 1◇ A	NT	XC 1◇ B ☕	TP 1◇ C	NT	TP 1◇ D	NT	XC 1◇ E ☕	TP 1◇ G	NT	TP 1◇ A	NT	XC 1◇ H ☕	TP 1◇ C	NT	TP 1◇ A	NT	TP 1◇ J	XC R 1 K ☕	TP 1◇ L
Liverpool Lime Street 10	90 d																					
Manchester Victoria	95 ⛴ d			11 15					12 15					13 15					14 15			
Moston	95 d			11 21					12 21					13 21					14 21			
Mills Hill	95 d			11 25					12 25					13 25					14 25			
Castleton	95 d			11 30					12 30					13 30					14 30			
Rochdale	95 a			11 34					12 34					13 34					14 34			
	d			11 34					12 34					13 34					14 34			
Smithy Bridge	d			11 38					12 38					13 38					14 38			
Littleborough	d			11 42					12 42					13 42					14 42			
Walsden	d			11 48					12 48					13 48					14 48			
Todmorden	d			11 51					12 51					13 51					14 51			
Blackpool North	97 d						11 12										13 12					
Poulton-le-Fylde	97 d						11 18										13 18					
Preston 8	97 d						11 37										13 37					
Blackburn	97 d						11 53										13 53					
Accrington	97 d						12 01										14 01					
Burnley Manchester Road	97 d						12 10										14 10					
Hebden Bridge	a			11 58			12 31		12 58					13 58			14 31		14 58			
	d			11 58			12 32		12 58					13 58			14 32		14 58			
Mytholmroyd	d			12 01					13 01					14 01					15 01			
Sowerby Bridge	d			12 07					13 07					14 07					15 07			
Huddersfield	39 d	11 20										13 20										
Brighouse	d	11 30										13 30										
Halifax	a	11 44		12 14			12 43		13 14			13 44		14 14			14 43		15 14			
	d	11 45		12 14			12 45		13 14			13 45		14 14			14 45		15 14			
Bradford Interchange	a	11 58		12 28			12 59		13 28			13 59		14 28			14 59		15 28			
	37 d	12 01		12 31			13 02		13 31			14 02		14 31			15 02		15 31			
New Pudsey	37 d	12 09		12 39			13 10		13 39			14 10		14 39			15 10		15 39			
Bramley	37 d	12 13		12 43					13 43			14 14		14 43					15 43			
Leeds 10	37, 39 a	12 21		12 52			13 21		13 52			14 22		14 53			15 21		15 52			
	d	12 25	12 40		13 08	13 10	13 25	13 40		14 08	14 10	14 25	14 40		15 08	15 10	15 25	15 40		15 55	16 08	16 10
Cross Gates	d	12 31					13 32					14 31					15 32					
Garforth	d	12 37				13 18	13 37					14 37				15 18	15 37					
East Garforth	d	12 39					13 39					14 39					15 39					
Micklefield	d	12 43					13 43					14 43					15 43					
South Milford	d										14 23											16 25
Selby	a										14 33											16 34
Church Fenton	33 a	12 49										14 49										
Ulleskelf	33 a																					
York 8	33 a	13 03	13 07		13 33	13 37	13 59	14 05		14 32		15 03	15 07		15 33	15 40	15 59	16 05		16 19	16 33	

		NT	TP 1◇ A	TP 1◇ G	NT	XC R 1 N ☕	TP 1◇ C	NT	TP 1◇ D	TP 1◇ G	NT	XC R 1 Q ☕	TP 1◇ U	NT	TP 1◇ A	NT	XC R 1 H ☕	TP 1◇ C	NT	TP 1◇ D	NT	TP 1◇ G	XC R 1 V
Liverpool Lime Street 10	90 d																						
Manchester Victoria	95 ⛴ d				15 15						16 15					17 15					18 15		
Moston	95 d				15 21						16 21					17 21					18 21		
Mills Hill	95 d				15 25						16 25					17 25					18 25		
Castleton	95 d				15 30						16 30					17 30					18 30		
Rochdale	95 a				15 34						16 34					17 34					18 34		
	d				15 34						16 34					17 34					18 34		
Smithy Bridge	d				15 38						16 38					17 38					18 38		
Littleborough	d				15 42						16 42					17 42					18 42		
Walsden	d				15 48						16 48					17 48					18 48		
Todmorden	d				15 51						16 51					17 51					18 51		
Blackpool North	97 d							15 12											17 10				
Poulton-le-Fylde	97 d							15 18											17 16				
Preston 8	97 d							15 37											17 37				
Blackburn	97 d							15 53											17 53				
Accrington	97 d							16 01											18 01				
Burnley Manchester Road	97 d							16 10											18 10				
Hebden Bridge	a				15 58			16 31			16 58					17 58			18 31		18 58		
	d				15 58			16 32			16 58					17 58			18 32		18 58		
Mytholmroyd	d				16 01						17 01					18 01					19 01		
Sowerby Bridge	d				16 07						17 07					18 07			18 39		19 07		
Huddersfield	39 d	15 20												17 20									
Brighouse	d	15 30												17 30									
Halifax	a	15 44			16 14			16 43			17 14			17 44		18 14			18 45		19 14		
	d	15 45			16 14			16 45			17 14			17 45		18 14			18 45		19 14		
Bradford Interchange	a	15 58			16 28			16 59			17 28			17 59		18 28			18 59		19 28		
	37 d	16 01			16 31			17 02			17 31			18 02		18 31			19 02		19 31		
New Pudsey	37 d	16 09			16 39			17 10			17 39			18 10		18 39			19 10		19 39		
Bramley	37 d	16 13			16 43						17 43			18 14		18 43					19 43		
Leeds 10	37, 39 a	16 21			16 54			17 21			17 52			18 22		18 54			19 21		19 53		
	d	16 25	16 40	16 54		17 08	17 10	17 25	17 40	17 54		18 08	18 10	18 25	18 40		19 08	19 10	19 25	19 40		19 56	20 08
Cross Gates	d	16 31						17 32						18 31					19 32				
Garforth	d	16 37					17 18	17 37						18 37				19 18	19 37				
East Garforth	d	16 39						17 39						18 39					19 39				
Micklefield	d	16 43						17 43						18 43					19 43				
South Milford	d									18 07												20 09	
Selby	a			17 13						18 16												20 19	
Church Fenton	33 a	16 49												18 49									
Ulleskelf	33 a																						
York 8	33 a	17 04	17 09			17 33	17 37	18 00	18 09			18 33	18 37	19 03	19 07		19 33	19 38	19 59	20 05			20 33

For general notes see front of timetable
For details of catering facilities see Directory of Train Operators

A From Manchester Airport to Newcastle (Table 39)
B From Birmingham New Street (Table 51) to Aberdeen (Table 229)
C From Liverpool Lime Street to Scarborough (Table 39)
D From Manchester Airport to Middlesbrough (Table 39)
E From Bristol Temple Meads to Edinburgh (Table 51)
G From Manchester Piccadilly to Hull (Table 39)
H From Oxford to Edinburgh (Table 51)
J From Manchester Piccadilly to Middlesbrough (Table 39)
K From Plymouth (Table 51) to Dundee (Table 229)
L From Liverpool Lime Street to Hull (Table 39)
N From Oxford to Glasgow Central (Table 51)
Q From Penzance (Table 135) to Glasgow Central (Table 51)
U From Liverpool Lime Street (Table 39)
V From Plymouth to Edinburgh (Table 51)

Table 41

Sundays

from 30 March

Manchester Victoria, Blackpool North and Huddersfield → Leeds, Selby and York via Halifax and Bradford Interchange

Network Diagram - see first page of Table 39

	TP	NT	NT	TP		NT	XC	TP	NT	TP	NT	XC	TP		TP	NT	NT	TP	NT	NT	TP	NT		
	1 ◇			1 ◇			R 1	1 ◇		1 ◇		R 1	1 ◇		1 ◇			1 ◇			1 ◇			
	A			B			C	D		E		G 🚲	H		J			K			D			
Liverpool Lime Street 10 90 d																								
Manchester Victoria 95 ⛴ d						19 15					20 15								21 15			22 15		
Moston 95 d						19 21					20 21								21 21			22 21		
Mills Hill 95 d						19 25					20 25								21 25			22 25		
Castleton 95 d						19 30					20 30								21 30			22 30		
Rochdale 95 a						19 34					20 34								21 34			22 34		
d						19 34					20 34								21 34			22 34		
Smithy Bridge d						19 38					20 38								21 38			22 38		
Littleborough d						19 42					20 42								21 42			22 42		
Walsden d						19 48					20 48								21 48			22 48		
Todmorden d						19 51					20 51								21 51			22 51		
Blackpool North 97 d		18 10							19 12											21 12				
Poulton-le-Fylde 97 d		18 16							19 18											21 18				
Preston 8 97 d		18 37							19 37											21 37				
Blackburn 97 d		18 53							19 53											21 53				
Accrington 97 d		19 01							20 01											22 01				
Burnley Manchester Road 97 d		19 10							20 10											22 10				
Hebden Bridge a		19 31				19 58			20 31		20 58								21 58	22 31		22 58		
d		19 32				19 58			20 32		20 58								21 58	22 32		22 58		
Mytholmroyd d						20 01					21 01								22 01			23 01		
Sowerby Bridge d						20 07					21 07								22 07			23 07		
Huddersfield 39 d			19 36													21 20								
Brighouse d			19 46													21 30								
Halifax a		19 43	19 55			20 14			20 43		21 14					21 45			22 14	22 43		23 14		
d		19 45	19 55			20 14			20 45		21 14					21 45			22 14	22 45		23 14		
Bradford Interchange a		19 59	20 11			20 28			20 59		21 28					21 59			22 28	22 59		23 28		
37 d		20 02	20 14			20 31			21 02		21 31					22 02			22 31	23 02		23 31		
New Pudsey 37 d		20 10	20 22			20 39			21 10		21 39					22 10			22 39	23 10		23 39		
Bramley 37 d			20 26			20 43					21 43					22 14			22 43			23 43		
Leeds 10 37, 39 a		20 22	20 34			20 54			21 21		21 54					22 22			22 53	23 21		23 52		
d	20 10	20 25		20 45			21 08	21 10	21 25	21 40		22 08	22 10		22 17		22 35	22 50			23 41			
Cross Gates d		20 32							21 32								22 41							
Garforth d		20 37						21 18	21 37								22 47							
East Garforth d		20 39							21 39								22 49							
Micklefield d		20 43							21 43								22 53							
South Milford d															22 30									
Selby a															22 39									
Church Fenton 33 a		20 48															22 59							
Ulleskelf 33 a																								
York 8 33 a	20 37	21 02		21 09			21 32	21 38	21 59	22 06		22 36	22 38				23 17	23 21			00 08			

For general notes see front of timetable
For details of catering facilities see Directory of Train Operators

- **A** From Liverpool Lime Street to Scarborough (Table 39)
- **B** From Manchester Airport to Newcastle (Table 39)
- **C** From Oxford to Newcastle (Table 51)
- **D** From Liverpool Lime Street (Table 39)
- **E** From Manchester Airport to Scarborough (Table 39)
- **G** From Plymouth (Table 51)
- **H** From Liverpool Lime Street to Newcastle (Table 39)
- **J** To Hull (Table 39)
- **K** From Manchester Airport (Table 39)

Hull → Beverley, Bridlington and Scarborough

Network Diagram - see first page of Table 39

Miles			NT	TP 1◇ A	TP 1◇ B	NT	NT	NT C	NT SO	NT SX	TP 1◇ D	NT E	NT G	NT C	TP 1◇ D	NT	NT C	TP 1◇ D	NT	TP 1◇ D	NT C
0	**Hull**	d	06 24			06 54	07 14	07 36	07 52	07 52		08 14	08 37	09 15		09 44	10 14		10 44		11 14
4	Cottingham	d	06 30			07 00	07 20	07 42	07 58	07 58		08 20	08 43	09 21		09 50	10 20		10 50		11 20
8¼	**Beverley**	d	06 37			07 07	07 27	07a48	08 05	08 05		08 27	08a49	09 28		09 57	10 27		10 57		11 27
11¼	Arram	d				07 11				08 09											
16¼	Hutton Cranswick	d				07 18	07 36		08 14	08 16		08 36		09 37		10 06			11 06		
19½	Driffield	d	06 49			07 24	07 41		08 19	08 22		08 41		09 42		10 11	10 39		11 11		11 39
21½	Nafferton	d				07 27	07 45		08 23	08 25		08 45		09 46		10 15			11 15		
31	**Bridlington**	a	07 04			07 39	07 58		08 36	08 39		08 56		10 01		10 26	10 54		11 28		11 52
—		d				07 49						09 00				10 36					12 04
34½	Bempton	d				07 56						09 07				10 43					12 11
41¾	Hunmanby	d				08 06						09 17				10 53					12 21
44½	Filey	d				08 11						09 22				10 58					12 26
51	Seamer	d		07 19	08 06	08 22					09 19	09 34			10 19	11 12		11 19		12 19	12 37
53¾	**Scarborough**	a		07 30	08 14	08 29					09 30	09 40			10 30	11 18		11 30		12 30	12 43

		NT	NT C	TP 1◇ D	NT	TP 1◇ D	NT C	NT	NT C	TP 1◇ D	NT	NT C	TP 1◇ D	TP 1◇ D	NT G	NT	NT	NT G	NT	TP 1◇ B	TP 1◇ B
Hull	d	11 44	12 14		12 44		13 14	13 44	14 14		14 44	15 20			16 00	16 14	16 29	16 52	17 07		
Cottingham	d	11 50	12 20		12 50		13 20	13 50	14 20		14 50	15 26			16 07	16 21	16 36	16 59	17 14		
Beverley	d	11 57	12 27		12 57		13 27	13 57	14 27		14 57	15 33			16 13	16a27	16a42	17 05	17a20		
Arram	d				13 01										16 18						
Hutton Cranswick	d	12 06			13 08			14 06			15 06				16 25			17 14			
Driffield	d	12 11	12 39		13 14		13 39	14 11	14 39		15 11	15 45			16 30			17 20			
Nafferton	d	12 15			13 17			14 15			15 15				16 34			17 23			
Bridlington	a	12 28	12 54		13 31		13 52	14 28	14 54		15 26	16 02			16 45			17 37			
	d						14 04				15 30				16 54						
Bempton	d						14 11				15 37				17 01						
Hunmanby	d						14 21				15 47				17 11						
Filey	d						14 26				15 52				17 16						
Seamer	d			13 19		14 19	14 37			15 19	16 03		16 19	17 19	17 27					18 07	18 41
Scarborough	a			13 30		14 30	14 45			15 30	16 10		16 30	17 30	17 35					18 17	18 51

		NT H	NT	NT G	NT SX	NT SO	NT SX	TP SO 1◇ D	TP SX 1◇ D	TP 1◇ D	NT J	NT SX C	NT SO C	TP 1◇ D	NT C	NT G	TP 1◇ B	NT C
Hull	d	17 30	17 44	18 00	18 25	18 45	18 50				19 14	20 10	20 14		21 09	21 48		23 00
Cottingham	d	17 37	17 51	18 07	18 31	18 51	18 56				19 20	20 16	20 21		21 15	21 54		23 06
Beverley	d	17 43	17a57	18 13	18a37	18a57	19a02				19 27	20 23	20 27		21a21	22 01		23a12
Arram	d	17 48										20 27	20 32					
Hutton Cranswick	d	17 55		18 22							19 36	20 34	20 39			22 10		
Driffield	d	18 00		18 28							19 41	20 40	20 44			22 15		
Nafferton	d	18 04		18 31							19 45	20 43	20 48			22 19		
Bridlington	a	18 15		18 45							19 57	20 57	21 01			22 32		
	d	18 18									19 59							
Bempton	d	18 25									20 06							
Hunmanby	d	18 35									20 16							
Filey	d	18 40									20 21							
Seamer	d	18 50						19 19	19 24	20 19	20 33			21 19			22 49	
Scarborough	a	18 57						19 30	19 30	20 30	20 39			21 30			23 02	

Sundays

until 16 March

		TP 1◇ K	TP 1◇ D	NT C	TP 1◇ D	NT C	NT C	TP 1◇ D	NT C	TP 1◇ D	NT C	NT C	TP 1◇ D	TP 1◇ D	TP 1◇ B
Hull	d			12 00		14 00	16 05		16 57		19 00	20 00			
Cottingham	d			12 06		14 06	16 11		17 03		19 06	20 06			
Beverley	d			12 13		14 13	16a17		17 10		19 13	20a12			
Arram	d														
Hutton Cranswick	d			12 22		14 22			17 19		19 22				
Driffield	d			12 27		14 27			17 24		19 27				
Nafferton	d			12 31		14 31			17 28		19 31				
Bridlington	a			12 44		14 44			17 41		19 44				
	d														
Bempton	d														
Hunmanby	d														
Filey	d														
Seamer	d	10 19	12 19		14 19			16 25		18 19			20 19	21 19	22 49
Scarborough	a	10 27	12 30		14 29			16 33		18 29			20 30	21 29	23 01

For general notes see front of timetable
For details of catering facilities see Directory of Train Operators

- **A** From York (Table 39)
- **B** From Manchester Airport (Table 39)
- **C** From Sheffield (Table 29)
- **D** From Liverpool Lime Street (Table 39)
- **E** From Gilberdyke (Table 29)
- **G** From Doncaster (Table 29)
- **H** From York via Selby (Table 29)
- **J** Mondays to Fridays from Doncaster (Table 29)
- **K** From Leeds (Table 39)

Table 43

Sundays

from 23 March

Hull → Beverley, Bridlington and Scarborough

Network Diagram - see first page of Table 39

		NT	TP 1◇ A	NT	NT B	NT C	TP 1◇ D	NT B	NT	TP 1◇ D	NT B	NT B	TP 1◇ D	NT B	NT B	NT	TP 1◇ D	NT B	NT B	NT B	TP 1◇ D	TP 1◇ D	TP 1◇ E
Hull	d	09 00		09 25	10 25	11 30		12 00	13 00		14 00	15 05		16 05	16 57	17 20		18 00	19 00	20 00			
Cottingham	d	09 06		09 31	10 31	11 36		12 06	13 06		14 06	15 11		16 11	17 03	17 26		18 06	19 06	20 06			
Beverley	d	09 13		09 38	10 38	11 43		12 13	13 13		14 13	15 18		16 18	17 10	17 33		18 13	19 13	20a12			
Arram	d			09 42																			
Hutton Cranswick	d			09 49	10 47			12 22			14 22			16 27		17 42			19 22				
Driffield	d	09 25		09 55	10 52	11 55		12 27	13 25		14 27	15 30		16 32	17 22	17 47		18 25	19 27				
Nafferton	d			09 58	10 56			12 31			14 31			16 36		17 51			19 31				
Bridlington	a	09 40		10 10	11 07	12 10		12 42	13 40		14 42	15 45		16 47	17 37	18 04		18 38	19 44				
	d			10 12	11 10			12 45			14 45			16 53				18 45					
Bempton	d			10 19	11 17			12 52			14 52			17 00				18 52					
Hunmanby	d			10 29	11 27			13 02			15 02			17 10				19 02					
Filey	d			10 34	11 32			13 07			15 07			17 15				19 07					
Seamer	d		10 19	10 45	11 43		12 19	13 22		14 19	15 18		16 25	17 26			18 19	19 22			20 19	21 19	22 49
Scarborough	a		10 27	10 52	11 50		12 30	13 28		14 29	15 25		16 33	17 33			18 29	19 27			20 30	21 29	23 01

For general notes see front of timetable
For details of catering facilities see Directory of Train Operators

A From Leeds (Table 39)
B From Sheffield (Table 29)
C From Doncaster (Table 29)
D From Liverpool Lime Street (Table 39)
E From Manchester Airport (Table 39)

Table 43

Mondays to Saturdays

Scarborough, Bridlington and Beverley → Hull

Network Diagram - see first page of Table 39

Miles			NT	NT	TP	TP	NT	NT	NT	NT	NT	TP	TP	TP	NT	TP	NT	NT	NT	TP	NT	NT	TP
			SO	SX	SX	SO	SX					SX	SO										
					1◇	1◇						1◇	1◇	1◇		1◇				1◇			1◇
			A	A	B	B		C	D		C	B	B	E	D	E	C	D		E	D		E
0	**Scarborough**	d			06 30	06 34					06 53	07 00	07 05	07 47		08 47			09 03	09 47		10 00	10 45
2¾	Seamer	d			06a35	06a39					06 59	07a05	07a10	07a52		08a52			09 08	09a52		10 05	10a50
9¼	Filey	d									07 08								09 17			10 14	
12	Hunmanby	d									07 13								09 21			10 18	
19¼	Bempton	d									07 23								09 31			10 28	
22¾	**Bridlington**	a									07 30								09 39			10 36	
—		d						06 46	07 14		07 38				08 08			09 06	09 42		10 12	10 42	
32¼	Nafferton	d						06 56	07 24		07 48				08 18			09 16	09 52			10 52	
34¼	Driffield	d						07 01	07 29		07 53				08 23			09 21	09 57		10 25	10 57	
37½	Hutton Cranswick	d						07 05	07 33		07 57				08 27			09 25	10 01			11 01	
42½	Arram	d									08 04							09 32					
45½	**Beverley**	d	06 30	06 40			06 58	07 15	07 43	07 58	08 09				08 37		09 00	09 37	10 11		10 37	11 11	
49¾	Cottingham	d	06 35	06 45			07 03	07 21	07 49	08 04	08 15				08 43		09 05	09 43	10 16		10 43	11 16	
53¾	**Hull**	a	06 44	06 53			07 12	07 31	07 59	08 13	08 25				08 53		09 14	09 53	10 26		10 53	11 26	

		NT	NT	NT	TP	TP	NT	TP	NT	NT	NT	TP	TP	NT	TP	TP	NT	NT	TP	NT	NT	NT
					SX	SO						SO	SX		SO	SX						
					1◇	1◇		1◇				1◇	1◇		1◇	1◇			1◇			
		D		D	E	E		E	D		D	E	E		E	E	D	C	E	D		A
Scarborough	d			11 28	11 45	11 47		12 47			13 28	13 45	13 47		14 45	14 47		14 54	15 47			
Seamer	d			11 33	11a50	11a52		12a52			13 33	13a50	13a52		14a50	14a52		14 59	15a52			
Filey	d			11 42							13 42							15 08				
Hunmanby	d			11 46							13 46							15 12				
Bempton	d			11 56							13 56							15 22				
Bridlington	a			12 04							14 04							15 30				
	d	11 12	11 42	12 12			12 42		13 12	13 42	14 12			14 42			15 12	15 40			16 14	
Nafferton	d		11 52				12 52			13 52				14 52				15 50			16 24	
Driffield	d	11 25	11 57	12 25			12 57		13 25	13 57	14 25			14 57			15 25	15 55			16 29	
Hutton Cranswick	d		12 01				13 01			14 01				15 01				15 59			16 33	
Arram	d		12 08																			
Beverley	d	11 37	12 13	12 37			13 11		13 37	14 11	14 37			15 11			15 37	16 09		16 32	16 43	17 00
Cottingham	d	11 43	12 19	12 43			13 16		13 43	14 16	14 43			15 16			15 43	16 14		16 37	16 48	17 05
Hull	a	11 53	12 29	12 54			13 26		13 53	14 26	14 53			15 29			15 53	16 24		16 46	16 58	17 14

		NT	NT	TP	NT	NT	NT	TP	TP	TP	NT	NT	TP	TP	NT	TP	NT	NT	TP	NT
									SO	SX			SX	SO						
				1◇				1◇	1◇	1◇			1◇	1◇		1◇			1◇	
		G	D	E			C	E	E	E		D	E	E		H		J	K	
Scarborough	d		16 18	16 47			17 38	17 45	18 45	18 46			19 45	19 47	20 00	20 37			22 07	
Seamer	d		16 22	16a52			17 43	17a50	18a50	18a51			19a50	19a52	20 05	20a42			22a12	
Filey	d		16 32				17 52								20 14					
Hunmanby	d		16 36				17 56								20 19					
Bempton	d		16 46				18 06								20 28					
Bridlington	a		16 53				18 14								20 36					
	d		17 06			17 46	18 25					19 10			20 38			21 35		22 40
Nafferton	d		17 16			17 56	18 36					19 20			20 48			21 45		22 50
Driffield	d		17 20			18 01	18 40					19 25			20 53			21 50		22 55
Hutton Cranswick	d		17 24			18 05	18 45					19 29			20 57			21 54		22 59
Arram	d					18 12														
Beverley	d	17 25	17 34		18 03	18 17	18 54				19 15	19 39			21 07		21 43	22 04		23 09
Cottingham	d	17 30	17 39		18 08	18 23	19 00				19 20	19 44			21 13		21 48	22 09		23 14
Hull	a	17 39	17 49		18 17	18 33	19 12				19 29	19 54			21 23		21 57	22 19		23 25

Sundays

until 16 March

		TP	TP	NT	TP	NT	TP	NT	TP	NT	TP	NT	TP	TP
		1◇	1◇		1◇		1◇		1◇		1◇		1◇	1◇
		B	E	D	E	D	E	D	E	D	E	D	L	L
Scarborough	d	09 20	10 45		12 45		14 45		16 45		18 45		20 45	21 45
Seamer	d	09a25	10a50		12a50		14a50		16a50		18a50		20a50	21a50
Filey	d													
Hunmanby	d													
Bempton	d													
Bridlington	a													
	d					12 53		14 53		17 50		20 15		
Nafferton	d					13 03		15 03		18 00		20 25		
Driffield	d					13 08		15 08		18 05		20 30		
Hutton Cranswick	d					13 12		15 12		18 09		20 34		
Arram	d													
Beverley	d			12 22		13 22		15 22		18 19		20 44		
Cottingham	d			12 27		13 27		15 27		18 24		20 49		
Hull	a			12 37		13 37		15 37		18 34		20 59		

For general notes see front of timetable
For details of catering facilities see Directory of Train Operators

- **A** To York via Selby (Table 29)
- **B** To Manchester Airport (Table 39)
- **C** To Doncaster (Table 29)
- **D** To Sheffield (Table 29)
- **E** To Liverpool Lime Street (Table 39)
- **G** To Sheffield (Saturdays to Doncaster) (Table 29)
- **H** To Leeds (Saturdays to York) (Table 39)
- **J** Saturdays to Sheffield (Table 29)
- **K** To York (Table 39)
- **L** To Manchester Piccadilly (Table 39)

Table 43

Sundays
from 23 March

Scarborough, Bridlington and Beverley → Hull

Network Diagram - see first page of Table 39

		TP	NT	TP	NT	NT	TP	NT	NT	TP	NT	NT
		1 ◇		1 ◇			1 ◇			1 ◇		
		A	B	C	B	B	C	B	B	C	B	B
Scarborough	d	09 20		10 45	11 14	12 08	12 45		14 08	14 45		16 08
Seamer	d	09a25		10a50	11 19	12 13	12a50		14 13	14a50		16 13
Filey	d				11 28	12 22			14 22			16 22
Hunmanby	d				11 32	12 26			14 26			16 26
Bempton	d				11 42	12 36			14 36			16 36
Bridlington	a				11 50	12 44			14 44			16 44
	d		09 53		11 53	12 53		13 53	14 53		15 50	16 53
Nafferton	d		10 03		12 03			14 03			16 00	
Driffield	d		10 08		12 08	13 06		14 08	15 06		16 05	17 06
Hutton Cranswick	d		10 12		12 12			14 12			16 09	
Arram	d											
Beverley	d		10 22		12 22	13 18		14 22	15 18		16 19	17 18
Cottingham	d		10 27		12 27	13 24		14 27	15 24		16 24	17 24
Hull	a		10 37		12 37	13 34		14 37	15 34		16 35	17 34

		TP	NT	NT	NT	NT	TP	NT	NT	TP	TP
		1 ◇					1 ◇			1 ◇	1 ◇
		C		B			C		B	D	D
Scarborough	d	16 45				18 08	18 45		19 37	20 45	21 45
Seamer	d	16a50				18 13	18a50		19 42	20a50	21a50
Filey	d					18 22			19 51		
Hunmanby	d					18 27			19 56		
Bempton	d					18 36			20 05		
Bridlington	a					18 44			20 13		
	d		17 21	17 53	18 14	18 53		19 57	20 15		
Nafferton	d		17 31			19 03			20 25		
Driffield	d		17 36	18 06	18 27	19 08		20 10	20 30		
Hutton Cranswick	d		17 40			19 12			20 34		
Arram	d					19 19					
Beverley	d		17 50	18 18	18 39	19 24		20 22	20 44		
Cottingham	d		17 55	18 24	18 45	19 30		20 28	20 49		
Hull	a		18 05	18 34	18 55	19 40		20 38	20 59		

For general notes see front of timetable
For details of catering facilities see Directory of Train Operators

A To Manchester Airport (Table 39)
B To Sheffield (Table 29)
C To Liverpool Lime Street (Table 39)
D To Manchester Piccadilly (Table 39)

Network Diagram for Tables 44, 45, 48

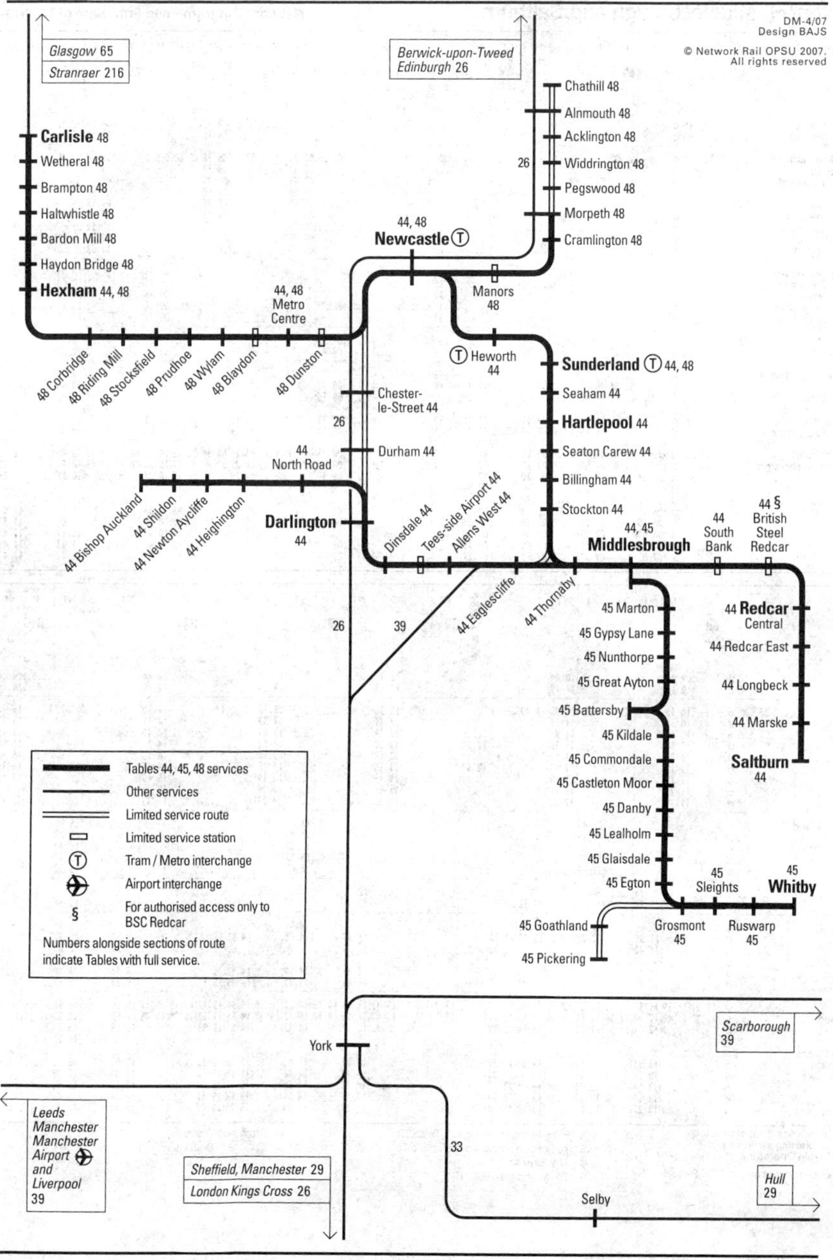

DM-4/07
Design BAJS
© Network Rail OPSU 2007. All rights reserved
Glasgow 65
Stranraer 216
Berwick-upon-Tweed
Edinburgh 26
Chathill 48
Alnmouth 48
Acklington 48
26
Widdrington 48
Pegswood 48
Morpeth 48
Cramlington 48
Carlisle 48
Wetheral 48
Brampton 48
Haltwhistle 48
Bardon Mill 48
Haydon Bridge 48
Hexham 44, 48
44, 48
Newcastle
Manors
48
44, 48
Metro
Centre
48 Corbridge
48 Riding Mill
48 Stocksfield
48 Prudhoe
48 Wylam
48 Blaydon
48 Dunston
Heworth
44
Sunderland 44, 48
Seaham 44
Chester-
le-Street 44
26
Hartlepool 44
Durham 44
Seaton Carew 44
44
North Road
Billingham 44
Stockton 44
44 Bishop Auckland
44 Shildon
44 Newton Aycliffe
44 Heighington
Darlington
44
Dinsdale 44
Tees-side Airport 44
Allens West 44
44, 45
Middlesbrough
44
South
Bank
44 §
British
Steel
Redcar
44 Eaglescliffe
44 Thornaby
26
39
45 Marton
45 Gypsy Lane
45 Nunthorpe
45 Great Ayton
45 Battersby
45 Kildale
45 Commondale
45 Castleton Moor
45 Danby
45 Lealholm
45 Glaisdale
45 Egton
44 Redcar
Central
44 Redcar East
44 Longbeck
44 Marske
Saltburn
44
45
Sleights
45
Whitby
45 Goathland
45 Pickering
Grosmont
45
Ruswarp
45
Tables 44, 45, 48 services
Other services
Limited service route
Limited service station
Tram / Metro interchange
Airport interchange
§ For authorised access only to BSC Redcar
Numbers alongside sections of route indicate Tables with full service.
York
Scarborough
39
Leeds
Manchester
Manchester
Airport
and
Liverpool
39
33
Sheffield, Manchester 29
London Kings Cross 26
Selby
Hull
29

Newcastle, Sunderland, Bishop Auckland and Darlington → Middlesbrough and Saltburn

Network Diagram - see first page of Table 44

Miles	Miles		NT	TP	NT	NT	NT	GC	NT	NT	NT	TP		NT	NT	TP	NT	NT	NT	NT	TP	NT	NT		NT
				1 ◇				R 1				1 ◇				1 ◇					1 ◇				
				A				B C ✕		D		E			D	A					A				
—	—	Hexham 48 d									06 13							07 42				08 44			
—	—	Metrocentre 48 d																08 15				09 15			
—	0	**Newcastle 8** 26 d		06 00		06 00	06 30		06 44	07b00	07 00			07 26	07 30		07 49	08 30	09 00	09b12		09 30	09b40		10 15
—	2¾	Heworth d				06 07					07 07				07 37			08 37				09 37			
—	12	**Sunderland** a				06 19					07 19				07 49			08 49				09 49			
—	—	d				06 20		06 46			07 20				07 50			08 50				09 50			
—	17¼	Seaham d				06 28					07 28				07 58			08 58				09 58			
—	30	**Hartlepool** d				06a46		07 10			07 45				08 15			09 15				10 15			
—	32¼	Seaton Carew d									07 49				08 19			09 19				10 19			
—	37¼	Billingham d									07 56				08 26			09 26				10 26			
—	41¾	Stockton d									08 04				08 33			09 33				10 33			
0	—	**Bishop Auckland** d								07 21										09 25			10 03		
2¾	—	Shildon d								07 26										09 30			10 08		
5	—	Newton Aycliffe d								07 31										09 35			10 13		
6½	—	Heighington d								07 34										09 38			10 16		
10¾	—	North Road d								07 43										09 47			10 25		
—	—	Chester-le-Street 26 d					06 31							07 37					08 33	09 21					
—	—	Durham 26 d		06 12			06 42		06 56	07 12				07 43			08 01		09 12	09 28			09 52		10 27
12	—	**Darlington 7** 26 a								07 46										09 50			10 28		
—	—	d		06 36	06 40		07 07		07 24	07 48				08 10			09 00		09 36	09 53			10 30		11 00
15¾	—	Dinsdale d			06 46				07 29					08 15			09 05			09 58					
17½	—	Tees-side Airport d																							
20	—	Allens West d			06 53		07 17		07 36	07 59				08 22			09 12			10 05			10 41		
20¾	—	Eaglescliffe d			06 55		07 20	07a28	07 38	08 01				08 24			09 14			10 08			10 43		
23¾	44	Thornaby d		06 53	07 01		07 25		07 45	08 07	08 12	08 25		08 33	08 39	09 12	09 20	09 39	09 52	10 18	10 21	10 39	10 48		11 17
27	47¼	**Middlesbrough** a		07 01	07 08		07 30		07 50	08 12	08 18	08 32		08 38	08 48	09 20	09 27	09 48	09 57	10 23	10 30	10 48	10 54		11 22
—	—	d	06 34		07 08		07 30		07 51					08 39			09 28		09 57	10 24			10 55		11 23
29½	—	South Bank d							07 56					08 43											
32¾	—	British Steel Redcar § d					07 38																		
34½	—	**Redcar Central** d	06 45		07 19		07 42		08 03					08 51			09 38		10 08	10 35			11 05		11 33
35½	—	Redcar East d	06 48		07 21		07 45		08 06					08 53			09 41		10 10	10 37			11 08		11 36
37	—	Longbeck d	06 52		07 25		07 49		08 10					08 57			09 45		10 14	10 41			11 12		11 40
37½	—	Marske d	06 54		07 27		07 50		08 11					08 59			09 46		10 16	10 43			11 13		11 41
39½	—	**Saltburn** a	07 03		07 35		07 58		08 19					09 07			09 54		10 24	10 52			11 22		11 49

	TP	NT	NT	TP	NT	NT	NT	NT	GC	TP		NT	NT	TP	NT	NT	NT	NT	TP	NT	NT		NT	TP	NT
	1 ◇			1 ◇					R 1	1 ◇				1 ◇					1 ◇					1 ◇	
	A			A					B ✕	A				A		D			A					A	D
Hexham 48 d		09 44				10 44						11 44				12 44				13 44					14 44
Metrocentre 48 d		10 15				11 15						12 15				13 15				14 15					15 15
Newcastle 8 26 d		10 30	11 00		11b25	11 30	11 40	12 15				12 30	12 40		13b29	13 30	13 40	14 12		14 30	14 40		15b22		15 30
Heworth d		10 37				11 37						12 37				13 37				14 37					15 37
Sunderland a		10 49				11 49						12 49				13 49				14 49					15 49
d		10 50				11 50			12 30			12 50				13 50				14 50					15 50
Seaham d		10 58				11 58						12 58				13 58				14 58					15 58
Hartlepool d		11 15				12 15			12 54			13 15				14 15				15 15					16 15
Seaton Carew d		11 19				12 19						13 19				14 19				15 19					16 19
Billingham d		11 26				12 26						13 26				14 26				15 26					16 26
Stockton d		11 33				12 33						13 33				14 33				15 33					16 33
Bishop Auckland d					11 40										13 40								15 30		
Shildon d					11 45										13 45								15 35		
Newton Aycliffe d					11 50										13 50								15 40		
Heighington d					11 53										13 53								15 43		
North Road d					12 02										14 02								15 52		
Chester-le-Street 26 d			10 34										12 32								14 33		15 21		
Durham 26 d			10 52		11 37		11 52	12 28					12 53		13 27		13 52	14 24			14 52		15 34		
Darlington 7 26 a					12 06										14 06								15 55		
d			11 35		12 07		12 30	12 56					13 30		14 08		14 32	15 00			15 30		15 57		
Dinsdale d			11 40										13 35								15 35		16 03		
Tees-side Airport d																									
Allens West d			11 47				12 40						13 42		14 18		14 42				15 42		16 10		
Eaglescliffe d			11 49				12 43		13a15				13 44		14 21		14 45	15 11			15 44		16 12		
Thornaby d	11 21	11 39	11 55	12 19	12 25	12 39	12 48	13 12		13 21		13 39	13 51	14 19	14 26	14 39	14 50	15 17	15 19	15 39	15 50		16 18	16 20	16 41
Middlesbrough a	11 30	11 48	12 00	12 30	12 31	12 49	12 53	13 17		13 30		13 48	13 56	14 30	14 32	14 48	14 55	15 22	15 30	15 48	15 55		16 23	16 30	16 47
d			12 01		12 32		12 54	13 20					13 57		14 33		14 56	15 23			15 56		16 24		
South Bank d																							16 29		
British Steel Redcar § d																									
Redcar Central d			12 11		12 42		13 04	13 30					14 07		14 43		15 06	15 33			16 06		16 36		
Redcar East d			12 14		12 45		13 07	13 33					14 10		14 46		15 09	15 36			16 09		16 39		
Longbeck d			12 18		12 49		13 11	13 37					14 14		14 50		15 13	15 40			16 13		16 43		
Marske d			12 19		12 50		13 12	13 38					14 15		14 51		15 14	15 41			16 14		16 44		
Saltburn a			12 27		12 58		13 20	13 46					14 23		14 59		15 22	15 49			16 22		16 53		

For general notes see front of timetable
For details of catering facilities see Directory of Train Operators

§ For authorised access only to BSC Redcar

A From Manchester Airport (Table 39)
B To London Kings Cross (Table 26)
C **The Zephyr**
D To Nunthorpe (Table 45)
E From York (Table 39)
b Change at Darlington

Newcastle, Sunderland, Bishop Auckland and Darlington → Middlesbrough and Saltburn

Network Diagram - see first page of Table 44

		NT	NT	TP 1◇ A	NT	NT B	NT C	GC R 1 D ✕	NT	TP 1◇ E	NT	NT	TP 1◇ A	NT B	NT	TP 1◇ A	NT	NT	NT	TP 1◇ A	NT	NT	NT G
Hexham	48 d					15 44	16 16				16 44			17 42				18 44					
Metrocentre	48 d					16 15	16 39				17 15			18 13				19 17			20 15		
Newcastle 8	26 d	15 40	16b06		16 27	16 30	16 53		17 17		17 30	17b40		18 30	18b40		19 08	19 30	19 40		20 30	20b37	22 00
Heworth	d					16 37	17 00				17 37			18 37				19 37			20 37		
Sunderland	a					16 49	17 13				17 49			18 49				19 49			20 49		
	d					16 50	17 15	17 30			17 50			18 50				19 50			20 50		
Seaham	d					16 58	17 22				17 58			18 58				19 58			20 58		
Hartlepool	d					17 15	17 39	17 56			18 15			19 15				20 15			21 15		
Seaton Carew	d					17 19	17 43				18 19			19 19				20 19			21 19		
Billingham	d					17 26	17 50				18 26			19 26				20 26			21 26		
Stockton	d					17 33	17 57				18 33			19 33				20 33			21 33		
Bishop Auckland	d		16 30									18 03			19 03							21 15	
Shildon	d		16 35									18 08			19 08							21 20	
Newton Aycliffe	d		16 40									18 13			19 13							21 25	
Heighington	d		16 43									18 16			19 16							21 28	
North Road	d		16 52									18 25			19 25							21 37	
Chester-le-Street	26 d		16 15		16 42				17 26						18 29				19 36				22 09
Durham	26 d	15 52	16 22		16 49				17 33			17 54			18 52		19 10		19 52			20 50	22 18
Darlington 7	26 a		16 57									18 31			19 30							21 40	22 38
	d	16 30	16 59		17 15				18 03			18 33			19 31		20 07		20 30			21 44	22 42
Dinsdale	d				17 20				18 08								20 12					21 49	
Tees-side Airport	d																						
Allens West	d	16 41	17 09		17 27				18 15			18 43			19 42		20 19					21 56	22 53
Eaglescliffe	d	16 44	17 12		17 29			18a14	18 17			18 46			19 44		20 21		20 41			21 58	22 55
Thornaby	d	16 49	17 17	17 19	17 35	17 39	18 03		18 23	18 32	18 39	18 51	19 18	19 39	19 50	20 21	20 26	20 39	20 50	21 15	21 39	22 04	23 00
Middlesbrough	a	16 54	17 23	17 30	17 41	17 49	18 12		18 28	18 42	18 48	18 56	19 30	19 48	19 55	20 31	20 35	20 50	20 55	21 25	21 48	22 09	23 10
	d	16 56	17 24		17 43				18 30			18 59			19 56				20 55			22 09	
South Bank	d				17 47																		
British Steel Redcar §	d																						
Redcar Central	d	17 06	17 35		17 55				18 40			19 09			20 06				21 05			22 20	
Redcar East	d	17 09	17 37		17 57				18 43			19 12			20 09				21 08			22 22	
Longbeck	d	17 13	17 41		18 01				18 47			19 16			20 13				21 12			22 26	
Marske	d	17 14	17 43		18 03				18 48			19 17			20 14				21 13			22 28	
Saltburn	a	17 22	17 52		18 11				18 56			19 26			20 23				21 22			22 37	

Saturdays

		NT	TP 1◇ A	NT	NT	NT	NT	GC R 1 D H	NT B	NT	TP 1◇ J	NT	NT B	NT	TP 1◇ A	NT	NT	NT	TP 1◇ A	NT	NT	NT	TP 1◇ A
Hexham	48 d									06 13										08 44			
Metrocentre	48 d																			09 15			
Newcastle 8	26 d		06 00		05 58	06 13	06 35		07 00	07 00		07b30	07 30	07 54		08 30	08 40	09b12		09 30	09b40	10 03	
Heworth	d				06 07					07 07			07 37			08 37				09 37			
Sunderland	a				06 19					07 19			07 49			08 49				09 49			
	d				06 20			06 53		07 20			07 50			08 50				09 50			
Seaham	d				06 28					07 28			07 58			08 58				09 58			
Hartlepool	d				06a46			07 17		07 45			08 15			09 15				10 15			
Seaton Carew	d									07 49			08 19			09 19				10 19			
Billingham	d									07 56			08 26			09 26				10 26			
Stockton	d									08 04			08 33			09 33				10 33			
Bishop Auckland	d											07 35						09 23			09 53		
Shildon	d											07 40						09 28			09 58		
Newton Aycliffe	d											07 45						09 33			10 03		
Heighington	d											07 48						09 36			10 06		
North Road	d											07 57						09 45			10 15		
Chester-le-Street	26 d													07 42			08 33	09 21					
Durham	26 d		06 12			06 29	06 47		07 12			07 42		07 54			08 52	09 27			09 52		
Darlington 7	26 a											08 00						09 48			10 18		
	d		06 36	06 40		06 58	07 19		07 38			08 10		09 00			09 23	09 51			10 20	10 47	
Dinsdale	d			06 46			07 24					08 15		09 05			09 28	09 56					
Tees-side Airport	d																				10 28		
Allens West	d			06 53		07 08	07 31		07 49			08 22		09 12			09 35	10 03			10 33		
Eaglescliffe	d			06 55		07 11	07 32	07a44	07 51			08 24		09 14			09 37	10 05			10 35		
Thornaby	d		06 53	07 01		07 16	07 39		07 56	08 09	08 25	08 30	08 39	09 20	09 23	09 39	09 45	10 11	10 21	10 39	10 45	11 03	11 21
Middlesbrough	a		07 01	07 09		07 21	07 44		08 02	08 17	08 32	08 36	08 48	09 25	09 32	09 48	09 52	10 16	10 30	10 48	10 52	11 08	11 30
	d	06 40		07 10		07 22	07 45					08 36		09 27			09 54	10 20			10 54	11 14	
South Bank	d						07 49					08 41											
British Steel Redcar §	d																						
Redcar Central	d	06 50		07 20		07 32	07 57					08 48		09 37			10 04	10 30			11 04	11 24	
Redcar East	d	06 53		07 23		07 35	07 59					08 51		09 40			10 07	10 33			11 07	11 27	
Longbeck	d	06 57		07 27		07 39	08 03					08 55		09 44			10 11	10 37			11 11	11 31	
Marske	d	06 58		07 28		07 40	08 05					08 56		09 45			10 12	10 38			11 12	11 32	
Saltburn	a	07 05		07 35		07 48	08 14					09 05		09 53			10 20	10 47			11 20	11 40	

For general notes see front of timetable
For details of catering facilities see Directory of Train Operators

§ For authorised access only to BSC Redcar

- **A** From Manchester Airport (Table 39)
- **B** To Nunthorpe (Table 45)
- **C** From Carlisle (Table 48)
- **D** To London Kings Cross (Table 26)
- **E** From Liverpool Lime Street (Table 39)
- **G** From Morpeth (Table 48)
- **H** **The Zephyr**
- **J** From York (Table 39)
- **b** Change at Darlington

Table 44

Saturdays

Newcastle, Sunderland, Bishop Auckland and Darlington → Middlesbrough and Saltburn

Network Diagram - see first page of Table 44

	NT A	NT	TP 1◇ B	NT	NT	NT	GC R 1 C		NT	TP 1◇ B	NT	NT	NT	TP 1◇ B	NT A		NT	NT	TP 1◇ B	NT	NT	NT	TP 1◇ B		NT A
Hexham 48 d	09 44				10 44						11 44				12 44					13 44					14 44
Metrocentre 48 d	10 15				11 15						12 15				13 15					14 15					15 15
Newcastle 8 26 d	10 30	10 40		11b25	11 30	11 40			12 17		12 30	12 40	13b15		13 30		13 40	14 22		14 30	14 59	15b22			15 30
Heworth d	10 37				11 37						12 37				13 37					14 37					15 37
Sunderland a	10 49				11 49						12 49				13 49					14 49					15 50
d	10 50				11 50		12 30				12 50				13 50					14 50					15 50
Seaham d	10 58				11 58						12 58				13 58					14 58					15 58
Hartlepool d	11 15				12 15		12 54				13 15				14 15					15 15					16 15
Seaton Carew d	11 19				12 19						13 19				14 19					15 19					16 19
Billingham d	11 26				12 26						13 26				14 26					15 26					16 26
Stockton d	11 33				12 33						13 33				14 33					15 33					16 33
Bishop Auckland d				11 40									13 26									15 32			
Shildon d				11 45									13 31									15 37			
Newton Aycliffe d				11 50									13 36									15 42			
Heighington d				11 53									13 39									15 45			
North Road d				12 02									13 48									15 54			
Chester-le-Street 26 d		10 34							12 29									14 31				15 18			
Durham 26 d		10 52		11 38		11 52			12 36			12 52	13 27				13 52	14 38			14 52	15 34			
Darlington 7 26 a				12 06									13 51									15 58			
d		11 30		12 06		12 35			12 58			13 31	13 53				14 35	15 04			15 32	16 00			
Dinsdale d		11 35							13 03			13 36									15 37				
Tees-side Airport d																									
Allens West d		11 42				12 45			13 10			13 43	14 04				14 45	15 14			15 44				
Eaglescliffe d		11 44				12 48	13a12		13 12			13 45	14 06				14 48	15 17			15 46	16 12			
Thornaby d	11 39	11 50	12 19	12 25	12 39	12 53			13 18	13 21	13 39	13 52	14 13	14 19	14 39		14 53	15 22	15 27	15 39	15 52	16 17	16 20		16 39
Middlesbrough a	11 48	11 55	12 30	12 32	12 49	12 58			13 23	13 30	13 48	13 57	14 18	14 30	14 48		14 58	15 27	15 34	15 48	15 57	16 22	16 30		16 47
d		11 56		12 33		12 58			13 24			13 58	14 20				14 58	15 28			15 58	16 23			
South Bank d																						16 27			
British Steel Redcar § d																									
Redcar Central d		12 06		12 43		13 09			13 34			14 08	14 31				15 09	15 39			16 08	16 35			
Redcar East d		12 09		12 46		13 11			13 37			14 11	14 33				15 11	15 41			16 11	16 37			
Longbeck d		12 13		12 50		13 15			13 41			14 15	14 37				15 15	15 45			16 15	16 41			
Marske d		12 14		12 51		13 17			13 42			14 16	14 39				15 17	15 47			16 16	16 43			
Saltburn a		12 22		12 59		13 25			13 50			14 24	14 48				15 25	15 55			16 24	16 52			

	NT	NT	TP 1◇ B	NT A	NT	NT D	NT		GC R 1 C	TP 1◇ E	NT	NT	TP 1◇ B	NT A	NT	TP 1◇ B	NT	NT	NT	TP 1◇ B	NT	NT	NT G		
Hexham 48 d				15 44		16 16					16 44			17 42				18 44							
Metrocentre 48 d				16 15		16 40					17 15			18 13				19 17			20 15				
Newcastle 8 26 d	15 40	16 20		16 30	16b40	16 53	17 19				17 29	17b40		18 30	18b52		19 06	19 28	19 45		20 30	20b46	21 50		
Heworth d				16 37		17 00					17 37			18 37				19 36			20 37				
Sunderland a				16 49		17 13					17 50			18 49				19 50			20 49				
d				16 50		17 15			17 30		17 50			18 50				19 50			20 50				
Seaham d				16 58		17 22					17 58			18 58				19 58			20 58				
Hartlepool d				17 15		17 39			17 56		18 15			19 15				20 15			21 15				
Seaton Carew d				17 19		17 43					18 19			19 19				20 19			21 19				
Billingham d				17 26		17 50					18 26			19 26				20 26			21 26				
Stockton d				17 33		17 57					18 33			19 33				20 33			21 33				
Bishop Auckland d					17 00							18 00			18 59							21 17			
Shildon d					17 05							18 05			19 04							21 22			
Newton Aycliffe d					17 10							18 10			19 09							21 27			
Heighington d					17 13							18 13			19 12							21 30			
North Road d					17 22							18 22			19 21							21 39			
Chester-le-Street 26 d		16 29					17 28								18 49								21 59		
Durham 26 d	15 52	16 36			16 52		17 35					17 54			19 04				19 57			20 59	22 08		
Darlington 7 26 a					17 26							18 25			19 25							21 42	22 28		
d	16 27	17 04			17 27		18 00					18 30			19 27		20 07		20 30			21 44	22 30		
Dinsdale d					17 33		18 05										20 12					21 49			
Tees-side Airport d																									
Allens West d	16 37				17 40		18 12					18 41			19 38		20 19					21 56	22 40		
Eaglescliffe d	16 40	17 15			17 42		18 14		18a27			18 45			19 40		20 21		20 41			21 58	22 43		
Thornaby d	16 45	17 21	17 24	17 39	17 47	18 03	18 20			18 32	18 39	18 50	19 18	19 39	19 45	20 13	20 27	20 39	20 48	21 15	21 39	22 04	22 48		
Middlesbrough a	16 52	17 26	17 34	17 49	17 54	18 12	18 25			18 42	18 48	19 00	19 30	19 48	19 52	20 23	20 38	20 50	20 55	21 25	21 48	22 09	22 57		
d	16 54	17 28			17 54		18 25					19 01			19 54				20 55			22 09			
South Bank d					17 59																				
British Steel Redcar § d																									
Redcar Central d	17 04	17 38			18 06		18 36					19 11			20 04				21 05			22 20			
Redcar East d	17 07	17 41			18 09		18 38					19 14			20 07				21 08			22 22			
Longbeck d	17 11	17 45			18 13		18 42					19 18			20 11				21 12			22 26			
Marske d	17 12	17 46			18 14		18 44					19 19			20 12				21 13			22 28			
Saltburn a	17 20	17 54			18 23		18 52					19 28			20 21				21 22			22 37			

For general notes see front of timetable
For details of catering facilities see Directory of Train Operators

§ For authorised access only to BSC Redcar

A To Nunthorpe (Table 45)
B From Manchester Airport (Table 39)
C To London Kings Cross (Table 26)
D From Carlisle (Table 48)
E From Liverpool Lime Street (Table 39)
G From Morpeth (Table 48)
b Change at Darlington

Table 44

Sundays

Newcastle, Sunderland, Bishop Auckland and Darlington → Middlesbrough and Saltburn

Network Diagram - see first page of Table 44

	TP	TP	NT	GC	NT	NT	TP	NT	NT	NT	NT	TP	NT	NT	NT	NT	NT	GC	TP	NT	NT
	1◇ A	1◇ B		R 1 C ☕			1◇ D					1◇ D						R 1 C ☕	1◇ D		
Hexham 48 d																					
Metrocentre 48 d										10 48			11 48		12 48					13 48	
Newcastle 8 26 d			07 58		08 55	09 00		10 00	10b25	11 00	11 25		12 00	12b32	13 00	13 32				14 00	14b32
Heworth d						09 07		10 07		11 06			12 06		13 06					14 06	
Sunderland a						09 22		10 21		11 22			12 21		13 22					14 21	
d				09 10				10 21					12 21					13 42		14 21	
Seaham d								10 29					12 29							14 29	
Hartlepool d				09 34				10 45					12 45				13 30	14 06		14 45	
Seaton Carew d								10 50					12 50				13 34			14 50	
Billingham d								10 57					12 57				13 41			14 57	
Stockton d								11 04					13 04				13 48			15 04	
Bishop Auckland d									10 29					12 40							14 49
Shildon d									10 34					12 45							14 54
Newton Aycliffe d									10 39					12 50							14 59
Heighington d									10 42					12 53							15 02
North Road d									10 51					13 02							15 11
Chester-le-Street 26 d									09 42							12 58					
Durham 26 d			08 10		09 07				10 37		11 37			12 45		13 45					14 38
Darlington 7 26 a									10 54					13 08			14 15				15 14
d			09 20		09 56				11 04		12 02			13 10		14 10					15 16
Dinsdale d			09 25						11 09					13 15							15 21
Tees-side Airport d																					
Allens West d			09 32						11 16					13 22							15 28
Eaglescliffe d			09 34	09a54	10 07				11 18		12 13			13 24		14 21		14a31			15 30
Thornaby d	08⟆58	09⟆22	09 43		10 13		10 58	11 09	11 24		12 19	12 58	13 09	13 30		14 27			14 58	15 09	15 36
Middlesbrough a	09⟆10	09⟆32	09 49		10 18		11 10	11 17	11 29		12 24	13 10	13 20	13 35		14 32			15 09	15 20	15 41
d			09 50		10 22				11 30		12 25			13 35		14 33					15 42
South Bank d																					
British Steel Redcar § d																					
Redcar Central d			10 00		10 33				11 41		12 35			13 46		14 43					15 52
Redcar East d			10 03		10 35				11 43		12 38			13 48		14 46					15 55
Longbeck d			10 07		10 39				11 47		12 42			13 52		14 50					15 59
Marske d			10 08		10 41				11 49		12 43			13 54		14 51					16 00
Saltburn a			10 15		10 48				11 57		12 50			14 02		14 58					16 08

	NT	NT	NT	NT	NT	TP	NT	NT	NT	TP	NT	NT	GC	NT	NT	NT	TP	NT	NT	NT
						1◇ E				1◇ D			R 1 C ☕				1◇ D			
Hexham 48 d																				
Metrocentre 48 d	14 48				15 48			16 48				17 48			18 48					
Newcastle 8 26 d	15 00	15 01	15 30		16 00		16b33	17 00	17 30			18 00		18 57	19 00	19 35		20 00	21 06	21 40
Heworth d	15 06				16 06			17 06				18 06			19 06			20 07		
Sunderland a	15 22				16 21			17 22				18 21			19 22			20 21		
d					16 21							18 21	18 42					20 21		
Seaham d					16 29							18 29						20 29		
Hartlepool d				16 22	16 45							18 45	19 06					20 45		
Seaton Carew d				16 26	16 50							18 50						20 50		
Billingham d				16 33	16 57							18 57						20 57		
Stockton d				16 40	17 04							19 04						21 04		
Bishop Auckland d							16 56				18 49									
Shildon d							17 01				18 54									
Newton Aycliffe d							17 06				18 59									
Heighington d							17 09				19 02									
North Road d							17 18				19 11									
Chester-le-Street 26 d									16 57										21 15	
Durham 26 d		15 15	15 37				16 46		17 37					19 10		19 48			21 24	21 53
Darlington 7 26 a				17 01			17 23				19 14								21 44	
d		15 42	16 19				17 24		18 31					19 36		20 30			21 45	22 45
Dinsdale d							17 30							19 41		20 35				
Tees-side Airport d																				
Allens West d							17 37							19 48		20 42				
Eaglescliffe d		15 53	16 30				17 39		18 42				19a24	19 50		20 44			21 57	22 56
Thornaby d		15 59	16 36		17 09	17 14	17 44		18 48	18 58		19 11		19 56		20 50	20 58	21 08	22 02	23 02
Middlesbrough a		16 04	16 41		17 17	17 24	17 49		18 53	19 10		19 20		20 01		20 55	21 10	21 20	22 07	23 10
d		16 05	16 45				17 50		18 54					20 02		20 56			22 08	
South Bank d																				
British Steel Redcar § d																				
Redcar Central d		16 15	16 55				18 01		19 04					20 12		21 06			22 18	
Redcar East d		16 18	16 58				18 03		19 07					20 15		21 09			22 21	
Longbeck d		16 22	17 02				18 07		19 11					20 19		21 13			22 25	
Marske d		16 23	17 03				18 09		19 12					20 20		21 14			22 26	
Saltburn a		16 30	17 11				18 17		19 19					20 27		21 21			22 34	

For general notes see front of timetable
For details of catering facilities see Directory of Train Operators

§ For authorised access only to BSC Redcar

A Until 27 January and from 30 March. From Manchester Airport (Table 39)
B 3 February to 23 March. From Leeds (Table 39)
C To London Kings Cross (Table 26)
D From Manchester Airport (Table 39)
E From Manchester Piccadilly (Table 39)
b Change at Darlington

Saltburn and Middlesbrough → Darlington, Bishop Auckland, Sunderland and Newcastle

Network Diagram - see first page of Table 44

Miles	Miles			NT	TP 1◇ A	NT	NT	NT	NT B	TP 1◇ A	NT C	NT	NT		NT	NT	NT	TP 1◇ A	NT C	NT	TP 1◇ A	NT	NT	GC R 1 D ✕		NT
0	—	**Saltburn**	d					06 24				07 17	07 38		08 02		08 30			09 21		10 00				10 30
2	—	Marske	d					06 28				07 21	07 42		08 06		08 34			09 25		10 04				10 34
2½	—	Longbeck	d					06 31				07 24	07 45		08 09		08 37			09 28		10 07				10 37
4	—	Redcar East	d					06 34				07 27	07 48		08 12		08 40			09 31		10 10				10 40
5	—	**Redcar Central**	d					06 37				07 30	07 51		08 15		08 43			09 34		10 13				10 43
6¾	—	British Steel Redcar §	d																							
10	—	South Bank	d														08 50									
12½	0	**Middlesbrough**	a					06 47				07 40	08 01		08 25		08 55			09 45		10 23				10 53
—	—		d	05 45	05 58			06 49	06 56	07 23	07 32	07 42	08 02		08 26	08 32	08 56	09 00	09 32	09 46	09 59	10 24	10 32			10 54
15¾	3½	Thornaby	d	05 50	06a03			06 54	07 02	07a28	07 37	07 47	08 07		08 31	08 37	09 01	09a04	09 37	09 51	10a04	10 29	10 37			10 59
18¾	—	Eaglescliffe	d	05 55				06 59				07 52	08 13		08 37		09 07			09 57		10 35		10 58		
19½	—	Allens West	d	05 58				07 02				07 55	08 15				09 09			09 59		10 37				
22	—	Tees-side Airport	d																							
23¾	—	Dinsdale	d					07 08				08 01	08 22									10 44				
27½	—	**Darlington 7**	a	06 14				07 19				08 11	08 31		08 52		09 24			10 17		10 53				11 19
—	—		26 d	06 14			06 47	07 20				08 15	08 33				09 26					10 55				
—	—	Durham	26 a	06 35				07 41				08 35	08 56		09 20		09 54			10 50		11 17				11 44
—	—	Chester-le-Street	26 a	06 42				07 48				08 43	09 02		09 44		10 40			10 56						
28¾	—	North Road	d				06 50						08 36				09 29					10 58				
33¼	—	Heighington	d				06 58						08 44				09 37					11 06				
34½	—	Newton Aycliffe	d				07 02						08 48				09 40					11 10				
36¾	—	Shildon	d				07 06						08 52				09 45					11 14				
39½	—	**Bishop Auckland**	a				07 16						08 59				09 52					11 21				
—	5½	Stockton	d						07 08		07 43					08 43			09 43				10 43			
—	10	Billingham	d						07 15		07 50					08 50			09 50				10 50			
—	15	Seaton Carew	d						07 21		07 56					08 56			09 56				10 56			
—	17¼	**Hartlepool**	d			07 03			07 27		08 02					09 02			10 02				11 02	11b23		
—	30	Seaham	d			07 18			07 42		08 17					09 17			10 17				11 17			
—	35¼	**Sunderland** ⛴	a			07 28			07 53		08 28					09 28			10 28				11 28	11 50		
—	—		d			07 30			07 55		08 30					09 30			10 30				11 30			
—	44¼	Heworth ⛴	d			07 41			08 06		08 41					09 42			10 42				11 42			
—	47¼	**Newcastle 8** ⛴	26 a	06 55		07 51		08 01	08 16		08 51	08 59	09c22		09 38	09 52	10c02		10 52	11 11		11c33	11 52			12 02
—	—	Metrocentre	48 a			08 03			08 31		09 01								11 01				12 01			
—	—	Hexham	48 a			08 40			08 58		09 37								11 36				12 36			

		TP 1◇ A	NT	NT	NT	TP 1◇ A	NT	NT	TP 1◇ A	NT	NT		NT	TP 1◇ A	NT	GC R 1 D ✕	NT	NT	TP 1◇ E	NT	NT	NT C		TP 1◇ A	NT	NT
Saltburn	d		11 00		11 30		12 00			12 30	13 00				13 30		14 00			14 30	15 03				15 30	16 00
Marske	d		11 04		11 34		12 04			12 34	13 04				13 34		14 04			14 35	15 07				15 34	16 04
Longbeck	d		11 07		11 37		12 07			12 37	13 07				13 37		14 07			14 38	15 10				15 37	16 07
Redcar East	d		11 10		11 40		12 10			12 40	13 10				13 40		14 10			14 41	15 13				15 40	16 10
Redcar Central	d		11 13		11 43		12 13			12 43	13 13				13 43		14 13			14 44	15 16				15 43	16 13
British Steel Redcar §	d																									
South Bank	d																									
Middlesbrough	a		11 23		11 55		12 23			12 56	13 24				13 54		14 23			14 54	15 26				15 54	16 23
	d	11 00	11 24	11 32	11 55	12 00	12 24	12 32	12 51	12 57	13 25		13 32	13 50	13 55		14 24	14 32	14 50	14 55	15 27	15 32		15 50	15 55	16 24
Thornaby	d	11a05	11 30	11 37	12 00	12a05	12 29	12 37	12a56	13 02	13 30		13 37	13a55	14 00		14 29	14 37	14a55	15 00	15 32	15 37		15a55	16 00	16 29
Eaglescliffe	d		11 35				12 35				13 35					14 05	14 35				15 37				16 05	16 35
Allens West	d		11 38				12 37				13 38						14 37				15 40				16 08	16 37
Tees-side Airport	d																									
Dinsdale	d						12 44				13 44										15 46				16 14	
Darlington 7	a		11 52		12 19		12 53			13 22	13 54				14 21		14 52			15 20	15 56				16 24	16 52
	26 d						12 55										14 54				15 57					
Durham	26 a		12 22		12 50		13 18			13 48	14 18				14 50		15 15			15 51	16 24				17 08	17 31
Chester-le-Street	26 a		12 50							13 54	14 41									15 57	16 36					
North Road	d						12 58										14 57				16 01					
Heighington	d						13 06										15 05				16 09					
Newton Aycliffe	d						13 10										15 09				16 12					
Shildon	d						13 14										15 13				16 16					
Bishop Auckland	a						13 21										15 19				16 24					
Stockton	d			11 43				12 43					13 43					14 43				15 43				
Billingham	d			11 50				12 50					13 50					14 50				15 50				
Seaton Carew	d			11 56				12 56					13 56					14 56				15 56				
Hartlepool	d			12 02				13 02					14 02			14 24		15 02				16 02				
Seaham	d			12 17				13 17					14 17					15 17				16 17				
Sunderland ⛴	a			12 29				13 28					14 28			14 50		15 28				16 27				
	d			12 30				13 30					14 30					15 30				16 30				
Heworth ⛴	d			12 42				13 42					14 42					15 42				16 42				
Newcastle 8 ⛴	26 a		12 37	12 51	12 55		13c34	13 51		14 10	14 37		14 51		15 06		15c32	15 51		15 57	16c39	16 51			17 26	17 28
Metrocentre	48 a			13 01				14 01					15 01					16 01				17 01				
Hexham	48 a			13 36				14 36					15 36					16 36				17 36				

For general notes see front of timetable
For details of catering facilities see Directory of Train Operators

§ For authorised access only to BSC Redcar

A To Manchester Airport (Table 39)
B To Carlisle (Table 48)
C From Nunthorpe (Table 45)
D From London Kings Cross (Table 26)
E To Manchester Piccadilly (Table 39)
b Arr. 1120
c Change at Darlington

Saltburn and Middlesbrough → Darlington, Bishop Auckland, Sunderland and Newcastle

Network Diagram - see first page of Table 44

		NT	TP	NT	NT	NT	TP	NT	NT	NT		NT	TP	NT	GC	NT	NT	TP	NT	TP	NT	TP	NT	NT
			1 ◇				1 ◇						1 ◇		R 1			1 ◇		1 ◇		1 ◇		
		A	B				C						D		E G ✕			C	H	B		D		
Saltburn	d			16 30	17 00			17 30	18 00			18 30				19 00	19 30				20 30		21 30	22 40
Marske	d			16 34	17 04			17 34	18 04			18 34				19 04	19 34				20 34		21 34	22 44
Longbeck	d			16 37	17 07			17 37	18 07			18 37				19 07	19 37				20 37		21 37	22 47
Redcar East	d			16 40	17 10			17 40	18 10			18 40				19 10	19 40				20 40		21 40	22 50
Redcar Central	d			16 43	17 13			17 43	18 13			18 43				19 13	19 43				20 43		21 43	22 53
British Steel Redcar §	d			16 46																				
South Bank	d			16 52																				
Middlesbrough	a			16 57	17 23			17 53	18 23			18 53				19 23	19 54				20 54		21 54	23 03
	d	16 32	16 50	16 57	17 24	17 32	17 50	17 55	18 24	18 30		18 54	19 00	19 20		19 25	19 55	20 10	20 30	20 50	20 55	21 40	21 55	23 05
Thornaby	d	16 37	16a55	17 02	17 29	17 37	17a55	18 00	18 29	18 35		18 59	19a05	19 25		19 30	20 00	20a15	20 35	20a55	21 00	21 45	22 00	23 10
Eaglescliffe	d			17 08	17 35			18 05				19 05			19 34	19 35	20 05				21 06		22 05	
Allens West	d			17 10	17 37			18 08				19 07				19 38	20 08				21 08		22 08	
Tees-side Airport	d																							
Dinsdale	d			17 17	17 44			18 14				19 14				19 44					21 15		22 14	
Darlington 7	a			17 26	17 54			18 24	18 49			19 29				19 56	20 25				21 24	22 02	22 28	23 31
	26 d			17 28				18 32									20 30							
Durham	26 a			*17 55*	*18 20*				*19 15*			*20 10*				*20 20*	*21 09*				*21 49*	*22 35*		*00 07*
Chester-le-Street	26 a			*18 01*	*18 40*				*19 57*							*20 37*	*21 45*					*22 45*		
North Road	d			17 31				18 35									20 33							
Heighington	d			17 39				18 43									20 41							
Newton Aycliffe	d			17 43				18 47									20 45							
Shildon	d			17 47				18 51									20 49							
Bishop Auckland	a			17 54				18 58									20 56							
Stockton	d	16 44				17 43				18 41				19 31					20 41					
Billingham	d	16 51				17 50				18 48				19 38					20 48					
Seaton Carew	d	16 57				17 56				18 54				19 44					20 54					
Hartlepool	d	17 03				18 02				19 00				19 49	20b08				21 00					
Seaham	d	17 18				18 18				19 15				20c10					21 15					
Sunderland	⛴ a	17 29				18 28				19 26				20 20	20 35				21 26					
	d	17 30				18 30				19 27				20 27					21 27					
Heworth	⛴ d	17 42				18 42				19 38				20 38					21 38					
Newcastle 8	26 ⛴ a	17 51		*18e16*	*18 37*	18 53			*19 35*	19 47		*20 26*		20 47		*20 37*	*21e27*		21 47		*22 07*	*23 00*		*00 42*
Metrocentre	48 a	18 01								19 57														
Hexham	48 a	18 31																						

Saturdays

		NT	TP	NT	NT	NT	NT	TP		NT	NT	NT	NT	NT	NT	TP		NT	NT	TP	NT	NT	GC	NT		TP
			1 ◇					1 ◇								1 ◇				1 ◇			R 1			1 ◇
			C				A	C		H						C		H		C			E 🍴			C
Saltburn	d					06 24					07 17	07 40	08 00		08 30				09 13		10 00			10 30		
Marske	d					06 28					07 21	07 44	08 04		08 34				09 17		10 04			10 34		
Longbeck	d					06 31					07 24	07 47	08 07		08 37				09 20		10 07			10 37		
Redcar East	d					06 34					07 27	07 50	08 10		08 40				09 23		10 10			10 40		
Redcar Central	d					06 37					07 30	07 53	08 13		08 43				09 26		10 13			10 43		
British Steel Redcar §	d																									
South Bank	d														08 50											
Middlesbrough	a					06 47					07 40	08 03	08 23		08 55				09 36		10 23			10 54		
	d	05 50	05 58			06 49	06 56	07 21		07 32	07 42	08 05	08 25	08 32	08 55	09 00		09 32	09 39	10 00	10 24	10 32		10 55		11 00
Thornaby	d	05 55	06a03			06 54	07 02	07a26		07 37	07 47	08 10	08 30	08 37	09 00	09a05		09 37	09 44	10a05	10 29	10 37		11 00		11a05
Eaglescliffe	d	06 00				07 01					07 56	08 12	08 35		09 06				09 49		10 34		10 49			
Allens West	d	06 03				07 03					07 59	08 15			09 08				09 52		10 37					
Tees-side Airport	d																									
Dinsdale	d					07 10					08 07	08 21									10 43					
Darlington 7	a	06 18				07 20					08 14	08 37	08 51		09 22				10 06		10 54			11 19		
	26 d				06 48	07 20					08 16	08 38			09 24						10 57					
Durham	26 a	*07 33*				07 40					08 36	*09 09*	*09 18*		*09 46*				*10 33*		*11 20*			*11 44*		
Chester-le-Street	26 a					07 48					08 44		*09 44*						*10 40*							
North Road	d				06 51							08 42			09 28						11 00					
Heighington	d				06 59							08 50			09 36						11 08					
Newton Aycliffe	d				07 02							08 53			09 39						11 12					
Shildon	d				07 07							08 57			09 43						11 16					
Bishop Auckland	a				07 17							09 04			09 51						11 23					
Stockton	d						07 08			07 43				08 43				09 43				10 43				
Billingham	d						07 15			07 50				08 50				09 50				10 50				
Seaton Carew	d						07 21			07 56				08 56				09 56				10 56				
Hartlepool	d			07 03			07 27			08 02				09 02				10 02				11 02	11 21			
Seaham	d			07 18			07 42			08 17				09 17				10 17				11 17				
Sunderland	⛴ a			07 28			07 53			08 28				09 28				10 28				11 28	11 50			
	d			07 30			07 55			08 30				09 30				10 30				11 30				
Heworth	⛴ d			07 42			08 07			08 42				09 42				10 42				11 42				
Newcastle 8	26 ⛴ a	*07 50*		07 53		08 01	08 17			08 53	08 56	*09e26*	*09 34*	09 54	*10e04*			10 52	*10 59*		*11e36*	11 52		*12 02*		
Metrocentre	48 a			08 03			08 31			09 02								11 01				12 01				
Hexham	48 a			08 40			08 58			09 38								11 36				12 36				

For general notes see front of timetable
For details of catering facilities see Directory of Train Operators

§ For authorised access only to BSC Redcar
A To Carlisle (Table 48)
B To Manchester Piccadilly (Table 39)
C To Manchester Airport (Table 39)
D To York (Table 39)
E From London Kings Cross (Table 26)
G **The 21st Century Limited**
H From Nunthorpe (Table 45)
b Arr. 2000
c Arr. 2005
e Change at Darlington

Table 44

Saturdays

Saltburn and Middlesbrough → Darlington, Bishop Auckland, Sunderland and Newcastle

Network Diagram - see first page of Table 44

	NT	NT	NT	TP	NT	NT	TP		NT	NT	NT	NT	TP	GC	NT		NT	TP	NT	NT	NT	TP	NT		NT
				1◇ A		B	1◇ A						1◇ A	R 1 C				1◇ D			B	1◇ A			
Saltburn d	11 00		11 30		11 56				12 30	13 00		13 30			13 58				14 30	15 00			15 30		16 00
Marske d	11 04		11 34		12 00				12 34	13 04		13 34			14 02				14 34	15 04			15 34		16 04
Longbeck d	11 07		11 37		12 03				12 37	13 07		13 37			14 05				14 37	15 07			15 37		16 07
Redcar East d	11 10		11 40		12 06				12 40	13 10		13 40			14 08				14 40	15 10			15 40		16 10
Redcar Central d	11 13		11 43		12 09				12 43	13 13		13 43			14 11				14 43	15 13			15 43		16 13
British Steel Redcar § d																									
South Bank d																									
Middlesbrough a	11 23		11 54		12 19				12 54	13 23		13 53			14 21				14 54	15 23			15 53		16 23
d	11 24	11 32	11 55	12 00	12 20	12 32	12 51		12 55	13 24	13 32	13 55	14 00		14 23		14 32	14 50	14 55	15 27	15 32	15 50	15 55		16 24
Thornaby d	11 29	11 37	12 00	12a05	12 25	12 37	12a56		13 00	13 29	13 37	14 00	14a05		14 28		14 37	14a55	15 00	15 32	15 37	15a55	16 00		16 29
Eaglescliffe d	11 35				12 30					13 34				14 27	14 33					15 37			16 05		16 34
Allens West d	11 37				12 33					13 37					14 36					15 40			16 08		16 37
Tees-side Airport d										13 41															
Dinsdale d					12 39					13 45										15 46			16 14		
Darlington 7 a	11 51		12 20		12 49				13 20	13 55		14 20			14 50				15 20	15 55			16 24		16 51
26 d					12 50										14 53								16 25		
Durham 26 a	12 18		12 45		13 18				13 52	14 18		14 51			15 17				15 45	16 17					17 17
Chester-le-Street 26 a	12 40								13 58										15 57						17 43
North Road d					12 54										14 57								16 28		
Heighington d					13 02										15 05								16 37		
Newton Aycliffe d					13 05										15 08								16 40		
Shildon d					13 09										15 12								16 44		
Bishop Auckland a					13 16										15 20								16 52		
Stockton d		11 43				12 43					13 43						14 43				15 43				
Billingham d		11 50				12 50					13 50						14 50				15 50				
Seaton Carew d		11 56				12 56					13 56						14 56				15 56				
Hartlepool d		12 02				13 02					14 02			14 46			15 02				16 02				
Seaham d		12 17				13 17					14 17						15 17				16 17				
Sunderland a		12 29				13 28					14 28			15 11			15 28				16 27				
d		12 30				13 30					14 30						15 30				16 30				
Heworth d		12 42				13 42					14 42						15 42				16 42				
Newcastle 8 26 a	12 35	12 52	13 01		13b35	13 52			14 13	14 35	14 51	15 12			15b34		15 52		16 01	16 34	16 52				17 34
Metrocentre 48 a		13 01				14 01					15 01						16 01				17 01				
Hexham 48 a		13 36				14 36					15 36						16 36				17 36				

	NT	NT	TP	NT	NT	NT	TP		NT	NT	NT	TP	NT	NT	GC	NT	TP	NT	TP	NT	TP	NT	NT		
	E		1◇ D		B		1◇ A					1◇ G			R 1 C H		1◇ A	B	1◇ D		1◇ J				
Saltburn d		16 30		16 59		17 28			18 00		18 28			19 00		19 35				20 30		21 30	22 40		
Marske d		16 34		17 03		17 32			18 04		18 32			19 04		19 39				20 34		21 34	22 44		
Longbeck d		16 37		17 06		17 35			18 07		18 35			19 07		19 42				20 37		21 37	22 47		
Redcar East d		16 40		17 09		17 38			18 10		18 38			19 10		19 45				20 40		21 40	22 50		
Redcar Central d		16 43		17 12		17 41			18 13		18 41			19 13		19 48				20 43		21 43	22 53		
British Steel Redcar § d																									
South Bank d				17 19																					
Middlesbrough a		16 54		17 24		17 55			18 23		18 51			19 23		19 58				20 54		21 53	23 04		
d	16 32	16 55	17 00	17 25	17 30	17 56	18 07		18 24	18 30	18 53	19 00	19 20	19 25		19 59	20 10	20 30	20 50	20 55	21 50	21 55	23 05		
Thornaby d	16 37	17 00	17a05	17 30	17 35	18 01	18a12		18 29	18 35	18 58	19a05	19 25	19 30		20 04	20a15	20 35	20a55	21 00	21 55	22 00	23 10		
Eaglescliffe d		17 05		17 35		18 06					19 03			19 35	19 50	20 10				21 06		22 05			
Allens West d		17 08		17 38		18 09					19 06			19 38		20 12				21 08		22 08			
Tees-side Airport d																									
Dinsdale d		17 14				18 15					19 12			19 44		20 19				21 15		22 14			
Darlington 7 a		17 24		17 52		18 25			18 49		19 23			19 54		20 28				21 24	22 15	22 24	23 30		
26 d		17 30				18 26										20 36									
Durham 26 a		17 57		18 17					19 17		19 51			20 22		21 21				21 56		23 25	00 19		
Chester-le-Street 26 a		18 03		18 39							19 57			20 41		22 17									
North Road d		17 34				18 30										20 39									
Heighington d		17 42				18 38										20 47									
Newton Aycliffe d		17 45				18 41										20 51									
Shildon d		17 49				18 45										20 55									
Bishop Auckland a		17 57				18 53										21 02									
Stockton d	16 43				17 41					18 41			19 31					20 41							
Billingham d	16 50				17 48					18 48			19 38					20 48							
Seaton Carew d	16 56				17 54					18 54			19 44					20 54							
Hartlepool d	17 02				18 02					19 00			19 49		20 09			21 00							
Seaham d	17 17				18 18					19 15			20c10					21 15							
Sunderland a	17 27				18 28					19 26			20 20		20 35			21 26							
d	17 30				18 30					19 27			20 27					21 27							
Heworth d	17 42				18 42					19 38			20 38					21 38							
Newcastle 8 26 a	17 52	18b18		18 34	18 53	19b05			19 34	19 48	20 12		20 48	20 36		21b41		21 48		22 14		23 46	00 52		
Metrocentre 48 a	18 01									19 58															
Hexham 48 a	18 32																								

For general notes see front of timetable
For details of catering facilities see Directory of Train Operators

§ For authorised access only to BSC Redcar
A To Manchester Airport (Table 39)
B From Nunthorpe (Table 45)
C From London Kings Cross (Table 26)
D To Manchester Piccadilly (Table 39)
E To Carlisle (Table 48)
G To York (Table 39)
H **The 21st Century Limited**
J To Manchester Airport (2 February to 22 March to Leeds) (Table 39)
b Change at Darlington
c Arr. 2005

Table 44

Sundays

Saltburn and Middlesbrough → Darlington, Bishop Auckland, Sunderland and Newcastle

Network Diagram - see first page of Table 44

	NT	NT	NT	NT		NT	TP	NT	NT		NT	NT	GC	NT		TP	NT	NT	NT		NT	TP	NT	NT	NT
							1 ◇ A						R 1 B ☕			1 ◇ A						1 ◇ C			
Saltburn d									10 28		11 00						12 01		13 00					14 14	
Marske d									10 32		11 04						12 05		13 04					14 18	
Longbeck d									10 35		11 07						12 08		13 07					14 21	
Redcar East d									10 38		11 10						12 11		13 10					14 24	
Redcar Central d									10 41		11 13						12 14		13 13					14 27	
British Steel Redcar § d																									
South Bank d																									
Middlesbrough a									10 51		11 23						12 24		13 23					14 37	
d		08 45	09 15	09 30		10 00	10 15		10 53		11 24	11 30				12 15	12 25		13 25		13 30	13 45		14 38	15 30
Thornaby d		08 50	09 20	09 35		10 05	10a20		10 58		11 29	11 35				12a20	12 30		13 30		13 35	13a50		14 43	15 35
Eaglescliffe d		08 55	09 25			10 10			11 03		11 34		11 40				12 36		13 35					14 49	
Allens West d		08 58	09 28								11 37								13 38						
Tees-side Airport d																									
Dinsdale d			09 34								11 43								13 45						
Darlington 7 a		09 12	09 49			10 26			11 22		11 54						12 52		13 54					15 06	
26 d			09 51								11 55			12 20					14 09						
Durham 26 a		*09 50*				*10 53*			*11 54*		*12 20*						*13 19*		*14 21*					*15b30*	
Chester-le-Street 26 a						*11 26*											*14 07*								
North Road d			09 54								11 58								14 12						
Heighington d			10 02								12 07								14 20						
Newton Aycliffe d			10 05								12 10								14 23						
Shildon d			10 10								12 14								14 28						
Bishop Auckland a			10 20								12 20								14 33						
Stockton d				09 41								11 41		12 36							13 41				15 41
Billingham d				09 48								11 48		12 43							13 48				15 48
Seaton Carew d				09 54								11 54		12 49							13 54				15 54
Hartlepool d				10 00								12 00	12c17	12a57							14 00				16 00
Seaham d				10 15								12 15									14 15				16 15
Sunderland ⛴ a				10 26								12 26	12 52								14 26				16 26
d	09 28			10 28				11 28				12 28						13 28			14 28		15 28		16 28
Heworth ⛴ d	09 39			10 39				11 39				12 39						13 39			14 39		15 39		16 39
Newcastle 8 26 ⛴ a	09 48	*10 06*		10 48		*11 09*		11 48	*12 10*		*12e37*	12 48					*13 36*	13 49	*14e37*		14 48		15 48	*15b51*	16 48
Metrocentre 48 a	10 01			10 59				11 57				12 59						13 59			14 59		15 59		16 57
Hexham 48 a																									

	NT		TP	NT	NT	GC		NT	NT	NT	TP		NT	NT	NT	NT		NT	TP	NT	NT	TP	NT		
			1 ◇ C			R 1 B ☕					1 ◇ C								1 ◇ A			1 ◇ A			
Saltburn d				15 20				16 21	16 48				17 20		18 27			19 23		20 31	21 30		22 38		
Marske d				15 24				16 25	16 52				17 24		18 31			19 27		20 35	21 34		22 42		
Longbeck d				15 27				16 28	16 55				17 27		18 34			19 30		20 38	21 37		22 45		
Redcar East d				15 30				16 31	16 58				17 30		18 37			19 33		20 41	21 40		22 48		
Redcar Central d				15 33				16 34	17 01				17 33		18 40			19 36		20 44	21 43		22 51		
British Steel Redcar § d																									
South Bank d																									
Middlesbrough a				15 48				16 44	17 11				17 48		18 52			19 46		20 54	21 53		23 01		
d			15 45	15 50				16 45	17 14	17 30	17 45		17 49		18 53	19 30		19 47	20 15	20 55	21 55	22 07	23 02		
Thornaby d			15a50	15 55				16 50	17 19	17 35	17a50		17 54		18 58	19 35		19 52	20a20	21 00	22 00	22a12	23 07		
Eaglescliffe d				16 00		16 40		16 56	17 25				17 59					19 58		21 06	22 05		23 12		
Allens West d				16 03									18 02					20 00			22 08				
Tees-side Airport d																									
Dinsdale d				16 09									18 08					20 07			22 14				
Darlington 7 a				16 20				17 15	17 42				18 18		19 25			20 17		21 22	22 25		23 29		
26 d	15 37			16 22									18 20												
Durham 26 a				*16 58*				*18 01*	*18 18*				*19 18*		*19 51*			*21 19*		*22 06*	*23 01*		*00 19*		
Chester-le-Street 26 a								*18 07*							*20 05*										
North Road d				16 25									18 23												
Heighington d				16 33									18 31												
Newton Aycliffe d				16 36									18 34												
Shildon d				16 41									18 39												
Bishop Auckland a				16 46									18 44												
Stockton d	15 53									17 41						19 41									
Billingham d	16 00									17 48						19 48									
Seaton Carew d	16 06									17 54						19 54									
Hartlepool d	16a14					17f10				18 00						20 00									
Seaham d										18 15						20 15									
Sunderland ⛴ a						17 36				18 26						20 25									
d					17 28					18 28				19 28		20 28									
Heworth ⛴ d					17 39					18 39				19 39		20 39									
Newcastle 8 26 ⛴ a				*17e04*	17 48			*18 01*	*18 35*	18 48			*19e05*	19 52	*20 07*	20 49		*21 06*		*22 02*	*23 34*		*00 52*		
Metrocentre 48 a					17 59					18 59															
Hexham 48 a																									

For general notes see front of timetable
For details of catering facilities see Directory of Train Operators

§ For authorised access only to BSC Redcar

A To Manchester Airport (Table 39)
B From London Kings Cross (Table 26)
C To Liverpool Lime Street (Table 39)

b 3 February to 23 March arr. Durham 1553, Newcastle 1610
c Arr. 1206
e Change at Darlington
f Arr. 1658

Middlesbrough and Pickering → Whitby

Network Diagram - see first page of Table 44

Mondays to Fridays

Miles	Station		NT	NT	NT	NY	NY	NY	NT	NY	NY	NY	NT	NT	NY	NY	NY	NT	NT	NT	NT
						ThFO	MFO	MFX		ThFO	MFO	MFX			ThFO	MFO	MFX				
				A		B	C	D		B	C	D		E	B	C	D	E		E	E
—	Newcastle 44	d	06b00	07 00	07 30				09b12				12b40	13 30				15 30	16b06	16 30	18 30
—	Darlington 44	d	06 36	07 48	08 10				09 53				13 30	14 08				15 57	16 59	17 15	18 33
0	**Middlesbrough**	d	07 08	08 13	08 49				10 38				14 16	14 49				16 47	17 40	17 54	19 49
3	Marton	d	07 13	08 18	08 54				10 43				14 21	14 54				16 52	17 45	17 59	19 54
4	Gypsy Lane	d	07 16	08 21	08 58				10 46				14 24	14 57				16 55	17 48	18 02	19 57
4½	Nunthorpe	d	07 19	08a26	09a01				10 49				14 27	15a03				16a59	17 51	18a05	20a03
8½	Great Ayton	d	07 25						10 55				14 33						17 57		
11	Battersby	a	07 31						11 01				14 39						18 03		
—		d	07 39						11 05				14 43						18 07		
12¾	Kildale	d	07 44						11 10				14 48						18 12		
16¾	Commondale	d	07 51						11 17				14 55						18 19		
18½	Castleton Moor	d	07 55						11 20				14 58						18 22		
20	Danby	d	07 58						11 23				15 01						18 25		
23½	Lealholm	d	08 05						11 30				15 08						18 32		
25½	Glaisdale	a	08 10						11 34				15 12						18 36		
—		d	08 12						11 37				15 15						18 39		
27¼	Egton	d	08 16						11 40				15 18						18 42		
—	**Pickering §**	d				08 45	09 00	09 00			12 00	12 00				16 00	16 00				
—	Goathland §	d				09 42	09 50	09 50		12 30	12 50	12 50			16 25	16 50	16 50				
28¾	Grosmont	d	08 20			10 00	10 10	10 10	11 44	13 10	13 10	13 10	15 22		16 45	17 10	17 10		18 46		
32	Sleights	d	08 29						11 53				15 31						18 55		
33½	Ruswarp	d	08 34						11 58				15 36						19 00		
35	**Whitby**	a	08 41			10 20	10 35	10 35	12 05	13 30	13 35	13 35	15 43		17 10	17 35	17 35		19 07		

Saturdays

Station		NT	NT	NT	NY	NY	NT	NT	NY	NY	NT	NT	NY	NY	NT	NT	NT	NT
					G	H		E	G	H		E	G	H	E		E	E
Newcastle 44	d	06b00	07 00	07 30			09b12	10 30			12b40	13 30			15 30	16b20	16 30	18 30
Darlington 44	d	06 36	07 38	08 10			09 51	10 47			13 31	13 53			16 00	17 04		18 30
Middlesbrough	d	07 06	08 04	08 49			10 38	11 49			14 12	14 49			16 47	17 38	17 50	19 48
Marton	d	07 11	08 09	08 54			10 43	11 54			14 17	14 54			16 52	17 43	17 55	19 53
Gypsy Lane	d	07 14	08 12	08 58			10 46	11 57			14 20	14 57			16 55	17 46	17 58	19 56
Nunthorpe	d	07 17	08a18	09a01			10 49	12a01			14 23	15a01			16a59	17 49	18a01	20a01
Great Ayton	d	07 23					10 55				14 29					17 55		
Battersby	a	07 29					11 01				14 35					18 01		
	d	07 33					11 05				14 39					18 05		
Kildale	d	07 38					11 10				14 44					18 10		
Commondale	d	07 45					11 17				14 51					18 17		
Castleton Moor	d	07 49					11 20				14 54					18 20		
Danby	d	07 52					11 23				14 57					18 23		
Lealholm	d	07 59					11 30				15 04					18 30		
Glaisdale	a	08 04					11 34				15 08					18 34		
	d	08 06					11 37				15 11					18 37		
Egton	d	08 10					11 40				15 14					18 40		
Pickering §	d				08 45	09 00				12 00				16 00				
Goathland §	d				09 42	09 50			12 30	12 50			16 25	16 50				
Grosmont	d	08 14			10 00	10 10	11 44		13 10	13 10	15 18		16 45	17 10		18 44		
Sleights	d	08 23					11 53				15 27					18 53		
Ruswarp	d	08 28					11 58				15 32					18 58		
Whitby	a	08 35			10 20	10 35	12 05		13 30	13 35	15 39		17 10	17 35		19 05		

For general notes see front of timetable
For details of catering facilities see Directory of Train Operators

§ North Yorkshire Moors Railway. For full service between Pickering, Goathland and Grosmont, please refer to separate publicity.

A From Bishop Auckland (Table 44)
B 27 and 28 December
C 21 to 28 March and 4 May
D From 25 March
E From Hexham (Table 48)
G 29 December
H 22 March to 5 April, 19 April and from 3 May
b Change at Darlington and Middlesbrough

Table 45

Sundays

Middlesbrough and Pickering → Whitby

Network Diagram - see first page of Table 44

		NY A ☕	NY B ☕	NY A ☕	NY B ☕	NY A ☕	NY B ☕
Newcastle 8	44 🚌 d						
Darlington 7	44 d						
Middlesbrough	d						
Marton	d						
Gypsy Lane	d						
Nunthorpe	d						
Great Ayton	d						
Battersby	a						
	d						
Kildale	d						
Commondale	d						
Castleton Moor	d						
Danby	d						
Lealholm	d						
Glaisdale	a						
	d						
Egton	d						
Pickering §	d	08 45	09 00		12 00		16 00
Goathland §	d	09 42	09 50	12 30	12 50	16 25	16 50
Grosmont	d	10 00	10 10	13 10	13 10	16 45	17 10
Sleights	d						
Ruswarp	d						
Whitby	a	10 20	10 35	13 30	13 35	17 10	17 35

For general notes see front of timetable
For details of catering facilities see Directory of Train Operators

§ North Yorkshire Moors Railway. For full service between Pickering, Goathland and Grosmont, please refer to separate publicity.

A 30 December
B From 23 March

No Sunday service operated by Northern Trains

Whitby → Pickering and Middlesbrough

Network Diagram - see first page of Table 44

Mondays to Fridays

Miles	Station		NT A	NT	NT A	NT	NY ThFO B ☕	NY MFO C ☕	NY MFX D ☕	NT	NY ThFO B ☕	NY MFO C ☕	NY MFX D ☕	NT A	NT	NT	NY ThFO B ☕	NY MFO C ☕	NY MFX D ☕	NT	NT	NT
0	**Whitby**	d				08 52	11 00	11 00	11 00	12 41	14 00	14 00	14 00			16 05	17 40	18 00	18 00			19 15
1½	Ruswarp	d				08 56				12 45						16 09						19 19
3	Sleights	d				09 01				12 50						16 14						19 24
6¼	Grosmont	d				09 09	11b30	11b30	11b30	12 58	14b30	14b30	14b30			16 22	18b10	18b30	18b30			19 32
—	Goathland §	a					11 45	11 45	11 45		14 45	14 45	14 45				18 25	18 45	18 45			
—	**Pickering §**	a						12 40	12 40			15 40	15 40				19 10	19 30	19 30			
7¾	Egton	d				09 12				13 01						16 26						19 35
9½	Glaisdale	a				09 16				13 05						16 30						19 39
—		d				09 19				13 08						16 33						19 42
11½	Lealholm	d				09 24				13 13						16 38						19 47
15	Danby	d				09 30				13 19						16 45						19 53
16½	Castleton Moor	d				09 33				13 22						16 49						19 56
18¼	Commondale	d				09 37				13 26						16 52						20 00
22¼	Kildale	d				09 44				13 33						16 59						20 07
24	Battersby	a				09 49				13 38						17 04						20 12
—		d				09 53				13 42						17 09						20 16
26½	Great Ayton	d				09 58				13 47						17 14						20 21
30½	Nunthorpe	d	07 19	08 30	09 16	10 05				13 54				15 16	17 02	17 21				18 24	20 14	20 28
31	Gypsy Lane	d	07 21	08 32	09 18	10 07				13 56				15 18	17 04	17 23				18 26	20 16	20 30
32	Marton	d	07 23	08 34	09 21	10 10				13 59				15 21	17 06	17 25				18 29	20 19	20 33
35	**Middlesbrough**	a	07 29	08 43	09 27	10 18				14 07				15 30	17 13	17 35				18 35	20 25	20 39
—	Darlington 7	44 a	*08 11*	*09 24*	*10 17*	*10 53*				*14 52*				*16 24*	*17 54*	*18 24*				*19 29*		*21 24*
—	Newcastle 8	44 ⛴ a	08 51	*10c02*	10 52	*11c33*				*15c32*				16 51	*18c37*	*19c35*				*20c26*	21 47	*22c07*

Saturdays

Station		NT A	NT	NT A	NT	NY E ☕	NY G ☕	NT A	NT	NY E ☕	NY G ☕	NT A	NT	NT	NY E ☕	NY G ☕	NT	NT	NT
Whitby	d				08 45	11 00	11 00		12 41	14 00	14 00		15 50		17 40	18 00			19 15
Ruswarp	d				08 49				12 45				15 54						19 19
Sleights	d				08 54				12 50				15 59						19 24
Grosmont	d				09 02	11b30	11b30		12 58	14b30	14b30		16 07		18b10	18b30			19 32
Goathland §	a					11 45	11 45			14 45	14 45				18 25	18 45			
Pickering §	a						12 40				15 40				19 10	19 30			
Egton	d				09 05				13 01				16 10						19 35
Glaisdale	a				09 09				13 05				16 14						19 39
	d				09 12				13 08				16 17						19 42
Lealholm	d				09 17				13 13				16 22						19 47
Danby	d				09 23				13 19				16 28						19 53
Castleton Moor	d				09 26				13 22				16 31						19 56
Commondale	d				09 30				13 26				16 35						20 00
Kildale	d				09 37				13 33				16 42						20 07
Battersby	a				09 42				13 38				16 47						20 12
	d				09 46				13 42				16 51						20 16
Great Ayton	d				09 51				13 47				16 56						20 21
Nunthorpe	d	07 19	08 26	09 16	09 58			12 16	13 54			15 16	17 03	17 16			18 24	20 14	20 28
Gypsy Lane	d	07 21	08 28	09 18	10 00			12 18	13 56			15 18	17 05	17 18			18 26	20 16	20 30
Marton	d	07 23	08 30	09 21	10 03			12 21	13 59			15 21	17 08	17 20			18 29	20 19	20 33
Middlesbrough	a	07 29	08 39	09 27	10 11			12 27	14 07			15 30	17 16	17 29			18 35	20 25	20 41
Darlington 7	44 a	*08 14*	*09 22*	*10 06*	*10 54*			*13 20*	*14 50*			*16 24*	*17 52*	*18 25*			*19 23*		*21 24*
Newcastle 8	44 ⛴ a	08 53	*10c04*	10 52	*11c36*			13 52	*15c34*			16 52	*18c34*	18 53			*20c12*	21 48	*22c14*

For general notes see front of timetable
For details of catering facilities see Directory of Train Operators

§ North Yorkshire Moors Railway. For full service between Grosmont, Goathland and Pickering, please refer to separate publicity.

- **A** To Hexham (Table 48)
- **B** 27 and 28 December
- **C** 21 to 28 March and 4 May
- **D** From 25 March
- **E** 29 December
- **G** 22 March to 5 April, 19 April and from 3 May
- **b** Arr. 10 minutes earlier
- **c** Change at Middlesbrough and Darlington

Table 45

Sundays

Whitby → Pickering and Middlesbrough

Network Diagram - see first page of Table 44

		NY A ☕	NY B ☕	NY A ☕	NY B ☕	NY A ☕	NY B ☕
Whitby	d	11}00	11}00	14}00	14}00	17}40	18}00
Ruswarp	d	}	}	}	}	}	}
Sleights	d	}	}	}	}	}	}
Grosmont	d	11b30	11b30	14b30	14b30	18b10	18b30
Goathland §	a	11}45	11}45	14}45	14}45	18}25	18}45
Pickering §	a		12}40		15}40	19}10	19}30
Egton	d						
Glaisdale	a						
	d						
Lealholm	d						
Danby	d						
Castleton Moor	d						
Commondale	d						
Kildale	d						
Battersby	a						
	d						
Great Ayton	d						
Nunthorpe	d						
Gypsy Lane	d						
Marton	d						
Middlesbrough	a						
Darlington 7 44	a						
Newcastle 8 44	a						

For general notes see front of timetable
For details of catering facilities see Directory of Train Operators

§ North Yorkshire Moors Railway. For full service between Grosmont, Goathland and Pickering, please refer to separate publicity.

A 30 December
B From 23 March
b Arr. 10 minutes earlier

No Sunday service operated by Northern Trains

Chathill and Morpeth → Newcastle → MetroCentre, Hexham and Carlisle

Network Diagram - see first page of Table 44

Miles	Miles			NT	NT A	GR R 1 B ✕	NT C	NT D	NT	NT E	NT	NT	NT	NT	NT	NT	NT E	NT	NT	XC R 1 G	NT	NT D	NT
0	—	**Chathill**	d						07 22														
11¼	—	Alnmouth	26 d			07 03			07 34											11 04			
17½	—	Acklington	d						07 42														
22¾	—	Widdrington	d						07 49														
27½	—	Pegswood	d						07 55														
29½	—	**Morpeth**	26 d			07 19			08 00		08 32			09 32				10 50		11 18			11 50
36¼	—	Cramlington	d						08 08		08 40			09 41				10 58					11 58
45½	—	Manors	d						08 21		08 53												
46	—	**Newcastle** 8	26 ⛴ a			07 38			08 25		08 57			09 55				11 14		11 35			12 13
—	—	Sunderland	44 ⛴ d				07 30	07 55		08 30				*09 30*			10 30					11 30	
—	—	London Kings Cross 15	⊖ 26 d											*06 15*	*07 00*		*07 30*	*08 00*				*08 30*	*09 00*
—	0	**Newcastle** 8	⛴ d	06 30	06 54		07 56	08 24		08 54		09 24	09 44	10 00	10 24	10 44	10 54	11 14	11 24		11 44	11 54	12 14
48¼	2¼	Dunston	d											10 05									
49½	3½	**Metrocentre**	a				08 03	08 31		09 01		09 31	09 51	10 08	10 32	10 52	11 01	11 21	11 32		11 53	12 01	12 22
—	—		d				08 04	08 32		09 02		09 32		10 09	10 33		11 02		11 33			12 02	
—	5½	Blaydon	d				08 08			09 05													
—	9¾	Wylam	d	06 44			08 14	08 40		09 12				10 17			11 10					12 10	
—	12	Prudhoe	d	06 48			08 18	08 44		09 15		09 42		10 21	10 43		11 14		11 43			12 14	
—	14½	Stocksfield	d	06 53			08 23	08 48		09 20				10 25			11 18					12 18	
—	16¾	Riding Mill	d	06 57			08 27			09 24				10 30			11 23					12 23	
—	19¼	Corbridge	d	07 01			08 31			09 28				10 33			11 26					12 26	
—	22¼	**Hexham**	a	07 10	07 20		08 40	08 58		09 37		09 55		10 42	10 56		11 36		11 56			12 36	
—	—		d		07 20			08 59				09 55			10 56				11 56				
—	30	Haydon Bridge	d		07 29			09 08											12 05				
—	33¾	Bardon Mill	d		07 36			09 14											12 12				
—	38½	Haltwhistle	d		07 43			09 21				10 14			11 15				12 19				
—	50¾	Brampton (Cumbria)	d		07 58			09 37											12 34				
—	57½	Wetheral	d		08 07			09 45											12 43				
—	61¾	**Carlisle** 8	a		08 17			09 56				10 44			11 46				12 53				

		NT	NT H	NT	NT D	NT	NT	XC R 1 J	NT	NT D	NT	NT	NT	NT D	NT	NT	XC 1 ◇ J	NT	NT D	NT	NT K	NT
Chathill	d																					
Alnmouth	26 d							13 04									15 05					
Acklington	d																					
Widdrington	d																					
Pegswood	d																					
Morpeth	26 d					12 50		13 19			13 50				14 50		15 21			15 50		
Cramlington	d					12 58					13 58				14 58					15 58		
Manors	d					13 11					14 10											
Newcastle 8	26 ⛴ a					13 13		13 37			14 13				15 13		15 38			16 13		
Sunderland	44 ⛴ d				12 30					13 30				14 30					15 30			
London Kings Cross 15	⊖ 26 d					*10 00*			*10 30*		*11 00*				*12 00*					*13 00*		*13 30*
Newcastle 8	⛴ d	12 24	12 39	12 44	12 54	13 14	13 24		13 44	13 54	14 14	14 24	14 44	14 54	15 14	15 24		15 44	15 54	16 14	16 24	16 44
Dunston	d																					
Metrocentre	a	12 32	12 46	12 52	13 01	13 22	13 31		13 51	14 01	14 22	14 31	14 52	15 01	15 21	15 32		15 51	16 01	16 21	16 31	16 51
	d		12 46		13 02		13 32			14 02		14 32		15 02		15 32			16 02		16 32	
Blaydon	d																					
Wylam	d				13 10					14 10		14 40		15 10					16 10		16 40	
Prudhoe	d				13 14		13 42			14 14		14 44		15 14					16 14		16 44	
Stocksfield	d				13 18					14 18				15 18					16 18		16 48	
Riding Mill	d				13 23					14 23				15 23					16 23		16 53	
Corbridge	d				13 26					14 26				15 26					16 26		16 56	
Hexham	a		13 06		13 36		13 55			14 36		14 56		15 36		15 54			16 36		17 02	
	d		13 08				13 55					14 57				15 54					17 03	
Haydon Bridge	d															16 04					17 12	
Bardon Mill	d															16 10						
Haltwhistle	d		13 26				14 14					15 16				16 17					17 23	
Brampton (Cumbria)	d															16 33						
Wetheral	d															16 42						
Carlisle 8	a		13 59				14 45					15 47				16 53					17 55	

For general notes see front of timetable
For details of catering facilities see Directory of Train Operators

- **A** To Glasgow Central (Table 216)
- **B** From Edinburgh to London Kings Cross (Table 26)
- **C** From Hartlepool (Table 44)
- **D** From Middlesbrough (Table 44)
- **E** From Nunthorpe (Table 45)
- **G** From Glasgow Central (Table 51) to Penzance (Table 135)
- **H** To Stranraer (Table 216)
- **J** From Edinburgh to Plymouth (Table 51)
- **K** To Whitehaven (Table 100)

For full service from Alnmouth to Newcastle, please see Table 26

Chathill and Morpeth → Newcastle → MetroCentre, Hexham and Carlisle

Network Diagram - see first page of Table 44

Mondays to Fridays

		NT	NT	NT	NT	XC	NT	NT	NT	NT	NT	NT	NT	NT	GR	NT	NT	NT	NT	NT	GR
						1 ◇									R 1						R 1
		A		B		C	D						D		E				G		H
Chathill	d													19 08							
Alnmouth	26 d					17 08								19 20	19 40						22 07
Acklington	d													19 28							
Widdrington	d													19 35							
Pegswood	d													19 41							
Morpeth	26 d		16 50			17 23				18 32		19 01		19 45	19 57				21 34		22 24
Cramlington	d		16 58							18 40		19 09		19 54					21 42		
Manors	d																				
Newcastle 8	26 a		17 12			17 38				18 55		19 25		20 06	20 18				21 56		22 45
Sunderland	44 d	16 30					17 30				18 30		19 27			20 27		21 27			
London Kings Cross 15	⊖ 26 d			14 00			15 00				16 00			17 00		17 30	18 00	18 20		19 00	
Newcastle 8	d	16 54		17 13	17 26		17 54	18 01	18 24		19 10		19 50	20 10		20 55	21 10	21 55		22 30	
Dunston	d							18 07													
Metrocentre	a	17 01		17 20	17 33		18 01	18 10	18 31		19 17		19 57	20 17		21 03	21 17	22 04		22 37	
	d	17 02		17 20	17 34		18 01		18 32		19 18			20 18			21 18			22 38	
Blaydon	d				17 39																
Wylam	d	17 10		17 29	17 46		18 09		18 40		19 26			20 26			21 26			22 46	
Prudhoe	d	17 14		17 32	17 49		18 13		18 44		19 30			20 30			21 30			22 50	
Stocksfield	d	17 18			17 54		18 18		18 48		19 34			20 34			21 34			22 54	
Riding Mill	d	17 23			17 58		18 22		18 53		19 39			20 39			21 39			22 59	
Corbridge	d	17 26			18 02		18 26		18 56		19 42			20 42			21 42			23 02	
Hexham	a	17 36		17 45	18 10		18 31		19 02		19 48			20 51			21 48			23 11	
	d			17 45			18 31		19 03		19 49						21 49				
Haydon Bridge	d			17 54			18 40				19 58						21 58				
Bardon Mill	d			18 01			18 47										22 04				
Haltwhistle	d			18 08			18 54		19 21		20 09						22 11				
Brampton (Cumbria)	d			18 23					19 37								22 27				
Wetheral	d			18 32					19 45								22 35				
Carlisle 8	a			18 43			19 26		19 57		20 42						22 45				

Saturdays

		NT	GR	NT	NT	NT	NT	NT	NT	NT	NT	NT	NT	NT	NT	XC	NT	NT	NT	NT	NT
			R 1													1 ◇					
		J	K	L	D		A						A			N		D			B
Chathill	d					07 22															
Alnmouth	26 d		07 19			07 34										11 04					
Acklington	d					07 42															
Widdrington	d					07 49															
Pegswood	d					07 55															
Morpeth	26 d		07 35			08 00				09 32				10 50		11 18			11 50		
Cramlington	d					08 08				09 40				10 58					11 58		
Manors	d					08 21															
Newcastle 8	26 a		07 53			08 25				09 55				11 14		11 36			12 13		
Sunderland	44 d			07 30	07 55		08 30				09 30		10 30					11 30			
London Kings Cross 15	⊖ 26 d								06 15		07 00			08 00				08 30	09 00		
Newcastle 8	d	06 34		07 56	08 24		08 54	09 24	09 44	10 00	10 24	10 44	10 54	11 14	11 22		11 44	11 54	12 14	12 24	12 39
Dunston	d									10 05											
Metrocentre	a			08 03	08 31		09 02	09 31	09 51	10 08	10 31	10 53	11 01	11 21	11 32		11 52	12 01	12 22	12 31	12 46
	d			08 04	08 32		09 02	09 32		10 09	10 32		11 02		11 33			12 02			12 46
Blaydon	d			08 08			09 05														
Wylam	d	06 49		08 14	08 40		09 11			10 17			11 10					12 10			
Prudhoe	d	06 53		08 18	08 44		09 15	09 42		10 21	10 42		11 14		11 43			12 14			
Stocksfield	d	06 57		08 23	08 48		09 20			10 25			11 18					12 18			
Riding Mill	d	07 02		08 27			09 24			10 30			11 23					12 23			
Corbridge	d	07 05		08 31			09 28			10 33			11 26					12 26			
Hexham	a	07 10		08 40	08 58		09 38	09 55		10 42	10 55		11 36		11 56			12 36			13 06
	d	07 11			08 59			09 56			10 55				11 57						13 08
Haydon Bridge	d	07 20			09 08										12 06						
Bardon Mill	d	07 26			09 14										12 12						
Haltwhistle	d	07 33			09 21			10 14			11 14				12 19						13 26
Brampton (Cumbria)	d	07 49			09 37										12 35						
Wetheral	d	07 57			09 45										12 44						
Carlisle 8	a	08 07			09 56			10 45			11 45				12 54						13 59

For general notes see front of timetable
For details of catering facilities see Directory of Train Operators

A From Nunthorpe (Table 45)
B To Stranraer (Table 216)
C From Edinburgh to Bristol Temple Meads (Table 51)
D From Middlesbrough (Table 44)
E From Edinburgh (Table 26)
G To Middlesbrough (Table 44)
H From Glasgow Central to York (Table 26)
J To Glasgow Central (Table 216)
K From Edinburgh to London Kings Cross (Table 26)
L From Hartlepool (Table 44)
N From Glasgow Central (from 29 March from Edinburgh) (Table 51) to Penzance (Table 135)

For full service from Alnmouth to Newcastle, please see Table 26

Chathill and Morpeth → Newcastle → MetroCentre, Hexham and Carlisle

Network Diagram - see first page of Table 44

	NT	NT A	NT	NT	XC [1]◇ B ☕	NT	NT C	NT	NT	NT	NT A	NT	NT	XC [1]◇ B ☕	NT	NT A	NT	NT D	NT
Chathill d																			
Alnmouth 26 d					13 03									15 04					
Acklington d																			
Widdrington d																			
Pegswood d																			
Morpeth 26 d			12 50		13 18			13 50				14 50		15 18			15 50		
Cramlington d			12 58					13 58				14 58					15 58		
Manors d			13 11																
Newcastle [8] 26 ⛴ a			13 13		13 36			14 13				15 13		15 37			16 13		
Sunderland 44 ⛴ d		12 30					13 30				14 30					15 30			
London Kings Cross [15] ⊖ 26 d		*09 30*	*10 00*			*10 30*		*11 00*			*11 30*	*12 00*				*12 30*	*13 00*		
Newcastle [8] ⛴ d	12 44	12 54	13 14	13 24		13 44	13 54	14 14	14 24	14 44	14 54	15 14	15 24		15 44	15 54	16 14	16 24	16 44
Dunston d																			
Metrocentre a	12 52	13 01	13 22	13 31		13 51	14 01	14 22	14 31	14 52	15 01	15 21	15 31		15 51	16 01	16 21	16 31	16 51
d		13 02		13 32			14 02		14 32		15 02		15 32			16 02		16 32	
Blaydon d																			
Wylam d		13 10					14 10		14 40		15 10					16 10		16 40	
Prudhoe d		13 14		13 42			14 14		14 44		15 14		15 42			16 14		16 44	
Stocksfield d		13 18					14 18				15 18					16 18		16 48	
Riding Mill d		13 23					14 23				15 23					16 23		16 53	
Corbridge d		13 26					14 26				15 26					16 26		16 56	
Hexham a		13 36		13 55			14 36		14 56		15 36		15 55			16 36		17 02	
d				13 56					14 57				15 56					17 03	
Haydon Bridge d													16 05					17 12	
Bardon Mill d													16 11						
Haltwhistle d				14 14					15 16				16 18					17 23	
Brampton (Cumbria) d													16 34						
Wetheral d													16 43						
Carlisle [8] a				14 45					15 47				16 54					17 55	

	NT C	NT E	NT	NT	XC [1]◇ G ☕	NT A	NT	NT	NT	NT	NT	NT A	NT	GR [R] [1] H ☕ ✕	NT	NT	NT J	NT
Chathill d													19 12					
Alnmouth 26 d					17 09								19 24	20 08				
Acklington d													19 32					
Widdrington d													19 39					
Pegswood d													19 45					
Morpeth 26 d			16 50		17 23				18 32		19 04		19 49	20 25			21 15	
Cramlington d			16 58						18 40		19 12		19 58				21 23	
Manors d																		
Newcastle [8] 26 ⛴ a			17 13		17 37				18 56		19 26		20 12	20 45			21 40	
Sunderland 44 ⛴ d	16 30					17 30				*18 30*		19 27			*20 27*			*21 27*
London Kings Cross [15] ⊖ 26 d	*13 30*	*14 00*						*15 00*				*16 00*	*17 00*			*18 00*		*18 35*
Newcastle [8] ⛴ d	16 54	17 11		17 24		17 54	18 02	18 24		19 10		19 50	20 14		20 56	21 10		21 56
Dunston d				17 30			18 07											
Metrocentre a	17 01	17 18		17 32		18 01	18 12	18 31		19 17		19 58	20 21		21 05	21 17		22 04
d	17 02	17 18		17 33		18 02		18 32		19 18			20 22			21 18		
Blaydon d				17 37														
Wylam d	17 10	17 27		17 44		18 10		18 40		19 26			20 30			21 26		
Prudhoe d	17 14	17 30		17 47		18 14		18 44		19 30			20 34			21 30		
Stocksfield d	17 18			17 52		18 18		18 48		19 34			20 38			21 34		
Riding Mill d	17 23			17 56		18 23		18 53		19 39			20 43			21 39		
Corbridge d	17 26			18 00		18 26		18 56		19 42			20 46			21 42		
Hexham a	17 36	17 45		18 08		18 32		19 02		19 48			20 55			21 48		
d		17 45				18 33		19 03		19 49						21 49		
Haydon Bridge d		17 54				18 42				19 58						21 58		
Bardon Mill d		18 01				18 48										22 04		
Haltwhistle d		18 08				18 55		19 21		20 09						22 11		
Brampton (Cumbria) d		18 23						19 37								22 27		
Wetheral d		18 32						19 45								22 35		
Carlisle [8] a		18 43				19 28		19 57		20 42						22 45		

For general notes see front of timetable
For details of catering facilities see Directory of Train Operators

- **A** From Middlesbrough (Table 44)
- **B** From Edinburgh to Plymouth (Table 51)
- **C** From Nunthorpe (Table 45)
- **D** To Whitehaven (Table 100)
- **E** To Stranraer (Table 216)
- **G** From Edinburgh (Table 26) to Bristol Temple Meads (Table 51)
- **H** From Glasgow Central (from 29 March from Edinburgh) to Leeds (Table 26)
- **J** To Middlesbrough (Table 44)

For full service from Alnmouth to Newcastle, please see Table 26

Table 48

Sundays

Newcastle → MetroCentre, Hexham and Carlisle

Network Diagram - see first page of Table 44

		NT	NT	NT	NT	NT A	NT	NT	NT	NT	NT	NT A	NT	NT	NT	NT	NT	NT A
Sunderland	44 d		09 28			10 28			11 28			12 28			13 28			14 28
London Kings Cross 15	⊖ 26 d										09 00	09 30		10 00	10 30		11 00	
Newcastle 8	d	09 10	09 53	10 10	10 30	10 50	11 10	11 30	11 50	12 10	12 30	12 50	13 10	13 30	13 50	14 10	14 30	14 50
Metrocentre	a	09 17	10 01	10 17	10 37	10 59	11 17	11 37	11 57	12 17	12 37	12 59	13 17	13 37	13 59	14 17	14 37	14 59
	d	09 18		10 18			11 18			12 18			13 18			14 18		
Wylam	d	09 26		10 26			11 26			12 26			13 26			14 26		
Prudhoe	d	09 30		10 30			11 30			12 30			13 30			14 30		
Stocksfield	d	09 34		10 34			11 34			12 34			13 34			14 34		
Riding Mill	d	09 39		10 39			11 39			12 39			13 39			14 39		
Corbridge	d	09 42		10 42			11 42			12 42			13 42			14 42		
Hexham	a	09 48		10 48			11 48			12 48			13 48			14 48		
	d	09 49		10 49			11 49			12 49			13 49			14 49		
Haydon Bridge	d	09 58		10 58						12 58								
Bardon Mill	d	10 04		11 04						13 04								
Haltwhistle	d	10 11		11 11			12 08			13 11			14 08			15 08		
Brampton (Cumbria)	d	10 27		11 27						13 27								
Wetheral	d	10 35		11 35						13 35								
Carlisle 8	a	10 45		11 45			12 38			13 45			14 38			15 38		

		NT	NT	NT	NT	NT	NT A	NT	NT	NT	NT	NT	NT A	NT
Sunderland	44 d			15 28			16 28			17 28			18 28	19 28
London Kings Cross 15	⊖ 26 d		12 00	12 30		13 00	13 30		14 00	14 30	15 00			17 00
Newcastle 8	d	15 10	15 30	15 50	16 10	16 30	16 50	17 10	17 30	17 50	18 10	18 30	18 50	20 15
Metrocentre	a	15 17	15 37	15 59	16 19	16 37	16 57	17 17	17 37	17 59	18 17	18 37	18 59	20 22
	d	15 18			16 20			17 18			18 18			20 23
Wylam	d	15 26			16 28			17 26			18 26			20 31
Prudhoe	d	15 30			16 32			17 30			18 30			20 35
Stocksfield	d	15 34			16 36			17 34			18 34			20 39
Riding Mill	d	15 39			16 41			17 39			18 39			20 44
Corbridge	d	15 42			16 44			17 42			18 42			20 47
Hexham	a	15 48			16 50			17 48			18 48			20 53
	d	15 49			16 51			17 49			18 49			20 54
Haydon Bridge	d	15 58									18 58			21 03
Bardon Mill	d	16 04									19 04			21 09
Haltwhistle	d	16 11			17 10			18 08			19 11			21 16
Brampton (Cumbria)	d	16 27									19 27			21 32
Wetheral	d	16 35									19 35			21 40
Carlisle 8	a	16 45			17 40			18 38			19 45			21 50

For general notes see front of timetable
For details of catering facilities see
Directory of Train Operators

A From Middlesbrough (Table 44)

For Sunday service from Morpeth to Newcastle, please see Table 26

Carlisle, Hexham and MetroCentre → Newcastle → Morpeth and Chathill

Network Diagram - see first page of Table 44

Miles	Miles	Station		NT	GR	NT	NT	NT	NT	GR	NT	NT	NT	XC	NT	NT	NT	NT	NT	NT	XC	NT	NT
					R 1					R 1				1 ◇							R 1		
					A	B			B	C	D		B	E			B	G		B	H		
0	—	**Carlisle** 8	d					06 25			07 13				08 30			09 33					10 36
4¼	—	Wetheral	d					06 32			07 20				08 37								
11	—	Brampton (Cumbria)	d					06 42			07 30				08 47								
23¼	—	Haltwhistle	d					06 56			07 45				09 01			10 01					11 04
28	—	Bardon Mill	d					07 04			07 52				09 09								
31¾	—	Haydon Bridge	d					07 09			07 57				09 14								
39½	—	**Hexham**	a					07 18			08 06				09 23			10 19					11 22
—	—		d			06 13		07 19	07 42		08 07		08 44		09 23		09 44	10 19		10 44			11 22
42½	—	Corbridge	d			06 17		07 23	07 46		08 11		08 48				09 48			10 48			
45	—	Riding Mill	d			06 22		07 28	07 51		08 16		08 53				09 53			10 53			
47½	—	Stocksfield	d			06 26		07 32	07 55		08 20		08 57				09 57			10 57			
49¾	—	Prudhoe	d			06 30		07 36	07 59		08 24		09 01		09 35		10 01			11 01			11 34
52	—	Wylam	d			06 34		07 40	08 03		08 28		09 05				10 05			11 05			
56¼	—	Blaydon	d						08 09		08 34												
58¼	0	**Metrocentre**	a					07 49	08 14		08 43		09 14		09 46		10 14	10 40		11 15			11 45
—	—		d					07 50	08 15		08 44		09 15		09 47		10 15	10 40	11 00	11 15		11 30	11 46
59½	1½	Dunston	d								08 47												
61¾	3½	**Newcastle** 8	⛴ a			06 52		08 03	08 25		08 57		09 27		09 58		10 25	10 51	11 09	11 25		11 39	11 59
—	—	London Kings Cross 15	⊖ 26 a			*09 54*		*11 50*	*12 17*		*12 42*		*12b44*				*13 43*	*14 10*	*14 44*			*14 57*	
—	—	Sunderland	44 ⛴ a			07 19			08 49				09 49				10 49			11 49			
—	—	**Newcastle** 8	26 ⛴ d	06 00	06 25		07 58			08 41		09 00		09 29		10 15			11 15		11 36		
—	4	Manors	d																				
—	13½	Cramlington	d	06 12			08 11					09 12				10 27			11 27				
—	20	**Morpeth**	26 d	06 20	06 38		08a21			08a55		09a20		09 42		10a35			11a35		11 49		
—	22	Pegswood	d																				
—	26¾	Widdrington	d																				
—	32	Acklington	d																				
—	38¼	Alnmouth	26 d	06 37	06a52									09a55							12a02		
—	49½	**Chathill**	a	06 53																			

Station		NT	NT	NT	NT	NT	NT	NT	NT	NT	NT	NT	NT	NT	NT	NT	XC	NT	NT	NT	NT	NT	NT
																	1 ◇						
			B					J				B		K		J	L				J		B
Carlisle 8	d				11 34					12 30				13 37					14 36				15 30
Wetheral	d									12 37													
Brampton (Cumbria)	d									12 47													
Haltwhistle	d				12 02					13 01				14 05					15 04				15 58
Bardon Mill	d									13 09													
Haydon Bridge	d				12 13					13 14													
Hexham	a				12 22					13 23				14 23					15 22				16 16
	d		11 44		12 23			12 44		13 23		13 44		14 24		14 44			15 22		15 44		16 16
Corbridge	d		11 48					12 48				13 48				14 48					15 48		
Riding Mill	d		11 53					12 53				13 53				14 53					15 53		
Stocksfield	d		11 57					12 57				13 57				14 57					15 57		
Prudhoe	d		12 01		12 34			13 01		13 35		14 01				15 01			15 34		16 01		16 28
Wylam	d		12 05					13 05				14 05				15 05					16 05		
Blaydon	d																						
Metrocentre	a		12 14		12 45			13 14		13 46		14 14		14 44		15 14			15 46		16 14		16 39
	d	12 05	12 15	12 30	12 45	12 40	13 00	13 15	13 30	13 47	14 00	14 15	14 30	14 45	15 00	15 15		15 30	15 46	16 00	16 15	16 30	16 39
Dunston	d															15 18							
Newcastle 8	⛴ a	12 13	12 28	12 40	12 57	12 51	13 10	13 26	13 38	13 57	14 09	14 26	14 40	14 55	15 09	15 27		15 38	15 58	16 11	16 25	16 40	16 50
London Kings Cross 15	⊖ 26 a	*15 44*				*15 51*	*16 46*		*16 57*	*17 30*		*17 41*	*18 04*		*18 45*			*19 11*		*19 18*		*20 18*	
Sunderland	44 ⛴ a		12 49					13 49				14 49				15 49					16 49		17 13
Newcastle 8	26 ⛴ d	12 15				13 03					14 15				15 15		15 35			16 15			
Manors	d																			16 17			
Cramlington	d	12 26				13 15					14 27				15 27					16 28			
Morpeth	26 d	12a36				13a23					14a35				15a35		15 48			16a36			
Pegswood	d																						
Widdrington	d																						
Acklington	d																						
Alnmouth	26 d																16a01						
Chathill	a																						

For general notes see front of timetable
For details of catering facilities see Directory of Train Operators

A To Glasgow Central (Table 26)
B To Middlesbrough (Table 44)
C From Leeds (Table 26) to Aberdeen (Table 229)
D From Dumfries (Table 216)
E From Birmingham New Street to Edinburgh (Table 51)
G From Girvan (Table 216)
H From Bristol Temple Meads to Edinburgh (Table 51)
J To Nunthorpe (Table 45)
K From Stranraer (Table 216)
L From Plymouth to Edinburgh (Table 51)
b Change at Newcastle and Doncaster

For full service from Newcastle to Alnmouth, please see Table 26

Carlisle, Hexham and MetroCentre → Newcastle → Morpeth and Chathill

Network Diagram - see first page of Table 44

		NT	NT	NT	NT	NT	NT	NT	NT	NT	NT	GR	NT	NT	NT	XC	NT	GR FO	NT	NT	NT
												R 1				R 1		R 1			
			A			B			A	C	A	D ✕				E		D ✕			
Carlisle 8	d				16 29			17 20		18 18			19 33							21 20	
Wetheral	d				16 36			17 27												21 27	
Brampton (Cumbria)	d				16 46			17 37												21 37	
Haltwhistle	d				17 00			17 52		18 46			20 01							21 52	
Bardon Mill	d				17 08			17 59												21 59	
Haydon Bridge	d				17 13			18 04												22 04	
Hexham	a				17 22			18 13		19 04			20 19							22 13	
	d		16 44		17 23	17 42		18 14	18 44	19 04			20 19				21 14			22 14	23 14
Corbridge	d		16 48			17 46		18 18	18 48	19 09			20 24				21 18			22 18	23 18
Riding Mill	d		16 53			17 51		18 23	18 53	19 13			20 28				21 23			22 23	23 23
Stocksfield	d		16 57		17 32	17 55		18 27	18 57	19 17			20 32				21 27			22 27	23 27
Prudhoe	d		17 01		17 36	17 59		18 31	19 01	19 22			20 37				21 31			22 31	23 31
Wylam	d		17 05			18 03		18 35	19 05	19 26			20 40				21 35			22 35	23 35
Blaydon	d								19 11												
Metrocentre	a		17 14		17 47	18 12		18 43	19 16	19 34			20 49				21 44			22 44	23 45
	d	17 00	17 15	17 35	17 47	18 13	18 18	18 44	19 17	19 34	20 15		20 50		21 10		21 45		22 15	22 45	23 45
Dunston	d																				
Newcastle 8	a	17 08	17 25	17 43	18 00	18 23	18 26	18 55	19 27	19 45	20 23		21 01		21 18		21 56		22 23	22 59	23 57
London Kings Cross 15 ⊖ 26	a	*20 42*			*21 17*		*21 44*	*22 19*			*00 15*										
Sunderland 44	a		17 49			18 49			19 49		20 49										
Newcastle 8 26	d	17 15		17 46			18 28					20 29		21 05		21 48		22 08			
Manors	d	17 17		17 48			18 30														
Cramlington	d	17 28		17 59			18 41							21 17							
Morpeth 26	d	17 36		18a07			18a49					20 44		21a26		22 01		22 22			
Pegswood	d	17 47																			
Widdrington	d	17 53																			
Acklington	d	18 10																			
Alnmouth 26	d	18 18										20a58				22a14		22a36			
Chathill	a	18 32																			

Saturdays

		NT	GR	NT	GR	NT	NT	NT	NT	XC	NT	NT	NT	NT	NT	NT	NT	XC	NT	NT	NT
			R 1		1					1 ◇								1 ◇			
			G	A	H			J	A	K			B	L		A		N			A
Carlisle 8	d					06 25		07 13			08 30			09 33					10 35		
Wetheral	d					06 32		07 20			08 37										
Brampton (Cumbria)	d					06 42		07 30			08 47										
Haltwhistle	d					06 56		07 45			09 01			10 01					11 03		
Bardon Mill	d					07 04		07 52			09 09										
Haydon Bridge	d					07 09		07 57			09 14										
Hexham	a					07 18		08 06			09 23			10 19					11 21		
	d			06 13		07 18		08 07	08 44		09 23		09 44	10 19		10 44			11 21		11 44
Corbridge	d			06 17		07 23		08 11	08 48				09 48			10 48					11 48
Riding Mill	d			06 22		07 27		08 16	08 53				09 53			10 53					11 53
Stocksfield	d			06 26		07 31		08 20	08 57				09 57			10 57					11 57
Prudhoe	d			06 30		07 36		08 24	09 01		09 35		10 01			11 01			11 33		12 01
Wylam	d			06 34		07 40		08 28	09 05		09 39		10 05			11 05					12 05
Blaydon	d							08 34													
Metrocentre	a					07 49		08 43	09 14		09 48		10 14	10 40		11 14			11 45		12 14
	d					07 49		08 44	09 15		09 49		10 15	10 40	11 00	11 15	11 30		11 45	12 00	12 15
Dunston	d							08 47													
Newcastle 8	a			06 52		08 03		08 57	09 25		10 01		10 25	10 51	11 10	11 25	11 38		11 59	12 08	12 25
London Kings Cross 15 ⊖ 26	a			*10 13*		*11 50*		*12 41*	*13 10*		*13 44*			*13 59*	*14 44*		*15 10*				*15 41*
Sunderland 44	a			07 19		*08 49*			09 49				10 49			11 49					12 49
Newcastle 8 26	d	06 05	06 30		07 52		08 24			09 29		10 15			11 15			11 39		12 15	
Manors	d																				
Cramlington	d	06 17					08 36					10 27			11 27					12 27	
Morpeth 26	d	06 25	06 43		08 06		08a44			09 42		10a35			11a35			11 52		12a35	
Pegswood	d																				
Widdrington	d																				
Acklington	d																				
Alnmouth 26	d	06 43	06a57		08a20					09a55								12a05			
Chathill	a	06 58																			

For general notes see front of timetable
For details of catering facilities see Directory of Train Operators

- **A** To Middlesbrough (Table 44)
- **B** To Nunthorpe (Table 45)
- **C** From Glasgow Central (Table 216)
- **D** From London Kings Cross to Edinburgh (Table 26)
- **E** From Plymouth to Edinburgh (Table 51)
- **G** To Glasgow Central (from 29 March to Edinburgh) (Table 26)
- **H** From Doncaster to Glasgow Central (from 29 March to Edinburgh) (Table 26)
- **J** From Dumfries (Table 216)
- **K** From Birmingham New Street to Edinburgh (Table 51)
- **L** From Girvan (Table 216)
- **N** From Bristol Temple Meads to Edinburgh (Table 51)

For full service from Newcastle to Alnmouth, please see Table 26

Table 48

Saturdays

Carlisle, Hexham and MetroCentre → Newcastle → Morpeth and Chathill

Network Diagram - see first page of Table 44

Station		NT	NT	NT	NT	NT	NT	NT	NT	NT	NT	NT	NT	NT	NT	NT	XC	NT	NT	NT
																	[1] ◇			
							A				B		C		A		D			A
																	🍴			
Carlisle [8]	d			11 34					12 30				13 36					14 36		
Wetheral	d								12 37											
Brampton (Cumbria)	d								12 47											
Haltwhistle	d			12 02					13 01				14 06					15 04		
Bardon Mill	d								13 09											
Haydon Bridge	d			12 13					13 14											
Hexham	a			12 22					13 23				14 24					15 22		
	d			12 23			12 44		13 23		13 44		14 24		14 44			15 22		15 44
Corbridge	d						12 48				13 48				14 48					15 48
Riding Mill	d						12 53				13 53				14 53					15 53
Stocksfield	d						12 57				13 57				14 57					15 57
Prudhoe	d			12 34			13 01		13 35		14 01				15 01			15 34		16 01
Wylam	d						13 05				14 05				15 05					16 05
Blaydon	d																			
Metrocentre	a			12 45			13 14		13 46		14 14		14 45		15 14			15 46		16 14
	d	12 30	12 40	12 45	13 00		13 15	13 30	13 47	14 00	14 15	14 30	14 45	15 00	15 15	15 30		15 46	16 00	16 15
Dunston	d														15 18					
Newcastle [8]	🚢 a	12 38	12 52	12 57	13 11		13 26	13 39	14 00	14 13	14 25	14 40	14 56	15 09	15 28	15 38		16 00	16 11	16 25
London Kings Cross [15]	⊖ 26 a		*15 58*		*16 47*			*16 57*		*17 43*		*18 10*		*18 46*					*19 40*	
Sunderland	44 🚢 a						13 49				14 49				15 50					16 49
Newcastle [8]	26 🚢 d					13 15				14 15				15 15			15 39		16 15	
Manors	d																		16 17	
Cramlington	d					13 26				14 26				15 27					16 28	
Morpeth	26 d					13a36				14a36				15a35			15 52		16a36	
Pegswood	d																			
Widdrington	d																			
Acklington	d																			
Alnmouth	26 d																16a05			
Chathill	a																			

Station		NT	NT	NT	NT	NT	NT	NT	NT	NT	NT	NT	NT	NT	NT	GR	NT	NT	NT	NT
																[R] [1]				
			B		B			A			B	E	B			G				
																🍴 H				
Carlisle [8]	d		15 30				16 29			17 20		18 18			19 33					21 20
Wetheral	d						16 36			17 27										21 27
Brampton (Cumbria)	d						16 46			17 37										21 37
Haltwhistle	d		15 58				17 00			17 52		18 46			20 01					21 52
Bardon Mill	d						17 08			17 59										21 59
Haydon Bridge	d						17 13			18 04										22 04
Hexham	a		16 16				17 22			18 13		19 04			20 19					22 13
	d		16 16		16 44		17 22	17 42		18 14	18 44	19 04			20 19			21 14		22 14
Corbridge	d				16 48			17 46		18 18	18 48	19 09			20 24			21 18		22 18
Riding Mill	d				16 53			17 51		18 23	18 53	19 13			20 28			21 23		22 23
Stocksfield	d				16 57		17 31	17 55		18 27	18 57	19 17			20 32			21 27		22 27
Prudhoe	d		16 28		17 01		17 35	17 59		18 31	19 01	19 22			20 37			21 31		22 31
Wylam	d				17 05			18 03		18 35	19 05	19 26			20 40			21 35		22 35
Blaydon	d										19 11									
Metrocentre	a		16 40		17 14		17 45	18 12		18 44	19 16	19 34			20 49			21 44		22 44
	d	16 30	16 40	17 00	17 15	17 35	17 45	18 13	18 18	18 45	19 17	19 34	20 15		20 50		21 10	21 45	22 10	22 45
Dunston	d																			
Newcastle [8]	🚢 a	16 38	16 50	17 08	17 26	17 43	18 00	18 23	18 26	18 55	19 27	19 45	20 23		21 01		21 18	21 55	22 20	22 59
London Kings Cross [15]	⊖ 26 a			*20 35*					*21 48*	*22 17*										
Sunderland	44 🚢 a		17 13		17 50			18 49			19 50		20 49							
Newcastle [8]	26 🚢 d			17 10		17 44			18 28					20 24		21 03				
Manors	d			17 13		17 47			18 30											
Cramlington	d			17 24		17 58			18 41					20 36						
Morpeth	26 d			17 32		18a06			18a49					20a45		21 18				
Pegswood	d			17 35																
Widdrington	d			17 41																
Acklington	d			17 48																
Alnmouth	26 d			18 09												21a33				
Chathill	a			18 24																

For general notes see front of timetable
For details of catering facilities see Directory of Train Operators

- **A** To Nunthorpe (Table 45)
- **B** To Middlesbrough (Table 44)
- **C** From Stranraer (Table 216)
- **D** From Plymouth to Edinburgh (Table 51)
- **E** From Glasgow Central (Table 216)
- **G** From London Kings Cross to Edinburgh (Table 26)

For full service from Newcastle to Alnmouth, please see Table 26

Table 48

Sundays

Carlisle, Hexham and MetroCentre → Newcastle

Network Diagram - see first page of Table 44

		NT	NT	NT	NT	NT	NT A	NT	NT	NT	NT	NT	NT A	NT	NT	NT	NT	NT
Carlisle 8	d		09 05			10 05			11 12			12 05			13 12			14 12
Wetheral	d		09 12			10 12						12 12						
Brampton (Cumbria)	d		09 22			10 22						12 22						
Haltwhistle	d		09 36			10 36			11 40			12 36			13 40			14 40
Bardon Mill	d		09 44			10 44						12 44						
Haydon Bridge	d		09 49			10 49						12 49						
Hexham	a		09 58			10 58			11 58			12 58			13 58			14 58
	d		09 59			10 59			11 59			12 59			13 59			14 59
Corbridge	d		10 03			11 03			12 03			13 03			14 03			15 03
Riding Mill	d		10 08			11 08			12 08			13 08			14 08			15 08
Stocksfield	d		10 12			11 12			12 12			13 12			14 12			15 12
Prudhoe	d		10 16			11 16			12 16			13 16			14 16			15 16
Wylam	d		10 20			11 20			12 20			13 20			14 20			15 20
Metrocentre	a		10 29			11 29			12 29			13 29			14 29			15 29
	d	10 10	10 30	10 48	11 10	11 30	11 48	12 10	12 30	12 48	13 10	13 30	13 48	14 10	14 30	14 48	15 10	15 30
Newcastle 8	a	10 18	10 40	10 56	11 18	11 40	11 56	12 18	12 40	12 57	13 18	13 40	13 56	14 18	14 40	14 56	15 18	15 40
London Kings Cross 15	⊖ 26 a	*13 36*	*14 04*		*14 42*	*15 11*		*15 38*	*16 11*	*16 29*	*16 45*	*17 11*		*17 49*	*18 15*		*18 38*	*19 12*
Sunderland	44 a			11 22			12 21			13 22			14 21			15 22		

		NT A	NT	NT	NT	NT	NT	NT A	NT	NT	NT	NT	NT	NT
Carlisle 8	d			15 05			16 12			17 12			18 05	20 15
Wetheral	d			15 12									18 12	
Brampton (Cumbria)	d			15 22									18 22	
Haltwhistle	d			15 36			16 40			17 40			18 36	20 43
Bardon Mill	d			15 44									18 44	
Haydon Bridge	d			15 49									18 49	
Hexham	a			15 58			16 58			17 58			18 58	20 58
	d			15 59			16 59			17 59			18 59	20 59
Corbridge	d			16 03			17 03			18 03			19 03	21 03
Riding Mill	d			16 08			17 08			18 08			19 08	21 08
Stocksfield	d			16 12			17 12			18 12			19 12	21 12
Prudhoe	d			16 16			17 16			18 16			19 16	21 16
Wylam	d			16 20			17 20			18 20			19 20	21 20
Metrocentre	a			16 29			17 29			18 29			19 29	21 29
	d	15 48	16 10	16 30	16 48	17 10	17 30	17 48	18 10	18 30	18 48	19 10	19 30	21 30
Newcastle 8	a	15 57	16 18	16 40	16 56	17 18	17 40	17 56	18 18	18 40	18 56	19 18	19 40	21 43
London Kings Cross 15	⊖ 26 a		*19 47*		*20 12*	*20 42*		*21 25*	*21 47*	*22 16*		*23 14*	*23 50*	
Sunderland	44 a	16 21			17 22			18 21			19 22		*20 21*	

For general notes see front of timetable
For details of catering facilities see Directory of Train Operators

A To Middlesbrough (Table 44)

For Sunday service from Newcastle to Morpeth, please see Table 26

Route Diagram for Table 49

DM-7/05
Design BAJS

This table summarises through services which, with their associated connecting services at Peterborough, link together The North, Midlands and East Anglia. In certain instances a faster journey is possible via London and the relevant Table(s) should be consulted.

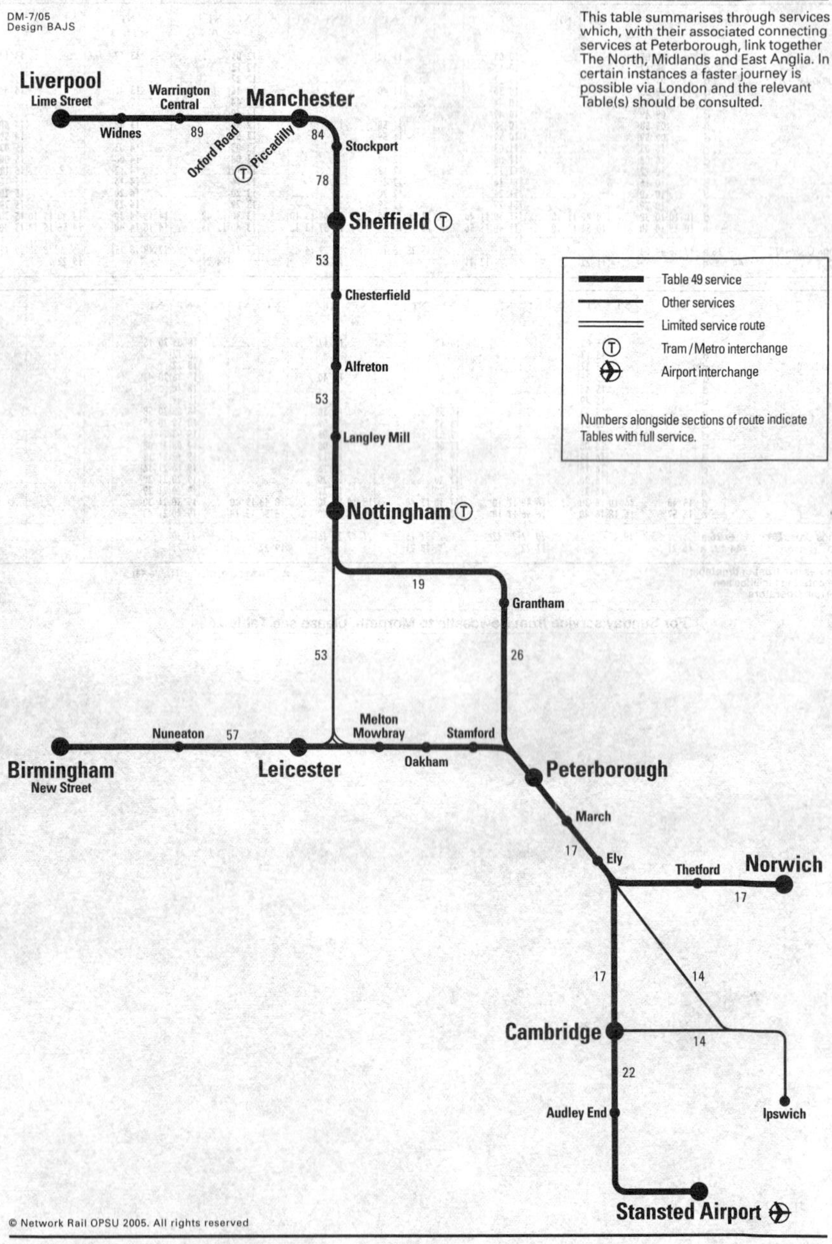

Stansted Airport → East Anglia → East Midlands → Birmingham and North West England

Route Diagram - see first page of Table 49

Miles	Miles	Miles	Miles			EM	EM	XC	XC	EM		EM	XC	EM	XC	EM		XC	EM	XC	EM	XC		EM	XC
						◇	◇	◇	◇	◇		◇	◇	◇	◇	◇		◇	◇	◇	◇	◇		◇	◇
						🛒	🛒			🛒								🛒		🛒		🛒			🛒
0	0	—	0	**Norwich**	d							05 52				07 57			08 57		09 57			10 57	
30½	30½	—	30½	Thetford	d							06 25				08 24			09 24		10 24			11 24	
—	—	—	—	Ipswich	d								*06b01*		*06c13*	*06e13*		*08b03*		*08c16*	*08e16*	*10b03*			*10c16*
—	—	0	—	**Stansted Airport** ✈	d				05 21						07 25			08 21		09 25		10 20			11 25
—	—	10¾	—	Audley End	d				05 33						07 38			08 36		09 38		10 38			11 38
—	—	24¾	—	**Cambridge**	d			05 07	05 58			*06 23*	06 50	07 27	07 59	*08 12*		09 04	*09 12*	10 04	*10 12*	11 04		*11 12*	12 04
53¾	53¾	39½	53¾	Ely 6	d			05 24	06 13			06 51	07 05	07 44	08 16	08 51		09 19	09 51	10 19	10 52	11 19		11 52	12 19
61¼	61¼	—	61¼	March	d			05 40	06 32			07 07	07 21	08 01	08 33	09 07		09 35		10 35		11 35			12 35
75¼	75¼	—	75¼	**Peterborough** 8	a			06 02	06 54			07 25	07 43	08 23	08 50	09 25		09 53	10 25	10 53	11 24	11 53		12 24	12 53
—	—	—	—		d			06 08	06 55			07 27	07 46	08 30	08 54	09 27		09 54	10 30	10 54	11 25	11 54		12 25	12 54
87¾	—	—	—	Stamford	d			06 20	07 08				07 59		09 07			10 07		11 07		12 07			13 07
101¼	—	—	—	Oakham	d			06 39	07 24				08 15		09 23			10 23		11 23		12 23			13 23
112¾	—	—	—	Melton Mowbray	d			06 50	07 35				08 26		09 34			10 34		11 34		12 34			13 34
127¾	—	—	—	**Leicester**	d			07 07	07 51				08 52		09 52			10 52		11 52		12 52			13 52
146½	—	—	—	Nuneaton	a			07 33	08 16				09 12		10 14			11 13		12 13		13 13			14 13
167½	—	—	—	**Birmingham New Street** 12	a			08 09	08 48				09 47		10 47			11 47		12 47		13 47			14 47
—	104½	—	—	Grantham 7	d							07 59		09 00		09 59			11 12		11 57			12 59	
—	127¼	—	145	**Nottingham** 8	a			*08f20*	*09f20*			08 39	*09f26*	09 39	*10f36*	10 28		*11f36*	11 41	*12f35*	12 34	*13f36*		13 28	*14f36*
—	—	—	—		d	05 19	06 34			07 42		08 42		09 40		10 42			11 42		12 42			13 45	
—	139¼	—	157	Langley Mill	d		06 53			07 58		08 58		09 57		10 58					12 58				
—	145½	—	163¼	Alfreton	d		07 01			08 06		09 06		10 05		11 06			12 04		13 06			14 07	
—	155½	—	173¼	Chesterfield	d	05 54	07 14			08 18		09 18		10 18		11 18			12 18		13 18			14 18	
—	167¼	—	185½	**Sheffield** 7	a	06 10	07 32			08 38		09 38		10 38		11 38			12 38		13 38			14 38	
—	—	—	—		d	06 20	07 37			08 42		09 42		10 42		11 42			12 42		13 42			14 42	
—	204½	—	222½	Stockport	a	07 23	08 26			09 24		10 24		11 24		12 24			13 24		14 24			15 24	
—	210½	—	228½	**Manchester Piccadilly** 10	a	07 35	08 36			09 36		10 36		11 36		12 36			13 36		14 36			15 36	
—	211	—	228¾	Manchester Oxford Road	a	07 38	08 40			09 40		10 40		11 40		12 40			13 40		14 40			15 40	
—	226¾	—	244½	Warrington Central	a	07 54	08 57			09 57		10 57		11 57		12 57			13 57		14 57			15 57	
—	233	—	250¾	Widnes	a	08 02	09 05			10 05		11 05		12 05		13 05			14 05		15 05			16 05	
—	245¼	—	263	**Liverpool Lime Street** 10	a	08 29	09 29			10 29		11 29		12 29		13 29			14 29		15 29			16 27	

		EM	XC	EM	XC	EM		XC	EM	XC	EM	XC		EM	XC	EM	XC	EM		XC	EM	XC	EM
		◇	◇	◇	◇	◇		◇	◇	◇	◇	◇		◇	◇	◇	◇	◇		◇		◇	
																					A		
			🛒		🛒			🛒		🛒		🛒			🛒		🛒			🛒		🛒	
Norwich	d	11 57		12 57		13 57			14 57		15 52			16 57		17 54		18 57					22 10
Thetford	d	12 24		13 24		14 24			15 24		16 27			17 24		18 24		19 24					22a43
Ipswich	d	*10e16*	*12b03*		*12c16*	*12e16*		*14b03*		*14c16*	*14e16*	*16b03*			*16c16*	*16e16*	*17b49*			*18c16*		*19c16*	
Stansted Airport ✈	d		12 25		13 25			14 25		15 25		16 20			17 17		18 20			19 18		20 20	
Audley End	d		12 38		13 38			14 38		15 38		16 33			17 32		18 32			19 32		20 32	
Cambridge	d	*12 12*	13 04	*13 12*	14 04	*14 12*		15 04	*15 12*	16 04	*16 24*	17 04		*17 22*	17 49	*18 25*	19 04	*19 25*		19 50		20 57	
Ely 6	d	12 51	13 19	13 52	14 19	14 52		15 19	15 52	16 19	16 52	17 19		17 50	18 06	18 52	19 19	19 52		20 05		21 14	
March	d		13 35		14 35			15 35		16 35		17 35		18 07	18 24		19 35			20 22		21 30	
Peterborough 8	a	13 24	13 53	14 25	14 53	15 25		15 53	16 25	16 53	17 26	17 53		18 24	18 43	19 31	19 53	20 25		20 39		21 52	
	d	13 25	13 54	14 26	14 54	15 26		15 54	16 27	16 54	17 27	17 54		18 26	18 44	19 31	19 54	20 26		20 41	21 30	21 54	
Stamford	d		14 07		15 07			16 07		17 07		18 07			18 57		20 07			20 54	21 43	22 07	
Oakham	d		14 23		15 23			16 23		17 23		18 23			19 13		20 23			21 09	21 58	22 23	
Melton Mowbray	d		14 34		15 34			16 34		17 34		18 34			19 24		20 34			21 20	22 11	22 34	
Leicester	d		14 52		15 52			16 52		17 52		18 52			19 41		20 52			21 36		22 49	
Nuneaton	a		15 13		16 13			17 13		18 17		19 13			20 00		21 13			21 57		23 08	
Birmingham New Street 12	a		15 47		16 47			17 47		18 48		19 47			20 37		21 47			22 36		23 43	
Grantham 7	d	13 57		14 58		15 56			17 02		18 00			18 56		20 04		20 56					
Nottingham 8	a	14 33	*15f36*	15 27	*16f35*	16 26		*17f50*	17 38	*18f48*	18 30	*19f35*		19 25	*20f27*	20 44	*21f37*	21 35		*22f28*	22 56	*00g35*	
	d	14 42		15 42		16 42			17 42		18 40			19 27									
Langley Mill	d	14 58				16 58			17 58		18 56												
Alfreton	d	15 06		16 06		17 06			18 06		19 06			19 57									
Chesterfield	d	15 18		16 18		17 18			18 18		19 18			20 08									
Sheffield 7	a	15 38		16 38		17 34			18 38		19 39			20 27									
	d	15 42		16 42		17 42			18 42		19 42			20 31									
Stockport	a	16 24		17 25		18 26			19 24		20 26			21 17									
Manchester Piccadilly 10	a	16 35		17 36		18 36			19 36		20 36			21 30									
Manchester Oxford Road	a	16 39		17 39		18 39			19 40		20 39												
Warrington Central	a	16 57		18 02		18 57			19 57		20 57												
Widnes	a	17 05		18 10		19 05			20 05		21 05												
Liverpool Lime Street 10	a	17 27		18 32		19 29			20 29		21 29												

For general notes see front of timetable
For details of catering facilities see Directory of Train Operators

A From Spalding (Table 18)
b Change at Ely
c Change at Cambridge
e Change at Cambridge and Ely
f Change at Leicester
g Tuesdays to Saturdays. Change at Leicester. From 24 March arr. 2331

Table 49

Saturdays

until 22 March

Stansted Airport → East Anglia → East Midlands → Birmingham and North West England

Route Diagram - see first page of Table 49

		EM ◇	EM ◇	XC ◇	XC ◇	EM ◇	EM ◇	XC ◇	EM ◇	XC ◇	EM ◇	XC ◇	EM ◇	XC ◇	EM ◇	XC ◇	EM ◇	XC ◇
Norwich	d						05 52				07 57		08 57		09 57		10 57	
Thetford	d						06 25				08 24		09 24		10 24		11 24	
Ipswich	d							*06b00*		*06c14*	*06e14*	*08b03*		*08c16*	*08e16*	*10b03*		*10c16*
Stansted Airport ✈	d				05 21					07 27		08 25		09 25		10 25		11 25
Audley End	d				05 33					07 40		08 38		09 38		10 38		11 38
Cambridge	d			05 11	05 51		*06 20*	06 55	07 25	08 04	*08 20*	09 04	*09 12*	10 04	*10 12*	11 04	*11 12*	12 04
Ely 6	d			05 28	06 08		06 51	07 10	07 44	08 19	08 52	09 19	09 53	10 19	10 53	11 19	11 52	12 19
March	d			05 44	06 27		07 07	07 26	08 01	08 35	09 09	09 35		10 35		11 35		12 35
Peterborough 8	a			06 06	06 48		07 25	07 52	08 24	08 54	09 27	09 53	10 25	10 53	11 25	11 53	12 25	12 53
	d			06 08	06 50		07 28	07 54	08 25	08 54	09 29	09 54	10 26	10 54	11 27	11 54	12 27	12 54
Stamford	d			06 21	07 03			08 07		09 07		10 07		11 07		12 07		13 07
Oakham	d			06 35	07 18			08 23		09 23		10 23		11 23		12 23		13 23
Melton Mowbray	d			06 46	07 29			08 34		09 34		10 34		11 34		12 34		13 34
Leicester	d			07 08	07 46			08 52		09 52		10 52		11 52		12 52		13 52
Nuneaton	a			07 32	08 11			09 14		10 14		11 13		12 14		13 14		14 14
Birmingham New Street 12	a			08 08	08 48			09 47		10 47		11 47		12 47		13 47		14 47
Grantham 7	d						08 01		08 57		10 00		10 58		11 58		12 59	
Nottingham 8 🚋	a			*08f16*	*08f56*		08 37	*09f37*	09 27	*10f34*	10 37	*11f27*	11 28	*12f27*	12 38	*13f36*	13 28	*14f37*
	d	05 23	06 37			07 42	08 42		09 42		10 42		11 42		12 47		13 42	
Langley Mill	d		06 53			07 58	08 58		09 59						13 03		13 59	
Alfreton	d		07 01			08 06	09 06		10 07		11 04		12 04		13 11		14 07	
Chesterfield	d	05 54	07 14			08 18	09 18		10 18		11 18		12 18		13 22		14 18	
Sheffield 7 🚋	a	06 10	07 31			08 38	09 38		10 38		11 38		12 38		13 39		14 38	
	d	06 20	07 36			08 42	09 42		10 42		11 42		12 42		13 42		14 42	
Stockport	a	07 23	08 25			09 25	10 24		11 24		12 24		13 24		14 25		15 24	
Manchester Piccadilly 10 🚋	a	07 35	08 36			09 36	10 36		11 36		12 36		13 36		14 36		15 36	
Manchester Oxford Road	a	07 38	08 40			09 40	10 40		11 40		12 40		13 40		14 40		15 40	
Warrington Central	a	07 54	08 57			09 57	10 57		11 57		12 57		13 57		14 57		15 57	
Widnes	a	08 02	09 05			10 05	11 05		12 05		13 05		14 05		15 05		16 05	
Liverpool Lime Street 10	a	08 29	09 27			10 27	11 29		12 29		13 27		14 27		15 25		16 29	

		EM ◇	XC ◇	EM ◇	XC ◇	EM ◇	XC ◇	EM ◇	XC ◇	EM ◇	XC ◇	EM ◇	XC ◇	EM ◇	XC ◇	EM ◇	XC ◇	EM
Norwich	d	11 57		12 57		13 57		14 57		15 52		16 57		17 57		18 57		22 10
Thetford	d	12 24		13 24		14 24		15 24		16 22		17 24		18 24		19 24		22a43
Ipswich	d	*10e16*	*12b03*		*12c16*	*12e16*	*14b03*		*14c16*	*14e16*	*16b03*		*16c16*	*16e16*	*18b03*		*18c16*	
Stansted Airport ✈	d		12 25		13 25		14 25		15 25		16 25		17 25		18 25		19 18	
Audley End	d		12 38		13 38		14 38		15 38		16 38		17 38		18 38		19 32	
Cambridge	d	*12 12*	13 04	*13 12*	14 04	*14 12*	15 04	*15 12*	16 04	*16 12*	17 04	*17 12*	18 02	*18 12*	19 04	*19 12*	19 50	
Ely 6	d	12 53	13 19	13 52	14 19	14 52	15 19	15 55	16 19	16 51	17 19	17 51	18 17	18 52	19 19	19 52	20 05	
March	d		13 35		14 35		15 35		16 35		17 35		18 35	19 09	19 35		20 21	
Peterborough 8	a	13 25	13 53	14 23	14 53	15 25	15 53	16 27	16 53	17 24	17 53	18 24	18 53	19 26	19 53	20 25	20 39	
	d	13 26	13 54	14 24	14 54	15 26	15 54	16 30	16 54	17 25	17 54	18 25	18 54	19 28	19 54	20 27	20 45	
Stamford	d		14 07		15 07		16 07		17 07		18 07		19 07		20 07		20 58	
Oakham	d		14 23		15 23		16 23		17 23		18 23		19 23		20 23		21 13	
Melton Mowbray	d		14 34		15 34		16 34		17 34		18 34		19 34		20 34		21 24	
Leicester	d		14 52		15 52		16 52		17 52		18 52		19 52		20 52		21 39	
Nuneaton	a		15 13		16 13		17 14		18 13		19 14		20 13		21 13		22 00	
Birmingham New Street 12	a		15 47		16 47		17 47		18 47		19 47		20 47		21 47		22 35	
Grantham 7	d	13 56		14 58		15 56		17 02		17 55		18 57		20 02		21 00		
Nottingham 8 🚋	a	14 26	*15f26*	15 28	*16f26*	16 25	*17f28*	17 38	*18f26*	18 28	*19f52*	19 26	*20f39*	20 44	*21f39*	21 30	*22f29*	
	d	14 42		15 44		16 42		17 42		18 42		19 28						
Langley Mill	d	14 59				16 58		17 58		18 59								
Alfreton	d	15 07		16 06		17 06		18 06		19 07		19 52						
Chesterfield	d	15 18		16 18		17 18		18 18		19 18		20 08						
Sheffield 7 🚋	a	15 38		16 38		17 34		18 38		19 39		20 25						
	d	15 42		16 42		17 42		18 42		19 42		20 29						
Stockport	a	16 24		17 24		18 26		19 24		21 24		21 11						
Manchester Piccadilly 10 🚋	a	16 37		17 35		18 35		19 35		20 36		21 25						
Manchester Oxford Road	a	16 40		17 39		18 39				20 39								
Warrington Central	a	16 57		18 02		18 57												
Widnes	a	17 05		18 10		19 05												
Liverpool Lime Street 10	a	17 29		18 32		19 29												

For general notes see front of timetable
For details of catering facilities see Directory of Train Operators

b Change at Ely
c Change at Cambridge
e Change at Cambridge and Ely
f Change at Leicester

Table 49

from 29 March

Stansted Airport → East Anglia → East Midlands → Birmingham and North West England

Route Diagram - see first page of Table 49

		EM	XC	EM	XC	EM	EM	XC	EM	XC	EM	XC	EM	XC	EM	XC	EM	XC
		◇	◇	◇	◇	◇	◇	◇	◇	◇	◇	◇	◇	◇	◇	◇	◇	◇
Norwich	d						05 52				07 57		08 57		09 57		10 57	
Thetford	d						06 25				08 24		09 24		10 24		11 24	
Ipswich	d							06b00		06c14	06e14	08b03		08c16	08e16	10b03		10c16
Stansted Airport ✈	d				05 21					07 27		08 25		09 25		10 25		11 25
Audley End	d				05 33					07 40		08 38		09 38		10 38		11 38
Cambridge	d		05 11		05 51		06 20	06 55	07 25	08 04	08 20	09 04	09 12	10 04	10 12	11 04	11 12	12 04
Ely [6]	d		05 28		06 08		06 51	07 10	07 44	08 19	08 52	09 19	09 53	10 19	10 53	11 19	11 52	12 19
March	d		05 44		06 27		07 07	07 26	08 01	08 35	09 09	09 35		10 35		11 35		12 35
Peterborough [8]	a		06 06		06 48		07 25	07 52	08 24	08 54	09 27	09 53	10 25	10 53	11 25	11 53	12 25	12 53
	d		06 08		06 50		07 28	07 54	08 25	08 54	09 29	09 54	10 26	10 54	11 27	11 54	12 27	12 54
Stamford	d		06 21		07 03			08 07		09 07		10 07		11 07		12 07		13 07
Oakham	d		06 35		07 18			08 23		09 23		10 23		11 23		12 23		13 23
Melton Mowbray	d		06 46		07 29			08 34		09 34		10 34		11 34		12 34		13 34
Leicester	d		07a05		07a47			08a52		09a52		10a49		11a49		12a50		13a51
Nuneaton	a		07f55		08f50			09f50		10f50		11f50		12f50		13f50		14f50
Birmingham New Street [12]	a		08f47		09f57			11f01		11f57		13f01		13f57		15f01		15f57
Grantham [7]	d						08 01		08 57		10 00		10 58		11 58		12 59	
Nottingham [8]	a		08 16		08 56		08 37	09 37	09 27	10 34	10 37	11 27	11 28	12 27	12 38	13 36	13 28	14 37
	d	05 23		06 37		07 42	08 42		09 42		10 42		11 42		12 47		13 42	
Langley Mill	d			06 53		07 58	08 58		09 59						13 03		13 59	
Alfreton	d			07 01		08 06	09 06		10 07		11 04		12 04		13 11		14 07	
Chesterfield	d	05 54		07 14		08 18	09 18		10 18		11 18		12 18		13 22		14 18	
Sheffield [7]	a	06 10		07 31		08 38	09 38		10 38		11 38		12 38		13 39		14 38	
	d	06 20		07 36		08 42	09 42		10 42		11 42		12 42		13 42		14 42	
Stockport	a	07 23		08 25		09 25	10 24		11 24		12 24		13 24		14 25		15 24	
Manchester Piccadilly [10]	a	07 35		08 36		09 36	10 36		11 36		12 36		13 36		14 36		15 36	
Manchester Oxford Road	a	07 38		08 40		09 40	10 40		11 40		12 40		13 40		14 40		15 40	
Warrington Central	a	07 54		08 57		09 57	10 57		11 57		12 57		13 57		14 57		15 57	
Widnes	a	08 02		09 05		10 05	11 05		12 05		13 05		14 05		15 05		16 05	
Liverpool Lime Street [10]	a	08 29		09 27		10 27	11 29		12 29		13 27		14 27		15 25		16 29	

		EM	XC	EM	XC	EM	XC	EM	XC	EM	XC	EM	XC	EM	XC	EM	XC	EM
		◇	◇	◇	◇	◇	◇	◇	◇	◇	◇	◇	◇	◇	◇	◇	◇	
Norwich	d	11 57		12 57		13 57		14 57		15 52		16 57		17 57		18 57		22 10
Thetford	d	12 24		13 24		14 24		15 24		16 22		17 24		18 24		19 24		22a43
Ipswich	d	10e16	12b03		12c16	12e16	14b03		14c16	14e16	16b03		16c16	16e16	18b03		18c16	
Stansted Airport ✈	d		12 25		13 25		14 25		15 25		16 25		17 25		18 25		19 18	
Audley End	d		12 38		13 38		14 38		15 38		16 38		17 38		18 38		19 32	
Cambridge	d	12 12	13 04	13 12	14 04	14 12	15 04	15 12	16 04	16 12	17 04	17 12	18 02	18 12	19 04	19 12	19 50	
Ely [6]	d	12 53	13 19	13 52	14 19	14 52	15 19	15 55	16 19	16 51	17 19	17 51	18 17	18 52	19 19	19 52	20 05	
March	d		13 35		14 35		15 35		16 35		17 35		18 35	19 09	19 35		20 21	
Peterborough [8]	a	13 25	13 53	14 23	14 53	15 25	15 53	16 27	16 53	17 24	17 53	18 24	18 53	19 26	19 53	20 25	20 39	
	d	13 26	13 54	14 24	14 54	15 26	15 54	16 30	16 54	17 25	17 54	18 25	18 54	19 28	19 54	20 27	20 45	
Stamford	d		14 07		15 07		16 07		17 07		18 07		19 07		20 07		20 58	
Oakham	d		14 23		15 23		16 23		17 24		18 23		19 23		20 23		21 13	
Melton Mowbray	d		14 34		15 34		16 34		17 34		18 34		19 34		20 34		21 24	
Leicester	d		14a49		15a49		16a50		17a50		18a50		19a50		20a50		21a40	
Nuneaton	a		15f50		16f50		17f50		18f50		19f50		20f50		21f50		22f35	
Birmingham New Street [12]	a		17f01		17f57		18f50		19f57		20f57		21f57		22f57		23f42	
Grantham [7]	d	13 56		14 58		15 56		17 02		17 55		18 57		20 02		21 00		
Nottingham [8]	a	14 26	15 26	15 28	16 26	16 25	17 34	17 38	18 41	18 28	19 52	19 26	20 39	20 44	21 39	21 30	22 29	
	d	14 42		15 44		16 42		17 42		18 42		19 28						
Langley Mill	d	14 59				16 58		17 58		18 59								
Alfreton	d	15 07		16 06		17 06		18 06		19 07		19 52						
Chesterfield	d	15 18		16 18		17 18		18 18		19 18		20 08						
Sheffield [7]	a	15 38		16 38		17 34		18 38		19 39		20 25						
	d	15 42		16 42		17 42		18 42		19 42		20 29						
Stockport	a	16 24		17 24		18 26		19 24		20 25		21 11						
Manchester Piccadilly [10]	a	16 37		17 35		18 35		19 35		20 36		21 25						
Manchester Oxford Road	a	16 40		17 39		18 39				20 39								
Warrington Central	a	16 57		18 02		18 57												
Widnes	a	17 05		18 10		19 05												
Liverpool Lime Street [10]	a	17 29		18 32		19 29												

For general notes see front of timetable
For details of catering facilities see Directory of Train Operators

b Change at Ely
c Change at Cambridge
e Change at Cambridge and Ely
f By bus.

Table 49

Sundays

until 27 January

Stansted Airport → East Anglia → East Midlands → Birmingham and North West England

Route Diagram - see first page of Table 49

		EM	EM	EM	EM	XC	EM	GM	EM	XC	XC	EM	EM	XC	XC	EM	XC	EM	XC	EM	XC	EM	EM	EM
		bus	bus	◇	◇	◇	◇	◇	◇	◇	◇	◇	◇	◇	◇	◇	◇	◇	◇	◇	◇	◇	◇	◇
Norwich	d						10 47					13 49				15 53		16 57		17 54		18 57	19 44	20 52
Thetford	d						11 14					14 16				16 20		17 24		18 21		19 24	20 11	21 19
Ipswich	d					09b55				11c02	11e02			13c02	13e02		15b55				17b55	17e02		19e02
Stansted Airport ✈	d									12 05				14 05	15 18		16 12		17 35		18 35			
Audley End	d									12 18				14 18	15 31		16 24		17 48		18 48			
Cambridge	d					10 48	11 07			12 36	13 43			14 36	15 47		16 47	17 02	18 09		19 08		20 02	21 02
Ely 6	d					11 09	11 39			12 54	14 00	14 45		14 53	16 04		17 04	17 51	18 26	18 48	19 28	19 56	20 35	21 44
March	d					11 25				13 10	14 16			15 10	16 21		17 20		18 42		19 44			
Peterborough 8	a					11 50	12 16			13 31	14 39	15 24		15 31	16 38	17 10	17 40	18 23	19 00	19 20	20 02	20 29	21 08	22 20
	d					11 52	12 18			13 35	14 41	15 26		15 33	16 40	17 15	17 41	18 30	19 01	19 22	20 06	20 32	21 10	22 22
Stamford	d					12 05				13 48	14 54			15 46	16 53		17 54		19 14		20 19		21 23	
Oakham	d					12 19				14 09	15 08			16 00	17 07		18 08		19 28		20 33		21 37	
Melton Mowbray	d					12 30				14 21	15 19			16 11	17 18		18 19		19 39		20 44		21 48	
Leicester	d					12 48				14 40	15 44			16 34	17 43		18 38		20 09		21 02			
Nuneaton	a					13 11				15 01	16 11			16 54	18 03		18 58		20 29		21 22			
Birmingham New Street 12	a					13 47				15 37	16 48			17 32	18 38		19 36		21 06		22 00			
Grantham 7	d						12 51					15 59				17 49		19 00		19 57		21 03		22 51
Nottingham 8	a					13f59	13 29			15f57	16f51	16 29		17f51	18f49	18 27	19f50	19 30	20f49	20 31	21f54	21 32	22 31	23 29
	d	09 05	10 05	11 46	12 39		13 33	14 36	15 35			16 42	17 31			18 33		19 39						
Langley Mill	d				12 56		13 54	14 53				16 59	17 52			18 52								
Alfreton	d	09 45	10 45	12 08	13 04		14 02	15 02	15 54			17 07	18 00			19 00		20 01						
Chesterfield	d	10 05	11 05	12 21	13 17		14 17	15 14	16 14			17 20	18 14			19 14		20 14						
Sheffield 7	a	10 40	11 40	12 37	13 34		14 33	15 31	16 32			17 44	18 31			19 32		20 31						
	d	10 45	11 45																					
Stockport	a	12 10	13 10	14g15	15g10		16g10	17g10	18g10			19g15	20g10			21g10		22g15						
Manchester Piccadilly 10	a	12 36	13 36	14 31	15 33		16 32	17 36	18 36			19 33	20g35			21g35		22g40						
Manchester Oxford Road	a	12 39	13 39	14 39	15 39		16 39	17 39	18 38			19 39												
Warrington Central	a	12 58	13 56	14 56	15 56		16 56	17 56	18 57			19 56												
Widnes	a	13 04	14 04	15 04	16 04		17 04	18 04	19 05			20 04												
Liverpool Lime Street 10	a	13 31	14 28	15 28	16 29		17 29	18 29	19 29			20 29												

Sundays

3 February to 23 March

		EM	EM	EM	XC	EM	EM	EM	XC	XC	EM	EM	XC	XC	EM	EM	XC	EM	XC	EM	XC	EM	EM	EM
		◇	◇	◇	◇	◇	◇	◇	◇	◇	◇	◇	◇	◇	◇	◇	◇	◇	◇	◇	◇	◇	◇	◇
Norwich	d						10 47					13 49				15 53		16 57		17 54		18 57	19 44	20 52
Thetford	d						11 14					14 16				16 20		17 24		18 21		19 24	20 11	21 19
Ipswich	d				09b55				11c02	11e02			13c02	13e02			15b55				17b55	17e02		19e02
Stansted Airport ✈	d								12 05				14 05	15 18			16 12		17 35		18 35			
Audley End	d								12 18				14 18	15 31			16 24		17 48		18 48			
Cambridge	d				10 48		11 07		12 36	13 43			14 36	15 47			16 47	17 02	18 09		19 08		20 02	21 02
Ely 6	d				11 09		11 39		12 54	14 00		14 45	14 53	16 04			17 04	17 51	18 26	18 48	19 28	19 56	20 35	21 44
March	d				11 25				13 10	14 16			15 10	16 21			17 20		18 42		19 44			
Peterborough 8	a				11 50		12 16		13 31	14 39		15 24	15 31	16 38		17 10	17 40	18 23	19 00	19 20	20 02	20 29	21 08	22 20
	d				11 52		12 18		13 35	14 41		15 26	15 33	16 40		17 15	17 41	18 30	19 01	19 22	20 06	20 32	21 10	22 22
Stamford	d				12 05				13 48	14 54			15 46	16 53			17 54		19 14		20 19		21 23	
Oakham	d				12 19				14 09	15 08			16 00	17 07			18 08		19 28		20 33		21 37	
Melton Mowbray	d				12 30				14 21	15 19			16 11	17 18			18 19		19 39		20 44		21 48	
Leicester	d				12 48				14 40	15 44			16 34	17 43			18 38		20 09		21 02			
Nuneaton	a				13 11				15 01	16 11			16 54	18 03			18 58		20 29		21 22			
Birmingham New Street 12	a				13 47				15 37	16 48			17 32	18 38			19 36		21 06		22 00			
Grantham 7	d						12 51					15 59				17 49		19 00		19 57		21 03		22 51
Nottingham 8	a				13f59		13 29		15f57	16f51		16 29	17f51	18f49		18 27	19f50	19 30	20f49	20 31	21f54	21 32	22 31	23 29
	d	09 15	10 36	11 46		12 39	13 33	14 36			15 35	16 42			17 31	18 33		19 39						
Langley Mill	d					12 56	13 54	14 53				16 59			17 52	18 52								
Alfreton	d		10 58	12 08		13 04	14 03	15 02			15 54	17 07			18 00	19 00		20 01						
Chesterfield	d	09 54	11 15	12 21		13 17	14 17	15 14			16 13	17 20			18 14	19 14		20 14						
Sheffield 7	a	10 14	11 33	12 37		13 34	14 33	15 31			16 32	17 38			18 31	19 32		20 31						
	d	10 26	11 40	12 40		13 39	14 37	15 35			16 36	17 42			18 35	19 35		20 35						
Stockport	a	11 18	12 23	13 24		14 21	15 22	16 19			17 22	18 24			19 21	20 24		21 18						
Manchester Piccadilly 10	a	11 33	12 36	13 36		14 31	15 33	16 32			17 36	18 36			19 33	20 35		21 33						
Manchester Oxford Road	a	11 39	12 39	13 39		14 39	15 39	16 39			17 39	18 38			19 39									
Warrington Central	a	11 56	12 56	13 56		14 56	15 56	16 56			17 56	18 57			19 56									
Widnes	a	12 04	13 04	14 04		15 04	16 04	17 04			18 04	19 05			20 04									
Liverpool Lime Street 10	a	12 29	13 31	14 28		15 28	16 29	17 29			18 29	19 29			20 29									

For general notes see front of timetable
For details of catering facilities see Directory of Train Operators

b Change at Ely
c Change at Cambridge
e Change at Cambridge and Ely
f Change at Leicester
g By bus.

Table 49

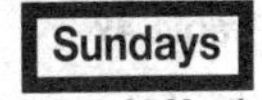

from 30 March

Stansted Airport → East Anglia → East Midlands → Birmingham and North West England

Route Diagram - see first page of Table 49

		EM ◇	EM ◇	EM ◇	XC ◇	EM ◇	EM ◇	XC ◇	EM ◇	XC ◇	EM ◇	EM ◇	XC ◇	XC ◇	XC ◇	EM ◇	EM ◇	XC ◇	EM ◇	XC ◇	EM ◇	XC ◇	EM ◇	EM ◇	EM ◇
Norwich	d						10 47					13 49					15 53		16 57		17 54		18 57	19 44	20 52
Thetford	d						11 14					14 16					16 20		17 24		18 21		19 24	20 11	21 19
Ipswich	d				*09b55*			*11c02*		*11e02*			*13c02*	*13e02*	*15b55*				*15 55*			*17b55*	*17e02*		*19e02*
Stansted Airport ✈	d							12 05					14 05	15 18	16 12			16 12		17 35		18 35			
Audley End	d							12 18					14 18	15 31	16 24			16 24		17 48		18 48			
Cambridge	d				10 48		*11 07*	12 36		13 43			14 36	15 47	16 47			16 47	*17 02*	18 09		19 08		*20 02*	*21 02*
Ely 6	d				11 09		11 39	12 54		14 00		14 45	14 53	16 04	17 04			17 04	17 51	18 26	18 48	19 28	19 56	20 35	21 44
March	d				11 25			13 10		14 16			15 10	16 21	17 20			17 20		18 42		19 44			
Peterborough 8	a				11 50		12 16	13 31		14 39		15 24	15 31	16 38	17 40		17 10	17 40	18 23	19 00	19 20	20 02	20 29	21 08	22 20
	d				11 52		12 18	13 35		14 41		15 26	15 33	16 40	17 41		17 15	17 41	18 30	19 01	19 22	20 06	20 32	21 10	22 22
Stamford	d				12 05			13 48		14 54			15 46	16 53	17 54			17 54		19 14		20 19		21 23	
Oakham	d				12 19			14 07		15 08			16 00	17 07	18 08			18 08		19 28		20 33		21 37	
Melton Mowbray	d				12 30			14 19		15 19			16 11	17 18	18 19			18 19		19 39		20 44		21 48	
Leicester	d				12a48			14a37		15a40			16a29	17a43	18a37			18a37		20a06		21a02			
Nuneaton	a				*13f35*			*15f30*		*16f30*			*17f30*	*18f30*						*20f55*		*22f24*			
Birmingham New Street 12	a				*14f42*			*16f37*		*17f37*			*18f37*	*19f37*						*22f02*		*23f31*			
Grantham 7	d						12 51					15 59					17 49		19 00		19 57		21 03		22 51
Nottingham 8 🚃	a				*14 17*		13 29	*15 12*				16 29	*17 17*	*19 15*			18 27		19 30	*20 37*	20 31	*22 11*	21 32	22 31	23 29
	d	09 15	10 36	11 46		12 39	13 33		14 36		15 35	16 42				17 31	18 33		19 39						
Langley Mill	d					12 56	13 54		14 53			16 59				17 52	18 52								
Alfreton	d		10 58	12 08		13 04	14 03		15 02		15 54	17 07				18 00	19 00		20 01						
Chesterfield	d	09 54	11 15	12 21		13 17	14 17		15 14		16 13	17 20				18 14	19 14		20 14						
Sheffield 7 🚃	a	10 14	11 33	12 37		13 34	14 33		15 31		16 32	17 38				18 31	19 32		20 31						
	d	10 26	11 40	12 40		13 39	14 37		15 35		16 36	17 42				18 35	19 35		20 35						
Stockport	a	11 18	12 23	13 24		14 21	15 22		16 19		17 22	18 24				19 21	20 24		21 18						
Manchester Piccadilly 10 🚃	a	11 33	12 36	13 36		14 31	15 33		16 32		17 36	18 36				19 33	20 35		21 33						
Manchester Oxford Road	a	11 39	12 39	13 39		14 39	15 39		16 39		17 39	18 38				19 39									
Warrington Central	a	11 56	12 56	13 56		14 56	15 56		16 56		17 56	18 57				19 56									
Widnes	a	12 04	13 04	14 04		15 04	16 04		17 04		18 04	19 05				20 04									
Liverpool Lime Street 10	a	12 29	13 31	14 28		15 28	16 29		17 29		18 29	19 29				20 29									

For general notes see front of timetable
For details of catering facilities see Directory of Train Operators

b Change at Ely
c Change at Cambridge
e Change at Cambridge and Ely
f By bus.

North West England and Birmingham → East Midlands → East Anglia → Stansted Airport

Route Diagram - see first page of Table 49

Miles	Miles	Miles	Miles			EM ◇	EM	XC ◇	EM ◇	XC ◇	EM ◇ A	XC ◇	EM ◇	XC ◇	EM ◇	XC ◇	EM ◇	XC ◇	EM ◇	XC ◇	EM ◇	XC ◇	EM ◇
—	0	—	0	**Liverpool Lime Street 10**	d										06 47		07 47		08 52		09 52		10 52
—	12¼	—	12¼	Widnes	d										07 07		08 08		09 09		10 09		11 09
—	18½	—	18½	Warrington Central	d										07 15		08 16		09 17		10 17		11 17
—	34¼	—	34¼	Manchester Oxford Road	d										07 39		08 38		09 38		10 38		11 38
—	34¾	—	34¾	**Manchester Piccadilly 10**	d										07 43		08 42		09 42		10 42		11 42
—	40¾	—	40¾	Stockport	d										07 54		08 53		09b55		10 55		11 55
—	77½	—	77½	**Sheffield 7**	a										08 34		09 35		10 35		11 35		12 35
—	—	—	—		d								07 40		08 38		09 38		10 38		11 38		12 38
—	89¾	—	89¾	Chesterfield	d								07 53		08 52		09 53		10 53		11 53		12 53
—	99¾	—	99¾	Alfreton	d								08 06		09 07		10 04		11 04		12 04		13 04
—	106	—	106	Langley Mill	d								08 13		09 14				11 11				13 11
—	118	—	118	**Nottingham 8**	a								08 29		09 30		10 25		11 30		12 29		13 29
—	—	—	—		d	04 56	05 09	05c30	06 13	06c53	07 52	07c30	08 31	08c26	09 35	09c30	10 31	10c30	11 32	11c30	12 34	12c30	13 31
—	140¾	—	—	Grantham 7	d		05 51				08 26		09 11		10 08		11 04		12 07		13 08		14 06
0	—	—	—	**Birmingham New Street 12**	d			05 20		06 37		07 21		08 24		09 24		10 24		11 24		12 24	
21	—	—	—	Nuneaton	d			05 48		07 05		07 48		08 53		09 53		10 53		11 53		12 53	
39¾	—	—	—	**Leicester**	d			06 12		07 29		08 14		09 14		10 14		11 14		12 14		13 14	
54¾	—	—	—	Melton Mowbray	d	05 29		06 28	06 52	07 45		08 30		09 30		10 30		11 30		12 30		13 30	
66¼	—	—	—	Oakham	d	05 41		06 41	07 04	07 57		08 41		09 41		10 41		11 41		12 41		13 41	
79¾	—	—	—	Stamford	d	06 02		06 55	07 18	08 13		08 57		09 57		10 57		11 57		12 57		13 57	
92¼	170	—	187¾	**Peterborough 8**	a	06 17	06 27	07 08	07 33	08 28	08 57	09 14	09 38	10 14	10 42	11 14	11 34	12 14	12 42	13 14	13 38	14 14	14 38
—	—	—	—		d	06 27		07 10	07 35	08 31	08 59	09 18	09 41	10 18	10 43	11 18	11 36	12 18	12 43	13 18	13 40	14 18	14 40
106¼	184	—	201¾	March	a	06 42		07 30	07 50	08 46		09 33		10 33		11 33		12 33		13 33		14 33	
113¾	191½	0	209¼	Ely 6	a	07 01		07 51	08 13	09 05	09 35	09 52	10 14	10 52	11 16	11 52	12 14	12 52	13 16	13 52	14 13	14 52	15 13
—	—	14¾	—	**Cambridge**	a	07 44		08 07	08 44	09 21		10 08	10 44	11 08	11 44	12 08	12 44	13 08	13 44	14 08	14 44	15 08	15 44
—	—	28¾	—	Audley End	a			08 23		09 36		10 22		11 22		12 22		13 22		14 23		15 23	
—	—	39½	—	**Stansted Airport** ✈	a			08 43		09 58		10 49		11 49		12 49		13 49		14 49		15 49	
—	—	—	—	Ipswich	a	10e02			09 26	11f02			11 25	13f02	14e02		13 25	15f02	16e02		15 25	17f02	18e03
137	214¾	—	232¾	Thetford	a	07 28			08 37		10 04		10 38		11 40		12 38		13 40		14 37		15 37
167½	245¼	—	263	**Norwich**	a	08 10			09 16		10 43		11 14		12 15		13 13		14 14		15 13		16 13

		XC ◇	EM ◇	XC ◇	EM ◇	XC ◇	XC ◇	XC ◇	EM ◇ 🚲	EM ◇	XC ◇	EM ◇	XC ◇	XC ◇	EM ◇ 🚲	EM ◇	XC ◇	EM ◇ 🚲	EM ◇ 🚲	EM ◇
Liverpool Lime Street 10	d		11 52		12 52				13 52	14 52		15 52			16 52	17 52		18 52	19 52	21 35
Widnes	d		12 09		13 09				14 09	15 09		16 09			17 09	18 09		19 09	20 09	21 53
Warrington Central	d		12 17		13 17				14 17	15 17		16 17			17 17	18 17		19 17	20 17	22 01
Manchester Oxford Road	d		12 38		13 38				14 38	15 38		16 38			17 38	18 40		19 38	20 38	22 23
Manchester Piccadilly 10	d		12 42		13 42				14 42	15 42		16 42			17 42	18 44		19 42	20 42	22 27
Stockport	d		12 55		13 55				14 55	15 51		16 53			17 53	18 55		19 55	20 55	22 38
Sheffield 7	a		13 35		14 35				15 35	16 35		17 37			18 41	19 36		20 39	21 34	23 35
	d		13 38		14 38				15 38	16 38		17 41			18 45	19 38		20 40	21 38	23 38
Chesterfield	d		13 53		14 53				15 55	16 55		17 55			19 01	19 56		20 55	21 53	23 59
Alfreton	d		14 04		15 04				16 06	17 06		18 06			19 12	20 07		21 06	22 04	
Langley Mill	d				15 11					17 13		18 13				20 16		21 13	22 11	
Nottingham 8	a		14 29		15 29				16 34	17 29		18 29			19 37	20 31		21 38	22 36	00 46
	d	13c30	14 31	14c30	15 31	15c30	16c07	16c30		17 39	17c30	18 31	18c30	19c30		20 36	20c07			
Grantham 7	d		15 07		16 07					18 16		19 09				21 08				
Birmingham New Street 12	d	13 24		14 24		15 24	16 12	16 24			17 24		18 24	19 26			20 27			
Nuneaton	d	13 53		14 53		15 53	16 41	16 56			17 55		18 53	19 51			20 54			
Leicester	d	14 14		15 14		16 14	17 03	17 31			18 16		19 14	20 17			21 15			
Melton Mowbray	d	14 30		15 30		16 30	17 19	17 46			18 32		19 30	20 32			21 32			
Oakham	d	14 41		15 41		16 41	17 30	17 57			18 44		19 41	20 44			21 44			
Stamford	d	14 57		15 57		16 57	17 45	18 14			19 02		19 57	21 00			21 59			
Peterborough 8	a	15 14	15 34	16 14	16 34	17 16	17 58	18 32		18 49	19 19	19 36	20 22	21 16		21 36	22 15			
	d	15 18	15 35	16 18	16 36	17 18	18 00	18 33		18 50	19 19	19 37	20 24	21 18		21 37	22 17			
March	a	15 33		16 33		17 37	18 15	18 51		19 06	19 36		20 39	21 33			22 36			
Ely 6	a	15 52	16 08	16 52	17 09	17 58	18 34	19 09		19 25	19 56	20 13	20 58	21 52		22 10	22 55			
Cambridge	a	16 08	16 44	17 08	17 43	18 16	18 51	19 29		19 55	20 11	21 01	21 16	22 08		22 29	23 14			
Audley End	a	16 22		17 23				19 43												
Stansted Airport ✈	a	16 49		17 43		18 47		20 05												
Ipswich	a		17 27	19f03	20e02	19g25		21f02		22e03		21 25	00e03			23g37				
Thetford	a		16 33		17 33					19 49		20 36				23g09				
Norwich	a		17 13		18 13					20 22		21 13				23g45				

For general notes see front of timetable
For details of catering facilities see Directory of Train Operators

A From Mansfield Woodhouse (Table 55)
b Arr. 0951
c Change at Leicester
e Change at Ely and Cambridge
f Change at Cambridge
g Change at Ely

Table 49

until 22 March

North West England and Birmingham → East Midlands → East Anglia → Stansted Airport

Route Diagram - see first page of Table 49

		EM	XC ◇	EM ◇		XC ◇	EM ◇	XC ◇		EM ◇	XC ◇	EM ◇		XC ◇	EM ◇	XC ◇		EM ◇	XC ◇	EM ◇		XC ◇	EM ◇	XC ◇	EM ◇
Liverpool Lime Street 10	d											06 47			07 47			08 52		09 52			10 52		11 52
Widnes	d											07 07			08 08			09 09		10 09			11 09		12 09
Warrington Central	d											07 15			08 16			09 17		10 17			11 17		12 17
Manchester Oxford Road	d											07 39			08 38			09 38		10 38			11 38		12 38
Manchester Piccadilly 10	d											07 43			08 42			09 42		10 42			11 42		12 42
Stockport	d											07 54			08 55			09 55		10 55			11 55		12 55
Sheffield 7	a											08 35			09 35			10 35		11 35			12 35		13 35
	d											08 38			09 38			10 38		11 38			12 38		13 38
Chesterfield	d											08 54			09 53			10 53		11 53			12 53		13 53
Alfreton	d											09 07			10 04			11 04		12 04			13 04		14 04
Langley Mill	d											09 14						11 11					13 11		
Nottingham 8	a											09 30			10 24			11 30		12 29			13 29		14 30
	d	05 09	*05*b*29*	06 19		*06*b*25*	07 39	*07*b*30*		08 33	*08*b*35*	09 32		*09*b*30*	10 31	*10*b*30*		11 32	*11*b*30*	12 31		*12*b*30*	13 31	*13*b*30*	14 32
Grantham 7	d	05 53					08 17			09 10		10 16			11 07			12 06		13 08			14 08		15 06
Birmingham New Street 12	d		05 20			06 36		07 24			08 24			09 24		10 24			11 24			12 24		13 24	
Nuneaton	d		05 46			07 04		07 53			08 53			09 53		10 53			11 53			12 53		13 53	
Leicester	d		06 07			07 29		08 14			09 14			10 14		11 14			12 14			13 14		14 14	
Melton Mowbray	d		06 25	06 56		07 45		08 30			09 30			10 30		11 30			12 30			13 30		14 30	
Oakham	d		06 37	07 08		07 57		08 41			09 41			10 41		11 41			12 41			13 41		14 41	
Stamford	d		06 53	07 23		08 13		08 57			09 57			10 57		11 57			12 57			13 57		14 57	
Peterborough 8	a	06 25	07 08	07 38		08 31	08 44	09 14		09 44	10 14	10 43		11 14	11 36	12 14		12 37	13 14	13 35		14 14	14 39	15 14	15 33
	d		07 10	07 39		08 32	08 46	09 18		09 46	10 18	10 46		11 18	11 38	12 18		12 39	13 18	13 37		14 18	14 40	15 18	15 36
March	a		07 29	07 55		08 48		09 33			10 33			11 33		12 33			13 33			14 33		15 33	
Ely 6	a		07 50	08 17		09 06	09 19	09 52		10 19	10 52	11 19		11 52	12 11	12 52		13 12	13 52	14 10		14 52	15 12	15 52	16 09
Cambridge	a		08 06	*08 44*		09 22	*09 44*	10 08		*10 44*	11 08	*11 44*		12 08	*12 44*	13 08		*13 44*	14 08	*14 44*		15 08	*15 44*	16 08	*16 44*
Audley End	a		08 22			09 37		10 22			11 22			12 22		13 22			14 22			15 22		16 22	
Stansted Airport ✈	a		08 49			09 58		10 49			11 49			12 49		13 49			14 49			15 49		16 49	
Ipswich	a			*09 25*		*11*c*02*	*12*e*02*			*11 27*	*13*c*02*	*14*e*02*			*13 27*	*15*c*02*		*16*e*02*		*15 25*		*17*c*02*	*18*e*03*		*17 27*
Thetford	a			08 38			09 44			10 44		11 44			12 37			13 36		14 37			15 37		16 35
Norwich	a			09 12			10 17			11 17		12 17			13 13			14 13		15 13			16 13		17 13

		XC ◇		EM ◇	XC ◇	XC ◇		EM ◇	EM ◇	XC ◇		EM ◇	XC ◇	XC ◇		EM ◇	EM ◇	XC ◇		EM ◇	EM ◇	EM ◇			
Liverpool Lime Street 10	d			12 52				13 52	14 52			15 52				16 52	17 52			18 52	19 52				
Widnes	d			13 09				14 09	15 09			16 09				17 09	18 09			19 09	20 09				
Warrington Central	d			13 17				14 17	15 17			16 17				17 17	18 17			19 17	20 17				
Manchester Oxford Road	d			13 38				14 38	15 38			16 38				17 38	18 39			19 38	20 38				
Manchester Piccadilly 10	d			13 42				14 42	15 42			16 42				17 42	18 44			19 42	20 42	21 42			
Stockport	d			13 55				14 55	15 55			16 53				17 55	18 55			19 55	20 55	21 52			
Sheffield 7	a			14 35				15 35	16 35			17 37				18 35	19 35			20 34	21 34	22 31			
	d			14 38				15 38	16 38			17 41				18 38	19 38			20 40	21 37	22 36			
Chesterfield	d			14 53				15 53	16 55			17 55				18 53	19 53			20 55	21 53	22 50			
Alfreton	d			15 04				16 04	17 06			18 06				19 04	20 04			21 06	22 04				
Langley Mill	d			15 11				16 11	17 13			18 13								21 13	22 11				
Nottingham 8	a			15 30				16 35	17 31			18 29				19 29	20 29			21 35	22 38	23 26			
	d	*14*b*30*		15 32	*15*b*30*	*16*b*30*			17 36	*17*b*30*		18 31	*18*b*30*	*19*b*30*		19 32	20 32	*20*b*30*							
Grantham 7	d			16 06					18 13			19 06				20f11	21 10								
Birmingham New Street 12	d	14 24			15 24	16 24				17 24			18 24	19 24				20 27							
Nuneaton	d	14 53			15 53	16 53				17 53			18 53	19 53				20 54							
Leicester	d	15 14			16 14	17 14				18 14			19 14	20 19				21 15							
Melton Mowbray	d	15 30			16 30	17 30				18 30			19 30	20 36				21 33							
Oakham	d	15 41			16 41	17 41				18 41			19 41	20 47				21 45							
Stamford	d	15 57			16 57	17 57				18 57			19 57	21 04				21 59							
Peterborough 8	a	16 14		16 37	17 14	18 14			18 40	19 14		19 33	20 14	21 20		20 38	21 37	22 15							
	d	16 18		16 38	17 18	18 18			18 42	19 18		19 35	20 18	21 21		20 39	21 39	22 17							
March	a	16 33			17 37	18 33			18 57	19 33			20 33	21 37		20 55	21 54	22 36							
Ely 6	a	16 52		17 11	17 58	18 52			19 16	19 52		20 08	20 52	21 55		21 15	22 13	22 54							
Cambridge	a	17 08		*17 44*	18 15	19 08			*19 55*	20 08		*20 55*	21 11	22 16		21 31	22 33	23 11							
Audley End	a	17 22			18 31					20 27															
Stansted Airport ✈	a	17 49			18 58					20 49															
Ipswich	a	*19*c*03*		*20*e*02*	*19*g*25*	*21 02*			*22*e*02*			*21 27*	*23 03*			*23 03*	*23*g*32*								
Thetford	a			17 38					19 40			20 36				*21*g*52*	*23*g*09*								
Norwich	a			18 13					20 13			21 13				*22*g*30*	*23*g*45*								

For general notes see front of timetable
For details of catering facilities see Directory of Train Operators

b Change at Leicester
c Change at Cambridge
e Change at Ely and Cambridge
f Arr. 9 minutes earlier
g Change at Ely

Table 49

Saturdays

from 29 March

North West England and Birmingham → East Midlands → East Anglia → Stansted Airport

Route Diagram - see first page of Table 49

		EM	XC ◇	EM ◇		XC ◇	EM ◇	XC ◇		EM ◇	XC ◇	EM ◇		XC ◇	EM ◇	XC ◇		EM ◇	XC ◇	EM ◇		XC ◇	EM ◇	XC ◇	EM ◇
Liverpool Lime Street 10	d											06 47			07 47			08 52		09 52			10 52		11 52
Widnes	d											07 07			08 08			09 09		10 09			11 09		12 09
Warrington Central	d											07 15			08 16			09 17		10 17			11 17		12 17
Manchester Oxford Road	d											07 39			08 38			09 38		10 38			11 38		12 38
Manchester Piccadilly 10	d											07 43			08 42			09 42		10 42			11 42		12 42
Stockport	d											07 54			08 55			09 55		10 55			11 55		12 55
Sheffield 7	a											08 35			09 35			10 35		11 35			12 35		13 35
	d											08 38			09 38			10 38		11 38			12 38		13 38
Chesterfield	d											08 54			09 53			10 53		11 53			12 53		13 53
Alfreton	d											09 07			10 04			11 04		12 04			13 04		14 04
Langley Mill	d											09 14						11 11					13 11		
Nottingham 8	a											09 30			10 24			11 30		12 29			13 29		14 30
	d	05 09	05 29	06 19		06 25	07 39	07 30		08 33	08 35	09 32		09 30	10 31	10 30		11 32	11 30	12 31		12 30	13 31	13 30	14 32
Grantham 7	d	05 53					08 17			09 10		10 16			11 07			12 06		13 08			14 08		15 06
Birmingham New Street 12	d					05b03		06b13			07b13			08b09		09b13			10b09			11b13		12b09	
Nuneaton	d					06b10		07b20			08b20			09b20		10b20			11b20			12b20		13b20	
Leicester	d		06 07			07 29		08 14			09 14			10 14		11 14			12 14			13 14		14 14	
Melton Mowbray	d		06 25	06 56		07 45		08 30			09 30			10 30		11 30			12 30			13 30		14 30	
Oakham	d		06 37	07 08		07 57		08 41			09 41			10 41		11 41			12 41			13 41		14 41	
Stamford	d		06 53	07 23		08 13		08 57			09 57			10 57		11 57			12 57			13 57		14 57	
Peterborough 8	a	06 25	07 08	07 38		08 31	08 44	09 14		09 44	10 14	10 43		11 14	11 36	12 14		12 37	13 14	13 35		14 14	14 39	15 14	15 33
	d		07 10	07 39		08 32	08 46	09 18		09 46	10 18	10 46		11 18	11 38	12 18		12 39	13 18	13 37		14 18	14 40	15 18	15 36
March	a		07 29	07 55		08 48		09 33			10 33			11 33		12 33			13 33			14 33		15 33	
Ely 6	a		07 50	08 17		09 06	09 19	09 52		10 19	10 52	11 19		11 52	12 11	12 52		13 12	13 52	14 10		14 52	15 12	15 52	16 09
Cambridge	a		08 06	08 44		09 22	09 44	10 08		10 44	11 08	11 44		12 08	12 44	13 08		13 44	14 08	14 44		15 08	15 44	16 08	16 44
Audley End	a		08 22			09 37		10 22			11 22			12 22		13 22			14 22			15 22		16 22	
Stansted Airport ✈	a		08 49			09 58		10 49			11 49			12 49		13 49			14 49			15 49		16 49	
Ipswich	a			09 25		11c02	12e02			11 27	13c02	14e02			13 27	15c02		16e02		15 25		17c02	18e03		17 27
Thetford	a			08 38			09 44			10 44		11 44			12 37			13 36		14 37			15 37		16 35
Norwich	a			09 12			10 17			11 17		12 17			13 13			14 13		15 13			16 13		17 13

		XC ◇		EM ◇	XC ◇	EM ◇		XC ◇	EM ◇	XC ◇		EM ◇	XC ◇	EM ◇		XC ◇	EM ◇	XC ◇		EM ◇	EM ◇	EM ◇			
Liverpool Lime Street 10	d			12 52		13 52			14 52			15 52		16 52			17 52			18 52	19 52				
Widnes	d			13 09		14 09			15 09			16 09		17 09			18 09			19 09	20 09				
Warrington Central	d			13 17		14 17			15 17			16 17		17 17			18 17			19 17	20 17				
Manchester Oxford Road	d			13 38		14 38			15 38			16 38		17 38			18 39			19 38	20 38				
Manchester Piccadilly 10	d			13 42		14 42			15 42			16 42		17 42			18 44			19 42	20 42	21 42			
Stockport	d			13 55		14 55			15 55			16 53		17 55			18 55			19 55	20 55	21 52			
Sheffield 7	a			14 35		15 35			16 35			17 37		18 35			19 35			20 34	21 34	22 31			
	d			14 38		15 38			16 38			17 41		18 38			19 38			20 40	21 37	22 36			
Chesterfield	d			14 53		15 53			16 55			17 55		18 53			19 53			20 55	21 53	22 50			
Alfreton	d			15 04		16 04			17 06			18 06		19 04			20 04			21 06	22 04				
Langley Mill	d			15 11		16 11			17 13			18 13								21 13	22 11				
Nottingham 8	a			15 30		16 35			17 31			18 29		19 29			20 29			21 35	22 38	23 26			
	d	14 30		15 32	15 30			16 30	17 36	17 30		18 31	18 30	19 32		19 30	20 32	20 30							
Grantham 7	d			16 06					18 13			19 06		20f11			21 10								
Birmingham New Street 12	d	13b13			14b09			15b13		16b09			17b13			18b13		19b09							
Nuneaton	d	13b20			15b20			16b20		17b20			18b20			19b20		20b20							
Leicester	d	15 14			16 15			17 14		18 14			19 14			20 19		21 15							
Melton Mowbray	d	15 30			16 30			17 30		18 30			19 30			20 36		21 33							
Oakham	d	15 41			16 41			17 41		18 41			19 41			20 47		21 45							
Stamford	d	15 57			16 57			17 57		18 57			19 57			21 04		21 59							
Peterborough 8	a	16 14		16 37	17 14			18 14	18 40	19 14		19 33	20 14	20 38		21 20	21 37	22 15							
	d	16 18		16 38	17 18			18 18	18 42	19 18		19 35	20 18	20 39		21 21	21 39	22 17							
March	a	16 33			17 37			18 33	18 57	19 33			20 33	20 55		21 37	21 54	22 36							
Ely 6	a	16 52		17 11	17 58			18 52	19 16	19 52		20 08	20 52	21 15		21 55	22 13	22 54							
Cambridge	a	17 08		17 44	18 15			19 08	19 55	20 08		20 55	21 11	21 31		22 16	22 33	23 11							
Audley End	a	17 22			18 31					20 27															
Stansted Airport ✈	a	17 49			18 58					20 49															
Ipswich	a	19c03		20e02	19g25			21 02	22e02			21 27	23 03	23 03			23g32								
Thetford	a			17 38					19 40			20 36		21g52			23 09								
Norwich	a			18 13					20 13			21 13		22g30			23 45								

For general notes see front of timetable
For details of catering facilities see Directory of Train Operators

b By bus.
c Change at Cambridge
e Change at Ely and Cambridge
f Arr. 9 minutes earlier
g Change at Ely

Table 49

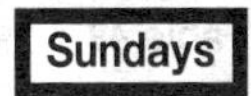

until 27 January

North West England and Birmingham → East Midlands → East Anglia → Stansted Airport

Route Diagram - see first page of Table 49

		XC ◇	EM ◇	EM ◇	XC ◇	EM ◇	XC ◇	EM ◇	XC ◇	EM ◇	XC ◇	EM ◇	XC ◇	EM ◇	XC ◇	EM	EM ◇	XC ◇		EM	EM 🚌
Liverpool Lime Street 10	d									12 52		12 52		14 52		15 52	16 52		17 52	18 52	19 52
Widnes	d									13 10		13 10		15 10		16 10	17 10		18 10	19 10	20 10
Warrington Central	d									13 18		14 18		15 18		16 18	17 18		18 18	19 18	20 18
Manchester Oxford Road	d									13 44		14 39		15 39		16 39	17 39		18 39	19 39	20 39
Manchester Piccadilly 10	d					11b35		12b35		13 49		14 43		15 43		16 43	17 43		18 42	19 42	20 43
Stockport	d					12b00		12b00		14b05		15b00		16b00		17b00	18b00		19b05	20b00	21 00
Sheffield 7	a																				22 25
	d			12 52		13 58		14 41		15 39		16 39		17 39		18 40	19 37		20 38	21 41	22 30
Chesterfield	d			13 06		14 13		14 56		15 54		16 54		17 53		18 54	19 53		20 54	21 56	23 05
Alfreton	d			13 21		14 24		15 07		16 05		17 08		18 04		19 05	20 05		21 05	22 08	23 25
Langley Mill	d							15 15		16 12		17 16		18 13		19 13			21 12	22 15	23 45
Nottingham 8	a			13 42		14 46		15 34		16 30		17 31		18 30		19 34	20 30		21 35	22 38	00 10
	d	11c43	12 32	13 44	13c31	14 54	14c48	15 48	15c40	16 40	16c30	17 38	17c24	18 46	18c41		20 35	20c30			
Grantham 7	d		13 14	14 20				16 24		17e24		18 18		19 22			21 19				
Birmingham New Street 12	d	11 26			13 36		14 34		15 32		16 34		17 34		18 34			20 28			
Nuneaton	d	11 53			14 04		15 02		16 01		17 03		18 03		19 02			20 58			
Leicester	d	12 21			14 28		15 24		16 27		17 28		18 28		19 26			21 21			
Melton Mowbray	d	12 38			14 45		15 43		16 44		17 46		18 46		19 41			21 41			
Oakham	d	12 51			14 57		15 55		16 56		17 58		18 59		19 52			21 53			
Stamford	d	13 04			15 11		16 09		17 10		18 12		19 13		20 08			22 07			
Peterborough 8	a	13 19	13 41	14 53	15 25	16 04	16 26	16 55	17 26	17 51	18 27	18 52	19 28	19 51	20 23		21 51	22 23			
	d	13 21	13 43	14 56	15 28	16 05	16 28	17 00	17 28	17 53	18 29	18 55	19 29	19 55	20 25		21 55	22 24			
March	a	13 36			15 43		16 43		17 43		18 44		19 45		20 45			22 40			
Ely 6	a	14 02	14 21	15 34	16 06	16 38	17 06	17 33	18 02	18 31	19 03	19 28	20 04	20 28	21 04		22 28	22 59			
Cambridge	a	14 19	15 09	16 14	16 22	17 14	17 23	18 14	18 21	19 14	19 20	20 14	20 21	21 14	21 19		23 13	23 17			
Audley End	a	14 34			16 39		17 38				19 38		20 38		21 34						
Stansted Airport ✈	a	14 58			16 59		17 58				19 58		20 58		21 53						
Ipswich	a		15 27		17f25		20g34		19f27		22g34		21f18		00g21						
Thetford	a		14 48	15 58		17 02		18 00		18 55		19 54		20 52			22 52				
Norwich	a		15 28	16 37		17 35		18 35		19 29		20 28		21 25			23 35				

Sundays

3 February to 23 March

		XC ◇	EM ◇	EM ◇	XC ◇	EM ◇	XC ◇	EM ◇	XC ◇	EM ◇	XC ◇	EM ◇	XC ◇	EM ◇	XC ◇	EM ◇	EM ◇	XC ◇	EM ◇	EM ◇	EM ◇
Liverpool Lime Street 10	d							12 52		13 52		14 52		15 52		16 52	17 52		18 52	19 52	21 22
Widnes	d							13 10		14 10		15 10		16 10		17 10	18 10		19 10	20 10	21 40
Warrington Central	d							13 18		14 18		15 18		16 18		17 18	18 18		19 18	20 18	21 47
Manchester Oxford Road	d							13 41		14 39		15 39		16 39		17 39	18 39		19 39	20 39	22 08
Manchester Piccadilly 10	d					12 44		13 49		14 43		15 43		16 43		17 43	18 42		19 42	20 43	22 12
Stockport	d					12 54		13 58		14 54		15 54		16 55		17 54	18 56		19 54	20 53	22 26
Sheffield 7	a					13 37		14 37		15 35		16 35		17 35		18 36	19 35		20 35	21 38	23 23
	d			12 52		13 58		14 41		15 39		16 39		17 39		18 40	19 37		20 38	21 41	23 27
Chesterfield	d			13 06		14 13		14 56		15 54		16 54		17 53		18 54	19 53		20 54	21 56	23 41
Alfreton	d			13 21		14 24		15 07		16 05		17 08		18 04		19 05	20 05		21 05	22 08	23 52
Langley Mill	d							15 15		16 12		17 16		18 13		19 13			21 12	22 15	00 02
Nottingham 8	a			13 42		14 46		15 34		16 30		17 31		18 30		19 34	20 30		21 35	22 38	00 22
	d	11c43	12 32	13 44	13c31	14 54	14c48	15 48	15c40	16 40	16c30	17 38	17c24	18 46	18c41		20 35	20c30			
Grantham 7	d		13 14	14 20				16 24		17e24		18 18		19 22			21 19				
Birmingham New Street 12	d	11 26			13 36		14 34		15 32		16 34		17 34		18 34			20 28			
Nuneaton	d	11 53			14 04		15 02		16 01		17 03		18 03		19 02			20 58			
Leicester	d	12 21			14 28		15 24		16 27		17 28		18 28		19 26			21 21			
Melton Mowbray	d	12 38			14 45		15 43		16 44		17 46		18 46		19 41			21 41			
Oakham	d	12 51			14 57		15 55		16 56		17 58		18 59		19 52			21 53			
Stamford	d	13 04			15 11		16 09		17 10		18 12		19 13		20 08			22 07			
Peterborough 8	a	13 19	13 41	14 53	15 25	16 04	16 26	16 55	17 26	17 51	18 27	18 52	19 28	19 51	20 23		21 51	22 23			
	d	13 21	13 43	14 56	15 28	16 05	16 28	17 00	17 28	17 53	18 29	18 55	19 29	19 55	20 25		21 55	22 24			
March	a	13 36			15 43		16 43		17 43		18 44		19 45		20 45			22 40			
Ely 6	a	14 02	14 21	15 34	16 06	16 38	17 06	17 33	18 02	18 31	19 03	19 28	20 04	20 28	21 04		22 28	22 59			
Cambridge	a	14 19	15 09	16 14	16 22	17 14	17 23	18 14	18 21	19 14	19 20	20 14	20 21	21 14	21 19		23 13	23 17			
Audley End	a	14 34			16 39		17 38				19 38		20 38		21 34						
Stansted Airport ✈	a	14 58			16 59		17 58				19 58		20 58		21 53						
Ipswich	a		15 27		17f25		20g34		19f27		22g34		21f18		00g21						
Thetford	a		14 48	15 58		17 02		18 00		18 55		19 54		20 52			22 52				
Norwich	a		15 28	16 37		17 35		18 35		19 29		20 28		21 25			23 35				

For general notes see front of timetable
For details of catering facilities see Directory of Train Operators

b By bus.
c Change at Leicester
e Arr. 1715
f Change at Ely
g Change at Ely and Cambridge

Table 49

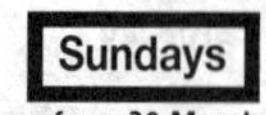

Sundays

from 30 March

North West England and Birmingham → East Midlands → East Anglia → Stansted Airport

Route Diagram - see first page of Table 49

		XC ◇	EM ◇	EM ◇	XC ◇	EM ◇		XC ◇	EM ◇	XC ◇	EM ◇	XC ◇		EM ◇	XC ◇	EM ◇	XC ◇	EM ◇	EM ◇	XC ◇	EM ◇	EM ◇	EM ◇		
Liverpool Lime Street 10	d								12 52		13 52			14 52		15 52		16 52	17 52		18 52	19 52	21 22		
Widnes	d								13 10		14 10			15 10		16 10		17 10	18 10		19 10	20 10	21 40		
Warrington Central	d								13 18		14 18			15 18		16 18		17 18	18 18		19 18	20 18	21 47		
Manchester Oxford Road	d								13 41		14 39			15 39		16 39		17 39	18 39		19 39	20 39	22 08		
Manchester Piccadilly 10	d					12 44			13 49		14 43			15 43		16 43		17 43	18 42		19 42	20 43	22 12		
Stockport	d					12 54			13 58		14 54			15 54		16 55		17 54	18 56		19 54	20 53	22 26		
Sheffield 7	a					13 37			14 37		15 35			16 35		17 35		18 36	19 35		20 35	21 38	23 23		
	d			12 52		13 58			14 41		15 39			16 39		17 39		18 40	19 37		20 38	21 41	23 27		
Chesterfield	d			13 06		14 13			14 56		15 54			16 54		17 53		18 54	19 53		20 54	21 56	23 41		
Alfreton	d			13 21		14 24			15 07		16 05			17 08		18 04		19 05	20 05		21 05	22 08	23 52		
Langley Mill	d								15 15		16 12			17 16		18 13		19 13			21 12	22 15	00 02		
Nottingham 8	a			13 42		14 46			15 34		16 30			17 31		18 30		19 34	20 30		21 35	22 38	00 22		
	d	*11 19*	12 32	13 44	*13 26*	14 50		*14 18*	15 48	*15 39*	16 40	*16 39*		17 38	*17 09*	18 46	*18 17*		20 35	*19 33*					
Grantham 7	d		13 14	14 20					16 24		17b24			18 18		19 22			21 19						
Birmingham New Street 12	d	*10c25*			*12c25*			*13c25*		*14c25*		*15c25*			*16c25*		*17c25*			*19c25*					
Nuneaton	d	*11c19*			*13c19*			*14c19*		*15c19*		*16c19*			*17c19*		*18c19*			*20c19*					
Leicester	d	12 21			14 28			15 24		16 25		17 27			18 27		19 26			21 21					
Melton Mowbray	d	12 38			14 45			15 43		16 44		17 45			18 45		19 41			21 41					
Oakham	d	12 50			14 57			15 55		16 56		17 58			18 58		19 52			21 53					
Stamford	d	13 04			15 11			16 09		17 10		18 12			19 12		20 08			22 07					
Peterborough 8	a	13 19	13 41	14 53	15 25	16 04		16 26	16 55	17 26	17 51	18 27		18 52	19 28	19 51	20 23		21 51	22 23					
	d	13 21	13 43	14 56	15 28	16 05		16 28	17 00	17 28	17 53	18 29		18 55	19 29	19 55	20 25		21 55	22 24					
March	a	13 36			15 43			16 43		17 43		18 44			19 45		20 45			22 40					
Ely 6	a	14 02	14 21	15 34	16 06	16 38		17 06	17 33	18 02	18 31	19 03		19 28	20 04	20 28	21 04		22 28	22 59					
Cambridge	a	14 19	*15 09*	*16 14*	16 22	*17 14*		17 23	*18 14*	18 21	*19 14*	19 20		*20 14*	20 21	*21 14*	21 19		*23 13*	23 17					
Audley End	a	14 34			16 39			17 38				19 38			20 38		21 34								
Stansted Airport ✈	a	14 58			16 59			17 58				19 58			20 58		21 53								
Ipswich	a		*15 27*		*17e25*			*20f34*		*19e27*		*22f34*			*21e18*		*00f21*								
Thetford	a		14 48	15 58		17 02			18 00		18 55			19 54		20 52			22 52						
Norwich	a		15 28	16 37		17 35			18 35		19 29			20 28		21 25			23 35						

For general notes see front of timetable
For details of catering facilities see Directory of Train Operators

b Arr. 1715
c By bus.
e Change at Ely
f Change at Ely and Cambridge

Network Diagram for Tables 50, 55, 56, 57

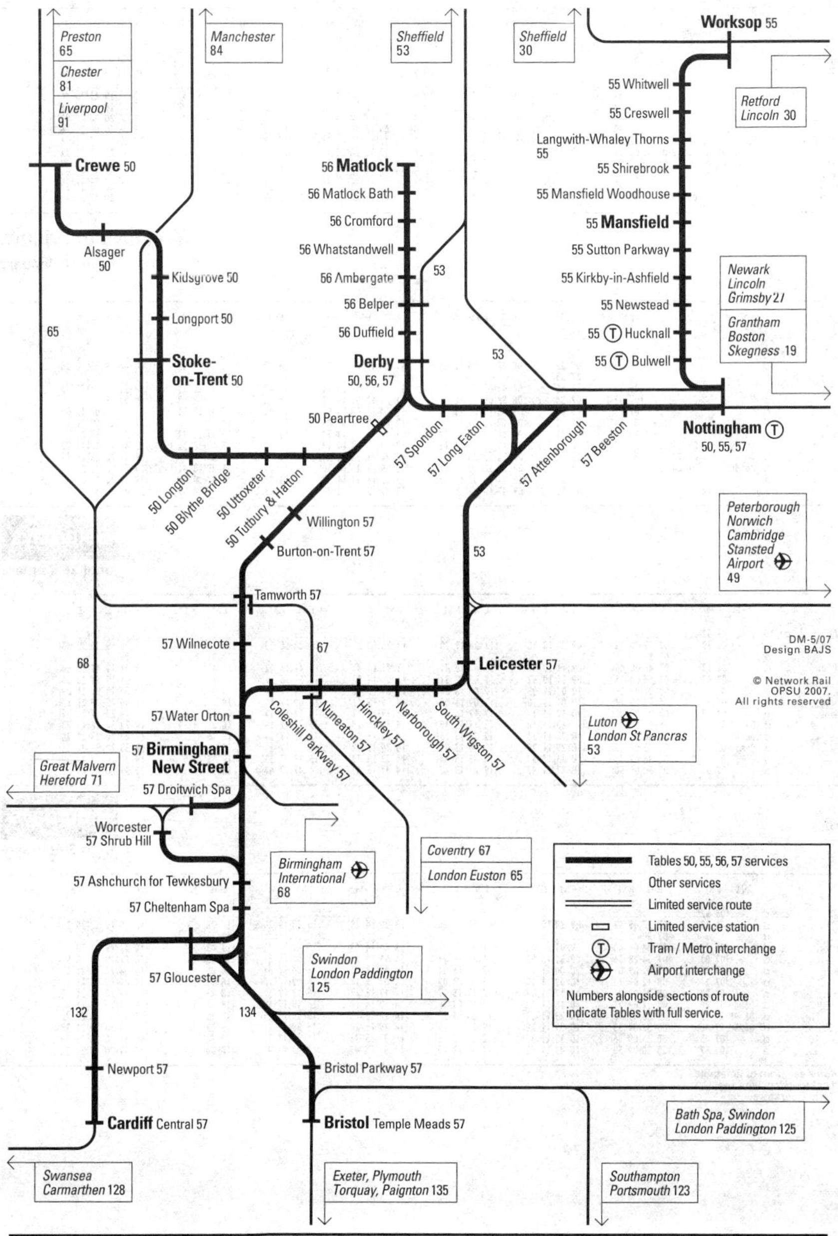

Preston 65
Chester 81
Liverpool 91
Manchester 84
Sheffield 53
Sheffield 30
Worksop 55
Retford Lincoln 30
55 Whitwell
55 Creswell
Langwith-Whaley Thorns 55
55 Shirebrook
55 Mansfield Woodhouse
55 Mansfield
55 Sutton Parkway
55 Kirkby-in-Ashfield
55 Newstead
55 Hucknall
55 Bulwell
Newark Lincoln Grimsby 27
Grantham Boston Skegness 19
Crewe 50
Alsager 50
Kidsgrove 50
Longport 50
Stoke-on-Trent 50
65
56 Matlock
56 Matlock Bath
56 Cromford
56 Whatstandwell
56 Ambergate
56 Belper
56 Duffield
Derby 50, 56, 57
53
50 Peartree
Nottingham 50, 55, 57
50 Longton
50 Blythe Bridge
50 Uttoxeter
50 Tutbury & Hatton
57 Spondon
57 Long Eaton
57 Attenborough
57 Beeston
Willington 57
Burton-on-Trent 57
Peterborough Norwich Cambridge Stansted Airport 49
Tamworth 57
57 Wilnecote
67
68
Leicester 57
DM-5/07 Design BAJS
57 Water Orton
57 Birmingham New Street
Coleshill Parkway 57
Nuneaton 57
Hinckley 57
Narborough 57
South Wigston 57
Luton London St Pancras 53
Great Malvern Hereford 71
57 Droitwich Spa
Worcester 57 Shrub Hill
Birmingham International 68
Coventry 67
London Euston 65
57 Ashchurch for Tewkesbury
57 Cheltenham Spa
57 Gloucester
Swindon London Paddington 125
132
134
Newport 57
Bristol Parkway 57
Cardiff Central 57
Bristol Temple Meads 57
Bath Spa, Swindon London Paddington 125
Swansea Carmarthen 128
Exeter, Plymouth Torquay, Paignton 135
Southampton Portsmouth 123
Tables 50, 55, 56, 57 services
Other services
Limited service route
Limited service station
Tram / Metro interchange
Airport interchange
Numbers alongside sections of route indicate Tables with full service.

Mondays to Fridays

until 25 January

Nottingham and Derby → Stoke-on-Trent and Crewe

Network Diagram - see first page of Table 50

Miles			NT	XC 1 ◇	NT	EM	NT	EM	EM	EM	EM	EM	EM	EM	EM	EM	EM	EM	NT	EM	EM	EM
0	**Nottingham** 8	d				05 55																
16	**Derby** 10	d				06 39		07 30	08 28	09 28	10 28	11 28	12 28	13 28	14 28	15 28	16 28	17 44		18 44	19 28	20 28
17¼	Peartree	d						07 33									16 31					
27½	Tutbury & Hatton	d				06 52		07 45	08 44	09 41	10 41	11 41	12 41	13 41	14 42	15 41	16 43	17 58		18 57	19 41	20 46
35¼	Uttoxeter	d				07 02		07 54	08 53	09 51	10 51	11 51	12 51	13 51	14 52	15 51	16 52	18 08		19 07	19 51	20 55
46¼	Blythe Bridge	d				07 15		08 07	09 06	10 04	11 04	12 04	13 04	14 04	15 05	16 04	17 05	18 21		19 20	20 04	21 08
49½	Longton	d				07 20		08 13	09 12	10 09	11 09	12 09	13 09	14 09	15 10	16 09	17 11			19 25	20 09	21 14
51	**Stoke-on-Trent**	a				07 27		08 21	09 18	10 17	11 17	12 17	13 17	14 18	15 17	16 17	17 17	18 32		19 32	20 17	21 21
—		d	06 40	06 53	07 13	07 27	07 40	08 21	09 19	10 18	11 18	12 18	13 18	14 18	15 18	16 18	17 18	18 32	19 19	19 32	20 18	21 22
55	Longport	d	06 44		07 20	07 32		08 26	09 24	10 23	11 23	12 24	13 24	14 24	15 24	16 23	17 23			19 37	20 23	21 27
58¼	Kidsgrove	d	06a49		07a24	07 39	07a48	08 33	09 29	10 29	11 29	12 29	13 29	14 30	15 29	16 29	17 29	18 41	19a27	19 44	20 29	21 33
60½	Alsager	d				07 42		08 36	09 33	10 33	11 33	12 33	13 33	14 33	15 33	16 33	17 33	18 45		19 47	20 33	21 37
66¾	**Crewe** 10	a		07 14		07 56		08 50	09 47	10 47	11 47	12 47	13 47	14 47	15 47	16 47	17 47	18 59		20 01	20 47	21 51

Mondays to Fridays

from 28 January

		NT	XC 1 ◇	NT	EM	NT	EM	EM	EM	EM	EM	EM	EM	EM	EM	EM	EM	NT	EM	EM	EM
Nottingham 8	d				05 55																
Derby 10	d				06 39		07 28	08 28	09 28	10 28	11 28	12 28	13 28	14 28	15 28	16 28	17 44		18 44	19 28	20 28
Peartree	d						07 33									16 31					
Tutbury & Hatton	d				06 52		07 45	08 44	09 41	10 41	11 41	12 41	13 41	14 42	15 41	16 43	17 58		18 57	19 41	20 46
Uttoxeter	d				07 02		07 54	08 53	09 51	10 51	11 51	12 51	13 51	14 52	15 51	16 52	18 08		19 07	19 51	20 55
Blythe Bridge	d				07 15		08 07	09 06	10 04	11 04	12 04	13 04	14 04	15 05	16 04	17 05	18 21		19 20	20 04	21 08
Longton	d				07 20		08 13	09 12	10 09	11 09	12 09	13 09	14 09	15 10	16 09	17 11			19 25	20 09	21 14
Stoke-on-Trent	a				07 27		08 21	09 18	10 17	11 17	12 17	13 17	14 18	15 17	16 17	17 17	18 32		19 32	20 17	21 21
	d	06 40	06 53	07 13	07 27	07 40	08 21	09 19	10 18	11 18	12 18	13 18	14 18	15 18	16 18	17 18	18 32	19 19	19 32	20 18	21 22
Longport	d	06 44		07 20	07 32		08 26	09 24	10 23	11 23	12 24	13 24	14 24	15 24	16 23	17 23			19 37	20 23	21 27
Kidsgrove	d	06a49		07a24	07 39	07a48	08 33	09 29	10 29	11 29	12 29	13 29	14 30	15 29	16 29	17 29	18 41	19a27	19 44	20 29	21 33
Alsager	d				07 42		08 36	09 33	10 33	11 33	12 33	13 33	14 33	15 33	16 33	17 33	18 45		19 47	20 33	21 37
Crewe 10	a		07 14		07 56		08 50	09 47	10 47	11 47	12 47	13 47	14 47	15 47	16 47	17 47	18 59		20 01	20 47	21 51

Saturdays

until 26 January

		NT	EM	EM	EM	EM	EM	EM	EM	EM	EM	EM	EM	EM	NT	EM	EM	EM
Nottingham 8	d		05 52															
Derby 10	d		06 39	07 27	08 32	09 28	10 28	11 28	12 28	13 28	14 28	15 28	16 28	17 28		18 28	19 28	20 33
Peartree	d			07 30										17 31				
Tutbury & Hatton	d		06 53	07 44	08 46	09 41	10 42	11 41	12 41	13 41	14 43	15 41	16 42	17 43		18 41	19 41	20 46
Uttoxeter	d		07 03	07 54	08 56	09 51	10 52	11 51	12 51	13 51	14 52	15 51	16 51	17 52		18 51	19 51	20 56
Blythe Bridge	d		07 16	08 07	09 09	10 04	11 05	12 04	13 04	14 04	15 05	16 04	17 04	18 05		19 04	20 04	21 09
Longton	d		07 21	08 12	09 14	10 09	11 10	12 09	13 09	14 09	15 11	16 09	17 10	18 11		19 09	20 09	21 14
Stoke-on-Trent	a		07 28	08 21	09 21	10 17	11 17	12 17	13 17	14 17	15 17	16 17	17 17	18 21		19 17	20 17	21 22
	d	06 45	07 28	08 21	09 21	10 18	11 18	12 18	13 18	14 18	15 18	16 18	17 18	18 21	19 19	19 22	20 18	21 23
Longport	d	06 49	07 33	08 26	09 26	10 23	11 23	12 23	13 23	14 23	15 23	16 23	17 23	18 26		19 27	20 23	21 28
Kidsgrove	d	06a54	07 40	08 33	09 33	10 29	11 29	12 29	13 29	14 29	15 28	16 29	17 29	18 33	19a27	19 33	20 29	21 33
Alsager	d		07 43	08 36	09 36	10 33	11 33	12 33	13 33	14 33	15 33	16 33	17 33	18 36		19 37	20 33	21 38
Crewe 10	a		07 57	08 50	09 50	10 47	11 47	12 47	13 47	14 47	15 47	16 47	17 47	18 50		19 51	20 47	21 52

Saturdays

from 2 February

		NT	EM	EM	EM	EM	EM	EM	EM	EM	EM	EM	EM	EM	NT	EM	EM	EM
Nottingham 8	d		05 52															
Derby 10	d		06 39	07 27	08 32	09 28	10 28	11 28	12 28	13 28	14 28	15 28	16 28	17 28		18 28	19 28	20 33
Peartree	d			07 30										17 31				
Tutbury & Hatton	d		06 53	07 44	08 46	09 41	10 42	11 41	12 41	13 41	14 43	15 41	16 42	17 43		18 41	19 41	20 46
Uttoxeter	d		07 03	07 54	08 56	09 51	10 52	11 51	12 51	13 51	14 52	15 51	16 51	17 52		18 51	19 51	20 56
Blythe Bridge	d		07 16	08 07	09 09	10 04	11 05	12 04	13 04	14 04	15 05	16 04	17 04	18 05		19 04	20 04	21 09
Longton	d		07 21	08 12	09 14	10 09	11 10	12 09	13 09	14 09	15 11	16 09	17 10	18 11		19 09	20 09	21 14
Stoke-on-Trent	a		07 28	08 21	09 21	10 17	11 17	12 17	13 17	14 17	15 17	16 17	17 17	18 21		19 17	20 17	21 22
	d	06 45	07 28	08 21	09 21	10 18	11 18	12 18	13 18	14 18	15 18	16 18	17 18	18 21	19 19	19 22	20 18	21 23
Longport	d	06 49	07 33	08 26	09 26	10 23	11 23	12 23	13 23	14 23	15 23	16 23	17 23	18 26		19 27	20 23	21 28
Kidsgrove	d	06a54	07 40	08 33	09 33	10 29	11 29	12 29	13 29	14 29	15 28	16 29	17 29	18 33	19a27	19 33	20 29	21 33
Alsager	d		07 43	08 36	09 36	10 33	11 33	12 33	13 33	14 33	15 33	16 33	17 33	18 36		19 37	20 33	21 38
Crewe 10	a		07 57	08 50	09 50	10 47	11 47	12 47	13 47	14 47	15 47	16 47	17 47	18 50		19 51	20 47	21 52

For general notes see front of timetable
For details of catering facilities see
Directory of Train Operators

Sundays

until 27 January

Nottingham and Derby → Stoke-on-Trent and Crewe

Network Diagram - see first page of Table 50

		EM	NT	EM	EM	EM	NT	EM	EM	EM	NT
Nottingham 8 🚢	d										
Derby 10	d	14 43		15 43	16 38	17 45		18 44	19 44	20 44	
Peartree	d										
Tutbury & Hatton	d	14 56		15 56	16 54	17 59		18 57	19 57	20 57	
Uttoxeter	d	15 06		16 06	17 04	18 08		19 07	20 07	21 07	
Blythe Bridge	d	15 19		16 19	17 17	18 21		19 20	20 20	21 20	
Longton	d	15 24		16 24	17 22	18 27		19 25	20 25	21 25	
Stoke-on-Trent	a	15 31		16 31	17 30	18 33		19 32	20 32	21 32	
	d	15 31	16 19	16 31	17 30	18 34	19 20	19 32	20 32	21 32	22 15
Longport	d	15 36	16 23	16 36	17 35	18 39	19 24	19 38	20 37	21 37	22 19
Kidsgrove	d	15 42	16a27	16 41	17 41	18 45	19a28	19 43	20 44	21 43	22a23
Alsager	d	15 46		16 45	17 45	18 48		19 47	20 47	21 47	
Crewe 10	a	16 03		17 02	17 59	19 05		20 03	21 05	22 04	

Sundays

3 February to 23 March

		EM 🚌	EM 1	NT	EM 🚌	EM 1	EM 🚌	EM 1	EM 🚌	EM 1	NT	EM 🚌	EM 1	EM 🚌	EM 1	EM 🚌	EM 1	NT
Nottingham 8 🚢	d																	
Derby 10	d	13 35			14 35		15 35		16 35			17 35		18 35		19 35		
Peartree	d																	
Tutbury & Hatton	d	14 05			15 05		16 05		17 05			18 05		19 05		20 05		
Uttoxeter	d	14 30			15 30		16 30		17 30			18 30		19 30		20 30		
Blythe Bridge	d	14 55			15 55		16 55		17 55			18 55		19 55		20 55		
Longton	d	15 05			16 05		17 05		18 05			19 05		20 05		21 05		
Stoke-on-Trent	a	15 20			16 20		17 20		18 20			19 20		20 20		21 20		
	d		15 31	16 19		16 31		17 30		18 34	19 20		19 32		20 32		21 32	22 15
Longport	d		15 36	16 23		16 36		17 35		18 39	19 24		19 37		20 37		21 37	22 19
Kidsgrove	d		15 42	16a27		16 41		17 41		18 45	19a28		19 44		20 44		21 43	22a23
Alsager	d		15 46			16 45		17 45		18 48			19 47		20 47		21 47	
Crewe 10	a		16 03			17 02		18 02		19 05			20 05		21 05		22 04	

Sundays

from 30 March

		EM	NT 🚌	EM 🚌	EM	EM 🚌	EM	EM 🚌	EM	NT 🚌	EM 🚌	EM	EM 🚌	EM	EM 🚌	EM	NT 🚌	EM 🚌
Nottingham 8 🚢	d																	
Derby 10	d	14 43			15 43		16 41		17 45			18 44		19 44		20 44		
Peartree	d																	
Tutbury & Hatton	d	14 56			15 56		16 54		17 59			18 57		19 57		20 57		
Uttoxeter	d	15 06			16 06		17 04		18 08			19 07		20 07		21 07		
Blythe Bridge	d	15a19		15 30	16a22	16 30	17a20	17 30	18a24		18 30	19a23	19 30	20a23	20 30	21a20		21 30
Longton	d			15 40		16 40		17 40			18 40		19 40		20 40			21 40
Stoke-on-Trent	a			15 55		16 55		17 55			18 55		19 55		20 55			21 55
	d		15 52	15 56		16 56		17 56		18 52	18 56		19 56		20 56		21 35	21 56
Longport	d			16 05		17 05		18 05			19 05		20 05		21 05			22 05
Kidsgrove	d		16a14	16 25		17 25		18 25		19a14	19 25		20 25		21 25		21a54	22 25
Alsager	d			16 38		17 38		18 38			19 38		20 38		21 38			22 38
Crewe 10	a			16 53		17 53		18 53			19 53		20 53		21 53			22 53

For general notes see front of timetable
For details of catering facilities see Directory of Train Operators

Table 50

Mondays to Fridays
until 25 January

Crewe and Stoke-on-Trent → Derby and Nottingham

Network Diagram - see first page of Table 50

Miles			XC [1] ◇	EM	NT	EM	NT	EM	EM	EM	EM	EM	EM	EM	EM	EM	EM	EM	NT	EM	EM	VT [1] ◇
0	**Crewe** [10]	d	05 45	05 50		06 40		08 07	09 07	10 07	11 07	12 07	13 07	14 07	15 07	16 07	17 07	18 07		19 07	20 50	21 34
6¼	Alsager	d		06 01		06 49		08 15	09 15	10 15	11 15	12 15	13 15	14 15	15 15	16 15	17 15	18 15		19 15	20 58	
8½	Kidsgrove	d		06 07	06 17	06 54	07 10	08 21	09 21	10 21	11 21	12 21	13 21	14 21	15 21	16 21	17 21	18 21	18 52	19 21	21 03	
11¾	Longport	d		06 13			07 14	08 27	09 27	10 27	11 27	12 27	13 27	14 27	15 27	16 27	17 27	18 27	18 57	19 27	21 08	
15¾	**Stoke-on-Trent**	a	06 03	06 22	06 27	07 02	07 19	08 32	09 32	10 32	11 32	12 32	13 32	14 32	15 32	16 32	17 32	18 32	19 02	19 32	21 13	21 51
—		d		06 23		07 02		08 33	09 33	10 33	11 33	12 33	13 33	14 33	15 33	16 33	17 33	18 33		19 33	21 14	
17½	Longton	d		06 28				08 39	09 39	10 39	11 39	12 39	13 39	14 39	15 39	16 39	17 39	18 39		19 39	21 19	
20½	Blythe Bridge	d		06 34		07 12		08 45	09 45	10 45	11 45	12 45	13 45	14 45	15 45	16 45	17 45	18 45		19 45	21 25	
31½	Uttoxeter	d		06 46		07 25		08 58	09 58	10 58	11 58	12 58	13 58	14 58	15 58	16 58	17 58	18 58		19 58	21 37	
39¼	Tutbury & Hatton	d		06 55		07 33		09 06	10 06	11 06	12 06	13 06	14 06	15 06	16 06	17 06	18 06	19 06		20 06	21 46	
49½	Peartree	d				07 48									16 19							
50¾	**Derby** [10]	a		07 12		07 51		09 26	10 26	11 26	12 26	13 26	14 26	15 26	16 28	17 26	18 26	19 26		20 26	22 11	
66¾	**Nottingham** [8]	a																				

Mondays to Fridays
from 28 January

		XC [1] ◇	EM	NT	EM	NT	EM	EM	EM	EM	EM	EM	EM	EM	EM	EM	EM	NT	EM	EM	VT [1] ◇
Crewe [10]	d	05 45	05 50		06 40		08 07	09 07	10 07	11 07	12 07	13 07	14 07	15 07	16 07	17 07	18 07		19 07	20 50	21 34
Alsager	d		06 01		06 49		08 15	09 15	10 15	11 15	12 15	13 15	14 15	15 15	16 15	17 15	18 15		19 15	20 58	
Kidsgrove	d		06 07	06 17	06 54	07 10	08 21	09 21	10 21	11 21	12 21	13 21	14 21	15 21	16 21	17 21	18 21	18 52	19 21	21 03	
Longport	d		06 13			07 14	08 27	09 27	10 27	11 27	12 27	13 27	14 27	15 27	16 27	17 27	18 27	18 57	19 27	21 08	
Stoke-on-Trent	a	06 03	06 22	06 27	07 02	07 19	08 32	09 32	10 32	11 32	12 32	13 32	14 32	15 32	16 32	17 32	18 32	19 02	19 32	21 13	21 51
	d		06 23		07 02		08 33	09 33	10 33	11 33	12 33	13 33	14 33	15 33	16 33	17 33	18 33		19 33	21 14	
Longton	d		06 28				08 39	09 39	10 39	11 39	12 39	13 39	14 39	15 39	16 39	17 39	18 39		19 39	21 19	
Blythe Bridge	d		06 34		07 12		08 45	09 45	10 45	11 45	12 45	13 45	14 45	15 45	16 45	17 45	18 45		19 45	21 25	
Uttoxeter	d		06 46		07 25		08 58	09 58	10 58	11 58	12 58	13 58	14 58	15 58	16 58	17 58	18 58		19 58	21 37	
Tutbury & Hatton	d		06 55		07 33		09 06	10 06	11 06	12 06	13 06	14 06	15 06	16 06	17 06	18 06	19 06		20 06	21 46	
Peartree	d				07 48									16 19							
Derby [10]	a		07 15		07 51		09 26	10 26	11 26	12 26	13 26	14 26	15 26	16 28	17 26	18 26	19 26		20 26	22 11	
Nottingham [8]	a																				

Saturdays
until 26 January

		XC ◇	NT	EM	EM	EM	EM	EM	EM	EM	EM	EM	EM	EM	EM	EM	NT	EM	EM
Crewe [10]	d	05 42		06 07	06 52	08 07	09 07	10 07	11 07	12 07	13 07	14 07	15 07	16 07	17 07	18 07		19 07	20 50
Alsager	d			06 15	07 00	08 15	09 15	10 15	11 15	12 15	13 15	14 15	15 15	16 15	17 15	18 15		19 15	20 58
Kidsgrove	d		06 15	06 21	07 05	08 22	09 22	10 22	11 22	12 22	13 22	14 22	15 22	16 22	17 22	18 22	18 44	19 22	21 03
Longport	d			06 27	07 10	08 28	09 27	10 28	11 28	12 28	13 27	14 28	15 28	16 28	17 28	18 28	18 48	19 28	21 08
Stoke-on-Trent	a	06 01	06 25	06 32	07 15	08 33	09 32	10 33	11 33	12 33	13 32	14 33	15 33	16 33	17 33	18 33	18 53	19 33	21 13
	d			06 33	07 16	08 34	09 33	10 33	11 33	12 33	13 33	14 33	15 33	16 33	17 33	18 33		19 33	21 14
Longton	d			06 38	07 21	08 39	09 38	10 38	11 38	12 38	13 38	14 38	15 38	16 38	17 38	18 38		19 38	21 19
Blythe Bridge	d			06 44	07 27	08 45	09 44	10 44	11 44	12 44	13 44	14 44	15 44	16 44	17 44	18 44		19 44	21 25
Uttoxeter	d			06 56	07 39	08 58	09 56	10 57	11 57	12 57	13 56	14 57	15 57	16 57	17 57	18 57		19 57	21 37
Tutbury & Hatton	d			07 05	07 48	09 06	10 05	11 05	12 05	13 05	14 05	15 05	16 05	17 05	18 05	19 05		20 05	21 46
Peartree	d			07 18									16 20						
Derby [10]	a			07 26	08 10	09 28	10 26	11 27	12 27	13 27	14 26	15 27	16 29	17 27	18 27	19 27		20 27	22 07
Nottingham [8]	a																		

Saturdays
from 2 February

		XC [1] ◇	NT	EM	EM	EM	EM	EM	EM	EM	EM	EM	EM	EM	EM	EM	NT	EM	EM
Crewe [10]	d	05 42		06 07	06 52	08 07	09 07	10 07	11 07	12 07	13 07	14 07	15 07	16 07	17 07	18 07		19 07	20 50
Alsager	d			06 15	07 00	08 15	09 15	10 15	11 15	12 15	13 15	14 15	15 15	16 15	17 15	18 15		19 15	20 58
Kidsgrove	d		06 15	06 21	07 05	08 22	09 22	10 22	11 22	12 22	13 22	14 22	15 22	16 22	17 22	18 22	18 44	19 22	21 03
Longport	d			06 27	07 10	08 28	09 27	10 28	11 28	12 28	13 27	14 28	15 28	16 28	17 28	18 28	18 48	19 28	21 08
Stoke-on-Trent	a	06 01	06 25	06 32	07 15	08 33	09 32	10 33	11 33	12 33	13 32	14 33	15 33	16 33	17 33	18 33	18 53	19 33	21 13
	d			06 33	07 16	08 34	09 33	10 33	11 33	12 33	13 33	14 33	15 33	16 33	17 33	18 33		19 33	21 14
Longton	d			06 38	07 21	08 39	09 38	10 38	11 38	12 38	13 38	14 38	15 38	16 38	17 38	18 38		19 38	21 19
Blythe Bridge	d			06 44	07 27	08 45	09 44	10 44	11 44	12 44	13 44	14 44	15 44	16 44	17 44	18 44		19 44	21 25
Uttoxeter	d			06 56	07 39	08 58	09 56	10 57	11 57	12 57	13 56	14 57	15 57	16 57	17 57	18 57		19 57	21 37
Tutbury & Hatton	d			07 05	07 48	09 06	10 05	11 05	12 05	13 05	14 05	15 05	16 05	17 05	18 05	19 05		20 05	21 46
Peartree	d			07 18									16 20						
Derby [10]	a			07 26	08 10	09 28	10 26	11 27	12 27	13 27	14 26	15 27	16 29	17 27	18 27	19 27		20 27	22 07
Nottingham [8]	a																		

For general notes see front of timetable
For details of catering facilities see
Directory of Train Operators

Table 50

Sundays until 27 January

Crewe and Stoke-on-Trent → Derby and Nottingham

Network Diagram - see first page of Table 50

		XC [1] ◇ (catering)	EM	EM	NT	EM	EM	EM	NT	EM	EM	EM	NT
Crewe [10]	d	08 46	14 16	15 16		16 16	17 16	18 16		19 16	20 16	21 23	
Alsager	d		14 25	15 25		16 24	17 26	18 25		19 25	20 25	21 31	
Kidsgrove	d		14 29	15 29	15 44	16 30	17 31	18 30	18 42	19 31	20 30	21 36	21 42
Longport	d		14 34	15 34	15 49	16 35	17 36	18 36	18 46	19 36	20 35	21 41	21 46
Stoke-on-Trent	a	09 04	14 39	15 39	15 54	16 40	17 41	18 41	18 52	19 41	20 40	21 46	21 51
	d		14 40	15 40		16 40	17 41	18 41		19 41	20 40	21 47	
Longton	d		14 45	15 45		16 45	17 47	18 46		19 46	20 45	21 53	
Blythe Bridge	d		14 51	15 51		16 51	17 53	18 52		19 52	20 51	21 59	
Uttoxeter	d		15 03	16 03		17 04	18 05	19 05		20 05	21 04	22 11	
Tutbury & Hatton	d		15 12	16 12		17 12	18 14	19 13		20 13	21 12	22 20	
Peartree	d												
Derby [10]	a		15 33	16 34		17 32	18 32	19 37		20 35	21 32	22 34	
Nottingham [8] (ferry)	a											23 06	

Sundays 3 February to 23 March

		XC [1] ◇ (catering)	EM	EM (bus)	EM	EM (bus)	NT	EM	EM (bus)	EM	EM (bus)	EM	EM (bus)	NT	EM	EM (bus)	EM [1]	EM (bus)	EM	NT	EM (bus)
Crewe [10]	d	08 46	14 16		15 16			16 16		17 16		18 16			19 16		20 16		21 23		
Alsager	d		14 25		15 25			16 24		17 26		18 25			19 25		20 25		21 32		
Kidsgrove	d		14 30		15 29		15 44	16 30		17 31		18 30		18 42	19 30		20 32		21 37	21 42	
Longport	d		14 35		15 34		15 49	16 35		17 36		18 35		18 46	19 35		20 37		21 42	21 46	
Stoke-on-Trent	a	09 04	14 42		15 41		15 54	16 42		17 43		18 42		18 52	19 42		20 44		21 49	21 51	
	d			14 50		15 50			16 50		17 50		18 50			19 50		20 50			21 58
Longton	d			15 05		16 05			17 05		18 05		19 05			20 05		21 05			22 13
Blythe Bridge	d			15 21		16 21			17 21		18 21		19 21			20 21		21 21			22 29
Uttoxeter	d			15 41		16 41			17 41		18 41		19 41			20 41		21 41			22 49
Tutbury & Hatton	d			15 59		16 59			17 59		18 59		19 59			20 59		21 59			23 07
Peartree	d																				
Derby [10]	a			16 24		17 24			18 24		19 24		20 24			21 24		22 24			23 32
Nottingham [8] (ferry)	a																				00 45

Sundays from 30 March

		EM (bus)	EM	EM (bus)	EM	EM (bus)	NT (bus)	EM	EM (bus)	EM	EM (bus)	EM	EM (bus)	NT (bus)	EM	EM (bus)	EM	EM (bus)	EM	NT (bus)
Crewe [10]	d	13 19		14 19		15 19			16 19		17 19		18 19			19 19		20 19		
Alsager	d	13 35		14 35		15 35			16 35		17 35		18 35			19 35		20 35		
Kidsgrove	d	13 48		14 48		15 48	16 13		16 48		17 48		18 48	19 13		19 48		20 48		22 13
Longport	d	14 03		15 03		16 03			17 03		18 03		19 03			20 03		21 03		
Stoke-on-Trent	a	14 11		15 11		16 11	16 39		17 11		18 11		19 11	19 39		20 11		21 11		22 39
	d	14 12		15 12		16 12			17 12		18 12		19 12			20 12		21 12		
Longton	d	14 27		15 27		16 27			17 27		18 27		19 27			20 27		21 27		
Blythe Bridge	d	14a43	14 51	15a43	15 51	16a43		16 51	17a43	17 53	18a43	18 52	19a43		19 52	20a43	20 51	21a43	21 59	
Uttoxeter	d		15 03		16 03			17 04		18 05		19 05			20 05		21 04		22 11	
Tutbury & Hatton	d		15 12		16 12			17 12		18 14		19 13			20 13		21 12		22 20	
Peartree	d																			
Derby [10]	a		15 33		16 34			17 32		18 32		19 37			20 35		21 32		22 34	
Nottingham [8] (ferry)	a																		23 06	

For general notes see front of timetable
For details of catering facilities see
Directory of Train Operators

Route Diagram for Table 51

This Table summarises through services which, with their associated connecting services at Birmingham New Street, link centres in the North and South of the country. In certain instances a faster journey is possible via London and the relevant Table(s) should be consulted.

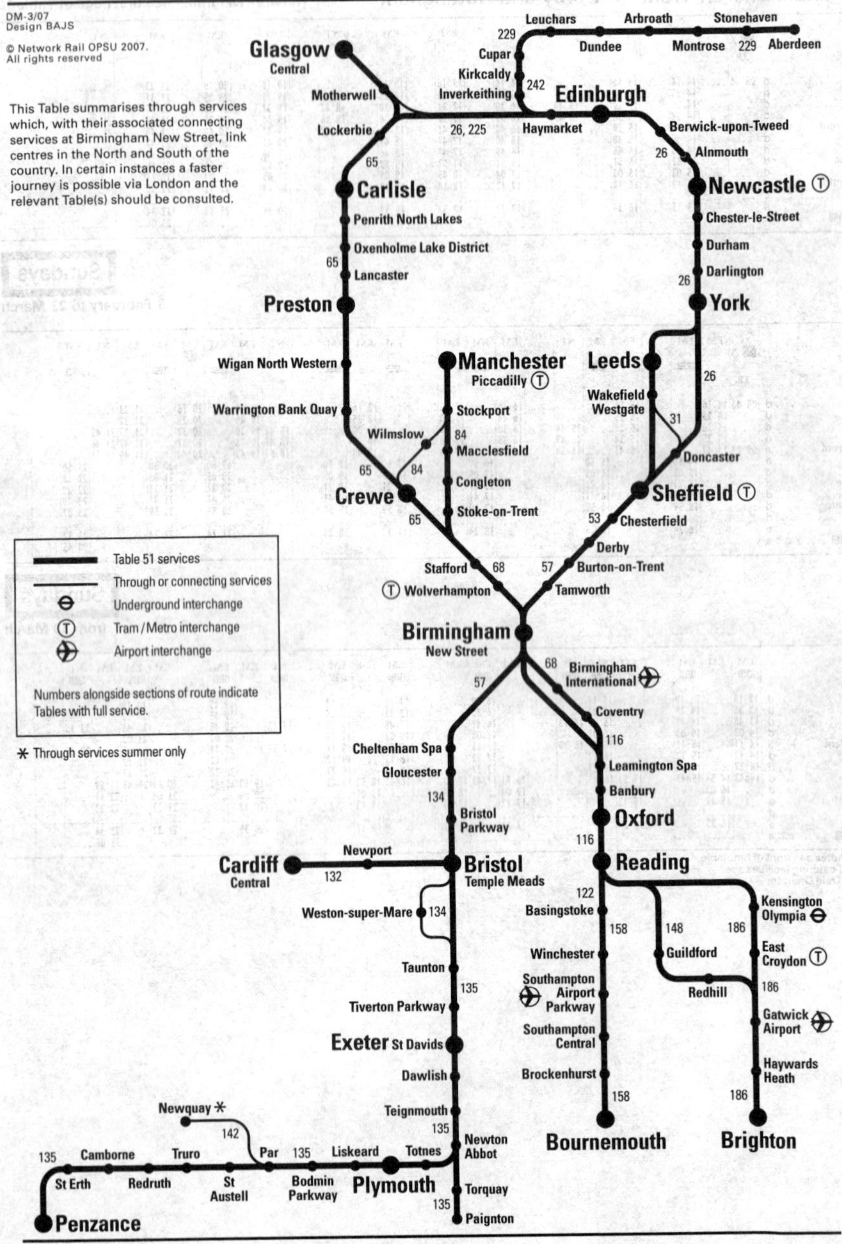

Scotland, The North East, North West England → The South West and South Coast

Route Diagram - See first page of Table 51

		XC	XC	XC	XC	XC	XC	XC	XC	VT	XC	XC	VT	XC	XC	XC	XC	VT	XC	XC	XC	XC	VT	XC
																R	R			R	R			
		1 ◇	1 ◇	1 ◇	1 ◇	1 ◇	1 ◇	1 ◇	1 ◇	1 ◇	1 ◇	1 ◇	1 ◇	1 ◇	1 ◇	1	1	1 ◇	1 ◇	1	1	1 ◇	1 ◇	1 ◇
		☕	☕	☕	☕	☕	☕	☕	☕	⊠	☕	☕	☕	☕	☕	☕	☕	☕	☕	☕	☕	☕	☕	☕
Aberdeen	d																							
Stonehaven	d																							
Montrose	d																							
Arbroath	d																							
Dundee	d																							
Leuchars 8	d																							
Cupar	d																							
Markinch	d																							
Kirkcaldy	d																							
Inverkeithing	d																							
Glasgow Central 15	d																							
Motherwell	d																							
Haymarket	d																							
Edinburgh 10	d																							
Haymarket	d																							
Lockerbie	d																							
Carlisle 8	d																							
Penrith North Lakes	d																							
Oxenholme Lake District	d																							
Lancaster 6	d																							
Preston 8	d												06 15					07 29					08 29	
Wigan North Western	d												06 27					07 41					08 41	
Warrington Bank Quay	d												06 45					07 53					08 52	
Manchester Piccadilly 10 ⛴	d					05b20				06 17				06 54		07 24			07 54			08 24		08 54
Stockport	d					05b31				06 25						07 33			08 03			08 33		09 03
Wilmslow	d					05b39																		
Crewe 10	d					05 45							07 10					08 15					09 15	
Macclesfield	d									06 38						07 47			08 16			08 47		09 16
Congleton	d													07 21		07 55			08 24					09 24
Stoke-on-Trent	d					06 04				06 54				07 33		08 08			08 39			09 04		09 39
Stafford	d					06 24				07 15				07 54		08 26			08 57			09 26		
Wolverhampton 7 ⛴	d					06 41				07 35			07 49	08 13		08 41		08 49	09 13			09 41	09 49	10 13
Dunbar	d																							
Berwick-upon-Tweed	d																							
Alnmouth	d																							
Newcastle 8	d																			06 19	06 44			
Chester-le-Street	d																			06 31				
Durham	d																			06 38	06 56			
Darlington 7	d																			06 55	07 14			
York 8	d														06 16					07 27	07 44			
Leeds 10	d										06 00						07 05				08 10			
Wakefield Westgate 7	d										06 12						07 19				08 23			
Doncaster 7	d																			07 52				
Sheffield 7	d										06 45				07 23		07 53			08 23	08 53			
Chesterfield	d										06 57				07 35		08 05			08 35				
Derby 10	d				06 10				06 57		07 20	07 24			07 57		08 27			08 57	09 24			
Burton-on-Trent	d				06 20				07 07			07 35					08 37							
Tamworth	d				06 31				07 18			07 46					08 48							
Birmingham New Street 12	a				06 51	06 58	←		07 36	07 55	07 58	08 07	08 11	08 30	08 36	08 58	09 06	09 11	09 30	09 36	09 58	09 58	10 11	10 30
Birmingham New Street 12	d	06 03	06 10	06 33	07 10	07 03	07 10	07 33	07 40	08 00	08 03	08 10		08 33	08 40	09 03	09 10		09 33	09 40	10 03	10 10		10 33
Cheltenham Spa	a		07 21		→		07 51		08 21			08 51			09 21		09 51			10 21		10 51		
Gloucester 7	a																							
Bristol Parkway 7	a		07 54				08 25		08 54			09 25			09 54		10 25			10 54		11 25		
Bristol Temple Meads 10	a		08 11				08 41		09 11			09 41			10 11		10 41			11 11		11 41		
Newport (South Wales)	a																							
Cardiff Central 7	a																							
Weston-super-Mare	a																			11 32				
Taunton	a		08 42				09 15					10 15					11 15			12 03		12 15		
Tiverton Parkway	a						09 28					10 28					11 28			12 16		12 28		
Exeter St Davids 6	a		09 07				09 43					10 43					11 43			12 31		12 43		
Dawlish	a																			12 44				
Teignmouth	a																			12 49				
Newton Abbot	a						10 02					11 02					12 02			12 56		13 02		
Torquay	a		09 34																	13 07				
Paignton	a		09 47																	13 20				
Totnes	a						10 16					11 16					12 16					13 16		
Plymouth	a						10 48					11 48					12 48					13 48		
Liskeard 8	a																							
Bodmin Parkway	a																							
Par 8	a																							
St Austell	a																							
Truro	a																							
Redruth	a																							
Camborne	a																							
St Erth 2	a																							
Penzance	a																							
Birmingham International ✈	d	06 15				07 15				08 10	08 15					09 15					10 15			
Coventry	d	06 25				07 25				08a20	08 25					09 25					10 25			
Leamington Spa 8	d	06 38		07 00		07 38		08 00			08 38			09 00		09 38			10 00		10 38			11 00
Banbury	a	06 54		07 18		07 54		08 18			08 54			09 18		09 54			10 18		10 54			11 18
Oxford	a	07 14		07 41		08 14		08 41			09 14			09 41		10 14			10 41		11 14			11 41
Reading 7	a	07 39		08 13		08 39		09 13			09 39			10 13		10 39			11 08		11 39			12 13
Kensington Olympia	a																		11 56					
East Croydon ⛴	a																		12 16					
Guildford	a																							
Redhill	a																							
Basingstoke	a	08 08				09 08					10 08					11 08					12 08			
Winchester	a	08 24				09 24					10 24					11 24					12 24			
Southampton Airport Parkwy ✈	a	08 33				09 33					10 33					11 33					12 33			
Southampton Central	a	08 40				09 40					10 40					11 40					12 40			
Brockenhurst 3	a	08 56				09 56					10 56					11 56					12 56			
Bournemouth	a	09 15				10 15					11 15					12 15					13 15			
Gatwick Airport 10 ✈	a																		12 33					
Haywards Heath 3	a																		12 49					
Brighton 10	a																		13 15					

For general notes see front of timetable
For details of catering facilities see Directory of Train Operators

b Change at Stafford

until 25 January

Scotland, The North East, North West England → The South West and South Coast

Route Diagram - See first page of Table 51

		XC		XC	XC	VT	XC	XC	XC	XC	VT	XC	XC	XC	XC	VT	XC	XC	XC	XC	XC	XC	XC	VT
				R					R					R		R		R	R	R	R			R
		1 ◇		1	1 ◇	1 ◇	1 ◇	1 ◇	1	1 ◇	1 ◇	1 ◇	1 ◇	1	1 ◇	1	1 ◇	1	1	1	1	1 ◇	1 ◇	1
Aberdeen	d																							
Stonehaven	d																							
Montrose	d																							
Arbroath	d																							
Dundee	d														06 38				07 33					
Leuchars 3	d														06 51				07 46					
Cupar	d														06 58				07 55					
Markinch	d														07 13				08 09					
Kirkcaldy	d														07 25				08 18					
Inverkeithing	d														07 43				08 37					
Glasgow Central 15	d								06 00		07 45										09 00			10 10
Motherwell	d																				09u14			
Haymarket	d								06 52						08 00				08 58		09 55			
Edinburgh 10	d				06 05	06 36			07 05						08 13	08 51			09 05		10 05 →			
Haymarket	d					06u40										08u57								
Lockerbie	d																							
Carlisle 8	d					07 53					09 14					10 17								11 22
Penrith North Lakes	d					08 09					09 29													
Oxenholme Lake District	d					08 33					09 54					10 53								
Lancaster 6	d					09 09					10 09					11 10								12 12
Preston 8	d					09 29					10 28					11 29								12 32
Wigan North Western	d					09 41					10 42					11 41								12 45
Warrington Bank Quay	d					09 53					10 53					11 52								12 59
Manchester Piccadilly 10	d			09 24			09 54			10 24		10 54		11 24			11 54			12 24		12 54		
Stockport	d			09 33			10 03			10 33		11 03		11 33			12 03			12 33		13 03		
Wilmslow	d																							
Crewe 10	d					10 15					11 14					12 13								13 33
Macclesfield	d			09 47			10 16			10 47		11 16		11 47			12 16			12 47		13 16		
Congleton	d											11 24										13 24		
Stoke-on-Trent	d			10 04			10 39			11 04		11 39		12 04			12 39			13 04		13 39		
Stafford	d			10 26						11 26				12 26						13 26				
Wolverhampton 7	d			10 41		10 49	11 13			11 41	11 49	12 13		12 41		12 49	13 13			13 41		14 13		14 18
Dunbar	d								07 25										09 25					
Berwick-upon-Tweed	d				06 49				07 49						08 52				09 49					
Alnmouth	d				07 11				08 08						09 12									
Newcastle 8	d	07 23			07 44			08 24	08 40				09 35		09 40			10 25	10 40				11 25	
Chester-le-Street	d							08 33										10 34						
Durham	d	07 37			07 56			08 40	08 52				09 47		09 52			10 41	10 52				11 37	
Darlington 7	d	07 54			08 14			08 57	09 10				10 04		10 10			10 58	11 10				11 56	
York 8	d	08 27			08 44			09 27	09 44				10 34		10 44			11 27	11 44				12 25	
Leeds 10	d				09 10				10 10						11 10				12 10					
Wakefield Westgate 7	d				09 23				10 23						11 23				12 23					
Doncaster 7	d	08 51						09 56					10 58					11 54					12 55	
Sheffield 7	d	09 23			09 53			10 23	10 53				11 23		11 53			12 23	12 53				13 23	
Chesterfield	d	09 35						10 35					11 35					12 35					13 35	
Derby 10	d	09 57			10 24			10 57	11 24				11 57		12 24			12 57	13 24				13 57	
Burton-on-Trent	d	10 07											12 07										14 07	
Tamworth	d	10 18											12 18										14 18	
Birmingham New Street 12	a	10 36		10 58	11 04	11 11	11 30	11 36	11 58	11 58	12 11	12 30	12 36	12 58	13 04	13 11	13 30	13 36	13 58	13 58		14 30	14 36	14 41
Birmingham New Street 12	d	10 40		11 03	11 10		11 33	11 40	12 03	12 10		12 33	12 40	13 03	13 10		13 33	13 40	14 03	14 10		14 33	14 40	
Cheltenham Spa	a	11 21			11 51			12 21		12 51			13 21		13 51			14 21		14 51			15 21	
Gloucester 7	a																							
Bristol Parkway 7	a	11 54			12 25			12 54		13 25			13 54		14 25			14 54		15 25			15 54	
Bristol Temple Meads 10	a	12 11			12 41			13 11		13 41			14 11		14 41			15 11		15 41			16 11	
Newport (South Wales)	a																							
Cardiff Central 7	a																							
Weston-super-Mare	a																							
Taunton	a				13 15			13 42		14 15					15 15			15 42		16 15				
Tiverton Parkway	a				13 28			14 01		14 28					15 28			15 54		16 28				
Exeter St Davids 6	a				13 43			14 16		14 43					15 43			16 10		16 43				
Dawlish	a							14 29																
Teignmouth	a							14 34																
Newton Abbot	a				14 02			14 41		15 02					16 02			16 30		17 02				
Torquay	a							14 52																
Paignton	a							15 05																
Totnes	a				14 16					15 16					16 16			16 43		17 16				
Plymouth	a				14 48					15 48					16 48			17 15		17 48				
Liskeard 3	a																			18 17				
Bodmin Parkway	a																			18 29				
Par 3	a																			18 40				
St Austell	a																			18 46				
Truro	a																			19 04				
Redruth	a																			19 16				
Camborne	a																			19 23				
St Erth 2	a																			19 33				
Penzance	a																			19 49				
Birmingham International ✈	d			11 15					12 15					13 15					14 15					
Coventry	d			11 25					12 25					13 25					14 25					
Leamington Spa 8	d			11 38			12 00		12 38			13 00		13 38			14 00		14 38			15 00		
Banbury	a			11 54			12 18		12 54			13 18		13 54			14 18		14 54			15 18		
Oxford	a			12 14			12 41		13 14			13 41		14 14			14 41		15 14			15 41		
Reading 7	a			12 39			13 13		13 39			14 13		14 39			15 13		15 39			16 11		
Kensington Olympia	a																							
East Croydon	a																							
Guildford	a																					16 59		
Redhill	a																					*17 38*		
Basingstoke	a			13 08					14 08					15 08					16 08					
Winchester	a			13 24					14 24					15 24					16 24					
Southampton Airport Parkwy ✈	a			13 33					14 33					15 33					16 33					
Southampton Central	a			13 40					14 40					15 40					16 40					
Brockenhurst 3	a			13 56					14 56					15 56					16 56					
Bournemouth	a			14 15					15 15					16 15					17 15					
Gatwick Airport 10 ✈	a																					*17 50*		
Haywards Heath 3	a																							
Brighton 10	a																							

For general notes see front of timetable
For details of catering facilities see Directory of Train Operators

Scotland, The North East, North West England → The South West and South Coast

Route Diagram - See first page of Table 51

		XC	XC	VT	XC	XC	XC	XC	VT	XC	XC	XC	XC	VT	XC	XC	XC	XC	VT	XC	XC	XC	XC
			R				R	R	R	R		R	R	R	R	R	R			R	R	R	
		1◇	1	1◇	1◇	1◇	1	1	1	1	1◇	1	1	1	1	1	1	1◇	1◇	1	1	1	1◇
Aberdeen	d						08 20																
Stonehaven	d						08 37																
Montrose	d						08 59																
Arbroath	d						09 15																
Dundee	d						09 33																
Leuchars 3	d						09 46																
Cupar	d						09 53																
Markinch	d						10 04																
Kirkcaldy	d						10 13																
Inverkeithing	d						10 28																
Glasgow Central 15	d								12 10										14 10				
Motherwell	d																						
Haymarket	d		←				10 47																
Edinburgh 10	d		10 05	10 51			11b05						12 05	12 51			13 05						14 05
Haymarket	d			10u56										12u56									
Lockerbie	d													13 53									
Carlisle 8	d			12 13					13 21					14 14					15 21				
Penrith North Lakes	d			12 29										14 29									
Oxenholme Lake District	d			12 53					13 59					14 53									
Lancaster 6	d			13 09										15 08					16 09				
Preston 8	d			13 29					14 30					15 29					16 29				
Wigan North Western	d			13 41					14 42					15 41					16 41				
Warrington Bank Quay	d			13 53					14 54					15 52					16 53				
Manchester Piccadilly 10	d	13 24			13 54			14 24		14 54		15 24			15 54			16 24		16 54		17 24	
Stockport	d	13 33			14 03			14 33		15 03		15 33			16 03			16 33		17 03		17 33	
Wilmslow	d																						
Crewe 10	d			14 14					15 15					16 11					17 15				
Macclesfield	d	13 47			14 16			14 47		15 16		15 47			16 16			16 47		17 16		17 47	
Congleton	d									15 24										17 24			
Stoke-on-Trent	d	14 04			14 39			15 04		15 39		16 04			16 39			17 04		17 39		18 04	
Stafford	d	14 26						15 26				16 26						17 26				18 26	
Wolverhampton 7	d	14 41		14 49	15 13			15 41	15 49	16 13		16 41		16 49	17 13			17 41	17 49	18 13		18 41	
Dunbar	d						11 25										13 25						
Berwick-upon-Tweed	d						11 49										13 49						
Alnmouth	d		11 04										13 04										15 05
Newcastle 8	d		11 40			12 19	12 40				13 33		13 40			14 22	14 40				15 22		15 40
Chester-le-Street	d					12 32										14 33							
Durham	d		11 52			12 40	12 53				13 46		13 52			14 40	14 52				15 34		15 52
Darlington 7	d		12 10			13 00	13 10				14 03		14 10			14 57	15 10				15 51		16 10
York 8	d		12 44			13 29	13 44				14 32		14 44			15 29	15 44				16 25		16 44
Leeds 10	d		13 10				14 10						15 10				16 10						17 10
Wakefield Westgate 7	d		13 23				14 23						15 23				16 23						17 23
Doncaster 7	d					13 54					14 57					15 55					16 53		
Sheffield 7	d		13 53			14 23	14 53				15 23		15 53			16 23	16 53				17 20		17 53
Chesterfield	d					14 35					15 35					16 35					17 35		
Derby 10	d		14 24			14 57	15 24				15 57		16 24			16 57	17 24				17 57		18 24
Burton-on-Trent	d										16 07										18 07		
Tamworth	d										16 18										18 18		
Birmingham New Street 12	a	14 58	15 04	15 11	15 30	15 36	15 58	15 58	16 11	16 30	16 36	16 58	17 04	17 11	17 30	17 36	17 58	17 58	18 11	18 30	18 36	18 58	19 08
Birmingham New Street 12	d	15 03	15 10		15 33	15 40	16 03	16 10		16 33	16 40	17 03	17 10		17 33	17 40	18 03	18 10		18 33	18 40	19 03	19 10
Cheltenham Spa	a		15 51			16 21		16 51			17 21		17 51			18 21		18 51			19 21		19 51
Gloucester 7	a															18 34							
Bristol Parkway 7	a		16 25			16 54		17 25			17 54		18 25			19 05		19 25			19 54		20 25
Bristol Temple Meads 10	a		16 41			17 11		17 41			18 11		18 41			19 22		19 41			20 11		20 41
Newport (South Wales)	a															19 59							
Cardiff Central 7	a															20 19							
Weston-super-Mare	a																				20 39		
Taunton	a		17 15			17 42		18 15					19 15					20 15					21 15
Tiverton Parkway	a		17 28			17 55		18 28					19 28					20 28					21 28
Exeter St Davids 6	a		17 43			18 10		18 43					19 43					20 43					21 43
Dawlish	a					18 23																	
Teignmouth	a					18 28																	
Newton Abbot	a		18 08			18 35		19 02					20 02					21 02					22 02
Torquay	a																						
Paignton	a																						
Totnes	a		18 21			18 48		19 16					20 16					21 16					22 16
Plymouth	a		18 52			19 20		19 48					20 48					21 48					22 48
Liskeard 3	a		19 22					20 12															
Bodmin Parkway	a		19 34					20 24															
Par 3	a		19 46					20 35															
St Austell	a		19 53					20 41															
Truro	a		20 10					20 59															
Redruth	a		20 21					21 13															
Camborne	a		20 28					21 20															
St Erth 2	a		20 39					21 30															
Penzance	a		20 56					21 47															
Birmingham International ✈	d	15 15					16 15					17 15					18 15					19 15	
Coventry	d	15 25					16 25					17 25					18 25					19 25	
Leamington Spa 8	d	15 38			16 00		16 38			17 00		17 38			18 00		18 38			19 00		19 38	
Banbury	a	15 54			16 18		16 54			17 18		17 54			18 18		18 54			19 18		19 54	
Oxford	a	16 14			16 41		17 14			17 41		18 14			18 41		19 14			19 41		20 14	
Reading 7	a	16 39			17 13		17 39			18 11		18 39			19 13		19 39			20 09		20 39	
Kensington Olympia	a									19 01										20 52			
East Croydon	a									19 33										21 15			
Guildford	a																						
Redhill	a																			21 34			
Basingstoke	a	17 08					18 08					19 08					20 08					21 08	
Winchester	a	17 24					18 24					19 24					20 24					21 24	
Southampton Airport Parkwy ✈	a	17 33					18 33					19 33					20 33					21 33	
Southampton Central	a	17 40					18 40					19 40					20 40					21 40	
Brockenhurst 3	a	17 56					18 56					19 56					20 56					21 56	
Bournemouth	a	18 15					19 15					20 24					21 26					22 26	
Gatwick Airport 10 ✈	a									19 52										21 47			
Haywards Heath 3	a									20 04										21c45			
Brighton 10	a									20 30										22c00			

For general notes see front of timetable
For details of catering facilities see Directory of Train Operators

b Arr. 1051
c Change at East Croydon

Scotland, The North East, North West England → The South West and South Coast

Route Diagram - See first page of Table 51

Station		VT	XC	XC	XC	XC	VT	XC	XC	XC	XC	VT	XC	XC	XC	XC	VT	XC	VT	XC	XC	XC
				R	R													R				
		1◇	1◇	1	1	1◇	1◇	1◇	1◇	1◇	1◇	1◇	1◇	1◇	1◇	1◇	1◇	1	1◇	1◇	1◇	1◇
		☕	☕	☕	☕	☕	☕	☕	☕		☕	☕		☕		☕	☕	☕	☕	☕		
Aberdeen	d																					
Stonehaven	d																					
Montrose	d																					
Arbroath	d																					
Dundee	d																					
Leuchars 3	d																					
Cupar	d																					
Markinch	d																					
Kirkcaldy	d																					
Inverkeithing	d																					
Glasgow Central 15	d						16 10										18 10					
Motherwell	d																18u27					
Haymarket	d																					
Edinburgh 10	d	14 51			15 05						16 05	16 51				17 05		18 05	18 51			
Haymarket	d	14u56										16u56							18u56			
Lockerbie	d	15 53										17 49							19 49			
Carlisle 8	d	16 14					17 21					18 11					19 32		20 11			
Penrith North Lakes	d	16 29					17 36					18 27							20 27			
Oxenholme Lake District	d	16 53					18 00					18 51					20 07		20 52			
Lancaster 6	d	17 09										19 08					20 23		21 07			
Preston 8	d	17 29					18 29					19 29					20 49		21 29			
Wigan North Western	d	17 41					18 42					19 41					21 01		21 42			
Warrington Bank Quay	d	17 53					18 53					19 53					21 13		21 54			
Manchester Piccadilly 10 🚊	d		17 54			18 24		18 54		19 24			19 54		20 24						21 54	
Stockport	d		18 03			18 33		19 03		19 33			20 03		20 33						22 03	
Wilmslow	d																					
Crewe 10	d	18 15					19 15					20 15					21 35		22 16			
Macclesfield	d		18 16			18 47		19 16		19 47			20 16		20 47						22 16	
Congleton	d		18 24					19 24					20 24								22 24	
Stoke-on-Trent	d		18 39			19 04		19 39		20 04			20 39		21 04						22 39	
Stafford	d					19 26		19 58		20 26			20 57		21 26		21 55		22 36		22 57	
Wolverhampton 7 🚊	d	18 49	19 13			19 41	19 49	20 13		20 41		20 49	21 13		21 41		22 16		22 49		23 13	
Dunbar	d				15 25											17 25		18 25				
Berwick-upon-Tweed	d				15 49											17 49				←		
Alnmouth	d										17 08							19 05		19 05		
Newcastle 8	d			16 27	16 40				17 17		17 40			18 20		18 40		→		19 40		20 26
Chester-le-Street	d			16 42					17 26					18 29								
Durham	d			16 49	16 52				17 33		17 54			18 36		18 52				19 52		20 38
Darlington 7	d			17 06					17 50		18 11			18 56		19 10				20 10		20 55
York 8	d			17 34	17 44				18 24		18 44			19 29		19 44				20 44		21 24
Leeds 10	d				18 10						19 10					20 10				21 10		
Wakefield Westgate 7	d				18 23						19 23					20 23				21 23		
Doncaster 7	d			17 58					18 52					19 57								
Sheffield 7	d			18 23	18 53				19 23		19 53			20 23		20 53				21 53		22 27
Chesterfield	d			18 35					19 35		20 05			20 35		21 05				22 05		22 53
Derby 10	d			18 57	19 24				19 57		20 27			20 57		21 27				22 27		23 15
Burton-on-Trent	d								20 07							21 37				22 37		23 26
Tamworth	d								20 18							21 48				22 48		23 37
Birmingham New Street 12	a	19 11	19 30	19 36	19 58	19 58	20 11	20 35	20 43	20 58	21 04	21 11	21 35	21 44	22 04	22 08	22 38		23 11	23 21	23 47	23 59
Birmingham New Street 12	d		19 33	19 40	20 03	20 10				21 03	21 10					22 10						
Cheltenham Spa	a			20 21		20 51					21 51					22 51						
Gloucester 7	a																					
Bristol Parkway 7	a			20 54		21 25					22 25					23 25						
Bristol Temple Meads 10	a			21 11		21 41					22 41					23 41						
Newport (South Wales)	a																					
Cardiff Central 7	a																					
Weston-super-Mare	a																					
Taunton	a					22s15																
Tiverton Parkway	a					22s45																
Exeter St Davids 6	a					23 10																
Dawlish	a																					
Teignmouth	a																					
Newton Abbot	a					23 33																
Torquay	a																					
Paignton	a																					
Totnes	a					23 46																
Plymouth	a					00 18																
Liskeard 3	a																					
Bodmin Parkway	a																					
Par 3	a																					
St Austell	a																					
Truro	a																					
Redruth	a																					
Camborne	a																					
St Erth 2	a																					
Penzance	a																					
Birmingham International ✈	d				20 15					21 15												
Coventry	d				20 25					21 25												
Leamington Spa 8	d		20 00		20 38					21 38												
Banbury	a		20 18		20 54					21 54												
Oxford	a		20 41		21 14					22 14												
Reading 7	a		21 06		21 39					22 39												
Kensington Olympia	a																					
East Croydon 🚊	a																					
Guildford	a		21 33																			
Redhill	a		22 10																			
Basingstoke	a				22 08					23 08												
Winchester	a				22 24					23 24												
Southampton Airport Parkwy ✈	a				22 33					23 33												
Southampton Central	a				22 46					23 47												
Brockenhurst 3	a				23b04					00b04												
Bournemouth	a				23b23					00b22												
Gatwick Airport 10 ✈	a		22 32																			
Haywards Heath 3	a		22c52																			
Brighton 10	a		23c15																			

For general notes see front of timetable
For details of catering facilities see Directory of Train Operators

b Change at Winchester
c Change at Redhill

from 28 January

Scotland, The North East, North West England → The South West and South Coast

Route Diagram - See first page of Table 51

		XC	XC	XC	XC	XC	XC	XC	XC	VT	XC	XC	VT	XC	XC	XC	XC	VT	XC	XC	XC	XC	VT	XC
		1 ◇	1 ◇	1 ◇	1 ◇	1 ◇	1 ◇	1 ◇	1 ◇	1 ◇	1 ◇	1 ◇	1 ◇	1 ◇	1 ◇	R 1	R 1	1 ◇	1 ◇	R 1	R 1	1 ◇	1 ◇	1 ◇
		☕	☕	☕	☕	☕	☕	☕	☕	⊠	☕	☕	☕	☕	☕	☕	☕	☕	☕	☕	☕	☕	☕	☕
Aberdeen	d																							
Stonehaven	d																							
Montrose	d																							
Arbroath	d																							
Dundee	d																							
Leuchars 3	d																							
Cupar	d																							
Markinch	d																							
Kirkcaldy	d																							
Inverkeithing	d																							
Glasgow Central 15	d																							
Motherwell	d																							
Haymarket	d																							
Edinburgh 10	d																							
Haymarket	d																							
Lockerbie	d																							
Carlisle 8	d																							
Penrith North Lakes	d																							
Oxenholme Lake District	d																							
Lancaster 6	d																							
Preston 8	d												06 15					07 29					08 29	
Wigan North Western	d												06 27					07 41					08 41	
Warrington Bank Quay	d												06 45					07 53					08 52	
Manchester Piccadilly 10	d					05b20				06 17				06 54		07 24			07 54			08 24		08 54
Stockport	d					05b31				06 25						07 33			08 03			08 33		09 03
Wilmslow	d					05b39																		
Crewe 10	d					05 45							07 10					08 15					09 15	
Macclesfield	d									06 38						07 47			08 16			08 47		09 16
Congleton	d													07 21		07 55			08 24					09 24
Stoke-on-Trent	d					06 04				06 54				07 33		08 08			08 39			09 04		09 39
Stafford	d					06 24				07 15				07 54		08 26			08 57			09 26		
Wolverhampton 7	d					06 41				07 35			07 49	08 13		08 41		08 49	09 13			09 41	09 49	10 13
Dunbar	d																							
Berwick-upon-Tweed	d																							
Alnmouth	d																							
Newcastle 8	d																			06 19	06 44			
Chester-le-Street	d																			06 31				
Durham	d																			06 38	06 56			
Darlington 7	d																			06 55	07 14			
York 8	d														06 16					07 27	07 44			
Leeds 10	d										06 00						07 05				08 10			
Wakefield Westgate 7	d										06 12						07 19				08 23			
Doncaster 7	d																			07 52				
Sheffield 7	d										06 45				07 23		07 53			08 23	08 53			
Chesterfield	d										06 57				07 35		08 05			08 35				
Derby 10	d				06 10				06 57		07 20	07 24			07 57		08 27			08 57	09 24			
Burton-on-Trent	d				06 20				07 07			07 35					08 37							
Tamworth	d				06 31				07 18			07 46					08 48							
Birmingham New Street 12	a				06 51	06 58	←		07 36	07 55	07 58	08 07	08 11	08 30	08 36	08 58	09 06	09 11	09 30	09 36	09 58	09 58	10 11	10 30
Birmingham New Street 12	d	06 03	06 10	06 33	07 10 →	07 03	07 10	07 33	07 40	08 00	08 03	08 10		08 33	08 40	09 03	09 10		09 33	09 40	10 03	10 10		10 33
Cheltenham Spa	a		07 21				07 51		08 21			08 51			09 21		09 51			10 21		10 51		
Gloucester 7	a																							
Bristol Parkway 7	a		07 54				08 25		08 54			09 25			09 54		10 25			10 54		11 25		
Bristol Temple Meads 10	a		08 11				08 41		09 11			09 41			10 11		10 41			11 11		11 41		
Newport (South Wales)	a																							
Cardiff Central 7	a																							
Weston-super-Mare	a																			11 32				
Taunton	a		08 42				09 15					10 15					11 15			12 03		12 15		
Tiverton Parkway	a						09 28					10 28					11 28			12 16		12 28		
Exeter St Davids 6	a		09 07				09 43					10 43					11 43			12 31		12 43		
Dawlish	a																			12 44				
Teignmouth	a																			12 49				
Newton Abbot	a						10 02					11 02					12 02			12 56		13 02		
Torquay	a		09 34																	13 07				
Paignton	a		09 47																	13 20				
Totnes	a						10 16					11 16					12 16					13 16		
Plymouth	a						10 48					11 48					12 48					13 48		
Liskeard 3	a																							
Bodmin Parkway	a																							
Par 3	a																							
St Austell	a																							
Truro	a																							
Redruth	a																							
Camborne	a																							
St Erth 2	a																							
Penzance	a																							
Birmingham International ✈	d	06 15				07 15				08 10	08 15					09 15					10 15			
Coventry	d	06 25				07 25				08a20	08 25					09 25					10 25			
Leamington Spa 8	d	06 38		07 00		07 38		08 00			08 38			09 00		09 38			10 00		10 38			11 00
Banbury	a	06 54		07 18		07 54		08 18			08 54			09 18		09 54			10 18		10 54			11 18
Oxford	a	07 14		07 41		08 14		08 41			09 14			09 41		10 14			10 41		11 14			11 41
Reading 7	a	07 39		08 13		08 39		09 13			09 39			10 13		10 39			11 08		11 39			12 13
Kensington Olympia	a																		11 56					
East Croydon	a																		12 16					
Guildford	a																							
Redhill	a																							
Basingstoke	a	08 08				09 08					10 08					11 08					12 08			
Winchester	a	08 24				09 24					10 24					11 24					12 24			
Southampton Airport Parkwy ✈	a	08 33				09 33					10 33					11 33					12 33			
Southampton Central	a	08 40				09 40					10 40					11 40					12 40			
Brockenhurst 3	a	08 56				09 56					10 56					11 56					12 56			
Bournemouth	a	09 15				10 15					11 15					12 15					13 15			
Gatwick Airport 10 ✈	a																		12 33					
Haywards Heath 3	a																		12 49					
Brighton 10	a																		13 15					

For general notes see front of timetable
For details of catering facilities see Directory of Train Operators

b Change at Stafford

from 28 January

Scotland, The North East, North West England → The South West and South Coast

Route Diagram - See first page of Table 51

	XC		XC	XC	VT	XC	XC	XC	XC	VT	XC	XC	XC	XC	VT	XC	XC	XC	XC	XC	XC	XC	VT
	1◇ ☕		R 1 ☕	1◇ ☕	1◇ ☕	1◇ ☕	1◇ ☕	R 1 ☕	1◇ ☕	1◇ ☕	1◇ ☕	1◇ ☕	R 1 ☕	1◇ ☕	R 1 ☕	1◇ ☕	R 1 ☕	R 1 ☕	R 1 ☕	R 1 ☕	1◇ ☕	1◇ ☕	R 1 ☕
Aberdeen d																							
Stonehaven d																							
Montrose d																							
Arbroath d																							
Dundee d														06 38				07 33					
Leuchars 3 d														06 51				07 46					
Cupar d														06 58				07 55					
Markinch d														07 13				08 09					
Kirkcaldy d														07 25				08 18					
Inverkeithing d														07 43				08 37					
Glasgow Central 15 d								06 00		07 45										09 00			10 10
Motherwell d																				09u14			
Haymarket d								06 52						08 00				08 58		09 55			
Edinburgh 10 d				06 05	06 36			07 05						08 13	08 51			09 05		10 05 →			
Haymarket d					06u40										08u57								
Lockerbie d																							
Carlisle 8 d					07 53					09 14					10 17								11 22
Penrith North Lakes d					08 09					09 29													
Oxenholme Lake District d					08 33					09 54					10 53								
Lancaster 6 d					09 09					10 09					11 10								12 12
Preston 8 d					09 29					10 28					11 29								12 32
Wigan North Western d					09 41					10 42					11 41								12 45
Warrington Bank Quay d					09 53					10 53					11 52								12 59
Manchester Piccadilly 10 d			09 24			09 54			10 24		10 54		11 24			11 54			12 24		12 54		
Stockport d			09 33			10 03			10 33		11 03		11 33			12 03			12 33		13 03		
Wilmslow d																							
Crewe 10 d					10 15					11 14					12 13								13 33
Macclesfield d			09 47			10 16			10 47		11 16		11 47			12 16			12 47		13 16		
Congleton d											11 24										13 24		
Stoke-on-Trent d			10 04			10 39			11 04		11 39		12 04			12 39			13 04		13 39		
Stafford d			10 26						11 26				12 26						13 26				
Wolverhampton 7 d			10 41		10 49	11 13			11 41	11 49	12 13		12 41		12 49	13 13			13 41		14 13		14 18
Dunbar d								07 25										09 25					
Berwick-upon-Tweed d				06 49				07 49						08 52				09 49					
Alnmouth d				07 11				08 08						09 12									
Newcastle 8 d	07 23			07 44			08 24	08 40				09 35		09 40			10 25	10 40				11 25	
Chester-le-Street d							08 33										10 34						
Durham d	07 37			07 56			08 40	08 52				09 47		09 52			10 41	10 52				11 37	
Darlington 7 d	07 54			08 14			08 57	09 10				10 04		10 10			10 58	11 10				11 56	
York 8 d	08 27			08 44			09 27	09 44				10 34		10 44			11 27	11 44				12 25	
Leeds 10 d				09 10				10 10						11 10				12 10					
Wakefield Westgate 7 d				09 23				10 23						11 23				12 23					
Doncaster 7 d	08 51						09 56					10 58					11 54					12 55	
Sheffield 7 d	09 23			09 53			10 23	10 53				11 23		11 53			12 23	12 53				13 23	
Chesterfield d	09 35						10 35					11 35					12 35					13 35	
Derby 10 d	09 57			10 24			10 57	11 24				11 57		12 24			12 57	13 24				13 57	
Burton-on-Trent d	10 07											12 07										14 07	
Tamworth d	10 18											12 18										14 18	
Birmingham New Street 12 a	10 36		10 58	11 04	11 11	11 30	11 36	11 58	11 58	12 11	12 30	12 36	12 58	13 04	13 11	13 30	13 36	13 58	13 58		14 30	14 36	14 41
Birmingham New Street 12 d	10 40		11 03	11 10		11 33	11 40	12 03	12 10		12 33	12 40	13 03	13 10		13 33	13 40	14 03	14 10		14 33	14 40	
Cheltenham Spa a	11 21			11 51			12 21		12 51			13 21		13 51			14 21		14 51			15 21	
Gloucester 7 a																							
Bristol Parkway 7 a	11 54			12 25			12 54		13 25			13 54		14 25			14 54		15 25			15 54	
Bristol Temple Meads 10 a	12 11			12 41			13 11		13 41			14 11		14 41			15 11		15 41			16 11	
Newport (South Wales) a																							
Cardiff Central 7 a																							
Weston-super-Mare a																							
Taunton a				13 15			13 42		14 15					15 15			15 42		16 15				
Tiverton Parkway a				13 28			14 01		14 28					15 28			15 54		16 28				
Exeter St Davids 6 a				13 43			14 16		14 43					15 43			16 10		16 43				
Dawlish a							14 29																
Teignmouth a							14 34																
Newton Abbot a				14 02			14 41		15 02					16 02			16 30		17 02				
Torquay a							14 52																
Paignton a							15 05																
Totnes a				14 16					15 16					16 16			16 43		17 16				
Plymouth a				14 48					15 48					16 48			17 15		17 48				
Liskeard 3 a																			18 17				
Bodmin Parkway a																			18 29				
Par 3 a																			18 40				
St Austell a																			18 46				
Truro a																			19 04				
Redruth a																			19 16				
Camborne a																			19 23				
St Erth 2 a																			19 33				
Penzance a																			19 49				
Birmingham International ✈ d			11 15					12 15					13 15					14 15					
Coventry d			11 25					12 25					13 25					14 25					
Leamington Spa 8 d			11 38			12 00		12 38			13 00		13 38			14 00		14 38			15 00		
Banbury a			11 54			12 18		12 54			13 18		13 54			14 18		14 54			15 18		
Oxford a			12 14			12 41		13 14			13 41		14 14			14 41		15 14			15 41		
Reading 7 a			12 39			13 13		13 39			14 13		14 39			15 13		15 39			16 11		
Kensington Olympia a																							
East Croydon a																							
Guildford a																					16 59		
Redhill a																					*17 38*		
Basingstoke a			13 08					14 08					15 08					16 08					
Winchester a			13 24					14 24					15 24					16 24					
Southampton Airport Parkwy ✈ a			13 33					14 33					15 33					16 33					
Southampton Central a			13 40					14 40					15 40					16 40					
Brockenhurst 3 a			13 56					14 56					15 56					16 56					
Bournemouth a			14 15					15 15					16 15					17 15					
Gatwick Airport 10 ✈ a																					*17 50*		
Haywards Heath 3 a																							
Brighton 10 a																							

For general notes see front of timetable
For details of catering facilities see Directory of Train Operators

from 28 January

Scotland, The North East, North West England → The South West and South Coast

Route Diagram - See first page of Table 51

		XC	XC	VT	XC	XC	XC	XC	VT	XC	XC	XC	XC	VT	XC	XC	XC	XC	VT	XC	XC	XC	XC
			R				R	R	R	R		R	R	R	R	R	R			R	R	R	
		1 ◇	1	1 ◇	1 ◇	1 ◇	1	1	1	1	1 ◇	1	1	1	1	1	1	1 ◇	1 ◇	1	1	1	1 ◇
		☕	☕	☕	☕	☕	☕	☕	☕	☕	☕	☕	☕	☕	☕	☕	☕	☕	☕	☕	☕	☕	☕
Aberdeen	d						08 20																
Stonehaven	d						08 37																
Montrose	d						08 59																
Arbroath	d						09 15																
Dundee	d						09 33																
Leuchars 3	d						09 46																
Cupar	d						09 53																
Markinch	d						10 04																
Kirkcaldy	d						10 13																
Inverkeithing	d						10 28																
Glasgow Central 15	d								12 10										14 10				
Motherwell	d																						
Haymarket	d		←				10 47																
Edinburgh 10	d		10 05	10 51			11b05						12 05	12 51			13 05						14 05
Haymarket	d			10u56										12u56									
Lockerbie	d													13 53									
Carlisle 8	d			12 13					13 21					14 14					15 21				
Penrith North Lakes	d			12 29										14 29									
Oxenholme Lake District	d			12 53					13 59					14 53									
Lancaster 6	d			13 09										15 08					16 09				
Preston 8	d			13 29					14 30					15 29					16 29				
Wigan North Western	d			13 41					14 42					15 41					16 41				
Warrington Bank Quay	d			13 53					14 54					15 52					16 53				
Manchester Piccadilly 10	d	13 24			13 54			14 24		14 54		15 24			15 54			16 24		16 54		17 24	
Stockport	d	13 33			14 03			14 33		15 03		15 33			16 03			16 33		17 03		17 33	
Wilmslow	d																						
Crewe 10	d			14 14					15 15					16 11					17 15				
Macclesfield	d	13 47			14 16			14 47		15 16		15 47			16 16			16 47		17 16		17 47	
Congleton	d									15 24										17 24			
Stoke-on-Trent	d	14 04			14 39			15 04		15 39		16 04			16 39			17 04		17 39		18 04	
Stafford	d	14 26						15 26				16 26						17 26				18 26	
Wolverhampton 7	d	14 41		14 49	15 13			15 41	15 49	16 13		16 41		16 49	17 13			17 41	17 49	18 13		18 41	
Dunbar	d						11 25										13 25						
Berwick-upon-Tweed	d						11 49										13 49						
Alnmouth	d		11 04										13 04										15 05
Newcastle 8	d		11 40			12 19	12 40				13 33		13 40			14 22	14 40				15 22		15 40
Chester-le-Street	d					12 32										14 33							
Durham	d		11 52			12 40	12 53				13 46		13 52			14 40	14 52				15 34		15 52
Darlington 7	d		12 10			13 00	13 10				14 03		14 10			14 57	15 10				15 51		16 10
York 8	d		12 44			13 29	13 44				14 32		14 44			15 29	15 44				16 25		16 44
Leeds 10	d		13 10				14 10						15 10				16 10						17 10
Wakefield Westgate 7	d		13 23				14 23						15 23				16 23						17 23
Doncaster 7	d					13 54					14 57					15 55					16 53		
Sheffield 7	d		13 53			14 23	14 53				15 23		15 53			16 23	16 53				17 20		17 53
Chesterfield	d					14 35					15 35					16 35					17 35		
Derby 10	d		14 24			14 57	15 24				15 57		16 24			16 57	17 24				17 57		18 24
Burton-on-Trent	d										16 07										18 07		
Tamworth	d										16 18										18 18		
Birmingham New Street 12	a	14 58	15 04	15 11	15 30	15 36	15 58	15 58	16 11	16 30	16 36	16 58	17 04	17 11	17 30	17 36	17 58	17 58	18 11	18 30	18 36	18 58	19 08
Birmingham New Street 12	d	15 03	15 10		15 33	15 40	16 03	16 10		16 33	16 40	17 03	17 10		17 33	17 40	18 03	18 10		18 33	18 40	19 03	19 10
Cheltenham Spa	a		15 51			16 21		16 51			17 21		17 51			18 21		18 51			19 21		19 51
Gloucester 7	a															18 34							
Bristol Parkway 7	a		16 25			16 54		17 25			17 54		18 25			19 05		19 25			19 54		20 25
Bristol Temple Meads 10	a		16 41			17 11		17 41			18 11		18 41			19 22		19 41			20 11		20 41
Newport (South Wales)	a															19 59							
Cardiff Central 7	a															20 19							
Weston-super-Mare	a																				20 39		
Taunton	a		17 15			17 42		18 15					19 15					20 15					21 15
Tiverton Parkway	a		17 28			17 55		18 28					19 28					20 28					21 28
Exeter St Davids 6	a		17 43			18 10		18 43					19 43					20 43					21 43
Dawlish	a					18 23																	
Teignmouth	a					18 28																	
Newton Abbot	a		18 08			18 35		19 02					20 02					21 02					22 02
Torquay	a																						
Paignton	a																						
Totnes	a		18 21			18 48		19 16					20 16					21 16					22 16
Plymouth	a		18 52			19 20		19 48					20 48					21 48					22 48
Liskeard 3	a		19 22					20 12															
Bodmin Parkway	a		19 34					20 24															
Par 3	a		19 46					20 35															
St Austell	a		19 53					20 41															
Truro	a		20 10					20 59															
Redruth	a		20 21					21 13															
Camborne	a		20 28					21 20															
St Erth 2	a		20 39					21 30															
Penzance	a		20 56					21 47															
Birmingham International ✈	d	15 15					16 15					17 15					18 15					19 15	
Coventry	d	15 25					16 25					17 25					18 25					19 25	
Leamington Spa 8	d	15 38			16 00		16 38			17 00		17 38			18 00		18 38			19 00		19 38	
Banbury	a	15 54			16 18		16 54			17 18		17 54			18 18		18 54			19 18		19 54	
Oxford	a	16 14			16 41		17 14			17 41		18 14			18 41		19 14			19 41		20 14	
Reading 7	a	16 39			17 13		17 39			18 11		18 39			19 13		19 39			20 09		20 39	
Kensington Olympia	a									19 01										20 52			
East Croydon	a									19 33										21 15			
Guildford	a																						
Redhill	a																			21 34			
Basingstoke	a	17 08					18 08					19 08					20 08					21 08	
Winchester	a	17 24					18 24					19 24					20 24					21 24	
Southampton Airport Parkwy ✈	a	17 33					18 33					19 33					20 33					21 33	
Southampton Central	a	17 40					18 40					19 40					20 40					21 40	
Brockenhurst 3	a	17 56					18 56					19 56					20 56					21 56	
Bournemouth	a	18 15					19 15					20 24					21 26					22 26	
Gatwick Airport 10 ✈	a									19 52										21 47			
Haywards Heath 3	a									20 04										21c45			
Brighton 10	a									20 30										22c00			

For general notes see front of timetable
For details of catering facilities see Directory of Train Operators

b Arr. 1051
c Change at East Croydon

from 28 January

Scotland, The North East, North West England → The South West and South Coast

Route Diagram - See first page of Table 51

		VT	XC	XC	XC	XC	VT	XC	XC	XC	XC	VT	XC	XC	XC	XC	VT	XC	VT	XC	XC	XC
				R	R													R				
		1 ◇	1 ◇	1	1	1 ◇	1 ◇	1 ◇	1 ◇	1 ◇	1 ◇	1 ◇	1 ◇	1 ◇	1 ◇	1 ◇	1 ◇	1	1 ◇	1 ◇	1 ◇	1 ◇
		🍴	🍴	🍴	🍴	🍴	🍴	🍴	🍴		🍴	🍴		🍴		🍴	🍴	🍴	🍴	🍴		
Aberdeen	d																					
Stonehaven	d																					
Montrose	d																					
Arbroath	d																					
Dundee	d																					
Leuchars 3	d																					
Cupar	d																					
Markinch	d																					
Kirkcaldy	d																					
Inverkeithing	d																					
Glasgow Central 15	d						16 10										18 10					
Motherwell	d																18u27					
Haymarket	d																					
Edinburgh 10	d	14 51			15 05						16 05	16 51				17 05		18 05	18 51			
Haymarket	d	14u56										16u56							18u56			
Lockerbie	d	15 53										17 49							19 49			
Carlisle 8	d	16 14					17 21					18 11					19 32		20 11			
Penrith North Lakes	d	16 29					17 36					18 27							20 27			
Oxenholme Lake District	d	16 53					18 00					18 51					20 07		20 52			
Lancaster 6	d	17 09										19 08					20 23		21 07			
Preston 8	d	17 29					18 29					19 29					20 49		21 29			
Wigan North Western	d	17 41					18 42					19 41					21 01		21 42			
Warrington Bank Quay	d	17 53					18 53					19 53					21 13		21 54			
Manchester Piccadilly 10	d		17 54			18 24		18 54		19 24			19 54		20 24						21 54	
Stockport	d		18 03			18 33		19 03		19 33			20 03		20 33						22 03	
Wilmslow	d																					
Crewe 10	d	18 15					19 15					20 15					21 35		22 16			
Macclesfield	d		18 16			18 47		19 16		19 47			20 16		20 47						22 16	
Congleton	d		18 24					19 24					20 24								22 24	
Stoke-on-Trent	d		18 39			19 04		19 39		20 04			20 39		21 04						22 39	
Stafford	d					19 26		19 58		20 26			20 57		21 26		21 55		22 36		22 57	
Wolverhampton 7	d	18 49	19 13			19 41	19 49	20 13		20 41		20 49	21 13		21 41		22 16		22 49		23 13	
Dunbar	d				15 25											17 25		18 25				
Berwick-upon-Tweed	d				15 49											17 49				←		
Alnmouth	d										17 08							19 05		19 05		
Newcastle 8	d			16 27	16 40				17 17		17 40			18 20		18 40		→		19 40		20 26
Chester-le-Street	d			16 42					17 26					18 29								
Durham	d			16 49	16 52				17 33		17 54			18 36		18 52				19 52		20 38
Darlington 7	d			17 06					17 50		18 11			18 56		19 10				20 10		20 55
York 8	d			17 34	17 44				18 24		18 44			19 29		19 44				20 44		21 24
Leeds 10	d				18 10						19 10					20 10				21 10		
Wakefield Westgate 7	d				18 23						19 23					20 23				21 23		
Doncaster 7	d			17 58					18 52					19 57								
Sheffield 7	d			18 23	18 53				19 23		19 53			20 23		20 53				21 53		22 27
Chesterfield	d			18 35					19 35		20 05			20 35		21 05				22 05		22 53
Derby 10	d			18 57	19 24				19 57		20 27			20 57		21 27				22 27		23 15
Burton-on-Trent	d								20 07							21 37				22 37		23 26
Tamworth	d								20 18							21 48				22 48		23 37
Birmingham New Street 12	a	19 11	19 30	19 36	19 58	19 58	20 11	20 35	20 43	20 58	21 04	21 11	21 35	21 44	22 04	22 08	22 38		23 11	23 21	23 47	23 59
Birmingham New Street 12	d		19 33	19 40	20 03	20 10				21 03	21 10					22 10						
Cheltenham Spa	a			20 21		20 51					21 51					22 51						
Gloucester 7	a																					
Bristol Parkway 7	a			20 54		21 25					22 25					23 25						
Bristol Temple Meads 10	a			21 11		21 41					22 41					23 41						
Newport (South Wales)	a																					
Cardiff Central 7	a																					
Weston-super-Mare	a																					
Taunton	a					22s15																
Tiverton Parkway	a					22s45																
Exeter St Davids 6	a					23 10																
Dawlish	a																					
Teignmouth	a																					
Newton Abbot	a					23 33																
Torquay	a																					
Paignton	a																					
Totnes	a					23 46																
Plymouth	a					00 18																
Liskeard 3	a																					
Bodmin Parkway	a																					
Par 3	a																					
St Austell	a																					
Truro	a																					
Redruth	a																					
Camborne	a																					
St Erth 2	a																					
Penzance	a																					
Birmingham International ✈	d				20 15					21 15												
Coventry	d				20 25					21 25												
Leamington Spa 8	d		20 00		20 38					21 38												
Banbury	a		20 18		20 54					21 54												
Oxford	a		20 41		21 14					22 14												
Reading 7	a		21 06		21 39					22 39												
Kensington Olympia	a																					
East Croydon	a																					
Guildford	a		21 33																			
Redhill	a		22 10																			
Basingstoke	a				22 08					23 08												
Winchester	a				22 24					23 24												
Southampton Airport Parkwy ✈	a				22 33					23 33												
Southampton Central	a				22 46					23 47												
Brockenhurst 3	a				23b04					00b04												
Bournemouth	a				23b23					00b22												
Gatwick Airport 10 ✈	a		22 32																			
Haywards Heath 3	a		22c52																			
Brighton 10	a		23c15																			

For general notes see front of timetable
For details of catering facilities see
Directory of Train Operators

b Change at Winchester
c Change at Redhill

until 26 January

Scotland, The North East, North West England → The South West and South Coast

Route Diagram - See first page of Table 51

		XC	XC	XC	XC	XC	VT	XC	XC	VT	XC	VT	XC	XC	XC	VT	VT	VT	XC	XC	XC	XC
		1◇	1◇	1◇	1◇	1◇	1◇	1◇	1◇	1◇	1◇	1◇	1◇	1◇	1◇	R 1	1◇	1◇	1◇	1◇	1◇	1◇
			☕	☕	☕	☕	☕	☕	☕	☕	☕	☕	☕	☕	☕	☕	☕	☕	☕	☕	☕	☕
Aberdeen	d																					
Stonehaven	d																					
Montrose	d																					
Arbroath	d																					
Dundee	d																					
Leuchars 8	d																					
Cupar	d																					
Markinch	d																					
Kirkcaldy	d																					
Inverkeithing	d																					
Glasgow Central 15	d																					
Motherwell	d																					
Haymarket	d																					
Edinburgh 10	d																					
Haymarket	d																					
Lockerbie	d																					
Carlisle 8	d																06 30					
Penrith North Lakes	d																06 44					
Oxenholme Lake District	d																07 08					
Lancaster 6	d																07 24					
Preston 8	d									06 15						07 20	07 44					
Wigan North Western	d									06 27						07 32	07 56					
Warrington Bank Quay	d									06 47						07 44	08 07					
Manchester Piccadilly 10	d			*05b05*			06 21					06 55		07 24				07 55				08 24
Stockport	d			*05b15*			06 30					07 04		07 33				08 04				08 33
Wilmslow	d			*05b23*																		
Crewe 10	d			05 42						07 10						08 11	08 29					
Macclesfield	d						06 43					07 17		07 46				08 17				08 46
Congleton	d																					08 54
Stoke-on-Trent	d			06 01			06 59					07 33		08 04				08 39				09 07
Stafford	d			06 20			07 19							08 26			08 48					09 26
Wolverhampton 7	d			06 41			07 35			07 48		08 11		08 41		08 48		09 11				09 41
Dunbar	d																					
Berwick-upon-Tweed	d																					
Alnmouth	d																					
Newcastle 8	d																				06 08	
Chester-le-Street	d																					
Durham	d																				06 23	
Darlington 7	d																				07 12	
York 8	d																			07 27	07 44	
Leeds 10	d												06 00		06 48						08 10	
Wakefield Westgate 7	d												06 12		*06 32*						08 23	
Doncaster 7	d														07 26					07 52		
Sheffield 7	d							06 01					06 48		07 53					08 23	08 53	
Chesterfield	d							06 24					07 16		08 05					08 35		
Derby 10	d		06 10					07 17					07 57		08 27					08 57	09 24	
Burton-on-Trent	d		06 20					07 27					08 07		08 37							
Tamworth	d		06 31					07 38					08 18		08 48							
Birmingham New Street 12	a		06 51	06 58	←		07 56	07 58		08 10		08 30	08 36	08 58	09 06	09 10	09 24	09 30		09 36	09 58	09 58
Birmingham New Street 12	d	06 03	07 10	07 03	07 10	07 33	08 00	08 03	08 10		08 33	08 33	08 40	09 03	09 10		09 30	09 33	09 33	09 40	10 03	10 10
Cheltenham Spa	a		→		07 51				08 51				09 21		09 51					10 21		10 51
Gloucester 7	a																					
Bristol Parkway 7	a				08 25				09 25				09 56		10 25					10 56		11 25
Bristol Temple Meads 10	a				08 41				09 41				10 13		10 41					11 13		11 41
Newport (South Wales)	a																					
Cardiff Central 7	a																					
Weston-super-Mare	a																			11 31		
Taunton	a				09 15				10 15						11 15					12 03		12 15
Tiverton Parkway	a				09 28				10 28						11 28					12 16		12 28
Exeter St Davids 6	a				09 43				10 43						11 43					12 31		12 43
Dawlish	a																			12 44		
Teignmouth	a																			12 49		
Newton Abbot	a				10 03				11 03						12 03					12 56		13 03
Torquay	a																			13 07		
Paignton	a																			13 20		
Totnes	a				10 16				11 16						12 16							13 16
Plymouth	a				10 48				11 48						12 48							13 48
Liskeard 3	a																					
Bodmin Parkway	a																					
Par 3	a																					
St Austell	a																					
Truro	a																					
Redruth	a																					
Camborne	a																					
St Erth 2	a																					
Penzance	a																					
Birmingham International ✈	d	06 15		07 15			08 10	08 15				08 43		09 15			09 40	09 45			10 15	
Coventry	d	06 25		07 25			08a19	08 25				08a54		09 25			09a49	09a54			10 25	
Leamington Spa 8	d	06 38		07 38		08 00		08 38			09 00			09 38					10 00		10 38	
Banbury	a	06 54		07 54		08 17		08 54			09 17			09 54					10 17		10 54	
Oxford	a	07 14		08 14		08 41		09 14			09 41			10 14					10 41		11 14	
Reading 7	a	07 44		08 39		09 13		09 39			10 13			10 39					11 13		11 39	
Kensington Olympia	a																		11 56			
East Croydon	a																		12 37			
Guildford	a																					
Redhill	a																					
Basingstoke	a			09 08				10 08						11 06							12 08	
Winchester	a			09 24				10 24						11 24							12 24	
Southampton Airport Parkwy ✈	a			09 33				10 33						11 33							12 33	
Southampton Central	a			09 40				10 40						11 40							12 40	
Brockenhurst 3	a			09 56				10 56						11 56							12 56	
Bournemouth	a			10 15				11 15						12 15							13 15	
Gatwick Airport 10 ✈	a																		12 53			
Haywards Heath 3	a																		13 13			
Brighton 10	a																		13 37			

For general notes see front of timetable
For details of catering facilities see Directory of Train Operators

b Change at Stafford

SUMMARY OF SERVICES

Saturdays

until 26 January

Scotland, The North East, North West England → The South West and South Coast

Route Diagram - See first page of Table 51

		XC	VT	VT	VT	XC	XC	XC	XC	VT	VT	VT	XC	XC	XC	XC	VT	VT	VT	XC	XC	XC
																	R					
		1 ◇	1 ◇	1 ◇	1 ◇	1 ◇	1 ◇	1 ◇	1 ◇	1 ◇	1 ◇	1 ◇	1 ◇	1 ◇	1 ◇	1 ◇	1	1 ◇	1 ◇	1 ◇	1 ◇	1 ◇
Aberdeen	d																					
Stonehaven	d																					
Montrose	d																					
Arbroath	d																					
Dundee	d																					
Leuchars 3	d																					
Cupar	d																					
Markinch	d																					
Kirkcaldy	d																					
Inverkeithing	d																					
Glasgow Central 15	d	05 50		06 10							07 10						07 40	08 06				
Motherwell	d	06u10		06u25							07u28				←			08u26				
Haymarket	d	06 51													06 51							
Edinburgh 10	d	→							06 05	06 52					07 05							
Haymarket	d									06u56												
Lockerbie	d									07 52												
Carlisle 8	d			07 28						08 13	08 32						09 14	09 23				
Penrith North Lakes	d			07 43						08 29	08 47						09 30	09 38				
Oxenholme Lake District	d			08 07						08 53	09 11						09 54	10 06				
Lancaster 6	d			08 27						09 09	09 27						10 09	10 22				
Preston 8	d		08 29	08 47						09 29	09 47						10 29	10 47				
Wigan North Western	d		08 40	08 59						09 41	09 59						10 41	10 59				
Warrington Bank Quay	d		08 52	09 10						09 53	10 10						10 53	11 10				
Manchester Piccadilly 10	d				08 54			09 24				09 54				10 24			10 58			11 24
Stockport	d				09 04			09 33				10 03				10 33			11 07			11 33
Wilmslow	d																					
Crewe 10	d		09 13	09 31						10 15	10 31						11 15	11 31				
Macclesfield	d				09 20			09 46				10 20				10 46			11 20			11 46
Congleton	d															10 54						
Stoke-on-Trent	d				09 39			10 04				10 39				11 07			11 39			12 04
Stafford	d							10 26								11 26						12 26
Wolverhampton 7	d		09 48		10 11			10 41		10 49		11 11				11 41	11 49		12 11			12 41
Dunbar	d														07 25							
Berwick-upon-Tweed	d								06 47						07 51							
Alnmouth	d								07 07						08 11							
Newcastle 8	d						06 50		07 40					08 24	08 40						09 25	
Chester-le-Street	d													08 33								
Durham	d						07 02		07 54					08 40	08 52						09 37	
Darlington 7	d								08 12					08 57	09 11						09 56	
York 8	d						08 19		08 44					09 27	09 44						10 25	
Leeds 10	d								09 10						10 10							
Wakefield Westgate 7	d								09 23						10 23							
Doncaster 7	d													09 51							10 53	
Sheffield 7	d						09 23		09 53					10 23	10 53						11 23	
Chesterfield	d						09 35							10 35							11 35	
Derby 10	d						09 57		10 24					10 57	11 24						11 57	
Burton-on-Trent	d						10 07														12 07	
Tamworth	d						10 18														12 18	
Birmingham New Street 12	a		10 11	10 24	10 30		10 36	10 58	11 04	11 11	11 24	11 30		11 36	11 58	11 58	12 11	12 24	12 30		12 36	12 58
Birmingham New Street 12	d			10 30	10 33	10 33	10 40	11 03	11 10		11 30	11 33	11 33	11 40	12 03	12 10		12 30	12 33	12 33	12 40	13 03
Cheltenham Spa	a						11 21		11 51					12 21		12 51					13 21	
Gloucester 7	a																					
Bristol Parkway 7	a						11 56		12 25					12 56		13 25					13 56	
Bristol Temple Meads 10	a						12 13		12 41					13 13		13 41					14 13	
Newport (South Wales)	a																					
Cardiff Central 7	a																					
Weston-super-Mare	a																					
Taunton	a								13 15							14 15						
Tiverton Parkway	a								13 28							14 28						
Exeter St Davids 6	a								13 43							14 43						
Dawlish	a																					
Teignmouth	a																					
Newton Abbot	a								14 03							15 03						
Torquay	a																					
Paignton	a																					
Totnes	a								14 16							15 16						
Plymouth	a								14 48							15 48						
Liskeard 3	a																					
Bodmin Parkway	a																					
Par 3	a																					
St Austell	a																					
Truro	a																					
Redruth	a																					
Camborne	a																					
St Erth 2	a																					
Penzance	a																					
Birmingham International ✈	d			10 40	10 45			11 15			11 40	11 45			12 15			12 40	12 46			13 15
Coventry	d			10a49	10a54			11 25			11a49	11a54			12 25			12a49	12a55			13 25
Leamington Spa 8	d					11 00		11 38					12 00		12 38					13 00		13 38
Banbury	a					11 17		11 54					12 17		12 54					13 17		13 54
Oxford	a					11 41		12 14					12 41		13 14					13 41		14 14
Reading 7	a					12 13		12 39					13 13		13 39					14 13		14 39
Kensington Olympia	a																					
East Croydon	a																					
Guildford	a																					
Redhill	a																					
Basingstoke	a							13 08							14 08							15 08
Winchester	a							13 24							14 24							15 24
Southampton Airport Parkwy ✈	a							13 33							14 33							15 33
Southampton Central	a							13 40							14 40							15 40
Brockenhurst 3	a							13 56							14 56							15 56
Bournemouth	a							14 15							15 15							16 15
Gatwick Airport 10 ✈	a																					
Haywards Heath 3	a																					
Brighton 10	a																					

For general notes see front of timetable
For details of catering facilities see Directory of Train Operators

until 26 January

Scotland, The North East, North West England → The South West and South Coast

Route Diagram - See first page of Table 51

		XC	VT	VT	VT	XC	XC	XC	XC	XC	VT	VT	VT	XC	XC	XC	XC	VT	VT	VT	XC	XC
			R								R											
		1 ◇	1	1 ◇	1 ◇	1 ◇	1 ◇	1 ◇	1 ◇	1 ◇	1	1 ◇	1 ◇	1 ◇	1 ◇	1 ◇	1 ◇	1 ◇	1 ◇	1 ◇	1 ◇	1 ◇
		☕	☕	☕	☕	☕	☕	☕	☕	☕	☕	☕	☕	☕	☕	☕	☕	☕	☕	☕	☕	☕
Aberdeen	d																					
Stonehaven	d																					
Montrose	d																					
Arbroath	d																					
Dundee	d							07 35														
Leuchars 3	d							07 48														
Cupar	d							07 56														
Markinch	d							08 11														
Kirkcaldy	d							08 20														
Inverkeithing	d							08 36														
Glasgow Central 15	d								09 00		10 10	10 20							11 10			
Motherwell	d								09u14										11u25			
Haymarket	d							08 57	09 55													
Edinburgh 10	d	08 05	08 51					09 05	10 05									10 51				
Haymarket	d		08u56															10u56				
Lockerbie	d																					
Carlisle 8	d		10 10								11 22	11 32						12 13	12 32			
Penrith North Lakes	d											11 47						12 29	12 47			
Oxenholme Lake District	d		10 47									12 11						12 53	13 11			
Lancaster 6	d		11 06								12 11	12 27						13 09	13 27			
Preston 8	d		11 28	11 47							12 29	12 47						13 29	13 47			
Wigan North Western	d		11 40	11 59							12 41	12 59						13 41	13 59			
Warrington Bank Quay	d		11 53	12 10							12 53	13 10						13 53	14 10			
Manchester Piccadilly 10	d				11 58					12 24			12 58			13 24				13 58		
Stockport	d				12 07					12 33			13 07			13 33				14 07		
Wilmslow	d																					
Crewe 10	d		12 13	12 31							13 15	13 31						14 15	14 31			
Macclesfield	d				12 20					12 46			13 20			13 46				14 20		
Congleton	d									12 54												
Stoke-on-Trent	d				12 39					13 07			13 39			14 04				14 39		
Stafford	d									13 26						14 26						
Wolverhampton 7	d		12 49		13 11					13 41	13 49		14 11			14 41		14 49		15 11		
Dunbar	d							09 25														
Berwick-upon-Tweed	d	08 46						09 49									←					
Alnmouth	d	09 06							11 04								11 04					
Newcastle 8	d	09 40					10 25	10 40	→						11 25		11 40					12 17
Chester-le-Street	d						10 34															12 29
Durham	d	09 52					10 41	10 52							11 38		11 52					12 36
Darlington 7	d	10 11					10 58	11 11							11 57		12 11					12 53
York 8	d	10 44					11 27	11 44							12 25		12 44					13 28
Leeds 10	d	11 10						12 10									13 10					
Wakefield Westgate 7	d	11 23						12 23									13 23					
Doncaster 7	d						11 55								12 52							13 54
Sheffield 7	d	11 53					12 23	12 53							13 23		13 53					14 23
Chesterfield	d						12 35								13 35							14 35
Derby 10	d	12 24					12 57	13 24							13 57		14 24					14 57
Burton-on-Trent	d														14 07							
Tamworth	d														14 18							
Birmingham New Street 12	a	13 04	13 11	13 24	13 30		13 36	13 58		13 58	14 11	14 24	14 30		14 36	14 58	15 04	15 11	15 24	15 30		15 36
Birmingham New Street 12	d	13 10		13 30	13 33	13 33	13 40	14 03		14 10		14 30	14 33	14 33	14 40	15 03	15 10		15 30	15 33	15 33	15 40
Cheltenham Spa	a	13 51					14 21			14 51					15 21		15 51					16 21
Gloucester 7	a																					
Bristol Parkway 7	a	14 25					14 56			15 25					15 56		16 25					16 56
Bristol Temple Meads 10	a	14 41					15 11			15 41					16 13		16 41					17 13
Newport (South Wales)	a																					
Cardiff Central 7	a																					
Weston-super-Mare	a																					
Taunton	a	15 15					15 42			16 15							17 15					
Tiverton Parkway	a	15 28					15 54			16 28							17 28					
Exeter St Davids 6	a	15 43					16 10			16 43							17 43					
Dawlish	a																					
Teignmouth	a																					
Newton Abbot	a	16 03					16 30			17 03							18 03					
Torquay	a																					
Paignton	a																					
Totnes	a	16 16					16 43			17 16							18 16					
Plymouth	a	16 48					17 15			17 48							18 48					
Liskeard 3	a									18 17							19 22					
Bodmin Parkway	a									18 30							19 34					
Par 3	a									18 40							19 44					
St Austell	a									18 47							19 51					
Truro	a									19 04							20 08					
Redruth	a									19 16							20 21					
Camborne	a									19 22							20 27					
St Erth 2	a									19 32							20 37					
Penzance	a									19 49							20 59					
Birmingham International ✈	d			13 40	13 45			14 15				14 40	14 46			15 15			15 40	15 46		
Coventry	d			13a49	13a55			14 25				14a49	14a55			15 25			15a49	15a55		
Leamington Spa 8	d					14 00		14 38						15 00		15 38					16 00	
Banbury	a					14 17		14 54						15 17		15 54					16 17	
Oxford	a					14 41		15 14						15 41		16 14					16 41	
Reading 7	a					15 13		15 39						16 13		16 39					17 13	
Kensington Olympia	a																					
East Croydon	a																					
Guildford	a													16 58								
Redhill	a													17 38								
Basingstoke	a							16 08								17 08						
Winchester	a							16 24								17 24						
Southampton Airport Parkwy ✈	a							16 33								17 33						
Southampton Central	a							16 40								17 40						
Brockenhurst 3	a							16 56								17 56						
Bournemouth	a							17 15								18 15						
Gatwick Airport 10 ✈	a													17 50								
Haywards Heath 3	a																					
Brighton 10	a																					

For general notes see front of timetable
For details of catering facilities see
Directory of Train Operators

Table 51

SUMMARY OF SERVICES

Saturdays

until 26 January

Scotland, The North East, North West England → The South West and South Coast

Route Diagram - See first page of Table 51

		XC	XC	VT	VT	VT	XC	XC	XC	XC	VT	VT	VT	XC	XC	XC	XC	VT	VT	VT	XC	XC
		1 ◇	1 ◇	R 1	1 ◇	1 ◇	1 ◇	1 ◇	1 ◇	1 ◇	R 1	1 ◇	1 ◇	1 ◇	1 ◇	1 ◇	1 ◇	1 ◇	1 ◇	1 ◇	1 ◇	1 ◇
		☕	☕	☕	☕	☕	☕	☕	☕	☕	☕	☕	☕	☕	☕	☕	☕	☕	☕	☕	☕	☕
Aberdeen	d	08 20																				
Stonehaven	d	08 37																				
Montrose	d	08 58																				
Arbroath	d	09 15																				
Dundee	d	09 32																				
Leuchars 3	d	09 45																				
Cupar	d	09 52																				
Markinch	d	10 04																				
Kirkcaldy	d	10 12																				
Inverkeithing	d	10 27																				
Glasgow Central 15	d			12 10								13 10						14 10				
Motherwell	d											13u24										
Haymarket	d	10 46																				
Edinburgh 10	d	11b05								12 05	12 51					13 05						
Haymarket	d										12u56											
Lockerbie	d											14 11										
Carlisle 8	d			13 21							14 13	14 32						15 21				
Penrith North Lakes	d										14 28	14 47										
Oxenholme Lake District	d			13 58							14 53	15 11										
Lancaster 6	d										15 09	15 27						16 10				
Preston 8	d			14 29	14 47						15 29	15 47						16 29	16 47			
Wigan North Western	d			14 41	14 59						15 41	15 59						16 41	16 59			
Warrington Bank Quay	d			14 52	15 10						15 53	16 10						16 52	17 10			
Manchester Piccadilly 10	d		14 24			14 58			15 24				15 58				16 24			16 58		
Stockport	d		14 33			15 07			15 33				16 07				16 33			17 07		
Wilmslow	d																					
Crewe 10	d			15 13	15 31						16 13	16 31						17 15	17 31			
Macclesfield	d		14 46			15 20			15 46				16 20				16 46			17 20		
Congleton	d		14 54														16 54					
Stoke-on-Trent	d		15 07			15 39			16 04				16 39				17 07			17 39		
Stafford	d		15 26						16 26								17 26					
Wolverhampton 7	d		15 41	15 47		16 11			16 41		16 49		17 11				17 41	17 49		18 11		
Dunbar	d	11 25														13 25						
Berwick-upon-Tweed	d	11 49														13 49						
Alnmouth	d									13 03												
Newcastle 8	d	12 40						13 27		13 40					14 22	14 40						15 22
Chester-le-Street	d														14 31							
Durham	d	12 52						13 39		13 52					14 38	14 52						15 34
Darlington 7	d	13 09						13 58		14 09					14 55	15 09						15 52
York 8	d	13 44						14 30		14 44					15 27	15 44						16 25
Leeds 10	d	14 10								15 10						16 10						
Wakefield Westgate 7	d	14 22								15 23						16 23						
Doncaster 7	d							14 55							15 55							16 53
Sheffield 7	d	14 53						15 23		15 53					16 23	16 53						17 20
Chesterfield	d							15 35							16 35							17 35
Derby 10	d	15 24						15 57		16 24					16 57	17 24						17 57
Burton-on-Trent	d							16 07														18 07
Tamworth	d							16 18														18 18
Birmingham New Street 12	a	15 58	15 58	16 11	16 24	16 30		16 36	16 58	17 04	17 11	17 24	17 30		17 36	17 58	17 58	18 11	18 24	18 30		18 36
Birmingham New Street 12	d	16 03	16 10		16 30	16 33	16 33	16 40	17 03	17 10		17 30	17 33	17 33	17 40	18 03	18 10		18 30	18 33	18 33	18 40
Cheltenham Spa	a		16 51					17 21		17 51					18 21		18 51					19 21
Gloucester 7	a														18 35							
Bristol Parkway 7	a		17 25					17 56		18 25					19 06		19 25					19 56
Bristol Temple Meads 10	a		17 41					18 13		18 41					19 24		19 41					20 13
Newport (South Wales)	a														19 59							
Cardiff Central 7	a														20 19							
Weston-super-Mare	a																					
Taunton	a		18 15							19 15							20 15					
Tiverton Parkway	a		18 28							19 28							20 28					
Exeter St Davids 6	a		18 43							19 43							20 43					
Dawlish	a																					
Teignmouth	a																					
Newton Abbot	a		19 03							20 03							21 03					
Torquay	a																					
Paignton	a																					
Totnes	a		19 16							20 16							21 16					
Plymouth	a		19 48							20 48							21 48					
Liskeard 3	a		20 12																			
Bodmin Parkway	a		20 24																			
Par 3	a		20 35																			
St Austell	a		20 41																			
Truro	a		20 58																			
Redruth	a		21 10																			
Camborne	a		21 16																			
St Erth 2	a		21 26																			
Penzance	a		21 43																			
Birmingham International ✈	d	16 15			16 40	16 46			17 15			17 40	17 45			18 15			18 40	18 45		
Coventry	d	16 25			16a49	16a55			17 25			17a49	17a55			18 25			18a49	18a55		
Leamington Spa 8	d	16 38					17 00		17 38					18 00		18 38					19 00	
Banbury	a	16 54					17 17		17 54					18 17		18 54					19 17	
Oxford	a	17 14					17 41		18 14					18 41		19 14					19 41	
Reading 7	a	17 39					18 13		18 39					19 13		19 39					20 13	
Kensington Olympia	a						19 01															
East Croydon	a						19 36															
Guildford	a																				20 58	
Redhill	a																				21 28	
Basingstoke	a	18 08							19 08							20 08						
Winchester	a	18 24							19 24							20 24						
Southampton Airport Parkwy ✈	a	18 33							19 33							20 33						
Southampton Central	a	18 40							19 40							20 40						
Brockenhurst 3	a	18 56							19 56							20 56						
Bournemouth	a	19 15							20 15							21 15						
Gatwick Airport 10 ✈	a						19 52														21 47	
Haywards Heath 3	a						20 04														22 24	
Brighton 10	a						20 28														22 50	

For general notes see front of timetable
For details of catering facilities see Directory of Train Operators

b Arr. 1055

until 26 January

Scotland, The North East, North West England → The South West and South Coast

Route Diagram - See first page of Table 51

		XC	XC	VT	VT	XC	XC	XC	VT	VT	XC	XC	XC	VT	VT	VT	XC	VT	XC	VT	XC
		1◇	1◇	1◇	1◇	1◇	1◇	1◇	1◇	1◇	1◇	1◇	1◇	1◇	1◇	1◇	1◇	1◇	1◇	1◇	1◇
Aberdeen	d																				
Stonehaven	d																				
Montrose	d																				
Arbroath	d																				
Dundee	d																				
Leuchars 3	d																				
Cupar	d																				
Markinch	d																				
Kirkcaldy	d																				
Inverkeithing	d																				
Glasgow Central 15	d								16 03									18 10			
Motherwell	d																	18u27			
Haymarket	d																				
Edinburgh 10	d		14 05	14 51			15 05						16 05	16 51							18 05
Haymarket	d			14u56										16u56							
Lockerbie	d													17 50				19 12			
Carlisle 8	d			16 09					17 21					18 11				19 32			
Penrith North Lakes	d			16 24					17 36					18 27							
Oxenholme Lake District	d			16 48					18 00					18 51				20 08			
Lancaster 6	d			17 04										19 07				20 21			
Preston 8	d			17 24					18 30					19 29				20 43		21 28	
Wigan North Western	d			17 36					18 42					19 41				20 55		21 40	
Warrington Bank Quay	d			17 48					18 53					19 53				21 06		21 52	
Manchester Piccadilly 10	d	17 24			17 58			18 24		18 58		19 24			19 58	20 17			20 54		
Stockport	d	17 33			18 07			18 33		19 07		19 33			20 07	20 26			21 04		
Wilmslow	d																				
Crewe 10	d			18 13					19 15					20 15				21 28		22 13	
Macclesfield	d	17 46			18 20			18 46		19 20		19 46			20 20	20 40			21 17		
Congleton	d							18 54				19 54							21 25		
Stoke-on-Trent	d	18 04			18 39			19 07		19 39		20 07			20 36	20 58			21 39		
Stafford	d	18 26						19 26				20 26				21 18		21 51	21 58	22 33	
Wolverhampton 7	d	18 41		18 49	19 11			19 41	19 49	20 11		20 41		20 49	21 11	21 35		22 09	22 13	22 49	
Dunbar	d						15 25														18 25
Berwick-upon-Tweed	d						15 49														18 51
Alnmouth	d		15 04										17 09								19 11
Newcastle 8	d		15 40			16 20	16 40				17 19		17 40				18 40				19 45
Chester-le-Street	d					16 29					17 28						18 49				
Durham	d		15 52			16 36	16 52				17 35		17 54				18 56				19 57
Darlington 7	d		16 09			16 54	17 09				17 52		18 11				19 13				20 14
York 8	d		16 44			17 25	17 44				18 25		18 44				19 44				20 44
Leeds 10	d		17 10				18 10						19 10				20 10				21 10
Wakefield Westgate 7	d		17 23				18 23						19 23				20 23				21 23
Doncaster 7	d					17 55					18 51										
Sheffield 7	d		17 53			18 23	18 53				19 23		19 53				20 53				21 53
Chesterfield	d					18 35					19 35		20 05				21 05				22 05
Derby 10	d		18 24			18 57	19 24				19 57		20 27				21 27				22 27
Burton-on-Trent	d										20 07						21 37				22 37
Tamworth	d										20 18						21 48				22 48
Birmingham New Street 12	a	18 58	19 04	19 11	19 30	19 36	19 58	19 58	20 11	20 30	20 42	20 58	21 04	21 11	21 30	21 56	22 13	22 30	22 37	23 10	23 20
Birmingham New Street 12	d	19 03	19 10		19 33	19 40	20 03	20 10		20 33		21 03	21 10		21 33	22 00					
Cheltenham Spa	a		19 51			20 21		20 51					21 51								
Gloucester 7	a																				
Bristol Parkway 7	a		20 25			20 56		21 25					22 25								
Bristol Temple Meads 10	a		20 41			21 13		21 41					22 41								
Newport (South Wales)	a																				
Cardiff Central 7	a																				
Weston-super-Mare	a																				
Taunton	a		21 15					22 15													
Tiverton Parkway	a		21 28					22 28													
Exeter St Davids 6	a		21 43					22 43													
Dawlish	a																				
Teignmouth	a																				
Newton Abbot	a		22 05					23 11													
Torquay	a																				
Paignton	a																				
Totnes	a		22 21					23 26													
Plymouth	a		22 55					23 59													
Liskeard 3	a																				
Bodmin Parkway	a																				
Par 3	a																				
St Austell	a																				
Truro	a																				
Redruth	a																				
Camborne	a																				
St Erth 2	a																				
Penzance	a																				
Birmingham International	d	19 15			19 43		20 15			20 43		21 15			21 43	22 10					
Coventry	d	19 25			19a52		20 25			20a52		21 25			21a52	22a19					
Leamington Spa 8	d	19 38					20 38					21 38									
Banbury	a	19 54					20 54					21 55									
Oxford	a	20 14					21 14					22 14									
Reading 7	a	20 39					21 39					22 39									
Kensington Olympia	a																				
East Croydon	a																				
Guildford	a																				
Redhill	a																				
Basingstoke	a	21 08					22 08					23 08									
Winchester	a	21 24					22 24					23 23									
Southampton Airport Parkwy	a	21 33					22 33					23 33									
Southampton Central	a	21 40					22 48					23 45									
Brockenhurst 3	a	21 56					23b04					00b04									
Bournemouth	a	22 15					23b23					00b22									
Gatwick Airport 10	a																				
Haywards Heath 3	a																				
Brighton 10	a																				

For general notes see front of timetable
For details of catering facilities see Directory of Train Operators

b Change at Winchester

Table 51

SUMMARY OF SERVICES

Saturdays

Scotland, The North East, North West England → The South West and South Coast

2 February to 22 March

Route Diagram - See first page of Table 51

		XC	XC	XC	XC	XC	VT	XC	XC	VT	XC	VT	XC	XC	XC	VT	VT	VT	XC	XC	XC	XC
																R						
		1◇	1◇	1◇	1◇	1◇	1◇	1◇	1◇	1◇	1◇	1◇	1◇	1◇	1◇	1	1◇	1◇	1◇	1◇	1◇	1◇
			☕	☕	☕	☕	☕	☕	☕	☕	☕	☕	☕	☕	☕	☕	☕	☕	☕	☕	☕	☕
Aberdeen	d																					
Stonehaven	d																					
Montrose	d																					
Arbroath	d																					
Dundee	d																					
Leuchars [3]	d																					
Cupar	d																					
Markinch	d																					
Kirkcaldy	d																					
Inverkeithing	d																					
Glasgow Central [15]	d																					
Motherwell	d																					
Haymarket	d																					
Edinburgh [10]	d																					
Haymarket	d																					
Lockerbie	d																					
Carlisle [8]	d																06 30					
Penrith North Lakes	d																06 44					
Oxenholme Lake District	d																07 08					
Lancaster [6]	d																07 24					
Preston [8]	d									06 15						07 20	07 44					
Wigan North Western	d									06 27						07 32	07 56					
Warrington Bank Quay	d									06 47						07 44	08 07					
Manchester Piccadilly [10]	d			05b05			06 21					06 55		07 24				07 55				08 24
Stockport	d			05b15			06 30					07 04		07 33				08 04				08 33
Wilmslow	d			05b23																		
Crewe [10]	d			05 42						07 10						08 11	08 29					
Macclesfield	d						06 43					07 17		07 46				08 17				08 46
Congleton	d																					08 54
Stoke-on-Trent	d			06 01			06 59					07 33		08 04				08 39				09 07
Stafford	d			06 20			07 19							08 26			08 48					09 26
Wolverhampton [7]	d			06 41			07 35			07 48		08 11		08 41		08 48		09 11				09 41
Dunbar	d																					
Berwick-upon-Tweed	d																					
Alnmouth	d																					
Newcastle [8]	d																				06 08	
Chester-le-Street	d																					
Durham	d																				06 23	
Darlington [7]	d																				07 12	
York [8]	d																			07 27	07 44	
Leeds [10]	d												06 00		06 48						08 10	
Wakefield Westgate [7]	d												06 12		*06 32*						08 23	
Doncaster [7]	d														07 26					07 52		
Sheffield [7]	d							06 01					06 48		07 53					08 23	08 53	
Chesterfield	d							06 24					07 16		08 05					08 35		
Derby [10]	d		06 10					07 17					07 57		08 27					08 57	09 24	
Burton-on-Trent	d		06 20					07 27					08 07		08 37							
Tamworth	d		06 31					07 38					08 18		08 48							
Birmingham New Street [12]	a		06 51	06 58	⟵		07 56	07 58		08 10		08 30	08 36	08 58	09 06	09 10	09 24	09 30		09 36	09 58	09 58
Birmingham New Street [12]	d	06 03	07 10 ⟶	07 03	07 10	07 33	08 00	08 03	08 10		08 33	08 33	08 40	09 03	09 10		09 30	09 33	09 33	09 40	10 03	10 10
Cheltenham Spa	a				07 51				08 51				09 21		09 51					10 21		10 51
Gloucester [7]	a																					
Bristol Parkway [7]	a				08 25				09 25				09 56		10 25					10 56		11 25
Bristol Temple Meads [10]	a				08 41				09 41				10 13		10 41					11 13		11 41
Newport (South Wales)	a																					
Cardiff Central [7]	a																					
Weston-super-Mare	a																			11 31		
Taunton	a				09 15				10 15						11 15					12 03		12 15
Tiverton Parkway	a				09 28				10 28						11 28					12 16		12 28
Exeter St Davids [6]	a				09 43				10 43						11 43					12 31		12 43
Dawlish	a																			12 44		
Teignmouth	a																			12 49		
Newton Abbot	a				10 03				11 03						12 03					12 56		13 03
Torquay	a																			13 07		
Paignton	a																			13 20		
Totnes	a				10 16				11 16						12 16							13 16
Plymouth	a				10 48				11 48						12 48							13 48
Liskeard [3]	a																					
Bodmin Parkway	a																					
Par [3]	a																					
St Austell	a																					
Truro	a																					
Redruth	a																					
Camborne	a																					
St Erth [2]	a																					
Penzance	a																					
Birmingham International ✈	d	06 15		07 15			08 10	08 15				08 43		09 15			09 40	09 45			10 15	
Coventry	d	06 25		07 25			08a19	08 25				08a54		09 25			09a49	09a54			10 25	
Leamington Spa [8]	d	06 38		07 38		08 00		08 38			09 00			09 38					10 00		10 38	
Banbury	a	06 54		07 54		08 17		08 54			09 17			09 54					10 17		10 54	
Oxford	a	07 14		08 14		08 41		09 14			09 41			10 14					10 41		11 14	
Reading [7]	a	07 44		08 39		09 13		09 39			10 13			10 39					11 13		11 39	
Kensington Olympia	a																		11 56			
East Croydon	a																		12 37			
Guildford	a																					
Redhill	a																					
Basingstoke	a			09 08				10 08						11 06							12 08	
Winchester	a			09 24				10 24						11 24							12 24	
Southampton Airport Parkwy ✈	a			09 33				10 33						11 33							12 33	
Southampton Central	a			09 40				10 40						11 40							12 40	
Brockenhurst [3]	a			09 56				10 56						11 56							12 56	
Bournemouth	a			10 15				11 15						12 15							13 15	
Gatwick Airport [10] ✈	a																		12 53			
Haywards Heath [3]	a																		13 13			
Brighton [10]	a																		13 37			

For general notes see front of timetable
For details of catering facilities see Directory of Train Operators

b Change at Stafford

Scotland, The North East, North West England → The South West and South Coast

2 February to 22 March

Route Diagram - See first page of Table 51

		VT	VT	VT	XC	XC	XC	XC	VT	VT	VT	XC	XC	XC	XC	VT	VT	VT	XC	XC	XC	XC
		1 ◇	1 ◇	1 ◇	1 ◇	1 ◇	1 ◇	1 ◇	1 ◇	1 ◇	1 ◇	1 ◇	1 ◇	1 ◇	1 ◇	R 1	1 ◇	1 ◇	1 ◇	1 ◇	1 ◇	1 ◇
		☕	☕	☕	☕	☕	☕	☕	☕	☕	☕	☕	☕	☕	☕	☕	☕	☕	☕	☕	☕	☕
Aberdeen	d																					
Stonehaven	d																					
Montrose	d																					
Arbroath	d																					
Dundee	d																					
Leuchars [3]	d																					
Cupar	d																					
Markinch	d																					
Kirkcaldy	d																					
Inverkeithing	d																					
Glasgow Central [15]	d													05 50								
Motherwell	d													06u10								
Haymarket	d													06 51								
Edinburgh [10]	d							06 05						07 05								08 05
Haymarket	d																					
Lockerbie	d																					
Carlisle [8]	d		07 28							08 32						09 14	09 23					
Penrith North Lakes	d		07 43							08 47						09 30	09 38					
Oxenholme Lake District	d		08 07							09 11						09 54	10 06					
Lancaster [6]	d		08 27							09 27						10 09	10 22					
Preston [8]	d	08 29	08 47						09 29	09 47						10 29	10 47					
Wigan North Western	d	08 40	08 59						09 41	09 59						10 41	10 59					
Warrington Bank Quay	d	08 52	09 10						09 53	10 10						10 53	11 10					
Manchester Piccadilly [10]	d			08 54			09 24				09 54				10 24			10 58			11 24	
Stockport	d			09 04			09 33				10 03				10 33			11 07			11 33	
Wilmslow	d																					
Crewe [10]	d	09 13	09 31						10 15	10 31						11 15	11 31					
Macclesfield	d			09 20			09 46				10 20				10 46			11 20			11 46	
Congleton	d														10 54							
Stoke-on-Trent	d			09 39			10 04				10 39				11 07			11 39			12 04	
Stafford	d						10 26								11 26						12 26	
Wolverhampton [7]	d	09 48		10 11			10 41		10 49		11 11				11 41	11 49		12 11			12 41	
Dunbar	d													07 25								
Berwick-upon-Tweed	d							06 47						07 51								08 46
Alnmouth	d							07 07						08 11								09 06
Newcastle [8]	d					06 50		07 40					08 24	08 40						09 25		09 40
Chester-le-Street	d												08 33									
Durham	d					07 02		07 54					08 40	08 52						09 37		09 52
Darlington [7]	d							08 12					08 57	09 11						09 56		10 11
York [8]	d					08 19		08 44					09 27	09 44						10 25		10 44
Leeds [10]	d							09 10						10 10								11 10
Wakefield Westgate [7]	d							09 23						10 23								11 23
Doncaster [7]	d												09 51							10 53		
Sheffield [7]	d					09 23		09 53					10 23	10 53						11 23		11 53
Chesterfield	d					09 35							10 35							11 35		
Derby [10]	d					09 57		10 24					10 57	11 24						11 57		12 24
Burton-on-Trent	d					10 07														12 07		
Tamworth	d					10 18														12 18		
Birmingham New Street [12]	a	10 11	10 24	10 30		10 36	10 58	11 04	11 11	11 24	11 30		11 36	11 58	11 58	12 11	12 24	12 30		12 36	12 58	13 04
Birmingham New Street [12]	d		10 30	10 33	10 33	10 40	11 03	11 10		11 30	11 33	11 33	11 40	12 03	12 10		12 30	12 33	12 33	12 40	13 03	13 10
Cheltenham Spa	a					11 21		11 51					12 21		12 51					13 21		13 51
Gloucester [7]	a																					
Bristol Parkway [7]	a					11 56		12 25					12 56		13 25					13 56		14 25
Bristol Temple Meads [10]	a					12 13		12 41					13 13		13 41					14 13		14 41
Newport (South Wales)	a																					
Cardiff Central [7]	a																					
Weston-super-Mare	a																					
Taunton	a							13 15							14 15							15 15
Tiverton Parkway	a							13 28							14 28							15 28
Exeter St Davids [6]	a							13 43							14 43							15 43
Dawlish	a																					
Teignmouth	a																					
Newton Abbot	a							14 03							15 03							16 03
Torquay	a																					
Paignton	a																					
Totnes	a							14 16							15 16							16 16
Plymouth	a							14 48							15 48							16 48
Liskeard [3]	a																					
Bodmin Parkway	a																					
Par [3]	a																					
St Austell	a																					
Truro	a																					
Redruth	a																					
Camborne	a																					
St Erth [2]	a																					
Penzance	a																					
Birmingham International ✈	d		10 40	10 45			11 15			11 40	11 45			12 15			12 40	12 46			13 15	
Coventry	d		10a49	10a54			11 25			11a49	11a54			12 25			12a49	12a55			13 25	
Leamington Spa [8]	d				11 00		11 38					12 00		12 38					13 00		13 38	
Banbury	a				11 17		11 54					12 17		12 54					13 17		13 54	
Oxford	a				11 41		12 14					12 41		13 14					13 41		14 14	
Reading [7]	a				12 13		12 39					13 13		13 39					14 13		14 39	
Kensington Olympia	a																					
East Croydon	a																					
Guildford	a																					
Redhill	a																					
Basingstoke	a						13 08							14 08							15 08	
Winchester	a						13 24							14 24							15 24	
Southampton Airport Parkwy ✈	a						13 33							14 33							15 33	
Southampton Central	a						13 40							14 40							15 40	
Brockenhurst [3]	a						13 56							14 56							15 56	
Bournemouth	a						14 15							15 15							16 15	
Gatwick Airport [10] ✈	a																					
Haywards Heath [3]	a																					
Brighton [10]	a																					

For general notes see front of timetable
For details of catering facilities see Directory of Train Operators

Scotland, The North East, North West England → The South West and South Coast

2 February to 22 March

Route Diagram - See first page of Table 51

		VT	VT	VT	XC	XC	XC	XC	VT	VT	VT	XC	XC	XC	XC	VT	VT	VT	XC	XC	XC
		R 1	1◇	1◇	1◇	1◇	1◇	1◇	R 1	1◇	1◇	1◇	1◇	1◇	1◇	1◇	1◇	1◇	1◇	1◇	1◇
Aberdeen	d																				08 20
Stonehaven	d																				08 37
Montrose	d																				08 58
Arbroath	d																				09 15
Dundee	d						07 35														09 32
Leuchars [3]	d						07 48														09 45
Cupar	d						07 56														09 52
Markinch	d						08 11														10 04
Kirkcaldy	d						08 20														10 12
Inverkeithing	d						08 36														10 27
Glasgow Central [15]	d														09 00						
Motherwell	d														09u14						
Haymarket	d						08 57								09 55						10 46
Edinburgh [10]	d						09 05								10 05						11b05
Haymarket	d																				
Lockerbie	d															11 51					
Carlisle [8]	d								11 22							12 13	12 32				
Penrith North Lakes	d															12 29	12 47				
Oxenholme Lake District	d															12 53	13 11				
Lancaster [6]	d								12 11							13 09	13 27				
Preston [8]	d	11 28	11 47						12 29	12 47						13 29	13 47				
Wigan North Western	d	11 40	11 59						12 41	12 59						13 41	13 59				
Warrington Bank Quay	d	11 53	12 10						12 53	13 10						13 53	14 10				
Manchester Piccadilly [10]	d			11 58				12 24			12 58			13 24				13 58			
Stockport	d			12 07				12 33			13 07			13 33				14 07			
Wilmslow	d																				
Crewe [10]	d	12 13	12 31						13 15	13 31						14 15	14 31				
Macclesfield	d			12 20				12 46			13 20			13 46				14 20			
Congleton	d							12 54													
Stoke-on-Trent	d			12 39				13 07			13 39			14 04				14 39			
Stafford	d							13 26						14 26							
Wolverhampton [7]	d	12 49		13 11				13 41	13 49		14 11			14 41		14 49		15 11			
Dunbar	d						09 25														11 25
Berwick-upon-Tweed	d						09 49														11 49
Alnmouth	d														11 04						
Newcastle [8]	d					10 25	10 40						11 25		11 40					12 17	12 40
Chester-le-Street	d					10 34														12 29	
Durham	d					10 41	10 52						11 38		11 52					12 36	12 52
Darlington [7]	d					10 58	11 11						11 57		12 11					12 53	13 09
York [8]	d					11 27	11 44						12 25		12 44					13 28	13 44
Leeds [10]	d						12 10								13 10						14 10
Wakefield Westgate [7]	d						12 23								13 23						14 22
Doncaster [7]	d					11 55							12 52							13 54	
Sheffield [7]	d					12 23	12 53						13 23		13 53					14 23	14 53
Chesterfield	d					12 35							13 35							14 35	
Derby [10]	d					12 57	13 24						13 57		14 24					14 57	15 24
Burton-on-Trent	d												14 07								
Tamworth	d												14 18								
Birmingham New Street [12]	a	13 11	13 24	13 30		13 36	13 58	13 58	14 11	14 24	14 30		14 36	14 58	15 04	15 11	15 24	15 30		15 36	15 58
Birmingham New Street [12]	d		13 30	13 33	13 33	13 40	14 03	14 10		14 30	14 33	14 33	14 40	15 03	15 10		15 30	15 33	15 33	15 40	16 03
Cheltenham Spa	a					14 21		14 51					15 21		15 51					16 21	
Gloucester [7]	a																				
Bristol Parkway [7]	a					14 56		15 25					15 56		16 25					16 56	
Bristol Temple Meads [10]	a					15 11		15 41					16 13		16 41					17 13	
Newport (South Wales)	a																				
Cardiff Central [7]	a																				
Weston-super-Mare	a																				
Taunton	a					15 42		16 15							17 15						
Tiverton Parkway	a					15 54		16 28							17 28						
Exeter St Davids [6]	a					16 10		16 43							17 43						
Dawlish	a																				
Teignmouth	a																				
Newton Abbot	a					16 30		17 03							18 03						
Torquay	a																				
Paignton	a																				
Totnes	a					16 43		17 16							18 16						
Plymouth	a					17 15		17 48							18 48						
Liskeard [3]	a							18 17							19 22						
Bodmin Parkway	a							18 30							19 34						
Par [3]	a							18 40							19 44						
St Austell	a							18 47							19 51						
Truro	a							19 04							20 08						
Redruth	a							19 16							20 21						
Camborne	a							19 22							20 27						
St Erth [2]	a							19 32							20 37						
Penzance	a							19 49							20 59						
Birmingham International ✈	d		13 40	13 45			14 15			14 40	14 46			15 15			15 40	15 46			16 15
Coventry	d		13a49	13a55			14 25			14a49	14a55			15 25			15a49	15a55			16 25
Leamington Spa [8]	d				14 00		14 38					15 00		15 38					16 00		16 38
Banbury	a				14 17		14 54					15 17		15 54					16 17		16 54
Oxford	a				14 41		15 14					15 41		16 14					16 41		17 14
Reading [7]	a				15 13		15 39					16 13		16 39					17 13		17 39
Kensington Olympia	a																				
East Croydon	a																				
Guildford	a											16 58									
Redhill	a											*17 38*									
Basingstoke	a						16 08							17 08							18 08
Winchester	a						16 24							17 24							18 24
Southampton Airport Parkwy ✈	a						16 33							17 33							18 33
Southampton Central	a						16 40							17 40							18 40
Brockenhurst [3]	a						16 56							17 56							18 56
Bournemouth	a						17 15							18 15							19 15
Gatwick Airport [10] ✈	a											*17 50*									
Haywards Heath [3]	a																				
Brighton [10]	a																				

For general notes see front of timetable
For details of catering facilities see Directory of Train Operators

b Arr. 1055

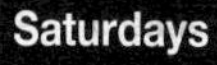

Scotland, The North East, North West England → The South West and South Coast

2 February to 22 March

Route Diagram - See first page of Table 51

Station		XC	VT	VT	VT	XC	XC	XC	XC	VT	VT	VT	XC	XC	XC	XC	VT	VT	VT	XC	XC	XC
		1◇	R 1	1◇	1◇	1◇	1◇	1◇	1◇	R 1	1◇	1◇	1◇	1◇	1◇	1◇	1◇	1◇	1◇	1◇	1◇	1◇
Aberdeen	d																					
Stonehaven	d																					
Montrose	d																					
Arbroath	d																					
Dundee	d																					
Leuchars 3	d																					
Cupar	d																					
Markinch	d																					
Kirkcaldy	d																					
Inverkeithing	d																					
Glasgow Central 15	d																					
Motherwell	d																					
Haymarket	d																					
Edinburgh 10	d								12 05						13 05							
Haymarket	d																					
Lockerbie	d		13 00							13 50							15 00					
Carlisle 8	d		13 21							14 13	14 32						15 21					
Penrith North Lakes	d									14 28	14 47											
Oxenholme Lake District	d		13 58							14 53	15 11											
Lancaster 6	d									15 09	15 27						16 10					
Preston 8	d		14 29	14 47						15 29	15 47						16 29	16 47				
Wigan North Western	d		14 41	14 59						15 41	15 59						16 41	16 59				
Warrington Bank Quay	d		14 52	15 10						15 53	16 10						16 52	17 10				
Manchester Piccadilly 10	d	14 24			14 58			15 24				15 58				16 24			16 58			17 24
Stockport	d	14 33			15 07			15 33				16 07				16 33			17 07			17 33
Wilmslow	d																					
Crewe 10	d		15 13	15 31						16 13	16 31						17 15	17 31				
Macclesfield	d	14 46			15 20			15 46				16 20				16 46			17 20			17 46
Congleton	d	14 54														16 54						
Stoke-on-Trent	d	15 07			15 39			16 04				16 39				17 07			17 39			18 04
Stafford	d	15 26						16 26								17 26						18 26
Wolverhampton 7	d	15 41	15 47		16 11			16 41		16 49		17 11				17 41	17 49		18 11			18 41
Dunbar	d														13 25							
Berwick-upon-Tweed	d														13 49							
Alnmouth	d								13 03													
Newcastle 8	d						13 27		13 40					14 22	14 40						15 22	
Chester-le-Street	d													14 31								
Durham	d						13 39		13 52					14 38	14 52						15 34	
Darlington 7	d						13 58		14 09					14 55	15 09						15 52	
York 8	d						14 30		14 44					15 27	15 44						16 25	
Leeds 10	d								15 10						16 10							
Wakefield Westgate 7	d								15 23						16 23							
Doncaster 7	d						14 55							15 55							16 53	
Sheffield 7	d						15 23		15 53					16 23	16 53						17 20	
Chesterfield	d						15 35							16 35							17 35	
Derby 10	d						15 57		16 24					16 57	17 24						17 57	
Burton-on-Trent	d						16 07														18 07	
Tamworth	d						16 18														18 18	
Birmingham New Street 12	a	15 58	16 11	16 24	16 30		16 36	16 58	17 04	17 11	17 24	17 30		17 36	17 58	17 58	18 11	18 24	18 30		18 36	18 58
Birmingham New Street 12	d	16 10		16 30	16 33	16 33	16 40	17 03	17 10		17 30	17 33	17 33	17 40	18 03	18 10		18 30	18 33	18 33	18 40	19 03
Cheltenham Spa	a	16 51					17 21		17 51					18 21		18 51					19 21	
Gloucester 7	a													18 35								
Bristol Parkway 7	a	17 25					17 56		18 25					19 06		19 25					19 56	
Bristol Temple Meads 10	a	17 41					18 13		18 41					19 24		19 41					20 13	
Newport (South Wales)	a													19 59								
Cardiff Central 7	a													20 19								
Weston-super-Mare	a																					
Taunton	a	18 15							19 15							20 15						
Tiverton Parkway	a	18 28							19 28							20 28						
Exeter St Davids 6	a	18 43							19 43							20 43						
Dawlish	a																					
Teignmouth	a																					
Newton Abbot	a	19 03							20 03							21 03						
Torquay	a																					
Paignton	a																					
Totnes	a	19 16							20 16							21 16						
Plymouth	a	19 48							20 48							21 48						
Liskeard 3	a	20 12																				
Bodmin Parkway	a	20 24																				
Par 3	a	20 35																				
St Austell	a	20 41																				
Truro	a	20 58																				
Redruth	a	21 10																				
Camborne	a	21 16																				
St Erth 2	a	21 26																				
Penzance	a	21 43																				
Birmingham International ✈	d			16 40	16 46			17 15			17 40	17 45			18 15			18 40	18 45			19 15
Coventry	d			16a49	16a55			17 25			17a49	17a55			18 25			18a49	18a55			19 25
Leamington Spa 8	d					17 00		17 38					18 00		18 38					19 00		19 38
Banbury	a					17 17		17 54					18 17		18 54					19 17		19 54
Oxford	a					17 41		18 14					18 41		19 14					19 41		20 14
Reading 7	a					18 13		18 39					19 13		19 39					20 13		20 39
Kensington Olympia	a					19 01																
East Croydon	a					19 36																
Guildford	a																			20 58		
Redhill	a																			21 28		
Basingstoke	a							19 08							20 08							21 08
Winchester	a							19 24							20 24							21 24
Southampton Airport Parkwy ✈	a							19 33							20 33							21 33
Southampton Central	a							19 40							20 40							21 40
Brockenhurst 3	a							19 56							20 56							21 56
Bournemouth	a							20 15							21 15							22 15
Gatwick Airport 10 ✈	a					19 52														21 47		
Haywards Heath 3	a					20 04														22 24		
Brighton 10	a					20 28														22 50		

For general notes see front of timetable
For details of catering facilities see Directory of Train Operators

Scotland, The North East, North West England → The South West and South Coast

2 February to 22 March

Route Diagram - See first page of Table 51

		XC	VT	VT	XC	XC		XC	VT	VT	XC	XC	XC	VT	VT		VT	XC	VT	XC	VT	XC
		1◇	1◇	1◇	1◇	1◇		1◇	1◇	1◇	1◇	1◇	1◇	1◇	1◇		1◇	1◇	1◇	1◇	1◇	1◇
		☕	☕	☕	☕	☕		☕	☕	☕	☕		☕	☕	☕		☕	☕	☕		☕	☕
Aberdeen	d																					
Stonehaven	d																					
Montrose	d																					
Arbroath	d																					
Dundee	d																					
Leuchars 3	d																					
Cupar	d																					
Markinch	d																					
Kirkcaldy	d																					
Inverkeithing	d																					
Glasgow Central 15	d																					
Motherwell	d																					
Haymarket	d																					
Edinburgh 10	d	14 05				15 05							16 05									18 05
Haymarket	d																					
Lockerbie	d		15 47						17 00					17 50					19 08		19 50	
Carlisle 8	d		16 09						17 21					18 11					19 29		20 11	
Penrith North Lakes	d		16 24						17 36					18 27							20 26	
Oxenholme Lake District	d		16 48						18 00					18 51					20 04		20 51	
Lancaster 6	d		17 04											19 07					20 21		21 07	
Preston 8	d		17 24						18 30					19 29					20 43		21 28	
Wigan North Western	d		17 36						18 42					19 41					20 55		21 40	
Warrington Bank Quay	d		17 48						18 53					19 53					21 06		21 52	
Manchester Piccadilly 10	d			17 58				18 24		18 58		19 24			19 58		20 17			20 54		
Stockport	d			18 07				18 33		19 07		19 33			20 07		20 26			21 04		
Wilmslow	d																					
Crewe 10	d		18 13						19 15					20 15					21 28		22 13	
Macclesfield	d			18 20				18 46		19 20		19 46			20 20		20 40			21 17		
Congleton	d							18 54				19 54								21 25		
Stoke-on-Trent	d			18 39				19 07		19 39		20 07			20 36		20 58			21 39		
Stafford	d							19 26				20 26					21 18		21 51	21 58	22 33	
Wolverhampton 7	d		18 49	19 11				19 41	19 49	20 11		20 41		20 49	21 11		21 35		22 09	22 13	22 49	
Dunbar	d					15 25																18 25
Berwick-upon-Tweed	d					15 49																18 51
Alnmouth	d	15 04											17 09									19 11
Newcastle 8	d	15 40			16 20	16 40					17 19		17 40					18 40				19 45
Chester-le-Street	d				16 29						17 28							18 49				
Durham	d	15 52			16 36	16 52					17 35		17 54					18 56				19 57
Darlington 7	d	16 09			16 54	17 09					17 52		18 11					19 13				20 14
York 8	d	16 44			17 25	17 44					18 25		18 44					19 44				20 44
Leeds 10	d	17 10				18 10							19 10					20 10				21 10
Wakefield Westgate 7	d	17 23				18 23							19 23					20 23				21 23
Doncaster 7	d				17 55						18 51											
Sheffield 7	d	17 53			18 23	18 53					19 23		19 53					20 53				21 53
Chesterfield	d				18 35						19 35		20 05					21 05				22 05
Derby 10	d	18 24			18 57	19 24					19 57		20 27					21 27				22 27
Burton-on-Trent	d										20 07							21 37				22 37
Tamworth	d										20 18							21 48				22 48
Birmingham New Street 12	a	19 04	19 11	19 30	19 36	19 58		19 58	20 11	20 30	20 42	20 58	21 04	21 11	21 30		21 56	22 13	22 30	22 37	23 10	23 20
Birmingham New Street 12	d	19 10		19 33	19 40	20 03		20 10		20 33		21 03	21 10		21 33		22 00					
Cheltenham Spa	a	19 51			20 21			20 51					21 51									
Gloucester 7	a																					
Bristol Parkway 7	a	20 25			20 56			21 25					22 25									
Bristol Temple Meads 10	a	20 41			21 13			21 41					22 41									
Newport (South Wales)	a																					
Cardiff Central 7	a																					
Weston-super-Mare	a																					
Taunton	a	21 15						22 15														
Tiverton Parkway	a	21 28						22 28														
Exeter St Davids 6	a	21 43						22 43														
Dawlish	a																					
Teignmouth	a																					
Newton Abbot	a	22 05						23 11														
Torquay	a																					
Paignton	a																					
Totnes	a	22 21						23 26														
Plymouth	a	22 55						23 59														
Liskeard 3	a																					
Bodmin Parkway	a																					
Par 3	a																					
St Austell	a																					
Truro	a																					
Redruth	a																					
Camborne	a																					
St Erth 2	a																					
Penzance	a																					
Birmingham International ✈	d			19 43		20 15				20 43		21 15			21 43		22 10					
Coventry	d			19a52		20 25				20a52		21 25			21a52		22a19					
Leamington Spa 8	d					20 38						21 38										
Banbury	a					20 54						21 55										
Oxford	a					21 14						22 14										
Reading 7	a					21 39						22 39										
Kensington Olympia	a																					
East Croydon	a																					
Guildford	a																					
Redhill	a																					
Basingstoke	a					22 08						23 08										
Winchester	a					22 24						23 23										
Southampton Airport Parkwy ✈	a					22 33						23 33										
Southampton Central	a					22 48						23 45										
Brockenhurst 3	a					23b04						00b04										
Bournemouth	a					23b23						00b22										
Gatwick Airport 10 ✈	a																					
Haywards Heath 3	a																					
Brighton 10	a																					

For general notes see front of timetable
For details of catering facilities see Directory of Train Operators

b Change at Winchester

Scotland, The North East, North West England → The South West and South Coast

from 29 March

Route Diagram - See first page of Table 51

		XC	XC	XC	XC	XC	VT	XC	XC	VT	XC	VT	XC	XC	XC	VT	VT	VT	XC	XC	XC	XC
		1◇	1◇	1◇	1◇	1◇	1◇	1◇	1◇	1◇	1◇	1◇	1◇	1◇	1◇	R 1	1◇	1◇	1◇	1◇	1◇	1◇
			⊡	⊡	⊡	⊡	⊡	⊡	⊡	⊡	⊡	⊡	⊡	⊡	⊡	⊡	⊡	⊡	⊡	⊡	⊡	⊡
Aberdeen	d																					
Stonehaven	d																					
Montrose	d																					
Arbroath	d																					
Dundee	d																					
Leuchars 8	d																					
Cupar	d																					
Markinch	d																					
Kirkcaldy	d																					
Inverkeithing	d																					
Glasgow Central 15	d																					
Motherwell	d																					
Haymarket	d																					
Edinburgh 10	d																					
Haymarket	d																					
Lockerbie	d																					
Carlisle 8	d																					
Penrith North Lakes	d																					
Oxenholme Lake District	d																					
Lancaster 6	d																					
Preston 8	d									06 15						07 20	07 44					
Wigan North Western	d									06 27						07 32	07 56					
Warrington Bank Quay	d									06 47						07 44	08 07					
Manchester Piccadilly 10	d			05b05			06 21					06 55		07 24				07 55				08 24
Stockport	d			05b15			06 30					07 04		07 33				08 04				08 33
Wilmslow	d			05b23																		
Crewe 10	d			05 42						07 10						08 11	08 29					
Macclesfield	d						06 43					07 17		07 46				08 17				08 46
Congleton	d																					08 54
Stoke-on-Trent	d			06 01			06 59					07 33		08 04				08 39				09 07
Stafford	d			06 20			07 19							08 26			08 48					09 26
Wolverhampton 7	d			06 41			07 35			07 48		08 11		08 41		08 48		09 11				09 41
Dunbar	d																					
Berwick-upon-Tweed	d																					
Alnmouth	d																					
Newcastle 8	d																				06 08	
Chester-le-Street	d																					
Durham	d																				06 23	
Darlington 7	d																				07 12	
York 8	d																			07 27	07 44	
Leeds 10	d												06 00		06 48						08 10	
Wakefield Westgate 7	d												06 12		*06 32*						08 23	
Doncaster 7	d														07 26					07 52		
Sheffield 7	d							06 01					06 48		07 53					08 23	08 53	
Chesterfield	d							06 24					07 16		08 05					08 35		
Derby 10	d		06 10					07 17					07 57		08 27					08 57	09 24	
Burton-on-Trent	d		06 20					07 27					08 07		08 37							
Tamworth	d		06 31					07 38					08 18		08 48							
Birmingham New Street 12	a		06 51	06 58	←		07 56	07 58		08 10		08 30	08 36	08 58	09 06	09 10	09 24	09 30		09 36	09 58	09 58
Birmingham New Street 12	d	06 03	07 10 →	07 03	07 10	07 33	08 00	08 03	08 10		08 33	08 33	08 40	09 03	09 10		09 30	09 33	09 33	09 40	10 03	10 10
Cheltenham Spa	a				07 51				08 51				09 21		09 51					10 21		10 51
Gloucester 7	a																					
Bristol Parkway 7	a				08 25				09 25				09 56		10 25					10 56		11 25
Bristol Temple Meads 10	a				08 41				09 41				10 13		10 41					11 13		11 41
Newport (South Wales)	a																					
Cardiff Central 7	a																					
Weston-super-Mare	a																			11 31		
Taunton	a				09 15				10 15						11 15					12 03		12 15
Tiverton Parkway	a				09 28				10 28						11 28					12 16		12 28
Exeter St Davids 6	a				09 43				10 43						11 43					12 31		12 43
Dawlish	a																			12 44		
Teignmouth	a																			12 49		
Newton Abbot	a				10 03				11 03						12 03					12 56		13 03
Torquay	a																			13 07		
Paignton	a																			13 20		
Totnes	a				10 16				11 16						12 16							13 16
Plymouth	a				10 48				11 48						12 48							13 48
Liskeard 3	a																					
Bodmin Parkway	a																					
Par 3	a																					
St Austell	a																					
Truro	a																					
Redruth	a																					
Camborne	a																					
St Erth 2	a																					
Penzance	a																					
Birmingham International ✈	d	06 15		07 15			08 10	08 15				08 43		09 15			09 40	09 45			10 15	
Coventry	d	06 25		07 25			08a19	08 25				08a54		09 25			09a49	09a54			10 25	
Leamington Spa 8	d	06 38		07 38		08 00		08 38			09 00			09 38					10 00		10 38	
Banbury	a	06 54		07 54		08 17		08 54			09 17			09 54					10 17		10 54	
Oxford	a	07 14		08 14		08 41		09 14			09 41			10 14					10 41		11 14	
Reading 7	a	07 44		08 39		09 13		09 39			10 13			10 39					11 13		11 39	
Kensington Olympia	a																		11 56			
East Croydon	a																		12 37			
Guildford	a																					
Redhill	a																					
Basingstoke	a			09 08				10 08						11 06							12 08	
Winchester	a			09 24				10 24						11 24							12 24	
Southampton Airport Parkwy ✈	a			09 33				10 33						11 33							12 33	
Southampton Central	a			09 40				10 40						11 40							12 40	
Brockenhurst 3	a			09 56				10 56						11 56							12 56	
Bournemouth	a			10 15				11 15						12 15							13 15	
Gatwick Airport 10 ✈	a																		12 53			
Haywards Heath 3	a																		13 13			
Brighton 10	a																		13 37			

For general notes see front of timetable
For details of catering facilities see Directory of Train Operators

b Change at Stafford

Scotland, The North East, North West England → The South West and South Coast

from 29 March

Route Diagram - See first page of Table 51

		VT	VT	VT	XC	XC	XC	XC	VT	VT	VT	XC	XC	XC	XC	VT	VT	VT	XC	XC	XC
		1◇ ☕	1◇ ☕	1◇ ☕	1◇ ☕	1◇ ☕	1◇ ☕	1◇ ☕	1◇ ☕	1◇ ☕	1◇ ☕	1◇ ☕	1◇ ☕	1◇ ☕	1◇ ☕	R 1 ☕	1◇ ☕	1◇ ☕	1◇ ☕	1◇ ☕	1◇ ☕
Aberdeen	d																				
Stonehaven	d																				
Montrose	d																				
Arbroath	d																				
Dundee	d																				
Leuchars 3	d																				
Cupar	d																				
Markinch	d																				
Kirkcaldy	d																				
Inverkeithing	d																				
Glasgow Central 15	d													05 50							
Motherwell	d													06u10							
Haymarket	d													06 51							
Edinburgh 10	d							06 05						07 05							
Haymarket	d																				
Lockerbie	d																				
Carlisle 8	d																				
Penrith North Lakes	d																				
Oxenholme Lake District	d																				
Lancaster 6	d																				
Preston 8	d	08 29	08 47						09 29	09 47						10 29	10 47				
Wigan North Western	d	08 40	08 59						09 41	09 59						10 41	10 59				
Warrington Bank Quay	d	08 52	09 10						09 53	10 10						10 53	11 10				
Manchester Piccadilly 10	d			08 54			09 24				09 54				10 24			10 58			11 24
Stockport	d			09 04			09 33				10 03				10 33			11 07			11 33
Wilmslow	d																				
Crewe 10	d	09 13	09 31						10 15	10 31						11 15	11 31				
Macclesfield	d			09 20			09 46				10 20				10 46			11 20			11 46
Congleton	d														10 54						
Stoke-on-Trent	d			09 39			10 04				10 39				11 07			11 39			12 04
Stafford	d						10 26								11 26						12 26
Wolverhampton 7	d	09 48		10 11			10 41		10 49		11 11				11 41	11 49		12 11			12 41
Dunbar	d													07 25							
Berwick-upon-Tweed	d							06 47						07 51							
Alnmouth	d							07 07						08 11							
Newcastle 8	d					06 50		07 40					08 24	08 40						09 25	
Chester-le-Street	d												08 33								
Durham	d					07 02		07 54					08 40	08 52						09 37	
Darlington 7	d							08 12					08 57	09 11						09 56	
York 8	d					08 19		08 44					09 27	09 44						10 25	
Leeds 10	d							09 10						10 10							
Wakefield Westgate 7	d							09 23						10 23							
Doncaster 7	d												09 51							10 53	
Sheffield 7	d					09 23		09 53					10 23	10 53						11 23	
Chesterfield	d					09 35							10 35							11 35	
Derby 10	d					09 57		10 24					10 57	11 24						11 57	
Burton-on-Trent	d					10 07														12 07	
Tamworth	d					10 18														12 18	
Birmingham New Street 12	a	10 11	10 24	10 30		10 36	10 58	11 04	11 11	11 24	11 30		11 36	11 58	11 58	12 11	12 24	12 30		12 36	12 58
Birmingham New Street 12	d		10 30	10 33	10 33	10 40	11 03	11 10		11 30	11 33	11 33	11 40	12 03	12 10		12 30	12 33	12 33	12 40	13 03
Cheltenham Spa	a					11 21		11 51					12 21		12 51					13 21	
Gloucester 7	a																				
Bristol Parkway 7	a					11 56		12 25					12 56		13 25					13 56	
Bristol Temple Meads 10	a					12 13		12 41					13 13		13 41					14 13	
Newport (South Wales)	a																				
Cardiff Central 7	a																				
Weston-super-Mare	a																				
Taunton	a							13 15							14 15						
Tiverton Parkway	a							13 28							14 28						
Exeter St Davids 6	a							13 43							14 43						
Dawlish	a																				
Teignmouth	a																				
Newton Abbot	a							14 03							15 03						
Torquay	a																				
Paignton	a																				
Totnes	a							14 16							15 16						
Plymouth	a							14 48							15 48						
Liskeard 3	a																				
Bodmin Parkway	a																				
Par 3	a																				
St Austell	a																				
Truro	a																				
Redruth	a																				
Camborne	a																				
St Erth 2	a																				
Penzance	a																				
Birmingham International ✈	d		10 40	10 45			11 15			11 40	11 45			12 15			12 40	12 46			13 15
Coventry	d		10a49	10a54			11 25			11a49	11a54			12 25			12a49	12a55			13 25
Leamington Spa 8	d				11 00		11 38					12 00		12 38					13 00		13 38
Banbury	a				11 17		11 54					12 17		12 54					13 17		13 54
Oxford	a				11 41		12 14					12 41		13 14					13 41		14 14
Reading 7	a				12 13		12 39					13 13		13 39					14 13		14 39
Kensington Olympia	a																				
East Croydon	a																				
Guildford	a																				
Redhill	a																				
Basingstoke	a						13 08							14 08							15 08
Winchester	a						13 24							14 24							15 24
Southampton Airport Parkway ✈	a						13 33							14 33							15 33
Southampton Central	a						13 40							14 40							15 40
Brockenhurst 3	a						13 56							14 56							15 56
Bournemouth	a						14 15							15 15							16 15
Gatwick Airport 10 ✈	a																				
Haywards Heath 3	a																				
Brighton 10	a																				

For general notes see front of timetable
For details of catering facilities see Directory of Train Operators

from 29 March

Scotland, The North East, North West England → The South West and South Coast

Route Diagram - See first page of Table 51

		XC	VT	VT	XC	XC	XC	XC	VT	VT	VT	XC	XC	XC	XC	VT	VT	VT	XC	XC	XC
									R												
		1 ◇	1 ◇	1 ◇	1 ◇	1 ◇	1 ◇	1 ◇	1	1 ◇	1 ◇	1 ◇	1 ◇	1 ◇	1 ◇	1 ◇	1 ◇	1 ◇	1 ◇	1 ◇	1 ◇
		☕	☕	☕	☕	☕	☕	☕	☕	☕	☕	☕	☕	☕	☕	☕	☕	☕	☕	☕	☕
Aberdeen	d																				08 20
Stonehaven	d																				08 37
Montrose	d																				08 58
Arbroath	d																				09 15
Dundee	d						07 35														09 32
Leuchars 3	d						07 48														09 45
Cupar	d						07 56														09 52
Markinch	d						08 11														10 04
Kirkcaldy	d						08 20														10 12
Inverkeithing	d						08 36														10 27
Glasgow Central 15	d								07 50												
Motherwell	d								08u04												
Haymarket	d						08 57														10 46
Edinburgh 10	d	08 05					09 05								10 05						11b05
Haymarket	d																				
Lockerbie	d								08 47												
Carlisle 8	d								09 09												
Penrith North Lakes	d																				
Oxenholme Lake District	d																				
Lancaster 6	d																				
Preston 8	d		11 47						12 27	12 47						13 29	13 47				
Wigan North Western	d		11 59						12 39	12 59						13 41	13 59				
Warrington Bank Quay	d		12 10						12 53	13 10						13 53	14 10				
Manchester Piccadilly 10	d			11 58				12 24			12 58			13 24				13 58			
Stockport	d			12 07				12 33			13 07			13 33				14 07			
Wilmslow	d																				
Crewe 10	d		12 31						13 15	13 31						14 15	14 31				
Macclesfield	d			12 20				12 46			13 20			13 46				14 20			
Congleton	d							12 54													
Stoke-on-Trent	d			12 39				13 07			13 39			14 04				14 39			
Stafford	d							13 26						14 26							
Wolverhampton 7	d			13 11				13 41	13 49		14 11			14 41		14 49		15 11			
Dunbar	d						09 25														11 25
Berwick-upon-Tweed	d	08 46					09 49														11 49
Alnmouth	d	09 06													11 04						
Newcastle 8	d	09 40				10 25	10 40						11 25		11 40					12 17	12 40
Chester-le-Street	d					10 34														12 29	
Durham	d	09 52				10 41	10 52						11 38		11 52					12 36	12 52
Darlington 7	d	10 11				10 58	11 11						11 57		12 11					12 53	13 09
York 8	d	10 44				11 27	11 44						12 25		12 44					13 28	13 44
Leeds 10	d	11 10					12 10								13 10						14 10
Wakefield Westgate 7	d	11 23					12 23								13 23						14 22
Doncaster 7	d					11 55							12 52							13 54	
Sheffield 7	d	11 53				12 23	12 53						13 23		13 53					14 23	14 53
Chesterfield	d					12 35							13 35							14 35	
Derby 10	d	12 24				12 57	13 24						13 57		14 24					14 57	15 24
Burton-on-Trent	d												14 07								
Tamworth	d												14 18								
Birmingham New Street 12	a	13 04	13 24	13 30		13 36	13 58	13 58	14 11	14 24	14 30		14 36	14 58	15 04	15 11	15 24	15 30		15 36	15 58
Birmingham New Street 12	d	13 10	13 30	13 33	13 33	13 40	14 03	14 10		14 30	14 33	14 33	14 40	15 03	15 10		15 30	15 33	15 33	15 40	16 03
Cheltenham Spa	a	13 51				14 21		14 51					15 21		15 51					16 21	
Gloucester 7	a																				
Bristol Parkway 7	a	14 25				14 56		15 25					15 56		16 25					16 56	
Bristol Temple Meads 10	a	14 41				15 11		15 41					16 13		16 41					17 13	
Newport (South Wales)	a																				
Cardiff Central 7	a																				
Weston-super-Mare	a																				
Taunton	a	15 15				15 42		16 15							17 15						
Tiverton Parkway	a	15 28				15 54		16 28							17 28						
Exeter St Davids 6	a	15 43				16 10		16 43							17 43						
Dawlish	a																				
Teignmouth	a																				
Newton Abbot	a	16 03				16 30		17 03							18 03						
Torquay	a																				
Paignton	a																				
Totnes	a	16 16				16 43		17 16							18 16						
Plymouth	a	16 48				17 15		17 48							18 48						
Liskeard 3	a							18 17							19 22						
Bodmin Parkway	a							18 30							19 34						
Par 3	a							18 40							19 44						
St Austell	a							18 47							19 51						
Truro	a							19 04							20 08						
Redruth	a							19 16							20 21						
Camborne	a							19 22							20 27						
St Erth 2	a							19 32							20 37						
Penzance	a							19 49							20 59						
Birmingham International	d		13 40	13 45			14 15			14 40	14 46			15 15			15 40	15 46			16 15
Coventry	d		13a49	13a55			14 25			14a49	14a55			15 25			15a49	15a55			16 25
Leamington Spa 8	d				14 00		14 38					15 00		15 38					16 00		16 38
Banbury	a				14 17		14 54					15 17		15 54					16 17		16 54
Oxford	a				14 41		15 14					15 41		16 14					16 41		17 14
Reading 7	a				15 13		15 39					16 13		16 39					17 13		17 39
Kensington Olympia	a																				
East Croydon	a																				
Guildford	a											16 58									
Redhill	a											*17 38*									
Basingstoke	a						16 08							17 08							18 08
Winchester	a						16 24							17 24							18 24
Southampton Airport Parkwy	a						16 33							17 33							18 33
Southampton Central	a						16 40							17 40							18 40
Brockenhurst 3	a						16 56							17 56							18 56
Bournemouth	a						17 15							18 15							19 15
Gatwick Airport 10	a											*17 50*									
Haywards Heath 3	a																				
Brighton 10	a																				

For general notes see front of timetable
For details of catering facilities see Directory of Train Operators

b Arr. 1055

from 29 March

Scotland, The North East, North West England → The South West and South Coast

Route Diagram - See first page of Table 51

		XC	VT	VT	VT	XC	XC	XC	XC	VT	VT	VT	XC	XC	XC	XC	VT	VT	VT	XC	XC	XC
			R							R												
		1◇	1	1◇	1◇	1◇	1◇	1◇	1◇	1	1◇	1◇	1◇	1◇	1◇	1◇	1◇	1◇	1◇	1◇	1◇	1◇
Aberdeen	d																					
Stonehaven	d																					
Montrose	d																					
Arbroath	d																					
Dundee	d																					
Leuchars 3	d																					
Cupar	d																					
Markinch	d																					
Kirkcaldy	d																					
Inverkeithing	d																					
Glasgow Central 15	d			09 18													11 48					
Motherwell	d			09u43													12u08					
Haymarket	d																					
Edinburgh 10	d								12 05						13 05							
Haymarket	d																					
Lockerbie	d			10 26													12 58					
Carlisle 8	d			11 00													13 30					
Penrith North Lakes	d																					
Oxenholme Lake District	d																					
Lancaster 6	d																					
Preston 8	d		14 29	14 47						15 29	15 47						16 29	16 47				
Wigan North Western	d		14 41	14 59						15 41	15 59						16 41	16 59				
Warrington Bank Quay	d		14 52	15 10						15 53	16 10						16 52	17 10				
Manchester Piccadilly 10	d	14 24			14 58			15 24				15 58				16 24			16 58			17 24
Stockport	d	14 33			15 07			15 33				16 07				16 33			17 07			17 33
Wilmslow	d																					
Crewe 10	d		15 13	15 31						16 13	16 31						17 15	17 31				
Macclesfield	d	14 46			15 20			15 46				16 20				16 46			17 20			17 46
Congleton	d	14 54														16 54						
Stoke-on-Trent	d	15 07			15 39			16 04				16 39				17 07			17 39			18 04
Stafford	d	15 26						16 26								17 26						18 26
Wolverhampton 7	d	15 41	15 47		16 11			16 41		16 49		17 11				17 41	17 49		18 11			18 41
Dunbar	d														13 25							
Berwick-upon-Tweed	d														13 49							
Alnmouth	d								13 03													
Newcastle 8	d						13 27		13 40					14 22	14 40						15 22	
Chester-le-Street	d													14 31								
Durham	d						13 39		13 52					14 38	14 52						15 34	
Darlington 7	d						13 58		14 09					14 55	15 09						15 52	
York 8	d						14 30		14 44					15 27	15 44						16 25	
Leeds 10	d								15 10						16 10							
Wakefield Westgate 7	d								15 23						16 23							
Doncaster 7	d						14 55							15 55							16 53	
Sheffield 7	d						15 23		15 53					16 23	16 53						17 20	
Chesterfield	d						15 35							16 35							17 35	
Derby 10	d						15 57		16 24					16 57	17 24						17 57	
Burton-on-Trent	d						16 07														18 07	
Tamworth	d						16 18														18 18	
Birmingham New Street 12	a	15 58	16 11	16 24	16 30		16 36	16 58	17 04	17 11	17 24	17 30		17 36	17 58	17 58	18 11	18 24	18 30		18 36	18 58
Birmingham New Street 12	d	16 10		16 30	16 33	16 33	16 40	17 03	17 10		17 30	17 33	17 33	17 40	18 03	18 10		18 30	18 33	18 33	18 40	19 03
Cheltenham Spa	a	16 51					17 21		17 51					18 21		18 51					19 21	
Gloucester 7	a																					
Bristol Parkway 7	a	17 25					17 56		18 25					18 56		19 25					19 56	
Bristol Temple Meads 10	a	17 41					18 13		18 41					19 13		19 41					20 13	
Newport (South Wales)	a																					
Cardiff Central 7	a																					
Weston-super-Mare	a																					
Taunton	a	18 15							19 15							20 15						
Tiverton Parkway	a	18 28							19 28							20 28						
Exeter St Davids 6	a	18 43							19 43							20 43						
Dawlish	a																					
Teignmouth	a																					
Newton Abbot	a	19 03							20 03							21 03						
Torquay	a																					
Paignton	a																					
Totnes	a	19 16							20 16							21 16						
Plymouth	a	19 48							20 48							21 48						
Liskeard 3	a	20 12																				
Bodmin Parkway	a	20 24																				
Par 3	a	20 35																				
St Austell	a	20 41																				
Truro	a	20 58																				
Redruth	a	21 10																				
Camborne	a	21 16																				
St Erth 2	a	21 26																				
Penzance	a	21 43																				
Birmingham International	d			16 40	16 46			17 15			17 40	17 45			18 15			18 40	18 45			19 15
Coventry	d			16a49	16a55			17 25			17a49	17a55			18 25			18a49	18a55			19 25
Leamington Spa 8	d					17 00		17 38					18 00		18 38					19 00		19 38
Banbury	a					17 17		17 54					18 17		18 54					19 17		19 54
Oxford	a					17 41		18 14					18 41		19 14					19 41		20 14
Reading 7	a					18 13		18 39					19 13		19 39					20 13		20 39
Kensington Olympia	a					19 01																
East Croydon	a					19 36																
Guildford	a																			20 58		
Redhill	a																			21 28		
Basingstoke	a							19 08							20 08							21 08
Winchester	a							19 24							20 24							21 24
Southampton Airport Parkwy	a							19 33							20 33							21 33
Southampton Central	a							19 40							20 40							21 40
Brockenhurst 3	a							19 56							20 56							21 56
Bournemouth	a							20 15							21 15							22 15
Gatwick Airport 10	a					19 52														21 47		
Haywards Heath 3	a					20 04														22 24		
Brighton 10	a					20 28														22 50		

For general notes see front of timetable
For details of catering facilities see
Directory of Train Operators

from 29 March

Scotland, The North East, North West England → The South West and South Coast

Route Diagram - See first page of Table 51

		XC 1◇ ☕	VT 1◇ ☕		VT 1◇ ☕	XC 1◇ ☕	XC 1◇ ☕	XC 1◇ ☕	VT 1◇ ☕	VT 1◇ ☕	XC 1◇ ☕		XC 1◇	XC 1◇ ☕	VT 1◇ ☕	VT 1◇ ☕	VT 1◇ ☕	XC 1◇ ☕	VT 1◇ ☕	XC 1◇	VT 1◇ ☕	XC 1◇ ☕		
Aberdeen	d																							
Stonehaven	d																							
Montrose	d																							
Arbroath	d																							
Dundee	d																							
Leuchars 3	d																							
Cupar	d																							
Markinch	d																							
Kirkcaldy	d																							
Inverkeithing	d																							
Glasgow Central 15	d																		16 10					
Motherwell	d																		16u25					
Haymarket	d																							
Edinburgh 10	d	14 05					15 05							16 05								18 05		
Haymarket	d																							
Lockerbie	d																		17 13					
Carlisle 8	d																		17 36					
Penrith North Lakes	d																							
Oxenholme Lake District	d																							
Lancaster 6	d																							
Preston 8	d		17 24						18 30						19 29				20 43		21 28			
Wigan North Western	d		17 36						18 42						19 41				20 55		21 40			
Warrington Bank Quay	d		17 48						18 53						19 53				21 06		21 52			
Manchester Piccadilly 10 🚊	d				17 58			18 24		18 58			19 24			19 58	20 17			20 54				
Stockport	d				18 07			18 33		19 07			19 33			20 07	20 26			21 04				
Wilmslow	d																							
Crewe 10	d		18 13						19 15						20 15				21 28		22 13			
Macclesfield	d				18 20			18 46		19 20			19 46			20 20	20 40			21 17				
Congleton	d							18 54					19 54							21 25				
Stoke-on-Trent	d				18 39			19 07		19 39			20 07			20 36	20 58			21 39				
Stafford	d							19 26					20 26				21 18		21 51	21 58	22 33			
Wolverhampton 7 🚊	d		18 49		19 11			19 41	19 49	20 11			20 41		20 49	21 11	21 35		22 09	22 13	22 49			
Dunbar	d						15 25															18 25		
Berwick-upon-Tweed	d						15 49															18 51		
Alnmouth	d	15 04												17 09								19 11		
Newcastle 8	d	15 40				16 20	16 40				17 19			17 40				18 40				19 45		
Chester-le-Street	d					16 29					17 28							18 49						
Durham	d	15 52				16 36	16 52				17 35			17 54				18 56				19 57		
Darlington 7	d	16 09				16 54	17 09				17 52			18 11				19 13				20 14		
York 8	d	16 44				17 25	17 44				18 25			18 44				19 44				20 44		
Leeds 10	d	17 10					18 10							19 10				20 10				21 10		
Wakefield Westgate 7	d	17 23					18 23							19 23				20 23				21 23		
Doncaster 7	d					17 55					18 51													
Sheffield 7	d	17 53				18 23	18 53				19 23			19 53				20 53				21 53		
Chesterfield	d					18 35					19 35			20 05				21 05				22 05		
Derby 10	d	18 24				18 57	19 24				19 57			20 27				21 27				22 27		
Burton-on-Trent	d										20 07							21 37				22 37		
Tamworth	d										20 18							21 48				22 48		
Birmingham New Street 12	a	19 04	19 11		19 30	19 36	19 58	19 58	20 11	20 30	20 42		20 58	21 04	21 11	21 30	21 56	22 13	22 30	22 37	23 10	23 20		
Birmingham New Street 12	d	19 10			19 33	19 40	20 03	20 10		20 33			21 03	21 10		21 33	22 00							
Cheltenham Spa	a	19 51				20 21		20 51						21 51										
Gloucester 7	a																							
Bristol Parkway 7	a	20 25				20 56		21 25						22 25										
Bristol Temple Meads 10	a	20 41				21 13		21 41						22 41										
Newport (South Wales)	a																							
Cardiff Central 7	a																							
Weston-super-Mare	a																							
Taunton	a	21 15						22 15																
Tiverton Parkway	a	21 28						22 28																
Exeter St Davids 6	a	21 43						22 43																
Dawlish	a																							
Teignmouth	a																							
Newton Abbot	a	22 05						23 11																
Torquay	a																							
Paignton	a																							
Totnes	a	22 21						23 26																
Plymouth	a	22 55						23 59																
Liskeard 3	a																							
Bodmin Parkway	a																							
Par 3	a																							
St Austell	a																							
Truro	a																							
Redruth	a																							
Camborne	a																							
St Erth 2	a																							
Penzance	a																							
Birmingham International ✈	d				19 43		20 15			20 43			21 15			21 43	22 10							
Coventry	d				19a52		20 25			20a52			21 25			21a52	22a19							
Leamington Spa 8	d						20 38						21 38											
Banbury	a						20 54						21 55											
Oxford	a						21 14						22 14											
Reading 7	a						21 39						22 39											
Kensington Olympia	a																							
East Croydon 🚊	a																							
Guildford	a																							
Redhill	a																							
Basingstoke	a						22 08						23 08											
Winchester	a						22 24						23 23											
Southampton Airport Parkwy ✈	a						22 33						23 33											
Southampton Central	a						22 48						23 45											
Brockenhurst 3	a						23b04						00b04											
Bournemouth	a						23b23						00b22											
Gatwick Airport 10 ✈	a																							
Haywards Heath 3	a																							
Brighton 10	a																							

For general notes see front of timetable
For details of catering facilities see Directory of Train Operators

b Change at Winchester

Scotland, The North East, North West England → The South West and South Coast

until 27 January

Route Diagram - See first page of Table 51

		XC 1◇	XC 1◇	XC 1◇	XC 1◇	XC 1◇	XC 1◇		VT 1◇	XC 1◇	XC 1◇	XC 1◇	XC 1◇	VT 1◇		VT 1◇	XC 1◇	XC 1◇	XC 1◇	XC 1◇	XC 1◇		VT 1◇	VT 1◇
Aberdeen	d																							
Stonehaven	d																							
Montrose	d																							
Arbroath	d																							
Dundee	d																							
Leuchars 3	d																							
Cupar	d																							
Markinch	d																							
Kirkcaldy	d																							
Inverkeithing	d																							
Glasgow Central 15	d																							
Motherwell	d																							
Haymarket	d																							
Edinburgh 10	d																							
Haymarket	d																							
Lockerbie	d																							
Carlisle 8	d																							
Penrith North Lakes	d																							
Oxenholme Lake District	d																							
Lancaster 6	d																							
Preston 8	d													10 28									11 25	
Wigan North Western	d													10 40									11 37	
Warrington Bank Quay	d													10 51									11 49	
Manchester Piccadilly 10	d			08 08		09 24			09 53				10 24			10 53				11 24				11 53
Stockport	d					09 33			10 02				10 33			11 02				11 33				12 02
Wilmslow	d			08 24																				
Crewe 10	d			08 46	09 33									11 13									12 12	
Macclesfield	d					09 46			10 15				10 46			11 15				11 46				12 15
Congleton	d																							
Stoke-on-Trent	d			09 05		10 05			10 31				11 05			11 31				12 05				12 31
Stafford	d			09 26	09 53	10 26							11 26							12 26				
Wolverhampton 7	d			09 43	10 09	10 43			11 05				11 43	11 49		12 05				12 43			12 49	13 05
Dunbar	d																							
Berwick-upon-Tweed	d																							
Alnmouth	d																							
Newcastle 8	d																		09 28					
Chester-le-Street	d																							
Durham	d																		09 41					
Darlington 7	d																		09 58					
York 8	d										09 20							10 20	10 28					
Leeds 10	d						08 45					10 00							11 00					
Wakefield Westgate 7	d						08 57					10 12							11 12					
Doncaster 7	d										09 50							10 50						
Sheffield 7	d						09 35				10 23	10 48						11 23	11 48					
Chesterfield	d						09 47				10 35							11 35						
Derby 10	d		09 05				10 09				10 57	11 20						11 57	12 20					
Burton-on-Trent	d		09 15				10 19				11 07							12 07						
Tamworth	d		09 26								11 18							12 18						
Birmingham New Street 12	a		09 44	09 58	10 30	10 58	11 04		11 26		11 36	11 53	11 58	12 11		12 26		12 36	12 53	12 58	←		13 11	13 26
Birmingham New Street 12	d	09 03	09 48	10 10	10 33	11 03	11 10		11 30	11 33	11 40	12 03	12 10			12 30	12 33	12 40	13 10	13 03	13 10			13 30
Cheltenham Spa	a			10 51			11 51				12 21		12 51					13 21	→		13 51			
Gloucester 7	a																							
Bristol Parkway 7	a			11 25			12 25				12 55		13 25					13 55			14 25			
Bristol Temple Meads 10	a			11 38			12 38				13 14		13 38					14 14			14 38			
Newport (South Wales)	a																							
Cardiff Central 7	a																							
Weston-super-Mare	a			12 01																				
Taunton	a			12 23			13 15						14 15								15 15			
Tiverton Parkway	a						13 28						14 28								15 28			
Exeter St Davids 6	a			12 48			13 43						14 43								15 43			
Dawlish	a			13 00																				
Teignmouth	a			13 06																				
Newton Abbot	a			13 13			14 03						15 03								16 03			
Torquay	a			13 24																				
Paignton	a			13 37																				
Totnes	a						14 16						15 16								16 16			
Plymouth	a						14 48						15 48								16 48			
Liskeard 3	a																							
Bodmin Parkway	a																							
Par 3	a																							
St Austell	a																							
Truro	a																							
Redruth	a																							
Camborne	a																							
St Erth 2	a																							
Penzance	a																							
Birmingham International ✈	d	09 15	10 15		10 45	11 15			11 41	11 45		12 15				12 41	12 45			13 15				13 41
Coventry	d	09 25	10 25		10 54	11 25			11a51	11 56		12 25				12a51	12 56			13 25				13a51
Leamington Spa 8	d	09 38	10 38		11 07	11 38				12 09		12 38					13 09			13 38				
Banbury	a	09 54	10 54		11 23	11 54				12 26		12 54					13 26			13 54				
Oxford	a	10 14	11 14		11 43	12 14				12 53		13 14					13 45			14 14				
Reading 7	a	10 44	11 44		12 15	12 44				13 28		13 44					14 22			14 44				
Kensington Olympia	a																							
East Croydon	a																							
Guildford	a																							
Redhill	a																							
Basingstoke	a	11 08	12 08			13 08						14 08								15 08				
Winchester	a	11 24	12 24			13 24						14 24								15 24				
Southampton Airport Parkwy ✈	a	11 33	12 33			13 33						14 33								15 33				
Southampton Central	a	11 42	12 42			13 42						14 42								15 42				
Brockenhurst 3	a	12 02	13 02			14 02						15 02								16 02				
Bournemouth	a	12 32	13 32			14 32						15 32								16 32				
Gatwick Airport 10 ✈	a																							
Haywards Heath 3	a																							
Brighton 10	a																							

For general notes see front of timetable
For details of catering facilities see Directory of Train Operators

Table 51 SUMMARY OF SERVICES

Sundays until 27 January

Scotland, The North East, North West England → The South West and South Coast

Route Diagram - See first page of Table 51

		XC	XC	XC	XC	VT	VT	XC	XC	XC	XC	XC	VT	VT	XC	XC	XC	XC	VT	VT	XC
				R	R					R	R	R					R	R	R		
		1 ◇	1 ◇	1	1	1 ◇	1 ◇	1 ◇	1 ◇	1	1	1	1 ◇	1 ◇	1 ◇	1 ◇	1	1	1	1 ◇	1 ◇
Aberdeen	d																				
Stonehaven	d																				
Montrose	d																				
Arbroath	d																				
Dundee	d																				
Leuchars 3	d																				
Cupar	d																				
Markinch	d																				
Kirkcaldy	d																				
Inverkeithing	d																				
Glasgow Central 15	d																		11 55		
Motherwell	d																		12u13		
Haymarket	d																				
Edinburgh 10	d			08 50						09 50			10 56				10 50				
Haymarket	d												11u01								
Lockerbie	d																				
Carlisle 8	d												12 14						13 15		
Penrith North Lakes	d												12 29						13 30		
Oxenholme Lake District	d												12 53								
Lancaster 6	d												13 09						14 07		
Preston 8	d					12 28							13 29						14 27		
Wigan North Western	d					12 40							13 40						14 40		
Warrington Bank Quay	d					12 52							13 53						14 52		
Manchester Piccadilly 10	d				12 08		12 53				13 24			13 53				14 24		14 53	
Stockport	d				12 22		13 02				13 33			14 03				14 33		15 02	
Wilmslow	d																				
Crewe 10	d					13 13							14 17						15 13		
Macclesfield	d				12 35		13 15				13 46			14 16				14 46		15 15	
Congleton	d																				
Stoke-on-Trent	d				12 58		13 31				14 05			14 32				15 05		15 31	
Stafford	d				13 26						14 26							15 26			
Wolverhampton 7	d				13 43	13 49	14 05				14 43		14 55	15 04				15 43	15 49	16 04	
Dunbar	d																11 11				
Berwick-upon-Tweed	d			09 31													11 35				
Alnmouth	d									10 48											
Newcastle 8	d		10 16	10 25					11 16	11 25						12 16	12 25				
Chester-le-Street	d																				
Durham	d		10 28	10 37					11 28	11 37						12 28	12 37				
Darlington 7	d		10 45	10 54					11 45	11 54						12 45	12 54				
York 8	d		11 20	11 28					12 20	12 28						13 20	13 28				
Leeds 10	d			12 00						13 00							14 00				
Wakefield Westgate 7	d			12 12						13 12							14 12				
Doncaster 7	d		11 50						12 50							13 50					
Sheffield 7	d		12 23	12 48					13 23	13 48						14 23	14 48				
Chesterfield	d		12 35						13 35							14 35					
Derby 10	d		12 57	13 20					13 57	14 20						14 57	15 20				
Burton-on-Trent	d								14 07												
Tamworth	d								14 18												
Birmingham New Street 12	a		13 36	13 53	13 58	14 11	14 26		14 36	14 53	14 58	←	15 16	15 26		15 36	15 53	15 58	16 11	16 26	
Birmingham New Street 12	d	13 33	13 40	14 03	14 10		14 30	14 33	14 40	15 10	15 03	15 10		15 30	15 33	15 40	16 03	16 10		16 30	16 33
Cheltenham Spa	a		14 21		14 51				15 21	→		15 51				16 21		16 51			
Gloucester 7	a																				
Bristol Parkway 7	a		14 55		15 25				15 55			16 25				16 55		17 25			
Bristol Temple Meads 10	a		15 11		15 38				16 14			16 38				17 14		17 38			
Newport (South Wales)	a																				
Cardiff Central 7	a																				
Weston-super-Mare	a																				
Taunton	a		15 43		16 15							17 15						18 15			
Tiverton Parkway	a		15 55		16 28							17 28						18 28			
Exeter St Davids 6	a		16 11		16 43							17 43						18 43			
Dawlish	a																				
Teignmouth	a																				
Newton Abbot	a		16 32		17 03							18 03						19 03			
Torquay	a																				
Paignton	a																				
Totnes	a		16 45		17 16							18 16						19 16			
Plymouth	a		17 18		17 48							18 48						19 48			
Liskeard 3	a				18 23							19 17						20 17			
Bodmin Parkway	a				18 35							19 29						20 29			
Par 3	a				18 46							19 40						20 40			
St Austell	a				18 52							19 46						20 46			
Truro	a				19 10							20 04						21 04			
Redruth	a				19 21							20 15						21 15			
Camborne	a				19 28							20 22						21 26			
St Erth 2	a				19 38							20 32						21 36			
Penzance	a				19 54							20 48						21 52			
Birmingham International	d	13 45		14 15			14 41	14 45			15 15			15 41	15 45		16 15			16 41	16 45
Coventry	d	13 56		14 25			14a51	14 56			15 25			15a51	15 56		16 25			16a51	16 56
Leamington Spa 8	d	14 09		14 38				15 09			15 38				16 09		16 38				17 09
Banbury	a	14 26		14 54				15 26			15 54				16 26		16 54				17 26
Oxford	a	14 45		15 14				15 53			16 14				16 53		17 14				17 53
Reading 7	a	15 22		15 44				16 28			16 44				17 28		17 44				18 28
Kensington Olympia	a																				
East Croydon	a																				
Guildford	a																				
Redhill	a																				
Basingstoke	a			16 08							17 08						18 08				
Winchester	a			16 24							17 24						18 24				
Southampton Airport Parkwy	a			16 33							17 33						18 33				
Southampton Central	a			16 42							17 42						18 42				
Brockenhurst 3	a			17 02							18 02						19 02				
Bournemouth	a			17 32							18 32						19 32				
Gatwick Airport 10	a																				
Haywards Heath 3	a																				
Brighton 10	a																				

For general notes see front of timetable
For details of catering facilities see Directory of Train Operators

until 27 January

Scotland, The North East, North West England → The South West and South Coast

Route Diagram - See first page of Table 51

		XC	XC	XC	XC	VT	VT	XC	XC	XC	XC	VT	VT	XC	XC	XC	XC	XC	VT	VT	XC
		1 ◇	R 1	R 1	R 1	R 1	1 ◇	1 ◇	R 1	R 1	R 1	R 1	1 ◇	1 ◇	1 ◇	R 1	R 1	R 1	R 1	1 ◇	1 ◇
		☕	☕	☕	☕	☕	☕	☕	☕	☕	☕	☕	☕	☕	☕	☕	☕	☕	☕	☕	☕
Aberdeen	d																				
Stonehaven	d																				
Montrose	d																				
Arbroath	d																				
Dundee	d																				
Leuchars 3	d																				
Cupar	d																				
Markinch	d																				
Kirkcaldy	d																				
Inverkeithing	d																				
Glasgow Central 15	d		10 30							11 30		14 03									
Motherwell	d		10u52							11u56											
Haymarket	d		11 37							12 37											
Edinburgh 10	d		11 50			12 52				12 50						13 50			14 53		
Haymarket	d					12u57													14u58		
Lockerbie	d					13 51													15 53		
Carlisle 8	d					14 13						15 16							16 14		
Penrith North Lakes	d					14 28													16 29		
Oxenholme Lake District	d					14 53													16 53		
Lancaster 6	d					15 09						16 04							17 09		
Preston 8	d					15 28						16 23							17 29		
Wigan North Western	d					15 41						16 36							17 41		
Warrington Bank Quay	d					15 52						16 47							17 53		
Manchester Piccadilly 10	d			15 24			15 53				16 24		16 53				17 24			17 53	
Stockport	d			15 33			16 02				16 33		17 02				17 33			18 02	
Wilmslow	d																				
Crewe 10	d					16 13						17 09							18 15		
Macclesfield	d			15 46			16 15				16 46		17 15				17 46			18 15	
Congleton	d																				
Stoke-on-Trent	d			16 05			16 31				17 05		17 31				18 05			18 31	
Stafford	d			16 26							17 26						18 26				
Wolverhampton 7	d			16 43		16 49	17 04				17 43	17 49	18 04				18 43		18 52	19 04	
Dunbar	d									13 12											
Berwick-upon-Tweed	d									13 35											
Alnmouth	d		12 48													14 48					
Newcastle 8	d	13 23	13 25						14 16	14 25					15 16	15 25					16 16
Chester-le-Street	d																				
Durham	d	13 36	13 37						14 28	14 38					15 28	15 37					16 29
Darlington 7	d	13 53	13 54						14 45	14 55					15 45	15 54					16 48
York 8	d	14 24	14 28						15 21	15 28					16 20	16 28					17 20
Leeds 10	d		15 00							16 00						17 00					
Wakefield Westgate 7	d		15 12							16 12						17 12					
Doncaster 7	d	14 50							15 50						16 50						17 50
Sheffield 7	d	15 23	15 48						16 23	16 48					17 23	17 48					18 23
Chesterfield	d	15 35							16 35						17 35						18 35
Derby 10	d	15 57	16 20						16 57	17 20					17 57	18 20					18 57
Burton-on-Trent	d	16 07													18 07						19 07
Tamworth	d	16 18													18 18						19 18
Birmingham New Street 12	a	16 36	16 53	16 58	←	17 11	17 26		17 36	17 53	17 58	18 11	18 26		18 36	18 53	18 58	←	19 14	19 26	19 36
Birmingham New Street 12	d	16 40	17 10	17 03	17 10		17 30	17 33	17 40	18 03	18 10		18 30	18 33	18 40	19 10	19 03	19 10		19 30	19 40
Cheltenham Spa	a	17 21	→		17 51				18 21		18 51				19 21	→		19 51			20 21
Gloucester 7	a								18 32												
Bristol Parkway 7	a	17 55			18 25				19 07		19 25				20 00			20 25			20 58
Bristol Temple Meads 10	a	18 14			18 38				19 24		19 38				20 16			20 38			21 14
Newport (South Wales)	a								19 51												
Cardiff Central 7	a								20 11												
Weston-super-Mare	a																				
Taunton	a				19 15						20 15							21 15			
Tiverton Parkway	a				19 28						20 28							21 28			
Exeter St Davids 6	a				19 45						20 45							21 43			
Dawlish	a																				
Teignmouth	a																				
Newton Abbot	a				20 06						21 06							22 03			
Torquay	a																				
Paignton	a																				
Totnes	a				20 19						21 22							22 16			
Plymouth	a				20 51						21 56							22 48			
Liskeard 3	a																				
Bodmin Parkway	a																				
Par 3	a																				
St Austell	a																				
Truro	a																				
Redruth	a																				
Camborne	a																				
St Erth 2	a																				
Penzance	a																				
Birmingham International ✈	d			17 15			17 41	17 45		18 15			18 40	18 45			19 15			19 41	
Coventry	d			17 25			17a51	17 56		18 25			18a49	18 56			19 25			19a51	
Leamington Spa 8	d			17 38				18 09		18 38				19 09			19 38				
Banbury	a			17 54				18 26		18 54				19 26			19 54				
Oxford	a			18 14				18 45		19 14				19 53			20 14				
Reading 7	a			18 44				19 11		19 44				20 19			20 44				
Kensington Olympia	a																				
East Croydon	a																				
Guildford	a							19 45						20 50							
Redhill	a							20 26						21 31							
Basingstoke	a			19 08						20 08							21 08				
Winchester	a			19 24						20 24							21 24				
Southampton Airport Parkwy ✈	a			19 33						20 33							21 33				
Southampton Central	a			19 42						20 44							21 42				
Brockenhurst 3	a			20 02						21 02							22 02				
Bournemouth	a			20 32						21 32							22 32				
Gatwick Airport 10 ✈	a							20 43						21 46							
Haywards Heath 3	a							20 54						22 06							
Brighton 10	a							21 13						22 50							

For general notes see front of timetable
For details of catering facilities see Directory of Train Operators

until 27 January

Scotland, The North East, North West England → The South West and South Coast

Route Diagram - See first page of Table 51

Station		XC	XC	VT	VT	XC	XC	XC	XC	VT	VT	XC	VT	XC	VT	XC	XC	VT	XC	XC
		R	R	R																
		1	1	1	1◊	1◊	1◊	1◊	1◊	1◊	1◊	1◊	1◊	1◊	1◊	1◊	1◊	1◊	1◊	1◊
		☕	☕	☕	☕	☕	☕		☕	☕	☕	☕	☕	☕	☕		☕	☕		☕
Aberdeen	d	11 58																		
Stonehaven	d	12 16																		
Montrose	d	12 39																		
Arbroath	d	12 56																		
Dundee	d	13 14																		
Leuchars 3	d	13 27																		
Cupar	d	13 35																		
Markinch	d	13 49																		
Kirkcaldy	d	13 58																		
Inverkeithing	d	14 14																		
Glasgow Central 15	d			16 03										15 45	18 03					
Motherwell	d													15u59						
Haymarket	d	14 29												16 39						
Edinburgh 10	d	14b50					15 50			16 53				16 50			17 50	18 52		18 50
Haymarket	d									16u59								18u57		
Lockerbie	d									17 56								19 58		
Carlisle 8	d			17 18						18 19					19 15			20 18		
Penrith North Lakes	d									18 34								20 34		
Oxenholme Lake District	d			17 55						18 58					19 52			20 58		
Lancaster 6	d			18 10						19 16					20 08			21 14		
Preston 8	d			18 30						19 35					20 28			21 34		
Wigan North Western	d			18 42						19 47					20 40			21 46		
Warrington Bank Quay	d			18 53						19 58					20 52			21 58		
Manchester Piccadilly 10 🚢	d		18 24		18 53			19 24			19 55		20 23			20 55			21 55	
Stockport	d		18 33		19 02			19 33			20 04		20 32			21 04			22 04	
Wilmslow	d																			
Crewe 10	d			19 15						20 20					21 13			22 20		
Macclesfield	d		18 46		19 15			19 46			20 17		20 45			21 17			22 17	
Congleton	d																			
Stoke-on-Trent	d		19 05		19 31			20 05			20 33		21 01			21 34			22 34	
Stafford	d		19 26					20 26			20 53		21 21		21 32	21 53		22 40	22 53	
Wolverhampton 7 🚢	d		19 43	19 49	20 04			20 43		20 52	21 10		21 35		21 56	22 09		22 55	23 09	
Dunbar	d	15 10												17 10			18 10			
Berwick-upon-Tweed	d	15 35												17 33						
Alnmouth	d						16 48										18 52			
Newcastle 8	d	16 25				17 16	17 25					18 16		18 25			19 25			20 25
Chester-le-Street	d																			
Durham	d	16 37				17 31	17 37					18 28		18 37			19 37			20 37
Darlington 7	d	16 54				17 48	17 54					18 45		18 54			19 54			20 54
York 8	d	17 28				18 20	18 28					19 20		19 28			20 28			21 26
Leeds 10	d	18 00					19 00							20 00			21 00			
Wakefield Westgate 7	d	18 12					19 12							20 12			21 12			
Doncaster 7	d					18 50						19 50								21 50
Sheffield 7	d	18 48				19 23	19 48					20 23		20 48			21 48			22 23
Chesterfield	d					19 35	20 00					20 35		21 00			22 00			22 35
Derby 10	d	19 20				19 57	20 24					20 57		21 24			22 24			22 57
Burton-on-Trent	d					20 07						21 07		21 34			22 34			23 07
Tamworth	d					20 18						21 18		21 45			22 45			23 18
Birmingham New Street 12	a	19 53	19 58	20 11	20 26	20 41	20 57	20 58	←	21 15	21 32	21 41	21 56	22 04	22 17	22 30	23 16	23 17	23 30	23 51
Birmingham New Street 12	d	20 03	20 10		20 30		21 10 →	21 03	21 10				22 00	22 10						
Cheltenham Spa	a		20 51						21 51					22 51						
Gloucester 7	a																			
Bristol Parkway 7	a		21 25						22 25					23 25						
Bristol Temple Meads 10	a		21 38						22 41					23 41						
Newport (South Wales)	a																			
Cardiff Central 7	a																			
Weston-super-Mare	a																			
Taunton	a		22 15																	
Tiverton Parkway	a		22 28																	
Exeter St Davids 6	a		22 45																	
Dawlish	a																			
Teignmouth	a																			
Newton Abbot	a		23 10																	
Torquay	a																			
Paignton	a																			
Totnes	a		23 25																	
Plymouth	a		23 59																	
Liskeard 3	a																			
Bodmin Parkway	a																			
Par 3	a																			
St Austell	a																			
Truro	a																			
Redruth	a																			
Camborne	a																			
St Erth 2	a																			
Penzance	a																			
Birmingham International ✈	d	20 15			20 41			21 15					22 10							
Coventry	d	20 25			20a51			21 25					22a19							
Leamington Spa 8	d	20 38						21 38												
Banbury	a	20 54						21 54												
Oxford	a	21 14						22 14												
Reading 7	a	21 44						22 49												
Kensington Olympia	a																			
East Croydon 🚢	a																			
Guildford	a																			
Redhill	a																			
Basingstoke	a	22 08						23 08												
Winchester	a	*22 44*						23 24												
Southampton Airport Parkwy ✈	a	23 18						23 33												
Southampton Central	a	23 31						23 45												
Brockenhurst 3	a	*23c16*						*00 53*												
Bournemouth	a	*23c35*						*01 16*												
Gatwick Airport 10 ✈	a																			
Haywards Heath 3	a																			
Brighton 10	a																			

For general notes see front of timetable
For details of catering facilities see Directory of Train Operators

b Arr. 1433
c Change at Basingstoke

Scotland, The North East, North West England → The South West and South Coast

3 February to 23 March

Route Diagram - See first page of Table 51

		XC	XC	XC	XC	XC	VT	XC	XC	VT	VT	XC	XC	XC	VT	VT	XC	XC	VT	VT	XC
		1◇	1◇	1◇	1◇	1◇	1◇	1◇	1◇	1◇	1◇	1◇	1◇	1◇	1◇	1◇	R 1	R 1	1◇	1◇	R 1
Aberdeen	d																				
Stonehaven	d																				
Montrose	d																				
Arbroath	d																				
Dundee	d																				
Leuchars [3]	d																				
Cupar	d																				
Markinch	d																				
Kirkcaldy	d																				
Inverkeithing	d																				
Glasgow Central [15]	d																				
Motherwell	d																				
Haymarket	d																				
Edinburgh [10]	d																				08 50
Haymarket	d																				
Lockerbie	d																				
Carlisle [8]	d																				
Penrith North Lakes	d																				
Oxenholme Lake District	d																				
Lancaster [6]	d																				
Preston [8]	d									10 28					11 25				12 28		
Wigan North Western	d									10 40					11 37				12 40		
Warrington Bank Quay	d									10 51					11 49				12 52		
Manchester Piccadilly [10]	d			08 08	09 24		09 53		10 24		10 53		11 24			11 53		12 08		12 53	
Stockport	d				09 33		10 02		10 33		11 02		11 33			12 02		12 22		13 02	
Wilmslow	d			08 24																	
Crewe [10]	d			08 46						11 13					12 12				13 13		
Macclesfield	d				09 46		10 15		10 46		11 15		11 46			12 15		12 35		13 15	
Congleton	d																				
Stoke-on-Trent	d			09 05	10 05		10 31		11 05		11 31		12 05			12 31		12 58		13 31	
Stafford	d			09 26	10 26				11 26				12 26					13 26			
Wolverhampton [7]	d			09 43	10 43		11 05		11 43	11 49	12 05		12 43		12 49	13 05		13 43	13 49	14 05	
Dunbar	d																				
Berwick-upon-Tweed	d																				09 31
Alnmouth	d																				
Newcastle [8]	d																09 28				10 25
Chester-le-Street	d																				
Durham	d																09 42				10 37
Darlington [7]	d																09 59				10 54
York [8]	d																10 28				11 28
Leeds [10]	d							09 00				10 00					11 00				12 00
Wakefield Westgate [7]	d							09 12				10 12					11 12				12 12
Doncaster [7]	d							09 34				10 35					11 30				12 33
Sheffield [7]	d							10 05				11 05					12 05				13 05
Chesterfield	d							10 17				11 17					12 17				13 17
Derby [10]	d					09 50		10 40				11 40					12 40				13 40
Burton-on-Trent	d																				
Tamworth	d																				
Birmingham New Street [12]	a			09 58	10 58	11 03	11 26	11 53	11 58	12 11	12 26	12 53	12 58	←	13 11	13 26	13 53	13 58	14 11	14 26	14 53
Birmingham New Street [12]	d	09 03	09 48	10 10	11 03	11 10	11 30	12 03	12 10		12 30	13 10	13 03	13 10		13 30	14 03	14 10		14 30	15 10
Cheltenham Spa	a			10 51		11 51			12 51			→		13 51				14 51			→
Gloucester [7]	a																				
Bristol Parkway [7]	a			11 25		12 25			13 25					14 25				15 25			
Bristol Temple Meads [10]	a			11 38		12 38			13 38					14 38				15 38			
Newport (South Wales)	a																				
Cardiff Central [7]	a																				
Weston-super-Mare	a																	16 08			
Taunton	a			12 59		14 15			15 15					16 15				16 33			
Tiverton Parkway	a			13 13		14 28			15 28					16 28				16 46			
Exeter St Davids [6]	a			13 28		14 43			15 43					16 43				17 01			
Dawlish	a			13 42														17 16			
Teignmouth	a			13 47														17 21			
Newton Abbot	a			13 55		15 03			16 03					17 03				17 28			
Torquay	a																				
Paignton	a																				
Totnes	a			14 08		15 16			16 16					17 16				17 41			
Plymouth	a			14 40		15 48			16 48					17 48				18 13			
Liskeard [3]	a																	18 35			
Bodmin Parkway	a																	18 47			
Par [3]	a																				
St Austell	a																	19 01			
Truro	a																	19 18			
Redruth	a																	19 30			
Camborne	a																	19 36			
St Erth [2]	a																				
Penzance	a																	20 00			
Birmingham International ✈	d	09 15	10 15		11 15		11 41	12 15			12 41		13 15			13 41	14 15			14 41	
Coventry	d	09 25	10 25		11 25		11a51	12 25			12a51		13 25			13a51	14 25			14a51	
Leamington Spa [8]	d	09 38	10 38		11 38			12 38					13 38				14 38				
Banbury	a	09 54	10 54		11 54			12 54					13 54				14 54				
Oxford	a	10 14	11 14		12 14			13 14					14 14				15 14				
Reading [7]	a	10 44	11 44		12 44			13 44					14 44				15 44				
Kensington Olympia	a																				
East Croydon	a																				
Guildford	a																				
Redhill	a																				
Basingstoke	a	11 08	12 08		13 08			14 08					15 08				16 08				
Winchester	a	11 24	12 24		13 24			14 24					15 24				16 24				
Southampton Airport Parkwy ✈	a	11 33	12 33		13 33			14 33					15 33				16 33				
Southampton Central	a	11 42	12 42		13 42			14 42					15 42				16 42				
Brockenhurst [3]	a	12 02	13 02		14 02			15 02					16 02				17 02				
Bournemouth	a	12 32	13 32		14 32			15 32					16 32				17 32				
Gatwick Airport [10] ✈	a																				
Haywards Heath [3]	a																				
Brighton [10]	a																				

For general notes see front of timetable
For details of catering facilities see Directory of Train Operators

Scotland, The North East, North West England → The South West and South Coast

3 February to 23 March

Route Diagram - See first page of Table 51

		XC	XC	VT	VT	XC	XC	VT	VT	XC	XC	XC	VT	VT	XC	XC	VT	XC	XC	XC
		R 1	R 1	1 ◇	1 ◇	R 1	R 1	R 1	1 ◇	R 1	R 1	R 1	R 1	1 ◇	R 1	R 1	1 ◇	1 ◇	R 1	R 1
Aberdeen	d																			
Stonehaven	d																			
Montrose	d																			
Arbroath	d																			
Dundee	d																			
Leuchars 3	d																			
Cupar	d																			
Markinch	d																			
Kirkcaldy	d																			
Inverkeithing	d																			
Glasgow Central 15	d														10 30				11 30	
Motherwell	d														10u56				11u56	
Haymarket	d														11 37				12 37	
Edinburgh 10	d					09 50				10 50					11 50				12 50	
Haymarket	d																			
Lockerbie	d							12 52					13 52							
Carlisle 8	d							13 15					14 13							
Penrith North Lakes	d							13 30					14 28							
Oxenholme Lake District	d												14 53							
Lancaster 6	d							14 07					15 09							
Preston 8	d			13 29				14 27					15 28							
Wigan North Western	d			13 40				14 40					15 41							
Warrington Bank Quay	d			13 53				14 52					15 52							
Manchester Piccadilly 10 ⇌	d	13 24			13 53		14 24		14 53		15 24			15 53		16 24	16 53			17 24
Stockport	d	13 33			14 03		14 33		15 02		15 33			16 02		16 33	17 02			17 33
Wilmslow	d																			
Crewe 10	d			14 17				15 13					16 13							
Macclesfield	d	13 46			14 16		14 46		15 15		15 46			16 15		16 46	17 15			17 46
Congleton	d																			
Stoke-on-Trent	d	14 05			14 32		15 05		15 31		16 05			16 31		17 05	17 31			18 05
Stafford	d	14 26					15 26				16 26					17 26				18 26
Wolverhampton 7 ⇌	d	14 43		14 55	15 04		15 43	15 49	16 04		16 43		16 49	17 04		17 43	18 04			18 43
Dunbar	d									11 11									13 10	
Berwick-upon-Tweed	d									11 35									13 33	
Alnmouth	d					10 48									12 48					
Newcastle 8	d					11 25				12 25					13 25				14 25	
Chester-le-Street	d																			
Durham	d					11 37				12 37					13 37				14 37	
Darlington 7	d					11 54				12 54					13 55				14 54	
York 8	d					12 28				13 28					14 28				15 28	
Leeds 10	d					13 00				14 00					15 00				16 00	
Wakefield Westgate 7	d					13 12				14 12					15 12				16 12	
Doncaster 7	d					13 30				14 30					15 30				16 30	
Sheffield 7	d					14 05				15 05					16 05				17 05	
Chesterfield	d					14 17				15 17					16 17				17 17	
Derby 10	d					14 40				15 40					16 40				17 40	
Burton-on-Trent	d																			
Tamworth	d																			
Birmingham New Street 12	a	14 58	←	15 16	15 26	15 53	15 58	16 11	16 26	16 53	16 58	←	17 11	17 26	17 53	17 58	18 26		18 53	18 58
Birmingham New Street 12	d	15 03	15 10		15 30	16 03	16 10		16 30	17 10	17 03	17 10		17 30	18 03	18 10	18 30	18 33	19 10	19 03
Cheltenham Spa	a		15 51				16 51			→		17 51				18 51			→	
Gloucester 7	a											18 02								
Bristol Parkway 7	a		16 25				17 25					18 35				19 25				
Bristol Temple Meads 10	a		16 38				17 38					18 47				19 38				
Newport (South Wales)	a																			
Cardiff Central 7	a																			
Weston-super-Mare	a																			
Taunton	a		17 15				18 15					19 21				20 15				
Tiverton Parkway	a		17 28				18 28					19 34				20 28				
Exeter St Davids 6	a		17 43				18 43					19 48				20 45				
Dawlish	a																			
Teignmouth	a																			
Newton Abbot	a		18 03				19 03					20 09				21 06				
Torquay	a																			
Paignton	a																			
Totnes	a		18 16				19 16					20 22				21 22				
Plymouth	a		18 48				19 48					20 54				21 56				
Liskeard 3	a		19 17				20 17													
Bodmin Parkway	a		19 29				20 29													
Par 3	a		19 40				20 40													
St Austell	a		19 46				20 46													
Truro	a		20 04				21 04													
Redruth	a		20 15				21 15													
Camborne	a		20 28				21 26													
St Erth 2	a		20 38				21 36													
Penzance	a		20 54				21 52													
Birmingham International ✈	d	15 15			15 41	16 15			16 41		17 15			17 41	18 15		18 40	18 46		19 15
Coventry	d	15 25			15a51	16 25			16a51		17 25			17a51	18 25		18a49	18 55		19 25
Leamington Spa 8	d	15 38				16 38					17 38				18 38			19 08		19 38
Banbury	a	15 54				16 54					17 54				18 54			19 24		19 54
Oxford	a	16 14				17 14					18 14				19 14			19 44		20 14
Reading 7	a	16 44				17 44					18 44				19 44			20 11		20 44
Kensington Olympia	a																			
East Croydon ⇌	a																			
Guildford	a																	20 50		
Redhill	a																	21 31		
Basingstoke	a	17 08				18 08					19 08				20 08					21 08
Winchester	a	17 24				18 24					19 24				20 24					21 24
Southampton Airport Parkwy ✈	a	17 33				18 33					19 33				20 33					21 33
Southampton Central	a	17 42				18 42					19 42				20 44					21 42
Brockenhurst 3	a	18 02				19 02					20 02				21 02					22 02
Bournemouth	a	18 32				19 32					20 32				21 32					22 32
Gatwick Airport 10 ✈	a																	21 46		
Haywards Heath 3	a																	22 06		
Brighton 10	a																	22 50		

For general notes see front of timetable
For details of catering facilities see Directory of Train Operators

Scotland, The North East, North West England → The South West and South Coast

3 February to 23 March

Route Diagram - See first page of Table 51

		XC	VT	VT	XC	XC	VT	VT	XC	XC	XC	VT	VT	XC	VT	XC	XC	VT	XC	XC
		R	R		R	R	R		R		R									
		1	1	1 ◊	1	1	1	1 ◊	1	1 ◊	1	1 ◊	1 ◊	1 ◊	1 ◊	1 ◊	1 ◊	1 ◊	1 ◊	1 ◊
Aberdeen	d								11 58											
Stonehaven	d								12 16											
Montrose	d								12 39											
Arbroath	d								12 56											
Dundee	d								13 14											
Leuchars 3	d								13 27											
Cupar	d								13 35											
Markinch	d								13 49											
Kirkcaldy	d								13 58											
Inverkeithing	d								14 14											
Glasgow Central 15	d																15 45			
Motherwell	d																15u59			
Haymarket	d								14 29								16 39			
Edinburgh 10	d				13 50				14b50					15 50			16 50			17 50
Haymarket	d																			
Lockerbie	d		15 52				16 52								18 52			19 58		
Carlisle 8	d		16 14				17 18								19 15			20 18		
Penrith North Lakes	d		16 29															20 34		
Oxenholme Lake District	d		16 53				17 55								19 52			20 58		
Lancaster 6	d		17 09				18 10								20 08			21 14		
Preston 8	d		17 29				18 30								20 28			21 34		
Wigan North Western	d		17 41				18 42								20 40			21 46		
Warrington Bank Quay	d		17 53				18 53								20 52			21 58		
Manchester Piccadilly 10	d			17 53		18 24		18 53		19 24		19 55	20 23			20 55			21 55	
Stockport	d			18 02		18 33		19 02		19 33		20 04	20 32			21 04			22 04	
Wilmslow	d																			
Crewe 10	d		18 15				19 15								21 13			22 20		
Macclesfield	d			18 15		18 46		19 15		19 46		20 17	20 45			21 17			22 17	
Congleton	d																			
Stoke-on-Trent	d			18 31		19 05		19 31		20 05		20 33	21 01			21 34			22 34	
Stafford	d					19 26				20 26		20 53	21 21		21 32	21 53		22 40	22 53	
Wolverhampton 7	d		18 52	19 04		19 43	19 49	20 04		20 43		21 10	21 35		21 56	22 09		22 55	23 09	
Dunbar	d								15 10								17 10			18 10
Berwick-upon-Tweed	d								15 35								17 33			
Alnmouth	d				14 48									16 48						18 52
Newcastle 8	d				15 25				16 25					17 25			18 25			19 25
Chester-le-Street	d																			
Durham	d				15 37				16 37					17 37			18 37			19 37
Darlington 7	d				15 54				16 54					17 54			18 54			19 54
York 8	d				16 28				17 28					18 28			19 28			20 28
Leeds 10	d				17 00				18 00					19 00			20 00			21 00
Wakefield Westgate 7	d				17 12				18 12					19 12			20 12			21 12
Doncaster 7	d				17 30				18 30					19 30			20 31			21 30
Sheffield 7	d				18 05				19 05					20 05			21 05			22 05
Chesterfield	d				18 17				19 17					20 17			21 17			22 17
Derby 10	d				18 40				19 40					20 40			21 40			22 40
Burton-on-Trent	d																			
Tamworth	d																			
Birmingham New Street 12	a	←	19 14	19 26	19 53	19 58	20 11	20 26	20 57	20 58	←	21 32	21 56	22 01	22 17	22 30	22 55	23 17	23 30	23 55
Birmingham New Street 12	d	19 10		19 30	20 03	20 10		20 30	21 10	21 03	21 10		22 00	22 10						
Cheltenham Spa	a	19 51				20 51			→		21 51			22 51						
Gloucester 7	a																			
Bristol Parkway 7	a	20 25				21 25					22 25			23 25						
Bristol Temple Meads 10	a	20 38				21 38					22 41			23 41						
Newport (South Wales)	a																			
Cardiff Central 7	a																			
Weston-super-Mare	a																			
Taunton	a	21 15				22 15														
Tiverton Parkway	a	21 28				22 28														
Exeter St Davids 6	a	21 43				22 45														
Dawlish	a																			
Teignmouth	a																			
Newton Abbot	a	22 03				23 10														
Torquay	a																			
Paignton	a																			
Totnes	a	22 16				23 25														
Plymouth	a	22 48				23 59														
Liskeard 3	a																			
Bodmin Parkway	a																			
Par 3	a																			
St Austell	a																			
Truro	a																			
Redruth	a																			
Camborne	a																			
St Erth 2	a																			
Penzance	a																			
Birmingham International	d			19 41	20 15			20 41		21 15			22 10							
Coventry	d			19a51	20 25			20a51		21 25			22a19							
Leamington Spa 8	d				20 38					21 38										
Banbury	a				20 54					21 54										
Oxford	a				21 14					22 14										
Reading 7	a				21 44					22 49										
Kensington Olympia	a																			
East Croydon	a																			
Guildford	a																			
Redhill	a																			
Basingstoke	a				22 08					23 08										
Winchester	a				22 44					23 24										
Southampton Airport Parkwy	a				23 18					23 33										
Southampton Central	a				23 31					23 45										
Brockenhurst 3	a				23c16					00 53										
Bournemouth	a				23c35					01 16										
Gatwick Airport 10	a																			
Haywards Heath 3	a																			
Brighton 10	a																			

For general notes see front of timetable
For details of catering facilities see Directory of Train Operators

b Arr. 1433
c Change at Basingstoke

Sundays

from 30 March

Scotland, The North East, North West England → The South West and South Coast

Route Diagram - See first page of Table 51

		XC	XC	XC	XC	XC	XC	XC	XC	XC	XC	VT	XC	XC	XC	XC	VT	VT	XC	XC	XC	XC
		1 ◊	1 ◊	1 ◊	1 ◊	1 ◊	1 ◊	1 ◊	1 ◊	1 ◊	1 ◊	1 ◊	1 ◊	1 ◊	1 ◊	1 ◊	1 ◊	1 ◊	1 ◊	1 ◊	1 ◊	1 ◊
		A		A		A				A					A							A
		🍴	🍴	🍴	🍴	🍴	🍴	🍴	🍴	🍴	🍴	🍴	🍴	🍴	🍴	🍴	🍴	🍴	🍴	🍴	🍴	🍴
Aberdeen	d																					
Stonehaven	d																					
Montrose	d																					
Arbroath	d																					
Dundee	d																					
Leuchars 3	d																					
Cupar	d																					
Markinch	d																					
Kirkcaldy	d																					
Inverkeithing	d																					
Glasgow Central 15	d																					
Motherwell	d																					
Haymarket	d																					
Edinburgh 10	d																					
Haymarket	d																					
Lockerbie	d																					
Carlisle 8	d																					
Penrith North Lakes	d																					
Oxenholme Lake District	d																					
Lancaster 6	d																					
Preston 8	d																10 28					
Wigan North Western	d																10 40					
Warrington Bank Quay	d																10 51					
Manchester Piccadilly 10 🚢	d						08 08		09 24			09 53				10 24		10 53			11 24	
Stockport	d								09 33			10 02				10 33		11 02			11 33	
Wilmslow	d						08 24		09 41			10 10				10 41		11 10			11 41	
Crewe 10	d						08 59		10 02							11 02	11 13				12 02	
Macclesfield	d																					
Congleton	d																					
Stoke-on-Trent	d																					
Stafford	d						09b26		10c26			10 48				11e26		11 49			12 26	
Wolverhampton 7 🚢	d						09 43		10 43			11 05				11 43	11 49	12 05			12 43	
Dunbar	d																					
Berwick-upon-Tweed	d																					
Alnmouth	d																					
Newcastle 8	d																			09 28		
Chester-le-Street	d																					
Durham	d																			09 41		
Darlington 7	d																			09 58		
York 8	d												09 20						10 20	10 28		
Leeds 10	d							08 45						10 00						11 00		
Wakefield Westgate 7	d							08 57						10 12						11 12		
Doncaster 7	d												09 50						10 50			
Sheffield 7	d							09 37					10 23	10 48					11 23	11 48		
Chesterfield	d							09 49					10 35						11 35			
Derby 10	d				09 05			10 10					10 57	11 20					11 57	12 20		
Burton-on-Trent	d				09 15			10 21					11 07						12 07			
Tamworth	d				09 26			10 32					11 18						12 18			
Birmingham New Street 12	a				09 44		09 58	10 51	10 58		←	11 26	11 36	11 53		11 58	12 11	12 26	12 36	12 53	12 58	
Birmingham New Street 12	d		09 03		09 48		10 10	11 10	11 03		11 10	11 30	11 40	12 03		12 10		12 30	12 40	13 10	13 03	
Cheltenham Spa	a						10 51	→			11 51		12 21			12 51			13 21	→		
Gloucester 7	a																					
Bristol Parkway 7	a						11 25				12 25		12 57			13 25			13 57			
Bristol Temple Meads 10	a						11 38				12 38		13 13			13 38			14 13			
Newport (South Wales)	a																					
Cardiff Central 7	a																					
Weston-super-Mare	a						12 01															
Taunton	a						12 26				13 15					14 15						
Tiverton Parkway	a										13 28					14 28						
Exeter St Davids 6	a						12 55				13 43					14 43						
Dawlish	a						13 07															
Teignmouth	a						13 13															
Newton Abbot	a						13 20				14 03					15 03						
Torquay	a						13 31															
Paignton	a						13 44															
Totnes	a										14 16					15 16						
Plymouth	a										14 48					15 48						
Liskeard 8	a																					
Bodmin Parkway	a																					
Par 3	a																					
St Austell	a																					
Truro	a																					
Redruth	a																					
Camborne	a																					
St Erth 2	a																					
Penzance	a																					
Birmingham International ✈	d		09 15		10 15				11 15			11 41		12 15				12 41			13 15	
Coventry	d		09 25		10 25				11 25			11a51		12 25				12a51			13 25	
Leamington Spa 8	d		09 38		10 38				11 38					12 38							13 38	
Banbury	a		09 54		10 54				11 54					12 54							13 54	
Oxford	a	*09f30*	10 19	*10f30*	11 19	*11f30*			12 19	*12f30*				13 19	*13f30*						14 19	*14f30*
Reading 7	a	10d50		11d50		12d50				13d50					14d50							15d50
Kensington Olympia	a																					
East Croydon 🚢	a																					
Guildford	a																					
Redhill	a																					
Basingstoke	a	11 08		12 08		13 08				14 08					15 08							16 08
Winchester	a	11 24		12 24		13 24				14 24					15 24							16 24
Southampton Airport Parkwy ✈	a	11 33		12 33		13 33				14 33					15 33							16 33
Southampton Central	a	11 42		12 42		13 42				14 42					15 42							16 42
Brockenhurst 3	a	12 02		13 02		14 02				15 02					16 02							17 02
Bournemouth	a	12 32		13 32		14 32				15 32					16 32							17 32
Gatwick Airport 10 ✈	a																					
Haywards Heath 3	a																					
Brighton 10	a																					

For general notes see front of timetable
For details of catering facilities see Directory of Train Operators

A From Didcot Parkway (Table 116)
b Arr. 0918
c Arr. 1021
e Arr. 1121
f Departure time. By bus to Didcot Parkway (Table 116)

Scotland, The North East, North West England → The South West and South Coast

Route Diagram - See first page of Table 51

	XC	VT	VT	XC	XC	XC	XC	VT	VT	XC	XC	XC	XC	XC	VT	XC	XC	XC	XC	VT	VT
					R		R				R	R		R			R		R	R	
	1◇	1◇	1◇	1◇	1	1◇	1	1◇	1◇	1◇	1	1	1◇	1	1◇	1◇	1	1◇	1	1	1◇
						A							A					A			
Aberdeen d																					
Stonehaven d																					
Montrose d																					
Arbroath d																					
Dundee d																					
Leuchars 8 d																					
Cupar d																					
Markinch d																					
Kirkcaldy d																					
Inverkeithing d																					
Glasgow Central 15 d																					
Motherwell d																					
Haymarket d																					
Edinburgh 10 d					08 50						09 50						10 50				
Haymarket d																					
Lockerbie d																					
Carlisle 8 d																					
Penrith North Lakes d																					
Oxenholme Lake District d																					
Lancaster 6 d																					
Preston 8 d		11 25						12 28												14 27	
Wigan North Western d		11 37						12 40												14 40	
Warrington Bank Quay d		11 49						12 52												14 52	
Manchester Piccadilly 10 d			11 53				12 08		12 53			13 24			13 53				14 24		14 53
Stockport d			12 02				12 22		13 02			13 33			14 03				14 33		15 02
Wilmslow d			12 10				12 30		13 11			13 41			14 11				14 41		15 10
Crewe 10 d		12 12					13 02	13 13				14 02							15 02	15 13	
Macclesfield d																					
Congleton d																					
Stoke-on-Trent d																					
Stafford d			12 49				13b26		13 48			14c26			14 49				15e26		15 49
Wolverhampton 7 d		12 49	13 05				13 43	13 49	14 05			14 43			15 04				15 43	15 49	16 04
Dunbar d																	11 11				
Berwick-upon-Tweed d					09 31												11 35				
Alnmouth d											10 48										
Newcastle 8 d				10 16	10 25					11 16	11 25					12 16	12 25				
Chester-le-Street d																					
Durham d				10 28	10 37					11 28	11 37					12 28	12 37				
Darlington 7 d				10 45	10 54					11 45	11 54					12 45	12 54				
York 8 d				11 20	11 28					12 20	12 28					13 20	13 28				
Leeds 10 d					12 00						13 00						14 00				
Wakefield Westgate 7 d					12 12						13 12						14 12				
Doncaster 7 d				11 50						12 50						13 50					
Sheffield 7 d				12 23	12 48					13 23	13 48					14 23	14 48				
Chesterfield d				12 35						13 35						14 35					
Derby 10 d				12 57	13 20					13 57	14 20					14 57	15 20				
Burton-on-Trent d										14 07											
Tamworth d										14 18											
Birmingham New Street 12 a	←	13 11	13 26	13 36	13 53		13 58	14 11	14 26	14 36	14 53	14 58		←	15 26	15 30	15 53		15 58	16 11	16 26
Birmingham New Street 12 d	13 10		13 30	13 40	14 03		14 10		14 30	14 40	15 10 →	15 03		15 10	15 30	15 40	16 03		16 10		16 30
Cheltenham Spa a	13 51			14 21			14 51			15 21				15 51		16 21			16 51		
Gloucester 7 a																					
Bristol Parkway 7 a	14 25			14 57			15 25			15 57				16 25		16 57			17 25		
Bristol Temple Meads 10 a	14 38			15 11			15 38			16 13				16 38		17 13			17 38		
Newport (South Wales) a																					
Cardiff Central 7 a																					
Weston-super-Mare a																					
Taunton a	15 15			15 43			16 15							17 15					18 15		
Tiverton Parkway a	15 28			15 55			16 28							17 28					18 28		
Exeter St Davids 6 a	15 43			16 11			16 43							17 43					18 43		
Dawlish a																					
Teignmouth a																					
Newton Abbot a	16 03			16 32			17 03							18 03					19 03		
Torquay a																					
Paignton a																					
Totnes a	16 16			16 45			17 16							18 16					19 16		
Plymouth a	16 48			17 18			17 48							18 48					19 48		
Liskeard 3 a							18 23							19 17					20 17		
Bodmin Parkway a							18 35							19 29					20 29		
Par 3 a							18 46							19 40					20 40		
St Austell a							18 52							19 46					20 46		
Truro a							19 10							20 04					21 04		
Redruth a							19 21							20 21					21 15		
Camborne a							19 28							20 35					21 26		
St Erth 2 a							19 38							20 45					21 36		
Penzance a							19 54							21 01					21 52		
Birmingham International ✈ d			13 41		14 15				14 41			15 15			15 41		16 15				16 41
Coventry d			13a51		14 25				14a51			15 25			15a51		16 25				16a51
Leamington Spa 8 d					14 38							15 38					16 38				
Banbury a					14 54							15 54					16 54				
Oxford a					15 19	*15f30*						16 19	*16f30*				17 19	*17f30*			
Reading 7 a						16d50							17d50					18d50			
Kensington Olympia a																					
East Croydon a																					
Guildford a																					
Redhill a																					
Basingstoke a						17 08							18 08					19 08			
Winchester a						17 24							18 24					19 24			
Southampton Airport Parkwy ✈ a						17 33							18 33					19 33			
Southampton Central a						17 42							18 42					19 42			
Brockenhurst 3 a						18 02							19 02					20 02			
Bournemouth a						18 32							19 32					20 32			
Gatwick Airport 10 ✈ a																					
Haywards Heath 3 a																					
Brighton 10 a																					

For general notes see front of timetable
For details of catering facilities see Directory of Train Operators

A From Didcot Parkway (Table 116)
b Arr. 1321
c Arr. 1422
e Arr. 1521
f Departure time. By bus to Didcot Parkway (Table 116)

SUMMARY OF SERVICES

Sundays from 30 March

Scotland, The North East, North West England → The South West and South Coast

Route Diagram - See first page of Table 51

		XC	XC	XC	XC	XC	VT	VT		XC	XC	XC	XC	VT	VT	XC	XC	XC		XC	XC	VT	VT	XC
		1◇	R 1	R 1	1◇	R 1	R 1	1◇		R 1	R 1	1◇	R 1	R 1	1◇	1◇	R 1	R 1		1◇	R 1	R 1	1◇	1◇
					A							A								A				
Aberdeen	d																							
Stonehaven	d																							
Montrose	d																							
Arbroath	d																							
Dundee	d																							
Leuchars 3	d																							
Cupar	d																							
Markinch	d																							
Kirkcaldy	d																							
Inverkeithing	d																							
Glasgow Central 15	d		10 30								11 30													
Motherwell	d		10u53								11u56													
Haymarket	d		11 37								12 37													
Edinburgh 10	d		11 50								12 50						13 50							
Haymarket	d																							
Lockerbie	d																							
Carlisle 8	d																							
Penrith North Lakes	d																							
Oxenholme Lake District	d																							
Lancaster 6	d																							
Preston 8	d						15 27							16 23								17 29		
Wigan North Western	d						15 41							16 35								17 41		
Warrington Bank Quay	d						15 53							16 47								17 53		
Manchester Piccadilly 10	d			15 24				15 53					16 24		16 53			17 24					17 53	
Stockport	d			15 33				16 02					16 33		17 02			17 33					18 02	
Wilmslow	d			15 41				16 13					16 41		17 12			17 41					18 12	
Crewe 10	d			16 02			16 13						17 02	17 09				18 02				18 16		
Macclesfield	d																							
Congleton	d																							
Stoke-on-Trent	d																							
Stafford	d			16 26				16 48					17 26		17 49			18b26					18 49	
Wolverhampton 7	d			16 43			16 49	17 04					17 43	17 49	18 04			18 43				18 52	19 04	
Dunbar	d										13 12													
Berwick-upon-Tweed	d										13 35													
Alnmouth	d		12 48														14 48							
Newcastle 8	d	13 23	13 25							14 16	14 25					15 16	15 25							16 16
Chester-le-Street	d																							
Durham	d	13 36	13 37							14 28	14 37					15 28	15 37							16 29
Darlington 7	d	13 53	13 54							14 45	14 54					15 45	15 54							16 48
York 8	d	14 24	14 28							15 21	15 28					16 20	16 28							17 20
Leeds 10	d		15 00								16 00						17 00							
Wakefield Westgate 7	d		15 12								16 12						17 12							
Doncaster 7	d	14 50								15 50						16 50								17 50
Sheffield 7	d	15 23	15 48							16 23	16 48					17 23	17 48							18 23
Chesterfield	d	15 35								16 35						17 35								18 35
Derby 10	d	15 57	16 20							16 57	17 20					17 57	18 20							18 57
Burton-on-Trent	d	16 07														18 07								19 07
Tamworth	d	16 18														18 18								19 18
Birmingham New Street 12	a	16 36	16 53	16 58		←	17 11	17 26		17 36	17 53		17 58	18 11	18 26	18 36	18 53	18 58			←	19 14	19 26	19 36
Birmingham New Street 12	d	16 40	17 10	17 03		17 10		17 30		17 40	18 03		18 10		18 30	18 40	19 10	19 03			19 10		19 30	19 40
Cheltenham Spa	a	17 21	→			17 51				18 21			18 51			19 21	→				19 51			20 21
Gloucester 7	a									18 32														
Bristol Parkway 7	a	18 01				18 25				19 07			19 25			20 00					20 25			20 58
Bristol Temple Meads 10	a	18 17				18 38				19 24			19 38			20 16					20 38			21 14
Newport (South Wales)	a																							
Cardiff Central 7	a																							
Weston-super-Mare	a																							
Taunton	a					19 15							20 15								21 15			
Tiverton Parkway	a					19 28							20 28								21 28			
Exeter St Davids 6	a					19 45							20 45								21 43			
Dawlish	a																							
Teignmouth	a																							
Newton Abbot	a					20 06							21 06								22 03			
Torquay	a																							
Paignton	a																							
Totnes	a					20 19							21 22								22 16			
Plymouth	a					20 51							21 56								22 48			
Liskeard 3	a																							
Bodmin Parkway	a																							
Par 3	a																							
St Austell	a																							
Truro	a																							
Redruth	a																							
Camborne	a																							
St Erth 2	a																							
Penzance	a																							
Birmingham International	d			17 15				17 41			18 15				18 40			19 15					19 41	
Coventry	d			17 25				17a51			18 25				18a49			19 25					19a51	
Leamington Spa 8	d			17 38							18 38							19 38						
Banbury	a			17 54							18 54							19 54						
Oxford	a			18 19	18c30						19 19	19c30						20 19		20c30				
Reading 7	a				19d50							20d50								21d50				
Kensington Olympia	a																							
East Croydon	a																							
Guildford	a																							
Redhill	a																							
Basingstoke	a				20 08							21 08								22 08				
Winchester	a				20 24							21 24								22 44				
Southampton Airport Parkwy	a				20 33							21 33								23 18				
Southampton Central	a				20 44							21 42								23 31				
Brockenhurst 3	a				21 02							22 02								23e16				
Bournemouth	a				21 32							22 32								23e35				
Gatwick Airport 10	a																							
Haywards Heath 3	a																							
Brighton 10	a																							

For general notes see front of timetable
For details of catering facilities see Directory of Train Operators

A From Didcot Parkway (Table 116)
b Arr. 1821
c Departure time. By bus to Didcot Parkway (Table 116)
e Change at Basingstoke

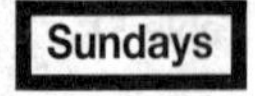

from 30 March

Scotland, The North East, North West England → The South West and South Coast

Route Diagram - See first page of Table 51

		XC	XC	XC	VT	VT	XC	XC	XC	XC	VT	VT	XC	VT	XC	VT	XC	XC	VT	XC	XC
		R 1	1 ◇	R 1	R 1	1 ◇	1 ◇	1 ◇	1 ◇	1 ◇	1 ◇	1 ◇	1 ◇	1 ◇	1 ◇	1 ◇	1 ◇	1 ◇	1 ◇	1 ◇	1 ◇
			A						A												
Aberdeen	d	11 58																			
Stonehaven	d	12 16																			
Montrose	d	12 39																			
Arbroath	d	12 56																			
Dundee	d	13 14																			
Leuchars 3	d	13 27																			
Cupar	d	13 35																			
Markinch	d	13 49																			
Kirkcaldy	d	13 58																			
Inverkeithing	d	14 14																			
Glasgow Central 15	d				14 05										15 45	16 05					
Motherwell	d				14u27										15u59	16u23					
Haymarket	d	14 29													16 39						
Edinburgh 10	d	14b50								15 50					16 50			17 50			18 50
Haymarket	d																				
Lockerbie	d				15 15											17 06					
Carlisle 8	d				15 37											17 39					
Penrith North Lakes	d																				
Oxenholme Lake District	d																				
Lancaster 6	d																				
Preston 8	d				18 30						19 29					20 38			21 34		
Wigan North Western	d				18 42						19 41					20 50			21 45		
Warrington Bank Quay	d				18 53						19 52					21 02			21 58		
Manchester Piccadilly 10	d			18 24		18 53		19 24				19 55		20 23			20 55			21 55	
Stockport	d			18 33		19 02		19 33				20 04		20 32			21 04			22 04	
Wilmslow	d			18 41		19 12		19 41				20 13		20 40			21 12			22 12	
Crewe 10	d			19 02	19 15			20 02			20 14					21 24	21 32		22 20	22 32	
Macclesfield	d																				
Congleton	d																				
Stoke-on-Trent	d																				
Stafford	d			19c26		19 49		20e26				20 53		21 21		21 43	21 53		22 40	22 53	
Wolverhampton 7	d			19 43	19 49	20 04		20 43			20 52	21 10		21 35		22 01	22 09		22 55	23 09	
Dunbar	d	15 10													17 10			18 10			
Berwick-upon-Tweed	d	15 35													17 33						
Alnmouth	d									16 48								18 52			
Newcastle 8	d	16 25					17 16			17 25			18 16		18 25			19 25			20 25
Chester-le-Street	d																				
Durham	d	16 37					17 31			17 37			18 28		18 37			19 37			20 37
Darlington 7	d	16 54					17 48			17 54			18 45		18 54			19 54			20 54
York 8	d	17 28					18 20			18 28			19 20		19 28			20 28			21 26
Leeds 10	d	18 00								19 00					20 00			21 00			
Wakefield Westgate 7	d	18 12								19 12					20 12			21 12			
Doncaster 7	d						18 50						19 50								21 50
Sheffield 7	d	18 48					19 23			19 48			20 23		20 48			21 48			22 23
Chesterfield	d						19 35			20 00			20 35		21 00			22 00			22 35
Derby 10	d	19 20					19 57			20 24			20 57		21 24			22 24			22 57
Burton-on-Trent	d						20 07						21 07		21 34			22 34			23 07
Tamworth	d						20 18						21 18		21 45			22 45			23 18
Birmingham New Street 12	a	19 53		19 58	20 11	20 26	20 41	20 58		20 57	21 15	21 32	21 41	21 56	22 04	22 22	22 30	23 16	23 17	23 30	23 51
Birmingham New Street 12	d	20 03		20 10		20 30		21 03		21 10				22 00	22 10						
Cheltenham Spa	a			20 51						21 51					22 51						
Gloucester 7	a																				
Bristol Parkway 7	a			21 25						22 25					23 25						
Bristol Temple Meads 10	a			21 38						22 41					23 41						
Newport (South Wales)	a																				
Cardiff Central 7	a																				
Weston-super-Mare	a																				
Taunton	a			22 15																	
Tiverton Parkway	a			22 28																	
Exeter St Davids 6	a			22 43																	
Dawlish	a																				
Teignmouth	a																				
Newton Abbot	a			23 03																	
Torquay	a																				
Paignton	a																				
Totnes	a			23 16																	
Plymouth	a			23 48																	
Liskeard 3	a																				
Bodmin Parkway	a																				
Par 3	a																				
St Austell	a																				
Truro	a																				
Redruth	a																				
Camborne	a																				
St Erth 2	a																				
Penzance	a																				
Birmingham International	d	20 15				20 41		21 15						22 10							
Coventry	d	20 25				20a51		21 25						22a19							
Leamington Spa 8	d	20 38						21 38													
Banbury	a	20 54						21 54													
Oxford	a	21 19	*21f30*					22 19	*22f30*												
Reading 7	a		22d50						23d45												
Kensington Olympia	a																				
East Croydon	a																				
Guildford	a								00 25												
Redhill	a								00 58												
Basingstoke	a		23 08																		
Winchester	a		23 24																		
Southampton Airport Parkwy	a		23 33																		
Southampton Central	a		23 45																		
Brockenhurst 3	a		*00 53*																		
Bournemouth	a		*01 16*																		
Gatwick Airport 10	a								01 17												
Haywards Heath 3	a								*02 02*												
Brighton 10	a								*02 30*												

For general notes see front of timetable
For details of catering facilities see Directory of Train Operators

A From Didcot Parkway (Table 116)
b Arr. 1433
c Arr. 1921
e Arr. 2022
f Departure time. By bus to Didcot Parkway (Table 116)

South Coast and the South West → North West England, The North East and Scotland

Route Diagram - See first page of Table 51

		VT	XC	XC	XC	XC	XC	VT	XC	XC	XC	VT	XC	XC	XC	XC	XC	VT	XC	XC
							R						R							
		1 ◇	1 ◇	1 ◇	1 ◇	1 ◇	1	1 ◇	1 ◇	1 ◇	1 ◇	1 ◇	1	1 ◇	1 ◇	1 ◇	1 ◇	1 ◇	1 ◇	1 ◇
																A				
		⊠	☕		☕	☕	☕	☕	☕	☕	☕	☕	☕	☕	☕	☕	☕	☕	☕	☕
Brighton 10	d													*03 50*						
Haywards Heath 3	d													*04 25*						
Gatwick Airport 10 ✈	d													05 15						05 45
Bournemouth	d																*05 15*			
Brockenhurst 3	d																*05 38*			
Southampton Central	d										05 15						06 15			
Southampton Airport Parkwy ✈	d										05 22						06 22			
Winchester	d										05 31						06 31			
Basingstoke	d										05 47						06 47			
Redhill	d													05 33						06 04
Guildford	d													06 00						06 51
East Croydon ⛴	d																			
Kensington Olympia	d																			
Reading 7	d										06 10			06 40			07 10			07 40
Oxford	d										06 36			07 07			07 36			08 07
Banbury	d										06 53			07 25			07 53			08 25
Leamington Spa 8	d										07 11			07 43			08 11			08 43
Coventry	d										07 23						08 23			
Birmingham International ✈	d										07 34						08 34			
Penzance	d																			
St Erth 2	d																			
Camborne	d																			
Redruth	d																			
Truro	d																			
St Austell	d																			
Par 3	d																			
Bodmin Parkway	d																			
Liskeard 3	d																			
Plymouth	d																			
Totnes	d																			
Paignton	d																			
Torquay	d																			
Newton Abbot	d																			
Teignmouth	d																			
Dawlish	d																			
Exeter St Davids 6	d																		06 23	
Tiverton Parkway	d																		06 37	
Taunton	d																		06 51	
Weston-super-Mare	d																			
Cardiff Central 7	d																			
Newport (South Wales)	d																			
Bristol Temple Meads 10	d												06 15		07 00				07 30	
Bristol Parkway 7	d												06 25		07 10				07 40	
Gloucester 7	d												07 02							
Cheltenham Spa	d												07 12		07 42				08 12	
Birmingham New Street 12	a										07 45		07 57	08 18	08 26		08 48		08 57	09 18
Birmingham New Street 12	d	05 30	06 00	06 03	06 30	06 30	07 03	07 03	07 18	07 30	07 48	08 03	08 03	08 18	08 30	08 48	09 03	09 03	09 18	
Tamworth	d		06 15		06 47		07 19			07 47			08 19		08 47					
Burton-on-Trent	d		06 25		06 58		07 29			07 58			08 29		08 58					
Derby 10	a		06 38		07 11		07 42			08 11			08 42		09 11		09 39			
Chesterfield	a				07 32		08 02			08 32					09 34					
Sheffield 7	a		07 09		07 51		08 17			08 50			09 18		09 50		10 15			
Doncaster 7	a				08 24					09 19					10 15					
Wakefield Westgate 7	a		07 36				08 46						09 46				10 46			
Leeds 10	a		07 52				09 02						10 02				11 02			
York 8	a		08 24		08 48		09 33			09 48			10 29		10 40		11 29			
Darlington 7	a		08 53		09 20		10 01			10 16			10 59		11 12		11 58			
Durham	a		09 08		09 37		10 18			10 33			11 17		11 29		12 22			
Chester-le-Street	a				09 44					10 40										
Newcastle 8	a		09 26		10 01		10 35			10 59			11 33		11 54		12 37			
Alnmouth	a		09 55										12 02							
Berwick-upon-Tweed	a						11 20										13 21			
Dunbar	a						11 43										13 44			
Wolverhampton 7 ⛴	d	05 49		06 21		07b06		07 21	07 39		08 06	08 21		08 39		09 06		09 21	09 39	
Stafford	a	06 04		06 33		07 17		07 33	07 53		08 17			08 53		09 17				
Stoke-on-Trent	a			06 52		07 36			08 12		08 36			09 12		09 36			10 12	
Congleton	a					07 48			08 24										10 24	
Macclesfield	a					07 56			08 32		08 52			09 31		09 52			10 32	
Crewe 10	a	06 25		07 14				07 53				08 54						09 53		
Wilmslow	a			07 33																
Stockport	a					08 09			08 46		09 05			09 46		10 05			10 46	
Manchester Piccadilly 10 ⛴	a			08 02		08 27			09 02		09 20			10 02		10 20			11 02	
Warrington Bank Quay	a	06 44						08 12				09 12						10 11		
Wigan North Western	a	07 03						08 23				09 23						10 22		
Preston 8	a	07 17						08 41				09 38						10 37		
Lancaster 6	a	07 34						09 00				09 55								
Oxenholme Lake District	a	07 47						09 17				10 10						11 11		
Penrith North Lakes	a	08 13						09 43				10 35								
Carlisle 8	a	08 34						10 01				10 52						11 56		
Lockerbie	a	08 54						10 21				11 12								
Haymarket	a											12s08								
Edinburgh 10	a		11 02				12 13					12 19	13 16				14 16			
Haymarket	a																			
Motherwell	a	09s50						11s04												
Glasgow Central 15	a	10 18						11 28										13 22		
Inverkeithing	a																			
Kirkcaldy	a																			
Markinch	a																			
Cupar	a																			
Leuchars 3	a																			
Dundee	a																			
Arbroath	a																			
Montrose	a																			
Stonehaven	a																			
Aberdeen	a																			

For general notes see front of timetable
For details of catering facilities see Directory of Train Operators

A From Derby (Table 57)
b Arr. 0700

until 25 January

South Coast and the South West → North West England, The North East and Scotland

Route Diagram - See first page of Table 51

Station		XC	XC	VT	XC	XC	XC	XC	XC	VT	XC	XC	XC	XC	VT	XC	XC	XC	XC	XC
											R			R						R
		1◇	1◇	1◇	1◇	1◇	1◇	1◇	1◇	1◇	1	1◇	1◇	1	1◇	1◇	1◇	1◇	1◇	1
		☕	☕	☕	☕	☕	☕	☕	☕	☕	☕	☕	☕	☕	☕	☕	☕	☕	☕	☕
Brighton 10	d																			
Haywards Heath 3	d																			
Gatwick Airport 10 ✈	d																			
Bournemouth	d		06 30						07 30					08 45						09 45
Brockenhurst 3	d		06 48						07 47					09 00						10 00
Southampton Central	d		07 15						08 15					09 15						10 15
Southampton Airport Parkwy ✈	d		07 22						08 22					09 22						10 22
Winchester	d		07 31						08 31					09 31						10 31
Basingstoke	d		07 47						08 47					09 47						10 47
Redhill	d																			
Guildford	d																			
East Croydon	d																			
Kensington Olympia	d																			
Reading 7	d		08 10			08 40			09 10			09 40		10 10			10 40			11 10
Oxford	d		08 36			09 07			09 36			10 07		10 36			11 07			11 36
Banbury	d		08 53			09 25			09 53			10 25		10 53			11 25			11 53
Leamington Spa 8	d		09 11			09 43			10 11			10 43		11 11			11 43			12 11
Coventry	d		09 23						10 23					11 23						12 23
Birmingham International ✈	d		09 34					10 18	10 34					11 34					12 18	12 34
Penzance	d																			
St Erth 2	d																			
Camborne	d																			
Redruth	d																			
Truro	d																			
St Austell	d																			
Par 3	d																			
Bodmin Parkway	d																			
Liskeard 3	d																			
Plymouth	d				06 25		06 40				07 25					08 25				
Totnes	d				06 50		07 05				07 50					08 50				
Paignton	d																			
Torquay	d																			
Newton Abbot	d				07 03		07 18				08 03					09 03				
Teignmouth	d																			
Dawlish	d																			
Exeter St Davids 6	d				07 23		07 38				08 23					09 23				
Tiverton Parkway	d				07 37		07 52				08 37					09 37				
Taunton	d				07 51		08 06				08 51					09 51				
Weston-super-Mare	d						08 30													
Cardiff Central 7	d	07 00																		
Newport (South Wales)	d	07 15																		
Bristol Temple Meads 10	d	08 00			08 30		09 00				09 30		10 00			10 30		11 00		
Bristol Parkway 7	d	08 10			08 40		09 10				09 40		10 10			10 40		11 10		
Gloucester 7	d																			
Cheltenham Spa	d	08 42			09 12		09 42				10 12		10 42			11 12		11 42		
Birmingham New Street 12	a	09 26	09 45		09 57	10 18	10 26	10 30	10 46		10 57	11 18	11 26	11 45		11 57	12 18	12 26	12 30	12 45
Birmingham New Street 12	d	09 30	09 48	10 03	10 03	10 18	10 30	10 48	11 03	11 03	11 18		11 30	11 48	12 03	12 03	12 18	12 30	12 48	13 03
Tamworth	d						10 47											12 47		
Burton-on-Trent	d						10 58											12 58		
Derby 10	a	10 11			10 39		11 11		11 39				12 11			12 39		13 11		13 39
Chesterfield	a	10 32					11 32						12 32					13 32		
Sheffield 7	a	10 51			11 15		11 50		12 15				12 51			13 15		13 50		14 15
Doncaster 7	a	11 15					12 15						13 22					14 18		
Wakefield Westgate 7	a				11 46				12 46							13 46				14 46
Leeds 10	a				12 02				13 02							14 02				15 02
York 8	a	11 41			12 29		12 43		13 29				13 46			14 29		14 45		15 29
Darlington 7	a	12 20			13 00		13 11		14 00				14 16			14 58		15 16		16 06
Durham	a	12 38			13 18		13 28		14 18				14 34			15 15		15 34		16 24
Chester-le-Street	a	12 50											14 41							
Newcastle 8	a	13 07			13 34		13 50		14 37				14 57			15 32		16 00		16 39
Alnmouth	a				14 00											16 01				
Berwick-upon-Tweed	a								15 21											17 24
Dunbar	a								15 44											17 47
Wolverhampton 7	d		10 06	10 21		10 39		11 06		11 21	11 39				12 21		12 39		13 06	
Stafford	a		10 17					11 17						12 17					13 17	
Stoke-on-Trent	a		10 36			11 12		11 36			12 12			12 36			13 12		13 36	
Congleton	a										12 24									
Macclesfield	a		10 52			11 31		11 52			12 32			12 52			13 31		13 52	
Crewe 10	a			10 53						11 55					12 53					
Wilmslow	a																			
Stockport	a		11 05			11 46		12 05			12 46			13 05			13 46		14 05	
Manchester Piccadilly 10	a		11 20			12 02		12 20			13 02			13 20			14 02		14 20	
Warrington Bank Quay	a			11 11						12 13					13 11					
Wigan North Western	a			11 22						12 24					13 22					
Preston 8	a			11 37						12 47					13 37					
Lancaster 6	a			11 54						13 04					13 54					
Oxenholme Lake District	a														14 08					
Penrith North Lakes	a			12 33						13 43										
Carlisle 8	a			12 51						14 00					14 51					
Lockerbie	a			13 10						14 21					15 12					
Haymarket	a			14s08											16s08					
Edinburgh 10	a			14 19	15 16				16b16						16 16	17 16				18 16
Haymarket	a								16 33											
Motherwell	a																			
Glasgow Central 15	a									15 25										
Inverkeithing	a								16 47											
Kirkcaldy	a								17 02											
Markinch	a								17 11											
Cupar	a								17 24											
Leuchars 3	a								17 31											
Dundee	a								17 44											
Arbroath	a								18 03											
Montrose	a								18 17											
Stonehaven	a								18 37											
Aberdeen	a								19 02											

For general notes see front of timetable
For details of catering facilities see Directory of Train Operators

b Dep. 1630

until 25 January

South Coast and the South West → North West England, The North East and Scotland

Route Diagram - See first page of Table 51

		VT	XC	XC	XC	XC	VT	XC	XC	XC	XC	XC	VT	XC	XC	XC	XC	VT	XC	XC
		1◇ ☕	R 1 ☕	1◇ ☕	1◇ ☕	R 1 ☕	1◇ ☕	R 1 ☕	1◇ ☕	1◇ ☕	1◇ ☕	R 1 ☕	1◇ ☕	R 1 ☕	1◇ ☕	1◇ ☕	R 1 ☕	1◇ ☕	R 1 ☕	R 1 ☕
Brighton [10]	d			09 21																
Haywards Heath [3]	d			09 33																
Gatwick Airport [10] ✈	d			09 46																
Bournemouth	d					10 45						11 45					12 45			
Brockenhurst [3]	d					11 00						12 00					13 00			
Southampton Central	d					11 15						12 15					13 15			
Southampton Airport Parkwy ✈	d					11 22						12 22					13 22			
Winchester	d					11 31						12 31					13 31			
Basingstoke	d					11 47						12 47					13 47			
Redhill	d																			
Guildford	d																			
East Croydon 🚋	d			10 08																
Kensington Olympia	d			10 37																
Reading [7]	d			11 40		12 10			12 40			13 10			13 40		14 10			14 40
Oxford	d			12 07		12 36			13 07			13 36			14 07		14 36			15 07
Banbury	d			12 25		12 53			13 25			13 53			14 25		14 53			15 25
Leamington Spa [8]	d			12 43		13 11			13 43			14 11			14 43		15 11			15 43
Coventry	d					13 23						14 23					15 23			
Birmingham International ✈	d					13 34					14 18	14 34					15 34			
Penzance	d		07 30					08 30						09 30						
St Erth [2]	d		07 38					08 38						09 38						
Camborne	d		07 48					08 48						09 48						
Redruth	d		07 54					08 54						09 54						
Truro	d		08 06					09 06						10 06						
St Austell	d		08 22					09 22						10 22						
Par [3]	d		08 29					09 29						10 29						
Bodmin Parkway	d		08 40					09 40						10 40						
Liskeard [3]	d		08 52					09 52						10 52						
Plymouth	d		09 25					10 25						11 25		11 50			12 25	
Totnes	d		09 50					10 50						11 50		12 15			12 50	
Paignton	d				10 02															
Torquay	d				10 08															
Newton Abbot	d		10 03		10 19			11 03						12 03		12 28			13 03	
Teignmouth	d				10 26															
Dawlish	d				10 31															
Exeter St Davids [6]	d		10 23		10 48			11 23						12 23		12 48			13 23	
Tiverton Parkway	d		10 37		11 01			11 37						12 37		13 02			13 37	
Taunton	d		10 51		11 16			11 51						12 51		13 16			13 51	
Weston-super-Mare	d																			
Cardiff Central [7]	d																			
Newport (South Wales)	d																			
Bristol Temple Meads [10]	d		11 30		12 00			12 30		13 00				13 30		14 00			14 30	
Bristol Parkway [7]	d		11 40		12 10			12 40		13 10				13 40		14 10			14 40	
Gloucester [7]	d																			
Cheltenham Spa	d		12 12		12 42			13 12		13 42				14 12		14 42			15 12	
Birmingham New Street [12]	a		12 57	13 18	13 26	13 45		13 57	14 18	14 26	14 30	14 45		14 57	15 18	15 26	15 45		15 57	16 18
Birmingham New Street [12]	d	13 03	13 18		13 30	13 48	14 03	14 03	14 18	14 30	14 48	15 03	15 03	15 18		15 30	15 48	16 03	16 03	16 18
Tamworth	d									14 47										
Burton-on-Trent	d									14 58										
Derby [10]	a				14 11			14 39		15 11		15 39				16 11			16 39	
Chesterfield	a				14 32					15 32						16 32				
Sheffield [7]	a				14 50			15 15		15 50		16 15				16 51			17 15	
Doncaster [7]	a				15 15					16 15						17 15				
Wakefield Westgate [7]	a							15 46				16 46							17 46	
Leeds [10]	a							16 02				17 02							18 02	
York [8]	a				15 40			16 29		16 40		17 29				17 40			18 29	
Darlington [7]	a				16 11			16 57		17 08		18 02				18 15			18 58	
Durham	a				16 29					17 31		18 20				18 33			19 15	
Chester-le-Street	a				16 36											18 40				
Newcastle [8]	a				16 52			17 28		17 54		18 37				18 56			19 35	
Alnmouth	a							17 54											20 03	
Berwick-upon-Tweed	a											19 22							20 24	
Dunbar	a											19 45								
Wolverhampton [7] 🚋	d	13 21	13 39			14 06	14 21		14 39		15 06		15 21	15 39				16 21		16 39
Stafford	a					14 17					15 17						16 17			
Stoke-on-Trent	a		14 12			14 36			15 12		15 36			16 12			16 36			17 12
Congleton	a		14 24											16 24						17 24
Macclesfield	a		14 32			14 52			15 31		15 52			16 32			16 52			17 32
Crewe [10]	a	13 53					14 53						15 55					16 53		
Wilmslow	a																			
Stockport	a		14 46			15 05			15 46		16 05			16 46			17 05			17 46
Manchester Piccadilly [10] 🚋	a		15 02			15 20			16 02		16 20			17 02			17 20			18 02
Warrington Bank Quay	a	14 14					15 11						16 14					17 11		
Wigan North Western	a	14 26					15 22						16 25					17 22		
Preston [8]	a	14 41					15 37						16 40					17 37		
Lancaster [6]	a	14 57					15 56						16 58					17 54		
Oxenholme Lake District	a	15 12											17 15					18 11		
Penrith North Lakes	a						16 33											18 37		
Carlisle [8]	a	15 55					16 51						17 57					18 55		
Lockerbie	a																			
Haymarket	a						18s09											20s08		
Edinburgh [10]	a						18 19	18 57				20 11						20 19	21 08	
Haymarket	a							19 04				20 18							→	
Motherwell	a											→	19s13							
Glasgow Central [15]	a	17 21											19 37							
Inverkeithing	a							19 18												
Kirkcaldy	a							19 34												
Markinch	a							19 43												
Cupar	a							19 57												
Leuchars [3]	a							20 04												
Dundee	a							20 25												
Arbroath	a																			
Montrose	a																			
Stonehaven	a																			
Aberdeen	a																			

For general notes see front of timetable
For details of catering facilities see Directory of Train Operators

until 25 January

South Coast and the South West → North West England, The North East and Scotland

Route Diagram - See first page of Table 51

		XC	XC	LM	XC	VT	XC	XC	XC	XC	XC	XC	XC	VT	XC	XC	XC	VT	XC
		R 1 ⊡	1◇ ⊡	1◇ ⊥	R 1 ⊡	1◇ ⊡	R 1 ⊡	R 1 ⊡	R 1 ⊡	R 1 ⊡	R 1 ⊡	R 1 ⊡	R 1 ⊡	1◇ ⊡	R 1 ⊡	R 1 ⊡	R 1 ⊡	1◇ ⊡	R 1 ⊡
Brighton 10	d															14 22			
Haywards Heath 3	d															14b31			
Gatwick Airport 10 ✈	d															14 51			
Bournemouth	d				13 45								14 45						15 45
Brockenhurst 3	d				14 00								15 00						16 00
Southampton Central	d				14 15								15 15						16 15
Southampton Airport Parkwy ✈	d				14 22								15 22						16 22
Winchester	d				14 31								15 31						16 31
Basingstoke	d				14 47								15 47						16 47
Redhill	d																		
Guildford	d																		
East Croydon	d															15 09			
Kensington Olympia	d															15 36			
Reading 7	d				15 10					15 40			16 10			16 40			17 10
Oxford	d				15 36					16 07			16 36			17 07			17 36
Banbury	d				15 53					16 25			16 53			17 25			17 53
Leamington Spa 8	d				16 11					16 43			17 11			17 43			18 11
Coventry	d				16 23								17 23					18 14	18 23
Birmingham International ✈	d		16 18		16 34								17 34					18 28	18 34
Penzance	d																		
St Erth 2	d																		
Camborne	d																		
Redruth	d																		
Truro	d																		
St Austell	d																		
Par 3	d																		
Bodmin Parkway	d																		
Liskeard 3	d																		
Plymouth	d							13 25							14 25				
Totnes	d							13 50							14 50				
Paignton	d										14 03								
Torquay	d										14 09								
Newton Abbot	d							14 03			14 21				15 03				
Teignmouth	d										14 28								
Dawlish	d										14 33								
Exeter St Davids 6	d							14 23			14 46				15 23				
Tiverton Parkway	d							14 37			15 00				15 37				
Taunton	d							14 51			15 14				15 51				
Weston-super-Mare	d										15 36								
Cardiff Central 7	d																		
Newport (South Wales)	d																		
Bristol Temple Meads 10	d	15 00						15 30			16 00				16 30		17 00		
Bristol Parkway 7	d	15 10						15 40			16 10				16 40		17 10		
Gloucester 7	d																		
Cheltenham Spa	d	15 42						16 12			16 42				17 12		17 42		
Birmingham New Street 12	a	16 26	16 30		16 45			16 57		17 18	17 26	←	17 45		17 57	18 18	18 26	18 39	18 45
Birmingham New Street 12	d	16 30	16 48	16 51	17 03	17 03		17 18		17 39 →	17 30	17 39	17 48	18 03	18 03	18 18	18 30	18 43	19 03
Tamworth	d											18 06					18 47		
Burton-on-Trent	d											18 16					18 58		
Derby 10	a	17 14			17 39						18 11	18 34			18 39		19 11		19 39
Chesterfield	a	17 37									18 34				19 02		19 32		20 02
Sheffield 7	a	17 50			18 17						18 50				19 17		19 47		20 17
Doncaster 7	a	18 16									19 17						20 20		
Wakefield Westgate 7	a				18 46										19 49				20 53
Leeds 10	a				19 02										20 06				21 09
York 8	a	18 41			19 29						19 44				20 33		20 46		21 34
Darlington 7	a	19 17			20 03						20 12				21 07		21 20		22 03
Durham	a	19 35			20 20						20 30				21 25		21 38		22 20
Chester-le-Street	a										20 37						21 45		
Newcastle 8	a	20 04			20 37						20 54				21 42		22 01		22 42
Alnmouth	a				21 07										22 14				
Berwick-upon-Tweed	a				21 29										22 35				
Dunbar	a														22 58				
Wolverhampton 7	d		17 06	17 10				17 39					18 06	18 21		18 39		19 06	
Stafford	a		17 17	17 26									18 17					19 21	
Stoke-on-Trent	a		17 36					18 12					18 36			19 12		19 45	
Congleton	a							18 24											
Macclesfield	a		17 52					18 32					18 52			19 31		20 01	
Crewe 10	a			17 48		17 53								18 54					
Wilmslow	a																		
Stockport	a		18 05					18 46					19 05			19 46		20 16	
Manchester Piccadilly 10	a		18 20					19 02					19 20			20 02		20 35	
Warrington Bank Quay	a			18 06										19 12					
Wigan North Western	a			18 17										19 23					
Preston 8	a			18 39		18 39								19 42					
Lancaster 6	a					18 58								19 59					
Oxenholme Lake District	a					19 13								20 13					
Penrith North Lakes	a													20 39					
Carlisle 8	a					19 54								20 58					
Lockerbie	a																		
Haymarket	a								←					22s13					
Edinburgh 10	a				22 24		←		21 08					22 25	23 28				
Haymarket	a						20 18		21 18										
Motherwell	a								21s59										
Glasgow Central 15	a					21 11	21 28		22 42										
Inverkeithing	a																		
Kirkcaldy	a																		
Markinch	a																		
Cupar	a																		
Leuchars 3	a																		
Dundee	a																		
Arbroath	a																		
Montrose	a																		
Stonehaven	a																		
Aberdeen	a																		

For general notes see front of timetable
For details of catering facilities see Directory of Train Operators

b Change at East Croydon

until 25 January

South Coast and the South West → North West England, The North East and Scotland

Route Diagram - See first page of Table 51

		VT	XC	XC	XC	XC	XC	XC	XC	XC	VT	XC	XC	XC	XC	XC	XC	XC
			R	R		R												
		1◇	1	1	1◇	1	1◇	1◇	1◇	1◇	1◇	1◇	1◇	1◇	1◇	1◇	1◇	1◇
		☕	☕	☕	☕	☕	☕	☕	☕	☕	☕	☕		☕	☕	☕		
Brighton 10	d																	
Haywards Heath 3	d																	
Gatwick Airport 10 ✈	d							*17 03*										
Bournemouth	d					16 45				17 45				18 45			19 45	
Brockenhurst 3	d					17 00				18 00				19 00			20 00	
Southampton Central	d					17 15				18 15				19 15			20 15	
Southampton Airport Parkwy ✈	d					17 22				18 22				19 22			20 22	
Winchester	d					17 31				18 31				19 31			20 31	
Basingstoke	d					17 47				18 47				19 47			20 47	
Redhill	d							*17 14*										
Guildford	d							*17 57*										
East Croydon 🚊	d																	
Kensington Olympia	d																	
Reading 7	d			17 40		18 10		18 40		19 10			19 40	20 10			21 10	
Oxford	d			18 07		18 36		19 07		19 36			20 07	20 36			21 36	
Banbury	d			18 25		18 53		19 25		19 53			20 25	20 53			21 53	
Leamington Spa 8	d			18 43		19 11		19 43		20 11			20 43	21 11			22 11	
Coventry	d					19 23				20 23				21 23			22 23	
Birmingham International ✈	d					19 34				20 34				21 34			22 34	
Penzance	d																	
St Erth 2	d																	
Camborne	d																	
Redruth	d																	
Truro	d																	
St Austell	d																	
Par 3	d																	
Bodmin Parkway	d																	
Liskeard 3	d																	
Plymouth	d		15 25				16 25					17 25			18 25			
Totnes	d		15 50				16 50					17 50			18 50			
Paignton	d				16 15													
Torquay	d				16 21													
Newton Abbot	d		16 03		16 33		17 03					18 03			19 03			
Teignmouth	d																	
Dawlish	d																	
Exeter St Davids 6	d		16 23		16 53		17 23					18 23			19 23			
Tiverton Parkway	d		16 37		17 07		17 37					18 38			19 37			
Taunton	d		16 51		17 21		17 51					18 52			19 51			
Weston-super-Mare	d																	
Cardiff Central 7	d																	
Newport (South Wales)	d																	
Bristol Temple Meads 10	d		17 30		18 00		18 30		19 00			19 30			20 30			22 00
Bristol Parkway 7	d		17 40		18 10		18 40		19 10			19 40			20 40			22 10
Gloucester 7	d																	
Cheltenham Spa	d		18 12		18 42		19 12		19 42			20 12			21 12			22 42
Birmingham New Street 12	a		18 57	19 18	19 26	19 45	19 57	20 18	20 42	20 48		20 57	21 18	21 45	21 57	←	22 52	23 43
Birmingham New Street 12	d	19 03	19 18		19 30	20 03	20 03	20 18	20 48	21 03	21 03	21 18		22 18	22 03	22 18		
Tamworth	d				19 47		20 19			21 19				↪ →	22 19			
Burton-on-Trent	d				19 58		20 29			21 29					22 29			
Derby 10	a				20 11		20 42			21 42					22 42			
Chesterfield	a				20 32		21 02			22 02					23 27			
Sheffield 7	a				20 48		21 18			22 17					23 54			
Doncaster 7	a																	
Wakefield Westgate 7	a						21 49			22s46								
Leeds 10	a						22 05			23 05					01 01			
York 8	a				21 48		22 58											
Darlington 7	a				22 18													
Durham	a				22 35													
Chester-le-Street	a				22 45													
Newcastle 8	a				23 00													
Alnmouth	a																	
Berwick-upon-Tweed	a																	
Dunbar	a																	
Wolverhampton 7 🚊	d	19 21	19 39			20 21		20 39	21 11		21 21	21 39				22 39		
Stafford	a	19 36				20 34			21 23		21 36	21 53				22 53		
Stoke-on-Trent	a		20 12					21 12	21 45			22 12				23s12		
Congleton	a		20 24									22 24						
Macclesfield	a		20 32					21 28	22 02			22 32						
Crewe 10	a	19 58				20 54					21 58							
Wilmslow	a					21 15												
Stockport	a		20 46			21 25		21 46	22 15			22 46						
Manchester Piccadilly 10 🚊	a		21 02			21 48		22 02	22 32			23 02				00 07		
Warrington Bank Quay	a	20 16									22 17							
Wigan North Western	a	20 27									22 43							
Preston 8	a	20 42									23 04							
Lancaster 6	a	21 00																
Oxenholme Lake District	a	21 14																
Penrith North Lakes	a	21 41																
Carlisle 8	a	21 58																
Lockerbie	a	22 17																
Haymarket	a																	
Edinburgh 10	a																	
Haymarket	a																	
Motherwell	a	23s04																
Glasgow Central 15	a	23 33																
Inverkeithing	a																	
Kirkcaldy	a																	
Markinch	a																	
Cupar	a																	
Leuchars 3	a																	
Dundee	a																	
Arbroath	a																	
Montrose	a																	
Stonehaven	a																	
Aberdeen	a																	

For general notes see front of timetable
For details of catering facilities see Directory of Train Operators

South Coast and The South West → North West England, The North East and Scotland

Route Diagram - See first page of Table 51

		VT	XC	XC	XC	XC	XC	VT	XC	XC	XC	VT	XC	XC	XC	XC	XC	VT	XC	XC
							R						R							
		1◇	1◇	1◇	1◇	1◇	1	1◇	1◇	1◇	1◇	1◇	1	1◇	1◇	1◇	1◇	1◇	1◇	1◇
																A				
		⊠	☕		☕	☕	☕	☕	☕	☕	☕	☕	☕	☕	☕	☕	☕	☕	☕	☕
Brighton [10]	d													*03 50*						
Haywards Heath [3]	d													*04 25*						
Gatwick Airport [10] ✈	d													05 15						05 45
Bournemouth	d																*05 15*			
Brockenhurst [3]	d																*05 38*			
Southampton Central	d										05 15						06 15			
Southampton Airport Parkwy ✈	d										05 22						06 22			
Winchester	d										05 31						06 31			
Basingstoke	d										05 47						06 47			
Redhill	d													05 33						06 04
Guildford	d													06 00						06 51
East Croydon	d																			
Kensington Olympia	d																			
Reading [7]	d										06 10			06 40			07 10			07 40
Oxford	d										06 36			07 07			07 36			08 07
Banbury	d										06 53			07 25			07 53			08 25
Leamington Spa [8]	d										07 11			07 43			08 11			08 43
Coventry	d										07 23						08 23			
Birmingham International ✈	d										07 34						08 34			
Penzance	d																			
St Erth [2]	d																			
Camborne	d																			
Redruth	d																			
Truro	d																			
St Austell	d																			
Par [3]	d																			
Bodmin Parkway	d																			
Liskeard [3]	d																			
Plymouth	d																			
Totnes	d																			
Paignton	d																			
Torquay	d																			
Newton Abbot	d																			
Teignmouth	d																			
Dawlish	d																			
Exeter St Davids [6]	d																		06 23	
Tiverton Parkway	d																		06 37	
Taunton	d																		06 51	
Weston-super-Mare	d																			
Cardiff Central [7]	d																			
Newport (South Wales)	d																			
Bristol Temple Meads [10]	d												06 15		07 00				07 30	
Bristol Parkway [7]	d												06 25		07 10				07 40	
Gloucester [7]	d												07 02							
Cheltenham Spa	d												07 12		07 42				08 12	
Birmingham New Street [12]	a										07 45		07 57	08 18	08 26		08 48		08 57	09 18
Birmingham New Street [12]	d	05 30	06 00	06 03	06 30	06 30	07 03	07 03	07 18	07 30	07 48	08 03	08 03	08 18	08 30	08 48	09 03	09 03	09 18	
Tamworth	d		06 15		06 47		07 19			07 47			08 19		08 47					
Burton-on-Trent	d		06 25		06 58		07 29			07 58			08 29		08 58					
Derby [10]	a		06 38		07 11		07 42			08 11			08 42		09 11		09 39			
Chesterfield	a				07 32		08 02			08 32					09 34					
Sheffield [7]	a		07 09		07 51		08 17			08 50			09 18		09 50		10 15			
Doncaster [7]	a				08 24					09 19					10 15					
Wakefield Westgate [7]	a		07 36				08 46						09 46				10 46			
Leeds [10]	a		07 52				09 02						10 02				11 02			
York [8]	a		08 24		08 48		09 33			09 48			10 29		10 40		11 29			
Darlington [7]	a		08 53		09 20		10 01			10 16			10 59		11 12		11 58			
Durham	a		09 08		09 37		10 18			10 33			11 17		11 29		12 22			
Chester-le-Street	a				09 44					10 40										
Newcastle [8]	a		09 26		10 01		10 35			10 59			11 33		11 54		12 37			
Alnmouth	a		09 55										12 02							
Berwick-upon-Tweed	a						11 20										13 21			
Dunbar	a						11 43										13 44			
Wolverhampton [7]	d	05 49		06 21		07b06		07 21	07 39		08 06	08 21		08 39		09 06		09 21	09 39	
Stafford	a	06 04		06 33		07 17		07 33	07 53		08 17			08 53		09 17				
Stoke-on-Trent	a			06 52		07 36			08 12		08 36			09 12		09 36			10 12	
Congleton	a					07 48			08 24										10 24	
Macclesfield	a					07 56			08 32		08 52			09 31		09 52			10 32	
Crewe [10]	a	06 25		07 14				07 53				08 54						09 53		
Wilmslow	a			07 33																
Stockport	a					08 09			08 46		09 05			09 46		10 05			10 46	
Manchester Piccadilly [10]	a			08 02		08 27			09 02		09 20			10 02		10 20			11 02	
Warrington Bank Quay	a	06 44						08 12				09 12						10 11		
Wigan North Western	a	07 03						08 23				09 23						10 22		
Preston [8]	a	07 17						08 41				09 38						10 37		
Lancaster [6]	a	07 34						09 00				09 55								
Oxenholme Lake District	a	07 47						09 17				10 10						11 11		
Penrith North Lakes	a	08 13						09 43				10 35								
Carlisle [8]	a	08 34						10 01				10 52						11 56		
Lockerbie	a	08 54						10 21				11 12								
Haymarket	a											12s08								
Edinburgh [10]	a		11 02				12 13					12 19	13 16				14 16			
Haymarket	a																			
Motherwell	a	09s50						11s04												
Glasgow Central [15]	a	10 18						11 28										13 22		
Inverkeithing	a																			
Kirkcaldy	a																			
Markinch	a																			
Cupar	a																			
Leuchars [3]	a																			
Dundee	a																			
Arbroath	a																			
Montrose	a																			
Stonehaven	a																			
Aberdeen	a																			

For general notes see front of timetable
For details of catering facilities see Directory of Train Operators

A From Derby (Table 57)
b Arr. 0700

South Coast and The South West → North West England, The North East and Scotland

Route Diagram - See first page of Table 51

		XC	XC	VT	XC	XC	XC	XC	XC	VT	XC	XC	XC	XC	VT	XC	XC	XC	XC	XC
		1◇	1◇	1◇	1◇	1◇	1◇	1◇	1◇	1◇	R 1	1◇	1◇	R 1	1◇	1◇	1◇	1◇	1◇	R 1
Brighton 10	d																			
Haywards Heath 3	d																			
Gatwick Airport 10	d																			
Bournemouth	d		06 30						07 30					08 45						09 45
Brockenhurst 3	d		06 48						07 47					09 00						10 00
Southampton Central	d		07 15						08 15					09 15						10 15
Southampton Airport Parkwy	d		07 22						08 22					09 22						10 22
Winchester	d		07 31						08 31					09 31						10 31
Basingstoke	d		07 47						08 47					09 47						10 47
Redhill	d																			
Guildford	d																			
East Croydon	d																			
Kensington Olympia	d																			
Reading 7	d		08 10			08 40			09 10			09 40		10 10			10 40			11 10
Oxford	d		08 36			09 07			09 36			10 07		10 36			11 07			11 36
Banbury	d		08 53			09 25			09 53			10 25		10 53			11 25			11 53
Leamington Spa 8	d		09 11			09 43			10 11			10 43		11 11			11 43			12 11
Coventry	d		09 23						10 23					11 23						12 23
Birmingham International	d		09 34					10 18	10 34					11 34					12 18	12 34
Penzance	d																			
St Erth 2	d																			
Camborne	d																			
Redruth	d																			
Truro	d																			
St Austell	d																			
Par 3	d																			
Bodmin Parkway	d																			
Liskeard 3	d																			
Plymouth	d				06 25		06 40				07 25					08 25				
Totnes	d				06 50		07 05				07 50					08 50				
Paignton	d																			
Torquay	d																			
Newton Abbot	d				07 03		07 18				08 03					09 03				
Teignmouth	d																			
Dawlish	d																			
Exeter St Davids 6	d				07 23		07 38				08 23					09 23				
Tiverton Parkway	d				07 37		07 52				08 37					09 37				
Taunton	d				07 51		08 06				08 51					09 51				
Weston-super-Mare	d						08 30													
Cardiff Central 7	d	07 00																		
Newport (South Wales)	d	07 15																		
Bristol Temple Meads 10	d	08 00			08 30		09 00				09 30		10 00			10 30		11 00		
Bristol Parkway 7	d	08 10			08 40		09 10				09 40		10 10			10 40		11 10		
Gloucester 7	d																			
Cheltenham Spa	d	08 42			09 12		09 42				10 12		10 42			11 12		11 42		
Birmingham New Street 12	a	09 26	09 45		09 57	10 18	10 26	10 30	10 46		10 57	11 18	11 26	11 45		11 57	12 18	12 26	12 30	12 45
Birmingham New Street 12	d	09 30	09 48	10 03	10 03	10 18	10 30	10 48	11 03	11 03	11 18		11 30	11 48	12 03	12 03	12 18	12 30	12 48	13 03
Tamworth	d						10 47											12 47		
Burton-on-Trent	d						10 58											12 58		
Derby 10	a	10 11			10 39		11 11		11 39				12 11			12 39		13 11		13 39
Chesterfield	a	10 32					11 32						12 32					13 32		
Sheffield 7	a	10 51			11 15		11 50		12 15				12 51			13 15		13 50		14 15
Doncaster 7	a	11 15					12 15						13 22					14 18		
Wakefield Westgate 7	a				11 46				12 46							13 46				14 46
Leeds 10	a				12 02				13 02							14 02				15 02
York 8	a	11 41			12 29		12 43		13 29				13 46			14 29		14 45		15 29
Darlington 7	a	12 20			13 00		13 11		14 00				14 16			14 58		15 16		16 06
Durham	a	12 38			13 18		13 28		14 18				14 34			15 15		15 34		16 24
Chester-le-Street	a	12 50											14 41							
Newcastle 8	a	13 07			13 34		13 50		14 37				14 57			15 32		16 00		16 39
Alnmouth	a				14 00											16 01				
Berwick-upon-Tweed	a								15 21											17 24
Dunbar	a								15 44											17 47
Wolverhampton 7	d		10 06	10 21		10 39		11 06		11 21	11 39				12 21		12 39		13 06	
Stafford	a		10 17					11 17						12 17					13 17	
Stoke-on-Trent	a		10 36			11 12		11 36			12 12			12 36			13 12		13 36	
Congleton	a										12 24									
Macclesfield	a		10 52			11 31		11 52			12 32			12 52			13 31		13 52	
Crewe 10	a			10 53						11 55					12 53					
Wilmslow	a																			
Stockport	a		11 05			11 46		12 05			12 46			13 05			13 46		14 05	
Manchester Piccadilly 10	a		11 20			12 02		12 20			13 02			13 20			14 02		14 20	
Warrington Bank Quay	a			11 11						12 13					13 11					
Wigan North Western	a			11 22						12 24					13 22					
Preston 8	a			11 37						12 47					13 37					
Lancaster 6	a			11 54						13 04					13 54					
Oxenholme Lake District	a														14 08					
Penrith North Lakes	a			12 33						13 43										
Carlisle 8	a			12 51						14 00					14 51					
Lockerbie	a			13 10						14 21					15 12					
Haymarket	a			14s08											16s08					
Edinburgh 10	a			14 19	15 16				16b16						16 16	17 16				18 16
Haymarket	a								16 33											
Motherwell	a																			
Glasgow Central 15	a									15 25										
Inverkeithing	a								16 47											
Kirkcaldy	a								17 02											
Markinch	a								17 11											
Cupar	a								17 24											
Leuchars 3	a								17 31											
Dundee	a								17 44											
Arbroath	a								18 03											
Montrose	a								18 17											
Stonehaven	a								18 37											
Aberdeen	a								19 02											

For general notes see front of timetable
For details of catering facilities see Directory of Train Operators

b Dep. 1630

from 28 January

South Coast and The South West → North West England, The North East and Scotland

Route Diagram - See first page of Table 51

		VT	XC	XC	XC	XC	VT	XC	XC	XC	XC	XC	VT	XC	XC	XC	XC	VT	XC	XC
			R			R		R				R		R			R		R	R
		1 ◇	1	1 ◇	1 ◇	1	1 ◇	1	1 ◇	1 ◇	1 ◇	1	1 ◇	1	1 ◇	1 ◇	1	1 ◇	1	1
		☕	☕	☕	☕	☕	☕	☕	☕	☕	☕	☕	☕	☕	☕	☕	☕	☕	☕	☕
Brighton 10	d			09 21																
Haywards Heath 3	d			09 33																
Gatwick Airport 10 ✈	d			09 46																
Bournemouth	d					10 45						11 45					12 45			
Brockenhurst 3	d					11 00						12 00					13 00			
Southampton Central	d					11 15						12 15					13 15			
Southampton Airport Parkwy ✈	d					11 22						12 22					13 22			
Winchester	d					11 31						12 31					13 31			
Basingstoke	d					11 47						12 47					13 47			
Redhill	d																			
Guildford	d																			
East Croydon	d			10 08																
Kensington Olympia	d			10 37																
Reading 7	d			11 40		12 10			12 40			13 10			13 40		14 10			14 40
Oxford	d			12 07		12 36			13 07			13 36			14 07		14 36			15 07
Banbury	d			12 25		12 53			13 25			13 53			14 25		14 53			15 25
Leamington Spa 8	d			12 43		13 11			13 43			14 11			14 43		15 11			15 43
Coventry	d					13 23						14 23					15 23			
Birmingham International ✈	d					13 34					14 18	14 34					15 34			
Penzance	d		07 30					08 30						09 30						
St Erth 2	d		07 38					08 38						09 38						
Camborne	d		07 48					08 48						09 48						
Redruth	d		07 54					08 54						09 54						
Truro	d		08 06					09 06						10 06						
St Austell	d		08 22					09 22						10 22						
Par 3	d		08 29					09 29						10 29						
Bodmin Parkway	d		08 40					09 40						10 40						
Liskeard 3	d		08 52					09 52						10 52						
Plymouth	d		09 25					10 25						11 25		11 50			12 25	
Totnes	d		09 50					10 50						11 50		12 15			12 50	
Paignton	d				10 02															
Torquay	d				10 08															
Newton Abbot	d		10 03		10 19			11 03						12 03		12 28			13 03	
Teignmouth	d				10 26															
Dawlish	d				10 31															
Exeter St Davids 6	d		10 23		10 48			11 23						12 23		12 48			13 23	
Tiverton Parkway	d		10 37		11 01			11 37						12 37		13 02			13 37	
Taunton	d		10 51		11 16			11 51						12 51		13 16			13 51	
Weston-super-Mare	d																			
Cardiff Central 7	d																			
Newport (South Wales)	d																			
Bristol Temple Meads 10	d		11 30		12 00			12 30		13 00				13 30		14 00			14 30	
Bristol Parkway 7	d		11 40		12 10			12 40		13 10				13 40		14 10			14 40	
Gloucester 7	d																			
Cheltenham Spa	d		12 12		12 42			13 12		13 42				14 12		14 42			15 12	
Birmingham New Street 12	a		12 57	13 18	13 26	13 45		13 57	14 18	14 26	14 30	14 45		14 57	15 18	15 26	15 45		15 57	16 18
Birmingham New Street 12	d	13 03	13 18		13 30	13 48	14 03	14 03	14 18	14 30	14 48	15 03	15 03	15 18		15 30	15 48	16 03	16 03	16 18
Tamworth	d									14 47										
Burton-on-Trent	d									14 58										
Derby 10	a				14 11			14 39		15 11		15 39				16 11			16 39	
Chesterfield	a				14 32					15 32						16 32				
Sheffield 7	a				14 50			15 15		15 51		16 15				16 51			17 15	
Doncaster 7	a				15 15					16 15						17 15				
Wakefield Westgate 7	a							15 46				16 46							17 46	
Leeds 10	a							16 02				17 02							18 02	
York 8	a				15 40			16 29		16 40		17 29				17 40			18 29	
Darlington 7	a				16 11			16 57		17 08		18 02				18 15			18 58	
Durham	a				16 29					17 31		18 20				18 33			19 15	
Chester-le-Street	a				16 36											18 40				
Newcastle 8	a				16 52			17 28		17 54		18 37				18 56			19 35	
Alnmouth	a							17 54											20 03	
Berwick-upon-Tweed	a											19 22							20 24	
Dunbar	a											19 45								
Wolverhampton 7	d	13 21	13 39			14 06	14 21		14 39		15 06		15 21	15 39				16 21		16 39
Stafford	a					14 17					15 17						16 17			
Stoke-on-Trent	a		14 12			14 36			15 12		15 36			16 12			16 36			17 12
Congleton	a		14 24											16 24						17 24
Macclesfield	a		14 32			14 52			15 31		15 52			16 32			16 52			17 32
Crewe 10	a	13 53					14 53						15 55					16 53		
Wilmslow	a																			
Stockport	a		14 46			15 05			15 46		16 05			16 46			17 05			17 46
Manchester Piccadilly 10	a		15 02			15 20			16 02		16 20			17 02			17 20			18 02
Warrington Bank Quay	a	14 14					15 11						16 14					17 11		
Wigan North Western	a	14 26					15 22						16 25					17 22		
Preston 8	a	14 41					15 37						16 40					17 37		
Lancaster 6	a	14 57					15 56						16 58					17 54		
Oxenholme Lake District	a	15 12											17 15					18 11		
Penrith North Lakes	a						16 33											18 37		
Carlisle 8	a	15 55					16 51						17 57					18 55		
Lockerbie	a																			
Haymarket	a						18s09											20s08		
Edinburgh 10	a						18 19	18 57				20 11						20 19	21 08	
Haymarket	a							19 04				20 18							→	
Motherwell	a											→	19s13							
Glasgow Central 15	a	17 21											19 37							
Inverkeithing	a							19 18												
Kirkcaldy	a							19 34												
Markinch	a							19 43												
Cupar	a							19 57												
Leuchars 3	a							20 04												
Dundee	a							20 25												
Arbroath	a																			
Montrose	a																			
Stonehaven	a																			
Aberdeen	a																			

For general notes see front of timetable
For details of catering facilities see
Directory of Train Operators

from 28 January

South Coast and The South West → North West England, The North East and Scotland

Route Diagram - See first page of Table 51

		XC	XC	LM	XC	VT	XC	XC	XC	XC	XC	XC	XC	VT	XC	XC	XC	VT	XC
		R			R		R	R	R	R	R	R	R		R	R	R		R
		1	1 ◇	1 ◇	1	1 ◇	1	1	1	1	1	1	1	1 ◇	1	1	1	1 ◇	1
		⊡	⊡	⊼	⊡	⊡	⊡	⊡	⊡	⊡	⊡	⊡	⊡	⊡	⊡	⊡	⊡	⊡	⊡
Brighton 10	d															14 22			
Haywards Heath 3	d															14b31			
Gatwick Airport 10 ✈	d															14 51			
Bournemouth	d				13 45								14 45						15 45
Brockenhurst 3	d				14 00								15 00						16 00
Southampton Central	d				14 15								15 15						16 15
Southampton Airport Parkwy ✈	d				14 22								15 22						16 22
Winchester	d				14 31								15 31						16 31
Basingstoke	d				14 47								15 47						16 47
Redhill	d																		
Guildford	d																		
East Croydon	d															15 09			
Kensington Olympia	d															15 36			
Reading 7	d				15 10					15 40			16 10			16 40			17 10
Oxford	d				15 36					16 07			16 36			17 07			17 36
Banbury	d				15 53					16 25			16 53			17 25			17 53
Leamington Spa 8	d				16 11					16 43			17 11			17 43			18 11
Coventry	d				16 23								17 23					18 14	18 23
Birmingham International ✈	d		16 18		16 34								17 34					18 28	18 34
Penzance	d																		
St Erth 2	d																		
Camborne	d																		
Redruth	d																		
Truro	d																		
St Austell	d																		
Par 3	d																		
Bodmin Parkway	d																		
Liskeard 3	d																		
Plymouth	d							13 25							14 25				
Totnes	d							13 50							14 50				
Paignton	d										14 03								
Torquay	d										14 09								
Newton Abbot	d							14 03			14 21				15 03				
Teignmouth	d										14 28								
Dawlish	d										14 33								
Exeter St Davids 6	d							14 23			14 46				15 23				
Tiverton Parkway	d							14 37			15 00				15 37				
Taunton	d							14 51			15 14				15 51				
Weston-super-Mare	d										15 36								
Cardiff Central 7	d																		
Newport (South Wales)	d																		
Bristol Temple Meads 10	d	15 00						15 30			16 00				16 30		17 00		
Bristol Parkway 7	d	15 10						15 40			16 10				16 40		17 10		
Gloucester 7	d																		
Cheltenham Spa	d	15 42						16 12			16 42				17 12		17 42		
Birmingham New Street 12	a	16 26	16 30		16 45			16 57		17 18	17 26	⟵	17 45		17 57	18 18	18 26	18 39	18 45
Birmingham New Street 12	d	16 30	16 48	16 51	17 03	17 03		17 18		17 39 ⟶	17 30	17 39	17 48	18 03	18 03	18 18	18 30	18 43	19 03
Tamworth	d											18 06					18 47		
Burton-on-Trent	d											18 16					18 58		
Derby 10	a	17 14			17 39						18 11	18 34			18 39		19 11		19 39
Chesterfield	a	17 37									18 34				19 02		19 32		20 02
Sheffield 7	a	17 50			18 17						18 50				19 17		19 47		20 17
Doncaster 7	a	18 16									19 17						20 20		
Wakefield Westgate 7	a				18 46										19 49				20 53
Leeds 10	a				19 02										20 06				21 09
York 8	a	18 41			19 29						19 44				20 33		20 46		21 34
Darlington 7	a	19 17			20 03						20 12				21 07		21 20		22 03
Durham	a	19 35			20 20						20 30				21 25		21 38		22 20
Chester-le-Street	a										20 37						21 45		
Newcastle 8	a	20 04			20 37						20 54				21 42		22 01		22 42
Alnmouth	a				21 07										22 14				
Berwick-upon-Tweed	a				21 29										22 35				
Dunbar	a														22 58				
Wolverhampton 7	d		17 06	17 10				17 39					18 06	18 21		18 39		19 06	
Stafford	a		17 17	17 26									18 17					19 21	
Stoke-on-Trent	a		17 36					18 12					18 36			19 12		19 45	
Congleton	a							18 24											
Macclesfield	a		17 52					18 32					18 52			19 31		20 01	
Crewe 10	a			17 48		17 53								18 54					
Wilmslow	a																		
Stockport	a		18 05					18 46					19 05			19 46		20 16	
Manchester Piccadilly 10	a		18 20					19 02					19 20			20 02		20 35	
Warrington Bank Quay	a			18 06										19 12					
Wigan North Western	a			18 17										19 23					
Preston 8	a			18 39		18 39								19 42					
Lancaster 6	a					18 58								19 59					
Oxenholme Lake District	a					19 13								20 13					
Penrith North Lakes	a													20 39					
Carlisle 8	a					19 54								20 58					
Lockerbie	a																		
Haymarket	a								⟵					22s13					
Edinburgh 10	a				22 24		⟵		21 08					22 25	23 28				
Haymarket	a						20 18		21 18										
Motherwell	a								21s59										
Glasgow Central 15	a					21 11	21 28		22 42										
Inverkeithing	a																		
Kirkcaldy	a																		
Markinch	a																		
Cupar	a																		
Leuchars 3	a																		
Dundee	a																		
Arbroath	a																		
Montrose	a																		
Stonehaven	a																		
Aberdeen	a																		

For general notes see front of timetable
For details of catering facilities see Directory of Train Operators

b Change at East Croydon

from 28 January

South Coast and The South West → North West England, The North East and Scotland

Route Diagram - See first page of Table 51

		VT	XC	XC	XC		XC	XC	XC	XC		XC	VT	XC	XC		XC	XC	XC	XC		XC		
			R	R			R																	
		1◇	1	1	1◇		1	1◇	1◇	1◇		1◇	1◇	1◇	1◇		1◇	1◇	1◇	1◇		1◇		
		🍴	🍴	🍴	🍴		🍴	🍴	🍴	🍴		🍴	🍴	🍴			🍴	🍴	🍴					
Brighton 10	d																							
Haywards Heath 3	d																							
Gatwick Airport 10 ✈	d								*17 03*															
Bournemouth	d						16 45					17 45					18 45			19 45				
Brockenhurst 3	d						17 00					18 00					19 00			20 00				
Southampton Central	d						17 15					18 15					19 15			20 15				
Southampton Airport Parkwy ✈	d						17 22					18 22					19 22			20 22				
Winchester	d						17 31					18 31					19 31			20 31				
Basingstoke	d						17 47					18 47					19 47			20 47				
Redhill	d								*17 14*															
Guildford	d								17 57															
East Croydon	d																							
Kensington Olympia	d																							
Reading 7	d			17 40			18 10		18 40			19 10			19 40		20 10			21 10				
Oxford	d			18 07			18 36		19 07			19 36			20 07		20 36			21 36				
Banbury	d			18 25			18 53		19 25			19 53			20 25		20 53			21 53				
Leamington Spa 8	d			18 43			19 11		19 43			20 11			20 43		21 11			22 11				
Coventry	d						19 23					20 23					21 23			22 23				
Birmingham International ✈	d						19 34					20 34					21 34			22 34				
Penzance	d																							
St Erth 2	d																							
Camborne	d																							
Redruth	d																							
Truro	d																							
St Austell	d																							
Par 3	d																							
Bodmin Parkway	d																							
Liskeard 3	d																							
Plymouth	d		15 25					16 25						17 25				18 25						
Totnes	d		15 50					16 50						17 50				18 50						
Paignton	d				16 15																			
Torquay	d				16 21																			
Newton Abbot	d		16 03		16 33			17 03						18 03				19 03						
Teignmouth	d																							
Dawlish	d																							
Exeter St Davids 6	d		16 23		16 53			17 23						18 23				19 23						
Tiverton Parkway	d		16 37		17 07			17 37						18 38				19 37						
Taunton	d		16 51		17 21			17 51						18 52				19 51						
Weston-super-Mare	d																							
Cardiff Central 7	d																							
Newport (South Wales)	d																							
Bristol Temple Meads 10	d		17 30		18 00			18 30		19 00				19 30				20 30				22 00		
Bristol Parkway 7	d		17 40		18 10			18 40		19 10				19 40				20 40				22 10		
Gloucester 7	d																							
Cheltenham Spa	d		18 12		18 42			19 12		19 42				20 12				21 12				22 42		
Birmingham New Street 12	a		18 57	19 18	19 26		19 45	19 57	20 18	20 42		20 48		20 57	21 18		21 45	21 57	←	22 52		23 43		
Birmingham New Street 12	d	19 03	19 18		19 30		20 03	20 03	20 18	20 48		21 03	21 03	21 18			22 18	22 03	22 18					
Tamworth	d				19 47			20 19				21 19					→	22 19						
Burton-on-Trent	d				19 58			20 29				21 29						22 29						
Derby 10	a				20 11			20 42				21 42						22 42						
Chesterfield	a				20 32			21 02				22 02						23 27						
Sheffield 7	a				20 48			21 18				22 17						23 54						
Doncaster 7	a																							
Wakefield Westgate 7	a							21 49				22s46												
Leeds 10	a							22 05				23 05						01 01						
York 8	a				21 48			22 58																
Darlington 7	a				22 18																			
Durham	a				22 35																			
Chester-le-Street	a				22 45																			
Newcastle 8	a				23 00																			
Alnmouth	a																							
Berwick-upon-Tweed	a																							
Dunbar	a																							
Wolverhampton 7	d	19 21	19 39				20 21		20 39	21 11			21 21	21 39					22 39					
Stafford	a	19 36					20 34			21 23			21 36	21 53					22 53					
Stoke-on-Trent	a		20 12						21 12	21 45				22 12					23s12					
Congleton	a		20 24											22 24										
Macclesfield	a		20 32						21 28	22 02				22 32										
Crewe 10	a	19 58					20 54						21 58											
Wilmslow	a						21 15																	
Stockport	a		20 46				21 25		21 46	22 15				22 46										
Manchester Piccadilly 10	a		21 02				21 48		22 02	22 32				23 02					00 07					
Warrington Bank Quay	a	20 16											22 17											
Wigan North Western	a	20 27											22 43											
Preston 8	a	20 42											23 04											
Lancaster 6	a	21 00																						
Oxenholme Lake District	a	21 14																						
Penrith North Lakes	a	21 41																						
Carlisle 8	a	21 58																						
Lockerbie	a	22 17																						
Haymarket	a																							
Edinburgh 10	a																							
Haymarket	a																							
Motherwell	a	23s04																						
Glasgow Central 15	a	23 33																						
Inverkeithing	a																							
Kirkcaldy	a																							
Markinch	a																							
Cupar	a																							
Leuchars 3	a																							
Dundee	a																							
Arbroath	a																							
Montrose	a																							
Stonehaven	a																							
Aberdeen	a																							

For general notes see front of timetable
For details of catering facilities see Directory of Train Operators

South Coast and The South West → North West England, The North East and Scotland

Route Diagram - See first page of Table 51

		VT 1◇	XC 1◇	XC 1◇	XC 1◇	XC 1◇	VT 1◇	XC 1◇	XC 1◇	VT 1◇	XC 1◇	XC 1◇	XC 1◇	VT 1◇	XC 1◇	VT 1◇	XC 1◇	XC 1◇	XC 1◇	VT 1◇	VT 1◇	XC 1◇	VT 1◇
Brighton 10	d											*03 50*											
Haywards Heath 3	d											*04 25*											
Gatwick Airport 10 ✈	d											05 15						05 45					
Bournemouth	d																					06 37	
Brockenhurst 3	d																					06 54	
Southampton Central	d														06 15							07 15	
Southampton Airport Parkway ✈	d														06 22							07 22	
Winchester	d														06 31							07 31	
Basingstoke	d														06 47							07 47	
Redhill	d											05 33						05 52					
Guildford	d											06 00											
East Croydon	d																	06 06					
Kensington Olympia	d																	06 50					
Reading 7	d											06 40			07 10			07 40				08 10	
Oxford	d											07 07			07 36			08 04				08 36	
Banbury	d											07 25			07 53			08 25				08 53	
Leamington Spa 8	d											07 43			08 11			08 43				09 11	
Coventry	d													08 15	08 23					09 10	09 16	09 23	
Birmingham International ✈	d													08 28	08 34					09 22	09 28	09 34	
Penzance	d																						
St Erth 2	d																						
Camborne	d																						
Redruth	d																						
Truro	d																						
St Austell	d																						
Par 3	d																						
Bodmin Parkway	d																						
Liskeard 3	d																						
Plymouth	d																						
Totnes	d																						
Paignton	d																						
Torquay	d																						
Newton Abbot	d																						
Teignmouth	d																						
Dawlish	d																						
Exeter St Davids 6	d																06 10						
Tiverton Parkway	d																06 24						
Taunton	d																06 38						
Weston-super-Mare	d																07 00						
Cardiff Central 7	d																						
Newport (South Wales)	d																						
Bristol Temple Meads 10	d										06 15						07 30		08 00				
Bristol Parkway 7	d										06 25						07 40		08 10				
Gloucester 7	d										07 01												
Cheltenham Spa	d										07 12						08 12		08 42				
Birmingham New Street 12	a										07 57	08 18		08 39	08 46		08 57	09 18	09 26	09 36	09 39	09 45	
Birmingham New Street 12	d	05 30	06 00	06 20	06 30	07 03	07 03	07 20	07 30	08 03	08 03	08 20	08 30	08 48	09 03	09 03	09 20		09 30	09 40	09 48	10 20 →	10 03
Tamworth	d		06 16		06 47	07 19			07 47		08 19		08 47										
Burton-on-Trent	d		06 26		06 58	07 29			07 58		08 29		08 58										
Derby 10	a		06 39		07 11	07 42			08 11		08 42		09 11		09 39				10 11				
Chesterfield	a				07 32	08 01			08 32		09 01		09 32						10 32				
Sheffield 7	a		07 09		07 49	08 17			08 46		09 17		09 50		10 15				10 50				
Doncaster 7	a				08 23				09 21				10 18						11 16				
Wakefield Westgate 7	a		07 36			08 46					09 46				10 46								
Leeds 10	a		07 52			09 04					10 02				11 02								
York 8	a		08 24		08 49	09 31			09 48		10 31		10 44		11 29				11 45				
Darlington 7	a		08 52		09 19	10 00			10 16		11 01		11 16		12 01				12 15				
Durham	a		09 09		09 37	10 17			10 33		11 20		11 33		12 18				12 33				
Chester-le-Street	a				09 44				10 40										12 40				
Newcastle 8	a		09 26		09 59	10 34			10 59		11 36		11 57		12 35				12 57				
Alnmouth	a		09 55								12 05												
Berwick-upon-Tweed	a					11 20									13 20								
Dunbar	a					11 43									13 43								
Wolverhampton 7	d	05 49		06 40			07 21	07 40		08 21		08 40		09 09		09 21	09 40				10 09		10 21
Stafford	a	06 04		06 53			07 33	07 53				08 53		09 24			09 53			10 17	10 24		
Stoke-on-Trent	a			07 12				08 12				09 12		09 43			10 12				10 42		
Congleton	a			07 24				08 24									10 24						
Macclesfield	a			07 32				08 32				09 29		09 59			10 32				10 58		
Crewe 10	a	06 25					07 54			08 54						09 54				10 38			10 54
Wilmslow	a																						
Stockport	a			07 46				08 46				09 46		10 13			10 46				11 13		
Manchester Piccadilly 10	a			08 02				09 02				10 02		10 28			11 02				11 28		
Warrington Bank Quay	a	06 43					08 12			09 11						10 12				10 57			11 11
Wigan North Western	a	07 02					08 23			09 22						10 23				11 08			11 22
Preston 8	a	07 18					08 39			09 38						10 38				11 22			11 37
Lancaster 6	a	07 33					08 59			09 53										11 40			11 54
Oxenholme Lake District	a	07 47					09 16			10 08						11 08				11 53			
Penrith North Lakes	a	08 13					09 42			10 34										12 19			12 31
Carlisle 8	a	08 31					10 00			10 52						11 50				12 37			12 49
Lockerbie	a	08 51					10 20			11 11													13 09
Haymarket	a									12s08													14s04
Edinburgh 10	a		11 02			12 13				12 19	13 13				14 13								14 16
Haymarket	a																						
Motherwell	a	09s34					11s03																
Glasgow Central 15	a	09 59					11 27									13 18				13 59			
Inverkeithing	a																						
Kirkcaldy	a																						
Markinch	a																						
Cupar	a																						
Leuchars 3	a																						
Dundee	a																						
Arbroath	a																						
Montrose	a																						
Stonehaven	a																						
Aberdeen	a																						

For general notes see front of timetable
For details of catering facilities see Directory of Train Operators

until 26 January

South Coast and The South West → North West England, The North East and Scotland

Route Diagram - See first page of Table 51

		XC	XC	XC	XC	VT	VT	XC	VT	XC	XC	XC	VT	VT	XC	VT	XC	XC	XC	XC	VT	VT	XC
		1◇	1◇	1◇	1◇	1◇	1◇	1◇	R 1	1◇	1◇	1◇	1◇	1◇	1◇	1◇	1◇	1◇	1◇	1◇	1◇	1◇	1◇
Brighton 10	d																						
Haywards Heath 3	d																						
Gatwick Airport 10 ✈	d																						
Bournemouth	d							07 45							08 45								09 45
Brockenhurst 3	d							08 00							09 00								10 00
Southampton Central	d							08 15							09 15								10 15
Southampton Airport Parkwy ✈	d							08 22							09 22								10 22
Winchester	d							08 31							09 31								10 31
Basingstoke	d							08 47							09 47								10 47
Redhill	d																						
Guildford	d																						
East Croydon	d																						
Kensington Olympia	d																						
Reading 7	d			08 40				09 10			09 40				10 10				10 40				11 10
Oxford	d			09 07				09 36			10 07				10 36				11 07				11 36
Banbury	d			09 25				09 53			10 25				10 53				11 25				11 53
Leamington Spa 8	d			09 43				10 11			10 43				11 11				11 43				12 11
Coventry	d					10 10	10 16	10 23					11 10	11 16	11 23						12 10	12 16	12 23
Birmingham International ✈	d					10 22	10 28	10 34					11 22	11 28	11 34						12 22	12 28	12 34
Penzance	d																						
St Erth 2	d																						
Camborne	d																						
Redruth	d																						
Truro	d																						
St Austell	d																						
Par 3	d																						
Bodmin Parkway	d																						
Liskeard 3	d																						
Plymouth	d	06 25								07 25							08 25						
Totnes	d	06 50								07 50							08 50						
Paignton	d																						
Torquay	d																						
Newton Abbot	d	07 03								08 03							09 03						
Teignmouth	d																						
Dawlish	d																						
Exeter St Davids 6	d	07 23								08 23							09 23						
Tiverton Parkway	d	07 37								08 37							09 37						
Taunton	d	07 51								08 51							09 51						
Weston-super-Mare	d																						
Cardiff Central 7	d											09 00											
Newport (South Wales)	d											09 15											
Bristol Temple Meads 10	d	08 30			09 00					09 30		10 00					10 30			11 00			
Bristol Parkway 7	d	08 40			09 10					09 40		10 10					10 40			11 10			
Gloucester 7	d																						
Cheltenham Spa	d	09 12			09 42					10 12		10 42					11 12			11 42			
Birmingham New Street 12	a	09 57	←	10 18	10 26	10 36	10 39	10 45		10 58	11 18	11 26	11 36	11 39	11 45		11 57	←	12 18	12 26	12 36	12 39	12 45
Birmingham New Street 12	d	10 03	10 20		10 30	10 40	10 48	11 03	11 03	11 20		11 30	11 40	11 48	12 20 →	12 03	12 03	12 20		12 30	12 40	12 48	13 03
Tamworth	d				10 47															12 47			
Burton-on-Trent	d				10 58															12 58			
Derby 10	a	10 39			11 11			11 39				12 11					12 39			13 11			13 39
Chesterfield	a				11 32							12 32								13 32			
Sheffield 7	a	11 15			11 50			12 15				12 50					13 15			13 51			14 15
Doncaster 7	a				12 15							13 19								14 15			
Wakefield Westgate 7	a	11 46						12 46									13 46						14 46
Leeds 10	a	12 02						13 02									14 02						15 02
York 8	a	12 29			12 43			13 29				13 44					14 29			14 43			15 29
Darlington 7	a	13 01			13 11			14 01				14 17					14 59			15 15			16 00
Durham	a	13 18			13 28			14 18				14 35					15 17			15 33			16 17
Chester-le-Street	a																						
Newcastle 8	a	13 35			13 50			14 35				14 54					15 34			15 55			16 34
Alnmouth	a	14 02															16 05						
Berwick-upon-Tweed	a							15 20															17 20
Dunbar	a							15 43															17 43
Wolverhampton 7	d		10 40				11 09		11 21	11 40				12 09		12 21		12 40				13 09	
Stafford	a		10 53			11 19	11 24			11 53			12 17	12 24				12 53			13 17	13 24	
Stoke-on-Trent	a		11 12				11 43			12 12				12 43				13 12				13 43	
Congleton	a									12 24													
Macclesfield	a		11 29				11 59			12 32				12 59				13 29				13 59	
Crewe 10	a					11 40			11 54				12 38			12 54					13 38		
Wilmslow	a																						
Stockport	a		11 46				12 13			12 46				13 13				13 46				14 13	
Manchester Piccadilly 10	a		12 02				12 28			13 02				13 28				14 02				14 28	
Warrington Bank Quay	a					11 59			12 13				12 56			13 11					13 57		
Wigan North Western	a					12 10			12 24				13 07			13 22					14 08		
Preston 8	a					12 24			12 39				13 26			13 36					14 23		
Lancaster 6	a					12 41			12 55							13 53					14 39		
Oxenholme Lake District	a					12 54										14 07					14 53		
Penrith North Lakes	a					13 20			13 32												15 19		
Carlisle 8	a					13 38			13 50							14 48					15 37		
Lockerbie	a								14 12							15 08							
Haymarket	a															16s09							
Edinburgh 10	a	15 13						16b19								16 19	17 14						18 16
Haymarket	a							16 34															
Motherwell	a																				16s34		
Glasgow Central 15	a					14 58			15 17												16 58		
Inverkeithing	a							16 47															
Kirkcaldy	a							17 02															
Markinch	a							17 11															
Cupar	a							17 24															
Leuchars 3	a							17 31															
Dundee	a							17 44															
Arbroath	a							18 03															
Montrose	a							18 17															
Stonehaven	a							18 37															
Aberdeen	a							19 02															

For general notes see front of timetable
For details of catering facilities see Directory of Train Operators

b Dep. 1630

until 26 January

South Coast and The South West → North West England, The North East and Scotland

Route Diagram - See first page of Table 51

		VT	XC	XC	XC	VT	VT	XC	VT	XC	XC	XC	XC	VT	VT	XC	VT	XC	XC	XC	VT	VT	XC
		R 1	1 ◇	1 ◇	1 ◇	1 ◇	1 ◇	1 ◇	R 1	1 ◇	1 ◇	1 ◇	1 ◇	1 ◇	1 ◇	1 ◇	R 1	1 ◇	1 ◇	1 ◇	1 ◇	1 ◇	1 ◇
Brighton [10]	d			09 15																			
Haywards Heath [3]	d			09 34																			
Gatwick Airport [10] ✈	d			09 47																			
Bournemouth	d							10 45								11 45							12 45
Brockenhurst [3]	d							11 00								12 00							13 00
Southampton Central	d							11 15								12 15							13 15
Southampton Airport Parkwy ✈	d							11 22								12 22							13 22
Winchester	d							11 31								12 31							13 31
Basingstoke	d							11 47								12 47							13 47
Redhill	d																						
Guildford	d																						
East Croydon	d			10 03																			
Kensington Olympia	d			10 34																			
Reading [7]	d			11 40				12 10				12 40				13 10			13 40				14 10
Oxford	d			12 07				12 35				13 07				13 36			14 07				14 36
Banbury	d			12 25				12 53				13 25				13 53			14 25				14 53
Leamington Spa [8]	d			12 43				13 11				13 43				14 11			14 43				15 11
Coventry	d					13 10	13 16	13 23						14 10	14 16	14 23					15 10	15 16	15 23
Birmingham International ✈	d					13 22	13 28	13 34						14 22	14 28	14 34					15 22	15 28	15 34
Penzance	d		07 30							08 30								09 30					
St Erth [2]	d		07 38							08 38								09 38					
Camborne	d		07 48							08 48								09 48					
Redruth	d		07 54							08 54								09 54					
Truro	d		08 06							09 06								10 06					
St Austell	d		08 22							09 22								10 22					
Par [3]	d		08 29							09 29								10 29					
Bodmin Parkway	d		08 40							09 40								10 40					
Liskeard [3]	d		08 52							09 52								10 52					
Plymouth	d		09 25							10 25								11 25					
Totnes	d		09 50							10 50								11 50					
Paignton	d				10 05																		
Torquay	d				10 11																		
Newton Abbot	d		10 03		10 22					11 03								12 03					
Teignmouth	d				10 29																		
Dawlish	d				10 34																		
Exeter St Davids [6]	d		10 23		10 48					11 23								12 23					
Tiverton Parkway	d		10 37		11 01					11 37								12 37					
Taunton	d		10 51		11 16					11 51								12 51					
Weston-super-Mare	d																						
Cardiff Central [7]	d																						
Newport (South Wales)	d																						
Bristol Temple Meads [10]	d		11 30		12 00					12 30			13 00					13 30		14 00			
Bristol Parkway [7]	d		11 40		12 10					12 40			13 10					13 40		14 10			
Gloucester [7]	d																						
Cheltenham Spa	d		12 12		12 42					13 12			13 42					14 12		14 42			
Birmingham New Street [12]	a		12 57	13 18	13 26	13 36	13 39	13 45		13 57	←	14 18	14 26	14 36	14 39	14 46		14 57	15 18	15 27	15 36	15 39	15 45
Birmingham New Street [12]	d	13 03	13 20		13 30	13 40	13 48	14 20 →	14 03	14 03	14 20		14 30	14 40	14 48	15 03	15 03	15 20		15 30	15 40	15 48	16 20 →
Tamworth	d												14 47										
Burton-on-Trent	d												14 58										
Derby [10]	a				14 11					14 39			15 11			15 39				16 11			
Chesterfield	a				14 32								15 32							16 32			
Sheffield [7]	a				14 50					15 15			15 50			16 15				16 50			
Doncaster [7]	a				15 15								16 15							17 19			
Wakefield Westgate [7]	a									15 46						16 46							
Leeds [10]	a									16 02						17 04							
York [8]	a				15 43					16 29			16 45			17 30				17 45			
Darlington [7]	a				16 12					17 00			17 16			18 00				18 15			
Durham	a				16 29					17 17			17 33			18 17				18 32			
Chester-le-Street	a												17 43							18 39			
Newcastle [8]	a				16 51					17 34			17 58			18 34				18 56			
Alnmouth	a									18 02													
Berwick-upon-Tweed	a															19 20							
Dunbar	a															19 43							
Wolverhampton [7]	d	13 21	13 40				14 09		14 21		14 40				15 09		15 21	15 40				16 09	
Stafford	a		13 53			14 17	14 24				14 53			15 17	15 24			15 53			16 17	16 24	
Stoke-on-Trent	a		14 12				14 43				15 12				15 43			16 12				16 43	
Congleton	a		14 24															16 24					
Macclesfield	a		14 32				14 59				15 29				15 59			16 33				16 59	
Crewe [10]	a	13 54				14 38			14 54					15 38			15 54				16 38		
Wilmslow	a																						
Stockport	a		14 46				15 13				15 46				16 13			16 46				17 13	
Manchester Piccadilly [10]	a		15 02				15 28				16 02				16 28			17 02				17 28	
Warrington Bank Quay	a	14 12				14 57			15 12					15 56			16 12				16 57		
Wigan North Western	a	14 23				15 08			15 23					16 07			16 23				17 08		
Preston [8]	a	14 39				15 22			15 39					16 22			16 39				17 23		
Lancaster [6]	a	14 54				15 39			15 54					16 38			16 57				17 40		
Oxenholme Lake District	a	15 09				15 52								16 52			17 12				17 53		
Penrith North Lakes	a	15 36				16 18			16 33					17 18			17 38				18 19		
Carlisle [8]	a	15 54				16 36			16 49					17 36			17 56				18 37		
Lockerbie	a																18 17						
Haymarket	a								18s06														
Edinburgh [10]	a								18 16	19 12						20 13							
Haymarket	a									19 16						20 17 →							
Motherwell	a	16s53				17s34											19s00						
Glasgow Central [15]	a	17 17				17 57								18 58			19 27				19 58		
Inverkeithing	a									19 32													
Kirkcaldy	a									19 49													
Markinch	a									19 58													
Cupar	a									20 19													
Leuchars [3]	a									20 27													
Dundee	a									20 50													
Arbroath	a																						
Montrose	a																						
Stonehaven	a																						
Aberdeen	a																						

For general notes see front of timetable
For details of catering facilities see Directory of Train Operators

until 26 January

South Coast and The South West → North West England, The North East and Scotland

Route Diagram - See first page of Table 51

		VT	XC	XC	XC	XC	VT	VT	XC	VT	XC	XC	XC	XC	XC	VT	VT	XC	XC	VT	XC	XC	XC
										R										R			
		1 ◇	1 ◇	1 ◇	1 ◇	1 ◇	1 ◇	1 ◇	1 ◇	1	1 ◇	1 ◇	1 ◇	1 ◇	1 ◇	1 ◇	1 ◇	1 ◇	1 ◇	1	1 ◇	1 ◇	1 ◇
Brighton 10	d																					14 22	
Haywards Heath 3	d																					14b32	
Gatwick Airport 10	d																					14 54	
Bournemouth	d								13 45									14 45					
Brockenhurst 3	d								14 00									15 00					
Southampton Central	d								14 15									15 15					
Southampton Airport Parkwy	d								14 22									15 22					
Winchester	d								14 31									15 31					
Basingstoke	d								14 47									15 47					
Redhill	d																						
Guildford	d																						
East Croydon	d																					15 08	
Kensington Olympia	d																					15 40	
Reading 7	d				14 40				15 10				15 40					16 10				16 40	
Oxford	d				15 07				15 36				16 07					16 36				17 07	
Banbury	d				15 25				15 53				16 25					16 53				17 25	
Leamington Spa 8	d				15 43				16 11				16 43					17 11				17 43	
Coventry	d						16 10	16 16	16 23							17 10	17 16	17 23					
Birmingham International	d						16 22	16 28	16 34							17 22	17 28	17 34					
Penzance	d																						
St Erth 2	d																						
Camborne	d																						
Redruth	d																						
Truro	d																						
St Austell	d																						
Par 3	d																						
Bodmin Parkway	d																						
Liskeard 3	d																						
Plymouth	d		12 25									13 25							14 25				
Totnes	d		12 50									13 50							14 50				
Paignton	d													14 05									
Torquay	d													14 11									
Newton Abbot	d		13 03									14 03		14 22					15 03				
Teignmouth	d													14 29									
Dawlish	d													14 34									
Exeter St Davids 6	d		13 23									14 23		14 48					15 23				
Tiverton Parkway	d		13 37									14 37		15 01					15 37				
Taunton	d		13 51									14 51		15 16					15 51				
Weston-super-Mare	d																						
Cardiff Central 7	d																						
Newport (South Wales)	d																						
Bristol Temple Meads 10	d		14 30			15 00						15 30		16 00					16 30				17 00
Bristol Parkway 7	d		14 40			15 10						15 40		16 10					16 40				17 10
Gloucester 7	d																						
Cheltenham Spa	d		15 12			15 42						16 12		16 42					17 12				17 42
Birmingham New Street 12	a		15 57	←	16 18	16 26	16 36	16 39	16 46			16 57	17 18	17 26		17 36	17 39	17 45	17 57		←	18 18	18 26
Birmingham New Street 12	d	16 03	16 03	16 20		16 30	16 40	16 48	17 03	17 03		17 20		17 30		17 40	17 48	18 20 →	18 03	18 03	18 20		18 30
Tamworth	d					16 47																	18 47
Burton-on-Trent	d					16 58																	18 58
Derby 10	a		16 39			17 11			17 39					18 11					18 39				19 11
Chesterfield	a					17 32								18 32					19 01				19 32
Sheffield 7	a		17 15			17 48			18 17					18 46					19 16				19 47
Doncaster 7	a					18 21								19 18									20 16
Wakefield Westgate 7	a		17 46						18 46										19 46				
Leeds 10	a		18 02						19 02										20 02				
York 8	a		18 29			18 46			19 32					19 49					20 29				20 42
Darlington 7	a		19 00			19 14			20 02					20 17					21 03				21 14
Durham	a		19 17			19 31			20 22					20 34					21 21				22 10
Chester-le-Street	a													20 41									22 17
Newcastle 8	a		19 34			19 53			20 36					20 54					21 41				22 34
Alnmouth	a		20 02						21 02														
Berwick-upon-Tweed	a		20 23						21 23					21 38									
Dunbar	a													22 01									
Wolverhampton 7	d	16 21		16 40				17 09		17 21		17 40					18 09			18 20	18 40		
Stafford	a			16 53			17 17	17 24				17 53				18 17	18 24				18 53		
Stoke-on-Trent	a			17 12				17 43				18 12					18 43				19 12		
Congleton	a											18 24											
Macclesfield	a			17 29				17 59				18 32					18 59				19 29		
Crewe 10	a	16 54					17 38			17 54						18 38				18 54			
Wilmslow	a																						
Stockport	a			17 46				18 13				18 46					19 13				19 46		
Manchester Piccadilly 10	a			18 02				18 28				19 02					19 28				20 02		
Warrington Bank Quay	a	17 12					17 57			18 12						18 57				19 12			
Wigan North Western	a	17 23					18 08			18 23						19 08				19 24			
Preston 8	a	17 39					18 22			18 39						19 25				19 43			
Lancaster 6	a	17 55					18 39			18 58						19 39							
Oxenholme Lake District	a	18 09					18 52			19 13						19 52							
Penrith North Lakes	a						19 19									20 18							
Carlisle 8	a	18 55					19 36			19 54						20 41							
Lockerbie	a	19 15																					
Haymarket	a	20s12																					
Edinburgh 10	a	20 22	21 13						22 13		←			22 31	←								
Haymarket	a		21 18 →								20 17				21 18								
Motherwell	a						20s39				21s00				22s04								
Glasgow Central 15	a						20 59			21 18	21 27				22 43								
Inverkeithing	a																						
Kirkcaldy	a																						
Markinch	a																						
Cupar	a																						
Leuchars 3	a																						
Dundee	a																						
Arbroath	a																						
Montrose	a																						
Stonehaven	a																						
Aberdeen	a																						

For general notes see front of timetable
For details of catering facilities see Directory of Train Operators

b Change at East Croydon

until 26 January

South Coast and The South West → North West England, The North East and Scotland

Route Diagram - See first page of Table 51

Station		VT	VT	XC	VT	XC	XC	XC	VT	XC	XC	XC	XC	XC	VT	XC	XC	XC	XC	XC	XC	XC
		1 ◇	1 ◇	1 ◇	R 1	1 ◇	1 ◇	1 ◇	1 ◇	1 ◇	1 ◇	1 ◇	1 ◇	1 ◇	1 ◇	1 ◇	1 ◇	1 ◇	1 ◇	1 ◇	1 ◇	1 ◇
		☕	☕	☕	☕	☕	☕	☕	☕	☕	☕	☕	☕		☕	☕	☕		☕	☕	☕	
Brighton 10	d																					
Haywards Heath 3	d																					
Gatwick Airport 10 ✈	d												17 03									
Bournemouth	d			15 45						16 45						17 45			18 45			19 45
Brockenhurst 3	d			16 00						17 00						18 00			19 00			20 00
Southampton Central	d			16 15						17 15						18 15			19 15			20 15
Southampton Airport Parkwy ✈	d			16 22						17 22						18 22			19 22			20 22
Winchester	d			16 31						17 31						18 31			19 31			20 31
Basingstoke	d			16 47						17 47						18 47			19 47			20 47
Redhill	d												17 14									
Guildford	d												17 58									
East Croydon 🚌	d																					
Kensington Olympia	d																					
Reading 7	d			17 10			17 40			18 10			18 40			19 10		19 40	20 10			21 10
Oxford	d			17 36			18 07			18 36			19 07			19 36		20 07	20 36			21 36
Banbury	d			17 53			18 25			18 53			19 25			19 53		20 25	20 53			21 53
Leamington Spa 8	d			18 11			18 43			19 11			19 43			20 11		20 43	21 11			22 11
Coventry	d	18 10	18 16	18 23					19 16	19 23					20 16	20 23			21 23			22 23
Birmingham International ✈	d	18 22	18 28	18 34					19 28	19 34					20 28	20 34			21 34			22 34
Penzance	d																					
St Erth 2	d																					
Camborne	d																					
Redruth	d																					
Truro	d																					
St Austell	d																					
Par 3	d																					
Bodmin Parkway	d																					
Liskeard 3	d																					
Plymouth	d					15 25					16 25						17 25			18 25		
Totnes	d					15 50					16 50						17 50			18 50		
Paignton	d																					
Torquay	d																					
Newton Abbot	d					16 03					17 03						18 03			19 03		
Teignmouth	d																					
Dawlish	d																					
Exeter St Davids 6	d					16 23					17 23						18 23			19 23		
Tiverton Parkway	d					16 37					17 37						18 37			19 37		
Taunton	d					16 51					17 51						18 51			19 51		
Weston-super-Mare	d																					
Cardiff Central 7	d																					
Newport (South Wales)	d																					
Bristol Temple Meads 10	d					17 30		18 00			18 30			19 00			19 30			20 30		
Bristol Parkway 7	d					17 40		18 10			18 40			19 10			19 40			20 40		
Gloucester 7	d																					
Cheltenham Spa	d					18 12		18 42			19 12			19 42			20 12			21 12		
Birmingham New Street 12	a	18 36	18 39	18 45		18 57	19 18	19 27	19 39	19 45	19 57	←	20 18	20 31	20 39	20 45	20 57	21 22	21 45	21 57	←	22 50
Birmingham New Street 12	d	18 40	18 48	19 03	19 03	19 20		19 30	19 48	20 20 →	20 03	20 20			20 48	20 50	21 20		22 20 →	22 03	22 20	
Tamworth	d							19 47			20 19					21 23				22 19		
Burton-on-Trent	d							19 58			20 29					21 33				22 29		
Derby 10	a			19 39				20 11			20 42					21 45				22 47		
Chesterfield	a			20 00				20 36			21 01					22 04						
Sheffield 7	a			20 18				20 51			21 16					22 19						
Doncaster 7	a																					
Wakefield Westgate 7	a			20 48							21 46					22s46						
Leeds 10	a			21 05							22 01					23 09						
York 8	a			21 35				21 54			22 38											
Darlington 7	a																					
Durham	a			22 48																		
Chester-le-Street	a																					
Newcastle 8	a			23 11																		
Alnmouth	a																					
Berwick-upon-Tweed	a																					
Dunbar	a																					
Wolverhampton 7 🚌	d		19 09		19 21	19 40			20 09			20 40			21 10		21 40				22 40	
Stafford	a	19 17	19 24		19 33	19 53			20 24			20 53			21 24		21 53				22 53	
Stoke-on-Trent	a		19 43			20 12			20 43			21 12			21 44		22 12				23s13	
Congleton	a					20 24											22 24					
Macclesfield	a		19 59			20 32			20 59			21 29			22 00		22 32				23s30	
Crewe 10	a	19 38			19 54																	
Wilmslow	a																					
Stockport	a		20 13			20 46			21 13			21 46			22 12		22 46				23s46	
Manchester Piccadilly 10 🚌	a		20 28			21 02			21 28			22 02			22 25		23 02				00 02	
Warrington Bank Quay	a	19 57			20 12																	
Wigan North Western	a	20 08			20 23																	
Preston 8	a	20 26			20 43																	
Lancaster 6	a																					
Oxenholme Lake District	a																					
Penrith North Lakes	a																					
Carlisle 8	a																					
Lockerbie	a																					
Haymarket	a																					
Edinburgh 10	a																					
Haymarket	a																					
Motherwell	a																					
Glasgow Central 15	a																					
Inverkeithing	a																					
Kirkcaldy	a																					
Markinch	a																					
Cupar	a																					
Leuchars 8	a																					
Dundee	a																					
Arbroath	a																					
Montrose	a																					
Stonehaven	a																					
Aberdeen	a																					

For general notes see front of timetable
For details of catering facilities see Directory of Train Operators

South Coast and The South West → North West England, The North East and Scotland

2 February to 22 March

Route Diagram - See first page of Table 51

		VT	XC	XC	XC	XC	VT	XC	XC	XC	VT	XC	XC	VT	XC	VT	XC	XC	XC	VT	VT	XC	XC
		1 ◇	1 ◇	1 ◇	1 ◇	1 ◇	1 ◇	1 ◇	1 ◇	1 ◇	1 ◇	1 ◇	1 ◇	1 ◇	1 ◇	1 ◇	1 ◇	1 ◇	1 ◇	1 ◇	1 ◇	1 ◇	1 ◇
Brighton 10	d											03 50											
Haywards Heath 3	d											04 25											
Gatwick Airport 10 ✈	d											05 15						05 45					
Bournemouth	d																					06 37	
Brockenhurst 3	d																					06 54	
Southampton Central	d														06 15							07 15	
Southampton Airport Parkwy ✈	d														06 22							07 22	
Winchester	d														06 31							07 31	
Basingstoke	d														06 47							07 47	
Redhill	d											05 33						05 52					
Guildford	d											06 00											
East Croydon	d																	06 06					
Kensington Olympia	d																	06 50					
Reading 7	d											06 40			07 10			07 40				08 10	
Oxford	d											07 07			07 36			08 04				08 36	
Banbury	d											07 25			07 53			08 25				08 53	
Leamington Spa 8	d											07 43			08 11			08 43				09 11	
Coventry	d													08 15	08 23					09 10	09 16	09 23	
Birmingham International ✈	d													08 28	08 34					09 22	09 28	09 34	
Penzance	d																						
St Erth 2	d																						
Camborne	d																						
Redruth	d																						
Truro	d																						
St Austell	d																						
Par 3	d																						
Bodmin Parkway	d																						
Liskeard 3	d																						
Plymouth	d																						06 25
Totnes	d																						06 50
Paignton	d																						
Torquay	d																						
Newton Abbot	d																						07 03
Teignmouth	d																						
Dawlish	d																						
Exeter St Davids 6	d																06 10						07 23
Tiverton Parkway	d																06 24						07 37
Taunton	d																06 38						07 51
Weston-super-Mare	d																07 00						
Cardiff Central 7	d																						
Newport (South Wales)	d																						
Bristol Temple Meads 10	d									06 15							07 30		08 00				08 30
Bristol Parkway 7	d									06 25							07 40		08 10				08 40
Gloucester 7	d									07 01													
Cheltenham Spa	d									07 12							08 12		08 42				09 12
Birmingham New Street 12	a									07 57		08 18		08 39	08 46		08 57	09 18	09 26	09 36	09 39	09 45	09 57
Birmingham New Street 12	d	05 30	06 00	06 20	06 30	07 03	07 03	07 20	07 30	08 03	08 03	08 20	08 30	08 48	09 03	09 03	09 20		09 30	09 40	09 48	10 20 →	10 03
Tamworth	d		06 16		06 47	07 19			07 47	08 19			08 47										
Burton-on-Trent	d		06 26		06 58	07 29			07 58	08 29			08 58										
Derby 10	a		06 39		07 11	07 42			08 11	08 42			09 11		09 39				10 11				10 39
Chesterfield	a				07 32	08 01			08 32	09 01			09 32						10 32				
Sheffield 7	a		07 09		07 49	08 17			08 46	09 17			09 50		10 15				10 50				11 15
Doncaster 7	a				08 23				09 21				10 18						11 16				
Wakefield Westgate 7	a		07 36			08 46				09 46					10 46								11 46
Leeds 10	a		07 52			09 04				10 02					11 02								12 02
York 8	a		08 24		08 49	09 31			09 48	10 31			10 44		11 29				11 45				12 29
Darlington 7	a		08 52		09 19	10 00			10 16	11 01			11 16		12 01				12 15				13 01
Durham	a		09 09		09 37	10 17			10 33	11 20			11 33		12 18				12 33				13 18
Chester-le-Street	a				09 44				10 40										12 40				
Newcastle 8	a		09 26		09 59	10 34			10 59	11 36			11 57		12 35				12 57				13 35
Alnmouth	a		09 55							12 05													14 02
Berwick-upon-Tweed	a					11 20									13 20								
Dunbar	a					11 43									13 43								
Wolverhampton 7	d	05 49		06 40			07 21	07 40			08 21	08 40		09 09		09 21	09 40				10 09		
Stafford	a	06 04		06 53			07 33	07 53				08 53		09 24			09 53			10 17	10 24		
Stoke-on-Trent	a			07 12				08 12				09 12		09 43			10 12				10 42		
Congleton	a			07 24				08 24									10 24						
Macclesfield	a			07 32				08 32				09 29		09 59			10 32				10 58		
Crewe 10	a	06 25					07 54				08 54					09 54				10 38			
Wilmslow	a																						
Stockport	a			07 46				08 46				09 46		10 13			10 46				11 13		
Manchester Piccadilly 10	a			08 02				09 02				10 02		10 28			11 02				11 28		
Warrington Bank Quay	a	06 43					08 12				09 11					10 12				10 57			
Wigan North Western	a	07 02					08 23				09 22					10 23				11 08			
Preston 8	a	07 18					08 39				09 38					10 38				11 25			
Lancaster 6	a	07 33									09 53												
Oxenholme Lake District	a	07 47									10 08												
Penrith North Lakes	a	08 13									10 34												
Carlisle 8	a	08 31									10 52												
Lockerbie	a										11 11												
Haymarket	a																						
Edinburgh 10	a		11 02			12 13				13 13					14 13								15 13
Haymarket	a																						
Motherwell	a																						
Glasgow Central 15	a																						
Inverkeithing	a																						
Kirkcaldy	a																						
Markinch	a																						
Cupar	a																						
Leuchars 3	a																						
Dundee	a																						
Arbroath	a																						
Montrose	a																						
Stonehaven	a																						
Aberdeen	a																						

For general notes see front of timetable
For details of catering facilities see Directory of Train Operators

SUMMARY OF SERVICES

South Coast and The South West → North West England, The North East and Scotland

2 February to 22 March

Route Diagram - See first page of Table 51

		VT	XC	XC	XC	VT	VT	XC	VT	XC	XC	XC	VT	VT	XC	XC	VT	XC	XC	XC	VT	VT	XC
		1 ◇	1 ◇	1 ◇	1 ◇	1 ◇	1 ◇	1 ◇	R 1	1 ◇	1 ◇	1 ◇	1 ◇	1 ◇	1 ◇	1 ◇	1 ◇	1 ◇	1 ◇	1 ◇	1 ◇	1 ◇	1 ◇
Brighton 10	d																						
Haywards Heath 3	d																						
Gatwick Airport 10 ✈	d																						
Bournemouth	d							07 45							08 45								09 45
Brockenhurst 3	d							08 00							09 00								10 00
Southampton Central	d							08 15							09 15								10 15
Southampton Airport Parkwy ✈	d							08 22							09 22								10 22
Winchester	d							08 31							09 31								10 31
Basingstoke	d							08 47							09 47								10 47
Redhill	d																						
Guildford	d																						
East Croydon	d																						
Kensington Olympia	d																						
Reading 7	d			08 40				09 10			09 40				10 10				10 40				11 10
Oxford	d			09 07				09 36			10 07				10 36				11 07				11 36
Banbury	d			09 25				09 53			10 25				10 53				11 25				11 53
Leamington Spa 8	d			09 43				10 11			10 43				11 11				11 43				12 11
Coventry	d					10 10	10 16	10 23					11 10	11 16	11 23						12 10	12 16	12 23
Birmingham International ✈	d					10 22	10 28	10 34					11 22	11 28	11 34						12 22	12 28	12 34
Penzance	d																						
St Erth 2	d																						
Camborne	d																						
Redruth	d																						
Truro	d																						
St Austell	d																						
Par 3	d																						
Bodmin Parkway	d																						
Liskeard 3	d																						
Plymouth	d									07 25						08 25							
Totnes	d									07 50						08 50							
Paignton	d																						
Torquay	d																						
Newton Abbot	d									08 03						09 03							
Teignmouth	d																						
Dawlish	d																						
Exeter St Davids 6	d									08 23						09 23							
Tiverton Parkway	d									08 37						09 37							
Taunton	d									08 51						09 51							
Weston-super-Mare	d																						
Cardiff Central 7	d											09 00											
Newport (South Wales)	d											09 15											
Bristol Temple Meads 10	d				09 00					09 30		10 00				10 30				11 00			
Bristol Parkway 7	d				09 10					09 40		10 10				10 40				11 10			
Gloucester 7	d																						
Cheltenham Spa	d				09 42					10 12		10 42				11 12				11 42			
Birmingham New Street 12	a		⟵	10 18	10 26	10 36	10 39	10 45		10 58	11 18	11 26	11 36	11 39	11 45	11 57		⟵	12 18	12 26	12 36	12 39	12 45
Birmingham New Street 12	d	10 03	10 20		10 30	10 40	10 48	11 03	11 03	11 20		11 30	11 40	11 48	12 20 ⟶	12 03	12 03	12 20		12 30	12 40	12 48	13 03
Tamworth	d				10 47															12 47			
Burton-on-Trent	d				10 58															12 58			
Derby 10	a				11 11			11 39				12 11				12 39				13 11			13 39
Chesterfield	a				11 32							12 32								13 32			
Sheffield 7	a				11 50			12 15				12 50				13 15				13 51			14 15
Doncaster 7	a				12 15							13 19								14 15			
Wakefield Westgate 7	a							12 46								13 46							14 46
Leeds 10	a							13 02								14 02							15 02
York 8	a				12 43			13 29				13 44				14 29				14 43			15 29
Darlington 7	a				13 11			14 01				14 17				14 59				15 15			16 00
Durham	a				13 28			14 18				14 35				15 17				15 33			16 17
Chester-le-Street	a																						
Newcastle 8	a				13 50			14 35				14 54				15 34				15 55			16 34
Alnmouth	a															16 05							
Berwick-upon-Tweed	a							15 20															17 20
Dunbar	a							15 43															17 43
Wolverhampton 7	d	10 21	10 40				11 09		11 21	11 40				12 09			12 21	12 40				13 09	
Stafford	a		10 53			11 19	11 24			11 53			12 17	12 24				12 53			13 17	13 24	
Stoke-on-Trent	a		11 12				11 43			12 12				12 43				13 12				13 43	
Congleton	a									12 24													
Macclesfield	a		11 29				11 59			12 32				12 59				13 29				13 59	
Crewe 10	a	10 54				11 40			11 54				12 38				12 54				13 38		
Wilmslow	a																						
Stockport	a		11 46				12 13			12 46				13 13				13 46				14 13	
Manchester Piccadilly 10	a		12 02				12 28			13 02				13 28				14 02				14 28	
Warrington Bank Quay	a	11 11				11 59			12 13				12 56				13 11				13 57		
Wigan North Western	a	11 22				12 10							13 07				13 22				14 08		
Preston 8	a	11 37				12 24			12 36				13 26				13 36				14 23		
Lancaster 6	a	11 54				12 41			12 54								13 53				14 39		
Oxenholme Lake District	a					12 54			13 08								14 07				14 53		
Penrith North Lakes	a	12 31				13 20			13 35												15 19		
Carlisle 8	a	12 49				13 38			13 52								14 51				15 37		
Lockerbie	a	13 09							14 11								15 11						
Haymarket	a																						
Edinburgh 10	a							16b19								17 14							18 16
Haymarket	a							16 34															
Motherwell	a																						
Glasgow Central 15	a																						
Inverkeithing	a							16 47															
Kirkcaldy	a							17 02															
Markinch	a							17 11															
Cupar	a							17 24															
Leuchars 8	a							17 31															
Dundee	a							17 44															
Arbroath	a							18 03															
Montrose	a							18 17															
Stonehaven	a							18 37															
Aberdeen	a							19 02															

For general notes see front of timetable
For details of catering facilities see Directory of Train Operators

b Dep. 1630

South Coast and The South West → North West England, The North East and Scotland

2 February to 22 March

Route Diagram - See first page of Table 51

		VT	XC	XC	XC	VT	VT	XC	XC	VT	XC	XC	XC	VT	VT	XC	VT	XC	XC	XC	VT	VT
		R 1	1 ◇	1 ◇	1 ◇	1 ◇	1 ◇	1 ◇	1 ◇	R 1	1 ◇	1 ◇	1 ◇	1 ◇	1 ◇	1 ◇	R 1	1 ◇	1 ◇	1 ◇	1 ◇	1 ◇
Brighton 10	d			09 15																		
Haywards Heath 3	d			09 34																		
Gatwick Airport 10 ✈	d			09 47																		
Bournemouth	d							10 45								11 45						
Brockenhurst 3	d							11 00								12 00						
Southampton Central	d							11 15								12 15						
Southampton Airport Parkwy ✈	d							11 22								12 22						
Winchester	d							11 31								12 31						
Basingstoke	d							11 47								12 47						
Redhill	d																					
Guildford	d																					
East Croydon	d			10 03																		
Kensington Olympia	d			10 34																		
Reading 7	d			11 40				12 10				12 40				13 10			13 40			
Oxford	d			12 07				12 35				13 07				13 36			14 07			
Banbury	d			12 25				12 53				13 25				13 53			14 25			
Leamington Spa 8	d			12 43				13 11				13 43				14 11			14 43			
Coventry	d					13 10	13 16	13 23						14 10	14 16	14 23					15 10	15 16
Birmingham International ✈	d					13 22	13 28	13 34						14 22	14 28	14 34					15 22	15 28
Penzance	d		07 30						08 30									09 30				
St Erth 2	d		07 38						08 38									09 38				
Camborne	d		07 48						08 48									09 48				
Redruth	d		07 54						08 54									09 54				
Truro	d		08 06						09 06									10 06				
St Austell	d		08 22						09 22									10 22				
Par 3	d		08 29						09 29									10 29				
Bodmin Parkway	d		08 40						09 40									10 40				
Liskeard 3	d		08 52						09 52									10 52				
Plymouth	d		09 25						10 25									11 25				
Totnes	d		09 50						10 50									11 50				
Paignton	d				10 05																	
Torquay	d				10 11																	
Newton Abbot	d		10 03		10 22				11 03									12 03				
Teignmouth	d				10 29																	
Dawlish	d				10 34																	
Exeter St Davids 6	d		10 23		10 48				11 23									12 23				
Tiverton Parkway	d		10 37		11 01				11 37									12 37				
Taunton	d		10 51		11 16				11 51									12 51				
Weston-super-Mare	d																					
Cardiff Central 7	d																					
Newport (South Wales)	d																					
Bristol Temple Meads 10	d		11 30		12 00				12 30				13 00					13 30		14 00		
Bristol Parkway 7	d		11 40		12 10				12 40				13 10					13 40		14 10		
Gloucester 7	d																					
Cheltenham Spa	d		12 12		12 42				13 12				13 42					14 12		14 42		
Birmingham New Street 12	a		12 57	13 18	13 26	13 36	13 39	13 45	13 57		←	14 18	14 26	14 36	14 39	14 46		14 57	15 18	15 27	15 36	15 39
Birmingham New Street 12	d	13 03	13 20		13 30	13 40	13 48	14 20 →	14 03	14 03	14 20		14 30	14 40	14 48	15 03	15 03	15 20		15 30	15 40	15 48
Tamworth	d												14 47									
Burton-on-Trent	d												14 58									
Derby 10	a				14 11				14 39				15 11			15 39				16 11		
Chesterfield	a				14 32								15 32							16 32		
Sheffield 7	a				14 50				15 15				15 50			16 15				16 50		
Doncaster 7	a				15 15								16 15							17 19		
Wakefield Westgate 7	a								15 46							16 46						
Leeds 10	a								16 02							17 04						
York 8	a				15 43				16 29				16 45			17 30				17 45		
Darlington 7	a				16 12				17 00				17 16			18 00				18 15		
Durham	a				16 29				17 17				17 33			18 17				18 32		
Chester-le-Street	a												17 43							18 39		
Newcastle 8	a				16 51				17 34				17 58			18 34				18 56		
Alnmouth	a								18 02													
Berwick-upon-Tweed	a															19 20						
Dunbar	a															19 43						
Wolverhampton 7	d	13 21	13 40				14 09			14 21	14 40				15 09		15 21	15 40				16 09
Stafford	a		13 53			14 17	14 24				14 53			15 17	15 24			15 53			16 17	16 24
Stoke-on-Trent	a		14 12				14 43				15 12				15 43			16 12				16 43
Congleton	a		14 24															16 24				
Macclesfield	a		14 32				14 59				15 29				15 59			16 33				16 59
Crewe 10	a	13 54				14 38				14 54				15 38			15 54				16 38	
Wilmslow	a																					
Stockport	a		14 46				15 13				15 46				16 13			16 46				17 13
Manchester Piccadilly 10	a		15 02				15 28				16 02				16 28			17 02				17 28
Warrington Bank Quay	a	14 12				14 57				15 12				15 56			16 12				16 57	
Wigan North Western	a	14 23				15 08				15 23				16 07			16 23				17 08	
Preston 8	a	14 39				15 22				15 39				16 22			16 39				17 23	
Lancaster 6	a	14 54				15 39				15 54				16 38			16 57				17 40	
Oxenholme Lake District	a	15 09				15 52								16 52			17 12				17 53	
Penrith North Lakes	a	15 36				16 18				16 33				17 18			17 38				18 19	
Carlisle 8	a	15 54				16 36				16 49				17 36			17 56				18 37	
Lockerbie	a	16 13								17 10							18 17					
Haymarket	a																					
Edinburgh 10	a								19 12							20 13						
Haymarket	a								19 16							20 17						
Motherwell	a															21s00						
Glasgow Central 15	a															21 27						
Inverkeithing	a								19 32													
Kirkcaldy	a								19 49													
Markinch	a								19 58													
Cupar	a								20 19													
Leuchars 3	a								20 27													
Dundee	a								20 50													
Arbroath	a																					
Montrose	a																					
Stonehaven	a																					
Aberdeen	a																					

For general notes see front of timetable
For details of catering facilities see Directory of Train Operators

South Coast and The South West → North West England, The North East and Scotland

2 February to 22 March

Route Diagram - See first page of Table 51

		XC	XC	VT	XC	XC	XC	VT	VT	XC	VT	XC	XC	XC	VT	VT		XC	XC	VT	XC	XC	XC	VT
		1◇	1◇	1◇	1◇	1◇	1◇	1◇	1◇	1◇	R 1	1◇	1◇	1◇	1◇	1◇		1◇	1◇	R 1	1◇	1◇	1◇	1◇
Brighton 10	d																					14 22		
Haywards Heath 3	d																					14b32		
Gatwick Airport 10 ✈	d																					14 54		
Bournemouth	d	12 45								13 45								14 45						
Brockenhurst 3	d	13 00								14 00								15 00						
Southampton Central	d	13 15								14 15								15 15						
Southampton Airport Parkwy ✈	d	13 22								14 22								15 22						
Winchester	d	13 31								14 31								15 31						
Basingstoke	d	13 47								14 47								15 47						
Redhill	d																							
Guildford	d																							
East Croydon ⛴	d																					15 08		
Kensington Olympia	d																					15 40		
Reading 7	d	14 10				14 40				15 10			15 40					16 10				16 40		
Oxford	d	14 36				15 07				15 36			16 07					16 36				17 07		
Banbury	d	14 53				15 25				15 53			16 25					16 53				17 25		
Leamington Spa 8	d	15 11				15 43				16 11			16 43					17 11				17 43		
Coventry	d	15 23						16 10	16 16	16 23					17 10	17 16		17 23						18 10
Birmingham International ✈	d	15 34						16 22	16 28	16 34					17 22	17 28		17 34						18 22
Penzance	d																							
St Erth 2	d																							
Camborne	d																							
Redruth	d																							
Truro	d																							
St Austell	d																							
Par 3	d																							
Bodmin Parkway	d																							
Liskeard 3	d																							
Plymouth	d		12 25									13 25							14 25					
Totnes	d		12 50									13 50							14 50					
Paignton	d													14 05										
Torquay	d													14 11										
Newton Abbot	d		13 03									14 03		14 22					15 03					
Teignmouth	d													14 29										
Dawlish	d													14 34										
Exeter St Davids 6	d		13 23									14 23		14 48					15 23					
Tiverton Parkway	d		13 37									14 37		15 01					15 37					
Taunton	d		13 51									14 51		15 16					15 51					
Weston-super-Mare	d																							
Cardiff Central 7	d																							
Newport (South Wales)	d																							
Bristol Temple Meads 10	d		14 30				15 00					15 30		16 00					16 30				17 00	
Bristol Parkway 7	d		14 40				15 10					15 40		16 10					16 40				17 10	
Gloucester 7	d																							
Cheltenham Spa	d		15 12				15 42					16 12		16 42					17 12				17 42	
Birmingham New Street 12	a	15 45	15 57		←	16 18	16 26	16 36	16 39	16 46		16 57	17 18	17 26	17 36	17 39		17 45	17 57		←	18 18	18 26	18 36
Birmingham New Street 12	d	16 20 →	16 03	16 03	16 20		16 30	16 40	16 48	17 03	17 03	17 20		17 30	17 40	17 48		18 20 →	18 03	18 03	18 20		18 30	18 40
Tamworth	d						16 47																18 47	
Burton-on-Trent	d						16 58																18 58	
Derby 10	a		16 39				17 11			17 39				18 11					18 39				19 11	
Chesterfield	a						17 32							18 32					19 01				19 32	
Sheffield 7	a		17 15				17 48			18 17				18 46					19 16				19 47	
Doncaster 7	a						18 21							19 18									20 16	
Wakefield Westgate 7	a		17 46							18 46									19 46					
Leeds 10	a		18 02							19 02									20 02					
York 8	a		18 29				18 46			19 32				19 49					20 29				20 42	
Darlington 7	a		19 00				19 14			20 02				20 17					21 03				21 14	
Durham	a		19 17				19 31			20 22				20 34					21 21				22 10	
Chester-le-Street	a													20 41									22 17	
Newcastle 8	a		19 34				19 53			20 36				20 54					21 41				22 34	
Alnmouth	a		20 02							21 02														
Berwick-upon-Tweed	a		20 23							21 23				21 38										
Dunbar	a													22 01										
Wolverhampton 7 ⛴	d			16 21	16 40				17 09		17 21	17 40				18 09				18 20	18 40			
Stafford	a				16 53			17 17	17 24			17 53			18 17	18 24					18 53			19 17
Stoke-on-Trent	a				17 12				17 43			18 12				18 43					19 12			
Congleton	a											18 24												
Macclesfield	a				17 29				17 59			18 32				18 59					19 29			
Crewe 10	a			16 54				17 38			17 54				18 38					18 54				19 38
Wilmslow	a																							
Stockport	a				17 46				18 13			18 46				19 13					19 46			
Manchester Piccadilly 10 ⛴	a				18 02				18 28			19 02				19 28					20 02			
Warrington Bank Quay	a			17 12				17 57			18 12				18 57					19 12				19 57
Wigan North Western	a			17 23				18 08			18 23				19 08					19 24				20 08
Preston 8	a			17 39				18 22			18 39				19 25					19 43				20 26
Lancaster 6	a			17 55				18 39			18 58				19 39									
Oxenholme Lake District	a			18 09				18 52			19 13				19 52									
Penrith North Lakes	a							19 19							20 18									
Carlisle 8	a			18 55				19 36			19 54				20 41									
Lockerbie	a			19 15							20 14													
Haymarket	a																							
Edinburgh 10	a		21 13							22 13				22 31										
Haymarket	a		21 18																					
Motherwell	a		22s04																					
Glasgow Central 15	a		22 43																					
Inverkeithing	a																							
Kirkcaldy	a																							
Markinch	a																							
Cupar	a																							
Leuchars 3	a																							
Dundee	a																							
Arbroath	a																							
Montrose	a																							
Stonehaven	a																							
Aberdeen	a																							

For general notes see front of timetable
For details of catering facilities see Directory of Train Operators

b Change at East Croydon

South Coast and The South West → North West England, The North East and Scotland

2 February to 22 March

Route Diagram - See first page of Table 51

		VT	XC	VT	XC	XC	XC	VT	XC	XC	XC	XC	XC		VT	XC	XC	XC	XC	XC	XC	XC
				R																		
		1 ◇	1 ◇	1	1 ◇	1 ◇	1 ◇	1 ◇	1 ◇	1 ◇	1 ◇	1 ◇	1 ◇		1 ◇	1 ◇	1 ◇	1 ◇	1 ◇	1 ◇	1 ◇	1 ◇
Brighton 10	d																					
Haywards Heath 3	d																					
Gatwick Airport 10 ✈	d											17 03										
Bournemouth	d		15 45						16 45							17 45			18 45			19 45
Brockenhurst 3	d		16 00						17 00							18 00			19 00			20 00
Southampton Central	d		16 15						17 15							18 15			19 15			20 15
Southampton Airport Parkwy ✈	d		16 22						17 22							18 22			19 22			20 22
Winchester	d		16 31						17 31							18 31			19 31			20 31
Basingstoke	d		16 47						17 47							18 47			19 47			20 47
Redhill	d											17 14										
Guildford	d											17 58										
East Croydon	d																					
Kensington Olympia	d																					
Reading 7	d		17 10			17 40			18 10			18 40				19 10		19 40	20 10			21 10
Oxford	d		17 36			18 07			18 36			19 07				19 36		20 07	20 36			21 36
Banbury	d		17 53			18 25			18 53			19 25				19 53		20 25	20 53			21 53
Leamington Spa 8	d		18 11			18 43			19 11			19 43				20 11		20 43	21 11			22 11
Coventry	d	18 16	18 23					19 16	19 23						20 16	20 23			21 23			22 23
Birmingham International ✈	d	18 28	18 34					19 28	19 34						20 28	20 34			21 34			22 34
Penzance	d																					
St Erth 2	d																					
Camborne	d																					
Redruth	d																					
Truro	d																					
St Austell	d																					
Par 3	d																					
Bodmin Parkway	d																					
Liskeard 3	d																					
Plymouth	d				15 25					16 25							17 25			18 25		
Totnes	d				15 50					16 50							17 50			18 50		
Paignton	d																					
Torquay	d																					
Newton Abbot	d				16 03					17 03							18 03			19 03		
Teignmouth	d																					
Dawlish	d																					
Exeter St Davids 6	d				16 23					17 23							18 23			19 23		
Tiverton Parkway	d				16 37					17 37							18 37			19 37		
Taunton	d				16 51					17 51							18 51			19 51		
Weston-super-Mare	d																					
Cardiff Central 7	d																					
Newport (South Wales)	d																					
Bristol Temple Meads 10	d				17 30		18 00			18 30			19 00				19 30			20 30		
Bristol Parkway 7	d				17 40		18 10			18 40			19 10				19 40			20 40		
Gloucester 7	d																					
Cheltenham Spa	d				18 12		18 42			19 12			19 42				20 12			21 12		
Birmingham New Street 12	a	18 39	18 45		18 57	19 18	19 27	19 39	19 45	19 57	←	20 18	20 31		20 39	20 45	20 57	21 22	21 45	21 57	←	22 50
Birmingham New Street 12	d	18 48	19 03	19 03	19 20		19 30	19 48	20 20	20 03	20 20				20 48	20 50	21 20		22 20	22 03	22 20	
Tamworth	d						19 47		→	20 19						21 23			→	22 19		
Burton-on-Trent	d						19 58			20 29						21 33				22 29		
Derby 10	a		19 39				20 11			20 42						21 45				22 47		
Chesterfield	a		20 00				20 36			21 01						22 04						
Sheffield 7	a		20 18				20 51			21 16						22 19						
Doncaster 7	a																					
Wakefield Westgate 7	a		20 48							21 46						22s46						
Leeds 10	a		21 05							22 01						23 09						
York 8	a		21 35				21 54			22 38												
Darlington 7	a																					
Durham	a		22 48																			
Chester-le-Street	a																					
Newcastle 8	a		23 11																			
Alnmouth	a																					
Berwick-upon-Tweed	a																					
Dunbar	a																					
Wolverhampton 7	d	19 09		19 21	19 40			20 09			20 40				21 10		21 40				22 40	
Stafford	a	19 24		19 33	19 53			20 24			20 53				21 24		21 53				22 53	
Stoke-on-Trent	a	19 43			20 12			20 43			21 12				21 44		22 12				23s13	
Congleton	a				20 24												22 24					
Macclesfield	a	19 59			20 32			20 59			21 29				22 00		22 32				23s30	
Crewe 10	a			19 54																		
Wilmslow	a																					
Stockport	a	20 13			20 46			21 13			21 46				22 12		22 46				23s46	
Manchester Piccadilly 10	a	20 28			21 02			21 28			22 02				22 25		23 02				00 02	
Warrington Bank Quay	a			20 12																		
Wigan North Western	a			20 23																		
Preston 8	a			20 43																		
Lancaster 6	a																					
Oxenholme Lake District	a																					
Penrith North Lakes	a																					
Carlisle 8	a																					
Lockerbie	a																					
Haymarket	a																					
Edinburgh 10	a																					
Haymarket	a																					
Motherwell	a																					
Glasgow Central 15	a																					
Inverkeithing	a																					
Kirkcaldy	a																					
Markinch	a																					
Cupar	a																					
Leuchars 3	a																					
Dundee	a																					
Arbroath	a																					
Montrose	a																					
Stonehaven	a																					
Aberdeen	a																					

For general notes see front of timetable
For details of catering facilities see Directory of Train Operators

Saturdays

from 29 March

South Coast and The South West → North West England, The North East and Scotland

Route Diagram - See first page of Table 51

		VT	XC	XC	XC	XC	VT	XC	XC	XC	VT	XC	XC	VT	XC	VT	XC	XC	XC	VT	VT	XC	XC
		1◇	1◇	1◇	1◇	1◇	1◇	1◇	1◇	1◇	1◇	1◇	1◇	1◇	1◇	1◇	1◇	1◇	1◇	1◇	1◇	1◇	1◇
Brighton 10	d											03 50											
Haywards Heath 3	d											04 25											
Gatwick Airport 10 ✈	d											05 15						05 45					
Bournemouth	d																					06 37	
Brockenhurst 3	d																					06 54	
Southampton Central	d														06 15							07 15	
Southampton Airport Parkwy ✈	d														06 22							07 22	
Winchester	d														06 31							07 31	
Basingstoke	d														06 47							07 47	
Redhill	d											05 33						05 52					
Guildford	d											06 00											
East Croydon	d																	06 06					
Kensington Olympia	d																	06 50					
Reading 7	d											06 40			07 10			07 40				08 10	
Oxford	d											07 07			07 36			08 04				08 36	
Banbury	d											07 25			07 53			08 25				08 53	
Leamington Spa 8	d											07 43			08 11			08 43				09 11	
Coventry	d													08 15	08 23					09 10	09 16	09 23	
Birmingham International ✈	d													08 28	08 34					09 22	09 28	09 34	
Penzance	d																						
St Erth 2	d																						
Camborne	d																						
Redruth	d																						
Truro	d																						
St Austell	d																						
Par 3	d																						
Bodmin Parkway	d																						
Liskeard 3	d																						
Plymouth	d																						06 25
Totnes	d																						06 50
Paignton	d																						
Torquay	d																						
Newton Abbot	d																						07 03
Teignmouth	d																						
Dawlish	d																						
Exeter St Davids 6	d																06 10						07 23
Tiverton Parkway	d																06 24						07 37
Taunton	d																06 38						07 51
Weston-super-Mare	d																07 00						
Cardiff Central 7	d																						
Newport (South Wales)	d																						
Bristol Temple Meads 10	d									06 15							07 30		08 00				08 30
Bristol Parkway 7	d									06 25							07 40		08 10				08 40
Gloucester 7	d									07 01													
Cheltenham Spa	d									07 12							08 12		08 42				09 12
Birmingham New Street 12	a									07 57		08 18		08 39	08 46		08 57	09 18	09 26	09 36	09 39	09 45	09 57
Birmingham New Street 12	d	05 30	06 00	06 20	06 30	07 03	07 03	07 20	07 30	08 03	08 03	08 20	08 30	08 48	09 03	09 03	09 20		09 30	09 40	09 48	10 20 ↪	10 03
Tamworth	d		06 16		06 47	07 19			07 47	08 19			08 47										
Burton-on-Trent	d		06 26		06 58	07 29			07 58	08 29			08 58										
Derby 10	a		06 39		07 11	07 42			08 11	08 42			09 11		09 39				10 11				10 39
Chesterfield	a				07 32	08 01			08 32	09 01			09 32						10 32				
Sheffield 7	a		07 09		07 49	08 17			08 46	09 17			09 50		10 15				10 50				11 15
Doncaster 7	a				08 23				09 21				10 18						11 16				
Wakefield Westgate 7	a		07 36			08 46				09 46					10 46								11 46
Leeds 10	a		07 52			09 04				10 02					11 02								12 02
York 8	a		08 24		08 49	09 31			09 48	10 31			10 44		11 29				11 45				12 29
Darlington 7	a		08 52		09 19	10 00			10 16	11 01			11 16		12 01				12 15				13 01
Durham	a		09 09		09 37	10 17			10 33	11 20			11 33		12 18				12 33				13 18
Chester-le-Street	a				09 44				10 40										12 40				
Newcastle 8	a		09 26		09 59	10 34			10 59	11 36			11 57		12 35				12 57				13 35
Alnmouth	a		09 55							12 05													14 02
Berwick-upon-Tweed	a					11 20									13 20								
Dunbar	a					11 43									13 43								
Wolverhampton 7	d	05 49		06 40			07 21	07 40			08 21	08 40		09 09		09 21	09 40				10 09		
Stafford	a	06 04		06 53			07 33	07 53				08 53		09 24			09 53			10 17	10 24		
Stoke-on-Trent	a			07 12				08 12				09 12		09 43			10 12				10 42		
Congleton	a			07 24				08 24									10 24						
Macclesfield	a			07 32				08 32				09 29		09 59			10 32				10 58		
Crewe 10	a	06 25					07 54				08 54					09 54				10 38			
Wilmslow	a																						
Stockport	a			07 46				08 46				09 46		10 13			10 46				11 13		
Manchester Piccadilly 10	a			08 02				09 02				10 02		10 28			11 02				11 28		
Warrington Bank Quay	a	06 43					08 12				09 11					10 12				10 57			
Wigan North Western	a	07 02					08 23				09 22					10 23				11 08			
Preston 8	a	07 18					08 44				09 44					10 44				11 25			
Lancaster 6	a																						
Oxenholme Lake District	a																						
Penrith North Lakes	a																						
Carlisle 8	a															13 49							
Lockerbie	a															14 12							
Haymarket	a																						
Edinburgh 10	a		11 02			12 13				13 13					14 13								15 13
Haymarket	a																						
Motherwell	a															14s55							
Glasgow Central 15	a															15 19							
Inverkeithing	a																						
Kirkcaldy	a																						
Markinch	a																						
Cupar	a																						
Leuchars 3	a																						
Dundee	a																						
Arbroath	a																						
Montrose	a																						
Stonehaven	a																						
Aberdeen	a																						

For general notes see front of timetable
For details of catering facilities see Directory of Train Operators

South Coast and The South West → North West England, The North East and Scotland

from 29 March

Route Diagram - See first page of Table 51

		VT	XC	XC	XC		VT	VT	XC	VT	XC	XC	XC	VT	VT	XC	XC	VT		XC	XC	XC	VT	VT
		1 ◇ ☕	1 ◇ ☕	1 ◇ ☕	1 ◇ ☕		1 ◇ ☕	1 ◇ ☕	1 ◇ ☕	R 1 ☕	1 ◇ ☕	1 ◇ ☕	1 ◇ ☕	1 ◇ ☕	1 ◇ ☕	1 ◇ ☕	1 ◇ ☕	1 ◇ ☕		1 ◇ ☕	1 ◇ ☕	1 ◇ ☕	1 ◇ ☕	1 ◇ ☕
Brighton 10	d																							
Haywards Heath 3	d																							
Gatwick Airport 10 ✈	d																							
Bournemouth	d								07 45							08 45								
Brockenhurst 3	d								08 00							09 00								
Southampton Central	d								08 15							09 15								
Southampton Airport Parkwy ✈	d								08 22							09 22								
Winchester	d								08 31							09 31								
Basingstoke	d								08 47							09 47								
Redhill	d																							
Guildford	d																							
East Croydon	d																							
Kensington Olympia	d																							
Reading 7	d			08 40					09 10			09 40				10 10					10 40			
Oxford	d			09 07					09 36			10 07				10 36					11 07			
Banbury	d			09 25					09 53			10 25				10 53					11 25			
Leamington Spa 8	d			09 43					10 11			10 43				11 11					11 43			
Coventry	d						10 10	10 16	10 23					11 10	11 16	11 23							12 10	12 16
Birmingham International ✈	d						10 22	10 28	10 34					11 22	11 28	11 34							12 22	12 28
Penzance	d																							
St Erth 2	d																							
Camborne	d																							
Redruth	d																							
Truro	d																							
St Austell	d																							
Par 3	d																							
Bodmin Parkway	d																							
Liskeard 3	d																							
Plymouth	d										07 25						08 25							
Totnes	d										07 50						08 50							
Paignton	d																							
Torquay	d																							
Newton Abbot	d										08 03						09 03							
Teignmouth	d																							
Dawlish	d																							
Exeter St Davids 6	d										08 23						09 23							
Tiverton Parkway	d										08 37						09 37							
Taunton	d										08 51						09 51							
Weston-super-Mare	d																							
Cardiff Central 7	d																							
Newport (South Wales)	d																							
Bristol Temple Meads 10	d				09 00						09 30		10 00				10 30					11 00		
Bristol Parkway 7	d				09 10						09 40		10 10				10 40					11 10		
Gloucester 7	d																							
Cheltenham Spa	d				09 42						10 12		10 42				11 12					11 42		
Birmingham New Street 12	a		←	10 18	10 26		10 36	10 39	10 45		10 58	11 18	11 26	11 36	11 39	11 45	11 57			←	12 18	12 26	12 36	12 39
Birmingham New Street 12	d	10 03	10 20		10 30		10 40	10 48	11 03	11 03	11 20		11 30	11 40	11 48	12 20 →	12 03	12 03		12 20		12 30	12 40	12 48
Tamworth	d				10 47																	12 47		
Burton-on-Trent	d				10 58																	12 58		
Derby 10	a				11 11				11 39				12 11				12 39					13 11		
Chesterfield	a				11 32								12 32									13 32		
Sheffield 7	a				11 50				12 15				12 50				13 15					13 51		
Doncaster 7	a				12 15								13 19									14 15		
Wakefield Westgate 7	a								12 46								13 46							
Leeds 10	a								13 02								14 02							
York 8	a				12 43				13 29				13 44				14 29					14 43		
Darlington 7	a				13 11				14 01				14 17				14 59					15 15		
Durham	a				13 28				14 18				14 35				15 17					15 33		
Chester-le-Street	a																							
Newcastle 8	a				13 50				14 35				14 54				15 34					15 55		
Alnmouth	a																16 05							
Berwick-upon-Tweed	a								15 20															
Dunbar	a								15 43															
Wolverhampton 7 🚢	d	10 21	10 40					11 09		11 21	11 40				12 09			12 21		12 40				13 09
Stafford	a		10 53				11 19	11 24			11 53			12 17	12 24					12 53			13 17	13 24
Stoke-on-Trent	a		11 12					11 43			12 12				12 43					13 12				13 43
Congleton	a										12 24													
Macclesfield	a		11 29					11 59			12 32				12 59					13 29				13 59
Crewe 10	a	10 54					11 40			11 54				12 38				12 54					13 38	
Wilmslow	a																							
Stockport	a		11 46					12 13			12 46				13 13					13 46				14 13
Manchester Piccadilly 10 🚢	a		12 02					12 28			13 02				13 28					14 02				14 28
Warrington Bank Quay	a	11 11					11 59			12 13				12 56				13 11					13 57	
Wigan North Western	a	11 22					12 10			12 24				13 07				13 22					14 08	
Preston 8	a	11 44					12 24			12 40				13 26				13 44					14 28	
Lancaster 6	a																							
Oxenholme Lake District	a																							
Penrith North Lakes	a																							
Carlisle 8	a						15 53																	
Lockerbie	a						16 25																	
Haymarket	a																							
Edinburgh 10	a								16b19								17 14							
Haymarket	a								16 34															
Motherwell	a						17s22																	
Glasgow Central 15	a						17 47																	
Inverkeithing	a								16 47															
Kirkcaldy	a								17 02															
Markinch	a								17 11															
Cupar	a								17 24															
Leuchars 3	a								17 31															
Dundee	a								17 44															
Arbroath	a								18 03															
Montrose	a								18 17															
Stonehaven	a								18 37															
Aberdeen	a								19 02															

For general notes see front of timetable
For details of catering facilities see Directory of Train Operators

b Dep. 1630

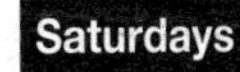

from 29 March

South Coast and The South West → North West England, The North East and Scotland

Route Diagram - See first page of Table 51

		XC	VT	XC	XC	XC	VT	VT	XC	XC	XC	XC	XC	VT	VT	XC	VT	XC	XC	XC	VT	VT	XC
			R														R						
		1 ◇	1	1 ◇	1 ◇	1 ◇	1 ◇	1 ◇	1 ◇	1 ◇	1 ◇	1 ◇	1 ◇	1 ◇	1 ◇	1 ◇	1	1 ◇	1 ◇	1 ◇	1 ◇	1 ◇	1 ◇
Brighton 10	d				09 15																		
Haywards Heath 3	d				09 34																		
Gatwick Airport 10	d				09 47																		
Bournemouth	d	09 45							10 45							11 45							12 45
Brockenhurst 3	d	10 00							11 00							12 00							13 00
Southampton Central	d	10 15							11 15							12 15							13 15
Southampton Airport Parkwy	d	10 22							11 22							12 22							13 22
Winchester	d	10 31							11 31							12 31							13 31
Basingstoke	d	10 47							11 47							12 47							13 47
Redhill	d																						
Guildford	d																						
East Croydon	d				10 03																		
Kensington Olympia	d				10 34																		
Reading 7	d	11 10			11 40				12 10			12 40				13 10			13 40				14 10
Oxford	d	11 36			12 07				12 35			13 07				13 36			14 07				14 36
Banbury	d	11 53			12 25				12 53			13 25				13 53			14 25				14 53
Leamington Spa 8	d	12 11			12 43				13 11			13 43				14 11			14 43				15 11
Coventry	d	12 23					13 10	13 16	13 23					14 10	14 16	14 23					15 10	15 16	15 23
Birmingham International	d	12 34					13 22	13 28	13 34					14 22	14 28	14 34					15 22	15 28	15 34
Penzance	d			07 30						08 30								09 30					
St Erth 2	d			07 38						08 38								09 38					
Camborne	d			07 48						08 48								09 48					
Redruth	d			07 54						08 54								09 54					
Truro	d			08 06						09 06								10 06					
St Austell	d			08 22						09 22								10 22					
Par 3	d			08 29						09 29								10 29					
Bodmin Parkway	d			08 40						09 40								10 40					
Liskeard 3	d			08 52						09 52								10 52					
Plymouth	d			09 25						10 25								11 25					
Totnes	d			09 50						10 50								11 50					
Paignton	d					10 05																	
Torquay	d					10 11																	
Newton Abbot	d			10 03		10 22				11 03								12 03					
Teignmouth	d					10 29																	
Dawlish	d					10 34																	
Exeter St Davids 6	d			10 23		10 48				11 23								12 23					
Tiverton Parkway	d			10 37		11 01				11 37								12 37					
Taunton	d			10 51		11 16				11 51								12 51					
Weston-super-Mare	d																						
Cardiff Central 7	d																						
Newport (South Wales)	d																						
Bristol Temple Meads 10	d			11 30		12 00				12 30			13 00					13 30		14 00			
Bristol Parkway 7	d			11 40		12 10				12 40			13 10					13 40		14 10			
Gloucester 7	d																						
Cheltenham Spa	d			12 12		12 42				13 12			13 42					14 12		14 42			
Birmingham New Street 12	a	12 45		12 57	13 18	13 26	13 36	13 39	13 45	13 57	←	14 18	14 26	14 36	14 39	14 46		14 57	15 18	15 27	15 36	15 39	15 45
Birmingham New Street 12	d	13 03	13 03	13 20		13 30	13 40	13 48	14 20 →	14 03	14 20		14 30	14 40	14 48	15 03	15 03	15 20		15 30	15 40	15 48	16 20 →
Tamworth	d												14 47										
Burton-on-Trent	d												14 58										
Derby 10	a	13 39				14 11				14 39			15 11			15 39				16 11			
Chesterfield	a					14 32							15 32							16 32			
Sheffield 7	a	14 15				14 50				15 15			15 50			16 15				16 50			
Doncaster 7	a					15 15							16 15							17 19			
Wakefield Westgate 7	a	14 46								15 46						16 46							
Leeds 10	a	15 02								16 02						17 04							
York 8	a	15 29				15 43				16 29			16 45			17 30				17 45			
Darlington 7	a	16 00				16 12				17 00			17 16			18 00				18 15			
Durham	a	16 17				16 29				17 17			17 33			18 17				18 32			
Chester-le-Street	a												17 43							18 39			
Newcastle 8	a	16 34				16 51				17 34			17 58			18 34				18 56			
Alnmouth	a									18 02													
Berwick-upon-Tweed	a	17 20														19 20							
Dunbar	a	17 43														19 43							
Wolverhampton 7	d		13 21	13 40				14 09			14 40				15 09		15 21	15 40				16 09	
Stafford	a			13 53			14 17	14 24			14 53			15 17	15 24			15 53			16 17	16 24	
Stoke-on-Trent	a			14 12				14 43			15 12				15 43			16 12				16 43	
Congleton	a			14 24														16 24					
Macclesfield	a			14 32				14 59			15 29				15 59			16 33				16 59	
Crewe 10	a		13 54				14 38							15 38			15 54				16 38		
Wilmslow	a																						
Stockport	a			14 46				15 13			15 46				16 13			16 46				17 13	
Manchester Piccadilly 10	a			15 02				15 28			16 02				16 28			17 02				17 28	
Warrington Bank Quay	a		14 12				14 57							15 56			16 12				16 57		
Wigan North Western	a		14 23				15 08							16 07			16 23				17 08		
Preston 8	a		14 44				15 26							16 25			16 44				17 28		
Lancaster 6	a																						
Oxenholme Lake District	a																						
Penrith North Lakes	a																						
Carlisle 8	a		17 43											19 39									
Lockerbie	a		18 03											20 10									
Haymarket	a																						
Edinburgh 10	a	18 16								19 12						20 13							
Haymarket	a									19 16													
Motherwell	a		18s51											20s59									
Glasgow Central 15	a		19 19											21 23									
Inverkeithing	a									19 32													
Kirkcaldy	a									19 49													
Markinch	a									19 58													
Cupar	a									20 19													
Leuchars 3	a									20 27													
Dundee	a									20 50													
Arbroath	a																						
Montrose	a																						
Stonehaven	a																						
Aberdeen	a																						

For general notes see front of timetable
For details of catering facilities see Directory of Train Operators

SUMMARY OF SERVICES

from 29 March

South Coast and The South West → North West England, The North East and Scotland

Route Diagram - See first page of Table 51

Station		XC		VT	XC	XC	XC	VT	VT	XC	VT	XC	XC	XC	VT		VT	XC	XC	VT	XC	XC	XC	VT
Brighton	d																					14 22		
Haywards Heath	d																					14b32		
Gatwick Airport	d																					14 54		
Bournemouth	d									13 45								14 45						
Brockenhurst	d									14 00								15 00						
Southampton Central	d									14 15								15 15						
Southampton Airport Parkwy	d									14 22								15 22						
Winchester	d									14 31								15 31						
Basingstoke	d									14 47								15 47						
Redhill	d																							
Guildford	d																							
East Croydon	d																					15 08		
Kensington Olympia	d																					15 40		
Reading	d					14 40				15 10			15 40					16 10				16 40		
Oxford	d					15 07				15 36			16 07					16 36				17 07		
Banbury	d					15 25				15 53			16 25					16 53				17 25		
Leamington Spa	d					15 43				16 11			16 43					17 11				17 43		
Coventry	d							16 10	16 16	16 23					17 10		17 16	17 23						18 10
Birmingham International	d							16 22	16 28	16 34					17 22		17 28	17 34						18 22
Penzance	d																							
St Erth	d																							
Camborne	d																							
Redruth	d																							
Truro	d																							
St Austell	d																							
Par	d																							
Bodmin Parkway	d																							
Liskeard	d																							
Plymouth	d	12 25										13 25							14 25					
Totnes	d	12 50										13 50							14 50					
Paignton	d													14 05										
Torquay	d													14 11										
Newton Abbot	d	13 03										14 03		14 22					15 03					
Teignmouth	d													14 29										
Dawlish	d													14 34										
Exeter St Davids	d	13 23										14 23		14 48					15 23					
Tiverton Parkway	d	13 37										14 37		15 01					15 37					
Taunton	d	13 51										14 51		15 16					15 51					
Weston-super-Mare	d																							
Cardiff Central	d																							
Newport (South Wales)	d																							
Bristol Temple Meads	d	14 30					15 00					15 30		16 00					16 30				17 00	
Bristol Parkway	d	14 40					15 10					15 40		16 10					16 40				17 10	
Gloucester	d																							
Cheltenham Spa	d	15 12					15 42					16 12		16 42					17 12				17 42	
Birmingham New Street	a	15 57			←	16 18	16 26	16 36	16 39	16 46		16 57	17 18	17 26	17 36		17 39	17 45	17 57		←	18 18	18 26	18 36
Birmingham New Street	d	16 03		16 03	16 20		16 30	16 40	16 48	17 03	17 03	17 20		17 30	17 40		17 48	18 20	18 03	18 03	18 20		18 30	18 40
Tamworth	d						16 47											→					18 47	
Burton-on-Trent	d						16 58																18 58	
Derby	a	16 39					17 11			17 39				18 11					18 39				19 11	
Chesterfield	a						17 32							18 32					19 01				19 32	
Sheffield	a	17 15					17 48			18 17				18 46					19 16				19 47	
Doncaster	a						18 21							19 18									20 16	
Wakefield Westgate	a	17 46								18 46									19 46					
Leeds	a	18 02								19 02									20 02					
York	a	18 29					18 46			19 32				19 49					20 29				20 42	
Darlington	a	19 00					19 14			20 02				20 17					21 03				21 14	
Durham	a	19 17					19 31			20 22				20 34					21 21				22 10	
Chester-le-Street	a													20 41									22 17	
Newcastle	a	19 34					19 53			20 36				20 54					21 41				22 34	
Alnmouth	a	20 02								21 02														
Berwick-upon-Tweed	a	20 23								21 23				21 38										
Dunbar	a													22 01										
Wolverhampton	d			16 21	16 40				17 09		17 21	17 40					18 09			18 20	18 40			
Stafford	a				16 53			17 17	17 24			17 53			18 17		18 24				18 53			19 17
Stoke-on-Trent	a				17 12				17 43			18 12					18 43				19 12			
Congleton	a											18 24												
Macclesfield	a				17 29				17 59			18 32					18 59				19 29			
Crewe	a			16 54				17 38			17 54				18 38					18 58				19 38
Wilmslow	a																							
Stockport	a				17 46				18 13			18 46					19 13				19 46			
Manchester Piccadilly	a				18 02				18 28			19 02					19 28				20 02			
Warrington Bank Quay	a			17 12				17 57			18 12				18 57					19 15				19 57
Wigan North Western	a			17 23				18 08			18 23				19 08					19 27				20 08
Preston	a			17 42				18 28			18 44				19 25					19 43				20 26
Lancaster	a																							
Oxenholme Lake District	a																							
Penrith North Lakes	a																							
Carlisle	a																							
Lockerbie	a																							
Haymarket	a																							
Edinburgh	a	21 13								22 13				22 31										
Haymarket	a																							
Motherwell	a																							
Glasgow Central	a																							
Inverkeithing	a																							
Kirkcaldy	a																							
Markinch	a																							
Cupar	a																							
Leuchars	a																							
Dundee	a																							
Arbroath	a																							
Montrose	a																							
Stonehaven	a																							
Aberdeen	a																							

For general notes see front of timetable
For details of catering facilities see Directory of Train Operators

b Change at East Croydon

from 29 March

South Coast and The South West → North West England, The North East and Scotland

Route Diagram - See first page of Table 51

		VT	XC	VT	XC	XC	XC		VT	XC	XC	XC	XC	XC	VT	XC	XC	XC	XC	XC	XC	XC
		1 ◇	1 ◇	1 ◇	1 ◇	1 ◇	1 ◇		1 ◇	1 ◇	1 ◇	1 ◇	1 ◇	1 ◇	1 ◇	1 ◇	1 ◇	1 ◇	1 ◇	1 ◇	1 ◇	1 ◇
		☕	☕	☕	☕	☕	☕		☕	☕	☕	☕	☕		☕	☕	☕		☕	☕	☕	
Brighton 10	d																					
Haywards Heath 3	d																					
Gatwick Airport 10 ✈	d												*17 03*									
Bournemouth	d		15 45							16 45						17 45			18 45			19 45
Brockenhurst 3	d		16 00							17 00						18 00			19 00			20 00
Southampton Central	d		16 15							17 15						18 15			19 15			20 15
Southampton Airport Parkwy ✈	d		16 22							17 22						18 22			19 22			20 22
Winchester	d		16 31							17 31						18 31			19 31			20 31
Basingstoke	d		16 47							17 47						18 47			19 47			20 47
Redhill	d												*17 14*									
Guildford	d												17 58									
East Croydon 🚌	d																					
Kensington Olympia	d																					
Reading 7	d		17 10			17 40				18 10			18 40			19 10		19 40	20 10			21 10
Oxford	d		17 36			18 07				18 36			19 07			19 36		20 07	20 36			21 36
Banbury	d		17 53			18 25				18 53			19 25			19 53		20 25	20 53			21 53
Leamington Spa 8	d		18 11			18 43				19 11			19 43			20 11		20 43	21 11			22 11
Coventry	d	18 16	18 23						19 16	19 23					20 16	20 23			21 23			22 23
Birmingham International ✈	d	18 28	18 34						19 28	19 34					20 28	20 34			21 34			22 34
Penzance	d																					
St Erth 2	d																					
Camborne	d																					
Redruth	d																					
Truro	d																					
St Austell	d																					
Par 3	d																					
Bodmin Parkway	d																					
Liskeard 3	d																					
Plymouth	d				15 25						16 25						17 25			18 25		
Totnes	d				15 50						16 50						17 50			18 50		
Paignton	d																					
Torquay	d																					
Newton Abbot	d				16 03						17 03						18 03			19 03		
Teignmouth	d																					
Dawlish	d																					
Exeter St Davids 6	d				16 23						17 23						18 23			19 23		
Tiverton Parkway	d				16 37						17 37						18 37			19 37		
Taunton	d				16 51						17 51						18 51			19 51		
Weston-super-Mare	d																					
Cardiff Central 7	d																					
Newport (South Wales)	d																					
Bristol Temple Meads 10	d				17 30		18 00				18 30			19 00			19 30			20 30		
Bristol Parkway 7	d				17 40		18 10				18 40			19 10			19 40			20 40		
Gloucester 7	d																					
Cheltenham Spa	d				18 12		18 42				19 12			19 42			20 12			21 12		
Birmingham New Street 12	a	18 39	18 45		18 57	19 18	19 27		19 39	19 45	19 57	⟵	20 18	20 31	20 39	20 45	20 57	21 22	21 45	21 57	⟵	22 50
Birmingham New Street 12	d	18 48	19 03	19 03	19 20		19 30		19 48	20 20	20 03	20 20			20 48	20 50	21 20		22 20	22 03	22 20	
Tamworth	d						19 47			⟶	20 19					21 23			⟶	22 19		
Burton-on-Trent	d						19 58				20 29					21 33				22 29		
Derby 10	a		19 39				20 11				20 42					21 45				22 47		
Chesterfield	a		20 00				20 36				21 01					22 04						
Sheffield 7	a		20 18				20 51				21 16					22 19						
Doncaster 7	a																					
Wakefield Westgate 7	a		20 48								21 46					22s46						
Leeds 10	a		21 05								22 01					23 09						
York 8	a		21 35				21 54				22 38											
Darlington 7	a																					
Durham	a		22 48																			
Chester-le-Street	a																					
Newcastle 8	a		23 11																			
Alnmouth	a																					
Berwick-upon-Tweed	a																					
Dunbar	a																					
Wolverhampton 7 🚌	d	19 09		19 21	19 40				20 09			20 40			21 10		21 40				22 40	
Stafford	a	19 24		19 33	19 53				20 24			20 53			21 24		21 53				22 53	
Stoke-on-Trent	a	19 43			20 12				20 43			21 12			21 44		22 12				23s13	
Congleton	a				20 24												22 24					
Macclesfield	a	19 59			20 32				20 59			21 29			22 00		22 32				23s30	
Crewe 10	a			19 54																		
Wilmslow	a																					
Stockport	a	20 13			20 46				21 13			21 46			22 12		22 46				23s46	
Manchester Piccadilly 10 🚌	a	20 28			21 02				21 28			22 02			22 25		23 02				00 02	
Warrington Bank Quay	a			20 12																		
Wigan North Western	a			20 23																		
Preston 8	a			20 43																		
Lancaster 6	a																					
Oxenholme Lake District	a																					
Penrith North Lakes	a																					
Carlisle 8	a																					
Lockerbie	a																					
Haymarket	a																					
Edinburgh 10	a																					
Haymarket	a																					
Motherwell	a																					
Glasgow Central 15	a																					
Inverkeithing	a																					
Kirkcaldy	a																					
Markinch	a																					
Cupar	a																					
Leuchars 8	a																					
Dundee	a																					
Arbroath	a																					
Montrose	a																					
Stonehaven	a																					
Aberdeen	a																					

For general notes see front of timetable
For details of catering facilities see Directory of Train Operators

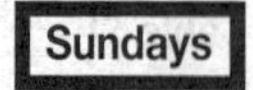

until 27 January

South Coast and The South West → North West England, The North East and Scotland

Route Diagram - See first page of Table 51

		XC	VT	XC	XC	VT	XC	XC	XC	VT	XC	XC	VT	XC	XC	VT	XC	XC	VT	XC	XC	XC	XC	VT
Brighton 10	d																							
Haywards Heath 3	d																							
Gatwick Airport 10	d																							
Bournemouth	d																08b06							
Brockenhurst 3	d																08b34							
Southampton Central	d																08 39							
Southampton Airport Parkway	d																08 46							
Winchester	d																09 23							
Basingstoke	d																09 47							
Redhill	d																							
Guildford	d																							
East Croydon	d																							
Kensington Olympia	d																							
Reading 7	d																10 10							
Oxford	d																10 36							
Banbury	d																10 53							
Leamington Spa 8	d																11 11							
Coventry	d									10 25						11 15	11 25							12 15
Birmingham International	d									10 36						11 26	11 36							12 26
Penzance	d																							
St Erth 2	d																							
Camborne	d																							
Redruth	d																							
Truro	d																							
St Austell	d																							
Par 3	d																							
Bodmin Parkway	d																							
Liskeard 3	d																							
Plymouth	d																							
Totnes	d																							
Paignton	d																							
Torquay	d																							
Newton Abbot	d																							
Teignmouth	d																							
Dawlish	d																							
Exeter St Davids 6	d																							
Tiverton Parkway	d																							
Taunton	d																							
Weston-super-Mare	d																							
Cardiff Central 7	d																							
Newport (South Wales)	d																							
Bristol Temple Meads 10	d										09 15							10 30					11 00	
Bristol Parkway 7	d										09 25							10 40					11 10	
Gloucester 7	d										10 00													
Cheltenham Spa	d										10 12			←				11 12			←		11 42	
Birmingham New Street 12	a									10 45	10 51			10 51		11 39	11 46	11 51			11 51	←	12 26	12 39
Birmingham New Street 12	d	09 03	09 03	09 18	09 30	10 03	10 03	10 18	10 30	10 48	→	11 03	11 03	11 18	11 30	11 48	12 18	→	12 03		12 03	12 18	12 30	12 48
Tamworth	d	09 19			09 47		10 19		10 47						11 47		→						12 47	
Burton-on-Trent	d	09 29			09 58		10 29		10 58						11 58								12 58	
Derby 10	a	09 42			10 11		10 42		11 11			11 39			12 11						12 39		13 11	
Chesterfield	a	10 02			10 32				11 32						12 32								13 32	
Sheffield 7	a	10 18			10 46		11 18		11 50			12 12			12 46						13 12		13 46	
Doncaster 7	a				11 16				12 16						13 15								14 16	
Wakefield Westgate 7	a	10 44					11 44					12 44									13 44			
Leeds 10	a	11 01					12 01					13 01									14 01			
York 8	a	11 33			11 44		12 33		12 45			13 33			13 44						14 32		14 41	
Darlington 7	a	12 03			12 13		13 02		13 15			14 04			14 13						15 08		15 13	
Durham	a	12 20			12 31		13 19		13 33			14 21			14 30						15 25		15 30	
Chester-le-Street	a																							
Newcastle 8	a	12 37			12 51		13 36		13 53			14 37			14 51						15 42		15 51	
Alnmouth	a						14 14														16 11			
Berwick-upon-Tweed	a	13 21										15 23								←				
Dunbar	a	13 44										15 54								15 54				
Wolverhampton 7	d		09 21	09 38		10 21		10 38		11 10		→	11 21	11 38		12 10			12 21			12 38		13 10
Stafford	a		09 33	09 51				10 51						11 51								12 51		
Stoke-on-Trent	a			10 10				11 10		11 42				12 10		12 40						13 10		13 43
Congleton	a																							
Macclesfield	a			10 27				11 27		11 58				12 27		12 56						13 27		13 59
Crewe 10	a		09 55			10 53							11 53						12 53					
Wilmslow	a																							
Stockport	a			10 41				11 41		12 15				12 41		13 10						13 41		14 13
Manchester Piccadilly 10	a			10 57				11 57		12 30				12 57		13 23						13 57		14 26
Warrington Bank Quay	a		10 12			11 11							12 11						13 12					
Wigan North Western	a		10 23			11 22							12 23						13 23					
Preston 8	a		10 40			11 36							12 39						13 37					
Lancaster 6	a					11 53							12 55						13 54					
Oxenholme Lake District	a					12 07													14 09					
Penrith North Lakes	a					12 35							13 33											
Carlisle 8	a					12 53							13 50						14 50					
Lockerbie	a					13 15													15 10					
Haymarket	a																		16s08					
Edinburgh 10	a	14 12				14 20	15 21												16 14	16c24	17 18			
Haymarket	a	14 18																		16 38				
Motherwell	a	14s53																						
Glasgow Central 15	a	15 17											15 09											
Inverkeithing	a																			16 52				
Kirkcaldy	a																			17 08				
Markinch	a																			17 17				
Cupar	a																			17 29				
Leuchars 3	a																			17 36				
Dundee	a																			17 49				
Arbroath	a																			18 06				
Montrose	a																			18 20				
Stonehaven	a																			18 40				
Aberdeen	a																			19 05				

For general notes see front of timetable
For details of catering facilities see Directory of Train Operators

b Change at Basingstoke
c Dep. 1635

South Coast and The South West → North West England, The North East and Scotland

Route Diagram - See first page of Table 51

		XC	XC	VT	XC	XC	XC	VT	XC	XC	VT	XC	XC	XC	XC	VT	VT	XC	XC	XC	XC	VT	XC	XC
									R	R	R	R	R				R	R	R				R	R
		1 ◇	1 ◇	1 ◇	1 ◇	1 ◇	1 ◇	1 ◇	1	1	1	1	1	1 ◇	1 ◇	1 ◇	1	1	1	1 ◇	1 ◇	1 ◇	1	1
Brighton 10	d					09 40																		
Haywards Heath 3	d					09 52																		
Gatwick Airport 10 ✈	d					10 11																		
Bournemouth	d		09 40						10 40									11 40					12 40	
Brockenhurst 3	d		09 57						10 57									11 57					12 57	
Southampton Central	d		10 15						11 15									12 15					13 15	
Southampton Airport Parkwy ✈	d		10 22						11 22									12 22					13 22	
Winchester	d		10 31						11 31									12 31					13 31	
Basingstoke	d		10 47						11 47									12 47					13 47	
Redhill	d					10 33																		
Guildford	d					10 58																		
East Croydon	d																							
Kensington Olympia	d																							
Reading 7	d		11 10			11 39			12 10					12 40				13 10		13 40			14 10	
Oxford	d		11 36			12 06			12 36					13 06				13 36		14 06			14 36	
Banbury	d		11 53			12 25			12 53					13 25				13 53		14 25			14 53	
Leamington Spa 8	d		12 11			12 43			13 11					13 43				14 11		14 43			15 11	
Coventry	d		12 25			12 55		13 15	13 25					13 55		14 15		14 25		14 55		15 15	15 25	
Birmingham International ✈	d		12 36			13 05		13 26	13 36					14 05		14 26		14 36		15 05		15 26	15 36	
Penzance	d																		09 30					10 30
St Erth 2	d																		09 38					10 38
Camborne	d																		09 48					10 48
Redruth	d																		09 54					10 54
Truro	d																		10 06					11 06
St Austell	d																		10 22					11 22
Par 3	d																		10 29					11 29
Bodmin Parkway	d																		10 40					11 40
Liskeard 3	d																		10 52					11 52
Plymouth	d	09 25								10 25									11 25					12 25
Totnes	d	09 50								10 50									11 50					12 50
Paignton	d																							
Torquay	d																							
Newton Abbot	d	10 03								11 03									12 03					13 03
Teignmouth	d																							
Dawlish	d																							
Exeter St Davids 6	d	10 23					10 48			11 23									12 23					13 23
Tiverton Parkway	d	10 37					11 01			11 37									12 37					13 37
Taunton	d	10 51					11 16			11 51									12 51					13 51
Weston-super-Mare	d																							
Cardiff Central 7	d														12 00									
Newport (South Wales)	d														12 15									
Bristol Temple Meads 10	d	11 30					12 00			12 30					13 00				13 30		14 00			14 30
Bristol Parkway 7	d	11 40					12 10			12 40					13 10				13 40		14 10			14 40
Gloucester 7	d																							
Cheltenham Spa	d	12 12			←		12 42			13 12		←			13 42				14 12		14 42			15 12
Birmingham New Street 12	a	12 51	12 46		12 51	13 18	13 26	13 39	13 46	13 51		13 51	←	14 18	14 26	14 39		14 46	14 57	15 18	15 26	15 39	15 46	15 51
Birmingham New Street 12	d	→	13 03	13 03	13 18		13 30	13 48	14 18	→	14 03	14 03	14 18		14 30	14 48	15 03	15 03	15 18		15 30	15 51	16 18	→
Tamworth	d								→						14 47								→	
Burton-on-Trent	d														14 58									
Derby 10	a		13 39				14 11					14 39			15 11			15 39			16 11			
Chesterfield	a						14 32								15 32						16 32			
Sheffield 7	a		14 12				14 51					15 18			15 50			16 16			16 49			
Doncaster 7	a						15 16								16 16						17 14			
Wakefield Westgate 7	a		14 44									15 44						16 44						
Leeds 10	a		15 01									16 01						17 01						
York 8	a		15 33				15 43					16 33			16 44			17 33			17 40			
Darlington 7	a		16 02				16 13					17 01			17 12			18 01			18 08			
Durham	a		16 19				16 31					17 19			17 29			18 18			18 25			
Chester-le-Street	a																							
Newcastle 8	a		16 35				16 52					17 41			17 52			18 35			18 47			
Alnmouth	a											18 09												
Berwick-upon-Tweed	a		17 21															19 20						
Dunbar	a		17 44															19 43						
Wolverhampton 7 ⛴	d			13 21	13 38			14 10			14 21		14 38			15 10	15 21		15 38			16 13		
Stafford	a				13 51								14 51						15 51					
Stoke-on-Trent	a				14 10			14 42					15 10			15 43			16 10			16 44		
Congleton	a																							
Macclesfield	a				14 27			14 58					15 27			15 59			16 27			17 00		
Crewe 10	a			13 53							14 52						15 53							
Wilmslow	a																							
Stockport	a				14 41			15 13					15 41			16 14			16 41			17 13		
Manchester Piccadilly 10 ⛴	a				14 57			15 27					15 57			16 27			16 57			17 27		
Warrington Bank Quay	a			14 11							15 11						16 11							
Wigan North Western	a			14 22							15 22						16 22							
Preston 8	a			14 37							15 38						16 37							
Lancaster 6	a			14 53							15 55						16 53							
Oxenholme Lake District	a			15 08													17 08							
Penrith North Lakes	a			15 36							16 31													
Carlisle 8	a			15 52							16 48						17 49							
Lockerbie	a																							
Haymarket	a										18s03													
Edinburgh 10	a		18 14								18 14	19b11						20 13						
Haymarket	a											19 28						20 17						
Motherwell	a																18s51	20s53						
Glasgow Central 15	a			17 11													19 16	→						
Inverkeithing	a											19 42												
Kirkcaldy	a											20 05												
Markinch	a											20 14												
Cupar	a											20 33												
Leuchars 3	a											20 45												
Dundee	a											21 05												
Arbroath	a																							
Montrose	a																							
Stonehaven	a																							
Aberdeen	a																							

For general notes see front of timetable
For details of catering facilities see
Directory of Train Operators

b Dep. 1925

Sundays

until 27 January

South Coast and The South West → North West England, The North East and Scotland

Route Diagram - See first page of Table 51

		VT	XC	XC	XC	XC	VT	XC	VT	XC	XC	XC	XC	VT	XC	XC	XC	VT	XC	XC	XC	XC	VT	XC
		R 1	R 1	R 1	1 ◇	1 ◇	1 ◇	R 1	R 1	R 1	R 1	1 ◇	R 1	1 ◇	R 1	R 1	R 1	R 1	R 1	R 1	1 ◇	1 ◇	1 ◇	R 1
Brighton 10	d																							
Haywards Heath 3	d																							
Gatwick Airport 10	d																							
Bournemouth	d							13 40								14 40								15 40
Brockenhurst 3	d							13 57								14 57								15 57
Southampton Central	d							14 15								15 15								16 15
Southampton Airport Parkwy	d							14 22								15 22								16 22
Winchester	d							14 31								15 31								16 31
Basingstoke	d							14 47								15 47								16 47
Redhill	d																							
Guildford	d																							
East Croydon	d																							
Kensington Olympia	d																							
Reading 7	d				14 40			15 10				15 40				16 10					16 40			17 10
Oxford	d				15 06			15 36				16 06				16 36					17 06			17 36
Banbury	d				15 25			15 53				16 25				16 53					17 25			17 53
Leamington Spa 8	d				15 43			16 11				16 43				17 11					17 43			18 11
Coventry	d				15 55		16 15	16 25				16 55		17 15		17 25					17 55		18 15	18 25
Birmingham International	d				16 05		16 26	16 36				17 05		17 26		17 36					18 05		18 26	18 36
Penzance	d										11 30													
St Erth 2	d										11 38													
Camborne	d										11 48													
Redruth	d										11 54													
Truro	d										12 06													
St Austell	d										12 22													
Par 3	d										12 29													
Bodmin Parkway	d										12 40													
Liskeard 3	d										12 52													
Plymouth	d										13 25						14 25							
Totnes	d										13 50						14 50							
Paignton	d												13 59											
Torquay	d												14 05											
Newton Abbot	d										14 03		14 16				15 03							
Teignmouth	d												14 24											
Dawlish	d												14 29											
Exeter St Davids 6	d										14 23		14 43				15 23							
Tiverton Parkway	d										14 37						15 37							
Taunton	d										14 51		15 06				15 51							
Weston-super-Mare	d												15 29											
Cardiff Central 7	d																							
Newport (South Wales)	d																							
Bristol Temple Meads 10	d					15 00					15 30		16 00				16 30					17 00		
Bristol Parkway 7	d					15 10					15 40		16 10				16 40					17 10		
Gloucester 7	d																							
Cheltenham Spa	d		←			15 42					16 12		16 42				17 12		←			17 42		
Birmingham New Street 12	a		15 51	←	16 18	16 26	16 39	16 46			16 57	17 18	17 26	17 39		17 46	17 51		17 51	←	18 18	18 26	18 39	18 46
Birmingham New Street 12	d	16 03	16 03	16 18		16 30	16 48	17 03	17 03		17 18		17 30	17 48		18 18 →	→	18 03	18 03	18 18		18 30	18 48	19 03
Tamworth	d					16 47																18 47		
Burton-on-Trent	d					16 58																18 58		
Derby 10	a		16 39			17 11		17 39					18 11						18 39			19 11		19 39
Chesterfield	a					17 32							18 32						19 01			19 32		20 01
Sheffield 7	a		17 12			17 47		18 14					18 48						19 16			19 48		20 16
Doncaster 7	a					18 16							19 16									20 16		
Wakefield Westgate 7	a		17 44					18 44											19 44					20 44
Leeds 10	a		18 01					19 01											20 01					21 01
York 8	a		18 33			18 41		19 33					19 43						20 33			20 42		21 32
Darlington 7	a		19 01			19 15		20 02					20 13						21 03			21 18		22 03
Durham	a		19 18			19 32		20 19					20 31						21 20			21 35		22 20
Chester-le-Street	a																							
Newcastle 8	a		19 35			19 54		20 36					20 51						21 37			21 57		22 42
Alnmouth	a		20 07					21 08											22 08					
Berwick-upon-Tweed	a		20 27					21 29											22 29					
Dunbar	a							21 52																
Wolverhampton 7	d	16 21		16 38			17 10		17 21		17 38			18 10				18 21		18 38			19 10	
Stafford	a			16 51							17 51									18 51				
Stoke-on-Trent	a			17 10			17 43				18 10			18 43						19 10			19 43	
Congleton	a																							
Macclesfield	a			17 27			17 59				18 27			18 59						19 27			19 59	
Crewe 10	a	16 53							17 53									18 52						
Wilmslow	a																							
Stockport	a			17 41			18 14				18 41			19 13						19 41			20 14	
Manchester Piccadilly 10	a			17 57			18 27				18 57			19 26						19 57			20 26	
Warrington Bank Quay	a	17 09							18 12									19 11						
Wigan North Western	a	17 20							18 23									19 22						
Preston 8	a	17 36							18 37									19 41						
Lancaster 6	a	17 53							18 53									19 56						
Oxenholme Lake District	a								19 08									20 10						
Penrith North Lakes	a	18 29							19 35									20 36						
Carlisle 8	a	18 48							19 52									20 52						
Lockerbie	a																							
Haymarket	a	20s04																22s08						
Edinburgh 10	a	20 14	21 13					22 22							←			22 18	23 18					
Haymarket	a		21 17 →							←					21 17									
Motherwell	a									20s53					21s59									
Glasgow Central 15	a								21 14	21 19					22 23									
Inverkeithing	a																							
Kirkcaldy	a																							
Markinch	a																							
Cupar	a																							
Leuchars 3	a																							
Dundee	a																							
Arbroath	a																							
Montrose	a																							
Stonehaven	a																							
Aberdeen	a																							

For general notes see front of timetable
For details of catering facilities see Directory of Train Operators

Table 51

South Coast and The South West → North West England, The North East and Scotland

Route Diagram - See first page of Table 51

		VT	XC	XC	XC	VT	XC	XC	XC	XC	XC	VT	XC	XC	VT	VT	XC	XC	XC	XC	XC	XC
		[R]	[R]				[R]	[R]	[R]													
		[1]	[1]	[1] ◇	[1] ◇	[1] ◇	[1]	[1]	[1]	[1] ◇	[1] ◇	[1] ◇	[1] ◇	[1] ◇	[1] ◇	[1] ◇	[1] ◇	[1] ◇	[1] ◇	[1] ◇	[1] ◇	[1] ◇
		☕	☕	☕	☕	☕	☕	☕	☕	☕		☕	☕	☕	☕	☕	☕	☕	☕			
Brighton [10]	d																					
Haywards Heath [3]	d																					
Gatwick Airport [10] ✈	d																					
Bournemouth	d						16 40						17 40				18 40			19 40		20 40
Brockenhurst [3]	d						16 57						17 57				18 57			19 57		20 57
Southampton Central	d						17 15						18 15				19 15			20 15		21 15
Southampton Airport Parkwy ✈	d						17 22						18 22				19 22			20 22		21 22
Winchester	d						17 31						18 31				19 31			20 31		21 31
Basingstoke	d						17 47						18 47				19 47			20 47		21 47
Redhill	d																					
Guildford	d																					
East Croydon 🚊	d																					
Kensington Olympia	d																					
Reading [7]	d			17 40			18 10			18 40			19 10				20 10			21 10		22 10
Oxford	d			18 06			18 36			19 06			19 36				20 36			21 36		22 36
Banbury	d			18 25			18 53			19 25			19 53				20 53			21 53		22 53
Leamington Spa [8]	d			18 43			19 11			19 43			20 11				21 11			22 11		23 11
Coventry	d			18 55		19 15	19 25			19 55		20 15	20 25		21 09	21 15	21 25			22 25		23 29
Birmingham International ✈	d			19 05		19 26	19 36			20 05		20 26	20 36			21 26	21 35			22 36		23 39
Penzance	d																					
St Erth [2]	d																					
Camborne	d																					
Redruth	d																					
Truro	d																					
St Austell	d																					
Par [3]	d																					
Bodmin Parkway	d																					
Liskeard [3]	d																					
Plymouth	d		15 25					16 25						17 25				18 25				
Totnes	d		15 50					16 50						17 50				18 50				
Paignton	d																					
Torquay	d																					
Newton Abbot	d		16 03					17 03						18 03				19 03				
Teignmouth	d																					
Dawlish	d																					
Exeter St Davids [6]	d		16 23					17 23						18 23				19 23				
Tiverton Parkway	d		16 37					17 37						18 37				19 37				
Taunton	d		16 51					17 51						18 51				19 51				
Weston-super-Mare	d																					
Cardiff Central [7]	d																					
Newport (South Wales)	d																					
Bristol Temple Meads [10]	d		17 30		18 00			18 30			19 00			19 30				20 30			22 10	
Bristol Parkway [7]	d		17 40		18 10			18 40			19 10			19 40				20 40			22 20	
Gloucester [7]	d																					
Cheltenham Spa	d		18 12		18 42			19 12			19 42			20 12				21 12			22 52	
Birmingham New Street [12]	a		18 57	19 18	19 26	19 39	19 46	19 51	←	20 21	20 34	20 39	20 46	20 57	21 32	21 39	21 46	21 51	←	23 13	23 44	23 55
Birmingham New Street [12]	d	19 03	19 18		19 30	19 48	20 18	20 03	20 18			20 48	21 03	21 18	21 35	21 48	22 18	22 03	22 18	23 13		
Tamworth	d				19 47		→	20 19					21 19				→			23 31		
Burton-on-Trent	d				19 58			20 29					21 29					22 39		23 42		
Derby [10]	a				20 11			20 42					21 42					22 50		23 59		
Chesterfield	a				20 32			21 01					22 01					23 12				
Sheffield [7]	a				20 48			21 17					22 18					23 26				
Doncaster [7]	a				21 16																	
Wakefield Westgate [7]	a							21 44					22s45					23s52				
Leeds [10]	a							22 01					23 09					00 34				
York [8]	a				21 41			22 36														
Darlington [7]	a				22 11																	
Durham	a				22 28																	
Chester-le-Street	a																					
Newcastle [8]	a				22 50																	
Alnmouth	a																					
Berwick-upon-Tweed	a																					
Dunbar	a																					
Wolverhampton [7] 🚊	d	19 21	19 38			20 10			20 38			21 10		21 38	21 54	22 10			22 38			
Stafford	a	19 33	19 51						20 51					21 51	22 09				22 51			
Stoke-on-Trent	a		20 10			20 44			21 10			21 44		22 10		22 40			23s10			
Congleton	a																					
Macclesfield	a		20 27			21 00			21 27			22 00		22 27		22 56			23s27			
Crewe [10]	a	19 54													22 35							
Wilmslow	a																					
Stockport	a		20 41			21 13			21 41			22 14		22 41		23 11			23s41			
Manchester Piccadilly [10] 🚊	a		20 57			21 26			21 57			22 27		22 57		23 26			23 57			
Warrington Bank Quay	a	20 12													22 53							
Wigan North Western	a	20 23													23 04							
Preston [8]	a	20 38													23 36							
Lancaster [6]	a	20 54																				
Oxenholme Lake District	a	21 09																				
Penrith North Lakes	a	21 35																				
Carlisle [8]	a	22 13																				
Lockerbie	a	22 33																				
Haymarket	a																					
Edinburgh [10]	a																					
Haymarket	a																					
Motherwell	a	23s16																				
Glasgow Central [15]	a	23 38																				
Inverkeithing	a																					
Kirkcaldy	a																					
Markinch	a																					
Cupar	a																					
Leuchars [8]	a																					
Dundee	a																					
Arbroath	a																					
Montrose	a																					
Stonehaven	a																					
Aberdeen	a																					

For general notes see front of timetable
For details of catering facilities see Directory of Train Operators

South Coast and The South West → North West England, The North East and Scotland

3 February to 23 March

Route Diagram - See first page of Table 51

		XC 1◇	VT 1◇	XC 1◇	XC 1◇	XC 1◇	VT 1◇	XC 1◇	VT 1◇	XC 1◇	XC 1◇	VT 1◇	XC 1◇	VT 1◇		XC 1◇	XC 1◇	VT 1◇	XC 1◇	VT 1◇	XC 1◇	VT 1◇	XC 1◇	XC 1◇
Brighton 10	d																							
Haywards Heath 3	d																							
Gatwick Airport 10 ✈	d																							
Bournemouth	d															08b06							09 40	
Brockenhurst 3	d															08b34							09 57	
Southampton Central	d															08 39							10 15	
Southampton Airport Parkwy ✈	d															08 46							10 22	
Winchester	d															09 23							10 31	
Basingstoke	d															09 47							10 47	
Redhill	d																							
Guildford	d																							
East Croydon	d																							
Kensington Olympia	d																							
Reading 7	d															10 10							11 10	
Oxford	d															10 36							11 36	
Banbury	d															10 53							11 53	
Leamington Spa 8	d															11 11							12 11	
Coventry	d								10 25					11 15		11 25				12 15			12 25	
Birmingham International ✈	d								10 36					11 26		11 36				12 26			12 36	
Penzance	d																							
St Erth 2	d																							
Camborne	d																							
Redruth	d																							
Truro	d																							
St Austell	d																							
Par 3	d																							
Bodmin Parkway	d																							
Liskeard 3	d																							
Plymouth	d																				08 35			
Totnes	d																				09 00			
Paignton	d																							
Torquay	d																							
Newton Abbot	d																				09 13			
Teignmouth	d																							
Dawlish	d																							
Exeter St Davids 6	d																				09 33			
Tiverton Parkway	d																				09 47			
Taunton	d																				10 01			
Weston-super-Mare	d																							
Cardiff Central 7	d																							
Newport (South Wales)	d																							
Bristol Temple Meads 10	d									09 15							10 30				11 30			
Bristol Parkway 7	d									09 25							10 40				11 40			
Gloucester 7	d									10 00														
Cheltenham Spa	d									10 12			←				11 12				12 12			←
Birmingham New Street 12	a								10 45	10 51			10 51	11 39		11 46	11 51		←	12 39	12 51		12 46	12 51
Birmingham New Street 12	d	08 30	09 03	09 18	09 30	10 03	10 03	10 18	10 48	→	11 03	11 03	11 18	11 48		12 18 →	12 03	12 03	12 18	12 48	→	13 03	13 03	13 18
Tamworth	d																							
Burton-on-Trent	d																							
Derby 10	a	09 42			10 42	11 23					12 23						13 23						14 23	
Chesterfield	a	10 02			11 02	11 44					12 44						13 44						14 44	
Sheffield 7	a	10 18			11 18	11 58					12 58						14 02						14 58	
Doncaster 7	a					12 27					13 26						14 27						15 26	
Wakefield Westgate 7	a	10 44			11 44	12 44					13 44						14 44						15 44	
Leeds 10	a	11 01			12 01	13 01					14 01						15 01						16 01	
York 8	a	11 33			12 33	13 33					14 32						15 32						16 33	
Darlington 7	a	12 03			13 02	14 03					15 08						16 02						17 03	
Durham	a	12 19			13 19	14 19					15 26						16 19						17 19	
Chester-le-Street	a																							
Newcastle 8	a	12 37			13 36	14 37					15 40						16 36						17 35	
Alnmouth	a				14 14						16 13												18 09	
Berwick-upon-Tweed	a	13 21				15 25											17 21							
Dunbar	a	13 44				15 54											17 44							
Wolverhampton 7	d		09 21	09 38			10 21	10 38	11 10			11 21	11 38	12 10				12 21	12 38	13 10		13 21		13 38
Stafford	a		09 33	09 51				10 51					11 51						12 51					13 51
Stoke-on-Trent	a			10 10				11 10	11 42				12 10	12 40					13 10	13 43				14 10
Congleton	a																							
Macclesfield	a			10 27				11 27	11 58				12 27	12 56					13 27	13 59				14 27
Crewe 10	a		09 55				10 53					11 53						12 53				13 53		
Wilmslow	a																							
Stockport	a			10 41				11 41	12 15				12 41	13 10					13 41	14 13				14 41
Manchester Piccadilly 10	a			10 57				11 57	12 30				12 57	13 23					13 57	14 26				14 57
Warrington Bank Quay	a		10 12				11 11					12 11						13 12				14 11		
Wigan North Western	a		10 23				11 22					12 23						13 23				14 22		
Preston 8	a		10 40				11 38					12 39						13 37				14 37		
Lancaster 6	a						11 53					12 55						13 54				14 53		
Oxenholme Lake District	a						12 07											14 09				15 08		
Penrith North Lakes	a						12 35					13 33										15 36		
Carlisle 8	a						12 53					13 50						14 50				15 52		
Lockerbie	a						13 16					14 10						15 10				16 12		
Haymarket	a																						19e11	
Edinburgh 10	a	14 14			15 21	16c24					17 20						18 14						19 28	
Haymarket	a	14 18				16 38																		
Motherwell	a	14s53																						
Glasgow Central 15	a	15 17																						
Inverkeithing	a					16 52																	19 42	
Kirkcaldy	a					17 08																	20 05	
Markinch	a					17 17																	20 14	
Cupar	a					17 29																	20 33	
Leuchars 3	a					17 36																	20 45	
Dundee	a					17 49																	21 05	
Arbroath	a					18 06																		
Montrose	a					18 20																		
Stonehaven	a					18 40																		
Aberdeen	a					19 05																		

For general notes see front of timetable
For details of catering facilities see Directory of Train Operators

b Change at Basingstoke
c Dep. 1635
e Dep. 1925

South Coast and The South West → North West England, The North East and Scotland

3 February to 23 March

Route Diagram - See first page of Table 51

Station		XC	VT	XC	XC	VT	XC	VT	XC	VT	XC	VT	XC	XC	VT	XC	VT	XC	VT	XC	VT	XC
				R	R	R	R		R	R	R		R	R	R	R		R	R	R		R
		1◇	1◇	1	1	1	1	1◇	1	1	1	1◇	1	1	1	1	1◇	1	1	1	1◇	1
Brighton 10	d	09 40																				
Haywards Heath 3	d	09 52																				
Gatwick Airport 10 ✈	d	10 11																				
Bournemouth	d			10 40					11 40				12 40					13 40				14 40
Brockenhurst 3	d			10 57					11 57				12 57					13 57				14 57
Southampton Central	d			11 15					12 15				13 15					14 15				15 15
Southampton Airport Parkway ✈	d			11 22					12 22				13 22					14 22				15 22
Winchester	d			11 31					12 31				13 31					14 31				15 31
Basingstoke	d			11 47					12 47				13 47					14 47				15 47
Redhill	d	10 33																				
Guildford	d	10 58																				
East Croydon	d																					
Kensington Olympia	d																					
Reading 7	d	11 40		12 10					13 10				14 10					15 10				16 10
Oxford	d	12 07		12 36					13 36				14 36					15 36				16 36
Banbury	d	12 25		12 53					13 53				14 53					15 53				16 53
Leamington Spa 3	d	12 43		13 11					14 11				15 11					16 11				17 11
Coventry	d	13 03	13 15	13 25				14 15	14 25			15 15	15 25				16 15	16 25			17 15	17 25
Birmingham International ✈	d	13 14	13 26	13 36				14 26	14 36			15 26	15 36				16 26	16 36			17 26	17 36
Penzance	d													09 30						10 30		
St Erth 2	d													09 38						10 38		
Camborne	d													09 48						10 48		
Redruth	d													09 54						10 54		
Truro	d													10 06						11 06		
St Austell	d													10 22						11 22		
Par 3	d													10 29						11 29		
Bodmin Parkway	d													10 40						11 40		
Liskeard 3	d													10 52						11 52		
Plymouth	d				09 40						10 25			11 30						12 30		
Totnes	d				10 05						10 50			11 55						12 55		
Paignton	d																					
Torquay	d																					
Newton Abbot	d				10 18						11 03			12 08						13 08		
Teignmouth	d										11 10											
Dawlish	d										11 15											
Exeter St Davids 6	d				10 38						11 28			12 28						13 28		
Tiverton Parkway	d				10 52						11 42			12 42						13 42		
Taunton	d				11 06						11 56			12 56						13 56		
Weston-super-Mare	d																					
Cardiff Central 7	d																					
Newport (South Wales)	d																					
Bristol Temple Meads 10	d				12 30						13 30			14 30						15 30		
Bristol Parkway 7	d				12 40						13 40			14 40						15 40		
Gloucester 7	d																					
Cheltenham Spa	d				13 12						14 12			15 12						16 12		
Birmingham New Street 12	a	13 30	13 39	13 46	13 51		←	14 39	14 46		14 57	15 39	15 46	15 51		←	16 39	16 46		16 57	17 39	17 46
Birmingham New Street 12	d		13 48	14 18 →	14 03	14 03	14 18	14 48	15 03	15 03	15 18	15 51	16 18 →	16 03	16 03	16 18	16 48	17 03	17 03	17 18	17 48	18 18 →
Tamworth	d																					
Burton-on-Trent	d																					
Derby 10	a				15 23				16 23					17 23				18 20				
Chesterfield	a				15 44				16 44					17 44				18 44				
Sheffield 7	a				15 58				16 58					17 58				18 58				
Doncaster 7	a				16 26				17 26					18 26				19 27				
Wakefield Westgate 7	a				16 44				17 44					18 44				19 44				
Leeds 10	a				17 01				18 01					19 01				20 01				
York 8	a				17 33				18 33					19 33				20 33				
Darlington 7	a				18 01				19 01					20 01				21 02				
Durham	a				18 18				19 18					20 18				21 19				
Chester-le-Street	a																					
Newcastle 8	a				18 35				19 35					20 35				21 36				
Alnmouth	a								20 07					21 08				22 08				
Berwick-upon-Tweed	a				19 23				20 27					21 29				22 29				
Dunbar	a				19 46									21 52								
Wolverhampton 7	d		14 10			14 21	14 38	15 10		15 21	15 38	16 13			16 21	16 38	17 10		17 21	17 38	18 10	
Stafford	a						14 51				15 51					16 51				17 51		
Stoke-on-Trent	a		14 42				15 10	15 43			16 10	16 44				17 10	17 43			18 10	18 43	
Congleton	a																					
Macclesfield	a		14 58				15 27	15 59			16 27	17 00				17 27	17 59			18 27	18 59	
Crewe 10	a					14 52				15 53					16 53				17 53			
Wilmslow	a																					
Stockport	a		15 13				15 41	16 14			16 41	17 13				17 41	18 14			18 41	19 13	
Manchester Piccadilly 10	a		15 27				15 57	16 27			16 57	17 27				17 57	18 27			18 57	19 26	
Warrington Bank Quay	a					15 11				16 11					17 09				18 12			
Wigan North Western	a					15 22				16 22					17 20				18 23			
Preston 8	a					15 38				16 37					17 36				18 37			
Lancaster 6	a					15 55				16 53					17 53				18 53			
Oxenholme Lake District	a									17 08									19 08			
Penrith North Lakes	a					16 31									18 29				19 35			
Carlisle 8	a					16 48				17 49					18 48				19 52			
Lockerbie	a					17 10				18 09					19 08				20 12			
Haymarket	a																					
Edinburgh 10	a				20 14				21 14					22 22				23 18				
Haymarket	a				20 17				21 17													
Motherwell	a				20s53				21s59													
Glasgow Central 15	a				21 19				22 23													
Inverkeithing	a																					
Kirkcaldy	a																					
Markinch	a																					
Cupar	a																					
Leuchars 3	a																					
Dundee	a																					
Arbroath	a																					
Montrose	a																					
Stonehaven	a																					
Aberdeen	a																					

For general notes see front of timetable
For details of catering facilities see Directory of Train Operators

South Coast and The South West → North West England, The North East and Scotland

3 February to 23 March

Route Diagram - See first page of Table 51

		XC	VT	XC	VT	XC	VT	XC	VT	XC	XC	XC	VT	XC	XC	VT	VT	XC	XC	XC	XC	XC
		R 1 ☕	R 1 ☕	R 1 ☕	1◇ ☕	R 1 ☕	R 1 ☕	R 1 ☕	1◇ ☕	R 1 ☕	R 1 ☕	R 1 ☕	1◇ ☕	1◇ ☕	1◇ ☕	1◇ ☕	1◇ ☕	1◇ ☕	1◇ ☕	1◇	1◇	1◇
Brighton 10	d																					
Haywards Heath 3	d																					
Gatwick Airport 10 ✈	d																					
Bournemouth	d					15 40				16 40				17 40				18 40		19 40		20 40
Brockenhurst 3	d					15 57				16 57				17 57				18 57		19 57		20 57
Southampton Central	d					16 15				17 15				18 15				19 15		20 15		21 15
Southampton Airport Parkwy ✈	d					16 22				17 22				18 22				19 22		20 22		21 22
Winchester	d					16 31				17 31				18 31				19 31		20 31		21 31
Basingstoke	d					16 47				17 47				18 47				19 47		20 47		21 47
Redhill	d																					
Guildford	d																					
East Croydon	d																					
Kensington Olympia	d																					
Reading 7	d					17 10				18 10				19 10				20 10		21 10		22 10
Oxford	d					17 36				18 36				19 36				20 36		21 36		22 36
Banbury	d					17 53				18 53				19 53				20 53		21 53		22 53
Leamington Spa 8	d					18 11				19 11				20 11				21 11		22 11		23 11
Coventry	d				18 15	18 25			19 15	19 25			20 15	20 25		21 09	21 15	21 25		22 25		23 29
Birmingham International ✈	d				18 26	18 36			19 26	19 36			20 26	20 36			21 26	21 36		22 36		23 39
Penzance	d	12 00																				
St Erth 2	d	12 08																				
Camborne	d	12 18																				
Redruth	d	12 24																				
Truro	d	12 36																				
St Austell	d	12 52																				
Par 3	d	12 59																				
Bodmin Parkway	d	13 10																				
Liskeard 3	d	13 22																				
Plymouth	d	13 55						15 25			16 25				17 25				18 25			
Totnes	d	14 20						15 50			16 50				17 50				18 50			
Paignton	d																					
Torquay	d																					
Newton Abbot	d	14 33						16 03			17 03				18 03				19 03			
Teignmouth	d	14 40																				
Dawlish	d	14 45																				
Exeter St Davids 6	d	15 00						16 23			17 23				18 23				19 23			
Tiverton Parkway	d	15 14						16 37			17 37				18 37				19 37			
Taunton	d	15 28						16 51			17 51				18 51				19 51			
Weston-super-Mare	d	16 00																				
Cardiff Central 7	d																					
Newport (South Wales)	d																					
Bristol Temple Meads 10	d	16 30						17 30			18 30				19 30				20 30		22 10	
Bristol Parkway 7	d	16 40						17 40			18 40				19 40				20 40		22 20	
Gloucester 7	d																					
Cheltenham Spa	d	17 12						18 12			19 12				20 12				21 12		22 52	
Birmingham New Street 12	a	17 51		←	18 39	18 46		18 57	19 39	19 46	19 51	←	20 39	20 46	20 57	21 32	21 39	21 46	21 55	23 13	23 44	23 55
Birmingham New Street 12	d	18 03	18 03	18 18	18 48	19 03	19 03	19 18	19 48	20 18 →	20 03	20 18	20 48	21 03	21 18	21 35	21 48	22 18				
Tamworth	d																					
Burton-on-Trent	d																					
Derby 10	a	19 23				20 16					21 22			22 13								
Chesterfield	a	19 45				20 44					21 44			22 37								
Sheffield 7	a	20 00				21 01					22 01			22 52								
Doncaster 7	a	20 32				21 26					22 26			23 16								
Wakefield Westgate 7	a	20 50				21 44					22s45			23s34								
Leeds 10	a	21 06				22 01					23 09			00 16								
York 8	a	21 33				22 36																
Darlington 7	a	22 10																				
Durham	a	22 29																				
Chester-le-Street	a																					
Newcastle 8	a	22 51																				
Alnmouth	a																					
Berwick-upon-Tweed	a																					
Dunbar	a																					
Wolverhampton 7	d		18 21	18 38	19 10		19 21	19 38	20 10			20 38	21 10		21 38	21 54	22 10	22 38				
Stafford	a			18 51			19 33	19 51				20 51			21 51	22 09		22 51				
Stoke-on-Trent	a			19 10	19 43			20 10	20 44			21 10	21 44		22 10		22 40	23s10				
Congleton	a																					
Macclesfield	a			19 27	19 59			20 27	21 00			21 27	22 00		22 27		22 56	23s27				
Crewe 10	a		18 52				19 54									22 35						
Wilmslow	a																					
Stockport	a			19 41	20 14			20 41	21 13			21 41	22 14		22 41		23 11	23s41				
Manchester Piccadilly 10	a			19 57	20 26			20 57	21 26			21 57	22 27		22 57		23 26	23 57				
Warrington Bank Quay	a		19 11													22 53						
Wigan North Western	a		19 22													23 04						
Preston 8	a		19 41													23 36						
Lancaster 6	a																					
Oxenholme Lake District	a																					
Penrith North Lakes	a																					
Carlisle 8	a																					
Lockerbie	a																					
Haymarket	a																					
Edinburgh 10	a																					
Haymarket	a																					
Motherwell	a																					
Glasgow Central 15	a																					
Inverkeithing	a																					
Kirkcaldy	a																					
Markinch	a																					
Cupar	a																					
Leuchars 3	a																					
Dundee	a																					
Arbroath	a																					
Montrose	a																					
Stonehaven	a																					
Aberdeen	a																					

For general notes see front of timetable
For details of catering facilities see Directory of Train Operators

Table 51

SUMMARY OF SERVICES

Sundays

from 30 March

South Coast and The South West → North West England, The North East and Scotland

Route Diagram - See first page of Table 51

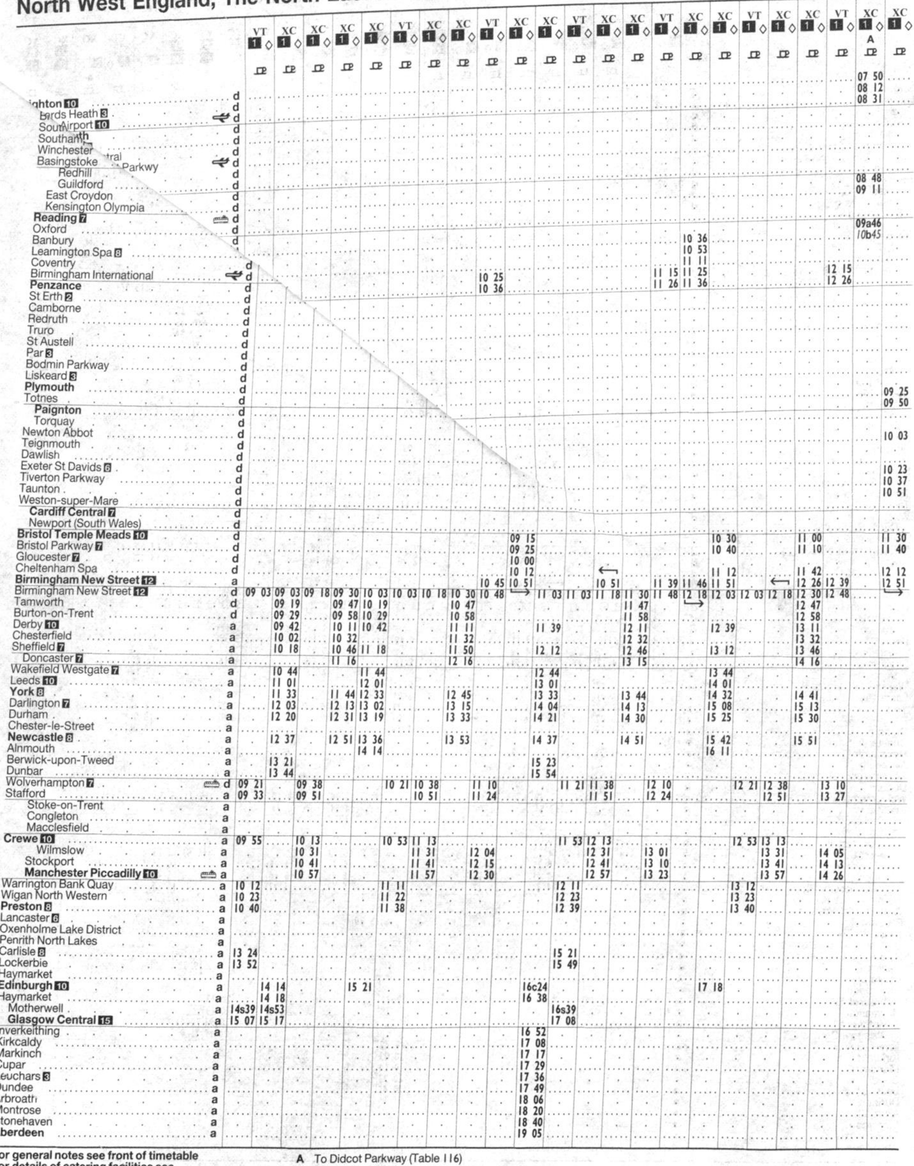

		VT	XC	XC	XC	XC	VT	XC	XC	VT	XC	XC	VT	XC	XC	VT	XC	XC	VT	XC	XC	VT	XC	XC
		1 ◇	1 ◇	1 ◇	1 ◇	1 ◇	1 ◇	1 ◇	1 ◇	1 ◇	1 ◇	1 ◇	1 ◇	1 ◇	1 ◇	1 ◇	1 ◇	1 ◇	1 ◇	1 ◇	1 ◇	1 ◇	1 ◇	1 ◇
																							A	
		☕	☕	☕	☕	☕	☕	☕	☕	☕	☕	☕	☕	☕	☕	☕	☕	☕	☕	☕	☕	☕	☕	☕
ighton 10	d																						07 50	
Birds Heath 3	d																						08 12	
SouAirport 10 ✈	d																						08 31	
Southamth	d																							
Winchester	d																							
Basingstoke tral Parkwy ✈	d																							
Redhill	d																						08 48	
Guildford	d																						09 11	
East Croydon	d																							
Kensington Olympia	d																							
Reading 7	d																						09a46	
Oxford	d															10 36							10b45	
Banbury	d															10 53								
Leamington Spa 8	d															11 11								
Coventry	d									10 25						11 15	11 25					12 15		
Birmingham International ✈	d									10 36						11 26	11 36					12 26		
Penzance	d																							
St Erth 2	d																							
Camborne	d																							
Redruth	d																							
Truro	d																							
St Austell	d																							
Par 3	d																							
Bodmin Parkway	d																							
Liskeard 3	d																							
Plymouth	d																							09 25
Totnes	d																							09 50
Paignton	d																							
Torquay	d																							
Newton Abbot	d																							10 03
Teignmouth	d																							
Dawlish	d																							
Exeter St Davids 6	d																							10 23
Tiverton Parkway	d																							10 37
Taunton	d																							10 51
Weston-super-Mare	d																							
Cardiff Central 7	d																							
Newport (South Wales)	d																							
Bristol Temple Meads 10	d										09 15							10 30			11 00			11 30
Bristol Parkway 7	d										09 25							10 40			11 10			11 40
Gloucester 7	d										10 00													
Cheltenham Spa	d										10 12							11 12			11 42			12 12
Birmingham New Street 12	a									10 45	10 51			← 10 51		11 39	11 46	11 51		←	12 26	12 39		12 51
Birmingham New Street 12	d	09 03	09 03	09 18	09 30	10 03	10 03	10 18	10 30	10 48	→	11 03	11 03	11 18	11 30	11 48	12 18	12 03	12 03	12 18	12 30	12 48		→
Tamworth	d		09 19		09 47	10 19			10 47						11 47		→				12 47			
Burton-on-Trent	d		09 29		09 58	10 29			10 58						11 58						12 58			
Derby 10	a		09 42		10 11	10 42			11 11			11 39			12 11			12 39			13 11			
Chesterfield	a		10 02		10 32				11 32						12 32						13 32			
Sheffield 7	a		10 18		10 46	11 18			11 50			12 12			12 46			13 12			13 46			
Doncaster 7	a				11 16				12 16						13 15						14 16			
Wakefield Westgate 7	a		10 44			11 44						12 44						13 44						
Leeds 10	a		11 01			12 01						13 01						14 01						
York 8	a		11 33		11 44	12 33			12 45			13 33			13 44			14 32			14 41			
Darlington 7	a		12 03		12 13	13 02			13 15			14 04			14 13			15 08			15 13			
Durham	a		12 20		12 31	13 19			13 33			14 21			14 30			15 25			15 30			
Chester-le-Street	a																							
Newcastle 8	a		12 37		12 51	13 36			13 53			14 37			14 51			15 42			15 51			
Alnmouth	a					14 14												16 11						
Berwick-upon-Tweed	a		13 21									15 23												
Dunbar	a		13 44									15 54												
Wolverhampton 7 🚌	d	09 21		09 38			10 21	10 38		11 10			11 21	11 38		12 10			12 21	12 38		13 10		
Stafford	a	09 33		09 51				10 51		11 24				11 51		12 24				12 51		13 27		
Stoke-on-Trent	a																							
Congleton	a																							
Macclesfield	a																							
Crewe 10	a	09 55		10 13			10 53	11 13					11 53	12 13					12 53	13 13				
Wilmslow	a			10 31				11 31		12 04				12 31		13 01				13 31		14 05		
Stockport	a			10 41				11 41		12 15				12 41		13 10				13 41		14 13		
Manchester Piccadilly 10 🚌	a			10 57				11 57		12 30				12 57		13 23				13 57		14 26		
Warrington Bank Quay	a	10 12					11 11						12 11						13 12					
Wigan North Western	a	10 23					11 22						12 23						13 23					
Preston 8	a	10 40					11 38						12 39						13 40					
Lancaster 6	a																							
Oxenholme Lake District	a																							
Penrith North Lakes	a																							
Carlisle 8	a	13 24											15 21											
Lockerbie	a	13 52											15 49											
Haymarket	a																							
Edinburgh 10	a		14 14			15 21						16c24						17 18						
Haymarket	a		14 18									16 38												
Motherwell	a	14s39	14s53										16s39											
Glasgow Central 15	a	15 07	15 17										17 08											
Inverkeithing	a											16 52												
Kirkcaldy	a											17 08												
Markinch	a											17 17												
Cupar	a											17 29												
Leuchars 3	a											17 36												
Dundee	a											17 49												
Arbroath	a											18 06												
Montrose	a											18 20												
Stonehaven	a											18 40												
Aberdeen	a											19 05												

For general notes see front of timetable
For details of catering facilities see Directory of Train Operators

A To Didcot Parkway (Table 116)
b Arrival time. By bus from Didcot Parkway (Table 116)
c Dep. 1635

South Coast and The South West → North West England, The North East and Scotland

Sundays from 30 March

Route Diagram - See first page of Table 51

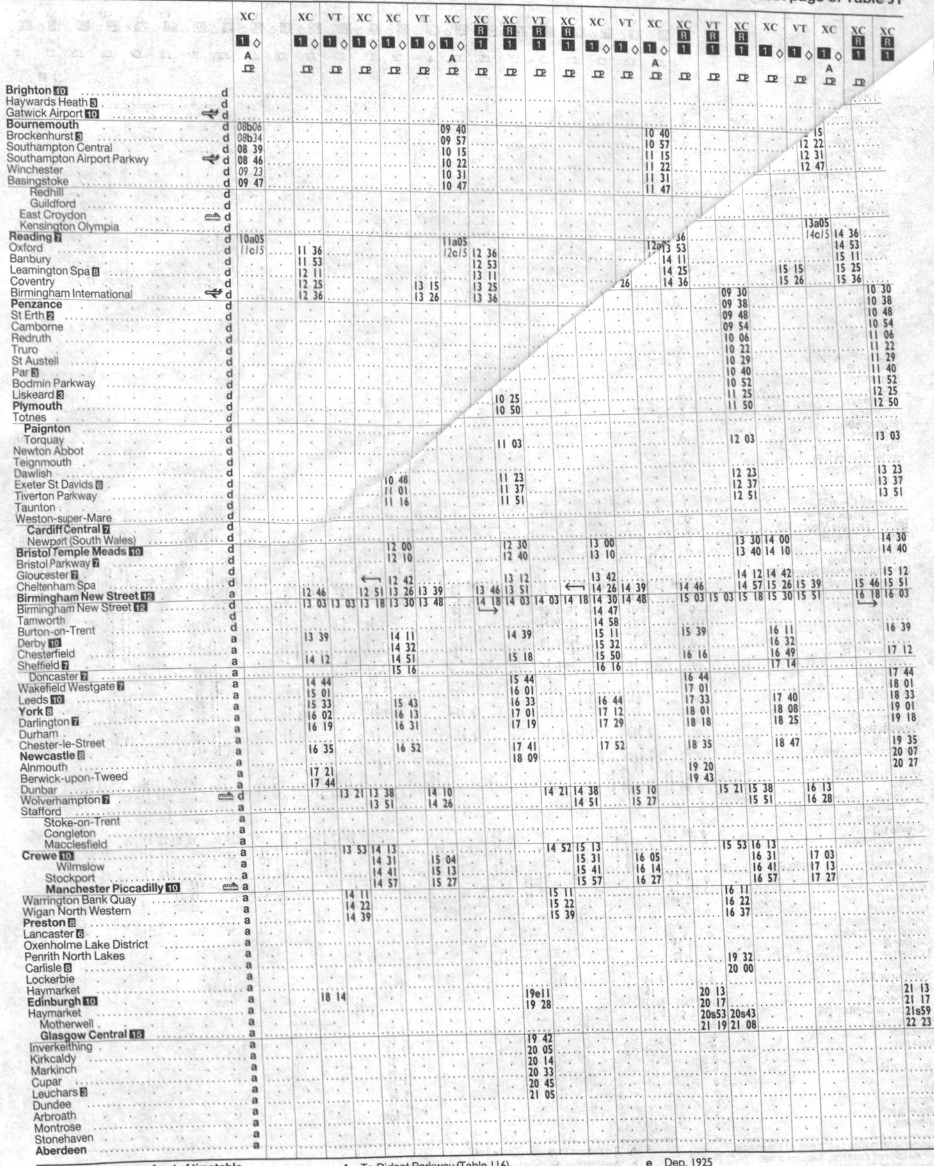

		XC		XC	VT	XC	XC	VT	XC	XC	XC	VT	XC	XC	VT	XC	XC	VT	XC	XC	VT	XC	XC	XC
		1 ◇		1 ◇	1 ◇	1 ◇	1 ◇	1 ◇	1 ◇	R 1	R 1	R 1	R 1	1 ◇	1 ◇	1 ◇	R 1	R 1	R 1	1 ◇	1 ◇	1 ◇	R 1	R 1
		A							A							A						A		
Brighton 10	d																							
Haywards Heath 3	d																							
Gatwick Airport 10 ✈	d																							
Bournemouth	d	08b06							09 40							10 40								
Brockenhurst 3	d	08b34							09 57							10 57								
Southampton Central	d	08 39							10 15							11 15						15		
Southampton Airport Parkway ✈	d	08 46							10 22							11 22						12 22		
Winchester	d	09 23							10 31							11 31						12 31		
Basingstoke	d	09 47							10 47							11 47						12 47		
Redhill	d																							
Guildford	d																							
East Croydon	d																							
Kensington Olympia	d																							
Reading 7	d	10a05							11a05							12a0						13a05		
Oxford	d	11c15		11 36					12c15	12 36							36					14c15	14 36	
Banbury	d			11 53						12 53							13 53						14 53	
Leamington Spa 8	d			12 11						13 11							14 11						15 11	
Coventry	d			12 25				13 15		13 25							14 25				15 15		15 25	
Birmingham International ✈	d			12 36				13 26		13 36					26		14 36				15 26		15 36	
Penzance	d																		09 30					10 30
St Erth 2	d																		09 38					10 38
Camborne	d																		09 48					10 48
Redruth	d																		09 54					10 54
Truro	d																		10 06					11 06
St Austell	d																		10 22					11 22
Par 3	d																		10 29					11 29
Bodmin Parkway	d																		10 40					11 40
Liskeard 3	d																		10 52					11 52
Plymouth	d										10 25								11 25					12 25
Totnes	d										10 50								11 50					12 50
Paignton	d																							
Torquay	d																							
Newton Abbot	d										11 03								12 03					13 03
Teignmouth	d																							
Dawlish	d																							
Exeter St Davids 6	d						10 48				11 23								12 23					13 23
Tiverton Parkway	d						11 01				11 37								12 37					13 37
Taunton	d						11 16				11 51								12 51					13 51
Weston-super-Mare	d																							
Cardiff Central 7	d																							
Newport (South Wales)	d																							
Bristol Temple Meads 10	d						12 00				12 30			13 00					13 30	14 00				14 30
Bristol Parkway 7	d						12 10				12 40			13 10					13 40	14 10				14 40
Gloucester 7	d																							
Cheltenham Spa	d					←	12 42				13 12		←	13 42					14 12	14 42				15 12
Birmingham New Street 12	a			12 46		12 51	13 26	13 39		13 46	13 51			14 26	14 39		14 46		14 57	15 26	15 39		15 46	15 51
Birmingham New Street 12	d			13 03	13 03	13 18	13 30	13 48		14 18	14 03	14 03	14 18	14 30	14 48		15 03	15 03	15 18	15 30	15 51		16 18	16 03
Tamworth	d									→				14 47									→	
Burton-on-Trent	d													14 58										
Derby 10	a			13 39			14 11				14 39			15 11			15 39			16 11				16 39
Chesterfield	a						14 32							15 32						16 32				
Sheffield 7	a			14 12			14 51				15 18			15 50			16 16			16 49				17 12
Doncaster 7	a						15 16							16 16						17 14				
Wakefield Westgate 7	a			14 44							15 44						16 44							17 44
Leeds 10	a			15 01							16 01						17 01							18 01
York 8	a			15 33			15 43				16 33			16 44			17 33			17 40				18 33
Darlington 7	a			16 02			16 13				17 01			17 12			18 01			18 08				19 01
Durham	a			16 19			16 31				17 19			17 29			18 18			18 25				19 18
Chester-le-Street	a																							
Newcastle 8	a			16 35			16 52				17 41			17 52			18 35			18 47				19 35
Alnmouth	a										18 09													20 07
Berwick-upon-Tweed	a			17 21													19 20							20 27
Dunbar	a			17 44													19 43							
Wolverhampton 7	d				13 21	13 38		14 10				14 21	14 38		15 10			15 21	15 38		16 13			
Stafford	a					13 51		14 26					14 51		15 27				15 51		16 28			
Stoke-on-Trent	a																							
Congleton	a																							
Macclesfield	a																							
Crewe 10	a				13 53	14 13						14 52	15 13					15 53	16 13					
Wilmslow	a					14 31		15 04					15 31		16 05				16 31		17 03			
Stockport	a					14 41		15 13					15 41		16 14				16 41		17 13			
Manchester Piccadilly 10	a					14 57		15 27					15 57		16 27				16 57		17 27			
Warrington Bank Quay	a				14 11							15 11						16 11						
Wigan North Western	a				14 22							15 22						16 22						
Preston 8	a				14 39							15 39						16 37						
Lancaster 6	a																							
Oxenholme Lake District	a																							
Penrith North Lakes	a																							
Carlisle 8	a																	19 32						
Lockerbie	a																	20 00						
Haymarket	a																							
Edinburgh 10	a			18 14							19e11						20 13							21 13
Haymarket	a										19 28						20 17							21 17
Motherwell	a																20s53	20s43						21s59
Glasgow Central 15	a																21 19	21 08						22 23
Inverkeithing	a										19 42													
Kirkcaldy	a										20 05													
Markinch	a										20 14													
Cupar	a										20 33													
Leuchars 3	a										20 45													
Dundee	a										21 05													
Arbroath	a																							
Montrose	a																							
Stonehaven	a																							
Aberdeen	a																							

For general notes see front of timetable
For details of catering facilities see Directory of Train Operators

A To Didcot Parkway (Table 116)
b Change at Basingstoke
c Arrival time. By bus from Didcot Parkway (Table 116)
e Dep. 1925

Table 51

SUMMARY OF SERVICES

Sundays
from 30 March

South Coast and The South West → North West England, The North East and Scotland

Route Diagram - See first page of Table 51

		XC	XC	VT		XC	XC	VT	XC	XC	VT	XC	XC	XC	VT	XC	XC	VT	XC	XC	VT	XC	XC	VT
		R 1	1 ◇	1 ◇		1 ◇	R 1	R 1	R 1	R 1	1 ◇	1 ◇	R 1	R 1	R 1	R 1	1 ◇	1 ◇	1 ◇	R 1	R 1	R 1	1 ◇	1 ◇
						A						A							A					
Brighton 10	d																							
Haywards Heath 3	d																							
Gatwick Airport 10 ✈	d																							
Bournemouth	d					12 40						13 40							14 40					
Brockenhurst 3	d					12 57						13 57							14 57					
Southampton Central	d					13 15						14 15							15 15					
Southampton Airport Parkway ✈	d					13 22						14 22							15 22					
Winchester	d					13 31						14 31							15 31					
Basingstoke	d					13 47						14 47							15 47					
Redhill	d																							
Guildford	d																							
East Croydon	d																							
Kensington Olympia	d																							
Reading 7	d					14a05						15a05							16a05					
Oxford	d					15b15	15 36					16b15	16 36						17b15	17 36				
Banbury	d						15 53						16 53							17 53				
Leamington Spa 8	d						16 11						17 11							18 11				
Coventry	d			16 15			16 25				17 15		17 25					18 15		18 25				19 15
Birmingham International ✈	d			16 26			16 36				17 26		17 36					18 26		18 36				19 26
Penzance	d								11 30															
St Erth 2	d								11 38															
Camborne	d								11 48															
Redruth	d								11 54															
Truro	d								12 06															
St Austell	d								12 22															
Par 3	d								12 29															
Bodmin Parkway	d								12 40															
Liskeard 3	d								12 52															
Plymouth	d								13 25					14 25								15 25		
Totnes	d								13 50					14 50								15 50		
Paignton	d									13 59														
Torquay	d									14 05														
Newton Abbot	d								14 03	14 16				15 03								16 03		
Teignmouth	d									14 24														
Dawlish	d									14 29														
Exeter St Davids 6	d								14 23	14 43				15 23								16 23		
Tiverton Parkway	d								14 37					15 37								16 37		
Taunton	d								14 51	15 06				15 51								16 51		
Weston-super-Mare	d									15 29														
Cardiff Central 7	d																							
Newport (South Wales)	d																							
Bristol Temple Meads 10	d		15 00						15 30	16 00				16 30			17 00					17 30	18 00	
Bristol Parkway 7	d		15 10						15 40	16 10				16 40			17 10					17 40	18 10	
Gloucester 7	d																							
Cheltenham Spa	d		15 42						16 12	16 42				17 12			17 42					18 12	18 42	
Birmingham New Street 12	a	←	16 26	16 39			16 46		16 57	17 26	17 39		17 46	17 51		←	18 26	18 39		18 46		18 57	19 26	19 39
Birmingham New Street 12	d	16 18	16 30	16 48			17 03	17 03	17 18	17 30	17 48		18 18 →	18 03	18 03	18 18	18 30	18 48		19 03	19 03	19 18	19 30	19 48
Tamworth	d		16 47														18 47						19 47	
Burton-on-Trent	d		16 58														18 58						19 58	
Derby 10	a		17 11				17 39			18 11				18 39			19 11			19 39			20 11	
Chesterfield	a		17 32							18 32				19 01			19 32			20 01			20 32	
Sheffield 7	a		17 47				18 14			18 48				19 16			19 48			20 16			20 48	
Doncaster 7	a		18 16							19 16							20 16						21 16	
Wakefield Westgate 7	a						18 44							19 44						20 44				
Leeds 10	a						19 01							20 01						21 01				
York 8	a		18 41				19 33			19 43				20 33			20 42			21 32			21 41	
Darlington 7	a		19 15				20 02			20 13				21 03			21 18			22 03			22 11	
Durham	a		19 32				20 19			20 31				21 20			21 35			22 20			22 28	
Chester-le-Street	a																							
Newcastle 8	a		19 54				20 36			20 51				21 37			21 57			22 45			22 50	
Alnmouth	a						21 08							22 08										
Berwick-upon-Tweed	a						21 29							22 29										
Dunbar	a						21 52																	
Wolverhampton 7	d	16 38		17 10				17 21	17 38		18 10				18 21	18 38		19 10			19 21	19 38		20 10
Stafford	a	16 51		17 27					17 51		18 27					18 51		19 27			19 33	19 51		20 28
Stoke-on-Trent	a																							
Congleton	a																							
Macclesfield	a																							
Crewe 10	a	17 13						17 53	18 13						18 52	19 13					19 54	20 13		
Wilmslow	a	17 31		18 04					18 31		19 04					19 31		20 03				20 31		21 03
Stockport	a	17 41		18 14					18 41		19 13					19 41		20 14				20 41		21 13
Manchester Piccadilly 10	a	17 57		18 27					18 57		19 26					19 57		20 26				20 57		21 26
Warrington Bank Quay	a							18 11							19 11						20 12			
Wigan North Western	a							18 22							19 22						20 23			
Preston 8	a							18 43							19 41						20 38			
Lancaster 6	a																							
Oxenholme Lake District	a																							
Penrith North Lakes	a																							
Carlisle 8	a																							
Lockerbie	a																							
Haymarket	a																							
Edinburgh 10	a						22 22							23 18										
Haymarket	a																							
Motherwell	a																							
Glasgow Central 15	a																							
Inverkeithing	a																							
Kirkcaldy	a																							
Markinch	a																							
Cupar	a																							
Leuchars 3	a																							
Dundee	a																							
Arbroath	a																							
Montrose	a																							
Stonehaven	a																							
Aberdeen	a																							

For general notes see front of timetable
For details of catering facilities see Directory of Train Operators

A To Didcot Parkway (Table 116)
b Arrival time. By bus from Didcot Parkway (Table 116)

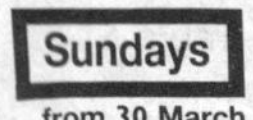

from 30 March

South Coast and The South West → North West England, The North East and Scotland

Route Diagram - See first page of Table 51

		XC	XC	XC	XC	XC	VT	XC	XC	XC	VT	VT	XC	XC	XC	XC	XC	XC	XC	XC	XC	XC
			R	R	R																	
		1◇	1	1	1	1◇	1◇	1◇	1◇	1◇	1◇	1◇	1◇	1◇	1◇	1◇	1◇	1◇	1◇	1◇	1◇	1◇
		A						A					A				A			A		A
		☕	☕	☕	☕		☕	☕		☕	☕	☕	☕		☕		☕					
Brighton [10]	d																					
Haywards Heath [3]	d																					
Gatwick Airport [10] ✈	d																					
Bournemouth	d	15 40						16 40					17 40				18 40			19 40		20 40
Brockenhurst [3]	d	15 57						16 57					17 57				18 57			19 57		20 57
Southampton Central	d	16 15						17 15					18 15				19 15			20 15		21 15
Southampton Airport Parkwy ✈	d	16 22						17 22					18 22				19 22			20 22		21 22
Winchester	d	16 31						17 31					18 31				19 31			20 31		21 31
Basingstoke	d	16 47						17 47					18 47				19 47			20 47		21 47
Redhill	d																					
Guildford	d																					
East Croydon ⛴	d																					
Kensington Olympia	d																					
Reading [7]	d	17a05						18a05					19a05				20a05			21a05		22a05
Oxford	d	18b15	18 36					19b15	19 36				20b15	20 36			21b15	21 36		22b15	22 36	23b15
Banbury	d		18 53						19 53					20 53				21 53			22 53	
Leamington Spa [8]	d		19 11						20 11					21 11				22 11			23 11	
Coventry	d		19 25				20 15		20 25		21 09	21 15		21 25				22 25			23 29	
Birmingham International ✈	d		19 36				20 26		20 36			21 26		21 36				22 36			23 39	
Penzance	d																					
St Erth [2]	d																					
Camborne	d																					
Redruth	d																					
Truro	d																					
St Austell	d																					
Par [3]	d																					
Bodmin Parkway	d																					
Liskeard [3]	d																					
Plymouth	d			16 25						17 25					18 25							
Totnes	d			16 50						17 50					18 50							
Paignton	d																					
Torquay	d																					
Newton Abbot	d			17 03						18 03					19 03							
Teignmouth	d																					
Dawlish	d																					
Exeter St Davids [6]	d			17 23						18 23					19 23							
Tiverton Parkway	d			17 37						18 37					19 37							
Taunton	d			17 51						18 51					19 51							
Weston-super-Mare	d																					
Cardiff Central [7]	d																					
Newport (South Wales)	d																					
Bristol Temple Meads [10]	d			18 30		19 00				19 30					20 30				22 10			
Bristol Parkway [7]	d			18 40		19 10				19 40					20 40				22 20			
Gloucester [7]	d																					
Cheltenham Spa	d			19 12		19 42				20 12					21 12				22 52			
Birmingham New Street [12]	a		19 46	19 51	←	20 34	20 39		20 46	20 57	21 32	21 39		21 46	21 51	←		23 13	23 44		23 55	
Birmingham New Street [12]	d		20 18	20 03	20 18		20 48		21 03	21 18	21 35	21 48		22 18	22 03	22 18		23 13				
Tamworth	d		→	20 19					21 19					→	22 27			23 31				
Burton-on-Trent	d			20 29					21 29						22 38			23 42				
Derby [10]	a			20 42					21 42						22 50			23 59				
Chesterfield	a			21 01					22 01						23 12							
Sheffield [7]	a			21 17					22 18						23 26							
Doncaster [7]	a																					
Wakefield Westgate [7]	a			21 44					22s45						23s52							
Leeds [10]	a			22 01					23 09						00 34							
York [8]	a			22 36																		
Darlington [7]	a																					
Durham	a																					
Chester-le-Street	a																					
Newcastle [8]	a																					
Alnmouth	a																					
Berwick-upon-Tweed	a																					
Dunbar	a																					
Wolverhampton [7] ⛴	d				20 38		21 10			21 38	21 54	22 10				22 38						
Stafford	a				20 51		21 28			21 51	22 09	22 24				22 51						
Stoke-on-Trent	a																					
Congleton	a																					
Macclesfield	a																					
Crewe [10]	a				21 13					22 13	22 35					23 17						
Wilmslow	a				21 31		22 03			22 31		22 59				23 35						
Stockport	a				21 41		22 14			22 41		23 09				23s41						
Manchester Piccadilly [10] ⛴	a				21 57		22 27			22 57		23 21				23 57						
Warrington Bank Quay	a										22 53											
Wigan North Western	a										23 04											
Preston [8]	a										23 36											
Lancaster [6]	a																					
Oxenholme Lake District	a																					
Penrith North Lakes	a																					
Carlisle [8]	a																					
Lockerbie	a																					
Haymarket	a																					
Edinburgh [10]	a																					
Haymarket	a																					
Motherwell	a																					
Glasgow Central [15]	a																					
Inverkeithing	a																					
Kirkcaldy	a																					
Markinch	a																					
Cupar	a																					
Leuchars [3]	a																					
Dundee	a																					
Arbroath	a																					
Montrose	a																					
Stonehaven	a																					
Aberdeen	a																					

For general notes see front of timetable
For details of catering facilities see Directory of Train Operators

A To Didcot Parkway (Table 116)
b Arrival time. By bus from Didcot Parkway (Table 116)

Network Diagram for Table 52

DM-4/07
Design BAJS

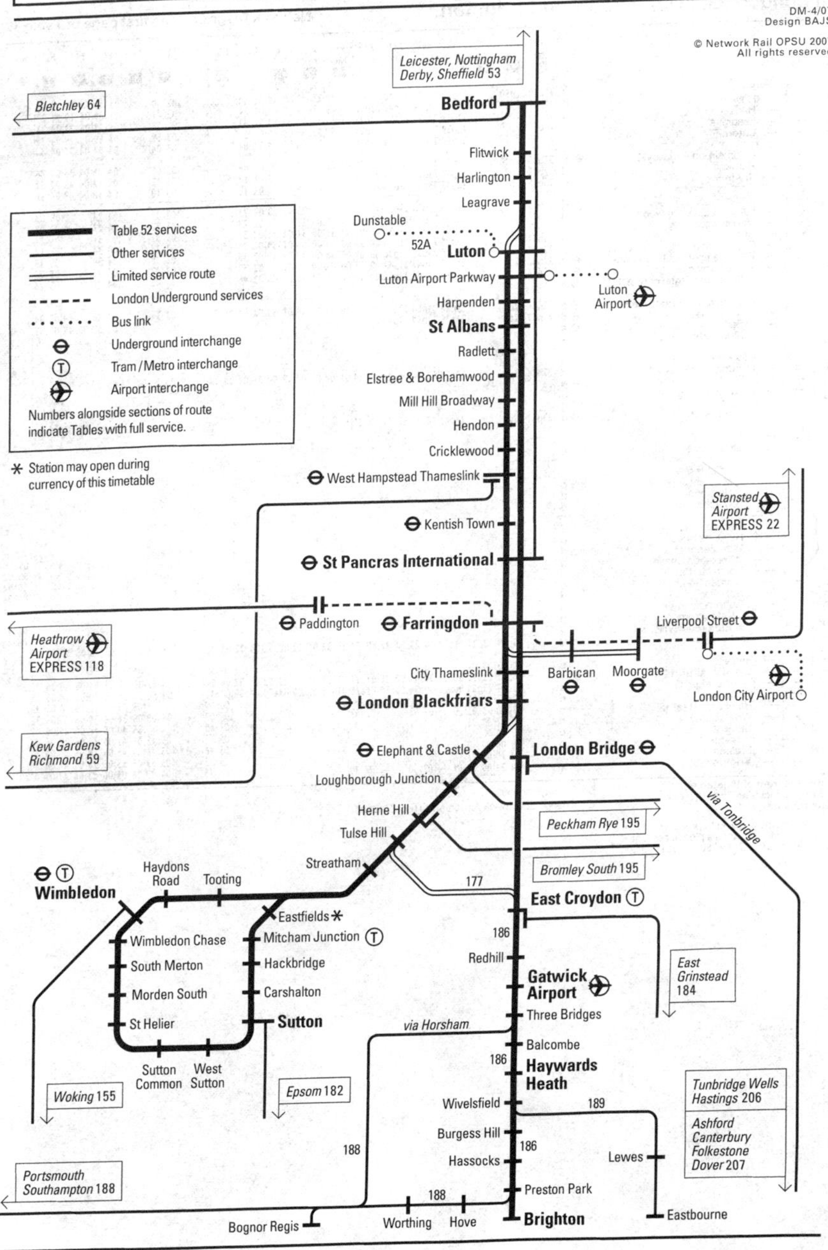
Leicester, Nottingham
Derby, Sheffield 53
Bletchley 64
Bedford
Flitwick
Harlington
Leagrave
Dunstable
52A
Luton
Luton Airport Parkway
Luton
Airport
Harpenden
St Albans
Radlett
Elstree & Borehamwood
Mill Hill Broadway
Hendon
Cricklewood
West Hampstead Thameslink
Kentish Town
St Pancras International
Table 52 services
Other services
Limited service route
London Underground services
Bus link
Underground interchange
Tram / Metro interchange
Airport interchange
Numbers alongside sections of route indicate Tables with full service.
* Station may open during currency of this timetable
Stansted
Airport
EXPRESS 22
Paddington
Farringdon
Liverpool Street
Heathrow
Airport
EXPRESS 118
City Thameslink
Barbican
Moorgate
London City Airport
London Blackfriars
Kew Gardens
Richmond 59
Elephant & Castle
London Bridge
Loughborough Junction
via Tonbridge
Herne Hill
Tulse Hill
Peckham Rye 195
Streatham
Bromley South 195
Haydons
Road
Tooting
177
Wimbledon
East Croydon
Eastfields *
Wimbledon Chase
Mitcham Junction
186
South Merton
Hackbridge
Redhill
Morden South
Carshalton
Gatwick
Airport
East
Grinstead
184
St Helier
Sutton
Three Bridges
via Horsham
Balcombe
Sutton
Common
West
Sutton
186
Haywards
Heath
Woking 155
Epsom 182
Tunbridge Wells
Hastings 206
Wivelsfield
189
Ashford
Canterbury
Folkestone
Dover 207
Burgess Hill
188
186
Lewes
Hassocks
Portsmouth
Southampton 188
Preston Park
188
Bognor Regis
Worthing
Hove
Brighton
Eastbourne

Bedford, Luton, St.Albans and City of London → South London, Gatwick Airport and Brighton

Network Diagram - see first page of Table 52

Miles	Miles	Miles	Miles	Miles			FC	FC	FC	FC	FC	FC	FC	FC	FC	FC	FC	FC		FC	FC	FC	FC	FC	SN
							MO	MX	MO		MO	MX	MX	MO	MX										
							1	1	1					1	1	1		1		1	1	1	1	1	
0	0	—	—	—	**Bedford** 7	d	21p40	21p50		22p10	22p40	22p40	23p10	23p40	23p40	00 40	01 40			02 40		03 40	04 10	04 20	
9½	—	—	—	—	Flitwick	d	21p49	21p59		22p19	22p49	22p49	23p19	23p49	23p49	00 49	01 49			02 49		03 49	04 19	04 29	
12½	—	—	—	—	Harlington	d	21p53	22p03		22p23	22p53	22p53	23p23	23p53	23p53	00 53	01 53			02 53		03 53	04 23	04 33	
17	—	—	—	—	Leagrave	d	21p59	22p09		22p29	22p59	22p59	23p29	23p59	23p59	00 59	01 59			02 59		03 59	04 29	04 39	
19½	19½	—	—	—	**Luton** 10	d	22p04	22p14		22p34	23p04	23p04	23p34	00 04	00 04	01 04	02 04			03 04		04 04	04 34	04 44	
20½	—	—	—	—	Luton Airport Parkway 7 ✈	d	22p06	22p16		22p36	23p06	23p06	23p36	00 06	00 06	01 06	02 06			03 06		04 06	04 36	04 46	
25	—	—	—	—	Harpenden	d	22p12	22p22		22p42	23p12	23p12	23p42	00 12	00 12	01 12	02 12			03 12		04 12	04 42	04 52	
29¾	—	—	—	—	**St Albans**	d	22p18	22p29		22p48	23p18	23p18	23p48	00 18	00 18	01 18	02 18			03 18		04 18	04 48	04 58	
34¼	—	—	—	—	Radlett	d	22p23			22p53	23p23	23p23	23p53	00 23	00 23	01 23	02 23			03 23		04 23		05 03	
37¼	—	—	—	—	Elstree & Borehamwood	d	22p27			22p57	23p27	23p27	23p57	00 27	00 27	01 27	02 27			03 27		04 27		05 07	
40½	—	—	—	—	Mill Hill Broadway	d	22p31			23p01	23p31	23p31	00 01	00 31	00 31	01 31	02 31			03 31		04 31		05 11	
42¾	—	—	—	—	Hendon	d	22p34			23p04	23p34	23p34	00 04	00 34	00 34	01 34	02 34			03 34		04 34		05 14	
44¾	—	—	—	—	Cricklewood	d	22p38			23p08	23p38	23p38	00 08	00 38	00 38	01 38	02 38			03 38		04 38		05 18	
45¾	—	—	—	—	West Hampstead Thameslink ⊖	d	22p42	22p42		23p12	23p42	23p42	00 12	00 42	00 42	01 42	02 42			03 42		04 42	05 02	05 22	
48¼	—	—	—	—	Kentish Town ⊖	d	22p46			23p16	23p46	23p46	00 16	00 46	00 46	01 46	02 46			03 46		04 46		05 26	
—	49¾	—	—	—	**St Pancras International** 15 ⊖	a																			
50	0	—	—	—	**St Pancras International** 15 ⊖	d	22p54	22p54		23p24	23p54	23p54	00 24	00 54	00 54	01 54	02 54	03 25		03 54	04 25	04 54	05 14	05 34	
51	0	—	—	—	Farringdon 3 ⊖	d	22p59	22p59		23p29	23p59	23p59	00 29									04 59	05 19	05 39	
—	½	—	—	—	Barbican ⊖	a																			
—	¾	—	—	—	**Moorgate** ⊖	a																			
51¾	—	—	—	—	City Thameslink 3	d		23p01																	
52¼	0	0	0	—	**London Blackfriars** 3 ⊖	d	23p04	23p04		23p34	00 04	00 04	00 34	01 04	01 04	02 04	03 04	03 34		04 04	04 34	05 04	05 24	05 44	
—	1	1	—	—	Elephant & Castle ⊖	d																			
—	3	3	—	—	Loughborough Jn	d																			
—	4	4	—	—	Herne Hill 4	d			←																
53	—	—	—	—	**London Bridge** 4 ⊖	d	23p11	23p11	23p11	23p41	00 11	00 11	00 41										05 31	05 50	
—	5	5	5	—	Tulse Hill 3	d	→																		
—	6½	6½	—	0	Streatham 4	d																			
—	—	—	—	1	Eastfields §	d																			
—	—	—	—	2	Mitcham Junction 🚋	d																			
—	—	—	—	4	Hackbridge	d																			
—	—	—	—	4¾	Carshalton	d																			
—	8	—	—	—	Tooting	d																			
—	9½	—	—	—	Haydons Road	d																			
—	10½	—	—	—	**Wimbledon** 6 ⊖ 🚋	d																			05 59
—	11½	—	—	—	Wimbledon Chase	d																			06 02
—	12	—	—	—	South Merton	d																			06 04
—	12½	—	—	—	Morden South	d																			06 06
—	13	—	—	—	St Helier	d																			06 08
—	14	—	—	—	Sutton Common	d																			06 10
—	15	—	—	—	West Sutton	d																			06 13
—	16	12½	—	6	**Sutton (Surrey)** 4	a																			06 16
63¼	—	—	10	—	**East Croydon** 🚋	d		23p24	23p27	23p57	00 27	00 27	00 57	01 32	01 32	02 32	03 32	04 02		04 32	05 02	05 32	05 52	06 04	
73¾	—	—	—	—	Redhill	d		00b03	00 03		00 50										05 39	06 06		06 36	
79¾	—	—	—	—	**Gatwick Airport** 10 ✈	d		23p41	23p50	00 17	00 47	00 50	01 17	01 52	01 52	02 52	03 52	04 24		04 52	05 22	05 54	06 08	06 20	
82¼	—	—	—	—	Three Bridges 4	d		23p47	23p54	00a26	00a56	00a56	01a26	01a58	02a00	03a00	04a00	04a32		04 58	05 26	06 00	06 14	06 26	
86¾	—	—	—	—	Balcombe	d		23p53	00 25									06c00			06 00		06 20	06 32	
90¾	—	—	—	—	**Haywards Heath** 3	d		23p58	00 03	00 56	02 02		02 02					05 00		05 08	05 36	06 10	06 25	06 38	
93¾	—	—	—	—	Wivelsfield 4	d		00 02	00 34									05 40			05 40	06 14	06 29	06 42	
94¾	—	—	—	—	Burgess Hill 4	d		00 04	00 08									05 42		05 42	05 42	06 16	06 32	06 44	
96¾	—	—	—	—	Hassocks 4	d		00 08	00 40									05 46		05 46	05 46	06 19	06 35	06 47	
102¼	—	—	—	—	Preston Park	d		00 15	00 47									05 53		05 53	05 53	06 26	06 42	06 [illegible]	
103¾	—	—	—	—	**Brighton** 10	a		00 22	00 24	01 14	02 30		02 30					05 16		05 29	06 01	06 33	06 47	[illegible]	

For general notes see front of timetable
For details of catering facilities see
Directory of Train Operators

§ It is unknown at the time of going to press, when this station will open. For further details please contact National Rail Enquiries 08457-484950 or see local publicity.

b Sundays arr. 0005

c Change at Gatwick Airport and Three Bridges

Bedford, Luton, St.Albans and City of London → South London, Gatwick Airport and Brighton

Network Diagram - see first page of Table 52

		SN	FC	FC 1	SN	FC 1	FC	FC 1	FC	EM 1 ◇ A	FC	FC 1	FC 1	EM 1 ◇ B	SN	FC	FC 1	FC 1	FC 1	FC	FC	SN	FC
Bedford 7	d			04 50		05 20		05 40	05 48	05 50		06 00		06 19			06 16		06 20		06 26		06 36
Flitwick	d			04 59		05 29		05 49	05 56			06 09					06 25		06 29		06 35		06 46
Harlington	d			05 03		05 33		05 53	06 01			06 13							06 33		06 39		
Leagrave	d			05 09		05 39		05 59	06 07			06 19							06 39		06 45		
Luton 10	d			05 14		05 44	05 48	06 04	06 12		06 18	06 24	06 30	06 35			06 36		06 44		06 50		06 56
Luton Airport Parkway 7 ✈	d			05 16		05 46	05 50	06 06		06 08	06 20	06 26	06 32						06 46		06 52		
Harpenden	d			05 22		05 52	05 56	06 12	06 18		06 26	06 32	06 38				06 42		06 52		06 58		07 02
St Albans	d			05 28		05 58	06 02	06 18	06 24		06 32	06 38	06 44				06 48		06 58	06 52	07 04		07 08
Radlett	d			05 33			06 07				06 37		06 49					←		06 57	07 09		
Elstree & Borehamwood	d			05 37			06 11				06 41		06 54			←		06 54		07 01	07 14		
Mill Hill Broadway	d			05 41			06 15				06 45		→			06 45		06 57		07 05	→		
Hendon	d			05 44			06 18				→					06 48				07 08			
Cricklewood	d			05 48			06 22									06 52				07 12			
West Hampstead Thameslink ⊖	d			05 52		06 12	06 25	06 32				06 50				06 55		07 04	07 10	07 15			
Kentish Town ⊖	d			05 56			06 29									06 59				07 19			
St Pancras International 15 ⊖	a									06 41				07 05									
St Pancras International 15 ⊖	d			06 04		06 24	06 33	06 39	06 44			06 57				07 03	07 07	07 12	07 17	07 24			07 28
Farringdon 3 ⊖	d			06 09		06 29	06 38	06 44	06 48			07 02				07 08	07 12	07 16	07 22	07 28			07 32
Barbican ⊖	a								06 49									07 18		07 30			
Moorgate ⊖	a								06 53									07 26		07 36			
City Thameslink 3	d			06 11		06 31	06 41	06 47				07 07				07 11	07 17		07 27				07 35
London Blackfriars 3 ⊖	d		06 11	06 14		06 36	06 46	06 50				07 10				07 16	07 23		07 32				07b43
Elephant & Castle ⊖	d		06 14				06 49									07 19	07 27						07 47
Loughborough Jn	d		06 18				06 53									07 23	07 31						07 51
Herne Hill 4	d		06c25				06 57									07 27	07 35						07 55
London Bridge 4 ⊖	d	06 00		06 21	06 30	06 43		07e00				07 16			07 00				07 40			07 31	
Tulse Hill 3	d	06 17	06 30		06 47		07 02								07 17	07 32	07 39					07 48	07 59
Streatham 4	d	06 21	06 33		06 51		07 05								07 21	07 35	07 42					07 52	08 02
Eastfields §	d																						
Mitcham Junction (tram)	d		06 38				07 10									07 40							08 06
Hackbridge	d		06 42				07 14									07 44							08 10
Carshalton	d		06 44				07 16									07 46							08 12
Tooting	d	06 27			06 57										07 25		07 46					07 56	
Haydons Road	d	06 30			07 00										07 28		07 49					07 59	
Wimbledon 6 ⊖ (tram)	d	06 33			07 03										07 32		07a54					08 02	
Wimbledon Chase	d	06 36			07f11										07 35							08 05	
South Merton	d	06 38			07 13										07 37							08 07	
Morden South	d	06 40			07 15										07 39							08 09	
St Helier	d	06 42			07 17										07 41							08 11	
Sutton Common	d	06 44			07 20										07 43							08 13	
West Sutton	d	06 47			07 22										07 46							08 16	
Sutton (Surrey) 4	a	06 50	06 48		07 26		07 20								07 49	07 50						08 19	08 16
East Croydon (tram)	d			06 36		06 56		07 16				07 32							07 56				
Redhill	d			*07 06*				*07 39*				*08 05*							*08 31*				
Gatwick Airport 10 ✈	d			06 52		07 12		07 32				07 50							08 12				
Three Bridges 4	d			06 56		07 18		07 38				07 54							08 16				
Balcombe	d			*07 15*		*07 35*						08 00							08 22				
Haywards Heath 3	d			07 06		07 28		07 48				08 06							08 28				
Wivelsfield 4	d			07 10		07 32						08 10							08 32				
Burgess Hill 4	d			07 12		07 34		07 54				08 12							08 34				
Hassocks 4	d			07 15		07 37						08 15							08 37				
Preston Park	d			07 22		07 44		*08 22*				08 22							08 44				
Brighton 10	a			07 29		07 51		08 06				08 28							08 51				

For general notes see front of timetable
For details of catering facilities see Directory of Train Operators

§ It is unknown at the time of going to press, when this station will open. For further details please contact National Rail Enquiries 08457-484950 or see local publicity.

A From 24 March. From Leicester (Table 53)
B From Derby (Table 53)
b Arr. 0740
c Arr. 0622
e Arr. 0656
f Arr. 0706

Bedford, Luton, St.Albans and City of London → South London, Gatwick Airport and Brighton

Network Diagram - see first page of Table 52

		FC	FC	FC	FC	EM	FC	FC	SN	FC	FC	EM	FC		EM	FC	SN	FC	FC	FC	FC	EM	FC	FC	FC
						1 ◇ A ⊠ ⌶	1		B		1	1 ◇ C ⊠ ⌶	1		1 ◇ A ⊏				1	1	1	1 ◇ A ⊠ ⌶		1	
Bedford [7]	d			06 40		06 51	06 56				07 00		07 08						07 16	07 22	07 28				07 32
Flitwick	d			06 49			07 05				07 09								07 25	07 31	07 37				07 41
Harlington	d			06 53							07 13								07 29	07 35					07 45
Leagrave	d			07 00							07 19		07 25						07 35	07 41					07 51
Luton [10]	d		06 56	07 04	07 08	07 08	07 16	07 20			07 24	07 29	07 30						07 40	07 46	07 48	07 52			07 56
Luton Airport Parkway [7] ✈	d		06 58	07 06	07 10			07 22			07 26				07 38				07 42	07 48					07 58
Harpenden	d		07 04	07 12	07 16		07 22	07 28			07 32		07 36						07 48	07 54	07 54				08 04
St Albans	d		07 10	07 18	07 22		07 28	07 34			07 38		07 44					07 44	07 56	08 00	08 00		07 54		08 12
Radlett	d	←	07 15		07 27			07 39										07 49		08 05			07 59	←	
Elstree & Borehamwood	d	07 14	07 19		07 31			07 43										07 54		08 10			08 03	08 10	
Mill Hill Broadway	d		07 23		07 35			07 47		←						←				→			08 07		
Hendon	d		07 27		07 39			07 51		07 39						07 51							08 10		
Cricklewood	d		07 30		→			→		07 42						07 54							08 14		
West Hampstead Thameslink	⊖ d	07 23	07 33							07 45						07 57		08 03					08 17	08 20	
Kentish Town	⊖ d		07 37							07 49						08 01							08 21		
St Pancras International [15]	⊖ a					07 36						07 59			08 06							08 24			
St Pancras International [15]	⊖ d	07 32	07 44				07 48			07 56	08 00		08 04			08 08		08 12	08 16		08 20		08 26	08 29	08 33
Farringdon [3]	⊖ d	07 37	07 48	07 44			07 52			08 00	08 04		08 08			08 12		08 16	08 20		08 24		08 30	08 33	08 37
Barbican	⊖ a	07 38	07 51	07 46												08 15			08 23				08 33	08 36	
Moorgate	⊖ a	07 42	07 57	07 53												08 21			08 29				08 38	08 40	
City Thameslink [3]	d						07 55			08 03	08 09		08 13					08 19			08 27				08 40
London Blackfriars [3]	⊖ d						08 00			08 08	08 12		08a19					08 24			08 32				08 45
Elephant & Castle	⊖ d									08 11								08 27			08 35				
Loughborough Jn	d									08 15								08 31			08 39				
Herne Hill [4]	d						08 09			08b23								08c39			08 43				08 54
London Bridge [4]	⊖ d								08 02		08 19						08 24								
Tulse Hill [3]	d						08 13		08 19	08 27							08 38	08e47			08 47				09f02
Streatham [4]	d								08 23	08 30							08 42	08 50							09 05
Eastfields §	d																								
Mitcham Junction ⇌	d									08 34								08 56							
Hackbridge	d									08 38								08 59							
Carshalton	d									08 40								09 02							
Tooting	d								08 27								08 46								09 10
Haydons Road	d								08 30								08 49								09 13
Wimbledon [6]	⊖ ⇌ d								08 32								08 55								09 16
Wimbledon Chase	d								08 35								08 58								09 19
South Merton	d								08 37								09 00								09 21
Morden South	d								08 39								09 02								09 23
St Helier	d								08 41								09 04								09 25
Sutton Common	d								08 44								09 06								09 27
West Sutton	d								08 46								09 09								09 30
Sutton (Surrey) [4]	a								08 50	08 44							09 13	09 05							09 38
East Croydon ⇌	d						08 26				08 36										09 06				
Redhill	d										08 49										09 30				
Gatwick Airport [10] ✈	d						08 42				08 56										09 23				
Three Bridges [4]	d						08 46				09 00										09 28				
Balcombe	d						08 52																		
Haywards Heath [3]	d						08 58				09 10										09g40				
Wivelsfield [4]	d						09 02				09 17														
Burgess Hill [4]	d						09 04				09 24										10 03				
Hassocks [4]	d						09 07				09 27										10 06				
Preston Park	d						09 14				09 34										10 13				
Brighton [10]	a						09 22				09 24										09 54				

For general notes see front of timetable
For details of catering facilities see Directory of Train Operators

§ It is unknown at the time of going to press, when this station will open. For further details please contact National Rail Enquiries 08457-484950 or see local publicity.

A From Nottingham (Table 53)
B To London Bridge (Table 179)
C From Sheffield (Table 53)
b Arr. 0819
c Arr. 0835
e Arr. 0843
f Arr. 0858
g Arr. 0936

Table 52

Bedford, Luton, St.Albans and City of London → South London, Gatwick Airport and Brighton

Network Diagram - see first page of Table 52

		FC	FC	FC		EM 1 ◇ A ⊠ ✠	FC 1	FC 1	EM 1 ◇ B ⊠ ✠	FC	FC	FC 1	FC 1	FC	FC 1	EM 1 ◇ C ☕	FC		FC	FC 1	FC	FC	FC 1	EM 1 ◇ D ☕	FC
Bedford 7	d	07 42					07 48	07 52	07 53	07 58			08 04		08 20	08 25			08 32	08 40			08 55	09 03	
Flitwick	d						07 57	08 01		08 07			08 13		08 29				08 41	08 49			09 04		
Harlington	d						08 01	08 05					08 17		08 33					08 53			09 08		
Leagrave	d	07 57					08 07	08 11					08 23		08 39					08 59			09 14		
Luton 10	d	08 02		08 02		08 10	08 12	08 16		08 20			08 28		08 44				08 54	09 04		09 14	09 19		
Luton Airport Parkway 7	✈ d			08 04			08 14	08 18					08 30		08 46					09 06		09 16	09 21	09 21	
Harpenden	d	08 09		08 10			08 20	08 24		08 26			08 36		08 52				09 00	09 12		09 22	09 27		
St Albans	d	08 16	08 07	08 16			08 27	08 32		08 32	08 22		08 44	08 40	09 00		08 56		09 06	09 18	09 12	09 28	09 33		
Radlett	d		08 12	08 21				08 37			08 27	←		08 45			09 01				09 17	09 33			
Elstree & Borehamwood	d		08 16	08 26				08 42			08 31	08 42		08 49			09 05				09 21	09 37			
Mill Hill Broadway	d		08 21					→			08 36			08 54			09 10				09 26	09 42			←
Hendon	d		08 24								08 39			08 57			09 13				09 29	09 45			09 45
Cricklewood	d		08 28								08 43			09 01			09 17				09 33	→			09 49
West Hampstead Thameslink	⊖ d		08 31	08 35							08 47	08 51		09 05			09 21				09 36				09 52
Kentish Town	⊖ d		08 35								08 51			09 09			09 25				09 40				09 56
St Pancras International 15	⊖ a					08 42			08 38							09 06								09 45	
St Pancras International 15	⊖ d	08 36	08 40	08 44			08 47			08 52	08 56	09 00	09 04	09 14	09 20		09 32			09 39	09 48		09 54		10 02
Farringdon 3	⊖ d	08 40	08 44	08 48			08 52			08 56	09 00	09 04	09 08	09 18	09 24		09 36		09 30	09 44	09 52		09 59		10 07
Barbican	⊖ a	08 43		08 51								09 07							09 33						
Moorgate	⊖ a	08 49		08 57								09 13							09 39						
City Thameslink 3	d		08 47				08 55			08 59	09 03		09 13	09 21	09 27		09 39			09 46	09 55		10 01		10 09
London Blackfriars 3	⊖ d		08 52				08 58			09 02	09 08		09 17	09 28	09 34		09 44			09 49	10 00		10 05		10b16
Elephant & Castle	⊖ d		08 55							09 05	09 11			09 31			09 47				10 03				10 19
Loughborough Jn	d		08 59							09 09	09 15			09 35			09 51				10 07				10 23
Herne Hill 4	d		09c06							09 13	09 21			09 41			09e59				10 11				10 27
London Bridge 4	⊖ d						09 06						09 25		09 42					09 56			10 11		
Tulse Hill 3	d		09 10							09 17	09 26			09 47			10 02				10 17				10 32
Streatham 4	d		09 15							09 20	09 30			09 50			10 05				10 20				10 35
Eastfields §	d																								
Mitcham Junction	🚋 d									09 26				09 56							10 26				
Hackbridge	d									09 29				09 59							10 29				
Carshalton	d									09 32				10 02							10 32				
Tooting	d		09 23								09 40						10 10								10 40
Haydons Road	d		09 26								09 43						10 13								10 43
Wimbledon 6	⊖ 🚋 d		09a29								09 46						10 16								10 46
Wimbledon Chase	d										09 49						10 19								10 49
South Merton	d										09 51						10 21								10 51
Morden South	d										09 53						10 23								10 53
St Helier	d										09 55						10 25								10 55
Sutton Common	d										09 57						10 27								10 57
West Sutton	d										10 00						10 30								11 00
Sutton (Surrey) 4	a									09 36	10 05			10 05			10 35				10 35				11 05
East Croydon	🚋 d						09 24						09 39		09 54					10 09			10 24		
Redhill	d												*10 00*							*10 30*					
Gatwick Airport 10	✈ d						09 41						09 56		10 11					10 26			10 41		
Three Bridges 4	d						09 45						10 00		10 15					*10 44*			10 45		
Balcombe	d						09 51								10 21										
Haywards Heath 3	d						09 57						10 10		10 27					10 38			10 55		
Wivelsfield 4	d						10 01						*10 22*		10 31					*10 50*			10 59		
Burgess Hill 4	d						10 03						*10 24*		10 33					*10 52*			11 01		
Hassocks 4	d						10 06						*10 27*		10 36					*10 55*			11 04		
Preston Park	d						10 13						*10 34*		10 43					*11 02*			11 11		
Brighton 10	a						10 21						10 24		10 51					10 56			11 19		

For general notes see front of timetable
For details of catering facilities see Directory of Train Operators

§ It is unknown at the time of going to press, when this station will open. For further details please contact National Rail Enquiries 08457-484950 or see local publicity.

A From Sheffield (Table 53)
B From Derby (Table 53)
C From Nottingham (Table 53)
D From Burton-on-Trent (Table 53)

b Arr. 1013
c Arr. 0903
e Arr. 0955

Table 52

Mondays to Fridays

Bedford, Luton, St.Albans and City of London → South London, Gatwick Airport and Brighton

Network Diagram - see first page of Table 52

Station		FC 1	EM 1 ◇ A ☕	FC 1	FC	FC	FC 1	FC		FC 1	FC 1	EM 1 ◇ B ☕	FC	FC	FC 1	FC	FC 1	FC	EM 1 ◇ A ☕	FC	FC		FC 1	FC	[illegible]
Bedford 7	d	09 10	09 23	09 20			09 25			09 40	09 50	09 53			09 57		10 10	10 20	10 21				[illegible]		10 40
Flitwick	d	09 19		09 29			09 34			09 49	09 59				10 06		10 19	10 29					[illegible] 36		10 49
Harlington	d	09 23					09 38			09 53					10 10		10 23						10 40		10 53
Leagrave	d	09 29					09 44			09 59					10 15		10 29						10 45		10 59
Luton 10	d	09 34	09 38	09 39		09 44	09 49			10 04	10 09			10 14	10 19		10 34	10 39	10 39				10 49		11 04
Luton Airport Parkway 7 ✈	d	09 36				09 46	09 51			10 06		10 09		10 16	10 21		10 36				10 46		10 51		11 06
Harpenden	d	09 42		09 47		09 52	09 57			10 12	10 17			10 22	10 27		10 42	10 47			10 52		10 57		11 12
St Albans	d	09 48		09 53	09 43	09 58	10 03			10 18	10 23		10 13	10 28	10 33		10 48	10 53		10 43	10 58		11 03		11 18
Radlett	d				09 48	10 03							10 18	10 33						10 48	11 03				
Elstree & Borehamwood	d				09 53	10 08							10 23	10 38						10 53	11 08				
Mill Hill Broadway	d				09 57	10 12		←					10 27	10 42		←				10 57	11 12			←	
Hendon	d				10 01	10 16 →		10 16					10 31	10 46 →		10 46				11 01	11 16 →			11 16	
Cricklewood	d				10 04			10 19					10 34			10 49				11 04				11 19	
West Hampstead Thameslink	⊖ d				10 08			10 22					10 38			10 52				11 08				11 22	
Kentish Town	⊖ d				10 12			10 26					10 42			10 56				11 12				11 26	
St Pancras International 15	⊖ a		10 04									10 34							11 04						
St Pancras International 15	⊖ d	10 09		10 14	10 17		10 24	10 32		10 39	10 44		10 47		10 54	11 02	11 09	11 14		11 18			11 24	11 32	11 39
Farringdon 3	⊖ d	10 14		10 18	10 22		10 29	10 37		10 44	10 48		10 52		10 59	11 07	11 14	11 18		11 22			11 29	11 37	11 44
Barbican	⊖ a			10 20							10 50							11 20							
Moorgate	⊖ a			10 25							10 55							11 25							
City Thameslink 3	d	10 16			10 26		10 31	10 39		10 46			10 56		11 01	11 09	11 16			11 26			11 31	11 39	11 46
London Blackfriars 3	⊖ d	10 20			10 30		10 35	10b46		10 50			11 00		11 05	11c16	11 20			11 30			11 35	11e46	11 50
Elephant & Castle	⊖ d				10 33			10 49					11 03			11 19				11 33				11 49	
Loughborough Jn	d				10 37			10 53					11 07			11 23				11 37				11 53	
Herne Hill 4	d				10 41			10 57					11 11			11 27				11 41				11 57	
London Bridge 4	⊖ d	10 26					10 41			10 56					11 11		11 26						11 41		11 56
Tulse Hill 3	d				10 47			11 02					11 17			11 32				11 47				12 02	
Streatham 4	d				10 50			11 05					11 20			11 35				11 50				12 05	
Eastfields §	d																								
Mitcham Junction	d				10 56								11 26							11 56					
Hackbridge	d				10 59								11 29							11 59					
Carshalton	d				11 02								11 32							12 02					
Tooting	d							11 10								11 40								12 10	
Haydons Road	d							11 13								11 43								12 13	
Wimbledon 6	⊖ d							11 16								11 46								12 16	
Wimbledon Chase	d							11 19								11 49								12 19	
South Merton	d							11 21								11 51								12 21	
Morden South	d							11 23								11 53								12 23	
St Helier	d							11 25								11 55								12 [illegible]	
Sutton Common	d							11 27								11 57								[illegible] 27	
West Sutton	d							11 30								12 00								12 30	
Sutton (Surrey) 4	a				11 05			11 35					11 35			12 05				12 05				12 35	
East Croydon	d	10 39					10 54			11 09					11 24		11 39						[illegible] 54		[illegible] 09
Redhill	d	11 00								11 30							12 00								[illegible]
Gatwick Airport 10 ✈	d	10 56					11 11			11 26					11 41		11 56						12 [illegible]		[illegible]
Three Bridges 4	d	11 14					11 15			11 44					11 45		12 14						[illegible]		[illegible] 44
Balcombe	d	11 21					11 21										12 21						[illegible]		
Haywards Heath 3	d	11 08					11 27			11 38					11 55		12 08						[illegible]		12 38
Wivelsfield 4	d						11 31			11 50					11 59								[illegible]		12 50
Burgess Hill 4	d	11 33					11 33			11 52					12 01		12 33						[illegible] 33		12 52
Hassocks 4	d	11 36					11 36			11 55					12 04		12 36						12 36		12 55
Preston Park	d	11 43					11 43			12 02					12 11		12 4[illegible]						12 43		13 02
Brighton 10	a	11 26					11 51			11 56					12 19		[illegible]						12 51		12 56

For general notes see front of timetable
For details of catering facilities see Directory of Train Operators

§ It is unknown at the time of going to press, when this station will open. For further details please contact National Rail Enquiries 08457-484950 or see local publicity.

A From Nottingham (Table 53)
B From Burton-on-Trent (Table 53)
b Arr. 1043
c Arr. 1113
e Arr. 1143

Bedford, Luton, St.Albans and City of London → South London, Gatwick Airport and Brighton

Network Diagram - see first page of Table 52

	EM 1 ◇ A	FC	FC	FC 1	FC	FC 1	EM 1 ◇ B	EM 1 ◇ C	FC	FC	FC 1		FC	FC 1	EM 1 ◇ D	FC	FC	FC 1	EM 1 ◇ E	FC	FC 1	EM 1 ◇ C	FC	FC
Bedford 7 d	10 51			10 55		11 10	11 12	11 21			11 25			11 40	11 51			11 55			12 10	12 21		
Flitwick d				11 04		11 19					11 34			11 49				12 04			12 19			
Harlington d				11 08		11 23					11 38			11 53				12 08			12 23			
Leagrave d				11 14		11 29					11 44			11 59				12 14			12 29			
Luton 10 d			11 14	11 19		11 34		11 36		11 44	11 49			12 04			12 14	12 19	12 20		12 34	12 36		12 44
Luton Airport Parkway 7 ✈ d	11 07		11 16	11 21		11 36				11 46	11 51			12 06	12 07		12 16	12 21			12 36			12 46
Harpenden d			11 22	11 27		11 42				11 52	11 57			12 12			12 22	12 27			12 42			12 52
St Albans d		11 13	11 28	11 33		11 48			11 43	11 58	12 03			12 18		12 13	12 28	12 33			12 48		12 43	12 58
Radlett d		11 18	11 33						11 48	12 03						12 18	12 33						12 48	13 03
Elstree & Borehamwood d		11 23	11 38						11 53	12 08						12 23	12 38						12 53	13 08
Mill Hill Broadway d		11 27	11 42		←				11 57	12 12			←			12 27	12 42			←			12 57	13 12
Hendon d		11 31	11 46		11 46				12 01	12 16			12 16			12 31	12 46			12 46			13 01	13 16
Cricklewood d		11 34	→		11 49				12 04	→			12 19			12 34	→			12 49			13 04	→
West Hampstead Thameslink ⊖ d		11 37			11 52				12 07				12 22			12 37				12 52			13 07	
Kentish Town ⊖ d		11 41			11 56				12 11				12 26			12 41				12 56			13 11	
St Pancras International 15 ⊖ a	11 34						11 51	12 04							12 34				12 51			13 04		
St Pancras International 15 ⊖ d		11 47		11 54	12 02	12 09			12 17		12 24		12 32	12 39		12 47		12 54		13 02	13 09		13 17	
Farringdon 3 ⊖ d		11 52		11 59	12 07	12 14			12 22		12 29		12 37	12 44		12 52		12 59		13 07	13 14		13 22	
Barbican ⊖ a																								
Moorgate ⊖ a																								
City Thameslink 3 d		11 54		12 01	12 09	12 16			12 24		12 31		12 39	12 46		12 54		13 01		13 09	13 16		13 24	
London Blackfriars 3 ⊖ d		12 00		12 05	12b16	12 20			12 30		12 35		12c46	12 50		13 00		13 05		13e16	13 20		13 30	
Elephant & Castle ⊖ d		12 03			12 19				12 33				12 49			13 03				13 19			13 33	
Loughborough Jn d		12 07			12 23				12 37				12 53			13 07				13 23			13 37	
Herne Hill 4 d		12 11			12 27				12 41				12 57			13 11				13 27			13 41	
London Bridge 4 ⊖ d				12 11		12 26					12 41			12 56				13 11			13 26			
Tulse Hill 3 d		12 17			12 32				12 47				13 02			13 17				13 32			13 47	
Streatham 4 d		12 20			12 35				12 50				13 05			13 20				13 35			13 50	
Eastfields § d																								
Mitcham Junction 🚋 d		12 26							12 56							13 26							13 56	
Hackbridge d		12 29							12 59							13 29							13 59	
Carshalton d		12 32							13 02							13 32							14 02	
Tooting d					12 40								13 10							13 40				
Haydons Road d					12 43								13 13							13 43				
Wimbledon 6 ⊖ 🚋 d					12 46								13 16							13 46				
Wimbledon Chase d					12 49								13 19							13 49				
South Merton d					12 51								13 21							13 51				
Morden South d					12 53								13 23							13 53				
St Helier d					12 55								13 25							13 55				
Sutton Common d					12 57								13 27							13 57				
West Sutton d					13 00								13 30							14 00				
Sutton (Surrey) 4 a		12 35			13 05				13 05				13 35			13 35				14 05			14 05	
East Croydon 🚋 d				12 24		12 39					12 54			13 09				13 24			13 39			
Redhill d						*13 00*								*13 30*							*14 00*			
Gatwick Airport 10 ✈ d				12 41		12 56					13 11			13 26				13 41			13 56			
Three Bridges 4 d				12 45		*13 14*					13 15			*13 44*				13 45			*14 14*			
Balcombe d						*13 21*					13 21										*14 21*			
Haywards Heath 3 d				12 55		13 08					13 27			13 38				13 55			14 08			
Wivelsfield 4 d				12 59							13 31			*13 50*				13 59						
Burgess Hill 4 d				13 01		*13 33*					13 33			*13 52*				14 01			*14 33*			
Hassocks 4 d				13 04		*13 36*					13 36			*13 55*				14 04			*14 36*			
Preston Park d				13 11		*13 43*					13 43			*14 02*				14 11			*14 43*			
Brighton 10 a				13 19		13 26					13 51			13 56				14 19			14 27			

For general notes see front of timetable
For details of catering facilities see Directory of Train Operators

§ It is unknown at the time of going to press, when this station will open. For further details please contact National Rail Enquiries 08457-484950 or see local publicity.

A From Barnsley (Table 53)
B From Leeds (Table 53)
C From Nottingham (Table 53)
D From Derby (Table 53)
E From Sheffield (Table 53)
b Arr. 1213
c Arr. 1243
e Arr. 1313

Table 52

Bedford, Luton, St.Albans and City of London → South London, Gatwick Airport and Brighton

Network Diagram - see first page of Table 52

Station		FC 1	FC		FC 1	EM 1 ◇ A ☕	FC	FC	FC 1	FC	FC 1	EM 1 ◇ B ☕	FC	FC	FC 1	FC		FC 1	EM 1 ◇ A ☕	FC	FC	FC 1	FC	FC 1	EM 1 ◇ B ☕
Bedford 7	d	12 25			12 40	12 51			12 55		13 10	13 21			13 25			13 40	13 51			13 55		14 10	14 21
Flitwick	d	12 34			12 49				13 04		13 19				13 34			13 49				14 04		14 19	
Harlington	d	12 38			12 53				13 08		13 23				13 38			13 53				14 08		14 23	
Leagrave	d	12 44			12 59				13 14		13 29				13 44			13 59				14 14		14 29	
Luton 10	d	12 49			13 04			13 14	13 19		13 34	13 36		13 44	13 49			14 04			14 14	14 19		14 34	14 36
Luton Airport Parkway 7 ✈	d	12 51			13 06	13 07		13 16	13 21		13 36			13 46	13 51			14 06	14 07		14 16	14 21		14 36	
Harpenden	d	12 57			13 12			13 22	13 27		13 42			13 52	13 57			14 12			14 22	14 27		14 42	
St Albans	d	13 03			13 18		13 13	13 28	13 33		13 48		13 43	13 58	14 03			14 18		14 13	14 28	14 33		14 48	
Radlett	d						13 18	13 33					13 48	14 03						14 18	14 33				
Elstree & Borehamwood	d						13 23	13 38					13 53	14 08						14 23	14 38				
Mill Hill Broadway	d		←				13 27	13 42		←			13 57	14 12		←				14 27	14 42		←		
Hendon	d		13 16				13 31	13 46		13 46			14 01	14 16		14 16				14 31	14 46		14 46		
Cricklewood	d		13 19				13 34	→		13 49			14 04	→		14 19				14 34	→		14 49		
West Hampstead Thameslink	⊖ d		13 22				13 37			13 52			14 07			14 22				14 37			14 52		
Kentish Town	⊖ d		13 26				13 41			13 56			14 11			14 26				14 41			14 56		
St Pancras International 15	⊖ a					13 34						14 04							14 34						15 04
St Pancras International 15	⊖ d	13 24	13 32		13 39		13 47		13 54	14 02	14 09		14 17		14 24	14 32		14 39		14 47		14 54	15 02	15 09	
Farringdon 3	⊖ d	13 29	13 37		13 44		13 52		13 59	14 07	14 14		14 22		14 29	14 37		14 44		14 52		14 59	15 07	15 14	
Barbican	⊖ a																								
Moorgate	⊖ a																								
City Thameslink 3	d	13 31	13 39		13 46		13 54		14 01	14 09	14 16		14 24		14 31	14 39		14 46		14 54		15 01	15 09	15 16	
London Blackfriars 3	⊖ d	13 35	13b46		13 50		14 00		14 05	14c16	14 20		14 30		14 35	14e46		14 50		15 00		15 05	15f16	15 20	
Elephant & Castle	⊖ d		13 49				14 03			14 19			14 33			14 49				15 03			15 19		
Loughborough Jn	d		13 53				14 07			14 23			14 37			14 53				15 07			15 23		
Herne Hill 4	d		13 57				14 11			14 27			14 41			14 57				15 11			15 27		
London Bridge 4	⊖ d	13 41			13 56				14 11		14 26				14 41			14 56				15 11		15 26	
Tulse Hill 3	d		14 02				14 17			14 32			14 47			15 02				15 17			15 32		
Streatham 4	d		14 05				14 20			14 35			14 50			15 05				15 20			15 35		
Eastfields §	d																								
Mitcham Junction	🚋 d						14 26						14 56							15 26					
Hackbridge	d						14 29						14 59							15 29					
Carshalton	d						14 32						15 02							15 32					
Tooting	d		14 10							14 40						15 10							15 40		
Haydons Road	d		14 13							14 43						15 13							15 43		
Wimbledon 6	⊖ 🚋 d		14 16							14 46						15 16							15 46		
Wimbledon Chase	d		14 19							14 49						15 19							15 49		
South Merton	d		14 21							14 51						15 21							15 51		
Morden South	d		14 23							14 53						15 23							15 53		
St Helier	d		14 25							14 55						15 25							15 55		
Sutton Common	d		14 27							14 57						15 27							15 57		
West Sutton	d		14 30							15 00						15 30							16 00		
Sutton (Surrey) 4	a		14 35				14 35			15 05			15 05			15 35				15 35			16 05		
East Croydon	🚋 d	13 54			14 09				14 24		14 39				14 54			15 09				15 24		15 39	
Redhill	d				14 30						15 00							15 30						16 00	
Gatwick Airport 10	✈ d	14 11			14 26				14 41		14 56				15 11			15 26				15 41		15 56	
Three Bridges 4	d	14 15			14 44				14 45		15 14				15 15			15 44				15 45		16 00	
Balcombe	d	14 21									15 21				15 21			16 21							
Haywards Heath 3	d	14 27			14 38				14 55		15 08				15 27			15 38				15 55		16 10	
Wivelsfield 4	d	14 31			14 50				14 59						15 31			15 50				15 59			
Burgess Hill 4	d	14 33			14 52				15 01		15 33				15 33			15 52				16 01		16 33	
Hassocks 4	d	14 36			14 55				15 04		15 36				15 36			15 55				16 04		16 36	
Preston Park	d	14 43			15 02				15 11		15 43				15 43			16 02				16 11		16 43	
Brighton 10	a	14 51			14 56				15 19		15 26				15 51			15 56				16 19		16 26	

For general notes see front of timetable
For details of catering facilities see Directory of Train Operators

§ It is unknown at the time of going to press, when this station will open. For further details please contact National Rail Enquiries 08457-484950 or see local publicity.

A From Derby (Table 53)
B From Nottingham (Table 53)
b Arr. 1343
c Arr. 1413
e Arr. 1443
f Arr. 1513

Bedford, Luton, St.Albans and City of London → South London, Gatwick Airport and Brighton

Network Diagram - see first page of Table 52

	FC	FC	FC 1	FC	FC 1	EM 1 ◇ A ☕	FC	FC	FC 1	EM 1 ◇ B ☕	FC	FC 1	EM 1 ◇ C ☕	FC	FC	FC 1	FC	FC 1	FC 1	EM 1 ◇ A ☕	FC	FC
Bedford 7 d			14 25		14 40	14 51			14 55			15 10	15 21			15 25		15 35	15 40	15 51		
Flitwick d			14 34		14 49				15 04			15 19				15 34			15 49			
Harlington d			14 38		14 53				15 08			15 23				15 38			15 53			
Leagrave d			14 44		14 59				15 14			15 29				15 44			15 59			
Luton 10 d		14 44	14 49		15 04			15 14	15 19	15 20		15 34	15 36		15 44	15 49		15 55	16 04			16 14
Luton Airport Parkway 7 ✈ d		14 46	14 51		15 06	15 07		15 16	15 21			15 36			15 46	15 51		15 57	16 06	16 07		16 16
Harpenden d		14 52	14 57		15 12			15 22	15 27			15 42			15 52	15 57		16 03	16 12			16 22
St Albans d	14 43	14 58	15 03		15 18		15 13	15 28	15 33			15 48		15 43	15 58	16 03		16 10	16 18		16 13	16 28
Radlett d	14 48	15 03					15 18	15 33						15 48	16 03						16 18	16 33
Elstree & Borehamwood d	14 53	15 08					15 23	15 38						15 53	16 08		←				16 23	16 38
Mill Hill Broadway d	14 57	15 12		←			15 27	15 42			←			15 57	16 12		16 12				16 27	16 42
Hendon d	15 01	15 16		15 16			15 31	15 46			15 46			16 01	→		16 16				16 31	→
Cricklewood d	15 04	→		15 19			15 34	→			15 49			16 04			16 19				16 34	
West Hampstead Thameslink ⊖ d	15 07			15 22			15 37				15 52			16 07		16 16	16 22				16 37	
Kentish Town ⊖ d	15 11			15 26			15 41				15 56			16 11			16 26				16 41	
St Pancras International 15 ⊖ a						15 34				15 50			16 04							16 34		
St Pancras International 15 ⊖ d	15 17		15 24	15 32	15 39		15 47		15 54		16 02	16 09		16 15		16 27	16 32	16 36	16 39		16 47	
Farringdon 3 ⊖ d	15 22		15 29	15 37	15 44		15 52		15 59		16 07	16 14		16 20		16 32	16 37	16 40	16 44		16 52	
Barbican ⊖ a																			16 46			
Moorgate ⊖ a																			16 52			
City Thameslink 3 d	15 24		15 31	15 39	15 46		15 54		16 01		16 09	16 16		16 22		16 34	16 39	16 43			16 54	
London Blackfriars 3 ⊖ d	15 30		15 35	15b46	15 50		16 00		16 05		16c16	16 20		16 26		16 37	16 42	16 46			16 58	
Elephant & Castle ⊖ d	15 33			15 49			16 03				16 19			16 29			16 45	16 50			17 01	
Loughborough Jn d	15 37			15 53			16 07				16 23			16 33			16 49	16 54			17 05	
Herne Hill 4 d	15 41			15 57			16 11				16 27			16 37			16 53	16 58			17 09	
London Bridge 4 ⊖ d			15 41		15 56				16 11			16 26				16e46						
Tulse Hill 3 d	15 47			16 02			16 16				16 32			16 42			16 58	17f08			17 16	
Streatham 4 d	15 50			16 05			16 20				16 35			16 45			17 01	17 12			17 20	
Eastfields § d																						
Mitcham Junction 🚋 d	15 56						16 25							16 50							17 25	
Hackbridge d	15 59													16 54							17 28	
Carshalton d	16 02													16 56							17 30	
Tooting d				16 10							16 38						17 06	17 15				
Haydons Road d				16 13							16 41						17 09	17 18				
Wimbledon 6 ⊖ 🚋 d				16 16							16 44						17 12	17a21				
Wimbledon Chase d				16 19							16 47						17 15					
South Merton d				16 21							16 49						17 17					
Morden South d				16 23							16 51						17 19					
St Helier d				16 25							16 53						17 21					
Sutton Common d				16 27							16 55						17 23					
West Sutton d				16 30							16 58						17 26					
Sutton (Surrey) 4 a	16 05			16 35			16 32				17 03			17 00			17 31				17 38	
East Croydon 🚋 d			15 54		16 09				16 24			16 40				17 00						
Redhill d					*16 30*							*17 00*				*17 27*						
Gatwick Airport 10 ✈ d			16 11		16 26				16 41			16 56				17 16						
Three Bridges 4 d			16 15		16 30				16 45			17 00				17 20						
Balcombe d			16 21													17 26						
Haywards Heath 3 d			16 27		16 40				16 55			17 10				17 32						
Wivelsfield 4 d			16 31		*16 50*				16 59			*17 28*				17 36						
Burgess Hill 4 d			16 33		*16 52*				17 01			*17 30*				17 39						
Hassocks 4 d			16 36		*16 55*				17 04			*17 34*				17 43						
Preston Park d			16 43		*17 02*				17 11			*17 41*				17 50						
Brighton 10 a			16 51		16 56				17 19			17 28				17 56						

For general notes see front of timetable
For details of catering facilities see Directory of Train Operators

§ It is unknown at the time of going to press, when this station will open. For further details please contact National Rail Enquiries 08457-484950 or see local publicity.

A From Derby (Table 53)
B From Sheffield (Table 53)
C From Nottingham (Table 53)
b Arr. 1543
c Arr. 1613
e Arr. 1643
f Arr. 1702

Bedford, Luton, St.Albans and City of London → South London, Gatwick Airport and Brighton

Network Diagram - see first page of Table 52

	FC	FC	FC	EM	FC	FC	FC	FC	FC	FC		EM	SE	FC	FC	FC	FC	FC	EM	EM	FC	FC	FC	FC
	1		1	1 ◊ A			1		1			1 ◊ B	3	1				1	1 ◊ C	1 ◊ A		1		1
Bedford 7 d	15 55		16 10	16 21			16 25		16 36	16 50		16 51		17 00				17 10	17 12	17 21		17 20		17 36
Flitwick d	16 04		16 19				16 34		16 45	16 59								17 19				17 29		17 45
Harlington d	16 08		16 23				16 38		16 49	17 03								17 23				17 33		17 49
Leagrave d	16 14		16 29				16 44		16 55	17 09								17 29				17 39		17 55
Luton 10 d	16 19		16 34	16 36		16 44	16 49		17 00	17 14				17 18			17 18	17 34		17 36		17 44	17 48	18 00
Luton Airport Parkway 7 ✈ d	16 21		16 36			16 46	16 51		17 02	17 16		17 07				←	17 20	17 36				17 46	17 50	18 02
Harpenden d	16 27		16 42			16 52	16 57		17 08	17 22						17 22	17 26	17 42				17 52	17 56	18 08
St Albans d	16 33		16 48		16 43	16 58	17 03		17 14	→				17 28	17 18	17 28	17 32	17 48			17 44	17 58	18 02	18 14
Radlett d					16 48	17 03									17 23		17 37				17 49		18 07	
Elstree & Borehamwood d		←			16 53	17 08		←							17 28		17 41				17 53		18 11	
Mill Hill Broadway d		16 42			16 57	17 12		17 12							17 32		17 45				17 57		18 15	
Hendon d		16 46			17 01	→		17 16							17 36		17 48				18 00		18 18	
Cricklewood d		16 49			17 04			17 19							17 39		17 52				18 04		18 22	
West Hampstead Thameslink ⊖ d	16 48	16 52			17 08		17 16	17 22							17 42	17 46	17 55				18 07	18 12	18 25	
Kentish Town ⊖ d		16 56			17 12			17 26							17 46		17 59				18 11		18 29	
St Pancras International 15 ⊖ a				17 04								17 34							17 53	18 04				
St Pancras International 15 ⊖ d	16 55	17 01	17 09		17 17		17 25	17 31	17 35					17 46	17 51	17 55	18 03	18 09			18 15	18 19	18 33	18 39
Farringdon 3 ⊖ d	17 00	17 06	17 14		17 22		17 30	17 36	17 40					17 50	17 56	18 00	18 08	18 14			18 20	18 24	18 38	18 44
Barbican ⊖ a	17 02						17 34									18 04						18 26		
Moorgate ⊖ a	17 08						17 39									18 08						18 32		
City Thameslink 3 d		17 11	17 16		17 24			17 38	17 42				17 47	17 53	17 58		18 10	18 16			18 22		18 40	18 46
London Blackfriars 3 ⊖ d		17 14	17 20		17 30			17 42	17 46				17 52	17 57	18 02		18 14	18 20			18 26		18 44	18 49
Elephant & Castle ⊖ d		17 17			17 33			17 45					17 56		18 05		18 17				18 29		18 47	
Loughborough Jn d		17 21			17 37			17 49					18 00		18 09		18 21				18 33		18 51	
Herne Hill 4 d		17 25			17 41			17 53					18a03	18 06	18 13		18 27				18 37		18 57	
London Bridge 4 ⊖ d			17 32						17 52									18 26						18 56
Tulse Hill 3 d		17 30			17 46			17 58							18 18		18 30				18 42		19 02	
Streatham 4 d		17 33			17 50			18 01							18 22		18 33				18 45		19 05	
Eastfields § d																								
Mitcham Junction 🚋 d					17 57										18 27						18 50			
Hackbridge d					18 00										18 30						18 54			
Carshalton d					18 02										18 32						18 56			
Tooting d		17 38						18 06									18 38						19 08	
Haydons Road d		17 41						18 09									18 41						19 11	
Wimbledon 6 ⊖ 🚋 d		17 44						18b14									18 44						19 16	
Wimbledon Chase d		17 47						18 17									18 47						19 19	
South Merton d		17 49						18 19									18 49						19 21	
Morden South d		17 51						18 21									18 51						19 23	
St Helier d		17 53						18 23									18 53						19 25	
Sutton Common d		17 55						18 25									18 55						19 27	
West Sutton d		17 58						18 28									18 58						19 30	
Sutton (Surrey) 4 a		18 05			18 06			18 33							18 36		19 03				19 02		19 40	
East Croydon 🚋 d			17 50						18 08					18 20				18 40						19 10
Redhill d			18 02						*18 29*					18 32				*19 07*						*19 30*
Gatwick Airport 10 ✈ d			18 12						18 24					18 42				18 56						19 26
Three Bridges 4 d			18 18						*18c35*					18a53				19 02						19 32
Balcombe d			18 24						*18c50*									19 08						
Haywards Heath 3 d			18 30						18 36					*18e58*				19 12						19 40
Wivelsfield 4 d			18 34						18 42					*19e09*				*19 28*						
Burgess Hill 4 d			18 37						18 43					*19e04*				19 17						19 46
Hassocks 4 d			18 41						18 47					*19e08*				19 21						19 50
Preston Park d			18 48						18 56					*19e15*				*19 43*						
Brighton 10 a			18 54						19 02					*19e25*				19 32						20 00

For general notes see front of timetable
For details of catering facilities see Directory of Train Operators

§ It is unknown at the time of going to press, when this station will open. For further details please contact National Rail Enquiries 08457-484950 or see local publicity.

A From Nottingham (Table 53)
B From Derby (Table 53)
C From Sheffield (Table 53)
b Arr. 1811
c Change at East Croydon
e Change at Gatwick Airport

Bedford, Luton, St.Albans and City of London → South London, Gatwick Airport and Brighton

Network Diagram - see first page of Table 52

		FC	FC 1	EM 1 ◇ A	FC	EM 1 ◇ B	FC 1	EM 1 ◇ C	FC	FC	FC 1	FC	FC 1	FC	FC 1	EM 1 ◇ A	FC	EM 1 ◇ B	EM 1 ◇ C	FC	FC 1	FC	FC 1
Bedford 7	d		17 50	17 51			18 10	18 23			18 30		18 40		18 50	18 53			19 23		19 20		19 50
Flitwick	d		17 59				18 19				18 39		18 49		18 59						19 29		19 59
Harlington	d		18 03				18 23						18 53		19 03						19 33		20 03
Leagrave	d		18 09				18 29						18 59		19 09						19 39		20 09
Luton 10	d		18 14		18 20	18 21	18 34	18 39		18 50	18 52	←	19 04		19 14		19 20	19 22	19 39		19 44	19 50	20 14
Luton Airport Parkway 7 ✈	d		18 16	18 07	18 22		18 36			18 52		18 52	19 06		19 16	19 07	19 22				19 46	19 52	20 16
Harpenden	d		18 22		18 28		18 42			→	18 58	18 58	19 12		19 22		19 28				19 52	19 58	20 22
St Albans	d	18 18	18 28		18 34		18 48		18 52		19 03	19 04	19 18	19 22	19 28		19 34			19 52	19 58	20 04	20 28
Radlett	d	18 23			18 39				18 57			19 09		19 27			19 39			19 57		20 09	
Elstree & Borehamwood	d	18 27			18 43				19 01			19 13		19 31			19 43			20 01		20 13	
Mill Hill Broadway	d				18 47							19 17					19 47					20 17	
Hendon	d				18 50							19 20					19 50					20 20	
Cricklewood	d				18 54							19 24					19 54					20 24	
West Hampstead Thameslink ⊖	d	18 35	18 42		18 57				19 09			19 27		19 39	19 42		19 57			20 09	20 12	20 27	20 42
Kentish Town ⊖	d				19 01							19 31					20 01					20 31	
St Pancras International 15 ⊖	a			18 34		18 51		19 04								19 34		19 52	20 04				
St Pancras International 15 ⊖	d	18 45	18 54		19 05		19 09		19 17		19 24	19 35	19 39	19 48	19 54		20 05			20 17	20 24	20 35	20 54
Farringdon 3 ⊖	d	18 50	18 59		19 10		19 14		19 22		19 29	19 40	19 44	19 52	19 59		20 10			20 22	20 29	20 40	20 59
Barbican ⊖	a																						
Moorgate ⊖	a																						
City Thameslink 3	d	18 52	19 01		19 12		19 16		19 24		19 31	19 42	19 47	19 55	20 01		20 12			20 24	20 31	20 42	21 01
London Blackfriars 3 ⊖	d	18 56	19 04		19 16		19 19		19 30		19 34	19 46	19b54	20 00	20 04		20 16			20 30	20 34	20 46	21 04
Elephant & Castle ⊖	d	18 59			19 19				19 33			19 49		20 03			20 19			20 33		20 49	
Loughborough Jn	d	19 03			19 23				19 37			19 53		20 07			20 23			20 37		20 53	
Herne Hill 4	d	19 07			19 27				19 41			19 57		20 11			20 27			20 41		20 57	
London Bridge 4 ⊖	d		19 12				19 27				19 41		20 01		20 11						20 41		21 11
Tulse Hill 3	d	19 12			19 32				19 47			20 02		20 17			20 32			20 47		21 02	
Streatham 4	d	19 15			19 35				19 50			20 05		20 20			20 35			20 50		21 05	
Eastfields §	d																						
Mitcham Junction 🚊	d	19 20							19 56					20 26						20 56			
Hackbridge	d	19 24							19 59					20 29						20 59			
Carshalton	d	19 26							20 02					20 32						21 02			
Tooting	d				19 40							20 10					20 40					21 10	
Haydons Road	d				19 43							20 13					20 43					21 13	
Wimbledon 6 ⊖ 🚊	d				19 46							20 16					20 46					21 16	
Wimbledon Chase	d				19 49							20 19					20 49					21 19	
South Merton	d				19 51							20 21					20 51					21 21	
Morden South	d				19 53							20 23					20 53					21 23	
St Helier	d				19 55							20 25					20 55					21 25	
Sutton Common	d				19 57							20 27					20 57					21 27	
West Sutton	d				20c05							20 30					21 00					21 30	
Sutton (Surrey) 4	a	19 31			20 10				20 05			20 35		20 35			21 05			21 05		21 35	
East Croydon 🚊	d		19 24				19 39				19 54		20 14		20 23						20 54		21 24
Redhill	d						*20 00*				*20 24*		*20 30*		*20 46*						*21 30*		*21 59*
Gatwick Airport 10 ✈	d		19 41				19 55				20 11		20 31		20 40						21 11		21 41
Three Bridges 4	d		19 45				20 01				20 15		*20 40*		20 43						21 15		21 45
Balcombe	d		19 51										*20 49*		20 49								21 51
Haywards Heath 3	d		19 58				20 09				20 26		20 42		20 58						21 26		21 58
Wivelsfield 4	d		20 02				*20 17*				20 30				21 02						21 30		22 02
Burgess Hill 4	d		20 04				20 15				20 32		*21 04*		21 04						21 32		22 04
Hassocks 4	d		20 07				20 19				20 35		*21 07*		21 07						21 35		22 08
Preston Park	d		20 14								20 42		*21 14*		21 15						21 42		22 15
Brighton 10	a		20 22				20 29				20 48		21 00		21 22						21 48		22 22

For general notes see front of timetable
For details of catering facilities see Directory of Train Operators

§ It is unknown at the time of going to press, when this station will open. For further details please contact National Rail Enquiries 08457-484950 or see local publicity.

A From Derby (Table 53)
B From Sheffield (Table 53)
C From Nottingham (Table 53)

b Arr. 1950
c Arr. 2000

Table 52

Mondays to Fridays

Bedford, Luton, St.Albans and City of London → South London, Gatwick Airport and Brighton

Network Diagram - see first page of Table 52

		EM	FC	EM	FC	FC		FC	EM	EM	FC	EM	FC	FC	FC	EM	FC	FC	EM		FC	FC	FC		
		1 ◇		1 ◇	1			1	1 ◇	1 ◇		1 ◇	1		1	1 ◇		1	1 ◇				1		
		A		B					A	C		B				B			B						
		☕		☕					☕	☕		☕				☕			☕						
Bedford 7	d	19 51		20 23	20 20			20 50	20 51	21 11		21 23	21 20		21 50	22 00		22 10	22 45		22 40	23 10	23 40		
Flitwick	d				20 29			20 59					21 29		21 59			22 19			22 49	23 19	23 49		
Harlington	d				20 33			21 03					21 33		22 03			22 23			22 53	23 23	23 53		
Leagrave	d				20 39			21 09					21 39		22 09			22 29			22 59	23 29	23 59		
Luton 10	d		20 20	20 39	20 44	20 50		21 14			21 20	21 39	21 44	21 50	22 14	22 16	22 20	22 34	23 01		23 04	23 34	00 04		
Luton Airport Parkway 7 ✈	d	20 07	20 22		20 46	20 52		21 16	21 07		21 22		21 46	21 52	22 16		22 22	22 36			23 06	23 36	00 06		
Harpenden	d		20 28		20 52	20 58		21 22			21 28		21 52	21 58	22 22		22 28	22 42			23 12	23 42	00 12		
St Albans	d		20 34		20 58	21 04		21 28			21 34		21 59	22 04	22 29		22 34	22 48			23 18	23 48	00 18		
Radlett	d		20 39			21 09					21 39			22 09			22 39	22 53			23 23	23 53	00 23		
Elstree & Borehamwood	d		20 43			21 13					21 43			22 13			22 43	22 57			23 27	23 57	00 27		
Mill Hill Broadway	d		20 47			21 17					21 47			22 17			22 47	23 01			23 31	00 01	00 31		
Hendon	d		20 50			21 20					21 50			22 20			22 50	23 04			23 34	00 04	00 34		
Cricklewood	d		20 54			21 24					21 54			22 24			22 54	23 08			23 38	00 08	00 38		
West Hampstead Thameslink ⊖	d		20 57		21 12	21 27		21 42			21 57		22 12	22 27	22 42		22 57	23 12			23 42	00 12	00 42		
Kentish Town ⊖	d		21 01			21 31					22 01			22 31			23 01	23 16			23 46	00 16	00 46		
St Pancras International 15 ⊖	a	20 34		21 04					21 34	21 53		22 04				22 40			23 32						
St Pancras International 15 ⊖	d		21 05		21 24	21 35		21 54			22 05		22 24	22 36	22 54		23 06	23 24			23 54	00 24	00 54		
Farringdon 3 ⊖	d		21 10		21 29	21 40		21 59			22 10		22 29	22 40	22 59		23 10	23 29			23 59	00 29			
Barbican ⊖	a																								
Moorgate ⊖	a																								
City Thameslink 3	d		21 12		21 31	21 42		22 01			22 12		22 31	22 42	23 01										
London Blackfriars 3 ⊖	d		21 16		21 34	21 46		22 04			22 16		22 34	22 46	23 04		23 16	23 34			00 04	00 34	01 04		
Elephant & Castle ⊖	d		21 19			21 49					22 19			22 49			23 19								
Loughborough Jn	d		21 23			21 53					22 23			22 53			23s23								
Herne Hill 4	d		21 27			21 57					22 27			22 57			23 27								
London Bridge 4 ⊖	d				21 41			22 11					22 41		23 11			23 41			00 11	00 41			
Tulse Hill 3	d		21 32			22 02					22 32			23 02			23 32								
Streatham 4	d		21 35			22 05					22 35			23 04			23 35								
Eastfields §	d																								
Mitcham Junction 🚊	d																								
Hackbridge	d																								
Carshalton	d																								
Tooting	d		21 40			22 10					22 40			23 10			23 40								
Haydons Road	d		21 43			22 13					22 43			23 13			23 43								
Wimbledon 6 ⊖ 🚊	d		21 46			22 16					22 46			23 16			23 46								
Wimbledon Chase	d		21 49			22 19					22 49			23 19			23 49								
South Merton	d		21 51			22 21					22 51			23 21			23 51								
Morden South	d		21 53			22 23					22 53			23 23			23 53								
St Helier	d		21 55			22 25					22 55			23 25			23 55								
Sutton Common	d		21 57			22 27					22 57			23 27			23 57								
West Sutton	d		22 00			22 30					23 00			23 30			23 59								
Sutton (Surrey) 4	a		22 05			22 35					23 05			23 33			00 05								
East Croydon 🚊	d				21 54			22 24					22 54		23 24			23 57			00 27	00 57	01 32		
Redhill	d				*22 30*			*23 00*					*23 30*		*00 03*			*00 24*			*00 50*				
Gatwick Airport 10 ✈	d				22 11			22 41					23 11		23 41			00 17			00 50	01 17	01 52		
Three Bridges 4	d				22 15			22 45					23 15		23 47			00a26			00a56	01a26	02a00		
Balcombe	d							22 51							23 53										
Haywards Heath 3	d				22 26			22 58					23 26		23 58			*00 56*				*02b02*			
Wivelsfield 4	d				22 30			23 02					23 30		00 02										
Burgess Hill 4	d				22 32			23 04					23 32		00 04										
Hassocks 4	d				22 35			23 08					23 35		00 08										
Preston Park	d				22 42			23 15					23 42		00 15										
Brighton 10	a				22 48			23 22					23 48		00 22			*01 14*				*02c30*			

For general notes see front of timetable
For details of catering facilities see Directory of Train Operators

§ It is unknown at the time of going to press, when this station will open. For further details please contact National Rail Enquiries 08457-484950 or see local publicity.

A From Derby (Table 53)
B From Nottingham (Table 53)
C From Sheffield (Table 53)

b Fridays arr. 0204
c Fridays arr. 0232

Bedford, Luton, St.Albans and City of London → South London, Gatwick Airport and Brighton

Network Diagram - see first page of Table 52

		FC 1	FC 1	FC	FC	FC 1	FC 1	FC 1	FC 1	FC 1	FC 1	FC 1	FC	FC 1		FC 1	FC	FC 1	FC 1	FC	FC 1	EM 1 ◇ A ☕	FC	FC	FC 1
Bedford 7	d	21p50	22p10	22p40	23p10	23p40	00 40	01 40	02 40	03 10	03 40	04 20		04 50		05 20		05 40	05 50		06 10	06 16			06 25
Flitwick	d	21p59	22p19	22p49	23p19	23p49	00 49	01 49	02 49	03 19	03 49	04 29		04 59		05 29		05 49	05 59		06 19				06 34
Harlington	d	22p03	22p23	22p53	23p23	23p53	00 53	01 53	02 53	03 23	03 53	04 33		05 03		05 33		05 53	06 03		06 23				06 38
Leagrave	d	22p09	22p29	22p59	23p29	23p59	00 59	01 59	02 59	03 29	03 59	04 39		05 09		05 39		05 59	06 09		06 29				06 44
Luton 10	d	22p14	22p34	23p04	23p34	00 04	01 04	02 04	03 04	03 34	04 04	04 44		05 14		05 44	05 50	06 04	06 14	06 20	06 34	06 37	06 44		06 49
Luton Airport Parkway 7 ✈	d	22p16	22p36	23p06	23p36	00 06	01 06	02 06	03 06	03 36	04 06	04 46		05 16		05 46	05 52	06 06	06 16	06 22	06 36		06 46		06 51
Harpenden	d	22p22	22p42	23p12	23p42	00 12	01 12	02 12	03 12	03 42	04 12	04 52		05 22		05 52	05 58	06 12	06 22	06 28	06 42		06 52		06 57
St Albans	d	22p29	22p48	23p18	23p48	00 18	01 18	02 18	03 18	03 48	04 18	04 58		05 28		05 58	06 04	06 18	06 28	06 34	06 48		06 58		07 03
Radlett	d		22p53	23p23	23p53	00 23	01 23	02 23	03 23	03 53	04 23	05 03		05 33			06 09			06 39			07 03		
Elstree & Borehamwood	d		22p57	23p27	23p57	00 27	01 27	02 27	03 27	03 57	04 27	05 07		05 37			06 13			06 43			07 08		
Mill Hill Broadway	d		23p01	23p31	00 01	00 31	01 31	02 31	03 31	04 01	04 31	05 11		05 41			06 17			06 47			07 12		
Hendon	d		23p04	23p34	00 04	00 34	01 34	02 34	03 34	04 04	04 34	05 14		05 44			06 20			06 50			07 16		
Cricklewood	d		23p08	23p38	00 08	00 38	01 38	02 38	03 38	04 08	04 38	05 18		05 48			06 24			06 54			→		
West Hampstead Thameslink	⊖ d	22p42	23p12	23p42	00 12	00 42	01 42	02 42	03 42	04 12	04 42	05 22		05 52		06 12	06 27		06 42	06 57					
Kentish Town	⊖ d		23p16	23p46	00 16	00 46	01 46	02 46	03 46	04 16	04 46	05 26		05 56			06 31			07 01					
St Pancras International 15	⊖ a																					07 05			
St Pancras International 15	⊖ d	22p54	23p24	23p54	00 24	00 54	01 54	02 54	03 54	04 23	04 54	05 34		06 04		06 24	06 35	06 39	06 54	07 05	07 09				07 24
Farringdon 3	⊖ d	22p59	23p29	23p59	00 29						04 59	05 39		06 09		06 29	06 40	06 44	06 59	07 10	07 14				07 29
Barbican	⊖ a																								
Moorgate	⊖ a																								
City Thameslink 3	d	23p01																							
London Blackfriars 3	⊖ d	23p04	23p34	00 04	00 34	01 04	02 04	03 04	04 04	04 34	05 04	05 44	06 16	06b20		06 35	06 46	06 50	07 05	07 16	07 20			07 30	07 35
Elephant & Castle	⊖ d												06 19				06 49			07 19				07 33	
Loughborough Jn	d																06 53			07 23				07 37	
Herne Hill 4	d												06 27				06 57			07 27				07 41	
London Bridge 4	⊖ d	23p11	23p41	00 11	00 41							05 50		06 26		06 41		06 56	07 11		07 26				07 41
Tulse Hill 3	d												06 32				07 02			07 32				07 47	
Streatham 4	d												06 35				07 05			07 35				07 50	
Eastfields §	d																								
Mitcham Junction 🚋	d																							07 56	
Hackbridge	d																							07 59	
Carshalton	d																							08 02	
Tooting	d												06 40				07 10			07 40					
Haydons Road	d												06 43				07 13			07 43					
Wimbledon 6	⊖ 🚋 d												06 46				07 16			07 46					
Wimbledon Chase	d												06 49				07 19			07 49					
South Merton	d												06 51				07 21			07 51					
Morden South	d												06 53				07 23			07 53					
St Helier	d												06 55				07 25			07 55					
Sutton Common	d												06 57				07 27			07 57					
West Sutton	d												07 00				07 30			08 00					
Sutton (Surrey) 4	a												07 05				07 35			08 05				08 05	
East Croydon	🚋 d	23p24	23p57	00 27	00 57	01 32	02 32	03 32	04 32	05 02	05 32	06 05		06 39		06 54		07 09	07 24		07 39				07 54
Redhill	d	*00 03*	*00 24*	*00 50*						*05 39*	*06 06*	*06 45*		*07 15*					*07 48*		*08 00*				
Gatwick Airport 10	✈ d	23p41	00 17	00 50	01 17	01 52	02 52	03 52	04 52	05 22	05 54	06 20		06 56		07 11		07 26	07 41		07 56				08 11
Three Bridges 4	d	23p47	00a26	00a56	01a26	02a00	03a00	04a00	05a00	05 28	06 00	06 26		07 00		07 15		*07 39*	07 45		*08 14*				08 15
Balcombe	d	23p53						*05c35*		05 35	06 06	06 32				07 21					*08 21*				08 21
Haywards Heath 3	d	23p58	*00 56*		*02 04*			*05 00*	*05 40*	05 42	06 12	06 38		07 08		07 27		07 38	07 55		08 08				08 27
Wivelsfield 4	d	00 02							*05 46*	05 46	06 16	*06 45*				07 31		*07 50*	07 59						08 31
Burgess Hill 4	d	00 04							*05 48*	05 48	06 18	*06 47*		*07 33*		07 33		*07 52*	08 01		*08 33*				08 33
Hassocks 4	d	00 08							*05 52*	05 52	06 22	*06 51*		*07 36*		07 36		*07 55*	08 04		*08 36*				08 36
Preston Park	d	00 15							*05 59*	05 59	06 29	*06 58*		*07 43*		07 43		*08 02*	08 11		*08 43*				08 43
Brighton 10	a	00 22	*01 14*		*02 32*			*05 16*	*06 07*	06 07	06 34	06 53		07 24		07 49		07 56	08 19		08 26				08 51

For general notes see front of timetable
For details of catering facilities see Directory of Train Operators

§ It is unknown at the time of going to press, when this station will open. For further details please contact National Rail Enquiries 08457-484950 or see local publicity.

A From Derby (Table 53)
b Arr. 0613
c Change at Gatwick Airport and Three Bridges

Bedford, Luton, St.Albans and City of London → South London, Gatwick Airport and Brighton

Network Diagram - see first page of Table 52

		FC	FC	FC 1	EM 1 ◇ A 🍴	FC		FC	FC 1	FC	FC	EM 1 ◇ B 🍴	FC 1	FC	EM 1 ◇ A 🍴	FC	FC 1	FC	FC	FC 1		FC	FC	FC 1	FC
Bedford 7	d			06 40	06 50				06 55				07 10		07 26		07 25			07 40				07 55	
Flitwick	d			06 49					07 04				07 19				07 34			07 49				08 04	
Harlington	d			06 53					07 08				07 23				07 38			07 53				08 08	
Leagrave	d			06 59					07 14				07 29				07 44			07 59				08 14	
Luton 10	d		06 59	07 04	07 08			07 14	07 19		07 26	07 31	07 34			07 44	07 49		07 59	08 04			08 14	08 19	
Luton Airport Parkway 7 ✈	d		07 01	07 06				07 16	07 21		07 28		07 36		07 42	07 46	07 51		08 01	08 06			08 16	08 21	
Harpenden	d		07 07	07 12				07 22	07 27		07 34		07 42			07 52	07 57		08 07	08 12			08 22	08 27	
St Albans	d		07 13	07 18				07 28	07 33		07b43		07 48			07 58	08 03		08 13	08 18			08 28	08 33	
Radlett	d		07 18					07 33			07 48					08 03			08 18				08 33		
Elstree & Borehamwood	d		07 23					07 38			07 53					08 08			08 23				08 38		
Mill Hill Broadway	d	←	07 27			←		07 42		←	07 57			←		08 12		←	08 27			←	08 42		←
Hendon	d	07 16	07 31			07 31		07 46		07 46	08 01			08 01		08 16		08 16	08 31			08 31	08 46		08 46
Cricklewood	d	07 19	→			07 34		→		07 50	→			08 04		→		08 19	→			08 34	→		08 49
West Hampstead Thameslink	⊖ d	07 22				07 37				07 52				08 07				08 22				08 37			08 52
Kentish Town	⊖ d	07 26				07 41				07 56				08 11				08 26				08 41			08 56
St Pancras International 15	⊖ a				07 38							08 05			08 09										
St Pancras International 15	⊖ d	07 32		07 39		07 47			07 54	08 02			08 10	08 17			08 24	08 32		08 39		08 47		08 54	09 02
Farringdon 3	⊖ d	07 37		07 44		07 52			07 59	08 07			08 14	08 22			08 29	08 37		08 44		08 52		08 59	09 07
Barbican	⊖ a																								
Moorgate	⊖ a																								
City Thameslink 3	d																							09 01	09 09
London Blackfriars 3	⊖ d	07c46		07 50		08e00			08 05	08f16			08 20	08g30			08 35	08h46		08 50		09j00		09 05	09k16
Elephant & Castle	⊖ d	07 49				08 03				08 19				08 33				08 49				09 03			09 19
Loughborough Jn	d	07 53				08 07				08 23				08 37				08 53				09 07			09 23
Herne Hill 4	d	07 57				08 11				08 27				08 41				08 57				09 11			09 27
London Bridge 4	⊖ d			07 56					08 11				08 26				08 41			08 56				09 11	
Tulse Hill 3	d	08 02				08 17				08 32				08 47				09 02				09 17			09 32
Streatham 4	d	08 05				08 20				08 35				08 50				09 05				09 20			09 35
Eastfields §	d																								
Mitcham Junction 🚋	d					08 26								08 56								09 26			
Hackbridge	d					08 29								08 59								09 29			
Carshalton	d					08 32								09 02								09 32			
Tooting	d	08 10								08 40								09 10							09 40
Haydons Road	d	08 13								08 43								09 13							09 43
Wimbledon 6	⊖ 🚋 d	08 16								08 46								09 16							09 46
Wimbledon Chase	d	08 19								08 49								09 19							09 49
South Merton	d	08 21								08 51								09 21							09 51
Morden South	d	08 23								08 53								09 23							09 53
St Helier	d	08 25								08 55								09 25							09 55
Sutton Common	d	08 27								08 57								09 27							09 57
West Sutton	d	08 30								09 00								09 30							10 00
Sutton (Surrey) 4	a	08 35				08 35				09 05				09 05				09 35				09 35			10 05
East Croydon	🚋 d			08 09					08 24				08 39				08 54			09 09				09 24	
Redhill	d			*08 30*									*09 00*							*09 30*					
Gatwick Airport 10	✈ d			08 26					08 41				08 56				09 11			09 26				09 41	
Three Bridges 4	d			*08 44*					08 45				*09 14*				09 15			*09 44*				09 45	
Balcombe	d												*09 21*				09 21								
Haywards Heath 3	d			08 38					08 55				09 08				09 27			09 38				09 55	
Wivelsfield 4	d			*08 50*					08 59								09 31			*09 50*				09 59	
Burgess Hill 4	d			*08 54*					09 01				*09 33*				09 33			*09 52*				10 01	
Hassocks 4	d			*08 57*					09 04				*09 36*				09 36			*09 55*				10 04	
Preston Park	d			*09 04*					09 11				*09 43*				09 43			*10 02*				10 11	
Brighton 10	a			08 56					09 20				09 26				09 51			09 56				10 19	

For general notes see front of timetable
For details of catering facilities see Directory of Train Operators

§ It is unknown at the time of going to press, when this station will open. For further details please contact National Rail Enquiries 08457-484950 or see local publicity.

A From Nottingham (Table 53)

B From Sheffield (Table 53)

b Arr. 0739

c Arr. 0742

e Arr. 0757

f Arr. 0812

g Arr. 0827

h Arr. 0842

j Arr. 0857

k Arr. 0913

Bedford, Luton, St.Albans and City of London → South London, Gatwick Airport and Brighton

Network Diagram - see first page of Table 52

		FC	EM	FC	FC	FC	FC	FC	EM	FC	FC	FC		FC	FC	EM	FC	FC	FC	FC	FC	EM	EM	FC	FC
		1	1 ◇			1		1	1 ◇			1			1	1 ◇			1		1	1 ◇	1 ◇		
			A						B							A						C	D		
			🍴						🍴							🍴						🍴	🍴		
Bedford 7	d	08 10	08 21			08 25		08 40	08 51			08 55			09 10	09 21			09 25		09 40	09 46	09 51		
Flitwick	d	08 19				08 34		08 49				09 04			09 19				09 34		09 49				
Harlington	d	08 23				08 38		08 53				09 08			09 23				09 38		09 53				
Leagrave	d	08 29				08 44		08 59				09 14			09 29				09 44		09 59				
Luton 10	d	08 34	08 36		08 44	08 49		09 04			09 14	09 19			09 34	09 36		09 44	09 49		10 04				10 14
Luton Airport Parkway 7 ✈	d	08 36			08 46	08 51		09 06	09 07		09 16	09 21			09 36			09 46	09 51		10 06		10 07		10 16
Harpenden	d	08 42			08 52	08 57		09 12			09 22	09 27			09 42			09 52	09 57		10 12				10 22
St Albans	d	08 48		08 43	08 58	09 03		09 18		09 13	09 28	09 33			09 48		09 43	09 58	10 03		10 18			10 13	10 28
Radlett	d			08 48	09 03					09 18	09 33						09 48	10 03						10 18	10 33
Elstree & Borehamwood	d			08 53	09 08					09 23	09 38						09 53	10 08						10 23	10 38
Mill Hill Broadway	d			08 57	09 12		←			09 27	09 42			←			09 57	10 12		←				10 27	10 42
Hendon	d			09 01	09 16		09 16			09 31	09 46			09 46			10 01	10 16		10 16				10 31	10 46
Cricklewood	d			09 04	→		09 19			09 34	→			09 49			10 04	→		10 19				10 34	→
West Hampstead Thameslink	⊖ d			09 07			09 22			09 37				09 52			10 07			10 22				10 37	
Kentish Town	⊖ d			09 11			09 26			09 41				09 56			10 11			10 26				10 41	
St Pancras International 15	⊖ a		09 04						09 34							10 04						10 29	10 36		
St Pancras International 15	⊖ d	09 09		09 17		09 24	09 32	09 39		09 47		09 54		10 02	10 09		10 17		10 24	10 32	10 39			10 47	
Farringdon 3	⊖ d	09 14		09 22		09 29	09 37	09 44		09 52		09 59		10 07	10 14		10 22		10 29	10 37	10 44			10 52	
Barbican	⊖ a																								
Moorgate	⊖ a																								
City Thameslink 3	d	09 16		09 24		09 31	09 39	09 46		09 54		10 01		10 09	10 16		10 24		10 31	10 39	10 46			10 54	
London Blackfriars 3	⊖ d	09 20		09 30		09 35	09b46	09 50		10 00		10 05		10c16	10 20		10 30		10 35	10e46	10 50			11 00	
Elephant & Castle	⊖ d			09 33			09 49			10 03				10 19			10 33			10 49				11 03	
Loughborough Jn	d			09 37			09 53			10 07				10 23			10 37			10 53				11 07	
Herne Hill 4	d			09 41			09 57			10 11				10 27			10 41			10 57				11 11	
London Bridge 4	⊖ d	09 26				09 41		09 56				10 11			10 26				10 41		10 56				
Tulse Hill 3	d			09 47			10 02			10 17				10 32			10 47			11 02				11 17	
Streatham 4	d			09 50			10 05			10 20				10 35			10 50			11 05				11 20	
Eastfields §	d																								
Mitcham Junction	🚋 d			09 56						10 26							10 56							11 26	
Hackbridge	d			09 59						10 29							10 59							11 29	
Carshalton	d			10 02						10 32							11 02							11 32	
Tooting	d						10 10							10 40						11 10					
Haydons Road	d						10 13							10 43						11 13					
Wimbledon 6	⊖ 🚋 d						10 16							10 46						11 16					
Wimbledon Chase	d						10 19							10 49						11 19					
South Merton	d						10 21							10 51						11 21					
Morden South	d						10 23							10 53						11 23					
St Helier	d						10 25							10 55						11 25					
Sutton Common	d						10 27							10 57						11 27					
West Sutton	d						10 30							11 00						11 30					
Sutton (Surrey) 4	a			10 05			10 35			10 35				11 05			11 05			11 35				11 35	
East Croydon	🚋 d	09 39				09 54		10 09				10 24			10 39				10 54		11 09				
Redhill	d	*10 00*						*10 30*							*11 00*						*11 30*				
Gatwick Airport 10	✈ d	09 56				10 11		10 26				10 41			10 56				11 11		11 26				
Three Bridges 4	d	*10 14*				10 15		*10 44*				10 45			*11 14*				11 15		*11 44*				
Balcombe	d	*10 21*				10 21									*11 21*				11 21						
Haywards Heath 3	d	10 08				10 27		10 38				10 55			11 08				11 27		11 38				
Wivelsfield 4	d					10 31		*10 50*				10 59							11 31		*11 50*				
Burgess Hill 4	d	*10 33*				10 33		*10 52*				11 01			*11 33*				11 33		*11 52*				
Hassocks 4	d	*10 36*				10 36		*10 55*				11 04			*11 36*				11 36		*11 55*				
Preston Park	d	*10 43*				10 43		*11 02*				11 11			*11 43*				11 43		*12 02*				
Brighton 10	a	10 26				10 51		10 56				11 19			11 26				11 51		11 56				

For general notes see front of timetable
For details of catering facilities see Directory of Train Operators

§ It is unknown at the time of going to press, when this station will open. For further details please contact National Rail Enquiries 08457-484950 or see local publicity.

A From Nottingham (Table 53)
B From Derby (Table 53)
C From Sheffield (Table 53)
D From Burton-on-Trent (Table 53)

b Arr. 0943
c Arr. 1013
e Arr. 1043

Bedford, Luton, St.Albans and City of London → South London, Gatwick Airport and Brighton

Network Diagram - see first page of Table 52

		FC ■1	FC	FC ■1		EM ■1 ◇	FC	FC	FC ■1	FC	FC ■1	EM ■1 ◇	FC	FC	FC ■1	FC	FC ■1	EM ■1 ◇		EM ■1 ◇	FC	FC	FC ■1	FC	FC ■1
						A						B						C		A					
						⊡						⊡						⊡		⊡					
Bedford ■7	d	09 55		10 10		10 21			10 25		10 40	10 51			10 55		11 10	11 17		11 21			11 25		11 40
Flitwick	d	10 04		10 19					10 34		10 49				11 04		11 19						11 34		11 49
Harlington	d	10 08		10 23					10 38		10 53				11 08		11 23						11 38		11 53
Leagrave	d	10 14		10 29					10 44		10 59				11 14		11 29						11 44		11 59
Luton ■10	d	10 19		10 34		10 36		10 44	10 49		11 04			11 14	11 19		11 34			11 36		11 44	11 49		12 04
Luton Airport Parkway ■7 ✈	d	10 21		10 36				10 46	10 51		11 06	11 07		11 16	11 21		11 36					11 46	11 51		12 06
Harpenden	d	10 27		10 42				10 52	10 57		11 12			11 22	11 27		11 42					11 52	11 57		12 12
St Albans	d	10 33		10 48			10 43	10 58	11 03		11 18		11 13	11 28	11 33		11 48				11 43	11 58	12 03		12 18
Radlett	d						10 48	11 03					11 18	11 33							11 48	12 03			
Elstree & Borehamwood	d						10 53	11 08					11 23	11 38							11 53	12 08			
Mill Hill Broadway	d		←				10 57	11 12		←			11 27	11 42		←					11 57	12 12		←	
Hendon	d		10 46				11 01	11 16		11 16			11 31	11 46		11 46					12 01	12 16		12 16	
Cricklewood	d		10 49				11 04	→		11 19			11 34	→		11 49					12 04	→		12 19	
West Hampstead Thameslink	⊖ d		10 52				11 07			11 22			11 37			11 52					12 07			12 22	
Kentish Town	⊖ d		10 56				11 11			11 26			11 41			11 56					12 11			12 26	
St Pancras International ■15	⊖ a					11 04						11 34						11 59		12 04					
St Pancras International ■15	⊖ d	10 54	11 02	11 09			11 17		11 24	11 32	11 39		11 47		11 54	12 02	12 09				12 17		12 24	12 32	12 39
Farringdon ■3	⊖ d	10 59	11 07	11 14			11 22		11 29	11 37	11 44		11 52		11 59	12 07	12 14				12 22		12 29	12 37	12 44
Barbican	⊖ a																								
Moorgate	⊖ a																								
City Thameslink ■3	d	11 01	11 09	11 16			11 24		11 31	11 39	11 46		11 54		12 01	12 09	12 16				12 24		12 31	12 39	12 46
London Blackfriars ■3	⊖ d	11 05	11b16	11 20			11 30		11 35	11c46	11 50		12 00		12 05	12e16	12 20				12 30		12 35	12f46	12 50
Elephant & Castle	⊖ d		11 19				11 33			11 49			12 03			12 19					12 33			12 49	
Loughborough Jn	d		11 23				11 37			11 53			12 07			12 23					12 37			12 53	
Herne Hill ■4	d		11 27				11 41			11 57			12 11			12 27					12 41			12 57	
London Bridge ■4	⊖ d	11 11		11 26					11 41		11 56				12 11		12 26						12 41		12 56
Tulse Hill ■3	d		11 32				11 47			12 02			12 17			12 32					12 47			13 02	
Streatham ■4	d		11 35				11 50			12 05			12 20			12 35					12 50			13 05	
Eastfields §	d																								
Mitcham Junction 🚋	d						11 56						12 26								12 56				
Hackbridge	d						11 59						12 29								12 59				
Carshalton	d						12 02						12 32								13 02				
Tooting	d		11 40							12 10						12 40								13 10	
Haydons Road	d		11 43							12 13						12 43								13 13	
Wimbledon ■6	⊖ 🚋 d		11 46							12 16						12 46								13 16	
Wimbledon Chase	d		11 49							12 19						12 49								13 19	
South Merton	d		11 51							12 21						12 51								13 21	
Morden South	d		11 53							12 23						12 53								13 23	
St Helier	d		11 55							12 25						12 55								13 25	
Sutton Common	d		11 57							12 27						12 57								13 27	
West Sutton	d		12 00							12 30						13 00								13 30	
Sutton (Surrey) ■4	a		12 05				12 05			12 35			12 35			13 05					13 05			13 35	
East Croydon	🚋 d	11 24		11 39					11 54		12 09				12 24		12 39						12 54		13 09
Redhill	d			*12 00*							*12 30*						*13 00*								*13 30*
Gatwick Airport ■10	✈ d	11 41		11 56					12 11		12 26				12 40		12 56						13 11		13 26
Three Bridges ■4	d	11 45		*12 14*					12 15		*12 44*				12 45		*13 14*						13 15		*13 44*
Balcombe	d			*12 21*					12 21								*13 21*						13 21		
Haywards Heath ■3	d	11 55		12 08					12 27		12 38				12 55		13 08						13 27		13 38
Wivelsfield ■4	d	11 59							12 31		*12 50*				12 59								13 31		*13 50*
Burgess Hill ■4	d	12 01		*12 33*					12 33		*12 52*				13 01		*13 33*						13 33		*13 52*
Hassocks ■4	d	12 04		*12 36*					12 36		*12 55*				13 04		*13 36*						13 36		*13 55*
Preston Park	d	12 11		*12 43*					12 43		*13 02*				13 11		*13 43*						13 43		*14 02*
Brighton ■10	a	12 19		12 26					12 51		12 56				13 17		13 26						13 51		13 56

For general notes see front of timetable
For details of catering facilities see Directory of Train Operators

§ It is unknown at the time of going to press, when this station will open. For further details please contact National Rail Enquiries 08457-484950 or see local publicity.

A From Nottingham (Table 53)
B From Barnsley (Table 53)
C From Leeds (Table 53)
b Arr. 1113
c Arr. 1143
e Arr. 1213
f Arr. 1243

Bedford, Luton, St.Albans and City of London → South London, Gatwick Airport and Brighton

Network Diagram - see first page of Table 52

		EM 1 ◇ A	FC	FC	FC 1	EM 1 ◇ B	FC	FC 1	EM 1 ◇ C	FC		FC	FC 1	FC	FC 1	EM 1 ◇ A	FC	FC	FC 1	FC	FC 1	EM 1 ◇ C	FC	FC	FC 1
Bedford 7	d	11 51			11 55			12 10	12 21				12 25		12 40	12 51			12 55		13 10	13 21			13 25
Flitwick	d				12 04			12 19					12 34		12 49				13 04		13 19				13 34
Harlington	d				12 08			12 23					12 38		12 53				13 08		13 23				13 38
Leagrave	d				12 14			12 29					12 44		12 59				13 14		13 29				13 44
Luton 10	d			12 14	12 19	12 21		12 34	12 36			12 44	12 49		13 04			13 14	13 19		13 34	13 36		13 44	13 49
Luton Airport Parkway 7 ✈	d	12 07		12 16	12 21			12 36				12 46	12 51		13 06	13 07		13 16	13 21		13 36			13 46	13 51
Harpenden	d			12 22	12 27			12 42				12 52	12 57		13 12			13 22	13 27		13 42			13 52	13 57
St Albans	d		12 13	12 28	12 33			12 48		12 43		12 58	13 03		13 18		13 13	13 28	13 33		13 48		13 43	13 58	14 03
Radlett	d		12 18	12 33						12 48		13 03					13 18	13 33					13 48	14 03	
Elstree & Borehamwood	d		12 23	12 38						12 53		13 08					13 23	13 38					13 53	14 08	
Mill Hill Broadway	d		12 27	12 42			←			12 57		13 12		←			13 27	13 42		←			13 57	14 12	
Hendon	d		12 31	12 46			12 46			13 01		13 16		13 16			13 31	13 46		13 46			14 01	14 16	
Cricklewood	d		12 34	→			12 49			13 04		→		13 19			13 34	→		13 49			14 04	→	
West Hampstead Thameslink	⊖ d		12 37				12 52			13 07				13 22			13 37			13 52			14 07		
Kentish Town	⊖ d		12 41				12 56			13 11				13 26			13 41			13 56			14 11		
St Pancras International 15	⊖ a	12 34				12 51			13 04							13 34						14 04			
St Pancras International 15	⊖ d		12 47		12 54		13 02	13 09		13 17			13 24	13 32	13 39		13 47		13 54	14 02	14 09		14 17		14 24
Farringdon 3	⊖ d		12 52		12 59		13 07	13 14		13 22			13 29	13 37	13 44		13 52		13 59	14 07	14 14		14 22		14 29
Barbican	⊖ a																								
Moorgate	⊖ a																								
City Thameslink 3	d		12 54		13 01		13 09	13 16		13 24			13 31	13 39	13 46		13 54		14 01	14 09	14 16		14 24		14 31
London Blackfriars 3	⊖ d		13 00		13 05		13b16	13 20		13 30			13 35	13c46	13 50		14 00		14 05	14e16	14 20		14 30		14 35
Elephant & Castle	⊖ d		13 03				13 19			13 33				13 49			14 03			14 19			14 33		
Loughborough Jn	d		13 07				13 23			13 37				13 53			14 07			14 23			14 37		
Herne Hill 4	d		13 11				13 27			13 41				13 57			14 11			14 27			14 41		
London Bridge 4	⊖ d				13 11			13 26					13 41		13 56				14 11		14 26				14 41
Tulse Hill 3	d		13 17				13 32			13 47				14 02			14 17			14 32			14 47		
Streatham 4	d		13 20				13 35			13 50				14 05			14 20			14 35			14 50		
Eastfields §	d																								
Mitcham Junction	🚋 d		13 26							13 56							14 26						14 56		
Hackbridge	d		13 29							13 59							14 29						14 59		
Carshalton	d		13 32							14 02							14 32						15 02		
Tooting	d						13 40							14 10						14 40					
Haydons Road	d						13 43							14 13						14 43					
Wimbledon 6	⊖ 🚋 d						13 46							14 16						14 46					
Wimbledon Chase	d						13 49							14 19						14 49					
South Merton	d						13 51							14 21						14 51					
Morden South	d						13 53							14 23						14 53					
St Helier	d						13 55							14 25						14 55					
Sutton Common	d						13 57							14 27						14 57					
West Sutton	d						14 00							14 30						15 00					
Sutton (Surrey) 4	a		13 35				14 05			14 05				14 35			14 35			15 05			15 05		
East Croydon	🚋 d				13 24			13 39					13 54		14 09				14 24		14 39				14 54
Redhill	d							*14 00*							*14 30*						*15 00*				
Gatwick Airport 10	✈ d				13 41			13 56					14 11		14 26				14 41		14 56				15 11
Three Bridges 4	d				13 45			*14 14*					14 15		*14 44*				14 45		*15 14*				15 15
Balcombe	d							*14 21*					14 21								*15 21*				15 21
Haywards Heath 3	d				13 55			14 08					14 27		14 38				14 55		15 08				15 27
Wivelsfield 4	d				13 59								14 31		*14 50*				14 59						15 31
Burgess Hill 4	d				14 01			*14 33*					14 33		*14 52*				15 01		*15 33*				15 33
Hassocks 4	d				14 04			*14 36*					14 36		*14 55*				15 04		*15 36*				15 36
Preston Park	d				14 11			*14 43*					14 43		*15 02*				15 11		*15 43*				15 43
Brighton 10	a				14 19			14 26					14 51		14 56				15 19		15 26				15 51

For general notes see front of timetable
For details of catering facilities see Directory of Train Operators

§ It is unknown at the time of going to press, when this station will open. For further details please contact National Rail Enquiries 08457-484950 or see local publicity.

A From Derby (Table 53)
B From Sheffield (Table 53)
C From Nottingham (Table 53)
b Arr. 1313
c Arr. 1343
e Arr. 1413

Bedford, Luton, St.Albans and City of London → South London, Gatwick Airport and Brighton

Network Diagram - see first page of Table 52

		FC		FC	EM	FC	FC	FC	FC	FC	EM	FC	FC	FC	FC	FC		EM	FC	FC	FC	EM	FC	FC	EM
				1	1 ◇			1		1	1 ◇			1		1		1 ◇			1	1 ◇		1	1 ◇
					A						B							A				C			B
					☕						☕							☕				☕			☕
Bedford [7]	d			13 40	13 51			13 55		14 10	14 21			14 25		14 40		14 51			14 55			15 10	15 21
Flitwick	d			13 49				14 04		14 19				14 34		14 49					15 04			15 19	
Harlington	d			13 53				14 08		14 23				14 38		14 53					15 08			15 23	
Leagrave	d			13 59				14 14		14 29				14 44		14 59					15 14			15 29	
Luton [10]	d			14 04			14 14	14 19		14 34	14 36		14 44	14 49		15 04				15 14	15 19	15 21		15 34	15 36
Luton Airport Parkway [7]	✈ d			14 06	14 07		14 16	14 21		14 36			14 46	14 51		15 06		15 07		15 16	15 21			15 36	
Harpenden	d			14 12			14 22	14 27		14 42			14 52	14 57		15 12				15 22	15 27			15 42	
St Albans	d			14 18		14 13	14 28	14 33		14 48		14 43	14 58	15 03		15 18			15 13	15 28	15 33			15 48	
Radlett	d					14 18	14 33					14 48	15 03						15 18	15 33					
Elstree & Borehamwood	d					14 23	14 38					14 53	15 08						15 23	15 38					
Mill Hill Broadway	d	←				14 27	14 42		←			14 57	15 12		←				15 27	15 42			←		
Hendon	d	14 16				14 31	14 46 →		14 46			15 01	15 16 →		15 16				15 31	15 46 →			15 46		
Cricklewood	d	14 19				14 34			14 49			15 04			15 19				15 34				15 49		
West Hampstead Thameslink	⊖ d	14 22				14 37			14 52			15 07			15 22				15 37				15 52		
Kentish Town	⊖ d	14 26				14 41			14 56			15 11			15 26				15 41				15 56		
St Pancras International [15]	⊖ a				14 34						15 04							15 34				15 51			16 04
St Pancras International [15]	⊖ d	14 32		14 39		14 47		14 54	15 02	15 09		15 17		15 24	15 32	15 39			15 47		15 54		16 02	16 09	
Farringdon [3]	⊖ d	14 37		14 44		14 52		14 59	15 07	15 14		15 22		15 29	15 37	15 44			15 52		15 59		16 07	16 14	
Barbican	⊖ a																								
Moorgate	⊖ a																								
City Thameslink [3]	d	14 39		14 46		14 54		15 01	15 09	15 16		15 24		15 31	15 39	15 46			15 54		16 01		16 09	16 16	
London Blackfriars [3]	⊖ d	14b46		14 50		15 00		15 05	15c16	15 20		15 30		15 35	15e46	15 50			16 00		16 05		16f16	16 20	
Elephant & Castle	⊖ d	14 49				15 03			15 19			15 33			15 49				16 03				16 19		
Loughborough Jn	d	14 53				15 07			15 23			15 37			15 53				16 07				16 23		
Herne Hill [4]	d	14 57				15 11			15 27			15 41			15 57				16 11				16 27		
London Bridge [4]	⊖ d			14 56				15 11		15 26				15 41		15 56					16 11			16 26	
Tulse Hill [3]	d	15 02				15 17			15 32			15 47			16 02				16 17				16 32		
Streatham [4]	d	15 05				15 20			15 35			15 50			16 05				16 20				16 35		
Eastfields §	d																								
Mitcham Junction	🚊 d					15 26						15 56							16 26						
Hackbridge	d					15 29						15 59							16 29						
Carshalton	d					15 32						16 02							16 32						
Tooting	d	15 10							15 40						16 10								16 40		
Haydons Road	d	15 13							15 43						16 13								16 43		
Wimbledon [6]	⊖ 🚊 d	15 16							15 46						16 16								16 46		
Wimbledon Chase	d	15 19							15 49						16 19								16 49		
South Merton	d	15 21							15 51						16 21								16 51		
Morden South	d	15 23							15 53						16 23								16 53		
St Helier	d	15 25							15 55						16 25								16 55		
Sutton Common	d	15 27							15 57						16 27								16 57		
West Sutton	d	15 30							16 00						16 30								17 00		
Sutton (Surrey) [4]	a	15 35				15 35			16 05			16 05			16 35				16 35				17 05		
East Croydon	🚊 d			15 09				15 24		15 39				15 54		16 09					16 24			16 39	
Redhill	d			*15 30*						*16 00*						*16 30*								*17 00*	
Gatwick Airport [10]	✈ d			15 26				15 41		15 56				16 11		16 26					16 41			16 56	
Three Bridges [4]	d			*15 44*				15 45		*16 14*				16 15		*16 44*					16 45			*17 14*	
Balcombe	d									*16 21*				16 21										*17 21*	
Haywards Heath [3]	d			15 38				15 55		16 08				16 27		16 38					16 55			17 08	
Wivelsfield [4]	d			*15 50*				15 59						16 31		*16 50*					16 59				
Burgess Hill [4]	d			*15 52*				16 01		*16 33*				16 33		*16 52*					17 01			*17 33*	
Hassocks [4]	d			*15 55*				16 04		*16 36*				16 36		*16 55*					17 04			*17 36*	
Preston Park	d			*16 02*				16 11		*16 43*				16 43		*17 02*					17 11			*17 43*	
Brighton [10]	a			15 56				16 19		16 26				16 51		16 56					17 19			17 26	

For general notes see front of timetable
For details of catering facilities see Directory of Train Operators

§ It is unknown at the time of going to press, when this station will open. For further details please contact National Rail Enquiries 08457-484950 or see local publicity.

A From Derby (Table 53)
B From Nottingham (Table 53)
C From Sheffield (Table 53)
b Arr. 1443
c Arr. 1513
e Arr. 1543
f Arr. 1613

Bedford, Luton, St.Albans and City of London → South London, Gatwick Airport and Brighton

Network Diagram - see first page of Table 52

	FC	FC	FC 1	FC	FC 1	EM 1 ◇ A	FC	FC	FC 1	FC	FC 1	EM 1 ◇ B	FC	FC	FC 1	FC	FC 1	EM 1 ◇ A	FC	FC	FC 1	FC
Bedford 7 d			15 25		15 40	15 51			15 55		16 10	16 21			16 25		16 40	16 51			16 55	
Flitwick d			15 34		15 49				16 04		16 19				16 34		16 49				17 04	
Harlington d			15 38		15 53				16 08		16 23				16 38		16 53				17 08	
Leagrave d			15 44		15 59				16 14		16 29				16 44		16 59				17 14	
Luton 10 d		15 44	15 49		16 04			16 14	16 19		16 34	16 36		16 44	16 49		17 04			17 14	17 19	
Luton Airport Parkway 7 ✈ d		15 46	15 51		16 06	16 07		16 16	16 21		16 36			16 46	16 51		17 06	17 07		17 16	17 21	
Harpenden d		15 52	15 57		16 12			16 22	16 27		16 42			16 52	16 57		17 12			17 22	17 27	
St Albans d	15 43	15 58	16 03		16 18		16 13	16 28	16 33		16 48		16 43	16 58	17 03		17 18		17 13	17 28	17 33	
Radlett d	15 48	16 03					16 18	16 33					16 48	17 03					17 18	17 33		
Elstree & Borehamwood d	15 53	16 08					16 23	16 38					16 53	17 08					17 23	17 38		
Mill Hill Broadway d	15 57	16 12		←			16 27	16 42		←			16 57	17 12		←			17 27	17 42		←
Hendon d	16 01	16 16		16 16			16 31	16 46		16 46			17 01	17 16		17 16			17 31	17 46		17 46
Cricklewood d	16 04	→		16 19			16 34	→		16 49			17 04	→		17 19			17 34	→		17 49
West Hampstead Thameslink ⊖ d	16 07			16 22			16 37			16 52			17 07			17 22			17 37			17 52
Kentish Town ⊖ d	16 11			16 26			16 41			16 56			17 11			17 26			17 41			17 56
St Pancras International 15 ⊖ a						16 34						17 04						17 34				
St Pancras International 15 ⊖ d	16 17		16 24	16 32	16 39		16 47		16 54	17 02	17 09		17 17		17 24	17 32	17 39		17 47		17 54	18 02
Farringdon 3 ⊖ d	16 22		16 29	16 37	16 44		16 52		16 59	17 07	17 14		17 22		17 29	17 37	17 44		17 52		17 59	18 07
Barbican ⊖ a																						
Moorgate ⊖ a																						
City Thameslink 3 d	16 24		16 31	16 39	16 46		16 54		17 01	17 09	17 16		17 24		17 31	17 39	17 46		17 54		18 01	18 09
London Blackfriars 3 ⊖ d	16 30		16 35	16b46	16 50		17 00		17 05	17c16	17 20		17 30		17 35	17e46	17 50		18 00		18 05	18f16
Elephant & Castle ⊖ d	16 33			16 49			17 03			17 19			17 33			17 49			18 03			18 19
Loughborough Jn d	16 37			16 53			17 07			17 23			17 37			17 53			18 07			18 23
Herne Hill 4 d	16 41			16 57			17 11			17 27			17 41			17 57			18 11			18 27
London Bridge 4 ⊖ d			16 41		16 56				17 11		17 26				17 41		17 56				18 11	
Tulse Hill 3 d	16 47			17 02			17 17			17 32			17 47			18 02			18 17			18 32
Streatham 4 d	16 50			17 05			17 20			17 35			17 50			18 05			18 20			18 35
Eastfields § d																						
Mitcham Junction 🚋 d	16 56						17 26						17 56						18 26			
Hackbridge d	16 59						17 29						17 59						18 29			
Carshalton d	17 02						17 32						18 02						18 32			
Tooting d				17 10						17 40						18 10						18 40
Haydons Road d				17 13						17 43						18 13						18 43
Wimbledon 6 ⊖ 🚋 d				17 16						17 46						18 16						18 46
Wimbledon Chase d				17 19						17 49						18 19						18 49
South Merton d				17 21						17 51						18 21						18 51
Morden South d				17 23						17 53						18 23						18 53
St Helier d				17 25						17 55						18 25						18 55
Sutton Common d				17 27						17 57						18 27						18 57
West Sutton d				17 30						18 00						18 30						19 00
Sutton (Surrey) 4 a	17 05			17 35			17 35			18 05			18 05			18 35			18 35			19 05
East Croydon 🚋 d			16 54		17 09				17 24		17 39				17 54		18 09				18 24	
Redhill d					*17 30*						*18 00*						*18 30*					
Gatwick Airport 10 ✈ d			17 11		17 26				17 41		17 56				18 11		18 26				18 41	
Three Bridges 4 d			17 15		*17 44*				17 45		*18 14*				18 15		*18 40*				18 45	
Balcombe d			17 21								*18 21*				18 21							
Haywards Heath 3 d			17 27		17 38				17 55		18 08				18 27		18 38				18 55	
Wivelsfield 4 d			17 31		*17 50*				17 59						18 31		*18 50*				18 59	
Burgess Hill 4 d			17 33		*17 52*				18 01		*18 33*				18 33		*18 52*				19 01	
Hassocks 4 d			17 36		*17 55*				18 04		*18 36*				18 36		*18 55*				19 04	
Preston Park d			17 43		*18 02*				18 11		*18 43*				18 43		*19 02*				19 11	
Brighton 10 a			17 51		17 56				18 19		18 26				18 51		18 56				19 19	

For general notes see front of timetable
For details of catering facilities see Directory of Train Operators

§ It is unknown at the time of going to press, when this station will open. For further details please contact National Rail Enquiries 08457-484950 or see local publicity.

A From Derby (Table 53)
B From Nottingham (Table 53)
b Arr. 1643
c Arr. 1713
e Arr. 1743
f Arr. 1813

Bedford, Luton, St.Albans and City of London → South London, Gatwick Airport and Brighton

Network Diagram - see first page of Table 52

		FC 1	EM 1 ◇ A ☕	EM 1 ◇ A ☕	FC	FC	FC 1	FC	FC 1	FC	FC 1	EM 1 ◇ B ☕	FC	EM 1 ◇ A ☕	FC 1	EM 1 ◇ C ☕	FC 1	FC	FC 1	FC 1	EM 1 ◇ B ☕	FC	EM 1 ◇ C ☕	FC 1
Bedford 7	d	17 10	17 13	17 21			17 25		17 40		17 50	17 51			18 10	18 21	18 20		18 40	18 50	18 51		19 25	19 20
Flitwick	d	17 19					17 34		17 49		17 59				18 19		18 29		18 49	18 59				19 29
Harlington	d	17 23					17 38		17 53		18 03				18 23		18 33		18 53	19 03				19 33
Leagrave	d	17 29					17 44		17 59		18 09				18 29		18 39		18 59	19 09				19 39
Luton 10	d	17 34		17 36		17 44	17 49		18 04		18 14		18 20	18 21	18 34	18 36	18 44	18 50	19 04	19 14		19 20	19 41	19 44
Luton Airport Parkway 7 ✈	d	17 36				17 46	17 51		18 06		18 16	18 07	18 22		18 36		18 46	18 52	19 06	19 16	19 07	19 22		19 46
Harpenden	d	17 42				17 52	17 57		18 12		18 22		18 28		18 42		18 52	18 58	19 12	19 22		19 28		19 52
St Albans	d	17 48			17 43	17 58	18 03		18 18	18 13	18 28		18 34		18 48		18 58	19 04	19 18	19 28		19 34		19 58
Radlett	d				17 48	18 03				18 18			18 39					19 09				19 39		
Elstree & Borehamwood	d				17 53	18 08				18 23			18 43					19 13				19 43		
Mill Hill Broadway	d				17 57	18 12		←		18 27			18 47					19 17				19 47		
Hendon	d				18 01	18 16		18 16		18 31			18 50					19 20				19 50		
Cricklewood	d				18 04	→		18 19		18 34			18 54					19 24				19 54		
West Hampstead Thameslink ⊖	d				18 07			18 22		18 37	18 42		18 57				19 12	19 27		19 42		19 57		20 12
Kentish Town ⊖	d				18 11			18 26		18 41			19 01					19 31				20 01		
St Pancras International 15 ⊖	a		17 51	18 04								18 34		18 51		19 04					19 35		20 09	
St Pancras International 15 ⊖	d	18 09			18 17		18 24	18 32	18 39	18 47	18 54		19 05		19 09		19 24	19 35	19 39	19 54		20 05		20 24
Farringdon 3 ⊖	d	18 14			18 22		18 29	18 37	18 44	18 52	18 59		19 10		19 14		19 29	19 40	19 44	19 59		20 10		20 29
Barbican ⊖	a																							
Moorgate ⊖	a																							
City Thameslink 3	d	18 16			18 24		18 31	18 39	18 46	18 54	19 01		19 12		19 16		19 31	19 42	19 46	20 01		20 12		20 31
London Blackfriars 3 ⊖	d	18 20			18 30		18 35	18b46	18 50	19 00	19 04		19 16		19 20		19 34	19 46	19 50	20 04		20 16		20 34
Elephant & Castle ⊖	d				18 33			18 49		19 03			19 19					19 49				20 19		
Loughborough Jn	d				18 37			18 53		19 07			19 23					19 53				20 23		
Herne Hill 4	d				18 41			18 57		19 11			19 27					19 57				20 27		
London Bridge 4 ⊖	d	18 26					18 41		18 56		19 11				19 26		19 41		19 56	20 11				20 41
Tulse Hill 3	d				18 47			19 02		19 17			19 32					20 02				20 32		
Streatham 4	d				18 50			19 05		19 20			19 35					20 05				20 35		
Eastfields §	d																							
Mitcham Junction 🚊	d				18 56					19 26														
Hackbridge	d				18 59					19 29														
Carshalton	d				19 02					19 32														
Tooting	d							19 10					19 40					20 10				20 40		
Haydons Road	d							19 13					19 43					20 13				20 43		
Wimbledon 6 ⊖ 🚊	d							19 16					19 46					20 16				20 46		
Wimbledon Chase	d							19 19					19 49					20 19				20 49		
South Merton	d							19 21					19 51					20 21				20 51		
Morden South	d							19 23					19 53					20 23				20 53		
St Helier	d							19 25					19 55					20 25				20 55		
Sutton Common	d							19 27					19 57					20 27				20 57		
West Sutton	d							19 30					20 00					20 30				21 00		
Sutton (Surrey) 4	a				19 05			19 35		19 35			20 05					20 35				21 05		
East Croydon 🚊	d	18 39					18 54		19 09		19 24				19 39		19 54		20 09	20 24				20 54
Redhill	d	*19 00*							*19 30*						*20 00*				*20 30*	*21 00*				*21 30*
Gatwick Airport 10 ✈	d	18 56					19 11		19 26		19 41				19 56		20 11		20 26	20 41				21 11
Three Bridges 4	d	*19 14*					19 15		*19 40*		19 45				*20 14*		20 15		*20 40*	20 45				21 15
Balcombe	d	*19 21*					19 21								*20 21*		20 21		*20 51*	20 51				
Haywards Heath 3	d	19 08					19 27		19 38		19 55				20 10		20 27		20 38	20 58				21 26
Wivelsfield 4	d						19 31		*19 50*		19 59						20 31		*20 50*	21 02				21 30
Burgess Hill 4	d	*19 33*					19 33		*19 52*		20 01				*20 33*		20 33		*20 52*	21 04				21 32
Hassocks 4	d	*19 36*					19 36		*19 55*		20 04				*20 36*		20 36		*20 55*	21 08				21 35
Preston Park	d	*19 43*					19 43		*20 02*		20 11				*20 43*		20 43		*21 02*	21 15				21 42
Brighton 10	a	19 26					19 51		19 56		20 19				20 28		20 51		20 56	21 22				21 50

For general notes see front of timetable
For details of catering facilities see Directory of Train Operators

§ It is unknown at the time of going to press, when this station will open. For further details please contact National Rail Enquiries 08457-484950 or see local publicity.

A From Sheffield (Table 53)
B From Derby (Table 53)
C From Nottingham (Table 53)

b Arr. 1843

Table 52

Bedford, Luton, St.Albans and City of London → South London, Gatwick Airport and Brighton

Network Diagram - see first page of Table 52

		FC	FC	EM	FC	EM		FC	FC	FC	EM	FC	EM	EM	FC	FC	EM	FC	FC	FC	FC	FC	FC		
			1	1 ◇		1 ◇		1	1	1	1 ◇		1 ◇	1 ◇	1		1 ◇	1				1	1		
				A		B					A		C	B			B								
				🍴		🍴					🍴		🍴	🍴			🍴								
Bedford 7	d		19 50	19 51		20 25		20 20		20 50	20 51		21 13	21 23	21 20		21 52	21 50		22 10	22 40	23 10	23 40		
Flitwick	d		19 59					20 29		20 59					21 29			21 59		22 19	22 49	23 19	23 49		
Harlington	d		20 03					20 33		21 03					21 33			22 03		22 23	22 53	23 23	23 53		
Leagrave	d		20 09					20 39		21 09					21 39			22 09		22 29	22 59	23 29	23 59		
Luton 10	d	19 50	20 14		20 20	20 41		20 44	20 50	21 14		21 20	21 29	21 39	21 44	21 50	22 09	22 14	22 20	22 34	23 04	23 34	00 04		
Luton Airport Parkway 7 ✈	d	19 52	20 16	20 07	20 22			20 46	20 52	21 16	21 09	21 22			21 46	21 52		22 16	22 22	22 36	23 06	23 36	00 06		
Harpenden	d	19 58	20 22		20 28			20 52	20 58	21 22		21 28			21 52	21 58		22 22	22 28	22 42	23 12	23 42	00 12		
St Albans	d	20 04	20 28		20 34			20 58	21 04	21 28		21 34			21 58	22 04		22 28	22 34	22 48	23 18	23 48	00 18		
Radlett	d	20 09			20 39				21 09			21 39				22 09			22 39	22 53	23 23	23 53	00 23		
Elstree & Borehamwood	d	20 13			20 43				21 13			21 43				22 13			22 43	22 57	23 27	23 57	00 27		
Mill Hill Broadway	d	20 17			20 47				21 17			21 47				22 17			22 47	23 01	23 31	00 01	00 31		
Hendon	d	20 20			20 50				21 20			21 50				22 20			22 50	23 04	23 34	00 04	00 34		
Cricklewood	d	20 24			20 54				21 24			21 54				22 24			22 54	23 08	23 38	00 08	00 38		
West Hampstead Thameslink ⊖	d	20 27	20 42		20 57			21 12	21 27	21 42		21 57			22 12	22 27		22 42	22 57	23 12	23 42	00 12	00 42		
Kentish Town ⊖	d	20 31			21 01				21 31			22 01				22 31			23 01	23 16	23 46	00 16	00 46		
St Pancras International 15 ⊖	a			20 35		21 08					21 35		21 52	22 04			22 43								
St Pancras International 15 ⊖	d	20 35	20 54		21 05			21 24	21 35	21 54		22 05			22 24	22 36		22 54	23 06	23 24	23 54	00 24	00 54		
Farringdon 3 ⊖	d	20 40	20 59		21 10			21 29	21 40	21 59		22 10			22 29	22 40		22 59	23 10	23 29	23 59	00 29			
Barbican ⊖	a																								
Moorgate ⊖	a																								
City Thameslink 3	d	20 42	21 01																						
London Blackfriars 3 ⊖	d	20 46	21 04		21 16			21 34	21 46	22 04		22 16			22 34	22 46		23 04	23 16	23 34	00 04	00 34	01a03		
Elephant & Castle ⊖	d	20 49			21 19				21 49			22 19				22 49			23 19						
Loughborough Jn	d	20 53			21 23				21 53			22 23				22 53			23s23						
Herne Hill 4	d	20 57			21 27				21 57			22 27				22 57			23 27						
London Bridge 4 ⊖	d		21 11					21 41		22 11					22 41			23 11		23 41	00 16	00 41			
Tulse Hill 3	d	21 02			21 32				22 02			22 32				23 02			23 32						
Streatham 4	d	21 05			21 35				22 05			22 35				23 05			23 35						
Eastfields §	d																								
Mitcham Junction 🚋	d																								
Hackbridge	d																								
Carshalton	d																								
Tooting	d	21 10			21 40				22 10			22 40				23 10			23 40						
Haydons Road	d	21 13			21 43				22 13			22 43				23 13			23 43						
Wimbledon 6 ⊖ 🚋	d	21 16			21 46				22 16			22 46				23 16			23 46						
Wimbledon Chase	d	21 19			21 49				22 19			22 49				23 19			23 49						
South Merton	d	21 21			21 51				22 21			22 51				23 21			23 51						
Morden South	d	21 23			21 53				22 23			22 53				23 23			23 53						
St Helier	d	21 25			21 55				22 25			22 55				23 25			23 55						
Sutton Common	d	21 27			21 57				22 27			22 57				23 27			23 57						
West Sutton	d	21 30			22 00				22 30			23 00				23 30			23 59						
Sutton (Surrey) 4	a	21 35			22 05				22 35			23 05				23 35			00 05						
East Croydon 🚋	d		21 24					21 54		22 24					22 54			23 24		23 57	00 29	00 57			
Redhill	d		*21 59*					*22 30*		*23 00*					*23 30*			*00 03*		*00 24*					
Gatwick Airport 10 ✈	d		21 41					22 11		22 41					23 11			23 41		00 18	00 47	01 17			
Three Bridges 4	d		21 45					22 15		22 45					23 15			23 45		00a26	00a56	01a26			
Balcombe	d		21 51							22 51								23 53							
Haywards Heath 3	d		21 58					22 26		22 58					23 26			23 58		*00 56*					
Wivelsfield 4	d		22 02					22 30		23 02					23 30			00 02							
Burgess Hill 4	d		22 04					22 32		23 04					23 32			00 04							
Hassocks 4	d		22 08					22 35		23 08					23 35			00 08							
Preston Park	d		22 15					22 42		23 15					23 42			00 15							
Brighton 10	a		22 22					22 50		23 22					23 50			00 22		*01 14*		*02 20*			

For general notes see front of timetable
For details of catering facilities see Directory of Train Operators

§ It is unknown at the time of going to press, when this station will open. For further details please contact National Rail Enquiries 08457-484950 or see local publicity.

A From Derby (Table 53)
B From Nottingham (Table 53)
C From York (Table 53)

Table 52

Sundays

Bedford, Luton, St.Albans and City of London → South London, Gatwick Airport and Brighton

Network Diagram - see first page of Table 52

		FC 1	FC	FC	FC 1	FC 1	FC 1	FC 1	FC 1	FC 1	FC 1	FC	FC	EM 1 ◇ A	FC 1	FC	FC 1	EM 1 ◇ B	FC 1	FC	FC 1	EM 1 ◇ A	FC 1
Bedford 7	d	21p50	22p10	22p40	23p10	23p40	05 40	06 10	06 40	07 10	07 50		08 10	08 16	08 20		08 40	08 46	08 50		09 10	09 15	09 20
Flitwick	d	21p59	22p19	22p49	23p19	23p49	05 49	06 19	06 49	07 19	07 59		08 19		08 29		08 50		08 59		09 19		09 29
Harlington	d	22p03	22p23	22p53	23p23	23p53	05 53	06 23	06 53	07 23	08 03		08 23		08 33		08 54		09 03		09 23		09 33
Leagrave	d	22p09	22p29	22p59	23p29	23p59	05 59	06 29	06 59	07 29	08 09		08 29		08 39		09 00		09 09		09 29		09 39
Luton 10	d	22p14	22p34	23p04	23p34	00 04	06 04	06 34	07 04	07 34	08 14	08 20	08 34	08 37	08 44	08 50	09 04	09 08	09 14	09 20	09 34		09 44
Luton Airport Parkway 7 ✈	d	22p16	22p36	23p06	23p36	00 06	06 06	06 36	07 06	07 36	08 16	08 22	08 36		08 46	08 52	09 06		09 16	09 22	09 36	09 43	09 46
Harpenden	d	22p22	22p42	23p12	23p42	00 12	06 12	06 42	07 12	07 42	08 22	08 28	08 42		08 52	08 58	09 12		09 22	09 28	09 42		09 52
St Albans	d	22p28	22p48	23p18	23p48	00 18	06 18	06 48	07 18	07 48	08 28	08 34	08 48		08 58	09 04	09 18		09 28	09 34	09 48		09 58
Radlett	d		22p53	23p23	23p53	00 23	06 23	06 53	07 23	07 53		08 39				09 09				09 39			
Elstree & Borehamwood	d		22p57	23p27	23p57	00 27	06 27	06 57	07 27	07 57		08 43				09 13				09 43			
Mill Hill Broadway	d		23p01	23p31	00 01	00 31	06 31	07 01	07 31	08 01		08 47				09 17				09 47			
Hendon	d		23p04	23p34	00 04	00 34	06 34	07 04	07 34	08 04		08 50				09 20				09 50			
Cricklewood	d		23p08	23p38	00 08	00 38	06 38	07 08	07 38	08 08		08 54				09 24				09 54			
West Hampstead Thameslink	⊖ d	22p42	23p12	23p42	00 12	00 42	06 42	07 12	07 42	08 12	08 44	08 57			09 14	09 27			09 44	09 57			10 14
Kentish Town	⊖ d		23p16	23p46	00 16	00 46	06 46	07 16	07 46	08 16		09 01				09 31				10 01			
St Pancras International 15	⊖ a													09 16				09 45				10 16	
St Pancras International 15	⊖ d	22p54	23p24	23p54	00 24	00 54	06 54	07 24	07 54	08 24	08 54	09 06	09 10		09 24	09 36	09 40		09 54	10 06	10 10		10 24
Farringdon 3	⊖ d	22p59	23p29	23p59	00 29		06 59	07 29	07 59	08 29	08 59	09 10	09 14		09 29	09 40	09 44		09 59	10 10	10 14		10 29
Barbican	⊖ a																						
Moorgate	⊖ a																						
City Thameslink 3	d																						
London Blackfriars 3	⊖ d	23p04	23p34	00 04	00 34	01a03	07 04	07 34	08 04	08 34	09 04	09 16	09 19		09 34	09 46	09 49		10 04	10 16	10 19		10 34
Elephant & Castle	⊖ d											09 19				09 49				10 19			
Loughborough Jn	d											09 23				09 53				10 23			
Herne Hill 4	d											09 27				09 57				10 27			
London Bridge 4	⊖ d	23p11	23p41	00 16	00 41		07 11	07 41	08 11	08 41	09 11		09 26		09 41		09 56		10 11		10 26		10 41
Tulse Hill 3	d											09 31				10 01				10 31			
Streatham 4	d											09 34				10 04				10 34			
Eastfields §	d																						
Mitcham Junction	🚊 d																						
Hackbridge	d																						
Carshalton	d																						
Tooting	d											09 38				10 08				10 38			
Haydons Road	d											09 41				10 11				10 41			
Wimbledon 6	⊖ 🚊 d											09 44				10 14				10 44			
Wimbledon Chase	d											09 47				10 17				10 47			
South Merton	d											09 49				10 19				10 49			
Morden South	d											09 51				10 21				10 51			
St Helier	d											09 53				10 23				10 53			
Sutton Common	d											09 55				10 25				10 55			
West Sutton	d											09 58				10 28				10 58			
Sutton (Surrey) 4	a											10 03				10 33				11 03			
East Croydon	🚊 d	23p24	23p57	00 29	00 57		07 27	07 57	08 27	08 57	09 27		09a47		09 57		10a17		10 27		10a47		10 57
Redhill	d	00 03					08 03	08 37	09 03	09 37	10 03		10 12				10 37		11 03		11 12		
Gatwick Airport 10	✈ d	23p41	00 18	00 47	01 17		07 50	08 20	08 50	09 20	09 50				10 20		10 46		10 50				11 20
Three Bridges 4	d	23p45	00a26	00a56	01a26		07 54	08 24	08 54	09 24	09 54		10 24		10 24		10 52		10 54		11 24		11 24
Balcombe	d	23p53					08 23		09 23		10 23						11 23		11 23				
Haywards Heath 3	d	23p58	00 56				08 03	08 33	09 03	09 33	10 03		10 33		10 33		11 03		11 03		11 33		11 33
Wivelsfield 4	d	00 02					08 32		09 32	09 45	10 32		10 45		10 45		11 32		11 32		11 45		11 45
Burgess Hill 4	d	00 04					08 08	08 38	09 08	09 38	10 08		10 38		10 38		11 08		11 08		11 38		11 38
Hassocks 4	d	00 08					08 38	08 42	09 38	09 42	10 38		10 42		10 42		11 38		11 38		11 42		11 42
Preston Park	d	00 15					08 45	09 45	09 45	10 45	10 45				11 45		11 45		11 45				12 45
Brighton 10	a	00 22	01 14		02 20		08 24	08 54	09 24	09 54	10 24		10 54		10 54		11 24		11 24		11 54		11 54

For general notes see front of timetable
For details of catering facilities see Directory of Train Operators

§ It is unknown at the time of going to press, when this station will open. For further details please contact National Rail Enquiries 08457-484950 or see local publicity.

A From Derby (Table 53)

B Until 27 January from Nottingham (Table 53). 3 February to 23 March from Leicester (Table 53). From 30 March from Nottingham (Table 53)

Table 52

Sundays

Bedford, Luton, St.Albans and City of London → South London, Gatwick Airport and Brighton

Network Diagram - see first page of Table 52

	FC	FC 1	EM 1 ◇	FC 1	FC	FC 1	EM 1 ◇	FC 1	FC	FC 1	EM 1 ◇	FC 1	FC	FC 1	EM 1 ◇	FC 1	FC	FC 1	EM 1 ◇	EM 1 ◇	FC 1
			A				B				C				B				D	E	
			☕				☕				☕				☕				☕	☕	
Bedford 7 d		09 40	09 45	09 50		10 10	10 15	10 20		10 40	10 46	10 50		11 10	11 16	11 20		11 40	11 46	11 46	11 50
Flitwick d		09 49		09 59		10 19		10 29		10 49		10 59		11 19		11 29		11 49			11 59
Harlington d		09 53		10 03		10 23		10 33		10 53		11 03		11 23		11 33		11 53			12 03
Leagrave d		09 59		10 09		10 29		10 39		10 59		11 09		11 29		11 39		11 59			12 09
Luton 10 d	09 50	10 04	10 08	10 14	10 20	10 34		10 44	10 50	11 04	11 07	11 14	11 20	11 34		11 44	11 50	12 04	12 08	12 11	12 14
Luton Airport Parkway 7 ✈ d	09 52	10 06		10 16	10 22	10 36		10 46	10 52	11 06		11 16	11 22	11 36	11 41	11 46	11 52	12 06			12 16
Harpenden d	09 58	10 12		10 22	10 28	10 42		10 52	10 58	11 12		11 22	11 28	11 42		11 52	11 58	12 12			12 22
St Albans d	10 04	10 18		10 28	10 34	10 48		10 58	11 04	11 18		11 28	11 34	11 48		11 58	12 04	12 18			12 28
Radlett d	10 09				10 39				11 09				11 39				12 09				
Elstree & Borehamwood d	10 13				10 43				11 13				11 43				12 13				
Mill Hill Broadway d	10 17				10 47				11 17				11 47				12 17				
Hendon d	10 20				10 50				11 20				11 50				12 20				
Cricklewood d	10 24				10 54				11 24				11 54				12 24				
West Hampstead Thameslink ⊖ d	10 27			10 44	10 57			11 14	11 27			11 44	11 57			12 14	12 27				12 44
Kentish Town ⊖ d	10 31				11 01				11 31				12 01				12 31				
St Pancras International 15 ⊖ a			10 46				11 19				11 49				12 19				12 50	12 50	
St Pancras International 15 ⊖ d	10 36	10 40		10 54	11 06	11 10		11 24	11 36	11 40		11 54	12 06	12 10		12 24	12 36	12 40			12 54
Farringdon 3 ⊖ d	10 40	10 44		10 59	11 10	11 14		11 29	11 40	11 44		11 59	12 10	12 14		12 29	12 40	12 44			12 59
Barbican ⊖ a																					
Moorgate ⊖ a																					
City Thameslink 3 d																					
London Blackfriars 3 ⊖ d	10 46	10 49		11 04	11 16	11 19		11 34	11 46	11 49		12 04	12 16	12 19		12 34	12 46	12 49			13 04
Elephant & Castle ⊖ d	10 49				11 19				11 49				12 19				12 49				
Loughborough Jn d	10 53				11 23				11 53				12 23				12 53				
Herne Hill 4 d	10 57				11 27				11 57				12 27				12 57				
London Bridge 4 ⊖ d		10 56		11 11		11 26		11 41		11 56		12 11		12 26		12 41		12 56			13 11
Tulse Hill 3 d	11 01				11 31				12 01				12 31				13 01				
Streatham 4 d	11 04				11 34				12 04				12 34				13 04				
Eastfields § d																					
Mitcham Junction 🚊 d																					
Hackbridge d																					
Carshalton d																					
Tooting d	11 08				11 38				12 08				12 38				13 08				
Haydons Road d	11 11				11 41				12 11				12 41				13 11				
Wimbledon 6 ⊖ 🚊 d	11 14				11 44				12 14				12 44				13 14				
Wimbledon Chase d	11 17				11 47				12 17				12 47				13 17				
South Merton d	11 19				11 49				12 19				12 49				13 19				
Morden South d	11 21				11 51				12 21				12 51				13 21				
St Helier d	11 23				11 53				12 23				12 53				13 23				
Sutton Common d	11 25				11 55				12 25				12 55				13 25				
West Sutton d	11 28				11 58				12 28				12 58				13 28				
Sutton (Surrey) 4 a	11 33				12 03				12 33				13 03				13 33				
East Croydon 🚊 d		11a17		11 27		11a47		11 57		12a17		12 27		12a47		12 57		13a17			13 27
Redhill d		11 37		12 03		12 12				12 37		13 03		13 12				13 37			14 03
Gatwick Airport 10 ✈ d		11 46		11 50				12 20		12 46		12 50				13 20		13 46			13 50
Three Bridges 4 d		11 52		11 54		12 24		12 24		12 52		12 54		13 24		13 24		13 52			13 54
Balcombe d		12 23		12 23						13 23		13 23						14 23			14 23
Haywards Heath 3 d		12 03		12 03		12 33		12 33		13 03		13 03		13 33		13 33		14 03			14 03
Wivelsfield 4 d		12 32		12 32		12 45		12 45		13 32		13 32		13 45		13 45		14 32			14 32
Burgess Hill 4 d		12 08		12 08		12 38		12 38		13 08		13 08		13 38		13 38		14 08			14 08
Hassocks 4 d		12 38		12 38		12 42		12 42		13 38		13 38		13 42		13 42		14 38			14 38
Preston Park d		12 45		12 45				13 45		13 45		13 45				14 45		14 45			14 45
Brighton 10 a		12 24		12 24		12 54		12 54		13 24		13 24		13 54		13 54		14 24			14 24

For general notes see front of timetable
For details of catering facilities see Directory of Train Operators

§ It is unknown at the time of going to press, when this station will open. For further details please contact National Rail Enquiries 08457-484950 or see local publicity.

A Until 27 January from Nottingham (Table 53). 3 February to 23 March from Leicester (Table 53). From 30 March from Nottingham (Table 53)

B From Derby (Table 53)

C Until 27 January from Nottingham (Table 53). 3 February to 23 March from Loughborough (Table 53). From 30 March from Nottingham (Table 53)

D From 30 March. From Nottingham (Table 53)

E Until 23 March. From Nottingham (Table 53)

Table 52

Sundays

Bedford, Luton, St.Albans and City of London → South London, Gatwick Airport and Brighton

Network Diagram - see first page of Table 52

		FC	FC	EM 1 ◇ A ☕	FC 1	FC	FC 1	EM 1 ◇ B ☕	EM 1 ◇ C ☕	FC 1	FC	FC 1	EM 1 ◇ D ☕	EM 1 ◇ E ☕	FC 1	FC	FC 1	EM 1 ◇ G ☕	FC 1	FC	EM 1 ◇ C ☕	FC 1
Bedford 7	d		12 10	12 16	12 20		12 40	12 45	12 45	12 50	13 00	13 10	13 13	13 16	13 20	13 30	13 40	13 45	13 50	14 00	14 07	14 10
Flitwick	d		12 19		12 29		12 49			12 59		13 19			13 29		13 49		13 59			14 19
Harlington	d		12 23		12 33		12 53			13 03		13 23			13 33		13 53		14 03			14 23
Leagrave	d		12 29		12 39		12 59			13 09		13 29			13 39		13 59		14 09			14 29
Luton 10	d	12 20	12 34	12 38	12 44	12 50	13 04	13 08	13 08	13 14	13 20	13 34			13 44	13 50	14 04	14 09	14 14	14 18		14 34
Luton Airport Parkway 7 ✈	d	12 22	12 36		12 46	12 52	13 06			13 16	13 22	13 36			13 46	13 52	14 06		14 16	14 20		14 36
Harpenden	d	12 28	12 42		12 52	12 58	13 12			13 22	13 28	13 42			13 52	13 58	14 12		14 22	14 26		14 42
St Albans	d	12 34	12 48		12 58	13 04	13 18			13 28	13 34	13 48			13 58	14 04	14 18		14 28	14 32		14 48
Radlett	d	12 39				13 09					13 39					14 09				14 37		
Elstree & Borehamwood	d	12 43				13 13					13 43					14 13				14 43		
Mill Hill Broadway	d	12 47				13 17					13 47					14 17				14 47		
Hendon	d	12 50				13 20					13 50					14 20				14 50		
Cricklewood	d	12 54				13 24					13 54					14 24				14 54		
West Hampstead Thameslink ⊖	d	12 57			13 14	13 27				13 44	13 57				14 14	14 27			14 44	14 57		
Kentish Town ⊖	d	13 01				13 31					14 01					14 31				15 01		
St Pancras International 15 ⊖	a			13 18				13 48	13 48				14 18	14 18				14 44			14 55	
St Pancras International 15 ⊖	d	13 06	13 10		13 24	13 36	13 40			13 54	14 06	14 10			14 24	14 36	14 40		14 54	15 06		15 10
Farringdon 3 ⊖	d	13 10	13 14		13 29	13 40	13 44			13 59	14 10	14 14			14 29	14 40	14 44		14 59	15 10		15 14
Barbican ⊖	a																					
Moorgate ⊖	a																					
City Thameslink 3	d																					
London Blackfriars 3 ⊖	d	13 16	13 19		13 34	13 46	13 49			14 04	14 16	14 19			14 34	14 46	14 49		15 04	15 16		15 19
Elephant & Castle ⊖	d	13 19				13 49					14 19					14 49				15 19		
Loughborough Jn	d	13 23				13 53					14 23					14 53				15 23		
Herne Hill 4	d	13 27				13 57					14 27					14 57				15 27		
London Bridge 4 ⊖	d		13 26		13 41		13 56			14 11		14 26			14 41		14 56		15 11			15 26
Tulse Hill 3	d	13 31				14 01					14 31					15 01				15 31		
Streatham 4	d	13 34				14 04					14 34					15 04				15 34		
Eastfields §	d																					
Mitcham Junction 🚊	d																					
Hackbridge	d																					
Carshalton	d																					
Tooting	d	13 38				14 08					14 38					15 08				15 38		
Haydons Road	d	13 41				14 11					14 41					15 11				15 41		
Wimbledon 6 ⊖ 🚊	d	13 44				14 14					14 44					15 14				15 44		
Wimbledon Chase	d	13 47				14 17					14 47					15 17				15 47		
South Merton	d	13 49				14 19					14 49					15 19				15 49		
Morden South	d	13 51				14 21					14 51					15 21				15 51		
St Helier	d	13 53				14 23					14 53					15 23				15 53		
Sutton Common	d	13 55				14 25					14 55					15 25				15 55		
West Sutton	d	13 58				14 28					14 58					15 28				15 58		
Sutton (Surrey) 4	a	14 03				14 33					15 03					15 33				16 03		
East Croydon 🚊	d		13a47		13 57		14a17			14 27		14a47			14 57		15a17		15 27			15a47
Redhill	d		*14 12*				*14 37*			*15 03*		*15 12*					*15 37*		*16 03*			*16 12*
Gatwick Airport 10 ✈	d				14 20		*14 46*			14 50					15 20		*15 46*		15 50			
Three Bridges 4	d		*14 24*		14 24		*14 52*			14 54		*15 24*			15 24		*15 52*		15 54			*16 24*
Balcombe	d						*15 23*			*15 23*							*16 23*		*16 23*			
Haywards Heath 3	d		*14 33*		14 33		*15 03*			15 03		*15 33*			15 33		*16 03*		16 03			*16 33*
Wivelsfield 4	d		*14 45*		*14 45*		*15 32*			*15 32*		*15 45*			*15 45*		*16 32*		*16 32*			*16 45*
Burgess Hill 4	d		*14 38*		14 38		*15 08*			15 08		*15 38*			15 38		*16 08*		16 08			*16 38*
Hassocks 4	d		*14 42*		14 42		*15 38*			*15 38*		*15 42*			15 42		*16 38*		*16 38*			*16 42*
Preston Park	d				*15 45*		*15 45*			*15 45*					*16 45*		*16 45*		*16 45*			
Brighton 10	a		*14 54*		14 54		*15 24*			15 24		*15 54*			15 54		*16 24*		16 24			*16 54*

For general notes see front of timetable
For details of catering facilities see Directory of Train Operators

§ It is unknown at the time of going to press, when this station will open. For further details please contact National Rail Enquiries 08457-484950 or see local publicity.

A From Sheffield (Table 53)

B Until 23 March. From Leeds (Table 53)

C From 30 March. From Leeds (Table 53)

D Until 23 March. From Sheffield (Table 53)

E From 30 March. From Sheffield (Table 53)

G From Nottingham (Table 53)

Table 52

Sundays

Bedford, Luton, St.Albans and City of London → South London, Gatwick Airport and Brighton

Network Diagram - see first page of Table 52

Station		EM	FC	FC	EM	FC	FC	FC	FC	EM	FC	FC	EM	EM	FC	FC	FC	EM	EM	FC	FC	FC
		1 ◇	1		1 ◇	1	1		1	1 ◇	1		1 ◇	1 ◇	1	1		1 ◇	1 ◇		1	
		A			B					C			D	E				G	H			
		⊏P			⊏P					⊏P			⊏P	⊏P				⊏P	⊏P			
Bedford [7]	d	14 16	14 20	14 30	14 44	14 40	14 50	15 00	15 10	15 15	15 20	15 30	15 35	15 34	15 40	15 50	16 00			16 10	16 20	16 30
Flitwick	d		14 29			14 49	14 59		15 19		15 29				15 49	15 59				16 20	16 29	
Harlington	d		14 33			14 53	15 03		15 23		15 33				15 53	16 03				16 24	16 33	
Leagrave	d		14 39			14 59	15 09		15 30		15 39				15 59	16 09				16 29	16 39	
Luton [10]	d		14 44	14 50	14 59	15 04	15 14	15 20	15 34		15 44	15 50	15 55	15 58	16 04	16 14	16 20			16 35	16 44	16 50
Luton Airport Parkway [7] ✈	d		14 46	14 52		15 06	15 16	15 22	15 36		15 46	15 52			16 06	16 16	16 22	16 34	16 35	16 38	16 46	16 52
Harpenden	d		14 52	14 58		15 12	15 22	15 28	15 42		15 52	15 58			16 12	16 22	16 28			16 43	16 52	16 58
St Albans	d		14 58	15 04		15 18	15 28	15 34	15 48		15 58	16 04			16 18	16 28	16 34			16 49	16 58	17 04
Radlett	d			15 09				15 39				16 09					16 39					17 09
Elstree & Borehamwood	d			15 13				15 43				16 13					16 43					17 13
Mill Hill Broadway	d			15 17				15 47				16 17					16 47					17 17
Hendon	d			15 20				15 50				16 20					16 50					17 20
Cricklewood	d			15 24				15 54				16 24					16 54					17 24
West Hampstead Thameslink	⊖ d		15 14	15 27			15 44	15 57			16 14	16 27				16 44	16 57				17 14	17 27
Kentish Town	⊖ d			15 31				16 01				16 31					17 01					17 31
St Pancras International [15]	⊖ a	15 11			15 29					16 06			16 27	16 27				17 06	17 06			
St Pancras International [15]	⊖ d		15 24	15 36		15 40	15 54	16 06	16 10		16 24	16 36			16 40	16 54	17 06			17 09	17 24	17 36
Farringdon [3]	⊖ d		15 29	15 40		15 44	15 59	16 10	16 14		16 29	16 40			16 44	16 59	17 10			17 14	17 29	17 40
Barbican	⊖ a																					
Moorgate	⊖ a																					
City Thameslink [3]	d																					
London Blackfriars [3]	⊖ d		15 34	15 46		15 49	16 04	16 16	16 19		16 34	16 46			16 49	17 04	17 16			17 19	17 34	17 46
Elephant & Castle	⊖ d			15 49				16 19				16 49					17 19					17 49
Loughborough Jn	d			15 53				16 23				16 53					17 23					17 53
Herne Hill [4]	d			15 57				16 27				16 57					17 27					17 57
London Bridge [4]	⊖ d		15 41			15 56	16 11		16 26		16 41				16 56	17 11				17 26	17 41	
Tulse Hill [3]	d			16 01				16 31				17 01					17 31					18 01
Streatham [4]	d			16 04				16 34				17 04					17 34					18 04
Eastfields §	d																					
Mitcham Junction	🚋 d																					
Hackbridge	d																					
Carshalton	d																					
Tooting	d			16 08				16 38				17 08					17 38					18 08
Haydons Road	d			16 11				16 41				17 11					17 41					18 11
Wimbledon [6]	⊖ 🚋 d			16 14				16 44				17 14					17 44					18 14
Wimbledon Chase	d			16 17				16 47				17 17					17 47					18 17
South Merton	d			16 19				16 49				17 19					17 49					18 19
Morden South	d			16 21				16 51				17 21					17 51					18 21
St Helier	d			16 23				16 53				17 23					17 53					18 23
Sutton Common	d			16 25				16 55				17 25					17 55					18 25
West Sutton	d			16 28				16 58				17 28					17 58					18 28
Sutton (Surrey) [4]	a			16 33				17 03				17 33					18 01					18 31
East Croydon	🚋 d		15 57			16a17	16 27		16a47		16 57				17a17	17 27				17a47	17 57	
Redhill	d					16 37	17 03		17 12						17 37	18 03				18 12	18 37	
Gatwick Airport [10]	✈ d		16 20			16 46	16 50				17 20				17 46	17 50					18 20	
Three Bridges [4]	d		16 24			16 52	16 54		17 24		17 24				17 52	17 54				18 24	18 24	
Balcombe	d					17 23	17 23								18 23	18 23				19b23		
Haywards Heath [3]	d		16 33			17 03	17 03		17 33		17 33				18 03	18 03				18 33	18 33	
Wivelsfield [4]	d		16 45			17 32	17 32		17 45		17 45				18 32	18 32				18 45	18 45	
Burgess Hill [4]	d		16 38			17 08	17 08		17 38		17 38				18 08	18 08				18 38	18 38	
Hassocks [4]	d		16 42			17 38	17 38		17 42		17 42				18 38	18 38				18 42	18 42	
Preston Park	d		17 45			17 45	17 45				18 45				18 45	18 45				19c45	19 45	
Brighton [10]	a		16 54			17 24	17 24		17 54		17 54				18 24	18 24				18 54	18 54	

For general notes see front of timetable
For details of catering facilities see Directory of Train Operators

§ It is unknown at the time of going to press, when this station will open. For further details please contact National Rail Enquiries 08457-484950 or see local publicity.

A Until 23 March. From Leeds (Table 53)

B From Nottingham (Table 53)

C From Sheffield (Table 53)

D From 30 March. From Nottingham (Table 53)

E Until 23 March. From Nottingham (Table 53)

G Until 23 March. From Sheffield (Table 53)

H From 30 March. From Sheffield (Table 53)

b Change at East Croydon and Gatwick Airport

c Change at East Croydon and Burgess Hill

Bedford, Luton, St.Albans and City of London → South London, Gatwick Airport and Brighton

Network Diagram - see first page of Table 52

		EM 1 ◊ A ☕	EM 1 ◊ B ☕	FC 1	FC	EM 1 ◊ C ☕	EM 1 ◊ D ☕	FC 1		EM 1 ◊ A ☕	FC	EM 1 ◊ B ☕	FC 1	FC	EM 1 ◊ C ☕	EM 1 ◊ D ☕		FC 1	FC	EM 1 ◊ C ☕	EM 1 ◊ E ☕	EM 1 ◊ G ☕	FC 1	EM 1 ◊ H ☕	FC
Bedford 7	d	16 54	16 55	16 50	17 00	17 09	17 10	17 20		17 25		17 41	17 50		18 06	18 08		18 20		18 34	18 40	18 40	18 50	19 10	
Flitwick	d			16 59				17 29					17 59					18 29					18 59		
Harlington	d			17 03				17 33					18 03					18 33					19 03		
Leagrave	d			17 09				17 39					18 09					18 39					19 09		
Luton 10	d	17 11	17 12	17 14	17 20			17 44			17 50		18 14	18 20	18 27	18 28		18 44	18 50	18 55	19 01	19 01	19 14		19 20
Luton Airport Parkway 7 ✈	d			17 16	17 22			17 46		17 42	17 52	17 59	18 16	18 22				18 46	18 52				19 16		19 22
Harpenden	d			17 22	17 28			17 52			17 58		18 22	18 28				18 52	18 58				19 22		19 28
St Albans	d			17 28	17 34			17 58			18 04		18 28	18 34				18 58	19 04				19 28		19 34
Radlett	d				17 39						18 09			18 39					19 09						19 39
Elstree & Borehamwood	d				17 43						18 14			18 44					19 14						19 44
Mill Hill Broadway	d				17 47						18 18			18 48					19 18						19 48
Hendon	d				17 50						18 21			18 51					19 21						19 51
Cricklewood	d				17 54						18 25			18 55					19 25						19 55
West Hampstead Thameslink ⊖	d			17 44	17 57			18 14			18 27		18 44	18 57				19 14	19 27				19 44		19 57
Kentish Town ⊖	d				18 01						18 31			19 01					19 31						19 59
St Pancras International 15 ⊖	a	17 41	17 42			17 55	17 55			18 11		18 28			18 57	18 57				19 24	19 29	19 30		19 56	
St Pancras International 15 ⊖	d			17 54	18 06			18 24			18 36		18 54	19 06				19 24	19 36				19 54		20 06
Farringdon 3 ⊖	d			17 59	18 10			18 29			18 40		18 59	19 10				19 29	19 40				19 59		20 10
Barbican ⊖	a																								
Moorgate ⊖	a																								
City Thameslink 3	d																								
London Blackfriars 3 ⊖	d			18 04	18 16			18 34			18 46		19 04	19 16				19 34	19 46				20 04		20 16
Elephant & Castle ⊖	d				18 19						18 49			19 19					19 49						20 19
Loughborough Jn	d				18 23						18 53			19 23					19 53						20 23
Herne Hill 4	d				18 27						18 57			19 27					19 57						20 27
London Bridge 4 ⊖	d			18 11				18 41					19 11					19 41					20 11		
Tulse Hill 3	d				18 31						19 01			19 31					20 01						20 31
Streatham 4	d				18 34						19 04			19 34					20 04						20 34
Eastfields §	d																								
Mitcham Junction 🚋	d																								
Hackbridge	d																								
Carshalton	d																								
Tooting	d				18 38						19 08			19 38					20 08						20 38
Haydons Road	d				18 41						19 11			19 41					20 11						20 41
Wimbledon 6 ⊖ 🚋	d				18 44						19 14			19 44					20 14						20 44
Wimbledon Chase	d				18 47						19 17			19 47					20 17						20 47
South Merton	d				18 49						19 19			19 49					20 19						20 49
Morden South	d				18 51						19 21			19 51					20 21						20 51
St Helier	d				18 53						19 23			19 53					20 23						20 53
Sutton Common	d				18 55						19 25			19 55					20 25						20 55
West Sutton	d				18 58						19 28			19 58					20 28						20 58
Sutton (Surrey) 4	a				19 01						19 31			20 01					20 31						21 01
East Croydon 🚋	d			18 27				18 57					19 27					19 57					20 27		
Redhill	d			*19 03*				*19 37*					*20 03*					*20 37*					*21 03*		
Gatwick Airport 10 ✈	d			18 50				19 20					19 50					20 20					20 50		
Three Bridges 4	d			18 54				19 24					19 54					20 24					20 54		
Balcombe	d			*19 23*									*20 23*										*21 23*		
Haywards Heath 3	d			19 03				19 33					20 03					20 33					21 03		
Wivelsfield 4	d			*19 32*				*19 45*					*20 32*					*20 45*					*21 32*		
Burgess Hill 4	d			19 08				19 38					20 08					20 38					21 08		
Hassocks 4	d			*19 38*				19 42					*20 38*					20 42					*21 38*		
Preston Park	d			*19 45*				*20 45*					*20 45*					*21 45*					*21 45*		
Brighton 10	a			19 24				19 54					20 24					20 54					21 24		

For general notes see front of timetable
For details of catering facilities see Directory of Train Operators

§ It is unknown at the time of going to press, when this station will open. For further details please contact National Rail Enquiries 08457-484950 or see local publicity.

A From 30 March. From Nottingham (Table 53)

B Until 23 March. From Nottingham (Table 53)

C From 30 March. From Sheffield (Table 53)

D Until 23 March. From Sheffield (Table 53)

E 3 February to 23 March. From Sheffield (Table 53)

G Until 27 January. From Sheffield (Table 53)

H From Sheffield (Table 53)

Table 52

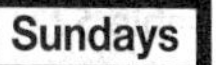

Sundays

Bedford, Luton, St.Albans and City of London → South London, Gatwick Airport and Brighton

Network Diagram - see first page of Table 52

Station		FC 1	FC	EM 1 ◇ A ☕	EM 1 ◇ B ☕	FC 1	EM 1 ◇ C ☕	FC 1	EM 1 ◇ D ☕	FC 1	FC 1	EM 1 ◇ E ☕	FC 1	EM 1 ◇ C ☕	EM 1 ◇ D ☕	FC 1	FC	EM 1 ◇ A ☕	EM 1 ◇ B ☕	FC	FC 1
Bedford 7	d	19 20		19 33	19 36	19 50	19 55	20 00	20 05	20 10	20 40	20 49	21 10	21 30	21 31	21 40	22 10	22 30	22 31	22 40	23 40
Flitwick	d	19 29				19 59				20 19	20 49		21 19			21 49	22 19			22 49	23 49
Harlington	d	19 33				20 03				20 23	20 53		21 23			21 53	22 23			22 53	23 53
Leagrave	d	19 39				20 09				20 29	20 59		21 29			21 59	22 29			22 59	23 59
Luton 10	d	19 44	19 50	19 51	19 52	20 14		20 20		20 34	21 04	21 08	21 34	21 49	21 50	22 04	22 34	22 50	22 50	23 04	00 04
Luton Airport Parkway 7 ✈	d	19 46	19 52			20 16		20 22		20 36	21 06		21 36			22 06	22 36			23 06	00 06
Harpenden	d	19 52	19 58			20 22		20 28		20 42	21 12		21 42			22 12	22 42			23 12	00 12
St Albans	d	19 58	20 04			20 28		20 34		20 48	21 18		21 48			22 18	22 48			23 18	00 18
Radlett	d		20 09					20 39		20 53	21 23		21 53			22 23	22 53			23 23	00 23
Elstree & Borehamwood	d		20 14					20 43		20 57	21 27		21 57			22 27	22 57			23 27	00 27
Mill Hill Broadway	d		20 18					20 47		21 01	21 31		22 01			22 31	23 01			23 31	00 31
Hendon	d		20 21					20 50		21 04	21 34		22 04			22 34	23 04			23 34	00 34
Cricklewood	d		20 25					20 54		21 08	21 38		22 08			22 38	23 08			23 38	00 38
West Hampstead Thameslink ⊖	d	20 14	20 27			20 44		20 57		21 12	21 42		22 12			22 42	23 12			23 42	00 42
Kentish Town ⊖	d		20 31					21 01		21 16	21 46		22 16			22 46	23 16			23 46	00 46
St Pancras International 15 ⊖	a			20 22	20 21		20 49		20 49			21 37		22 18	22 19			23 22	23 22		
St Pancras International 15 ⊖	d	20 24	20 36			20 54		21b10		21 24	21 54		22 24			22 54	23 24			23 54	00 54
Farringdon 3 ⊖	d	20 29	20 40			20 59		21 14		21 29	21 59		22 29			22 59	23 29			23 59	
Barbican ⊖	a																				
Moorgate ⊖	a																				
City Thameslink 3	d																				
London Blackfriars 3 ⊖	d	20 34	20 46			21 04		21 19		21 34	22 04		22 34			23 04	23 34			00 04	01 04
Elephant & Castle ⊖	d		20 49																		
Loughborough Jn	d		20 53																		
Herne Hill 4	d		20 57																		
London Bridge 4 ⊖	d	20 41				21 11		21 26		21 41	22 11		22 41			23 11	23 41			00 11	
Tulse Hill 3	d		21 01																		
Streatham 4	d		21 04																		
Eastfields §	d																				
Mitcham Junction 🚋	d																				
Hackbridge	d																				
Carshalton	d																				
Tooting	d		21 08																		
Haydons Road	d		21 11																		
Wimbledon 6 ⊖ 🚋	d		21 14																		
Wimbledon Chase	d		21 17																		
South Merton	d		21 19																		
Morden South	d		21 21																		
St Helier	d		21 23																		
Sutton Common	d		21 25																		
West Sutton	d		21 28																		
Sutton (Surrey) 4	a		21 33																		
East Croydon 🚋	d	20 57				21 27		21a49		21 57	22 27		22 57			23 27	23 57			00 27	01 32
Redhill	d	21 37				22 03		22 12		22 37	23 03		23 42			00 05	00 50			00 50	
Gatwick Airport 10 ✈	d	21 20				21 50				22 20	22 50		23 20			23 50	00 17			00 47	01 52
Three Bridges 4	d	21 24				21 54		22 24		22 24	22 54		23 24			23 54	00a26			00a56	01a58
Balcombe	d					22 23		23c23			23 23					00 25					
Haywards Heath 3	d	21 33				22 03		22 33		22 33	23 03		23 33			00 03	02c02			02 02	
Wivelsfield 4	d	21 45				22 32		22 45		22 45	23 32		23 45			00 34					
Burgess Hill 4	d	21 38				22 08		22 38		22 38	23 08		23 38			00 08					
Hassocks 4	d	21 42				22 38		22 42		22 42	23 38		23 42			00 40					
Preston Park	d	22 45				22 45		23e45		23 45	23 45		00 47			00 47					
Brighton 10	a	21 54				22 24		22 54		22 54	23 24		23 54			00 24	02c30			02 30	

For general notes see front of timetable
For details of catering facilities see Directory of Train Operators

§ It is unknown at the time of going to press, when this station will open. For further details please contact National Rail Enquiries 08457-484950 or see local publicity.

A Until 23 March. From Nottingham (Table 53)
B From 30 March. From Nottingham (Table 53)
C From 30 March. From Sheffield (Table 53)
D Until 23 March. From Sheffield (Table 53)
E From York (Table 53)
b Arr. 2107
c Change at East Croydon and Gatwick Airport
e Change at East Croydon and Burgess Hill

Brighton, Gatwick Airport and South London → City of London, St.Albans, Luton and Bedford

Network Diagram - see first page of Table 52

Miles	Miles	Miles	Miles	Miles	Station		FC MO [1]	FC MX	FC MX [1]	FC MO [1]	FC MX [1]	FC MO [1]	FC MX	FC MX [1]	FC MO [1]	FC MX [1]	FC MO [1]	FC MO	FC MX	FC MX [1]	FC MO [1]	FC [1]	FC [1]	FC	EM [1] ◇ A ☕
0	—	—	—	—	**Brighton [10]**	d	21p44		22p07	22p16				22p33	22p44					23p37	23p44				
1½	—	—	—	—	Preston Park	d			22p11					22p37						23p41	*23 06*				
7¾	—	—	—	—	Hassocks [4]	d	21p52		22p17					22p43	22p52					23p47	23p52				
9¼	—	—	—	—	Burgess Hill [4]	d	21p56		22p21	22p26				22p47	22p56					23p51	23p56				
10	—	—	—	—	Wivelsfield [4]	d			22p23					22p49						23p53	*23 19*				
13	—	—	—	—	**Haywards Heath [3]**	d	22p01		22p32	22p31				22p54	23p01					23p59	00 01				
17	—	—	—	—	Balcombe	d			22p37					23p00						00 04	*23 29*				
21½	—	—	—	—	Three Bridges [4]	d	22p10		22p42	22p40				23p12	23p10					00 10	00 10	02 25	03 25	04 25	
24¼	—	—	—	—	**Gatwick Airport [10]** ✈	d	22p15		22p46	22p45				23p16	23p15					00 15	00 15	02 30	03 30	04 30	
30	—	—	—	—	Redhill	d														00 22	00 22				
40½	—	—	0	—	**East Croydon** 🚋	d	22p32		23p02	23p02				23p32	23p32					00 36	00 36	02 47	03 47	04 47	
—	0	0	—	0	**Sutton (Surrey) [4]**	d																			
—	1	—	—	—	West Sutton	d																			
—	2	—	—	—	Sutton Common	d																			
—	3	—	—	—	St Helier	d																			
—	3½	—	—	—	Morden South	d																			
—	4	—	—	—	South Merton	d																			
—	4½	—	—	—	Wimbledon Chase	d																			
—	5½	—	—	—	**Wimbledon [6]** ⊖ 🚋	d																			
—	6¾	—	—	—	Haydons Road	d																			
—	8	—	—	—	Tooting	d																			
—	—	—	—	1¼	Carshalton	d																			
—	—	—	—	2	Hackbridge	d																			
—	—	—	—	4	Mitcham Junction 🚋	d																			
—	—	—	—	5	Eastfields §	d																			
—	9½	6	—	6	Streatham [4]	d																			
—	11	7½	5	—	Tulse Hill [3]	d																			
50¾	—	—	—	—	**London Bridge [4]** ⊖	d	22p45		23p15	23p15				23p45	23p45			00 20	00 20	00 52	00 52				
—	12	8½	—	—	Herne Hill [4]	d																			
—	13	9½	—	—	Loughborough Jn	d																			
—	15	11½	—	—	Elephant & Castle	d					←					←									
51½	16	12½	10	—	**London Blackfriars [3]** ⊖	d	22p53	23p08	23p23 →	23p23	23p23		23p38	23p53 →	23p53	23p53		00 28	00 28	01 00	01 00	03 13	04 13	05 13	
52	—	—	—	—	City Thameslink [3]	d																			
—	0	—	—	—	**Moorgate** ⊖	d																			
—	½	—	—	—	Barbican ⊖	d																			
52¾	¾	—	—	—	Farringdon [3] ⊖	d	22p58	23p14		23p28	23p29		23p44		23p58	23p59		00 30	00 34					05 18	
533	0	—	—	—	**St Pancras International [15]** ⊖	d	23p02	23p18		23p32	23p33		23p48		00 02	00 03		00b38	00 38	01 08	01 08	03 22	04 22	05 22	06 10
55½	—	—	—	—	Kentish Town ⊖	d	23p06	23p22		23p36			23p52		00 06			00 42	00 42	01 12	01 12	03 26	04 26	05 26	
58	—	—	—	—	West Hampstead Thameslink ⊖	d	23p10	23p26		23p40	23p40		23p56		00 10	00 10		00 46	00 46	01 16	01 16	03 30	04 30	05 30	
59	—	—	—	—	Cricklewood	d	23p13	23p29		23p43		←	23p59		00 13		←	00 49	00 49	01 19	01 19	03 33	04 33	05 33	
61	—	—	—	—	Hendon	d	23p16	23p32		23p46 →		23p46	00 02		00 16 →		00 16	00 52	00 52	01 22	01 22	03 36	04 36	05 36	
63¼	—	—	—	—	Mill Hill Broadway	d	23p19	23p35				23p49	00 05				00 19	00 55	00 55	01 25	01 25	03 39	04 39	05 39	
66½	—	—	—	—	Elstree & Borehamwood	d	23p24	23p40				23p54	00 10				00 24	01 00	01 00	01 30	01 30	03 44	04 44	05 44	
69½	—	—	—	—	Radlett	d	23p28	23p44				23p58	00 14				00 28	01 04	01 04	01 34	01 34	03 48	04 48	05 48	
74	—	—	—	—	**St Albans**	d	23p34	23p50			23p54	00 04	00 20			00 24	00 34	01 10	01 10	01 40	01 40	03 54	04 54	05 54	
78¾	—	—	—	—	Harpenden	d	23p39	23p55			00 01	00 09	00 25			00 31	00 39	01 15	01 15	01 45	01 45	03 59	04 59	05 59	
83¼	—	—	—	—	Luton Airport Parkway [7] ✈	d	23p45	00 01			00 07	00 15	00 31			00 37	00 45	01 21	01 21	01 51	01 51	04 05	05 05	06 05	
84¼	30¼	—	—	—	**Luton [10]**	d	23p49	00 05			00 10	00 19	00 35			00 40	00 49	01 25	01 25	01 55	01 55	04 10	05 10	06 10	06 33
86¾	—	—	—	—	Leagrave	d	23p53	00 09			00 14	00 23	00 39			00 44	00 53	01 29	01 29	01 59	01 59	04 14	05 14	06 14	
91¼	—	—	—	—	Harlington	d	23p59	00 14			00 20	00 29	00 44			00 50	00 59	01 34	01 34	02 04	02 04	04 20	05 20	06 20	
94¼	—	—	—	—	Flitwick	d	00 03	00 18			00 24	00 33	00 48			00 54	01 03	01 38	01 38	02 08	02 08	04 24	05 24	06 24	
103¾	49¾	—	—	—	**Bedford [7]**	a	00 15	00 30			00 35	00 45	01 00			01 07	01 15	01 52	01 52	02 20	02 20	04 37	05 37	06 37	06 47

For general notes see front of timetable
For details of catering facilities see Directory of Train Operators

§ It is unknown at the time of going to press, when this station will open. For further details please contact National Rail Enquiries 08457-484950 or see local publicity.

A To Sheffield (Table 53)
b Arr. 0035

Brighton, Gatwick Airport and South London → City of London, St.Albans, Luton and Bedford

Network Diagram - see first page of Table 52

		FC	EM	FC	FC		FC	EM	FC	FC	EM	FC	EM	FC	FC	FC	FC	FC	FC	EM	FC	FC	EM	FC	FC
		1	1 ◇		1			1 ◇	1		1 ◇	1	1 ◇				1			1 ◇		1	1 ◇	1	
			A					B			C		A			D		D		B			C		
Brighton 10	d	*03 50*			05 09				05 39			05 49					06 09							06 24	
Preston Park	d				05 13				05 43			05 53					06 13							06 28	
Hassocks 4	d				05 19				05 49			05 59					06 19							06 34	
Burgess Hill 4	d				05 23				05 53			06 03					06 23							06 38	
Wivelsfield 4	d				05 26				05 56			06 05					*06 15*							06 40	
Haywards Heath 3	d	*04 25*			05 30				06 00			06 09					06 30							06 45	
Balcombe	d								06 05								06 35							06 51	
Three Bridges 4	d	04 55			05 40				06 12			06 20					06 40							06 56	
Gatwick Airport 10 ✈	d	05 00			05 46				06 16			06 24					06 46							07 01	
Redhill	d				*05 28*				*05 48*			06 33												07 10	
East Croydon	d	05 17			06 02				06 32			06 44					07 02							07 24	
Sutton (Surrey) 4	d														06 23						06 48				
West Sutton	d														06 26						06 51				
Sutton Common	d														06 28						06 54				
St Helier	d														06 31						06 56				
Morden South	d														06 33						06 58				
South Merton	d														06 35						07 00				
Wimbledon Chase	d														06 37						07 02				
Wimbledon 6 ⊖	d									06 28					06 40						07 06				
Haydons Road	d									06 30					06 43						07 08				
Tooting	d									06 33					06 46						07 11				
Carshalton	d																								
Hackbridge	d																								
Mitcham Junction	d																								
Eastfields §	d																								
Streatham 4	d			05 46			06 06			06 36					06 50	06 56					07 16				
Tulse Hill 3	d			05 50			06 10			06 40					06 54	07 00					07 20			07 35	
London Bridge 4 ⊖	d	05 34			06 15				06 46			06 59					07 16								
Herne Hill 4	d			05 54			06 14			06 44					06 59	07 04					07 24				
Loughborough Jn	d						06 17			06 47					07 02	07 07					07 27				
Elephant & Castle	d			06 02			06 22			06 52					07 07	07 12					07 32				
London Blackfriars 3 ⊖	d	05 43		06b08	06 24		06 28		06 53	06 58		07 07			07 12	07 18	07 23				07 38			07c53	
City Thameslink 3	d			06 10	06 25		06 30		06 56	07 00		07 09			07 14	07 20	07 25				07 40			07 55	
Moorgate ⊖	d																		07 30			07 50			08 00
Barbican ⊖	d																								
Farringdon 3 ⊖	d	05 48		06 14	06 29		06 34		06 59	07 04		07 12			07 16	07 24	07 28		07 32		07 44	07 52		07 58	08 04
St Pancras International 15 ⊖	d	05 52	06 35	06 18	06 33		06 38	07 00	07 03	07 08	07 25	07 16	07 30		07 21	07 28	07 32		07 36	08 00	07 48	07 56	08 25	08 02	08 08
Kentish Town ⊖	d	05 56		06 22			06 42			07 12									07 40			08 00			08 12
West Hampstead Thameslink ⊖	d	06 00		06 26	06 40		06 46		07 10	07 16						07 36	07 40		07 44		07 56	08 04		08 09	08 16
Cricklewood	d	06 03		06 29			06 49			07 19				←					07 47			08 07			08 19
Hendon	d	06 06		06 32			06 52			07 22				07 22					07 50			08 10			08 22
Mill Hill Broadway	d	06 09		06 35			06 55			→				07 25				←	07 53			08 13			→
Elstree & Borehamwood	d	06 14		06 40			07 00							07 30		07 46		07 46	07 58		08 06	→			
Radlett	d	06 18		06 44			07 04							07 34		→		07 50	08 02		08 10				
St Albans	d	06 24		06 50	06 54		07 10		07 24			07 36		07 40	07a45		07 54	07a59	08a12		08 16			08 23	
Harpenden	d	06 29		06 55	07 01		07 15		07 29			07 43		07 47			07 59				08 21			08 30	
Luton Airport Parkway 7 ✈	d	06 35	06a56	07 01	07 07		07 21	07 22	07 35			07 49		07 54			08 05			08 22	08 27			08 36	
Luton 10	d	06 40		07 04	07 10		07 24		07 38		07a49	07 52	07 53	07 57			08 08				08 30			08 39	
Leagrave	d	06 44		07 08	07 14		07 28		07 43			07 56		08 00			08 12				08 34				
Harlington	d	06 50		07 14	07 20		07 34		07 48			08 02		08 06			08 18				08 40				
Flitwick	d	06 54		07 18	07 24		07 38		07 52			08 06		08 10			08 22				08 44			08 49	
Bedford 7	a	07 07		07 32	07 37		07 52	07 37	08 05			08 19	08 08	08 22			08 35			08 37	08 57		09 00	09 01	

For general notes see front of timetable
For details of catering facilities see Directory of Train Operators

§ It is unknown at the time of going to press, when this station will open. For further details please contact National Rail Enquiries 08457-484950 or see local publicity.

A To Nottingham (Table 53)
B To Derby (Table 53)
C To Sheffield (Table 53)
D From Selhurst (Table 177)

b Arr. 0605
c Arr. 0750

Brighton, Gatwick Airport and South London → City of London, St.Albans, Luton and Bedford

Network Diagram - see first page of Table 52

		FC	EM	FC	FC		FC	FC	FC	FC	FC	FC	EM	FC	FC	FC	FC	EM	EM	FC	FC	FC	FC	FC	FC
		1	1 ◇	1				1					1 ◇		1	1		1 ◇	1 ◇			1			1
			A				B					B	C					D	A						
Brighton 10	d							07 00								07 26						07 50			08 02
Preston Park	d							07 04								07 30						07 54			08 06
Hassocks 4	d							07 10								07 36						08 00			08 12
Burgess Hill 4	d							07 14								07 40						*08 00*			08 16
Wivelsfield 4	d							07 18								*07 39*						*07 49*			08 18
Haywards Heath 3	d							07 23								07 47						08 09			08 23
Balcombe	d							*07 19*														08 14			*08 21*
Three Bridges 4	d							07 32								07 56						*08 09*			08 34
Gatwick Airport 10 ✈	d							07 37								08 01						08 22			08 38
Redhill	d							*07 26*								08 14									*08 18*
East Croydon	d							07 54								08 28						08 38			08 54
Sutton (Surrey) 4	d						07 20					07 50									08 16				
West Sutton	d						07 23					07 53									08 19				
Sutton Common	d						07 26					07 56									08 21				
St Helier	d						07 28					07 58									08 24				
Morden South	d						07 30					08 00									08 26				
South Merton	d						07 32					08 02									08 28				
Wimbledon Chase	d						07 34					08 04									08 30				
Wimbledon 6 ⊖	d						07 38				07 58	08 08									08 36				
Haydons Road	d						07 40				08 00	08 10									08 38				
Tooting	d						07 43				08 03	08 13									08 41				
Carshalton	d																								
Hackbridge	d																								
Mitcham Junction	d																								
Eastfields §	d																								
Streatham 4	d						07 46				08 11	08 17									08 45				
Tulse Hill 3	d						07 50	08 05			08 15	08 23				08 39					08 49	08 55			
London Bridge 4 ⊖	d																								09 11
Herne Hill 4	d						07 54				08 22	08 28				08 43					08 53	08 59			
Loughborough Jn	d						07 57				08 25	08 31									08 56				
Elephant & Castle	d						08 02				08 30	08 36									09 00				
London Blackfriars 3 ⊖	d						08b13	08c23			08 37	08 43				08e57					09 05	09 09			09 18
City Thameslink 3	d						08 15	08 25			08 39	08 45				08 59					09 07	09 11			09 21
Moorgate ⊖	d			08 10					08 32						08 52					09 04			09 14		
Barbican ⊖	d																								
Farringdon 3 ⊖	d			08 12			08 20	08 29	08 34		08 42	08 50			08 58	09 02				09 06	09 10	09 14	09f20		09g29
St Pancras International 15 ⊖	d		08 30	08 16			08 24	08 33	08 38		08 46	08 54	09 00		09 02	09 06		09 25	09 30	09 10	09 14	09 18	09 24		09 33
Kentish Town ⊖	d						08 28		08 42			08 58									09 18		09 28		
West Hampstead Thameslink ⊖	d						08 32		08 48			09 02								09 16	09 22		09 32		
Cricklewood	d				←		08 35		08 51	←		09 05		←			←				09 25		09 35	←	
Hendon	d	←			08 22		08 38		08 54	08 38		09 08		08 54			09 08				09 28		09 38	09 28	
Mill Hill Broadway	d	08 13			08 25		→		→	08 41		→		08 57			09 11				→		→	09 31	
Elstree & Borehamwood	d	08 18			08 30					08 46				09 02			09 16			09 26				09 36	
Radlett	d	08 22			08 36					08 50				09 08			09 20			09 30				09 40	
St Albans	d	08a31		08 36	08a44			08 54		08a59	09 09			09 14	09 22	09 28	09a29			09 38		09 42		09a51	09 54
Harpenden	d			08 43				08 59			09 14			09 19	09 28	09 34				09 43		09 47			09 59
Luton Airport Parkway 7 ✈	d			08 49				09 05			09 20		09 22	09 25		09 40				09 49		09 53			10 05
Luton 10	d		08 53	08 54				09 08			09 24			09a31	09 34	09 44		09a48	09 53	09a54		09 56			10 08
Leagrave	d			08 57				09 12			09 27					09 47						09 59			10 12
Harlington	d			09 03				09 18			09 33					09 53						10 05			10 18
Flitwick	d			09 07				09 22			09 37				09 45	09 57						10 09			10 22
Bedford 7	a		09 07	09 18				09 35			09 49		09 37		10 00	10 09			10 08			10 21			10 37

For general notes see front of timetable
For details of catering facilities see Directory of Train Operators

§ It is unknown at the time of going to press, when this station will open. For further details please contact National Rail Enquiries 08457-484950 or see local publicity.

A To Nottingham (Table 53)
B From Luton
C To Derby (Table 53)
D To Sheffield (Table 53)
b Arr. 0807
c Arr. 0819
e Arr. 0852
f Arr. 0917
g Arr. 0926

Table 52

Brighton, Gatwick Airport and South London → City of London, St.Albans, Luton and Bedford

Network Diagram - see first page of Table 52

		FC	FC	FC 1	FC	EM 1 ◇ A 🍴	FC	FC 1	FC	FC	EM 1 ◇ B 🍴	FC 1	FC	FC	FC 1	FC	FC	FC 1	FC	EM 1 ◇ A 🍴	FC	FC 1	FC	FC
Brighton 10	d			08 16				08 36				09 00			09 04			09 34				09 37		
Preston Park	d			08 20				08 40							09 08			*09 08*				09 41		
Hassocks 4	d			08 26				08 46				09 08			09 14			*09 14*				09 47		
Burgess Hill 4	d			08 30				08 50				09 12			09 18			*09 35*				09 51		
Wivelsfield 4	d			08 33				*08 39*				*08 59*			09 20			*09 33*				09 53		
Haywards Heath 3	d			08 38				09 00				09 16			09 25			09 48				09 58		
Balcombe	d							09 06							09 31			*09 31*						
Three Bridges 4	d			08 47				09 12				09 27			09 37			*09 48*				10 10		
Gatwick Airport 10 ✈	d			08 52				09 16				09 31			09 41			10 01				10 16		
Redhill	d			*08 32*				*08 51*				*09 22*						*09 48*				*10 05*		
East Croydon ⛴	d			09 08				09 32				09 47			09 57			10 17				10 32		
Sutton (Surrey) 4	d		08 46						09 06					09 37		09 36			10 04				10 06	
West Sutton	d		08 49						09 09							09 39							10 09	
Sutton Common	d		08 51						09 11							09 41							10 11	
St Helier	d		08 54						09 14							09 44							10 14	
Morden South	d		08 56						09 16							09 46							10 16	
South Merton	d		08 58						09 18							09 48							10 18	
Wimbledon Chase	d		09 00						09 20							09 50							10 20	
Wimbledon 6 ⊖ ⛴	d		09 04						09 23							09 53							10 23	
Haydons Road	d		09 06						09 25							09 55							10 25	
Tooting	d		09 09						09 28							09 58							10 28	
Carshalton	d													09 40					10 07					
Hackbridge	d													09 42					10 09					
Mitcham Junction ⛴	d													09 45					10 12					
Eastfields §	d																							
Streatham 4	d		09 15						09 33					09 52		10 03			10 19				10 33	
Tulse Hill 3	d		09 19	09 25					09 37					09 55		10 07			10 23				10 37	
London Bridge 4 ⊖	d							09 45				10 00			10 15			10 30				10 45		
Herne Hill 4	d		09 23						09 41					09 59		10 11			10 26				10 41	
Loughborough Jn	d		09 26						09 45					10 02		10 15			10 30				10 45	
Elephant & Castle	d		09 30						09 50					10 07		10 20			10 35				10 50	
London Blackfriars 3 ⊖	d		09 34	09 38				09 53	09 58			10 08		10b13	10 23	10 28		10 38	10 43			10 53	10 58	
City Thameslink 3	d		09 36	09 40				09 55	10 00			10 10		10 15	10 25	10 30		10 40	10 45			10 55	11 00	
Moorgate ⊖	d				09 48																			
Barbican ⊖	d																							
Farringdon 3 ⊖	d		09 40	09 44	09 50			09 59	10 04			10 14		10 19	10 29	10 34		10 44	10 49			10 59	11 04	
St Pancras International 15 ⊖	d		09 44	09 48	09 54	10 00		10 03	10 08		10 30	10 18		10 23	10 33	10 38		10 48	10 53	11 00		11 03	11 08	
Kentish Town ⊖	d		09 48		09 58				10 12					10 27		10 42			10 57				11 12	
West Hampstead Thameslink ⊖	d		09 52		10 02				10 16					10 31		10 46			11 01				11 16	
Cricklewood	d	←	09 55		10 05		←		10 19	←			←	10 34		10 49	←		11 04		←		11 19	←
Hendon	d	09 38	09 58		10 08		09 58		10 22	10 08			10 22	10 37		10 52	10 37		11 07		10 52		11 22	11 07
Mill Hill Broadway	d	09 41	→		→		10 01		→	10 11			10 25	→		→	10 40		→		10 55		→	11 10
Elstree & Borehamwood	d	09 46					10 06			10 16			10 30				10 45				11 00			11 15
Radlett	d	09 50					10 10			10 20			10 38				10 50				11 08			11 20
St Albans	d	09 58		10 09			10a19	10 24		10 28		10 39	10 44		10 54		10a58	11 09			11 14	11 24		11a29
Harpenden	d	10 03		10 14				10 29		10 37		10 44	10 51		10 59			11 14			11 19	11 29		
Luton Airport Parkway 7 ✈	d	10 09		10 20		10 22		10 35		10 43		10 50	10 57		11 05			11 20		11 22	11 25	11 35		
Luton 10	d	10a18		10 24				10 38		10a49	10 53	10 54	11a02		11 08			11 24			11a31	11 38		
Leagrave	d			10 28				10 42				10 58			11 12			11 28				11 42		
Harlington	d			10 34				10 48				11 04			11 18			11 34				11 48		
Flitwick	d			10 38				10 52				11 08			11 22			11 38				11 52		
Bedford 7	a			10 50		10 37		11 05			11 07	11 20			11 35			11 50		11 37		12 05		

For general notes see front of timetable
For details of catering facilities see Directory of Train Operators

§ It is unknown at the time of going to press, when this station will open. For further details please contact National Rail Enquiries 08457-484950 or see local publicity.

A To Derby (Table 53)
B To Nottingham (Table 53)
b Arr. 1010

Brighton, Gatwick Airport and South London → City of London, St.Albans, Luton and Bedford

Network Diagram - see first page of Table 52

Station		EM	FC	FC	FC		FC	FC	FC	FC	FC	EM	FC	FC	FC	FC	EM	FC	FC	FC	FC	FC	FC	FC	FC
		1 ◇	1				1			1		1 ◇		1			1 ◇	1			1			1	
		A										B					A								
		🍴										🍴					🍴								
Brighton 10	d		10 04				10 07			10 34				10 37				11 04			11 07			11 34	
Preston Park	d		*09 58*				10 11			*10 11*				10 41				*10 58*			11 11			*11 11*	
Hassocks 4	d		*10 05*				10 17			*10 17*				10 47				*11 05*			11 17			*11 17*	
Burgess Hill 4	d		*10 08*				10 21			*10 21*				10 51				*11 08*			11 21			*11 21*	
Wivelsfield 4	d		*10 11*				10 23			*10 35*				10 53				*11 11*			11 23			*11 34*	
Haywards Heath 3	d		10 18				10 32			10 48				11 02				11 18			11 32			11 48	
Balcombe	d						10 37			*10 37*											11 37			*11 37*	
Three Bridges 4	d		*10 18*				10 42			*10 48*				11 12				*11 18*			11 42			*11 48*	
Gatwick Airport 10 ✈	d		10 31				10 46			11 01				11 16				11 31			11 46			12 01	
Redhill	d		*10 16*				*10 37*			*10 48*				*11 16*							*11 37*			*11 49*	
East Croydon 🚊	d		10 47				11 02			11 17				11 32				11 47			12 02			12 17	
Sutton (Surrey) 4	d			10 34				10 36			11 04				11 06				11 34			11 36			12 04
West Sutton	d							10 39							11 09							11 39			
Sutton Common	d							10 41							11 11							11 41			
St Helier	d							10 44							11 14							11 44			
Morden South	d							10 46							11 16							11 46			
South Merton	d							10 48							11 18							11 48			
Wimbledon Chase	d							10 50							11 20							11 50			
Wimbledon 6 ⊖ 🚊	d							10 53							11 23							11 53			
Haydons Road	d							10 55							11 25							11 55			
Tooting	d							10 58							11 28							11 58			
Carshalton	d			10 37							11 07								11 37						12 07
Hackbridge	d			10 39							11 09								11 39						12 09
Mitcham Junction 🚊	d			10 42							11 12								11 42						12 12
Eastfields §	d																								
Streatham 4	d			10 49				11 03			11 19				11 33				11 49			12 03			12 19
Tulse Hill 3	d			10 53				11 07			11 23				11 37				11 53			12 07			12 23
London Bridge 4 ⊖	d		11 00				11 15			11 30				11 45				12 00			12 15			12 30	
Herne Hill 4	d			10 56				11 11			11 26				11 41				11 56			12 11			12 26
Loughborough Jn	d			11 00				11 15			11 30				11 45				12 00			12 15			12 30
Elephant & Castle	d			11 05				11 20			11 35				11 50				12 05			12 20			12 35
London Blackfriars 3 ⊖	d		11 08	11 13			11 23	11 28		11 38	11 43			11 53	11 58			12 08	12 13		12 23	12 28		12 38	12 43
City Thameslink 3	d		11 10	11 15			11 25	11 30		11 40	11 45			11 55	12 00			12 10	12 15		12 25	12 30		12 40	12 45
Moorgate ⊖	d																								
Barbican ⊖	d																								
Farringdon 3 ⊖	d		11 14	11 19			11 29	11 34		11 44	11 49			11 59	12 04			12 14	12 19		12 29	12 34		12 44	12 49
St Pancras International 15 ⊖	d	11 30	11 18	11 23			11 33	11 38		11 48	11 53	12 00		12 03	12 08		12 30	12 18	12 23		12 33	12 38		12 48	12 53
Kentish Town ⊖	d			11 27				11 42			11 57				12 12				12 27			12 42			12 57
West Hampstead Thameslink ⊖	d			11 31				11 46			12 01				12 16				12 31			12 46			13 01
Cricklewood	d			11 34	←			11 49	←		12 04		←		12 19	←			12 34	←		12 49	←		13 04
Hendon	d			11 37	11 22			11 52	11 37		12 07		11 52		12 22	12 07			12 37	12 22		12 52	12 37		13 07
Mill Hill Broadway	d			→	11 25			→	11 40		→		11 55		→	12 10			→	12 25		→	12 40		→
Elstree & Borehamwood	d				11 30				11 45				12 00			12 15				12 30			12 45		
Radlett	d				11 38				11 50				12 08			12 20				12 38			12 50		
St Albans	d		11 39		11 44		11 54		11a59	12 09			12 14	12 24		12a29		12 39		12 44	12 54		12a59	13 09	
Harpenden	d		11 44		11 49		11 59			12 14			12 19	12 29				12 44		12 49	12 59			13 14	
Luton Airport Parkway 7 ✈	d		11 50		11 55		12 05			12 20		12 22	12 25	12 35				12 50		12 55	13 05			13 20	
Luton 10	d	11 53	11 54		12a01		12 08			12 24			12a31	12 38			12 53	12 54		13a01	13 08			13 24	
Leagrave	d		11 58				12 12			12 28				12 42				12 58			13 12			13 28	
Harlington	d		12 04				12 18			12 34				12 48				13 04			13 18			13 34	
Flitwick	d		12 08				12 22			12 38				12 52				13 08			13 22			13 38	
Bedford 7	a	12 07	12 20				12 35			12 50		12 37		13 05			13 07	13 20			13 35			13 50	

For general notes see front of timetable
For details of catering facilities see Directory of Train Operators

§ It is unknown at the time of going to press, when this station will open. For further details please contact National Rail Enquiries 08457-484950 or see local publicity.

A To Nottingham (Table 53)
B To Derby (Table 53)

Brighton, Gatwick Airport and South London → City of London, St.Albans, Luton and Bedford

Network Diagram - see first page of Table 52

		EM 1 ◇ A ☕	FC	FC 1	FC		FC	EM 1 ◇ B ☕	FC 1	FC	FC	FC 1	FC	FC	FC 1	FC	EM 1 ◇ A ☕	FC	EM 1 ◇ C ☕	FC 1	FC	FC	EM 1 ◇ B ☕	FC 1	FC
Brighton 10	d			11 37					12 04			12 07			12 34					12 37				13 04	
Preston Park	d			11 41					11 58			12 11			12 11					12 41				12 58	
Hassocks 4	d			11 47					12 05			12 17			12 17					12 47				13 05	
Burgess Hill 4	d			11 51					12 08			12 21			12 21					12 51				13 08	
Wivelsfield 4	d			11 53					12 11			12 23			12 34					12 53				13 11	
Haywards Heath 3	d			12 02					12 18			12 32			12 48					13 02				13 18	
Balcombe	d											12 37			12 37										
Three Bridges 4	d			12 12					12 18			12 42			12 48					13 12				13 18	
Gatwick Airport 10 ✈	d			12 16					12 31			12 46			13 01					13 16				13 31	
Redhill	d			12 16								12 37			12 48					13 05				13 18	
East Croydon	d			12 32					12 47			13 02			13 17					13 32				13 47	
Sutton (Surrey) 4	d				12 06					12 34			12 36			13 04					13 06				13 34
West Sutton	d				12 09								12 39								13 09				
Sutton Common	d				12 11								12 41								13 11				
St Helier	d				12 14								12 44								13 14				
Morden South	d				12 16								12 46								13 16				
South Merton	d				12 18								12 48								13 18				
Wimbledon Chase	d				12 20								12 50								13 20				
Wimbledon 6 ⊖	d				12 23								12 53								13 23				
Haydons Road	d				12 25								12 55								13 25				
Tooting	d				12 28								12 58								13 28				
Carshalton	d									12 37						13 07									13 37
Hackbridge	d									12 39						13 09									13 39
Mitcham Junction	d									12 42						13 12									13 42
Eastfields §	d																								
Streatham 4	d				12 33					12 49			13 03			13 19					13 33				13 49
Tulse Hill 3	d				12 37					12 53			13 07			13 23					13 37				13 53
London Bridge 4 ⊖	d			12 45					13 00			13 15			13 30					13 45				14 00	
Herne Hill 4	d				12 41					12 56			13 11			13 26					13 41				13 56
Loughborough Jn	d				12 45					13 00			13 15			13 30					13 45				14 00
Elephant & Castle	d				12 50					13 05			13 20			13 35					13 50				14 05
London Blackfriars 3 ⊖	d			12 53	12 58				13 08	13 13		13 23	13 28		13 38	13 43				13 53	13 58			14 08	14 13
City Thameslink 3	d			12 55	13 00				13 10	13 15		13 25	13 30		13 40	13 45				13 55	14 00			14 10	14 15
Moorgate ⊖	d																								
Barbican ⊖	d																								
Farringdon 3 ⊖	d			12 59	13 04				13 14	13 19		13 29	13 34		13 44	13 49				13 59	14 04			14 14	14 19
St Pancras International 15 ⊖	d	13 00		13 03	13 08			13 30	13 18	13 23		13 33	13 38		13 48	13 53	14 00		14 25	14 03	14 08		14 30	14 18	14 23
Kentish Town ⊖	d				13 12					13 27			13 42			13 57					14 12				14 27
West Hampstead Thameslink ⊖	d				13 16					13 31			13 46			14 01					14 16				14 31
Cricklewood	d		←		13 19		←			13 34	←		13 49	←		14 04		←			14 19	←			14 34
Hendon	d		12 52		13 22		13 07			13 37	13 22		13 52	13 37		14 07		13 52			14 22	14 07			14 37
Mill Hill Broadway	d		12 55		→		13 10			→	13 25		→	13 40		→		13 55			→	14 10			→
Elstree & Borehamwood	d		13 00				13 15				13 30			13 45				14 00				14 15			
Radlett	d		13 08				13 20				13 38			13 50				14 08				14 20			
St Albans	d		13 14	13 24			13a29		13 39		13 44	13 54		13a59	14 09			14 14		14 24		14a29		14 39	
Harpenden	d		13 19	13 29					13 44		13 49	13 59			14 14			14 19		14 29				14 44	
Luton Airport Parkway 7 ✈	d	13 22	13 25	13 35					13 50		13 55	14 05			14 20		14 22	14 25		14 35				14 50	
Luton 10	d		13a31	13 38				13 53	13 54		14a01	14 08			14 24			14a31		14 38			14 53	14 54	
Leagrave	d			13 42					13 58			14 12			14 28					14 42				14 58	
Harlington	d			13 48					14 04			14 18			14 34					14 48				15 04	
Flitwick	d			13 52					14 08			14 22			14 38					14 52				15 08	
Bedford 7	a	13 37		14 05				14 07	14 20			14 35			14 50		14 37		15 00	15 05			15 07	15 20	

For general notes see front of timetable
For details of catering facilities see Directory of Train Operators

§ It is unknown at the time of going to press, when this station will open. For further details please contact National Rail Enquiries 08457-484950 or see local publicity.

A To Derby (Table 53)
B To Nottingham (Table 53)
C To Sheffield (Table 53)

Brighton, Gatwick Airport and South London → City of London, St.Albans, Luton and Bedford

Network Diagram - see first page of Table 52

		FC	FC 1	FC	FC		FC 1	FC	EM 1 ◇ A ☕	FC	FC 1	FC	FC	FC	EM 1 ◇ B ☕	EM 1 ◇ C ☕	FC 1	FC	FC	FC 1	FC	FC	FC 1	EM 1 ◇ C ☕	FC 1
Brighton 10	d		13 07				13 34				13 37						14 04			14 07					14 34
Preston Park	d		13 11				*13 11*				13 41						*13 58*			14 11					*14 11*
Hassocks 4	d		13 17				*13 17*				13 47						*14 05*			14 17					*14 17*
Burgess Hill 4	d		13 21				*13 21*				13 51						*14 08*			14 21					*14 21*
Wivelsfield 4	d		13 23				*13 34*				13 53						*14 11*			14 23					*14 34*
Haywards Heath 3	d		13 32				13 48				14 02						14 18			14 31					14 48
Balcombe	d		13 37				*13 37*													14 37					*14 37*
Three Bridges 4	d		13 42				*13 48*				14 12						*14 18*			14 41					*14 48*
Gatwick Airport 10 ✈	d		13 46				14 01				14 16						14 31			14 46					15 01
Redhill	d		*13 37*				*13 48*				*14 16*									*14 37*					*14 48*
East Croydon 🚋	d		14 02				14 17				14 32						14 47			15 01					15 17
Sutton (Surrey) 4	d			13 36				14 04				14 06						14 34			14 36				
West Sutton	d			13 39								14 09									14 39				
Sutton Common	d			13 41								14 11									14 41				
St Helier	d			13 44								14 14									14 44				
Morden South	d			13 46								14 16									14 46				
South Merton	d			13 48								14 18									14 48				
Wimbledon Chase	d			13 50								14 20									14 50				
Wimbledon 6 ⊖ 🚋	d			13 53								14 23									14 53				
Haydons Road	d			13 55								14 25									14 55				
Tooting	d			13 58								14 28									14 58				
Carshalton	d							14 07										14 37							
Hackbridge	d							14 09										14 39							
Mitcham Junction 🚋	d							14 12										14 42							
Eastfields §	d																								
Streatham 4	d			14 03				14 19				14 33						14 49			15 03				
Tulse Hill 3	d			14 07				14 23				14 37						14 53			15 07				
London Bridge 4 ⊖	d		14 15				14 30				14 45						15 00			15 15					15 30
Herne Hill 4	d			14 11				14 26				14 41						14 56			15 11				
Loughborough Jn	d			14 15				14 30				14 45						15 00			15 15				
Elephant & Castle	d			14 20				14 35				14 50						15 05			15 20				
London Blackfriars 3 ⊖	d		14 23	14 28			14 38	14 43			14 53	14 58					15 08	15 13		15 22	15 28				15 38
City Thameslink 3	d		14 25	14 30			14 40	14 45			14 55	15 00					15 10	15 15		15 25	15 30				15 40
Moorgate ⊖	d													15 06									15 35		
Barbican ⊖	d																								
Farringdon 3 ⊖	d		14 29	14 34			14 44	14 49			14 59	15 04		15 10			15 14	15 19		15 29	15 34		15 39		15 44
St Pancras International 15 ⊖	d		14 33	14 38			14 48	14 53	15 00		15 03	15 08		15 15	15 25	15 30	15 18	15 23		15 33	15 38		15 44	15 55	15 48
Kentish Town ⊖	d			14 42				14 57				15 12						15 27			15 42				
West Hampstead Thameslink ⊖	d			14 46				15 01				15 16						15 31			15 46				
Cricklewood	d	←		14 49	←			15 04		←		15 19	←					15 34	←		15 49	←			
Hendon	d	14 22		14 52	14 37			15 07		14 52		15 22	15 07					15 37	15 22		15 52	15 37			
Mill Hill Broadway	d	14 25		→	14 40			→		14 55		→	15 10					→	15 25		→	15 40			
Elstree & Borehamwood	d	14 30			14 45					15 00			15 15						15 30			15 45			
Radlett	d	14 38			14 50					15 08			15 20						15 38			15 50			
St Albans	d	14 44	14 54		14a59		15 09			15 14	15 24		15a29	15 34			15 39		15 44	15 54		15a59	16 02		16 09
Harpenden	d	14 49	14 59				15 14			15 20	15 29			15 40			15 44		15 49	15 59			16 09		16 14
Luton Airport Parkway 7 ✈	d	14 55	15 05				15 20		15 22	15 25	15 35						15 50		15 55	16 05					16 20
Luton 10	d	15a01	15 08				15 24			15a31	15 38			15 47	15a48	15 53	15 54		16a01	16 08			16 17	16a18	16 24
Leagrave	d		15 12				15 28				15 42						15 58			16 12					16 28
Harlington	d		15 18				15 34				15 48						16 04			16 18					16 34
Flitwick	d		15 22				15 38				15 52			15 58			16 08			16 22			16 27		16 38
Bedford 7	a		15 35				15 50		15 37		16 05			16 12		16 08	16 20			16 35			16 42		16 50

For general notes see front of timetable
For details of catering facilities see Directory of Train Operators

§ It is unknown at the time of going to press, when this station will open. For further details please contact National Rail Enquiries 08457-484950 or see local publicity.

A To Derby (Table 53)
B To Sheffield (Table 53)
C To Nottingham (Table 53)

Brighton, Gatwick Airport and South London → City of London, St.Albans, Luton and Bedford

Network Diagram - see first page of Table 52

		FC	EM	FC	EM		FC	FC	FC	EM	FC	FC	FC	FC	FC	FC	FC	FC	FC	FC	FC	EM	EM	FC	FC
			1 ◇ A ☕		1 ◇ ☕		1			1 ◇ B ☕	1			1	1			1			1	1 ◇ A ☕	1 ◇ C ☕	1	
Brighton 10	d						14 37				15 04				15 07						15 34			15 37	
Preston Park	d						14 41				*14 58*				15 11						*15 11*			15 41	
Hassocks 4	d						14 47				*15 05*				15 17						*15 17*			15 47	
Burgess Hill 4	d						14 51				*15 08*				15 21						*15 21*			15 51	
Wivelsfield 4	d						14 53				*15 11*				15 23						*15 35*			15 53	
Haywards Heath 3	d						15 02				15 18				15 32						15 48			15 58	
Balcombe	d														15 37						*15 37*				
Three Bridges 4	d						15 12				*15 18*				15 42						*15 48*			16 07	
Gatwick Airport 10	✈ d						15 16				15 31				15 46						16 01			16 11	
Redhill	d						*15 16*								*15 37*						*15 48*				
East Croydon	🚋 d						15 32				15 47				16 02						16 17			16 27	
Sutton (Surrey) 4	d	15 04						15 06				15 34				15 36			16 04						
West Sutton	d							15 09								15 39									
Sutton Common	d							15 11								15 41									
St Helier	d							15 14								15 44									
Morden South	d							15 16								15 46									
South Merton	d							15 18								15 48									
Wimbledon Chase	d							15 20								15 50									
Wimbledon 6	⊖ 🚋 d							15 23								15 53									
Haydons Road	d							15 25								15 55									
Tooting	d							15 28								15 58									
Carshalton	d	15 07										15 37							16 07						
Hackbridge	d	15 09										15 39							16 09						
Mitcham Junction	🚋 d	15 12										15 42							16 12						
Eastfields §	d																								
Streatham 4	d	15 19						15 33				15 49				16 03			16 19						
Tulse Hill 3	d	15 23						15 37				15 53				16 07			16 23		16 33				
London Bridge 4	⊖ d						15 45				16 00				16 15									16 42	
Herne Hill 4	d	15 26						15 41				15 56				16 11			16 27		16 37				
Loughborough Jn	d	15 30						15 45				16 00				16 15			16 30						
Elephant & Castle	d	15 35						15 50				16 05				16 20			16 35		16 43				
London Blackfriars 3	⊖ d	15 43					15 53	15 58			16 08	16b14			16 25	16 30			16c44		16 50			16 54	
City Thameslink 3	d	15 45					15 55	16 00			16 10	16 16			16 28	16 32			16 46		16 52			16 56	
Moorgate	⊖ d													16 24				16 38							
Barbican	⊖ d																								
Farringdon 3	⊖ d	15 49					15 59	16 04			16 14	16 20		16 28	16 32	16 36		16 42	16 50		16 58			17 02	
St Pancras International 3	⊖ d	15 53	16 00		16 08		16 03	16 08		16 30	16 18	16 25		16 32	16 36	16 40		16 46	16 54		17 02	17 15	17 30	17 06	
Kentish Town	⊖ d	15 57						16 12				16 28				16 44			16 58						
West Hampstead Thameslink	⊖ d	16 01						16 16				16 32				16 48			17 02						
Cricklewood	d	16 04		←				16 19	←			16 35	←			16 51	←		17 05	←					←
Hendon	d	16 07		15 52				16 22	16 07			16 38	16 22			16 54	16 38		17 08	16 54					17 08
Mill Hill Broadway	d	→		15 55				→	16 11			→	16 27			→	16 43		→	16 59					17 13
Elstree & Borehamwood	d			16 00					16 16				16 32				16 48			17 04					17 18
Radlett	d			16 08					16 20				16 38				16 52			17 08					17 22
St Albans	d			16 14			16 24		16a29		16 40		16 44	16 52	16 56		17a02	17 06		17 14	17 22			17 26	17a32
Harpenden	d			16 19			16 30				16 46		16 50	16 58	17 04			17 14		17 20	17 28			17 34	
Luton Airport Parkway 7	✈ d		16a21	16 25			16 36				16 52		16 56		17 10			17 20		17 26	17 34	17a38		17 40	
Luton 10	d			16a31	16 38		16 40			16 53	16 55		17a01	17 04	17 13			17 23		17a31	17 36			17 43	
Leagrave	d						16 44				16 58				17 16			17 26						17 46	
Harlington	d						16 50				17 04				17 22			17 32						17 52	
Flitwick	d						16 54				17 08			17 15	17 26			17 36			17 47			17 56	
Bedford 7	a				16 56		17 05			17 07	17 20			17 30	17 38			17 48			18 00		18 07	18 10	

For general notes see front of timetable
For details of catering facilities see Directory of Train Operators

§ It is unknown at the time of going to press, when this station will open. For further details please contact National Rail Enquiries 08457-484950 or see local publicity.

A To Derby (Table 53)
B To Nottingham (Table 53)
C To Sheffield (Table 53)

b Arr. 1611
c Arr. 1638

Brighton, Gatwick Airport and South London → City of London, St.Albans, Luton and Bedford

Network Diagram - see first page of Table 52

		FC	FC	FC 1	FC 1		FC	FC	FC 1	EM 1 ◇ A ☕	FC 1	FC	FC	EM 1 ◇ B ☕	FC 1	EM 1 ◇ C ☕	FC	EM 1 ◇ D ☕	FC	FC	FC 1	FC 1	FC	FC	FC 1
Brighton 10	d										16 07				16 14										16 29
Preston Park	d										16 11				*16 11*										16 33
Hassocks 4	d										16 17														16 39
Burgess Hill 4	d										16 21				16 25										16 43
Wivelsfield 4	d										*16 11*														16 46
Haywards Heath 3	d										16 26				16 38										16 50
Balcombe	d										16 31														16 56
Three Bridges 4	d										16 37				16 47										17 02
Gatwick Airport 10 ✈	d										16 41				16 53										17 07
Redhill	d										*16 18*				*16 48*										
East Croydon 🚋	d										16 57				17 09										17 27
Sutton (Surrey) 4	d	16 06	16 33				16 32												17 03	17 00					
West Sutton	d	16 09					16 35													17 03					
Sutton Common	d	16 11					16 37													17 05					
St Helier	d	16 14					16 40													17 08					
Morden South	d	16 16					16 42													17 10					
South Merton	d	16 18					16 44													17 12					
Wimbledon Chase	d	16 20					16 46													17 14					
Wimbledon 6 ⊖ 🚋	d	16 23					16 50													17 18					
Haydons Road	d	16 25					16 52													17 20					
Tooting	d	16 28					16 55													17 23					
Carshalton	d		16 36																17 06						
Hackbridge	d		16 38																17 08						
Mitcham Junction 🚋	d		16 41																17 11						
Eastfields §	d																								
Streatham 4	d	16 33	16 47				16 59												17 17	17 29					
Tulse Hill 3	d	16 37	16 50				17 02				17 12								17 22	17 32					
London Bridge 4 ⊖	d														17 29										
Herne Hill 4	d	16 42	16 54				17 06												17 26	17 36					
Loughborough Jn	d	16 45					17 09												17 29	17 39					
Elephant & Castle	d	16 50	17 00				17 14												17 34	17 44					17 52
London Blackfriars 3 ⊖	d	17b00	17 04				17 18				17 26				17 36				17 40	17 48	17 52				18c06
City Thameslink 3	d	17 02	17 06				17 20				17 28				17 39				17 42	17 50	17 54				18 08
Moorgate ⊖	d			17 10	17 14				17 24			17 32										17 58		18 04	
Barbican ⊖	d																								
Farringdon 3 ⊖	d	17 06	17 10	17 14	17 18		17 24		17 28		17 32	17e38			17 42				17f50	17 54	17 58	18 02		18 08	18 12
St Pancras International 15 ⊖	d	17 10	17 14	17 18	17 22		17 28		17 32	17 45	17 36	17 42		17 55	17 46	18 00		18 15	17 54	17 58	18 02	18 06		18 12	18 16
Kentish Town ⊖	d		17 18				17 32					17 46								18 02				18 16	
West Hampstead Thameslink ⊖	d	17 18	17 22				17 36					17 50							18 02	18 06				18 20	
Cricklewood	d		17 25				17 39	←				17 53	←				←			18 09			←	18 23	
Hendon	d		17 28				17 42	17 28				17 56	17 42				17 56			18 12			18 12	18 26	
Mill Hill Broadway	d		→				→	17 33				→	17 47				18 01			→			18 17	→	
Elstree & Borehamwood	d	17 28						17 38					17 52				18 06		18 12				18 22		
Radlett	d	17 32						17 42					17 56				18 10		18 16				18 26		
St Albans	d	17 38		17 38	17 42			17 48	17 52		17 56		18a06		18 06		18 16		18 22		18 22	18 26	18a36		18 36
Harpenden	d	17 44		17 44	17 50			17 54	17 58		18 04				18 14		18 22		18 28		18 28	18 34			18 44
Luton Airport Parkway 7 ✈	d	17 50			17 56			18 00			18 10				18 20	18 23	18 28		18 34			18 40			18 50
Luton 10	d	17 54		17 50	17 59			18a07	18 04	18a09	18 13			18a19	18 23		18a35		18 38		18 34	18 43			18 53
Leagrave	d	17 58			18 02						18 16				18 26				18 42			18 46			18 56
Harlington	d	18 04			18 08						18 22				18 32				18 48			18 52			19 02
Flitwick	d	18 08		18 01	18 12				18 15		18 26				18 36				18 52		18 45	18 56			19 06
Bedford 7	a	18 22		18 16	18 26				18 30		18 38				18 48	18 38		18 54	19 04		19 00	19 10			19 18

For general notes see front of timetable
For details of catering facilities see Directory of Train Operators

§ It is unknown at the time of going to press, when this station will open. For further details please contact National Rail Enquiries 08457-484950 or see local publicity.

A To Leeds (Table 53)
B To Nottingham (Table 53)
C To Burton-on-Trent (Table 53)
D To Sheffield (Table 53)

b Arr. 1657
c Arr. 1756
e Arr. 1734
f Arr. 1747

Brighton, Gatwick Airport and South London → City of London, St.Albans, Luton and Bedford

Network Diagram - see first page of Table 52

		EM	FC	EM	FC		FC	FC	FC	SN	FC	FC	FC	FC	EM	FC	FC	SN	FC	FC	FC	FC	SN	EM	EM
		1 ◇ A		1 ◇ A				1	1			1			1 ◇ B		1		1			1		1 ◇ C	1 ◇ A
Brighton 10	d								17 03								17 23		17 37						
Preston Park	d								16 58								17 27		17 41						
Hassocks 4	d								17 05								17 33		17 47						
Burgess Hill 4	d								17 13								17 37		17 51						
Wivelsfield 4	d								17 11								17 40								
Haywards Heath 3	d								17 18								17 46		17 56						
Balcombe	d																17 27		18 02						
Three Bridges 4	d								17 27								17 56		18 12						
Gatwick Airport 10 ✈	d								17 31								18 01		18 16						
Redhill	d								17 22								17 53		18 07						
East Croydon	d								17 47								18 17		18 32						
Sutton (Surrey) 4	d						17 31			17 30	17 39			18 06						18 08			18 31		
West Sutton	d									17 34	17 42									18 13			18 34		
Sutton Common	d									17 36	17 45									18 14			18 37		
St Helier	d									17 39	17 47									18 18			18 39		
Morden South	d									17 41	17 49									18 20			18 41		
South Merton	d									17 43	17 51									18 22			18 43		
Wimbledon Chase	d									17 45	17 53									18 24			18 45		
Wimbledon 6 ⊖	d									17 51	17 56							18 23		18 27			18 50		
Haydons Road	d									17 53	17 59							18 25		18 29			18 52		
Tooting	d									17 56	18 02							18 28		18 32			18 55		
Carshalton	d						17 34							18 09											
Hackbridge	d						17 36							18 11											
Mitcham Junction	d						17 39							18 14											
Eastfields §	d																								
Streatham 4	d						17 46			18 01	18 06			18 20				18 32		18 36			18 59		
Tulse Hill 3	d						17 50			18 05	18 10			18 24			18 32	18 36		18 40			19 05		
London Bridge 4 ⊖	d								18 11	18a24								18a53	18 45				19a22		
Herne Hill 4	d						17 54				18 14			18 27			18 37			18 44					
Loughborough Jn	d						17 57				18 17			18 30			18 40			18 47					
Elephant & Castle	d						18 02				18 22			18 35			18 45			18 52					
London Blackfriars 3 ⊖	d						18b14		18c26		18e32			18f46			18g52		18 56	19h02					
City Thameslink 3	d						18j20		18 28		18 34			18 48			18 54		18 58	19 04					
Moorgate ⊖	d				18 16			18 24				18 38										19 08			
Barbican ⊖	d																								
Farringdon 3 ⊖	d				18 20		18 24	18 28	18 32		18 38	18 42		18 52			18 58		19 02	19 08		19 12			
St Pancras International 15 ⊖	d	18 30		18 55	18 24		18 28	18 32	18 36		18 42	18 46		18 56	19 00		19 02		19 06	19 12		19 16		19 25	19 30
Kentish Town ⊖	d						18 32				18 46			19 00						19 16					
West Hampstead Thameslink ⊖	d				18 32		18 36				18 50			19 04					19 14	19 20					
Cricklewood	d		←				18 39				18 53		←	19 07		←				19 23	←				
Hendon	d		18 26				18 42 →				18 56 →		18 42	19 10 →		18 56				19 26 →	19 10				
Mill Hill Broadway	d		18 31										18 47			19 01					19 15				
Elstree & Borehamwood	d		18 36		18 42								18 52			19 06					19 20				
Radlett	d		18 40		18 46								18 56			19 10					19 24				
St Albans	d		18 46		18 52			18 52	18 56			19 06	19a06			19 16	19 22		19 28		19a34	19 36			
Harpenden	d		18 52		18 58			18 58	19 04			19 14				19 22	19 28		19 34			19 44			
Luton Airport Parkway 7 ✈	d		18 58		19 04				19 10			19 20			19 22	19 28			19 40						
Luton 10	d	18a54	19a05		19 08			19 04	19 13			19 23				19a35	19 34		19 43			19 50		19a50	19 53
Leagrave	d				19 12				19 16			19 26							19 46			19 54			
Harlington	d				19 18				19 22			19 32							19 52						
Flitwick	d				19 22			19 15	19 26			19 36					19 45		19 56						
Bedford 7	a			19 30	19 36			19 30	19 38			19 50			19 37		20 00		20 09			20 14			20 08

For general notes see front of timetable
For details of catering facilities see Directory of Train Operators

§ It is unknown at the time of going to press, when this station will open. For further details please contact National Rail Enquiries 08457-484950 or see local publicity.

A To Nottingham (Table 53)

B To Burton-on-Trent (Table 53)

C To Leeds (Table 53)

b Arr. 1809

c Arr. 1819

e Arr. 1829

f Arr. 1840

g Arr. 1849

h Arr. 1859

j Arr. 1816

Brighton, Gatwick Airport and South London → City of London, St.Albans, Luton and Bedford

Network Diagram - see first page of Table 52

	FC 1	FC	FC	FC 1		FC	FC	FC 1	EM 1 ◇ A ☕	FC	FC	FC 1	FC	FC	EM 1 ◇ B ☕	FC 1	FC	FC 1	FC	FC 1	EM 1 ◇ A ☕	FC	FC 1	FC
Brighton 10 d	18 03			18 07				18 34				18 37				18b49		19 07		19 34			19 37	
Preston Park d	17 58			18 11				18 11				18 41				18 41		19 11		19 11			19 41	
Hassocks 4 d	18 05			18 17				18 17				18 47				18 47		19 17		19 17			19 47	
Burgess Hill 4 d	18 13			18 21				18 33				18 51				18 51		19 21		19 33			19 51	
Wivelsfield 4 d	18 11			18 23				18 34				18 53				19c05		19 23					19 53	
Haywards Heath 3 d	18 18			18 32				18 48				19 02				19c14		19 32		19 48			20 02	
Balcombe d	18 02			18 37				18 37										19 37		19 37				
Three Bridges 4 d	18 18			18 42				18 48				19 12				19 27		19 42		19 51			20 12	
Gatwick Airport 10 ✈ d	18 31			18 46				19 01				19 16				19 31		19 46		20 01			20 16	
Redhill d	18 21			18 37				18 47				19 07				19 18		19 37		19 47			20 08	
East Croydon 🚋 d	18 47			19 02				19 17				19 32				19 47		20 02		20 17			20 32	
Sutton (Surrey) 4 d						18 37					19 02		19 02						19 36					20 06
West Sutton d						18 41							19 05						19 39					20 09
Sutton Common d						18 42							19 07						19 42					20 11
St Helier d						18 46							19 10						19 44					20 14
Morden South d						18 48							19 12						19 46					20 16
South Merton d						18 50							19 14						19 48					20 18
Wimbledon Chase d						18 52							19 16						19 50					20 20
Wimbledon 6 ⊖ 🚋 d						18 55							19 23						19 54					20 23
Haydons Road d						18 57							19 25						19 56					20 25
Tooting d						19 00							19 28						19 59					20 28
Carshalton d											19 05													
Hackbridge d											19 07													
Mitcham Junction 🚋 d											19 10													
Eastfields § d																								
Streatham 4 d						19 05					19 17		19 33						20 04					20 33
Tulse Hill 3 d						19 08					19 23		19 37						20 07					20 37
London Bridge 4 ⊖ d	19 00			19 16				19 30				19 45				20 00		20 15		20 30			20 45	
Herne Hill 4 d						19 11					19 27		19 41						20 11					20 41
Loughborough Jn d						19 15					19 30		19 45						20 15					20 45
Elephant & Castle d						19 20					19 35		19 50						20 20					20 50
London Blackfriars 3 ⊖ d	19e10			19 23		19 28		19 38			19 43	19 53	19 58			20 08		20 23	20 28	20 38			20 53	20 58
City Thameslink 3 d	19 12			19 25		19 30		19 40			19 45	19 55	20 00			20 10		20 25	20 30	20 40			20 55	21 00
Moorgate ⊖ d			19 18																					
Barbican ⊖ d																								
Farringdon 3 ⊖ d	19 16		19 22	19 29		19 34		19 44			19 50	19 59	20 04			20 14		20 29	20 34	20 44			20 59	21 04
St Pancras International 15 ⊖ d	19 20		19 26	19 33		19 38		19 48	20 00		19 54	20 03	20 08		20 30	20 18		20 33	20 38	20 48	21 00		21 03	21 08
Kentish Town ⊖ d			19 30			19 42					19 58		20 12						20 42					21 12
West Hampstead Thameslink ⊖ d			19 34	19 40		19 46					20 02	20 10	20 16					20 40	20 46				21 10	21 16
Cricklewood d		←	19 37			19 49				←	20 05		20 19				←		20 49			←		21 19
Hendon d		19 26	19 40			19 52	←			19 52	20 08		20 22	←			20 22		20 52			20 52		21 22
Mill Hill Broadway d		19 31	19 45			→	19 45			19 57	20 13		→	20 13			20 25		→			20 55		→
Elstree & Borehamwood d		19 36	→				19 50			20 02	→			20 18			20 30					21 00		
Radlett d		19 40					19 54			20 08				20 22			20 38					21 08		
St Albans d	19 42	19 46		19 54			20 00	20 09		20 14		20 24		20 30		20 39	20 44	20 54		21 09		21 14	21 24	
Harpenden d	19 48	19 52		20 01			20 06	20 14		20 19		20 31		20 36		20 44	20 49	21 01		21 14		21 19	21 31	
Luton Airport Parkway 7 ✈ d	19 54	19 58		20 07			20 12	20 20	20 22	20 25		20 37		20 42		20 50	20 55	21 07		21 20	21 22	21 25	21 37	
Luton 10 d	19 57	20a03		20 10			20 15	20 24		20a31		20 40		20 45	20 53	20 54	21a01	21 10		21 24		21a31	21 40	
Leagrave d	20 00			20 14			20 18	20 28				20 44		20 48		20 58		21 14		21 28			21 44	
Harlington d	20 06			20 20			20 24	20 34				20 50		20 54		21 04		21 20		21 34			21 50	
Flitwick d	20 10			20 24			20 28	20 38				20 54		20 58		21 08		21 24		21 38			21 54	
Bedford 7 a	20 22			20 35			20 40	20 50	20 37			21 05		21 10	21 07	21 20		21 35		21 50	21 37		22 05	

For general notes see front of timetable
For details of catering facilities see Directory of Train Operators

§ It is unknown at the time of going to press, when this station will open. For further details please contact National Rail Enquiries 08457-484950 or see local publicity.

A To Derby (Table 53)
B To Nottingham (Table 53)
b Change at East Croydon
c Change at Gatwick Airport
e Arr. 1907

Table 52 — Mondays to Fridays

Brighton, Gatwick Airport and South London → City of London, St.Albans, Luton and Bedford

Network Diagram - see first page of Table 52

		EM	FC	FC	FC		FC	EM	FC	FC	FC	EM	FC	FC	FC	FC	EM	FC	FC	FC	FC	FC	FC
																						FX	FO
		1 ◇	1		1			1 ◇	1		1	1 ◇		1		1	1 ◇		1		1	1	1
		A						A				B					C						
		☕						☕				☕					☕						
Brighton 10	d		20 04		20 07				20 34		20 37			21 07		21 37			22 07		22 33	23 37	23b02
Preston Park	d		19 41		20 11				20 11		20 41			21 11		21 41			22 11		22 37	23 41	23b06
Hassocks 4	d		19 47		20 17				20 17		20 47			21 17		21 47			22 17		22 43	23 47	23b12
Burgess Hill 4	d		19 51		20 21				20 33		20 51			21 21		21 51			22 21		22 47	23 51	23b16
Wivelsfield 4	d		20 05		20 23						20 53			21 23		21 53			22 23		22 49	23 53	23b19
Haywards Heath 3	d		20 18		20 32				20 48		21 02			21 32		22 02			22 32		22 54	23 59	23 59
Balcombe	d				20 37				20 37					21 37					22 37		23 00	00 04	00 04
Three Bridges 4	d		20 18		20 42				20 51		21 12			21 42		22 12			22 42		23 12	00 10	00 10
Gatwick Airport 10 ✈	d		20 31		20 46				21 01		21 16			21 46		22 16			22 46		23 16	00 15	00 15
Redhill	d		20 18		20 37				20 47		21 08			21 37		22 08			22 40		22 47	00 22	00 22
East Croydon	d		20 47		21 02				21 17		21 32			22 02		22 32			23 02		23 32	00 36	00 36
Sutton (Surrey) 4	d						20 36						21 06		21 53								
West Sutton	d						20 39						21 09		21 56								
Sutton Common	d						20 41						21 11		21 58								
St Helier	d						20 44						21 14		22 01								
Morden South	d						20 46						21 16		22 02								
South Merton	d						20 48						21 18		22 04								
Wimbledon Chase	d						20 50						21 20		22 06								
Wimbledon 6 ⊖	d						20 53						21c39		22 09								
Haydons Road	d						20 55						21 41		22 11								
Tooting	d						20 58						21 44		22 14								
Carshalton	d																						
Hackbridge	d																						
Mitcham Junction	d																						
Eastfields §	d																						
Streatham 4	d						21 03						21 49		22 19								
Tulse Hill 3	d						21 07						21 53		22 23								
London Bridge 4 ⊖	d		21 00		21 15				21 30		21 45			22 15		22 45			23 15		23 45	00 52	00 52
Herne Hill 4	d						21 11						21 56		22 26								
Loughborough Jn	d						21 15						22 00		22 30								
Elephant & Castle	d						21 19						22 05		22 35								
London Blackfriars 3 ⊖	d		21 08		21 23		21e33		21 38		21 53		22 08	22 23	22 38	22 53		23 08	23 23	23 38	23 53	01 00	01 00
City Thameslink 3	d		21 10		21 25		21 35		21 40		21 55		22 10	22 25	22 40	22 55							
Moorgate ⊖	d																						
Barbican ⊖	d																						
Farringdon 3 ⊖	d		21 14		21 29		21 39		21 44		21 59		22 14	22 29	22 44	22 59		23 14	23 29	23 44	23 59		
St Pancras International 15 ⊖	d	21 30	21 18		21 33		21 43	22 00	21 48		22 03	22 25	22 18	22 33	22 48	23 03	23 15	23 18	23 33	23 48	00 03	01 08	01 08
Kentish Town ⊖	d						21 47						22 22		22 52			23 22		23 52		01 12	01 12
West Hampstead Thameslink ⊖	d				21 40		21 51				22 10		22 26	22 40	22 56	23 10		23 26	23 40	23 56	00 10	01 16	01 16
Cricklewood	d			←			21 54			←			22 29		22 59			23 29		23 59		01 19	01 19
Hendon	d			21 22			21 57			21 57			22 32		23 02			23 32		00 02		01 22	01 22
Mill Hill Broadway	d			21 25			→			22 00			22 35		23 05			23 35		00 05		01 25	01 25
Elstree & Borehamwood	d			21 30						22 05			22 40		23 10			23 40		00 10		01 30	01 30
Radlett	d			21 38						22 09			22 44		23 14			23 44		00 14		01 34	01 34
St Albans	d		21 39	21 44	21 54				22 08	22 14	22 24		22 50	22 54	23 20	23 24		23 50	23 54	00 20	00 24	01 40	01 40
Harpenden	d		21 44	21 49	22 01				22 14	22 19	22 31		22 55	23 01	23 25	23 31		23 55	00 01	00 25	00 31	01 45	01 45
Luton Airport Parkway 7 ✈	d		21 50	21 56	22 07				22 20	22 25	22 37		23 01	23 07	23 31	23 37		00 01	00 07	00 31	00 37	01 51	01 51
Luton 10	d	21 53	21 54	22 00	22 10			22 22	22 24	22 30	22 40	22 48	23 05	23 10	23 35	23 40	23 45	00 05	00 10	00 35	00 40	01 55	01 55
Leagrave	d		21 58	22 04	22 14				22 28	22 34	22 44		23 09	23 14	23 39	23 44		00 09	00 14	00 39	00 44	01 59	01 59
Harlington	d		22 04	22 10	22 20				22 34	22 40	22 50		23 14	23 20	23 44	23 50		00 14	00 20	00 44	00 50	02 04	02 04
Flitwick	d		22 08	22 14	22 24				22 38	22 44	22 54		23 18	23 24	23 48	23 54		00 18	00 24	00 48	00 54	02 08	02 08
Bedford 7	a	22 07	22 20	22 25	22 35			22 37	22 50	22 55	23 05	23 04	23 30	23 35	00 01	00 07	00 09	00 30	00 35	01 00	01 07	02 20	02 20

For general notes see front of timetable
For details of catering facilities see Directory of Train Operators

§ It is unknown at the time of going to press, when this station will open. For further details please contact National Rail Enquiries 08457-484950 or see local publicity.

A To Nottingham (Table 53)
B To Sheffield (Table 53)
C To Derby (Table 53)
b Change at Three Bridges

c Arr. 2125
e Arr. 2126

Table 52

Saturdays

Brighton, Gatwick Airport and South London → City of London, St.Albans, Luton and Bedford

Network Diagram - see first page of Table 52

	FC	FC 1	FC	FC 1	FC	FC 1	FC	FC 1	FC 1	FC 1	FC 1	EM 1 ◇ A	FC 1	FC B	FC 1	EM 1 ◇ C	FC B	EM 1 ◇ D	EM 1 ◇ C	FC 1	FC B	FC	FC 1	FC
Brighton 10 d		22p07		22p33		*23 02*					*03 50*				05 24					06 04			06 24	
Preston Park d		22p11		22p37		*23 06*									05 28					*06b00*			06 28	
Hassocks 4 d		22p17		22p43		*23 12*									05 34					*06b06*			06 34	
Burgess Hill 4 d		22p21		22p47		*23 16*									05 38					06 14			06 38	
Wivelsfield 4 d		22p23		22p49		*23 19*									05 40					*06 11*			06 40	
Haywards Heath 3 d		22p32		22p54		23p59					*04 25*				05 45					06 18			06 45	
Balcombe d		22p37		23p00		00 04									05 51					*05 51*			06 51	
Three Bridges 4 d		22p42		23p12		00 10		02 25	03 25	04 25	04 55		05 20		05 56					*06 20*			06 56	
Gatwick Airport 10 ✈ d		22p46		23p16		00 15		02 30	03 30	04 30	05 00		05 25		06 01					06 31			07 01	
Redhill d						00 22									*05 52*					*06 08*			*06 37*	
East Croydon 🚋 d		23p02		23p32		00 36		02 47	03 47	04 47	05 17		05 42		06 17					06 47			07 17	
Sutton (Surrey) 4 d																								07 04
West Sutton d																								
Sutton Common d																								
St Helier d																								
Morden South d																								
South Merton d																								
Wimbledon Chase d																								
Wimbledon 6 ⊖ 🚋 d																						06 53		
Haydons Road d																						06 55		
Tooting d																						06 58		
Carshalton d																								07 07
Hackbridge d																								07 09
Mitcham Junction 🚋 d																								07 12
Eastfields § d																								
Streatham 4 d														05 49			06 19				06 49	07 03		07 19
Tulse Hill 3 d														05 58			06 23				06 53	07 07		07 23
London Bridge 4 ⊖ d		23p15		23p45	00 20	00 52									06 31					07 01			07 31	
Herne Hill 4 d														06 02			06 26				06 56	07 11		07 26
Loughborough Jn d																	06 30				07 00	07 15		07 30
Elephant & Castle d														06 07			06 35				07 05	07 20		07 35
London Blackfriars 3 ⊖ d	23p08	23p23	23p38	23p53	00 28	01 00		03 13	04 13	05 13	05 43		06 08	06 13	06 38		06 43			07 08	07 13	07 28	07 38	07 43
City Thameslink 3 d																								
Moorgate ⊖ d																								
Barbican ⊖ d																								
Farringdon 3 ⊖ d	23p14	23p29	23p44	23p59	00 34					05 18	05 48		06 14	06 19	06 42		06 49			07 14	07 19	07 34	07 44	07 49
St Pancras International 15 ⊖ d	23p18	23p33	23p48	00 03	00 38	01 08	01 52	03 22	04 22	05 22	05 52	06 20	06 18	06 23	06 46	07 00	06 53	07 25	07 30	07 18	07 23	07 38	07 48	07 53
Kentish Town ⊖ d	23p22		23p52		00 42	01 12	01 56	03 26	04 26	05 26	05 56			06 27			06 57				07 27	07 42		07 57
West Hampstead Thameslink ⊖ d	23p26	23p40	23p56	00 10	00 46	01 16	02 00	03 30	04 30	05 30	06 00		06 25	06 31	06 53		07 01			07 25	07 31	07 46		08 01
Cricklewood d	23p29		23p59		00 49	01 19	02 03	03 33	04 33	05 33	06 03			06 34			07 04				07 34	07 49		08 04
Hendon d	23p32		00 02		00 52	01 22	02 06	03 36	04 36	05 36	06 06			06 37			07 07				07 37	07 52		08 07
Mill Hill Broadway d	23p35		00 05		00 55	01 25	02 09	03 39	04 39	05 39	06 09			06 40			07 10				07 40	⟶		⟶
Elstree & Borehamwood d	23p40		00 10		01 00	01 30	02 14	03 44	04 44	05 44	06 14			06 45			07 15				07 45			
Radlett d	23p44		00 14		01 04	01 34	02 18	03 48	04 48	05 48	06 18			06 49			07 19				07 49			
St Albans d	23p50	23p54	00 20	00 24	01 10	01 40	02 24	03 54	04 54	05 54	06 24		06 41	06 55	07 09		07 25			07 41	07 57		08 09	
Harpenden d	23p55	00 01	00 25	00 31	01 15	01 45	02 29	03 59	04 59	05 59	06 29		06 47	07 00	07 15		07 30			07 47	08 02		08 14	
Luton Airport Parkway 7 ✈ d	00 01	00 07	00 31	00 37	01 21	01 51	02 35	04 05	05 05	06 05	06 35		06 52	07 06	07 20	07 25	07 36			07 52	08 08		08 20	
Luton 10 d	00 05	00 10	00 35	00 40	01 25	01 55	02 40	04 10	05 10	06 10	06 40	06 44	06 56	07a12	07 24		07a42	07a49	07 53	07 56	08 11		08 24	
Leagrave d	00 09	00 14	00 39	00 44	01 29	01 59	02 44	04 14	05 14	06 14	06 44		07 00		07 28					08 00	08 14		08 28	
Harlington d	00 14	00 20	00 44	00 50	01 34	02 04	02 50	04 20	05 20	06 20	06 50		07 06		07 34					08 06	08 20		08 34	
Flitwick d	00 18	00 24	00 48	00 54	01 38	02 08	02 54	04 24	05 24	06 24	06 54		07 10		07 38					08 10	08 24		08 38	
Bedford 7 a	00 30	00 35	01 00	01 07	01 52	02 20	03 07	04 37	05 37	06 37	07 07	07 01	07 23		07 52	07 41			08 08	08 23	08 39		08 52	

For general notes see front of timetable
For details of catering facilities see Directory of Train Operators

§ It is unknown at the time of going to press, when this station will open. For further details please contact National Rail Enquiries 08457-484950 or see local publicity.

A To York (Table 53)
B From Selhurst (Table 177)
C To Nottingham (Table 53)
D To Sheffield (Table 53)
b Change at Haywards Heath

Table 52

Brighton, Gatwick Airport and South London → City of London, St.Albans, Luton and Bedford

Network Diagram - see first page of Table 52

		EM	FC	EM	FC	FC	FC	EM	FC	FC	FC	FC	FC	FC	FC	FC	EM	FC	FC	FC	FC	EM	EM	FC
		1 ◇		1 ◇	1			1 ◇	1			1			1		1 ◇		1			1 ◇	1 ◇	1
		A		B				C									A					B	C	
		ꟾP		ꟾP				ꟾP									ꟾP					ꟾP	ꟾP	
Brighton 10	d				06 37				07 04			07 07			07 34				07 37					08 04
Preston Park	d				06 41				*06 58*			07 11			*07 11*				07 41					*07 58*
Hassocks 4	d				06 47				*07 05*			07 17			*07 17*				07 47					*08 05*
Burgess Hill 4	d				06 51				*07 08*			07 21			*07 21*				07 51					*08 08*
Wivelsfield 4	d				06 53				*07 11*			07 23			*07 34*				07 53					*08 11*
Haywards Heath 3	d				07 02				07 18			07 32			07 48				08 02					08 18
Balcombe	d								*06 51*			07 37			*07 37*									
Three Bridges 4	d				07 12				*07 18*			07 42			*07 48*				08 12					*08 18*
Gatwick Airport 10 ✈	d				07 16				07 31			07 46			08 01				08 16					08 31
Redhill	d				*07 16*							*07 37*			*07 48*				*08 16*					
East Croydon 🚋	d				07 32				07 47			08 02			08 17				08 32					08 47
Sutton (Surrey) 4	d						07 06				07 34		07 36			08 04				08 06				
West Sutton	d						07 09						07 39							08 09				
Sutton Common	d						07 11						07 41							08 11				
St Helier	d						07 14						07 44							08 14				
Morden South	d						07 16						07 46							08 16				
South Merton	d						07 18						07 48							08 18				
Wimbledon Chase	d						07 20						07 50							08 20				
Wimbledon 6 ⊖ 🚋	d						07 23						07 53							08 23				
Haydons Road	d						07 25						07 55							08 25				
Tooting	d						07 28						07 58							08 28				
Carshalton	d										07 37					08 07								
Hackbridge	d										07 39					08 09								
Mitcham Junction 🚋	d										07 42					08 12								
Eastfields §	d																							
Streatham 4	d						07 33				07 49		08 03			08 19				08 33				
Tulse Hill 3	d						07 37				07 53		08 07			08 23				08 37				
London Bridge 4 ⊖	d				07 45				08 01			08 15			08 31				08 45					09 01
Herne Hill 4	d						07 41				07 56		08 11			08 26				08 41				
Loughborough Jn	d						07 45				08 00		08 15			08 30				08 45				
Elephant & Castle	d						07 50				08 05		08 20			08 35				08 50				
London Blackfriars 3 ⊖	d				07 53		07 58		08 08		08 13	08 23	08 28		08 38	08 43			08 53	08 58				09 08
City Thameslink 3	d																			09 00				09 10
Moorgate ⊖	d																							
Barbican ⊖	d																							
Farringdon 3 ⊖	d				07 59		08 04		08 14		08 19	08 29	08 34		08 44	08 49			08 59	09 04				09 14
St Pancras International 15 ⊖	d	08 00		08 25	08 03		08 08	08 30	08 18		08 23	08 33	08 38		08 48	08 53	09 00		09 03	09 08		09 25	09 30	09 18
Kentish Town ⊖	d						08 12				08 27		08 42			08 57				09 12				
West Hampstead Thameslink ⊖	d						08 16				08 31		08 46			09 01				09 16				
Cricklewood	d		←			←	08 19			←	08 34		08 49	←		09 04		←		09 19	←			
Hendon	d		07 52			08 07	08 22			08 22	08 37		08 52	08 37		09 07		08 52		09 22	09 07			
Mill Hill Broadway	d		07 55			08 10	→			08 25	→		→	08 40		→		08 55		→	09 10			
Elstree & Borehamwood	d		08 00			08 15				08 30				08 45				09 00			09 15			
Radlett	d		08 08			08 20				08 38				08 50				09 08			09 20			
St Albans	d		08 14		08 24	08a29			08 39	08 44		08 54		08a59	09 09			09 14	09 24		09a29			09 39
Harpenden	d		08 19		08 29				08 44	08 49		08 59			09 14			09 19	09 29					09 44
Luton Airport Parkway 7 ✈	d	08 22	08 25		08 35				08 50	08 55		09 05			09 20		09 22	09 25	09 35					09 50
Luton 10	d		08a31		08 38			08 53	08 54	09a01		09 08			09 24			09a31	09 38			09a48	09 53	09 54
Leagrave	d				08 42				08 58			09 12			09 28				09 42					09 58
Harlington	d				08 48				09 04			09 18			09 34				09 48					10 04
Flitwick	d				08 52				09 08			09 22			09 38				09 52					10 08
Bedford 7	a	08 37		09 00	09 07			09 07	09 22			09 37			09 52		09 37		10 07				10 07	10 22

For general notes see front of timetable
For details of catering facilities see Directory of Train Operators

§ It is unknown at the time of going to press, when this station will open. For further details please contact National Rail Enquiries 08457-484950 or see local publicity.

A To Derby (Table 53)
B To Sheffield (Table 53)
C To Nottingham (Table 53)

Table 52

Saturdays

Brighton, Gatwick Airport and South London → City of London, St.Albans, Luton and Bedford

Network Diagram - see first page of Table 52

		FC	FC	FC 1	FC	FC	FC 1	FC	EM 1 ◇ A ☕	FC	FC 1	FC	FC	EM 1 ◇ B ☕	FC 1	FC	FC	FC 1	FC	FC	FC 1	FC	EM 1 ◇ A ☕	FC	FC 1
Brighton 10	d			08 07			08 34				08 37				09 04			09 07			09 34				09 37
Preston Park	d			08 11			*08 11*				08 41				*08 58*			09 11			*09 11*				09 41
Hassocks 4	d			08 17			*08 17*				08 47				*09 05*			09 17			*09 17*				09 47
Burgess Hill 4	d			08 21			*08 21*				08 51				*09 08*			09 21							09 51
Wivelsfield 4	d			08 23			*08 34*				08 53				*09 11*						*09 34*				09 53
Haywards Heath 3	d			08 32			08 49				09 02				09 18			09 26			09 48				10 02
Balcombe	d			08 37			*08 37*											09 32			*09 32*				
Three Bridges 4	d			08 42			*08 48*				09 12				*09 18*			09 37			*09 48*				10 12
Gatwick Airport 10 ✈	d			08 46			09 01				09 16				09 31			09 41			10 01				10 16
Redhill	d			*08 37*			*08 48*				*09 16*										*09 48*				*10 16*
East Croydon ⛴	d			09 02			09 17				09 32				09 47			09 57			10 17				10 32
Sutton (Surrey) 4	d	08 34			08 36			09 04				09 06				09 34			09 36			10 04			
West Sutton	d				08 39							09 09							09 39						
Sutton Common	d				08 41							09 11							09 41						
St Helier	d				08 44							09 14							09 44						
Morden South	d				08 46							09 16							09 46						
South Merton	d				08 48							09 18							09 48						
Wimbledon Chase	d				08 50							09 20							09 50						
Wimbledon 6 ⊖ ⛴	d				08 53							09 23							09 53						
Haydons Road	d				08 55							09 25							09 55						
Tooting	d				08 58							09 28							09 58						
Carshalton	d	08 37						09 07								09 37						10 07			
Hackbridge	d	08 39						09 09								09 39						10 09			
Mitcham Junction ⛴	d	08 42						09 12								09 42						10 12			
Eastfields §	d																								
Streatham 4	d	08 49			09 03			09 19				09 33				09 49			10 03			10 19			
Tulse Hill 3	d	08 53			09 07			09 23				09 37				09 53			10 07			10 23			
London Bridge 4 ⊖	d			09 15			09 30				09 45				10 00			10 15			10 30				10 45
Herne Hill 4	d	08 56			09 11			09 26				09 41				09 56			10 11			10 26			
Loughborough Jn	d	09 00			09 15			09 30				09 46				10 00			10 15			10 30			
Elephant & Castle	d	09 05			09 20			09 35				09 50				10 05			10 20			10 35			
London Blackfriars 3 ⊖	d	09 13		09 23	09 28		09 38	09 43			09 53	09 58			10 08	10 13		10 23	10 28		10 38	10 43			10 53
City Thameslink 3	d	09 15		09 25	09 30		09 40	09 45			09 55	10 00			10 10	10 15		10 25	10 30		10 40	10 45			10 55
Moorgate ⊖	d																								
Barbican ⊖	d																								
Farringdon 3 ⊖	d	09 19		09 29	09 34		09 44	09 49			09 59	10 04			10 14	10 19		10 29	10 34		10 44	10 49			10 59
St Pancras International 15 ⊖	d	09 23		09 33	09 38		09 48	09 53	10 00		10 03	10 08		10 30	10 18	10 23		10 33	10 38		10 48	10 53	11 00		11 03
Kentish Town ⊖	d	09 27			09 42			09 57				10 12				10 27			10 42			10 57			
West Hampstead Thameslink ⊖	d	09 31			09 46			10 01				10 16				10 31			10 46			11 01			
Cricklewood	d	09 34	←		09 49	←		10 04		←		10 19	←			10 34	←		10 49	←		11 04		←	
Hendon	d	09 37	09 22		09 52	09 37		10 07		09 52		10 22	10 07			10 37	10 22		10 52	10 37		11 07		10 52	
Mill Hill Broadway	d	→	09 25		→	09 40		→		09 55		→	10 10			→	10 25		→	10 40		→		10 55	
Elstree & Borehamwood	d		09 30			09 45				10 00			10 15				10 30			10 45				11 00	
Radlett	d		09 38			09 50				10 08			10 20				10 38			10 50				11 08	
St Albans	d		09 44	09 54		09a59	10 09			10 14	10 24		10a29		10 39		10 44	10 54		10a59	11 09			11 14	11 24
Harpenden	d		09 49	09 59			10 14			10 19	10 29				10 44		10 49	10 59			11 14			11 19	11 29
Luton Airport Parkway 7 ✈	d		09 55	10 05			10 20		10 22	10 25	10 35				10 50		10 55	11 05			11 20		11 22	11 25	11 35
Luton 10	d		10a01	10 08			10 24			10a31	10 38			10 53	10 54		11a01	11 08			11 24			11a31	11 38
Leagrave	d			10 12			10 28				10 42				10 58			11 12			11 28				11 42
Harlington	d			10 18			10 34				10 48				11 04			11 18			11 34				11 48
Flitwick	d			10 22			10 38				10 52				11 08			11 22			11 38				11 52
Bedford 7	a			10 37			10 52		10 37		11 07			11 07	11 22			11 37			11 52		11 37		12 07

For general notes see front of timetable
For details of catering facilities see Directory of Train Operators

§ It is unknown at the time of going to press, when this station will open. For further details please contact National Rail Enquiries 08457-484950 or see local publicity.

A To Derby (Table 53)
B To Sheffield (Table 53)

Brighton, Gatwick Airport and South London → City of London, St.Albans, Luton and Bedford

Network Diagram - see first page of Table 52

		FC		FC	EM	FC	FC	FC	FC	FC	FC	FC	FC	EM	FC	FC	FC	FC	EM	FC	FC	FC	FC	FC	FC
					1 ◇	1			1			1		1 ◇		1			1 ◇	1			1		
					A									B					A						
					☕									☕					☕						
Brighton 10	d					10 04			10 07			10 34				10 37				11 04			11 07		
Preston Park	d					09 58			10 11			10 11				10 41				10 58			11 11		
Hassocks 4	d					10 05			10 17			10 17				10 47				11 05			11 17		
Burgess Hill 4	d					10 08			10 21			10 21				10 51				11 08			11 21		
Wivelsfield 4	d					10 11			10 23			10 34				10 53				11 11			11 23		
Haywards Heath 3	d					10 18			10 32			10 48				11 02				11 18			11 32		
Balcombe	d								10 37			10 37											11 37		
Three Bridges 4	d					10 18			10 42			10 48				11 12				11 18			11 42		
Gatwick Airport 10 ✈	d					10 31			10 46			11 01				11 16				11 31			11 46		
Redhill	d								10 37			10 48				11 16							11 37		
East Croydon 🚌	d					10 47			11 02			11 17				11 32				11 47			12 02		
Sutton (Surrey) 4	d	10 06					10 34			10 36			11 04				11 06				11 34			11 36	
West Sutton	d	10 09								10 39							11 09							11 39	
Sutton Common	d	10 11								10 41							11 11							11 41	
St Helier	d	10 14								10 44							11 14							11 44	
Morden South	d	10 16								10 46							11 16							11 46	
South Merton	d	10 18								10 48							11 18							11 48	
Wimbledon Chase	d	10 20								10 50							11 20							11 50	
Wimbledon 6 ⊖ 🚌	d	10 23								10 53							11 23							11 53	
Haydons Road	d	10 25								10 55							11 25							11 55	
Tooting	d	10 28								10 58							11 28							11 58	
Carshalton	d						10 37						11 07								11 37				
Hackbridge	d						10 39						11 09								11 39				
Mitcham Junction 🚌	d						10 42						11 12								11 42				
Eastfields §	d																								
Streatham 4	d	10 33					10 49			11 03			11 19				11 33				11 49			12 03	
Tulse Hill 3	d	10 37					10 53			11 07			11 23				11 37				11 53			12 07	
London Bridge 4 ⊖	d					11 00			11 15			11 30				11 45				12 00			12 15		
Herne Hill 4	d	10 41					10 56			11 11			11 26				11 41				11 56			12 11	
Loughborough Jn	d	10 45					11 00			11 15			11 30				11 45				12 00			12 15	
Elephant & Castle	d	10 50					11 05			11 20			11 35				11 50				12 05			12 20	
London Blackfriars 3 ⊖	d	10 58				11 08	11 13		11 23	11 28		11 38	11 43			11 53	11 58			12 08	12 13		12 23	12 28	
City Thameslink 3	d	11 00				11 10	11 15		11 25	11 30		11 40	11 45			11 55	12 00			12 10	12 15		12 25	12 30	
Moorgate ⊖	d																								
Barbican ⊖	d																								
Farringdon 3 ⊖	d	11 04				11 14	11 19		11 29	11 34		11 44	11 49			11 59	12 04			12 14	12 19		12 29	12 34	
St Pancras International 15 ⊖	d	11 08			11 30	11 18	11 23		11 33	11 38		11 48	11 53	12 00		12 03	12 08		12 30	12 18	12 23		12 33	12 38	
Kentish Town ⊖	d	11 12					11 27			11 42			11 57				12 12				12 27			12 42	
West Hampstead Thameslink ⊖	d	11 16					11 31			11 46			12 01				12 16				12 31			12 46	
Cricklewood	d	11 19		←			11 34	←		11 49	←		12 04		←		12 19	←			12 34	←		12 49	←
Hendon	d	11 22		11 07			11 37	11 22		11 52	11 37		12 07		11 52		12 22	12 07			12 37	12 22		12 52	12 37
Mill Hill Broadway	d	→		11 10			→	11 25		→	11 40		→		11 55		→	12 10			→	12 25		→	12 40
Elstree & Borehamwood	d			11 15				11 30			11 45				12 00			12 15				12 30			12 45
Radlett	d			11 20				11 38			11 50				12 08			12 20				12 38			12 50
St Albans	d			11a29		11 39		11 44	11 54		11a59	12 09			12 14	12 24		12a29		12 39		12 44	12 54		12a59
Harpenden	d					11 44		11 49	11 59			12 14			12 19	12 29				12 44		12 49	12 59		
Luton Airport Parkway 7 ✈	d					11 50		11 55	12 05			12 20		12 22	12 25	12 35				12 50		12 55	13 05		
Luton 10	d				11 53	11 54		12a01	12 08			12 24			12a31	12 38			12 53	12 54		13a01	13 08		
Leagrave	d					11 58			12 12			12 28				12 42				12 58			13 12		
Harlington	d					12 04			12 18			12 34				12 48				13 04			13 18		
Flitwick	d					12 08			12 22			12 38				12 52				13 08			13 22		
Bedford 7	a				12 07	12 22			12 37			12 52		12 37		13 07			13 07	13 22			13 37		

For general notes see front of timetable
For details of catering facilities see Directory of Train Operators

§ It is unknown at the time of going to press, when this station will open. For further details please contact National Rail Enquiries 08457-484950 or see local publicity.

A To Nottingham (Table 53)
B To Derby (Table 53)

Table 52

Brighton, Gatwick Airport and South London → City of London, St.Albans, Luton and Bedford

Network Diagram - see first page of Table 52

		FC 1	FC	EM 1 ◇ A ☕	FC	FC 1	FC	FC	EM 1 ◇ B ☕	FC 1	FC	FC	FC 1	FC		FC	FC 1	FC	EM 1 ◇ A ☕	FC	EM 1 ◇ C ☕	FC 1	FC	FC	EM 1 ◇ B ☕
Brighton 10	d	11 34				11 37				12 04			12 07				12 34					12 37			
Preston Park	d	*11 11*				11 41				*11 58*			12 11				*12 11*					12 41			
Hassocks 4	d	*11 17*				11 47				*12 05*			12 17				*12 17*					12 47			
Burgess Hill 4	d	*11 21*				11 51				*12 08*			12 21				*12 21*					12 51			
Wivelsfield 4	d	*11 34*				11 53				*12 11*			12 23				*12 34*					12 53			
Haywards Heath 3	d	11 48				12 02				12 18			12 32				12 48					13 02			
Balcombe	d	*11 37*											12 37				*12 37*								
Three Bridges 4	d	*11 48*				12 12				*12 18*			12 42				*12 48*					13 12			
Gatwick Airport 10	✈ d	12 01				12 16				12 31			12 46				13 01					13 16			
Redhill	d	*11 48*				*12 16*							*12 37*				*12 48*					*13 16*			
East Croydon	🚢 d	12 17				12 32				12 47			13 02				13 17					13 32			
Sutton (Surrey) 4	d		12 04				12 06				12 34			12 36				13 04					13 06		
West Sutton	d						12 09							12 39									13 09		
Sutton Common	d						12 11							12 41									13 11		
St Helier	d						12 14							12 44									13 14		
Morden South	d						12 16							12 46									13 16		
South Merton	d						12 18							12 48									13 18		
Wimbledon Chase	d						12 20							12 50									13 20		
Wimbledon 6	⊖ 🚢 d						12 23							12 53									13 23		
Haydons Road	d						12 25							12 55									13 25		
Tooting	d						12 28							12 58									13 28		
Carshalton	d		12 07								12 37							13 07							
Hackbridge	d		12 09								12 39							13 09							
Mitcham Junction	🚢 d		12 12								12 42							13 12							
Eastfields §	d																								
Streatham 4	d		12 19				12 33				12 49			13 03				13 19					13 33		
Tulse Hill 3	d		12 23				12 37				12 53			13 07				13 23					13 37		
London Bridge 4	⊖ d	12 30				12 45				13 00			13 15				13 30					13 45			
Herne Hill 4	d		12 26				12 41				12 56			13 11				13 26					13 41		
Loughborough Jn	d		12 30				12 45				13 00			13 15				13 30					13 45		
Elephant & Castle	d		12 35				12 50				13 05			13 20				13 35					13 50		
London Blackfriars 3	⊖ d	12 38	12 43			12 53	12 58			13 08	13 13		13 23	13 28			13 38	13 43				13 53	13 58		
City Thameslink 3	d	12 40	12 45			12 55	13 00			13 10	13 15		13 25	13 30			13 40	13 45				13 55	14 00		
Moorgate	⊖ d																								
Barbican	⊖ d																								
Farringdon 3	⊖ d	12 44	12 49			12 59	13 04			13 14	13 19		13 29	13 34			13 44	13 49				13 59	14 04		
St Pancras International 15	⊖ d	12 48	12 53	13 00		13 03	13 08		13 30	13 18	13 23		13 33	13 38			13 48	13 53	14 00		14 25	14 03	14 08		14 30
Kentish Town	⊖ d		12 57				13 12				13 27			13 42				13 57					14 12		
West Hampstead Thameslink	⊖ d		13 01				13 16				13 31			13 46				14 01					14 16		
Cricklewood	d		13 04		←		13 19	←			13 34	←		13 49		←		14 04		←			14 19	←	
Hendon	d		13 07		12 52		13 22	13 07			13 37	13 22		13 52		13 37		14 07		13 52			14 22	14 07	
Mill Hill Broadway	d		→		12 55		→	13 10			→	13 25		→		13 40		→		13 55			→	14 10	
Elstree & Borehamwood	d				13 00			13 15				13 30				13 45				14 00				14 15	
Radlett	d				13 08			13 20				13 38				13 50				14 08				14 20	
St Albans	d	13 09			13 14	13 24		13a29		13 39		13 44	13 54			13a59	14 09			14 14		14 24		14a29	
Harpenden	d	13 14			13 19	13 29				13 44		13 49	13 59				14 14			14 19		14 29			
Luton Airport Parkway 7	✈ d	13 20		13 22	13 25	13 35				13 50		13 55	14 05				14 20		14 22	14 25		14 35			
Luton 10	d	13 24			13a31	13 38			13 53	13 54		14a01	14 08				14 24			14a31		14 38			14 53
Leagrave	d	13 28				13 42				13 58			14 12				14 28					14 42			
Harlington	d	13 34				13 48				14 04			14 18				14 34					14 48			
Flitwick	d	13 38				13 52				14 08			14 22				14 38					14 52			
Bedford 7	a	13 52		13 37		14 07			14 07	14 22			14 37				14 52		14 37		15 00	15 07			15 07

For general notes see front of timetable
For details of catering facilities see
Directory of Train Operators

§ It is unknown at the time of going to press, when this station will open. For further details please contact National Rail Enquiries 08457-484950 or see local publicity.

A To Derby (Table 53)
B To Nottingham (Table 53)
C To Sheffield (Table 53)

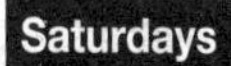

Brighton, Gatwick Airport and South London → City of London, St.Albans, Luton and Bedford

Network Diagram - see first page of Table 52

		FC	FC	FC	FC	FC	FC	FC	FC	EM	FC	FC	FC	FC	EM	EM	FC	FC	FC	FC	FC	FC	EM	FC	FC
		1			1			1		1 ◇ A		1			1 ◇ B	1 ◇ C	1			1			1 ◇ C	1	
Brighton 10	d	13 04			13 07			13 34				13 37					14 04			14 07				14 34	
Preston Park	d	*12 58*			13 11			*13 11*				13 41					*13 58*			14 11				*14 11*	
Hassocks 4	d	*13 05*			13 17			*13 17*				13 47					*14 05*			14 17				*14 17*	
Burgess Hill 4	d	*13 08*			13 21			*13 21*				13 51					*14 08*			14 21				*14 21*	
Wivelsfield 4	d	*13 11*			13 23			*13 34*				13 53					*14 11*			14 23				*14 34*	
Haywards Heath 3	d	13 18			13 32			13 48				14 02					14 18			14 32				14 48	
Balcombe	d				13 37			*13 37*												14 37				*14 37*	
Three Bridges 4	d	*13 18*			13 42			*13 48*				14 12					*14 18*			14 42				*14 48*	
Gatwick Airport 10	✈ d	13 31			13 46			14 01				14 16					14 31			14 46				15 01	
Redhill	d				*13 37*			*13 48*				*14 16*								*14 37*				*14 48*	
East Croydon	d	13 47			14 02			14 17				14 32					14 47			15 02				15 17	
Sutton (Surrey) 4	d		13 34			13 36			14 04				14 06					14 34			14 36				15 04
West Sutton	d					13 39							14 09								14 39				
Sutton Common	d					13 41							14 11								14 41				
St Helier	d					13 44							14 14								14 44				
Morden South	d					13 46							14 16								14 46				
South Merton	d					13 48							14 18								14 48				
Wimbledon Chase	d					13 50							14 20								14 50				
Wimbledon 6	⊖ d					13 53							14 23								14 53				
Haydons Road	d					13 55							14 25								14 55				
Tooting	d					13 58							14 28								14 58				
Carshalton	d		13 37						14 07									14 37							15 07
Hackbridge	d		13 39						14 09									14 39							15 09
Mitcham Junction	d		13 42						14 12									14 42							15 12
Eastfields §	d																								
Streatham 4	d		13 49			14 03			14 19				14 33					14 49			15 03				15 19
Tulse Hill 3	d		13 53			14 07			14 23				14 37					14 53			15 07				15 23
London Bridge 4	⊖ d	14 00			14 15			14 30				14 45					15 00			15 15				15 30	
Herne Hill 4	d		13 56			14 11			14 26				14 41					14 56			15 11				15 26
Loughborough Jn	d		14 00			14 15			14 30				14 45					15 00			15 15				15 30
Elephant & Castle	d		14 05			14 20			14 35				14 50					15 05			15 20				15 35
London Blackfriars 3	⊖ d	14 08	14 13		14 23	14 28		14 38	14 43			14 53	14 58				15 08	15 13		15 23	15 28			15 38	15 43
City Thameslink 3	d	14 10	14 15		14 25	14 30		14 40	14 45			14 55	15 00				15 10	15 15		15 25	15 30			15 40	15 45
Moorgate	⊖ d																								
Barbican	⊖ d																								
Farringdon 3	⊖ d	14 14	14 19		14 29	14 34		14 44	14 49			14 59	15 04				15 14	15 19		15 29	15 34			15 44	15 49
St Pancras International 15	⊖ d	14 18	14 23		14 33	14 38		14 48	14 53	15 00		15 03	15 08		15 25	15 30	15 18	15 23		15 33	15 38		15 55	15 48	15 53
Kentish Town	⊖ d		14 27			14 42			14 57				15 12					15 27			15 42				15 57
West Hampstead Thameslink	⊖ d		14 31			14 46			15 01				15 16					15 31			15 46				16 01
Cricklewood	d		14 34	←		14 49	←		15 04		←		15 19	←				15 34	←		15 49	←			16 04
Hendon	d		14 37	14 22		14 52	14 37		15 07		14 52		15 22	15 07				15 37	15 22		15 52	15 37			16 07
Mill Hill Broadway	d		→	14 25		→	14 40		→		14 55		→	15 10				→	15 25		→	15 40			→
Elstree & Borehamwood	d			14 30			14 45				15 00			15 15					15 30			15 45			
Radlett	d			14 38			14 50				15 08			15 20					15 38			15 50			
St Albans	d	14 39		14 44	14 54		14a59	15 09			15 14	15 24		15a29			15 39		15 44	15 54		15a59		16 09	
Harpenden	d	14 44		14 49	14 59			15 14			15 19	15 29					15 44		15 49	15 59				16 14	
Luton Airport Parkway 7	✈ d	14 50		14 55	15 05			15 20		15 22	15 25	15 35					15 50		15 55	16 05				16 20	
Luton 10	d	14 54		15a01	15 08			15 24			15a31	15 38			15a48	15 53	15 54		16a01	16 08			16a18	16 24	
Leagrave	d	14 58			15 12			15 28				15 42					15 58			16 12				16 28	
Harlington	d	15 04			15 18			15 34				15 48					16 04			16 18				16 34	
Flitwick	d	15 08			15 22			15 38				15 52					16 08			16 22				16 38	
Bedford 7	a	15 22			15 37			15 52		15 37		16 07				16 07	16 22			16 37				16 52	

For general notes see front of timetable
For details of catering facilities see Directory of Train Operators

§ It is unknown at the time of going to press, when this station will open. For further details please contact National Rail Enquiries 08457-484950 or see local publicity.

A To Derby (Table 53)
B To Sheffield (Table 53)
C To Nottingham (Table 53)

Table 52

Brighton, Gatwick Airport and South London → City of London, St.Albans, Luton and Bedford

Network Diagram - see first page of Table 52

		EM [1] ◇ A	FC	FC [1]		FC	FC	EM [1] ◇ B	FC [1]	FC	FC	FC [1]	FC	FC	FC [1]	FC	EM [1] ◇ C	FC	FC [1]	FC	FC	EM [1] ◇ D	EM [1] ◇ E	FC [1]	FC
Brighton [10]	d			14 37					15 04			15 07			15 34				15 37					16 04	
Preston Park	d			14 41					*14 58*			15 11			*15 11*				15 41					*15 58*	
Hassocks [4]	d			14 47					*15 05*			15 17			*15 17*				15 47					*16 05*	
Burgess Hill [4]	d			14 51					*15 08*			15 21			*15 21*				15 51					*16 08*	
Wivelsfield [4]	d			14 53					*15 11*			15 23			*15 34*				15 53					*16 11*	
Haywards Heath [3]	d			15 02					15 18			15 32			15 48				16 02					16 18	
Balcombe	d											15 37			*15 37*										
Three Bridges [4]	d			15 12					*15 18*			15 42			*15 48*				16 12					*16 18*	
Gatwick Airport [10] ✈	d			15 16					15 31			15 46			16 01				16 16					16 31	
Redhill	d			*15 16*								*15 37*			*15 48*				*16 16*						
East Croydon	d			15 32					15 47			16 02			16 17				16 32					16 47	
Sutton (Surrey) [4]	d					15 06				15 34			15 36			16 04				16 06					16 34
West Sutton	d					15 09							15 39							16 09					
Sutton Common	d					15 11							15 41							16 11					
St Helier	d					15 14							15 44							16 14					
Morden South	d					15 16							15 46							16 16					
South Merton	d					15 18							15 48							16 18					
Wimbledon Chase	d					15 20							15 50							16 20					
Wimbledon [6] ⊖	d					15 23							15 53							16 23					
Haydons Road	d					15 25							15 55							16 25					
Tooting	d					15 28							15 58							16 28					
Carshalton	d									15 37						16 07									16 37
Hackbridge	d									15 39						16 09									16 39
Mitcham Junction	d									15 42						16 12									16 42
Eastfields §	d																								
Streatham [4]	d					15 33				15 49			16 03			16 19				16 33					16 49
Tulse Hill [3]	d					15 37				15 53			16 07			16 23				16 37					16 53
London Bridge [4] ⊖	d			15 45					16 00			16 15			16 30				16 45					17 00	
Herne Hill [4]	d					15 41				15 56			16 11			16 26				16 41					16 56
Loughborough Jn	d					15 45				16 00			16 15			16 30				16 45					17 00
Elephant & Castle	d					15 50				16 05			16 20			16 35				16 50					17 05
London Blackfriars [3] ⊖	d			15 53		15 58			16 08	16 13		16 23	16 28		16 38	16 43			16 53	16 58				17 08	17 13
City Thameslink [3]	d			15 55		16 00			16 10	16 15		16 25	16 30		16 40	16 45			16 55	17 00				17 10	17 15
Moorgate ⊖	d																								
Barbican ⊖	d																								
Farringdon [3] ⊖	d			15 59		16 04			16 14	16 19		16 29	16 34		16 44	16 49			16 59	17 04				17 14	17 19
St Pancras International [15] ⊖	d	16 00		16 03		16 08		16 30	16 18	16 23		16 33	16 38		16 48	16 53	17 00		17 03	17 08		17 30	17 40	17 18	17 23
Kentish Town ⊖	d					16 12				16 27			16 42			16 57				17 12					17 27
West Hampstead Thameslink ⊖	d					16 16				16 31			16 46			17 01				17 16					17 31
Cricklewood	d		←			16 19	←			16 34	←		16 49	←		17 04		←		17 19	←				17 34
Hendon	d		15 52			16 22	16 07			16 37	16 22		16 52	16 37		17 07		16 52		17 22	17 07				17 37
Mill Hill Broadway	d		15 55			→	16 10			→	16 25		→	16 40		→		16 55		→	17 10				→
Elstree & Borehamwood	d		16 00				16 15				16 30			16 45				17 00			17 15				
Radlett	d		16 08				16 20				16 38			16 50				17 08			17 20				
St Albans	d		16 14	16 24			16a29		16 39		16 44	16 54		16a59	17 09			17 14	17 24		17a29			17 39	
Harpenden	d		16 19	16 29					16 44		16 49	16 59			17 14			17 19	17 29					17 44	
Luton Airport Parkway [7] ✈	d	16 22	16 25	16 35					16 50		16 55	17 05			17 20		17 22	17 25	17 35					17 50	
Luton [10]	d		16a31	16 38				16 53	16 54		17a01	17 08			17 24			17a31	17 38			17 53		17 54	
Leagrave	d			16 42					16 58			17 12			17 28				17 42					17 58	
Harlington	d			16 48					17 04			17 18			17 34				17 48					18 04	
Flitwick	d			16 52					17 08			17 22			17 38				17 52					18 08	
Bedford [7]	a	16 37		17 07				17 07	17 22			17 37			17 52		17 37		18 07			18 07	18 19	18 22	

For general notes see front of timetable
For details of catering facilities see Directory of Train Operators

§ It is unknown at the time of going to press, when this station will open. For further details please contact National Rail Enquiries 08457-484950 or see local publicity.

A To Burton-on-Trent (Table 53)
B To Nottingham (Table 53)
C To Derby (Table 53)
D To Sheffield (Table 53)
E To Leeds (Table 53)

Brighton, Gatwick Airport and South London → City of London, St.Albans, Luton and Bedford

Network Diagram - see first page of Table 52

		FC	FC	FC	FC	EM	FC	FC	EM	FC	FC	FC	FC	EM	FC	FC		FC	FC	FC	FC	EM	FC	FC	EM
			1			1 ◇	1		1 ◇		1			1 ◇	1				1			1 ◇	1		1 ◇
						A			B					A								A			C
						☕			☕					☕								☕			☕
Brighton 10	d		16 07				16 34				16 37				17 04				17 07				17 34		
Preston Park	d		16 11				16 11				16 41				16 58				17 11				17 11		
Hassocks 4	d		16 17				16 17				16 47				17 05				17 17				17 17		
Burgess Hill 4	d		16 21				16 21				16 51				17 08				17 21				17 21		
Wivelsfield 4	d		16 23				16 34				16 53				17 11				17 23				17 34		
Haywards Heath 3	d		16 32				16 48				17 02				17 18				17 32				17 48		
Balcombe	d		16 37				16 37												17 37				17 37		
Three Bridges 4	d		16 42				16 48				17 12				17 18				17 42				17 48		
Gatwick Airport 10 ✈	d		16 46				17 01				17 16				17 31				17 46				18 01		
Redhill	d		16 37				16 48				17 16								17 37				17 48		
East Croydon	d		17 02				17 17				17 32				17 47				18 02				18 17		
Sutton (Surrey) 4	d			16 36				17 04				17 06				17 34				17 36				18 04	
West Sutton	d			16 39								17 09								17 39					
Sutton Common	d			16 41								17 11								17 41					
St Helier	d			16 44								17 14								17 44					
Morden South	d			16 46								17 16								17 46					
South Merton	d			16 48								17 18								17 48					
Wimbledon Chase	d			16 50								17 20								17 50					
Wimbledon 6 ⊖	d			16 53								17 23								17 53					
Haydons Road	d			16 55								17 25								17 55					
Tooting	d			16 58								17 28								17 58					
Carshalton	d							17 07								17 37								18 07	
Hackbridge	d							17 09								17 39								18 09	
Mitcham Junction	d							17 12								17 42								18 12	
Eastfields §	d																								
Streatham 4	d			17 03				17 19				17 33				17 49				18 03				18 19	
Tulse Hill 3	d			17 07				17 23				17 37				17 53				18 07				18 23	
London Bridge 4 ⊖	d		17 15				17 30				17 45				18 00				18 15				18 30		
Herne Hill 4	d			17 11				17 26				17 41				17 56				18 11				18 26	
Loughborough Jn	d			17 15				17 30				17 45				18 00				18 15				18 30	
Elephant & Castle	d			17 20				17 35				17 50				18 05				18 20				18 35	
London Blackfriars 3 ⊖	d		17 23	17 28			17 38	17 43			17 53	17 58			18 08	18 13			18 23	18 28			18 38	18 43	
City Thameslink 3	d		17 25	17 30			17 40	17 45			17 55	18 00			18 10	18 15			18 25	18 30			18 40	18 45	
Moorgate ⊖	d																								
Barbican ⊖	d																								
Farringdon 3 ⊖	d		17 29	17 34			17 44	17 49			17 59	18 04			18 14	18 19			18 29	18 34			18 44	18 49	
St Pancras International 15 ⊖	d		17 33	17 38		17 55	17 48	17 53	18 00		18 03	18 08		18 30	18 18	18 23			18 33	18 38		18 55	18 48	18 53	19 00
Kentish Town ⊖	d			17 42				17 57				18 12				18 27				18 42				18 57	
West Hampstead Thameslink ⊖	d			17 46				18 01				18 16				18 31				18 46				19 01	
Cricklewood	d	←		17 49	←			18 04		←		18 19	←			18 34		←		18 49	←			19 04	
Hendon	d	17 22		17 52	17 37			18 07		17 52		18 22	18 07			18 37		18 22		18 52	18 37			19 07	
Mill Hill Broadway	d	17 25		→	17 40			→		17 55		→	18 10			→		18 25		→	18 40			→	
Elstree & Borehamwood	d	17 30			17 45					18 00			18 15					18 30			18 45				
Radlett	d	17 38			17 50					18 08			18 20					18 38			18 50				
St Albans	d	17 44	17 54		17a59		18 09			18 14	18 24		18b29		18 39			18 44	18 54		18c59		19 09		
Harpenden	d	17 49	17 59				18 14			18 19	18 29		18 34		18 44			18 49	18 59		19 04		19 14		
Luton Airport Parkway 7 ✈	d	17 55	18 05				18 20		18 22	18 25	18 35		18 40		18 50			18 55	19 05		19 10		19 20		19 22
Luton 10	d	18a01	18 08			18a18	18 24			18a31	18 38		18 44	18 53	18 54			19a01	19 08		19 14	19a18	19 24		
Leagrave	d		18 12				18 28				18 42		18 48		18 58				19 12		19 18		19 28		
Harlington	d		18 18				18 34				18 48		18 54		19 04				19 18		19 24		19 34		
Flitwick	d		18 22				18 38				18 52		18 58		19 08				19 22		19 28		19 38		
Bedford 7	a		18 37				18 52		18 37		19 07		19 11	19 07	19 22				19 37		19 41		19 52		19 37

For general notes see front of timetable
For details of catering facilities see Directory of Train Operators

§ It is unknown at the time of going to press, when this station will open. For further details please contact National Rail Enquiries 08457-484950 or see local publicity.

A To Nottingham (Table 53)
B To Barnsley (Table 53)
C To Derby (Table 53)

b Arr. 1826
c Arr. 1856

Table 52

Saturdays

Brighton, Gatwick Airport and South London → City of London, St.Albans, Luton and Bedford

Network Diagram - see first page of Table 52

	FC	FC 1	FC	FC	EM 1 ◇ A 🍴	EM 1 ◇ B 🍴	FC 1	FC	FC	FC 1	FC	FC	FC 1	EM 1 ◇ C 🍴	FC	FC	FC 1	FC	FC	EM 1 ◇ B 🍴	FC 1	FC	FC 1	FC
Brighton 10 d		17 37					18 04			18 07			18 34				18 37				19 04		19 07	
Preston Park d		17 41					17 58			18 11			18 11				18 41				18 58		19 11	
Hassocks 4 d		17 47					18 05			18 17			18 17				18 47				19 05		19 17	
Burgess Hill 4 d		17 51					18 08			18 21			18 21				18 51				19 08		19 21	
Wivelsfield 4 d		17 53					18 11			18 23			18 34				18 53				19 11		19 23	
Haywards Heath 3 d		18 02					18 18			18 32			18 48				19 02				19 18		19 32	
Balcombe d										18 37			18 37										19 37	
Three Bridges 4 d		18 12					18 18			18 42			18 51				19 12				19 18		19 42	
Gatwick Airport 10 ✈ d		18 16					18 31			18 46			19 01				19 16				19 31		19 46	
Redhill d		18 16								18 37			18 48				19 06				19 18		19 37	
East Croydon d		18 32					18 47			19 02			19 17				19 32				19 47		20 02	
Sutton (Surrey) 4 d			18 06					18 34			18 36					19 04		19 06						19 36
West Sutton d			18 09								18 39							19 09						19 39
Sutton Common d			18 11								18 41							19 11						19 41
St Helier d			18 14								18 44							19 14						19 44
Morden South d			18 16								18 46							19 16						19 46
South Merton d			18 18								18 48							19 18						19 48
Wimbledon Chase d			18 20								18 50							19 20						19 50
Wimbledon 6 ⊖ d			18 23								18 53							19 23						19 53
Haydons Road d			18 25								18 55							19 25						19 55
Tooting d			18 28								18 58							19 28						19 58
Carshalton d								18 37								19 07								
Hackbridge d								18 39								19 09								
Mitcham Junction d								18 42								19 12								
Eastfields § d																								
Streatham 4 d			18 33					18 49			19 03					19 19		19 33						20 03
Tulse Hill 3 d			18 37					18 53			19 07					19 23		19 37						20 07
London Bridge 4 ⊖ d		18 45					19 00			19 15			19 30				19 45				20 00		20 15	
Herne Hill 4 d			18 41					18 56			19 11					19 26		19 41						20 11
Loughborough Jn d			18 45					19 00			19 15					19 30		19 45						20 15
Elephant & Castle d			18 50					19 05			19 20					19 35		19 50						20 20
London Blackfriars 3 ⊖ d		18 53	18 58				19 08	19 13		19 23	19 28		19 38			19 43	19 53	19 58			20 08		20 23	20 28
City Thameslink 3 d		18 55	19 00				19 10	19 15		19 25	19 30		19 40			19 45	19 55	20 00			20 10		20 25	20 30
Moorgate ⊖ d																								
Barbican ⊖ d																								
Farringdon 3 ⊖ d		18 59	19 04				19 14	19 19		19 29	19 34		19 44			19 49	19 59	20 04			20 14		20 29	20 34
St Pancras International 15 ⊖ d		19 03	19 08		19 25	19 30	19 18	19 23		19 33	19 38		19 48	20 00		19 53	20 03	20 08		20 30			20 33	20 38
Kentish Town ⊖ d			19 12					19 27			19 42					19 57		20 12						20 42
West Hampstead Thameslink ⊖ d			19 16					19 31			19 46					20 01	20 10	20 16				←	20 40	20 46
Cricklewood d	←		19 19	←				19 34	←		19 49	←			←	20 04		20 19				20 19		20 49
Hendon d	18 52		19 22	19 07				19 37	19 22		19 52	19 37			19 52	20 07		→	←			20 22		20 52
Mill Hill Broadway d	18 55		→	19 10				→	19 25		→	19 40			19 55	20 10			20 10			20 25		→
Elstree & Borehamwood d	19 00			19 15					19 30			19 45			20 00	→			20 15			20 30		
Radlett d	19 08			19 20					19 38			19 50			20 08				20 20			20 38		
St Albans d	19 14	19 24		19b29			19 39		19 44	19 54		19c59	20 09		20 14		20 24		20e29		20 40	20 44	20 54	
Harpenden d	19 19	19 31		19 35			19 44		19 49	20 01		20 04	20 14		20 19		20 31		20 35		20 44	20 49	21 01	
Luton Airport Parkway 7 ✈ d	19 25	19 37		19 41			19 50		19 55	20 07		20 10	20 20	20 22	20 25		20 37		20 41		20 50	20 55	21 07	
Luton 10 d	19a31	19 40		19 44	19a48	19 53	19 54		20a01	20 10		20 14	20 24		20a31		20 40		20a45	20 53	20 54	21a01	21 10	
Leagrave d		19 44		19 48			19 58			20 14		20 18	20 28				20 44				20 58		21 14	
Harlington d		19 50		19 54			20 04			20 20		20 24	20 34				20 50				21 04		21 20	
Flitwick d		19 54		19 58			20 08			20 24		20 28	20 38				20 54				21 08		21 24	
Bedford 7 a		20 07		20 11		20 07	20 22			20 37		20 42	20 52	20 37			21 07			21 07	21 22		21 37	

For general notes see front of timetable
For details of catering facilities see Directory of Train Operators

§ It is unknown at the time of going to press, when this station will open. For further details please contact National Rail Enquiries 08457-484950 or see local publicity.

A To Leeds (Table 53)
B To Nottingham (Table 53)
C To Derby (Table 53)
b Arr. 1926
c Arr. 1956
e Arr. 2026

Brighton, Gatwick Airport and South London → City of London, St.Albans, Luton and Bedford

Network Diagram - see first page of Table 52

		FC	EM	FC	FC	FC	FC	FC	FC	FC	FC	FC	FC	EM	FC	FC	FC	FC	FC	FC	FC	FC	FC
		1	1 ◇		1		1		1		1		1	1 ◇		1		1		1		1	1
			A											A									
			☕											☕									
Brighton 10	d	19 34			19 37		20 04		20 07		20 34		20 37			21 07		21 37		22 07		22 33	23b02
Preston Park	d	19 11			19 41		19 41		20 11		20 11		20 41			21 11		21 41		22 11		22 37	23b06
Hassocks 4	d	19 17			19 47		19 47		20 17		20 17		20 47			21 17		21 47		22 17		22 43	23b12
Burgess Hill 4	d	19 21			19 51		20 02		20 21		20 21		20 51			21 21		21 51		22 21		22 47	23b16
Wivelsfield 4	d	19 34			19 53		20 03		20 23				20 53			21 23		21 53		22 23		22 49	23b19
Haywards Heath 3	d	19 48			20 02		20 18		20 32		20 48		21 02			21 32		22 02		22 32		22 54	23 59
Balcombe	d	19 37							20 37		20 37					21 37				22 37		23 00	00 04
Three Bridges 4	d	19 51			20 12		20 18		20 42		20 51		21 12			21 42		22 12		22 42		23 12	00 10
Gatwick Airport 10 ✈	d	20 01			20 16		20 31		20 46		21 01		21 16			21 46		22 16		22 46		23 16	00 15
Redhill	d	19 47			20 08		20 18		20 37		20 47		21 08			21 38		22 08		22 40		22 47	00 22
East Croydon	d	20 17			20 32		20 47		21 02		21 17		21 32			22 02		22 32		23 02		23 32	00 36
Sutton (Surrey) 4	d					20 06				20 36					21 06		21 52						
West Sutton	d					20 09				20 39					21 09		21 55						
Sutton Common	d					20 11				20 41					21 11		21 57						
St Helier	d					20 14				20 44					21 14		22 00						
Morden South	d					20 16				20 46					21 16		22 02						
South Merton	d					20 18				20 48					21 18		22 04						
Wimbledon Chase	d					20 20				20 50					21 20		22 06						
Wimbledon 6 ⊖	d					20 23				20 53					21c39		22 09		22 39				
Haydons Road	d					20 25				20 55					21 41		22 11		22 41				
Tooting	d					20 28				20 58					21 44		22 14		22 44				
Carshalton	d																						
Hackbridge	d																						
Mitcham Junction	d																						
Eastfields §	d																						
Streatham 4	d					20 33				21 03					21 49		22 19		22 49				
Tulse Hill 3	d					20 37				21 07					21 53		22 23		22 53				
London Bridge 4 ⊖	d	20 30			20 45		21 00		21 15		21 30		21 45			22 15		22 45		23 15		23 45	00 52
Herne Hill 4	d					20 41				21 11					21 56		22 26		22 56				
Loughborough Jn	d					20 45				21 15					22 00		22 30						
Elephant & Castle	d					20 50				21 20					22 05		22 35		23 05				
London Blackfriars 3 ⊖	d	20 38			20 53	20 58	21 08		21 23	21e33	21 38		21 53		22 08	22 23	22 38	22 53	23 08	23 23	23 38	23 53	01 00
City Thameslink 3	d	20 40			20 55	21 00																	
Moorgate ⊖	d																						
Barbican ⊖	d																						
Farringdon 3 ⊖	d	20 44			20 59	21 04	21 14		21 29	21 39	21 44		21 59		22 14	22 29	22 44	22 59	23 14	23 29	23 44	23 59	
St Pancras International 15 ⊖	d	20 48	21 00		21 03	21 08	21 18		21 33	21 43	21 48		22 03	22 10	22 18	22 33	22 48	23 03	23 18	23 33	23 48	00 03	01 08
Kentish Town ⊖	d					21 12				21 47					22 22		22 52		23 22		23 52		01 12
West Hampstead Thameslink ⊖	d				21 10	21 16			21 40	21 51			22 10		22 26	22 40	22 56	23 10	23 26	23 40	23 56	00 10	01 16
Cricklewood	d			←		21 19		←		21 54		←			22 29		22 59		23 29		23 59		01 19
Hendon	d			20 52		21 22		21 22		21 57		21 57			22 32		23 02		23 32		00 02		01 22
Mill Hill Broadway	d			20 55		→		21 25		→		22 00			22 35		23 05		23 35		00 05		01 25
Elstree & Borehamwood	d			21 00				21 30				22 05			22 40		23 10		23 40		00 10		01 30
Radlett	d			21 08				21 38				22 09			22 44		23 14		23 44		00 14		01 34
St Albans	d	21 09		21 14	21 24		21 39	21 44	21 54		22 10	22 15	22 24		22 50	22 54	23 20	23 24	23 50	23 54	00 20	00 24	01 40
Harpenden	d	21 14		21 19	21 31		21 44	21 49	22 01		22 14	22 21	22 31		22 55	23 01	23 25	23 31	23 55	00 01	00 25	00 31	01 45
Luton Airport Parkway 7 ✈	d	21 20	21 22	21 25	21 37		21 50	21 55	22 07		22 20	22 27	22 37		23 01	23 07	23 31	23 37	00 01	00 07	00 31	00 37	01 51
Luton 10	d	21 24		21a31	21 40		21 54	22 00	22 10		22 24	22 30	22 40	22 47	23 05	23 10	23 35	23 40	00 05	00 10	00 35	00 40	01 55
Leagrave	d	21 28			21 44		21 58	22 04	22 14		22 28	22 34	22 44		23 09	23 14	23 39	23 44	00 09	00 14	00 39	00 44	01 59
Harlington	d	21 34			21 50		22 04	22 10	22 20		22 34	22 40	22 50		23 14	23 20	23 44	23 50	00 14	00 20	00 44	00 50	02 04
Flitwick	d	21 38			21 54		22 08	22 14	22 24		22 38	22 44	22 54		23 18	23 24	23 48	23 54	00 18	00 24	00 48	00 54	02 08
Bedford 7	a	21 52	21 37		22 07		22 22	22 26	22 37		22 52	22 55	23 07	23 07	23 30	23 37	00 01	00 07	00 30	00 37	01 00	01 07	02 20

For general notes see front of timetable
For details of catering facilities see Directory of Train Operators

§ It is unknown at the time of going to press, when this station will open. For further details please contact National Rail Enquiries 08457-484950 or see local publicity.

A To Derby (Table 53)
b Change at Three Bridges
c Arr. 2123
e Arr. 2126

Table 52

Sundays

Brighton, Gatwick Airport and South London → City of London, St.Albans, Luton and Bedford

Network Diagram - see first page of Table 52

		FC	FC 1	FC	FC 1	FC	FC 1	FC 1	FC 1	FC 1	FC 1	FC 1	EM 1 ◇ A	FC 1	EM 1 ◇ B	FC 1	EM 1 ◇ A	FC 1	EM 1 ◇ B	FC 1	FC	EM 1 ◇ A	FC 1	FC	FC 1
Brighton 10	d		22p07		22p33		23 02	03 50	05 44	06 13	06 44	07 16		07 44		08 16		08 44		09 16	09 16		09 44		09 44
Preston Park	d		22p11		22p37		23 06				06 19	07 03		07 03		08 03		08 03		09 03	09 03		09 03		09 03
Hassocks 4	d		22p17		22p43		23 12		05 52		06 52	07 10		07 52		08 10		08 52		09 10	09 10		09 52		09 52
Burgess Hill 4	d		22p21		22p47		23 16		05 56	06 26	06 56	07 26		07 56		08 26		08 56		09 26	09 26		09 56		09 56
Wivelsfield 4	d		22p23		22p49		23 19				06 32	07 16		07 32		08 16		08 31		09 16	09 16		09 31		09 31
Haywards Heath 3	d		22p32		22p54		23p59		06 01	06 31	07 01	07 31		08 01		08 31		09 01		09 31	09 31		10 01		10 01
Balcombe	d		22p37		23p00		00 04					07 26				08 26				09 26	09 26				09 26
Three Bridges 4	d		22p42		23p12		00 10	05 10	06 10	06 40	07 10	07 40		08 10		08 40		09 10		09 40	09 40		10 10		10 10
Gatwick Airport 10 ✈	d		22p46		23p16		00 15	05 15	06 15	06 45	07 15	07 45		08 15		08 45		09 15		09 45			10 15		
Redhill	d						00 22		05 46		07 07			08 09				09 09			09 46		10 09		
East Croydon	d		23p02		23p32		00 36	05 32	06 32	07 02	07 32	08 02		08 32		09 02		09 32		10 02	10 12		10 32		10 42
Sutton (Surrey) 4	d																							10 10	
West Sutton	d																							10 13	
Sutton Common	d																							10 15	
St Helier	d																							10 17	
Morden South	d																							10 19	
South Merton	d																							10 21	
Wimbledon Chase	d																							10 22	
Wimbledon 6 ⊖	d	22p39																						10 26	
Haydons Road	d	22p41																						10 28	
Tooting	d	22p44																						10 31	
Carshalton	d																								
Hackbridge	d																								
Mitcham Junction	d																								
Eastfields §	d																								
Streatham 4	d	22p49																						10 35	
Tulse Hill 3	d	22p53																						10 38	
London Bridge 4 ⊖	d		23p15		23p45	00 20	00 52			07 15	07 45	08 15		08 45		09 15		09 45		10 15	10 30		10 45		11 00
Herne Hill 4	d	22p56																						10 42	
Loughborough Jn	d																							10 45	
Elephant & Castle	d	23p05																						10 50	
London Blackfriars 3 ⊖	d	23p08	23p23	23p38	23p53	00 28	01 00	05 55	06 55	07 23	07 53	08 23		08 53		09 23		09 53		10 23	10 38		10 53	10 58	11 08
City Thameslink 3	d																								
Moorgate ⊖	d																								
Barbican ⊖	d																								
Farringdon 3 ⊖	d	23p14	23p29	23p44	23p59	00 34			06 58	07 28	07 58	08 28		08 58		09 28		09 58		10 28	10 44		10 58	11 02	11 14
St Pancras International 15 ⊖	d	23p18	23p33	23p48	00 03	00 38	01 08	06 02	07 02	07 32	08 02	08 32	09 00	09 02	09 30	09 32	10 00	10 02	10 30	10 32	10 48	11 00	11 02	11 06	11 18
Kentish Town ⊖	d	23p22		23p52		00 42	01 12	06 06	07 06	07 36	08 06	08 36		09 06		09 36		10 06		10 36				11 10	
West Hampstead Thameslink ⊖	d	23p26	23p40	23p56	00 10	00 46	01 16	06 10	07 10	07 40	08 10	08 40		09 10		09 40		10 10		10 40	10 55			11 14	11 25
Cricklewood	d	23p29		23p59		00 49	01 19	06 13	07 13	07 43	08 13	08 43		09 13		09 43		10 13		10 43				11 17	
Hendon	d	23p32		00 02		00 52	01 22	06 16	07 16	07 46	08 16	08 46		09 16		09 46		10 16		10 46				11 20	
Mill Hill Broadway	d	23p35		00 05		00 55	01 25	06 19	07 19	07 49	08 19	08 49		09 19		09 49		10 19		10 49				11 23	
Elstree & Borehamwood	d	23p40		00 10		01 00	01 30	06 24	07 24	07 54	08 24	08 54		09 24		09 54		10 24		10 54				11 28	
Radlett	d	23p44		00 14		01 04	01 34	06 28	07 28	07 58	08 28	08 58		09 28		09 58		10 28		10 58				11 32	
St Albans	d	23p50	23p54	00 20	00 24	01 10	01 40	06 34	07 34	08 04	08 34	09 04		09 34		10 04		10 34		11 04	11 11		11 24	11 37	11 41
Harpenden	d	23p55	00 01	00 25	00 31	01 15	01 45	06 39	07 39	08 09	08 39	09 09		09 39		10 09		10 39		11 09	11 17		11 29	11 43	11 47
Luton Airport Parkway 7 ✈	d	00 01	00 07	00 31	00 37	01 21	01 51	06 45	07 45	08 15	08 45	09 15		09 45		10 15		10 45		11 15	11 22	11 28	11 35	11 48	11 52
Luton 10	d	00 05	00 10	00 35	00 40	01 25	01 55	06 49	07 49	08 19	08 49	09 19	09 30	09 49	10 02	10 19	10 30	10 49		11 19	11 26	11 33	11 39	11a55	11 56
Leagrave	d	00 09	00 14	00 39	00 44	01 29	01 59	06 53	07 53	08 23	08 53	09 23		09 53		10 23		10 53		11 23	11 30		11 43		12 00
Harlington	d	00 14	00 20	00 44	00 50	01 34	02 04	06 59	07 59	08 29	08 59	09 29		09 59		10 29		10 59		11 29	11 36		11 49		12 06
Flitwick	d	00 18	00 24	00 48	00 54	01 38	02 08	07 03	08 03	08 33	09 03	09 33		10 03		10 33		11 03		11 33	11 40		11 53		12 10
Bedford 7	a	00 30	00 37	01 00	01 07	01 52	02 20	07 19	08 17	08 47	09 17	09 47	09 50	10 17	10 22	10 47	10 50	11 17	11 24	11 47	11 53	11 55	12 07		12 23

For general notes see front of timetable
For details of catering facilities see Directory of Train Operators

§ It is unknown at the time of going to press, when this station will open. For further details please contact National Rail Enquiries 08457-484950 or see local publicity.

A To Nottingham (Table 53)
B To Sheffield (Table 53)

Table 52

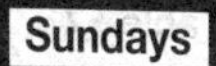
Sundays

Brighton, Gatwick Airport and South London → City of London, St.Albans, Luton and Bedford

Network Diagram - see first page of Table 52

		EM 1◇ A	FC 1	FC	FC 1	EM 1◇ B	FC 1	FC	FC 1	EM 1◇ B	FC 1	FC	FC 1	EM 1◇ B	FC 1	FC	EM 1◇ A	FC 1	EM 1◇ C	FC 1	FC	FC 1	EM 1◇ B	FC 1	FC
Brighton 10	d		10 16		10 16		10 44		10 44		11 16		11 16		11 44			11 44		12 16		12 16		12 44	
Preston Park	d		10 03		10 03		10 03				11 03		11 03		11 03					12 03		12 03		12 03	
Hassocks 4	d		10 10		10 10		10 52		10 52		11 10		11 10		11 52			11 52		12 10		12 10		12 52	
Burgess Hill 4	d		10 26		10 26		10 56		10 56		11 26		11 26		11 56			11 56		12 26		12 26		12 56	
Wivelsfield 4	d		10 16		10 16		10 31		10 31		11 16		11 16		11 31			11 31		12 16		12 16		12 31	
Haywards Heath 3	d		10 31		10 31		11 01		11 01		11 31		11 31		12 01			12 01		12 31		12 31		13 01	
Balcombe	d		10 26		10 26						11 26		11 26							12 26		12 26			
Three Bridges 4	d		10 40		10 40		11 10		11 10		11 40		11 40		12 10			12 10		12 40		12 40		13 10	
Gatwick Airport 10 ✈	d		10 45				11 15				11 45				12 15					12 45				13 15	
Redhill	d				10 46		11 09						11 46		12 09							12 46		13 09	
East Croydon	d		11 02		11 12		11 32		11 42		12 02		12 12		12 32			12 42		13 02		13 12		13 32	
Sutton (Surrey) 4	d			10 40				11 10				11 40				12 10					12 40				13 10
West Sutton	d			10 43				11 13				11 43				12 13					12 43				13 13
Sutton Common	d			10 45				11 15				11 45				12 15					12 45				13 15
St Helier	d			10 47				11 17				11 47				12 17					12 47				13 17
Morden South	d			10 49				11 19				11 49				12 19					12 49				13 19
South Merton	d			10 51				11 21				11 51				12 21					12 51				13 21
Wimbledon Chase	d			10 52				11 22				11 52				12 22					12 52				13 22
Wimbledon 6 ⊖	d			10 56				11 26				11 56				12 26					12 56				13 26
Haydons Road	d			10 58				11 28				11 58				12 28					12 58				13 28
Tooting	d			11 01				11 31				12 01				12 31					13 01				13 31
Carshalton	d																								
Hackbridge	d																								
Mitcham Junction	d																								
Eastfields §	d																								
Streatham 4	d			11 05				11 35				12 05				12 35					13 05				13 35
Tulse Hill 3	d			11 08				11 38				12 08				12 38					13 08				13 38
London Bridge 4 ⊖	d		11 15		11 30		11 45		12 00		12 15		12 30		12 45			13 00		13 15		13 30		13 45	
Herne Hill 4	d			11 12				11 42				12 14				12 44					13 12				13 42
Loughborough Jn	d			11 15				11 45				12 17				12 47					13 15				13 45
Elephant & Castle	d			11 20				11 50				12 22				12 52					13 20				13 50
London Blackfriars 3 ⊖	d		11 23	11 28	11 38		11 53	11 58	12 08		12 23	12 28	12 38		12 53	12 58		13 08		13 23	13 28	13 38		13 53	13 58
City Thameslink 3	d																								
Moorgate ⊖	d																								
Barbican ⊖	d																								
Farringdon 3 ⊖	d		11 28	11 32	11 44		11 58	12 02	12 14		12 28	12 32	12 44		12 58	13 02		13 14		13 28	13 32	13 44		13 58	14 02
St Pancras International 15 ⊖	d	11 30	11 32	11 36	11 48	12 00	12 02	12 06	12 18	12 30	12 32	12 36	12 48	13 00	13 02	13 06	13 30	13 18	13 30	13 32	13 36	13 48	14 00	14 02	14 06
Kentish Town ⊖	d			11 40				12 10				12 40				13 10					13 40				14 10
West Hampstead Thameslink ⊖	d			11 44	11 55			12 14	12 25			12 44	12 55			13 14		13 25			13 44	13 55			14 14
Cricklewood	d			11 47				12 17				12 47				13 17					13 47				14 17
Hendon	d			11 50				12 20				12 50				13 20					13 50				14 20
Mill Hill Broadway	d			11 53				12 23				12 53				13 23					13 53				14 23
Elstree & Borehamwood	d			11 58				12 28				12 58				13 28					13 58				14 28
Radlett	d			12 02				12 32				13 02				13 32					14 02				14 32
St Albans	d		11 54	12 07	12 11		12 24	12 37	12 41		12 54	13 07	13 11		13 24	13 37		13 41		13 54	14 07	14 11		14 24	14 37
Harpenden	d		11 59	12 13	12 17		12 29	12 43	12 47		12 59	13 13	13 17		13 29	13 43		13 47		13 59	14 13	14 17		14 29	14 43
Luton Airport Parkway 7 ✈	d		12 05	12 18	12 22		12 35	12 48	12 52		13 05	13 18	13 23	13 27	13 35	13 48		13 53		14 05	14 18	14 23		14 35	14 48
Luton 10	d		12 09	12a25	12 26	12 31	12 39	12 52	12 56		13 09	13 22	13 26	13 33	13 39	13 52		13 56		14 09	14 22	14 26	14 32	14 39	14 52
Leagrave	d		12 13		12 30		12 43		13 00		13 13		13 30		13 43			14 00		14 13		14 30		14 43	
Harlington	d		12 19		12 36		12 49		13 06		13 19		13 36		13 49			14 06		14 19		14 36		14 49	
Flitwick	d		12 23		12 40		12 53		13 10		13 23		13 40		13 53			14 10		14 23		14 40		14 53	
Bedford 7	a	12 23	12 37		12 53	12 55	13 07	13 13	13 23	13 23	13 37	13 43	13 53	13 54	14 07	14 12	14 22	14 23	14 23	14 37	14 43	14 53	14 46	15 07	15 13

For general notes see front of timetable
For details of catering facilities see Directory of Train Operators

§ It is unknown at the time of going to press, when this station will open. For further details please contact National Rail Enquiries 08457-484950 or see local publicity.

A Until 23 March
To Sheffield (Table 53)

B To Nottingham (Table 53)

C From 30 March.
To Sheffield (Table 53)

Table 52

Sundays

Brighton, Gatwick Airport and South London → City of London, St.Albans, Luton and Bedford

Network Diagram - see first page of Table 52

		EM	FC	FC	FC	FC	EM	FC	FC	EM	FC	FC	FC	FC	EM	FC	FC	FC	EM	FC	FC	FC	EM	FC	EM
		1 ◇	1	1			1 ◇	1		1 ◇	1	1		1	1 ◇	1		1	1 ◇	1		1	1 ◇	1	1 ◇
		A					B			A					B				A				B		C
		☕					☕			☕					☕				☕				☕		☕
Brighton 10	d		12 44	13 16		13 16		13 44			13 44	14 16		14 16		14 44		14 44		15 16		15 16		15 44	
Preston Park	d			13 03		13 03		13 03			13 03	14 03		14 03		14 03				15 03		15 03		15 03	
Hassocks 4	d		12 52	13 10		13 10		13 52			13 52	14 10		14 10		14 52		14 52		15 10		15 10		15 52	
Burgess Hill 4	d		12 56	13 26		13 26		13 56			13 56	14 26		14 26		14 56		14 56		15 26		15 26		15 56	
Wivelsfield 4	d		12 31	13 16		13 16		13 31			13 31	14 16		14 16		14 31		14 31		15 16		15 16		15 31	
Haywards Heath 3	d		13 01	13 31		13 31		14 01			14 01	14 31		14 31		15 01		15 01		15 31		15 31		16 01	
Balcombe	d			13 26		13 26					13 26	14 26		14 26						15 26		15 26			
Three Bridges 4	d		13 10	13 40		13 40		14 10			14 10	14 40		14 40		15 10		15 10		15 40		15 40		16 10	
Gatwick Airport 10 ✈	d			13 45				14 15				14 45				15 15				15 45				16 15	
Redhill	d					13 46		14 09						14 46		15 09						15 46		16 09	
East Croydon	d		13 42	14 02		14 12		14 32			14 42	15 02		15 12		15 32		15 42		16 02		16 12		16 32	
Sutton (Surrey) 4	d				13 40				14 10				14 40				15 10				15 40				
West Sutton	d				13 43				14 13				14 43				15 13				15 43				
Sutton Common	d				13 45				14 15				14 45				15 15				15 45				
St Helier	d				13 47				14 17				14 47				15 17				15 47				
Morden South	d				13 49				14 19				14 49				15 19				15 49				
South Merton	d				13 51				14 21				14 51				15 21				15 51				
Wimbledon Chase	d				13 52				14 22				14 52				15 22				15 52				
Wimbledon 6 ⊖	d				13 56				14 26				14 56				15 26				15 56				
Haydons Road	d				13 58				14 28				14 58				15 28				15 58				
Tooting	d				14 01				14 31				15 01				15 31				16 01				
Carshalton	d																								
Hackbridge	d																								
Mitcham Junction	d																								
Eastfields §	d																								
Streatham 4	d				14 05				14 35				15 05				15 35				16 05				
Tulse Hill 3	d				14 08				14 38				15 08				15 38				16 08				
London Bridge 4 ⊖	d		14 00	14 15		14 30		14 45			15 00	15 15		15 30		15 45		16 00		16 15		16 30		16 45	
Herne Hill 4	d				14 12				14 42				15 12				15 42				16 14				
Loughborough Jn	d				14 15				14 45				15 15				15 45				16 17				
Elephant & Castle	d				14 20				14 50				15 20				15 50				16 22				
London Blackfriars 3 ⊖	d		14 08	14 23	14 28	14 38		14 53	14 58		15 08	15 23	15 28	15 38		15 53	15 58	16 08		16 23	16 28	16 38		16 53	
City Thameslink 3	d																								
Moorgate ⊖	d																								
Barbican ⊖	d																								
Farringdon 3 ⊖	d		14 14	14 28	14 32	14 44		14 58	15 02		15 14	15 28	15 32	15 44		15 58	16 02	16 14		16 28	16 32	16 44		16 58	
St Pancras International 15 ⊖	d	14 30	14 18	14 32	14 36	14 48	15 00	15 02	15 06	15 30	15 18	15 32	15 36	15 48	16 00	16 02	16 06	16 18	16 30	16 32	16 36	16 48	17 00	17 02	17 30
Kentish Town ⊖	d				14 40				15 10				15 40				16 10				16 40				
West Hampstead Thameslink ⊖	d		14 25		14 44	14 55			15 14		15 25		15 44	15 55			16 14	16 25			16 44	16 55			
Cricklewood	d				14 47				15 17				15 47				16 17				16 47				
Hendon	d				14 50				15 20				15 50				16 20				16 50				
Mill Hill Broadway	d				14 53				15 23				15 53				16 23				16 53				
Elstree & Borehamwood	d				14 58				15 28				15 58				16 28				16 58				
Radlett	d				15 02				15 32				16 02				16 32				17 02				
St Albans	d		14 41	14 54	15 07	15 11		15 24	15 37		15 41	15 54	16 07	16 11		16 24	16 37	16 41		16 54	17 07	17 11		17 24	
Harpenden	d		14 47	14 59	15 13	15 17		15 29	15 43		15 47	15 59	16 13	16 17		16 29	16 43	16 47		16 59	17 13	17 17		17 29	
Luton Airport Parkway 7 ✈	d		14 53	15 05	15 18	15 23	15 29	15 35	15 48		15 53	16 05	16 18	16 23		16 35	16 48	16 53		17 05	17 18	17 22		17 35	
Luton 10	d		14 56	15 09	15 22	15 26	15 34	15 39	15 52		15 56	16 09	16 22	16 26	16 32	16 39	16 52	16 56	17 01	17 09	17a25	17 26	17 31	17 39	17 51
Leagrave	d		15 00	15 13		15 30		15 43			16 00	16 13		16 30		16 43		17 00		17 13		17 30		17 43	
Harlington	d		15 06	15 19		15 36		15 49			16 06	16 19		16 36		16 49		17 06		17 19		17 36		17 49	
Flitwick	d		15 10	15 23		15 40		15 53			16 10	16 23		16 40		16 53		17 10		17 23		17 40		17 53	
Bedford 7	a	15 15	15 23	15 37	15 42	15 53	15 51	16 07	16 13	16 15	16 23	16 38	16 43	16 53	16 47	17 08	17 13	17 23	17 15	17 37		17 53	17 47	18 07	18 15

For general notes see front of timetable
For details of catering facilities see Directory of Train Operators

§ It is unknown at the time of going to press, when this station will open. For further details please contact National Rail Enquiries 08457-484950 or see local publicity.

A To Sheffield (Table 53)
B To Nottingham (Table 53)
C From 30 March. To Derby (Table 53)

Brighton, Gatwick Airport and South London → City of London, St.Albans, Luton and Bedford

Network Diagram - see first page of Table 52

		EM 1◇ A	FC	FC 1	FC 1	EM 1◇ B	FC	FC 1	FC 1	FC	FC 1	EM 1◇ C	EM 1◇ D	EM 1◇ E	FC 1	FC	FC	EM 1◇ G	EM 1◇ H	FC 1	FC	EM 1◇ J	EM 1◇ K	FC 1	FC
Brighton 10	d			15 51	16 16			16 16	16 44		16 51				17 16		17 16			17 44				18 16	
Preston Park	d				16 03			16 03	16 03						17 03		17 03			17 03				18 03	
Hassocks 4	d			15 52	16 10			16 10	16 52		16 52				17 10		17 10			17 52				18 10	
Burgess Hill 4	d			15 56	16 26			16 26	16 56		16 56				17 26		17 26			17 56				18 26	
Wivelsfield 4	d			15 31	16 16			16 16	16 31		16 31				17 16		17 16			17 31				18 16	
Haywards Heath 3	d			16 01	16 31			16 31	17 01		17 01				17 31		17 31			18 01				18 31	
Balcombe	d				16 26			16 26							17 26		17 26							18 26	
Three Bridges 4	d			16 10	16 40			16 40	17 10		17 10				17 40		17 40			18 10				18 40	
Gatwick Airport 10 ✈	d			16 18	16 45				17 15		17 18				17 45					18 15				18 45	
Redhill	d							16 46	17 09								17 46			18 09					
East Croydon	d			16 42	17 02			17 12	17 32		17 42				18 02		18 12			18 32				19 02	
Sutton (Surrey) 4	d		16 10				16 40			17 10						17 40					18 10				18 40
West Sutton	d		16 13				16 43			17 13						17 43					18 13				18 43
Sutton Common	d		16 15				16 45			17 15						17 45					18 15				18 45
St Helier	d		16 17				16 47			17 17						17 47					18 17				18 47
Morden South	d		16 19				16 49			17 19						17 49					18 19				18 49
South Merton	d		16 21				16 51			17 21						17 51					18 21				18 51
Wimbledon Chase	d		16 22				16 52			17 22						17 52					18 22				18 52
Wimbledon 6 ⊖	d		16 26				16 56			17 26						17 56					18 26				18 56
Haydons Road	d		16 28				16 58			17 28						17 58					18 28				18 58
Tooting	d		16 31				17 01			17 31						18 01					18 31				19 01
Carshalton	d																								
Hackbridge	d																								
Mitcham Junction	d																								
Eastfields §	d																								
Streatham 4	d		16 35				17 05			17 35						18 05					18 35				19 05
Tulse Hill 3	d		16 38				17 08			17 38						18 08					18 38				19 08
London Bridge 4 ⊖	d			17 00	17 15			17 30	17 45		18 00				18 15		18 30			18 45				19 15	
Herne Hill 4	d		16 42				17 14			17 42						18 12					18 42				19 12
Loughborough Jn	d		16 45				17 17			17 45						18 15					18 44				19 14
Elephant & Castle	d		16 50				17 22			17 50						18 20					18 50				19 20
London Blackfriars 3 ⊖	d		16 58	17 08	17 23		17 28	17 38	17 53	17 58	18 08				18 23	18 28	18 38			18 53	18 58			19 23	19 28
City Thameslink 3	d																								
Moorgate ⊖	d																								
Barbican ⊖	d																								
Farringdon 3 ⊖	d		17 02	17 14	17 28		17 32	17 44	17 58	18 02	18 14				18 28	18 32	18 44			18 58	19 02			19 28	19 32
St Pancras International 15 ⊖	d	17 30	17 06	17 18	17 32	18 00	17 36	17 48	18 02	18 06	18 18	18 30	18 30	18 30	18 32	18 36	18 48	19 00	19 00	19 02	19 06	19 30	19 30	19 32	19 36
Kentish Town ⊖	d		17 10				17 40			18 10						18 40					19 10				19 40
West Hampstead Thameslink ⊖	d		17 14	17 25			17 44	17 55		18 14	18 25					18 44	18 55			19 10	19 14			19 40	19 44
Cricklewood	d		17 17				17 47			18 17						18 47					19 17				19 47
Hendon	d		17 20				17 50			18 20						18 50					19 20				19 50
Mill Hill Broadway	d		17 23				17 53			18 23						18 53					19 23				19 53
Elstree & Borehamwood	d		17 28				17 58			18 28						18 58					19 28				19 58
Radlett	d		17 32				18 02			18 32						19 02					19 31				20 01
St Albans	d		17 37	17 41	17 54		18 07	18 11	18 24	18 37	18 41				18 54	19 07	19 11			19 24	19 36			19 54	20 06
Harpenden	d		17 43	17 47	17 59		18 13	18 17	18 29	18 43	18 47				18 59	19 13	19 17			19 29	19 42			19 59	20 12
Luton Airport Parkway 7 ✈	d		17 48	17 52	18 05		18 18	18 22	18 35	18 48	18 52	18 56	18 57		19 05	19 18	19 22	19 26		19 35	19 47			20 05	20 17
Luton 10	d	17 53	17a55	17 56	18 09	18 22	18a25	18 26	18 39	18a55	18 56		19 01	19 01	19 09	19a25	19 26		19 27	19 39	19 52	19 55	19 56	20 09	20 22
Leagrave	d			18 00	18 13			18 30	18 43		19 00				19 13		19 30			19 43				20 13	
Harlington	d			18 06	18 19			18 36	18 49		19 06				19 19		19 36			19 49				20 19	
Flitwick	d			18 10	18 23			18 40	18 53		19 10				19 23		19 40			19 53				20 23	
Bedford 7	a	18 17		18 23	18 37	18 46		18 53	19 07		19 23	19 17	19 19	19 19	19 37		19 53	19 45	19 45	20 07	20 13	20 17	20 17	20 37	20 43

For general notes see front of timetable
For details of catering facilities see Directory of Train Operators

§ It is unknown at the time of going to press, when this station will open. For further details please contact National Rail Enquiries 08457-484950 or see local publicity.

A Until 23 March. To Leeds (Table 53)

B To Sheffield (Table 53)

C From 30 March. To Derby (Table 53)

D Until 27 January. To Leeds (Table 53)

E 3 February to 23 March. To Leeds (Table 53)

G Until 23 March. To Nottingham (Table 53)

H From 30 March. To Nottingham (Table 53)

J From 30 March. To Sheffield (Table 53)

K Until 23 March. To Sheffield (Table 53)

Brighton, Gatwick Airport and South London → City of London, St.Albans, Luton and Bedford

Network Diagram - see first page of Table 52

		EM	FC	FC	EM	FC	FC	EM	EM	FC	FC	EM	FC	FC	FC	FC	EM	FC	EM	FC	FC	FC	FC
		1 ◇	1		1 ◇	1		1 ◇	1 ◇	1		1 ◇	1		1		1 ◇	1	1 ◇	1	1	1	1
		A			B			C	D			E					A		G				
Brighton 10	d		18 44			19 16				19 44			20 16		20 44			21 16		21 44	22 16	22 44	23 44
Preston Park	d		*18 03*			*19 03*				*19 03*			*20 03*		*20 03*			*21 03*		*21 03*	*22 03*	*22 03*	*23 06*
Hassocks 4	d		18 52			*19 10*				19 52			*20 10*		20 52			*21 10*		21 52	*22 10*	22 52	23 52
Burgess Hill 4	d		18 56			19 26				19 56			20 26		20 56			21 26		21 56	22 26	22 56	23 56
Wivelsfield 4	d		*18 31*			*19 16*				*19 31*			*20 16*		*20 31*			*21 16*		*21 31*	*22 16*		*23 19*
Haywards Heath 3	d		19 01			19 31				20 01			20 31		21 01			21 31		22 01	22 31	23 01	00 01
Balcombe	d					*19 26*							*20 26*					*21 26*			*22 26*		*23 29*
Three Bridges 4	d		19 10			19 40				20 10			20 40		21 10			21 40		22 10	22 40	23 10	00 10
Gatwick Airport 10 ✈	d		19 15			19 45				20 15			20 45		21 15			21 45		22 15	22 45	23 15	00 15
Redhill	d		*19 09*							*20 09*					*21 13*					*22 09*		*23 09*	00 22
East Croydon	d		19 32			20 02				20 32			21 02		21 32			22 02		22 32	23 02	23 32	00 36
Sutton (Surrey) 4	d			19 10			19 40				20 10			20 40		21 10							
West Sutton	d			19 13			19 43				20 13			20 43		21 13							
Sutton Common	d			19 15			19 45				20 15			20 45		21 15							
St Helier	d			19 17			19 47				20 17			20 47		21 17							
Morden South	d			19 19			19 49				20 19			20 49		21 19							
South Merton	d			19 21			19 51				20 21			20 51		21 21							
Wimbledon Chase	d			19 22			19 52				20 22			20 52		21 22							
Wimbledon 6 ⊖	d			19 26			19 56				20 26			20 56		21 26							
Haydons Road	d			19 28			19 58				20 28			20 58		21 28							
Tooting	d			19 31			20 01				20 31			21 01		21 31							
Carshalton	d																						
Hackbridge	d																						
Mitcham Junction	d																						
Eastfields §	d																						
Streatham 4	d			19 35			20 05				20 35			21 05		21 35							
Tulse Hill 3	d			19 38			20 08				20 38			21 08		21 38							
London Bridge 4 ⊖	d		19 45			20 15				20 45			21 15		21 45			22 15		22 45	23 15	23 45	00 52
Herne Hill 4	d			19 42			20 12				20 42			21 12		21 42							
Loughborough Jn	d			19 44			20 14				20 44			21 14		21 44							
Elephant & Castle	d			19 50			20 20				20 50			21 20		21 50							
London Blackfriars 3 ⊖	d		19 53	19 58		20 23	20 28			20 53	20 58		21 23	21 28	21 53	21 58		22 23		22 53	23 23	23 53	01 00
City Thameslink 3	d																						
Moorgate ⊖	d																						
Barbican ⊖	d																						
Farringdon 3 ⊖	d		19 58	20 02		20 28	20 32			20 58	21 02		21 28	21 32	21 58	22 02		22 28		22 58	23 28	23 58	
St Pancras International 15 ⊖	d	20 00	20 02	20 06	20 30	20 32	20 36	21 00	21 00	21 02	21 06	21 30	21 32	21 36	22 02	22 06	22 30	22 32	23 00	23 02	23 32	00 02	01 08
Kentish Town ⊖	d			20 10			20 40				21 10			21 40		22 10		22 36		23 06	23 36	00 06	01 12
West Hampstead Thameslink ⊖	d		20 10	20 14		20 40	20 44			21 10	21 14		21 40	21 44	22 10	22 14		22 40		23 10	23 40	00 10	01 16
Cricklewood	d			20 17			20 47				21 17			21 47		22 17		22 43		23 13	23 43	00 13	01 19
Hendon	d			20 20			20 50				21 20			21 50		22 20		22 46		23 16	23 46	00 16	01 22
Mill Hill Broadway	d			20 23			20 53				21 23			21 53		22 23		22 49		23 19	23 49	00 19	01 25
Elstree & Borehamwood	d			20 28			20 58				21 28			21 58		22 28		22 54		23 24	23 54	00 24	01 30
Radlett	d			20 31			21 01				21 31			22 01		22 31		22 58		23 28	23 58	00 28	01 34
St Albans	d		20 24	20 36		20 54	21 06			21 24	21 36		21 54	22 06	22 24	22 36		23 04		23 34	00 04	00 34	01 40
Harpenden	d		20 29	20 42		20 59	21 12			21 29	21 42		21 59	22 12	22 29	22 42		23 09		23 39	00 09	00 39	01 45
Luton Airport Parkway 7 ✈	d		20 35	20 47		21 05	21 17			21 35	21 47		22 05	22 17	22 35	22 47		23 15		23 45	00 15	00 45	01 51
Luton 10	d	20 26	20 39	20 52		21 09	21 22	21 23	21 25	21 39	21 50		22 09	22 22	22 39	22 50	22 55	23 19	23 26	23 49	00 19	00 49	01 55
Leagrave	d		20 43			21 13				21 43			22 13		22 43			23 23		23 53	00 23	00 53	01 59
Harlington	d		20 49			21 19				21 49			22 19		22 49			23 29		23 59	00 29	00 59	02 04
Flitwick	d		20 53			21 23				21 53			22 23		22 53			23 33		00 03	00 33	01 03	02 08
Bedford 7	a	20 47	21 07	21 13	21 13	21 37	21 43	21 47	21 49	22 07	22 13	22 18	22 37	22 43	23 07	23 13	23 18	23 45	23 52	00 15	00 45	01 15	02 20

For general notes see front of timetable
For details of catering facilities see Directory of Train Operators

§ It is unknown at the time of going to press, when this station will open. For further details please contact National Rail Enquiries 08457-484950 or see local publicity.

A To Nottingham (Table 53)
B To Leeds (Table 53)
C From 30 March. To Nottingham (Table 53)
D Until 23 March. To Nottingham (Table 53)
E Until 23 March to Derby (Table 53). From 30 March to Sheffield (Table 53)
G To Derby (Table 53)

Table 52A

Mondays to Fridays

Luton → Dunstable

Bus Service

	FC	FC		FC	FC		FC	FC		FC	FC		FC	FC		FC	FC		FC	FC		FC	FC		FC	FC		FC
Luton d	05 57	06 15		06 40	07 10		07 32	07 53		08 06	08 27		08 47	09 08		09 27	09 34		09 52	10 04		10 22	10 34		10 52	11 04		11 22
Dunstable a	06 20	06 50		07 10	07 45		08 05	08 25		08 45	09 00		09 25	09 40		09 55	10 10		10 25	10 40		10 55	11 10		11 25	11 40		11 55

	FC	FC		FC	FC		FC	FC		FC	FC		FC	FC		FC	FC		FC	FC		FC	FC		FC	FC		FC
Luton d	11 34	11 52		12 04	12 22		12 34	12 52		13 04	13 22		13 34	13 52		14 04	14 22		14 34	14 52		15 04	15 22		15 36	15 52		16 04
Dunstable a	12 10	12 29		12 40	12 55		13 10	13 25		13 40	13 55		14 10	14 29		14 40	14 55		15 10	15 25		15 40	15 55		16 10	16 25		16 40

	FC	FC		FC	FC		FC	FC		FC	FC		FC	FC		FC	FC		FC	FC		FC	FC		FC	FC		
Luton d	16 22	16 37		16 50	17 07		17 25	17 40		17 57	18 27		18 43	19 15		19 30	20 02		20 32	21 00		21 17	21 45		22 15	22 45		
Dunstable a	16 59	17 14		17 34	17 46		18 00	18 12		18 32	18 55		19 08	19 42		19 54	20 32		21 02	21 20		21 41	22 09		22 37	23 08		

Saturdays

	FC	FC		FC	FC		FC	FC		FC	FC		FC	FC		FC	FC		FC	FC		FC	FC		FC	FC		FC
Luton d	05 55	06 30		07 07	07 37		08 07	08 37		09 07	09 27		09 42	10 02		10 22	10 42		11 02	11 22		11 42	12 02		12 22	12 42		13 02
Dunstable a	06 13	06 48		07 35	08 05		08 40	09 10		09 40	09 57		10 15	10 35		10 55	11 15		11 35	11 55		12 15	12 39		12 55	13 15		13 35

	FC	FC		FC	FC		FC	FC		FC	FC		FC	FC		FC	FC		FC	FC	FC	FC	FC	FC	FC	FC		
Luton d	13 22	13 42		14 02	14 22		14 42	15 02		15 22	15 42		16 02	16 13		16 22	16 42		17 12	17 42	19 00	19 30	20 02	20 30	21 17	21 45		
Dunstable a	13 55	14 15		14 39	14 55		15 15	15 35		15 55	16 15		16 31	16 47		17 00	17 11		17 45	18 11	19 18	19 54	20 32	21 02	21 41	21 59		

Sundays

	FC					FC					FC					FC					FC							
Luton d	18 42					19 42					20 42					21 42					22 42							
Dunstable a	19 04					20 04					21 04					22 04					23 06							

For general notes see front of timetable
For details of catering facilities see
Directory of Train Operators

Dunstable → Luton
Bus Service

		FC	FC	FC	FC	FC	FC	FC	FC	FC	FC	FC	FC	FC	FC	FC	FC	FC	FC	FC	FC	FC	FC	FC	FC	FC	FC	FC	FC
Dunstable	d	05 15	05 45	05 50	06 00	06 05	06 25	06 40	06 50	06 55	07 15	07 30	07 36	07 53	08 00	08 08	08 10	08 18	08 28	08 30	08 49	09 00	09 05	09 17	09 30	09 35	09 47	10 00	10 05
Luton	a	05 40	06 04	06 04	06 15	06 30	06 40	07 06	07 04	07 10	07 32	08 04	07 53	08 12	08 36	08 27	08 46	08 37	08 47	09 06	09 08	09 34	09 27	09 34	10 04	09 52	10 04	10 34	10 22

		FC		FC	FC	FC	FC	FC	FC	FC	FC	FC	FC	FC	FC	FC	FC	FC	FC	FC	FC	FC	FC	FC	FC	FC	FC	FC	FC
Dunstable	d	10 17	.....	10 30	10 35	10 47	11 00	11 05	11 17	11 30	11 35	11 47	12 00	12 05	12 17	12 30	12 35	12 47	13 00	13 05	13 17	13 35	13 47	14 00	14 05	14 17	14 30	14 35	14 47
Luton	a	10 34	.	11 04	10 52	11 04	11 34	11 22	11 34	12 04	11 52	12 04	12 34	12 22	12 34	13 04	12 52	13 04	13 34	13 22	13 34	13 52	14 04	14 34	14 22	14 34	15 04	14 52	15 04

		FC	FC	FC	FC	FC	FC	FC	FC	FC	FC	FC	FC	FC	FC	FC	FC	FC	FC	FC	FC	FC	FC	FC	FC	FC	FC		
Dunstable	d	15 00	15 05	15 19	15 35	15 40	15 47	16 05	16 10	16 20	16 33	16 40	16 50	17 08	17 10	17 20	17 23	17 40	17 40	18 10	18 20	18 45	19 15	20 15	20 45	21 45	23 08	.....	.....
Luton	a	15 34	15 22	15 36	15 52	16 15	16 04	16 22	16 47	16 37	16 50	17 17	17 07	17 25	17 47	17 59	17 40	17 57	18 17	18 27	18 51	19 16	19 44	20 35	21 10	22 07	23 31	.	.

Saturdays

		FC	FC	FC		FC	FC	FC		FC	FC	FC		FC	FC	FC		FC	FC	FC		FC	FC	FC		FC	FC	FC	FC
Dunstable	d	06 00	06 15	06 20	.....	06 50	07 00	07 15	.....	07 40	07 50	08 10	.....	08 20	08 40	08 50	.....	09 05	09 10	09 25	.....	09 30	09 45	10 00	.....	10 05	10 25	10 30	10 45
Luton	a	06 26	06 30	06 44	.	07 07	07 34	07 28	.	08 10	08 07	08 40	.	08 37	09 10	09 07	.	09 27	09 34	09 42	.	10 04	10 02	10 34	.	10 22	10 42	11 04	11 02

		FC		FC	FC	FC		FC	FC	FC		FC	FC	FC		FC	FC	FC		FC	FC	FC		FC	FC	FC		FC	FC
Dunstable	d	11 00	.....	11 05	11 25	11 30	.....	11 45	12 00	12 05	.....	12 25	12 30	12 45	.....	13 00	13 05	13 25	.....	13 30	13 45	14 00	.....	14 05	14 25	14 30	.....	14 45	15 00
Luton	a	11 34	.	11 22	11 42	12 04	.	12 02	12 34	12 22	.	12 42	13 04	13 02	.	13 34	13 22	13 42	.	14 04	14 02	14 34	.	14 22	14 42	15 04	.	15 02	15 34

		FC	FC	FC		FC	FC	FC		FC	FC	FC		FC	FC	FC		FC	FC	FC		FC	FC						
Dunstable	d	15 05	15 25	15 30	.....	15 45	16 00	16 05	.....	16 25	16 40	16 55	.....	17 10	17 23	17 40	.....	18 00	18 45	19 15	.....	20 45	23 08	.....	.....	.....	.....	.....	.....
Luton	a	15 22	15 42	16 04	.	16 02	16 34	16 22	.	16 42	17 14	17 12	.	17 44	17 40	18 10	.	18 33	19 16	19 44	.	21 10	23 31	.	.	.	.	.	.

Sundays

Dunstable	d	.....	.....	.....	.....	.....	.....	.....	.....	.....	.....	.....	.....	.....	.....	.....	.....	.....	.....	.....	.....	.....	.....	.....	.....	.....	.....	.....	.....
Luton	a	.	.	.	.	.	.	.	.	.	.	.	.	.	.	.	.	.	.	.	.	.	.	.	.	.	.	.	.

For general notes see front of timetable
For details of catering facilities see
Directory of Train Operators

Route Diagram for Table 53

DM-5/07
Design BAJS

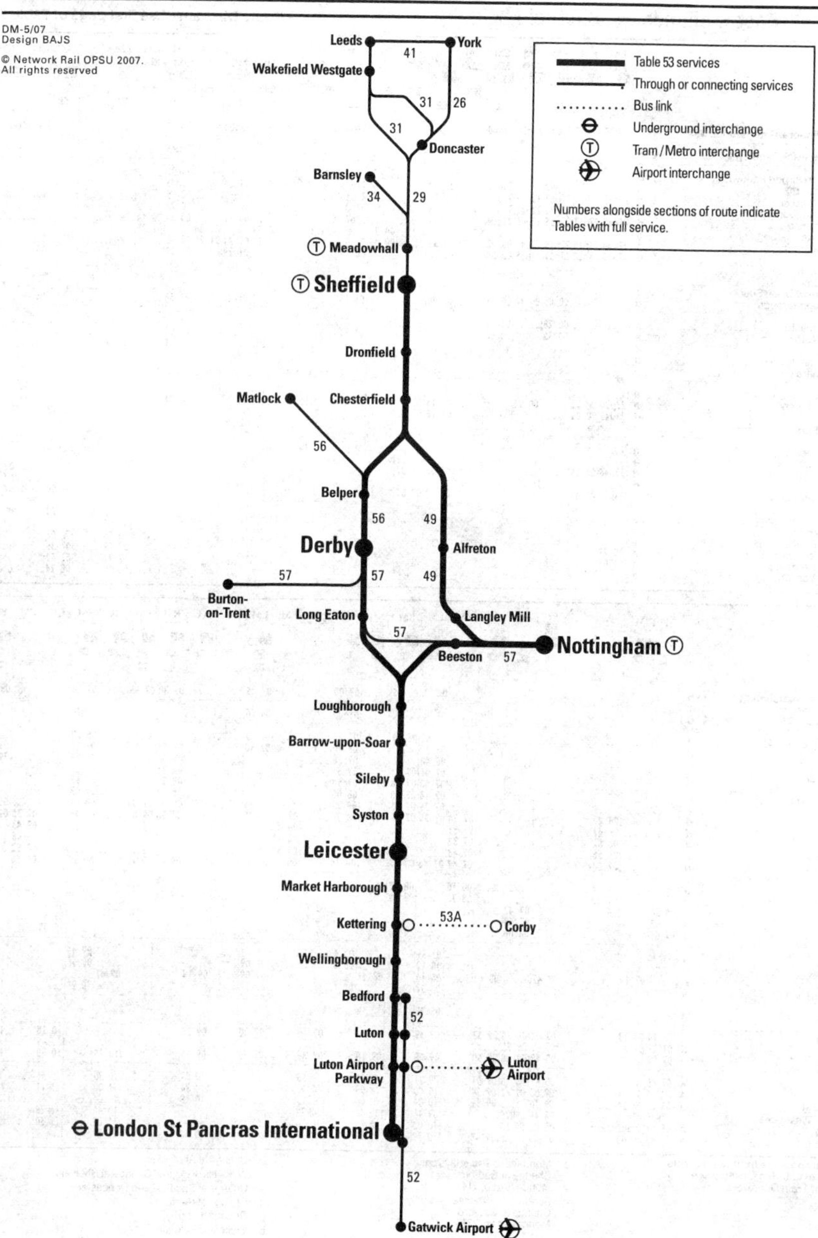
Table 53 services
Through or connecting services
Bus link
Underground interchange
Tram / Metro interchange
Airport interchange
Numbers alongside sections of route indicate Tables with full service.
Leeds
York
41
Wakefield Westgate
31
26
31
Doncaster
Barnsley
34
29
Meadowhall
Sheffield
Dronfield
Matlock
Chesterfield
56
Belper
56
49
Derby
Alfreton
57
57
49
Burton-on-Trent
Long Eaton
Langley Mill
57
Beeston
57
Nottingham
Loughborough
Barrow-upon-Soar
Sileby
Syston
Leicester
Market Harborough
Kettering
53A
Corby
Wellingborough
Bedford
52
Luton
Luton Airport Parkway
Luton Airport
London St Pancras International
52
Gatwick Airport

Table 53

Mondays to Fridays
until 25 January

London → East Midlands → Sheffield

Route Diagram - See first page of Table 53

Miles	Miles	Station		EM	EM	EM	EM	EM	EM	EM	EM	EM	EM	EM		EM	EM	EM	EM	EM	EM		XC	XC	EM
				MO	MX	MX	MO	MX	MX	MX	MO	MO	MO	MO		MO	MO	MX	MX	MX					
				1 ◇	1 ◇	1 ◇	1 ◇	1 ◇		1 ◇			1 ◇				1 ◇		1 ◇		◇		1 ◇		1 ◇
									🚌		🚌	🚌		🚌		🚌		🚌		🚌					
				☕	☕	☕	☕	☕		☕			☕				☕		☕		trolley		☕		☕
0	0	**St Pancras International** 15 ⊖	d	20p30	21p25	21p30	21p30	22p00		22p25			22p30				23p00		23p15						
—	—	Gatwick Airport 10 ✈	d																21b46						
—	—	Luton Airport Parkway 7	d																23c31						
30¼	30¼	**Luton** 10	d			21p53		22p22		22p48			22p55				23p26		23p45						
49¾	49¾	Bedford 7	d	21p13		22p07	22p19	22p38		23p05			23p19				23p52		00 09						
65¼	65¼	Wellingborough	d	21p27		22p20	22p32	22p51		23p18			23p31				00 05		00 22						
72	72	Kettering	d	21p40	22p17	22p35	22p46	23p04		23p29			23p44	00 27			00 19		00 34	00 44					
83	83	Market Harborough	d						00 01			00 23		00a52		00 54		01 04		01a09					
99¼	99¼	**Leicester**	a	22p44	23p19	23p46	23p49	00 02	00 26	00 31		00 48	00 53			01 19	01 24	01 29	01 33						
—	—		d	22p50	23p24	23p51	23p55	00 08		00 36			00 58				01 29		01 39					06 30	
103	103	Syston	d																						
105¾	105¾	Sileby	d																						
107¾	107¾	Barrow Upon Soar	d																						
111¾	111¾	Loughborough	d		23p35	00 06	00 10	00 21		00 48			01 15				01 46		01 56					06 45	
123¼	—	Beeston	a			00 28		00 39																	
126½	—	**Nottingham** 8 🚋	a			00 35		00 46					01 41						02 12						
—	—		d																02 19		05 19				
138½	—	Langley Mill	d																						
144¾	—	Alfreton	d																						
—	120½	Long Eaton	a																					06 56	
—	128½	**Derby** 10	a	23p20	00 02		00 36			01 15							02 06		02 36					07 11	
—	—		d	23p25	00 05					01 16	00 46												06 39		06 43
—	—	Burton-on-Trent	a																						
—	136½	Belper	a																						
—	—	Matlock	a																						
—	152¾	Chesterfield	d	23p46	00 25					01 36	01 32										05 54				07 04
160¼	158	Dronfield	d																						07 11
167¼	165	**Sheffield** 7 🚋	a	23p59	00 41					01 52	02 02										06 10		07 09		07 23
—	—	Meadowhall 🚋	a																		06 23		07 28		07 31
—	—	Barnsley	a																		07 00				07 48
—	—	Doncaster 7	a																		06 56		08 02		08e20
—	—	Wakefield Westgate 7	a	00 29																	07 19		07 36		08f28
—	—	Leeds 10	a	01 06																	07 44		07 52		08e51
—	—	York 8	a																		08g10		08 24		08e48

Station		EM	XC	EM		XC	EM	XC	EM	EM	EM	XC	EM	EM	EM	EM		XC	EM	EM	XC	EM	EM	EM	EM
						R						R													
		◇	1 ◇			1	◇	1 ◇		1 ◇	1 ◇	1	1 ◇	◇		1 ◇		1 ◇	1 ◇	1 ◇	1 ◇	1 ◇	◇		1 ◇
		trolley	☕			☕	trolley	☕		☕	☕	☕	☕			⊠ trolley		☕	☕	⊠ trolley	☕	☕			⊠ trolley
St Pancras International 15 ⊖	d									06 10	06 35		07 00			07 25			07 30	07 55		08 00			08 25
Gatwick Airport 10 ✈	d									04 30			05h00			06 16						06h24			06 46
Luton Airport Parkway 7	d									06 05	06 57		07 22			07 35						08 22			
Luton 10	d									06 33			06 40			07 50			07 53			07 57			08 08
Bedford 7	d									06 48			07 38						08 08			08 38			09 00
Wellingborough	d									07 01	07 21		07 51						08 21			08 51			
Kettering	d									07 08	07 28		07 58						08 28			08 58			
Market Harborough	d									07 18	07 38		08 08						08 38			09 08			
Leicester	a									07 35	07 55		08 23			08 38			08 55	09 04		09 23			09 38
	d			06 40					07 24	07 35	07 56		08 24		08 35	08 39			08 56	09 05		09 24		09 36	09 39
Syston	d			06 47					07 31						08 42									09 43	
Sileby	d			06 52					07 38						08 47									09 48	
Barrow Upon Soar	d			06 56					07 43						08 51									09 52	
Loughborough	d			07 00					07 47	07 46	08 07		08 34		08 55	08 50			09 07	09 16		09 34		09 56	
Beeston	a			07 21					08 10		08 19								09 19						
Nottingham 8 🚋	a			07 30					08 20		08 29				09 20				09 26	09 36				10 20	
	d	06 34					07 42							08 42									09 40		
Langley Mill	d	06 53					07 58							08 58									09 57		
Alfreton	d	07 01					08 06							09 06									10 05		
Long Eaton	a									07 59			08 43									09 43			
Derby 10	a									08 12			08 55			09 09						09 56			10 05
	d		07 14			07 42		08 14		08 16		08 42				09 09		09 14			09 42				10 07
Burton-on-Trent	a									08 37			09 17			09 51						10 21			10 51
Belper	a									08 25															10 38
Matlock	a									08j59															10 58
Chesterfield	d	07 14	07 33			08 03	08 18	08 33		08 39				09 18		09 30		09 35					10 18		10 27
Dronfield	d	07 21	07 39				08 25																		
Sheffield 7 🚋	a	07 32	07 51			08 17	08 38	08 50		09 05		09 18		09 38		09 46		09 50			10 15		10 38		10 46
Meadowhall 🚋	a	07 46	08 13			08 41	08 56	09 03		09 21		09 30		09 56				10 03			10 30		10 56		11 03
Barnsley	a	08 11	08 34			09 00	09 11	09 34		10 00		10 00		10 11				10 34			11 00		11 11		
Doncaster 7	a	08 20	08 24			09 10		09 19		10 04		10 04						10 15			11 04				
Wakefield Westgate 7	a	08k28	08e46			08 46	09k29			09 46		09 46		10k29							10 46		11k29		
Leeds 10	a	08 51	09e02			09 02	09 50			10 02		10 02		10 50							11 02		11 50		
York 8	a	08 48	08 48			09 33	09 48	09 48		10 29		10 29				10 40		10 40			11 29				11 41

For general notes see front of timetable
For details of catering facilities see Directory of Train Operators

b Mondays to Thursdays only. Change at Bedford. Mondays dep. 2145

c Sundays to Wednesdays only. Change at Bedford. Mondays dep. 2315

e Change at Sheffield

f Wakefield Kirkgate. Change at Sheffield

g Change at Sheffield and Doncaster

h Change at Bedford

j Change at Derby

k Wakefield Kirkgate

London → East Midlands → Sheffield

Route Diagram - See first page of Table 53

Station		XC 1◇	EM 1◇	EM 1◇	XC 1◇	EM 1◇		EM ◇	EM	EM 1◇	XC 1◇	EM 1◇	EM 1◇	XC 1◇	EM 1◇	EM ◇	EM 1◇	XC 1◇		EM	EM 1◇	EM 1◇	XC 1◇	EM 1◇	EM ◇
St Pancras International 15	⊖ d		08 30	08 55		09 00				09 25		09 30	09 55		10 00		10 25				10 30	10 55		11 00	
Gatwick Airport 10	✈ d		07 01			07b01				07 37		08 01			08b22						09 16			09b31	
Luton Airport Parkway 7	d		08 36			09 22				09 25		09 40			10 22						10 35			11 22	
Luton 10	d		08 53			08 54				09 48		09 53			09 56						10 53			10 54	
Bedford 7	d		09 08			09 38						10 08			10 38						11 08			11 38	
Wellingborough	d		09 21			09 51						10 21			10 51						11 21			11 51	
Kettering	d		09 28			09 58						10 28			10 58						11 28			11 58	
Market Harborough	d		09 38			10 08						10 38			11 08						11 38			12 08	
Leicester	a		09 55	10 04		10 23				10 36		10 55	11 04		11 23		11 34				11 55	12 04		12 23	
	d		09 56	10 05		10 24			10 35	10 39		10 56	11 05		11 24		11 35			11 35	11 56	12 05		12 24	
Syston	d								10 42											11 42					
Sileby	d								10 47											11 47					
Barrow Upon Soar	d								10 51											11 51					
Loughborough	d		10 07			10 34			10 55			11 07	11 16		11 34					11 55	12 07			12 34	
Beeston	a		10 19									11 20									12 19				
Nottingham 8	a		10 26	10 36					11 20			11 27	11 36							12 19	12 26	12 35			
	d							10 42								11 42									12 42
Langley Mill	d							10 58																	12 58
Alfreton	d							11 06								12 04									13 06
Long Eaton	a					10 43									11 43									12 43	
Derby 10	a					10 56				11 05					11 56		12 05							12 56	
	d	10 14			10 42					11 07	11 14			11 42			12 07	12 14					12 42		
Burton-on-Trent	a					11 21				11 51					12 19		12 51							13 19	
Belper	a																12 38								
Matlock	a																12 58								
Chesterfield	d	10 33						11 18		11 27	11 33					12 18	12 27	12 33							13 18
Dronfield	d																								
Sheffield 7	a	10 51			11 15			11 38		11 46	11 50			12 15		12 38	12 46	12 51					13 15		13 38
Meadowhall	a	11 13			11 30			11 56			12 03			12 30		12 56	13 03	13 13					13 30		13 57
Barnsley	a	11 34			12 00			12 11			12 34			13 00		13 11		13 34					14 00		14 12
Doncaster 7	a	11 15			12 04						12 15			13 04				13 22					14 04		
Wakefield Westgate 7	a				11 46			12c29						12 46		13c29							13 46		14c28
Leeds 10	a				12 02			12 50						13 02		13 50							14 02		14 50
York 8	a	11 41			12 29					12 43	12 43			13 29			13 46	13 46					14 29		

Station		EM	EM 1◇	XC 1◇	EM 1◇	EM 1◇	XC R 1	EM 1◇		EM ◇	EM	EM 1◇	XC 1◇	EM 1◇	EM 1◇	XC R 1	EM 1◇	EM ◇	EM	EM 1◇		XC 1◇	EM 1◇	EM 1◇	XC R 1
St Pancras International 15	⊖ d		11 25		11 30	11 55		12 00				12 25		12 30	12 55		13 00			13 25			13 30	13 55	
Gatwick Airport 10	✈ d				10 16			10b31						11 16			11b31						12 16		
Luton Airport Parkway 7	d				11 35			12 22						12 35			13 22						13 35		
Luton 10	d				11 53			11 54						12 53			12 54						13 53		
Bedford 7	d				12 08			12 38						13 08			13 38						14 08		
Wellingborough	d				12 21			12 51						13 21			13 51						14 21		
Kettering	d				12 28			12 58						13 28			13 58						14 28		
Market Harborough	d				12 38			13 08						13 38			14 08						14 38		
Leicester	a		12 34		12 55	13 04		13 23				13 34		13 55	14 04		14 23			14 35			14 55	15 05	
	d	12 35	12 36		12 56	13 05		13 24			13 35	13 36		13 56	14 05		14 24		14 35	14 36			14 56	15 05	
Syston	d	12 42									13 42								14 42						
Sileby	d	12 47									13 47								14 47						
Barrow Upon Soar	d	12 51									13 51								14 51						
Loughborough	d	12 55			13 07	13 15		13 34			13 55			14 07			14 34		14 55				15 07	15 17	
Beeston	a				13 19									14 19									15 19		
Nottingham 8	a	13 18			13 26	13 36					14 21			14 26	14 36				15 18				15 26	15 36	
	d									13 45								14 42							
Langley Mill	d																	14 58							
Alfreton	d									14 07								15 06							
Long Eaton	a							13 43									14 43								
Derby 10	a		13 05					13 56				14 05					14 56			15 05					
	d		13 07	13 14			13 42					14 07	14 14			14 42				15 07		15 14			15 42
Burton-on-Trent	a		13 51					14 21				14 51					15 19			15 51					
Belper	a											14 37													
Matlock	a											14 57													
Chesterfield	d		13 27	13 33						14 18		14 27	14 33					15 18		15 27		15 33			
Dronfield	d																								
Sheffield 7	a		13 46	13 50			14 15			14 38		14 46	14 50			15 15		15 38		15 46		15 50			16 15
Meadowhall	a			14 03			14 30			14 56			15 03			15 30		15 56				16 03			16 30
Barnsley	a			14 34			15 00			15 11			15 34			16 00		16 11				16 34			17 02
Doncaster 7	a			14 18			15 04						15 15			16 04						16 15			17 07
Wakefield Westgate 7	a			14e46			14 46			15c29			15e46			15 46		16c27				16e46			16 46
Leeds 10	a			15e02			15 02			15 50			16e02			16 02		16 50				17e02			17 02
York 8	a		14 45	14 45			15 29					15 40	15 40			16 29				16 40		16 40			17 29

For general notes see front of timetable
For details of catering facilities see Directory of Train Operators

b Change at Bedford
c Wakefield Kirkgate
e Change at Sheffield

London → East Midlands → Sheffield

Route Diagram - See first page of Table 53

	EM 1 ◇ ☕	EM ◇	EM	EM 1 ◇ ☕	XC 1 ◇ ☕	EM 1 ◇ ☕	EM 1 ◇ ☕	XC R 1 ☕	EM 1 ◇ ☕		EM ◇	EM	EM 1 ◇ ☕	XC R 1 ☕	EM 1 ◇ ☕	XC R 1 ☕	EM ◇	EM 1 ◇ ☕	EM 1 ◇ ☕	EM 1 ◇ ☕	EM		EM 1 ◇ ☕	XC R 1 ☕
St Pancras International 15 ⊖ d	14 00			14 25		14 30	14 55		15 00				15 25		15 30			15 55	16 00	16 08			16 25	
Gatwick Airport 10 ✈ d	12b31			13 01		13 16			13b31				14 16					14 46						
Luton Airport Parkway 7 d	14 22					14 35			15 22				15 35					16 05	16 22					
Luton 10 d	13 54			14 24		14 53			14 54				15 48		15 53			16 18		16 38				
Bedford 7 d	14 38			15 00		15 08			15 38						16 08					16a56				
Wellingborough d	14 51					15 21			15 51						16 21			16 43	16 51					
Kettering d	14 58					15 28			15 58				16 18		16 28				16 58				17 14	
Market Harborough d	15 08					15 38			16 08						16 38				17 08					
Leicester a	15 24			15 39		15 56	16 04		16 23				16 40		16 55			17 13	17 23				17 39	
Leicester d	15 24		15 35	15 40		15 56	16 05		16 24			16 35	16 44		16 56			17 13	17 24		17 35		17 40	
Syston d			15 42									16 42									17 42			
Sileby d			15 47									16 47									17 47			
Barrow Upon Soar d			15 51									16 51									17 51			
Loughborough d	15 34		15 55			16 07	16 16		16 34			16 55			17 07			17 24	17 34		17 55		17 51	
Beeston a						16 19									17 19			17 38						
Nottingham 8 a			16 18			16 26	16 35					17 18			17 26			17 50			18 18			
Nottingham 8 d		15 42									16 42						17 42							
Langley Mill d											16 58						17 58							
Alfreton d		16 06									17 06						18 06							
Long Eaton a	15 44								16 43										17 43				18 10	
Derby 10 a	15 56			16 05					16 56				17 08						17 56				18 10	
Derby 10 d				16 07	16 14			16 42					17 09	17 14		17 42							18 10	18 14
Burton-on-Trent a	16 20			16 51					17 19				17 51						18 19				18 51	
Belper a				16 32									17 47											
Matlock a				16 52									18 07											
Chesterfield d		16 18		16 27	16 33						17 18		17 31	17 38			18 18						18 31	18 35
Dronfield d																	18 26							
Sheffield 7 a		16 38		16 46	16 51			17 15			17 34		17 48	17 50		18 17	18 38						18 47	18 50
Meadowhall a		16 56		17 03	17 13			17 31			17 46		18 03	18 03		18 29	18 56						19 03	19 03
Barnsley a		17 11			17 34			18 02			18 11		18 34	18 34		19 02	19 15						19 34	19 34
Doncaster 7 a					17 15			18 07			18 13		18 35	18 16		18 54							19 17	19 17
Wakefield Westgate 7 a		17c29			17e46			17 46			18c36		18 46			18 46	19c36							
Leeds 10 a		17 50			18e02			18 02			18 55		19 02			19 02	19 56							
York 8 a				17 40	17 40			18 29			18 41		19 29	18 41		19 29							19 44	19 44

	EM 1 ◇ ☕	EM 1 ◇ A ☕	XC R 1 ☕	EM ◇	EM 1 ◇ B ☕	EM	EM 1 ◇ ☕	XC R 1 ☕	EM 1 ◇ ☕	XC R 1 ☕	EM ◇		EM 1 ◇ ☕	EM 1 ◇ ☕	EM 1 ◇ ☕	XC 1 ◇	EM	EM 1 ◇ ☕	EM 1 ◇ ☕	EM 1 ◇ ☕	EM 1 ◇ ☕	XC 1 ◇	EM 1 ◇ ☕	EM
St Pancras International 15 ⊖ d	16 30	16 55			17 00		17 15		17 30				17 45	17 55	18 00			18 15	18 25	18 30	18 55		19 00	
Gatwick Airport 10 ✈ d	15 16								16 01				16 11		16b11			16 41		16 53	17 07			
Luton Airport Parkway 7 d	16 36						17 39		17 34				17 56	18 00	18 23					18 40	18 50		19 22	
Luton 10 d	16 53								17 36				18 10	18 20	18 04			18 13		18 54	18 53		19 04	
Bedford 7 d	17 08								18 10						18 38			18 54			19 30		19 38	
Wellingborough d	17 21				17 44		18 03		18 23				18 34	18 44	18 51				19 12	19 18	19 42		19 51	
Kettering d	17 28				17 51		18 10		18 33				18 41	18 53	18 58			19 12	19 19	19 26			19 58	
Market Harborough d	17 38				18 01		18 20						18 53		19 09			19 23	19 31	19 38			20 08	
Leicester a	17 56	18 04			18 21		18 35		18 57				19 08	19 18	19 25			19 38	19 48	19 55	20 10		20 23	
Leicester d	17 57	18 06			18 21	18 33	18 36		18 57				19 09	19 19	19 26		19 36	19 42	19 48	19 56	20 10		20 24	20 34
Syston d						18 42											19 44							20 41
Sileby d						18 47											19 49							20 45
Barrow Upon Soar d						18 51											19 53							20 50
Loughborough d	18 08					18 55	18 46							19 32	19 37		19 57		19 59	20 07	20 23		20 34	20 54
Beeston a	18 19				18 42									19 45			20 16			20 19				21 18
Nottingham 8 a	18 26				18 48	19 20							19 35	19 53			20 22			20 27	20 38			21 23
Nottingham 8 d				18 40							19 27		19 42											
Langley Mill d				18 56									19 59											
Alfreton d				19 06							19 57		20 07											
Long Eaton a							18 55								19 46			20 03					20 43	
Derby 10 a		18 35					19 09		19 25						19 59			20 15	20 22				20 56	
Derby 10 d		18 36	18 42					19 14	19 25	19 42					20 11	20 14		20 18	20 22			20 42	21 03	
Burton-on-Trent a		19 19							20 06						20 26								21 16	
Belper a		19 07																20 42						
Matlock a		19 27																21 02						
Chesterfield d		18 57	19 03	19 18				19 33	19 46	20 03	20 08		20 18			20 33		20 39	20 44			21 03		
Dronfield d																								
Sheffield 7 a		19 13	19 17	19 39				19 47	20 02	20 17	20 27		20 33			20 48		20 53	20 59			21 18		
Meadowhall a		19 35	19 35	19 56				20 03	20 16	20 34	20 44		20 47						21 14			21 36		
Barnsley a		20 04	20 04	20 12				20 34					21 06						21 35			22 05		
Doncaster 7 a		20 08	20 08	20 20				20 20	20 41	21 18	21 18								21 25					
Wakefield Westgate 7 a		19 44	19 49	20c28				20f51	20 53	20 53			21 01					21 44	21 44			21 49		
Leeds 10 a		20 06	20 06	20 50					21 09	21 09			21 21						22 05			22 05		
York 8 a		20e33	20 33	20 46				20 46	21 34	21 34						21 48		21g59	23 12			22 58		

For general notes see front of timetable
For details of catering facilities see Directory of Train Operators

- **A** The Master Cutler
- **B** The Robin Hood
- **b** Change at Bedford
- **c** Wakefield Kirkgate
- **e** Change at Sheffield
- **f** Wakefield Kirkgate. Change at Sheffield
- **g** Change at Sheffield and Doncaster

Mondays to Fridays
until 25 January

London → East Midlands → Sheffield

Route Diagram - See first page of Table 53

		EM	EM	XC	EM	EM	EM	EM	EM	XC	EM	EM	EM	EM	EM	EM	EM	EM	EM	EM
		1 ◇	1 ◇	1 ◇	1 ◇	1 ◇	1 ◇	1 ◇	1 ◇	1 ◇	1 ◇	1 ◇	bus	bus	1 ◇	bus	1 ◇	bus	1 ◇	bus	1 ◇
St Pancras International 15	d	19 25	19 30		19 55	20 00	20 25	20 30	20 55		21 00	21 25			21 30		22 00		22 25		23 15
Gatwick Airport 10	d	*18 01*	*18 16*			*18b31*		*19 16*			*19b31*				*20 16*		*20 46*		*21 01*		*21 46*
Luton Airport Parkway 7	d	*19 28*	*19 40*			20 22		*20 37*			21 22				*21 37*		*22 07*		*22 25*		*23 31*
Luton 10	d	19 51	19 53			*19 57*		20 53			*20 54*				21 53		22 22		22 48		23 45
Bedford 7	d		20 08			20 38		21 08			21 38				22 07		22 38		23 05		00 09
Wellingborough	d		20 21		20 39	20 51		21 21			21 51				22 20		22 51		23 18		00 22
Kettering	d	20 19	20 28			20 58	21 15	21 28			21 58	22 17	22 45		22 35		23 04	23 14	23 29	23 39	00 34
Market Harborough	d		20 38			21 08		21 38	21 51		22 08		23a10	23 19		23 33		23a39		00a04	
Leicester	a	20 44	20 56		21 06	21 23	21 39	21 55	22 06		22 23	23 19		23 44	23 46	23 58	00 02		00 31		01 33
	d	20 44	20 56		21 07	21 24	21 39	21 56	22 06		22 24	23 24			23 51		00 08		00 36		01 39
Syston	d																				
Sileby	d																				
Barrow Upon Soar	d																				
Loughborough	d		21 07		21 18	21 34		22 07	22 17		22 34	23 35			00 06		00 21		00 48		01 56
Beeston	a		21 21					22 19			22 45				00 28		00 40				
Nottingham 8	a		21 28		21 37			22 28	22 39		22 52				00 35		00 46				02 12
	d				21 42						22 58										02 19
Langley Mill	d				22 01																
Alfreton	d				22 10																
Long Eaton	a					21 43					23 13										
Derby 10	a	21 12				21 56	22 08				23 26	00 02							01 15		02 36
	d	21 13		21 42			22 09			22 49		00 05							01 16		
Burton-on-Trent	a	*21 37*				*22 19*	*22 37*														
Belper	a						*22 32*														
Matlock	a						*22 52*														
Chesterfield	d	21 34		22 03	22 21		22 30			23 28		00 25							01 36		
Dronfield	d																				
Sheffield 7	a	21 49		22 17	22 38		22 46			23 54		00 41							01 52		
Meadowhall	a	*22 13*		*22 46*			*23 20*														
Barnsley	a	*22 34*		*23 06*			*23c50*														
Doncaster 7	a	22 12					*00 07*														
Wakefield Westgate 7	a	22 30		22s46			*00 09*														
Leeds 10	a	22 50		23 05			*00 30*			01 01											
York 8	a	*23e12*		*00 08*			*01f29*														

Mondays to Fridays
from 28 January

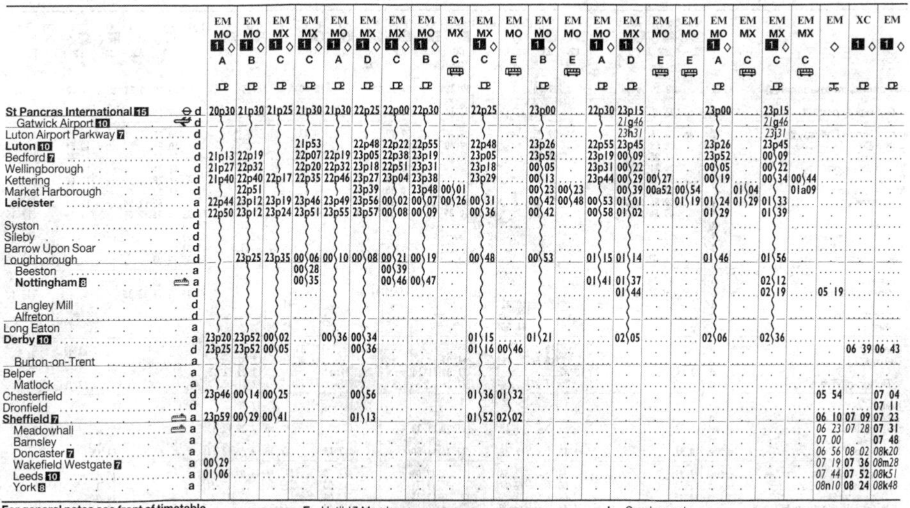

		EM	EM	EM	EM	EM	EM	EM	EM	EM	EM	EM	EM	EM	EM	EM	EM	EM	EM	EM	EM	EM	EM	XC	EM
		MO	MO	MX	MX	MO	MX	MX	MO	MX	MX	MO	MO	MO	MO	MX	MO	MO	MO	MX	MX	MX			
		1 ◇	1 ◇	1 ◇	1 ◇	1 ◇	1 ◇	1 ◇	1 ◇		1 ◇		1 ◇		1 ◇	1 ◇			1 ◇		1 ◇		◇	1 ◇	1 ◇
		A	B	C	C	A	D	C	B	C bus	C	E bus	B	E bus	A	D	E bus	E bus	A	C bus	C	C bus			
St Pancras International 15	d	20p30	21p30	21p25	21p30	21p30	22p25	22p00	22p30		22p25		23p00		22p30	23p15			23p00		23p15				
Gatwick Airport 10	d															*21g46*					*21g46*				
Luton Airport Parkway 7	d															*23h31*					*23j31*				
Luton 10	d				21p53		22p48	22p22	22p55		22p48		23p26		22p55	23p45			23p26		23p45				
Bedford 7	d	21p13	22p19		22p07	22p19	23p05	22p38	23p19		23p05		23p52		23p19	00 09			23p52		00 09				
Wellingborough	d	21p27	22p32		22p20	22p32	23p18	22p51	23p31		23p18		00 05		23p31	00 22			00 05		00 22				
Kettering	d	21p40	22p40	22p17	22p35	22p46	23p27	23p04	23p38		23p29		00 13		23p44	00 29	00 27		00 19		00 34	00 44			
Market Harborough	d		22p51				23p39		23p48	00 01			00 23	00 23		00 39	00a52	00 54		01 04		01a09			
Leicester	a	22p44	23p12	23p19	23p46	23p49	23p56	00 02	00 07	00 26	00 31		00 42	00 48	00 53	01 01		01 19	01 24	01 29	01 33				
	d	22p50	23p12	23p24	23p51	23p55	23p57	00 08	00 09		00 36		00 42		00 58	01 02			01 29		01 39				
Syston	d																								
Sileby	d																								
Barrow Upon Soar	d																								
Loughborough	d		23p25	23p35	00 06	00 10	00 08	00 21	00 19		00 48		00 53		01 15	01 14			01 46		01 56				
Beeston	a				00 28			00 39																	
Nottingham 8	a				00 35			00 46	00 47						01 41	01 37					02 12				
	d															01 44					02 19		05 19		
Langley Mill	d																								
Alfreton	d																								
Long Eaton	a																								
Derby 10	a	23p20	23p52	00 02		00 36	00 34				01 15		01 21			02 05			02 06		02 36				
	d	23p25	23p52	00 05			00 36				01 16	00 46												06 39	06 43
Burton-on-Trent	a																								
Belper	a																								
Matlock	a																								
Chesterfield	d	23p46	00 14	00 25			00 56				01 36	01 32											05 54		07 04
Dronfield	d																								07 11
Sheffield 7	a	23p59	00 29	00 41			01 13				01 52	02 02											06 10	07 09	07 23
Meadowhall	a																						*06 23*	*07 28*	07 31
Barnsley	a																						*07 00*		07 48
Doncaster 7	a																						*06 56*	*08 02*	*08k20*
Wakefield Westgate 7	a	00 29																					*07 19*	07 36	*08m28*
Leeds 10	a	01 06																					*07 44*	07 52	*08k51*
York 8	a																						*08n10*	08 24	*08k48*

For general notes see front of timetable
For details of catering facilities see Directory of Train Operators

A Until 24 March
B From 31 March
C Until 21 March
D From 25 March
E Until 17 March
b Change at Bedford
c Mondays to Thursdays only
e Change at Doncaster
f Change at Sheffield and Leeds
g Mondays to Thursdays only. Change at Bedford. Mondays dep. 2145
h Sundays only. Change at Bedford. Mondays dep. 2315
j Sundays to Wednesdays only. Change at Bedford. Mondays dep. 2315
k Change at Sheffield
m Wakefield Kirkgate. Change at Sheffield
n Change at Sheffield and Doncaster

London → East Midlands → Sheffield

Route Diagram - See first page of Table 53

		XC		EM ◇	XC 1 ◇	EM	XC R 1	EM ◇	XC 1 ◇	EM	EM 1 ◇	EM 1 ◇	XC R 1	EM 1 ◇	EM ◇	EM	EM 1 ◇ ⊠	XC 1 ◇	EM 1 ◇	EM 1 ◇ ⊠	XC 1 ◇	EM 1 ◇	EM ◇	EM	EM 1 ◇ ⊠
St Pancras International 15 ⊖	d										06 10	06 35		07 00			07 25		07 30	07 55		08 00			08 25
Gatwick Airport 10 ✈	d										04 30			05b00			06 16					06b24			06 46
Luton Airport Parkway 7	d										06 05	06 57		07 22			07 35					08 22			
Luton 10	d										06 33			06 40			07 50		07 53			07 57			08 08
Bedford 7	d										06 48			07 38					08 08			08 38			09 00
Wellingborough	d										07 01	07 21		07 51					08 21			08 51			
Kettering	d										07 08	07 28		07 58					08 28			08 58			
Market Harborough	d										07 18	07 38		08 08					08 38			09 08			
Leicester	a										07 35	07 55		08 23			08 38		08 55	09 04		09 23			09 38
	d	06 30				06 40				07 24	07 35	07 56		08 24		08 35	08 39		08 56	09 05		09 24		09 36	09 39
Syston	d					06 47				07 31						08 42								09 43	
Sileby	d					06 52				07 38						08 47								09 48	
Barrow Upon Soar	d					06 56				07 43						08 51								09 52	
Loughborough	d	06 45				07 00				07 47	07 46	08 07		08 34		08 55	08 50		09 07	09 16		09 34		09 56	
Beeston	a	06 45				07 21				08 10		08 19							09 19						
Nottingham 8	a					07 30				08 20		08 29				09 20			09 26	09 36				10 20	
	d			06 34				07 42							08 42								09 40		
Langley Mill	d			06 53				07 58							08 58								09 57		
Alfreton	d			07 01				08 06							09 06								10 05		
Long Eaton	a	06 56									07 59			08 43								09 43			
Derby 10	a	07 11									08 12			08 55			09 09					09 56			10 07
	d				07 14		07 42		08 14		08 16		08 42				09 09	09 14			09 42				10 09
Burton-on-Trent	a										08 37			09 17			09 51					10 21			10 51
Belper	a										08 25														10 38
Matlock	a										08c59														10 58
Chesterfield	d			07 14	07 33		08 03	08 18	08 33		08 39				09 18		09 31	09 35					10 18		10 29
Dronfield	d			07 21	07 39			08 25																	
Sheffield 7	a			07 32	07 51		08 17	08 38	08 50		09 05		09 18		09 38		09 46	09 50			10 15		10 38		10 46
Meadowhall	a			07 46	08 13		08 41	08 56	09 03		09 21		09 30		09 56			10 03			10 30		10 56		11 03
Barnsley	a			08 11	08 34		09 00	09 11	09 34		10 00		10 00		10 11			10 34			11 00		11 11		
Doncaster 7	a			08 20	08 24		09 10		09 19		10 04		10 04					10 15			11 04				
Wakefield Westgate 7	a			08e28	08f46		08 46	09e29			09 46		09 46		10e29						10 46		11e29		
Leeds 10	a			08 51	09f02		09 02	09 50			10 02		10 02		10 50						11 02		11 50		
York 8	a			08 48	08 48		09 33	09 48	09 48		10 29		10 29				10 40	10 40			11 29				11 41

		XC 1 ◇	EM 1 ◇	EM 1 ◇ ⊠		XC 1 ◇	EM 1 ◇	EM ◇	EM	EM 1 ◇ ⊠	XC 1 ◇	EM 1 ◇	EM 1 ◇ ⊠	XC 1 ◇	EM 1 ◇	EM ◇	EM 1 ◇ ⊠	XC 1 ◇	EM	EM 1 ◇	EM 1 ◇	XC 1 ◇	EM 1 ◇	EM ◇	EM
St Pancras International 15 ⊖	d		08 30	08 55			09 00			09 25		09 30	09 55		10 00		10 25			10 30	10 55		11 00		
Gatwick Airport 10 ✈	d		07 01				07b01			07 37		08 01			08b22					09 16			09b31		
Luton Airport Parkway 7	d		08 36				09 22			09 25		09 40			10 22					10 35			11 22		
Luton 10	d		08 53				08 54			09 48		09 53			09 56					10 53			10 54		
Bedford 7	d		09 08				09 38					10 08			10 38					11 08			11 38		
Wellingborough	d		09 21				09 51					10 21			10 51					11 21			11 51		
Kettering	d		09 28				09 58					10 28			10 58					11 28			11 58		
Market Harborough	d		09 38				10 08					10 38			11 08					11 38			12 08		
Leicester	a		09 55	10 04			10 23			10 36		10 55	11 04		11 23		11 34			11 55	12 04		12 23		
	d		09 56	10 05			10 24		10 35	10 39		10 56	11 05		11 24		11 35		11 35	11 56	12 05		12 24		12 35
Syston	d								10 42										11 42						12 42
Sileby	d								10 47										11 47						12 47
Barrow Upon Soar	d								10 51										11 51						12 51
Loughborough	d		10 07				10 34		10 55			11 07	11 16		11 34				11 55	12 07			12 34		12 55
Beeston	a		10 19									11 20								12 19					
Nottingham 8	a		10 26	10 36					11 20			11 27	11 36						12 19	12 26	12 35				13 18
	d							10 42								11 42								12 42	
Langley Mill	d							10 58																12 58	
Alfreton	d							11 06								12 04								13 06	
Long Eaton	a						10 43								11 43								12 43		
Derby 10	a						10 54			11 07					11 56		12 07						12 54		
	d	10 14				10 42				11 09	11 14			11 42			12 09	12 15				12 42			
Burton-on-Trent	a						11 21			11 51					12 19		12 51						13 19		
Belper	a																12 38								
Matlock	a																12 58								
Chesterfield	d	10 33						11 18		11 28	11 33					12 18	12 29	12 33						13 18	
Dronfield	d																								
Sheffield 7	a	10 51				11 15		11 38		11 46	11 50			12 15		12 38	12 46	12 51				13 15		13 38	
Meadowhall	a	11 13				11 30		11 56			12 03			12 30		12 56	13 03	13 13				13 30		13 57	
Barnsley	a	11 34				12 00		12 11			12 34			13 00		13 11		13 34				14 00		14 12	
Doncaster 7	a	11 15				12 04					12 15			13 04				13 22				14 04			
Wakefield Westgate 7	a					11 46		12e29						12 46		13e29						13 46		14e28	
Leeds 10	a					12 02		12 50						13 02		13 50						14 02		14 50	
York 8	a	11 41				12 29				12 43	12 43			13 29			13 46	13 46				14 29			

For general notes see front of timetable
For details of catering facilities see Directory of Train Operators

- b Change at Bedford
- c Change at Derby
- e Wakefield Kirkgate
- f Change at Sheffield

Table 53

Mondays to Fridays
from 28 January

London → East Midlands → Sheffield

Route Diagram - See first page of Table 53

		EM	XC	EM	EM	XC		EM	EM	EM	EM	XC	EM	EM	XC	EM	EM	EM	EM	XC	EM	EM	XC	EM	EM
		1 ◇	1 ◇	1 ◇	1 ◇	R 1		1 ◇	◇		1 ◇	1 ◇	1 ◇	1 ◇	R 1	1 ◇	◇		1 ◇	1 ◇	1 ◇	1 ◇	R 1	1 ◇	◇
		☕	☕	☕	☕	☕		☕	🚲		☕	☕	☕	☕	☕	☕			☕	☕	☕	☕	☕	☕	
St Pancras International [15]	⊖ d	11 25		11 30	11 55			12 00			12 25		12 30	12 55		13 00			13 25		13 30	13 55		14 00	
Gatwick Airport [10]	✈ d			*10 16*				*10b31*					*11 16*			*11b31*					*12 16*			*12b31*	
Luton Airport Parkway [7]	d			*11 35*				12 22					*12 35*			13 22					*13 35*			14 22	
Luton [10]	d			11 53				*11 54*					12 53			*12 54*					13 53			*13 54*	
Bedford [7]	d			12 08				12 38					13 08			13 38					14 08			14 38	
Wellingborough	d			12 21				12 51					13 21			13 51					14 21			14 51	
Kettering	d			12 28				12 58					13 28			13 58					14 28			14 58	
Market Harborough	d			12 38				13 08					13 38			14 08					14 38			15 08	
Leicester	a	12 34		12 55	13 04			13 23			13 34		13 55	14 04		14 23			14 35		14 55	15 05		15 24	
	d	12 36		12 56	13 05			13 24		13 35	13 36		13 56	14 05		14 24		14 35	14 36		14 56	15 05		15 24	
Syston	d									13 42								14 42							
Sileby	d									13 47								14 47							
Barrow Upon Soar	d									13 51								14 51							
Loughborough	d			13 07	13 15			13 34		13 55			14 07			14 34		14 55			15 07	15 17		15 34	
Beeston	a			13 19									14 19								15 19				
Nottingham [8]	🚢 a			13 26	13 36					14 21			14 26	14 36				15 18			15 26	15 36			
	d								13 45								14 42								15 42
Langley Mill	d																14 58								
Alfreton	d								14 07								15 06								16 06
Long Eaton	a							13 43								14 43								15 44	
Derby [10]	a	13 07						13 56			14 07					14 56			15 07					15 56	
	d	13 09	13 14			13 42					14 09	14 15			14 42				15 09	15 14			15 42		
Burton-on-Trent	a	*13 51*						*14 21*			*14 51*					*15 19*			*15 51*					*16 20*	
Belper	a										*14 37*														
Matlock	a										*14 57*														
Chesterfield	d	13 30	13 33						14 18		14 30	14 33					15 18		15 30	15 33					16 18
Dronfield	d																								
Sheffield [7]	🚢 a	13 46	13 50			14 15			14 38		14 46	14 50			15 15		15 38		15 46	15 51			16 15		16 38
Meadowhall	🚢 a		*14 03*			*14 30*			*14 56*			*15 03*			*15 30*		*15 56*		*16 03*	*16 13*			*16 30*		*16 56*
Barnsley	a		*14 34*			*15 00*			*15 11*			*15 34*			*16 00*		*16 11*			*16 34*			*17 02*		*17 11*
Doncaster [7]	a		14 18			*15 04*						15 15			*16 04*					16 15			*17 07*		
Wakefield Westgate [7]	a		*14c46*			14 46			*15e29*			*15c46*			15 46		*16e27*			*16c46*			16 46		*17e29*
Leeds [10]	a		*15c02*			15 02			*15 50*			*16c02*			16 02		*16 50*			*17c02*			17 02		*17 50*
York [8]	a	*14 45*	14 45			15 29					*15 40*	15 40			16 29				*16 40*	16 40			17 29		

		EM	EM	XC	EM	EM	XC	EM		EM	EM	EM	XC	EM	XC	EM	EM	EM	EM	EM	EM	XC	EM	EM	XC
			1 ◇	1 ◇	1 ◇	1 ◇	R 1	1 ◇		◇		1 ◇	R 1	1 ◇	R 1	◇	1 ◇	1 ◇	1 ◇		1 ◇	R 1	1 ◇	1 ◇	R 1
																								A	B
			☕	☕	☕	☕	☕	☕				☕	☕	☕	☕		☕	☕	☕		☕	☕	☕	☕	☕
St Pancras International [15]	⊖ d		14 25		14 30	14 55		15 00				15 25		15 30			15 55	16 00	16 08		16 25		16 30	16 55	
Gatwick Airport [10]	✈ d		*13 01*		*13 16*			*13b31*				*14 16*					*14 46*						*15 16*		
Luton Airport Parkway [7]	d				*14 35*			15 22				*15 35*					*16 05*	16 22					*16 36*		
Luton [10]	d		*14 24*		14 53			*14 54*				15 48		15 53			16 18						16 53		
Bedford [7]	d		15 00		15 08			15 38						16 08					16 38				17 08		
Wellingborough	d				15 21			15 51						16 21			16 43	16 51	16a56				17 21		
Kettering	d				15 28			15 58				16 18		16 28				16 58			17 14		17 28		
Market Harborough	d				15 38			16 08						16 38				17 08					17 38		
Leicester	a		15 39		15 56	16 04		16 23				16 40		16 55			17 13	17 23			17 39		17 56	18 04	
	d	15 35	15 40		15 56	16 05		16 24			16 35	16 44		16 56			17 13	17 24		17 35	17 40		17 57	18 06	
Syston	d	15 42									16 42									17 42					
Sileby	d	15 47									16 47									17 47					
Barrow Upon Soar	d	15 51									16 51									17 51					
Loughborough	d	15 55			16 07	16 16		16 34			16 55			17 07			17 24	17 34		17 55	17 51		18 08		
Beeston	a				16 19									17 19			17 38						18 19		
Nottingham [8]	🚢 a	16 18			16 26	16 35					17 18			17 26			17 50			18 18			18 26		
	d									16 42						17 42									
Langley Mill	d									16 58						17 58									
Alfreton	d									17 06						18 06									
Long Eaton	a							16 43										17 43							
Derby [10]	a		16 07					16 56				17 08						17 56			18 10			18 35	
	d		16 09	16 14			16 42					17 09	17 14		17 42						18 10	18 14		18 36	18 42
Burton-on-Trent	a		*16 51*					*17 19*				*17 51*						*18 19*			*18 51*			*19 19*	
Belper	a		*16 32*									*17 47*												*19 07*	
Matlock	a		*16 52*									*18 07*												*19 27*	
Chesterfield	d		16 30	16 33						17 18		17 31	17 38			18 18					18 31	18 35		18 57	19 03
Dronfield	d															18 26									
Sheffield [7]	🚢 a		16 46	16 51			17 15			17 34		17 48	17 50		18 17	18 38					18 47	18 50		19 13	19 17
Meadowhall	🚢 a		*17 03*	*17 13*			*17 31*			*17 46*		*18 03*	*18 03*		*18 29*	*18 56*					*19 03*	*19 03*		*19 35*	*19 35*
Barnsley	a			*17 34*			*18 02*			*18 11*		*18 34*	*18 34*		*19 02*	*19 15*					*19 34*	*19 34*		*20 04*	*20 04*
Doncaster [7]	a			17 15			*18 07*			*18 13*		*18 35*	18 16		*18 54*						*19 17*	19 17		*20 08*	*20 08*
Wakefield Westgate [7]	a			*17c46*			17 46			*18e36*		*18 46*			18 46	*19e36*								19 44	19 49
Leeds [10]	a			*18c02*			18 02			*18 55*		*19 02*			19 02	*19 56*								20 06	20 06
York [8]	a		*17 40*	17 40			18 29			*18 41*		*19 29*	18 41		19 29						*19 44*	19 44		*20c33*	20 33

For general notes see front of timetable
For details of catering facilities see Directory of Train Operators

- **A** The Master Cutler
- **B** ☕ to Leeds
- **b** Change at Bedford
- **c** Change at Sheffield
- **e** Wakefield Kirkgate

London → East Midlands → Sheffield

Route Diagram - See first page of Table 53

Station		EM	EM	EM	EM	XC	EM	XC	EM	EM	EM	EM	XC	EM	EM	EM	EM	EM	XC	EM	EM	EM	EM	XC
		◇	1 ◇		1 ◇	R 1	1 ◇	R 1	◇	1 ◇	1 ◇	1 ◇	1 ◇		1 ◇	1 ◇	1 ◇	1 ◇	1 ◇	1 ◇		1 ◇	1 ◇	1 ◇
			A					B					B											
			☕		☕	☕	☕	☕		☕	☕	☕			☕	☕	☕	☕		☕		☕	☕	
St Pancras International 15 ⊖	d		17 00		17 15		17 30			17 45	17 55	18 00			18 15	18 25	18 30	18 55		19 00		19 25	19 30	
Gatwick Airport 10 ✈	d						16 01			16 11		16b11			16 41		16 53	17 07				18 01	18 16	
Luton Airport Parkway 7	d				17 39		17 34			17 56	18 00	18 23					18 40	18 50		19 22		19 28	19 40	
Luton 10	d						17 36			18 10	18 20	18 04			18 13		18 54	18 53		19 04		19 51	19 53	
Bedford 7	d						18c10					18 38			18 54			19 30		19 38			20 08	
Wellingborough	d		17 44		18 03		18 23			18 34	18 44	18 51				19 12	19 18	19 42		19 51			20 21	
Kettering	d		17 51		18 10		18 33			18 41	18 53	18 58			19 12	19 19	19 26			19 58		20 19	20 28	
Market Harborough	d		18 01		18 20					18 53		19 09			19 23	19 31	19 38			20 08			20 38	
Leicester	a		18 21		18 35		18 57			19 08	19 18	19 25			19 38	19 48	19 55	20 10		20 23		20 44	20 56	
	d		18 21	18 33	18 36		18 57			19 09	19 19	19 26		19 36	19 42	19 48	19 56	20 10		20 24	20 34	20 44	20 56	
Syston	d			18 42										19 44							20 41			
Sileby	d			18 47										19 49							20 45			
Barrow Upon Soar	d			18 51										19 53							20 50			
Loughborough	d			18 55	18 46						19 32	19 37		19 57		19 59	20 07	20 23		20 34	20 54		21 07	
Beeston	a		18 42								19 45			20 16			20 19				21 18		21 21	
Nottingham 8 🚢	a		18 48	19 20						19 35	19 53			20 22			20 27	20 38			21 23		21 28	
	d	18 40							19 27	19 42														
Langley Mill	d	18 56								19 59														
Alfreton	d	19 06							19 57	20 07														
Long Eaton	a				18 55							19 46			20 03					20 43				
Derby 10	a				19 09		19 25					20 00			20 15	20 22				20 56		21 12		
	d					19 14	19 25	19 42				20 11	20 14		20 18	20 22			20 42	21 03		21 13		21 42
Burton-on-Trent	a						20 06					20 26								21 16		21 37		
Belper	a														20 42									
Matlock	a														21 02									
Chesterfield	d	19 18				19 33	19 46	20 03	20 08	20 18				20 33	20 39	20 44			21 03			21 34		22 03
Dronfield	d																							
Sheffield 7 🚢	a	19 39				19 47	20 02	20 17	20 27	20 33				20 48	20 53	20 59			21 18			21 49		22 17
Meadowhall 🚢	a	19 56				20 03	20 16	20 34	20 44	20 47						21 14			21 36			22 13		22 46
Barnsley	a	20 12				20 34				21 06						21 35			22 05			22 34		23 06
Doncaster 7	a	20 20				20 20	20 41	21 18	21 18							21 25						22 12		
Wakefield Westgate 7	a	20e28				20f51	20 53	20 53		21 01					21 44	21 44			21 49			22 30		22s46
Leeds 10	a	20 50					21 09	21 09		21 21						22 05			22 05			22 50		23 05
York 8	a	20 46				20 46	21 34	21 34						21 48	21g59	23 12			22 58			23h12		00 08

Station		EM	EM	EM	EM	EM	EM	EM	XC	EM	EM	EM	EM	EM	EM	EM	EM	EM	EM	EM	EM	EM	EM
		1 ◇	1 ◇	1 ◇	1 ◇	1 ◇	1 ◇	1 ◇	1 ◇	1 ◇	1 ◇	1 ◇			1 ◇	1 ◇		1 ◇		1 ◇		1 ◇	1 ◇
								C		C	D	C	D 🚌	D 🚌	D	C	D 🚌	D	D 🚌	D	D 🚌	C	D
		☕	☕	☕	☕	☕	☕	☕		☕	☕	☕			☕	☕		☕		☕		☕	☕
St Pancras International 15 ⊖	d	19 55	20 00	20 25	20 30	20 55	21 00	21 25		21 30	21 25	22 00			21 30	22 25		22 00		22 25		23 15	23 15
Gatwick Airport 10 ✈	d		18b31		19 16		19b31			20 16		20 46			20 16	21 01		20 46		21 01		21 46	21 46
Luton Airport Parkway 7	d		20 22		20 37		21 22			21 37		22 07			21 37	22 25		22 07		22 25		23 31	23 31
Luton 10	d		19 57		20 53		20 54			21 53		22 22			21 53	22 48		22 22		22 48		23 45	23 45
Bedford 7	d		20 38		21 08		21 38			22 07		22 38			22 07	23 05		22 38		23 05		00 09	00 09
Wellingborough	d	20 39	20 51		21 21		21 51			22 20		22 51			22 20	23 18		22 51		23 18		00 22	00 22
Kettering	d		20 58	21 15	21 28		21 58	22 14		22 27	22 17	22 59	22 45		22 35	23 27		23 04	23 14	23 29	23 39	00 29	00 34
Market Harborough	d		21 08		21 38	21 51	22 08			22 37		23 09	23a10	23 19		23 39	23 33		23a39		00a04	00 39	
Leicester	a	21 06	21 23	21 39	21 55	22 06	22 23	22 38		22 55	23 19	23 29		23 44	23 46	23 56	23 58	00 02		00 31		01 01	01 33
	d	21 07	21 24	21 39	21 56	22 06	22 24	22 39		22 56	23 24	23 30			23 51	23 57		00 08		00 36		01 02	01 39
Syston	d																						
Sileby	d																						
Barrow Upon Soar	d																						
Loughborough	d	21 18	21 34		22 07	22 17	22 34	22 50		23 07	23 35	23 49			00 06	00 08		00 21		00 48		01 14	01 56
Beeston	a				22 19		22 45			23 19		23 59			00 28			00 39					
Nottingham 8 🚢	a	21 37			22 28	22 39	22 52			23 31		00 06			00 35			00 46				01 37	02 12
	d	21 42					22 58															01 44	02 19
Langley Mill	d	22 01																					
Alfreton	d	22 10																					
Long Eaton	a		21 43				23 13																
Derby 10	a		21 56	22 08			23 26	23 06			00 02					00 34				01 15		02 05	02 36
	d			22 09				23 11	22 49		00 05					00 36				01 16			
Burton-on-Trent	a		22 19	22 37																			
Belper	a			22 32																			
Matlock	a			22 52																			
Chesterfield	d	22 21		22 30				23 33	23 28		00 25					00 56				01 36			
Dronfield	d																						
Sheffield 7 🚢	a	22 38		22 46				23 49	23 54		00 41					01 13				01 52			
Meadowhall 🚢	a			23 20																			
Barnsley	a			23j50																			
Doncaster 7	a			00 07																			
Wakefield Westgate 7	a			00 09																			
Leeds 10	a			00 30					01 01														
York 8	a			01k29																			

For general notes see front of timetable
For details of catering facilities see Directory of Train Operators

A The Robin Hood

B ☕ to Sheffield
C From 24 March
D Until 21 March
b Change at Bedford
c Arr. 1807
e Wakefield Kirkgate

f Wakefield Kirkgate. Change at Sheffield
g Change at Sheffield and Doncaster
h Change at Doncaster
j Mondays to Thursdays only
k Change at Sheffield and Leeds

London → East Midlands → Sheffield

Route Diagram - See first page of Table 53

		EM	EM	EM	EM	EM	EM	EM	EM	EM	EM	XC	EM	XC	EM	XC		EM	XC	EM	EM	XC	EM	EM	XC
		1 ◇	1 ◇	1 ◇	🚌	1 ◇	🚌	1 ◇	🚌	◇	1 ◇	1 ◇	◇	1 ◇		1 ◇		◇	1 ◇		1 ◇	1 ◇	◇	1 ◇	1 ◇
		☕	☕	☕		☕		☕			☕	☕		☕		☕			☕		☕	☕		☕	☕
St Pancras International 15	⊖ d	21p25	21p30	22p00		22p25		23p15													06 20			07 00	
Gatwick Airport 10	✈ d							21b46													04 30			05c25	
Luton Airport Parkway 7	d							23e31													06 05			07 25	
Luton 10	d		21p53	22p22		22p48		23p45													06 44			06 56	
Bedford 7	d		22p07	22p38		23p05		00 09													07 01			07 41	
Wellingborough	d		22p20	22p51		23p18		00 22													07 16			07 53	
Kettering	d	22p17	22p35	23p04		23p29		00 34	00 44												07 24			08 01	
Market Harborough	d				00 01		01 04		01a09												07 36			08 11	
Leicester	a	23p19	23p46	00 02	00 26	00 31	01 29	01 33													07 54			08 27	
	d	23p24	23p51	00 08		00 36		01 39							06 40					07 28	07 54			08 27	
Syston	d														06 47					07 39					
Sileby	d														06 52					07 45					
Barrow Upon Soar	d														06 56					07 49					
Loughborough	d	23p35	00 06	00 21		00 48		01 56							07 00					07 53	08 06			08 38	
Beeston	a		00 28	00 39											07 20									08 48	
Nottingham 8	a		00 35	00 46				02 12							07 27					08 16				08 56	
	d							02 19		05 23			06 37					07 42					08 42		
Langley Mill	d												06 53					07 58					08 58		
Alfreton	d												07 01					08 06					09 06		
Long Eaton	a																				08 21				
Derby 10	a	00 02				01 15		02 36													08 32				
	d	00 05				01 16					06 30	06 39		07 14		07 42			08 14		08 34	08 42			09 14
Burton-on-Trent	a																				09 19				
Belper	a																								
Matlock	a																								
Chesterfield	d	00 25				01 36				05 54	06 49		07 14	07 33		08 01		08 18	08 33		08 56	09 01	09 18		09 33
Dronfield	d												07 21	07 39				08 25							
Sheffield 7	a	00 41				01 52				06 10	07 05	07 09	07 31	07 49		08 17		08 38	08 46		09 13	09 17	09 38		09 50
Meadowhall	a									06 23	07 23	07 23	07 46	08 13		08 41		08 56	09 03		09 28	09 32	09 56		10 03
Barnsley	a									07 00	07 43	07 43	08 11	08 34		09 00		09 11	09 34			10 00	10 11		
Doncaster 7	a									06 57		08 02	08 20	08 23		09 09			09 21		09 52	10 05			10 18
Wakefield Westgate 7	a									07 19		07 36	08f28			08 46		09f29				09 46	10f29		
Leeds 10	a									07 44		07 52	08 51			09 04		09 50				10 02	10 50		
York 8	a										08g24	08 24	08 49	08 49		09 31		09 48	09 48		10 16	10 31	10 44		10 44

		EM	EM	EM	EM	XC	EM	EM	EM	EM		EM	XC	EM	EM	XC	EM	EM	EM	EM	XC	EM	EM	XC	EM
			1 ◇	1 ◇	1 ◇	1 ◇		1 ◇	◇			1 ◇	1 ◇	1 ◇	1 ◇	1 ◇	1 ◇	◇		1 ◇	1 ◇	1 ◇	1 ◇	1 ◇	1 ◇
			☕	☕	☕	☕		☕				☕	☕	☕	☕	☕	☕			☕	☕	☕	⊠	☕	☕
St Pancras International 15	⊖ d		07 25	07 30	07 55			08 00				08 25		08 30	08 55		09 00			09 25		09 30	09 55		10 00
Gatwick Airport 10	✈ d		06 01					06c31				07 01		07 16			07c31			08 16					08c31
Luton Airport Parkway 7	d		07 20	07 36				08 22						08 35			09 22			09 35					10 22
Luton 10	d		07 49	07 53				07 56				08 24		08 53			08 54			09 49		09 53			09 54
Bedford 7	d			08 08				08 38				09 00		09 08			09 38					10 08			10 38
Wellingborough	d			08 21				08 51						09 21			09 51					10 21			10 51
Kettering	d			08 28				08 58						09 28			09 58					10 28			10 58
Market Harborough	d			08 38				09 08						09 38			10 08					10 38			11 08
Leicester	a		08 39	08 55	09 04			09 23				09 38		09 55	10 04		10 23			10 38		10 55	11 04		11 23
	d	08 32	08 40	08 56	09 05			09 25		09 30		09 39		09 56	10 05		10 25		10 30	10 39		10 56	11 05		11 24
Syston	d	08 39								09 39									10 39						
Sileby	d	08 44								09 44									10 44						
Barrow Upon Soar	d	08 48								09 48									10 48						
Loughborough	d	08 52	08 51	09 07	09 16			09 34		09 52				10 07			10 34		10 52			11 07	11 16		11 34
Beeston	a			09 19										10 19								11 19			
Nottingham 8	a	09 16		09 26	09 37					10 18				10 27	10 34				11 17			11 27	11 35		
	d								09 42									10 42							
Langley Mill	d								09 59																
Alfreton	d								10 07									11 04							
Long Eaton	a							09 43									10 43								11 44
Derby 10	a		09 14					09 56				10 05					10 56			11 05					11 56
	d		09 17			09 42	09 49					10 07	10 14			10 42				11 07	11 14			11 42	
Burton-on-Trent	a		09 51					10 21				10 53					11 19			11 50					12 20
Belper	a		10 01				10 01													12 04					
Matlock	a		10 21				10 21													12 24					
Chesterfield	d		09 38						10 18			10 27	10 33					11 18		11 27	11 33				
Dronfield	d																								
Sheffield 7	a		09 56			10 15			10 38			10 46	10 50			11 15		11 38		11 46	11 50			12 15	
Meadowhall	a		10 13			10 30			10 56				11 03			11 30		11 56			12 03			12 30	
Barnsley	a		10 34			11 00			11 11				11 34			12 00		12 11			12 34			13 00	
Doncaster 7	a		10 40			11 04							11 16			12 04					12 15			13 04	
Wakefield Westgate 7	a					10 46			11f29							11 46		12f29						12 46	
Leeds 10	a					11 02			11 50							12 02		12 50						13 02	
York 8	a		11 29			11 29						11 45	11 45			12 29				12 43	12 43			13 29	

For general notes see front of timetable
For details of catering facilities see Directory of Train Operators

b Fridays. Change at Bedford
c Change at Bedford
e Thursdays. Change at Bedford
f Wakefield Kirkgate
g Change at Sheffield

Table 53

Saturdays

until 26 January

London → East Midlands → Sheffield

Route Diagram - See first page of Table 53

		EM ◇	EM	EM 1◇ ⊠		XC 1◇	EM 1◇	EM 1◇	XC 1◇	EM 1◇	EM ◇	EM	EM 1◇	XC 1◇	EM 1◇	EM 1◇	EM 1◇	XC 1◇	EM 1◇	EM ◇		EM	EM 1◇	XC 1◇	EM 1◇
St Pancras International 15 ⊖	d			10 25			10 30	10 55		11 00			11 25		11 30		11 55		12 00				12 25		12 30
Gatwick Airport 10 ✈	d						09 16			09b31					10 16				10b31						11 16
Luton Airport Parkway 7	d						10 35			11 22					11 35				12 22						12 35
Luton 10	d						10 53			10 54					11 53				11 54						12 53
Bedford 7	d						11 08			11 38					12 08				12 38						13 08
Wellingborough	d						11 21			11 51					12 21				12 51						13 21
Kettering	d						11 28			11 58					12 28				12 58						13 28
Market Harborough	d						11 38			12 08					12 38				13 08						13 38
Leicester	a			11 34			11 55	12 03		12 23			12 34		12 55		13 04		13 23				13 34		13 55
	d		11 30	11 36			11 56	12 05		12 24		12 30	12 36		12 56		13 05		13 24			13 30	13 36		13 56
Syston	d		11 39									12 39										13 39			
Sileby	d		11 44									12 44										13 44			
Barrow Upon Soar	d		11 48									12 48										13 48			
Loughborough	d		11 52				12 07			12 34		12 52			13 07		13 17		13 34			13 52			14 07
Beeston	a						12 19								13 19										14 19
Nottingham 8	a		12 16				12 27	12 34				13 16			13 25	←	13 36					14 18			14 25
	d	11 42					12 45 →				12 47					12 45				13 42					
Langley Mill	d										13 03					13 22				13 59					
Alfreton	d	12 04									13 11					13 30				14 07					
Long Eaton	a									12 43									13 43						
Derby 10	a			12 05						12 56			13 05						13 56				14 05		
	d			12 07		12 14			12 42				13 07	13 14				13 42					14 07	14 14	
Burton-on-Trent	a			12 50						13 19			13 51						14 21				14 50		
Belper	a												13 42										15 00		
Matlock	a												14 02										15 20		
Chesterfield	d	12 18		12 27		12 33					13 22		13 28	13 33		13 41				14 18			14 27	14 33	
Dronfield	d															13 49									
Sheffield 7	a	12 38		12 46		12 50			13 15		13 39		13 47	13 51		14 00		14 15		14 38			14 46	14 50	
Meadowhall	a	12 56				13 03			13 30		13 57		14 03			14 13		14 30		14 56				15 03	
Barnsley	a	13 11				13 34			14 00		14 12					14 34		15 00		15 11				15 34	
Doncaster 7	a					13 19			14 04					14 15		14 38		15 04						15 15	
Wakefield Westgate 7	a	13c29							13 46		14c28							14 46		15c29					
Leeds 10	a	13 50							14 02		14 50							15 02		15 50					
York 8	a			13 44		13 44			14 29				14 43	14 43		15 29		15 29					15 43	15 43	

		EM 1◇	XC 1◇	EM 1◇	EM ◇	EM	EM 1◇	XC 1◇	EM 1◇	EM 1◇	XC 1◇	EM 1◇	EM ◇	EM		EM 1◇	XC 1◇	EM 1◇	EM 1◇	XC 1◇	EM 1◇	EM ◇	EM	EM 1◇	XC 1◇
St Pancras International 15 ⊖	d	12 55		13 00			13 25		13 30	13 55		14 00				14 25		14 30	14 55		15 00			15 25	
Gatwick Airport 10 ✈	d			11b31					12 16			12b31				13 01		13 16			13b31			14 16	
Luton Airport Parkway 7	d			13 22					13 35			14 22				14 24		14 35			15 22			15 35	
Luton 10	d			12 54					13 53			13 54				15 00		14 53			14 54			15 48	
Bedford 7	d			13 38					14 08			14 38						15 08			15 38				
Wellingborough	d			13 51					14 21			14 51						15 21			15 51				
Kettering	d			13 58					14 28			14 58						15 28			15 58				
Market Harborough	d			14 08					14 38			15 08						15 38			16 08				
Leicester	a	14 04		14 23			14 34		14 55	15 05		15 23				15 36		15 55	16 03		16 23			16 38	
	d	14 05		14 24		14 30	14 36		14 56	15 05		15 24		15 30		15 39		15 56	16 05		16 24		16 30	16 39	
Syston	d					14 39								15 39									16 39		
Sileby	d					14 44								15 44									16 44		
Barrow Upon Soar	d					14 48								15 48									16 4[illegible]		
Loughborough	d			14 34		14 52			15 07	15 16		15 34		15 52				16 07			16 34		[illegible]52		
Beeston	a								15 19									16 20							
Nottingham 8	a	14 37				15 18			15 26	15 34				16 16				16 26	16 36				[illegible]16		
	d				14 42								15 44									16 [illegible]			
Langley Mill	d				14 59																	[illegible]58			
Alfreton	d				15 07								16 06									17 06			
Long Eaton	a			14 43								15 43									16 43				
Derby 10	a			14 56			15 05					15 56				16 05					16 56			17 05	
	d		14 42				15 07	15 14			15 42					16 07	[illegible] 14			16 42				17 07	17 14
Burton-on-Trent	a			15 19			15 50					16 19				16 [illegible]					17 21			17 49	
Belper	a															16 34								18 00	
Matlock	a															16 [illegible]								18 20	
Chesterfield	d				15 18		15 27	15 33					16 18			[illegible] 27	16 33					17 18		17 27	17 33
Dronfield	d																								
Sheffield 7	a		15 15		15 38		15 46	15 50			16 15		[illegible] 38			16 46	16 50			17 15		17 34		17 43	17 48
Meadowhall	a		15 30		15 56			16 03			16 [illegible]		1[illegible]				17 03			17 31		17 46		17 56	18 03
Barnsley	a		16 00		16 11			16 34			[illegible] 02		[illegible] 11				17 34			18 02				18 11	18 34
Doncaster 7	a		16 04					16 15			17 08						17 19			18 07		18 10			18 21
Wakefield Westgate 7	a		15 46		16c27						16[illegible]		17c29							17 46		18e35		18c36	
Leeds 10	a		16 02		16 50						[illegible] 04		17 50							18 02		18e53		18 55	
York 8	a		16 29				16 45	16[illegible]			17 30					17 45	17 45			18 29				18 46	18 46

For general notes see front of timetable
For details of catering facilities see Directory of Train Operators

b Change at Bedford
c Wakefield Kirkgate
e Change at Sheffield and Doncaster

London → East Midlands → Sheffield

Route Diagram - See first page of Table 53

		EM	EM	XC	EM	EM	XC	EM		EM	EM	EM	XC	EM	EM	XC	EM	EM	EM	XC	EM	EM	EM	EM	EM
		1 ◇	1 ◇	1 ◇	1 ◇	◇	1 ◇			1 ◇	1 ◇	1 ◇	1 ◇	1 ◇	◇	1 ◇		1 ◇	1 ◇	1 ◇	◇	1 ◇	1 ◇	1 ◇	
		☕	☕	☕	☕		☕			☕	☕	☕	☕	☕		☕		☕	☕	☕		☕	☕	☕	
St Pancras International 15	⊖ d	15 30	15 55		16 00					16 25	16 30	16 55		17 00				17 30	17 40			17 55		18 00	
Gatwick Airport 10	✈ d		*14 46*		*14b31*						*15 16*			*15b31*				*16 16*	*16 16*			*16 46*		*16b31*	
Luton Airport Parkway 7	d		*16 05*		16 22						*16 35*			17 22				*17 35*	*17 35*			*18 05*		18 22	
Luton 10	d	15 53	16 18		*15 54*						16 53			*16 54*				17 53				18 19		*17 54*	
Bedford 7	d	16 08			16 38						17 08			17 38				18 08	18 19					18 38	
Wellingborough	d	16 21			16 51						17 21	17 39		17 51				18 21	18 33					18 51	
Kettering	d	16 28			16 58					17 15	17 28	17 47		17 58				18 28	18 41			18 49		18 58	
Market Harborough	d	16 38			17 08						17 38	17 57		18 08				18 38				19 00		19 08	
Leicester	a	16 55	17 06		17 23					17 39	17 56	18 17		18 24				18 55	19 05			19 21		19 26	
	d	16 56	17 10		17 24			17 30		17 39	17 56	18 17		18 24			18 30	18 56	19 06			19 22		19 27	19 29
Syston	d							17 39									18 39								19 39
Sileby	d							17 44									18 44								19 44
Barrow Upon Soar	d							17 48									18 48								19 48
Loughborough	d	17 07			17 34			17 52		17 51	18 07			18 34			18 52	19 07				19 33		19 37	19 52
Beeston	a	17 19									18 19							19 19							20 13
Nottingham 8	🚢 a	17 28	17 34					18 16			18 26	18 41					19 16	19 26				19 52	←		20 19
	d					17 42									18 42			19 37 →			19 28		19 37		
Langley Mill	d					17 58									18 59								19 53		
Alfreton	d					18 06									19 07						19 52		20 02		
Long Eaton	a				17 43									18 43										19 46	
Derby 10	a				17 54					18 16				18 56					19 31					19 57	
	d			17 42	18 01		18 14			18 18			18 42			19 14			19 32	19 42				19 58	
Burton-on-Trent	a				18 15					*18 51*				*19 21*					*20 07*					*20 19*	
Belper	a													*19 33*										20 06	
Matlock	a													*19 53*											
Chesterfield	d					18 18	18 33			18 39			19 01		19 18	19 33			19 53	20 01	20 08		20 14	20 21	
Dronfield	d					18 26																			
Sheffield 7	🚢 a			18 17		18 38	18 46			18 59			19 16		19 39	19 47			20 08	20 18	20 25		20 28	20 38	
Meadowhall	🚢 a			*18 29*		*18 56*	*19 06*			*19 13*			*19 35*		*19 56*	*20 03*			*20 20*	*20 36*			*20 43*	20 53	
Barnsley	a			*19 02*		*19 15*				*19 34*			*20 04*		*20 12*	*20 34*							*21 06*	21 14	
Doncaster 7	a			*18 53*			19 18			19 29			*20 09*			20 16			20 36						
Wakefield Westgate 7	a			18 46		*19c36*				19 59			19 46		*20c28*				20 53	20 48				*21e34*	
Leeds 10	a			19 02		*19 57*				20 22			20 02		*20 50*				21 15	21 05				*21e54*	
York 8	a			19 32		*19 49*	19 49			*20e29*			20 29		*20 42*	20 42			*21e35*	21 35					

		EM		XC	EM	EM	XC	EM	EM	EM	EM	XC	EM	EM	EM	EM	EM	EM	EM	EM	EM	EM	EM		
		1 ◇		1 ◇	1 ◇	1 ◇	1 ◇	1 ◇		1 ◇	1 ◇	1 ◇	1 ◇	1 ◇	1 ◇	1 ◇	1 ◇	1 ◇	1 ◇	🚌	1 ◇	1 ◇	🚌		
		☕			☕	☕		☕		☕	☕		☕	☕	☕	☕	☕	☕	☕		☕	☕			
St Pancras International 15	⊖ d	18 25			18 30	18 55		19 00		19 25	19 30		19 55	20 00	20 25	20 30	20 55	21 00	21 25		21 35	22 10			
Gatwick Airport 10	✈ d				*17 16*	*17 46*		*17b31*		*18 16*				*18b31*		*19 16*		*19b31*				*21 01*			
Luton Airport Parkway 7	d				*18 40*	*19 05*		19 22		*19 37*	*19 41*			20 22		*20 37*		21 22				*22 27*			
Luton 10	d				18 53	19 18		*18 54*		19 49	19 53			*19 54*		20 53		*20 54*				22 45			
Bedford 7	d				19 08			19 38			20 08			20 38		21 08		21 38				23 08			
Wellingborough	d				19 21	19 42		19 51			20 21		20 39	20 51		21 21		21 51			22 20	23 21			
Kettering	d	19 15			19 28			19 58		20 19	20 28			20 58	21 14	21 28		21 58	22 15		22 27	23 34	23 43		
Market Harborough	d	19 26			19 38			20 08			20 38			21 08		21 38	21 51	22 08			22 37		00a08		
Leicester	a	19 42			19 55	20 13		20 23		20 43	20 55		21 06	21 23	21 36	21 55	22 07	22 23	22 39		22 52	00 36			
	d	19 43			19 56	20 14		20 24	20 30	20 43	20 56		21 07	21 24	21 39	21 57	22 09	22 24	22 40		22 57	00 42			
Syston	d								20 39																
Sileby	d								20 44																
Barrow Upon Soar	d								20 48																
Loughborough	d				20 07	20 24		20 34	20 52		21 07		21 18	21 34		22 10	22 22	22 36	22 53		23 09				
Beeston	a				20 22				21 11		21 19					22 19									
Nottingham 8	🚢 a				20 34	20 39			21 17		21 26		21 39			22 29	22 38				23 25				
	d												21 47												
Langley Mill	d												22 04												
Alfreton	d												22 12												
Long Eaton	a							20 43						21 43				22 44				00 59			
Derby 10	a	20 09						20 56		21 10				21 56	22 05			22 56	23 12			01 12			
	d	20 11		20 15			20 42			21 11		21 45			22 07					23 21					
Burton-on-Trent	a	*20 52*								*21 37*					22 29										
Belper	a									*22 03*															
Matlock	a									*22 23*															
Chesterfield	d	20 31		20 37			21 01			21 31		22 04	22 24		22 30					00 07					
Dronfield	d																								
Sheffield 7	🚢 a	20 47		20 51			21 16			21 47		22 19	22 40		22 44					00 37					
Meadowhall	🚢 a			*21 14*			*21 31*			*22 13*		*22 31*			*23 30*										
Barnsley	a			*21 35*			*22 05*			*22 34*		*23 06*													
Doncaster 7	a	21 13		*21 40*						22 21		*23 04*			*00 03*										
Wakefield Westgate 7	a	21 34					21 46			22 38		22s46													
Leeds 10	a	21 54					22 01			23 00		23 09													
York 8	a			21 54			22 38					*00 08*													

For general notes see front of timetable
For details of catering facilities see Directory of Train Operators

- b Change at Bedford
- c Wakefield Kirkgate
- e Change at Sheffield

London → East Midlands → Sheffield

Route Diagram - See first page of Table 53

		EM 1◇ A	EM 1◇ A	EM 1◇ B	EM 1◇ A	EM A	EM 1◇ A	EM 1◇ B	EM A	EM 1◇ A	EM A	EM ◇	EM 1◇	XC 1◇	EM ◇	XC 1◇	EM	XC 1◇	EM ◇	XC 1◇	EM		EM 1◇	XC 1◇	EM ◇
St Pancras International 15	d	21p25	21p30	22p25	22p00		22p25	23p15		23p15													06 20		
Gatwick Airport 10	d							21b46		21b46													04 30		
Luton Airport Parkway 7	d							23c31		23c31													06 05		
Luton 10	d		21p53	22p48	22p22		22p48	23p45		23p45													06 44		
Bedford 7	d		22p07	23p05	22p38		23p05	00 09		00 09													07 01		
Wellingborough	d		22p20	23p18	22p51		23p18	00 22		00 22													07 16		
Kettering	d	22p17	22p35	23p27	23p04		23p29	00 29		00 34	00 44												07 24		
Market Harborough	d			23p39		00 01		00 39	01 04		01a09												07 36		
Leicester	a	23p19	23p46	23p56	00 02	00 26	00 31	01 01	01 29	01 33													07 54		
	d	23p24	23p51	23p57	00 08		00 36	01 02		01 39							06 40				07 28		07 54		
Syston	d																06 47				07 39				
Sileby	d																06 52				07 45				
Barrow Upon Soar	d																06 56				07 49				
Loughborough	d	23p35	00 06	00 08	00 21		00 48	01 14		01 56							07 00				07 53		08 06		
Beeston	a		00 28		00 39												07 20								
Nottingham 8	a		00 35		00 46			01 37		02 12							07 27				08 16				
	d							01 44		02 19		05 23			06 37				07 42						08 42
Langley Mill	d														06 53				07 58						08 58
Alfreton	d														07 01				08 06						09 06
Long Eaton	a																						08 21		
Derby 10	a	00 02		00 34			01 15	02 05		02 36													08 32		
	d	00 05		00 36			01 16						06 30	06 39		07 14		07 42		08 14			08 34	08 42	
Burton-on-Trent	a																						09 19		
Belper	a																								
Matlock	a																								
Chesterfield	d	00 25		00 56			01 36					05 54	06 49		07 14	07 33		08 01	08 18	08 33			08 56	09 01	09 18
Dronfield	d														07 21	07 39			08 25						
Sheffield 7	a	00 41		01 13			01 52					06 10	07 05	07 09	07 31	07 49		08 17	08 38	08 46			09 13	09 17	09 38
Meadowhall	a											06 23	07 23	07 23	07 46	08 13		08 41	08 56	09 03			09 28	09 32	09 56
Barnsley	a											07 00	07 43	07 43	08 11	08 34		09 00	09 11	09 34				10 00	10 11
Doncaster 7	a											06 57		08 02	08 20	08 23		09 09		09 21			09 52	10 05	
Wakefield Westgate 7	a											07 19		07 36	08e28			08 46	09e29				10f29	09 46	10e29
Leeds 10	a											07 44		07 52	08 51			09 04	09 50					10 02	10 50
York 8	a												08g24	08 24	08 49	08 49		09 31	09 48	09 48			10 16	10 31	10 44

		EM 1◇	XC 1◇	EM	EM 1◇	EM 1◇	EM 1◇	XC 1◇	EM 1◇	EM ◇	EM	EM 1◇	XC 1◇	EM 1◇	EM 1◇	XC 1◇	EM 1◇	EM ◇	EM	EM 1◇		XC 1◇	EM 1◇	EM 1◇	XC 1◇
St Pancras International 15	d	07 00			07 25	07 30	07 55		08 00			08 25		08 30	08 55		09 00			09 25			09 30	09 55	
Gatwick Airport 10	d	05h25			06 01				06h31			07 01		07 16			07h31			08 16					
Luton Airport Parkway 7	d	07 25			07 20	07 36			08 22					08 35			09 22			09 35					
Luton 10	d	06 56			07 49	07 53			07 56			08 24		08 53			08 54			09 49			09 53		
Bedford 7	d	07 41				08 08			08 38			09 00		09 08			09 38						10 08		
Wellingborough	d	07 53				08 21			08 51					09 21			09 51						10 21		
Kettering	d	08 01				08 28			08 58					09 28			09 58						10 28		
Market Harborough	d	08 11				08 38			09 08					09 38			10 08						10 38		
Leicester	a	08 27			08 39	08 55	09 04		09 23			09 38		09 55	10 04		10 23			10 38			10 55	11 04	
	d	08 27		08 32	08 40	08 56	09 05		09 25		09 30	09 39		09 56	10 05		10 25		10 30	10 39			10 56	11 05	
Syston	d			08 39							09 39								10 39						
Sileby	d			08 44							09 44								10 44						
Barrow Upon Soar	d			08 48							09 48								10 48						
Loughborough	d	08 38		08 52	08 51	09 07	09 16		09 34		09 52			10 07			10 34		10 52				11 07	11 16	
Beeston	a	08 48				09 19								10 19									11 19		
Nottingham 8	a	08 56		09 16		09 26	09 37				10 18			10 27	10 34				11 17				11 27	11 35	
	d									09 42								10 42							
Langley Mill	d									09 59															
Alfreton	d									10 07								11 04							
Long Eaton	a								09 43								10 43								
Derby 10	a				09 16				09 56			10 07					10 56			11 07					
	d		09 14		09 18			09 42				10 09	10 14			10 42				11 09		11 14			11 42
Burton-on-Trent	a				09 51				10 21			10 53					11 19			11 50					
Belper	a				10 01															12 04					
Matlock	a				10 21															12 24					
Chesterfield	d		09 33		09 38					10 18		10 30	10 33					11 18		11 30		11 33			
Dronfield	d																								
Sheffield 7	a		09 50		09 56			10 15		10 38		10 46	10 50			11 15		11 38		11 46		11 50			12 15
Meadowhall	a		10 03		10 13			10 30		10 56			11 03			11 30		11 56				12 03			12 30
Barnsley	a				10 34			11 00		11 11			11 34			12 00		12 11				12 34			13 00
Doncaster 7	a		10 18		10 40			11 04					11 16			12 04						12 15			13 04
Wakefield Westgate 7	a							10 46		11e29						11 46		12e29							12 46
Leeds 10	a							11 02		11 50						12 02		12 50							13 02
York 8	a		10 44		11 29			11 29				11 45	11 45			12 29				12 43		12 43			13 29

For general notes see front of timetable
For details of catering facilities see Directory of Train Operators

A Until 22 March

B From 29 March

b Fridays. Change at Bedford

c Thursdays. Change at Bedford

e Wakefield Kirkgate

f Wakefield Kirkgate. Change at Sheffield

g Change at Sheffield

h Change at Bedford

Table 53

Saturdays

from 2 February

London → East Midlands → Sheffield

Route Diagram - See first page of Table 53

		EM	EM	EM	EM	XC	EM	EM	XC	EM	EM	EM	EM	XC	EM	EM	EM	XC	EM		EM	EM	EM	XC	EM
		1 ◇ ☕	◇		1 ◇ ☒ 🚲	1 ◇ ☕	1 ◇ ☕	1 ◇ ☕	1 ◇ ☕	1 ◇ ☕	◇		1 ◇ ☕	1 ◇ ☕	1 ◇ ☕	1 ◇ ☕	1 ◇ ☕	1 ◇ ☕	1 ◇ ☕		◇		1 ◇ ☕	1 ◇ ☕	1 ◇ ☕
St Pancras International [15] ⊖	d	10 00			10 25		10 30	10 55		11 00			11 25		11 30		11 55		12 00				12 25		12 30
Gatwick Airport [10] ✈	d	08b31					09 16			09b31					10 16				10b31						11 16
Luton Airport Parkway [7]	d	10 22					10 35			11 22					11 35				12 22						12 35
Luton [10]	d	09 54					10 53			10 54					11 53				11 54						12 53
Bedford [7]	d	10 38					11 08			11 38					12 08				12 38						13 08
Wellingborough	d	10 51					11 21			11 51					12 21				12 51						13 21
Kettering	d	10 58					11 28			11 58					12 28				12 58						13 28
Market Harborough	d	11 08					11 38			12 08					12 38				13 08						13 38
Leicester	a	11 23			11 34		11 55	12 03		12 23			12 34		12 55		13 04		13 23				13 34		13 55
	d	11 24		11 30	11 36		11 56	12 05		12 24		12 30	12 36		12 56		13 05		13 24			13 30	13 36		13 56
Syston	d			11 39								12 39										13 39			
Sileby	d			11 44								12 44										13 44			
Barrow Upon Soar	d			11 48								12 48										13 48			
Loughborough	d	11 34		11 52			12 07			12 34		12 52			13 07		13 17		13 34			13 52			14 07
Beeston	a						12 19								13 19										14 19
Nottingham [8]	a			12 16			12 27	12 34				13 16			13 25	←	13 36					14 18			14 25
	d		11 42				12 45 →				12 47					12 45					13 42				
Langley Mill	d										13 03					13 22					13 59				
Alfreton	d		12 04								13 11					13 30					14 07				
Long Eaton	a	11 44								12 43									13 43						
Derby [10]	a	11 56			12 07					12 56			13 07						13 56				14 07		
	d				12 09	12 14			12 42				13 09	13 14				13 42					14 09	14 14	
Burton-on-Trent	a	12 20			12 50					13 19			13 51						14 21				14 50		
Belper	a												13 42										15 00		
Matlock	a												14 02										15 20		
Chesterfield	d		12 18		12 30	12 33					13 22		13 30	13 33		13 41					14 18		14 30	14 33	
Dronfield	d															13 49									
Sheffield [7]	a		12 38		12 46	12 50			13 15		13 39		13 47	13 51		14 00		14 15			14 38		14 46	14 50	
Meadowhall	a		12 56			13 03			13 30		13 57		14 03			14 13		14 30			14 56			15 03	
Barnsley	a		13 11			13 34			14 00		14 12					14 34		15 00			15 11			15 34	
Doncaster [7]	a					13 19			14 04					14 15		14 38		15 04						15 15	
Wakefield Westgate [7]	a		13c29						13 46		14c28							14 46			15c29				
Leeds [10]	a		13 50						14 02		14 50							15 02			15 50				
York [8]	a				13 44	13 44			14 29				14 43	14 43		15 29		15 29					15 43	15 43	

		EM	XC	EM	EM	EM	EM	XC	EM	EM	XC	EM	EM	EM	EM	XC	EM	EM		XC	EM	EM	EM	EM	XC
		1 ◇ ☕	1 ◇ ☕	1 ◇ ☕	◇		1 ◇ ☕	1 ◇ ☕	1 ◇ ☕	1 ◇ ☕	1 ◇ ☕	1 ◇ ☕	◇		1 ◇ ☕	1 ◇ ☕	1 ◇ ☕	1 ◇ ☕		1 ◇ ☕	1 ◇ ☕	◇		1 ◇ ☕	1 ◇ ☕
St Pancras International [15] ⊖	d	12 55		13 00			13 25		13 30	13 55		14 00			14 25		14 30	14 55			15 00			15 25	
Gatwick Airport [10] ✈	d			11b31					12 16			12b31			13 01		13 16				13b31			14 16	
Luton Airport Parkway [7]	d			13 22					13 35			14 22					14 35				15 22			15 35	
Luton [10]	d			12 54					13 53			13 54			14 24		14 53				14 54			15 48	
Bedford [7]	d			13 38					14 08			14 38			15 00		15 08				15 38				
Wellingborough	d			13 51					14 21			14 51					15 21				15 51				
Kettering	d			13 58					14 28			14 58					15 28				15 58				
Market Harborough	d			14 08					14 38			15 08					15 38				16 08				
Leicester	a	14 04		14 23			14 34		14 55	15 05		15 23			15 36		15 55	16 03			16 23			16 38	
	d	14 05		14 24		14 30	14 36		14 56	15 05		15 24		15 30	15 39		15 56	16 05			16 24		16 30	16 39	
Syston	d					14 39								15 39									16 39		
Sileby	d					14 44								15 44									16 44		
Barrow Upon Soar	d					14 48								15 48									16 48		
Loughborough	d			14 34		14 52			15 07	15 16		15 34		15 52			16 07				16 34		16 52		
Beeston	a								15 19								16 20								
Nottingham [8]	a	14 37				15 18			15 26	15 34				16 16			16 26	16 36					17 16		
	d				14 42								15 44									16 42			
Langley Mill	d				14 59																	16 58			
Alfreton	d				15 07								16 06									17 06			
Long Eaton	a			14 43								15 43									16 43				
Derby [10]	a			14 56			15 07					15 56			16 07						16 56			17 07	
	d		14 42				15 09	15 14			15 42				16 09	16 14				16 42				17 09	17 14
Burton-on-Trent	a			15 19			15 50					16 19			16 51						17 21			17 49	
Belper	a														16 34									18 00	
Matlock	a														16 54									18 20	
Chesterfield	d				15 18		15 29	15 33					16 18		16 29	16 33						17 18		17 30	17 33
Dronfield	d																								
Sheffield [7]	a		15 15		15 38		15 46	15 50			16 15		16 38		16 46	16 50				17 15		17 34		17 43	17 48
Meadowhall	a		15 30		15 56			16 03			16 30		16 56			17 03				17 31		17 46		17 56	18 03
Barnsley	a		16 00		16 11			16 34			17 02		17 11			17 34				18 02				18 11	18 34
Doncaster [7]	a		16 04					16 15			17 08					17 19				18 07		18 10			18 21
Wakefield Westgate [7]	a		15 46		16c27						16 46		17c29							17 46		18e35		18c36	
Leeds [10]	a		16 02		16 50						17 04		17 50							18 02		18e53		18 55	
York [8]	a		16 29				16 45	16 45			17 30				17 45	17 45				18 29				18 46	18 46

For general notes see front of timetable
For details of catering facilities see
Directory of Train Operators

b Change at Bedford
c Wakefield Kirkgate
e Change at Sheffield and Doncaster

London → East Midlands → Sheffield

Route Diagram - See first page of Table 53

		EM	EM	XC	EM	EM	XC	EM	EM	EM	EM	XC	EM	EM	XC	EM	EM		EM	XC	EM	EM	EM	EM	EM
		1◇	1◇	1◇	1◇	◇	1◇		1◇	1◇	1◇	1◇	1◇	◇	1◇		1◇		1◇	1◇	◇	1◇	1◇	1◇	
		☕	☕	☕	☕		☕		☕	☕	☕	☕	☕		☕		☕		☕	☕		☕	☕	☕	
St Pancras International 15	⊖ d	15 30	15 55		16 00				16 25	16 30	16 55		17 00				17 30		17 40			17 55		18 00	
Gatwick Airport 10	✈ d		14 46		14b31					15 16			15b31				16 16		16 16			16 46		16b31	
Luton Airport Parkway 7	d		16 05		16 22					16 35			17 22				17 35		17 35			18 05		18 22	
Luton 10	d	15 53	16 18		15 54					16 53			16 54				17 53					18 19		17 54	
Bedford 7	d	16 08			16 38					17 08			17 38				18 08		18 19					18 38	
Wellingborough	d	16 21			16 51					17 21	17 39		17 51				18 21		18 33					18 51	
Kettering	d	16 28			16 58				17 15	17 28	17 47		17 58				18 28		18 41			18 49		18 58	
Market Harborough	d	16 38			17 08					17 38	17 57		18 08				18 38					19 00		19 08	
Leicester	a	16 55	17 06		17 23				17 39	17 56	18 17		18 24				18 55		19 05			19 21		19 26	
	d	16 56	17 10		17 24			17 30	17 39	17 56	18 17		18 24			18 30	18 56		19 06			19 22		19 27	19 29
Syston	d							17 39								18 39									19 39
Sileby	d							17 44								18 44									19 44
Barrow Upon Soar	d							17 48								18 48									19 48
Loughborough	d	17 07			17 34			17 52	17 51	18 07			18 34			18 52	19 07					19 33		19 37	19 52
Beeston	a	17 19								18 19							19 19								20 13
Nottingham 8	🚋 a	17 28	17 34					18 16		18 26	18 41					19 16	19 26					19 52	←		20 19
	d					17 42								18 42			19 37 →				19 28		19 37		
Langley Mill	d					17 58								18 59							19 52		19 53		
Alfreton	d					18 06								19 07									20 02		
Long Eaton	a				17 43								18 43											19 46	
Derby 10	a				17 54				18 16				18 56						19 31					19 57	
	d			17 42	18 01		18 14		18 18			18 42			19 14				19 32	19 42				19 58	
Burton-on-Trent	a				18 15				18 51				19 21						20 07					20 19	
Belper	a												19 33											20 06	
Matlock	a												19 53												
Chesterfield	d					18 18	18 33		18 39			19 01		19 18	19 33				19 53	20 01	20 08		20 14	20 21	
Dronfield	d					18 26																			
Sheffield 7	🚋 a			18 17		18 38	18 46		18 59			19 16		19 39	19 47				20 08	20 18	20 25		20 28	20 38	
Meadowhall	🚋 a			18 29		18 56	19 06		19 13			19 35		19 56	20 03				20 20	20 36			20 43	20 53	
Barnsley	a			19 02		19 15			19 34			20 04		20 12	20 34								21 06	21 14	
Doncaster 7	a			18 53			19 18		19 29			20 09			20 16				20 36					21e34	
Wakefield Westgate 7	a			18 46		19c36			19 59			19 46		20c28					20 53	20 48				21e54	
Leeds 10	a			19 02		19 57			20 22			20 02		20 50					21 15	21 05					
York 8	a			19 32		19 49	19 49		20e29			20 29		20 42	20 42				21e35	21 35					

		EM	XC	EM	EM	XC	EM	EM	EM	EM	XC	EM	EM	EM	EM	EM	EM	EM	EM	EM	EM	EM	EM
		1◇	1◇	1◇	1◇	1◇	1◇		1◇	1◇	1◇	1◇	1◇	1◇	1◇	1◇	1◇	1◇	🚌	1◇	1◇ A	1◇ B	B 🚌
		☕		☕	☕		☕		☕	☕		☕	☕	☕	☕	☕	☕	☕		☕	☕	☕	
St Pancras International 15	⊖ d	18 25		18 30	18 55		19 00		19 25	19 30		19 55	20 00	20 25	20 30	20 55	21 00	21 25		21 35	22 10	22 10	
Gatwick Airport 10	✈ d			17 16	17 46		17b31		18 16				18b31		19 16		19b31				21 01	21 01	
Luton Airport Parkway 7	d			18 40	19 05		19 22		19 37	19 41			20 22		20 37		21 22				22 27	22 27	
Luton 10	d			18 53	19 18		18 54		19 49	19 53			19 54		20 53		20 54				22 45	22 45	
Bedford 7	d			19 08			19 38			20 08			20 38		21 08		21 38				23 08	23 08	
Wellingborough	d			19 21	19 42		19 51			20 21		20 39	20 51		21 21		21 51			22 20	23 21	23 21	
Kettering	d	19 15		19 28			19 58		20 19	20 28			20 58	21 14	21 28		21 58	22 15		22 27	23 30	23 34	23 43
Market Harborough	d	19 26		19 38			20 08			20 38			21 08		21 38	21 51	22 08			22 37	23 40		00a08
Leicester	a	19 42		19 55	20 13		20 23		20 43	20 55		21 06	21 23	21 36	21 55	22 07	22 23	22 39		22 52	23 55	00 36	
	d	19 43		19 56	20 14		20 24	20 30	20 43	20 56		21 07	21 24	21 39	21 57	22 09	22 24	22 40		22 57	23 56	00 42	
Syston	d							20 39															
Sileby	d							20 44															
Barrow Upon Soar	d							20 48															
Loughborough	d			20 07	20 24		20 34	20 52		21 07		21 18	21 34		22 10	22 22	22 36	22 53		23 09			
Beeston	a			20 22				21 11		21 19					22 19								
Nottingham 8	🚋 a			20 34	20 39			21 17		21 26		21 39			22 29	22 38				23 25			
	d											21 47											
Langley Mill	d											22 04											
Alfreton	d											22 12											
Long Eaton	a						20 43						21 43				22 44				00 13	00 59	
Derby 10	a	20 09					20 56		21 10				21 56	22 05			22 56	[illegible] 12			00 26	01 12	
	d	20 11	20 15			20 42			21 11		21 45			22 07					23 21				
Burton-on-Trent	a	20 52							21 37					22 29									
Belper	a								22 03														
Matlock	a								22 23														
Chesterfield	d	20 31	20 37			21 01			21 31		22 04	22 24		22 [illegible]					00 07				
Dronfield	d																						
Sheffield 7	🚋 a	20 47	20 51			21 16			21 47		22 19	22 40		22 44					00 37				
Meadowhall	🚋 a		21 14			21 31			22 13		22 31			23 30									
Barnsley	a		21 35			22 05			22 34		23 [illegible]												
Doncaster 7	a	21 13	21 40						22 21		[illegible] 04			00 03									
Wakefield Westgate 7	a	21 34				21 46			22 38		22s46												
Leeds 10	a	21 54				22 01			23 0[illegible]		23 09												
York 8	a		21 54			22 38					00 08												

For general notes see front of timetable
For details of catering facilities see Directory of Train Operators

- **A** From 29 M[illegible]
- **B** Until 2[illegible] [illegible]arch
- **b** Ch[illegible]ge at Bedford
- **c** Wakefield Kirkgate
- **e** Change at Sheffield

Table 53

Sundays

until 27 January

London → East Midlands → Sheffield

Route Diagram - See first page of Table 53

		EM	EM	EM	EM	EM	EM	EM	EM	XC		EM	EM	XC	EM	EM	XC	EM	XC	XC		EM	XC	EM	EM
		🚌	🚌	1 ◇ ☕	🚌	🚌	🚌	🚌	🚌	1 ◇ ☕		🚌	🚌	1 ◇ ☕	1 ◇ ☕	🚌	1 ◇ ☕	🚌	1 ◇ ☕	1 ◇ ☕		◇	1 ◇ ☕	🚌	🚌
St Pancras International 15	⊖ d			22p10																					
Gatwick Airport 10	✈ d																								
Luton Airport Parkway 7	d																								
Luton 10	d			22p47																					
Bedford 7	d			23p08																					
Wellingborough	d			23p21																					
Kettering	d			23p34	06 52	07 22	07 51	08 17	08 51				09 11			09 52								10 20	
Market Harborough	d		00 07		07a17	07a47	08a16	08a42	09a16				09a36			10a17								10a45	10 50
Leicester	a		00 32	00 36																					11 15
	d			00 42											10 05										
Syston	d																								
Sileby	d																								
Barrow Upon Soar	d																								
Loughborough	d														10 15										
Beeston	a																								
Nottingham 8	a																								
	d											09 05						10 05				11 46			
Langley Mill	d																								
Alfreton	d											09 45						10 45				12 08			
Long Eaton	a			00 59											10 23										
Derby 10	a			01 12											10 34										
	d	23p21								09 42				10 14	10 35		10 42		11 14	11 42			12 14		
Burton-on-Trent	a														*11 07*										
Belper	a														*11 44*										
Matlock	a														*12 04*										
Chesterfield	d	00 07								10 03		10 05		10 33	10 55			11 05	11 33			12 21	12 33		
Dronfield	d																								
Sheffield 7	a	00 37								10 18		10 40		10 46	11 09		11 18	11 40	11 50	12 12		12 37	12 46		
Meadowhall	a									*10 31*				*11 11*			*11 37*		*12 13*	*12 29*					
Barnsley	a									*11 05*							*11 52*			*13 05*					
Doncaster 7	a									*10 51*				11 16	11 34				12 16	*12 54*			13 15		
Wakefield Westgate 7	a									10 44							11 44			12 44					
Leeds 10	a									11 01							12 01			13 01					
York 8	a									11 33		*11 44*		11 44	11 57		12 33	*12 45*	12 45	13 33		*13 44*	13 44		

		EM	EM	EM	EM	EM	EM	XC		EM	XC	EM	EM	EM	EM	EM	EM	EM		EM	EM	EM	XC	EM	EM
		1 ◇ ☕	🚌	🚌	🚌	🚌	1 ◇ ☕	1 ◇ ☕		◇	1 ◇ ☕	🚌	🚌	🚌	1 ◇ ☕	🚌	🚌	🚌		1 ◇ ☕	🚌	🚌	1 ◇ ☕	◇	1 ◇ ☕
St Pancras International 15	⊖ d	09 00					09 30								10 00					10 30					11 00
Gatwick Airport 10	✈ d	*07 45*					*08 15*								*08 45*					*09 15*					09b45
Luton Airport Parkway 7	d	*09 15*					*09 45*								*10 15*					*10 45*					11 28
Luton 10	d	09 30					10 02								10 30					*10 49*					11 33
Bedford 7	d	09 50					10 22								10 50					11 24					11 55
Wellingborough	d	10 03					10 36								11 05					11 36					12 09
Kettering	d	10 17	10 25	10 49	10 57		10 48					11 21	11 26		11 17	11 44	11 57			11 49	12 21				12 21
Market Harborough	d		10a50	11a14	11a22	11 25						11a46	11a51	11 54		12a09	12a22	12 29			12a46	12 54			
Leicester	a	11 19				11 50	11 52							12 19	12 23			12 54		12 59		13 19			13 23
	d	11 24					12 00								12 29					13 04					13 29
Syston	d																								
Sileby	d																								
Barrow Upon Soar	d																								
Loughborough	d	11 39					12 11								12 40					13 16					13 41
Beeston	a	11 48																							13 51
Nottingham 8	a	11 56													12 56										13 59
	d									12 39														13 33	
Langley Mill	d									12 56														13 54	
Alfreton	d									13 04														14 02	
Long Eaton	a						12 19																		
Derby 10	a						12 31													13 32					
	d						12 31	12 42			13 14									13 33			13 42		
Burton-on-Trent	a																			*14 07*					
Belper	a																			*14 03*					
Matlock	a																			*14 23*					
Chesterfield	d						12 52			13 17	13 33									13 53				14 17	
Dronfield	d																								
Sheffield 7	a						13 05	13 12		13 34	13 46									14 07			14 12	14 33	
Meadowhall	a							*13 29*			*14 13*												*14 29*		
Barnsley	a							*13 52*															*15 05*		
Doncaster 7	a							*14 01*			14 16												*14 56*		
Wakefield Westgate 7	a							13 44															14 44		
Leeds 10	a							14 01															15 01		
York 8	a						*14 32*	14 32		*14 41*	14 41									*15 33*			15 33	*15 43*	

For general notes see front of timetable
For details of catering facilities see
Directory of Train Operators

b Change at Luton

Table 53

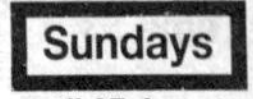
Sundays

until 27 January

London → East Midlands → Sheffield

Route Diagram - See first page of Table 53

	EM	EM	XC	EM	EM	EM	EM	XC	EM	XC	EM	EM	EM	EM	EM	EM	EM	EM	EM	XC	EM	EM
			1 ◇			1 ◇		R 1	◇	1 ◇			1 ◇				1 ◇			R 1	◇	1 ◇
St Pancras International 15 ⊖ d						11 30							12 00				12 30					13 00
Gatwick Airport 10 ✈ d						10 15							10 45				11 15					11b45
Luton Airport Parkway 7 d						11 35							12 05				12 48					13 27
Luton 10 d						11 39							12 31				12 52					13 33
Bedford 7 d						12 23							12 55				13 24					13 54
Wellingborough d						12 37							13 08				13 37					14 07
Kettering d	12 30	12 45		12 58		12 50	13 20				13 30		13 22	13 48	13 59		13 50	14 09				14 19
Market Harborough d	12a55	13a10		13a23	13 25		13a45				13a55	13 58		14a13	14a24	14 25		14a34	14 52			
Leicester a					13 50	13 53						14 23	14 28			14 50	14 54		15 17			15 23
Leicester d						14 00							14 33				15 00					15 29
Syston d																						
Sileby d																						
Barrow Upon Soar d																						
Loughborough d						14 13							14 45				15 14					15 40
Beeston a																						15 50
Nottingham 8 a													14 59									15 57
Nottingham 8 d									14 36												15 35	
Langley Mill d									14 53													
Alfreton d									15 02												15 54	
Long Eaton a						14 23																
Derby 10 a						14 34											15 34					
Derby 10 d			14 14			14 35		14 42		15 14							15 35			15 42		
Burton-on-Trent a						15 51											16 07					
Belper a																	15 58					
Matlock a																	16 18					
Chesterfield d			14 33			14 56			15 14	15 33							15 56				16 13	
Dronfield d																						
Sheffield 7 a			14 51			15 15		15 18	15 31	15 50							16 13			16 16	16 32	
Meadowhall a			15 13			15 29		15 33	15 44	16 13							16 29			16 29	16 44	
Barnsley a						15 52		15 52	16 06								17 05			17 05	17 05	
Doncaster 7 a			15 16			15 54		15 54		16 16							16 54			16 54		
Wakefield Westgate 7 a			15c44			16e11		15 44									16 44			16 44	17e29	
Leeds 10 a			16c01			16 31		16 01									17 01			17 01		
York 8 a			15 43			16f34		16 33	16 44	16 44							17 33			17 33	17 40	

	EM	XC	EM	EM	EM	EM	XC	EM	XC	EM	EM	EM	EM	EM	EM	EM	EM	XC	EM	XC	EM
		1 ◇				1 ◇	R 1	◇	1 ◇				1 ◇				1 ◇	R 1	◇	R 1	
St Pancras International 15 ⊖ d						13 30							14 00				14 30				
Gatwick Airport 10 ✈ d						12 15							12 45				13 15				
Luton Airport Parkway 7 d						13 48							14 18				14 35				
Luton 10 d						13 52							14 32				14 39				
Bedford 7 d						14 22							14 46				15 16				
Wellingborough d						14 35							15 00				15 29				
Kettering d	14 28		14 54	14 56		14 43				15 21	15 22		15 13	15 44	15 51		15g50				16 17
Market Harborough d	14a53		15a19	15a21	15 22					15a46	15a47	15 48		16a09	16a16	16 25					16a42
Leicester a					15 47	15 50						16 13	16 17			16 50	16 54				
Leicester d						15 57							16 23				17 00				
Syston d																					
Sileby d																					
Barrow Upon Soar d																					
Loughborough d						16 10							16 34				17 13				
Beeston a																					
Nottingham 8 a													16 51								
Nottingham 8 d								16 42											17 31		
Langley Mill d								16 59											17 52		
Alfreton d								17 07											18 00		
Long Eaton a						16 17															
Derby 10 a						16 28											17 31				
Derby 10 d		16 14				16 29	16 42		17 14								17 31	17 42		18 14	
Burton-on-Trent a						16 49											17 53				
Belper a																	18 08				
Matlock a																	18 28				
Chesterfield d		16 33				16 50		17 20	17 33								17 52		18 14	18 33	
Dronfield d																					
Sheffield 7 a		16 49				17 08	17 12	17 44	17 47								18 08	18 14	18 31	18 48	
Meadowhall a		17 13				17 29	17 29		18 14								18 29	18 29	18 44	19 03	
Barnsley a						18 05	18 05										19 05	19 05	19 05		
Doncaster 7 a		17 14				17 57	17 57		18 16								18 54	18 54	19 16	19 16	
Wakefield Westgate 7 a						17 44	17 44										18 44	18 44	19e29		
Leeds 10 a						18 01	18 01										19 01	19 01			
York 8 a		17 40				18 33	18 33	18 41	18 41								19 33	19 33	19 43	19 43	

For general notes see front of timetable
For details of catering facilities see Directory of Train Operators

b Change at Luton
c Change at Sheffield
e Wakefield Kirkgate
f Change at Sheffield and Doncaster
g Arr. 1540

London → East Midlands → Sheffield

Route Diagram - See first page of Table 53

		EM 🚌		EM 1 ◇ ☕	EM 🚌	EM 🚌	EM 🚌	EM 🚌	EM 1 ◇ ☕	EM 🚌	XC R 1 ☕	EM ◇		XC 1 ◇ ☕	EM 🚌	EM 🚌	EM 1 ◇ ☕	EM 🚌	EM 🚌	EM 🚌	EM 1 ◇ ☕	EM 🚌		EM 🚌	XC R 1 ☕
St Pancras International 15	⊖ d			15 00					15 30								16 00				16 30				
Gatwick Airport 10	✈ d			13b45					14 15								14 45				15 15				
Luton Airport Parkway 7	d			15 29					15 35								16 18				16 35				
Luton 10	d			15 34					15 39								16 32				17 01				
Bedford 7	d			15 51					16 16								16 48				17 15				
Wellingborough	d			16 04					16 28								17 01				17 28				
Kettering	d			16 16	16 25	16 31	16 49		16c48	17 08					17 22		17 14	17 46	17 49		17 41	18 04			
Market Harborough	d	16 48			16a50	16a56	17a14	17 22		17a33					17a47	17 49		18a11	18a14	18 15		18a29		18 46	
Leicester	a	17 13		17 17				17 47	17 50							18 14	18 18			18 40	18 45			19 11	
	d			17 23					17 57								18 24				18 50				
Syston	d																								
Sileby	d																								
Barrow Upon Soar	d																								
Loughborough	d			17 34					18 09												19 03				
Beeston	a			17 44																					
Nottingham 8	🚢 a			17 51													18 49								
	d											18 33													
Langley Mill	d											18 52													
Alfreton	d											19 00													
Long Eaton	a								18 17																
Derby 10	a								18 28												19 19				
	d								18 29		18 42			19 14							19 19				19 42
Burton-on-Trent	a								18 51												19 50				
Belper	a																				20 01				
Matlock	a																				20 21				
Chesterfield	d								18 51		19 01	19 14		19 33							19 40				20 01
Dronfield	d																								
Sheffield 7	🚢 a								19 07		19 16	19 32		19 48							19 56				20 16
Meadowhall	🚢 a								19 32		19 32	19 44									20 08				20 32
Barnsley	a								20 05		20 05	20 05									21 05				21 05
Doncaster 7	a								20 05		20 05			20 16							20 30				21 04
Wakefield Westgate 7	a								19 44		19 44										20 44				20 44
Leeds 10	a								20 01		20 01										21 01				21 01
York 8	a								20 33		20 33	20 42		20 42							21 32				21 32

		EM ◇	EM 1 ◇ ☕	EM 🚌	EM 🚌	XC 1 ◇	EM 🚌	EM 🚌	EM 1 ◇ ☕	XC R 1		EM 🚌	EM 🚌	EM 1 ◇ ☕	EM 🚌	EM 1 ◇ ☕	EM 🚌	EM 🚌	EM 🚌	XC 1 ◇		EM 🚌	EM 🚌	EM 1 ◇ ☕	EM ◇
St Pancras International 15	⊖ d		17 00						17 30					18 00		18 30								19 00	
Gatwick Airport 10	✈ d		15 45						16 15					16 45		17b15								17e45	
Luton Airport Parkway 7	d		17 05						17 35					18 05										19 26	
Luton 10	d		17 31						17 53					18 22		19 01								19 09	
Bedford 7	d		17 47						18 17					18 46		19 19								19 45	
Wellingborough	d		18 01						18 30					18 59		19 33								19 58	
Kettering	d		18 14	18 23	18 33		18 52		18 43			19 17		19 11	19 20	19 47	19 55		20 06			20 20		20 12	
Market Harborough	d			18a48	18a58		19a17	19 18				19a42	19 44		19a45		20a20	20 26	20a31			20a45	20 48		
Leicester	a		19 15					19 43	19 48				20 09	20 13		20 50		20 51					21 13	21 16	
	d		19 20						19 53					20 19		21 01								21 23	
Syston	d																								
Sileby	d																								
Barrow Upon Soar	d																								
Loughborough	d		19 33						20 04					20 30		21 12								21 37	22 10
Beeston	a		19 44											20 42										21 47	
Nottingham 8	🚢 a		19 50											20 49										21 54	22 31
	d	19 39												20 55											
Langley Mill	d													21 12											
Alfreton	d	20 01												21 19											
Long Eaton	a								20 14							21 22									
Derby 10	a								20 27							21 36									
	d					20 14			20 32	20 42						21 38				21 42					
Burton-on-Trent	a								21 07							22 21									
Belper	a															22 05									
Matlock	a															22 25									
Chesterfield	d	20 14				20 33			20 52	21 01				21 31		21 58				22 01					
Dronfield	d																								
Sheffield 7	🚢 a	20 31				20 48			21 10	21 17				21 46		22 13				22 18					
Meadowhall	🚢 a	20 44				21 14			21 29	21 29						22 31				22 31					
Barnsley	a	21 05							22 09	22 09						23 05				23 05					
Doncaster 7	a					21 16			21 38	22 02						22 38				22 55					
Wakefield Westgate 7	a	21f29				21g44			22 01	21 44				22 45		22 56				22s45					
Leeds 10	a					22g01			22 22	22 01				23 09		23 12				23 09					
York 8	a	21 41				21 41			22g36	22 36				00h08		00 08				00 08					

For general notes see front of timetable
For details of catering facilities see Directory of Train Operators

- b Change at Luton
- c Arr. 1639
- e Change at Bedford
- f Wakefield Kirkgate
- g Change at Sheffield
- h Change at Sheffield and Leeds

Sundays

until 27 January

London → East Midlands → Sheffield

Route Diagram - See first page of Table 53

	EM	EM	EM	EM	EM	EM	EM		XC	EM	EM	EM	EM	EM	EM	EM	EM		EM	EM	EM	EM		
	🚌	🚌	1 ◇	🚌	🚌	1 ◇	🚌		1 ◇	🚌	🚌	1 ◇	🚌	1 ◇	🚌	🚌	🚌		1 ◇	1 ◇	🚌	1 ◇		
St Pancras International 15 ⊖ d			19 30			20 00						20 30		21 00					21 30	22 30		23 00		
Gatwick Airport 10 ✈ d			18 15			18 45						18 45		19 45					20 15	21 15		21b45		
Luton Airport Parkway 7 d			19 35			20 05						20 17		21b17					21 35	22 35		23b15		
Luton 10 d			19 56			20 26								21 25					21 39	22 55		23 26		
Bedford 7 d			20 17			20 47						21 13		21 50					22 19	23 19		23 52		
Wellingborough d			20 31			21 01						21 27		22 02					22 32	23 31		00 05		
Kettering d	20 50		20 41	21 05		21 15	21 24			21 49		21 40		22 15	22 24	22 54			22 46	23 44	23 53	00 19		
Market Harborough d	21a15	21 20		21a30	21 49		21a49			22a14	22 15		22 49		22a49	23a19	23 20				00a18			
Leicester a		21 45	21 46		22 14	22 19					22 40	22 44	23 14	23 19			23 45		23 49	00 53		01 24		
d			21 55			22 24						22 50		23 24					23 55	00 58		01 29		
Syston d																								
Sileby d																								
Barrow Upon Soar d																								
Loughborough d						22 38													00 10	01 15		01 46		
Beeston a														23 55										
Nottingham 8 a						22 56								00 02						01 41				
d																								
Langley Mill d																								
Alfreton d																								
Long Eaton a			22 10																					
Derby 10 a			22 23									23 20							00 36			02 06		
d			22 27						22 53			23 25												
Burton-on-Trent a			23 07																					
Belper a																								
Matlock a																								
Chesterfield d			22 49						23 13			23 46												
Dronfield d																								
Sheffield 7 a			23 08						23 26			23 59												
Meadowhall a			23 25																					
Barnsley a																								
Doncaster 7 a			23 58																					
Wakefield Westgate 7 a									23s52			00 29												
Leeds 10 a									00 34			01 06												
York 8 a																								

Sundays

3 February to 23 March

	EM	EM	EM	EM	EM	EM	EM	EM	EM	EM	XC	EM	EM	XC	EM	XC	EM	XC	EM	EM	EM	EM	EM	EM
	🚌	🚌	1 ◇	🚌	🚌	🚌	🚌	◇	🚌	🚌	1 ◇	1 ◇	🚌	1 ◇	◇	1 ◇	◇	1 ◇	🚌	🚌	1 ◇	🚌	🚌	🚌
St Pancras International 15 ⊖ d			22p10																		09 00			
Gatwick Airport 10 ✈ d																					07 45			
Luton Airport Parkway 7 d																					09 15			
Luton 10 d			22p45																		09 30			
Bedford 7 d			23p08																		09 5[illegible]			
Wellingborough d			23p21																		[illegible]			
Kettering d			23p34	06 52	07 22	07 51	08 17		08 51	09 11			09 52						10 20		[illegible] 17	10 25	10 49	10 57
Market Harborough d		00 07		07a17	07a47	08a16	08a42		09a16	09a36			10a17						10a45	[illegible]		10a50	11a14	11a22
Leicester a		00 32	00 36																	[illegible] 15	11 19			
d			00 42									10 05									11 24			
Syston d																								
Sileby d																								
Barrow Upon Soar d																								
Loughborough d												[illegible] 15									11 39			
Beeston a																					11 48			
Nottingham 8 a																					11 56			
d								09 15							[illegible] 36		11 46							
Langley Mill d																								
Alfreton d															10 58		12 08							
Long Eaton a			00 59									10 2[illegible]												
Derby 10 a			01 12									[illegible]												
d	23p21										09 4[illegible]	[illegible] 35		10 42		11 26		12 26						
Burton-on-Trent a												11c20												
Belper a												11 44												
Matlock a												12 04												
Chesterfield d	00 07							09 54			10 03	10 55		11 03	11 15	11 45	12 21	12 45						
Dronfield d																								
Sheffield 7 a	00 37							[illegible] 14			10 18	11 09		11 18	11 33	11 58	12 37	12 58						
Meadowhall a											10 31			11 37		12 13								
Barnsley a											11 05			11 52		13 05								
Doncaster 7 a											10 51	11 34				12 27		13 26						
Wakefield Westgate 7 a											10 44			11 44	12 44	12 44	13 44	13 44						
Leeds 10 a											11 01			12 01	13 01	13 01	14 01	14 01						
York 8 a								11e29			11 33	11 57		12 33	13e05	13 33	14e04	14 32						

For general notes se[illegible]ont of timetable
For details of cate[illegible]g facilities see
Directory of T[illegible] Operators

b Change at Bedford
c By bus
e Change at Sheffield and Doncaster

Table 53

London → East Midlands → Sheffield

Sundays

3 February to 23 March

Route Diagram - See first page of Table 53

	EM	EM 1 ◇	EM	EM ◇	XC 1 ◇	EM		EM	EM 1 ◇	EM	EM	EM	EM 1 ◇	EM	EM	EM ◇	EM 1 ◇	EM	EM	XC 1 ◇	EM	EM	EM 1 ◇	EM
St Pancras International 15 ⊖ d		09 30							10 00				10 30				11 00						11 30	
Gatwick Airport 10 ✈ d		*08 15*							*08 45*				*09 15*				*09b45*						*10 15*	
Luton Airport Parkway 7 d		*09 45*							*10 15*				*10 45*				11 28						*11 35*	
Luton 10 d		10 02							10 30				*10 49*				11 33						*11 39*	
Bedford 7 d		10 22							10 50				11 24				11 55						12 23	
Wellingborough d		10 36							11 05				11 36				12 09						12 37	
Kettering d		10 48	11 10			11 26			11 17	11 44	11 57		11 49	12 21			12 21	12 30	12 45		12 58		12 50	13 20
Market Harborough d	11 25		11a35			11a51		11 54		12a09	12a22	12 29		12a46	12 54			12a55	13a10		13a23	13 25		13a45
Leicester a	11 50	11 52						12 19	12 23			12 54	12 59		13 19		13 23					13 50	13 53	
d		12 00							12 29				13 04				13 29						14 00	
Syston d																								
Sileby d																								
Barrow Upon Soar d																								
Loughborough d		12 11							12 40				13 16				13 41						14 13	
Beeston a																	13 51							
Nottingham 8 a									12 56								13 59							
d				12 39												13 33								
Langley Mill d				12 56												13 54								
Alfreton d				13 04												14 03								
Long Eaton a		12 19																					14 23	
Derby 10 a		12 31											13 32										14 34	
d		12 31			13 26								13 33							14 26			14 35	
Burton-on-Trent a		*13c05*											*14c20*										*15c20*	
Belper a													*14 03*											
Matlock a													*14 23*											
Chesterfield d		12 52		13 17	13 45								13 53			14 17				14 45			14 56	
Dronfield d																								
Sheffield 7 a		13 05		13 34	14 02								14 09			14 33				14 58			15 15	
Meadowhall a		*13 29*		*14 13*									*14 29*			*15 13*				*15 13*			*15 29*	
Barnsley a		*13 52*											*15 05*										*15 52*	
Doncaster 7 a		*14 01*			14 27								*14 56*			*15 26*				15 26			*15 54*	
Wakefield Westgate 7 a		*14e11*		*14 44*	14 44								*15e29*			*15 44*				15 44			*16e11*	
Leeds 10 a		*14 31*		*15 01*	15 01								*15f58*			*16 01*				16 01			*16 31*	
York 8 a		*14f33*		*15f05*	15 32								*15f36*			*16f04*				16 33			*16f34*	

	EM ◇	XC R 1	EM	EM	EM 1 ◇	EM	EM	EM	EM 1 ◇	EM	EM	EM ◇	EM 1 ◇		EM	XC R 1	EM	EM	EM	EM 1 ◇	EM ◇	XC R 1	EM	EM
St Pancras International 15 ⊖ d					12 00				12 30				13 00							13 30				
Gatwick Airport 10 ✈ d					*10 45*				*11 15*				*11b45*							*12 15*				
Luton Airport Parkway 7 d					*12 05*				*12 48*				13 27							*13 48*				
Luton 10 d					12 31				*12 52*				13 33							*13 52*				
Bedford 7 d					12 55				13 24				13 54							14 22				
Wellingborough d					13 08				13 37				14 07							14 35				
Kettering d			13 30		13 22	13 48	13 59		13 50	14 09			14 19		14 28		14 54	14 56		14 43			15 21	15 22
Market Harborough d			13a55	13 58		14a13	14a24	14 25		14a34	14 52				14a53		15a19	15a21	15 22				15a46	15a47
Leicester a				14 23	14 28			14 50	14 54		15 17		15 23						15 47	15 50				
d					14 33				15 00				15 29							15 57				
Syston d																								
Sileby d																								
Barrow Upon Soar d																								
Loughborough d					14 45				15 14				15 40							16 10				
Beeston a													15 50											
Nottingham 8 a					14 59								15 57											
d	14 36											15 35									16 42			
Langley Mill d	14 53																				16 59			
Alfreton d	15 02											15 54									17 07			
Long Eaton a																				16 17				
Derby 10 a									15 34											16 28				
d		15 26							15 35							16 26				16 29		17 26		
Burton-on-Trent a									*16c20*											*17c05*				
Belper a									*15 58*															
Matlock a									*16 18*															
Chesterfield d	15 14	15 45							15 56			16 13				16 45				16 50	17 20	17 45		
Dronfield d																								
Sheffield 7 a	15 31	15 58							16 13			16 32				16 58				17 08	17 38	17 58		
Meadowhall a	*15 44*	*16 13*							*16 29*			*16 44*				*17 13*				*17 29*	*18 14*	*18 14*		
Barnsley a	*16 06*								*17 05*			*17 05*								*18 05*				
Doncaster 7 a	*16 26*	16 26							*16 54*			*17 26*				17 26				*17 57*	*18 26*	18 26		
Wakefield Westgate 7 a	*16 44*	16 44							*17e29*			*17e29*				17 44				*18 27*	*18 44*	18 44		
Leeds 10 a	*17 01*	17 01							*17f58*			*18 01*				18 01				*18 52*	*19 01*	19 01		
York 8 a	*17 01*	17 33							*17f45*			*18f05*				18 33				*18f34*	*19f03*	19 33		

For general notes see front of timetable
For details of catering facilities see Directory of Train Operators

b Change at Luton
c By bus
e Wakefield Kirkgate
f Change at Sheffield and Doncaster

Sundays

3 February to 23 March

London → East Midlands → Sheffield

Route Diagram - See first page of Table 53

		EM	EM	EM	EM	EM	EM	EM	XC	EM	EM	EM	EM	EM	EM	EM	EM	EM	EM	EM	EM		EM	EM	EM
		🚌	1 ◇ ☕	🚌	🚌	🚌	1 ◇ ☕	◇	R 1 ☕	🚌	🚌	1 ◇ ☕	🚌	🚌	🚌	🚌	1 ◇ ☕	🚌	◇	🚌	🚌		1 ◇ ☕	🚌	🚌
St Pancras International 15 ⊖	d		14 00				14 30					15 00					15 30						16 00		
Gatwick Airport 10 ✈	d		12 45				13 15					13b45					14 15						14 45		
Luton Airport Parkway 7	d		14 18				14 35					15 29					15 35						16 18		
Luton 10	d		14 32				14 39					15 34					15 39						16 32		
Bedford 7	d		14 46				15 16					15 51					16 16						16 48		
Wellingborough	d		15 00				15 29					16 04					16 28						17 01		
Kettering	d		15 13	15 44	15 51		15c50			16 17		16 16	16 25	16 31	16 49		16e48	17 08		17 22			17 14	17 46	17 49
Market Harborough	d	15 48		16a09	16a16	16 25				16a42	16 48		16a50	16a56	17a14	17 22		17a33		17a47	17 49			18a11	18a14
Leicester	a	16 13	16 17			16 50	16 54				17 13	17 17				17 47	17 50				18 14		18 18		
	d		16 23				17 00					17 23					17 57						18 24		
Syston	d																								
Sileby	d																								
Barrow Upon Soar	d																								
Loughborough	d		16 34				17 13					17 34					18 09								
Beeston	a											17 44													
Nottingham 8 🚢	a		16 51									17 51											18 49		
	d							17 31											18 33						
Langley Mill	d							17 52											18 52						
Alfreton	d							18 00											19 00						
Long Eaton	a																18 17								
Derby 10	a						17 31										18 28								
	d						17 31		18 26								18 29								
Burton-on-Trent	a						18f10										19f05								
Belper	a						18 08																		
Matlock	a						18 28																		
Chesterfield	d						17 52	18 14	18 45								18 51		19 14						
Dronfield	d																								
Sheffield 7 🚢	a						18 11	18 31	18 58								19 07		19 32						
Meadowhall 🚢	a						18 29	18 44	19 13								19 32		19 44						
Barnsley	a						19 05	19 05									20 05		20 05						
Doncaster 7	a						18 54	19 27	19 27								20 05								
Wakefield Westgate 7	a						19g29	19g29	19 44								20 26								
Leeds 10	a						20 01	20 01	20 01								20 52								
York 8	a						19h46	20h07	20 33								20h38								

		EM	EM	EM	EM	XC	EM	EM	EM	EM	XC	EM	EM	EM	EM	EM	EM	EM	XC	EM	EM	EM	EM	XC	EM
		🚌	1 ◇ ☕	🚌	🚌	R 1 ☕	◇	1 ◇ ☕	🚌	🚌	R 1	🚌	🚌	1 ◇ ☕	🚌	🚌	1 ◇ ☕	🚌	R 1	1 ◇ ☕	🚌	🚌	🚌	1 ◇	🚌
St Pancras International 15 ⊖	d		16 30					17 00						17 30			18 00			18 30					
Gatwick Airport 10 ✈	d		15 15					15 45						16 15			16 45			17 15					
Luton Airport Parkway 7	d		16 35					17 05						17 35			18 05			18 35					
Luton 10	d		17 01					17 31						17 53			18 22			19 01					
Bedford 7	d		17 15					17 47						18 17			18 46			19 19					
Wellingborough	d		17 28					18 01						18 30			18 59			19 33					
Kettering	d		17 41	18 04				18 14	18 23	18 33		18 52		18 43	19 17		19 11	19 20		19 47	19 55		20 06		20 20
Market Harborough	d	18 15		18a29	18 46				18a48	18a58		19a17	19 18		19a42	19 44		19a45			20a20	20 26	20a31		20a45
Leicester	a	18 40	18 45		19 11			19 15					19 43	19 48		20 09	20 13			20 50		20 51			
	d		18 50					19 20						19 53			20 19			21 01					
Syston	d																								
Sileby	d																								
Barrow Upon Soar	d																								
Loughborough	d		19 03					19 33						20 04			20 30			21 12					
Beeston	a							19 44									20 42								
Nottingham 8 🚢	a							19 50									20 49								
	d						19 39										20 55								
Langley Mill	d																21 12								
Alfreton	d						20 01										21 19								
Long Eaton	a													20 14						21 22					
Derby 10	a		19 19											20 27						21 36					
	d		19 19			19 26					20 26			20 32					21 26	21 38				22 19	
Burton-on-Trent	a		20f00											21f05						22f20					
Belper	a		20 01																	22 05					
Matlock	a		20 21																	22 25					
Chesterfield	d		19 40			19 45	20 14				20 45			20 52			21 31		21 45	21 58				22 38	
Dronfield	d																								
Sheffield 7 🚢	a		19 56			20 00	20 31				21 01			21 10			21 46		22 01	22 13				22 52	
Meadowhall 🚢	a		20 08			20 13	20 44				21 14			21 29						22 31					
Barnsley	a		21 05			21 05	21 05							22 09						23 05					
Doncaster 7	a		20 30			20 32	21 26				21 26			21 42			22 26		22 26	22 38				23 16	
Wakefield Westgate 7	a		20 50			20 50	21g29				21 44			22 01			22 45		22s45	22 56				23s34	
Leeds 10	a		21 06			21 06	22 01				22 01			22 22			23 09		23 09	23 17				00 16	
York 8	a		21 33			21 33	22h00				22 36			23j11			23h11		23j11	00 08				01 02	

For general notes see front of timetable
For details of catering facilities see Directory of Train Operators

- b Change at Luton
- c Arr. 1540
- e Arr. 1639
- f By bus
- g Wakefield Kirkgate
- h Change at Sheffield and Doncaster
- j Change at Doncaster

Table 53

Sundays

3 February to 23 March

…don → East Midlands → Sheffield

Route Diagram - See first page of Table 53

		EM	EM	EM	EM	EM	EM	EM	EM	EM	EM	EM	EM	EM	EM	EM	EM	EM	EM	EM	EM	EM	EM
			1 ◇	◇			1 ◇			1 ◇				1 ◇		1 ◇				1 ◇	1 ◇		1 ◇
		🚌			🚌	🚌		🚌	🚌		🚌	🚌	🚌		🚌		🚌	🚌	🚌			🚌	
St Pancras Interna…			☕				☕			☕				☕		☕				☕	☕		☕
Gatwick Airport 10	⊖ d		19 00				19 30			20 00				20 30		21 00				21 30	22 30		23 00
Luton Airport Parkway 7	✈ d		17b45				18 15			18 45				18 45		19 45				20 15	21 15		21b45
Luton 10	d		19 26				19 35			20 05				20 17		21b17				21 35	22 35		23b15
Bedford 7	d		19 09				19 56			20 26						21 25				21 39	22 55		23 26
Wellingborough	d		19 45				20 17			20 47				21 13		21 50				22 19	23 19		23 52
Kettering	d		19 58				20 31			21 01				21 27		22 02				22 32	23 31		00 05
Market Harborough	d	2[illegible]	20 12		20 50		20 41	21 05		21 15	21 24	21 49		21 40		22 15	22 24	22 54		22 46	23 44	23 53	00 19
Leicester	a	21 [illegible]			21a15	21 20		21a30	21 49		21a49	22a14	22 15		22 49		22a49	23a19	23 20			00a18	
	d		[illegible]46			21 45	21 46		22 14	22 19			22 40	22 44	23 14	23 19			23 45	23 49	00 53		01 24
Syston	d						21 55			22 24				22 50		23 24				23 55	00 58		01 29
Sileby	d																						
Barrow Upon Soar	d																						
Loughborough	d		21 37	22 [illegible]						22 38										00 10	01 15		01 46
Beeston	a		21 47																				
Nottingham 8	🚋 a		21 54	22 31												23 55							
	d									22 56						00 02					01 41		
Langley Mill	d																						
Alfreton	d																						
Long Eaton	a						22 10																
Derby 10	a						22 23							23 20						00 36			02 06
	d						22 27							23 25									
Burton-on-Trent	a						23c20																
Belper	a																						
Matlock	a																						
Chesterfield	d						22 49							23 46									
Dronfield	d																						
Sheffield 7	🚋 a						23 08							23 59									
Meadowhall	🚋 a						23 25																
Barnsley	a																						
Doncaster 7	a																						
Wakefield Westgate 7	a						23 58																
Leeds 10	a						00 29							00 29									
York 8	a						01 06							01 06									

Sundays

from 30 March

		EM	EM	EM		XC	XC	XC		EM	EM	XC		EM	XC	EM		EM	XC	EM		XC	EM	EM	XC
			1 ◇	◇		1 ◇	1 ◇	1 ◇		1 ◇	◇	1 ◇		1 ◇	1 ◇	1 ◇		◇	1 ◇	1 ◇		1 ◇	1 ◇	◇	1 ◇
		🚌	☕			☕	☕	☕		☕		☕		☕	☕	☕			☕	☕		☕	☕		☕
St Pancras International 15	⊖ d		22p10											09 00		09 30				10 00			10 30		
Gatwick Airport 10	✈ d													07 45		08 15				08 45			09 15		
Luton Airport Parkway 7	d													09 15		09 45				10 15			10 45		
Luton 10	d		22p45											09 30		10 02				10 30			10 49		
Bedford 7	d		23p08											09 50		10 22				10 50			11 24		
Wellingborough	d		23p21											10 03		10 35				11 04			11 35		
Kettering	d		23p30											10 14		10 43				11 12			11 43		
Market Harborough	d		23p40											10 24		10 53				11 22			11 53		
Leicester	a		23p55											10 37		11 12				11 42			12 12		
	d		23p56							10 12				10 37		11 13				11 43			12 12		
Syston	d																								
Sileby	d																								
Barrow Upon Soar	d																								
Loughborough	d									10 23				10 49		11 26				11 57			12 25		
Beeston	a													10 58											
Nottingham 8	🚋 a													11 07						12 15					
	d			09 15							10 36							11 46						12 39	
Langley Mill	d																							12 56	
Alfreton	d										10 58							12 08						13 04	
Long Eaton	a		00 13							10 31						11 33									
Derby 10	a		00 26							10 42						11 45							12 44		
	d	23p21				09 42	10 14	10 42		10 48		11 14			11 42	11 46			12 14			12 42	12 46		13 14
Burton-on-Trent	a									11 07						12 07							14 07		
Belper	a									11 4[illegible]													14 03		
Matlock	a									12 04													14 23		
Chesterfield	d	00 07		09 54		10 03	10 33			11 09	11 [illegible]	[illegible] 33				12 07		12 21	12 33				13 06	13 17	13 33
Dronfield	d																								
Sheffield 7	🚋 a	00 37		10 14		10 18	10 46	11 18		11 23	11 33	11 5[illegible]			12 12	12 25		12 37	12 46			13 12	13 20	13 34	13 46
Meadowhall	🚋 a					10 31	11 11			11 37		12 13			12 29	12 44						13 29	13 37		14 13
Barnsley	a					11 05				11 52						13 05							13 52		15 05
Doncaster 7	a					10 51	11 16			11 54		12 16			[illegible]54				13 15			14 01			14 16
Wakefield Westgate 7	a					10 44		11 44		12e11					12 [illegible]	13f29						13 44	14f11		14g44
Leeds 10	a					11 01		12 01		12g31					13 01							14 01	14 31		15g01
York 8	a			11h29		11 33	11 44	12 33		12 19	12 45	12 45			13 33	13 4[illegible]		13 44	13 44			14 32	14 41	14 41	14 41

For general notes see front of timetable
For details of catering facilities see Directory of Train Operators

- **b** Change at Bedford
- **c** By bus
- **e** Wakefield Kirkgate. Change at Sheffield
- **f** Wakefield Kirkgate
- **g** Change at Sheffield
- **h** Change at Sheffield and Doncaster

Sundays

from 30 March

London → East Midlands → Sheffield

Route Diagram - See first page of Table [illegible]

		XC		EM	EM	EM		XC	EM	XC		EM	EM	EM		XC	XC	EM		EM	EM	XC	[illegible]	[illegible]
		1 ◇ ☕		1 ◇ ☕	◇	1 ◇ ☕		1 ◇ ☕	1 ◇ ☕	R 1 ☕		◇	1 ◇ ☕	1 ◇ ☕		1 ◇ ☕	R 1 ☕			◇	1 ◇ ☕	1 ◇ ☕	☕	1 ◇ ☕
St Pancras International 15	⊖ d			11 00		11 30			12 00				12 30	13 00							13 30			14 30
Gatwick Airport 10	✈ d			09b45		10 15			10 45				11 15	11b45										13 15
Luton Airport Parkway 7	d			11 28		11 35			12 05				12 48	13 27							[illegible]			14 35
Luton 10	d			11 33		11 39			12 31				12 52	13 33							[illegible]3 52			14 39
Bedford 7	d			11 55		12 23			12 55				13 24	13 54							14 23			15 16
Wellingborough	d			12 08		12 36			13 08				13 36	14 06							14 36			15 28
Kettering	d			12 16		12 44			13 16				13 45	14 13							14 44			15 40
Market Harborough	d			12 26		12 55			13 26				13 56	14 23							14 55			15 51
Leicester	a			12 45		13 17			13 45				14 20	14 43							15 19			16 09
	d			12 49		13 17			13 45				14 20	14 44							15 19			16 10
Syston	d																							
Sileby	d																							
Barrow Upon Soar	d																							
Loughborough	d			13 00		13 31			14 00				14 31	14 55							15 33			16 22
Beeston	a			13 12										15 05										
Nottingham 8	a			13 20					14 17					15 1[illegible]										
	d				13 33							14 36						15 14		15 35				
Langley Mill	d				13 54							14 53								15 54				
Alfreton	d				14 03							15 02												
Long Eaton	a					13 44												15 30			15 43			
Derby 10	a					13 56							14 50					15 41			15 56			16 46
	d	13 42				13 57		14 14		14 42			14 51			15 14	15 42	15 46			15 56	16 14	16 42	16 47
Burton-on-Trent	a					14 51							15 51					16 07			16 49			17 53
Belper	a												15 58					15 58						
Matlock	a												16 18					16 18						
Chesterfield	d				14 17	14 22		14 33				15 14	15 20			15 33				16 13	16 25	16 33		17 10
Dronfield	d																							
Sheffield 7	a	14 12			14 33	14 40		14 51		15 18		15 31	15 39			15 50	16 16			16 32	16 43	16 49	17 12	17 26
Meadowhall	a	14 29						15 13		15 29		15 44	15 51			16 13	16 29			16 44		17 13	17 29	17 41
Barnsley	a	15 05						15 52		15 52		16 06				17 05	17 05			17 05				18 05
Doncaster 7	a	14 56						15 16		15 54						16 16	16 54					17 14	17 57	
Wakefield Westgate 7	a	14 44						15c44		15 44						16c44	16 44			17e29		17c44	17 44	18 27
Leeds 10	a	15 01						16c01		16 01						17c01	17 01					18c01	18 01	18 52
York 8	a	15 33				15 43		15 43		16 33			16 44			16 44	17 33				17 40	17 40	18 33	18 41

		EM	XC	EM		XC	EM	EM		EM	XC	XC		EM	EM	XC		EM	EM	EM		XC	EM	EM	XC
		◇	1 ◇ ☕	1 ◇ ☕		R 1 ☕	1 ◇ ☕	◇		1 ◇ ☕	R 1 ☕	R 1 ☕		1 ◇ ☕	◇	1 ◇ ☕		1 ◇ ☕	1 ◇ ☕	1 ◇ ☕		R 1 ☕	◇	1 ◇ ☕	1 ◇
St Pancras International 15	⊖ d			15 00			15 30			16 00				16 30				17 00	17 25	17 30				18 00	
Gatwick Airport 10	✈ d			13b45			14 15			14 45				15 15				15 45		16 15				16 45	
Luton Airport Parkway 7	d			15 29			15 35			16 18				16 35				17 05		17 35				18 05	
Luton 10	d			15 34			15 39			16 32				17 01				17 31		17 51				18 22	
Bedford 7	d			15 51			16 16			16 48				17 15				17 47		18 15				18 46	
Wellingborough	d			16 04			16 28			17 01				17 28				18 01		18 28				18 59	
Kettering	d			16 12			16 35			17 09				17 36				18 08		18 35				19 06	
Market Harborough	d			16 22			16 48			17 20				17 49				18 18		18 45				19 17	
Leicester	a			16 42			17 04			17 36				18 04				18 37	18 46	19 05				19 36	
	d			16 42			17 05			17 36				18 04				18 38	18 49	19 06				19 [illegible]	
Syston	d																								
Sileby	d																								
Barrow Upon Soar	d																								
Loughborough	d			16 53			17 15							18 17				18 49		19 16				19 47	
Beeston	a			17 09														19 09						19 59	
Nottingham 8	a			17 17						18 01								19 15						20 05	
	d	16 42						17 31							18 33								19 39	20 12 →	
Langley Mill	d	16 59						17 52							18 52										
Alfreton	d	17 07						18 00							19 00								20 01		
Long Eaton	a						17 24													19 25					
Derby 10	a						17 35							18 43					19 18	19 36					
	d		17 14			17 42	17 48				18 14	18 42		18 47		19 1[illegible]			19 19			19 42			20 14
Burton-on-Trent	a						18 07							19 07					19 50	20 07					
Belper	a						18 08													20 01					
Matlock	a						18 28													20 21					
Chesterfield	d	17 20	17 33				18 08	18 14			18 33	19 01		[illegible] 08	19 14	19 33			19 41			20 01	20 14		20 33
Dronfield	d																								
Sheffield 7	a	17 38	17 47			18 14	18 22	18 31			18 48	19 16		19 25	19 32	19 48			19 57			20 16	20 31		20 48
Meadowhall	a		18 14			18 29	18 44	18 44			19 0[illegible]	[illegible] 32		19 41	19 44	20 08			20 13			20 32	20 44		
Barnsley	a						19 05	19 05						20 05	20 05				21 05			21 05	21 05		
Doncaster 7	a		18 16			18 54	19 16	19 16			[illegible] 16	20 05		20 16	20 16	20 16			20 22			21 04			21 16
Wakefield Westgate 7	a		18c44			18 44	19e29	19e29				19 44		20 26	20 44				20 49			20 44	21e29		21c39
Leeds 10	a		19c01			19 01	20 01	20 01				20 01		20 52	21 01				21 10			21 01			
York 8	a	18 41	18 41			19 33	19 43	19 43			19 43	20 33		20 42	20 42	20 42			21f00			21 32	21 41		21 41

For general notes see front of timetable
For details of catering facilities see
Directory of Train Operators

b Change at Luton
c Change at Sheffield
e Wakefield Kirkgate
f Change at Doncaster

Table 53

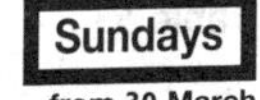

Sundays

from 30 March

London → East Midlands → Sheffield

Route Diagram - See first page of Table 53

		EM	EM	EM	EM	XC	EM	EM	XC	EM	EM	EM	EM	XC	EM	EM	EM	EM
		1 ◇ ☕	1 ◇ ☕	1 ◇ ☕	1 ◇ ☕	R 1	1 ◇ ☕	1 ◇ ☕	1 ◇	1 ◇ ☕	1 ◇ ☕	1 ◇ ☕	◇	1 ◇	1 ◇ ☕	1 ◇ ☕	1 ◇ ☕	1 ◇ ☕
St Pancras International 15	⊖ d	18 25	18 30		18 55		19 00	19 25		19 30	20 00	20 30			21 00	21 30	22 30	23 00
Gatwick Airport 10	✈ d		17b15				17 45			18 15	18 45	18 45			19 45	20 15	21 15	21b45
Luton Airport Parkway 7	d		18 56				19 05			19 35	20 05	20 17			21 05	21 35	22 35	23b15
Luton 10	d		18 39				19 27			19 55	20 26				21 23	21 39	22 55	23 26
Bedford 7	d		19 17				19 45			20 17	20 47	21 13			21 48	22 19	23 19	23 52
Wellingborough	d		19 29				19 58			20 31	21 01	21 26			22 00	22 32	23 31	00 05
Kettering	d		19 37				20 08			20 39	21 10	21 36			22 07	22 40	23 38	00 13
Market Harborough	d		19 51				20 22			20 53	21 21	21 50			22 18	22 51	23 48	00 23
Leicester	a	19 51	20 07		20 14		20 35	20 46		21 09	21 41	22 08			22 37	23 12	00 07	00 42
	d	19 51	20 07		20 14		20 35	20 47		21 10	21 42	22 09			22 37	23 12	00 09	00 42
Syston	d																	
Sileby	d																	
Barrow Upon Soar	d																	
Loughborough	d		20 18				20 46				21 53		22 10			23 25	00 19	00 53
Beeston	a						20 56								23 05			
Nottingham 8	🚋 a			←	20 37		21 03				22 11		22 31		23 11		00 47	
	d			20 12														
Langley Mill	d			20 28														
Alfreton	d			20 36														
Long Eaton	a		20 26							21 28								
Derby 10	a	20 19	20 39					21 12		21 45		22 35				23 52		01 21
	d	20 19				20 42		21 13	21 42	21 46		22 36		22 53		23 52		
Burton-on-Trent	a	20 50	21 07					21 33		22 21		23 07						
Belper	a							22 05										
Matlock	a							22 25										
Chesterfield	d	20 40		20 47		21 01		21 34	22 01	22 09		22 59		23 13		00 14		
Dronfield	d																	
Sheffield 7	🚋 a	20 56		21 02		21 17		21 49	22 18	22 27		23 12		23 26		00 29		
Meadowhall	🚋 a	21 14		21 29		21 29			22 31	22 44		23 25						
Barnsley	a			22 09		22 09				23 05								
Doncaster 7	a	21 20		22 02		22 02			22 55			23 58						
Wakefield Westgate 7	a	21 39		21 44		21 44			22s45	23c28		23 39		23s52				
Leeds 10	a	22 02		22 01		22 01			23 09	00 04		00 16		00 34				
York 8	a	23 17		22 36		22 36		00e08	00 08	01e02		01 02						

For general notes see front of timetable
For details of catering facilities see Directory of Train Operators

b Change at Bedford
c Wakefield Kirkgate
e Change at Sheffield and Leeds

Sheffield → East Midlands → London

Route Diagram - See first page of Table 53

Miles	Miles			EM 1◇ ⊠⚲	EM ◇	EM 1◇ ⊠⚲	EM 1◇ ⊠⚲	EM 1◇ ⊠⚲	EM	EM 1◇ ☕	EM ◇	EM	EM 1◇ ⊠⚲	EM 1◇ ⊠⚲	EM	EM 1◇ ⊠⚲	EM 1◇ ⊠⚲	EM 1◇ ☕	EM 1◇ A ⊠⚲	XC 1◇ ☕		EM 1◇ ☕	EM 1◇ B ⊠⚲	EM	EM 1◇ ☕
—	—	York 8	d																	04b09			04c09		
—	—	Leeds 10	d														05e05			06 00					
—	—	Wakefield Westgate 7	d														05e17			06 12					
—	—	Doncaster 7	d														05 42			06 00					
—	—	Barnsley	d													05 18				05 53			06 27		
—	—	Meadowhall	d													05 41	06 00			06 27			06 49		
0	0	**Sheffield 7**	d					05 20								06 00	06 25		06 30	06 45			07 05		
7	7	Dronfield	d																						
12¼	12¼	Chesterfield	d					05 33								06 14	06 38		06 45	06 57			07 19		
—	—	Matlock	d														06 20								
—	28½	Belper	d														06 40								
—	—	Burton-on-Trent	d														06 25					07 10			
—	36½	**Derby 10**	a					05 54									07 00			07 16		07 26	07 46		
—	—		d			05 00		05 56				06 16		06 39			07 01					07 34	07 46		
—	44	Long Eaton	d					06 06				06 25										07 43			
22½	—	Alfreton	d																06 57						
34¾	—	Langley Mill	d																07 05						
40¾	—	**Nottingham 8**	a													06 45			07 23						
—	—		d		04 56		05 30			06 07	06 13		06 25			06 53		07 07	07 30					07 38	08 07
44	—	Beeston	d							06 13			06 31					07 13	07 36					07 44	08 13
55½	53¼	Loughborough	d		05a10		05 45	06 15	06 08		06a26	06 39	06 41		←		07 18	07 22				07 52		08 01	08 22
59½	57¼	Barrow Upon Soar	d						06 12			06 44			06 44									08 06	
61½	59¼	Sileby	d						06 17			→			06 48									08 10	
64¼	62	Syston	d						06 22						06 53									08 15	
68	65¾	**Leicester**	a			05 25	05 58	06 28	06 31	06 34			06 53	07 01	07 06	07 13	07 30	07 37	07 55			08 04	08 12	08 25	08 34
—	—		d	05 00		05 25	06 00	06 30		06 35			06 55	07 04		07 15	07 30	07 37	07 57			08 05	08 14		08 35
84¼	82	Market Harborough	d			05 41	06 15	06 45		06 50			07 10			07 29	07 47	07 53				08 19			08 49
95¼	93	Kettering	d	05 21		05 52	06 26	06 56		07 02			07 20	07 28		07 39	07 58	08 03	08 17			08 29			08 59
102¼	100	Wellingborough	d	05 29		06 00	06 34	07 04		07 10			07 28	07 37		07 46	08 06	08 12				08 40			09 06
117½	115¼	Bedford 7	d	05 50		06 19	06 51							07 53				08 25				09 03			09 23
137	134¾	**Luton 10**	d			06 35	07 08	07 29					07 52	08 27		08 10		08 53				09 33			09 38
—	—	Luton Airport Parkway 7	d	06 08		06 52	07 22	07 42		07 38			08 04	08 30		08 30		09 06				09 21			09 51
—	—	Gatwick Airport 10	a			08 40	08 56	09 22					09 40	09 55		09 55		10 25				10f55			11 10
167¼	165	**St Pancras International 15**	a	06 41		07 06	07 36	07 59		08 06			08 24	08 38		08 42	08 55	09 06	09 12			09 45	09 29		10 04

		EM 1◇ ☕	XC 1◇ ☕	EM 1◇ C ⊠⚲	EM ◇	EM 1◇ ☕	XC R 1 ☕	EM	XC R 1 ☕	EM 1◇ ☕	EM 1◇ ☕	EM 1◇ ☕	EM 1◇ ☕	EM ◇ ⚲	XC R 1 ☕	EM		XC 1◇ ☕	EM 1◇ ☕	EM 1◇ ☕	EM ◇ ⚲	XC 1◇ ☕	EM 1◇ ☕	EM 1◇ ☕	EM
York 8	d	06e00	06 16				06e30		07 27	07g27			07h27		07 44			08 27	08h27			08 44			
Leeds 10	d		06 14	06 14			07 05		07h16	07 26			07h26		08 10			08h28	08 28			09 10			
Wakefield Westgate 7	d		06 26	06 26			07 19		07j32	07 38			07h38		08 23			08h39	08 39			09 23			
Doncaster 7	d	06 40	06 45	06 45			07 02		07 52	07 59								08 51			08 57	09 01			
Barnsley	d		06 46		06 58		06 58		07 48	07 48			08 06	07 58	08 14			08 48			08 58	08 58			
Meadowhall	d	06 59	07 04		07 19		07 33		08 07	08 07			08 24	08 22	08 34			09 03			09 21	09 33			
Sheffield 7	d	07 14	07 23	07 27	07 40		07 53		08 23	08 27			08 36	08 38	08 53			09 23	09 27		09 38	09 53			
Dronfield	d																								
Chesterfield	d	07 27	07 35	07 40	07 53		08 05		08 35	08 40			08 48	08 52				09 35	09 40		09 53				
Matlock	d					07k38													09 04						
Belper	d					07k58							09 03						09 25						
Burton-on-Trent	d					08 10				08 29			08 58						09 20						
Derby 10	a		07 55			08 25	08 26		08 55	09 01			09 13		09 22			09 55	10 01			10 22			
	d					08 34				09 03			09 34						10 03					10 34	
Long Eaton	d					08 43							09 43											10 43	
Alfreton	d	07 40			08 06									09 07											
Langley Mill	d	07 50			08 13									09 14											
Nottingham 8	a	08 09			08 29									09 30							10 25				
	d	08 26						08 36			09 07	09 30				09 38				10 07			10 30		10 38
Beeston	d	08 34									09 13									10 13					
Loughborough	d	08 43				08 52		09 01			09 23	09 44	09 52			10 0[illegible]				10 22				10 52	11 00
Barrow Upon Soar	d							09 06								[illegible]									11 06
Sileby	d							09 10								[illegible]									11 10
Syston	d							09 15								10 15									11 15
Leicester	a	08 55				09 04		09 25		09 28	09 35	09 57	10 04			10 25			10 28	10 34			10 57	11 04	11 25
	d	08 56				09 05				09 30	09 35	10 00	10 [illegible]						10 30	10 35			11 00	11 05	
Market Harborough	d					09 19					09 49									10 49				11 19	
Kettering	d	09 18				09 29					09 59		[illegible] 29							10 59				11 29	
Wellingborough	d					09 36					10 [illegible]		10 36							11 06				11 36	
Bedford 7	d					09 53					[illegible]		10 51						11 12	11 21				11 51	
Luton 10	d					10 33					[illegible] 39		11 33							11 36				12 33	
Luton Airport Parkway 7	d					10 09					10 51		11 07						11 51	11 51				12 07	
Gatwick Airport 10	a					11f55					12 10		12f55						13 10	13 10				13f55	
St Pancras International 15	a	10 19		09 33		10 34				10 48	11 04	11 17	11 34						11 51	12 04			12 15	12 34	

For general notes see front of timetable
For details of catering facilities see Directory of Train Operators

A **The Robin Hood**

R **[illegible]idland Express**
[illegible] **[illegible]he Master Cutler**
b Mondays dep. 0411
c Change at Leeds and Sheffield. Mondays dep. 0411
e Change at Doncaster and Sheffield

f Change at Bedford
g Change at Doncaster
h Change at Sheffield
j Wakefield Kirkgate. Change at Sheffield
k Change at Derby

Sheffield → East Midlands → London

Route Diagram - See first page of Table 53

		XC	EM	EM	EM	EM	XC	EM	EM	XC	EM	EM		EM	XC	EM	EM	EM	XC	EM	EM	EM	XC	EM	EM
		1 ◇ ☕	1 ◇ ☕	1 ◇ ☕	1 ◇ ☕	◇ 🛒	R 1 ☕	1 ◇ ☕		1 ◇ ☕	1 ◇ ☕	1 ◇ ☕		◇ 🛒	1 ◇ ☕	1 ◇ ☕	1 ◇ ☕		R 1 ☕	1 ◇ ☕	1 ◇ ☕	◇ 🛒	R 1 ☕	1 ◇ ☕	1 ◇ ☕
York [8]	d	09 27	09 27				09 44			10 34	10 34				10 44				11 27	11 27			11 44		
Leeds [10]	d	09b16					10 10			10b16					11 10				11b16	11 16			12 10		
Wakefield Westgate [7]	d	09c32					10 23			10c32					11 23				11c32	11e32			12 23		
Doncaster [7]	d	09 56					10 02			10 58					11 02				11 54	11 54			11 58		
Barnsley	d	09 48				10 01	10 01			10 48				11 01	11 01				11 48	11 48		12 01	12 01		
Meadowhall 🚊	d	10 03	10 07			10 19	10 33			11 04	11 07			11 19	11 33				12 03	12 06		12 19	12 33		
Sheffield [7] 🚊	d	10 23	10 27			10 38	10 53			11 23	11 27			11 38	11 53				12 23	12 27		12 38	12 53		
Dronfield	d																					12 49			
Chesterfield	d	10 35	10 40			10 53				11 35	11 40			11 53					12 35	12 40		12 53			
Matlock	d										11 12														
Belper	d										11 33														
Burton-on-Trent	d		10 18					10 58			11 19						11 44			12 19					12 58
Derby [10]	a	10 55	11 01				11 22			11 55	12 01				12 22				12 55	13 01			13 22		
	d		11 03					11 34			12 03						12 34			13 03					13 34
Long Eaton	d							11 43									12 43								13 43
Alfreton	d					11 04								12 04								13 04			
Langley Mill	d					11 11																13 11			
Nottingham [8] 🚊	a					11 30								12 29								13 29			
	d			11 07	11 30				11 38			12 07				12 30		12 38			13 07			13 30	
Beeston	d			11 13								12 13									13 13				
Loughborough	d			11 22	11 44			11 52	12 00			12 22					12 52	13 00			13 22			13 44	13 52
Barrow Upon Soar	d								12 06									13 06							
Sileby	d								12 10									13 10							
Syston	d								12 15									13 15							
Leicester	a		11 28	11 34	11 57			12 04	12 25		12 28	12 34				12 57	13 04	13 25		13 26	13 34			13 57	14 04
	d		11 30	11 35	12 00			12 05			12 30	12 35				13 00	13 05			13 30	13 35			14 00	14 05
Market Harborough	d			11 49				12 19				12 49					13 19				13 49				14 19
Kettering	d			11 59				12 29				12 59					13 29				13 59				14 29
Wellingborough	d			12 06				12 36				13 06					13 36				14 06				14 36
Bedford [7]	d			12 21				12 51				13 21					13 51				14 21				14 51
Luton [10]	d		12 20	12 36				13 33				13 36					14 33				14 36				15 33
Luton Airport Parkway [7]	d		12 36	12 51				13 07				13 51					14 07				14 51				15 07
Gatwick Airport [10] ✈	a		13 55	14 10				14f55				15 10					15f55				16 10				16f55
St Pancras International [15] ⊖	a		12 51	13 04	13 15			13 34			13 45	14 04				14 14	14 34			14 44	15 04			15 14	15 34

		EM	XC	EM	EM	EM	XC	EM		EM	EM	XC	EM	EM	EM	XC	EM	EM	EM	XC	EM	EM	EM	EM	XC
			1 ◇ ☕	1 ◇ ☕	1 ◇ ☕	◇ 🛒	R 1 ☕	1 ◇ ☕		1 ◇ ☕		1 ◇ ☕	1 ◇ ☕	1 ◇ ☕	◇ 🛒	R 1 ☕	1 ◇ ☕	1 ◇ ☕		1 ◇ ☕	1 ◇ ☕	1 ◇ ☕	1 ◇ ☕	◇ 🛒	R 1 ☕
York [8]	d		12 25	12 25			12 44					13 29	13 29			13 44				14 32	14 32				14 44
Leeds [10]	d		12b16				13 10					13b16				14 10				14b16					15 10
Wakefield Westgate [7]	d		12c32				13 23					13c32				14 23				14c32					15 23
Doncaster [7]	d		12 55				13 02					13 54				14 01				14 57					15 02
Barnsley	d		12 48			13 01	13 01					13 48			14 01	14 01				14 48				15 01	15 01
Meadowhall 🚊	d		13 04	13 07		13 21	13 33					14 03	14 06		14 19	14 33				15 03	15 06			15 19	15 33
Sheffield [7] 🚊	d		13 23	13 27		13 38	13 53					14 23	14 27		14 38	14 53				15 23	15 27			15 38	15 53
Dronfield	d																							15 49	
Chesterfield	d		13 35	13 40		13 53						14 35	14 40		14 53					15 35	15 40			15 55	
Matlock	d			13 12																	15 17				
Belper	d			13 33																	15 38				
Burton-on-Trent	d			13 21						13 44			14 18					14 58			15 20				
Derby [10]	a		13 55	14 01			14 22					14 55	15 01			15 22				15 55	16 01				16 22
	d			14 03						14 34			15 03					15 34			16 03				
Long Eaton	d									14 43								15 43							
Alfreton	d					14 04									15 04									16 06	
Langley Mill	d														15 11										
Nottingham [8] 🚊	a					14 29									15 29									16 34	
	d	13 38			14 07			14 30			14 38			15 07			15 30		15 38			16 07	16 30		
Beeston	d				14 13									15 13								16 13			
Loughborough	d	14 00			14 22					14 52	15 00			15 22			15 44	15 52	16 00			16 22	16 44		
Barrow Upon Soar	d	14 06									15 06								16 06						
Sileby	d	14 10									15 10								16 10						
Syston	d	14 15									15 15								16 15						
Leicester	a	14 25		14 28	14 34			14 57		15 04	15 25		15 28	15 34			15 58	16 04	16 25		16 28	16 34	16 58		
	d			14 30	14 35			15 00		15 05			15 30	15 35			16 00	16 05			16 30	16 35	17 00		
Market Harborough	d				14 49					15 19				15 49				16 19				16 49			
Kettering	d				14 59					15 29				15 59				16 29				16 59	17 21		
Wellingborough	d				15 06					15 36				16 06				16 36				17 06			
Bedford [7]	d				15 21					15 51				16 21				16 51			17 12	17 21			
Luton [10]	d			15 20	15 36					16 33				16 36				17 17				17 36			
Luton Airport Parkway [7]	d			15 36	15 51					16 07				16 51				17 07			17 46	17 50			
Gatwick Airport [10] ✈	a			16 55	17 15					18f12				18 24				18f41			19 26	19 26			
St Pancras International [15] ⊖	a			15 50	16 04			16 15		16 34			16 45	17 04			17 13	17 34			17 53	18 04	18 19		

For general notes see front of timetable
For details of catering facilities see Directory of Train Operators

b Change at Sheffield
c Wakefield Kirkgate. Change at Sheffield
e Wakefield Kirkgate
f Change at Bedford

Table 53

Mondays to Fridays
until 25 January

Sheffield → East Midlands → London

Route Diagram - See first page of Table 53

		EM	EM	XC		EM	EM	EM	XC	EM	EM	EM	XC	EM	EM	EM	XC	EM	EM	EM	XC	EM		EM	EM
		1◇ ⊡		R 1 ⊡		1◇ ⊡	1◇ ⊡	◇ ⊼	R 1 ⊡	1◇ ⊡	1◇ ⊡		R 1 ⊡	1◇ ⊡	1◇ ⊡	◇ ⊼	1◇ ⊡	1◇ ⊡	1◇ ⊡		R 1 ⊡	1◇ ⊡		1◇ ⊡	1◇ ⊡
York 8	d			15 29		15 29			15 44				16 25	16 25			16 44				17 34	17 34			
Leeds 10	d			15b16		15 16			16 10					16 16			17 10				17b16	17 16			
Wakefield Westgate 7	d			15c32		15e32			16 23					16e32			17 23				17c32	17e32			
Doncaster 7	d			15 55		15 55			16 02				16 53	16 53			17 00				17 58	17 58			
Barnsley	d			15 48		15 48		16 01	16 01				16 26	16 48		17 01	17 01				17 48	17 48			
Meadowhall	d			16 06		16 09		16 19	16 33				17 00	17 07		17 19	17 33				18 04	18 07			
Sheffield 7	d			16 23		16 27		16 38	16 53				17 20	17 27		17 41	17 53				18 23	18 27			
Dronfield	d							16 49					17 28												
Chesterfield	d			16 35		16 40		16 55					17 35	17 40		17 55					18 35	18 40			
Matlock	d													16 58								18 13			
Belper	d													17 19								18 33			
Burton-on-Trent	d	15 44				16 20					16 48			17 20					17 40			18 22			
Derby 10	a			16 55		17 01			17 22				17 55	18 01			18 22				18 55	19 01			
	d	16 34				17 03					17 34			18 02					18 34			19 02			
Long Eaton	d	16 43									17 43								18 43						
Alfreton	d							17 06								18 06									
Langley Mill	d							17 13								18 13									
Nottingham 8	a							17 29								18 29									
	d		16 38				17 07			17 30		17 38			18 07			18 30		18 38				19 07	19 30
Beeston	d						17 13								18 13									19 13	
Loughborough	d	16 52	17 02				17 22			17 44	17 52	18 02		18 18	18 22			18 44	18 52	19 00		19 17		19 22	19 44
Barrow Upon Soar	d		17 07									18 08								19 06					
Sileby	d		17 11									18 12								19 10					
Syston	d		17 16									18 17								19 15					
Leicester	a	17 04	17 25			17 30	17 33			17 58	18 04	18 26		18 30	18 35			18 57	19 04	19 25		19 28		19 35	19 55
	d	17 05				17 30	17 35			18 00	18 05			18 30	18 35			19 00	19 05			19 30		19 35	20 00
Market Harborough	d	17 19					17 49				18 19				18 51				19 19					19 51	
Kettering	d	17 29					17 59				18 29				19 01				19 29					20 01	
Wellingborough	d	17 36					18 06				18 36				19 09				19 36					20 09	
Bedford 7	d	17 51					18 23				18 53				19 23				19 51					20 23	
Luton 10	d	18 33				18 21	18 39							19 22	19 39									20 39	
Luton Airport Parkway 7	d	18 07				18 36	18 52				19 07			19 46	19 52				20 07					20 52	
Gatwick Airport 10 ✈	a	19f55				19 55	20 10				21f10			21 10	21 41				22f10					22 41	
St Pancras International 15 ⊖	a	18 34				18 51	19 04			19 17	19 34			19 52	20 04			20 11	20 34			20 41		21 04	21 11

		EM	XC	EM	EM	XC	EM	EM	EM	XC	EM	EM	XC	EM	EM	EM	XC	EM	EM	XC	XC	EM	EM		
		◇ ⊼	R 1 ⊡	1◇ ⊡		1◇ ⊡	1◇ ⊡	1◇ ⊡	◇ ⊼	1◇ ⊡	1◇ ⊡		1◇ ⊡	1◇ ⊡	1◇ ⊡	◇ ⊼	1◇		◇ ⊼	1◇	1◇	1◇ ⊡	◇		
York 8	d		17 44			18 24	18 24			18 44			19 29	19 29			19 44		20 31	20 44	21 24	21g38			
Leeds 10	d		18 10			18b16				19 10			19b16				20 10		20 16	21 10		21 34	21 48		
Wakefield Westgate 7	d		18 23			18c32				19 23			19c32				20 23		20e32	21 23		22e03			
Doncaster 7	d		18 02			18 52				18 55			19 57				20 03		20 56	21 07	21 48	22 13			
Barnsley	d	18 01	18 01			18 48			18 58	19 16			19 48				20 06		20 48	21 06	21 26	22 26			
Meadowhall	d	18 19	18 33			19 04	19 07		19 16	19 34			20 04	20 08			20 33		21 07	21 34	22 10	22 49	22 51		
Sheffield 7	d	18 45	18 53			19 23	19 27		19 38	19 53			20 23	20 39		20 40	20 53		21 38	21 53	22 27	23 08	23 38		
Dronfield	d								19 50																
Chesterfield	d	19 01				19 35	19 40		19 56	20 05			20 35	20 51		20 55	21 05		21 53	22 05	22 53	23 21	23 59		
Matlock	d													19 38											
Belper	d													19 58											
Burton-on-Trent	d			18 58			19 20							20 29											
Derby 10	a		19 22			19 55	20 01			20 26			20 55	21 14			21 27			22 26	23 13	23 46			
	d			19 34			20 02							21 16											
Long Eaton	d			19 43																					
Alfreton	d	19 12							20 07							21 06			22 04						
Langley Mill	d								20 16							21 13			22 11						
Nottingham 8	a	19 37							20 31							21 38			22 36				00 46		
	d				19 38			20 07			20 47	20 38			21 30			21 54							
Beeston	d				19 44			20 13																	
Loughborough	d			19 52	20 01		20 18	20 22			21 00	21 00		21 30	21 45			22 10							
Barrow Upon Soar	d				20 06							21 06													
Sileby	d				20 10							21 10													
Syston	d				20 15							21 15													
Leicester	a			20 04	20 25		20 29	20 35			21 12	21 25		21 43	21 56			22 23							
	d			20 05			20 30	20 35			21 15			21 45	22 00										
Market Harborough	d			20 19				20 51			21 28			21 59	22 13										
Kettering	d			20 29				21 01			21 38			22 09	22 23										
Wellingborough	d			20 36				21 09			21 45			22 16	22 30										
Bedford 7	d			20 51			21 11	21 23			22 00				22 45										
Luton 10	d							21 39			22 16				23 01										
Luton Airport Parkway 7	d			21 07			21 46	21 52			22 36				23 36										
Gatwick Airport 10 ✈	a						23 10	23 41			00 16				01 16										
St Pancras International 15 ⊖	a			21 34			21 53	22 04			22 40			23 04	23 32										

For general notes see front of timetable
For details of catering facilities see Directory of Train Operators

b Change at Sheffield
c Wakefield Kirkgate. Change at Sheffield
e Wakefield Kirkgate
f Change at Bedford
g Change at Doncaster and Sheffield

Sheffield → East Midlands → London

Route Diagram - See first page of Table 53

Station		EM 1◇ A	EM ◇	EM 1◇ B	EM 1◇	EM 1◇	EM	EM 1◇	EM ◇	EM	EM 1◇	EM 1◇	EM	EM 1◇		EM 1◇	EM 1◇	EM 1◇ C	XC 1◇	EM 1◇	EM 1◇ D	EM	EM 1◇	EM 1◇	XC 1◇
York 8	d																		04b09		04c09			06e00	06 16
Leeds 10	d															05e05			06 00						06 14
Wakefield Westgate 7	d															05e17			06 12						06 26
Doncaster 7	d															05 42			06 00					06 40	06 45
Barnsley	d													05 18					05 53		06 27				06 46
Meadowhall	d													05 41		06 00			06 27		06 49			06 59	07 04
Sheffield 7	d					05 20								06 00		06 25		06 30	06 45		07 05			07 14	07 23
Dronfield	d																								
Chesterfield	d					05 33								06 14		06 38		06 45	06 57		07 19			07 27	07 35
Matlock	d															06 20									
Belper	d															06 40									
Burton-on-Trent	d															06 25				07 10					
Derby 10	a					05 54										07 00				07 26	07 46				
	d			05 00		05 56				06 16		06 39				07 01			07 16	07 34	07 46				07 55
Long Eaton	d					06 06				06 25										07 43					
Alfreton	d																	06 57						07 40	
Langley Mill	d																	07 05						07 50	
Nottingham 8	a													06 45				07 23						08 09	
	d		04 56		05 30			06 07	06 13		06 25			06 53			07 07	07 30				07 38	08 07	08 26	
Beeston	d							06 13			06 31						07 13	07 36				07 44	08 13	08 34	
Loughborough	d		05a10		05 45	06 15	06 08		06a26	06 39	06 41		←			07 18	07 22			07 52		08 01	08 22	08 43	
Barrow Upon Soar	d						06 12			06 44 →			06 44									08 06			
Sileby	d						06 17						06 48									08 10			
Syston	d						06 22						06 53									08 15			
Leicester	a			05 25	05 58	06 28	06 31	06 34			06 53	07 01	07 06	07 13		07 30	07 37	07 55		08 04	08 12	08 25	08 34	08 55	
	d	05 00		05 25	06 00	06 30		06 35			06 55	07 04		07 15		07 30	07 37	07 57		08 05	08 14		08 35	08 56	
Market Harborough	d			05 41	06 15	06 45		06 50			07 10			07 29		07 47	07 53			08 19			08 49		
Kettering	d	05 21		05 52	06 26	06 56		07 02			07 20	07 28		07 39		07 58	08 03	08 17		08 29			08 59	09 18	
Wellingborough	d	05 29		06 00	06 34	07 04		07 10			07 28	07 37		07 46		08 06	08 12			08 40			09 06		
Bedford 7	d	05 50		06 19	06 51							07 53					08 25			09 03			09 23		
Luton 10	d	06 23		06 35	07 08	07 29					07 52	08 27		08 10			08 53			09 33			09 38		
Luton Airport Parkway 7	d	06 08		06 52	07 22	07 42		07 38			08 04	08 30		08 30			09 06			09 21			09 51		
Gatwick Airport 10	a	07f48		08 40	08 56	09 22					09 40	09 55		09 55			10 25			10f55			11 10		
St Pancras International 15	a	06 41		07 06	07 36	07 59		08 06			08 24	08 38		08 42		08 55	09 06	09 12		09 45	09 29		10 04	10 19	

Station		EM 1◇ E	EM ◇	EM 1◇	XC R 1	EM		XC R 1	EM 1◇	EM 1◇	EM 1◇	EM 1◇	EM ◇	XC R 1	EM	XC 1◇	EM 1◇	EM 1◇	EM ◇	XC 1◇		EM 1◇	EM 1◇	EM	XC 1◇
York 8	d				06e30			07 27	07g27			07h27		07 44		08 27	08h27			08 44					09 27
Leeds 10	d	06 14			07 05			07h16	07 26			07h26		08 10		08h28	08 28			09 10					09h16
Wakefield Westgate 7	d	06 26			07 19			07j32	07 38			07h38		08 23		08h39	08 39			09 23					09j32
Doncaster 7	d	06 45			07 02			07 52	07 59							08 51			08 57	09 01					09 56
Barnsley	d		06 58		06 58			07 48	07 48			08 06	07 58	08 14		08 48			08 58	08 58					09 48
Meadowhall	d		07 19		07 33			08 07	08 07			08 24	08 22	08 34		09 03			09 21	09 33					10 03
Sheffield 7	d	07 27	07 40		07 53			08 23	08 27			08 36	08 38	08 53		09 23	09 27		09 38	09 53					10 23
Dronfield	d																								
Chesterfield	d	07 40	07 53		08 05			08 35	08 40			08 48	08 52			09 35	09 40		09 53						10 35
Matlock	d			07k38													09 04								
Belper	d			07k58								09 03					09 25								
Burton-on-Trent	d			08 10					08 29			08 58					09 20						09 47		
Derby 10	a			08 25	08 26			08 55	09 01			09 13		09 22		09 55	10 01			10 22					10 55
	d			08 34					09 03			09 34					10 03						10 34		
Long Eaton	d			08 43								09 43											10 43		
Alfreton	d		08 06										09 07						10 04						
Langley Mill	d		08 13										09 14												
Nottingham 8	a		08 29										09 30						10 25						
	d					08 36				09 07	09 30				09 38			10 07				10 30		10 38	
Beeston	d									09 13								10 13							
Loughborough	d			08 52		09 01				09 23	09 44	09 52			10 00			10 22					10 52	11 00	
Barrow Upon Soar	d					09 06									10 06									11 06	
Sileby	d					09 10									10 10									11 10	
Syston	d					09 15									10 15									11 15	
Leicester	a			09 04		09 25			09 28	09 35	09 57	10 04			10 25		10 28	10 34				10 57	11 04	11 25	
	d			09 05					09 30	09 35	10 00	10 05					10 30	10 35				11 00	11 05		
Market Harborough	d			09 19						09 49		10 19						10 49					11 19		
Kettering	d			09 29						09 59		10 29						10 59					11 29		
Wellingborough	d			09 36						10 06		10 36						11 06					11 36		
Bedford 7	d			09 53						10 21		10 51					11 12	11 21					11 51		
Luton 10	d			10 33						10 39		11 33						11 36					12 33		
Luton Airport Parkway 7	d			10 09						10 51		11 07					11 51	11 51					12 07		
Gatwick Airport 10	a			11f55						12 10		12f55					13 10	13 10					13f55		
St Pancras International 15	a	09 33		10 34					10 48	11 04	11 17	11 34					11 51	12 04				12 15	12 34		

For general notes see front of timetable
For details of catering facilities see Directory of Train Operators

A From 24 March
B All Tuesdays to Fridays, also Mondays until 17 March
C **The Robin Hood**
D **The Midland Express**
E **The Master Cutler**
b Mondays dep. 0411
c Change at Leeds and Sheffield. Mondays dep. 0411
e Change at Doncaster and Sheffield
f Change at Bedford
g Change at Doncaster
h Change at Sheffield
j Wakefield Kirkgate. Change at Sheffield
k Change at Derby

Sheffield → East Midlands → London

Route Diagram - See first page of Table 53

Station		EM	EM	EM	EM	XC	EM	EM	XC	EM	EM	EM		XC	EM	EM	EM	XC	EM	EM	EM	XC	EM	EM	EM
						R												R				R			
		1 ◇	1 ◇	1 ◇	◇	1	1 ◇		1 ◇	1 ◇	1 ◇	◇		1 ◇	1 ◇	1 ◇		1	1 ◇	1 ◇	◇	1	1 ◇	1 ◇	
		☕	☕	☕	🚌	☕	☕		☕	☕	☕	🚌		☕	☕	☕		☕	☕	☕	🚌	☕	☕	☕	
York 8	d	09 27				09 44			10 34	10 34				10 44				11 27	11 27			11 44			
Leeds 10	d					10 10			10b16					11 10				11b16	11 16			12 10			
Wakefield Westgate 7	d					10 23			10c32					11 23				11c32	11e32			12 23			
Doncaster 7	d					10 02			10 58					11 02				11 54	11 54			11 58			
Barnsley	d				10 01	10 01			10 48			11 01		11 01				11 48	11 48		12 01	12 01			
Meadowhall	d	10 07			10 19	10 33			11 04	11 07		11 19		11 33				12 03	12 06		12 19	12 33			
Sheffield 7	d	10 27			10 38	10 53			11 23	11 27		11 38		11 53				12 23	12 27		12 38	12 53			
Dronfield	d																				12 49				
Chesterfield	d	10 40			10 53				11 35	11 40		11 53						12 35	12 40		12 53				
Matlock	d									11 12															
Belper	d									11 33															
Burton-on-Trent	d	10 18					10 58			11 19						11 44			12 19					12 58	
Derby 10	a	11 01				11 22			11 55	12 01				12 22				12 55	13 01			13 22			
	d	11 03					11 34			12 03						12 34			13 03					13 34	
Long Eaton	d						11 43									12 43								13 43	
Alfreton	d				11 04							12 04									13 04				
Langley Mill	d				11 11																13 11				
Nottingham 8	a				11 30							12 29									13 29				
	d		11 07	11 30				11 38			12 07				12 30		12 38			13 07			13 30		13 38
Beeston	d		11 13								12 13									13 13					
Loughborough	d		11 22	11 44			11 52	12 00			12 22					12 52	13 00			13 22			13 44	13 52	14 00
Barrow Upon Soar	d							12 06									13 06								14 06
Sileby	d							12 10									13 10								14 10
Syston	d							12 15									13 15								14 15
Leicester	a	11 28	11 34	11 57			12 04	12 25		12 28	12 34				12 57	13 04	13 25		13 26	13 34			13 57	14 04	14 25
	d	11 30	11 35	12 00			12 05			12 30	12 35				13 00	13 05			13 30	13 35			14 00	14 05	
Market Harborough	d		11 49				12 19				12 49					13 19				13 49				14 19	
Kettering	d		11 59				12 29				12 59					13 29				13 59				14 29	
Wellingborough	d		12 06				12 36				13 06					13 36				14 06				14 36	
Bedford 7	d		12 21				12 51				13 21					13 51				14 21				14 51	
Luton 10	d	12 20	12 36				13 33				13 36					14 33				14 36				15 33	
Luton Airport Parkway 7	d	12 36	12 51				13 07				13 51					14 07				14 51				15 07	
Gatwick Airport 10	a	13 55	14 10				14f55				15 10					15f55				16 10				16f55	
St Pancras International 15	a	12 51	13 04	13 15			13 34			13 45	14 04				14 14	14 34			14 44	15 04			15 14	15 34	

Station		XC	EM	EM		EM	XC	EM	EM	EM	XC	EM	EM	EM	XC	EM	EM	EM		XC	EM	EM	EM	EM	XC
							R								R										R
		1 ◇	1 ◇	1 ◇		◇	1	1 ◇	1 ◇		1 ◇	1 ◇	1 ◇	◇	1	1 ◇	1 ◇			1 ◇	1 ◇	1 ◇	1 ◇	◇	1
		☕	☕	☕		🚌	☕	☕	☕		☕	☕	☕	🚌	☕	☕	☕			☕	☕	☕	☕	🚌	☕
York 8	d	12 25	12 25				12 44				13 29	13 29			13 44					14 32	14 32				14 44
Leeds 10	d	12b16					13 10				13b16				14 10					14b16					15 10
Wakefield Westgate 7	d	12c32					13 23				13c32				14 23					14c32					15 23
Doncaster 7	d	12 55					13 02				13 54				14 01					14 57					15 02
Barnsley	d	12 48				13 01	13 01				13 48			14 01	14 01					14 48				15 01	15 01
Meadowhall	d	13 04	13 07			13 21	13 33				14 03	14 06		14 19	14 33					15 03	15 06			15 19	15 33
Sheffield 7	d	13 23	13 27			13 38	13 53				14 23	14 27		14 38	14 53					15 23	15 27			15 38	15 53
Dronfield	d																							15 49	
Chesterfield	d	13 35	13 40			13 53					14 35	14 40		14 53						15 35	15 40			15 55	
Matlock	d		13 12																		15 17				
Belper	d		13 33																		15 38				
Burton-on-Trent	d		13 21						13 44			14 18					14 58				15 20				
Derby 10	a	13 55	14 01				14 22				14 55	15 01			15 22					15 55	16 01				16 22
	d		14 03						14 34			15 03					15 34				16 03				
Long Eaton	d								14 43								15 43								
Alfreton	d					14 04								15 04										16 06	
Langley Mill	d													15 11											
Nottingham 8	a					14 29								15 29										16 34	
	d			14 07				14 30		14 38			15 07			15 30		15 38				16 07	16 30		
Beeston	d			14 13									15 13									16 13			
Loughborough	d			14 22					14 52	15 00			15 22			15 44	15 52	16 00				16 22	16 44		
Barrow Upon Soar	d									15 06								16 06							
Sileby	d									15 10								16 10							
Syston	d									15 15								16 15							
Leicester	a		14 28	14 34				14 57	15 04	15 25		15 28	15 34			15 58	16 04	16 25			16 28	16 34	16 58		
	d		14 30	14 35				15 00	15 05			15 30	15 35			16 00	16 05				16 30	16 35	17 00		
Market Harborough	d			14 49					15 19				15 49				16 19					16 49			
Kettering	d			14 59					15 29				15 59				16 29					16 59	17 21		
Wellingborough	d			15 06					15 36				16 06				16 36					17 06			
Bedford 7	d			15 21					15 51				16 21				16 51				17 12	17 21			
Luton 10	d		15 20	15 36					16 33				16 36				17 17					17 36			
Luton Airport Parkway 7	d		15 36	15 51					16 07				16 51				17 07				17 46	17 50			
Gatwick Airport 10	a		16 55	17 15					18f12				18 24				18f41				19 26	19 26			
St Pancras International 15	a		15 50	16 04				16 15	16 34			16 45	17 04			17 13	17 34				17 53	18 04	18 19		

For general notes see front of timetable
For details of catering facilities see Directory of Train Operators

b Change at Sheffield
c Wakefield Kirkgate. Change at Sheffield
e Wakefield Kirkgate
f Change at Bedford

Table 53

Mondays to Fridays
from 28 January

Sheffield → East Midlands → London

Route Diagram - See first page of Table 53

	EM	EM	XC	EM	EM	EM	XC	EM	EM		EM	XC	EM	EM	EM	XC	EM	EM	EM	XC	EM	EM	EM	EM
	1◇ ☕		R 1 ☕	1◇ ☕	1◇ ☕	◇ 🛒	R 1 ☕	1◇ ☕	1◇ ☕			R 1 ☕	1◇ ☕	1◇ ☕	◇ 🛒	1◇ ☕	1◇ ☕	1◇ ☕		R 1 ☕	1◇ ☕	1◇ ☕	1◇ ☕	◇ 🛒
York 8 d			15 29	15 29			15 44					16 25	16 25			16 44				17 34	17 34			
Leeds 10 d			15b16	15 16			16 10						16 16			17 10				17b16	17 16			
Wakefield Westgate 7 d			15c32	15e32			16 23						16e32			17 23				17c32	17e32			
Doncaster 7 d			15 55	15 55			16 02					16 53	16 53			17 00				17 58	17 58			
Barnsley d			15 48	15 48		16 01	16 01					16 26	16 48		17 01	17 01				17 48	17 48			18 01
Meadowhall d			16 06	16 09		16 19	16 33					17 00	17 07		17 19	17 33				18 04	18 07			18 19
Sheffield 7 d			16 23	16 27		16 38	16 53					17 20	17 27		17 41	17 53				18 23	18 27			18 45
Dronfield d						16 49						17 28												
Chesterfield d			16 35	16 40		16 55						17 35	17 40		17 55					18 35	18 40			19 01
Matlock d													16 58								18 13			
Belper d													17 19								18 33			
Burton-on-Trent d	15 44			16 20					16 48				17 20					17 40			18 22			
Derby 10 a			16 55	17 01			17 22					17 55	18 01			18 22				18 55	19 01			
d	16 34			17 03					17 34				18 02					18 34			19 02			
Long Eaton d	16 43								17 43									18 43						
Alfreton d						17 06									18 06									19 12
Langley Mill d						17 13									18 13									
Nottingham 8 a						17 29									18 29									19 37
d		16 38			17 07			17 30			17 38			18 07			18 30		18 38			19 07	19 30	
Beeston d					17 13									18 13								19 13		
Loughborough d	16 52	17 02			17 22			17 44	17 52		18 02		18 18	18 22			18 44	18 52	19 00		19 17	19 22	19 44	
Barrow Upon Soar d		17 07									18 08								19 06					
Sileby d		17 11									18 12								19 10					
Syston d		17 16									18 17								19 15					
Leicester a	17 04	17 25		17 30	17 33			17 58	18 04		18 26		18 30	18 35			18 57	19 04	19 25		19 28	19 35	19 55	
d	17 05			17 30	17 35			18 00	18 05				18 30	18 35			19 00	19 05			19 30	19 35	20 00	
Market Harborough d	17 19				17 49				18 19					18 51				19 19				19 51		
Kettering d	17 29				17 59				18 29					19 01				19 29				20 01		
Wellingborough d	17 36				18 06				18 36					19 09				19 36				20 09		
Bedford 7 d	17 51				18 23				18 53					19 23				19 51				20 23		
Luton 10 d	18 33			18 21	18 39								19 22	19 39								20 39		
Luton Airport Parkway 7 d	18 07			18 36	18 52				19 07				19 46	19 52				20 07				20 52		
Gatwick Airport 10 a	19f55			19 55	20 10				21f10				21 10	21 41				22f10				22 41		
St Pancras International 15 a	18 34			18 51	19 04			19 17	19 34				19 52	20 04			20 11	20 34			20 41	21 04	21 11	

	XC		EM	EM	XC	EM	EM	EM	XC	EM	EM	XC	EM	EM	EM	XC	EM	EM	XC	XC	EM	EM		
	R 1 ☕		1◇ ☕		1◇ ☕	1◇ ☕	1◇ ☕	◇ 🛒	1◇ ☕	1◇ ☕		1◇ ☕	1◇ ☕	1◇ ☕	◇ 🛒	1◇		◇ 🛒	1◇	1◇	1◇ ☕	◇		
York 8 d	17 44				18 24	18 24			18 44			19 29	19 29			19 44		20 31	20 44	21 24	21g38			
Leeds 10 d	18 10				18b16				19 10			19b16				20 10		20 16	21 10		21 34	21 48		
Wakefield Westgate 7 d	18 23				18c32				19 23			19c32				20 23		20e32	21 23		22e03			
Doncaster 7 d	18 02				18 52				18 55			19 57				20 03		20 56	21 07	21 48	22 13			
Barnsley d	18 01				18 48			18 58	19 16			19 48				20 06		20 48	21 06	21 26	22 26			
Meadowhall d	18 33				19 04	19 07		19 16	19 34			20 04	20 08			20 33		21 07	21 34	22 10	22 49	22 51		
Sheffield 7 d	18 53				19 23	19 27		19 38	19 53			20 23	20 39		20 40	20 53		21 38	21 53	22 27	23 08	23 38		
Dronfield d								19 50																
Chesterfield d					19 35	19 40		19 56	20 05			20 35	20 51		20 55	21 05		21 53	22 05	22 53	23 21	23 59		
Matlock d													19 38											
Belper d													19 58											
Burton-on-Trent d			18 58			19 20							20 29											
Derby 10 a	19 22				19 55	20 01			20 26			20 55	21 14			21 27			22 26	23 13	23 46			
d			19 34			20 02							21 16											
Long Eaton d			19 43																					
Alfreton d								20 07							21 06			22 04						
Langley Mill d								20 16							21 13			22 11						
Nottingham 8 a								20 31							21 38			22 36				00 46		
d				19 38			20 07			20 47	20 38			21 30			21 54							
Beeston d				19 44			20 13																	
Loughborough d			19 52	20 01		20 18	20 22			21 00	21 00		21 30	21 45			22 10							
Barrow Upon Soar d				20 06							21 06													
Sileby d				20 10							21 10													
Syston d				20 15							21 15													
Leicester a			20 04	20 25		20 29	20 35			21 12	21 25		21 43	21 56			22 23							
d			20 05			20 30	20 35			21 15			21 45	22 00										
Market Harborough d			20 19				20 51			21 28			21 59	22 13										
Kettering d			20 29				21 01			21 38			22 09	22 23										
Wellingborough d			20 36				21 09			21 45			22 16	22 30										
Bedford 7 d			20 51			21 11	21 23			22 00				22 45										
Luton 10 d							21 39			22 16				23 01										
Luton Airport Parkway 7 d			21 07			21 46	21 52			22 36				23 36										
Gatwick Airport 10 a						23 10	23 41			00 16				01 16										
St Pancras International 15 a			21 34			21 53	22 04			22 40			23 04	23 32										

For general notes see front of timetable
For details of catering facilities see Directory of Train Operators

b Change at Sheffield
c Wakefield Kirkgate. Change at Sheffield
e Wakefield Kirkgate
f Change at Bedford
g Change at Doncaster and Sheffield

Saturdays
until 26 January

Sheffield → East Midlands → London

Route Diagram - See first page of Table 53

		EM 1◇	EM 1◇	EM 1◇	EM 1◇	EM ◇	XC 1◇		EM 1◇	EM	EM 1◇	EM 1◇	EM 1◇ ⊠	XC 1◇		EM 1◇	EM	XC 1◇	EM 1◇ ⊠	EM 1◇	EM 1◇		XC 1◇	EM 1◇	EM
York 8	d																	04 19	06b00				06c00		
Leeds 10	d										05b05							06 00					06 48		
Wakefield Westgate 7	d										05b17							06 12					06 32		
Doncaster 7	d										05 42							06 00	06 40				07 26		
Barnsley	d						05 18						05 53						06 27				06 58		
Meadowhall	d						05 39				06 00		06 13					06 27	07 00				07 33		
Sheffield 7	d			05 00			06 01				06 16		06 34	⟵				06 48	07 27		07 32		07 53		
Dronfield	d																								
Chesterfield	d			05 13			06 24 ⟶				06 29		06 46	06 24				07 16	07 40		07 45		08 05		
Matlock	d															06 14								07e39	
Belper	d															06 34								07e59	
Burton-on-Trent	d										06 26					06 58			07 29					08 08	
Derby 10	a			05 53							06 51			07 09				07 53	08 01				08 25	08 25	
	d	05 00		06 00						06 26	06 53					07 34			08 03					08 34	
Long Eaton	d			06 10						06 36						07 43								08 43	
Alfreton	d												06 58								07 57				
Langley Mill	d												07 07								08 06				
Nottingham 8	a												07 23								08 26				
	d		05 29		06 07	06 19			06 25			07 07	07 30				07 38			08 07	08 35				08 38
Beeston	d				06 13							07 13					07 44			08 13					
Loughborough	d		05 44	06 20	06 26	06a35			06 40	06 55	07 10	07 23				07 52	08 01			08 22				08 52	09 01
Barrow Upon Soar	d									06 59							08 06								09 06
Sileby	d									07 05							08 10								09 10
Syston	d									07 10							08 15								09 15
Leicester	a	05 29	05 57	06 32	06 35				06 51	07 18	07 22	07 34	07 56			08 04	08 25		08 27	08 34	08 57			09 04	09 25
	d	05 30	05 57	06 32	06 35				06 55		07 23	07 35	08 00			08 05			08 28	08 35	09 00			09 05	
Market Harborough	d		06 13		06 53				07 10			07 49				08 19			08 43	08 49				09 19	
Kettering	d	05 54	06 24	06 57	07 03				07 21		07 47	07 59	08 23			08 29			08 54	08 59	09 23			09 29	
Wellingborough	d	06 02	06 32	07 05	07 11				07 29		07 55	08 06				08 36				09 06	09 31			09 36	
Bedford 7	d	06 16	06 50		07 26							08 21				08 51				09 21	09 46			09 51	
Luton 10	d	06 37	07 08	07 30	08 03							08 36				09 33				09 36	10 18			10 33	
Luton Airport Parkway 7	d	06 51	07 21	07 46	07 42							08 51				09 07				09 51				10 07	
Gatwick Airport 10	a	08 10	08 40	09 10	09f25							10 10				10f55				11 10	11 40			11f55	
St Pancras International 15	a	07 05	07 38	08 05	08 09				08 21		08 45	09 04	09 17			09 34			09 49	10 04	10 29			10 36	

		XC 1◇	EM 1◇	EM 1◇	EM 1◇	EM ◇		XC 1◇	EM 1◇	EM	XC 1◇	EM 1◇	EM 1◇		EM ◇	XC 1◇	EM 1◇	EM 1◇	EM	XC 1◇		EM 1◇	EM 1◇	EM 1◇	EM ◇
York 8	d	07 27				07 27		07 44	07g27		08 19					08 44				09 27		09 27			
Leeds 10	d	07g16	07 19			07 19		08 10	07g23		08 16	08 40				09 10				09g16					
Wakefield Westgate 7	d	07h32	07 32					08 23	07h55		08j32	08 52				09 23				09h32					
Doncaster 7	d	07 52	07 59								08 42				08 59	09 02				09 51					
Barnsley	d	07 48				07 58		07 58	08 30		08 48				08 58	08 58				09 48					10 01
Meadowhall	d	08 06				08 22		08 22	08 47		09 03				09 22	09 33				10 03		10 07			10 19
Sheffield 7	d	08 23	08 27			08 38		08 53	08 56		09 23	09 27			09 38	09 53				10 23		10 27			10 38
Dronfield	d																								
Chesterfield	d	08 35	08 39			08 54			09 09		09 35	09 40			09 53					10 35		10 40			10 53
Matlock	d											08 58													
Belper	d								09 26																
Burton-on-Trent	d		08 29						08 58			09 20						09 41				10 20			
Derby 10	a	08 55	09 01					09 22	09 33		09 55	10 01				10 22				10 55		11 01			
	d		09 02						09 34			10 03						10 34				11 03			
Long Eaton	d								09 43									10 43							
Alfreton	d					09 07									10 04										11 04
Langley Mill	d					09 14																			11 11
Nottingham 8	a					09 30									10 24										11 30
	d			09 07	09 30					09 38			10 07				10 30		10 38				11 07	11 30	
Beeston	d			09 13									10 13										11 13		
Loughborough	d			09 22	09 45				09 52	10 01			10 22					10 52	11 01				11 22	11 45	
Barrow Upon Soar	d									10 06									11 06						
Sileby	d									10 10									11 10						
Syston	d									10 15									11 15						
Leicester	a		09 27	09 34	09 56				10 04	10 25		10 28	10 34				10 53	11 04	11 25			11 28	11 34	11 55	
	d		09 28	09 35	10 00				10 05			10 30	10 35				11 00	11 05				11 30	11 35	12 00	
Market Harborough	d			09 49	10 15				10 19				10 49					11 19					11 49		
Kettering	d		09 51	09 59					10 29			10 53	10 59					11 29					11 59		
Wellingborough	d			10 06					10 36			11 01	11 06					11 36					12 06		
Bedford 7	d			10 21					10 51			11 17	11 21					11 51					12 21		
Luton 10	d			10 36					11 33			11 48	11 36					12 33				12 21	12 36		
Luton Airport Parkway 7	d			10 51					11 07			11 51	11 51					12 07				12 36	12 51		
Gatwick Airport 10	a			12 10					12f56			13 10	13 10					13f55				13 55	14 10		
St Pancras International 15	a		10 46	11 04	11 17				11 34			11 59	12 04				12 15	12 34				12 51	13 04	13 15	

For general notes see front of timetable
For details of catering facilities see Directory of Train Operators

b Change at Doncaster and Sheffield
c Change at Doncaster
e Change at Derby
f Change at Bedford
g Change at Sheffield
h Wakefield Kirkgate. Change at Sheffield
j Wakefield Kirkgate

Table 53

Saturdays

until 26 January

Sheffield → East Midlands → London

Route Diagram - See first page of Table 53

		XC 1◇ ☕	EM 1◇ ☕	EM	XC 1◇ ☕		EM 1◇ ☕	EM 1◇ ☕	EM ◇	XC 1◇ ☕	EM 1◇ ☕	EM 1◇ ☕		EM	XC 1◇ ☕	EM 1◇ ☕	EM 1◇ ☕	EM ◇	XC 1◇ ☕		EM 1◇ ☕	EM 1◇ ☕	EM	XC 1◇ ☕	EM 1◇ ☕
York 8	d	09 44			10 25		10 25			10 44					11 27	11 27			11 44					12 25	12 25
Leeds 10	d	10 10			10b16					11 10					11b16				12 10					12b16	
Wakefield Westgate 7	d	10 23			10c32					11 23					11c32				12 23					12c32	
Doncaster 7	d	10 02			10 53					11 02					11 55				12 02					12 52	
Barnsley	d	10 01			10 48				11 01	11 01					11 48			12 01	12 01					12 48	
Meadowhall	d	10 33			11 04		11 06		11 19	11 33					12 03	12 06		12 19	12 33					13 03	13 06
Sheffield 7	d	10 53			11 23		11 27		11 38	11 53					12 23	12 27		12 38	12 53					13 23	13 27
Dronfield	d																	12 49							
Chesterfield	d				11 35		11 40		11 53						12 35	12 40		12 53						13 35	13 40
Matlock	d		10 38																			12 38			
Belper	d		10 58																			12 58			
Burton-on-Trent	d		10 58				11 20					11 44				12 20						12 58			13 20
Derby 10	a	11 22			11 55		12 01			12 22					12 55	13 01			13 22					13 55	14 01
	d		11 34				12 03					12 34				13 03						13 34			14 03
Long Eaton	d		11 43									12 43										13 43			
Alfreton	d								12 04									13 04							
Langley Mill	d																	13 11							
Nottingham 8	a								12 29									13 29							
	d			11 38				12 07			12 30			12 38			13 07				13 30		13 38		
Beeston	d							12 13									13 13								
Loughborough	d		11 52	12 01				12 22				12 52		13 01			13 22				13 45	13 52	14 01		
Barrow Upon Soar	d			12 06										13 06									14 06		
Sileby	d			12 10										13 10									14 10		
Syston	d			12 15										13 15									14 15		
Leicester	a		12 04	12 25			12 26	12 34			12 57	13 04		13 25		13 28	13 34				13 55	14 04	14 25		14 28
	d		12 05				12 30	12 35			13 00	13 05				13 30	13 35				14 00	14 05			14 30
Market Harborough	d		12 19					12 49				13 19					13 49					14 19			
Kettering	d		12 29					12 59				13 29					13 59					14 29			
Wellingborough	d		12 36					13 06				13 36					14 06					14 36			
Bedford 7	d		12 51					13 21				13 51					14 21					14 51			
Luton 10	d		13 33					13 36				14 33					14 36					15 33			15 21
Luton Airport Parkway 7	d		13 07					13 51				14 07					14 51					15 07			15 36
Gatwick Airport 10	a		14e55					15 10				15e55					16 10					16e55			16 55
St Pancras International 15	a		13 34				13 44	14 04			14 15	14 34				14 45	15 04				15 15	15 34			15 51

		EM 1◇ ☕	EM 1◇ ☕	EM ◇		XC 1◇ ☕	EM 1◇ ☕	EM	XC 1◇ ☕	EM 1◇ ☕	EM 1◇ ☕		EM 1◇ ☕	EM ◇	XC 1◇ ☕	EM 1◇ ☕	EM 1◇ ☕	EM		XC 1◇ ☕	EM 1◇ ☕	EM 1◇ ☕	EM 1◇ ☕	EM ◇	XC 1◇ ☕
York 8	d					12 44			13 28	13 28					13 44	13 44				14 30	14 30				14 44
Leeds 10	d					13 10			13b16						14 10					14b16					15 10
Wakefield Westgate 7	d					13 23			13c32						14 22					14c32					15 23
Doncaster 7	d					13 01			13 54						14 02					14 55					15 02
Barnsley	d			13 01		13 01			13 48					14 01	14 01					14 48				15 01	15 01
Meadowhall	d			13 21		13 33			14 03	14 07				14 19	14 33					15 03	15 06			15 19	15 33
Sheffield 7	d			13 38		13 53			14 23	14 27				14 38	14 53	15 02				15 23	15 27			15 38	15 53
Dronfield	d																								
Chesterfield	d			13 53					14 35	14 40				14 53		15 14				15 35	15 40			15 53	
Matlock	d									14 10															
Belper	d									14 30															
Burton-on-Trent	d						13 42			14 20							14 58				15 20				
Derby 10	a					14 22			14 55	15 01					15 22					15 55	16 01				16 22
	d						14 34			15 03							15 34				16 03				
Long Eaton	d						14 43										15 43								
Alfreton	d			14 04										15 04		15 27						←		16 04	
Langley Mill	d													15 11		15 35						15 35		16 11	
Nottingham 8	a			14 30										15 30		→						16 00		16 35	
	d	14 07	14 30					14 38			15 07		15 30					15 38				16 07	16 30		
Beeston	d	14 13									15 13											16 13			
Loughborough	d	14 22					14 52	15 01			15 22		15 46				15 52	16 01				16 22			
Barrow Upon Soar	d							15 06										16 06							
Sileby	d							15 10										16 10							
Syston	d							15 15										16 15							
Leicester	a	14 34	14 53				15 04	15 25		15 28	15 34		15 58				16 04	16 25			16 28	16 34	16 55		
	d	14 35	15 00				15 05			15 30	15 35		16 00				16 05				16 30	16 35	17 00		
Market Harborough	d	14 49					15 19				15 49						16 19					16 49			
Kettering	d	14 59					15 29				15 59						16 29					16 59			
Wellingborough	d	15 06					15 36				16 06						16 36					17 06			
Bedford 7	d	15 21					15 51				16 21						16 51				17 13	17 21			
Luton 10	d	15 36					16 33				16 36						17 33					17 36			
Luton Airport Parkway 7	d	15 51					16 07				16 51						17 07				17 51	17 51			
Gatwick Airport 10	a	17 10					17e55				18 10						18e55				19 10	19 10			
St Pancras International 15	a	16 04	16 15				16 34			16 45	17 04		17 17				17 34				17 51	18 04	18 15		

For general notes see front of timetable
For details of catering facilities see
Directory of Train Operators

b Change at Sheffield
c Wakefield Kirkgate. Change at Sheffield
e Change at Bedford

Table 53

Saturdays

until 26 January

Sheffield → East Midlands → London

Route Diagram - See first page of Table 53

		EM 1 ◇ ☕	EM		XC 1 ◇ ☕	EM 1 ◇ ☕	EM 1 ◇ ☕	EM 1 ◇ ☕	EM ◇	XC 1 ◇ ☕		EM 1 ◇ ☕	EM	XC 1 ◇ ☕	EM 1 ◇ ☕	EM 1 ◇ ☕	EM ◇		XC 1 ◇ ☕	EM 1 ◇ ☕	EM 1 ◇ ☕	EM	XC 1 ◇ ☕	EM 1 ◇ ☕	EM 1 ◇ ☕
York [8]	d				15 27	15 27				15 44				16 25	16 25				16 44				17 25	17 25	
Leeds [10]	d				15b16					16 10					16 16				17 10				17b16		
Wakefield Westgate [7]	d				15c32					16 23					16e32				17 23				17c32		
Doncaster [7]	d				15 55					16 02				16 53					17 02				17 55		
Barnsley	d				15 48				16 01	16 01				16 26	16 48		17 01		17 01				17 48		
Meadowhall	d				16 06	16 09			16 19	16 33				17 00	17 06		17 19		17 33				18 04	18 06	
Sheffield [7]	d				16 23	16 27			16 38	16 53				17 20	17 27		17 41		17 53				18 23	18 27	
Dronfield	d								16 49					17 28											
Chesterfield	d				16 35	16 40			16 55					17 35	17 40		17 55						18 35	18 40	
Matlock	d	15 38													17 01										
Belper	d	15 58													17 21										
Burton-on-Trent	d	15 44				16 20						16 58			17 20						17 47			18 20	
Derby [10]	a				16 55	17 01				17 22				17 55	18 01				18 22				18 55	19 01	
	d	16 34				17 03						17 34			18 03						18 34			19 03	
Long Eaton	d	16 43										17 43									18 43				
Alfreton	d								17 06								18 06								
Langley Mill	d								17 13								18 13								
Nottingham [8]	a								17 31								18 29								
	d		16 38				17 07	17 30					17 38			18 07				18 30		18 38			19 07
Beeston	d						17 13									18 13									19 13
Loughborough	d	16 52	17 03				17 22	17 45				17 52	18 03		18 20	18 25				18 45	18 52	19 01		19 18	19 24
Barrow Upon Soar	d		17 07										18 07									19 06			
Sileby	d		17 11										18 11									19 10			
Syston	d		17 16										18 16									19 15			
Leicester	a	17 04	17 25			17 28	17 34	17 56				18 04	18 25		18 33	18 39				18 56	19 04	19 25		19 30	19 38
	d	17 05				17 30	17 35	18 00				18 05			18 34	18 40				19 00	19 05			19 30	19 39
Market Harborough	d	17 19					17 49					18 19				18 51					19 19				19 53
Kettering	d	17 29					17 59					18 29				19 01					19 29				20 03
Wellingborough	d	17 36					18 06					18 36				19 11					19 36				20 11
Bedford [7]	d	17 51					18 21					18 51				19 25					19 51				20 25
Luton [10]	d	18 33				18 21	18 36									19 41									20 41
Luton Airport Parkway [7]	d	18 07				18 36	18 52					19 07									20 07				20 52
Gatwick Airport [10]	a	19f56				19 56	20 25					21f10				21 40					22f10				22 40
St Pancras International [15]	a	18 34				18 51	19 04	19 08				19 35			19 45	20 09				20 15	20 35			20 48	21 08

		EM ◇		XC 1 ◇ ☕	EM 1 ◇ ☕	EM 1 ◇ ☕	EM	EM 1 ◇ ☕	XC 1 ◇ ☕		EM 1 ◇ ☕	EM ◇	XC 1 ◇ ☕	EM 1 ◇ ☕	EM ◇	EM 1 ◇ ☕		XC 1 ◇	EM	EM ◇	XC 1 ◇	EM 1 ◇ ☕	EM ◇		
York [8]	d			17 44				17 49	18 25			18 25	18 44		18 44	18 44		19 44		20g05	20 44	20 44			
Leeds [10]	d			18 10					18b16				19 10		19 16	19 16		20 10		20 16	21 10				
Wakefield Westgate [7]	d			18 23					18c32				19 23		19e32	19e32		20 23		20e32	21 23				
Doncaster [7]	d			18 15				18 15	18 51				19 03		19 49	19 49		20 03		20 42	21 07		21 49		
Barnsley	d	18 01		18 01				18b26	18 48			19 01	19 01		19 48	20 06				20 48	21 06		21 26		
Meadowhall	d	18 19		18 38				18 38	19 06			19 19	19 33		20 07	20 24		20 35		21 07	21 35		22 09		
Sheffield [7]	d	18 38		18 53				19 07	19 23			19 38	19 53		20 40	20 47		20 53		21 37	21 53	22 00	22 36		
Dronfield	d																								
Chesterfield	d	18 53						19 19	19 35			19 53	20 05		20 55	21 00		21 05		21 53	22 05	22 12	22 50		
Matlock	d					18 38										20 20									
Belper	d					18 58										20 40									
Burton-on-Trent	d					18 58		19 20								20 29									
Derby [10]	a			19 22				19 40	19 55				20 26			21 22		21 27			22 26	22 35			
	d					19 34		19 51								21 22									
Long Eaton	d					19 43		20 02																	
Alfreton	d	19 04										20 04			21 06					22 04					
Langley Mill	d														21 13					22 11					
Nottingham [8]	a	19 29										20 29			21 35					22 38			23 26		
	d				19 30		19 33				20 07			20 30					21 30						
Beeston	d						19 39				20 13														
Loughborough	d				19 45	19 54	19 57	20 15						20 49		21 41			21 46						
Barrow Upon Soar	d						20 02																		
Sileby	d						20 06																		
Syston	d						20 12																		
Leicester	a				19 56	20 04	20 22	20 26			20 34			21 02		21 56			22 00						
	d				20 00	20 05		20 27			20 35			21 03											
Market Harborough	d					20 19		20 41			20 49			21 18											
Kettering	d					20 29		20 51			20 59			21 28											
Wellingborough	d					20 36		20 59			21 07			21 36											
Bedford [7]	d					20 51		21 13			21 23			21 52											
Luton [10]	d							21 29			21 39			22 09											
Luton Airport Parkway [7]	d					21 09		21 46			21 52			22 22											
Gatwick Airport [10]	a					23f10		23 10			23 40			00 17											
St Pancras International [15]	a				21 12	21 35		21 52			22 04			22 43											

For general notes see front of timetable
For details of catering facilities see Directory of Train Operators

b Change at Sheffield
c Wakefield Kirkgate. Change at Sheffield
e Wakefield Kirkgate
f Change at Bedford
g Change at Doncaster and Sheffield

Saturdays
from 2 February

Sheffield → East Midlands → London

Route Diagram - See first page of Table 53

Station	EM 1◇	EM 1◇	EM 1◇	EM 1◇	EM ◇	XC 1◇	EM 1◇		EM	EM 1◇	EM 1◇	EM 1◇ ⊠	XC 1◇	EM 1◇	EM		XC 1◇	EM 1◇ ⊠	EM 1◇	EM 1◇	XC 1◇	EM 1◇	EM	XC 1◇
York 8 d																	04 19	06b00			06c00			07 27
Leeds 10 d										05b05							06 00				06 48			07e16
Wakefield Westgate 7 d										05b17							06 12				06 32			07f32
Doncaster 7 d										05 42							06 00	06 40			07 26			07 52
Barnsley d						05 18						05 53						06 27			06 58			07 48
Meadowhall d						05 39				06 00		06 13					06 27	07 00			07 33			08 06
Sheffield 7 d			05 00			06 01				06 16		06 34					06 48	07 27		07 32	07 53			08 23
Dronfield d													←											
Chesterfield d			05 13			06 24				06 29		06 46	06 24				07 16	07 40		07 45	08 05			08 35
Matlock d						→								06 14								07g39		
Belper d														06 34								07g59		
Burton-on-Trent d										06 26				06 58				07 29				08 08		
Derby 10 a			05 53							06 51			07 09				07 53	08 01			08 25	08 25		08 55
d	05 00		06 00						06 26	06 53				07 34				08 03				08 34		
Long Eaton d			06 10						06 36					07 43								08 43		
Alfreton d												06 58								07 57				
Langley Mill d												07 07								08 06				
Nottingham 8 a												07 23								08 26				
d		05 29		06 07	06 19		06 25				07 07	07 30			07 38				08 07	08 35			08 38	
Beeston d				06 13							07 13				07 44				08 13					
Loughborough d		05 44	06 20	06 26	06a35		06 40		06 55	07 10	07 23			07 52	08 01				08 22			08 52	09 01	
Barrow Upon Soar d									06 59						08 06								09 06	
Sileby d									07 05						08 10								09 10	
Syston d									07 10						08 15								09 15	
Leicester a	05 29	05 57	06 32	06 35			06 51		07 18	07 22	07 34	07 56		08 04	08 25			08 27	08 34	08 57		09 04	09 25	
d	05 30	05 57	06 32	06 35			06 55			07 23	07 35	08 00		08 05				08 28	08 35	09 00		09 05		
Market Harborough d		06 13		06 53			07 10				07 49			08 19				08 43	08 49			09 19		
Kettering d	05 54	06 24	06 57	07 03			07 21			07 47	07 59	08 23		08 29				08 54	08 59	09 23		09 29		
Wellingborough d	06 02	06 32	07 05	07 11			07 29			07 55	08 06			08 36					09 06	09 31		09 36		
Bedford 7 d	06 16	06 50		07 26							08 21			08 51					09 21	09 46		09 51		
Luton 10 d	06 37	07 08	07 30	08 03							08 36			09 33					09 36	10 18		10 33		
Luton Airport Parkway 7 d	06 51	07 21	07 46	07 42							08 51			09 07					09 51			10 07		
Gatwick Airport 10 a	08 10	08 40	09 10	09h25							10 10			10h55					11 10	11 40		11h55		
St Pancras International 15 a	07 05	07 38	08 05	08 09			08 21			08 45	09 04	09 17		09 34				09 49	10 04	10 29		10 36		

Station	EM 1◇		EM 1◇	EM 1◇	EM ◇	XC 1◇	EM 1◇	EM	XC 1◇		EM 1◇	EM 1◇	EM ◇	XC 1◇	EM 1◇	EM 1◇	EM		XC 1◇	EM 1◇	EM 1◇	EM 1◇	EM ◇	XC 1◇
York 8 d					07 27	07 44	07e27		08 19					08 44					09 27	09 27				09 44
Leeds 10 d	07 19				07 19	08 10	07e23		08 16		08 40			09 10					09e16					10 10
Wakefield Westgate 7 d	07 32					08 23	07f55		08j32		08 52			09 23					09f32					10 23
Doncaster 7 d	07 59								08 42				08 59	09 02					09 51					10 02
Barnsley d					07 58	07 58	08 30		08 48				08 58	08 58					09 48				10 01	10 01
Meadowhall d					08 22	08 22	08 47		09 03				09 22	09 33					10 03	10 07			10 19	10 33
Sheffield 7 d	08 27				08 38	08 53	08 56		09 23		09 27		09 38	09 53					10 23	10 27			10 38	10 53
Dronfield d																								
Chesterfield d	08 39				08 54		09 09		09 35		09 40		09 53						10 35	10 40			10 53	
Matlock d											08 58													
Belper d							09 26																	
Burton-on-Trent d	08 29						08 58				09 20					09 41				10 20				
Derby 10 a	09 01					09 22	09 33		09 55		10 01			10 22					10 55	11 01				11 22
d	09 02						09 34				10 03					10 34				11 03				
Long Eaton d							09 43									10 43								
Alfreton d					09 07								10 04										11 04	
Langley Mill d					09 14																		11 11	
Nottingham 8 a					09 30								10 24										11 30	
d			09 07	09 30				09 38				10 07			10 30		10 38				11 07	11 30		
Beeston d			09 13									10 13									11 13			
Loughborough d			09 22	09 45			09 52	10 01				10 22				10 52	11 01				11 22	11 45		
Barrow Upon Soar d								10 06									11 06							
Sileby d								10 10									11 10							
Syston d								10 15									11 15							
Leicester a	09 27		09 34	09 56			10 04	10 25			10 28	10 34			10 53	11 04	11 25			11 28	11 34	11 55		
d	09 28		09 35	10 00			10 05				10 30	10 35			11 00	11 05				11 30	11 35	12 00		
Market Harborough d			09 49	10 15			10 19					10 49				11 19					11 49			
Kettering d	09 51		09 59				10 29				10 53	10 59				11 29					11 59			
Wellingborough d			10 06				10 36				11 01	11 06				11 36					12 06			
Bedford 7 d			10 21				10 51				11 17	11 21				11 51					12 21			
Luton 10 d			10 36				11 33				11 48	11 36				12 33				12 21	12 36			
Luton Airport Parkway 7 d			10 51				11 07				11 51	11 51				12 07				12 36	12 51			
Gatwick Airport 10 a			12 10				12h56				13 10	13 10				13h55				13 55	14 10			
St Pancras International 15 a	10 46		11 04	11 17			11 34				11 59	12 04			12 15	12 34				12 51	13 04	13 15		

For general notes see front of timetable
For details of catering facilities see Directory of Train Operators

b Change at Doncaster and Sheffield
c Change at Doncaster
e Change at Sheffield
f Wakefield Kirkgate. Change at Sheffield
g Change at Derby
h Change at Bedford
j Wakefield Kirkgate

Sheffield → East Midlands → London

Route Diagram - See first page of Table 53

		EM	EM	XC		EM	EM	EM	XC	EM	EM	EM		XC	EM	EM	EM	XC	EM	EM		EM	XC	EM	EM
		1 ◇ ☕		1 ◇ ☕		1 ◇ ☕	1 ◇ ☕	◇	1 ◇ ☕	1 ◇ ☕	1 ◇ ☕			1 ◇ ☕	1 ◇ ☕	1 ◇ ☕	◇	1 ◇ ☕	1 ◇ ☕	1 ◇ ☕			1 ◇ ☕	1 ◇ ☕	1 ◇ ☕
York 8	d			10 25		10 25			10 44					11 27	11 27			11 44					12 25	12 25	
Leeds 10	d			10b16					11 10					11b16				12 10					12b16		
Wakefield Westgate 7	d			10c32					11 23					11c32				12 23					12c32		
Doncaster 7	d			10 53					11 02					11 55				12 02					12 52		
Barnsley	d			10 48				11 01	11 01					11 48			12 01	12 01					12 48		
Meadowhall	d			11 04		11 06		11 19	11 33					12 03	12 06		12 19	12 33					13 03	13 06	
Sheffield 7	d			11 23		11 27		11 38	11 53					12 23	12 27		12 38	12 53					13 23	13 27	
Dronfield	d																12 49								
Chesterfield	d			11 35		11 40		11 53						12 35	12 40		12 53						13 35	13 40	
Matlock	d	10 38																		12 38					
Belper	d	10 58																		12 58					
Burton-on-Trent	d	10 58				11 20					11 44				12 20					12 58				13 20	
Derby 10	a			11 55		12 01			12 22					12 55	13 01			13 22					13 55	14 01	
	d	11 34				12 03					12 34				13 03					13 34				14 03	
Long Eaton	d	11 43									12 43									13 43					
Alfreton	d							12 04									13 04								
Langley Mill	d																13 11								
Nottingham 8	a							12 29									13 29								
	d		11 38				12 07			12 30		12 38				13 07			13 30			13 38			14 07
Beeston	d						12 13									13 13									14 13
Loughborough	d	11 52	12 01				12 22				12 52	13 01				13 22			13 45	13 52		14 01			14 22
Barrow Upon Soar	d		12 06									13 06										14 06			
Sileby	d		12 10									13 10										14 10			
Syston	d		12 15									13 15										14 15			
Leicester	a	12 04	12 25			12 26	12 34			12 57	13 04	13 25			13 28	13 34			13 55	14 04		14 25		14 28	14 34
	d	12 05				12 30	12 35			13 00	13 05				13 30	13 35			14 00	14 05				14 30	14 35
Market Harborough	d	12 19					12 49				13 19					13 49				14 19					14 49
Kettering	d	12 29					12 59				13 29					13 59				14 29					14 59
Wellingborough	d	12 36					13 06				13 36					14 06				14 36					15 06
Bedford 7	d	12 51					13 21				13 51					14 21				14 51					15 21
Luton 10	d	13 33					13 36				14 33					14 36				15 33				15 21	15 36
Luton Airport Parkway 7	d	13 07					13 51				14 07					14 51				15 07				15 36	15 51
Gatwick Airport 10 ✈	a	14e55					15 10				15e55					16 10				16e55				16 55	17 10
St Pancras International 15 ⊖	a	13 34				13 44	14 04			14 15	14 34				14 45	15 04			15 15	15 34				15 51	16 04

		EM	EM	XC	EM	EM		XC	EM	EM	EM	EM	XC	EM		EM	EM	XC	EM	EM	EM	EM		XC	EM
		1 ◇ ☕	◇	1 ◇ ☕	1 ◇ ☕			1 ◇ ☕	1 ◇ ☕	1 ◇ ☕	1 ◇ ☕	◇	1 ◇ ☕	1 ◇ ☕		1 ◇ ☕		1 ◇ ☕	1 ◇ ☕	1 ◇ ☕	1 ◇ ☕	◇		1 ◇ ☕	1 ◇ ☕
York 8	d			12 44				13 28	13 28				13 44	13 44				14 30	14 30					14 44	
Leeds 10	d			13 10				13b16					14 10					14b16						15 10	
Wakefield Westgate 7	d			13 23				13c32					14 22					14c32						15 23	
Doncaster 7	d			13 01				13 54					14 02					14 55						15 02	
Barnsley	d		13 01	13 01				13 48				14 01	14 01					14 48				15 01		15 01	
Meadowhall	d		13 21	13 33				14 03	14 07			14 19	14 33					15 03	15 06			15 19		15 33	
Sheffield 7	d		13 38	13 53				14 23	14 27			14 38	14 53	15 02				15 23	15 27			15 38		15 53	
Dronfield	d																								
Chesterfield	d		13 53					14 35	14 40			14 53		15 14				15 35	15 40			15 53			
Matlock	d								14 10																15 38
Belper	d								14 30																15 58
Burton-on-Trent	d				13 42				14 20							14 58			15 20						15 44
Derby 10	a			14 22				14 55	15 01				15 21					15 55	16 01					16 22	
	d				14 34				15 03							15 34			16 03						16 34
Long Eaton	d				14 43											15 43									16 43
Alfreton	d		14 04									15 04		15 27						←		16 04			
Langley Mill	d											15 11		15 35 →						15 35		16 11			
Nottingham 8	a		14 30									15 30								16 00		16 35			
	d	14 30				14 38				15 07	15 30						15 38			16 07	16 30				
Beeston	d									15 13										16 13					
Loughborough	d				14 52	15 01				15 22	15 46					15 52	16 01			16 22					16 52
Barrow Upon Soar	d					15 06											16 06								
Sileby	d					15 10											16 10								
Syston	d					15 15											16 15								
Leicester	a	14 53			15 04	15 25			15 28	15 34	15 58					16 04	16 25		16 28	16 34	16 55				17 04
	d	15 00			15 05				15 30	15 35	16 00					16 05			16 30	16 35	17 00				17 05
Market Harborough	d				15 19					15 49						16 19				16 49					17 19
Kettering	d				15 29					15 59						16 29				16 59					17 29
Wellingborough	d				15 36					16 06						16 36				17 06					17 36
Bedford 7	d				15 51					16 21						16 51			17 13	17 21					17 51
Luton 10	d				16 33					16 36						17 33				17 36					18 33
Luton Airport Parkway 7	d				16 07					16 51						17 07			17 51	17 51					18 07
Gatwick Airport 10 ✈	a				17e55					18 10						18e55			19 10	19 10					19e56
St Pancras International 15 ⊖	a	16 15			16 34				16 45	17 04	17 17					17 34			17 51	18 04	18 15				18 34

For general notes see front of timetable
For details of catering facilities see Directory of Train Operators

b Change at Sheffield
c Wakefield Kirkgate. Change at Sheffield
e Change at Bedford

Table 53

Saturdays

from 2 February

Sheffield → East Midlands → London

Route Diagram - See first page of Table 53

		EM	XC 1 ◇ ☕	EM 1 ◇ ☕	EM 1 ◇ ☕	EM 1 ◇ ☕	EM ◇	XC 1 ◇ ☕		EM 1 ◇ ☕	EM	XC 1 ◇ ☕	EM 1 ◇ ☕	EM 1 ◇ ☕	EM ◇	XC 1 ◇ ☕		EM 1 ◇ ☕	EM 1 ◇ ☕	EM	XC 1 ◇ ☕	EM 1 ◇ ☕	EM 1 ◇ ☕	EM ◇	XC 1 ◇ ☕
York 8	d		15 27	15 27				15 44				16 25	16 25			16 44					17 25	17 25			17 44
Leeds 10	d		15b16					16 10					16 16			17 10					17b16				18 10
Wakefield Westgate 7	d		15c32					16 23					16e32			17 23					17c32				18 23
Doncaster 7	d		15 55					16 02				16 53				17 02					17 55				18 15
Barnsley	d		15 48				16 01	16 01				16 26	16 48		17 01	17 01					17 48			18 01	18 01
Meadowhall	d		16 06	16 09			16 19	16 33				17 00	17 06		17 19	17 33					18 04	18 06		18 19	18 38
Sheffield 7	d		16 23	16 27			16 38	16 53				17 20	17 27		17 41	17 53					18 23	18 27		18 38	18 53
Dronfield	d						16 49					17 28													
Chesterfield	d		16 35	16 40			16 55					17 35	17 40		17 55						18 35	18 40		18 53	
Matlock	d												17 01												
Belper	d												17 21												
Burton-on-Trent	d			16 20						16 58			17 20						17 47			18 20			
Derby 10	a		16 55	17 01				17 22				17 55	18 01			18 22					18 55	19 01			19 22
	d			17 03						17 34			18 03						18 34			19 03			
Long Eaton	d									17 43									18 43						
Alfreton	d						17 06								18 06									19 04	
Langley Mill	d						17 13								18 13										
Nottingham 8	a						17 31								18 29									19 29	
	d	16 38			17 07	17 30					17 38			18 07				18 30		18 38			19 07		
Beeston	d				17 13									18 13									19 13		
Loughborough	d	17 03			17 22	17 45				17 52	18 03		18 20	18 25				18 45	18 52	19 01		19 18	19 24		
Barrow Upon Soar	d	17 07									18 07									19 06					
Sileby	d	17 11									18 11									19 10					
Syston	d	17 16									18 16									19 15					
Leicester	a	17 25		17 28	17 34	17 56				18 04	18 25		18 33	18 39				18 56	19 04	19 25		19 30	19 38		
	d			17 30	17 35	18 00				18 05			18 34	18 40				19 00	19 05			19 30	19 39		
Market Harborough	d				17 49					18 19				18 51					19 19				19 53		
Kettering	d				17 59					18 29				19 01					19 29				20 03		
Wellingborough	d				18 06					18 36				19 11					19 36				20 11		
Bedford 7	d				18 21					18 51				19 25					19 51				20 25		
Luton 10	d			18 21	18 36									19 41									20 41		
Luton Airport Parkway 7	d			18 36	18 52					19 07									20 07				20 52		
Gatwick Airport 10	a			19 56	20 25					21f10				21 40					22f10				22 40		
St Pancras International 15	a			18 51	19 04	19 08				19 35			19 45	20 09				20 15	20 35			20 48	21 08		

		EM 1 ◇ ☕		EM 1 ◇ ☕	EM	EM 1 ◇ ☕	XC 1 ◇ ☕	EM 1 ◇ ☕	EM ◇	XC 1 ◇ ☕		EM 1 ◇ ☕	EM ◇	EM 1 ◇ ☕	XC 1 ◇	EM	EM ◇	XC 1 ◇		EM 1 ◇ ☕	EM ◇	EM			
York 8	d					17 49	18 25		18 25	18 44			18 44	18 44	19 44		20g05	20 44		20 44					
Leeds 10	d						18b16			19 10			19 16	19 16	20 10		20 16	21 10							
Wakefield Westgate 7	d						18c32			19 23			19e32	19e32	20 23		20e32	21 23							
Doncaster 7	d					18 15	18 51			19 03			19 49	19 49	20 03		20 42	21 07			21 49				
Barnsley	d					18b26	18 48		19 01	19 01			19 48	20 06			20 48	21 06			21 26				
Meadowhall	d					18 38	19 06		19 19	19 33			20 07	20 24	20 35		21 07	21 35			22 09				
Sheffield 7	d					19 07	19 23		19 38	19 53			20 40	20 47	20 53		21 37	21 53		22 00	22 36				
Dronfield	d																								
Chesterfield	d					19 19	19 35		19 53	20 05			20 55	21 00	21 05		21 53	22 05		22 12	22 50				
Matlock	d			18 38										20 20								22 28			
Belper	d			18 58										20 40								22 48			
Burton-on-Trent	d			18 58		19 20								20 29								22 29			
Derby 10	a					19 40	19 55			20 26				21 22	21 27			22 26		22 35		23 00			
	d			19 34		19 51								21 22								23 04			
Long Eaton	d			19 43		20 02																23 14			
Alfreton	d								20 04				21 06				22 04								
Langley Mill	d												21 13				22 11								
Nottingham 8	a								20 29				21 35				22 38				23 26	23 37			
	d	19 30			19 33			20 07				20 30				21 30									
Beeston	d				19 39			20 13																	
Loughborough	d	19 45		19 54	19 57	20 15						20 49		21 41		21 46									
Barrow Upon Soar	d				20 02																				
Sileby	d				20 06																				
Syston	d				20 12																				
Leicester	a	19 56		20 04	20 22	20 26		20 34				21 02		21 56		22 00									
	d	20 00		20 05		20 27		20 35				21 03													
Market Harborough	d			20 19		20 41		20 49				21 18													
Kettering	d			20 29		20 51		20 59				21 28													
Wellingborough	d			20 36		20 59		21 07				21 36													
Bedford 7	d			20 51		21 13		21 23				21 52													
Luton 10	d					21 29		21 39				22 09													
Luton Airport Parkway 7	d			21 09		21 46		21 52				22 22													
Gatwick Airport 10	a			23f10		23 10		23 40				00 17													
St Pancras International 15	a	21 12		21 35		21 52		22 04				22 43													

For general notes see front of timetable
For details of catering facilities see Directory of Train Operators

b Change at Sheffield
c Wakefield Kirkgate. Change at Sheffield
e Wakefield Kirkgate
f Change at Bedford
g Change at Doncaster and Sheffield

Table 53

Sundays

until 27 January

Sheffield → East Midlands → London

Route Diagram - See first page of Table 53

Station		EM	EM	EM	EM	EM	EM	EM	EM	EM	EM	EM	EM	EM	EM	EM	EM	EM	EM	XC	EM	EM	XC	EM	EM
		1 ◇ ☕	Bus	1 ◇ ☕	Bus	1 ◇ ☕	Bus	1 ◇ ☕	Bus	1 ◇ ☕	Bus	Bus	1 ◇ ☕	Bus	1 ◇ ☕	Bus	1 ◇ ☕	Bus	1 ◇ ☕	1 ◇ ☕	Bus	1 ◇ ☕	1 ◇ ☕	Bus	1 ◇ ☕
York 8	d																			*07 22*		*07 22*	09 20		*09 20*
Leeds 10	d																			08 45		08 35	*09 05*		*09b05*
Wakefield Westgate 7	d																			08 57		08 47	*09 17*		*09b17*
Doncaster 7	d																		*08 03*			09 07	09 50		
Barnsley	d																						*09 21*		
Meadowhall	d																		*09 00*				*10 00*		
Sheffield 7	d										07 46								09 26	09 35		09 40	10 23		10 30
Dronfield	d																								
Chesterfield	d										08 17								09 40	09 47		09 53	10 35		10 42
Matlock	d																								
Belper	d																								
Burton-on-Trent	d																		*09 29*						*10 29*
Derby 10	a										09 02								10 01	10 07		10 15	10 55		11 03
	d	06 17				07 11				08 14					09 12				10 03			10 16			11 04
Long Eaton	d					07 21									09 22				10 13						11 14
Alfreton	d																								
Langley Mill	d																								
Nottingham 8	a																					10 36			
	d			06 51				07 40					08 28				09 42					10 44			
Beeston	d							07 48									09 48								
Loughborough	d					07 29				08 30			08 49		09 32		09 59		10 26			10 59			11 24
Barrow Upon Soar	d																								
Sileby	d																								
Syston	d																								
Leicester	a	06 42		07 12		07 41		08 07		08 41			09 01		09 42		10 10		10 39			11 11			11 34
	d	06 47		07 18		07 45		08 13		08 46			09 06		09 47		10 16		10 43			11 16			11 39
Market Harborough	d		07 47		08 15		08 44		09 16			09 44		10 17		10 46		11 15			11 46			12 13	
Kettering	d	07 51	08a12	08 22	08a40	08 50	09a09	09 19	09a41	09 51		10a09	10 19	10a42	10 52	11a11	11 21	11a40	11 50		12a11	12 21		12a38	12 48
Wellingborough	d	08 00		08 31		09 00		09 29		10 00			10 29		11 01		11 31		12 00			12 31			12 58
Bedford 7	d	08 16		08 46		09 15		09 45		10 15			10 46		11 16		11 46		12 16			12 45			13 13
Luton 10	d	08 37		09 08		*10 03*		10 08		*11 03*			11 07		*12 03*		12 11		12 38			13 08			*13 43*
Luton Airport Parkway 7	d	*08 52*		*09 22*		09 43		*10 22*		*11 06*			*11 22*		11 41		*12 22*		*12 52*			*13 22*			*13 46*
Gatwick Airport 10	a	*10 48*		*11 18*		*11c48*		*12 18*		*12 48*			*13 18*		*13c48*		*14 18*		*14 48*			*15 18*			*15 18*
St Pancras International 15	a	09 16		09 45		10 16		10 46		11 19			11 49		12 19		12 50		13 18			13 48			14 18

Station		EM	EM	XC	XC	EM	EM	XC	XC	EM		EM	EM	EM	EM	EM	EM	XC	EM	XC	EM	XC	EM	XC	EM
		Bus	1 ◇ ☕	1 ◇ ☕	1 ◇ ☕	Bus	1 ◇ ☕	1 ◇ ☕	1 ◇ ☕	Bus		1 ◇ ☕	Bus	1 ◇ ☕	Bus	1 ◇ ☕	Bus	R 1 ☕	◇	1 ◇ ☕	1 ◇ ☕	R 1 ☕	◇	1 ◇ ☕	Bus
York 8	d				10 20		*10e20*	10 28	11 20					*11 20*				11 28	*11 28*	12 20	*12 20*	12 28	*12 28*	13 20	
Leeds 10	d			10 00	*10e25*		10 25	11 00	*11e14*									12 00	*12 00*	*12e00*		13 00	*13 00*	*13e14*	
Wakefield Westgate 7	d			10 12	*10e36*		10 36	11 12	*11f30*									12 12	*12 12*	*12e12*		13 12	*13 12*	*13f30*	
Doncaster 7	d				10 50			*10 55*	11 50											12 50				13 50	
Barnsley	d				*10 49*				*11 49*										*12 12*	*12 12*			*13 12*	*13 49*	
Meadowhall	d				*11 05*			*11 13*	*12 05*									*12 11*	*12 33*	*13 00*			*13 33*	*14 05*	
Sheffield 7	d			10 48	11 23		11 27	11 48	12 23					12 27				12 48	12 52	13 23	13 34	13 48	13 58	14 23	
Dronfield	d																								
Chesterfield	d				11 35		11 40		12 35					12 40					13 06	13 35	13 47		14 13	14 35	
Matlock	d						*10 42*														*12 41*				
Belper	d						*11 02*														*13 02*				
Burton-on-Trent	d						*10 58*							*11 58*							*12 58*				
Derby 10	a			11 18	11 55		12 01	12 18	12 55					13 01				13 18		13 55	14 08	14 18		14 55	
	d						12 03							13 02							14 14				
Long Eaton	d													13 12											
Alfreton	d																		13 21				14 24		
Langley Mill	d																								
Nottingham 8	a																		13 42				14 46		
	d		11 43									12 46				13 31									
Beeston	d		11 49													13 37									
Loughborough	d		11 59				12 21					13 00		13 23		13 48					14 35				
Barrow Upon Soar	d																								
Sileby	d																								
Syston	d																								
Leicester	a		12 11				12 35					13 10		13 38		13 59					14 44				
	d		12 15				12 39					13 15		13 43		14 06					14 49				
Market Harborough	d	12 46				13 13				13 45			14 15		14 36		15 20								15 52
Kettering	d	13a11	13 21			13a38	13 48			14a10		14 20	14a40	14 50	15a01	15 11	15a45				15 55				16a17
Wellingborough	d		13 31				13 58					14 29		15 00		15 21					16 05				
Bedford 7	d		13 45				14 16					14 44		15 15		15 34									
Luton 10	d		14 09				*14 49*					14 59		*15 49*		15 58									
Luton Airport Parkway 7	d		*14c20*				*14 52*					*15 16*		*15 52*		*16 16*					16 34				
Gatwick Airport 10	a		*16 18*				*16 48*					*16 48*		*17 48*		*17 48*									
St Pancras International 15	a		14 44				15 11					15 29		16 06		16 27					17 06				

For general notes see front of timetable
For details of catering facilities see Directory of Train Operators

b Change at Doncaster and Sheffield
c Change at Bedford
e Change at Sheffield
f Wakefield Kirkgate. Change at Sheffield

Table 53

Sundays

until 27 January

Sheffield → East Midlands → London

Route Diagram - See first page of Table 53

		EM	EM	EM	EM	EM	EM	XC	EM	EM	XC	EM	EM	EM	XC	XC	EM	EM	EM	EM	EM	XC	EM	EM	XC
		1 ◇	Bus	1 ◇	◇	Bus	1 ◇	R 1	Bus	1 ◇	1 ◇	Bus	1 ◇	◇	R 1	R 1	Bus	1 ◇	Bus	1 ◇	◇	R 1	Bus	1 ◇	1 ◇
		☕		☕			☕	☕		☕	☕		☕		☕	☕		☕		☕		☕		☕	☕
York 8	d			12b57	13 20			13 28		13b33	14 24		14 24		14 28	15 21		14b36			15 21	15 28		15b34	16 23
Leeds 10	d							14 00		14 00					15 00			15 00			15 09	16 00		16 00	
Wakefield Westgate 7	d							14 12		14 12					15 12			15 12			15 24	16 12		16 12	
Doncaster 7	d			13 42						14 13	14 50					15 50		15 42			15 50			16 13	16 50
Barnsley	d									14 12						15 12		15 12						16 12	
Meadowhall	d				14 14			14 14		14 42	15 00					16 00		16 00			16 11	16 11		16 42	17 00
Sheffield 7	d			14 25	14 41			14 48		15 10	15 23		15 27	15 39	15 48	16 23		16 26			16 39	16 48		17 09	17 23
Dronfield	d																								
Chesterfield	d			14 40	14 56					15 23	15 35		15 40	15 54		16 35		16 40			16 54			17 22	17 35
Matlock	d									14 36															
Belper	d									14 58															
Burton-on-Trent	d			14 18						14 58								16 23						17 23	
Derby 10	a			15 01				15 18		15 44	15 55				16 18	16 55		17 01				17 18		17 46	17 55
	d			15 01						15 53								17 02						17 46	
Long Eaton	d			15 11														17 14							
Alfreton	d				15 07								15 52	16 05							17 08				
Langley Mill	d				15 15								16 01	16 12							17 16				
Nottingham 8	a				15 34								16 18	16 30							17 31				
	d	14 48					15 40						16 30							17 24					
Beeston	d						15 45						16 37							17 30					
Loughborough	d	15 02		15 21			15 58			16 07								17 22		17 43				18 08	
Barrow Upon Soar	d																								
Sileby	d																								
Syston	d																								
Leicester	a	15 12		15 34			16 07			16 21			16 58					17 36		17 54				18 23	
	d	15 17		15 39			16 12			16 30			17 07					17 40		17 59				18 32	
Market Harborough	d		16 09			16 42			17 09			17 39					18 10		18 32				19 03		
Kettering	d	16c29	16a34	16 44		17a07	17 17		17a34	17 44		18a04	18 13				18a35	18 45	18a57	19 07			19a28	19 38	
Wellingborough	d	16 39		16 54			17 27			17 53			18 23					18 55		19 17				19 48	
Bedford 7	d	16 55		17 10			17 41			18 08			18 40					19 10		19 33				20 05	
Luton 10	d	17 12		17 43			18 13			18 28			19 01					19 43		19 51				21 03	
Luton Airport Parkway 7	d	17 46		17 46			17 59			18 46			19 16					19 46		20 16				21 06	
Gatwick Airport 10 ✈	a	19 18		19 18			19e48			20 18			20 48					21 18		21 48				22 48	
St Pancras International 15 ⊖	a	17 42		17 55			18 28			18 57			19 30					19 56		20 22				20 49	

		EM	EM	EM	XC	XC	EM	XC	EM	EM	XC	EM	EM	EM	XC	XC	EM	XC	EM	XC	EM	XC	EM		
		Bus	1 ◇	◇	R 1	1 ◇	◇	R 1	Bus	1 ◇	1 ◇	Bus	1 ◇	◇	1 ◇	1 ◇	◇	1 ◇	◇	1 ◇	1 ◇	1 ◇	Bus		
			☕		☕	☕		☕		☕	☕		☕		☕	☕		☕			☕				
York 8	d		16 40	16 40	16 28	17 20	17 20	17 28		17 28	18 20			18 20	18 28	19 20	19 20	19 28	20b02	20 28	20b40	21 26	21 26		
Leeds 10	d		16 09	16b09	17 00	17 05	17 09	18 00		18 00					19 00		19 09	20 00		21 00					
Wakefield Westgate 7	d		16 22	16b22	17 12	17 18	17 24	18 12		18 12					19 12		19 24	20 12		21 12					
Doncaster 7	d		17 06			17 50					18 50					19 50			20 42	20 42	21 23	21 50			
Barnsley	d					17 12					18 12					19 12			20 12	20 12	21 12				
Meadowhall	d					18 00	18 11	18 26		18 26	19 00					20 00	20 11	20 11	21 08	21 08	21 45	22 00			
Sheffield 7	d		17 35	17 39	17 48	18 23	18 40	18 48		18 51	19 23			19 37	19 48	20 23	20 38	20 48	21 41	21 48	22 06	22 23	22 30		
Dronfield	d																								
Chesterfield	d		17 47	17 53		18 35	18 54			19 04	19 35			19 53	20 00	20 35	20 54	21 00	21 56	22 00	22 18	22 35	23 05		
Matlock	d									18 38															
Belper	d									19 00															
Burton-on-Trent	d									18 58															
Derby 10	a				18 18	18 55		19 18		19 24	19 55				20 20	20 55		21 20		22 22	22 43	22 55			
	d									19 25															
Long Eaton	d									19 35															
Alfreton	d		17 58	18 04			19 05							20 05			21 05		22 08				23 25		
Langley Mill	d		18 06	18 13			19 13										21 12		22 15				23 45		
Nottingham 8	a		18 24	18 30			19 34							20 30			21 35		22 38				00 10		
	d		18 41										20 30												
Beeston	d		18 48																						
Loughborough	d									19 44			20 43												
Barrow Upon Soar	d																								
Sileby	d																								
Syston	d																								
Leicester	a		19 07							19 57			20 55												
	d		19 12							20 02			21 03												
Market Harborough	d	19 42							20 31			21 31													
Kettering	d	20a07	20 17						20a56	21 07		21a56	22 06												
Wellingborough	d		20 32							21 16			22 16												
Bedford 7	d		20 49							21 31			22 30												
Luton 10	d		21 08							21 50			22 50												
Luton Airport Parkway 7	d		21 36							22 06			23 06												
Gatwick Airport 10 ✈	a		23 18							23 48			00 46												
St Pancras International 15 ⊖	a		21 37							22 19			23 22												

For general notes see front of timetable
For details of catering facilities see Directory of Train Operators

b Change at Doncaster and Sheffield
c Arr. 1619
e Change at Bedford

Table 53

3 February to 23 March

Sheffield → East Midlands → London

Route Diagram - See first page of Table 53

		EM	EM	EM	EM	EM	EM	EM		EM	EM	EM	EM	EM	EM	EM		EM	EM	EM	EM	EM	EM	EM	EM
		1 ◇			1 ◇		1 ◇				1 ◇		1 ◇					1 ◇		1 ◇		1 ◇		1 ◇	
			🚌	🚌		🚌		🚌		🚌		🚌		🚌	🚌	🚌			🚌		🚌		🚌		🚌
		☕			☕		☕				☕		☕					☕		☕		☕		☕	
York 8	d																								
Leeds 10	d																								
Wakefield Westgate 7	d																								
Doncaster 7	d																							*08 03*	
Barnsley	d																								
Meadowhall 🚋	d																							*09 00*	
Sheffield 7 🚋	d														07 46									09 26	
Dronfield	d																								
Chesterfield	d														08 17									09 40	
Matlock	d																								
Belper	d																								
Burton-on-Trent	d																							*09b00*	
Derby 10	a														09 02									10 01	
	d	06 17					07 11						08 14							09 12				10 03	
Long Eaton	d						07 21													09 22				10 13	
Alfreton	d																								
Langley Mill	d																								
Nottingham 8 🚋	a																								
	d		06 18					06 52						07 59								09 42			
Beeston	d							07 13														09 48			
Loughborough	d						07 29						08 30	08a39				08 49		09 32		09 59		10 26	
Barrow Upon Soar	d																								
Sileby	d																								
Syston	d																								
Leicester	a	06 42	07 08				07 41	08 03					08 41					09 01		09 42		10 10		10 39	
	d	06 47			07 18		07 45				08 13		08 46					09 06		09 47		10 16		10 43	
Market Harborough	d			07 47		08 15				08 44		09 16				09 44			10 17		10 46		11 15		11 41
Kettering	d	07 51		08a12	08 22	08a40	08 50			09a09	09 19	09a41	09 51			10a09		10 19	10a42	10 52	11a11	11 21	11a40	11 50	12a06
Wellingborough	d	08 00			08 31		09 00				09 29		10 00					10 29		11 01		11 31		12 00	
Bedford 7	d	08 16			08 46		09 15				09 45		10 15					10 46		11 16		11 46		12 16	
Luton 10	d	08 37			09 08		*10 03*				10 08		*11 03*					11 07		*12 03*		12 11		12 38	
Luton Airport Parkway 7	d	*08 52*			*09 22*		09 43				*10 22*		*11 06*					*11 22*		11 41		*12 22*		*12 52*	
Gatwick Airport 10 ✈	a	*10 48*			*11 18*		*11c48*				*12 18*		*12 48*					*13 18*		*13c48*		*14 18*		*14 48*	
St Pancras International 15 ⊖	a	09 16			09 45		10 16				10 46		11 19					11 49		12 19		12 50		13 18	

		EM		XC	EM	EM	EM	EM	XC	EM		EM	XC	EM	EM	EM	EM	EM		EM	EM	XC	EM	EM	EM
													R									R			
		1 ◇		1 ◇		1 ◇		1 ◇	1 ◇			1 ◇	1		1 ◇		1 ◇			1 ◇	◇	1		1 ◇	◇
					🚌		🚌			🚌				🚌		🚌		🚌					🚌		
		☕		☕		☕		☕	☕			☕	☕		☕		☕			☕		☕		☕	
York 8	d	*06 42*		*08e58*		*08f58*			*09 15*			*10f02*	10 28				*10 28*					11 28		*11f29*	*11g40*
Leeds 10	d	08 35		09 00		*09 00*			10 00			10 25	11 00				*11 14*					12 00		*12 00*	*12 17*
Wakefield Westgate 7	d	08 47		09 12		*09 12*			10 12			10 36	11 12				*11h30*					12 12		*12 12*	12h46
Doncaster 7	d	09 07		09 34		*09 39*			10 35			*10 42*	11 30				*11 42*					12 33		*12 42*	
Barnsley	d			*09 21*					*10 12*			*10 49*	*11 12*				*11 49*				*12 12*	*12 12*		*12 12*	*13 12*
Meadowhall 🚋	d			*09 41*		*10 00*			*10 42*			*11 05*	*11 44*				*12 05*				*12 33*	*12 43*		*13 00*	*13 33*
Sheffield 7 🚋	d	09 40		10 05		10 30			11 05			11 27	12 05				12 27				12 52	13 05		13 34	13 58
Dronfield	d																								
Chesterfield	d	09 53		10 17		10 42			11 17			11 40	12 17				12 40				13 06	13 17		13 47	14 13
Matlock	d											*10 42*												*12 41*	
Belper	d											*11 02*												*13 02*	
Burton-on-Trent	d					*10b00*						*10b40*					*11b40*							*12b40*	
Derby 10	a			10 37		11 03			11 37			12 01	12 37				13 01					13 37		14 08	
	d					11 04						12 03					13 02							14 14	
Long Eaton	d					11 14											13 12								
Alfreton	d																				13 21				14 24
Langley Mill	d																								
Nottingham 8 🚋	a	10 24																			13 42				14 46
	d	10 31						11 43							12 46					13 31					
Beeston	d							11 49												13 37					
Loughborough	d	10 47				11 24		11 59				12 21			13 00		13 23			13 48				14 35	
Barrow Upon Soar	d																								
Sileby	d																								
Syston	d																								
Leicester	a	11 00				11 34		12 11				12 35			13 10		13 38			13 59				14 44	
	d	11 09				11 39		12 15				12 39			13 15		13 43			14 06				14 49	
Market Harborough	d				12 13		12 46			13 13				13 45		14 15		14 36					15 20		
Kettering	d	12 16			12a38	12 48	13a11	13 21		13a38		13 48		14a10	14 20	14a40	14 50	15a01		15 11			15a45	15 55	
Wellingborough	d	12 26				12 58		13 31				13 58			14 29		15 00			15 21				16 05	
Bedford 7	d	12 45				13 13		13 45				14 16			14 44		15 15			15 34					
Luton 10	d	13 08				*13 43*		14 09				*14 49*			14 59		*15 49*			15 58					
Luton Airport Parkway 7	d	*13 22*				*13 46*		*14c20*				*14 52*			*15 16*		*15 52*			*16 16*				16 34	
Gatwick Airport 10 ✈	a	*15 18*				*15 18*		*16 18*				*16 48*			*16 48*		*17 48*			*17 48*					
St Pancras International 15 ⊖	a	13 48				14 18		14 44				15 11			15 29		16 06			16 27				17 06	

For general notes see front of timetable
For details of catering facilities see Directory of Train Operators

- **b** By bus
- **c** Change at Bedford
- **e** Change at Doncaster
- **f** Change at Doncaster and Sheffield
- **g** Change at Leeds and Sheffield
- **h** Wakefield Kirkgate

Table 53

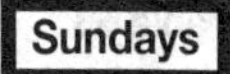

3 February to 23 March

Sheffield → East Midlands → London

Route Diagram - See first page of Table 53

		XC R 1 ☕	EM 🚌	EM 1 ◇ ☕		EM 🚌	EM 1 ◇ ☕	EM ◇	EM 🚌	EM 1 ◇ ☕	XC R 1 ☕	EM 🚌		EM 1 ◇ ☕	EM 🚌	EM 1 ◇ ☕	EM ◇	XC R 1 ☕	EM 🚌	EM 1 ◇ ☕		EM 🚌	EM 1 ◇ ☕	EM ◇	XC R 1 ☕
York [8]	d	12 28					12b57				13 28			13b33		14b05		14 28		14b36					15 28
Leeds [10]	d	13 00					13 14				14 00			14 00				15 00		15 00				15 09	16 00
Wakefield Westgate [7]	d	13 12					13c30				14 12			14 12				15 12		15 12				15 24	16 12
Doncaster [7]	d	13 30					13 42				14 30			14 33		14 42		15 30		15 42					16 30
Barnsley	d	13 12					13 49				14 12			14 12				15 12		15 12					16 12
Meadowhall	d	13 43					14 05	14 14			14 42			14 51		15 00		15 42		16 00				16 11	16 42
Sheffield [7]	d	14 05					14 25	14 41			15 05			15 10		15 27	15 39	16 05		16 26				16 39	17 05
Dronfield	d																								
Chesterfield	d	14 17					14 40	14 56			15 17			15 23		15 40	15 54	16 17		16 40				16 54	17 17
Matlock	d													14 36											
Belper	d													14 58											
Burton-on-Trent	d						13e52							14e40						16e08					
Derby [10]	a	14 37					15 00				15 37			15 44				16 37		17 01					17 37
	d						15 01							15 53						17 02					
Long Eaton	d						15 11													17 14					
Alfreton	d							15 07								15 52	16 05							17 08	
Langley Mill	d							15 15								16 01	16 12							17 16	
Nottingham [8]	a							15 34								16 18	16 30							17 31	
	d			14 48						15 40						16 30							17 24		
Beeston	d									15 45						16 37							17 30		
Loughborough	d			15 02			15 21			15 58				16 07						17 22			17 43		
Barrow Upon Soar	d																								
Sileby	d																								
Syston	d																								
Leicester	a			15 12			15 34			16 07				16 21		16 58				17 36			17 54		
	d			15 17			15 39			16 12				16 30		17 07				17 40			17 59		
Market Harborough	d		15 52			16 09			16 42			17 09			17 39				18 10			18 32			
Kettering	d		16a17	16f29		16a34	16 44		17a07	17 17		17a34		17 44	18a04	18 13			18a35	18 45		18a57	19 07		
Wellingborough	d			16 39			16 54			17 27				17 53		18 23				18 55			19 17		
Bedford [7]	d			16 55			17 10			17 41				18 08		18 40				19 10			19 33		
Luton [10]	d			17 12			17 43			18 13				18 28		19 01				19 43			19 51		
Luton Airport Parkway [7]	d			17 46			17 46			17 59				18 46		19 16				19 46			20 16		
Gatwick Airport [10] ✈	a			19 18			19 18			19g48				20 18		20 48				21 18			21 48		
St Pancras International [15] ⊖	a			17 42			17 55			18 28				18 57		19 30				19 56			20 22		

		EM 🚌	EM 1 ◇ ☕	EM 🚌	EM 1 ◇ ☕	EM ◇		XC R 1 ☕	EM ◇	EM 🚌	EM 1 ◇ ☕	XC R 1 ☕	EM 🚌	EM 1 ◇ ☕		EM ◇	XC 1 ◇ ☕	EM ◇	XC 1 ◇	EM ◇	XC 1 ◇	EM 1 ◇ ☕	EM ◇		
York [8]	d		15b34		16 40	16 40		16 28	17b01		17 17	17 28				18b07	18 28	19b05	19 28	20b02	20 28	20b40	21b28		
Leeds [10]	d		16 00		16 09	16b09		17 00	17 09		17 09	18 00				18 00	19 00	19 09	20 00	20 00	21 00	21 00	21 40		
Wakefield Westgate [7]	d		16 12		16 22	16b22		17 12	17 24		17 24	18 12				18 12	19 12	19 24	20 12	20 12	21 12	21 12	21 55		
Doncaster [7]	d		16 33		17 06			17 30	17 42		17 42	18 30				18 42	19 30	19 42	20 31	20 42	21 30		22 20		
Barnsley	d		16 12					17 12	17 12		17 12	18 12				18 12	19 12		20 12		21 12		22 21		
Meadowhall	d		16 51		17 00			17 42	18 11		18 26	18 42				19 00	19 44	20 11	20 45	21 08	21 45		22 50		
Sheffield [7]	d		17 09		17 35	17 39		18 05	18 40		18 51	19 05				19 37	20 05	20 38	21 05	21 41	22 05	22 08	23 27		
Dronfield	d																								
Chesterfield	d		17 22		17 47	17 53		18 17	18 54		19 04	19 17				19 53	20 17	20 54	21 17	21 56	22 17	22 18	23 41		
Matlock	d										18 38														
Belper	d										19 00														
Burton-on-Trent	d		17e08								18e40														
Derby [10]	a		17 46					18 37			19 24	19 37					20 37		21 37		22 37	22 43			
	d		17 46								19 25														
Long Eaton	d										19 35														
Alfreton	d				17 58	18 04			19 05							20 05		21 05		22 08			23 52		
Langley Mill	d				18 06	18 13			19 13									21 12		22 15			00 02		
Nottingham [8]	a				18 24	18 30			19 34							20 30		21 35		22 38			00 22		
	d				18 41									20 30											
Beeston	d				18 48																				
Loughborough	d		18 08								19 44			20 43											
Barrow Upon Soar	d																								
Sileby	d																								
Syston	d																								
Leicester	a		18 23		19 07						19 57			20 55											
	d		18 32		19 12						20 02			21 03											
Market Harborough	d	19 03		19 42						20 31			21 31												
Kettering	d	19a28	19 38	20a07	20 17					20a56	21 07		21a56	22 06											
Wellingborough	d		19 48		20 32						21 16			22 16											
Bedford [7]	d		20 05		20 49						21 31			22 30											
Luton [10]	d		21 03		21 08						21 50			22 50											
Luton Airport Parkway [7]	d		21 06		21 36						22 06			23 06											
Gatwick Airport [10] ✈	a		22 48		23 18						23 48			00 46											
St Pancras International [15] ⊖	a		20 49		21 37						22 19			23 22											

For general notes see front of timetable
For details of catering facilities see Directory of Train Operators

b Change at Doncaster and Sheffield
c Wakefield Kirkgate
e By bus
f Arr. 1619
g Change at Bedford

Table 53

Sundays
from 30 March

Sheffield → East Midlands → London

Route Diagram - See first page of Table 53

		EM	EM	EM	EM	EM	EM	EM	EM	XC	EM	EM	EM	XC	XC	EM	XC	XC	EM	EM	XC	EM	XC	EM	EM
		1◇	1◇	1◇	1◇	1◇	1◇	🚌	1◇	1◇	1◇	1◇	1◇	1◇	1◇	1◇	1◇	1◇	1◇	1◇	1◇	1◇	R 1	◇	1◇
		☕	☕	☕	☕	☕	☕		☕	☕	☕	☕	☕	☕	☕	☕	☕	☕	☕	☕	☕	☕	☕		☕
York [8]	d									07 22		07b22	09c00	09 20	09e20		10 20	10 28		10 28	11 20		11 28	11 28	11f29
Leeds [10]	d									08 45			09 18	09e18	10 00		10e14	11 00		11 06	11e14		12 00	12 00	12 00
Wakefield Westgate [7]	d									08 57		09g00	09 29	09e29	10 12		10h30	11 12		11 17	11h30		12 12	12 12	12 12
Doncaster [7]	d									08 03		09 13	09 48	09 50		10 13	10 50	10 55		10 55	11 50				12 16
Barnsley	d											09 21				10 12	10 49			11 12	11 49			12 12	12 12
Meadowhall	d									09 00		09 41	09 54	10 00		10 42	11 05	11 13		11 33	12 05		12 11	12 33	12 43
Sheffield [7]	d							08 25		09 37		10 08	10 14	10 23	10 48	11 13	11 23	11 48		11 52	12 23		12 48	12 52	13 09
Dronfield	d																								
Chesterfield	d							08 56		09 49		10 22	10 28	10 35		11 25	11 35			12 05	12 35			13 06	13 22
Matlock	d															10 42									12 41
Belper	d															11 02									13 02
Burton-on-Trent	d								09 29			09 58				10 58				11 58					12 58
Derby [10]	a							09 41		10 09		10 43	10 50	10 55	11 18	11 46	11 55	12 18		12 27	12 55		13 18		13 45
	d	06 56		07 50		08 53			09 51			10 44	10 51			11 49				12 33					13 46
Long Eaton	d			08 00					10 01			10 54				11 59									13 56
Alfreton	d																							13 21	
Langley Mill	d																								
Nottingham [8]	a												11 11											13 42	
	d		07 29		08 19		09 19				10 16		11 19						12 24			13 26			
Beeston	d				08 27						10 22								12 30						
Loughborough	d			08 09		09 08	09 36		10 11		10 35	11 06	11 34			12 09			12 41	12 50		13 41			14 07
Barrow Upon Soar	d																								
Sileby	d																								
Syston	d																								
Leicester	a	07 19	07 50	08 20	08 47	09 19	09 48		10 22		10 47	11 19	11 47			12 20			12 52	13 03		13 51			14 20
	d	07 19	07 50	08 20	08 47	09 19	09 48		10 22		10 47	11 19	11 47			12 20			12 52	13 03		13 52			14 20
Market Harborough	d	07 39	08 09	08 39	09 06	09 39	10 08		10 41		11 07	11 38	12 07			12 39			13 11	13 23		14 06			14 38
Kettering	d	07 49	08 19	08 49	09 17	09 49	10 19		10 51		11 18	11 49	12 17			12 49			13 21	13 34		14 16			14 49
Wellingborough	d	08 01	08 31	09 01	09 29	10 01	10 30		10 58		11 26	11 57	12 28			12 58			13 28	13 44		14 23			14 57
Bedford [7]	d	08 16	08 46	09 15	09 45	10 15	10 46		11 16		11 46	12 16	12 45			13 16			13 45	14 07		14 44			15 15
Luton [10]	d	08 37	09 08	10 03	10 08	11 03	11 07		12 03		12 08	12 38	13 08			13 49			14 09	14 43		14 59			15 49
Luton Airport Parkway [7]	d	08 52	09 22	09 43	10 22	11 06	11 22		11 41		12 22	12 52	13 22			13 52			14j20	14 46		15 16			15 52
Gatwick Airport [10] ✈	a	10 48	11 18	11j48	12 18	12 48	13 18		13j48		14 18	14 48	15 18			15 48			16 18	16 18		16 48			17 48
St Pancras International [15] ⊖	a	09 16	09 45	10 16	10 46	11 19	11 49		12 19		12 50	13 18	13 48			14 18			14 44	14 55		15 29			16 06

		XC		EM	XC	EM	XC	EM	EM	XC	EM	EM	EM	XC	EM	EM	XC	EM	EM	EM	EM	XC	EM	XC	EM
		1◇		1◇	R 1	◇	1◇	1◇	◇	R 1	1◇	1◇	1◇	1◇	1◇	◇	R 1	1◇	1◇	1◇	1◇	R 1	◇	R 1	1◇
		☕		☕	☕		☕	☕		☕	☕	☕	☕	☕	☕		☕	☕	☕	☕	☕	☕		☕	☕
York [8]	d	12 20			12 28	12 28	13 20	13 20		13 28	13 28		13f33	14 24		14 24	14 28		14f36			15 21	15 21	15 28	15f34
Leeds [10]	d				13 00	13 00	13e14			14 00	14 00						15 00		15 00				15 09	16 00	16 00
Wakefield Westgate [7]	d				13 12	13 12	13h30			14 12	14 12						15 12		15 12				15 24	16 12	16 12
Doncaster [7]	d	12 50					13 50						14 13	14 50					15 13			15 50	15 50		16 13
Barnsley	d					13 12	13 49				14 12								15 12						16 12
Meadowhall	d	13 00				13 33	14 05		14 14	14 14	14 33		14 42	15 00					15 42			16 00	16 11	16 11	16 42
Sheffield [7]	d	13 23			13 48	13 58	14 23	14 27	14 41	14 48	14 55		15 10	15 23		15 39	15 48		16 04		16 09	16 23	16 39	16 48	17 08
Dronfield	d																								
Chesterfield	d	13 35				14 13	14 35	14 41	14 56		15 08		15 25	15 35		15 54			16 18		16 24	16 35	16 54		17 22
Matlock	d										14 36														
Belper	d										14 58														
Burton-on-Trent	d							14 18			14 58														
Derby [10]	a	13 55			14 18		14 55	15 02		15 18	15 29		15 50	15 55			16 18		16 40			16 55		17 18	17 43
	d							15 03			15 30		15 50						16 41						17 44
Long Eaton	d												16 02												17 56
Alfreton	d					14 24			15 07							16 05					16 36		17 08		
Langley Mill	d								15 15							16 12					16 46		17 16		
Nottingham [8]	a					14 46			15 34							16 30					17 03		17 31		
	d			14 18								15 39			16 03			16 39		17 02	17 09				
Beeston	d			14 24											16 08						17 16				
Loughborough	d			14 34				15 19				15 53	16 11		16 22				16 57	17 19					18 04
Barrow Upon Soar	d																								
Sileby	d																								
Syston	d																								
Leicester	a			14 45				15 29			15 56	16 03	16 24		16 33			17 03	17 10	17 31	17 37				18 16
	d			14 47				15 31			15 57	16 04	16 25		16 34			17 03	17 12	17 31	17 39				18 17
Market Harborough	d			15 00				15 45				16 19			16 49				17 29		17 55				18 32
Kettering	d			15 10				15 55				16 29			16 59				17 40		18 06				18 43
Wellingborough	d			15 17				16 02				16 36			17 06				17 48		18 14				18 52
Bedford [7]	d			15 35								16 54	17 09		17 25				18 06		18 34				19 10
Luton [10]	d			15 55								17 11	17 43		18 13				18 27		18 55				19 43
Luton Airport Parkway [7]	d			16 16				16 35				17 22			17 42				18 46		19 16				19 46
Gatwick Airport [10] ✈	a			17 48								19 18	19 18		19j48				20 18		20 48				21 18
St Pancras International [15] ⊖	a			16 27				17 06			17 24	17 41	17 55		18 11			18 28	18 57	19 04	19 24				19 56

For general notes see front of timetable
For details of catering facilities see Directory of Train Operators

b Change at Leeds and Sheffield
c Change at Doncaster
e Change at Sheffield
f Change at Doncaster and Sheffield
g Wakefield Kirkgate
h Wakefield Kirkgate. Change at Sheffield
j Change at Bedford

Table 53

Sundays

from 30 March

Sheffield → East Midlands → London

Route Diagram - See first page of Table 53

	XC	EM	EM	XC	EM	XC	EM	EM	XC	XC	EM	EM	XC	XC	EM	EM	XC	EM	XC	EM	XC	EM		
				R					R															
	1 ◇ ☕	1 ◇ ☕	◇	1 ☕	1 ◇ ☕	1 ◇ ☕	1 ◇ ☕	◇	1 ☕	1 ◇ ☕	1 ◇ ☕	◇	1 ◇ ☕	1 ◇ ☕	1 ◇ ☕	◇	1 ◇	◇	1 ◇	1 ◇ ☕	1 ◇	◇		
York 8 d	16 20		16 20	16 28	16 28	17 20	17 25	17 25	17 28	18 20	18b07	18 20	18 28	19 20		19 20	19 28	20b02	20 28	20b40	21 26	21b28		
Leeds 10 d				17 00	17 00	17 05	17c09		18 00	18c00			19 00			19 09	20 00		21 00			21 40		
Wakefield Westgate 7 d				17 12	17 12	17 18	17c24		18 12	18c12			19 12			19 24	20 12		21 12			21 55		
Doncaster 7 d	16 50					17 50	18 00			18 50	18 42			19 50				20 42	20 42	21 23	21 50	22 20		
Barnsley d					17 12					18 12				19 12				20 12	20 12	21 12		22 21		
Meadowhall d	17 00				17 33	18 00	18 11		18 26	19 00				20 00		20 11	20 11	21 08	21 08	21 45	22 00	22 50		
Sheffield 7 d	17 23		17 39	17 48	17 52	18 23	18 30	18 40	18 48	19 23	19 26	19 37	19 48	20 23		20 38	20 48	21 41	21 48	22 06	22 23	23 27		
Dronfield d																								
Chesterfield d	17 35		17 53		18 05	18 35	18 43	18 54		19 35	19 41	19 53	20 00	20 35		20 54	21 00	21 56	22 00	22 18	22 35	23 41		
Matlock d											18 38													
Belper d											19 00													
Burton-on-Trent d					17 23						19 21													
Derby 10 a	17 55			18 18	18 27	18 55			19 18	19 55	20 01		20 20	20 55			21 20		22 22	22 43	22 55			
d					18 28						20 02													
Long Eaton d											20 12													
Alfreton d			18 04				18 54	19 05				20 05				21 05		22 08				23 52		
Langley Mill d			18 13				19 02	19 13								21 12		22 15				00 02		
Nottingham 8 a			18 30				19 20	19 34				20 30				21 35		22 38				00 22		
d		18 17					19 33								21 14									
Beeston d		18 22					19 40																	
Loughborough d		18 34			18 47						20 25				21 28									
Barrow Upon Soar d																								
Sileby d																								
Syston d																								
Leicester a		18 44			19 00		20 00				20 36				21 40									
d		18 45			19 00		20 00				20 38				21 41									
Market Harborough d		18 59			19 18		20 14				20 54				21 55									
Kettering d		19 09			19 29		20 24				21 04				22 05									
Wellingborough d		19 16			19 37		20 32				21 11				22 13									
Bedford 7 d		19 36			19 55		20 49				21 30				22 31									
Luton 10 d		19 52			20 33		21 08				21 49				22 50									
Luton Airport Parkway 7 d		20 16			20 36		21 36				22 06				23 06									
Gatwick Airport 10 ✈ a		21 48			22 18		23 18				23 48				00 46									
St Pancras International 15 ⊖ a		20 21			20 49		21 37				22 18				23 22									

For general notes see front of timetable
For details of catering facilities see Directory of Train Operators

b Change at Doncaster and Sheffield
c Change at Sheffield

Kettering → Corby

Bus Service

Mondays to Fridays

	EM MO A 🚌	EM MO B 🚌	EM MX C 🚌	EM MX D 🚌	EM 🚌	EM 🚌	EM 🚌	EM 🚌	EM 🚌	EM 🚌	EM 🚌		EM 🚌	EM 🚌	EM 🚌	EM 🚌	EM 🚌	EM 🚌	EM 🚌	EM 🚌	EM 🚌	EM 🚌	EM 🚌	EM 🚌
St Pancras International 15 53 d	23b00	23b00	23c15	23c15					06 10	07 00	07 30		08 00	08 30	09 00	09 30	10 00	10 30	11 00	11 30	12 00	12 30	13 00	13 30
Sheffield 53 d	⌇	⌇	⌇	⌇				05 20		06 25	06 30			07 14		08 36								
Leicester 53 d	⌇	⌇	⌇	⌇	05e00	05f25	06 00	06 30	06 55	07 30	08 05		08 35	09 05	09 35	10 05	10 35	11 05	11 35	12 05	12 35	13 05	13 35	14 05
Kettering d	00⌇23	00⌇29	00⌇36	00⌇41	05 28	05 59	06 33	07 03	07 25	08 03	08 34		09 04	09 34	10 04	10 34	11 04	11 34	12 04	12 34	13 04	13 34	14 04	14 34
Corby Town Centre a	00⌇43	00⌇49	00⌇56	01⌇01	05 48	06 19	06 53	07 23	07 45	08 23	08 56		09 24	09 54	10 24	10 54	11 24	11 54	12 24	12 54	13 24	13 54	14 24	14 54

	EM 🚌		EM 🚌	EM 🚌	EM 🚌	EM 🚌	EM 🚌	EM 🚌	EM 🚌	EM 🚌	EM 🚌	EM 🚌	EM 🚌	EM 🚌	EM 🚌	EM 🚌	EM D 🚌	EM A 🚌	EM A 🚌	EM D 🚌	EM A 🚌	EM D 🚌		
St Pancras International 15 53 d	14 00		14 30	15 00	15 30	16 00	16 30	17 00	17 30	18 00	18 30	19 00	19 30	20 00	20 30	21 00	21⌇25	21⌇30	22⌇00	22⌇00	22⌇25	22⌇25		
Sheffield 53 d																	20⌇39	20⌇39	⌇	⌇	⌇	⌇		
Leicester 53 d	14 35		15 05	15 35	16 05	16 35	17 05	17 35	18 05	18 35	19 05	19 35	20 05	20 35		21 15	22⌇00	22⌇00	⌇	⌇	⌇	⌇		
Kettering d	15 04		15 34	16 04	16 34	17 04	17 34	18 04	18 38	19 06	19 34	20 06	20 36	21 06	21 33	22 04	22⌇30	22⌇32	23⌇06	23⌇11	23⌇34	23⌇36		
Corby Town Centre a	15 24		15 54	16 24	16 56	17 26	17 56	18 24	18 58	19 26	19 54	20 26	20 56	21 26	21 53	22 24	22⌇50	22⌇52	23⌇26	23⌇31	23⌇54	23⌇56		

Saturdays

	EM E 🚌	EM G 🚌	EM 🚌	EM 🚌		EM 🚌	EM 🚌	EM 🚌	EM 🚌		EM 🚌	EM 🚌	EM 🚌	EM 🚌		EM 🚌	EM 🚌	EM 🚌	EM 🚌		EM 🚌	EM 🚌	EM 🚌	EM 🚌
St Pancras International 15 53 d	23g15	23g15					06 20	07 00	07 30		08 00	08 30	09 00	09 30		10 00	10 30	11 00	11 30		12 00	12 30	13 00	13 30
Sheffield 53 d	⌇	⌇				05 00		06 16	06 34		07 27	07 32	08 27	08 56		09 27								
Leicester 53 d	⌇	⌇	05 30	05 57		06 32	06 55	07 35	08 05		08 35	09 05	09 35	10 05		10 35	11 05	11 35	12 05		12 35	13 05	13 35	14 05
Kettering d	00⌇39	00⌇44	06 01	06 29		07 03	07 29	08 06	08 34		09 04	09 34	10 04	10 34		11 04	11 34	12 04	12 34		13 04	13 34	14 04	14 34
Corby Town Centre a	00⌇59	01⌇04	06 21	06 49		07 23	07 49	08 26	08 54		09 24	09 54	10 24	10 54		11 24	11 54	12 24	12 54		13 24	13 54	14 24	14 54

	EM 🚌	EM 🚌		EM 🚌	EM 🚌	EM 🚌	EM 🚌		EM 🚌	EM 🚌	EM 🚌	EM 🚌		EM 🚌	EM 🚌	EM 🚌	EM 🚌		EM 🚌	EM 🚌	EM E 🚌	EM G 🚌		
St Pancras International 15 53 d	14 00	14 30		15 00	15 30	16 00	16 30		17 00	17 30	18 00	18 30		19 00	19 30	20 00	20 30		21 25	21 35	22⌇10	22⌇10		
Sheffield 53 d						15 02										19 07					⌇	⌇		
Leicester 53 d	14 35	15 05		15 35	16 05	16 35	17 05		17 35	18 05		19 05		19 39	20 05	20 35	21 03				⌇	⌇		
Kettering d	15 04	15 34		16 04	16 34	17 04	17 34		18 04	18 34	19 04	19 34		20 08	20 34	21 04	21 33		22 22	22 34	23⌇40	23⌇44		
Corby Town Centre a	15 24	15 54		16 24	16 54	17 24	17 54		18 24	18 54	19 24	19 54		20 28	20 54	21 24	21 53		22 42	22 54	23⌇59	00⌇04		

Sundays

	EM H 🚌	EM J 🚌	EM H 🚌	EM J 🚌	EM H 🚌	EM J 🚌		EM H 🚌	EM J 🚌	EM H 🚌	EM J 🚌	EM H 🚌	EM J 🚌		EM H 🚌	EM J 🚌	EM H 🚌	EM J 🚌	EM J 🚌	EM H 🚌		EM H 🚌	EM J 🚌	EM H 🚌
St Pancras International 15 53 d												09⌇00	09⌇00		09⌇30	09⌇30	10⌇00	10⌇00	10⌇30	10⌇30		11⌇00	11⌇00	11⌇30
Sheffield 53 d												⌇	⌇		⌇	⌇	⌇	⌇	09⌇26	10⌇08		10⌇14	09⌇40	11⌇13
Leicester 53 d	07⌇19	06⌇47	07⌇50	07h18	08⌇20	07⌇45		08⌇47	08j13	09⌇19	08⌇46	⌇	09⌇06		10⌇22	09⌇47	10⌇47	10⌇16	10⌇43	11⌇19		11⌇47	11k16	12⌇20
Kettering d	07⌇56	07⌇57	08⌇24	08⌇27	08⌇56	08⌇57		09⌇22	09⌇24	09⌇55	09⌇58	10⌇21	10⌇24		10⌇56	10⌇57	11⌇24	11⌇28	11⌇55	11⌇56		12⌇24	12⌇28	12⌇54
Corby Town Centre a	08⌇16	08⌇17	08⌇44	08⌇47	09⌇16	09⌇17		09⌇42	09⌇44	10⌇15	10⌇18	10⌇41	10⌇44		11⌇16	11⌇17	11⌇44	11⌇48	12⌇15	12⌇16		12⌇44	12⌇48	13⌇14

	EM J 🚌	EM H 🚌	EM J 🚌	EM H 🚌	EM J 🚌		EM H 🚌	EM J 🚌	EM H 🚌	EM J 🚌	EM H 🚌	EM J 🚌		EM H 🚌	EM J 🚌	EM H 🚌	EM J 🚌	EM H 🚌	EM J 🚌		EM H 🚌	EM J 🚌	EM H 🚌	EM J 🚌
St Pancras International 15 53 d	11⌇30	12⌇00	12⌇00	12⌇30	12⌇30		13⌇00	13⌇00	13⌇30	13⌇30	14⌇00	14⌇00		14⌇30	14⌇30	15⌇30	15⌇30	16⌇00	16⌇00		16⌇30	16⌇30	17⌇00	17⌇00
Sheffield 53 d	10⌇30	⌇	⌇	11⌇52	11⌇27		⌇	⌇	⌇	12⌇27	13⌇09	⌇		⌇	⌇	14⌇27	14⌇25	⌇	⌇		⌇	15⌇10	16⌇09	15⌇27
Leicester 53 d	11⌇39	⌇	12⌇15	13⌇03	12⌇39		⌇	13⌇15	13⌇52	13⌇43	14⌇47	14⌇06		⌇	⌇	16⌇04	15⌇39	16⌇34	⌇		⌇	16m31	17⌇39	17⌇07
Kettering d	12⌇55	13⌇23	13⌇27	13⌇52	13⌇57		14⌇18	14⌇24	14⌇51	14⌇55	15⌇19	15⌇20		15⌇47	15⌇57	16⌇42	16⌇53	17⌇14	17⌇19		17⌇43	17⌇48	18⌇13	18⌇19
Corby Town Centre a	13⌇15	13⌇43	13⌇47	14⌇12	14⌇17		14⌇38	14⌇42	15⌇11	15⌇15	15⌇39	15⌇40		16⌇07	16⌇17	17⌇02	17⌇13	17⌇34	17⌇39		18⌇03	18⌇08	18⌇33	18⌇39

	EM J 🚌	EM H 🚌	EM H 🚌	EM J 🚌		EM H 🚌	EM J 🚌	EM H 🚌	EM J 🚌	EM H 🚌	EM J 🚌		EM J 🚌	EM H 🚌	EM H 🚌	EM J 🚌	EM H 🚌	EM J 🚌	EM H 🚌	EM J 🚌	EM H 🚌	EM J 🚌		
St Pancras International 15 53 d		17⌇30	18⌇00	18⌇00		18⌇30	18⌇30	19⌇00	19⌇00	19⌇30	19⌇30			20⌇00	20⌇30	20⌇30	21⌇00	21⌇00	21⌇30	21⌇30	22⌇30	22⌇30		
Sheffield 53 d		17⌇08	⌇	16⌇26		17⌇52	17⌇09	⌇	⌇	18⌇30	17⌇35		18⌇51	19⌇26	⌇	⌇	⌇	⌇	⌇	⌇	⌇	⌇		
Leicester 53 d		18⌇17	18⌇45	17⌇59		19⌇00	18⌇32	⌇	⌇	20⌇00	19⌇12		20⌇02	20⌇38	⌇	⌇	21⌇41	21⌇03	⌇	⌇	⌇	⌇		
Kettering d	18⌇48	18⌇50	19⌇16	19⌇18		19⌇44	19⌇52	20⌇13	20⌇17	20⌇44	20⌇47		21⌇13	21⌇15	21⌇43	21⌇47	22⌇14	22⌇22	22⌇47	22⌇53	23⌇45	23⌇54		
Corby Town Centre a	19⌇08	19⌇10	19⌇36	19⌇38		20⌇04	20⌇11	20⌇33	20⌇36	21⌇04	21⌇07		21⌇33	21⌇35	22⌇03	22⌇07	22⌇34	22⌇42	23⌇07	23⌇13	00⌇05	00⌇14		

For general notes see front of timetable
For details of catering facilities see Directory of Train Operators

- **A** From 24 March
- **B** Until 17 March
- **C** From 25 March
- **D** Until 21 March
- **E** From 29 March
- **G** Until 22 March
- **H** From 30 March
- **J** Until 23 March
- **b** Mondays
- **c** Tuesdays to Fridays
- **e** From 24 March only
- **f** Mondays from 24 March dep. 0500
- **g** Saturdays
- **h** 3 February to 23 March dep. 0719
- **j** 3 February to 23 March dep. 0814
- **k** 3 February to 23 March dep. 1109
- **m** 3 February to 23 March dep. 1630

Corby → Kettering
Bus Service

Mondays to Fridays

	EM 🚌	EM 🚌	EM 🚌	EM 🚌	EM 🚌	EM 🚌		EM 🚌	EM 🚌	EM 🚌	EM 🚌	EM 🚌	EM 🚌		EM 🚌	EM 🚌	EM 🚌	EM 🚌	EM 🚌	EM 🚌		EM 🚌	EM 🚌	EM 🚌
Corby Town Centre 🚌 d	04 49	05 20	05 54	06 24	06 56	07 26	.....	07 47	08 23	08 56	09 26	09 56	10 26	.....	10 56	11 26	11 56	12 26	12 56	13 26	.....	13 56	14 26	14 56
Kettering 🚌 a	05 11	05 42	06 16	06 46	07 18	07 48		08 07	08 48	09 18	09 48	10 18	10 48		11 18	11 48	12 18	12 48	13 18	13 48		14 18	14 48	15 18
Leicester 53 a	.....	.....	.....	07 35	07 55	08 23	.....	08 55	09 23	09 55	10 23	10 55	11 23	.....	11 55	12 23	12 55	13 23	13 55	14 23	.....	14 55	15 24	15 56
Sheffield 53 a				09 05																				
St Pancras International 15 53 a	07b05	07c05	07 36	07 59	08 38	08 55	.....	09 12	10 04	10 34	11 04	11 34	12 04	.....	12 34	13 04	13 34	14 04	14 34	15 04	.....	15 34	16 04	16 34

	EM 🚌	EM 🚌	EM 🚌	EM 🚌	EM 🚌		EM 🚌	EM 🚌	EM 🚌	EM 🚌	EM 🚌	EM 🚌		EM 🚌	EM 🚌	EM 🚌	EM A 🚌	EM B 🚌	EM A 🚌	EM B 🚌	EM A 🚌	EM B 🚌		
Corby Town Centre 🚌 d	15 26	15 56	16 26	16 58	17 28	.....	17 58	18 26	18 58	19 26	19 56	20 26	.....	21 06	21 37	21 53	22 27	22 32	22 55	22 57	23 57	00 02	.....	.....
Kettering 🚌 a	15 48	16 18	16 48	17 20	17 50		18 20	18 48	19 18	19 48	20 18	20 48		21 28	21 59	22 13	22 49	22 54	23 17	23 19	00 19	00 24		
Leicester 53 a	16 23	16 55	17 23	17 56	18 35	.....	18 57	19 18	19 55	20 23	20 56	21 23	.....	22 23	23e19	23f46	23 29	00 02	23 56	00 31	01 01	01 33	.....	.....
Sheffield 53 a	17 48		18 47				20 02	20 53		21 49		22 46			00g41	01h52			01 13	01 52				
St Pancras International 15 53 a	17 04	17 34	18 04	18 34	19 04	.....	19 34	20 04	20 34	21 04	21 34	22 04	.....	22 40	23 04	23 32	.....	.....	.....	.....	.....	.....	.....	.....

Saturdays

	EM 🚌	EM 🚌	EM 🚌		EM 🚌	EM 🚌	EM 🚌		EM 🚌	EM 🚌	EM 🚌		EM 🚌	EM 🚌	EM 🚌		EM 🚌	EM 🚌	EM 🚌		EM 🚌	EM 🚌	EM 🚌	EM 🚌
Corby Town Centre 🚌 d	05 22	05 52	06 25	.....	06 51	07 26	07 51	.....	08 28	08 56	09 26	.....	09 56	10 26	10 56	.....	11 26	11 56	12 26	.....	12 56	13 26	13 56	14 26
Kettering 🚌 a	05 44	06 14	06 47		07 11	07 48	08 13		08 48	09 18	09 48		10 18	10 48	11 18		11 48	12 18	12 48		13 18	13 48	14 18	14 48
Leicester 53 a	.....	.....	.....	.....	07 54	08 27	08 55	.....	09 23	09 55	10 23	.....	10 55	11 23	11 55	.....	12 23	12 55	13 23	.....	13 55	14 23	14 55	15 23
Sheffield 53 a					09 13										14 00									
St Pancras International 15 53 a	07 05	07 38	08 05	.....	08 21	09 04	09 17	.....	09 49	10 29	11 04	.....	11 34	11 59	12 34	.....	13 04	13 34	14 04	.....	14 34	15 04	15 34	16 04

	EM 🚌		EM 🚌	EM 🚌	EM 🚌		EM 🚌	EM 🚌	EM 🚌		EM 🚌	EM 🚌	EM 🚌		EM 🚌	EM 🚌	EM 🚌		EM 🚌	EM 🚌	EM C 🚌	EM D 🚌		
Corby Town Centre 🚌 d	14 56	.....	15 26	15 56	16 26	.....	16 56	17 26	17 56	.....	18 26	18 56	19 26	.....	19 56	20 28	20 56	.....	21 26	21 56	22 58	23 02	.....	.....
Kettering 🚌 a	15 18		15 48	16 18	16 48		17 18	17 48	18 18		18 48	19 18	19 48		20 18	20 48	21 18		21 48	22 17	23 20	23 24		
Leicester 53 a	15 55	.....	16 23	16 55	17 23	.....	17 56	18 24	18 55	.....	19 26	19 55	20 23	.....	20 55	21 23	21 55	.....	22 23	22 52	23 55	00 36	.....	.....
Sheffield 53 a					18 59				20 08		20 38		21 47			22 44								
St Pancras International 15 53 a	16 34	.....	17 04	17 34	18 04	.....	18 34	19 04	19 35	.....	20 09	20 35	21 08	.....	21 35	22 04	22 43	.....	.....	.....	.....	.....	.....	.....

Sundays

	EM E 🚌	EM G 🚌	EM E 🚌	EM G 🚌	EM E 🚌	EM G 🚌		EM E 🚌	EM G 🚌	EM E 🚌	EM G 🚌	EM E 🚌	EM G 🚌		EM E 🚌	EM G 🚌	EM G 🚌	EM E 🚌	EM 🚌	EM E 🚌		EM G 🚌	EM G 🚌	EM E 🚌
Corby Town Centre 🚌 d	07 19	07 21	07 49	07 52	08 19	08 20	.....	08 47	08 50	09 19	09 21	09 44	09 47	.....	10 21	10 22	10 47	10 48	11 19	11 47	.....	11 51	12 18	12 19
Kettering 🚌 a	07 39	07 41	08 09	08 12	08 39	08 40		09 07	09 09	09 39	09 41	10 04	10 07		10 41	10 42	11 07	11 08	11 39	12 07		12 11	12 38	12 39
Leicester 53 a							.....					10 37	11 19	.....	11 42	11 52	12 23	12 12	12j59	12 45	.....	13 23	13 53	13 17
Sheffield 53 a												12 25				13 05	14k07	13 20	14m07				15 15	14 40
St Pancras International 15 53 a	09 16	09 16	09 45	09 45	10 16	10 16	.....	10 46	10 46	11 19	11 19	11 49	11 49	.....	12 19	12 19	12 50	12 50	13 18	13 48	.....	13 48	14 18	14 18

	EM 🚌	EM E 🚌	EM G 🚌	EM E 🚌	EM G 🚌		EM E 🚌	EM G 🚌	EM E 🚌	EM G 🚌	EM 🚌	EM G 🚌		EM E 🚌	EM E 🚌	EM G 🚌	EM E 🚌	EM G 🚌	EM E 🚌		EM G 🚌	EM E 🚌	EM G 🚌	EM E 🚌
Corby Town Centre 🚌 d	12 51	13 15	13 18	13 46	13 49	.....	14 19	14 20	14 40	14 42	15 25	15 57	.....	15 59	16 29	16 42	17 11	17 14	17 36	.....	17 44	18 13	18 15	18 36
Kettering 🚌 a	13 11	13 35	13 38	14 06	14 09		14 39	14 40	15 00	15 02	15 45	16 17		16 19	16 49	17 02	17 31	17 34	17 56		18 04	18 33	18 35	18 56
Leicester 53 a	14n28	14 20	14 54	14 43	15 23	.....	15 19		15 42	16 17	16q54	17 50	.....	17 04	17 36	18 18	18 04	18 45	18 37	.....	19 15		19 48	19 36
Sheffield 53 a	16r13	15 39	16 13		17t07		16 43		17 26	18v08	18w08	19 07		18 22			19 25	19 56					21 10	21 02
St Pancras International 15 53 a	14 44	.....	15 11	15 29	15 29	.....	16 06	16 06	16 27	16 27	17 06	17 42	.....	17 41	18 11	18 28	18 57	18 57	19 24	.....	19y30	19 56	19 56	20 21

	EM G 🚌	EM G 🚌	EM E 🚌	EM G 🚌		EM E 🚌	EM E 🚌	EM G 🚌	EM E 🚌	EM G 🚌	EM E 🚌		EM G 🚌	EM E 🚌	EM G 🚌	EM E 🚌	EM G 🚌	EM E 🚌		EM G 🚌	EM E 🚌	EM G 🚌		
Corby Town Centre 🚌 d	18 39	19 08	19 24	19 47	.....	19 54	20 09	20 11	20 34	20 36	21 06	.....	21 10	21 35	21 36	22 10	22 16	23 08	.....	23 14	23 43	23 49	.....	.....
Kettering 🚌 a	18 59	19 28	19 44	20 07		20 14	20 29	20 31	20 54	20 56	21 26		21 30	21 55	21 56	22 30	22 36	23 28		23 34	00 03	00 09		
Leicester 53 a	20z13	20 50	20 35	21 16	.....		21 09	21 46	21 41	22 19	22 08	.....	22 44	22 37	23H19	23 12	23 49	00 07	.....	00 53	00 42	01 24	.....	.....
Sheffield 53 a	21 46	22 13					22 27	23 08			23 12		23 59		00 29	00 29								
St Pancras International 15 53 a	20 22	20 49	.....	21 37	.....	21 37	.....	.....	22 18	22 19	.....	.....	.....	23 22	23 22	.....	.....	.....	.....	.....	.....	.....	.....	.....

For general notes see front of timetable
For details of catering facilities see Directory of Train Operators

- **A** From 24 March
- **B** Until 21 March
- **C** From 29 March
- **D** Until 22 March
- **E** From 30 March
- **G** Until 23 March
- **H** 23 March arr. 2312
- **b** From 24 March arr. 0641
- **c** Mondays from 24 March arr. 0736
- **e** From 24 March arr. 2238
- **f** From 24 March arr. 2255
- **g** Tuesdays to Saturdays. From 24 March arr. 2349
- **h** From 24 March arr. 0113
- **j** From 30 March arr. 1245
- **k** 3 February to 23 March arr. 1409
- **m** 3 February to 23 March arr. 1409. From 30 March arr. 1440
- **n** From 30 March arr. 1345
- **q** From 30 March arr. 1642
- **r** From 30 March arr. 1539
- **t** 3 February to 23 March arr. 1708
- **v** 3 February to 23 March arr. 1811
- **w** 3 February to 23 March arr. 1811. From 30 March arr. 1822
- **y** 3 February to 23 March arr. 1929
- **z** 3 February to 23 March arr. 2012

Nottingham → Mansfield → Worksop

Network Diagram - see first page of Table 50

Miles			EM	EM	EM	EM	EM	EM	EM	EM	EM	EM	EM	EM	EM
0	**Nottingham** 8	d	05 44	06 10	07 03	08 23	08 47	09 26	09 56	10 26	10 56	11 26	11 56	12 26	12 56
5½	Bulwell	d	05 53		07 12	08 35	08 56		10 06		11 06		12 06		13 06
8¼	Hucknall	d	05 58		07 18	08 40	09 01	09 39	10 11	10 39	11 11	11 39	12 11	12 39	13 11
10¾	Newstead	d	06 03		07 24	08 45	09 06	09 44		10 44		11 44		12 44	
13¾	Kirkby In Ashfield	d	06 09	06 30	07 30	08 51	09 12	09 49	10 19	10 49	11 19	11 49	12 19	12 49	13 19
14½	Sutton Parkway	d	06 12	06 33	07 34	08 54	09 15	09 52	10 22	10 52	11 22	11 52	12 22	12 52	13 22
17½	**Mansfield**	d	06 18	06 39	07 40	08 59	09 20	09 57	10 27	10 57	11 27	11 57	12 27	12 57	13 27
18¾	Mansfield Woodhouse	d	06 22	06 44	07 45	09 03	09a27	10 02	10a34	11 02	11a34	12 02	12a34	13 02	13a34
21½	Shirebrook	d	06 29	06 50	07 52	09 10		10 08		11 08		12 08		13 08	
22¼	Langwith - Whaley Thorns	d	06 33	06 54	07 56	09 14		10 12		11 12		12 12		13 12	
25½	Creswell (Derbys)	d	06 37	06 58	08 00	09 18		10 16		11 16		12 16		13 16	
26¾	Whitwell	d	06 40	07 02	08 03	09 21		10 20		11 20		12 20		13 20	
31½	**Worksop**	a	06 52	07 20	08 21	09 33		10 31		11 31		12 31		13 31	

		EM	EM	EM	EM	EM	EM	EM	EM	EM	EM	EM	EM	EM
Nottingham 8	d	13 26	13 56	14 26	14 56	15 26	15 56	16 26	16 56	17 26	17 55	18 56	19 56	21 05
Bulwell	d		14 06		15 06		16 06		17 06	17 39	18 11	19 05	20 05	21 14
Hucknall	d	13 39	14 11	14 39	15 11	15 39	16 11	16 38	17 12	17 44	18 16	19 10	20 11	21 19
Newstead	d	13 44		14 44		15 44		16 43	17 17	17 49	18 21	19 15	20 16	21 24
Kirkby In Ashfield	d	13 49	14 19	14 49	15 19	15 49	16 19	16 49	17 23	17 55	18 27	19 21	20 27	21 30
Sutton Parkway	d	13 52	14 22	14 52	15 22	15 52	16 22	16 52	17 27	17 58	18 30	19 24	20 30	21 33
Mansfield	d	13 57	14 27	14 57	15 27	15 57	16 27	16 57	17 32	18 03	18 35	19 29	20 35	21 38
Mansfield Woodhouse	d	14 02	14a34	15 02	15a34	16 02	16a34	17 02	17a39	18 08	18 39	19 33	20 39	21 43
Shirebrook	d	14 08		15 08		16 08		17 08		18 14	18 46	19 40	20 46	21 49
Langwith - Whaley Thorns	d	14 12		15 12		16 12		17 12		18 18	18 50	19 44	20 50	21 53
Creswell (Derbys)	d	14 16		15 16		16 16		17 16		18 22	18 54	19 48	20 54	21 57
Whitwell	d	14 20		15 20		16 20		17 20		18 26	18 57	19 51	20 57	22 01
Worksop	a	14 31		15 31		16 31		17 31		18 37	19 09	20 03	21 09	22 12

Saturdays

		EM	EM	EM	EM	EM	EM	EM	EM	EM	EM	EM	EM	EM
Nottingham 8	d	05 39	06 12	07 14	08 23	08 48	09 26	09 56	10 26	10 56	11 26	11 56	12 26	12 56
Bulwell	d	05 48	06 21	07 23	08 35	08 57		10 06		11 06		12 06		13 06
Hucknall	d	05 53	06 26	07 28	08 40	09 02	09 39	10 11	10 39	11 11	11 39	12 11	12 39	13 11
Newstead	d	05 58	06 31	07 33	08 45	09 07	09 44		10 44		11 44		12 44	
Kirkby In Ashfield	d	06 04	06 37	07 39	08 50	09 13	09 49	10 19	10 49	11 19	11 49	12 19	12 49	13 19
Sutton Parkway	d	06 07	06 40	07 42	08 53	09 16	09 52	10 22	10 52	11 22	11 52	12 22	12 52	13 22
Mansfield	d	06 13	06 45	07 47	08 59	09 21	09 57	10 27	10 57	11 27	11 57	12 27	12 57	13 27
Mansfield Woodhouse	d	06 17	06 50	07 52	09 03	09a28	10 02	10a34	11 02	11a34	12 02	12a34	13 02	13a34
Shirebrook	d	06 24	06 56	07 58	09 10		10 08		11 08		12 08		13 08	
Langwith - Whaley Thorns	d	06 28	07 00	08 02	09 14		10 12		11 12		12 12		13 12	
Creswell (Derbys)	d	06 32	07 04	08 06	09 18		10 16		11 16		12 16		13 16	
Whitwell	d	06 35	07 08	08 10	09 21		10 20		11 20		12 20		13 20	
Worksop	a	06 47	07 20	08 21	09 33		10 31		11 31		12 31		13 31	

		EM	EM	EM	EM	EM	EM	EM	EM	EM	EM	EM	EM	EM
Nottingham 8	d	13 26	13 56	14 26	14 56	15 26	15 56	16 26	16 56	17 26	17 56	18 56	19 56	21 05
Bulwell	d		14 06		15 06		16 06		17 06	17 40	18 12	19 05	20 05	21 14
Hucknall	d	13 39	14 11	14 39	15 11	15 39	16 11	16 39	17 11	17 45	18 17	19 10	20 11	21 19
Newstead	d	13 44		14 44		15 44		16 44	17 16	17 50	18 22	19 15	20 16	21 24
Kirkby In Ashfield	d	13 49	14 19	14 49	15 19	15 49	16 19	16 49	17 22	17 55	18 28	19 21	20 27	21 30
Sutton Parkway	d	13 52	14 22	14 52	15 22	15 52	16 22	16 52	17 26	17 58	18 31	19 24	20 30	21 33
Mansfield	d	13 57	14 27	14 57	15 27	15 57	16 27	16 57	17 31	18 03	18 36	19 29	20 35	21 38
Mansfield Woodhouse	d	14 02	14a34	15 02	15a34	16 02	16a34	17 02	17a38	18 08	18 39	19 33	20 39	21 43
Shirebrook	d	14 08		15 08		16 08		17 08		18 14	18 46	19 40	20 46	21 49
Langwith - Whaley Thorns	d	14 12		15 12		16 12		17 12		18 18	18 50	19 44	20 50	21 53
Creswell (Derbys)	d	14 16		15 16		16 16		17 16		18 22	18 54	19 48	20 54	21 57
Whitwell	d	14 20		15 20		16 20		17 20		18 26	18 57	19 51	20 57	22 01
Worksop	a	14 31		15 31		16 31		17 31		18 37	19 09	20 03	21 09	22 12

For general notes see front of timetable
For details of catering facilities see Directory of Train Operators

No Sunday Service

Worksop → Mansfield → Nottingham

Network Diagram - see first page of Table 50

Miles			EM	EM ◇ A	EM B	EM	EM	EM	EM	EM	EM	EM	EM	EM	EM
0	**Worksop**	d	05 50		06 56		07 37	08 38		09 40		10 40		11 40	
4¾	Whitwell	d	05 59		07 06		07 46	08 47		09 49		10 49		11 49	
6	Creswell (Derbys)	d	06 02		07 09		07 49	08 50		09 52		10 52		11 52	
9¼	Langwith - Whaley Thorns	d	06 06		07 13		07 54	08 55		09 57		10 57		11 57	
10	Shirebrook	d	06 10		07 17		07 57	08 58		10 00		11 00		12 00	
12¾	Mansfield Woodhouse	d	06 18	07 06	07 25	07 39	08 05	09 06	09 37	10 08	10 37	11 08	11 37	12 08	12 37
14¼	**Mansfield**	d	06 21	07 10	07 29	07 43	08 09	09 10	09 40	10 12	10 40	11 12	11 40	12 12	12 40
17	Sutton Parkway	d	06 27	07 15	07 35	07 48	08 14	09 15	09 46	10 17	10 46	11 17	11 46	12 17	12 46
17¾	Kirkby In Ashfield	d	06 30	07 18	07 38	07 52	08 17	09 18	09 49	10 20	10 49	11 20	11 49	12 20	12 49
20¾	Newstead	d	06 35	07 29	07 43	07 57	08 22	09 23	09 54		10 54		11 54		12 54
23¼	Hucknall	d	06 39	07 35	07 48	08 02	08 27	09 27	09 58	10 27	10 58	11 27	11 58	12 27	12 58
26	Bulwell	d	06 43	07 40	07 53	08 06	08 31	09 31		10 31		11 31		12 31	
31½	**Nottingham** 8	a	06 57	07 50	08 05	08 18	08 45	09 46	10 16	10 45	11 15	11 45	12 15	12 45	13 15

		EM	EM	EM	EM	EM	EM	EM	EM	EM	EM	EM	EM	EM	EM	EM
Worksop	d	12 40		13 40		14 40		15 40		16 42		17 45	18 52	19 21	20 15	21 21
Whitwell	d	12 49		13 49		14 49		15 49		16 51		17 54	19 01	19 30	20 24	21 30
Creswell (Derbys)	d	12 52		13 52		14 52		15 52		16 54		17 57	19 04	19 33	20 27	21 33
Langwith - Whaley Thorns	d	12 57		13 57		14 57		15 57		16 59		18 01	19 09	19 37	20 31	21 38
Shirebrook	d	13 00		14 00		15 00		16 00		17 02		18 07	19 12	19 41	20 35	21 41
Mansfield Woodhouse	d	13 08	13 37	14 08	14 37	15 08	15 37	16 08	16 37	17 10	17 43	18 14	19 20	19 48	20 43	21 49
Mansfield	d	13 12	13 40	14 12	14 40	15 12	15 40	16 11	16 41	17 14	17 46	18 18	19 24	19 52	20 47	21 53
Sutton Parkway	d	13 17	13 46	14 17	14 46	15 17	15 46	16 17	16 46	17 19	17 52	18 24	19 29	19 57	20 52	21 58
Kirkby In Ashfield	d	13 20	13 49	14 20	14 49	15 20	15 49	16 20	16 49	17 22	17 55	18 27	19 32	20 00	20 55	22 01
Newstead	d		13 54		14 54		15 54		16 54		17 59	18 32	19 37	20 05	21 00	22 06
Hucknall	d	13 27	13 58	14 27	14 58	15 27	15 58	16 27	16 58	17 30	18 04	18 36	19 41	20 09	21 04	22 10
Bulwell	d	13 31		14 31		15 31		16 31		17 34		18 40	19 45	20 13	21 08	22 14
Nottingham 8	a	13 46	14 16	14 45	15 15	15 45	16 15	16 45	17 16	17 48	18 23	18 52	20 01	20 26	21 22	22 26

Saturdays

		EM	EM	EM	EM	EM	EM	EM	EM	EM	EM	EM	EM	EM
Worksop	d	06 03	07 01	07 37	08 38		09 40		10 40		11 40		12 40	
Whitwell	d	06 12	07 10	07 46	08 47		09 49		10 49		11 49		12 49	
Creswell (Derbys)	d	06 15	07 13	07 49	08 50		09 52		10 52		11 52		12 52	
Langwith - Whaley Thorns	d	06 19	07 18	07 54	08 55		09 57		10 57		11 57		12 57	
Shirebrook	d	06 23	07 21	07 57	08 58		10 00		11 00		12 00		13 00	
Mansfield Woodhouse	d	06 31	07 29	08 05	09 06	09 37	10 08	10 37	11 08	11 37	12 08	12 37	13 08	13 37
Mansfield	d	06 34	07 33	08 08	09 09	09 40	10 11	10 40	11 11	11 40	12 11	12 40	13 11	13 40
Sutton Parkway	d	06 40	07 38	08 14	09 15	09 46	10 17	10 46	11 17	11 46	12 17	12 46	13 17	13 46
Kirkby In Ashfield	d	06 43	07 41	08 17	09 18	09 49	10 20	10 49	11 20	11 49	12 20	12 49	13 20	13 49
Newstead	d	06 48	07 46	08 22	09 23	09 54		10 54		11 54		12 54		13 54
Hucknall	d	06 52	07 51	08 26	09 27	09 58	10 27	10 58	11 27	11 58	12 27	12 58	13 27	13 58
Bulwell	d	06 56	07 55	08 30	09 31		10 31		11 31		12 31		13 31	
Nottingham 8	a	07 10	08 08	08 45	09 45	10 15	10 45	11 15	11 46	12 15	12 45	13 16	13 45	14 15

		EM	EM	EM	EM	EM	EM	EM	EM	EM	EM	EM	EM	EM
Worksop	d	13 40		14 40		15 40		16 42		17 45	18 52	19 21	20 15	21 21
Whitwell	d	13 49		14 49		15 49		16 51		17 54	19 01	19 30	20 24	21 30
Creswell (Derbys)	d	13 52		14 52		15 52		16 54		17 57	19 04	19 33	20 27	21 33
Langwith - Whaley Thorns	d	13 57		14 57		15 57		16 59		18 02	19 09	19 37	20 31	21 38
Shirebrook	d	14 00		15 00		16 00		17 02		18 07	19 12	19 41	20 35	21 41
Mansfield Woodhouse	d	14 08	14 37	15 08	15 37	16 08	16 37	17 10	17 43	18 14	19 20	19 48	20 43	21 49
Mansfield	d	14 11	14 40	15 11	15 40	16 11	16 40	17 13	17 46	18 18	19 24	19 52	20 47	21 53
Sutton Parkway	d	14 17	14 46	15 17	15 46	16 17	16 46	17 19	17 52	18 24	19 29	19 57	20 52	21 58
Kirkby In Ashfield	d	14 20	14 49	15 20	15 49	16 20	16 49	17 22	17 55	18 27	19 32	20 00	20 55	22 01
Newstead	d		14 54		15 54		16 54	17 27	18 00	18 32	19 37	20 05	21 00	22 06
Hucknall	d	14 27	14 58	15 27	15 58	16 27	16 58	17 31	18 04	18 37	19 42	20 09	21 05	22 11
Bulwell	d	14 31		15 31		16 31		17 35		18 41	19 46	20 13	21 09	22 15
Nottingham 8	a	14 45	15 15	15 45	16 15	16 45	17 15	17 49	18 19	18 55	20 01	20 27	21 23	22 29

For general notes see front of timetable
For details of catering facilities see Directory of Train Operators

A To Norwich (Table 49)
B To Lincoln (Table 27)

No Sunday Service

Table 56

Derby → Matlock

Mondays to Fridays
until 25 January

Network Diagram - see first page of Table 50

Miles			EM	EM	EM 1 ◇	EM	EM	EM	EM	EM	EM	EM	EM	EM
0	**Derby 10**	d	05 42	06 57	08 16	08 27	10 26	12 26	14 25	16 20	17 35	18 55	20 30	22 20
5¼	Duffield	d	05 49	07 04	.	08 34	10 33	12 33	14 32	16 27	17 42	19 02	20 37	22 27
7¾	Belper	d	05 54	07 08	08a25	08 39	10 38	12 38	14 37	16 32	17 47	19 07	20 42	22 32
10½	Ambergate	d	06 00	07 14	.	08 45	10 44	12 44	14 43	16 38	17 52	19 13	20 48	22 38
12½	Whatstandwell	d	06 04	07 18	.	08 49	10 48	12 48	14 47	16 42	17 56	19 17	20 52	22 42
15½	Cromford	d	06 09	07 22	.	08 54	10 53	12 53	14 52	16 47	18 01	19 22	20 57	22 47
16¼	Matlock Bath	d	06 11	07 25	.	08 56	10 55	12 55	14 54	16 49	18 04	19 24	20 59	22 49
17¼	**Matlock**	a	06 14	07 27	.	08 59	10 58	12 58	14 57	16 52	18 07	19 27	21 02	22 52

Mondays to Fridays
from 28 January

		EM	EM	EM 1 ◇	EM	EM	EM	EM	EM	EM	EM	EM	EM
Derby 10	d	05 42	06 57	08 16	08 27	10 26	12 26	14 25	16 20	17 35	18 55	20 30	22 20
Duffield	d	05 49	07 04	.	08 34	10 33	12 33	14 32	16 27	17 42	19 02	20 37	22 27
Belper	d	05 54	07 08	08a25	08 39	10 38	12 38	14 37	16 32	17 47	19 07	20 42	22 32
Ambergate	d	06 00	07 14	.	08 45	10 44	12 44	14 43	16 38	17 52	19 13	20 48	22 38
Whatstandwell	d	06 04	07 18	.	08 49	10 48	12 48	14 47	16 42	17 56	19 17	20 52	22 42
Cromford	d	06 09	07 22	.	08 54	10 53	12 53	14 52	16 47	18 01	19 22	20 57	22 47
Matlock Bath	d	06 11	07 25	.	08 56	10 55	12 55	14 54	16 49	18 04	19 24	20 59	22 49
Matlock	a	06 14	07 27	.	08 59	10 58	12 58	14 57	16 52	18 07	19 27	21 02	22 52

Saturdays
until 26 January

		EM	EM	EM	EM	EM	EM	EM	EM	EM	EM	EM 1 ◇	EM
Derby 10	d	05 37	07 02	08 21	09 49	11 52	13 30	14 48	16 22	17 48	19 21	19 58	21 51
Duffield	d	05 44	07 09	08 28	09 56	11 59	13 37	14 55	16 29	17 55	19 28	.	21 58
Belper	d	05 49	07 14	08 33	10 01	12 04	13 42	15 00	16 34	18 00	19 33	20a06	22 03
Ambergate	d	05 55	07 20	08 39	10 07	12 10	13 48	15 06	16 40	18 06	19 39	.	22 09
Whatstandwell	d	05 59	07 24	08 43	10 11	12 14	13 52	15 10	16 44	18 10	19 43	.	22 13
Cromford	d	06 04	07 29	08 48	10 16	12 19	13 57	15 15	16 49	18 15	19 48	.	22 18
Matlock Bath	d	06 06	07 31	08 50	10 18	12 21	13 59	15 17	16 51	18 17	19 50	.	22 20
Matlock	a	06 09	07 34	08 53	10 21	12 24	14 02	15 20	16 54	18 20	19 53	.	22 23

Saturdays
from 2 February

		EM	EM	EM	EM	EM	EM	EM	EM	EM	EM	EM 1 ◇	EM
Derby 10	d	05 37	07 02	08 21	09 49	11 52	13 30	14 48	16 22	17 48	19 21	19 58	21 51
Duffield	d	05 44	07 09	08 28	09 56	11 59	13 37	14 55	16 29	17 55	19 28	.	21 58
Belper	d	05 49	07 14	08 33	10 01	12 04	13 42	15 00	16 34	18 00	19 33	20a06	22 03
Ambergate	d	05 55	07 20	08 39	10 07	12 10	13 48	15 06	16 40	18 06	19 39	.	22 09
Whatstandwell	d	05 59	07 24	08 43	10 11	12 14	13 52	15 10	16 44	18 10	19 43	.	22 13
Cromford	d	06 04	07 29	08 48	10 16	12 19	13 57	15 15	16 49	18 15	19 48	.	22 18
Matlock Bath	d	06 06	07 31	08 50	10 18	12 21	13 59	15 17	16 51	18 17	19 50	.	22 20
Matlock	a	06 09	07 34	08 53	10 21	12 24	14 02	15 20	16 54	18 20	19 53	.	22 23

Sundays
until 27 January

		EM A	EM A	EM A	EM A	EM A	EM A	EM A
Derby 10	d	09 59	11 32	13 51	15 46	17 56	19 49	21 53
Duffield	d	10 06	11 39	13 58	15 53	18 03	19 56	22 00
Belper	d	10 11	11 44	14 03	15 58	18 08	20 01	22 05
Ambergate	d	10 17	11 50	14 09	16 04	18 14	20 07	22 11
Whatstandwell	d	10 21	11 54	14 13	16 08	18 18	20 11	22 15
Cromford	d	10 26	11 59	14 18	16 13	18 23	20 16	22 20
Matlock Bath	d	10 28	12 01	14 20	16 15	18 25	20 18	22 22
Matlock	a	10 31	12 04	14 23	16 18	18 28	20 21	22 25

For general notes see front of timetable
For details of catering facilities see Directory of Train Operators

A From Nottingham (Table 57)

Table 56

from 3 February

Derby → Matlock

Network Diagram - see first page of Table 50

		EM A	EM A	EM A	EM A	EM A	EM A	EM A
Derby 10	d	09 59	11 32	13 51	15 46	17 56	19 49	21 53
Duffield	d	10 06	11 39	13 58	15 53	18 03	19 56	22 00
Belper	d	10 11	11 44	14 03	15 58	18 08	20 01	22 05
Ambergate	d	10 17	11 50	14 09	16 04	18 14	20 07	22 11
Whatstandwell	d	10 21	11 54	14 13	16 08	18 18	20 11	22 15
Cromford	d	10 26	11 59	14 18	16 13	18 23	20 16	22 20
Matlock Bath	d	10 28	12 01	14 20	16 15	18 25	20 18	22 22
Matlock	a	10 31	12 04	14 23	16 18	18 28	20 21	22 25

For general notes see front of timetable
For details of catering facilities see Directory of Train Operators

A From Nottingham (Table 57)

Table 56

Mondays to Fridays
until 25 January

Matlock → Derby

Network Diagram - see first page of Table 50

Miles			EM	EM	EM [1] ◇ ☕	EM	EM	EM	EM	EM	EM	EM	EM	EM A
0	**Matlock**	d	06 20	07 38		09 04	11 12	13 12	15 17	16 58	18 13	19 38	21 10	22 59
1	Matlock Bath	d	06 22	07 40		09 06	11 14	13 14	15 19	17 00	18 15	19 40	21 12	23 01
1¾	Cromford	d	06 25	07 43		09 09	11 17	13 17	15 22	17 03	18 18	19 43	21 15	23 04
4¾	Whatstandwell	d	06 30	07 48		09 14	11 22	13 22	15 27	17 08	18 23	19 48	21 20	23 09
6¾	Ambergate	d	06 35	07 53		09 20	11 27	13 27	15 32	17 13	18 28	19 53	21 25	23 14
9½	Belper	d	06 40	07 58	09 03	09 25	11 33	13 33	15 38	17 19	18 33	19 58	21 30	23 19
12	Duffield	d	06 45	08 03		09 29	11 37	13 37	15 42	17 23	18 37	20 02	21 34	23 23
17¼	**Derby [10]**	a	06 51	08 09	09 13	09 36	11 45	13 45	15 49	17 30	18 47	20 10	21 42	23 31

Mondays to Fridays
from 28 January

		EM	EM	EM [1] ◇ ☕	EM	EM	EM	EM	EM	EM	EM	EM	EM A
Matlock	d	06 20	07 38		09 04	11 12	13 12	15 17	16 58	18 13	19 38	21 10	22 59
Matlock Bath	d	06 22	07 40		09 06	11 14	13 14	15 19	17 00	18 15	19 40	21 12	23 01
Cromford	d	06 25	07 43		09 09	11 17	13 17	15 22	17 03	18 18	19 43	21 15	23 04
Whatstandwell	d	06 30	07 48		09 14	11 22	13 22	15 27	17 08	18 23	19 48	21 20	23 09
Ambergate	d	06 35	07 53		09 20	11 27	13 27	15 32	17 13	18 28	19 53	21 25	23 14
Belper	d	06 40	07 58	09 03	09 25	11 33	13 33	15 38	17 19	18 33	19 58	21 30	23 19
Duffield	d	06 45	08 03		09 29	11 37	13 37	15 42	17 23	18 37	20 02	21 34	23 23
Derby [10]	a	06 51	08 09	09 13	09 37	11 45	13 45	15 49	17 30	18 47	20 10	21 42	23 31

Saturdays
until 26 January

		EM	EM	EM	EM [1] ◇ ☕	EM	EM	EM	EM	EM	EM	EM	EM A
Matlock	d	06 14	07 39	08 58		10 38	12 38	14 10	15 38	17 01	18 38	20 20	22 28
Matlock Bath	d	06 16	07 41	09 00		10 40	12 40	14 12	15 40	17 03	18 40	20 22	22 30
Cromford	d	06 19	07 44	09 03		10 43	12 43	14 15	15 43	17 06	18 43	20 25	22 33
Whatstandwell	d	06 24	07 49	09 08		10 48	12 48	14 20	15 48	17 11	18 48	20 30	22 38
Ambergate	d	06 29	07 54	09 13		10 53	12 53	14 25	15 53	17 16	18 53	20 35	22 43
Belper	d	06 34	07 59	09 18	09 26	10 58	12 58	14 30	15 58	17 21	18 58	20 40	22 48
Duffield	d	06 38	08 03	09 22		11 02	13 02	14 34	16 02	17 25	19 02	20 44	22 53
Derby [10]	a	06 46	08 11	09 30	09 33	11 10	13 10	14 42	16 10	17 33	19 10	20 52	23 00

Saturdays
from 2 February

		EM	EM	EM	EM [1] ◇ ☕	EM	EM	EM	EM	EM	EM	EM	EM A
Matlock	d	06 14	07 39	08 58		10 38	12 38	14 10	15 38	17 01	18 38	20 20	22 28
Matlock Bath	d	06 16	07 41	09 00		10 40	12 40	14 12	15 40	17 03	18 40	20 22	22 30
Cromford	d	06 19	07 44	09 03		10 43	12 43	14 15	15 43	17 06	18 43	20 25	22 33
Whatstandwell	d	06 24	07 49	09 08		10 48	12 48	14 20	15 48	17 11	18 48	20 30	22 38
Ambergate	d	06 29	07 54	09 13		10 53	12 53	14 25	15 53	17 16	18 53	20 35	22 43
Belper	d	06 34	07 59	09 18	09 26	10 58	12 58	14 30	15 58	17 21	18 58	20 40	22 48
Duffield	d	06 38	08 03	09 22		11 02	13 02	14 34	16 02	17 25	19 02	20 44	22 53
Derby [10]	a	06 46	08 11	09 30	09 33	11 10	13 10	14 42	16 10	17 33	19 10	20 52	23 00

Sundays
until 27 January

		EM A	EM A	EM A	EM A	EM A	EM A	EM
Matlock	d	10 42	12 41	14 36	16 40	18 38	20 40	22 33
Matlock Bath	d	10 44	12 43	14 38	16 42	18 40	20 42	22 35
Cromford	d	10 46	12 46	14 41	16 45	18 43	20 45	22 38
Whatstandwell	d	10 51	12 51	14 46	16 50	18 48	20 50	22 43
Ambergate	d	10 57	12 56	14 51	16 55	18 53	20 55	22 48
Belper	d	11 02	13 02	14 58	17 00	19 00	21 00	22 53
Duffield	d	11 06	13 06	15 02	17 04	19 04	21 04	22 57
Derby [10]	a	11 13	13 14	15 10	17 12	19 12	21 12	23 04

For general notes see front of timetable
For details of catering facilities see Directory of Train Operators

A To Nottingham (Table 57)

Table 56

Sundays

from 3 February

Matlock → Derby

Network Diagram - see first page of Table 50

		EM A	EM A	EM A	EM A	EM A	EM A	EM
Matlock	d	10 42	12 41	14 36	16 40	18 38	20 40	22 33
Matlock Bath	d	10 44	12 43	14 38	16 42	18 40	20 42	22 35
Cromford	d	10 46	12 46	14 41	16 45	18 43	20 45	22 38
Whatstandwell	d	10 51	12 51	14 46	16 50	18 48	20 50	22 43
Ambergate	d	10 57	12 56	14 51	16 55	18 53	20 55	22 48
Belper	d	11 02	13 02	14 58	17 00	19 00	21 00	22 53
Duffield	d	11 06	13 06	15 02	17 04	19 04	21 04	22 57
Derby 10	a	11 13	13 14	15 10	17 12	19 12	21 12	23 04

For general notes see front of timetable
For details of catering facilities see
Directory of Train Operators

A To Nottingham (Table 57)

Nottingham, Derby and Leicester → Birmingham → Cardiff and Bristol

Network Diagram - see first page of Table 50

Miles	Miles	Miles			EM	AW	GW	XC	GW	XC	GW	XC	GW		GW	AW	XC	XC	EM	EM	EM	XC	XC		XC
					MX ■1 ◇	A	■1 ◇		■1 ◇			■1 ◇	◇ B		■1 ◇	A	■1 ◇ C		D	■1 ◇	■1 ◇	◇	■1 ◇		
0	—	—	**Nottingham** 8	d	02 19														05 55	06 07	06 25				
3¼	—	—	Beeston	d															06 00	06a12	06a30				
4¾	—	—	Attenborough	d															06 04						
7¾	—	—	Long Eaton	d															06 13						
13½	—	—	Spondon	d															06 19						
16	—	—	**Derby** 10	a	02 36														06 26						
—	—	—		d													06 10					06 35	06 57		
22¼	—	—	Willington	d																		06 45			
27	—	—	Burton-on-Trent	d													06 20					06 51	07 07		
40	—	—	Tamworth	d													06 31					07 03	07 18		
41¾	—	—	Wilnecote	d																		07 06			
—	0	—	**Leicester**	d														06 03							06 52
—	1¾	—	South Wigston	d														06 11							06 57
—	4¾	—	Narborough	d														06 16							07 02
—	13½	—	Hinckley	d														06 24							07 10
—	18¾	—	Nuneaton	d														06 31							07 17
—	29¼	—	Coleshill Parkway	d														06 47							07 33
—	31	—	Water Orton	d																					07 36
56¾	38¾	—	**Birmingham New Street** 12	a													06 51	07 05				07 27	07 36		07 50
—	—	0		d						05 30		06 10					07 10					07 30	07 40		
83¾	—	—	Worcester Shrub Hill 7	d				05 40		06 17			06 49												
98½	—	39¼	Ashchurch for Tewkesbury	d				05 55		06 33			07 05												
105¾	—	46½	Cheltenham Spa	d		05 37	05 58	06 04	06 31	06 43	07 02	07 22	07 15		07 27	07 45	07 52					08 11	08 22		
112¼	—	—	Gloucester 7	a		05 48	06 08	06 14	06 41	06 52	07 12		07 25		07 36	07 56						08 23			
—	—	87	Bristol Parkway 7	a							07 51	07 54	08 24				08 25						08 54		
—	—	92¾	**Bristol Temple Meads** 10	a							08 03	08 11	08 36				08 41						09 11		
157	—	—	Newport (South Wales)	a		06 41		07 06		07 50						08 49						09 07			
168¾	—	—	**Cardiff Central** 7	a		07 00		07 27		08 12						09 10						09 29			

		XC	XC	XC	GW	AW	XC	XC	XC	XC		EM	EM	XC	XC	XC	XC	XC	EM	EM		GW	GW	XC	XC
			E	■1 ◇	■1 ◇	A	■1 ◇ C	◇ G		◇		■1 ◇	■1 ◇ H	■1 ◇ J		■1 ◇	◇ K			■1 ◇ L		N		R ■1 Q	
Nottingham 8	d	06 38								07 00		07 07	07 30					07 34	07 38						
Beeston	d									07 06		07a12	07a35					07 40	07a44						
Attenborough	d									07 09															
Long Eaton	d	06 52	06 57							07 16								07 50		08 00					
Spondon	d		07 03																						
Derby 10	a	07 03	07 11							07 28								08 00		08 12					
	d	07 08		07 20			07 24			07 39				07 47		07 57		08 05						08 27	
Willington	d																	08 13							
Burton-on-Trent	d	07 19					07 35			07 51				07 58				08 19						08 37	
Tamworth	d	07 31					07 46			08 02				08 12				08 31						08 48	
Wilnecote	d	07 34																08 35							
Leicester	d							07 07	07 24								07 51								08 08
South Wigston	d																07 56								
Narborough	d							07 17									08 01								08 19
Hinckley	d							07 26									08 09								08 28
Nuneaton	d							07 33	07 43								08 17								08 35
Coleshill Parkway	d							07 52	07 58																08 56
Water Orton	d								08 02																
Birmingham New Street 12	a	07 57		07 58			08 07	08 09	08 15	08 25				08 36		08 36	08 48	08 54						09 06	09 09
	d						08 10			08 30					06 10	08 40								09 10	
Worcester Shrub Hill 7	d																					09 05			
Ashchurch for Tewkesbury	d																					09 21			
Cheltenham Spa	d				08 31	08 45	08 52			09 11					07 22	09 22						09 31	09 38	09 52	
Gloucester 7	a				08 40	08 56				09 21												09 39	09 48		
Bristol Parkway 7	a						09 25								07 56	09 54						10 19		10 25	
Bristol Temple Meads 10	a						09 41								08 11	10 11						10 34		10 41	
Newport (South Wales)	a					09 50				10 09															
Cardiff Central 7	a					10 10				10 30															

For general notes see front of timetable
For details of catering facilities see Directory of Train Operators

- **A** To Maesteg (Table 128)
- **B** To Weymouth (Table 123)
- **C** To Plymouth (Table 51)
- **D** To Crewe (Table 50)
- **E** From Leicester
- **G** From Cambridge (Table 49)
- **H** From Sheffield (Table 53)
- **J** To Manchester Piccadilly (Table 65)
- **K** From Stansted Airport (Table 49)
- **L** To Sheffield (Table 53)
- **N** From Great Malvern (Table 71) to Westbury (Table 123)
- **Q** From Leeds to Plymouth (Table 51)

Nottingham, Derby and Leicester → Birmingham → Cardiff and Bristol

Network Diagram - see first page of Table 50

		XC	EM	EM	EM	XC	XC	XC		XC	XC	GW	AW	XC	XC	EM	EM	XC		XC	XC	GW	GW	AW	XC
		◇	1 ◇	1 ◇	1 ◇	R 1	◇			R 1		1 ◇		1 ◇	◇	1 ◇	1 ◇	1 ◇		◇		◇			1 ◇
				A		B	C						D	E				G		H		J		D	E
Nottingham 8	d	08 00	08 07	08 26				08 34							09 00	09 07					09 34				
Beeston	d	08 06	08a12	08a33											09 06	09a12					09 41				
Attenborough	d	08 09													09 09										
Long Eaton	d	08 17			08 44			08 50							09 18		09 44				09 50				
Spondon	d	08 24													09 25										
Derby 10	a	08 30			08 55			09 00							09 30		09 56				10 00				
	d	08 38				08 57		09 06		09 24					09 38			09 57			10 08				10 24
Willington	d																				10 15				
Burton-on-Trent	d	08 51						09 17							09 51			10 07			10 21				
Tamworth	d	09 03						09 31							10 03			10 18			10 33				
Wilnecote	d							09 35																	
Leicester	d						08 52				09 09									09 52					
South Wigston	d																								
Narborough	d										09 18														
Hinckley	d										09 27														
Nuneaton	d						09 14				09 34									10 14					
Coleshill Parkway	d						09 29				09 52									10 29					
Water Orton	d										09 56														
Birmingham New Street 12	a	09 27				09 36	09 47	09 54		09 58	10 09				10 27			10 36		10 47	10 54				11 04
	d	09 30				09 40								10 10	10 30			10 40							11 10
Worcester Shrub Hill 7	d																					11 05			
Ashchurch for Tewkesbury	d																					11 21			
Cheltenham Spa	d	10 11				10 22						10 31	10 45	10 52	11 11			11 22				11 31	11 38	11 45	11 52
Gloucester 7	a	10 21										10 40	10 56		11 21							11 39	11 48	11 56	
Bristol Parkway 7	a					10 54								11 25				11 54				12 19			12 25
Bristol Temple Meads 10	a					11 11								11 41				12 11				12 35			12 41
Newport (South Wales)	a	11 10											11 50		12 09									12 50	
Cardiff Central 7	a	11 32											12 10		12 32									13 10	

		XC	XC	EM	EM	XC		XC	XC	XC	XC	GW	XC	XC	EM	EM		XC	XC	XC	GW	GW	AW	XC	XC
			◇	1 ◇	1 ◇	1 ◇		◇		R 1		1 ◇	1 ◇	◇	1 ◇	1 ◇		1 ◇	◇		◇			1 ◇	
						B		H					E					G	H		K		D	E	
Nottingham 8	d		10 02	10 07					10 34					11 00	11 07					11 34					
Beeston	d		10 08	10a12					10 40					11 06	11a12					11 40					
Attenborough	d								10 43					11 09											
Long Eaton	d		10 18		10 44				10 49					11 19		11 44				11 50					
Spondon	d																								
Derby 10	a		10 31		10 56				11 00					11 29		11 56				12 00					
	d		10 38			10 57			11 08	11 24				11 38				11 57		12 08				12 24	
Willington	d								11 15																
Burton-on-Trent	d		10 51						11 21					11 51				12 07		12 19					
Tamworth	d		11 03						11 33					12 03				12 18		12 31					
Wilnecote	d																			12 35					
Leicester	d	10 09						10 52			11 09								11 52						12 09
South Wigston	d	10 15																							12 15
Narborough	d	10 20									11 18														12 20
Hinckley	d	10 28									11 26														12 28
Nuneaton	d	10 35						11 14			11 34								12 14						12 35
Coleshill Parkway	d	10 52						11 29			11 50								12 29						12 52
Water Orton	d										11 54														
Birmingham New Street 12	a	11 09	11 27			11 36		11 47	11 54	11 58	12 09			12 27				12 36	12 47	12 54				13 04	13 09
	d		11 30			11 40							12 10	12 30				12 40						13 10	
Worcester Shrub Hill 7	d																				13 05				
Ashchurch for Tewkesbury	d																				13 21				
Cheltenham Spa	d		12 11			12 22						12 31	12 52	13 11				13 22			13 31	13 38	13 45	13 52	
Gloucester 7	a		12 21									12 40		13 21							13 39	13 48	13 56		
Bristol Parkway 7	a					12 54							13 25					13 54			14 19			14 25	
Bristol Temple Meads 10	a					13 11							13 41					14 11			14 34			14 41	
Newport (South Wales)	a		13 09											14 10									14 51		
Cardiff Central 7	a		13 34											14 32									15 10		

For general notes see front of timetable
For details of catering facilities see Directory of Train Operators

- **A** From Sheffield (Table 53)
- **B** To Paignton (Table 51)
- **C** From Cambridge (Table 49)
- **D** To Maesteg (Table 128)
- **E** To Plymouth (Table 51)
- **G** From Newcastle (Table 51)
- **H** From Stansted Airport (Table 49)
- **J** From Great Malvern (Table 71) to Brighton (Table 123)
- **K** From Great Malvern (Table 71) to Weymouth (Table 123)

Table 57

Mondays to Fridays

until 25 January

Nottingham, Derby and Leicester → Birmingham → Cardiff and Bristol

Network Diagram - see first page of Table 50

		XC	EM	EM		XC	XC	XC	XC	XC	GW	AW	XC	XC		EM	EM	XC	XC	XC	GW	XC	XC	XC	EM
		◇	1 ◇	1 ◇		R 1	◇		R 1		1 ◇		R 1	◇		1 ◇	1 ◇	1 ◇	◇			R 1		◇	1 ◇
						A	B				C	D	E					G	B			H			
			☕	☕		☕	🛒		☕		🛒		☕	🛒		☕	☕	☕	🛒			☕		🛒	☕
Nottingham [8]	d	12 02	12 07					12 34						13 00		13 07				13 34				14 00	14 07
Beeston	d	12 08	12a12					12 40						13 06		13a12				13 40				14 06	14a12
Attenborough	d													13 09											
Long Eaton	d	12 18		12 44				12 50						13 18			13 44			13 50				14 17	
Spondon	d	12 24																							
Derby [10]	a	12 31		12 56				13 00						13 31			13 56			14 00				14 31	
	d	12 38				12 57		13 08	13 24					13 38				13 57		14 08		14 24		14 38	
Willington	d	12 45																		14 15					
Burton-on-Trent	d	12 51						13 19						13 51				14 07		14 21				14 51	
Tamworth	d	13 03						13 31						14 03				14 18		14 33				15 03	
Wilnecote	d							13 35																15 07	
Leicester	d						12 52			13 09									13 52				14 09		
South Wigston	d																						14 15		
Narborough	d									13 18													14 20		
Hinckley	d									13 26													14 28		
Nuneaton	d						13 14			13 35									14 14				14 35		
Coleshill Parkway	d						13 29			13 51									14 29				14 53		
Water Orton	d									13 54															
Birmingham New Street [12]	a	13 27				13 36	13 47	13 54	13 58	14 09				14 27				14 36	14 47	14 54		15 04	15 09	15 27	
	d	13 30				13 40							14 10	14 30				14 40				15 10		15 30	
Worcester Shrub Hill [7]	d																								
Ashchurch for Tewkesbury	d																							16 06	
Cheltenham Spa	d	14 11				14 22					14 31	14 45	14 52	15 11				15 22			15 38	15 52		16 15	
Gloucester [7]	a	14 21									14 40	14 56		15 21							15 48			16 24	
Bristol Parkway [7]	a					14 54							15 25					15 54				16 25			
Bristol Temple Meads [10]	a					15 11							15 41					16 11				16 41			
Newport (South Wales)	a	15 09										15 51		16 09										17 09	
Cardiff Central [7]	a	15 32										16 09		16 32										17 32	

		EM		XC	XC	XC	XC	XC	GW	AW	XC	XC		EM	EM	XC	XC	XC	GW	GW	AW	XC		XC	XC
		1 ◇		1 ◇	◇		R 1		1 ◇		R 1	◇		1 ◇	1 ◇	1 ◇	◇					R 1			◇
				A	B					D	E					G	B		J	K	D	A			L
		☕		☕	🛒		☕		🛒		☕	🛒		☕	☕	☕	🛒					☕			🛒
Nottingham [8]	d					14 34						15 00		15 07				15 34							16 00
Beeston	d					14 40						15 06		15a12				15 40							16 06
Attenborough	d											15 09													16 09
Long Eaton	d	14 44				14 50						15 16			15 45			15 50							16 17
Spondon	d																								16 24
Derby [10]	a	14 56				15 00						15 30			15 56			16 00							16 33
	d			14 57		15 08	15 24					15 38				15 57		16 08				16 24			16 38
Willington	d																								
Burton-on-Trent	d					15 19						15 51				16 07		16 20							16 51
Tamworth	d					15 31						16 03				16 18		16 34							17 03
Wilnecote	d																	16 37							
Leicester	d				14 52			15 09									15 52							16 09	
South Wigston	d																							16 15	
Narborough	d							15 21																16 20	
Hinckley	d							15 29																16 28	
Nuneaton	d				15 14			15 37									16 14							16 35	
Coleshill Parkway	d				15 29			15 53									16 29							16 52	
Water Orton	d							15 56																	17 16
Birmingham New Street [12]	a			15 36	15 47	15 54	15 58	16 09				16 26				16 36	16 47	16 54				17 04		17 12	17 27
	d			15 40							16 10	16 30				16 40						17 10			17 30
Worcester Shrub Hill [7]	d																		17 05						
Ashchurch for Tewkesbury	d																		17 21						18 09
Cheltenham Spa	d			16 22					16 31	16 45	16 52	17 14				17 22			17 31	17 38	17 45	17 52			18 18
Gloucester [7]	a								16 40	16 56		17 23							17 39	17 48	17 56				18 29
Bristol Parkway [7]	a			16 54							17 25					17 54			18 19			18 25			
Bristol Temple Meads [10]	a			17 11							17 41					18 11			18 34			18 41			
Newport (South Wales)	a									17 51		18 09									18 50				19 14
Cardiff Central [7]	a									18 10		18 32									19 10				19 36

For general notes see front of timetable
For details of catering facilities see Directory of Train Operators

- **A** To Plymouth (Table 51)
- **B** From Stansted Airport (Table 49)
- **C** **The Cheltenham Spa Express**
- **D** To Maesteg (Table 128)
- **E** To Penzance (Table 51)
- **G** From Newcastle (Table 51)
- **H** To Penzance (Table 135)
- **J** From Worcester Foregate Street (Table 71) to Westbury (Table 123)
- **K** To Westbury (Table 123)
- **L** 🛒 to Newport (South Wales)

Nottingham, Derby and Leicester → Birmingham → Cardiff and Bristol

Network Diagram - see first page of Table 50

		EM	EM	XC	XC	XC	EM	XC	XC	GW		AW	XC	XC	EM	EM	XC	XC	XC	EM		AW	XC	XC	GW
		1◇	1◇	R 1	◇			R 1		1◇			1◇	◇	1◇	1◇	R 1	◇					1◇		
					A		B					C	D				E	A		B		C	D		
		☕	☕	☕	trolley			☕		trolley			☕		☕	☕	☕	trolley					☕		
Nottingham 8	d	16 07				16 34	16 38							17 00	17 07				17 34	17 38					
Beeston	d	16a12				16 40								17 06	17a12				17 40						
Attenborough	d						16a45							17 09						17a45					
Long Eaton	d		16 44			16 48								17 17		17 44			17 50						
Spondon	d													17 23											
Derby 10	a		16 56			17 00								17 31		17 56			18 01						
	d			16 57		17 06		17 24						17 38			17 57		18 06				18 24		
Willington	d													17 45											
Burton-on-Trent	d					17 20								17 51			18 07		18 19						
Tamworth	d					17 31								18 03			18 18		18 31						
Wilnecote	d																								
Leicester	d				16 52				17 11									17 52						18 23	
South Wigston	d								17 16									17 58						18 29	
Narborough	d								17 21									18 02						18 33	
Hinckley	d								17 29									18 10						18 42	
Nuneaton	d				17 14				17 36									18 18						18 51	
Coleshill Parkway	d				17 29				17 52																
Water Orton	d																		18 44						
Birmingham New Street 12	a			17 36	17 47	17 54		17 58	18 09					18 27			18 36	18 48	18 56				19 08	19 18	
	d			17 40									18 10	18 30			18 40						19 10		
Worcester Shrub Hill 7	d																								
Ashchurch for Tewkesbury	d																								
Cheltenham Spa	d			18 22						18 31		18 45	18 52	19 14			19 22					19 45	19 52		20 00
Gloucester 7	a			18 34						18 40		18 56		19 23								19 56			20 10
Bristol Parkway 7	a			19 05									19 25				19 54						20 25		
Bristol Temple Meads 10	a			19 22									19 41				20 11						20 41		
Newport (South Wales)	a			19 59								19 50		20 10								20 50			
Cardiff Central 7	a			20 19								20 11		20 29								21 10			

		XC	EM	XC	XC	XC	EM	EM		XC	XC	GW	XC	XC	XC	EM	XC	EM		EM	EM	EM	GW	AW	XC
		◇	1◇	R 1	◇		1◇	1◇		R 1		1◇	1◇	◇	1◇	1◇				1◇	1◇	1◇			1◇
					A								D	A	G	H		B		H	J		K		
			☕	☕	trolley		☕	☕		☕		trolley		trolley	☕	☕				☕	☕	☕			
Nottingham 8	d	18 00	18 07			18 34		19 07									19 34	19 38				20 07			
Beeston	d	18 06	18a12					19a12									19 40	19a44				20a12			
Attenborough	d	18 09																							
Long Eaton	d	18 17				18 46	18 56									19 47	19 51				20 03				
Spondon	d																								
Derby 10	a	18 29				18 56	19 09									19 59	20 02			←	20 15				
	d	18 39		18 57		19 06				19 24					19 57	20 11	20 08			20 11					20 27
Willington	d					19 14										→				20 21					
Burton-on-Trent	d	18 51				19 20									20 07		20 19			20a26					
Tamworth	d	19 03				19 31									20 18		20 31								
Wilnecote	d	19 06																							
Leicester	d				18 52						19 09			19 41											
South Wigston	d										19 16														
Narborough	d										19 20														
Hinckley	d										19 30														
Nuneaton	d				19 14						19 38			20 01											
Coleshill Parkway	d				19 29						19 55			20 16											
Water Orton	d																								
Birmingham New Street 12	a	19 27		19 36	19 47	19 54				19 58	20 09			20 37	20 43		20 58								21 04
	d	19 30		19 40									20 10												21 10
Worcester Shrub Hill 7	d																						21 08		
Ashchurch for Tewkesbury	d	20 06																					21 24		
Cheltenham Spa	d	20 15		20 22								20 48	20 52										21 34	21 45	21 52
Gloucester 7	a	20 24										20 58											21 45	21 56	
Bristol Parkway 7	a			20 54									21 25												22 25
Bristol Temple Meads 10	a			21 11									21 41												22 41
Newport (South Wales)	a	21 10																						22 57	
Cardiff Central 7	a	21 31																						23 18	

For general notes see front of timetable
For details of catering facilities see Directory of Train Operators

- **A** From Stansted Airport (Table 49)
- **B** From Lincoln (Table 27)
- **C** To Maesteg (Table 128)
- **D** To Plymouth (Table 51)
- **E** From Newcastle to Weston-super-Mare (Table 51)
- **G** From Newcastle (Table 51)
- **H** From St Pancras International (Table 53)
- **J** To Sheffield (Table 53)
- **K** From Great Malvern (Table 71)

Nottingham, Derby and Leicester → Birmingham → Cardiff and Bristol

Mondays to Fridays
until 25 January

Network Diagram - see first page of Table 50

		XC	XC	XC	EM	XC		XC	GW	GW	AW	XC	XC	EM	GW	XC		LM FO	XC	XC	XC	XC	EM		
			1 ◇	◇	1 ◇					◇		1 ◇	◇	1 ◇					1 ◇		◇	1 ◇	1 ◇		
				A	B							C	A						C		A	D	B		
				🛒	☕					🛒			🛒	☕							🛒		☕		
Nottingham 8	d					20 34										21 36							22 58		
Beeston	d					20 40										21 41							23 04		
Attenborough	d															21 44									
Long Eaton	d				20 44	20 49								21 44		21 52							23 14		
Spondon	d															21 59									
Derby 10	a				20 56	21 01								21 56		22 04							23 26		
	d		20 57		21 03	21 09						21 27				22 08			22 27			23 15			
Willington	d				21 11																				
Burton-on-Trent	d				21a16	21 18						21 37				22 19			22 37			23 26			
Tamworth	d					21 30						21 48				22 31			22 48			23 37			
Wilnecote	d					21 34										22 34									
Leicester	d	20 09		20 52				21 09					21 36							22 27	22 49				
South Wigston	d	20 15						21 15												22 33					
Narborough	d	20 20						21 19												22 37					
Hinckley	d	20 28						21 28												22 46					
Nuneaton	d	20 37		21 14				21 37					21 58							22 54	23 09				
Coleshill Parkway	d	20 57		21 29									22 17							23 14	23 26				
Water Orton	d					21 42																			
Birmingham New Street 12	a	21 09	21 44	21 47		21 57		22 04				22 08	22 36			22 54			23 21	23 34	23 43	23 59			
	d											22 10						23 04							
Worcester Shrub Hill 7	d														22 32			23 44							
Ashchurch for Tewkesbury	d														22 50			23 58							
Cheltenham Spa	d								22 00	22 31	22 45	22 52			23 00			00 07							
Gloucester 7	a								22 10	22 41	22 56				23 13			00 16							
Bristol Parkway 7	a									23 16		23 25													
Bristol Temple Meads 10	a									23 30		23 41													
Newport (South Wales)	a										23 59														
Cardiff Central 7	a										00 22														

Mondays to Fridays
from 28 January

		XC	XC	XC	EM	EM	AW	GW	XC	GW	XC	GW	XC	GW		XC	GW	AW	XC	XC	EM	EM	EM	XC	XC
		MO	MO	MO	MX	MX																			
					1 ◇	1 ◇		1 ◇		1 ◇			1 ◇	◇		1 ◇	1 ◇		1 ◇			1 ◇	1 ◇	◇	1 ◇
		E	E	E	G	H	J							K				J	L		N				
		🚌	🚌	🚌	☕	☕		🛒		🛒			☕			☕	🛒		☕			☕	⊠ 🛒		☕
Nottingham 8	d				01 44	02 19															05 55	06 07	06 25		
Beeston	d																				06 00	06a12	06a30		
Attenborough	d																				06 04				
Long Eaton	d																				06 13				
Spondon	d																				06 19				
Derby 10	a				02 05	02 36															06 26				
	d																		06 10					06 35	06 57
Willington	d																							06 45	
Burton-on-Trent	d																		06 20					06 51	07 07
Tamworth	d																		06 31					07 03	07 18
Wilnecote	d																							07 06	
Leicester	d	23p10	23p10	23p10																06 03					
South Wigston	d	23p26	23p26	23p26																06 11					
Narborough	d	23p37	23p37	23p37																06 16					
Hinckley	d	00 01	00 02	00 02																06 24					
Nuneaton	d	00 20	00 20	00 21																06 31					
Coleshill Parkway	d																			06 47					
Water Orton	d																								
Birmingham New Street 12	a	01 05	01 05	01 06															06 51	07 05				07 27	07 36
	d										05 30		06 10			06 10			07 10					07 30	07 40
Worcester Shrub Hill 7	d								05 40		06 17			06 49											
Ashchurch for Tewkesbury	d								05 55		06 33			07 05											
Cheltenham Spa	d						05 37	05 58	06 04	06 31	06 43	07 02	07 22	07 15		07 22	07 27	07 45	07 52					08 11	08 22
Gloucester 7	a						05 48	06 08	06 14	06 41	06 52	07 12		07 25			07 36	07 56						08 23	
Bristol Parkway 7	a											07 51	07 54	08 24		07 56			08 25						08 54
Bristol Temple Meads 10	a											08 03	08 11	08 36		08 11			08 41						09 11
Newport (South Wales)	a						06 41		07 06		07 50							08 49						09 07	
Cardiff Central 7	a						07 00		07 27		08 12							09 10						09 29	

For general notes see front of timetable
For details of catering facilities see Directory of Train Operators

- **A** From Stansted Airport (Table 49)
- **B** From St Pancras International (Table 53)
- **C** From Edinburgh (Table 51)
- **D** From Newcastle (Table 51)
- **E** From 31 March
- **G** From 25 March
- **H** Until 21 March
- **J** To Maesteg (Table 128)
- **K** To Weymouth (Table 123)
- **L** To Plymouth (Table 51)
- **N** To Crewe (Table 50)

Table 57

Nottingham, Derby and Leicester → Birmingham → Cardiff and Bristol

Mondays to Fridays
from 28 January

Network Diagram - see first page of Table 50

		XC	XC	XC	XC	GW		AW	XC	XC	XC	XC	XC	EM	EM	XC	XC	XC	XC	XC		EM	EM	GW	GW
											MO		MX			MO									
					1 ◇	1 ◇			1 ◇	◇	◇		◇	1 ◇	1 ◇	◇	1 ◇	1 ◇	◇				1 ◇		
				A				B	C	D					E		G		H				J	K	
					☕	🍴			☕		🍴		🍴	☕	⊠ 🍴	🍴	☕	☕					☕		
Nottingham 8 🚌	d		06 38								07 00		07 00	07 07	07 30					07 34		07 38			
Beeston	d										07 06		07 06	07a12	07a35					07 40		07a44			
Attenborough	d										07 09		07 09												
Long Eaton	d		06 52	06 57							07 16		07 16							07 50			08 00		
Spondon	d			07 03																					
Derby 10	a		07 03	07 11							07 28		07 31			←				08 00			08 12		
	d		07 08		07 20				07 24		07 39 →		07 38			07 39	07 47	07 57		08 05					
Willington	d																			08 13					
Burton-on-Trent	d		07 19						07 35				07 51			07 51	07 58			08 19					
Tamworth	d		07 31						07 46				08 03			08 03	08 12			08 31					
Wilnecote	d		07 34																	08 35					
Leicester	d	06 52								07 07		07 24							07 51						
South Wigston	d	06 57																	07 56						
Narborough	d	07 02								07 17									08 01						
Hinckley	d	07 10								07 26									08 09						
Nuneaton	d	07 17								07 33		07 43							08 17						
Coleshill Parkway	d	07 33								07 52		07 58													
Water Orton	d	07 36										08 02													
Birmingham New Street 12	a	07 50	07 57		07 58				08 07	08 09		08 15	08 25			08 25	08 36	08 36	08 48	08 54					
	d								08 10				08 30			08 30		08 40							
Worcester Shrub Hill 7	d																							09 05	
Ashchurch for Tewkesbury	d																							09 21	
Cheltenham Spa	d					08 31		08 45	08 52				09 11			09 11		09 22						09 31	09 38
Gloucester 7	a					08 40		08 56					09 21			09 21								09 39	09 48
Bristol Parkway 7	a								09 25									09 54						10 19	
Bristol Temple Meads 10	a								09 41									10 11						10 34	
Newport (South Wales)	a							09 50					10 09			10 09									
Cardiff Central 7	a							10 10					10 30			10 30									

		XC	XC	XC	EM	EM	EM	XC	XC	XC	XC	XC		GW	AW	XC	XC	EM	EM	XC	XC	XC	GW	GW	AW
		R						R			R														
		1		◇	1 ◇	1 ◇	1 ◇	1	◇		1			1 ◇		1 ◇	◇	1 ◇	1 ◇	1 ◇	◇		◇		
		L				E		N	D						B	C				Q	H		U		B
		☕		🍴	☕	☕	☕	☕			☕			🍴		☕	🍴	☕	☕	☕					
Nottingham 8 🚌	d			08 00	08 07	08 26				08 34							09 00	09 07				09 34			
Beeston	d			08 06	08a12	08a33											09 06	09a12				09 41			
Attenborough	d			08 09													09 09								
Long Eaton	d			08 17			08 44			08 50							09 18		09 44			09 50			
Spondon	d			08 24													09 25								
Derby 10	a			08 30			08 55			09 00							09 30		09 54			10 00			
	d	08 27		08 38				08 57		09 06	09 24						09 38			09 57		10 08			
Willington	d																					10 15			
Burton-on-Trent	d	08 37		08 51						09 17							09 51			10 07		10 21			
Tamworth	d	08 48		09 03						09 31							10 03			10 18		10 33			
Wilnecote	d									09 35															
Leicester	d		08 08						08 52			09 09									09 52				
South Wigston	d																								
Narborough	d		08 19									09 18													
Hinckley	d		08 28									09 27													
Nuneaton	d		08 35						09 14			09 34									10 14				
Coleshill Parkway	d		08 56						09 29			09 52									10 29				
Water Orton	d											09 56													
Birmingham New Street 12	a	09 06	09 09	09 27				09 36	09 47	09 54	09 58	10 09					10 27			10 36	10 47	10 54			
	d	09 10		09 30				09 40								10 10	10 30			10 40					
Worcester Shrub Hill 7	d																						11 05		
Ashchurch for Tewkesbury	d																						11 21		
Cheltenham Spa	d	09 52		10 11				10 22						10 31	10 45	10 52	11 11			11 22			11 31	11 38	11 45
Gloucester 7	a			10 21										10 40	10 56		11 21						11 39	11 48	11 56
Bristol Parkway 7	a	10 25						10 54								11 25				11 54			12 19		
Bristol Temple Meads 10	a	10 41						11 11								11 41				12 11			12 35		
Newport (South Wales)	a			11 10											11 50		12 09								12 50
Cardiff Central 7	a			11 32											12 10		12 32								13 10

For general notes see front of timetable
For details of catering facilities see Directory of Train Operators

- **A** From Leicester
- **B** To Maesteg (Table 128)
- **C** To Plymouth (Table 51)
- **D** From Cambridge (Table 49)
- **E** From Sheffield (Table 53)
- **G** To Manchester Piccadilly (Table 65)
- **H** From Stansted Airport (Table 49)
- **J** To Sheffield (Table 53)
- **K** From Great Malvern (Table 71) to Westbury (Table 123)
- **L** From Leeds to Plymouth (Table 51)
- **N** To Paignton (Table 51)
- **Q** From Newcastle (Table 51)
- **U** From Great Malvern (Table 71) to Brighton (Table 123)

Table 57

Mondays to Fridays

from 28 January

Nottingham, Derby and Leicester → Birmingham → Cardiff and Bristol

Network Diagram - see first page of Table 50

		XC	XC	XC		EM	EM	XC	XC	XC	XC	XC	GW	XC	XC	EM	EM	XC		XC	XC	GW	GW	AW	XC
		1 ◇		◇		1 ◇	1 ◇	1 ◇	◇		R 1		1 ◇	1 ◇	◇	1 ◇	1 ◇	1 ◇		◇		◇			1 ◇
		A						B	C					A				D		C		E		G	A
		☕		🛒		☕	☕	☕	🛒		☕		🛒	☕	🛒	☕	☕	☕		🛒					☕
Nottingham 8 ⛴	d			10 02		10 07				10 34					11 00	11 07					11 34				
Beeston	d			10 08		10a12				10 40					11 06	11a12					11 40				
Attenborough	d									10 43					11 09										
Long Eaton	d			10 18			10 44			10 49					11 19		11 44				11 50				
Spondon	d																								
Derby 10	a			10 31			10 54			11 00					11 31		11 54				12 00				
	d	10 24		10 38				10 57		11 08	11 24				11 38			11 57			12 08				12 24
Willington	d									11 15															
Burton-on-Trent	d			10 51						11 21					11 51			12 07			12 19				
Tamworth	d			11 03						11 33					12 03			12 18			12 31				
Wilnecote	d																				12 35				
Leicester	d		10 09						10 52			11 09								11 52					
South Wigston	d		10 15																						
Narborough	d		10 20									11 18													
Hinckley	d		10 28									11 26													
Nuneaton	d		10 35						11 14			11 34								12 14					
Coleshill Parkway	d		10 52						11 29			11 50								12 29					
Water Orton	d											11 54													
Birmingham New Street 12	a	11 04	11 09	11 27				11 36	11 47	11 54	11 58	12 09			12 27			12 36		12 47	12 54				13 04
	d	11 10		11 30				11 40						12 10	12 30			12 40							13 10
Worcester Shrub Hill 7	d																					13 05			
Ashchurch for Tewkesbury	d																					13 21			
Cheltenham Spa	d	11 52		12 11				12 22					12 31	12 52	13 11			13 22				13 31	13 38	13 45	13 52
Gloucester 7	a			12 21									12 40		13 21							13 39	13 48	13 56	
Bristol Parkway 7	a	12 25						12 54						13 25				13 54				14 19			14 25
Bristol Temple Meads 10	a	12 41						13 11						13 41				14 11				14 34			14 41
Newport (South Wales)	a			13 09											14 10									14 51	
Cardiff Central 7	a			13 34											14 32									15 10	

		XC	XC	EM	EM	XC	XC	XC	XC	XC		GW	AW	XC	XC	EM	EM	XC	XC	XC	GW	GW	XC	XC	XC
			◇	1 ◇	1 ◇	R 1	◇		R 1			1 ◇		R 1	◇	1 ◇	1 ◇	1 ◇	◇		◇		R 1		◇
						A	C					H	G	J				D	C				K		
				☕	☕	☕	🛒		☕			🛒		☕	🛒	☕	☕	☕	🛒				☕		🛒
Nottingham 8 ⛴	d		12 02	12 07				12 34							13 00	13 07				13 34					14 00
Beeston	d		12 08	12a12				12 40							13 06	13a12				13 40					14 06
Attenborough	d														13 09										
Long Eaton	d		12 18		12 44			12 50							13 18		13 44			13 50					14 17
Spondon	d		12 24																						
Derby 10	a		12 31		12 54			13 00							13 31		13 54			14 00					14 31
	d		12 38			12 57		13 08	13 24						13 38			13 57		14 08			14 24		14 38
Willington	d		12 45																	14 15					
Burton-on-Trent	d		12 51					13 19							13 51			14 07		14 21					14 51
Tamworth	d		13 03					13 31							14 03			14 18		14 33					15 03
Wilnecote	d							13 35																	15 07
Leicester	d	12 09					12 52			13 09									13 52					14 09	
South Wigston	d	12 15																						14 15	
Narborough	d	12 20								13 18														14 20	
Hinckley	d	12 28								13 26														14 28	
Nuneaton	d	12 35					13 14			13 35									14 14					14 35	
Coleshill Parkway	d	12 52					13 29			13 51									14 29					14 53	
Water Orton	d									13 54															
Birmingham New Street 12	a	13 09	13 27			13 36	13 47	13 54	13 58	14 09					14 27			14 36	14 47	14 54			15 04	15 09	15 27
	d		13 30			13 40								14 10	14 30			14 40					15 10		15 30
Worcester Shrub Hill 7	d																				15 05				
Ashchurch for Tewkesbury	d																				15 21				16 06
Cheltenham Spa	d		14 11			14 22						14 31	14 45	14 52	15 11			15 22			15 31	15 38	15 52		16 15
Gloucester 7	a		14 21									14 40	14 56		15 21						15 39	15 48			16 24
Bristol Parkway 7	a					14 54								15 25				15 54			16 19		16 25		
Bristol Temple Meads 10	a					15 11								15 41				16 11			16 34		16 41		
Newport (South Wales)	a		15 09										15 51		16 09										17 09
Cardiff Central 7	a		15 32										16 09		16 32										17 32

For general notes see front of timetable
For details of catering facilities see Directory of Train Operators

- **A** To Plymouth (Table 51)
- **B** To Paignton (Table 51)
- **C** From Stansted Airport (Table 49)
- **D** From Newcastle (Table 51)
- **E** From Great Malvern (Table 71) to Weymouth (Table 123)
- **G** To Maesteg (Table 128)
- **H** **The Cheltenham Spa Express**
- **J** To Penzance (Table 51)
- **K** To Penzance (Table 135)

Nottingham, Derby and Leicester → Birmingham → Cardiff and Bristol

Network Diagram - see first page of Table 50

		EM		EM	XC	XC	XC	XC	XC	GW	AW	XC	XC	EM	EM	XC		XC	XC	GW	GW	AW	XC	XC	XC
								[R]				[R]											[R]		
		[1] ◇		[1] ◇	[1] ◇	◇		[1]		[1] ◇		[1]	◇	[1] ◇	[1] ◇	[1] ◇		◇					[1]		◇
					A	B					C	D				E		B		G	H	C	A		J
		⊡		⊡	⊡	☕		⊡		☕		⊡	☕	⊡	⊡	⊡		☕					⊡		☕
Nottingham [8] 🚊	d	14 07					14 34						15 00	15 07					15 34						16 00
Beeston	d	14a12					14 40						15 06	15a12					15 40						16 06
Attenborough	d												15 09												16 09
Long Eaton	d			14 44			14 50						15 16		15 45				15 50						16 17
Spondon	d																								16 24
Derby [10]	a			14 54			15 00						15 30		15 55				16 00						16 33
	d				14 57		15 08	15 24					15 38			15 57			16 08				16 24		16 38
Willington	d																								
Burton-on-Trent	d						15 19						15 51			16 07			16 20						16 51
Tamworth	d						15 31						16 03			16 18			16 34						17 03
Wilnecote	d																		16 37						
Leicester	d					14 52			15 09									15 52						16 09	
South Wigston	d																							16 15	
Narborough	d								15 21															16 20	
Hinckley	d								15 29															16 28	
Nuneaton	d					15 14			15 37									16 14						16 35	
Coleshill Parkway	d					15 29			15 53									16 29						16 52	
Water Orton	d								15 56																17 16
Birmingham New Street [12]	a				15 36	15 47	15 54	15 58	16 09				16 26			16 36		16 47	16 54				17 04	17 12	17 27
	d				15 40							16 10	16 30			16 40							17 10		17 30
Worcester Shrub Hill [7]	d																			17 05					
Ashchurch for Tewkesbury	d																			17 21					18 09
Cheltenham Spa	d				16 22					16 31	16 45	16 52	17 14			17 22				17 31	17 38	17 45	17 52		18 18
Gloucester [7]	a									16 40	16 56		17 23							17 39	17 48	17 56			18 29
Bristol Parkway [7]	a				16 54							17 25				17 54				18 19			18 25		
Bristol Temple Meads [10]	a				17 11							17 41				18 11				18 34			18 41		
Newport (South Wales)	a										17 51		18 09									18 50			19 14
Cardiff Central [7]	a										18 10		18 32									19 10			19 36

		EM	EM	XC	XC	XC	EM	XC		XC	GW	AW	XC	XC	EM	EM	XC	XC	XC	EM	GW	AW		XC	XC
				[R]				[R]									[R]								
		[1] ◇	[1] ◇	[1]	◇			[1]			[1] ◇		[1] ◇	◇	[1] ◇	[1] ◇	[1]	◇			◇			[1] ◇	
					B		K					C	A				L	B		K		C		A	
		⊡	⊡	⊡	☕			⊡			☕		⊡		⊡	⊡	⊡	☕						⊡	
Nottingham [8] 🚊	d	16 07				16 34	16 38							17 00	17 07				17 34	17 38					
Beeston	d	16a12				16 40								17 06	17a12				17 40						
Attenborough	d						16a45							17 09						17a45					
Long Eaton	d		16 44			16 48								17 17		17 44			17 50						
Spondon	d													17 23											
Derby [10]	a		16 54			17 00								17 31		17 54			18 01						
	d			16 57		17 07		17 24						17 38			17 57		18 06					18 24	
Willington	d													17 45											
Burton-on-Trent	d					17 20								17 51			18 07		18 19						
Tamworth	d					17 31								18 03			18 18		18 31						
Wilnecote	d																								
Leicester	d				16 52					17 11								17 52							18 23
South Wigston	d									17 16								17 58							18 29
Narborough	d									17 21								18 02							18 33
Hinckley	d									17 29								18 10							18 42
Nuneaton	d				17 14					17 36								18 18							18 51
Coleshill Parkway	d				17 29					17 52															
Water Orton	d																		18 44						
Birmingham New Street [12]	a			17 36	17 47	17 54		17 58		18 09				18 27			18 36	18 48	18 56					19 08	19 18
	d			17 40									18 10	18 30			18 40							19 10	
Worcester Shrub Hill [7]	d																				19 05				
Ashchurch for Tewkesbury	d																				19 21				
Cheltenham Spa	d			18 22							18 31	18 45	18 52	19 14			19 22				19 31	19 45		19 52	
Gloucester [7]	a			18 34							18 40	18 56		19 23							19 40	19 56			
Bristol Parkway [7]	a			19 05									19 25				19 54				20 19			20 25	
Bristol Temple Meads [10]	a			19 22									19 41				20 11				20 34			20 41	
Newport (South Wales)	a			19 59								19 50		20 10								20 50			
Cardiff Central [7]	a			20 19								20 11		20 29								21 10			

For general notes see front of timetable
For details of catering facilities see Directory of Train Operators

A To Plymouth (Table 51)
B From Stansted Airport (Table 49)
C To Maesteg (Table 128)
D To Penzance (Table 51)
E From Newcastle (Table 51)
G From Worcester Foregate Street (Table 71) to Westbury (Table 123)
H To Westbury (Table 123)
J ☕ to Newport (South Wales)
K From Lincoln (Table 27)
L From Newcastle to Weston-super-Mare (Table 51)

Table 57

Nottingham, Derby and Leicester → Birmingham → Cardiff and Bristol

Mondays to Fridays
from 28 January

Network Diagram - see first page of Table 50

Station		GW	XC	EM	XC	XC	XC	EM	EM	XC	XC	GW	XC	XC		XC	EM	XC	EM	EM	EM	EM	GW	AW	XC
			◇	1 ◇	R 1	◇ A		1 ◇	1 ◇	R 1		1 ◇	1 ◇ B	◇ A		1 ◇ C	1 ◇ D		E	1 ◇ D	1 ◇ G	1 ◇	H		1 ◇
Nottingham [8]	d		18 00	18 07			18 34		19 07									19 34	19 38			20 07			
Beeston	d		18 06	18a12					19a12									19 40	19a44			20a12			
Attenborough	d		18 09																						
Long Eaton	d		18 17				18 46	18 56									19 47	19 51			20 03				
Spondon	d																								
Derby [10]	a		18 29				18 56	19 09									20 00	20 02		←	20 15				
	d		18 39		18 57		19 06			19 24						19 57	20 11 →	20 08		20 11					20 27
Willington	d						19 14													20 21					
Burton-on-Trent	d		18 51				19 20									20 07		20 19		20a26					
Tamworth	d		19 03				19 31									20 18		20 31							
Wilnecote	d		19 06																						
Leicester	d					18 52					19 09			19 41											
South Wigston	d										19 16														
Narborough	d										19 20														
Hinckley	d										19 30														
Nuneaton	d					19 14					19 38			20 01											
Coleshill Parkway	d					19 29					19 55			20 16											
Water Orton	d																								
Birmingham New Street [12]	a		19 27		19 36	19 47	19 54			19 58	20 09			20 37		20 43		20 58							21 04
	d		19 30		19 40								20 10												21 10
Worcester Shrub Hill [7]	d																						21 08		
Ashchurch for Tewkesbury	d		20 06																				21 24		
Cheltenham Spa	d	20 00	20 15		20 22							20 48	20 52										21 34	21 45	21 52
Gloucester [7]	a	20 10	20 24									20 58											21 45	21 56	
Bristol Parkway [7]	a				20 54								21 25												22 25
Bristol Temple Meads [10]	a				21 11								21 41												22 41
Newport (South Wales)	a		21 10																					22 57	
Cardiff Central [7]	a		21 31																					23 18	

Station		XC	XC	XC	EM	XC		XC	GW	GW	AW	XC	XC	EM	GW	XC	LM FO	XC	XC	XC		XC	EM		
			1 ◇	◇ A	1 ◇ D					1 ◇		1 ◇ J	◇ A	1 ◇				1 ◇ J		◇ A		1 ◇ C	1 ◇ D		
Nottingham [8]	d					20 34										21 36							22 58		
Beeston	d					20 40										21 41							23 04		
Attenborough	d															21 44									
Long Eaton	d				20 44	20 49								21 44		21 52							23 14		
Spondon	d															21 59									
Derby [10]	a				20 56	21 01								21 56		22 04							23 26		
	d		20 57		21 03	21 09						21 27				22 08		22 27				23 15			
Willington	d				21 11																				
Burton-on-Trent	d				21a16	21 18						21 37				22 19		22 37				23 26			
Tamworth	d					21 30						21 48				22 31		22 48				23 37			
Wilnecote	d					21 34										22 34									
Leicester	d	20 09		20 52				21 09					21 36						22 27	22 49					
South Wigston	d	20 15						21 15											22 33						
Narborough	d	20 20						21 19											22 37						
Hinckley	d	20 28						21 28											22 46						
Nuneaton	d	20 37		21 14				21 37					21 58						22 54	23 09					
Coleshill Parkway	d	20 57		21 29									22 17						23 14	23 26					
Water Orton	d					21 42																			
Birmingham New Street [12]	a	21 09	21 44	21 47		21 57		22 04				22 08	22 36			22 54		23 21	23 34	23 43		23 59			
	d											22 10					23 04								
Worcester Shrub Hill [7]	d														22 32		23 44								
Ashchurch for Tewkesbury	d														22 50		23 58								
Cheltenham Spa	d								22 00	22 31	22 45	22 52			23 00		00 07								
Gloucester [7]	a								22 10	22 41	22 56				23 13		00 16								
Bristol Parkway [7]	a									23 16		23 25													
Bristol Temple Meads [10]	a									23 30		23 41													
Newport (South Wales)	a										23 59														
Cardiff Central [7]	a										00 22														

For general notes see front of timetable
For details of catering facilities see Directory of Train Operators

- **A** From Stansted Airport (Table 49)
- **B** To Plymouth (Table 51)
- **C** From Newcastle (Table 51)
- **D** From St Pancras International (Table 53)
- **E** From Lincoln (Table 27)
- **G** To Sheffield (Table 53)
- **H** From Great Malvern (Table 71)
- **J** From Edinburgh (Table 51)

until 26 January

Nottingham, Derby and Leicester → Birmingham → Cardiff and Bristol

Network Diagram - see first page of Table 50

		LM	EM	GW	AW	XC	XC	XC	GW	GW		AW	XC	EM	EM	XC	XC	XC	XC	XC		AW	XC	GW	XC
			1 ◇							1 ◇			1 ◇		1 ◇	◇			1 ◇	◇			1 ◇	1 ◇	◇
					A				B			A	C	D					E	G		A	C		
			☕							☕			☕		☕				☕				☕	☕	🛒
Nottingham [8]	d		02 19											05 52	06 07			06 34							06 58
Beeston	d													05 58	06a12			06 40							07 03
Attenborough	d													06 01											07 06
Long Eaton	d													06 11				06 50							07 14
Spondon	d													06 17											
Derby [10]	a		02 36											06 23				07 00							07 24
	d												06 10			06 34		07 06	07 17						07 38
Willington	d															06 45									
Burton-on-Trent	d												06 20			06 51		07 19	07 27						07 51
Tamworth	d												06 31			07 03		07 31	07 38						08 03
Wilnecote	d															07 06									
Leicester	d							05 45									06 47			07 08					
South Wigston	d							05 50									06 53								
Narborough	d							05 55									06 58			07 17					
Hinckley	d							06 03									07 07			07 26					
Nuneaton	d							06 10									07 15			07 34					
Coleshill Parkway	d							06 32									07 31								
Water Orton	d																07 36			07 53					
Birmingham New Street [12]	a							06 46					06 51			07 27	07 46	07 54	07 58	08 08					08 28
	d	23p04					05 30						07 10			07 30							08 10		08 30
Worcester Shrub Hill [7]	d	23p44				05 40	06 17		06 40																
Ashchurch for Tewkesbury	d	23p58				05 56	06 33		06 56																
Cheltenham Spa	d	00 07		05 30	05 37	06 05	06 43		07 06	07 27		07 45	07 52			08 11						08 45	08 52	09 00	09 11
Gloucester [7]	a	00 16		05 40	05 48	06 15	06 52		07 14	07 36		07 56				08 20						08 56		09 10	09 21
Bristol Parkway [7]	a								08 15				08 25										09 25		
Bristol Temple Meads [10]	a								08 34				08 41										09 41		
Newport (South Wales)	a				06 42	07 05	07 50					08 50				09 06						09 50			10 04
Cardiff Central [7]	a				07 00	07 26	08 12					09 10				09 29						10 10			10 25

		EM	XC	XC	XC	EM	GW	XC		XC	XC	EM	EM	XC	XC	XC	XC	XC		AW	XC	GW	XC	EM	EM
		1 ◇	1 ◇	◇				1 ◇			◇	1 ◇	1 ◇	1 ◇	◇		1 ◇				1 ◇	1 ◇	◇	1 ◇	1 ◇
			H	J			K	L					N	Q	G					A	C				
		☕	☕					☕				☕	☕	☕			☕				☕	☕		☕	☕
Nottingham [8]	d	07 07			07 34	07 38					08 00	08 07				08 32							09 00	09 07	
Beeston	d	07a12			07 40	07a44					08 06	08a12											09 06	09a12	
Attenborough	d										08 09												09 09		
Long Eaton	d				07 50						08 16		08 22			08 50							09 17		09 44
Spondon	d										08 23												09 23		
Derby [10]	a				08 02						08 29		08 32			09 00							09 28		09 56
	d		07 57		08 06			08 27			08 38			08 57		09 08	09 24						09 37		
Willington	d				08 13																				
Burton-on-Trent	d		08 07		08 19			08 37			08 51					09 19							09 51		
Tamworth	d		08 18		08 31			08 48			09 03					09 33							10 03		
Wilnecote	d				08 35																				
Leicester	d			07 46						08 09					08 52			09 09							
South Wigston	d									08 16															
Narborough	d			07 55						08 20								09 18							
Hinckley	d			08 04						08 29								09 26							
Nuneaton	d			08 11						08 41					09 14			09 33							
Coleshill Parkway	d			08 30						08 57					09 29			09 50							
Water Orton	d																	09 53							
Birmingham New Street [12]	a		08 36	08 48	08 54			09 06		09 09	09 27			09 36	09 47	09 54	09 58	10 09					10 27		
	d		08 40					09 10			09 30			09 40							10 10		10 30		
Worcester Shrub Hill [7]	d						09 05																		
Ashchurch for Tewkesbury	d						09 21																		
Cheltenham Spa	d		09 22				09 31	09 52			10 11			10 22						10 45	10 52	11 00	11 11		
Gloucester [7]	a						09 39				10 21									10 56		11 10	11 21		
Bristol Parkway [7]	a		09 56				10 19	10 25						10 56							11 25				
Bristol Temple Meads [10]	a		10 13				10 35	10 41						11 13							11 41				
Newport (South Wales)	a										11 04									11 50			12 04		
Cardiff Central [7]	a										11 25									12 10			12 25		

For general notes see front of timetable
For details of catering facilities see Directory of Train Operators

A To Maesteg (Table 128)
B To Weymouth (Table 123)
C To Plymouth (Table 51)
D To Crewe (Table 50)
E From Sheffield (Table 51)
G From Cambridge (Table 49)
H From Leeds (Table 51)
J From Stansted Airport (Table 49)
K From Great Malvern (Table 71) to Westbury (Table 123)
L From Leeds to Plymouth (Table 51)
N To York (Table 53)
Q To Paignton (Table 51)

Nottingham, Derby and Leicester → Birmingham → Cardiff and Bristol

Saturdays

until 26 January

Network Diagram - see first page of Table 50

		XC	XC	XC	GW	AW		XC	XC	XC	EM	EM	XC	XC	XC	XC		XC	XC	GW	XC	EM	EM	XC	XC
		1 ◇	◇					1 ◇		◇	1 ◇	1 ◇	1 ◇	◇		1 ◇			1 ◇	◇ 1	◇	1 ◇	1 ◇	1 ◇	◇
		A	B		C	D		E						B					E					A	B
		☕						☕			☕	☕	☕			☕			☕	☕		☕	☕	☕	
Nottingham 8	d			09 34						10 02	10 07				10 34						11 00	11 07			
Beeston	d			09 40						10 08	10a12				10 40						11 06	11a12			
Attenborough	d																				11 09				
Long Eaton	d			09 50						10 17		10 44			10 50						11 17		11 45		
Spondon	d																								
Derby 10	a			10 00						10 29		10 56			11 00						11 28		11 56		
	d	09 57		10 08				10 24		10 38			10 57		11 08	11 24					11 39			11 57	
Willington	d			10 16																					
Burton-on-Trent	d	10 07		10 22						10 54					11 19						11 51			12 07	
Tamworth	d	10 18		10 33						11 05					11 31						12 03			12 18	
Wilnecote	d														11 35										
Leicester	d		09 52						10 09					10 52				11 09							11 52
South Wigston	d								10 15																
Narborough	d								10 20									11 18							
Hinckley	d								10 28									11 26							
Nuneaton	d		10 14						10 35					11 14				11 35							12 14
Coleshill Parkway	d		10 29						10 54					11 29				11 52							12 29
Water Orton	d																	11 56							
Birmingham New Street 12	a	10 36	10 47	10 55				11 04	11 09	11 27			11 36	11 47	11 54	11 58		12 09			12 27			12 36	12 47
	d	10 40						11 10		11 30			11 40						12 10		12 30			12 40	
Worcester Shrub Hill 7	d				11 05																				
Ashchurch for Tewkesbury	d				11 21																				
Cheltenham Spa	d	11 22			11 31	11 45		11 52		12 11			12 22						12 52	13 00	13 11			13 22	
Gloucester 7	a				11 39	11 56				12 21										13 10	13 21				
Bristol Parkway 7	a	11 56			12 19			12 25					12 56						13 25					13 56	
Bristol Temple Meads 10	a	12 13			12 35			12 41					13 13						13 41					14 13	
Newport (South Wales)	a					12 50				13 04											14 04				
Cardiff Central 7	a					13 10				13 25											14 25				

		XC	GW	AW		XC	XC	XC	EM	EM	XC	XC	XC	XC		XC	AW	XC	GW	XC	EM	EM	XC	XC	XC
			◇			1 ◇		◇	1 ◇	1 ◇	1 ◇	◇		1 ◇				1 ◇	1 ◇	◇	1 ◇	1 ◇	1 ◇	◇	
			G	D		E					E	B					D	H					A	B	
			trolley			☕			☕	☕	☕			☕				☕	☕		☕	☕	☕		
Nottingham 8	d	11 34						12 02	12 07				12 34							13 00	13 07				13 34
Beeston	d	11 40						12 07	12a12				12 40							13 06	13a12				13 40
Attenborough	d																			13 09					
Long Eaton	d	11 50						12 17		12 44			12 50							13 16		13 44			13 50
Spondon	d							12 24																	
Derby 10	a	12 00						12 31		12 56			13 00							13 28		13 56			14 00
	d	12 08				12 24		12 39			12 57		13 08	13 24						13 39			13 57		14 08
Willington	d																								14 16
Burton-on-Trent	d	12 20						12 51					13 19							13 51			14 07		14 22
Tamworth	d	12 32						13 03					13 31							14 03			14 18		14 33
Wilnecote	d	12 36																							
Leicester	d						12 09					12 52				13 09								13 52	
South Wigston	d						12 15																		
Narborough	d						12 20									13 18									
Hinckley	d						12 28									13 26									
Nuneaton	d						12 35					13 14				13 35								14 14	
Coleshill Parkway	d						12 54					13 29				13 53								14 29	
Water Orton	d												13 44			13 56									
Birmingham New Street 12	a	12 55				13 04	13 09	13 27			13 36	13 47	13 54	13 58		14 09				14 28			14 36	14 47	14 54
	d					13 10		13 30			13 40							14 10		14 30			14 40		
Worcester Shrub Hill 7	d		13 05																						
Ashchurch for Tewkesbury	d		13 21																						
Cheltenham Spa	d		13 31	13 45		13 52		14 11			14 22						14 45	14 52	15 00	15 11			15 22		
Gloucester 7	a		13 39	13 56				14 21									14 56		15 10	15 21					
Bristol Parkway 7	a		14 19			14 25					14 56							15 25					15 56		
Bristol Temple Meads 10	a		14 34			14 41					15 11							15 41					16 13		
Newport (South Wales)	a			14 52				15 04									15 50			16 04					
Cardiff Central 7	a			15 11				15 25									16 07			16 25					

For general notes see front of timetable
For details of catering facilities see Directory of Train Operators

- **A** From Newcastle (Table 51)
- **B** From Stansted Airport (Table 49)
- **C** From Great Malvern (Table 71) to Brighton (Table 123)
- **D** To Maesteg (Table 128)
- **E** To Plymouth (Table 51)
- **G** From Great Malvern (Table 71) to Weymouth (Table 123)
- **H** To Penzance (Table 51)

Table 57

Saturdays

until 26 January

Nottingham, Derby and Leicester → Birmingham → Cardiff and Bristol

Network Diagram - see first page of Table 50

		GW ◇ A		XC 1 ◇ B ☕	XC	GW	XC ◇	EM 1 ◇ ☕	EM 1 ◇ ☕	XC 1 ◇ ☕	XC ◇ C	XC		XC 1 ◇ ☕	XC	AW D	XC 1 ◇ B ☕	GW 1 ◇ ☕	XC ◇	EM 1 ◇ ☕	EM 1 ◇ ☕	XC 1 ◇ E ☕		XC ◇ C	XC
Nottingham 8	d						14 02	14 07				14 34							15 00	15 07					15 34
Beeston	d						14 08	14a12				14 40							15 06	15a12					15 40
Attenborough	d																		15 09						
Long Eaton	d						14 22		14 44			14 50							15 17		15 44				15 50
Spondon	d																								
Derby 10	a						14 32		14 56			15 00							15 28		15 56				16 00
	d			14 24			14 39			14 57		15 08		15 24					15 39			15 57			16 08
Willington	d																								
Burton-on-Trent	d						14 51					15 19							15 51			16 07			16 19
Tamworth	d						15 03					15 31							16 03			16 18			16 31
Wilnecote	d											15 35													16 35
Leicester	d				14 09						14 52				15 09									15 52	
South Wigston	d				14 15																				
Narborough	d				14 20										15 18										
Hinckley	d				14 28										15 26										
Nuneaton	d				14 35						15 14				15 34									16 14	
Coleshill Parkway	d				14 54						15 29				15 50									16 29	
Water Orton	d														15 56										
Birmingham New Street 12	a			15 04	15 09		15 27			15 36	15 47	15 54		15 58	16 09				16 27			16 36		16 47	16 54
	d			15 10			15 30			15 40							16 10		16 30			16 40			
Worcester Shrub Hill 7	d	15 05																							
Ashchurch for Tewkesbury	d	15 21					16 06																		
Cheltenham Spa	d	15 31		15 52		16 01	16 15			16 22						16 45	16 52	17 00	17 14			17 22			
Gloucester 7	a	15 40				16 11	16 24									16 56		17 10	17 23						
Bristol Parkway 7	a	16 19		16 25						16 56							17 25					17 56			
Bristol Temple Meads 10	a	16 34		16 41						17 13							17 41					18 13			
Newport (South Wales)	a						17 07									17 50			18 06						
Cardiff Central 7	a						17 25									18 10			18 25						

		GW G	AW D	XC 1 ◇ H ☕	XC	GW	XC ◇	EM 1 ◇ J ☕	EM 1 ◇ ☕	XC 1 ◇ ☕		XC ◇ C	XC	EM K	XC 1 ◇ ☕	XC	AW D	XC 1 ◇ H ☕	GW 1 ◇ ☕	XC ◇		EM 1 ◇ ☕	XC 1 ◇ E ☕	XC ◇ C	EM 1 ◇ L ☕
Nottingham 8	d						16 00	16 07					16 34	16 38						17 00		17 07			
Beeston	d						16 06	16a12					16 40							17 06		17a12			
Attenborough	d						16 09							16a47						17 09					
Long Eaton	d						16 17		16 44				16 48							17 18					17 44
Spondon	d						16 23													17 27					
Derby 10	a						16 29		16 56				17 00							17 33					17 54
	d			16 24			16 39			16 57			17 07		17 24					17 38			17 57		18 01
Willington	d												17 16												18 10
Burton-on-Trent	d						16 51						17 22							17 50			18 07		18a15
Tamworth	d						17 03						17 33							18 03			18 18		
Wilnecote	d																								
Leicester	d				16 09							16 52				17 09								17 52	
South Wigston	d				16 15											17 15									
Narborough	d				16 20											17 20									
Hinckley	d				16 28											17 28									
Nuneaton	d				16 35							17 14				17 35								18 14	
Coleshill Parkway	d				16 54							17 29				17 52								18 29	
Water Orton	d																								
Birmingham New Street 12	a			17 04	17 12		17 27			17 36		17 47	17 54		17 58	18 09				18 27			18 36	18 47	
	d			17 10			17 30			17 40								18 10		18 30			18 40		
Worcester Shrub Hill 7	d	17 05																							
Ashchurch for Tewkesbury	d	17 21					18 09																		
Cheltenham Spa	d	17 31	17 45	17 52		18 01	18 18			18 22							18 45	18 52	19 00	19 14			19 22		
Gloucester 7	a	17 39	17 56			18 11	18 29			18 35							18 56		19 10	19 23					
Bristol Parkway 7	a	18 19		18 25						19 06								19 25					19 56		
Bristol Temple Meads 10	a	18 35		18 41						19 24								19 41					20 13		
Newport (South Wales)	a		18 50				19 12			19 59							19 50			20 06					
Cardiff Central 7	a		19 10				19 33			20 19							20 10			20 25					

For general notes see front of timetable
For details of catering facilities see Directory of Train Operators

A From Worcester Foregate Street (Table 71) to Weymouth (Table 123)
B To Penzance (Table 51)
C From Stansted Airport (Table 49)
D To Maesteg (Table 128)
E From Newcastle (Table 51)
G From Great Malvern (Table 71) to Westbury (Table 123)
H To Plymouth (Table 51)
J From Sheffield (Table 53)
K From Lincoln (Table 27)
L From St Pancras International (Table 53)

Table 57

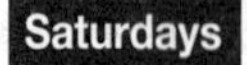

Saturdays

until 26 January

Nottingham, Derby and Leicester → Birmingham → Cardiff and Bristol

Network Diagram - see first page of Table 50

		XC	EM A	GW ◇ B	AW C	XC 1◇ D ☕	XC	XC		EM 1◇ ☕	EM 1◇ ☕	GW E	XC 1◇ ☕	XC ◇ G	XC	EM 1◇ ☕	XC 1◇ ☕	XC		EM	XC 1◇ D	XC 1◇ H ☕	XC ◇ G	EM 1◇ J ☕	XC
Nottingham 8	d	17 34	17 38					18 00		18 07					18 34	19 07				19 33					19 40
Beeston	d	17 40						18 06		18a12					18 40	19a12				19a39					
Attenborough	d		17a47					18 09																	19 46
Long Eaton	d	17 51						18 18			18 43				18 50									19 47	19 53
Spondon	d																								
Derby 10	a	18 00						18 31			18 56				19 00									19 57	20 03
	d	18 08				18 24		18 38					18 57		19 08		19 24					19 57			20 07
Willington	d														19 16										
Burton-on-Trent	d	18 20						18 51							19 22							20 07			20 20
Tamworth	d	18 33						19 03							19 33							20 18			20 32
Wilnecote	d							19 06																	
Leicester	d						18 09							18 52				19 09					19 52		
South Wigston	d						18 16											19 15							
Narborough	d						18 21											19 20							
Hinckley	d						18 29											19 28							
Nuneaton	d						18 36							19 14				19 38					20 14		
Coleshill Parkway	d						18 52							19 29				19 54					20 29		
Water Orton	d																								
Birmingham New Street 12	a	18 54				19 04	19 08	19 27					19 36	19 47	19 54		19 58	20 09				20 42	20 47		20 54
	d					19 10							19 40		20 00						20 10				
Worcester Shrub Hill 7	d			19 10																					
Ashchurch for Tewkesbury	d			19 26											20 36										
Cheltenham Spa	d			19 35	19 45	19 52						20 01	20 22		20 49						20 52				
Gloucester 7	a			19 43	19 56							20 10			21 01										
Bristol Parkway 7	a			20 19		20 25							20 56								21 25				
Bristol Temple Meads 10	a			20 36		20 41							21 13								21 41				
Newport (South Wales)	a				20 50																				
Cardiff Central 7	a				21 10																				

		XC	EM 1◇ ☕	GW	GW	AW		XC 1◇	XC	EM 1◇ ☕	GW ◇ K	XC ◇ G	XC	XC 1◇ H	XC ◇ G	EM 1◇ ☕		AW	XC	XC 1◇ L	XC	EM 1◇ ☕			
Nottingham 8	d		20 07						20 11										21 45						
Beeston	d		20a12						20 17										21 51						
Attenborough	d																		21 55						
Long Eaton	d								20 24	20 44						21 44			22 01			22 45			
Spondon	d								20 32										22 07						
Derby 10	a								20 37	20 56						21 56			22 13			22 56			
	d							20 27	20 40					21 27					22 17	22 27					
Willington	d																								
Burton-on-Trent	d								20 52					21 37					22 29	22 37					
Tamworth	d								21 05					21 48					22 42	22 48					
Wilnecote	d								21 08																
Leicester	d	20 09										20 52	21 10		21 39						22 26				
South Wigston	d	20 14											21 15								22 31				
Narborough	d	20 19											21 20								22 36				
Hinckley	d	20 27											21 28								22 44				
Nuneaton	d	20 34										21 14	21 35		22 01						22 51				
Coleshill Parkway	d	20 49										21 29	21 52		22 18						23 10				
Water Orton	d																								
Birmingham New Street 12	a	21 01						21 04	21 28			21 47	22 04	22 13	22 35				23 03	23 20	23 22				
	d							21 10																	
Worcester Shrub Hill 7	d										21 34														
Ashchurch for Tewkesbury	d										21 52														
Cheltenham Spa	d			21 02	21 28	21 45		21 52			22 01														
Gloucester 7	a			21 12	21 38	21 56					22 09							22d58							
Bristol Parkway 7	a			21 51				22 25																	
Bristol Temple Meads 10	a			22 04				22 41																	
Newport (South Wales)	a					22 55												23 57							
Cardiff Central 7	a					23 18												00 18							

For general notes see front of timetable
For details of catering facilities see Directory of Train Operators

A From Lincoln (Table 27)
B To Weymouth (Table 123)
C To Maesteg (Table 128)
D To Plymouth (Table 51)
E To Westbury (Table 123)
G From Stansted Airport (Table 49)
H From Newcastle (Table 51)
J To Barnsley (Table 53)
K From Great Malvern (Table 71)
L From Edinburgh (Table 51)

Table 57

Nottingham, Derby and Leicester → Birmingham → Cardiff and Bristol

2 February to 22 March

Network Diagram - see first page of Table 50

		LM	EM	GW	AW	XC	XC	XC	GW	GW	AW	XC	EM	EM	XC	XC	XC	XC	XC	AW	XC	XC	EM	XC	XC
			1◇							1◇		1◇		1◇	◇			1◇	◇		1◇	◇	1◇	1◇	◇
					A				B		A	C	D					E	G	A	C			H	J
			☕							☕		☕		☕				☕			☕	🍴	☕	☕	
Nottingham 8 🚌	d		02 19										05 52	06 07			06 34					06 58	07 07		
Beeston	d												05 58	06a12			06 40					07 03	07a12		
Attenborough	d												06 01									07 06			
Long Eaton	d												06 11				06 50					07 14			
Spondon	d												06 17												
Derby 10	a		02 36										06 23				07 00					07 24			
	d											06 10			06 34		07 06	07 17				07 38		07 57	
Willington	d														06 45										
Burton-on-Trent	d											06 20			06 51		07 19	07 27				07 51		08 07	
Tamworth	d											06 31			07 03		07 31	07 38				08 03		08 18	
Wilnecote	d														07 06										
Leicester	d							05 45								06 47			07 08						07 46
South Wigston	d							05 50								06 53									
Narborough	d							05 55								06 58			07 17						07 55
Hinckley	d							06 03								07 07			07 26						08 04
Nuneaton	d							06 10								07 15			07 34						08 11
Coleshill Parkway	d							06 32								07 31									08 30
Water Orton	d															07 36			07 53						
Birmingham New Street 12	a							06 46				06 51			07 27	07 46	07 54	07 58	08 08			08 28		08 36	08 48
	d	23p04					05 30					07 10			07 30						08 10	08 30		08 40	
Worcester Shrub Hill 7	d	23p44				05 40	06 17		06 40																
Ashchurch for Tewkesbury	d	23p58				05 56	06 33		06 56																
Cheltenham Spa	d	00 07		05 30	05 37	06 05	06 43		07 06	07 27	07 45	07 52			08 11					08 45	08 52	09 11		09 22	
Gloucester 7	a	00 16		05 40	05 48	06 15	06 52		07 14	07 36	07 56				08 20					08 56		09 21			
Bristol Parkway 7	a								08 15			08 25									09 25			09 56	
Bristol Temple Meads 10	a								08 34			08 41									09 41			10 13	
Newport (South Wales)	a				06 42	07 05	07 50				08 50				09 06					09 50		10 04			
Cardiff Central 7	a				07 00	07 26	08 12				09 10				09 29					10 10		10 25			

		XC	EM	GW	XC	XC	XC	EM	EM	XC	XC	XC	XC	XC	AW	XC	XC	EM	EM	XC	XC	XC	GW	AW	XC
					1◇		◇	1◇	1◇	1◇	◇		1◇			1◇	◇	1◇	1◇	1◇	◇				1◇
				K	L				N	Q	G				A	C				U	J		V	A	C
					☕			☕	☕	☕			☕			☕		☕	☕	☕					☕
Nottingham 8 🚌	d	07 34	07 38				08 00	08 07				08 32					09 00	09 07				09 34			
Beeston	d	07 40	07a44				08 06	08a12									09 06	09a12				09 40			
Attenborough	d						08 09										09 09								
Long Eaton	d	07 50					08 16		08 22			08 50					09 17		09 44			09 50			
Spondon	d						08 23										09 23								
Derby 10	a	08 02					08 29		08 32			09 00					09 28		09 56			10 00			
	d	08 06			08 27		08 38			08 57		09 08	09 24				09 37			09 57		10 08			10 24
Willington	d	08 13																				10 16			
Burton-on-Trent	d	08 19			08 37		08 51					09 19					09 51			10 07		10 22			
Tamworth	d	08 31			08 48		09 03					09 33					10 03			10 18		10 33			
Wilnecote	d	08 35																							
Leicester	d					08 09					08 52			09 09							09 52				
South Wigston	d					08 16																			
Narborough	d					08 20								09 17											
Hinckley	d					08 29								09 26											
Nuneaton	d					08 41					09 14			09 33							10 14				
Coleshill Parkway	d					08 57					09 29			09 50							10 29				
Water Orton	d													09 53											
Birmingham New Street 12	a	08 54			09 06	09 09	09 27			09 36	09 47	09 54	09 58	10 09			10 27			10 36	10 47	10 55			11 04
	d				09 10		09 30			09 40						10 10	10 30			10 40					11 10
Worcester Shrub Hill 7	d			09 05																			11 05		
Ashchurch for Tewkesbury	d			09 21																			11 21		
Cheltenham Spa	d			09 31	09 52		10 11			10 22					10 45	10 52	11 11			11 22			11 31	11 45	11 52
Gloucester 7	a			09 39			10 21								10 56		11 21						11 39	11 56	
Bristol Parkway 7	a			10 19	10 25					10 56						11 25				11 56			12 19		12 25
Bristol Temple Meads 10	a			10 35	10 41					11 13						11 41				12 13			12 35		12 41
Newport (South Wales)	a						11 04								11 50		12 04							12 50	
Cardiff Central 7	a						11 25								12 10		12 25							13 10	

For general notes see front of timetable
For details of catering facilities see Directory of Train Operators

- A To Maesteg (Table 128)
- B To Weymouth (Table 123)
- C To Plymouth (Table 51)
- D To Crewe (Table 50)
- E From Sheffield (Table 51)
- G From Cambridge (Table 49)
- H From Leeds (Table 51)
- J From Stansted Airport (Table 49)
- K From Great Malvern (Table 71) to Westbury (Table 123)
- L From Leeds to Plymouth (Table 51)
- N To York (Table 53)
- Q To Paignton (Table 51)
- U From Newcastle (Table 51)
- V From Great Malvern (Table 71) to Brighton (Table 123)

Table 57

Saturdays

2 February to 22 March

Nottingham, Derby and Leicester → Birmingham → Cardiff and Bristol

Network Diagram - see first page of Table 50

		XC	XC ◇	EM [1] ◇ 🍴	EM [1] ◇ 🍴	XC [1] ◇ 🍴	XC ◇ A	XC	XC [1] ◇ 🍴	XC	XC [1] ◇ B 🍴	XC ◇	EM [1] ◇ 🍴	EM [1] ◇ 🍴	XC [1] ◇ C 🍴	XC ◇ A	XC	GW ◇ D 🛒	AW E	XC [1] ◇ B 🍴	XC	XC ◇	EM [1] ◇ 🍴	EM [1] ◇ 🍴	XC [1] ◇ B 🍴
Nottingham [8] 🚌	d		10 02	10 07				10 34				11 00	11 07				11 34					12 02	12 07		
Beeston	d		10 08	10a12				10 40				11 06	11a12				11 40					12 07	12a12		
Attenborough	d											11 09													
Long Eaton	d		10 17		10 44			10 50				11 17		11 45			11 50					12 17		12 44	
Spondon	d																					12 24			
Derby [10]	a		10 29		10 56			11 00				11 28		11 56			12 00					12 31		12 56	
	d		10 38			10 57		11 08	11 24			11 39			11 57		12 08			12 24		12 39			12 57
Willington	d																								
Burton-on-Trent	d		10 54					11 19				11 51			12 07		12 20					12 51			
Tamworth	d		11 05					11 31				12 03			12 18		12 32					13 03			
Wilnecote	d							11 35									12 36								
Leicester	d	10 09					10 52			11 09						11 52					12 09				
South Wigston	d	10 15																			12 15				
Narborough	d	10 20								11 18											12 20				
Hinckley	d	10 28								11 26											12 28				
Nuneaton	d	10 35					11 14			11 35						12 14					12 35				
Coleshill Parkway	d	10 54					11 29			11 52						12 29					12 54				
Water Orton	d									11 56															
Birmingham New Street [12]	a	11 09	11 27			11 36	11 47	11 54	11 58	12 09		12 27			12 36	12 47	12 55			13 04	13 09	13 27			13 36
	d		11 30			11 40					12 10	12 30			12 40					13 10		13 30			13 40
Worcester Shrub Hill [7]	d																	13 05							
Ashchurch for Tewkesbury	d																	13 21							
Cheltenham Spa	d		12 11			12 22					12 52	13 11			13 22			13 31	13 45	13 52		14 11			14 22
Gloucester [7]	a		12 21									13 21						13 39	13 56			14 21			
Bristol Parkway [7]	a					12 56					13 25				13 56			14 19		14 25					14 56
Bristol Temple Meads [10]	a					13 13					13 41				14 13			14 34		14 41					15 11
Newport (South Wales)	a		13 04									14 04							14 52			15 04			
Cardiff Central [7]	a		13 25									14 25							15 11			15 25			

		XC ◇ A	XC	XC [1] ◇ 🍴	XC	AW E	XC [1] ◇ G 🍴	XC ◇	EM [1] ◇ 🍴	EM [1] ◇ 🍴	XC [1] ◇ C 🍴	XC ◇ A	XC	GW ◇ H	XC [1] ◇ G 🍴	XC	GW	XC ◇	EM [1] ◇ 🍴	EM [1] ◇ 🍴	XC [1] ◇ 🍴	XC ◇ A	XC	XC [1] ◇ 🍴	XC
Nottingham [8] 🚌	d		12 34					13 00	13 07				13 34					14 02	14 07				14 34		
Beeston	d		12 40					13 06	13a12				13 40					14 08	14a12				14 40		
Attenborough	d							13 09																	
Long Eaton	d		12 50					13 16		13 44			13 50					14 22		14 44			14 50		
Spondon	d																								
Derby [10]	a		13 00					13 28		13 56			14 00					14 32		14 56			15 00		
	d		13 08	13 24				13 39			13 57		14 08		14 24			14 39			14 57		15 08	15 24	
Willington	d												14 16												
Burton-on-Trent	d		13 19					13 51			14 07		14 22					14 51					15 19		
Tamworth	d		13 31					14 03			14 18		14 33					15 03					15 31		
Wilnecote	d																						15 35		
Leicester	d	12 52			13 09							13 52				14 09						14 52			15 09
South Wigston	d															14 15									
Narborough	d				13 18											14 20									15 18
Hinckley	d				13 26											14 28									15 26
Nuneaton	d	13 14			13 35							14 14				14 35						15 14			15 34
Coleshill Parkway	d	13 29			13 53							14 29				14 54						15 29			15 50
Water Orton	d		13 44		13 56																				15 56
Birmingham New Street [12]	a	13 47	13 54	13 58	14 09			14 28			14 36	14 47	14 54		15 04	15 09		15 27			15 36	15 47	15 54	15 58	16 09
	d						14 10	14 30			14 40				15 10			15 30			15 40				
Worcester Shrub Hill [7]	d													15 05											
Ashchurch for Tewkesbury	d													15 21				16 06							
Cheltenham Spa	d					14 45	14 52	15 11			15 22			15 31	15 52		16 01	16 15			16 22				
Gloucester [7]	a					14 56		15 21						15 40			16 11	16 24							
Bristol Parkway [7]	a						15 25				15 56			16 19	16 25						16 56				
Bristol Temple Meads [10]	a						15 41				16 13			16 34	16 41						17 13				
Newport (South Wales)	a					15 50		16 04										17 07							
Cardiff Central [7]	a					16 07		16 25										17 25							

For general notes see front of timetable
For details of catering facilities see Directory of Train Operators

- **A** From Stansted Airport (Table 49)
- **B** To Plymouth (Table 51)
- **C** From Newcastle (Table 51)
- **D** From Great Malvern (Table 71) to Weymouth (Table 123)
- **E** To Maesteg (Table 128)
- **G** To Penzance (Table 51)
- **H** From Worcester Foregate Street (Table 71) to Weymouth (Table 123)

Table 57

Saturdays

Nottingham, Derby and Leicester → Birmingham → Cardiff and Bristol

2 February to 22 March

Network Diagram - see first page of Table 50

		GW	AW	XC	XC	EM	EM	XC	XC	XC	GW	AW	XC	XC	GW	XC	EM	EM	XC	XC	XC	EM	XC	XC	AW
		1 ◇		1 ◇	◇	1 ◇	1 ◇	1 ◇	◇				1 ◇			◇	1 ◇	1 ◇	1 ◇	◇			1 ◇		
			A	B				C	D		E	A	G				H			D		J			A
		☕		☕		☕	☕	☕					☕				☕	☕	☕				☕		
Nottingham 8	d				15 00	15 07				15 34						16 00	16 07				16 34	16 38			
Beeston	d				15 06	15a12				15 40						16 06	16a12				16 40				
Attenborough	d				15 09											16 09						16a47			
Long Eaton	d				15 17		15 44			15 50						16 17		16 44			16 48				
Spondon	d															16 23									
Derby 10	a				15 28		15 56			16 00						16 29		16 56			17 00				
	d				15 39			15 57		16 08			16 24			16 39			16 57		17 07		17 24		
Willington	d																				17 16				
Burton-on-Trent	d				15 51			16 07		16 19						16 51					17 22				
Tamworth	d				16 03			16 18		16 31						17 03					17 33				
Wilnecote	d									16 35															
Leicester	d								15 52					16 09						16 52				17 09	
South Wigston	d													16 15										17 15	
Narborough	d													16 20										17 20	
Hinckley	d													16 28										17 28	
Nuneaton	d								16 14					16 35						17 14				17 35	
Coleshill Parkway	d								16 29					16 54						17 29				17 52	
Water Orton	d																								
Birmingham New Street 12	a				16 27			16 36	16 47	16 54			17 04	17 12		17 27			17 36	17 47	17 54		17 58	18 09	
	d			16 10	16 30			16 40					17 10			17 30			17 40						
Worcester Shrub Hill 7	d										17 05														
Ashchurch for Tewkesbury	d										17 21					18 09									
Cheltenham Spa	d	16 31	16 45	16 52	17 14			17 22			17 31	17 45	17 52		18 01	18 18			18 22						18 45
Gloucester 7	a	16 40	16 56		17 23						17 39	17 56			18 11	18 29			18 35						18 56
Bristol Parkway 7	a			17 25				17 56			18 19		18 25						19 06						
Bristol Temple Meads 10	a			17 41				18 13			18 35		18 41						19 24						
Newport (South Wales)	a		17 50		18 06							18 50				19 12		20 00	19 59						19 50
Cardiff Central 7	a		18 10		18 25							19 10				19 33		20 19	20 19						20 10

		XC	XC	EM	XC	XC	EM	XC	EM	GW	AW	XC	XC	XC	EM	EM	GW	XC	XC	XC	EM	XC	XC	EM	XC
		1 ◇	◇	1 ◇	1 ◇	◇	1 ◇			◇		1 ◇			1 ◇	1 ◇		1 ◇	◇		1 ◇	1 ◇			1 ◇
		G			C	D	K		J	L	A	G					N		D						G
		☕		☕	☕		☕					☕			☕	☕		☕			☕	☕			
Nottingham 8	d		17 00	17 07				17 34	17 38					18 00	18 07					18 34	19 07			19 33	
Beeston	d		17 06	17a12				17 40						18 06	18a12					18 40	19a12			19a39	
Attenborough	d		17 09						17a47					18 09											
Long Eaton	d		17 18				17 44	17 51						18 18		18 43				18 50					
Spondon	d		17 27																						
Derby 10	a		17 33				17 54	18 00						18 31		18 56				19 00					
	d		17 38		17 57		18 01	18 08				18 24		18 38				18 57		19 08		19 24			
Willington	d						18 10													19 16					
Burton-on-Trent	d		17 50		18 07		18a15	18 20						18 51						19 22					
Tamworth	d		18 03		18 18			18 33						19 03						19 33					
Wilnecote	d													19 06											
Leicester	d					17 52							18 09						18 52				19 09		
South Wigston	d												18 16										19 15		
Narborough	d												18 21										19 20		
Hinckley	d												18 29										19 28		
Nuneaton	d					18 14							18 36						19 14				19 38		
Coleshill Parkway	d					18 29							18 52						19 29				19 54		
Water Orton	d																								
Birmingham New Street 12	a		18 27		18 36	18 47		18 54				19 04	19 08	19 27				19 36	19 47	19 54		19 58	20 09		
	d	18 10	18 30		18 40							19 10						19 40		20 00					20 10
Worcester Shrub Hill 7	d									19 10															
Ashchurch for Tewkesbury	d									19 26										20 36					
Cheltenham Spa	d	18 52	19 14		19 22					19 35	19 45	19 52					20 01	20 22		20 49					20 52
Gloucester 7	a		19 23							19 43	19 56						20 10			21 01					
Bristol Parkway 7	a	19 25			19 56					20 19		20 25						20 56							21 25
Bristol Temple Meads 10	a	19 41			20 13					20 36		20 41						21 13							21 41
Newport (South Wales)	a		20 06								20 52														
Cardiff Central 7	a		20 25								21 11														

For general notes see front of timetable
For details of catering facilities see Directory of Train Operators

A To Maesteg (Table 128)
B To Penzance (Table 51)
C From Newcastle (Table 51)
D From Stansted Airport (Table 49)
E From Great Malvern (Table 71) to Westbury (Table 123)
G To Plymouth (Table 51)
H From Sheffield (Table 53)
J From Lincoln (Table 27)
K From St Pancras International (Table 53)
L To Weymouth (Table 123)
N To Westbury (Table 123)

Table 57

Saturdays

2 February to 22 March

Nottingham, Derby and Leicester → Birmingham → Cardiff and Bristol

Network Diagram - see first page of Table 50

		XC	XC	EM	XC	XC	EM	GW	GW	AW	XC	XC	EM	GW	XC	XC	XC	XC	EM	AW	XC	XC	XC	EM
		1 ◇	◇	1 ◇			1 ◇				1 ◇		1 ◇	◇	◇		1 ◇	◇	1 ◇			1 ◇		1 ◇
		A	B	C										D	B		A	B				E		
		☕		☕			☕						☕						☕					☕
Nottingham 8	d				19 40		20 07					20 11									21 45			
Beeston	d						20a12					20 17									21 51			
Attenborough	d				19 46																21 55			
Long Eaton	d			19 47	19 53							20 24	20 44						21 44		22 01			22 45
Spondon	d											20 32									22 07			
Derby 10	a			19 57	20 03							20 37	20 56						21 56		22 13			22 56
	d	19 57			20 07						20 27	20 40					21 27				22 17	22 27		
Willington	d																							
Burton-on-Trent	d	20 07			20 20							20 52					21 37				22 29	22 37		
Tamworth	d	20 18			20 32							21 05					21 48				22 42	22 48		
Wilnecote	d											21 08												
Leicester	d		19 52			20 09									20 52	21 10		21 39					22 26	
South Wigston	d					20 14										21 15							22 31	
Narborough	d					20 19										21 20							22 36	
Hinckley	d					20 27										21 28							22 44	
Nuneaton	d		20 14			20 34									21 14	21 35		22 01					22 51	
Coleshill Parkway	d		20 29			20 49									21 29	21 52		22 18					23 10	
Water Orton	d																							
Birmingham New Street 12	a	20 42	20 47		20 54	21 01					21 04	21 28			21 47	22 04	22 13	22 35			23 03	23 20	23 22	
	d										21 10													
Worcester Shrub Hill 7	d													21 34										
Ashchurch for Tewkesbury	d													21 52										
Cheltenham Spa	d							21 02	21 28	21 45	21 52			22 01										
Gloucester 7	a							21 12	21 38	21 56				22 09										
Bristol Parkway 7	a							21 51			22 25									22d58				
Bristol Temple Meads 10	a							22 04			22 41													
Newport (South Wales)	a									22 55										23 57				
Cardiff Central 7	a									23 15										00 18				

Saturdays

from 29 March

		LM	EM	AW	XC	XC	GW	AW	XC	XC		EM	EM	XC	XC		XC	AW	XC	XC	XC		XC	EM	XC
			1 ◇						1 ◇				1 ◇	◇			1 ◇		1 ◇				◇	1 ◇	1 ◇
				G			H	G	J			K					L	G	J						N
			☕						☕	🚌			☕				☕		☕	🚌	🚌		🛒	☕	☕
Nottingham 8	d		01 44									05 52	06 07		06 34								06 58	07 07	
Beeston	d											05 58	06a12		06 40								07 03	07a12	
Attenborough	d											06 01											07 06		
Long Eaton	d											06 11			06 50								07 14		
Spondon	d											06 17													
Derby 10	a		02 05									06 23			07 00								07 24		
	d								06 10					06 34	07 06		07 17						07 38		07 57
Willington	d													06 45											
Burton-on-Trent	d								06 20					06 51	07 19		07 27						07 51		08 07
Tamworth	d								06 31					07 03	07 31		07 38						08 03		08 18
Wilnecote	d													07 06											
Leicester	d									05 30										05 45	06 20				
South Wigston	d																			06 01					
Narborough	d																			06 12					
Hinckley	d																			06 36					
Nuneaton	d									06 11										06a54	07 01				
Coleshill Parkway	d									06 47											07 37				
Water Orton	d																				07 46				
Birmingham New Street 12	a								06 51	07 17				07 27	07 54		07 58				08 11		08 28		08 36
	d	23p04				05 30			07 10					07 30					08 10				08 30		08 40
Worcester Shrub Hill 7	d	23p44			05 40	06 17	06 40																		
Ashchurch for Tewkesbury	d	23p58			05 56	06 33	06 56																		
Cheltenham Spa	d	00 07		05 37	06 05	06 43	07 06	07 45	07 52					08 11				08 45	08 52				09 11		09 22
Gloucester 7	a	00 16		05 48	06 15	06 52	07 14	07 56						08 20				08 56					09 21		
Bristol Parkway 7	a						08 15		08 25										09 25						09 56
Bristol Temple Meads 10	a						08 34		08 41										09 41						10 13
Newport (South Wales)	a			06 42	07 05	07 50		08 50						09 06				09 50					10 04		
Cardiff Central 7	a			07 00	07 26	08 12		09 10						09 29				10 10					10 25		

For general notes see front of timetable
For details of catering facilities see Directory of Train Operators

A From Newcastle (Table 51)
B From Stansted Airport (Table 49)
C To Barnsley (Table 53)
D From Great Malvern (Table 71)
E From Edinburgh (Table 51)
G To Maesteg (Table 128)
H To Weymouth (Table 123)
J To Plymouth (Table 51)
K To Crewe (Table 50)
L From Sheffield (Table 51)
N From Leeds (Table 51)

Table 57

Saturdays

from 29 March

Nottingham, Derby and Leicester → Birmingham → Cardiff and Bristol

Network Diagram - see first page of Table 50

		XC	XC		XC	EM	GW	XC		XC	EM	EM	XC	XC	XC	XC		XC	AW	XC	XC	EM	EM		XC
								1◇		◇	1◇	1◇	1◇					1◇		1◇	◇	1◇	1◇		1◇
							A	B				C	D						E	G					H
		🚌	🚌												🚌	🚌									
								☕			☕	☕	☕					☕		☕		☕	☕		☕
Nottingham 8	d				07 34	07 38				08 00	08 07			08 32							09 00	09 07			
Beeston	d				07 40	07a44				08 06	08a12										09 06	09a12			
Attenborough	d									08 09											09 09				
Long Eaton	d				07 50					08 16		08 22		08 50							09 17		09 44		
Spondon	d									08 23											09 23				
Derby 10	a				08 02					08 29		08 32		09 00							09 28		09 56		
	d				08 06			08 27		08 38			08 57	09 08				09 24			09 37				09 57
Willington	d				08 13																				
Burton-on-Trent	d				08 19			08 37		08 51				09 19							09 51				10 07
Tamworth	d				08 31			08 48		09 03				09 33							10 03				10 18
Wilnecote	d				08 35																				
Leicester	d	06 40	07 15												07 37	08 10									
South Wigston	d	06 56													07 53										
Narborough	d	07 07													08 04										
Hinckley	d	07 31													08 28										
Nuneaton	d	07a49	07 56												08a46	08 51									
Coleshill Parkway	d																								
Water Orton	d		08 22													09 27									
Birmingham New Street 12	a		08 47		08 54			09 06		09 27			09 36	09 54		09 57		09 58			10 27				10 36
	d							09 10		09 30			09 40							10 10	10 30				10 40
Worcester Shrub Hill 7	d						09 05																		
Ashchurch for Tewkesbury	d						09 21																		
Cheltenham Spa	d						09 31	09 52		10 11			10 22						10 45	10 52	11 11				11 22
Gloucester 7	a						09 39			10 21									10 56		11 21				
Bristol Parkway 7	a						10 19	10 25					10 56							11 25					11 56
Bristol Temple Meads 10	a						10 35	10 41					11 13							11 41					12 13
Newport (South Wales)	a									11 04									11 50		12 04				
Cardiff Central 7	a									11 25									12 10		12 25				

		XC	XC	XC		GW	AW	XC	XC	EM	EM	XC	XC	XC	XC			XC	XC	XC	EM	EM	XC	XC	XC
								1◇	◇	1◇	1◇	1◇						1◇	1◇	◇	1◇	1◇	1◇		
						J	E	G											G				H		
			🚌	🚌										🚌	🚌										🚌
								☕		☕	☕	☕						☕	☕		☕	☕	☕		
Nottingham 8	d	09 34							10 02	10 07			10 34							11 00	11 07			11 34	
Beeston	d	09 40							10 08	10a12			10 40							11 06	11a12			11 40	
Attenborough	d																			11 09					
Long Eaton	d	09 50							10 17		10 44		10 50							11 17		11 45		11 50	
Spondon	d																								
Derby 10	a	10 00							10 29		10 56		11 00							11 28		11 56		12 00	
	d	10 08						10 24	10 38			10 57	11 08					11 24		11 39			11 57	12 08	
Willington	d	10 16																							
Burton-on-Trent	d	10 22							10 54				11 19							11 51			12 07	12 20	
Tamworth	d	10 33							11 05				11 31							12 03			12 18	12 32	
Wilnecote	d												11 35											12 36	
Leicester	d		08 37	09 10										09 37	10 10										10 37
South Wigston	d		08 53											09 53											10 53
Narborough	d		09 04											10 04											11 04
Hinckley	d		09 28											10 28											11 28
Nuneaton	d		09a46	09 51										10a46	10 51										11a46
Coleshill Parkway	d			10 27											11 27										
Water Orton	d			10 36																					
Birmingham New Street 12	a	10 55		11 01				11 04	11 27			11 36	11 54		11 57			11 58		12 27			12 36	12 55	
	d							11 10	11 30			11 40							12 10	12 30			12 40		
Worcester Shrub Hill 7	d					11 05																			
Ashchurch for Tewkesbury	d					11 21																			
Cheltenham Spa	d					11 31	11 45	11 52	12 11			12 22							12 52	13 11			13 22		
Gloucester 7	a					11 39	11 56		12 21											13 21					
Bristol Parkway 7	a					12 19		12 25				12 56							13 25				13 56		
Bristol Temple Meads 10	a					12 35		12 41				13 13							13 41				14 13		
Newport (South Wales)	a						12 50		13 04											14 04					
Cardiff Central 7	a						13 10		13 25											14 25					

For general notes see front of timetable
For details of catering facilities see Directory of Train Operators

- **A** From Great Malvern (Table 71) to Westbury (Table 123)
- **B** From Leeds to Plymouth (Table 51)
- **C** To York (Table 53)
- **D** To Paignton (Table 51)
- **E** To Maesteg (Table 128)
- **G** To Plymouth (Table 51)
- **H** From Newcastle (Table 51)
- **J** From Great Malvern (Table 71) to Brighton (Table 123)

Nottingham, Derby and Leicester → Birmingham → Cardiff and Bristol

Network Diagram - see first page of Table 50

Station		XC Bus		GW ◇ A trolley	AW B	XC 1 ◇ C catering	XC ◇	EM 1 ◇ catering		EM 1 ◇ catering	XC 1 ◇ C catering	XC	XC Bus	XC Bus		XC 1 ◇ catering	AW B	XC 1 ◇ D catering	XC ◇	EM 1 ◇ catering	EM 1 ◇ catering	XC 1 ◇ E catering	XC		XC Bus
Nottingham [8]	d						12 02	12 07				12 34							13 00	13 07			13 34		
Beeston	d						12 07	12a12				12 40							13 06	13a12			13 40		
Attenborough	d																		13 09						
Long Eaton	d						12 17			12 44		12 50							13 16		13 44		13 50		
Spondon	d						12 24																		
Derby [10]	a						12 31			12 56		13 00							13 28		13 56		14 00		
	d					12 24	12 39				12 57	13 08				13 24			13 39			13 57	14 08		
Willington	d																						14 16		
Burton-on-Trent	d						12 51					13 19							13 51			14 07	14 22		
Tamworth	d						13 03					13 31							14 03			14 18	14 33		
Wilnecote	d																								
Leicester	d	11 10											11 37	12 10											12 37
South Wigston	d												11 53												12 53
Narborough	d												12 04												13 04
Hinckley	d												12 28												13 28
Nuneaton	d	11 51											12a46	12 51											13a46
Coleshill Parkway	d	12 27												13 27											
Water Orton	d	12 36										13 44													
Birmingham New Street [12]	a	13 01				13 04	13 27				13 36	13 54		13 57		13 58			14 28			14 36	14 54		
	d					13 10	13 30				13 40							14 10	14 30			14 40			
Worcester Shrub Hill [7]	d			13 05																					
Ashchurch for Tewkesbury	d			13 21																					
Cheltenham Spa	d			13 31	13 45	13 52	14 11				14 22						14 45	14 52	15 11			15 22			
Gloucester [7]	a			13 39	13 56		14 21										14 56		15 21						
Bristol Parkway [7]	a			14 19		14 25					14 56							15 25				15 56			
Bristol Temple Meads [10]	a			14 34		14 41					15 11							15 41				16 13			
Newport (South Wales)	a				14 52		15 04										15 50		16 04						
Cardiff Central [7]	a				15 11		15 25										16 07		16 25						

Station		XC Bus		GW ◇ G	XC 1 ◇ D catering	XC ◇	EM 1 ◇ catering	EM 1 ◇ catering	XC 1 ◇ catering	XC	XC Bus	XC Bus		XC 1 ◇ catering	AW B		XC 1 ◇ D catering	XC ◇	EM 1 ◇ catering	EM 1 ◇ catering	XC 1 ◇ E catering	XC	XC Bus	XC Bus	
Nottingham [8]	d					14 02	14 07			14 34								15 00	15 07			15 34			
Beeston	d					14 08	14a12			14 40								15 06	15a12			15 40			
Attenborough	d																	15 09							
Long Eaton	d					14 22		14 44		14 50								15 17		15 44		15 50			
Spondon	d																								
Derby [10]	a					14 32		14 56		15 00								15 28		15 56		16 00			
	d				14 24	14 39			14 57	15 08				15 24				15 39			15 57	16 08			
Willington	d																								
Burton-on-Trent	d					14 51				15 19								15 51			16 07	16 19			
Tamworth	d					15 03				15 31								16 03			16 18	16 31			
Wilnecote	d									15 35												16 35			
Leicester	d	13 10									13 37	14 10											14 37	15 10	
South Wigston	d										13 53												14 53		
Narborough	d										14 04												15 04		
Hinckley	d										14 28												15 28		
Nuneaton	d	13 51									14a46	14 51											15a46	15 51	
Coleshill Parkway	d	14 27										15 27												16 27	
Water Orton	d	14 36																						16 36	
Birmingham New Street [12]	a	15 01			15 04	15 27			15 36	15 54		15 57		15 58				16 27			16 36	16 54		17 01	
	d				15 10	15 30			15 40								16 10	16 30			16 40				
Worcester Shrub Hill [7]	d			15 05																					
Ashchurch for Tewkesbury	d			15 21		16 06																			
Cheltenham Spa	d			15 31	15 52	16 15			16 22						16 45		16 52	17 14			17 22				
Gloucester [7]	a			15 40		16 24									16 56			17 23							
Bristol Parkway [7]	a			16 19	16 25				16 56								17 25				17 56				
Bristol Temple Meads [10]	a			16 34	16 41				17 13								17 41				18 13				
Newport (South Wales)	a					17 07									17 50			18 06							
Cardiff Central [7]	a					17 25									18 10			18 25							

For general notes see front of timetable
For details of catering facilities see Directory of Train Operators

A From Great Malvern (Table 71) to Westbury (Table 123)
B To Maesteg (Table 128)
C To Plymouth (Table 51)
D To Penzance (Table 51)
E From Newcastle (Table 51)
G From Worcester Foregate Street (Table 71) to Westbury (Table 123)

Table 57

Saturdays

from 29 March

Nottingham, Derby and Leicester → Birmingham → Cardiff and Bristol

Network Diagram - see first page of Table 50

Station		GW A	AW B	XC 1◇ C ☕	XC ◇	EM 1◇ D ☕	EM 1◇ ☕	XC 1◇ ☕	XC	XC 🚌	XC 🚌	EM E	XC 1◇ ☕	AW B	XC 1◇ C ☕	XC ◇	EM 1◇ ☕	XC 1◇ G ☕	EM 1◇ H ☕	XC	XC 🚌	XC 🚌
Nottingham 8 ⛴	d				16 00	16 07			16 34			16 38				17 00	17 07			17 34		
Beeston	d				16 06	16a12			16 40							17 06	17a12			17 40		
Attenborough	d				16 09							16a47				17 09						
Long Eaton	d				16 17		16 44		16 48							17 18			17 44	17 51		
Spondon	d				16 23											17 27						
Derby 10	a				16 29		16 56		17 00							17 33			17 54	18 00		
	d			16 24	16 39			16 57	17 07				17 24			17 38		17 57	18 01	18 08		
Willington	d								17 16										18 10			
Burton-on-Trent	d				16 51				17 22							17 50		18 07	18a15	18 20		
Tamworth	d				17 03				17 33							18 03		18 18		18 33		
Wilnecote	d																					
Leicester	d									15 37	16 10										16 37	17 10
South Wigston	d									15 53											16 53	
Narborough	d									16 04											17 04	
Hinckley	d									16 28											17 28	
Nuneaton	d									16a46	16 51										17a46	17 51
Coleshill Parkway	d										17 27											18 27
Water Orton	d																					
Birmingham New Street 12	a			17 04	17 27			17 36	17 54		17 57		17 58			18 27		18 36		18 54		18 57
	d			17 10	17 30			17 40							18 10	18 30		18 40				
Worcester Shrub Hill 7	d	17 05																				
Ashchurch for Tewkesbury	d	17 21			18 09																	
Cheltenham Spa	d	17 31	17 45	17 52	18 18			18 22						18 45	18 52	19 14		19 22				
Gloucester 7	a	17 39	17 56		18 29									18 56		19 23						
Bristol Parkway 7	a	18 19		18 25				18 56							19 25			19 56				
Bristol Temple Meads 10	a	18 35		18 41				19 13							19 41			20 13				
Newport (South Wales)	a		18 50		19 12									19 50		20 06						
Cardiff Central 7	a		19 10		19 33									20 10		20 25						

Station		EM E	AW B	XC 1◇ C ☕	XC	EM 1◇ ☕	EM 1◇ ☕	XC 1◇ ☕	XC	XC 🚌	XC 🚌	XC 1◇ ☕	EM 1◇ ☕	XC 1◇ C	XC 1◇ G ☕	EM	EM 1◇ J ☕	XC	XC 🚌	XC 🚌	EM 1◇ ☕
Nottingham 8 ⛴	d	17 38			18 00	18 07			18 34				19 07			19 33		19 40			20 07
Beeston	d				18 06	18a12			18 40				19a12			19a39					20a12
Attenborough	d	17a47			18 09													19 46			
Long Eaton	d				18 18		18 43		18 50								19 47	19 53			
Spondon	d																				
Derby 10	a				18 31		18 56		19 00								19 57	20 03			
	d			18 24	18 38			18 57	19 08			19 24			19 57			20 07			
Willington	d								19 16												
Burton-on-Trent	d				18 51				19 22						20 07			20 20			
Tamworth	d				19 03				19 33						20 18			20 32			
Wilnecote	d				19 06																
Leicester	d									17 37	18 10								18 37	19 10	
South Wigston	d									17 53									18 53		
Narborough	d									18 04									19 04		
Hinckley	d									18 28									19 28		
Nuneaton	d									18a46	18 51								19a46	19 51	
Coleshill Parkway	d										19 27									20 27	
Water Orton	d																				
Birmingham New Street 12	a			19 04	19 27			19 36	19 54		19 57	19 58			20 42			20 54		20 57	
	d			19 10				19 40	20 00					20 10							
Worcester Shrub Hill 7	d																				
Ashchurch for Tewkesbury	d								20 36												
Cheltenham Spa	d		19 45	19 52				20 22	20 49					20 52							
Gloucester 7	a		19 56						21 01												
Bristol Parkway 7	a			20 25				20 56						21 25							
Bristol Temple Meads 10	a			20 41				21 13						21 41							
Newport (South Wales)	a		20 50																		
Cardiff Central 7	a		21 10																		

For general notes see front of timetable
For details of catering facilities see Directory of Train Operators

- **A** From Great Malvern (Table 71) to Westbury (Table 123)
- **B** To Maesteg (Table 128)
- **C** To Plymouth (Table 51)
- **D** From Sheffield (Table 53)
- **E** From Lincoln (Table 27)
- **G** From Newcastle (Table 51)
- **H** From St Pancras International (Table 53)
- **J** To Barnsley (Table 53)

Table 57

Saturdays
from 29 March

Nottingham, Derby and Leicester → Birmingham → Cardiff and Bristol

Network Diagram - see first page of Table 50

		GW	AW	XC	XC	XC	XC			EM	GW	XC	GW	XC	XC	AW	EM	XC	XC	XC	XC	XC	EM		
				1 ◇						1 ◇	◇	1 ◇					1 ◇		1 ◇				1 ◇		
											A	B							C						
						🚌	🚌			☕				🚌	🚌		☕			🚌	🚌	🚌	☕		
Nottingham 8 🚢	d				20 11													21 45							
Beeston	d				20 17													21 51							
Attenborough	d																	21 55							
Long Eaton	d				20 24					20 44							21 44	22 01					22 45		
Spondon	d				20 32													22 07							
Derby 10	a				20 37					20 56							21 56	22 13					22 56		
	d			20 27	20 40							21 27						22 17	22 27						
Willington	d																								
Burton-on-Trent	d				20 52							21 37						22 29	22 37						
Tamworth	d				21 05							21 48						22 42	22 48						
Wilnecote	d				21 08																				
Leicester	d					19 37	20 10							20 37	21 10					21 55	21 37	22 26			
South Wigston	d					19 53								20 53							21 53	22 42			
Narborough	d					20 04								21 04							22 04	22 53			
Hinckley	d					20 28								21 28							22 28	23 17			
Nuneaton	d					20a46	20 51							21a46	21 51					22 36	22 47	23 36			
Coleshill Parkway	d						21 27								22 27					23 12	23 23	00 12			
Water Orton	d																								
Birmingham New Street 12	a			21 04	21 28		21 57					22 13			22 57			23 03	23 20	23 42	23 53	00 42			
	d			21 10																					
Worcester Shrub Hill 7	d										21 34		22 16												
Ashchurch for Tewkesbury	d										21 52		22 32												
Cheltenham Spa	d	21 02	21 45	21 52							22 01		22 40												
Gloucester 7	a	21 12	21 56								22 09		22 49			22a58									
Bristol Parkway 7	a	21 51		22 25																					
Bristol Temple Meads 10	a	22 04		22 41																					
Newport (South Wales)	a		22 55													23 57									
Cardiff Central 7	a		23 18													00 18									

Sundays
until 27 January

		EM	EM	GW	XC	XC	EM	EM	XC	XC	GW		XC	EM	GW	AW	XC	GW	XC	XC	EM	EM		XC	XC
		1 ◇	1 ◇			1 ◇		1 ◇	1 ◇	◇	1 ◇		1 ◇	1 ◇			1 ◇			1 ◇		1 ◇		1 ◇	
							D		E				G	H			J				D			K	
		☕	☕			☕		☕	☕		☕		☕	☕			☕			☕		☕		☕	
Nottingham 8 🚢	d		07 40				09 25	09 42													11 03	11 43			
Beeston	d		07a47				09 31	09a47													11 09	11a48			
Attenborough	d						09 34														11 12				
Long Eaton	d	01 00					09 41							10 23							11 19				
Spondon	d																								
Derby 10	a	01 12					09 55							10 34							11 30				
	d					09 05							10 09				10 57			11 20					
Willington	d																								
Burton-on-Trent	d					09 15							10 19				11 07								
Tamworth	d					09 26											11 18								
Wilnecote	d																								
Leicester	d																								11 15
South Wigston	d																								11 21
Narborough	d																								11 26
Hinckley	d																								11 35
Nuneaton	d																								11 46
Coleshill Parkway	d																								12 03
Water Orton	d																								
Birmingham New Street 12	a					09 44							11 04				11 36			11 53					12 17
	d								10 10	10 30			11 10				11 40		11 46					12 10	
Worcester Shrub Hill 7	d				09 35														12 24						
Ashchurch for Tewkesbury	d				09 49																				
Cheltenham Spa	d			09 35	09 58				10 52	11 11	11 46		11 52		12 00	12 16	12 22	12 35	12 45					12 52	
Gloucester 7	a			09 45	10 08					11 21	11 56				12 10	12 27		12 45	12 55						
Bristol Parkway 7	a								11 25				12 25		12 48		12 55							13 25	
Bristol Temple Meads 10	a								11 38				12 38		13 00		13 14							13 38	
Newport (South Wales)	a				10 54					12 04						13 25									
Cardiff Central 7	a				11 13					12 25						13 45									

For general notes see front of timetable
For details of catering facilities see Directory of Train Operators

A From Great Malvern (Table 71)
B From Newcastle (Table 51)
C From Edinburgh (Table 51)
D To Matlock (Table 56)
E To Paignton (Table 51)
G From Leeds to Plymouth (Table 51)
H To York (Table 53)
J From York (Table 51)
K To Plymouth (Table 51)

Table 57

Sundays

until 27 January

Nottingham, Derby and Leicester → Birmingham → Cardiff and Bristol

Network Diagram - see first page of Table 50

		XC	XC	GW	XC	XC	EM	XC	AW	XC	XC	XC	EM	EM	XC	XC	GW	XC	XC	GW	XC	XC	XC
		◇	[1]◇ A ☕	[1]◇ ☕	[1]◇ B ☕		[1]◇ C ☕	◇		[1]◇ B ☕	◇ D	[R] [1] ☕	E	[1]◇ ☕	[R] [1] G ☕		H	◇	[1]◇ J ☕	[1]◇ ☕	[R] [1] G ☕		◇
Nottingham [8]	d							12 09					13 16	13 31									14 01
Beeston	d												13 21	13a37									14 07
Attenborough	d												13 24										14 10
Long Eaton	d						12 19	12 24					13 32										14 18
Spondon	d																						
Derby [10]	a						12 31	12 34					13 43										14 28
	d		11 57		12 20			12 39		12 57		13 20							13 57		14 20		14 35
Willington	d																						
Burton-on-Trent	d		12 07					12 50											14 07				14 51
Tamworth	d		12 18					13 03											14 18				15 03
Wilnecote	d																						15 06
Leicester	d					12 15					12 48					13 15						14 15	
South Wigston	d					12 22										13 22						14 21	
Narborough	d					12 27										13 27						14 27	
Hinckley	d					12 36										13 36						14 36	
Nuneaton	d					12 44					13 13					13 44						14 44	
Coleshill Parkway	d					13 02					13 29					14 00						15 01	
Water Orton	d																						
Birmingham New Street [12]	a		12 36		12 53	13 17		13 24		13 36	13 47	13 53				14 17			14 36		14 53	15 17	15 27
	d	12 30	12 40		13 10			13 30		13 40					14 10			14 30	14 40		15 10		15 30
Worcester Shrub Hill [7]	d																14 36						
Ashchurch for Tewkesbury	d																14 52	15 06					
Cheltenham Spa	d	13 12	13 22	13 46	13 52			14 11	14 16	14 22					14 52		15 01	15 15	15 22	15 46	15 52		16 12
Gloucester [7]	a	13 24		13 56				14 21	14 27								15 10	15 25		15 57			16 21
Bristol Parkway [7]	a		13 55		14 25					14 55					15 25		15 49		15 55		16 25		
Bristol Temple Meads [10]	a		14 14		14 38					15 11					15 38		16 10		16 14		16 38		
Newport (South Wales)	a	14 08						15 04	15 24									16 08					17 08
Cardiff Central [7]	a	14 29						15 25	15 45									16 29					17 29

		EM	AW	XC	XC	XC	GW	XC	XC	GW	XC	EM	EM	XC	XC	GW	XC	XC	EM	XC	XC	EM	AW
		[1]◇ C ☕		[1]◇ ☕	◇ K	[R] [1] ☕		[R] [1] G ☕			◇	E	[1]◇ ☕	[1]◇ J ☕	◇ D	[1]◇ ☕	[R] [1] B ☕		[1]◇ C ☕	◇	◇ K	[1]◇ L ☕	
Nottingham [8]	d										15 02	15 14	15 40							16 09		16 30	
Beeston	d											15 19	15a45									16a37	
Attenborough	d											15 23											
Long Eaton	d	14 24									15 15	15 30							16 17	16 23			
Spondon	d																						
Derby [10]	a	14 34									15 25	15 41							16 28	16 33			
	d			14 57		15 20					15 37			15 57			16 20			16 38			
Willington	d																						
Burton-on-Trent	d										15 52			16 07						16 49			
Tamworth	d										16 04			16 18						17 01			
Wilnecote	d																			17 05			
Leicester	d				14 40				15 15						15 44			16 15			16 34		
South Wigston	d								15 22									16 21					
Narborough	d								15 27									16 26					
Hinckley	d								15 36									16 35					
Nuneaton	d				15 01				15 44						16 12			16 43			16 55		
Coleshill Parkway	d				15 18				16 00						16 29			16 59			17 15		
Water Orton	d																						
Birmingham New Street [12]	a			15 36	15 37	15 53			16 13		16 27			16 36	16 48		16 53	17 13		17 24	17 32		
	d			15 40				16 10			16 30			16 40			17 10			17 30			
Worcester Shrub Hill [7]	d									16 39													
Ashchurch for Tewkesbury	d									16 55													
Cheltenham Spa	d		16 16	16 22			16 35	16 52		17 04	17 15			17 22		17 46	17 52			18 12			18 16
Gloucester [7]	a		16 27				16 45			17 12	17 25					17 56				18 22			18 27
Bristol Parkway [7]	a			16 55				17 25		17 51				17 55			18 25						
Bristol Temple Meads [10]	a			17 14				17 38		18 07				18 14			18 38						
Newport (South Wales)	a		17 27								18 08									19 05			19 26
Cardiff Central [7]	a		17 45								18 26									19 26			19 45

For general notes see front of timetable
For details of catering facilities see Directory of Train Operators

A From York (Table 51)
B To Plymouth (Table 51)
C To Sheffield (Table 53)
D From Cambridge (Table 49)
E To Matlock (Table 56)
G To Penzance (Table 51)
H To Weston-super-Mare (Table 134)
J From Newcastle (Table 51)
K From Stansted Airport (Table 49)
L From Sheffield (Table 53)

Table 57

until 27 January

Nottingham, Derby and Leicester → Birmingham → Cardiff and Bristol

Network Diagram - see first page of Table 50

		XC	XC	XC	XC	XC	EM	EM	XC	XC	GW		XC	XC	EM	XC	XC	EM	AW	XC	XC	XC		XC	GW
		R 1	R 1	R 1		◇		1 ◇	1 ◇	◇	1 ◇		R 1		1 ◇	◇	◇	1 ◇		1 ◇	R 1	R 1			
				A			B		C	D			A		E		D	G		C		A			
		☕	☕	☕				☕	☕		☕		☕		☕			☕		☕	☕				
Nottingham 8	d					17 13	17 18	17 24								18 06		18 41							
Beeston	d					17 19	17 24	17a30								18 11		18a47							
Attenborough	d						17 27									18 14									
Long Eaton	d					17 29	17 34								18 17	18 23									
Spondon	d																								
Derby 10	a					17 38	17 49								18 28	18 32									
	d	16 57	17 20			17 42			17 57				18 20			18 39				18 57	19 20				
Willington	d																								
Burton-on-Trent	d					17 53			18 07							18 51				19 07					
Tamworth	d					18 05			18 18							19 03				19 18					
Wilnecote	d															19 06									
Leicester	d				17 15					17 43				18 13			18 38							19 14	
South Wigston	d				17 21									18 20										19 20	
Narborough	d				17 26									18 25										19 25	
Hinckley	d				17 35									18 34										19 34	
Nuneaton	d				17 43					18 04				18 42			18 59							19 42	
Coleshill Parkway	d				18 00					18 20				18 59			19 18							20 00	
Water Orton	d																								
Birmingham New Street 12	a	17 36	17 53		18 14	18 27			18 36	18 38			18 53	19 14		19 26	19 36			19 36	19 53			20 14	
	d	17 40		18 10		18 30			18 40				19 10			19 30				19 40		20 10			
Worcester Shrub Hill 7	d																								20 36
Ashchurch for Tewkesbury	d																								20 53
Cheltenham Spa	d	18 22		18 52		19 15			19 22		19 46		19 52			20 12			20 20	20 22		20 52			21 02
Gloucester 7	a	18 32				19 25					19 57					20 23			20 31						21 11
Bristol Parkway 7	a	19 07		19 25					20 00				20 25							20 58		21 25			21 50
Bristol Temple Meads 10	a	19 24		19 38					20 16				20 38							21 14		21 38			22 03
Newport (South Wales)	a	19 51				20 12													21 25						
Cardiff Central 7	a	20 11				20 33													21 46						

		XC	EM	XC	GW	XC	XC	EM	XC	XC	XC		GW	AW	XC	XC	EM	EM	XC	EM	XC	XC	XC		
				1 ◇		1 ◇	◇	1 ◇		1 ◇	◇				1 ◇		1 ◇			1 ◇	1 ◇	1 ◇			
			B	C			D	H		C	D				J		H	B		E	K	K			
				☕				☕									☕			☕					
Nottingham 8	d	19 08	19 19						20 08									21 23	21 41						
Beeston	d		19 24						20 14									21 29	21 47						
Attenborough	d		19 28															21 32							
Long Eaton	d	19 20	19 34					20 15	20 21								21 22	21 39	21 55	22 10					
Spondon	d																								
Derby 10	a	19 29	19 48					20 27	20 33								21 36	21 50	22 05	22 23					
	d	19 39		19 57		20 24			20 36	20 57					21 24				22 09		22 24	22 57			
Willington	d																								
Burton-on-Trent	d	19 50		20 07					20 51	21 07					21 34				22 21		22 34	23 07			
Tamworth	d	20 02		20 18					21 04	21 18					21 45				22 34		22 45	23 18			
Wilnecote	d								21 07																
Leicester	d						20 09				21 02					21 12							23 08		
South Wigston	d															21 21							23 17		
Narborough	d															21 26							23 24		
Hinckley	d															21 35							23 35		
Nuneaton	d						20 30				21 22					21 43							23 43		
Coleshill Parkway	d						20 49				21 43					21 59									
Water Orton	d																								
Birmingham New Street 12	a	20 29		20 41		20 57	21 06		21 27	21 41	22 00				22 04	22 12			22 55		23 16	23 51	00 12		
	d	20 30				21 10									22 10										
Worcester Shrub Hill 7	d																								
Ashchurch for Tewkesbury	d	21 05																							
Cheltenham Spa	d	21 14			21 42	21 52							22 01		22 52										
Gloucester 7	a	21 28			21 52								22 11	22 33											
Bristol Parkway 7	a					22 25									23 25										
Bristol Temple Meads 10	a					22 41									23 41										
Newport (South Wales)	a													23 35											
Cardiff Central 7	a													23 56											

For general notes see front of timetable
For details of catering facilities see Directory of Train Operators

- **A** To Plymouth (Table 51)
- **B** To Matlock (Table 56)
- **C** From Newcastle (Table 51)
- **D** From Stansted Airport (Table 49)
- **E** To Sheffield (Table 53)
- **G** From York (Table 53)
- **H** To Leeds (Table 53)
- **J** From Glasgow Central (Table 51)
- **K** From Edinburgh (Table 51)

Table 57

Nottingham, Derby and Leicester → Birmingham → Cardiff and Bristol

3 February to 23 March

Network Diagram - see first page of Table 50

	EM	EM	XC	XC	GW	GW		XC	XC	XC	XC	XC	GW		XC	XC	EM	EM	EM	GW		AW	XC	XC
	1◇ ☕	🚌	🚌	🚌					🚌	1◇ A ☕	◇	🚌	1◇ ☕		1◇ A ☕	🚌	B	1◇ ☕	1◇ C ☕					🚌
Nottingham 8 🚊 d		06 52															09 25	09 42						
Beeston d		07a12															09 31	09a47						
Attenborough d																	09 34							
Long Eaton d	01 00																09 41		10 23					
Spondon d																								
Derby 10 a	01 12																09 55		10 34					
d				08 30					08 55						09 50	09 55								
Willington d																								
Burton-on-Trent d			08 15						09 20			09 35				10 20								10 35
Tamworth d			08 50						09a55			10 10				10a55								11 10
Wilnecote d																								
Leicester d																								
South Wigston d																								
Narborough d																								
Hinckley d																								
Nuneaton d																								
Coleshill Parkway d																								
Water Orton d																								
Birmingham New Street 12 a			09 30	09 30								10 50			11 03									11 50
d										10 10	10 30				11 10									
Worcester Shrub Hill 7 d								09 35															11 46	
Ashchurch for Tewkesbury d								09 49															12 24	
Cheltenham Spa d						09 35		09 58		10 52	11 11		11 46		11 52					12 00		12 16	12 45	
Gloucester 7 a						09 45		10 08			11 21		11 56							12 10		12 27	12 55	
Bristol Parkway 7 a										11 25					12 25					12 48				
Bristol Temple Meads 10 a					09 50					11 38					12 38					13 00				
Newport (South Wales) a					10 21			10 54			12 04											13 25		
Cardiff Central 7 a					10 37			11 13			12 25											13 45		

	XC	XC	EM	XC	XC		EM	GW	XC	XC	XC	XC		XC	EM	XC	XC	XC	XC		XC	AW	GW	XC
	1◇ ☕	🚌	B	1◇ A ☕			1◇ ☕		◇	🚌	1◇ A ☕			🚌	1◇ D ☕		◇	◇ E	🚌		R 1 ☕		1◇ ☕	R 1 G ☕
Nottingham 8 🚊 d			11 03				11 43									12 09								
Beeston d			11 09				11a48																	
Attenborough d			11 12																					
Long Eaton d			11 19												12 19	12 24								
Spondon d																								
Derby 10 a			11 30												12 31	12 34								
d	10 40	10 55									11 40			11 55							12 40			
Willington d																								
Burton-on-Trent d		11 20								11 35				12 20					12 35					
Tamworth d		11a55								12 10				12a55					13 10					
Wilnecote d																								
Leicester d					11 15							12 15						12 48						
South Wigston d					11 21							12 22												
Narborough d					11 26							12 27												
Hinckley d					11 35							12 36												
Nuneaton d					11 46							12 44						13 13						
Coleshill Parkway d					12 03							13 02						13 29						
Water Orton d																								
Birmingham New Street 12 a	11 53				12 17					12 50	12 53	13 17						13 47	13 50		13 53			
d				12 10					12 30		13 10						13 30							14 10
Worcester Shrub Hill 7 d																								
Ashchurch for Tewkesbury d																								
Cheltenham Spa d				12 52				13 05	13 12		13 52						14 11					14 16	14 46	14 52
Gloucester 7 a								13 15	13 24								14 21					14 27	14 56	
Bristol Parkway 7 a				13 25							14 25													15 25
Bristol Temple Meads 10 a				13 38							14 38													15 38
Newport (South Wales) a									14 08								15 04					15 24		
Cardiff Central 7 a									14 29								15 25					15 45		

For general notes see front of timetable
For details of catering facilities see Directory of Train Operators

A To Plymouth (Table 51)
B To Matlock (Table 56)
C To York (Table 53)
D To Sheffield (Table 53)
E From Cambridge (Table 49)
G To Penzance (Table 51)

Nottingham, Derby and Leicester → Birmingham → Cardiff and Bristol

3 February to 23 March

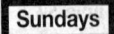

Network Diagram - see first page of Table 50

		XC	XC	XC	GW		XC	XC	XC	EM	EM	XC		XC	XC	EM	XC	XC	XC		XC	XC	XC	XC	AW
		bus		bus	A		◇	bus	R 1 B cup	C	1 ◇ cup			bus		1 ◇ D cup	◇	◇ E	bus		R 1 cup	bus	bus	◇	
Nottingham 8	d									13 16	13 31				14 01									15 02	
Beeston	d									13 21	13a37				14 07										
Attenborough	d									13 24					14 10										
Long Eaton	d									13 32					14 18	14 24								15 20	
Spondon	d																								
Derby 10	a									13 43					14 28	14 34								15 29	
	d	12 45		12 55					13 40					13 55							14 40	14 40	14 55		
Willington	d																								
Burton-on-Trent	d	13 06		13 20				13 35						14 20					14 35			15 01	15 20		
Tamworth	d	13 32		13a55				14 10						14a55					15 10			15 27	15a55		
Wilnecote	d																					15 38			
Leicester	d		13 15									14 15						14 40							
South Wigston	d		13 22									14 21													
Narborough	d		13 27									14 27													
Hinckley	d		13 36									14 36													
Nuneaton	d		13 44									14 44						15 01							
Coleshill Parkway	d		14 00									15 01						15 18							
Water Orton	d																								
Birmingham New Street 12	a	14 12	14 17					14 50	14 53			15 17						15 37	15 50		15 53	16 08			
	d						14 30		15 10								15 30								
Worcester Shrub Hill 7	d				14 36																				
Ashchurch for Tewkesbury	d				14 52		15 06																		
Cheltenham Spa	d				15 01		15 15		15 52								16 12								16 16
Gloucester 7	a				15 10		15 25										16 21								16 27
Bristol Parkway 7	a				15 49				16 25																
Bristol Temple Meads 10	a				16 10				16 38																
Newport (South Wales)	a						16 08										17 08								17 27
Cardiff Central 7	a						16 29										17 29								17 45

		GW	XC	XC		GW	XC	XC	XC	GW	XC		XC	EM	EM	XC	XC	EM		XC	XC	XC	XC	EM	XC
			R 1 B cup				◇	◇ G	bus	1 ◇ cup	R 1 H cup		bus	C	1 ◇ cup		bus	1 ◇ D cup			◇	◇ E	bus	1 ◇ J cup	R 1 cup
Nottingham 8	d													15 14	15 40					16 09				16 30	
Beeston	d													15 19	15a45									16a37	
Attenborough	d													15 23											
Long Eaton	d													15 30				16 17		16 22					
Spondon	d																								
Derby 10	a													15 41				16 28		16 32					
	d										15 40		15 40				15 55								16 40
Willington	d																								
Burton-on-Trent	d								15 35				16 01				16 20						16 35		
Tamworth	d								16 10				16 27				16a55						17 10		
Wilnecote	d																								
Leicester	d			15 15				15 44								16 15						16 34			
South Wigston	d			15 22												16 21									
Narborough	d			15 27												16 26									
Hinckley	d			15 36												16 35									
Nuneaton	d			15 44				16 12								16 43						16 55			
Coleshill Parkway	d			16 00				16 29								16 59						17 15			
Water Orton	d																								
Birmingham New Street 12	a			16 13				16 48	16 50		16 53		17 07			17 13						17 32	17 50		17 53
	d		16 10				16 30				17 10										17 30				
Worcester Shrub Hill 7	d					16 39																			
Ashchurch for Tewkesbury	d					16 55																			
Cheltenham Spa	d	16 30	16 52			17 04	17 15			17 35	17 52										18 12				
Gloucester 7	a	16 40				17 12	17 25			17 45	18 02										18 22				
Bristol Parkway 7	a		17 25			17 51					18 35														
Bristol Temple Meads 10	a		17 38			18 07					18 47														
Newport (South Wales)	a						18 08														19 05				
Cardiff Central 7	a						18 26														19 26				

For general notes see front of timetable
For details of catering facilities see Directory of Train Operators

- **A** To Weston-super-Mare (Table 134)
- **B** To Penzance (Table 51)
- **C** To Matlock (Table 56)
- **D** To Sheffield (Table 53)
- **E** From Stansted Airport (Table 49)
- **G** From Cambridge (Table 49)
- **H** To Plymouth (Table 51)
- **J** From Sheffield (Table 53)

Table 57

Sundays

Nottingham, Derby and Leicester → Birmingham → Cardiff and Bristol

3 February to 23 March

Network Diagram - see first page of Table 50

Station		AW	XC R 1 A ☕		XC 🚌	XC	XC 🚌	XC	XC ◇	XC ◇ B		XC 🚌	XC R 1 A ☕	EM C	EM 1 ◇ ☕	XC	XC 🚌		XC 🚌	EM 1 ◇ D ☕	XC ◇	XC ◇	XC ◇ B	XC 🚌	XC R 1 ☕
Nottingham 8 🚋	d							17 13						17 18	17 24						18 06				
Beeston	d							17 19						17 24	17a30						18 11				
Attenborough	d													17 27							18 14				
Long Eaton	d							17 29						17 34						18 17	18 23				
Spondon	d																								
Derby 10	a							17 38						17 49						18 28	18 32				
	d				16 45		16 55						17 40				17 50		17 55						18 40
Willington	d																								
Burton-on-Trent	d				17 06		17 20					17 35					18 11		18 20					18 35	
Tamworth	d				17 32		17a55					18 10					18 37		18a55					19 10	
Wilnecote	d				17 43																				
Leicester	d					17 15				17 43						18 13							18 38		
South Wigston	d					17 21										18 20									
Narborough	d					17 26										18 25									
Hinckley	d					17 35										18 34									
Nuneaton	d					17 43				18 04						18 42							18 59		
Coleshill Parkway	d					18 00				18 20						18 59							19 18		
Water Orton	d																								
Birmingham New Street 12	a				18 13	18 14				18 38		18 50	18 53			19 14	19 17						19 36	19 50	19 53
	d		18 10						18 30				19 10									19 30			
Worcester Shrub Hill 7	d																								
Ashchurch for Tewkesbury	d																								
Cheltenham Spa	d	18 16	18 52						19 15				19 52									20 12			
Gloucester 7	a	18 27							19 25													20 23			
Bristol Parkway 7	a		19 25										20 25												
Bristol Temple Meads 10	a		19 38										20 38												
Newport (South Wales)	a	19 26							20 12																
Cardiff Central 7	a	19 45							20 33																

Station		EM 1 ◇ E ☕		AW	GW 1 ◇ ☕	XC R 1 A	XC 🚌	XC	XC 🚌		XC	GW	XC	XC 🚌	GW	XC R 1		XC ◇ B	XC 🚌	EM C	XC 🚌	EM 1 ◇ G ☕	XC		XC 🚌
Nottingham 8 🚋	d	18 41									19 08									19 19			20 08		
Beeston	d	18a47																		19 24			20 14		
Attenborough	d																			19 28					
Long Eaton	d										19 20									19 34		20 15	20 21		
Spondon	d																								
Derby 10	a										19 29									19 48		20 27	20 33		
	d						18 45		18 55							19 40			19 40		19 55				
Willington	d																								
Burton-on-Trent	d						19 06		19 20					19 35					20 01		20 20				20 35
Tamworth	d						19 32		19a55					20 10					20 27		20a55				21 10
Wilnecote	d						19 43																		
Leicester	d							19 14										20 09							
South Wigston	d							19 20																	
Narborough	d							19 25																	
Hinckley	d							19 34																	
Nuneaton	d							19 42										20 30							
Coleshill Parkway	d							20 00										20 49							
Water Orton	d																								
Birmingham New Street 12	a						20 13	20 14						20 50		20 57		21 06	21 07						21 50
	d					20 10							20 30			21 10									
Worcester Shrub Hill 7	d											20 36													
Ashchurch for Tewkesbury	d											20 53	21 05												
Cheltenham Spa	d			20 20	20 35	20 52						21 02	21 14		21 42	21 52									
Gloucester 7	a			20 31	20 45							21 11	21 28		21 52										
Bristol Parkway 7	a					21 25						21 50				22 25									
Bristol Temple Meads 10	a					21 38						22 03				22 41									
Newport (South Wales)	a			21 25																					
Cardiff Central 7	a			21 46																					

For general notes see front of timetable
For details of catering facilities see Directory of Train Operators

- **A** To Plymouth (Table 51)
- **B** From Stansted Airport (Table 49)
- **C** To Matlock (Table 56)
- **D** To Sheffield (Table 53)
- **E** From York (Table 53)
- **G** To Leeds (Table 53)

Table 57

Sundays

3 February to 23 March

Nottingham, Derby and Leicester → Birmingham → Cardiff and Bristol

Network Diagram - see first page of Table 50

		XC ◇ A	GW	AW	XC [1] ◇	XC	XC (bus)		XC (bus)	XC (bus)	EM [1] ◇ B (cup)	XC [1] ◇	EM C	XC (bus)		XC	XC (bus)	EM [1] ◇ D (cup)	XC (bus)	XC [1] ◇	XC		XC (bus)		
Nottingham [8] (ship)	d												21 23			21 41									
Beeston	d												21 29			21 47									
Attenborough	d												21 32												
Long Eaton	d										21 22		21 39			21 55		22 10							
Spondon	d																								
Derby [10]	a										21 36		21 50			22 05		22 23							
	d				20 40		20 45		20 55			21 40		21 55			22 15			22 40			22 55		
Willington	d																								
Burton-on-Trent	d						21 06		21 20	21 35				22 20			22 36		22 35				23 20		
Tamworth	d						21 32		21a55	22 10				22a55			23 02		23 10				23a55		
Wilnecote	d						21 43																		
Leicester	d	21 02				21 12															23 08				
South Wigston	d					21 21															23 17				
Narborough	d					21 26															23 24				
Hinckley	d					21 35															23 35				
Nuneaton	d	21 22				21 43															23 43				
Coleshill Parkway	d	21 43				21 59																			
Water Orton	d																								
Birmingham New Street [12]	a	22 00			22 01	22 12	22 13			22 50		22 55					23 42		23 50	23 55	00 12				
	d				22 10																				
Worcester Shrub Hill [7]	d																								
Ashchurch for Tewkesbury	d																								
Cheltenham Spa	d		22 01		22 52																				
Gloucester [7]	a		22 11	22d33																					
Bristol Parkway [7]	a				23 25																				
Bristol Temple Meads [10]	a				23 41																				
Newport (South Wales)	a			23 35																					
Cardiff Central [7]	a			23 56																					

Sundays

from 30 March

		XC (bus)	EM [1] ◇ (cup)	EM [1] ◇ (cup)	XC	XC [1] ◇ (cup)	EM C	XC [1] ◇ E (cup)	EM [1] ◇ (cup)	XC ◇	XC [1] ◇ G (cup)	EM [1] ◇ H (cup)	GW		AW	XC [1] ◇ J (cup)	XC	XC [1] ◇ (cup)	EM C	EM [1] ◇ D (cup)	XC [1] ◇ K (cup)	XC ◇	XC [1] ◇ J (cup)	XC [1] ◇ K (cup)	XC ◇
Nottingham [8] (ship)	d			08 19			09 25		10 16										11 03						12 09
Beeston	d			08a26			09 31		10a22										11 09						
Attenborough	d						09 34												11 12						
Long Eaton	d		00 14				09 41					10 31							11 19	11 33					12 24
Spondon	d																								
Derby [10]	a		00 26				09 55					10 42							11 30	11 45					12 34
	d					09 05					10 10					10 57		11 20					11 57	12 20	12 39
Willington	d																								
Burton-on-Trent	d					09 15					10 21					11 07							12 07		12 50
Tamworth	d					09 26					10 32					11 18							12 18		13 03
Wilnecote	d																								
Leicester	d	22p26																							
South Wigston	d	22p42																							
Narborough	d	22p53																							
Hinckley	d	23p17																							
Nuneaton	d	23p36																							
Coleshill Parkway	d	00 12																							
Water Orton	d																								
Birmingham New Street [12]	a	00 42				09 44					10 51					11 36		11 53					12 36	12 53	13 24
	d							10 10		10 30	11 10					11 40	11 46				12 10	12 30	12 40	13 10	13 30
Worcester Shrub Hill [7]	d				09 35												12 24								
Ashchurch for Tewkesbury	d				09 49																				
Cheltenham Spa	d				09 58			10 52		11 11	11 52		11 57		12 16	12 22	12 45				12 52	13 12	13 22	13 52	14 11
Gloucester [7]	a				10 08					11 21			12 07		12 29		12 55					13 24			14 21
Bristol Parkway [7]	a							11 25			12 25		12 46			12 57					13 25		13 57	14 25	
Bristol Temple Meads [10]	a							11 38			12 38		12 58			13 13					13 38		14 13	14 38	
Newport (South Wales)	a				10 54					12 04					13 29							14 08			15 04
Cardiff Central [7]	a				11 13					12 25					13 49							14 29			15 25

For general notes see front of timetable
For details of catering facilities see Directory of Train Operators

A From Stansted Airport (Table 49)
B To Leeds (Table 53)
C To Matlock (Table 56)
D To Sheffield (Table 53)
E To Paignton (Table 51)
G From Leeds to Plymouth (Table 51)
H To York (Table 53)
J From York (Table 51)
K To Plymouth (Table 51)

Table 57

Sundays

from 30 March

Nottingham, Derby and Leicester → Birmingham → Cardiff and Bristol

Network Diagram - see first page of Table 50

		EM		AW	XC	XC	XC		XC	XC	EM	GW	XC	EM	XC	XC	XC		XC	XC	XC	XC	XC		EM
		1 ◇			1 ◇				R 1	R 1			◇	1 ◇	1 ◇				R 1	◇	1 ◇				1 ◇
					A					B	C	D		E	G				B						
						bus	bus									bus	bus					bus	bus		
		buffet			buffet				buffet	buffet				buffet	buffet				buffet	trolley	buffet				buffet
Nottingham 8 (tram)	d	12 24									13 16									14 01					14 18
Beeston	d	12a29									13 21									14 07					14a24
Attenborough	d										13 24									14 10					
Long Eaton	d										13 32			13 45						14 18					
Spondon	d																								
Derby 10	a										13 43			13 56						14 28					
	d				12 57				13 20						13 57				14 20	14 35	14 57				
Willington	d																								
Burton-on-Trent	d														14 07					14 51					
Tamworth	d														14 18					15 03					
Wilnecote	d																			15 06					
Leicester	d					11 15	11 50									12 15	12 55					13 15	13 50		
South Wigston	d					11 31										12 31						13 31			
Narborough	d					11 42										12 42						13 42			
Hinckley	d					12 06										13 06						14 06			
Nuneaton	d					12a24	12 31									13a24	13 36					14a24	14 31		
Coleshill Parkway	d						13 07										14 12						15 07		
Water Orton	d																								
Birmingham New Street 12	a				13 36		13 37		13 53						14 36		14 42		14 53	15 27	15 30		15 37		
	d				13 40					14 10			14 30		14 40				15 10	15 30	15 40				
Worcester Shrub Hill 7	d											14 34													
Ashchurch for Tewkesbury	d											14 49	15 06												
Cheltenham Spa	d			14 16	14 22					14 52		14 58	15 15		15 22				15 52	16 12	16 22				
Gloucester 7	a			14 29								15 07	15 25							16 21					
Bristol Parkway 7	a				14 57					15 25		15 46			15 57				16 25		16 57				
Bristol Temple Meads 10	a				15 11					15 38		15 59			16 13				16 38		17 13				
Newport (South Wales)	a			15 29									16 08							17 08					
Cardiff Central 7	a			15 49									16 29							17 29					

		XC	AW	XC		GW	XC	EM	EM	XC	XC	XC		EM	GW	XC	XC	XC	XC	XC		XC	EM	EM	AW
		R 1		R 1			◇		1 ◇	1 ◇				1 ◇	1 ◇	R 1	◇	R 1				R 1	1 ◇	1 ◇	
				B				C	E	G					H	A							J	E	
											bus	bus							bus	bus					
		buffet		buffet					buffet	buffet				buffet	buffet	buffet	trolley	buffet				buffet	buffet	buffet	
Nottingham 8 (tram)	d						15 02	15 14						16 03			16 09						17 09		
Beeston	d							15 19						16a08									17a16		
Attenborough	d							15 23																	
Long Eaton	d						15 18	15 30	15 43								16 23							17 24	
Spondon	d																								
Derby 10	a						15 30	15 41	15 56								16 33							17 35	
	d	15 20					15 37			15 57						16 20	16 38	16 57				17 20			
Willington	d																								
Burton-on-Trent	d						15 52			16 07							16 49								
Tamworth	d						16 04			16 18							17 01								
Wilnecote	d																17 05								
Leicester	d										14 15	14 50							15 15	15 50					
South Wigston	d										14 31								15 31						
Narborough	d										14 42								15 42						
Hinckley	d										15 06								16 06						
Nuneaton	d										15a24	15 31							16a24	16 31					
Coleshill Parkway	d											16 07								17 07					
Water Orton	d																								
Birmingham New Street 12	a	15 53					16 27			16 36		16 37				16 53	17 24	17 36		17 37		17 53			
	d			16 10			16 30			16 40						17 10	17 30	17 40							
Worcester Shrub Hill 7	d					16 39									17 25										
Ashchurch for Tewkesbury	d					16 55																			
Cheltenham Spa	d		16 26	16 52		17 04	17 15			17 22					17a42	17 52	18 12	18 22							18 26
Gloucester 7	a		16 36			17 12	17 25										18 22	18 32							18 41
Bristol Parkway 7	a			17 25		17 53				18 01						18 25		19 07							
Bristol Temple Meads 10	a			17 38		18 08				18 17						18 38		19 24							
Newport (South Wales)	a		17 30				18 08										19 05								19 34
Cardiff Central 7	a		17 48				18 26										19 26								19 53

For general notes see front of timetable
For details of catering facilities see Directory of Train Operators

- **A** To Plymouth (Table 51)
- **B** To Penzance (Table 51)
- **C** To Matlock (Table 56)
- **D** To Weston-super-Mare (Table 134)
- **E** To Sheffield (Table 53)
- **G** From Newcastle (Table 51)
- **H** From Hereford (Table 71)
- **J** From Sheffield (Table 53)

Table 57

Sundays

from 30 March

Nottingham, Derby and Leicester → Birmingham → Cardiff and Bristol

Network Diagram - see first page of Table 50

		XC	XC	EM	XC	XC	XC	GW	XC	XC	EM	AW	XC	XC	XC	XC	XC	GW	XC	XC	XC
		R 1	◇		1 ◇			1 ◇	R 1	◇	1 ◇		1 ◇			R 1	R 1				
		A		B	C			D	A				C				A				
						bus	bus							bus	bus					bus	bus
		catering			catering			catering	catering		catering		catering			catering					
Nottingham 8	d		17 13	17 18						18 06	18 17								19 08		
Beeston	d		17 19	17 24						18 11	18a22										
Attenborough	d			17 27						18 14											
Long Eaton	d		17 29	17 34						18 23									19 20		
Spondon	d																				
Derby 10	a		17 38	17 49						18 32									19 29		
	d		17 42		17 57				18 20	18 39			18 57			19 20			19 39		
Willington	d																				
Burton-on-Trent	d		17 53		18 07					18 51			19 07						19 50		
Tamworth	d		18 05		18 18					19 03			19 18						20 02		
Wilnecote	d									19 06											
Leicester	d					16 15	16 50							17 15	17 50					18 15	18 50
South Wigston	d					16 31								17 31						18 31	
Narborough	d					16 42								17 42						18 42	
Hinckley	d					17 06								18 06						19 06	
Nuneaton	d					17a24	17 31							18a24	18 31					19a24	19 31
Coleshill Parkway	d						18 07								19 07						20 07
Water Orton	d																				
Birmingham New Street 12	a		18 27		18 36		18 37		18 53	19 26			19 36		19 37	19 53			20 29		20 37
	d	18 10	18 30		18 40				19 10	19 30			19 40				20 10		20 30		
Worcester Shrub Hill 7	d							19 24										20 36			
Ashchurch for Tewkesbury	d																	20 53	21 05		
Cheltenham Spa	d	18 52	19 15		19 22			19a41	19 52	20 12		20 20	20 22				20 52	21 02	21 14		
Gloucester 7	a		19 25							20 23		20 31						21 11	21 28		
Bristol Parkway 7	a	19 25			20 00				20 25				20 58				21 25	21 50			
Bristol Temple Meads 10	a	19 38			20 16				20 38				21 14				21 38	22 03			
Newport (South Wales)	a		20 08									21 25									
Cardiff Central 7	a		20 29									21 46									

		EM	EM	EM	XC	XC	XC	XC	XC	EM	XC	XC	GW	AW	XC	EM	EM	XC	XC	XC	XC	XC	XC
		1 ◇		1 ◇	1 ◇	1 ◇				1 ◇	1 ◇				1 ◇	1 ◇				1 ◇		1 ◇	
			B	E	C						C				G	H	B			J		J	
								bus	bus			bus							bus		bus		bus
		catering		catering	catering					catering						catering							
Nottingham 8	d		19 19	19 33			20 08										21 23	21 41					
Beeston	d		19 24	19a39			20 14										21 29	21 47					
Attenborough	d		19 28														21 32						
Long Eaton	d	19 26	19 34				20 21			20 26						21 28	21 39	21 55					
Spondon	d																						
Derby 10	a	19 36	19 48				20 33			20 39						21 45	21 50	22 05					
	d				19 57	20 24	20 36				20 57				21 24			22 09		22 24		22 57	
Willington	d																						
Burton-on-Trent	d				20 07		20 51				21 07				21 34			22 21		22 34		23 07	
Tamworth	d				20 18		21 04				21 18				21 45			22 34		22 45		23 18	
Wilnecote	d						21 07																
Leicester	d							19 15	19 50			20 15							21 15		21 15		23 10
South Wigston	d							19 31													21 31		23 26
Narborough	d							19 42													21 42		23 37
Hinckley	d							20 06													22 06		00 02
Nuneaton	d							20a24	20 31			20 56							21 56		22 25		00 21
Coleshill Parkway	d								21 07			21 32							22 32		23 01		
Water Orton	d																						
Birmingham New Street 12	a				20 41	20 57	21 27		21 37		21 41	22 02			22 04			22 55	23 02	23 16	23 31	23 51	01 06
	d					21 10									22 10								
Worcester Shrub Hill 7	d																						
Ashchurch for Tewkesbury	d																						
Cheltenham Spa	d					21 52							22 01		22 52								
Gloucester 7	a												22 11	22 37									
Bristol Parkway 7	a					22 25									23 25								
Bristol Temple Meads 10	a					22 41									23 41								
Newport (South Wales)	a													23 36									
Cardiff Central 7	a													23 57									

For general notes see front of timetable
For details of catering facilities see Directory of Train Operators

- **A** To Plymouth (Table 51)
- **B** To Matlock (Table 56)
- **C** From Newcastle (Table 51)
- **D** From Hereford (Table 71)
- **E** From York (Table 53)
- **G** From Glasgow Central (Table 51)
- **H** To Sheffield (Table 53)
- **J** From Edinburgh (Table 51)

Table 57

Mondays to Fridays

until 25 January

Bristol and Cardiff → Birmingham → Leicester, Derby and Nottingham

Network Diagram - see first page of Table 50

Miles	Miles	Miles			EM	EM	AW	EM	XC	EM	XC	XC	XC	EM	XC	XC	GW		XC	EM	XC	XC	XC	EM	EM
					MX	MX	MX																		
					1 ◇	1 ◇		1 ◇	◇				1 ◇			1 ◇				1 ◇	◇		R 1		1 ◇
							A	B												C	D				
					☕	☕		⊠ 🛒					☕			☕				☕			☕		☕
0	—	—	**Cardiff Central 7**	d			23p20																		
11¾	—	—	Newport (South Wales)	d			23p39																		
—	—	0	**Bristol Temple Meads 10**	d																					
—	—	5¾	Bristol Parkway 7	d																					
56½	—	—	Gloucester 7	d			00 39										06 02								
63	—	46¼	Cheltenham Spa	d			00a52										06 12								
70¼	—	53½	Ashchurch for Tewkesbury	d													06 20								
85	—	—	Worcester Shrub Hill 7	a													06 40								
112	—	92¾	**Birmingham New Street 12**	a																					
—	0	—		d					05 20			05 55	06 00		06 09	06 30					06 37	06 54	07 03		
119¾	7¾	—	Water Orton	d											06 19										
—	9½	—	Coleshill Parkway	d																	06 49				
—	20	—	Nuneaton	d					05 48			06 21									07 05	07 22			
—	25¼	—	Hinckley	d								06 28										07 28			
—	34	—	Narborough	d								06 36										07 37			
—	37	—	South Wigston	d								06 40										07 42			
—	38¾	—	**Leicester**	a					06 08			06 46									07 28	07 48			
127	—	—	Wilnecote	d											06 27										
128¾	—	—	Tamworth	d									06 15		06 31	06 47							07 19		
141¾	—	—	Burton-on-Trent	d									06 25		06 42	06 58				07 10			07 29		
146½	—	—	Willington	d																07 16					
152¾	—	—	**Derby 10**	a									06 38		06 58	07 11				07 25			07 42		
—	—	—		d				05 56		06 16	06 28				07 11				07 22	07 34					
155¼	—	—	Spondon	d							06 33								07 27						
161	—	—	Long Eaton	d				06a05		06a25	06 40				07 20				07 35	07a43					
164	—	—	Attenborough	d							06 49			07 18					07 42					08 07	
165½	—	—	Beeston	d	00 28	00 40					06 52			07 21	07 28				07 45					08 10	08 20
168¾	—	—	**Nottingham 8**	🚋 a	00 35	00 46					06 59			07 30	07 34				07 53					08 20	08 29

		XC	XC	XC	EM	EM	XC	XC	XC		XC	GW	AW	EM	XC	XC	XC	EM	XC	GW	XC	XC	AW		XC
			◇	1 ◇		1 ◇			R 1					1 ◇		◇	1 ◇	1 ◇		1 ◇		1 ◇			1 ◇
			D			C						E				D		G				H			
				☕		☕			☕					☕			☕	☕		🛒		☕			☕
Cardiff Central 7	d												06 12										07 12		
Newport (South Wales)	d												06 27										07 27		
Bristol Temple Meads 10	d								06 15								07 00					07 30			
Bristol Parkway 7	d								06 25								07 10					07 40			
Gloucester 7	d								07 02		07 09	07 15	07 21						07 46	07 55			08 21		
Cheltenham Spa	d								07 12		07 19	07 25	07a34				07 42		07 57	08a03		08 12	08a34		
Ashchurch for Tewkesbury	d										07 28	07 33							08 04						
Worcester Shrub Hill 7	a											07 54													
Birmingham New Street 12	a								07 57		08 16						08 26		08 46			08 57			
	d	07 10	07 21	07 30			07 49	07 54	08 03						08 19	08 24	08 30		08 49		08 54				09 03
Water Orton	d	07 21																			09 06				
Coleshill Parkway	d															08 37									
Nuneaton	d		07 48					08 24								08 53					09 26				
Hinckley	d		07 55					08 31													09 33				
Narborough	d		08 03					08 39													09 41				
South Wigston	d		08 07					08 44																	
Leicester	a		08 13					08 50								09 13					09 51				
Wilnecote	d						08 05																		
Tamworth	d	07 30		07 47			08 09		08 19						08 36		08 47		09 08						
Burton-on-Trent	d	07 42		07 58		08 10	08 20		08 29						08 48		08 58		09 20						
Willington	d	07 47				08 16																			
Derby 10	a	07 56		08 11		08 25	08 36		08 42						09 01		09 11		09 36						09 39
	d	08 03			08 22	08 34	08 39								09 11			09 34	09 40						
Spondon	d	08 08													09 16										
Long Eaton	d	08 15			08 32	08a43	08 49								09 23			09a43	09 50						
Attenborough	d	08 23													09 31										
Beeston	d	08 26			08 39		08 57							09 20	09 35				09 56						
Nottingham 8	🚋 a	08 32			08 45		09 04							09 26	09 41				10 05						

For general notes see front of timetable
For details of catering facilities see Directory of Train Operators

- **A** From Maesteg (Table 128)
- **B** From Sheffield (Table 53)
- **C** To St Pancras International (Table 53)
- **D** To Stansted Airport (Table 49)
- **E** To Great Malvern (Table 71)
- **G** From Barnsley (Table 53)
- **H** From Exeter St Davids (Table 51)

Table 57

Mondays to Fridays

until 25 January

Bristol and Cardiff → Birmingham → Leicester, Derby and Nottingham

Network Diagram - see first page of Table 50

		EM	XC	XC	XC	EM	XC	GW	XC	XC	EM	XC	XC	GW		XC	GW	EM	XC	GW	XC	XC	AW	XC	EM
		1◇		◇	1◇	1◇	◇			1◇	1◇		◇			1◇		1◇	◇	1◇		R 1		1◇	1◇
				A			B	C		D			A	E		D	E		B			D			
		☕			☕	☕	🛒			☕	☕	🛒				☕		☕	🛒	🛒		☕		☕	☕
Cardiff Central [7]	d				07 00		07 45												08 45				09 12		
Newport (South Wales)	d				07 15		07 59												08 59				09 27		
Bristol Temple Meads [10]	d				08 00					08 30				08 41		09 00						09 30			
Bristol Parkway [7]	d				08 10					08 40				08 52		09 10	←					09 40			
Gloucester [7]	d						08 46	08 50						09 38 →			09 38		09 46	09 50			10 21		
Cheltenham Spa	d				08 42		08 57	09a03		09 12						09 42	09 48		09 56	10a03		10 12	10a34		
Ashchurch for Tewkesbury	d																09 56		10 04						
Worcester Shrub Hill [7]	a																10 13								
Birmingham New Street [12]	a				09 26		09 45			09 57						10 26			10 45			10 57			
	d		09 19	09 24	09 30		09 49		09 54	10 03		10 13	10 24			10 30			10 49		10 54			11 03	
Water Orton	d																				11 05				
Coleshill Parkway	d			09 37					10 08				10 37								11 08				
Nuneaton	d			09 53					10 25				10 53								11 25				
Hinckley	d								10 32												11 32				
Narborough	d								10 40												11 40				
South Wigston	d								10 45																
Leicester	a			10 13					10 50				11 13								11 50				
Wilnecote	d											10 29													
Tamworth	d		09 36				10 06					10 33				10 47			11 06						
Burton-on-Trent	d		09 47				10 18					10 44				10 58			11 19						
Willington	d						10 25																		
Derby [10]	a		10 02		10 11		10 36			10 39		11 02				11 11			11 36					11 39	
	d		10 11			10 34	10 41					11 11						11 34	11 41						
Spondon	d																								
Long Eaton	d		10 20			10a43	10 50					11 20						11a43	11 51						
Attenborough	d		10 27									11 31													
Beeston	d	10 20	10 30				10 57				11 21	11 34							11 59						12 20
Nottingham [8]	a	10 26	10 37				11 04				11 27	11 42							12 05						12 26

		XC	XC	XC	EM	XC		GW	XC	XC	AW	EM	XC	XC	GW	XC	GW	EM	XC	GW		XC	XC	XC	EM
			◇	1◇	1◇	◇				1◇		1◇		◇	◇	1◇	◇	1◇	◇	1◇			R 1	R 1	1◇
			A			B				D	G			A	H		H		B				J		
				☕	☕	🛒				☕		☕				☕		☕	🛒	🛒			☕	☕	☕
Cardiff Central [7]	d					09 45					10 12								10 45						
Newport (South Wales)	d					09 59					10 27								10 59						
Bristol Temple Meads [10]	d			10 00						10 30					10 41	11 00							11 30		
Bristol Parkway [7]	d			10 10						10 40					10 52	11 10	←						11 40		
Gloucester [7]	d					10 46		10 50			11 21				11 36 →		11 36		11 46	11 50					
Cheltenham Spa	d			10 42		10 57		11a03		11 12	11a34					11 42	11 47		11 57	12a03			12 12		
Ashchurch for Tewkesbury	d																11 55								
Worcester Shrub Hill [7]	a																12 13								
Birmingham New Street [12]	a			11 26		11 45				11 57						12 26			12 46				12 57		
	d	11 13	11 24	11 30		11 49			11 54	12 03			12 13	12 24		12 30			12 49			12 54		13 03	
Water Orton	d																					13 06			
Coleshill Parkway	d		11 37						12 08					12 37								13 10			
Nuneaton	d		11 53						12 24					12 53								13 26			
Hinckley	d								12 31													13 33			
Narborough	d								12 39													13 41			
South Wigston	d								12 44																
Leicester	a		12 13						12 50					13 13								13 50			
Wilnecote	d	11 29											12 28												
Tamworth	d	11 33				12 07							12 32			12 47			13 09						
Burton-on-Trent	d	11 44				12 19							12 46			12 58			13 21						
Willington	d												12 56												
Derby [10]	a	12 02		12 11		12 36				12 39			13 03			13 11			13 36					13 39	
	d	12 11			12 34	12 41							13 11					13 34	13 41						
Spondon	d	12 16																							
Long Eaton	d	12 22			12a43	12 50							13 20					13a43	13 50						
Attenborough	d												13 31												
Beeston	d	12 31				12 57						13 20	13 34						13 57						14 20
Nottingham [8]	a	12 40				13 04						13 26	13 41						14 05						14 26

For general notes see front of timetable
For details of catering facilities see Directory of Train Operators

- A To Stansted Airport (Table 49)
- B 🛒 from Newport (South Wales)
- C From Westbury (Table 123)
- D From Plymouth (Table 51)
- E From Warminster (Table 123) to Great Malvern (Table 71)
- G From Maesteg (Table 128)
- H From Weymouth (Table 123) to Great Malvern (Table 71)
- J From Penzance (Table 51)

Bristol and Cardiff → Birmingham → Leicester, Derby and Nottingham

Network Diagram - see first page of Table 50

		XC	XC ◇ A	XC 1 ◇ B ☕	EM 1 ◇ ☕	XC ◇ C 🛒	GW	XC	XC R 1 D ☕	AW E	EM 1 ◇ ☕	XC		XC ◇ A	XC 1 ◇ ☕	GW ◇ G	EM 1 ◇ ☕	XC ◇	GW 1 ◇ H 🛒	XC	XC R 1 D ☕	AW E	XC R 1 ☕	EM 1 ◇ ☕	XC
Cardiff Central 7	d					11 45				12 12								12 45				13 12			
Newport (South Wales)	d					11 59				12 27								12 59				13 27			
Bristol Temple Meads 10	d			12 00					12 30						13 00	12 41					13 30				
Bristol Parkway 7	d			12 10					12 40						13 10	12 52					13 40				
Gloucester 7	d					12 46	12 50			13 21						13 38		13 46	13 50			14 21			
Cheltenham Spa	d			12 42		12 57	13a03		13 12	13a34					13 42	13 49		13 57	14a03		14 12	14a34			
Ashchurch for Tewkesbury	d															13 57									
Worcester Shrub Hill 7	a															14 20									
Birmingham New Street 12	a			13 26		13 45			13 57						14 26			14 45			14 57				
	d	13 13	13 24	13 30		13 49		13 54	14 03			14 13		14 24	14 30			14 49		14 54			15 03		15 13
Water Orton	d																			15 05					
Coleshill Parkway	d		13 37					14 08						14 37						15 09					
Nuneaton	d		13 53					14 24						14 53						15 25					
Hinckley	d							14 31												15 32					
Narborough	d							14 39												15 40					
South Wigston	d							14 44																	
Leicester	a		14 13					14 50						15 13						15 50					
Wilnecote	d	13 29																							15 29
Tamworth	d	13 33				14 06						14 30			14 47			15 08							15 33
Burton-on-Trent	d	13 44				14 18						14 42			14 58			15 20							15 44
Willington	d											14 47													
Derby 10	a	14 02		14 11		14 36			14 39			15 02			15 11			15 36					15 39		16 02
	d	14 11			14 34	14 41						15 11					15 34	15 41							16 11
Spondon	d																								
Long Eaton	d	14 20			14a43	14 50						15 20					15a43	15 50							16 20
Attenborough	d											15 31													
Beeston	d	14 29				14 57					15 20	15 34						15 57						16 20	16 31
Nottingham 8	a	14 39				15 04					15 26	15 41						16 04						16 26	16 39

		XC ◇	XC 1 ◇ J ☕	EM 1 ◇ ☕		XC ◇	GW	XC	XC R 1 J ☕	XC ◇ K	EM 1 ◇ ☕	XC	XC ◇ A	GW L	XC R 1 ☕	GW L	EM 1 ◇ ☕	EM 1 ◇ ☕		XC ◇	GW 1 ◇ 🛒	XC	XC R 1 J ☕	AW E	XC R 1 ☕
Cardiff Central 7	d					13 45														14 45				15 12	
Newport (South Wales)	d					13 59														14 59				15 27	
Bristol Temple Meads 10	d		14 00						14 30					14 41	15 00								15 30		
Bristol Parkway 7	d		14 10						14 40					14 52	15 10	←							15 40		
Gloucester 7	d					14 46	14 50							15 38		15 38				15 46	15 50			16 22	
Cheltenham Spa	d		14 42			14 56	15a03		15 12					→	15 42	15 49				15 57	16a03		16 12	16a34	
Ashchurch for Tewkesbury	d															15 57				16 04					
Worcester Shrub Hill 7	a															16 22									
Birmingham New Street 12	a		15 26			15 45			15 57						16 26					16 45			16 57		
	d	15 24	15 30			15 49		15 54	16 03	16 12		16 19	16 24		16 30					16 49		16 54			17 03
Water Orton	d																					17 05			
Coleshill Parkway	d							16 08		16 26			16 40									17 08			
Nuneaton	d	15 53						16 24		16 41			16 56									17 25			
Hinckley	d							16 31														17 32			
Narborough	d							16 39														17 40			
South Wigston	d							16 44														17 44			
Leicester	a	16 13						16 50		17 01			17 27									17 50			
Wilnecote	d					16 05														17 05					
Tamworth	d					16 09						16 36								17 09					
Burton-on-Trent	d					16 20						16 48								17 20					
Willington	d																			17 26					
Derby 10	a		16 11			16 36			16 39			17 02			17 14					17 36					17 39
	d			16 34		16 41						17 10					17 34			17 41					
Spondon	d											17 15													
Long Eaton	d			16a43		16 50						17 22					17a43			17 50					
Attenborough	d											17 29													
Beeston	d					16 57					17 20	17 33						17 39		17 57					
Nottingham 8	a					17 04					17 26	17 39						17 50		18 04					

For general notes see front of timetable
For details of catering facilities see Directory of Train Operators

A To Stansted Airport (Table 49)
B From Paignton (Table 51)
C 🛒 from Newport (South Wales)
D From Penzance (Table 51)
E From Maesteg (Table 128)
G From Brighton (Table 123) to Great Malvern (Table 71)
H **The Cheltenham Spa Express**
J From Plymouth (Table 51)
K To Cambridge (Table 49)
L From Westbury (Table 123) to Worcester Foregate Street (Table 71)

Table 57

Mondays to Fridays

until 25 January

Bristol and Cardiff → Birmingham → Leicester, Derby and Nottingham

Network Diagram - see first page of Table 50

		EM	XC	XC	XC	XC	EM	XC	EM	XC		GW	XC	XC	AW	XC	XC	GW	XC	GW	EM	EM	XC	GW	XC
		1 ◇			◇	R 1	1 ◇	R 1	1 ◇	◇				R 1			◇		R 1		1 ◇	1 ◇	◇	1 ◇	
					A	B		C						D	E		A	G		G					
		🍴				🍴	🍴	🍴	🍴					🍴					🍴		🍴	🍴		🛒	
Cardiff Central 7	d									15 45					16 12								16 45		
Newport (South Wales)	d									15 59					16 27								16 59		
Bristol Temple Meads 10	d					16 00								16 30				16 41	17 00						
Bristol Parkway 7	d					16 10								16 40				16 52	17 10	←					
Gloucester 7	d									16 46		16 50			17 22			17 38 →		17 38			17 46	17 54	
Cheltenham Spa	d					16 42				16 57		17a03		17 12	17a34			→	17 42	17 49			17 57	18a03	
Ashchurch for Tewkesbury	d									17 04										17 57			18 04		
Worcester Shrub Hill 7	a																			18 17					
Birmingham New Street 12	a					17 26				17 45				17 57					18 26				18 45		
	d		17 09	17 12	17 24	17 30		17 39		17 49			17 59	18 03		18 09	18 24		18 30				18 49		18 54
Water Orton	d			17 25												18 21									
Coleshill Parkway	d			17 28	17 39			17 53								18 24	18 37								19 07
Nuneaton	d			17 46	17 55								18 27				18 53								19 24
Hinckley	d			17 53									18 34												19 31
Narborough	d												18 42												19 39
South Wigston	d												18 47												19 44
Leicester	a			18 12	18 16								18 53				19 13								19 51
Wilnecote	d									18 07															
Tamworth	d		17 29					18 06		18 11						18 36			18 47				19 08		
Burton-on-Trent	d		17 40					18 16		18 22						18 48			18 58				19 20		
Willington	d									18 27															
Derby 10	a		17 59			18 11		18 34		18 37				18 39		19 02			19 11				19 36		
	d		18 11				18 34			18 41						19 13					19 34		19 41		
Spondon	d															19 18									
Long Eaton	d		18 20				18a43			18 50						19 25					19a43		19 50		
Attenborough	d		18 29													19 32							19 57		
Beeston	d	18 20	18 32						18 43	18 57						19 36						19 46	20 00		
Nottingham 8	a	18 26	18 37						18 48	19 04						19 42						19 53	20 06		

		XC		AW	XC	XC	XC	EM	EM	XC	GW	XC	XC	AW	XC	GW		XC	GW	XC	GW	EM	EM	XC	XC
		R 1			R 1	◇	1 ◇		1 ◇	◇			1 ◇		◇			1 ◇		◇	1 ◇		1 ◇		
		D		E			B	H					D	E		G			G						
		🍴			🍴		🍴		🍴				🍴					🍴		🛒	🛒		🍴		
Cardiff Central 7	d			17 12						17 45				18 12						18 45					
Newport (South Wales)	d			17 27						17 59				18 27						18 59					
Bristol Temple Meads 10	d	17 30					18 00						18 30			18 41		19 00							
Bristol Parkway 7	d	17 40					18 10						18 40			18 52		19 10	←						
Gloucester 7	d			18 22						18 46	18 50			19 21		19 38 →			19 38	19 46	19 54				
Cheltenham Spa	d	18 12		18a34			18 42			18 57	19a03		19 12	19a34		→		19 42	19 49	19 57	20a03				
Ashchurch for Tewkesbury	d																		19 57	20 04					
Worcester Shrub Hill 7	a																		20 14						
Birmingham New Street 12	a	18 57					19 26			19 46			19 57					20 42		20 43					
	d				19 03	19 26	19 30			19 49		19 54	20 03		20 27									20 49	20 54
Water Orton	d											20 05													
Coleshill Parkway	d																								21 08
Nuneaton	d					19 51						20 25			20 54										21 24
Hinckley	d											20 32													21 31
Narborough	d											20 40													21 39
South Wigston	d											20 45													21 44
Leicester	a					20 15						20 50			21 14										21 51
Wilnecote	d									20 05														21 05	
Tamworth	d						19 47			20 09			20 19											21 09	
Burton-on-Trent	d						19 58			20 20			20 29											21 20	
Willington	d																								
Derby 10	a				19 39		20 11			20 35			20 42											21 36	
	d									20 40														21 41	
Spondon	d									20 45															
Long Eaton	d									20 51														21 50	
Attenborough	d									20 58															
Beeston	d							20 16	20 20	21 01												21 18	21 22	21 57	
Nottingham 8	a							20 22	20 27	21 07												21 23	21 28	22 04	

For general notes see front of timetable
For details of catering facilities see Directory of Train Operators

A To Cambridge (Table 49)
B From Paignton (Table 51)
C From Reading (Table 51)
D From Plymouth (Table 51)
E From Maesteg (Table 128)
G From Warminster (Table 123) to Great Malvern (Table 71)
H To Lincoln (Table 27)

Table 57

Bristol and Cardiff → Birmingham → Leicester, Derby and Nottingham

Mondays to Fridays
until 25 January

Network Diagram - see first page of Table 50

		XC	GW	XC	GW	EM	EM	XC		XC	GW	AW	GW	XC	XC	GW	AW	EM	XC	XC	XC	GW	AW		
		1 ◇	◇	1 ◇	1 ◇	1 ◇	1 ◇	◇		1 ◇			◇		◇	1 ◇				1 ◇					
		A					B			A	C	D	E				D	G					D		
Cardiff Central 7	d							20 00				20 15			20 50		21 14						23 20		
Newport (South Wales)	d							20 15				20 30			21 04		21 29						23 39		
Bristol Temple Meads 10	d	19 30	19 41							20 30			20 41							22 00					
Bristol Parkway 7	d	19 40	19 52							20 40			20 52							22 10					
Gloucester 7	d		20 33		20 50			20 57			21 16	21 23	21 34		21 46	21 54	22 23				22 41	22 50	00 39		
Cheltenham Spa	d	20 12	20a42		21a03			21 07		21 12	21a26	21a34	21 44		21 57	22a05	22a36			22 42	22 52	23a03	00a52		
Ashchurch for Tewkesbury	d												21 52												
Worcester Shrub Hill 7	a												22 10								23 15				
Birmingham New Street 12	a	20 57						21 52		21 57					22 48					23 43					
	d			21 03				21 54		22 03				22 15					23 10						
Water Orton	d																		23 21						
Coleshill Parkway	d																								
Nuneaton	d													22 45											
Hinckley	d													22 52											
Narborough	d													23 00											
South Wigston	d													23 04											
Leicester	a													23 10											
Wilnecote	d																		23 29						
Tamworth	d			21 19				22 12		22 19									23 33						
Burton-on-Trent	d			21 29				22 23		22 29									23 44						
Willington	d																		23 50						
Derby 10	a			21 42				22 37		22 42									23s59						
	d							22 41										23 36							
Spondon	d																								
Long Eaton	d							22 50										23 46							
Attenborough	d																								
Beeston	d					22 20	22 46	22 58										23 54							
Nottingham 8	a					22 28	22 52	23 05										00 01	00 23						

Mondays to Fridays
from 28 January

		EM	EM	EM		XC	EM	AW	EM	XC	EM	XC	XC	XC	EM	XC	XC	GW	XC	EM		XC	XC	XC	EM
		MX	MO	MX		MO	MX	MX																	
		1 ◇		1 ◇			1 ◇		1 ◇	◇				1 ◇			1 ◇			1 ◇		◇		R 1	
		H	J	K		L	K	D	N											Q		U			
Cardiff Central 7	d							23p20																	
Newport (South Wales)	d							23p39																	
Bristol Temple Meads 10	d																								
Bristol Parkway 7	d																								
Gloucester 7	d							00 39										06 02							
Cheltenham Spa	d							00a52										06 12							
Ashchurch for Tewkesbury	d																	06 20							
Worcester Shrub Hill 7	a																	06 40							
Birmingham New Street 12	a																								
	d					22p20				05 20			05 55	06 00		06 09	06 30					06 37	06 54	07 03	
Water Orton	d															06 19									
Coleshill Parkway	d																					06 49			
Nuneaton	d									05 48			06 21									07 05	07 22		
Hinckley	d												06 28										07 28		
Narborough	d												06 36										07 37		
South Wigston	d												06 40										07 42		
Leicester	a									06 08			06 46									07 28	07 48		
Wilnecote	d					22p51										06 27									
Tamworth	d					23p02								06 15		06 31	06 47							07 19	
Burton-on-Trent	d					23p28								06 25		06 42	06 58			07 10				07 29	
Willington	d																			07 16					
Derby 10	a					23b53								06 38		06 58	07 11			07 26				07 42	
	d		23p34						05 56		06 16	06 28				07 11			07 22	07 34					
Spondon	d											06 33							07 27						
Long Eaton	d		00 04			00s23			06a05		06a25	06 40				07 20			07 35	07a43					
Attenborough	d		00 15									06 49			07 18				07 42						08 07
Beeston	d	00 01	00 25	00 28		00s35	00 40					06 52			07 21	07 28			07 45						08 10
Nottingham 8	a	00 06	00 45	00 35		00 55	00 46					06 59			07 30	07 34			07 53						08 20

For general notes see front of timetable
For details of catering facilities see Directory of Train Operators

- **A** From Plymouth (Table 51)
- **B** To Derby
- **C** From Westbury (Table 123)
- **D** From Maesteg (Table 128)
- **E** From Brighton (Table 123)
- **G** From Matlock (Table 56)
- **H** From 25 March
- **J** 4 February to 24 March. From Stoke-on-Trent (Table 50)
- **K** Until 21 March
- **L** 4 February to 24 March
- **N** From Sheffield (Table 53)
- **Q** To St Pancras International (Table 53)
- **U** To Stansted Airport (Table 49)
- **b** Previous night. Stops to set down only

Table 57

Mondays to Fridays

from 28 January

Bristol and Cardiff → Birmingham → Leicester, Derby and Nottingham

Network Diagram - see first page of Table 50

		EM	XC	XC	XC	EM	EM	XC	XC	XC	XC	GW	AW	EM	XC	XC	XC	EM		XC	GW	XC	XC	AW MO	AW
		1 ◇		◇	1 ◇		1 ◇			R 1				1 ◇		◇	1 ◇	1 ◇			1 ◇		1 ◇		
				A			B					C				A		D					E	G	H
		☕			☕		☕			☕				☕			☕	☕			🛒		☕		
Cardiff Central 7	d												06 12											07 05	07 12
Newport (South Wales)	d												06 27											07 27	07 27
Bristol Temple Meads 10	d									06 15							07 00						07 30		
Bristol Parkway 7	d									06 25							07 10						07 40		
Gloucester 7	d									07 02	07 09	07 15	07 21							07 46	07 55			08 21	08 21
Cheltenham Spa	d									07 12	07 19	07 25	07a34				07 42			07 57	08a03		08 12	08a34	08a34
Ashchurch for Tewkesbury	d										07 28	07 33								08 04					
Worcester Shrub Hill 7	a											07 54													
Birmingham New Street 12	a									07 57	08 16						08 26			08 46			08 57		
	d		07 10	07 21	07 30			07 49	07 54	08 03					08 19	08 24	08 30			08 49		08 54			
Water Orton	d		07 21																			09 06			
Coleshill Parkway	d															08 37									
Nuneaton	d			07 48					08 24							08 53						09 26			
Hinckley	d			07 55					08 31													09 33			
Narborough	d			08 03					08 39													09 41			
South Wigston	d			08 07					08 44																
Leicester	a			08 13					08 50							09 13						09 51			
Wilnecote	d							08 05																	
Tamworth	d		07 30		07 47			08 09		08 19					08 36		08 47			09 08					
Burton-on-Trent	d		07 42		07 58		08 10	08 20		08 29					08 48		08 58			09 20					
Willington	d		07 47				08 16																		
Derby 10	a		07 56		08 11		08 25	08 36		08 42					09 01		09 11			09 36					
	d		08 03			08 22	08 34	08 39							09 11			09 34		09 40					
Spondon	d		08 08												09 16										
Long Eaton	d		08 15			08 32	08a43	08 49							09 23			09a43		09 50					
Attenborough	d		08 23												09 31										
Beeston	d	08 20	08 26			08 39		08 57						09 20	09 35					09 56					
Nottingham 8 🚊	a	08 29	08 32			08 45		09 04						09 26	09 41					10 05					

		XC	EM	XC	XC	XC	EM	XC	GW	XC	XC	EM	XC	XC	GW	XC		GW	EM	XC	GW	XC	XC	AW	XC
		1 ◇	1 ◇		◇	1 ◇	1 ◇	◇			1 ◇	1 ◇		◇		1 ◇			1 ◇	◇	1 ◇		R 1		1 ◇
					A			J	K		L			A	N	L		N		J			L		
		☕	☕			☕	☕	🛒			☕	☕	🛒			☕			☕	🛒	🛒		☕		☕
Cardiff Central 7	d					07 00		07 45												08 45				09 12	
Newport (South Wales)	d					07 15		07 59												08 59				09 27	
Bristol Temple Meads 10	d					08 00					08 30				08 41	09 00							09 30		
Bristol Parkway 7	d					08 10					08 40				08 52	09 10		←					09 40		
Gloucester 7	d							08 46	08 50						09 38			09 38		09 46	09 50			10 21	
Cheltenham Spa	d					08 42		08 57	09a03		09 12				→	09 42		09 48		09 56	10a03		10 12	10a34	
Ashchurch for Tewkesbury	d																	09 57		10 04					
Worcester Shrub Hill 7	a																	10 13							
Birmingham New Street 12	a					09 26		09 45			09 57					10 26				10 45			10 57		
	d	09 03		09 19	09 24	09 30		09 49		09 54	10 03		10 13	10 24		10 30				10 49		10 54			11 03
Water Orton	d																					11 05			
Coleshill Parkway	d				09 37					10 08				10 37								11 08			
Nuneaton	d				09 53					10 25				10 53								11 25			
Hinckley	d									10 32												11 32			
Narborough	d									10 40												11 40			
South Wigston	d									10 45															
Leicester	a				10 13					10 50				11 13								11 50			
Wilnecote	d												10 29												
Tamworth	d			09 36				10 06					10 33			10 47				11 06					
Burton-on-Trent	d			09 47				10 18					10 44			10 58				11 19					
Willington	d							10 25																	
Derby 10	a	09 39		10 02		10 11		10 36			10 39		11 02			11 11				11 36					11 39
	d			10 11			10 34	10 41					11 11						11 34	11 41					
Spondon	d																								
Long Eaton	d			10 20			10a43	10 50					11 20						11a43	11 51					
Attenborough	d			10 27									11 31												
Beeston	d		10 20	10 30				10 57				11 21	11 34							11 59					
Nottingham 8 🚊	a		10 26	10 37				11 04				11 27	11 42							12 05					

For general notes see front of timetable
For details of catering facilities see Directory of Train Operators

- **A** To Stansted Airport (Table 49)
- **B** To St Pancras International (Table 53)
- **C** To Great Malvern (Table 71)
- **D** From Barnsley (Table 53)
- **E** From Exeter St Davids (Table 51)
- **G** From 24 March
- **H** All Tuesdays to Fridays, also Mondays until 17 March
- **J** 🛒 from Newport (South Wales)
- **K** From Westbury (Table 123)
- **L** From Plymouth (Table 51)
- **N** From Warminster (Table 123) to Great Malvern (Table 71)

Bristol and Cardiff → Birmingham → Leicester, Derby and Nottingham

Network Diagram - see first page of Table 50

		EM	XC	XC	XC	EM	XC	GW	XC	XC	AW	EM	XC	XC		GW	XC	GW	EM	XC	GW	XC	XC	XC	EM
		1 ◇		◇	1 ◇	1 ◇	◇			1 ◇		1 ◇		◇		◇	1 ◇	◇	1 ◇	◇	1 ◇		R 1	R 1	1 ◇
				A			B			C	D			A		E		E		B			G		
		☕			☕	☕	🛒			☕		☕					☕		☕	🛒	🛒		☕	☕	☕
Cardiff Central [7]	d						09 45				10 12									10 45					
Newport (South Wales)	d						09 59				10 27									10 59					
Bristol Temple Meads [10]	d				10 00					10 30						10 41	11 00						11 30		
Bristol Parkway [7]	d				10 10					10 40						10 52	11 10	←					11 40		
Gloucester [7]	d						10 46	10 50			11 21					11 36		11 36		11 46	11 50				
Cheltenham Spa	d				10 42		10 57	11a03		11 12	11a34					↪	11 42	11 47		11 57	12a03		12 12		
Ashchurch for Tewkesbury	d																	11 55							
Worcester Shrub Hill [7]	a																	12 13							
Birmingham New Street [12]	a				11 26		11 45			11 57							12 26			12 46			12 57		
	d		11 13	11 24	11 30		11 49		11 54	12 03			12 13	12 24			12 30			12 49		12 54		13 03	
Water Orton	d																					13 06			
Coleshill Parkway	d			11 37					12 08					12 37								13 10			
Nuneaton	d			11 53					12 24					12 53								13 26			
Hinckley	d								12 31													13 33			
Narborough	d								12 39													13 41			
South Wigston	d								12 44																
Leicester	a			12 13					12 50					13 13								13 50			
Wilnecote	d		11 29										12 28												
Tamworth	d		11 33				12 07						12 32				12 47			13 09					
Burton-on-Trent	d		11 44				12 19						12 46				12 58			13 21					
Willington	d												12 56												
Derby [10]	a		12 02		12 11		12 36			12 39			13 03				13 11			13 36				13 39	
	d		12 11			12 34	12 41						13 11						13 34	13 41					
Spondon	d		12 16																						
Long Eaton	d		12 22			12a43	12 50						13 20						13a43	13 50					
Attenborough	d												13 31												
Beeston	d	12 20	12 31				12 57					13 20	13 34							13 57					14 20
Nottingham [8]	a	12 26	12 40				13 04					13 26	13 41							14 05					14 26

		XC	XC	XC	EM	XC	GW	XC	XC	AW	EM	XC		XC	GW	XC	GW	EM	XC	GW	XC	XC	AW	XC	EM
			◇	1 ◇	1 ◇	◇			R 1		1 ◇			◇	◇	1 ◇	◇	1 ◇	◇	1 ◇		R 1		R 1	1 ◇
			A	H		B			G	D				A	J		J			K		G	D		
				☕	☕	🛒			☕		☕					☕		☕		🛒		☕		☕	☕
Cardiff Central [7]	d					11 45				12 12									12 45				13 12		
Newport (South Wales)	d					11 59				12 27									12 59				13 27		
Bristol Temple Meads [10]	d			12 00					12 30						12 41	13 00						13 30			
Bristol Parkway [7]	d			12 10					12 40						12 52	13 10	←					13 40			
Gloucester [7]	d					12 46	12 50			13 21					13 38		13 38		13 46	13 50			14 21		
Cheltenham Spa	d			12 42		12 57	13a03		13 12	13a34					↪	13 42	13 49		13 57	14a03		14 12	14a34		
Ashchurch for Tewkesbury	d																13 57								
Worcester Shrub Hill [7]	a																14 20								
Birmingham New Street [12]	a			13 26		13 45			13 57							14 26			14 45			14 57			
	d	13 13	13 24	13 30		13 49		13 54	14 03			14 13		14 24		14 30			14 49		14 54			15 03	
Water Orton	d																				15 05				
Coleshill Parkway	d		13 37					14 08						14 37							15 09				
Nuneaton	d		13 53					14 24						14 53							15 25				
Hinckley	d							14 31													15 32				
Narborough	d							14 39													15 40				
South Wigston	d							14 44																	
Leicester	a		14 13					14 50						15 13							15 50				
Wilnecote	d	13 29																							
Tamworth	d	13 33				14 06						14 30				14 47			15 08						
Burton-on-Trent	d	13 44				14 18						14 42				14 58			15 20						
Willington	d											14 47													
Derby [10]	a	14 02		14 11		14 36			14 39			15 02				15 11			15 36					15 39	
	d	14 11			14 34	14 41						15 11						15 34	15 41						
Spondon	d																								
Long Eaton	d	14 20			14a43	14 50						15 20						15a43	15 50						
Attenborough	d											15 31													
Beeston	d	14 29				14 57					15 20	15 34							15 57						16 20
Nottingham [8]	a	14 39				15 04					15 26	15 41							16 04						16 26

For general notes see front of timetable
For details of catering facilities see Directory of Train Operators

- **A** To Stansted Airport (Table 49)
- **B** 🛒 from Newport (South Wales)
- **C** From Plymouth (Table 51)
- **D** From Maesteg (Table 128)
- **E** From Weymouth (Table 123) to Great Malvern (Table 71)
- **G** From Penzance (Table 51)
- **H** From Paignton (Table 51)
- **J** From Brighton (Table 123) to Great Malvern (Table 71)
- **K** **The Cheltenham Spa Express**

Table 57

Bristol and Cardiff → Birmingham → Leicester, Derby and Nottingham

Mondays to Fridays

from 28 January

Network Diagram - see first page of Table 50

		XC	XC	XC	EM	XC	GW	XC	XC	XC		EM	XC	XC	GW	XC	GW	EM	EM	XC	GW	XC	XC	AW	XC
			◇	1 ◇	1 ◇	◇			R 1	◇		1 ◇		◇		R 1		1 ◇	1 ◇	◇	1 ◇		R 1		R 1
				A					A	B				C	D		D						A	E	
Cardiff Central 7	d					13 45														14 45				15 12	
Newport (South Wales)	d					13 59														14 59				15 27	
Bristol Temple Meads 10	d			14 00					14 30						14 41	15 00							15 30		
Bristol Parkway 7	d			14 10					14 40						14 52	15 10	←						15 40		
Gloucester 7	d					14 46	14 50								15 38		15 38			15 46	15 50			16 22	
Cheltenham Spa	d			14 42		14 56	15a03		15 12						→	15 42	15 49			15 57	16a03		16 12	16a34	
Ashchurch for Tewkesbury	d																15 57			16 04					
Worcester Shrub Hill 7	a																16 22								
Birmingham New Street 12	a			15 26		15 45			15 57							16 26				16 45			16 57		
	d	15 13	15 24	15 30		15 49		15 54	16 03	16 12			16 19	16 24		16 30				16 49		16 54			17 03
Water Orton	d																					17 05			
Coleshill Parkway	d							16 08		16 26				16 40								17 08			
Nuneaton	d		15 53					16 24		16 41				16 56								17 25			
Hinckley	d							16 31														17 32			
Narborough	d							16 39														17 40			
South Wigston	d							16 44														17 44			
Leicester	a		16 13					16 50		17 01				17 27								17 50			
Wilnecote	d	15 29				16 05														17 05					
Tamworth	d	15 33				16 09							16 36							17 09					
Burton-on-Trent	d	15 44				16 20							16 48							17 20					
Willington	d																			17 26					
Derby 10	a	16 02		16 11		16 36			16 39				17 03			17 14				17 36					17 39
	d	16 11			16 34	16 41							17 10					17 34		17 41					
Spondon	d												17 15												
Long Eaton	d	16 20			16a43	16 50							17 22					17a43		17 50					
Attenborough	d												17 29												
Beeston	d	16 31				16 57						17 20	17 33						17 39	17 57					
Nottingham 8	a	16 39				17 04						17 26	17 39						17 50	18 04					

		EM	XC	XC	XC	XC	EM	XC		EM	XC	GW	XC	XC	AW	XC	XC	GW	XC	GW	EM	EM	XC	GW	XC
		1 ◇			◇	R 1	1 ◇	R 1		1 ◇	◇			R 1			◇		R 1		1 ◇	1 ◇	◇	1 ◇	
					B	G		H						A	E		B	J		J					
Cardiff Central 7	d										15 45				16 12								16 45		
Newport (South Wales)	d										15 59				16 27								16 59		
Bristol Temple Meads 10	d					16 00								16 30				16 41	17 00						
Bristol Parkway 7	d					16 10								16 40				16 52	17 10	←					
Gloucester 7	d										16 46	16 50			17 22			17 38		17 38			17 46	17 54	
Cheltenham Spa	d					16 42					16 57	17a03		17 12	17a34			→	17 42	17 49			17 57	18a03	
Ashchurch for Tewkesbury	d										17 04									17 57			18 04		
Worcester Shrub Hill 7	a																			18 17					
Birmingham New Street 12	a					17 26					17 45			17 57					18 26				18 45		
	d		17 09	17 12	17 24	17 30		17 39			17 49		17 59	18 03		18 09	18 24		18 30				18 49		18 54
Water Orton	d			17 25												18 21									
Coleshill Parkway	d			17 28	17 39			17 53								18 24	18 37								19 07
Nuneaton	d			17 46	17 55								18 27				18 53								19 24
Hinckley	d			17 53									18 34												19 31
Narborough	d												18 42												19 39
South Wigston	d												18 47												19 44
Leicester	a			18 12	18 16								18 53				19 13								19 51
Wilnecote	d										18 07														
Tamworth	d		17 29					18 06			18 11					18 36			18 47				19 08		
Burton-on-Trent	d		17 40					18 16			18 22					18 48			18 58				19 20		
Willington	d										18 27														
Derby 10	a		17 59			18 11		18 34			18 37			18 39		19 02			19 11				19 36		
	d		18 11				18 34				18 41					19 13					19 34		19 41		
Spondon	d															19 18									
Long Eaton	d		18 20				18a43				18 50					19 25					19a43		19 50		
Attenborough	d		18 29													19 32							19 57		
Beeston	d	18 20	18 32							18 43	18 57					19 36						19 46	20 00		
Nottingham 8	a	18 26	18 37							18 48	19 04					19 42						19 53	20 06		

For general notes see front of timetable
For details of catering facilities see Directory of Train Operators

- A From Plymouth (Table 51)
- B To Cambridge (Table 49)
- C To Stansted Airport (Table 49)
- D From Westbury (Table 123) to Worcester Foregate Street (Table 71)
- E From Maesteg (Table 128)
- G From Paignton (Table 51)
- H From Reading (Table 51)
- J From Warminster (Table 123) to Great Malvern (Table 71)

Bristol and Cardiff → Birmingham → Leicester, Derby and Nottingham

Network Diagram - see first page of Table 50

		XC	AW	XC	XC	XC		EM	EM	XC	GW	XC	XC	AW	XC	GW	XC	GW	XC	GW	EM	EM	XC	XC	XC
		[R] [1]		[R] [1]	◇	[1] ◇			[1] ◇	◇			[1] ◇		◇		[1] ◇		◇	[1] ◇		[1] ◇			[1] ◇
		A	B			C		D					E	B		G		G							A
		☕		☕		☕			☕				☕				☕		🛒	🛒		☕			☕
Cardiff Central [7]	d		17 12							17 45				18 12					18 45						
Newport (South Wales)	d		17 27							17 59				18 27					18 59						
Bristol Temple Meads [10]	d	17 30				18 00							18 30			18 41	19 00								19 30
Bristol Parkway [7]	d	17 40				18 10							18 40			18 52	19 10	←							19 40
Gloucester [7]	d		18 22							18 46	18 50			19 21		19 38		19 38	19 46	19 54					
Cheltenham Spa	d	18 12	18a34			18 42				18 57	19a03		19 12	19a34		→	19 42	19 49	19 57	20a03					20 12
Ashchurch for Tewkesbury	d																	19 57	20 04						
Worcester Shrub Hill [7]	a																	20 14							
Birmingham New Street [12]	a	18 57				19 26				19 46			19 57				20 42		20 43						20 57
	d			19 03	19 26	19 30				19 49		19 54	20 03		20 27								20 49	20 54	
Water Orton	d											20 05													
Coleshill Parkway	d																							21 08	
Nuneaton	d				19 51							20 25			20 54									21 24	
Hinckley	d											20 32												21 31	
Narborough	d											20 40												21 39	
South Wigston	d											20 45												21 44	
Leicester	a				20 15							20 50			21 14									21 51	
Wilnecote	d									20 05													21 05		
Tamworth	d					19 47				20 09			20 19										21 09		
Burton-on-Trent	d					19 58				20 20			20 29										21 20		
Willington	d																								
Derby [10]	a			19 39		20 11				20 35			20 42										21 36		
	d									20 40													21 41		
Spondon	d									20 45															
Long Eaton	d									20 51													21 50		
Attenborough	d									20 58															
Beeston	d							20 16	20 20	21 01											21 18	21 22	21 57		
Nottingham [8] 🚌	a							20 22	20 27	21 07											21 23	21 28	22 04		

		GW	XC	GW		EM	EM	XC	XC	GW	AW	GW	XC	XC	GW	AW	EM	EM	XC	XC	XC	GW	AW		
		◇	[1] ◇	[1] ◇		[1] ◇	[1] ◇	◇	[1] ◇			◇		◇	[1] ◇		[1] ◇			[1] ◇					
							H		J	K	B	L				B	N	Q					B		
				🛒		☕	☕								🛒		☕								
Cardiff Central [7]	d							20 00			20 15			20 50		21 14							23 20		
Newport (South Wales)	d							20 15			20 30			21 04		21 29							23 39		
Bristol Temple Meads [10]	d	19 41							20 30			20 41								22 00					
Bristol Parkway [7]	d	19 52							20 40			20 52								22 10					
Gloucester [7]	d	20 33		20 50				20 57		21 16	21 23	21 34		21 46	21 54	22 23					22 41	22 50	00 39		
Cheltenham Spa	d	20a42		21a03				21 07	21 12	21a26	21a34	21 44		21 57	22a05	22a36				22 42	22 52	23a03	00a52		
Ashchurch for Tewkesbury	d											21 52													
Worcester Shrub Hill [7]	a											22 10									23 15				
Birmingham New Street [12]	a							21 52	21 57					22 48						23 43					
	d		21 03					21 54	22 03				22 15						23 10						
Water Orton	d																		23 21						
Coleshill Parkway	d																								
Nuneaton	d												22 45												
Hinckley	d												22 52												
Narborough	d												23 00												
South Wigston	d												23 04												
Leicester	a												23 10												
Wilnecote	d																		23 29						
Tamworth	d		21 19					22 12	22 19										23 33						
Burton-on-Trent	d		21 29					22 23	22 29										23 44						
Willington	d																		23 50						
Derby [10]	a		21 42					22 37	22 42										23s59						
	d							22 41										23 36							
Spondon	d																								
Long Eaton	d							22 50										23 46							
Attenborough	d																								
Beeston	d					22 20	22 46	22 58									23}19	23 54							
Nottingham [8] 🚌	a					22 28	22 52	23 05									23}31	00 01	00 23						

For general notes see front of timetable
For details of catering facilities see Directory of Train Operators

- **A** From Plymouth (Table 51)
- **B** From Maesteg (Table 128)
- **C** From Paignton (Table 51)
- **D** To Lincoln (Table 27)
- **E** From Plymouth (Table 51). ☕ to Birmingham New Street
- **G** From Warminster (Table 123) to Great Malvern (Table 71)
- **H** To Derby
- **J** From Plymouth (Table 51). ☕ to Bristol Temple Meads
- **K** From Westbury (Table 123)
- **L** From Brighton (Table 123)
- **N** From 24 March
- **Q** From Matlock (Table 56)

Bristol and Cardiff → Birmingham → Leicester, Derby and Nottingham

Network Diagram - see first page of Table 50

Station		EM	EM	AW	EM	XC	EM	XC	XC	XC	GW	EM	XC		XC	XC	EM	XC	XC	XC	XC	XC	EM	EM	XC
		1 ◇ ☕	1 ◇ ☕	A	1 ◇ B ☕	◇				1 ◇ ☕					1 ◇ ☕	◇	1 ◇ ☕		1 ◇ ☕	◇	◇ C	1 ◇ ☕	1 ◇ D ☕	1 ◇ ☕	
Cardiff Central [7]	d			23p20																					
Newport (South Wales)	d			23p39																					
Bristol Temple Meads [10]	d																								
Bristol Parkway [7]	d																								
Gloucester [7]	d			00 39							05 50														06 46
Cheltenham Spa	d			00a52							06 00														06 57
Ashchurch for Tewkesbury	d										06 08														07 04
Worcester Shrub Hill [7]	a										06 30														
Birmingham New Street [12]	a																								07 45
	d					05 20			05 54	06 00			06 09		06 30	06 36		06 52	07 03	07 10	07 24	07 30			07 49
Water Orton	d												06 19												
Coleshill Parkway	d								06 07									07 06			07 37				
Nuneaton	d					05 46			06 24							07 04		07 24			07 53				
Hinckley	d								06 31									07 31							
Narborough	d								06 39									07 39							
South Wigston	d								06 44									07 44							
Leicester	a					06 06			06 50							07 25		07 50			08 13				
Wilnecote	d												06 27												08 06
Tamworth	d									06 16			06 31		06 47				07 19	07 28		07 47			08 10
Burton-on-Trent	d									06 26			06 42		06 58				07 29	07 39		07 58	08 08		08 22
Willington	d																			07 45			08 13		
Derby [10]	a									06 39			06 58		07 11				07 42	07 58		08 11	08 25		08 35
	d				06 00		06 26	06 29					07 06				07 34			08 08			08 34		08 42
Spondon	d							06 34					07 11												08 48
Long Eaton	d				06a09		06a35	06 41					07 18				07a43			08 17			08a43		08 54
Attenborough	d							06 47				07 17	07 27							08 23					
Beeston	d	00 28	00 40					06 50				07 20	07 31							08 27				08 48	09 01
Nottingham [8] 🚌	a	00 35	00 46					06 56				07 27	07 37							08 32				08 56	09 10

Station		XC	XC	AW		EM	XC	XC	XC	EM	XC	XC	XC	GW	AW	XC	EM		XC	XC	XC	EM	XC	XC	XC
			1 ◇ ☕			1 ◇ ☕		◇ C	1 ◇ ☕	1 ◇ E ☕			1 ◇ G ☕			1 ◇ ☕	1 ◇ ☕			◇ C	1 ◇ ☕	1 ◇ ☕	◇ H 🍴		1 ◇ J ☕
Cardiff Central [7]	d			06 12											07 12								07 45		
Newport (South Wales)	d			06 27											07 27								07 59		
Bristol Temple Meads [10]	d		06 15										07 30								08 00				08 30
Bristol Parkway [7]	d		06 25										07 40								08 10				08 40
Gloucester [7]	d		07 01	07 21							07 46			08 10	08 22								08 46		
Cheltenham Spa	d		07 12	07a34							07 57		08 12	08a23	08a32						08 42		08 57		09 12
Ashchurch for Tewkesbury	d										08 04														
Worcester Shrub Hill [7]	a																								
Birmingham New Street [12]	a		07 57								08 46		08 57								09 26		09 45		09 57
	d	07 54	08 03				08 13	08 24	08 30		08 49	08 54				09 03			09 13	09 24	09 30		09 49	09 54	10 03
Water Orton	d											09 07													
Coleshill Parkway	d	08 07						08 37				09 10								09 37				10 07	
Nuneaton	d	08 24						08 53				09 25								09 53				10 23	
Hinckley	d	08 31										09 32												10 30	
Narborough	d	08 39										09 40												10 38	
South Wigston	d	08 44																						10 43	
Leicester	a	08 50						09 13				09 51								10 13				10 50	
Wilnecote	d																								
Tamworth	d		08 19				08 34		08 47		09 08								09 30				10 08		
Burton-on-Trent	d		08 29				08 46		08 58		09 20								09 41				10 20		
Willington	d																		09 49						
Derby [10]	a		08 42				09 02		09 11		09 36					09 39			10 02		10 11		10 35		10 39
	d						09 06			09 34	09 43								10 11			10 34	10 43		
Spondon	d																								
Long Eaton	d						09 16			09a43	09 52								10 20			10a43	10 52		
Attenborough	d																		10 28						
Beeston	d					09 20	09 24				09 59						10 20		10 31				10 59		
Nottingham [8] 🚌	a					09 26	09 35				10 05						10 27		10 37				11 04		

For general notes see front of timetable
For details of catering facilities see Directory of Train Operators

A From Maesteg (Table 128)
B From Sheffield (Table 53)
C To Stansted Airport (Table 49)
D To St Pancras International (Table 53)
E From Barnsley (Table 53)
G From Exeter St Davids (Table 51)
H 🍴 from Newport (South Wales)
J From Plymouth (Table 51)

Table 57

Saturdays

until 26 January

Bristol and Cardiff → Birmingham → Leicester, Derby and Nottingham

Network Diagram - see first page of Table 50

		EM	XC	XC	GW	XC	GW	EM		XC	XC	XC	GW	AW	XC	EM	XC	XC	XC	EM	XC		XC	XC	GW
		1 ◇		◇		1 ◇		1 ◇		◇		1 ◇	1 ◇		1 ◇	1 ◇		◇	1 ◇	1 ◇	◇			1 ◇	
				A	B		B			C		D				E		A			C			D	
		☕				☕		☕		🛒		☕	☕		☕	☕			☕	☕	🛒			☕	
Cardiff Central 7	d									08 45				09 12					09 00		09 45				
Newport (South Wales)	d									08 59				09 27					09 15		09 59				
Bristol Temple Meads 10	d				08 41	09 00						09 30							10 00					10 30	
Bristol Parkway 7	d				08 52	09 10	←					09 40							10 10					10 40	
Gloucester 7	d				09 38		09 38			09 46			10 11	10 21							10 46				11 08
Cheltenham Spa	d				→	09 42	09 48			09 57		10 12	10a23	10a34					10 42		10 57			11 12	11a20
Ashchurch for Tewkesbury	d						09 56			10 04															
Worcester Shrub Hill 7	a						10 13																		
Birmingham New Street 12	a					10 26				10 45		10 58							11 26		11 45			11 57	
	d		10 13	10 24		10 30				10 49	10 54				11 03		11 13	11 24	11 30		11 49		11 54	12 03	
Water Orton	d										11 05														
Coleshill Parkway	d			10 37							11 08							11 37					12 07		
Nuneaton	d			10 53							11 25							11 53					12 24		
Hinckley	d										11 32												12 31		
Narborough	d										11 40												12 39		
South Wigston	d																						12 43		
Leicester	a			11 13							11 50							12 13					12 50		
Wilnecote	d		10 31														11 29								
Tamworth	d		10 35			10 47				11 08							11 33				12 08				
Burton-on-Trent	d		10 46			10 58				11 20							11 44				12 20				
Willington	d																								
Derby 10	a		11 02			11 11				11 35					11 39		12 02		12 11		12 36			12 39	
	d		11 11					11 34		11 43							12 11			12 34	12 43				
Spondon	d																12 16								
Long Eaton	d		11 20					11a43		11 52							12 22			12a43	12 52				
Attenborough	d		11 31																						
Beeston	d	11 19	11 34													12 19	12 30				12 59				
Nottingham 8	a	11 27	11 41							12 06						12 27	12 38				13 05				

		AW	EM	XC	XC	GW	XC	GW	EM	XC	XC	XC		GW	XC	EM	XC	XC	XC	EM	XC	XC	XC	GW	AW
			1 ◇		◇	◇	1 ◇	◇	1 ◇	◇		1 ◇		1 ◇	1 ◇	1 ◇		◇	1 ◇	1 ◇	◇		1 ◇		
		G			A	H		H		C		J							K		C		J		G
			☕				☕		☕	🛒		☕		☕	☕	☕			☕	☕	🛒		☕		
Cardiff Central 7	d	10 12								10 45											11 45				12 12
Newport (South Wales)	d	10 27								10 59											11 59				12 27
Bristol Temple Meads 10	d					10 41	11 00					11 30							12 00				12 30		
Bristol Parkway 7	d					10 52	11 10	←				11 40							12 10				12 40		
Gloucester 7	d	11 22				11 36		11 36		11 46				12 12							12 46			13 08	13 21
Cheltenham Spa	d	11a34				→	11 42	11 47		11 57		12 12		12a23					12 42		12 57		13 12	13a20	13a34
Ashchurch for Tewkesbury	d							11 55																	
Worcester Shrub Hill 7	a							12 15																	
Birmingham New Street 12	a						12 26			12 46		12 57							13 26		13 45		13 57		
	d			12 13	12 24		12 30			12 49	12 54				13 03		13 13	13 24	13 30		13 49	13 54	14 03		
Water Orton	d										13 05														
Coleshill Parkway	d				12 37						13 09											14 07			
Nuneaton	d				12 53						13 25							13 53				14 24			
Hinckley	d										13 32											14 31			
Narborough	d										13 40											14 39			
South Wigston	d																					14 44			
Leicester	a				13 13						13 50							14 13				14 50			
Wilnecote	d			12 29																					
Tamworth	d			12 33			12 47			13 08							13 30				14 08				
Burton-on-Trent	d			12 43			12 58			13 20							13 42				14 20				
Willington	d																13 48								
Derby 10	a			13 02			13 11			13 36					13 39		14 02		14 11		14 35		14 39		
	d			13 11					13 34	13 43							14 11			14 34	14 43				
Spondon	d																								
Long Eaton	d			13 20					13a43	13 52							14 20			14a43	14 52				
Attenborough	d			13 30																					
Beeston	d		13 20	13 33						14 00						14 19	14 27				15 00				
Nottingham 8	a		13 25	13 40						14 05						14 25	14 35				15 05				

For general notes see front of timetable
For details of catering facilities see Directory of Train Operators

A To Stansted Airport (Table 49)
B From Warminster (Table 123) to Great Malvern (Table 71)
C 🛒 from Newport (South Wales)
D From Plymouth (Table 51)
E To Sheffield (Table 53)
G From Maesteg (Table 128)
H From Weymouth (Table 123) to Great Malvern (Table 71)
J From Penzance (Table 51)
K From Paignton (Table 51)

Table 57

Saturdays

until 26 January

Bristol and Cardiff → Birmingham → Leicester, Derby and Nottingham

Network Diagram - see first page of Table 50

		EM	XC	XC	GW	XC	GW	EM	XC	XC	XC	GW	AW	XC	EM	XC	XC	XC	EM	XC	XC	XC	GW
		[1] ◇		◇	◇	[1] ◇	◇	[1] ◇	◇		[1] ◇	[1] ◇		[1] ◇	[1] ◇		◇	[1] ◇	[1] ◇	◇		[1] ◇	
				A	B		B				C		D				A					E	
		🍴				🍴		🍴			🍴	🍴		🍴	🍴			🍴	🍴			🍴	
Cardiff Central [7]	d								12 45				13 12							13 45			
Newport (South Wales)	d								12 59				13 27							13 59			
Bristol Temple Meads [10]	d				12 41	13 00					13 30							14 00				14 30	
Bristol Parkway [7]	d				12 52	13 10	←				13 40							14 10				14 40	
Gloucester [7]	d				13 40		13 40		13 46			14 11	14 21							14 46			15 08
Cheltenham Spa	d				→	13 42	13 50		13 57		14 12	14a23	14a34					14 42		14 57		15 12	15a20
Ashchurch for Tewkesbury	d						13 58																
Worcester Shrub Hill [7]	a						14 26																
Birmingham New Street [12]	a					14 26			14 45		14 57							15 27		15 45		15 57	
	d		14 13	14 24		14 30			14 49	14 54				15 03		15 13	15 24	15 30		15 49	15 54	16 03	
Water Orton	d									15 06													
Coleshill Parkway	d			14 37						15 10							15 37				16 07		
Nuneaton	d			14 53						15 25							15 53				16 23		
Hinckley	d									15 32											16 30		
Narborough	d									15 40											16 38		
South Wigston	d																				16 42		
Leicester	a			15 13						15 50							16 13				16 50		
Wilnecote	d		14 29													15 29							
Tamworth	d		14 33			14 47			15 08							15 33				16 08			
Burton-on-Trent	d		14 46			14 58			15 20							15 44				16 20			
Willington	d																						
Derby [10]	a		15 02			15 11			15 34					15 39		16 02		16 11		16 36		16 39	
	d		15 11					15 34	15 43							16 11			16 34	16 43			
Spondon	d																						
Long Eaton	d		15 20					15a43	15 53							16 20			16a43	16 53			
Attenborough	d		15 30																				
Beeston	d	15 20	15 33						16 00						16 21	16 27				17 01			
Nottingham [8]	a	15 26	15 41						16 05						16 26	16 33				17 06			

		EM	XC	XC	GW	XC	GW	EM	XC	XC	XC	GW	AW	XC	EM	XC	XC	XC	EM	XC	XC	GW	AW
		[1] ◇		◇		[1] ◇		[1] ◇	◇		[1] ◇	[1] ◇		[1] ◇	[1] ◇		◇	[1] ◇	[1] ◇	◇	[1] ◇		
				G	H		H				E		D				A	J			E		D
		🍴				🍴		🍴			🍴	🍴		🍴	🍴			🍴	🍴		🍴		
Cardiff Central [7]	d								14 45				15 12							15 45			16 12
Newport (South Wales)	d								14 59				15 27							15 59			16 26
Bristol Temple Meads [10]	d				14 41	15 00					15 30							16 00			16 30		
Bristol Parkway [7]	d				14 52	15 10	←				15 40							16 10			16 40		
Gloucester [7]	d				15 38		15 38		15 46			16 11	16 21							16 46		17 08	17 21
Cheltenham Spa	d				→	15 42	15 48		15 57		16 12	16a23	16a34					16 42		16 57	17 12	17a20	17a34
Ashchurch for Tewkesbury	d						15 56		16 04											17 04			
Worcester Shrub Hill [7]	a						16 13																
Birmingham New Street [12]	a					16 26			16 45		16 57							17 26		17 45	17 57		
	d		16 13	16 24		16 30			16 49	16 54				17 03		17 13	17 24	17 30		17 49	18 03		
Water Orton	d									17 05						17 23				17 59			
Coleshill Parkway	d			16 37						17 08							17 37						
Nuneaton	d			16 53						17 25							17 53						
Hinckley	d									17 32													
Narborough	d									17 40													
South Wigston	d									17 44													
Leicester	a			17 13						17 50							18 13						
Wilnecote	d		16 31													17 31							
Tamworth	d		16 35			16 47			17 08							17 35				18 09			
Burton-on-Trent	d		16 46			16 58			17 20							17 47				18 20			
Willington	d															17 53							
Derby [10]	a		17 02			17 11			17 36					17 39		18 07		18 11		18 35	18 39		
	d		17 11					17 34	17 43							18 11			18 34	18 41			
Spondon	d		17 16																				
Long Eaton	d		17 22					17a43	17 52							18 20			18a43	18 50			
Attenborough	d		17 30													18 26							
Beeston	d	17 20	17 33						18 01						18 20	18 29				18 59			
Nottingham [8]	a	17 28	17 40						18 06						18 26	18 38				19 05			

For general notes see front of timetable
For details of catering facilities see Directory of Train Operators

A To Stansted Airport (Table 49)
B From Brighton (Table 123) to Worcester Foregate Street (Table 71)
C From Penzance (Table 51)
D From Maesteg (Table 128)
E From Plymouth (Table 51)
G To Cambridge (Table 49)
H From Southampton Central (Table 123) to Great Malvern (Table 71)
J From Paignton (Table 51)

Table 57

Bristol and Cardiff → Birmingham → Leicester, Derby and Nottingham

Network Diagram - see first page of Table 50

		XC	EM 1◇ A ☕	XC	XC ◇ B	XC 1◇ ☕	EM 1◇ ☕	XC ◇	XC	XC 1◇ C ☕	GW 1◇ ☕		AW D	XC 1◇ ☕	EM 1◇ E ☕	XC ◇	XC 1◇ ☕	EM G	EM 1◇ ☕	XC ◇	XC	XC 1◇ C ☕	GW	AW D	XC ◇
Cardiff Central 7	d							16 45					17 12							17 45				18 12	
Newport (South Wales)	d							16 59					17 27							17 59				18 27	
Bristol Temple Meads 10	d					17 00				17 30							18 00					18 30			
Bristol Parkway 7	d					17 10				17 40							18 10					18 40			
Gloucester 7	d							17 46			18 11		18 23							18 46			19 08	19 21	
Cheltenham Spa	d					17 42		17 57		18 12	18a23		18a33				18 42			18 57		19 12	19a20	19a34	
Ashchurch for Tewkesbury	d							18 04																	
Worcester Shrub Hill 7	a																								
Birmingham New Street 12	a					18 26		18 46		18 57							19 27			19 45		19 57			
	d	18 05		18 13	18 24	18 30		18 49	18 54					19 03		19 24	19 30			19 49	19 55	20 03			20 27
Water Orton	d			18 26																	20 05				
Coleshill Parkway	d				18 37				19 07																
Nuneaton	d	18 33			18 53				19 24							19b53					20 24				20 54
Hinckley	d	18 40							19 31												20 31				
Narborough	d	18 48							19 39												20 39				
South Wigston	d	18 53							19 44												20 44				
Leicester	a	18 59			19 13				19 50							20 16					20 50				21 14
Wilnecote	d			18 34				19 06												20 05					
Tamworth	d			18 38		18 47		19 10									19 47			20 09		20 19			
Burton-on-Trent	d			18 50		18 58		19 20									19 58			20 20		20 29			
Willington	d			18 56																					
Derby 10	a			19 06		19 11		19 35						19 39			20 11			20 36		20 42			
	d			19 12			19 34	19 43							19 51					20 42					
Spondon	d			19 17																20 47					
Long Eaton	d			19 23			19a43	19 52							20a01					20 53					
Attenborough	d			19 29				19 58												21 00					
Beeston	d		19 20	19 32				20 02										20 13	20 22	21 03					
Nottingham 8 🚌	a		19 26	19 40				20 10										20 19	20 34	21 11					

		XC 1◇		EM	EM 1◇ ☕	XC ◇	XC 1◇	XC 1◇ C ☕	GW 1◇ ☕	GW ◇ H	XC	EM 1◇ ☕	XC ◇	XC 1◇ C ☕	XC		AW D	XC	GW J	XC ◇	GW 1◇ ☕	AW D	EM K		
Cardiff Central 7	d					18 45							20 00				20 15			20 50		21 15			
Newport (South Wales)	d					18 59							20 15				20 30			21 04		21 30			
Bristol Temple Meads 10	d	19 00						19 30		19 40				20 30					20 41						
Bristol Parkway 7	d	19 10						19 40		19 52				20 40					20 52						
Gloucester 7	d					19 46			20 11	20 38			20 57		21 17		21 23		21 34	21 46	22 11	22a22			
Cheltenham Spa	d	19 42				19 57		20 12	20a23	20a45			21 07	21 12	21 27		21a34		21 42	21 57	22a23				
Ashchurch for Tewkesbury	d					20 04																			
Worcester Shrub Hill 7	a														21 54					22 20					
Birmingham New Street 12	a	20 31				20 41		20 57					21 52	21 57						23 02					
	d					20 44	20 50				21 15		21 54	22 03				22 09							
Water Orton	d																								
Coleshill Parkway	d										21 28														
Nuneaton	d										21 44							22 36							
Hinckley	d										21 50							22 43							
Narborough	d										21 58							22 51							
South Wigston	d										22 03							22 56							
Leicester	a										22 11							23 02							
Wilnecote	d												22 09												
Tamworth	d					21 03	21 23						22 13	22 19											
Burton-on-Trent	d					21 14	21 33						22 25	22 29											
Willington	d																								
Derby 10	a					21 36	21 45						22 38	22 47											
	d					21 41							22 42										23 04		
Spondon	d																								
Long Eaton	d					21 50							22 51										23 14		
Attenborough	d																						23 26		
Beeston	d			21 11	21 20	21 58						22 20	22 57										23 30		
Nottingham 8 🚌	a			21 17	21 26	22 04						22 29	23 04										23 37		

For general notes see front of timetable
For details of catering facilities see Directory of Train Operators

A To Sheffield (Table 53)
B To Cambridge (Table 49)
C From Plymouth (Table 51)
D From Maesteg (Table 128)
E From York (Table 53)
G To Lincoln (Table 27)
H From Weymouth (Table 123)
J From Brighton (Table 123)
K From Matlock (Table 56)
b Arr. 1950

Table 57

Saturdays

Bristol and Cardiff → Birmingham → Leicester, Derby and Nottingham

2 February to 22 March

Network Diagram - see first page of Table 50

		EM 1◇ 🍴	EM 1◇ 🍴	AW A	EM 1◇ B 🍴	XC ◇	EM	XC	XC	XC 1◇ 🍴	GW	EM	XC		XC 1◇ 🍴	XC ◇	EM 1◇ 🍴	XC	XC 1◇ 🍴	XC ◇	XC ◇ C	XC 1◇ 🍴	EM 1◇ D 🍴	EM 1◇ 🍴	XC
Cardiff Central 7	d			23p20																					
Newport (South Wales)	d			23p39																					
Bristol Temple Meads 10	d																								
Bristol Parkway 7	d																								
Gloucester 7	d			00 39							05 50														06 46
Cheltenham Spa	d			00a52							06 00														06 57
Ashchurch for Tewkesbury	d										06 08														07 04
Worcester Shrub Hill 7	a										06 30														
Birmingham New Street 12	a																								07 45
	d					05 20			05 54	06 00			06 09		06 30	06 36		06 52	07 03	07 10	07 24	07 30			07 49
Water Orton	d												06 19												
Coleshill Parkway	d								06 07									07 06			07 37				
Nuneaton	d					05 46			06 24							07 04		07 24			07 53				
Hinckley	d								06 31									07 31							
Narborough	d								06 39									07 39							
South Wigston	d								06 44									07 44							
Leicester	a					06 06			06 50							07 25		07 50			08 13				
Wilnecote	d												06 27												08 06
Tamworth	d									06 16			06 31		06 47				07 19	07 28		07 47			08 10
Burton-on-Trent	d									06 26			06 42		06 58				07 29	07 39		07 58	08 08		08 22
Willington	d																			07 45			08 13		
Derby 10	a									06 39			06 58		07 11				07 42	07 58		08 11	08 25		08 35
	d				06 00		06 26	06 29					07 06				07 34			08 08			08 34		08 42
Spondon	d							06 34					07 11												08 48
Long Eaton	d				06a09		06a35	06 41					07 18				07a43			08 17			08a43		08 54
Attenborough	d							06 47				07 17	07 27							08 23					
Beeston	d	00 28	00 40					06 50				07 20	07 31							08 27				08 48	09 01
Nottingham 8 🚢	a	00 35	00 46					06 56				07 27	07 37							08 32				08 56	09 10

		XC	XC 1◇ 🍴	AW		EM 1◇ 🍴	XC	XC ◇ C	XC 1◇ 🍴	EM 1◇ E 🍴	XC	XC	XC 1◇ G 🍴	GW	AW	XC 1◇ 🍴	EM 1◇ 🍴		XC	XC ◇ C	XC 1◇ 🍴	EM 1◇ 🍴	XC ◇ H	XC	XC 1◇ J 🍴
Cardiff Central 7	d			06 12											07 12								07 45		
Newport (South Wales)	d			06 27											07 27								07 59		
Bristol Temple Meads 10	d		06 15										07 30								08 00				08 30
Bristol Parkway 7	d		06 25										07 40								08 10				08 40
Gloucester 7	d		07 01	07 21							07 46			08 10	08 22								08 46		
Cheltenham Spa	d		07 12	07a34							07 57		08 12	08a23	08a32						08 42		08 57		09 12
Ashchurch for Tewkesbury	d										08 04														
Worcester Shrub Hill 7	a																								
Birmingham New Street 12	a		07 57								08 46		08 57								09 26		09 45		09 57
	d	07 54	08 03				08 13	08 24	08 30		08 49	08 54				09 03			09 13	09 24	09 30		09 49	09 54	10 03
Water Orton	d											09 07													
Coleshill Parkway	d	08 07						08 37				09 10								09 37				10 07	
Nuneaton	d	08 24						08 53				09 25								09 53				10 23	
Hinckley	d	08 31										09 32												10 30	
Narborough	d	08 39										09 40												10 38	
South Wigston	d	08 44																						10 43	
Leicester	a	08 50						09 13				09 51								10 13				10 50	
Wilnecote	d																								
Tamworth	d		08 19				08 34		08 47		09 08								09 30				10 08		
Burton-on-Trent	d		08 29				08 46		08 58		09 20								09 41				10 20		
Willington	d																		09 49						
Derby 10	a		08 42				09 02		09 11		09 36					09 39			10 02		10 11		10 35		10 39
	d						09 06			09 34	09 43								10 11			10 34	10 43		
Spondon	d																								
Long Eaton	d						09 16			09a43	09 52								10 20			10a43	10 52		
Attenborough	d																		10 28						
Beeston	d					09 20	09 24				09 59						10 20		10 31				10 59		
Nottingham 8 🚢	a					09 26	09 35				10 05						10 27		10 37				11 04		

For general notes see front of timetable
For details of catering facilities see Directory of Train Operators

A From Maesteg (Table 128)
B From Sheffield (Table 53)
C To Stansted Airport (Table 49)
D To St Pancras International (Table 53)
E From Barnsley (Table 53)
G From Exeter St Davids (Table 51)
H 🍴 from Newport (South Wales)
J From Plymouth (Table 51)

Saturdays

Bristol and Cardiff → Birmingham → Leicester, Derby and Nottingham

2 February to 22 March

Network Diagram - see first page of Table 50

		EM 1◇ ☕	XC	XC ◇ A	GW B	XC 1◇ ☕	GW B	EM 1◇ ☕		XC ◇ C 🍴	XC	XC 1◇ D ☕	GW 1◇ ☕	AW	XC 1◇ ☕	EM 1◇ E ☕	XC	XC ◇ A	XC 1◇ ☕	EM 1◇ ☕	XC ◇ C 🍴		XC	XC 1◇ D ☕	GW
Cardiff Central 7	d									08 45				09 12					09 00		09 45				
Newport (South Wales)	d									08 59				09 27					09 15		09 59				
Bristol Temple Meads 10	d				08 41	09 00						09 30							10 00					10 30	
Bristol Parkway 7	d				08 52	09 10	←					09 40							10 10					10 40	
Gloucester 7	d				09 38		09 38			09 46			10 07	10 21							10 46				11 08
Cheltenham Spa	d				→	09 42	09 48			09 57		10 12	10a18	10a34					10 42		10 57			11 12	11a20
Ashchurch for Tewkesbury	d						09 56			10 04															
Worcester Shrub Hill 7	a						10 13																		
Birmingham New Street 12	a					10 26				10 45		10 58							11 26		11 45			11 57	
	d		10 13	10 24		10 30				10 49	10 54				11 03		11 13	11 24	11 30		11 49		11 54	12 03	
Water Orton	d										11 05														
Coleshill Parkway	d			10 37							11 08							11 37					12 07		
Nuneaton	d			10 53							11 25							11 53					12 24		
Hinckley	d										11 32												12 31		
Narborough	d										11 40												12 39		
South Wigston	d																						12 44		
Leicester	a			11 13							11 50							12 13					12 50		
Wilnecote	d		10 31														11 29								
Tamworth	d		10 35			10 47				11 08							11 33				12 08				
Burton-on-Trent	d		10 46			10 58				11 20							11 44				12 20				
Willington	d																								
Derby 10	a		11 02			11 11				11 35					11 39		12 02		12 11		12 36			12 39	
	d		11 11					11 34		11 43							12 11			12 34	12 43				
Spondon	d																12 16								
Long Eaton	d		11 20					11a43		11 52							12 22			12a43	12 52				
Attenborough	d		11 31																						
Beeston	d	11 19	11 34													12 19	12 30				12 59				
Nottingham 8	a	11 27	11 41							12 06						12 27	12 38				13 05				

		AW G	EM 1◇ ☕	XC	XC ◇ A	GW ◇ H	XC 1◇ ☕	GW ◇ H	EM 1◇ ☕	XC ◇ C 🍴	XC	XC 1◇ J ☕		GW 1◇ ☕	XC 1◇ ☕	EM 1◇ ☕	XC	XC ◇	XC 1◇ K ☕	EM 1◇ ☕	XC ◇ C 🍴	XC	XC 1◇ J ☕	GW	AW G
Cardiff Central 7	d	10 12								10 45											11 45				12 12
Newport (South Wales)	d	10 27								10 59											11 59				12 27
Bristol Temple Meads 10	d					10 41	11 00					11 30							12 00				12 30		
Bristol Parkway 7	d					10 52	11 10	←				11 40							12 10				12 40		
Gloucester 7	d	11 22				11 36		11 36		11 46				12 07							12 46			13 08	13 21
Cheltenham Spa	d	11a34				→	11 42	11 47		11 57		12 12		12a18					12 42		12 57		13 12	13a20	13a34
Ashchurch for Tewkesbury	d							11 55																	
Worcester Shrub Hill 7	a							12 15																	
Birmingham New Street 12	a						12 26			12 46		12 57							13 26		13 45		13 57		
	d			12 13	12 24		12 30			12 49	12 54				13 03		13 13	13 24	13 30		13 49	13 54	14 03		
Water Orton	d										13 05														
Coleshill Parkway	d				12 37						13 09											14 07			
Nuneaton	d				12 53						13 25							13 53				14 24			
Hinckley	d										13 32											14 31			
Narborough	d										13 40											14 39			
South Wigston	d																					14 44			
Leicester	a				13 13						13 50							14 13				14 50			
Wilnecote	d			12 29																					
Tamworth	d			12 33			12 47			13 08							13 30				14 08				
Burton-on-Trent	d			12 44			12 58			13 20							13 42				14 20				
Willington	d																13 48								
Derby 10	a			13 02			13 11			13 36					13 39		14 02		14 11		14 35		14 39		
	d			13 11					13 34	13 43							14 11			14 34	14 43				
Spondon	d																								
Long Eaton	d			13 20					13a43	13 52							14 20			14a43	14 52				
Attenborough	d			13 30																					
Beeston	d		13 20	13 33						14 00						14 19	14 27				15 00				
Nottingham 8	a		13 25	13 40						14 05						14 25	14 35				15 05				

For general notes see front of timetable
For details of catering facilities see Directory of Train Operators

- **A** To Stansted Airport (Table 49)
- **B** From Warminster (Table 123) to Great Malvern (Table 71)
- **C** 🍴 from Newport (South Wales)
- **D** From Plymouth (Table 51)
- **E** To Sheffield (Table 53)
- **G** From Maesteg (Table 128)
- **H** From Weymouth (Table 123) to Great Malvern (Table 71)
- **J** From Penzance (Table 51)
- **K** From Paignton (Table 51)

Table 57

Bristol and Cardiff → Birmingham → Leicester, Derby and Nottingham

2 February to 22 March

Network Diagram - see first page of Table 50

		EM	XC		XC	GW	XC	GW	EM	XC	XC	XC	GW	AW	XC	EM		XC	XC	XC	EM	XC	XC	XC	GW
		1 ◇			◇	◇	1 ◇	◇	1 ◇	◇		1 ◇	1 ◇		1 ◇	1 ◇			◇	1 ◇	1 ◇	◇		1 ◇	
					A	B		B				C		D					A					E	
		☕					☕		☕			☕	☕		☕	☕				☕	☕			☕	
Cardiff Central 7	d									12 45				13 12								13 45			
Newport (South Wales)	d									12 59				13 27								13 59			
Bristol Temple Meads 10	d					12 41	13 00					13 30								14 00				14 30	
Bristol Parkway 7	d					12 52	13 10	⟵				13 40								14 10				14 40	
Gloucester 7	d					13 40		13 40		13 46			14 07	14 21								14 46			15 08
Cheltenham Spa	d					⟶	13 42	13 50		13 57		14 12	14a18	14a34						14 42		14 57		15 12	15a20
Ashchurch for Tewkesbury	d							13 58																	
Worcester Shrub Hill 7	a							14 26																	
Birmingham New Street 12	a						14 26			14 45		14 57								15 27		15 45		15 57	
	d		14 13		14 24		14 30			14 49	14 54				15 03			15 13	15 24	15 30		15 49	15 54	16 03	
Water Orton	d										15 06														
Coleshill Parkway	d				14 37						15 10								15 37				16 07		
Nuneaton	d				14 53						15 25								15 53				16 23		
Hinckley	d										15 32												16 30		
Narborough	d										15 40												16 38		
South Wigston	d																						16 42		
Leicester	a				15 13						15 50								16 13				16 50		
Wilnecote	d		14 29															15 29							
Tamworth	d		14 33				14 47			15 08								15 33				16 08			
Burton-on-Trent	d		14 46				14 58			15 20								15 44				16 20			
Willington	d																								
Derby 10	a		15 02				15 11			15 34					15 39			16 02		16 11		16 36		16 39	
	d		15 11						15 34	15 43								16 11			16 34	16 43			
Spondon	d																								
Long Eaton	d		15 20						15a43	15 53								16 20			16a43	16 53			
Attenborough	d		15 30																						
Beeston	d	15 20	15 33							16 00						16 21		16 27				17 01			
Nottingham 8	a	15 26	15 41							16 05						16 26		16 33				17 06			

		EM	XC	XC	GW	XC	GW		EM	XC	XC	XC	GW	AW	XC	EM	XC	XC	XC	EM		XC	XC	GW	AW
		1 ◇		◇		1 ◇			1 ◇	◇		1 ◇	1 ◇		1 ◇	1 ◇		◇	1 ◇	1 ◇		◇	1 ◇		
				G	H		H					E		D				A	J				E		D
		☕				☕			☕			☕	☕		☕	☕			☕	☕			☕		
Cardiff Central 7	d									14 45				15 12								15 45			16 12
Newport (South Wales)	d									14 59				15 27								15 59			16 26
Bristol Temple Meads 10	d				14 41	15 00						15 30							16 00				16 30		
Bristol Parkway 7	d				14 52	15 10	⟵					15 40							16 10				16 40		
Gloucester 7	d				15 38		15 38			15 46			16 07	16 21								16 46		17 08	17 21
Cheltenham Spa	d				⟶	15 42	15 48			15 57		16 12	16a18	16a34					16 42			16 57	17 12	17a20	17a34
Ashchurch for Tewkesbury	d						15 56			16 04												17 04			
Worcester Shrub Hill 7	a						16 13																		
Birmingham New Street 12	a					16 26				16 45		16 57							17 26			17 45	17 57		
	d		16 13	16 24		16 30				16 49	16 54				17 03		17 13	17 24	17 30			17 49	18 03		
Water Orton	d										17 05						17 23					17 59			
Coleshill Parkway	d			16 37							17 08							17 37							
Nuneaton	d			16 53							17 25							17 53							
Hinckley	d										17 32														
Narborough	d										17 40														
South Wigston	d										17 44														
Leicester	a			17 13							17 50							18 13							
Wilnecote	d		16 31														17 31								
Tamworth	d		16 35			16 47				17 08							17 35					18 09			
Burton-on-Trent	d		16 46			16 58				17 20							17 47					18 20			
Willington	d																17 53								
Derby 10	a		17 02			17 11				17 36					17 39		18 07		18 11			18 35	18 39		
	d		17 11						17 34	17 43							18 11			18 34		18 41			
Spondon	d		17 16																						
Long Eaton	d		17 22						17a43	17 52							18 20			18a43		18 50			
Attenborough	d		17 30														18 26								
Beeston	d	17 20	17 33							18 01						18 20	18 29					18 59			
Nottingham 8	a	17 28	17 40							18 06						18 26	18 38					19 05			

For general notes see front of timetable
For details of catering facilities see Directory of Train Operators

A To Stansted Airport (Table 49)

B From Brighton (Table 123) to Worcester Foregate Street (Table 71)

C From Penzance (Table 51)

D From Maesteg (Table 128)

E From Plymouth (Table 51)

G To Cambridge (Table 49)

H From Southampton Central (Table 123) to Great Malvern (Table 71)

J From Paignton (Table 51)

Saturdays

2 February to 22 March

Bristol and Cardiff → Birmingham → Leicester, Derby and Nottingham

Network Diagram - see first page of Table 50

		XC	EM 1◇ A ☕	XC	XC ◇ B	XC 1◇ ☕	EM 1◇ ☕	XC ◇	XC	XC 1◇ C ☕	GW 1◇ ☕		AW D	XC 1◇ ☕	EM 1◇ E ☕	XC ◇	XC 1◇ ☕	EM G	EM 1◇ ☕	XC ◇	XC	XC 1◇ C ☕	GW	AW D	XC ◇
Cardiff Central 7	d							16 45					17 12							17 45				18 12	
Newport (South Wales)	d							16 59					17 27							17 59				18 27	
Bristol Temple Meads 10	d					17 00				17 30							18 00					18 30			
Bristol Parkway 7	d					17 10				17 40							18 10					18 40			
Gloucester 7	d							17 46			18 07		18 23							18 46			19 08	19 21	
Cheltenham Spa	d					17 42		17 57		18 12	18a18		18a33				18 42			18 57		19 12	19a20	19a34	
Ashchurch for Tewkesbury	d							18 04																	
Worcester Shrub Hill 7	a																								
Birmingham New Street 12	a					18 26		18 46		18 57							19 27			19 45		19 57			
	d	18 05		18 13	18 24	18 30		18 49	18 54					19 03		19 24	19 30			19 49	19 55	20 03			20 27
Water Orton	d			18 26																	20 05				
Coleshill Parkway	d				18 37				19 07																
Nuneaton	d	18 33			18 53				19 24							19b53					20 24				20 54
Hinckley	d	18 40							19 31												20 31				
Narborough	d	18 48							19 39												20 39				
South Wigston	d	18 53							19 44												20 44				
Leicester	a	18 59			19 13				19 50							20 16					20 50				21 14
Wilnecote	d			18 34				19 06												20 05					
Tamworth	d			18 38		18 47		19 10									19 47			20 09		20 19			
Burton-on-Trent	d			18 50		18 58		19 20									19 58			20 20		20 29			
Willington	d			18 56																					
Derby 10	a			19 06		19 11		19 35						19 39			20 11			20 36		20 42			
	d			19 12			19 34	19 43							19 51					20 42					
Spondon	d			19 17																20 47					
Long Eaton	d			19 23			19a43	19 52							20a01					20 53					
Attenborough	d			19 29				19 58												21 00					
Beeston	d		19 20	19 32				20 02										20 13	20 22	21 03					
Nottingham 8 ⛴	a		19 26	19 40				20 10										20 19	20 34	21 11					

		XC 1◇		EM	EM 1◇ ☕	XC ◇	XC 1◇	XC 1◇ C ☕	GW 1◇ ☕	GW ◇ H	XC	EM 1◇ ☕	XC ◇	XC 1◇ C ☕	XC		AW D	XC	GW J	XC ◇	GW 1◇ ☕	AW D	EM K		
Cardiff Central 7	d					18 45							20 00				20 15			20 50		21 15			
Newport (South Wales)	d					18 59							20 15				20 30			21 04		21 30			
Bristol Temple Meads 10	d	19 00						19 30		19 40				20 30					20 41						
Bristol Parkway 7	d	19 10						19 40		19 52				20 40					20 52						
Gloucester 7	d					19 46			20 11	20 38			20 57		21 17		21 23		21 34	21 46	22 11	22a22			
Cheltenham Spa	d	19 42				19 57		20 12	20a23	20a45			21 07	21 12	21 27		21a34		21 42	21 57	22a23				
Ashchurch for Tewkesbury	d					20 04																			
Worcester Shrub Hill 7	a														21 54					22 20					
Birmingham New Street 12	a	20 31				20 41		20 57					21 52	21 57						23 02					
	d					20 44	20 50				21 15		21 54	22 03				22 09							
Water Orton	d																								
Coleshill Parkway	d										21 28														
Nuneaton	d										21 44							22 36							
Hinckley	d										21 50							22 43							
Narborough	d										21 58							22 51							
South Wigston	d										22 03							22 56							
Leicester	a										22 11							23 02							
Wilnecote	d												22 09												
Tamworth	d					21 03	21 23						22 13	22 19											
Burton-on-Trent	d					21 14	21 33						22 25	22 29											
Willington	d																								
Derby 10	a					21 36	21 45						22 38	22 47											
	d					21 41							22 42										23 04		
Spondon	d																								
Long Eaton	d					21 50							22 51										23 14		
Attenborough	d																						23 26		
Beeston	d			21 11	21 20	21 58						22 20	22 57										23 30		
Nottingham 8 ⛴	a			21 17	21 26	22 04						22 29	23 04										23 37		

For general notes see front of timetable
For details of catering facilities see Directory of Train Operators

A To Sheffield (Table 53)
B To Cambridge (Table 49)
C From Plymouth (Table 51)
D From Maesteg (Table 128)
E From York (Table 53)
G To Lincoln (Table 27)
H From Weymouth (Table 123)
J From Brighton (Table 123)
K From Matlock (Table 56)
b Arr. 1950

Table 57

Saturdays
from 29 March

Bristol and Cardiff → Birmingham → Leicester, Derby and Nottingham

Network Diagram - see first page of Table 50

		EM	AW	EM	EM	XC	XC	XC	EM	XC	XC	XC	XC	GW	EM	XC	XC	XC	XC	XC	EM	EM	XC	XC	AW
		1 ◇		1 ◇				1 ◇					1 ◇		1 ◇	1 ◇	◇			1 ◇	1 ◇	1 ◇		1 ◇	
			A	B																	C				
							🚌				🚌	🚌						🚌	🚌						
		☕		☕				☕					☕		☕	☕				☕	☕	☕		☕	
Cardiff Central [7]	d		23p20																						06 12
Newport (South Wales)	d		23p39																						06 27
Bristol Temple Meads [10]	d																							06 15	
Bristol Parkway [7]	d																							06 25	
Gloucester [7]	d		00 39											05 50									06 46	07 01	07 21
Cheltenham Spa	d		00a52											06 00									06 57	07 12	07a34
Ashchurch for Tewkesbury	d													06 08									07 04		
Worcester Shrub Hill [7]	a													06 30											
Birmingham New Street [12]	a																						07 45	07 57	
	d						05 03	06 00		06 09	06 13		06 30			07 03	07 10	07 13		07 30			07 49	08 03	
Water Orton	d									06 19															
Coleshill Parkway	d						05 34				06 44							07 44							
Nuneaton	d						06 10				07 20	07 24						08 20	08 24						
Hinckley	d						06 29					07 43							08 43						
Narborough	d						06 53					08 07							09 07						
South Wigston	d						07 04					08 18							09 18						
Leicester	a						07 19				08 00	08 33						09 00	09 33						
Wilnecote	d									06 27													08 06		
Tamworth	d							06 16		06 31			06 47			07 19	07 28			07 47			08 10	08 19	
Burton-on-Trent	d							06 26		06 42			06 58			07 29	07 39			07 58	08 08		08 22	08 29	
Willington	d																07 45				08 13				
Derby [10]	a							06 39		06 58			07 11			07 42	07 58			08 11	08 25		08 35	08 42	
	d			06 00	06 26	06 29				07 06					07 34		08 08				08 34		08 42		
Spondon	d					06 34				07 11													08 48		
Long Eaton	d			06a09	06a35	06 41				07 18					07a43		08 17				08a43		08 54		
Attenborough	d					06 47			07 17	07 27							08 23								
Beeston	d	00 01				06 50			07 20	07 31							08 27					08 48	09 01		
Nottingham [8] 🚊	a	00 06				06 56			07 27	07 37							08 32					08 56	09 10		

		XC	XC	EM	XC	XC	EM	XC	XC	AW	XC	EM		XC	XC	XC	XC	EM	XC	XC	XC	XC	EM	XC	GW
				1 ◇		1 ◇	1 ◇		1 ◇		1 ◇	1 ◇					1 ◇	1 ◇	◇	1 ◇			1 ◇		
							D		E										G	H					J
		🚌	🚌												🚌	🚌					🚌	🚌			
				☕		☕	☕		☕		☕	☕					☕	☕	🛒	☕			☕		
Cardiff Central [7]	d									07 12									07 45						
Newport (South Wales)	d									07 27									07 59						
Bristol Temple Meads [10]	d								07 30								08 00			08 30					08 41
Bristol Parkway [7]	d								07 40								08 10			08 40					08 52
Gloucester [7]	d							07 46		08 22									08 46						09 38
Cheltenham Spa	d							07 57	08 12	08a32							08 42		08 57	09 12					→
Ashchurch for Tewkesbury	d							08 04																	
Worcester Shrub Hill [7]	a																								
Birmingham New Street [12]	a							08 46	08 57								09 26		09 45	09 57					
	d	08 09			08 13	08 30		08 49			09 03			09 13	09 13		09 30		09 49	10 03	10 09			10 13	
Water Orton	d	08 35																			10 35				
Coleshill Parkway	d	08 44													09 44						10 44				
Nuneaton	d	09 20	09 24												10 20	10 24					11 20	11 24			
Hinckley	d		09 43													10 43						11 43			
Narborough	d		10 07													11 07						12 07			
South Wigston	d		10 18													11 18						12 18			
Leicester	a	10 00	10 33												11 00	11 33					12 00	12 33			
Wilnecote	d																							10 31	
Tamworth	d				08 34	08 47		09 08						09 30					10 08					10 35	
Burton-on-Trent	d				08 46	08 58		09 20						09 41					10 20					10 46	
Willington	d													09 49											
Derby [10]	a				09 02	09 11		09 36			09 39			10 02			10 11		10 35	10 39				11 02	
	d				09 06		09 34	09 43						10 11				10 34	10 43					11 11	
Spondon	d																								
Long Eaton	d				09 16		09a43	09 52						10 20				10a43	10 52					11 20	
Attenborough	d													10 28										11 31	
Beeston	d			09 20	09 24			09 59				10 20		10 31					10 59				11 19	11 34	
Nottingham [8] 🚊	a			09 26	09 35			10 05				10 27		10 37					11 04				11 27	11 41	

For general notes see front of timetable
For details of catering facilities see Directory of Train Operators

- **A** From Maesteg (Table 128)
- **B** From Sheffield (Table 53)
- **C** To St Pancras International (Table 53)
- **D** From Barnsley (Table 53)
- **E** From Exeter St Davids (Table 51)
- **G** 🛒 from Newport (South Wales)
- **H** From Plymouth (Table 51)
- **J** From Warminster (Table 123) to Great Malvern (Table 71)

Table 57

Saturdays

from 29 March

Bristol and Cardiff → Birmingham → Leicester, Derby and Nottingham

Network Diagram - see first page of Table 50

		XC	GW	EM	XC	XC	AW	XC	XC	XC	EM	XC	XC	EM	XC	XC	AW	XC	XC	EM	XC	GW	XC	GW	EM
		1 ◇		1 ◇	◇	1 ◇		1 ◇			1 ◇		1 ◇	1 ◇	◇	1 ◇				1 ◇		◇	1 ◇	◇	1 ◇
			A		B	C					D				B	C	E					G		G	
									(bus)	(bus)								(bus)	(bus)						
		(buffet)		(buffet)	(trolley)	(buffet)		(buffet)			(buffet)		(buffet)	(buffet)	(trolley)	(buffet)				(buffet)			(buffet)		(buffet)
Cardiff Central 7	d				08 45		09 12								09 45		10 12								
Newport (South Wales)	d				08 59		09 27								09 59		10 27								
Bristol Temple Meads 10	d	09 00				09 30							10 00			10 30						10 41	11 00		
Bristol Parkway 7	d	09 10	←			09 40							10 10			10 40						10 52	11 10	←	
Gloucester 7	d		09 38		09 46		10 21								10 46		11 22					11 36		11 36	
Cheltenham Spa	d	09 42	09 48		09 57	10 12	10a34						10 42		10 57	11 12	11a34					→	11 42	11 47	
Ashchurch for Tewkesbury	d		09 56		10 04																			11 55	
Worcester Shrub Hill 7	a		10 13																					12 15	
Birmingham New Street 12	a	10 26			10 45	10 58							11 26		11 45	11 57							12 26		
	d	10 30			10 49			11 03	11 13			11 13	11 30		11 49	12 03		12 09			12 13		12 30		
Water Orton	d																	12 35							
Coleshill Parkway	d								11 44									12 44							
Nuneaton	d								12 20	12 24								13 20	13 24						
Hinckley	d									12 43									13 43						
Narborough	d									13 07									14 07						
South Wigston	d									13 18									14 18						
Leicester	a								13 00	13 33								14 00	14 33						
Wilnecote	d											11 29									12 29				
Tamworth	d	10 47			11 08							11 33			12 08						12 33		12 47		
Burton-on-Trent	d	10 58			11 20							11 44			12 20						12 44		12 58		
Willington	d																								
Derby 10	a	11 11			11 35			11 39				12 02	12 11		12 36	12 39					13 02		13 11		
	d			11 34	11 43							12 11		12 34	12 43						13 11				13 34
Spondon	d											12 16													
Long Eaton	d			11a43	11 52							12 22		12a43	12 52						13 20				13a43
Attenborough	d																				13 30				
Beeston	d										12 19	12 30			12 59					13 20	13 33				
Nottingham 8 (ferry)	a				12 06						12 27	12 38			13 05					13 25	13 40				

		XC		XC	XC	EM	XC	XC	XC	XC	EM	XC	XC	AW	XC	XC	EM	XC	GW	XC	GW	EM	XC	XC	AW
		◇		1 ◇	1 ◇	1 ◇				1 ◇	1 ◇	◇	1 ◇				1 ◇		◇	1 ◇	◇	1 ◇	◇	1 ◇	
		B		H						J		B	H	E					K		K			H	E
								(bus)	(bus)						(bus)	(bus)									
		(trolley)		(buffet)	(buffet)	(buffet)				(buffet)	(buffet)	(trolley)	(buffet)				(buffet)			(buffet)		(buffet)		(buffet)	
Cardiff Central 7	d	10 45										11 45		12 12									12 45		13 12
Newport (South Wales)	d	10 59										11 59		12 27									12 59		13 27
Bristol Temple Meads 10	d			11 30						12 00			12 30						12 41	13 00				13 30	
Bristol Parkway 7	d			11 40						12 10			12 40						12 52	13 10	←			13 40	
Gloucester 7	d	11 46										12 46		13 21					13 40		13 40		13 46		14 21
Cheltenham Spa	d	11 57		12 12						12 42		12 57	13 12	13a34					→	13 42	13 50		13 57	14 12	14a34
Ashchurch for Tewkesbury	d																				13 58				
Worcester Shrub Hill 7	a																				14 26				
Birmingham New Street 12	a	12 46		12 57						13 26		13 45	13 57							14 26			14 45	14 57	
	d	12 49			13 03		13 13	13 13		13 30		13 49	14 03		14 09			14 13		14 30			14 49		
Water Orton	d														14 35										
Coleshill Parkway	d							13 44							14 44										
Nuneaton	d							14 20	14 24						15 20	15 24									
Hinckley	d								14 43							15 43									
Narborough	d								15 07							16 07									
South Wigston	d								15 18							16 18									
Leicester	a							15 00	15 33						16 00	16 33									
Wilnecote	d																	14 29							
Tamworth	d	13 08					13 30					14 08						14 33		14 47			15 08		
Burton-on-Trent	d	13 20					13 42					14 20						14 46		14 58			15 20		
Willington	d						13 48																		
Derby 10	a	13 36			13 39		14 02			14 11		14 35	14 39					15 02		15 11			15 34		
	d	13 43					14 11				14 34	14 43						15 11				15 34	15 43		
Spondon	d																								
Long Eaton	d	13 52					14 20				14a43	14 52						15 20				15a43	15 53		
Attenborough	d																	15 30							
Beeston	d	14 00				14 19	14 27					15 00					15 20	15 33					16 00		
Nottingham 8 (ferry)	a	14 05				14 25	14 35					15 05					15 26	15 41					16 05		

For general notes see front of timetable
For details of catering facilities see Directory of Train Operators

A From Warminster (Table 123) to Great Malvern (Table 71)
B (trolley) from Newport (South Wales)
C From Plymouth (Table 51)
D To Sheffield (Table 53)
E From Maesteg (Table 128)
G From Weymouth (Table 123) to Great Malvern (Table 71)
H From Penzance (Table 51)
J From Paignton (Table 51)
K From Brighton (Table 123) to Worcester Foregate Street (Table 71)

from 29 March

Bristol and Cardiff → Birmingham → Leicester, Derby and Nottingham

Network Diagram - see first page of Table 50

		XC	EM	XC	XC	XC	XC	EM	XC	XC	XC	XC	EM	XC	GW	XC	GW	EM	XC	XC	AW	XC	EM	XC
		1◇	1◇				1◇	1◇	◇	1◇			1◇			1◇		1◇	◇	1◇		1◇	1◇	
										A					B		B			A	C			
					🚌	🚌					🚌	🚌												
		☕	☕				☕	☕		☕			☕			☕		☕		☕		☕	☕	
Cardiff Central [7]	d								13 45										14 45		15 12			
Newport (South Wales)	d								13 59										14 59		15 27			
Bristol Temple Meads [10]	d						14 00			14 30					14 41	15 00				15 30				
Bristol Parkway [7]	d						14 10			14 40					14 52	15 10	←			15 40				
Gloucester [7]	d								14 46						15 38 →		15 38		15 46		16 21			
Cheltenham Spa	d						14 42		14 57	15 12						15 42	15 48		15 57	16 12	16a34			
Ashchurch for Tewkesbury	d																15 56		16 04					
Worcester Shrub Hill [7]	a																16 13							
Birmingham New Street [12]	a						15 27		15 45	15 57						16 26			16 45	16 57				
	d	15 03		15 13	15 13		15 30		15 49	16 03	16 09			16 13		16 30			16 49			17 03		17 13
Water Orton	d										16 35													17 23
Coleshill Parkway	d				15 44						16 44													
Nuneaton	d				16 20	16 24					17 20	17 24												
Hinckley	d					16 43						17 43												
Narborough	d					17 07						18 07												
South Wigston	d					17 18						18 18												
Leicester	a				17 00	17 33					18 00	18 33												
Wilnecote	d			15 29										16 31										17 31
Tamworth	d			15 33					16 08					16 35		16 47			17 08					17 35
Burton-on-Trent	d			15 44					16 20					16 46		16 58			17 20					17 47
Willington	d																							17 53
Derby [10]	a	15 39		16 02			16 11		16 36	16 39				17 02		17 11			17 36			17 39		18 07
	d			16 11				16 34	16 43					17 11				17 34	17 43					18 11
Spondon	d													17 16										
Long Eaton	d			16 20				16a43	16 53					17 22				17a43	17 52					18 20
Attenborough	d													17 30										18 26
Beeston	d		16 21	16 27					17 01				17 20	17 33					18 01				18 20	18 29
Nottingham [8] ⛴	a		16 26	16 33					17 06				17 28	17 40					18 06				18 26	18 38

		XC	XC	XC	EM	XC	XC	AW	EM	XC	XC	XC	XC	EM	XC	XC	AW	XC	EM	XC	XC	XC	EM	EM	XC
				1◇	1◇	◇	1◇		1◇				1◇	1◇	◇	1◇		1◇	1◇			1◇		1◇	◇
				D			A	C	E							A	C		G				H		
		🚌	🚌								🚌	🚌								🚌	🚌				
				☕	☕		☕		☕				☕	☕		☕		☕	☕			☕		☕	
Cardiff Central [7]	d					15 45		16 12							16 45		17 12								17 45
Newport (South Wales)	d					15 59		16 26							16 59		17 27								17 59
Bristol Temple Meads [10]	d			16 00			16 30						17 00			17 30						18 00			
Bristol Parkway [7]	d			16 10			16 40						17 10			17 40						18 10			
Gloucester [7]	d					16 46		17 21							17 46		18 23								18 46
Cheltenham Spa	d			16 42		16 57	17 12	17a34					17 42		17 57	18 12	18a33					18 42			18 57
Ashchurch for Tewkesbury	d					17 04									18 04										
Worcester Shrub Hill [7]	a																								
Birmingham New Street [12]	a			17 26		17 45	17 57						18 26		18 46	18 57						19 27			19 45
	d	17 13		17 30		17 49	18 03			18 13	18 13		18 30		18 49			19 03		19 09		19 30			19 49
Water Orton	d					17 59				18 26										19 35					
Coleshill Parkway	d	17 44									18 44									19 44					
Nuneaton	d	18 20	18 24								19 20	19 24								20 20	20 24				
Hinckley	d		18 43									19 43									20 43				
Narborough	d		19 07									20 07									21 07				
South Wigston	d		19 18									20 18									21 18				
Leicester	a	19 00	19 33								20 00	20 33								21 00	21 33				
Wilnecote	d									18 34					19 06										20 05
Tamworth	d					18 09				18 38			18 47		19 10							19 47			20 09
Burton-on-Trent	d					18 20				18 50			18 58		19 20							19 58			20 20
Willington	d									18 56															
Derby [10]	a			18 11		18 35	18 39			19 06			19 11		19 35			19 39				20 11			20 36
	d				18 34	18 41				19 12				19 34	19 43				19 51						20 42
Spondon	d									19 17															20 47
Long Eaton	d				18a43	18 50				19 23				19a43	19 52				20a01						20 53
Attenborough	d									19 29					19 58										21 00
Beeston	d					18 59			19 20	19 32					20 02								20 13	20 22	21 03
Nottingham [8] ⛴	a					19 05			19 26	19 40					20 10								20 19	20 34	21 11

For general notes see front of timetable
For details of catering facilities see Directory of Train Operators

- A From Plymouth (Table 51)
- B From Southampton Central (Table 123) to Great Malvern (Table 71)
- C From Maesteg (Table 128)
- D From Paignton (Table 51)
- E To Sheffield (Table 53)
- G From York (Table 53)
- H To Lincoln (Table 27)

Table 57

Saturdays from 29 March

Bristol and Cardiff → Birmingham → Leicester, Derby and Nottingham

Network Diagram - see first page of Table 50

		XC 1◇ A ☕	AW B	XC 🚌	XC 🚌	XC 1◇	EM	EM 1◇ ☕	XC ◇	XC 1◇	XC 1◇ A ☕	GW ◇ C	XC 🚌	EM 1◇ ☕	XC ◇	XC 1◇ A ☕	XC	AW B	XC 🚌	GW D	XC ◇	AW B	EM E		
Cardiff Central 7	d		18 12						18 45						20 00			20 15			20 50	21 15			
Newport (South Wales)	d		18 27						18 59						20 15			20 30			21 04	21 30			
Bristol Temple Meads 10	d	18 30				19 00					19 30	19 40				20 30				20 41					
Bristol Parkway 7	d	18 40				19 10					19 40	19 52				20 40				20 52					
Gloucester 7	d		19 21						19 46			20 37			20 57		21 17	21 23		21 34	21 46	22a22			
Cheltenham Spa	d	19 12	19a34			19 42			19 57		20 12	20a45			21 07	21 12	21 27	21a34		21a42	21 57				
Ashchurch for Tewkesbury	d								20 04																
Worcester Shrub Hill 7	a																21 54				22 20				
Birmingham New Street 12	a	19 57				20 31			20 41		20 57				21 52	21 57					23 02				
	d	20 03		20 03					20 44	20 50			21 04		21 54	22 03			22 04						
Water Orton	d																								
Coleshill Parkway	d			20 34									21 35						22 35						
Nuneaton	d			21 10	21 14								22 11						23 11						
Hinckley	d				21 33								22 30						23 30						
Narborough	d				21 57								22 54						23 54						
South Wigston	d				22 08								23 05						00 05						
Leicester	a			21 50	22 23								23 20						00 20						
Wilnecote	d														22 09										
Tamworth	d	20 19							21 03	21 23					22 13	22 19									
Burton-on-Trent	d	20 29							21 14	21 33					22 25	22 29									
Willington	d																								
Derby 10	a	20 42							21 36	21 45					22 38	22 47									
	d								21 41						22 42								23 04		
Spondon	d																								
Long Eaton	d								21 50						22 51								23 14		
Attenborough	d																						23 26		
Beeston	d						21 11	21 20	21 58					22 20	22 57								23 30		
Nottingham 8 ⛴	a						21 17	21 26	22 04					22 29	23 04								23 37		

Sundays until 27 January

		EM 1◇ ☕	EM 1◇ ☕	XC 1◇ ☕	EM 1◇ G ☕	XC 1◇ ☕	EM 1◇ ☕	XC	XC 1◇ ☕	EM 1◇ G ☕	XC 1◇ ☕	XC 1◇ ☕	GW	GW 1◇ ☕	EM E	XC	XC 1◇ ☕	XC ◇ H	XC 1◇ ☕	EM 1◇ ☕	XC	XC 1◇ ☕	EM 1◇ G ☕	XC	XC 1◇ ☕
Cardiff Central 7	d																								
Newport (South Wales)	d																								
Bristol Temple Meads 10	d											09 15	09 44									10 30			11 00
Bristol Parkway 7	d											09 25	09 55									10 40			11 10
Gloucester 7	d											10 00	10 36	10 50											
Cheltenham Spa	d											10 12	10a46	11a00								11 12			11 42
Ashchurch for Tewkesbury	d																								
Worcester Shrub Hill 7	a																								
Birmingham New Street 12	a											10 51										11 51			12 26
	d			09 03		09 30		09 53	10 03		10 30					10 55	11 03	11 26	11 30		11 55	12 03		12 12	12 30
Water Orton	d																								
Coleshill Parkway	d							10 07								11 09		11 39			12 09				
Nuneaton	d							10 23								11 25		11 53			12 25				
Hinckley	d							10 31								11 32					12 32				
Narborough	d							10 40								11 41					12 41				
South Wigston	d							10 46								11 46					12 46				
Leicester	a							10 52								11 53		12 19			12 52				
Wilnecote	d																								
Tamworth	d			09 19		09 47			10 19		10 47								11 47					12 33	12 47
Burton-on-Trent	d			09 29		09 58			10 29		10 58								11 58					12 46	12 58
Willington	d																								
Derby 10	a			09 42		10 11			10 42		11 11						11 39		12 11			12 39		13 00	13 11
	d	07 11	09 12		10 03		10 16			11 04					11 15								13 02	13 06	
Spondon	d																								
Long Eaton	d	07a20	09a22		10a13					11a14					11 25								13a12	13 18	
Attenborough	d														11 33										
Beeston	d														11 36					11 49					
Nottingham 8 ⛴	a						10 36								11 43					11 56				13 30	

For general notes see front of timetable
For details of catering facilities see Directory of Train Operators

- **A** From Plymouth (Table 51)
- **B** From Maesteg (Table 128)
- **C** From Westbury (Table 123)
- **D** From Brighton (Table 123)
- **E** From Matlock (Table 56)
- **G** From Sheffield (Table 53)
- **H** To Stansted Airport (Table 49)

Table 57

Sundays

until 27 January

Bristol and Cardiff → Birmingham → Leicester, Derby and Nottingham

Network Diagram - see first page of Table 50

		GW	AW	XC	EM	XC	XC	XC	GW	EM	XC	XC	XC	XC	XC	EM	GW	XC	GW	AW	XC	EM	XC	XC	XC
														R										R	R
				1 ◇			1 ◇	1 ◇	1 ◇	1 ◇	◇	◇		1		1 ◇		1 ◇			◇			1	1
				A	B			C			D			A		E					D	B		G	
				☕			☕	☕	☕	☕				☕		☕		☕						☕	☕
Cardiff Central 7	d		10 30									11 50						12 00		12 30					
Newport (South Wales)	d		10 45									12 04						12 15		12 45					
Bristol Temple Meads 10	d			11 30				12 00						12 30			12 44	13 00						13 30	
Bristol Parkway 7	d			11 40				12 10						12 40			12 55	13 10	←					13 40	
Gloucester 7	d	11 38	11 44						12 37			12 46			13 16		13 36		13 36	13 44					
Cheltenham Spa	d	11a48	12a04	12 12				12 42	12a46			12 58		13 12	13 27		→	13 42	13 48	13a57				14 12	
Ashchurch for Tewkesbury	d																		13 56						
Worcester Shrub Hill 7	a																		14 25						
Birmingham New Street 12	a			12 51				13 26				13 40		13 51	14 19			14 26						14 57	
	d					12 55	13 03	13 30			13 36	13 49	13 53	14 03				14 30			14 34		14 55		15 03
Water Orton	d																								
Coleshill Parkway	d					13 10					13 49		14 06								14 47		15 08		
Nuneaton	d					13 26					14 04		14 23								15 02		15 25		
Hinckley	d					13 33							14 30										15 32		
Narborough	d					13 41							14 38										15 40		
South Wigston	d					13 47							14 44										15 46		
Leicester	a					13 53					14 26		14 50								15 23		15 51		
Wilnecote	d																								
Tamworth	d											14 06						14 47							
Burton-on-Trent	d											14 18						14 58							
Willington	d																								
Derby 10	a						13 39	14 11				14 29		14 39				15 11							15 39
	d				13 16							14 34				15 01						15 12			
Spondon	d																								
Long Eaton	d				13 26							14 44				15a12						15 22			
Attenborough	d				13 34																	15 32			
Beeston	d				13 38					13 51												15 36			
Nottingham 8	a				13 46					13 59		15 01										15 43			

		XC	GW	XC	EM	XC	XC	XC	GW	EM	GW	XC	AW	XC	EM	EM	XC	GW	XC	XC	XC	XC	GW	XC	XC
								R												R	R	R			
		1 ◇	1 ◇	◇	1 ◇	◇		1		1 ◇		1 ◇		◇	1 ◇		◇			1	1	1	1 ◇	◇	◇
				H				G		E				D		B				G		J		D	
		☕	☕		☕			☕		☕		☕			☕					☕	☕	☕	☕		
Cardiff Central 7	d					13 50							14 30				14 50								15 50
Newport (South Wales)	d					14 04							14 45				15 04								16 04
Bristol Temple Meads 10	d	14 00						14 30			14 44	15 00								15 30		16 00			
Bristol Parkway 7	d	14 10						14 40			14 55	15 10						←		15 40		16 10			
Gloucester 7	d		14 37			14 46			15 23		15 51		15 38				15 46	15 51					16 37		16 44
Cheltenham Spa	d	14 42	14a46			14 57		15 12	15a33		→	15 42	15a51				15 57	16 01		16 12		16 42	16a46		16 57
Ashchurch for Tewkesbury	d					15 04												16 09							
Worcester Shrub Hill 7	a																	16 29							
Birmingham New Street 12	a	15 26				15 44		15 51				16 26					16 39			16 57		17 26			17 45
	d	15 30		15 32		15 52	15 55	16 03				16 30		16 34			16 49		16 55		17 03	17 30		17 34	17 49
Water Orton	d																								
Coleshill Parkway	d			15 47			16 09							16 48					17 08					17 47	
Nuneaton	d			16 01			16 25							17 03					17 24					18 03	
Hinckley	d						16 31												17 31						
Narborough	d						16 40												17 40						
South Wigston	d						16 45												17 45						
Leicester	a			16 25			16 52							17 26					17 51					18 25	
Wilnecote	d					16 08											17 07								
Tamworth	d					16 12						16 47					17 11								18 09
Burton-on-Trent	d					16 23						16 58					17 23								18 21
Willington	d																								
Derby 10	a	16 11				16 35		16 39				17 11					17 36				17 39	18 11			18 35
	d					16 45				17 02						17 22	17 40								18 45
Spondon	d																								
Long Eaton	d					16 54				17a13						17 32	17 50								18 54
Attenborough	d					17 01										17 48									19 02
Beeston	d				15 50	17 04									17 45	17 51									19 05
Nottingham 8	a				15 57	17 10									17 51	17 57	18 04								19 11

For general notes see front of timetable
For details of catering facilities see Directory of Train Operators

A From Plymouth (Table 51)
B From Matlock (Table 56)
C From Exeter St Davids (Table 51)
D To Stansted Airport (Table 49)
E From Sheffield (Table 53)
G From Penzance (Table 51)
H To Cambridge (Table 49)
J From Paignton (Table 51)

Table 57

Sundays

until 27 January

Bristol and Cardiff → Birmingham → Leicester, Derby and Nottingham

Network Diagram - see first page of Table 50

		XC	XC	GW	XC	AW	XC	EM	EM	EM	XC	GW	XC	XC	XC	GW	EM	XC	XC	XC	GW	XC	GW	AW	XC
			R 1		1 ◇		◇		1 ◇	1 ◇	◇		R 1	R 1	1 ◇	1 ◇	1 ◇	◇		R 1		1 ◇			◇
			A				B	C	D				A				E			A					G
			☕		☕				☕	☕			☕	☕	☕	☕	☕			☕					
Cardiff Central 7	d					16 30					16 50							17 50						18 30	
Newport (South Wales)	d					16 45					17 04							18 04						18 45	
Bristol Temple Meads 10	d		16 30	16 44	17 00								17 30		18 00					18 30	18 44	19 00			
Bristol Parkway 7	d		16 40	16 55	17 10							←	17 40		18 10					18 40	18 55	19 10			
Gloucester 7	d			17 51		17 38					17 46	17 51				18 38		18 46			19 38		←	19 42	
Cheltenham Spa	d		17 12	→	17 42	17a51					17 57	18 02	18 12		18 42	18a47		18 57		19 12	19 48	19 42	19 48	19a55	
Ashchurch for Tewkesbury	d											18 10									→		19 56		
Worcester Shrub Hill 7	a											18 29											20 14		
Birmingham New Street 12	a		17 51		18 26						18 45		18 57		19 26			19 45		19 51		20 34			
	d	17 55	18 03		18 30		18 34				18 49			19 03	19 30			19 49	19 55	20 03					20 28
Water Orton	d																								
Coleshill Parkway	d	18 09					18 47												20 08						20 42
Nuneaton	d	18 25					19 02												20 25						20 58
Hinckley	d	18 32																	20 32						
Narborough	d	18 41																	20 40						
South Wigston	d	18 46																	20 45						
Leicester	a	18 53					19 24												20 54						21 19
Wilnecote	d																								
Tamworth	d				18 47						19 10				19 47			20 09		20 19					
Burton-on-Trent	d				18 58						19 21				19 58			20 21		20 29					
Willington	d																								
Derby 10	a		18 39		19 11						19 35			19 39	20 11			20 35		20 42					
	d							19 14	19 25		19 41							20 41							
Spondon	d																								
Long Eaton	d							19 24	19a35									20 52							
Attenborough	d							19 30										20 59							
Beeston	d							19 34		19 44							20 43	21 02							
Nottingham 8	a							19 41		19 50	20 00						20 49	21 07							

		EM	EM	XC	XC	GW	XC	XC	XC	EM	XC	GW	GW	XC	XC	AW	GW	XC	XC	XC	EM	AW	GW		
			1 ◇	◇	1 ◇	1 ◇	1 ◇	◇			1 ◇						1 ◇	1 ◇	1 ◇		1 ◇				
		C			A					H	A	J													
			☕		☕	☕					☕						☕				☕				
Cardiff Central 7	d			18 50				19 50								20 30				21 40		22 30			
Newport (South Wales)	d			19 04				20 04								20 45				21 55		22 49			
Bristol Temple Meads 10	d				19 30						20 30		20 44						22 10						
Bristol Parkway 7	d				19 40						20 40		20 55						22 20						
Gloucester 7	d			19 46		20 36		20 46				21 20	21 36		21 46	21a37	22 36			22 44		23a47	23 53		
Cheltenham Spa	d			19 57	20 12	20a45		21 00			21 12	21a30	21a45		21 59		22a45		22 52	22 56			00a04		
Ashchurch for Tewkesbury	d																			23 04					
Worcester Shrub Hill 7	a																			23 21					
Birmingham New Street 12	a			20 45	20 57			21 44			21 51				22 45				23 44						
	d			20 49			21 03		21 53		22 03			22 20				23 13							
Water Orton	d																								
Coleshill Parkway	d								22 07																
Nuneaton	d								22 23																
Hinckley	d								22 31																
Narborough	d								22 39																
South Wigston	d								22 44																
Leicester	a								22 51																
Wilnecote	d													22 36											
Tamworth	d			21 09			21 19							22 40				23 31							
Burton-on-Trent	d			21 21			21 29				22 39			22 53				23 42							
Willington	d																								
Derby 10	a			21 35			21 42				22 50			23 08				23 59							
	d	21 14		21 41						22 39				23 15											
Spondon	d																								
Long Eaton	d	21 26		21 50						22 50				23 24											
Attenborough	d	21 32		21 57						22 57															
Beeston	d	21 36	21 48	22 01						23 00				23 32							23 56				
Nottingham 8	a	21 43	21 54	22 07						23 06				23 40							00 02				

For general notes see front of timetable
For details of catering facilities see Directory of Train Operators

- A From Plymouth (Table 51)
- B To Stansted Airport (Table 49)
- C From Matlock (Table 56)
- D From Sheffield (Table 53)
- E To Sheffield (Table 53)
- G To Cambridge (Table 49)
- H From Crewe (Table 50)
- J From Westbury (Table 123)

Table 57

Bristol and Cardiff → Birmingham → Leicester, Derby and Nottingham

3 February to 23 March

Network Diagram - see first page of Table 50

		EM	EM	XC	XC	EM	XC	XC	XC	XC	EM		XC	EM	XC	XC	XC	GW	GW	EM	XC	XC		XC	XC
		1 ◇	1 ◇		1 ◇	1 ◇			1 ◇		1 ◇				1 ◇		1 ◇		1 ◇	1 ◇				1 ◇	
						A					A			B											
				bus			bus	bus					bus			bus					bus				bus
		☕	☕		☕	☕			☕		☕				☕		☕		☕	☕				☕	
Cardiff Central 7	d																								
Newport (South Wales)	d																								
Bristol Temple Meads 10	d																09 15	09 44							
Bristol Parkway 7	d																09 25	09 55							
Gloucester 7	d																10 00	10 36	10 50						
Cheltenham Spa	d																10 12	10a46	11a00						
Ashchurch for Tewkesbury	d																								
Worcester Shrub Hill 7	a																								
Birmingham New Street 12	a																10 51								
	d				08 30			09 10	09 30	09 53					10 03	10 10						10 55		11 03	11 10
Water Orton	d																								
Coleshill Parkway	d									10 07												11 09			
Nuneaton	d									10 23												11 25			
Hinckley	d									10 31												11 32			
Narborough	d									10 40												11 41			
South Wigston	d									10 46												11 46			
Leicester	a									10 52												11 53			
Wilnecote	d																								
Tamworth	d			08 25			09 25	09 50					10 05			10 50					11 05				11 50
Burton-on-Trent	d			09 00			10 00	10a25					10 40			11a25					11 40				12a25
Willington	d																								
Derby 10	a			09 30	09 42		10 30		10 42				11 10		11 23						12 10			12 23	
	d	07 11	09 12			10 03					11 04			11 15											
Spondon	d																								
Long Eaton	d	07a20	09a22			10a13					11a14			11 25											
Attenborough	d													11 33											
Beeston	d													11 36						11 49					
Nottingham 8 ⛴	a													11 43						11 56					

		XC	XC	XC	EM	XC	XC	EM	XC	AW	XC		XC	XC	XC	GW	XC	XC	XC	EM	XC	XC		XC	XC
			◇		1 ◇				1 ◇						1 ◇	1		1 ◇		1 ◇	◇	◇			
			C		A			B							D						C				
		bus					bus				bus		bus	bus					bus						
					☕				☕						☕			☕		☕					
Cardiff Central 7	d									10 30												11 50			
Newport (South Wales)	d									10 45												12 04			
Bristol Temple Meads 10	d								10 30						11 30										
Bristol Parkway 7	d								10 40						11 40										
Gloucester 7	d									11 44						12 25						12 46			
Cheltenham Spa	d								11 12	11a57					12 12	12a35						12 58			
Ashchurch for Tewkesbury	d																								
Worcester Shrub Hill 7	a																								
Birmingham New Street 12	a								11 51						12 51							13 40			
	d	11 25	11 26	11 55					12 03		12 10			12 45			12 55	13 03	13 10		13 36			13 53	
Water Orton	d																								
Coleshill Parkway	d		11 39	12 09													13 10				13 49			14 06	
Nuneaton	d		11 53	12 25													13 26				14 04			14 23	
Hinckley	d			12 32													13 33							14 30	
Narborough	d			12 41													13 41							14 38	
South Wigston	d			12 46													13 47							14 44	
Leicester	a		12 19	12 52													13 53				14 26			14 50	
Wilnecote	d																								
Tamworth	d	12 06					12 05				12 50		13 05	13 26					13 50						
Burton-on-Trent	d	12 32					12 40				13a25		13 40	13 52					14a25						
Willington	d																								
Derby 10	a	12 57					13 10		13 23				14 10	14 17				14 23							
	d				13 02	13 09		13 16																	14 30
Spondon	d																								
Long Eaton	d				13a12	13 18		13 26																	14 40
Attenborough	d							13 34																	
Beeston	d							13 38												13 51					
Nottingham 8 ⛴	a					13 30		13 46												13 59					14 51

For general notes see front of timetable
For details of catering facilities see Directory of Train Operators

A From Sheffield (Table 53)
B From Matlock (Table 56)
C To Stansted Airport (Table 49)
D From Plymouth (Table 51)

Bristol and Cardiff → Birmingham → Leicester, Derby and Nottingham

Sundays

3 February to 23 March

Network Diagram - see first page of Table 50

		EM	XC	EM	XC	XC	XC	GW	AW	XC	XC	XC	GW	XC	XC	XC	EM	XC	XC	XC	XC	XC	XC
					R							R				R							
		1 ◇			1					◇		1	1 ◇			1	1 ◇			◇	◇		
		A		B	C					D		C								E			
			🚌			🚌								🚌	🚌			🚌	🚌				
		☕			☕							☕	☕			☕	☕						
Cardiff Central 7	d								12 30												13 50		
Newport (South Wales)	d								12 45												14 04		
Bristol Temple Meads 10	d				12 30			12 44				13 30											
Bristol Parkway 7	d				12 40			12 55				13 40											
Gloucester 7	d						13 16	13 36	13 44				14 05								14 46		
Cheltenham Spa	d				13 12		13 27	13 48	13a57			14 12	14a16								14 57		
Ashchurch for Tewkesbury	d							13 56													15 04		
Worcester Shrub Hill 7	a							14 25															
Birmingham New Street 12	a				13 51		14 19					14 57									15 44		
	d				14 03	14 10				14 34	14 55				15 00	15 03			15 10	15 32		15 55	
Water Orton	d																						
Coleshill Parkway	d									14 47	15 08									15 47		16 09	
Nuneaton	d									15 02	15 25									16 01		16 25	
Hinckley	d										15 32											16 31	
Narborough	d										15 40											16 40	
South Wigston	d										15 46											16 45	
Leicester	a									15 23	15 51									16 25		16 52	
Wilnecote	d														15 31			←					
Tamworth	d		14 05			14 50								15 05	15 42			15 42	15 50				
Burton-on-Trent	d		14 40			15a25								15 40	→			16 08	16a25				
Willington	d																						
Derby 10	a		15 10		15 23									16 10		16 23		16 33					
	d	15 01		15 12																			16 45
Spondon	d																						
Long Eaton	d	15a11		15 22																			16 54
Attenborough	d			15 32																			17 01
Beeston	d			15 36													15 50						17 04
Nottingham 8	⛴ a			15 43													15 57						17 10

		EM	XC	XC	EM	EM	XC	GW	AW	XC	XC	XC	XC	GW	XC	XC	XC	XC	XC	XC	XC	XC	XC
							R									R				R			
		1 ◇			1 ◇		1					◇	◇			1				1			◇
		A				B	G					D				G							D
			🚌	🚌						🚌	🚌							🚌	🚌		🚌	🚌	
		☕			☕		☕									☕				☕			
Cardiff Central 7	d								14 30				14 50										
Newport (South Wales)	d								14 45				15 04										
Bristol Temple Meads 10	d						14 30							14 44		15 30							
Bristol Parkway 7	d						14 40							14 55		15 40							
Gloucester 7	d							15 23	15 38				15 46	15 51									
Cheltenham Spa	d						15 12	15a33	15a51				15 57	16 01		16 12							
Ashchurch for Tewkesbury	d													16 09									
Worcester Shrub Hill 7	a													16 29									
Birmingham New Street 12	a						15 51						16 39			16 57							
	d			16 00			16 03				16 10	16 34			16 55				17 00	17 03		17 10	17 34
Water Orton	d																						
Coleshill Parkway	d											16 48			17 08								17 47
Nuneaton	d											17 03			17 24								18 03
Hinckley	d														17 31								
Narborough	d														17 40								
South Wigston	d														17 45								
Leicester	a											17 26			17 51								18 25
Wilnecote	d			16 31						←											←		
Tamworth	d		16 05	16 42						16 42	16 50							17 05	17 42		17 42	17 50	
Burton-on-Trent	d		16 40	→						17 08	17a25							17 40	→		18 08	18a25	
Willington	d																						
Derby 10	a		17 10				17 23			17 33								18 10		18 20	18 33		
	d	17 02				17 22											17 44						
Spondon	d																						
Long Eaton	d	17a13				17 32											17 54						
Attenborough	d					17 48																	
Beeston	d				17 45	17 51																	
Nottingham 8	⛴ a				17 51	17 57											18 07						

For general notes see front of timetable
For details of catering facilities see Directory of Train Operators

- A From Sheffield (Table 53)
- B From Matlock (Table 56)
- C From Plymouth (Table 51)
- D To Stansted Airport (Table 49)
- E To Cambridge (Table 49)
- G From Penzance (Table 51)

Table 57

Bristol and Cardiff → Birmingham → Leicester, Derby and Nottingham

3 February to 23 March

Network Diagram - see first page of Table 50

		XC	GW	XC	XC	XC	XC	EM	XC	AW	EM		XC	XC	XC	XC	GW	XC	EM	XC	XC	XC		XC	XC
		◇	1 ◇						R 1		1 ◇				◇	◇		R 1	1 ◇					R 1	
								A	B		C				D			E							
			☕			🚌	🚌		☕		☕		🚌	🚌				☕	☕		🚌	🚌		☕	🚌
Cardiff Central 7	d	15 50								16 30						16 50									
Newport (South Wales)	d	16 04								16 45						17 04									
Bristol Temple Meads 10	d								16 30								16 44	17 30							
Bristol Parkway 7	d								16 40								16 55	17 40							
Gloucester 7	d	16 46	16 55							17 38						17 46	17 51								
Cheltenham Spa	d	16 57	17a05						17 12	17a51						17 57	18 02	18 12							
Ashchurch for Tewkesbury	d																18 10								
Worcester Shrub Hill 7	a																18 29								
Birmingham New Street 12	a	17 45							17 51							18 45		18 57							
	d			17 55			18 00		18 03					18 10	18 34							19 00		19 03	
Water Orton	d																								
Coleshill Parkway	d			18 09											18 47										
Nuneaton	d			18 25											19 02										
Hinckley	d			18 32																					
Narborough	d			18 41																					
South Wigston	d			18 46																					
Leicester	a			18 53											19 24										
Wilnecote	d												←												←
Tamworth	d					18 05	18 42						18 42	18 50							19 05	19 42			19 42
Burton-on-Trent	d					18 40	→						19 08	19a25							19 40	→			20 08
Willington	d																								
Derby 10	a					19 10			19 23				19 33								20 10			20 16	20 33
	d				18 45			19 14			19 25									19 45					
Spondon	d																								
Long Eaton	d				18 54			19 24			19a35														
Attenborough	d				19 02			19 30																	
Beeston	d				19 05			19 34											19 44						
Nottingham 8 ⛴	a				19 11			19 41											19 50	20 04					

		XC	XC	XC	EM	XC	XC	XC	EM	XC	GW		AW	XC	XC	XC	XC	GW	XC	EM	XC	XC		XC	XC
			◇		1 ◇					R 1						◇	◇	1 ◇	1 ◇	1 ◇				1 ◇	
					G				A	E						H			E						
		🚌			☕		🚌	🚌		☕				🚌	🚌			☕	☕	☕		🚌			🚌
Cardiff Central 7	d		17 50										18 30				18 50								
Newport (South Wales)	d		18 04										18 45				19 04								
Bristol Temple Meads 10	d									18 30	18 44								19 30						
Bristol Parkway 7	d									18 40	18 55								19 40						
Gloucester 7	d		18 46								19 38		19 42				19 46	19 55							
Cheltenham Spa	d		18 57							19 12	19 48		19a55				19 57	20a06	20 12						
Ashchurch for Tewkesbury	d										19 56														
Worcester Shrub Hill 7	a										20 14														
Birmingham New Street 12	a		19 45							19 51							20 45		20 57						
	d	19 10		19 55				20 00		20 03					20 10	20 28								21 03	21 10
Water Orton	d																								
Coleshill Parkway	d			20 08												20 42									
Nuneaton	d			20 25												20 58									
Hinckley	d			20 32																					
Narborough	d			20 40																					
South Wigston	d			20 45																					
Leicester	a			20 54												21 19									
Wilnecote	d													←											
Tamworth	d	19 50					20 05	20 42						20 42	20 50							20 55			21 50
Burton-on-Trent	d	20a25					20 40	→						21 08	21a25							21 30			22a25
Willington	d																								
Derby 10	a						21 10			21 22				21 33								22 00		22 13	
	d					20 45			21 14												21 45				
Spondon	d																								
Long Eaton	d					20 54			21 26												21 54				
Attenborough	d					21 01			21 32												22 01				
Beeston	d				20 43	21 04			21 36											21 48	22 05				
Nottingham 8 ⛴	a				20 49	21 10			21 43											21 54	22 11				

For general notes see front of timetable
For details of catering facilities see Directory of Train Operators

A From Matlock (Table 56)
B From Penzance (Table 51)
C From Sheffield (Table 53)
D To Stansted Airport (Table 49)
E From Plymouth (Table 51)
G To Sheffield (Table 53)
H To Cambridge (Table 49)

Table 57

Sundays

3 February to 23 March

Bristol and Cardiff → Birmingham → Leicester, Derby and Nottingham

Network Diagram - see first page of Table 50

		XC	XC	XC	XC	GW	GW	XC	XC	XC	EM		EM	XC	XC	AW	XC	XC	XC	XC	GW	AW	GW		
			◇		1◇						1◇								1◇		1◇				
					A	B							C												
		🚌						🚌	🚌		☕		🚌	🚌			🚌	🚌			☕				
Cardiff Central 7	d		19 50													20 30				21 40		22 30			
Newport (South Wales)	d		20 04													20 45				21 55		22 49			
Bristol Temple Meads 10	d				20 30		20 44												22 10						
Bristol Parkway 7	d				20 40		20 55												22 20						
Gloucester 7	d		20 46			21 20	21 36								21 46	21a37				22 44	23 00	23a47	23 53		
Cheltenham Spa	d		20 57		21 12	21a30	21a45								21 59				22 52	22 56	23a10		00a04		
Ashchurch for Tewkesbury	d																			23 04					
Worcester Shrub Hill 7	a																			23 21					
Birmingham New Street 12	a		21 44		21 55										22 45				23 44						
	d	21 30		21 53					22 10					22 20				23 25							
Water Orton	d																								
Coleshill Parkway	d			22 07																					
Nuneaton	d			22 23																					
Hinckley	d			22 31																					
Narborough	d			22 39																					
South Wigston	d			22 44																					
Leicester	a			22 51																					
Wilnecote	d	22 01												22 51											
Tamworth	d	22 12						22 05	22 50					23 02			23 05	00a05							
Burton-on-Trent	d	22 38						22 40	23a25					23 28			23 40								
Willington	d																								
Derby 10	a	23 03						23 10						23s53			00 10								
	d									23 15			23 34												
Spondon	d																								
Long Eaton	d									23 24			00 04	00s23											
Attenborough	d												00 15												
Beeston	d									23 32	23 56		00 25	00s35											
Nottingham 8	a									23 40	00 02		00 45	00 55											

Sundays

from 30 March

		XC	XC	EM	XC	EM	XC	XC	XC	EM	EM	EM		XC	XC	XC	GW	EM	XC	EM	XC	XC	XC	EM	XC
				1◇	1◇	1◇	1◇		1◇	1◇	1◇	1◇			1◇	1◇			1◇	1◇	1◇		1◇	1◇	
										D								E		D					
		🚌	🚌					🚌						🚌								🚌			
				☕	☕	☕	☕		☕	☕	☕	☕			☕	☕			☕	☕	☕		☕	☕	
Cardiff Central 7	d																								
Newport (South Wales)	d																								
Bristol Temple Meads 10	d															09 15	09 44						10 30		
Bristol Parkway 7	d															09 25	09 55						10 40		
Gloucester 7	d															10 00	10 36								
Cheltenham Spa	d															10 12	10a46						11 12		
Ashchurch for Tewkesbury	d																								
Worcester Shrub Hill 7	a																								
Birmingham New Street 12	a															10 51							11 51		
	d	22p04	22p04		09 03		09 30	09 43	10 03					10 25	10 30				11 03		11 30		12 03		12 12
Water Orton	d																								
Coleshill Parkway	d	22p35	22p35					10 14						10 56											
Nuneaton	d	23p11	23p11					10 37						11 19								11 37			
Hinckley	d	23p30	23p30					10 56														11 56			
Narborough	d	23p54	23p54					11 20														12 20			
South Wigston	d	00 05	00 05					11 31														12 31			
Leicester	a	00 20	00 20					11 46						11 59								12 46			
Wilnecote	d																								
Tamworth	d				09 19		09 47		10 19						10 47						11 47				12 33
Burton-on-Trent	d				09 29		09 58		10 29						10 58						11 58				12 46
Willington	d																								
Derby 10	a				09 42		10 11		10 42						11 11				11 39		12 11		12 39		13 00
	d			07 50		09 51				10 44		10 51						11 15		11 49					13 06
Spondon	d																								
Long Eaton	d			07a59		10a01				10a54								11 25		11a59					13 18
Attenborough	d																	11 33							
Beeston	d										10 59							11 36						13 12	
Nottingham 8	a										11 07	11 11						11 43						13 20	13 30

For general notes see front of timetable
For details of catering facilities see Directory of Train Operators

A From Plymouth (Table 51)
B From Westbury (Table 123)
C From Stoke-on-Trent (Table 50)
D From Sheffield (Table 53)
E From Matlock (Table 56)

Sundays

from 30 March

Bristol and Cardiff → Birmingham → Leicester, Derby and Nottingham

Network Diagram - see first page of Table 50

		XC		XC	XC	AW	XC	EM	XC	EM	XC	XC	XC	XC		XC	XC	EM	XC	XC	GW	XC	GW	AW	XC
																R									R
					1 ◇		1 ◇		1 ◇	1 ◇			1 ◇	◇		1		1 ◇				1 ◇			1
							A	B		C			D			A									E
		🚌		🚌							🚌	🚌							🚌	🚌					
					☕		☕		☕	☕			☕			☕		☕				☕			☕
Cardiff Central 7	d					10 30								11 50										12 30	
Newport (South Wales)	d					10 45								12 04										12 45	
Bristol Temple Meads 10	d				11 00		11 30						12 00			12 30					12 44	13 00			13 30
Bristol Parkway 7	d				11 10		11 40						12 10			12 40					12 55	13 10	←		13 40
Gloucester 7	d					11 44								12 46			13 16				13 39 →		13 39	13 44	
Cheltenham Spa	d				11 42	11a57	12 12						12 42	12 58		13 12	13 27					13 42	13 50	13a57	14 12
Ashchurch for Tewkesbury	d																						13 58		
Worcester Shrub Hill 7	a																						14 25		
Birmingham New Street 12	a				12 26		12 51						13 26	13 40		13 51	14 19					14 26			14 57
	d			12 25	12 30				13 03			13 25	13 30	13 49		14 03				14 25		14 30			
Water Orton	d																								
Coleshill Parkway	d			12 56								13 56								14 56					
Nuneaton	d	12 37		13 19							13 37	14 19							14 37	15 19					
Hinckley	d	12 56									13 56								14 56						
Narborough	d	13 20									14 20								15 20						
South Wigston	d	13 31									14 31								15 31						
Leicester	a	13 46		13 59							14 46	14 59							15 46	15 59					
Wilnecote	d																								
Tamworth	d				12 47									14 06								14 47			
Burton-on-Trent	d				12 58									14 18								14 58			
Willington	d																								
Derby 10	a				13 11				13 39				14 11	14 29		14 39						15 11			
	d							13 16		13 46				14 34											
Spondon	d																								
Long Eaton	d							13 26		13a56				14 44											
Attenborough	d							13 34																	
Beeston	d							13 38										15 05							
Nottingham 8 ⛴	a							13 46						15 02				15 12							

		EM	XC	EM		XC	XC	XC	XC	XC	EM	XC	XC	GW	XC	AW		EM	XC	GW	XC	XC	EM	XC	XC
			R							R											R	R			
			1	1 ◇				1 ◇	◇	1	1 ◇				1 ◇				◇		1	1	1 ◇		
		B		C						E								B			E		C		
						🚌	🚌					🚌	🚌											🚌	🚌
			☕	☕				☕		☕	☕				☕						☕	☕	☕		
Cardiff Central 7	d								13 50							14 30			14 50						
Newport (South Wales)	d								14 04							14 45			15 04						
Bristol Temple Meads 10	d							14 00		14 30				14 44	15 00						15 30				
Bristol Parkway 7	d							14 10		14 40				14 55	15 10					←	15 40				
Gloucester 7	d								14 46					15 51 →		15 38			15 46	15 51					
Cheltenham Spa	d							14 42	14 57	15 12					15 42	15a51			15 57	16 01	16 12				
Ashchurch for Tewkesbury	d								15 04											16 09					
Worcester Shrub Hill 7	a																			16 29					
Birmingham New Street 12	a							15 26	15 44	15 51					16 26				16 39		16 57				
	d		15 03				15 25	15 30	15 52	16 03			16 25		16 30				16 49			17 03			17 25
Water Orton	d																								
Coleshill Parkway	d						15 56						16 56												17 56
Nuneaton	d					15 37	16 19					16 37	17 19											17 37	18 19
Hinckley	d					15 56						16 56												17 56	
Narborough	d					16 20						17 20												18 20	
South Wigston	d					16 31						17 31												18 31	
Leicester	a					16 46	16 59					17 46	17 59											18 46	18 59
Wilnecote	d								16 08										17 07						
Tamworth	d								16 12						16 47				17 11						
Burton-on-Trent	d								16 23						16 58				17 23						
Willington	d																								
Derby 10	a		15 39					16 11	16 35	16 39					17 11				17 36			17 39			
	d	15 12		15 50					16 45									17 22	17 40				17 44		
Spondon	d																								
Long Eaton	d	15 22		16a02					16 54									17 32	17 50				17a55		
Attenborough	d	15 32							17 01									17 48							
Beeston	d	15 36							17 04		17 10							17 51							
Nottingham 8 ⛴	a	15 43							17 10		17 17							17 57	18 04						

For general notes see front of timetable
For details of catering facilities see Directory of Train Operators

A From Plymouth (Table 51)
B From Matlock (Table 56)
C From Sheffield (Table 53)
D From Exeter St Davids (Table 51)
E From Penzance (Table 51)

Table 57

Sundays
from 30 March

Bristol and Cardiff → Birmingham → Leicester, Derby and Nottingham

Network Diagram - see first page of Table 50

		XC	XC	XC	GW	XC		AW	EM	XC	EM	XC	GW	XC	XC	EM	EM	XC		XC	EM	XC	XC	GW	XC
		[R] [1] A (cafe)	◇	[R] [1] B (cafe)		[1] ◇ (cafe)			[1] ◇ (cafe)	(bus)	C	◇		[R] [1] B (cafe)	[R] [1] (cafe)	[1] ◇ D (cafe)	[1] ◇ E (cafe)	(bus)		[1] ◇ (cafe)	[1] ◇ (cafe)	◇	[R] [1] B (cafe)		[1] ◇
Cardiff Central [7]	d		15 50					16 30				16 50										17 50			
Newport (South Wales)	d		16 04					16 45				17 04										18 04			
Bristol Temple Meads [10]	d	16 00		16 30	16 44	17 00								17 30						18 00			18 30	18 44	19 00
Bristol Parkway [7]	d	16 10		16 40	16 55	17 10							←	17 40						18 10			18 40	18 55	19 10
Gloucester [7]	d		16 44		17 51			17 38				17 46	17 51									18 46		19 39	
Cheltenham Spa	d	16 42	16 57	17 12	→	17 42		17a51				17 57	18 02	18 12						18 42		18 57	19 12	→	19 42
Ashchurch for Tewkesbury	d												18 10												
Worcester Shrub Hill [7]	a												18 29												
Birmingham New Street [12]	a	17 26	17 45	17 51		18 26						18 45		18 57						19 26		19 45	19 51		20 34
	d	17 30	17 49	18 03		18 30						18 49			19 03			19 25		19 30		19 49	20 03		
Water Orton	d																								
Coleshill Parkway	d																	19 56							
Nuneaton	d									18 37								20 19							
Hinckley	d									18 56															
Narborough	d									19 20															
South Wigston	d									19 31															
Leicester	a									19 46								20 59							
Wilnecote	d																								
Tamworth	d		18 09			18 47						19 10								19 47		20 09	20 19		
Burton-on-Trent	d		18 21			18 58						19 21								19 58		20 21	20 29		
Willington	d																								
Derby [10]	a	18 11	18 35	18 39		19 11						19 35			19 39					20 11		20 35	20 42		
	d		18 45								19 14	19 41					20 02					20 41			
Spondon	d																								
Long Eaton	d		18 54								19 24						20a12					20 52			
Attenborough	d		19 02								19 30											20 59			
Beeston	d		19 05						19 09		19 34					20 00					20 57	21 02			
Nottingham [8] (train)	a		19 11						19 15		19 41	20 00				20 05					21 03	21 07			

		GW	AW	XC	EM	XC	XC	XC		XC	XC	EM	XC	GW	AW	EM	XC	XC	XC	XC	XC	XC	AW		
				(bus)	C	◇	[1] ◇ B (cafe)	[1] ◇		(bus)	◇	G	[1] ◇ B (cafe)			[1] ◇ (cafe)		(bus)		[1] ◇	[1] ◇				
Cardiff Central [7]	d		18 30			18 50					19 50				20 30							21 40	22 30		
Newport (South Wales)	d		18 45			19 04					20 04				20 45							21 55	22 49		
Bristol Temple Meads [10]	d						19 30						20 30	20 44							22 10				
Bristol Parkway [7]	d	←					19 40						20 40	20 55							22 20				
Gloucester [7]	d	19 39	19 42			19 46					20 46			21 39	21a37				21 45			22 44	23a47		
Cheltenham Spa	d	19 48	19a56			19 57	20 12				21 00		21 12	21a47					21 57		22 52	22 56			
Ashchurch for Tewkesbury	d	19 56																				23 04			
Worcester Shrub Hill [7]	a	20 14																				23 21			
Birmingham New Street [12]	a					20 45	20 57				21 44		21 51						22 45		23 44				
	d					20 49		21 03		21 25			22 03				22 20			23 13					
Water Orton	d																								
Coleshill Parkway	d									21 56															
Nuneaton	d			20 37						22 19								22 37							
Hinckley	d			20 56														22 56							
Narborough	d			21 20														23 20							
South Wigston	d			21 31														23 31							
Leicester	a			21 46						22 59								23 46							
Wilnecote	d																22 36								
Tamworth	d					21 09		21 19					22 27				22 40			23 31					
Burton-on-Trent	d					21 21		21 29					22 38				22 53			23 42					
Willington	d																								
Derby [10]	a					21 35		21 42					22 50				23 08			23 59					
	d				21 14	21 41						22 40					23 15								
Spondon	d																								
Long Eaton	d				21 26	21 50						22 50					23 24								
Attenborough	d				21 32	21 57						22 57													
Beeston	d				21 36	22 01						23 00				23 06	23 32								
Nottingham [8] (train)	a				21 43	22 07						23 06				23 11	23 40								

For general notes see front of timetable
For details of catering facilities see Directory of Train Operators

- **A** From Paignton (Table 51)
- **B** From Plymouth (Table 51)
- **C** From Matlock (Table 56)
- **D** To Sheffield (Table 53)
- **E** From Sheffield (Table 53)
- **G** From Blythe Bridge (Table 50)

Network Diagram for Tables 59, 60, 61, 62, 64, 66

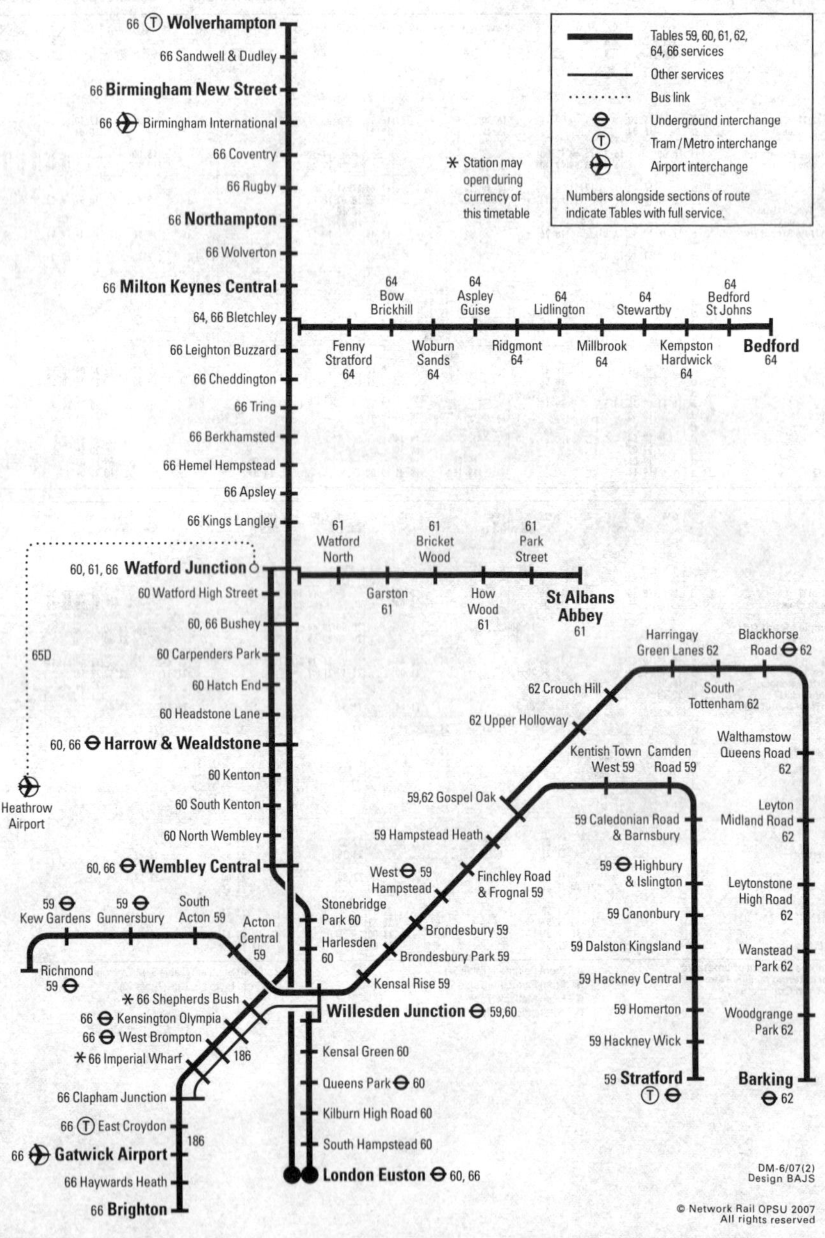

Tables 59, 60, 61, 62, 64, 66 services
Other services
Bus link
Underground interchange
Tram / Metro interchange
Airport interchange
Numbers alongside sections of route indicate Tables with full service.
* Station may open during currency of this timetable
66 Wolverhampton
66 Sandwell & Dudley
66 Birmingham New Street
66 Birmingham International
66 Coventry
66 Rugby
66 Northampton
66 Wolverton
66 Milton Keynes Central
64, 66 Bletchley
66 Leighton Buzzard
66 Cheddington
66 Tring
66 Berkhamsted
66 Hemel Hempstead
66 Apsley
66 Kings Langley
60, 61, 66 Watford Junction
60 Watford High Street
60, 66 Bushey
60 Carpenders Park
60 Hatch End
60 Headstone Lane
60, 66 Harrow & Wealdstone
60 Kenton
60 South Kenton
60 North Wembley
60, 66 Wembley Central
Stonebridge Park 60
Harlesden 60
Willesden Junction 59,60
Kensal Green 60
Queens Park 60
Kilburn High Road 60
South Hampstead 60
London Euston 60, 66
64 Bow Brickhill
64 Aspley Guise
64 Lidlington
64 Stewartby
64 Bedford St Johns
Fenny Stratford 64
Woburn Sands 64
Ridgmont 64
Millbrook 64
Kempston Hardwick 64
Bedford 64
61 Watford North
61 Bricket Wood
61 Park Street
Garston 61
How Wood 61
St Albans Abbey 61
65D
Heathrow Airport
59 Kew Gardens
59 Gunnersbury
South Acton 59
Acton Central 59
Richmond 59
* 66 Shepherds Bush
66 Kensington Olympia
66 West Brompton
* 66 Imperial Wharf
186
66 Clapham Junction
66 East Croydon
186
66 Gatwick Airport
66 Haywards Heath
66 Brighton
Harringay Green Lanes 62
Blackhorse Road 62
62 Crouch Hill
South Tottenham 62
62 Upper Holloway
Kentish Town West 59
Camden Road 59
59,62 Gospel Oak
59 Hampstead Heath
West Hampstead 59
Finchley Road & Frognal 59
Brondesbury 59
Brondesbury Park 59
Kensal Rise 59
59 Caledonian Road & Barnsbury
59 Highbury & Islington
59 Canonbury
59 Dalston Kingsland
59 Hackney Central
59 Homerton
59 Hackney Wick
59 Stratford
Walthamstow Queens Road 62
Leyton Midland Road 62
Leytonstone High Road 62
Wanstead Park 62
Woodgrange Park 62
Barking 62
DM-6/07(2)
Design BAJS

North Woolwich → Silvertown & City Airport, Stratford, Highbury, West Hampstead, Willesden Junction and Richmond.

Network diagram - see first page of Table 59

Miles	Station		LO	LO	LO	LO	LO	LO	LO	LO A	LO	LO	LO	LO	LO	LO	LO A	LO	LO	LO	LO	LO
0	**Stratford Low Level** 7 ⊖	d			06 07	06 22	06 37	06 52	07 07	07 12	07 22	07 37	07 52	07 59	08 06	08 22	08 30	08 37	08 52	09 03	09 07	09 22
1	Hackney Wick	d			06 11	06 26	06 41	06 56	07 10	07 16	07 26	07 41	07 56	08 03	08 11	08 26	08 34	08 41	08 56	09 07	09 11	09 26
1¾	Homerton	d			06 13	06 28	06 43	06 58	07 13	07 18	07 28	07 43	07 58	08 05	08 13	08 28	08 36	08 43	08 58	09 09	09 13	09 28
2½	Hackney Central	d			06 15	06 30	06 45	07 00	07 15	07 20	07 30	07 45	08 00	08 07	08 15	08 30	08 38	08 45	09 00	09 11	09 15	09 30
3¼	Dalston Kingsland	d			06 18	06 33	06 48	07 03	07 17	07 23	07 33	07 48	08 03	08 10	08 18	08 33	08 41	08 48	09 03	09 14	09 18	09 33
4¼	Canonbury	d			06 20	06 35	06 50	07 05	07 20	07 25	07 35	07 50	08 05	08 12	08 20	08 35	08 43	08 50	09 05	09 16	09 20	09 35
4¾	**Highbury & Islington** ⊖	d			06 23	06 38	06 53	07 08	07 23	07 28	07 38	07 53	08 08	08 15	08 23	08 38	08 46	08 53	09 08	09 19	09 23	09 38
5¼	Caledonian Rd & Barnsbury	d			06 25	06 40	06 55	07 10	07 25	07 30	07 40	07 55	08 10	08 17	08 25	08 40	08 49	08 55	09 10	09 22	09 25	09 40
6¼	Camden Road	d			06 29	06 44	06 59	07 14	07 28	07 34	07 44	07 59	08 14	08a22	08 29	08 44	08 52	08 59	09 14	09 25	09 29	09 44
6½	Kentish Town West	d			06 31	06 46	07 01	07 16	07 30	07 36	07 46	08 01	08 16		08 31	08 46	08 54	09 01	09 16	09 27	09 31	09 46
7½	**Gospel Oak**	d			06 34	06 49	07 04	07 19	07 33	07 39	07 49	08 04	08 19		08 34	08 49	08 57	09 04	09 19	09 31	09 34	09 49
8	Hampstead Heath	d			06 35	06 51	07 06	07 21	07 35	07 41	07 51	08 06	08 21		08 36	08 51	08 59	09 06	09 20	09 33	09 36	09 50
9	Finchley Road & Frognal	d			06 38	06 53	07 08	07 23	07 37	07 43	07 53	08 08	08 23		08 38	08 53	09 01	09 08	09 23	09 36	09 38	09 53
9½	West Hampstead ⊖	d			06 39	06 55	07 10	07 25	07 39	07 45	07 55	08 10	08 25		08 40	08 55	09 03	09 10	09 24	09 37	09 40	09 54
10	Brondesbury	d			06 41	06 56	07 11	07 26	07 40	07 46	07 56	08 11	08 26		08 41	08 56	09 04	09 11	09 26	09 39	09 41	09 56
10¼	Brondesbury Park	d			06 42	06 58	07 13	07 28	07 42	07 48	07 58	08 13	08 28		08 43	08 58	09 06	09 13	09 27	09 40	09 43	09 57
11	Kensal Rise	d			06 44	07 00	07 15	07 30	07 44	07 50	08 00	08 15	08 30		08 45	09 00	09 08	09 15	09 29	09 42	09 45	09 59
12	**Willesden Jn. High Level** ⊖	a			06 47	07 03	07 18	07 33	07 47	07 53	08 03	08 18	08 33		08 49	09 03	09 09	09 18	09 33	09 45	09 49	10 02
—		d	06 19	06 32	06 48	07 04	07 19	07 34	07 48		08 04	08 19	08 34		08 49	09 04		09 19	09 33	09 46	09 49	10 03
13½	Acton Central	d	06 24	06 37	06 53	07 09	07 24	07 39	07 53		08 09	08 24	08 39		08 54	09 09		09 24	09 39	09 51	09 54	10 08
14½	South Acton	d	06 28	06 41	06 57	07 13	07 28	07 43	07 57		08 13	08 28	08 43		08 58	09 13		09 28	09 42	09 55	09 58	10 12
15¼	Gunnersbury ⊖	d	06 30	06 43	07 00	07 15	07 30	07 45	07 59		08 15	08 30	08 45		09 00	09 15		09 30	09 45	09 58	10 00	10 15
16¼	Kew Gardens ⊖	d	06 33	06 46	07 02	07 18	07 33	07 48	08 02		08 18	08 33	08 48		09 03	09 18		09 33	09 47	10 01	10 03	10 17
17½	**Richmond** ⊖	a	06 38	06 51	07 08	07 23	07 38	07 53	08 07		08 23	08 38	08 53		09 10	09 23		09 38	09 54	10 07	10 12	10 23

Station		LO	LO	LO	LO	LO	LO	LO	LO	LO	LO	LO	LO	LO	LO	LO	LO	LO	LO	LO	LO
Stratford Low Level 7 ⊖	d	09 31	09 37	09 52	10 07	10 22	10 37	10 52	11 07	11 22	11 37	11 52	12 07	12 22	12 37	12 52	13 07	13 22	13 37	13 52	14 07
Hackney Wick	d	09 34	09 41	09 56	10 11	10 26	10 41	10 56	11 11	11 26	11 41	11 56	12 11	12 26	12 41	12 56	13 11	13 26	13 41	13 56	14 11
Homerton	d	09 37	09 43	09 58	10 13	10 28	10 43	10 58	11 13	11 28	11 43	11 58	12 13	12 28	12 43	12 58	13 13	13 28	13 43	13 58	14 13
Hackney Central	d	09 39	09 45	10 00	10 15	10 30	10 45	11 00	11 15	11 30	11 45	12 00	12 15	12 30	12 45	13 00	13 15	13 30	13 45	14 00	14 15
Dalston Kingsland	d	09 41	09 48	10 03	10 18	10 33	10 48	11 03	11 18	11 33	11 48	12 03	12 18	12 33	12 48	13 03	13 18	13 33	13 48	14 03	14 18
Canonbury	d	09 44	09 50	10 05	10 20	10 35	10 50	11 05	11 20	11 35	11 50	12 05	12 20	12 35	12 50	13 05	13 20	13 35	13 50	14 05	14 20
Highbury & Islington ⊖	d	09 46	09 53	10 08	10 23	10 38	10 53	11 08	11 23	11 38	11 53	12 08	12 23	12 38	12 53	13 08	13 23	13 38	13 53	14 08	14 23
Caledonian Rd & Barnsbury	d	09 48	09 55	10 10	10 25	10 40	10 55	11 10	11 25	11 40	11 55	12 10	12 25	12 40	12 55	13 10	13 25	13 40	13 55	14 10	14 25
Camden Road	d	09a53	09 59	10 14	10 29	10 44	10 59	11 14	11 29	11 44	11 59	12 14	12 29	12 44	12 59	13 14	13 29	13 44	13 59	14 14	14 29
Kentish Town West	d		10 01	10 16	10 31	10 46	11 01	11 16	11 31	11 46	12 01	12 16	12 31	12 46	13 01	13 16	13 31	13 46	14 01	14 16	14 31
Gospel Oak	d		10 04	10 19	10 34	10 49	11 04	11 19	11 34	11 49	12 04	12 19	12 34	12 49	13 04	13 19	13 34	13 49	14 04	14 19	14 34
Hampstead Heath	d		10 06	10 20	10 36	10 50	11 06	11 20	11 36	11 50	12 06	12 20	12 36	12 50	13 06	13 20	13 36	13 50	14 06	14 20	14 36
Finchley Road & Frognal	d		10 08	10 23	10 38	10 53	11 08	11 23	11 38	11 53	12 08	12 23	12 38	12 53	13 08	13 23	13 38	13 53	14 08	14 23	14 38
West Hampstead ⊖	d		10 10	10 24	10 40	10 54	11 10	11 24	11 40	11 54	12 10	12 24	12 40	12 54	13 10	13 24	13 40	13 54	14 10	14 24	14 40
Brondesbury	d		10 11	10 26	10 41	10 56	11 11	11 26	11 41	11 56	12 11	12 26	12 41	12 56	13 11	13 26	13 41	13 56	14 11	14 26	14 41
Brondesbury Park	d		10 13	10 27	10 43	10 57	11 13	11 27	11 43	11 57	12 13	12 27	12 43	12 57	13 13	13 27	13 43	13 57	14 13	14 27	14 43
Kensal Rise	d		10 15	10 29	10 45	10 59	11 15	11 29	11 45	11 59	12 15	12 29	12 45	12 59	13 15	13 29	13 45	13 59	14 15	14 29	14 45
Willesden Jn. High Level ⊖	a		10 19	10 32	10 48	11 02	11 18	11 32	11 48	12 02	12 18	12 33	12 48	13 02	13 18	13 32	13 48	14 02	14 18	14 32	14 49
	d		10 19	10 33	10 49	11 03	11 19	11 33	11 49	12 03	12 19	12 33	12 49	13 03	13 19	13 33	13 49	14 03	14 19	14 33	14 49
Acton Central	d		10 24	10 38	10 54	11 08	11 24	11 38	11 54	12 08	12 24	12 38	12 54	13 08	13 24	13 38	13 54	14 08	14 24	14 38	14 54
South Acton	d		10 28	10 42	10 58	11 12	11 28	11 42	11 58	12 12	12 28	12 42	12 58	13 12	13 28	13 42	13 58	14 12	14 28	14 42	14 58
Gunnersbury ⊖	d		10 30	10 45	11 02	11 15	11 32	11 45	12 02	12 15	12 32	12 45	13 02	13 15	13 32	13 45	14 02	14 15	14 32	14 45	15 00
Kew Gardens ⊖	d		10 33	10 47	11 05	11 17	11 35	11 47	12 05	12 17	12 35	12 47	13 05	13 17	13 35	13 47	14 05	14 17	14 35	14 47	15 03
Richmond ⊖	a		10 41	10 53	11 10	11 23	11 40	11 53	12 10	12 23	12 40	12 54	13 10	13 23	13 40	13 53	14 10	14 23	14 40	14 53	15 10

Station		LO	LO	LO	LO	LO	LO	LO	LO	LO	LO	LO	LO	LO A	LO	LO	LO	LO	LO	LO	LO	LO
Stratford Low Level 7 ⊖	d	14 22	14 37	14 52	15 07	15 22	15 37	15 52	16 07	16 22	16 37	16 52	17 07	17 13	17 22	17 37	17 44	17 52	18 07	18 22	18 31	18 36
Hackney Wick	d	14 26	14 41	14 56	15 11	15 26	15 41	15 56	16 11	16 26	16 41	16 56	17 11	17 17	17 26	17 41	17 48	17 56	18 11	18 26	18 35	18 41
Homerton	d	14 28	14 43	14 58	15 13	15 28	15 43	15 58	16 13	16 28	16 43	16 58	17 13	17 19	17 28	17 43	17 50	17 58	18 13	18 28	18 37	18 43
Hackney Central	d	14 30	14 45	15 00	15 15	15 30	15 45	16 00	16 15	16 30	16 45	17 00	17 15	17 21	17 30	17 45	17 52	18 00	18 15	18 30	18 39	18 45
Dalston Kingsland	d	14 33	14 48	15 03	15 18	15 33	15 48	16 03	16 18	16 33	16 48	17 03	17 18	17 24	17 33	17 48	17 55	18 03	18 18	18 33	18 42	18 48
Canonbury	d	14 35	14 50	15 05	15 20	15 35	15 50	16 05	16 20	16 35	16 50	17 05	17 20	17 26	17 35	17 50	17 57	18 05	18 20	18 35	18 44	18 50
Highbury & Islington ⊖	d	14 38	14 53	15 08	15 23	15 38	15 53	16 08	16 23	16 38	16 53	17 08	17 23	17 29	17 38	17 53	18 00	18 08	18 23	18 38	18 47	18 53
Caledonian Rd & Barnsbury	d	14 40	14 55	15 10	15 25	15 40	15 55	16 10	16 25	16 40	16 55	17 10	17 25	17 31	17 40	17 55	18 02	18 10	18 25	18 40	18 49	18 55
Camden Road	d	14 44	14 59	15 14	15 29	15 44	15 59	16 14	16 29	16 44	16 59	17 14	17 29	17 35	17 44	17 59	18a07	18 14	18 29	18 43	18a54	18 59
Kentish Town West	d	14 46	15 01	15 16	15 31	15 46	16 01	16 16	16 31	16 46	17 01	17 16	17 31	17 37	17 46	18 01		18 16	18 31	18 45		19 01
Gospel Oak	d	14 49	15 04	15 19	15 34	15 49	16 04	16 19	16 34	16 49	17 04	17 19	17 34	17 40	17 49	18 04		18 19	18 34	18 48		19 04
Hampstead Heath	d	14 50	15 06	15 20	15 35	15 51	16 06	16 21	16 36	16 51	17 06	17 21	17 36	17 42	17 50	18 05		18 22	18 36	18 50		19 06
Finchley Road & Frognal	d	14 53	15 08	15 23	15 38	15 54	16 08	16 23	16 38	16 54	17 08	17 23	17 38	17 45	17 53	18 08		18 25	18 38	18 52		19 08
West Hampstead ⊖	d	14 54	15 10	15 24	15 39	15 55	16 10	16 25	16 40	16 55	17 10	17 25	17 40	17 46	17 54	18 09		18 26	18 40	18 54		19 10
Brondesbury	d	14 56	15 11	15 26	15 41	15 57	16 11	16 26	16 41	16 57	17 11	17 26	17 41	17 48	17 56	18 11		18 28	18 41	18 55		19 11
Brondesbury Park	d	14 57	15 13	15 27	15 42	15 58	16 13	16 28	16 43	16 58	17 13	17 28	17 43	17 49	17 57	18 12		18 29	18 43	18 57		19 13
Kensal Rise	d	14 59	15 15	15 29	15 44	16 00	16 15	16 30	16 45	17 00	17 15	17 30	17 45	17 51	17 59	18 14		18 31	18 45	18 59		19 15
Willesden Jn. High Level ⊖	a	15 02	15 18	15 32	15 47	16 03	16 19	16 33	16 48	17 03	17 18	17 33	17 48	17 53	18 03	18 17		18 34	18 48	19 02		19 18
	d	15 03	15 19	15 33	15 48	16 04	16 19	16 34	16 49	17 04	17 19	17 34	17 49		18 03	18 18		18 35	18 49	19 03		19 19
Acton Central	d	15 08	15 24	15 38	15 53	16 09	16 24	16 39	16 54	17 09	17 24	17 39	17 54		18 08	18 23		18 40	18 54	19 08		19 24
South Acton	d	15 12	15 28	15 42	15 57	16 13	16 28	16 43	16 58	17 13	17 28	17 43	17 58		18 12	18 27		18 44	18 58	19 12		19 28
Gunnersbury ⊖	d	15 15	15 32	15 45	16 00	16 16	16 32	16 45	17 00	17 16	17 30	17 45	18 00		18 15	18 30		18 47	19 00	19 14		19 32
Kew Gardens ⊖	d	15 17	15 35	15 47	16 02	16 18	16 35	16 48	17 03	17 18	17 33	17 48	18 03		18 17	18 32		18 49	19 03	19 17		19 35
Richmond ⊖	a	15 23	15 40	15 53	16 08	16 24	16 40	16 53	17 08	17 24	17 38	17 53	18 08		18 25	18 38		18 55	19 08	19 22		19 42

For general notes see front of timetable
For details of catering facilities see Directory of Train Operators

A To Clapham Junction (Table 186)

North Woolwich → Silvertown & City Airport, Stratford, Highbury, West Hampstead, Willesden Junction and Richmond.

Network diagram - see first page of Table 59

	LO		LO	LO	LO	LO		LO	LO	LO	LO		LO	LO	LO	LO		LO	LO	LO	LO				
Stratford Low Level 7 ⊖ d	18 52		19 01	19 06	19 23	19 33		19 52	20 12	20 32	20 52		21 12	21 32	21 52	22 12		22 32	22 52	23 12	23 32				
Hackney Wick d	18 56		19 05	19 10	19 27	19 37		19 56	20 16	20 36	20 56		21 16	21 36	21 56	22 16		22 36	22 56	23 16	23 36				
Homerton d	18 58		19 07	19 12	19 30	19 39		19 58	20 18	20 38	20 58		21 18	21 38	21 58	22 18		22 38	22 58	23 18	23 38				
Hackney Central d	19 00		19 09	19 14	19 32	19 41		20 00	20 20	20 40	21 00		21 20	21 40	22 00	22 20		22 40	23 00	23 20	23 40				
Dalston Kingsland d	19 03		19 12	19 17	19 34	19 44		20 03	20 23	20 43	21 03		21 23	21 43	22 03	22 23		22 43	23 03	23 23	23 43				
Canonbury d	19 05		19 14	19 19	19 37	19 46		20 05	20 25	20 45	21 05		21 25	21 45	22 05	22 25		22 45	23 05	23 25	23 45				
Highbury & Islington ⊖ d	19 08		19 17	19 22	19 40	19 49		20 08	20 28	20 48	21 08		21 28	21 48	22 08	22 28		22 48	23 08	23 28	23 48				
Caledonian Rd & Barnsbury d	19 10		19 19	19 24	19 42	19 51		20 10	20 30	20 50	21 10		21 30	21 50	22 10	22 30		22 50	23 10	23 30	23 50				
Camden Road d	19 14		19a24	19 27	19 45	19 54		20 13	20 33	20 53	21 13		21 33	21 53	22 13	22 33		22 53	23 13	23 33	23a55				
Kentish Town West d	19 16			19 29	19 47	19 56		20 15	20 35	20 55	21 15		21 35	21 55	22 15	22 35		22 55	23 15	23 35					
Gospel Oak d	19 19			19 32	19 52	19 59		20 18	20 38	20 58	21 18		21 38	21 58	22 18	22 38		22 58	23 18	23 38					
Hampstead Heath d	19 21			19 33	19 54	20 00		20 19	20 39	20 59	21 19		21 39	21 59	22 19	22 39		22 59	23 19	23 39					
Finchley Road & Frognal d	19 23			19 36	19 56	20 03		20 22	20 42	21 02	21 22		21 42	22 02	22 22	22 42		23 02	23 22	23 42					
West Hampstead ⊖ d	19 25			19 37	19 58	20 04		20 23	20 43	21 03	21 23		21 43	22 03	22 23	22 43		23 03	23 23	23 43					
Brondesbury d	19 26			19 39	19 59	20 06		20 25	20 45	21 05	21 25		21 45	22 05	22 25	22 45		23 05	23 25	23 45					
Brondesbury Park d	19 28			19 40	20 01	20 07		20 26	20 46	21 06	21 26		21 46	22 06	22 26	22 46		23 06	23 26	23 46					
Kensal Rise d	19 30			19 42	20 03	20 09		20 28	20 48	21 08	21 28		21 48	22 08	22 28	22 48		23 08	23 28	23 49					
Willesden Jn. High Level ⊖ a	19 33			19 44	20 06	20 13		20 32	20 52	21 12	21 32		21 52	22 12	22 32	22 52		23 12	23 32	23b53					
d	19 34			19 44	20 07	20 13		20 32	20 52	21 12	21 32		21 52	22 12	22 32	22 52		23 12	23 32						
Acton Central d	19 39			19 49	20 14	20 18		20 37	20 57	21 17	21 37		21 57	22 17	22 37	22 57		23 17	23 37						
South Acton d	19 43			19 53	20 16	20 22		20 41	21 01	21 21	21 41		22 01	22 21	22 41	23 01		23 21	23 41						
Gunnersbury ⊖ d	19 45			19 57	20 18	20 25		20 44	21 04	21 24	21 44		22 04	22 24	22 44	23 04		23 24	23 44						
Kew Gardens ⊖ d	19 48			19 58	20 21	20 27		20 46	21 06	21 26	21 46		22 06	22 26	22 46	23 06		23 26	23 46						
Richmond ⊖ a	19 53			20 09	20 26	20 37		20 55	21 13	21 36	21 53		22 14	22 32	22 53	23 12		23 33	23 53						

Saturdays

	LO	LO	LO	LO	LO	LO	LO	LO	LO	LO	LO	LO		LO	LO	LO	LO	LO	LO	LO	LO	LO	LO	LO	LO
Stratford Low Level 7 ⊖ d			06 07	06 22	06 37	06 52	07 07	07 23	07 37	07 52	08 09	08 22		08 37	08 52	09 07	09 22	09 37	09 52	10 07	10 22	10 37	10 52	11 07	11 22
Hackney Wick d			06 11	06 26	06 41	06 56	07 11	07 27	07 41	07 56	08 13	08 26		08 41	08 56	09 11	09 26	09 41	09 56	10 11	10 26	10 41	10 56	11 11	11 26
Homerton d			06 13	06 28	06 43	06 58	07 13	07 29	07 43	07 58	08 15	08 28		08 43	08 58	09 13	09 28	09 43	09 58	10 13	10 28	10 43	10 58	11 13	11 28
Hackney Central d			06 15	06 30	06 45	07 00	07 15	07 31	07 45	08 00	08 17	08 30		08 45	09 00	09 15	09 30	09 45	10 00	10 15	10 30	10 45	11 00	11 15	11 30
Dalston Kingsland d			06 18	06 33	06 48	07 03	07 18	07 34	07 48	08 03	08 20	08 33		08 48	09 03	09 18	09 33	09 48	10 03	10 18	10 33	10 48	11 03	11 18	11 33
Canonbury d			06 20	06 35	06 50	07 05	07 20	07 36	07 50	08 05	08 22	08 35		08 50	09 05	09 20	09 35	09 50	10 05	10 20	10 35	10 50	11 05	11 20	11 35
Highbury & Islington ⊖ d			06 23	06 38	06 53	07 08	07 23	07 39	07 53	08 08	08 25	08 38		08 53	09 08	09 23	09 38	09 53	10 08	10 23	10 38	10 53	11 08	11 23	11 38
Caledonian Rd & Barnsbury d			06 25	06 40	06 55	07 10	07 25	07 41	07 55	08 10	08 27	08 40		08 55	09 10	09 25	09 40	09 55	10 10	10 25	10 40	10 55	11 10	11 25	11 40
Camden Road d			06 29	06 44	06 59	07 14	07 29	07 45	07 59	08 14	08 31	08 44		08 59	09 14	09 29	09 44	09 59	10 14	10 29	10 44	10 59	11 14	11 29	11 44
Kentish Town West d			06 31	06 46	07 01	07 16	07 31	07 47	08 01	08 16	08 33	08 46		09 01	09 16	09 31	09 46	10 01	10 16	10 31	10 46	11 01	11 16	11 31	11 46
Gospel Oak d			06 34	06 49	07 04	07 19	07 34	07 50	08 04	08 19	08 36	08 49		09 04	09 19	09 34	09 49	10 04	10 19	10 34	10 49	11 04	11 19	11 34	11 49
Hampstead Heath d			06 36	06 50	07 06	07 21	07 36	07 51	08 06	08 21	08 38	08 50		09 06	09 21	09 36	09 50	10 06	10 21	10 36	10 50	11 06	11 21	11 36	11 50
Finchley Road & Frognal d			06 38	06 53	07 08	07 23	07 38	07 54	08 08	08 23	08 40	08 53		09 08	09 23	09 38	09 53	10 08	10 23	10 38	10 53	11 08	11 23	11 38	11 53
West Hampstead ⊖ d			06 40	06 54	07 10	07 25	07 40	07 55	08 10	08 25	08 42	08 54		09 10	09 25	09 40	09 54	10 10	10 25	10 40	10 54	11 10	11 25	11 40	11 54
Brondesbury d			06 41	06 56	07 11	07 26	07 41	07 57	08 11	08 26	08 43	08 56		09 11	09 26	09 41	09 56	10 11	10 26	10 41	10 56	11 11	11 26	11 41	11 56
Brondesbury Park d			06 43	06 57	07 13	07 28	07 43	07 58	08 13	08 28	08 45	08 57		09 13	09 28	09 43	09 57	10 13	10 28	10 43	10 57	11 13	11 28	11 43	11 57
Kensal Rise d			06 45	06 59	07 15	07 30	07 45	08 00	08 15	08 30	08 47	08 59		09 15	09 30	09 45	09 59	10 15	10 30	10 45	10 59	11 15	11 30	11 45	11 59
Willesden Jn. High Level ⊖ a			06 48	07 02	07 18	07 33	07 48	08 03	08 18	08 33	08 50	09 02		09 18	09 33	09 48	10 02	10 18	10 33	10 48	11 02	11 18	11 33	11 48	12 02
d	06 17	06 33	06 48	07 03	07 19	07 34	07 49	08 04	08 19	08 34	08 51	09 03		09 19	09 34	09 49	10 03	10 19	10 34	10 49	11 03	11 19	11 34	11 49	12 03
Acton Central d	06 22	06 38	06 53	07 08	07 23	07 39	07 54	08 09	08 24	08 39	08 56	09 08		09 24	09 39	09 54	10 08	10 24	10 39	10 54	11 08	11 24	11 39	11 54	12 08
South Acton d	06 26	06 42	06 57	07 12	07 27	07 43	07 58	08 13	08 28	08 43	09 00	09 12		09 28	09 43	09 58	10 12	10 28	10 43	10 58	11 12	11 28	11 43	11 58	12 12
Gunnersbury ⊖ d	06 29	06 45	07 02	07 15	07 32	07 45	08 02	08 16	08 32	08 45	09 02	09 15		09 32	09 45	10 02	10 15	10 32	10 45	11 02	11 15	11 32	11 45	12 02	12 15
Kew Gardens ⊖ d	06 31	06 47	07 05	07 17	07 35	07 48	08 05	08 18	08 35	08 48	09 05	09 17		09 35	09 48	10 05	10 17	10 35	10 48	11 05	11 17	11 35	11 48	12 05	12 17
Richmond ⊖ a	06 37	06 53	07 10	07 23	07 40	07 53	08 10	08 24	08 40	08 53	09 10	09 23		09 40	09 53	10 10	10 23	10 40	10 53	11 10	11 23	11 40	11 53	12 10	12 23

	LO	LO		LO	LO	LO	LO	LO	LO	LO	LO	LO	LO	LO	LO		LO	LO	LO	LO	LO	LO	LO	LO	LO
Stratford Low Level 7 ⊖ d	11 37	11 52		12 07	12 22	12 37	12 52	13 07	13 22	13 37	13 52	14 07	14 22	14 37	14 52		15 07	15 22	15 37	15 52	16 07	16 22	16 37	16 52	17 07
Hackney Wick d	11 41	11 56		12 11	12 26	12 41	12 56	13 11	13 26	13 41	13 56	14 11	14 26	14 41	14 56		15 11	15 26	15 41	15 56	16 11	16 26	16 41	16 56	17 11
Homerton d	11 43	11 58		12 13	12 28	12 43	12 58	13 13	13 28	13 43	13 58	14 13	14 28	14 43	14 58		15 13	15 28	15 43	15 58	16 13	16 28	16 43	16 58	17 13
Hackney Central d	11 45	12 00		12 15	12 30	12 45	13 00	13 15	13 30	13 45	14 00	14 15	14 30	14 45	15 00		15 15	15 30	15 45	16 00	16 15	16 30	16 45	17 00	17 15
Dalston Kingsland d	11 48	12 03		12 18	12 33	12 48	13 03	13 18	13 33	13 48	14 03	14 18	14 33	14 48	15 03		15 18	15 33	15 48	16 03	16 18	16 33	16 48	17 03	17 18
Canonbury d	11 50	12 05		12 20	12 35	12 50	13 05	13 20	13 35	13 50	14 05	14 20	14 35	14 50	15 05		15 20	15 35	15 50	16 05	16 20	16 35	16 50	17 05	17 20
Highbury & Islington ⊖ d	11 53	12 08		12 23	12 38	12 53	13 08	13 23	13 38	13 53	14 08	14 23	14 38	14 53	15 08		15 23	15 38	15 53	16 08	16 23	16 38	16 53	17 08	17 23
Caledonian Rd & Barnsbury d	11 55	12 10		12 25	12 40	12 55	13 10	13 25	13 40	13 55	14 10	14 25	14 40	14 55	15 10		15 25	15 40	15 55	16 10	16 25	16 40	16 55	17 10	17 25
Camden Road d	11 59	12 14		12 29	12 44	12 59	13 14	13 29	13 44	13 59	14 14	14 29	14 44	14 59	15 14		15 29	15 44	15 59	16 14	16 29	16 44	16 59	17 14	17 29
Kentish Town West d	12 01	12 16		12 31	12 46	13 01	13 16	13 31	13 46	14 01	14 16	14 31	14 46	15 01	15 16		15 31	15 46	16 01	16 16	16 31	16 46	17 01	17 16	17 31
Gospel Oak d	12 04	12 19		12 34	12 49	13 04	13 19	13 34	13 49	14 04	14 19	14 34	14 49	15 04	15 19		15 34	15 49	16 04	16 19	16 34	16 49	17 04	17 19	17 34
Hampstead Heath d	12 06	12 21		12 36	12 50	13 06	13 21	13 36	13 50	14 06	14 21	14 36	14 50	15 06	15 21		15 36	15 50	16 06	16 21	16 36	16 50	17 06	17 21	17 36
Finchley Road & Frognal d	12 08	12 23		12 38	12 53	13 08	13 23	13 38	13 53	14 08	14 23	14 38	14 53	15 08	15 23		15 38	15 53	16 08	16 23	16 38	16 53	17 08	17 23	17 38
West Hampstead ⊖ d	12 10	12 25		12 40	12 54	13 10	13 25	13 40	13 54	14 10	14 25	14 40	14 54	15 10	15 25		15 40	15 54	16 10	16 25	16 40	16 54	17 10	17 25	17 40
Brondesbury d	12 11	12 26		12 41	12 56	13 11	13 26	13 41	13 56	14 11	14 26	14 41	14 56	15 11	15 26		15 41	15 56	16 11	16 26	16 41	16 56	17 11	17 26	17 41
Brondesbury Park d	12 13	12 28		12 43	12 57	13 13	13 28	13 43	13 57	14 13	14 28	14 43	14 57	15 13	15 28		15 43	15 57	16 13	16 28	16 43	16 57	17 13	17 28	17 43
Kensal Rise d	12 15	12 30		12 45	12 59	13 15	13 30	13 45	13 59	14 15	14 30	14 45	14 59	15 15	15 30		15 45	15 59	16 15	16 30	16 45	16 59	17 15	17 30	17 45
Willesden Jn. High Level ⊖ a	12 18	12 33		12 48	13 02	13 18	13 33	13 48	14 02	14 18	14 33	14 48	15 02	15 18	15 33		15 48	16 02	16 18	16 33	16 48	17 02	17 18	17 33	17 48
d	12 19	12 34		12 49	13 03	13 19	13 34	13 49	14 03	14 19	14 34	14 49	15 03	15 19	15 34		15 49	16 03	16 19	16 34	16 49	17 03	17 19	17 34	17 49
Acton Central d	12 24	12 39		12 54	13 08	13 24	13 39	13 54	14 08	14 24	14 39	14 54	15 08	15 24	15 39		15 54	16 08	16 24	16 39	16 54	17 08	17 24	17 39	17 54
South Acton d	12 28	12 43		12 58	13 12	13 28	13 43	13 58	14 12	14 28	14 43	14 58	15 12	15 28	15 43		15 58	16 12	16 28	16 43	16 58	17 12	17 28	17 43	17 58
Gunnersbury ⊖ d	12 32	12 45		13 02	13 15	13 32	13 45	14 02	14 15	14 32	14 45	15 02	15 15	15 32	15 45		16 02	16 15	16 32	16 45	17 02	17 15	17 32	17 45	18 02
Kew Gardens ⊖ d	12 35	12 48		13 05	13 17	13 35	13 48	14 05	14 17	14 35	14 48	15 05	15 17	15 35	15 48		16 05	16 17	16 35	16 48	17 05	17 17	17 35	17 48	18 05
Richmond ⊖ a	12 40	12 53		13 10	13 23	13 40	13 53	14 10	14 23	14 40	14 53	15 10	15 23	15 40	15 53		16 10	16 23	16 40	16 53	17 10	17 23	17 40	17 53	18 10

For general notes see front of timetable
For details of catering facilities see
Directory of Train Operators

b Willesden Jn Low Level

Table 59

Saturdays

North Woolwich → Silvertown & City Airport, Stratford, Highbury, West Hampstead, Willesden Junction and Richmond.

Network diagram - see first page of Table 59

		LO	LO	LO	LO	LO		LO	LO	LO	LO	LO	LO	LO	LO	LO	LO	LO	LO	LO	LO	LO	LO	LO
Stratford Low Level 7 ⊖	d	17 22	17 37	17 52	18 12	18 22		18 35	18 52	19 07	19 22	19 37	19 52	20 12	20 32	20 52	21 12	21 32	21 52	22 12	22 32	22 52	23 12	23 32
Hackney Wick	d	17 26	17 41	17 56	18 16	18 26		18 38	18 56	19 11	19 26	19 41	19 56	20 16	20 36	20 56	21 16	21 36	21 56	22 16	22 36	22 56	23 16	23 36
Homerton	d	17 28	17 43	17 58	18 18	18 28		18 41	18 58	19 13	19 28	19 43	19 58	20 18	20 38	20 58	21 18	21 38	21 58	22 18	22 38	22 58	23 18	23 38
Hackney Central	d	17 30	17 45	18 00	18 20	18 30		18 43	19 00	19 15	19 30	19 45	20 00	20 20	20 40	21 00	21 20	21 40	22 00	22 20	22 40	23 00	23 20	23 40
Dalston Kingsland	d	17 33	17 48	18 03	18 23	18 33		18 45	19 03	19 18	19 33	19 48	20 03	20 23	20 43	21 03	21 23	21 43	22 03	22 23	22 43	23 03	23 23	23 43
Canonbury	d	17 35	17 50	18 05	18 25	18 35		18 48	19 05	19 20	19 35	19 50	20 05	20 25	20 45	21 05	21 25	21 45	22 05	22 25	22 45	23 05	23 25	23 45
Highbury & Islington ⊖	d	17 38	17 53	18 08	18 28	18 38		18 51	19 08	19 23	19 38	19 53	20 08	20 28	20 48	21 08	21 28	21 48	22 08	22 28	22 48	23 08	23 28	23 48
Caledonian Rd & Barnsbury	d	17 40	17 55	18 10	18 30	18 40		18 53	19 10	19 25	19 40	19 55	20 10	20 30	20 50	21 10	21 30	21 50	22 10	22 30	22 50	23 10	23 30	23 50
Camden Road	d	17 44	17 59	18 14	18 34	18 44		18 56	19 14	19 29	19 44	19 59	20 14	20 34	20 54	21 14	21 34	21 54	22 14	22 34	22 54	23 14	23 34	23a55
Kentish Town West	d	17 46	18 01	18 16	18 36	18 46		18 58	19 16	19 31	19 46	20 01	20 16	20 36	20 56	21 16	21 36	21 56	22 16	22 36	22 56	23 16	23 36	
Gospel Oak	d	17 49	18 04	18 19	18 39	18 49		19 01	19 19	19 34	19 49	20 04	20 19	20 39	20 59	21 19	21 39	21 59	22 19	22 39	22 59	23 19	23 39	
Hampstead Heath	d	17 50	18 06	18 21	18 41	18 51		19 03	19 21	19 36	19 51	20 06	20 21	20 40	21 01	21 21	21 40	22 00	22 21	22 40	23 01	23 21	23 41	
Finchley Road & Frognal	d	17 53	18 08	18 23	18 43	18 53		19 06	19 23	19 38	19 53	20 08	20 23	20 43	21 03	21 23	21 43	22 03	22 23	22 43	23 03	23 23	23 43	
West Hampstead ⊖	d	17 54	18 10	18 25	18 45	18 55		19 07	19 25	19 40	19 55	20 10	20 25	20 44	21 05	21 25	21 44	22 04	22 25	22 44	23 05	23 25	23 45	
Brondesbury	d	17 56	18 11	18 26	18 46	18 56		19 09	19 26	19 41	19 56	20 11	20 26	20 46	21 06	21 26	21 46	22 06	22 26	22 46	23 06	23 26	23 46	
Brondesbury Park	d	17 57	18 13	18 28	18 48	18 58		19 10	19 28	19 43	19 58	20 13	20 28	20 47	21 08	21 28	21 47	22 07	22 28	22 47	23 08	23 28	23 48	
Kensal Rise	d	17 59	18 15	18 30	18 50	19 00		19 12	19 30	19 45	20 00	20 15	20 30	20 49	21 10	21 30	21 49	22 09	22 30	22 49	23 10	23 30	23 50	
Willesden Jn. High Level ⊖	a	18 02	18 18	18 33	18 53	19 05		19 15	19 33	19 48	20 03	20 18	20 33	20 52	21 14	21 33	21 52	22 12	22 33	22 52	23 13	23 33	23b53	
	d	18 03	18 19	18 34	18 54			19 16	19 34	19 49	20 05	20 19	20 34	20 53	21 15	21 34	21 53	22 13	22 34	22 53	23 14	23 34		
Acton Central	d	18 08	18 24	18 39	18 59			19 21	19 39	19 54	20 13	20 24	20 39	20 58	21 20	21 38	21 58	22 18	22 39	22 58	23 19	23 39		
South Acton	d	18 12	18 28	18 43	19 03			19 25	19 43	19 58	20 17	20 28	20 43	21 02	21 24	21 42	22 02	22 22	22 43	23 02	23 23	23 43		
Gunnersbury ⊖	d	18 15	18 32	18 45	19 05			19 28	19 45	20 02	20 22	20 31	20 45	21 05	21 28	21 45	22 04	22 24	22 45	23 05	23 25	23 45		
Kew Gardens ⊖	d	18 17	18 35	18 48	19 08			19 31	19 48	20 05	20 25	20 33	20 48	21 07	21 31	21 47	22 07	22 27	22 48	23 07	23 28	23 48		
Richmond ⊖	a	18 23	18 41	18 53	19 13			19 36	19 53	20 10	20 30	20 40	20 53	21 13	21 36	21 53	22 12	22 32	22 53	23 13	23 33	23 53		

Sundays

		LO			LO	LO			LO		LO		LO
Stratford Low Level 7 ⊖	d				08 49	09 19			21 49		22 19		22 49
Hackney Wick	d				08 53	09 23			21 53		22 23		22 53
Homerton	d				08 55	09 25			21 55		22 25		22 55
Hackney Central	d				08 57	09 27			21 57		22 27		22 57
Dalston Kingsland	d				09 00	09 30			22 00		22 30		23 00
Canonbury	d				09 02	09 32			22 02		22 32		23 02
Highbury & Islington ⊖	d				09 05	09 35			22 05		22 35		23 05
Caledonian Rd & Barnsbury	d				09 07	09 37			22 07		22 37		23 07
Camden Road	d				09 11	09 41	and		22 11		22 41		23 11
Kentish Town West	d				09 13	09 43	every 30		22 13		22 43		23 13
Gospel Oak	d				09 16	09 46	minutes		22 16		22 46		23 16
Hampstead Heath	d				09 18	09 48	until		22 18		22 48		23 18
Finchley Road & Frognal	d				09 20	09 50			22 20		22 50		23 20
West Hampstead ⊖	d				09 22	09 52			22 22		22 52		23 22
Brondesbury	d				09 23	09 53			22 23		22 53		23 23
Brondesbury Park	d				09 25	09 55			22 25		22 55		23 25
Kensal Rise	d				09 27	09 57			22 27		22 57		23 27
Willesden Jn. High Level ⊖	a				09 30	10 00			22 30		23 00		23b32
	d	09 00			09 31	10 01			22 31		23 01		
Acton Central	d	09 05			09 36	10 06			22 36		23 06		
South Acton	d	09 09			09 40	10 10			22 40		23 10		
Gunnersbury ⊖	d	09 11			09 42	10 12			22 42		23 12		
Kew Gardens ⊖	d	09 14			09 45	10 15			22 45		23 15		
Richmond ⊖	a	09 19			09 50	10 20			22 50		23 20		

For general notes see front of timetable
For details of catering facilities see Directory of Train Operators

b Willesden Jn Low Level

Richmond → Willesden Junction, West Hampstead, Highbury, Stratford, Silvertown & City Airport and North Woolwich.

Network diagram - see first page of Table 59

Miles	Station		LO	LO	LO	LO	LO	LO	LO	LO	LO	LO A	LO	LO	LO	LO	LO	LO A	LO	LO	LO	LO
0	**Richmond**	⊖ d				06 12	06 27	06 42		06 58	07 13		07 29	07 46		07 59	08 13		08 29	08 42	08 59	09 14
1½	Kew Gardens	⊖ d				06 15	06 30	06 45		07 01	07 16		07 32	07 49		08 02	08 16		08 32	08 45	09 02	09 17
2¼	Gunnersbury	⊖ d				06 18	06 33	06 48		07 04	07 19		07 35	07 52		08 05	08 19		08 35	08 48	09 05	09 20
3¼	South Acton	d				06 20	06 35	06 50		07 06	07 21		07 37	07 54		08 07	08 21		08 37	08 50	09 07	09 22
4	Acton Central	d				06b25	06 38	06 53		07 09	07 24		07 40	07 57		08 10	08 24		08 40	08 53	09 10	09 25
5¾	**Willesden Jn. High Level**	⊖ a				06 31	06 43	06 58		07 14	07 29		07 45	08 02		08 15	08 29		08 45	08 58	09 15	09 30
—		d	05c58	06c11		06 32	06 44	06 59		07 15	07 30	07 39	07 46	08 03		08 16	08 30	08 38	08 46	08 59	09 16	09 31
6¾	Kensal Rise	d	06 03	06 17		06 34	06 47	07 02		07 18	07 33	07 42	07 49	08 06		08 19	08 33	08 41	08 49	09 02	09 19	09 34
7½	Brondesbury Park	d	06 05	06 19		06 36	06 49	07 04		07 20	07 35	07 44	07 51	08 08		08 21	08 35	08 43	08 51	09 04	09 21	09 36
7¾	Brondesbury	d	06 07	06 21		06 38	06 51	07 06		07 22	07 37	07 46	07 53	08 10		08 23	08 37	08 45	08 53	09 06	09 23	09 38
8¼	West Hampstead	⊖ d	06 09	06 22		06 40	06 52	07 07		07 23	07 38	07 47	07 54	08 11		08 24	08 38	08 46	08 54	09 07	09 24	09 39
8¾	Finchley Road & Frognal	d	06 10	06 24		06 41	06 54	07 09		07 25	07 40	07 49	07 56	08 13		08 26	08 40	08 48	08 56	09 09	09 26	09 41
9¾	Hampstead Heath	d	06 13	06 27		06 44	06 57	07 12		07 28	07 43	07 52	07 59	08 16		08 29	08 43	08 51	08 59	09 12	09 29	09 44
10¼	**Gospel Oak**	d	06 15	06 29		06 46	06 59	07 14		07 30	07 45	07 54	08 01	08 18		08 31	08 45	08 53	09 01	09 14	09 31	09 46
11	Kentish Town West	d	06 17	06 31		06 48	07 01	07 16		07 32	07 47	07 56	08 03	08 20		08 33	08 47	08 55	09 03	09 16	09 33	09 48
11¼	Camden Road	d	06 20	06 33	06 39	06 51	07 03	07 18	07 27	07 34	07 49	07 58	08 05	08 22	08 30	08 35	08 49	08 57	09 05	09 18	09 35	09 50
12½	Caledonian Rd & Barnsbury	d	06 23	06 36	06 42	06 54	07 06	07 21	07 30	07 37	07 52	08 01	08 08	08 25	08 33	08 38	08 52	09 00	09 08	09 21	09 38	09 53
13	**Highbury & Islington**	⊖ d	06 25	06 39	06 45	06 56	07 09	07 24	07 32	07 40	07 55	08 04	08 11	08 27	08 35	08 41	08 54	09 03	09 11	09 24	09 40	09 56
13½	Canonbury	⊖ d	06 27	06 41	06 47	06 58	07 11	07 26	07 34	07 42	07 57	08 06	08 13	08 29	08 37	08 43	08 56	09 05	09 13	09 26	09 42	09 58
14¼	Dalston Kingsland	d	06 30	06 44	06 50	07 01	07 14	07 29	07 37	07 45	08 00	08 09	08 16	08 32	08 40	08 46	08 59	09 08	09 16	09 29	09 45	10 01
15¼	Hackney Central	d	06 32	06 46	06 52	07 03	07 16	07 31	07 39	07 47	08 02	08 11	08 18	08 34	08 42	08 48	09 01	09 10	09 18	09 31	09 47	10 03
16	Homerton	d	06 34	06 48	06 54	07 05	07 18	07 33	07 41	07 49	08 04	08 13	08 20	08 36	08 44	08 50	09 03	09 12	09 20	09 33	09 49	10 05
16¾	Hackney Wick	d	06 37	06 51	06 57	07 08	07 21	07 36	07 44	07 52	08 07	08 16	08 23	08 38	08 47	08 53	09 06	09 15	09 23	09 36	09 52	10 08
17¼	**Stratford Low Level** 7	⊖ a	06 44	06 58	07 04	07 15	07 28	07 43	07 51	07 59	08 14	08 23	08 30	08 45	08 54	09 00	09 13	09 22	09 30	09 43	09 59	10 15

Station		LO	LO	LO	LO	LO	LO	LO	LO	LO	LO	LO	LO	LO	LO	LO	LO	LO	LO	LO	LO
Richmond	⊖ d	09 27	09 41	09 57	10 11	10 27	10 41	10 57	11 11	11 27	11 41	11 57	12 11	12 27	12 41	12 57	13 11	13 27	13 41	13 57	14 11
Kew Gardens	⊖ d	09 30	09 44	10 00	10 14	10 30	10 44	11 00	11 14	11 30	11 44	12 00	12 14	12 30	12 44	13 00	13 14	13 30	13 44	14 00	14 14
Gunnersbury	⊖ d	09 33	09 47	10 03	10 17	10 33	10 47	11 03	11 17	11 33	11 47	12 03	12 17	12 33	12 47	13 03	13 17	13 33	13 47	14 03	14 17
South Acton	d	09 35	09 49	10 05	10 19	10 35	10 49	11 05	11 19	11 35	11 49	12 05	12 19	12 35	12 49	13 05	13 19	13 35	13 49	14 05	14 19
Acton Central	d	09 38	09 53	10 08	10 23	10 38	10 53	11 08	11 23	11 38	11 53	12 08	12 23	12 38	12 53	13 08	13 23	13 38	13 53	14 08	14 23
Willesden Jn. High Level	⊖ a	09 43	10 00	10 14	10 29	10 43	11 00	11 13	11 29	11 43	11 59	12 13	12 30	12 43	12 58	13 13	13 29	13 43	13 59	14 13	14 29
	d	09 44	10 00	10 14	10 29	10 44	11 00	11 14	11 30	11 44	12 00	12 14	12 30	12 44	13 00	13 14	13 30	13 44	14 00	14 14	14 30
Kensal Rise	d	09 47	10 03	10 17	10 33	10 47	11 03	11 17	11 33	11 47	12 03	12 17	12 33	12 47	13 03	13 17	13 33	13 47	14 03	14 17	14 33
Brondesbury Park	d	09 49	10 05	10 19	10 35	10 49	11 05	11 19	11 35	11 49	12 05	12 19	12 35	12 49	13 05	13 19	13 35	13 49	14 05	14 19	14 35
Brondesbury	d	09 51	10 07	10 21	10 37	10 51	11 07	11 21	11 37	11 51	12 07	12 21	12 37	12 51	13 07	13 21	13 37	13 51	14 07	14 21	14 37
West Hampstead	⊖ d	09 52	10 08	10 22	10 38	10 52	11 08	11 22	11 38	11 52	12 08	12 22	12 38	12 52	13 08	13 22	13 38	13 52	14 08	14 22	14 38
Finchley Road & Frognal	d	09 54	10 10	10 24	10 40	10 54	11 10	11 24	11 40	11 54	12 10	12 24	12 40	12 54	13 10	13 24	13 40	13 54	14 10	14 24	14 40
Hampstead Heath	d	09 57	10 13	10 27	10 43	10 57	11 13	11 27	11 43	11 57	12 13	12 27	12 43	12 57	13 13	13 27	13 43	13 57	14 13	14 27	14 43
Gospel Oak	d	09 59	10 15	10 29	10 45	10 59	11 15	11 29	11 45	11 59	12 15	12 29	12 45	12 59	13 15	13 29	13 45	13 59	14 15	14 29	14 45
Kentish Town West	d	10 01	10 17	10 31	10 47	11 01	11 17	11 31	11 47	12 01	12 17	12 31	12 47	13 01	13 17	13 31	13 47	14 01	14 17	14 31	14 47
Camden Road	d	10 03	10 19	10 33	10 49	11 03	11 19	11 33	11 49	12 03	12 19	12 33	12 49	13 03	13 19	13 33	13 49	14 03	14 19	14 33	14 49
Caledonian Rd & Barnsbury	d	10 06	10 22	10 36	10 52	11 06	11 22	11 36	11 52	12 06	12 22	12 36	12 52	13 06	13 22	13 36	13 52	14 06	14 22	14 36	14 52
Highbury & Islington	⊖ d	10 09	10 25	10 39	10 55	11 09	11 25	11 39	11 55	12 09	12 25	12 39	12 55	13 09	13 25	13 39	13 55	14 09	14 25	14 39	14 55
Canonbury	⊖ d	10 11	10 27	10 41	10 57	11 11	11 27	11 41	11 57	12 11	12 27	12 41	12 57	13 11	13 27	13 41	13 57	14 11	14 27	14 41	14 57
Dalston Kingsland	d	10 14	10 30	10 44	11 00	11 14	11 30	11 44	12 00	12 14	12 30	12 44	13 00	13 14	13 30	13 44	14 00	14 14	14 30	14 44	15 00
Hackney Central	d	10 16	10 32	10 46	11 02	11 16	11 32	11 46	12 02	12 16	12 32	12 46	13 02	13 16	13 32	13 46	14 02	14 16	14 32	14 46	15 02
Homerton	d	10 18	10 34	10 48	11 04	11 18	11 34	11 48	12 04	12 18	12 34	12 48	13 04	13 18	13 34	13 48	14 04	14 18	14 34	14 48	15 04
Hackney Wick	d	10 21	10 37	10 51	11 07	11 21	11 37	11 51	12 07	12 21	12 37	12 51	13 07	13 21	13 37	13 51	14 07	14 21	14 37	14 51	15 07
Stratford Low Level 7	⊖ a	10 28	10 45	10 59	11 14	11 28	11 45	11 58	12 14	12 29	12 44	12 58	13 15	13 28	13 44	13 58	14 14	14 28	14 44	14 58	15 14

Station		LO	LO	LO	LO	LO	LO	LO	LO	LO	LO	LO	LO	LO	LO	LO A	LO	LO	LO	LO	LO	LO A
Richmond	⊖ d	14 27	14 41	14 57	15 11	15 27	15 41	15 57		16 15	16 27	16 35	16 44	16 59	17 12		17 29	17 44		18 00	18 15	
Kew Gardens	⊖ d	14 30	14 44	15 00	15 14	15 30	15 44	16 00		16 18	16 30	16 38	16 47	17 02	17 15		17 32	17 47		18 03	18 18	
Gunnersbury	⊖ d	14 33	14 47	15 03	15 17	15 33	15 47	16 03		16 21	16 33	16 41	16 50	17 05	17 18		17 35	17 50		18 06	18 21	
South Acton	d	14 35	14 49	15 05	15 19	15 35	15 49	16 05		16 23	16 35	16 43	16 52	17 07	17 20		17 37	17 52		18 08	18 23	
Acton Central	d	14 38	14 53	15 08	15 23	15 38	15 53	16 08		16 26	16 38	16 46	16 55	17 10	17 23		17 40	17 55		18 11	18 26	
Willesden Jn. High Level	⊖ a	14 44	14 59	15 13	15 30	15 43	15 59	16 13		16 31	16 43	16 51	17 00	17 15	17 30		17 45	18 00		18 16	18 32	
	d	14 44	15 00	15 14	15 30	15 44	16 00	16 14		16 32	16 44	16 52	17 01	17 16	17 31	17 39	17 46	18 01		18 17	18 32	18 39
Kensal Rise	d	14 47	15 03	15 17	15 33	15 47	16 03	16 17		16 35	16 47	16 55	17 04	17 19	17 34	17 42	17 49	18 04		18 20	18 35	18 42
Brondesbury Park	d	14 49	15 05	15 19	15 35	15 49	16 05	16 19		16 37	16 49	16 57	17 06	17 21	17 36	17 44	17 51	18 06		18 22	18 37	18 44
Brondesbury	d	14 51	15 07	15 21	15 37	15 51	16 07	16 21		16 39	16 51	16 59	17 08	17 23	17 38	17 46	17 53	18 08		18 24	18 39	18 46
West Hampstead	⊖ d	14 52	15 08	15 22	15 38	15 52	16 08	16 22		16 40	16 52	17 00	17 09	17 24	17 39	17 47	17 54	18 09		18 25	18 40	18 47
Finchley Road & Frognal	d	14 54	15 10	15 24	15 40	15 54	16 10	16 24		16 42	16 54	17 02	17 11	17 26	17 41	17 49	17 56	18 11		18 27	18 42	18 49
Hampstead Heath	d	14 57	15 13	15 27	15 43	15 57	16 13	16 27		16 45	16 57	17 05	17 14	17 29	17 44	17 52	17 59	18 14		18 30	18 45	18 52
Gospel Oak	d	14 59	15 15	15 29	15 45	15 59	16 15	16 29		16 47	16 59	17 07	17 16	17 31	17 46	17 54	18 01	18 16		18 32	18 47	18 54
Kentish Town West	d	15 01	15 17	15 31	15 47	16 01	16 17	16 31		16 49	17 01	17 09	17 18	17 33	17 48	17 56	18 03	18 18		18 34	18 49	18 56
Camden Road	d	15 03	15 19	15 33	15 49	16 03	16 19	16 33	16 40	16 51	17 03	17 12	17 21	17 35	17 51	17 58	18 05	18 20	18 27	18 37	18 51	18 58
Caledonian Rd & Barnsbury	d	15 06	15 22	15 36	15 52	16 06	16 22	16 36	16 43	16 54	17 06	17 15	17 24	17 39	17 54	18 01	18 08	18 23	18 30	18 40	18 54	19 01
Highbury & Islington	⊖ d	15 09	15 25	15 39	15 55	16 09	16 24	16 39	16 45	16 57	17 09	17 18	17 26	17 41	17 56	18 04	18 11	18 26	18 33	18 43	18 57	19 04
Canonbury	⊖ d	15 11	15 27	15 41	15 57	16 11	16 26	16 41	16 47	16 59	17 11	17 20	17 28	17 43	17 58	18 06	18 13	18 28	18 35	18 45	18 59	19 06
Dalston Kingsland	d	15 14	15 30	15 44	16 00	16 14	16 29	16 44	16 50	17 02	17 14	17 23	17 31	17 46	18 01	18 09	18 16	18 31	18 38	18 48	19 02	19 09
Hackney Central	d	15 16	15 32	15 46	16 02	16 16	16 31	16 46	16 52	17 04	17 16	17 25	17 33	17 48	18 03	18 11	18 18	18 33	18 41	18 50	19 04	19 11
Homerton	d	15 18	15 34	15 48	16 04	16 18	16 33	16 48	16 54	17 06	17 18	17 27	17 35	17 50	18 05	18 13	18 20	18 35	18 43	18 52	19 06	19 13
Hackney Wick	d	15 21	15 37	15 51	16 07	16 21	16 35	16 51	16 57	17 08	17 21	17 30	17 38	17 53	18 08	18 16	18 23	18 38	18 46	18 55	19 09	19 16
Stratford Low Level 7	⊖ a	15 30	15 44	15 59	16 14	16 28	16 42	16 58	17 04	17 15	17 28	17 37	17 45	18 00	18 15	18 23	18 30	18 45	18 53	19 02	19 16	19 23

For general notes see front of timetable
For details of catering facilities see Directory of Train Operators

A From Clapham Junction (Table 186)
b Arr. 0622
c Willesden Jn Low Level

Richmond → Willesden Junction, West Hampstead, Highbury, Stratford, Silvertown & City Airport and North Woolwich.

Network diagram - see first page of Table 59

Station	LO	LO	LO	LO	LO	LO	LO	LO	LO	LO	LO	LO	LO	LO	LO	LO	LO
Richmond ⊖ d	18 31	18 44	18 55	19 15	19 26	19 41	19 59	20 15	20 35	20 55	21 15	21 35	21 55	22 15	22 35	22 55	23 15
Kew Gardens ⊖ d	18 34	18 47	18a58	19 18	19 29	19 44	20 02	20 18	20 38	20 58	21 18	21 38	21 58	22 18	22 38	22 58	23 18
Gunnersbury ⊖ d	18 37	18 50	19 01	19 21	19 32	19 47	20 05	20 21	20 41	21 01	21 21	21 41	22 01	22 21	22 41	23 01	23 21
South Acton d	18 39	18 52	19 03	19 23	19 34	19 49	20 07	20 23	20 43	21 03	21 23	21 43	22 03	22 23	22 43	23 03	23 23
Acton Central d	18 43	18 55	19 06	19 26	19 37	19 52	20 10	20 26	20 46	21 06	21 26	21 46	22 06	22 26	22 46	23 06	23 26
Willesden Jn. High Level ⊖ a	18 49	19 00	19 12	19 32	19 42	19 58	20 15	20 32	20 52	21 12	21 31	21 52	22 12	22 32	22 52	23 12	23 35
d	18 50	19 01	19 12	19 32	19 43	19 58	20 16	20 32	20 52	21 12	21 32	21 52	22 12	22 32	22 52	23 12	
Kensal Rise d	18 53	19 04	19 15	19 35	19 46	20 01	20 19	20 35	20 55	21 15	21 35	21 55	22 15	22 35	22 55	23 15	
Brondesbury Park d	18 55	19 06	19 17	19 37	19 48	20 03	20 21	20 37	20 57	21 17	21 37	21 57	22 17	22 37	22 57	23 17	
Brondesbury d	18 57	19 08	19 19	19 39	19 50	20 05	20 23	20 39	20 59	21 19	21 39	21 59	22 19	22 39	22 59	23 19	
West Hampstead ⊖ d	18 58	19 09	19 20	19 40	19 51	20 06	20 24	20 40	21 00	21 20	21 40	22 00	22 20	22 40	23 00	23 20	
Finchley Road & Frognal d	19 00	19 11	19 22	19 42	19 53	20 08	20 26	20 42	21 02	21 22	21 42	22 02	22 22	22 42	23 02	23 22	
Hampstead Heath d	19 03	19 14	19 25	19 45	19 56	20 11	20 29	20 45	21 05	21 25	21 45	22 05	22 25	22 45	23 05	23 25	
Gospel Oak d	19 05	19 16	19 27	19 47	19 58	20 13	20 31	20 47	21 07	21 27	21 47	22 07	22 27	22 47	23 07	23 27	
Kentish Town West d	19 07	19 18	19 29	19 49	20 00	20 15	20 33	20 49	21 09	21 29	21 49	22 09	22 29	22 49	23 09	23 29	
Camden Road d	19 09	19 20	19 31	19 51	20 02	20 17	20 35	20 51	21 11	21 31	21 51	22 11	22 31	22 51	23 11	23 31	
Caledonian Rd & Barnsbury d	19 12	19 23	19 34	19 54	20 05	20 20	20 38	20 54	21 14	21 34	21 54	22 14	22 34	22 54	23 14	23 34	
Highbury & Islington ⊖ d	19 15	19 26	19 37	19 57	20 08	20 23	20 41	20 57	21 17	21 37	21 57	22 17	22 37	22 57	23 17	23 37	
Canonbury ⊖ d	19 17	19 28	19 39	19 59	20 10	20 25	20 43	20 59	21 19	21 39	21 59	22 19	22 39	22 59	23 19	23 39	
Dalston Kingsland d	19 20	19 31	19 42	20 02	20 13	20 28	20 46	21 02	21 22	21 42	22 02	22 22	22 42	23 02	23 22	23 42	
Hackney Central d	19 23	19 33	19 44	20 04	20 15	20 30	20 48	21 04	21 24	21 44	22 04	22 24	22 44	23 04	23 24	23 44	
Homerton d	19 25	19 35	19 46	20 06	20 17	20 32	20 50	21 06	21 26	21 46	22 06	22 26	22 46	23 06	23 26	23 46	
Hackney Wick d	19 29	19 38	19 49	20 09	20 20	20 35	20 53	21 09	21 29	21 49	22 09	22 29	22 49	23 09	23 29	23 49	
Stratford Low Level 7 ⊖ ⛴ a	19 36	19 45	20 00	20 17	20 27	20 43	21 01	21 16	21 38	21 58	22 16	22 37	22 57	23 17	23 37	23 59	

Saturdays

Station	LO	LO	LO	LO	LO	LO	LO	LO	LO	LO	LO	LO	LO	LO	LO	LO	LO	LO	LO	LO	LO	LO	LO
Richmond ⊖ d			06 11	06 27	06 41	06 57	07 11	07 27	07 41	07 57	08 11	08 27	08 41	08 57	09 11	09 27	09 41	09 57	10 11	10 27	10 41	10 57	11 11
Kew Gardens ⊖ d			06 14	06 30	06 44	07 00	07 14	07 30	07 44	08 00	08 14	08 30	08 44	09 00	09 14	09 30	09 44	10 00	10 14	10 30	10 44	11 00	11 14
Gunnersbury ⊖ d			06 17	06 33	06 47	07 03	07 17	07 33	07 47	08 03	08 17	08 33	08 47	09 03	09 17	09 33	09 47	10 03	10 17	10 33	10 47	11 03	11 17
South Acton d			06 19	06 35	06 49	07 05	07 19	07 35	07 49	08 05	08 19	08 35	08 49	09 05	09 19	09 35	09 49	10 05	10 19	10 35	10 49	11 05	11 19
Acton Central d			06 23	06 38	06 53	07 08	07 23	07 38	07 53	08 08	08 23	08 38	08 53	09 08	09 23	09 38	09 53	10 08	10 23	10 38	10 53	11 08	11 23
Willesden Jn. High Level ⊖ a			06 29	06 43	06 58	07 14	07 29	07 43	07 58	08 13	08 29	08 43	08 58	09 13	09 29	09 43	09 58	10 13	10 29	10 43	10 59	11 13	11 29
d	05b58	06b11	06 29	06 44	06 59	07 14	07 29	07 44	07 59	08 14	08 29	08 44	08 59	09 14	09 29	09 44	09 59	10 14	10 29	10 44	10 59	11 14	11 29
Kensal Rise d	06 02	06 17	06 32	06 47	07 02	07 17	07 32	07 47	08 02	08 17	08 32	08 47	09 02	09 17	09 32	09 47	10 02	10 17	10 32	10 47	11 02	11 17	11 32
Brondesbury Park d	06 04	06 19	06 34	06 49	07 04	07 19	07 34	07 49	08 04	08 19	08 34	08 49	09 04	09 19	09 34	09 49	10 04	10 19	10 34	10 49	11 04	11 19	11 34
Brondesbury d	06 06	06 21	06 36	06 51	07 06	07 21	07 36	07 51	08 06	08 21	08 36	08 51	09 06	09 21	09 36	09 51	10 06	10 21	10 36	10 51	11 06	11 21	11 36
West Hampstead ⊖ d	06 07	06 22	06 37	06 52	07 07	07 22	07 37	07 52	08 07	08 22	08 37	08 52	09 07	09 22	09 37	09 52	10 07	10 22	10 37	10 52	11 07	11 22	11 37
Finchley Road & Frognal d	06 09	06 24	06 39	06 54	07 09	07 24	07 39	07 54	08 09	08 24	08 39	08 54	09 09	09 24	09 39	09 54	10 09	10 24	10 39	10 54	11 09	11 24	11 39
Hampstead Heath d	06 12	06 27	06 42	06 57	07 12	07 27	07 42	07 57	08 12	08 27	08 42	08 57	09 12	09 27	09 42	09 57	10 12	10 27	10 42	10 57	11 12	11 27	11 42
Gospel Oak d	06 14	06 29	06 44	06 59	07 14	07 29	07 44	07 59	08 14	08 29	08 44	08 59	09 14	09 29	09 44	09 59	10 14	10 29	10 44	10 59	11 14	11 29	11 44
Kentish Town West d	06 16	06 31	06 46	07 01	07 16	07 31	07 46	08 01	08 16	08 31	08 46	09 01	09 16	09 31	09 46	10 01	10 16	10 31	10 46	11 01	11 16	11 31	11 46
Camden Road d	06 18	06 33	06 48	07 03	07 18	07 33	07 48	08 03	08 18	08 33	08 48	09 03	09 18	09 33	09 48	10 03	10 18	10 33	10 48	11 03	11 18	11 33	11 48
Caledonian Rd & Barnsbury d	06 21	06 36	06 51	07 06	07 21	07 36	07 51	08 06	08 21	08 36	08 51	09 06	09 21	09 36	09 51	10 06	10 21	10 36	10 51	11 06	11 21	11 36	11 51
Highbury & Islington ⊖ d	06 24	06 39	06 54	07 09	07 24	07 39	07 54	08 09	08 24	08 39	08 54	09 09	09 24	09 39	09 54	10 09	10 24	10 39	10 54	11 09	11 24	11 39	11 54
Canonbury ⊖ d	06 26	06 41	06 56	07 11	07 26	07 41	07 56	08 11	08 26	08 41	08 56	09 11	09 26	09 41	09 56	10 11	10 26	10 41	10 56	11 11	11 26	11 41	11 56
Dalston Kingsland d	06 29	06 44	06 59	07 14	07 29	07 44	07 59	08 14	08 29	08 44	08 59	09 14	09 29	09 44	09 59	10 14	10 29	10 44	10 59	11 14	11 29	11 44	11 59
Hackney Central d	06 31	06 46	07 01	07 16	07 31	07 46	08 01	08 16	08 31	08 46	09 01	09 16	09 31	09 46	10 01	10 16	10 31	10 46	11 01	11 16	11 31	11 46	12 01
Homerton d	06 33	06 48	07 03	07 18	07 33	07 48	08 03	08 18	08 33	08 48	09 03	09 18	09 33	09 48	10 03	10 18	10 33	10 48	11 03	11 18	11 33	11 48	12 03
Hackney Wick d	06 36	06 51	07 06	07 21	07 36	07 51	08 06	08 21	08 36	08 51	09 06	09 21	09 36	09 51	10 06	10 21	10 36	10 51	11 06	11 21	11 36	11 51	12 06
Stratford Low Level 7 ⊖ ⛴ a	06 44	06 58	07 14	07 28	07 43	08 01	08 13	08 28	08 43	08 58	09 13	09 28	09 43	09 58	10 13	10 28	10 43	10 58	11 13	11 28	11 43	11 59	12 13

Station	LO	LO	LO	LO	LO	LO	LO	LO	LO	LO	LO	LO	LO	LO	LO	LO	LO	LO	LO	LO	LO	LO	LO
Richmond ⊖ d	11 27	11 41	11 57	12 11	12 27	12 41	12 57	13 11	13 27	13 41	13 57	14 11	14 27	14 41	14 57	15 11	15 27	15 41	15 57	16 11	16 27	16 41	16 57
Kew Gardens ⊖ d	11 30	11 44	12 00	12 14	12 30	12 44	13 00	13 14	13 30	13 44	14 00	14 14	14 30	14 44	15 00	15 14	15 30	15 44	16 00	16 14	16 30	16 44	17 00
Gunnersbury ⊖ d	11 33	11 47	12 03	12 17	12 33	12 47	13 03	13 17	13 33	13 47	14 03	14 17	14 33	14 47	15 03	15 17	15 33	15 47	16 03	16 17	16 33	16 47	17 03
South Acton d	11 35	11 49	12 05	12 19	12 35	12 49	13 05	13 19	13 35	13 49	14 05	14 19	14 35	14 49	15 05	15 19	15 35	15 49	16 05	16 19	16 35	16 49	17 05
Acton Central d	11 38	11 53	12 08	12 23	12 38	12 53	13 08	13 23	13 38	13 53	14 08	14 23	14 38	14 53	15 08	15 23	15 38	15 53	16 08	16 23	16 38	16 53	17 08
Willesden Jn. High Level ⊖ a	11 43	11 58	12 13	12 29	12 43	12 58	13 13	13 29	13 43	13 59	14 13	14 29	14 43	14 58	15 13	15 29	15 43	15 59	16 13	16 29	16 43	16 58	17 13
d	11 44	11 59	12 14	12 29	12 44	12 59	13 14	13 29	13 44	13 59	14 14	14 29	14 44	14 59	15 14	15 29	15 44	15 59	16 14	16 29	16 44	16 59	17 14
Kensal Rise d	11 47	12 02	12 17	12 32	12 47	13 02	13 17	13 32	13 47	14 02	14 17	14 32	14 47	15 02	15 17	15 32	15 47	16 02	16 17	16 32	16 47	17 02	17 17
Brondesbury Park d	11 49	12 04	12 19	12 34	12 49	13 04	13 19	13 34	13 49	14 04	14 19	14 34	14 49	15 04	15 19	15 34	15 49	16 04	16 19	16 34	16 49	17 04	17 19
Brondesbury d	11 51	12 06	12 21	12 36	12 51	13 06	13 21	13 36	13 51	14 06	14 21	14 36	14 51	15 06	15 21	15 36	15 51	16 06	16 21	16 36	16 51	17 06	17 21
West Hampstead ⊖ d	11 52	12 07	12 22	12 37	12 52	13 07	13 22	13 37	13 52	14 07	14 22	14 37	14 52	15 07	15 22	15 37	15 52	16 07	16 22	16 37	16 52	17 07	17 22
Finchley Road & Frognal d	11 54	12 09	12 24	12 39	12 54	13 09	13 24	13 39	13 54	14 09	14 24	14 39	14 54	15 09	15 24	15 39	15 54	16 09	16 24	16 39	16 54	17 09	17 24
Hampstead Heath d	11 57	12 12	12 27	12 42	12 57	13 12	13 27	13 42	13 57	14 12	14 27	14 42	14 57	15 12	15 27	15 42	15 57	16 12	16 27	16 42	16 57	17 12	17 27
Gospel Oak d	11 59	12 14	12 29	12 44	12 59	13 14	13 29	13 44	13 59	14 14	14 29	14 44	14 59	15 14	15 29	15 44	15 59	16 14	16 29	16 44	16 59	17 14	17 29
Kentish Town West d	12 01	12 16	12 31	12 46	13 01	13 16	13 31	13 46	14 01	14 16	14 31	14 46	15 01	15 16	15 31	15 46	16 01	16 16	16 31	16 46	17 01	17 16	17 31
Camden Road d	12 03	12 18	12 33	12 48	13 03	13 18	13 33	13 48	14 03	14 18	14 33	14 48	15 03	15 18	15 33	15 48	16 03	16 18	16 33	16 48	17 03	17 18	17 33
Caledonian Rd & Barnsbury d	12 06	12 21	12 36	12 51	13 06	13 21	13 36	13 51	14 06	14 21	14 36	14 51	15 06	15 21	15 36	15 51	16 06	16 21	16 36	16 51	17 06	17 21	17 36
Highbury & Islington ⊖ d	12 09	12 24	12 39	12 54	13 09	13 24	13 39	13 54	14 09	14 24	14 39	14 54	15 09	15 24	15 39	15 54	16 09	16 24	16 39	16 54	17 09	17 24	17 39
Canonbury ⊖ d	12 11	12 26	12 41	12 56	13 11	13 26	13 41	13 56	14 11	14 26	14 41	14 56	15 11	15 26	15 41	15 56	16 11	16 26	16 41	16 56	17 11	17 26	17 41
Dalston Kingsland d	12 14	12 29	12 44	12 59	13 14	13 29	13 44	13 59	14 14	14 29	14 44	14 59	15 14	15 29	15 44	15 59	16 14	16 29	16 44	16 59	17 14	17 29	17 44
Hackney Central d	12 16	12 31	12 46	13 01	13 16	13 31	13 46	14 01	14 16	14 31	14 46	15 01	15 16	15 31	15 46	16 01	16 16	16 31	16 46	17 01	17 16	17 31	17 46
Homerton d	12 18	12 33	12 48	13 03	13 18	13 33	13 48	14 03	14 18	14 33	14 48	15 03	15 18	15 33	15 48	16 03	16 18	16 33	16 48	17 03	17 18	17 33	17 48
Hackney Wick d	12 21	12 36	12 51	13 06	13 21	13 36	13 51	14 06	14 21	14 36	14 51	15 06	15 21	15 36	15 51	16 06	16 21	16 36	16 51	17 06	17 21	17 36	17 51
Stratford Low Level 7 ⊖ ⛴ a	12 29	12 43	12 58	13 13	13 28	13 43	13 58	14 13	14 28	14 43	14 58	15 13	15 28	15 43	15 58	16 13	16 28	16 43	16 58	17 13	17 28	17 43	17 58

For general notes see front of timetable
For details of catering facilities see Directory of Train Operators

b Willesden Jn Low Level

Table 59

Saturdays

Richmond → Willesden Junction, West Hampstead, Highbury, Stratford, Silvertown & City Airport and North Woolwich.

Network diagram - see first page of Table 59

Station		LO	LO	LO	LO	LO	LO	LO	LO	LO	LO	LO	LO	LO	LO	LO	LO	LO	LO	LO	LO	LO	LO
Richmond	⊖ d	17 11	17 27	17 41	17 57	18 11	18 26	18 41	18 56	19 16	19 26	19 40	19 57	20 16	20 36	20 56	21 16	21 36	21 56	22 16	22 36	22 56	23 16
Kew Gardens	⊖ d	17 14	17 30	17 44	18 00	18 14	18 29	18 44	18 59	19 19	19 29	19 43	20 00	20 19	20 39	20 59	21 19	21 39	21 59	22 19	22 39	22 59	23 19
Gunnersbury	⊖ d	17 17	17 33	17 47	18 03	18 17	18 32	18 47	19 02	19 22	19 32	19 46	20 03	20 22	20 42	21 02	21 22	21 42	22 02	22 22	22 42	23 02	23 22
South Acton	d	17 19	17 35	17 49	18 05	18 19	18 34	18 49	19 04	19 24	19 34	19 48	20 05	20 24	20 44	21 04	21 24	21 44	22 04	22 24	22 44	23 04	23 24
Acton Central	d	17 23	17 38	17 53	18 08	18 23	18 38	18 52	19 07	19 27	19 38	19 51	20 08	20 27	20 47	21 07	21 27	21 47	22 07	22 27	22 47	23 07	23 27
Willesden Jn. High Level	⊖ a	17 29	17 43	17 58	18 13	18 29	18 43	18 57	19 12	19 32	19 43	19 59	20 13	20 32	20 52	21 12	21 32	21 52	22 12	22 32	22 52	23 13	23 35
	d	17 29	17 44	17 59	18 14	18 29	18 44	18 58	19 13	19 33	19 44	20 00	20 14	20 33	20 53	21 13	21 33	21 53	22 13	22 33	22 53	23 13	
Kensal Rise	d	17 32	17 47	18 02	18 17	18 32	18 47	19 01	19 16	19 36	19 47	20 03	20 17	20 36	20 56	21 16	21 36	21 56	22 16	22 36	22 56	23 16	
Brondesbury Park	d	17 34	17 49	18 04	18 19	18 34	18 49	19 03	19 18	19 38	19 49	20 05	20 19	20 38	20 58	21 18	21 38	21 58	22 18	22 38	22 58	23 18	
Brondesbury	d	17 36	17 51	18 06	18 21	18 36	18 51	19 05	19 20	19 40	19 51	20 07	20 21	20 40	21 00	21 20	21 40	22 00	22 20	22 40	23 00	23 20	
West Hampstead	⊖ d	17 37	17 52	18 07	18 22	18 37	18 52	19 06	19 21	19 41	19 52	20 08	20 22	20 41	21 01	21 21	21 41	22 01	22 21	22 41	23 01	23 21	
Finchley Road & Frognal	d	17 39	17 54	18 09	18 24	18 39	18 54	19 08	19 23	19 43	19 54	20 10	20 24	20 43	21 03	21 23	21 43	22 03	22 23	22 43	23 03	23 23	
Hampstead Heath	d	17 42	17 57	18 12	18 27	18 42	18 57	19 11	19 26	19 46	19 57	20 13	20 27	20 46	21 06	21 26	21 46	22 06	22 26	22 46	23 06	23 26	
Gospel Oak	d	17 44	17 59	18 14	18 29	18 44	18 59	19 13	19 28	19 48	19 59	20 15	20 29	20 48	21 08	21 28	21 48	22 08	22 28	22 48	23 08	23 28	
Kentish Town West	d	17 46	18 01	18 16	18 31	18 46	19 01	19 15	19 30	19 50	20 01	20 17	20 31	20 50	21 10	21 30	21 50	22 10	22 30	22 50	23 10	23 30	
Camden Road	d	17 48	18 03	18 18	18 33	18 48	19 03	19 17	19 32	19 52	20 03	20 19	20 33	20 52	21 12	21 32	21 52	22 12	22 32	22 52	23 12	23 32	
Caledonian Rd & Barnsbury	d	17 51	18 06	18 21	18 36	18 51	19 06	19 20	19 35	19 55	20 06	20 22	20 36	20 55	21 15	21 35	21 55	22 15	22 35	22 55	23 15	23 35	
Highbury & Islington	⊖ d	17 54	18 09	18 24	18 39	18 54	19 09	19 23	19 38	19 57	20 09	20 24	20 38	20 57	21 17	21 37	21 57	22 17	22 37	22 57	23 17	23 37	
Canonbury	⊖ d	17 56	18 11	18 26	18 41	18 56	19 11	19 24	19 39	19 59	20 11	20 26	20 40	20 59	21 19	21 39	21 59	22 19	22 39	22 59	23 19	23 39	
Dalston Kingsland	d	17 59	18 14	18 29	18 44	18 59	19 14	19 27	19 42	20 02	20 14	20 29	20 43	21 02	21 22	21 42	22 02	22 22	22 42	23 02	23 22	23 42	
Hackney Central	d	18 01	18 16	18 31	18 46	19 01	19 16	19 29	19 44	20 04	20 16	20 31	20 45	21 04	21 24	21 44	22 04	22 24	22 44	23 04	23 24	23 44	
Homerton	d	18 03	18 18	18 33	18 48	19 03	19 18	19 31	19 46	20 06	20 18	20 33	20 47	21 06	21 26	21 46	22 06	22 26	22 46	23 06	23 26	23 46	
Hackney Wick	d	18 06	18 21	18 36	18 51	19 06	19 21	19 34	19 49	20 09	20 21	20 35	20 50	21 09	21 29	21 49	22 09	22 29	22 49	23 09	23 29	23 49	
Stratford Low Level 7	⊖ a	18 13	18 28	18 43	18 59	19 13	19 28	19 44	19 59	20 16	20 28	20 42	20 57	21 19	21 39	21 59	22 16	22 36	22 56	23 16	23 36	23 59	

Sundays

Station		LO A	LO	LO	LO		LO	LO	LO
Richmond	⊖ d			09 08	09 38		22 08	22 38	23 08
Kew Gardens	⊖ d			09 11	09 41		22 11	22 41	23 11
Gunnersbury	⊖ d			09 14	09 44		22 14	22 44	23 14
South Acton	d			09 16	09 46		22 16	22 46	23 16
Acton Central	d			09 19	09 49		22 19	22 49	23 19
Willesden Jn. High Level	⊖ a			09 24	09 54		22 24	22 54	23 26
	d	08 55	08 55	09 25	09 55	and	22 25	22 55	
Kensal Rise	d	08 57	08 57	09 28	09 58		22 28	22 58	
Brondesbury Park	d	08 59	08 59	09 30	10 00	every 30	22 30	23 00	
Brondesbury	d	09 01	09 01	09 32	10 02		22 32	23 02	
West Hampstead	⊖ d	09 03	09 03	09 33	10 03	minutes	22 33	23 03	
Finchley Road & Frognal	d	09 04	09 04	09 35	10 05		22 35	23 05	
Hampstead Heath	d	09 07	09 07	09 38	10 08	until	22 38	23 08	
Gospel Oak	d	09 09	09 09	09 40	10 10		22 40	23 10	
Kentish Town West	d	09 11	09 11	09 42	10 12		22 42	23 12	
Camden Road	d	09 14	09 14	09 44	10 14		22 44	23 14	
Caledonian Rd & Barnsbury	d	09 17	09 17	09 47	10 17		22 47	23 17	
Highbury & Islington	⊖ d	09 19	09 19	09 50	10 20		22 50	23 20	
Canonbury	⊖ d	09 21	09 21	09 52	10 22		22 52	23 22	
Dalston Kingsland	d	09 24	09 24	09 55	10 25		22 55	23 25	
Hackney Central	d	09 26	09 26	09 57	10 27		22 57	23 27	
Homerton	d	09 28	09 28	09 59	10 29		22 59	23 29	
Hackney Wick	d	09 31	09 31	10 02	10 32		23 02	23 32	
Stratford Low Level 7	⊖ a	09 38	09 38	10 09	10 39		23 09	23 39	

For general notes see front of timetable
For details of catering facilities see Directory of Train Operators

A From Clapham Junction (Table 186)

London, Queens Park and Harrow & Wealdstone → Watford Junction

Network Diagram - See first page of Table 59

Mondays to Fridays

Miles	Station		LO MO	LO MX	LO MO	LO MX	LO	LO	LO	LO	LO	LO	LO	LO	LO	LO	LO	LO	LO	LO	LO
0	**London Euston** 15	⊖ d	23p17	23p27	23p47	23p57	05 27	05 57	06 27	06 57	07 17	07 37	07 57	08 17	08 37	08 57	09 17	09 37	09 57	10 17	10 37
2½	South Hampstead	d	23p23	23p33	23p53	00 03	05 33	06 03	06 33	07 03	07 23	07 43	08 03	08 23	08 43	09 03	09 23	09 43	10 03	10 23	10 43
3	Kilburn High Road	d	23p24	23p34	23p54	00 04	05 34	06 04	06 34	07 04	07 24	07 44	08 04	08 24	08 44	09 04	09 24	09 44	10 04	10 24	10 44
3¾	**Queens Park (Dc)**	⊖ d	23p26	23p36	23p56	00 06	05 36	06 06	06 36	07 06	07 26	07 46	08 06	08 26	08 46	09 06	09 26	09 46	10 06	10 26	10 46
4½	Kensal Green	d	23p28	23p38	23p58	00 08	05 38	06 08	06 38	07 08	07 28	07 48	08 08	08 28	08 48	09 08	09 28	09 48	10 08	10 28	10 48
5½	**Willesden Jn Low Level**	d	23p31	23p41	00 01	00 11	05 41	06 11	06 41	07 11	07 31	07 51	08 11	08 31	08 51	09 11	09 31	09 51	10 11	10 31	10 51
6	Harlesden	d	23p33	23p43	00 03	00 13	05 43	06 13	06 43	07 13	07 33	07 53	08 13	08 33	08 53	09 13	09 33	09 53	10 13	10 33	10 53
7	Stonebridge Park	d	23p35	23p45	00 05	00 15	05 45	06 15	06 45	07 15	07 35	07 55	08 15	08 35	08 55	09 15	09 35	09 55	10 15	10 35	10 55
8	Wembley Central Dc	d	23p38	23p48	00 08	00 18	05 48	06 18	06 48	07 18	07 38	07 58	08 18	08 38	08 58	09 18	09 38	09 58	10 18	10 38	10 58
9	North Wembley	d	23p40	23p50	00 10	00 20	05 50	06 20	06 50	07 20	07 40	08 00	08 20	08 40	09 00	09 20	09 40	10 00	10 20	10 40	11 00
9½	South Kenton	d	23p42	23p52	00 12	00 22	05 52	06 22	06 52	07 22	07 42	08 02	08 22	08 42	09 02	09 22	09 42	10 02	10 22	10 42	11 02
10¼	Kenton	d	23p44	23p54	00 14	00 24	05 54	06 24	06 54	07 24	07 44	08 04	08 24	08 44	09 04	09 24	09 44	10 04	10 24	10 44	11 04
11¼	**Harrow & Wealdstone D.C.**	d	23p46	23p56	00 16	00 26	05 56	06 26	06 56	07 26	07 46	08 06	08 26	08 46	09 06	09 26	09 46	10 06	10 26	10 46	11 06
12½	Headstone Lane	d	23p49	23p59	00 19	00 29	05 59	06 29	06 59	07 29	07 49	08 09	08 29	08 49	09 09	09 29	09 49	10 09	10 29	10 49	11 09
13¼	Hatch End	d	23p51	00 01	00 21	00 31	06 01	06 31	07 01	07 31	07 51	08 11	08 31	08 51	09 11	09 31	09 51	10 11	10 31	10 51	11 11
14¾	Carpenders Park	d	23p54	00 04	00 24	00 34	06 04	06 34	07 04	07 34	07 54	08 14	08 34	08 54	09 14	09 34	09 54	10 14	10 34	10 54	11 14
16	Bushey Dc	d	23p57	00 07	00 27	00 37	06 07	06 37	07 07	07 37	07 57	08 17	08 37	08 57	09 17	09 37	09 57	10 17	10 37	10 57	11 17
16¾	Watford High Street	d	00 01	00 10	00 30	00 40	06 10	06 40	07 10	07 40	08 00	08 20	08 40	09 00	09 20	09 40	10 00	10 20	10 40	11 00	11 20
17¾	**Watford Junction Dc**	a	00 04	00 14	00 34	00 44	06 14	06 44	07 14	07 44	08 04	08 24	08 44	09 04	09 24	09 44	10 04	10 24	10 45	11 04	11 24

Station		LO	LO	LO	LO	LO	LO	LO	LO	LO	LO	LO	LO	LO	LO	LO	LO	LO	LO	LO
London Euston 15	⊖ d	10 57	11 17	11 37	11 57	12 17	12 37	12 57	13 17	13 37	13 57	14 17	14 37	14 57	15 17	15 37	15 57	16 17	16 37	16 57
South Hampstead	d	11 03	11 23	11 43	12 03	12 23	12 43	13 03	13 23	13 43	14 03	14 23	14 43	15 03	15 23	15 43	16 03	16 23	16 43	17 03
Kilburn High Road	d	11 04	11 24	11 44	12 04	12 24	12 44	13 04	13 24	13 44	14 04	14 24	14 44	15 04	15 24	15 44	16 04	16 24	16 44	17 04
Queens Park (Dc)	⊖ d	11 06	11 26	11 46	12 06	12 26	12 46	13 06	13 26	13 46	14 06	14 26	14 46	15 06	15 26	15 46	16 06	16 27	16 47	17 07
Kensal Green	d	11 08	11 28	11 48	12 08	12 28	12 48	13 08	13 28	13 48	14 08	14 28	14 48	15 08	15 28	15 48	16 08	16 29	16 49	17 09
Willesden Jn Low Level	d	11 11	11 31	11 51	12 11	12 31	12 51	13 11	13 31	13 51	14 11	14 31	14 51	15 11	15 31	15 51	16 11	16 32	16 52	17 12
Harlesden	d	11 13	11 33	11 53	12 13	12 33	12 53	13 13	13 33	13 53	14 13	14 33	14 53	15 13	15 33	15 53	16 13	16 34	16 54	17 14
Stonebridge Park	d	11 15	11 35	11 55	12 15	12 35	12 55	13 15	13 35	13 55	14 15	14 35	14 55	15 15	15 35	15 55	16 15	16 36	16 56	17 16
Wembley Central Dc	d	11 18	11 38	11 58	12 18	12 38	12 58	13 18	13 38	13 58	14 18	14 38	14 58	15 18	15 38	15 58	16 18	16 39	16 59	17 19
North Wembley	d	11 20	11 40	12 00	12 20	12 40	13 00	13 20	13 40	14 00	14 20	14 40	15 00	15 20	15 40	16 00	16 20	16 41	17 01	17 21
South Kenton	d	11 22	11 42	12 02	12 22	12 42	13 02	13 22	13 42	14 02	14 22	14 42	15 02	15 22	15 42	16 02	16 22	16 43	17 03	17 23
Kenton	d	11 24	11 44	12 04	12 24	12 44	13 04	13 24	13 44	14 04	14 24	14 44	15 04	15 24	15 44	16 04	16 24	16 45	17 05	17 25
Harrow & Wealdstone D.C.	d	11 26	11 46	12 06	12 26	12 46	13 06	13 26	13 46	14 06	14 26	14 46	15 06	15 26	15 46	16 06	16 26	16 48	17 08	17 28
Headstone Lane	d	11 29	11 49	12 09	12 29	12 49	13 09	13 29	13 49	14 09	14 29	14 49	15 09	15 29	15 49	16 09	16 29	16 51	17 11	17 31
Hatch End	d	11 31	11 51	12 11	12 31	12 51	13 11	13 31	13 51	14 11	14 31	14 51	15 11	15 31	15 51	16 11	16 31	16 53	17 13	17 33
Carpenders Park	d	11 34	11 54	12 14	12 34	12 54	13 14	13 34	13 54	14 14	14 34	14 54	15 14	15 34	15 54	16 14	16 34	16 56	17 16	17 36
Bushey Dc	d	11 37	11 57	12 17	12 37	12 57	13 17	13 37	13 57	14 17	14 37	14 57	15 17	15 37	15 57	16 17	16 37	16 59	17 19	17 39
Watford High Street	d	11 40	12 00	12 20	12 40	13 00	13 20	13 40	14 00	14 20	14 40	15 00	15 20	15 40	16 00	16 20	16 40	17 01	17 21	17 41
Watford Junction Dc	a	11 44	12 04	12 24	12 44	13 04	13 24	13 44	14 04	14 24	14 44	15 04	15 24	15 44	16 04	16 24	16 44	17 06	17 26	17 48

Station		LO	LO	LO	LO	LO	LO	LO	LO	LO	LO	LO	LO	LO	LO	LO	LO	LO	LO
London Euston 15	⊖ d	17 17	17 37	17 57	18 17	18 37	18 57	19 17	19 37	19 57	20 17	20 37	20 57	21 27	21 57	22 27	22 57	23 27	23 57
South Hampstead	d	17 23	17 43	18 03	18 23	18 43	19 03	19 23	19 43	20 03	20 23	20 43	21 03	21 33	22 03	22 33	23 03	23 33	00 03
Kilburn High Road	d	17 24	17 44	18 04	18 24	18 44	19 04	19 24	19 44	20 04	20 24	20 44	21 04	21 34	22 04	22 34	23 04	23 34	00 04
Queens Park (Dc)	⊖ d	17 27	17 47	18 07	18 27	18 47	19 07	19 26	19 46	20 06	20 26	20 46	21 06	21 36	22 06	22 36	23 06	23 36	00 06
Kensal Green	d	17 29	17 49	18 09	18 29	18 49	19 09	19 28	19 48	20 08	20 28	20 48	21 08	21 38	22 08	22 38	23 08	23 38	00 08
Willesden Jn Low Level	d	17 32	17 52	18 12	18 32	18 52	19 12	19 31	19 51	20 11	20 31	20 51	21 11	21 41	22 11	22 41	23 11	23 41	00 11
Harlesden	d	17 34	17 54	18 14	18 34	18 54	19 14	19 33	19 53	20 13	20 33	20 53	21 13	21 43	22 13	22 43	23 13	23 43	00 13
Stonebridge Park	d	17 36	17 56	18 16	18 36	18 56	19 16	19 35	19 55	20 15	20 35	20 55	21 15	21 45	22 15	22 45	23 15	23 45	00 15
Wembley Central Dc	d	17 39	17 59	18 19	18 39	18 59	19 19	19 38	19 58	20 18	20 38	20 58	21 18	21 48	22 18	22 48	23 18	23 48	00 18
North Wembley	d	17 41	18 01	18 21	18 41	19 01	19 21	19 40	20 00	20 20	20 40	21 00	21 20	21 50	22 20	22 50	23 20	23 50	00 20
South Kenton	d	17 43	18 03	18 23	18 43	19 03	19 23	19 42	20 02	20 22	20 42	21 02	21 22	21 52	22 22	22 52	23 22	23 52	00 22
Kenton	d	17 45	18 05	18 25	18 45	19 05	19 25	19 44	20 04	20 24	20 44	21 04	21 24	21 54	22 24	22 54	23 24	23 54	00 24
Harrow & Wealdstone D.C.	d	17 48	18 08	18 28	18 48	19 08	19 28	19 46	20 06	20 26	20 46	21 06	21 26	21 56	22 26	22 56	23 26	23 56	00 26
Headstone Lane	d	17 51	18 11	18 31	18 51	19 11	19 31	19 49	20 09	20 29	20 49	21 09	21 29	21 59	22 29	22 59	23 29	23 59	00 29
Hatch End	d	17 53	18 13	18 33	18 53	19 13	19 33	19 51	20 11	20 31	20 51	21 11	21 31	22 01	22 31	23 01	23 31	00 01	00 31
Carpenders Park	d	17 56	18 16	18 36	18 56	19 16	19 36	19 54	20 14	20 34	20 54	21 14	21 34	22 04	22 34	23 04	23 34	00 04	00 34
Bushey Dc	d	17 59	18 19	18 39	18 59	19 19	19 39	19 57	20 17	20 37	20 57	21 17	21 37	22 07	22 37	23 07	23 37	00 07	00 37
Watford High Street	d	18 01	18 21	18 41	19 01	19 21	19 41	20 00	20 20	20 40	21 00	21 20	21 40	22 10	22 40	23 10	23 40	00 10	00 40
Watford Junction Dc	a	18 08	18 28	18 48	19 08	19 28	19 48	20 04	20 24	20 44	21 04	21 24	21 44	22 14	22 44	23 14	23 44	00 14	00 44

Saturdays

Station		LO	LO	LO	LO	LO	LO	LO	LO	LO	LO	LO	LO	LO	LO	LO	LO	LO	LO	LO
London Euston 15	⊖ d	23p27	23p57	05 27	05 57	06 27	06 57	07 17	07 37	07 57	08 17	08 37	08 57	09 17	09 37	09 57	10 17	10 37	10 57	11 17
South Hampstead	d	23p33	00 03	05 33	06 03	06 33	07 03	07 23	07 43	08 03	08 23	08 43	09 03	09 23	09 43	10 03	10 23	10 43	11 03	11 23
Kilburn High Road	d	23p34	00 04	05 34	06 04	06 34	07 04	07 24	07 44	08 04	08 24	08 44	09 04	09 24	09 44	10 04	10 24	10 44	11 04	11 24
Queens Park (Dc)	⊖ d	23p36	00 06	05 36	06 06	06 36	07 06	07 26	07 46	08 06	08 26	08 46	09 06	09 26	09 46	10 06	10 26	10 46	11 06	11 26
Kensal Green	d	23p38	00 08	05 38	06 08	06 38	07 08	07 28	07 48	08 08	08 28	08 48	09 08	09 28	09 48	10 08	10 28	10 48	11 08	11 28
Willesden Jn Low Level	d	23p41	00 11	05 41	06 11	06 41	07 11	07 31	07 51	08 11	08 31	08 51	09 11	09 31	09 51	10 11	10 31	10 51	11 11	11 31
Harlesden	d	23p43	00 13	05 43	06 13	06 43	07 13	07 33	07 53	08 13	08 33	08 53	09 13	09 33	09 53	10 13	10 33	10 53	11 13	11 33
Stonebridge Park	d	23p45	00 15	05 45	06 15	06 45	07 15	07 35	07 55	08 15	08 35	08 55	09 15	09 35	09 55	10 15	10 35	10 55	11 15	11 35
Wembley Central Dc	d	23p48	00 18	05 48	06 18	06 48	07 18	07 38	07 58	08 18	08 38	08 58	09 18	09 38	09 58	10 18	10 38	10 58	11 18	11 38
North Wembley	d	23p50	00 20	05 50	06 20	06 50	07 20	07 40	08 00	08 20	08 40	09 00	09 20	09 40	10 00	10 20	10 40	11 00	11 20	11 40
South Kenton	d	23p52	00 22	05 52	06 22	06 52	07 22	07 42	08 02	08 22	08 42	09 02	09 22	09 42	10 02	10 22	10 42	11 02	11 22	11 42
Kenton	d	23p54	00 24	05 54	06 24	06 54	07 24	07 44	08 04	08 24	08 44	09 04	09 24	09 44	10 04	10 24	10 44	11 04	11 24	11 44
Harrow & Wealdstone D.C.	d	23p56	00 26	05 56	06 26	06 56	07 26	07 46	08 06	08 26	08 46	09 06	09 26	09 46	10 06	10 26	10 46	11 06	11 26	11 46
Headstone Lane	d	23p59	00 29	05 59	06 29	06 59	07 29	07 49	08 09	08 29	08 49	09 09	09 29	09 49	10 09	10 29	10 49	11 09	11 29	11 49
Hatch End	d	00 01	00 31	06 01	06 31	07 01	07 31	07 51	08 11	08 31	08 51	09 11	09 31	09 51	10 11	10 31	10 51	11 11	11 31	11 51
Carpenders Park	d	00 04	00 34	06 04	06 34	07 04	07 34	07 54	08 14	08 34	08 54	09 14	09 34	09 54	10 14	10 34	10 54	11 14	11 34	11 54
Bushey Dc	d	00 07	00 37	06 07	06 37	07 07	07 37	07 57	08 17	08 37	08 57	09 17	09 37	09 57	10 17	10 37	10 57	11 17	11 37	11 57
Watford High Street	d	00 10	00 40	06 10	06 40	07 10	07 40	08 00	08 20	08 40	09 00	09 20	09 40	10 00	10 20	10 40	11 00	11 20	11 40	12 00
Watford Junction Dc	a	00 14	00 44	06 14	06 44	07 18	07 44	08 04	08 24	08 44	09 04	09 24	09 44	10 04	10 24	10 44	11 04	11 24	11 44	12 04

For general notes see front of timetable
For details of catering facilities see
Directory of Train Operators

Stations Queen's Park to Harrow & Wealdstone inclusive are also served by London Underground Bakerloo line services

Table 60

Saturdays

London, Queens Park and Harrow & Wealdstone → Watford Junction

Network Diagram - See first page of Table 59

	LO	LO	LO		LO	LO	LO		LO	LO	LO		LO	LO	LO		LO	LO	LO		LO	LO	LO		LO
London Euston 15 ⊖ d	11 37	11 57	12 17		12 37	12 57	13 17		13 37	13 57	14 17		14 37	14 57	15 17		15 37	15 57	16 17		16 37	16 57	17 17		17 37
South Hampstead d	11 43	12 03	12 23		12 43	13 03	13 23		13 43	14 03	14 23		14 43	15 03	15 23		15 43	16 03	16 23		16 43	17 03	17 23		17 43
Kilburn High Road d	11 44	12 04	12 24		12 44	13 04	13 24		13 44	14 04	14 24		14 44	15 04	15 24		15 44	16 04	16 24		16 44	17 04	17 24		17 44
Queens Park (Dc) ⊖ d	11 46	12 06	12 26		12 46	13 06	13 26		13 46	14 06	14 26		14 46	15 06	15 26		15 46	16 06	16 26		16 46	17 06	17 26		17 46
Kensal Green d	11 48	12 08	12 28		12 48	13 08	13 28		13 48	14 08	14 28		14 48	15 08	15 28		15 48	16 08	16 28		16 48	17 08	17 28		17 48
Willesden Jn Low Level d	11 51	12 11	12 31		12 51	13 11	13 31		13 51	14 11	14 31		14 51	15 11	15 31		15 51	16 11	16 31		16 51	17 11	17 31		17 51
Harlesden d	11 53	12 13	12 33		12 53	13 13	13 33		13 53	14 13	14 33		14 53	15 13	15 33		15 53	16 13	16 33		16 53	17 13	17 33		17 53
Stonebridge Park d	11 55	12 15	12 35		12 55	13 15	13 35		13 55	14 15	14 35		14 55	15 15	15 35		15 55	16 15	16 35		16 55	17 15	17 35		17 55
Wembley Central Dc d	11 58	12 18	12 38		12 58	13 18	13 38		13 58	14 18	14 38		14 58	15 18	15 38		15 58	16 18	16 38		16 58	17 18	17 38		17 58
North Wembley d	12 00	12 20	12 40		13 00	13 20	13 40		14 00	14 20	14 40		15 00	15 20	15 40		16 00	16 20	16 40		17 00	17 20	17 40		18 00
South Kenton d	12 02	12 22	12 42		13 02	13 22	13 42		14 02	14 22	14 42		15 02	15 22	15 42		16 02	16 22	16 42		17 02	17 22	17 42		18 02
Kenton d	12 04	12 24	12 44		13 04	13 24	13 44		14 04	14 24	14 44		15 04	15 24	15 44		16 04	16 24	16 44		17 04	17 24	17 44		18 04
Harrow & Wealdstone D.C. d	12 06	12 26	12 46		13 06	13 26	13 46		14 06	14 26	14 46		15 06	15 26	15 46		16 06	16 26	16 46		17 06	17 26	17 46		18 06
Headstone Lane d	12 09	12 29	12 49		13 09	13 29	13 49		14 09	14 29	14 49		15 09	15 29	15 49		16 09	16 29	16 49		17 09	17 29	17 49		18 09
Hatch End d	12 11	12 31	12 51		13 11	13 31	13 51		14 11	14 31	14 51		15 11	15 31	15 51		16 11	16 31	16 51		17 11	17 31	17 51		18 11
Carpenders Park d	12 14	12 34	12 54		13 14	13 34	13 54		14 14	14 34	14 54		15 14	15 34	15 54		16 14	16 34	16 54		17 14	17 34	17 54		18 14
Bushey Dc d	12 17	12 37	12 57		13 17	13 37	13 57		14 17	14 37	14 57		15 17	15 37	15 57		16 17	16 37	16 57		17 17	17 37	17 57		18 17
Watford High Street d	12 20	12 40	13 00		13 20	13 40	14 00		14 20	14 40	15 00		15 20	15 40	16 00		16 20	16 40	17 00		17 20	17 40	18 00		18 20
Watford Junction Dc a	12 24	12 44	13 04		13 24	13 44	14 04		14 24	14 44	15 04		15 24	15 44	16 04		16 24	16 44	17 04		17 24	17 44	18 04		18 24

	LO	LO	LO		LO	LO	LO		LO	LO	LO		LO	LO	LO		LO	LO	LO		LO				
London Euston 15 ⊖ d	17 57	18 17	18 37		18 57	19 17	19 37		19 57	20 17	20 37		20 57	21 27	21 57		22 27	22 57	23 27		23 57				
South Hampstead d	18 03	18 23	18 43		19 03	19 23	19 43		20 03	20 23	20 43		21 03	21 33	22 03		22 33	23 03	23 33		00 03				
Kilburn High Road d	18 04	18 24	18 44		19 04	19 24	19 44		20 04	20 24	20 44		21 04	21 34	22 04		22 34	23 04	23 34		00 04				
Queens Park (Dc) ⊖ d	18 06	18 26	18 46		19 06	19 26	19 46		20 06	20 26	20 46		21 06	21 36	22 06		22 36	23 06	23 36		00 06				
Kensal Green d	18 08	18 28	18 48		19 08	19 28	19 48		20 08	20 28	20 48		21 08	21 38	22 08		22 38	23 08	23 38		00 08				
Willesden Jn Low Level d	18 11	18 31	18 51		19 11	19 31	19 51		20 11	20 31	20 51		21 11	21 41	22 11		22 41	23 11	23 41		00 11				
Harlesden d	18 13	18 33	18 53		19 13	19 33	19 53		20 13	20 33	20 53		21 13	21 43	22 13		22 43	23 13	23 43		00 13				
Stonebridge Park d	18 15	18 35	18 55		19 15	19 35	19 55		20 15	20 35	20 55		21 15	21 45	22 15		22 45	23 15	23 45		00 15				
Wembley Central Dc d	18 18	18 38	18 58		19 18	19 38	19 58		20 18	20 38	20 58		21 18	21 48	22 18		22 48	23 18	23 48		00 18				
North Wembley d	18 20	18 40	19 00		19 20	19 40	20 00		20 20	20 40	21 00		21 20	21 50	22 20		22 50	23 20	23 50		00 20				
South Kenton d	18 22	18 42	19 02		19 22	19 42	20 02		20 22	20 42	21 02		21 22	21 52	22 22		22 52	23 22	23 52		00 22				
Kenton d	18 24	18 44	19 04		19 24	19 44	20 04		20 24	20 44	21 04		21 24	21 54	22 24		22 54	23 24	23 54		00 24				
Harrow & Wealdstone D.C. d	18 26	18 46	19 06		19 26	19 46	20 06		20 26	20 46	21 06		21 26	21 56	22 26		22 56	23 26	23 56		00 26				
Headstone Lane d	18 29	18 49	19 09		19 29	19 49	20 09		20 29	20 49	21 09		21 29	21 59	22 29		22 59	23 29	23 59		00 29				
Hatch End d	18 31	18 51	19 11		19 31	19 51	20 11		20 31	20 51	21 11		21 31	22 01	22 31		23 01	23 31	00 01		00 31				
Carpenders Park d	18 34	18 54	19 14		19 34	19 54	20 14		20 34	20 54	21 14		21 34	22 04	22 34		23 04	23 34	00 04		00 34				
Bushey Dc d	18 37	18 57	19 17		19 37	19 57	20 17		20 37	20 57	21 17		21 37	22 07	22 37		23 07	23 37	00 07		00 37				
Watford High Street d	18 40	19 00	19 20		19 40	20 00	20 20		20 40	21 00	21 20		21 40	22 10	22 40		23 10	23 40	00 10		00 40				
Watford Junction Dc a	18 44	19 04	19 24		19 44	20 04	20 24		20 44	21 04	21 24		21 44	22 14	22 44		23 14	23 44	00 14		00 44				

Sundays

	LO	LO	LO	LO		LO	LO	LO	LO		LO	LO	LO	LO		LO	LO	LO	LO		LO	LO	LO A	LO A	LO
London Euston 15 ⊖ d	23p27	23p57	00 22	02 00		06 47	07 17	07 47	08 17		08 47	09 17	09 47	10 17		10 47	11 17	11 47	12 17		12 47	13 17	13⌇47	14⌇17	14 47
South Hampstead d	23p33	00 03				06 53	07 23	07 53	08 23		08 53	09 23	09 53	10 23		10 53	11 23	11 53	12 23		12 53	13 23	13⌇53	14⌇23	14 53
Kilburn High Road d	23p34	00 04				06 54	07 24	07 54	08 24		08 54	09 24	09 54	10 24		10 54	11 24	11 54	12 24		12 54	13 24	13⌇54	14⌇24	14 54
Queens Park (Dc) ⊖ d	23p36	00 06	00 30			06 56	07 26	07 56	08 26		08 56	09 26	09 56	10 26		10 56	11 26	11 56	12 26		12 56	13 26	13⌇56	14⌇26	14 56
Kensal Green d	23p38	00 08				06 58	07 28	07 58	08 28		08 58	09 28	09 58	10 28		10 58	11 28	11 58	12 28		12 58	13 28	13⌇58	14⌇28	14 58
Willesden Jn Low Level d	23p41	00 11				07 01	07 31	08 01	08 31		09 01	09 31	10 01	10 31		11 01	11 31	12 01	12 31		13 01	13 31	14⌇01	14⌇31	15 01
Harlesden d	23p43	00 13				07 03	07 33	08 03	08 33		09 03	09 33	10 03	10 33		11 03	11 33	12 03	12 33		13 03	13 33	14⌇03	14⌇33	15 03
Stonebridge Park d	23p45	00 15				07 05	07 35	08 05	08 35		09 05	09 35	10 05	10 35		11 05	11 35	12 05	12 35		13 05	13 35	14⌇05	14⌇35	15 05
Wembley Central Dc d	23p48	00 18	00 38	02 18		07 08	07 38	08 08	08 38		09 08	09 38	10 08	10 38		11 08	11 38	12 08	12 38		13 08	13 38	14⌇08	14⌇38	15 08
North Wembley d	23p50	00 20				07 10	07 40	08 10	08 40		09 10	09 40	10 10	10 40		11 10	11 40	12 10	12 40		13 10	13 40	14⌇10	14⌇40	15 10
South Kenton d	23p52	00 22				07 12	07 42	08 12	08 42		09 12	09 42	10 12	10 42		11 12	11 42	12 12	12 42		13 12	13 42	14⌇12	14⌇42	15 12
Kenton d	23p54	00 24				07 14	07 44	08 14	08 44		09 14	09 44	10 14	10 44		11 14	11 44	12 14	12 44		13 14	13 44	14⌇14	14⌇44	15 14
Harrow & Wealdstone D.C. d	23p56	00 26	00 45	02 27		07 16	07 46	08 16	08 46		09 16	09 46	10 16	10 46		11 16	11 46	12 16	12 46		13 16	13 46	14⌇16	14⌇46	15 16
Headstone Lane d	23p59	00 29				07 19	07 49	08 19	08 49		09 19	09 49	10 19	10 49		11 19	11 49	12 19	12 49		13 19	13 49	14⌇19	14⌇49	15 19
Hatch End d	00 01	00 31				07 21	07 51	08 21	08 51		09 21	09 51	10 21	10 51		11 21	11 51	12 21	12 51		13 21	13 51	14⌇21	14⌇51	15 21
Carpenders Park d	00 04	00 34				07 24	07 54	08 24	08 54		09 24	09 54	10 24	10 54		11 24	11 54	12 24	12 54		13 24	13 54	14⌇24	14⌇54	15 24
Bushey Dc d	00 07	00 37				07 27	07 57	08 27	08 57		09 27	09 57	10 27	10 57		11 27	11 57	12 27	12 57		13 27	13 57	14⌇27	14⌇57	15 27
Watford High Street d	00 10	00 40				07 30	08 00	08 30	09 00		09 30	10 00	10 30	11 00		11 30	12 00	12 30	13 00		13 30	14 00	14⌇30	15⌇00	15 30
Watford Junction Dc a	00 14	00 44	00 59	02 40		07 34	08 04	08 34	09 04		09 34	10 04	10 34	11 04		11 34	12 04	12 34	13 04		13 34	14 04	14⌇34	15⌇04	15 34

	LO		LO A	LO	LO A	LO		LO	LO	LO	LO		LO	LO	LO	LO		LO	LO	LO	LO		LO		
London Euston 15 ⊖ d	15 17		15⌇47	16 17	16⌇47	17 17		17 47	18 17	18 47	19 17		19 47	20 17	20 47	21 17		21 47	22 17	22 47	23 17		23 47		
South Hampstead d	15 23		15⌇53	16 23	16⌇53	17 23		17 53	18 23	18 53	19 23		19 53	20 23	20 53	21 23		21 53	22 23	22 53	23 23		23 53		
Kilburn High Road d	15 24		15⌇54	16 24	16⌇54	17 24		17 54	18 24	18 54	19 24		19 54	20 24	20 54	21 24		21 54	22 24	22 54	23 24		23 54		
Queens Park (Dc) ⊖ d	15 26		15⌇56	16 26	16⌇56	17 26		17 56	18 26	18 56	19 26		19 56	20 26	20 56	21 26		21 56	22 26	22 56	23 26		23 56		
Kensal Green d	15 28		15⌇58	16 28	16⌇58	17 28		17 58	18 28	18 58	19 28		19 58	20 28	20 58	21 28		21 58	22 28	22 58	23 28		23 58		
Willesden Jn Low Level d	15 31		16⌇01	16 31	17⌇01	17 31		18 01	18 31	19 01	19 31		20 01	20 31	21 01	21 31		22 01	22 31	23 01	23 31		00 01		
Harlesden d	15 33		16⌇03	16 33	17⌇03	17 33		18 03	18 33	19 03	19 33		20 03	20 33	21 03	21 33		22 03	22 33	23 03	23 33		00 03		
Stonebridge Park d	15 35		16⌇05	16 35	17⌇05	17 35		18 05	18 35	19 05	19 35		20 05	20 35	21 05	21 35		22 05	22 35	23 05	23 35		00 05		
Wembley Central Dc d	15 38		16⌇08	16 38	17⌇08	17 38		18 08	18 38	19 08	19 38		20 08	20 38	21 08	21 38		22 08	22 38	23 08	23 38		00 08		
North Wembley d	15 40		16⌇10	16 40	17⌇10	17 40		18 10	18 40	19 10	19 40		20 10	20 40	21 10	21 40		22 10	22 40	23 10	23 40		00 10		
South Kenton d	15 42		16⌇12	16 42	17⌇12	17 42		18 12	18 42	19 12	19 42		20 12	20 42	21 12	21 42		22 12	22 42	23 12	23 42		00 12		
Kenton d	15 44		16⌇14	16 44	17⌇14	17 44		18 14	18 44	19 14	19 44		20 14	20 44	21 14	21 44		22 14	22 44	23 14	23 44		00 14		
Harrow & Wealdstone D.C. d	15 46		16⌇16	16 46	17⌇16	17 46		18 16	18 46	19 16	19 46		20 16	20 46	21 16	21 46		22 16	22 46	23 16	23 46		00 16		
Headstone Lane d	15 49		16⌇19	16 49	17⌇19	17 49		18 19	18 49	19 19	19 49		20 19	20 49	21 19	21 49		22 19	22 49	23 19	23 49		00 19		
Hatch End d	15 51		16⌇21	16 51	17⌇21	17 51		18 21	18 51	19 21	19 51		20 21	20 51	21 21	21 51		22 21	22 51	23 21	23 51		00 21		
Carpenders Park d	15 54		16⌇24	16 54	17⌇24	17 54		18 24	18 54	19 24	19 54		20 24	20 54	21 24	21 54		22 24	22 54	23 24	23 54		00 24		
Bushey Dc d	15 57		16⌇27	16 57	17⌇27	17 57		18 27	18 57	19 27	19 57		20 27	20 57	21 27	21 57		22 27	22 57	23 27	23 57		00 27		
Watford High Street d	16 00		16⌇30	17 00	17⌇30	18 00		18 30	19 00	19 30	20 00		20 30	21 00	21 30	22 00		22 30	23 00	23 30	00 01		00 30		
Watford Junction Dc a	16 04		16⌇34	17 04	17⌇34	18 04		18 34	19 04	19 34	20 04		20 34	21 04	21 34	22 04		22 34	23 04	23 34	00 04		00 34		

For general notes see front of timetable
For details of catering facilities see
Directory of Train Operators

A 3 February to 23 March

Stations Queen's Park to Harrow & Wealdstone inclusive are also served by London Underground Bakerloo line services

Watford Junction → Harrow & Wealdstone, Queens Park and London

Network Diagram - See first page of Table 59

Miles			LO MO	LO	LO	LO	LO	LO	LO	LO	LO	LO	LO	LO	LO	LO	LO	LO	LO
0	**Watford Junction Dc**	d	23p21	05 05	05 31	06 01	06 20	06 40	07 00	07 20	07 40	08 00	08 20	08 40	09 00	09 21	09 41	10 01	10 21
1	Watford High Street	d	23p24	05 08	05 34	06 04	06 23	06 43	07 03	07 23	07 43	08 03	08 23	08 43	09 03	09 24	09 44	10 04	10 24
1¾	Bushey Dc	d	23p26	05 10	05 36	06 06	06 25	06 45	07 05	07 25	07 45	08 05	08 25	08 45	09 05	09 26	09 46	10 06	10 26
3	Carpenders Park	d	23p29	05 13	05 39	06 09	06 28	06 48	07 08	07 28	07 48	08 08	08 28	08 48	09 08	09 29	09 49	10 09	10 29
4½	Hatch End	d	23p32	05 16	05 42	06 12	06 31	06 51	07 11	07 31	07 51	08 11	08 31	08 51	09 11	09 32	09 52	10 12	10 32
5¼	Headstone Lane	d	23p34	05 18	05 44	06 14	06 33	06 53	07 13	07 33	07 53	08 13	08 33	08 53	09 13	09 34	09 54	10 14	10 34
6½	**Harrow & Wealdstone D.C.**	d	23p37	05 21	05 47	06 17	06 36	06 56	07 16	07 36	07 56	08 16	08 36	08 56	09 16	09 37	09 57	10 17	10 37
7½	Kenton	d	23p39	05 23	05 49	06 19	06 39	06 59	07 19	07 39	07 59	08 19	08 39	08 59	09 19	09 39	09 59	10 19	10 39
8¼	South Kenton	d	23p41	05 25	05 51	06 21	06 41	07 01	07 21	07 41	08 01	08 21	08 41	09 01	09 21	09 41	10 01	10 21	10 41
8¾	North Wembley	d	23p43	05 27	05 53	06 23	06 43	07 03	07 23	07 43	08 03	08 23	08 43	09 03	09 23	09 43	10 03	10 23	10 43
9¾	Wembley Central Dc	d	23p45	05 29	05 57	06 25	06 45	07 05	07 25	07 45	08 05	08 25	08 45	09 05	09 25	09 45	10 05	10 25	10 45
10¾	Stonebridge Park	d	23p48	05 32	05 58	06 28	06 48	07 08	07 28	07 48	08 08	08 28	08 48	09 08	09 28	09 48	10 08	10 28	10 48
11¾	Harlesden	d	23p50	05 34	06 00	06 30	06 50	07 10	07 30	07 50	08 10	08 30	08 50	09 10	09 30	09 50	10 10	10 30	10 50
12¼	**Willesden Jn Low Level**	d	23p52	05 36	06 02	06 32	06 53	07 13	07 33	07 53	08 13	08 33	08 53	09 13	09 33	09 52	10 12	10 32	10 52
13¼	Kensal Green	d	23p55	05 39	06 05	06 35	06 55	07 15	07 35	07 55	08 15	08 35	08 55	09 15	09 35	09 55	10 15	10 35	10 55
14	**Queens Park (Dc)**	⊖ d	23p57	05 41	06 07	06 38	06 58	07 18	07 38	07 58	08 18	08 38	08 58	09 18	09 38	09 57	10 17	10 37	10 57
14¾	Kilburn High Road	d	23p59	05 43	06 09	06 40	07 00	07 20	07 40	08 00	08 20	08 40	09 00	09 20	09 40	09 59	10 19	10 39	10 59
15¼	South Hampstead	d	00 01	05 45	06 11	06 42	07 02	07 22	07 42	08 02	08 22	08 42	09 02	09 22	09 42	10 01	10 21	10 41	11 01
17¾	**London Euston** 15	⊖ a	00 08	05 52	06 20	06 50	07 12	07 32	07 52	08 12	08 32	08 52	09 12	09 32	09 52	10 10	10 30	10 50	11 11

		LO	LO	LO	LO	LO	LO	LO	LO	LO	LO	LO	LO	LO	LO	LO	LO	LO
Watford Junction Dc	d	10 41	11 01	11 21	11 41	12 01	12 21	12 41	13 01	13 21	13 41	14 01	14 21	14 41	15 01	15 21	15 41	16 01
Watford High Street	d	10 44	11 04	11 24	11 44	12 04	12 24	12 44	13 04	13 24	13 44	14 04	14 24	14 44	15 04	15 24	15 44	16 04
Bushey Dc	d	10 46	11 06	11 26	11 46	12 06	12 26	12 46	13 06	13 26	13 46	14 06	14 26	14 46	15 06	15 26	15 46	16 06
Carpenders Park	d	10 49	11 09	11 29	11 49	12 09	12 29	12 49	13 09	13 29	13 49	14 09	14 29	14 49	15 09	15 29	15 49	16 09
Hatch End	d	10 52	11 12	11 32	11 52	12 12	12 32	12 52	13 12	13 32	13 52	14 12	14 32	14 52	15 12	15 32	15 52	16 12
Headstone Lane	d	10 54	11 14	11 34	11 54	12 14	12 34	12 54	13 14	13 34	13 54	14 14	14 34	14 54	15 14	15 34	15 54	16 14
Harrow & Wealdstone D.C.	d	10 57	11 17	11 37	11 57	12 17	12 37	12 57	13 17	13 37	13 57	14 17	14 37	14 57	15 17	15 37	15 57	16 17
Kenton	d	10 59	11 19	11 39	11 59	12 19	12 39	12 59	13 19	13 39	13 59	14 19	14 39	14 59	15 19	15 39	15 59	16 19
South Kenton	d	11 01	11 21	11 41	12 01	12 21	12 41	13 01	13 21	13 41	14 01	14 21	14 41	15 01	15 21	15 41	16 01	16 21
North Wembley	d	11 03	11 23	11 43	12 03	12 23	12 43	13 03	13 23	13 43	14 03	14 23	14 43	15 03	15 23	15 43	16 03	16 23
Wembley Central Dc	d	11 05	11 25	11 45	12 05	12 25	12 45	13 05	13 25	13 45	14 05	14 25	14 45	15 05	15 25	15 45	16 05	16 25
Stonebridge Park	d	11 08	11 28	11 48	12 08	12 28	12 48	13 08	13 28	13 48	14 08	14 28	14 48	15 08	15 28	15 48	16 08	16 28
Harlesden	d	11 10	11 30	11 50	12 10	12 30	12 50	13 10	13 30	13 50	14 10	14 30	14 50	15 10	15 30	15 50	16 10	16 30
Willesden Jn Low Level	d	11 12	11 32	11 52	12 12	12 32	12 52	13 12	13 32	13 52	14 12	14 32	14 52	15 12	15 32	15 52	16 12	16 32
Kensal Green	d	11 15	11 35	11 55	12 15	12 35	12 55	13 15	13 35	13 55	14 15	14 35	14 55	15 15	15 35	15 55	16 15	16 35
Queens Park (Dc)	⊖ d	11 17	11 37	11 57	12 17	12 37	12 57	13 17	13 37	13 57	14 17	14 37	14 57	15 17	15 37	15 57	16 17	16 37
Kilburn High Road	d	11 19	11 39	11 59	12 19	12 39	12 59	13 19	13 39	13 59	14 19	14 39	14 59	15 19	15 39	15 59	16 19	16 39
South Hampstead	d	11 21	11 41	12 01	12 21	12 41	13 01	13 21	13 41	14 01	14 21	14 41	15 01	15 21	15 41	16 01	16 21	16 41
London Euston 15	⊖ a	11 30	11 50	12 11	12 30	12 50	13 11	13 30	13 50	14 11	14 30	14 50	15 11	15 30	15 50	16 11	16 30	16 50

		LO	LO	LO	LO	LO	LO	LO	LO	LO	LO	LO	LO	LO	LO	LO	LO	LO	LO
Watford Junction Dc	d	16 21	16 41	17 01	17 21	17 41	18 01	18 21	18 41	19 01	19 21	19 41	20 01	20 31	21 01	21 31	22 01	22 31	23 01
Watford High Street	d	16 24	16 44	17 04	17 24	17 44	18 04	18 24	18 44	19 04	19 24	19 44	20 04	20 34	21 04	21 34	22 04	22 34	23 04
Bushey Dc	d	16 26	16 46	17 06	17 26	17 46	18 06	18 26	18 46	19 06	19 26	19 46	20 06	20 36	21 06	21 36	22 06	22 36	23 06
Carpenders Park	d	16 29	16 49	17 09	17 29	17 49	18 09	18 29	18 49	19 09	19 29	19 49	20 09	20 39	21 09	21 39	22 09	22 39	23 09
Hatch End	d	16 32	16 52	17 12	17 32	17 52	18 12	18 32	18 52	19 12	19 32	19 52	20 12	20 42	21 12	21 42	22 12	22 42	23 12
Headstone Lane	d	16 34	16 54	17 14	17 34	17 54	18 14	18 34	18 54	19 14	19 34	19 54	20 14	20 44	21 14	21 44	22 14	22 44	23 14
Harrow & Wealdstone D.C.	d	16 37	16 57	17 17	17 37	17 57	18 17	18 37	18 57	19 17	19 37	19 57	20 17	20 47	21 17	21 47	22 17	22 47	23 17
Kenton	d	16 39	16 59	17 19	17 39	17 59	18 19	18 39	18 59	19 19	19 39	19 59	20 19	20 49	21 19	21 49	22 19	22 49	23 19
South Kenton	d	16 41	17 01	17 21	17 41	18 01	18 21	18 41	19 01	19 21	19 41	20 01	20 21	20 51	21 21	21 51	22 21	22 51	23 21
North Wembley	d	16 43	17 03	17 23	17 43	18 03	18 23	18 43	19 03	19 23	19 43	20 03	20 23	20 53	21 23	21 53	22 23	22 53	23 23
Wembley Central Dc	d	16 45	17 05	17 25	17 45	18 05	18 25	18 45	19 05	19 25	19 45	20 05	20 25	20 55	21 25	21 55	22 25	22 55	23 25
Stonebridge Park	d	16 48	17 08	17 28	17 48	18 08	18 28	18 48	19 08	19 28	19 48	20 08	20 28	20 58	21 28	21 58	22 28	22 58	23 28
Harlesden	d	16 50	17 10	17 30	17 50	18 10	18 30	18 50	19 10	19 30	19 50	20 10	20 30	21 00	21 30	22 00	22 30	23 00	23 30
Willesden Jn Low Level	d	16 52	17 12	17 32	17 52	18 12	18 32	18 52	19 12	19 32	19 52	20 12	20 32	21 02	21 32	22 02	22 32	23 02	23 32
Kensal Green	d	16 55	17 15	17 35	17 55	18 15	18 35	18 55	19 15	19 35	19 55	20 15	20 35	21 05	21 35	22 05	22 35	23 05	23 35
Queens Park (Dc)	⊖ d	16 57	17 17	17 37	17 57	18 17	18 37	18 57	19 17	19 37	19 57	20 17	20 37	21 07	21 37	22 07	22 37	23 07	23 37
Kilburn High Road	d	16 59	17 19	17 39	17 59	18 19	18 39	18 59	19 19	19 39	19 59	20 19	20 39	21 09	21 39	22 09	22 39	23 09	23 39
South Hampstead	d	17 01	17 21	17 41	18 01	18 21	18 41	19 01	19 21	19 41	20 01	20 21	20 41	21 11	21 41	22 11	22 41	23 11	23 41
London Euston 15	⊖ a	17 11	17 30	17 50	18 10	18 30	18 50	19 10	19 30	19 50	20 10	20 30	20 51	21 20	21 51	22 18	22 50	23 20	23 50

Saturdays

		LO	LO	LO	LO	LO	LO	LO	LO	LO	LO	LO	LO	LO	LO	LO	LO	LO
Watford Junction Dc	d	05 01	05 31	06 01	06 21	06 41	07 01	07 21	07 41	08 01	08 21	08 41	09 01	09 21	09 41	10 01	10 21	10 41
Watford High Street	d	05 04	05 34	06 04	06 24	06 44	07 04	07 24	07 44	08 04	08 24	08 44	09 04	09 24	09 44	10 04	10 24	10 44
Bushey Dc	d	05 06	05 36	06 06	06 26	06 46	07 06	07 26	07 46	08 06	08 26	08 46	09 06	09 26	09 46	10 06	10 26	10 46
Carpenders Park	d	05 09	05 39	06 09	06 29	06 49	07 09	07 29	07 49	08 09	08 29	08 49	09 09	09 29	09 49	10 09	10 29	10 49
Hatch End	d	05 12	05 42	06 12	06 32	06 52	07 12	07 32	07 52	08 12	08 32	08 52	09 12	09 32	09 52	10 12	10 32	10 52
Headstone Lane	d	05 14	05 44	06 14	06 34	06 54	07 14	07 34	07 54	08 14	08 34	08 54	09 14	09 34	09 54	10 14	10 34	10 54
Harrow & Wealdstone D.C.	d	05 17	05 47	06 17	06 37	06 57	07 17	07 37	07 57	08 17	08 37	08 57	09 17	09 37	09 57	10 17	10 37	10 57
Kenton	d	05 19	05 49	06 19	06 39	06 59	07 19	07 39	07 59	08 19	08 39	08 59	09 19	09 39	09 59	10 19	10 39	10 59
South Kenton	d	05 21	05 51	06 21	06 41	07 01	07 21	07 41	08 01	08 21	08 41	09 01	09 21	09 41	10 01	10 21	10 41	11 01
North Wembley	d	05 23	05 53	06 23	06 43	07 03	07 23	07 43	08 03	08 23	08 43	09 03	09 23	09 43	10 03	10 23	10 43	11 03
Wembley Central Dc	d	05 25	05 55	06 25	06 45	07 05	07 25	07 45	08 05	08 25	08 45	09 05	09 25	09 45	10 05	10 25	10 45	11 05
Stonebridge Park	d	05 28	05 58	06 28	06 48	07 08	07 28	07 48	08 08	08 28	08 48	09 08	09 28	09 48	10 08	10 28	10 48	11 08
Harlesden	d	05 30	06 00	06 30	06 50	07 10	07 30	07 50	08 10	08 30	08 50	09 10	09 30	09 50	10 10	10 30	10 50	11 10
Willesden Jn Low Level	d	05 32	06 02	06 32	06 52	07 12	07 32	07 52	08 12	08 32	08 52	09 12	09 32	09 52	10 12	10 32	10 52	11 12
Kensal Green	d	05 35	06 05	06 35	06 55	07 15	07 35	07 55	08 15	08 35	08 55	09 15	09 35	09 55	10 15	10 35	10 55	11 15
Queens Park (Dc)	⊖ d	05 37	06 07	06 37	06 57	07 17	07 37	07 57	08 17	08 37	08 57	09 17	09 37	09 57	10 17	10 37	10 57	11 17
Kilburn High Road	d	05 39	06 09	06 39	06 59	07 19	07 39	07 59	08 19	08 39	08 59	09 19	09 39	09 59	10 19	10 39	10 59	11 19
South Hampstead	d	05 41	06 11	06 41	07 01	07 21	07 41	08 01	08 21	08 41	09 01	09 21	09 41	10 01	10 21	10 41	11 01	11 21
London Euston 15	⊖ a	05 50	06 20	06 50	07 10	07 30	07 50	08 10	08 30	08 50	09 10	09 30	09 50	10 10	10 30	10 50	11 10	11 30

For general notes see front of timetable
For details of catering facilities see Directory of Train Operators

Stations Harrow & Wealdstone to Queen's Park inclusive are also served by London Underground Bakerloo Line services

Table 60

Saturdays

Watford Junction → Harrow & Wealdstone, Queens Park and London

Network Diagram - See first page of Table 59

		LO	LO	LO	LO	LO	LO	LO	LO	LO	LO	LO	LO	LO	LO	LO	LO	LO
Watford Junction Dc	d	11 01	11 21	11 41	12 01	12 21	12 41	13 01	13 21	13 41	14 01	14 21	14 41	15 01	15 21	15 41	16 01	16 21
Watford High Street	d	11 04	11 24	11 44	12 04	12 24	12 44	13 04	13 24	13 44	14 04	14 24	14 44	15 04	15 24	15 44	16 04	16 24
Bushey Dc	d	11 06	11 26	11 46	12 06	12 26	12 46	13 06	13 26	13 46	14 06	14 26	14 46	15 06	15 26	15 46	16 06	16 26
Carpenders Park	d	11 09	11 29	11 49	12 09	12 29	12 49	13 09	13 29	13 49	14 09	14 29	14 49	15 09	15 29	15 49	16 09	16 29
Hatch End	d	11 12	11 32	11 52	12 12	12 32	12 52	13 12	13 32	13 52	14 12	14 32	14 52	15 12	15 32	15 52	16 12	16 32
Headstone Lane	d	11 14	11 34	11 54	12 14	12 34	12 54	13 14	13 34	13 54	14 14	14 34	14 54	15 14	15 34	15 54	16 14	16 34
Harrow & Wealdstone D.C.	d	11 17	11 37	11 57	12 17	12 37	12 57	13 17	13 37	13 57	14 17	14 37	14 57	15 17	15 37	15 57	16 17	16 37
Kenton	d	11 19	11 39	11 59	12 19	12 39	12 59	13 19	13 39	13 59	14 19	14 39	14 59	15 19	15 39	15 59	16 19	16 39
South Kenton	d	11 21	11 41	12 01	12 21	12 41	13 01	13 21	13 41	14 01	14 21	14 41	15 01	15 21	15 41	16 01	16 21	16 41
North Wembley	d	11 23	11 43	12 03	12 23	12 43	13 03	13 23	13 43	14 03	14 23	14 43	15 03	15 23	15 43	16 03	16 23	16 43
Wembley Central Dc	d	11 25	11 45	12 05	12 25	12 45	13 05	13 25	13 45	14 05	14 25	14 45	15 05	15 25	15 45	16 05	16 25	16 45
Stonebridge Park	d	11 28	11 48	12 08	12 28	12 48	13 08	13 28	13 48	14 08	14 28	14 48	15 08	15 28	15 48	16 08	16 28	16 48
Harlesden	d	11 30	11 50	12 10	12 30	12 50	13 10	13 30	13 50	14 10	14 30	14 50	15 10	15 30	15 50	16 10	16 30	16 50
Willesden Jn Low Level	d	11 32	11 52	12 12	12 32	12 52	13 12	13 32	13 52	14 12	14 32	14 52	15 12	15 32	15 52	16 12	16 32	16 52
Kensal Green	d	11 35	11 55	12 15	12 35	12 55	13 15	13 35	13 55	14 15	14 35	14 55	15 15	15 35	15 55	16 15	16 35	16 55
Queens Park (Dc) ⊖	d	11 37	11 57	12 17	12 37	12 57	13 17	13 37	13 57	14 17	14 37	14 57	15 17	15 37	15 57	16 17	16 37	16 57
Kilburn High Road	d	11 39	11 59	12 19	12 39	12 59	13 19	13 39	13 59	14 19	14 39	14 59	15 19	15 39	15 59	16 19	16 39	16 59
South Hampstead	d	11 41	12 01	12 21	12 41	13 01	13 21	13 41	14 01	14 21	14 41	15 01	15 21	15 41	16 01	16 21	16 41	17 01
London Euston 15 ⊖	a	11 50	12 10	12 30	12 50	13 10	13 30	13 50	14 10	14 30	14 50	15 10	15 30	15 50	16 10	16 30	16 50	17 10

		LO	LO	LO	LO	LO	LO	LO	LO	LO	LO	LO	LO	LO	LO	LO	LO	LO
Watford Junction Dc	d	16 41	17 01	17 21	17 41	18 01	18 21	18 41	19 01	19 21	19 41	20 01	20 31	21 01	21 31	22 01	22 31	23 01
Watford High Street	d	16 44	17 04	17 24	17 44	18 04	18 24	18 44	19 04	19 24	19 44	20 04	20 34	21 04	21 34	22 04	22 34	23 04
Bushey Dc	d	16 46	17 06	17 26	17 46	18 06	18 26	18 46	19 06	19 26	19 46	20 06	20 36	21 06	21 36	22 06	22 36	23 06
Carpenders Park	d	16 49	17 09	17 29	17 49	18 09	18 29	18 49	19 09	19 29	19 49	20 09	20 39	21 09	21 39	22 09	22 39	23 09
Hatch End	d	16 52	17 12	17 32	17 52	18 12	18 32	18 52	19 12	19 32	19 52	20 12	20 42	21 12	21 42	22 12	22 42	23 12
Headstone Lane	d	16 54	17 14	17 34	17 54	18 14	18 34	18 54	19 14	19 34	19 54	20 14	20 44	21 14	21 44	22 14	22 44	23 14
Harrow & Wealdstone D.C.	d	16 57	17 17	17 37	17 57	18 17	18 37	18 57	19 17	19 37	19 57	20 17	20 47	21 17	21 47	22 17	22 47	23 17
Kenton	d	16 59	17 19	17 39	17 59	18 19	18 39	18 59	19 19	19 39	19 59	20 19	20 49	21 19	21 49	22 19	22 49	23 19
South Kenton	d	17 01	17 21	17 41	18 01	18 21	18 41	19 01	19 21	19 41	20 01	20 21	20 51	21 21	21 51	22 21	22 51	23 21
North Wembley	d	17 03	17 23	17 43	18 03	18 23	18 43	19 03	19 23	19 43	20 03	20 23	20 53	21 23	21 53	22 23	22 53	23 23
Wembley Central Dc	d	17 05	17 25	17 45	18 05	18 25	18 45	19 05	19 25	19 45	20 05	20 25	20 55	21 25	21 55	22 25	22 55	23 25
Stonebridge Park	d	17 08	17 28	17 48	18 08	18 28	18 48	19 08	19 28	19 48	20 08	20 28	20 58	21 28	21 58	22 28	22 58	23 28
Harlesden	d	17 10	17 30	17 50	18 10	18 30	18 50	19 10	19 30	19 50	20 10	20 30	21 00	21 30	22 00	22 30	23 00	23 30
Willesden Jn Low Level	d	17 12	17 32	17 52	18 12	18 32	18 52	19 12	19 32	19 52	20 12	20 32	21 02	21 32	22 02	22 32	23 02	23 32
Kensal Green	d	17 15	17 35	17 55	18 15	18 35	18 55	19 15	19 35	19 55	20 15	20 35	21 05	21 35	22 05	22 35	23 05	23 35
Queens Park (Dc) ⊖	d	17 17	17 37	17 57	18 17	18 37	18 57	19 17	19 37	19 57	20 17	20 37	21 07	21 37	22 07	22 37	23 07	23 37
Kilburn High Road	d	17 19	17 39	17 59	18 19	18 39	18 59	19 19	19 39	19 59	20 19	20 39	21 09	21 39	22 09	22 39	23 09	23 39
South Hampstead	d	17 21	17 41	18 01	18 21	18 41	19 01	19 21	19 41	20 01	20 21	20 41	21 11	21 41	22 11	22 41	23 11	23 41
London Euston 15 ⊖	a	17 30	17 50	18 10	18 30	18 50	19 10	19 30	19 50	20 10	20 30	20 50	21 20	21 50	22 20	22 50	23 22	23 50

Sundays

		LO	LO	LO	LO	LO	LO	LO	LO	LO	LO	LO	LO	LO	LO	LO	LO	LO	LO	LO
Watford Junction Dc	d	00 10	01 07	06 51	07 21	07 51	08 21	08 51	09 21	09 51	10 21	10 51	11 21	11 51	12 21	12 51	13 21	13 51	14 21	14 51
Watford High Street	d			06 54	07 24	07 54	08 24	08 54	09 24	09 54	10 24	10 54	11 24	11 54	12 24	12 54	13 24	13 54	14 24	14 54
Bushey Dc	d			06 56	07 26	07 56	08 26	08 56	09 26	09 56	10 26	10 56	11 26	11 56	12 26	12 56	13 26	13 56	14 26	14 56
Carpenders Park	d			06 59	07 29	07 59	08 29	08 59	09 29	09 59	10 29	10 59	11 29	11 59	12 29	12 59	13 29	13 59	14 29	14 59
Hatch End	d			07 02	07 32	08 02	08 32	09 02	09 32	10 02	10 32	11 02	11 32	12 02	12 32	13 02	13 32	14 02	14 32	15 02
Headstone Lane	d			07 04	07 34	08 04	08 34	09 04	09 34	10 04	10 34	11 04	11 34	12 04	12 34	13 04	13 34	14 04	14 34	15 04
Harrow & Wealdstone D.C.	d	00 22	01 19	07 07	07 37	08 07	08 37	09 07	09 37	10 07	10 37	11 07	11 37	12 07	12 37	13 07	13 37	14 07	14 37	15 07
Kenton	d			07 09	07 39	08 09	08 39	09 09	09 39	10 09	10 39	11 09	11 39	12 09	12 39	13 09	13 39	14 09	14 39	15 09
South Kenton	d			07 11	07 41	08 11	08 41	09 11	09 41	10 11	10 41	11 11	11 41	12 11	12 41	13 11	13 41	14 11	14 41	15 11
North Wembley	d			07 13	07 43	08 13	08 43	09 13	09 43	10 13	10 43	11 13	11 43	12 13	12 43	13 13	13 43	14 13	14 43	15 13
Wembley Central Dc	d	00 28	01 25	07 15	07 45	08 15	08 45	09 15	09 45	10 15	10 45	11 15	11 45	12 15	12 45	13 15	13 45	14 15	14 45	15 15
Stonebridge Park	d			07 18	07 48	08 18	08 48	09 18	09 48	10 18	10 48	11 18	11 48	12 18	12 48	13 18	13 48	14 18	14 48	15 18
Harlesden	d			07 20	07 50	08 20	08 50	09 20	09 50	10 20	10 50	11 20	11 50	12 20	12 50	13 20	13 50	14 20	14 50	15 20
Willesden Jn Low Level	d			07 22	07 52	08 22	08 52	09 22	09 52	10 22	10 52	11 22	11 52	12 22	12 52	13 22	13 52	14 22	14 52	15 22
Kensal Green	d			07 25	07 55	08 25	08 55	09 25	09 55	10 25	10 55	11 25	11 55	12 25	12 55	13 25	13 55	14 25	14 55	15 25
Queens Park (Dc) ⊖	d			07 27	07 57	08 27	08 57	09 27	09 57	10 27	10 57	11 27	11 57	12 27	12 57	13 27	13 57	14 27	14 57	15 27
Kilburn High Road	d			07 29	07 59	08 29	08 59	09 29	09 59	10 29	10 59	11 29	11 59	12 29	12 59	13 29	13 59	14 29	14 59	15 29
South Hampstead	d			07 31	08 01	08 31	09 01	09 31	10 01	10 31	11 01	11 31	12 01	12 31	13 01	13 31	14 01	14 31	15 01	15 31
London Euston 15 ⊖	a	00 44	01 41	07 38	08 08	08 38	09 08	09 38	10 08	10 38	11 08	11 38	12 08	12 38	13 08	13 38	14 08	14 38	15 08	15 38

		LO	LO	LO	LO	LO	LO	LO	LO	LO	LO	LO	LO	LO	LO	LO	LO	LO
Watford Junction Dc	d	15 21	15 51	16 21	16 51	17 21	17 51	18 21	18 51	19 21	19 51	20 21	20 51	21 21	21 51	22 21	22 51	23 21
Watford High Street	d	15 24	15 54	16 24	16 54	17 24	17 54	18 24	18 54	19 24	19 54	20 24	20 54	21 24	21 54	22 24	22 54	23 24
Bushey Dc	d	15 26	15 56	16 26	16 56	17 26	17 56	18 26	18 56	19 26	19 56	20 26	20 56	21 26	21 56	22 26	22 56	23 26
Carpenders Park	d	15 29	15 59	16 29	16 59	17 29	17 59	18 29	18 59	19 29	19 59	20 29	20 59	21 29	21 59	22 29	22 59	23 29
Hatch End	d	15 32	16 02	16 32	17 02	17 32	18 02	18 32	19 02	19 32	20 02	20 32	21 02	21 32	22 02	22 32	23 02	23 32
Headstone Lane	d	15 34	16 04	16 34	17 04	17 34	18 04	18 34	19 04	19 34	20 04	20 34	21 04	21 34	22 04	22 34	23 04	23 34
Harrow & Wealdstone D.C.	d	15 37	16 07	16 37	17 07	17 37	18 07	18 37	19 07	19 37	20 07	20 37	21 07	21 37	22 07	22 37	23 07	23 37
Kenton	d	15 39	16 09	16 39	17 09	17 39	18 09	18 39	19 09	19 39	20 09	20 39	21 09	21 39	22 09	22 39	23 09	23 39
South Kenton	d	15 41	16 11	16 41	17 11	17 41	18 11	18 41	19 11	19 41	20 11	20 41	21 11	21 41	22 11	22 41	23 11	23 41
North Wembley	d	15 43	16 13	16 43	17 13	17 43	18 13	18 43	19 13	19 43	20 13	20 43	21 13	21 43	22 13	22 43	23 13	23 43
Wembley Central Dc	d	15 45	16 15	16 45	17 15	17 45	18 15	18 45	19 15	19 45	20 15	20 45	21 15	21 45	22 15	22 45	23 15	23 45
Stonebridge Park	d	15 48	16 18	16 48	17 18	17 48	18 18	18 48	19 18	19 48	20 18	20 48	21 18	21 48	22 18	22 48	23 18	23 48
Harlesden	d	15 50	16 20	16 50	17 20	17 50	18 20	18 50	19 20	19 50	20 20	20 50	21 20	21 50	22 20	22 50	23 20	23 50
Willesden Jn Low Level	d	15 52	16 22	16 52	17 22	17 52	18 22	18 52	19 22	19 52	20 22	20 52	21 22	21 52	22 22	22 52	23 22	23 52
Kensal Green	d	15 55	16 25	16 55	17 25	17 55	18 25	18 55	19 25	19 55	20 25	20 55	21 25	21 55	22 25	22 55	23 25	23 55
Queens Park (Dc) ⊖	d	15 57	16 27	16 57	17 27	17 57	18 27	18 57	19 27	19 57	20 27	20 57	21 27	21 57	22 27	22 57	23 27	23 57
Kilburn High Road	d	15 59	16 29	16 59	17 29	17 59	18 29	18 59	19 29	19 59	20 29	20 59	21 29	21 59	22 29	22 59	23 29	23 59
South Hampstead	d	16 01	16 31	17 01	17 31	18 01	18 31	19 01	19 31	20 01	20 31	21 01	21 31	22 01	22 31	23 01	23 31	00 01
London Euston 15 ⊖	a	16 08	16 38	17 08	17 38	18 08	18 38	19 08	19 38	20 08	20 38	21 08	21 38	22 08	22 38	23 08	23 38	00 08

For general notes see front of timetable
For details of catering facilities see Directory of Train Operators

Stations Harrow & Wealdstone to Queen's Park inclusive are also served by London Underground Bakerloo Line services

Table 61

Mondays to Fridays

Watford Junction — St. Albans

Network Diagram - See first page of Table 59

Miles			LM	LM	LM	LM	LM	LM	LM	LM	LM	LM	LM	LM	LM	LM	LM	LM	LM	LM	LM	LM	LM	LM
—	London Euston 15	⊖ d	*05 24*	*05 55*	*06 37*	*07 34*	*08 34*	*09 24*	*10 04*	*10 54*	*11 34*	*12 24*	*13 04*	*13 54*	*14 34*	*15 24*	*16 04*	*16 54*	*17 40*	*18 24*	*19 04*	*20 04*	*21 04*
0	**Watford Junction**	d	06 00	06 42	07 24	08 09	09 01	09 46	10 31	11 16	12 01	12 46	13 31	14 16	15 01	15 46	16 31	17 21	18 06	18 51	19 36	20 31	21 31
¾	Watford North	d	06 02	06 44	07 26	08 11	09 03	09 48	10 33	11 18	12 03	12 48	13 33	14 18	15 03	15 48	16 33	17 23	18 08	18 53	19 38	20 33	21 33
1¾	Garston (Hertfordshire)	d	06 05	06 47	07 29	08 14	09 06	09 51	10 36	11 21	12 06	12 51	13 36	14 21	15 06	15 51	16 36	17 26	18 11	18 56	19 41	20 36	21 36
3¼	Bricket Wood	d	06 08	06 50	07 32	08 17	09 09	09 54	10 39	11 24	12 09	12 54	13 39	14 24	15 09	15 54	16 39	17 29	18 14	18 59	19 44	20 39	21 39
4½	How Wood	d	06 10	06 52	07 34	08 19	09 11	09 56	10 41	11 26	12 11	12 56	13 41	14 26	15 11	15 56	16 41	17 31	18 16	19 01	19 46	20 41	21 41
5	Park Street	d	06 12	06 54	07 36	08 21	09 13	09 58	10 43	11 28	12 13	12 58	13 43	14 28	15 13	15 58	16 43	17 33	18 18	19 03	19 48	20 43	21 43
6½	**St Albans Abbey**	a	06 16	06 58	07 40	08 25	09 17	10 03	10 47	11 32	12 17	13 02	13 47	14 32	15 17	16 03	16 47	17 37	18 22	19 07	19 52	20 47	21 47

Saturdays

		LM	LM	LM	LM	LM	LM	LM	LM	LM	LM	LM	LM	LM	LM	LM	LM	LM	LM	LM	LM	LM
London Euston 15	⊖ d	*05 34*		*07 04*	*07 54*	*08 34*	*09 24*	*10 04*	*10 54*	*11 34*	*12 24*	*13 04*	*13 54*	*14 34*	*15 24*	*16 04*	*16 54*	*17 34*	*18 24*	*19 04*	*20 04*	*21 04*
Watford Junction	d	06 01	06 46	07 31	08 16	09 01	09 46	10 31	11 16	12 01	12 46	13 31	14 16	15 01	15 46	16 31	17 16	18 01	18 46	19 31	20 31	21 31
Watford North	d	06 03	06 48	07 33	08 18	09 03	09 48	10 33	11 18	12 03	12 48	13 33	14 18	15 03	15 48	16 33	17 18	18 03	18 48	19 33	20 33	21 33
Garston (Hertfordshire)	d	06 06	06 51	07 36	08 21	09 06	09 51	10 36	11 21	12 06	12 51	13 36	14 21	15 06	15 51	16 36	17 21	18 06	18 51	19 36	20 36	21 36
Bricket Wood	d	06 09	06 54	07 39	08 24	09 09	09 54	10 39	11 24	12 09	12 54	13 39	14 24	15 09	15 54	16 39	17 24	18 09	18 54	19 39	20 39	21 39
How Wood	d	06 11	06 56	07 41	08 26	09 11	09 56	10 41	11 26	12 11	12 56	13 41	14 26	15 11	15 56	16 41	17 26	18 11	18 56	19 41	20 41	21 41
Park Street	d	06 13	06 58	07 43	08 28	09 13	09 58	10 43	11 28	12 13	12 58	13 43	14 28	15 13	15 58	16 43	17 28	18 13	18 58	19 43	20 43	21 43
St Albans Abbey	a	06 17	07 02	07 47	08 32	09 17	10 02	10 47	11 32	12 17	13 02	13 47	14 32	15 17	16 02	16 47	17 32	18 17	19 02	19 47	20 47	21 47

Sundays

		LM	LM	LM	LM	LM	LM	LM	LM	LM	LM	LM	LM	LM	LM	LM
London Euston 15	⊖ d	*06***b***24*	*07***b***24*	*09 13*	*10 13*	*11 13*	*12 13*	*13 13*	*14 13*	*15 13*	*16 13*	*17 13*	*18 13*	*19 13*	*20 13*	*21 13*
Watford Junction	d	08 06	09 06	10 06	11 06	12 06	13 06	14 06	15 06	16 06	17 06	18 06	19 06	20 06	21 06	22 06
Watford North	d	08 08	09 08	10 08	11 08	12 08	13 08	14 08	15 08	16 08	17 08	18 08	19 08	20 08	21 08	22 08
Garston (Hertfordshire)	d	08 11	09 11	10 11	11 11	12 11	13 11	14 11	15 11	16 11	17 11	18 11	19 11	20 11	21 11	22 11
Bricket Wood	d	08 14	09 14	10 14	11 14	12 14	13 14	14 14	15 14	16 14	17 14	18 14	19 14	20 14	21 14	22 14
How Wood	d	08 16	09 16	10 16	11 16	12 16	13 16	14 16	15 16	16 16	17 16	18 16	19 16	20 16	21 16	22 16
Park Street	d	08 18	09 18	10 18	11 18	12 18	13 18	14 18	15 18	16 18	17 18	18 18	19 18	20 18	21 18	22 18
St Albans Abbey	a	08 22	09 22	10 22	11 22	12 22	13 22	14 22	15 22	16 22	17 22	18 22	19 22	20 22	21 22	22 22

Mondays to Fridays

Miles			LM	LM	LM	LM	LM	LM	LM	LM	LM	LM	LM	LM	LM	LM	LM	LM	LM	LM	LM	LM	LM
0	**St Albans Abbey**	d	06 21	07 03	07 45	08 30	09 22	10 07	10 52	11 37	12 22	13 07	13 52	14 37	15 22	16 07	16 52	17 42	18 27	19 12	19 57	20 52	21 52
1½	Park Street	d	06 24	07 06	07 48	08 33	09 25	10 10	10 55	11 40	12 25	13 10	13 55	14 40	15 25	16 10	16 55	17 45	18 30	19 15	20 00	20 55	21 55
2¼	How Wood	d	06 26	07 08	07 50	08 35	09 27	10 12	10 57	11 42	12 27	13 12	13 57	14 42	15 27	16 12	16 57	17 47	18 32	19 17	20 02	20 57	21 57
3	Bricket Wood	d	06 29	07 11	07 53	08 38	09 30	10 15	11 00	11 45	12 30	13 15	14 00	14 45	15 30	16 15	17 00	17 50	18 35	19 20	20 05	21 00	22 00
4¾	Garston (Hertfordshire)	d	06 32	07 14	07 56	08 41	09 33	10 18	11 03	11 48	12 33	13 18	14 03	14 48	15 33	16 18	17 03	17 53	18 38	19 23	20 08	21 03	22 03
5½	Watford North	d	06 34	07 16	07 58	08 43	09 35	10 20	11 05	11 50	12 35	13 20	14 05	14 50	15 35	16 20	17 05	17 55	18 40	19 25	20 10	21 05	22 05
6½	**Watford Junction**	a	06 37	07 19	08 01	08 46	09 38	10 24	11 08	11 53	12 38	13 23	14 08	14 53	15 38	16 24	17 08	17 58	18 43	19 28	20 13	21 08	22 08
—	London Euston 15	⊖ a	*07 00*	*07 50*	*08 30*	*09 16*	*10 11*	*11 08*	*11 38*	*12 38*	*13 08*	*14 08*	*14 38*	*15 38*	*16 08*	*17 08*	*17 38*	*18 43*	*19 15*	*20 11*	*20 48*	*21 37*	*22 41*

Saturdays

		LM	LM	LM	LM	LM	LM	LM	LM	LM	LM	LM	LM	LM	LM	LM	LM	LM	LM	LM	LM	LM
St Albans Abbey	d	06 22	07 07	07 52	08 37	09 22	10 07	10 52	11 37	12 22	13 07	13 52	14 37	15 22	16 07	16 52	17 37	18 22	19 07	19 52	20 52	21 52
Park Street	d	06 25	07 10	07 55	08 40	09 25	10 10	10 55	11 40	12 25	13 10	13 55	14 40	15 25	16 10	16 55	17 40	18 25	19 10	19 55	20 55	21 55
How Wood	d	06 27	07 12	07 57	08 42	09 27	10 12	10 57	11 42	12 27	13 12	13 57	14 42	15 27	16 12	16 57	17 42	18 27	19 12	19 57	20 57	21 57
Bricket Wood	d	06 30	07 15	08 00	08 45	09 30	10 15	11 00	11 45	12 30	13 15	14 00	14 45	15 30	16 15	17 00	17 45	18 30	19 15	20 00	21 00	22 00
Garston (Hertfordshire)	d	06 33	07 18	08 03	08 48	09 33	10 18	11 03	11 48	12 33	13 18	14 03	14 48	15 33	16 18	17 03	17 48	18 33	19 18	20 03	21 03	22 03
Watford North	d	06 35	07 20	08 05	08 50	09 35	10 20	11 05	11 50	12 35	13 20	14 05	14 50	15 35	16 20	17 05	17 50	18 35	19 20	20 05	21 05	22 05
Watford Junction	a	06 38	07 23	08 08	08 53	09 38	10 23	11 08	11 53	12 38	13 23	14 08	14 53	15 38	16 23	17 08	17 53	18 38	19 23	20 08	21 08	22 08
London Euston 15	⊖ a	*07 11*	*08 11*	*08 39*	*09 37*	*10 11*	*11 11*	*11 38*	*12 37*	*13 11*	*14 11*	*14 37*	*15 37*	*16 11*	*17 11*	*17 37*	*18 37*	*19 11*	*19 51*	*20 42*	*21 52*	*22 52*

Sundays

		LM	LM	LM	LM	LM	LM	LM	LM	LM	LM	LM	LM	LM	LM	LM
St Albans Abbey	d	08 27	09 27	10 27	11 27	12 27	13 27	14 27	15 27	16 27	17 27	18 27	19 27	20 27	21 27	22 27
Park Street	d	08 30	09 30	10 30	11 30	12 30	13 30	14 30	15 30	16 30	17 30	18 30	19 30	20 30	21 30	22 30
How Wood	d	08 32	09 32	10 32	11 32	12 32	13 32	14 32	15 32	16 32	17 32	18 32	19 32	20 32	21 32	22 32
Bricket Wood	d	08 35	09 35	10 35	11 35	12 35	13 35	14 35	15 35	16 35	17 35	18 35	19 35	20 35	21 35	22 35
Garston (Hertfordshire)	d	08 38	09 38	10 38	11 38	12 38	13 38	14 38	15 38	16 38	17 38	18 38	19 38	20 38	21 38	22 38
Watford North	d	08 40	09 40	10 40	11 40	12 40	13 40	14 40	15 40	16 40	17 40	18 40	19 40	20 40	21 40	22 40
Watford Junction	a	08 43	09 43	10 43	11 43	12 43	13 43	14 43	15 43	16 43	17 43	18 43	19 43	20 43	21 43	22 43
London Euston 15	⊖ a	*10 08*	*10 30*	*11 20*	*12 20*	*13 20*	*14 20*	*15 20*	*16 20*	*17 20*	*18 20*	*19 20*	*20 20*	*21 20*	*22 20*	*23 20*

For general notes see front of timetable
For details of catering facilities see
Directory of Train Operators

b By bus

Gospel Oak → Barking

Network diagram - see first page of Table 59

Mondays to Fridays

Miles			LO	LO	LO	LO		LO	LO	LO	LO		LO	LO	LO		LO	LO			LO	LO	LO	LO	LO
0	**Gospel Oak**	d	06 25	06 55	07 15	07 40		08 00	08 20	08 40	09 00		09 20	09 40	10 00		10 25	10 55			14 25	14 55	15 12	15 35	15 55
1¼	Upper Holloway	d	06 29	06 59	07 19	07 44		08 04	08 24	08 44	09 04		09 24	09 44	10 04		10 29	10 59	and		14 29	14 59	15b19	15 39	15 59
2	Crouch Hill	d	06 32	07 02	07 22	07 47		08 07	08 27	08 48	09 07		09 27	09 47	10 07		10 32	11 02			14 32	15 02	15 22	15 42	16 02
3	Harringay Green Lanes	d	06 35	07 05	07 25	07 50		08 10	08 30	08 51	09 10		09 30	09 50	10 10		10 35	11 05	every 30		14 35	15 05	15 25	15 45	16 05
4½	South Tottenham	d	06 38	07 08	07 28	07 53		08 13	08 33	08 54	09 13		09 33	09 53	10 13		10 38	11 08			14 38	15 08	15 28	15 48	16 08
5¾	Blackhorse Road ⊖	d	06 41	07 11	07 31	07 56		08 16	08 36	08 57	09 16		09 36	09 56	10 16		10 41	11 11	minutes		14 41	15 11	15 31	15 51	16 11
6½	Walthamstow Queens Road	d	06 44	07 14	07 34	07 59		08 19	08 39	09 00	09 19		09 39	09 59	10 19		10 44	11 14			14 44	15 14	15 34	15 54	16 14
7½	Leyton Midland Road	d	06 47	07 17	07 37	08 02		08 22	08 42	09 03	09 22		09 42	10 02	10 22		10 47	11 17	until		14 47	15 17	15 37	15 57	16 17
8¼	Leytonstone High Road	d	06 50	07 20	07 40	08 05		08 25	08 45	09 06	09 25		09 45	10 05	10 25		10 50	11 20			14 50	15 20	15 40	16 00	16 20
9½	Wanstead Park	d	06 53	07 23	07 43	08 08		08 28	08 48	09 09	09 28		09 48	10 08	10 28		10 53	11 23			14 53	15 23	15 43	16 03	16 23
10½	Woodgrange Park	d	06 55	07 25	07 45	08 10		08 30	08 50	09 11	09 30		09 50	10 10	10 30		10 55	11 25			14 55	15 25	15 45	16 05	16 25
12¼	**Barking** ⊖	a	06 59	07 31	07 51	08 16		08 36	08 56	09 16	09 36		09 56	10 16	10 36		10 59	11 29			14 59	15 29	15 49	16 09	16 29

		LO		LO	LO	LO	LO		LO	LO	LO	LO		LO	LO	LO	LO		LO	LO	LO	LO		LO		
Gospel Oak	d	16 15		16 35	16 55	17 15	17 35		17 55	18 15	18 35	18 55		19 25	19 58	20 25	20 55		21 25	21 55	22 25	22 55		23 25		
Upper Holloway	d	16 19		16 39	16 59	17 19	17 39		17 59	18 19	18 39	18 59		19 29	20 02	20 29	20 59		21 29	21 59	22 29	22 59		23 29		
Crouch Hill	d	16 22		16 42	17 02	17 22	17 42		18 02	18 22	18 42	19 02		19 32	20 05	20 32	21 02		21 32	22 02	22 32	23 02		23 32		
Harringay Green Lanes	d	16 25		16 45	17 05	17 25	17 45		18 05	18 25	18 45	19 05		19 35	20 08	20 35	21 05		21 35	22 05	22 35	23 05		23 35		
South Tottenham	d	16 28		16 48	17 08	17 28	17 48		18 08	18 28	18 48	19 08		19 38	20 11	20 38	21 08		21 38	22 08	22 38	23 08		23 38		
Blackhorse Road ⊖	d	16 31		16 51	17 11	17 31	17 51		18 11	18 31	18 51	19 11		19 41	20 14	20 41	21 11		21 41	22 11	22 41	23 11		23 41		
Walthamstow Queens Road	d	16 34		16 54	17 14	17 34	17 54		18 14	18 34	18 54	19 14		19 44	20 17	20 44	21 14		21 44	22 14	22 44	23 14		23 44		
Leyton Midland Road	d	16 37		16 57	17 17	17 37	17 57		18 17	18 37	18 57	19 17		19 47	20 20	20 47	21 17		21 47	22 17	22 47	23 17		23 47		
Leytonstone High Road	d	16 40		17 00	17 20	17 40	18 00		18 20	18 40	19 00	19 20		19 50	20 23	20 50	21 20		21 50	22 20	22 50	23 20		23 50		
Wanstead Park	d	16 43		17 03	17 23	17 43	18 03		18 23	18 43	19 03	19 23		19 53	20 26	20 53	21 23		21 53	22 23	22 53	23 23		23 53		
Woodgrange Park	d	16 45		17 05	17 25	17 45	18 05		18 25	18 45	19 05	19 25		19 55	20 28	20 55	21 25		21 55	22 25	22 55	23 25		23 55		
Barking ⊖	a	16 51		17 11	17 31	17 51	18 11		18 31	18 51	19 11	19 31		19 59	20 32	20 59	21 29		21 59	22 29	22 59	23 29		23 59		

Saturdays

		LO	LO	LO	LO		LO	LO	LO	LO		LO	LO	LO		LO	LO			LO	LO	LO	LO		LO
Gospel Oak	d	06 25	06 55	07 15	07 40		08 00	08 20	08 40	09 00		09 20	09 40	10 00		10 25	10 55			14 25	14 55	15 12	15 35		15 55
Upper Holloway	d	06 29	06 59	07 19	07 44		08 04	08 24	08 44	09 04		09 24	09 44	10 04		10 29	10 59	and		14 29	14 59	15b19	15 39		15 59
Crouch Hill	d	06 32	07 02	07 22	07 47		08 07	08 27	08 47	09 07		09 27	09 47	10 07		10 32	11 02			14 32	15 02	15 22	15 42		16 02
Harringay Green Lanes	d	06 35	07 05	07 25	07 50		08 10	08 30	08 50	09 10		09 30	09 50	10 10		10 35	11 05	every 30		14 35	15 05	15 25	15 45		16 05
South Tottenham	d	06 38	07 08	07 28	07 53		08 13	08 33	08 53	09 13		09 33	09 53	10 13		10 38	11 08			14 38	15 08	15 28	15 48		16 08
Blackhorse Road ⊖	d	06 41	07 11	07 31	07 56		08 16	08 36	08 56	09 16		09 36	09 56	10 16		10 41	11 11	minutes		14 41	15 11	15 31	15 51		16 11
Walthamstow Queens Road	d	06 44	07 14	07 34	07 59		08 19	08 39	08 59	09 19		09 39	09 59	10 19		10 44	11 14			14 44	15 14	15 34	15 54		16 14
Leyton Midland Road	d	06 47	07 17	07 37	08 02		08 22	08 42	09 02	09 22		09 42	10 02	10 22		10 47	11 17	until		14 47	15 17	15 37	15 57		16 17
Leytonstone High Road	d	06 50	07 20	07 40	08 05		08 25	08 45	09 05	09 25		09 45	10 05	10 25		10 50	11 20			14 50	15 20	15 40	16 00		16 20
Wanstead Park	d	06 53	07 23	07 43	08 08		08 28	08 48	09 08	09 28		09 48	10 08	10 28		10 53	11 23			14 53	15 23	15 43	16 03		16 23
Woodgrange Park	d	06 55	07 25	07 45	08 10		08 30	08 50	09 10	09 30		09 50	10 10	10 30		10 55	11 25			14 55	15 25	15 45	16 05		16 25
Barking ⊖	a	06 59	07 29	07 49	08 14		08 34	08 54	09 14	09 34		09 54	10 14	10 34		10 59	11 29			14 59	15 29	15 49	16 09		16 29

		LO	LO	LO	LO		LO	LO	LO	LO		LO	LO	LO	LO		LO	LO	LO	LO		LO	LO			
Gospel Oak	d	16 15	16 35	16 55	17 15		17 35	17 55	18 16	18 35		18 55	19 25	19 58	20 25		20 55	21 25	21 55	22 25		22 55	23 25			
Upper Holloway	d	16 19	16 39	16 59	17 19		17 39	17 59	18 20	18 39		18 59	19 29	20 02	20 29		20 59	21 29	21 59	22 29		22 59	23 29			
Crouch Hill	d	16 22	16 42	17 02	17 22		17 42	18 02	18 23	18 42		19 02	19 32	20 05	20 32		21 02	21 32	22 02	22 32		23 02	23 32			
Harringay Green Lanes	d	16 25	16 45	17 05	17 25		17 45	18 05	18 26	18 45		19 05	19 35	20 08	20 35		21 05	21 35	22 05	22 35		23 05	23 35			
South Tottenham	d	16 28	16 48	17 08	17 28		17 48	18 08	18 29	18 48		19 08	19 38	20 11	20 38		21 08	21 38	22 08	22 38		23 08	23 38			
Blackhorse Road ⊖	d	16 31	16 51	17 11	17 31		17 51	18 11	18 32	18 51		19 11	19 41	20 14	20 41		21 11	21 41	22 11	22 41		23 11	23 41			
Walthamstow Queens Road	d	16 34	16 54	17 14	17 34		17 54	18 14	18 35	18 54		19 14	19 44	20 17	20 44		21 14	21 44	22 14	22 44		23 14	23 44			
Leyton Midland Road	d	16 37	16 57	17 17	17 37		17 57	18 17	18 38	18 57		19 17	19 47	20 20	20 47		21 17	21 47	22 17	22 47		23 17	23 47			
Leytonstone High Road	d	16 40	17 00	17 20	17 40		18 00	18 20	18 41	19 00		19 20	19 50	20 23	20 50		21 20	21 50	22 20	22 50		23 20	23 50			
Wanstead Park	d	16 43	17 03	17 23	17 43		18 03	18 23	18 44	19 03		19 23	19 53	20 26	20 53		21 23	21 53	22 23	22 53		23 23	23 53			
Woodgrange Park	d	16 45	17 05	17 25	17 45		18 05	18 25	18 46	19 05		19 25	19 55	20 28	20 55		21 25	21 55	22 25	22 55		23 25	23 55			
Barking ⊖	a	16 49	17 09	17 29	17 49		18 09	18 29	18 50	19 09		19 29	19 59	20 32	20 59		21 29	21 59	22 29	22 59		23 29	23 59			

Sundays

			LO	LO				LO			LO
Gospel Oak	d		08 50	09 20				22 50			23 20
Upper Holloway	d		08 54	09 24	and			22 54			23 24
Crouch Hill	d		08 57	09 27				22 57			23 27
Harringay Green Lanes	d		09 00	09 30	every 30			23 00			23 30
South Tottenham	d		09 03	09 33				23 03			23 33
Blackhorse Road ⊖	d		09 06	09 36	minutes			23 06			23 36
Walthamstow Queens Road	d		09 09	09 39				23 09			23 39
Leyton Midland Road	d		09 12	09 42	until			23 12			23 42
Leytonstone High Road	d		09 15	09 45				23 15			23 45
Wanstead Park	d		09 18	09 48				23 18			23 48
Woodgrange Park	d		09 20	09 50				23 20			23 50
Barking ⊖	a		09 24	09 54				23 24			23 54

For general notes see front of timetable
For details of catering facilities see
Directory of Train Operators

b Arr. 1516

Barking → Gospel Oak

Network diagram - see first page of Table 59

Miles			LO	LO	LO	LO		LO	LO	LO	LO		LO	LO	LO	LO		LO		LO	LO		LO		LO
0	**Barking**	⊖ d	06 32	06 54	07 20	07 40		08 00	08 20	08 40	09 00		09 20	09 40	10 00	10 22		10 40		11 08	11 38		15 08		15 34
1¾	Woodgrange Park	d	06 35	06 57	07 23	07 43		08 03	08 23	08 43	09 03		09 23	09 43	10 03	10 25		10 43		11 11	11 41	and	15 11		15 37
2¾	Wanstead Park	d	06 38	07 00	07 26	07 46		08 06	08 26	08 46	09 06		09 26	09 46	10 06	10 28		10 46		11 14	11 44		15 14		15 40
4	Leytonstone High Road	d	06 42	07 04	07 30	07 50		08 10	08 30	08 50	09 10		09 30	09 50	10 10	10 32		10 50		11 18	11 48	every 30	15 18		15 44
4¾	Leyton Midland Road	d	06 44	07 06	07 32	07 52		08 12	08 32	08 52	09 12		09 32	09 52	10 12	10 34		10 52		11 20	11 50		15 20		15 46
5¾	Walthamstow Queens Road	d	06 47	07 09	07 35	07 55		08 15	08 35	08 55	09 15		09 35	09 55	10 15	10 37		10 55		11 23	11 53	minutes	15 23		15 49
6½	Blackhorse Road	⊖ d	06 50	07 12	07 38	07 58		08 18	08 38	08 58	09 18		09 38	09 58	10 18	10 40		10 58		11 26	11 56		15 26		15 52
8¼	South Tottenham	d	06 54	07 16	07 42	08 02		08 22	08 42	09 02	09 22		09 42	10 02	10 22	10 44		11 02		11 30	12 00	until	15 30		15 56
9¼	Harringay Green Lanes	d	06 57	07 19	07 45	08 05		08 25	08 45	09 05	09 25		09 45	10 05	10 25	10 47		11 05		11 33	12 03		15 33		15 59
10¼	Crouch Hill	d	07 00	07 22	07 48	08 08		08 28	08 48	09 08	09 28		09 48	10 08	10 28	10 50		11 08		11 36	12 06		15 36		16 02
11	Upper Holloway	d	07 02	07 24	07 50	08 10		08 30	08 50	09 10	09 30		09 50	10 10	10 30	10 52		11 10		11 38	12 08		15 38		16 04
12¼	**Gospel Oak**	a	07 07	07 29	07 55	08 17		08 37	08 57	09 17	09 37		09 57	10 17	10 37	10 58		11 15		11 44	12 13		15 43		16 11

		LO	LO	LO	LO		LO	LO	LO	LO		LO	LO	LO	LO		LO	LO	LO	LO		LO	LO	LO		
Barking	⊖ d	15 54	16 14	16 34	16 54		17 14	17 34	17 54	18 14		18 34	18 54	19 18	19 43		20 08	20 38	21 08	21 38		22 08	22 38	23 08		
Woodgrange Park	d	15 57	16 17	16 37	16 57		17 17	17 37	17 57	18 17		18 37	18 57	19 21	19 46		20 11	20 41	21 11	21 41		22 11	22 41	23 11		
Wanstead Park	d	16 00	16 20	16 40	17 00		17 20	17 40	18 00	18 20		18 40	19 00	19 24	19 49		20 14	20 44	21 14	21 44		22 14	22 44	23 14		
Leytonstone High Road	d	16 04	16 24	16 44	17 04		17 24	17 44	18 04	18 24		18 44	19 04	19 28	19 53		20 18	20 48	21 18	21 48		22 18	22 48	23 18		
Leyton Midland Road	d	16 06	16 26	16 46	17 06		17 26	17 46	18 06	18 26		18 46	19 06	19 30	19 55		20 20	20 50	21 20	21 50		22 20	22 50	23 20		
Walthamstow Queens Road	d	16 09	16 29	16 49	17 09		17 29	17 49	18 09	18 29		18 49	19 09	19 33	19 58		20 23	20 53	21 23	21 53		22 23	22 53	23 23		
Blackhorse Road	⊖ d	16 12	16 32	16 52	17 12		17 32	17 52	18 12	18 32		18 52	19 12	19 36	20 01		20 26	20 56	21 26	21 56		22 26	22 56	23 26		
South Tottenham	d	16 16	16 36	16 56	17 16		17 36	17 56	18 16	18 36		18 56	19 16	19 40	20 05		20 30	21 00	21 30	22 00		22 30	23 00	23 30		
Harringay Green Lanes	d	16 19	16 39	16 59	17 19		17 39	17 59	18 19	18 39		18 59	19 19	19 43	20 08		20 33	21 03	21 33	22 03		22 33	23 03	23 33		
Crouch Hill	d	16 22	16 42	17 02	17 22		17 42	18 02	18 22	18 42		19 02	19 22	19 46	20 11		20 36	21 06	21 36	22 06		22 36	23 06	23 36		
Upper Holloway	d	16 24	16 44	17 04	17 24		17 44	18 04	18 24	18 44		19 04	19 24	19 48	20 13		20 38	21 08	21 38	22 08		22 38	23 08	23 38		
Gospel Oak	a	16 31	16 51	17 11	17 31		17 51	18 11	18 31	18 51		19 11	19 31	19 53	20 18		20 43	21 13	21 43	22 13		22 43	23 13	23 43		

Saturdays

		LO	LO	LO	LO		LO	LO	LO	LO		LO	LO	LO	LO		LO		LO	LO		LO		LO	LO
Barking	⊖ d	06 32	06 54	07 20	07 40		08 00	08 20	08 40	09 00		09 20	09 40	10 00	10 22		10 40		11 08	11 38		15 08		15 34	15 54
Woodgrange Park	d	06 35	06 57	07 23	07 43		08 03	08 23	08 43	09 03		09 23	09 43	10 03	10 25		10 43		11 11	11 41	and	15 11		15 37	15 57
Wanstead Park	d	06 38	07 00	07 26	07 46		08 06	08 26	08 46	09 06		09 26	09 46	10 06	10 28		10 46		11 14	11 44		15 14		15 40	16 00
Leytonstone High Road	d	06 42	07 04	07 30	07 50		08 10	08 30	08 50	09 10		09 30	09 50	10 10	10 32		10 50		11 18	11 48	every 30	15 18		15 44	16 04
Leyton Midland Road	d	06 44	07 06	07 32	07 52		08 12	08 32	08 52	09 12		09 32	09 52	10 12	10 34		10 52		11 20	11 50		15 20		15 46	16 06
Walthamstow Queens Road	d	06 47	07 09	07 35	07 55		08 15	08 35	08 55	09 15		09 35	09 55	10 15	10 37		10 55		11 23	11 53	minutes	15 23		15 49	16 09
Blackhorse Road	⊖ d	06 50	07 12	07 38	07 58		08 18	08 38	08 58	09 18		09 38	09 58	10 18	10 40		10 58		11 26	11 56		15 26		15 52	16 12
South Tottenham	d	06 54	07 16	07 42	08 02		08 22	08 42	09 02	09 22		09 42	10 02	10 22	10 44		11 02		11 30	12 00	until	15 30		15 56	16 16
Harringay Green Lanes	d	06 57	07 19	07 45	08 05		08 25	08 45	09 05	09 25		09 45	10 05	10 25	10 47		11 05		11 33	12 03		15 33		15 59	16 19
Crouch Hill	d	07 00	07 22	07 48	08 08		08 28	08 48	09 08	09 28		09 48	10 08	10 28	10 50		11 08		11 36	12 06		15 36		16 02	16 22
Upper Holloway	d	07 02	07 24	07 50	08 10		08 30	08 50	09 10	09 30		09 50	10 10	10 30	10 52		11 10		11 38	12 08		15 38		16 04	16 24
Gospel Oak	a	07 07	07 29	07 55	08 15		08 35	08 55	09 15	09 35		09 55	10 15	10 35	10 57		11 15		11 43	12 13		15 43		16 09	16 29

		LO	LO	LO	LO		LO	LO	LO	LO		LO	LO	LO	LO		LO	LO	LO	LO		LO	LO			
Barking	⊖ d	16 14	16 34	16 54	17 14		17 34	17 54	18 14	18 34		18 55	19 18	19 43	20 08		20 38	21 08	21 38	22 08		22 38	23 08			
Woodgrange Park	d	16 17	16 37	16 57	17 17		17 37	17 57	18 17	18 37		18 58	19 21	19 46	20 11		20 41	21 11	21 41	22 11		22 41	23 11			
Wanstead Park	d	16 20	16 40	17 00	17 20		17 40	18 00	18 20	18 40		19 01	19 24	19 49	20 14		20 44	21 14	21 44	22 14		22 44	23 14			
Leytonstone High Road	d	16 24	16 44	17 04	17 24		17 44	18 04	18 24	18 44		19 05	19 28	19 53	20 18		20 48	21 18	21 48	22 18		22 48	23 18			
Leyton Midland Road	d	16 26	16 46	17 06	17 26		17 46	18 06	18 26	18 46		19 07	19 30	19 55	20 20		20 50	21 20	21 50	22 20		22 50	23 20			
Walthamstow Queens Road	d	16 29	16 49	17 09	17 29		17 49	18 09	18 29	18 49		19 10	19 33	19 58	20 23		20 53	21 23	21 53	22 23		22 53	23 23			
Blackhorse Road	⊖ d	16 32	16 52	17 12	17 32		17 52	18 12	18 32	18 52		19 13	19 36	20 01	20 26		20 56	21 26	21 56	22 26		22 56	23 26			
South Tottenham	d	16 36	16 56	17 16	17 36		17 56	18 16	18 36	18 56		19 17	19 40	20 05	20 30		21 00	21 30	22 00	22 30		23 00	23 30			
Harringay Green Lanes	d	16 39	16 59	17 19	17 39		17 59	18 19	18 39	18 59		19 20	19 43	20 08	20 33		21 03	21 33	22 03	22 33		23 03	23 33			
Crouch Hill	d	16 42	17 02	17 22	17 42		18 02	18 22	18 42	19 02		19 23	19 46	20 11	20 36		21 06	21 36	22 06	22 36		23 06	23 36			
Upper Holloway	d	16 44	17 04	17 24	17 44		18 04	18 24	18 44	19 04		19 25	19 48	20 13	20 38		21 08	21 38	22 08	22 38		23 08	23 38			
Gospel Oak	a	16 49	17 09	17 29	17 49		18 11	18 29	18 49	19 09		19 30	19 53	20 18	20 43		21 13	21 43	22 13	22 43		23 13	23 43			

Sundays

			LO	LO				LO			LO			LO
Barking	⊖ d		09 05	09 35				22 05			22 35			23 05
Woodgrange Park	d		09 08	09 38	and			22 08			22 38			23 08
Wanstead Park	d		09 11	09 41				22 11			22 41			23 11
Leytonstone High Road	d		09 15	09 45	every 30			22 15			22 45			23 15
Leyton Midland Road	d		09 17	09 47				22 17			22 47			23 17
Walthamstow Queens Road	d		09 20	09 50	minutes			22 20			22 50			23 20
Blackhorse Road	⊖ d		09 23	09 53				22 23			22 53			23 23
South Tottenham	d		09 27	09 57	until			22 27			22 57			23 27
Harringay Green Lanes	d		09 30	10 00				22 30			23 00			23 30
Crouch Hill	d		09 33	10 03				22 33			23 03			23 33
Upper Holloway	d		09 35	10 05				22 35			23 05			23 35
Gospel Oak	a		09 40	10 10				22 40			23 10			23 40

For general notes see front of timetable
For details of catering facilities see
Directory of Train Operators

Table 64

Mondays to Fridays

Bletchley — Bedford

Network Diagram - See first page of Table 59

Miles			LM	LM	LM	LM	LM	LM	LM	LM	LM	LM	LM	LM	LM	LM	LM	LM
—	Milton Keynes Central 3	d	*05 24*	*06 25*	*07 22*	*08 25*	*09 49*	*10 49*	*11 49*	*12 49*	*13 49*	*14 49*	*15 25*	*16 25*	*17 19*	*18 15*	*19 19*	*20 19*
0	**Bletchley**	d	05 39	06 39	07 39	08 39	09 59	10 59	11 59	12 59	13 59	14 59	15 44	16 44	17 29	18 29	19 51	20 49
1	Fenny Stratford	d	05 41	06 41	07 41	08 41	10 01	11 01	12 01	13 01	14 01	15 01	15 46	16 46	17 31	18 31	19 53	20 51
2	Bow Brickhill	d	05 45	06 45	07 45	08 45	10 05	11 05	12 05	13 05	14 05	15 05	15 50	16 50	17 35	18 35	19 57	20 55
4	Woburn Sands	d	05 49	06 49	07 49	08 49	10 09	11 09	12 09	13 09	14 09	15 09	15 54	16 54	17 39	18 39	20 01	20 59
5	Aspley Guise	d	05 51	06 51	07 51	08 51	10 11	11 11	12 11	13 11	14 11	15 11	15 56	16 56	17 41	18 41	20 03	21 01
6¾	Ridgmont	d	05 55	06 55	07 55	08 55	10 15	11 15	12 15	13 15	14 15	15 15	16 00	17 00	17 45	18 45	20 07	21 05
8½	Lidlington	d	05 59	06 59	07 59	08 59	10 19	11 19	12 19	13 19	14 19	15 19	16 04	17 04	17 49	18 49	20 11	21 09
10	Millbrook (Bedfordshire)	d	06 02	07 02	08 02	09 02	10 22	11 22	12 22	13 22	14 22	15 22	16 07	17 07	17 52	18 52	20 14	21 12
11¼	Stewartby	d	06 05	07 05	08 05	09 05	10 25	11 25	12 25	13 25	14 25	15 25	16 10	17 10	17 55	18 55	20 17	21 15
13	Kempston Hardwick	d	06 09	07 09	08 09	09 09	10 29	11 29	12 29	13 29	14 29	15 29	16 14	17 14	17 59	18 59	20 21	21 19
16	Bedford St Johns	d	06 14	07 14	08 14	09 14	10 34	11 34	12 34	13 34	14 34	15 34	16 19	17 19	18 04	19 04	20 26	21 24
16¾	**Bedford 7**	a	06 21	07 21	08 21	09 21	10 41	11 41	12 41	13 41	14 41	15 41	16 26	17 26	18 11	19 11	20 33	21 31

Saturdays

		LM	LM	LM	LM	LM	LM	LM	LM	LM	LM	LM	LM	LM	LM	LM	LM
Milton Keynes Central 5	d	*04 35*	*06 18*	*07 18*	*08 18*	*09 45*	*10 45*	*11 45*	*12 45*	*13 45*	*14 45*	*15 18*	*16 18*	*17 18*	*18 18*	*19 18*	*20 02*
Bletchley	d	05 41	06 39	07 39	08 39	09 59	10 59	11 57	12 57	13 57	14 57	15 47	16 47	17 29	18 29	19 47	20 49
Fenny Stratford	d	05 43	06 41	07 41	08 41	10 01	11 01	11 59	12 59	13 59	14 59	15 49	16 49	17 31	18 31	19 49	20 51
Bow Brickhill	d	05 47	06 45	07 45	08 45	10 05	11 05	12 03	13 03	14 03	15 03	15 53	16 53	17 35	18 35	19 53	20 55
Woburn Sands	d	05 51	06 49	07 49	08 49	10 09	11 09	12 07	13 07	14 07	15 07	15 57	16 57	17 39	18 39	19 57	20 59
Aspley Guise	d	05 53	06 51	07 51	08 51	10 11	11 11	12 09	13 09	14 09	15 09	15 59	16 59	17 41	18 41	19 59	21 01
Ridgmont	d	05 57	06 55	07 55	08 55	10 15	11 15	12 13	13 13	14 13	15 13	16 03	17 03	17 45	18 45	20 03	21 05
Lidlington	d	06 01	06 59	07 59	08 59	10 19	11 19	12 17	13 17	14 17	15 17	16 07	17 07	17 49	18 49	20 07	21 09
Millbrook (Bedfordshire)	d	06 04	07 02	08 02	09 02	10 22	11 22	12 20	13 20	14 20	15 20	16 10	17 10	17 52	18 52	20 10	21 12
Stewartby	d	06 07	07 05	08 05	09 05	10 25	11 25	12 23	13 23	14 23	15 23	16 13	17 13	17 55	18 55	20 13	21 15
Kempston Hardwick	d	06 11	07 09	08 09	09 09	10 29	11 29	12 27	13 27	14 27	15 27	16 17	17 17	17 59	18 59	20 17	21 19
Bedford St Johns	d	06 16	07 14	08 14	09 14	10 34	11 34	12 32	13 32	14 32	15 32	16 22	17 22	18 04	19 04	20 22	21 24
Bedford 7	a	06 23	07 21	08 21	09 21	10 41	11 41	12 39	13 39	14 39	15 39	16 29	17 29	18 11	19 11	20 29	21 31

Mondays to Fridays

Miles			LM	LM	LM	LM	LM	LM	LM	LM	LM	LM	LM	LM	LM	LM	LM	LM
0	**Bedford 7**	d	06 31	07 31	08 31	09 31	10 51	11 51	12 51	13 51	14 51	15 51	16 36	17 36	18 21	19 21	20 42	21 41
¾	Bedford St Johns	d	06 34	07 34	08 34	09 34	10 54	11 54	12 54	13 54	14 54	15 54	16 39	17 39	18 24	19 24	20 45	21 44
3¾	Kempston Hardwick	d	06 40	07 40	08 40	09 40	11 00	12 00	13 00	14 00	15 00	16 00	16 45	17 45	18 30	19 30	20 51	21 50
5½	Stewartby	d	06 44	07 44	08 44	09 44	11 04	12 04	13 04	14 04	15 04	16 04	16 49	17 49	18 34	19 34	20 55	21 54
6¾	Millbrook (Bedfordshire)	d	06 47	07 47	08 47	09 47	11 07	12 07	13 07	14 07	15 07	16 07	16 52	17 52	18 37	19 37	20 58	21 57
8¼	Lidlington	d	06 50	07 50	08 50	09 50	11 10	12 10	13 10	14 10	15 10	16 10	16 55	17 55	18 40	19 40	21 01	22 00
10	Ridgmont	d	06 54	07 54	08 54	09 54	11 14	12 14	13 14	14 14	15 14	16 14	16 59	17 59	18 44	19 44	21 05	22 04
11¾	Aspley Guise	d	06 57	07 57	08 57	09 57	11 17	12 17	13 17	14 17	15 17	16 17	17 02	18 02	18 47	19 47	21 08	22 07
12¾	Woburn Sands	d	07 00	08 00	09 00	10 00	11 20	12 20	13 20	14 20	15 20	16 20	17 05	18 05	18 50	19 50	21 11	22 10
14¾	Bow Brickhill	d	07 04	08 04	09 04	10 04	11 24	12 24	13 24	14 24	15 24	16 24	17 09	18 09	18 54	19 54	21 15	22 14
15¾	Fenny Stratford	d	07 07	08 07	09 07	10 07	11 27	12 27	13 27	14 27	15 27	16 27	17 12	18 12	18 57	19 57	21 18	22 17
16¾	**Bletchley**	a	07 13	08 13	09 13	10 13	11 33	12 33	13 33	14 33	15 33	16 33	17 18	18 18	19 03	20 03	21 24	22 23
—	Milton Keynes Central 3	a	*07 36*	*08 37*	*09 36*	*10 33*	*11 53*	*12 53*	*13 53*	*14 53*	*15 53*	*16 53*	*18 02*	*18 35*	*19 17*	*20 25*	*21 37*	*22 43*

Saturdays

		LM	LM	LM	LM	LM	LM	LM	LM	LM	LM	LM	LM	LM	LM	LM	LM
Bedford 7	d	06 33	07 31	08 31	09 31	10 49	11 49	12 49	13 49	14 49	15 49	16 39	17 39	18 19	19 21	20 39	21 41
Bedford St Johns	d	06 36	07 34	08 34	09 34	10 52	11 52	12 52	13 52	14 52	15 52	16 42	17 42	18 22	19 24	20 42	21 44
Kempston Hardwick	d	06 42	07 40	08 40	09 40	10 58	11 58	12 58	13 58	14 58	15 58	16 48	17 48	18 28	19 30	20 48	21 50
Stewartby	d	06 46	07 44	08 44	09 44	11 02	12 02	13 02	14 02	15 02	16 02	16 52	17 52	18 32	19 34	20 52	21 54
Millbrook (Bedfordshire)	d	06 49	07 47	08 47	09 47	11 05	12 05	13 05	14 05	15 05	16 05	16 55	17 55	18 35	19 37	20 55	21 57
Lidlington	d	06 52	07 50	08 50	09 50	11 08	12 08	13 08	14 08	15 08	16 08	16 58	17 58	18 38	19 40	20 58	22 00
Ridgmont	d	06 56	07 54	08 54	09 54	11 12	12 12	13 12	14 12	15 12	16 12	17 02	18 02	18 42	19 44	21 02	22 04
Aspley Guise	d	06 59	07 57	08 57	09 57	11 15	12 15	13 15	14 15	15 15	16 15	17 05	18 05	18 45	19 47	21 05	22 07
Woburn Sands	d	07 02	08 00	09 00	10 00	11 18	12 18	13 18	14 18	15 18	16 18	17 08	18 08	18 48	19 50	21 08	22 10
Bow Brickhill	d	07 06	08 04	09 04	10 04	11 22	12 22	13 22	14 22	15 22	16 22	17 12	18 12	18 52	19 54	21 12	22 14
Fenny Stratford	d	07 09	08 07	09 07	10 07	11 25	12 25	13 25	14 25	15 25	16 25	17 15	18 15	18 55	19 57	21 15	22 17
Bletchley	a	07 15	08 13	09 13	10 13	11 31	12 31	13 31	14 31	15 31	16 31	17 21	18 21	19 01	20 03	21 21	22 23
Milton Keynes Central 5	a	*07 40*	*08 49*	*09 49*	*10 49*	*11 49*	*12 49*	*13 49*	*14 49*	*15 49*	*16 49*	*17 49*	*18 49*	*19 23*	*20 22*	*21b58*	*23c34*

For general notes see front of timetable
For details of catering facilities see
Directory of Train Operators

b 2 February to 22 March arr. 2200
c 2 February to 22 March arr. 2306

No Sunday Service

Route Diagram for Table 65

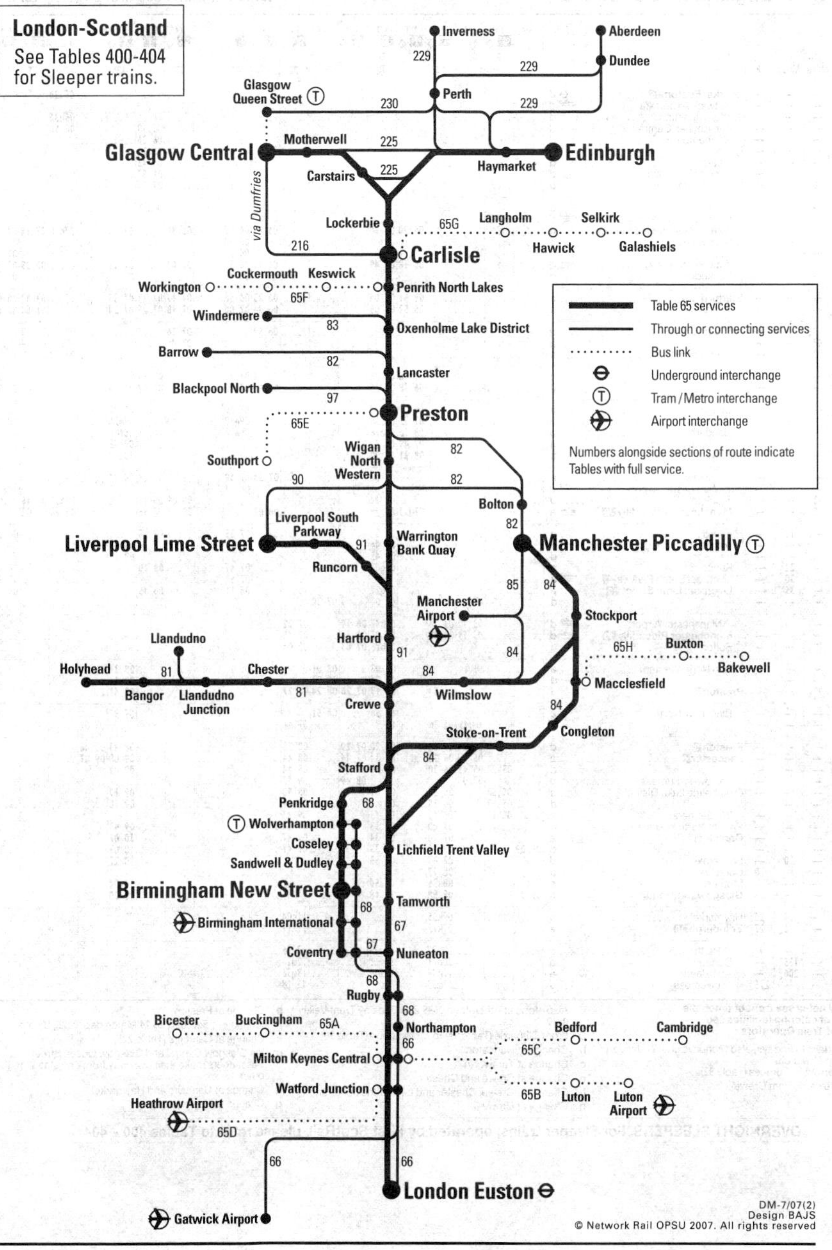

London-Scotland
See Tables 400-404 for Sleeper trains.
Inverness
Aberdeen
Dundee
Perth
Glasgow Queen Street
Glasgow Central
Motherwell
Carstairs
Haymarket
Edinburgh
via Dumfries
Lockerbie
Langholm
Selkirk
Hawick
Galashiels
Carlisle
Cockermouth
Keswick
Workington
Penrith North Lakes
Windermere
Oxenholme Lake District
Barrow
Lancaster
Blackpool North
Preston
Southport
Wigan North Western
Bolton
Liverpool South Parkway
Liverpool Lime Street
Warrington Bank Quay
Manchester Piccadilly
Runcorn
Manchester Airport
Stockport
Llandudno
Hartford
Buxton
Bakewell
Holyhead
Chester
Macclesfield
Bangor
Llandudno Junction
Crewe
Wilmslow
Stoke-on-Trent
Congleton
Stafford
Penkridge
Wolverhampton
Coseley
Sandwell & Dudley
Lichfield Trent Valley
Birmingham New Street
Tamworth
Birmingham International
Coventry
Nuneaton
Rugby
Bicester
Buckingham
Northampton
Bedford
Cambridge
Milton Keynes Central
Watford Junction
Luton
Luton Airport
Heathrow Airport
London Euston
Gatwick Airport
Table 65 services
Through or connecting services
Bus link
Underground interchange
Tram / Metro interchange
Airport interchange
Numbers alongside sections of route indicate Tables with full service.
DM-7/07(2)
Design BAJS

London and West Midlands → North West England and Scotland

Route Diagram - see first page of Table 65

Miles	Miles	Miles	Miles	Miles			SR	TP **1** ◇ A	NT	VT **1** ◇ 🍽	VT **1** ◇	VT **1** ◇ B ⊠	TP **1** ◇	NT	TP **1** ◇ 🛒	XC **1** ◇	LM **1** ◇ 🛒		XC **1** ◇ 🍽	LM **1** C	VT **1** ◇ 🍽	NT D	VT **1** ◇ ⊠	XC **1** ◇ 🍽	LM **1** ◇ 🛒
0	—	—	—	—	**London Euston 15** ⊖	d																	06 20		
—	—	—	—	—	Gatwick Airport 10 ✈	d																			
17½	—	—	—	—	Watford Junction	d																	06u36		
49¾	—	—	—	—	Milton Keynes Central	d														*05 30*			06 56		
—	—	—	—	—	Northampton	d														06 06					
82½	0	—	—	—	Rugby	d														06 29					
97	—	—	—	—	Nuneaton	d														06 43					
110	—	—	—	—	Tamworth Low Level	d														06 57			07 35		
116¼	—	0	—	—	Lichfield Trent Valley	d														07 04					
—	11½	—	—	—	Coventry	d														*06b15*				*06 27*	
—	22	—	—	—	Birmingham International ✈	d															*06 23*			*06 45*	
—	30½	—	—	—	**Birmingham New Street 12**	d				05 20	05 30				06 03	06 07		06 30		07 03		*07c10*	07 18	07 21
35¾	—	—	—	—	Sandwell & Dudley	d										06 18								
39	—	—	—	—	Coseley	d										06 27								07 34
—	43¼	—	—	—	Wolverhampton 7 ⛴	d				05 38	05 49				06 21	06 39		07 06		07 21			07 39	07 44
—	53¼	—	—	—	Penkridge	d										06 49								07 54
133½	59½	—	—	—	**Stafford**	a				05 51	06 04				06 33	06 56		07 17	07 23	07 33			07 53	08 01
—	—	—	—	—		d				05 52	06 05				06 34	07 00		07 18	07 25	07 34			07 54	08 01
—	75¾	30¼	—	—	**Stoke-on-Trent**	a									06 52			07 36				08 04	08 12	
—	87½	42	—	—	Congleton	a												07 48					08 24	
—	95¼	50¼	—	—	Macclesfield	a												07 56				08 20	08 32	
158	—	—	—	—	**Crewe 10**	a				06 16	06 25				07 14	07 21			07 45	07 53				08 22
—	—	—	0	—		d				06 18	06 26				07 15	07 23			07 47	07 56				08 24
—	—	—	—	—	Chester	a				06 37	*07 00*					*07 59*				*08 27*				*08 57*
—	—	—	—	—	Llandudno Junction	a				07 33	*07e58*					*09e19*				*09e26*				*10e17*
—	—	—	—	—	Llandudno	a				*08 16*	*08e16*					*09e37*				*10f01*				*10e37*
—	—	—	—	—	Bangor (Gwynedd)	a				07 49	*08 43*									*09e43*				
—	—	—	—	—	Holyhead	a				08 21	*09 30*									*10e20*				
—	—	—	—	—	Wilmslow	a					*07 01*				07 33	*07 59*			*08 26*	*08 44*				
—	—	—	—	—	Manchester Airport ✈	a										*08 14*								
—	107¼	62¼	—	—	Stockport	a					*07 14*							08 09	*08 41*			08s35	08 46	
—	113	68	—	—	**Manchester Piccadilly 10** ⛴	a				*07g13*	*07 28*				08 02			08 27	*08 56*			08 48	09 02	
169¾	—	—	11¾	—	Hartford	a										07 35			07 58					08 35
182	—	—	—	—	Warrington Bank Quay	a					06 44									08 12				
—	—	—	—	—		d					06 45									08 13				
—	—	—	22½	—	Runcorn	a					*07g03*					07 47			08 10					08 45
—	—	—	30	—	Liverpool South Parkway 7 ✈	a										07 53								08 53
—	—	—	35½	—	**Liverpool Lime Street 10**	a					*07g27*					08 11			08 35					09 09
—	—	—	—	—		d					*06 04*		07 30											
—	—	—	—	—	Manchester Airport ✈	d			*03 40*	*04 34*		*05h47*	06 19		07 22										
—	—	—	—	—	**Manchester Piccadilly 10** ⛴	d			*03 55*	04 58		*06h05*	06 44		07 45										
—	—	79¼	—	—	Bolton	d						*06h26*	07 03		08 04										
193¾	—	—	—	—	Wigan North Western	a						07 03		08 01							08 23				
—	—	—	—	—		d						07 04		08 02							08 24				
209	—	99¼	—	—	**Preston 8**	a				05 54		07 17	07 26	08 24	08 27						08 41				
—	—	—	—	—	Blackpool North	a						*07 56*		08 51							*09 33*				
—	—	—	—	—		d			*04j45*	*05 30*		*06 34*			*07 41*							*08 09*			
—	—	—	—	—	**Preston 8**	d			05 24	06 04		07 20	07 29		08 28						08 43	08 46			
230	—	—	—	—	**Lancaster 6**	a			05 44	06 18		07 34	07 44		08 44						09 00	09 07			
—	—	—	—	—		d		05{22	05 45	06 20		07 35	07 45		08 44						09 02				
—	—	—	—	—	Barrow-in-Furness	a			07 05				08 49		*09 57*										
249	—	—	—	—	Oxenholme Lake District	a		05{53		06 34		07 47			08 58						09 17				
—	—	—	—	—		d		05{53		06 35		07 49			08 59						09 18				
—	—	—	—	—	Windermere	a		06{12		*07 10*		*08 15*			*09 22*										
281¼	—	—	—	—	Penrith North Lakes	d				07 00		08 13			09 24						09 43				
299	—	—	—	—	**Carlisle 8**	a				07 18		08 34			09 47						10 01				
—	—	—	—	—		d	06 09			07 21		08 35			09 47						10 03				
324¼	—	—	0	—	Lockerbie	d				07 43		08 55									10 22				
372½	—	—	—	0	Carstairs	a				08 17															
388½	—	—	—	—	Motherwell	a				08s35		09s50									11s04				
401¼	—	—	—	—	**Glasgow Central 15**	a	08 37			08 58		10 18									11 28				
—	—	—	75	26¼	Haymarket	a				*09k05*					11s04										
—	—	—	76¼	27½	**Edinburgh 10**	a				*09k12*					11 11										
—	—	—	—	97¼	Perth	a				*10m37*		*12m37*			*12 56*										
—	—	—	135½	—	Dundee	a				*10n21*		*13m00*			*12q23*										
—	—	—	206¾	—	Aberdeen	a				*11n34*		*14m13*			*13q36*										
—	—	—	—	215¼	Inverness	a				*13m35*					*15 18*										

For general notes see front of timetable
For details of catering facilities see Directory of Train Operators

A All Tuesdays to Fridays, also Mondays until 21 January and from 31 March. From Barrow-in-Furness (Table 82)

B 🍽 to Crewe, ⊠ from Crewe

C Also stops at Atherstone 0649 and Rugeley Trent Valley 0712

D From Clitheroe (Table 94) to Morecambe (Table 98)

b Change at Nuneaton

c Change at Tamworth

e Change at Crewe and Chester

f Change at Crewe, Chester and Llandudno Junction

g Change at Crewe

h Change at Preston

j Mondays 4 February to 24 March dep. 0325, by bus

k Change at Carstairs (Table 225)

m Via Glasgow Central and Glasgow Queen Street. Passengers make their own way from one station to the other

n Change at Carstairs and Haymarket

q Change at Haymarket

OVERNIGHT SLEEPERS. For Sleeper trains, operated by First ScotRail, please refer to Tables 400 - 404

London and West Midlands → North West England and Scotland

Route Diagram - see first page of Table 65

		VT	TP	XC	VT	LM	NT	VT	NT	NT	TP	VT	NT	VT	XC	LM	VT	TP	XC	VT	LM	VT	NT
		1 ◇	1 ◇	1 ◇	1 ◇	1 ◇		1 ◇			1 ◇	1 ◇		1 ◇	1 ◇	1	1 ◇	1 ◇	1 ◇	1 ◇	1 ◇	1 ◇	
			A	B		C	D		D		A		E		G	H			J				
		⊠	⊼	⫐	⊠	⊼		⫐			⊼	⊠		⊠	⫐	⊼	⊠	⊼	⫐	⊠	⊼	⫐	
London Euston 15 ⊖	d	06 46			07 03							07 13		07 35			07 46			08 05			
Gatwick Airport 10 ✈	d				05 53										05 15								
Watford Junction	d	06 51			07u18							07u28					08u01			07 31			
Milton Keynes Central	d	07 17										07 48								08 36			
Northampton	d	07 00														07 22	08 00						
Rugby	d	07 39														07 43	08 39						
Nuneaton	d											08 21											
Tamworth Low Level	d																		08b12				
Lichfield Trent Valley	d																						
Coventry	d			07 23		07 10						07c14			07 32	07 56					08 01	08 23	
Birmingham International ✈	d			07 34		07 20									07 51	08 09					08 19	08 34	
Birmingham New Street 12	d			07 48		07 51		08 03							08 18	08 26			08 48		08 51	09 03	
Sandwell & Dudley	d																				08 59		
Coseley	d															08 37							
Wolverhampton 7	d			08 06		08 09		08 21							08 39	08 44			09 06		09 10	09 21	
Penkridge	d					08 19										08 54							
Stafford	a			08 17		08 25						08 47			08 53	09 01			09 17		09 24		
	d			08 18		08 26						08 47			08 54	09 01			09 18		09 24		
Stoke-on-Trent	a			08 36	08 41									09 06	09 12				09 36	09 41			
Congleton	a																						
Macclesfield	a			08 52	08 57										09 31				09 52	09 57			
Crewe 10	a	08 30				08 51		08 54				09 07				09 22	09 30				09 46	09 53	
	d	08 31				08 52		08 56				09 08				09 24	09 31				09 47	09 56	
Chester	a					09 26										09 57						10 27	
Llandudno Junction	a					10 24										11e17						11e24	
Llandudno	a															11e35							
Bangor (Gwynedd)	a					10 46																11e41	
Holyhead	a					11 30																12e20	
Wilmslow	a	09 03										09 44				10 01					10 26		
Manchester Airport ✈	a	09 15														10 11							
Stockport	a	09 39		09 05	09s12									09s34	09 46				10 05	10s12	10 39		
Manchester Piccadilly 10	a	09 41		09 20	09 25									09 46	10 02				10 20	10 24	10 54		
Hartford	a															09 35							
Warrington Bank Quay	a	08 49						09 12									09 49					10 11	
	d	08 50						09 13									09 50					10 13	
Runcorn	a					09 08						09 25				09 45					10 03		
Liverpool South Parkway 7 ✈	a															09 53							
Liverpool Lime Street 10	a					09 31						09 47				10 09					10 26		
	d	08 04					08 28			08 57							09 04						09 57
Manchester Airport ✈	d	07f47	08 27								08 47							09 27					
Manchester Piccadilly 10	d	08f11	08 45								09 11							09 45					
Bolton	d	08f32	09 05								09 32							10 05					
Wigan North Western	a	09 00					09 12	09 23		09 30							10 00					10 22	10 31
	d	09 01					09 13	09 24		09 31							10 01					10 24	10 31
Preston 8	a	09 14	09 29				09 38	09 38		09 54	09 58						10 14	10 27				10 37	10 54
Blackpool North	a	09 57								10 21							10 57						11 21
	d	08 41							←		09 30						09 38						
Preston 8	d	09 18	09 34				09 44 →	09 40	09 44		10 04		10 10				10 18	10 29				10 40	
Lancaster 6	a	09 31	09 49					09 55	10 03		10 21		10 30				10 35	10 44					
	d	09 33	09 50					09 57			10 23		10 30					10 45					
Barrow-in-Furness	a		10 47								11 33		11 33					12 16					
Oxenholme Lake District	a	09 45						10 10			10 44							11 03				11 11	
	d	09 46						10 11			10 44							11 03				11 12	
Windermere	a	10 12									11 01												
Penrith North Lakes	d	10 12						10 35										11 30					
Carlisle 8	a	10 29						10 52										11 48				11 56	
	d	10 30						10 54										11 52				11 59	
Lockerbie	d							11 12										12 11					
Carstairs	a																						
Motherwell	a	11s27																12s57					
Glasgow Central 15	a	11 50																13 14				13 22	
Haymarket	a							12s08															
Edinburgh 10	a							12 19															
Perth	a	13g37						14 54															
Dundee	a	14g00						14 23															
Aberdeen	a	15g13						15 36															
Inverness	a							17 07															

For general notes see front of timetable
For details of catering facilities see Directory of Train Operators

A ⊼ to Preston
B From Southampton Central (Table 51)
C From Walsall (Table 70)
D To Morecambe (Table 98)
E To Carlisle via Whitehaven (Table 100)
G ⫐ from Reading
H ⊼ from Birmingham New Street
J From Derby (Table 57)
b Tamworth High Level
c Change at Nuneaton
e Change at Crewe and Chester
f Change at Preston
g Via Glasgow Central and Glasgow Queen Street. Passengers make their own way from one station to the other

OVERNIGHT SLEEPERS. For Sleeper trains, operated by First ScotRail, please refer to Tables 400 - 404

London and West Midlands → North West England and Scotland

Route Diagram - see first page of Table 65

		VT	VT	XC	LM	VT	TP	VT	XC	VT	LM	VT	NT	VT	VT	VT	XC	LM	VT	TP	XC	LM	VT
		1 ◇	1 ◇	1 ◇	1 ◇	1 ◇	1 ◇	1 ◇	1 ◇	1 ◇	1 ◇	1 ◇		1 ◇	1 ◇	1 ◇	1 ◇	1 ◇	1 ◇	1 ◇	1 ◇	1 ◇	1 ◇
				A			B		C								D						
		⊠	⊠	⊐	⊤	⊠	⊤	⊠	⊐	⊠	⊤	⊐		⊠	⊠	⊠	⊐	⊤	⊠		⊐	⊤	⊠
London Euston 15 ⊖	d	08 17	08 35			08 46		09 00		09 05				09 17	09 35	09 38			09 46				10 05
Gatwick Airport 10 ✈	d																						
Watford Junction	d	08u32				09u01				09u20				08 41					09 11				09 41
Milton Keynes Central	d							08b37						09 48					10 17				10 36
Northampton	d							09 00								10 26 →			10 00				
Rugby	d							09 49											10 39				
Nuneaton	d	09 21												10 21									
Tamworth Low Level	d																						
Lichfield Trent Valley	d																						
Coventry	d	08c11		08 32	08 44				09 23								09 32	09 44			10e02		
Birmingham International ✈	d			08 50	08 58				09 34								09 50	09 58			10 18	10 20	
Birmingham New Street 12	d			09 18	09 21				09 48		09 51	10 03					10 18	10 21			10 48	10 51	
Sandwell & Dudley	d										09 59											10 59	
Coseley	d				09 34													10 34					
Wolverhampton 7	d			09 39	09 44				10 06		10 10	10 21					10 39	10 44			11 06	11 10	
Penkridge	d				09 54													10 54					
Stafford	a	09 47			10 01				10 17		10 24			10 47				11 01			11 17	11 24	
	d	09 47			10 01				10 18		10 24			10 47				11 01			11 18	11 24	
Stoke-on-Trent	a		10 06	10 12					10 36	10 41					11 06		11 12				11 36		11 41
Congleton	a			10 24																			
Macclesfield	a			10 32					10 52	10 57							11 31				11 52		11 57
Crewe 10	a	10 07			10 21	10 31		10 41			10 46	10 53		11 07				11 22	11 31			11 50	
	d	10 08			10 24	10 32		10 50			10 47	10 56		11 08				11 24	11 32				
Chester	a				10 57			11 17				11 29						11 59				12 27	
Llandudno Junction	a				11f55			12 07				12 25						13f17				13f24	
Llandudno	a							12 35				13g01						13f35					
Bangor (Gwynedd)	a				12f12			12 26				12 48										13f48	
Holyhead	a				12f47			13 03				13 30										14f30	
Wilmslow	a	10 44			11 01						11 26			11 44				12 01				12 26	
Manchester Airport ✈	a				11 11													12 11					
Stockport	a	10 53	10s34	10 46					11 05	11s12	11 39			11 53	11s34		11 46				12 05	12 39	12s12
Manchester Piccadilly 10	a	11 13	10 46	11 02					11 20	11 24	11 54			12 13	11 46		12 02				12 20	12 54	12 24
Hartford	a				10 33													11 35					
Warrington Bank Quay	a					10 50						11 11							11 50				
	d					10 51						11 13							11 51				
Runcorn	a	10 25			10 45						11 03			11 25				11 45					
Liverpool South Parkway 7 ✈	a				10 53													11 53					
Liverpool Lime Street 10	a	10 47			11 09						11 26			11 47				12 09					
	d					10 04							10 57						11 04				
Manchester Airport ✈	d					09h47	10 27												10h47				
Manchester Piccadilly 10	d					10h11	10 45												11h11				
Bolton	d					10h32	11 05												11h32				
Wigan North Western	a					11 01						11 22	11 30						12 01				
	d					11 02						11 24	11 30						12 02				
Preston 8	a					11 15	11 27					11 37	11 53						12 15				
Blackpool North	a					11 54							12 20						12 54				
	d					10 41													11 41				
Preston 8	d					11 19	11 29					11 40							12 19	12 23			
Lancaster 6	a					11 32	11 44					11 54							12 32	12 38			
	d					11 34	11 45					11 55							12 34	12 39			
Barrow-in-Furness	a						12 49																
Oxenholme Lake District	a					11 46													12 46	12 54			
	d					11 47													12 47	12 57			
Windermere	a					12 14														13 18			
Penrith North Lakes	d											12 33							13 12				
Carlisle 8	a					12 28						12 51							13 36				
	d					12 29						12 53											
Lockerbie	d											13 11											
Carstairs	a																						
Motherwell	a																						
Glasgow Central 15	a					13 46																	
Haymarket	a											14s08											
Edinburgh 10	a											14 19											
Perth	a					15j36																	
Dundee	a					15j59						16 17											
Aberdeen	a					17j09						17 38											
Inverness	a																						

For general notes see front of timetable
For details of catering facilities see Directory of Train Operators

A From Exeter St Davids (Table 51)
B ⊤ to Preston
C From Bournemouth (Table 51)
D From Reading (Table 51)
b Change at Northampton and Rugby
c Change at Nuneaton
e Change at Birmingham New Street
f Change at Crewe and Chester
g Change at Crewe and Llandudno Junction
h Change at Preston
j Via Glasgow Central and Glasgow Queen Street. Passengers make their own way from one station to the other

OVERNIGHT SLEEPERS. For Sleeper trains, operated by First ScotRail, please refer to Tables 400 - 404

London and West Midlands → North West England and Scotland

Route Diagram - see first page of Table 65

		TP	VT	VT	VT	VT	TP	VT	NT	VT	VT		XC	LM	VT	TP	XC	LM	VT	NT	TP	VT	VT		VT
		1◇	1◇	1◇	1◇	1◇	1◇	1◇		1◇	1◇		R 1	1◇	1◇	1◇	R 1	1◇	1◇		1◇	1◇	1◇		1◇
													A			B	C				B				
		⊤	⊏	⊠	⊠	⊠	⊤	⊏		⊠	⊠		⊏	⊤	⊠	⊤	⊏	⊤	⊏		⊤	⊏	⊏		⊏
London Euston 15 ⊖	d				10 15	10 29				10 35					10 46							11 05	11 17		11 28
Gatwick Airport 10 ✈	d														*09 37*										
Watford Junction	d				10u30										11u01							11u20	*10 41*		
Milton Keynes Central	d			←											*10b33*								11 48		
Northampton	d			10 26											*11 00*										
Rugby	d			10 47											11 39										
Nuneaton	d			11 00	11 19																				
Tamworth Low Level	d			11c15																			12 22		
Lichfield Trent Valley	d			11 22																					
Coventry	d		*10 23*										*10 32*	*10 44*			11 23								
Birmingham International ✈	d		*10 34*										*10 50*	*10 58*			11 34								
Birmingham New Street 12	d		11 03										11 18	11 21			11 48	11 51	12 03						
Sandwell & Dudley	d																	11 59							
Coseley	d													11 34											
Wolverhampton 7	d		11 21										11 39	11 44				12 10	12 21						
Penkridge	d													11 54											
Stafford	a				11 45									12 01			12 17	12 24					12 48		
	d				11 45									12 01			12 18	12 24					12 48		
Stoke-on-Trent	a									12 06			12 12				12 36					12 41			
Congleton	a												12 24												
Macclesfield	a												12 32				12 52					12 57			
Crewe 10	a		11 55	12 04	12 07						←			12 22	12 31			12 45	12 53				13 09		13 12
	d		11 56	12 08	12 08						12 08			12 24	12 32			12 48	12 56				13 10		13 12
Chester	a			→										*12 59*									*13 43*		13 32
Llandudno Junction	a													*14e09*									*14 38*		14 22
Llandudno	a													*14e27*											14 44
Bangor (Gwynedd)	a																						*14 55*		*14f55*
Holyhead	a																						*15 30*		*15f30*
Wilmslow	a				*12 44*						12 28			*13 01*				*13 26*							*13g44*
Manchester Airport ✈	a													*13 11*											
Stockport	a				*12 53*					12s34	12s41		12 46				13 05	*13 39*				13s12			
Manchester Piccadilly 10	a				*13 13*					12 46	12 55		13 02				13 20	*13 54*				13 24			
Hartford	a													12 33											
Warrington Bank Quay	a		12 13												12 50				13 11						
	d		12 14												12 51				13 13						
Runcorn	a				12 25									12 45				13 03					13 26		
Liverpool South Parkway 7 ✈	a													12 53											
Liverpool Lime Street 10	a				12 47									13 09				13 26					13 49		
	d								11 57						*12 04*					12 57					
Manchester Airport ✈	d	11 27														12 27					12 47				
Manchester Piccadilly 10	d	11 45														12 45					13 11				
Bolton	d	12 05														13 05					13 32				
Wigan North Western	a		12 24					←	12 31						13 01				13 22	13 31					
	d		12 26					12 26	12 31						13 02				13 24	13 31					
Preston 8	a	12 27	→			12 43		12 47	12 56						13 15	13 27			13 37	13 54	14 01				
Blackpool North	a								13 21						*13 54*					14 21					
	d							*12 11*							*12 41*						*13 30*				
Preston 8	d	12 29				12 44		12 50							13 19	13 29			13 40		14 09				
Lancaster 6	a	12 44						13 04							13 38	13 44			13 54		14 24				
	d	12 45						13 06								13 46			13 55		14 26				
Barrow-in-Furness	a							*14 07*								14 43			*15 21*						
Oxenholme Lake District	a	12 59																	14 08		14 41				
	d	12 59																	14 10		14 51				
Windermere	a	*14 13*																			→				
Penrith North Lakes	d							13 44																	
Carlisle 8	a	13 40				13 43	←	14 00											14 51						
	d	13 47				13 43	13 47	14 03											14 54						
Lockerbie	d	→						14 22											15 13						
Carstairs	a																								
Motherwell	a																								
Glasgow Central 15	a					14 54		15 25																	
Haymarket	a						15s04												16s08						
Edinburgh 10	a						15 11												16 16						
Perth	a					*16h37*		*17h20*											*17 55*						
Dundee	a					*16h59*	*17 26*												*17 44*						
Aberdeen	a					*18h15*	*18 46*												*19 02*						
Inverness	a							*19h34*											*20 08*						

For general notes see front of timetable
For details of catering facilities see Directory of Train Operators

A From Plymouth (Table 51)
B ⊤ to Preston
C From Bournemouth (Table 51)
b Change at Northampton and Rugby
c Arr. 1112
e Change at Crewe and Chester
f Change at Llandudno Junction
g Change at Crewe
h Via Glasgow Central and Glasgow Queen Street. Passengers make their own way from one station to the other

OVERNIGHT SLEEPERS. For Sleeper trains, operated by First ScotRail, please refer to Tables 400 - 404

London and West Midlands → North West England and Scotland

Route Diagram - see first page of Table 65

		VT	XC	LM	VT	TP	TP	XC	LM	VT	NT	VT	VT	VT	XC	LM	VT	TP	XC	LM	VT	LM	NT	VT
		1◇	1◇	1◇	1◇	1◇	1◇	1◇	1◇	1◇		1◇	1◇	1◇	R 1	1◇	1◇	1◇	R 1	1◇	1◇	1		1◇
			A												B			C	D			E		
		🍽	🍽	🛒	🍽		🛒	🍽	🛒	🍽		🍽	🍽	🍽	🍽	🛒	🍽	🛒	🍽	🛒	🍽	🛒		🍽
London Euston [15] ⊖	d	11 35			11 46							12 05	12 17	12 35			12 46					12 49		13 05
Gatwick Airport [10] ✈	d												10 37											11 37
Watford Junction	d				11 11							11 41	12u32											13u20
Milton Keynes Central	d				12 17							12 36					13 17							
Northampton	d				12 00												13 00							
Rugby	d				12 39												13 39					13 47		
Nuneaton	d												13 21									14 01		
Tamworth Low Level	d																					14 17		
Lichfield Trent Valley	d																					14 23		
Coventry	d		11 32	11 44				12b02		12 23					12 32	12 46			13 23					
Birmingham International ✈	d		11 50	11 58				12 18	12 20	12 34					12 50	12 58			13 34					
Birmingham New Street [12]	d		12 18	12 21				12 48	12 51	13 03					13 18	13 21			13 48	13 51	14 03			
Sandwell & Dudley	d								12 59											13 59				
Coseley	d			12 34												13 34								
Wolverhampton [7] 🚌	d		12 39	12 44				13 06	13 10	13 21					13 39	13 44			14 06	14 10	14 21			
Penkridge	d			12 54												13 54								
Stafford	a			13 01				13 17	13 24				13 47			14 01			14 17	14 24		14 43		
	d			13 01				13 18	13 24				13 47			14 01			14 18	14 24		14 44		
Stoke-on-Trent	a	13 06	13 12					13 36				13 41		14 06	14 12				14 36					14 41
Congleton	a														14 24									
Macclesfield	a		13 31					13 52				13 57			14 32				14 52					14 57
Crewe [10]	a			13 22	13 31				13 50	13 53			14 07			14 22	14 31			14 45	14 53	15 09		
	d			13 24	13 32					13 56			14 08			14 24	14 32			14 47	14 56			
Chester	a			13 57						14 27						14 57					15 26			
Llandudno Junction	a			15c18						15c25						16c17					16 24			
Llandudno	a			15c36						16e01						16c35								
Bangor (Gwynedd)	a									15c47											16 46			
Holyhead	a									16c30											17 20			
Wilmslow	a			14 01					14 26				14 44			15 01				15 26		15 44		
Manchester Airport ✈	a			14 11												15 11								
Stockport	a	13s34	13 46					14 05	14 39			14s12	14 53	14s34	14 46				15 05	15 39		15 33		15s12
Manchester Piccadilly [10] 🚌	a	13 46	14 02					14 20	14 54			14 24	15 13	14 46	15 02				15 20	15 54		16 13		15 24
Hartford	a			13 35												14 35								
Warrington Bank Quay	a				13 49					14 14							14 50				15 11			
	d				13 51					14 15							14 51				15 13			
Runcorn	a			13 45									14 25			14 45				15 03				
Liverpool South Parkway [7] ✈	a			13 53												14 53								
Liverpool Lime Street [10]	a			14 09									14 47			15 09				15 26				
	d				13 04						13 57						14 04						14 57	
Manchester Airport ✈	d						13 27											14 27						
Manchester Piccadilly [10] 🚌	d						13 45											14 45						
Bolton	d						14 05											15 05						
Wigan North Western	a				14 00					14 26	14 31						15 01				15 22		15 31	
	d				14 02					14 27	14 31						15 02				15 24		15 31	
Preston [8]	a				14 15		14 27			14 41	14 54						15 15	15 27			15 37		15 54	
Blackpool North	a				14 54						15 21						15 54						16 21	
	d				13 41												14 41							
Preston [8]	d				14 19		14 29			14 43							15 19	15 29			15 40			
Lancaster [6]	a				14 32		14 44			14 57							15 38	15 44			15 56			
	d				14 34		14 45			14 59								15 52			15 58			
Barrow-in-Furness	a																	16 56						
Oxenholme Lake District	a				14 46	⟵	14 59			15 12														
	d				14 47	14 51	14 59			15 13														
Windermere	a					15 09				16 10														
Penrith North Lakes	d				15 12		15 24														16 33			
Carlisle [8]	a				15 30		15 42			15 55											16 51			
	d				15 30		15 43			15 56											16 53			
Lockerbie	d						16 02																	
Carstairs	a																							
Motherwell	a				16s27																			
Glasgow Central [15]	a				16 55					17 21														
Haymarket	a						17s08														18s09			
Edinburgh [10]	a						17 14														18 19			
Perth	a				18f48		18 54			19f19											19 49			
Dundee	a				19f15		19 27														21 10			
Aberdeen	a				20f33		20 44																	
Inverness	a						20 58																	

For general notes see front of timetable
For details of catering facilities see Directory of Train Operators

A From Reading (Table 51)
B From Penzance (Table 135)
C 🛒 to Preston
D From Bournemouth (Table 51)
E Also stops at Atherstone 1407, Polesworth 1412 and Rugeley Trent Valley 1431
b Change at Birmingham New Street
c Change at Crewe and Chester
e Change at Crewe, Chester and Llandudno Junction
f Via Glasgow Central and Glasgow Queen Street. Passengers make their own way from one station to the other

OVERNIGHT SLEEPERS. For Sleeper trains, operated by First ScotRail, please refer to Tables 400 - 404

London and West Midlands → North West England and Scotland

Route Diagram - see first page of Table 65

		VT	VT	XC	LM	VT	TP	XC	LM	VT	VT	NT	VT	VT	XC	LM	VT	TP	XC	VT	LM	NT	VT
		1◇	1◇	1◇	1◇	1◇	1◇	1◇	1◇	1◇	1◇		1◇	1◇	R 1	1◇	1◇	1◇	R 1	1◇	1◇		1◇
				A											B			C	D				
		☕	☕	☕	🛒	☕	🛒	☕	🛒	☕	☕		☕	☕	☕	🛒	☕	🛒	☕	☕	🛒		☕
London Euston 15 ⊖	d	13 17	13 35			13 46				14 05			14 17	14 35			14 46			15 05			
Gatwick Airport 10 ✈	d					*12 37*														*13 37*			
Watford Junction	d	*12 41*				14u01				*13 41*			14u32							15u20			
Milton Keynes Central	d	13 48								14 36							15u17						
Northampton	d					*14 00*											*15 00*						
Rugby	d					14 39											15 39						
Nuneaton	d	14 21											15 21										
Tamworth Low Level	d																						
Lichfield Trent Valley	d																						
Coventry	d			*13 32*	*13 44*			14b02			*14 23*				*14 32*	*14 44*			15 23				
Birmingham International ✈	d			*13 50*	*13 58*			14 18	*14 20*		*14 34*				*14 50*	*14 58*			15 34				
Birmingham New Street 12	d			14 18	14 21			14 48	14 51		15 03				15 18	15 21			15 48		15 51		16 03
Sandwell & Dudley	d								14 59												15 59		
Coseley	d				14 34											15 34							
Wolverhampton 7 ⛴	d			14 39	14 44			15 06	15 10		15 21				15 39	15 44					16 10		16 21
Penkridge	d				14 54											15 54							
Stafford	a	14 47			15 01			15 17	15 24				15 47			16 01			16 17		16 24		
	d	14 47			15 01			15 18	15 24				15 47			16 01			16 18		16 24		
Stoke-on-Trent	a		15 06	15 12				15 36		15 41				16 06	16 12				16 36	16 41			
Congleton	a														16 24								
Macclesfield	a			15 31				15 52		15 57					16 32				16 52	16 57			
Crewe 10	a	15 07			15 22	15 31			15 50		15 55		16 07			16 22	16 31				16 45		16 53
	d	15 08			15 24	15 32					15 57		16 08			16 24	16 32				16 47		16 56
Chester	a				*15 57*				*16 27*							*16 57*							*17 26*
Llandudno Junction	a				*17c17*				*17c24*							*18c17*							*18 25*
Llandudno	a				*17c35*											*18c35*							
Bangor (Gwynedd)	a								*17c47*														*18 47*
Holyhead	a								*18c30*														*19 20*
Wilmslow	a				*16 01*				*16 26*				*16 44*				*17 05*				*17 26*		
Manchester Airport ✈	a				*16 11*												*17 15*						
Stockport	a		15s34	15 46				16 05	*16 40*	16s12			*16 53*	16s34	16 46				17 05	17s12	*17 38*		
Manchester Piccadilly 10 ⛴	a		15 46	16 02				16 20	*16 54*	16 24			*17 11*	16 46	17 02		*17 41*		17 20	17 24	*17 54*		
Hartford	a				15 35											16 33							
Warrington Bank Quay	a					15 50					16 14						16 50						17 11
	d					15 51					16 15						16 51						17 13
Runcorn	a	15 25			15 45								16 25			16 45					17 03		
Liverpool South Parkway 7 ✈	a				15 53											16 53							
Liverpool Lime Street 10	a	15 48			16 09								16 48			17 09					17 26		
	d					*15 04*						15 57					*16 04*					16 30	
Manchester Airport ✈	d					*14e47*	15 27										*15e47*	16 27					
Manchester Piccadilly 10 ⛴	d					*15e11*	15 45										*16e11*	16 44					
Bolton	d					*15e32*	16 05										*16e32*	17 05					
Wigan North Western	a					16 01					16 25	16 31					17 01					17 09	17 22
	d					16 02					16 27	16 31					17 02					17 10	17 24
Preston 8	a					16 15	16 27				16 40	16 54					17 15	17 27				→	17 37
Blackpool North	a					*16 54*						*17 34*					*17 58*						
	d					*15 41*						*16 25*					*16 38*						
Preston 8	d					16 19	16 29				16 43	16 56					17 18	17 29					17 40
Lancaster 6	a					16 32	16 44				16 58	17 16					17 32	17 44					17 54
	d					16 34	16 45				16 59	17 16					17 34	17 45					17 55
Barrow-in-Furness	a					*17 44*						18 23						18 50					
Oxenholme Lake District	a					16 46	16 59				17 15												18 11
	d					16 47	16 59				17 17												18 12
Windermere	a						*17 23*				*18 04*												
Penrith North Lakes	d					17 12	17 25																18 37
Carlisle 8	a					17 29	17 43				17 57						18 26						18 55
	d					17 29	17 44				17 59						18 27						18 58
Lockerbie	d						18 04																
Carstairs	a																						
Motherwell	a										19s13												
Glasgow Central 15	a					18 46					19 37						19 47						
Haymarket	a						19s04																20s08
Edinburgh 10	a						19 11																20 19
Perth	a					20f37	20 51										21f42						
Dundee	a						20g26																*21 53*
Aberdeen	a						21g39																*23 13*
Inverness	a						23 10																

For general notes see front of timetable
For details of catering facilities see Directory of Train Operators

A From Reading (Table 51)
B From Penzance (Table 135)
C 🛒 to Preston
D From Bournemouth (Table 51)
b Change at Birmingham New Street
c Change at Crewe and Chester
e Change at Preston
f Via Glasgow Central and Glasgow Queen Street. Passengers make their own way from one station to the other
g Change at Haymarket

OVERNIGHT SLEEPERS. For Sleeper trains, operated by First ScotRail, please refer to Tables 400 - 404

London and West Midlands → North West England and Scotland

Route Diagram - see first page of Table 65

	NT	TP	VT	VT	XC	LM	NT	TP	VT	TP	NT	TP	XC	VT	LM	VT	NT	VT	VT	VT	XC	LM
		1 ◇	1 ◇	1 ◇	R 1	1 ◇		1 ◇	1 ◇	1 ◇		1 ◇	1 ◇	1 ◇	1 ◇	1 ◇		1 ◇	1 ◇	1 ◇	R 1	1 ◇
					A							B									C	
		🛒	⊠	⊠	☕	🛒			⊠			🛒	☕	☕	🛒	☕		☕	☕	☕	☕	🛒
London Euston 15 ⊖ d			15 17	15 35					15 46					15 49				16 05	16 17	16 35		
Gatwick Airport 10 ✈ d																		13b37	14 37			
Watford Junction d			14 41															15 41	16u32			
Milton Keynes Central d			15 48															16u36				
Northampton d														16 00								
Rugby d														16 39								
Nuneaton d			16 21																17 21			
Tamworth Low Level d									16 53													
Lichfield Trent Valley d																						
Coventry d					15 32	15 44							16c02			16 23					16 32	16 44
Birmingham International ✈ d					15 50	15 58							16 18		16 20	16 34					16 50	16 58
Birmingham New Street 12 d					16 18	16 21							16 48		16 51	17 03					17 18	17 21
Sandwell & Dudley d															16 59							
Coseley d						16 34																17 35
Wolverhampton 7 d					16 39	16 44							17 06		17 10						17 39	17 44
Penkridge d						16 54									17 20							17 54
Stafford a			16 47			17 01							17 17		17 26				17 47			18 01
d			16 47			17 01							17 18		17 27				17 47			18 01
Stoke-on-Trent a				17 06	17 12								17 36					17 41		18 06	18 12	
Congleton a					17 24																18 24	
Macclesfield a				17 21	17 32								17 52					17 57		18 21	18 32	
Crewe 10 a			17 07			17 22			17 31					17 34	17 48	17 53			18 07			18 22
d			17 08			17 24			17 32					17 35	17 49	17 56			18 08			18 24
Chester a			17 53											17 58		18 29						18 57
Llandudno Junction a														18 49		19e26						20e18
Llandudno a														19 37								20e35
Bangor (Gwynedd) a														19 05		19e49						
Holyhead a														19 41		20e30						
Wilmslow a			17 44			18 04									18 26				18 42			
Manchester Airport ✈ a						18 15													18 54			
Stockport a			17 54	17s35	17 46								18 05		18 39			18s11	18 53	18s35	18 46	
Manchester Piccadilly 10 a			18 12	17 49	18 02								18 20		18 56			18 25	19 13	18 49	19 02	
Hartford a						17 35																18 35
Warrington Bank Quay a									17 49						18 06							
d									17 51						18 07							
Runcorn a			17 25			17 45													18 25			18 45
Liverpool South Parkway 7 ✈ a						17 53																18 53
Liverpool Lime Street 10 a			17 47			18 09													18 47			19 09
d							17 20										17 45					
Manchester Airport ✈ d		16 47										17 32										
Manchester Piccadilly 10 d		17 11										17 50										
Bolton d		17 30										18 10										
Wigan North Western a	←						17 54		18 00		←				18 17		18 28					
d	17 10						17 54		18 02		17 54				18 17		18 28					
Preston 8 a	17 40	17 53					→		18 15		18 17	18 34			18 39	18 39	18 54					
Blackpool North a	18 22	18 30							19 00		18 48	19 09					19 23					
d		17 19							17 38													
Preston 8 d		17 58							18 18			18 38				18 40						
Lancaster 6 a		18 13							18 31			18 53				18 58						
d		18 14						18 22	18 33			18 54				19 00						
Barrow-in-Furness a												19 59										
Oxenholme Lake District a		18 28						18 43	18 47	←						19 13						
d		18 28						18 52	18 49	18 52						19 14						
Windermere a								→		19 13												
Penrith North Lakes d		18 53							19 13													
Carlisle 8 a		19 11							19 31							19 54						
d		19 13							19 32							19 56						
Lockerbie d		19 32																				
Carstairs a																						
Motherwell a									20s30													
Glasgow Central 15 a		20 31							20 57							21 11						
Haymarket a																						
Edinburgh 10 a																						
Perth a									22f36													
Dundee a									22f59													
Aberdeen a									00f17													
Inverness a																						

For general notes see front of timetable
For details of catering facilities see Directory of Train Operators

- A From Reading (Table 51)
- B 🛒 to Preston
- C From Plymouth (Table 51)
- b Change at Watford Junction and Milton Keynes Central
- c Change at Birmingham New Street
- e Change at Crewe and Chester
- f Via Glasgow Central and Glasgow Queen Street. Passengers make their own way from one station to the other

OVERNIGHT SLEEPERS. For Sleeper trains, operated by First ScotRail, please refer to Tables 400 - 404

London and West Midlands → North West England and Scotland

Route Diagram - see first page of Table 65

		NT	VT	NT	XC	VT	LM	VT	VT	VT	VT	TP	XC	VT	VT	LM	VT	NT	VT	NT	TP	VT	VT
			1◇		R 1	1◇	1◇	1◇	1◇	1◇	1◇	1◇	R 1	1◇	1◇	1◇	1◇		1◇		1◇	1◇	1◇
					A								B										
			☕		☕	☕	🛒	☕	☕	⊠	☕	🛒	☕	⊠	⊠	🛒	⊠		⊠			☕	⊠
London Euston 15 ⊖	d		16 46			16 49		17 05	17 10	17 15				17 17	17 21		17 35		17 45				17 48
Gatwick Airport 10 ✈	d							15 37					14 51										16 37
Watford Junction	d							17u20											16b42				18u03
Milton Keynes Central	d					17u20									16c37				17c39				
Northampton	d														17 00				18 05				
Rugby	d														18 10				18 34				
Nuneaton	d														18 24								
Tamworth Low Level	d													18 24									
Lichfield Trent Valley	d					18 03																←	18e25 19 00
Coventry	d				17 23				18 14 →				17 32			17 44						18 14	
Birmingham International ✈	d				17 34								17 50			17 58						18 28	
Birmingham New Street 12	d				17 48		17 51				18 03		18 18			18 21						18 43	
Sandwell & Dudley	d						17 59															18 53	
Coseley	d															18 34							
Wolverhampton 7	d				18 06		18 10				18 21		18 39			18 44						19 06	
Penkridge	d						18 20									18 54							
Stafford	a		18 11		18 17		18 26								18 50	19 01			19 10			19 21	
	d		18 11		18 18		18 27								18 50	19 03			19 10			19 27	
Stoke-on-Trent	a				18 36			18 41					19 12				19 06					→	
Congleton	a																						
Macclesfield	a				18 52			18 57					19 31				19 22						
Crewe 10	a		18 31			18 41	18 48				18 54			19 07	19 11	19 29							19 34
	d		18 32			18 42	18 49				18 56			19 08	19 22	19 31							19 35
Chester	a						19 25								19 49								
Llandudno Junction	a														20 44								
Llandudno	a														21 08								
Bangor (Gwynedd)	a														21 03								
Holyhead	a														21 40								
Wilmslow	a					18 58	19 26								19f44								
Manchester Airport ✈	a														20g02								19 51
Stockport	a				19 05	19s09	19 39	19s12					19 46		19f53		19s36						20s02
Manchester Piccadilly 10	a				19 20	19 21	19 57	19 24					20 02				19 50						20 14
Hartford	a															19 44							
Warrington Bank Quay	a		18 51							19 09	19 12								19 45				
	d		18 52							19 09	19 13								19 47				
Runcorn	a						19 05							19 25		19 53							
Liverpool South Parkway 7 ✈	a															20 01							
Liverpool Lime Street 10	a						19 29							19 45		20 18							
	d	18 04																19 04					
Manchester Airport ✈	d		17h47							17j52		18 27									19 27		
Manchester Piccadilly 10	d		18h11							18h31		18 45									19 44		
Bolton	d		18h32							18h51		19 12									20 04		
Wigan North Western	a	18 51	19 02	←						19 20	19 23							19 51	19 56	←			
	d	18 51	19 03	18 51						19 20	19 24							19 51	19 58	19 51			
Preston 8	a	→	19 15	19 17						19 37	19 42	19 44						→	20 13	20 17	20 26		
Blackpool North	a			19 57							20 36									20 56			
	d		18 38								19 10								19 25		19 42		
Preston 8	d		19 18							19 40	19 45	19 50							20 16		20 27		
Lancaster 6	a		19 33								19 59	20 05							20 32		20 44		
	d		19 34								20 00	20 06									20 51		
Barrow-in-Furness	a		20 42																		21 56		
Oxenholme Lake District	a		19 46								20 13	20 20											
	d		19 48								20 15	20 21											
Windermere	a		20 18									21 24											
Penrith North Lakes	d		20 12								20 40	20 46											
Carlisle 8	a		20 29							20 39	20 58	21 03											
	d		20 30							20 40	20 59	21 05											
Lockerbie	d		20 52									21 24											
Carstairs	a																						
Motherwell	a																						
Glasgow Central 15	a									21 55		22 31											
Haymarket	a		21s47								22s13												
Edinburgh 10	a		21 56								22 25												
Perth	a									00k15													
Dundee	a										00m07												
Aberdeen	a																						
Inverness	a																						

For general notes see front of timetable
For details of catering facilities see Directory of Train Operators

A From Bournemouth (Table 51)
B From Brighton (Table 51)

b Change at Milton Keynes Central, Northampton and Rugby
c Change at Northampton and Rugby
e By bus
f Change at Crewe
g Change at Crewe and Wilmslow

h Change at Preston
j Change at Manchester Piccadilly and Preston
k Via Glasgow Central and Glasgow Queen Street. Passengers make their own way from one station to the other
m Change at Haymarket

OVERNIGHT SLEEPERS. For Sleeper trains, operated by First ScotRail, please refer to Tables 400 - 404

London and West Midlands → North West England and Scotland

Route Diagram - see first page of Table 65

		LM	VT	VT	VT	VT	VT	VT	VT	XC	VT	LM	VT	VT	NT	XC	VT	VT	XC	LM	VT	VT	TP
								FO			FO												
		1◇	1◇	R 1	1◇	1◇	1◇	1◇	1◇	R 1	1◇	1◇	R 1	1◇		R 1	1◇	1◇	1◇	1◇	1◇	1◇	1◇
										A						B			C				
		⚯	⊠	⊠	⊏	⊏	⊠	⊏	⊠	⊏	⊏	⚯	⊏	⊏		⊏	⊏	⊏		⚯	⊏	⊏	
London Euston 15 ⊖	d		18 05	18 08			18 17	18 20	18 35				18 45	19 05			19 17	19 35			19 38	19 46	
Gatwick Airport 10 ✈	d												17 37										
Watford Junction	d						17 51						19u00				19u32					20 19	
Milton Keynes Central	d						18u49															20 00	
Northampton	d																					20 41	
Rugby	d			18 56																			
Nuneaton	d		19 04														20 20					21 00	
Tamworth Low Level	d												19 55										
Lichfield Trent Valley	d																				20 48		
Coventry	d		18b17			18 23				18 34		18 36				19 23			19 32	19 44			
Birmingham International ✈	d					18 34				18 46		18 54				19 34			19 50	19 58			
Birmingham New Street 12	d	18 51				19 03				19 18		19 21	19c30			20 03			20 18	20 21			
Sandwell & Dudley	d	18 59																					
Coseley	d											19 34								20 34			
Wolverhampton 7	d	19 10				19 21				19 39		19 44				20 21			20 39	20 44			
Penkridge	d											19 54								20 54			
Stafford	a	19 24			←	19 36	19 44	19 51				20 01				20 34		20 57		21 01			
	d	19 24			19 27	19 36	19 45	19 52				20 01				20 34		20 57		21 01			
Stoke-on-Trent	a		19 39		19 45				20 06	20 12				20 40					21 12				
Congleton	a									20 24													
Macclesfield	a		19 57		20 01				20 23	20 32				20 57					21 28				
Crewe 10	a	19 49		19 52		19 58	20 07	20 14			←	20 22	20 31			20 54	21 03			21 23	21 29	21 37	
	d			19 54		19 59	20 08	20 16			20 16	20 24	20 32			20 56	21 04			21 24	21 29	21 38	
Chester	a			20 27				→				20 57	21 27								21 49	22 11	
Llandudno Junction	a			21e28																	22 39		
Llandudno	a			21f43																			
Bangor (Gwynedd)	a			21e51																	22 55		
Holyhead	a			22e35																	23 30		
Wilmslow	a	20 26					20 45				20 32					21 15	21 44	21 31				22 26	
Manchester Airport ✈	a						21g02				21 02						22g07	22 07				23g02	
Stockport	a	20 39	20s12		20 16		20 53		20s36	20 46	20s44			21s12		21 25	21 53	21s42	21 46			22 39	
Manchester Piccadilly 10	a	20 54	20 20		20 35		21 13		20 51	21 02	21 04			21 24		21 48	22 12	21 54	22 02			22 52	
Hartford	a											20 35								21 36			
Warrington Bank Quay	a					20 16							20 50									21 56	
	d					20 17							20 51									21 57	
Runcorn	a						20 25					20 45					21 21			21 45			
Liverpool South Parkway 7 ✈	a											20 53								21 53			
Liverpool Lime Street 10	a						20 47					21 09					21 45			22 09			
	d												19 48									20 48	
Manchester Airport ✈	d												19h47									20h47	21 27
Manchester Piccadilly 10	d												20h11									21h11	21 43
Bolton	d												20h32									21h32	22 02
Wigan North Western	a					20 27							21 01									22 07	
	d					20 29							21 02									22 08	
Preston 8	a			20 32		20 42							21 15									22 21	22 32
Blackpool North	a					21 36							21 56										
	d												20 28		20 53							20 53	22 03
Preston 8	d			20 35		20 45							21 19		21 29							22 24	22 34
Lancaster 6	a					21 00							21 34		21 49							22 38	22 49
	d					21 01							21 36		21 49							22 39	22 50
Barrow-in-Furness	a														22 54								23 54
Oxenholme Lake District	a			20 59		21 14							21 48									22 51	
	d			21 00		21 16							21 49									22 53	
Windermere	a			21 24									22 12										
Penrith North Lakes	d			21 25		21 42							22 14									23 22	
Carlisle 8	a			21 43		21 58							22 37									23 45	
	d			21 43		22 00																	
Lockerbie	d					22 18																	
Carstairs	a																						
Motherwell	a			22s49		23s04																	
Glasgow Central 15	a			23 04		23 33																	
Haymarket	a																						
Edinburgh 10	a																						
Perth	a			01j19																			
Dundee	a																						
Aberdeen	a																						
Inverness	a																						

For general notes see front of timetable
For details of catering facilities see Directory of Train Operators

A From Plymouth (Table 51)
B From Bournemouth (Table 51). ⊏ to Birmingham New Street
C From Guildford (Table 51)
b Change at Nuneaton
c Change at Tamworth
e Change at Crewe and Chester
f Change at Crewe, Chester and Llandudno Junction
g Change at Crewe and Wilmslow
h Change at Preston
j Via Glasgow Central and Glasgow Queen Street. Passengers make their own way from one station to the other

OVERNIGHT SLEEPERS. For Sleeper trains, operated by First ScotRail, please refer to Tables 400 - 404

London and West Midlands → North West England and Scotland

Route Diagram - see first page of Table 65

		NT	VT	XC	VT	VT	XC	LM	VT	NT		VT	VT	XC	SR	AW	LM	VT	SR FO		SR FX	
			1 ◇	1 ◇	1 ◇	1 ◇	1 ◇	1 ◇	1 ◇			1 ◇	1 ◇	1 ◇	R	◇	1 ◇	1 ◇	R		R	
				A			B							C	D							
			☕		☕	☕		🚲	☕			☕	☕		☕			☕	☕		☕	
London Euston [15] ⊖	d		20 05			20 17			20 46			21 05	21 10		21 15			22 05	23 00		23 45	
Gatwick Airport [10] ✈	d								19 37									20 37	21 37		22 37	
Watford Junction	d		19 43						21u01			21u20	21u25		21u33			22u20	23u19		00u04	
Milton Keynes Central	d		20 36			20 48												22 40				
Northampton	d								21 00									22 00				
Rugby	d								21 38									23 21				
Nuneaton	d					21 21							22 15					23 32				
Tamworth Low Level	d																	23 43				
Lichfield Trent Valley	d								22 01													
Coventry	d			20 02	20 23			20 44					21b50	21 23		21 44	22 23					
Birmingham International ✈	d			20 20	20 34			20 58						21 34		21 58	22 34					
Birmingham New Street [12]	d			20 48	21 03		21 18	21 21						22 18		22 33	23 07	23c10				
Sandwell & Dudley	d																23 18					
Coseley	d							21 34									23 27					
Wolverhampton [7] 🚋	d			21 11	21 21		21 39	21 44						22 39		22 48	23 34					
Penkridge	d							21 54									23 43					
Stafford	a			21 23	21 36	21 47	21 53	22 01					22 41	22 53			23 50	00s03				
	d			21 24	21 36	21 47	21 54	22 01					22 41	22 54			23 51					
Stoke-on-Trent	a		21 39	21 45			22 12					22 44		23s12								
Congleton	a						22 24															
Macclesfield	a		21 57	22 02			22 32					23 00										
Crewe [10]	a				21 58	22 07		22 22	22 35				23 01			00 01	00 21	00s32				
	d				21 59	22 08		22 24	22 36				23 02		23u45	00 02						
Chester	a					22 40			23 09				23 35			00 26						
Llandudno Junction	a					23e38										01 25						
Llandudno	a																					
Bangor (Gwynedd)	a					00e01										01 42						
Holyhead	a					00e47										02 15						
Wilmslow	a								23 23													
Manchester Airport ✈	a																	01 14				
Stockport	a		22s12	22 15			22 46		23 33			23s15						00s58				
Manchester Piccadilly [10] 🚋	a		22 24	22 32			23 02		23 49			23 29		00 07				01 10				
Hartford	a							22 35														
Warrington Bank Quay	a				22 17				22 53													
	d				22 17				22 54													
Runcorn	a					22 25		22 45					23 19									
Liverpool South Parkway [7] ✈	a							22 54														
Liverpool Lime Street [10]	a					22 47		23 12					23 47									
	d	21 48								23 05												
Manchester Airport ✈	d														22 47							
Manchester Piccadilly [10] 🚋	d														23 11							
Bolton	d														23 32							
Wigan North Western	a	22 37			22 43				23 04	23 51												
	d	22 38			22 44				23 04	23 51												
Preston [8]	a	23 02			23 04				23 24	00 15												
Blackpool North	a	23 28							23 59													
	d														23 13							
Preston [8]	d														00u44							
Lancaster [6]	a																					
	d																					
Barrow-in-Furness	a																					
Oxenholme Lake District	a																					
	d																					
Windermere	a																					
Penrith North Lakes	d																					
Carlisle [8]	a																		04s27		05s03	
	d																					
Lockerbie	d																					
Carstairs	a																		05s32		06s24	
Motherwell	a																		06s10		06s58	
Glasgow Central [15]	a																		06 30		07 17	
Haymarket	a																					
Edinburgh [10]	a																			06 40		07 15
Perth	a														05s44				08f04		09f37	
Dundee	a														06s08					08 26		09 25
Aberdeen	a														07 37					09 40		10 38
Inverness	a														08 30				10f26			11 59

For general notes see front of timetable
For details of catering facilities see Directory of Train Operators

A From Bristol Temple Meads (Table 51)
B From Plymouth (Table 51)
C From Bournemouth (Table 51)
D Also conveys portion to Fort William (Table 227)
b Change at Nuneaton
c Change at Tamworth
e Change at Crewe and Chester
f Via Glasgow Central and Glasgow Queen Street. Passengers make their own way from one station to the other

OVERNIGHT SLEEPERS. For Sleeper trains, operated by First ScotRail, please refer to Tables 400 - 404

Table 65

Saturdays

until 26 January

London and West Midlands → North West England and Scotland

Route Diagram - see first page of Table 65

		SR	TP	VT	VT	VT	TP	LM	NT	TP	XC	LM	VT	NT	XC	LM	VT	TP	VT	VT	NT	TP	VT	XC	LM
			1◇	1◇	1◇	1◇	1◇	1◇		1◇	1◇	1◇	1◇		1◇	1◇	1◇	1◇	1◇	1◇		1◇	1◇	1◇	1◇
			A											B				C				C		D	
London Euston 15 ⊖	d																05 25		05 31				06 30		
Gatwick Airport 10 ✈	d																							05 15	
Watford Junction	d																05u40						06u46		
Milton Keynes Central	d																06 10		06 16						
Northampton	d																		05 58						
Rugby	d																		07 11						
Nuneaton	d																								
Tamworth Low Level	d																								
Lichfield Trent Valley	d																								
Coventry	d												06 04		06 32					07 04				07 32	
Birmingham International ✈	d												06 20		06 50					07 20				07 50	
Birmingham New Street 12	d				05 20	05 30		06 07			06 20		07 03		07 20	07 21				08 03				08 20	08 21
Sandwell & Dudley	d							06 18																	
Coseley	d							06 27								07 34									08 34
Wolverhampton 7	d				05 38	05 49		06 33			06 40		07 21		07 40	07 44				08 21				08 40	08 44
Penkridge	d							06 43								07 53									08 53
Stafford	a				05 51	06 04		06 50			06 53	←	07 33		07 53	08 01	08 16							08 53	09 01
	d				05 52	06 05		07 00			06 54	07 00	07 33		07 54	08 02	08 18							08 54	09 02
Stoke-on-Trent	a							→			07 12				08 12								09 03	09 12	
Congleton	a										07 24				08 24										
Macclesfield	a										07 32				08 32								09 19	09 29	
Crewe 10	a				06 16	06 25						07 22	07 54			08 23	08 36		08 46	08 54					09 23
	d				06 18	06 28						07 22	07 55			08 24	08 39		08 49	08 55					09 24
Chester	a				06 37	07 03						07 57				08 57			09 26						09 57
Llandudno Junction	a				07 33	08 20						09b19				10b17			10 24						11b17
Llandudno	a				08 16							09b37				10b37									11b35
Bangor (Gwynedd)	a				07 49	08 43						09b43							10 46						
Holyhead	a				08 21	09 30						10b20							11 30						
Wilmslow	a					07 01						07 59	08 48			09 03			09 26	09 48					10 01
Manchester Airport ✈	a											08 14				09 15									10 11
Stockport	a					07 13					07 46	08 13			08 46				09 39				09s34	09 46	
Manchester Piccadilly 10	a					07 28					08 02	08 28			09 02	09 40			09 54				09 48	10 02	
Hartford	a											07 34				08 36									09 36
Warrington Bank Quay	a					06 43							08 12				08 55			09 11					
	d					06 45							08 13				08 56			09 12					
Runcorn	a											07 46				08 46			09 04						09 45
Liverpool South Parkway 7 ✈	a											07 54				08 56									09 54
Liverpool Lime Street 10	a											08 10				09 10			09 31						10 09
	d					06 04			07 30								08 04				08 57				
Manchester Airport ✈	d			04 35		05c47	06 19			07 22							07c47	08 27				08 47			
Manchester Piccadilly 10	d			05 10		06c05	06 44			07 45							08c11	08 45				09 11			
Bolton	d					06c26	07 05			08 04							08c32	09 05				09 32			
Wigan North Western	a					07 02			08 01				08 23				09 06			09 22	09 30				
	d					07 04			08 02				08 24				09 07			09 23	09 31				
Preston 8	a			05 47		07 18	07 27		08 24	08 27			08 39				09 20	09 30		09 38	09 54	10 01			
Blackpool North	a					07 56			08 51				09 32				09 57				10 21				
	d			05 30		06 34				07 41				08 09			08 41					09 30			
Preston 8	d			06 04		07 20	07 29			08 28			08 40	08 46			09 23	09 32		09 39		10 06			
Lancaster 6	a			06 18		07 33	07 44			08 44			08 59	09 07			09 37	09 48		09 53		10 24			
	d		05 50	06 19		07 35	07 45			08 44			09 01				09 38	09 48		09 55		10 25			
Barrow-in-Furness	a						08 49			09 54								10 45							
Oxenholme Lake District	a		06 04	06 33		07 47				08 58			09 16				09 50			10 08		10 43			
	d		06 04	06 34		07 49				08 59			09 17				09 51			10 09		10 50			
Windermere	a		06 25	07 19		08 15				09 21							10 14					11 11			
Penrith North Lakes	d			06 59		08 13				09 24			09 42				10 16			10 34					
Carlisle 8	a			07 19		08 31				09 41			10 00				10 33			10 52					
	d	06 09		07 21		08 34				09 43			10 03				10 35			10 53					
Lockerbie	d			07 41		08 52							10 21				10 56			11 12					
Carstairs	a			08 15																					
Motherwell	a			08s30		09s34							11s03												
Glasgow Central 15	a	08 37		09 00		09 59							11 27				11 57								
Haymarket	a									11s04										12s08					
Edinburgh 10	a									11 11										12 19					
Perth	a			10e37		11e37				12 56							13e37			14 54					
Dundee	a			11e00		12e00				12f23							14e00			14 23					
Aberdeen	a			12e19		13e13				13f36							15e13			15 36					
Inverness	a			13e35						15 18										17 07					

For general notes see front of timetable
For details of catering facilities see Directory of Train Operators

A From Barrow-in-Furness (Table 82)
B From Clitheroe (Table 94) to Morecambe (Table 98)
C to Preston
D from Reading
b Change at Crewe and Chester
c Change at Preston
e Via Glasgow Central and Glasgow Queen Street. Passengers make their own way from one station to the other
f Change at Haymarket

Saturdays

until 26 January

London and West Midlands → North West England and Scotland

Route Diagram - see first page of Table 65

Station		VT	TP	VT	VT	VT	TP	NT	VT	XC	LM	VT	TP	VT	XC	VT	VT	NT	TP	VT	XC	LM	VT	TP	TP
		1◇	1◇	1◇	1◇	1◇	1◇		1◇	1◇	1◇	1◇	1◇	1◇	1◇	1◇	1◇		1◇	1◇	1◇	1◇	1◇	1◇	1◇
										A			B		C						C				
		🍽	🛒	🍽	🍽	🍽	🛒		🍽	🍽		🍽	🛒	🍽	🍽	🍽	🍽			🍽	🍽		🍽		🛒
London Euston 15 ⊖	d	06 59		07 06	07 15				07 52			08 03		08 10		08 17				08 53			09 03		
Gatwick Airport 10 ✈	d	05 52										06 37								07 37					
Watford Junction	d	07u14		07u21	07u31				07 25			08u18		08u26						09u08			08 41		
Milton Keynes Central	d	07 34		07 42					08 23							08 49							09 34		
Northampton	d				06 58							07 58											08 58		
Rugby	d				08 12							08 57				09 13							09 58		
Nuneaton	d																								
Tamworth Low Level	d																								
Lichfield Trent Valley	d																								
Coventry	d	08 08		08 15	08 27					08 32		09 10		09 16	09b23	09 27						09 32	10 10		
Birmingham International ✈	d			08 28	08u41					08 50		09 22		09 28	09b34	09 39					←	09 50	10 22		
Birmingham New Street 12	d			08 48	08s50	09 03				09 20	09 21	09 40		09 48	10 20	09s50	10 03				10 20	10 21	10 40		
Sandwell & Dudley	d														→										
Coseley	d										09 34											10 34			
Wolverhampton 7 ⛴	d			09 09		09 21				09 40	09 44			10 09			10 21				10 40	10 44			
Penkridge	d										09 53											10 53			
Stafford	a	09 14		09 24						09 53	10 01	10 17		10 24							10 53	11 01	11 19		
	d	09 16		09 26						09 54	10 02	10 19		10 26							10 54	11 02	11 21		
Stoke-on-Trent	a			09 43					10 05	10 12				10 42						11 05	11 12				
Congleton	a									10 24															
Macclesfield	a			09 59					10 21	10 32				10 58						11 21	11 29				
Crewe 10	a	09 34			09 49	09 54					10 22	10 38				10 49	10 54					11 23	11 40		
	d	09 37			09 52	09 55					10 24	10 41				10 52	10 55					11 24	11 43		
Chester	a				10 27						10 57					11 29						11 59			
Llandudno Junction	a				11c26						12 02					12 25						13c17			
Llandudno	a										12e35					13e01						13c35			
Bangor (Gwynedd)	a				11c43						12 18					12 48									
Holyhead	a				12c20						12 53					13 30									
Wilmslow	a				10 26	10 48					11 01					11 26	11 48					12 01			
Manchester Airport ✈	a										11 11											12 11			
Stockport	a			10 13	10 39				10s34	10 46				11 13		11 39				11s34	11 46				
Manchester Piccadilly 10 ⛴	a			10 28	10 54				10 48	11 02				11 28		11 54				11 48	12 02				
Hartford	a										10 33											11 36			
Warrington Bank Quay	a	09 55				10 12						10 57					11 11						11 59		
	d	09 57				10 13						10 58					11 13						12 00		
Runcorn	a				10 09						10 45					11 08						11 45			
Liverpool South Parkway 7 ✈	a										10 54											11 54			
Liverpool Lime Street 10	a				10 31						11 09					11 31						12 09			
	d	09 04						09 57				10 04						10 57					11 04		
Manchester Airport ✈	d		09 27									09f47	10 27												11 27
Manchester Piccadilly 10 ⛴	d		09 45									10f11	10 45												11 45
Bolton	d		10 05									10f32	11 05												12 05
Wigan North Western	a	10 06				10 23		10 31				11 08					11 22	11 30					12 10		
	d	10 08				10 24		10 31				11 09					11 24	11 30					12 11		
Preston 8	a	10 26	10 27			10 38		10 55				11 22	11 27				11 37	11 53					12 24		12 27
Blackpool North	a							11 23				12 01						12 20					13 01		
	d		09 40									10 41							11 41						
Preston 8	d		10 29			10 40						11 25	11 29				11 40		12 19				12 27		12 29
Lancaster 6	a		10 44									11 40	11 44				11 54		12 34				12 41		12 44
	d		10 45									11 41	11 45				11 55		12 35				12 42		12 45
Barrow-in-Furness	a		11 56										12 49												
Oxenholme Lake District	a		11 03			11 08						11 53							12 50				12 54	←	12 59
	d		11 03			11 09						11 55							12 59				12 56	12 59	12 59
Windermere	a											12 17							→					13 20	14 14
Penrith North Lakes	d		11 30									12 19					12 33						13 20		
Carlisle 8	a		11 46			11 50	←					12 37					12 49						13 38		13 43
	d		11 56			11 52	11 56					12 40					12 50						13 41		13 45
Lockerbie	d		→				12 16										13 09								
Carstairs	a																								14 04
Motherwell	a						13s00																		
Glasgow Central 15	a					13 16	13 18					13 59											14 58		
Haymarket	a																14s04								15s04
Edinburgh 10	a																14 16								15 11
Perth	a											15g36											16g37		
Dundee	a																15h24						16g59		17 26
Aberdeen	a																16h37						18g15		18 44
Inverness	a																								

For general notes see front of timetable
For details of catering facilities see Directory of Train Operators

A From Exeter St Davids (Table 51)

B 🛒 to Preston

C From Bournemouth (Table 51)

b By changing at Birmingham New Street, passengers may depart Coventry at 0932, Birmingham International at 0950

c Change at Crewe and Chester

e Change at Crewe and Llandudno Junction

f Change at Preston

g Via Glasgow Central and Glasgow Queen Street. Passengers make their own way from one station to the other

h Change at Haymarket

London and West Midlands → North West England and Scotland

Route Diagram - see first page of Table 65

		VT	VT	VT	NT	VT	XC	LM	VT	TP	VT	XC	VT	VT	NT	TP	VT	XC	LM	VT	TP	VT	VT	VT	NT
		1 ◇	1 ◇	R 1		1 ◇	1 ◇	1 ◇	1 ◇	1 ◇	1 ◇	1 ◇	1 ◇	1 ◇		1 ◇	1 ◇	1 ◇	1 ◇	1 ◇	1 ◇	1 ◇	1 ◇	R 1	
							A			B		C				B		C							
		☕	☕	☕		☕	☕		☕	🛒	☕	☕	☕	☕		🛒	☕	☕		☕	🛒	☕	☕	☕	
London Euston 15 ⊖	d	09 10	09 17			09 53			10 03		10 10		10 17				10 53			11 03		11 10	11 17		
Gatwick Airport 10 ✈	d								08 37								09 37			09b37					
Watford Junction	d	09u25	09u32						10u18		10u25						11u08			10 41		11u25	11u32		
Milton Keynes Central	d					10 24							10 48							11 34					
Northampton	d								09 58											10 58					
Rugby	d		10 12						10 57				11 12							11 58			12 12		
Nuneaton	d						09c39																		
Tamworth Low Level	d						10c27																		
Lichfield Trent Valley	d						10c48																		
Coventry	d	10 16	10 27				10 32		11 10		11 16	11e23	11 27					←	11 32	12 10		12 16	12u27		
Birmingham International ✈	d	10 28	10 39				10 50		11 22		11 28	11e34	11 39						11 50	12 22		12 28	12 39		
Birmingham New Street 12	d	10 48	10s50	11 03			11 20	11 21	11 40		11 48	12 20 →	11s50	12 03				12 20	12 21	12 40		12 48	12s50	13 03	
Sandwell & Dudley	d																								
Coseley	d							11 34											12 34						
Wolverhampton 7	d	11 09		11 21			11 40	11 44			12 09			12 21				12 40	12 44			13 09		13 21	
Penkridge	d							11 53											12 53						
Stafford	a	11 24					11 53	12 01	12 17		12 24							12 53	13 01	13 17		13 24			
	d	11 26					11 54	12 02	12 19		12 26							12 54	13 02	13 19		13 26			
Stoke-on-Trent	a	11 43				12 05	12 12				12 43						13 05	13 12				13 43			
Congleton	a						12 24																		
Macclesfield	a	11 59				12 21	12 32				12 59						13 21	13 29				13 59			
Crewe 10	a		11 49	11 54				12 23	12 38				12 48	12 54					13 23	13 38			13 50	13 54	
	d		11 52	11 55				12 24	12 41				12 51	12 55					13 24	13 41			13 52	13 55	
Chester	a		12 27					12 59						13 31					13 57				14 27		
Llandudno Junction	a		13f24					14f09						14 21					15f18				15f25		
Llandudno	a							14f27						14 33					15f36				16g01		
Bangor (Gwynedd)	a		13f48											14 54									15f47		
Holyhead	a		14f30											15 30									16f30		
Wilmslow	a		12 26	12 48				13 01					13 26	13 48					14 01				14 26	14 48	
Manchester Airport ✈	a							13 11											14 11						
Stockport	a	12 13	12 39			12s34	12 46				13 13		13 39				13s34	13 46				14 13	14 39		
Manchester Piccadilly 10	a	12 28	12 54			12 48	13 02				13 28		13 54				13 48	14 02				14 28	14 54		
Hartford	a							12 34											13 36						
Warrington Bank Quay	a			12 13					12 56					13 11						13 57				14 12	
	d			12 13					12 58					13 12						13 58				14 13	
Runcorn	a		12 09					12 46					13 08						13 45				14 08		
Liverpool South Parkway 7 ✈	a							12 54											13 54						
Liverpool Lime Street 10	a		12 31					13 09					13 30						14 09				14 32		
	d				11 57				12 04						12 57					13 04					13 57
Manchester Airport ✈	d									12 27						12 47					13 27				
Manchester Piccadilly 10	d									12 45						13 11					13 45				
Bolton	d									13 05						13 32					14 05				
Wigan North Western	a			12 24	12 31				13 07					13 22	13 31					14 08				14 23	14 31
	d			12 25	12 31				13 09					13 23	13 31					14 09				14 24	14 31
Preston 8	a			12 39	12 56				13 26	13 27				13 36	13 54	14 01				14 23	14 27			14 39	14 54
Blackpool North	a				13 21				14 00						14 21					15 01					15 21
	d									12 41						13 30				13 41					
Preston 8	d			12 41						13 29				13 38		14 09				14 26	14 29			14 40	
Lancaster 6	a			12 55						13 44				13 53		14 24				14 39	14 44			14 54	
	d			12 56						13 45				13 53		14 25				14 41	14 45			14 56	
Barrow-in-Furness	a									14 42				15 23											
Oxenholme Lake District	a													14 07		14 42				14 53	14 59			15 09	
	d													14 08		14 43				14 54	14 59			15 10	
Windermere	a															15 01									
Penrith North Lakes	d			13 34																15 19	15 25			15 37	
Carlisle 8	a			13 50										14 48						15 37	15 43			15 54	
	d			13 55										14 50						15 39	15 44			15 55	
Lockerbie	d			14 13										15 09							16 04				
Carstairs	a																								
Motherwell	a																			16s34				16s53	
Glasgow Central 15	a			15 17																16 58				17 17	
Haymarket	a													16s09							17s08				
Edinburgh 10	a													16 19							17 14				
Perth	a			17h20										17 55						18h42	18 54			19h19	
Dundee	a													17 44							18j48				
Aberdeen	a													19 02							20k27				
Inverness	a			19h34										20 08							20 58				

For general notes see front of timetable
For details of catering facilities see Directory of Train Operators

- **A** From Plymouth (Table 51)
- **B** 🛒 to Preston
- **C** From Bournemouth (Table 51)
- **b** Change at Watford Junction and Milton Keynes Central
- **c** Change at Stafford. By bus
- **e** By changing at Birmingham New Street, passengers may depart Coventry at 1132, Birmingham International at 1150
- **f** Change at Crewe and Chester
- **g** Change at Crewe, Chester and Llandudno Junction
- **h** Via Glasgow Central and Glasgow Queen Street. Passengers make their own way from one station to the other
- **j** Change at Haymarket
- **k** Change at Haymarket and Dundee

London and West Midlands → North West England and Scotland

until 26 January

Route Diagram - see first page of Table 65

		VT	XC	LM	VT	TP	VT	XC	VT	VT	NT	VT	XC	LM	VT	TP	VT	VT	VT	NT	VT	XC	LM	VT	TP
										R									R						
		1 ◇	1 ◇	1 ◇	1 ◇	1 ◇	1 ◇	1 ◇	1 ◇	1		1 ◇	1 ◇	1 ◇	1 ◇	1 ◇	1 ◇	1 ◇	1		1 ◇	1 ◇	1 ◇	1 ◇	1 ◇
			A			B		C					C							D		A			B
		🍴	🍴		🍴	🛒	🍴	🍴	🍴	🍴		🍴	🍴		🍴	🛒	🍴	🍴	🍴		🍴	🍴		🍴	🛒
London Euston [15] ⊖	d	11 53			12 03		12 10		12 17			12 53			13 03		13 10	13 17			13 53			14 03	
Gatwick Airport [10] ✈	d				*10 37*							*11 37*			*11b37*									*12 37*	
Watford Junction	d				12u18		12u25					13u08			*12 41*		13u25	13u32						14u18	
Milton Keynes Central	d	12 24							12 48						13 34						14 24				
Northampton	d				*11 58*										*12 58*									*13 58*	
Rugby	d				12 57				13 12						13 58			14 11						14 57	
Nuneaton	d						*12c32*																		
Tamworth Low Level	d						*13c20*																		
Lichfield Trent Valley	d						*13c41*																		
Coventry	d		*12 32*		13 10		13 16	13e23	13 27					*13 42*	14 10		14 16	14u27				*14 32*		15 10	
Birmingham International ✈	d		*12 50*		13 22		13 28	13e34	13 39				←	*13 57*	14 22		14 28	14 39				*14 50*		15 22	
Birmingham New Street [12]	d		13 20	13 21	13 40		13 48	14 20 →	13s50	14 03			14 20	14 21	14 40		14 48	14s50	15 03			15 20	15 21	15 40	
Sandwell & Dudley	d																								
Coseley	d			13 34										14 34									15 34		
Wolverhampton [7] ⛴	d		13 40	13 44			14 09			14 21			14 40	14 44			15 09		15 21			15 40	15 44		
Penkridge	d			13 53										14 53									15 53		
Stafford	a		13 53	14 01	14 17		14 24						14 53	15 01	15 17		15 24					15 53	16 01	16 17	
	d		13 54	14 02	14 19		14 26						14 54	15 02	15 19		15 26					15 54	16 02	16 19	
Stoke-on-Trent	a	14 05	14 12				14 43					15 05	15 12				15 43				16 05	16 12			
Congleton	a		14 24																			16 24			
Macclesfield	a	14 21	14 32				14 59					15 21	15 29				15 59				16 21	16 33			
Crewe [10]	a			14 23	14 38				14 49	14 54				15 23	15 38			15 49	15 54				16 23	16 38	
	d			14 24	14 41				14 52	14 55				15 24	15 41			15 52	15 55				16 24	16 41	
Chester	a			*14 57*					*15 26*					*15 57*				*16 27*					*16 56*		
Llandudno Junction	a			*16f17*					*16 24*					*17f17*				*17f24*					*18f17*		
Llandudno	a			*16f35*										*17f35*									*18f35*		
Bangor (Gwynedd)	a								*16 46*									*17f47*							
Holyhead	a								*17 20*									*18f30*							
Wilmslow	a			*15 01*					*15 26*	*15 48*				*16 01*				*16 26*	*16 48*				*17 05*		
Manchester Airport ✈	a			*15 11*										*16 11*									*17 15*		
Stockport	a	14s34	14 46				15 13		*15 39*			15s34	15 46				16 13	*16 40*			16s34	16 46			
Manchester Piccadilly [10] ⛴	a	14 48	15 02				15 28		*15 54*			15 48	16 02				16 28	*16 54*			16 48	17 02			
Hartford	a			14 36										15 36									16 34		
Warrington Bank Quay	a				14 57					15 12					15 56				16 12					16 57	
	d				14 58					15 13					15 58				16 13					16 58	
Runcorn	a			14 45					15 09					15 45				16 09					16 46		
Liverpool South Parkway [7] ✈	a			14 54										15 54									16 54		
Liverpool Lime Street [10]	a			15 09					15 31					16 09				16 33					17 09		
	d				*14 04*						14 57				*15 04*					15 57				*16 04*	
Manchester Airport ✈	d				*13g47*	14 27									*14g47*	15 27								*15g47*	16 27
Manchester Piccadilly [10] ⛴	d				*14g11*	14 45									*15g11*	15 45								*16g11*	16 44
Bolton	d				*14g32*	15 05									*15g32*	16 05								*16g32*	17 05
Wigan North Western	a				15 08					15 23	15 31				16 07				16 23	16 31				17 08	
	d				15 09					15 24	15 31				16 09				16 24	16 31				17 09	
Preston [8]	a				15 22	15 27				15 39	15 54				16 22	16 27			16 39	16 54				17 23	17 27
Blackpool North	a				*16 01*						16 21				*17 01*					*17 34*				*18 03*	
	d				*14 41*										*15 41*					*16 25*				*16 38*	
Preston [8]	d				15 25	15 30				15 40					16 25	16 29			16 40	16 56				17 26	17 29
Lancaster [6]	a				15 39	15 45				15 54					16 38	16 44			16 57	17 16				17 40	17 44
	d				15 40	15 50				15 56					16 40	16 45			16 59	17 17				17 41	17 45
Barrow-in-Furness	a					16 53				*17 17*										18 21					18 50
Oxenholme Lake District	a				15 52										16 52	16 59			17 12					17 53	
	d				15 54										16 53	16 59			17 13					17 55	
Windermere	a				*16 17*											*17 23*			*18 04*						
Penrith North Lakes	d				16 18					16 33					17 18	17 25			17 38					18 19	
Carlisle [8]	a				16 36					16 49					17 36	17 43			17 56					18 37	
	d				16 39					16 53					17 39	17 44			18 00					18 40	
Lockerbie	d															18 04			18 18						
Carstairs	a																								
Motherwell	a				17s34														19s00						
Glasgow Central [15]	a				17 57										18 58				19 27					19 58	
Haymarket	a									18s06						19s04									
Edinburgh [10]	a									18 16						19 11									
Perth	a				*19h42*										*20h37*	*20 51*								*21h42*	
Dundee	a									*19 49*						*20j26*								*22h08*	
Aberdeen	a									*21 10*						*21j39*								*23h21*	
Inverness	a															*23 13*									

For general notes see front of timetable
For details of catering facilities see Directory of Train Operators

A From Penzance (Table 135)
B 🛒 to Preston
C From Bournemouth (Table 51)
D To Millom (Table 100)
b Change at Watford Junction and Milton Keynes Central
c Change at Stafford. By bus
e By changing at Birmingham New Street, passengers may depart Coventry at 1332, Birmingham International at 1350
f Change at Crewe and Chester
g Change at Preston
h Via Glasgow Central and Glasgow Queen Street. Passengers make their own way from one station to the other
j Change at Haymarket

Table 65

Saturdays

until 26 January

London and West Midlands → North West England and Scotland

Route Diagram - see first page of Table 65

		VT	NT	XC	VT	VT	NT	TP	NT	TP	VT	XC	LM	VT	TP	VT	VT	VT	NT	SR	NT	VT	XC	LM	VT
																		R							
		1◇		1◇	1◇	1◇		1◇		1◇	1◇	1◇	1◇	1◇	1◇	1◇	1◇	1				1◇	1◇	1◇	1◇
				A								A			B								C		
		☕		☕	☕	☕		🛒			☕	☕		☕	🛒	☕	☕	☕				☕	☕		☕
London Euston 15 ⊖	d	14 10			14 17						14 53			15 03		15 10	15 17					15 53			16 03
Gatwick Airport 10 ✈	d										*13 37*														*14 37*
Watford Junction	d	14u25									15u08			*14 41*		15u25	15u32								16u18
Milton Keynes Central	d				14 48									15 34								16 24			
Northampton	d													*14 58*											*15 58*
Rugby	d				15 12									15 58			16 12								16 57
Nuneaton	d																								
Tamworth Low Level	d																								
Lichfield Trent Valley	d																								
Coventry	d	15 16		15b23	15 27								*15 32*	16 10		16 16	16u27						*16 32*		17 10
Birmingham International ✈	d	15 28		15b34	15 39							←	*15 50*	16 22		16 28	16 39						*16 50*		17 22
Birmingham New Street 12	d	15 48		16 20	15s50	16 03						16 20	16 21	16 40		16 48	16s50	17 03					17 20	17 21	17 40
Sandwell & Dudley	d			→																					
Coseley	d												16 34											17 34	
Wolverhampton 7	d	16 09				16 21						16 40	16 44			17 09		17 21					17 40	17 44	
Penkridge	d												16 53											17 53	
Stafford	a	16 24										16 53	17 01	17 17		17 24							17 53	18 01	18 17
	d	16 26										16 54	17 02	17 19		17 26							17 54	18 02	18 19
Stoke-on-Trent	a	16 43									17 05	17 12				17 43						18 05	18 12		
Congleton	a																						18 24		
Macclesfield	a	16 59									17 21	17 29				17 59						18 21	18 32		
Crewe 10	a				16 49	16 54							17 23	17 38			17 50	17 54						18 23	18 38
	d				16 52	16 55							17 24	17 41			17 52	17 55						18 24	18 41
Chester	a				*17 26*	*17 54*							*17 59*				*18 29*							*18 57*	
Llandudno Junction	a				*18 25*								*18 49*				*19c26*							*20c18*	
Llandudno	a												*19e37*											*20c35*	
Bangor (Gwynedd)	a				*18 47*								*19 05*				*19c49*								
Holyhead	a				*19 20*								*19 36*				*20c30*								
Wilmslow	a				*17 26*	*17 48*							*18 04*				*18 26*	*18 48*						*19 05*	
Manchester Airport ✈	a												*18 15*											*19 16*	
Stockport	a	17 13			*17 39*						17s34	17 46				18 13	*18 39*					18s34	18 46		
Manchester Piccadilly 10	a	17 28			*17 54*						17 48	18 02				18 28	*18 54*					18 48	19 02		
Hartford	a												17 36											18 34	
Warrington Bank Quay	a					17 12								17 57				18 12							18 57
	d					17 13								17 58				18 13							18 58
Runcorn	a				17 09								17 45				18 09							18 43	
Liverpool South Parkway 7 ✈	a												17 53											18 54	
Liverpool Lime Street 10	a				17 30								18 09				18 28							19 09	
	d		16 30						17 20									*17 25*	17 45		18 04				
Manchester Airport ✈	d							16 47							17 32										*17f47*
Manchester Piccadilly 10	d							17 11						*17f15*	17 50										*18f11*
Bolton	d							17 30						*17f37*	18 10										*18f32*
Wigan North Western	a		17 11			17 23	←		17 54					18 08				18 23	18 28		18 51				19 08
	d		17 12			17 24	17 12		17 54					18 09				18 24	18 28		18 51				19 09
Preston 8	a		→			17 39	17 40	17 53	18 17					18 22	18 34			18 39	18 52		19 17				19 25
Blackpool North	a						*18 30*		18 48					*18 59*					19 21						*20 01*
	d							*17 19*						*17 38*											*18 42*
Preston 8	d					17 40		17 58						18 25	18 38			18 40							19 25
Lancaster 6	a					17 55		18 13						18 39	18 53			18 58							19 39
	d					17 56		18 14		18 21				18 40	18 54			19 00							19 40
Barrow-in-Furness	a														19 59										
Oxenholme Lake District	a					18 09		18 28		18 40				18 52				19 13							19 52
	d					18 11		18 28		18 40				18 54				19 14							19 54
Windermere	a									19 02															*20 19*
Penrith North Lakes	d													19 19											20 18
Carlisle 8	a					18 55		19 09						19 36				19 54							20 41
	d					18 58		19 10						19 41				19 56		20 08					
Lockerbie	d					19 16		19 29																	
Carstairs	a																								
Motherwell	a													20s39											
Glasgow Central 15	a							20 28						20 59				21 18		22 27					
Haymarket	a					20s12																			
Edinburgh 10	a					20 22																			
Perth	a													*22g36*				*00g15*							
Dundee	a					*22 26*								*22g59*											
Aberdeen	a					*23 40*								*00g17*											
Inverness	a																								

For general notes see front of timetable
For details of catering facilities see Directory of Train Operators

A From Bournemouth (Table 51)

B 🛒 to Preston

C From Plymouth (Table 51)

b By changing at Birmingham New Street, passengers may depart Coventry at 1532, Birmingham International at 1550

c Change at Crewe and Chester

e Change at Crewe and Llandudno Junction

f Change at Preston

g Via Glasgow Central and Glasgow Queen Street. Passengers make their own way from one station to the other

Table 65

Saturdays

until 26 January

London and West Midlands → North West England and Scotland

Route Diagram - see first page of Table 65

		VT	VT	TP	VT		VT	VT	VT	VT	VT	NT	VT	XC	LM	VT	TP	VT	VT	VT	VT	VT	XC	LM	VT
						_5 B_Q																			
				1◇	1◇	1◇	1◇	R 1					1◇	1◇	1◇	1◇	1◇	1◇	1◇	R 1		1◇	1◇	1◇	
						A								A									B		
		bus	bus						bus	bus	bus										bus				bus
					catering	catering	catering	catering					catering	catering		catering		catering	catering	catering		catering	catering		
London Euston 15 ⊖	d				16 10		16 17						16 53			17 03		17 10	17 17			17 53			
Gatwick Airport 10 ✈	d												15 37												
Watford Junction	d				16u25								17u08			16 41		17u25	17u32						
Milton Keynes Central	d						16 48									17 34						18 24			
Northampton	d															16 58									
Rugby	d						17 12									17 58			18 12						
Nuneaton	d																			17b42					
Tamworth Low Level	d																			18b30					
Lichfield Trent Valley	d																			18b51					
Coventry	d				17 16	17c23	17 27								17 32	18 10		18 16	18u27				18 32		
Birmingham International ✈	d				17 28	17c34	17 39							←	17 50	18 22		18 28	18 41				18 50		
Birmingham New Street 12	d				17 48	18 20 →	17s50	18 03						18 20	18 21	18 40		18 48	18s50	19 03			19 20	19 21	
Sandwell & Dudley	d																								
Coseley	d														18 34									19 34	
Wolverhampton 7	d				18 09			18 20						18 40	18 44			19 09		19 21			19 40	19 44	
Penkridge	d														18 53									19 53	
Stafford	a				18 24									18 53	19 01	19 17		19 24		19 33			19 53	20 01	
	d				18 26									18 54	19 02	19 19		19 26		19 33			19 54	20 02	
Stoke-on-Trent	a				18 43								19 05	19 12				19 43				20 05	20 12		
Congleton	a																						20 24		
Macclesfield	a				18 59								19 21	19 29				19 59				20 21	20 32		
Crewe 10	a						18 49	18 54							19 23	19 38			19 49	19 54				20 23	
	d						18 52	18 55							19 24	19 41			19 52	19 55				20 24	
Chester	a						19 25	19 46							20 02				20 27					20 57	
Llandudno Junction	a							20 37											21e28						
Llandudno	a							21f08											21g43						
Bangor (Gwynedd)	a							20 55																	
Holyhead	a							21 33																	
Wilmslow	a						19 26	19 48											20 26	20 45					
Manchester Airport ✈	a						20h02													21h02					
Stockport	a				19 13		19 39						19s34	19 46				20 13	20 39			20s34	20 46		
Manchester Piccadilly 10	a				19 28		19 57						19 48	20 02				20 28	20 54			20 48	21 02		
Hartford	a														19 36									20 36	
Warrington Bank Quay	a							19 12								19 57				20 12					
	d							19 13								19 58				20 13					
Runcorn	a						19 08								19 45				20 08					20 45	
Liverpool South Parkway 7 ✈	a														19 54									20 54	
Liverpool Lime Street 10	a						19 32								20 09				20 30					21 09	
	d											19 04													
Manchester Airport ✈	d			18 27													19 27								
Manchester Piccadilly 10	d			18 45													19 44								
Bolton	d			19 12													20 05								
Wigan North Western	a							19 24				19 51				20 08				20 23					
	d							19 24				19 51				20 09				20 24					
Preston 8	a			19 36				19 43				20 17				20 26	20 27			20 43					
Blackpool North	a							20 36				20 56								21 36					
	d								19 10	19 25							19 42								
Preston 8	d			19 38					19 55	20 00	←						20 29				20 55				21 00
Lancaster 6	a			19 53					20 45								20 43				21 45				
	d			19 55					20 45		20 45						20 43				21 45				
Barrow-in-Furness	a			20 51					22 50 →		22 50						21 50								
Oxenholme Lake District	a										21 30										22 30				
	d										21 30										22 30				
Windermere	a																								
Penrith North Lakes	d										22 25										23 25 →				
Carlisle 8	a									22 00	23 00														
	d	20 55	20 55																						23 00
Lockerbie	d																								
Carstairs	a																								
Motherwell	a		22 35																						
Glasgow Central 15	a	22 50																							
Haymarket	a																								
Edinburgh 10	a																								
Perth	a	01j16																							
Dundee	a																								
Aberdeen	a																								
Inverness	a																								

For general notes see front of timetable
For details of catering facilities see Directory of Train Operators

A From Bournemouth (Table 51)
B From Plymouth (Table 51)
b Change at Stafford. By bus
c By changing at Birmingham New Street, passengers may depart Coventry at 1732, Birmingham International at 1750
e Change at Crewe and Chester
f Change at Crewe and Llandudno Junction
g Change at Crewe, Chester and Llandudno Junction
h Change at Crewe and Wilmslow
j Via Glasgow Central and Glasgow Queen Street. Passengers make their own way from one station to the other

Table 65

Saturdays

until 26 January

London and West Midlands → North West England and Scotland

Route Diagram - see first page of Table 65

		VT	VT	VT	VT	VT	VT	VT	XC	LM	VT	VT	VT	NT	VT	VT	XC	LM	NT	XC	VT	VT	XC	AW
			1 ◇		1 ◇	1	1 ◇	1 ◇	1 ◇	1 ◇	1 ◇		1 ◇		1 ◇	1 ◇	1 ◇	1 ◇		1 ◇	1 ◇	1 ◇	1 ◇	◇
									A								B			C			C	
		🚌		🚌								🚌												
			☕		☕	☕	☕	☕	☕		☕		☕		☕	☕					☕	☕		
London Euston 15 ⊖	d		18 03		18 10	18 17	18 53	18 57			19 02				19 05	19 20					19 36	20 00		
Gatwick Airport 10 ✈	d		*16 37*				*17 37*						←								*18 37*			
Watford Junction	d		18u18		18u25		19u08	19u11			*18 41*		19u11		19u19						19u50	20u14		
Milton Keynes Central	d					18 48		→			19 35				19 41	19 55					20 38	21 01		
Northampton	d					*17 58*									*18 58*						*19 58*	*20 58*		
Rugby	d					19 12									20 17						21 16	21 39		
Nuneaton	d																							
Tamworth Low Level	d																							
Lichfield Trent Valley	d																							
Coventry	d		19 10		19 16				19b23	*19 32*	20 10		20 16		20 29		*20 32*			21c33	21 28			*21 32*
Birmingham International ✈	d				19 28				19b34	*19 50*			20 28				*20 50*			21c34			←	*21 50*
Birmingham New Street 12	d				19 48				20 20	20 21			20 48				21 20	21 21		22 20			22 20	22 33
Sandwell & Dudley	d												20 57							→				
Coseley	d									20 34								21 35						
Wolverhampton 7	d				20 09				20 40	20 44			21 10				21 40	21 44					22 40	22 48
Penkridge	d									20 53								21 54						
Stafford	a		20 13		20 24				20 53	21 01	21 13		21 24				21 53	22 01			22 16	22 47	22 53	
	d		20 15		20 26				20 54	21 02	21 15		21 26				21 54	22 02			22 17	22 49	22 54	
Stoke-on-Trent	a				20 43		21 05		21 12				21 44			22 01	22 12					23 07	23s13	
Congleton	a																22 24							
Macclesfield	a				20 59		21 21		21 29				22 00			22 17	22 32					23 23	23s30	
Crewe 10	a		20 34			20 50				21 32	21 34				21 49			22 30			22 36			00 01
	d		20 37			20 52					21 37				21 52						22 39			00 02
Chester	a					*21 27*					*22 09*				22 30						*23 10*			00 24
Llandudno Junction	a					*22 25*									23e33									
Llandudno	a																							
Bangor (Gwynedd)	a					*22 42*									*00f25*									
Holyhead	a					*23 30*									*01f45*									
Wilmslow	a					*21 26*									*22 26*						*23 22*			
Manchester Airport ✈	a					22g05									23g05									
Stockport	a				21 13	*21 39*	21s34		21 46				22 12		*22 39*	22s32	22 46				*23 33*	23s37	23s46	
Manchester Piccadilly 10	a				21 28	*21 53*	21 51		22 02				22 25		*22 52*	22 45	23 02				*23 50*	23 51	00 02	
Hartford	a																							
Warrington Bank Quay	a		20 53								21 53													
	d		20 54								21 54													
Runcorn	a					21 08									22 08						22 54			
Liverpool South Parkway 7 ✈	a																							
Liverpool Lime Street 10	a					21 27									22 27						23 15			
	d		*19 48*								*20 48*			21 48					23 05					
Manchester Airport ✈	d																							
Manchester Piccadilly 10	d																							
Bolton	d																							
Wigan North Western	a		21 04								22 04			22 37					23 51					
	d		21 05								22 05			22 38					23 51					
Preston 8	a		21 24								22 24			23 02					00 15					
Blackpool North	a		*21 56*											23 28										
	d			*20 53*								*22 03*												
Preston 8	d			21 40								22 40												
Lancaster 6	a			22 30								23 30												
	d																							
Barrow-in-Furness	a			*23 50*																				
Oxenholme Lake District	a																							
	d																							
Windermere	a	←																						
Penrith North Lakes	d	23 25																						
Carlisle 8	a	23 59																						
	d																							
Lockerbie	d																							
Carstairs	a																							
Motherwell	a																							
Glasgow Central 15	a																							
Haymarket	a																							
Edinburgh 10	a																							
Perth	a																							
Dundee	a																							
Aberdeen	a																							
Inverness	a																							

For general notes see front of timetable
For details of catering facilities see Directory of Train Operators

A From Bournemouth (Table 51). ☕ to Birmingham New Street

B From Plymouth (Table 51)

C From Bournemouth (Table 51)

b By changing at Birmingham New Street, passengers may depart Coventry at 1932, Birmingham International at 1950

c By changing at Birmingham New Street, passengers may depart Coventry at 2132, Birmingham International at 2150

e Change at Crewe and Chester

f Change at Crewe, Chester and Llandudno Junction. By bus from Llandudno Junction

g Change at Crewe and Wilmslow

Table 65

Saturdays

London and West Midlands → North West England and Scotland

2 February to 22 March

Route Diagram - see first page of Table 65

		SR	TP	VT	VT	VT	VT	VT	TP	NT	TP	VT	VT	LM	XC	LM	VT	NT	XC	LM	VT	TP	VT	VT
			1 ◇	1 ◇		1 ◇	1 ◇		1 ◇		1 ◇			1 ◇	1 ◇	1 ◇	1 ◇		1 ◇	1 ◇	1 ◇	1 ◇	1 ◇	1 ◇
			A															B				C		
				☕	bus		☕	bus			trolley	bus	bus				☕		☕		☕	trolley	☕	☕
London Euston 15 ⊖	d																				05 25		05 31	
Gatwick Airport 10 ✈	d																							
Watford Junction	d																				05u40			
Milton Keynes Central	d																				06 10		06 16	
Northampton	d																						05 58	
Rugby	d																						07 11	
Nuneaton	d																							
Tamworth Low Level	d																							
Lichfield Trent Valley	d																							
Coventry	d																06 04		06 32					07 04
Birmingham International ✈	d																06 20		06 50					07 20
Birmingham New Street 12	d					05 20	05 30							06 07	06 20		07 03		07 20	07 21				08 03
Sandwell & Dudley	d													06 18										
Coseley	d													06 27						07 34				
Wolverhampton 7	d					05 38	05 49							06 33	06 40		07 21		07 40	07 44				08 21
Penkridge	d													06 43						07 53				
Stafford	a					05 51	06 04							06 50	06 53	⟵	07 33		07 53	08 01	08 16			
	d					05 52	06 05							07 00	06 54	07 00	07 33		07 54	08 02	08 18			
Stoke-on-Trent	a													⟶	07 12				08 12					
Congleton	a														07 24				08 24					
Macclesfield	a														07 32				08 32					
Crewe 10	a					06 16	06 25									07 22	07 54			08 23	08 36		08 46	08 54
	d					06 18	06 28									07 22	07 55			08 24	08 39		08 49	08 55
Chester	a					06 37	07 03									07 57				08 57			09 26	
Llandudno Junction	a					07 33	08 20									09b19				10b17			10 24	
Llandudno	a					08 16										09b37				10b37				
Bangor (Gwynedd)	a					07 49	08 43									09b43							10 46	
Holyhead	a					08 21	09 30									10b20							11 30	
Wilmslow	a						07 01									07 59	08 48			09 03			09 26	09 48
Manchester Airport ✈	a															08 14				09 15				
Stockport	a						07 13								07 46	08 13			08 46				09 39	
Manchester Piccadilly 10	a						07 28								08 02	08 28			09 02	09 40			09 54	
Hartford	a															07 34				08 36				
Warrington Bank Quay	a						06 43										08 12				08 55			09 11
	d						06 45										08 13				08 56			09 12
Runcorn	a															07 46				08 46			09 04	
Liverpool South Parkway 7 ✈	a															07 54				08 56				
Liverpool Lime Street 10	a															08 10				09 10			09 31	
	d						06 04			07 30											08 04			
Manchester Airport ✈	d			04 35			05c47		06 19		07 22										07c47	08 27		
Manchester Piccadilly 10	d			05 10			06c05		06 44		07 45										08c11	08 45		
Bolton	d						06c26		07 05		08 04										08c32	09 05		
Wigan North Western	a						07 02			08 01							08 23				09 06			09 22
	d						07 04			08 02							08 24				09 07			09 23
Preston 8	a			05 47			07 18		07 27	08 24	08 27						08 39				09 20	09 30		09 38
Blackpool North	a						07 56			08 51							09 32				09 57			
	d			05 30			06 34				07 41							08 09			08 41			
Preston 8	d			06 04			07 20		07 29		08 28							08 46			09 23	09 32		09 39
Lancaster 6	a			06 18			07 33		07 44		08 44							09 07			09 37	09 48		09 53
	d		05 50	06 19			07 35		07 45		08 44										09 38	09 48		09 55
Barrow-in-Furness	a								08 49		09 54											10 45		
Oxenholme Lake District	a		06 04	06 33			07 47				08 58										09 50			10 08
	d		06 04	06 34			07 49				08 59										09 51			10 09
Windermere	a		06 25	07 19			08 15				09 21										10 14			
Penrith North Lakes	d			06 59			08 13				09 24										10 16			10 34
Carlisle 8	a			07 19			08 31				09 42										10 38			10 52
	d	06 09			07 30			08 40				09 50												10 53
Lockerbie	d											10 30	10 40											11a11
Carstairs	a																							
Motherwell	a																							
Glasgow Central 15	a	08 37			09 25			10 35				12 05												
Haymarket	a																							
Edinburgh 10	a												12 50											
Perth	a	10e37			11e18			12e37				13e37												
Dundee	a	11e00			12e00			13e00				14e00												
Aberdeen	a	12e19			13e13			14e13				15e13												
Inverness	a				13e35			15f18																

For general notes see front of timetable
For details of catering facilities see Directory of Train Operators

A From Barrow-in-Furness (Table 82)

B From Clitheroe (Table 94) to Morecambe (Table 98)

C trolley to Preston

b Change at Crewe and Chester

c Change at Preston

e Via Glasgow Central and Glasgow Queen Street. Passengers make their own way from one station to the other

f Change at Glasgow Central, Glasgow Queen Street and Perth. Passengers make their own way between Glasgow Central and Glasgow Queen Street

2 February to 22 March

London and West Midlands → North West England and Scotland

Route Diagram - see first page of Table 65

		VT	SR	VT		NT	TP	VT	XC	LM	VT	TP	VT	VT	VT	VT	VT		VT	VT	NT	VT	XC	LM	VT
							1◇	1◇	1◇	1◇	1◇	1◇	1◇	1◇	1◇					1◇		1◇	1◇	1◇	1◇
							A		B														C		
		🚌		🚌												🚌	🚌		🚌						
							🛒	☕	☕		☕	🛒	☕	☕						☕		☕	☕		☕
London Euston 15 ⊖	d							06 30			06 59		07 06	07 15								07 52			08 03
Gatwick Airport 10 ✈	d								05 15		05 52														06 37
Watford Junction	d							06u46			07u14		07u21	07u31								07 25			08u18
Milton Keynes Central	d										07 34		07 42									08 23			
Northampton	d													06 58											07 58
Rugby	d													08 12											08 57
Nuneaton	d																								
Tamworth Low Level	d																								
Lichfield Trent Valley	d																								
Coventry	d								07 32		08 08		08 15	08 27									08 32		09 10
Birmingham International ✈	d								07 50				08 28	08u41									08 50		09 22
Birmingham New Street 12	d								08 20	08 21			08 48	08s50						09 03			09 20	09 21	09 40
Sandwell & Dudley	d																								
Coseley	d									08 34														09 34	
Wolverhampton 7	d								08 40	08 44			09 09							09 21			09 40	09 44	
Penkridge	d									08 53														09 53	
Stafford	a								08 53	09 01	09 14		09 24										09 53	10 01	10 17
	d								08 54	09 02	09 16		09 26										09 54	10 02	10 19
Stoke-on-Trent	a							09 03	09 12				09 43									10 05	10 12		
Congleton	a																						10 24		
Macclesfield	a							09 19	09 29				09 59									10 21	10 32		
Crewe 10	a									09 23	09 34			09 49						09 54				10 22	10 38
	d									09 24	09 37			09 52						09 55				10 24	10 41
Chester	a									09 57				10 27										10 57	
Llandudno Junction	a									11b17				11b26										12 02	
Llandudno	a									11b35														12c35	
Bangor (Gwynedd)	a													11b43										12 18	
Holyhead	a													12b20										12 53	
Wilmslow	a									10 01				10 26						10 48				11 01	
Manchester Airport ✈	a									10 11														11 11	
Stockport	a							09s34	09 46				10 13	10 39								10s34	10 46		
Manchester Piccadilly 10	a							09 48	10 02				10 28	10 54								10 48	11 02		
Hartford	a									09 36														10 33	
Warrington Bank Quay	a										09 55									10 12					10 57
	d										09 57									10 13					10 58
Runcorn	a									09 45				10 09										10 45	
Liverpool South Parkway 7 ✈	a									09 54														10 54	
Liverpool Lime Street 10	a									10 09				10 31										11 09	
	d					08 57					09 04										09 57				10 04
Manchester Airport ✈	d						08 47					09 27													
Manchester Piccadilly 10	d						09 11					09 45													
Bolton	d						09 32					10 05													
Wigan North Western	a					09 30					10 06									10 23	10 31				11 08
	d					09 31					10 08									10 24	10 31				11 09
Preston 8	a					09 54	10 01				10 26	10 27								10 38	10 55				11 25
Blackpool North	a					10 21															11 23				12 01
	d						09 30					09 40													
Preston 8	d						10 06					10 29													
Lancaster 6	a						10 24					10 44													
	d						10 25					10 45													
Barrow-in-Furness	a											11 56													
Oxenholme Lake District	a						10 43					11 03													
	d						10 50					11 03													
Windermere	a						11 11																		
Penrith North Lakes	d											11 30													
Carlisle 8	a											11 48													
	d	11 00	11 07												11 56	12 00									
Lockerbie	d			11 30											12a14		12 30		12 35						
Carstairs	a																								
Motherwell	a																		13 50						
Glasgow Central 15	a	12 55	13 29													13 55			14e46						
Haymarket	a																								
Edinburgh 10	a			13 40													14 40								
Perth	a	14f37														15f36									
Dundee	a	15f00		15 24												15f59	16 17								
Aberdeen	a	16f21		16 37												17f09	17 38								
Inverness	a	17g07																							

For general notes see front of timetable
For details of catering facilities see Directory of Train Operators

A 🛒 to Preston
B ☕ from Reading
C From Exeter St Davids (Table 51)
b Change at Crewe and Chester
c Change at Crewe and Llandudno Junction
e Glasgow Central Low Level
f Via Glasgow Central and Glasgow Queen Street. Passengers make their own way from one station to the other
g Change at Glasgow Central, Glasgow Queen Street and Perth. Passengers make their own way between Glasgow Central and Glasgow Queen Street

Table 65

Saturdays

London and West Midlands → North West England and Scotland

2 February to 22 March

Route Diagram - see first page of Table 65

		TP	VT	XC	VT	VT	VT	SR	VT	NT	VT	XC	TP	LM	VT	TP	TP	VT	VT	VT	VT	VT	VT
		1◇	1◇	1◇	1◇	1◇					1◇	1◇	1◇	1◇	1◇	1◇	1◇	1◇	1◇	R 1			
		A		B								B											
							bus		bus												bus	bus	bus
		trolley	restaurant	restaurant	restaurant	restaurant					restaurant	restaurant			restaurant		trolley	restaurant	restaurant	restaurant			
London Euston 15 ⊖	d		08 10		08 17						08 53				09 03			09 10	09 17				
Gatwick Airport 10 ✈	d										07 37												
Watford Junction	d		08u26								09u08				08 41			09u25	09u32				
Milton Keynes Central	d				08 49										09 34								
Northampton	d														08 58								
Rugby	d				09 13										09 58				10 12				
Nuneaton	d																						
Tamworth Low Level	d																						
Lichfield Trent Valley	d																						
Coventry	d		09 16	09b23	09 27									09 32	10 10			10 16	10 27				
Birmingham International ✈	d		09 28	09b34	09 39							←		09 50	10 22			10 28	10 39				
Birmingham New Street 12	d		09 48	10 20	09s50	10 03						10 20		10 21	10 40			10 48	10s50	11 03			
Sandwell & Dudley	d			→																			
Coseley	d													10 34									
Wolverhampton 7	d		10 09			10 21						10 40		10 44				11 09		11 21			
Penkridge	d													10 53									
Stafford	a		10 24									10 53		11 01	11 19			11 24					
	d		10 26									10 54		11 02	11 21			11 26					
Stoke-on-Trent	a		10 42								11 05	11 12						11 43					
Congleton	a																						
Macclesfield	a		10 58								11 21	11 29						11 59					
Crewe 10	a				10 49	10 54								11 23	11 40				11 49	11 54			
	d				10 52	10 55								11 24	11 43				11 52	11 55			
Chester	a				11 29									11 59					12 27				
Llandudno Junction	a				12 25									13c17					13c24				
Llandudno	a				13e01									13c35									
Bangor (Gwynedd)	a				12 48														13c48				
Holyhead	a				13 30														14c30				
Wilmslow	a				11 26	11 48								12 01					12 26	12 48			
Manchester Airport ✈	a													12 11									
Stockport	a		11 13		11 39						11s34	11 46						12 13	12 39				
Manchester Piccadilly 10	a		11 28		11 54						11 48	12 02						12 28	12 54				
Hartford	a													11 36									
Warrington Bank Quay	a					11 11									11 59					12 13			
	d					11 13									12 00					12 13			
Runcorn	a				11 08									11 45					12 09				
Liverpool South Parkway 7 ✈	a													11 54									
Liverpool Lime Street 10	a				11 31									12 09					12 31				
	d									10 57					11 04								
Manchester Airport ✈	d	10 27															11 27						
Manchester Piccadilly 10	d	10 45															11 45						
Bolton	d	11 05															12 05						
Wigan North Western	a					11 22				11 30					12 10								
	d					11 24				11 30					12 11								
Preston 8	a	11 27				11 37				11 53					12 24		12 27			12 36			
Blackpool North	a									12 20					13 01								
	d	10 41											11 41										
Preston 8	d	11 29				11 40							12 19		12 27		12 29			12 40			
Lancaster 6	a	11 44				11 54							12 34		12 41		12 44			12 54			
	d	11 45				11 55							12 35		12 42		12 45			12 55			
Barrow-in-Furness	a	12 49																					
Oxenholme Lake District	a												12 50		12 54	←	12 59			13 08			
	d												12 59		12 56	12 59	12 59			13 09			
Windermere	a												→			13 20				14 14			
Penrith North Lakes	d					12 33									13 20					13 36			
Carlisle 8	a					12 49									13 38		13 43			13 52			
	d					12 51	13 00	13 09												13 53	14 00		
Lockerbie	d					13a09			13 30											14a11		14 30	14 35
Carstairs	a																						
Motherwell	a																						15 50
Glasgow Central 15	a						14 55	15 33													15 55		16f46
Haymarket	a																						
Edinburgh 10	a								15 40													16 40	
Perth	a						16g37														17g36		
Dundee	a						16g59		17 26												17g59	18 22	
Aberdeen	a						18g15		18 44												19g15	19 38	
Inverness	a						19g34														20h08		

For general notes see front of timetable
For details of catering facilities see Directory of Train Operators

A trolley to Preston
B From Bournemouth (Table 51)

b By changing at Birmingham New Street, passengers may depart Coventry at 0932, Birmingham International at 0950
c Change at Crewe and Chester
e Change at Crewe and Llandudno Junction
f Glasgow Central Low Level

g Via Glasgow Central and Glasgow Queen Street. Passengers make their own way from one station to the other
h Change at Glasgow Central, Glasgow Queen Street and Perth. Passengers make their own way between Glasgow Central and Glasgow Queen Street

Saturdays

London and West Midlands → North West England and Scotland

2 February to 22 March

Route Diagram - see first page of Table 65

		NT	VT	XC	LM	VT	TP	VT	XC	VT	VT	VT		SR	VT	NT	TP	VT	XC	LM	VT	TP	VT	VT	VT
			1◇	1◇	1◇	1◇	1◇	1◇	1◇	1◇	1◇						1◇	1◇	1◇	1◇	1◇	1◇	1◇	1◇	R 1
				A			B		C										C						
												🚌			🚌										
			☕	☕		☕	🍴	☕	☕	☕	☕							☕	☕		☕	🍴	☕	☕	☕
London Euston [15] ⊖	d		09 53			10 03		10 10		10 17								10 53			11 03		11 10	11 17	
Gatwick Airport [10] ✈	d					*08 37*												*09 37*			*09b37*				
Watford Junction	d					10u18		10u25										11u08			*10 41*		11u25	11u32	
Milton Keynes Central	d		10 24							10 48											11 34				
Northampton	d					*09 58*															*10 58*				
Rugby	d					10 57				11 12											11 58			12 12	
Nuneaton	d			*09c39*																					
Tamworth Low Level	d			*10c27*																					
Lichfield Trent Valley	d			*10c48*																					
Coventry	d			*10 32*		11 10		11 16	11e23	11 27										*11 32*	12 10		12 16	12u27	
Birmingham International ✈	d			*10 50*		11 22		11 28	11e34	11 39									←	*11 50*	12 22		12 28	12 39	
Birmingham New Street [12]	d			11 20	11 21	11 40		11 48	12 20 →	11s50	12 03								12 20	12 21	12 40		12 48	12s50	13 03
Sandwell & Dudley	d																								
Coseley	d				11 34															12 34					
Wolverhampton [7] 🚊	d			11 40	11 44			12 09			12 21								12 40	12 44			13 09		13 21
Penkridge	d				11 53															12 53					
Stafford	a			11 53	12 01	12 17		12 24											12 53	13 01	13 17		13 24		
	d			11 54	12 02	12 19		12 26											12 54	13 02	13 19		13 26		
Stoke-on-Trent	a		12 05	12 12				12 43										13 05	13 12				13 43		
Congleton	a			12 24																					
Macclesfield	a		12 21	12 32				12 59										13 21	13 29				13 59		
Crewe [10]	a				12 23	12 38				12 48	12 54									13 23	13 38			13 50	13 54
	d				12 24	12 41				12 51	12 55									13 24	13 41			13 52	13 55
Chester	a				*12 59*						*13 31*									*13 57*				*14 27*	
Llandudno Junction	a				*14f09*						*14 21*									*15f18*				*15f25*	
Llandudno	a				*14f27*						*14 33*									*15f36*				*16g01*	
Bangor (Gwynedd)	a										*14 54*													*15f47*	
Holyhead	a										*15 30*													*16f30*	
Wilmslow	a				*13 01*					*13 26*	*13 48*									*14 01*				*14 26*	*14 48*
Manchester Airport ✈	a				*13 11*															*14 11*					
Stockport	a		12s34	12 46				13 13		*13 39*								13s34	13 46				14 13	*14 39*	
Manchester Piccadilly [10] 🚊	a		12 48	13 02				13 28		*13 54*								13 48	14 02				14 28	*14 54*	
Hartford	a				12 34															13 36					
Warrington Bank Quay	a					12 56					13 11										13 57				14 12
	d					12 58					13 12										13 58				14 13
Runcorn	a				12 46					13 08										13 45				14 08	
Liverpool South Parkway [7] ✈	a				12 54															13 54					
Liverpool Lime Street [10]	a				13 09					13 30										14 09				14 32	
	d	11 57				*12 04*										12 57					*13 04*				
Manchester Airport ✈	d						12 27										*12 47*					13 27			
Manchester Piccadilly [10] 🚊	d						12 45										*13 11*					13 45			
Bolton	d						13 05										*13 32*					14 05			
Wigan North Western	a	12 31				13 07					13 22					13 31					14 08				14 23
	d	12 31				13 09					13 23					13 31					14 09				14 24
Preston [8]	a	12 56				13 26	13 27				13 36					13 54					14 23	14 27			14 39
Blackpool North	a	13 21				*14 00*										14 21					*15 01*				
	d						*12 41*										*13 30*				*13 41*				
Preston [8]	d						13 29				13 38						14 09				14 26	14 29			14 40
Lancaster [6]	a						13 44				13 53						14 24				14 39	14 44			14 54
	d						13 45				13 53						14 25				14 41	14 45			14 56
Barrow-in-Furness	a						14 42				*15 23*														
Oxenholme Lake District	a										14 07						14 42				14 53	14 59			15 09
	d										14 08						14 43				14 54	14 59			15 10
Windermere	a																15 01								
Penrith North Lakes	d																				15 19	15 25			15 37
Carlisle [8]	a										14 51										15 37	15 43			15 54
	d										14 53	15 00		15 00											15 55
Lockerbie	d										15a11				15 30										16a13
Carstairs	a																								
Motherwell	a																								
Glasgow Central [15]	a											16 55		17 31											
Haymarket	a																								
Edinburgh [10]	a														17 40										
Perth	a											*18h42*		*19h19*											
Dundee	a											*19h06*			*19 27*										
Aberdeen	a											*20h27*			*20 41*										
Inverness	a											*20j58*													

For general notes see front of timetable
For details of catering facilities see Directory of Train Operators

- **A** From Plymouth (Table 51)
- **B** 🍴 to Preston
- **C** From Bournemouth (Table 51)

- **b** Change at Watford Junction and Milton Keynes Central
- **c** Change at Stafford. By bus
- **e** By changing at Birmingham New Street, passengers may depart Coventry at 1132, Birmingham International at 1150
- **f** Change at Crewe and Chester
- **g** Change at Crewe, Chester and Llandudno Junction

- **h** Via Glasgow Central and Glasgow Queen Street. Passengers make their own way from one station to the other
- **j** Change at Glasgow Central, Glasgow Queen Street and Perth. Passengers make their own way between Glasgow Central and Glasgow Queen Street

Saturdays

London and West Midlands → North West England and Scotland

2 February to 22 March

Route Diagram - see first page of Table 65

		VT	VT	VT	NT	VT	XC	LM	VT	TP	VT	XC	VT	VT	VT	VT	NT	VT	XC	LM	VT	TP	VT
														R									
						1◇	1◇	1◇	1◇	1◇	1◇	1◇	1◇	1				1◇	1◇	1◇	1◇	1◇	1◇
							A			B		C							C				
		bus	bus	bus											bus	bus							
						buffet	buffet		buffet	trolley	buffet	buffet	buffet	buffet				buffet	buffet		buffet	trolley	buffet
London Euston 15 ⊖	d					11 53			12 03		12 10		12 17					12 53			13 03		13 10
Gatwick Airport 10 ✈	d								10 37									11 37			11b37		
Watford Junction	d								12u18		12u25							13u08			12 41		13u25
Milton Keynes Central	d					12 24							12 48								13 34		
Northampton	d								11 58												12 58		
Rugby	d								12 57				13 12								13 58		
Nuneaton	d										12c32												
Tamworth Low Level	d										13c20												
Lichfield Trent Valley	d										13c41												
Coventry	d						12 32		13 10		13 16	13e23	13 27							13 42	14 10		14 16
Birmingham International ✈	d						12 50		13 22		13 28	13e34	13 39						←	13 57	14 22		14 28
Birmingham New Street 12	d						13 20	13 21	13 40		13 48	14 20 →	13s50	14 03					14 20	14 21	14 40		14 48
Sandwell & Dudley	d																						
Coseley	d							13 34												14 34			
Wolverhampton 7	d						13 40	13 44			14 09			14 21					14 40	14 44			15 09
Penkridge	d							13 53												14 53			
Stafford	a						13 53	14 01	14 17		14 24								14 53	15 01	15 17		15 24
	d						13 54	14 02	14 19		14 26								14 54	15 02	15 19		15 26
Stoke-on-Trent	a					14 05	14 12				14 43							15 05	15 12				15 43
Congleton	a						14 24																
Macclesfield	a					14 21	14 32				14 59							15 21	15 29				15 59
Crewe 10	a							14 23	14 38				14 49	14 54						15 23	15 38		
	d							14 24	14 41				14 52	14 55						15 24	15 41		
Chester	a							14 57					15 26							15 57			
Llandudno Junction	a							16f17					16 24							17f17			
Llandudno	a							16f35												17f35			
Bangor (Gwynedd)	a												16 46										
Holyhead	a												17 20										
Wilmslow	a							15 01					15 26	15 48						16 01			
Manchester Airport ✈	a							15 11												16 11			
Stockport	a					14s34	14 46				15 13		15 39					15s34	15 46				16 13
Manchester Piccadilly 10	a					14 48	15 02				15 28		15 54					15 48	16 02				16 28
Hartford	a							14 36												15 36			
Warrington Bank Quay	a								14 57					15 12							15 56		
	d								14 58					15 13							15 58		
Runcorn	a							14 45					15 09							15 45			
Liverpool South Parkway 7 ✈	a							14 54												15 54			
Liverpool Lime Street 10	a							15 09					15 31							16 09			
	d				13 57				14 04								14 57				15 04		
Manchester Airport ✈	d								13g47	14 27											14g47	15 27	
Manchester Piccadilly 10	d								14g11	14 45											15g11	15 45	
Bolton	d								14g32	15 05											15g32	16 05	
Wigan North Western	a				14 31				15 08					15 23			15 31				16 07		
	d				14 31				15 09					15 24			15 31				16 09		
Preston 8	a				14 54				15 22	15 27				15 39			15 54				16 22	16 27	
Blackpool North	a				15 21				16 01								16 21				17 01		
	d								14 41												15 41		
Preston 8	d								15 25	15 30				15 40							16 25	16 29	
Lancaster 6	a								15 39	15 45				15 54							16 38	16 44	
	d								15 40	15 50				15 56							16 40	16 45	
Barrow-in-Furness	a									16 53				17 17									
Oxenholme Lake District	a								15 52												16 52	16 59	
	d								15 54												16 53	16 59	
Windermere	a								16 17													17 23	
Penrith North Lakes	d								16 18					16 33							17 18	17 25	
Carlisle 8	a								16 36					16 49							17 36	17 43	
	d	16 05												16 53	17 05								
Lockerbie	d		16 30	16 35										17a10		17 30							
Carstairs	a																						
Motherwell	a			17 50																			
Glasgow Central 15	a	18 00		18h46											19 00								
Haymarket	a																						
Edinburgh 10	a		18 40													19 40							
Perth	a	19j42	20 51												20j37								
Dundee	a	20j08	20 26												21j00	21 41							
Aberdeen	a	21j20	21 39												22j15	23k21							
Inverness	a														23m13								

For general notes see front of timetable
For details of catering facilities see Directory of Train Operators

A From Penzance (Table 135)
B trolley to Preston
C From Bournemouth (Table 51)

b Change at Watford Junction and Milton Keynes Central
c Change at Stafford. By bus
e By changing at Birmingham New Street, passengers may depart Coventry at 1332, Birmingham International at 1350
f Change at Crewe and Chester
g Change at Preston
h Glasgow Central Low Level
j Via Glasgow Central and Glasgow Queen Street. Passengers make their own way from one station to the other
k Change at Edinburgh and Dundee
m Change at Glasgow Central, Glasgow Queen Street and Perth. Passengers make their own way between Glasgow Central and Glasgow Queen Street

Table 65

Saturdays

London and West Midlands → North West England and Scotland

2 February to 22 March

Route Diagram - see first page of Table 65

		SR	VT	VT	VT	VT	VT		NT	VT	XC	LM	VT	TP	VT	XC	VT	NT	VT	VT		VT	NT	TP	VT
			1 ◇	R 1						1 ◇	1 ◇	1 ◇	1 ◇	1 ◇	1 ◇	1 ◇	1 ◇		1 ◇					1 ◇	
									A		B			C		D									
					🚌	🚌	🚌													🚌		🚌			🚌
			🍴	🍴						🍴	🍴		🍴	🛒	🍴	🍴	🍴		🍴					🛒	
London Euston 15 ⊖	d		13 17							13 53			14 03		14 10		14 17								
Gatwick Airport 10 ✈	d												12 37												
Watford Junction	d		13u32										14u18		14u25										
Milton Keynes Central	d									14 24							14 48								
Northampton	d												13 58												
Rugby	d		14 11										14 57				15 12								
Nuneaton	d																								
Tamworth Low Level	d																								
Lichfield Trent Valley	d																								
Coventry	d		14u27								14 32		15 10		15 16	15b23	15 27								
Birmingham International ✈	d		14 39								14 50		15 22		15 28	15b34	15 39								
Birmingham New Street 12	d		14s50	15 03							15 20	15 21	15 40		15 48	16 20 →	15s50		16 03						
Sandwell & Dudley	d																								
Coseley	d											15 34													
Wolverhampton 7 🚢	d			15 21							15 40	15 44			16 09				16 21						
Penkridge	d											15 53													
Stafford	a										15 53	16 01	16 17		16 24										
	d										15 54	16 02	16 19		16 26										
Stoke-on-Trent	a									16 05	16 12				16 43										
Congleton	a										16 24														
Macclesfield	a									16 21	16 33				16 59										
Crewe 10	a		15 49	15 54								16 23	16 38				16 49		16 54						
	d		15 52	15 55								16 24	16 41				16 52		16 55						
Chester	a		16 27									16 56					17 26		17 54						
Llandudno Junction	a		17c24									18c17					18 25								
Llandudno	a											18c35													
Bangor (Gwynedd)	a		17c47														18 47								
Holyhead	a		18c30														19 20								
Wilmslow	a		16 26	16 48								17 05					17 26		17 48						
Manchester Airport ✈	a											17 15													
Stockport	a		16 40							16s34	16 46				17 13		17 39								
Manchester Piccadilly 10 🚢	a		16 54							16 48	17 02				17 28		17 54								
Hartford	a											16 34													
Warrington Bank Quay	a			16 12									16 57						17 12						
	d			16 13									16 58						17 13						
Runcorn	a		16 09									16 46					17 09								
Liverpool South Parkway 7 ✈	a											16 54													
Liverpool Lime Street 10	a		16 33									17 09					17 30								
	d								15 57				16 04					16 30							
Manchester Airport ✈	d												15e47	16 27										16 47	
Manchester Piccadilly 10 🚢	d												16e11	16 44										17 11	
Bolton	d												16e32	17 05										17 30	
Wigan North Western	a			16 23					16 31				17 08					17 11	17 23				←		
	d			16 24					16 31				17 09					17 12	17 24				17 12		
Preston 8	a			16 39					16 54				17 23	17 27				→	17 39				17 40	17 53	
Blackpool North	a								17 34				18 03												
	d								16 25				16 38											17 19	
Preston 8	d			16 40					16 56				17 26	17 29					17 40					17 58	
Lancaster 6	a			16 57					17 16				17 40	17 44					17 55					18 13	
	d			16 59					17 17				17 41	17 45					17 56					18 14	
Barrow-in-Furness	a								18 21					18 50											
Oxenholme Lake District	a			17 12									17 53						18 09					18 28	
	d			17 13									17 55						18 11					18 28	
Windermere	a			18 04																					
Penrith North Lakes	d			17 38									18 19												
Carlisle 8	a			17 56									18 37						18 55					19 09	
	d	17 51		18 00	18 05														18 58	19 05					19 30
Lockerbie	d			18a17		18 30	18 35												19a15			19 30			
Carstairs	a																								
Motherwell	a						19 50																		
Glasgow Central 15	a	20 27			20 00		20 44													21 00					21 25
Haymarket	a																								
Edinburgh 10	a					20 40																21 40			
Perth	a				21f42															22f36					
Dundee	a				22f08	22 26														22f59		00 07			
Aberdeen	a				23f21	23 40														00f17					
Inverness	a																								

For general notes see front of timetable
For details of catering facilities see Directory of Train Operators

A To Millom (Table 100)

B From Penzance (Table 135)

C 🛒 to Preston

D From Bournemouth (Table 51)

b By changing at Birmingham New Street, passengers may depart Coventry at 1532, Birmingham International at 1550

c Change at Crewe and Chester

e Change at Preston

f Via Glasgow Central and Glasgow Queen Street. Passengers make their own way from one station to the other

Table 65

Saturdays

London and West Midlands → North West England and Scotland

2 February to 22 March

Route Diagram - see first page of Table 65

		TP	NT	VT	XC	LM	VT	TP	VT	VT	VT		VT	SR	NT	VT	NT	XC	LM	VT	VT	VT	TP	VT	XC
		1 ◇		1 ◇	1 ◇	1 ◇	1 ◇	1 ◇	1 ◇	1 ◇	R 1					1 ◇		1 ◇	1 ◇	1 ◇			1 ◇	1 ◇	1 ◇
					A			B										C							A
													🚌								🚌	🚌			
				☕	☕		☕	🛒	☕	☕	☕					☕		☕		☕				☕	☕
London Euston 15 ⊖	d			14 53			15 03		15 10	15 17						15 53				16 03				16 10	
Gatwick Airport 10 ✈	d			*13 37*																*14 37*					
Watford Junction	d			15u08			*14 41*		15u25	15u32										16u18				16u25	
Milton Keynes Central	d						15 34									16 24									
Northampton	d						*14 58*													*15 58*					
Rugby	d						15 58			16 12										16 57					
Nuneaton	d																								
Tamworth Low Level	d																								
Lichfield Trent Valley	d																								
Coventry	d					*15 32*	16 10		16 16	16u27								*16 32*		17 10				17 16	17b23
Birmingham International ✈	d				←	*15 50*	16 22		16 28	16 39								*16 50*		17 22				17 28	17b34
Birmingham New Street 12	d				16 20	16 21	16 40		16 48	16s50	17 03							17 20	17 21	17 40				17 48	18 20 →
Sandwell & Dudley	d																								
Coseley	d					16 34													17 34						
Wolverhampton 7 ⛴	d				16 40	16 44			17 09		17 21							17 40	17 44					18 09	
Penkridge	d					16 53													17 53						
Stafford	a				16 53	17 01	17 17		17 24									17 53	18 01	18 17				18 24	
	d				16 54	17 02	17 19		17 26									17 54	18 02	18 19				18 26	
Stoke-on-Trent	a			17 05	17 12				17 43							18 05		18 12						18 43	
Congleton	a																	18 24							
Macclesfield	a			17 21	17 29				17 59							18 21		18 32						18 59	
Crewe 10	a					17 23	17 38			17 50	17 54								18 23	18 38					
	d					17 24	17 41			17 52	17 55								18 24	18 41					
Chester	a					*17 59*				*18 29*									*18 57*						
Llandudno Junction	a					*18 49*				*19c26*									*20c18*						
Llandudno	a					*19e37*													*20c35*						
Bangor (Gwynedd)	a					*19 05*				*19c49*															
Holyhead	a					*19 36*				*20c30*															
Wilmslow	a					*18 04*				*18 26*	*18 48*								*19 05*						
Manchester Airport ✈	a					*18 15*													*19 16*						
Stockport	a			17s34	17 46				18 13	*18 39*						18s34		18 46						19 13	
Manchester Piccadilly 10 ⛴	a			17 48	18 02				18 28	*18 54*						18 48		19 02						19 28	
Hartford	a					17 36													18 34						
Warrington Bank Quay	a						17 57				18 12									18 57					
	d						17 58				18 13									18 58					
Runcorn	a					17 45				18 09									18 43						
Liverpool South Parkway 7 ✈	a					17 53													18 54						
Liverpool Lime Street 10	a					18 09				18 28									19 09						
	d		17 20								*17 25*				17 45		18 04								
Manchester Airport ✈	d							17 32												*17f47*			18 27		
Manchester Piccadilly 10 ⛴	d						*17f15*	17 50												*18f11*			18 45		
Bolton	d						*17f37*	18 10												*18f32*			19 12		
Wigan North Western	a		17 54				18 08				18 23				18 28		18 51			19 08					
	d		17 54				18 09				18 24				18 28		18 51			19 09					
Preston 8	a		18 17				18 22	18 34			18 39				18 52		19 17			19 25			19 36		
Blackpool North	a		18 48				*18 59*								19 21					*20 01*					
	d						*17 38*													*18 42*					
Preston 8	d						18 25	18 38			18 40									19 25			19 38		
Lancaster 6	a						18 39	18 53			18 58									19 39			19 53		
	d	18 21					18 40	18 54			19 00									19 40			19 55		
Barrow-in-Furness	a							19 59															20 51		
Oxenholme Lake District	a	18 40					18 52				19 13									19 52					
	d	18 40					18 54				19 14									19 54					
Windermere	a	19 02																		*20 19*					
Penrith North Lakes	d						19 19													20 18					
Carlisle 8	a						19 36				19 54									20 41					
	d										19 57		20 05	20 08							20 55	20 55			
Lockerbie	d										20a14														
Carstairs	a																								
Motherwell	a																					22 35			
Glasgow Central 15	a												22 00	22 27							22 50				
Haymarket	a																								
Edinburgh 10	a																								
Perth	a												*00g15*	*01g16*							*01g16*				
Dundee	a																								
Aberdeen	a																								
Inverness	a																								

For general notes see front of timetable
For details of catering facilities see Directory of Train Operators

A From Bournemouth (Table 51)

B 🛒 to Preston

C From Plymouth (Table 51)

b By changing at Birmingham New Street, passengers may depart Coventry at 1732, Birmingham International at 1750

c Change at Crewe and Chester

e Change at Crewe and Llandudno Junction

f Change at Preston

g Via Glasgow Central and Glasgow Queen Street. Passengers make their own way from one station to the other

Table 65

Saturdays

London and West Midlands → North West England and Scotland

2 February to 22 March

Route Diagram - see first page of Table 65

Station		VT		VT	VT	VT	NT	VT	XC	LM	VT	TP	VT	VT	VT		VT	VT	VT	XC	LM	VT	VT	VT	VT
		1◇		R 1				1◇	1◇	1◇	1◇	1◇		1◇	1◇		R 1		1◇	1◇	1◇			1◇	
									A											B					
					🚌	🚌							🚌					🚌				🚌	🚌		🚌
		☕		☕				☕	☕		☕			☕	☕		☕		☕	☕				☕	
London Euston 15 ⊖	d	16 17						16 53			17 03			17 10	17 17				17 53					18 03	
Gatwick Airport 10 ✈	d							*15 37*																*16 37*	
Watford Junction	d							17u08			*16 41*			17u25	17u32									18u18	
Milton Keynes Central	d	16 48									17 34								18 24						
Northampton	d										*16 58*														
Rugby	d	17 12									17 58				18 12										
Nuneaton	d																*17b42*								
Tamworth Low Level	d																*18b30*								
Lichfield Trent Valley	d																*18b51*								
Coventry	d	17 27								*17 32*	18 10			18 16	18u27					*18 32*				19 10	
Birmingham International ✈	d	17 39							←	*17 50*	18 22			18 28	18 41					*18 50*					
Birmingham New Street 12	d	17s50		18 03					18 20	18 21	18 40			18 48	18s50		19 03			19 20	19 21				
Sandwell & Dudley	d																								
Coseley	d									18 34											19 34				
Wolverhampton 7 ⛴	d			18 20					18 40	18 44				19 09			19 21			19 40	19 44				
Penkridge	d									18 53											19 53				
Stafford	a								18 53	19 01	19 17			19 24			19 33			19 53	20 01			20 13	
	d								18 54	19 02	19 19			19 26			19 33			19 54	20 02			20 15	
Stoke-on-Trent	a							19 05	19 12					19 43					20 05	20 12					
Congleton	a																			20 24					
Macclesfield	a							19 21	19 29					19 59					20 21	20 32					
Crewe 10	a	18 49		18 54						19 23	19 38				19 49		19 54				20 23			20 34	
	d	18 52		18 55						19 24	19 41				19 52		19 55				20 24			20 37	
Chester	a	*19 25*		*19 46*						*20 02*					*20 27*						*20 57*				
Llandudno Junction	a			*20 37*											*21c28*										
Llandudno	a			*21e08*											*21f43*										
Bangor (Gwynedd)	a			*20 55*																					
Holyhead	a			*21 33*																					
Wilmslow	a	*19 26*		*19 48*											*20 26*		*20 45*								
Manchester Airport ✈	a	*20g02*															*21g02*								
Stockport	a	*19 39*						19s34	19 46					20 13	*20 39*				20s34	20 46					
Manchester Piccadilly 10 ⛴	a	*19 57*						19 48	20 02					20 28	*20 54*				20 48	21 02					
Hartford	a									19 36											20 36				
Warrington Bank Quay	a			19 12							19 57						20 12							20 53	
	d			19 13							19 58						20 13							20 54	
Runcorn	a	19 08								19 45					20 08						20 45				
Liverpool South Parkway 7 ✈	a									19 54											20 54				
Liverpool Lime Street 10	a	19 32								20 09					20 30						21 09				
	d						19 04																	*19 48*	
Manchester Airport ✈	d											19 27													
Manchester Piccadilly 10 ⛴	d											19 44													
Bolton	d											20 05													
Wigan North Western	a			19 24			19 51				20 08						20 23							21 04	
	d			19 24			19 51				20 09						20 24							21 05	
Preston 8	a			19 43			20 17				20 26	20 27					20 43							21 24	
Blackpool North	a			*20 36*			*20 56*										*21 36*							*21 56*	
	d				*19 10*	*19 25*						*19 42*													
Preston 8	d				19 55	20 00						20 29						20 55				21 00			21 40
Lancaster 6	a				20 45							20 43	←					21 45							22 30
	d				20 45 →							20 43	20 45					21 45							
Barrow-in-Furness	a											21 50													*23 50*
Oxenholme Lake District	a												21 30					22 30							
	d												21 30					22 30							
Windermere	a																						←		
Penrith North Lakes	d												22 25					23 25 →					23 25		
Carlisle 8	a					22 00							23 00									23 00	23 59		
	d																								
Lockerbie	d																								
Carstairs	a																								
Motherwell	a																								
Glasgow Central 15	a																								
Haymarket	a																								
Edinburgh 10	a																								
Perth	a																								
Dundee	a																								
Aberdeen	a																								
Inverness	a																								

For general notes see front of timetable
For details of catering facilities see Directory of Train Operators

- **A** From Bournemouth (Table 51)
- **B** From Plymouth (Table 51)
- **b** Change at Stafford. By bus
- **c** Change at Crewe and Chester
- **e** Change at Crewe and Llandudno Junction
- **f** Change at Crewe, Chester and Llandudno Junction
- **g** Change at Crewe and Wilmslow

London and West Midlands → North West England and Scotland

Saturdays

2 February to 22 March

Route Diagram - see first page of Table 65

	VT	VT	VT	VT	XC		LM	VT	VT	VT	NT	VT	VT	XC	LM	NT	XC	VT		VT	XC	AW		
	1 ◇	1 ◇	1 ◇	1 ◇	1 ◇		1 ◇	1 ◇	1 ◇			1 ◇	1 ◇	1 ◇	1 ◇		1 ◇	1 ◇		1 ◇	1 ◇	◇		
					A									B			C				C			
										🚌														
	☕	☕	☕	☕	☕			☕	☕			☕	☕					☕		☕				
London Euston 15 ⊖ d	18 10	18 17	18 53	18 57				19 02				19 05	19 20					19 36		20 00				
Gatwick Airport 10 ✈ d			17 37						←									18 37						
Watford Junction d	18u25		19u08	19u11				18 41	19u11			19u19						19u50		20u14				
Milton Keynes Central d		18 48		→				19 35				19 41	19 55					20 38		21 01				
Northampton d		17 58										18 58						19 58		20 58				
Rugby d		19 12										20 17						21 16		21 39				
Nuneaton d																								
Tamworth Low Level d																								
Lichfield Trent Valley d																								
Coventry d	19 16				19b23		19 32	20 10	20 16			20 29		20 32			21c23	21 28				21 32		
Birmingham International ✈ d	19 28				19b34		19 50		20 28					20 50			21c34				←	21 50		
Birmingham New Street 12 d	19 48				20 20		20 21		20 48					21 20	21 21		22 20				22 20	22 33		
Sandwell & Dudley d									20 57								→							
Coseley d							20 34								21 35									
Wolverhampton 7 d	20 09				20 40		20 44		21 10					21 40	21 44						22 40	22 48		
Penkridge d							20 53								21 54									
Stafford a	20 24				20 53		21 01	21 13	21 24					21 53	22 01			22 16		22 47	22 53			
d	20 26				20 54		21 02	21 15	21 26					21 54	22 02			22 17		22 49	22 54			
Stoke-on-Trent a	20 43		21 05		21 12				21 44				22 01	22 12						23 07	23s13			
Congleton a														22 24										
Macclesfield a	20 59		21 21		21 29				22 00				22 17	22 32						23 23	23s30			
Crewe 10 a		20 50					21 32	21 34				21 49			22 30			22 36				00 01		
d		20 52						21 37				21 52						22 39				00 02		
Chester a		21 27						22 09				22 30						23 10				00 24		
Llandudno Junction a		22 25										23e33												
Llandudno a																								
Bangor (Gwynedd) a		22 42										00f25												
Holyhead a		23 30										01f45												
Wilmslow a		21 26										22 26						23 22						
Manchester Airport ✈ a		22g05										23g05												
Stockport a	21 13	21 39	21s34		21 46				22 12			22 39	22s32	22 46				23 33		23s37	23s46			
Manchester Piccadilly 10 a	21 28	21 53	21 51		22 02				22 25			22 52	22 45	23 02				23 50		23 51	00 02			
Hartford a																								
Warrington Bank Quay a								21 53																
d								21 54																
Runcorn a		21 08										22 08						22 54						
Liverpool South Parkway 7 ✈ a																								
Liverpool Lime Street 10 a		21 27										22 27						23 15						
d								20 48			21 48					23 05								
Manchester Airport ✈ d																								
Manchester Piccadilly 10 d																								
Bolton d																								
Wigan North Western a								22 04			22 37					23 51								
d								22 05			22 38					23 51								
Preston 8 a								22 24			23 02					00 15								
Blackpool North a											23 28													
d										22 03														
Preston 8 d										22 40														
Lancaster 6 a										23 30														
d																								
Barrow-in-Furness a																								
Oxenholme Lake District a																								
d																								
Windermere a																								
Penrith North Lakes d																								
Carlisle 8 a																								
d																								
Lockerbie d																								
Carstairs a																								
Motherwell a																								
Glasgow Central 15 a																								
Haymarket a																								
Edinburgh 10 a																								
Perth a																								
Dundee a																								
Aberdeen a																								
Inverness a																								

For general notes see front of timetable
For details of catering facilities see Directory of Train Operators

A From Bournemouth (Table 51). ☕ to Birmingham New Street

B From Plymouth (Table 51)

C From Bournemouth (Table 51)

b By changing at Birmingham New Street, passengers may depart Coventry at 1932, Birmingham International at 1950

c By changing at Birmingham New Street, passengers may depart Coventry at 2132, Birmingham International at 2150

e Change at Crewe and Chester

f Change at Crewe, Chester and Llandudno Junction. By bus from Llandudno Junction

g Change at Crewe and Wilmslow

Table 65

London and West Midlands → North West England and Scotland

Route Diagram - see first page of Table 65

		SR	TP	VT	TP	TP	TP	TP	TP	VT	VT	VT	TP	VT	VT	VT	VT		NT	TP	LM	XC	NT	LM	VT
			1		1		1 ◇	1		1 ◇	1 ◇		1						A		1 ◇	1 ◇		1 ◇	1 ◇
				bus		bus	bike		bus		catering	bus		bus	bus	bus	bus			bus					catering
London Euston 15 ⊖	d																								
Gatwick Airport 10 ✈	d																								
Watford Junction	d																								
Milton Keynes Central	d																								
Northampton	d																								
Rugby	d																								
Nuneaton	d																								
Tamworth Low Level	d																								
Lichfield Trent Valley	d																								
Coventry	d																								
Birmingham International ✈	d																								
Birmingham New Street 12	d									05 20	05 30										06 07	06 20			
Sandwell & Dudley	d																				06 18				
Coseley	d																				06 27				
Wolverhampton 7	d									05 38	05 49										06 33	06 40			
Penkridge	d																				06 43				
Stafford	a									05 51	06 04										06 50	06 53		←	
	d									05 52	06 05										07 00	06 54		07 00	
Stoke-on-Trent	a																				→	07 12			
Congleton	a																					07 24			
Macclesfield	a																					07 32			
Crewe 10	a									06 16	06 25													07 22	
	d									06 18	06 28													07 22	
Chester	a									06 37	*07 03*													07 57	
Llandudno Junction	a									07 33	*08 20*													09b19	
Llandudno	a									*08 16*														09b37	
Bangor (Gwynedd)	a									07 49	*08 43*													09b43	
Holyhead	a									08 21	*09 30*													10b20	
Wilmslow	a										*07 01*													*07 59*	
Manchester Airport ✈	a																							*08 14*	
Stockport	a										*07 13*											07 46		*08 13*	
Manchester Piccadilly 10	a										*07 28*											08 02		*08 28*	
Hartford	a																							07 34	
Warrington Bank Quay	a										06 43														
	d										06 45														
Runcorn	a																							07 46	
Liverpool South Parkway 7 ✈	a																							07 54	
Liverpool Lime Street 10	a																							08 10	
	d										*06 04*												07 30		
Manchester Airport ✈	d					*04c35*										*06 19*									
Manchester Piccadilly 10	d					*05 10*										*06 44*									
Bolton	d															*07 05*									
Wigan North Western	a										07 02												08 01		
	d										07 04												08 02		
Preston 8	a										07 18												08 24		
Blackpool North	a										*07 56*												08 51		
	d			*05 30*					*06 34*							*07 03*				*07 30*					
Preston 8	d			06 15		06 20		*06e55*	07 13						07 30	08 00			*08e00*	08 13					
Lancaster 6	a			07 05					08 03						08 20					09 03					
	d		06 10		07 10			07 44					08 10		08 20				08 50						
Barrow-in-Furness	a							08 48											09 54						
Oxenholme Lake District	a		06 25		07 25	07 30							08 25		09 05										
	d		06 26		07 26	07 30							08 26	09 00	09 05										
Windermere	a		06 47		07 47								08 47				←								
Penrith North Lakes	d					08 15								09 55 →	10a00		09 55								
Carlisle 8	a					08 50										10 00	10 30								
	d	06 09					09 02					09 30													10 40
Lockerbie	d						09 22					10 05													11 01
Carstairs	a																								
Motherwell	a																								11s53
Glasgow Central 15	a	08 37					10 29																		12 17
Haymarket	a																								
Edinburgh 10	a											12 15													
Perth	a	*10f37*					*12f37*																		*14f37*
Dundee	a	*11f00*					*13f00*					*14 23*													*15f00*
Aberdeen	a	*12f19*					*14f13*					*15 36*													*16f21*
Inverness	a	*13f35*					*15g18*																		

For general notes see front of timetable
For details of catering facilities see Directory of Train Operators

A To Carlisle via Whitehaven (Table 100)

b Change at Crewe and Chester

c Change at Manchester Piccadilly and Preston

e Change at Carnforth. By bus

f Via Glasgow Central and Glasgow Queen Street. Passengers make their own way from one station to the other

g Change at Glasgow Central, Glasgow Queen Street and Perth. Passengers make their own way between Glasgow Central and Glasgow Queen Street

Table 65

Saturdays
from 29 March

London and West Midlands → North West England and Scotland

Route Diagram - see first page of Table 65

		VT	VT	TP	XC	TP	TP	TP	TP	TP	LM	VT		VT	VT	NT	VT	VT	XC	TP	TP	TP	VT	NT	LM
		1◇		1	1◇	1		1		1◇	1◇	1◇		1◇	1◇		1◇		1◇	1		1			1◇
																			A						
			🚌				🚌		🚌									🚌			🚌		🚌		
		☕			☕					🛒		☕		☕	☕		☕		☕						
London Euston 15 ⊖	d											05 25		05 31			06 30								
Gatwick Airport 10 ✈	d																		05 15						
Watford Junction	d											05u40					06u46								
Milton Keynes Central	d											06 10		06 16											
Northampton	d													05 58											
Rugby	d													07 11											
Nuneaton	d																								
Tamworth Low Level	d																								
Lichfield Trent Valley	d																								
Coventry	d	06 04			06 32										07 04				07 32						
Birmingham International ✈	d	06 20			06 50										07 20				07 50						
Birmingham New Street 12	d	07 03			07 20						07 21				08 03				08 20						08 21
Sandwell & Dudley	d																								
Coseley	d										07 34														08 34
Wolverhampton 7 ⛴	d	07 21			07 40						07 44				08 21				08 40						08 44
Penkridge	d										07 53														08 53
Stafford	a	07 33			07 53						08 01	08 16							08 53						09 01
	d	07 33			07 54						08 02	08 18							08 54						09 02
Stoke-on-Trent	a				08 12												09 03		09 12						
Congleton	a				08 24																				
Macclesfield	a				08 32												09 19		09 29						
Crewe 10	a	07 54									08 23	08 36		08 46	08 54										09 23
	d	07 55									08 24	08 39		08 49	08 55										09 24
Chester	a										08 57			09 26											09 57
Llandudno Junction	a										10b17			10 24											11b17
Llandudno	a										10b37														11b35
Bangor (Gwynedd)	a													10 46											
Holyhead	a													11 30											
Wilmslow	a	08 48									09 03			09 26	09 48										10 01
Manchester Airport ✈	a										09 15														10 11
Stockport	a	08 56			08 46									09 39			09s34		09 46						
Manchester Piccadilly 10 ⛴	a	09 12			09 02						09 40			09 54			09 48		10 02						
Hartford	a										08 36														09 36
Warrington Bank Quay	a	08 12										08 55			09 11										
	d	08 13										08 56			09 12										
Runcorn	a										08 46			09 04											09 45
Liverpool South Parkway 7 ✈	a										08 56														09 54
Liverpool Lime Street 10	a										09 10			09 31											10 09
	d											08 04				08 57									
Manchester Airport ✈	d								07 47									08 27							
Manchester Piccadilly 10 ⛴	d								08 11									08 45							
Bolton	d								08 32									09 05							
Wigan North Western	a	08 23										09 06			09 22	09 30									
	d	08 24										09 07			09 23	09 31									
Preston 8	a	08 44										09 25			09 44	09 54									
Blackpool North	a	09 32										10 02				10 21									
	d						08 41											09 11			09 40				
Preston 8	d					08c55	09 13		09 15									09 55		10c10	10 13			10c55	
Lancaster 6	a						10 03											10 45			11 03				
	d			09 10		09 48		10 10										10 45		11 02		11 10		11 45	
Barrow-in-Furness	a					10 46														11 54				12 51	
Oxenholme Lake District	a			09 25				10 25	10 30									11 30				11 25			
	d			09 26				10 26	10 30									11 30				11 26	12 10		
Windermere	a			09 47				10 47														11 47			
Penrith North Lakes	d								11 15									12a25					13 05		
Carlisle 8	a								11 50														13 40		
	d									12 04															
Lockerbie	d		11 10							12 23															
Carstairs	a																								
Motherwell	a																								
Glasgow Central 15	a									13 29															
Haymarket	a																								
Edinburgh 10	a		13 20																						
Perth	a		14 54							15e36															
Dundee	a		15 24							15e59															
Aberdeen	a		16 37							17e09															
Inverness	a		17 07																						

For general notes see front of timetable
For details of catering facilities see Directory of Train Operators

A ☕ from Reading
b Change at Crewe and Chester
c Change at Carnforth. By bus
e Via Glasgow Central and Glasgow Queen Street. Passengers make their own way from one station to the other

Table 65

Saturdays
from 29 March

London and West Midlands → North West England and Scotland

Route Diagram - see first page of Table 65

Station		VT	VT	VT	VT	VT	VT		VT	NT	VT	XC	TP	TP	LM	VT	XC	VT	VT	VT	NT	VT	VT	XC	TP
		1 ◇	1 ◇	1 ◇	1 ◇		1 ◇				1 ◇	1 ◇		1	1 ◇	1 ◇	1 ◇	1 ◇	1 ◇	1 ◇		1 ◇		1 ◇	
												A					B							B	
						bus			bus				bus										bus		bus
		catering	catering	catering	catering		catering				catering	catering				catering	catering	catering	catering	catering		catering		catering	
London Euston 15 ⊖	d	06 59	07 06	07 15							07 52					08 03		08 10	08 17			08 53			
Gatwick Airport 10 ✈	d	05 52														06 37						07 37			
Watford Junction	d	07u14	07u21	07u31							07 25					08u18		08u26				09u08			
Milton Keynes Central	d	07 34	07 42								08 23								08 49						
Northampton	d			06 58												07 58									
Rugby	d			08 12												08 57			09 13						
Nuneaton	d																								
Tamworth Low Level	d																								
Lichfield Trent Valley	d																								
Coventry	d	08 08	08 15	08 27								08 32				09 10	09b23	09 16	09 27						
Birmingham International ✈	d		08 28	08u41								08 50				09 22	09b34	09 28	09 39					←	
Birmingham New Street 12	d		08 48	08s50	09 03							09 20			09 21	09 40	10 20 →	09 48	09s50	10 03				10 20	
Sandwell & Dudley	d																								
Coseley	d														09 34										
Wolverhampton 7	d		09 09		09 21							09 40			09 44			10 09		10 21				10 40	
Penkridge	d														09 53										
Stafford	a	09 14	09 24									09 53			10 01	10 17		10 24						10 53	
	d	09 16	09 26									09 54			10 02	10 19		10 26						10 54	
Stoke-on-Trent	a		09 43								10 05	10 12						10 42				11 05		11 12	
Congleton	a											10 24													
Macclesfield	a		09 59								10 21	10 32						10 58				11 21		11 29	
Crewe 10	a	09 34		09 49	09 54										10 22	10 38			10 49	10 54					
	d	09 37		09 52	09 55										10 24	10 41			10 52	10 55					
Chester	a			10 27											10 57				11 29						
Llandudno Junction	a			11c26											12 02				12 25						
Llandudno	a														12e35				13e01						
Bangor (Gwynedd)	a			11c43											12 18				12 48						
Holyhead	a			12c20											12 53				13 30						
Wilmslow	a			10 26	10 48										11 01				11 26	11 48					
Manchester Airport ✈	a														11 11										
Stockport	a		10 13	10 39							10s34	10 46						11 13	11 39			11s34		11 46	
Manchester Piccadilly 10	a		10 28	10 54							10 48	11 02						11 28	11 54			11 48		12 02	
Hartford	a														10 33										
Warrington Bank Quay	a	09 55			10 12											10 57				11 11					
	d	09 57			10 13											10 58				11 13					
Runcorn	a			10 09											10 45				11 08						
Liverpool South Parkway 7 ✈	a														10 54										
Liverpool Lime Street 10	a			10 31											11 09				11 31						
	d	09 04								09 57						10 04					10 57				
Manchester Airport ✈	d					09 27																	10 27		
Manchester Piccadilly 10	d					09 45																	10 45		
Bolton	d					10 05																	11 05		
Wigan North Western	a	10 06			10 23					10 31						11 08				11 22	11 30				
	d	10 08			10 24					10 31						11 09				11 24	11 30				
Preston 8	a	10 26			10 44					10 55						11 25				11 44	11 53				
Blackpool North	a						←			11 23						12 01					12 20				
	d					10 11	10 25						10 41										11 11		11 41
Preston 8	d				11 00 →	10 55	11 00						11 13										11 55		12 13
Lancaster 6	a					11 45							12 03										12 45		13 03
	d					11 45								12 10									12 45		
Barrow-in-Furness	a																								
Oxenholme Lake District	a					12 30								12 25									13 30		
	d					12 30								12 26									13 30 →		
Windermere	a													12 47											
Penrith North Lakes	d					13a25																			
Carlisle 8	a						13 49																		
	d						13 55																		
Lockerbie	d						14 13		14 25																
Carstairs	a																								
Motherwell	a						14s55																		
Glasgow Central 15	a						15 19																		
Haymarket	a																								
Edinburgh 10	a								16 35																
Perth	a						17f20																		
Dundee	a						17f59		18 22																
Aberdeen	a						19f15		19 38																
Inverness	a						19 34																		

For general notes see front of timetable
For details of catering facilities see Directory of Train Operators

A From Exeter St Davids (Table 51)

B From Bournemouth (Table 51)

b By changing at Birmingham New Street, passengers may depart Coventry at 0932, Birmingham International at 0950

c Change at Crewe and Chester

e Change at Crewe and Llandudno Junction

f Via Glasgow Central and Glasgow Queen Street. Passengers make their own way from one station to the other

Table 65

Saturdays

from 29 March

London and West Midlands → North West England and Scotland

Route Diagram - see first page of Table 65

		TP		TP	VT	TP	SR	VT	LM	VT	VT	VT	VT	VT	TP	VT	NT	VT	XC		TP	TP	NT	LM	VT
		1				1 ◇			1 ◇	1 ◇	1 ◇		1 ◇	R 1	1			1 ◇	1 ◇ A			1	B	1 ◇	1 ◇
				🚌	🚌	⚲		🚌		☕	☕	🚌	☕	☕		🚌		☕	☕		🚌				☕
London Euston 15 ⊖	d									09 03	09 10		09 17					09 53							10 03
Gatwick Airport 10 ✈	d																								*08 37*
Watford Junction	d									*08 41*	09u25		09u32												10u18
Milton Keynes Central	d									09 34								10 24							
Northampton	d									*08 58*															*09 58*
Rugby	d									09 58			10 12												10 57
Nuneaton	d																		*09b39*						
Tamworth Low Level	d																		*10b27*						
Lichfield Trent Valley	d																		*10b48*						
Coventry	d								*09 32*	10 10	10 16		10 27						*10 32*						11 10
Birmingham International ✈	d								*09 50*	10 22	10 28		10 39						*10 50*						11 22
Birmingham New Street 12	d								10 21	10 40	10 48		10s50	11 03					11 20					11 21	11 40
Sandwell & Dudley	d																								
Coseley	d								10 34															11 34	
Wolverhampton 7	d								10 44		11 09			11 21					11 40					11 44	
Penkridge	d								10 53															11 53	
Stafford	a								11 01	11 19	11 24								11 53					12 01	12 17
	d								11 02	11 21	11 26								11 54					12 02	12 19
Stoke-on-Trent	a										11 43							12 05	12 12						
Congleton	a																		12 24						
Macclesfield	a										11 59							12 21	12 32						
Crewe 10	a								11 23	11 40			11 49	11 54										12 23	12 38
	d								11 24	11 43			11 52	11 55										12 24	12 41
Chester	a								*11 59*				*12 27*											*12 59*	
Llandudno Junction	a								*13c17*				*13c24*											*14c09*	
Llandudno	a								*13c35*															*14c27*	
Bangor (Gwynedd)	a												*13c48*												
Holyhead	a												*14c30*												
Wilmslow	a								*12 01*				*12 26*	*12 48*										*13 01*	
Manchester Airport ✈	a								*12 11*															*13 11*	
Stockport	a										12 13		*12 39*					12s34	12 46						
Manchester Piccadilly 10	a										12 28		*12 54*					12 48	13 02						
Hartford	a								11 36															12 34	
Warrington Bank Quay	a									11 59				12 13											12 56
	d									12 00				12 13											12 58
Runcorn	a								11 45				12 09											12 46	
Liverpool South Parkway 7 ✈	a								11 54															12 54	
Liverpool Lime Street 10	a								12 09				12 31											13 09	
	d									*11 04*							11 57								*12 04*
Manchester Airport ✈	d			*10 47*						*11e27*															
Manchester Piccadilly 10	d			*11 11*						*11e45*															
Bolton	d			*11 32*						*12e05*															
Wigan North Western	a									12 10				12 24			12 31								13 07
	d									12 11				12 25			12 31								13 09
Preston 8	a									12 24				12 40			12 56								13 26
Blackpool North	a									*13 01*							13 21								*14 00*
	d									*11 41*						*12 11*					*12 41*				
Preston 8	d			12 15						12 38					*12f55*	12 55					13 13		*13f30*		
Lancaster 6	a															13 45					14 03				
	d	13 10						13 35							13 45	13 45						14 10	14 18		
Barrow-in-Furness	a														14 48								15 23		
Oxenholme Lake District	a	13 25		13 30	⟵			14 20								14 30						14 25			
	d	13 26		13 30	13 30			14 20								14 30						14 26			
Windermere	a	13 47																				14 47			
Penrith North Lakes	d			14 15	14a25			15 15								15a25									
Carlisle 8	a			14 50				15 50		15 53															
	d					14 58	15 00			16 03															
Lockerbie	d					15 17				16 26		16 40													
Carstairs	a																								
Motherwell	a									17s22															
Glasgow Central 15	a					16 16	17 31			17 47															
Haymarket	a																								
Edinburgh 10	a											18 50													
Perth	a					*18g42*	*19g19*			*19g42*															
Dundee	a					*19g06*				*20g08*		*20 26*													
Aberdeen	a					*20g27*				*21g20*		*21 39*													
Inverness	a					*20h58*																			

For general notes see front of timetable
For details of catering facilities see Directory of Train Operators

A From Plymouth (Table 51)

B To Carlisle via Whitehaven (Table 100)

b Change at Stafford. By bus

c Change at Crewe and Chester

e Change at Preston

f Change at Carnforth. By bus

g Via Glasgow Central and Glasgow Queen Street. Passengers make their own way from one station to the other

h Change at Glasgow Central, Glasgow Queen Street and Perth. Passengers make their own way between Glasgow Central and Glasgow Queen Street

Table 65

Saturdays

from 29 March

London and West Midlands → North West England and Scotland

Route Diagram - see first page of Table 65

		VT	XC	VT	VT	NT	VT	VT	XC	TP	TP	TP	TP	VT		VT	LM	VT	VT	VT	VT	NT	VT	TP	VT
		1 ◇	1 ◇	1 ◇	1 ◇		1 ◇		1 ◇		1		1 ◇				1 ◇	1 ◇	1 ◇	1 ◇	R 1			1	R 1
			A						A																
								bus		bus		bus		bus		bus							bus		
		☕	☕	☕	☕		☕		☕				trolley					☕	☕	☕	☕				☕
London Euston 15 ⊖	d	10 10		10 17			10 53											11 03	11 10	11 17					
Gatwick Airport 10 ✈	d						09 37											09b37							
Watford Junction	d	10u25					11u08											10 41	11u25	11u32					
Milton Keynes Central	d			10 48														11 34							
Northampton	d																	10 58							
Rugby	d			11 12														11 58		12 12					
Nuneaton	d																								
Tamworth Low Level	d																								
Lichfield Trent Valley	d																								
Coventry	d	11 16	11c23	11 27													11 32	12 10	12 16	12u27					
Birmingham International ✈	d	11 28	11c34	11 39					←								11 50	12 22	12 28	12 39					
Birmingham New Street 12	d	11 48	12 20 →	11s50	12 03				12 20								12 21	12 40	12 48	12s50	13 03				
Sandwell & Dudley	d																								
Coseley	d																12 34								
Wolverhampton 7	d	12 09			12 21				12 40								12 44		13 09		13 21				
Penkridge	d																12 53								
Stafford	a	12 24							12 53								13 01	13 17	13 24						
	d	12 26							12 54								13 02	13 19	13 26						
Stoke-on-Trent	a	12 43					13 05		13 12										13 43						
Congleton	a																								
Macclesfield	a	12 59					13 21		13 29										13 59						
Crewe 10	a			12 48	12 54												13 23	13 38		13 50	13 54				
	d			12 51	12 55												13 24	13 41		13 52	13 55				
Chester	a				13 31												13 57			14 27					
Llandudno Junction	a				14 21												15e18			15e25					
Llandudno	a				14 33												15e36			16f01					
Bangor (Gwynedd)	a				14 54															15e47					
Holyhead	a				15 30															16e30					
Wilmslow	a			13 26	13 48												14 01			14 26	14 48				
Manchester Airport ✈	a																14 11								
Stockport	a	13 13		13 39			13s34		13 46										14 13	14 39					
Manchester Piccadilly 10	a	13 28		13 54			13 48		14 02										14 28	14 54					
Hartford	a																13 36								
Warrington Bank Quay	a				13 11													13 57			14 12				
	d				13 12													13 58			14 13				
Runcorn	a			13 08													13 45			14 08					
Liverpool South Parkway 7 ✈	a																13 54								
Liverpool Lime Street 10	a			13 30													14 09			14 32					
	d					12 57												13 04				13 57			
Manchester Airport ✈	d							12 27				12 47											13 27		
Manchester Piccadilly 10	d							12 45				13 11											13 45		
Bolton	d							13 05				13 32											14 05		
Wigan North Western	a				13 22	13 31												14 08			14 23	14 31			
	d				13 23	13 31												14 09			14 24	14 31			
Preston 8	a				13 44	13 54												14 28			14 44	14 54			
Blackpool North	a					14 21																15 21			←
	d							13 11		13 41													14 11		14 25
Preston 8	d							13 55		14 13		14 15									15 00 →		14 55	14g55	15 00
Lancaster 6	a							14 45		15 03													15 45		
	d							14 45			15 10												15 45	15 54	
Barrow-in-Furness	a																							16 56	
Oxenholme Lake District	a							15 30			15 25	15 30		←									16 30		
	d							15 30 →			15 26	15 30		15 30		16 00							16 30		
Windermere	a										15 47														
Penrith North Lakes	d											16 15		16a25		16 55							17a25		
Carlisle 8	a											16 50				17 30									17 43
	d												17 00												17 46
Lockerbie	d												17 19												18 04
Carstairs	a																								
Motherwell	a																								18s51
Glasgow Central 15	a												18 29												19 19
Haymarket	a																								
Edinburgh 10	a																								
Perth	a												20h37												21h42
Dundee	a												21h00												22h08
Aberdeen	a												22h15												23h21
Inverness	a												23j13												

For general notes see front of timetable
For details of catering facilities see Directory of Train Operators

A From Bournemouth (Table 51)

b Change at Watford Junction and Milton Keynes Central

c By changing at Birmingham New Street, passengers may depart Coventry at 1132, Birmingham International at 1150

e Change at Crewe and Chester

f Change at Crewe, Chester and Llandudno Junction

g Change at Carnforth. By bus

h Via Glasgow Central and Glasgow Queen Street. Passengers make their own way from one station to the other

j Change at Glasgow Central, Glasgow Queen Street and Perth. Passengers make their own way between Glasgow Central and Glasgow Queen Street

Table 65

London and West Midlands → North West England and Scotland

Saturdays

from 29 March

Route Diagram - see first page of Table 65

		VT	VT	XC	TP	TP	SR	LM	NT		VT	NT	VT	VT	TP	TP	TP	VT	TP	TP	VT	XC	VT	VT	XC
			1 ◇	1 ◇		1		1 ◇			1 ◇		1 ◇			1			1 ◇	1		1 ◇	1 ◇	1 ◇	1 ◇
				A																		B			B
		bus			bus									bus	bus		bus	bus			bus				
			catering	catering							catering		catering						trolley			catering	catering	catering	catering
London Euston [15] ⊖	d		11 53								12 03		12 10										12 17	12 53	
Gatwick Airport [10] ✈	d										10 37													11 37	
Watford Junction	d		11 11								12u18		12u25											13u08	
Milton Keynes Central	d		12 24																				12 48		
Northampton	d										11 58														
Rugby	d										12 57												13 12		
Nuneaton	d												12b32												
Tamworth Low Level	d												13b20												
Lichfield Trent Valley	d												13b41												
Coventry	d			12 32							13 10		13 16									13c23	13 27		
Birmingham International ✈	d			12 50							13 22		13 28									13c34	13 39		←
Birmingham New Street [12]	d			13 20				13 21			13 40		13 48									14 20 →	13s50		14 20
Sandwell & Dudley	d																								
Coseley	d							13 34																	
Wolverhampton [7]	d			13 40				13 44					14 09												14 40
Penkridge	d							13 53																	
Stafford	a			13 53				14 01			14 17		14 24												14 53
	d			13 54				14 02			14 19		14 26												14 54
Stoke-on-Trent	a		14 05	14 12									14 43											15 05	15 12
Congleton	a			14 24																					
Macclesfield	a		14 21	14 32									14 59											15 21	15 29
Crewe [10]	a							14 23			14 38												14 49		
	d							14 24			14 41												14 52		
Chester	a							14 57															15 26		
Llandudno Junction	a							16e17															16 24		
Llandudno	a							16e35																	
Bangor (Gwynedd)	a																						16 46		
Holyhead	a																						17 20		
Wilmslow	a							15 01															15 26		
Manchester Airport ✈	a							15 11																	
Stockport	a		14s34	14 46									15 13										15 39	15s34	15 46
Manchester Piccadilly [10]	a		14 48	15 02									15 28										15 54	15 48	16 02
Hartford	a							14 36																	
Warrington Bank Quay	a										14 57														
	d										14 58														
Runcorn	a							14 45															15 09		
Liverpool South Parkway [7] ✈	a							14 54																	
Liverpool Lime Street [10]	a							15 09															15 31		
	d										14 04	14 57													
Manchester Airport ✈	d													14 27			14 47								
Manchester Piccadilly [10]	d													14 45			15 11								
Bolton	d													15 05			15 32								
Wigan North Western	a										15 08	15 31													
	d										15 09	15 31													
Preston [8]	a										15 26	15 54													
Blackpool North	a										16 01	16 21													
	d				14 41									15 11	15 41										
Preston [8]	d				15 13				15f25					15 55	16 13		16 15			16f25					
Lancaster [6]	a				16 03									16 45	17 03										
	d					16 10			16 14					16 45		17 10				17 17					
Barrow-in-Furness	a								17 17											18 18					
Oxenholme Lake District	a					16 25								17 30		17 25	17 30	←							
	d					16 26								17 30 →		17 26	17 30	17 30			18 05				
Windermere	a					16 47										17 47									
Penrith North Lakes	d																18 15	18a25			19 00				
Carlisle [8]	a																18 50				19 35				
	d						17 51												19 10						
Lockerbie	d	18 15																	19 29						
Carstairs	a																								
Motherwell	a																								
Glasgow Central [15]	a						20 27												20 31						
Haymarket	a																								
Edinburgh [10]	a	20 25																							
Perth	a																		22g36						
Dundee	a	22 26																	22g59						
Aberdeen	a	23 40																	00g17						
Inverness	a																								

For general notes see front of timetable
For details of catering facilities see Directory of Train Operators

A From Penzance (Table 135)

B From Bournemouth (Table 51)

b Change at Stafford. By bus

c By changing at Birmingham New Street, passengers may depart Coventry at 1332, Birmingham International at 1350

e Change at Crewe and Chester

f Change at Carnforth. By bus

g Via Glasgow Central and Glasgow Queen Street. Passengers make their own way from one station to the other

Table 65

Saturdays

from 29 March

London and West Midlands → North West England and Scotland

Route Diagram - see first page of Table 65

		LM	VT	VT		VT	VT	VT	TP	VT	NT	VT	XC	TP	TP	LM	VT	NT	VT	XC	VT		VT	VT	XC
								R																	
		1 ◇	1 ◇			1 ◇	1 ◇	1	1			1 ◇	1 ◇		1	1 ◇	1 ◇		1 ◇	1 ◇	1 ◇		1 ◇	1 ◇	1 ◇
													A		B					C					C
				bus						bus				bus											
			catering			catering	catering	catering				catering	catering				catering		catering	catering	catering		catering	catering	catering
London Euston 15 ⊖	d		13 03			13 10	13 17					13 53					14 03		14 10		14 17			14 53	
Gatwick Airport 10 ✈	d		11b37														12 37							13 37	
Watford Junction	d		12 41			13u25	13u32										14u18		14u25					15u08	
Milton Keynes Central	d		13 34									14 24									14 48				
Northampton	d		12 58														13 58								
Rugby	d		13 58				14 11										14 57				15 12				
Nuneaton	d																								
Tamworth Low Level	d																								
Lichfield Trent Valley	d																								
Coventry	d	13 42	14 10			14 16	14u27						14 32				15 10		15 16	15c23	15 27				←
Birmingham International ✈	d	13 57	14 22			14 28	14 39						14 50				15 22		15 28	15c34	15 39				
Birmingham New Street 12	d	14 21	14 40			14 48	14s50	15 03					15 20			15 21	15 40		15 48	16 20 →	15s50		16 03		16 20
Sandwell & Dudley	d																								
Coseley	d	14 34														15 34									
Wolverhampton 7	d	14 44				15 09		15 21					15 40			15 44			16 09				16 21		16 40
Penkridge	d	14 53														15 53									
Stafford	a	15 01	15 17			15 24							15 53			16 01	16 17		16 24						16 53
	d	15 02	15 19			15 26							15 54			16 02	16 19		16 26						16 54
Stoke-on-Trent	a					15 43						16 05	16 12						16 43					17 05	17 12
Congleton	a												16 24												
Macclesfield	a					15 59						16 21	16 33						16 59					17 21	17 29
Crewe 10	a	15 23	15 38				15 49	15 54								16 23	16 38				16 49		16 54		
	d	15 24	15 41				15 52	15 55								16 24	16 41				16 52		16 55		
Chester	a	15 57					16 27									16 56					17 26		17 54		
Llandudno Junction	a	17e17					17e24									18e17					18 25				
Llandudno	a	17e35														18e35									
Bangor (Gwynedd)	a						17e47														18 47				
Holyhead	a						18e30														19 20				
Wilmslow	a	16 01					16 26	16 48								17 05					17 26		17 48		
Manchester Airport ✈	a	16 11														17 15									
Stockport	a					16 13	16 40					16s34	16 46						17 13		17 39		17 58	17s34	17 46
Manchester Piccadilly 10	a					16 28	16 54					16 48	17 02						17 28		17 54		18 10	17 48	18 02
Hartford	a	15 36														16 34									
Warrington Bank Quay	a		15 56					16 12									16 57						17 12		
	d		15 58					16 13									16 58						17 13		
Runcorn	a	15 45					16 09									16 46					17 09				
Liverpool South Parkway 7 ✈	a	15 54														16 54									
Liverpool Lime Street 10	a	16 09					16 33									17 09					17 30				
	d		15 04								15 57						16 04	16 30							
Manchester Airport ✈	d		15f27																						
Manchester Piccadilly 10	d		15f45																						
Bolton	d		16f05																						
Wigan North Western	a		16 07					16 23			16 31						17 08	17 11					17 23		
	d		16 09					16 24			16 31						17 09	17 12					17 24		
Preston 8	a		16 25					16 44			16 56						17 28	17 40					17 42		
Blackpool North	a		17 01								17 34						18 03						18 30		
	d									16 10				16 30											
Preston 8	d		16 41						16g55	16 55				17 13											
Lancaster 6	a									17 45				18 03											
	d								17 45	17 45					18 10										
Barrow-in-Furness	a								18 50																
Oxenholme Lake District	a									18 30					18 25										
	d									18 30					18 26										
Windermere	a														18 47										
Penrith North Lakes	d									19 25															
Carlisle 8	a		19 39							20 00															
	d		19 48																						
Lockerbie	d		20 12	20 20																					
Carstairs	a																								
Motherwell	a		20s59																						
Glasgow Central 15	a		21 23																						
Haymarket	a																								
Edinburgh 10	a			22 30																					
Perth	a		00h15																						
Dundee	a			00 36																					
Aberdeen	a																								
Inverness	a																								

For general notes see front of timetable
For details of catering facilities see Directory of Train Operators

- **A** From Penzance (Table 51)
- **B** From Barrow-in-Furness (Table 82)
- **C** From Bournemouth (Table 51)
- **b** Change at Watford Junction and Milton Keynes Central
- **c** By changing at Birmingham New Street, passengers may depart Coventry at 1532, Birmingham International at 1550
- **e** Change at Crewe and Chester
- **f** Change at Preston
- **g** Change at Carnforth. By bus
- **h** Via Glasgow Central and Glasgow Queen Street. Passengers make their own way from one station to the other

Table 65

London and West Midlands → North West England and Scotland

Saturdays

from 29 March

Route Diagram - see first page of Table 65

		VT	TP	VT	SR	VT	TP	NT	LM	VT	VT	VT	VT	NT	VT	VT		VT	VT	XC	TP	TP	NT	LM	VT
			1						**1** ◇	**1** ◇	**1** ◇	**1** ◇	**1** ◇						**1** ◇	**1** ◇		**1**		**1** ◇	**1** ◇
																				A		B			
London Euston [15]	d									15 03	15 10	15 17							15 53						16 03
Gatwick Airport [10]	d																								14 37
Watford Junction	d									14 41	15u25	15u32													16u18
Milton Keynes Central	d									15 34									16 24						
Northampton	d									14 58															15 58
Rugby	d									15 58		16 12													16 57
Nuneaton	d																								
Tamworth Low Level	d																								
Lichfield Trent Valley	d																								
Coventry	d								15 32	16 10	16 16	16u27								16 32					17 10
Birmingham International	d								15 50	16 22	16 28	16 39								16 50					17 22
Birmingham New Street [12]	d								16 21	16 40	16 48	16s50	17 03							17 20				17 21	17 40
Sandwell & Dudley	d																								
Coseley	d								16 34															17 34	
Wolverhampton [7]	d								16 44		17 09		17 21							17 40				17 44	
Penkridge	d								16 53															17 53	
Stafford	a								17 01	17 17	17 24									17 53				18 01	18 17
	d								17 02	17 19	17 26									17 54				18 02	18 19
Stoke-on-Trent	a										17 43								18 05	18 12					
Congleton	a																			18 24					
Macclesfield	a										17 59								18 21	18 32					
Crewe [10]	a								17 23	17 38		17 50	17 54											18 23	18 38
	d								17 24	17 41		17 52	17 55											18 24	18 41
Chester	a								17 59			18 29												18 57	
Llandudno Junction	a								18 49			19b26												20b18	
Llandudno	a								19c37															20b35	
Bangor (Gwynedd)	a								19 05			19b49													
Holyhead	a								19 36			20b30													
Wilmslow	a								18 04			18 26	18 48											19 05	
Manchester Airport	a								18 15															19 16	
Stockport	a										18 13	18 39							18s34	18 46					
Manchester Piccadilly [10]	a										18 28	18 54							18 48	19 02					
Hartford	a								17 36															18 34	
Warrington Bank Quay	a									17 57			18 12												18 57
	d									17 58			18 13												18 58
Runcorn	a								17 45			18 09												18 43	
Liverpool South Parkway [7]	a								17 53															18 54	
Liverpool Lime Street [10]	a								18 09			18 28												19 09	
	d							17 20					17 25	17 45									18 04		
Manchester Airport	d	16 27													17 32										
Manchester Piccadilly [10]	d	16 44		16 52											17 50										
Bolton	d	17 05		17 13											18 10										
Wigan North Western	a							17 54		18 08			18 23	18 28									18 51		19 08
	d							17 54		18 09			18 24	18 28									18 51		19 09
Preston [8]	a							18 17		18 28			18 44	18 52									19 17		19 25
Blackpool North	a							18 48						19 21											20 01
	d	17 19													18 11	18 25					18 30				
Preston [8]	d	17 55	17e55	18 00			18 13								18 55	19 00					19 13				
Lancaster [6]	a	18 45					19 03								19 45						20 03				
	d	18 45	18 54												19 45										
Barrow-in-Furness	a		19 59												20 52							20 15			
Oxenholme Lake District	a	19 30				←									20 30			←				20 30			
	d	19 30 →				19 30									20 30 →			20 30				20 31			
Windermere	a																					20 52			
Penrith North Lakes	d					20 25												21 25							
Carlisle [8]	a			20 00		21 00										21 00		22 00							
	d				20 08											21 10									
Lockerbie	d																								
Carstairs	a																								
Motherwell	a																								
Glasgow Central [15]	a				22 27											23 05									
Haymarket	a																								
Edinburgh [10]	a																								
Perth	a				01f16											01f16									
Dundee	a																								
Aberdeen	a																								
Inverness	a																								

For general notes see front of timetable
For details of catering facilities see Directory of Train Operators

A From Plymouth (Table 51)
B From Barrow-in-Furness (Table 82)
b Change at Crewe and Chester
c Change at Crewe and Llandudno Junction
e Change at Carnforth. By bus
f Via Glasgow Central and Glasgow Queen Street. Passengers make their own way from one station to the other

Table 65

Saturdays

from 29 March

London and West Midlands → North West England and Scotland

Route Diagram - see first page of Table 65

		VT	XC	VT	VT	TP	VT	VT	VT	NT	VT	XC	LM	VT	VT	VT	VT	TP	VT	VT	VT	VT	XC	LM
		1 ◇	1 ◇	1 ◇	1 ◇	1					1 ◇	1 ◇	1 ◇	1 ◇	1 ◇	1 ◇	1 ◇		1 ◇				1 ◇	1 ◇
			A									A											B	
							bus	bus	bus									bus		bus	bus	bus		
		🍽	🍽	🍽	🍽						🍽	🍽		🍽	🍽	🍽	🍽		🍽				🍽	
London Euston 15 ⊖	d	16 10		16 17							16 53			17 03	17 10	17 17			17 53					
Gatwick Airport 10 ✈	d										15 37													
Watford Junction	d	16u25									17u08			16 41	17u25	17u32								
Milton Keynes Central	d			16 48										17 34					18 24					
Northampton	d													16 58										
Rugby	d			17 12										17 58		18 12								
Nuneaton	d																17b42							
Tamworth Low Level	d																18b30							
Lichfield Trent Valley	d																18b51							
Coventry	d	17 16	17c23	17 27									17 32	18 10	18 16	18u27							18 32	
Birmingham International ✈	d	17 28	17c34	17 39								←	17 50	18 22	18 28	18 41							18 50	
Birmingham New Street 12	d	17 48	18 20	17s50	18 03							18 20	18 21	18 40	18 48	18s50	19 03						19 20	19 21
Sandwell & Dudley	d		→																					
Coseley	d												18 34											19 34
Wolverhampton 7	d	18 09			18 20							18 40	18 44		19 09		19 21						19 40	19 44
Penkridge	d												18 53											19 53
Stafford	a	18 24										18 53	19 01	19 17	19 24		19 33						19 53	20 01
	d	18 26										18 54	19 02	19 19	19 26		19 33						19 54	20 02
Stoke-on-Trent	a	18 43									19 05	19 12			19 43				20 05				20 12	
Congleton	a																						20 24	
Macclesfield	a	18 59									19 21	19 29			19 59				20 21				20 32	
Crewe 10	a			18 49	18 58								19 23	19 38		19 49	19 54							20 23
	d			18 52	18 58								19 24	19 41		19 52	19 55							20 24
Chester	a			19 25	19 46								20 02			20 27								20 57
Llandudno Junction	a				20 37											21e28								
Llandudno	a				21f08											21g43								
Bangor (Gwynedd)	a				20 55																			
Holyhead	a				21 33											22e35								
Wilmslow	a			19 26	19 48											20 26	20 48							
Manchester Airport ✈	a			20h02												21h02								
Stockport	a	19 13		19 39							19s34	19 46			20 13	20 39			20s34				20 46	
Manchester Piccadilly 10	a	19 28		19 57							19 48	20 02			20 28	20 54			20 48				21 02	
Hartford	a												19 36											20 36
Warrington Bank Quay	a				19 15									19 57			20 12							
	d				19 16									19 58			20 13							
Runcorn	a			19 08									19 45			20 08								20 45
Liverpool South Parkway 7 ✈	a												19 54											20 54
Liverpool Lime Street 10	a			19 32									20 09			20 30								21 09
	d									19 04														
Manchester Airport ✈	d						18 27													19 27				
Manchester Piccadilly 10	d						18 45													19 44				
Bolton	d						19 12													20 05				
Wigan North Western	a				19 27					19 51				20 08			20 23							
	d				19 27					19 51				20 09			20 24							
Preston 8	a				19 43					20 17				20 26			20 43							
Blackpool North	a				20 36					20 56							21 36							
	d						19 10	19 25										19 42						
Preston 8	d					19j55	19 55	20 00										20 45		20 55	21 00			
Lancaster 6	a						20 45											21 35		21 45				
	d					20 43	20 45													21 45				
Barrow-in-Furness	a					21 50												22 50						
Oxenholme Lake District	a						21 30		←											22 30		←		
	d						21 30 →		21 30											22 30 →		22 30		
Windermere	a																							
Penrith North Lakes	d								22 25													23 25		
Carlisle 8	a							22 00	23 00												23 00	23 59		
	d																							
Lockerbie	d																							
Carstairs	a																							
Motherwell	a																							
Glasgow Central 15	a																							
Haymarket	a																							
Edinburgh 10	a																							
Perth	a																							
Dundee	a																							
Aberdeen	a																							
Inverness	a																							

For general notes see front of timetable
For details of catering facilities see Directory of Train Operators

A From Bournemouth (Table 51)
B From Plymouth (Table 51)
b Change at Stafford. By bus
c By changing at Birmingham New Street, passengers may depart Coventry at 1732, Birmingham International at 1750
e Change at Crewe and Chester
f Change at Crewe and Llandudno Junction
g Change at Crewe, Chester and Llandudno Junction
h Change at Crewe and Wilmslow
j Change at Carnforth. By bus

Table 65

Saturdays

from 29 March

London and West Midlands → North West England and Scotland

Route Diagram - see first page of Table 65

		VT	LM	VT	VT	VT		XC	VT	VT	VT	VT	NT	VT	VT	XC	LM	NT	XC	VT	VT	XC	AW		
		1 ◇	1 ◇	1 ◇	1 ◇	1 ◇		1 ◇		1 ◇	1 ◇			1 ◇	1 ◇	1 ◇	1 ◇		1 ◇	1 ◇	1 ◇	1 ◇	◇		
								A								B			C			C			
									🚌			🚌													
		☕		☕	☕	☕		☕		☕	☕			☕	☕					☕	☕				
London Euston 15 ⊖	d	18 03		18 10	18 17	18 53				19 02	19 10			19 17	19 25					19 50	20 12				
Gatwick Airport 10 ✈	d	*16 37*				*17 37*														*18 37*					
Watford Junction	d	18u18		18u25		19u08				*18 41*	19u25			19u32						20u05	20u31				
Milton Keynes Central	d				18 48					19 35				19 52	20 04					20 50	21 19				
Northampton	d				*17 58*									*18 58*						*19 58*	*20 58*				
Rugby	d				19 12									20 17						21 16	21 45				
Nuneaton	d																								
Tamworth Low Level	d																								
Lichfield Trent Valley	d																								
Coventry	d	19 10	*19 32*	19 16				19b23		20 10	20 16			20 29		*20 32*			21c23	21 28			*21 32*		
Birmingham International ✈	d		*19 50*	19 28				19b34			20 28					*20 50*			21c34			←	*21 50*		
Birmingham New Street 12	d		20 21	19 48				20 20			20 48					21 20	21 21		→			22 20	22 33		
Sandwell & Dudley	d										20 57														
Coseley	d		20 34														21 35								
Wolverhampton 7	d		20 44	20 09				20 40			21 10					21 40	21 44					22 40	22 48		
Penkridge	d		20 53														21 54								
Stafford	a	20 13	21 01	20 24				20 53		21 13	21 24					21 53	22 01			22 16	22 47	22 53			
	d	20 15	21 02	20 26				20 54		21 15	21 26					21 54	22 02			22 17	22 49	22 54			
Stoke-on-Trent	a			20 43		21 05		21 12			21 44				22 01	22 12					23 07	23s13			
Congleton	a															22 24									
Macclesfield	a			20 59		21 21		21 29			22 00				22 17	22 32					23 23	23s30			
Crewe 10	a	20 34	21 32		20 50					21 34				21 49			22 30			22 36			00 01		
	d	20 37			20 52					21 37				21 52						22 39			00 02		
Chester	a				*21 27*					*22 09*				*22 30*						*23 10*			00 24		
Llandudno Junction	a				*22 25*									23e33											
Llandudno	a																								
Bangor (Gwynedd)	a				*22 42*									*00f25*											
Holyhead	a				*23 30*									*01f45*											
Wilmslow	a				*21 26*									*22 26*						*23 22*					
Manchester Airport ✈	a				22g05									23g05											
Stockport	a			21 13	*21 39*	21s34		21 46			22 12			*22 39*	22s32	22 46				*23 33*	23s37	23s46			
Manchester Piccadilly 10	a			21 28	*21 53*	21 51		22 02			22 25			*22 52*	22 45	23 02				*23 50*	23 51	00 02			
Hartford	a																								
Warrington Bank Quay	a	20 53								21 53															
	d	20 54								21 54															
Runcorn	a				21 08									22 08						22 54					
Liverpool South Parkway 7 ✈	a																								
Liverpool Lime Street 10	a				21 27									22 27						23 15					
	d	*19 48*								*20 48*			21 48					23 05							
Manchester Airport ✈	d																								
Manchester Piccadilly 10	d																								
Bolton	d																								
Wigan North Western	a	21 04								22 04			22 37					23 51							
	d	21 05								22 05			22 38					23 51							
Preston 8	a	21 24								22 24			23 02					00 15							
Blackpool North	a	*21 56*											23 28												
	d								*20 53*			*22 03*													
Preston 8	d								21 35			22 40													
Lancaster 6	a								22 20			23 30													
	d																								
Barrow-in-Furness	a								*23 35*																
Oxenholme Lake District	a																								
	d																								
Windermere	a																								
Penrith North Lakes	d																								
Carlisle 8	a																								
	d																								
Lockerbie	d																								
Carstairs	a																								
Motherwell	a																								
Glasgow Central 15	a																								
Haymarket	a																								
Edinburgh 10	a																								
Perth	a																								
Dundee	a																								
Aberdeen	a																								
Inverness	a																								

For general notes see front of timetable
For details of catering facilities see Directory of Train Operators

A From Bournemouth (Table 51). ☕ to Birmingham New Street
B From Plymouth (Table 51)
C From Bournemouth (Table 51)
b By changing at Birmingham New Street, passengers may depart Coventry at 1932, Birmingham International at 1950
c By changing at Birmingham New Street, passengers may depart Coventry at 2132, Birmingham International at 2150
e Change at Crewe and Chester
f Change at Crewe, Chester and Llandudno Junction. By bus from Llandudno Junction
g Change at Crewe and Wilmslow

until 27 January

London and West Midlands → North West England and Scotland

Route Diagram - see first page of Table 65

		NT	VT	XC	TP	NT	LM	VT	TP	TP	XC	VT	VT	XC	NT	VT	NT	LM	VT	VT	TP	VT	VT
			1 ◇	1 ◇	1 ◇		1 ◇	1 ◇	1 ◇	1 ◇	1 ◇	1 ◇	1 ◇	1 ◇		1 ◇		1 ◇	1 ◇	1 ◇	1 ◇	1 ◇	1 ◇
														A									
			☕	☕				☕		🛒	☕	☕	☕	☕		☕			☕	☕		☕	☕
London Euston 15 ⊖	d											08 40				09 31			09 36	09 40			10 10
Gatwick Airport 10 ✈	d																						
Watford Junction	d											08u58				09u46			09u52	09u57			10u27
Milton Keynes Central	d											09 46				10 31			10 37	10 43			11 12
Northampton	d															09b21							
Rugby	d															10 57				11 08			
Nuneaton	d																						
Tamworth Low Level	d																						
Lichfield Trent Valley	d																						
Coventry	d			08 30				09 04			09 30	10 25		10 30		11 09			11 15	11 21		11 25	
Birmingham International ✈	d			08 46				09 14			09 46	10 36		10 46					11 26			11 36	
Birmingham New Street 12	d		09 03	09 18			09 30	10 03			10 18	10 48	11 03	11 18				11 30	11 48			12 03	
Sandwell & Dudley	d											10 57							11 57				
Coseley	d																						
Wolverhampton 7	d		09 21	09 38			09 46	10 21			10 38	11 10	11 21	11 38				11 48	12 10			12 21	
Penkridge	d						09 55																
Stafford	a		09 33	09 51			10 02				10 51			11 51		12 00		12 06					12 39
	d		09 35	09 53			10 03				10 53			11 53		12 01		12 06					12 40
Stoke-on-Trent	a			10 10							11 10	11 42		12 10					12 40				12 58
Congleton	a																						
Macclesfield	a			10 27							11 27	11 58		12 27					12 56				13 14
Crewe 10	a		09 55				10 25	10 53					11 53			12 20		12 25		12 37		12 53	
	d		09 57				10 26	10 55					11 55			12 23		12 28		12 40		12 55	
Chester	a		10 28				11 20	11 36										13 00		13 20		13 50	
Llandudno Junction	a		11 25					12 31															
Llandudno	a							13c30															
Bangor (Gwynedd)	a		11 46					12 48															
Holyhead	a							13 22															
Wilmslow	a		10 51					11 50					12 50										
Manchester Airport ✈	a		10 59										12 59										
Stockport	a			10 41				12 01			11 41	12 15	13e28	12 41					13 10				13s30
Manchester Piccadilly 10	a			10 57				12 16			11 57	12 30	13 28	12 57					13 23				13 44
Hartford	a						10 38																
Warrington Bank Quay	a		10 12					11 11					12 11			12 38						13 12	
	d		10 14					11 12					12 12			12 40						13 12	
Runcorn	a						10 47											12 45		12 55			
Liverpool South Parkway 7 ✈	a						10 54											12 54					
Liverpool Lime Street 10	a						11 13											13 11		13 18			
	d	08 00	09 00			10 00							11 00		12 00								
Manchester Airport ✈	d							09f47		11 27			11f27			11f47							
Manchester Piccadilly 10	d							10f25		11 42			11f42			12f03						12f25	
Bolton	d							10f45		12 00						12f22						12f45	
Wigan North Western	a	08 41	10 23			10 41		11 22					12 23		12 42	12 49	←					13 23	
	d	08 42	10 25			10 42		11 23					12 23		12 42	12 51	12 42					13 23	
Preston 8	a	09 05	10 40			11 05		11 36		12 20			12 39		→	13 04	13 06					13 37	
Blackpool North	a	09 34	11 16			11 34		12 16					13 16			13 38	13 34					14 16	
	d				10 28			11 02	11 12	11 28			12 02			12 28						13 02	
Preston 8	d				11 00			11 39	11 59	12 25			12 40			13 07					13 25	13 40	
Lancaster 6	a				11 15			11 53	12 14	12 40			12 55			13 20					13 40	13 54	
	d				11 16			11 54	12 15	12 41			12 56			13 22					13 41	13 56	
Barrow-in-Furness	a				12 18																14 44		
Oxenholme Lake District	a							12 07	12 31	12 55						13 34						14 09	
	d							12 10	12 31	12 55						13 35						14 10	
Windermere	a								12 52							13 58						14 55	
Penrith North Lakes	d							12 35		13 22			13 33			14 00							
Carlisle 8	a							12 53		13 38			13 50			14 18						14 50	
	d							12 57		13 42			13 52			14 20						14 52	
Lockerbie	d							13 16		14 03												15 11	
Carstairs	a																						
Motherwell	a																						
Glasgow Central 15	a												15 09			15 37							
Haymarket	a									15s01												16s08	
Edinburgh 10	a							14 20		15 08												16 14	
Perth	a												16g46										
Dundee	a									16h48			17g09									17 49	
Aberdeen	a												18g23									19 05	
Inverness	a																						

For general notes see front of timetable
For details of catering facilities see Directory of Train Operators

A From Bristol Temple Meads (Table 51)

b By bus

c Change at Crewe and Llandudno Junction. By bus from Llandudno Junction

e Change at Crewe and Wilmslow

f Change at Preston

g Via Glasgow Central and Glasgow Queen Street. Passengers make their own way from one station to the other

h Change at Haymarket

OVERNIGHT SLEEPERS. For Sleeper trains, operated by First ScotRail, please refer to Tables 400 - 404

Sundays until 27 January

London and West Midlands → North West England and Scotland

Route Diagram - see first page of Table 65

		XC	VT	TP	VT	VT	VT	XC	NT	VT	NT	TP	LM	VT	VT	VT	VT	XC	VT	TP	VT	VT	VT
																R		R					R
		1◇	1◇	1◇	1◇	1◇	1◇	1◇		1◇		1◇	1◇	1◇	1◇	1	1◇	1	1◇	1◇	1◇	1◇	1
		A						B										C					
London Euston 15 ⊖	d		10 31		10 36		11 10			11 31				11 36	11 40		12 10		12 31		12 36	12 40	
Gatwick Airport 10 ✈	d																						
Watford Junction	d		10 32		10u52		11 02			11u46				11u52	11u57		12u27		12 32		12u52		
Milton Keynes Central	d		11 31		11 37		12 12							12 37	12 43				13 31		13 37	13 43	
Northampton	d		10b21							11b21									12b21				
Rugby	d		11 57							12 57					13 08				13 57			14 08	
Nuneaton	d																						
Tamworth Low Level	d																						
Lichfield Trent Valley	d																						
Coventry	d	11c25	12 09		12 15	12 25		12 30		13 09				13 15		13 25		13e25	14 09		14 15	14 21	14 25
Birmingham International ✈	d	11c36			12 26	12 36		12 46					13 05	13 26		13 36		13e36			14 26		14 36
Birmingham New Street 12	d	12 18			12 48	13 03		13 18					13 30	13 48		14 03		14 18			14 48		15 03
Sandwell & Dudley	d				12 57									13 57							14 57		
Coseley	d																						
Wolverhampton 7	d	12 38			13 10	13 21		13 38					13 52	14 10		14 21		14 38			15 10		15 21
Penkridge	d												14 01										
Stafford	a	12 51	13 00				13 39	13 51		14 00			14 08					14 51	15 00			15 18	
	d	12 53	13 01				13 40	13 53		14 01			14 09					14 53	15 01			15 20	
Stoke-on-Trent	a	13 10			13 43		13 58	14 10						14 42			14 56	15 10			15 43		
Congleton	a																						
Macclesfield	a	13 27			13 59		14 14	14 27						14 58			15 12	15 27			15 59		
Crewe 10	a		13 20			13 53				14 20			14 31		14 39	14 52			15 20			15 41	15 53
	d		13 23			13 55				14 23			14 31		14 42	14 55			15 22			15 44	15 55
Chester	a		14 15			14 50									15 20							16 17	
Llandudno Junction	a		15 10			15f59																17 09	
Llandudno	a					16g30																	
Bangor (Gwynedd)	a		15 34			16f22																17 26	
Holyhead	a					16f58																18 02	
Wilmslow	a		13 54			14 44										15 44							16 50
Manchester Airport ✈	a					15 04																	16 59
Stockport	a	13 41	14 05		14 13		14s30	14 41						15 13	15 55		15s30	15 41			16 14		
Manchester Piccadilly 10	a	13 57	14 20		14 26		14 44	14 57						15 27	16 12		15 46	15 57			16 27		
Hartford	a												14 43										
Warrington Bank Quay	a		13 38			14 11				14 39						15 11			15 38				16 11
	d		13 40			14 11				14 40						15 11			15 39				16 11
Runcorn	a												14 52		15 00							16 00	
Liverpool South Parkway 7 ✈	a												15 01										
Liverpool Lime Street 10	a												15 18		15 26							16 24	
	d		13 00						14 00										15 00				
Manchester Airport ✈	d			13 27						13h47		14 27							14h47	15 27			
Manchester Piccadilly 10	d			13 42						14h03		14 42							15h03	15 42			
Bolton	d			14 00						14h22		15 00							15h22	16 00			
Wigan North Western	a		13 49			14 22			14 42	14 50	←					15 22			15 49				16 22
	d		13 51			14 22			14 42	14 51	14 42					15 22			15 50				16 23
Preston 8	a		14 08	14 23		14 37			→	15 04	15 07	15 20				15 38			16 03	16 20			16 37
Blackpool North	a		14 47			15 16				15 38	15 34					16 16			16 47	17 16			17 16
	d			13 28		13 57				14 28						15 02			15 28				16 02
Preston 8	d			14 25		14 39				15 07		15 25				15 39			16 06	16 25			16 39
Lancaster 6	a			14 40		14 53				15 21		15 40				15 55			16 20	16 40			16 53
	d			14 41		14 55				15 22		15 41				15 56			16 21	16 41			16 55
Barrow-in-Furness	a											16 44							17 51				
Oxenholme Lake District	a			14 55		15 08				15 34									16 33	16 55			17 08
	d			14 55		15 09				15 36									16 35	16 55			17 09
Windermere	a									15 58									16 55				
Penrith North Lakes	d			15 22		15 37				16 00						16 32			16 59	17 22			
Carlisle 8	a			15 38		15 52				16 18						16 48			17 17	17 38			17 49
	d			15 42		15 55				16 21						16 51			17 21	17 42			17 51
Lockerbie	d			16 03																18 03			
Carstairs	a																						
Motherwell	a																						18s51
Glasgow Central 15	a					17 11				17 37									18 40				19 16
Haymarket	a			17s01												18s03				19s01			
Edinburgh 10	a			17 08												18 14				19 08			
Perth	a			18j27		18k44				19k15									20k47				
Dundee	a			18j14		19k08										20 01				20j46			
Aberdeen	a			19j30		20k26										21 21				22m24			
Inverness	a			20j44						21k34													

For general notes see front of timetable
For details of catering facilities see Directory of Train Operators

- **A** From Southampton Central (Table 51)
- **B** From Plymouth (Table 51)
- **C** From Bournemouth (Table 51)
- **b** By bus
- **c** By changing at Birmingham New Street, passengers may depart Coventry at 1130, Birmingham International at 1146
- **e** By changing at Birmingham New Street, passengers may depart Coventry at 1330, Birmingham International at 1346
- **f** Change at Crewe and Chester
- **g** Change at Crewe, Chester and Llandudno Junction. By bus from Llandudno Junction
- **h** Change at Preston
- **j** Change at Haymarket
- **k** Via Glasgow Central and Glasgow Queen Street. Passengers make their own way from one station to the other
- **m** Change at Edinburgh and Dundee

OVERNIGHT SLEEPERS. For Sleeper trains, operated by First ScotRail, please refer to Tables 400 - 404

Table 65

Sundays

until 27 January

London and West Midlands → North West England and Scotland

Route Diagram - see first page of Table 65

		NT	VT	XC	VT	TP	LM	VT	VT	VT	VT	XC	NT	VT	NT	TP	VT	VT	VT	XC	NT	VT	NT
			1◇	R 1	1◇	1◇	1◇	1◇	1◇	R 1	1◇	R 1		1◇		1◇	1◇	R 1	1◇	R 1		1◇	
				A								B								A			
London Euston 15 ⊖	d		13 10		13 40			13 50	13 55		14 36			14 50			14 53		15 36			15 50	
Gatwick Airport 10 ✈	d																						
Watford Junction	d		*13 02*		13u58			14u07	14u11		14u52			*14 32*			15u10		*15 32*			16u06	
Milton Keynes Central	d		14 13						14 44					15 35					16 22				
Northampton	d				*13b21*									*14b21*								*15b21*	
Rugby	d				14 57				15 09					15 57								16 57	
Nuneaton	d																						
Tamworth Low Level	d																						
Lichfield Trent Valley	d																						
Coventry	d			*14 30*	15 09			15 15		*15 25*		15c25		16 09			16 15	*16 25*		*16 30*		17 09	
Birmingham International ✈	d			*14 46*			*15 05*	15 26		*15 36*		15c36					16 26	*16 36*		*16 46*			
Birmingham New Street 12	d			15 18			15 30	15 51		16 03		16 18					16 48	17 03		17 18			
Sandwell & Dudley	d							16 00									16 57						
Coseley	d																						
Wolverhampton 7	d			15 38			15 50	16 13		16 21		16 38					17 10	17 21		17 38			
Penkridge	d																						
Stafford	a			15 51	16 00		16 05					16 51		17 00						17 51		18 00	
	d			15 53	16 01		16 05					16 53		17 01						17 53		18 01	
Stoke-on-Trent	a		15 58	16 10				16 44			16 59	17 10					17 43		17 58	18 10			
Congleton	a																						
Macclesfield	a		16 14	16 27				17 00			17 15	17 27					17 59		18 14	18 27			
Crewe 10	a				16 20		16 26		16 42	16 53				17 20				17 53				18 20	
	d				16 23		16 28		16 45	16 55				17 23				17 55				18 23	
Chester	a				*16 54*					*17 29*				*18 01*								*18 55*	
Llandudno Junction	a									*18 29*				*18 54*									
Llandudno	a													*19e30*									
Bangor (Gwynedd)	a									*18 51*				*19 14*									
Holyhead	a													*20 00*									
Wilmslow	a													*17 58*				*18 50*					
Manchester Airport ✈	a													*19 00*				*19 00*					
Stockport	a		16s30	16 41				17 13			17s30	17 41		*18 11*			18 14		18s30	18 41			
Manchester Piccadilly 10	a		16 44	16 57				17 27			17 44	17 57		*18 26*			18 27		18 45	18 57			
Hartford	a																						
Warrington Bank Quay	a				16 38					17 09				17 38				18 12				18 38	
	d				16 40					17 11				17 40				18 12				18 40	
Runcorn	a						16 44		17 01														
Liverpool South Parkway 7 ✈	a						16 52																
Liverpool Lime Street 10	a						17 09		17 27														
	d	16 00											17 00								18 00		
Manchester Airport ✈	d				*15f47*	16 27								*16f47*		17 27						*17f47*	
Manchester Piccadilly 10	d				*16f03*	16 42								*17f03*		17 42						*18f03*	
Bolton	d				*16f22*	17 00								*17f22*		18 00						*18f22*	
Wigan North Western	a	16 41			16 49					17 20			17 41	17 49	←			18 23			18 41	18 49	←
	d	16 42			16 51					17 22			17 42	17 51	17 42			18 23			18 42	18 51	18 42
Preston 8	a	17 04			17 04	17 22				17 36			→	18 04	18 05	18 23		18 37			→	19 04	19 05
Blackpool North	a	17 35			*17 38*					*18 16*				*18 47*	18 34			*19 16*				19 47	19 32
	d				*16 28*	*16 45*				*17 02*				*17 25*		*17 45*		*18 02*				*18 28*	
Preston 8	d				17 07	17 25				17 39				18 07		18 25		18 39				19 07	
Lancaster 6	a				17 21	17 40				17 53				18 20		18 40		18 53				19 20	
	d				17 22	17 41				17 54				18 22		18 41		18 55				19 22	
Barrow-in-Furness	a					18 44																	
Oxenholme Lake District	a				17 34									18 34		18 55		19 08				19 34	
	d				17 36									18 35		18 55		19 09				19 35	
Windermere	a				*17 58*									*18 58*								*19 58*	
Penrith North Lakes	d				18 00					18 30				19 00		19 22		19 36				20 00	
Carlisle 8	a				18 18					18 48				19 18		19 38		19 52				20 18	
	d				18 21					18 50				19 20		19 42		19 55				20 20	
Lockerbie	d															20 03							
Carstairs	a																						
Motherwell	a															20s47							
Glasgow Central 15	a				19 36									20 48		21 07		21 14				21 37	
Haymarket	a									20s04													
Edinburgh 10	a									20 14													
Perth	a																	22g47					
Dundee	a									*22 17*								23g09					
Aberdeen	a									*23 33*								00g25					
Inverness	a																						

For general notes see front of timetable
For details of catering facilities see Directory of Train Operators

A From Penzance (Table 135)

B From Bournemouth (Table 51)

b By bus

c By changing at Birmingham New Street, passengers may depart Coventry at 1530, Birmingham International at 1546

e Change at Crewe and Llandudno Junction. By bus from Llandudno Junction

f Change at Preston

g Via Glasgow Central and Glasgow Queen Street. Passengers make their own way from one station to the other

OVERNIGHT SLEEPERS. For Sleeper trains, operated by First ScotRail, please refer to Tables 400 - 404

Sundays

until 27 January

London and West Midlands → North West England and Scotland

Route Diagram - see first page of Table 65

		TP	LM	VT	VT	VT	VT	XC	VT	VT	TP	VT	VT	NT	VT	XC	VT	TP	LM	VT	VT	VT	VT
						R		R					R			R							
		1 ◇	1 ◇	1 ◇	1 ◇	1	1 ◇	1	1 ◇	1 ◇	1	1 ◇	1		1 ◇	1	1 ◇	1 ◇	1 ◇	1 ◇	1 ◇	1 ◇	1 ◇
								A								B							
				☕	☕	☕	☕	☕	☕	☕		☕	☕		☕	☕	☕			☕	☕	☕	☕
London Euston 15 ⊖	d			15 53	15 58		16 36		16 50	16 53		16 58			17 36		17 50			17 53	17 58	18 36	
Gatwick Airport 10 ✈	d																						
Watford Junction	d			16u11	16u14		16u52		16 32	17u10					17 32		18u06			18u11	18u14	18u56	
Milton Keynes Central	d				16 43				17 32			17 42			18 22								
Northampton	d								16b21								17b21						
Rugby	d				17 09				17 57			18 08					18 57				19 09		
Nuneaton	d																						
Tamworth Low Level	d																						
Lichfield Trent Valley	d																						
Coventry	d			17 15		17 25		17c25	18 09	18 15		18 21	18 25			18 30	19 09			19 15			19 25
Birmingham International ✈	d		17 05	17 26		17 36		17c36		18 26			18 36			18 46			19 05	19 26			19 36
Birmingham New Street 12	d		17 30	17 48		18 03		18 18		18 48			19 03			19 18			19 30	19 48			20 03
Sandwell & Dudley	d			17 57						18 57										19 57			
Coseley	d																						
Wolverhampton 7	d		17 50	18 10		18 21		18 38		19 10			19 21			19 38			19 50	20 10			20 22
Penkridge	d		17 59																19 59				
Stafford	a		18 06					18 51	19 01			19 18	19 33			19 51	20 00		20 06				20 37
	d		18 07					18 53	19 03			19 20	19 34			19 53	20 01		20 07				20 38
Stoke-on-Trent	a			18 43			18 58	19 10		19 43					19 58	20 10				20 44		20 59	
Congleton	a																						
Macclesfield	a			18 59			19 14	19 27		19 59					20 14	20 27				21 00		21 15	
Crewe 10	a		18 28		18 39	18 52			19 23			19 41	19 54				20 20		20 27		20 43		20 57
	d		18 29		18 42	18 55			19 26			19 44	19 55				20 23		20 28		20 46		21 06
Chester	a				19 20				19 52			20 20					20 56				21 20		21 33
Llandudno Junction	a								20 40								21 51						22 23
Llandudno	a																						
Bangor (Gwynedd)	a								20 57								22 14						22 42
Holyhead	a								21 26								22 50						23 14
Wilmslow	a					19 48							20 50										21e45
Manchester Airport ✈	a												20 59										
Stockport	a			19 13	19 59		19s30	19 41		20 14					20s30	20 41				21 13		21s30	
Manchester Piccadilly 10	a			19 26	20 14		19 44	19 57		20 26					20 44	20 57				21 26		21 44	
Hartford	a		18 41																20 40				
Warrington Bank Quay	a					19 11			19 41				20 12				20 38						
	d					19 11			19 43				20 12				20 40						
Runcorn	a		18 50		18 58							20 00							20 49		21 02		
Liverpool South Parkway 7 ✈	a		18 58																21 00				
Liverpool Lime Street 10	a		19 13		19 26							20 24							21 15		21 25		
	d								19 00					20 00									
Manchester Airport ✈	d	18 27											19f01				19g47	20 27					
Manchester Piccadilly 10	d	18 42											19g26				20g03	20 42					
Bolton	d	19 00											19g45				20g22	21 00					
Wigan North Western	a					19 22			19 52				20 23	20 41			20 49						
	d					19 22			19 54				20 23	20 42			20 51						
Preston 8	a	19 21				19 41			20 11				20 38	21 05			21 05	21 21					
Blackpool North	a								20 47				21 16	21 34			21 38						
	d					19 02			19 28				20 02				20 28						
Preston 8	d	19 25				19 42			20 14				20 40				21 08	21 25					
Lancaster 6	a	19 40				19 56			20 31				20 54				21 22	21 40					
	d	19 41				19 57					20 42		20 56				21 23	21 41					
Barrow-in-Furness	a	20 44																22 44					
Oxenholme Lake District	a					20 10					20 57		21 09				21 35						
	d					20 12					20 58		21 10				21 37						
Windermere	a										21 16												
Penrith North Lakes	d					20 36							21 35				22 01						
Carlisle 8	a					20 52							22 13				22 19						
	d					20 55							22 16				22 22						
Lockerbie	d												22 34										
Carstairs	a																						
Motherwell	a												23s16										
Glasgow Central 15	a												23 38				23 41						
Haymarket	a					22s08																	
Edinburgh 10	a					22 18																	
Perth	a					00 06																	
Dundee	a					23h56																	
Aberdeen	a																						
Inverness	a																						

For general notes see front of timetable
For details of catering facilities see Directory of Train Operators

A From Bournemouth (Table 51)
B From Plymouth (Table 51)
b By bus
c By changing at Birmingham New Street, passengers may depart Coventry at 1730, Birmingham International at 1746
e Change at Crewe
f Change at Manchester Piccadilly and Preston
g Change at Preston
h Change at Haymarket

OVERNIGHT SLEEPERS. For Sleeper trains, operated by First ScotRail, please refer to Tables 400 - 404

Table 65

Sundays

until 27 January

London and West Midlands → North West England and Scotland

Route Diagram - see first page of Table 65

		XC	VT	VT	NT	VT	VT	XC	VT	LM	VT		VT	XC	SR	VT	VT	VT	VT	AW	VT	SR		
		R 1	1 ◇	1 ◇		1 ◇	1 ◇	1 ◇	1 ◇	1 ◇	1 ◇		1 ◇	1 ◇	R	1 ◇	1 ◇	1 ◇	1 ◇	◇	1 ◇	R		
		A						B						C	D									
		🛒	🛒	🛒		🛒	🛒		🛒		🛒		🛒		🛒	🛒	🛒	🛒	🛒		🛒	🛒		
London Euston 15 ⊖	d		18 50	18 53		18 58	19 36		19 50		19 53		19 58		20 01	20 10	20 31	20 40	21 10		21 40	23 30		
Gatwick Airport 10 ✈	d																							
Watford Junction	d		18 32	19u10			19 32		20u06		20u11		20u14		20u25	20u27	20u46	20u58	21 02		21u57	23u51		
Milton Keynes Central	d		19 32			19 43	20 22		20 34				20 43				21 31	21 43	22 12		22 43			
Northampton	d		18b21						19b21							20b21					21b21			
Rugby	d		19 57			20 08			20 57				21 09			21 41	21 57	22 07			23 14			
Nuneaton	d																							
Tamworth Low Level	d																							
Lichfield Trent Valley	d																							
Coventry	d	19c25	20 09	20 15		20 21		20 30	21 09		21 15			21e25		21 30	22 09	22 21						
Birmingham International ✈	d	19c36		20 26				20 46	21 09		21 26			21e35		22 03				22 28				
Birmingham New Street 12	d	20 18		20 48				21 18	21 35	21 40	21 48			22 18						22 54				
Sandwell & Dudley	d			20 57							21 57													
Coseley	d																							
Wolverhampton 7 🚢	d	20 38		21 10				21 38	21 54	21 57	22 10			22 38						23 11				
Penkridge	d									22 07														
Stafford	a	20 51	21 00			21 21	21 42	21 51	22 09	22 16				22 51		22 57	23 03	23 16	23 48		00 13			
	d	20 53	21 01			21 22	21 43	21 53	22 10	22 17				22 53		22 58	23 04	23 18	23 50		00 14			
Stoke-on-Trent	a	21 10		21 44			22 01	22 10			22 40			23s10		23 16								
Congleton	a																							
Macclesfield	a	21 27		22 00			22 17	22 27			22 56			23s27		23 32								
Crewe 10	a		21 20			21 41			22 35	22 42			22 49				23 30	23 42	00s15	00 20	00s39			
	d		21 23			21 44			22 38				22 52		23u14		23 33	23 45		00 30				
Chester	a					22 20				23 19										00 48				
Llandudno Junction	a					23 33														01 39				
Llandudno	a																							
Bangor (Gwynedd)	a					23 50														01 56				
Holyhead	a					00 26														02 27				
Wilmslow	a					22 51													00s33					
Manchester Airport ✈	a					22 59																		
Stockport	a	21 41		22 14			22s30	22 41			23 11			23s41		23s47			00s43		01s04			
Manchester Piccadilly 10 🚢	a	21 57		22 27			22 42	22 57			23 26			23 57		23 59			00 55		01 16			
Hartford	a																							
Warrington Bank Quay	a		21 38						22 53								23 48							
	d		21 40						22 55								23 50							
Runcorn	a					21 59							23 07					00 01						
Liverpool South Parkway 7 ✈	a																							
Liverpool Lime Street 10	a					22 24							23 35					00 39						
	d		21 00		22 00												23 00							
Manchester Airport ✈	d		20f47												22 47									
Manchester Piccadilly 10 🚢	d		21f03												23 03									
Bolton	d		21f22												23 22									
Wigan North Western	a		21 49		22 41				23 04								23 59							
	d		21 51		22 42				23 06								00 01							
Preston 8	a		22 08		23 15				23 36								00 27							
Blackpool North	a		22 47		23 43				00 16															
	d		21 28																					
Preston 8	d		22 11												00u33									
Lancaster 6	a		22 24																					
	d		22 26																					
Barrow-in-Furness	a		00 13																					
Oxenholme Lake District	a		22 38																					
	d		22 39																					
Windermere	a																							
Penrith North Lakes	d		23 06																					
Carlisle 8	a		23 42																			04s58		
	d																							
Lockerbie	d																							
Carstairs	a																					06s28		
Motherwell	a																					06s58		
Glasgow Central 15	a																					07 17		
Haymarket	a																							
Edinburgh 10	a																					07 16		
Perth	a														05s44							09g37		
Dundee	a														06s08							09 25		
Aberdeen	a														07 37							10 38		
Inverness	a														08 30							11 59		

For general notes see front of timetable
For details of catering facilities see Directory of Train Operators

- **A** From Bournemouth (Table 51). 🛒 to Birmingham New Street
- **B** From Plymouth (Table 51)
- **C** From Bournemouth (Table 51)
- **D** Also conveys portion to Fort William (Table 227)
- **b** By bus
- **c** By changing at Birmingham New Street, passengers may depart Coventry at 1930, Birmingham International at 1946
- **e** By changing at Birmingham New Street, passengers may depart Coventry at 2130, Birmingham International at 2146
- **f** Change at Preston
- **g** Via Glasgow Central and Glasgow Queen Street. Passengers make their own way from one station to the other

OVERNIGHT SLEEPERS. For Sleeper trains, operated by First ScotRail, please refer to Tables 400 - 404

London and West Midlands → North West England and Scotland

3 February to 23 March

Route Diagram - see first page of Table 65

		NT	VT	XC	TP	NT	LM	VT	VT	VT	VT	TP	TP	XC		VT	VT	VT	VT	XC	NT	VT	VT	NT	LM
			1◇	1◇	1◇		1◇	1◇				1◇	1◇	1◇		1◇	1◇			1◇		1◇			1◇
																				A					
									🚌	🚌	🚌							🚌	🚌				🚌		
			☕	☕				☕					🍴	☕		☕	☕			☕		☕			
London Euston 15 ⊖	d															08 40						09 31			
Gatwick Airport 10 ✈	d																								
Watford Junction	d															08u58						09u46			
Milton Keynes Central	d															09 46						10 31			
Northampton	d																					09b21			
Rugby	d																					10 57			
Nuneaton	d																								
Tamworth Low Level	d																								
Lichfield Trent Valley	d																								
Coventry	d			08 30				09 04						09 30		10 25				10 30		11 09			
Birmingham International ✈	d			08 46				09 14						09 46		10 36				10 46					
Birmingham New Street 12	d		09 03	09 18			09 30	10 03						10 18		10 48	11 03			11 18					11 30
Sandwell & Dudley	d															10 57									
Coseley	d																								
Wolverhampton 7	d		09 21	09 38			09 46	10 21						10 38		11 10	11 21			11 38					11 48
Penkridge	d						09 55																		
Stafford	a		09 33	09 51			10 02							10 51						11 51		12 00			12 06
	d		09 35	09 53			10 03							10 53						11 53		12 01			12 06
Stoke-on-Trent	a			10 10										11 10		11 42				12 10					
Congleton	a																								
Macclesfield	a			10 27										11 27		11 58				12 27					
Crewe 10	a		09 55				10 25	10 53									11 53					12 20			12 25
	d		09 57				10 26	10 55									11 55					12 23			12 28
Chester	a		10 28				11 20	11 36																	13 00
Llandudno Junction	a		11 25					12 31																	
Llandudno	a							13c30																	
Bangor (Gwynedd)	a		11 46					12 48																	
Holyhead	a							13 22																	
Wilmslow	a		10 51					11 50									12 50								
Manchester Airport ✈	a		10 59														12 59								
Stockport	a		11e28	10 41										11 41		12 15				12 41					
Manchester Piccadilly 10	a		11 21	10 57										11 57		12 30				12 57					
Hartford	a						10 38																		
Warrington Bank Quay	a		10 12					11 11									12 11					12 38			
	d		10 14					11 12									12 12					12 40			
Runcorn	a						10 47																		12 45
Liverpool South Parkway 7 ✈	a						10 54																		12 54
Liverpool Lime Street 10	a						11 13																		13 11
	d	08 00	09 00			10 00											11 00				12 00				
Manchester Airport ✈	d												11 27									11f47			
Manchester Piccadilly 10	d							10f25					11 42									12f03			
Bolton	d							10f45					12 00									12f22			
Wigan North Western	a	08 41	10 23			10 41		11 22									12 23				12 42	12 49		←	
	d	08 42	10 25			10 42		11 23									12 23				12 42	12 51		12 42	
Preston 8	a	09 05	10 40			11 05		11 38					12 20				12 39				→	13 04		13 06	
Blackpool North	a	09b55				11b55		13b00																13b55	
	d				09b50			10b30				10b45					11b50								
Preston 8	d				11 00			11 39				11 59	12 25				12 40					13 07			
Lancaster 6	a				11 15			11 53				12 14	12 40				12 55					13 20			
	d				11 16			11 54				12 15	12 41				12 56					13 22			
Barrow-in-Furness	a				12 18																				
Oxenholme Lake District	a							12 07				12 31	12 55									13 34			
	d							12 10				12 31	12 55									13 35			
Windermere	a											12 52										13 58			
Penrith North Lakes	d							12 35					13 22				13 33					14 00			
Carlisle 8	a							12 53					13 38				13 50					14 18			
	d							12 57	13 05								13 52	14 05					14 30		
Lockerbie	d							13a16		13 30	13 35						14a10		14 25						
Carstairs	a																								
Motherwell	a										14 50														
Glasgow Central 15	a								15 00		15g34							16 00					16 25		
Haymarket	a																								
Edinburgh 10	a									15 40									16 35						
Perth	a								16h46										18 27						
Dundee	a								17h09	17 24									18 14						
Aberdeen	a								18h23	18 44									19 30						
Inverness	a																		20 44						

For general notes see front of timetable
For details of catering facilities see Directory of Train Operators

A From Bristol Temple Meads (Table 51)

b By bus
c Change at Crewe and Llandudno Junction. By bus from Llandudno Junction
e Change at Crewe and Wilmslow
f Change at Preston
g Glasgow Central Low Level
h Via Glasgow Central and Glasgow Queen Street. Passengers make their own way from one station to the other

OVERNIGHT SLEEPERS. For Sleeper trains, operated by First ScotRail, please refer to Tables 400 - 404

Table 65

Sundays

London and West Midlands → North West England and Scotland

3 February to 23 March

Route Diagram - see first page of Table 65

		VT	VT	TP	VT	VT		VT	VT	XC	VT	TP	VT	VT	VT	VT	VT	VT	XC	NT		VT	VT	NT	LM
		1 ◇	1 ◇	1 ◇	1 ◇				1 ◇	1 ◇	1 ◇	1 ◇	1 ◇	1 ◇				1 ◇	1 ◇			1 ◇			1 ◇
										A									B						
						Bus		Bus							Bus	Bus	Bus						Bus		
London Euston 15	⊖ d	09 36	09 40						10 10		10 31		10 36					11 10				11 31			
Gatwick Airport 10	✈ d																								
Watford Junction	d	09u52	09u57						10u27		10 32		10u52					11 02				11u46			
Milton Keynes Central	d	10 37	10 43						11 12		11 31		11 37					12 12							
Northampton	d										10b21											11b21			
Rugby	d		11 08								11 57											12 57			
Nuneaton	d																								
Tamworth Low Level	d																								
Lichfield Trent Valley	d																								
Coventry	d	11 15	11 21		11 25					11c25	12 09		12 15	12 25					12 30			13 09			
Birmingham International	✈ d	11 26			11 36					11c36			12 26	12 36					12 46						
Birmingham New Street 12	d	11 48			12 03					12 18			12 48	13 03					13 18						13 30
Sandwell & Dudley	d	11 57											12 57												
Coseley	d																								
Wolverhampton 7	🚢 d	12 10			12 21					12 38			13 10	13 21					13 38						13 52
Penkridge	d																								14 01
Stafford	a								12 39	12 51	13 00							13 39	13 51			14 00			14 08
	d								12 40	12 53	13 01							13 40	13 53			14 01			14 09
Stoke-on-Trent	a	12 40							12 58	13 10			13 43					13 58	14 10						
Congleton	a																								
Macclesfield	a	12 56							13 14	13 27			13 59					14 14	14 27						
Crewe 10	a		12 37		12 53						13 20			13 53								14 20			14 31
	d		12 40		12 55						13 23			13 55								14 23			14 31
Chester	a		13 20		13 50						14 15			14 50											
Llandudno Junction	a										15 10			15e59											
Llandudno	a													16f30											
Bangor (Gwynedd)	a										15 34			16e22											
Holyhead	a													16e58											
Wilmslow	a										13 54			14 44											
Manchester Airport	✈ a													15 04											
Stockport	a	13 10							13s30	13 41	14 05		14 13					14s30	14 41						
Manchester Piccadilly 10	🚢 a	13 23							13 44	13 57	14 20		14 26					14 44	14 57						
Hartford	a																								14 43
Warrington Bank Quay	a				13 12						13 38			14 11								14 39			
	d				13 12						13 40			14 11								14 40			
Runcorn	a		12 55																						14 52
Liverpool South Parkway 7	✈ a																								15 01
Liverpool Lime Street 10	a		13 18																						15 18
	d										13 00									14 00					
Manchester Airport	✈ d											13 27										13g47			
Manchester Piccadilly 10	🚢 d				12g25							13 42										14g03			
Bolton	d				12g45							14 00										14g22			
Wigan North Western	a				13 23						13 49			14 22						14 42		14 50		←	
	d				13 23						13 51			14 22						14 42 →		14 51		14 42	
Preston 8	a				13 37						14 08	14 23		14 37								15 04		15 07	
Blackpool North	a				15b00																			15b55	
	d				12b30							12b45		13b50											
Preston 8	d			13 25	13 40							14 25		14 39								15 07			
Lancaster 6	a			13 40	13 54							14 40		14 53								15 21			
	d			13 41	13 56							14 41		14 55								15 22			
Barrow-in-Furness	a			14 44																					
Oxenholme Lake District	a				14 09							14 55		15 08								15 34			
	d				14 10							14 55		15 09								15 36			
Windermere	a				14 55																	15 58			
Penrith North Lakes	d											15 22		15 37								16 00			
Carlisle 8	a				14 50							15 38		15 52								16 18			
	d				14 52	15 05								15 55	16 05								16 30		
Lockerbie	d				15a10			15 25						16a12		16 25	16 30								
Carstairs	a																								
Motherwell	a																17 45								
Glasgow Central 15	a					17 00									18 00		18h34						18 25		
Haymarket	a																								
Edinburgh 10	a							17 35								18 35									
Perth	a					18j44																			
Dundee	a					19j08		20 01								20 46									
Aberdeen	a					20j26		21 21																	
Inverness	a					21j34																			

For general notes see front of timetable
For details of catering facilities see Directory of Train Operators

A From Southampton Central (Table 51)
B From Plymouth (Table 51)

b By bus
c By changing at Birmingham New Street, passengers may depart Coventry at 1130, Birmingham International at 1146
e Change at Crewe and Chester
f Change at Crewe, Chester and Llandudno Junction. By bus from Llandudno Junction
g Change at Preston
h Glasgow Central Low Level
j Via Glasgow Central and Glasgow Queen Street. Passengers make their own way from one station to the other

OVERNIGHT SLEEPERS. For Sleeper trains, operated by First ScotRail, please refer to Tables 400 - 404

Table 65

Sundays

London and West Midlands → North West England and Scotland

3 February to 23 March

Route Diagram - see first page of Table 65

		TP	VT	VT	VT	VT	VT	VT	XC	VT	VT	TP	VT	VT	VT	VT	VT	NT	VT	XC	VT	TP	LM	VT
					R				R						R					R				
		1 ◇	1 ◇	1 ◇	1			1 ◇	1	1 ◇		1 ◇	1 ◇	1 ◇	1				1 ◇	1	1 ◇	1 ◇	1 ◇	1 ◇
									A											B				
						bus	bus				bus					bus	bus							
			catering	catering	catering			catering	catering	catering		trolley	catering	catering	catering				catering	catering	catering			catering
London Euston 15 ⊖	d		11 36	11 40				12 10		12 31			12 36	12 40					13 10		13 40			13 50
Gatwick Airport 10 ✈	d																							
Watford Junction	d		11u52	11u57				12u27		*12 32*			12u52						*13 02*		13u58			14u07
Milton Keynes Central	d		12 37	12 43						13 31			13 37	13 43					14 13					
Northampton	d									*12b21*											*13b21*			
Rugby	d			13 08						13 57				14 08							14 57			
Nuneaton	d																							
Tamworth Low Level	d																							
Lichfield Trent Valley	d																							
Coventry	d		13 15		*13 25*				13c25	14 09			14 15	14 21	*14 25*					*14 30*	15 09			15 15
Birmingham International ✈	d		13 26		*13 36*				13c36				14 26		*14 36*					*14 46*			*14 54*	15 26
Birmingham New Street 12	d		13 48		14 03				14 18				14 48		15 03					15 18			15 30	15 51
Sandwell & Dudley	d		13 57										14 57											
Coseley	d																							16 00
Wolverhampton 7	d		14 10		14 21				14 38				15 10		15 21					15 38			15 50	16 13
Penkridge	d																							
Stafford	a								14 51	15 00				15 18						15 51	16 00		16 05	
	d								14 53	15 01				15 20						15 53	16 01		16 05	
Stoke-on-Trent	a		14 42					14 56	15 10				15 43						15 58	16 10				16 44
Congleton	a																							
Macclesfield	a		14 58					15 12	15 27				15 59						16 14	16 27				17 00
Crewe 10	a			14 39	14 52					15 20				15 41	15 53						16 20		16 26	
	d			14 42	14 55					15 22				15 44	15 55						16 23		16 28	
Chester	a			*15 20*										*16 17*							*16 54*			
Llandudno Junction	a													*17 09*										
Llandudno	a																							
Bangor (Gwynedd)	a													*17 26*										
Holyhead	a													*18 02*										
Wilmslow	a				*15 44*										*16 50*									
Manchester Airport ✈	a														*16 59*									
Stockport	a		15 13	*15 55*				15s30	15 41				16 14						16s30	16 41				17 13
Manchester Piccadilly 10	a		15 27	*16 12*				15 46	15 57				16 27						16 44	16 57				17 27
Hartford	a																							
Warrington Bank Quay	a				15 11					15 38					16 11						16 38			
	d				15 11					15 39					16 11						16 40			
Runcorn	a			15 00										16 00									16 44	
Liverpool South Parkway 7 ✈	a																						16 52	
Liverpool Lime Street 10	a			15 26										16 24									17 09	
	d									*15 00*								16 00						
Manchester Airport ✈	d	14 27								*14e47*		15 27										16 27		
Manchester Piccadilly 10	d	14 42								*15e03*		15 42										16 42		
Bolton	d	15 00								*15e22*		16 00										17 00		
Wigan North Western	a				15 22					15 49					16 22			16 41			16 49			
	d				15 22					15 50					16 23			16 42			16 51			
Preston 8	a	15 20			15 38					16 03		16 20			16 37			17 04			17 05	17 22		
Blackpool North	a				*17b00*																*17b55*			
	d				*14b30*					*14b45*					*15b50*									
Preston 8	d	15 25			15 39					16 06		16 25			16 39							17 25		
Lancaster 6	a	15 40			15 55					16 20		16 40			16 53							17 40		
	d	15 41			15 56					16 21		16 41			16 55							17 41		
Barrow-in-Furness	a	16 44								*17 51*												18 44		
Oxenholme Lake District	a									16 33		16 55			17 08									
	d									16 35		16 55			17 09									
Windermere	a									*16 55*					*17 58*									
Penrith North Lakes	d				16 32					16 59		17 22												
Carlisle 8	a				16 48					17 17		17 38			17 49									
	d				16 51	17 05					17 30				17 51	18 05								
Lockerbie	d				17a10		17 25								18a09		18 25							
Carstairs	a																							
Motherwell	a																							
Glasgow Central 15	a					19 00					19 25					20 00								
Haymarket	a																							
Edinburgh 10	a						19 35										20 35							
Perth	a					*20f47*																		
Dundee	a					*21f10*											*22 17*							
Aberdeen	a					*22f24*											*23 33*							
Inverness	a																							

For general notes see front of timetable
For details of catering facilities see Directory of Train Operators

A From Bournemouth (Table 51)

B From Plymouth (Table 51)

b By bus

c By changing at Birmingham New Street, passengers may depart Coventry at 1330, Birmingham International at 1346

e Change at Preston

f Via Glasgow Central and Glasgow Queen Street. Passengers make their own way from one station to the other

OVERNIGHT SLEEPERS. For Sleeper trains, operated by First ScotRail, please refer to Tables 400 - 404

Table 65

Sundays

3 February to 23 March

London and West Midlands → North West England and Scotland

Route Diagram - see first page of Table 65

Station		VT	VT	VT		VT	VT	VT	XC	NT	VT	VT	NT	SR	TP	VT	VT	VT		VT	VT	XC	NT	VT	NT
		1 ◇	R 1	bus		bus	bus	1 ◇	R 1 A		1 ◇	bus			1 ◇	1 ◇	R 1	bus		bus	1 ◇	R 1 B		1 ◇	
London Euston 15 ⊖	d	13 55						14 36			14 50					14 53					15 36			15 50	
Gatwick Airport 10 ✈	d																								
Watford Junction	d	14u11						14u52			14 32					15u10					15 02			16u06	
Milton Keynes Central	d	14 44									15 35										16 22				
Northampton	d										14b21													15b21	
Rugby	d	15 09									15 57													16 57	
Nuneaton	d																								
Tamworth Low Level	d																								
Lichfield Trent Valley	d																								
Coventry	d		15 25						15c25		16 09					16 15	16 25					16 30		17 09	
Birmingham International ✈	d		15 36						15c36							16 26	16 36					16 46			
Birmingham New Street 12	d		16 03						16 18							16 48	17 03					17 18			
Sandwell & Dudley	d															16 57									
Coseley	d																								
Wolverhampton 7	d		16 21						16 38							17 10	17 21					17 38			
Penkridge	d																								
Stafford	a								16 51		17 00											17 51		18 00	
	d								16 53		17 01											17 53		18 01	
Stoke-on-Trent	a							16 59	17 10							17 43					17 58	18 10			
Congleton	a																								
Macclesfield	a							17 15	17 27							17 59					18 14	18 27			
Crewe 10	a	16 42	16 53								17 20						17 53							18 20	
	d	16 45	16 55								17 23						17 55							18 23	
Chester	a		17 29								18 01													18 55	
Llandudno Junction	a		18 29								18 54														
Llandudno	a										19e30														
Bangor (Gwynedd)	a		18 51								19 14														
Holyhead	a										20 00														
Wilmslow	a										17 58						18 50								
Manchester Airport ✈	a										19 00						19 00								
Stockport	a							17s30	17 41		18 11					18 14					18s30	18 41			
Manchester Piccadilly 10	a							17 44	17 57		18 26					18 27					18 45	18 57			
Hartford	a																								
Warrington Bank Quay	a		17 09								17 38						18 12							18 38	
	d		17 11								17 40						18 12							18 40	
Runcorn	a	17 01																							
Liverpool South Parkway 7 ✈	a																								
Liverpool Lime Street 10	a	17 27																							
	d									17 00													18 00		
Manchester Airport ✈	d										16f47				17 27									17f47	
Manchester Piccadilly 10	d										17f03				17 42									18f03	
Bolton	d										17f22				18 00									18f22	
Wigan North Western	a		17 20							17 41	17 49		←				18 23						18 41	18 49	←
	d		17 22							17 42 →	17 51		17 42				18 23						18 42 →	18 51	18 42
Preston 8	a		17 36								18 04		18 05		18 23		18 37							19 04	19 05
Blackpool North	a												18b55												19b55
	d		16b50														17b50								
Preston 8	d		17 39								18 07				18 25		18 39							19 07	
Lancaster 6	a		17 53								18 20				18 40		18 53							19 20	
	d		17 54								18 22				18 41		18 55							19 22	
Barrow-in-Furness	a																								
Oxenholme Lake District	a										18 34				18 55		19 08							19 34	
	d										18 35				18 55		19 09							19 35	
Windermere	a										18 58													19 58	
Penrith North Lakes	d		18 30								19 00				19 22		19 36							20 00	
Carlisle 8	a		18 48								19 18				19 38		19 52							20 18	
	d		18 50	19 05								19 30		19 35			19 55	20 05							
Lockerbie	d		19a08			19 25	19 30										20a12			20 25					
Carstairs	a																								
Motherwell	a						20 45																		
Glasgow Central 15	a			21 00			21g34					21 25		21 55				22 00							
Haymarket	a																								
Edinburgh 10	a					21 35														22 35					
Perth	a			22h47		00 06																			
Dundee	a			23h09		23 56																			
Aberdeen	a			00h25																					
Inverness	a																								

For general notes see front of timetable
For details of catering facilities see Directory of Train Operators

A From Bournemouth (Table 51)
B From Penzance (Table 135)

b By bus
c By changing at Birmingham New Street, passengers may depart Coventry at 1530, Birmingham International at 1546
e Change at Crewe and Llandudno Junction. By bus from Llandudno Junction
f Change at Preston
g Glasgow Central Low Level
h Via Glasgow Central and Glasgow Queen Street. Passengers make their own way from one station to the other

OVERNIGHT SLEEPERS. For Sleeper trains, operated by First ScotRail, please refer to Tables 400 - 404

Table 65

Sundays

London and West Midlands → North West England and Scotland

3 February to 23 March

Route Diagram - see first page of Table 65

		VT	LM	TP	VT	VT	VT	VT	XC	VT	VT	TP	VT	VT	NT	VT	XC	VT	VT	VT	LM	TP	VT	VT
								R	R					R			R							
			1 ◇	1 ◇	1 ◇	1 ◇	1 ◇	1	1	1 ◇	1 ◇	1	1 ◇	1		1 ◇	1	1 ◇			1 ◇	1 ◇	1 ◇	1 ◇
									A								B							
		🚌																	🚌	🚌				
					☕	☕	☕	☕	☕	☕	☕		☕	☕		☕	☕	☕					☕	☕
London Euston 15 ⊖	d				15 53	15 58	16 36			16 50	16 53		16 58			17 36		17 50					17 53	17 58
Gatwick Airport 10 ✈	d																							
Watford Junction	d				16u11	16u14	16u52			16 32	17u10					17 02		18u06					18u11	18u14
Milton Keynes Central	d					16 43				17 32			17 42			18 22								
Northampton	d									16b21								17b21						
Rugby	d					17 09				17 57			18 08					18 57						19 09
Nuneaton	d																							
Tamworth Low Level	d																							
Lichfield Trent Valley	d																							
Coventry	d		16 46		17 15			17 25	17c25	18 09	18 15		18 21	18 25			18 30	19 09			18 46		19 15	
Birmingham International ✈	d		16 58		17 26			17 36	17c36		18 26			18 36			18 46				18 58		19 26	
Birmingham New Street 12	d		17 30		17 48			18 03	18 18		18 48			19 03			19 18				19 30		19 48	
Sandwell & Dudley	d				17 57						18 57												19 57	
Coseley	d																							
Wolverhampton 7	d		17 50		18 10			18 21	18 38		19 10			19 21			19 38				19 50		20 10	
Penkridge	d		17 59																		19 59			
Stafford	a		18 06						18 51	19 01			19 18	19 33			19 51	20 00			20 06			
	d		18 07						18 53	19 03			19 20	19 34			19 53	20 01			20 07			
Stoke-on-Trent	a				18 43		18 58		19 10		19 43					19 58	20 10						20 44	
Congleton	a																							
Macclesfield	a				18 59		19 14		19 27		19 59					20 14	20 27						21 00	
Crewe 10	a		18 28			18 39		18 52		19 23			19 41	19 54				20 20			20 27			20 43
	d		18 29			18 42		18 55		19 26			19 44					20 23			20 28			20 46
Chester	a					19 20				19 52			20 20					20 56						21 20
Llandudno Junction	a									20 40								21 51						
Llandudno	a																							
Bangor (Gwynedd)	a									20 57								22 14						
Holyhead	a									21 26								22 50						
Wilmslow	a					19 48		19 48						20 50										
Manchester Airport ✈	a													20 59										
Stockport	a				19 13	19 59	19s30		19 41		20 14					20s30	20 41						21 13	
Manchester Piccadilly 10	a				19 26	20 14	19 44		19 57		20 26					20 44	20 57						21 26	
Hartford	a		18 41																		20 40			
Warrington Bank Quay	a							19 11		19 41				20 12				20 38						
	d							19 11		19 43				20 12				20 40						
Runcorn	a		18 50			18 58							20 00								20 49			21 02
Liverpool South Parkway 7 ✈	a		18 58																		21 00			
Liverpool Lime Street 10	a		19 13			19 26							20 24								21 15			21 25
	d									19 00					20 00									
Manchester Airport ✈	d			18 27														19e47				20 27		
Manchester Piccadilly 10	d			18 42														20e03				20 42		
Bolton	d			19 00														20e22				21 00		
Wigan North Western	a							19 22		19 52					20 41			20 49						
	d							19 22		19 54					20 42			20 51						
Preston 8	a			19 21				19 41		20 11					21 05			21 05				21 21		
Blackpool North	a							21b00		21b30								21b55				22b30		
	d									18b45								19b50						
Preston 8	d			19 25						20 14								21 08				21 25		
Lancaster 6	a			19 40						20 31								21 22				21 40		
	d			19 41								20 42						21 23				21 41		
Barrow-in-Furness	a			20 44																		22 44		
Oxenholme Lake District	a											20 57						21 35						
	d											20 58						21 37						
Windermere	a											21 16												
Penrith North Lakes	d																	22 01						
Carlisle 8	a																	22 19						
	d	20 30																	22 35	22 40				
Lockerbie	d																							
Carstairs	a																							
Motherwell	a																			00 20				
Glasgow Central 15	a	22 25																	00 30					
Haymarket	a																							
Edinburgh 10	a																							
Perth	a	00f56																						
Dundee	a																							
Aberdeen	a																							
Inverness	a																							

For general notes see front of timetable
For details of catering facilities see Directory of Train Operators

A From Bournemouth (Table 51)

B From Plymouth (Table 51)

b By bus

c By changing at Birmingham New Street, passengers may depart Coventry at 1730, Birmingham International at 1746

e Change at Preston

f Via Glasgow Central and Glasgow Queen Street. Passengers make their own way from one station to the other

OVERNIGHT SLEEPERS. For Sleeper trains, operated by First ScotRail, please refer to Tables 400 - 404

London and West Midlands → North West England and Scotland

3 February to 23 March

Route Diagram - see first page of Table 65

		VT	VT	XC	VT	VT	NT	VT	VT	XC	VT	LM	VT	VT	SR	XC	VT	VT	VT	VT	VT	SR
		1◇	1◇	R 1	1◇	1◇		1◇	1◇	1◇	1◇	1◇	1◇	1◇	R	1◇	1◇	1◇	1◇	1◇	1◇	R
				A						B					C	D						E
		🍴	🍴	🍴	🍴	🍴		🍴	🍴		🍴		🍴	🍴	🍴		🍴	🍴	🍴	🍴	🍴	🍴
London Euston 15 ⊖	d	18 36			18 50	18 53		18 58	19 36		19 50		19 53	19 58	20 01		20 10	20 31	20 40	21 10	21 40	22 26
Gatwick Airport 10 ✈	d																					
Watford Junction	d	18u56			*18 32*	19u10			*19 02*		20u06		20u11	20u14			20u27	20u46	20u58	*21 02*	21u57	
Milton Keynes Central	d				19 32			19 43	20 22		20 34			20 43				21 31	21 43	22 12	22 43	
Northampton	d				*18b21*						*19b21*						*20b21*				*21b21*	
Rugby	d				19 57			20 08			20 57			21 09			21 41	21 57	22 07		23 14	
Nuneaton	d																					
Tamworth Low Level	d																					
Lichfield Trent Valley	d																					
Coventry	d		*19 25*	19c25	20 09	20 15		20 21		*20 30*	21 09		21 15			21e25	*21 30*	22 09	22 21			
Birmingham International ✈	d		*19 36*	19c36		20 26				*20 46*	*21 09*		21 26			21e36	22 03					
Birmingham New Street 12	d		20 03	20 18		20 48				21 18	21 35	21 40	21 48			22 18						
Sandwell & Dudley	d					20 57							21 57									
Coseley	d																					
Wolverhampton 7	d		20 22	20 38		21 10				21 38	21 54	21 57	22 10			22 38						
Penkridge	d											22 07										
Stafford	a		20 37	20 51	21 00			21 21	21 42	21 51	22 09	22 16				22 51	22 57	23 03	23 16	23 48	00 13	
	d		20 38	20 53	21 01			21 22	21 43	21 53	22 10	22 17				22 53	22 58	23 04	23 18	23 50	00 14	
Stoke-on-Trent	a	20 59		21 10		21 44			22 01	22 10			22 40			23s10	23 16					
Congleton	a																					
Macclesfield	a	21 15		21 27		22 00			22 17	22 27			22 56			23s27	23 32					
Crewe 10	a		20 57		21 20			21 41			22 35	22 42		22 49				23 30	23 42	00s15	00s39	
	d		21 06		21 23			21 44			22 38			22 52				23 33	23 45			
Chester	a		21 33					*22 20*				*23 19*								*00 48*		
Llandudno Junction	a		22 23					*23 33*												*01 39*		
Llandudno	a																					
Bangor (Gwynedd)	a		22 42					*23 50*												*01 56*		
Holyhead	a		23 14					*00 26*												*02 27*		
Wilmslow	a		*21f45*					*22 51*												00s33		
Manchester Airport ✈	a							*22 59*														
Stockport	a	21s30		21 41		22 14			22s30	22 41			23 11			23s41	23s47			00s43	01s04	
Manchester Piccadilly 10	a	21 44		21 57		22 27			22 42	22 57			23 26			23 57	23 59			00 55	01 16	
Hartford	a																					
Warrington Bank Quay	a				21 38						22 53							23 48				
	d				21 40						22 55							23 50				
Runcorn	a							21 59						23 07					00 01			
Liverpool South Parkway 7 ✈	a																					
Liverpool Lime Street 10	a							22 24						23 35					00 39			
	d				*21 00*		22 00											*23 00*				
Manchester Airport ✈	d				*20g47*																	
Manchester Piccadilly 10	d				*21g03*																	
Bolton	d				*21g22*																	
Wigan North Western	a				21 49		22 41				23 04							23 59				
	d				21 51		22 42				23 06							00 01				
Preston 8	a				22 08		23 15				23 36							00 27				
Blackpool North	a				*23b30*		*00b05*				*01b05*											
	d				*20b45*																	
Preston 8	d				22 11																	
Lancaster 6	a				22 24																	
	d				22 26																	
Barrow-in-Furness	a				*00 13*																	
Oxenholme Lake District	a				22 38																	
	d				22 39																	
Windermere	a																					
Penrith North Lakes	d				23 06																	
Carlisle 8	a				23 42																	
	d																					
Lockerbie	d																					
Carstairs	a																					07s13
Motherwell	a																					07s39
Glasgow Central 15	a																					07 58
Haymarket	a																					
Edinburgh 10	a																					06s27
Perth	a														05s44							
Dundee	a														06s08							
Aberdeen	a														07 37							
Inverness	a														08 30							

For general notes see front of timetable
For details of catering facilities see Directory of Train Operators

- A From Bournemouth (Table 51). 🍴 to Birmingham New Street
- B From Plymouth (Table 51)
- C Also conveys portion to Fort William (Table 227)
- D From Bournemouth (Table 51)
- E Stops at Edinburgh before Carstairs, Motherwell and Glasgow Central
- b By bus
- c By changing at Birmingham New Street, passengers may depart Coventry at 1930, Birmingham International at 1946
- e By changing at Birmingham New Street, passengers may depart Coventry at 2130, Birmingham International at 2146
- f Change at Crewe
- g Change at Preston

OVERNIGHT SLEEPERS. For Sleeper trains, operated by First ScotRail, please refer to Tables 400 - 404

Table 65

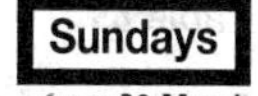

Sundays

from 30 March

London and West Midlands → North West England and Scotland

Route Diagram - see first page of Table 65

		NT	TP	VT	VT	VT	TP	TP	VT	VT	NT	XC	LM	VT	XC	VT	VT	VT	TP	TP	VT	VT	VT	VT	VT
			1		1 ◇			1	1 ◇	1 ◇		1 ◇	1 ◇	1 ◇	1 ◇	1 ◇				1 ◇		1 ◇		1 ◇	1 ◇
								A																	
				bus		bus	bus										bus	bus	bus		bus		bus		
					catering				catering	catering		catering		catering	catering	catering				trolley		catering		catering	catering
London Euston 15 ⊖	d															08 40									
Gatwick Airport 10 ✈	d																								
Watford Junction	d															08u58									
Milton Keynes Central	d															09 46									
Northampton	d																								
Rugby	d																								
Nuneaton	d																								
Tamworth Low Level	d																								
Lichfield Trent Valley	d																								
Coventry	d											08 30		09 04	09 30	10 25									
Birmingham International ✈	d											08 46		09 14	09 46	10 36									
Birmingham New Street 12	d				09 03							09 18	09 30	10 03	10 18	10 48						11 03			
Sandwell & Dudley	d															10 57									
Coseley	d																								
Wolverhampton 7	d				09 21							09 38	09 46	10 21	10 38	11 10						11 21			
Penkridge	d												09 55												
Stafford	a				09 33							09 51	10 02		10 51	11 24									
	d				09 35							09 53	10 03		10 53	11 26	11 35								
Stoke-on-Trent	a																12 05								
Congleton	a																								
Macclesfield	a																12 55								
Crewe 10	a				09 55							10 13	10 25	10 53	11 13							11 53			
	d				09 57							10 16	10 26	10 55	11 16							11 55			
Chester	a				10 28							10 50	11 20	11 36	12 20										
Llandudno Junction	a				11 25									12 31	13b25										
Llandudno	a				11c40									12e46	13f40										
Bangor (Gwynedd)	a				11 46									12 48	13b51										
Holyhead	a													13 22											
Wilmslow	a											10 31			11 31	12 04									
Manchester Airport ✈	a											10 59													
Stockport	a											10 41			11 41	12 15									
Manchester Piccadilly 10	a											10 57			11 57	12 30									
Hartford	a												10 38												
Warrington Bank Quay	a				10 12									11 11								12 11			
	d				10 14									11 12								12 12			
Runcorn	a												10 47												
Liverpool South Parkway 7 ✈	a												10 54												
Liverpool Lime Street 10	a												11 13												
	d	08 00			09 00				←		10 00											11 00		←	
Manchester Airport ✈	d					08g51			09 47										10 47				11g00	11 47	
Manchester Piccadilly 10	d					09 25			10 03										11 03				11 25	12 03	
Bolton	d					09 45			10 22										11 22				11 45	12 22	
Wigan North Western	a	08 41			10 23						10 41			11 22								12 23			
	d	08 42			10 25						10 42			11 23								12 23			
Preston 8	a	09 05			10 40						11 05			11 38								12 39			
Blackpool North	a	09 34			11 16						11 34			12 16								13 16			
	d					10 17			10 28										11 12					12 17	
Preston 8	d		10h00		11 03 →	10 50	10 57		11 03									11 50	11 57			12 57 →	12 50	12 57	
Lancaster 6	a						11 47											12 40							
	d		11 00	11 05				11 56													13 00				
Barrow-in-Furness	a		12 01																						
Oxenholme Lake District	a			11 50		12 05		12 11											13 05		13 45		14 05		
	d			11 50		12 05		12 12											13 05		13 45		14 05		
Windermere	a							12 33											13 26						
Penrith North Lakes	d			12 45		13a00													14 00		14 40		15a00		
Carlisle 8	a			13 20					13 24										14 35		15 15			15 21	
	d								13 33	13 41										14 48				15 30	15 42
Lockerbie	d								13 53	14 02										15 09				15 50	16 02
Carstairs	a																								
Motherwell	a								14s39															16s39	
Glasgow Central 15	a								15 07															17 08	
Haymarket	a									15s01										16 08					17s01
Edinburgh 10	a									15 08										16 16					17 08
Perth	a								16j46											18 27					18k27
Dundee	a									16k48										17 49					18k46
Aberdeen	a									18m23										19 05					20m26
Inverness	a																			20 44					20k44

For general notes see front of timetable
For details of catering facilities see Directory of Train Operators

- A From Barrow-in-Furness (Table 82)
- b Change at Crewe and Chester
- c From 6 April only. Change at Crewe and Llandudno Junction
- e Change at Crewe and Llandudno Junction. 30 March arr. 1330
- f From 6 April only. Change at Crewe, Chester and Llandudno Junction
- g Change at Manchester Piccadilly and Preston
- h Change at Carnforth. By bus
- j Via Glasgow Central and Glasgow Queen Street. Passengers make their own way from one station to the other
- k Change at Haymarket
- m Change at Haymarket and Dundee

OVERNIGHT SLEEPERS. For Sleeper trains, operated by First ScotRail, please refer to Tables 400 - 404

Table 65

Sundays

from 30 March

London and West Midlands → North West England and Scotland

Route Diagram - see first page of Table 65

		TP	TP	XC	NT	VT	LM	VT	TP	VT	VT	VT	VT	XC	TP	TP	TP	VT	VT	VT	VT	VT	VT	VT	VT
			1	1 ◇		1 ◇	1 ◇	1 ◇	1	1 ◇	1 ◇	1 ◇		1 ◇			1 ◇		1 ◇	1 ◇	1 ◇	1 ◇	1 ◇	1 ◇	
			A	B					C					D											
		bus											bus		bus	bus		bus							bus
				catering		catering		catering		catering	catering	catering		catering			trolley		catering	catering	catering	catering	catering	catering	
London Euston 15 ⊖	d					09 31		09 36		09 40		10 10							10 31			10 36		11 10	
Gatwick Airport 10 ✈	d																								
Watford Junction	d					09u46		09u52		09u57		10u27							*10 32*			10u52		*11 02*	
Milton Keynes Central	d					10 31		10 37		10 43		11 12							11 31			11 37		12 12	
Northampton	d					*10 28*													*11 24*						
Rugby	d					10 57				11 08									11 57						
Nuneaton	d																								
Tamworth Low Level	d																								
Lichfield Trent Valley	d																								
Coventry	d			*10 30*		11 09		11 15		11 21	*11 25*			11b25					12 09			12 15	*12 25*		
Birmingham International ✈	d			*10 46*				11 26			*11 36*			11b36								12 26	*12 36*		
Birmingham New Street 12	d			11 18			11 30	11 48			12 03			12 18								12 48	13 03		
Sandwell & Dudley	d							11 57														12 57			
Coseley	d																								
Wolverhampton 7	d			11 38			11 48	12 10			12 21			12 38								13 10	13 21		
Penkridge	d																								
Stafford	a			11 51		12 00	12 06	12 24				12 39		12 51					13 00			13 27		13 39	
	d			11 53		12 01	12 06	12 26				12 40	12 50	12 53					13 01			13 29		13 40	13 50
Stoke-on-Trent	a												13 20												14 20
Congleton	a																								
Macclesfield	a											*14c00*	14 10											*15c00*	15 10
Crewe 10	a			12 13		12 20	12 25			12 37	12 53			13 13					13 20				13 53		
	d			12 16		12 23	12 28			12 40	12 55			13 16					13 23				13 55		
Chester	a						*13 00*			*13 20*				*13 50*					*14 15*						
Llandudno Junction	a																		*15 10*						
Llandudno	a																		*15e26*						
Bangor (Gwynedd)	a																		*15 34*						
Holyhead	a																								
Wilmslow	a			12 31				13 01				13 17		13 31					*13 54*			14 05		14 17	
Manchester Airport ✈	a			*12 59*																					
Stockport	a			12 41				13 10				13s30		13 41					*14 05*			14 13		14s30	
Manchester Piccadilly 10	a			12 57				13 23				13 44		13 57					*14 20*			14 26		14 44	
Hartford	a																								
Warrington Bank Quay	a					12 38					13 12								13 38				14 11		
	d					12 40					13 12								13 40				14 11		
Runcorn	a						12 45			12 55															
Liverpool South Parkway 7 ✈	a						12 54																		
Liverpool Lime Street 10	a						13 11			13 18															
	d				12 00														*13 00*						
Manchester Airport ✈	d														*12 46*				*12f52*						
Manchester Piccadilly 10	d														*13 02*				*13g24*						
Bolton	d														*13 22*				*13g44*						
Wigan North Western	a				12 42	12 49					13 23								13 49				14 22		
	d				12 42	12 51					13 23								13 51				14 22		
Preston 8	a				13 06	13 06					13 40								14 07				14 39		
Blackpool North	a				13 34	*13 39*					*14 16*								*14 47*				*15 16*		
	d														*13 12*				*14 02*						
Preston 8	d	12 57							*13h27*						13 57	13 57			14 42						
Lancaster 6	a	13 47														14 47									
	d		13 56						14 15									15 15							
Barrow-in-Furness	a								15 16																
Oxenholme Lake District	a		14 11												15 05			16 00							
	d		14 12												15 05			16 00							
Windermere	a		14 33												*15 29*										
Penrith North Lakes	d														16 00			16 55							
Carlisle 8	a														16 35			17 30	17 36		←				
	d																16 48		17 46	17 44	17 46				
Lockerbie	d																17 09		→	18 02	18 10				
Carstairs	a																								
Motherwell	a																				18s52				
Glasgow Central 15	a																				19 15				
Haymarket	a																18 08			19 01					
Edinburgh 10	a																18 16			19 08					
Perth	a																				*20j47*				
Dundee	a																*20 01*			*20k46*	*21j10*				
Aberdeen	a																*21 21*				*22j24*				
Inverness	a																								

For general notes see front of timetable
For details of catering facilities see Directory of Train Operators

- **A** From Barrow-in-Furness (Table 82)
- **B** From Bristol Temple Meads (Table 51)
- **C** From Windermere (Table 83)
- **D** From Oxford (Table 51)
- **b** By changing at Birmingham New Street, passengers may depart Coventry at 1130, Birmingham International at 1146
- **c** Change at Wilmslow. By bus
- **e** From 6 April only. Change at Crewe and Llandudno Junction
- **f** Change at Manchester Piccadilly and Preston
- **g** Change at Preston
- **h** Change at Carnforth. By bus
- **j** Via Glasgow Central and Glasgow Queen Street. Passengers make their own way from one station to the other
- **k** Change at Haymarket

OVERNIGHT SLEEPERS. For Sleeper trains, operated by First ScotRail, please refer to Tables 400 - 404

Table 65

Sundays
from 30 March

London and West Midlands → North West England and Scotland

Route Diagram - see first page of Table 65

Station		VT	TP	TP	XC	NT	VT	LM	VT	VT	VT	VT	VT	TP	VT	TP	TP	XC	TP	VT	VT	VT	VT	VT	VT
				1	1◇		1◇	1◇	1◇	1◇	1◇			1	R 1		1◇	R 1		1◇		1◇	1◇	1◇	R 1
				A	B									C				D							
		bus	bus		☕		☕		☕	☕	☕	bus	bus		☕	bus	trolley	☕	bus	☕	bus	☕	☕	☕	☕
London Euston 15 ⊖	d						11 31		11 36	11 40	12 10									12 31		12 36	12 40		
Gatwick Airport 10 ✈	d																								
Watford Junction	d						11u46		11u52	11u57	12u27									12 32		12u52			
Milton Keynes Central	d								12 37	12 43										13 31		13 37	13 43		
Northampton	d						12 24													13 24					
Rugby	d						12 57			13 08										13 57			14 08		
Nuneaton	d																								
Tamworth Low Level	d																								
Lichfield Trent Valley	d																								
Coventry	d				12 30		13 09		13 15						13 25			13b25		14 09		14 15	14 21	←	14 25
Birmingham International ✈	d				12 46				13 26						13 36			13b36				14 26		14 26	14 36
Birmingham New Street 12	d				13 18			13 30	13 48						14 03			14 18				→		14 48	15 03
Sandwell & Dudley	d								13 57															14 57	
Coseley	d																								
Wolverhampton 7	d				13 38			13 52	14 10						14 21			14 38						15 10	15 21
Penkridge	d							14 01																	
Stafford	a				13 51		14 00	14 08	14 26		14 39							14 51		15 00			15 18	15 27	
	d				13 53		14 01	14 09	14 28		14 40	14 50						14 53		15 01			15 20	15 29	
Stoke-on-Trent	a											15 20													
Congleton	a																								
Macclesfield	a										16c00	16 10													
Crewe 10	a				14 13		14 20	14 31		14 39					14 52			15 13		15 20			15 41		15 53
	d				14 16		14 23	14 31		14 42					14 55			15 16		15 22			15 44		15 55
Chester	a				14 50					15 20													16 17		
Llandudno Junction	a				15e59																		17 09		
Llandudno	a				16f16																		17g27		
Bangor (Gwynedd)	a				16e22																		17 26		
Holyhead	a				16e58																		18 02		
Wilmslow	a				14 31				15 04		15 17							15 31						16 05	
Manchester Airport ✈	a				15 04																				
Stockport	a				14 41				15 13		15s30							15 41						16 14	
Manchester Piccadilly 10	a				14 57				15 27		15 46							15 57						16 27	
Hartford	a							14 43																	
Warrington Bank Quay	a						14 39								15 11					15 38					16 11
	d						14 40								15 11					15 39					16 11
Runcorn	a							14 52		15 00													16 00		
Liverpool South Parkway 7 ✈	a							15 01																	
Liverpool Lime Street 10	a							15 18		15 26													16 24		
	d					14 00														15 00					
Manchester Airport ✈	d												13 47			14 47									
Manchester Piccadilly 10	d												14 03			15 03									
Bolton	d												14 22			15 22									
Wigan North Western	a					14 42	14 50								15 22					15 49					16 22
	d					14 42	14 51								15 22					15 50					16 23
Preston 8	a					15 07	15 08								15 39					16 05					16 37
Blackpool North	a					15 34	15 47								16 16					16 47					17 16
	d		14 17										14 28			15 12					15 28				
Preston 8	d	14 50	14 57										15 20	15h27		15 57			15 57		16 20				16 57 →
Lancaster 6	a		15 47										16 10						16 47		17 10				
	d			15 56									16 10	16 15							17 10				
Barrow-in-Furness	a												17 51	17 16											
Oxenholme Lake District	a	16 05		16 11									16 55			17 05					17 55				
	d	16 05		16 12									16 55			17 05					17 55				
Windermere	a			16 33												17 26									
Penrith North Lakes	d	17a00											17a50			18 00					18 50				
Carlisle 8	a															18 35					19 25				
	d																18 50								
Lockerbie	d																19 09								
Carstairs	a																								
Motherwell	a																								
Glasgow Central 15	a																20 14								
Haymarket	a																								
Edinburgh 10	a																								
Perth	a																								
Dundee	a																								
Aberdeen	a																								
Inverness	a																								

For general notes see front of timetable
For details of catering facilities see Directory of Train Operators

A From Barrow-in-Furness (Table 82)
B From Plymouth (Table 51)
C From Windermere (Table 65)
D From Oxford (Table 51)
b By changing at Birmingham New Street, passengers may depart Coventry at 1330, Birmingham International at 1346
c Change at Wilmslow. By bus
e Change at Crewe and Chester
f Change at Crewe, Chester and Llandudno Junction. 30 March arr. 1630, by bus from Llandudno Junction
g From 6 April only. Change at Crewe and Llandudno Junction
h Change at Carnforth. By bus

OVERNIGHT SLEEPERS. For Sleeper trains, operated by First ScotRail, please refer to Tables 400 - 404

Table 65

Sundays

from 30 March

London and West Midlands → North West England and Scotland

Route Diagram - see first page of Table 65

		VT	VT	VT	TP	TP	VT	VT	XC	NT	VT	VT	TP	LM	VT	VT	TP	TP	TP	NT	VT	VT	XC	VT	VT
			R						R														R		
			1	1 ◇		1	1 ◇		1		1 ◇		1	1 ◇	1 ◇	1 ◇		1 ◇			1 ◇		1		1 ◇
						A			B				C										D		
		🚌			🚌			🚌				🚌					🚌		🚌			🚌		🚌	
			☕	☕			☕		☕		☕				☕	☕		🍴			☕		☕		☕
London Euston 15 ⊖	d						13 10				13 40				13 50	13 55					14 36				14 50
Gatwick Airport 10 ✈	d																								
Watford Junction	d						13 02				13u58				14u07	14u11					14u52				
Milton Keynes Central	d						14 13									14 44									15 35
Northampton	d										14 24														15 24
Rugby	d										14 57					15 09									15 57
Nuneaton	d																								
Tamworth Low Level	d																								
Lichfield Trent Valley	d																								
Coventry	d								14 30		15 09				15 15								15b25		16 09
Birmingham International ✈	d								14 46					14 54	15 26								15b36		
Birmingham New Street 12	d								15 18					15 30	15 51								16 18		
Sandwell & Dudley	d														16 00										
Coseley	d																								
Wolverhampton 7	d								15 38					15 50	16 13								16 38		
Penkridge	d																								
Stafford	a						15 41		15 51		16 00			16 05	16 28						16 41		16 51		17 00
	d						15 42	15 50	15 53		16 01			16 05	16 30						16 42	16 50	16 53		17 01
Stoke-on-Trent	a							16 20														17 20			
Congleton	a																								
Macclesfield	a						17c00	17 10													18c00	18 10			
Crewe 10	a								16 13		16 20			16 26		16 42							17 13		17 20
	d								16 16		16 23			16 28		16 45							17 16		17 23
Chester	a										16 54					17 29									18 01
Llandudno Junction	a															18 29									18 54
Llandudno	a																								19e30
Bangor (Gwynedd)	a															18 51									19 14
Holyhead	a																								20 00
Wilmslow	a						16 17		16 31						17 03						17 17		17 31		17 55
Manchester Airport ✈	a								16 59																
Stockport	a						16s30		16 41						17 13						17s30		17 41		18 06
Manchester Piccadilly 10	a						16 44		16 57						17 27						17 44		17 57		18 20
Hartford	a																								
Warrington Bank Quay	a										16 38														17 38
	d										16 40														17 40
Runcorn	a													16 44		17 01									
Liverpool South Parkway 7 ✈	a													16 52											
Liverpool Lime Street 10	a													17 09		17 27									
	d		←							16 00										17 00					
Manchester Airport ✈	d	14f52	15 47									16f01					16 47								
Manchester Piccadilly 10	d	15 25	16 03									16 25					17 03								
Bolton	d	15 45	16 22									16 45					17 22								
Wigan North Western	a									16 41	16 49									17 41					17 49
	d									16 42	16 51									17 42					17 51
Preston 8	a									17 04	17 04									18 05					18 09
Blackpool North	a									17 35	17 38									18 34					18 47
	d	16 17															17 17								
Preston 8	d	16 50	16 57		16 57							17 20	17g27				17 57		17 57						18 41 →
Lancaster 6	a				17 47							18 10							18 47						
	d					17 56						18 10	18 15											19 10	
Barrow-in-Furness	a												19 16												
Oxenholme Lake District	a	18 05				18 11						18 55					19 05							19 55	
	d	18 05				18 12						18 55					19 05							19 55	
Windermere	a					18 33											19 30								
Penrith North Lakes	d	19a00										19a50					20 00							20 40	
Carlisle 8	a		19 32														20 35							21 15	
	d		19 41	19 50														20 49							
Lockerbie	d		20 01	20 08														21 08							
Carstairs	a																								
Motherwell	a		20s43																						
Glasgow Central 15	a		21 08															22 09							
Haymarket	a			21s04																					
Edinburgh 10	a			21 12																					
Perth	a		22h47	00 06														00h56							
Dundee	a		23h09	23 56																					
Aberdeen	a		00h25																						
Inverness	a																								

For general notes see front of timetable
For details of catering facilities see Directory of Train Operators

- **A** From Barrow-in-Furness (Table 82)
- **B** From Penzance (Table 135)
- **C** From Windermere (Table 83)
- **D** From Oxford (Table 51)
- **b** By changing at Birmingham New Street, passengers may depart Coventry at 1530, Birmingham International at 1546
- **c** Change at Wilmslow. By bus
- **e** Change at Crewe and Llandudno Junction. By bus from Llandudno Junction
- **f** Change at Manchester Piccadilly and Preston
- **g** Change at Carnforth. By bus
- **h** Via Glasgow Central and Glasgow Queen Street. Passengers make their own way from one station to the other

OVERNIGHT SLEEPERS. For Sleeper trains, operated by First ScotRail, please refer to Tables 400 - 404

Table 65

Sundays
from 30 March

London and West Midlands → North West England and Scotland

Route Diagram - see first page of Table 65

		VT	VT	VT	VT	VT	VT	TP	TP	XC	NT	VT	NT	LM	VT	VT	TP	VT	VT	VT	VT	XC	VT	VT	VT
					R					R											R	R			
			1 ◇	1 ◇	1	1 ◇			1	1		1 ◇		1 ◇	1 ◇	1 ◇	1	1 ◇			1	1		1 ◇	
									A	B							C					D			
		bus					bus	bus											bus	bus			bus		bus
			catering	catering	catering	catering				catering		catering			catering	catering		catering			catering	catering		catering	
London Euston 15 ⊖	d			14 53		15 36						15 50			15 53	15 58		16 36						16 50	
Gatwick Airport 10 ✈	d																								
Watford Junction	d			15u10		*15 32*						16u06			16u11	16u14		16u52							
Milton Keynes Central	d					16 22										16 43								17 32	
Northampton	d											*16 24*												*17 24*	
Rugby	d											16 57				17 09								17 57	
Nuneaton	d																								
Tamworth Low Level	d																								
Lichfield Trent Valley	d																								
Coventry	d			16 15						*16 30*		17 09			17 15						*17 25*	17b25		18 09	
Birmingham International ✈	d			16 26						*16 46*				*16 58*	17 26						*17 36*	17b36			
Birmingham New Street 12	d			16 48	17 03					17 18				17 30	17 48						18 03	18 18			
Sandwell & Dudley	d			16 57											17 57										
Coseley	d																								
Wolverhampton 7	d			17 10	17 21					17 38				17 50	18 10						18 21	18 38			
Penkridge	d													17 59											
Stafford	a			17 27		17 41				17 51		18 00		18 06	18 27			18 41				18 51		19 01	
	d			17 29		17 42	17 50			17 53		18 01		18 07	18 29			18 42	18 50			18 53		19 03	
Stoke-on-Trent	a						18 20												19 20						
Congleton	a																								
Macclesfield	a					*19c00*	19 10											*20c00*	20 10						
Crewe 10	a				17 53					18 13		18 20		18 28		18 39					18 52	19 13		19 23	
	d				17 55					18 16		18 23		18 29		18 42					18 55	19 16		19 26	
Chester	a											*18 55*				*19 20*								*19 52*	
Llandudno Junction	a																							*20 40*	
Llandudno	a																								
Bangor (Gwynedd)	a																							*20 57*	
Holyhead	a																							*21 26*	
Wilmslow	a			18 04		18 17				18 31					19 04			19 17				19 31			
Manchester Airport ✈	a									*19 00*															
Stockport	a			18 14		18s30				18 41					19 13			19s30				19 41			
Manchester Piccadilly 10	a			18 27		18 45				18 57					19 26			19 44				19 57			
Hartford	a													18 41											
Warrington Bank Quay	a				18 11							18 38									19 11			19 41	
	d				18 11							18 40									19 11			19 43	
Runcorn	a													18 50		18 58									
Liverpool South Parkway 7 ✈	a													18 58											
Liverpool Lime Street 10	a													19 13		19 26									
	d										18 00													19 00	
Manchester Airport ✈	d	*17e01*																		*18e01*			*18 47*		*19e01*
Manchester Piccadilly 10	d	*17 25*																		*18 25*			*19 03*		*19 26*
Bolton	d	*17 45*																		*18 45*			*19 22*		*19 45*
Wigan North Western	a				18 22						18 41	18 49	←								19 22			19 52	
	d				18 22						18 42	18 51	18 42								19 22			19 54	
Preston 8	a				18 43						→	19 04	19 05								19 41			20 17	
Blackpool North	a		←									*19 38*	19 32								*20 47*			*21f03*	
	d		*18 02*					*18 17*												*18 28*			*19 28*		
Preston 8	d	18 30	18 41					18 57									*19g27*			19 30			20 00		20 30
Lancaster 6	a	19 20						19 47												20 20			20 50		21 20
	d	19 20							19 56								20 20			20 20			20 50		21 20
Barrow-in-Furness	a																21 21								
Oxenholme Lake District	a	20 05							20 11											21 05			21 35		22 05
	d	20 05							20 12											21 05			21 35		22 05
Windermere	a								20 33																→
Penrith North Lakes	d	21a00																		22 00			22a30		
Carlisle 8	a		21 32																	22 35					
	d		21 41																						
Lockerbie	d		22 05																						
Carstairs	a																								
Motherwell	a		22s47																						
Glasgow Central 15	a		23 06																						
Haymarket	a																								
Edinburgh 10	a																								
Perth	a																								
Dundee	a																								
Aberdeen	a																								
Inverness	a																								

For general notes see front of timetable
For details of catering facilities see Directory of Train Operators

A From Barrow-in-Furness (Table 82)
B From Penzance (Table 135)
C From Windermere (Table 83)
D From Oxford (Table 51)
b By changing at Birmingham New Street, passengers may depart Coventry at 1730, Birmingham International at 1746
c Change at Wilmslow. By bus
e Change at Manchester Piccadilly and Preston
f 4 May only
g Change at Carnforth. By bus

OVERNIGHT SLEEPERS. For Sleeper trains, operated by First ScotRail, please refer to Tables 400 - 404

Table 65

Sundays

from 30 March

London and West Midlands → North West England and Scotland

Route Diagram - see first page of Table 65

		VT	VT	VT	VT	VT	TP	VT	VT	NT	XC	VT	VT	VT	LM	VT	VT	VT	VT	VT	XC	VT	VT	VT	VT
			1 ◇	1 ◇	1 ◇	R 1		1 ◇			R 1	1 ◇			1 ◇	1 ◇	1 ◇		1 ◇	1 ◇	R 1	1 ◇		1 ◇	
											A										B				
London Euston 15	d		16 53	16 58				17 36				17 50				17 53	17 58			18 36		18 50		18 53	
Gatwick Airport 10	d																								
Watford Junction	d		17u10					17 32				18u06				18u11	18u14			18u52				19u10	
Milton Keynes Central	d			17 42				18 22														19 32			
Northampton	d											18 24										19 24			
Rugby	d			18 08								18 57					19 09					19 57			
Nuneaton	d																								
Tamworth Low Level	d																								
Lichfield Trent Valley	d																								
Coventry	d		18 15	18 21	←	18 25					18 30	19 09				19 15			19 25		19b25	20 09		20 15	
Birmingham International	d		18 26		18 26	18 36					18 46				18 58	19 26			19 36		19b36			20 26	
Birmingham New Street 12	d		→		18 48	19 03					19 18				19 30	19 48			20 03		20 18			→	
Sandwell & Dudley	d				18 57											19 57									
Coseley	d																								
Wolverhampton 7	d				19 10	19 21					19 38				19 50	20 10			20 22		20 38				
Penkridge	d														19 59										
Stafford	a			19 18	19 27	19 33		19 41			19 51	20 00			20 06	20 28			20 37	20 42	20 51	21 00			
	d			19 20	19 29	19 34		19 42	19 50		19 53	20 01			20 07	20 30			20 38	20 43	20 53	21 01	20 50		
Stoke-on-Trent	a								20 20														21 20		
Congleton	a																								
Macclesfield	a							21c00	21 10										23e00	22c00			22 10		
Crewe 10	a			19 41		19 54					20 13	20 20			20 27		20 43		20 57		21 13	21 20			
	d			19 44		19 55					20 16	20 23			20 28		20 46		21 06		21 16	21 23			
Chester	a			20 20								20 56					21 20		21 33						
Llandudno Junction	a											21 51							22 23						
Llandudno	a																								
Bangor (Gwynedd)	a											22 14							22 42						
Holyhead	a											22 50							23 14						
Wilmslow	a				20 03			20 17			20 31					21 03				21 17	21 31				
Manchester Airport	a										20 59														
Stockport	a				20 14			20s30			20 41					21 13				21s30	21 41				
Manchester Piccadilly 10	a				20 26			20 44			20 57					21 26				21 44	21 57				
Hartford	a														20 40										
Warrington Bank Quay	a					20 12						20 38										21 38			
	d					20 12						20 40										21 40			
Runcorn	a			20 00											20 49		21 02								
Liverpool South Parkway 7	a														21 00										
Liverpool Lime Street 10	a			20 24											21 15		21 25								
	d									20 00												21 00			
Manchester Airport	d																								20 47
Manchester Piccadilly 10	d																								21 03
Bolton	d																								21 22
Wigan North Western	a					20 23				20 41		20 49										21 49			
	d					20 23				20 42		20 51										21 51			
Preston 8	a					20 38				21 05		21 06										22 05			
Blackpool North	a					21 16				21 34		21 38										22 47			
	d						20 17						20 28												21 28
Preston 8	d	20 30					20 55						21 15					21 15							22 15
Lancaster 6	a						21 40											22 05							
	d																	22 05							
Barrow-in-Furness	a						22 52											00 13							
Oxenholme Lake District	a													←				22 50							
	d													22 05				22 50							
Windermere	a																								
Penrith North Lakes	d	22 10											22 55	23 00				23a45							23 55
Carlisle 8	a	22 45											23 30	23 35											00 30
	d																								
Lockerbie	d																								
Carstairs	a																								
Motherwell	a																								
Glasgow Central 15	a																								
Haymarket	a																								
Edinburgh 10	a																								
Perth	a																								
Dundee	a																								
Aberdeen	a																								
Inverness	a																								

For general notes see front of timetable
For details of catering facilities see Directory of Train Operators

A From Plymouth (Table 51)

B From Oxford (Table 51). to Birmingham New Street

b By changing at Birmingham New Street, passengers may depart Coventry at 1930, Birmingham International at 1946

c Change at Wilmslow. By bus

e Change at Crewe and Wilmslow. By bus from Wilmslow

OVERNIGHT SLEEPERS. For Sleeper trains, operated by First ScotRail, please refer to Tables 400 - 404

Table 65

Sundays
from 30 March

London and West Midlands → North West England and Scotland

Route Diagram - see first page of Table 65

		VT	VT	VT	NT	VT	VT	XC	VT	LM	VT	VT	VT	SR	XC	VT	VT	VT	VT	VT	AW	VT	SR
			1 ◇	1 ◇		1 ◇		1 ◇	1 ◇	1 ◇	1 ◇		1 ◇	R	1 ◇	1 ◇	1 ◇		1 ◇	1 ◇	◇	1 ◇	R
								A						B	C								
		🚌					🚌					🚌						🚌					
			☕	☕		☕			☕		☕		☕	☕		☕	☕		☕	☕		☕	☕
London Euston 15 ⊖	d		18 58			19 36			19 50		19 53		19 58	20 01		20 10	20 31		20 40	21 10		21 40	23 06
Gatwick Airport 10 ✈	d																						
Watford Junction	d					*19 32*			20u06		20u11		20u14	20u25		20u27	20u46		20u58	*21 02*		21u57	23u27
Milton Keynes Central	d		19 43			20 22			20 34				20 43				21 31		21 43	22 02		22 34	
Northampton	d								*20 24*								*21 24*					*22 24*	
Rugby	d		20 08						20 57				21 09			21 41	21 57		22 07			23 14	
Nuneaton	d																						
Tamworth Low Level	d																						
Lichfield Trent Valley	d																						
Coventry	d		20 21	←				*20 30*	21 09		21 15				21b25	*21 30*	22 09		22 21		*22 15*		
Birmingham International ✈	d			20 26				*20 46*	*21 09*		21 26				21b36	22 03					*22 28*		
Birmingham New Street 12	d			20 48				21 18	21 35	21 40	21 48				22 18						22 54		
Sandwell & Dudley	d			20 57							21 57												
Coseley	d																						
Wolverhampton 7	d			21 10				21 38	21 54	21 57	22 10				22 38						23 11		
Penkridge	d									22 07													
Stafford	a		21 21	21 28		21 42		21 51	22 09	22 16	22 24				22 51	22 57	23 03		23 16	23 48		00 13	
	d		21 22	21 30		21 43	21 50	21 53	22 10	22 17	22 26	22 35			22 53	22 58	23 04	23 10	23 18	23 50		00 14	
Stoke-on-Trent	a						22 20					23 05						23 40					
Congleton	a																						
Macclesfield	a					*23c00*	23 10				*23c40*	23 55				*00c20*		00 30		*01c15*			
Crewe 10	a		21 41					22 13	22 35	22 42			22 49		23 17		23 30		23 42	00s15	00 20	00s39	
	d		21 44					22 16	22 38				22 52	23u14	23 20		23 33		23 45		00 30		
Chester	a		*22 20*							*23 19*											00 48		
Llandudno Junction	a		*23 33*																		01 39		
Llandudno	a																						
Bangor (Gwynedd)	a		*23 50*																		01 56		
Holyhead	a		*00 26*																		02 27		
Wilmslow	a			22 03		22 17		22 31			22 59				23 35	23 40				00s33			
Manchester Airport ✈	a							*22 59*															
Stockport	a			22 14		22s30		22 41			23 09				23s41	23s50				00s43		01s04	
Manchester Piccadilly 10	a			22 27		22 42		22 57			23 21				23 57	00 04				00 55		01 16	
Hartford	a																						
Warrington Bank Quay	a								22 53								23 48						
	d								22 55								23 50						
Runcorn	a		21 59										23 07						00 01				
Liverpool South Parkway 7 ✈	a																						
Liverpool Lime Street 10	a		22 24										23 35						00 39				
	d				22 00												*23 00*						
Manchester Airport ✈	d													*22 47*									
Manchester Piccadilly 10	d													*23 03*									
Bolton	d													*23 22*									
Wigan North Western	a				22 41				23 04								23 59						
	d				22 42				23 06								00 01						
Preston 8	a				23 15				23 36								00 27						
Blackpool North	a				23 43				*00 16*														
	d																						
Preston 8	d	22 15												00u33									
Lancaster 6	a	23 05																					
	d	23 05																					
Barrow-in-Furness	a																						
Oxenholme Lake District	a	23 50																					
	d																						
Windermere	a																						
Penrith North Lakes	d																						
Carlisle 8	a																						04s58
	d																						
Lockerbie	d																						
Carstairs	a																						06s28
Motherwell	a																						06s58
Glasgow Central 15	a																						07 17
Haymarket	a																						
Edinburgh 10	a																						07 16
Perth	a													05s44									*09e37*
Dundee	a													06s08									*09 25*
Aberdeen	a													07 37									*10 38*
Inverness	a													08 30									*11 59*

For general notes see front of timetable
For details of catering facilities see Directory of Train Operators

A From Plymouth (Table 51)

B Also conveys portion to Fort William (Table 227)

C From Oxford (Table 51)

b By changing at Birmingham New Street, passengers may depart Coventry at 2130, Birmingham International at 2146

c Change at Wilmslow. By bus

e Via Glasgow Central and Glasgow Queen Street. Passengers make their own way from one station to the other

OVERNIGHT SLEEPERS. For Sleeper trains, operated by First ScotRail, please refer to Tables 400 - 404

Scotland and North West England → West Midlands and London

Route Diagram - see first page of Table 65

Miles	Miles	Miles	Miles	Miles			VT	XC	VT	XC	LM	VT	VT	TP	LM	TP	TP	VT	TP	LM	VT	VT	VT	VT	VT
																MO									
							1◇	1◇	1◇	1◇	1◇	1◇	1◇	1◇	1	1◇	1◇	1◇	1◇	1	1◇	1◇	1◇	1◇	1◇
								A		A				B	C	D		E			H				
								╤P	⊠	╤P	╤	⊠	⊠					⊠			⊠	⊠	╤P	⊠	⊠
—	0	—	—	—	Inverness	d																			
—	—	0	—	—	Aberdeen	d																			
—	—	71¼	—	—	Dundee	d																			
—	118	—	—	—	Perth	d																			
—	130¼	187¼	—	—	**Edinburgh** 10	d																			
—	131½	188½	—	—	Haymarket	d																			
0	—	—	—	—	**Glasgow Central** 15	d																			
12¾	—	—	—	—	Motherwell	d																			
28¾	158	—	—	—	Carstairs	d																			
77	—	263½	—	—	Lockerbie	d																			
102¼	—	—	—	—	**Carlisle** 8	a																			
—	—	—	—	—		d																			
120	—	—	—	—	Penrith North Lakes	d																			
—	—	—	—	—	Windermere	d																			
152¼	—	—	—	—	Oxenholme Lake District	a																			
—	—	—	—	—		d																			
—	—	—	—	—	Barrow-in-Furness	d								04 20		04 20									
171¼	—	—	—	—	Lancaster 6	a								05 14		05 22									
—	—	—	—	—		d										05 24		05b36							
192¼	—	—	—	—	**Preston** 8	a										05 42		05b51							
—	—	—	—	—	Blackpool North	a																			
—	—	—	—	—		d											05 19						05 30		
—	—	—	0	—	**Preston** 8	d											05 50	05 54	←				06 15		
207½	—	—	—	—	Wigan North Western	a											06 11	06 04	06 11				06 26		
—	—	—	—	—		d											→	06 06	06 13				06 27		
—	—	—	20	—	Bolton	a													06 29						
—	—	—	31¼	—	**Manchester Piccadilly** 10	a													06 56						
—	—	—	—	—	Manchester Airport	a													07 15						
—	—	—	—	—	**Liverpool Lime Street** 10	a																	07 29		
—	0	—	—	—		d						05 44										06 27			
—	5½	—	—	—	Liverpool South Parkway 7	d																			
—	13	—	—	—	Runcorn	d						06 00										06 43			
219¼	—	—	—	—	Warrington Bank Quay	a												06 25					06 44		
—	—	—	—	—		d												06 27					06 45		
231½	23¾	—	—	—	Hartford	d																			
—	—	—	—	0	**Manchester Piccadilly** 10	d			05 20				06 02								06 17			06 35	06 45
—	—	—	37	5¾	Stockport	d			05u31				06u11								06 25			06u44	06u53
—	—	—	—	—	Manchester Airport	d																05c53			
—	—	—	—	—	Wilmslow	d			05 39													06 05		06 51	
—	—	—	—	—	Holyhead	d	02 15															04e27			
—	—	—	—	—	Bangor (Gwynedd)	d	02 42															05e00			
—	—	—	—	—	Llandudno	d																			
—	—	—	—	—	Llandudno Junction	d	03 00					04 55										05e18			
—	—	—	—	—	Chester	d	03 40	04 55				05 51										06 30			
243¼	35½	—	—	—	**Crewe** 10	a	03 59		05 56			06 20						06 46				07 02	07 08	07 10	
—	—	—	—	—		d	04 02	05 45	05 59		06 09	06 24			06 37			06 49				07 05	07 10	07 13	
—	—	—	49	17¾	Macclesfield	d							06 24								06 38				07 09
—	—	—	57	25¾	Congleton	d				←															
—	—	—	68¾	37¼	**Stoke-on-Trent**	d		06 04		06 04			06 40								06 54				07 24
267¾	—	—	—	53½	**Stafford**	a	04 29	→	06 16	06 22	06 29	06 42			06 56						07 13	07 24			
—	—	—	—	—		d	04 30		06 18	06 24	06 30	06 43			06 57						07 15	07 26			
—	—	—	—	59¼	Penkridge	a					06 35														
—	—	—	—	69¾	Wolverhampton 7	a	04 44			06 41	06 47										07 32		07 48		
74	—	—	—	—	Coseley	a																			
77¼	—	—	—	—	Sandwell & Dudley	a															07 44				
—	—	—	—	82½	**Birmingham New Street** 12	a	05 12			06 58	07 08		07f36								07 55		08 11		
—	—	—	—	91	Birmingham International	a	05 39			07 14	07 40										08 09		08 39		
—	—	—	—	101½	Coventry	a	05 49			07 23	07 54		08g01		08h01						08 20		08 49		
285	—	—	99¼	—	Lichfield Trent Valley	a			06 32						07 15			07 19			→				
291¼	—	—	—	—	Tamworth Low Level	a			06 39				07 05		07 22					←					
304½	—	—	—	—	Nuneaton	a			06 50			07 05			07 37					07 37		07 48			
318¾	—	—	—	113	Rugby	a	06 02		07 04				07 27		→			07 45		07 54					
—	—	—	—	—	Northampton	a							08 05							08 29					
351½	—	—	—	—	Milton Keynes Central	a							08j24							08 57					
383½	—	—	—	—	Watford Junction	a			07s44			07s57	09j03												
—	—	—	—	—	Gatwick Airport 10	a							10k22												
401¼	—	—	—	—	**London Euston** 15	a			08 04			08 19	08 27					08 40				08 58		09 01	09 07

For general notes see front of timetable
For details of catering facilities see Directory of Train Operators

- **A** To Bournemouth (Table 51)
- **B** Not Mondays 28 January to 24 March. To Windermere (Table 83)
- **C** Also stops at Rugeley Trent Valley 0706 and Atherstone 0730
- **D** 28 January to 24 March
- **E** Until 25 January and from 31 March
- **H** ╤P to Wolverhampton, ⊠ from Wolverhampton
- **b** Not Mondays 28 January to 24 March
- **c** Change at Wilmslow and Crewe
- **e** Change at Chester and Crewe
- **f** Change at Tamworth
- **g** Change at Tamworth Low Level and Nuneaton
- **h** Change at Nuneaton
- **j** Change at Rugby and Northampton
- **k** Change at Rugby, Northampton and Watford Junction

OVERNIGHT SLEEPERS. For Sleeper trains, operated by First ScotRail, please refer to Tables 400 - 404

Scotland and North West England → West Midlands and London

Route Diagram - see first page of Table 65

		LM	XC		TP	VT	VT	VT	VT	VT	XC	VT MO	VT	VT	VT MO	LM	XC	VT	NT	VT	NT	LM	TP		VT
		1◇	1◇		1◇	1◇	1◇	1◇	1◇	1◇	1◇		1◇	1◇	1◇	1◇	R 1	1◇		1◇		1◇	1◇		1◇
			A								A	B [bus]		C	B		D						E		C
		[trolley]	[buffet]			⊠	⊠	⊠	⊠	⊠	[buffet]		⊠	⊠	⊠	[trolley]	[buffet]	⊠		[buffet]		[trolley]	[trolley]		⊠
Inverness	d																								
Aberdeen	d																								
Dundee	d																								
Perth	d																								
Edinburgh 10	d																								
Haymarket	d																								
Glasgow Central 15	d																								
Motherwell	d																								
Carstairs	d																								
Lockerbie	d																								
Carlisle 8	a																								
	d											04 35		05 44											06 09
Penrith North Lakes	d											05 10		05 58											06 23
Windermere	d																								06 20
Oxenholme Lake District	a											06 05		06 21											06 46
	d											06 05		06 22											06 47
Barrow-in-Furness	d				05b00																		06 15		
Lancaster 6	a				05b53							06 50		06 37									07 15		07 22
	d				05b53		06 33							06 38	06 58								07 16		07 23
Preston 8	a				06 27		06 48							07 15	07 15								07 35		07 40
Blackpool North	a						07 31							07 56	07 56										08 12
	d						06 09							06 34	06 34				06 57						07 03
Preston 8	d				06 28		06 51							07 18	07 18				07 25	07 29	←		07 40		07 43
Wigan North Western	a						07 01							07 29	07 29				07 44	07 40	07 44				07 55
	d						07 03							07 30	07 30				→	07 41	07 45				07 55
Bolton	a				06 52																		08 02		08c24
Manchester Piccadilly 10	a				07 15																		08 25		08c47
Manchester Airport ✈	a				07 40																		08 42		09c06
Liverpool Lime Street 10	a						07 59														08 27				09 19
	d	06 35						07 07								07 18						07 40			
Liverpool South Parkway 7 ✈	d	06 45																				07 50			
Runcorn	d	06 53						07u22								07 35						07 58			
Warrington Bank Quay	a						07 12							07 40	07 40					07 51					08 07
	d						07 14							07 41	07 41					07 53					08 07
Hartford	d	07 05																				08 08			
Manchester Piccadilly 10	d		06 54			07 05			06e38				07 15				07 24	07 45				07 28			
Stockport	d					07u14			06e48				07u23				07 33	07u55				07 37			
Manchester Airport ✈	d								06e57																
Wilmslow	d								07e04											07 27		07 46			
Holyhead	d								05 32																06f00
Bangor (Gwynedd)	d								06 01																06f28
Llandudno	d																								06g39
Llandudno Junction	d								06 21																06f53
Chester	d								07 15											07 30					08 00
Crewe 10	a	07 20							07 38							07 54				08 12		08 23			08 31
	d	07 23							07 48							07 56				08 15		08 25			08 34
Macclesfield	d												07 37				07 47	08 07							
Congleton	d		07 21								←						07 55								
Stoke-on-Trent	d		07 33								07 33		07 53				08 08	08 22							
Stafford	a	07 43	→				07 46				07 53			08 14	08 14	08 20	08 25					08 45			
	d	07 46					07 48				07 54			08 16	08 16	08 21	08 26					08 46			
Penkridge	a	07 51																				08 51			
Wolverhampton 7	a	08 05									08 12					08 37	08 41			08 48		09 06			
Coseley	a																					09 12			
Sandwell & Dudley	a															08 46									
Birmingham New Street 12	a	08 29									08 30					08 58	08 58			09 11		09 30			
Birmingham International ✈	a									←	08 57						09 14			09 39					
Coventry	a									08 20	09 15		09h00				09 23			09 49					
Lichfield Trent Valley	a																								
Tamworth Low Level	a																								
Nuneaton	a												08 29												
Rugby	a										09 27		09j27	08 49	08 49										09 23
Northampton	a													09 58	09 58										10 59
Milton Keynes Central	a												09 04					09 31							09 46
Watford Junction	a								09s14	09s20			09 54	09s28	09s28			10 25							
Gatwick Airport 10 ✈	a												11k22	11 22	11 22										
London Euston 15 ⊖	a					09 11	09 14	09 17	09 36	09 44			09 45	09 53	09 53			10 09							10 27

For general notes see front of timetable
For details of catering facilities see Directory of Train Operators

A To Reading (Table 51)
B 28 January to 24 March
C Not Mondays 28 January to 24 March
D To Bournemouth (Table 51)
E [trolley] from Preston
b 15 minutes later on Mondays
c Change at Preston
e Change at Crewe
f Change at Chester and Crewe
g Change at Llandudno Junction, Chester and Crewe
h Change at Nuneaton
j Change at Nuneaton and Coventry
k Change at Milton Keynes Central and Watford Junction

OVERNIGHT SLEEPERS. For Sleeper trains, operated by First ScotRail, please refer to Tables 400 - 404

Scotland and North West England → West Midlands and London

Route Diagram - see first page of Table 65

		VT	XC	VT	VT	VT	LM	XC	VT	LM	VT	TP	NT	VT	NT	XC	VT	VT	LM	XC		VT	NT	VT	LM
		MO																							
		1 ◇	1 ◇	1 ◇	1 ◇	1 ◇	1 ◇	1 ◇	1 ◇	1 ◇	1 ◇	1 ◇		1 ◇		1 ◇	1 ◇	1 ◇	1 ◇	R 1		1 ◇		1 ◇	1 ◇
		A	B					C				D				E				G			H		
		⊠	☕	⊠	☕	⊠	⌶	☕	☕	⌶	⊠	⌶		⊠		☕	⊠	⊠	⌶	☕		⊠		☕	⌶
Inverness	d																								
Aberdeen	d																								
Dundee	d																								
Perth	d																								
Edinburgh 10	d																							06 36	
Haymarket	d																							06u40	
Glasgow Central 15	d													05 55											
Motherwell	d													06u10											
Carstairs	d																								
Lockerbie	d																								
Carlisle 8	a													07 10										07 51	
	d	06 30												07 14										07 53	
Penrith North Lakes	d	06 44												07 29										08 09	
Windermere	d	06b20												07 24											
Oxenholme Lake District	a	07 07												07 51										08 32	
	d	07 08												07 53										08 33	
Barrow-in-Furness	d											07 01	07 17										07 58		
Lancaster 6	a	07 22										07 58	08 19	08 27									08 59	09 08	
	d	07 22										07 59	08 19	08 29									09 00	09 09	
Preston 8	a	07 40										08 17	08 42	08 46									09 25	09 26	
Blackpool North	a	08 12										08 51		09 33										10 02	
	d	07 03							07 41					08 09	←									08 41	
Preston 8	d	07 43							08 29			08 34	08 50	08 49	08 50									09 29	
Wigan North Western	a	07 55							08 39				→	08 59	09 10									09 40	
	d	07 55							08 41					09 01	09 11									09 41	
Bolton	a	08c24										08 58		09c34											
Manchester Piccadilly 10	a	08c47										09 20		09c57											
Manchester Airport	a	09c06										09 40		10c19											
Liverpool Lime Street 10	a	09 19							09 49						09 53									10 49	
	d			08 15			08 19			08 40								09 15	09 19						09 40
Liverpool South Parkway 7	d									08 50															09 50
Runcorn	d			08 31			08 35			08 58								09 31	09 35						09 58
Warrington Bank Quay	a	08 07							08 51					09 10										09 51	
	d	08 07							08 52					09 12										09 53	
Hartford	d									09 10															10 08
Manchester Piccadilly 10	d		07 54		07e34	08 15		08 24			08 45			08 34		08 54	09 15			09 24		09 45			09 34
Stockport	d		08 03		07f43	08u24		08 33			08u55			08 44		09 03	09u23			09 33		09u54			09 42
Manchester Airport	d				08e00													09 00							
Wilmslow	d				08e07	08 33								08 52				09 07						09 24	09 54
Holyhead	d	06g00			06 45													07 15							
Bangor (Gwynedd)	d	06g28			07 12													08 01							
Llandudno	d	06h39			07 03									07g47											
Llandudno Junction	d	06g53			07 31									07g56				08 27							
Chester	d	08 00			08 22				08 30					09 00				09 19							
Crewe 10	a	08 31			08 45	08 51	08 59		09 13	09 23				09 31				09 50	09 58					10 12	10 23
	d	08 34			08 50	08 54	09 00		09 15	09 25				09 34				09 53	10 00					10 15	10 25
Macclesfield	d		08 16					08 47			09 08					09 16				09 47		10 07			
Congleton	d		08 24													09 24									
Stoke-on-Trent	d		08 39					09 04			09 24					09 39	09 50			10 04		10 23			
Stafford	a		08 55			09 12	09 21	09 25		09 45								10 10	10 20	10 25					10 45
	d		08 57			09 13	09 21	09 26		09 46								10 12	10 21	10 26					10 46
Penkridge	a									09 51															10 52
Wolverhampton 7	a		09 12				09 36	09 41	09 48	10 06						10 12			10 36	10 41				10 47	11 07
Coseley	a									10 12															11 12
Sandwell & Dudley	a						09 46												10 46						
Birmingham New Street 12	a		09 30		09j54		09 58	09 58	10 11	10 30						10 30			10 58	10 58				11 11	11 30
Birmingham International	a		09 57					10 27	10 39							10 57				11 14				11 39	
Coventry	a		10 15	10k00				10 45	10 49							11 15		10k58		11 23				11 49	
Lichfield Trent Valley	a					09 26																			
Tamworth Low Level	a				09 22																				
Nuneaton	a			09 24														10 34							
Rugby	a	09 23	10 27	10m27										10 23		11 27									
Northampton	a	10 59												11 59											
Milton Keynes Central	a	09 46				10 11																11 28			
Watford Junction	a				10s21						10s46			11s02				11s25				12 25			
Gatwick Airport 10	a		12 33											12 22				13 22							
London Euston 15 ⊖	a	10 27		10 35	10 46	10 50					11 09			11 27			11 28	11 48				12 07			

For general notes see front of timetable
For details of catering facilities see Directory of Train Operators

- **A** 28 January to 24 March
- **B** To Brighton (Table 51)
- **C** To Plymouth (Table 51)
- **D** ⌶ from Preston
- **E** To Reading (Table 51)
- **G** To Bournemouth (Table 51)
- **H** From Maryport (Table 100)
- **b** By bus
- **c** Change at Preston
- **e** Change at Crewe
- **f** Change at Wilmslow and Crewe
- **g** Change at Chester and Crewe
- **h** Change at Llandudno Junction, Chester and Crewe
- **j** Change at Tamworth
- **k** Change at Nuneaton
- **m** Change at Nuneaton and Coventry

OVERNIGHT SLEEPERS. For Sleeper trains, operated by First ScotRail, please refer to Tables 400 - 404

Scotland and North West England → West Midlands and London

Route Diagram - see first page of Table 65

		TP	VT	NT	XC	VT	VT	LM	XC	VT	LM	NT	VT	LM	TP	VT	XC	VT		VT	VT	LM	XC	VT	NT
		1◇	1◇		1◇	1◇	1◇	1	1◇	1◇	1		1◇	1◇	1◇	1◇	1◇	1◇		1◇	1◇	1◇	R 1	1◇	
					A			B	C			D			E		A						G		
		🛒	⊠		☕	⊠	⊠	🛒	☕	⊠	🛒		☕	🛒	🛒	⊠	☕	☕		☕	☕	🛒	☕	☕	
Inverness	d																								
Aberdeen	d																								
Dundee	d																								
Perth	d		*05b15*													*06b09*									
Edinburgh 10	d																								
Haymarket	d																								
Glasgow Central 15	d	06 40	07 10										07 45			08 10									
Motherwell	d															08u28									
Carstairs	d																								
Lockerbie	d	07 40																							
Carlisle 8	a	08 02	08 19										09 11			09 30									
	d	08 04	08 21										09 14			09 34									
Penrith North Lakes	d	08 19											09 29			09 49									
Windermere	d	*08 20*											*09 28*												
Oxenholme Lake District	a	08 59											09 52			10 11									
	d	08 59											09 54			10 13									
Barrow-in-Furness	d														09 15										
Lancaster 6	a	09 14	09 27										10 08		10 15	10 27									
	d	09 14	09 29									09 35	10 09		10 16	10 29									
Preston 8	a	09 33	09 47									10 01	10 27		10 34	10 49									
Blackpool North	a		*10 21*									*10 57*			*11 21*	*11 32*									
	d		*09 11*	09 25									*09 38*			*10 11*									10 25
Preston 8	d	09 38	09 49	09 50									10 28		10 38	10 49									10 50
Wigan North Western	a		10 00	10 10									10 40			10 59									11 11
	d		10 02	10 11									10 42			11 01									11 11
Bolton	a	09 58	*10c34*												10 58	*11c34*									
Manchester Piccadilly 10	a	10 20	*10c57*												11 20	*11c57*									
Manchester Airport ✈	a	10 40	*11c19*												11 40	*12c19*									
Liverpool Lime Street 10	a			10 52									*11 49*												11 52
	d						10 15	10 19						10 40							11 15	11 19			
Liverpool South Parkway 7 ✈	d													10 50											
Runcorn	d						10 31	10 35						10 58							11 31	11 35			
Warrington Bank Quay	a		10 11										10 52			11 10									
	d		10 13										10 53			11 12									
Hartford	d							10 46						11 09											
Manchester Piccadilly 10	d				09 54	10 15			10 24	10 45						*10 34*	10 54	11 15					11 24	11 45	
Stockport	d				10 03	10u24			10 33	10u54						*10 42*	11 03	11u23					11 33	11u54	
Manchester Airport ✈	d						*10 00*													*11e00*					
Wilmslow	d						*10 06*						*10 24*			*10 54*				*11e06*					
Holyhead	d							*08f10*												09 50	*09 28*				
Bangor (Gwynedd)	d							*09f04*												10 18	*10 07*				
Llandudno	d		*08f47*													*09f47*				*10 14*	*10g14*				
Llandudno Junction	d		*08f56*					*09f27*								*09f56*				10 36	*10 30*				
Chester	d		*10 00*					*10 29*								*11 00*				11 28	*11 14*				
Crewe 10	a		10 32				10 50	10 58					11 13	11 23		11 31				11 47	11 50	11 58			
	d		10 34				10 53	11 00					11 14	11 25		11 34				11 49	11 53	12 00			
Macclesfield	d				10 16				10 47	11 07							11 16						11 47	12 07	
Congleton	d																11 24								
Stoke-on-Trent	d				10 39	10 50			11 04	11 23							11 39	11 50					12 04	12 23	
Stafford	a						11 10	11 19	11 25					11 45							12 10	12 20	12 25		
	d						11 12	11 21	11 26					11 46							12 12	12 21	12 26		
Penkridge	a													11 51											
Wolverhampton 7	a				11 12				11 41				11 48	12 06			12 12					12 36	12 41		
Coseley	a													12 12											
Sandwell & Dudley	a																					12 47			
Birmingham New Street 12	a				11 30				11 58				12 11	12 30			12 30					12 58	12 58		
Birmingham International ✈	a				*11 57*				*12 27*				*12 39*				*12 57*						13 14		
Coventry	a				*12 15*			*12h59*	*12 45*				*12 49*				*13 15*						13 23		
Lichfield Trent Valley	a							11 40															*13j25*		
Tamworth Low Level	a							11 47			←												*13j45*		
Nuneaton	a						11 34	12 02 →			12 02										12 34				
Rugby	a		11 23		*12 27*						12 16					12 23	*13 27*								
Northampton	a										*12 56*					*13 57*									
Milton Keynes Central	a		11 45				12 09				*13 25*														
Watford Junction	a						*12 56*			12s46						13s03					13s24				
Gatwick Airport 10 ✈	a															*14 22*					*15 22*				
London Euston 15 ⊖	a		12 26			12 26	12 48			13 09	13 18					13 27		13 28		13 40	13 47			14 04	

For general notes see front of timetable
For details of catering facilities see Directory of Train Operators

- **A** To Reading (Table 51)
- **B** Also stops at Rugeley Trent Valley 1132 and Atherstone 1156
- **C** To Plymouth (Table 51)
- **D** From Morecambe (Table 98)
- **E** 🛒 from Preston
- **G** To Bournemouth (Table 51)
- **b** Via Glasgow Queen Street and Glasgow Central. Passengers make their own way from one station to the other
- **c** Change at Preston
- **e** Change at Crewe
- **f** Change at Chester and Crewe
- **g** Change at Llandudno Junction and Crewe
- **h** Change at Nuneaton
- **j** Change at Stafford. By bus

OVERNIGHT SLEEPERS. For Sleeper trains, operated by First ScotRail, please refer to Tables 400 - 404

Scotland and North West England → West Midlands and London

Route Diagram - see first page of Table 65

		TP	TP	TP	VT	LM	TP	NT	VT	VT	XC	VT	VT	NT	VT	LM		XC	LM	VT	XC	VT	TP	VT	NT
		1◇	1◇	1◇	R 1	1◇	1◇		1◇	1◇	1◇	1◇	1◇		1◇	1◇		R 1	1◇	1◇	1◇	R 1	1◇	1◇	
											A							B			C		D		
			T	T	☕	T	T		☕	⊠	☕	☕	☕		☕	T		☕	T	☕	☕	☕	T	☕	
Inverness	d																							06b45	
Aberdeen	d				06 00																	06c34		07 20	
Dundee	d		06 38		07b17																	07c52		08 31	
Perth	d		06 14		07 03					07c14												08c13		08b48	
Edinburgh 10	d		08 21		08 51																			10 10	
Haymarket	d				08u57																			10u16	
Glasgow Central 15	d			08 40						09 39												10 10			
Motherwell	d																								
Carstairs	d																								
Lockerbie	d			09 40																				11 14	
Carlisle 8	a		09 54	10 02	10 16					10 47												11 22		11 32	
	d			10 06	10 17					10 50												11 22		11 34	
Penrith North Lakes	d			10 22																				11 49	
Windermere	d	10 18																						11 30	
Oxenholme Lake District	a	10 35		10 46	10 52																			12 11	
	d	10 37		10 46	10 53																			12 13	
Barrow-in-Furness	d				09 57																		11 18		
Lancaster 6	a	10 52		11 04	11 09																	12 12	12 17	12 27	
	d	10 53		11 05	11 10				11 29													12 12	12 18	12 29	
Preston 8	a	11 12		11 23	11 27				11 46	11 50												12 31	12 36	12 46	
Blackpool North	a	11 54			12 01				12 20	12 32			←											13 21	
	d				10 41		←	11 25		11 11			11 25									11 41		12 11	12 25
Preston 8	d			11 38 →	11 29		11 38	11 50	11 56 →	11 52			11 56	←								12 32	12 38	12 49	12 50
Wigan North Western	a				11 40			12 10					12 07	12 10								12 44		12 59	13 10
	d				11 41			→					12 08	12 11								12 45		13 01	13 11
Bolton	a						11 58			12 35													12 58	13e34	
Manchester Piccadilly 10	a						12 20			12 57													13 20	13e57	
Manchester Airport	a						12 40			13 19													13 40	14e19	
Liverpool Lime Street 10	a				12 49								13 19	12 52								13 49			13 52
	d					11 40									12 15				12 40						
Liverpool South Parkway 7	d					11 50													12 50						
Runcorn	d					11 58									12 31				12 58						
Warrington Bank Quay	a				11 51								12 18									12 57		13 10	
	d				11 52								12 20									12 59		13 12	
Hartford	d					12 08													13 10						
Manchester Piccadilly 10	d										11 54	12 15	11 34					12 24	12 34	12 45	12 54				
Stockport	d										12 03	12u24	11 42					12 33	12 42	12u54	13 03				
Manchester Airport	d												12 00												
Wilmslow	d				11 24	11 24							12 06						12 54						
Holyhead	d															10f30									
Bangor (Gwynedd)	d															11f03									
Llandudno	d												10f44											11f47	
Llandudno Junction	d												10f53			11f26								11f56	
Chester	d												12 00			12 29								13 00	
Crewe 10	a				12 12	12 24							12 41		12 50				13 23			13 27		13 32	
	d				12 13	12 24							12 44		12 53	13 00			13 25			13 33		13 34	
Macclesfield	d										12 16							12 47		13 07	13 16				
Congleton	d																				13 24				
Stoke-on-Trent	d										12 39	12 50						13 04		13 23	13 39				
Stafford	a					12 46									13 10	13 20		13 25	13 45						
	d					12 46									13 12	13 21		13 26	13 46						
Penkridge	a					12 52													13 51						
Wolverhampton 7	a				12 48	13 06					13 12					13 36		13 41	14 06		14 12	14 17			
Coseley	a					13 12													14 12						
Sandwell & Dudley	a															13 46									
Birmingham New Street 12	a				13 11	13 30					13 30					13 58		13 58	14 30		14 30	14 41			
Birmingham International	a				13 39						13 57							14 27			14 57	15 09			
Coventry	a				13 49						14 15				14g00			14 45			15 15	15 19			
Lichfield Trent Valley	a																								
Tamworth Low Level	a																								
Nuneaton	a														13 34										
Rugby	a										14 27		13 38		14h27						15 27			14 23	
Northampton	a												14 57											15 57	
Milton Keynes Central	a												14 01		14 09										
Watford Junction	a														14 54					14s46				15s02	
Gatwick Airport 10	a																							16 22	
London Euston 15	⊖ a									14 04		14 26	14 40		14 49					15 08				15 26	

For general notes see front of timetable
For details of catering facilities see Directory of Train Operators

A To Reading (Table 51)

B To Penzance (Table 135)

C To Guildford (Table 51)

D T from Preston

b Change at Haymarket

c Via Glasgow Queen Street and Glasgow Central. Passengers make their own way from one station to the other

e Change at Preston

f Change at Chester and Crewe

g Change at Nuneaton

h Change at Nuneaton and Coventry

OVERNIGHT SLEEPERS. For Sleeper trains, operated by First ScotRail, please refer to Tables 400 - 404

Scotland and North West England → West Midlands and London

Route Diagram - see first page of Table 65

		VT	VT	LM	XC	VT	TP	VT	TP	LM	VT	XC	VT	VT	VT	LM	XC	VT	NT	TP	VT	LM	TP	NT
																	R				R			
		1◇	1◇	1◇	1◇	1◇	1◇	1◇	1◇	1◇	1◇	1◇	1◇	1◇	1◇	1◇	1	1◇		1◇	1	1◇	1◇	
					A		B		B			C					D							
		☕	☕	🛒	☕	☕	🛒	☕	🛒	🛒	☕	☕	☕	☕	☕	🛒	☕	☕		🛒	☕	🛒	🛒	
Inverness	d																			07 55				
Aberdeen	d							08b20												08 50				
Dundee	d							09b33												09 59				
Perth	d										09c08									09 56	10c12			
Edinburgh 10	d							10 51												11 52				
Haymarket	d							10u56																
Glasgow Central 15	d										11 10										12 10			
Motherwell	d										11u26													
Carstairs	d																							
Lockerbie	d																							
Carlisle 8	a							12 11			12 32									13 09	13 21			
	d							12 13			12 34									13 11	13 21			
Penrith North Lakes	d							12 29			12 49									13 25				
Windermere	d						12 21													13 24				
Oxenholme Lake District	a						12 38	12 52			13 11									13 49	13 57			
	d						12 40	12 53			13 13									13 49	13 59			
Barrow-in-Furness	d										12 06									12 56				
Lancaster 6	a						12 58	13 08			13 28									14 05				
	d						12 59	13 09			13 29									14 06				
Preston 8	a						13 17	13 26			13 46									14 24	14 28			
Blackpool North	a						13 54	13 59			14 21									15 00				
	d							12 41	←		13 11								13 25		13 41		←	14 21
Preston 8	d						13 38	13 29	13 38		13 49								13 50	14 38	14 30		14 38	14 46
Wigan North Western	a						→	13 40			14 00								14 11	→	14 41			15 09
	d							13 41			14 01								14 11		14 42			→
Bolton	a								13 58		14e34												14 58	
Manchester Piccadilly 10	a								14 20		14e57												15 20	
Manchester Airport ✈	a								14 40		15e19												15 40	
Liverpool Lime Street 10	a							14 49											14 52		15 49			
	d		13 15	13 19						13 40					14 15							14 40		
Liverpool South Parkway 7 ✈	d									13 50												14 50		
Runcorn	d		13 31	13 35						13 58					14 31							14 58		
Warrington Bank Quay	a							13 51			14 11										14 52			
	d							13 53			14 12										14 54			
Hartford	d									14 08												15 08		
Manchester Piccadilly 10	d	13 15			13 24	13 45				13 34		13 54	14 05	14 15			14 24	14 45						
Stockport	d	13u24			13 33	13u54				13 42		14 03	14 15	14u24			14 33	14u54						
Manchester Airport ✈	d		13 00										14 00											
Wilmslow	d		13 06					13 24		13 54			14 25								14 26			
Holyhead	d							11 40													12f35			
Bangor (Gwynedd)	d							12 19													13f04			
Llandudno	d										12f47										13g14			
Llandudno Junction	d							12 42			12f56										13f27			
Chester	d							13 33			14 00										14 30	14 30		
Crewe 10	a		13 50	13 58				14 12		14 23	14 32		14 42		14 50						15 12	15 23		
	d		13 53	14 00				14 14		14 25	14 34		14 49		14 53	15 00					15 15	15 25		
Macclesfield	d				13 47	14 07						14 16					14 47	15 07						
Congleton	d																							
Stoke-on-Trent	d	13 49			14 04	14 23						14 39		14 50			15 04	15 23						
Stafford	a		14 10	14 20	14 25					14 45					15 10	15 20	15 25					15 45		
	d		14 12	14 21	14 26					14 46					15 12	15 21	15 26					15 46		
Penkridge	a									14 51												15 51		
Wolverhampton 7	a			14 36	14 41			14 47		15 06		15 12				15 36	15 41				15 48	16 06		
Coseley	a									15 12												16 12		
Sandwell & Dudley	a			14 46												15 46								
Birmingham New Street 12	a			14 58	14 58			15 11		15 30		15 30	15h54			15 58	15 58				16 11	16 30		
Birmingham International ✈	a				15 14			15 39				15 57					16 27				16 39			
Coventry	a				15 23			15 49				16 15			16j11		16 45				16 49			
Lichfield Trent Valley	a												15 17											
Tamworth Low Level	a												15 24											
Nuneaton	a		14 34										→		15 34									
Rugby	a										15 23	16 27												
Northampton	a																							
Milton Keynes Central	a					15 28					15 46				16 09									
Watford Junction	a		15s25			16 25									16 54			16s46						
Gatwick Airport 10 ✈	a																							
London Euston 15 ⊖	a	15 28	15 48			16 07					16 27			16 28	16 48			17 08						

For general notes see front of timetable
For details of catering facilities see Directory of Train Operators

- **A** To Bournemouth (Table 51)
- **B** 🛒 from Preston
- **C** To Reading (Table 51)
- **D** To Penzance (Table 135)
- **b** Change at Haymarket
- **c** Via Glasgow Queen Street and Glasgow Central. Passengers make their own way from one station to the other
- **e** Change at Preston
- **f** Change at Chester and Crewe
- **g** Change at Llandudno Junction, Chester and Crewe
- **h** Change at Tamworth
- **j** Change at Nuneaton

OVERNIGHT SLEEPERS. For Sleeper trains, operated by First ScotRail, please refer to Tables 400 - 404

Scotland and North West England → West Midlands and London

Route Diagram - see first page of Table 65

		VT	NT	VT	XC	VT	VT	VT	VT	LM	XC	VT		VT	LM	VT	VT	TP	TP	VT	NT	XC	VT	VT	VT
		1◇		1◇	R 1	1◇	1◇	1◇	1◇	1◇	R 1	R 1		1◇	1◇	1◇	1◇	1◇	1◇	1◇		R 1	1◇	1◇	1◇
					A						B							C	C			D			
		🍴		🍴	🍴	🍴	🍴	🍴	🍴	🛒	🍴	🍴		🍴	🛒	🍴	🍴	🛒	🛒	🍴		🍴	🍴	🍴	🍴
Inverness	d			07b55																					
Aberdeen	d			09c36								10e22													
Dundee	d			09c50								11e30													
Perth	d			11c12																					
Edinburgh 10	d											12 51													
Haymarket	d											12u56													
Glasgow Central 15	d			12 49																					
Motherwell	d																								
Carstairs	d																								
Lockerbie	d											13 53													
Carlisle 8	a			13 57								14 12													
	d			14 00								14 14								14 34					
Penrith North Lakes	d											14 29								14 48					
Windermere	d											14 18						14 18							
Oxenholme Lake District	a											14 52						14 35		15 11					
	d											14 53						14 37		15 12					
Barrow-in-Furness	d																		14 10						
Lancaster 6	a											15 07						14 54	15 03	15 27					
	d	14 29										15 08						15 16		15 28					
Preston 8	a	14 46		14 59								15 25						15 34		15 45					
Blackpool North	a	15 21		15 54								16 00								16 21					
	d	14 11		14 30								14 41								15 11	15 25				
Preston 8	d	14 49	←	15 02								15 29						15 38		15 48	15 50				
Wigan North Western	a	14 59	15 09									15 40								15 59	16 10				
	d	15 01	15 11									15 41								16 00	16 11				
Bolton	a			15 34														15 58		16f34					
Manchester Piccadilly 10	a			15 57														16 20		16f57					
Manchester Airport ✈	a			16 19														16 40		17f19					
Liverpool Lime Street 10	a		15 52									16 49									16 53				
	d								15 15	15 19					15 40										16 15
Liverpool South Parkway 7 ✈	d														15 50										
Runcorn	d								15 31	15 35					15 58										16 31
Warrington Bank Quay	a	15 10						←				15 51								16 10					
	d	15 12						15 12				15 52								16 11					
Hartford	d	→													16 08										
Manchester Piccadilly 10	d				14 54		15 15	14 34			15 24				15 34	15 45						15 54	16 15		
Stockport	d				15 03		15u24	14 42			15 33				15 42	15u54						16 03	16u24		
Manchester Airport ✈	d								15 00															16g00	
Wilmslow	d							14 54	15 06			15 24			15 54									16g06	
Holyhead	d							13h20				13 35		14 14											
Bangor (Gwynedd)	d							13h49				14 14		14 43											
Llandudno	d							13h47						14 35										15 08	
Llandudno Junction	d							14h07				14 37		15 03										15 17	
Chester	d							15 03				15 30		15 48						16 00				16 08	
Crewe 10	a							15 35	15 50	15 58		16 11		16 11	16 23		←			16 31				16 38	16 50
	d							15 38	15 53	16 00		16 11		16 28	16 25		16 28			16 34				16 49	16 53
Macclesfield	d				15 16						15 47			→		16 07						16 16			
Congleton	d				15 24																				
Stoke-on-Trent	d				15 39		15 50				16 04					16 23						16 39	16 50		
Stafford	a								16 10	16 20	16 25				16 45										17 10
	d								16 12	16 21	16 26				16 46										17 12
Penkridge	a														16 51										
Wolverhampton 7	a				16 12					16 36	16 41	16 48			17 05							17 12			
Coseley	a														17 12										
Sandwell & Dudley	a									16 47															
Birmingham New Street 12	a				16 30					16 58	16 58	17 11			17 30							17 30			
Birmingham International ✈	a				16 55						17 14	17 39										17 55			
Coventry	a				17 04				17j08		17 24	17 52										18 04			18j06
Lichfield Trent Valley	a					←																			
Tamworth Low Level	a					15 24																			
Nuneaton	a					15 38			16 34																17 34
Rugby	a				17 16	15 53		16 38			17 54									17 23		18 17			17 49
Northampton	a					16 16		17 46																	18 23
Milton Keynes Central	a					16 35										17 28	17 40			17 46					18 11
Watford Junction	a							17s17	17s25							18 21								18s17	
Gatwick Airport 10 ✈	a				19 52				19 23																
London Euston 15 ⊖	a			17 17		17 22	17 27	17 40	17 47							18 07	18 21			18 27			18 28	18 42	18 50

For general notes see front of timetable
For details of catering facilities see Directory of Train Operators

A To Brighton (Table 51)
B To Bournemouth (Table 51)
C 🛒 from Preston
D To Reading (Table 51)
b Change at Perth, Glasgow Queen Street and Glasgow Central. Passengers make their own way between Glasgow Queen Street and Glasgow Central
c Via Glasgow Queen Street and Glasgow Central. Passengers make their own way from one station to the other
e Change at Haymarket
f Change at Preston
g Change at Crewe
h Change at Chester and Crewe
j Change at Nuneaton

OVERNIGHT SLEEPERS. For Sleeper trains, operated by First ScotRail, please refer to Tables 400 - 404

Scotland and North West England → West Midlands and London

Route Diagram - see first page of Table 65

		LM	XC	TP	VT	TP	VT	LM	LM	VT		XC	VT	VT	LM	NT	XC	VT	VT	LM	TP	VT	XC	NT	VT
		1	1 ◇	1 ◇	1 ◇	1 ◇	1 ◇	1	1 ◇	1 ◇		R 1	1 ◇	1 ◇	1 ◇		R 1	1 ◇	1 ◇	1 ◇	1 ◇	1 ◇	1 ◇		1 ◇
		A	B									C					D				E		C		
		⚲	🍽	⚲	🍽	⚲	🍽	⚲	⚲	🍽		🍽	🍽	🍽	⚲		🍽	🍽	🍽	⚲	⚲	🍽	🍽		🍽
Inverness	d			*09b19*															*10 53*						
Aberdeen	d				*10b41*														*12c24*						
Dundee	d				*11b50*														*13c33*						
Perth	d			*11b39*	*12b12*														*13 04*			*13b12*			
Edinburgh 10	d																		14 51						
Haymarket	d																		14u56						
Glasgow Central 15	d			13 40	14 10																	15 10			
Motherwell	d																					15u29			
Carstairs	d																								
Lockerbie	d			14 37															15 53						
Carlisle 8	a			14 58	15 21														16 12			16 32			
	d			15 08	15 21														16 14			16 34			
Penrith North Lakes	d			15 23															16 29			16 49			
Windermere	d			*15 21*															*16 28*						
Oxenholme Lake District	a			15 46															16 52			17 11			
	d			15 47															16 53			17 13			
Barrow-in-Furness	d																		*15 28*		16 21				
Lancaster 6	a			16 02	16 09														17 08		17 14	17 27			
	d			16 03	16 09					16 29									17 09		17 15	17 29			
Preston 8	a			16 22	16 27					16 46									17 26		17 35	17 46			
Blackpool North	a			*17 00*						*17 34*									*18 03*			*18 22*			
	d				*15 41*	⟵				*16 10*						16 25			*16 38*			*17 10*			
Preston 8	d			16 38	16 29	16 38				16 49						16 50			17 29		17 35	17 49		17 50	
Wigan North Western	a			⟶	16 40					16 59						17 09			17 40			17 59		18 11	
	d				16 41					17 01						17 11			17 41			18 00		18 11	
Bolton	a					16 58															17 59	*18e34*			
Manchester Piccadilly 10	a					17 20															18 20	*18e59*			
Manchester Airport	a					17 40															18 42	*19e19*			
Liverpool Lime Street 10	a				*17 49*											17 53			*18 49*					18 55	
	d								16 40					17 15	17 18					17 37					
Liverpool South Parkway 7	d								16 50						17 28					17 47					
Runcorn	d								16 58					17 31	17 36					17 56					
Warrington Bank Quay	a				16 51					17 10									17 51			18 10			
	d				16 53					17 12									17 53			18 12			
Hartford	d								17 09											18 08					
Manchester Piccadilly 10	d		16 24				16 45			*16 34*		16 54	17 15				17 24	17 45		*17 34*			17 54		18 15
Stockport	d		16 33				16u54			*16 42*		17 03	17u23				17 33	17u55		*17 42*			18 03		18u24
Manchester Airport	d													*17 00*											
Wilmslow	d				*16 24*					*16 54*				*17 06*					*17 26*	*17 51*					
Holyhead	d				*14f35*														*15 39*						
Bangor (Gwynedd)	d				*15f04*														*16 17*						
Llandudno	d									*15f47*									*16g14*			*16f47*			
Llandudno Junction	d				*15f27*					*15f56*									*16 40*			*16f56*			
Chester	d				*16 31*					*17 00*									*17 31*			*17 59*			
Crewe 10	a				17 13				17 23	17 32				17 51	17 58				18 12	18 23		18 31			
	d	17 00			17 15				17 24	17 34				17 54	18 00				18 15	18 25		18 34			
Macclesfield	d		16 47				17 08					17 16					17 47	18 08					18 16		
Congleton	d											17 24											18 24		
Stoke-on-Trent	d		17 04				17 24					17 39	17 50				18 04	18 24					18 39		18 51
Stafford	a	17 19	17 25						17 45					18 11	18 20		18 25			18 45					
	d	17 20	17 26						17 46					18 13	18 21		18 26			18 46					
Penkridge	a								17 51											18 51					
Wolverhampton 7	a		17 41		17 48				18 06			18 12			18 36		18 41		18 48	19 05			19 12		
Coseley	a								18 12											19 12					
Sandwell & Dudley	a														18 46										
Birmingham New Street 12	a		17 58		18 11				18 30			18 30			18 58		18 58		19 11	19 30			19 30		
Birmingham International	a		*18 29*		*18 39*							*18 57*					19 14		*19 39*				*19 57*		
Coventry	a		*18 46*		*18 49*							*19 15*		*19h06*			19 24		*19 49*				*20 15*		
Lichfield Trent Valley	a	17 37																							
Tamworth Low Level	a	17 44																							
Nuneaton	a	17 59						⟵						18 35											
Rugby	a	18 14	*18 58*					18 14		18 23		*19 27*		*19j27*								19 23	*20 27*		
Northampton	a	⟶								*19 29*												*20 57*			
Milton Keynes Central	a																	19 28				19 46			
Watford Junction	a						18s49			19s02				19s28											20s10
Gatwick Airport 10	a									*20 23*		21 47		*21 23*									22 32		
London Euston 15 ⊖	a						19 11	19 18		19 25			19 28	19 50				20 07				20 26			20 33

For general notes see front of timetable
For details of catering facilities see
Directory of Train Operators

A Also stops at Rugeley Trent Valley 1729 and Atherstone 1753

B To Plymouth (Table 51)
C 🍽 to Reading
D To Bournemouth (Table 51)
E ⚲ from Preston
b Via Glasgow Queen Street and Glasgow Central. Passengers make their own way from one station to the other

c Change at Haymarket
e Change at Preston
f Change at Chester and Crewe
g Change at Llandudno Junction and Crewe
h Change at Nuneaton
j Change at Nuneaton and Coventry

OVERNIGHT SLEEPERS. For Sleeper trains, operated by First ScotRail, please refer to Tables 400 - 404

Scotland and North West England → West Midlands and London

Route Diagram - see first page of Table 65

		VT	XC	TP	VT	TP	LM	VT	XC	NT	VT	TP	VT	TP	LM	XC	VT	LM	XC	NT	VT	VT	XC	VT
		1 ◇	1 ◇	1 ◇	1 ◇	1 ◇	1 ◇	1 ◇	1 ◇		1 ◇	1 ◇	1 ◇	1 ◇	1 ◇	1 ◇	1 ◇	1 ◇	1 ◇		1 ◇	1 ◇	1 ◇	1 ◇
			A													B								
Inverness	d												12b40											
Aberdeen	d			13c21									13e42				14c25							
Dundee	d			14c30									14e50				15c32							
Perth	d				14e12								15e12											
Edinburgh 10	d			15 52													16 51							
Haymarket	d			15u56													16u56							
Glasgow Central 15	d				16 10								16 46											17 40
Motherwell	d																							
Carstairs	d																							
Lockerbie	d			16 52													17 49							18 47
Carlisle 8	a			17 13	17 21								17 56				18 11							19 03
	d			17 15	17 21								17 59				18 11							19 06
Penrith North Lakes	d			17 29	17 36												18 27							19 20
Windermere	d			17 27								18 09												19 18
Oxenholme Lake District	a			17 53	17 59							18 29	18 32	←			18 51							19 43
	d			17 53	18 00							18 38	18 34	18 38			18 51							19 44
Barrow-in-Furness	d			17 06								→	17 43											
Lancaster 6	a			18 09		←							18 49	18 55			19 08							19 59
	d			18 16		18 16							18 51	18 55			19 08							20 01
Preston 8	a			→	18 28	18 36							19 08	19 14			19 27							20 18
Blackpool North	a				19 09	19 23								19 57			20 03							20 56
	d				17 38					18 25			18 38							19 25				19 42
Preston 8	d				18 29	18 38				18 50			19 10	19 14			19 29			19 50				20 21
Wigan North Western	a				18 41					19 10			19 21				19 40			20 11				20 31
	d				18 42					19 11			19 22				19 41			20 11				20 33
Bolton	a					18 58								19 45			20f12							
Manchester Piccadilly 10	a					19 20								20 04			20f34							
Manchester Airport ✈	a					19 40								20 26			21g06							
Liverpool Lime Street 10	a									19 52			20 19							20 52				
	d	18 15					18 40								19 19			19 40				19 49		
Liverpool South Parkway 7 ✈	d						18 50											19 50						
Runcorn	d	18 31					18 58								19 35			19 58				20 05		
Warrington Bank Quay	a				18 52								19 32				19 51							20 42
	d				18 53								19 33				19 53							20 44
Hartford	d						19 12											20 08						
Manchester Piccadilly 10	d	17h39	18 24				18 34	18 45	18 54		19 15					19 24			19 54		20 15		20 24	
Stockport	d	17h51	18 33				18 42	18u54	19 03		19u24					19 33			20 03		20u24		20 33	
Manchester Airport ✈	d	18 00															19h01							
Wilmslow	d	18 11			18 24		18 54										19 26					19 54		
Holyhead	d				16j35								17 27											18j35
Bangor (Gwynedd)	d				17j04								18 06											19j14
Llandudno	d												17k47									18j47		
Llandudno Junction	d				17j27								18 29									18j56		19j32
Chester	d				18 30								19 22									20 05		20 30
Crewe 10	a	18 50			19 12		19 25						19 52		19 58		20 13	20 22				20 31		21 03
	d	18 53			19 15		19 27						19 54		20 00		20 15	20 24				20 39		21 05
Macclesfield	d		18 47					19 07	19 16		19 37					19 47			20 16		20 37		20 47	
Congleton	d								19 24										20 24					
Stoke-on-Trent	d		19 04					19 24	19 39		19 53					20 04			20 39		20 53		21 04	
Stafford	a	19 10	19 25				19 47		19 57				20 12		20 20	20 25		20 44	20 56			20 59	21 25	
	d	19 12	19 26				19 48		19 58				20 14		20 21	20 26		20 46	20 57			21 04	21 26	
Penkridge	a						19 53											20 51						
Wolverhampton 7	a		19 41		19 48		20 06		20 12						20 36	20 41	20 48	21 05	21 12				21 41	
Coseley	a						20 12											21 12						
Sandwell & Dudley	a														20 46									
Birmingham New Street 12	a		19 58		20 11		20 30		20 35						20 58	20 58	21 11	21 30	21 35				22 04	
Birmingham International ✈	a				20 39											21 14	21 39		22 20				22 52	
Coventry	a	20m08			20 49											21 23	21 49		22 39			22m48	23 12	
Lichfield Trent Valley	a												21n05											
Tamworth Low Level	a												21n25											
Nuneaton	a	19 34																				21 27		
Rugby	a	20q27											20 47			22 22						21 42		
Northampton	a												21 47									22 54		
Milton Keynes Central	a	20 09						20 28													21 55	22 05		22 16
Watford Junction	a	20 43									21s13		21s26									22s25		22 47
Gatwick Airport 10 ✈	a	22r23																						
London Euston 15 ⊖	a	20 48						21 07			21 36		21 51								22 52	23 05		23 14

For general notes see front of timetable
For details of catering facilities see Directory of Train Operators

A To Plymouth (Table 51)
B To Southampton Central (Table 51)

b Change at Perth, Glasgow Queen Street and Glasgow Central. Passengers make their own way between Glasgow Queen Street and Glasgow Central
c Change at Haymarket
e Via Glasgow Queen Street and Glasgow Central. Passengers make their own way from one station to the other
f Change at Preston
g Change at Preston and Manchester Piccadilly
h Change at Wilmslow and Crewe
j Change at Chester and Crewe
k Change at Llandudno Junction and Crewe
m Change at Nuneaton
n By bus
q Change at Nuneaton and Coventry
r Change at Milton Keynes Central and Watford Junction

OVERNIGHT SLEEPERS. For Sleeper trains, operated by First ScotRail, please refer to Tables 400 - 404

Scotland and North West England → West Midlands and London

Route Diagram - see first page of Table 65

		LM	VT	NT	TP	TP	VT	VT	LM	NT	XC	VT	NT	TP	NT	SR	SR	SR	SR	SR	SR	SR
																	FX	FX	FO	FO	FX	FO
																	R	R	R	R	R	R
		1 ◇	1 ◇		1 ◇	1 ◇	1 ◇	1 ◇	1 ◇		1 ◇	1 ◇		1 ◇								
														A							B	B
Inverness	d							14 41								16b56		18 27		18 27	20 40	20 40
Aberdeen	d				15c20			16c21				17e21				18b41		20 26		20 26	21 40	21 40
Dundee	d				16c31			17c31				18e35				19b50		21 38		21 38	23u06	23u06
Perth	d						16b12	16 48				18b12				20b12	21b18		21b18		23u18	23u18
Edinburgh 10	d				17 52			18 51				20f15						23 40		23 40		
Haymarket	d				17u56			18u56				20f19										
Glasgow Central 15	d						18 10					20 10				22 03	23 41		23 41			
Motherwell	d						18u27										23u56		23u56			
Carstairs	d											20u51					00u16		00u16			
Lockerbie	d				18 53			19 49				21 26										
Carlisle 8	a				19 15		19 30	20 11				21 45				00 34						
	d				19 16		19 32	20 11				21 47					01u39		01u39			
Penrith North Lakes	d				19 31			20 27				22 02										
Windermere	d							20 27				21 28		22 16								
Oxenholme Lake District	a				19 54		20 06	20 52				22 26		22 36								
	d				19 55		20 07	20 52				22 27		22 36								
Barrow-in-Furness	d					19 10							21 45									
Lancaster 6	a				20 10	20 15	20 22	21 07				22 42	22 49	22 53	←							
	d				20 11	20 17	20 23	21 07				22 44	23 01		23 01							
Preston 8	a				20 29	20 35	20 42	21 26				23 02	→		23 25						04s29	04s05
Blackpool North	a						21 36	22 12							23 59							
	d							20 53		22 03												
Preston 8	d			20 27	20 32	20 38	20 49	21 29		22 27		23 23			23 29							
Wigan North Western	a			20 46			21 00	21 41		22 47		23s39										
	d			20 47			21 01	21 42		22 47												
Bolton	a				20 53	21 08	21g54	22g53							23 51						05 39	05 39
Manchester Piccadilly 10	a				21 14	21 30	22g18	23g30				00 16			00h09						05 57	05 57
Manchester Airport ✈	a				21 37	21 51	22g39	23g58				00 45			00j45						06 14	06 14
Liverpool Lime Street 10	a			21 38				22 38		23 38												
	d	20 40							21 40													
Liverpool South Parkway 7 ✈	d	20 50							21 51													
Runcorn	d	20 58							21 59													
Warrington Bank Quay	a						21 11	21 52														
	d						21 13	21 54														
Hartford	d	21 08							22 09													
Manchester Piccadilly 10	d	20 34	20 45					21 03			21 54											
Stockport	d	20 46	20u54					21 15			22 03											
Manchester Airport ✈	d	19k56						21k10														
Wilmslow	d	20 54	21 05					21 26														
Holyhead	d							19 35														
Bangor (Gwynedd)	d							20 14														
Llandudno	d		19m47																			
Llandudno Junction	d		19m56					20 37														
Chester	d		21 00					21 33														
Crewe 10	a	21 23	21 28				21 32	22 13	22 24												05s30	05s02
	d	21 25	21 34				21 35	22 16	22 24													
Macclesfield	d										22 16											
Congleton	d										22 24											
Stoke-on-Trent	d		21 51								22 39											
Stafford	a	21 45					21 55	22 35	22 47		22 56										06 16	06 08
	d	21 46					21 55	22 36	22 47		22 57											
Penkridge	a	21 51							22 52													
Wolverhampton 7	a	22 08					22 16	22 48	23 06		23 12										06 41	06 41
Coseley	a																					
Sandwell & Dudley	a																					
Birmingham New Street 12	a	22 30	22n54				22 38	23 11	23 30		23 47										06 58	06 58
Birmingham International ✈	a						23 09				00q21										07 14	07 14
Coventry	a						23 19				00 37										07 23	07 23
Lichfield Trent Valley	a		22 15																		06 32	
Tamworth Low Level	a		22 22																		06 39	
Nuneaton	a		22 33																		06 50	
Rugby	a		22 48				23 32														07 04	07 24
Northampton	a		23 56																			
Milton Keynes Central	a		23 10																			
Watford Junction	a		23s30														06s34		06s50		07 44	08 03
Gatwick Airport 10 ✈	a																08r39		08 22			
London Euston 15 ⊖	a		00 09														07 00		07 18		07 43	08 04

For general notes see front of timetable
For details of catering facilities see Directory of Train Operators

A To Barrow-in-Furness (Table 82) via Morecambe (Table 98)
B Also conveys portion from Fort William (Table 227)

b Via Glasgow Queen Street and Glasgow Central. Passengers make their own way from one station to the other
c Change at Haymarket
e Change at Edinburgh and Carstairs
f Change at Carstairs
g Change at Preston

h Manchester Victoria. Connection arrives Manchester Piccadilly 0029, change at Bolton
j Change at Bolton
k Change at Wilmslow and Crewe
m Change at Chester and Crewe
n Change at Tamworth
q Saturday mornings arr. 0022
r Change at Watford Junction and Clapham Junction

OVERNIGHT SLEEPERS. For Sleeper trains, operated by First ScotRail, please refer to Tables 400 - 404

Table 65

until 26 January

Scotland and North West England → West Midlands and London

Route Diagram - see first page of Table 65

		VT	XC	VT	XC	LM	VT	TP	VT	VT	VT	VT	VT	LM	TP	VT	VT	VT	XC	VT	NT	VT	LM	TP	VT
		1 ◇	1 ◇	1 ◇	1 ◇	1 ◇	1 ◇	1 ◇	1 ◇	1 ◇	1 ◇	1 ◇	1 ◇	1 ◇	1 ◇	1 ◇	1 ◇	1 ◇	1 ◇	R 1		1 ◇	1 ◇	1 ◇	1 ◇
			A		A														A					B	
			☕	☕	☕		☕		☕	☕	☕	☕	☕			☕	☕	☕	☕	☕		☕		🍴	☕
Inverness	d																								
Aberdeen	d																								
Dundee	d																								
Perth	d																								
Edinburgh 10	d																								
Haymarket	d																								
Glasgow Central 15	d																								
Motherwell	d																								
Carstairs	d																								
Lockerbie	d																								
Carlisle 8	a																								
	d																								06 30
Penrith North Lakes	d																								06 44
Windermere	d																								06 35
Oxenholme Lake District	a																								07 07
	d																								07 08
Barrow-in-Furness	d						04 15								05 15									06 15	
Lancaster 6	a														06 08									07 15	07 23
	d						05 20								06 08	06 25								07 16	07 24
Preston 8	a						05 37								06 27	06 42								07 35	07 41
Blackpool North	a															07 31								08 12	08 36
	d						04 43	05 19					05 30			06 08				06 34	06 57				07 03
Preston 8	d						05 40	05 48					06 15		06 28	06 45				07 20	07 25			07 40	07 44
Wigan North Western	a						05 50	06 11					06 26			06 55				07 31	07 44				07 55
	d						05 52	06 13					06 27			06 57				07 32	07 45				07 56
Bolton	a							06 29							06 52									08 02	08b24
Manchester Piccadilly 10	a							06 56							07 15									08 25	08b47
Manchester Airport	a							07 15							07 40									08 42	09b06
Liverpool Lime Street 10	a						06 59						07 29			07 59					08 26				09 20
	d									06 07				06 33				07 12					07 39		
Liverpool South Parkway 7	d													06 45									07 49		
Runcorn	d									06 24				06 53				07 28					07 57		
Warrington Bank Quay	a						06 07						06 46			07 06				07 42					08 06
	d						06 09						06 47			07 08				07 44					08 07
Hartford	d													07 07									08 06		
Manchester Piccadilly 10	d			05 05					06 03		06 21	06 41				06 38	06 55		07 24			07 43	07 28		
Stockport	d			05u15					06u12		06 30	06u51				06 48	07 04		07 33			07u53	07 37		
Manchester Airport	d													05c53				06 57							
Wilmslow	d			05 23										06 36		06 55		07 04		07 27			07 46		
Holyhead	d	02 15											04e27							05 35					
Bangor (Gwynedd)	d	02 42											05e00							06 04					
Llandudno	d																								
Llandudno Junction	d	03 00					05 00						05e18			05 45				06 24					
Chester	d	03 40	04 55				06 00						06 30			06 56				07 30					
Crewe 10	a	03 59		05 41			06 30			06 43			07 08	07 23		07 28		07 48		08 03			08 21		08 27
	d	04 02	05 42	05 44		06 09	06 33			06 45			07 10	07 23		07 30		07 50		08 11			08 22		08 29
Macclesfield	d								06 25		06 43	07 05					07 17		07 46			08 05			
Congleton	d				←																				
Stoke-on-Trent	d		06 01		06 01				06 41		06 59	07 23					07 33		08 04			08 21			
Stafford	a	04 29	→	06 08	06 19	06 29				07 04	07 18			07 44		07 47			08 25				08 43		08 47
	d	04 30		06 10	06 20	06 30				07 06	07 19			07 44		07 47			08 26				08 44		08 48
Penkridge	a					06 35								07 49									08 50		
Wolverhampton 7	a	04 45			06 41	06 47					07 35		07 47	08 07			08 11		08 41	08 47			→		
Coseley	a													08 14											
Sandwell & Dudley	a										07 47														
Birmingham New Street 12	a	05 08			06 58	07 08					07 56		08 10	08 27			08 30		08 58	09 10					09 24
Birmingham International	a	06 09			07 14	07 40					08 09			09 09			08 42		09 14						09 39
Coventry	a	06 19			07 23	07 52	07 46			08 14	08 19					08 50	08 54	09 14	09 23						09 49
Lichfield Trent Valley	a	06f40																							
Tamworth Low Level	a	07f01																							
Nuneaton	a	07f49																							
Rugby	a	06 33		07 24		08 21	08 21			08 27							09 21	09 25							
Northampton	a			07 54						09 48															
Milton Keynes Central	a			08g17			08 21		08 32	08 51		09 17					09 29								10 24
Watford Junction	a			08s03			08s42		08s52		09s16					09s43		10s10				10s19			
Gatwick Airport 10	a			09 22					10 22							11 22						12 22			
London Euston 15	a			08 28			09 04		09 15	09 29	09 38	09 56				10 05	10 07	10 32				10 41			11 02

For general notes see front of timetable
For details of catering facilities see Directory of Train Operators

A To Bournemouth (Table 51)
B 🍴 from Preston
b Change at Preston
c Change at Wilmslow and Crewe
e Change at Chester and Crewe
f Change at Stafford. By bus
g Change at Rugby and Northampton

until 26 January

Scotland and North West England → West Midlands and London

Route Diagram - see first page of Table 65

		LM	VT	VT	XC	VT	VT	TP	LM	VT	LM	NT	VT	VT	XC	VT	VT	TP	LM	VT	LM	NT	VT	VT	XC
		1◇	1◇	1◇	1◇	1◇	1◇	1◇	1◇	1◇	1◇		1◇	1◇	1◇	1◇	1◇	1◇	1◇	1◇	1◇		1◇	1◇	1◇
					A			B							C										A
			☕	☕	☕	☕	☕	🍴		☕			☕	☕	☕	☕	☕	🍴		☕			☕	☕	☕
Inverness	d																								
Aberdeen	d																								
Dundee	d																								
Perth	d																			05b15					
Edinburgh 10	d																06 52								
Haymarket	d																06u56								
Glasgow Central 15	d									06 10								06 58		07 10					
Motherwell	d									06u25										07u28					
Carstairs	d																								
Lockerbie	d																07 52	07 56							
Carlisle 8	a									07 26							08 11	08 18		08 30					
	d									07 28							08 13	08 20		08 32					
Penrith North Lakes	d									07 43							08 29	08 35		08 47					
Windermere	d									*07 24*							*08 28*								
Oxenholme Lake District	a									08 05							08 52	08 59		09 09					
	d									08 07							08 53	08 59		09 11					
Barrow-in-Furness	d							07 05									*07 58*								
Lancaster 6	a							08 02		08 25							09 08	09 14		09 25					
	d							08 03		08 27							09 09	09 14		09 27					
Preston 8	a							08 21		08 44							09 26	09 35		09 44					
Blackpool North	a							*09 00*		*09 32*							*10 02*			*10 21*					
	d					*07 41*				*08 09*							*08 41*			*09 11*		09 25			
Preston 8	d					08 29		08 34		08 47		08 50					09 29	09 38		09 47		09 50			
Wigan North Western	a					08 39				08 57		09 10					09 40			09 57		10 09			
	d					08 40				08 59		09 11					09 41			09 59		10 11			
Bolton	a							08 58		*09c34*								09 58		*10c34*					
Manchester Piccadilly 10	a							09 20		*09c57*								10 20		*10c57*					
Manchester Airport ✈	a							09 40		*10c19*								10 40		*11c19*					
Liverpool Lime Street 10	a					*09 49*						09 52					*10 49*					10 52			
	d			08 12					08 38					09 15					09 37					10 15	
Liverpool South Parkway 7 ✈	d								08 47										09 47						
Runcorn	d			08 28					08 55					09 31					09 55					10 31	
Warrington Bank Quay	a					08 50				09 08							09 51			10 08					
	d					08 52				09 10							09 53			10 10					
Hartford	d								09 07										10 05						
Manchester Piccadilly 10	d		07 55	*07 34*	08 24		08 40			*08 34*			08 54		09 24	09 40				*09 34*			09 54		10 24
Stockport	d		08 04	*07e43*	08 33		08u49			*08 44*			09 04		09 33	09u49				*09 42*			10 03		10 33
Manchester Airport ✈	d			*08 00*										*09 00*										*10 00*	
Wilmslow	d			*08 07*		*08 21*				*08 52*				*09 07*			*09 24*			*09 51*				*10 06*	
Holyhead	d			*06f00*		*06 45*								*07 15*											
Bangor (Gwynedd)	d			*06f30*		*07 12*								*08 01*											
Llandudno	d			*06g39*		*07h03*								*07h47*										*08f47*	
Llandudno Junction	d			*06f54*		*07 30*								*08 27*										*08f56*	
Chester	d			*08 00*		*08 30*								*09 19*										*10 00*	
Crewe 10	a			08 47		09 11			09 21	09 29				09 50			10 12		10 21	10 29				10 50	
	d			08 49		09 13			09 22	09 31				09 53			10 15		10 22	10 31				10 53	
Macclesfield	d		08 17		08 46		09 05						09 20		09 46	10 05							10 20		10 46
Congleton	d				08 54																				10 54
Stoke-on-Trent	d		08 39		09 07		09 21						09 39		10 04	10 21							10 39		11 07
Stafford	a			09 08	09 25				09 43					10 11	10 25				10 43					11 11	11 25
	d	←		09 10	09 26				09 44		←			10 13	10 26				10 44		←			11 13	11 26
Penkridge	a	08 50							09 50 →		09 50								10 50 →		10 50				
Wolverhampton 7	a	09 05	09 11		09 41	09 47					10 05		10 11		10 41		10 48				11 05		11 11		11 41
Coseley	a	09 14									10 14										11 14				
Sandwell & Dudley	a																								
Birmingham New Street 12	a	09 27	09 30	09u50	09 58	10 11				10 24	10 27		10 30	10u50	10 58		11 11			11 24	11 27		11 30	11u50	11 58
Birmingham International ✈	a		09 44	09 59						10 39			10 44	10 59	11 14					11 39			11 44	11 59	
Coventry	a		09 54	10s13						10 49			10 54	11s13	11 23					11 49			11 54	12s13	
Lichfield Trent Valley	a																								
Tamworth Low Level	a																								
Nuneaton	a																								
Rugby	a		10 08	*10 33*									11 08	*11 33*									12 08	*12 34*	
Northampton	a		*10 46*										*11 46*										*12 46*		
Milton Keynes Central	a		10 31	10 49						11 25						12 00				12 25			12 31	12 48	
Watford Junction	a		*11j13*				11s17						11s52	12s05		*12 54*							*13j14*		
Gatwick Airport 10 ✈	a													*13 22*		*14k22*									
London Euston 15 ⊖	a		11 09	11 27			11 40			12 03			12 13	12 28		12 42				13 03			13 09	13 26	

For general notes see front of timetable
For details of catering facilities see Directory of Train Operators

- **A** To Plymouth (Table 51)
- **B** 🍴 from Preston
- **C** To Bournemouth (Table 51)
- **b** Via Glasgow Queen Street and Glasgow Central. Passengers make their own way from one station to the other
- **c** Change at Preston
- **e** Change at Wilmslow and Crewe
- **f** Change at Chester and Crewe
- **g** Change at Llandudno Junction, Chester and Crewe
- **h** Change at Llandudno Junction and Crewe
- **j** Change at Rugby
- **k** Change at Milton Keynes Central and Watford Junction

Scotland and North West England → West Midlands and London

Route Diagram - see first page of Table 65

		VT	VT	TP	LM	VT	LM	NT	VT	VT	XC	VT		TP	TP	TP	VT	TP	LM	VT	LM	NT	VT	VT	XC
			R														R								
		1 ◇	1	1 ◇	1 ◇	1 ◇	1 ◇		1 ◇	1 ◇	1 ◇	1 ◇		1 ◇	1 ◇	1 ◇	1	1 ◇	1 ◇	1 ◇	1 ◇		1 ◇	1 ◇	1 ◇
				A							B														C
		☕	☕	🍴		☕			☕	☕	☕	☕			🍴	🍴	☕	🍴		☕			☕	☕	☕
Inverness	d																								
Aberdeen	d															06 00									
Dundee	d															07 11									
Perth	d															07 03									
Edinburgh 10	d															08 42	08 51								
Haymarket	d																08u56								
Glasgow Central 15	d		07 40			08 06									08 40										
Motherwell	d					08u26																			
Carstairs	d																								
Lockerbie	d														09 36										
Carlisle 8	a		09 08			09 21									09 58	10 06	10 08	←							
	d		09 14			09 23									10 15 →		10 10	10 15							
Penrith North Lakes	d		09 30			09 38												10 30							
Windermere	d		09 26											10 18											
Oxenholme Lake District	a		09 53			10 00								10 35			10 45	10 53							
	d		09 54			10 06								10 37			10 47	10 54							
Barrow-in-Furness	d			09 15														09 58							
Lancaster 6	a		10 09	10 15		10 20								10 52			11 04	11 10							
	d		10 09	10 16		10 22								10 53			11 06	11 10							
Preston 8	a		10 27	10 34		10 43								11 13			11 23	11 32							
Blackpool North	a					11 23								11 56			12 01	12 20							
	d		09 40			10 11		10 25									10 41			11 11		11 25			
Preston 8	d		10 29	10 38		10 47		10 50									11 28	11 38		11 47		11 50			
Wigan North Western	a		10 40			10 57		11 11									11 39			11 57		12 09			
	d		10 41			10 59		11 11									11 40			11 59		12 11			
Bolton	a			10 58		11b34												11 58							
Manchester Piccadilly 10 🚊	a			11 20		11b57												12 20							
Manchester Airport ✈	a			11 40		12b19												12 40							
Liverpool Lime Street 10	a		11 49					11 52									12 49					12 52			
	d				10 37					11 15									11 37					12 15	
Liverpool South Parkway 7 ✈	d				10 47														11 47						
Runcorn	d				10 55					11 31									11 55					12 31	
Warrington Bank Quay	a		10 51			11 08											11 51			12 08					
	d		10 53			11 10											11 53			12 10					
Hartford	d				11 05														12 05						
Manchester Piccadilly 10 🚊	d	10 40				10 34			10 58		11 24	11 40								11 34			11 58		12 24
Stockport	d	10u49				10 43			11 07		11 33	11u49								11 42			12 07		12 33
Manchester Airport ✈	d									11 00														12 00	
Wilmslow	d		10 24			10 51				11 06							11 24			11 51				12 06	
Holyhead	d		08c25							09 28							09 50								
Bangor (Gwynedd)	d		09c04							10 07							10 18								
Llandudno	d									10e14														10c47	
Llandudno Junction	d		09c27							10 30							10 36							10c56	
Chester	d		10 29							11 14							11 28							12 00	
Crewe 10	a		11 13		11 21	11 29				11 50							12 12		12 21	12 29				12 50	
	d		11 15		11 22	11 31				11 53							12 13		12 22	12 31				12 53	
Macclesfield	d	11 05							11 20		11 46	12 05											12 20		12 46
Congleton	d																								12 54
Stoke-on-Trent	d	11 21							11 39		12 04	12 21											12 39		13 07
Stafford	a				11 43					12 11	12 25								12 43					13 11	13 25
	d				11 44		←			12 13	12 26								12 44		←			13 13	13 26
Penkridge	a				11 50 →		11 50												12 50 →		12 50				
Wolverhampton 7 🚊	a		11 48				12 06		12 11		12 41						12 48				13 05		13 11		13 41
Coseley	a						12 14														13 14				
Sandwell & Dudley	a																								
Birmingham New Street 12	a		12 11			12 24	12 27		12 30	12u50	12 58						13 11			13 24	13 27		13 30	13u50	13 58
Birmingham International ✈	a					12 39			12 45	12 59	13 14									13 39			13 44	13 59	
Coventry	a					12 49			12 55	13s13	13 23									13 49			13 55	14s13	
Lichfield Trent Valley	a										13f31														
Tamworth Low Level	a										13f52														
Nuneaton	a										14f40														
Rugby	a								13 09	13 33													14 09	14 33	
Northampton	a								13 47														14 46		
Milton Keynes Central	a					13 25						14 00								14 25			14 32	14 49	
Watford Junction	a	13s19							13s51	14s04		14 54											15g13		
Gatwick Airport 10 ✈	a									15 22		16h22													
London Euston 15 ⊖	a	13 41				14 03			14 12	14 27		14 43								15 03			15 09	15 27	

For general notes see front of timetable
For details of catering facilities see Directory of Train Operators

- **A** 🍴 from Preston
- **B** To Bournemouth (Table 51)
- **C** To Penzance (Table 135)
- **b** Change at Preston
- **c** Change at Chester and Crewe
- **e** Change at Llandudno Junction and Crewe
- **f** Change at Stafford. By bus
- **g** Change at Rugby
- **h** Change at Milton Keynes Central and Watford Junction

Table 65

Saturdays

until 26 January

Scotland and North West England → West Midlands and London

Route Diagram - see first page of Table 65

		VT	VT	TP	LM	VT	LM	NT	VT	VT	XC	VT	TP	VT	TP	LM	VT	LM	NT	VT	VT	XC	VT	TP	VT
		1◇	R 1	1◇	1◇	1◇	1◇		1◇	1◇	1◇	1◇	1◇	1◇	1◇	1◇	1◇	1◇		1◇	1◇	1◇	1◇	1◇	R 1
				A							B		A		A							C			
Inverness	d													06 45										07 55	
Aberdeen	d		06b34			07b07								08c20										08 50	
Dundee	d		07b52			08b21								09c32										09 59	
Perth	d		08b13			08b43								08 48			09b08							09 56	10b12
Edinburgh 10	d													10 51										11 52	
Haymarket	d													10u56											
Glasgow Central 15	d		10 10			10 20											11 10								12 10
Motherwell	d																11u25								
Carstairs	d																								
Lockerbie	d																								
Carlisle 8	a		11 20			11 31								12 11			12 30							13 09	13 20
	d		11 22			11 32								12 13			12 32							13 11	13 21
Penrith North Lakes	d					11 47								12 29			12 47							13 25	
Windermere	d					11 30							12 23											13 25	
Oxenholme Lake District	a					12 09							12 40	12 52			13 10							13 49	13 57
	d					12 11							12 42	12 53			13 11							13 50	13 58
Barrow-in-Furness	d			11 18																					
Lancaster 6	a		12 09	12 16		12 25							13 02	13 08			13 26							14 07	
	d		12 11	12 16		12 27							13 04	13 09			13 27							14 17 →	
Preston 8	a		12 28	12 35		12 44							13 22	13 26			13 44								14 26
Blackpool North	a					13 21								14 00			14 21								15 01
	d		11 41			12 11		12 25						12 41	←		13 11		13 25						13 41
Preston 8	d		12 29	12 38		12 47		12 50					13 38 →	13 29	13 38		13 47		13 50						14 29
Wigan North Western	a		12 40			12 57		13 09						13 40			13 57		14 11						14 40
	d		12 41			12 59		13 11						13 41			13 59		14 11						14 41
Bolton	a			12 58		13e34									13 58		14e34								
Manchester Piccadilly 10	a			13 20		13e57									14 20		14e57								
Manchester Airport	a			13 40		14e19									14 40		15e19								
Liverpool Lime Street 10	a		13 49					13 52						14 49					14 52						15 49
	d				12 37					13 15						13 37		13 37			14 15				
Liverpool South Parkway 7	d				12 47											13 47		13 47							
Runcorn	d				12 55					13 31						13 55		13 55			14 31				
Warrington Bank Quay	a		12 51			13 08								13 51			14 08								14 50
	d		12 53			13 10								13 53			14 10								14 52
Hartford	d				13 07											14 05		14 05							
Manchester Piccadilly 10	d	12 40				12 34			12 58		13 24	13 40					13 34			13 58		14 24	14 40		
Stockport	d	12u49				12 42			13 07		13 33	13u49					13 42			14 07		14 33	14u49		
Manchester Airport	d									13 00											14 00				
Wilmslow	d		12 24			12 51				13 06				13 24			13 54				14 06				14 24
Holyhead	d		10f30											11 40											12f35
Bangor (Gwynedd)	d		11f03											12 19											13f04
Llandudno	d									11f47											12f47				13g14
Llandudno Junction	d		11f26							11f56				12 42							12f56				13f27
Chester	d		12 29							13 00				13 33							14 00				14 30
Crewe 10	a		13 12		13 21	13 29				13 51				14 12		14 21	14 28	14 21			14 50				15 10
	d		13 15		13 22	13 31				13 54				14 15		14 22	14 31	14 22			14 53				15 13
Macclesfield	d	13 05							13 20		13 46	14 05								14 20		14 46	15 05		
Congleton	d																					14 54			
Stoke-on-Trent	d	13 21							13 39		14 04	14 21								14 39		15 07	15 21		
Stafford	a				13 43					14 13	14 25					14 43		14 43			15 11	15 25			
	d				13 44		←			14 14	14 26					14 44		14 44			15 13	15 26			
Penkridge	a				13 50 →		13 50									14 50 →		14 50							
Wolverhampton 7	a		13 48				14 05		14 11		14 41			14 48				15 05		15 11		15 41			15 46
Coseley	a						14 14											15 14							
Sandwell & Dudley	a																								
Birmingham New Street 12	a		14 11			14 24	14 27		14 30	14u50	14 58			15 11			15 24	15 27		15 30	15u50	15 58			16 11
Birmingham International	a					14 39			14 45	14 59	15 14						15 39			15 45	15 59				
Coventry	a					14 49			14 55	15s13	15 23						15 49			15 55	16s13				
Lichfield Trent Valley	a																					16h21			
Tamworth Low Level	a																					16h42			
Nuneaton	a																					17h30			
Rugby	a								15 09	15 33										16 09	16 33				
Northampton	a								15 46											16 46					
Milton Keynes Central	a					15 25			16j17			16 00					16 25			16 32	16 49				
Watford Junction	a	15s17							15s49	16s06		16 54								17k13			17s18		
Gatwick Airport 10	a									17 22		18m22													
London Euston 15	a	15 40				16 05			16 10	16 29		16 42					17 05			17 10	17 27		17 40		

For general notes see front of timetable
For details of catering facilities see Directory of Train Operators

- **A** from Preston
- **B** To Bournemouth (Table 51)
- **C** To Penzance (Table 135)
- **b** Via Glasgow Queen Street and Glasgow Central. Passengers make their own way from one station to the other
- **c** Change at Haymarket
- **e** Change at Preston
- **f** Change at Chester and Crewe
- **g** Change at Llandudno Junction, Chester and Crewe
- **h** Change at Stafford. By bus
- **j** Change at Rugby and Northampton
- **k** Change at Rugby
- **m** Change at Milton Keynes Central and Watford Junction

until 26 January

Scotland and North West England → West Midlands and London

Route Diagram - see first page of Table 65

		TP	LM	VT	LM	NT	VT	VT	XC	VT	TP	TP	VT	TP	LM	VT	LM	NT	VT	VT	XC	VT	TP	VT	TP
		1◇	1◇	1◇	1◇		1◇	1◇	1◇	1◇	1◇	1◇	R 1	1◇	1◇	1◇	1◇		1◇	1◇	1◇	1◇	1◇	1◇	1◇
									A					B							C				
		🛒		☕			☕	☕	☕	☕			☕	🛒		☕			☕	☕	☕	☕	🛒	☕	🛒
Inverness	d																						09b19		
Aberdeen	d												10c22											10b41	
Dundee	d												11c30											11b50	
Perth	d												11 08			11b12							11b39	12b12	
Edinburgh 10	d												12 51												
Haymarket	d												12u56												
Glasgow Central 15	d															13 10							13 40	14 10	
Motherwell	d															13u24									
Carstairs	d																								
Lockerbie	d															14 11							14 37		
Carlisle 8	a												14 10			14 30							14 58	15 20	
	d												14 13			14 32							15 08	15 21	
Penrith North Lakes	d												14 28			14 47							15 23		
Windermere	d										14 18												15 22		
Oxenholme Lake District	a										14 35		14 51			15 09							15 46		
	d	←									14 37		14 53			15 11							15 47		
Barrow-in-Furness	d	12 56										14 10													
Lancaster 6	a										14 54	15 03	15 07	←		15 25							16 02	16 09	
	d	14 17										15 16 →	15 09	15 16		15 27							16 03	16 10	
Preston 8	a	14 35											15 26	15 34		15 44							16 22	16 27	
Blackpool North	a	15 21											16 01			16 21							17 01	17 34	
	d			14 11		14 25							14 41			15 11		15 25						15 41	←
Preston 8	d	14 38		14 47		14 50							15 29	15 38		15 47		15 50					16 38 →	16 29	16 38
Wigan North Western	a			14 57		15 10							15 40			15 57		16 10						16 40	
	d			14 59		15 11							15 41			15 59		16 11						16 41	
Bolton	a	14 58												15 58		16e34									16 58
Manchester Piccadilly 10	a	15 20												16 20		16e57									17 20
Manchester Airport ✈	a	15 40												16 40		17e19									17 40
Liverpool Lime Street 10	a					15 52							16 49					16 54						17 49	
	d		14 37					15 10							15 37					16 15					
Liverpool South Parkway 7 ✈	d		14 47												15 47										
Runcorn	d		14 55					15 26							15 55					16 31					
Warrington Bank Quay	a			15 08									15 52			16 08								16 51	
	d			15 10									15 53			16 10								16 52	
Hartford	d		15 05												16 05										
Manchester Piccadilly 10	d			14 34			14 58		15 24	15 40						15 34			15 58		16 24	16 40			
Stockport	d			14 42			15 07		15 33	15u49						15 42			16 07		16 33	16u49			
Manchester Airport ✈	d							15 00												16 00					
Wilmslow	d			14 51				15 06					15 24			15 51				16 06				16 24	
Holyhead	d												13 35		14 13									14f35	
Bangor (Gwynedd)	d												14 14		14 41									15f04	
Llandudno	d							13f47							14g35					15 08					
Llandudno Junction	d							13f56					14 37		14 59					15 16				15f27	
Chester	d							15 03					15 30		15 48					16 12				16 31	
Crewe 10	a		15 21	15 28				15 45					16 12		16 21	16 29				16 50				17 13	
	d		15 22	15 31				15 48					16 13		16 22	16 31				16 53				17 15	
Macclesfield	d						15 20		15 46	16 05									16 20		16 46	17 05			
Congleton	d																				16 54				
Stoke-on-Trent	d						15 39		16 04	16 21									16 39		17 07	17 21			
Stafford	a		15 43					16 07	16 24						16 44					17 11	17 25				
	d		15 44		←			16 09	16 26						16 44		←			17 13	17 26				
Penkridge	a		15 50 →		15 50										16 50 →		16 50								
Wolverhampton 7	a				16 05		16 11		16 41				16 48				17 08		17 11		17 41			17 48	
Coseley	a				16 14												17 14								
Sandwell & Dudley	a																								
Birmingham New Street 12	a			16 24	16 27		16 30	16u50	16 58				17 11			17 24	17 27		17 30	17u50	17 58			18 11	
Birmingham International ✈	a			16 39			16 45	16 59	17 14							17 39			17 44	17 59					
Coventry	a			16 49			16 55	17s13	17 23							17 49			17 55	18s13					
Lichfield Trent Valley	a																								
Tamworth Low Level	a																								
Nuneaton	a																								
Rugby	a						17 09	17 33											18 09	18 28					
Northampton	a						17 46												18 46						
Milton Keynes Central	a									18 00						18 24			18 32	18 52					
Watford Junction	a			17s41			17s49	18s06		18 54										19h16		19s21			
Gatwick Airport 10 ✈	a							19 22		20j22															
London Euston 15 ⊖	a			18 03			18 10	18 29		18 44						19 03			19 10	19 30		19 42			

For general notes see front of timetable
For details of catering facilities see Directory of Train Operators

A To Bournemouth (Table 51)
B 🛒 from Preston
C To Plymouth (Table 51)
b Via Glasgow Queen Street and Glasgow Central. Passengers make their own way from one station to the other
c Change at Haymarket
e Change at Preston
f Change at Chester and Crewe
g Change at Llandudno Junction and Crewe
h Change at Rugby
j Change at Milton Keynes Central and Watford Junction

Scotland and North West England → West Midlands and London

Route Diagram - see first page of Table 65

		LM	VT	LM	NT	VT	VT	XC	VT	VT	LM	TP	VT	VT	VT	NT	XC	VT	TP	VT	LM	TP	VT	NT	VT
		1 ◇	1 ◇	1 ◇		1 ◇	1 ◇	1 ◇	1 ◇	1 ◇	1 ◇	1 ◇	1 ◇	1 ◇	1 ◇		1 ◇	1 ◇	1 ◇	1 ◇	1 ◇	1 ◇	1 ◇		1 ◇
								A				B					C								
			🍽			🍽	🍽	🍽	🍽	🍽		☕	🍽	🍽	🍽		🍽	🍽	☕	🍽		☕	🍽		🍽
Inverness	d									*10 53*															
Aberdeen	d									*12b24*									*13b21*						
Dundee	d									*13b33*									*14b30*						
Perth	d									*13 04*			*13c12*							*14c12*					
Edinburgh [10]	d									14 51									15 52						
Haymarket	d									14u56									15u56						
Glasgow Central [15]	d												15 10							16 03			16 10		
Motherwell	d												15u25												
Carstairs	d																								
Lockerbie	d																		16 52						
Carlisle [8]	a									16 07			16 29						17 13	17 20			17 30		
	d									16 09			16 31						17 15	17 21			17 33		
Penrith North Lakes	d									16 24			16 47						17 29	17 36			17 47		
Windermere	d									*16 22*									*17 27*						
Oxenholme Lake District	a									16 47			17 09						17 53	17 59			18 10		
	d									16 48			17 11						17 53	18 00		←	18 11		
Barrow-in-Furness	d									*15 28*		16 21										*17 06*			
Lancaster [6]	a									17 03		17 14	17 25						18 09				18 26		
	d									17 04		17 15	17 27						18 16			18 16	18 27		
Preston [8]	a									17 21		17 34	17 44						→	18 29		18 36	18 44		
Blackpool North	a									*18 03*			*18 30*										*19 21*		
	d		*16 10*		16 25					*16 38*			*17 10*							*17 38*			*18 11*	18 25	
Preston [8]	d		16 47		16 50					17 24		17 35	17 47			17 50				18 30		18 38	18 47	18 50	
Wigan North Western	a		16 57		17 09					17 35			17 57			18 11				18 41			18 58	19 10	
	d		16 59		17 11					17 36			17 58			18 11				18 42			18 59	19 11	
Bolton	a											17 59	*18e34*									18 58	*19e34*		
Manchester Piccadilly [10] 🚊	a											18 20	*18e59*									19 20	*19e58*		
Manchester Airport ✈	a											18 42	*19e19*									19 40	*20e19*		
Liverpool Lime Street [10]	a				17 53					*18 34*						18 55								19 52	
	d	16 37					17 15				17 37				18 10						18 40				
Liverpool South Parkway [7] ✈	d	16 47									17 47										18 50				
Runcorn	d	16 55					17 31				17 55				18 26						18 58				
Warrington Bank Quay	a		17 08							17 46			18 08							18 52			19 09		
	d		17 10							17 48			18 10							18 53			19 10		
Hartford	d	17 07									18 05										19 09				
Manchester Piccadilly [10] 🚊	d		*16 34*			16 58		17 24	17 40				*17 34*	17 58			18 24	18 40					*18 34*		18 58
Stockport	d		*16 43*			17 07		17 33	17u49				*17 42*	18 07			18 33	18u49					*18 43*		19 07
Manchester Airport ✈	d						*17 00*								*18 00*										
Wilmslow	d		*16 51*				*17 06*			*17 26*			*17 51*		*18 11*					*18 24*			*18 51*		
Holyhead	d									*15 39*										*16f35*					
Bangor (Gwynedd)	d									*16 17*										*17f04*					
Llandudno	d						*15f47*			*16g14*					*16f47*										
Llandudno Junction	d						*15f56*			*16 40*					*16f56*					*17f27*					
Chester	d						*17 00*			*17 31*					*18 00*					*18 30*					
Crewe [10]	a	17 21	17 29				17 50			18 07	18 21		18 29		18 45					19 13	19 22		19 29		
	d	17 22	17 31				17 53			18 13	18 21		18 32		18 48					19 15	19 23		19 31		
Macclesfield	d					17 20		17 46	18 05					18 20			18 46	19 05							19 20
Congleton	d																18 54								
Stoke-on-Trent	d					17 39		18 04	18 21					18 39			19 07	19 21							19 39
Stafford	a	17 43					18 11	18 25			18 43				19 06		19 25				19 44		19 50		
	d	17 44		←			18 13	18 26			18 43				19 08		19 26				19 45		19 52		
Penkridge	a	17 50		17 50							18 49										19 51				
Wolverhampton [7] 🚊	a	→		18 07		18 11		18 41		18 48	19 07			19 11			19 41			19 48	20 07				20 11
Coseley	a			18 14							19 14														
Sandwell & Dudley	a																								
Birmingham New Street [12]	a		18 24	18 27		18 30	18u50	18 58		19 11	19 27			19 30			19 58			20 11	20 30				20 30
Birmingham International ✈	a		18 39			18 44	18 59	19 14			*20 09*			19 42											20 42
Coventry	a		18 49			18 55	19s13	19 23						19 52	20 13						*21 23*				20 52
Lichfield Trent Valley	a																				*20h38*				
Tamworth Low Level	a																				*20h59*				
Nuneaton	a																				*21h47*				
Rugby	a					19 09	*19 33*						20 00	*20 21*	*20 33*								21 00		*21 21*
Northampton	a					*19 46*							*20 47*										*21 49*		
Milton Keynes Central	a								20 06				20 35	20 40	21 01										21 39
Watford Junction	a		19s41			19s49	20s22							21s18	*21 57*			22s08					22s16		22s22
Gatwick Airport [10] ✈	a					*21 22*	*22 23*																		
London Euston [15] ⊖	a		20 03			20 16	20 49		21 20				21 36	21 42	22 01			22 34					22 42		22 46

For general notes see front of timetable
For details of catering facilities see Directory of Train Operators

A To Bournemouth (Table 51)
B ☕ from Preston
C To Plymouth (Table 51)
b Change at Haymarket
c Via Glasgow Queen Street and Glasgow Central. Passengers make their own way from one station to the other
e Change at Preston
f Change at Chester and Crewe
g Change at Llandudno Junction and Crewe
h Change at Stafford. By bus

Saturdays

until 26 January

Scotland and North West England → West Midlands and London

Route Diagram - see first page of Table 65

		XC	TP	VT	LM	NT	VT	VT	VT	VT	NT	NT	TP	TP	VT	XC	LM	VT	TP	NT	NT	SR	SR
		1 ◇	1 ◇	1 ◇	1 ◇		1 ◇	1 ◇	1 ◇	1 ◇			1 ◇	1 ◇	1 ◇	1 ◇	1 ◇	1 ◇	1				
		A				B														C			
				⊡			⊡	⊡	⊡	⊡			🍴		⊡			⊡					
Inverness	d			12 40																		14b41	16c56
Aberdeen	d			14e25									15e20									16c41	18c41
Dundee	d			15e32									16e31									17c50	19c50
Perth	d			14 49			15c12								16c12							18c12	20c12
Edinburgh 10	d			16 51									17 52										
Haymarket	d			16u56									17u56										
Glasgow Central 15	d						17 07								18 10							20 03	22 03
Motherwell	d														18u27								
Carstairs	d																						
Lockerbie	d			17 50									18 53		19 12								
Carlisle 8	a			18 11			18 31						19 15		19 31							22 24	00 34
	d			18 11			18 33						19 16		19 32								
Penrith North Lakes	d			18 27			18 48						19 31										
Windermere	d		18 10										19 28						20 24				
Oxenholme Lake District	a		18 30	18 51			19 10						19 54		20 07				20 44				
	d		18 33	18 51			19 12						19 55		20 08				20 46				
Barrow-in-Furness	d					18 14								19 15									
Lancaster 6	a		18 49	19 07		19 17	19 26						20 10	20 16	20 20				21 03				
	d		18 51	19 07		19 18	19 28						20 11	20 16	20 21					21 20			
Preston 8	a		19 09	19 26		19 43	19 45						20 29	20 35	20 41					21 45			
Blackpool North	a		20 01	20 07			20 36								21 36					22 36			
	d			18 42			19 10				19 25	19 42						20 53			22 03		
Preston 8	d		19 14	19 29			19 48				19 50	20 27	20 32	20 37	20 43			21 28			22 28		
Wigan North Western	a			19 40			19 58				20 10	20 47			20 54			21 39			22 47		
	d			19 41			20 00				20 11	20 48			20 55			21 40			22 47		
Bolton	a		19 37	20f11			20f32						20 53	21 07	21f53					22 52			
Manchester Piccadilly 10 ⛴	a		20 04	20f34			20f58						21 14	21 30	22f18					23 30			
Manchester Airport ✈	a		20 26	21g06			21f19						21 37	21 51	22f39					23 55			
Liverpool Lime Street 10	a										20 52	21 39						22 38			23 38		
	d				19 37				20 10								21 16						
Liverpool South Parkway 7 ✈	d				19 47												21 26						
Runcorn	d				19 55				20 26								21 34						
Warrington Bank Quay	a			19 51			20 09								21 05			21 50					
	d			19 53			20 11								21 06			21 52					
Hartford	d				20 05												21 44						
Manchester Piccadilly 10 ⛴	d	19 24					19 34	19 58		20 17					20 34	20 54		20 58					
Stockport	d	19 33					19 42	20 07		20 26					20 46	21 04		21 15					
Manchester Airport ✈	d			19h02											19h56			21h10					
Wilmslow	d			19 26			19 54								20 54			21 26					
Holyhead	d			17 35											18j35			19 35					
Bangor (Gwynedd)	d			18 14											19j14			20 14					
Llandudno	d			17k47					18j47								19j47						
Llandudno Junction	d			18 37					18j56						19j32		19j56	20 37					
Chester	d			19 34					20 05						20 30		21 00	21 33					
Crewe 10	a			20 13	20 21		20 29		20 45						21 26		21 58	22 11					
	d			20 15	20 22		20 32		20 48						21 28		22 00	22 13					
Macclesfield	d	19 46						20 20		20 40						21 17							
Congleton	d	19 54														21 25							
Stoke-on-Trent	d	20 07						20 36		20 58						21 39							
Stafford	a	20 25			20 43					21 17					21 51	21 57	22 24	22 32					
	d	20 26			20 44					21 18					21 51	21 58	22 25	22 33					
Penkridge	a				20 50												22 30						
Wolverhampton 7 ⛴	a	20 41		20 48	21 08			21 11		21 35					22 09	22 13	22 43	22 48					
Coseley	a																						
Sandwell & Dudley	a									21 46													
Birmingham New Street 12	a	20 58		21 11	21 27			21 30		21 56					22 30	22 37	23 04	23 10					
Birmingham International ✈	a	21 14						21 42		22 09					23 04		23 33	00 21					
Coventry	a	21 23						21 52		22 19					23 22		23 49	00 37					
Lichfield Trent Valley	a																						
Tamworth Low Level	a																						
Nuneaton	a																						
Rugby	a						22 00	22 21	22 09	22 33					23 34								
Northampton	a								22 49	23 58													
Milton Keynes Central	a						22 35	22 41	22 47	23 08													
Watford Junction	a						23s10	23s19	23s25	23s52													
Gatwick Airport 10 ✈	a																						
London Euston 15 ⊖	a						23 36	23 43	23 49	00 16													

For general notes see front of timetable
For details of catering facilities see Directory of Train Operators

A To Southampton Central (Table 51)
B From Carlisle via Whitehaven (Table 100)
C From Morecambe (Table 98)
b Change at Perth, Glasgow Queen Street and Glasgow Central. Passengers make their own way between Glasgow Queen Street and Glasgow Central
c Via Glasgow Queen Street and Glasgow Central. Passengers make their own way from one station to the other
e Change at Haymarket
f Change at Preston
g Change at Preston and Manchester Piccadilly
h Change at Wilmslow and Crewe
j Change at Chester and Crewe
k Change at Llandudno Junction and Crewe

Table 65

Saturdays

Scotland and North West England → West Midlands and London

2 February to 22 March

Route Diagram - see first page of Table 65

		VT	XC	VT	XC	LM	VT	TP	VT	VT	VT		VT	VT	LM	TP	VT	VT	VT	XC	VT	NT		VT	LM
		1 ◇	1 ◇	1 ◇	1 ◇	1 ◇	1 ◇	1 ◇	1 ◇	1 ◇	1 ◇		1 ◇	1 ◇	1 ◇	1 ◇	1 ◇	1 ◇	1 ◇	1 ◇	R 1			1 ◇	1 ◇
			A		A															A					
			☕	☕	☕		☕		☕	☕	☕		☕	☕			☕	☕	☕	☕	☕			☕	
Inverness	d																								
Aberdeen	d																								
Dundee	d																								
Perth	d																								
Edinburgh 10	d																								
Haymarket	d																								
Glasgow Central 15	d																								
Motherwell	d																								
Carstairs	d																								
Lockerbie	d																								
Carlisle 8	a																								
	d																								
Penrith North Lakes	d																								
Windermere	d																								
Oxenholme Lake District	a																								
	d																								
Barrow-in-Furness	d						04 15									05 15									
Lancaster 6	a															06 08									
	d						05 20									06 08	06 25								
Preston 8	a						05 37									06 27	06 42								
Blackpool North	a																07 31								
	d						04 43	05 19						05 30			06 08				06 34	06 57			
Preston 8	d						05 40	05 48						06 15		06 28	06 45				07 20	07 25			
Wigan North Western	a						05 50	06 11						06 26			06 55				07 31	07 44			
	d						05 52	06 13						06 27			06 57				07 32	07 45			
Bolton	a							06 29								06 52									
Manchester Piccadilly 10	a							06 56								07 15									
Manchester Airport	a							07 15								07 40									
Liverpool Lime Street 10	a						06 59							07 29			07 59					08 26			
	d									06 07					06 33				07 12						07 39
Liverpool South Parkway 7	d														06 45										07 49
Runcorn	d									06 24					06 53				07 28						07 57
Warrington Bank Quay	a						06 07							06 46			07 06				07 42				
	d						06 09							06 47			07 08				07 44				
Hartford	d														07 07										08 06
Manchester Piccadilly 10	d			05 05					06 03		06 21		06 40				06 38	06 55		07 24				07 43	07 28
Stockport	d			05u15					06u12		06 30		06u49				06 48	07 04		07 33				07u53	07 37
Manchester Airport	d														05b53				06 57						
Wilmslow	d			05 23											06 36		06 55		07 04		07 27				07 46
Holyhead	d	02 15												04c27							05 35				
Bangor (Gwynedd)	d	02 42												05c00							06 04				
Llandudno	d																								
Llandudno Junction	d	03 00					05 00							05c18			05 45				06 24				
Chester	d	03 40	04 55				06 00							06 30			06 56				07 30				
Crewe 10	a	03 59		05 41			06 30			06 43				07 08	07 23		07 28		07 48		08 03				08 21
	d	04 02	05 42	05 44		06 09	06 33			06 45				07 10	07 23		07 30		07 50		08 11				08 22
Macclesfield	d								06 25		06 43		07 05					07 17		07 46				08 05	
Congleton	d				←																				
Stoke-on-Trent	d		06 01		06 01				06 41		06 59		07 21					07 33		08 04				08 21	
Stafford	a	04 29	→	06 08	06 19	06 29				07 04	07 18				07 44		07 47			08 25					08 43
	d	04 30		06 10	06 20	06 30				07 06	07 19				07 44		07 47			08 26					08 44
Penkridge	a					06 35									07 49										
Wolverhampton 7	a	04 45			06 41	06 47					07 35			07 47	08 07			08 11		08 41	08 47				08 50 →
Coseley	a														08 14										
Sandwell & Dudley	a										07 47														
Birmingham New Street 12	a	05 08			06 58	07 08					07 56			08 10	08 27			08 30		08 58	09 10				
Birmingham International	a	06 09			07 14	07 40					08 09				09 09			08 42		09 14					
Coventry	a	06 19			07 23	07 52	07 46			08 14	08 19						08 50	08 54	09 14	09 23					
Lichfield Trent Valley	a	06e40																							
Tamworth Low Level	a	07e01																							
Nuneaton	a	07e49																							
Rugby	a	06 33		07 24		08 21	08 21			08 27								09 21	09 25						
Northampton	a			07 54						09 48															
Milton Keynes Central	a			08f17			08 21		08 32	08 51			09 17					09 29							
Watford Junction	a			08s03			08s42		08s52		09s16						09s43		10s10					10s19	
Gatwick Airport 10	a			09 22					10 22								11 22							12 22	
London Euston 15	⊖ a			08 28			09 04		09 15	09 29	09 38		09 56				10 05	10 07	10 32					10 41	

For general notes see front of timetable
For details of catering facilities see Directory of Train Operators

A To Bournemouth (Table 51)
b Change at Wilmslow and Crewe
c Change at Chester and Crewe
e Change at Stafford. By bus
f Change at Rugby and Northampton

2 February to 22 March

Scotland and North West England → West Midlands and London

Route Diagram - see first page of Table 65

		TP	VT	LM	VT	VT	XC	VT	VT	TP	LM		VT	LM	NT	VT	VT	XC	VT	VT	VT	TP		LM	VT
		1◇	1◇	1◇	1◇	1◇	1◇	1◇	1◇	1◇	1◇		1◇	1◇		1◇	1◇	1◇	1◇	1◇		1◇		1◇	1◇
		A					B			A								C							
		🛒	☕		☕	☕	☕	☕	☕	🛒			☕			☕	☕	☕	☕	☕	🚌	🛒			☕
Inverness	d																								
Aberdeen	d																								
Dundee	d																								
Perth	d																								
Edinburgh 10	d																								
Haymarket	d																								
Glasgow Central 15	d																				06 15				05 51
Motherwell	d																								
Carstairs	d																								
Lockerbie	d																				08 10				08 17
Carlisle 8	a																								08 32
	d		06 30										07 28									08 20			08 47
Penrith North Lakes	d		06 44										07 43									08 35			
Windermere	d		*06 35*										*07 24*									*08 28*			
Oxenholme Lake District	a		07 07										08 05									08 59			09 09
	d		07 08										08 07									08 59			09 11
Barrow-in-Furness	d	06 15								07 05												*07 58*			
Lancaster 6	a	07 15	07 23							08 02			08 25									09 14			09 25
	d	07 16	07 24							08 03			08 27									09 14			09 27
Preston 8	a	07 35	07 41							08 21			08 44									09 35			09 44
Blackpool North	a	*08 12*	*08 36*							*09 00*			*09 32*												*10 21*
	d		*07 03*					*07 41*					*08 09*							*08 41*					*09 11*
Preston 8	d	07 40	07 44					08 29		08 34			08 47		08 50					09 29		09 38			09 47
Wigan North Western	a		07 55					08 39					08 57		09 10					09 40					09 57
	d		07 56					08 40					08 59		09 11					09 41					09 59
Bolton	a	08 02	*08b24*							08 58			*09b34*									09 58			*10b34*
Manchester Piccadilly 10	a	08 25	*08b47*							09 20			*09b57*									10 20			*10b57*
Manchester Airport ✈	a	08 42	*09b06*							09 40			*10b19*									10 40			*11b19*
Liverpool Lime Street 10	a		*09 20*					*09 49*							09 52					*10 49*					
	d					08 12					08 38						09 15							09 37	
Liverpool South Parkway 7 ✈	d										08 47													09 47	
Runcorn	d					08 28					08 55						09 31							09 55	
Warrington Bank Quay	a		08 06					08 50					09 08							09 51					10 08
	d		08 07					08 52					09 10							09 53					10 10
Hartford	d										09 07													10 05	
Manchester Piccadilly 10	d				07 55	*07 34*	08 24		08 40				*08 34*			08 54		09 24	09 40						*09 34*
Stockport	d				08 04	*07c43*	08 33		08u49				*08 44*			09 04		09 33	09u49						*09 42*
Manchester Airport ✈	d					*08 00*											*09 00*								
Wilmslow	d					*08 07*		*08 21*					*08 52*				*09 07*			*09 24*					*09 51*
Holyhead	d					*06e00*		*06 45*									*07 15*								
Bangor (Gwynedd)	d					*06e30*		*07 12*									*08 01*								
Llandudno	d					*06f39*		*07g03*									*07g47*								
Llandudno Junction	d					*06e54*		*07 30*									*08 27*								
Chester	d					*08 00*		*08 30*									*09 19*								
Crewe 10	a		08 27			08 47		09 11			09 21		09 29				09 50			10 12				10 21	10 29
	d		08 29			08 49		09 13			09 22		09 31				09 53			10 15				10 22	10 31
Macclesfield	d				08 17		08 46		09 05							09 20		09 46	10 05						
Congleton	d						08 54																		
Stoke-on-Trent	d				08 39		09 07		09 21							09 39		10 04	10 21						
Stafford	a		08 47			09 08	09 25				09 43						10 11	10 25						10 43	
	d		08 48	←		09 10	09 26				09 44			←			10 13	10 26						10 44	
Penkridge	a			08 50							09 50 →			09 50										10 50 →	
Wolverhampton 7	a			09 05	09 11		09 41	09 47						10 05		10 11		10 41		10 48					
Coseley	a			09 14										10 14											
Sandwell & Dudley	a																								
Birmingham New Street 12	a		09 24	09 27	09 30	09u50	09 58	10 11					10 24	10 27		10 30	10u50	10 58		11 11					11 24
Birmingham International ✈	a		09 39		09 44	09 59							10 39			10 44	10 59	11 14							11 39
Coventry	a		09 49		09 54	10s13							10 49			10 54	11s13	11 23							11 49
Lichfield Trent Valley	a																								
Tamworth Low Level	a																								
Nuneaton	a																								
Rugby	a				10 08	*10 33*										11 08	*11 33*								
Northampton	a				*10 46*											*11 46*									
Milton Keynes Central	a		10 24		10 31	10 49							11 25						12 00						12 25
Watford Junction	a				*11h13*				11s17							11s52	12s05		*12 54*						
Gatwick Airport 10 ✈	a																*13 22*		*14j22*						
London Euston 15 ⊖	a		11 02		11 09	11 27			11 40				12 03			12 13	12 28		12 42						13 03

For general notes see front of timetable
For details of catering facilities see Directory of Train Operators

A 🛒 from Preston
B To Plymouth (Table 51)
C To Bournemouth (Table 51)
b Change at Preston
c Change at Wilmslow and Crewe
e Change at Chester and Crewe
f Change at Llandudno Junction, Chester and Crewe
g Change at Llandudno Junction and Crewe
h Change at Rugby
j Change at Milton Keynes Central and Watford Junction

Table 65

Saturdays

Scotland and North West England → West Midlands and London

2 February to 22 March

Route Diagram - see first page of Table 65

		LM	NT	VT	VT	XC	VT	VT	VT	VT	TP	LM	VT	LM	NT	VT	VT	XC	VT	TP	VT	VT	VT
		1 ◇		1 ◇ ☕	1 ◇ ☕	1 ◇ A ☕	1 ◇ ☕	🚌	🚌	R 1 ☕	1 ◇ B 🛒	1 ◇	1 ◇ ☕	1 ◇		1 ◇ ☕	1 ◇ ☕	1 ◇ C ☕	1 ◇ ☕	1 ◇	R 1 ☕	🚌	🚌
Inverness	d																						
Aberdeen	d																						
Dundee	d																						
Perth	d								05b15														
Edinburgh [10]	d																						07 25
Haymarket	d																						
Glasgow Central [15]	d							06 50	07 15													08 00	
Motherwell	d							07u20															
Carstairs	d																						
Lockerbie	d																						
Carlisle [8]	a							09 00	09 10													09 55	10 05
	d									09 14			09 23										
Penrith North Lakes	d									09 30			09 38										
Windermere	d									*09 26*			*09 26*							10 18			
Oxenholme Lake District	a									09 53			10 00							10 35			
	d									09 54			10 06							10 37			
Barrow-in-Furness	d										09 15												
Lancaster [6]	a									10 09	10 15		10 20							10 52			
	d									10 09	10 16		10 22							10 53			
Preston [8]	a									10 27	10 34		10 43							11 13			
Blackpool North	a												*11 23*							*11 56*			
	d		09 25							*09 40*			*10 11*		10 25						*10 41*		
Preston [8]	d		09 50							10 29	10 38		10 47		10 50						11 28		
Wigan North Western	a		10 09							10 40			10 57		11 11						11 39		
	d		10 11							10 41			10 59		11 11						11 40		
Bolton	a										10 58		*11c34*										
Manchester Piccadilly [10] ⛴	a										11 20		*11c57*										
Manchester Airport ✈	a										11 40		*12c19*										
Liverpool Lime Street [10]	a		10 52							*11 49*					11 52						*12 49*		
	d				10 15							10 37					11 15						
Liverpool South Parkway [7] ✈	d											10 47											
Runcorn	d				10 31							10 55					11 31						
Warrington Bank Quay	a									10 51			11 08								11 51		
	d									10 53			11 10								11 53		
Hartford	d											11 05											
Manchester Piccadilly [10] ⛴	d			09 54		10 24	10 40						*10 34*			10 58		11 24	11 40				
Stockport	d			10 03		10 33	10u49						*10 43*			11 07		11 33	11u49				
Manchester Airport ✈	d				*10 00*												*11 00*						
Wilmslow	d				*10 06*					*10 24*			*10 51*				*11 06*				*11 24*		
Holyhead	d									*08e25*							*09 28*				*09 50*		
Bangor (Gwynedd)	d									*09e04*							*10 07*				*10 18*		
Llandudno	d				*08e47*												*10f14*						
Llandudno Junction	d				*08e56*					*09e27*							*10 30*				*10 36*		
Chester	d				*10 00*					*10 29*							*11 14*				*11 28*		
Crewe [10]	a				10 50					11 13		11 21	11 29				11 50				12 12		
	d				10 53					11 15		11 22	11 31				11 53				12 13		
Macclesfield	d			10 20		10 46	11 05									11 20		11 46	12 05				
Congleton	d					10 54																	
Stoke-on-Trent	d			10 39		11 07	11 21									11 39		12 04	12 21				
Stafford	a				11 11	11 25						11 43					12 11	12 25					
	d	←			11 13	11 26						11 44		←			12 13	12 26					
Penkridge	a	10 50										11 50 →		11 50									
Wolverhampton [7] ⛴	a	11 05		11 11		11 41				11 48				12 06		12 11		12 41			12 48		
Coseley	a	11 14												12 14									
Sandwell & Dudley	a																						
Birmingham New Street [12]	a	11 27		11 30	11u50	11 58				12 11			12 24	12 27		12 30	12u50	12 58			13 11		
Birmingham International ✈	a			11 44	11 59								12 39			12 45	12 59	13 14					
Coventry	a			11 54	12s13								12 49			12 55	13s13	13 23					
Lichfield Trent Valley	a																	*13g31*					
Tamworth Low Level	a																	*13g52*					
Nuneaton	a																	*14g40*					
Rugby	a			12 08	*12 34*											13 09	*13 33*						
Northampton	a			*12 46*												*13 47*							
Milton Keynes Central	a			12 31	12 48								13 25						14 00				
Watford Junction	a			*13h14*			13s19									13s51	14s04		*14 54*				
Gatwick Airport [10] ✈	a																*15 22*		*16j22*				
London Euston [15] ⊖	a			13 09	13 26		13 41						14 03			14 12	14 27		14 43				

For general notes see front of timetable
For details of catering facilities see Directory of Train Operators

A To Plymouth (Table 51)

B 🛒 from Preston

C To Bournemouth (Table 51)

b Via Glasgow Queen Street and Glasgow Central. Passengers make their own way from one station to the other

c Change at Preston

e Change at Chester and Crewe

f Change at Llandudno Junction and Crewe

g Change at Stafford. By bus

h Change at Rugby

j Change at Milton Keynes Central and Watford Junction

Table 65

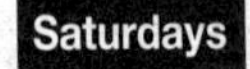

2 February to 22 March

Scotland and North West England → West Midlands and London

Route Diagram - see first page of Table 65

		TP	LM	VT	LM	NT	VT	VT	XC	VT	SR		VT	VT	VT	TP	LM	VT	LM	NT	VT	VT		XC	VT
															R										
		1 ◇	1 ◇	1 ◇	1 ◇		1 ◇	1 ◇	1 ◇	1 ◇					1	1 ◇	1 ◇	1 ◇	1 ◇		1 ◇	1 ◇		1 ◇	1 ◇
									A							B								C	
													🚌	🚌											
		🛒		☕			☕	☕	☕	☕					☕	🛒		☕			☕	☕		☕	☕
Inverness	d																								
Aberdeen	d																								
Dundee	d													*06 16*											
Perth	d																								
Edinburgh 10	d													08 30											
Haymarket	d																								
Glasgow Central 15	d										08 28		09 00												
Motherwell	d																								
Carstairs	d																								
Lockerbie	d																								
Carlisle 8	a										10 53		10 55	11 10											
	d	10 15													11 22										
Penrith North Lakes	d	10 30																							
Windermere	d																								
Oxenholme Lake District	a	10 53																							
	d	10 54																							
Barrow-in-Furness	d	*09 58*														11 18									
Lancaster 6	a	11 10													12 09	12 16									
	d	11 10													12 11	12 16									
Preston 8	a	11 31													12 28	12 35									
Blackpool North	a	*12 20*														*13 21*									
	d			*11 11*		11 25									*11 41*			*12 11*		12 25					
Preston 8	d	11 38		11 47		11 50									12 29	12 38		12 47		12 50					
Wigan North Western	a			11 57		12 09									12 40			12 57		13 09					
	d			11 59		12 11									12 41			12 59		13 11					
Bolton	a	11 58														12 58									
Manchester Piccadilly 10 ⛴	a	12 20														13 20									
Manchester Airport ✈	a	12 40														13 40									
Liverpool Lime Street 10	a					12 52									*13 49*					13 52					
	d		11 37					12 15									12 37					13 15			
Liverpool South Parkway 7 ✈	d		11 47														12 47								
Runcorn	d		11 55					12 31									12 55					13 31			
Warrington Bank Quay	a			12 08											12 51			13 08							
	d			12 10											12 53			13 10							
Hartford	d		12 05														13 07								
Manchester Piccadilly 10 ⛴	d			*11 34*			11 58		12 24	12 40								*12 34*			12 58			13 24	13 40
Stockport	d			*11 42*			12 07		12 33	12u49								*12 42*			13 07			13 33	13u49
Manchester Airport ✈	d							*12 00*														*13 00*			
Wilmslow	d			*11 51*				*12 06*							*12 24*			*12 51*				*13 06*			
Holyhead	d														*10b30*										
Bangor (Gwynedd)	d														*11b03*										
Llandudno	d							*10b47*														*11b47*			
Llandudno Junction	d							*10b56*							*11b26*							*11b56*			
Chester	d							*12 00*							*12 29*							*13 00*			
Crewe 10	a		12 21	12 29				12 50							13 12		13 21	13 29				13 51			
	d		12 22	12 31				12 53							13 15		13 22	13 31				13 54			
Macclesfield	d						12 20		12 46	13 05											13 20			13 46	14 05
Congleton	d								12 54																
Stoke-on-Trent	d						12 39		13 07	13 21											13 39			14 04	14 21
Stafford	a		12 43					13 11	13 25								13 43					14 13		14 25	
	d		12 44		←			13 13	13 26								13 44		←			14 14		14 26	
Penkridge	a		12 50 →		12 50												13 50 →		13 50						
Wolverhampton 7 ⛴	a				13 05		13 11		13 41						13 48				14 05		14 11			14 41	
Coseley	a				13 14														14 14						
Sandwell & Dudley	a																								
Birmingham New Street 12	a			13 24	13 27		13 30	13u50	13 58						14 11			14 24	14 27		14 30	14u50		14 58	
Birmingham International ✈	a			13 39			13 44	13 59										14 39			14 45	14 59		15 14	
Coventry	a			13 49			13 55	14s13										14 49			14 55	15s13		15 23	
Lichfield Trent Valley	a																								
Tamworth Low Level	a																								
Nuneaton	a																								
Rugby	a						14 09	*14 33*													15 09	*15 33*			
Northampton	a						*14 46*														*15 46*				
Milton Keynes Central	a			14 25			14 32	14 49										15 25							16 00
Watford Junction	a						*15c13*			15s17											15s49	16s06			*16 54*
Gatwick Airport 10 ✈	a																					*17 22*			*18e22*
London Euston 15 ⊖	a			15 03			15 09	15 27		15 40								16 05			16 10	16 29			16 42

For general notes see front of timetable
For details of catering facilities see Directory of Train Operators

A To Penzance (Table 135)
B 🛒 from Preston
C To Bournemouth (Table 51)
b Change at Chester and Crewe
c Change at Rugby
e Change at Milton Keynes Central and Watford Junction

Saturdays

Scotland and North West England → West Midlands and London

2 February to 22 March

Route Diagram - see first page of Table 65

		VT	VT	VT	TP	VT	TP	LM	VT	LM	NT		VT	VT	XC	VT	VT	TP	VT	VT	TP	LM		VT	LM
					1◇	1◇	1◇	1◇	1◇	1◇			1◇	1◇	1◇	1◇		1◇		R 1	1◇	1◇		1◇	1◇
					A		A								B										
		bus	bus	bus	trolley	cup	trolley		cup				cup	cup	cup	cup	bus	trolley	bus	cup	trolley			cup	
Inverness	d																		06 45						
Aberdeen	d	06 00		06b34															07 53						
Dundee	d	07 35		07b52															09 06						
Perth	d			08b13													09b08								
Edinburgh 10	d	09 20																	10 35						
Haymarket	d																								
Glasgow Central 15	d		09 50	10 00													11 00								
Motherwell	d		10 15																						
Carstairs	d																								
Lockerbie	d	11a30	11a30			11 51													12a45	13 00					
Carlisle 8	a			11 55		12 11											12 55			13 20					
	d					12 13			12 32									13 11		13 21					
Penrith North Lakes	d					12 29			12 47									13 25							
Windermere	d				12 23													13 25							
Oxenholme Lake District	a				12 40	12 52			13 10									13 49		13 57					
	d				12 42	12 53			13 11									13 50		13 58	⟵				
Barrow-in-Furness	d																				12 56				
Lancaster 6	a				13 02	13 08			13 26									14 07							
	d				13 04	13 09			13 27									14 17			14 17				
Preston 8	a				13 22	13 26			13 44									⟶		14 26	14 35				
Blackpool North	a					14 00			14 21											15 01	15 21				
	d					12 41	⟵		13 11		13 25									13 41				14 11	
Preston 8	d				13 38 ⟶	13 29	13 38		13 47		13 50									14 29	14 38			14 47	
Wigan North Western	a					13 40			13 57		14 11									14 40				14 57	
	d					13 41			13 59		14 11									14 41				14 59	
Bolton	a						13 58		14c34												14 58				
Manchester Piccadilly 10	a						14 20		14c57												15 20				
Manchester Airport	a						14 40		15c19												15 40				
Liverpool Lime Street 10	a					14 49					14 52									15 49					
	d							13 37						14 15								14 37			
Liverpool South Parkway 7	d							13 47														14 47			
Runcorn	d							13 55						14 31								14 55			
Warrington Bank Quay	a					13 51			14 08											14 50				15 08	
	d					13 53			14 10											14 52				15 10	
Hartford	d							14 05														15 05			
Manchester Piccadilly 10	d								13 34				13 58		14 24	14 40								14 34	
Stockport	d								13 42				14 07		14 33	14u49								14 42	
Manchester Airport	d													14 00											
Wilmslow	d					13 24			13 54					14 06						14 24				14 51	
Holyhead	d					11 40														12e35					
Bangor (Gwynedd)	d					12 19														13e04					
Llandudno	d													12e47						13f14					
Llandudno Junction	d					12 42								12e56						13e27					
Chester	d					13 33								14 00						14 30					
Crewe 10	a					14 12		14 21	14 28					14 50						15 10		15 21		15 28	
	d					14 15		14 22	14 31					14 53						15 13		15 22		15 31	
Macclesfield	d												14 20		14 46	15 05									
Congleton	d														14 54										
Stoke-on-Trent	d												14 39		15 07	15 21									
Stafford	a							14 43						15 11	15 25							15 43			
	d							14 44		⟵				15 13	15 26							15 44			⟵
Penkridge	a							14 50 ⟶		14 50												15 50 ⟶			15 50
Wolverhampton 7	a					14 48				15 05			15 11		15 41					15 46					16 05
Coseley	a									15 14															16 14
Sandwell & Dudley	a																								
Birmingham New Street 12	a					15 11			15 24	15 27			15 30	15u50	15 58					16 11				16 24	16 27
Birmingham International	a								15 39				15 45	15 59										16 39	
Coventry	a								15 49				15 55	16s13										16 49	
Lichfield Trent Valley	a														16g21										
Tamworth Low Level	a														16g42										
Nuneaton	a														17g30										
Rugby	a												16 09	16 33											
Northampton	a												16 46												
Milton Keynes Central	a								16 25				16 32	16 49											
Watford Junction	a												17h13			17s18								17s41	
Gatwick Airport 10	a																								
London Euston 15	a								17 05				17 10	17 27		17 40								18 03	

For general notes see front of timetable
For details of catering facilities see Directory of Train Operators

A trolley from Preston
B To Penzance (Table 135)
b Via Glasgow Queen Street and Glasgow Central. Passengers make their own way from one station to the other
c Change at Preston
e Change at Chester and Crewe
f Change at Llandudno Junction, Chester and Crewe
g Change at Stafford. By bus
h Change at Rugby

Saturdays

Scotland and North West England → West Midlands and London

2 February to 22 March

Route Diagram - see first page of Table 65

	NT	VT	VT	XC	VT	VT	VT	VT	TP	TP		VT	TP	SR	LM	VT	LM	NT	VT	VT	XC		VT	VT
												R												
		1 ◇	1 ◇	1 ◇	1 ◇				1 ◇	1 ◇		1	1 ◇		1 ◇	1 ◇	1 ◇		1 ◇	1 ◇	1 ◇		1 ◇	
				A									B								C			
						bus	bus	bus																bus
		⊡	⊡	⊡	⊡							⊡	⚲			⊡			⊡	⊡	⊡		⊡	
Inverness d								07b55																
Aberdeen d						08 20		08c39																09c36
Dundee d						09 32		09c50																10c50
Perth d								10c12																11c12
Edinburgh 10 d						11 20																		
Haymarket d																								
Glasgow Central 15 d							11 50	12 00						12 03										13 00
Motherwell d							12 15																	
Carstairs d																								
Lockerbie d						13a30	13a30					13 50												
Carlisle 8 a								13 55				14 10		14 26										14 55
d												14 13				14 32								
Penrith North Lakes d												14 28				14 47								
Windermere d									14 18															
Oxenholme Lake District a									14 35			14 51				15 09								
d									14 37			14 53				15 11								
Barrow-in-Furness d										14 10														
Lancaster 6 a									14 54	15 03		15 07	←			15 25								
d									15 16 →			15 09	15 16			15 27								
Preston 8 a												15 26	15 34			15 44								
Blackpool North a												16 01				16 21								
d	14 25											14 41				15 11		15 25						
Preston 8 d	14 50											15 29	15 38			15 47		15 50						
Wigan North Western a	15 10											15 40				15 57		16 10						
d	15 11											15 41				15 59		16 11						
Bolton a													15 58			16e34								
Manchester Piccadilly 10 a													16 20			16e57								
Manchester Airport a													16 40			17e19								
Liverpool Lime Street 10 a	15 52											16 49						16 54						
d			15 10												15 37					16 15				
Liverpool South Parkway 7 d															15 47									
Runcorn d			15 26												15 55					16 31				
Warrington Bank Quay a												15 52				16 08								
d												15 53				16 10								
Hartford d															16 05									
Manchester Piccadilly 10 d		14 58		15 24	15 40											15 34			15 58		16 24		16 40	
Stockport d		15 07		15 33	15u49											15 42			16 07		16 33		16u49	
Manchester Airport d			15 00																	16 00				
Wilmslow d			15 06									15 24				15 51				16 06				
Holyhead d												13 35			14 13									
Bangor (Gwynedd) d												14 14			14 41									
Llandudno d			13f47												14g35					15 08				
Llandudno Junction d			13f56									14 37			14 59					15 16				
Chester d			15 03									15 30			15 48					16 12				
Crewe 10 a			15 45									16 12			16 21	16 29				16 50				
d			15 48									16 13			16 22	16 31				16 53				
Macclesfield d		15 20		15 46	16 05														16 20		16 46		17 05	
Congleton d																					16 54			
Stoke-on-Trent d		15 39		16 04	16 21														16 39		17 07		17 21	
Stafford a			16 07	16 24											16 44					17 11	17 25			
d			16 09	16 26											16 44		←			17 13	17 26			
Penkridge a															16 50 →		16 50							
Wolverhampton 7 a		16 11		16 41								16 48					17 08		17 11		17 41			
Coseley a																	17 14							
Sandwell & Dudley a																								
Birmingham New Street 12 a		16 30	16u50	16 58								17 11				17 24	17 27		17 30	17u50	17 58			
Birmingham International a		16 45	16 59	17 14												17 39			17 44	17 59				
Coventry a		16 55	17s13	17 23												17 49			17 55	18s13				
Lichfield Trent Valley a																								
Tamworth Low Level a																								
Nuneaton a																								
Rugby a		17 09	17 33																18 09	18 28				
Northampton a		17 46																	18 46					
Milton Keynes Central a					18 00											18 24			18 32	18 52				
Watford Junction a		17s49	18s06		18 54															19h16			19s21	
Gatwick Airport 10 a			19 22		20j22																			
London Euston 15 ⊖ a		18 10	18 29		18 44											19 03			19 10	19 30			19 42	

For general notes see front of timetable
For details of catering facilities see Directory of Train Operators

A To Bournemouth (Table 51)
B ⚲ from Preston
C To Plymouth (Table 51)
b Change at Perth, Glasgow Queen Street and Glasgow Central. Passengers make their own way between Glasgow Queen Street and Glasgow Central
c Via Glasgow Queen Street and Glasgow Central. Passengers make their own way from one station to the other
e Change at Preston
f Change at Chester and Crewe
g Change at Llandudno Junction and Crewe
h Change at Rugby
j Change at Milton Keynes Central and Watford Junction

Scotland and North West England → West Midlands and London

2 February to 22 March

Route Diagram - see first page of Table 65

		TP	VT	VT	TP	SR	LM	VT	LM	NT	VT		VT	XC	VT	VT	VT	VT	VT	LM	TP	VT		NT	VT
		1 ◇		1 ◇	1 ◇		1 ◇	1 ◇	1 ◇		1 ◇		1 ◇	1 ◇	1 ◇				1 ◇	1 ◇	1 ◇	1 ◇			1 ◇
														A							B				
			🚌													🚌	🚌	🚌							
		🛒		☕	🛒			☕			☕		☕	☕	☕				☕		🛒	☕			☕
Inverness	d																	09b19							
Aberdeen	d		09 52															10b41							
Dundee	d		11 05															11b50							
Perth	d																	12b12							
Edinburgh 10	d		12 35													13 20									
Haymarket	d																								
Glasgow Central 15	d					13 03											13 50	14 00							
Motherwell	d																14 15								
Carstairs	d																								
Lockerbie	d		14a45	15 00												15a30	15a30		15 47						
Carlisle 8	a			15 20		15 28												15 55	16 07						
	d	15 08		15 21															16 09			16 31			
Penrith North Lakes	d	15 23																	16 24			16 47			
Windermere	d	15 22																	16 22						
Oxenholme Lake District	a	15 46																	16 47			17 09			
	d	15 47																	16 48			17 11			
Barrow-in-Furness	d																		15 28		16 21				
Lancaster 6	a	16 02		16 09															17 03		17 14	17 25			
	d	16 03		16 10															17 04		17 15	17 27			
Preston 8	a	16 22		16 27															17 21		17 34	17 44			
Blackpool North	a	17 01		17 34															18 03			18 30			
	d			15 41	←			16 10		16 25									16 38			17 10			
Preston 8	d	16 38 →		16 29	16 38			16 47		16 50									17 24		17 35	17 47		17 50	
Wigan North Western	a			16 40				16 57		17 09									17 35			17 57		18 11	
	d			16 41				16 59		17 11									17 36			17 58		18 11	
Bolton	a				16 58																17 59	18c34			
Manchester Piccadilly 10	a				17 20																18 20	18c59			
Manchester Airport	a				17 40																18 42	19c19			
Liverpool Lime Street 10	a			17 49						17 53									18 34					18 55	
	d						16 37						17 15							17 37					
Liverpool South Parkway 7	d						16 47													17 47					
Runcorn	d						16 55						17 31							17 55					
Warrington Bank Quay	a			16 51				17 08											17 46			18 08			
	d			16 52				17 10											17 48			18 10			
Hartford	d						17 07													18 05					
Manchester Piccadilly 10	d							16 34			16 58			17 24	17 40							17 34			17 58
Stockport	d							16 43			17 07			17 33	17u49							17 42			18 07
Manchester Airport	d												17 00												
Wilmslow	d			16 24				16 51					17 06						17 26			17 51			
Holyhead	d			14e35															15 39						
Bangor (Gwynedd)	d			15e04															16 17						
Llandudno	d												15e47						16f14						
Llandudno Junction	d			15e27									15e56						16 40						
Chester	d			16 31									17 00						17 31						
Crewe 10	a			17 13			17 21	17 29					17 50						18 07	18 21		18 29			
	d			17 15			17 22	17 31					17 53						18 13	18 21		18 32			
Macclesfield	d										17 20			17 46	18 05										18 20
Congleton	d																								
Stoke-on-Trent	d										17 39			18 04	18 21										18 39
Stafford	a						17 43						18 11	18 25						18 43					
	d						17 44		←				18 13	18 26						18 43					
Penkridge	a						17 50 →		17 50											18 49					
Wolverhampton 7	a			17 48					18 07		18 11			18 41					18 48	19 07					19 11
Coseley	a								18 14											19 14					
Sandwell & Dudley	a																								
Birmingham New Street 12	a			18 11				18 24	18 27		18 30		18u50	18 58					19 11	19 27					19 30
Birmingham International	a							18 39			18 44		18 59	19 14						20 09					19 42
Coventry	a							18 49			18 55		19s13	19 23											19 52
Lichfield Trent Valley	a																								
Tamworth Low Level	a																								
Nuneaton	a																								
Rugby	a										19 09		19 33									20 00			20 21
Northampton	a										19 46											20 47			
Milton Keynes Central	a														20 06							20 35			20 40
Watford Junction	a							19s41			19s49		20s22												21s18
Gatwick Airport 10	a										21 22		22 23												
London Euston 15	⊖ a							20 03			20 16		20 49		21 20							21 36			21 42

For general notes see front of timetable
For details of catering facilities see Directory of Train Operators

A To Bournemouth (Table 51)
B 🛒 from Preston

b Via Glasgow Queen Street and Glasgow Central. Passengers make their own way from one station to the other
c Change at Preston
e Change at Chester and Crewe
f Change at Llandudno Junction and Crewe

Scotland and North West England → West Midlands and London

2 February to 22 March

Route Diagram - see first page of Table 65

		VT	XC	VT	VT	TP	VT	VT	TP	LM	VT		VT	XC	NT	TP	VT	VT	VT	VT	LM	NT		VT	NT
		1 ◇	1 ◇	1 ◇		1 ◇		1 ◇	1 ◇	1 ◇	1 ◇		1 ◇	1 ◇		1 ◇				1 ◇	1 ◇			1 ◇	
			A											B								C			
					🚌		🚌										🚌	🚌	🚌						
		☕	☕	☕		🍴		☕	🍴		☕		☕							☕				☕	
Inverness	d				10b53																				
Aberdeen	d				11c42												12c42								
Dundee	d				12c50												13c50								
Perth	d				13c12												14c12								
Edinburgh 10	d						14 35											15 20							
Haymarket	d																								
Glasgow Central 15	d				15 00												16 00		15 50						
Motherwell	d																		16 15						
Carstairs	d																								
Lockerbie	d						16a45	17 00										17a30	17a30	17 50					
Carlisle 8	a				16 55			17 20									17 55			18 11					
	d					17 15		17 21			17 33									18 11				18 33	
Penrith North Lakes	d					17 29		17 36			17 47									18 27				18 48	
Windermere	d					17 27										18 10									
Oxenholme Lake District	a					17 53		17 59			18 10					18 30				18 51				19 10	
	d					17 53		18 00	←		18 11					18 33				18 51				19 12	
Barrow-in-Furness	d								17 06													18 14			
Lancaster 6	a					18 09					18 26					18 49				19 07		19 17		19 26	
	d					18 16 →			18 16		18 27					18 51				19 07		19 18		19 28	
Preston 8	a							18 29	18 36		18 44					19 09				19 26		19 43		19 45	
Blackpool North	a										19 21					20 01				20 07				20 36	
	d							17 38			18 11				18 25					18 42				19 10	19 25
Preston 8	d							18 30	18 38		18 47				18 50	19 14				19 29				19 48	19 50
Wigan North Western	a							18 41			18 58				19 10					19 40				19 58	20 10
	d							18 42			18 59				19 11					19 41				20 00	20 11
Bolton	a								18 58		19e34					19 37				20e11				20e32	
Manchester Piccadilly 10	a								19 20		19e58					20 04				20e34				20e58	
Manchester Airport ✈	a								19 40		20e19					20 26				21f06				21e19	
Liverpool Lime Street 10	a														19 52										20 52
	d	18 10								18 40											19 37				
Liverpool South Parkway 7 ✈	d									18 50											19 47				
Runcorn	d	18 26								18 58											19 55				
Warrington Bank Quay	a							18 52			19 09									19 51				20 09	
	d							18 53			19 10									19 53				20 11	
Hartford	d									19 09											20 05				
Manchester Piccadilly 10	d		18 24	18 40							18 34		18 58	19 24										19 34	
Stockport	d		18 33	18u49							18 43		19 07	19 33										19 42	
Manchester Airport ✈	d	18 00																		19g02					
Wilmslow	d	18 11						18 24			18 51									19 26				19 54	
Holyhead	d							16h35												17 35					
Bangor (Gwynedd)	d							17h04												18 14					
Llandudno	d	16h47																		17j47					
Llandudno Junction	d	16h56						17h27												18 37					
Chester	d	18 00						18 30												19 34					
Crewe 10	a	18 45						19 13		19 22	19 29									20 13	20 21			20 29	
	d	18 48						19 15		19 23	19 31									20 15	20 22			20 32	
Macclesfield	d		18 46	19 05									19 20	19 46											
Congleton	d		18 54											19 54											
Stoke-on-Trent	d		19 07	19 21									19 39	20 07											
Stafford	a	19 06	19 25							19 44	19 50			20 25							20 43				
	d	19 08	19 26							19 45	19 52			20 26							20 44				
Penkridge	a									19 51											20 50				
Wolverhampton 7	a		19 41					19 48		20 07			20 11	20 41						20 48	21 08				
Coseley	a																								
Sandwell & Dudley	a																								
Birmingham New Street 12	a		19 58					20 11		20 30			20 30	20 58						21 11	21 27				
Birmingham International ✈	a												20 42	21 14											
Coventry	a	20 13								21 23			20 52	21 23											
Lichfield Trent Valley	a									20k38															
Tamworth Low Level	a									20k59															
Nuneaton	a									21k47															
Rugby	a	20 33									21 00		21 21											22 00	
Northampton	a										21 49														
Milton Keynes Central	a	21 01											21 39											22 35	
Watford Junction	a	21 57		22s08							22s16		22s22											23s10	
Gatwick Airport 10 ✈	a																								
London Euston 15 ⊖	a	22 01		22 34							22 42		22 46											23 36	

For general notes see front of timetable
For details of catering facilities see Directory of Train Operators

A To Plymouth (Table 51)
B To Southampton Central (Table 51)
C From Carlisle via Whitehaven (Table 100)
b Change at Perth, Glasgow Queen Street and Glasgow Central. Passengers make their own way between Glasgow Queen Street and Glasgow Central
c Via Glasgow Queen Street and Glasgow Central. Passengers make their own way from one station to the other
e Change at Preston
f Change at Preston and Manchester Piccadilly
g Change at Wilmslow and Crewe
h Change at Chester and Crewe
j Change at Llandudno Junction and Crewe
k Change at Stafford. By bus

Table 65

Saturdays

Scotland and North West England → West Midlands and London

2 February to 22 March

Route Diagram - see first page of Table 65

		VT	VT	VT	NT	VT	TP	TP	VT	VT	XC		LM	TP	VT	VT	VT	VT	NT	NT	SR	SR			
		1 ◇	1 ◇	1 ◇			1 ◇	1 ◇		1 ◇	1 ◇		1 ◇	1				1 ◇							
																			A						
		☕	☕	☕		🚌	🛒		🚌	☕					🚌	🚌	🚌	☕							
Inverness	d					12b40															14b41	16c56			
Aberdeen	d					13c42											14c40				16c41	18c41			
Dundee	d					14c50											15c50				17c50	19c50			
Perth	d					15c12											16c12				18c12	20c12			
Edinburgh 10	d								16 45						17 20										
Haymarket	d																								
Glasgow Central 15	d					17 00										17 50	18 00				20 03	22 03			
Motherwell	d															18 15									
Carstairs	d																								
Lockerbie	d								18a55	19 08					19a30	19a30		19 50							
Carlisle 8	a					18 55				19 27							19 55	20 11			22 24	00 34			
	d						19 16			19 29								20 11							
Penrith North Lakes	d						19 31											20 26							
Windermere	d						19 28							20 24											
Oxenholme Lake District	a						19 54			20 03				20 44				20 51							
	d						19 54			20 04				20 46				20 51							
Barrow-in-Furness	d							19 15																	
Lancaster 6	a						20 10	20 16		20 20				21 03				21 07							
	d						20 11	20 16		20 21								21 07	21 20						
Preston 8	a						20 29	20 35		20 41								21 26	21 45						
Blackpool North	a									21 36									22 36						
	d				19 42													20 53		22 03					
Preston 8	d				20 27		20 32	20 37		20 43								21 28		22 28					
Wigan North Western	a				20 47					20 54								21 39		22 47					
	d				20 48					20 55								21 40		22 47					
Bolton	a						20 53	21 07		21e53									22 52						
Manchester Piccadilly 10	a						21 14	21 30		22e18									23 30						
Manchester Airport ✈	a						21 37	21 51		22e39									23 55						
Liverpool Lime Street 10	a				21 39													22 38		23 38					
	d		20 10										21 16												
Liverpool South Parkway 7 ✈	d												21 26												
Runcorn	d		20 26										21 34												
Warrington Bank Quay	a									21 05								21 50							
	d									21 06								21 52							
Hartford	d												21 44												
Manchester Piccadilly 10	d	19 58		20 17						20 34	20 54							20 58							
Stockport	d	20 07		20 26						20 46	21 04							21 15							
Manchester Airport ✈	d									19f56								21f10							
Wilmslow	d									20 54								21 26							
Holyhead	d									18g35								19 35							
Bangor (Gwynedd)	d									19g14								20 14							
Llandudno	d		18g47										19g47												
Llandudno Junction	d		18g56							19g32			19g56					20 37							
Chester	d		20 05							20 30			21 00					21 33							
Crewe 10	a		20 45							21 26			21 58					22 11							
	d		20 48							21 28			22 00					22 13							
Macclesfield	d	20 20		20 40							21 17														
Congleton	d										21 25														
Stoke-on-Trent	d	20 36		20 58							21 39														
Stafford	a			21 17						21 51	21 57		22 24					22 32							
	d			21 18						21 51	21 58		22 25					22 33							
Penkridge	a												22 30												
Wolverhampton 7	a	21 11		21 35						22 09	22 13		22 43					22 48							
Coseley	a																								
Sandwell & Dudley	a			21 46																					
Birmingham New Street 12	a	21 30		21 56						22 30	22 37		23 04					23 10							
Birmingham International ✈	a	21 42		22 09						23 04			23 33					00 21							
Coventry	a	21 52		22 19						23 22			23 49					00 37							
Lichfield Trent Valley	a																								
Tamworth Low Level	a																								
Nuneaton	a																								
Rugby	a	22 21	22 09	22 33						23 34															
Northampton	a		22 49	23 58																					
Milton Keynes Central	a	22 41	22 47	23 08																					
Watford Junction	a	23s19	23s25	23s52																					
Gatwick Airport 10 ✈	a																								
London Euston 15 ⊖	a	23 43	23 49	00 16																					

For general notes see front of timetable
For details of catering facilities see Directory of Train Operators

A From Morecambe (Table 98)

b Change at Perth, Glasgow Queen Street and Glasgow Central. Passengers make their own way between Glasgow Queen Street and Glasgow Central

c Via Glasgow Queen Street and Glasgow Central. Passengers make their own way from one station to the other

e Change at Preston

f Change at Wilmslow and Crewe

g Change at Chester and Crewe

Table 65

from 29 March

Scotland and North West England → West Midlands and London

Route Diagram - see first page of Table 65

		VT	XC	VT	XC	LM	VT	TP	VT	VT	VT	VT	VT	TP	LM	VT	VT	VT	VT	XC		VT	VT	NT	VT
		1 ◇	1 ◇	1 ◇	1 ◇	1 ◇	1 ◇	1 ◇	1 ◇	1 ◇	1 ◇	1 ◇	1 ◇	1	1 ◇		1 ◇	1 ◇	1 ◇	1 ◇		R 1	1 ◇		
			A		A											🚌				A					🚌
			☕	☕	☕		☕		☕	☕	☕	☕	☕				☕	☕	☕	☕		☕	☕		
Inverness	d																								
Aberdeen	d																								
Dundee	d																								
Perth	d																								
Edinburgh 10	d																								
Haymarket	d																								
Glasgow Central 15	d																								
Motherwell	d																								
Carstairs	d																								
Lockerbie	d																								
Carlisle 8	a																								
	d																								
Penrith North Lakes	d																								
Windermere	d																								
Oxenholme Lake District	a																								
	d																								05 55
Barrow-in-Furness	d													04 50											
Lancaster 6	a													05 45											06 40
	d															05 45									06 40
Preston 8	a													06b25		06 35									07 30
Blackpool North	a																								
	d						04 43	05 19					05 30				06 08					06 34		06 57	
Preston 8	d						05 40	05 48					06 15				06 45					07 20		07 25	
Wigan North Western	a						05 50	06 11					06 26				06 55					07 31		07 44	
	d						05 52	06 13					06 27				06 57					07 32		07 45	
Bolton	a							06 29																	
Manchester Piccadilly 10	a							06 56																	
Manchester Airport ✈	a							07 15																	
Liverpool Lime Street 10	a						06 59						07 29				07 59							08 26	
	d									06 07					06 33				07 12						
Liverpool South Parkway 7 ✈	d														06 45										
Runcorn	d									06 24					06 53				07 28						
Warrington Bank Quay	a						06 07						06 46				07 06					07 42			
	d						06 09						06 47				07 08					07 44			
Hartford	d														07 07										
Manchester Piccadilly 10 🚆	d			05 05					06 03		06 21	06 41					06 38	06 55		07 24			07 43		
Stockport	d			05u15					06u12		06 30	06u51					06 48	07 04		07 33			07u53		
Manchester Airport ✈	d														05c53				06 57						
Wilmslow	d			05 23											06 36		06 55		07 04			07 27			
Holyhead	d	02 15											04e27									05 35			
Bangor (Gwynedd)	d	02 42											05e00									06 04			
Llandudno	d																								
Llandudno Junction	d	03 00					05 00						05e18				05 45					06 24			
Chester	d	03 40	04 55				06 00						06 30				06 56					07 30			
Crewe 10	a	03 59		05 41			06 30			06 43			07 08		07 23		07 28		07 48			08 03			
	d	04 02	05 42	05 44		06 09	06 33			06 45			07 10		07 23		07 30		07 50			08 11			
Macclesfield	d								06 25		06 43	07 05						07 17		07 46			08 05		
Congleton	d				←																				
Stoke-on-Trent	d		06 01		06 01				06 41		06 59	07 23						07 33		08 04			08 21		
Stafford	a	04 29	→	06 08	06 19	06 29				07 04	07 18				07 44		07 47			08 25					
	d	04 30		06 10	06 20	06 30				07 06	07 19				07 44		07 47			08 26					
Penkridge	a					06 35									07 49										
Wolverhampton 7 🚆	a	04 45			06 41	06 47					07 35		07 47		08 07			08 11		08 41		08 47			
Coseley	a														08 14										
Sandwell & Dudley	a										07 47														
Birmingham New Street 12	a	05 08			06 58	07 08					07 56		08 10		08 27			08 30		08 58		09 10			
Birmingham International ✈	a	06 09			07 14	07 40					08 09				09 09			08 42		09 14					
Coventry	a	06 19			07 23	07 52	07 46			08 14	08 19						08 50	08 54	09 14	09 23					
Lichfield Trent Valley	a	06f40																							
Tamworth Low Level	a	07f01																							
Nuneaton	a	07f49																							
Rugby	a	06 33		07 24		08 21	08 21			08 27								09 21	09 25						
Northampton	a			07 54						09 48															
Milton Keynes Central	a			08g17			08 21		08 32	08 51		09 17						09 29							
Watford Junction	a			08s03			08s42		08s52		09s16						09s43		10s10				10s19		
Gatwick Airport 10 ✈	a			09 22					10 22								11 22						12 22		
London Euston 15 ⊖	a			08 28			09 04		09 15	09 29	09 38	09 56					10 05	10 07	10 32				10 41		

For general notes see front of timetable
For details of catering facilities see Directory of Train Operators

A To Bournemouth (Table 51)
b Change at Carnforth. By bus
c Change at Wilmslow and Crewe
e Change at Chester and Crewe
f Change at Stafford. By bus
g Change at Rugby and Northampton

Table 65

Saturdays

from 29 March

Scotland and North West England → West Midlands and London

Route Diagram - see first page of Table 65

		VT	VT	LM	VT	TP	LM	VT	VT	XC	TP	TP	VT	VT	VT	VT	LM	VT		LM	NT	VT	VT	XC	VT
				1◇	1◇	1	1◇	1◇	1◇	1◇	1		1◇			1◇	1◇	1◇		1◇		1◇	1◇	1◇	1◇
										A														B	
		🚌	🚌									🚌		🚌	🚌										
					☕			☕	☕	☕			☕			☕		☕				☕	☕	☕	☕
Inverness	d																								
Aberdeen	d																								
Dundee	d																								
Perth	d																								
Edinburgh 10	d																								
Haymarket	d																								
Glasgow Central 15	d																								
Motherwell	d																								
Carstairs	d																								
Lockerbie	d																								
Carlisle 8	a																								
	d	05 25	05 30											06 30	←										
Penrith North Lakes	d	06 00													06 00										
Windermere	d	→									06 51														
Oxenholme Lake District	a										07 11				06 55										
	d										07 12				06 55										
Barrow-in-Furness	d					06 00																			
Lancaster 6	a					07 02					07 29				07 40										
	d											07 35			07 40										
Preston 8	a		07 30			07b55						08 25		08 30	08 30										
Blackpool North	a		*08 12*									*09 03*			*09 32*										
	d				*07 03*								*07 41*					*08 09*							
Preston 8	d				07 44								08 29					08 47			08 50				
Wigan North Western	a				07 55								08 39					08 57			09 10				
	d				07 56								08 40					08 59			09 11				
Bolton	a		*08 02*												*09 12*										
Manchester Piccadilly 10	a		*08 25*												*09 35*										
Manchester Airport ✈	a		*08 42*												*10c02*										
Liverpool Lime Street 10	a				*09 20*								*09 49*								09 52				
	d			07 39					08 12								08 38						09 15		
Liverpool South Parkway 7 ✈	d			07 49													08 47								
Runcorn	d			07 57					08 28								08 55						09 31		
Warrington Bank Quay	a				08 06								08 50					09 08							
	d				08 07								08 52					09 10							
Hartford	d			08 06													09 07								
Manchester Piccadilly 10	d			*07 28*				07 55	*07 34*	08 24						08 40		*08 34*				08 54		09 24	09 40
Stockport	d			*07 37*				08 04	*07e43*	08 33						08u49		*08 44*				09 04		09 33	09u49
Manchester Airport ✈	d								*08 00*														*09 00*		
Wilmslow	d			*07 46*					*08 07*				*08 21*					*08 52*					*09 07*		
Holyhead	d								*06f00*				*06 45*										*07 15*		
Bangor (Gwynedd)	d								*06f30*				*07 12*										*08 01*		
Llandudno	d								*06g39*				*07h03*										*07h47*		
Llandudno Junction	d								*06f54*				*07 30*										*08 27*		
Chester	d								*08 00*				*08 30*										*09 19*		
Crewe 10	a			08 21	08 27				08 47				09 11				09 21	09 29					09 50		
	d			08 22	08 29				08 49				09 13				09 22	09 31					09 53		
Macclesfield	d							08 17		08 46						09 05						09 20		09 46	10 05
Congleton	d									08 54															
Stoke-on-Trent	d							08 39		09 07						09 21						09 39		10 04	10 21
Stafford	a			08 43	08 47				09 08	09 25							09 43						10 11	10 25	
	d			08 44	08 48		←		09 10	09 26							09 44			←			10 13	10 26	
Penkridge	a			08 50			08 50										09 50			09 50					
Wolverhampton 7	a			→			09 05	09 11		09 41			09 47				→			10 05		10 11		10 41	
Coseley	a						09 14													10 14					
Sandwell & Dudley	a																								
Birmingham New Street 12	a				09 24		09 27	09 30	09u50	09 58			10 11					10 24		10 27		10 30	10u50	10 58	
Birmingham International ✈	a				09 39			09 44	09 59									10 39				10 44	10 59	11 14	
Coventry	a				09 49			09 54	10s13									10 49				10 54	11s13	11 23	
Lichfield Trent Valley	a																								
Tamworth Low Level	a																								
Nuneaton	a																								
Rugby	a							10 08	*10 33*													11 08	*11 33*		
Northampton	a							*10 46*														*11 46*			
Milton Keynes Central	a				10 24			10 31	10 49									11 25							12 00
Watford Junction	a							*11j13*								11s17						11s52	12s05		*12 54*
Gatwick Airport 10 ✈	a																						*13 22*		*14k22*
London Euston 15 ⊖	a				11 02			11 09	11 27							11 40		12 03				12 13	12 28		12 42

For general notes see front of timetable
For details of catering facilities see Directory of Train Operators

A To Plymouth (Table 51)

B To Bournemouth (Table 51)
b Change at Carnforth. By bus
c Change at Preston and Manchester Piccadilly
e Change at Wilmslow and Crewe
f Change at Chester and Crewe

g Change at Llandudno Junction, Chester and Crewe
h Change at Llandudno Junction and Crewe
j Change at Rugby
k Change at Milton Keynes Central and Watford Junction

Table 65

Saturdays
from 29 March

Scotland and North West England → West Midlands and London

Route Diagram - see first page of Table 65

		TP	VT	VT	VT	TP	TP	VT	LM	VT	LM	NT	VT	NT	VT	XC		VT	VT	VT	TP	TP	VT	LM	VT
		1				1		1 ◇	1 ◇	1 ◇	1 ◇		1 ◇		1 ◇	1 ◇		1 ◇			1		R 1	1 ◇	1 ◇
														A		B									
			🚌	🚌	🚌		🚌												🚌	🚌		🚌			
								☕		☕			☕		☕	☕		☕					☕		☕
Inverness	d																								
Aberdeen	d																								
Dundee	d																								
Perth	d																								
Edinburgh 10	d																								
Haymarket	d																								
Glasgow Central 15	d																								
Motherwell	d																								
Carstairs	d																								
Lockerbie	d																								
Carlisle 8	a																								
	d			07 10	07 15														⟵	08 15					
Penrith North Lakes	d		06 45	07 45															07 45						
Windermere	d			⟶		07 51															08 51				
Oxenholme Lake District	a		07 40			08 11													08 40		09 11				
	d		07 40			08 12													08 40		09 12				
Barrow-in-Furness	d	07 05												07 58											
Lancaster 6	a	08 06	08 25			08 29								09 02					09 25		09 29				
	d		08 25				08 35												09 25			09 35			
Preston 8	a	08b55	09 15		09 15		09 25							09b50					10 15	10 15		10 25			
Blackpool North	a				09 57		10 02												10 57			11 03			
	d							08 41		09 11		09 25											09 40		10 11
Preston 8	d							09 29		09 47		09 50											10 29		10 47
Wigan North Western	a							09 40		09 57		10 09											10 40		10 57
	d							09 41		09 59		10 11											10 41		10 59
Bolton	a				09 58															10 58					
Manchester Piccadilly 10	a				10 20															11 20					
Manchester Airport	a				10 40															11 40					
Liverpool Lime Street 10	a							10 49				10 52											11 49		
	d								09 37						10 15									10 37	
Liverpool South Parkway 7	d								09 47															10 47	
Runcorn	d								09 55						10 31									10 55	
Warrington Bank Quay	a							09 51		10 08													10 51		11 08
	d							09 53		10 10													10 53		11 10
Hartford	d								10 05															11 05	
Manchester Piccadilly 10	d									09 34			09 54			10 24		10 40							10 34
Stockport	d									09 42			10 03			10 33		10u49							10 43
Manchester Airport	d														10 00										
Wilmslow	d							09 24		09 51					10 06								10 24		10 51
Holyhead	d																						08c25		
Bangor (Gwynedd)	d																						09c04		
Llandudno	d														08c47										
Llandudno Junction	d														08c56								09c27		
Chester	d														10 00								10 29		
Crewe 10	a							10 12	10 21	10 29					10 50								11 13	11 21	11 29
	d							10 15	10 22	10 31					10 53								11 15	11 22	11 31
Macclesfield	d												10 20			10 46		11 05							
Congleton	d															10 54									
Stoke-on-Trent	d												10 39			11 07		11 21							
Stafford	a								10 43						11 11	11 25								11 43	
	d								10 44		⟵				11 13	11 26								11 44	
Penkridge	a								10 50		10 50													11 50	
Wolverhampton 7	a							10 48	⟶		11 05		11 11			11 41							11 48	⟶	
Coseley	a										11 14														
Sandwell & Dudley	a																								
Birmingham New Street 12	a							11 11		11 24	11 27		11 30		11u50	11 58							12 11		12 24
Birmingham International	a									11 39			11 44		11 59										12 39
Coventry	a									11 49			11 54		12s13										12 49
Lichfield Trent Valley	a																								
Tamworth Low Level	a																								
Nuneaton	a																								
Rugby	a												12 08		12 34										
Northampton	a												12 46												
Milton Keynes Central	a									12 25			12 31		12 48										13 25
Watford Junction	a												13e14					13s19							
Gatwick Airport 10	a																								
London Euston 15	a									13 03			13 09		13 26			13 41							14 03

For general notes see front of timetable
For details of catering facilities see Directory of Train Operators

A From Maryport (Table 100)
B To Plymouth (Table 51)
b Change at Carnforth. By bus
c Change at Chester and Crewe
e Change at Rugby

Table 65

from 29 March

Scotland and North West England → West Midlands and London

Route Diagram - see first page of Table 65

		LM	NT	VT	VT	XC	VT	TP	VT	VT	VT	TP	TP	LM		VT	LM	NT	VT	VT	XC	VT	VT	VT	NT
		1 ◇		1 ◇	1 ◇	1 ◇	1 ◇	1		1 ◇		1		1 ◇		1 ◇	1 ◇		1 ◇	1 ◇	1 ◇	1 ◇		R 1	
						A															B				C
									🚌		🚌		🚌										🚌		
				☕	☕	☕	☕			☕						☕			☕	☕	☕	☕		☕	
Inverness	d																								
Aberdeen	d																								
Dundee	d																								
Perth	d									*05b15*															
Edinburgh 10	d																						06 25		
Haymarket	d																								
Glasgow Central 15	d									07 10														07 50	
Motherwell	d									07 26														08u04	
Carstairs	d																								
Lockerbie	d																						08a35	08 47	
Carlisle 8	a									08 22														09 07	
	d										08 35													09 09	
Penrith North Lakes	d								08 45		09 10														
Windermere	d											09 51													
Oxenholme Lake District	a								09 40		10 05	10 11													
	d								09 40			10 12													
Barrow-in-Furness	d							09 05																	09 58
Lancaster 6	a							10 09	10 25			10 29													11 01
	d								10 25				10 35												
Preston 8	a							*10c55*	11 15				11 25											11 49	*11c50*
Blackpool North	a								*11 56*				*12 01*											*12 32*	
	d		10 25													*11 11*		11 25							
Preston 8	d		10 50													11 47		11 50						12 27	
Wigan North Western	a		11 11													11 57		12 09							
	d		11 11													11 59		12 11							
Bolton	a								*11 58*															*12 35*	
Manchester Piccadilly 10	a								*12 20*															*12 57*	
Manchester Airport	a								*12 40*															*13 19*	
Liverpool Lime Street 10	a		11 52															12 52						↪	
	d				11 15									11 37						12 15					
Liverpool South Parkway 7	d													11 47											
Runcorn	d				11 31									11 55						12 31					
Warrington Bank Quay	a															12 08									
	d															12 10									
Hartford	d													12 05											
Manchester Piccadilly 10	d			10 58		11 24	11 40									*11 34*			11 58		12 24	12 40			
Stockport	d			11 07		11 33	11u49									*11 42*			12 07		12 33	12u49			
Manchester Airport	d				*11 00*															*12 00*					
Wilmslow	d				*11 06*									*11 24*		*11 51*				*12 06*					
Holyhead	d				*09 28*									*09 50*											
Bangor (Gwynedd)	d				*10 07*									*10 18*											
Llandudno	d				*10e14*															*10f47*					
Llandudno Junction	d				*10 30*									*10 36*						*10f56*					
Chester	d				*11 14*									*11 28*						*12 00*					
Crewe 10	a				11 50									12 21		12 29				12 50					
	d				11 53									12 22		12 31				12 53					
Macclesfield	d			11 20		11 46	12 05												12 20		12 46	13 05			
Congleton	d																				12 54				
Stoke-on-Trent	d			11 39		12 04	12 21												12 39		13 07	13 21			
Stafford	a				12 11	12 25								12 43						13 11	13 25				
	d	←			12 13	12 26								12 44			←			13 13	13 26				
Penkridge	a	11 50												12 50			12 50								
Wolverhampton 7	a	12 06		12 11		12 41								↪			13 05		13 11		13 41				
Coseley	a	12 14															13 14								
Sandwell & Dudley	a																								
Birmingham New Street 12	a	12 27		12 30	12u50	12 58										13 24	13 27		13 30	13u50	13 58				
Birmingham International	a			12 45	12 59	13 14										13 39			13 44	13 59					
Coventry	a			12 55	13s13	13 23										13 49			13 55	14s13					
Lichfield Trent Valley	a					*13g31*																			
Tamworth Low Level	a					*13g52*																			
Nuneaton	a					*14g40*																			
Rugby	a			13 09	*13 33*														14 09	*14 33*					
Northampton	a			*13 47*															*14 46*						
Milton Keynes Central	a						14 00									14 25			14 32	14 49					
Watford Junction	a			13s51	14s04		*14 54*												*15h13*			15s17			
Gatwick Airport 10	a				*15 22*		*16j22*																		
London Euston 15	a			14 12	14 27		14 43									15 03			15 09	15 27		15 40			

For general notes see front of timetable
For details of catering facilities see Directory of Train Operators

A To Bournemouth (Table 51)

B To Penzance (Table 135)

C From Millom (Table 100)

b Via Glasgow Queen Street and Glasgow Central. Passengers make their own way from one station to the other

c Change at Carnforth. By bus

e Change at Llandudno Junction and Crewe

f Change at Chester and Crewe

g Change at Stafford. By bus

h Change at Rugby

j Change at Milton Keynes Central and Watford Junction

Scotland and North West England → West Midlands and London

Route Diagram - see first page of Table 65

		VT	VT	TP	TP	VT	LM	VT	NT	LM	VT	VT		XC	VT	TP	VT	TP	TP	VT	TP	TP	VT	LM	VT
				1		R 1	1◇	1◇		1◇	1◇	1◇		1◇	1◇	1		1◇			1		1◇	1◇	1◇
														A											
		🚌	🚌		🚌												🚌		🚌	🚌		🚌			
						☕		☕			☕	☕		☕	☕			trolley					☕		☕
Inverness	d																								
Aberdeen	d																								
Dundee	d																								
Perth	d																								
Edinburgh 10	d																								
Haymarket	d																								
Glasgow Central 15	d																	08 40							
Motherwell	d																								
Carstairs	d																								
Lockerbie	d																	09 36							
Carlisle 8	a																	09 58							
	d		09 20																10 20						
Penrith North Lakes	d	09 45	09a55														10 45		10 55						
Windermere	d			10 51																	11 51				
Oxenholme Lake District	a	10 40		11 11													11 40		11 45		12 11				
	d	10 40		11 12													11 40		11 45		12 12				
Barrow-in-Furness	d	09 58														11 09									
Lancaster 6	a	11 25		11 29												12 09	12 25			←	12 29				
	d	11 25			11 35												12 25			12 25		12 35			
Preston 8	a	12 15			12 25											12b55	→		12 55	13 15		13 25			
Blackpool North	a	12 54			13 01	←													13 32	13 54		14 00			
	d					11 41		12 11	12 25														12 41		13 11
Preston 8	d					12 27		12 47	12 50														13 29		13 47
Wigan North Western	a					12 38		12 57	13 09														13 40		13 57
	d					12 39		12 59	13 11														13 41		13 59
Bolton	a	12 58																	13 34	13 58					
Manchester Piccadilly 10	a	13 20																	13 57	14 20					
Manchester Airport	a	13 40																	14 19	14 40					
Liverpool Lime Street 10	a					13 49			13 52														14 49		
	d						12 37					13 15												13 37	
Liverpool South Parkway 7	d						12 47																	13 47	
Runcorn	d						12 55					13 31												13 55	
Warrington Bank Quay	a					12 51		13 08															13 51		14 08
	d					12 53		13 10															13 53		14 10
Hartford	d						13 07																	14 05	
Manchester Piccadilly 10	d							12 34			12 58			13 24	13 40										13 34
Stockport	d							12 42			13 07			13 33	13u49										13 42
Manchester Airport	d											13 00													
Wilmslow	d					12 24		12 51				13 06											13 24		13 54
Holyhead	d					10c30																	11 40		
Bangor (Gwynedd)	d					11c03																	12 19		
Llandudno	d											11c47													
Llandudno Junction	d					11c26						11c56											12 42		
Chester	d					12 29						13 00											13 33		
Crewe 10	a					13 12	13 21	13 29				13 51											14 12	14 21	14 28
	d					13 15	13 22	13 31				13 54											14 15	14 22	14 31
Macclesfield	d										13 20			13 46	14 05										
Congleton	d																								
Stoke-on-Trent	d										13 39			14 04	14 21										
Stafford	a						13 43					14 13		14 25										14 43	
	d						13 44			←		14 14		14 26										14 44	
Penkridge	a						13 50			13 50														14 50	
Wolverhampton 7	a					13 48	→			14 05	14 11			14 41									14 48	→	
Coseley	a									14 14															
Sandwell & Dudley	a																								
Birmingham New Street 12	a					14 11		14 24		14 27	14 30	14u50		14 58									15 11		15 24
Birmingham International	a							14 39			14 45	14 59		15 14											15 39
Coventry	a							14 49			14 55	15s13		15 23											15 49
Lichfield Trent Valley	a																								
Tamworth Low Level	a																								
Nuneaton	a																								
Rugby	a										15 09	15 33													
Northampton	a										15 46														
Milton Keynes Central	a							15 25							16 00										16 25
Watford Junction	a										15s49	16s06			16 54										
Gatwick Airport 10	a											17 22			18e22										
London Euston 15	a							16 05			16 10	16 29			16 42										17 05

For general notes see front of timetable
For details of catering facilities see Directory of Train Operators

A To Bournemouth (Table 51)
b Change at Carnforth. By bus
c Change at Chester and Crewe
e Change at Milton Keynes Central and Watford Junction

Table 65

Saturdays

from 29 March

Scotland and North West England → West Midlands and London

Route Diagram - see first page of Table 65

	LM	NT	VT	VT	XC	VT	VT	VT	VT		VT	TP	TP	VT	LM	VT	LM	NT	VT	VT	XC	VT	NT	TP
	1 ◇		1 ◇	1 ◇	1 ◇	1 ◇		1 ◇				1		R 1	1 ◇	1 ◇	1 ◇		1 ◇	1 ◇	1 ◇	1 ◇		1 ◇
					A																B			
							bus		bus		bus		bus											
			☕	☕	☕	☕		☕						☕		☕			☕	☕	☕	☕		trolley
Inverness d																								
Aberdeen d								05b27																07b07
Dundee d							06 16	06b48																08b21
Perth d								07b14																08b43
Edinburgh 10 d							08 05																	
Haymarket d																								
Glasgow Central 15 d								09 18																10 40
Motherwell d								09u43																
Carstairs d																								
Lockerbie d							10a15	10 26																
Carlisle 8 a								10 48																11 59
d								11 00	11 00															
Penrith North Lakes d									11 35		11 45													
Windermere d												12 51												
Oxenholme Lake District a									12 30		12 40	13 11												
d									12 30		12 40	13 12												
Barrow-in-Furness d																							12 56	
Lancaster 6 a									13 15		13 25	13 29											14 00	
d											13 25		13 35											
Preston 8 a								14 15			14 15		14 25										14c50	
Blackpool North a								14 54					15 01			←								
d		13 25												13 41		14 11		14 25						
Preston 8 d		13 50						14 47						14 29		14 47		14 50						
Wigan North Western a		14 11												14 40		14 57		15 10						
d		14 11												14 41		14 59		15 11						
Bolton a								14 58																
Manchester Piccadilly 10 a								15 20																
Manchester Airport a								15 40																
Liverpool Lime Street 10 a		14 52						↪						15 49				15 52						
d				14 15											14 37					15 10				
Liverpool South Parkway 7 d															14 47									
Runcorn d				14 31											14 55					15 26				
Warrington Bank Quay a														14 50		15 08								
d														14 52		15 10								
Hartford d															15 05									
Manchester Piccadilly 10 d			13 58		14 24	14 40										14 34			14 58		15 24	15 40		
Stockport d			14 07		14 33	14u49										14 42			15 07		15 33	15u49		
Manchester Airport d				14 00																15 00				
Wilmslow d				14 06										14 24		14 51				15 06				
Holyhead d														12e35										
Bangor (Gwynedd) d														13e04										
Llandudno d				12e47										13f14						13e47				
Llandudno Junction d				12e56										13e27						13e56				
Chester d				14 00										14 30						15 03				
Crewe 10 a				14 50										15 10	15 21	15 28				15 45				
d				14 53										15 13	15 22	15 31				15 48				
Macclesfield d			14 20		14 46	15 05													15 20		15 46	16 05		
Congleton d					14 54																			
Stoke-on-Trent d			14 39		15 07	15 21													15 39		16 04	16 21		
Stafford a				15 11	15 25										15 43					16 07	16 24			
d	←			15 13	15 26										15 44		←			16 09	16 26			
Penkridge a	14 50														15 50		15 50							
Wolverhampton 7 a	15 05		15 11		15 41									15 46	→		16 05		16 11		16 41			
Coseley a	15 14																16 14							
Sandwell & Dudley a																								
Birmingham New Street 12 a	15 27		15 30	15u50	15 58									16 11		16 24	16 27		16 30	16u50	16 58			
Birmingham International a			15 45	15 59												16 39			16 45	16 59	17 14			
Coventry a			15 55	16s13												16 49			16 55	17s13	17 23			
Lichfield Trent Valley a					16g21																			
Tamworth Low Level a					16g42																			
Nuneaton a					17g30																			
Rugby a			16 09	16 33															17 09	17 33				
Northampton a			16 46																17 46					
Milton Keynes Central a			16 32	16 49																		18 00		
Watford Junction a			17h13			17s18										17s41			17s49	18s06		18 54		
Gatwick Airport 10 a																				19 22		20j22		
London Euston 15 a			17 10	17 27		17 40										18 03			18 10	18 29		18 44		

For general notes see front of timetable
For details of catering facilities see Directory of Train Operators

A To Penzance (Table 135)

B To Bournemouth (Table 51)

b Via Glasgow Queen Street and Glasgow Central. Passengers make their own way from one station to the other

c Change at Carnforth. By bus

e Change at Chester and Crewe

f Change at Llandudno Junction, Chester and Crewe

g Change at Stafford. By bus

h Change at Rugby

j Change at Milton Keynes Central and Watford Junction

Table 65

Saturdays

from 29 March

Scotland and North West England → West Midlands and London

Route Diagram - see first page of Table 65

		TP	VT	TP	TP	VT	LM	VT		LM	NT	VT	VT	XC	VT	TP	VT	VT	VT	VT	TP	TP	LM	VT	LM
						R																			
				1		1	1◇	1◇		1◇		1◇	1◇	1◇	1◇	1		1◇		1◇	1		1◇	1◇	1◇
														A											
		🚌	🚌		🚌												🚌		🚌			🚌			
						☕		☕				☕	☕	☕	☕			☕		☕				☕	
Inverness	d																06 45	07b55							
Aberdeen	d																07 53	08c39							
Dundee	d																09 06	09c50							
Perth	d																08 48	10c12							
Edinburgh [10]	d																10 35								
Haymarket	d																								
Glasgow Central [15]	d																	11 48							
Motherwell	d																	12u08							
Carstairs	d																								
Lockerbie	d																12a45	12 58							
Carlisle [8]	a																	13 20							
	d	12 20																13 30	13 30						
Penrith North Lakes	d	12 55																	14 05						
Windermere	d			13 51																	14 51				
Oxenholme Lake District	a	13 45		14 11															15 00		15 11				
	d	13 45		14 12																	15 12				
Barrow-in-Furness	d															14 10									
Lancaster [6]	a			14 29												15 05					15 29				
	d		14 25		14 35																	15 35			
Preston [8]	a	14 55	15 15		15 25											15e55		16 19				16 25			
Blackpool North	a	15 32	15 54		16 01															←		17 01			
	d					14 41		15 11			15 25									15 41				16 10	
Preston [8]	d					15 29		15 47			15 50							16 29		16 29				16 47	
Wigan North Western	a					15 40		15 57			16 10									16 40				16 57	
	d					15 41		15 59			16 11									16 41				16 59	
Bolton	a	15 34																16 58							
Manchester Piccadilly [10]	a	15 57																17 20							
Manchester Airport	a	16 19																17 40							
Liverpool Lime Street [10]	a					16 49					16 54							→		17 49					
	d						15 37						16 15										16 37		
Liverpool South Parkway [7]	d						15 47																16 47		
Runcorn	d						15 55						16 31										16 55		
Warrington Bank Quay	a					15 52		16 08												16 51				17 08	
	d					15 53		16 10												16 52				17 10	
Hartford	d						16 05																17 07		
Manchester Piccadilly [10]	d							15 34				15 58		16 24	16 40									16 34	
Stockport	d							15 42				16 07		16 33	16u49									16 43	
Manchester Airport	d												16 00												
Wilmslow	d					15 24		15 51					16 06							16 24				16 51	
Holyhead	d					13 35	14 13													14f35					
Bangor (Gwynedd)	d					14 14	14 41													15f04					
Llandudno	d						14g35						15 08												
Llandudno Junction	d					14 37	14 59						15 16							15f27					
Chester	d					15 30	15 48						16 12							16 31					
Crewe [10]	a					16 12	16 21	16 29					16 50							17 13			17 21	17 29	
	d					16 13	16 22	16 31					16 53							17 15			17 22	17 31	
Macclesfield	d											16 20		16 46	17 05										
Congleton	d													16 54											
Stoke-on-Trent	d											16 39		17 07	17 21										
Stafford	a						16 44						17 11	17 25									17 43		
	d						16 44			←			17 13	17 26									17 44		←
Penkridge	a						16 50			16 50													17 50		17 50
Wolverhampton [7]	a					16 48	→			17 08		17 11		17 41						17 48			→		18 07
Coseley	a									17 14															18 14
Sandwell & Dudley	a																								
Birmingham New Street [12]	a					17 11		17 24		17 27		17 30	17u40	17 58						18 11				18 24	18 27
Birmingham International	a							17 39				17 44	17 59											18 39	
Coventry	a							17 49				17 55	18s13											18 49	
Lichfield Trent Valley	a																								
Tamworth Low Level	a																								
Nuneaton	a																								
Rugby	a											18 09	18 28												
Northampton	a											18 46													
Milton Keynes Central	a							18 24				18 32	18 52												
Watford Junction	a												19h16		19s21									19s41	
Gatwick Airport [10]	a																								
London Euston [15]	a							19 03				19 10	19 30		19 42									20 03	

For general notes see front of timetable
For details of catering facilities see Directory of Train Operators

A To Plymouth (Table 51)

b Change at Perth, Glasgow Queen Street and Glasgow Central. Passengers make their own way between Glasgow Queen Street and Glasgow Central

c Via Glasgow Queen Street and Glasgow Central. Passengers make their own way from one station to the other

e Change at Carnforth. By bus

f Change at Chester and Crewe

g Change at Llandudno Junction and Crewe

h Change at Rugby

Scotland and North West England → West Midlands and London

Route Diagram - see first page of Table 65

		NT	VT	VT	XC	VT		VT	VT	TP	NT	TP	LM	VT	NT	VT	VT	SR	XC	VT	TP	VT	VT	VT	VT
			1 ◇	1 ◇	1 ◇	1 ◇			1 ◇	1			1 ◇	1 ◇		1 ◇	1 ◇		1 ◇	1 ◇	1			1 ◇	
					A						B								C						
								🚌				🚌										🚌	🚌		🚌
			☕	☕	☕	☕			☕					☕		☕	☕		☕	☕				☕	
Inverness	d																								
Aberdeen	d																						08 50	09b36	
Dundee	d																						09 59	10b50	
Perth	d																							11b12	
Edinburgh 10	d																						11 55		
Haymarket	d																								
Glasgow Central 15	d																	12 03						13 10	
Motherwell	d																							13u30	
Carstairs	d																								
Lockerbie	d																						14a05	14 17	
Carlisle 8	a																	14 26						14 36	
	d																							15 06	14 50
Penrith North Lakes	d							14 45																	15 25
Windermere	d									15 51															
Oxenholme Lake District	a							15 40		16 11															16 20
	d							15 40		16 12															16 20
Barrow-in-Furness	d										15 28										16 10				
Lancaster 6	a							16 25		16 29	16 34										17 06				17 05
	d							16 25				16 35										17 25			
Preston 8	a							17 15			17c20	17 25									17c55	18 15		18 16	
Blackpool North	a							17 58				18 03												18 59	
	d	16 25							16 38					17 10											
Preston 8	d	16 50							17 24					17 47	17 50									18 47	
Wigan North Western	a	17 09							17 35					17 57	18 11										
	d	17 11							17 36					17 58	18 11										
Bolton	a							17 59																18 58	
Manchester Piccadilly 10 🚊	a							18 20																19 20	
Manchester Airport ✈	a							18 42																19 40	
Liverpool Lime Street 10	a	17 53							18 34						18 55									↦	
	d			17 15									17 37				18 10								
Liverpool South Parkway 7 ✈	d												17 47												
Runcorn	d			17 31									17 55				18 26								
Warrington Bank Quay	a								17 46					18 08											
	d								17 48					18 10											
Hartford	d												18 05												
Manchester Piccadilly 10 🚊	d		16 58		17 24	17 40								17 34		17 58			18 24	18 40					
Stockport	d		17 07		17 33	17u49								17 42		18 07			18 33	18u49					
Manchester Airport ✈	d			17 00													18 00								
Wilmslow	d			17 06					17 26					17 51			18 11								
Holyhead	d								15 39																
Bangor (Gwynedd)	d								16 17																
Llandudno	d			15e47					16f14								16e47								
Llandudno Junction	d			15e56					16 40								16e56								
Chester	d			17 00					17 31								18 00								
Crewe 10	a			17 50					18 07				18 21	18 29			18 45								
	d			17 53					18 13				18 21	18 32			18 48								
Macclesfield	d		17 20		17 46	18 05										18 20			18 46	19 05					
Congleton	d																		18 54						
Stoke-on-Trent	d		17 39		18 04	18 21										18 39			19 07	19 21					
Stafford	a			18 11	18 25								18 43				19 06		19 25						
	d			18 13	18 26								18 43				19 08		19 26						
Penkridge	a												18 49												
Wolverhampton 7 🚊	a		18 11		18 41				18 48				19 07			19 11			19 41						
Coseley	a												19 14												
Sandwell & Dudley	a																								
Birmingham New Street 12	a		18 30	18u50	18 58				19 11				19 27			19 30			19 58						
Birmingham International ✈	a		18 44	18 59	19 14								20 09			19 42									
Coventry	a		18 55	19s13	19 23											19 52	20 13								
Lichfield Trent Valley	a																								
Tamworth Low Level	a																								
Nuneaton	a																								
Rugby	a		19 09	19 33										20 00		20 21	20 33								
Northampton	a		19 46											20 47											
Milton Keynes Central	a					20 06								20 26		20 32	20 53								
Watford Junction	a		19s49	20s22												21s06	21 44			22s01					
Gatwick Airport 10 ✈	a		21 22													22 23									
London Euston 15 ⊖	a		20 16	20 49		21 20								21 28		21 33	22 01			22 28					

For general notes see front of timetable
For details of catering facilities see Directory of Train Operators

- **A** To Bournemouth (Table 51)
- **B** From Carlisle via Whitehaven (Table 100)
- **C** To Plymouth (Table 51)
- **b** Via Glasgow Queen Street and Glasgow Central. Passengers make their own way from one station to the other
- **c** Change at Carnforth. By bus
- **e** Change at Chester and Crewe
- **f** Change at Llandudno Junction and Crewe

Table 65

Saturdays

from 29 March

Scotland and North West England → West Midlands and London

Route Diagram - see first page of Table 65

		TP	TP	VT		LM	VT	VT	XC	NT	TP	TP	VT	TP	VT	TP	TP	VT	LM	VT	VT	VT	NT	VT	VT
		1		1 ◇		1 ◇	1 ◇	1 ◇	1 ◇		1	1 ◇				1		1 ◇	1 ◇	1 ◇	1 ◇	1 ◇		1 ◇	
									A		B														
			🚌										🚌	🚌	🚌		🚌								🚌
				☕			☕	☕				🛒						☕		☕	☕	☕		☕	
Inverness	d											10b53													
Aberdeen	d											11c42													
Dundee	d											12c50													
Perth	d											13c12													
Edinburgh 10	d																								14 50
Haymarket	d																								
Glasgow Central 15	d											14 48													
Motherwell	d																								
Carstairs	d																								
Lockerbie	d											15 51													17a00
Carlisle 8	a											16 12													
	d													16 20											
Penrith North Lakes	d												16 45	16 55											
Windermere	d	16 51														17 51									
Oxenholme Lake District	a	17 11											17 40	17 45		18 11									
	d	17 12											17 40	17 45		18 12									
Barrow-in-Furness	d										17 06														
Lancaster 6	a	17 29									18 05		18 25		←	18 29									
	d		17 35										18 25		18 25		18 35								
Preston 8	a		18 25								18e55		→	18 55	19 15		19 25								
Blackpool North	a		19 04				←							19 35			20 01								
	d			17 38			18 11			18 25								18 42		19 10			19 25		
Preston 8	d			18 30			18 47			18 50								19 29		19 48			19 50		
Wigan North Western	a			18 41			18 58			19 10								19 40		19 58			20 10		
	d			18 42			18 59			19 11								19 41		20 00			20 11		
Bolton	a													19 34	20 11										
Manchester Piccadilly 10 🚊	a													19 58	20 34										
Manchester Airport ✈	a													20 19	21f06										
Liverpool Lime Street 10	a									19 52													20 52		
	d					18 40													19 37			20 10			
Liverpool South Parkway 7 ✈	d					18 50													19 47						
Runcorn	d					18 58													19 55			20 26			
Warrington Bank Quay	a			18 52			19 09											19 51		20 09					
	d			18 53			19 10											19 53		20 11					
Hartford	d					19 09													20 05						
Manchester Piccadilly 10 🚊	d						18 34	18 58	19 24											19 34	19 58			20 17	
Stockport	d						18 43	19 07	19 33											19 42	20 07			20 26	
Manchester Airport ✈	d																	19g02							
Wilmslow	d			18 24			18 51											19 26		19 54					
Holyhead	d			16h35														17 35							
Bangor (Gwynedd)	d			17h04														18 14							
Llandudno	d																	17j47				18h47			
Llandudno Junction	d			17h27														18 37				18h56			
Chester	d			18 30														19 34				20 05			
Crewe 10	a			19 13		19 22	19 29											20 13	20 21	20 29		20 45			
	d			19 15		19 23	19 31											20 15	20 22	20 32		20 48			
Macclesfield	d							19 20	19 46												20 20			20 40	
Congleton	d								19 54																
Stoke-on-Trent	d							19 39	20 07												20 36			20 58	
Stafford	a					19 44	19 50		20 25										20 43					21 17	
	d					19 45	19 52		20 26										20 44					21 18	
Penkridge	a					19 51													20 50						
Wolverhampton 7 🚊	a			19 48		20 07		20 11	20 41									20 48	21 08		21 11			21 35	
Coseley	a																								
Sandwell & Dudley	a																							21 46	
Birmingham New Street 12	a			20 11		20 30		20 30	20 58									21 11	21 27		21 30			21 56	
Birmingham International ✈	a							20 42	21 14												21 42			22 09	
Coventry	a					21 23		20 52	21 23												21 52			22 19	
Lichfield Trent Valley	a					20k38																			
Tamworth Low Level	a					20k59																			
Nuneaton	a					21k47																			
Rugby	a						21 00	21 21												22 00	22 21	22 09		22 33	
Northampton	a						21 49															22 49		23 58	
Milton Keynes Central	a							21 29												22 25	22 31	22 38		23 02	
Watford Junction	a						22s06	22s16												23s00	23s05	23s11		23s52	
Gatwick Airport 10 ✈	a																								
London Euston 15 ⊖	a						22 34	22 39												23 26	23 30	23 34		00 16	

For general notes see front of timetable
For details of catering facilities see Directory of Train Operators

A To Southampton Central (Table 51)
B To Windermere (Table 83)

b Change at Perth, Glasgow Queen Street and Glasgow Central. Passengers make their own way between Glasgow Queen Street and Glasgow Central
c Via Glasgow Queen Street and Glasgow Central. Passengers make their own way from one station to the other

e Change at Carnforth. By bus
f Change at Preston and Manchester Piccadilly
g Change at Wilmslow and Crewe
h Change at Chester and Crewe
j Change at Llandudno Junction and Crewe
k Change at Stafford. By bus

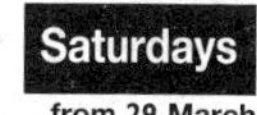

from 29 March

Scotland and North West England → West Midlands and London

Route Diagram - see first page of Table 65

		VT		VT	VT	TP	NT	VT	TP	VT	TP	TP	VT	VT	XC	LM	VT	NT	VT	TP	VT	SR	SR		
		1 ◇				1 ◇		1 ◇	1 A		1				1 ◇	1 ◇	1 ◇			1					
		☕		🚌	🚌	🛒		☕		🚌		🚌	🚌	🚌			☕		🚌		🚌				
Inverness	d					12b40																14b41	16c56		
Aberdeen	d	12c42				13c42															14 50	16c41	18c41		
Dundee	d	13c50				14c50															16 03	17c50	19c50		
Perth	d	14c12				15c12																18c12	20c12		
Edinburgh 10	d																				17 50				
Haymarket	d																								
Glasgow Central 15	d	16 10				17 40																20 03	22 03		
Motherwell	d	16u25																							
Carstairs	d																								
Lockerbie	d	17 13				18 36															20 00				
Carlisle 8	a	17 30				19 03															20 35	22 24	00 34		
	d	17 36			17 40								19 11	19 15											
Penrith North Lakes	d			17 45	18 15					19 05			19 46												
Windermere	d									18 51	19 45									20 56					
Oxenholme Lake District	a			18 40	19 10					20 00	20 05		20 41						←	21 16					
	d			18 40	19 10					20 00	20 06		20 41 →						20 41	21 17					
Barrow-in-Furness	d			18 14					19 09																
Lancaster 6	a			19 25	19 55				20 11		20 23								21 26	21 35					
	d			19 25								20 30							21 26						
Preston 8	a	19 57		20 15					21e05	21 15		21 15		21 15					22 11						
Blackpool North	a	20 36		20 56										21 56					23 28						
	d						19 42	←									20 53	22 03							
Preston 8	d	20 43					20 27	20 43									21 28	22 28							
Wigan North Western	a						20 47	20 54									21 39	22 47							
	d						20 48	20 55									21 40	22 47							
Bolton	a	20 32		20 53										21 53					22 52						
Manchester Piccadilly 10 🚊	a	20 58		21 14										22 18					23 30						
Manchester Airport ✈	a	21 19		21 37										22 39					23 55						
Liverpool Lime Street 10	a	↪					21 39										22 38	23 38							
	d															21 16									
Liverpool South Parkway 7 ✈	d															21 26									
Runcorn	d															21 34									
Warrington Bank Quay	a							21 05									21 50								
	d							21 06									21 52								
Hartford	d															21 44									
Manchester Piccadilly 10 🚊	d							20 34							20 54		20 58								
Stockport	d							20 46							21 04		21 15								
Manchester Airport ✈	d							19f56									21f10								
Wilmslow	d							20 54									21 26								
Holyhead	d							18g35									19 35								
Bangor (Gwynedd)	d							19g14									20 14								
Llandudno	d															19g47									
Llandudno Junction	d							19g32								19g56	20 37								
Chester	d							20 30								21 00	21 33								
Crewe 10	a							21 26								21 58	22 11								
	d							21 28								22 00	22 13								
Macclesfield	d														21 17										
Congleton	d														21 25										
Stoke-on-Trent	d														21 39										
Stafford	a							21 51							21 57	22 24	22 32								
	d							21 51							21 58	22 25	22 33								
Penkridge	a															22 30									
Wolverhampton 7 🚊	a							22 09							22 13	22 43	22 48								
Coseley	a																								
Sandwell & Dudley	a																								
Birmingham New Street 12	a							22 30							22 37	23 04	23 10								
Birmingham International ✈	a							23 04								23 33	00 21								
Coventry	a							23 22								23 49	00 37								
Lichfield Trent Valley	a																								
Tamworth Low Level	a																								
Nuneaton	a																								
Rugby	a							23 34																	
Northampton	a																								
Milton Keynes Central	a																								
Watford Junction	a																								
Gatwick Airport 10 ✈	a																								
London Euston 15 ⊖	a																								

For general notes see front of timetable
For details of catering facilities see Directory of Train Operators

A To Windermere (Table 83)

b Change at Perth, Glasgow Queen Street and Glasgow Central. Passengers make their own way between Glasgow Queen Street and Glasgow Central

c Via Glasgow Queen Street and Glasgow Central. Passengers make their own way from one station to the other

e Change at Carnforth. By bus

f Change at Wilmslow and Crewe

g Change at Chester and Crewe

Table 65

Sundays

until 27 January

Scotland and North West England → West Midlands and London

Route Diagram - see first page of Table 65

		XC	VT	XC	LM	VT	XC	NT	VT	VT	VT	VT	VT		VT	XC	VT	VT	VT	VT	XC	VT	NT	VT	TP
		1◇	1◇	1◇	1◇	1◇	1◇		1◇	1◇	1◇	1◇			1◇	1◇	1◇	1◇	1◇	1◇	1◇	1◇			1◇
		A		B			C						🚌			D					C			🚌	
		⊡	⊡	⊡		⊡	⊡		⊡	⊡	⊡	⊡			⊡	⊡	⊡	⊡	⊡	⊡	⊡	⊡			
Inverness	d																								
Aberdeen	d																								
Dundee	d																								
Perth	d																								
Edinburgh 10	d																								
Haymarket	d																								
Glasgow Central 15	d																								
Motherwell	d																								
Carstairs	d																								
Lockerbie	d																								
Carlisle 8	a																								
	d																								
Penrith North Lakes	d																								
Windermere	d																								
Oxenholme Lake District	a																								
	d																								
Barrow-in-Furness	d																								09 58
Lancaster 6	a																								10 57
	d												09 00											10 25	10 58
Preston 8	a												09 50											11 15	11 17
Blackpool North	a												*10 47*												*12 16*
	d							08 17							*09 28*								10 17		
Preston 8	d							08 42							10 03			10 28					10 42		
Wigan North Western	a							09 01							10 14			10 40					11 01		
	d							09 01							10 15			10 40					11 01		
Bolton	a																								
Manchester Piccadilly 10	a																								
Manchester Airport	a																								
Liverpool Lime Street 10	a							09 49										*11 49*					11 49		
	d										09 53								10 53						
Liverpool South Parkway 7	d																								
Runcorn	d										10 09								11 09						
Warrington Bank Quay	a														10 25			10 51							
	d														10 26			10 51							
Hartford	d																								
Manchester Piccadilly 10	d	08 08				09 00	09 24			09 44		09 53				10 24	10 44			10 53	11 24	11 44			
Stockport	d					09u10	09 33			09u53		10 02				10 33	10u52			11 02	11 33	11u52			
Manchester Airport	d										*09 33*														
Wilmslow	d	08 24				09 19					*09 41*														
Holyhead	d																								
Bangor (Gwynedd)	d																								
Llandudno	d																								
Llandudno Junction	d																								
Chester	d			*08 55*					*09 25*		*09 55*				*10 11*				*10 55*						
Crewe 10	a	08 43				09 36					10 29				10 45			11 12	11 28						
	d	08 46		09 33	09 40	09 48			10 12		10 35				10 48			11 13	11 35						
Macclesfield	d						09 46			10 06		10 15				10 46	11 05			11 15	11 46	12 05			
Congleton	d																								
Stoke-on-Trent	d	09 05					10 05			10 22		10 31				11 05	11 21			11 31	12 05	12 21			
Stafford	a	09 24		09 52	10 01	10 06	10 24		10 31	10 40	10 54				11 06	11 24			11 54		12 24				
	d	09 26	09 39	09 53	10 01	10 08	10 26		10 32	10 41	10 55				11 08	11 26			11 55		12 26				
Penkridge	a				10 07																				
Wolverhampton 7	a	09 40		10 09	10 23		10 40		10 48			11 05				11 40		11 48		12 05	12 40				
Coseley	a																								
Sandwell & Dudley	a											11 16								12 16					
Birmingham New Street 12	a	09 58		10 30	10 43		10 58		11 11			11 26				11 58		12 11		12 26	12 58				
Birmingham International	a	*10 24*		10 42		10 57	11 14					11 39				*12 30*				12 39	13 13				
Coventry	a		10 28	10 53		11 12	11 23				11 45	11 51			12 12	*12 40*			12 45	12 51	13 23				
Lichfield Trent Valley	a																								
Tamworth Low Level	a																								
Nuneaton	a																								
Rugby	a		10 41			11 26				11 39	11 58								12 58						
Northampton	a		*12b17*								*13b17*								*14b17*						
Milton Keynes Central	a		11 05			11 51					12 21	12 27			12 50		13 00		13 22	13 28					
Watford Junction	a		*11 55*			12s31				12s43	13s00	13s06			13s31		*13 55*			14s03		14s31			
Gatwick Airport 10	a																								
London Euston 15	a		12 00			12 51				13 04	13 23	13 29			13 56		14 00		14 23	14 29		14 56			

For general notes see front of timetable
For details of catering facilities see Directory of Train Operators

A To Paignton (Table 51)
B To Reading (Table 51)
C To Bournemouth (Table 51)
D To Plymouth (Table 51)
b By bus

OVERNIGHT SLEEPERS. For Sleeper trains, operated by First ScotRail, please refer to Tables 400 - 404

until 27 January

Scotland and North West England → West Midlands and London

Route Diagram - see first page of Table 65

		VT	LM	VT		VT	XC	VT	VT	VT	VT	VT	VT	NT	VT	XC	LM		TP	VT	VT	VT	VT	VT	XC
		1◇	1◇	1◇		1◇	R 1 A	🚌	1◇	1◇	1◇	1◇	1◇		1◇	R 1 B	1◇		1◇	1◇	1◇	1◇	1◇	1◇	R 1 A
		☕		☕		☕	☕		☕	☕	☕	☕	☕		☕	☕				☕	☕	☕	☕	☕	☕
Inverness	d																								
Aberdeen	d																								
Dundee	d																							08b45	
Perth	d																			09c27				09b05	
Edinburgh 10	d																			10 56					
Haymarket	d																			11u01					
Glasgow Central 15	d																							11 27	
Motherwell	d																							11u49	
Carstairs	d																								
Lockerbie	d																								
Carlisle 8	a																			12 12				12 43	
	d							09 15							11 51					12 14				12 45	
Penrith North Lakes	d							09 50							12 08					12 29				13 00	
Windermere	d																							12 59	
Oxenholme Lake District	a							10 45							12 30					12 52				13 22	
	d							10 45							12 32					12 53				13 24	
Barrow-in-Furness	d																		12 00						
Lancaster 6	a							11 30							12 46				12 59	13 08				13 38	
	d								11 43						12 48				13 00	13 09				13 40	
Preston 8	a								12 00						13 05				13 19	13 26				13 57	
Blackpool North	a								12 47						13 38					14 16				14 47	
	d	10 28							11 28					12 17	12 28									13 28	
Preston 8	d	11 25							12 03		12 28			12 42	13 08					13 29				14 00	
Wigan North Western	a	11 36							12 14		12 39			13 01	13 19					13 40				14 11	
	d	11 37							12 15		12 40			13 01	13 21					13 40				14 13	
Bolton	a								12e52						13e52					14e26					
Manchester Piccadilly 10	a								13e15						14e15					14e49					
Manchester Airport	a								13e33						14e33					15f21					
Liverpool Lime Street 10	a	12 49												13 50						14 49					
	d		11 35	11 56								12 56					13 26					13 56			
Liverpool South Parkway 7	d		11 45														13 36								
Runcorn	d		11 53	12 14								13 14					13 44					14 14			
Warrington Bank Quay	a	11 47							12 25		12 50				13 30					13 51				14 22	
	d	11 49							12 26		12 52				13 32					13 53				14 24	
Hartford	d		12 03														13 54								
Manchester Piccadilly 10	d					11 53	12 08			12 45		12 33	12 53			13 24					13 45		13 53		14 24
Stockport	d					12 02	12 22			12u56		12 42	13 02			13 33					13u55		14 03		14 33
Manchester Airport	d		11 32														13 26								
Wilmslow	d		11 40									12 54					13 33								
Holyhead	d			09 56							10g35														
Bangor (Gwynedd)	d			10 34							11g04				11 56		11 56								
Llandudno	d			10h15																					
Llandudno Junction	d			10 57							11g22				12 14		12 14								
Chester	d	11 25		11 48							12 25				13 08		13 25					13 55			
Crewe 10	a	12 08	12 17	12 33					12 45		13 11	13 33			13 50		14 08			14 13		14 33		14 43	
	d	12 12	12 19	12 35					12 48		13 13	13 38			13 53		14 10			14 17		14 37		14 45	
Macclesfield	d					12 15	12 35			13 09			13 15			13 46					14 08		14 16		14 46
Congleton	d																								
Stoke-on-Trent	d					12 31	12 58			13 25			13 31			14 05					14 24		14 32		15 05
Stafford	a		12 42	12 54			13 24					13 57				14 24	14 31					14 56		15 06	15 24
	d		12 43	12 56			13 26					13 58				14 26	14 31					14 58		15 07	15 26
Penkridge	a		12 49														14 37								
Wolverhampton 7	a	12 48	13 02			13 05	13 40				13 48		14 05			14 40	14 49			14 54			15 04		15 40
Coseley	a																								
Sandwell & Dudley	a					13 16							14 16										15 16		
Birmingham New Street 12	a	13 11	13 21			13 26	13 58				14 11		14 26			14 58	15 08			15 16			15 26		15 58
Birmingham International	a		13 45			13 39	14 30						14 39			15 14							15 39		16 30
Coventry	a			13 45		13 51	14 40					14 45	14 51			15 23						15 45	15 51	16 12	16 40
Lichfield Trent Valley	a																								
Tamworth Low Level	a																								
Nuneaton	a																								
Rugby	a			13 58					14 22			14 58			15 23							15 58		16 26	
Northampton	a			15j17								16j17										17j17			
Milton Keynes Central	a					14 26			14 50	15 00		15 21	15 27										16 25	16 51	
Watford Junction	a			14s46					15s13	15 55			16 26		16s12						16s32	16s46	17 26		
Gatwick Airport 10	a																								
London Euston 15	a			15 08		15 16			15 38	15 56		16 07	16 16		16 36						16 56	17 08	17 11	17 39	

For general notes see front of timetable
For details of catering facilities see Directory of Train Operators

A To Penzance (Table 135)

B To Bournemouth (Table 51)

b Via Glasgow Queen Street and Glasgow Central. Passengers make their own way from one station to the other

c Change at Haymarket

e Change at Preston

f Change at Preston and Manchester Piccadilly

g Change at Chester and Crewe

h Change at Llandudno Junction and Crewe. By bus to Llandudno Junction

j By bus

OVERNIGHT SLEEPERS. For Sleeper trains, operated by First ScotRail, please refer to Tables 400 - 404

Table 65

Sundays

until 27 January

Scotland and North West England → West Midlands and London

Route Diagram - see first page of Table 65

		TP	VT	TP	VT	VT	VT	XC	NT	VT	VT	TP	LM	VT	LM	VT	VT	VT	XC	VT	TP	VT	VT
		1◇	R 1	1◇	1◇	1◇	1◇	R 1		1◇	1◇	1◇	1◇	R 1	1◇	1◇	1◇	1◇	R 1	1◇	1◇	R 1	1◇
								A											B				
Inverness	d																						
Aberdeen	d													09 50									
Dundee	d	09 25												11 03									
Perth	d																	11b05					
Edinburgh 10	d	11 43												12 52									
Haymarket	d	11u47												12u57									
Glasgow Central 15	d		11 55															13 25			13 35	14 03	
Motherwell	d		12u13															13u45					
Carstairs	d																						
Lockerbie	d	12 44												13 51							14 34		
Carlisle 8	a	13 05	13 12											14 11				14 43			14 56	15 14	
	d	13 07	13 15											14 13				14 45			15 03	15 16	
Penrith North Lakes	d	13 21	13 30											14 28				15 00			15 17		
Windermere	d													14 15				14 59					
Oxenholme Lake District	a	13 45												14 51				15 22			15 41		
	d	13 45												14 53				15 24			15 41		
Barrow-in-Furness	d											14 00											
Lancaster 6	a	14 01	14 06									15 00		15 07				15 38			15 57	16 03	
	d	14 01	14 07									15 02		15 09				15 40			15 57	16 04	
Preston 8	a	14 20	14 25									15 20		15 26				15 57			16 16	16 21	
Blackpool North	a		15 16											16 16							16 47	17 16	
	d			←					14 17	14 28								15 28					
Preston 8	d	14 30	14 27	14 30					14 42	15 02		15 23		15 28				16 00			16 20	16 23	
Wigan North Western	a	→	14 40						15 00	15 12				15 39				16 12				16 34	
	d		14 40						15 01	15 14				15 41				16 13				16 36	
Bolton	a		15c26	14 52								15 41		16c26							16 42	16c51	
Manchester Piccadilly 10	a		15c49	15 15								16 01		16c49							17 01	17c15	
Manchester Airport	a			15 33								16 18									17 18	17c33	
Liverpool Lime Street 10	a								15 49					16 49									
	d					14 56							15 31			15 56							
Liverpool South Parkway 7	d												15 41										
Runcorn	d					15 14							15 49			16 14							
Warrington Bank Quay	a		14 51							15 23				15 51				16 23				16 46	
	d		14 52							15 25				15 52				16 24				16 47	
Hartford	d																						
Manchester Piccadilly 10	d				14 45	14 34	14 53	15 24			15 45						15 53	15 49	16 24	16 45			16 53
Stockport	d				14u55	14 42	15 02	15 33			15u55						16 02	15 58	16 33	16u55			17 02
Manchester Airport	d												15 25										
Wilmslow	d					14 55							15 33					16 06					
Holyhead	d					13 14							13e31										
Bangor (Gwynedd)	d		12 52			13 41							13e58										
Llandudno	d					13f15																	
Llandudno Junction	d		13 15			13 59							14e16										
Chester	d		14 12			14 55							15 25			16 00						16 25	
Crewe 10	a		15 12			15 33				15 44			16 08	16 12		16 33		16 43				17 07	
	d		15 13			15 35				15 46			16 11	16 13		16 35		16 46				17 09	
Macclesfield	d				15 08		15 15	15 46			16 08						16 15		16 46	17 08			17 15
Congleton	d																						
Stoke-on-Trent	d				15 24		15 31	16 05			16 24						16 31		17 05	17 24			17 31
Stafford	a					15 54		16 24					16 36			16 53		17 06	17 24				
	d					15 55		16 26					16 36		←	16 55		17 08	17 26				
Penkridge	a												16 42		16 42								
Wolverhampton 7	a		15 48				16 04	16 40					→	16 48	16 54		17 04		17 40			17 48	18 04
Coseley	a																						
Sandwell & Dudley	a						16 16										17 16						18 16
Birmingham New Street 12	a		16 11				16 26	16 58						17 11	17 14		17 26		17 58			18 11	18 26
Birmingham International	a						16 39	17 14									17 39		18 30				18 39
Coventry	a					16 45	16 51	17 23								17 45	17 51	18 12	18 40				18 49
Lichfield Trent Valley	a																						
Tamworth Low Level	a																						
Nuneaton	a																						
Rugby	a					16 58				17 23						17 58		18 26					
Northampton	a					18g17										19g17		20g17					
Milton Keynes Central	a				17 00	17 22	17 27									18 22	18 27	18 50		19 00			19 25
Watford Junction	a				17 55		18 26			18s12	18s30					18s45	19 26						19s50
Gatwick Airport 10	a																						
London Euston 15	a				17 56	18 08	18 11			18 38	18 51					19 14	19 17	19 33		19 53			20 11

For general notes see front of timetable
For details of catering facilities see Directory of Train Operators

A To Bournemouth (Table 51)

B To Plymouth (Table 51)

b Via Glasgow Queen Street and Glasgow Central. Passengers make their own way from one station to the other

c Change at Preston

e Change at Chester and Crewe

f Change at Llandudno Junction and Crewe. By bus to Llandudno Junction

g By bus

OVERNIGHT SLEEPERS. For Sleeper trains, operated by First ScotRail, please refer to Tables 400 - 404

Table 65

Sundays

until 27 January

Scotland and North West England → West Midlands and London

Route Diagram - see first page of Table 65

		XC	NT	VT	LM	VT	TP	VT	VT	VT	NT	VT		XC	VT	TP	VT	VT	VT	NT	VT	XC	LM	VT	TP
		R						R						R			R								
		1		1 ◇	1 ◇	1 ◇	1 ◇	1	1 ◇	1 ◇		1 ◇		1	1 ◇	1 ◇	1	1 ◇	1 ◇		1 ◇	1 ◇	1 ◇	1 ◇	1 ◇
		A												B								C			
		☕		☕		☕		☕	☕	☕		☕		☕	☕	🍴	☕	☕	☕		☕			☕	
Inverness	d							09 38													12b30				
Aberdeen	d							11 58																	
Dundee	d							13 14								13 25									
Perth	d							11 55				13b05									14b50				
Edinburgh 10	d							14 53								15 43									
Haymarket	d							14u58								15u47									
Glasgow Central 15	d			14 26								15 25					16 03				16 26				
Motherwell	d			14u45								15u45									16u45				
Carstairs	d																								
Lockerbie	d							15 53								16 44									
Carlisle 8	a			15 45				16 12				16 43				17 05	17 12				17 43				
	d			15 47				16 14				16 45				17 07	17 18				17 45				
Penrith North Lakes	d			16 02				16 29				17 00				17 21					18 00				
Windermere	d			*16 02*								*16 59*									*18 02*				
Oxenholme Lake District	a			16 24				16 52				17 22				17 45	17 55				18 22				
	d			16 26				16 53				17 24				17 45	17 55				18 24				
Barrow-in-Furness	d						16 00																		18 00
Lancaster 6	a			16 40			17 00	17 08				17 38				18 01	18 09				18 38				19 00
	d			16 42			17 02	17 09				17 40				18 01	18 10				18 40				19 02
Preston 8	a			16 59			17 20	17 26				17 57				18 20	18 28				18 57				19 20
Blackpool North	a			*17 35*				*18 16*				*18 34*					*19 05*				*19 32*				*20 03*
	d		16 17	*16 28*				*16 45*			17 17	*17 25*					*17 45*			18 17	*18 28*				
Preston 8	d		16 42	17 02			17 23	17 29			17 42	18 00				18 23	18 30			18 42	19 00				19 23
Wigan North Western	a		17 00	17 12				17 40			18 00	18 12					18 41			19 00	19 11				
	d		17 01	17 14				17 41			18 01	18 13					18 42			19 01	19 12				
Bolton	a						17 41	*18c26*								18 42	*19c26*								19 41
Manchester Piccadilly 10	a						18 01	*18c49*								19 01	*19c49*								20 01
Manchester Airport ✈	a						18 18									19 18									20 18
Liverpool Lime Street 10	a		17 49								18 49									19 49					
	d				17 25				17 56									18 56					19 30		
Liverpool South Parkway 7 ✈	d				17 35																		19 39		
Runcorn	d				17 43				18 14									19 14					19 47		
Warrington Bank Quay	a			17 23				17 51				18 23					18 52				19 22				
	d			17 25				17 53				18 24					18 53				19 23				
Hartford	d				17 52																				
Manchester Piccadilly 10	d	17 24		*16 37*		17 45				17 53				18 24	18 45			*18 37*	18 53			19 24		19 45	
Stockport	d	17 33		*16 45*		17u55				18 02				18 33	18u55			*18 45*	19 02			19 33		19u55	
Manchester Airport ✈	d							*17 24*																	
Wilmslow	d			*16 54*				*17 31*										*18 55*							
Holyhead	d				*15 57*												*16 48*						*17e25*		
Bangor (Gwynedd)	d			*15e42*	*16 24*				*16e32*								*17 27*						*17e53*		
Llandudno	d				*16f15*																				
Llandudno Junction	d			*16e00*	*16 42*				*16e54*								*17 46*						*18e11*		
Chester	d			*17 00*	*17 38*				*17 52*								*18 42*						*19 25*		
Crewe 10	a			17 44	18 07			18 12	18 33			18 44					19 12	19 33			19 42		20 07		
	d			17 47	18 09			18 15	18 35			18 47					19 15	19 36			19 45		20 08		
Macclesfield	d	17 46				18 08				18 15				18 46	19 08				19 15			19 46		20 08	
Congleton	d																								
Stoke-on-Trent	d	18 05				18 24				18 31				19 05	19 24				19 31			20 05		20 24	
Stafford	a	18 24			18 30				18 53			19 06		19 24				19 54			20 06	20 24	20 29		
	d	18 26			18 30				18 55			19 08		19 26				19 55			20 08	20 26	20 31		
Penkridge	a				18 36																				
Wolverhampton 7	a	18 40			18 48			18 51		19 04				19 40			19 48		20 04			20 40	20 47		
Coseley	a																								
Sandwell & Dudley	a									19 16									20 16						
Birmingham New Street 12	a	18 58			19 04			19 14		19 26				19 58			20 11		20 26			20 58	21 08		
Birmingham International ✈	a	19 13			*19 30*					19 39				*20 30*					20 39			21 14			
Coventry	a	19 23			*19 40*				19 45	19 51		20 12		*20 40*				20 45	20 51			21 23			
Lichfield Trent Valley	a																								
Tamworth Low Level	a																								
Nuneaton	a																								
Rugby	a			19 23					19 58			20 26						20 58			21 23			21 39	
Northampton	a								*21g17*									*22g17*							
Milton Keynes Central	a								20 22	20 27		20 51			21 01			21 22	21 28		21 50			22 04	
Watford Junction	a			20s12		20s31			20s47	20s51		21s31			*21 55*			22s00	22s06		22s31			22s41	
Gatwick Airport 10 ✈	a																								
London Euston 15 ⊖	a			20 38		20 53			21 14	21 17		21 54			21 57			22 23	22 27		22 51			23 00	

For general notes see front of timetable
For details of catering facilities see Directory of Train Operators

A To Bournemouth (Table 51)

B To Plymouth (Table 51)

C To Southampton Central (Table 51)

b Via Glasgow Queen Street and Glasgow Central. Passengers make their own way from one station to the other

c Change at Preston

e Change at Chester and Crewe

f Change at Llandudno Junction and Crewe. By bus to Llandudno Junction

g By bus

OVERNIGHT SLEEPERS. For Sleeper trains, operated by First ScotRail, please refer to Tables 400 - 404

Scotland and North West England → West Midlands and London

Sundays
until 27 January

Route Diagram - see first page of Table 65

		VT	VT		VT	VT	VT	TP	VT	TP	XC	NT	VT	XC	LM	TP	TP	NT	VT	SR	SR	SR	SR
		1◇	1◇		1◇	1◇	1◇	1◇	1◇	1	1◇		1◇	1◇	1◇	1◇	1◇		1◇		R	R	R
																							A
		☕	☕		☕	☕	☕	🛒	☕				☕						☕		☕	☕	☕
Inverness	d	13 25																		16b15		18 30	20 25
Aberdeen	d	13 50						15c10											15e30	17e50		20 10	21 40
Dundee	d	15c25						16c25											16e43	19e02		21 21	23u04
Perth	d	15 25																	17e05	19e24		20 46	22u59
Edinburgh 10	d	16 53						17 39					18 52									23 15	
Haymarket	d	16u59						17u43					18u57										
Glasgow Central 15	d					17 33			18 03										20 03	22 28	23 15		
Motherwell	d					17u50													20u22		23u30		
Carstairs	d																				23u50		
Lockerbie	d	17 56						18 44					19 58						21 07				
Carlisle 8	a	18 16				18 49		19 05	19 13				20 16						21 28	00 49			
	d	18 19				18 52		19 07	19 15				20 18						21 30		01u24		
Penrith North Lakes	d	18 34				19 06		19 21					20 34						21 45				
Windermere	d					19 02				20 02							21 20						
Oxenholme Lake District	a	18 57				19 29		19 45	19 51	20 19			20 57				21 40		22 08				
	d	18 58				19 30		19 45	19 52	20 21			20 58				21 40		22 09				
Barrow-in-Furness	d												19 57			20 50							
Lancaster 6	a	19 15				19 45		20 01	20 07	20 38			21 13			21 51	21 56		22 25				
	d	19 16				19 46		20 01	20 08				21 14				22 02		22 26				
Preston 8	a	19 33				20 03		20 20	20 25				21 31				22 20		22 58				04s22
Blackpool North	a	20 16				20 47			21 16				22 16				23 16		23 43				
	d					19 28						20 17	20 28					22 17					
Preston 8	d	19 35				20 06		20 23	20 28			20 42	21 34				22 23	22 42	23 01				
Wigan North Western	a	19 46				20 17			20 39			21 01	21 46					23 11	23s23				
	d	19 47				20 18			20 40			21 01	21 46					23 11					
Bolton	a	20f26						20 42	21f26				22f26				22 41		23s37				05 39
Manchester Piccadilly 10	a	20f49						21 01	21f49				22f49				23 01		23 59				05 57
Manchester Airport ✈	a							21 18	22f33								23 18		00 33				06 14
Liverpool Lime Street 10	a	20 49										21 49	22 49					23 59					
	d				19 56										21 47								
Liverpool South Parkway 7 ✈	d														21 57								
Runcorn	d				20 14										22 05								
Warrington Bank Quay	a	19 57				20 28			20 50				21 56										
	d	19 58				20 29			20 52				21 58										
Hartford	d														22 15								
Manchester Piccadilly 10	d		19 56				20 23				20 55		21 06	21 55									
Stockport	d		20 04				20 32				21 04		20 54	22 04									
Manchester Airport ✈	d	19 24											21 25										
Wilmslow	d	19 32											21 32										
Holyhead	d								18g40														
Bangor (Gwynedd)	d								19g09				19 55										
Llandudno	d																						
Llandudno Junction	d								19g27				20 18										
Chester	d				19 55				20 25				21 25		21 55								
Crewe 10	a	20 18			20 33	20 48			21 11				22 17		22 40								05s29
	d	20 20			20 35	20 51			21 13				22 20		22 43								
Macclesfield	d		20 17				20 45				21 16			22 17									
Congleton	d																						
Stoke-on-Trent	d		20 33				21 01				21 34			22 34									
Stafford	a		20 51		20 58	21 09	21 19		21 31		21 52		22 39	22 52	23 06								06 16
	d		20 53		20 59	21 11	21 21		21 32		21 53		22 40	22 53	23 07								
Penkridge	a														23 12								
Wolverhampton 7	a	20 52	21 08				21 35		21 54		22 09		22 54	23 09	23 25								06 41
Coseley	a																						
Sandwell & Dudley	a						21 47																
Birmingham New Street 12	a	21 15	21 32				21 56		22 17		22 30		23 17	23 30	23 45								06 58
Birmingham International ✈	a	21 52					22 09		22 52		23 09												07 14
Coventry	a				21 45	22 12	22 19		23 08		23 19												07 23
Lichfield Trent Valley	a																						06 32
Tamworth Low Level	a																						06 39
Nuneaton	a																						
Rugby	a				21 58		22 33				23 33												06 50
Northampton	a				23h17		00h17																
Milton Keynes Central	a				22 21	22 50	22 58																
Watford Junction	a				23s00	23s16	23s28															06s28	07 04
Gatwick Airport 10 ✈	a																					08j39	
London Euston 15 ⊖	a				23 25	23 41	23 48															06 54	07 43

For general notes see front of timetable
For details of catering facilities see Directory of Train Operators

A Also conveys portion from Fort William (Table 227)

b Change at Perth, Glasgow Queen Street and Glasgow Central. Passengers make their own way between Glasgow Queen Street and Glasgow Central

c Change at Haymarket

e Via Glasgow Queen Street and Glasgow Central. Passengers make their own way from one station to the other

f Change at Preston

g Change at Chester and Crewe

h By bus

j Change at Watford Junction and Clapham Junction

OVERNIGHT SLEEPERS. For Sleeper trains, operated by First ScotRail, please refer to Tables 400 - 404

Table 65

Sundays

Scotland and North West England → West Midlands and London

3 February to 23 March

Route Diagram - see first page of Table 65

		XC	VT	LM	VT	XC	NT	VT	VT	VT	VT	VT	VT	XC	VT	VT		VT	VT	XC	VT	NT	VT	TP	VT
		1 ◇	1 ◇	1 ◇	1 ◇	1 ◇		1 ◇	1 ◇	1 ◇	1 ◇		1 ◇	1 ◇	1 ◇	1 ◇		1 ◇	1 ◇	1 ◇	1 ◇			1 ◇	1 ◇
		A				B								A						B					
												bus											bus		
		catering	catering		catering	catering		catering	catering	catering	catering		catering	catering	catering	catering		catering	catering	catering	catering				catering
Inverness	d																								
Aberdeen	d																								
Dundee	d																								
Perth	d																								
Edinburgh 10	d																								
Haymarket	d																								
Glasgow Central 15	d																								
Motherwell	d																								
Carstairs	d																								
Lockerbie	d																								
Carlisle 8	a																								
	d																								
Penrith North Lakes	d																								
Windermere	d																								
Oxenholme Lake District	a																								
	d																								
Barrow-in-Furness	d																							09 58	
Lancaster 6	a																							10 57	
	d											09 00											10 25	10 58	
Preston 8	a											09 50											11 15	11 17	
Blackpool North	a											11b00											12b20	12b30	
	d						07b50						08b45			09b20						09b50			
Preston 8	d						08 42						10 03			10 28						10 42			11 25
Wigan North Western	a						09 01						10 14			10 40						11 01			11 36
	d						09 01						10 15			10 40						11 01			11 37
Bolton	a																								
Manchester Piccadilly 10	a																								
Manchester Airport	a																								
Liverpool Lime Street 10	a						09 49									*11 49*						11 49			*12 49*
	d									09 53								10 53							
Liverpool South Parkway 7	d																								
Runcorn	d									10 09								11 09							
Warrington Bank Quay	a												10 25			10 51									11 47
	d												10 26			10 51									11 49
Hartford	d																								
Manchester Piccadilly 10	d	08 08			09 00	09 24			09 44		09 53			10 24	10 44				10 53	11 24	11 44				
Stockport	d				09u10	09 33			09u53		10 02			10 33	10u52				11 02	11 33	11u52				
Manchester Airport	d									*09 33*															
Wilmslow	d	08 24			09 19					*09 41*															
Holyhead	d																								
Bangor (Gwynedd)	d																								
Llandudno	d																								
Llandudno Junction	d																								
Chester	d			*08 55*				*09 25*		*09 55*			*10 11*					*10 55*							*11 25*
Crewe 10	a	08 43			09 36					10 29			10 45			11 12		11 28							12 08
	d	08 46		09 40	09 48			10 12		10 35			10 48			11 13		11 35							12 12
Macclesfield	d					09 46			10 06		10 15			10 46	11 05				11 15	11 46	12 05				
Congleton	d																								
Stoke-on-Trent	d	09 05				10 05			10 22		10 31			11 05	11 21				11 31	12 05	12 21				
Stafford	a	09 24		10 01	10 06	10 24		10 31	10 40	10 54			11 06	11 24				11 54		12 24					
	d	09 26	09 39	10 01	10 08	10 26		10 32	10 41	10 55			11 08	11 26				11 55		12 26					
Penkridge	a			10 07																					
Wolverhampton 7	a	09 40		10 23		10 40		10 48			11 05			11 40		11 48			12 05	12 40					12 48
Coseley	a																								
Sandwell & Dudley	a										11 16								12 16						
Birmingham New Street 12	a	09 58		10 43		10 58		11 11			11 26			11 58		12 11			12 26	12 58					13 11
Birmingham International	a	*10 24*			10 57	11 14					11 39			*12 25*					12 39	13 13					
Coventry	a		10 28		11 12	11 23				11 45	11 51		12 12	*12 37*				12 45	12 51	13 23					
Lichfield Trent Valley	a																								
Tamworth Low Level	a																								
Nuneaton	a																								
Rugby	a		10 41		11 26				11 39	11 58								12 58							
Northampton	a		*12b17*							*13b17*								*14b17*							
Milton Keynes Central	a		11 05		11 51					12 21	12 27		12 50		13 00			13 22	13 28						
Watford Junction	a		*11 55*		12s31				12s43	13s00	13s06		13s31		*13 55*				14s03		14s31				
Gatwick Airport 10	a																								
London Euston 15	a		12 00		12 51				13 04	13 23	13 29		13 56		14 00			14 23	14 29		14 56				

For general notes see front of timetable
For details of catering facilities see Directory of Train Operators

A To Plymouth (Table 51)
B To Bournemouth (Table 51)
b By bus

OVERNIGHT SLEEPERS. For Sleeper trains, operated by First ScotRail, please refer to Tables 400 - 404

Table 65

Sundays

3 February to 23 March

Scotland and North West England → West Midlands and London

Route Diagram - see first page of Table 65

		LM	VT	VT	XC	VT	VT	VT	VT	VT		VT	XC	NT	VT	VT	TP	LM	VT	VT	VT	VT	VT	VT	XC
		1 ◇	1 ◇ ☕	1 ◇ ☕	R 1 A ☕	bus	1 ◇ ☕	1 ◇ ☕	1 ◇ ☕	1 ◇ ☕		1 ◇ ☕	R 1 B ☕		bus	1 ◇ ☕	1 ◇	1 ◇	1 ◇ ☕	1 ◇ ☕	1 ◇ ☕	1 ◇ ☕	bus	1 ◇ ☕	R 1 A ☕
Inverness	d																								
Aberdeen	d																								
Dundee	d																								
Perth	d																								
Edinburgh 10	d																								
Haymarket	d																								
Glasgow Central 15	d														09 40								10 35		
Motherwell	d																								
Carstairs	d																								
Lockerbie	d																								
Carlisle 8	a														11 35								12 30		
	d					09 15										11 51								12 45	
Penrith North Lakes	d					09 50										12 08								13 00	
Windermere	d																							12 59	
Oxenholme Lake District	a					10 45										12 30								13 22	
	d					10 45										12 32								13 24	
Barrow-in-Furness	d																12 00								
Lancaster 6	a					11 30										12 46	12 59							13 38	
	d						11 43									12 48	13 00							13 40	
Preston 8	a						12 00									13 05	13 19							13 57	
Blackpool North	a						13b30									13b55	14b30								
	d						10b45	11b20						11b50					12b20					12b45	
Preston 8	d						12 03	12 28						12 42		13 08			13 29					14 00	
Wigan North Western	a						12 14	12 39						13 01		13 19			13 40					14 11	
	d						12 15	12 40						13 01		13 21			13 40					14 13	
Bolton	a						12c52									13c52									
Manchester Piccadilly 10	a						13c15									14c15									
Manchester Airport ✈	a						13c33									14c33									
Liverpool Lime Street 10	a													13 50					14 49						
	d	11 35	11 56							12 56								13 26			13 56				
Liverpool South Parkway 7 ✈	d	11 45																13 36							
Runcorn	d	11 53	12 14							13 14								13 44			14 14				
Warrington Bank Quay	a						12 25	12 50								13 30			13 51					14 22	
	d						12 26	12 52								13 32			13 53					14 24	
Hartford	d	12 03																13 54							
Manchester Piccadilly 10	d			11 53	12 08				12 45	12 33		12 53	13 24							13 45		13 53			14 24
Stockport	d			12 02	12 22				12u56	12 42		13 02	13 33							13u55		14 03			14 33
Manchester Airport ✈	d	11 32																13 26							
Wilmslow	d	11 40								12 54								13 33							
Holyhead	d		09 56					10e35																	
Bangor (Gwynedd)	d		10 34					11e04								11 56									
Llandudno	d		10f15																						
Llandudno Junction	d		10 57					11e22								12 14									
Chester	d		11 48					12 25								13 08		13 25			13 55				
Crewe 10	a	12 17	12 33				12 45	13 11		13 33						13 50		14 08	14 13		14 33			14 43	
	d	12 19	12 35				12 48	13 13		13 38						13 53		14 10	14 17		14 37			14 45	
Macclesfield	d			12 15	12 35				13 09			13 15	13 46							14 08		14 16			14 46
Congleton	d																								
Stoke-on-Trent	d			12 31	12 58				13 25			13 31	14 05							14 24		14 32			15 05
Stafford	a	12 42	12 54		13 24					13 57			14 24					14 31			14 56			15 06	15 24
	d	12 43	12 56		13 26					13 58			14 26					14 31			14 58			15 07	15 26
Penkridge	a	12 49																14 37							
Wolverhampton 7	a	13 02		13 05	13 40			13 48				14 05	14 40					14 49	14 54			15 04			15 40
Coseley	a																								
Sandwell & Dudley	a			13 16								14 16										15 16			
Birmingham New Street 12	a	13 21		13 26	13 58			14 11				14 26	14 58					15 08	15 16			15 26			15 58
Birmingham International ✈	a	13 52		13 39	14 25							14 39	15 14									15 39			16 25
Coventry	a		13 45	13 51	14 37					14 45		14 51	15 23								15 45	15 51		16 12	16 37
Lichfield Trent Valley	a																								
Tamworth Low Level	a																								
Nuneaton	a																								
Rugby	a		13 58				14 22			14 58						15 23					15 58			16 26	
Northampton	a		15b17							16b17											17b17				
Milton Keynes Central	a			14 26			14 50		15 00	15 21		15 27										16 25		16 51	
Watford Junction	a		14s46				15s13		15 55			16 26				16s12				16s32	16s46	17 26			
Gatwick Airport 10 ✈	a																								
London Euston 15 ⊖	a		15 08	15 16			15 38		15 56	16 07		16 16				16 36				16 56	17 08	17 11		17 39	

For general notes see front of timetable
For details of catering facilities see Directory of Train Operators

A To Penzance (Table 135)
B To Bournemouth (Table 51)
b By bus
c Change at Preston
e Change at Chester and Crewe
f Change at Llandudno Junction and Crewe. By bus to Llandudno Junction

OVERNIGHT SLEEPERS. For Sleeper trains, operated by First ScotRail, please refer to Tables 400 - 404

Sundays

Scotland and North West England → West Midlands and London

3 February to 23 March

Route Diagram - see first page of Table 65

		VT	TP	VT	VT	VT	VT	VT	VT	XC	NT	VT	VT	TP	VT	VT	LM	VT	LM	VT	VT	VT	VT
							R			R								R					
		1 ◇	1 ◇				1	1 ◇	1 ◇	1		1 ◇	1 ◇	1 ◇			1 ◇	1	1 ◇	1 ◇	1 ◇		1 ◇
										A													
				bus	bus	bus									bus	bus						bus	
		☕	trolley				☕	☕	☕	☕		☕	☕					☕		☕	☕		☕
Inverness	d																						
Aberdeen	d																						
Dundee	d					08b45										09 25							
Perth	d					09b05										09 27							
Edinburgh 10	d			10 30												11 30							
Haymarket	d																						
Glasgow Central 15	d				10 50	11 00									12 05							12 35	
Motherwell	d				11 25																		
Carstairs	d																						
Lockerbie	d			12a40	12a40		12 52									13a40		13 52					
Carlisle 8	a					12 55	13 12								14 00			14 12				14 30	
	d		13 07				13 15											14 13					14 45
Penrith North Lakes	d		13 21				13 30											14 28					15 00
Windermere	d																	14 15					14 59
Oxenholme Lake District	a		13 44															14 51					15 22
	d		13 44															14 53					15 24
Barrow-in-Furness	d													14 00									
Lancaster 6	a		14 01				14 06							15 00				15 07					15 38
	d		14 01				14 07							15 02				15 09					15 40
Preston 8	a		14 20				14 25							15 20				15 26					15 57
Blackpool North	a						15c30											16c30					
	d										13c50							14c20					14c45
Preston 8	d		14 23				14 27				14 42	15 02		15 23				15 28					16 00
Wigan North Western	a						14 40				15 00	15 12						15 39					16 12
	d						14 40				15 01	15 14						15 41					16 13
Bolton	a		14 42				15e26							15 41				16e26					
Manchester Piccadilly 10	a		15 00				15e49							16 01				16e49					
Manchester Airport ✈	a		15 18											16 18									
Liverpool Lime Street 10	a										15 49							16 49					
	d							14 56									15 31			15 56			
Liverpool South Parkway 7 ✈	d																15 41						
Runcorn	d							15 14									15 49			16 14			
Warrington Bank Quay	a						14 51					15 23						15 51					16 23
	d						14 52					15 25						15 52					16 24
Hartford	d																						
Manchester Piccadilly 10	d	14 45						14 34	14 53	15 24			15 45								15 53		15 49
Stockport	d	14u55						14 42	15 02	15 33			15u55								16 02		15 58
Manchester Airport ✈	d																15 25						
Wilmslow	d							14 55									15 33						16 06
Holyhead	d							13 14									13f31						
Bangor (Gwynedd)	d						12 52	13 41									13f58						
Llandudno	d							13g15															
Llandudno Junction	d						13 15	13 59									14f16						
Chester	d						14 12	14 55									15 25			16 00			
Crewe 10	a						15 12	15 33				15 44					16 08	16 12		16 33			16 43
	d						15 13	15 35				15 46					16 11	16 13		16 35			16 46
Macclesfield	d	15 08							15 15	15 46			16 08								16 15		
Congleton	d																						
Stoke-on-Trent	d	15 24							15 31	16 05			16 24								16 31		
Stafford	a							15 54		16 24							16 36			16 53			17 06
	d							15 55		16 26							16 36		⟵	16 55			17 08
Penkridge	a																16 42		16 42				
Wolverhampton 7	a						15 48		16 04	16 40							⟶	16 48	16 54		17 04		
Coseley	a																						
Sandwell & Dudley	a								16 16												17 16		
Birmingham New Street 12	a						16 11		16 26	16 58								17 11	17 14		17 26		
Birmingham International ✈	a								16 39	17 14											17 39		
Coventry	a							16 45	16 51	17 23										17 45	17 51		18 12
Lichfield Trent Valley	a																						
Tamworth Low Level	a																						
Nuneaton	a																						
Rugby	a							16 58				17 23								17 58			18 26
Northampton	a							18c17												19c17			20c17
Milton Keynes Central	a	17 00						17 22	17 27											18 22	18 27		18 50
Watford Junction	a	17 55							18 26			18s12	18s30							18s45	19 26		
Gatwick Airport 10 ✈	a																						
London Euston 15 ⊖	a	17 56						18 08	18 11			18 38	18 51							19 14	19 17		19 33

For general notes see front of timetable
For details of catering facilities see Directory of Train Operators

A To Bournemouth (Table 51)
b Via Glasgow Queen Street and Glasgow Central. Passengers make their own way from one station to the other
c By bus
e Change at Preston
f Change at Chester and Crewe
g Change at Llandudno Junction and Crewe. By bus to Llandudno Junction

OVERNIGHT SLEEPERS. For Sleeper trains, operated by First ScotRail, please refer to Tables 400 - 404

Table 65

Sundays

Scotland and North West England → West Midlands and London

3 February to 23 March

Route Diagram - see first page of Table 65

		XC	VT	VT	TP	VT	VT	VT	NT	XC	VT	VT	LM	VT		TP	VT	VT	VT	VT	VT	VT	NT	VT	XC
		R 1	1 ◇		1 ◇		1 ◇	1 ◇		R 1		1 ◇	1 ◇	1 ◇		1 ◇				R 1	1 ◇	1 ◇		1 ◇	R 1
		A								B															A
				🚌		🚌					🚌						🚌	🚌	🚌						
		⫿P	⫿P		⫿⫿			⫿P		⫿P		⫿P		⫿P						⫿P	⫿P	⫿P		⫿P	⫿P
Inverness	d																09 38								
Aberdeen	d			09b30													09 50								
Dundee	d			10b43													11 25								
Perth	d			11b05													11 55								
Edinburgh 10	d					12 30											13 30								
Haymarket	d																								
Glasgow Central 15	d			13 00							13 35							13c34	14 05						
Motherwell	d																	14 25							
Carstairs	d																								
Lockerbie	d					14a40	14 52										15a40	15a40		15 52					
Carlisle 8	a			14 55			15 12				15 30								16 00	16 11					
	d				15 03							15 47								16 14					
Penrith North Lakes	d				15 17							16 02								16 29					
Windermere	d											16 02													
Oxenholme Lake District	a				15 41							16 24								16 52					
	d				15 41							16 26								16 53					
Barrow-in-Furness	d															16 00									
Lancaster 6	a				15 57							16 40				17 00				17 08					
	d				15 57							16 42				17 02				17 09					
Preston 8	a				16 16							16 59				17 20				17 26					
Blackpool North	a											17e55								18e30					
	d								15e50											16e20			16e50		
Preston 8	d				16 20				16 42			17 02				17 23				17 29				17 42	18 00
Wigan North Western	a								17 00			17 12								17 40				18 00	18 12
	d								17 01			17 14								17 41				18 01	18 13
Bolton	a				16 42											17 41				18f26					
Manchester Piccadilly 10	a				17 01											18 01				18f49					
Manchester Airport ✈	a				17 18											18 18				19f18					
Liverpool Lime Street 10	a								17 49														18 49		
	d												17 25								17 56				
Liverpool South Parkway 7 ✈	d												17 35												
Runcorn	d												17 43								18 14				
Warrington Bank Quay	a											17 23								17 51				18 23	
	d											17 25								17 53				18 24	
Hartford	d												17 52												
Manchester Piccadilly 10	d	16 24	16 45					16 53		17 24		16 37		17 45								17 53			18 24
Stockport	d	16 33	16u55					17 02		17 33		16 45		17u55								18 02			18 33
Manchester Airport ✈	d																			17 24					
Wilmslow	d											16 54								17 31					
Holyhead	d												15 57												
Bangor (Gwynedd)	d											15g42	16 24								16g32				
Llandudno	d												16h15												
Llandudno Junction	d											16g00	16 42								16g54				
Chester	d											17 00	17 38								17 52				
Crewe 10	a											17 44	18 07							18 12	18 33			18 44	
	d											17 47	18 09							18 15	18 35			18 47	
Macclesfield	d	16 46	17 08					17 15		17 46				18 08								18 15			18 46
Congleton	d																								
Stoke-on-Trent	d	17 05	17 24					17 31		18 05				18 24								18 31			19 05
Stafford	a	17 24								18 24			18 30								18 53			19 06	19 24
	d	17 26								18 26			18 30								18 55			19 08	19 26
Penkridge	a												18 36												
Wolverhampton 7	a	17 41						18 04		18 40			18 48							18 51		19 04			19 40
Coseley	a																								
Sandwell & Dudley	a							18 16														19 16			
Birmingham New Street 12	a	17 58						18 26		18 58			19 04							19 14		19 26			19 58
Birmingham International ✈	a	18 25						18 39		19 13			19 30									19 39			20 25
Coventry	a	18 37						18 49		19 23			19 40								19 45	19 51		20 12	20 37
Lichfield Trent Valley	a																								
Tamworth Low Level	a																								
Nuneaton	a																								
Rugby	a											19 23									19 58			20 26	
Northampton	a																				21e17				
Milton Keynes Central	a		19 00					19 25													20 22	20 27		20 51	
Watford Junction	a							19s50				20s12		20s31							20s47	20s51		21s31	
Gatwick Airport 10 ✈	a																								
London Euston 15 ⊖	a		19 53					20 11				20 38		20 53							21 14	21 17		21 54	

For general notes see front of timetable
For details of catering facilities see Directory of Train Operators

A To Plymouth (Table 51)

B To Bournemouth (Table 51)

b Via Glasgow Queen Street and Glasgow Central. Passengers make their own way from one station to the other

c Glasgow Central Low Level

e By bus

f Change at Preston

g Change at Chester and Crewe

h Change at Llandudno Junction and Crewe. By bus to Llandudno Junction

OVERNIGHT SLEEPERS. For Sleeper trains, operated by First ScotRail, please refer to Tables 400 - 404

Scotland and North West England → West Midlands and London

3 February to 23 March

Route Diagram - see first page of Table 65

Station		VT	VT	TP	VT	VT	VT	VT		NT	VT	VT	XC	LM	VT	TP	VT	VT	VT	VT	VT	VT	VT	VT	TP
						R																			
		1◇		1◇		1	1◇	1◇				1◇	1◇	1◇	1◇	1◇		1◇	1◇	1◇		1◇	1◇		1◇
													A												
			[bus]		[bus]						[bus]						[bus]				[bus]			[bus]	
		[catering]		[trolley]		[catering]	[catering]	[catering]				[catering]			[catering]				[catering]	[catering]		[catering]	[catering]		[trolley]
Inverness	d																				12b30				
Aberdeen	d		11b28														11 58							13b30	
Dundee	d		12b43														13 25							14b43	
Perth	d		13b05																		14b50			15b05	
Edinburgh 10	d				14 30												15 30								
Haymarket	d																								
Glasgow Central 15	d		15 00								15 35										16 40			16 55	
Motherwell	d																								
Carstairs	d																								
Lockerbie	d				16a40	16 52											17a40	17 52							
Carlisle 8	a		16 55			17 09					17 30							18 12			18 35			18 50	
	d			17 07		17 18						17 45										18 52			19 07
Penrith North Lakes	d			17 21								18 00										19 06			19 21
Windermere	d			16 59		16 59						18 02										19 02			
Oxenholme Lake District	a			17 44		17 55						18 22										19 29			19 44
	d			17 44		17 55						18 24										19 30			19 44
Barrow-in-Furness	d															18 00									
Lancaster 6	a			18 01		18 09						18 38				19 00						19 45			20 01
	d			18 01		18 10						18 40				19 02						19 46			20 01
Preston 8	a			18 20		18 28						18 57				19 20						20 03			20 20
Blackpool North	a			19c30								19c55				20c30									
	d					17c20				17c50												18c45			
Preston 8	d			18 23		18 30				18 42		19 00				19 23						20 06			20 23
Wigan North Western	a					18 41				19 00		19 11										20 17			
	d					18 42				19 01		19 12										20 18			
Bolton	a			18 42		19e26										19 41									20 42
Manchester Piccadilly 10	a			19 01		19e49										20 01									21 01
Manchester Airport	a			19 18												20 18									21 18
Liverpool Lime Street 10	a									19 49		20 49													
	d						18 56							19 30						19 56					
Liverpool South Parkway 7	d													19 39											
Runcorn	d						19 14							19 47						20 14					
Warrington Bank Quay	a					18 52						19 22										20 28			
	d					18 53						19 23										20 29			
Hartford	d																								
Manchester Piccadilly 10	d	18 45					18 37	18 53					19 24		19 45				19 56				20 23		
Stockport	d	18u55					18 45	19 02					19 33		19u55				20 04				20 32		
Manchester Airport	d																								
Wilmslow	d						18 55																		
Holyhead	d					16 48								17f25											
Bangor (Gwynedd)	d					17 27								17f53											
Llandudno	d																								
Llandudno Junction	d					17 46								18f11											
Chester	d					18 42								19 25						19 55					
Crewe 10	a					19 12	19 33					19 42		20 07						20 33		20 48			
	d					19 15	19 36					19 45		20 08						20 35		20 51			
Macclesfield	d	19 08						19 15					19 46		20 08				20 17				20 45		
Congleton	d																								
Stoke-on-Trent	d	19 24						19 31					20 05		20 24				20 33				21 01		
Stafford	a						19 54					20 06	20 24	20 29					20 51	20 58		21 09	21 19		
	d						19 55					20 08	20 26	20 31					20 53	20 59		21 11	21 21		
Penkridge	a																								
Wolverhampton 7	a					19 48		20 04					20 40	20 47					21 08				21 35		
Coseley	a																								
Sandwell & Dudley	a							20 16															21 47		
Birmingham New Street 12	a					20 11		20 26					20 58	21 08					21 32				21 56		
Birmingham International	a							20 39					21 14										22 09		
Coventry	a						20 45	20 51					21 23							21 45		22 12	22 19		
Lichfield Trent Valley	a																								
Tamworth Low Level	a																								
Nuneaton	a																								
Rugby	a						20 58					21 23			21 39					21 58			22 33		
Northampton	a						22c17													23c17			00c17		
Milton Keynes Central	a	21 01					21 22	21 28				21 50			22 04					22 21		22 50	22 58		
Watford Junction	a	21 55					22s00	22s06				22s31			22s41					23s00		23s16	23s28		
Gatwick Airport 10	a																								
London Euston 15	a	21 57					22 23	22 27				22 51			23 00					23 25		23 41	23 48		

For general notes see front of timetable
For details of catering facilities see Directory of Train Operators

- **A** To Southampton Central (Table 51)
- **b** Via Glasgow Queen Street and Glasgow Central. Passengers make their own way from one station to the other
- **c** By bus
- **e** Change at Preston
- **f** Change at Chester and Crewe

OVERNIGHT SLEEPERS. For Sleeper trains, operated by First ScotRail, please refer to Tables 400 - 404

Table 65

Sundays

3 February to 23 March

Scotland and North West England → West Midlands and London

Route Diagram - see first page of Table 65

		VT		VT	VT	VT	TP	XC	NT	VT	VT	VT	XC	LM	TP	TP	NT	VT	VT	VT	SR	SR	SR		
						1◇	1	1◇				1◇	1◇	1◇	1◇	1◇			1◇			R	R		
																						A	B		
Inverness	d									13 25											16b15	18 30	20 25		
Aberdeen	d									13 50								15c30		17 10	17c50	20 10	21 40		
Dundee	d									15 25								16c43		18 19	19c02	21 21	23u04		
Perth	d									15 25								17c05			19c24	20 46	22u59		
Edinburgh 10	d	16 30								17 30										19 45		23u16			
Haymarket	d																								
Glasgow Central 15	d			16e34	17 05						18 10							19 20			22 28	21 42			
Motherwell	d			17 25																		22u01			
Carstairs	d																					22u22			
Lockerbie	d	18a40		18a40		18 52				19a40		19 58							21 07	21a55					
Carlisle 8	a				19 00	19 10					20 05	20 16						21 15	21 28		00 49				
	d					19 15						20 18							21 30						
Penrith North Lakes	d											20 34							21 45						
Windermere	d						20 02									21 20									
Oxenholme Lake District	a					19 51	20 19					20 57				21 40			22 08						
	d					19 52	20 21					20 58				21 40			22 09						
Barrow-in-Furness	d											19 57			20 50										
Lancaster 6	a					20 07	20 38					21 13			21 51	21 56			22 25						
	d					20 08						21 14			22 02				22 26						
Preston 8	a					20 25						21 31			22 20				22 58						
Blackpool North	a					21f30						23f00			23f30				00f05						
	d					19f20			19f50			20f30					21f50								
Preston 8	d					20 28			20 42			21 34			22 23		22 42		23 01						
Wigan North Western	a					20 39			21 01			21 46					23 11		23s23						
	d					20 40			21 01			21 46					23 11								
Bolton	a					21g26						22g26			22 41				23s37						
Manchester Piccadilly 10	a					21g49						22g49			23 01				23 59						
Manchester Airport	a					22g33									23 18				00 33						
Liverpool Lime Street 10	a								21 49			22 49					23 59								
	d													21 47											
Liverpool South Parkway 7	d													21 57											
Runcorn	d													22 05											
Warrington Bank Quay	a					20 50						21 56													
	d					20 52						21 58													
Hartford	d													22 15											
Manchester Piccadilly 10	d							20 55				21 06	21 55												
Stockport	d							21 04				20 54	22 04												
Manchester Airport	d											21 25													
Wilmslow	d											21 32													
Holyhead	d					18h40																			
Bangor (Gwynedd)	d					19h09						19 55													
Llandudno	d																								
Llandudno Junction	d					19h27						20 18													
Chester	d					20 25						21 25		21 55											
Crewe 10	a					21 11						22 17		22 40											
	d					21 13						22 20		22 43											
Macclesfield	d							21 16					22 17												
Congleton	d																								
Stoke-on-Trent	d							21 34					22 34												
Stafford	a					21 31		21 52				22 39	22 52	23 06											
	d					21 32		21 53				22 40	22 53	23 07											
Penkridge	a													23 12											
Wolverhampton 7	a					21 54		22 09				22 54	23 09	23 25											
Coseley	a																								
Sandwell & Dudley	a																								
Birmingham New Street 12	a					22 17		22 30				23 17	23 30	23 45											
Birmingham International	a					22 52		23 09																	
Coventry	a					23 08		23 19																	
Lichfield Trent Valley	a																								
Tamworth Low Level	a																								
Nuneaton	a																								
Rugby	a							23 33																	
Northampton	a																								
Milton Keynes Central	a																								
Watford Junction	a																								
Gatwick Airport 10	a																								
London Euston 15	⊖ a																					07 11	09 28		

For general notes see front of timetable
For details of catering facilities see Directory of Train Operators

A Stops at Edinburgh after Glasgow Central, Motherwell and Carstairs

B Also conveys portion from Fort William (Table 227)

b Change at Perth, Glasgow Queen Street and Glasgow Central. Passengers make their own way between Glasgow Queen Street and Glasgow Central

c Via Glasgow Queen Street and Glasgow Central. Passengers make their own way from one station to the other

e Glasgow Central Low Level

f By bus

g Change at Preston

h Change at Chester and Crewe

OVERNIGHT SLEEPERS. For Sleeper trains, operated by First ScotRail, please refer to Tables 400 - 404

Table 65

Sundays

from 30 March

Scotland and North West England → West Midlands and London

Route Diagram - see first page of Table 65

		XC	VT	LM	VT	XC	NT	VT		VT	VT	VT	VT	VT	VT	VT		XC	VT	VT	VT	VT	VT	VT	XC
		1◇	1◇	1◇	1◇	1◇		1◇			1◇	1◇	1◇	1◇		1◇		1◇		1◇	1◇	1◇	1◇	1◇	1◇
		A				B												C							B
										🚌					🚌				🚌						
		☕	☕		☕	☕		☕			☕	☕	☕	☕		☕		☕		☕	☕	☕	☕	☕	☕
Inverness	d																								
Aberdeen	d																								
Dundee	d																								
Perth	d																								
Edinburgh 10	d																								
Haymarket	d																								
Glasgow Central 15	d																								
Motherwell	d																								
Carstairs	d																								
Lockerbie	d																								
Carlisle 8	a																								
	d																								
Penrith North Lakes	d																								
Windermere	d																								
Oxenholme Lake District	a																								
	d																								
Barrow-in-Furness	d																								
Lancaster 6	a																								
	d														09 00										
Preston 8	a														09 50										
Blackpool North	a														*10 47*										
	d						08 17									*09 28*									
Preston 8	d						08 42									10 03				10 28					
Wigan North Western	a						09 01									10 14				10 40					
	d						09 01									10 15				10 40					
Bolton	a																								
Manchester Piccadilly 10	a																								
Manchester Airport	a																								
Liverpool Lime Street 10	a						09 49																		
	d												09 53										10 53		
Liverpool South Parkway 7	d																								
Runcorn	d												10 09										11 09		
Warrington Bank Quay	a															10 25				10 51					
	d															10 26				10 51					
Hartford	d																								
Manchester Piccadilly 10	d	08 08			09 00	09 24					09 44	09 53						10 24			10 44	10 53			11 24
Stockport	d				09u10	09 33					09u53	10 02						10 33			10u52	11 02			11 33
Manchester Airport	d										*09 33*														*11 25*
Wilmslow	d	08 24			09 19	09 41					10 01	10 10						10 41			11 00	11 10			11 41
Holyhead	d																								
Bangor (Gwynedd)	d																								
Llandudno	d																								
Llandudno Junction	d																								
Chester	d			*08 55*		*09 25*							*09 55*			*10 11*							*10 55*		*11 25*
Crewe 10	a	08 43			09 36	09 59							10 29			10 45		10 59		11 12			11 28		12 01
	d	08 59		09 40	09 48	10 02		10 12					10 35			10 48		11 02		11 13			11 35		12 02
Macclesfield	d									09 10	09b20								10 10		10b20				
Congleton	d																								
Stoke-on-Trent	d									10 00									11 00						
Stafford	a	09 18		10 01	10 06	10 21		10 30		10 30	10 40	10 47	10 54			11 06		11 21	11 30		11 38	11 47	11 54		12 23
	d	09 26	09 39	10 01	10 08	10 26		10 31			10 41	10 48	10 55			11 08		11 26			11 41	11 49	11 55		12 26
Penkridge	a			10 07																					
Wolverhampton 7	a	09 40		10 23		10 40		10 48				11 05						11 40		11 48		12 05			12 40
Coseley	a																								
Sandwell & Dudley	a											11 16										12 16			
Birmingham New Street 12	a	09 58		10 43		10 58		11 11				11 26		←				11 58		12 11		12 26		←	12 58
Birmingham International	a	*10 24*			10 57	11 14						11 39		11 39				*12 25*				12 39		12 39	13 13
Coventry	a		10 28		11 12	11 23						→	11 45	11 51		12 12		*12 37*				→	12 45	12 51	13 23
Lichfield Trent Valley	a																								
Tamworth Low Level	a																								
Nuneaton	a																								
Rugby	a		10 41		11 26						11 39		11 58					*12 54*					12 58		*13 54*
Northampton	a		*11 15*								*12 20*		*13 20*										*14 20*		
Milton Keynes Central	a		11 05		11 51								12 21	12 27		12 50					13 00		13 22	13 28	
Watford Junction	a		*11 55*		12s31						12s43		13s00	13s06		13s31					*13 55*			14s03	
Gatwick Airport 10	a																								
London Euston 15	⊖ a		12 00		12 51						13 04		13 23	13 29		13 56					14 00		14 23	14 29	

For general notes see front of timetable
For details of catering facilities see Directory of Train Operators

A To Paignton (Table 51)
B To Oxford (Table 51)
C To Plymouth (Table 51)
b Change at Wilmslow. By bus

OVERNIGHT SLEEPERS. For Sleeper trains, operated by First ScotRail, please refer to Tables 400 - 404

Sundays from 30 March

Scotland and North West England → West Midlands and London

Route Diagram - see first page of Table 65

		VT		VT	NT	VT	VT	TP	LM	VT		VT	VT	VT		VT	XC	VT		VT	VT	VT	VT	VT	TP
				1 ◊			1 ◊	1	1 ◊	1 ◊		1 ◊	1 ◊			1 ◊	R 1 A	1 ◊			1 ◊	1 ◊	1 ◊	1 ◊	1 B
		[bus]				[bus]								[bus]	[bus]					[bus]					
				[catering]			[catering]			[catering]		[catering]	[catering]			[catering]	[catering]	[catering]			[catering]	[catering]	[catering]	[catering]	
Inverness	d																								
Aberdeen	d																								
Dundee	d																								
Perth	d																								
Edinburgh [10]	d																								
Haymarket	d																								
Glasgow Central [15]	d																								
Motherwell	d																								
Carstairs	d																								
Lockerbie	d																								
Carlisle [8]	a																								
	d														09 50										
Penrith North Lakes	d													09 20											
Windermere	d																								
Oxenholme Lake District	a													10 15											
	d													10 15											
Barrow-in-Furness	d							09 40																	10 50
Lancaster [6]	a							10 45						11 00											11 52
	d					10 25								11 00											
Preston [8]	a					11 15		*11b40*						11 50	11 50										*12b40*
Blackpool North	a					*12 16*								*12 47*											
	d				10 17		*10 28*									*11 28*									
Preston [8]	d				10 42		11 25									12 03		12 28							
Wigan North Western	a				11 01		11 36									12 14		12 39							
	d				11 01		11 37									12 15		12 40							
Bolton	a													*12 52*											
Manchester Piccadilly [10]	a													*13 15*											
Manchester Airport	a													*13 33*											
Liverpool Lime Street [10]	a				11 49		*12 49*																		
	d								11 35			11 56											12 56		
Liverpool South Parkway [7]	d								11 45																
Runcorn	d								11 53			12 14											13 14		
Warrington Bank Quay	a						11 47									12 25		12 50							
	d						11 49									12 26		12 52							
Hartford	d								12 03																
Manchester Piccadilly [10]	d			11 44						11 53							12 08				12 45	12 53			
Stockport	d			11u52						12 02							12 22				12u56	13 02			
Manchester Airport	d																								
Wilmslow	d			12 01						12 10							12 30				13 04	13 11			
Holyhead	d											*09 56*					*10c35*								
Bangor (Gwynedd)	d											*10 34*					*11c04*								
Llandudno	d											*10e15*													
Llandudno Junction	d											*10 57*					*11c22*								
Chester	d											*11 48*					*12 25*								
Crewe [10]	a						12 08		12 17			12 33				12 45	12 53	13 11					13 33		
	d						12 12		12 19			12 35				12 48	13 02	13 13					13 38		
Macclesfield	d	11 10		*11f20*																12 10	*12f20*				
Congleton	d																								
Stoke-on-Trent	d	12 00																		13 00					
Stafford	a	12 30		12 37					12 42	12 47		12 54					13 21			13 30	13 41	13 46	13 57		
	d			12 39					12 43	12 49		12 56					13 26				13 42	13 48	13 58		
Penkridge	a								12 49																
Wolverhampton [7]	a						12 48		13 02	13 05							13 40	13 48				14 05			
Coseley	a																								
Sandwell & Dudley	a									13 16												14 16			
Birmingham New Street [12]	a						13 11		13 21	13 26			←				13 58	14 11				14 26		←	
Birmingham International	a									13 39			13 39				*14 25*					14 39		14 39	
Coventry	a									→		13 45	13 51				*14 37*					→	14 45	14 51	
Lichfield Trent Valley	a																								
Tamworth Low Level	a																								
Nuneaton	a																								
Rugby	a											13 58				14 22	*14 54*						14 58		
Northampton	a															*15 20*									
Milton Keynes Central	a												14 26			14 50					15 00		15 21	15 27	
Watford Junction	a			14s31								14s46				15s13					*15 55*			*16 26*	
Gatwick Airport [10]	a																								
London Euston [15]	a			14 56								15 08	15 16			15 38					15 56		16 07	16 16	

For general notes see front of timetable
For details of catering facilities see Directory of Train Operators

A To Penzance (Table 135)
B To Windermere (Table 83)
b Change at Carnforth. By bus
c Change at Chester and Crewe
e Change at Llandudno Junction and Crewe. By bus to Llandudno Junction
f Change at Wilmslow. By bus

OVERNIGHT SLEEPERS. For Sleeper trains, operated by First ScotRail, please refer to Tables 400 - 404

Table 65

Sundays

from 30 March

Scotland and North West England → West Midlands and London

Route Diagram - see first page of Table 65

		NT	VT	VT	XC	VT	LM	VT	VT	VT	VT	VT	VT	XC	TP	VT	VT	VT	VT	VT	VT	TP
				1 ◇	R 1		1 ◇	1 ◇	1 ◇	1 ◇	1 ◇		1 ◇	R 1		R 1		1 ◇	1 ◇	1 ◇	1 ◇	1
					A									B								C
			Bus			Bus						Bus			Bus		Bus					
				Catering	Catering			Catering	Catering	Catering	Catering		Catering	Catering		Catering		Catering	Catering	Catering	Catering	
Inverness	d																					
Aberdeen	d																					
Dundee	d																					
Perth	d																					
Edinburgh 10	d																					
Haymarket	d																					
Glasgow Central 15	d																					
Motherwell	d																					
Carstairs	d																					
Lockerbie	d																					
Carlisle 8	a																					
	d																					
Penrith North Lakes	d		10 20									11 20										
Windermere	d																					
Oxenholme Lake District	a		11 15									12 15										
	d		11 15									12 15										
Barrow-in-Furness	d																					12 50
Lancaster 6	a		12 00									13 00										13 52
	d		12 00									13 00			13 25							
Preston 8	a		12 50									13 50			14 15							14b40
Blackpool North	a		13 34									14 47			15 16							
	d	12 17		12 28									13 28									
Preston 8	d	12 42		13 08									14 00									
Wigan North Western	a	13 01		13 19									14 11									
	d	13 01		13 21									14 13									
Bolton	a		13 52									14 52										
Manchester Piccadilly 10	a		14 15									15 15										
Manchester Airport	a		14 33									15 33										
Liverpool Lime Street 10	a	13 50		14 49																		
	d						13 26			13 56										14 56		
Liverpool South Parkway 7	d						13 36															
Runcorn	d						13 44			14 14										15 14		
Warrington Bank Quay	a			13 30									14 22									
	d			13 32									14 24									
Hartford	d						13 54															
Manchester Piccadilly 10	d				13 24			13 45	13 53					14 24				14 45	14 53			
Stockport	d				13 33			13u55	14 03					14 33				14u55	15 02			
Manchester Airport	d				13 26																	
Wilmslow	d				13 41			14 03	14 11					14 41				15 03	15 10			
Holyhead	d															13 14						
Bangor (Gwynedd)	d			11 56										12 52		13 41						
Llandudno	d			11c58												13e15						
Llandudno Junction	d			12 14										13 15		13 59						
Chester	d			13 08						13 55				14 12		14 46				14 55		
Crewe 10	a			13 50	14 01		14 08			14 33			14 43	15 00		15 06				15 33		
	d			13 53	14 02		14 10			14 37			14 45	15 02		15 13				15 35		
Macclesfield	d					13 10		13f20									14 10	14f20				
Congleton	d																					
Stoke-on-Trent	d					14 00											15 00					
Stafford	a				14 22	14 30	14 31	14 40	14 47	14 56			15 06	15 21			15 30	15 40	15 47	15 54		
	d				14 26		14 31	14 42	14 49	14 58			15 07	15 26				15 42	15 49	15 55		
Penkridge	a						14 37															
Wolverhampton 7	a				14 40		14 49		15 04					15 40		15 48			16 04			
Coseley	a																					
Sandwell & Dudley	a								15 16										16 16			
Birmingham New Street 12	a				14 58		15 08		15 26		←			15 58		16 11			16 26		←	
Birmingham International	a				15 14				15 39		15 39			16 25					16 39		16 39	
Coventry	a				15 23				→	15 45	15 51		16 12	16 37					→	16 45	16 51	
Lichfield Trent Valley	a																					
Tamworth Low Level	a																					
Nuneaton	a																					
Rugby	a			15 23	15 54					15 58			16 26	16 54						16 58		
Northampton	a			16 20									17 20									
Milton Keynes Central	a			16g41							16 25		16 51					17 00		17 22	17 27	
Watford Junction	a			16s12				16s32		16s46	17 26							17 55			18 26	
Gatwick Airport 10	a																					
London Euston 15	⊖ a			16 36				16 56		17 08	17 11		17 39					17 56		18 08	18 11	

For general notes see front of timetable
For details of catering facilities see Directory of Train Operators

- **A** To Oxford (Table 51)
- **B** To Penzance (Table 135)
- **C** To Windermere (Table 83)
- **b** Change at Carnforth. By bus
- **c** From 6 April only. Change at Llandudno Junction and Crewe
- **e** By bus
- **f** Change at Wilmslow. By bus
- **g** Change at Rugby and Northampton

OVERNIGHT SLEEPERS. For Sleeper trains, operated by First ScotRail, please refer to Tables 400 - 404

Table 65

Sundays

from 30 March

Scotland and North West England → West Midlands and London

Route Diagram - see first page of Table 65

		NT	VT	VT	XC	TP		TP	VT	LM	VT	LM	VT	VT		VT	VT	VT	VT	XC	TP	VT		VT	VT
				[1]◇	[R] [1]	[1]				[1]◇	[R] [1]	[1]◇	[1]◇	[1]◇		[1]◇	[1]◇		[1]◇	[R] [1]		[R] [1]			[1]◇
					A	B														C					
			bus					bus	bus									bus			bus			bus	
				catering	catering						catering		catering	catering		catering	catering		catering	catering		catering			catering
Inverness	d																								
Aberdeen	d																								
Dundee	d																								
Perth	d																								
Edinburgh [10]	d																								
Haymarket	d																								
Glasgow Central [15]	d																								
Motherwell	d																								
Carstairs	d																								
Lockerbie	d																								
Carlisle [8]	a																								
	d																								
Penrith North Lakes	d		12 20															13 20							
Windermere	d		*12 40*			13 33																			
Oxenholme Lake District	a		13 15			13 53												14 15							
	d		13 15			13 54												14 15							
Barrow-in-Furness	d																	*13 30*							
Lancaster [6]	a		14 00			14 11												15 00							
	d		14 00					14 25										15 00			15 25				
Preston [8]	a		14 50					15 15										15 50			16 15				
Blackpool North	a		*15 34*					*16 16*										*16 47*							
	d	14 17		*14 28*															*15 28*						
Preston [8]	d	14 42		15 02							15 27								16 00			16 23			
Wigan North Western	a	15 00		15 12							15 40								16 12			16 34			
	d	15 01		15 14							15 41								16 13			16 35			
Bolton	a		*15 52*															*16 51*							
Manchester Piccadilly [10] (tram)	a		*16 15*															*17 15*							
Manchester Airport (airport)	a		*16 33*															*17 33*							
Liverpool Lime Street [10]	a	15 49									*16 49*														
	d									15 31						15 56									
Liverpool South Parkway [7] (airport)	d									15 41															
Runcorn	d									15 49						16 14									
Warrington Bank Quay	a			15 23							15 51								16 23			16 45			
	d			15 25							15 53								16 24			16 47			
Hartford	d																								
Manchester Piccadilly [10] (tram)	d				15 24								15 45	15 53						16 24					16 45
Stockport	d				15 33								15u55	16 02						16 33					16u55
Manchester Airport (airport)	d				*15 25*																				
Wilmslow	d				15 41								16 03	16 13						16 41					17 03
Holyhead	d				*13b31*																				
Bangor (Gwynedd)	d				*13b58*																				
Llandudno	d				*14c00*																				
Llandudno Junction	d				*14b16*																				
Chester	d				*15 25*											*16 00*				*16 25*					
Crewe [10]	a			15 44	16 01					16 08	16 12					16 33			16 43	16 59		17 06			
	d			15 46	16 02					16 11	16 13					16 35			16 46	17 02		17 09			
Macclesfield	d								15 10				*15e20*											16 10	*16e20*
Congleton	d																								
Stoke-on-Trent	d								16 00															17 00	
Stafford	a				16 23				16 30	16 36			16 39	16 46		16 53			17 06	17 21				17 30	17 39
	d				16 26					16 36		←	16 41	16 48		16 55			17 08	17 26					17 41
Penkridge	a									16 42		16 42													
Wolverhampton [7] (tram)	a				16 40					→	16 48	16 54		17 04						17 40		17 48			
Coseley	a																								
Sandwell & Dudley	a													17 16											
Birmingham New Street [12]	a				16 58						17 11	17 14		17 26			←			17 58		18 11			
Birmingham International (airport)	a				17 14									17 39			17 39			*18 25*					
Coventry	a				17 23									→		17 45	17 51		18 12	*18 37*					
Lichfield Trent Valley	a																								
Tamworth Low Level	a																								
Nuneaton	a																								
Rugby	a			17 23	*17 54*											17 58			18 26	*18 54*					
Northampton	a			*18 20*															*19 20*						
Milton Keynes Central	a															18 22	18 27		18 50						19 00
Watford Junction	a			18s12									18s30			18s45	*19 26*								
Gatwick Airport [10] (airport)	a																								
London Euston [15] (Underground)	a			18 38									18 51			19 14	19 17		19 33						19 53

For general notes see front of timetable
For details of catering facilities see Directory of Train Operators

- **A** To Oxford (Table 51)
- **B** To Barrow-in-Furness (Table 82)
- **C** To Plymouth (Table 51)
- **b** Change at Chester and Crewe
- **c** From 6 April only. Change at Llandudno Junction, Chester and Crewe
- **e** Change at Wilmslow. By bus

OVERNIGHT SLEEPERS. For Sleeper trains, operated by First ScotRail, please refer to Tables 400 - 404

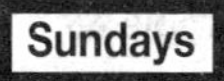

from 30 March

Scotland and North West England → West Midlands and London

Route Diagram - see first page of Table 65

		VT	NT	VT	VT	TP	VT	TP		TP	VT	XC	LM	TP	TP	VT		VT	VT	VT	VT	VT	NT	VT	VT
		1 ◇		1 ◇		1		1 ◇			1 ◇	R 1	1 ◇	1				R 1	1 ◇	1 ◇	1 ◇	1 ◇			1 ◇
						A						B		C											
					🚌		🚌			🚌					🚌	🚌								🚌	
		🛒		🛒				🍴			🛒	🛒						🛒	🛒	🛒	🛒	🛒			🛒
Inverness	d																								
Aberdeen	d							09b30																	
Dundee	d			08b45				10b43																	
Perth	d			09b05				11b05																	
Edinburgh 10	d																								
Haymarket	d																								
Glasgow Central 15	d			11 25				12 43																	
Motherwell	d			11u46																					
Carstairs	d																								
Lockerbie	d			12 33				13 48																	
Carlisle 8	a			12 56				14 09																	
	d			13 14	13 10					14 17															
Penrith North Lakes	d				13 45		14 15			14 50														15 20	
Windermere	d						14 40							15 35											
Oxenholme Lake District	a				14 40		15 10			15 40				15 52										16 15	
	d				14 40		15 10			15 40				15 54										16 15	
Barrow-in-Furness	d					14 50																			
Lancaster 6	a				15 25	15 52	15 55							16 11										17 00	
	d						15 55				←				16 25									17 00	
Preston 8	a			16 26		16c40	16 45			16 50	16 26				17 15									17 50	
Blackpool North	a			17 16						17 35					18 16									18 34	
	d		16 17	→														16 28					17 17		17 25
Preston 8	d		16 42								16 57							17 29					17 42		18 00
Wigan North Western	a		17 00								17 12							17 40					18 00		18 12
	d		17 01								17 14							17 41					18 01		18 13
Bolton	a									17 26															
Manchester Piccadilly 10	a									17 49															
Manchester Airport	a									18 33															
Liverpool Lime Street 10	a		17 49																				18 49		
	d												17 25								17 56				
Liverpool South Parkway 7	d												17 35												
Runcorn	d												17 43								18 14				
Warrington Bank Quay	a										17 23							17 51							18 23
	d										17 25							17 53							18 24
Hartford	d												17 52												
Manchester Piccadilly 10	d	16 53									16 37	17 24							17 45	17 53					
Stockport	d	17 02									16 45	17 33							17u55	18 02					
Manchester Airport	d											17 24													
Wilmslow	d	17 12									16 54	17 41							18 03	18 12					
Holyhead	d												15 57												
Bangor (Gwynedd)	d										15e42		16 24								16e32				
Llandudno	d										15f40		16g15								16f39				
Llandudno Junction	d										16e00		16 42								16e54				
Chester	d										17 00	17 25	17 38								17 52				
Crewe 10	a										17 44	17 59	18 07					18 14			18 33				18 44
	d										17 47	18 02	18 09					18 16			18 35				18 47
Macclesfield	d															17 10			17h20						
Congleton	d																								
Stoke-on-Trent	d															18 00									
Stafford	a	17 47										18 21	18 30			18 30			18 40	18 47	18 53				19 06
	d	17 49										18 26	18 30						18 41	18 49	18 55				19 08
Penkridge	a												18 36												
Wolverhampton 7	a	18 04										18 40	18 48					18 51		19 04					
Coseley	a																								
Sandwell & Dudley	a	18 16																		19 16					
Birmingham New Street 12	a	18 26										18 58	19 04					19 14		19 26		←			
Birmingham International	a	18 39										19 13	19 30							19 39		19 39			
Coventry	a	18 49										19 23	19 40							→	19 45	19 51			20 12
Lichfield Trent Valley	a																								
Tamworth Low Level	a																								
Nuneaton	a																								
Rugby	a										19 23		19 54								19 58				20 26
Northampton	a										20 20														21 20
Milton Keynes Central	a	19 25																			20 22	20 27			20 51
Watford Junction	a	19s50									20s12								20s31		20s47	20s51			21s31
Gatwick Airport 10	a																								
London Euston 15	⊖ a	20 11									20 38								20 53		21 14	21 17			21 54

For general notes see front of timetable
For details of catering facilities see Directory of Train Operators

A To Windermere (Table 83)
B To Oxford (Table 51)
C To Barrow-in-Furness (Table 82)
b Via Glasgow Queen Street and Glasgow Central. Passengers make their own way from one station to the other
c Change at Carnforth. By bus
e Change at Chester and Crewe
f From 6 April only. Change at Llandudno Junction, Chester and Crewe
g Change at Llandudno Junction and Crewe. By bus to Llandudno Junction
h Change at Wilmslow. By bus

OVERNIGHT SLEEPERS. For Sleeper trains, operated by First ScotRail, please refer to Tables 400 - 404

Table 65

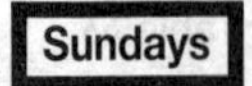

from 30 March

Scotland and North West England → West Midlands and London

Route Diagram - see first page of Table 65

		TP		VT	VT	VT	XC	VT	TP	VT		VT	VT	VT	VT	VT	NT	TP		TP	VT	VT	XC	LM	VT
							R	R																	
					1◇		1	1	1				1◇	1◇	1◇	1◇		1◇				1◇	1◇	1◇	
							A		B														C		
		🚌		🚌		🚌				🚌		🚌								🚌	🚌				🚌
					🍴		🍴	🍴					🍴	🍴	🍴	🍴		🛒				🍴			
Inverness	d				09 38																				
Aberdeen	d				09 50													11 58							
Dundee	d				11 25													13 14							
Perth	d				11 55																				
Edinburgh 10	d				13 49													14 43							
Haymarket	d				13u55													14 48							
Glasgow Central 15	d							14 05																	
Motherwell	d							14u27																	
Carstairs	d																								
Lockerbie	d				14 48			15 15										15 44							
Carlisle 8	a				15 10			15 35										16 06							
	d					15 20		15 37		15 45										16 15					
Penrith North Lakes	d			15 45		15 55				16 20										16 50					
Windermere	d									16 40															
Oxenholme Lake District	a			16 40		16 50				17 15										17 40					
	d			16 40		16 50				17 15										17 40					
Barrow-in-Furness	d								16 50																
Lancaster 6	a			17 25		17 35			17 52	18 00											←				
	d	17 25		17 25						18 00											18 00				
Preston 8	a	18 15		18 15				18 19	18b40	→										18 45	18 50				
Blackpool North	a							19 16													19 32				
	d																18 17					18 28			
Preston 8	d							18 30									18 42					19 00			
Wigan North Western	a							18 41									19 00					19 11			
	d							18 42									19 01					19 12			
Bolton	a							18c52												19 26					
Manchester Piccadilly 10	a							19c15												19 49					
Manchester Airport ✈	a							19c33												20 33					
Liverpool Lime Street 10	a																19 49								
	d														18 56									19 30	
Liverpool South Parkway 7 ✈	d																							19 39	
Runcorn	d														19 14									19 47	
Warrington Bank Quay	a							18 52														19 22			
	d							18 53														19 23			
Hartford	d																								
Manchester Piccadilly 10	d						18 24						18 45	18 53									19 24		
Stockport	d						18 33						18u55	19 02									19 33		
Manchester Airport ✈	d																						19 25		
Wilmslow	d						18 41						19 03	19 12									19 41		
Holyhead	d							16 48															17e25		
Bangor (Gwynedd)	d							17 27															17e53		
Llandudno	d							17f29																	
Llandudno Junction	d							17 46															18e11		
Chester	d						18 25	18 42															19 25		
Crewe 10	a						18 59	19 13							19 33							19 42	20 00	20 07	
	d						19 02	19 15							19 36							19 45	20 02	20 08	
Macclesfield	d											18 10	18g20												19 10
Congleton	d																								
Stoke-on-Trent	d											19 00													20 00
Stafford	a						19 21					19 30	19 40	19 47	19 54							20 06	20 22	20 29	20 30
	d						19 26						19 41	19 49	19 55							20 08	20 26	20 31	
Penkridge	a																								
Wolverhampton 7	a						19 40	19 48						20 04									20 40	20 47	
Coseley	a																								
Sandwell & Dudley	a													20 16											
Birmingham New Street 12	a						19 58	20 11						20 26		←							20 58	21 08	
Birmingham International ✈	a						20 25							20 39		20 39							21 14		
Coventry	a						20 37							→	20 45	20 51							21 23		
Lichfield Trent Valley	a																								
Tamworth Low Level	a																								
Nuneaton	a																								
Rugby	a						20 54								20 58							21 23			
Northampton	a																								
Milton Keynes Central	a												21 01		21 22	21 28						21 50			
Watford Junction	a												21 55		22s00	22s06						22s31			
Gatwick Airport 10 ✈	a																								
London Euston 15 ⊖	a												21 57		22 23	22 27						22 51			

For general notes see front of timetable
For details of catering facilities see Directory of Train Operators

- **A** To Plymouth (Table 51)
- **B** To Windermere (Table 83)
- **C** To Oxford (Table 51)
- **b** Change at Carnforth. By bus
- **c** Change at Preston
- **e** Change at Chester and Crewe
- **f** From 6 April only. Change at Llandudno Junction and Crewe
- **g** Change at Wilmslow. By bus

OVERNIGHT SLEEPERS. For Sleeper trains, operated by First ScotRail, please refer to Tables 400 - 404

Table 65

Sundays

Scotland and North West England → West Midlands and London

from 30 March

Route Diagram - see first page of Table 65

		TP	TP	VT	VT	VT	VT	VT	VT	VT	VT	VT	VT	VT	VT	VT	TP	XC	NT	TP	TP	TP
		1		1◇	1◇	1◇	1◇	1◇		1◇			1◇	1◇	1◇		1	1◇		1◇		1
		A															B					A
Inverness	d																			13b25		
Aberdeen	d																			13 50		
Dundee	d													13 25						15 03		
Perth	d							13c05												15b25		
Edinburgh 10	d													15 47						16 43		
Haymarket	d													15u53						16 48		
Glasgow Central 15	d							15 05							16 05							
Motherwell	d							15u23							16u23							
Carstairs	d																					
Lockerbie	d							16 11						16 46	17 06					17 44		
Carlisle 8	a							16 30						17 08	17 26					18 06		
	d							16 52	16 45						17 39	17 35					18 15	
Penrith North Lakes	d								17 20		17 50					18 10					18 50	
Windermere	d	17 33														18 40						19 40
Oxenholme Lake District	a	17 53							18 15		18 45					19 05					19 40	19 57
	d	17 54							18 15		18 45					19 05					19 40	19 59
Barrow-in-Furness	d																18 50					
Lancaster 6	a	18 11							19 00		19 30					19 50	19 52					20 16
	d		18 25						19 00		19 30											
Preston 8	a		19 15					19 45	19 50		20 20				20 31		20e40				20 45	
Blackpool North	a		20 16						20 47	←	21f03				21 16						21 34	
	d									19 28					20 02				20 17			
Preston 8	d			19 29				20 01		20 01					20 38				20 42			
Wigan North Western	a			19 40						20 17					20 49				21 01			
	d			19 41						20 18					20 50				21 01			
Bolton	a							20 26			20 51										21 26	
Manchester Piccadilly 10	a							20 49			21 15										21 49	
Manchester Airport	a							21 22			21 33										22 33	
Liverpool Lime Street 10	a			20 49				→											21 49			
	d						19 56															
Liverpool South Parkway 7	d																					
Runcorn	d						20 14															
Warrington Bank Quay	a			19 51						20 28					21 00							
	d			19 52						20 29					21 02							
Hartford	d																					
Manchester Piccadilly 10	d				19 45	19 56							20 23					20 55				
Stockport	d				19u55	20 04							20 32					21 04				
Manchester Airport	d																					
Wilmslow	d				20 03	20 13							20 40					21 12				
Holyhead	d														18g40							
Bangor (Gwynedd)	d														19g09							
Llandudno	d																					
Llandudno Junction	d														19g27							
Chester	d						19 55								20 25			20 55				
Crewe 10	a			20 11			20 33			20 48					21 22			21 31				
	d			20 14			20 35			20 51					21 24			21 32				
Macclesfield	d				19h20							19 50	20h00									
Congleton	d																					
Stoke-on-Trent	d											20 40										
Stafford	a				20 40	20 51	20 58			21 09		21 10	21 19		21 42			21 52				
	d				20 42	20 53	20 59			21 11			21 21		21 43			21 53				
Penkridge	a																					
Wolverhampton 7	a			20 52		21 08							21 35		21 59			22 09				
Coseley	a																					
Sandwell & Dudley	a												21 47									
Birmingham New Street 12	a			21 15		21 32							21 56		22 22			22 30				
Birmingham International	a			21 52									22 09		22 52			23 09				
Coventry	a						21 45			22 12			22 19		23 08			23 19				
Lichfield Trent Valley	a																					
Tamworth Low Level	a																					
Nuneaton	a																					
Rugby	a				21 39		21 58						22 32					23 32				
Northampton	a				22 20								23 15									
Milton Keynes Central	a				22 04		22 34			22 59			23 06									
Watford Junction	a				22s41		23s04			23s29			23s38									
Gatwick Airport 10	a																					
London Euston 15 ⊖	a				23 00		23 25			23 47			23 58									

For general notes see front of timetable
For details of catering facilities see Directory of Train Operators

A To Barrow-in-Furness (Table 82)
B To Windermere (Table 83)
b Change at Haymarket
c Via Glasgow Queen Street and Glasgow Central. Passengers make their own way from one station to the other
e Change at Carnforth. By bus
f 4 May only
g Change at Chester and Crewe
h Change at Wilmslow. By bus

OVERNIGHT SLEEPERS. For Sleeper trains, operated by First ScotRail, please refer to Tables 400 - 404

Table 65

Sundays

from 30 March

Scotland and North West England → West Midlands and London

Route Diagram - see first page of Table 65

		TP	VT	XC	LM	VT	VT	TP	VT	TP	TP	NT	VT	VT	VT	TP	SR	SR	SR	SR
			1 ◇	1 ◇	1 ◇	1 ◇	1 ◇	1 ◇		1			1 ◇		1 ◇			R	R	R
																				A
		[bus]							[bus]		[bus]			[bus]		[bus]				
			[sleeper/catering]			[sleeper/catering]	[sleeper/catering]	[trolley]					[sleeper/catering]		[sleeper/catering]			[sleeper/catering]	[sleeper/catering]	[sleeper/catering]
Inverness	d																16b15		18 30	20 25
Aberdeen	d					15 10											17c50		20 10	21 40
Dundee	d					16 25											19c02		21 21	23u04
Perth	d																19c24		20 46	22u59
Edinburgh 10	d					17 52		18 43											23 15	
Haymarket	d					17u58		18 48												
Glasgow Central 15	d						18 03										22 28	23 15		
Motherwell	d						18u19											23u30		
Carstairs	d																	23u50		
Lockerbie	d					18 51	19 06	19 44												
Carlisle 8	a					19 13	19 26	20 06					←				00 49			
	d						19 28 →		20 15				19 28	19 45		20 15		01u24		
Penrith North Lakes	d													20 20		20 50				
Windermere	d									20 40										
Oxenholme Lake District	a									21 00				21 15		21 40				
	d									21 01				21 15		21 40				
Barrow-in-Furness	d										20 30									
Lancaster 6	a									21 20				22 00		22 25				
	d	20 25									21 40			22 00		22 25				
Preston 8	a	21 15							22 15		22 20		22 24	22 50		23 10				04s22
Blackpool North	a	22 16											23 16	23 43		00 16				
	d		20 28									22 17			←					
Preston 8	d		21 34									22 42	23 01		23 01					
Wigan North Western	a		21 45									23 11	→		23s23					
	d		21 45									23 11								
Bolton	a								22 51						23s37	00 01				05 39
Manchester Piccadilly 10	a								23 15						23 59	00 17				05 57
Manchester Airport	a								23 33							00 33				06 14
Liverpool Lime Street 10	a		22 49									23 59								
	d				21 47															
Liverpool South Parkway 7	d				21 57															
Runcorn	d				22 05															
Warrington Bank Quay	a		21 55																	
	d		21 58																	
Hartford	d				22 15															
Manchester Piccadilly 10	d		21 06	21 55																
Stockport	d		21 04	22 04																
Manchester Airport	d		21 25																	
Wilmslow	d		21 32	22 12																
Holyhead	d																			
Bangor (Gwynedd)	d		19 55																	
Llandudno	d																			
Llandudno Junction	d		20 18																	
Chester	d		21 25	21 55																
Crewe 10	a		22 16	22 31	22 40															05s29
	d		22 20	22 32	22 43															
Macclesfield	d																			
Congleton	d																			
Stoke-on-Trent	d																			
Stafford	a		22 39	22 52	23 06															06 16
	d		22 40	22 53	23 07															
Penkridge	a				23 12															
Wolverhampton 7	a		22 54	23 09	23 25															06 41
Coseley	a																			
Sandwell & Dudley	a																			
Birmingham New Street 12	a		23 17	23 30	23 45															06 58
Birmingham International	a																			07 14
Coventry	a																			07 23
Lichfield Trent Valley	a																			06 32
Tamworth Low Level	a																			06 39
Nuneaton	a																			06 50
Rugby	a																			07 04
Northampton	a																			
Milton Keynes Central	a																			
Watford Junction	a																	06s28		07 44
Gatwick Airport 10	a																	08e39		
London Euston 15	a																	06 54		07 43

For general notes see front of timetable
For details of catering facilities see Directory of Train Operators

A Also conveys portion from Fort William (Table 227)

b Change at Perth, Glasgow Queen Street and Glasgow Central. Passengers make their own way between Glasgow Queen Street and Glasgow Central

c Via Glasgow Queen Street and Glasgow Central. Passengers make their own way from one station to the other

e Change at Watford Junction and Clapham Junction

OVERNIGHT SLEEPERS. For Sleeper trains, operated by First ScotRail, please refer to Tables 400 - 404

Milton Keynes Central → Buckingham and Bicester

Bus Service

		VT	VT	VT	VT	VT	VT	VT	VT	VT	VT	VT	VT	VT
Milton Keynes Central	d	05 50	06 20	06 50	07 20	07 40	08 20	08 45	09 15	09 45	10 15	10 45	11 15	11 45
Buckingham Tesco	d	06 10	06 40	07 10	07 40	08 00	08 40	09 05	09 35	10 05	10 35	11 05	11 35	12 05
Bicester Bure Place	a	06 30	07 00	07 30	08 00	08 25	09 00	09 25	09 55	10 25	10 55	11 25	11 55	12 25

		VT	VT	VT	VT	VT	VT	VT	VT	VT	VT	VT	VT	VT	VT	VT	VT	
Milton Keynes Central	d	12 15	12 45	13 15	13 45	14 15	14 45	15 15	15 45	16 15	16 45	17 15	17 45	18 15	18 45	19 45	20 45	
Buckingham Tesco	d	12 35	13 05	13 35	14 05	14 35	15 05	15 35	16 05	16 35	17 05	17 35	18 05	18 35	19 05	20 05	21 05	
Bicester Bure Place	a	12 55	13 25	13 55	14 25	14 55	15 25	15 55	16 25	16 55	17 25	17 55	18 25	18 55	19 25	20 25	21 25	

Saturdays

		VT	VT	VT	VT	VT	VT	VT	VT	VT	VT	VT	VT	VT
Milton Keynes Central	d	05 50	06 20	06 50	07 20	07 40	08 20	08 45	09 15	09 45	10 15	10 45	11 15	11 45
Buckingham Tesco	d	06 10	06 40	07 10	07 40	08 00	08 40	09 05	09 35	10 05	10 35	11 05	11 35	12 05
Bicester Bure Place	a	06 30	07 00	07 30	08 00	08 25	09 00	09 25	09 55	10 25	10 55	11 25	11 55	12 25

		VT	VT	VT	VT	VT	VT	VT	VT	VT	VT	VT	VT	VT	VT	VT	VT	
Milton Keynes Central	d	12 15	12 45	13 15	13 45	14 15	14 45	15 15	15 45	16 15	16 45	17 15	17 45	18 15	18 45	19 45	20 45	
Buckingham Tesco	d	12 35	13 05	13 35	14 05	14 35	15 05	15 35	16 05	16 35	17 05	17 35	18 05	18 35	19 05	20 05	21 05	
Bicester Bure Place	a	12 55	13 25	13 55	14 25	14 55	15 25	15 55	16 25	16 55	17 25	17 55	18 25	18 55	19 25	20 25	21 25	

Sundays

		VT	VT	VT	VT	VT	VT	VT	VT	VT	VT	VT	VT	VT	VT	VT	VT	VT	VT	VT	VT	VT	VT	VT	VT	VT
Milton Keynes Central	d	06 45	07 45	08 45	09 45	10 15	10 45	11 15	11 45	12 15	12 45	13 15	13 45	14 15	14 45	15 15	15 45	16 15	16 45	17 15	17 45	18 15	18 45	19 45	20 40	21 53
Buckingham Tesco	d	07 05	08 05	09 05	10 05	10 35	11 05	11 35	12 05	12 35	13 05	13 35	14 05	14 35	15 05	15 35	16 05	16 35	17 05	17 35	18 05	18 35	19 05	20 05	21 00	22 13
Bicester Bure Place	a	07 25	08 25	09 25	10 25	10 55	11 25	11 55	12 25	12 55	13 25	13 55	14 25	14 55	15 25	15 55	16 25	16 55	17 25	17 55	18 25	18 55	19 25	20 25	21 20	22 33

For general notes see front of timetable
For details of catering facilities see
Directory of Train Operators

This is the X5 service operated by Stagecoach East

Table 65A

Mondays to Fridays

Bicester and Buckingham → Milton Keynes Central

Bus Service

		VT	VT	VT	VT	VT	VT	VT	VT	VT	VT	VT	VT	VT
Bicester Bure Place	d	07 35	08 05	08 35	09 05	09 35	10 05	10 35	11 05	11 35	12 05	12 35	13 05	13 35
Buckingham Tesco	d	07 55	08 25	08 55	09 25	09 55	10 25	10 55	11 25	11 55	12 25	12 55	13 25	13 55
Milton Keynes Central	a	08 15	08 45	09 15	09 45	10 15	10 45	11 15	11 45	12 15	12 45	13 15	13 45	14 15

		VT	VT	VT	VT	VT	VT	VT	VT	VT	VT	VT	VT	VT	VT	VT	VT	VT
Bicester Bure Place	d	14 05	14 35	15 05	15 35	16 05	16 35	17 05	17 35	18 05	18 35	19 05	19 30	20 00	20 25	21 25	22 25	
Buckingham Tesco	d	14 25	14 55	15 25	15 55	16 25	16 55	17 25	17 55	18 25	18 55	19 25	19 50	20 20	20 45	21 45	22 45	
Milton Keynes Central	a	14 45	15 15	15 45	16 15	16 45	17 15	17 45	18 15	18 45	19 15	19 45	20 10	20 40	21 05	22 05	23 05	

Saturdays

		VT	VT	VT	VT	VT	VT	VT	VT	VT	VT	VT	VT	VT
Bicester Bure Place	d	07 35	08 05	08 35	09 05	09 35	10 05	10 35	11 05	11 35	12 05	12 35	13 05	13 35
Buckingham Tesco	d	07 55	08 25	08 55	09 25	09 55	10 25	10 55	11 25	11 55	12 25	12 55	13 25	13 55
Milton Keynes Central	a	08 15	08 45	09 15	09 45	10 15	10 45	11 15	11 45	12 15	12 45	13 15	13 45	14 15

		VT	VT	VT	VT	VT	VT	VT	VT	VT	VT	VT	VT	VT	VT	VT	VT
Bicester Bure Place	d	14 05	14 35	15 05	15 35	16 05	16 35	17 05	17 35	18 05	18 35	19 05	19 30	20 00	20 25	21 25	22 25
Buckingham Tesco	d	14 25	14 55	15 25	15 55	16 25	16 55	17 25	17 55	18 25	18 55	19 25	19 50	20 20	20 45	21 45	22 45
Milton Keynes Central	a	14 45	15 15	15 45	16 15	16 45	17 15	17 45	18 15	18 45	19 15	19 45	20 10	20 40	21 05	22 05	23 05

Sundays

		VT	VT	VT	VT	VT	VT	VT	VT	VT	VT	VT	VT	VT	VT	VT	VT	VT	VT	VT	VT	VT	VT	VT	VT
Bicester Bure Place	d	08 35	09 35	10 35	11 35	12 05	12 35	13 05	13 35	14 05	14 35	15 05	15 35	16 05	16 35	17 05	17 35	18 05	18 35	19 05	19 30	20 05	20 30	21 30	22 30
Buckingham Tesco	d	08 55	09 55	10 55	11 55	12 25	12 55	13 25	13 55	14 25	14 55	15 25	15 55	16 25	16 55	17 25	17 55	18 25	18 55	19 25	19 50	20 25	20 50	21 50	22 50
Milton Keynes Central	a	09 15	10 15	11 15	12 15	12 45	13 15	13 45	14 15	14 45	15 15	15 45	16 15	16 45	17 15	17 45	18 15	18 45	19 15	19 45	20 10	20 45	21 10	22 10	23 10

For general notes see front of timetable
For details of catering facilities see
Directory of Train Operators

This is the X5 service operated by Stagecoach East

Mondays to Saturdays

Milton Keynes Central — London Luton Airport

Bus Service

		VT	VT SX	VT SO	VT SX	VT	VT	VT	VT	VT	VT SX	VT	VT SX	VT	VT SX	VT	VT	VT SX	VT	VT	VT	VT	VT SX
Milton Keynes Central	d	06 40	07 10	07 55	07 55	08 55	09 55	10 55	11 55	12 55	13 25	13 55	14 25	14 55	15 25	15 55	16 55	17 25	17 55	18 55	19 55	20 55	21 55
Milton Keynes The Point	d	06 45	07 15	08 00	08 00	09 00	10 00	11 00	12 00	13 00	13 30	14 00	14 30	15 00	15 30	16 00	17 00	17 30	18 00	19 00	20 00	21 00	22 00
Luton	d	07 25	08 05	08 40	08 45	09 40	10 40	11 40	12 40	13 40	14 10	14 40	15 10	15 40	16 10	16 40	17 40	18 10	18 40	19 40	20 40	21 40	22 40
London Luton Airport	a	07 35	08 15	08 50	08 55	09 50	10 50	11 50	12 50	13 50	14 20	14 50	15 20	15 50	16 20	16 50	17 50	18 20	18 50	19 50	20 50	21 50	22 50

Sundays

		VT	VT	VT	VT	VT	VT	VT	VT	VT	VT	VT	VT	VT
Milton Keynes Central	d	09 20	10 20	11 20	12 20	13 20	14 20	15 20	16 20	17 20	18 20	19 20	20 20	21 20
Milton Keynes The Point	d	09 25	10 25	11 25	12 25	13 25	14 25	15 25	16 25	17 25	18 25	19 25	20 25	21 25
Luton	d	10 05	11 05	12 05	13 05	14 05	15 05	16 05	17 05	18 05	19 05	20 05	21 05	22 05
London Luton Airport	a	10 15	11 15	12 15	13 15	14 15	15 15	16 15	17 15	18 15	19 15	20 15	21 15	22 15

Mondays to Saturdays

		VT SO A	VT SX	VT SO	VT SX	VT SX	VT SO	VT SX	VT SX	VT	VT	VT	VT	VT
London Luton Airport	d	05 50	05 50	06 50	06 50	07 20	07 50	07 50	08 35	09 05	10 05	11 05	12 05	13 05
Luton	d	06 00	06 00	07 00	07 00	07 30	08 00	08 00	08 45	09 15	10 15	11 15	12 15	13 15
Luton Galaxy Centre	d	06 02	06 02	07 02	07 02	07 32	08 02	08 02	08 47	09 17	10 17	11 17	12 17	13 17
Milton Keynes The Point	d	.	06 40	07 40	07 45	08 18	08 40	08 48	09 25	09 55	10 55	11 55	12 55	13 55
Milton Keynes Central	a	06 40	06 45	07 45	07 50	08 30	08 45	09 00	09 30	10 00	11 00	12 00	13 00	14 00

		VT SX	VT	VT SX	VT	VT SX	VT	VT SX	VT	VT SX	VT	VT SO A	VT SX	VT SO A	VT SX A	VT SX A
London Luton Airport	d	13 35	14 05	14 35	15 05	15 35	16 05	16 35	17 05	17 35	18 05	19 05	19 05	20 05	20 05	21 05
Luton	d	13 45	14 15	14 45	15 15	15 45	16 15	16 45	17 15	17 45	18 15	19 15	19 15	20 15	20 15	21 15
Luton Galaxy Centre	d	13 47	14 17	14 47	15 17	15 47	16 17	16 47	17 17	17 47	18 17	19 17	19 17	20 17	20 17	21 17
Milton Keynes The Point	d	14 25	14 55	15 25	15 55	16 25	16 55	17 25	17 55	18 25	18 55	.	19 55	.	.	.
Milton Keynes Central	a	14 30	15 00	15 30	16 00	16 30	17 00	17 30	18 00	18 30	19 00	19 50	20 00	20 50	20 55	21 55

Sundays

		VT	VT	VT	VT	VT	VT	VT	VT	VT	VT	VT	VT	VT
London Luton Airport	d	08 20	09 20	10 20	11 20	12 20	13 20	14 20	15 20	16 20	17 20	18 20	19 20	20 20
Luton	d	08 30	09 30	10 30	11 30	12 30	13 30	14 30	15 30	16 30	17 30	18 30	19 30	20 30
Luton Galaxy Centre	d	08 32	09 32	10 32	11 32	12 32	13 32	14 32	15 32	16 32	17 32	18 32	19 32	20 32
Milton Keynes The Point	d	09 10	10 10	11 10	12 10	13 10	14 10	15 10	16 10	17 10	18 10	19 10	20 10	21 10
Milton Keynes Central	a	09 15	10 15	11 15	12 15	13 15	14 15	15 15	16 15	17 15	18 15	19 15	20 15	21 15

For general notes see front of timetable
For details of catering facilities see Directory of Train Operators

A To Milton Keynes The Point

Milton Keynes Central → Bedford and Cambridge

Bus Service

		VT	VT		VT	VT		VT	VT		VT	VT		VT	VT		VT	VT		VT	VT		VT	VT		VT
Milton Keynes Central	d	07 15	07 50		08 15	08 45		09 15	09 45		10 15	10 45		11 15	11 45		12 15	12 45		13 15	13 45		14 15	14 45		15 15
Bedford Bus Station	a	08 00	08 35		09 05	09 35		10 05	10 35		11 05	11 35		12 05	12 35		13 05	13 35		14 05	14 35		15 05	15 35		16 05
St Neots Cross Keys	a	08 42	09 17		09 47	10 17		10 47	11 17		11 47	12 17		12 47	13 17		13 47	14 17		14 47	15 17		15 47	16 17		16 47
Cambridge Bus Station	a	09 20	09 55		10 25	10 55		11 25	11 55		12 25	12 55		13 25	13 55		14 25	14 55		15 25	15 55		16 25	16 55		17 25

		VT	VT		VT	VT		VT	VT		VT	VT		VT	VT		VT	VT		VT	VT					
Milton Keynes Central	d	15 45	16 15		16 45	17 15		17 45	18 15		18 45	19 15		19 45	20 10		20 40	21 05		22 05	23 05					
Bedford Bus Station	a	16 35	17 05		17 35	18 05		18 35	19 05		19 35	20 05		20 35	20 55		21 25	21 50		22 50	23 50					
St Neots Cross Keys	a	17 17	17 47		18 17	18 47		19 17			20 10			21 10			22 10									
Cambridge Bus Station	a	17 55	18 25		18 55	19 25		19 48			20 43			21 43			22 43									

Saturdays

		VT	VT		VT	VT		VT	VT		VT	VT		VT	VT		VT	VT		VT	VT		VT	VT		VT
Milton Keynes Central	d	07 15	07 50		08 15	08 45		09 15	09 45		10 15	10 45		11 15	11 45		12 15	12 45		13 15	13 45		14 15	14 45		15 15
Bedford Bus Station	a	08 00	08 35		09 05	09 35		10 05	10 35		11 05	11 35		12 05	12 35		13 05	13 35		14 05	14 35		15 05	15 35		16 05
St Neots Cross Keys	a	08 42	09 17		09 47	10 17		10 47	11 17		11 47	12 17		12 47	13 17		13 47	14 17		14 47	15 17		15 47	16 17		16 47
Cambridge Bus Station	a	09 20	09 55		10 25	10 55		11 25	11 55		12 25	12 55		13 25	13 55		14 25	14 55		15 25	15 55		16 25	16 55		17 25

		VT	VT		VT	VT		VT	VT		VT	VT		VT	VT		VT	VT		VT	VT					
Milton Keynes Central	d	15 45	16 15		16 45	17 15		17 45	18 15		18 45	19 15		19 45	20 10		20 40	21 05		22 05	23 05					
Bedford Bus Station	a	16 35	17 05		17 35	18 05		18 35	19 05		19 35	20 05		20 30	20 55		21 25	21 50		22 50	23 50					
St Neots Cross Keys	a	17 17	17 47		18 17	18 47		19 15			20 10			21 10			22 10									
Cambridge Bus Station	a	17 55	18 25		18 55	19 25		19 48			20 43			21 43			22 43									

Sundays

		VT	VT	VT	VT	VT	VT	VT	VT	VT	VT	VT	VT	VT	VT	VT	VT	VT	VT	VT	VT	VT	VT	VT	VT	
Milton Keynes Central	d	09 15	10 15	11 15	12 15	12 45	13 15	13 45	14 15	14 45	15 15	15 45	16 15	16 45	17 15	17 45	18 15	18 45	19 15	19 45	20 10	20 45	21 10	22 10	23 10	
Bedford Bus Station	a	10 05	11 05	12 05	13 05	13 35	14 05	14 35	15 05	15 35	16 05	16 35	17 05	17 35	18 05	18 35	19 05	19 35	20 05	20 35	20 55	21 35	21 55	22 55	23 55	
St Neots Cross Keys	a	10 47	11 47	12 47	13 47	14 17	14 47	15 17	15 47	16 17	16 45	17 15	17 40	18 10	18 40	19 10		20 10		21 10		22 10				
Cambridge Bus Station	a	11 25	12 25	13 25	14 25	14 55	15 25	15 55	16 25	16 55	17 18	17 48	18 13	18 43	19 13	19 43		20 43		21 43		22 43				

For general notes see front of timetable
For details of catering facilities see
Directory of Train Operators

This is the X5 service operated by Stagecoach East

Cambridge and Bedford → Milton Keynes Central

Bus Service

		VT	VT	VT	VT	VT	VT	VT	VT	VT	VT	VT	VT	VT	VT	VT	VT	VT
Cambridge Bus Station	d					05 40		06 30	07 00	07 30	08 10	08 40	09 10	09 40	10 10	10 40	11 10	11 40
St Neots Sq (Bus)	d					06 15		07 05	07 35	08 05	08 45	09 15	09 45	10 15	10 45	11 15	11 45	12 15
Bedford Bus Station	d	05 05	05 35	06 05	06 35	06 55	07 30	07 55	08 25	09 00	09 30	10 00	10 30	11 00	11 30	12 00	12 30	13 00
Milton Keynes Central	a	05 50	06 20	06 50	07 20	07 40	08 20	08 45	09 15	09 45	10 15	10 45	11 15	11 45	12 15	12 45	13 15	13 45

		VT	VT	VT	VT	VT	VT	VT	VT	VT	VT	VT	VT	VT	VT
Cambridge Bus Station	d	12 10	12 40	13 10	13 40	14 10	14 40	15 10	15 40	16 10	16 40	17 10	17 40	18 10	18 40
St Neots Sq (Bus)	d	12 45	13 15	13 45	14 15	14 45	15 15	15 45	16 15	16 45	17 15	17 45	18 15	18 45	19 15
Bedford Bus Station	d	13 30	14 00	14 30	15 00	15 30	16 00	16 30	17 00	17 30	18 00	18 30	19 00	19 30	20 00
Milton Keynes Central	a	14 15	14 45	15 15	15 45	16 15	16 45	17 15	17 45	18 15	18 45	19 15	19 45	20 10	20 45

Saturdays

		VT	VT	VT	VT	VT	VT	VT	VT	VT	VT	VT	VT	VT	VT	VT	VT	VT
Cambridge Bus Station	d							06 30	07 00	07 30	08 10	08 40	09 10	09 40	10 10	10 40	11 10	11 40
St Neots Sq (Bus)	d							07 05	07 35	08 05	08 45	09 15	09 45	10 15	10 45	11 15	11 45	12 15
Bedford Bus Station	d	05 05	05 35	06 05	06 35	07 00	07 30	08 00	08 30	09 00	09 30	10 00	10 30	11 00	11 30	12 00	12 30	13 00
Milton Keynes Central	a	05 50	06 20	06 50	07 20	07 45	08 15	08 45	09 15	09 45	10 15	10 45	11 15	11 45	12 15	12 45	13 15	13 45

		VT	VT	VT	VT	VT	VT	VT	VT	VT	VT	VT	VT	VT	VT
Cambridge Bus Station	d	12 10	12 40	13 10	13 40	14 10	14 40	15 10	15 40	16 10	16 40	17 10	17 40	18 10	18 40
St Neots Sq (Bus)	d	12 45	13 15	13 45	14 15	14 45	15 15	15 45	16 15	16 45	17 15	17 45	18 15	18 45	19 15
Bedford Bus Station	d	13 30	14 00	14 30	15 00	15 30	16 00	16 30	17 00	17 30	18 00	18 30	19 00	19 30	20 00
Milton Keynes Central	a	14 15	14 45	15 15	15 45	16 15	16 45	17 15	17 45	18 15	18 45	19 15	19 45	20 10	20 45

Sundays

		VT	VT	VT	VT	VT	VT	VT	VT	VT	VT	VT	VT	VT	VT	VT	VT	VT	VT	VT	VT	VT	VT	VT	VT	VT
Cambridge Bus Station	d					08 10		09 10		10 10		11 10	11 40	12 10	12 40	13 10	13 40	14 10	14 40	15 10	15 40	16 10	16 40	17 10	17 40	18 40
St Neots Sq (Bus)	d					08 45		09 45		10 45		11 45	12 15	12 45	13 15	13 45	14 15	14 45	15 15	15 45	16 15	16 45	17 15	17 45	18 15	19 15
Bedford Bus Station	d	06 00	07 00	08 00	09 00	09 30	10 00	10 30	11 00	11 30	12 00	12 30	13 00	13 30	14 00	14 30	15 00	15 30	16 00	16 30	17 00	17 30	18 00	18 30	19 00	20 00
Milton Keynes Central	a	06 45	07 45	08 45	09 45	10 15	10 45	11 15	11 45	12 15	12 45	13 15	13 45	14 15	14 45	15 15	15 45	16 15	16 45	17 15	17 45	18 15	18 45	19 15	19 45	20 45

For general notes see front of timetable
For details of catering facilities see Directory of Train Operators

This is the X5 service operated by Stagecoach East

Mondays to Fridays

Watford Junction → Heathrow Airport

Bus Service

	VT	VT	VT	VT	VT	VT	VT	VT	VT	VT	VT	VT	VT	VT	VT	VT	VT
	MO	MX															
Watford Junction ... 65, 66 d	23p10	23p35	06 30	07 00	07 30	08 15	09 00	09 30	10 00	10 30	11 00	11 30	12 00	12 30	13 00	13 30	14 00
Heathrow Terminal 4 Bus a	23p45	00 10	07 15	07 50	08 30	09 15	09 50	10 10	10 40	11 10	11 40	12 10	12 40	13 10	13 40	14 10	14 40
Heathrow Terminal 1 Bus .. a	23b59	00s25	07s30	08s05	08s45	09s30	10s05	10s25	10s55	11s25	11s55	12s25	12s55	13s25	13s55	14s25	14s55
Heathrow Terminal 3 Bus a	00s05	00s30	07s35	08s10	08s50	09s35	10s10	10s30	11s00	11s30	12s00	12s30	13s00	13s30	14s00	14s30	15s00
Heathrow Central Bus Stn a	00 10	00 35	07 40	08 15	08 55	09 40	10 15	10 35	11 05	11 35	12 05	12 35	13 05	13 35	14 05	14 35	15 05

	VT	VT	VT	VT	VT	VT	VT	VT	VT	VT	VT	VT	VT	VT	VT	VT
Watford Junction ... 65, 66 d	14 30	15 00	15 30	16 00	16 30	17 00	17 45	18 30	19 00	19 30	20 00	20 30	21 30	22 00	22 30	23 35
Heathrow Terminal 4 Bus a	15 10	15 40	16 10	16 45	17 20	17 50	18 35	19 20	19 50	20 10	20 40	21 10	22 10	22 35	23 10	00 10
Heathrow Terminal 1 Bus .. a	15s25	15s55	16s25	17s00	17s35	18s05	18s50	19s35	20s05	20s25	20s55	21s25	22s25	22s50	23s25	00s25
Heathrow Terminal 3 Bus a	15s30	16s00	16s30	17s05	17s40	18s10	18s55	19s40	20s10	20s30	21s00	21s30	22s30	22s55	23s30	00s30
Heathrow Central Bus Stn a	15 35	16 05	16 35	17 10	17 45	18 15	19 00	19 45	20 15	20 35	21 05	21 35	22 35	23 00	23 35	00 35

Saturdays

	VT	VT	VT	VT	VT	VT	VT	VT	VT	VT	VT	VT	VT	VT	VT	VT	VT
Watford Junction ... 65, 66 d	23p35	07 00	07 30	08 00	08 30	09 00	09 30	10 00	10 30	11 00	11 30	12 00	12 30	13 00	13 30	14 00	14 30
Heathrow Terminal 4 Bus a	00 10	07 40	08 10	08 40	09 10	09 40	10 10	10 40	11 10	11 40	12 10	12 40	13 10	13 40	14 10	14 40	15 10
Heathrow Terminal 1 Bus .. a	00s25	07s55	08s25	08s55	09s25	09s55	10s25	10s55	11s25	11s55	12s25	12s55	13s25	13s55	14s25	14s55	15s25
Heathrow Terminal 3 Bus a	00s30	08s00	08s30	09s00	09s30	10s00	10s30	11s00	11s30	12s00	12s30	13s00	13s30	14s00	14s30	15s00	15s30
Heathrow Central Bus Stn a	00 35	08 05	08 35	09 05	09 35	10 05	10 35	11 05	11 35	12 05	12 35	13 05	13 35	14 05	14 35	15 05	15 35

	VT	VT	VT	VT	VT	VT	VT	VT	VT	VT	VT	VT	VT	VT
Watford Junction ... 65, 66 d	15 00	15 30	16 00	16 30	17 00	17 30	18 00	18 30	19 00	19 30	20 00	20 30	21 00	22 00
Heathrow Terminal 4 Bus a	15 40	16 10	16 40	17 10	17 40	18 10	18 40	19 10	19 40	20 10	20 40	21 10	21 40	22 35
Heathrow Terminal 1 Bus .. a	15s55	16s25	16s55	17s25	17s55	18s25	18s55	19s25	19s55	20s25	20s55	21s25	21s55	22s50
Heathrow Terminal 3 Bus a	16s00	16s30	17s00	17s30	18s00	18s30	19s00	19s30	20s00	20s30	21s00	21s30	22s00	22s55
Heathrow Central Bus Stn a	16 05	16 35	17 05	17 35	18 05	18 35	19 05	19 35	20 05	20 35	21 05	21 35	22 05	23 00

Sundays

	VT	VT	VT	VT	VT	VT	VT	VT	VT	VT	VT	VT	VT	VT	VT	VT	VT
Watford Junction ... 65, 66 d	06 50	07 20	07 50	08 20	08 50	09 20	09 50	10 20	10 50	11 20	11 50	12 20	12 50	13 20	13 50	14 20	14 50
Heathrow Terminal 4 Bus a	07 30	08 00	08 30	09 00	09 30	10 00	10 30	11 00	11 30	12 00	12 30	13 00	13 30	14 00	14 30	15 00	15 30
Heathrow Terminal 1 Bus .. a	07s45	08s15	08s45	09s15	09s45	10s15	10s45	11s15	11s45	12s15	12s45	13s15	13s45	14s15	14s45	15s15	15s45
Heathrow Terminal 3 Bus a	07s50	08s20	08s50	09s20	09s50	10s20	10s50	11s20	11s50	12s20	12s50	13s20	13s50	14s20	14s50	15s20	15s50
Heathrow Central Bus Stn a	07 55	08 25	08 55	09 25	09 55	10 25	10 55	11 25	11 55	12 25	12 55	13 25	13 55	14 25	14 55	15 25	15 55

	VT	VT	VT	VT	VT	VT	VT	VT	VT	VT	VT	VT	VT	VT	VT
Watford Junction ... 65, 66 d	15 20	15 50	16 20	16 50	17 20	17 50	18 20	18 50	19 20	19 50	20 20	20 50	21 20	22 10	23 10
Heathrow Terminal 4 Bus a	16 00	16 30	17 00	17 30	18 00	18 30	19 00	19 30	20 00	20 30	21 00	21 30	21 55	22 45	23 45
Heathrow Terminal 1 Bus .. a	16s15	16s45	17s15	17s45	18s15	18s45	19s15	19s45	20s15	20s45	21s15	21s45	22s10	23s00	23s59
Heathrow Terminal 3 Bus a	16s20	16s50	17s20	17s50	18s20	18s50	19s20	19s50	20s20	20s50	21s20	21s50	22s15	23s05	00s05
Heathrow Central Bus Stn a	16 25	16 55	17 25	17 55	18 25	18 55	19 25	19 55	20 25	20 55	21 25	21 55	22 20	23 10	00 10

For general notes see front of timetable
For details of catering facilities see
Directory of Train Operators

b Previous night.
Stops to set down only

Heathrow Airport → Watford Junction

Bus Service

	VT	VT	VT	VT	VT	VT	VT	VT	VT	VT	VT	VT	VT	VT	VT	VT	VT
Heathrow Terminal 4 Bus .. d	05 15	06 05	06 40	07 15	07 50	08 30	09 15	09 50	10 10	10 40	11 10	11 40	12 10	12 40	13 10	13 40	14 10
Heathrow Central Bus Stn d	05 40	06 30	07 05	07 40	08 15	08 55	09 40	10 15	10 35	11 05	11 35	12 05	12 35	13 05	13 35	14 05	14 35
Watford Junction .... 65, 66 a	06 20	07 10	07 50	08 30	09 05	09 40	10 25	11 00	11 15	11 45	12 15	12 45	13 15	13 45	14 15	14 45	15 15

	VT	VT	VT	VT	VT	VT	VT	VT	VT	VT	VT	VT	VT	VT			
Heathrow Terminal 4 Bus .. d	14 40	15 10	15 40	16 10	16 45	17 20	17 50	18 35	19 20	19 50	20 10	20 40	21 10	22 35			
Heathrow Central Bus Stn d	15 05	15 35	16 05	16 35	17 10	17 45	18 15	19 00	19 45	20 15	20 35	21 05	21 35	23 00			
Watford Junction .... 65, 66 a	15 45	16 15	16 55	17 35	18 10	18 45	19 15	19 55	20 25	20 55	21 15	21 45	22 15	23 30			

Saturdays

	VT	VT	VT	VT	VT	VT	VT	VT	VT	VT	VT	VT	VT	VT	VT	VT	VT
Heathrow Terminal 4 Bus .. d	05 45	06 40	07 40	08 10	08 40	09 10	09 40	10 10	10 40	11 10	11 40	12 10	12 40	13 10	13 40	14 10	14 40
Heathrow Central Bus Stn d	06 10	07 05	08 05	08 35	09 05	09 35	10 05	10 35	11 05	11 35	12 05	12 35	13 05	13 35	14 05	14 35	15 05
Watford Junction .... 65, 66 a	06 50	07 45	08 45	09 15	09 45	10 15	10 45	11 15	11 45	12 15	12 45	13 15	13 45	14 15	14 45	15 15	15 45

	VT	VT	VT	VT	VT	VT	VT	VT	VT	VT	VT	VT	VT	VT	VT		
Heathrow Terminal 4 Bus .. d	15 10	15 40	16 10	16 40	17 10	17 40	18 10	18 40	19 10	19 40	20 10	20 40	21 10	21 40	22 35		
Heathrow Central Bus Stn d	15 35	16 05	16 35	17 05	17 35	18 05	18 35	19 05	19 35	20 05	20 35	21 05	21 35	22 05	23 00		
Watford Junction .... 65, 66 a	16 15	16 55	17 15	17 45	18 15	18 45	19 15	19 45	20 15	20 45	21 15	21 45	22 15	22 45	23 30		

Sundays

	VT	VT	VT	VT	VT	VT	VT	VT	VT	VT	VT	VT	VT	VT	VT	VT	VT
Heathrow Terminal 4 Bus .. d	06 40	07 30	08 00	08 30	09 00	09 30	10 00	10 30	11 00	11 30	12 00	12 30	13 00	13 30	14 00	14 30	15 00
Heathrow Central Bus Stn d	07 05	07 55	08 25	08 55	09 25	09 55	10 25	10 55	11 25	11 55	12 25	12 55	13 25	13 55	14 25	14 55	15 25
Watford Junction .... 65, 66 a	07 45	08 35	09 05	09 35	10 05	10 35	11 05	11 35	12 05	12 35	13 05	13 35	14 05	14 35	15 05	15 35	16 05

	VT	VT	VT	VT	VT	VT	VT	VT	VT	VT	VT	VT	VT				
Heathrow Terminal 4 Bus .. d	15 30	16 00	16 30	17 00	17 30	18 00	18 30	19 00	19 30	20 00	20 30	21 30	21 55				
Heathrow Central Bus Stn d	15 55	16 25	16 55	17 25	17 55	18 25	18 55	19 25	19 55	20 25	20 55	21 55	22 20				
Watford Junction .... 65, 66 a	16 35	17 05	17 35	18 05	18 35	19 05	19 35	20 05	20 35	21 05	21 35	22 35	22 55				

For general notes see front of timetable
For details of catering facilities see
Directory of Train Operators

Table 65E

Mondays to Saturdays

Preston — Southport

Bus Service

		VT	VT	VT	VT	VT	VT	VT	VT	VT	VT	VT	VT	VT	VT	VT
Preston 8	d	06 13	07 00	08 09	09 09	10 09	11 09	12 09	13 09	14 09	15 09	16 09	17 19	18 19	19 34	20 19
Southport (Lord Street)	a	06 45	07 33	08 46	09 46	10 46	11 46	12 46	13 46	14 46	15 46	16 46	17 56	18 56	20 11	20 46

Sundays

		VT	VT	VT	VT	VT	VT
Preston 8	d	08 09	10 09	12 09	14 09	16 09	18 09
Southport (Lord Street)	a	08 46	10 46	12 46	14 46	16 46	18 46

Mondays to Saturdays

		VT SX	VT SO	VT SO	VT SX	VT	VT	VT	VT	VT	VT	VT	VT	VT SO	VT SX	VT	VT	VT	VT
Southport (Lord Street)	d	06 55	06 57	07 48	07 41	09 08	10 08	11 08	12 08	13 08	14 08	15 08	16 08	17 11	17 23	18 20	19 20	20 20	21 20
Preston (Fishergate)	a	07 31	07 31	08 28	08 41	09 55	10 55	11 55	12 55	13 55	14 55	15 55	16 55	17 58	18 10	18 57	19 57	20 57	21 57

Sundays

		VT	VT	VT	VT	VT	VT	VT
Southport (Lord Street)	d	09 05	11 05	13 05	15 05	17 05	19 05	21 05
Preston (Fishergate)	a	09 45	11 45	13 45	15 45	17 45	19 45	21 45

For general notes see front of timetable
For details of catering facilities see Directory of Train Operators

This is the X2 service operated jointly by Stagecoach in Lancashire and Stagecoach in Merseyside

Table 65F

Mondays to Saturdays

Penrith — Keswick, Cockermouth and Workington

Bus Service

		VT	VT		VT	VT		VT	VT		VT	VT		VT	VT		VT	VT	VT	VT	VT SX	VT SO	VT		
Penrith North Lakes	d	07 20	08 30		09 30	10 30		11 30	12 30		13 30	14 30		15 30	16 30		17 30	18 30	19 30	20 34	21 35	21 35	22 40		
Keswick (Bus Station)	a	07 55	09 05		10 05	11 05		12 05	13 05		14 05	15 05		16 05	17 05		18 05	19 05	20 05	21 03	22 10	22 10	23 15		
Cockermouth (Main Street)	a	08 31	09 41		10 41	11 41		12 41	13 41		14 41	15 41		16 41	17 41		18 41	19 41	20 41	21 36	22 44	22 46	23 45		
Workington (Bus Station)	a	08 52	10 02		11 02	12 02		13 02	14 02		15 02	16 02		17 02	18 02		19 02	20 02	21 02	21 53	23 07	23 07	00 07		

Sundays

		VT			VT			VT			VT			VT			VT			VT					
Penrith North Lakes	d	08 45			09 20			11 20			13 20			15 20			17 20			19 20					
Keswick (Bus Station)	a	09 20			09 55			11 55			13 55			15 55			17 55			19 55					
Cockermouth (Main Street)	a				10 31			12 31			14 31			16 31			18 31			20 31					
Workington (Bus Station)	a				10 52			12 52			14 52			16 52			18 52			20 52					

Mondays to Saturdays

		VT	VT		VT	VT		VT	VT		VT	VT		VT	VT		VT	VT	VT	VT	VT	VT	VT		
Workington (Bus Station)	d	05 15	06 15		07 15	08 15		09 15	10 15		11 15	12 15		13 15	14 15		15 15	16 15	17 15		18 15	19 15			
Cockermouth (Main Street)	d	05 36	06 36		07 36	08 36		09 36	10 36		11 36	12 36		13 36	14 36		15 36	16 36	17 36		18 36	19 36			
Keswick (Bus Station)	d	06 15	07 15		08 15	09 15		10 15	11 15		12 15	13 15		14 15	15 15		16 15	17 15	18 15	18 40	19 15	20 15	21 50		
Penrith North Lakes	a	06 50	07 50		08 50	09 50		10 50	11 50		12 50	13 50		14 50	15 50		16 50	17 50	18 50	19 17	19 50	20 50	22 25		

Sundays

		VT			VT			VT			VT			VT			VT			VT					
Workington (Bus Station)	d	07 15			09 15			11 15			13 15			15 15			17 15								
Cockermouth (Main Street)	d	07 36			09 36			11 36			13 36			15 36			17 36								
Keswick (Bus Station)	d	08 15			10 15			12 15			14 15			16 15			18 15			18 40					
Penrith North Lakes	a	08 50			10 50			12 50			14 50			16 50			18 50			19 15					

For general notes see front of timetable
For details of catering facilities see
Directory of Train Operators

This is an amalgamation of the X4/X5/X50 services operated by Stagecoach in Cumbria

Mondays to Saturdays

Carlisle — Scottish Border Towns

Bus Service

		VT SO 🚌	VT 🚌	VT 🚌	VT 🚌	VT 🚌	VT 🚌	VT 🚌	VT 🚌	VT 🚌	VT 🚌	VT 🚌	VT 🚌	VT FSO 🚌
Carlisle	d	22p50	09 10	10 10	11 10	12 10	13 10	14 10	15 10	16 10	17 10	18 50	20 50	22 50
Langholm	a	23p32	09 57	10 57	11 57	12 57	13 57	14 57	15 57	16 57	17 57	19 37	21 37	23 32
Hawick	a	00 07	10 32	11 32	12 32	13 32	14 32	15 32	16 32	17 32	18 32	20 12	22 12	00 07
Selkirk	a	00 30	10 55	11 55	12 55	13 55	14 55	15 55	16 55	17 55	18 55	20 35	22 35	00 30
Galashiels	a	00 45	11 15	12 15	13 15	14 15	15 15	16 15	17 15	18 15	19 15	20 50	22 50	00 45

Sundays

		VT 🚌	VT 🚌	VT 🚌	VT 🚌
Carlisle	d	22p50	14 05	18 05	21 20
Langholm	a	23p32	14 50	18 50	22 05
Hawick	a	00 07	15 25	19 25	22 40
Selkirk	a	00 30	15 45	19 45	23 00
Galashiels	a	00 45	16 00	20 00	23 15

Mondays to Saturdays

		VT 🚌	VT 🚌	VT 🚌	VT 🚌	VT 🚌	VT 🚌	VT 🚌	VT 🚌	VT 🚌	VT SX 🚌	VT SX 🚌	VT FSO 🚌
Galashiels	d	06 20	07 15	08 10	09 25	10 25	11 25	12 25	13 25	14 25	16 30	17 35	19 25
Selkirk	d	06 35	07 30	08 25	09 40	10 40	11 40	12 40	13 40	14 40	16 45	17 50	19 40
Hawick	d	06 55	07 50	08 45	10 00	11 00	12 00	13 00	14 00	15 00	17 05	18 10	19 58
Langholm	d	07 35	08 30	09 25	10 40	11 40	12 40	13 40	14 40	15 40	17 45	18 50	20 38
Carlisle	a	08 27	09 17	10 12	11 27	12 27	13 27	14 27	15 27	16 27	18 32	19 37	21 25

Sundays

		VT 🚌	VT 🚌	VT 🚌	VT 🚌
Galashiels	d	09 30	11 30	15 30	17 30
Selkirk	d	09 45	11 45	15 45	17 45
Hawick	d	10 05	12 05	16 05	18 05
Langholm	d	10 38	12 38	16 38	18 38
Carlisle	a	11 27	13 27	17 27	19 27

For general notes see front of timetable
For details of catering facilities see Directory of Train Operators

Mondays to Saturdays

Macclesfield — Buxton and Bakewell

Bus Service

		VT	VT	VT	VT	VT	VT	VT	VT
Macclesfield	d	07 25	08 30	10 55	12 30	14 50	16 30	17 30	18 35
Buxton (Market Place)	a	07 54	08 59	11 25	12 59	15 20	16 59	17 59	19 04
Bakewell Square	a		09 24						

Sundays

		VT	VT	VT	VT	VT	VT
Macclesfield	d	09 42	11 00	12 35	13 35	16 15	18 15
Buxton (Market Place)	a	10 12	11 30	13 00	14 00	16 40	18 45
Bakewell Square	a			13 30	14 30	17 10	

Mondays to Saturdays

		VT	VT	VT	VT	VT	VT	VT	VT
Bakewell Square	d					13 50			
Buxton (Market Place)	d	06 55	07 55	10 20	12 00	14 15	15 55	17 00	18 05
Macclesfield	a	07 24	08 24	10 50	12 29	14 44	16 25	17 29	18 34

Sundays

		VT	VT	VT
Bakewell Square	d	12 35	15 15	17 15
Buxton (Market Place)	d	13 00	15 40	17 40
Macclesfield	a	13 30	16 10	18 10

For general notes see front of timetable
For details of catering facilities see Directory of Train Operators

London → Watford Junction, Milton Keynes, Northampton and West Midlands

Network Diagram - See first page of Table 59

Miles	Miles	Miles			VT	VT	LM	LM	LM	LM	LM	VT	LM	VT	VT	LM	LM		LM	LM	LM	LM	LM	LM	LM	LM
					MX	MO	MO	MO	MO	MX	MX	MX	MO	MO	MO	MX	MO		MO	MO	MX	MO	MX	MO	MO	MO
					1◇	1◇		1	1	1	1	1◇		1◇	1◇	1	1		1		1	1	1	1	1	
						A	B	C	B				B	D	A		C		B	B		C		C	B	B
					☕	☕	🚌					☕	🚌	☕	☕					🚌						🚌
0	0	—	**London Euston 15** ⊖	d	22p40	22p40		23p13	23p13	23p24	23p34	23p40		23p40	23p40		23p43		23p43		00 04	00 34	00 34		00 34	
—	—	0	**Brighton 10**	d																						
—	—	13	Haywards Heath 3	d																						
—	—	24¼	Gatwick Airport 10 ✈	d																						
—	—	40½	East Croydon ⛴	d																						
—	—	48¼	Clapham Junction 10	d																						
—	—	49¼	Imperial Wharf §	d																						
—	—	49¾	West Brompton ⊖	d																						
—	—	51¾	Kensington Olympia ⊖	d																						
—	—	53	Shepherds Bush §	d																						
8	—	57¼	Wembley Central	d																		00 45	00 45		00 45	
11½	11½	—	Harrow & Wealdstone ⊖	d				23p25	23p25		23p46						23p55		23p55		00 16	00 50	00 50		00 50	
16	—	—	Bushey	d							23p51												00 55		00 55	
—	—	—	**Watford Junction**	a				23p32	23p32	23p41	23p54						00 02		00 02		00 23	00 56	00 58		00 58	
17½	17½	—		d	22b57	22b57		23p32	23p32	23p42	23p55			23b56	23b57		00 02		00 02		00 23	00 58	00 58		00 58	
21	—	—	Kings Langley	d				23p37	23p37		23p59											01 03	01 03		01 03	
23	—	—	Apsley	d				23p40	23p40		00 03											01 06	01 06		01 06	
—	—	—	Hemel Hempstead	a				23p43	23p43	23p49	00 06						00 10		00 10		00 31	01 09	01 09	←	01 09	
24½	—	—		d				23p43	23p43	23p49	00 06					←	00 10		00 10		00 31	01 09	01 09	01 09	01 09	
28	—	—	Berkhamsted	d				23p48	23p48	23p54	00 10					00 10	00 14		00 14		00 35	→	01 14	01 14	01 14	
31¾	—	—	Tring	d							→					00 15	00 19		00 19		00 40		01 19	01 19	01 19	
36	—	—	Cheddington	d												00 20	00 24		00 24				01 24	01 24	01 24	
40¼	—	—	Leighton Buzzard	d				00 01	00 01	00 05						00 25	00 31		00 31		00 48		01 29	01 31	01 31	
46¾	—	—	Bletchley	d				00 08	00 08	00 12						00 33	00 39		00 38		00 56		01 36	01 38	01 38	
—	—	—	**Milton Keynes Central 10**	a	23p23	23p29		00 17	00 19	00 20		00 23		00 27	00 30	00 43	00 47		00 49		01 06		01 45	01 47	01 47	
49¾	49¾	—		d	23p24	23p30	23p57	00 17		00 20		00 24	00 27	00 28	00 32		00 48			00 57	01 07		01 45	01 47		01 57
52½	52½	—	Wolverton	d			00 07	00 21		00 24			00 37				00 51			01 07	01 10		01 49	01 51		02 07
65¾	—	—	**Northampton**	a	23c38		00 42	00 39		00 42		00s50	01 12				01 10			01 42	01 27		02 07	02 07		02 42
—	—	—	**Rugby**	a	00s23	23p51						01s20		01 01	00 56											
84½	82½	—		d		23p53								01 02	00 57											
—	—	—	Nuneaton	a																						
96	—	—	Coventry	a	00s35	00 04						01s33		01 13	01 08											
106¾	—	—	Birmingham International ✈	a	00s47	00 16						01s46		01 25	01 20											
115¼	—	—	**Birmingham New Street 12**	a	01s01	00 28						01s58		01 38	01 33											
120½	—	—	Sandwell & Dudley	a																						
128	—	—	Wolverhampton 7 ⛴	a	01 34	00 53						02 32		02 00	01 55											

		LM	LM	LM	LM	LM	SN	LM		VT	LM	LM	VT	VT	LM	SN	LM	VT	VT	SN	LM	VT		LM	LM	VT
		MO	MO	MX																						
		1	1	1	1	1	1	1		1◇	1	1	1◇	1◇	1	1	1	1◇	1◇	1	1	1◇		1	1	1◇
		A	D													E										
										⊠			⊠	⊠				⊠	⊠			⊠				⊠
London Euston 15 ⊖	d	01 34	01 34	01 34		05 24		05 55		06 20		06 24	06 36	06 46	06 37		07 04	07 08	07 13		07 21	07 40		07 14	07 34	07 46
Brighton 10	d															05 22										
Haywards Heath 3	d															05 36										
Gatwick Airport 10 ✈	d															05 53										
East Croydon ⛴	d															06 10										
Clapham Junction 10	d															06 30				06 49						
Imperial Wharf §	d																									
West Brompton ⊖	d						05 31									06 35				06 54						
Kensington Olympia ⊖	d						05 34									06 39				06 57						
Shepherds Bush §	d																									
Wembley Central	d	01 45	01 47	01 48												06 57				07 17						
Harrow & Wealdstone ⊖	d	01 50	01 52	01 53		05 36	05 51	06 09				06 36				07 02	07 16			07 22					07 46	
Bushey	d																									
Watford Junction	a	01 56	01 58	01 59		05 43	05 58	06 15				06 43			06 53	07 09	07 23			07 30				07 31	07 53	
	d	01 57	01 59	02 00		05 43		06 16		06u36		06 43	06u51		06 54		07 23	07u23	07u28					07 31	07 53	08u01
Kings Langley	d					05 48		06 20				06 48					07 28								07 58	
Apsley	d					05 51		06 24				06 51					07 31								08 01	
Hemel Hempstead	a	02 04	02 06	02 07		05 54		06 27				06 54			07 01		07 34							07 39	08 04	
	d	02 04	02 06	02 07		05 54		06 27			←	06 54			07 01		07 34							07 39	08 04	
Berkhamsted	d	02 09	02 11	02 12		05 59		06 32			06 32	06 59			07 06		07 39							07 43	08 09	
Tring	d	02 14	02 16	02 17		06 06		→			06 40	07a07			07 13		07a47							07 50	08a17	
Cheddington	d					06 11									07 18											
Leighton Buzzard	d	02 26	02 24	02 25		06 16					06 48				07 23									07 58		
Bletchley	d	02 33	02 31	02 32	05 25	06 25					06 56				07 30									08 06		
Milton Keynes Central 10	a	02 42	02 42	02 44	05 29	06 32				06 55	07 02		07 10	07 16	07 36				07 47		08 01	08 10		08 11		
	d				05 30	06 32					07 02		07 11	07 17	07 36				07 48			08 10		08 12		
Wolverton	d				05 33	06 36					07 06				07 40									08 15		
Northampton	a				05 47	06 49					07 19				07 53									08 30		
Rugby	a													07 39												08 39
	d																									
Nuneaton	a																		08 21							
Coventry	a												07 44					08 11				08 44				
Birmingham International ✈	a												07 57					08 27				08 57				
Birmingham New Street 12	a												08 09					08 41				09 09				
Sandwell & Dudley	a												08 22									09 22				
Wolverhampton 7 ⛴	a												08 36									09 36				

For general notes see front of timetable
For details of catering facilities see Directory of Train Operators

§ This station may open during the currency of the Timetable

A Until 24 March
B 4 February to 24 March
C Until 28 January and from 31 March
D From 31 March
E Also stops at Selhurst 0613

b Previous night. Stops to pick up only
c Previous night. Stops to set down only

London → Watford Junction, Milton Keynes, Northampton and West Midlands

Network Diagram - See first page of Table 59

		VT 1 ◇ ⊠	LM 1	LM 1	LM 1	VT 1 ◇ ⊠	VT 1 ◇ ⊠	SN 1	LM 1	VT 1 ◇ ⊠	LM 1	LM 1	SN 1		LM 1	VT 1 ◇ ⊠	VT 1 ◇ ⊠	LM 1	LM 1	VT 1 ◇ ⊠	LM 1	VT 1 ◇ ⊠	VT 1 ◇ ⊠	VT 1 ◇ ⊠	LM 1	LM 1
London Euston 15 ⊖	d	08 05	07 49	07 54	08 04	08 10	08 17		08 25	08 40	08 24	08 34			08 50	09 00	09 17	08 54	09 04	09 10	09 22	09 38	09 40	09 46	09 24	09 34
Brighton 10	d																									
Haywards Heath 3	d																									
Gatwick Airport 10 ✈	d																									
East Croydon	d																									
Clapham Junction 10	d							07 57					08 24													
Imperial Wharf §	d																									
West Brompton ⊖	d							08 02					08 29													
Kensington Olympia ⊖	d							08 05					08 32													
Shepherds Bush §	d																									
Wembley Central	d							08 21					08 48													
Harrow & Wealdstone ⊖	d				08 16			08 26				08 46	08 53						09 16							09 46
Bushey	d				08 21							08 51							09 21							09 51
Watford Junction	a		08 05	08 10	08 24			08 33			08 40	08 54	09 00					09 10	09 24						09 40	09 54
	d		08 06	08 11	08 25	08u25	08u32				08 41	08 55						09 11	09 25	09u25					09 41	09 55
Kings Langley	d				08 29							08 59							09 29							09 59
Apsley	d				08 33							09 03							09 33							10 03
Hemel Hempstead	a			08 18	08 36						08 48	09 06						09 18	09 36						09 48	10 06
	d			08 18	08 36						08 48	09 06						09 18	09 36						09 48	10 06
Berkhamsted	d			08 23	08 40						08 53	09 10						09 23	09 40						09 53	10 10
Tring	d			08 30	08a47							09a18						09 30	09a48							10a17
Cheddington	d			08 35														09 35								
Leighton Buzzard	d		08 23	08 40							09 06				09 23			09 40							10 06	
Bletchley	d		08 32	08 47							09 13				09 31			09 47							10 13	
Milton Keynes Central 10	a	08 35	08 37	08 53					09 05	09 10	09 19				09 36		09 47	09 53			10 00		10 11	10 16	10 19	
	d		08 37	08 53					09 06	09 10	09 19				09 37		09 48				10 00		10 12	10 17	10 19	
Wolverton	d		08 41	08 57							09 23				09 40										10 23	
Northampton	a		08 55	09 10					09 21		09 36				09 55						10 16	10 24			10 36	
Rugby	a															09 49						10 46		10 39		
	d																					10 47				
Nuneaton	a						09 21										10 21					10 58				
Coventry	a					09 13				09 44										10 13			10 44			
Birmingham International ✈	a					09 26				09 57										10 26			10 57			
Birmingham New Street 12	a					09 41				10 09										10 41			11 09			
Sandwell & Dudley	a									10 22													11 22			
Wolverhampton 7	a									10 36													11 36			

		SN 1	LM 1	VT 1 ◇ ⊠		LM 1	LM 1	VT 1 ◇ ⊠	VT 1 ◇ ⊠	LM 1	VT 1 ◇ ☕	LM 1	SN 1	LM 1	VT 1 ◇ ⊠	LM 1	VT 1 ◇ ☕	LM 1		LM 1	VT 1 ◇ ☕	LM 1	VT 1 ◇ ☕	VT 1 ◇ ☕	LM 1	SN 1
London Euston 15 ⊖	d		09 51	10 05		09 54	10 04	10 10	10 15	10 22	10 40	10 24		10 34	10 46	10 53	11 17	10 54		11 04	11 10	11 22	11 40	11 46	11 24	
Brighton 10	d																									09 55
Haywards Heath 3	d																									10 16
Gatwick Airport 10 ✈	d												09 37													10 37
East Croydon	d												09 52													10 52
Clapham Junction 10	d	09 27											10 03													11 03
Imperial Wharf §	d																									
West Brompton ⊖	d	09 32											10 09													11 09
Kensington Olympia ⊖	d	09 35											10 12													11 12
Shepherds Bush §	d																									
Wembley Central	d	09 53																								
Harrow & Wealdstone ⊖	d	09 58					10 16						10 29	10 46						11 16						11 29
Bushey	d						10 21							10 51						11 21						
Watford Junction	a	10 05				10 10	10 24					10 40	10 45	10 54				11 10		11 24					11 40	11 45
	d					10 11	10 25	10u25	10u30			10 41		10 55	11u01			11 11		11 25	11u25				11 41	
Kings Langley	d						10 29							10 59						11 29						
Apsley	d						10 33							11 03						11 33						
Hemel Hempstead	a					10 18	10 36					10 48		11 06				11 18		11 36					11 48	
	d					10 18	10 36					10 48		11 06				11 18		11 36					11 48	
Berkhamsted	d					10 23	10 40					10 53		11 10				11 23		11 40					11 53	
Tring	d					10 30	10a48							11a18				11 30		11a48						
Cheddington	d					10 35												11 35								
Leighton Buzzard	d		10 20			10 40						11 06				11 22		11 40							12 06	
Bletchley	d		10 28			10 47						11 13				11 30		11 47							12 13	
Milton Keynes Central 10	a		10 33	10 35		10 53				10 59	11 10	11 19				11 35	11 47	11 53				12 01	12 10	12 16	12 19	
	d		10 33							10 59	11 10	11 19				11 35	11 48					12 02	12 10	12 17	12 19	
Wolverton	d		10 37									11 23				11 39									12 23	
Northampton	a		10 51							11 15		11 36				11 53						12 17			12 36	
Rugby	a														11 39									12 39		
	d																									
Nuneaton	a								11 19								12 22									
Coventry	a							11 13			11 44										12 13		12 44			
Birmingham International ✈	a							11 26			11 57										12 26		12 57			
Birmingham New Street 12	a							11 41			12 09										12 41		13 09			
Sandwell & Dudley	a										12 22												13 22			
Wolverhampton 7	a										12 36												13 36			

For general notes see front of timetable
For details of catering facilities see
Directory of Train Operators

§ This station may open during the currency of the Timetable

London → Watford Junction, Milton Keynes, Northampton and West Midlands

Network Diagram - See first page of Table 59

		LM	VT	LM	LM	LM	VT	VT	LM		VT	VT	LM	SN	LM	LM	LM	VT	LM	LM	VT	LM	VT		LM	SN
		1	1◇	1	1	1	1◇	1◇	1		1◇	1◇	1	1	1	1	1	1◇	1	1	1◇	1	1◇		1	1
			☕				☕	☕			☕	☕				🛒		☕			☕		☕			
London Euston 15 ⊖	d	11 34	12 05	11 53	11 54	12 04	12 10	12 17	12 22		12 40	12 46	12 24		12 34	12 49	12 53	13 17	12 54	13 04	13 10	13 22	13 40		13 24	
Brighton 10	d													10 55												11 55
Haywards Heath 3	d													11 16												12 16
Gatwick Airport 10 ✈	d													11 37												12 37
East Croydon 🚌	d													11 52												12 52
Clapham Junction 10	d													12 03												13 03
Imperial Wharf §	d																									
West Brompton ⊖	d													12 09												13 09
Kensington Olympia ⊖	d													12 12												13 12
Shepherds Bush §	d																									
Wembley Central	d																									
Harrow & Wealdstone ⊖	d	11 46				12 16								12 29	12 46					13 16						13 29
Bushey	d	11 51				12 21									12 51					13 21						
Watford Junction	a	11 54			12 10	12 24							12 40	12 45	12 54				13 10	13 24					13 40	13 45
	d	11 55			12 11	12 25	12u25	12u32					12 41		12 55				13 11	13 25	13u25				13 41	
Kings Langley	d	11 59				12 29									12 59					13 29						
Apsley	d	12 03				12 33									13 03					13 33						
Hemel Hempstead	a	12 06			12 18	12 36							12 48		13 06				13 18	13 36					13 48	
	d	12 06			12 18	12 36							12 48		13 06				13 18	13 36					13 48	
Berkhamsted	d	12 10			12 23	12 40							12 53		13 10				13 23	13 40					13 53	
Tring	d	12a18			12 30	12a48									13a18				13 30	13a48						
Cheddington	d				12 35														13 35							
Leighton Buzzard	d			12 24	12 40								13 06				13 22		13 40						14 06	
Bletchley	d			12 32	12 47								13 13				13 30		13 47						14 13	
Milton Keynes Central 10	a		12 35	12 37	12 53				13 00		13 10	13 16	13 19				13 35	13 47	13 53			14 01	14 10		14 19	
	d			12 37					13 00		13 10	13 17	13 19				13 35	13 48				14 02	14 10		14 19	
Wolverton	d			12 41									13 23				13 39								14 23	
Northampton	a			12 55					13 16				13 36				13 53					14 18			14 36	
Rugby	a											13 39				13 46										
	d															13 47										
Nuneaton	a							13 21								14 01		14 21								
Coventry	a						13 13				13 44										14 13		14 44			
Birmingham International ✈	a						13 26				13 57										14 27		14 57			
Birmingham New Street 12	a						13 41				14 09										14 41		15 09			
Sandwell & Dudley	a										14 22												15 22			
Wolverhampton 7 🚌	a										14 36												15 36			

		LM	VT	VT	LM	LM	LM	VT	VT	LM	VT	VT	LM	SN		LM	LM	VT	LM	LM	VT	LM	VT	LM	SN	LM
		1	1◇	1◇	1	1	1	1◇	1◇	1	1◇	1◇	1	1		1	1	1◇	1	1	1◇	1	1◇	1	1	1
			☕	☕				☕	☕		☕	☕						⊠			☕		☕			
London Euston 15 ⊖	d	13 34	13 46	14 05	13 53	13 54	14 04	14 10	14 17	14 22	14 40	14 46	14 24			14 34	14 53	15 17	14 54	15 04	15 10	15 26	15 40	15 24		15 34
Brighton 10	d													12 55											13 55	
Haywards Heath 3	d													13 16											14 16	
Gatwick Airport 10 ✈	d													13 37											14 37	
East Croydon 🚌	d													13 52											14 52	
Clapham Junction 10	d													14 03											15 03	
Imperial Wharf §	d																									
West Brompton ⊖	d													14 09											15 09	
Kensington Olympia ⊖	d													14 12											15 12	
Shepherds Bush §	d																									
Wembley Central	d																									
Harrow & Wealdstone ⊖	d	13 46					14 16							14 29		14 46				15 16					15 29	15 46
Bushey	d	13 51					14 21									14 51				15 21						15 51
Watford Junction	a	13 54				14 10	14 24						14 40	14 45		14 54			15 10	15 24				15 40	15 45	15 54
	d	13 55	14u01			14 11	14 25	14u25	14u32				14 41			14 55			15 11	15 25	15u25			15 41		15 55
Kings Langley	d	13 59					14 29									14 59				15 29						15 59
Apsley	d	14 03					14 33									15 03				15 33						16 03
Hemel Hempstead	a	14 06				14 18	14 36						14 48			15 06			15 18	15 36				15 48		16 06
	d	14 06				14 18	14 36						14 48			15 06			15 18	15 36				15 48		16 06
Berkhamsted	d	14 10				14 23	14 40						14 53			15 10			15 23	15 40				15 53		16 10
Tring	d	14a18				14 30	14a48									15a18			15 30	15a48						16a18
Cheddington	d					14 35													15 35							
Leighton Buzzard	d				14 24	14 40							15 06				15 22		15 40					16 06		
Bletchley	d				14 32	14 47							15 13				15 30		15 47					16 13		
Milton Keynes Central 10	a			14 35	14 37	14 53				15 01	15 10		15 19				15 35	15 47	15 53			16 03	16 10	16 19		
	d				14 37					15 02	15 10	15u17	15 19				15 35	15 48				16 03	16 10	16 19		
Wolverton	d				14 41								15 23				15 39							16 23		
Northampton	a				14 55					15 18			15 36				15 53					16 19		16 36		
Rugby	a		14 39									15 39														
	d																									
Nuneaton	a								15 21									16 21								
Coventry	a							15 13			15 44										16 13		16 44			
Birmingham International ✈	a							15 26			15 57										16 26		16 57			
Birmingham New Street 12	a							15 41			16 09										16 41		17 09			
Sandwell & Dudley	a										16 22												17 22			
Wolverhampton 7 🚌	a										16 36												17 36			

For general notes see front of timetable
For details of catering facilities see
Directory of Train Operators

§ This station may open during the currency of the Timetable

London → Watford Junction, Milton Keynes, Northampton and West Midlands

Network Diagram - See first page of Table 59

	VT	LM	LM	LM		VT	VT	LM	VT	LM	SN	LM	VT	LM	LM	LM	LM	VT		VT	LM	LM	SN	VT	VT
	■1◇ ☕	■1	■1	■1		■1◇ ☕	■1◇ ☕	■1	■1◇ ☕	■1	■1	■1	■1◇ ☕	■1	■1	■1	■1	■1◇ ☕		■1◇ A ⊠	■1	■1	■1	■1◇ ☕	■1◇ ⊠
London Euston 15 ⊖ d	15 49	15 53	15 54	16 04		16 10	16 17	16 22	16 40	16 24		16 34	16 51	16 54	16 55	17 04	17 09	17 10		17 21	17 23	17 24		17 30	17 45
Brighton 10 d											14 55												15 55		
Haywards Heath 3 d											15 16												16 16		
Gatwick Airport 10 ✈ d											15 37												16 37		
East Croydon 🚌 d											15 52												16 52		
Clapham Junction 10 d											16 03												17 03		
Imperial Wharf § d																									
West Brompton ⊖ d											16 09												17 09		
Kensington Olympia ⊖ d											16 12												17 12		
Shepherds Bush § d																									
Wembley Central d											16 26												17 26		
Harrow & Wealdstone ⊖ d				16 16							16 31	16 46				17 16						17 36	17 31		
Bushey d				16 21								16 51					17 25								
Watford Junction a			16 10	16 24						16 41	16 45	16 54		17 10		17 23	17 28					17 43	17 45		
d			16 11	16 25		16u25	16u32			16 42		16 55		17 11		17 23	17 28					17 43			
Kings Langley d				16 29								16 59					17 33								
Apsley d				16 33								17 03					17 36								
Hemel Hempstead a			16 18	16 36						16 49		17 06		17 18			17 39					17 51			
d			16 18	16 36						16 49		17 06		17 18			17 39					17 51			
Berkhamsted d			16 23	16 40						16 54		17 10		17 23			17 44					17 55			
Tring d			16 30	16a50						17 01		17a20		17a33		17 38	17a54								
Cheddington d			16 35							17 06						17 43									
Leighton Buzzard d		16 24	16 40					16 55		17 11					17 27	17 48					17 57				
Bletchley d		16 32	16 47					17 04		17 18						17 55						18 14			
Milton Keynes Central 10 a		16 37	16 53					17 09		17 25					17 38	18 02					18 08	18 20			
d		16 37						17 09	17u11						17 39						18 09	18 20			
Wolverton d		16 41						17 13							17 42						18 14				
Northampton a		16 55						17 27							17 57						18 28	18 36			
Rugby a	16 39												17 47							18 10					18 34
d													17 47							18 10					
Nuneaton a							17 21													18 24					
Coventry a						17 13			17 44				18 01					18 14						18 32	
Birmingham International ✈ a						17 26			17 56				18 12					18 26						18 44	
Birmingham New Street 12 a						17 41			18 09				18 29					18 39						18 57	
Sandwell & Dudley a									18 22									18 53						19 22	
Wolverhampton 7 🚌 a									18 36									19 06						19 36	

	VT	LM	LM	LM	LM	LM	VT	VT	VT		LM	LM	VT	LM	SN	LM	LM	LM	LM	VT	LM	VT	VT		LM
	■1◇ ☕	■1	■1	■1	■1	■1	■1◇ ⊠	R ■1 ⊠	■1◇ ☕		■1	■1	■1◇ ☕	■1	■1	■1	■1	■1	■1	■1◇ ☕	■1	■1◇ ☕	■1◇ ☕		■1
London Euston 15 ⊖ d	17 51	17 34	17 40	17 55	17 54	18 04	18 05	18 08	18 10		18 09	18 23	18 40	18 24		18 34	18 40	18 49	18 54	18 57	19 04	19 10	19 17		19 22
Brighton 10 d															16 55										
Haywards Heath 3 d															17 21										
Gatwick Airport 10 ✈ d															17 37										
East Croydon 🚌 d															17 52										
Clapham Junction 10 d															18 04										
Imperial Wharf § d																									
West Brompton ⊖ d															18 09										
Kensington Olympia ⊖ d															18 12										
Shepherds Bush § d																									
Wembley Central d															18 28										
Harrow & Wealdstone ⊖ d			17 52			18 16								18 37	18 33	18 47			19 06		19 16				
Bushey d			17 57								18 25						18 56				19 21				
Watford Junction a		17 50	18 00		18 10	18 23					18 28			18 44	18 45	18 54	18 59		19 13		19 24				
d		17 51	18 01		18 11	18 23			18u25		18 28			18 44		18 54	18 59		19 13		19 25	19u25	19u32		
Kings Langley d		17 55									18 33						19 04				19 29				
Apsley d		17 59									18 36						19 07				19 33				
Hemel Hempstead a		18 02			18 18						18 39			18 52			19 10		19 21		19 36				
d		18 02			18 18						18 39			18 52			19 10		19 21		19 36				
Berkhamsted d			18 11		18 23						18 44					19 03	19 15		19 25		19 40				
Tring d		18 11	18a21			18 38					18a54					19 11	19a25		19 32		19 47				
Cheddington d		18 16				18 43										19 17					19 52				
Leighton Buzzard d		18 21		18 28		18 48						18 58				19 25		19 21	19 40		20 00				19 55
Bletchley d		18 28			18 41	18 56								19 12		19a34			19 48		20a08				20 03
Milton Keynes Central 10 a		18 35		18 39	18 46	19 02						19 08		19 17				19 32	19 54						20 08
d	18u26			18 40	18 47							19 09	19u11	19 18				19 33							20 09
Wolverton d				18 45	18 50							19 13		19 21				19 36							20 12
Northampton a				18 59	19 04							19 28		19 35				19 51							20 27
Rugby a								18 56												19 47					
d																				19 47					
Nuneaton a							19 04																20 20		
Coventry a	18 58								19 14				19 44							20 00		20 13			
Birmingham International ✈ a	19 10								19 26				19 57							20 12		20 26			
Birmingham New Street 12 a	19 27								19 39				20 09							20 26		20 39			
Sandwell & Dudley a									19 59				20 22									20 52			
Wolverhampton 7 🚌 a									20 13				20 36									21 06			

For general notes see front of timetable
For details of catering facilities see Directory of Train Operators

§ This station may open during the currency of the Timetable

A To Holyhead (Table 81)

London → Watford Junction, Milton Keynes, Northampton and West Midlands

Network Diagram - See first page of Table 59

Station		VT	VT	LM	SN	LM	LM	VT	VT	LM	LM	VT	LM	VT		LM	SN	LM	VT	LM	LM	LM	VT	LM	SN	VT
		1 ◇	1 ◇	1	1	1	1	1 ◇	1 ◇	1	1	1 ◇	1	1 ◇		1	1	1	1 ◇	1	1	1	1 ◇	1	1	1 ◇
London Euston 15 ⊖	d	19 40	19 46	19 24		19 34	19 52	20 05	20 17	19 54	20 04	20 10	20 22	20 40		20 24		20 34	20 46	20 58	20 54	21 04	21 10	21 24		21 40
Brighton 10	d				17 55																					
Haywards Heath 3	d				18 22																					
Gatwick Airport 10 ✈	d				18 37												19 37								20 37	
East Croydon	d				18 52												19 52								20 52	
Clapham Junction 10	d				19 03												20 03								21 03	
Imperial Wharf §	d																									
West Brompton ⊖	d				19 08												20 09								21 09	
Kensington Olympia ⊖	d				19 11												20 12								21 12	
Shepherds Bush §	d																									
Wembley Central	d				19 26																					
Harrow & Wealdstone ⊖	d				19 31	19 46					20 16						20 30	20 46				21 16			21 29	
Bushey	d					19 51					20 21							20 51				21 21				
Watford Junction	a			19 42	19 45	19 54				20 12	20 24					20 40	20 45	20 54			21 10	21 24		21 42	21 45	
	d			19 43		19 55				20 12	20 25	20u25				20 41		20 55	21u01		21 11	21 25	21u25	21 43		21u54
Kings Langley	d					19 59					20 29							20 59				21 29				
Apsley	d					20 03					20 33							21 03				21 33				
Hemel Hempstead	a			19 50		20 06				20 20	20 36					20 48		21 06			21 18	21 36		21 50		
	d			19 50		20 06				20 20	20 36					20 48		21 06			21 18	21 36		21 50		
Berkhamsted	d			19 55		20 10				20 24	20 40					20 53		21 10			21 23	21 40		21 55		
Tring	d			20 02		20a18					20a48					21 00		21a18				21 47		→		
Cheddington	d			20 07												21 05										
Leighton Buzzard	d			20 12						20 38			20 50			21 10					21 37					
Bletchley	d			20 20						20 46			20 58			21 17				21 32	21 44	22a00				
Milton Keynes Central 10	a	20 11	20 18	20 25			20 31	20 35	20 47	20 52			21 03	21 10		21 23				21 37	21 50					22 14
	d	20 12	20 19				20 31		20 48				21 04	21 11						21 38	21 50					22 14
Wolverton	d						20 35						21 07							21 42	21 54					
Northampton	a						20 50						21 21							21 55	22 08					
Rugby	a		20 41																21 38							22 57
	d																									22 58
Nuneaton	a								21 21														22 15			
Coventry	a	20 44										21 13		21 44												23 10
Birmingham International ✈	a	20 57										21 26		21 57												23 27
Birmingham New Street 12	a	21 09										21 39		22 09												23 39
Sandwell & Dudley	a	21 22										21 59		22 22												23 51
Wolverhampton 7	a	21 36										22 13		22 36												00 05

Station		LM	LM	LM	LM		VT	LM	LM	LM	LM	SN	LM	VT FX	VT FO	LM	LM	LM	VT FO		LM	SN	VT FX	LM		
		1	1	1	1		1 ◇	1	1	1	1	1	1	1 ◇	1 ◇	1	1	1	1 ◇		1	1	1 ◇	1		
London Euston 15 ⊖	d	21 25		21 34	21 54		22 05		22 04		22 24		22 34	22 40	22 40			22 54	23 40		23 24		23 40	23 34		
Brighton 10	d																									
Haywards Heath 3	d																									
Gatwick Airport 10 ✈	d											21 37										22 37				
East Croydon	d											21 52										22 52				
Clapham Junction 10	d											22 03										23 03				
Imperial Wharf §	d																									
West Brompton ⊖	d											22 09										23 09				
Kensington Olympia ⊖	d											22 12										23 12				
Shepherds Bush §	d																									
Wembley Central	d																									
Harrow & Wealdstone ⊖	d			21 46					22 16			22 29	22 46									23 29		23 46		
Bushey	d			21 51					22 21				22 51											23 51		
Watford Junction	a			21 54	22 10				22 27		22 42	22 45	22 54					23 10			23 41	23 45		23 54		
	d			21 55	22 11		22u20				22 43		22 55	22u57	22u57			23 11			23 42			23 55		
Kings Langley	d			21 59									22 59											23 59		
Apsley	d			22 03									23 03											00 03		
Hemel Hempstead	a			22 06	22 18						22 50		23 06					23 18			23 49			00 06		
	d		←	22 06	22 18			←			22 50		23 06			←	←	23 18			23 49			00 06		
Berkhamsted	d		21 55	22 10	22 23			22 10		←	22 55		23 10			22 55	23 10	23 23			23 54			00 10		
Tring	d			→	22 28			22 15		22 28	→		→				23 15	23 28						00 15		
Cheddington	d				→			22 20									23 20							00 20		
Leighton Buzzard	d	22 01	22 06					22 25		22 36						23 06	23 25	23 36			00 05			00 25		
Bletchley	d	22 09	22 13					22 33		22 43						23 13	23 33	23 43			00 12			00 33		
Milton Keynes Central 10	a	22 15	22 22				22 39	22 43		22 54				23 23	23 24	23 24	23 43	23 54	00 16		00 20		00 23	00 43		
	d	22 15	22 22				22 40			22 54				23 24	23 24	23 24		23 54	00 18		00 20		00 24			
Wolverton	d	22 19	22 26							22 58						23 28		23 58			00 24					
Northampton	a	22 37	22 44							23 14				23s38	23s39	23 44		00 14	00s33		00 42		00s50			
Rugby	a						23 19							00s23	00s19				01s20				01s20			
	d						23 21																			
Nuneaton	a						23 32																			
Coventry	a													00s35	00s32				01s33				01s33			
Birmingham International ✈	a													00s47	00s47				01s46				01s46			
Birmingham New Street 12	a													01s01	01s01				01s57				01s58			
Sandwell & Dudley	a																									
Wolverhampton 7	a													01 34	01 32				02 31				02 32			

For general notes see front of timetable
For details of catering facilities see
Directory of Train Operators

§ This station may open during the currency of the Timetable

London → Watford Junction, Milton Keynes, Northampton and West Midlands

Network Diagram - See first page of Table 59

	VT	LM	LM	LM	LM	LM	LM	VT	VT	LM	VT	LM	SN	VT	LM	VT	VT		LM	VT	SN	VT	LM	LM	VT
	1◇ ☕	1	1	1	1	1	1	1◇ ☕	1◇ ☕	1	1◇ ☕	1	1	1◇ ☕	1	1◇ ☕	1◇ ☕		1	1◇ ☕	1	1◇ ☕	1	1	1◇ ☕
London Euston 15 ⊖ d	23p40	23p24	23p34	00 04	00 34	02 00		05 25	05 31	05 34	06 10	06 34		06 59		07 06	07 30		07 04	07 15		07 52	07 24	07 34	08 17
Brighton 10 d													05 21								05 56				
Haywards Heath 3 d													05 34								06 22				
Gatwick Airport 10 ✈ d													05 52								06 37				
East Croydon ⇌ d													06 10								06 53				
Clapham Junction 10 d													06 23								07 03				
Imperial Wharf § d																									
West Brompton ⊖ d													06 29								07 09				
Kensington Olympia ⊖ d													06 32								07 12				
Shepherds Bush § d																									
Wembley Central d					00 45	02 11																			
Harrow & Wealdstone ⊖ d			23p46	00 16	00 50	02 16				05 46		06 46	06 56						07 16		07 29			07 46	
Bushey d			23p51		00 55							06 51							07 21					07 51	
Watford Junction a		23p41	23p54	00 23	00 58	02 22				05 53		06 54	07 04						07 24		07 36		07 40	07 54	
d		23p42	23p55	00 23	00 58	02 23		05u40		05 53	06u29	06 55		07u14		07u21			07 25	07u31			07 41	07 55	
Kings Langley d			23p59		01 03					05 58		06 59							07 29					07 59	
Apsley d			00 03		01 06					06 01		07 03							07 33					08 03	
Hemel Hempstead a		23p49	00 06	00 31	01 09	02 30				06 04		07 06							07 36				07 48	08 06	
d		23p49	00 06	00 31	01 09	02 30				06 04		07 06			←				07 36				07 48	08 06	
Berkhamsted d		23p54	00 10	00 35	01 14	02 35				06 09		07 10			07 10				07 40				07 53	08 10	
Tring d			00 15	00 40	01 19	02 40				06 14		→			07 17				07 47				08 00	08a18	
Cheddington d			00 20		01 24					06 19					07 22								08 05		
Leighton Buzzard d		00 05	00 25	00 48	01 29	02 48				06 24					07 27				07 55				08 10		
Bletchley d		00 12	00 33	00 56	01 36	02 55	05 25			06 31					07 35				08 03				08 17		
Milton Keynes Central 10 a	00 16	00 20	00 43	01 04	01 45	03 06	05 29	06 09	06 15	06 40	06 56			07 33	07 40	07 40	08 00		08 08			08 22	08 23		08 48
d	00 18	00 20		01 05	01 45		05 30		06 16	06 40	06 58			07 34	07 41	07 42	08 01		08 09						08 49 →
Wolverton d		00 24		01 08	01 49		05 33			06 44					07 44				08 12						
Northampton a	00s33	00 42		01 27	02 09		05 49			07 03					08 00				08 26						
Rugby a	01s20								07 09											08 10					
d																				08 12					
Nuneaton a																									
Coventry a	01s33										07 40			08 07		08 14	08 41			08 23					
Birmingham International ✈ a	01s46										07 55					08 27	08 55								
Birmingham New Street 12 a	01s57										08 11					08 39	09 11			08s50					
Sandwell & Dudley a											08 21						09 21								
Wolverhampton 7 ⇌ a	02 31										08 33					09 07	09 33								

	LM	VT	LM	VT	VT	SN	VT	LM	LM	VT	LM	LM		VT	VT	SN	VT	LM	LM	VT	VT	LM	VT	LM	VT
	1	1◇ ☕	1	1◇ ☕	1◇ ☕	1	1◇ ☕	1	1	1◇ ☕	1	1		1◇ ☕	1◇ ☕	1	1◇ ☕	1	1	1◇ ☕	1◇ ☕	1	1◇ ☕	1	1◇ ☕
London Euston 15 ⊖ d	07 54	08 03	08 04	08 10			08 30	08 24	08 34	09 03	08 54	09 04		09 10	09 17		09 38	09 24	09 34	09 53	10 17	09 54	10 03	10 04	10 10
Brighton 10 d						06 55										07 55									
Haywards Heath 3 d						07 16										08 16									
Gatwick Airport 10 ✈ d						07 37										08 37									
East Croydon ⇌ d						07 52										08 52									
Clapham Junction 10 d						08 03										09 03									
Imperial Wharf § d																									
West Brompton ⊖ d						08 09										09 09									
Kensington Olympia ⊖ d						08 12										09 12									
Shepherds Bush § d																									
Wembley Central d																									
Harrow & Wealdstone ⊖ d			08 16			08 29			08 46			09 16				09 29			09 46					10 16	
Bushey d			08 21						08 51			09 21							09 51					10 21	
Watford Junction a	08 10		08 24			08 37		08 40	08 54		09 10	09 24				09 36		09 40	09 54			10 10		10 24	
d	08 11	08u18	08 25	08u26				08 41	08 55		09 11	09 25		09u25	09u32			09 41	09 55			10 11	10u18	10 25	10u25
Kings Langley d			08 29						08 59			09 29							09 59					10 29	
Apsley d			08 33						09 03			09 33							10 03					10 33	
Hemel Hempstead a	08 18		08 36					08 48	09 06		09 18	09 36						09 48	10 06			10 18		10 36	
d	08 18		08 36					08 48	09 06		09 18	09 36						09 48	10 06			10 18		10 36	
Berkhamsted d	08 23		08 40					08 53	09 10		09 23	09 40						09 53	10 10			10 23		10 40	
Tring d			08a48					09 00	09a18			09a48						10 00	10a18					10a48	
Cheddington d								09 05										10 05							
Leighton Buzzard d	08 36							09 10			09 36							10 10				10 36			
Bletchley d	08 43							09 17			09 43							10 17				10 43			
Milton Keynes Central 10 a	08 49				←		09 00	09 23		09 33	09 49						10 08	10 23		10 23	10 47	10 49			
d	08 49				08 49		09 01	09 23		09 34	09 49						10 10	10 23			10 48	10 49			
Wolverton d	08 53							09 27			09 53							10 27				10 53			
Northampton a	09 07							09 43			10 07							10 43				11 07			
Rugby a		08 56			09 11					09 56					10 10						11 10		10 56		
d		08 57			09 13					09 58					10 12						→		10 57		
Nuneaton a																									
Coventry a		09 09		09 15	09 24		09 40			10 09				10 15	10 23		10 42						11 09		11 15
Birmingham International ✈ a		09 21		09 27	09 38		09 55			10 21				10 27	10 38		10 55						11 21		11 27
Birmingham New Street 12 a		09 36		09 39	09s50		10 11			10 36				10 39	10s50		11 11						11 36		11 39
Sandwell & Dudley a							10 21										11 21								
Wolverhampton 7 ⇌ a				10 07			10 33							11 07			11 33								12 07

For general notes see front of timetable
For details of catering facilities see Directory of Train Operators

§ This station may open during the currency of the Timetable

London → Watford Junction, Milton Keynes, Northampton and West Midlands

Network Diagram - See first page of Table 59

	SN 1	VT 1◇ ☕	LM 1	VT 1◇ ☕	LM 1	LM 1	VT 1◇ ☕		LM 1	LM 1	VT 1◇ ☕	VT 1◇ ☕	SN 1	LM 1	VT 1◇ ☕	LM 1	LM 1	VT 1◇ ☕	VT 1◇ ☕	LM 1	VT 1◇ ☕	LM 1	VT 1◇ ☕	VT 1◇ ☕	SN 1
London Euston 15 ⊖ d			10 20	10 38	10 24	10 34	11 03		10 54	11 04	11 10	11 17		11 20	11 38	11 24	11 34	11 53	12 17	11 54	12 03	12 04	12 10		
Brighton 10 d	08 55												09 55												10 55
Haywards Heath 3 d	09 16												10 16												11 16
Gatwick Airport 10 ✈ d	09 37												10 37												11 37
East Croydon 🚋 d	09 52												10 52												11 52
Clapham Junction 10 d	10 03												11 03												12 03
Imperial Wharf § d																									
West Brompton ⊖ d	10 09												11 09												12 09
Kensington Olympia ⊖ d	10 12												11 12												12 12
Shepherds Bush § d																									
Wembley Central d																									
Harrow & Wealdstone ⊖ d	10 29					10 46				11 16			11 29				11 46					12 16			12 29
Bushey d						10 51				11 21							11 51					12 21			
Watford Junction a	10 35				10 40	10 54			11 10	11 24			11 36			11 40	11 54			12 10		12 24			12 36
d					10 41	10 55			11 11	11 25	11u25	11u32				11 41	11 55			12 11	12u18	12 25	12u25		
Kings Langley d						10 59				11 29							11 59					12 29			
Apsley d						11 03				11 33							12 03					12 33			
Hemel Hempstead a					10 48	11 06			11 18	11 36						11 48	12 06			12 18		12 36			
d					10 48	11 06			11 18	11 36						11 48	12 06			12 18		12 36			
Berkhamsted d					10 53	11 10			11 23	11 40						11 53	12 10			12 23		12 40			
Tring d					11 00	11a18				11a48						12 00	12a18					12a48			
Cheddington d					11 05											12 05									
Leighton Buzzard d			10 51		11 10				11 36					11 51		12 10				12 36					
Bletchley d			10 58		11 17				11 43					11 58		12 17				12 43					
Milton Keynes Central 10 a			11 04	11 08	11 23		11 33		11 49					12 04	12 08	12 23		12 23	12 47	12 49				←	
d			11 04	11 09			11 34		11 49					12 04	12 09				12 48 →	12 49				12 48	
Wolverton d			11 08						11 53					12 08						12 53					
Northampton a		←	11 21						12 07					12 21						13 07					
Rugby a		11 10					11 56					12 10									12 56			13 10	
d		11 12					11 58					12 12									12 57			13 12	
Nuneaton a																									
Coventry a		11 23		11 40			12 09				12 15				12 42						13 09		13 15	13 23	
Birmingham International ✈ a		11 38		11 55			12 21				12 27	12 38			12 55						13 21		13 27	13 38	
Birmingham New Street 12 a		11s50		12 11			12 36				12 39	12s50			13 11						13 36		13 39	13s50	
Sandwell & Dudley a				12 21											13 21										
Wolverhampton 7 🚋 a				12 33							13 07				13 33								14 07		

	LM 1	VT 1◇ ☕		LM 1	LM 1	VT 1◇ ☕	LM 1	LM 1	VT 1◇ ☕	VT 1◇ ☕	SN 1	LM 1	VT 1◇ ☕	LM 1	LM 1	VT 1◇ ☕	VT 1◇ ☕	LM 1	VT 1◇ ☕	LM 1		VT 1◇ ☕	VT 1◇ ☕	SN 1	LM 1
London Euston 15 ⊖ d	12 20	12 38		12 24	12 34	13 03	12 54	13 04	13 10	13 17		13 20	13 38	13 24	13 34	13 53	14 17	13 54	14 03	14 04		14 10			14 20
Brighton 10 d											11 55													12 55	
Haywards Heath 3 d											12 16													13 16	
Gatwick Airport 10 ✈ d											12 37													13 37	
East Croydon 🚋 d											12 52													13 52	
Clapham Junction 10 d											13 03													14 03	
Imperial Wharf § d																									
West Brompton ⊖ d											13 09													14 09	
Kensington Olympia ⊖ d											13 12													14 12	
Shepherds Bush § d																									
Wembley Central d																									
Harrow & Wealdstone ⊖ d					12 46			13 16			13 29				13 46					14 16				14 29	
Bushey d					12 51			13 21							13 51					14 21					
Watford Junction a				12 40	12 54		13 10	13 24			13 37			13 40	13 54			14 10		14 24				14 37	
d				12 41	12 55		13 11	13 25	13u25	13u32				13 41	13 55			14 11	14u18	14 25		14u25			
Kings Langley d					12 59			13 29							13 59					14 29					
Apsley d					13 03			13 33							14 03					14 33					
Hemel Hempstead a				12 48	13 06		13 18	13 36						13 48	14 06			14 18		14 36					
d				12 48	13 06		13 18	13 36						13 48	14 06			14 18		14 36					
Berkhamsted d				12 53	13 10		13 23	13 40						13 53	14 10			14 23		14 40					
Tring d				13 00	13a18			13a48						14 00	14a18					14a48					
Cheddington d				13 05										14 05											
Leighton Buzzard d	12 51			13 10			13 36					13 51		14 10				14 36							14 51
Bletchley d	12 58			13 17			13 43					13 58		14 17				14 43							14 58
Milton Keynes Central 10 a	13 03	13 08		13 23		13 33	13 49					14 03	14 08	14 23		14 23	14 47	14 49					←		15 03
d	13 04	13 09				13 34	13 49					14 04	14 09				14 48 →	14 49					14 48		15 04
Wolverton d	13 08						13 53					14 08						14 53							15 08
Northampton a	13 20						14 07					14 20						15 07							15 20
Rugby a						13 56				14 10									14 56				15 10		
d						13 58				14 11									14 57				15 12		
Nuneaton a																									
Coventry a		13 40				14 09			14 15				14 41						15 09			15 15	15 23		
Birmingham International ✈ a		13 55				14 21			14 27	14 38			14 55						15 21			15 27	15 38		
Birmingham New Street 12 a		14 09				14 36			14 39	14s50			15 11						15 36			15 39	15s50		
Sandwell & Dudley a		14 21											15 21												
Wolverhampton 7 🚋 a		14 33							15 07				15 33									16 07			

For general notes see front of timetable
For details of catering facilities see
Directory of Train Operators

§ This station may open during the currency of the Timetable

London → Watford Junction, Milton Keynes, Northampton and West Midlands

Network Diagram - See first page of Table 59

		VT	LM	LM	VT	LM	LM	VT	VT	SN	LM	VT	LM	LM	VT	VT		LM	VT	LM	VT	VT	SN	LM	VT	LM
		1◇	1	1	1◇	1	1	1◇	1◇	1	1	1◇	1	1	1◇	1◇		1	1◇	1	1◇	1◇	1	1	1◇	1
		☕			☕			☕	☕			☕			☕	☕			☕		☕	☕			☕	
London Euston 15 ⊖	d	14 38	14 24	14 34	15 03	14 54	15 04	15 10	15 17		15 20	15 38	15 24	15 34	15 53	16 17		15 54	16 03	16 04	16 10			16 20	16 38	16 24
Brighton 10	d									13 55													14 55			
Haywards Heath 3	d									14 16													15 16			
Gatwick Airport 10 ✈	d									14 37													15 37			
East Croydon	d									14 52													15 52			
Clapham Junction 10	d									15 03													16 03			
Imperial Wharf §	d																									
West Brompton ⊖	d									15 09													16 09			
Kensington Olympia ⊖	d									15 12													16 12			
Shepherds Bush §	d																									
Wembley Central	d																									
Harrow & Wealdstone ⊖	d			14 46			15 16			15 29				15 46						16 16			16 29			
Bushey	d			14 51			15 21							15 51						16 21						
Watford Junction	a		14 40	14 54		15 10	15 24			15 37			15 40	15 54				16 10		16 24			16 37			16 40
	d		14 41	14 55		15 11	15 25	15u25	15u32				15 41	15 55				16 11	16u18	16 25	16u25					16 41
Kings Langley	d			14 59			15 29							15 59						16 29						
Apsley	d			15 03			15 33							16 03						16 33						
Hemel Hempstead	a		14 48	15 06		15 18	15 36						15 48	16 06				16 18		16 36						16 48
	d		14 48	15 06		15 18	15 36						15 48	16 06				16 18		16 36						16 48
Berkhamsted	d		14 53	15 10		15 23	15 40						15 53	16 10				16 23		16 40						16 53
Tring	d		15 00	15a18			15a48						16 00	16a18						16a48						17 00
Cheddington	d		15 05										16 05													17 05
Leighton Buzzard	d		15 10			15 36					15 51		16 10					16 36						16 51		17 10
Bletchley	d		15 17			15 43					15 58		16 17					16 43						16 58		17 17
Milton Keynes Central 10	a	15 08	15 23		15 33	15 49					16 03	16 08	16 23		16 23	16 47		16 49				←		17 03	17 08	17 23
	d	15 09			15 34	15 49					16 04	16 09				16 48 →		16 49				16 48		17 04	17 09	
Wolverton	d					15 53					16 08							16 53						17 08		
Northampton	a					16 07					16 20							17 07						17 20		
Rugby	a				15 56				16 10										16 56			17 10				
	d				15 58				16 12										16 57			17 12				
Nuneaton	a																									
Coventry	a	15 41			16 09			16 15				16 41							17 09		17 15	17 23			17 41	
Birmingham International ✈	a	15 55			16 21			16 27	16 38			16 55							17 21		17 27	17 38			17 55	
Birmingham New Street 12	a	16 11			16 36			16 39	16s50			17 11							17 36		17 39	17s50			18 11	
Sandwell & Dudley	a	16 21										17 21													18 21	
Wolverhampton 7	a	16 33						17 07				17 33									18 07				18 33	

		LM	VT	LM	LM	VT	VT	SN	LM	VT	LM		LM	VT	VT	LM	VT	LM	VT	SN	LM	VT	LM	LM	LM	LM
															R											
		1	1◇	1	1	1◇	1◇	1	1	1◇	1		1	1◇	1	1	1◇	1	1◇	1	1	1◇	1	1	1	1
			☕			☕	☕			☕				☕	☕		☕		☕			☕				
London Euston 15 ⊖	d	16 34	17 03	16 54	17 04	17 10	17 17		17 20	17 38	17 24		17 34	17 53	18 17	17 54	18 03	18 04	18 10		18 20	18 38	18 24	18 34	18 50	18 54
Brighton 10	d							15 55												16 55						
Haywards Heath 3	d							16 16												17 16						
Gatwick Airport 10 ✈	d							16 37												17 37						
East Croydon	d							16 52												17 52						
Clapham Junction 10	d							17 03												18 03						
Imperial Wharf §	d																									
West Brompton ⊖	d							17 09												18 09						
Kensington Olympia ⊖	d							17 12												18 12						
Shepherds Bush §	d																									
Wembley Central	d																									
Harrow & Wealdstone ⊖	d	16 46			17 16			17 29					17 46					18 16		18 29				18 46		
Bushey	d	16 51			17 21								17 51					18 21						18 51		
Watford Junction	a	16 54		17 10	17 24			17 36			17 40		17 54			18 10		18 24		18 37			18 40	18 54		19 10
	d	16 55		17 11	17 25	17u25	17u32				17 41		17 55			18 11	18u18	18 25	18u25				18 41	18 55		19 11
Kings Langley	d	16 59			17 29								17 59					18 29						18 59		
Apsley	d	17 03			17 33								18 03					18 33						19 03		
Hemel Hempstead	a	17 06		17 18	17 36						17 48		18 06			18 18		18 36					18 48	19 06		19 18
	d	17 06		17 18	17 36						17 48		18 06			18 18		18 36					18 48	19 06		19 18
Berkhamsted	d	17 10		17 23	17 40						17 53		18 10			18 23		18 40					18 53	19 10		19 23
Tring	d	17a18			17a48						18 00		18a18					18a48					19 00	19a18		→
Cheddington	d										18 05												19 05			
Leighton Buzzard	d			17 36					17 51		18 10					18 36					18 51		19 10		19 19	
Bletchley	d			17 43					17 58		18 17					18 43					18 58		19 17		19 26	
Milton Keynes Central 10	a		17 33	17 49					18 03	18 08	18 23			18 23	18 47	18 49					19 03	19 08	19 23		19 31	
	d		17 34	17 49					18 04	18 09					18 48	18 49					19 04	19 10			19 32	
Wolverton	d			17 53					18 08							18 53					19 08				19 36	
Northampton	a			18 06					18 20							19 07					19 20				19 48	
Rugby	a		17 56				18 10								19 10											
	d		17 58				18 12																			
Nuneaton	a																									
Coventry	a		18 09			18 15				18 41							19 09		19 15			19 41				
Birmingham International ✈	a		18 21			18 27	18 39			18 55									19 27			19 55				
Birmingham New Street 12	a		18 36			18 39	18s50			19 11									19 39			20 11				
Sandwell & Dudley	a									19 21												20 21				
Wolverhampton 7	a					19 07				19 33									20 07			20 33				

For general notes see front of timetable
For details of catering facilities see Directory of Train Operators

§ This station may open during the currency of the Timetable

London → Watford Junction, Milton Keynes, Northampton and West Midlands

Network Diagram - See first page of Table 59

		VT	VT	VT	LM	VT		LM	VT	SN	VT	VT	VT	LM	VT	VT	LM	LM	VT	LM	VT	LM	LM	VT		VT
		1 ◇	1 ◇	1 ◇	1	1 ◇		1	1 ◇	1	1 ◇	1 ◇	1 ◇	1	1 ◇	1 ◇	1	1	1 ◇	1	1 ◇	1	1	1 ◇		1 ◇
		A		A		B			B		A	B	A		B	A	C	D	B		A	D	C	A		B
		☕	☕	☕		☕			☕		☕	☕	☕		☕	☕			☕		☕			☕		☕
London Euston 15 ⊖	d	18 57	19 02	19 05	19 04	19 10			19 17		19 20	19 25	19 24	19 24	19 31	19 36	19 34	19 34	19 50	19 54	20 00	20 04	20 04	20 13		20 12
Brighton 10	d									17 55																
Haywards Heath 3	d									18 16																
Gatwick Airport 10 ✈	d									18 37																
East Croydon	d									18 52																
Clapham Junction 10	d									19 03																
Imperial Wharf §	d																									
West Brompton ⊖	d									19 09																
Kensington Olympia ⊖	d									19 12																
Shepherds Bush §	d																									
Wembley Central	d																									
Harrow & Wealdstone ⊖	d				19 16					19 29							19 46	19 46				20 16	20 16			
Bushey	d				19 21												19 51	19 51					20 21			
Watford Junction	a				19 24					19 37				19 40			19 56	19 56		20 10		20 23	20 24			
	d	19u11		19u19	19 25	19u25			19u32				19u38	19 41	19u46	19u50	19 57	19 57	20u05	20 11	20u14	20 23	20 25	20u29 →		20u31
Kings Langley	d				19 29												20 01	20 01				20 28	20 29			
Apsley	d				19 33												20 05	20 05				20 31	20 33			
Hemel Hempstead	a				19 36									19 48			20 08	20 08		20 18		20 34	20 36			
	d				19 36			←						19 48			20 08	20 08		20 18		20 34	20 36			
Berkhamsted	d				19 40			19 23						19 53			20 12	20 12		20 23		20 39	20 40			
Tring	d				19a48												20 17	20 17				20 44	20 45			
Cheddington	d																20 22	20 22				20 53	20 54			
Leighton Buzzard	d							19 36						20 06			20 29	20 29		20 38		20 58	20 59			
Bletchley	d							19 43						20 13			20 37	20a37		20 45		21a05	21 07			
Milton Keynes Central 10	a		19 33	19 39				19 49	19 51		19 54	20 03	20 12	20 22	20 27	20 36	20 45		20 49	20 54	21 00		21 15			21 17
	d		19 35	19 41				19 49	19 52				20 14	20 22	20 28	20 38			20 50	20 54	21 01					21 19
Wolverton	d							19 53						20 26						20 58						
Northampton	a							20 07						20 42						21 14						
Rugby	a			20 15					20 15							21 14			21 14		21 38					21 44
	d			20 17					20 17							21 16			21 16							
Nuneaton	a																									
Coventry	a	20 15	20 09	20 28		20 15			20 28				21 10		21 10	21 27			21 27							
Birmingham International ✈	a	20 27				20 27							21 25		21 25											
Birmingham New Street 12	a	20 39				20 39							21 39		21 39											
Sandwell & Dudley	a	20 56				20 56							21 59		21 59											
Wolverhampton 7	a	21 08				21 08							22 14		22 14											

		SN	VT	LM	VT	LM	LM	LM	LM	VT	VT	SN	VT	LM	VT	LM	LM	VT	SN	LM	LM	LM	LM	LM		
		1	1 ◇	1	1 ◇	1	1	1	1	1 ◇	1 ◇	1	1 ◇	1	1 ◇	1	1	1 ◇	1	1	1	1	1	1		
			A		B	D	C	D	C	A	B		A		A	D	C	B			D	C	D	C		
			☕		☕					☕	☕		☕		☕			☕								
London Euston 15 ⊖	d			20 24	20 30	20 48	21 00	21 04	21 04	21 13	21 30			21 34	21 50	21 54	21 54	22 13		22 34	23 04	23 04	23 45	23 45		
Brighton 10	d	18 55																								
Haywards Heath 3	d	19 16																								
Gatwick Airport 10 ✈	d	19 37										20 37							21 37							
East Croydon	d	19 52										20 52							21 52							
Clapham Junction 10	d	20 03										21 03							22 03							
Imperial Wharf §	d																									
West Brompton ⊖	d	20 09										21 09							22 09							
Kensington Olympia ⊖	d	20 12										21 12							22 12							
Shepherds Bush §	d																									
Wembley Central	d																									
Harrow & Wealdstone ⊖	d	20 29				21 00			21 16			21 29				22 06	22 06		22 29		23 16	23 16	23 57	23 57		
Bushey	d								21 21								22 11					23 21		00 02		
Watford Junction	a	20 37	←	20 40		21 07	21 16	21 20	21 24			21 46	←	21 50		22 13	22 14		22 46	22 50	23 23	23 24	00 04	00 05		
	d		20u29	20 41	20u48	21 07	21 17	21 21	21 25	21u29 →	21u45		21u29	21 51	22u04	22 13	22 15	22u30		22 51	23 25	23 25	00 04	00 06		
Kings Langley	d					21 12			21 29							22 18	22 19				23 29	23 29	00 09	00 10		
Apsley	d					21 15			21 33							22 21	22 23				23 33	23 33	00 12	00 14		
Hemel Hempstead	a			20 48		21 18	21 24	21 28	21 36					21 58		22 24	22 26			22 58	23 36	23 36	00 15	00 17		
	d			20 48		21 18	21 24	21 28	21 36					21 58		22 24	22 26			22 58	23 36	23 36	00 15	00 17		
Berkhamsted	d			20 53		21 23	21 29	21 33	21 40					22 03		22 29	22 30			23 03	23 40	23 40	00 20	00 21		
Tring	d					21 28			21 45							22 34	22 35				23 47	23 47	00 27	00 28		
Cheddington	d					21 37			21 50							22 39	22 40				23 52	23 52	00 32	00 33		
Leighton Buzzard	d			21 08		21 42	21 44		21 59					22 18		22 48	22 49			23 18	23 57	23 57	00 37	00 38		
Bletchley	d			21 16		21 49	21 51	21a56	22a10					22 25		22a55	22 57			23 25	00 05	00 05	00 44	00 46		
Milton Keynes Central 10	a		21 18	21 24	21 29	21 58	22 00				22 18		22 19	22 34	22 39		23 06	23 10		23 34	00 10	00 10	00 50	00 51		
	d		21 20	21 25	21 31	21 58	22 00				22 19		22 20	22 34	22 40			23 12		23 34	00 11	00 11	00 50	00 52		
Wolverton	d			21 28		22 02	22 04							22 38						23 38	00 14	00 14	00 54	00 55		
Northampton	a			21 45		22 18	22 20							22 54						23 54	00 28	00 28	01 07	01 09		
Rugby	a		21 55		21 55						22 44		22 54		23 17			23 35								
	d		21 56		21 56						22 46		22 55		23 18			23 36								
Nuneaton	a																									
Coventry	a		22 07		22 07						22 58		23 06		23 30			23 48								
Birmingham International ✈	a		22 25		22 25						23 18		23 18		23 42			23 59								
Birmingham New Street 12	a		22 39		22 39						23 33		23 33		23 54			00 12								
Sandwell & Dudley	a		22 56		22 56																					
Wolverhampton 7	a		23 11		23 11						23 58		23 58		00 19			00 39								

For general notes see front of timetable
For details of catering facilities see Directory of Train Operators

§ This station may open during the currency of the Timetable

A Until 22 March
B From 29 March
C 2 February to 22 March
D Until 26 January and from 29 March

London → Watford Junction, Milton Keynes Northampton and West Midlands

Sundays

until 27 January and from 30 March

Network Diagram - See first page of Table 59

		LM [1]	LM [1]	LM 🚌	LM 🚌	LM 🚌	LM 🚌		LM 🚌	LM 🚌	LM 🚌	LM 🚌	LM 🚌	LM 🚌		LM 🚌	LM 🚌	VT [1] ◇ ☕	LM [1]	SN [1]	LM [1]		SN [1]	VT [1] ◇ ☕	VT [1] ◇ ☕	VT [1] ◇ ☕
London Euston [15] ⊖	d	23p04	23p45			00 34				02 00				05 24		06 24	07 24	08 40	08 43		09 13			09 31	09 36	09 40
Brighton [10]	d																									
Haywards Heath [3]	d																									
Gatwick Airport [10] ✈	d																									
East Croydon 🚌	d																									
Clapham Junction [10]	d																			08 35			09 05			
Imperial Wharf §	d																									
West Brompton ⊖	d																			08 40			09 10			
Kensington Olympia ⊖	d																			08 43			09 13			
Shepherds Bush §	d																									
Wembley Central	d																									
Harrow & Wealdstone ⊖	d	23p16	23p57											05 59		06 59	07 59		08 55	09 06	09 25		09 32			
Bushey	d																									
Watford Junction	a	23p23	00 04			01 19				02 45				06 19		07 19	08 19		09 02	09 14	09 32		09 42			
	d	23p25	00 04	01 06	01 06	01 19			02 43	02 45				06 19		07 19		08u58	09 02		09 32			09u46	09u52	09u57
Kings Langley	d	23p29	00 09		01 21				02 58					06 34		07 34			09 07		09 37					
Apsley	d	23p33	00 12		01 31				03 08					06 44		07 44			09 10		09 40					
Hemel Hempstead	a	23p36	00 15		01 36		←		03 13		←			06 49		07 49			09 13		09 43					
	d	23p36	00 15		01 36		01 36		03 13		03 13			06 49		07 49			09 13		09 43					
Berkhamsted	d	23p40	00 20		→		01 46		→		03 23			06 59		07 59			09 18		09 48					
Tring	d	23p47	00 27				02 01				03 38			07 14		08 14			09 23							
Cheddington	d	23p52	00 32				02 21				03 58			07 34		08 34			09 28							
Leighton Buzzard	d	23p57	00 37	01 51		02 04	02 41			03 30	04 18			07 54		08 54			09 35		10 01					
Bletchley	d	00 05	00 44	02 16		02 29	03 06			03 55	04 43	06 55	07 55	08 19		09 19			09 42		10 08					
Milton Keynes Central [10]	a	00 10	00 50	02 31		02 44	03 21			04 10	04 58	07 10	08 10	08 34		09 34		09 45	09 51		10 17			10 29	10 35	10 41
	d	00 11	00 50									07 10	08 10					09 46	09 51		10 17			10 31	10 37	10 43
Wolverton	d	00 14	00 54									07 20	08 20						09 54		10 21					
Northampton	a	00 28	01 07									07 55	08 55						10 13		10 39					
Rugby	a																							10 56		11 07
	d																							10 57		11 08
Nuneaton	a																									
Coventry	a																	10 24						11 07	11 13	11 19
Birmingham International ✈	a																	10 35							11 25	
Birmingham New Street [12]	a																	10 45							11 39	
Sandwell & Dudley	a																	10 56							11 56	
Wolverhampton [7] 🚌	a																	11 08							12 08	

		LM [1]	VT [1] ◇ ☕	LM [1]	SN [1]		VT [1] ◇ ☕	VT [1] ◇ ☕	LM [1]	VT [1] ◇ ☕	LM [1]	SN [1]		VT [1] ◇ ☕	VT [1] ◇ ☕	VT [1] ◇ ☕	LM [1]	LM [1]	SN [1]		VT [1] ◇ ☕	VT [1] ◇ ☕	VT [1] ◇ ☕	LM [1]	VT [1] ◇ ☕	VT [1] ◇ ☕
London Euston [15] ⊖	d	09 43	10 10	10 13			10 31	10 36	10 43	11 10	11 13			11 31	11 36	11 40	11 43	12 13			12 31	12 36	12 40	12 43	13 06	13 10
Brighton [10]	d																									
Haywards Heath [3]	d																									
Gatwick Airport [10] ✈	d																									
East Croydon 🚌	d																									
Clapham Junction [10]	d				10 05							11 05							12 05							
Imperial Wharf §	d																									
West Brompton ⊖	d				10 10							11 10							12 10							
Kensington Olympia ⊖	d				10 13							11 13							12 13							
Shepherds Bush §	d																									
Wembley Central	d																									
Harrow & Wealdstone ⊖	d	09 55		10 25	10 35				10 55		11 25	11 32					11 55	12 25	12 32					12 55		
Bushey	d																									
Watford Junction	a	10 02		10 32	10 42				11 02		11 32	11 42					12 02	12 32	12 41					13 02		
	d	10 02	10u27	10 32				10u52	11 02		11 32			11u46	11u52	11u57	12 02	12 32				12u52		13 02		
Kings Langley	d			10 37							11 37							12 37								
Apsley	d			10 40							11 40							12 40								
Hemel Hempstead	a	10 10		10 43					11 10		11 43						12 10	12 43						13 10		
	d	10 10		10 43					11 10		11 43						12 10	12 43						13 10		
Berkhamsted	d	10 14		10 48					11 14		11 48						12 14	12 48						13 14		
Tring	d	10 19							11 19								12 19							13 19		
Cheddington	d	10 24							11 24								12 24							13 24		
Leighton Buzzard	d	10 31		11 01					11 31		12 01						12 31	13 01						13 31		
Bletchley	d	10 39		11 08					11 39		12 08						12 39	13 08						13 39		
Milton Keynes Central [10]	a	10 47	11 11	11 17			11 29	11 35	11 47	12 11	12 17				12 35	12 41	12 47	13 17			13 29	13 35	13 41	13 47	14 05	14 11
	d	10 48		11 17			11 31	11 37	11 48		12 17				12 37	12 43	12 48	13 17			13 31	13 37	13 43	13 48	14 07	
Wolverton	d	10 51		11 21					11 51		12 21						12 51	13 21						13 51		
Northampton	a	11 10		11 39					12 10		12 39						13 10	13 39						14 10		
Rugby	a						11 56							12 56		13 07					13 56		14 07			
	d						11 57							12 57							13 57		14 08			
Nuneaton	a																									
Coventry	a						12 07	12 13						13 07	13 13						14 07	14 13	14 19		14 41	
Birmingham International ✈	a							12 25							13 25							14 25			14 53	
Birmingham New Street [12]	a							12 39							13 39							14 39			15 09	
Sandwell & Dudley	a							12 56							13 56							14 56				
Wolverhampton [7] 🚌	a							13 08							14 08							15 08				

For general notes see front of timetable
For details of catering facilities see
Directory of Train Operators

§ This station may open during the currency of the Timetable

Table 66

Sundays

London → Watford Junction, Milton Keynes Northampton and West Midlands

until 27 January and from 30 March

Network Diagram - See first page of Table 59

	LM	SN	VT	LM	VT	VT	LM	VT	VT	LM	SN	VT	LM	VT	VT	VT	LM	SN	VT	LM	VT
	1	1	1 ◇	1	1 ◇	1 ◇	1	1 ◇	1 ◇	1	1	1 ◇	1	1 ◇	1 ◇	1 ◇	1	1	1 ◇	1	1 ◇
								A	B						A	B					
			☕		☕	☕		☕	☕			☕		☕	☕	☕			☕		☕
London Euston 15 ⊖ d	13 13		13 40	13 43	13 50	13 55		14 27	14 27	14 13		14 50	14 43	14 53	15 27	15 27	15 13		15 36	15 43	15 50
Brighton 10 d																					
Haywards Heath 3 d																					
Gatwick Airport 10 ✈ d																					
East Croydon 🚌 d																					
Clapham Junction 10 d		13 05									14 05							15 05			
Imperial Wharf § d																					
West Brompton ⊖ d		13 10									14 10							15 10			
Kensington Olympia ⊖ d		13 13									14 13							15 13			
Shepherds Bush § d																					
Wembley Central d																					
Harrow & Wealdstone ⊖ d	13 25	13 32		13 55						14 25	14 32		14 55				15 25	15 32		15 55	
Bushey d																					
Watford Junction a	13 32	13 42		14 02						14 32	14 42		15 02				15 32	15 42		16 02	
d	13 32		13u58	14 02	14u07	14u11				14 32			15 02	15u10			15 32			16 02	16u06
Kings Langley d	13 37									14 37							15 37				
Apsley d	13 40									14 40							15 40				
Hemel Hempstead a	13 43			14 10						14 43			15 10				15 43			16 10	
d	13 43			14 10						14 43			15 10				15 43			16 10	
Berkhamsted d	13 48			14 14			←			14 48			15 14				15 48			16 14	
Tring d				14 19 →			14 19						15 19							16 19 →	
Cheddington d							14 24						15 24								
Leighton Buzzard d	14 01						14 32			15 01			15 31				16 01				
Bletchley d	14 08						14 40			15 08			15 39				16 08				
Milton Keynes Central 10 a	14 17					14 42	14 47	15 10	15 10	15 17		15 34	15 47		16 10	16 10	16 17		16 21		
d	14 17					14 44	14 48	15 11	15 11	15 17		15 35	15 48		16 11	16 11	16 17				
Wolverton d	14 21						14 51			15 21			15 51				16 21				
Northampton a	14 39						15 10			15 39			16 10				16 39				
Rugby a			14 56			15 07						15 56									16 56
d			14 57									15 57									16 57
Nuneaton a																					
Coventry a			15 07		15 13			15 42	15 45			16 07		16 13	16 42	16 45					17 07
Birmingham International ✈ a					15 25			15 54	15 57					16 25	16 54	16 57					
Birmingham New Street 12 a					15 39			16 09	16 09					16 39	17 09	17 09					
Sandwell & Dudley a					15 59									16 56							
Wolverhampton 7 🚌 a					16 11									17 08							

	VT	VT	LM	VT	VT	LM	SN	VT	VT	LM	VT	VT	VT	LM	SN	VT	LM	VT	VT	VT	VT	VT
	1 ◇	1 ◇	1	1 ◇	1 ◇	1	1	1 ◇	1 ◇	1	1 ◇	1 ◇	1 ◇	1	1	1 ◇	1	1 ◇	1 ◇	1 ◇	1 ◇	1 ◇
				A	B							A	B								A	B
	☕	☕		☕	☕			☕	☕		☕	☕	☕			☕		☕	☕	☕	☕	☕
London Euston 15 ⊖ d	15 53	15 58		16 27	16 27	16 13		16 50	16 58	16 43	16 53	17 27	17 27	17 13		17 36	17 43	17 50	17 53	17 58	18 27	18 27
Brighton 10 d																						
Haywards Heath 3 d																						
Gatwick Airport 10 ✈ d																						
East Croydon 🚌 d																						
Clapham Junction 10 d							16 05								17 05							
Imperial Wharf § d																						
West Brompton ⊖ d							16 10								17 10							
Kensington Olympia ⊖ d							16 13								17 13							
Shepherds Bush § d																						
Wembley Central d																						
Harrow & Wealdstone ⊖ d						16 25	16 32			16 55				17 25	17 32		17 55					
Bushey d																						
Watford Junction a						16 32	16 41			17 02				17 32	17 41		18 02					
d	16u11	16u14				16 32				17 02	17u10			17 32			18 02	18u06	18u11	18u14		
Kings Langley d						16 37								17 37								
Apsley d						16 40								17 40								
Hemel Hempstead a						16 43				17 10				17 43			18 10					
d						16 43				17 10				17 43			18 10					
Berkhamsted d			←			16 48				17 14				17 48			18 14					
Tring d			16 19							17 19							18 19					
Cheddington d			16 24							17 24							18 24					
Leighton Buzzard d			16 31			17 01				17 31				18 01			18 31					
Bletchley d			16 39			17 08				17 39				18 08			18 39					
Milton Keynes Central 10 a		16 41	16 47	17 10	17 10	17 17		17 31	17 41	17 47		18 10	18 10	18 17		18 21	18 47				19 10	19 10
d		16 43	16 48	17 11	17 11	17 17		17 32	17 42	17 48		18 11	18 11	18 17			18 48				19 11	19 11
Wolverton d			16 51			17 21				17 51				18 21			18 51					
Northampton a			17 10			17 39				18 10				18 39			19 10					
Rugby a		17 07						17 56	18 07									18 56		19 07		
d								17 57	18 08									18 57				
Nuneaton a																						
Coventry a	17 13			17 42	17 45			18 07	18 19		18 13	18 42	18 45					19 07	19 13		19 42	19 45
Birmingham International ✈ a	17 25			17 54	17 57						18 25	18 54	18 57						19 25		19 54	19 57
Birmingham New Street 12 a	17 39			18 09	18 09						18 39	19 09	19 09						19 39		20 09	20 09
Sandwell & Dudley a	17 56										18 56								19 56			
Wolverhampton 7 🚌 a	18 08										19 08								20 08			

For general notes see front of timetable
For details of catering facilities see
Directory of Train Operators

§ This station may open during the currency of the Timetable

A Until 27 January
B From 30 March

Table 66

Sundays

London → Watford Junction, Milton Keynes Northampton and West Midlands

until 27 January and from 30 March

Network Diagram - See first page of Table 59

Station		LM 1	SN 1	VT 1◇	VT 1◇		LM 1	VT 1◇	VT 1◇	LM 1	SN 1	VT 1◇		LM 1	VT 1◇	VT 1◇	VT 1◇	LM 1	VT 1◇		LM 1	SN 1	VT 1◇	VT 1◇	VT 1◇	LM 1
London Euston 15 ⊖	d	18 13		18 50	18 58		18 43	18 53	19 27	19 13		19 36		19 43	19 50	19 53	19 58		20 10		20 13		20 31	20 36	20 40	20 43
Brighton 10	d																									
Haywards Heath 3	d																									
Gatwick Airport 10 ✈	d																									
East Croydon	d																									
Clapham Junction 10	d		18 05								19 05											20 05				
Imperial Wharf §	d																									
West Brompton ⊖	d		18 10								19 10											20 10				
Kensington Olympia ⊖	d		18 13								19 13											20 13				
Shepherds Bush §	d																									
Wembley Central	d																									
Harrow & Wealdstone ⊖	d	18 25	18 32				18 55			19 25	19 32			19 55							20 25	20 32				20 55
Bushey	d																									
Watford Junction	a	18 32	18 41				19 02			19 32	19 41			20 02							20 32	20 42				21 02
	d	18 32					19 02	19u10		19 32				20 02	20u06	20u11	20u14		20u27		20 32		20u46	20u53	20u58	21 02
Kings Langley	d	18 37								19 37											20 37					
Apsley	d	18 40								19 40											20 40					
Hemel Hempstead	a	18 43					19 10			19 43				20 10							20 43					21 10
	d	18 43					19 10			19 43				20 10							20 43					21 10
Berkhamsted	d	18 48					19 14			19 48				20 14				←			20 48					21 14
Tring	d						19 19							20 19 →				20 19								21 19
Cheddington	d						19 24											20 24								21 24
Leighton Buzzard	d	19 01					19 31			20 01								20 31			21 01					21 31
Bletchley	d	19 08					19 39			20 08								20 39			21 08					21 39
Milton Keynes Central 10	a	19 17		19 31	19 41		19 47		20 10	20 17		20 21			20 32		20 42	20 47			21 17		21 29	21 35	21 41	21 47
	d	19 17		19 32	19 43		19 48		20 11	20 17					20 34		20 43	20 48			21 17		21 31	21 37	21 43	21 48
Wolverton	d	19 21					19 51			20 21								20 51			21 21					21 51
Northampton	a	19 39					20 10			20 39								21 10			21 39					22 10
Rugby	a			19 56	20 07										20 56		21 07		21 40				21 56	22 01	22 06	
	d			19 57	20 08										20 57				21 41				21 57	22 02	22 07	
Nuneaton	a																									
Coventry	a			20 07	20 19			20 13	20 42						21 07	21 13							22 07	22 13	22 19	
Birmingham International ✈	a							20 25	20 54							21 25			22 02					22 26		
Birmingham New Street 12	a							20 39	21 09						21 32	21 39								22 39		
Sandwell & Dudley	a							20 56								21 56								22 51		
Wolverhampton 7	a							21 08							21 53	22 08								23 03		

Station		VT 1◇ A	VT 1◇ B		LM 1	SN 1	VT 1◇ B	VT 1◇ A	VT 1◇ A	VT 1◇ B		VT 1◇ B	LM 1	LM 1	SN 1	VT 1◇ A	VT 1◇ B		LM 1	LM 1	VT 1◇ A	VT 1◇ B	LM 1
London Euston 15 ⊖	d	21 10	21 10		21 13		21 36	21 36	21 40			21 40	21 43	22 13		22 39	22 40		22 43	23 13	23 40	23 40	23 43
Brighton 10	d																						
Haywards Heath 3	d																						
Gatwick Airport 10 ✈	d																						
East Croydon	d																						
Clapham Junction 10	d					21 05									22 05								
Imperial Wharf §	d																						
West Brompton ⊖	d					21 10									22 10								
Kensington Olympia ⊖	d					21 13									22 13								
Shepherds Bush §	d																						
Wembley Central	d																						
Harrow & Wealdstone ⊖	d				21 25	21 32							21 55	22 25	22 32				22 55	23 25			23 55
Bushey	d																						
Watford Junction	a				21 32	21 42				←			22 02	22 32	22 40				23 02	23 32			00 02
	d				21 32		21u52 →	21u52	21u57	21u52		21u57	22 02	22 32		22u54	22u57		23 02	23 32	23u56	23u57	00 02
Kings Langley	d				21 37									22 37						23 37			
Apsley	d				21 40									22 40						23 40			
Hemel Hempstead	a				21 43								22 10	22 43					23 10	23 43			00 10
	d				21 43								22 10	22 43					23 10	23 43			00 10
Berkhamsted	d				21 48								22 14	22 48					23 14	23 48			00 14
Tring	d												22 19						23 19				00 19
Cheddington	d												22 24						23 24				00 24
Leighton Buzzard	d				22 01								22 31	23 01					23 31	00 01			00 31
Bletchley	d				22 08								22 39	23 08					23 39	00 08			00 39
Milton Keynes Central 10	a	22 01	22 11		22 17			22 26	22 33	22 35		22 41	22 47	23 17		23 25	23 29		23 47	00 17	00 27	00 30	00 47
	d				22 17			22 28	22 34	22 37		22 43	22 48	23 17		23 26	23 30		23 48	00 17	00 28	00 32	00 48
Wolverton	d				22 21								22 51	23 21					23 51	00 21			00 51
Northampton	a				22 39								23 10	23 39					00 10	00 39			01 10
Rugby	a								23 13			23 13				00 04	23 51				01 01	00 56	
	d															00 05	23 53				01 02	00 57	
Nuneaton	a																						
Coventry	a							23 15		23 15						00 16	00 04				01 13	01 08	
Birmingham International ✈	a							23 27		23 27						00 28	00 16				01 25	01 20	
Birmingham New Street 12	a							23 40		23 40						00 41	00 28				01 38	01 33	
Sandwell & Dudley	a																						
Wolverhampton 7	a							00 05		00 05						01 06	00 53				02 00	01 55	

For general notes see front of timetable
For details of catering facilities see Directory of Train Operators

§ This station may open during the currency of the Timetable

A From 30 March
B Until 27 January

Table 66

Sundays

3 February to 23 March

London → Watford Junction, Milton Keynes Northampton and West Midlands

Network Diagram - See first page of Table 59

		LM	LM	LM	LM	LM	LM	LM	LM	LM	LM	LM	LM	LM	LM	LM	VT	LM	SN	LM	LM	SN	LM	VT	VT	VT
		1	1	🚌	🚌	🚌	🚌	🚌	🚌	🚌	🚌	🚌	🚌	🚌	🚌	🚌	1 ◇ ☕	1	1	🚌	1	1	🚌	1 ◇ ☕	1 ◇ ☕	1 ◇ ☕
London Euston 15 ⊖	d	23p04	23p45			00 34			02 00				05 24		06 24	07 24	08 40	08 43			09 13			09 31	09 36	09 40
Brighton 10	d																									
Haywards Heath 3	d																									
Gatwick Airport 10 ✈	d																									
East Croydon	d																									
Clapham Junction 10	d																		08 35			09 05				
Imperial Wharf §	d																									
West Brompton ⊖	d																		08 40			09 10				
Kensington Olympia ⊖	d																		08 43			09 13				
Shepherds Bush §	d																									
Wembley Central	d																									
Harrow & Wealdstone ⊖	d	23p16	23p57										05 59		06 59	07 59		08 55	09 06		09 25	09 32				
Bushey	d	23p21	00 02																							
Watford Junction	a	23p24	00 05			01 19			02 45				06 19		07 19	08 19		09 02	09 14		09 32	09 42				
	d	23p25	00 06	01 06	01 06	01 19		02 43	02 45				06 19		07 19		08u58	09 02			09 32			09u46	09u52	09u57
Kings Langley	d	23p29	00 10		01 21			02 58					06 34		07 34			09 07			09 37					
Apsley	d	23p33	00 14		01 31			03 08					06 44		07 44			09 10			09 40					
Hemel Hempstead	a	23p36	00 17		01 36		←	03 13		←			06 49		07 49			09 13			09 43					
	d	23p36	00 17		01 36 →		01 36	03 13 →		03 13			06 49		07 49			09 13			09 43					
Berkhamsted	d	23p40	00 21				01 46			03 23			06 59		07 59			09 18			09 48					
Tring	d	23p47	00 28				02 01			03 38			07 14		08 14			09 23								
Cheddington	d	23p52	00 33				02 21			03 58			07 34		08 34			09 28								
Leighton Buzzard	d	23p57	00 38	01 51		02 04	02 41		03 30	04 18			07 54		08 54			09 35			10 01					
Bletchley	d	00 05	00 46	02 16		02 29	03 06		03 55	04 43	06 55	07 55	08 19		09 19			09 42			10 08					
Milton Keynes Central 10	a	00 10	00 51	02 31		02 44	03 21		04 10	04 58	07 10	08 10	08 34		09 34		09 45	09 53			10 19			10 29	10 35	10 41
	d	00 11	00 52								07 10	08 10		08 44			09 46			10 01			10 27	10 31	10 37	10 43
Wolverton	d	00 14	00 55								07 20	08 20		08 54						10 11			10 37			
Northampton	a	00 28	01 09								07 55	08 55		09 29						10 46			11 12			
Rugby	a																							10 56		11 07
	d																							10 57		11 08
Nuneaton	a																									
Coventry	a																10 24							11 07	11 13	11 19
Birmingham International ✈	a																10 35								11 25	
Birmingham New Street 12	a																10 45								11 39	
Sandwell & Dudley	a																10 56								11 56	
Wolverhampton 7	a																11 08								12 08	

		LM	LM	VT	LM	SN	LM	VT	VT	LM	LM	VT	LM	SN	VT	LM	VT	VT	LM	LM	LM	SN	LM	VT	VT	VT
		1	🚌	1 ◇ ☕	1	1	🚌	1 ◇ ☕	1 ◇ ☕	1	🚌	1 ◇ ☕	1	1	1 ◇ ☕	🚌	1 ◇ ☕	1 ◇ ☕	1	🚌	1	1	🚌	1 ◇ ☕	1 ◇ ☕	1 ◇ ☕
London Euston 15 ⊖	d	09 43		10 10	10 13			10 31	10 36	10 43		11 10	11 13		11 31		11 36	11 40	11 43		12 13			12 31	12 36	12 40
Brighton 10	d																									
Haywards Heath 3	d																									
Gatwick Airport 10 ✈	d																									
East Croydon	d																									
Clapham Junction 10	d					10 05								11 05								12 05				
Imperial Wharf §	d																									
West Brompton ⊖	d					10 10								11 10								12 10				
Kensington Olympia ⊖	d					10 13								11 13								12 13				
Shepherds Bush §	d																									
Wembley Central	d																									
Harrow & Wealdstone ⊖	d	09 55			10 25	10 35				10 55			11 25	11 32					11 55		12 25	12 32				
Bushey	d																									
Watford Junction	a	10 02			10 32	10 42				11 02			11 32	11 42					12 02		12 32	12 41				
	d	10 02		10u27	10 32				10u52	11 02			11 32		11u46		11u52	11u57	12 02		12 32				12u52	
Kings Langley	d				10 37								11 37								12 37					
Apsley	d				10 40								11 40								12 40					
Hemel Hempstead	a	10 10			10 43					11 10			11 43						12 10		12 43					
	d	10 10			10 43					11 10			11 43						12 10		12 43					
Berkhamsted	d	10 14			10 48					11 14			11 48						12 14		12 48					
Tring	d	10 19								11 19									12 19							
Cheddington	d	10 24								11 24									12 24							
Leighton Buzzard	d	10 31			11 01					11 31			12 01						12 31		13 01					
Bletchley	d	10 39			11 08					11 39			12 08						12 39		13 08					
Milton Keynes Central 10	a	10 49		11 11	11 19			11 29	11 35	11 49		12 11	12 19				12 35	12 41	12 49		13 19			13 29	13 35	13 41
	d		10 57				11 27	11 31	11 37		11 57					12 27	12 37	12 43		12 57			13 27	13 31	13 37	13 43
Wolverton	d		11 07				11 37				12 07					12 37				13 07			13 37			
Northampton	a		11 42				12 12				12 42					13 12				13 42			14 12			
Rugby	a							11 56							12 56			13 07						13 56		14 07
	d							11 57							12 57									13 57		14 08
Nuneaton	a																									
Coventry	a							12 07	12 13						13 07		13 13							14 07	14 13	14 19
Birmingham International ✈	a								12 25								13 25								14 25	
Birmingham New Street 12	a								12 39								13 39								14 39	
Sandwell & Dudley	a								12 56								13 56								14 56	
Wolverhampton 7	a								13 08								14 08								15 08	

For general notes see front of timetable
For details of catering facilities see
Directory of Train Operators

§ This station may open during the currency of the Timetable

Table 66

Sundays

London → Watford Junction, Milton Keynes Northampton and West Midlands

3 February to 23 March

Network Diagram - See first page of Table 59

		LM 1	LM 🚌	VT 1 ◇ ☕		VT 1 ◇ ☕	LM 1	SN 1	VT 1 ◇ ☕	LM 1	VT 1 ◇ ☕	LM 🚌	VT 1 ◇ ☕	LM 1	LM 🚌	VT 1 ◇ ☕	LM 1	SN 1	LM 🚌	VT 1 ◇ ☕	LM 1	VT 1 ◇ ☕	LM 🚌	VT 1 ◇ ☕	LM 1	SN 1
London Euston 15 ⊖	d	12 43		13 06		13 10	13 13		13 40	13 43	13 50		13 55			14 27	14 13			14 50	14 43	14 53		15 27	15 13	
Brighton 10	d																									
Haywards Heath 3	d																									
Gatwick Airport 10 ✈	d																									
East Croydon	d																									
Clapham Junction 10	d							13 05										14 05								15 05
Imperial Wharf §	d																									
West Brompton ⊖	d							13 10										14 10								15 10
Kensington Olympia ⊖	d							13 13										14 13								15 13
Shepherds Bush §	d																									
Wembley Central	d																									
Harrow & Wealdstone ⊖	d	12 55					13 25	13 32		13 55							14 25	14 32			14 55				15 25	15 32
Bushey	d																									
Watford Junction	a	13 02					13 32	13 42		14 02							14 32	14 42			15 02				15 32	15 42
	d	13 02					13 32		13u58	14 02	14u07		14u11				14 32				15 02	15u10			15 32	
Kings Langley	d						13 37										14 37								15 37	
Apsley	d						13 40										14 40								15 40	
Hemel Hempstead	a	13 10					13 43			14 10							14 43				15 10				15 43	
	d	13 10					13 43			14 10							14 43				15 10				15 43	
Berkhamsted	d	13 14					13 48			14 14				←			14 48				15 14				15 48	
Tring	d	13 19								14 19 →				14 19							15 19					
Cheddington	d	13 24												14 24							15 24					
Leighton Buzzard	d	13 31					14 01							14 32			15 01				15 31				16 01	
Bletchley	d	13 39					14 08							14 40			15 08				15 39				16 08	
Milton Keynes Central 10	a	13 49		14 05		14 11	14 19						14 42	14 49		15 10	15 19			15 34	15 49			16 10	16 19	
	d		13 57	14 07								14 27	14 44		14 57	15 11			15 27	15 35			15 57	16 11		
Wolverton	d		14 07									14 37			15 07				15 37				16 07			
Northampton	a		14 42									15 12			15 42				16 12				16 42			
Rugby	a								14 56				15 07							15 56						
	d								14 57											15 57						
Nuneaton	a																									
Coventry	a			14 41					15 07		15 13					15 45				16 07		16 13		16 45		
Birmingham International ✈	a			14 53							15 25					15 57						16 25		16 57		
Birmingham New Street 12	a			15 09							15 39					16 09						16 39		17 09		
Sandwell & Dudley	a										15 59											16 56				
Wolverhampton 7	a										16 11											17 08				

		VT 1 ◇ ☕	LM 1	VT 1 ◇ ☕	VT 1 ◇ ☕	LM 🚌	VT 1 ◇ ☕	LM 1	LM 🚌	VT 1 ◇ ☕	LM 1	SN 1	LM 🚌	VT 1 ◇ ☕	VT 1 ◇ ☕	LM 1	VT 1 ◇ ☕	LM 🚌	VT 1 ◇ ☕	LM 1	SN 1	VT 1 ◇ ☕	LM 🚌	LM 1	VT 1 ◇ ☕	VT 1 ◇ ☕
London Euston 15 ⊖	d	15 36	15 43	15 50	15 53		15 58			16 27	16 13			16 50	16 58	16 43	16 53		17 27	17 13		17 36		17 43	17 50	17 53
Brighton 10	d																									
Haywards Heath 3	d																									
Gatwick Airport 10 ✈	d																									
East Croydon	d																									
Clapham Junction 10	d											16 05									17 05					
Imperial Wharf §	d																									
West Brompton ⊖	d											16 10									17 10					
Kensington Olympia ⊖	d											16 13									17 13					
Shepherds Bush §	d																									
Wembley Central	d																									
Harrow & Wealdstone ⊖	d		15 55								16 25	16 32				16 55				17 25	17 32			17 55		
Bushey	d																									
Watford Junction	a		16 02								16 32	16 41				17 02				17 32	17 41			18 02		
	d		16 02	16u06	16u11		16u14				16 32					17 02	17u10			17 32				18 02	18u06	18u11
Kings Langley	d										16 37									17 37						
Apsley	d										16 40									17 40						
Hemel Hempstead	a		16 10								16 43					17 10				17 43				18 10		
	d		16 10								16 43					17 10				17 43				18 10		
Berkhamsted	d		16 14					←			16 48					17 14				17 48				18 14		
Tring	d		16 19 →					16 19								17 19								18 19		
Cheddington	d							16 24								17 24								18 24		
Leighton Buzzard	d							16 31			17 01					17 31				18 01				18 31		
Bletchley	d							16 39			17 08					17 39				18 08				18 39		
Milton Keynes Central 10	a	16 21					16 41	16 49		17 10	17 19			17 31	17 41	17 49			18 10	18 19		18 21		18 49		
	d					16 27	16 43		16 57	17 11			17 27	17 32	17 42			17 57	18 11				18 27			
Wolverton	d					16 37			17 07				17 37					18 07					18 37			
Northampton	a					17 12			17 42				18 12					18 42					19 12			
Rugby	a			16 56			17 07							17 56	18 07										18 56	
	d			16 57										17 57	18 08										18 57	
Nuneaton	a																									
Coventry	a			17 07	17 13					17 45				18 07	18 19		18 13		18 45						19 07	19 13
Birmingham International ✈	a				17 25					17 57							18 25		18 57							19 25
Birmingham New Street 12	a				17 39					18 09							18 39		19 09							19 39
Sandwell & Dudley	a				17 56												18 56									19 56
Wolverhampton 7	a				18 08												19 08									20 08

For general notes see front of timetable
For details of catering facilities see
Directory of Train Operators

§ This station may open during the currency of the Timetable

Table 66

Sundays

3 February to 23 March

London → Watford Junction, Milton Keynes Northampton and West Midlands

Network Diagram - See first page of Table 59

	VT	LM	VT	LM	SN	LM	VT	VT	LM	VT	LM	VT	LM	SN	VT	LM	LM	VT	VT	VT	LM	VT	LM	LM	SN
	1 ◇ ☕	🚌	1 ◇ ☕	1	1	🚌	1 ◇ ☕	1 ◇ ☕	1	1 ◇ ☕	🚌	1 ◇ ☕	1	1	1 ◇ ☕	1	🚌	1 ◇ ☕	1 ◇ ☕	1 ◇ ☕	1	1 ◇ ☕	🚌	1	1
London Euston 15 ⊖ d	17 58		18 27	18 13			18 50	18 58	18 43	18 53		19 27	19 13		19 36	19 43		19 50	19 53	19 58		20 10		20 13	
Brighton 10 d																									
Haywards Heath 3 d																									
Gatwick Airport 10 ✈ d																									
East Croydon 🚊 d																									
Clapham Junction 10 d					18 05									19 05											20 05
Imperial Wharf § d																									
West Brompton ⊖ d					18 10									19 10											20 10
Kensington Olympia ⊖ d					18 13									19 13											20 13
Shepherds Bush § d																									
Wembley Central d																									
Harrow & Wealdstone ⊖ d				18 25	18 32				18 55				19 25	19 32		19 55								20 25	20 32
Bushey d																									
Watford Junction a				18 32	18 41				19 02				19 32	19 41		20 02								20 32	20 42
d	18u14			18 32					19 02	19u10			19 32			20 02		20u06	20u11	20u14		20u27		20 32	
Kings Langley d				18 37									19 37											20 37	
Apsley d				18 40									19 40											20 40	
Hemel Hempstead a				18 43					19 10				19 43			20 10								20 43	
d				18 43					19 10				19 43			20 10								20 43	
Berkhamsted d				18 48					19 14				19 48			20 14					←			20 48	
Tring d									19 19							20 19					20 19				
Cheddington d									19 24							→					20 24				
Leighton Buzzard d				19 01					19 31				20 01								20 31			21 01	
Bletchley d				19 08					19 39				20 08								20 39			21 08	
Milton Keynes Central 10 a			19 10	19 19			19 31	19 41	19 49			20 10	20 19		20 21			20 32		20 42	20 49			21 19	
d		18 57	19 11			19 27	19 32	19 43			19 57	20 11					20 27	20 34		20 43			20 57		
Wolverton d		19 07				19 37					20 07						20 37						21 07		
Northampton a		19 42				20 12					20 42						21 12						21 42		
Rugby a	19 07						19 56	20 07										20 56		21 07		21 40			
d							19 57	20 08										20 57				21 41			
Nuneaton a																									
Coventry a			19 45				20 07	20 19		20 13		20 42						21 07	21 13			22 02			
Birmingham International ✈ a			19 57							20 25		20 54							21 25						
Birmingham New Street 12 a			20 09							20 39		21 09						21 32	21 39						
Sandwell & Dudley a										20 56									21 56						
Wolverhampton 7 🚊 a										21 08								21 53	22 08						

	LM	VT	VT	VT	LM	LM	VT	LM	SN	LM	VT	VT	LM	LM	LM	SN	LM	VT	LM	LM	LM	VT	LM
	🚌	1 ◇ ☕	1 ◇ ☕	1 ◇ ☕	1	🚌	1 ◇ ☕	1	1	🚌	1 ◇ ☕	1 ◇ ☕	1	🚌	1	1	🚌	1 ◇ ☕	1	🚌	1	1 ◇ ☕	1
London Euston 15 ⊖ d		20 31	20 36	20 40	20 43		21 10	21 13			21 36	21 40	21 43		22 13			22 40	22 43		23 13	23 40	23 43
Brighton 10 d																							
Haywards Heath 3 d																							
Gatwick Airport 10 ✈ d																							
East Croydon 🚊 d																							
Clapham Junction 10 d									21 05							22 05							
Imperial Wharf § d																							
West Brompton ⊖ d									21 10							22 10							
Kensington Olympia ⊖ d									21 13							22 13							
Shepherds Bush § d																							
Wembley Central d																							
Harrow & Wealdstone ⊖ d					20 55			21 25	21 32				21 55		22 25	22 32			22 55		23 25		23 55
Bushey d																							
Watford Junction a					21 02			21 32	21 42				22 02		22 32	22 40			23 02		23 32		00 02
d		20u46	20u53	20u58	21 02			21 32			21u52	21u57	22 02		22 32			22u57	23 02		23 32	23u57	00 02
Kings Langley d								21 37							22 37						23 37		
Apsley d								21 40							22 40						23 40		
Hemel Hempstead a					21 10			21 43					22 10		22 43				23 10		23 43		00 10
d					21 10			21 43					22 10		22 43				23 10		23 43		00 10
Berkhamsted d					21 14			21 48					22 14		22 48				23 14		23 48		00 14
Tring d					21 19								22 19						23 19				00 19
Cheddington d					21 24								22 24						23 24				00 24
Leighton Buzzard d					21 31			22 01					22 31		23 01				23 31		00 01		00 31
Bletchley d					21 39			22 08					22 39		23 08				23 39		00 08		00 38
Milton Keynes Central 10 a		21 29	21 35	21 41	21 49		22 11	22 19			22 35	22 41	22 49		23 19			23 29	23 49		00 19	00 30	00 49
d	21 27	21 31	21 37	21 43		21 57				22 27	22 37	22 43		22 57			23 27	23 30		23 57		00 32	
Wolverton d	21 37					22 07				22 37				23 07			23 37			00 07			
Northampton a	22 12					22 42				23 12				23 42			00 12			00 42			
Rugby a		21 56	22 01	22 06								23 13						23 51				00 56	
d		21 57	22 02	22 07														23 53				00 57	
Nuneaton a																							
Coventry a		22 07	22 13	22 19							23 15							00 04				01 08	
Birmingham International ✈ a			22 26								23 27							00 16				01 20	
Birmingham New Street 12 a			22 39								23 40							00 28				01 33	
Sandwell & Dudley a			22 51																				
Wolverhampton 7 🚊 a			23 03								00 05							00 53				01 55	

For general notes see front of timetable
For details of catering facilities see Directory of Train Operators

§ This station may open during the currency of the Timetable

Table 66

Mondays to Fridays

West Midlands, Northampton, Milton Keynes and Watford Junction → London

Network Diagram - See first page of Table 59

Miles	Miles	Miles		LM	LM	LM	VT	LM	LM	VT	LM	LM	LM	LM	LM		LM	SN	LM	LM	LM	LM	LM	VT
				MO	MO	MX	MO	MO	MO	MX	MX	MO	MO											
				1	1	1	1 ◇	1	1	1	1	1	1	1	1		1	1	1	1	1	1	1	1 ◇
				A	B		C	A	B			A	B											
							☕																	⊠
0	—	—	Wolverhampton 7 d				22p35			22p39														05 05
7½	—	—	Sandwell & Dudley d				22p47																	05 15
12¾	—	—	**Birmingham New Street 12** d				23p00			23p00														05 30
21¼	—	—	Birmingham International d				23p10			23p10														05 40
32	—	—	Coventry d				23p21			23p20														05 50
—	—	—	Nuneaton d																					
43½	0	—	**Rugby** a				23p32			23p32														06 02
—	—	—	d				23p34			23p34														06 04
62¼	—	—	**Northampton** d	22p56		23p46		23p56							04 15		04 43			05 35		05 58		
75¼	30	—	Wolverton d	23p08		23p58		00 08							04 27		04 55			05 47		06 10		
—	—	—	**Milton Keynes Central 10** a	23p11		00 01	00 06	00 11		00s15					04 30		04 58			05 50		06 14		06 25
78¼	32¾	—	d	23p12	23p12	00 02	00 08	00 12	00 12					03 31	04 31		04 59		05 24	05 51		06 14	06 25	06 26
81¼	—	—	Bletchley d	23p17	23p17	00 09		00 17	00 17					03 36	04 36		05 04		05 29	05 56	06 01		06 30	
87¾	—	—	Leighton Buzzard d	23p23	23p23	00 17		00 23	00 23		←			03 42	04 42		05 10		05 35	06 02	06 07	06 23		
92	—	—	Cheddington d	23p28	23p28	00 22		00 28	00 28		00 22	←	←				05 19		05 41		06 13			
96¼	—	—	Tring d	23p37	23p37	→		00 37	00 37		00 27	00 37	00 37	03 54	04 54		05 24		05 47		06 19			
100	—	—	Berkhamsted d	23p42	23p42			→	→		00 32	00 42	00 42	03 59	04 59		05 29		05 52	06 15	06 24		06 49	
—	—	—	Hemel Hempstead a	23p46	23p46						00 36	00 46	00 46	04 03	05 03		05 33		05 56	06 20	06 28		→	
103½	—	—	d	23p46	23p46						00 36	00 46	00 46	04 03	05 03		05 33		05 57	06 20	06 28			
105	—	—	Apsley d	23p49	23p49							00 49	00 49				05 36		06 00		06 31			
107	—	—	Kings Langley d	23p53	23p53							00 53	00 53				05 40		06 04		06 35			
—	—	—	**Watford Junction** a	23p58	23p58		00s38			00s38	00 43	00 59	00 59	04 10	05 10		05 44		06 09	06 27	06 39	06 41		06s47
110½	65	—	d	23p59	23p59						00 44	01 00	01 00	04 11	05 11		05 45	06 05	06 09	06 27	06 40	06 42		
112	—	—	Bushey d																		06 43			
116½	71	—	Harrow & Wealdstone ⊖ d	00 05	00 05						00 50	01 06	01 06	04 17	05 22		05 51	06 11	06 16		06 48			
119¾	—	0	Wembley Central d								00 54			04 21										
—	—	4¼	Shepherds Bush § a																					
—	—	5½	Kensington Olympia ⊖ a															06 30						
—	—	7½	West Brompton ⊖ a															06 33						
—	—	8	Imperial Wharf § a																					
—	—	9	Clapham Junction 10 a															06 42						
—	—	16¾	East Croydon a																					
—	—	33	Gatwick Airport 10 a																					
—	—	44¼	Haywards Heath 3 a																					
—	—	57¼	**Brighton 10** a																					
128	82½	—	**London Euston 15** ⊖ a	00 24	00 24		00 57			01 02	01 09	01 24	01 24	04 38	05 38		06 08		06 29	06 46	07 04	07 00		07 09

	LM	LM	LM	SN	LM	VT		LM	VT	LM	SN	VT	VT	LM	VT	LM	LM	VT	LM		VT	LM	LM	LM
	1	1	1	1	1	1 ◇		1	1 ◇	1	1	1 ◇	1	1	1 ◇	1	1	1 ◇	1		1 ◇	1	1	1
						☕			⊠			⊠			⊠			⊠			⊠			
Wolverhampton 7 d									05 45						06 15									
Sandwell & Dudley d									05 55						06 25									
Birmingham New Street 12 d									06 10						06 40									
Birmingham International d									06 21						06 50									
Coventry d									06 32						07 00									
Nuneaton d												06 51						07 07						
Rugby a												07 04			07 13									
d						06 20						07 04			07 14						07 28			
Northampton d		06 27				06 41		06 49					07 12				07 06		07 21					
Wolverton d		06 39						07 01									07 18							
Milton Keynes Central 10 a		06 43				06 55		07 05	07 07								07 22		07 35					
d		06 43			06 48	06 56		07 06	07 08	←						07 15	07 22		07 36					07 42
Bletchley d			06 34		06 53			07 11		07 11						07 20	07 27					07 34		07 47
Leighton Buzzard d		06 53	06 40		06 59			→		07 19						07 27			07 47			07 42		07 53
Cheddington d			06 46													07 33								07 59
Tring d	←		06 52		07 10									07 24		07 39							07 55	08 05
Berkhamsted d	06 49		06 57		07 15									07 29			07 47						07 59	08 10
Hemel Hempstead a	06 53		07 01		07 19									07 33								07 58	08 04	
d	06 53		07 01		07 20									07 34								07 58	08 04	
Apsley d			07 04											07 37									08 07	
Kings Langley d			07 08											07 40									08 11	
Watford Junction a	07 00		07 13		07 27				07s28	07 36		07s44		07 45		07 51	07 57	07s57				08 05	08 15	08 20
d	07 01		07 13	07 18	07 27					07 37	07 40			07 46		07 52	07 57					08 06	08 16	08 21
Bushey d			07 16											07 49								08 09		
Harrow & Wealdstone ⊖ d	07 07		07 21	07 25	07 34						07 46					07 58						08 14		08 27
Wembley Central d				07 29							07 51													
Shepherds Bush § a											08 05													
Kensington Olympia ⊖ a				07 43							08 07													
West Brompton ⊖ a				07 45							08 10													
Imperial Wharf § a																								
Clapham Junction 10 a				07 52							08 16													
East Croydon a																								
Gatwick Airport 10 a																								
Haywards Heath 3 a																								
Brighton 10 a																								
London Euston 15 ⊖ a	07 23	07 28	07 37		07 50	07 36			07 50	07 55		08 04	08 00	08 08	08 09	08 14	08 17	08 19	08 21		08 27	08 30	08 36	08 43

For general notes see front of timetable
For details of catering facilities see Directory of Train Operators

§ This station may open during the currency of the Timetable

A Until 28 January and from 31 March
B 4 February to 24 March
C From 31 March

West Midlands, Northampton, Milton Keynes and Watford Junction → London

Network Diagram - See first page of Table 59

		LM	VT	VT	VT	LM	LM	VT	VT	VT	SN		LM	LM	LM	LM	SN	LM	VT	VT	LM	VT	LM	LM	VT
		1	1 ◇	1 ◇	1 ◇	1	1	1 ◇	1 ◇	1 ◇	1		1	1	1	1	1	1	1 ◇	1 ◇	1	1 ◇	1	1	1 ◇
																				A					
			⊠	⊠	⊠			⊠	⊠	⊠									⊠	⊠		⊠			⊠
Wolverhampton 7	d		06 35						07 05										07 35						08 05
Sandwell & Dudley	d		06 45						07 15										07 45						08 15
Birmingham New Street 12	d		07 00		07 15				07 30	07 45									08 00						08 30
Birmingham International	d		07 10		07 28				07 40	07 56									08 10						08 40
Coventry	d		07 20		07 38				07 56										08 24						08 50
Nuneaton	d							07 49														08 31			
Rugby	a																								
	d			07 46																08 51					
Northampton	d	07 31					07 47								08 10	08 24					08 42				
Wolverton	d	07 44					07 59									08 36					08 54				
Milton Keynes Central 10	a	07 48	07s56				08 02								08 24	08 39					08 57	09 04			09 25
	d	07 49					08 03							08 21	08 25	08 40					08 58	09 05		09 15	09 26
Bletchley	d					07 56	08 08								08 30						09 03			09 20	
Leighton Buzzard	d	07 58				08 03								08 30	08 36	08 49					09 09			09 26	
Cheddington	d														08 42									09 32	
Tring	d												08 26		08 48			08 57					09 27	09 38	
Berkhamsted	d												08 31	08 43				09 01			09 22		09 31	09 43	
Hemel Hempstead	a					08 18							08 35		08 55			09 06			09 27		09 36	09 47	
	d					08 19							08 36		08 56			09 06			09 27		09 36	09 47	
Apsley	d												08 39					09 09					09 39		
Kings Langley	d												08 42					09 12					09 42		
Watford Junction	a					08 26	08 33						08 47	08 53	09 03			09 17	09s20	09s28	09 34		09 47	09 54	
	d					08 26	08 34				08 42		08 47	08 54	09 03		09 11	09 17			09 34		09 47	09 55	
Bushey	d												08 50					09 20					09 50		
Harrow & Wealdstone ⊖	d					08 32					08 48			09 00	09 09		09 17	09 25					09 55		
Wembley Central	d										08 53						09 22								
Shepherds Bush §	a																								
Kensington Olympia ⊖	a										09 08						09 37								
West Brompton ⊖	a										09 11						09 40								
Imperial Wharf §	a																								
Clapham Junction 10	a										09 18						09 50								
East Croydon	a																10 07								
Gatwick Airport 10	a																10 22								
Haywards Heath 3	a																10 42								
Brighton 10	a																11 07								
London Euston 15 ⊖	a	08 34	08 39	08 40	08 43	08 48	08 57	08 58	09 01	09 07			09 10	09 16	09 25	09 25		09 41	09 44	09 53	09 55	09 45	10 11	10 14	10 03

		LM		VT	VT	VT	VT	SN	LM	LM	LM	VT	LM	LM	VT		LM	VT	SN	VT	LM	LM	LM	VT	LM
		1		1 ◇	1 ◇	1 ◇	1 ◇	1	1	1	1	1 ◇	1	1	1 ◇		1	1 ◇	1	1 ◇	1	1	1	1 ◇	1
				⊠	⊠	⊠	⊠					⊠			⊠			⊠		⊠				⊠	
Wolverhampton 7	d														09 05										
Sandwell & Dudley	d														09 15										
Birmingham New Street 12	d					09 00									09 30					10 00					
Birmingham International	d					09 10									09 40					10 10					
Coventry	d					09 20									09 50					10 20					
Nuneaton	d						09 26																	10 35	
Rugby	a																								
	d				09 25													10 25							
Northampton	d	09 11								09 33	09 45						10 09					10 33	10 43		
Wolverton	d	09 23								09 45							10 21					10 45			
Milton Keynes Central 10	a	09 27			09 46					09 48	09 59				10 22		10 25					10 48	10 57		
	d	09 27		09 31	09 47					09 49	10 00	10 12		10 15	10 23		10 25					10 49	10 57		
Bletchley	d	09 32								09 54				10 20			10 30					10 54			
Leighton Buzzard	d	09 40								10 00				10 26			10 38					11 00			
Cheddington	d													10 32											
Tring	d								09 56				10 26	10 38							10 56				11 26
Berkhamsted	d								10 00	10 13			10 30	10 43							11 00	11 13			11 30
Hemel Hempstead	a								10 05	10 18			10 35	10 47							11 05	11 18			11 35
	d								10 05	10 18			10 35	10 47							11 05	11 18			11 35
Apsley	d								10 08				10 38								11 08				11 38
Kings Langley	d								10 11				10 41								11 11				11 41
Watford Junction	a					10s10			10 16	10 25			10 46	10 54				11s02		11s13	11 16	11 25		11s25	11 46
	d							10 11	10 16	10 25			10 46	10 55					11 11		11 16	11 25			11 46
Bushey	d								10 19				10 49								11 19				11 49
Harrow & Wealdstone ⊖	d							10 17	10 24				10 54						11 17		11 24				11 54
Wembley Central	d																								
Shepherds Bush §	a																								
Kensington Olympia ⊖	a							10 37											11 37						
West Brompton ⊖	a							10 39											11 39						
Imperial Wharf §	a																								
Clapham Junction 10	a							10 50											11 50						
East Croydon	a							11 07											12 07						
Gatwick Airport 10	a							11 22											12 22						
Haywards Heath 3	a							11 42											12 42						
Brighton 10	a							12 07											13 07						
London Euston 15 ⊖	a	10 13		10 09	10 27	10 31	10 35		10 38	10 44	10 44	10 50	11 08	11 14	11 00		11 11	11 27		11 35	11 38	11 44	11 38	11 48	12 08

For general notes see front of timetable
For details of catering facilities see Directory of Train Operators

§ This station may open during the currency of the Timetable

A All Mondays, also Tuesdays to Fridays until 25 January and from 1 April

West Midlands, Northampton, Milton Keynes and Watford Junction → London

Network Diagram - See first page of Table 59

		LM	VT	LM	VT	VT		SN	VT	LM	LM	LM	VT	LM	LM	VT	LM	LM	VT		SN	VT	LM	VT	LM
		1	1 ◇ ⊠	1	1 ◇ ⊠	1 ◇ ⊠		1	1 ◇ ☕	1	1	1	1 ◇ ⊠	1	1	1 ◇ ☕	1	1 🚌	1 ◇ ⊠		1	1 ◇ ☕	1	1 ◇ ☕	1
Wolverhampton 7 🚌	d		10 05													11 05									
Sandwell & Dudley	d		10 15													11 15									
Birmingham New Street 12	d		10 30						11 00							11 30						12 00			
Birmingham International ✈	d		10 40						11 10							11 40						12 10			
Coventry	d		10 50						11 20							11 50						12 20			
Nuneaton	d												11 35					12 02						12 35	
Rugby	a																	12 16							
	d					11 25												12 17	12 25						
Northampton	d			11 09							11 33	11 43					12 09								12 33
Wolverton	d			11 21							11 45						12 21								12 45
Milton Keynes Central 10	a		11 22	11 25		11 45					11 48	11 57	12 09			12 22	12 25								12 48
	d	11 15	11 23	11 25	11 29	11 46					11 49	11 57	12 10		12 15	12 23	12 25								12 49
Bletchley	d	11 20		11 30							11 54				12 20		12 30								12 54
Leighton Buzzard	d	11 26		11 38							12 00				12 26		12 38								13 00
Cheddington	d	11 32													12 32										
Tring	d	11 38								11 56				12 26	12 38								12 56		
Berkhamsted	d	11 43								12 00	12 13			12 30	12 43								13 00		13 13
Hemel Hempstead	a	11 47								12 05	12 18			12 35	12 47								13 05		13 18
	d	11 47								12 05	12 18			12 35	12 47								13 05		13 18
Apsley	d									12 08				12 38									13 08		
Kings Langley	d									12 11				12 41									13 11		
Watford Junction	a	11 54							12s12	12 16	12 25			12 46	12 56				13s03			13s13	13 16	13s24	13 25
	d	11 55						12 11		12 16	12 25			12 46	12 57						13 11		13 16		13 25
Bushey	d									12 19				12 49									13 19		
Harrow & Wealdstone ⊖	d							12 17		12 24				12 54							13 17		13 24		
Wembley Central	d																								
Shepherds Bush §	a																								
Kensington Olympia ⊖	a							12 37													13 37				
West Brompton ⊖	a							12 39													13 39				
Imperial Wharf §	a																								
Clapham Junction 10	a							12 50													13 50				
East Croydon 🚌	a							13 07													14 07				
Gatwick Airport 10 ✈	a							13 22													14 22				
Haywards Heath 3	a							13 42													14 42				
Brighton 10	a							14 07													15 07				
London Euston 15 ⊖	a	12 14	12 00	12 11	12 07	12 26			12 33	12 38	12 44	12 38	12 48	13 08	13 14	13 00	13 12	13 18	13 27			13 34	13 38	13 47	13 44

		LM	LM	LM	VT	LM	SN	VT	LM	LM		LM	VT	VT	LM	LM	VT	LM	VT	SN	VT	LM	LM		LM
		1	1	1	1 ◇ ☕	1	1	1 ◇ ☕	1	1		1	1 ◇ ☕	1 ◇ ☕	1	1	1 ◇ ☕	1	1 ◇ ☕	1	1 ◇ ☕	1	1		1
Wolverhampton 7 🚌	d				12 05												13 05								
Sandwell & Dudley	d				12 15												13 15								
Birmingham New Street 12	d				12 30			13 00									13 30				14 00				
Birmingham International ✈	d				12 40			13 10									13 40				14 10				
Coventry	d				12 50			13 20									13 50				14 20				
Nuneaton	d													13 35											
Rugby	a																								
	d												13 40						14 25						
Northampton	d	12 43				13 09				13 33		13 43						14 09					14 33		14 43
Wolverton	d					13 21				13 45								14 22					14 45		
Milton Keynes Central 10	a	12 57			13 22	13 25				13 48		13 57	14 01	14 09			14 22	14 25					14 48		14 57
	d	12 57		13 15	13 23	13 25				13 49		13 57	14 02	14 10		14 15	14 23	14 26					14 49		14 57
Bletchley	d			13 20		13 30				13 54						14 20		14 31					14 54		
Leighton Buzzard	d			13 26		13 38				14 00						14 26		14 39					15 00		
Cheddington	d			13 32												14 32									
Tring	d		13 26	13 38					13 56						14 26	14 38						14 56			
Berkhamsted	d		13 30	13 43					14 00	14 13					14 30	14 43						15 00	15 13		
Hemel Hempstead	a		13 35	13 47					14 05	14 18					14 35	14 47						15 05	15 18		
	d		13 35	13 47					14 05	14 18					14 35	14 47						15 05	15 18		
Apsley	d		13 38						14 08						14 38							15 08			
Kings Langley	d		13 41						14 11						14 41							15 11			
Watford Junction	a		13 46	13 54				14s12	14 16	14 25					14 46	14 54			15s02		15s13	15 16	15 25		
	d		13 46	13 55			14 11		14 16	14 25					14 46	14 55				15 11		15 16	15 25		
Bushey	d		13 49						14 19						14 49							15 19			
Harrow & Wealdstone ⊖	d		13 54				14 17		14 24						14 54					15 17		15 24			
Wembley Central	d																								
Shepherds Bush §	a																								
Kensington Olympia ⊖	a						14 37													15 39					
West Brompton ⊖	a						14 39													15 41					
Imperial Wharf §	a																								
Clapham Junction 10	a						14 50													15 47					
East Croydon 🚌	a						15 07													16 07					
Gatwick Airport 10 ✈	a						15 22													16 22					
Haywards Heath 3	a						15 42													16 39					
Brighton 10	a						16 07													17 07					
London Euston 15 ⊖	a	13 39	14 08	14 14	14 00	14 11		14 33	14 38	14 44		14 43	14 40	14 49	15 08	15 14	15 00	15 11	15 26		15 34	15 38	15 46		15 38

For general notes see front of timetable
For details of catering facilities see
Directory of Train Operators

§ This station may open during the currency of the Timetable

West Midlands, Northampton, Milton Keynes and Watford Junction → London

Network Diagram - See first page of Table 59

		VT 1◇	LM 1	LM 1	VT 1◇	LM 1	VT 1◇	VT 1◇	VT 1◇	LM 1	LM 1	LM 1	VT 1◇		SN 1	LM 1	LM 1	VT 1◇	LM 1	VT 1◇	VT 1◇	LM 1	VT 1◇	LM 1	LM 1
Wolverhampton 7	d				14 05													15 05							
Sandwell & Dudley	d				14 15													15 15							
Birmingham New Street 12	d				14 30				15 00									15 30			16 00				
Birmingham International	d				14 40				15 10									15 40			16 10				
Coventry	d				14 50				15 20									15 50			16 20				
Nuneaton	d	14 35											15 35							15 40					
Rugby	a																			15 53					
	d							15 25												15 55			16 40		
Northampton	d					15 09					15 33	15 43							16 09	16 17				16 33	16 43
Wolverton	d					15 21					15 45								16 21					16 45	
Milton Keynes Central 10	a				15 22	15 25		15 46			15 48	15 57	16 09					16 22	16 25	16 35				16 48	16 57
	d			15 15	15 23	15 25	15 29	15 47			15 49	15 57	16 10				16 15	16 23	16 25	16 36				16 49	16 57
Bletchley	d			15 20		15 31					15 54						16 20		16 30					16 54	
Leighton Buzzard	d			15 26		15 38					16 00						16 26		16 38					17 00	
Cheddington	d			15 32													16 32								
Tring	d		15 26	15 38						15 56						16 26	16 38					16 56			
Berkhamsted	d		15 30	15 43						16 00	16 13					16 30	16 43					17 00		17 13	
Hemel Hempstead	a		15 35	15 47						16 05	16 18					16 35	16 47					17 05		17 18	
	d		15 35	15 47						16 05	16 18					16 35	16 47					17 05		17 18	
Apsley	d		15 38							16 08						16 38						17 08			
Kings Langley	d		15 41							16 11						16 41						17 11			
Watford Junction	a	15s25	15 46	15 54					16s12	16 16	16 25					16 46	16 54				17s12	17 16	17s17	17 25	
	d		15 46	15 55						16 16	16 25				16 29	16 46	16 55					17 16		17 25	
Bushey	d		15 49							16 19						16 49						17 19			
Harrow & Wealdstone ⊖	d		15 54							16 24					16 35	16 54						17 24			
Wembley Central	d														16 40										
Shepherds Bush §	a																								
Kensington Olympia ⊖	a														16 53										
West Brompton ⊖	a														16 56										
Imperial Wharf §	a																								
Clapham Junction 10	a														17 02										
East Croydon	a																								
Gatwick Airport 10	a																								
Haywards Heath 3	a																								
Brighton 10	a																								
London Euston 15 ⊖	a	15 48	16 08	16 14	16 00	16 13	16 07	16 27	16 34	16 38	16 44	16 38	16 48			17 08	17 15	17 00	17 11	17 22	17 33	17 38	17 40	17 44	17 40

		VT 1◇	SN 1	LM 1		LM 1	VT 1◇	VT 1◇	SN 1	VT 1◇	LM 1	VT 1◇	VT 1◇	LM 1	LM 1	VT 1◇	LM 1		LM 1	LM 1	VT 1◇	LM 1	VT 1◇	SN 1	VT 1◇
Wolverhampton 7	d						16 05														17 05				
Sandwell & Dudley	d						16 15														17 15				
Birmingham New Street 12	d						16 30			17 00											17 30				18 00
Birmingham International	d						16 40			17 10											17 40				18 10
Coventry	d						16 50			17 20											17 52				18 20
Nuneaton	d	16 35														17 35						18 00			
Rugby	a															17 49						18 14			
	d												17 24			17 50						18 14	18 25		
Northampton	d					17 03								17 33	17 43					18 09					
Wolverton	d					17 15								17 45						18 21					
Milton Keynes Central 10	a					17 18	17 22						17 46	17 48	17 57	18 11				18 24	18 25				
	d			17 04		17 19	17 23	17 29			17 37	17 41	17 47	17 49	17 58	18 12			18 15	18 25	18 26				
Bletchley	d			17 09		17 24					17 42			17 54					18 20	18 30					
Leighton Buzzard	d			17 15		17 30					17 48			18 00					18 26	18 37					
Cheddington	d			17 21							17 54								18 32						
Tring	d			17 27							18 00						18 26		18 38						
Berkhamsted	d			17 32		17 43					18 05			18 13			18 30		18 43						
Hemel Hempstead	a			17 36		17 48					18 09			18 18			18 36		18 47						
	d			17 36		17 48					18 09			18 18			18 36		18 47						
Apsley	d			17 39							18 12						18 39								
Kings Langley	d			17 43							18 16						18 42								
Watford Junction	a	17s25		17 47		17 55				18s13	18 21			18 26			18 47		18 55				19s02		19s12
	d		17 29	17 48		17 55			18 12		18 21			18 26			18 47		18 55					19 11	
Bushey	d			17 51							18 24						18 52								
Harrow & Wealdstone ⊖	d		17 35	17 56					18 18		18 29						18 57							19 18	
Wembley Central	d		17 40						18 23															19 23	
Shepherds Bush §	a																							19 37	
Kensington Olympia ⊖	a		17 55						18 38															19 39	
West Brompton ⊖	a		17 58						18 41															19 41	
Imperial Wharf §	a																								
Clapham Junction 10	a		18 04						18 48															19 48	
East Croydon	a		18 28						19 07															20 07	
Gatwick Airport 10	a								19 23															20 23	
Haywards Heath 3	a																								
Brighton 10	a																								
London Euston 15 ⊖	a	17 47		18 11		18 14	18 00	18 07		18 34	18 43	18 21	18 27	18 47	18 42	18 50	19 11		19 15	19 12	19 03	19 18	19 25		19 34

For general notes see front of timetable
For details of catering facilities see
Directory of Train Operators

§ This station may open during the currency of the Timetable

West Midlands, Northampton, Milton Keynes and Watford Junction → London

Network Diagram - See first page of Table 59

	LM 1	LM 1	LM 1	VT 1 ◇ ☕	LM 1	LM 1	VT 1 ◇ ☕		VT 1 ◇ ☕	VT 1 ◇ ☕	SN 1	LM 1	VT 1 ◇ ☕	LM 1	VT 1 ◇ ☕	LM 1	VT 1 ◇ ☕	VT 1 ◇ ☕	LM 1	LM 1		SN 1	LM 1	VT 1 ◇ ☕
Wolverhampton 7 🚌 d							18 05										19 05							
Sandwell & Dudley d							18 15										19 15							
Birmingham New Street 12 d							18 30						19 00				19 30							
Birmingham International ✈ d							18 40						19 11				19 40							
Coventry d							18 50						19 20				19 50							
Nuneaton d				18 36											19 35									
Rugby a																								
d										19 25														20 49
Northampton d		18 33	18 43			19 01								19 33		20 03								
Wolverton d		18 45				19 15								19 45		20 15								
Milton Keynes Central 10 a		18 48	18 57			19 18	19 22			19 46				19 48	20 09	20 18	20 22							
d		18 49	18 58		19 03	19 19	19 23		19 29	19 47				19 49	20 10	20 19	20 23	20 29						
Bletchley d		18 54			19 08	19 24								19 54		20 24				←				
Leighton Buzzard d		19 00			19 14	19 30								20 00		20 30 →				20 30				
Cheddington d					19 20									20 07										
Tring d	18 59				19 26							19 55		20 12					20 26				20 55	
Berkhamsted d	19 03	19 13			19 31	19 43						19 59		20 17					20 30	20 43			20 59	
Hemel Hempstead a	19 08	19 18			19 35	19 48						20 04		20 21					20 35	20 48			21 04	
d	19 08	19 18			19 35	19 48						20 04		20 21					20 35	20 48			21 04	
Apsley d	19 11				19 38							20 07							20 38				21 07	
Kings Langley d	19 14				19 42							20 10							20 41				21 10	
Watford Junction a	19 19	19 25		19s28	19 46	19 55						20 15	20s19	20 28			20s43		20 46	20 55			21 15	21s26
d	19 19	19 25			19 47	19 55					20 11	20 15		20 29					20 46	20 55		21 11	21 15	
Bushey d	19 22				19 50							20 18							20 49				21 18	
Harrow & Wealdstone ⊖ d	19 27				19 55						20 17	20 23							20 54			21 17	21 23	
Wembley Central d																								
Shepherds Bush § a											20 36													
Kensington Olympia ⊖ a											20 38											21 36		
West Brompton ⊖ a											20 41											21 39		
Imperial Wharf § a																								
Clapham Junction 10 a											20 48											21 47		
East Croydon 🚌 a											21 07											22 07		
Gatwick Airport 10 ✈ a											21 23											22 23		
Haywards Heath 3 a																								
Brighton 10 a																								
London Euston 15 ⊖ a	19 41	19 45	19 41	19 50	20 11	20 14	20 00		20 07	20 26		20 37	20 41	20 48	20 48		21 04	21 07	21 08	21 14			21 37	21 51

	LM 1	LM 1	VT 1 ◇ ☕	LM 1	LM 1	SN 1	LM 1	VT 1 ◇ ☕	LM 1	VT 1 ◇ ☕	LM 1		VT 1 ◇ ☕	VT 1 ◇ ☕	LM 1	SN 1	LM 1	VT 1 ◇ ☕	LM 1	LM 1	VT 1	LM 1		
Wolverhampton 7 🚌 d			20 05											21 05							22 39			
Sandwell & Dudley d			20 15											21 15										
Birmingham New Street 12 d			20 30											21 30							23 00			
Birmingham International ✈ d			20 40											21 40							23 10			
Coventry d			20 50											21 50							23 20			
Nuneaton d										21 29								22 34						
Rugby a										21 42								22 48			23 32			
d										21 44								22 49			23 34			
Northampton d	20 33	21 03							21 46						22 16		22 47			23 46				
Wolverton d	20 45	21 15							21 58						22 28		22 59			23 58				
Milton Keynes Central 10 a	20 48	21 18	21 22						22 01	22 05				22 24	22 31		23 02	23 10		00 01	00s15			
d	20 49	21 19	21 23				21 32	21 57	22 02	22 06			22 17	22 25	22 32		23 03	23 10		00 02				
Bletchley d	20 54	21 24			←		21 37		22 07						22 37		23 08			00 09				
Leighton Buzzard d	21 00	21 30 →			21 30		21 43		22 13						22 43		23 14			00 17		←		
Cheddington d	21 07								22 22		←						23 23		←	00 22 →		00 22		
Tring d	21 12			21 26			21 55		22 27 →		22 27						23 28 →		23 28			00 27		
Berkhamsted d	21 17			21 30	21 43		21 59				22 32				22 58				23 33			00 32		
Hemel Hempstead a	21 21			21 35	21 48		22 04				22 36				23 03				23 37			00 36		
d	21 21			21 35	21 48		22 04				22 36				23 03				23 37			00 36		
Apsley d				21 38			22 07				22 39								23 40					
Kings Langley d				21 41			22 10				22 43								23 44					
Watford Junction a	21 28		21s43	21 46	21 55		22 15			22s25	22 47			22s47	23 10			23s30	23 48		00s38	00 43		
d	21 29			21 46	21 55	22 12	22 15				22 48				23 10	23 18			23 49			00 44		
Bushey d				21 49							22 51								23 52					
Harrow & Wealdstone ⊖ d				21 54		22 18	22 21				22 56					23 24			23 57			00 50		
Wembley Central d																						00 54		
Shepherds Bush § a																								
Kensington Olympia ⊖ a						22 41										23 44								
West Brompton ⊖ a						22 43										23 47								
Imperial Wharf § a																								
Clapham Junction 10 a						22 51										23 54								
East Croydon 🚌 a																								
Gatwick Airport 10 ✈ a																								
Haywards Heath 3 a																								
Brighton 10 a																								
London Euston 15 ⊖ a	21 48		22 04	22 08	22 18		22 41	22 52		23 05	23 13		23 14	23 26	23 32			00 09	00 14		01 02	01 09		

For general notes see front of timetable
For details of catering facilities see Directory of Train Operators

§ This station may open during the currency of the Timetable

West Midlands, Northampton, Milton Keynes and Watford Junction → London

Network Diagram - See first page of Table 59

		LM 1	LM 1	LM 1	SN 1	LM 1	LM 1	LM 1	SN 1	LM 1	LM 1	VT 1◇	LM 1	LM 1	VT 1◇	SN 1		VT 1◇	LM 1	VT 1◇ ⊠	LM 1	LM 1	VT 1◇	VT 1◇	LM 1
Wolverhampton 7	d											05 37						06 35		06 05				07 05	
Sandwell & Dudley	d											05 47						06 48		06 15				07 16	
Birmingham New Street 12	d											06 00						07 00		06 30				07 30	
Birmingham International	d											06 10						07 10		06 41				07 41	
Coventry	d											06 21						07 22		06 55			07 47	07 54	
Nuneaton	d																								
Rugby	a											06 33						07 35							
	d											06 35			07 26			07 36							
Northampton	d	23p46				05 15		06 02			06 32			07 02							07 32	08 02			
Wolverton	d	23p58				05 29		06 14			06 44			07 14							07 44	08 14			
Milton Keynes Central 10	a	00 01				05 32		06 17			06 47	07 11		07 17						07 41	07 47	08 17	08 21	08 28	
	d	00 02	03 40	04 35		05 33		06 18		06 34	06 48	07 12		07 18					07 33	07 42	07 48	08 18	08 23	08 29	
Bletchley	d	00 09	03 45	04 40		05 38	06 05	06 23		06 39	06 53		07 09	07 23					07 38		07 53	08 23			
Leighton Buzzard	d	00 17	03 51	04 46		05 44	06 11	06 29		06 45	06 59		07 15	07 29					07 44		07 59	08 29			
Cheddington	d	00 22				05 53				06 54									07 51			→			
Tring	d	00 27	04 03	04 58		05 58	06 23			06 59			07 24						07 56						08 26
Berkhamsted	d	00 32	04 08	05 03		06 03	06 28	06 44		07 04	07 12		07 29	07 42					08 01		08 12				08 30
Hemel Hempstead	a	00 36	04 12	05 07		06 07	06 32	06 49		07 08	07 17		07 33	07 47					08 05		08 17				08 35
	d	00 36	04 12	05 07		06 07	06 32	06 49		07 08	07 17		07 33	07 47					08 05		08 17				08 35
Apsley	d					06 10	06 35			07 11			07 36						08 08						08 38
Kings Langley	d					06 14	06 39			07 15			07 40						08 12						08 41
Watford Junction	a	00 43	04 19	05 14		06 18	06 43	06 56		07 19	07 24	07s31	07 44	07 54	08s03			08s15	08 16		08 24		08s42		08 46
	d	00 44	04 20	05 15	06 11	06 19	06 44	06 56	07 13	07 20	07 25		07 45	07 54		08 11			08 17		08 24				08 46
Bushey	d					06 22	06 47			07 23			07 48						08 20						08 49
Harrow & Wealdstone	⊖ d	00 50	04 26	05 21	06 17	06 27	06 52		07 19	07 28			07 53			08 17			08 25						08 54
Wembley Central	d	00 54	04 35	05 30																					
Shepherds Bush §	a																								
Kensington Olympia	⊖ a				06 42				07 42							08 42									
West Brompton	⊖ a				06 45				07 45							08 45									
Imperial Wharf §	a																								
Clapham Junction 10	a				06 53				07 53							08 53									
East Croydon	a				07 07				08 07							09 07									
Gatwick Airport 10	✈ a				07 22				08 22							09 22									
Haywards Heath 3	a				07 42				08 42							09 42									
Brighton 10	a				08 08				09 09							10 07									
London Euston 15	⊖ a	01 09	04 47	05 42		06 44	07 11	07 18		07 42	07 51	07 52	08 11	08 14	08 28			08 36	08 39	08 18	08 43		09 04	09 06	09 11

		VT 1◇	LM 1	SN 1	LM 1	VT 1◇	LM 1	VT 1◇	LM 1	VT 1◇		LM 1	LM 1	VT 1◇	VT 1◇	VT 1◇	SN 1	VT 1◇	LM 1	LM 1	LM 1	LM 1	LM 1	VT 1◇	VT 1◇
Wolverhampton 7	d					07 35									08 11			08 35							09 11
Sandwell & Dudley	d					07 48												08 48							
Birmingham New Street 12	d					08 00									08 33			09 00						09 30	09 33
Birmingham International	d					08 10									08 43			09 10						09 40	09 45
Coventry	d					08 21		08 15		08 52					08 56	09 16		09 22						09 51	09 56
Nuneaton	d																								
Rugby	a							08 27								09 25		09 34							10 08
	d							08 28								09 29		09 36							10 10
Northampton	d								08 42				09 02								09 42		10 02		
Wolverton	d								08 54				09 14								09 54		10 14		
Milton Keynes Central 10	a							08 51	08 57				09 17		09 29						09 57		10 17	10 24	10 31
	d	08 33					08 45	08 52	08 58				09 18	09 19	09 31					09 45	09 58		10 18	10 25	10 33
Bletchley	d		←				08 50		09 03				09 23							09 50	10 03		10 23		
Leighton Buzzard	d		08 29				08 56		09 10				09 29							09 56	10 11		10 29		
Cheddington	d						09 03													10 03					
Tring	d				08 56		09 08					09 26							09 56	10 08		10 26			
Berkhamsted	d		08 42		09 00		09 13					09 30	09 42						10 00	10 13		10 30	10 42		
Hemel Hempstead	a		08 47		09 05		09 17					09 35	09 47						10 05	10 17		10 35	10 47		
	d		08 47		09 05		09 17					09 35	09 47						10 05	10 17		10 35	10 47		
Apsley	d				09 08							09 38							10 08			10 38			
Kings Langley	d				09 11							09 41							10 11			10 41			
Watford Junction	a	08s52	08 55		09 16	09s16	09 24			09s43		09 46	09 54			10s10		10s14	10 16	10 24		10 46	10 54		
	d		08 55	09 11	09 16		09 25					09 46	09 54				10 11		10 16	10 25		10 46	10 54		
Bushey	d				09 19							09 49							10 19			10 49			
Harrow & Wealdstone	⊖ d			09 17	09 24							09 54					10 17		10 24			10 54			
Wembley Central	d																								
Shepherds Bush §	a																								
Kensington Olympia	⊖ a			09 42													10 42								
West Brompton	⊖ a			09 45													10 45								
Imperial Wharf §	a																								
Clapham Junction 10	a			09 53													10 53								
East Croydon	a			10 07													11 07								
Gatwick Airport 10	✈ a			10 22													11 22								
Haywards Heath 3	a			10 42													11 42								
Brighton 10	a			11 07													12 07								
London Euston 15	⊖ a	09 15	09 15		09 37	09 38	09 44	09 29	09 47	10 05		10 11	10 14	09 56	10 07	10 32		10 36	10 37	10 44	10 46	11 11	11 15	11 02	11 09

For general notes see front of timetable
For details of catering facilities see
Directory of Train Operators

§ This staion may open during the currency of the Timetable

Table 66

Saturdays

West Midlands, Northampton, Milton Keynes and Watford Junction → London

Network Diagram - See first page of Table 59

	SN 1	VT 1 ◇	LM 1		LM 1	VT 1 ◇	LM 1	LM 1	VT 1 ◇	LM 1	VT 1 ◇	VT 1 ◇	SN 1	VT 1 ◇	LM 1	LM 1	LM 1	VT 1 ◇	LM 1		LM 1	VT 1 ◇	VT 1 ◇	SN 1
Wolverhampton 7 d		09 35							10 11					10 35									11 11	
Sandwell & Dudley d		09 48												10 48										
Birmingham New Street 12 d		10 00				09u50			10 33		10 30	10u50		11 00								11 30	11 33	
Birmingham International d		10 10				10 00			10 45		10 40	11 00		11 10								11 40	11 45	
Coventry d		10 21							10 56		10 51			11 21								11 51	11 56	
Nuneaton d																								
Rugby a		10 33							11 08					11 33									12 08	
d		10 35							11 10					11 35									12 10	
Northampton d							10 42			11 02							11 42				12 02			
Wolverton d							10 54			11 14							11 54				12 14			
Milton Keynes Central 10 a						10 49	10 57			11 17	11 25						11 57				12 17	12 25	12 31	
d					10 45	10 50	10 58			11 18	11 26					11 45	11 58	12 02			12 18	12 26	12 33	
Bletchley d					10 50		11 03			11 23						11 50	12 03				12 23			
Leighton Buzzard d					10 56		11 11			11 29						11 56	12 11				12 29			
Cheddington d					11 03											12 03								
Tring d			10 56		11 08			11 26							11 56	12 08			12 26					
Berkhamsted d			11 00		11 13			11 30		11 42					12 00	12 13			12 30		12 42			
Hemel Hempstead a			11 05		11 17			11 35		11 47					12 05	12 17			12 35		12 47			
d			11 05		11 17			11 35		11 47					12 05	12 17			12 35		12 47			
Apsley d			11 08					11 38							12 08				12 38					
Kings Langley d			11 11					11 41							12 11				12 41					
Watford Junction a		11s13	11 16		11 24			11 46	11s52	11 54		12s05		12s13	12 16	12 24			12 46		12 54			
d	11 11		11 16		11 25			11 46		11 54			12 11		12 16	12 25			12 46		12 54			13 11
Bushey d			11 19					11 49							12 19				12 49					
Harrow & Wealdstone ⊖ d	11 17		11 24					11 54					12 17		12 24				12 54					13 17
Wembley Central d																								
Shepherds Bush § a																								
Kensington Olympia ⊖ a	11 42												12 42											13 42
West Brompton ⊖ a	11 45												12 45											13 45
Imperial Wharf § a																								
Clapham Junction 10 a	11 53												12 52											13 53
East Croydon a	12 07												13 07											14 07
Gatwick Airport 10 ✈ a	12 22												13 22											14 22
Haywards Heath 3 a	12 42												13 42											14 42
Brighton 10 a	13 07												14 07											15 07
London Euston 15 ⊖ a		11 36	11 38		11 44	11 27	11 46	12 11	12 13	12 14	12 03	12 28		12 36	12 37	12 44	12 43	12 42	13 11		13 14	13 03	13 09	

	VT 1 ◇	LM 1	LM 1	VT 1 ◇	LM 1	LM 1	VT 1 ◇	LM 1	VT 1 ◇	VT 1 ◇	SN 1	VT 1 ◇	LM 1		LM 1	LM 1	VT 1 ◇	LM 1	LM 1	VT 1 ◇	VT 1 ◇	SN 1	VT 1 ◇	LM 1
Wolverhampton 7 d	11 35						12 11					12 35									13 11		13 35	
Sandwell & Dudley d	11 48											12 48											13 48	
Birmingham New Street 12 d	12 00			11u50			12 33		12 30	12u50		13 00								13 30	13 33		14 00	
Birmingham International d	12 10			12 00			12 46		12 40	13 00		13 10								13 40	13 45		14 10	
Coventry d	12 21						12 57		12 51			13 21								13 51	13 57		14 21	
Nuneaton d																								
Rugby a	12 34						13 09					13 33									14 09		14 33	
d	12 36						13 11					13 35									14 11		14 35	
Northampton d					12 42			13 02								13 42			14 02					
Wolverton d					12 54			13 14								13 54			14 14					
Milton Keynes Central 10 a				12 48	12 57			13 17	13 25							13 57			14 17	14 25	14 32			
d			12 45	12 49	12 58			13 18	13 26						13 45	13 58	14 02		14 18	14 26	14 34			
Bletchley d			12 50		13 03			13 23							13 50	14 03			14 23					
Leighton Buzzard d			12 56		13 11			13 29							13 56	14 11			14 29					
Cheddington d			13 03												14 03									
Tring d		12 56	13 08			13 26							13 56		14 08			14 26						14 56
Berkhamsted d		13 00	13 13			13 30		13 42					14 00		14 13			14 30	14 42					15 00
Hemel Hempstead a		13 05	13 17			13 35		13 47					14 05		14 17			14 35	14 47					15 05
d		13 05	13 17			13 35		13 47					14 05		14 17			14 35	14 47					15 05
Apsley d		13 08				13 38							14 08					14 38						15 08
Kings Langley d		13 11				13 41							14 11					14 41						15 11
Watford Junction a	13s14	13 16	13 24			13 46	13s51	13 54		14s04		14s13	14 16		14 24			14 46	14 54				15s13	15 16
d		13 16	13 25			13 46		13 54			14 11		14 16		14 25			14 46	14 54			15 11		15 16
Bushey d		13 19				13 49							14 19					14 49						15 19
Harrow & Wealdstone ⊖ d		13 24				13 54					14 17		14 24					14 54				15 17		15 24
Wembley Central d																								
Shepherds Bush § a																								
Kensington Olympia ⊖ a											14 42											15 42		
West Brompton ⊖ a											14 45											15 45		
Imperial Wharf § a																								
Clapham Junction 10 a											14 53											15 53		
East Croydon a											15 07											16 07		
Gatwick Airport 10 ✈ a											15 22											16 22		
Haywards Heath 3 a											15 42											16 42		
Brighton 10 a											16 07											17 07		
London Euston 15 ⊖ a	13 37	13 38	13 44	13 26	13 43	14 11	14 12	14 14	14 03	14 27		14 36	14 37		14 44	14 43	14 43	15 11	15 14	15 03	15 09		15 36	15 37

For general notes see front of timetable
For details of catering facilities see
Directory of Train Operators

§ This staion may open during the currency of the Timetable

Table 66

West Midlands, Northampton, Milton Keynes and Watford Junction → London

Network Diagram - See first page of Table 59

		LM 1	VT 1◇	LM 1	LM 1	VT 1◇	LM 1	VT 1◇		VT 1◇	SN 1	VT 1◇	LM 1	LM 1	LM 1	VT 1◇	LM 1	LM 1	VT 1◇	VT 1◇	SN 1	VT 1◇	LM 1	LM 1	VT 1◇
Wolverhampton 7	d					14 11						14 35								15 11		15 35			
Sandwell & Dudley	d											14 48										15 48			
Birmingham New Street 12	d		13u50			14 33		14 30		14u50		15 00							15 30	15 33		16 00			15u50
Birmingham International	d		14 00			14 46		14 40		15 00		15 10							15 40	15 46		16 10			16 00
Coventry	d					14 57		14 51				15 21							15 51	15 57		16 21			
Nuneaton	d																								
Rugby	a					15 09						15 33								16 09		16 33			
	d					15 11						15 35								16 11		16 35			
Northampton	d			14 42			15 02								15 42			16 02							
Wolverton	d			14 54			15 14								15 54			16 14							
Milton Keynes Central 10	a		14 49	14 57			15 17	15 25							15 57			16 17	16 25	16 32					16 49
	d	14 45	14 50	14 58			15 18	15 26						15 45	15 58	16 02		16 18	16 26	16 34				16 45	16 50
Bletchley	d	14 50		15 03			15 23							15 50	16 03			16 23						16 50	
Leighton Buzzard	d	14 56		15 11			15 29							15 56	16 11			16 29						16 56	
Cheddington	d	15 03												16 03										17 03	
Tring	d	15 08			15 26								15 56	16 08			16 26						16 56	17 08	
Berkhamsted	d	15 13			15 30		15 42						16 00	16 13			16 30	16 42					17 00	17 13	
Hemel Hempstead	a	15 17			15 35		15 47						16 05	16 17			16 35	16 47					17 05	17 17	
	d	15 17			15 35		15 47						16 05	16 17			16 35	16 47					17 05	17 17	
Apsley	d				15 38								16 08				16 38						17 08		
Kings Langley	d				15 41								16 11				16 41						17 11		
Watford Junction	a	15 24			15 46	15s49	15 54			16s06		16s16	16 16	16 24			16 46	16 54				17s13	17 16	17 24	
	d	15 25			15 46		15 54				16 11		16 16	16 25			16 46	16 54			17 11		17 16	17 25	
Bushey	d				15 49								16 19				16 49						17 19		
Harrow & Wealdstone	⊖ d				15 54						16 17		16 24				16 54				17 17		17 24		
Wembley Central	d																								
Shepherds Bush §	a																								
Kensington Olympia	⊖ a										16 42										17 42				
West Brompton	⊖ a										16 45										17 45				
Imperial Wharf §	a																								
Clapham Junction 10	a										16 53										17 53				
East Croydon	a										17 07										18 07				
Gatwick Airport 10	a										17 22										18 22				
Haywards Heath 3	a										17 42										18 42				
Brighton 10	a										18 07										19 07				
London Euston 15	⊖ a	15 44	15 27	15 43	16 11	16 10	16 14	16 05		16 29		16 37	16 37	16 44	16 45	16 42	17 11	17 14	17 05	17 10		17 36	17 37	17 44	17 27

		LM 1		VT 1◇	LM 1	VT 1◇	LM 1	VT 1◇	SN 1	VT 1◇	LM 1	LM 1	LM 1	VT 1◇	LM 1	LM 1	VT 1◇	VT 1◇		SN 1	LM 1	VT 1◇	LM 1	VT 1◇	VT 1◇
Wolverhampton 7	d					16 11				16 35								17 11				17 35			
Sandwell & Dudley	d									16 48												17 48			
Birmingham New Street 12	d			16 30		16 33		16u50		17 00							17 30	17 33				18 00		17u50	18 30
Birmingham International	d			16 40		16 46		17 00		17 10							17 40	17 45				18 10		18 00	18 40
Coventry	d			16 51		16 57				17 21							17 51	17 57				18 21			18 51
Nuneaton	d																								
Rugby	a					17 09				17 33								18 09				18 33		18 28	
	d					17 11				17 35								18 11				18 35		18 30	
Northampton	d	16 42					17 02						17 42			18 02							18 32		
Wolverton	d	16 54					17 14						17 54			18 14							18 44		
Milton Keynes Central 10	a	16 57					17 17						17 57			18 17	18 24	18 32					18 47	18 52	
	d	16 58					17 18					17 45	17 58	18 02		18 18	18 25	18 34					18 48	18 54	
Bletchley	d	17 03					17 23					17 50	18 03			18 23							18 53		
Leighton Buzzard	d	17 11					17 29					17 56	18 11			18 29							18 59		
Cheddington	d											18 03											19 06		
Tring	d				17 26						17 56	18 08			18 26						18 56		19 11		
Berkhamsted	d				17 30		17 42				18 00	18 13			18 30	18 42					19 00		19 16		
Hemel Hempstead	a				17 35		17 47				18 05	18 17			18 35	18 47					19 05		19 20		
	d				17 35		17 47				18 05	18 17			18 35	18 47					19 05		19 20		
Apsley	d				17 38						18 08				18 38						19 08				
Kings Langley	d				17 41						18 11				18 41						19 11				
Watford Junction	a			17s41	17 46	17s49	17 54	18s06		18s14	18 16	18 24			18 46	18 54					19 16	19s16	19 27		19s41
	d				17 46		17 54		18 11		18 16	18 25			18 46	18 54				19 11	19 16		19 28		
Bushey	d				17 49						18 19				18 49						19 19				
Harrow & Wealdstone	⊖ d				17 54				18 17		18 24				18 54					19 17	19 24				
Wembley Central	d																								
Shepherds Bush §	a																								
Kensington Olympia	⊖ a								18 42											19 42					
West Brompton	⊖ a								18 45											19 45					
Imperial Wharf §	a																								
Clapham Junction 10	a								18 53											19 53					
East Croydon	a								19 07											20 07					
Gatwick Airport 10	a								19 22											20 22					
Haywards Heath 3	a								19 42											20 42					
Brighton 10	a								20 07											21 07					
London Euston 15	⊖ a	17 43		18 03	18 11	18 10	18 14	18 29		18 37	18 37	18 44	18 43	18 44	19 11	19 14	19 03	19 10			19 37	19 38	19 51	19 30	20 03

For general notes see front of timetable
For details of catering facilities see
Directory of Train Operators

§ This staion may open during the currency of the Timetable

Table 66

Saturdays

West Midlands, Northampton, Milton Keynes and Watford Junction → London

Network Diagram - See first page of Table 59

		LM	VT	LM	SN	LM	VT	LM	VT	LM	LM	VT		VT	VT	VT	SN	VT	LM	VT	VT	VT	LM	LM	VT
		1	1 ◇	1	1	1	1 ◇	1	1 ◇	1	1	1 ◇		1 ◇	1 ◇	1 ◇	1	1 ◇	1	1 ◇	1 ◇	1 ◇	1	1	1 ◇
										A	B			C	C	D		D		C	C	D	A	B	D
			☕				☕		☕			☕		☕	☕	☕		☕		☕	☕	☕			☕
Wolverhampton 7	d		18 11						18 35						19 11			19 11			19 35				19 35
Sandwell & Dudley	d								18 48												19 48				19 48
Birmingham New Street 12	d		18 33				18u50		19 00						19 33			19 33			20 00				20 00
Birmingham International	d		18 45				19 00		19 10						19 43			19 43			20 10				20 10
Coventry	d		18 57						19 21						19 54			19 54		20 15	20 21	20 15			20 21
Nuneaton	d																								
Rugby	a		19 09						19 33												20 33				20 33
	d		19 11						19 35					20 01		20 01					20 35				20 35
Northampton	d			19 02				19 32		19 47									20 32				20 50		
Wolverton	d			19 14				19 44											20 44						
Milton Keynes Central 10	a			19 17				19 47		20 01				20 26	20 32	20 35		20 40	20 48	20 53	20 59	21 01	21 05		21 11
	d			19 18				19 48		20 02	20 02	20 08		20 27	20 33	20 36		20 41	20 49	20 55	21 01	21 03	21 06	21 07	21 13
Bletchley	d			19 23				19 53		20 07	20 07								20 54				21 12	21 12	
Leighton Buzzard	d			19 29				19 59		20 13	20 13								21 00				21 19	21 19	
Cheddington	d									20 18	20 18												21 24	21 24	
Tring	d	19 26				19 53				20 27	20 27												21 33	21 33	
Berkhamsted	d	19 30		19 42		19 57		20 14		20 32	20 32								21 14				21 37	21 37	
Hemel Hempstead	a	19 35		19 47		20 02		20 19		20 36	20 36								21 19				21 42	21 42	
	d	19 35		19 47		20 02		20 19		20 36	20 36								21 19				21 42	21 42	
Apsley	d	19 38				20 05				20 39	20 39												21 45	21 45	
Kings Langley	d	19 41				20 08				20 43	20 43												21 48	21 48	
Watford Junction	a	19 46	19s49	19 54		20 17	20s22	20 30	20s35	20 51	20 51				21s06			21s18	21 30		21s44		21 57	21 57	22s02
	d	19 46		19 54	20 13	20 17		20 30		20 52	20 52						21 13		21 30				21 57	21 57	
Bushey	d	19 49				20 20				20 55	20 55												22 00	22 00	
Harrow & Wealdstone	⊖ d	19 54			20 19	20 25				21 00	21 00						21 19						22 05	22 05	
Wembley Central	d																								
Shepherds Bush §	a																								
Kensington Olympia	⊖ a				20 42												21 42								
West Brompton	⊖ a				20 45												21 45								
Imperial Wharf §	a																								
Clapham Junction 10	a				20 53												21 53								
East Croydon	a				21 07												22 07								
Gatwick Airport 10	a				21 22												22 23								
Haywards Heath 3	a																								
Brighton 10	a																								
London Euston 15	⊖ a	20 11	20 16	20 17		20 42	20 49	20 52	21 00	21 17	21 17	21 20		21 28	21 33	21 36		21 42	21 52	22 01	22 08	22 01	22 22	22 22	22 26

		VT	SN	VT	VT	VT		LM	LM	LM	VT	VT	VT	VT	SN	VT	VT	LM	VT	VT	LM	LM	LM
		1 ◇	1	1 ◇	1 ◇	1 ◇		1	1	1	1 ◇	1 ◇	1 ◇	1 ◇	1	1 ◇	1 ◇	1	1 ◇	1 ◇	1		
		C		C	D	D			A	B	C	C	D	C		D	D		C	D			
		☕		☕	☕	☕					☕	☕	☕	☕		☕	☕		☕	☕		🚌	🚌
Wolverhampton 7	d			20 11		20 11						21 11				21 11			21 35	21 35			
Sandwell & Dudley	d																		21 47	21 47			
Birmingham New Street 12	d			20 33		20 33						21 33				21 33			22 00	22 00			
Birmingham International	d			20 43		20 43						21 43				21 43			22 10	22 10			
Coventry	d			20 54		20 54						21 54				21 54			22 21	22 21			
Nuneaton	d																						
Rugby	a																		22 33	22 33			
	d	21 01			21 01						22 01		22 01	22 11			22 11		22 35	22 35			
Northampton	d							21 32	21 47									22 42			23 35		
Wolverton	d							21 44										22 54			23 47		
Milton Keynes Central 10	a			21 29		21 39		21 47	22 03		22 25	22 31	22 35	22 38		22 41	22 47	22 57	23 02	23 08	23 50		
	d			21 31		21 40		21 48	22 04	22 04	22 27	22 33	22 36	22 39		22 42	22 48	22 58	23 04	23 10	23 51	23 58	23 58
Bletchley	d							21 53	22 09	22 09								23 03			23a55	00 13	00 13
Leighton Buzzard	d							21 59	22 15	22 15								23 09				00 38	00 38
Cheddington	d								22 20	22 20								23 18					00 58
Tring	d								22 29	22 29								23 23					01 18
Berkhamsted	d							22 14	22 34	22 34								23 28					01 33
Hemel Hempstead	a							22 19	22 38	22 38								23 32					01 43
	d							22 19	22 38	22 38								23 32					01 43
Apsley	d								22 41	22 41								23 39					
Kings Langley	d								22 45	22 45								23 43					
Watford Junction	a	22s06		22s16	22s16	22s22		22 30	22 53	22 53	23s00	23s05	23s10	23s11		23s19	23s25	23 47	23s52	23s52		01 23	02 08
	d		22 11					22 30	22 54	22 54					23 13			23 48				01 23	02 08
Bushey	d								22 57	22 57								23 51					
Harrow & Wealdstone	⊖ d		22 17						23 02	23 02					23 19			23 56					02 28
Wembley Central	d																						02 43
Shepherds Bush §	a																						
Kensington Olympia	⊖ a		22 42												23 42								
West Brompton	⊖ a		22 45												23 45								
Imperial Wharf §	a																						
Clapham Junction 10	a		22 52												23 53								
East Croydon	a																						
Gatwick Airport 10	a																						
Haywards Heath 3	a																						
Brighton 10	a																						
London Euston 15	⊖ a	22 34		22 39	22 42	22 46		22 52	23 19	23 19	23 26	23 30	23 36	23 34		23 43	23 49	00 13	00 16	00 16		02 08	03 13

For general notes see front of timetable
For details of catering facilities see Directory of Train Operators

§ This staion may open during the currency of the Timetable

A Until 26 January and from 29 March
B 2 February to 22 March
C From 29 March
D Until 22 March

Table 66

Sundays

West Midlands, Northampton, Milton Keynes and Watford Junction → London

until 27 January and from 30 March

Network Diagram - See first page of Table 59

		LM	LM	LM	LM	LM	LM	LM	LM	LM	LM	SN	LM	LM	SN	LM	VT	LM	SN	LM	VT	VT	LM	SN	LM
		🚌	🚌	🚌	🚌	🚌	🚌	🚌	🚌	🚌	🚌	1	1	1	1	1	1 ◇ ☕	1	1	1	1 ◇ ☕	1 ◇ ☕	1	1	1
Wolverhampton 7	d																08 37				09 35				
Sandwell & Dudley	d																08 47				09 47				
Birmingham New Street 12	d																09 00				10 00				
Birmingham International	d																09 10				10 10				
Coventry	d																09 21				10 21	10 29			
Nuneaton	d																								
Rugby	a																					10 41			
	d																					10 42			
Northampton	d									06 45	08 10					09 30		09 56		10 26			10 56		11 26
Wolverton	d									07 20	08 45					09 43		10 08		10 38			11 08		11 38
Milton Keynes Central 10	a									07 30	08 55					09 46	10 01	10 11		10 41	10 55	11 05	11 11		11 41
	d	23p58	23p58		05 00	06 00	06 40		07 20	07 30	08 55					09 47	10 02	10 12		10 42	10 57	11 07	11 12		11 42
Bletchley	d	00 13	00 13		05 15	06 15	06 55		07 35	07 45	09a10			09 30		09 52		10 17		10 47			11 17		11 47
Leighton Buzzard	d	00 38	00 38		05 40	06 40			08 00					09 36		09 58		10 23		10 53			11 23		11 53
Cheddington	d		00 58		06 00	07 00			08 20					09 41				10 28					11 28		
Tring	d		01 18	05 20	06 20	07 20		←	08 40					09 50				10 37					11 37		
Berkhamsted	d		01 33	05 35	06 35	07 35 →		07 35	08 55					09 55		10 13		10 42		11 08			11 42		12 08
Hemel Hempstead	a		01 43	05 45	06 45			07 45	09 05					09 59		10 18		10 46		11 13			11 46		12 13
	d		01 43	05 45	06 45			07 45					09 27	09 59		10 18		10 46		11 13			11 46		12 13
Apsley	d			05 50	06 50			07 50					09 30			10 21				11 16					12 16
Kings Langley	d			06 00	07 00			08 00					09 33			10 24				11 19					12 19
Watford Junction	a	01 23	02 08	06 15	07 15		07 55	08 15		08 45			09 38	10 06		10 31	10s36	10 55		11 26	11s31		11 55		12 26
	d	01 23	02 08	06 15	07 15		07 55	08 15		08 45		09 22	09 38	10 07	10 22	10 31		10 56	11 22	11 26			11 56	12 22	12 26
Bushey	d																								
Harrow & Wealdstone ⊖	d		02 28	06 35	07 35		08 15	08 35		09 05		09 28	09 48	10 13	10 27	10 37		11 02	11 28	11 32			12 02	12 28	12 32
Wembley Central	d		02 43																						
Shepherds Bush §	a																								
Kensington Olympia ⊖	a											09 47			10 47				11 47					12 47	
West Brompton ⊖	a											09 49			10 49				11 49					12 49	
Imperial Wharf §	a																								
Clapham Junction 10	a											10 00			11 00				12 00					13 00	
East Croydon	a																								
Gatwick Airport 10	a																								
Haywards Heath 3	a																								
Brighton 10	a																								
London Euston 15 ⊖	a	02 08	03 13	07 10	08 10		08 50	09 10		09 40			10 08	10 33		10 55	10 56	11 20		11 50	11 51	12 00	12 20		12 50

		VT		VT	VT	LM	VT	VT	SN	LM	VT	VT	LM	VT	VT	SN	LM	VT	LM	VT	LM	VT	VT	SN	LM
		1 ◇ ☕		1 ◇ ☕	1 ◇ ☕	1	1 ◇ ☕	1 ◇ ☕	1	1	1 ◇ ☕	1 ◇ ☕	1	1 ◇ ☕	1 ◇ ☕	1	1	1 ◇ ☕	1	1 ◇ ☕	1	1 ◇ ☕	1 ◇ ☕	1	1
Wolverhampton 7	d			10 36				11 05							12 05					13 05					
Sandwell & Dudley	d			10 47				11 17							12 17					13 17					
Birmingham New Street 12	d			11 00				11 30							12 30					13 30			14 00		
Birmingham International	d	10 58		11 10				11 41							12 41					13 41			14 10		
Coventry	d	11 14		11 21			11 47	11 53			12 14			12 47	12 53			13 47		13 53			14 21		
Nuneaton	d																								
Rugby	a	11 26					11 58							12 58				13 58							
	d	11 28			11 41		11 59							12 59				13 59				14 24			
Northampton	d					11 56				12 26			12 56				13 26		13 56		14 26				
Wolverton	d					12 08				12 38			13 08				13 38		14 08		14 38				
Milton Keynes Central 10	a	11 51		11 57		12 11	12 21	12 27		12 41	12 50		13 11	13 22	13 28		13 41		14 11	14 26	14 41	14 50			
	d	11 52		11 58		12 12	12 23	12 29		12 42	12 51	13 02	13 12	13 24	13 30		13 42		14 12	14 28	14 42	14 51			
Bletchley	d					12 17				12 47			13 17				13 47		14 17		14 47				
Leighton Buzzard	d					12 23				12 53			13 23				13 53		14 23		14 53				
Cheddington	d					12 28							13 28						14 28						
Tring	d					12 37							13 37						14 37						←
Berkhamsted	d					12 42				13 08			13 42				14 08		14 42		15 08 →				15 08
Hemel Hempstead	a					12 46				13 13			13 46				14 13		14 46						15 13
	d					12 46				13 13			13 46				14 13		14 46						15 13
Apsley	d									13 16							14 16								15 16
Kings Langley	d									13 19							14 19								15 19
Watford Junction	a	12s31		12s36	12s43	12 55	13s00	13s06		13 26	13s31		13 55		14s03		14 26	14s46	14 55			15s13	15s17		15 26
	d					12 56			13 22	13 26			13 56			14 22	14 26		14 56					15 22	15 26
Bushey	d																								
Harrow & Wealdstone ⊖	d					13 02			13 28	13 32			14 02			14 28	14 32		15 02					15 28	15 32
Wembley Central	d																								
Shepherds Bush §	a																								
Kensington Olympia ⊖	a								13 47							14 47								15 47	
West Brompton ⊖	a								13 48							14 49								15 50	
Imperial Wharf §	a																								
Clapham Junction 10	a								14 00							15 00								16 00	
East Croydon	a																								
Gatwick Airport 10	a																								
Haywards Heath 3	a																								
Brighton 10	a																								
London Euston 15 ⊖	a	12 51		12 58	13 04	13 20	13 23	13 29		13 50	13 56	14 00	14 20	14 23	14 29		14 50	15 08	15 20	15 16		15 38	15 43		15 50

For general notes see front of timetable
For details of catering facilities see
Directory of Train Operators

§ This station may open during the currency of the Timetable

Table 66

Sundays

until 27 January and from 30 March

West Midlands, Northampton, Milton Keynes and Watford Junction → London

Network Diagram - See first page of Table 59

		VT	LM	VT		VT	VT	VT	SN	LM	VT	LM	VT	VT	VT	SN	LM	VT	VT	LM	VT	VT	VT	VT	VT
		1 ◇	1	1 ◇		1 ◇	1 ◇	1 ◇	1	1	1 ◇	1	1 ◇	1 ◇	1 ◇	1	1	1 ◇	1 ◇	1	1 ◇	1 ◇	1 ◇	1 ◇	1 ◇
														A	B									A	B
		🍴		🍴		🍴	🍴	🍴			🍴		🍴	🍴	🍴			🍴	🍴		🍴	🍴	🍴	🍴	🍴
Wolverhampton 7	d					14 05							15 04									16 04			
Sandwell & Dudley	d					14 17							15 17									16 17			
Birmingham New Street 12	d					14 30		15 00					15 30	16 00	16 00							16 30		17 00	17 00
Birmingham International	d					14 41		15 11					15 41	16 10	16 11							16 41		17 10	17 11
Coventry	d			14 47		14 53		15 22			15 47		15 53	16 21	16 22			16 14			16 47	16 53		17 21	17 22
Nuneaton	d																								
Rugby	a			14 58							15 58							16 26			16 58				
	d			14 59			15 25				15 59							16 28			16 59		17 25		
Northampton	d		14 56							15 26		15 56					16 26			16 56					
Wolverton	d		15 08							15 38		16 08					16 38			17 08					
Milton Keynes Central 10	a		15 11	15 21		15 27				15 41		16 11	16 25				16 41	16 51		17 11	17 22	17 27			
	d	15 02	15 12	15 23		15 29				15 42		16 12	16 26				16 42	16 52	17 02	17 12	17 24	17 28			
Bletchley	d		15 17							15 47		16 17					16 47			17 17					
Leighton Buzzard	d		15 23							15 53		16 23					16 53			17 23					
Cheddington	d		15 28									16 28								17 28					
Tring	d		15 37									16 37								17 37					
Berkhamsted	d		15 42							16 08		16 42					17 08			17 42					
Hemel Hempstead	a		15 46							16 13		16 46					17 13			17 46					
	d		15 46							16 13		16 46					17 13			17 46					
Apsley	d									16 16							17 16								
Kings Langley	d									16 19							17 19								
Watford Junction	a		15 55				16s12	16s18		16 26	16s46	16 55		17s18	17s18		17 26			17 55			18s12	18s17	18s17
	d		15 56						16 22	16 26		16 56				17 22	17 26			17 56					
Bushey	d																								
Harrow & Wealdstone ⊖	d		16 02						16 28	16 32		17 02				17 28	17 32			18 02					
Wembley Central	d																								
Shepherds Bush §	a																								
Kensington Olympia ⊖	a								16 47							17 47									
West Brompton ⊖	a								16 50							17 50									
Imperial Wharf §	a																								
Clapham Junction 10	a								17 00							18 00									
East Croydon	a																								
Gatwick Airport 10 ✈	a																								
Haywards Heath 3	a																								
Brighton 10	a																								
London Euston 15 ⊖	a	15 56	16 20	16 07	.	16 16	16 36	16 41	.	16 50	17 08	17 20	17 11	17 43	17 43	.	17 50	17 39	17 56	18 20	18 08	18 11	18 38	18 41	18 41

		SN	LM	LM	VT	VT		LM	VT	VT	SN	LM	VT	VT	LM	VT	LM	VT	SN	LM	LM	VT	VT	LM	SN
		1	1	1	1 ◇	1 ◇		1	1 ◇	1 ◇	1	1	1 ◇	1 ◇	1	1 ◇	1	1 ◇	1	1	1	1 ◇	1 ◇	1	1
									A	B															
					🍴	🍴			🍴	🍴			🍴	🍴		🍴		🍴				🍴	🍴		
Wolverhampton 7	d					17 04										18 04							19 04		
Sandwell & Dudley	d					17 17										18 17							19 17		
Birmingham New Street 12	d					17 30			18 00	18 00						18 30							19 30		
Birmingham International	d					17 41			18 10	18 11						18 40							19 41		
Coventry	d				17 47	17 53			18 21	18 22			18 14			18 51						19 47	19 53		
Nuneaton	d																								
Rugby	a				17 58								18 26									19 58			
	d				17 59								18 28					19 25				19 59			
Northampton	d		17 26	17 56								18 26			18 56					19 26	19 56				
Wolverton	d		17 38	18 08								18 38			19 08					19 38	20 08				
Milton Keynes Central 10	a		17 41	18 11	18 22	18 27						18 41	18 50		19 11	19 25				19 41	20 11	20 22	20 27		
	d		17 42	18 12	18 24	18 29						18 42	18 52	19 02	19 12	19 27				19 42	20 12	20 24	20 29		
Bletchley	d		17 47	18 17								18 47			19 17					19 47	20 17				
Leighton Buzzard	d		17 53	18 23				←				18 53			19 23		←			19 53	20 23			←	
Cheddington	d			18 28 →				18 28							19 28 →		19 28				20 28 →			20 28	
Tring	d							18 37									19 37							20 37	
Berkhamsted	d		18 08					18 42				19 08					19 42			20 08				20 42	
Hemel Hempstead	a		18 13					18 46				19 13					19 46			20 13				20 46	
	d		18 13					18 46				19 13					19 46			20 13				20 46	
Apsley	d		18 16									19 16								20 16					
Kings Langley	d		18 19									19 19								20 19					
Watford Junction	a		18 26		18s45			18 55	19 17	19 17		19 26				19s50	19 55	20s12		20 26		20s47	20s51	20 55	
	d	18 22	18 26					18 56	19 18	19 18	19 22	19 26					19 56		20 22	20 26				20 56	21 22
Bushey	d																								
Harrow & Wealdstone ⊖	d	18 28	18 32					19 02			19 28	19 32					20 02		20 28	20 32				21 02	21 28
Wembley Central	d																								
Shepherds Bush §	a																								
Kensington Olympia ⊖	a	18 47									19 47								20 47						21 47
West Brompton ⊖	a	18 50									19 50								20 50						21 50
Imperial Wharf §	a																								
Clapham Junction 10	a	19 00									20 00								21 00						22 00
East Croydon	a																								
Gatwick Airport 10 ✈	a																								
Haywards Heath 3	a																								
Brighton 10	a																								
London Euston 15 ⊖	a	.	18 50	.	19 14	19 17	.	19 20	19 41	19 41	.	19 50	19 33	19 53	.	20 11	20 20	20 38	.	20 50	.	21 14	21 17	21 20	.

For general notes see front of timetable
For details of catering facilities see Directory of Train Operators

§ This station may open during the currency of the Timetable

A From 30 March
B Until 27 January

Table 66

Sundays

until 27 January and from 30 March

West Midlands, Northampton, Milton Keynes and Watford Junction → London

Network Diagram - See first page of Table 59

	LM 1	VT 1 ◇ ☕	VT 1 ◇ ☕	LM 1	VT 1 ◇ ☕	VT 1 ◇ ☕	SN 1	LM 1	VT 1 ◇ ☕	VT 1 ◇ ☕	LM 1	VT 1 ◇ A ☕	VT 1 ◇ B ☕	VT 1 ◇ A ☕	SN 1	VT 1 ◇ A ☕	VT 1 ◇ B ☕	VT 1 ◇ B ☕	LM 1	VT 1 ◇ A ☕	VT 1 ◇ B ☕	LM 1
Wolverhampton 7 d						20 04										21 35		21 35		22 35	22 35	
Sandwell & Dudley d						20 17										21 48		21 48		22 47	22 47	
Birmingham New Street 12 d						20 30										22 00		22 00		23 00	23 00	
Birmingham International d						20 41										22 10		22 10		23 10	23 10	
Coventry d		20 14			20 47	20 53						21 47	21 47	22 14		22 21	22 14	22 21		23 21	23 21	
Nuneaton d																						
Rugby a		20 26			20 58							21 58	21 58			22 33		22 32		23 33	23 32	
d		20 28			20 59				21 25	21 41		21 59	21 59			22 35		22 34		23 35	23 34	
Northampton d	20 26			20 56				21 26			21 56								22 56			23 56
Wolverton d	20 38			21 08				21 38			22 08								23 08			00 08
Milton Keynes Central 10 a	20 41	20 51		21 11	21 22	21 28		21 41	21 50	22 04	22 11	22 21	22 34	22 50		22 58	22 59	23 06	23 11	23 58	00 06	00 11
d	20 42	20 52	21 02	21 12	21 24	21 30		21 42	21 51	22 05	22 12	22 23	22 35	22 52		22 59	23 00	23 08	23 12	23 59	00 08	00 12
Bletchley d	20 47			21 17				21 47			22 17								23 17			00 17
Leighton Buzzard d	20 53			21 23				21 53			22 23								23 23			00 23
Cheddington d				21 28							22 28								23 28			00 28
Tring d				21 37							22 37								23 37			00 37
Berkhamsted d	21 08			21 42				22 08			22 42								23 42			00 42
Hemel Hempstead a	21 13			21 46				22 13			22 46								23 46			00 46
d	21 13			21 46				22 13			22 46								23 46			00 46
Apsley d	21 16							22 16											23 49			00 49
Kings Langley d	21 19							22 19											23 53			00 53
Watford Junction a	21 26	21s31		21 55	22s00	22s06		22 26	22s31	22s41	22 55	23s00	23s04	23s16		23s28	23s29	23s38	23 58	00s28	00s38	00 59
d	21 26			21 56			22 22	22 26			22 56				23 22				23 59			01 00
Bushey d																						
Harrow & Wealdstone ⊖ d	21 32			22 02			22 28	22 32			23 02				23 28				00 05			01 06
Wembley Central d																						
Shepherds Bush § a																						
Kensington Olympia ⊖ a							22 47								23 47							
West Brompton ⊖ a							22 50								23 50							
Imperial Wharf § a																						
Clapham Junction 10 a							23 00								00 01							
East Croydon a															00 20							
Gatwick Airport 10 a																						
Haywards Heath 3 a																						
Brighton 10 a																						
London Euston 15 ⊖ a	21 50	21 54	21 57	22 20	22 23	22 27		22 50	22 51	23 00	23 20	23 25	23 25	23 41		23 48	23 47	23 58	00 24	00 47	00 57	01 24

Sundays

3 February to 23 March

	LM 🚌	LM 🚌	LM 🚌	LM 🚌	LM 🚌	LM 🚌	LM 🚌	LM 🚌	LM 🚌	LM 🚌	SN 1	LM 🚌	LM 1	LM 1	SN 1		LM 1	LM 🚌	VT 1 ◇ ☕	LM 1	LM 🚌	SN 1	LM 1	VT 1 ◇ ☕
Wolverhampton 7 d																			08 37					09 35
Sandwell & Dudley d																			08 47					09 47
Birmingham New Street 12 d																			09 00					10 00
Birmingham International d																			09 10					10 10
Coventry d																			09 21					10 21
Nuneaton d																								
Rugby a																								
d																								
Northampton d									06 45	08 10		08 40						09 10			09 40			
Wolverton d									07 20	08 45		09 15						09 45			10 15			
Milton Keynes Central 10 a									07 30	08 55		09 25						09 55	10 01		10 25			10 55
d	23p58	23p58		05 00	06 00	06 40		07 20	07 30	08 55							09 42		10 02	10 12			10 42	10 57
Bletchley d	00 13	00 13		05 15	06 15	06 55		07 35	07 45	09a10				09 30			09 47			10 17			10 47	
Leighton Buzzard d	00 38	00 38		05 40	06 40			08 00						09 36			09 53			10 23			10 53	
Cheddington d		00 58		06 00	07 00			08 20						09 41						10 28				
Tring d		01 18	05 20	06 20	07 20		←	08 40						09 50						10 37				
Berkhamsted d		01 33	05 35	06 35	07 35		07 35	08 55						09 55			10 08			10 42			11 08	
Hemel Hempstead a		01 43	05 45	06 45	→		07 45	09 05						09 59			10 13			10 46			11 13	
d		01 43	05 45	06 45			07 45						09 27	09 59			10 13			10 46			11 13	
Apsley d			05 50	06 50			07 50						09 30				10 16						11 16	
Kings Langley d			06 00	07 00			08 00						09 33				10 19						11 19	
Watford Junction a	01 23	02 08	06 15	07 15		07 55	08 15		08 45				09 38	10 06			10 27		10s36	10 55			11 26	11s31
d	01 23	02 08	06 15	07 15		07 55	08 15		08 45		09 22		09 38	10 07	10 22		10 27			10 56		11 22	11 26	
Bushey d																								
Harrow & Wealdstone ⊖ d		02 28	06 35	07 35		08 15	08 35		09 05		09 28		09 48	10 13	10 27		10 33			11 02		11 28	11 32	
Wembley Central d		02 43																						
Shepherds Bush § a																								
Kensington Olympia ⊖ a											09 47				10 47							11 47		
West Brompton ⊖ a											09 49				10 49							11 49		
Imperial Wharf § a																								
Clapham Junction 10 a											10 00				11 00							12 00		
East Croydon a																								
Gatwick Airport 10 a																								
Haywards Heath 3 a																								
Brighton 10 a																								
London Euston 15 ⊖ a	02 08	03 13	07 10	08 10		08 50	09 10		09 40				10 08	10 33			10 51		10 56	11 20			11 50	11 51

For general notes see front of timetable
For details of catering facilities see Directory of Train Operators

§ This station may open during the currency of the Timetable

A Until 27 January
B From 30 March

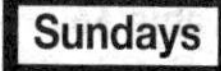

West Midlands, Northampton, Milton Keynes and Watford Junction → London

3 February to 23 March

Network Diagram - See first page of Table 59

	LM (bus)	VT 1 ◇	LM 1	LM (bus)	SN 1	LM 1	VT 1 ◇	LM (bus)	VT 1 ◇		VT 1 ◇	LM 1	VT 1 ◇	LM (bus)	VT 1 ◇	SN 1	LM 1	VT 1 ◇	LM (bus)	VT 1 ◇	LM 1	VT 1 ◇	LM (bus)	VT 1 ◇
Wolverhampton [7] d									10 36						11 05									12 05
Sandwell & Dudley d									10 47						11 17									12 17
Birmingham New Street [12] d									11 00						11 30									12 30
Birmingham International d							10 58		11 10						11 41									12 41
Coventry d		10 29					11 14		11 21				11 47		11 53			12 14				12 47		12 53
Nuneaton d																								
Rugby a		10 41					11 26						11 58									12 58		
d		10 42					11 28				11 41		11 59									12 59		
Northampton d	10 10			10 40				11 10						11 40					12 10				12 40	
Wolverton d	10 45			11 15				11 45						12 15					12 45				13 15	
Milton Keynes Central [10] a	10 55	11 05		11 25			11 51	11 55	11 57				12 21	12 25	12 27			12 50	12 55			13 22	13 25	13 28
d		11 07	11 12			11 42	11 52		11 58			12 12	12 23		12 29		12 42	12 51		13 02	13 12	13 24		13 30
Bletchley d			11 17			11 47						12 17					12 47				13 17			
Leighton Buzzard d			11 23			11 53						12 23					12 53				13 23			
Cheddington d			11 28									12 28									13 28			
Tring d			11 37									12 37									13 37			
Berkhamsted d			11 42			12 08						12 42					13 08				13 42			
Hemel Hempstead a			11 46			12 13						12 46					13 13				13 46			
d			11 46			12 13						12 46					13 13				13 46			
Apsley d						12 16											13 16							
Kings Langley d						12 19											13 19							
Watford Junction a			11 55			12 26	12s31		12s36		12s43	12 55	13s00		13s06		13 26	13s31			13 55			14s03
d			11 56		12 22	12 26						12 56				13 22	13 26				13 56			
Bushey d																								
Harrow & Wealdstone ⊖ d			12 02		12 28	12 32						13 02				13 28	13 32				14 02			
Wembley Central d																								
Shepherds Bush § a																								
Kensington Olympia ⊖ a					12 47											13 47								
West Brompton ⊖ a					12 49											13 48								
Imperial Wharf § a																								
Clapham Junction [10] a					13 00											14 00								
East Croydon a																								
Gatwick Airport [10] a																								
Haywards Heath [3] a																								
Brighton [10] a																								
London Euston [15] ⊖ a		12 00	12 20			12 50	12 51		12 58		13 04	13 20	13 23		13 29		13 50	13 56		14 00	14 20	14 23		14 29

	SN 1	LM 1	LM (bus)		VT 1 ◇	LM 1	LM (bus)	VT 1 ◇	LM 1	VT 1 ◇	LM (bus)	VT 1 ◇	SN 1	LM 1	VT 1 ◇	LM 1	VT 1 ◇	LM (bus)	VT 1 ◇		VT 1 ◇	VT 1 ◇	SN 1	LM 1
Wolverhampton [7] d								13 05											14 05					
Sandwell & Dudley d								13 17											14 17					
Birmingham New Street [12] d								13 30				14 00							14 30			15 00		
Birmingham International d								13 41				14 10							14 41			15 11		
Coventry d					13 47			13 53				14 21					14 47		14 53			15 22		
Nuneaton d																								
Rugby a					13 58												14 58							
d					13 59					14 24							14 59				15 25			
Northampton d			13 10				13 40				14 10							14 40						
Wolverton d			13 45				14 15				14 45							15 15						
Milton Keynes Central [10] a			13 55				14 25	14 26		14 50	14 55						15 21	15 25	15 27					
d		13 42				14 12		14 28	14 42	14 51					15 02	15 12	15 23		15 29					15 42
Bletchley d		13 47				14 17			14 47							15 17								15 47
Leighton Buzzard d		13 53				14 23			14 53							15 23								15 53
Cheddington d						14 28										15 28								
Tring d						14 37								←		15 37								
Berkhamsted d		14 08				14 42			15 08					15 08		15 42								16 08
Hemel Hempstead a		14 13				14 46			→					15 13		15 46								16 13
d		14 13				14 46								15 13		15 46								16 13
Apsley d		14 16												15 16										16 16
Kings Langley d		14 19												15 19										16 19
Watford Junction a		14 26			14s46	14 55				15s13		15s17		15 26		15 55					16s12	16s18		16 26
d	14 22	14 26				14 56							15 22	15 26		15 56							16 22	16 26
Bushey d																								
Harrow & Wealdstone ⊖ d	14 28	14 32				15 02							15 28	15 32		16 02							16 28	16 32
Wembley Central d																								
Shepherds Bush § a																								
Kensington Olympia ⊖ a	14 47												15 47										16 47	
West Brompton ⊖ a	14 49												15 50										16 50	
Imperial Wharf § a																								
Clapham Junction [10] a	15 00												16 00										17 00	
East Croydon a																								
Gatwick Airport [10] a																								
Haywards Heath [3] a																								
Brighton [10] a																								
London Euston [15] ⊖ a		14 50			15 08	15 20		15 16		15 38		15 43		15 50	15 56	16 20	16 07		16 16		16 36	16 41		16 50

For general notes see front of timetable
For details of catering facilities see
Directory of Train Operators

§ This station may open during the currency of the Timetable

Table 66

Sundays

3 February to 23 March

West Midlands, Northampton, Milton Keynes and Watford Junction → London

Network Diagram - See first page of Table 59

	LM	VT	LM	VT	LM	VT	SN	LM	VT	LM	VT	LM	VT		LM	VT	VT	VT	SN	LM	LM	LM	VT	LM
		1 ◇	1	1 ◇		1 ◇	1	1	1 ◇		1 ◇	1	1 ◇			1 ◇	1 ◇	1 ◇	1	1		1	1 ◇	
	🚌				🚌					🚌					🚌						🚌			🚌
		☕		☕		☕			☕		☕		☕			☕	☕	☕					☕	
Wolverhampton 7 ⛴ d				15 04												16 04								
Sandwell & Dudley d				15 17												16 17								
Birmingham New Street 12 d				15 30		16 00										16 30		17 00						
Birmingham International ✈ d				15 41		16 10										16 41		17 10						
Coventry d		15 47		15 53		16 21			16 14				16 47			16 53		17 21					17 47	
Nuneaton d																								
Rugby a		15 58							16 26				16 58										17 58	
d		15 59							16 28				16 59				17 25						17 59	
Northampton d	15 10				15 40					16 10					16 40						17 10			17 40
Wolverton d	15 45				16 15					16 45					17 15						17 45			18 15
Milton Keynes Central 10 a	15 55			16 25	16 25				16 51	16 55			17 22		17 25	17 27					17 55		18 22	18 25
d			16 12	16 26				16 42	16 52		17 02	17 12	17 24			17 28				17 42		18 12	18 24	
Bletchley d			16 17					16 47				17 17								17 47		18 17		
Leighton Buzzard d			16 23					16 53				17 23								17 53		18 23		
Cheddington d			16 28									17 28										18 28 →		
Tring d			16 37									17 37												
Berkhamsted d			16 42					17 08				17 42								18 08				
Hemel Hempstead a			16 46					17 13				17 46								18 13				
d			16 46					17 13				17 46								18 13				
Apsley d								17 16												18 16				
Kings Langley d								17 19												18 19				
Watford Junction a		16s46	16 55			17s18		17 26				17 55					18s12	18s17		18 26			18s45	
d			16 56				17 22	17 26				17 56							18 22	18 26				
Bushey d																								
Harrow & Wealdstone ⊖ d			17 02				17 28	17 32				18 02							18 28	18 32				
Wembley Central d																								
Shepherds Bush § a																								
Kensington Olympia ⊖ a							17 47												18 47					
West Brompton ⊖ a							17 50												18 50					
Imperial Wharf § a																								
Clapham Junction 10 a							18 00												19 00					
East Croydon ⛴ a																								
Gatwick Airport 10 ✈ a																								
Haywards Heath 3 a																								
Brighton 10 a																								
London Euston 15 ⊖ a		17 08	17 20	17 11		17 43		17 50	17 39		17 56	18 20	18 08			18 11	18 38	18 41		18 50			19 14	

	VT	LM	VT	SN	LM	VT	LM		VT	LM	VT	LM	LM	VT	SN	LM	LM	LM	VT	LM	VT	LM	SN	LM
	1 ◇	1	1 ◇	1	1	1 ◇			1 ◇	1	1 ◇		1	1 ◇	1	1		1	1 ◇		1 ◇	1	1	1
							🚌					🚌					🚌			🚌				
	☕		☕			☕			☕		☕			☕					☕		☕			
Wolverhampton 7 ⛴ d	17 04										18 04										19 04			
Sandwell & Dudley d	17 17										18 17										19 17			
Birmingham New Street 12 d	17 30		18 00								18 30										19 30			
Birmingham International ✈ d	17 41		18 10								18 40										19 41			
Coventry d	17 53		18 21			18 14					18 51								19 47		19 53			
Nuneaton d																								
Rugby a						18 26													19 58					
d						18 28								19 25					19 59					
Northampton d							18 10					18 40					19 10			19 40				
Wolverton d							18 45					19 15					19 45			20 15				
Milton Keynes Central 10 a	18 27					18 50	18 55				19 25	19 25					19 55		20 22	20 25	20 27			
d	18 29				18 42	18 52			19 02	19 12	19 27					19 42		20 12	20 24		20 29			20 42
Bletchley d					18 47					19 17						19 47		20 17						20 47
Leighton Buzzard d		←			18 53					19 23			←			19 53		20 23				←		20 53
Cheddington d		18 28								19 28 →			19 28					20 28 →				20 28		
Tring d		18 37											19 37									20 37		
Berkhamsted d		18 42			19 08								19 42			20 08						20 42		21 08
Hemel Hempstead a		18 46			19 13								19 46			20 13						20 46		21 13
d		18 46			19 13								19 46			20 13						20 46		21 13
Apsley d					19 16											20 16								21 16
Kings Langley d					19 19											20 19								21 19
Watford Junction a		18 55	19 17		19 26						19s50		19 55	20s12		20 26			20s47		20s51	20 55		21 26
d		18 56	19 18	19 22	19 26								19 56		20 22	20 26						20 56	21 22	21 26
Bushey d																								
Harrow & Wealdstone ⊖ d		19 02		19 28	19 32								20 02		20 28	20 32						21 02	21 28	21 32
Wembley Central d																								
Shepherds Bush § a																								
Kensington Olympia ⊖ a				19 47											20 47								21 47	
West Brompton ⊖ a				19 50											20 50								21 50	
Imperial Wharf § a																								
Clapham Junction 10 a				20 00											21 00								22 00	
East Croydon ⛴ a																								
Gatwick Airport 10 ✈ a																								
Haywards Heath 3 a																								
Brighton 10 a																								
London Euston 15 ⊖ a	19 17	19 20	19 41		19 50	19 33			19 53		20 11		20 20	20 38		20 50			21 14		21 17	21 20		21 50

For general notes see front of timetable
For details of catering facilities see Directory of Train Operators

§ This station may open during the currency of the Timetable

Table 66

Sundays

West Midlands, Northampton, Milton Keynes and Watford Junction → London

3 February to 23 March

Network Diagram - See first page of Table 59

		VT 1 ◇ ☕		LM 🚌	VT 1 ◇ ☕	LM 1	VT 1 ◇ ☕	LM 🚌	VT 1 ◇ ☕	SN 1	LM 1	VT 1 ◇ ☕	LM 🚌	VT 1 ◇ ☕	LM 1	VT 1 ◇ ☕	VT 1 ◇ ☕	LM 🚌	SN 1	VT 1 ◇ ☕	LM 1	LM 🚌	VT 1 ◇ ☕		
Wolverhampton 7	d								20 04											21 35			22 35		
Sandwell & Dudley	d								20 17											21 48			22 47		
Birmingham New Street 12	d								20 30											22 00			23 00		
Birmingham International	d								20 41											22 10			23 10		
Coventry	d	20 14					20 47		20 53							21 47	22 14			22 21			23 21		
Nuneaton	d																								
Rugby	a	20 26					20 58									21 58				22 33			23 33		
	d	20 28					20 59					21 25		21 41		21 59				22 35			23 35		
Northampton	d			20 10				20 40					21 10					22 10				23 10			
Wolverton	d			20 45				21 15					21 45					22 45				23 45			
Milton Keynes Central 10	a	20 51		20 55			21 22	21 25	21 28			21 50	21 55	22 04		22 21	22 50	22 55		22 58		23 55	23 58		
	d	20 52			21 02	21 12	21 24		21 30		21 42	21 51		22 05	22 12	22 23	22 52			22 59	23 12		23 59		
Bletchley	d					21 17					21 47				22 17						23 17				
Leighton Buzzard	d					21 23					21 53				22 23						23 23				
Cheddington	d					21 28									22 28						23 28				
Tring	d					21 37									22 37						23 37				
Berkhamsted	d					21 42					22 08				22 42						23 42				
Hemel Hempstead	a					21 46					22 13				22 46						23 46				
	d					21 46					22 13				22 46						23 46				
Apsley	d										22 16										23 49				
Kings Langley	d										22 19										23 53				
Watford Junction	a	21s31				21 55	22s00		22s06		22 26	22s31		22s41	22 55	23s00	23s16			23s28	23 58		00s28		
	d					21 56				22 22	22 26				22 56				23 22		23 59				
Bushey	d																								
Harrow & Wealdstone ⊖	d					22 02				22 28	22 32				23 02				23 28		00 05				
Wembley Central	d																								
Shepherds Bush §	a																								
Kensington Olympia ⊖	a									22 47									23 47						
West Brompton ⊖	a									22 50									23 50						
Imperial Wharf §	a																								
Clapham Junction 10	a									23 00									00 01						
East Croydon	a																		00 20						
Gatwick Airport 10	a																								
Haywards Heath 3	a																								
Brighton 10	a																								
London Euston 15 ⊖	a	21 54			21 57	22 20	22 23		22 27		22 50	22 51		23 00	23 20	23 25	23 41			23 48	00 24		00 47		

For general notes see front of timetable
For details of catering facilities see Directory of Train Operators

§ This station may open during the currency of the Timetable

Network Diagram for Tables 67, 68, 69, 70, 74, 75

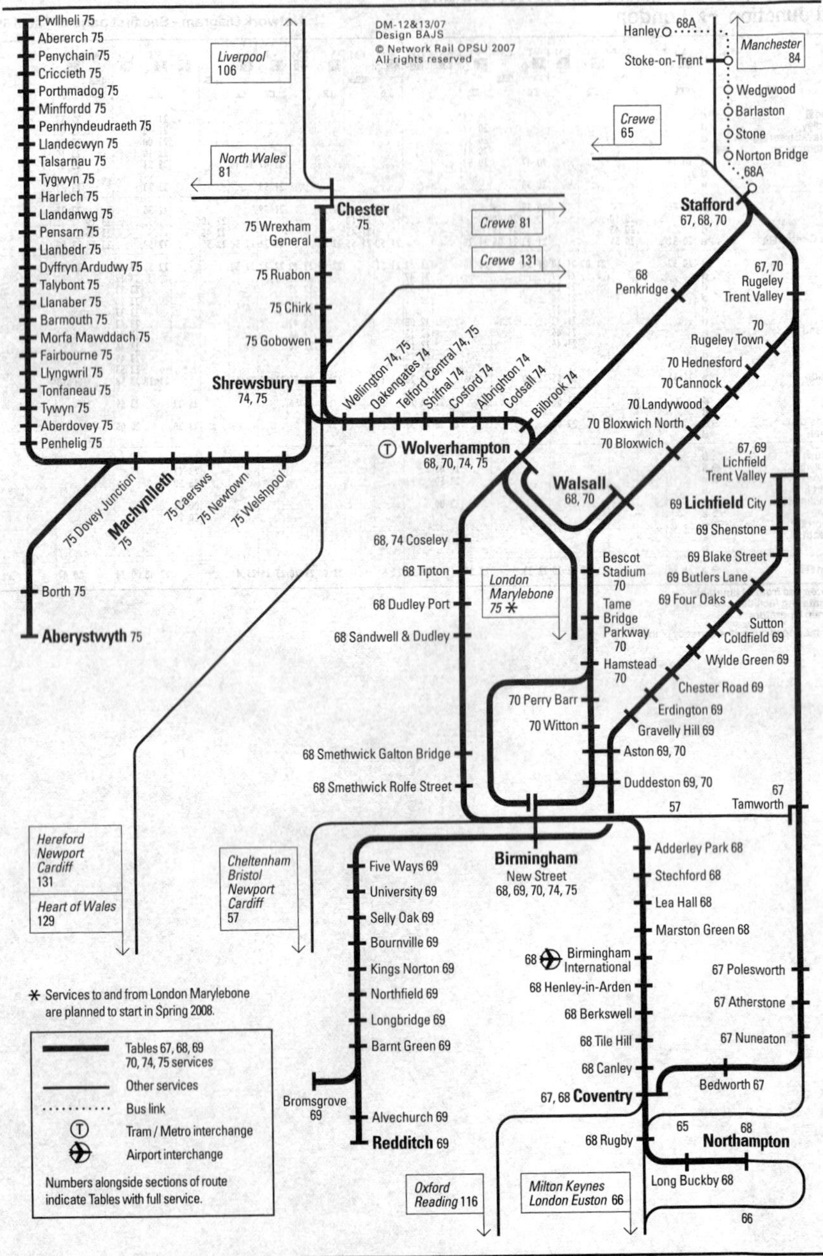

DM-12&13/07
Design BAJS
© Network Rail OPSU 2007
All rights reserved
Pwllheli 75
Abererch 75
Penychain 75
Criccieth 75
Porthmadog 75
Minffordd 75
Penrhyndeudraeth 75
Llandecwyn 75
Talsarnau 75
Tygwyn 75
Harlech 75
Llandanwg 75
Pensarn 75
Llanbedr 75
Dyffryn Ardudwy 75
Talybont 75
Llanaber 75
Barmouth 75
Morfa Mawddach 75
Fairbourne 75
Llyngwril 75
Tonfaneau 75
Tywyn 75
Aberdovey 75
Penhelig 75
Borth 75
Aberystwyth 75
75 Dovey Junction
Machynlleth 75
75 Caersws
75 Newtown
75 Welshpool
Liverpool 106
North Wales 81
Chester 75
75 Wrexham General
75 Ruabon
75 Chirk
75 Gobowen
Shrewsbury 74, 75
Crewe 81
Crewe 131
Wellington 74, 75
Oakengates 74
Telford Central 74, 75
Shifnal 74
Cosford 74
Albrighton 74
Codsall 74
Bilbrook 74
Wolverhampton 68, 70, 74, 75
Hanley
68A
Manchester 84
Stoke-on-Trent
Wedgwood
Barlaston
Stone
Norton Bridge
68A
Crewe 65
Stafford 67, 68, 70
68 Penkridge
67, 70 Rugeley Trent Valley
70 Rugeley Town
70 Hednesford
70 Cannock
70 Landywood
70 Bloxwich North
70 Bloxwich
67, 69 Lichfield Trent Valley
Walsall 68, 70
69 Lichfield City
69 Shenstone
69 Blake Street
69 Butlers Lane
69 Four Oaks
Sutton Coldfield 69
Wylde Green 69
Chester Road 69
Erdington 69
Gravelly Hill 69
68, 74 Coseley
68 Tipton
68 Dudley Port
68 Sandwell & Dudley
London Marylebone 75 *
Bescot Stadium 70
Tame Bridge Parkway 70
Hamstead 70
70 Perry Barr
70 Witton
Aston 69, 70
Duddeston 69, 70
68 Smethwick Galton Bridge
68 Smethwick Rolfe Street
57
67 Tamworth
Birmingham New Street 68, 69, 70, 74, 75
Hereford Newport Cardiff 131
Heart of Wales 129
Cheltenham Bristol Newport Cardiff 57
Five Ways 69
University 69
Selly Oak 69
Bournville 69
Kings Norton 69
Northfield 69
Longbridge 69
Barnt Green 69
Bromsgrove 69
Alvechurch 69
Redditch 69
Adderley Park 68
Stechford 68
Lea Hall 68
Marston Green 68
68 Birmingham International
68 Henley-in-Arden
68 Berkswell
68 Tile Hill
68 Canley
67, 68 Coventry
68 Rugby
67 Polesworth
67 Atherstone
67 Nuneaton
Bedworth 67
65
68
Northampton
Long Buckby 68
66
Oxford Reading 116
Milton Keynes London Euston 66
* Services to and from London Marylebone are planned to start in Spring 2008.
Tables 67, 68, 69 70, 74, 75 services
Other services
Bus link
Tram / Metro interchange
Airport interchange
Numbers alongside sections of route indicate Tables with full service.

Table 67

Mondays to Fridays

Coventry → Nuneaton → Stafford

Network Diagram - see first page of Table 67

Miles			LM	LM	VT	LM	VT	LM	VT	LM	LM	VT	LM	VT	VT	LM	VT	LM	VT	LM	LM	VT	LM	VT	LM	LM
				1 A	1◇		1◇		1◇			1◇		1◇	1◇		1◇		1◇		1 B	1◇		1◇		
					⊠		⊠		⊠		🚌	⊠		⊠	⊠		☕		☕		⌶	☕		☕		🚌
0	**Coventry**	d	06 15			07 14		08 11		09 10			10 10			11 12		12 06		13 06			14 10		15 08	
6¼	Bedworth	d	06 27			07 25		08 22		09 21			10 21			11 26		12 17		13 17			14 21		15 19	
—	London Euston 15	⊖ d			06 20		07 13		08 17			09 17		09 38	10 15		11 17		12 17		12 49	13 17		14 17		
—	Rugby	d		06 29										10 47							13 47					
10	**Nuneaton**	a	06 34	06 42		07 32	08 21	08 29	09 21	09 28		10 21	10 28	10 58	11 19	11 33	12 22	12 24	13 21	13 24	14 01	14 21	14 28	15 21	15 26	
—		d		06 43			08 21		09 21		09 39	10 21		11 00	11 19		12 22		13 21		14 01	14 21		15 21		
15	Atherstone	d		06 49							09 55										14 07					15 36
19	Polesworth	d									10 11										14 12					15 51
22½	Tamworth Low Level	d		06 57	07a35						10 27										14 17					16 04
28¾	Lichfield Trent Valley	d		07 04							10 48			11b15							14 23					16 19
36¾	Rugeley Trent Valley	d		07 12							11 04			11a22							14 31					16a39
46	**Stafford**	a		07 23			08 47		09 47		11 24	10 47			11 45		12 48		13 47		14 43	14 47		15 47		

		VT	VT	LM	VT	VT	VT	LM	LM	VT	VT	LM	VT	VT	LM	VT	VT	VT	LM	VT	VT	LM	VT	VT
		1◇	1◇		1◇	1◇	1◇			1◇	1◇		1◇	R 1		1◇	1◇	1◇		1◇	1◇		1◇	1◇
		⊠	⊠		☕	☕	⊠		🚌	⊠	⊠		⊠	☕		☕	☕	☕		☕	☕		☕	☕
Coventry	d			16 17				17 17				18 17			19 17				20 18			21 50		
Bedworth	d			16 29				17 29				18 32			19 29				20 29			22 01		
London Euston 15	⊖ d	15 17	15 46		16 17	16 49	17 17			17 21	17 48		18 05	18 45		19 17	19 38	19 46		20 17	20 46		21 10	22 05
Rugby	d									18 10								20 41			21 38			23 21
Nuneaton	a	16 21		16 36	17 21			17 36		18 24		18 39	19 04		19 36	20 20			20 36	21 21		22 08	22 15	23 32
	d	16 21			17 21				17 42	18 24										21 21			22 15	23 32
Atherstone	d								17 57															
Polesworth	d								18 10															
Tamworth Low Level	d		16a53				18a24		18 25					19a55				21a00						23 43
Lichfield Trent Valley	d					18a03			18 45		19a00						20a48				22a01			
Rugeley Trent Valley	d								19 05															
Stafford	a	16 47			17 47				19 32	18 50										21 47			22 41	00s03

Saturdays

		LM	LM	LM	LM	LM	LM	LM	LM	LM	LM	LM	LM	LM	LM	LM	LM	LM	LM	LM	LM	LM
		🚌	🚌	🚌	🚌	🚌	🚌	🚌	🚌	🚌	🚌	🚌	🚌	🚌	🚌	🚌	🚌	🚌	🚌	🚌	🚌	🚌
Coventry	d		06 35	07 35		08 35		09 35	10 35	11 35		12 35	13 35	14 35		15 35	16 35		17 15	18 35	20 05	21 35
Bedworth	d		06 56	07 56		08 56		09 56	10 56	11 56		12 56	13 56	14 56		15 56	16 56		17 36	18 56	20 26	21 56
London Euston 15	⊖ d																					
Rugby	d																					
Nuneaton	a		07 11	08 11		09 11		10 11	11 11	12 11		13 11	14 11	15 11		16 11	17 11		17 51	19 11	20 41	22 11
	d	05 54			08 39		09 39				12 32				15 36			17 42				
Atherstone	d	06 10			08 55		09 55				12 48				15 52			17 58				
Polesworth	d	06 26			09 11		10 11				13 04				16 08			18 14				
Tamworth Low Level	d	06 42			09 27		10 27				13 20				16 24			18 30				
Lichfield Trent Valley	d	07 03			09 48		10 48				13 41				16 45			18 51				
Rugeley Trent Valley	d	07a18			10a03		11 04				13 57				17a00			19 07				
Stafford	a						11 24				14 17							19 27				

Sundays

		LM	LM	LM	LM	LM	LM	LM	LM
		🚌	🚌	🚌	🚌	🚌	🚌	🚌	🚌
Coventry	d	11 35	13 35	14 35	15 35	16 35	17 35	19 35	21 35
Bedworth	d	11 56	13 56	14 56	15 56	16 56	17 56	19 56	21 56
London Euston 15	⊖ d								
Rugby	d								
Nuneaton	a	12 11	14 11	15 11	16 11	17 11	18 11	20 11	22 11
	d								
Atherstone	d								
Polesworth	d								
Tamworth Low Level	d								
Lichfield Trent Valley	d								
Rugeley Trent Valley	d								
Stafford	a								

For general notes see front of timetable
For details of catering facilities see Directory of Train Operators

A From Northampton (Table 68) to Liverpool Lime Street (Table 91)
B To Crewe (Table 65)
b Arr. 1112

Stafford → Nuneaton → Coventry

Network Diagram - see first page of Table 67

Miles			LM	VT 1 ◇ ⊠	VT 1 ◇ ⊠	VT 1 ◇ ⊠	LM 1 A	LM	VT 1 ◇ ⊠	VT 1 ◇ ⊠	VT 1 ◇ ⊠	LM	VT 1 ◇ ⊠	LM	VT 1 ◇ ☕	VT 1 ◇ ⊠	VT 1 ◇ ⊠	LM	VT 1 ◇ ⊠	LM	LM 1 B 🛒	VT 1 ◇ ☕	LM	VT 1 ◇ ☕
0	**Stafford**	d		06 18	06 43		06 57			07 26						09 13	10 12		11 12		11 21	12 12		13 12
9¼	Rugeley Trent Valley	d					07 07														11 32			
17¼	Lichfield Trent Valley	d		06 33			07 15		07 21							09 27					11 41			
23½	Tamworth Low Level	d		06 40		07 06	07 22								09 23						11 48			
27	Polesworth	d																						
31	Atherstone	d					07 31														11 56			
—	**Nuneaton**	a		06 50	07 05		07 37			07 48							10 34		11 34		12 02	12 34		13 34
36		d	06 46	06 51	07 07		07 37	07 42		07 49	08 31	08 42	09 26	09 42			10 35	10 40	11 35	11 38	12 02	12 35	12 38	13 35
—	Rugby	a		07 04		07 27	07 54		07 45												12 16			
—	London Euston 15	⊖ a		08 04	08 19	08 27			08 40	08 58	09 45		10 35		10 46	10 50	11 48		12 48		13 18	13 47		14 49
39½	Bedworth	d	06 52					07 49				08 48		09 48				10 46		11 44			12 44	
46	**Coventry**	a	07 04					08 01				09 00		10 00				10 58		11 56			12 59	

		LM	LM 🚌	VT 1 ◇ ☕	LM	VT 1 ◇ ☕	VT 1 ◇ ☕	LM	VT 1 ◇ ☕	LM	VT 1 ◇ ☕	LM	LM 1 C 🛒	VT 1 ◇ ☕	LM	VT 1 ◇ ☕	LM	LM	VT 1 ◇ ☕	LM 🚌	LM	VT 1 ◇ ☕
Stafford	d		12 45	14 12		15 12			16 12		17 12		17 20	18 13		19 12			21 04	20 22		
Rugeley Trent Valley	d		13 05										17 29							20 50		
Lichfield Trent Valley	d		13 25				15 18						17 38							21 05		22 16
Tamworth Low Level	d		13 45				15 25						17 45							21 25		22 23
Polesworth	d		14 00																	21 38		
Atherstone	d		14 13										17 53							21 51		
Nuneaton	a		14 25	14 34		15 34	15 38		16 34		17 34		17 59	18 35		19 34			21 27	22 03		22 33
	d	13 42		14 35	14 38	15 35	15 40	15 53	16 35	16 50	17 35	17 48	18 00	18 36	18 47	19 35	19 48	21 17	21 29		22 30	22 34
Rugby	a						15 53				17 49		18 14						21 42			22 48
London Euston 15	⊖ a			15 48		16 48	17 22		17 47		18 50		19 18	19 50		20 48			23 05			00 09
Bedworth	d	13 48			14 44			15 59		16 56		17 54			18 54		19 54	21 23			22 36	
Coventry	a	14 00			14 56			16 11		17 08		18 06			19 06		20 08	21 35			22 48	

Saturdays

		LM 🚌	LM 🚌	LM 🚌	LM 🚌	LM 🚌	LM 🚌	LM 🚌	LM 🚌	LM 🚌	LM 🚌	LM 🚌	LM 🚌	LM 🚌	LM 🚌	LM 🚌	LM 🚌	LM 🚌	LM 🚌	LM 🚌	LM 🚌	LM 🚌	LM 🚌
Stafford	d			05 54									12 45				15 35					19 52	
Rugeley Trent Valley	d			06 20		07 57				10 55			13 11				16 01			18 06		20 18	
Lichfield Trent Valley	d			06 41		08 18				11 16			13 32				16 22			18 27		20 39	
Tamworth Low Level	d			07 02		08 39				11 37			13 53				16 43			18 48		21 00	
Polesworth	d			07 18		08 55				11 53			14 09				16 59			19 04		21 16	
Atherstone	d			07 34		09 11				12 09			14 25				17 15			19 20		21 32	
Nuneaton	a			07 49		09 26				12 24			14 40				17 30			19 35		21 47	
	d	06 48	07 48		08 48		09 48	10 48	11 48		12 48	13 48		14 48	15 48	16 48		17 48	19 24		20 48		22 48
Rugby	a																						
London Euston 15	⊖ a																						
Bedworth	d	07 04	08 04		09 04		10 04	11 04	12 04		13 04	14 04		15 04	16 04	17 04		18 04	19 40		21 04		23 04
Coventry	a	07 24	08 24		09 24		10 24	11 24	12 24		13 24	14 24		15 24	16 24	17 24		18 24	20 00		21 24		23 24

Sundays

		LM 🚌	LM 🚌	LM 🚌	LM 🚌	LM 🚌	LM 🚌	LM 🚌	LM 🚌
Stafford	d								
Rugeley Trent Valley	d								
Lichfield Trent Valley	d								
Tamworth Low Level	d								
Polesworth	d								
Atherstone	d								
Nuneaton	a								
	d	11 48	13 48	14 48	15 48	16 48	17 48	19 48	21 48
Rugby	a								
London Euston 15	⊖ a								
Bedworth	d	12 04	14 04	15 04	16 04	17 04	18 04	20 04	22 04
Coventry	a	12 24	14 24	15 24	16 24	17 24	18 24	20 24	22 24

For general notes see front of timetable
For details of catering facilities see Directory of Train Operators

A From Crewe (Table 65) to Northampton (Table 68)
B From Liverpool Lime Street (Table 65)
C From Crewe (Table 65)

Northampton → Coventry → Birmingham → Wolverhampton → Stafford

Network Diagram - see first page of Table 67

Miles			VT MO [1] ◇ A ☕	VT MO [1] ◇ B ☕	VT MX [1] ◇ ☕	LM MO A 🚌	VT MO [1] ◇ A ☕	VT MO [1] ◇ B ☕	VT MX [1] ◇ ☕	VT [1] ◇ C	VT [1] ◇ ⊠	XC [1] ◇	LM [1] ◇ D 🛒	LM [1]	AW ◇	XC [1] ◇ ☕	LM	LM	LM	LM [1] D	VT [1] ◇ ☕	LM	LM [1]	AW ◇	XC [1] ◇ ☕
—	London Euston [15] ⊖	d	22p40	22p39	22p40		23p40	23p40	23p40																
0	**Northampton**	d				23p21								05 19						06 06			06 15		
9½	Long Buckby	d				23p42								05 29						06 17			06 25		
18¾	Rugby	d	23p53	00 05	00s23	00 13	00 57	01 02	01s20					05 43						06 29			06 36		
32¼	**Coventry**	a	00 04	00 16	00s35	00 53	01 08	01 13	01s33					05 54									06 48		
—		d	00 05	00 18			01 10	01 15						05 55				06 05	06 27				06 48		
34	Canley	d																06 08	06 30						
36	Tile Hill	d																06 12	06 34						
38	Berkswell	d																06 15	06 37						
41¼	Hampton-in-Arden	d																06 19	06 41						
43	**Birmingham International** ✈	a	00 16	00 28	00s47		01 20	01 25	01s46					06 04				06 23	06 45				06 58		
—		d	00 17	00 30			01 22	01 27						06 05				06 23	06 45				06 58		
45	Marston Green	d																06 26	06 48						
46½	Lea Hall	d																06 30	06 52						
47¾	Stechford	d																06 32	06 54						
49½	Adderley Park	d																06 36							
51½	**Birmingham New Street** [12]	a	00 28	00 41	01s01		01 33	01 38	01s58					06 22				06 42	07 01				07 15		
—		d	00 32	00 45			01 37	01 42		05 20	05 30	06 03	06 07		06 33	06 30	06 37				07 03	07 07		07 17	07 18
54¾	Smethwick Rolfe Street	d											06 13				06 43					07 13			
55½	Smethwick Galton Bdg L.L. [7]	d											06 15				06 45					07 15			
56¾	Sandwell & Dudley	d											06 18				06 47					07 17			
57¾	Dudley Port	d											06 22				06 50					07 20			
58½	Tipton	d											06 24				06 52					07 22			
60	Coseley	d											06 27				06 55					07 25			
—	Walsall	d																							
64¼	**Wolverhampton** [7] 🚌	a	00 53	01 06	01 34		01 55	02 00	02 32	05 37	05 48	06 20	06 32		06 48	07 00	07 01				07 20	07 31		07 33	07 39
—		d								05 38	05 49	06 21	06 39			07 06					07 21				07 39
74¼	Penkridge	d											06 49												
79½	**Stafford**	a								05 51	06 04	06 33	06 56			07 17				07 23	07 33				07 53

		LM [1] ◇ 🛒	LM [1]	LM E	LM [1]	LM	XC [1] ◇ ☕	LM [1] ◇ G	LM H	LM	LM	VT [1] ◇ ☕	LM [1]	LM	VT [1] ◇ ⊠	XC [1] ◇ ☕	LM H	LM [1] J 🛒	AW ◇ 🛒	LM	LM K	LM [1]	VT [1] ◇ ⊠	XC [1] ◇ ☕	XC [1] ◇ ☕
London Euston [15] ⊖	d														06 36								07 08		
Northampton	d				06 35								07 00					07 22							
Long Buckby	d				06 45								07 10					07 32							
Rugby	d				06 56								07 20					07 43							
Coventry	a				07 08								07 32		07 44			07 56					08 11		
	d		06 53		07 10		07 23						07 32		07 44			07 56				08 01	08 14		08 23
Canley	d		06 56										07 35									08 04			
Tile Hill	d		07 00										07 39					08 01				08 08			
Berkswell	d		07 03										07 42									08 11			
Hampton-in-Arden	d		07 07										07 47									08 15			
Birmingham International ✈	a		07 11		07 19		07 33						07 50		07 57			08 09				08 19	08 27		08 33
	d		07 11		07 20		07 34		07 37				07 51		07 58		08 04	08 09				08 19	08 28		08 34
Marston Green	d		07 14						07 40								08 07	08 12				08 22			
Lea Hall	d		07 18						07 43								08 10					08 26			
Stechford	d		07 20						07 45								08 13					08 28			
Adderley Park	d		07 24														08 16					08 32			
Birmingham New Street [12]	a		07 28		07 35		07 45		07 53				08 04		08 09		08 21	08 25				08 37	08 41		08 48
	d	07 21				07 37	07 48	07 51		07 57		08 03		08 07	08 13	08 18		08 26	08 33		08 37			08 48	
Smethwick Rolfe Street	d					07 43								08 13							08 43				
Smethwick Galton Bdg L.L. [7]	d					07 45								08 15							08 45				
Sandwell & Dudley	d					07 47								08 17	08 23						08 47				
Dudley Port	d					07 50								08 20							08 50				
Tipton	d					07 52								08 22							08 52				
Coseley	d	07 34								08 09				08 25				08 37							
Walsall	d			07 30							08 13									08 44					
Wolverhampton [7] 🚌	a	07 43		07 45		08 00	08 05	08 09		08 15	08 20	08 20		08 31	08 36	08 38		08 44	08 48	08 59	09 01			09 05	
	d	07 44					08 06	08 09								08 39		08 44						09 06	
Penkridge	d	07 54						08 19										08 54							
Stafford	a	08 01					08 17	08 25								08 53		09 01						09 17	

For general notes see front of timetable
For details of catering facilities see Directory of Train Operators

A Until 24 March
B From 31 March
C To Holyhead (Table 81)
D To Liverpool Lime Street (Table 91)
E To Shrewsbury (Table 74)
G To Liverpool Lime Street (Table 65)
H To Walsall (Table 70)
J To Liverpool Lime Street (Table 65). 🛒 from Birmingham New Street
K From Four Oaks (Table 69)

Northampton → Coventry → Birmingham → Wolverhampton → Stafford

Network Diagram - see first page of Table 67

		LM	LM	LM	VT	CH	LM	LM	VT	XC	LM	LM	AW	LM	LM	LM	VT	XC	LM	LM	LM	VT	LM	LM	VT
		1 ◇			1 ◇		1		1 ◇	1 ◇	1 ◇		◇	1			1 ◇	1 ◇	1 ◇			1 ◇	1		1 ◇
			A			B						A								A					
London Euston 15 ⊖	d								07 40								08 10								08 40
Northampton	d						08 00																09 00		
Long Buckby	d						08 10																09 10		
Rugby	d						08 20																09 20		
Coventry	a						08 32		08 44								09 13						09 31		09 44
	d						08 32		08 44					09 02			09 14	09 23					09 32		09 44
Canley	d						08 35							09 05									09 35		
Tile Hill	d						08 39							09 09									09 39		
Berkswell	d						08 42							09 12									09 42		
Hampton-in-Arden	d						08 46							09 16									09 46		
Birmingham International ✈	a						08 50		08 57					09 19			09 26	09 33					09 50		09 57
	d		08 37			08 42	08 50		08 58			09 05		09 20			09 28	09 34		09 37			09 50		09 58
Marston Green	d		08 40									09 08								09 40					
Lea Hall	d		08 43									09 11								09 43					
Stechford	d		08 45									09 13								09 45					
Adderley Park	d											09 16													
Birmingham New Street 12	a		08 52				09 06		09 09			09 21		09 34			09 41	09 45		09 52			10 06		10 09
	d	08 51		08 57	09 03			09 07	09 13	09 18	09 21		09 33			09 37		09 48	09 51		09 57	10 03		10 07	10 13
Smethwick Rolfe Street	d							09 13								09 43								10 13	
Smethwick Galton Bdg L.L. 7	d							09 15								09 45								10 15	
Sandwell & Dudley	d	08 59							09 23							09 47			09 59						10 23
Dudley Port	d							09 20								09 50								10 19	
Tipton	d							09 22								09 52								10 21	
Coseley	d			09 09				09 25			09 34										10 09			10 23	
Walsall	d														09 44										
Wolverhampton 7	a	09 09		09 15	09 20	09 25		09 31	09 36	09 38	09 44		09 48		09 59	10 00		10 05	10 09		10 15	10 20		10 30	10 36
	d	09 10									09 44							10 06	10 10						
Penkridge	d										09 54														
Stafford	a	09 24									10 01							10 17	10 24						

		XC	LM	LM	AW	LM	XC	LM	LM	VT	XC	XC	LM	LM	LM	VT	LM	VT	LM	VT	XC	LM	LM	AW	LM
		1 ◇	1 ◇		◇		1 ◇	1		1 ◇	1 ◇	1 ◇	1 ◇			1 ◇	1	1 ◇		1 ◇	R 1	1 ◇		◇	1
				A										A									A		
London Euston 15 ⊖	d									09 10								09 38		09 40					
Northampton	d																10 00	10 26							
Long Buckby	d																10 10								
Rugby	d																10 20	10a46							
Coventry	a									10 13							10 32			10 44					
	d							10 02		10 14	10 23						10 32			10 44					11 02
Canley	d							10 05									10 35								11 05
Tile Hill	d							10 09									10 39								11 09
Berkswell	d							10 12									10 42								11 12
Hampton-in-Arden	d							10 16									10 46								11 16
Birmingham International ✈	a							10 20		10 26	10 33						10 50			10 57					11 20
	d			10 05			10 18	10 20		10 28	10 34			10 37			10 50			10 58			11 05		11 20
Marston Green	d			10 08										10 40									11 08		
Lea Hall	d			10 11										10 43									11 11		
Stechford	d			10 13										10 45									11 13		
Adderley Park	d			10 16																			11 16		
Birmingham New Street 12	a			10 21			10 30	10 34		10 41	10 46	←		10 53			11 06			11 09			11 21		11 34
	d	10 18	10 21		10 33		10 48 →		10 37			10 48	10 51		10 57	11 03			11 07	11 13	11 18	11 21		11 33	
Smethwick Rolfe Street	d								10 43										11 13						
Smethwick Galton Bdg L.L. 7	d								10 45										11 15						
Sandwell & Dudley	d								10 47				10 59							11 23					
Dudley Port	d								10 50										11 19						
Tipton	d								10 52										11 21						
Coseley	d		10 34												11 09				11 23			11 34			
Walsall	d					10 44																			
Wolverhampton 7	a	10 38	10 44		10 48	10 59			11 00			11 05	11 09		11 15	11 20			11 30	11 36	11 38	11 44		11 48	
	d		10 44									11 06	11 10									11 44			
Penkridge	d		10 54																			11 54			
Stafford	a		11 01									11 17	11 24									12 01			

For general notes see front of timetable
For details of catering facilities see Directory of Train Operators

A To Walsall (Table 70)
B From London Marylebone (Table 71)

Northampton → Coventry → Birmingham → Wolverhampton → Stafford

Network Diagram - see first page of Table 67

		LM	LM	VT	XC	LM	LM	LM	VT	LM	LM	VT	XC	LM	LM	AW	LM	XC	LM	LM	VT	XC	XC	LM	LM
				1◇	R 1	1◇	A		1◇	1		1◇	1◇	1◇	A	◇		1◇	1		1◇	R 1	1◇	1◇	A
				⊠	☕	🛒			☕			☕	☕	🛒		🛒		☕			☕	☕	☕	🛒	
London Euston 15 ⊖	d			10 10								10 40									11 10				
Northampton	d									11 00															
Long Buckby	d									11 10															
Rugby	d									11 20															
Coventry	a			11 13						11 32		11 44									12 13				
	d			11 14	11 23					11 32		11 44							12 02		12 14	12 23			
Canley	d									11 35									12 05						
Tile Hill	d									11 39									12 09						
Berkswell	d									11 42									12 12						
Hampton-in-Arden	d									11 46									12 16						
Birmingham International ✈	a			11 26	11 33					11 50		11 57							12 20		12 26	12 33			
	d			11 28	11 34		11 37			11 50		11 58			12 05			12 18	12 20		12 28	12 34			12 37
Marston Green	d						11 40								12 08										12 40
Lea Hall	d						11 43								12 11										12 43
Stechford	d						11 45								12 13										12 45
Adderley Park	d														12 16										
Birmingham New Street 12	a			11 41	11 45		11 53			12 06		12 09			12 21			12 30	12 34		12 41	12 45	←		12 53
	d		11 37		11 48	11 51		11 57	12 03		12 07	12 13	12 18	12 21		12 33		12 48 →		12 37			12 48	12 51	
Smethwick Rolfe Street	d		11 43								12 13									12 43					
Smethwick Galton Bdg L.L. 7	d		11 45								12 15									12 45					
Sandwell & Dudley	d		11 47			11 59						12 23								12 47				12 59	
Dudley Port	d		11 50								12 19									12 50					
Tipton	d		11 52								12 21									12 52					
Coseley	d							12 09			12 23			12 34											
Walsall	d	11 44															12 44								
Wolverhampton 7 🚢	a	11 59	12 00			12 09		12 15	12 20		12 30	12 36	12 38	12 44		12 48	12 59			13 00			13 05	13 09	
	d					12 10								12 44									13 06	13 10	
Penkridge	d													12 54											
Stafford	a				12 17	12 24								13 01									13 17	13 24	

		LM	VT	LM	LM	VT	XC	LM	LM	AW	LM	LM	LM	VT	XC	LM	LM	LM	VT	LM	LM	VT	XC	LM	LM
			1◇	1		1◇	R 1	1◇	A	◇	1			1◇	R 1	1◇	A		1◇	1		1◇	1◇	1◇	A
			☕			☕	☕	🛒		🛒				☕	☕	🛒			☕			☕	☕	🛒	
London Euston 15 ⊖	d					11 40								12 10								12 40			
Northampton	d			12 00																13 00					
Long Buckby	d			12 10																13 10					
Rugby	d			12 20																13 20					
Coventry	a			12 32		12 44								13 13						13 32		13 44			
	d			12 32		12 46					13 02			13 14	13 23					13 32		13 44			
Canley	d			12 35							13 05									13 35					
Tile Hill	d			12 39							13 09									13 39					
Berkswell	d			12 42							13 12									13 42					
Hampton-in-Arden	d			12 46							13 16									13 46					
Birmingham International ✈	a			12 50		12 57					13 20			13 26	13 33					13 50		13 57			
	d			12 50		12 58			13 05		13 20			13 28	13 34		13 37			13 50		13 58			14 05
Marston Green	d								13 08								13 40								14 08
Lea Hall	d								13 11								13 43								14 11
Stechford	d								13 13								13 45								14 13
Adderley Park	d								13 16																14 16
Birmingham New Street 12	a			13 06		13 09			13 21		13 34			13 41	13 45		13 53			14 06		14 09			14 21
	d	12 57	13 03		13 07	13 13	13 18	13 21		13 33			13 37		13 48	13 51		13 57	14 03		14 07	14 13	14 18	14 21	
Smethwick Rolfe Street	d				13 13								13 43								14 13				
Smethwick Galton Bdg L.L. 7	d				13 15								13 45								14 15				
Sandwell & Dudley	d					13 23							13 47			13 59						14 23			
Dudley Port	d				13 19								13 50								14 19				
Tipton	d				13 21								13 52								14 21				
Coseley	d	13 09			13 23			13 34										14 09			14 23			14 34	
Walsall	d											13 44													
Wolverhampton 7 🚢	a	13 15	13 20		13 30	13 36	13 38	13 44		13 48		13 59	14 00		14 05	14 09		14 15	14 20		14 30	14 36	14 38	14 44	
	d							13 44							14 06	14 10								14 44	
Penkridge	d							13 54																14 54	
Stafford	a							14 01							14 17	14 24								15 01	

For general notes see front of timetable
For details of catering facilities see Directory of Train Operators

A To Walsall (Table 70)

Northampton → Coventry → Birmingham → Wolverhampton → Stafford

Network Diagram - see first page of Table 67

	AW	LM	XC	LM	LM	VT	XC	XC	LM	LM	LM	VT	LM	LM	VT	XC	LM	LM	AW	LM	LM	LM	VT	XC
	◇		1 ◇	1		1 ◇	R 1	1 ◇	1 ◇	A		1 ◇	1		1 ◇	R 1	1 ◇	A	◇	1			1 ◇	R 1
London Euston 15 ⊖ d						13 10									13 40								14 10	
Northampton d													14 00											
Long Buckby d													14 10											
Rugby d													14 20											
Coventry a						14 13							14 32		14 44								15 13	
d				14 02		14 14	14 23						14 32		14 44					15 02			15 14	15 23
Canley d				14 05									14 35							15 05				
Tile Hill d				14 09									14 39							15 09				
Berkswell d				14 12									14 42							15 12				
Hampton-in-Arden d				14 16									14 46							15 16				
Birmingham International ✈ a				14 20		14 27	14 33						14 50		14 57					15 20			15 26	15 33
d			14 18	14 20		14 28	14 34			14 37			14 50		14 58			15 05		15 20			15 28	15 34
Marston Green d										14 40								15 08						
Lea Hall d										14 43								15 11						
Stechford d										14 45								15 13						
Adderley Park d																		15 16						
Birmingham New Street 12 a			14 30	14 34		14 41	14 45	←		14 53			15 06		15 09			15 21		15 34			15 41	15 45
d	14 33		14 48 →		14 37			14 48	14 51		14 57	15 03		15 07	15 13	15 18	15 21		15 33			15 37		15 48
Smethwick Rolfe Street d					14 43									15 13								15 43		
Smethwick Galton Bdg L.L. 7 d					14 45									15 15								15 45		
Sandwell & Dudley d					14 47				14 59						15 23							15 47		
Dudley Port d					14 50									15 19								15 50		
Tipton d					14 52									15 21								15 52		
Coseley d											15 09			15 23			15 34							
Walsall d		14 44																			15 44			
Wolverhampton 7 a	14 48	14 59			15 00			15 05	15 09		15 15	15 20		15 30	15 36	15 38	15 44		15 48		15 59	16 00		
d								15 06	15 10								15 44							
Penkridge d																	15 54							
Stafford a								15 17	15 24								16 01							16 17

	LM	LM	LM	VT	LM	LM	VT	XC	LM	LM	AW	LM	XC	LM	LM	VT	XC	XC	LM	LM	LM	LM	LM	VT
	1 ◇	A		1 ◇	1		1 ◇	R 1	1 ◇	A	R		1 ◇	1		1 ◇	R 1	1 ◇	1 ◇	A		1		1 ◇
London Euston 15 ⊖ d							14 40									15 10								15 40
Northampton d					15 00																	16 00		
Long Buckby d					15 10																	16 10		
Rugby d					15 20																	16 20		
Coventry a					15 32		15 44									16 13						16 32		16 44
d					15 32		15 44							16 02		16 14	16 23					16 32		16 44
Canley d					15 35									16 05								16 35		
Tile Hill d					15 39									16 09								16 39		
Berkswell d					15 42									16 12								16 42		
Hampton-in-Arden d					15 46									16 16								16 46		
Birmingham International ✈ a					15 50		15 57							16 20		16 26	16 33					16 50		16 57
d		15 37			15 50		15 58			16 05			16 18	16 20		16 28	16 34			16 37		16 50		16 58
Marston Green d		15 40								16 08										16 40				
Lea Hall d		15 43								16 11										16 43				
Stechford d		15 45								16 13										16 45				
Adderley Park d										16 16														
Birmingham New Street 12 a		15 53			16 06		16 09			16 21			16 30	16 34		16 41	16 45	←		16 53		17 06		17 09
d	15 51		15 57	16 03		16 07	16 13	16 18	16 21		16 33		16 48 →		16 37			16 48	16 51		16 57		17 07	17 13
Smethwick Rolfe Street d						16 13									16 43								17 13	
Smethwick Galton Bdg L.L. 7 d						16 15									16 45								17 15	
Sandwell & Dudley d	15 59						16 23								16 47				16 59					17 23
Dudley Port d						16 19									16 50								17 19	
Tipton d						16 21									16 52								17 21	
Coseley d			16 09			16 23			16 34												17 09		17 23	
Walsall d												16 44												
Wolverhampton 7 a	16 09		16 15	16 20		16 30	16 36	16 38	16 43		16 48	16 59			17 00			17 05	17 09		17 15		17 30	17 36
d	16 10								16 44									17 06	17 10					
Penkridge d									16 54										17 20					
Stafford a	16 24								17 01									17 17	17 26					

For general notes see front of timetable
For details of catering facilities see Directory of Train Operators

A To Walsall (Table 70)

Northampton → Coventry → Birmingham → Wolverhampton → Stafford

Network Diagram - see first page of Table 67

	XC	LM	LM	LM	AW	LM	LM	LM	VT	XC	LM	LM	LM	VT	LM	LM	VT	XC	LM	LM	VT	AW	LM	LM
	R 1	1 ◇			◇	1			1 ◇	R 1	1 ◇			1 ◇	1		1 ◇	R 1	1 ◇		1 ◇	◇	1	
		A	B	C								B								B				
	☕	🛒			🛒				☕	☕	🛒			☕			☕	☕	🛒		☕	🛒		
London Euston 15 ⊖ d									16 10								16 40				16 51			
Northampton d						16 30									17 00									
Long Buckby d						16 40									17 10									
Rugby d						16 50									17 20						17 47			
Coventry a						17 01			17 13						17 32		17 44				18 01			
d						17 02			17 14	17 23					17 32		17 44				18 02		18 02	
Canley d						17 05									17 35								18 05	
Tile Hill d						17 09									17 39								18 09	
Berkswell d						17 12									17 42								18 12	
Hampton-in-Arden d						17 16									17 46								18 16	
Birmingham International ✈ a						17 20			17 26	17 33					17 50		17 56				18 12		18 20	
d			17 05			17 20			17 28	17 34		17 37			17 50		17 58			18 05	18 14		18 20	
Marston Green d			17 08									17 40								18 08				
Lea Hall d			17 11									17 43								18 11				
Stechford d			17 13									17 45								18 13				
Adderley Park d			17 16																	18 16				
Birmingham New Street 12 a			17 21			17 36			17 41	17 45		17 53			18 06		18 09			18 21	18 29		18 34	
d	17 18	17 21		17 24	17 33			17 37		17 48	17 51		17 57	18 03		18 07	18 13	18 18	18 21			18 33		
Smethwick Rolfe Street d								17 43								18 13								
Smethwick Galton Bdg L.L. 7 d				17 31				17 45								18 15								
Sandwell & Dudley d				17 34				17 47			17 59						18 23							
Dudley Port d				17 37				17 50								18 19								
Tipton d		17 32						17 52								18 21								
Coseley d		17 35						17 55					18 09			18 23			18 34					
Walsall d							17 44																	18 44
Wolverhampton 7 🚌 a	17 38	17 43		17 48	17 48		17 59	18 01		18 05	18 09		18 15	18 20		18 30	18 36	18 38	18 43			18 48		18 59
d		17 44								18 06	18 10								18 44					
Penkridge d		17 54									18 20								18 54					
Stafford a		18 01								18 17	18 26								19 01					

	LM	VT	XC	LM	LM	LM	VT	LM	VT	LM	LM	XC	LM	LM	VT	AW	LM	LM	LM	VT	XC	LM	LM	XC
		1 ◇	R 1	1 ◇	1		1 ◇		1 ◇	1	1	R 1	1 ◇	1	1 ◇	◇	1			1 ◇	R 1	1		R 1
		☕	☕	🛒			☕		☕			☕	🛒		☕					☕	☕			☕
London Euston 15 ⊖ d		17 10							17 30						17 51					18 10				
Northampton d											18 05													
Long Buckby d											18 15													
Rugby d											18 26													
Coventry a		18 14							18 32		18 41				18 58					19 14				
d		18 14	18 23						18 34	18 36					18 58		19 02			19 14	19 23			
Canley d										18 39							19 05							
Tile Hill d										18 43							19 09							
Berkswell d										18 46							19 12							
Hampton-in-Arden d										18 50							19 16							
Birmingham International ✈ a		18 26	18 33						18 44	18 54					19 10		19 19			19 26	19 33			
d		18 28	18 34		18 37				18 46	18 54				19 05	19 11		19 20			19 28	19 34	19 37		
Marston Green d					18 40									19 08								19 40		
Lea Hall d					18 43									19 11								19 43		
Stechford d					18 45									19 13								19 45		
Adderley Park d														19 16										
Birmingham New Street 12 a		18 39	18 45		18 53				18 57	19 08				19 21	19 27		19 34			19 39	19 45	19 53		←
d	18 37	18 43		18 51		18 57	19 03	19 07	19 13			19 18	19 21			19 33			19 37	19 51	20 03 →		19 57	20 03
Smethwick Rolfe Street d	18 43							19 13											19 43					
Smethwick Galton Bdg L.L. 7 d	18 45							19 15											19 45					
Sandwell & Dudley d	18 47	18 53		18 59					19 23										19 47	20 00				
Dudley Port d	18 50							19 19											19 50					
Tipton d	18 52							19 21											19 52					
Coseley d						19 09		19 23					19 34										20 09	
Walsall d																		19 44						
Wolverhampton 7 🚌 a	19 00	19 06		19 09		19 15	19 20	19 30	19 36			19 38	19 42			19 48		19 59	20 00	20 13			20 15	20 20
d		19 06		19 10			19 21						19 44											20 21
Penkridge d													19 54											
Stafford a		19 21		19 24			19 36						20 01											20 34

For general notes see front of timetable
For details of catering facilities see Directory of Train Operators

A To Liverpool Lime Street (Table 65)
B To Walsall (Table 70)
C To Shrewsbury (Table 74)

Northampton → Coventry → Birmingham → Wolverhampton → Stafford

Network Diagram - see first page of Table 67

		LM	LM	VT	LM	XC	LM	LM	VT	AW	LM	LM	VT	XC	XC	LM	LM	VT	LM	LM	VT	XC	LM	LM	LM
		1		1 ◇		1 ◇	1 ◇	1	1 ◇	◇	1		1 ◇	1 ◇	1 ◇			1 ◇		1	1 ◇	1 ◇	1 ◇		1
				buffet			trolley		buffet	trolley			buffet		buffet			buffet			buffet		trolley		
London Euston 15	⊖ d			18 40					18 57				19 10								19 40				
Northampton	d	19 00			19 14															20 00					
Long Buckby	d	19 10			19 24															20 10					
Rugby	d	19 20							19 47											20 20					
Coventry	a	19 32		19 44	19 55				20 00				20 13							20 32	20 44				
	d	19 32		19 44					20 00		20 02		20 14		20 23					20 32	20 44				21 02
Canley	d	19 35									20 04									20 34					21 04
Tile Hill	d	19 39									20 08									20 38					21 08
Berkswell	d	19 42									20 11									20 41					21 11
Hampton-in-Arden	d	19 46									20 15									20 45					21 15
Birmingham International ✈	a	19 50		19 57					20 12		20 20		20 26		20 33					20 50	20 57				21 18
	d	19 50		19 58				20 05	20 12		20 20		20 28		20 34					20 50	20 58				21 19
Marston Green	d							20 08			20 23									20 53					21 22
Lea Hall	d							20 11			20 26									20 56					21 25
Stechford	d							20 13			20 28									20 58					21 27
Adderley Park	d							20 16																	21 30
Birmingham New Street 12	a	20 06		20 09				20 21	20 26		20 36		20 39		20 48					21 08	21 09				21 38
	d		20 07	20 13		20 18	20 21			20 33		20 37	20 43	20 48			20 57	21 03	21 07		21 13	21 18	21 21	21 37	
Smethwick Rolfe Street	d		20 13									20 43							21 13					21 43	
Smethwick Galton Bdg L.L. 7	d		20 15									20 45							21 15					21 45	
Sandwell & Dudley	d			20 23								20 47	20 53								21 23			21 47	
Dudley Port	d		20 19									20 50							21 19					21 50	
Tipton	d		20 21									20 52							21 21					21 52	
Coseley	d		20 23				20 34										21 09		21 23				21 34		
Walsall	d															21 00									
Wolverhampton 7	a		20 30	20 36		20 38	20 43			20 49		21 00	21 06	21 08		21 13	21 16	21 20	21 30		21 36	21 38	21 43	22 00	
	d						20 44							21 11				21 21				21 39	21 44		
Penkridge	d						20 54																21 54		
Stafford	a						21 01							21 23				21 36				21 53	22 01		

		VT	XC	LM	LM	LM	LM	VT	XC	AW	LM	LM	XC	LM	LM	LM	AW	LM	VT	LM	VT FO	VT FX	VT FO	VT FX
		1 ◇	1 ◇			1		1 ◇	1 ◇	◇		1	1 ◇	1 ◇	1			1	1 ◇	1	1 ◇	1 ◇	1 ◇	1 ◇
			A											B										
		buffet	buffet					buffet	buffet										buffet		buffet	buffet	buffet	buffet
London Euston 15	⊖ d	20 10						20 40											21 40		22 40	22 40	23 40	23 40
Northampton	d					21 00									22 00					23 00				
Long Buckby	d					21 10									22 10					23 10				
Rugby	d					21 20									22 22				22 58	23 20	00s19	00s23	01s20	01s20
Coventry	a	21 13				21 32		21 44							22 32				23 10	23 36	00s32	00s35	01s33	01s33
	d	21 14	21 23			21 32		21 44				22 02	22 23		22 32			23 02	23 10					
Canley	d					21 34						22 04			22 34			23 04						
Tile Hill	d					21 38						22 08			22 38			23 08						
Berkswell	d					21 41						22 11			22 41			23 11						
Hampton-in-Arden	d					21 45						22 15			22 45			23 15						
Birmingham International ✈	a	21 26	21 33			21 50		21 57				22 18	22 33		22 50			23 18	23 27		00s47	00s47	01s46	01s46
	d	21 28	21 34			21 50		21 58				22 19	22 34		22 50			23 19	23 27					
Marston Green	d					21 53						22 22			22 53			23 22						
Lea Hall	d					21 56						22 25			22 56			23 25						
Stechford	d					21 58						22 27			22 58			23 27						
Adderley Park	d											22 30						23 30						
Birmingham New Street 12	a	21 39	21 45			22 08		22 09	←			22 38	22 52		23 08			23 38	23 39		01s01	01s01	01s57	01s58
	d	21 51	22 18	21 57	22 07			22 13	22 18	22 33	22 37			23 07			23 33		23 43					
Smethwick Rolfe Street	d		→		22 13						22 43			23 13										
Smethwick Galton Bdg L.L. 7	d				22 15						22 45			23 15										
Sandwell & Dudley	d	22 00			22 17			22 23			22 47			23 18					23 52					
Dudley Port	d				22 20						22 50			23 22										
Tipton	d				22 22						22 52			23 24										
Coseley	d			22 09	22 25						22 55			23 27										
Walsall	d						22 15									23 20								
Wolverhampton 7	a	22 13		22 16	22 31		22 32	22 36	22 38	22 48	23 01			23 33		23 34	23 49		00 05		01 32	01 34	02 31	02 32
	d								22 39					23 34										
Penkridge	d													23 43										
Stafford	a								22 53					23 50										

For general notes see front of timetable
For details of catering facilities see Directory of Train Operators

A From Bournemouth (Table 51). buffet to Reading
B To Crewe (Table 65)

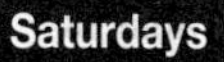

Northampton → Coventry → Birmingham → Wolverhampton → Stafford

Network Diagram - see first page of Table 67

		VT	VT	VT	VT	LM	XC	AW	LM	LM	LM	VT	LM	LM	XC	LM	AW		LM	LM	LM	LM	VT	LM	LM
		1 ◇	1 ◇	1 ◇	1 ◇	1 ◇	1 ◇	◇				1 ◇		1	1 ◇	1 ◇	◇						1 ◇		1
				A		B																			
		☕	☕		☕							☕			☕								☕		
London Euston 15 ⊖	d	22p40	23p40																						
Northampton	d													05 58											06 58
Long Buckby	d													06 08											07 08
Rugby	d	00s19	01s20											06 20											07 20
Coventry	a	00s32	01s33											06 31											07 31
	d								06 04					06 32					07 04						07 32
Canley	d								06 06					06 35					07 06						07 35
Tile Hill	d								06 10					06 39					07 10						07 39
Berkswell	d								06 13					06 42					07 13						07 42
Hampton-in-Arden	d								06 17					06 46					07 17						07 46
Birmingham International ✈	a	00s47	01s46						06 20					06 49					07 20						07 49
	d								06 20					06 50					07 20						07 50
Marston Green	d								06 23					06 53					07 23						07 53
Lea Hall	d								06 26					06 56					07 26						07 56
Stechford	d								06 29					06 59					07 29						07 59
Adderley Park	d								06 32										07 32						
Birmingham New Street 12	a	01s01	01s57						06 36					07 08					07 36						08 08
	d			05 20	05 30	06 07	06 20	06 33			06 37	07 03	07 07		07 20	07 21	07 33				07 37	07 57	08 03	08 07	
Smethwick Rolfe Street	d					06 13					06 43		07 13								07 43			08 13	
Smethwick Galton Bdg L.L. 7	d					06 15					06 45		07 15								07 45			08 15	
Sandwell & Dudley	d					06 18					06 47		07 17								07 47			08 17	
Dudley Port	d					06 22					06 50		07 20								07 50			08 20	
Tipton	d					06 24					06 52		07 22								07 52			08 22	
Coseley	d					06 27					06 55		07 25			07 34						08 09		08 25	
Walsall	d									06 42										07 44					
Wolverhampton 7	a	01 32	02 31	05 37	05 48	06 32	06 38	06 48		06 57	07 01	07 20	07 31		07 38	07 42	07 48			07 59	08 00	08 14	08 20	08 31	
	d			05 38	05 49	06 33	06 40					07 21			07 40	07 44									
Penkridge	d					06 43										07 53									
Stafford	a			05 51	06 04	06 50	06 53					07 33			07 53	08 01									

		VT	XC	LM	AW	LM	VT	LM	LM	VT	XC	VT		LM	VT	LM	LM	VT	XC	LM	AW	LM	LM	LM	VT
		1 ◇	1 ◇	1 ◇	◇		1 ◇			1 ◇	1 ◇	1 ◇			1 ◇		1	1 ◇	1 ◇	1 ◇	◇				1 ◇
		☕	☕		🛒		☕			☕	☕	☕			☕			☕	☕		🛒				☕
London Euston 15 ⊖	d	06 10					06 59			07 06		07 15						07 30							08 03
Northampton	d																07 58								
Long Buckby	d																08 08								
Rugby	d											08 12					08 20								08 57
Coventry	a	07 40					08 07			08 14		08 23					08 31	08 41							09 09
	d	07 42				08 00	08 08			08 15	08 23	08 27					08 32	08 43				09 00			09 10
Canley	d					08 02											08 35					09 02			
Tile Hill	d					08 06											08 39					09 06			
Berkswell	d					08 09											08 42					09 09			
Hampton-in-Arden	d					08 13											08 46					09 13			
Birmingham International ✈	a	07 55				08 16				08 27	08 33						08 49	08 55				09 16			09 21
	d	07 57				08 16				08 28	08 34	08u41					08 50	08 57				09 16			09 22
Marston Green	d					08 19											08 53					09 19			
Lea Hall	d					08 22											08 56					09 22			
Stechford	d					08 25											08 59					09 25			
Adderley Park	d					08 28																09 28			
Birmingham New Street 12	a	08 11				08 36				08 39	08 46	08s50					09 08	09 11				09 33			09 36
	d	08 13	08 20	08 21	08 33				08 37	08 48				08 57	09 03	09 07		09 13	09 20	09 21	09 33			09 37	09 40
Smethwick Rolfe Street	d								08 43							09 13								09 43	
Smethwick Galton Bdg L.L. 7	d								08 45							09 15								09 45	
Sandwell & Dudley	d	08 22							08 47							09 17		09 22						09 47	
Dudley Port	d								08 50							09 20								09 50	
Tipton	d								08 52							09 22								09 52	
Coseley	d			08 34										09 09		09 25				09 34					
Walsall	d							08 44															09 44		
Wolverhampton 7	a	08 33	08 38	08 42	08 48			08 59	09 01	09 07				09 15	09 20	09 30		09 33	09 38	09 42	09 48		09 59	10 00	
	d		08 40	08 44						09 09									09 40	09 44					
Penkridge	d			08 53																09 53					
Stafford	a		08 53	09 01			09 14			09 24									09 53	10 01					10 17

For general notes see front of timetable
For details of catering facilities see Directory of Train Operators

A To Holyhead (Table 81)
B To Liverpool Lime Street (Table 91)

Northampton → Coventry → Birmingham → Wolverhampton → Stafford

Network Diagram - see first page of Table 67

		VT	XC	VT	LM	VT	LM		LM	VT	XC	LM	AW	LM	LM	LM	VT	VT	XC	VT	LM	VT	LM	LM	VT
		1 ◇	1 ◇	1 ◇		1 ◇			1	1 ◇	1 ◇	1 ◇	◇				1 ◇	1 ◇	1 ◇	1 ◇		R 1		1	1 ◇
		☕	☕	☕		☕				☕	☕		🛒				☕	☕	☕	☕		☕			☕
London Euston 15 ⊖	d	08 10		08 17						08 30							09 03	09 10		09 17					09 38
Northampton	d								08 58															09 58	
Long Buckby	d								09 08															10 08	
Rugby	d			09 13					09 20								09 58			10 12				10 20	
Coventry	a	09 15		09 24					09 31	09 40							10 09	10 15		10 23				10 31	10 42
	d	09 16	09 23	09 27					09 32	09 42				10 00			10 10	10 16	10 23	10 27				10 32	10 43
Canley	d								09 35					10 02										10 35	
Tile Hill	d								09 39					10 06										10 39	
Berkswell	d								09 42					10 09										10 42	
Hampton-in-Arden	d								09 46					10 13										10 46	
Birmingham International ✈	a	09 27	09 33	09 38					09 49	09 55				10 16			10 21	10 27	10 33	10 38				10 49	10 55
	d	09 28	09 34	09 39					09 50	09 57				10 16			10 22	10 28	10 34	10 39				10 50	10 57
Marston Green	d								09 53					10 19										10 53	
Lea Hall	d								09 56					10 22										10 56	
Stechford	d								09 59					10 25										10 59	
Adderley Park	d													10 28											
Birmingham New Street 12	a	09 39	09 45	09s50					10 08	10 11	←			10 33			10 36	10 39	10 45	10s50				11 08	11 11
	d	09 48	10 20 →		09 57	10 03	10 07			10 13	10 20	10 21	10 33			10 37	10 40	10 48			10 57	11 03	11 07		11 13
Smethwick Rolfe Street	d						10 13									10 43							11 13		
Smethwick Galton Bdg L.L. 7	d						10 15									10 45							11 15		
Sandwell & Dudley	d						10 17			10 22						10 47							11 17		11 22
Dudley Port	d						10 20									10 50							11 20		
Tipton	d						10 22									10 52							11 22		
Coseley	d				10 09		10 25					10 34									11 09		11 25		
Walsall	d														10 44										
Wolverhampton 7	a	10 07			10 15	10 21	10 30			10 33	10 38	10 42	10 48		10 59	11 00		11 07			11 15	11 20	11 30		11 33
	d	10 09									10 40	10 44						11 09							
Penkridge	d											10 53													
Stafford	a	10 24									10 53	11 01					11 19	11 24							

		XC		LM	AW	LM	LM	LM	VT	VT	XC	VT	LM	VT	LM	LM	VT	XC	LM		AW	LM	LM	LM	VT
		1 ◇		1 ◇	◇				1 ◇	1 ◇	1 ◇	1 ◇		1 ◇		1	1 ◇	1 ◇	1 ◇		◇				1 ◇
		☕			🛒				☕	☕	☕	☕		☕			☕	☕			🛒				☕
London Euston 15 ⊖	d								10 03	10 10		10 17					10 38								11 03
Northampton	d															10 58									
Long Buckby	d															11 08									
Rugby	d								10 57			11 12				11 20									11 58
Coventry	a								11 09	11 15		11 23				11 31	11 40								12 09
	d					11 00			11 10	11 16	11 23	11 27				11 32	11 42					12 00			12 10
Canley	d					11 02										11 35						12 02			
Tile Hill	d					11 06										11 39						12 06			
Berkswell	d					11 09										11 42						12 09			
Hampton-in-Arden	d					11 13										11 46						12 13			
Birmingham International ✈	a					11 16			11 21	11 27	11 33	11 38				11 49	11 55					12 16			12 21
	d					11 16			11 22	11 28	11 34	11 39				11 50	11 57					12 16			12 22
Marston Green	d					11 19										11 53						12 19			
Lea Hall	d					11 22										11 56						12 22			
Stechford	d					11 25										11 59						12 25			
Adderley Park	d					11 28																12 28			
Birmingham New Street 12	a					11 33			11 36	11 39	11 45	11s50				12 08	12 11	←				12 33			12 36
	d	11 20		11 21	11 33			11 37	11 40	11 48	12 20 →		11 57	12 03	12 07		12 13	12 20	12 21		12 33			12 37	12 40
Smethwick Rolfe Street	d							11 43							12 13									12 43	
Smethwick Galton Bdg L.L. 7	d							11 45							12 15									12 45	
Sandwell & Dudley	d							11 47							12 17		12 22							12 47	
Dudley Port	d							11 50							12 20									12 50	
Tipton	d							11 52							12 22									12 52	
Coseley	d			11 34											12 25				12 34						
Walsall	d						11 44																12 44		
Wolverhampton 7	a	11 38		11 42	11 48		11 59	12 00		12 07			12 15	12 20	12 30		12 33	12 38	12 42		12 48		12 59	13 00	
	d	11 40		11 44						12 09								12 40	12 44						
Penkridge	d			11 53															12 53						
Stafford	a	11 53		12 01					12 17	12 24								12 53	13 01						13 17

For general notes see front of timetable
For details of catering facilities see Directory of Train Operators

Northampton → Coventry → Birmingham → Wolverhampton → Stafford

Network Diagram - see first page of Table 67

		VT	XC	VT	LM	VT	LM	LM	VT	XC	LM	AW	LM	LM		LM	VT	VT	XC	VT	LM	VT	LM	LM	VT
		1 ◇ ☕	1 ◇ ☕	1 ◇ ☕		R 1 ☕		1	1 ◇ ☕	1 ◇ ☕	1 ◇	◇ 🛒					1 ◇ ☕	1 ◇ ☕	1 ◇ ☕	1 ◇ ☕		R 1 A ☕		1	1 ◇ ☕
London Euston 15 ⊖	d	11 10		11 17					11 38								12 03	12 10		12 17					12 38
Northampton	d							11 58																12 58	
Long Buckby	d							12 08																13 08	
Rugby	d			12 12				12 20									12 57			13 12				13 20	
Coventry	a	12 15						12 31	12 42								13 09	13 15		13 23				13 31	13 40
	d	12 16	12 23	12u27				12 32	12 43				13 00				13 10	13 16	13 23	13 27				13 32	13 42
Canley	d							12 35					13 02											13 35	
Tile Hill	d							12 39					13 06											13 39	
Berkswell	d							12 42					13 09											13 42	
Hampton-in-Arden	d							12 46					13 13											13 46	
Birmingham International ✈	a	12 27	12 33	12 38				12 49	12 55				13 16				13 21	13 27	13 33	13 38				13 49	13 55
	d	12 28	12 34	12 39				12 50	12 57				13 16				13 22	13 28	13 34	13 39				13 50	13 57
Marston Green	d							12 53					13 19											13 53	
Lea Hall	d							12 56					13 22											13 56	
Stechford	d							12 59					13 25											13 59	
Adderley Park	d												13 28												
Birmingham New Street 12	a	12 39	12 45	12s50				13 08	13 11				13 33				13 36	13 39	13 45	13s50				14 08	14 09
	d	12 48			12 57	13 03	13 07		13 13	13 20	13 21	13 33				13 37	13 40	13 48	14 20 →		13 57	14 03	14 07		14 13
Smethwick Rolfe Street	d						13 13									13 43							14 13		
Smethwick Galton Bdg L.L. 7	d						13 15									13 45							14 15		
Sandwell & Dudley	d						13 17		13 22							13 47							14 17		14 22
Dudley Port	d						13 20									13 50							14 20		
Tipton	d						13 22									13 52							14 22		
Coseley	d				13 09		13 25				13 34										14 09		14 25		
Walsall	d													13 44											
Wolverhampton 7	a	13 07			13 15	13 20	13 30		13 33	13 38	13 42	13 48		13 59		14 00		14 07			14 15	14 20	14 30		14 33
	d	13 09								13 40	13 44							14 09							
Penkridge	d										13 53														
Stafford	a	13 24								13 53	14 01						14 17	14 24							

		XC	LM	AW	LM	LM	LM	VT	VT		XC	VT	LM	VT	LM	LM	VT	XC	LM	AW	LM	LM	LM	VT	VT
		1 ◇ ☕	1 ◇	◇ 🛒				1 ◇ ☕	1 ◇ ☕		1 ◇ ☕	1 ◇ ☕		R 1 ☕		1	1 ◇ ☕	1 ◇ ☕	1 ◇	◇ 🛒				1 ◇ ☕	1 ◇ ☕
London Euston 15 ⊖	d							13 03	13 10			13 17					13 38							14 03	14 10
Northampton	d															13 58									
Long Buckby	d															14 08									
Rugby	d							13 58				14 11				14 20								14 57	
Coventry	a							14 09	14 15							14 31	14 41							15 09	15 15
	d				14 00			14 10	14 16		14 23	14u27				14 32	14 43				15 00			15 10	15 16
Canley	d				14 02											14 35					15 02				
Tile Hill	d				14 06											14 39					15 06				
Berkswell	d				14 09											14 42					15 09				
Hampton-in-Arden	d				14 13											14 46					15 13				
Birmingham International ✈	a				14 16			14 21	14 27		14 33	14 38				14 49	14 55				15 16			15 21	15 27
	d				14 16			14 22	14 28		14 34	14 39				14 50	14 57				15 16			15 22	15 28
Marston Green	d				14 19											14 53					15 19				
Lea Hall	d				14 22											14 56					15 22				
Stechford	d				14 25											14 59					15 25				
Adderley Park	d				14 28																15 28				
Birmingham New Street 12	a	←			14 33			14 36	14 39		14 46	14s50				15 08	15 11				15 33			15 36	15 39
	d	14 20	14 21	14 33			14 37	14 40	14 48				14 57	15 03	15 07		15 13	15 20	15 21	15 33			15 37	15 40	15 48
Smethwick Rolfe Street	d						14 43								15 13								15 43		
Smethwick Galton Bdg L.L. 7	d						14 45								15 15								15 45		
Sandwell & Dudley	d						14 47								15 17		15 22						15 47		
Dudley Port	d						14 50								15 20								15 50		
Tipton	d						14 52								15 22								15 52		
Coseley	d		14 34										15 09		15 25				15 34						
Walsall	d					14 44																15 44			
Wolverhampton 7	a	14 38	14 42	14 48		14 59	15 00		15 07				15 15	15 20	15 30		15 33	15 38	15 42	15 48		15 59	16 00		16 07
	d	14 40	14 44						15 09									15 40	15 44						16 09
Penkridge	d		14 53																15 53						
Stafford	a	14 53	15 01					15 17	15 24									15 53	16 01					16 17	16 24

For general notes see front of timetable
For details of catering facilities see Directory of Train Operators

A Until 22 March

Northampton → Coventry → Birmingham → Wolverhampton → Stafford

Network Diagram - see first page of Table 67

		XC	VT	LM		VT	LM	LM	VT	XC	LM	AW	LM	LM	LM	VT	VT	XC	VT	LM	VT		LM	LM	VT
												R									R				
		1◇	1◇			1◇		1	1◇	1◇	1◇					1◇	1◇	1◇	1◇		1			1	1◇
		🍴	🍴			🍴			🍴	🍴		trolley				🍴	🍴	🍴	🍴		🍴				🍴
London Euston 15 ⊖	d		14 17						14 38							15 03	15 10		15 17						15 38
Northampton	d							14 58																15 58	
Long Buckby	d							15 08																16 08	
Rugby	d		15 12					15 20								15 58			16 12					16 20	
Coventry	a		15 23					15 31	15 41							16 09	16 15							16 31	16 41
	d	15 23	15 27					15 32	15 43				16 00			16 10	16 16	16 23	16u27					16 32	16 43
Canley	d							15 35					16 02											16 35	
Tile Hill	d							15 39					16 06											16 39	
Berkswell	d							15 42					16 09											16 42	
Hampton-in-Arden	d							15 46					16 13											16 46	
Birmingham International ✈	a	15 33	15 38					15 49	15 55				16 16			16 21	16 27	16 33	16 38					16 49	16 55
	d	15 34	15 39					15 50	15 57				16 16			16 22	16 28	16 34	16 39					16 50	16 57
Marston Green	d							15 53					16 19											16 53	
Lea Hall	d							15 56					16 22											16 56	
Stechford	d							15 59					16 25											16 59	
Adderley Park	d												16 28												
Birmingham New Street 12	a	15 45	15s50					16 08	16 11	←			16 33			16 36	16 39	16 46	16s50					17 08	17 11
	d	16 20 →		15 57		16 03	16 07		16 13	16 20	16 21	16 33			16 37	16 40	16 48			16 57	17 03		17 07		17 13
Smethwick Rolfe Street	d						16 13								16 43								17 13		
Smethwick Galton Bdg L.L. 7	d						16 15								16 45								17 15		
Sandwell & Dudley	d						16 17		16 22						16 47								17 17		17 22
Dudley Port	d						16 20								16 50								17 20		
Tipton	d						16 22								16 52								17 22		
Coseley	d						16 25				16 34									17 09			17 25		
Walsall	d													16 44											
Wolverhampton 7	a			16 15		16 20	16 30		16 33	16 38	16 42	16 48		16 59	17 00		17 07			17 15	17 20		17 30		17 33
	d									16 40	16 44						17 09								
Penkridge	d										16 53														
Stafford	a									16 53	17 01					17 17	17 24								

		XC	LM	AW	LM	LM	LM	VT	VT	XC	VT	LM	VT	LM	LM	VT		XC	LM	AW	LM	LM	LM	VT	VT
													R												
		1◇	1◇	◇				1◇	1◇	1◇	1◇		1		1	1◇		1◇	1◇	◇				1◇	1◇
		🍴		trolley				🍴	🍴	🍴	🍴		🍴			🍴		🍴		trolley				🍴	🍴
London Euston 15 ⊖	d							16 03	16 10		16 17					16 38								17 03	17 10
Northampton	d														16 58										
Long Buckby	d														17 08										
Rugby	d							16 57			17 12				17 20									17 58	
Coventry	a							17 09	17 15		17 23				17 31	17 41								18 09	18 15
	d				17 00			17 10	17 16	17 23	17 27				17 32	17 43					18 00			18 10	18 16
Canley	d				17 02										17 35						18 02				
Tile Hill	d				17 06										17 39						18 06				
Berkswell	d				17 09										17 42						18 09				
Hampton-in-Arden	d				17 13										17 46						18 13				
Birmingham International ✈	a				17 16			17 21	17 27	17 33	17 38				17 49	17 55					18 16			18 21	18 27
	d				17 16			17 22	17 28	17 34	17 39				17 50	17 57					18 16			18 22	18 28
Marston Green	d				17 19										17 53						18 19				
Lea Hall	d				17 22										17 56						18 22				
Stechford	d				17 25										17 59						18 25				
Adderley Park	d				17 28																18 28				
Birmingham New Street 12	a				17 33			17 36	17 39	17 45	17s50				18 08	18 11		←			18 33			18 36	18 39
	d	17 20	17 21	17 33			17 37	17 40	17 48	18 20 →		17 57	18 03	18 07		18 13		18 20	18 21	18 33			18 37	18 40	18 48
Smethwick Rolfe Street	d						17 43							18 13									18 43		
Smethwick Galton Bdg L.L. 7	d						17 45							18 15									18 45		
Sandwell & Dudley	d						17 47							18 17		18 22							18 47		
Dudley Port	d						17 50							18 20									18 50		
Tipton	d						17 52							18 22									18 52		
Coseley	d		17 34									18 09		18 25					18 34						
Walsall	d					17 44																18 44			
Wolverhampton 7	a	17 38	17 42	17 48		17 59	18 00		18 07			18 15	18 20	18 30		18 33		18 38	18 42	18 48		18 59	19 00		19 07
	d	17 40	17 44						18 09									18 40	18 44						19 09
Penkridge	d		17 53																18 53						
Stafford	a	17 53	18 01					18 17	18 24									18 53	19 01					19 17	19 24

For general notes see front of timetable
For details of catering facilities see Directory of Train Operators

Table 68

Northampton → Coventry → Birmingham → Wolverhampton → Stafford

Network Diagram - see first page of Table 67

	XC	VT	LM	VT	LM	LM	VT	XC	LM	AW		LM	VT	LM	LM	VT	XC	LM	LM	LM	VT	XC	LM	AW
	1 ◇ ☕	1 ◇ ☕		R 1 ☕		1	1 ◇ ☕	1 ◇ ☕	1 ◇	◇			1 ◇ ☕			1 ◇ ☕	1 ◇ ☕			1	1 ◇ ☕	1 ◇ ☕	1 ◇	◇ 🍴
London Euston 15 ⊖ d		17 17					17 38						18 03			18 10					18 38			
Northampton d						17 58														18 58				
Long Buckby d						18 08														19 08				
Rugby d		18 12				18 20														19 20				
Coventry a						18 31	18 41						19 09			19 15				19 31	19 41			
d	18 23	18u27				18 32	18 43					19 00	19 10			19 16	19 23			19 32	19 43			
Canley d						18 35						19 02								19 35				
Tile Hill d						18 39						19 06								19 39				
Berkswell d						18 42						19 09								19 42				
Hampton-in-Arden d						18 46						19 13								19 46				
Birmingham International ✈ a	18 33	18 39				18 49	18 55					19 16				19 27	19 33			19 49	19 55			
d	18 34	18 41				18 50	18 57					19 16				19 28	19 34			19 50	19 57			
Marston Green d						18 53						19 19								19 53				
Lea Hall d						18 56						19 22								19 56				
Stechford d						18 59						19 25								19 59				
Adderley Park d												19 28												
Birmingham New Street 12 a	18 45	18s50				19 08	19 11					19 36				19 39	19 45			20 08	20 11	←		
d			18 57	19 03	19 07		19 13	19 20	19 21	19 33					19 37	19 48	20 20 →	19 57	20 07		20 13	20 20	20 21	20 33
Smethwick Rolfe Street d					19 13										19 43				20 13					
Smethwick Galton Bdg L.L. 7 d					19 15										19 45				20 15					
Sandwell & Dudley d					19 17		19 22								19 47				20 17		20 22			
Dudley Port d					19 20										19 50				20 20					
Tipton d					19 22										19 52				20 22					
Coseley d			19 09		19 25				19 34									20 09	20 25				20 34	
Walsall d														19 44										
Wolverhampton 7 a			19 15	19 20	19 30		19 33	19 38	19 42	19 48				19 59	20 00	20 07		20 15	20 30		20 33	20 38	20 42	20 48
d				19 21				19 40	19 44							20 09						20 40	20 44	
Penkridge d									19 53														20 53	
Stafford a				19 33				19 53	20 01				20 13			20 24						20 53	21 01	

	LM	VT	LM	LM	VT		VT	XC	VT	VT	LM	LM	LM	XC	LM	AW	LM	LM	VT	VT	LM	LM		XC
		1 ◇ ☕			1 ◇ A ☕		1 ◇ B ☕	1 ◇ ☕	1 ◇ A ☕	1 ◇ B ☕			1	1 ◇	1 ◇	◇			1 ◇ A ☕	1 ◇ B ☕				1 ◇ ☕
London Euston 15 ⊖ d		19 02			18 57		19 10		19 05	19 17									19 24	19 31				
Northampton d													19 58											
Long Buckby d													20 08											
Rugby d									20 17	20 17			20 20											
Coventry a		20 09			20 15		20 15		20 28	20 28			20 32						21 10	21 10				
d	20 00	20 10			20 16		20 16	20 23					20 32				21 00		21 11	21 11				21 23
Canley d	20 02												20 35				21 02							
Tile Hill d	20 06												20 39				21 06							
Berkswell d	20 09												20 42				21 09							
Hampton-in-Arden d	20 13												20 46				21 13							
Birmingham International ✈ a	20 16				20 27		20 27	20 33					20 50				21 16		21 25	21 25				21 33
d	20 16				20 28		20 28	20 34					20 50				21 16		21 26	21 26				21 34
Marston Green d	20 19												20 53				21 19							
Lea Hall d	20 22												20 56				21 22							
Stechford d	20 25												20 59				21 25							
Adderley Park d	20 28																21 28							
Birmingham New Street 12 a	20 36				20 39		20 39	20 45					21 08				21 33		21 39	21 39				21 45
d				20 37	20 48		20 48				20 57	21 07		21 20	21 21	21 33		21 37	21 51	21 51	21 57	22 07		22 20 →
Smethwick Rolfe Street d				20 43								21 13						21 43				22 13		
Smethwick Galton Bdg L.L. 7 d				20 45								21 15						21 45				22 15		
Sandwell & Dudley d				20 47	20 57		20 57					21 17						21 47	22 00	22 00		22 17		
Dudley Port d				20 50								21 20						21 50				22 20		
Tipton d				20 52								21 22						21 52				22 22		
Coseley d											21 09	21 25			21 34						22 09	22 25		
Walsall d			20 44																					
Wolverhampton 7 a			20 59	21 00	21 08		21 08				21 15	21 30		21 38	21 42	21 48		22 00	22 14	22 14	22 15	22 30		
d					21 10		21 10							21 40	21 44									
Penkridge d															21 54									
Stafford a		21 13			21 24		21 24							21 53	22 01									

For general notes see front of timetable
For details of catering facilities see Directory of Train Operators

A Until 22 March
B From 29 March

Saturdays

Northampton → Coventry → Birmingham → Wolverhampton → Stafford

Network Diagram - see first page of Table 67

		VT 1◇ A	VT 1◇ B	LM 1	VT 1◇ A	VT 1◇ B	LM	XC 1◇	AW ◇	LM	VT 1◇ A	VT 1◇ B	XC 1◇	LM	LM	LM	LM		AW	VT 1◇ B	VT 1◇ A	VT 1◇ A	VT 1◇ B		
London Euston 15 ⊖	d	19 36	19 50		20 00	20 12					20 13	20 30								21 30	21 13	21 50	22 13		
Northampton	d			20 58																					
Long Buckby	d			21 08																					
Rugby	d	21 16	21 16	21 20	21 39	21 45					21 56	21 56								22 46	22 55	23 18	23 36		
Coventry	a	21 27	21 27	21 32							22 07	22 07								22 58	23 06	23 30	23 48		
	d	21 28	21 28	21 32						22 03	22 09	22 09	22 23		22 32		22 56			22 59	23 08	23 31	23 50		
Canley	d			21 35						22 05					22 35		22 59								
Tile Hill	d			21 39						22 09					22 39		23 02								
Berkswell	d			21 42						22 12					22 42		23 06								
Hampton-in-Arden	d			21 46						22 16					22 46		23 10								
Birmingham International ✈	a			21 50						22 19	22 25	22 25	22 33		22 49		23 13			23 18	23 18	23 42	23 59		
	d			21 50						22 19	22 26	22 26	22 34		22 50		23 13			23 20	23 20	23 43	00 01		
Marston Green	d			21 53						22 22					22 53		23 16								
Lea Hall	d			21 56						22 25					22 56		23 19								
Stechford	d			21 59						22 28					22 59		23 22								
Adderley Park	d									22 31							23 25								
Birmingham New Street 12	a			22 08				←		22 36	22 39	22 39	22 50		23 08		23 30			23 33	23 33	23 54	00 12		
	d							22 20	22 33	22 37	22 48	22 48		23 07					23 33	23 37	23 37	23 58	00 17		
Smethwick Rolfe Street	d									22 43				23 13											
Smethwick Galton Bdg L.L. 7	d									22 45				23 15											
Sandwell & Dudley	d									22 47	22 57	22 57		23 17											
Dudley Port	d									22 50				23 20											
Tipton	d									22 52				23 22											
Coseley	d									22 55				23 25											
Walsall	d						22 15									23 20									
Wolverhampton 7	a						22 32	22 38	22 48	23 01	23 11	23 11		23 30		23 39			23 49	23 58	23 58	00 19	00 39		
	d							22 40																	
Penkridge	d																								
Stafford	a	22 16	22 16		22 47	22 47		22 53																	

Sundays

until 27 January

		VT 1◇	LM	LM	XC 1◇	LM 1◇	LM	LM	VT 1◇	LM	LM (bus)	LM	XC 1◇	AW	LM 1	LM	VT 1◇	VT 1◇	LM	LM (bus)	LM	XC 1◇	AW ◇	LM 1◇	LM 1
London Euston 15 ⊖	d																08 40								
Northampton	d										08 21									09 21					
Long Buckby	d										08 42									09 42					
Rugby	d										09 13									10 13					
Coventry	a										09 53						10 24			10 53					
	d		08 30				09 04			09 30					10 04		10 25		10 30						11 04
Canley	d		08 32							09 32									10 32						
Tile Hill	d		08 36							09 36									10 36						
Berkswell	d		08 39							09 39									10 39						
Hampton-in-Arden	d		08 43							09 43									10 43						
Birmingham International ✈	a		08 46				09 13			09 46					10 13		10 35		10 46						11 13
	d		08 46				09 14			09 46					10 14		10 36		10 46						11 14
Marston Green	d		08 49							09 49									10 49						
Lea Hall	d		08 52							09 52									10 52						
Stechford	d		08 55							09 55									10 55						
Adderley Park	d		08 58							09 58									10 58						
Birmingham New Street 12	a		09 06				09 30			10 06					10 30		10 45		11 06						11 30
	d	09 03			09 18	09 30		09 40	10 00				10 18	10 27		10 40	10 48	11 03				11 18	11 27	11 30	
Smethwick Rolfe Street	d							09 46								10 46									
Smethwick Galton Bdg L.L. 7	d							09 48								10 48									
Sandwell & Dudley	d							09 50								10 50	10 57								
Dudley Port	d							09 53								10 53									
Tipton	d							09 55								10 55									
Coseley	d							09 58								10 58									
Walsall	d			09 20								10 20									11 20				
Wolverhampton 7	a	09 20		09 35	09 37	09 45		10 03	10 20			10 36	10 37	10 43		11 03	11 08	11 20			11 36	11 37	11 43	11 47	
	d	09 21			09 38	09 46							10 38									11 38		11 48	
Penkridge	d					09 55																			
Stafford	a	09 33			09 51	10 02							10 51									11 51		12 06	

For general notes see front of timetable
For details of catering facilities see
Directory of Train Operators

A Until 22 March
B From 29 March

Table 68

until 27 January

Northampton → Coventry → Birmingham → Wolverhampton → Stafford

Network Diagram - see first page of Table 67

		VT		CH	LM	VT	VT	VT	LM	XC	LM	LM	LM	VT	AW	LM	VT	XC	VT	LM	LM	LM	XC	XC	LM
		1◇		A		1◇	1◇	1◇		1◇		🚌	1	1◇			1◇	1◇	1◇		🚌		1◇	1◇	
		☕				☕	☕	☕		☕				☕			☕	☕	☕				☕	☕	
London Euston 15 ⊖	d	09 31				09 36	09 40							10 31			10 36								
Northampton	d											10 21									11 21				
Long Buckby	d											10 42									11 42				
Rugby	d	10 57					11 08					11 13		11 57							12 13				
Coventry	a	11 07				11 13	11 19					11 53		12 07			12 13				12 53				
	d	11 09				11 15				11 25	11 30		11 59	12 09			12 15	12 25		12 30				12 55	
Canley	d										11 32									12 32					
Tile Hill	d										11 36									12 36					
Berkswell	d										11 39									12 39					
Hampton-in-Arden	d										11 43									12 43					
Birmingham International ✈	a					11 25				11 35	11 46		12 08				12 25	12 35		12 46				13 04	
	d					11 26				11 36	11 46		12 09				12 26	12 36		12 46				13 05	
Marston Green	d										11 49									12 49					
Lea Hall	d										11 52									12 52					
Stechford	d										11 55									12 55					
Adderley Park	d										11 58									12 58					
Birmingham New Street 12	a					11 39				11 46	12 06		12 24				12 39	12 46		13 06				13 18	
	d			11 33	11 40	11 48		12 03		12 18					12 27	12 37	12 48		13 03				13 18		13 21
Smethwick Rolfe Street	d				11 46											12 43									13 27
Smethwick Galton Bdg L.L. 7	d				11 48											12 45									13 29
Sandwell & Dudley	d				11 50	11 57										12 47	12 57								13 31
Dudley Port	d				11 53											12 50									13 34
Tipton	d				11 55											12 52									13 36
Coseley	d				11 58											12 55									13 39
Walsall	d								12 20													13 20			
Wolverhampton 7	a			11 51	12 04	12 08		12 20	12 34	12 37					12 43	13 02	13 08		13 20			13 36	13 37		13 44
	d									12 38													13 38		
Penkridge	d																								
Stafford	a	12 00								12 51				13 00									13 51		

		LM	VT	AW		LM	VT	VT	LM	XC	LM	LM	XC	LM	LM	VT	AW	VT	VT	XC	VT	LM	AW	VT	LM
								R		R										R	R				
		1	1◇	◇		1◇	1◇	1		1		🚌	1◇		1	1◇	◇	1◇	1◇	1	1			1◇	🚌
			☕	🛒			☕	☕		☕			☕			☕		☕	☕	☕	☕			☕	
London Euston 15 ⊖	d		11 31				11 36									12 31		12 36	12 40					13 06	
Northampton	d											12 21													13 21
Long Buckby	d											12 42													13 42
Rugby	d		12 57									13 13				13 57			14 08						14 13
Coventry	a		13 07				13 13					13 53				14 07		14 13	14 19					14 41	14 53
	d	12 59	13 09				13 15			13 25	13 30		13 55		13 59	14 09		14 15	14 21	14 25		14 30		14 42	
Canley	d										13 32											14 32			
Tile Hill	d										13 36											14 36			
Berkswell	d										13 39											14 39			
Hampton-in-Arden	d										13 43											14 43			
Birmingham International ✈	a	13 09					13 25			13 35	13 46		14 04		14 09			14 25		14 35		14 46		14 53	
	d	13 09					13 26			13 36	13 46		14 05		14 09			14 26		14 36		14 46		14 54	
Marston Green	d										13 49											14 49			
Lea Hall	d										13 52											14 52			
Stechford	d										13 55											14 55			
Adderley Park	d										13 58											14 58			
Birmingham New Street 12	a	13 23					13 39			13 46	14 06		14 18		14 24			14 39		14 46		15 06		15 09	
	d			13 27		13 30	13 48	14 03		14 18				14 21			14 27	14 48			15 03		15 07		
Smethwick Rolfe Street	d													14 27											
Smethwick Galton Bdg L.L. 7	d													14 29											
Sandwell & Dudley	d						13 57							14 31				14 57							
Dudley Port	d													14 34											
Tipton	d													14 36											
Coseley	d													14 39											
Walsall	d								14 20																
Wolverhampton 7	a			13 47		13 51	14 08	14 20	14 36	14 37				14 44			14 47	15 08			15 20		15 25		
	d					13 52				14 38															
Penkridge	d					14 01																			
Stafford	a		14 00			14 08				14 51						15 00			15 18						

For general notes see front of timetable
For details of catering facilities see Directory of Train Operators

A From London Marylebone (Table 71)

Table 68

Sundays

until 27 January

Northampton → Coventry → Birmingham → Wolverhampton → Stafford

Network Diagram - see first page of Table 67

		LM	XC	XC	LM	LM		VT	LM	VT	VT	XC	LM	AW	VT	LM	LM	XC	XC	LM	LM	VT	VT	XC	AW
			R 1 ☕	1 ◇ ☕		1		1 ◇ ☕	1 ◇	1 ◇ ☕	R 1 ☕	R 1 ☕		◇ 🛒	1 ◇ ☕	🚌		R 1 ☕	1 ◇ ☕		1	1 ◇ ☕	1 ◇ ☕	R 1 ☕	◇
London Euston 15 ⊖	d							13 40		13 50					14 27							14 50	14 53		
Northampton	d															14 21									
Long Buckby	d															14 42									
Rugby	d							14 57								15 13						15 57			
Coventry	a							15 07		15 13					15 42	15 53						16 07	16 13		
	d			14 55		14 59		15 09		15 15		15 25	15 30		15 43				15 55		15 59	16 09	16 15	16 25	
Canley	d												15 32												
Tile Hill	d												15 36												
Berkswell	d												15 39												
Hampton-in-Arden	d												15 43												
Birmingham International ✈	a			15 04		15 09				15 25		15 35	15 46		15 54				16 04		16 09		16 25	16 35	
	d			15 05		15 09				15 26		15 36	15 46		15 55				16 05		16 09		16 26	16 36	
Marston Green	d												15 49												
Lea Hall	d												15 52												
Stechford	d												15 55												
Adderley Park	d												15 58												
Birmingham New Street 12	a			15 18		15 24				15 39		15 46	16 06		16 09			←	16 18		16 24		16 39	16 46	
	d		15 18		15 21				15 30	15 51	16 03	16 18 →		16 07				16 18		16 21			16 48		16 57
Smethwick Rolfe Street	d				15 27															16 27					
Smethwick Galton Bdg L.L. 7	d				15 29															16 29					
Sandwell & Dudley	d				15 31					16 00										16 31			16 57		
Dudley Port	d				15 34															16 34					
Tipton	d				15 36															16 36					
Coseley	d				15 39															16 39					
Walsall	d	15 20															16 20								
Wolverhampton 7 🚉	a	15 34	15 37		15 44				15 50	16 11	16 20			16 25			16 34	16 37		16 45			17 08		17 13
	d		15 38						15 50									16 38							
Penkridge	d																								
Stafford	a		15 51					16 00	16 05									16 51				17 00			

		VT	LM	VT	LM	LM	XC	XC		LM	LM	VT	LM	CH	VT	AW	VT	LM	XC	LM	VT	LM	XC	LM	LM
		R 1 ☕		1 ◇ ☕	🚌		R 1 ☕	1 ◇ ☕			1	1 ◇ ☕	1 ◇	A	1 ◇ ☕		R 1 ☕		R 1 ☕		1 ◇ ☕	🚌	1 ◇ ☕		1
London Euston 15 ⊖	d			15 27								15 50			15 53						16 27				
Northampton	d				15 21																	16 21			
Long Buckby	d				15 42																	16 42			
Rugby	d				16 13							16 57										17 13			
Coventry	a			16 42	16 53							17 07			17 13						17 42	17 53			
	d		16 30	16 43				16 55			16 59	17 09			17 15				17 25	17 30	17 43		17 55		17 59
Canley	d		16 32																	17 32					
Tile Hill	d		16 36																	17 36					
Berkswell	d		16 39																	17 39					
Hampton-in-Arden	d		16 43																	17 43					
Birmingham International ✈	a		16 46	16 54				17 04			17 09				17 25				17 35	17 46	17 54		18 04		18 09
	d		16 46	16 55				17 05			17 09				17 26				17 36	17 46	17 55		18 05		18 09
Marston Green	d		16 49																	17 49					
Lea Hall	d		16 52																	17 52					
Stechford	d		16 55																	17 55					
Adderley Park	d		16 58																	17 58					
Birmingham New Street 12	a		17 06	17 09				17 18			17 24				17 39				17 46	18 06	18 09		18 18		18 24
	d	17 03					17 18			17 21			17 30	17 26	17 48	17 57	18 03		18 18					18 21	
Smethwick Rolfe Street	d									17 27														18 27	
Smethwick Galton Bdg L.L. 7	d									17 29														18 29	
Sandwell & Dudley	d									17 31					17 57									18 31	
Dudley Port	d									17 34														18 34	
Tipton	d									17 36														18 36	
Coseley	d									17 39														18 39	
Walsall	d					17 20												18 20							
Wolverhampton 7 🚉	a	17 20				17 34	17 37			17 45			17 49	17 53	18 08	18 15	18 20	18 34	18 37					18 45	
	d						17 38						17 50						18 38						
Penkridge	d												17 59												
Stafford	a						17 51					18 00	18 06						18 51						

For general notes see front of timetable
For details of catering facilities see Directory of Train Operators

A From London Marylebone (Table 71)

Table 68

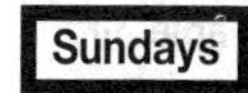

until 27 January

Northampton → Coventry → Birmingham → Wolverhampton → Stafford

Network Diagram - see first page of Table 67

	VT	VT	VT	XC	AW	VT	LM	VT	LM		LM	XC	XC	LM	LM	VT	LM	VT	AW	VT	LM	XC	LM	VT
	1 ◇	1 ◇	1 ◇	R 1	◇	R 1		1 ◇				R 1	1 ◇		1	1 ◇	1 ◇	1 ◇	◇	1 ◇		R 1		1 ◇
																				A				
									🚌															
	☕	☕	☕	☕	trolley	☕		☕				☕	☕			☕		☕	trolley	☕		☕		☕
London Euston 15 ⊖ d	16 50	16 53	16 58					17 27								17 50		17 53						18 27
Northampton d									17 21															
Long Buckby d									17 42															
Rugby d	17 57		18 08						18 13							18 57								
Coventry a	18 07	18 13	18 19					18 42	18 53							19 07		19 13						19 42
d	18 09	18 15	18 21	18 25			18 30	18 43					18 55		18 59	19 09		19 15				19 25	19 30	19 43
Canley d							18 32																19 32	
Tile Hill d							18 36																19 36	
Berkswell d							18 39																19 39	
Hampton-in-Arden d							18 43																19 43	
Birmingham International ✈ a		18 25		18 35			18 46	18 54					19 04		19 09			19 25				19 35	19 46	19 54
d		18 26		18 36			18 46	18 55					19 05		19 09			19 26				19 36	19 46	19 55
Marston Green d							18 49																19 49	
Lea Hall d							18 52																19 52	
Stechford d							18 55																19 55	
Adderley Park d							18 58																19 58	
Birmingham New Street 12 a		18 39		18 46			19 06	19 09					19 18		19 24			19 39				19 46	20 06	20 09
d		18 48			18 57	19 03						19 18		19 21			19 30	19 48	19 57	20 03		20 18		
Smethwick Rolfe Street d														19 27										
Smethwick Galton Bdg L.L. 7 d														19 29										
Sandwell & Dudley d		18 57												19 31				19 57						
Dudley Port d														19 34										
Tipton d														19 36										
Coseley d														19 39										
Walsall d											19 20										20 20			
Wolverhampton 7 a		19 08			19 13	19 20					19 34	19 37		19 45			19 49	20 08	20 15	20 20	20 34	20 37		
d						19 21						19 38					19 50			20 22		20 38		
Penkridge d																	19 59							
Stafford a	19 01		19 18			19 33						19 51				20 00	20 06			20 37		20 51		

	LM	LM	XC	LM	VT	CH	VT	VT	XC	AW	LM		VT	LM	LM	XC	LM	LM	VT	LM	VT	AW	LM	XC
			1 ◇	1	1 ◇		1 ◇	1 ◇	1 ◇				1 ◇			1 ◇		1	1 ◇	1 ◇	1 ◇			1 ◇
						B																		
	🚌													🚌										
			☕		☕		☕	☕	☕				☕						☕		☕			☕
London Euston 15 ⊖ d					18 50		18 53	18 58					19 27						19 50		19 53			
Northampton d	18 21													19 21										
Long Buckby d	18 42													19 42										
Rugby d	19 13				19 57			20 08						20 13					20 57					
Coventry a	19 53				20 07		20 13	20 19					20 42	20 53					21 07		21 13			
d			19 55	19 59	20 09		20 15	20 21	20 25		20 30		20 44					20 59	21 09		21 15			21 25
Canley d											20 32													
Tile Hill d											20 36													
Berkswell d											20 39													
Hampton-in-Arden d											20 43													
Birmingham International ✈ a			20 04	20 09			20 25		20 35		20 46		20 54					21 08			21 25			21 34
d			20 05	20 09			20 26		20 36		20 46		20 56					21 09			21 26			21 35
Marston Green d											20 49													
Lea Hall d											20 52													
Stechford d											20 55													
Adderley Park d											20 58													
Birmingham New Street 12 a			20 21	20 24			20 39		20 46		21 06		21 09					21 23	21 32		21 39			21 46
d		20 21				20 26	20 48			20 57						21 18	21 21		21 35	21 40	21 48	21 57		22 18
Smethwick Rolfe Street d		20 27															21 27							
Smethwick Galton Bdg L.L. 7 d		20 29															21 29							
Sandwell & Dudley d		20 31					20 57										21 31				21 57			
Dudley Port d		20 34															21 34							
Tipton d		20 36															21 36							
Coseley d		20 39															21 39							
Walsall d															21 20								22 20	
Wolverhampton 7 a		20 45				20 58	21 08			21 15					21 34	21 37	21 45		21 53	21 56	22 08	22 15	22 34	22 37
d																21 38			21 54	21 57				22 38
Penkridge d																				22 07				
Stafford a					21 00			21 21								21 51			22 09	22 16				22 51

For general notes see front of timetable
For details of catering facilities see
Directory of Train Operators

A To Holyhead (Table 81)
B From London Marylebone (Table 71)

Table 68

Sundays

until 27 January

Northampton → Coventry → Birmingham → Wolverhampton → Stafford

Network Diagram - see first page of Table 67

		LM	LM	VT	LM	LM	VT	VT	VT	XC	AW	LM	LM	LM	XC	LM	VT	XC	LM	VT	VT	LM	VT		
				1 ◇		1	1 ◇	1 ◇	1 ◇	1 ◇	◇				1 ◇		1 ◇	1 ◇		1 ◇	1 ◇		1 ◇		
			bus											bus					bus			bus			
				catering			catering	catering	catering								catering			catering	catering		catering		
London Euston 15 ⊖	d			20 10			20 31	20 36	20 40								21 36			21 40	22 40		23 40		
Northampton	d		20 21											21 21					22 21			23 21			
Long Buckby	d		20 42											21 42					22 42			23 42			
Rugby	d		21 13	21 41			21 57	22 02	22 07					22 13					23 13	23 14	23 53	00 13	00 57		
Coventry	a		21 53				22 07	22 13	22 19					22 53			23 15		23 53		00 04	00 53	01 08		
	d	21 30				21 59	22 09	22 15	22 21	22 25			22 37				23 17	23 29			00 05		01 10		
Canley	d	21 32											22 39												
Tile Hill	d	21 36											22 43												
Berkswell	d	21 39											22 46												
Hampton-in-Arden	d	21 43											22 50												
Birmingham International ✈	a	21 46		22 02		22 08		22 26		22 35			22 53		←		23 27	23 38			00 16		01 20		
	d	21 46		22 03		22 09		22 28		22 36 →			22 53		22 36		23 29	23 39			00 17		01 22		
Marston Green	d	21 49											22 56												
Lea Hall	d	21 52											22 59												
Stechford	d	21 55											23 02												
Adderley Park	d	21 58											23 05												
Birmingham New Street 12	a	22 06				22 23		22 39					23 12		23 13		23 40	23 55			00 28		01 33		
	d				22 21			22 43			22 54	23 10					23 44				00 32		01 37		
Smethwick Rolfe Street	d				22 27							23 16													
Smethwick Galton Bdg L.L. 7	d				22 29							23 18													
Sandwell & Dudley	d				22 31			22 52				23 20													
Dudley Port	d				22 34							23 23													
Tipton	d				22 36							23 25													
Coseley	d				22 39							23 28													
Walsall	d															23 20									
Wolverhampton 7	a				22 45			23 03			23 10	23 33				23 37	00 05				00 53		01 55		
	d																								
Penkridge	d																								
Stafford	a			22 57			23 03		23 16											00 13					

Sundays

3 February to 23 March

		VT	LM	LM	XC	LM	LM	LM	VT	LM		LM	LM	XC	CH	LM	LM	VT	VT	LM		LM	LM	XC	CH
		1 ◇			1 ◇	1 ◇			1 ◇					1 ◇	A	1		1 ◇	1 ◇					1 ◇	A
												bus										bus			
		catering			catering				catering					catering				catering	catering					catering	
London Euston 15 ⊖	d																	08 40							
Northampton	d											08 21										09 21			
Long Buckby	d											08 42										09 42			
Rugby	d											09 13										10 13			
Coventry	a											09 53						10 24				10 53			
	d		08 30				09 04			09 30					09 58	10 04		10 25		10 30					10 58
Canley	d		08 32							09 32										10 32					
Tile Hill	d		08 36							09 36										10 36					
Berkswell	d		08 39							09 39										10 39					
Hampton-in-Arden	d		08 43							09 43										10 43					
Birmingham International ✈	a		08 46				09 13			09 46					10 08	10 13		10 35		10 46					11 08
	d		08 46				09 14			09 46					10 09	10 14		10 36		10 46					11 09
Marston Green	d		08 49							09 49										10 49					
Lea Hall	d		08 52							09 52										10 52					
Stechford	d		08 55							09 55										10 55					
Adderley Park	d		08 58							09 58										10 58					
Birmingham New Street 12	a		09 06				09 30			10 06					10 28	10 30		10 45		11 06					11 28
	d	09 03			09 18	09 30		09 40	10 03					10 18			10 40	10 48	11 03					11 18	
Smethwick Rolfe Street	d							09 46									10 46								
Smethwick Galton Bdg L.L. 7	d							09 48									10 48								
Sandwell & Dudley	d							09 50									10 50	10 57							
Dudley Port	d							09 53									10 53								
Tipton	d							09 55									10 55								
Coseley	d							09 58									10 58								
Walsall	d			09 20									10 20										11 20		
Wolverhampton 7	a	09 20		09 35	09 37	09 45		10 03	10 20				10 36	10 37			11 03	11 08	11 20				11 36	11 37	
	d	09 21			09 38	09 46								10 38										11 38	
Penkridge	d					09 55																			
Stafford	a	09 33			09 51	10 02								10 51										11 51	

For general notes see front of timetable
For details of catering facilities see
Directory of Train Operators

A From London Marylebone (Table 115)

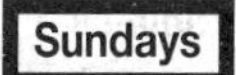

Northampton → Coventry → Birmingham → Wolverhampton → Stafford

3 February to 23 March

Network Diagram - see first page of Table 67

		LM	LM	VT	LM	VT	VT	LM		VT	LM	XC	LM	LM	LM	CH	VT	LM		VT	CH	XC	CH	VT	LM
		1 ◇	1	1 ◇		1 ◇	1 ◇	1 ◇		1 ◇		1 ◇			1	A	1 ◇			1 ◇	A	1 ◇	A	1 ◇	
														🚌											
				☕		☕	☕			☕		☕					☕			☕		☕		☕	
London Euston 15 ⊖	d			09 31		09 36	09 40										10 31			10 36					
Northampton	d													10 21											
Long Buckby	d													10 42											
Rugby	d			10 57			11 08							11 13			11 57								
Coventry	a			11 07		11 13	11 19							11 53			12 07			12 13					
	d		11 04	11 09		11 15						11 25	11 30		11 59	12 03	12 09			12 15	12 19	12 25			12 30
Canley	d												11 32												12 32
Tile Hill	d												11 36												12 36
Berkswell	d												11 39												12 39
Hampton-in-Arden	d												11 43												12 43
Birmingham International ✈	a		11 13			11 25						11 35	11 46		12 08	12 13				12 25	12 30	12 35	←		12 46
	d		11 14			11 26						11 36	11 46		12 09	12 14				12 26	12 30 →	12 36	12 30		12 46
Marston Green	d												11 49												12 49
Lea Hall	d												11 52												12 52
Stechford	d												11 55												12 55
Adderley Park	d												11 58												12 58
Birmingham New Street 12	a		11 30			11 39						11 46	12 06		12 24	12 38				12 39		12 46	12 48		13 06
	d	11 30			11 40	11 48				12 03		12 18						12 37		12 48				13 03	
Smethwick Rolfe Street	d				11 46													12 43							
Smethwick Galton Bdg L.L. 7	d				11 48													12 45							
Sandwell & Dudley	d				11 50	11 57												12 47		12 57					
Dudley Port	d				11 53													12 50							
Tipton	d				11 55													12 52							
Coseley	d				11 58													12 55							
Walsall	d										12 20														
Wolverhampton 7 ⛴	a	11 47			12 04	12 08		←		12 20	12 34	12 37						13 02		13 08				13 20	
	d	11 48 →						11 48				12 38													
Penkridge	d																								
Stafford	a			12 00				12 06				12 51					13 00								

		LM	LM	XC	LM	LM		LM	XC	VT	VT	VT	LM	LM	XC	LM		LM	LM	LM	CH	VT	VT	VT	XC
				1 ◇		1		1 ◇	1 ◇	1 ◇	1 ◇	R 1	1 ◇		R 1					1	A	1 ◇	1 ◇	1 ◇	R 1
		🚌																🚌							
				☕					☕	☕	☕	☕			☕							☕	☕	☕	☕
London Euston 15 ⊖	d									11 31	11 36											12 31	12 36	12 40	
Northampton	d	11 21																12 21							
Long Buckby	d	11 42																12 42							
Rugby	d	12 13								12 57								13 13				13 57		14 08	
Coventry	a	12 53								13 07	13 13							13 53				14 07	14 13	14 19	
	d					12 59			13 03	13 09	13 15				13 25	13 30				13 59	14 03	14 09	14 15	14 21	14 25
Canley	d															13 32									
Tile Hill	d															13 36									
Berkswell	d															13 39									
Hampton-in-Arden	d															13 43									
Birmingham International ✈	a					13 09			13 13		13 25				13 35	13 46				14 09	14 13		14 25		14 35
	d					13 09			13 14		13 26				13 36	13 46				14 09	14 14		14 26		14 36
Marston Green	d															13 49									
Lea Hall	d															13 52									
Stechford	d															13 55									
Adderley Park	d															13 58									
Birmingham New Street 12	a					13 23			13 30		13 39				13 46	14 06				14 24	14 38		14 39		14 46
	d			13 18	13 21			13 30			13 48	14 03			14 18				14 21				14 48		
Smethwick Rolfe Street	d				13 27														14 27						
Smethwick Galton Bdg L.L. 7	d				13 29														14 29						
Sandwell & Dudley	d				13 31						13 57								14 31				14 57		
Dudley Port	d				13 34														14 34						
Tipton	d				13 36														14 36						
Coseley	d				13 39														14 39						
Walsall	d		13 20											14 20											
Wolverhampton 7 ⛴	a		13 36	13 37	13 44			13 51			14 08	14 20		14 36	14 37				14 44				15 08		
	d			13 38				13 52					←		14 38										
Penkridge	d							14 01					14 01												
Stafford	a			13 51				→		14 00			14 08		14 51							15 00		15 18	

For general notes see front of timetable
For details of catering facilities see Directory of Train Operators

A From London Marylebone (Table 115)

Table 68

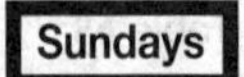

Northampton → Coventry → Birmingham → Wolverhampton → Stafford

3 February to 23 March

Network Diagram - see first page of Table 67

	VT	LM	VT		LM	LM	XC	LM	LM	LM	CH	VT	VT		VT	LM	XC	LM	VT	LM	LM	LM	CH	VT
	R						R								R		R							
	1		1 ◇				1		1	1 ◇		1 ◇	1 ◇		1		1		1 ◇			1		1 ◇
											A												A	
					🚌															🚌				
	☕		☕				☕					☕	☕		☕		☕		☕					☕
London Euston 15 ⊖ d			13 06									13 40	13 50						14 27					14 50
Northampton d					13 21															14 21				
Long Buckby d					13 42															14 42				
Rugby d					14 13							14 57								15 13				15 57
Coventry a			14 41		14 53							15 07	15 13						15 45	15 53				16 07
d		14 30	14 42						14 59		15 03	15 09	15 15				15 25	15 30	15 46			15 59	16 03	16 09
Canley d		14 32																15 32						
Tile Hill d		14 36																15 36						
Berkswell d		14 39																15 39						
Hampton-in-Arden d		14 43																15 43						
Birmingham International ✈ a		14 46	14 53						15 09		15 13		15 25				15 35	15 46	15 57			16 08	16 13	
d		14 46	14 54						15 09		15 14		15 26				15 36	15 46	15 58			16 09	16 14	
Marston Green d		14 49																15 49						
Lea Hall d		14 52																15 52						
Stechford d		14 55																15 55						
Adderley Park d		14 58																15 58						
Birmingham New Street 12 a		15 06	15 09						15 24		15 38		15 39				15 46	16 06	16 09			16 24	16 38	
d	15 03						15 18	15 21		15 30			15 51		16 03		16 18				16 21			
Smethwick Rolfe Street d								15 27													16 27			
Smethwick Galton Bdg L.L. 7 d								15 29													16 29			
Sandwell & Dudley d								15 31					16 00								16 31			
Dudley Port d								15 34													16 34			
Tipton d								15 36													16 36			
Coseley d								15 39													16 39			
Walsall d						15 20										16 20								
Wolverhampton 7 ⛴ a	15 20					15 34	15 37	15 44		15 50			16 11		16 20	16 34	16 37				16 45			
d							15 38			15 50							16 38							
Penkridge d																								
Stafford a							15 51			16 05		16 00					16 51							17 00

	VT		XC	VT	LM	VT	LM	LM	XC	LM	LM		LM	CH	VT	VT	VT	LM	XC	LM	VT		LM	LM
			R	R					R								R		R					
	1 ◇		1	1		1 ◇			1		1		1 ◇		1 ◇	1 ◇	1		1		1 ◇			
														A										
							🚌																🚌	
	☕		☕	☕		☕			☕						☕	☕	☕		☕		☕			
London Euston 15 ⊖ d	14 53					15 27									15 50	15 53					16 27			
Northampton d							15 21																16 21	
Long Buckby d							15 42																16 42	
Rugby d							16 13								16 57								17 13	
Coventry a	16 13					16 45	16 53								17 07	17 13					17 45		17 53	
d	16 15		16 25		16 30	16 46					16 59			17 03	17 09	17 15			17 25	17 30	17 46			
Canley d					16 32															17 32				
Tile Hill d					16 36															17 36				
Berkswell d					16 39															17 39				
Hampton-in-Arden d					16 43															17 43				
Birmingham International ✈ a	16 25		16 35		16 46	16 57					17 08			17 13		17 25			17 35	17 46	17 57			
d	16 26		16 36		16 46	16 58					17 09			17 14		17 26			17 36	17 46	17 58			
Marston Green d					16 49															17 49				
Lea Hall d					16 52															17 52				
Stechford d					16 55															17 55				
Adderley Park d					16 58															17 58				
Birmingham New Street 12 a	16 39		16 46		17 06	17 09					17 24			17 38		17 39			17 46	18 06	18 09			
d	16 48			17 03					17 18	17 21			17 30			17 48	18 03		18 18					18 21
Smethwick Rolfe Street d										17 27														18 27
Smethwick Galton Bdg L.L. 7 d										17 29														18 29
Sandwell & Dudley d	16 57									17 31						17 57								18 31
Dudley Port d										17 34														18 34
Tipton d										17 36														18 36
Coseley d										17 39														18 39
Walsall d								17 20										18 20						
Wolverhampton 7 ⛴ a	17 08			17 20				17 34	17 37	17 45			17 49			18 08	18 20	18 34	18 37					18 45
d									17 38				17 50						18 38					
Penkridge d													17 59											
Stafford a									17 51				18 06		18 00				18 51					

For general notes see front of timetable
For details of catering facilities see Directory of Train Operators

A From London Marylebone (Table 115)

Table 68

Sundays

3 February to 23 March

Northampton → Coventry → Birmingham → Wolverhampton → Stafford

Network Diagram - see first page of Table 67

	LM	CH	VT	VT	VT	XC	VT	LM	VT		LM	LM	XC	LM	LM	LM	CH	VT	VT		VT	LM	XC	LM
	[1]		[1] ◇	[1] ◇	[1] ◇	[R] [1]	[R] [1]		[1] ◇				[R] [1]		[1]	[1] ◇		[1] ◇	[1] ◇		[1] ◇		[R] [1]	
		A									🚌						A				B			
			☕	☕	☕	☕	☕		☕				☕					☕	☕		☕		☕	
London Euston [15] ⊖ d			16 50	16 53	16 58				17 27									17 50	17 53					
Northampton d											17 21													
Long Buckby d											17 42													
Rugby d			17 57		18 08						18 13							18 57						
Coventry a			18 07	18 13	18 19				18 45		18 53							19 07	19 13					
d	17 59	18 03	18 09	18 15	18 21	18 25		18 30	18 46						18 59		19 03	19 09	19 15				19 25	19 30
Canley d								18 32																19 32
Tile Hill d								18 36																19 36
Berkswell d								18 39																19 39
Hampton-in-Arden d								18 43																19 43
Birmingham International ✈ a	18 08	18 13		18 25		18 35		18 46	18 57						19 08		19 13		19 25				19 35	19 46
d	18 09	18 14		18 26		18 36		18 46	18 58						19 09		19 14		19 26				19 36	19 46
Marston Green d								18 49																19 49
Lea Hall d								18 52																19 52
Stechford d								18 55																19 55
Adderley Park d								18 58																19 58
Birmingham New Street [12] a	18 24	18 38		18 39		18 46		19 06	19 09						19 24		19 38		19 39				19 46	20 06
d				18 48			19 03						19 18	19 21		19 30			19 48		20 03		20 18	
Smethwick Rolfe Street d														19 27										
Smethwick Galton Bdg L.L. [7] d														19 29										
Sandwell & Dudley d				18 57										19 31					19 57					
Dudley Port d														19 34										
Tipton d														19 36										
Coseley d														19 39										
Walsall d												19 20										20 20		
Wolverhampton [7] ⛴ a				19 08			19 20					19 34	19 37	19 45		19 49			20 08		20 20	20 34	20 37	
d							19 21						19 38			19 50					20 22		20 38	
Penkridge d																19 59								
Stafford a			19 01		19 18		19 33						19 51			20 06		20 00			20 37		20 51	

	VT	LM	LM	LM	CH	VT	VT		VT	XC	LM	VT	LM	LM	XC	LM	LM		VT	LM	VT	LM	XC	LM
	[1] ◇			[1]		[1] ◇	[1] ◇		[1] ◇	[1] ◇		[1] ◇			[1] ◇		[1]		[1] ◇	[1] ◇	[1] ◇		[1] ◇	
		🚌			A								🚌											
	☕					☕	☕		☕	☕		☕							☕		☕		☕	
London Euston [15] ⊖ d	18 27					18 50	18 53		18 58			19 27							19 50		19 53			
Northampton d		18 21											19 21											
Long Buckby d		18 42											19 42											
Rugby d		19 13				19 57			20 08				20 13						20 57					
Coventry a	19 45	19 53				20 07	20 13		20 19			20 42	20 53						21 07		21 13			
d	19 46			19 59	20 03	20 09	20 15		20 21	20 25	20 30	20 44					20 59		21 09		21 15		21 25	21 30
Canley d											20 32													21 32
Tile Hill d											20 36													21 36
Berkswell d											20 39													21 39
Hampton-in-Arden d											20 43													21 43
Birmingham International ✈ a	19 57			20 08	20 13		20 25			20 35	20 46	20 54					21 08				21 25		21 35	21 46
d	19 58			20 09	20 14		20 26			20 36	20 46	20 56					21 09				21 26		21 36	21 46
Marston Green d											20 49													21 49
Lea Hall d											20 52													21 52
Stechford d											20 55													21 55
Adderley Park d											20 58													21 58
Birmingham New Street [12] a	20 09			20 23	20 38		20 39			20 46	21 06	21 09					21 23		21 32		21 39		21 46	22 06
d			20 21				20 48								21 18	21 21			21 35	21 40	21 48		22 18	
Smethwick Rolfe Street d			20 27													21 27								
Smethwick Galton Bdg L.L. [7] d			20 29													21 29								
Sandwell & Dudley d			20 31				20 57									21 31					21 57			
Dudley Port d			20 34													21 34								
Tipton d			20 36													21 36								
Coseley d			20 39													21 39								
Walsall d														21 20								22 20		
Wolverhampton [7] ⛴ a			20 45				21 08							21 34	21 37	21 45			21 53	21 56	22 08	22 34	22 37	
d															21 38				21 54	21 57			22 38	
Penkridge d																				22 07				
Stafford a						21 00			21 21						21 51				22 09	22 16			22 51	

For general notes see front of timetable
For details of catering facilities see Directory of Train Operators

A From London Marylebone (Table 115)
B To Holyhead (Table 81)

Table 68

Sundays

3 February to 23 March

Northampton → Coventry → Birmingham → Wolverhampton → Stafford

Network Diagram - see first page of Table 67

		LM	VT	LM	LM	VT		VT	VT	XC	LM	LM	LM	XC	LM	VT		XC	LM	VT	VT	LM	VT		
			1 ◇		**1**	**1** ◇		**1** ◇	**1** ◇	**1** ◇				**1** ◇		**1** ◇		**1** ◇		**1** ◇	**1** ◇		**1** ◇		
		🚌											🚌						🚌			🚌			
			☕			☕		☕	☕							☕				☕	☕		☕		
London Euston **15** ⊖	d		20 10			20 31		20 36	20 40							21 36				21 40	22 40		23 40		
Northampton	d	20 21											21 21						22 21			23 21			
Long Buckby	d	20 42											21 42						22 42			23 42			
Rugby	d	21 13	21 41			21 57		22 02	22 07				22 13						23 13	23 14	23 53	00 13	00 57		
Coventry	a	21 53				22 07		22 13	22 19				22 53			23 15			23 53		00 04	00 53	01 08		
	d				21 59	22 09		22 15	22 21	22 25		22 37				23 17		23 29			00 05		01 10		
Canley	d											22 39													
Tile Hill	d											22 43													
Berkswell	d											22 46													
Hampton-in-Arden	d											22 50													
Birmingham International ✈	a		22 02		22 08			22 26		22 35		22 53		←		23 27		23 38			00 16		01 20		
	d		22 03		22 09			22 28		22 36 →		22 53		22 36		23 29		23 39			00 17		01 22		
Marston Green	d											22 56													
Lea Hall	d											22 59													
Stechford	d											23 02													
Adderley Park	d											23 05													
Birmingham New Street 12	a				22 23			22 39				23 12		23 13		23 40		23 55			00 28		01 33		
	d			22 21				22 43			23 10					23 44					00 32		01 37		
Smethwick Rolfe Street	d			22 27							23 16														
Smethwick Galton Bdg L.L. **7**	d			22 29							23 18														
Sandwell & Dudley	d			22 31				22 52			23 20														
Dudley Port	d			22 34							23 23														
Tipton	d			22 36							23 25														
Coseley	d			22 39							23 28														
Walsall	d														23 20										
Wolverhampton 7 🚌	a			22 45				23 03			23 33				23 37	00 05					00 53		01 55		
	d																								
Penkridge	d																								
Stafford	a		22 57			23 03			23 16											00 13					

Sundays

from 30 March

		VT	VT	LM	LM	XC	LM	LM	LM	VT	LM	LM	XC		AW	CH	LM	LM	VT	VT	LM	LM	XC	AW	CH
		1 ◇	**1** ◇			**1** ◇	**1** ◇			**1** ◇			**1** ◇				**1**		**1** ◇	**1** ◇			**1** ◇	◇	
																A									A
		☕	☕			☕				☕			☕						☕	☕			☕		
London Euston **15** ⊖	d	22p13																	08 40						
Northampton	d																09 30								
Long Buckby	d																09 40								
Rugby	d	23p36															09 52								
Coventry	a	23p48															10 03		10 24						
	d	23p50		08 30				09 04			09 30					09 58	10 04		10 25		10 30				10 58
Canley	d			08 32							09 32										10 32				
Tile Hill	d			08 36							09 36										10 36				
Berkswell	d			08 39							09 39										10 39				
Hampton-in-Arden	d			08 43							09 43										10 43				
Birmingham International ✈	a	23p59		08 46				09 13			09 46					10 08	10 14		10 35		10 46				11 08
	d	00 01		08 46				09 14			09 46					10 09	10 14		10 36		10 46				11 09
Marston Green	d			08 49							09 49										10 49				
Lea Hall	d			08 52							09 52										10 52				
Stechford	d			08 55							09 55										10 55				
Adderley Park	d			08 58							09 58										10 58				
Birmingham New Street 12	a	00 12		09 06				09 30			10 06					10 28	10 30		10 45		11 06				11 28
	d	00 17	09 03			09 18	09 30		09 40	10 03			10 18		10 27			10 40	10 48	11 03			11 18	11 27	
Smethwick Rolfe Street	d								09 46									10 46							
Smethwick Galton Bdg L.L. **7**	d								09 48									10 48							
Sandwell & Dudley	d								09 50									10 50	10 57						
Dudley Port	d								09 53									10 53							
Tipton	d								09 55									10 55							
Coseley	d								09 58									10 58							
Walsall	d				09 20							10 20										11 20			
Wolverhampton 7 🚌	a	00 39	09 20		09 35	09 37	09 45		10 03	10 20		10 36	10 37		10 43			11 03	11 08	11 20		11 36	11 37	11 43	
	d		09 21			09 38	09 46						10 38						11 10				11 38		
Penkridge	d						09 55																		
Stafford	a		09 33			09 51	10 02						10 51						11 24				11 51		

For general notes see front of timetable
For details of catering facilities see
Directory of Train Operators

A From London Marylebone (Table 115)

Table 68

Sundays
from 30 March

Northampton → Coventry → Birmingham → Wolverhampton → Stafford

Network Diagram - see first page of Table 67

		LM	LM	VT		LM	LM	VT	VT	VT	LM	XC	LM	LM	AW	CH	VT		LM	VT	XC	VT	LM	LM	XC
		1 ◇	1	1 ◇			1 ◇	1 ◇	1 ◇	1 ◇		1 ◇		1			1 ◇			1 ◇	1 ◇	1 ◇			1 ◇
																A									
				☕				☕	☕	☕		☕					☕			☕	☕	☕			☕
London Euston 15 ⊖	d			09 31				09 36	09 40								10 31			10 36					
Northampton	d		10 28											11 24											
Long Buckby	d		10 38											11 34											
Rugby	d		10 52	10 57					11 08					11 47			11 57								
Coventry	a		11 03	11 07				11 13	11 19					11 58			12 07			12 13					
	d		11 04	11 09				11 15				11 25	11 30	11 59		12 03	12 09			12 15	12 25		12 30		
Canley	d												11 32										12 32		
Tile Hill	d												11 36										12 36		
Berkswell	d												11 39										12 39		
Hampton-in-Arden	d												11 43										12 43		
Birmingham International ✈	a		11 13					11 25				11 35	11 46	12 08		12 13				12 25	12 35		12 46		
	d		11 14					11 26				11 36	11 46	12 09		12 14				12 26	12 36		12 46		
Marston Green	d												11 49										12 49		
Lea Hall	d												11 52										12 52		
Stechford	d												11 55										12 55		
Adderley Park	d												11 58										12 58		
Birmingham New Street 12	a		11 30					11 39				11 46	12 06	12 23		12 38				12 39	12 46		13 06		
	d	11 30				11 40		11 48		12 03		12 18			12 27				12 37	12 48		13 03			13 18
Smethwick Rolfe Street	d					11 46													12 43						
Smethwick Galton Bdg L.L. 7	d					11 48													12 45						
Sandwell & Dudley	d					11 50		11 57											12 47	12 57					
Dudley Port	d					11 53													12 50						
Tipton	d					11 55													12 52						
Coseley	d					11 58													12 55						
Walsall	d										12 20													13 20	
Wolverhampton 7	a	11 47				12 04	←	12 08		12 20	12 34	12 37			12 43				13 02	13 08		13 20		13 36	13 37
	d	11 48					11 48	12 10				12 38								13 10					13 38
Penkridge	d	→																							
Stafford	a			12 00			12 06	12 24				12 51					13 00			13 27					13 51

		LM	LM	AW	LM	CH	VT	LM		VT	VT	LM	XC	LM	LM	LM	AW	CH	VT	VT	VT		XC	VT	VT
											R		R										R		R
			1	◇	1 ◇		1 ◇	1 ◇		1 ◇	1		1			1	◇		1 ◇	1 ◇	1 ◇		1	1 ◇	1
						A												A							
				[trolley]			☕			☕	☕		☕						☕	☕	☕		☕	☕	☕
London Euston 15 ⊖	d						11 31			11 36									12 31	12 36	12 40				
Northampton	d		12 24													13 24									
Long Buckby	d		12 34													13 34									
Rugby	d		12 47				12 57									13 47			13 57		14 08				
Coventry	a		12 58				13 07			13 13						13 58			14 07	14 13	14 19				
	d		12 59			13 03	13 09			13 15			13 25	13 30		13 59		14 03	14 09	14 15	14 21		14 25		
Canley	d													13 32											
Tile Hill	d													13 36											
Berkswell	d													13 39											
Hampton-in-Arden	d													13 43											
Birmingham International ✈	a		13 08			13 13				13 25			13 35	13 46		14 08		14 13		14 25			14 35		
	d		13 09			13 14				13 26			13 36	13 46		14 09		14 14		14 26			14 36		
Marston Green	d													13 49											
Lea Hall	d													13 52											
Stechford	d													13 55											
Adderley Park	d													13 58											
Birmingham New Street 12	a		13 23			13 33				13 39			13 46	14 06		14 23		14 38		14 39			14 46	←	
	d	13 21		13 27	13 30					13 48	14 03		14 18		14 21		14 27			14 48				14 48	15 03
Smethwick Rolfe Street	d	13 27													14 27					→					
Smethwick Galton Bdg L.L. 7	d	13 29													14 29										
Sandwell & Dudley	d	13 31								13 57					14 31									14 57	
Dudley Port	d	13 34													14 34										
Tipton	d	13 36													14 36										
Coseley	d	13 39													14 39										
Walsall	d											14 20													
Wolverhampton 7	a	13 44		13 47	13 51					14 08	14 20	14 36	14 37		14 44		14 47							15 08	15 20
	d				13 52			←		14 10			14 38											15 10	
Penkridge	d				14 01			14 01																	
Stafford	a				→		14 00	14 08		14 26			14 51						15 00		15 18			15 27	

For general notes see front of timetable
For details of catering facilities see Directory of Train Operators

A From London Marylebone (Table 115)

Northampton → Coventry → Birmingham → Wolverhampton → Stafford

from 30 March

Network Diagram - see first page of Table 67

		LM	AW	VT	LM	XC	LM	LM	LM	CH	VT	LM		VT	XC	LM	AW	VT	LM	XC	LM	LM	CH	VT	VT
				1 ◇		R 1		1	1 ◇		1 ◇	1 ◇		1 ◇	R 1		◇	1 ◇		R 1		1		1 ◇	1 ◇
										A													A		
				☕		☕					☕			☕	☕		🛒	☕		☕				☕	☕
London Euston 15 ⊖	d			13 06							13 40			13 50				14 27						14 50	14 53
Northampton	d							14 24														15 24			
Long Buckby	d							14 34														15 34			
Rugby	d							14 47			14 57											15 47		15 57	
Coventry	a			14 41				14 58			15 07			15 13				15 45				15 58		16 07	16 13
	d	14 30		14 42				14 59		15 03	15 09			15 15	15 25	15 30		15 46				15 59	16 03	16 09	16 15
Canley	d	14 32														15 32									
Tile Hill	d	14 36														15 36									
Berkswell	d	14 39														15 39									
Hampton-in-Arden	d	14 43														15 43									
Birmingham International ✈	a	14 46		14 53				15 08		15 13				15 25	15 35	15 46		15 57				16 08	16 13		16 25
	d	14 46		14 54				15 09		15 14				15 26	15 36	15 46		15 58				16 09	16 14		16 26
Marston Green	d	14 49														15 49									
Lea Hall	d	14 52														15 52									
Stechford	d	14 55														15 55									
Adderley Park	d	14 58														15 58									
Birmingham New Street 12	a	15 06		15 09				15 23		15 38				15 39	15 46	16 06		16 09		←		16 23	16 38		16 39
	d		15 07			15 18	15 21		15 30					15 51	16 18 →		16 07			16 18	16 21				16 48
Smethwick Rolfe Street	d						15 27														16 27				
Smethwick Galton Bdg L.L. 7	d						15 29														16 29				
Sandwell & Dudley	d						15 31							16 00							16 31				16 57
Dudley Port	d						15 34														16 34				
Tipton	d						15 36														16 36				
Coseley	d						15 39														16 39				
Walsall	d				15 20														16 20						
Wolverhampton 7 🚌	a		15 25		15 34	15 37	15 44		15 50			←		16 11			16 25		16 34	16 37	16 45				17 08
	d					15 38			15 50 →			15 50		16 13						16 38					17 10
Penkridge	d																								
Stafford	a					15 51					16 00	16 05		16 28						16 51				17 00	17 27

		XC	AW		VT	LM	VT	LM	XC	LM	LM	LM	CH	VT	LM	VT		AW	VT	LM	XC	LM	VT	LM	LM
		R 1	◇		R 1		1 ◇		R 1		1	1 ◇		1 ◇	1 ◇	1 ◇			R 1		R 1		1 ◇		1
													A												
		☕			☕		☕		☕					☕		☕			☕		☕		☕		
London Euston 15 ⊖	d						15 27							15 50		15 53							16 27		
Northampton	d										16 24														17 24
Long Buckby	d										16 34														17 34
Rugby	d										16 47			16 57											17 47
Coventry	a						16 45				16 58			17 07		17 13							17 45		17 58
	d	16 25				16 30	16 46				16 59		17 03	17 09		17 15					17 25	17 30	17 46		17 59
Canley	d					16 32																17 32			
Tile Hill	d					16 36																17 36			
Berkswell	d					16 39																17 39			
Hampton-in-Arden	d					16 43																17 43			
Birmingham International ✈	a	16 35				16 46	16 57				17 08		17 13			17 25					17 35	17 46	17 57		18 08
	d	16 36				16 46	16 58				17 09		17 14			17 26					17 36	17 46	17 58		18 09
Marston Green	d					16 49																17 49			
Lea Hall	d					16 52																17 52			
Stechford	d					16 55																17 55			
Adderley Park	d					16 58																17 58			
Birmingham New Street 12	a	16 46				17 06	17 09				17 23		17 38			17 39					17 46	18 06	18 09		18 23
	d		16 57		17 03				17 18	17 21		17 30				17 48		17 57	18 03		18 18			18 21	
Smethwick Rolfe Street	d									17 27														18 27	
Smethwick Galton Bdg L.L. 7	d									17 29														18 29	
Sandwell & Dudley	d									17 31						17 57								18 31	
Dudley Port	d									17 34														18 34	
Tipton	d									17 36														18 36	
Coseley	d									17 39														18 39	
Walsall	d							17 20												18 20					
Wolverhampton 7 🚌	a		17 13		17 20			17 34	17 37	17 45		17 49				18 08		18 15	18 20	18 34	18 37			18 45	
	d								17 38			17 50			←	18 10					18 38				
Penkridge	d											17 59 →			17 59										
Stafford	a								17 51					18 00	18 06	18 27					18 51				

For general notes see front of timetable
For details of catering facilities see Directory of Train Operators

A From London Marylebone (Table 115)

Table 68

Sundays

from 30 March

Northampton → Coventry → Birmingham → Wolverhampton → Stafford

Network Diagram - see first page of Table 67

		CH	VT	VT	VT	XC	VT		AW	VT	LM	VT	LM	XC	LM	LM	LM	CH	VT	LM		VT	AW	VT	LM
			1 ◇	1 ◇	1 ◇	R 1	1 ◇		◇	R 1		1 ◇		R 1		1	1 ◇		1 ◇	1 ◇		1 ◇	◇	1 ◇	
		A																A						B	
			☕	☕	☕	☕	☕		trolley	☕		☕		☕					☕			☕	trolley	☕	
London Euston 15 ⊖	d		16 50	16 53	16 58							17 27							17 50			17 53			
Northampton	d															18 24									
Long Buckby	d															18 34									
Rugby	d		17 57		18 08											18 47			18 57						
Coventry	a		18 07	18 13	18 19							18 45				18 58			19 07			19 13			
	d	18 03	18 09	18 15	18 21	18 25					18 30	18 46				18 59		19 03	19 09			19 15			
Canley	d										18 32														
Tile Hill	d										18 36														
Berkswell	d										18 39														
Hampton-in-Arden	d										18 43														
Birmingham International ✈	a	18 13		18 25		18 35					18 46	18 57				19 08		19 13				19 25			
	d	18 14		18 26		18 36					18 46	18 58				19 09		19 14				19 26			
Marston Green	d										18 49														
Lea Hall	d										18 52														
Stechford	d										18 55														
Adderley Park	d										18 58														
Birmingham New Street 12	a	18 38		18 39		18 46	←				19 06	19 09				19 23		19 38				19 39			
	d			18 48 →			18 48		18 57	19 03				19 18	19 21		19 30					19 48	19 57	20 03	
Smethwick Rolfe Street	d														19 27										
Smethwick Galton Bdg L.L. 7	d														19 29										
Sandwell & Dudley	d						18 57								19 31							19 57			
Dudley Port	d														19 34										
Tipton	d														19 36										
Coseley	d														19 39										
Walsall	d												19 20												20 20
Wolverhampton 7 ⛴	a						19 08		19 13	19 20			19 34	19 37	19 45		19 49					20 08	20 15	20 20	20 34
	d						19 10			19 21				19 38			19 50			←		20 10		20 22	
Penkridge	d																19 59 →			19 59					
Stafford	a		19 01		19 18		19 27			19 33				19 51					20 00	20 06		20 28		20 37	

		XC	LM	VT	LM	LM	CH	VT	VT	VT	XC		VT	AW	LM	VT	LM	XC	LM	LM	VT	LM	VT	AW	LM
		R 1		1 ◇		1		1 ◇	1 ◇	1 ◇	1 ◇		1 ◇			1 ◇		1 ◇		1	1 ◇	1 ◇	1 ◇		
		C					A																		
		☕		☕				☕	☕	☕			☕			☕					☕		☕		
London Euston 15 ⊖	d			18 27				18 50	18 53	18 58						19 27					19 50		19 53		
Northampton	d					19 24														20 24					
Long Buckby	d					19 34														20 34					
Rugby	d					19 47		19 57		20 08										20 47	20 57				
Coventry	a			19 45		19 58		20 07	20 13	20 19						20 42				20 58	21 07		21 13		
	d	19 25	19 30	19 46		19 59	20 03	20 09	20 15	20 21	20 25				20 30	20 44				20 59	21 09		21 15		
Canley	d		19 32												20 32										
Tile Hill	d		19 36												20 36										
Berkswell	d		19 39												20 39										
Hampton-in-Arden	d		19 43												20 43										
Birmingham International ✈	a	19 35	19 46	19 57		20 09	20 13		20 25		20 35				20 46	20 54				21 09			21 25		
	d	19 36	19 46	19 58		20 09	20 14		20 26		20 36				20 46	20 56				21 09			21 26		
Marston Green	d		19 49												20 49										
Lea Hall	d		19 52												20 52										
Stechford	d		19 55												20 55										
Adderley Park	d		19 58												20 58										
Birmingham New Street 12	a	19 46	20 06	20 09		20 23	20 38		20 39		20 46		←		21 06	21 09				21 23	21 32		21 39		
	d	20 18			20 21				20 48 →				20 48	20 57				21 18	21 21		21 35	21 40	21 48	21 57	
Smethwick Rolfe Street	d				20 27														21 27						
Smethwick Galton Bdg L.L. 7	d				20 29														21 29						
Sandwell & Dudley	d				20 31								20 57						21 31				21 57		
Dudley Port	d				20 34														21 34						
Tipton	d				20 36														21 36						
Coseley	d				20 39														21 39						
Walsall	d																21 20								22 20
Wolverhampton 7 ⛴	a	20 37			20 45								21 08	21 15			21 34	21 37	21 45		21 53	21 56	22 08	22 15	22 34
	d	20 38											21 10					21 38			21 54	21 57	22 10		
Penkridge	d																					22 07			
Stafford	a	20 51						21 00		21 21			21 28					21 51			22 09	22 16	22 24		

For general notes see front of timetable
For details of catering facilities see Directory of Train Operators

A From London Marylebone (Table 115)
B To Holyhead (Table 81)
C ☕ to Birmingham New Street

Table 68

from 30 March

Northampton → Coventry → Birmingham → Wolverhampton → Stafford

Network Diagram - see first page of Table 67

		XC 1 ◇		LM	VT 1 ◇ 🍴	LM	LM 1	VT 1 ◇ 🍴	VT 1 ◇ 🍴	VT 1 ◇ 🍴	XC 1 ◇	AW ◇	LM	LM	LM 1		XC 1 ◇	LM	VT 1 ◇ 🍴	XC 1 ◇	LM 1	VT 1 ◇ 🍴	VT 1 ◇ 🍴		
London Euston 15 ⊖	d				20 10			20 31	20 36	20 40									21 36			22 39	23 40		
Northampton	d						21 24								22 24						23 35				
Long Buckby	d						21 34								22 35						23 45				
Rugby	d				21 41		21 47	21 57	22 02	22 07					22 47						23 58	00 05	01 02		
Coventry	a						21 58	22 07	22 13	22 19					23 04				23 15		00 13	00 16	01 13		
	d	21 25		21 30			21 59	22 09	22 15	22 21	22 25			22 37					23 17	23 29		00 18	01 15		
Canley	d			21 32										22 39											
Tile Hill	d			21 36										22 43											
Berkswell	d			21 39										22 46											
Hampton-in-Arden	d			21 43										22 50											
Birmingham International ✈	a	21 35		21 46	22 02		22 09		22 26		22 35			22 53			←		23 27	23 38		00 28	01 25		
	d	21 36		21 46	22 03		22 09		22 28		22 36 →			22 53			22 36		23 29	23 39		00 30	01 27		
Marston Green	d			21 49										22 56											
Lea Hall	d			21 52										22 59											
Stechford	d			21 55										23 02											
Adderley Park	d			21 58										23 05											
Birmingham New Street 12	a	21 46		22 06			22 23		22 39					23 12			23 13		23 40	23 55		00 41	01 38		
	d	22 18				22 21			22 43			22 54	23 10						23 44			00 45	01 42		
Smethwick Rolfe Street	d					22 27							23 16												
Smethwick Galton Bdg L.L. 7	d					22 29							23 18												
Sandwell & Dudley	d					22 31			22 52				23 20												
Dudley Port	d					22 34							23 23												
Tipton	d					22 36							23 25												
Coseley	d					22 39							23 28												
Walsall	d																	23 20							
Wolverhampton 7	a	22 37				22 45			23 03			23 10	23 33					23 37	00 05			01 06	02 00		
	d	22 38																							
Penkridge	d																								
Stafford	a	22 51			22 57			23 03		23 16															

For general notes see front of timetable
For details of catering facilities see
Directory of Train Operators

Stafford → Wolverhampton → Birmingham → Coventry → Northampton

Network Diagram - see first page of Table 67

Miles	Station		LM	VT	LM	VT	VT	LM	XC	VT	LM	AW	VT	LM	LM	AW	VT	LM	XC		LM	LM	LM	LM	VT
			MX	1 ◇	1	1 ◇	1 ◇	1	1 ◇	1 ◇			1 ◇				1 ◇		1 ◇			1 ◇		1	1 ◇
																								A	
						☒	☕		☕	☒			☒				☒		☕			trolley			☒
0	**Stafford**	d		04 30															06 24			06 30		06 57	
5¾	Penkridge	d																				06 36			
10¼	**Wolverhampton** 7	a		04 44															06 41			06 47			
—		d		04 45		05 05				05 45		06 01	06 15		06 22	06 31	06 35	06 38	06 41			06 47			
—	Walsall	a																06 50							
18½	Coseley	d													06 27										
20	Tipton	d													06 29										
20¾	Dudley Port	d													06 31										
22¾	Sandwell & Dudley	d				05 15				05 55			06 25		06 35		06 45								
24	Smethwick Galton Bdg L.L. 7	d													06 37										
24¾	Smethwick Rolfe Street	d													06 39										
28	**Birmingham New Street** 12	a		05 12		05 26				06 05		06 18	06 34		06 45	06 48	06 56		06 58			07 08			
—		d	00 10			05 30			06 03	06 10	06 13		06 40	06 43			07 00		07 03		07 06				07 15
30	Adderley Park	d									06 17														
32	Stechford	d									06 21			06 49							07 13				
33	Lea Hall	d									06 23			06 52							07 15				
34½	Marston Green	d	00 18								06 27			06 55							07 18				
36¼	**Birmingham International** ✈	a	00 21			05 39			06 14	06 21	06 30		06 49	06 58			07 09		07 14		07 23				07 27
—		d	00 22			05 40			06 15	06 21	06 30		06 50	06 59			07 10		07 15						07 28
38¼	Hampton-in-Arden	d									06 33			07 02											
41½	Berkswell	d									06 38			07 07											
43½	Tile Hill	d									06 41			07 10											
45½	Canley	d									06 45			07 13											
47¼	**Coventry**	a	00 37			05 49			06 23	06 32	06 48		06 59	07 16			07 19		07 23				←		07 38
—		d			05 15	05 50		06 18		06 32			07 00	07 27			07 20						07 27		07 38
60¾	Rugby	d			05 26	06 04	06 20	06 32					07 14	→									07 41	07 55	
70	Long Buckby	d			05 37			06 43															07 51	08 07	
79½	**Northampton**	a			05 51		06 39	07 00															08 05	08 29	
—	London Euston 15	⊖ a				07 09	07 36			07 50			08 09				08 39								08 43

Station		LM	LM	LM	VT	LM	VT	LM	LM	LM	VT	LM	XC	LM	VT		LM	LM	AW	VT	LM	XC	LM	LM	LM
					1 ◇		1 ◇		1		1 ◇		1 ◇		1 ◇				◇	1 ◇	1 ◇	1 ◇			
			B																		C		D		
					☒		☒				☒		☕		☕				trolley	☒	trolley	☕			
Stafford	d										07 15	07 20									07 46	07 54			
Penkridge	d											07 26									07 52				
Wolverhampton 7	a										07 32	07 37									08 05	08 12			
	d	06 52	06 56		07 05			07 22		07 29	07 35	07 38			07 49		07 52		07 59	08 05	08 08	08 13		08 19	08 22
Walsall	a		07 12																						
Coseley	d	06 57						07 27				07 43					07 57								08 27
Tipton	d	06 59						07 29				07 45					07 59								08 29
Dudley Port	d	07 01						07 31				07 47					08 01								08 31
Sandwell & Dudley	d	07 05			07 15			07 35			07 45						08 05			08 15					08 35
Smethwick Galton Bdg L.L. 7	d	07 07						07 37				07 51					08 07								08 37
Smethwick Rolfe Street	d	07 09						07 39				07 53					08 09								08 39
Birmingham New Street 12	a	07 15			07 24			07 45		07 48	07 55	08 00			08 11		08 15		08 18	08 24	08 30	08 30		08 36	08 45
	d			07 18	07 30	07 33	07 45		07 48		08 00		08 03	08 06				08 18		08 30			08 33		
Adderley Park	d					07 37																	08 37		
Stechford	d					07 40								08 13									08 40		
Lea Hall	d					07 43								08 15									08 43		
Marston Green	d					07 46								08 18									08 46		
Birmingham International ✈	a			07 30	07 40	07 51	07 54		07 59		08 09		08 14	08 23				08 27		08 39			08 51		
	d			07 31	07 40		07 56		07 59		08 10		08 15					08 27		08 40					
Hampton-in-Arden	d			07 34					08 02									08 30							
Berkswell	d			07 39					08 07									08 35							
Tile Hill	d			07 42					08 10									08 38							
Canley	d			07 45					08 14									08 41							
Coventry	a			07 50	07 54				08 17		08 20		08 23					08 45		08 49					
	d				07 56				08 17		08 24									08 50					
Rugby	d								08 28																
Long Buckby	d								08 39																
Northampton	a								08 59																
London Euston 15	⊖ a				09 01		09 07				09 44									10 03					

For general notes see front of timetable
For details of catering facilities see Directory of Train Operators

A From Crewe (Table 65)
B From Shrewsbury (Table 74)
C From Liverpool Lime Street (Table 91)
D From Walsall (Table 70)

Stafford → Wolverhampton → Birmingham → Coventry → Northampton

Network Diagram - see first page of Table 67

	LM	LM	LM	LM	VT	XC	LM	VT	LM	LM		AW	VT	LM	XC	LM	LM	LM	LM	LM	LM	XC	VT	XC
		1		1 ◇	1 ◇	R 1	A	1 ◇				◇	1 ◇	1 ◇	1 ◇		1				1 ◇	1 ◇	1 ◇	R 1
				⊤	⊠	☕		☕				⊤	⊠	⊤	☕						⊤	☕	⊠	☕
Stafford d				08 21		08 26								08 46	08 57						09 21	09 26		
Penkridge d														08 52										
Wolverhampton 7 a				08 37		08 41								09 06	09 12						09 36	09 41		
d	08 23		08 35	08 37		08 41		08 49	08 52			08 59	09 05	09 08	09 13			09 22	09 25	09 30	09 37	09 41		
Walsall a	08 38																		09 38					
Coseley d									08 57					09 12						09 35				
Tipton d									08 59									09 28						
Dudley Port d									09 01									09 30						
Sandwell & Dudley d				08 46									09 15					09 33			09 46			
Smethwick Galton Bdg L.L. 7 d									09 06									09 36						
Smethwick Rolfe Street d									09 08									09 38						
Birmingham New Street 12 a			08 55	08 58		08 58		09 11	09 15			09 18	09 24	09 30	09 30			09 48		09 51	09 58	09 58		
d		08 48			09 00	09 03	09 06			09 18			09 30			09 34	09 48						10 00	10 03
Adderley Park d																09 39								
Stechford d							09 13									09 42								
Lea Hall d							09 15									09 44								
Marston Green d							09 18									09 47								
Birmingham International ✈ a		08 57			09 09	09 14	09 23			09 27			09 39			09 52	09 57						10 09	10 14
d		08 57			09 10	09 15				09 27			09 40				09 57						10 10	10 15
Hampton-in-Arden d		09 00								09 30							10 00							
Berkswell d		09 05								09 35							10 05							
Tile Hill d		09 08								09 38							10 08							
Canley d		09 12								09 42							10 12							
Coventry a		09 15			09 19	09 23				09 45			09 49				10 15						10 19	10 23
d		09 15			09 20								09 50				10 15						10 20	
Rugby d		09 27															10 27							
Long Buckby d		09 37															10 37							
Northampton a		09 58															10 58							
London Euston 15 ⊖ a					10 31								11 00										11 35	

	LM	VT	LM	LM	AW	VT		LM	XC	LM	LM	LM	LM	LM	LM	VT	XC	LM	VT	LM	LM	AW	VT	LM
		1 ◇			◇	1 ◇		1 ◇	1 ◇				1		1 ◇	1 ◇	R 1	A	1 ◇			◇	1 ◇	1 ◇
		☕			⊤	⊠		⊤	☕						⊤	☕	☕		☕			⊤	☕	⊤
Stafford d								09 46							10 21		10 26							10 46
Penkridge d								09 52																10 52
Wolverhampton 7 a								10 06							10 36		10 41							11 07
d		09 49	09 52		09 59	10 05		10 08	10 13		10 22	10 25		10 28	10 37		10 41		10 49	10 52		10 59	11 05	11 08
Walsall a												10 38												
Coseley d			09 57					10 12						10 33						10 57				11 12
Tipton d			10 00								10 28									10 59				
Dudley Port d			10 01								10 30									11 01				
Sandwell & Dudley d						10 15					10 33				10 46								11 15	
Smethwick Galton Bdg L.L. 7 d			10 07								10 36									11 06				
Smethwick Rolfe Street d			10 09								10 38									11 08				
Birmingham New Street 12 a		10 11	10 16		10 18	10 24		10 30	10 30		10 45			10 48	10 58		10 58		11 11	11 15		11 18	11 24	11 30
d	10 06			10 18		10 30				10 34			10 48			11 00	11 03	11 06			11 18		11 30	
Adderley Park d										10 39														
Stechford d	10 13									10 42								11 13						
Lea Hall d	10 15									10 44								11 15						
Marston Green d	10 18									10 47								11 18						
Birmingham International ✈ a	10 23			10 27		10 39				10 52			10 57			11 09	11 14	11 23			11 27		11 39	
d				10 27		10 40							10 57			11 10	11 15				11 27		11 40	
Hampton-in-Arden d				10 30									11 00								11 30			
Berkswell d				10 35									11 05								11 35			
Tile Hill d				10 38									11 08								11 38			
Canley d				10 42									11 12								11 42			
Coventry a				10 45		10 49							11 15			11 19	11 23				11 45		11 49	
d						10 50							11 15			11 20							11 50	
Rugby d													11 27											
Long Buckby d													11 37											
Northampton a													11 58											
London Euston 15 ⊖ a						12 00										12 33							13 00	

For general notes see front of timetable
For details of catering facilities see Directory of Train Operators

A From Walsall (Table 70)

Stafford → Wolverhampton → Birmingham → Coventry → Northampton

Network Diagram - see first page of Table 67

		XC	LM		LM	LM	LM	LM	XC	VT	XC	LM	VT	LM	LM	AW	VT	LM	XC	LM	LM		LM	LM	LM
		1◇ ☕	A				1		1◇ ☕	1◇ ☕	R 1 ☕	A	1◇ ☕			◇ ⊼	1◇ ☕	1◇ ⊼	1◇ ☕	A				1	
Stafford	d								11 26									11 46							
Penkridge	d																	11 52							
Wolverhampton 7	a								11 41									12 06							
	d	11 13			11 22	11 25		11 28	11 41				11 49	11 52		11 59	12 05	12 08	12 13		12 22		12 25		12 28
Walsall	a					11 38																	12 39		
Coseley	d							11 33						11 57				12 12							12 33
Tipton	d				11 28									11 59							12 28				
Dudley Port	d				11 30									12 01							12 30				
Sandwell & Dudley	d				11 33									12 05			12 15				12 33				
Smethwick Galton Bdg L.L. 7	d				11 36									12 07							12 36				
Smethwick Rolfe Street	d				11 38									12 09							12 38				
Birmingham New Street 12	a	11 30			11 45			11 48	11 58				12 11	12 15		12 18	12 24	12 30	12 30		12 45				12 48
	d		11 34				11 48			12 00	12 03	12 06			12 18		12 30			12 34				12 48	
Adderley Park	d		11 39																	12 39					
Stechford	d		11 42									12 13								12 42					
Lea Hall	d		11 44									12 15								12 44					
Marston Green	d		11 47									12 18								12 47					
Birmingham International ✈	a		11 52				11 57			12 09	12 14	12 23			12 27		12 39			12 52				12 57	
	d						11 57			12 10	12 15				12 27		12 40							12 57	
Hampton-in-Arden	d						12 00								12 30									13 00	
Berkswell	d						12 05								12 35									13 05	
Tile Hill	d						12 08								12 38									13 08	
Canley	d						12 12								12 42									13 12	
Coventry	a						12 15			12 19	12 23				12 45		12 49							13 15	
	d						12 15			12 20							12 50							13 15	
Rugby	d						12 27																	13 27	
Long Buckby	d						12 37																	13 37	
Northampton	a						12 56																	13 57	
London Euston 15 ⊖	a									13 34							14 00								

		LM	VT	XC	LM	VT	LM	LM	AW	VT	LM	XC	LM	LM	LM	LM	LM		LM	XC	VT	XC	LM	LM	LM
		1◇ ⊼	1◇ ☕	R 1 ☕	A	R 1 ☕			◇ ⊼	1◇ ☕	1◇ ⊼	1◇ ☕	A			1			1◇ ⊼	R 1 ☕	1◇ ☕	R 1 ☕	A		
Stafford	d	12 21		12 26							12 46								13 21	13 26					
Penkridge	d										12 52														
Wolverhampton 7	a	12 36		12 41							13 06								13 36	13 41					
	d	12 38		12 41		12 49	12 52		12 59	13 05	13 08	13 13		13 22	13 25		13 28		13 37	13 41				13 52	
Walsall	a														13 38										
Coseley	d						12 57				13 12						13 33							13 57	
Tipton	d						12 59							13 28										13 59	
Dudley Port	d						13 01							13 30										14 01	
Sandwell & Dudley	d	12 47								13 15				13 33					13 46						
Smethwick Galton Bdg L.L. 7	d						13 06							13 36										14 06	
Smethwick Rolfe Street	d						13 08							13 38										14 08	
Birmingham New Street 12	a	12 58		12 58		13 11	13 15		13 18	13 24	13 30	13 30		13 45			13 48		13 58	13 58				14 15	
	d		13 00	13 03	13 06			13 18		13 30			13 34			13 48					14 00	14 03	14 06		14 18
Adderley Park	d												13 39												
Stechford	d				13 13								13 42										14 13		
Lea Hall	d				13 15								13 44										14 15		
Marston Green	d				13 18								13 47										14 18		
Birmingham International ✈	a		13 09	13 14	13 23			13 27		13 39			13 52			13 57					14 09	14 14	14 23		14 27
	d		13 10	13 15				13 27		13 40						13 57					14 10	14 15			14 27
Hampton-in-Arden	d							13 30								14 00									14 30
Berkswell	d							13 35								14 05									14 35
Tile Hill	d							13 38								14 08									14 38
Canley	d							13 42								14 12									14 42
Coventry	a		13 19	13 23				13 45		13 49						14 15					14 19	14 23			14 45
	d		13 20							13 50						14 15					14 20				
Rugby	d															14 27									
Long Buckby	d															14 37									
Northampton	a															14 57									
London Euston 15 ⊖	a		14 33							15 00											15 34				

For general notes see front of timetable
For details of catering facilities see Directory of Train Operators

A From Walsall (Table 70)

Stafford → Wolverhampton → Birmingham → Coventry → Northampton

Network Diagram - see first page of Table 67

		AW	VT	LM	XC	LM	VT	LM	LM	LM	LM	LM	VT		XC	LM	VT	LM	LM	AW	VT	LM	XC	LM	LM
		◇	[1] ◇	[1] ◇	[1] ◇	A	[R] [1]			[1]		[1] ◇	[1] ◇		[1] ◇	A	[1] ◇			◇	[1] ◇	[1] ◇	[1] ◇	A	
		[trolley]	[restaurant]	[trolley]	[restaurant]		[restaurant]					[trolley]	[restaurant]		[restaurant]		[restaurant]			[trolley]	[restaurant]	[trolley]	[restaurant]		
Stafford	d			13 46								14 21			14 26							14 46			
Penkridge	d			13 52																		14 52			
Wolverhampton [7]	a			14 06								14 36			14 41							15 06			
	d	13 59	14 05	14 08	14 13		14 18	14 22	14 25		14 28	14 37			14 41		14 49	14 52		14 59	15 05	15 08	15 13		15 22
Walsall	a								14 38																
Coseley	d			14 12							14 33							14 57				15 12			
Tipton	d							14 28										14 59							15 28
Dudley Port	d							14 30										15 01							15 30
Sandwell & Dudley	d		14 15					14 33				14 46									15 15				15 33
Smethwick Galton Bdg L.L. [7]	d							14 36										15 06							15 36
Smethwick Rolfe Street	d							14 38										15 08							15 38
Birmingham New Street [12]	a	14 18	14 24	14 30	14 30		14 41	14 45			14 48	14 58			14 58		15 11	15 15		15 18	15 24	15 30	15 30		15 45
	d		14 30			14 34				14 48			15 00		15 03	15 06			15 18		15 30			15 34	
Adderley Park	d					14 39																		15 39	
Stechford	d					14 42										15 13								15 42	
Lea Hall	d					14 44										15 15								15 44	
Marston Green	d					14 47										15 18								15 47	
Birmingham International ✈	a		14 39			14 52				14 57			15 09		15 14	15 23			15 27		15 39			15 52	
	d		14 40							14 57			15 10		15 15				15 27		15 40				
Hampton-in-Arden	d									15 00									15 30						
Berkswell	d									15 05									15 35						
Tile Hill	d									15 08									15 38						
Canley	d									15 12									15 42						
Coventry	a		14 49							15 15			15 19		15 23				15 45		15 49				
	d		14 50							15 15			15 20								15 50				
Rugby	d									15 27															
Long Buckby	d									15 37															
Northampton	a									15 57															
London Euston [15] ⊖	a		16 00										16 34								17 00				

		LM	VT	LM	LM	LM	XC	VT	XC		LM	VT	LM	LM	AW	VT	LM	XC	LM	LM	LM	LM	LM	LM	LM
			[1] ◇	[1]		[1] ◇	[R] [1]	[1] ◇	[R] [1]		A	[R] [1]			◇	[1] ◇	[1] ◇	[R] [1]	A				[1]		[1] ◇
			[restaurant]			[trolley]	[restaurant]	[restaurant]	[restaurant]			[restaurant]			[trolley]	[restaurant]	[trolley]	[restaurant]							[trolley]
Stafford	d					15 21	15 26										15 46								16 21
Penkridge	d																15 52								
Wolverhampton [7]	a					15 36	15 41										16 06								16 36
	d	15 25			15 28	15 37	15 41					15 49	15 52		15 59	16 05	16 08	16 13			16 22	16 25		16 28	16 38
Walsall	a	15 38																				16 40			
Coseley	d				15 33								15 57				16 12							16 33	
Tipton	d												15 59								16 28				
Dudley Port	d												16 01								16 30				
Sandwell & Dudley	d					15 46										16 15					16 33				16 47
Smethwick Galton Bdg L.L. [7]	d												16 06								16 36				
Smethwick Rolfe Street	d												16 08								16 38				
Birmingham New Street [12]	a				15 48	15 58	15 58					16 11	16 15		16 18	16 24	16 30	16 30			16 45			16 48	16 58
	d			15 48				16 00	16 03		16 06			16 18		16 30			16 34	16 45			16 48		
Adderley Park	d																		16 39						
Stechford	d										16 13								16 42						
Lea Hall	d										16 15								16 44						
Marston Green	d										16 18								16 47				16 56		
Birmingham International ✈	a			15 57				16 09	16 14		16 23			16 27		16 39			16 52	16 55			16 59		
	d			15 57				16 10	16 15					16 27		16 40				16 56			17 00		
Hampton-in-Arden	d			16 00										16 30									17 03		
Berkswell	d			16 05										16 35									17 08		
Tile Hill	d			16 08										16 38									17 11		
Canley	d			16 12										16 42									17 14		
Coventry	a			16 15				16 19	16 23					16 45		16 49				17 04			17 20		
	d			16 15				16 20								16 50				17 05					
Rugby	d		15 55	16 27																17 17					
Long Buckby	d			16 37																17 28					
Northampton	a		16 16	16 57																17 46					
London Euston [15] ⊖	a		17 22					17 33								18 00									

For general notes see front of timetable
For details of catering facilities see Directory of Train Operators

A From Walsall (Table 70)

Table 68 — Mondays to Fridays

Stafford → Wolverhampton → Birmingham → Coventry → Northampton

Network Diagram - see first page of Table 67

		VT	XC	LM	VT		LM	LM	LM	AW	VT	LM	XC	LM	LM	LM	LM	LM	LM	XC	VT	XC	LM		VT
		1 ◇	R 1		R 1		1			◇	1 ◇	1 ◇	R 1		1					1 ◇	1 ◇	R 1			1 ◇
														A									A		
		☕	☕		☕					🛒	☕	🛒	☕							☕	☕	☕			☕
Stafford	d		16 26									16 46								17 26					
Penkridge	d											16 52													
Wolverhampton 7	a		16 41									17 05								17 41					
	d		16 41		16 49			16 52		16 59	17 05	17 08	17 13			17 22	17 25		17 28	17 41					17 49
Walsall	a																17 40								
Coseley	d							16 57				17 12							17 33						
Tipton	d							16 59								17 28									
Dudley Port	d							17 01								17 30									
Sandwell & Dudley	d										17 15					17 33									
Smethwick Galton Bdg L.L. 7	d							17 06								17 36									
Smethwick Rolfe Street	d							17 08								17 38									
Birmingham New Street 12	a		16 58		17 11			17 15		17 18	17 24	17 30	17 30			17 45			17 48	17 58					18 11
	d	17 00	17 03	17 06			17 15		17 18		17 30			17 34	17 45			17 48			18 00	18 03	18 06		
Adderley Park	d													17 39											
Stechford	d			17 13										17 42									18 13		
Lea Hall	d			17 15					17 25					17 44									18 15		
Marston Green	d			17 18					17 28					17 47				17 56					18 18		
Birmingham International ✈	a	17 09	17 14	17 23			17 26		17 31		17 39			17 52	17 55			17 59			18 09	18 14	18 23		
	d	17 10	17 15				17 27		17 32		17 40				17 56			18 00			18 10	18 15			
Hampton-in-Arden	d								17 35									18 03							
Berkswell	d								17 40									18 07							
Tile Hill	d								17 43									18 10							
Canley	d								17 46									18 14							
Coventry	a	17 20	17 24				17 35		17 52		17 52				18 04			18 20			18 20	18 24			
	d	17 20					17 37				17 52				18 05						18 20				
Rugby	d						17 54								18 17										
Long Buckby	d						18 04								18 27										
Northampton	a						18 23								18 53										
London Euston 15 ⊖	a	18 34									19 03										19 34				

		LM	LM	AW	VT	LM	XC	LM	LM	LM	LM	LM	LM	VT	XC	LM	VT	LM		LM	AW	VT	LM	XC	LM
			1	◇	1 ◇	1 ◇	R 1				1		1 ◇	1 ◇	R 1		1 ◇				◇	1 ◇	1 ◇	1 ◇	
								A								A							B		A
				🛒	☕	🛒	☕						🛒	☕	☕		☕				🛒	☕	🛒	☕	
Stafford	d					17 46							18 21		18 26								18 46		
Penkridge	d					17 52																	18 52		
Wolverhampton 7	a					18 06							18 36		18 41								19 05		
	d	17 52		17 59	18 05	18 08	18 13		18 22	18 25		18 28	18 37		18 41		18 49	18 52			18 59	19 05	19 08	19 13	
Walsall	a									18 40															
Coseley	d	17 57				18 12						18 33						18 57					19 12		
Tipton	d	17 59							18 28									18 59							
Dudley Port	d	18 01							18 30									19 01							
Sandwell & Dudley	d	18 05			18 15				18 33				18 46									19 15			
Smethwick Galton Bdg L.L. 7	d	18 07							18 36									19 06							
Smethwick Rolfe Street	d	18 09							18 38									19 08							
Birmingham New Street 12	a	18 15		18 18	18 24	18 30	18 30		18 45			18 48	18 58		18 58		19 11	19 15			19 18	19 24	19 30	19 30	
	d		18 18		18 30			18 34			18 48			19 00	19 03	19 06				19 18		19 30			19 34
Adderley Park	d							18 39																	19 39
Stechford	d							18 42								19 13									19 42
Lea Hall	d							18 44								19 15									19 44
Marston Green	d		18 26					18 47								19 18									19 47
Birmingham International ✈	a		18 29		18 39			18 52			18 57			19 09	19 14	19 24				19 27		19 39			19 52
	d		18 30		18 40						18 57			19 11	19 15					19 27		19 40			
Hampton-in-Arden	d		18 33								19 00									19 30					
Berkswell	d		18 37								19 05									19 35					
Tile Hill	d		18 40								19 08									19 38					
Canley	d		18 44								19 12									19 42					
Coventry	a		18 46		18 49						19 15			19 20	19 24					19 45		19 49			
	d		18 47		18 50						19 15			19 20								19 50			
Rugby	d		18 58								19 27														
Long Buckby	d		19 08								19 37														
Northampton	a		19 29								19 56														
London Euston 15 ⊖	a				20 00									20 41								21 04			

For general notes see front of timetable
For details of catering facilities see
Directory of Train Operators

A From Walsall (Table 70)
B From Liverpool Lime Street (Table 91)

Stafford → Wolverhampton → Birmingham → Coventry → Northampton

Network Diagram - see first page of Table 67

Station		LM	LM	LM	LM	XC	XC	LM	VT	LM	AW	VT	LM	XC	LM	LM	LM	LM	XC	LM	VT	LM	VT	LM
				1		1 ◇ ☕	R 1		1 ◇ ☕		◇ 🛒	1 ◇ ☕	1 ◇ 🛒	1 ◇ ☕	1			1 ◇ 🛒	1 ◇		1 ◇ ☕		1 ◇ ☕	1 ◇ 🛒
Stafford	d					19 26							19 48	19 58				20 21	20 26					20 46
Penkridge	d												19 54											20 52
Wolverhampton 7	a					19 41							20 06	20 12				20 36	20 41					21 05
	d	19 22	19 25		19 30	19 41			19 49	19 52	19 59	20 05	20 08	20 13		20 22	20 34	20 37	20 41		20 49	20 52	21 05	21 08
Walsall	a		19 40														20 49							
Coseley	d				19 35					19 57			20 12									20 57		21 12
Tipton	d	19 28								19 59						20 28						20 59		
Dudley Port	d	19 30								20 01						20 30						21 01		
Sandwell & Dudley	d	19 33								20 05		20 15				20 33		20 46				21 05	21 15	
Smethwick Galton Bdg L.L. 7	d	19 36								20 07						20 36						21 07		
Smethwick Rolfe Street	d	19 38								20 09						20 38						21 09		
Birmingham New Street 12	a	19 45			19 48	19 58			20 11	20 15	20 18	20 24	20 30	20 35		20 45		20 58	20 58		21 11	21 16	21 24	21 30
	d			19 48			20 03	20 06				20 30			20 36				21 03	21 06			21 30	
Adderley Park	d														20 40									
Stechford	d							20 12							20 44					21 12				
Lea Hall	d							20 15							20 46					21 15				
Marston Green	d							20 17							20 50					21 17				
Birmingham International ✈	a			19 57			20 14	20 21				20 39			20 53				21 14	21 20			21 39	
	d			19 57			20 15	20 21				20 40			20 53				21 15	21 21			21 40	
Hampton-in-Arden	d			20 00				20 24							20 56					21 24				
Berkswell	d			20 05				20 28							21 01					21 28				
Tile Hill	d			20 08				20 31							21 04					21 31				
Canley	d			20 12				20 34							21 08					21 34				
Coventry	a			20 15			20 23	20 39				20 49			21 11				21 23	21 39			21 49	
	d			20 15								20 50			21 11								21 50	
Rugby	d			20 27											21 22									
Long Buckby	d			20 37											21 33									
Northampton	a			20 57											21 47									
London Euston 15 ⊖	a											22 04											23 26	

Station		XC	LM	LM	LM	LM	XC	LM	LM	AW	LM	LM	VT	LM	VT	VT	LM	LM	LM	AW	LM	XC
		1 ◇		1			1 ◇			◇ 🛒	1 ◇ 🛒	1	1 ◇ ☕		1	1 ◇ ☕			A		1 ◇ B 🛒	1 ◇
Stafford	d	20 57					21 26				21 46		21 55			22 36					22 47	22 57
Penkridge	d										21 52										22 52	
Wolverhampton 7	a	21 12					21 41				22 08		22 16			22 48					23 06	23 12
	d	21 13	21 19		21 22	21 25	21 41		21 52	22 03	22 08		22 16	22 22	22 39	22 49		22 52	22 55	22 59	23 08	23 13
Walsall	a		21 32																23 12			
Coseley	d					21 30			21 57					22 27				22 57				
Tipton	d					21 32			21 59					22 29				22 59				
Dudley Port	d					21 34			22 01					22 31				23 01				
Sandwell & Dudley	d					21 38			22 05					22 35				23 05				
Smethwick Galton Bdg L.L. 7	d					21 40			22 07					22 37				23 07				
Smethwick Rolfe Street	d					21 42			22 09					22 39				23 09				
Birmingham New Street 12	a	21 35			21 44	21 48	22 04		22 15	22 18	22 30		22 38	22 45	22 56	23 11		23 15		23 18	23 30	23 47
	d			21 36				22 06				22 36			23 00		23 15					
Adderley Park	d			21 40								22 41					23 19					
Stechford	d			21 44				22 12				22 44					23 23					
Lea Hall	d			21 46				22 15				22 46					23 25					
Marston Green	d			21 50				22 17				22 49					23 29					
Birmingham International ✈	a			21 53				22 20				22 52			23 09		23 32					
	d			21 53				22 21				22 52			23 10		23 32					
Hampton-in-Arden	d			21 56				22 24				22 55					23 35					
Berkswell	d			22 01				22 28				22 59					23 40					
Tile Hill	d			22 04				22 31				23 02					23 43					
Canley	d			22 08				22 34				23 05					23 47					
Coventry	a			22 11				22 39				23 12			23 19		23 52					
	d			22 11											23 20							
Rugby	d			22 22											23 34							
Long Buckby	d			22 34																		
Northampton	a			22 54											23s56							
London Euston 15 ⊖	a														01 02							

For general notes see front of timetable
For details of catering facilities see Directory of Train Operators

A From Shrewsbury (Table 74)
B From Liverpool Lime Street (Table 91)

Stafford → Wolverhampton → Birmingham → Coventry → Northampton

Network Diagram - see first page of Table 67

		LM	VT	VT	XC	LM	AW	VT	LM	LM	LM	VT	XC	LM	LM	LM	AW	VT	VT	LM	VT	LM	LM	LM	VT
			1 ◇	1 ◇	1 ◇			1 ◇		1		1 ◇	1 ◇	1 ◇				1 ◇	1 ◇	1	1 ◇				1 ◇
				☕				⊠				☕	☕					☕	☕		☕				☕
Stafford	d		04 30										06 20	06 30							07 06				07 19
Penkridge	d													06 36											
Wolverhampton 7	a		04 45										06 41	06 47											07 35
	d		04 46	05 37			06 01	06 05	06 08		06 22	06 35	06 41	06 47		06 52	06 59		07 05			07 22	07 25	07 31	07 35
Walsall	a								06 22														07 38		
Coseley	d										06 27					06 57						07 27			
Tipton	d										06 29					06 59						07 29			
Dudley Port	d										06 31					07 01						07 31			
Sandwell & Dudley	d			05 47				06 15			06 35	06 48				07 05			07 16			07 35			07 48
Smethwick Galton Bdg L.L. 7	d										06 37					07 07						07 37			
Smethwick Rolfe Street	d										06 39					07 09						07 39			
Birmingham New Street 12	a		05 08	05 56			06 18	06 24			06 45	06 56	06 58	07 08		07 15	07 18		07 24			07 45		07 51	07 56
	d	00 10		06 00	06 03	06 13		06 30		06 43		07 00	07 03		07 09				07 30	07 36					08 00
Adderley Park	d					06 18									07 14										
Stechford	d					06 21				06 49					07 17					07 42					
Lea Hall	d					06 24				06 52					07 20					07 45					
Marston Green	d	00 18				06 26				06 55					07 22					07 48					
Birmingham International ✈	a	00 22		06 09	06 14	06 29		06 39		06 59		07 09	07 14		07 25				07 40	07 51					08 09
	d	00 22		06 10	06 15	06 30		06 41		06 59		07 10	07 15		07 26				07 41	07 52					08 10
Hampton-in-Arden	d					06 33				07 02					07 29					07 55					
Berkswell	d					06 37				07 07					07 33					08 00					
Tile Hill	d					06 40				07 10					07 36					08 03					
Canley	d					06 43				07 13					07 39					08 06					
Coventry	a	00 37		06 19	06 23	06 45		06 54		07 17		07 20	07 23		07 41				07 52	08 09	08 14				08 19
	d			06 21				06 55		07 17		07 22						07 47	07 54	08 10	08 15				08 21
Rugby	d			06 35						07 30		07 36								08 21	08 28				
Long Buckby	d									07 40										08 31					
Northampton	a									07 53										08 46					
London Euston 15 ⊖	a			07 52				08 18				08 36						09 04	09 06		09 29				09 38

		XC	LM	VT	LM	AW	LM	VT	VT	LM	LM	LM	LM	VT	VT	XC	LM	VT	LM	AW	LM	VT	LM	VT	LM
																		R							
		1 ◇		1 ◇		◇	1 ◇	1 ◇	1 ◇	1				1 ◇	1 ◇	1 ◇		1		◇	1 ◇	1 ◇	1 ◇	1 ◇	1
							A																		
		☕		☕		🛒		☕	☕					☕	☕	☕		☕		🛒		☕		☕	
Stafford	d						07 44	07 47								08 26					08 44	08 48			
Penkridge	d						07 50														08 50				
Wolverhampton 7	a						08 07									08 41					09 05		←		
	d			07 48	07 52	07 59	08 09		08 11		08 22	08 25	08 31		08 35	08 41		08 48	08 52	08 59	09 09		09 09	09 11	
Walsall	a											08 40									→				
Coseley	d				07 57		08 14						08 37						08 57				09 14		
Tipton	d				07 59						08 28								08 59						
Dudley Port	d				08 01						08 30								09 01						
Sandwell & Dudley	d				08 05						08 33				08 48				09 05						
Smethwick Galton Bdg L.L. 7	d				08 07						08 36								09 07						
Smethwick Rolfe Street	d				08 09						08 38								09 09						
Birmingham New Street 12	a			08 10	08 15	08 18	08 27		08 30		08 45		08 51		08 56	08 58		09 10	09 15	09 18		09 24	09 27	09 30	
	d	08 03	08 09						08 33	08 36					09 00	09 03	09 09					09 30		09 33	09 36
Adderley Park	d		08 14														09 14								
Stechford	d		08 17							08 42							09 17								09 42
Lea Hall	d		08 20							08 45							09 20								09 45
Marston Green	d		08 22							08 48							09 22								09 48
Birmingham International ✈	a	08 14	08 25						08 42	08 51					09 09	09 14	09 25					09 39		09 44	09 52
	d	08 15	08 26						08 43	08 52					09 10	09 15	09 26					09 40		09 45	09 52
Hampton-in-Arden	d		08 29							08 55							09 29								09 55
Berkswell	d		08 33							09 00							09 33								10 00
Tile Hill	d		08 36							09 03							09 36								10 03
Canley	d		08 39							09 06							09 39								10 06
Coventry	a	08 23	08 42					08 50	08 54	09 09					09 20	09 23	09 41					09 49		09 54	10 10
	d							08 52	08 56	09 10				09 16	09 22							09 51		09 56	10 10
Rugby	d									09 21				09b29	09 36									10 10	10 21
Long Buckby	d									09 31															10 31
Northampton	a									09 48															10 46
London Euston 15 ⊖	a							10 05	10 07					10 32	10 36							11 02		11 09	

For general notes see front of timetable
For details of catering facilities see Directory of Train Operators

A From Liverpool Lime Street (Table 91)
b Arr. 0925

Table 68

Saturdays

Stafford → Wolverhampton → Birmingham → Coventry → Northampton

Network Diagram - see first page of Table 67

		LM	VT	LM	LM	VT	XC	XC	LM	VT	LM	AW	LM	VT	VT	LM	LM	VT	LM	LM	VT	XC	LM	VT	LM
			1 ◇ ☕			1 ◇ ☕	1 ◇ ☕	1 ◇ ☕		1 ◇ ☕		◇ 🛒	1 ◇	1 ◇ ☕	1 ◇ ☕	1		1 ◇ ☕			1 ◇ ☕	1 ◇ ☕		1 ◇ ☕	
Stafford	d		09 10				09 26						09 44					10 13				10 26			
Penkridge	d												09 50												
Wolverhampton 7	🚌 a						09 41						10 05									10 41			
	d	09 22		09 25	09 31	09 35	09 41			09 48	09 52	09 59	10 09		10 11		10 22		10 25	10 31	10 35	10 41		10 49	10 52
Walsall	a			09 40															10 40						
Coseley	d				09 37						09 57		10 14							10 37					10 57
Tipton	d	09 28									09 59						10 28								10 59
Dudley Port	d	09 30									10 01						10 30								11 01
Sandwell & Dudley	d	09 33				09 48					10 05						10 33				10 48				11 05
Smethwick Galton Bdg L.L. 7	d	09 36									10 07						10 36								11 07
Smethwick Rolfe Street	d	09 38									10 09						10 38								11 09
Birmingham New Street 12	a	09 45			09 51	09 56	09 58			10 11	10 15	10 18	10 27		10 30		10 45			10 51	10 56	10 58		11 11	11 15
	d		09u50			10 00		10 03	10 09					10 30	10 33	10 36		10u50			11 00	11 03	11 09		
Adderley Park	d								10 14														11 14		
Stechford	d								10 17							10 42							11 17		
Lea Hall	d								10 20							10 45							11 20		
Marston Green	d								10 22							10 48							11 22		
Birmingham International	✈ a		09 59			10 09		10 14	10 25					10 39	10 44	10 52		10 59			11 09	11 14	11 25		
	d		10 00			10 10		10 15	10 26					10 40	10 45	10 52		11 00			11 10	11 15	11 26		
Hampton-in-Arden	d								10 29							10 55							11 29		
Berkswell	d								10 33							11 00							11 33		
Tile Hill	d								10 36							11 03							11 36		
Canley	d								10 39							11 06							11 39		
Coventry	a		10s13			10 19		10 23	10 41					10 49	10 54	11 10		11s13			11 19	11 23	11 41		
	d					10 21								10 51	10 56	11 10					11 21				
Rugby	d					10 35									11 10	11 21					11 35				
Long Buckby	d															11 31									
Northampton	a															11 46									
London Euston 15	⊖ a		11 27			11 36								12 03	12 13			12 28			12 36				

		AW	LM	VT	VT	LM	LM	VT	LM	LM	VT	XC	XC	LM	VT	LM	AW	LM	VT	VT	LM	LM	VT	LM	LM
		◇ 🛒	1 ◇	1 ◇ ☕	1 ◇ ☕	1		1 ◇ ☕			1 ◇ ☕	1 ◇ ☕	1 ◇ ☕		R 1 ☕		◇ 🛒	1 ◇	1 ◇ ☕	1 ◇ ☕	1		1 ◇ ☕		
Stafford	d		10 44					11 13				11 26						11 44					12 13		
Penkridge	d		10 50															11 50							
Wolverhampton 7	🚌 a		11 05									11 41						12 06							
	d	10 59	11 09		11 11		11 22		11 25	11 31	11 35	11 41			11 49	11 52	11 59	12 09		12 11		12 22		12 25	12 31
Walsall	a								11 40															12 40	
Coseley	d		11 14							11 37						11 57		12 14							12 37
Tipton	d						11 28									11 59						12 28			
Dudley Port	d						11 30									12 01						12 30			
Sandwell & Dudley	d						11 33				11 48					12 05						12 33			
Smethwick Galton Bdg L.L. 7	d						11 36									12 07						12 36			
Smethwick Rolfe Street	d						11 38									12 09						12 38			
Birmingham New Street 12	a	11 18	11 27		11 30		11 45			11 51	11 56	11 58			12 11	12 15	12 18	12 27		12 30		12 45			12 51
	d			11 30	11 33	11 36		11u50			12 00		12 03	12 09					12 30	12 33	12 36		12u50		
Adderley Park	d													12 14											
Stechford	d					11 42								12 17							12 42				
Lea Hall	d					11 45								12 20							12 45				
Marston Green	d					11 48								12 22							12 48				
Birmingham International	✈ a			11 39	11 44	11 51		11 59			12 09		12 14	12 25					12 39	12 45	12 51		12 59		
	d			11 40	11 45	11 52		12 00			12 10		12 15	12 26					12 40	12 46	12 52		13 00		
Hampton-in-Arden	d					11 55								12 29							12 55				
Berkswell	d					12 00								12 33							13 00				
Tile Hill	d					12 03								12 36							13 03				
Canley	d					12 06								12 39							13 06				
Coventry	a			11 49	11 54	12 09		12s13			12 19		12 23	12 41					12 49	12 55	13 09		13s13		
	d			11 51	11 56	12 10					12 21								12 51	12 57	13 10				
Rugby	d				12 10	12 21					12 36									13 11	13 21				
Long Buckby	d					12 31															13 31				
Northampton	a					12 46															13 47				
London Euston 15	⊖ a			13 03	13 09			13 26			13 37								14 03	14 12			14 27		

For general notes see front of timetable
For details of catering facilities see Directory of Train Operators

Table 68

Saturdays

Stafford → Wolverhampton → Birmingham → Coventry → Northampton

Network Diagram - see first page of Table 67

	VT	XC	LM	VT	LM	AW	LM	VT	VT	LM	LM	VT	LM	LM	VT	XC	XC	LM	VT	LM	AW	LM	VT	VT
				R															R					
	1 ◇	1 ◇		1		◇	1 ◇	1 ◇	1 ◇	1		1 ◇			1 ◇	1 ◇	1 ◇		1		◇	1 ◇	1 ◇	1 ◇
				A																				
	☕	☕		☕		🛒		☕	☕			☕			☕	☕	☕		☕		🛒		☕	☕
Stafford d		12 26					12 44					13 13				13 26						13 44		
Penkridge d							12 50															13 50		
Wolverhampton 7 a		12 41					13 05									13 41						14 05		
d	12 35	12 41		12 49	12 52	12 59	13 09		13 11		13 22		13 25	13 31	13 35	13 41			13 49	13 52	13 59	14 09		14 11
Walsall a													13 40											
Coseley d					12 57		13 14							13 37						13 57		14 14		
Tipton d					12 59						13 28									13 59				
Dudley Port d					13 01						13 30									14 01				
Sandwell & Dudley d	12 48				13 05						13 33				13 48					14 05				
Smethwick Galton Bdg L.L. 7 d					13 07						13 36									14 07				
Smethwick Rolfe Street d					13 09						13 38									14 09				
Birmingham New Street 12 a	12 56	12 58		13 11	13 15	13 18	13 27		13 30		13 45			13 51	13 56	13 58			14 11	14 15	14 18	14 27		14 30
d	13 00	13 03	13 09					13 30	13 33	13 36		13u50			14 00		14 03	14 09					14 30	14 33
Adderley Park d			13 14															14 14						
Stechford d			13 17							13 42								14 17						
Lea Hall d			13 20							13 45								14 20						
Marston Green d			13 22							13 48								14 22						
Birmingham International ✈ a	13 09	13 14	13 25					13 39	13 44	13 52		13 59			14 09		14 14	14 25					14 39	14 45
d	13 10	13 15	13 26					13 40	13 45	13 52		14 00			14 10		14 15	14 26					14 40	14 46
Hampton-in-Arden d			13 29							13 55								14 29						
Berkswell d			13 33							14 00								14 33						
Tile Hill d			13 36							14 03								14 36						
Canley d			13 39							14 06								14 39						
Coventry a	13 19	13 23	13 41					13 49	13 55	14 10		14s13			14 19		14 23	14 41					14 49	14 55
d	13 21							13 51	13 57	14 10					14 21								14 51	14 57
Rugby d	13 35								14 11	14 21					14 35									15 11
Long Buckby d										14 31														
Northampton a										14 46														
London Euston 15 ⊖ a	14 36							15 03	15 09			15 27			15 36								16 05	16 10

	LM	LM	VT	LM	LM	VT	XC	LM	VT	LM	AW	LM	VT	VT	LM	LM	VT	LM	LM	VT	XC	XC	LM	VT
																								R
	1		1 ◇			1 ◇	1 ◇		1 ◇		◇	1 ◇	1 ◇	1 ◇	1		1 ◇			1 ◇	1 ◇	1 ◇		1
			☕			☕	☕		☕		🛒		☕	☕			☕			☕	☕	☕		☕
Stafford d			14 14				14 26					14 44					15 13				15 26			
Penkridge d												14 50												
Wolverhampton 7 a							14 41					15 05									15 41			
d		14 22		14 25	14 31	14 35	14 41		14 49	14 52	14 59	15 09		15 11		15 22		15 25	15 31	15 35	15 41			15 47
Walsall a				14 40														15 40						
Coseley d					14 37					14 57		15 14							15 37					
Tipton d		14 28								14 59						15 28								
Dudley Port d		14 30								15 01						15 30								
Sandwell & Dudley d		14 33				14 48				15 05						15 33				15 48				
Smethwick Galton Bdg L.L. 7 d		14 36								15 07						15 36								
Smethwick Rolfe Street d		14 38								15 09						15 38								
Birmingham New Street 12 a		14 45			14 51	14 56	14 58		15 11	15 15	15 18	15 27		15 30		15 45			15 51	15 56	15 58			16 11
d	14 36		14u50			15 00	15 03	15 09					15 30	15 33	15 36		15u50			16 00		16 03	16 09	
Adderley Park d								15 14															16 14	
Stechford d	14 42							15 17							15 42								16 17	
Lea Hall d	14 45							15 20							15 45								16 20	
Marston Green d	14 48							15 22							15 48								16 22	
Birmingham International ✈ a	14 51		14 59			15 09	15 14	15 25					15 39	15 45	15 51		15 59			16 09		16 14	16 25	
d	14 52		15 00			15 10	15 15	15 26					15 40	15 46	15 52		16 00			16 10		16 15	16 26	
Hampton-in-Arden d	14 55							15 29							15 55								16 29	
Berkswell d	15 00							15 33							16 00								16 33	
Tile Hill d	15 03							15 36							16 03								16 36	
Canley d	15 06							15 39							16 06								16 39	
Coventry a	15 09		15s13			15 19	15 23	15 41					15 49	15 55	16 09		16s13			16 19		16 23	16 41	
d	15 10					15 21							15 51	15 57	16 10					16 21				
Rugby d	15 21					15 35								16 11	16 21					16 35				
Long Buckby d	15 31														16 31									
Northampton a	15 46														16 46									
London Euston 15 ⊖ a			16 29			16 37							17 05	17 10			17 27			17 36				

For general notes see front of timetable
For details of catering facilities see Directory of Train Operators

A Until 22 March

Stafford → Wolverhampton → Birmingham → Coventry → Northampton

Network Diagram - see first page of Table 67

		LM	AW	LM	VT	VT	LM	LM	VT	LM	LM	VT	XC	LM	VT	LM	AW	LM	VT	VT	LM	LM	VT	LM	LM
			◇	1 ◇	1 ◇	1 ◇	1		1 ◇			1 ◇	1 ◇		R 1		◇	1 ◇	1 ◇	1 ◇	1		1 ◇		
Stafford	d			15 44					16 09				16 26					16 44					17 13		
Penkridge	d			15 50														16 50							
Wolverhampton 7	a			16 05									16 41					17 08							
	d	15 52	15 59	16 09		16 11		16 22		16 25	16 31	16 35	16 41		16 49	16 52	16 59	17 09		17 11		17 22		17 25	17 31
Walsall	a									16 40														17 40	
Coseley	d	15 57		16 14							16 37					16 57		17 14							17 37
Tipton	d	15 59						16 28								16 59						17 28			
Dudley Port	d	16 01						16 30								17 01						17 30			
Sandwell & Dudley	d	16 05						16 33				16 48				17 05						17 33			
Smethwick Galton Bdg L.L. 7	d	16 07						16 36								17 07						17 36			
Smethwick Rolfe Street	d	16 09						16 38								17 09						17 38			
Birmingham New Street 12	a	16 15	16 18	16 27		16 30		16 45			16 51	16 56	16 58		17 11	17 15	17 18	17 27		17 30		17 45			17 51
	d				16 30	16 33	16 36		16u50			17 00	17 03	17 09					17 30	17 33	17 36		17u50		
Adderley Park	d													17 14											
Stechford	d						16 42							17 17							17 42				
Lea Hall	d						16 45							17 20							17 45				
Marston Green	d						16 48							17 22							17 48				
Birmingham International	a				16 39	16 45	16 51		16 59			17 09	17 14	17 25					17 39	17 44	17 52		17 59		
	d				16 40	16 46	16 52		17 00			17 10	17 15	17 26					17 40	17 45	17 52		18 00		
Hampton-in-Arden	d						16 55							17 29							17 55				
Berkswell	d						17 00							17 33							18 00				
Tile Hill	d						17 03							17 36							18 03				
Canley	d						17 06							17 39							18 06				
Coventry	a				16 49	16 55	17 09		17s13			17 19	17 23	17 41					17 49	17 55	18 10		18s13		
	d				16 51	16 57	17 10					17 21							17 51	17 57	18 10				
Rugby	d					17 11	17 21					17 35								18 11	18 21		18 30		
Long Buckby	d						17 31														18 31				
Northampton	a						17 46														18 46				
London Euston 15 ⊖	a				18 03	18 10			18 29			18 37							19 03	19 10			19 30		

		VT	XC	XC	LM	VT	LM	AW	LM	VT	VT	LM	LM	VT	LM	LM	VT	XC	LM	VT	LM	AW	LM	VT	VT
		1 ◇	1 ◇	1 ◇		1 ◇		◇	1 ◇	1 ◇	1 ◇	1		1 ◇			1 ◇	1 ◇		1 ◇		◇	1 ◇	1 ◇	1 ◇
																							A	B	C
Stafford	d		17 26						17 44					18 13				18 26					18 44		
Penkridge	d								17 50														18 50		
Wolverhampton 7	a		17 41						18 07									18 41					19 07		
	d	17 35	17 41			17 49	17 52	17 59	18 09		18 11		18 22		18 25	18 31	18 35	18 41		18 49	18 52	18 59	19 09	19 11	19 11
Walsall	a														18 40										
Coseley	d						17 57		18 14							18 37					18 57		19 14		
Tipton	d						17 59						18 28								18 59				
Dudley Port	d						18 01						18 30								19 01				
Sandwell & Dudley	d	17 48					18 05						18 33				18 48				19 05				
Smethwick Galton Bdg L.L. 7	d						18 07						18 36								19 07				
Smethwick Rolfe Street	d						18 09						18 38								19 09				
Birmingham New Street 12	a	17 56	17 58			18 11	18 16	18 19	18 27		18 30		18 45			18 51	18 56	18 58		19 11	19 15	19 18	19 27	19 30	19 30
	d	18 00		18 03	18 09					18 30	18 33	18 36		18u50			19 00	19 03	19 09					19 33	19 33
Adderley Park	d				18 14														19 14						
Stechford	d				18 17							18 42							19 17						
Lea Hall	d				18 20							18 45							19 20						
Marston Green	d				18 22							18 48							19 22						
Birmingham International	a	18 09		18 14	18 25					18 39	18 44	18 52		18 59			19 09	19 14	19 25					19 42	19 42
	d	18 10		18 15	18 26					18 40	18 45	18 52		19 00			19 10	19 15	19 26					19 43	19 43
Hampton-in-Arden	d				18 29							18 55							19 29						
Berkswell	d				18 33							19 00							19 33						
Tile Hill	d				18 36							19 03							19 36						
Canley	d				18 39							19 06							19 39						
Coventry	a	18 19		18 23	18 41					18 49	18 55	19 10		19s13			19 19	19 23	19 41					19 52	19 52
	d	18 21								18 51	18 57	19 10					19 21							19 54	19 54
Rugby	d	18 35									19 11	19 21					19 35								
Long Buckby	d											19 31													
Northampton	a											19 46													
London Euston 15 ⊖	a	19 38								20 03	20 16			20 49			21 00							21 33	21 42

For general notes see front of timetable
For details of catering facilities see Directory of Train Operators

A From Liverpool Lime Street (Table 91)
B From 29 March
C Until 22 March

Table 68

Saturdays

Stafford → Wolverhampton → Birmingham → Coventry → Northampton

Network Diagram - see first page of Table 67

		LM	VT	LM	LM	LM	VT	VT	XC	XC	LM	VT	LM	AW	LM	VT	VT	VT	VT	LM	LM	LM	XC	LM	VT
		1	1 ◇				1 ◇	1 ◇	1 ◇	1 ◇		1 ◇		◇	1 ◇	1 ◇	1 ◇	1 ◇	1 ◇	1			1 ◇		1 ◇
							A	B								A	A	B	B						
			☕				☕	☕	☕			☕		🛒		☕	☕	☕	☕						☕
Stafford	d		19 08						19 26						19 44	19 52		19 52					20 26		
Penkridge	d														19 50										
Wolverhampton 7	a								19 41						20 07								20 41		
	d			19 22	19 25	19 31	19 35	19 35	19 41			19 49	19 52	19 59	20 09		20 11		20 11		20 22	20 25	20 41		20 49
Walsall	a				19 39																	20 39			
Coseley	d					19 37							19 57								20 27				
Tipton	d			19 28									19 59								20 29				
Dudley Port	d			19 30									20 01								20 31				
Sandwell & Dudley	d			19 33			19 48	19 48					20 05								20 35				
Smethwick Galton Bdg L.L. 7	d			19 36									20 07								20 37				
Smethwick Rolfe Street	d			19 38									20 09								20 39				
Birmingham New Street 12	a			19 45		19 51	19 56	19 56	19 58			20 11	20 15	20 18	20 30		20 30		20 30		20 45		20 58		21 11
	d	19 36					20 00	20 00		20 03	20 09						20 33		20 33	20 36			21 03	21 09	
Adderley Park	d										20 14													21 14	
Stechford	d	19 42									20 17									20 42				21 17	
Lea Hall	d	19 45									20 20									20 45				21 20	
Marston Green	d	19 48									20 22									20 48				21 22	
Birmingham International ✈	a	19 51					20 09	20 09		20 14	20 25						20 42		20 42	20 51			21 14	21 25	
	d	19 52					20 10	20 10		20 15	20 26						20 43		20 43	20 52			21 15	21 26	
Hampton-in-Arden	d	19 55									20 29									20 55				21 29	
Berkswell	d	20 00									20 33									21 00				21 33	
Tile Hill	d	20 03									20 36									21 03				21 36	
Canley	d	20 06									20 39									21 06				21 39	
Coventry	a	20 09	20 13				20 19	20 19		20 23	20 41						20 52		20 52	21 09			21 23	21 41	
	d	20 10	20 15				20 21	20 21									20 54		20 54	21 10					
Rugby	d	20 21					20 35	20 35								21 01		21 01		21 21					
Long Buckby	d	20 31																		21 31					
Northampton	a	20 47																		21 49					
London Euston 15 ⊖	a		22 01				22 08	22 26								22 34	22 39	22 42	22 46						

		LM	AW	LM	LM	VT	VT	LM	LM	LM	VT	LM	LM	AW	VT	XC	LM	LM	LM	VT	LM	LM	LM	AW	
					1 ◇	1 ◇	1 ◇	1			1 ◇			◇	1 ◇	1 ◇		1	1 ◇	1 ◇					
						A	B															C			
						☕	☕				☕			🛒	☕					☕					
Stafford	d				20 44						21 18				21 51	21 58			22 25	22 33					
Penkridge	d				20 50														22 31						
Wolverhampton 7	a				21 08						21 35				22 09	22 13			22 43	22 48					
	d	20 52	20 59	21 03	21 09	21 11	21 11		21 22	21 31	21 35	21 52		22 03	22 09	22 13	22 22		22 43	22 49	22 52	22 55		22 59	
Walsall	a			21 18																		23 12			
Coseley	d	20 57							21 27			21 57					22 27				22 57				
Tipton	d	20 59							21 29			21 59					22 29				22 59				
Dudley Port	d	21 01							21 31			22 01					22 31				23 01				
Sandwell & Dudley	d	21 05							21 35		21 47	22 05					22 35				23 05				
Smethwick Galton Bdg L.L. 7	d	21 07							21 37			22 07					22 37				23 07				
Smethwick Rolfe Street	d	21 09							21 39			22 09					22 39				23 09				
Birmingham New Street 12	a	21 15	21 18		21 27	21 30	21 30		21 45	21 53	21 56	22 15		22 18	22 30	22 37	22 45		23 04	23 10	23 15			23 18	
	d					21 33	21 33	21 36			22 00		22 18					22 48					23 17		
Adderley Park	d												22 23										23 22		
Stechford	d							21 42					22 26					22 55					23 25		
Lea Hall	d							21 45					22 29					22 58					23 28		
Marston Green	d							21 48					22 31					23 01					23 30		
Birmingham International ✈	a					21 42	21 42	21 52			22 09		22 34					23 04					23 33		
	d					21 43	21 43	21 52			22 10		22 35					23 04					23 34		
Hampton-in-Arden	d							21 55					22 38					23 07					23 37		
Berkswell	d							22 00					22 42					23 12					23 41		
Tile Hill	d							22 03					22 45					23 15					23 44		
Canley	d							22 06					22 48					23 19					23 47		
Coventry	a					21 52	21 52	22 10			22 19		22 50					23 22					23 49		
	d					21 54	21 54	22 10			22 21							23 22							
Rugby	d							22 21			22 35							23 34							
Long Buckby	d							22 31										23 44							
Northampton	a							22 49										23 58							
London Euston 15 ⊖	a					23 30	23 43				00 16														

For general notes see front of timetable
For details of catering facilities see Directory of Train Operators

A From 29 March
B Until 22 March
C From Shrewsbury (Table 74)

Table 68

Sundays

until 27 January

Stafford → Wolverhampton → Birmingham → Coventry → Northampton

Network Diagram - see first page of Table 67

		LM	LM 🚌	VT 1◇ ☕	XC 1◇ ☕	LM 1	LM	LM	LM 🚌	LM	AW	XC 1◇ ☕	VT 1◇ ☕	LM	XC 1◇ ☕	XC 1◇ ☕		VT 1◇ ☕	LM 1	LM	LM 🚌	XC 1◇ ☕	LM	LM 1◇	VT 1◇ ☕
Stafford	d														09 26			09 39				09 53		10 01	10 08
Penkridge	d																							10 07	
Wolverhampton 7	a														09 40							10 09		10 23	
	d			08 37			08 52	09 01			09 31		09 35	09 41	09 43					09 52		10 09		10 24	
Walsall	a							09 15						09 56											
Coseley	d						08 57													09 57					
Tipton	d						08 59													09 59					
Dudley Port	d						09 01													10 01					
Sandwell & Dudley	d			08 47			09 05						09 47							10 05					
Smethwick Galton Bdg L.L. 7	d						09 07													10 07					
Smethwick Rolfe Street	d						09 09													10 09					
Birmingham New Street 12	a			08 56			09 16				09 47		09 56		09 58	←				10 16		10 30		10 43	
	d	00 10		09 00	09 03	09 15				09 36		09 48 →	10 00			09 48			10 15			10 33	10 36		
Adderley Park	d									09 41													10 41		
Stechford	d									09 44													10 44		
Lea Hall	d									09 46													10 46		
Marston Green	d	00 18								09 49													10 49		
Birmingham International ✈	a	00 21		09 09	09 14	09 24				09 52			10 09			10 13			10 24			10 42	10 52		10 57
	d	00 22		09 10	09 15	09 25				09 52			10 10			10 15			10 25			10 45	10 52		10 58
Hampton-in-Arden	d									09 55													10 55		
Berkswell	d									09 59													10 59		
Tile Hill	d									10 02													11 02		
Canley	d									10 05													11 05		
Coventry	a	00 37		09 19	09 23	09 34				10 09			10 19			10 23		10 28	10 34			10 53	11 08		11 12
	d		08 45	09 21					09 45				10 21					10 29			10 45				11 14
Rugby	d		09 26						10 26									10 42			11 26				11 28
Long Buckby	d		09 52						10 52												11 52				
Northampton	a		10 17						11 17												12 17				
London Euston 15 ⊖	a			10 56									11 51					12 00							12 51

		AW	VT 1◇ ☕	LM	XC 1◇ ☕	VT 1◇ ☕	LM	LM 1	LM 🚌	VT 1◇ ☕		VT 1◇ ☕	XC 1◇ ☕	LM	VT 1◇ ☕	LM	AW	LM	XC 1◇ ☕	XC 1◇ ☕	VT 1◇ ☕	LM 1	LM 🚌	VT 1◇ ☕	VT 1◇ ☕
Stafford	d				10 26	10 32				10 55					11 08				11 26					11 55	
Penkridge	d																								
Wolverhampton 7	a				10 40	10 48													11 40						
	d	10 31	10 36	10 40	10 43	10 49	10 52					11 05				11 22	11 31	11 40	11 43		11 49				12 05
Walsall	a			10 55														11 56							
Coseley	d						10 57									11 27									
Tipton	d						10 59									11 29									
Dudley Port	d						11 01									11 31									
Sandwell & Dudley	d		10 47				11 05					11 17				11 35									12 17
Smethwick Galton Bdg L.L. 7	d						11 07									11 37									
Smethwick Rolfe Street	d						11 09									11 39									
Birmingham New Street 12	a	10 47	10 56		10 58	11 11	11 16					11 26				11 46	11 48		11 58		12 11				12 26
	d		11 00		11 03			11 18				11 30	11 33	11 36						12 03		12 18			12 30
Adderley Park	d													11 41											
Stechford	d													11 44											
Lea Hall	d													11 46											
Marston Green	d													11 49											
Birmingham International ✈	a		11 09		11 14			11 30				11 39	11 45	11 52						12 13		12 30			12 39
	d		11 10		11 15			11 31				11 41	11 45	11 52						12 15		12 31			12 41
Hampton-in-Arden	d													11 55											
Berkswell	d													11 59											
Tile Hill	d													12 02											
Canley	d													12 05											
Coventry	a		11 19		11 23			11 40		11 45		11 51	11 55	12 08	12 12					12 23		12 40		12 45	12 51
	d		11 21						11 45	11 47		11 53			12 14								12 45	12 47	12 53
Rugby	d								12 26	11 59													13 26	12 59	
Long Buckby	d								12 52														13 52		
Northampton	a								13 17														14 17		
London Euston 15 ⊖	a		12 58							13 23		13 29			13 56									14 23	14 29

For general notes see front of timetable
For details of catering facilities see
Directory of Train Operators

Table 68

Sundays

until 27 January

Stafford → Wolverhampton → Birmingham → Coventry → Northampton

Network Diagram - see first page of Table 67

		XC	LM	LM		LM	XC	VT	AW	LM	LM	LM	VT	VT	XC	LM	LM	AW	LM	XC		VT	XC	VT	LM
		1 ◇					1 ◇	1 ◇	◇	1	1 ◇	bus	1 ◇	1 ◇	1 ◇					R 1		1 ◇	R 1	1 ◇	1
		☕					☕	☕	trolley				☕	☕	☕					☕		☕	☕	☕	
Stafford	d						12 26				12 43		12 56							13 26					
Penkridge	d										12 49														
Wolverhampton 7	a						12 40				13 02									13 40					
	d			12 22		12 40	12 43	12 49	12 58		13 02			13 05			13 22	13 31	13 40	13 43				13 49	
Walsall	a					12 55													13 56						
Coseley	d			12 27													13 27								
Tipton	d			12 29													13 29								
Dudley Port	d			12 31													13 31								
Sandwell & Dudley	d			12 35										13 17			13 35								
Smethwick Galton Bdg L.L. 7	d			12 37													13 37								
Smethwick Rolfe Street	d			12 39													13 39								
Birmingham New Street 12	a			12 46			12 58	13 11	13 15		13 21			13 26			13 46	13 49		13 58				14 11	
	d	12 33	12 36				13 03			13 18				13 30	13 33	13 36						14 00	14 03		14 18
Adderley Park	d		12 41													13 41									
Stechford	d		12 44													13 44									
Lea Hall	d		12 46													13 46									
Marston Green	d		12 49													13 49									
Birmingham International ✈	a	12 44	12 52				13 13			13 30				13 39	13 45	13 52						14 09	14 14		14 30
	d	12 45	12 52				13 15			13 31				13 41	13 45	13 52						14 10	14 15		14 31
Hampton-in-Arden	d		12 55													13 55									
Berkswell	d		12 59													13 59									
Tile Hill	d		13 02													14 02									
Canley	d		13 05													14 05									
Coventry	a	12 55	13 08				13 23			13 40			13 45	13 51	13 55	14 08						14 19	14 23		14 40
	d											13 45	13 47	13 53								14 21			
Rugby	d											14 26	13 59												
Long Buckby	d											14 52													
Northampton	a											15 17													
London Euston 15 ⊖	a												15 08	15 16								15 43			

		LM	VT	VT	XC	LM	LM	AW	LM	VT	XC	LM	VT	LM		AW	LM	VT	VT	XC	LM	VT	LM	LM	XC
		bus	1 ◇	1 ◇	1 ◇					1 ◇	R 1	1 ◇	1 ◇	1		◇	bus	1 ◇	1 ◇	1 ◇		1 ◇			R 1
			☕	☕	☕					☕	☕		☕			trolley		☕	☕	☕		☕			☕
Stafford	d		13 58								14 26	14 31						14 58				15 07			15 26
Penkridge	d											14 37													
Wolverhampton 7	a										14 40	14 49													15 40
	d			14 05			14 22	14 32	14 40		14 43	14 50	14 55			15 02			15 04				15 22	15 40	15 43
Walsall	a								14 56															15 55	
Coseley	d						14 27																15 27		
Tipton	d						14 29																15 29		
Dudley Port	d						14 31																15 31		
Sandwell & Dudley	d			14 17			14 35												15 17				15 35		
Smethwick Galton Bdg L.L. 7	d						14 37																15 37		
Smethwick Rolfe Street	d						14 39																15 39		
Birmingham New Street 12	a			14 26			14 46	14 49			14 58	15 08	15 16			15 18			15 26				15 46		15 58
	d			14 30	14 33	14 36				15 00	15 03			15 18					15 30	15 33	15 36				
Adderley Park	d					14 41															15 41				
Stechford	d					14 44															15 44				
Lea Hall	d					14 46															15 46				
Marston Green	d					14 49															15 49				
Birmingham International ✈	a			14 39	14 45	14 52				15 10	15 14			15 30					15 39	15 45	15 52				
	d			14 41	14 45	14 52				15 11	15 15			15 31					15 41	15 45	15 52				
Hampton-in-Arden	d					14 55															15 55				
Berkswell	d					14 59															15 59				
Tile Hill	d					15 02															16 02				
Canley	d					15 05															16 05				
Coventry	a		14 45	14 51	14 55	15 08				15 20	15 23			15 40				15 45	15 51	15 55	16 08	16 12			
	d	14 45	14 47	14 53						15 22							15 45	15 47	15 53			16 14			
Rugby	d	15 26	14 59														16 26	15 59				16 28			
Long Buckby	d	15 52															16 52								
Northampton	a	16 17															17 17								
London Euston 15 ⊖	a		16 07	16 16						16 41								17 08	17 11			17 39			

For general notes see front of timetable
For details of catering facilities see Directory of Train Operators

Table 68

Sundays

until 27 January

Stafford → Wolverhampton → Birmingham → Coventry → Northampton

Network Diagram - see first page of Table 67

		VT	XC	VT	LM	LM	VT	VT		XC	AW	LM	LM	LM	VT	XC	VT	LM	LM	LM	VT	VT	XC	AW	LM
		1 ◇	R 1	R 1	1	🚌	1 ◇	1 ◇		1 ◇	◇				1 ◇	R 1	R 1	1 ◇	1	🚌	1 ◇	1 ◇	1 ◇		
		☕	☕	☕			☕	☕		☕					☕	☕	☕				☕	☕	☕		
Stafford	d						15 55									16 26		16 36			16 55				
Penkridge	d																	16 42							
Wolverhampton 7	a															16 40		16 54							
	d			15 49				16 04			16 17		16 22	16 40		16 43	16 49	16 54				17 04		17 18	
Walsall	a													16 55											
Coseley	d												16 27												
Tipton	d												16 29												
Dudley Port	d												16 31												
Sandwell & Dudley	d							16 17					16 35									17 17			
Smethwick Galton Bdg L.L. 7	d												16 37												
Smethwick Rolfe Street	d												16 39												
Birmingham New Street 12	a			16 11				16 26			16 33		16 46			16 58	17 11	17 14				17 26		17 34	
	d	16 00	16 03		16 18			16 30		16 33		16 36			17 00	17 03			17 18			17 30	17 33		17 36
Adderley Park	d											16 41													17 41
Stechford	d											16 44													17 44
Lea Hall	d											16 46													17 46
Marston Green	d											16 49													17 49
Birmingham International ✈	a	16 10	16 14		16 30			16 39		16 44		16 52			17 10	17 14			17 30			17 39	17 45		17 52
	d	16 11	16 15		16 31			16 41		16 45		16 52			17 11	17 15			17 31			17 41	17 45		17 52
Hampton-in-Arden	d											16 55													17 55
Berkswell	d											16 59													17 59
Tile Hill	d											17 02													18 02
Canley	d											17 05													18 05
Coventry	a	16 20	16 23		16 40		16 45	16 51		16 55		17 08			17 20	17 23			17 40		17 45	17 51	17 55		18 08
	d	16 22				16 45	16 47	16 53							17 22					17 45	17 47	17 53			
Rugby	d					17 26	16 59													18 26	17 59				
Long Buckby	d					17 52														18 52					
Northampton	a					18 17														19 17					
London Euston 15	⊖ a	17 43					18 08	18 11							18 41						19 14	19 17			

		VT		LM	LM	XC	VT	XC	VT	LM	LM	VT	XC	AW	LM	LM	CH	LM		XC	LM	VT	LM	LM	VT
		1 ◇				R 1	1 ◇	R 1	R 1	1	🚌	1 ◇	1 ◇	◇			A			R 1	1 ◇	R 1	1	🚌	1 ◇
		☕				☕	☕	☕	☕			☕	☕	🛒						☕		☕			☕
Stafford	d	17 08				17 26														18 26	18 30				18 55
Penkridge	d																				18 36				
Wolverhampton 7	a					17 40														18 40	18 48				
	d			17 22	17 40	17 43			17 49			18 04		18 18		18 22	18 34	18 40		18 43	18 48	18 52			
Walsall	a				17 55													18 55							
Coseley	d			17 27												18 27									
Tipton	d			17 29												18 29									
Dudley Port	d			17 31												18 31									
Sandwell & Dudley	d			17 35								18 17				18 35									
Smethwick Galton Bdg L.L. 7	d			17 37												18 37									
Smethwick Rolfe Street	d			17 39												18 39									
Birmingham New Street 12	a			17 46		17 58			18 11			18 26		18 35		18 46	18 50			18 58	19 04	19 14			
	d						18 00	18 03		18 18		18 30	18 33		18 36					19 03			19 18		
Adderley Park	d														18 41										
Stechford	d														18 44										
Lea Hall	d														18 46										
Marston Green	d														18 49										
Birmingham International ✈	a						18 10	18 14		18 30		18 39	18 45		18 52					19 13			19 30		
	d						18 11	18 15		18 31		18 40	18 45		18 52					19 15			19 31		
Hampton-in-Arden	d														18 55										
Berkswell	d														18 59										
Tile Hill	d														19 02										
Canley	d														19 05										
Coventry	a	18 12					18 20	18 23		18 40		18 49	18 55		19 08					19 23			19 40		19 45
	d	18 14					18 22				18 45	18 51												19 45	19 47
Rugby	d	18 28									19 26													20 26	19 59
Long Buckby	d										19 52													20 52	
Northampton	a										20 17													21 17	
London Euston 15	⊖ a	19 33					19 41					20 11													21 14

For general notes see front of timetable
For details of catering facilities see
Directory of Train Operators

A To London Marylebone (Table 71)

Table 68

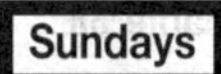

Sundays

until 27 January

Stafford → Wolverhampton → Birmingham → Coventry → Northampton

Network Diagram - see first page of Table 67

		VT	AW	LM	VT	LM	LM	XC	XC	VT	LM	AW		LM	VT	VT	VT	LM	LM	LM	XC	LM	VT	LM	VT
		1 ◇ ☕	◇		1 ◇ ☕			R 1 ☕	R 1	R 1 ☕	1	◇ 🛒		🚌	1 ◇ ☕	1 ◇ ☕	1 ◇ ☕				1 ◇	1 ◇	1 ◇ ☕	1	1 ◇ ☕
Stafford	d				19 08			19 26							19 55		20 08				20 26	20 31			20 53
Penkridge	d																								
Wolverhampton 7 🚢	a							19 40													20 40	20 47			21 08
	d	19 04	19 18			19 22	19 40	19 43		19 49		20 02				20 04			20 22	20 40	20 43	20 47	20 52		21 10
Walsall	a						19 55													20 55					
Coseley	d					19 27													20 27						
Tipton	d					19 29													20 29						
Dudley Port	d					19 31													20 31						
Sandwell & Dudley	d	19 17				19 35										20 17			20 35						
Smethwick Galton Bdg L.L. 7	d					19 37													20 37						
Smethwick Rolfe Street	d					19 39													20 39						
Birmingham New Street 12	a	19 26	19 34			19 46		19 58		20 11		20 19				20 26			20 46		20 58	21 08	21 15		21 32
	d	19 30		19 36					20 03		20 18					20 30		20 36			21 03			21 18	
Adderley Park	d			19 41														20 41							
Stechford	d			19 44														20 44							
Lea Hall	d			19 46														20 46							
Marston Green	d			19 49														20 49							
Birmingham International ✈	a	19 39		19 52					20 14		20 30					20 39		20 52			21 14			21 30	
	d	19 41		19 52					20 15		20 31					20 41		20 52			21 15			21 31	
Hampton-in-Arden	d			19 55														20 55							
Berkswell	d			19 59														20 59							
Tile Hill	d			20 02														21 02							
Canley	d			20 05														21 05							
Coventry	a	19 51		20 08	20 12				20 23		20 40				20 45	20 51		21 08			21 23			21 40	
	d	19 53			20 14									20 45	20 47	20 53									
Rugby	d				20 28									21 26	20 59		21 25								
Long Buckby	d													21 52											
Northampton	a													22 17											
London Euston 15 ⊖	a	21 17			21 54										22 23	22 27	22 51								

		LM	VT	AW	LM	VT		LM	VT	LM	LM	VT	XC	LM	LM	AW	LM	VT	LM	LM	VT	XC	LM		
		🚌	1 ◇ ☕	◇		1 ◇ ☕			1 ◇ ☕		1	1 ◇ ☕	1 ◇	🚌		◇ 🛒		1 ◇ ☕			1 ◇ ☕	1 ◇	1 ◇		
Stafford	d		20 59			21 11			21 21			21 32	21 53								22 40	22 53	23 07		
Penkridge	d																						23 12		
Wolverhampton 7 🚢	a								21 35			21 54	22 09								22 54	23 09	23 25		
	d			21 16				21 22	21 35	21 40		21 56	22 09			22 19	22 22	22 35	22 40		22 55	23 09	23 25		
Walsall	a									21 55									22 55						
Coseley	d							21 27									22 27								
Tipton	d							21 29									22 29								
Dudley Port	d							21 31									22 31								
Sandwell & Dudley	d							21 35	21 48								22 35	22 47							
Smethwick Galton Bdg L.L. 7	d							21 37									22 37								
Smethwick Rolfe Street	d							21 39									22 39								
Birmingham New Street 12	a			21 32				21 46	21 56			22 17	22 30			22 36	22 46	22 56			23 17	23 30	23 45		
	d				21 36				22 00		22 15				22 36			23 00		23 15					
Adderley Park	d				21 41										22 41					23 20					
Stechford	d				21 44										22 44					23 23					
Lea Hall	d				21 46										22 46					23 25					
Marston Green	d				21 49										22 49					23 28					
Birmingham International ✈	a				21 52				22 09		22 24				22 52			23 09		23 31					
	d				21 52				22 10		22 25				22 52			23 10		23 31					
Hampton-in-Arden	d				21 55										22 55					23 34					
Berkswell	d				21 59										22 59					23 38					
Tile Hill	d				22 02										23 02					23 41					
Canley	d				22 05										23 05					23 44					
Coventry	a		21 45		22 08	22 12			22 19		22 34				23 08			23 19		23 47					
	d	21 45	21 47			22 14			22 21					22 45				23 21							
Rugby	d	22 26	21 59						22 35					23 26				23 35							
Long Buckby	d	22 52												23 52											
Northampton	a	23 17												00 17											
London Euston 15 ⊖	a		23 25			23 41			23 48									00 47							

For general notes see front of timetable
For details of catering facilities see Directory of Train Operators

Table 68

Stafford → Wolverhampton → Birmingham → Coventry → Northampton

3 February to 23 March

Network Diagram - see first page of Table 67

		LM	LM	VT	XC	LM	LM	LM	LM	LM	XC	VT	LM	XC	XC	VT	LM	LM	LM	LM	LM	VT	VT	LM	XC
				1 ◇	1 ◇	1					1 ◇	1 ◇		1 ◇	1 ◇	1 ◇	1				1 ◇	1 ◇	1 ◇		1 ◇
			🚌						🚌										🚌						
				☕	☕						☕	☕		☕	☕	☕						☕	☕		☕
Stafford	d													09 26		09 39					10 01	10 08			10 26
Penkridge	d																				10 07				
Wolverhampton 7	a													09 40							10 23				10 40
	d			08 37			08 52	09 01				09 35	09 41	09 43				09 52			10 24		10 36	10 40	10 43
Walsall	a							09 15					09 56											10 55	
Coseley	d						08 57											09 57							
Tipton	d						08 59											09 59							
Dudley Port	d						09 01											10 01							
Sandwell & Dudley	d			08 47			09 05					09 47						10 05					10 47		
Smethwick Galton Bdg L.L. 7	d						09 07											10 07							
Smethwick Rolfe Street	d						09 09											10 09							
Birmingham New Street 12	a			08 56			09 16					09 56		09 58				10 16			10 43		10 56		10 58
	d	00 10		09 00	09 03	09 15				09 36	09 48	10 00					10 15			10 36			11 00		11 03
Adderley Park	d									09 41										10 41					
Stechford	d									09 44										10 44					
Lea Hall	d									09 46										10 46					
Marston Green	d	00 18								09 49					←					10 49					
Birmingham International ✈	a	00 21		09 09	09 14	09 24				09 52	10 13	10 09			10 13		10 24			10 52		10 57	11 09		11 14
	d	00 22		09 10	09 15	09 25				09 52	→	10 10			10 15		10 25			10 52		10 58	11 10		11 15
Hampton-in-Arden	d									09 55										10 55					
Berkswell	d									09 59										10 59					
Tile Hill	d									10 02										11 02					
Canley	d									10 05										11 05					
Coventry	a	00 37		09 19	09 23	09 34				10 09		10 19			10 23	10 28	10 34			11 08		11 12	11 19		11 23
	d		08 45	09 21					09 45			10 21				10 29			10 45			11 14	11 21		
Rugby	d		09 26						10 26							10 42			11 26			11 28			
Long Buckby	d		09 52						10 52										11 52						
Northampton	a		10 17						11 17										12 17						
London Euston 15 ⊖	a			10 56								11 51				12 00						12 51	12 58		

		VT	VT	CH	LM	LM	LM	VT	VT	LM	VT	LM	LM	XC	XC	VT	CH	LM	LM	VT	VT	LM	LM	LM	XC
		1 ◇	1 ◇			1		1 ◇	1 ◇		1 ◇			1 ◇	1 ◇	1 ◇		1		1 ◇	1 ◇				1 ◇
				A													A								
							🚌												🚌						
		☕	☕					☕	☕		☕			☕	☕	☕				☕	☕				☕
Stafford	d	10 32	10 41					10 55			11 08			11 26						11 55					12 26
Penkridge	d																								
Wolverhampton 7	a	10 48												11 40											12 40
	d	10 49			10 52				11 05			11 22	11 40	11 43		11 49					12 05		12 22	12 40	12 43
Walsall	a												11 56											12 55	
Coseley	d				10 57							11 27											12 27		
Tipton	d				10 59							11 29											12 29		
Dudley Port	d				11 01							11 31											12 31		
Sandwell & Dudley	d				11 05				11 17			11 35									12 17		12 35		
Smethwick Galton Bdg L.L. 7	d				11 07							11 37											12 37		
Smethwick Rolfe Street	d				11 09							11 39											12 39		
Birmingham New Street 12	a	11 11			11 16				11 26			11 46		11 58		12 11					12 26		12 46		12 58
	d			11 15		11 18			11 30	11 36					12 03		12 15	12 18			12 30	12 36			13 03
Adderley Park	d									11 41												12 41			
Stechford	d									11 44												12 44			
Lea Hall	d									11 46												12 46			
Marston Green	d									11 49												12 49			
Birmingham International ✈	a			11 25		11 30			11 39	11 52					12 13		12 25	12 30			12 39	12 52			13 13
	d			11 26		11 31			11 41	11 52					12 15		12 26	12 31			12 41	12 52			13 15
Hampton-in-Arden	d									11 55												12 55			
Berkswell	d									11 59												12 59			
Tile Hill	d									12 02												13 02			
Canley	d									12 05												13 05			
Coventry	a			11 37		11 40		11 45	11 51	12 08	12 12				12 23		12 37	12 40		12 45	12 51	13 08			13 23
	d						11 45	11 47	11 53		12 14								12 45	12 47	12 53				
Rugby	d		11 41				12 26	11 59											13 26	12 59					
Long Buckby	d						12 52												13 52						
Northampton	a						13 17												14 17						
London Euston 15 ⊖	a		13 04					13 23	13 29		13 56									14 23	14 29				

For general notes see front of timetable
For details of catering facilities see Directory of Train Operators

A To London Marylebone (Table 115)

Table 68

Sundays

Stafford → Wolverhampton → Birmingham → Coventry → Northampton

3 February to 23 March

Network Diagram - see first page of Table 67

	VT	CH	LM	LM	LM	VT	VT	LM	LM	LM	XC	VT	XC	VT	CH	LM	LM	VT	VT	LM	LM	LM	VT	XC
	1 ◇	A	1	1 ◇	🚌	1 ◇	1 ◇				R 1	1 ◇	R 1	1 ◇	A	1	🚌	1 ◇	1 ◇				1 ◇	R 1
	☕					☕	☕				☕	☕	☕	☕				☕	☕				☕	☕
Stafford d				12 43		12 56					13 26							13 58						14 26
Penkridge d				12 49																				
Wolverhampton 7 🚌 a				13 02							13 40													14 40
d	12 49			13 02			13 05		13 22	13 40	13 43			13 49					14 05		14 22	14 40		14 43
Walsall a										13 56												14 56		
Coseley d									13 27												14 27			
Tipton d									13 29												14 29			
Dudley Port d									13 31												14 31			
Sandwell & Dudley d							13 17		13 35										14 17		14 35			
Smethwick Galton Bdg L.L. 7 d									13 37												14 37			
Smethwick Rolfe Street d									13 39												14 39			
Birmingham New Street 12 a	13 11			13 21			13 26		13 46		13 58			14 11					14 26		14 46			14 58
d		13 15	13 18				13 30	13 36				14 00	14 03		14 15	14 18			14 30	14 36			15 00	15 03
Adderley Park d								13 41												14 41				
Stechford d								13 44												14 44				
Lea Hall d								13 46												14 46				
Marston Green d								13 49												14 49				
Birmingham International ✈ a		13 25	13 30				13 39	13 52				14 09	14 14		14 25	14 30			14 39	14 52			15 10	15 14
d		13 26	13 31				13 41	13 52				14 10	14 15		14 26	14 31			14 41	14 52			15 11	15 15
Hampton-in-Arden d								13 55												14 55				
Berkswell d								13 59												14 59				
Tile Hill d								14 02												15 02				
Canley d								14 05												15 05				
Coventry a		13 37	13 40			13 45	13 51	14 08				14 19	14 23		14 37	14 40		14 45	14 51	15 08			15 20	15 23
d					13 45	13 47	13 53					14 21					14 45	14 47	14 53				15 22	
Rugby d					14 26	13 59											15 26	14 59						
Long Buckby d					14 52												15 52							
Northampton a					15 17												16 17							
London Euston 15 ⊖ a						15 08	15 16					15 43						16 07	16 16				16 41	

	LM	CH	VT	LM	LM	VT	VT	LM	VT	LM	LM	XC	VT	XC	VT	CH	LM	LM	VT	VT	LM	LM	LM	VT
	1 ◇	A	1 ◇	1	🚌	1 ◇	1 ◇		1 ◇			R 1	1 ◇	R 1	R 1	A	1	🚌	1 ◇	1 ◇				1 ◇
			☕			☕	☕		☕			☕	☕	☕	☕				☕	☕				☕
Stafford d	14 31					14 58			15 07			15 26							15 55					
Penkridge d	14 37																							
Wolverhampton 7 🚌 a	14 49											15 40												
d	14 50		14 55				15 04			15 22	15 40	15 43			15 49					16 04		16 22	16 40	
Walsall a											15 55												16 55	
Coseley d										15 27												16 27		
Tipton d										15 29												16 29		
Dudley Port d										15 31												16 31		
Sandwell & Dudley d							15 17			15 35										16 17		16 35		
Smethwick Galton Bdg L.L. 7 d										15 37												16 37		
Smethwick Rolfe Street d										15 39												16 39		
Birmingham New Street 12 a	15 08		15 16				15 26			15 46		15 58			16 11					16 26		16 46		
d		15 15		15 18			15 30	15 36					16 00	16 03		16 15	16 18			16 30	16 36			17 00
Adderley Park d								15 41													16 41			
Stechford d								15 44													16 44			
Lea Hall d								15 46													16 46			
Marston Green d								15 49													16 49			
Birmingham International ✈ a		15 25		15 30			15 39	15 52					16 09	16 14		16 25	16 30			16 39	16 52			17 09
d		15 26		15 31			15 41	15 52					16 10	16 15		16 26	16 31			16 41	16 52			17 10
Hampton-in-Arden d								15 55													16 55			
Berkswell d								15 59													16 59			
Tile Hill d								16 02													17 02			
Canley d								16 05													17 05			
Coventry a		15 37		15 40		15 45	15 51	16 08	16 12				16 19	16 23		16 37	16 40		16 45	16 51	17 08			17 19
d					15 45	15 47	15 53		16 14				16 21					16 45	16 47	16 53				17 21
Rugby d					16 26	15 59			16 28									17 26	16 59					
Long Buckby d					16 52													17 52						
Northampton a					17 17													18 17						
London Euston 15 ⊖ a						17 08	17 11		17 39				17 43						18 08	18 11				18 41

For general notes see front of timetable
For details of catering facilities see Directory of Train Operators

A To London Marylebone (Table 115)

Sundays

Stafford → Wolverhampton → Birmingham → Coventry → Northampton

3 February to 23 March

Network Diagram - see first page of Table 67

		XC	VT	LM	CH	LM	LM	VT	VT	LM	VT	LM	LM	XC	VT	XC	CH	LM	LM	VT	XC	LM	LM	LM	XC
		R	R											R		R									R
		1	1	1 ◇		1		1 ◇	1 ◇		1 ◇			1	1 ◇	1		1		1 ◇	1 ◇				1
					A												A								
							bus												bus						
		catering	catering					catering	catering		catering			catering	catering	catering				catering	catering				catering
Stafford	d	16 26		16 36				16 55			17 08			17 26											18 26
Penkridge	d			16 42																					
Wolverhampton 7	a	16 40		16 54										17 40											18 40
	d	16 43	16 49	16 54					17 04			17 22	17 40	17 43						18 04			18 22	18 40	18 43
Walsall	a												17 55											18 55	
Coseley	d											17 27											18 27		
Tipton	d											17 29											18 29		
Dudley Port	d											17 31											18 31		
Sandwell & Dudley	d								17 17			17 35								18 17			18 35		
Smethwick Galton Bdg L.L. 7	d											17 37											18 37		
Smethwick Rolfe Street	d											17 39											18 39		
Birmingham New Street 12	a	16 58	17 11	17 14					17 26			17 46		17 58						18 26			18 46		18 58
	d	17 03			17 15	17 18			17 30	17 36					18 00	18 03	18 15	18 18		18 30	18 33	18 36			19 03
Adderley Park	d									17 41												18 41			
Stechford	d									17 44												18 44			
Lea Hall	d									17 46												18 46			
Marston Green	d									17 49												18 49			
Birmingham International ✈	a	17 14			17 25	17 30			17 39	17 52					18 09	18 14	18 25	18 30		18 39	18 45	18 52			19 13
	d	17 15			17 26	17 31			17 41	17 52					18 10	18 15	18 26	18 31		18 40	18 46	18 52			19 15
Hampton-in-Arden	d									17 55												18 55			
Berkswell	d									17 59												18 59			
Tile Hill	d									18 02												19 02			
Canley	d									18 05												19 05			
Coventry	a	17 23			17 37	17 40		17 45	17 51	18 08	18 12				18 19	18 23	18 37	18 40		18 49	18 54	19 08			19 23
	d						17 45	17 47	17 53		18 14				18 21				18 45	18 51					
Rugby	d						18 26	17 59			18 28								19 26						
Long Buckby	d						18 52												19 52						
Northampton	a						19 17												20 17						
London Euston 15 ⊖	a							19 14	19 17		19 33				19 41					20 11					

		LM	VT	CH	LM	LM	VT	VT	LM	VT	LM	LM	XC	XC	VT	CH	LM	LM	VT	VT	VT	LM	LM	LM	XC
			R										R	R	R										
		1 ◇	1		1		1 ◇	1 ◇		1 ◇			1	1	1		1		1 ◇	1 ◇	1 ◇				1 ◇
				A												A									
						bus												bus							
			catering				catering	catering		catering			catering		catering				catering	catering	catering				
Stafford	d	18 30					18 55			19 08			19 26						19 55		20 08				20 26
Penkridge	d	18 36																							
Wolverhampton 7	a	18 48											19 40												20 40
	d	18 48	18 52					19 04			19 22	19 40	19 43		19 49					20 04			20 22	20 40	20 43
Walsall	a											19 55												20 55	
Coseley	d										19 27												20 27		
Tipton	d										19 29												20 29		
Dudley Port	d										19 31												20 31		
Sandwell & Dudley	d							19 17			19 35									20 17			20 35		
Smethwick Galton Bdg L.L. 7	d										19 37												20 37		
Smethwick Rolfe Street	d										19 39												20 39		
Birmingham New Street 12	a	19 04	19 14					19 26			19 46		19 58		20 11					20 26			20 46		20 58
	d			19 15	19 18			19 30	19 36					20 03		20 15	20 18			20 30		20 36			21 03
Adderley Park	d								19 41													20 41			
Stechford	d								19 44													20 44			
Lea Hall	d								19 46													20 46			
Marston Green	d								19 49													20 49			
Birmingham International ✈	a			19 25	19 30			19 39	19 52					20 14		20 25	20 30			20 39		20 52			21 14
	d			19 26	19 31			19 41	19 52					20 15		20 26	20 31			20 41		20 52			21 15
Hampton-in-Arden	d								19 55													20 55			
Berkswell	d								19 59													20 59			
Tile Hill	d								20 02													21 02			
Canley	d								20 05													21 05			
Coventry	a			19 37	19 40		19 45	19 51	20 08	20 12				20 23		20 37	20 40		20 45	20 51		21 08			21 23
	d					19 45	19 47	19 53		20 14								20 45	20 47	20 53					
Rugby	d					20 26	19 59			20 28								21 26	20 59		21 25				
Long Buckby	d					20 52												21 52							
Northampton	a					21 17												22 17							
London Euston 15 ⊖	a						21 14	21 17		21 54									22 23	22 27	22 51				

For general notes see front of timetable
For details of catering facilities see Directory of Train Operators

A To London Marylebone (Table 115)

Stafford → Wolverhampton → Birmingham → Coventry → Northampton

Sundays

3 February to 23 March

Network Diagram - see first page of Table 67

		LM	CH	LM	VT	LM	VT	LM	VT	LM	VT	LM	LM	VT	XC	LM	LM	LM	VT	LM	LM	VT	XC	LM
		1◇	A	1	1◇ ☕	🚌	1◇ ☕		1◇ ☕		1◇ ☕		1	1◇ ☕	1◇	🚌			1◇ ☕			1◇ ☕	1◇	1◇
Stafford	d	20 31			20 53		20 59		21 11		21 21			21 32	21 53							22 40	22 53	23 07
Penkridge	d																							23 12
Wolverhampton 7	a	20 47			21 08						21 35			21 54	22 09							22 54	23 09	23 25
	d	20 47			21 10					21 22	21 35	21 40		21 56	22 09			22 22	22 35	22 40		22 55	23 09	23 25
Walsall	a											21 55								22 55				
Coseley	d									21 27								22 27						
Tipton	d									21 29								22 29						
Dudley Port	d									21 31								22 31						
Sandwell & Dudley	d									21 35	21 48							22 35	22 47					
Smethwick Galton Bdg L.L. 7	d									21 37								22 37						
Smethwick Rolfe Street	d									21 39								22 39						
Birmingham New Street 12	a	21 08			21 32					21 46	21 56			22 17	22 30			22 46	22 56			23 17	23 30	23 45
	d		21 15	21 18				21 36			22 00		22 15				22 36		23 00		23 15			
Adderley Park	d							21 41									22 41				23 20			
Stechford	d							21 44									22 44				23 23			
Lea Hall	d							21 46									22 46				23 25			
Marston Green	d							21 49									22 49				23 28			
Birmingham International ✈	a		21 25	21 30				21 52			22 09		22 24				22 52		23 09		23 31			
	d		21 26	21 31				21 52			22 10		22 25				22 52		23 10		23 31			
Hampton-in-Arden	d							21 55									22 55				23 34			
Berkswell	d							21 59									22 59				23 38			
Tile Hill	d							22 02									23 02				23 41			
Canley	d							22 05									23 05				23 44			
Coventry	a		21 37	21 40			21 45	22 08	22 12		22 19		22 34				23 08		23 19		23 47			
	d					21 45	21 47		22 14		22 21					22 45			23 21					
Rugby	d					22 26	21 59				22 35					23 26			23 35					
Long Buckby	d					22 52										23 52								
Northampton	a					23 17										00 17								
London Euston 15 ⊖	a						23 25		23 41		23 48								00 47					

Sundays

from 30 March

		LM	VT	XC	LM	LM	LM	LM	AW	XC	VT		LM	XC	XC	VT	LM	LM	LM	LM	VT	AW		VT	LM
			1◇ ☕	1◇ ☕	1					1◇ ☕	1◇ ☕			1◇ ☕	1◇ ☕	1◇ ☕	1			1◇	1◇ ☕			1◇ ☕	
Stafford	d													09 26		09 39				10 01	10 08				
Penkridge	d																			10 07					
Wolverhampton 7	a													09 40						10 23					
	d		08 37			08 52	09 01		09 31		09 35		09 41	09 43				09 52		10 24		10 31		10 36	10 40
Walsall	a						09 15						09 56												10 55
Coseley	d					08 57												09 57							
Tipton	d					08 59												09 59							
Dudley Port	d					09 01												10 01							
Sandwell & Dudley	d		08 47			09 05					09 47							10 05						10 47	
Smethwick Galton Bdg L.L. 7	d					09 07												10 07							
Smethwick Rolfe Street	d					09 09												10 09							
Birmingham New Street 12	a		08 56			09 16			09 47		09 56			09 58				10 16		10 43		10 47		10 56	
	d	00 10	09 00	09 03	09 15			09 36		09 48	10 00						10 15		10 36					11 00	
Adderley Park	d							09 41											10 41						
Stechford	d							09 44											10 44						
Lea Hall	d							09 46											10 46						
Marston Green	d	00 18						09 49							←				10 49						
Birmingham International ✈	a	00 21	09 09	09 14	09 24			09 52		10 13	10 09				10 13		10 24		10 52		10 57			11 09	
	d	00 22	09 10	09 15	09 25			09 52		→	10 10				10 15		10 25		10 52		10 58			11 10	
Hampton-in-Arden	d							09 55											10 55						
Berkswell	d							09 59											10 59						
Tile Hill	d							10 02											11 02						
Canley	d							10 05											11 05						
Coventry	a	00 37	09 19	09 23	09 34			10 09			10 19				10 23	10 28	10 34		11 08		11 12			11 19	
	d		09 21		09 35						10 21					10 29	10 35				11 14			11 21	
Rugby	d				09 48											10 42	10 48				11 28				
Long Buckby	d				09 59												10 59								
Northampton	a				10 15												11 15								
London Euston 15 ⊖	a		10 56								11 51					12 00					12 51			12 58	

For general notes see front of timetable
For details of catering facilities see Directory of Train Operators

A To London Marylebone (Table 115)

Table 68

Stafford → Wolverhampton → Birmingham → Coventry → Northampton

Sundays

from 30 March

Network Diagram - see first page of Table 67

		XC	VT	CH	LM	VT	LM	VT	VT	LM	VT		LM	AW	LM	XC	XC	VT	CH	VT	LM	VT		VT	LM
		1 ◇	1 ◇			1 ◇	1	1 ◇	1 ◇		1 ◇					1 ◇	1 ◇	1 ◇		1 ◇	1	1 ◇		1 ◇	
				A															A						
		☕	☕			☕		☕	☕		☕					☕	☕	☕		☕		☕		☕	
Stafford	d	10 26	10 31			10 48		10 55			11 08					11 26				11 49		11 55			
Penkridge	d																								
Wolverhampton 7	a	10 40	10 48			11 05										11 40				12 05					
	d	10 43	10 49		10 52	11 05							11 22	11 31	11 40	11 43		11 49		12 05					
Walsall	a														11 56										
Coseley	d				10 57								11 27												
Tipton	d				10 59								11 29												
Dudley Port	d				11 01								11 31												
Sandwell & Dudley	d				11 05	11 17 →			← 11 17				11 35							12 17 →				← 12 17	
Smethwick Galton Bdg L.L. 7	d				11 07								11 37												
Smethwick Rolfe Street	d				11 09								11 39												
Birmingham New Street 12	a	10 58	11 11		11 16				11 26				11 46	11 48		11 58		12 11						12 26	
	d	11 03		11 15			11 18		11 30	11 36							12 03		12 15		12 18			12 30	12 36
Adderley Park	d									11 41															12 41
Stechford	d									11 44															12 44
Lea Hall	d									11 46															12 46
Marston Green	d									11 49															12 49
Birmingham International ✈	a	11 14		11 25			11 30		11 39	11 52							12 13		12 25		12 30			12 39	12 52
	d	11 15		11 26			11 31		11 41	11 52							12 15		12 26		12 31			12 41	12 52
Hampton-in-Arden	d									11 55															12 55
Berkswell	d									11 59															12 59
Tile Hill	d									12 02															13 02
Canley	d									12 05															13 05
Coventry	a	11 23		11 37			11 40	11 45	11 51	12 08	12 12						12 23		12 37		12 40	12 45		12 51	13 08
	d						11 41	11 47	11 53		12 14										12 41	12 47		12 53	
Rugby	d						11 54	11 59													12 54	12 59			
Long Buckby	d						12 04														13 04				
Northampton	a						12 20														13 20				
London Euston 15 ⊖	a							13 23	13 29		13 56											14 23		14 29	

		LM	LM	XC	VT	CH	AW	LM	LM	VT	VT		VT	LM	LM	AW	LM	XC	VT	XC	VT	CH		VT	LM
																		R		R					
				1 ◇	1 ◇		◇	1	1 ◇	1 ◇	1 ◇		1 ◇					1	1 ◇	1	1 ◇			1 ◇	1
						A																A			
				☕	☕		🍴			☕	☕		☕					☕	☕	☕	☕			☕	
Stafford	d			12 26					12 43	12 49	12 56							13 26						13 48	
Penkridge	d								12 49																
Wolverhampton 7	a			12 40					13 02	13 05								13 40						14 05	
	d	12 22	12 40	12 43	12 49		12 58		13 02	13 05					13 22	13 31	13 40	13 43			13 49			14 05	
Walsall	a		12 55														13 56								
Coseley	d	12 27													13 27										
Tipton	d	12 29													13 29										
Dudley Port	d	12 31													13 31										
Sandwell & Dudley	d	12 35								13 17 →			← 13 17		13 35									14 17 →	
Smethwick Galton Bdg L.L. 7	d	12 37													13 37										
Smethwick Rolfe Street	d	12 39													13 39										
Birmingham New Street 12	a	12 46		12 58	13 11		13 15		13 21				13 26		13 46	13 49		13 58			14 11				
	d			13 03		13 15		13 18					13 30	13 36					14 00	14 03		14 15			14 18
Adderley Park	d													13 41											
Stechford	d													13 44											
Lea Hall	d													13 46											
Marston Green	d													13 49											
Birmingham International ✈	a			13 13		13 25		13 30					13 39	13 52					14 09	14 14		14 25			14 30
	d			13 15		13 26		13 31					13 41	13 52					14 10	14 15		14 26			14 31
Hampton-in-Arden	d													13 55											
Berkswell	d													13 59											
Tile Hill	d													14 02											
Canley	d													14 05											
Coventry	a			13 23		13 37		13 40			13 45		13 51	14 08					14 19	14 23		14 37			14 40
	d							13 41			13 47		13 53						14 21						14 41
Rugby	d							13 54			13 59														14 54
Long Buckby	d							14 04																	15 04
Northampton	a							14 20																	15 20
London Euston 15 ⊖	a										15 08		15 16						15 43						

For general notes see front of timetable
For details of catering facilities see Directory of Train Operators

A To London Marylebone (Table 115)

Table 68

Sundays

from 30 March

Stafford → Wolverhampton → Birmingham → Coventry → Northampton

Network Diagram - see first page of Table 67

		VT	VT	LM	LM	AW	LM	VT	XC	LM	CH	LM	AW	VT	VT	VT	LM	VT	LM	LM	XC	VT	XC
		1 ◇	1 ◇					1 ◇	R 1	1 ◇	A	1	◇	1 ◇	1 ◇	1 ◇		1 ◇			R 1	1 ◇	R 1
		☕	☕					☕	☕				🛒	☕	☕	☕		☕			☕	☕	☕
Stafford	d	13 58							14 26	14 31				14 49	14 58			15 07			15 26		
Penkridge	d									14 37													
Wolverhampton 7	a								14 40	14 49				15 04							15 40		
	d				14 22	14 32	14 40		14 43	14 50			15 02	15 04					15 22	15 40	15 43		
Walsall	a						14 56													15 55			
Coseley	d				14 27														15 27				
Tipton	d				14 29														15 29				
Dudley Port	d		←		14 31											←			15 31				
Sandwell & Dudley	d		14 17		14 35									15 17 →		15 17			15 35				
Smethwick Galton Bdg L.L. 7	d				14 37														15 37				
Smethwick Rolfe Street	d				14 39														15 39				
Birmingham New Street 12	a		14 26		14 46	14 49			14 58	15 08			15 18			15 26			15 46		15 58		
	d		14 30	14 36				15 00	15 03		15 15	15 18				15 30	15 36					16 00	16 03
Adderley Park	d			14 41													15 41						
Stechford	d			14 44													15 44						
Lea Hall	d			14 46													15 46						
Marston Green	d			14 49													15 49						
Birmingham International ✈	a		14 39	14 52				15 10	15 14		15 25	15 30				15 39	15 52					16 09	16 14
	d		14 41	14 52				15 11	15 15		15 26	15 31				15 41	15 52					16 10	16 15
Hampton-in-Arden	d			14 55													15 55						
Berkswell	d			14 59													15 59						
Tile Hill	d			15 02													16 02						
Canley	d			15 05													16 05						
Coventry	a	14 45	14 51	15 08				15 20	15 23		15 37	15 40			15 45	15 51	16 08	16 12				16 19	16 23
	d	14 47	14 53					15 22				15 41			15 47	15 53		16 14				16 21	
Rugby	d	14 59										15 54			15 59			16 28					
Long Buckby	d											16 04											
Northampton	a											16 20											
London Euston 15 ⊖	a	16 07	16 16					16 41							17 08	17 11		17 39				17 43	

		VT	CH	VT	LM	VT	VT	AW	LM	LM	LM	VT	XC	VT	LM	CH	VT	LM	VT	VT	AW	LM	VT
		R 1	A	1 ◇	1	1 ◇	1 ◇	◇				1 ◇	R 1	R 1	1 ◇	A	1 ◇	1	1 ◇	1 ◇			1 ◇
		☕		☕		☕	☕					☕	☕	☕			☕		☕	☕			☕
Stafford	d			15 49		15 55							16 26		16 36		16 48		16 55				17 08
Penkridge	d														16 42								
Wolverhampton 7	a			16 04									16 40		16 54		17 04						
	d	15 49		16 04				16 17		16 22	16 40		16 43	16 49	16 54		17 04				17 18		
Walsall	a										16 55												
Coseley	d									16 27													
Tipton	d									16 29													
Dudley Port	d						←			16 31										←			
Sandwell & Dudley	d			16 17 →			16 17			16 35							17 17 →			17 17			
Smethwick Galton Bdg L.L. 7	d									16 37													
Smethwick Rolfe Street	d									16 39													
Birmingham New Street 12	a	16 11					16 26	16 33		16 46			16 58	17 11	17 14					17 26	17 34		
	d		16 15		16 18		16 30		16 36			17 00	17 03			17 15		17 18		17 30		17 36	
Adderley Park	d								16 41													17 41	
Stechford	d								16 44													17 44	
Lea Hall	d								16 46													17 46	
Marston Green	d								16 49													17 49	
Birmingham International ✈	a		16 25		16 30		16 39		16 52			17 09	17 14			17 25		17 30		17 39		17 52	
	d		16 26		16 31		16 41		16 52			17 10	17 15			17 26		17 31		17 41		17 52	
Hampton-in-Arden	d								16 55													17 55	
Berkswell	d								16 59													17 59	
Tile Hill	d								17 02													18 02	
Canley	d								17 05													18 05	
Coventry	a		16 37		16 40	16 45	16 51		17 08			17 19	17 23			17 37		17 40	17 45	17 51		18 08	18 12
	d				16 41	16 47	16 53					17 21						17 41	17 47	17 53			18 14
Rugby	d				16 54	16 59												17 54	17 59				18 28
Long Buckby	d				17 04													18 04					
Northampton	a				17 20													18 20					
London Euston 15 ⊖	a					18 08	18 11					18 41							19 14	19 17			19 33

For general notes see front of timetable
For details of catering facilities see
Directory of Train Operators

A To London Marylebone (Table 115)

Table 68

Sundays

from 30 March

Stafford → Wolverhampton → Birmingham → Coventry → Northampton

Network Diagram - see first page of Table 67

		LM	LM	XC	VT	XC	VT	CH	LM	VT	AW
				R 1	1 ◇	R 1	R 1	A	1	1 ◇	◇
Stafford	d			17 26						17 49	
Penkridge	d										
Wolverhampton [7]	a			17 40						18 04	
	d	17 22	17 40	17 43			17 49			18 04	18 18
Walsall	a		17 55								
Coseley	d	17 27									
Tipton	d	17 29									
Dudley Port	d	17 31									
Sandwell & Dudley	d	17 35								18 17	
Smethwick Galton Bdg L.L. [7]	d	17 37									
Smethwick Rolfe Street	d	17 39									
Birmingham New Street [12]	a	17 46		17 58			18 11			18 26	18 35
	d				18 00	18 03		18 15	18 18	18 30	
Adderley Park	d										
Stechford	d										
Lea Hall	d										
Marston Green	d										
Birmingham International ✈	a				18 09	18 14		18 25	18 30	18 39	
	d				18 10	18 15		18 26	18 31	18 40	
Hampton-in-Arden	d										
Berkswell	d										
Tile Hill	d										
Canley	d										
Coventry	a				18 19	18 23		18 37	18 40	18 49	
	d				18 21				18 41	18 51	
Rugby	d								18 54		
Long Buckby	d								19 04		
Northampton	a								19 20		
London Euston [15] ⊖	a				19 41					20 11	

		LM	LM	LM	XC	LM	VT	CH	VT	LM	VT	VT	AW
					R 1	1 ◇	R 1	A	1 ◇	1	1 ◇	1 ◇	◇
Stafford	d				18 26	18 30			18 49		18 55		
Penkridge	d					18 36							
Wolverhampton [7]	a				18 40	18 48			19 04				
	d		18 22	18 40	18 43	18 48	18 52		19 04				19 18
Walsall	a			18 55									
Coseley	d		18 27										
Tipton	d		18 29										
Dudley Port	d		18 31										
Sandwell & Dudley	d		18 35						19 17 →			← 19 17	
Smethwick Galton Bdg L.L. [7]	d		18 37										
Smethwick Rolfe Street	d		18 39										
Birmingham New Street [12]	a		18 46		18 58	19 04	19 14					19 26	19 34
	d	18 36			19 03			19 15		19 18		19 30	
Adderley Park	d	18 41											
Stechford	d	18 44											
Lea Hall	d	18 46											
Marston Green	d	18 49											
Birmingham International ✈	a	18 52			19 13			19 25		19 30		19 39	
	d	18 52			19 15			19 26		19 31		19 41	
Hampton-in-Arden	d	18 55											
Berkswell	d	18 59											
Tile Hill	d	19 02											
Canley	d	19 05											
Coventry	a	19 08			19 23			19 37		19 40	19 45	19 51	
	d									19 41	19 47	19 53	
Rugby	d									19 54	19 59		
Long Buckby	d									20 04			
Northampton	a									20 20			
London Euston [15] ⊖	a										21 14	21 17	

		LM	VT	LM	LM	XC	XC	VT	CH	LM	AW
			1 ◇			R 1	R 1	R 1	A	1	◇
Stafford	d		19 08			19 26					
Penkridge	d										
Wolverhampton [7]	a					19 40					
	d			19 22	19 40	19 43		19 49			20 02
Walsall	a				19 55						
Coseley	d			19 27							
Tipton	d			19 29							
Dudley Port	d			19 31							
Sandwell & Dudley	d			19 35							
Smethwick Galton Bdg L.L. [7]	d			19 37							
Smethwick Rolfe Street	d			19 39							
Birmingham New Street [12]	a			19 46		19 58		20 11			20 19
	d	19 36					20 03		20 15	20 18	
Adderley Park	d	19 41									
Stechford	d	19 44									
Lea Hall	d	19 46									
Marston Green	d	19 49									
Birmingham International ✈	a	19 52					20 14		20 25	20 30	
	d	19 52					20 15		20 26	20 31	
Hampton-in-Arden	d	19 55									
Berkswell	d	19 59									
Tile Hill	d	20 02									
Canley	d	20 05									
Coventry	a	20 08	20 12				20 23		20 37	20 40	
	d		20 14							20 41	
Rugby	d		20 28							20 54	
Long Buckby	d									21 04	
Northampton	a									21 20	
London Euston [15] ⊖	a		21 54								

		VT	VT	VT	VT	LM	LM	LM	XC	LM	CH	VT	LM
		1 ◇	1 ◇	1 ◇	1 ◇				1 ◇	1 ◇	A	1 ◇	1
Stafford	d	19 49	19 55		20 08				20 26	20 31			
Penkridge	d												
Wolverhampton [7]	a	20 04							20 40	20 47			
	d	20 04					20 22	20 40	20 43	20 47		20 52	
Walsall	a							20 55					
Coseley	d						20 27						
Tipton	d						20 29						
Dudley Port	d						20 31						
Sandwell & Dudley	d	20 17 →		← 20 17			20 35						
Smethwick Galton Bdg L.L. [7]	d						20 37						
Smethwick Rolfe Street	d						20 39						
Birmingham New Street [12]	a			20 26			20 46		20 58	21 08		21 15	
	d			20 30		20 36			21 03		21 15		21 18
Adderley Park	d					20 41							
Stechford	d					20 44							
Lea Hall	d					20 46							
Marston Green	d					20 49							
Birmingham International ✈	a			20 39		20 52			21 14		21 25		21 30
	d			20 41		20 52			21 15		21 26		21 31
Hampton-in-Arden	d					20 55							
Berkswell	d					20 59							
Tile Hill	d					21 02							
Canley	d					21 05							
Coventry	a		20 45	20 51		21 08			21 23		21 37		21 40
	d		20 47	20 53									21 41
Rugby	d		20 59		21 25								21 54
Long Buckby	d												22 04
Northampton	a												22 20
London Euston [15] ⊖	a		22 23	22 27	22 51								

For general notes see front of timetable
For details of catering facilities see
Directory of Train Operators

A To London Marylebone (Table 115)

Table 68

Sundays

from 30 March

Stafford → Wolverhampton → Birmingham → Coventry → Northampton

Network Diagram - see first page of Table 67

		VT	VT	AW	LM	VT	LM	VT	LM	LM	VT		XC	LM	AW	LM	VT	LM	LM	VT	XC	LM			
		1 ◇	1 ◇	◇		1 ◇		1 ◇		1	1 ◇		1 ◇		◇		1 ◇			1 ◇	1 ◇	1 ◇			
		☕	☕			☕		☕			☕				🛒		☕			☕					
Stafford	d	20 53	20 59			21 11		21 21			21 43		21 53							22 40	22 53	23 07			
Penkridge	d																					23 12			
Wolverhampton 7	a	21 08						21 35			21 59		22 09							22 54	23 09	23 25			
	d	21 10		21 16			21 22	21 35	21 40		22 01		22 09		22 19	22 22	22 35	22 40		22 55	23 09	23 25			
Walsall	a								21 55									22 55							
Coseley	d						21 27									22 27									
Tipton	d						21 29									22 29									
Dudley Port	d						21 31									22 31									
Sandwell & Dudley	d						21 35	21 48								22 35	22 47								
Smethwick Galton Bdg L.L. 7	d						21 37									22 37									
Smethwick Rolfe Street	d						21 39									22 39									
Birmingham New Street 12	a	21 32		21 32			21 46	21 56			22 22		22 30		22 36	22 46	22 56			23 17	23 30	23 45			
	d				21 36			22 00		22 15				22 36			23 00		23 15						
Adderley Park	d				21 41									22 41					23 20						
Stechford	d				21 44									22 44					23 23						
Lea Hall	d				21 46									22 46					23 25						
Marston Green	d				21 49									22 49					23 28						
Birmingham International ✈	a				21 52			22 09		22 24				22 52			23 09		23 31						
	d				21 52			22 10		22 25				22 52			23 10		23 31						
Hampton-in-Arden	d				21 55									22 55					23 34						
Berkswell	d				21 59									22 59					23 38						
Tile Hill	d				22 02									23 02					23 41						
Canley	d				22 05									23 05					23 44						
Coventry	a		21 45		22 08	22 12		22 19		22 34				23 08			23 19		23 47						
	d		21 47			22 14		22 21		22 35							23 21								
Rugby	d		21 59					22 34		22 48							23 34								
Long Buckby	d									22 58															
Northampton	a									23 15															
London Euston 15 ⊖	a		23 25			23 47		23 58									00 57								

For general notes see front of timetable
For details of catering facilities see Directory of Train Operators

Table 68A

Mondays to Fridays

Stafford — Stoke-on-Trent

Bus Service

Network Diagram - see first page of Table 67

		LM	LM	LM	LM	LM		LM	LM	LM	LM	LM		LM	LM	LM	LM	LM	LM	LM	LM	LM	LM		
Stafford	d		07 20	08 15	08 35	09 35		10 05	10 35	11 35	12 25	12 35		13 35	14 15	14 35	15 35	16 30	16 35	17 25	17 35	18 35	19 25		
Norton Bridge Station Drv	d			08 37				10 27			12 47				14 37			16a52		18a02					
Stone Granville Square	d	07 00	08 10	09a00	09 20	10 20		10a52	11 20	12 20	13a29	13 20		14 20	14a52	15 20	16 20		17 20		18 20	19 20	20 05		
Barlaston Orchard Place	d	07 10	08 20		09 30	10 30			11 30	12 30		13 30		14 30		15 30	16 30		17 30		18 30	19 30	20 15		
Wedgwood Old Road Bridge	d	07 12	08 22		09 32	10 32			11 32	12 32		13 32		14 32		15 32	16 32		17 32		18 32	19 32	20 17		
Stoke-on-Trent	a	07 35	08 48		09 48	10 48			11 48	12 48		13 48		14 48		15 48	16 48		17 48		18 48	19 48	20 33		
Hanley Bus Station	a	07 44	08 57		09 57	10 57			11 57	12 57		13 57		14 57		15 57	16 57		17 57		18 57	19 55	20 45		

Saturdays

		LM		LM		LM		LM		LM		LM		LM		LM		LM	LM	LM	LM	LM	LM		
Stafford	d			08 15		08 35		09 35		10 05		11 35		12 25		13 35		14 15	15 35	16 30	17 25	17 35	19 35		
Norton Bridge Station Drv	d			08 37						10 27				12 47				14 37		16a52	18a02				
Stone Granville Square	d	07 00		09a00		09 20		10 20		10a52		12 20		13a29		14 20		14a52	16 20			18 20	19 55		
Barlaston Orchard Place	d	07 10				09 30		10 30				12 30				14 30			16 30			18 30	20 05		
Wedgwood Old Road Bridge	d	07 12				09 32		10 32				12 32				14 32			16 32			18 32	20 07		
Stoke-on-Trent	a	07 35				09 48		10 48				12 48				14 48			16 48			18 48	20 23		
Hanley Bus Station	a	07 44				09 57		10 57				12 57				14 57			16 57			18 57	20 30		

Mondays to Fridays

		LM	LM	LM	LM	LM		LM	LM	LM	LM	LM		LM	LM	LM	LM	LM	LM	LM	LM	LM	LM		
Hanley Bus Station	d		06 55		07 50			09 00	10 00	11 00		12 00			13 00	14 00	15 00		16 00		17 00	18 00	19 00		
Stoke-on-Trent	d		07 01		08 01			09 11	10 11	11 11		12 11			13 11	14 11	15 11		16 11		17 11	18 11	19 11		
Wedgwood Old Road Bridge	d		07 10		08 10			09 22	10 22	11 22		12 22			13 22	14 22	15 22		16 22		17 22	18 22	19 22		
Barlaston Orchard Place	d		07 12		08 12			09 25	10 25	11 25		12 25			13 25	14 25	15 25		16 25		17 25	18 25	19 25		
Stone Granville Square	d	06 40	07 25		08 25	08 56		09 35	10 35	11 35	11 39	12 35		13 39	13 35	14 35	15 35	15 41	16 35		17 35	18 35	19a32		
Norton Bridge Station Drv	d			07 56		09 46					12 06			13 56				16 11		17 06					
Stafford	a	06 58	08 03	08 15	09 08	10 05		10 18	11 18	12 18	12 25	13 18		14 15	14 18	15 18	16 18	16 30	17 18	17 25	18 18	19 18			

Saturdays

		LM		LM		LM		LM		LM		LM		LM		LM		LM	LM	LM	LM	LM	LM		
Hanley Bus Station	d	06 55				07 50				10 00				12 00				14 00		16 00		18 00	19 00		
Stoke-on-Trent	d	07 01				08 01				10 11				12 11				14 11		16 11		18 11	19 11		
Wedgwood Old Road Bridge	d	07 10				08 10				10 22				12 22				14 22		16 22		18 22	19 22		
Barlaston Orchard Place	d	07 12				08 12				10 25				12 25				14 25		16 25		18 25	19 25		
Stone Granville Square	d	07 25				08 25		08 56		10 35		11 39		12 35		13 39		14 35	15 41	16 35		18 35	19a32		
Norton Bridge Station Drv	d			07 56				09 46				12 06				13 56			16 11		17 06				
Stafford	a	08 05		08 15		09 10		10 05		11 18		12 25		13 18		14 15		15 18	16 30	17 18	17 25	19 18			

For general notes see front of timetable
For details of catering facilities see
Directory of Train Operators

No Sunday Service

Lichfield → Birmingham → Longbridge and Redditch

Network Diagram - see first page of Table 67

Miles	Miles			LM	LM	LM	LM	LM	LM	LM		LM	LM	LM	LM	LM	LM	LM		LM	LM	LM	LM	LM	XC	LM
																									◇ A	
0	—	**Lichfield Trent Valley**	d							06 09			06 23				06 52			07 10		07 22		07 40		07 54
1¼	—	**Lichfield City**	d							06 12			06 26			06 43	06 55			07 14		07 25		07 45		07 57
4¼	—	Shenstone	d							06 17						06 48				07 19				07 50		
6¾	—	Blake Street	d					06 04		06 21			06 34			06 51	07 03			07 23		07 33		07 54		08 05
8½	—	Butlers Lane	d					06 06		06 23			06 36			06 53	07 05			07 25		07 35		07 56		08 07
9½	—	Four Oaks	d					06 09	06 18	06 25			06 39	06 48		06 56	07 08	07 18		07 28		07 38	07 48	07 59		08 10
11	—	Sutton Coldfield	d					06 12	06 21	06 29			06 42	06 51		07 00	07 11	07 21		07 31		07 41	07 51	08 02		08 13
12	—	Wylde Green	d					06 15	06 24	06 31			06 45	06 54		07 02	07 14	07 24		07 34		07 44	07 54	08 05		08 16
12¾	—	Chester Road	d					06 17	06 26	06 34			06 47	06 56		07 04	07 16	07 26		07 36		07 46	07 56	08 07		08 18
13¾	—	Erdington	d					06 18	06 27	06 35			06 48	06 57		07 06	07 17	07 27		07 37		07 47	07 57	08 08		08 19
14½	—	Gravelly Hill	d					06 21	06 30	06 38			06 51	07 00		07 08	07 20	07 30		07 40		07 50	08 00	08 11		08 22
15¾	—	Aston	d					06 24	06 33	06 41			06 54	07 03		07 11	07 23	07 33		07 43		07 53	08 03	08 14		08 25
17	—	Duddeston	d					06 26	06 36	06 44				07 06				07 36		07 45			08 06	08 17		
18½	—	**Birmingham New Street** 12	a					06 31	06 42	06 48			07 00	07 11		07 19	07 30	07 42		07 51		08 01	08 11	08 21		08 31
—	0		d	05 54	06 04	06 14	06 24	06 34	06 44	06 54		06 59	07 04	07 14	07 20	07 24	07 34	07 44		07 54	07 59	08 04	08 14	08 24	08 30	08 34
19½	—	Five Ways	d	05 57	06 07	06 17	06 27	06 37	06 47	06 57			07 07	07 17		07 27	07 37	07 47		07 57		08 07	08 17	08 27		08 37
20	1½	University	d	06 01	06 11	06 21	06 31	06 41	06 51	07 01		07 05	07 11	07 21	07 26	07 31	07 41	07 51		08 01	08 05	08 11	08 21	08 31	08a36	08 41
20¾	—	Selly Oak	d	06 03	06 13	06 23	06 33	06 43	06 53	07 03			07 13	07 23		07 33	07 43	07 53		08 03		08 13	08 23	08 33		08 43
21¾	—	Bournville	d	06 05	06 15	06 25	06 35	06 45	06 55	07 05			07 15	07 25		07 35	07 45	07 55		08 05		08 15	08 25	08 35		08 45
22¾	—	Kings Norton	d	06 07	06 17	06 27	06 37	06 47	06 57	07 07			07 17	07 27		07 37	07 47	07 57		08 07		08 17	08 27	08 37		08 47
24¼	—	Northfield	d	06 10	06 20	06 30	06 40	06 50	07 00	07 10			07 20	07 30		07 40	07 50	08 00		08 10		08 20	08 30	08 40		08 50
25¼	—	Longbridge	d	06a14	06a24	06 34	06a44	06a54	07 04	07a14			07a24	07 34		07a44	07a54	08 04		08a14		08a24	08 34	08a44		08a54
28	9½	Barnt Green	d			06 39			07 09					07 39	07 42			08 09					08 39			
29¾	—	Alvechurch	d			06 43			07 13					07 43				08 13					08 43			
33	—	**Redditch**	a			06 53			07 23					07 53				08 23					08 53			
—	13	Bromsgrove	a									07 23			07 47						08 21					

		LM	LM		LM	LM	LM	LM	LM	LM	LM		LM	LM	LM	LM	LM	XC	LM		LM	LM	LM	LM	LM	LM
		B																◇ A								
Lichfield Trent Valley	d				08 12				08 40	08 52					09 22				09 52					10 22		
Lichfield City	d		08 09		08 15		08 26		08 45	08 55			09 16		09 25		09 46		09 55			10 16		10 25		10 46
Shenstone	d				08 20				08 50				09 21				09 51					10 21				10 51
Blake Street	d				08 24		08 33		08 54	09 03			09 24		09 33		09 54		10 03			10 24		10 33		10 54
Butlers Lane	d				08 26		08 35		08 56	09 05			09 26		09 35		09 56		10 05			10 26		10 35		10 56
Four Oaks	d	08 15	08 19		08 29		08 38	08 48	08 59	09 08	09 18		09 29		09 38	09 48	09 59		10 08		10 18	10 29		10 38	10 48	10 59
Sutton Coldfield	d	08 18	08 22		08 32		08 42	08 51	09 02	09 11	09 21		09 33		09 41	09 51	10 03		10 11		10 21	10 33		10 41	10 51	11 03
Wylde Green	d	08 21	08 25		08 35		08 45	08 54	09 05	09 14	09 24		09 35		09 44	09 54	10 05		10 14		10 24	10 35		10 44	10 54	11 05
Chester Road	d	08 23	08 27		08 37		08 47	08 56	09 07	09 16	09 26		09 37		09 46	09 56	10 06		10 16		10 26	10 36		10 46	10 56	11 07
Erdington	d	08 25	08 28		08 38		08 48	08 57	09 08	09 17	09 27		09 38		09 47	09 57	10 08		10 17		10 27	10 38		10 47	10 57	11 09
Gravelly Hill	d		08 31		08 41		08 51	09 00	09 11	09 20	09 30		09 41		09 50	10 00	10 10		10 20		10 30	10 40		10 50	11 00	11 11
Aston	d		08 34		08 44		08 54	09 03	09 14	09 24	09 33		09 45		09 54	10 03	10 15		10 24		10 33	10 45		10 54	11 03	11 15
Duddeston	d		08 36		08 46			09 06			09 36					10 06					10 36				11 06	
Birmingham New Street 12	a	08 35	08 41		08 51		09 02	09 12	09 21	09 31	09 41		09 51		10 01	10 12	10 21		10 30		10 41	10 51		11 01	11 12	11 21
	d		08 44		08 54	08 59	09 04	09 14	09 24	09 34	09 44		09 54	09 59	10 04	10 14	10 24	10 30	10 34		10 44	10 54	10 59	11 04	11 14	11 24
Five Ways	d		08 47		08 57		09 07	09 17	09 27	09 37	09 47		09 57		10 07	10 17	10 27		10 37		10 47	10 57		11 07	11 17	11 27
University	d		08 51		09 01	09 05	09 11	09 21	09 31	09 41	09 51		10 01	10 05	10 11	10 21	10 31	10a36	10 41		10 51	11 01	11 05	11 11	11 21	11 31
Selly Oak	d		08 53		09 03		09 13	09 23	09 33	09 43	09 53		10 03		10 13	10 23	10 33		10 43		10 53	11 03		11 13	11 23	11 33
Bournville	d		08 55		09 05		09 15	09 25	09 35	09 45	09 55		10 05		10 15	10 25	10 35		10 45		10 55	11 05		11 15	11 25	11 35
Kings Norton	d		08 57		09 07		09 17	09 27	09 37	09 47	09 57		10 07		10 17	10 27	10 37		10 47		10 57	11 07		11 17	11 27	11 37
Northfield	d		09 00		09 10		09 20	09 30	09 40	09 50	10 00		10 10		10 20	10 30	10 40		10 50		11 00	11 10		11 20	11 30	11 40
Longbridge	d		09 04		09a14		09a24	09 34	09a44	09a54	10 04		10a14		10a24	10 34	10a44		10a54		11 04	11a14		11a24	11 34	11a44
Barnt Green	d		09 09					09 39			10 09					10 39					11 09				11 39	
Alvechurch	d		09 13					09 43			10 13					10 43					11 13				11 43	
Redditch	a		09 23					09 53			10 23					10 53					11 23				11 53	
Bromsgrove	a					09 21								10 21									11 21			

		LM	LM	LM		LM	LM	LM	LM	XC	LM	LM		LM	LM	LM	LM	LM	LM	LM		LM	LM	LM	LM	LM
										◇ A																
Lichfield Trent Valley	d	10 52					11 22				11 52					12 22			12 52					13 22		
Lichfield City	d	10 55		11 16			11 25		11 46		11 55			12 16		12 25		12 46	12 55			13 16		13 25		13 46
Shenstone	d			11 21					11 51					12 21				12 51				13 21				13 51
Blake Street	d	11 03		11 24			11 33		11 54		12 03			12 24		12 33		12 54	13 03			13 24		13 33		13 54
Butlers Lane	d	11 05		11 26			11 35		11 56		12 05			12 26		12 35		12 56	13 05			13 26		13 35		13 56
Four Oaks	d	11 08	11 18	11 29			11 38	11 48	11 59		12 08	12 18		12 29		12 38	12 48	12 59	13 08	13 18		13 29		13 38	13 48	13 59
Sutton Coldfield	d	11 11	11 21	11 33			11 41	11 51	12 03		12 11	12 21		12 33		12 41	12 51	13 03	13 11	13 21		13 33		13 41	13 51	14 03
Wylde Green	d	11 14	11 24	11 35			11 44	11 54	12 05		12 14	12 24		12 35		12 44	12 54	13 05	13 14	13 24		13 35		13 44	13 54	14 05
Chester Road	d	11 16	11 26	11 37			11 46	11 56	12 07		12 16	12 26		12 37		12 46	12 56	13 07	13 16	13 26		13 37		13 46	13 56	14 07
Erdington	d	11 17	11 27	11 39			11 47	11 57	12 09		12 17	12 27		12 39		12 47	12 57	13 09	13 17	13 27		13 39		13 47	13 57	14 09
Gravelly Hill	d	11 20	11 30	11 41			11 50	12 00	12 11		12 20	12 30		12 41		12 50	13 00	13 11	13 20	13 30		13 41		13 50	14 00	14 11
Aston	d	11 24	11 33	11 45			11 54	12 03	12 15		12 24	12 33		12 45		12 54	13 03	13 15	13 24	13 33		13 45		13 54	14 03	14 15
Duddeston	d		11 36					12 06				12 36					13 06			13 36					14 06	
Birmingham New Street 12	a	11 30	11 41	11 51			12 01	12 12	12 21		12 30	12 41		12 51		13 01	13 12	13 21	13 30	13 41		13 51		14 01	14 12	14 21
	d	11 34	11 44	11 54		11 59	12 04	12 14	12 24	12 30	12 34	12 44		12 54	12 59	13 04	13 14	13 24	13 34	13 44		13 54	13 59	14 04	14 14	14 24
Five Ways	d	11 37	11 47	11 57			12 07	12 17	12 27		12 37	12 47		12 57		13 07	13 17	13 27	13 37	13 47		13 57		14 07	14 17	14 27
University	d	11 41	11 51	12 01		12 05	12 11	12 21	12 31	12a36	12 41	12 51		13 01	13 05	13 11	13 21	13 31	13 41	13 51		14 01	14 05	14 11	14 21	14 31
Selly Oak	d	11 43	11 53	12 03			12 13	12 23	12 33		12 43	12 53		13 03		13 13	13 23	13 33	13 43	13 53		14 03		14 13	14 23	14 33
Bournville	d	11 45	11 55	12 05			12 15	12 25	12 35		12 45	12 55		13 05		13 15	13 25	13 35	13 45	13 55		14 05		14 15	14 25	14 35
Kings Norton	d	11 47	11 57	12 07			12 17	12 27	12 37		12 47	12 57		13 07		13 17	13 27	13 37	13 47	13 57		14 07		14 17	14 27	14 37
Northfield	d	11 50	12 00	12 10			12 20	12 30	12 40		12 50	13 00		13 10		13 20	13 30	13 40	13 50	14 00		14 10		14 20	14 30	14 40
Longbridge	d	11a54	12 04	12a14			12a24	12 34	12a44		12a54	13 04		13a14		13a24	13 34	13a44	13a54	14 04		14a14		14a24	14 34	14a44
Barnt Green	d		12 09					12 39				13 09					13 39			14 09					14 39	
Alvechurch	d		12 13					12 43				13 13					13 43			14 13					14 43	
Redditch	a		12 23					12 53				13 23					13 53			14 23					14 53	
Bromsgrove	a					12 21									13 21								14 21			

For general notes see front of timetable
For details of catering facilities see Directory of Train Operators

A From Nottingham (Table 57)
B To Wolverhampton (Table 68)

Lichfield → Birmingham → Longbridge and Redditch

Network Diagram - see first page of Table 67

		XC	LM	LM	LM	LM	LM	LM	LM	LM	LM	LM	LM	LM	LM	LM	LM	XC	LM	LM	LM	LM	LM
		◇ A ⚲																◇ B ⚲					
Lichfield Trent Valley	d		13 52				14 22			14 52				15 22					15 51				16 22
Lichfield City	d		13 55		14 16		14 25		14 46	14 55		15 16		15 25			15 46		15 54		16 16		16 25
Shenstone	d				14 21				14 51			15 21					15 51		15 59		16 21		
Blake Street	d		14 03		14 24		14 33		14 54	15 03		15 24		15 33			15 54		16 03		16 24		16 33
Butlers Lane	d		14 05		14 26		14 35		14 56	15 05		15 27		15 35			15 56		16 05		16 26		16 35
Four Oaks	d		14 08	14 18	14 29		14 38	14 48	14 59	15 08	15 18	15 29		15 38	15 48		15 59		16 08	16 18	16 29		16 38
Sutton Coldfield	d		14 11	14 21	14 33		14 41	14 51	15 03	15 11	15 21	15 33		15 41	15 51		16 03		16 11	16 21	16 33		16 41
Wylde Green	d		14 14	14 24	14 35		14 44	14 54	15 05	15 14	15 24	15 35		15 44	15 54		16 05		16 14	16 24	16 35		16 44
Chester Road	d		14 16	14 26	14 37		14 46	14 56	15 07	15 16	15 26	15 37		15 46	15 56		16 07		16 16	16 26	16 37		16 46
Erdington	d		14 17	14 27	14 39		14 48	14 57	15 09	15 17	15 27	15 39		15 48	15 57		16 09		16 17	16 27	16 39		16 47
Gravelly Hill	d		14 20	14 30	14 41		14 50	15 00	15 11	15 20	15 30	15 41		15 50	16 00		16 11		16 20	16 30	16 41		16 50
Aston	d		14 24	14 33	14 45		14 54	15 03	15 15	15 24	15 33	15 45		15 54	16 03		16 15		16 24	16 33	16 45		16 54
Duddeston	d			14 36				15 06			15 36				16 06					16 36			
Birmingham New Street 12	a		14 30	14 41	14 51		15 03	15 12	15 21	15 30	15 41	15 51		16 01	16 12		16 21		16 30	16 42	16 51		17 02
	d	14 30	14 34	14 44	14 54	14 59	15 04	15 14	15 24	15 34	15 44	15 54	15 59	16 04	16 14	16 19	16 24	16 30	16 34	16 44	16 54	16 59	17 04
Five Ways	d		14 37	14 47	14 57		15 07	15 17	15 27	15 37	15 47	15 57		16 07	16 17		16 27		16 37	16 47	16 57		17 07
University	d	14a36	14 41	14 51	15 01	15 05	15 11	15 21	15 31	15 41	15 51	16 01	16 05	16 11	16 21	16a25	16 31	16 36	16 41	16 51	17 01	17 05	17 11
Selly Oak	d		14 43	14 53	15 03		15 13	15 23	15 33	15 43	15 53	16 04		16 14	16 23		16 34		16 44	16 53	17 04		17 14
Bournville	d		14 45	14 55	15 05		15 15	15 25	15 35	15 45	15 55	16 06		16 16	16 25		16 36		16 46	16 55	17 06		17 16
Kings Norton	d		14 47	14 57	15 07		15 17	15 27	15 37	15 47	15 57	16 09		16 19	16 27		16 39		16 49	16 57	17 09		17 19
Northfield	d		14 50	15 00	15 10		15 20	15 30	15 40	15 50	16 00	16 11		16 21	16 30		16 41		16 51	17 00	17 11		17 21
Longbridge	d		14a54	15 04	15a14		15a24	15 34	15a44	15a54	16 04	16a14		16a24	16 36		16a44		16a54	17 04	17a14		17a24
Barnt Green	d			15 09				15 39			16 09				16 40					17 09			
Alvechurch	d			15 13				15 43			16 13				16 45					17 13			
Redditch	a			15 23				15 53			16 23				16 55					17 23			
Bromsgrove	a					15 21							16 21					16 50				17 21	

		LM	LM	LM	XC	LM	LM	LM	LM	LM	LM	LM	LM	XC	LM	LM	LM	LM	LM	LM	LM	LM	LM
					◇ C ⚲									◇ A									
Lichfield Trent Valley	d					16 52				17 21			17 40		17 52		18 10	18 22				18 52	
Lichfield City	d			16 46		16 55	17 05			17 24			17 45		17 55		18 15	18 25			18 46	18 55	
Shenstone	d			16 51						17 29			17 50				18 20				18 51		
Blake Street	d			16 54		17 03	17 12			17 33			17 54		18 03		18 24	18 33			18 54	19 03	
Butlers Lane	d			16 56		17 05	17 14			17 35			17 56		18 05		18 26	18 35			18 56	19 05	
Four Oaks	d	16 48		16 59		17 08	17 18	17 29		17 38	17 48		17 59		18 08	18 18	18 29	18 38	18 48		18 59	19 08	19 18
Sutton Coldfield	d	16 51		17 03		17 11	17 21	17 33		17 41	17 51		18 02		18 11	18 21	18 32	18 41	18 51		19 03	19 11	19 21
Wylde Green	d	16 54		17 05		17 14	17 24	17 35		17 44	17 54		18 05		18 14	18 24	18 35	18 44	18 54		19 05	19 14	19 24
Chester Road	d	16 56		17 07		17 16	17 26	17 37		17 46	17 56		18 07		18 16	18 26	18 37	18 46	18 56		19 07	19 16	19 26
Erdington	d	16 57		17 09		17 17	17 27	17 39		17 47	17 57		18 09		18 17	18 27	18 39	18 47	18 57		19 09	19 17	19 27
Gravelly Hill	d	17 00		17 11		17 20	17 30	17 41		17 50	18 00		18 11		18 20	18 30	18 41	18 50	19 00		19 11	19 20	19 30
Aston	d	17 03		17 14		17 24	17 33	17 44		17 54	18 03		18 15		18 24	18 33	18 45	18 54	19 03		19 15	19 24	19 33
Duddeston	d	17 06					17 36				18 06					18 36			19 06				19 36
Birmingham New Street 12	a	17 11		17 21		17 30	17 41	17 51		18 01	18 11		18 21		18 30	18 41	18 51	19 01	19 11		19 21	19 31	19 41
	d	17 14	17 19	17 24	17 30	17 34	17 44	17 54	17 59	18 04	18 14	18 19	18 24	18 30	18 34	18 44	18 54	19 04	19 14	19 19	19 24	19 34	19 44
Five Ways	d	17 17		17 27		17 37	17 47	17 57		18 07	18 17		18 27		18 37	18 47	18 57	19 07	19 17		19 27	19 37	19 47
University	d	17 21	17 25	17 31	17 36	17 41	17 51	18 01	18 05	18 11	18 21		18 31		18 41	18 51	19 01	19 11	19 21	19 25	19 31	19 41	19 51
Selly Oak	d	17 23		17 34		17 44	17 53	18 04		18 14	18 23		18 33		18 43	18 53	19 03	19 13	19 23		19 33	19 43	19 53
Bournville	d	17 25		17 36		17 46	17 55	18 06		18 16	18 25		18 35		18 45	18 55	19 05	19 15	19 25		19 35	19 45	19 55
Kings Norton	d	17 27		17 39		17 49	17 57	18 08		18 18	18 27		18 37		18 47	18 57	19 07	19 17	19 27		19 37	19 47	19 57
Northfield	d	17 30		17 41		17 51	18 00	18 11		18 21	18 30		18 40		18 50	19 00	19 10	19 20	19 30		19 40	19 50	20 00
Longbridge	d	17 34		17a45		17a54	18 06	18a15		18a24	18 34		18a44		18a54	19 04	19a14	19a24	19 35		19a44	19a54	20 04
Barnt Green	d	17 39					18 10				18 39					19 09			19 40				20 09
Alvechurch	d	17 43					18 15				18 43					19 13			19 44				20 13
Redditch	a	17 55					18 25				18 53					19 23			19 54				20 23
Bromsgrove	a		17 45		17 51				18 21			18 46		18 50						19 40			

		LM	LM	LM	LM	LM	LM	LM	LM	LM	LM	LM	LM	LM	LM	LM	LM	LM	LM	LM	LM
Lichfield Trent Valley	d		19 22			20 00			20 30		21 00			21 30		22 00			22 30	22 57	
Lichfield City	d	19 16	19 25		19 46	20 03			20 33		21 03			21 33		22 03			22 33	23 00	
Shenstone	d	19 21			19 51	20 08			20 38		21 08			21 38		22 08			22 38	23 05	
Blake Street	d	19 24	19 33		19 54	20 12			20 42		21 12			21 42		22 12			22 42	23 09	23 36
Butlers Lane	d	19 26	19 35		19 56	20 14			20 44		21 14			21 44		22 14			22 44	23 11	23 38
Four Oaks	d	19 29	19 38	19 48	19 59	20 17			20 47		21 17			21 47		22 17			22 47	23 14	23 41
Sutton Coldfield	d	19 33	19 41	19 51	20 03	20 20			20 50		21 20			21 50		22 20			22 50	23 17	23 44
Wylde Green	d	19 35	19 44	19 54	20 05	20 23			20 53		21 23			21 53		22 23			22 53	23 20	
Chester Road	d	19 37	19 46	19 56	20 07	20 25			20 55		21 25			21 55		22 25			22 55		
Erdington	d	19 39	19 48	19 57	20 09	20 26			20 56		21 26			21 56		22 26			22 56		
Gravelly Hill	d	19 41	19 50	20 00	20 11	20 29			20 59		21 29			21 59		22 29			22 59		
Aston	d	19 45	19 54	20 03	20 15	20 32			21 02		21 32			22 02		22 32			23 02		
Duddeston	d			20 06		20 35			21 05		21 35			22 05		22 35			23 05		
Birmingham New Street 12	a	19 51	20 03	20 12	20 21	20 41			21 12		21 41			22 12		22 41			23 11	23 31	23 58
	d	19 54		20 14	20 24	20 44	20 59	20 54	21 14	21 24	21 44	21 54	21 59	22 14	22 24	22 44	22 55	23 04	23 14	23 35	
Five Ways	d	19 57		20 17	20 27	20 47		20 57	21 17	21 27	21 47	21 57		22 17	22 27	22 47	22 58		23 17	23 38	
University	d	20 01		20 21	20 31	20 51	21 05	21 01	21 21	21 31	21 51	22 01	22 05	22 21	22 31	22 51	23 02	23 10	23 21	23 42	
Selly Oak	d	20 03		20 23	20 33	20 53		21 03	21 23	21 33	21 53	22 03		22 23	22 33	22 53	23 04		23 23	23 45	
Bournville	d	20 05		20 25	20 35	20 55		21 05	21 25	21 35	21 55	22 05		22 25	22 35	22 55	23 06		23 25	23 47	
Kings Norton	d	20 07		20 27	20 37	20 57		21 07	21 27	21 37	21 57	22 07		22 27	22 37	22 57	23 08		23 27	23 49	
Northfield	d	20 10		20 30	20 40	21 00		21 10	21 30	21 40	22 00	22 10		22 30	22 40	23 00	23 11		23 30	23 52	
Longbridge	d	20a14		20 34	20a44	21 04		21a14	21 34	21a44	22 04	22a14		22 34	22a44	23 04	23a15		23 34	23a55	
Barnt Green	d			20 39		21 09			21 39		22 09			22 39		23 09			23 39		
Alvechurch	d			20 43		21 13			21 43		22 13			22 43		23 13			23 43		
Redditch	a			20 53		21 23			21 53		22 23			22 53		23 23			23 53		
Bromsgrove	a						21 21						22 21					23 23			

For general notes see front of timetable
For details of catering facilities see Directory of Train Operators

A From Nottingham (Table 57)
B From Nottingham to Cardiff Central (Table 57)
C From Nottingham to Cardiff Central (Table 57).
⚲ to Newport (South Wales)

Table 69

Saturdays

Lichfield → Birmingham → Longbridge and Redditch

Network Diagram - see first page of Table 67

		LM	LM	LM	LM	LM	LM	LM	LM	LM	LM	LM	LM	LM	LM	LM	LM	LM	LM	XC ◇ A	LM	LM	LM	LM	LM	LM
Lichfield Trent Valley	d									06 21			06 50				07 22				07 52				08 22	
Lichfield City	d									06 24	06 40		06 54	07 11			07 25	07 36			07 55	08 06			08 25	08 36
Shenstone	d									06 29			06 59				07 30	07 41			08 00	08 11			08 30	08 41
Blake Street	d					06 04				06 33			07 03				07 34	07 44			08 04	08 14			08 34	08 44
Butlers Lane	d					06 06				06 35			07 05				07 36	07 46			08 06	08 16			08 36	08 46
Four Oaks	d					06 09				06 38	06 50		07 08	07 21			07 39	07 50			08 09	08 20			08 39	08 49
Sutton Coldfield	d					06 12				06 41	06 53		07 11	07 24			07 42	07 53			08 12	08 23			08 42	08 53
Wylde Green	d					06 15				06 44	06 56		07 14	07 27			07 45	07 56			08 15	08 26			08 45	08 56
Chester Road	d					06 17				06 46	06 58		07 16	07 29			07 47	07 58			08 17	08 28			08 47	08 58
Erdington	d					06 18				06 47	06 59		07 17	07 30			07 48	07 59			08 18	08 29			08 48	08 59
Gravelly Hill	d					06 21				06 50	07 02		07 20	07 33			07 51	08 02			08 21	08 32			08 51	09 02
Aston	d					06 24				06 53	07 05		07 23	07 35			07 54	08 05			08 24	08 35			08 54	09 05
Duddeston	d					06 26				06 56	07 08		07 26	07 38				08 08				08 38				09 08
Birmingham New Street 12	a					06 31				07 00	07 13		07 30	07 43			08 00	08 12			08 30	08 43			09 00	09 12
	d	05 54	06 04	06 14	06 24	06 34	06 44	06 54	06 59	07 04	07 14	07 24	07 34	07 44	07 54	07 59	08 04	08 14	08 24	08 30	08 34	08 44	08 54	08 59	09 04	09 14
Five Ways	d	05 57	06 07	06 17	06 27	06 37	06 47	06 57		07 07	07 17	07 27	07 37	07 47	07 57		08 07	08 17	08 27		08 37	08 47	08 57		09 07	09 17
University	d	06 01	06 11	06 21	06 31	06 41	06 51	07 01	07 05	07 11	07 21	07 31	07 41	07 51	08 01	08 05	08 11	08 21	08 31	08a36	08 41	08 51	09 01	09 05	09 11	09 21
Selly Oak	d	06 03	06 13	06 23	06 33	06 43	06 53	07 03		07 13	07 23	07 33	07 43	07 53	08 03		08 13	08 23	08 33		08 43	08 53	09 03		09 13	09 23
Bournville	d	06 05	06 15	06 25	06 35	06 45	06 55	07 05		07 15	07 25	07 35	07 45	07 55	08 05		08 15	08 25	08 35		08 45	08 55	09 05		09 15	09 25
Kings Norton	d	06 07	06 17	06 27	06 37	06 47	06 57	07 07		07 17	07 27	07 37	07 47	07 57	08 07		08 17	08 27	08 37		08 47	08 57	09 07		09 17	09 27
Northfield	d	06 10	06 20	06 30	06 40	06 50	07 00	07 10		07 20	07 30	07 40	07 50	08 00	08 10		08 20	08 30	08 40		08 50	09 00	09 10		09 20	09 30
Longbridge	d	06a14	06a24	06 34	06a44	06a54	07 04	07a14		07a24	07 34	07a44	07a54	08 04	08a14		08a24	08 34	08a44		08a54	09 04	09a14		09a24	09 34
Barnt Green	d			06 39			07 09				07 39			08 09				08 39				09 09				09 39
Alvechurch	d			06 43			07 13				07 43			08 13				08 43				09 13				09 43
Redditch	a			06 53			07 23				07 53			08 23				08 53				09 23				09 53
Bromsgrove	a								07 22							08 21								09 21		

		LM	LM	LM	LM	LM	LM	LM		LM	XC ◇ A	LM	LM	LM	LM	LM	LM	LM	LM	LM	LM	LM	LM	LM	LM	LM
Lichfield Trent Valley	d		08 52				09 22					09 52				10 22			10 52				11 22			11 52
Lichfield City	d		08 55	09 06			09 25	09 36				09 55	10 06			10 25	10 36		10 55	11 06			11 25	11 36		11 55
Shenstone	d		09 00	09 11			09 30	09 41				10 00	10 11			10 30	10 41		11 00	11 11			11 30	11 41		12 00
Blake Street	d		09 04	09 14			09 34	09 44				10 04	10 14			10 34	10 44		11 04	11 14			11 34	11 44		12 04
Butlers Lane	d		09 06	09 16			09 36	09 46				10 06	10 16			10 36	10 46		11 06	11 16			11 36	11 46		12 06
Four Oaks	d		09 09	09 20			09 39	09 50				10 09	10 20			10 39	10 50		11 09	11 20			11 39	11 50		12 09
Sutton Coldfield	d		09 12	09 23			09 42	09 53				10 12	10 23			10 42	10 53		11 12	11 23			11 42	11 53		12 12
Wylde Green	d		09 15	09 26			09 45	09 56				10 15	10 26			10 45	10 56		11 15	11 26			11 45	11 56		12 15
Chester Road	d		09 17	09 28			09 47	09 58				10 17	10 28			10 47	10 58		11 17	11 28			11 47	11 58		12 17
Erdington	d		09 18	09 29			09 48	09 59				10 18	10 29			10 48	10 59		11 18	11 29			11 48	11 59		12 18
Gravelly Hill	d		09 21	09 32			09 51	10 02				10 21	10 32			10 51	11 02		11 21	11 32			11 51	12 02		12 21
Aston	d		09 24	09 35			09 54	10 05				10 24	10 35			10 54	11 05		11 24	11 35			11 54	12 05		12 24
Duddeston	d			09 38				10 08					10 38				11 08			11 38				12 08		
Birmingham New Street 12	a		09 30	09 43			10 01	10 12				10 30	10 42			11 01	11 12		11 30	11 43			12 01	12 12		12 30
	d	09 24	09 34	09 44	09 54	09 59	10 04	10 14		10 24	10 30	10 34	10 44	10 54	10 59	11 04	11 14	11 24	11 34	11 44	11 54	11 59	12 04	12 14	12 24	12 34
Five Ways	d	09 27	09 37	09 47	09 57		10 07	10 17		10 27		10 37	10 47	10 57		11 07	11 17	11 27	11 37	11 47	11 57		12 07	12 17	12 27	12 37
University	d	09 31	09 41	09 51	10 01	10 05	10 11	10 21		10 31	10a36	10 41	10 51	11 01	11 05	11 11	11 21	11 31	11 41	11 51	12 01	12 05	12 11	12 21	12 31	12 41
Selly Oak	d	09 33	09 43	09 53	10 03		10 13	10 23		10 33		10 43	10 53	11 03		11 13	11 23	11 33	11 43	11 53	12 03		12 13	12 23	12 33	12 43
Bournville	d	09 35	09 45	09 55	10 05		10 15	10 25		10 35		10 45	10 55	11 05		11 15	11 25	11 35	11 45	11 55	12 05		12 15	12 25	12 35	12 45
Kings Norton	d	09 37	09 47	09 57	10 07		10 17	10 27		10 37		10 47	10 57	11 07		11 17	11 27	11 37	11 47	11 57	12 07		12 17	12 27	12 37	12 47
Northfield	d	09 40	09 50	10 00	10 10		10 20	10 30		10 40		10 50	11 00	11 10		11 20	11 30	11 40	11 50	12 00	12 10		12 20	12 30	12 40	12 50
Longbridge	d	09a44	09a54	10 04	10a14		10a24	10 34		10a44		10a54	11 04	11a14		11a24	11 34	11a44	11a54	12 04	12a14		12a24	12 34	12a44	12a54
Barnt Green	d			10 09				10 39					11 09				11 39			12 09				12 39		
Alvechurch	d			10 13				10 43					11 13				11 43			12 13				12 43		
Redditch	a			10 23				10 53					11 23				11 53			12 23				12 53		
Bromsgrove	a					10 21									11 21							12 21				

		LM	LM	LM	LM	LM	LM	LM	LM	LM	LM	LM	LM	LM	XC ◇ A	LM		LM	LM	LM	LM	LM	LM	LM	LM	LM
Lichfield Trent Valley	d				12 22			12 52				13 22				13 52					14 22			14 52		
Lichfield City	d	12 06			12 25	12 36		12 55	13 06			13 25	13 36			13 55		14 06			14 25	14 36		14 55	15 06	
Shenstone	d	12 11			12 30	12 41		13 00	13 11			13 30	13 41			14 00		14 11			14 30	14 41		15 00	15 11	
Blake Street	d	12 14			12 34	12 44		13 04	13 14			13 34	13 44			14 04		14 14			14 34	14 44		15 04	15 14	
Butlers Lane	d	12 16			12 36	12 46		13 06	13 16			13 36	13 46			14 06		14 16			14 36	14 46		15 06	15 16	
Four Oaks	d	12 20			12 39	12 50		13 09	13 20			13 39	13 50			14 09		14 20			14 39	14 50		15 09	15 20	
Sutton Coldfield	d	12 23			12 42	12 53		13 12	13 23			13 42	13 53			14 12		14 23			14 42	14 53		15 12	15 23	
Wylde Green	d	12 26			12 45	12 56		13 15	13 26			13 45	13 56			14 15		14 26			14 45	14 56		15 15	15 26	
Chester Road	d	12 28			12 47	12 58		13 17	13 28			13 47	13 58			14 17		14 28			14 47	14 58		15 17	15 28	
Erdington	d	12 29			12 48	12 59		13 18	13 29			13 48	13 59			14 18		14 29			14 48	14 59		15 18	15 29	
Gravelly Hill	d	12 32			12 51	13 02		13 21	13 32			13 51	14 02			14 21		14 32			14 51	15 02		15 21	15 32	
Aston	d	12 35			12 54	13 05		13 24	13 35			13 54	14 05			14 24		14 35			14 54	15 05		15 24	15 35	
Duddeston	d	12 38				13 08			13 38				14 08					14 38				15 08			15 38	
Birmingham New Street 12	a	12 42			13 01	13 12		13 30	13 43			14 01	14 12			14 31		14 43			15 01	15 12		15 30	15 43	
	d	12 44	12 54	12 59	13 04	13 14	13 24	13 34	13 44	13 54	13 59	14 04	14 14	14 24	14 30	14 34		14 44	14 54	14 59	15 04	15 14	15 24	15 34	15 44	15 54
Five Ways	d	12 47	12 57		13 07	13 17	13 27	13 37	13 47	13 57		14 07	14 17	14 27		14 37		14 47	14 57		15 07	15 17	15 27	15 37	15 47	15 57
University	d	12 51	13 01	13 05	13 11	13 21	13 31	13 41	13 51	14 01	14 05	14 11	14 21	14 31	14a36	14 41		14 51	15 01	15 05	15 11	15 21	15 31	15 41	15 51	16 01
Selly Oak	d	12 53	13 03		13 13	13 23	13 33	13 43	13 53	14 03		14 13	14 23	14 33		14 43		14 53	15 03		15 13	15 23	15 33	15 43	15 53	16 03
Bournville	d	12 55	13 05		13 15	13 25	13 35	13 45	13 55	14 05		14 15	14 25	14 35		14 45		14 55	15 05		15 15	15 25	15 35	15 45	15 55	16 05
Kings Norton	d	12 57	13 07		13 17	13 27	13 37	13 47	13 57	14 07		14 17	14 27	14 37		14 47		14 57	15 07		15 17	15 27	15 37	15 47	15 57	16 07
Northfield	d	13 00	13 10		13 20	13 30	13 40	13 50	14 00	14 10		14 20	14 30	14 40		14 50		15 00	15 10		15 20	15 30	15 40	15 50	16 00	16 10
Longbridge	d	13 04	13a14		13a24	13 34	13a44	13a54	14 04	14a14		14a24	14 34	14a44		14a54		15 04	15a14		15a24	15 34	15a44	15a54	16 04	16a14
Barnt Green	d	13 09				13 39			14 09				14 39					15 09				15 39			16 09	
Alvechurch	d	13 13				13 43			14 13				14 43					15 13				15 43			16 13	
Redditch	a	13 23				13 53			14 23				14 53					15 23				15 53			16 23	
Bromsgrove	a			13 21							14 21									15 21						

For general notes see front of timetable
For details of catering facilities see
Directory of Train Operators

A From Nottingham (Table 57)

Table 69

Saturdays

Lichfield → Birmingham → Longbridge and Redditch

Network Diagram - see first page of Table 67

		LM	LM	LM	LM	XC ◇ A	LM	LM	LM	LM	LM	LM	LM	XC ◇ A	LM	LM	LM	LM	LM	LM	LM	XC ◇ B	LM	LM	LM	LM
Lichfield Trent Valley	d		15 22				15 52				16 22				16 52				17 22				17 52			18 22
Lichfield City	d		15 25	15 36			15 55	16 06			16 25	16 36			16 55	17 06			17 25	17 36			17 55	18 06		18 25
Shenstone	d		15 30	15 41			16 00	16 11			16 30	16 41			17 00	17 11			17 30	17 41			18 00	18 11		18 30
Blake Street	d		15 34	15 44			16 04	16 14			16 34	16 44			17 04	17 14			17 34	17 44			18 04	18 14		18 34
Butlers Lane	d		15 36	15 46			16 06	16 16			16 36	16 46			17 06	17 16			17 36	17 46			18 06	18 16		18 36
Four Oaks	d		15 39	15 50			16 09	16 20			16 39	16 50			17 09	17 20			17 39	17 50			18 09	18 20		18 39
Sutton Coldfield	d		15 42	15 53			16 12	16 23			16 42	16 53			17 12	17 23			17 42	17 53			18 12	18 23		18 42
Wylde Green	d		15 45	15 56			16 15	16 26			16 45	16 56			17 15	17 26			17 45	17 56			18 15	18 26		18 45
Chester Road	d		15 47	15 58			16 17	16 28			16 47	16 58			17 17	17 28			17 47	17 58			18 17	18 28		18 47
Erdington	d		15 48	15 59			16 18	16 29			16 48	16 59			17 18	17 29			17 48	17 59			18 18	18 29		18 48
Gravelly Hill	d		15 51	16 02			16 21	16 32			16 51	17 02			17 21	17 32			17 51	18 02			18 21	18 32		18 51
Aston	d		15 54	16 05			16 24	16 35			16 54	17 05			17 24	17 35			17 54	18 05			18 24	18 35		18 54
Duddeston	d			16 08				16 38				17 08				17 38				18 08				18 38		
Birmingham New Street 12	a		16 01	16 12			16 30	16 43			17 01	17 12			17 30	17 42			18 01	18 12			18 30	18 43		19 00
	d	15 59	16 04	16 14	16 24	16 30	16 34	16 44	16 54	16 59	17 04	17 14	17 24	17 30	17 34	17 44	17 54	17 59	18 04	18 14	18 24	18 30	18 34	18 44	18 54	19 04
Five Ways	d		16 07	16 17	16 27		16 37	16 47	16 57		17 07	17 17	17 27		17 37	17 47	17 57		18 07	18 17	18 27		18 37	18 47	18 57	19 07
University	d	16 05	16 11	16 21	16 31	16 36	16 41	16 51	17 01	17 05	17 11	17 21	17 31	17 36	17 41	17 51	18 01	18 05	18 11	18 21	18 31		18 41	18 51	19 01	19 11
Selly Oak	d		16 13	16 23	16 33		16 43	16 53	17 03		17 13	17 23	17 33		17 43	17 53	18 03		18 13	18 23	18 33		18 43	18 53	19 03	19 13
Bournville	d		16 15	16 25	16 35		16 45	16 55	17 05		17 15	17 25	17 35		17 45	17 55	18 05		18 15	18 25	18 35		18 45	18 55	19 05	19 15
Kings Norton	d		16 17	16 27	16 37		16 47	16 57	17 07		17 17	17 27	17 37		17 47	17 57	18 07		18 17	18 27	18 37		18 47	18 57	19 07	19 17
Northfield	d		16 20	16 30	16 40		16 50	17 00	17 10		17 20	17 30	17 40		17 50	18 00	18 10		18 20	18 30	18 40		18 50	19 00	19 10	19 20
Longbridge	d		16a24	16 34	16a44		16a54	17 04	17a14		17a24	17 34	17a44		17a54	18 04	18a14		18a24	18 34	18a44		18a54	19 04	19a14	19a24
Barnt Green	d			16 39				17 09				17 39				18 09				18 39				19 09		
Alvechurch	d			16 43				17 13				17 43				18 13				18 43				19 13		
Redditch	a			16 53				17 23				17 53				18 23				18 53				19 23		
Bromsgrove	a	16 21				16 50				17 21				17 51				18 20				18 50				

		LM	LM	LM 🚲	LM	LM	LM	LM	LM	LM	LM	LM	LM	LM	LM	LM	LM	LM	LM	LM	LM	LM	LM	LM
Lichfield Trent Valley	d				18 52			19 22			20 00			20 30		21 00		21 30		22 00		22 30	22 57	
Lichfield City	d	18 36			18 55	19 06		19 25	19 36		20 03			20 33		21 03		21 33		22 03		22 33	23 00	
Shenstone	d	18 41			19 00	19 11		19 30	19 41		20 08			20 38		21 08		21 38		22 08		22 38	23 05	
Blake Street	d	18 44			19 04	19 14		19 34	19 44		20 12			20 42		21 12		21 42		22 12		22 42	23 09	23 36
Butlers Lane	d	18 46			19 06	19 16		19 36	19 46		20 14			20 44		21 14		21 44		22 14		22 44	23 11	23 38
Four Oaks	d	18 50			19 09	19 20		19 39	19 50		20 17			20 47		21 17		21 47		22 17		22 47	23 14	23 41
Sutton Coldfield	d	18 53			19 12	19 23		19 42	19 53		20 20			20 50		21 20		21 50		22 20		22 50	23 17	23 44
Wylde Green	d	18 56			19 15	19 26		19 45	19 56		20 23			20 53		21 23		21 53		22 23		22 53	23 20	
Chester Road	d	18 58			19 17	19 28		19 47	19 58		20 25			20 55		21 25		21 55		22 25		22 55		
Erdington	d	18 59			19 18	19 29		19 48	19 59		20 26			20 56		21 26		21 56		22 26		22 56		
Gravelly Hill	d	19 02			19 21	19 32		19 51	20 02		20 29			20 59		21 29		21 59		22 29		22 59		
Aston	d	19 05			19 24	19 35		19 54	20 05		20 32			21 02		21 32		22 02		22 32		23 02		
Duddeston	d	19 08				19 38			20 08		20 35			21 05		21 35		22 05		22 35		23 05		
Birmingham New Street 12	a	19 12			19 30	19 42		20 03	20 12		20 41			21 11		21 42		22 13		22 41		23 12	23 31	23 58
	d	19 14	19 24	19 30	19 34	19 44	19 54		20 14	20 24	20 44	20 54	20 59	21 14	21 24	21 44	21 54	22 14	22 24	22 44	22 55	23 14	23 35	
Five Ways	d	19 17	19 27		19 37	19 47	19 57		20 17	20 27	20 47	20 57		21 17	21 27	21 47	21 57	22 17	22 27	22 47	22 58	23 17	23 38	
University	d	19 21	19 31	19 36	19 41	19 51	20 01		20 21	20 31	20 51	21 01	21 05	21 21	21 31	21 51	22 01	22 21	22 31	22 51	23 02	23 21	23 42	
Selly Oak	d	19 23	19 33		19 43	19 53	20 03		20 23	20 33	20 53	21 03		21 23	21 33	21 53	22 03	22 23	22 33	22 53	23 04	23 23	23 45	
Bournville	d	19 25	19 35		19 45	19 55	20 05		20 25	20 35	20 55	21 05		21 25	21 35	21 55	22 05	22 25	22 35	22 55	23 06	23 25	23 47	
Kings Norton	d	19 27	19 37		19 47	19 57	20 07		20 27	20 37	20 57	21 07		21 27	21 37	21 57	22 07	22 27	22 37	22 57	23 08	23 27	23 49	
Northfield	d	19 30	19 40		19 50	20 00	20 10		20 30	20 40	21 00	21 10		21 30	21 40	22 00	22 10	22 30	22 40	23 00	23 11	23 30	23 52	
Longbridge	d	19 34	19a44		19a54	20 04	20a14		20 34	20a44	21 04	21a14		21 34	21a44	22 04	22a14	22 34	22a44	23 04	23a15	23 34	23a55	
Barnt Green	d	19 39				20 09			20 39		21 09			21 39		22 09		22 39		23 09		23 39		
Alvechurch	d	19 43				20 13			20 43		21 13			21 43		22 13		22 43		23 13		23 43		
Redditch	a	19 53				20 23			20 53		21 23			21 53		22 23		22 53		23 23		23 53		
Bromsgrove	a			19 50									21 21											

Sundays

until 23 March

		LM	LM	LM	LM	LM	XC	LM	LM	LM	LM	LM	LM	LM	LM	LM	LM	LM	LM	LM
Lichfield Trent Valley	d			09 37	10 07	10 37		11 07	11 37	12 07	12 37		13 07	13 37	14 07	14 37	15 07		15 37	16 07
Lichfield City	d			09 40	10 10	10 40		11 10	11 40	12 10	12 40		13 10	13 40	14 10	14 40	15 10		15 40	16 10
Shenstone	d			09 45	10 15	10 45		11 15	11 45	12 15	12 45		13 15	13 45	14 15	14 45	15 15		15 45	16 15
Blake Street	d			09 49	10 19	10 49		11 19	11 49	12 19	12 49		13 19	13 49	14 19	14 49	15 19		15 49	16 19
Butlers Lane	d			09 51	10 21	10 51		11 21	11 51	12 21	12 51		13 21	13 51	14 21	14 51	15 21		15 51	16 21
Four Oaks	d		09 24	09 54	10 24	10 54		11 24	11 54	12 24	12 54		13 24	13 54	14 24	14 54	15 24		15 54	16 24
Sutton Coldfield	d		09 27	09 57	10 27	10 57		11 27	11 57	12 27	12 57		13 27	13 57	14 27	14 57	15 27		15 57	16 27
Wylde Green	d		09 30	10 00	10 30	11 00		11 30	12 00	12 30	13 00		13 30	14 00	14 30	15 00	15 30		16 00	16 30
Chester Road	d		09 32	10 02	10 32	11 02		11 32	12 02	12 32	13 02		13 32	14 02	14 32	15 02	15 32		16 02	16 32
Erdington	d		09 33	10 03	10 33	11 03		11 33	12 03	12 33	13 03		13 33	14 03	14 33	15 03	15 33		16 03	16 33
Gravelly Hill	d		09 36	10 06	10 36	11 06		11 36	12 06	12 36	13 06		13 36	14 06	14 36	15 06	15 36		16 06	16 36
Aston	d		09 39	10 09	10 39	11 09		11 39	12 09	12 39	13 09		13 39	14 09	14 39	15 09	15 39		16 09	16 39
Duddeston	d		09 41	10 11	10 41	11 11		11 41	12 11	12 41	13 11		13 41	14 11	14 41	15 11	15 41		16 11	16 41
Birmingham New Street 12	a		09 47	10 17	10 47	11 18		11 47	12 17	12 47	13 17		13 47	14 17	14 47	15 17	15 47		16 17	16 47
	d	09 20	09 50	10 20	10 50	11 20	11 46	11 50	12 20	12 50	13 20	13 45	13 50	14 20	14 50	15 20	15 50	16 00	16 20	16 50
Five Ways	d	09 23	09 53	10 23	10 53	11 23		11 53	12 23	12 53	13 23		13 53	14 23	14 53	15 23	15 53		16 23	16 53
University	d	09 27	09 57	10 27	10 57	11 27		11 57	12 27	12 57	13 27		13 57	14 27	14 57	15 27	15 57		16 27	16 57
Selly Oak	d	09 29	09 59	10 29	10 59	11 29		11 59	12 29	12 59	13 29		13 59	14 29	14 59	15 29	15 59		16 29	16 59
Bournville	d	09 31	10 01	10 31	11 01	11 31		12 01	12 31	13 01	13 31		14 01	14 31	15 01	15 31	16 01		16 31	17 01
Kings Norton	d	09 33	10 03	10 33	11 03	11 33		12 03	12 33	13 03	13 33		14 03	14 33	15 03	15 33	16 03		16 33	17 03
Northfield	d	09 36	10 06	10 36	11 06	11 36		12 06	12 36	13 06	13 36		14 06	14 36	15 06	15 36	16 06		16 36	17 06
Longbridge	d	09 39	10 09	10 39	11 09	11 39		12 09	12 39	13 09	13 39		14 09	14 39	15 09	15 39	16 09		16 39	17 09
Barnt Green	d	09 43	10 13	10 43	11 13	11 43		12 13	12 43	13 13	13 43		14 13	14 43	15 13	15 43	16 13		16 43	17 13
Alvechurch	d	09 48	10 18	10 48	11 18	11 48		12 18	12 48	13 18	13 48		14 18	14 48	15 18	15 48	16 18		16 48	17 18
Redditch	a	09 57	10 27	10 57	11 27	11 57		12 27	12 57	13 27	13 57		14 27	14 57	15 27	15 57	16 27		16 57	17 27
Bromsgrove	a						12 04					14 05						16 20		

For general notes see front of timetable
For details of catering facilities see Directory of Train Operators

A From Nottingham to Cardiff Central (Table 57)
B From Nottingham (Table 57)

Table 69

until 23 March

Lichfield → Birmingham → Longbridge and Redditch

Network Diagram - see first page of Table 67

		LM	LM	LM	LM	LM	LM	LM	LM	LM	LM	LM	LM	LM	LM	LM	LM	LM
Lichfield Trent Valley	d	16 37	17 07		17 37	18 07		18 37	19 07	19 37	20 07		20 37	21 07	21 37	22 07	22 37	23 07
Lichfield City	d	16 40	17 10		17 40	18 10		18 40	19 10	19 40	20 10		20 40	21 10	21 40	22 10	22 40	23 10
Shenstone	d	16 45	17 15		17 45	18 15		18 45	19 15	19 45	20 15		20 45	21 15	21 45	22 15	22 45	23 15
Blake Street	d	16 49	17 19		17 49	18 19		18 49	19 19	19 49	20 19		20 49	21 19	21 49	22 19	22 49	23 19
Butlers Lane	d	16 51	17 21		17 51	18 21		18 51	19 21	19 51	20 21		20 51	21 21	21 51	22 21	22 51	23 21
Four Oaks	d	16 54	17 24		17 54	18 24		18 54	19 24	19 54	20 24		20 54	21 24	21 54	22 24	22 54	23 24
Sutton Coldfield	d	16 57	17 27		17 57	18 27		18 57	19 27	19 57	20 27		20 57	21 27	21 57	22 27	22 57	23 27
Wylde Green	d	17 00	17 30		18 00	18 30		19 00	19 30	20 00	20 30		21 00	21 30	22 00	22 30	23 00	23 30
Chester Road	d	17 02	17 32		18 02	18 32		19 02	19 32	20 02	20 32		21 02	21 32	22 02	22 32	23 02	
Erdington	d	17 03	17 33		18 03	18 33		19 03	19 33	20 03	20 33		21 03	21 33	22 03	22 33	23 03	
Gravelly Hill	d	17 06	17 36		18 06	18 36		19 06	19 36	20 06	20 36		21 06	21 36	22 06	22 36	23 06	
Aston	d	17 09	17 39		18 09	18 39		19 09	19 39	20 09	20 39		21 09	21 39	22 09	22 39	23 09	
Duddeston	d	17 11	17 41		18 11	18 41		19 11	19 41	20 11	20 41		21 11	21 41	22 11	22 41	23 11	
Birmingham New Street 12	a	17 17	17 47		18 17	18 47		19 17	19 47	20 18	20 47		21 17	21 47	22 17	22 47	23 17	23 44
	d	17 20	17 50	18 00	18 20	18 50	19 00	19 20	19 50	20 20	20 50	21 00	21 20	21 50	22 20	22 50	23 20	
Five Ways	d	17 23	17 53		18 23	18 53		19 23	19 53	20 23	20 53		21 23	21 53	22 23	22 53	23 23	
University	d	17 27	17 57		18 27	18 57		19 27	19 57	20 27	20 57		21 27	21 57	22 27	22 57	23 27	
Selly Oak	d	17 29	17 59		18 29	18 59		19 29	19 59	20 29	20 59		21 29	21 59	22 29	22 59	23 29	
Bournville	d	17 31	18 01		18 31	19 01		19 31	20 01	20 31	21 01		21 31	22 01	22 31	23 01	23 31	
Kings Norton	d	17 33	18 03		18 33	19 03		19 33	20 03	20 33	21 03		21 33	22 03	22 33	23 03	23 33	
Northfield	d	17 36	18 06		18 36	19 06		19 36	20 06	20 36	21 06		21 36	22 06	22 36	23 06	23 36	
Longbridge	d	17 39	18 09		18 39	19 09		19 39	20 09	20 39	21 09		21 39	22 09	22 39	23 09	23 39	
Barnt Green	d	17 43	18 13		18 43	19 13		19 43	20 13	20 43	21 13		21 43	22 13	22 43	23 13	23 43	
Alvechurch	d	17 48	18 18		18 48	19 18		19 48	20 18	20 48	21 18		21 48	22 18	22 48	23 18	23 48	
Redditch	a	17 57	18 27		18 57	19 27		19 57	20 27	20 57	21 27		21 57	22 27	22 57	23 27	23 57	
Bromsgrove	a			18 20			19 21					21 20						

Sundays

from 30 March

		LM	LM	LM 🚌	LM	LM 🚌	LM	LM 🚌	LM	XC	LM 🚌	LM	LM 🚌	LM	LM 🚌	LM	LM 🚌	LM	LM	LM 🚌	LM	LM 🚌	LM
Lichfield Trent Valley	d			09 15		09 45		10 15			10 45		11 15		11 45		12 15			12 45		13 15	
Lichfield City	d			09 21		09 51		10 21			10 51		11 21		11 51		12 21			12 51		13 21	
Shenstone	d			09 30		10 00		10 30			11 00		11 30		12 00		12 30			13 00		13 30	
Blake Street	d			09 37		10 07		10 37			11 07		11 37		12 07		12 37			13 07		13 37	
Butlers Lane	d			09 41		10 11		10 41			11 11		11 41		12 11		12 41			13 11		13 41	
Four Oaks	d		09 24	09a47	09 54	10a17	10 24	10a47	10 54		11a17	11 24	11a47	11 54	12a17	12 24	12a47	12 54		13a17	13 24	13a47	13 54
Sutton Coldfield	d		09 27		09 57		10 27		10 57			11 27		11 57		12 27		12 57			13 27		13 57
Wylde Green	d		09 30		10 00		10 30		11 00			11 30		12 00		12 30		13 00			13 30		14 00
Chester Road	d		09 32		10 02		10 32		11 02			11 32		12 02		12 32		13 02			13 32		14 02
Erdington	d		09 33		10 03		10 33		11 03			11 33		12 03		12 33		13 03			13 33		14 03
Gravelly Hill	d		09 36		10 06		10 36		11 06			11 36		12 06		12 36		13 06			13 36		14 06
Aston	d		09 39		10 09		10 39		11 09			11 39		12 09		12 39		13 09			13 39		14 09
Duddeston	d		09 41		10 11		10 41		11 11			11 41		12 11		12 41		13 11			13 41		14 11
Birmingham New Street 12	a		09 47		10 17		10 47		11 18			11 47		12 17		12 47		13 17			13 47		14 17
	d	09 20	09 50		10 20		10 50		11 20	11 46		11 50		12 20		12 50		13 20	13 45		13 50		14 20
Five Ways	d	09 23	09 53		10 23		10 53		11 23			11 53		12 23		12 53		13 23			13 53		14 23
University	d	09 27	09 57		10 27		10 57		11 27			11 57		12 27		12 57		13 27			13 57		14 27
Selly Oak	d	09 29	09 59		10 29		10 59		11 29			11 59		12 29		12 59		13 29			13 59		14 29
Bournville	d	09 31	10 01		10 31		11 01		11 31			12 01		12 31		13 01		13 31			14 01		14 31
Kings Norton	d	09 33	10 03		10 33		11 03		11 33			12 03		12 33		13 03		13 33			14 03		14 33
Northfield	d	09 36	10 06		10 36		11 06		11 36			12 06		12 36		13 06		13 36			14 06		14 36
Longbridge	d	09 39	10 09		10 39		11 09		11 39			12 09		12 39		13 09		13 39			14 09		14 39
Barnt Green	d	09 43	10 13		10 43		11 13		11 43			12 13		12 43		13 13		13 43			14 13		14 43
Alvechurch	d	09 48	10 18		10 48		11 18		11 48			12 18		12 48		13 18		13 48			14 18		14 48
Redditch	a	09 57	10 27		10 57		11 27		11 57			12 27		12 57		13 27		13 57			14 27		14 57
Bromsgrove	a									12 04									14 05				

		LM 🚌	LM	LM 🚌	LM	LM 🚌	LM	LM	LM 🚌	LM	LM 🚌	LM	LM 🚌	LM	LM 🚌	LM	LM	LM 🚌	LM	LM 🚌	LM	LM	LM 🚌
Lichfield Trent Valley	d	13 45		14 15		14 45			15 15		15 45		16 15		16 45			17 15		17 45			18 15
Lichfield City	d	13 51		14 21		14 51			15 21		15 51		16 21		16 51			17 21		17 51			18 21
Shenstone	d	14 00		14 30		15 00			15 30		16 00		16 30		17 00			17 30		18 00			18 30
Blake Street	d	14 07		14 37		15 07			15 37		16 07		16 37		17 07			17 37		18 07			18 37
Butlers Lane	d	14 11		14 41		15 11			15 41		16 11		16 41		17 11			17 41		18 11			18 41
Four Oaks	d	14a17	14 24	14a47	14 54	15a17	15 24		15a47	15 54	16a17	16 24	16a47	16 54	17a17	17 24		17a47	17 54	18a17	18 24		18a47
Sutton Coldfield	d		14 27		14 57		15 27			15 57		16 27		16 57		17 27			17 57		18 27		
Wylde Green	d		14 30		15 00		15 30			16 00		16 30		17 00		17 30			18 00		18 30		
Chester Road	d		14 32		15 02		15 32			16 02		16 32		17 02		17 32			18 02		18 32		
Erdington	d		14 33		15 03		15 33			16 03		16 33		17 03		17 33			18 03		18 33		
Gravelly Hill	d		14 36		15 06		15 36			16 06		16 36		17 06		17 36			18 06		18 36		
Aston	d		14 39		15 09		15 39			16 09		16 39		17 09		17 39			18 09		18 39		
Duddeston	d		14 41		15 11		15 41			16 11		16 41		17 11		17 41			18 11		18 41		
Birmingham New Street 12	a		14 47		15 17		15 47			16 17		16 47		17 17		17 47			18 17		18 47		
	d		14 50		15 20		15 50	16 00		16 20		16 50		17 20		17 50	18 00		18 20		18 50	19 00	
Five Ways	d		14 53		15 23		15 53			16 23		16 53		17 23		17 53			18 23		18 53		
University	d		14 57		15 27		15 57			16 27		16 57		17 27		17 57			18 27		18 57		
Selly Oak	d		14 59		15 29		15 59			16 29		16 59		17 29		17 59			18 29		18 59		
Bournville	d		15 01		15 31		16 01			16 31		17 01		17 31		18 01			18 31		19 01		
Kings Norton	d		15 03		15 33		16 03			16 33		17 03		17 33		18 03			18 33		19 03		
Northfield	d		15 06		15 36		16 06			16 36		17 06		17 36		18 06			18 36		19 06		
Longbridge	d		15 09		15 39		16 09			16 39		17 09		17 39		18 09			18 39		19 09		
Barnt Green	d		15 13		15 43		16 13			16 43		17 13		17 43		18 13			18 43		19 13		
Alvechurch	d		15 18		15 48		16 18			16 48		17 18		17 48		18 18			18 48		19 18		
Redditch	a		15 27		15 57		16 27			16 57		17 27		17 57		18 27			18 57		19 27		
Bromsgrove	a							16 20									18 20					19 21	

For general notes see front of timetable
For details of catering facilities see Directory of Train Operators

Table 69

Sundays

from 30 March

Lichfield → Birmingham → Longbridge and Redditch

Network Diagram - see first page of Table 67

		LM	LM 🚌	LM	LM 🚌	LM	LM 🚌	LM	LM	LM 🚌	LM	LM 🚌	LM	LM 🚌	LM	LM 🚌	LM	LM 🚌	LM	LM 🚌	LM
Lichfield Trent Valley	d		18 45		19 15		19 45			20 15		20 45		21 15		21 45		22 15		22 45	
Lichfield City	d		18 51		19 21		19 51			20 21		20 51		21 21		21 51		22 21		22 51	
Shenstone	d		19 00		19 30		20 00			20 30		21 00		21 30		22 00		22 30		23 00	
Blake Street	d		19 07		19 37		20 07			20 37		21 07		21 37		22 07		22 37		23 07	
Butlers Lane	d		19 11		19 41		20 11			20 41		21 11		21 41		22 11		22 41		23 11	
Four Oaks	d	18 54	19a17	19 24	19a47	19 54	20a17	20 24		20a47	20 54	21a17	21 24	21a47	21 54	22a17	22 24	22a47	22 54	23a17	23 24
Sutton Coldfield	d	18 57		19 27		19 57		20 27			20 57		21 27		21 57		22 27		22 57		23 27
Wylde Green	d	19 00		19 30		20 00		20 30			21 00		21 30		22 00		22 30		23 00		23 30
Chester Road	d	19 02		19 32		20 02		20 32			21 02		21 32		22 02		22 32		23 02		
Erdington	d	19 03		19 33		20 03		20 33			21 03		21 33		22 03		22 33		23 03		
Gravelly Hill	d	19 06		19 36		20 06		20 36			21 06		21 36		22 06		22 36		23 06		
Aston	d	19 09		19 39		20 09		20 39			21 09		21 39		22 09		22 39		23 09		
Duddeston	d	19 11		19 41		20 11		20 41			21 11		21 41		22 11		22 41		23 11		
Birmingham New Street 12	a	19 17		19 47		20 18		20 47			21 17		21 47		22 17		22 47		23 17		23 44
	d	19 20		19 50		20 20		20 50	21 00		21 20		21 50		22 20		22 50		23 20		
Five Ways	d	19 23		19 53		20 23		20 53			21 23		21 53		22 23		22 53		23 23		
University	d	19 27		19 57		20 27		20 57			21 27		21 57		22 27		22 57		23 27		
Selly Oak	d	19 29		19 59		20 29		20 59			21 29		21 59		22 29		22 59		23 29		
Bournville	d	19 31		20 01		20 31		21 01			21 31		22 01		22 31		23 01		23 31		
Kings Norton	d	19 33		20 03		20 33		21 03			21 33		22 03		22 33		23 03		23 33		
Northfield	d	19 36		20 06		20 36		21 06			21 36		22 06		22 36		23 06		23 36		
Longbridge	d	19 39		20 09		20 39		21 09			21 39		22 09		22 39		23 09		23 39		
Barnt Green	d	19 43		20 13		20 43		21 13			21 43		22 13		22 43		23 13		23 43		
Alvechurch	d	19 48		20 18		20 48		21 18			21 48		22 18		22 48		23 18		23 48		
Redditch	a	19 57		20 27		20 57		21 27			21 57		22 27		22 57		23 27		23 57		
Bromsgrove	a								21 20												

For general notes see front of timetable
For details of catering facilities see
Directory of Train Operators

Redditch and Longbridge → Birmingham → Lichfield

Network Diagram - see first page of Table 67

Miles	Miles			LM MO A 🚌	LM	LM	LM	LM	LM	LM	LM	LM	LM	LM	LM	LM	LM	LM	LM	LM	LM	LM	XC B
—	0	Bromsgrove	d						06 21			06 42					07 23						07 50
0	—	**Redditch**	d								06 27				06 57					07 27			
3¼	—	Alvechurch	d								06 32				07 02					07 32			
5	3½	Barnt Green	d								06 38				07 08					07 38			
7¾	—	Longbridge	d				06 13	06 23		06 33	06 43		06 53	07 03	07 13	07 23			07 33	07 43		07 53	
8¾	—	Northfield	d				06 15	06 25		06 35	06 45		06 55	07 05	07 15	07 25			07 35	07 45		07 55	
10¼	—	Kings Norton	d				06 17	06 27		06 37	06 47		06 57	07 07	07 17	07 27			07 37	07 47		07 57	
11¼	—	Bournville	d				06 20	06 30		06 40	06 50		07 00	07 10	07 20	07 30			07 40	07 50		08 00	
12¼	—	Selly Oak	d				06 22	06 32		06 42	06 52		07 02	07 12	07 22	07 32			07 42	07 52		08 02	
13	11½	University	d				06 25	06 35	06 39	06 45	06 55	06 59	07 05	07 15	07 25	07 35			07 45	07 55	07 59	08 05	08 09
13½	—	Five Ways	d				06 28	06 38		06 48	06 58		07 08	07 18	07 28	07 38			07 48	07 58		08 08	
14½	13	**Birmingham New Street** 12	a				06 33	06 43	06 45	06 53	07 03	07 07	07 14	07 23	07 33	07 43	07 45		07 53	08 03	08 09	08 13	08 16
—	—		d		06 03	06 24	06 35	06 45		06 55	07 05		07 15	07 25	07 35	07 45		07 51	07 55	08 05		08 15	
16	—	Duddeston	d		06 07	06 28		06 49					07 19			07 49						08 19	
17¼	—	Aston	d		06 10	06 31	06 41	06 52		07 01	07 12		07 22	07 31	07 41	07 52		07 57	08 00	08 12		08 22	
18½	—	Gravelly Hill	d		06 13	06 34	06 45	06 56		07 04	07 15		07 25	07 34	07 44	07 55		08 00	08 04	08 15		08 25	
19¼	—	Erdington	d		06 15	06 36	06 47	06 58		07 06	07 17		07 28	07 37	07 47	07 58		08 02	08 07	08 17		08 28	
20¼	—	Chester Road	d		06 17	06 38	06 49	07 00		07 08	07 19		07 30	07 39	07 48	07 59		08 04	08 09	08 19		08 30	
21	—	Wylde Green	d		06 19	06 40	06 51	07 02		07 10	07 21		07 32	07 41	07 50	08 01		08 06	08 11	08 21		08 32	
22	—	Sutton Coldfield	d		06 22	06 43	06 54	07 05		07 13	07 24		07 35	07 44	07 53	08 03		08 09	08 14	08 24		08 35	
23½	—	Four Oaks	d	23p38	06 25	06 46	06 58	07a11		07 16	07 27		07a42	07 47		08a08		08 12	08 17	08 28		08a41	
24½	—	Butlers Lane	d	23p41	06 27	06 48	07 00			07 18	07 29			07 49					08 19	08 30			
26¼	—	Blake Street	d	23p45	06 29	06 50	07 02			07 20	07 31			07 51					08 21	08 32			
28¾	—	Shenstone	d	23p52	06 33	06 54				07 24				07 55					08 25	08 36			
31¾	—	**Lichfield City**	d	00 02	06a41	06 59	07b12			07 29	07c42			08 00	08a07			08a24	08 30	08 42			
33	—	**Lichfield Trent Valley**	a	00 08		07 05	07 16			07 35	07 47			08 05					08 35	08 46			

		LM	LM	LM	LM	XC C	LM	LM	LM	LM	LM	LM	LM	XC ◇ D	LM	LM	LM	LM	LM	LM	LM	LM	LM
Bromsgrove	d					08 23			08 41					09 21				09 50					
Redditch	d		07 57					08 27				08 57				09 27				09 57			10 27
Alvechurch	d		08 02					08 32				09 02				09 32				10 02			10 32
Barnt Green	d		08 08					08 38				09 08				09 38				10 08			10 38
Longbridge	d	08 03	08 13		08 23		08 33	08 43		08 53	09 03	09 13	09 23		09 33	09 43	09 53		10 03	10 13	10 23	10 33	10 43
Northfield	d	08 05	08 15		08 25		08 35	08 45		08 55	09 05	09 15	09 25		09 35	09 45	09 55		10 05	10 15	10 25	10 35	10 45
Kings Norton	d	08 07	08 17		08 27		08 37	08 48		08 57	09 07	09 17	09 27		09 37	09 47	09 57		10 07	10 17	10 27	10 37	10 47
Bournville	d	08 10	08 20		08 30		08 40	08 50		09 00	09 10	09 20	09 30		09 40	09 50	10 00		10 10	10 20	10 30	10 40	10 50
Selly Oak	d	08 12	08 22		08 32		08 42	08 52		09 02	09 12	09 22	09 32		09 42	09 52	10 02		10 12	10 22	10 32	10 42	10 52
University	d	08 15	08 25	08 29	08 35	08 39	08 45	08 55	08 59	09 05	09 15	09 25	09 35		09 45	09 55	10 05	10 09	10 15	10 25	10 35	10 44	10 55
Five Ways	d	08 18	08 28		08 38		08 48	08 58		09 08	09 18	09 28	09 38		09 48	09 58	10 08		10 18	10 28	10 38	10 47	10 58
Birmingham New Street 12	a	08 23	08 34	08 37	08 43	08 46	08 53	09 03	09 07	09 13	09 23	09 34	09 43	09 45	09 53	10 03	10 13	10 24	10 23	10 33	10 43	10 53	11 03
	d	08 25	08 35		08 45		08 55	09 05		09 15	09 25	09 35	09 45		09 55	10 05	10 15		10 25	10 35	10 45	10 55	11 05
Duddeston	d				08 49					09 19			09 49				10 19				10 49		
Aston	d	08 30	08 41		08 52		09 00	09 11		09 23	09 31	09 41	09 52		10 00	10 11	10 22		10 30	10 41	10 52	11 00	11 11
Gravelly Hill	d	08 33	08 44		08 55		09 04	09 15		09 26	09 34	09 45	09 55		10 03	10 15	10 25		10 34	10 45	10 55	11 04	11 15
Erdington	d	08 36	08 47		08 58		09 06	09 17		09 29	09 36	09 47	09 58		10 06	10 17	10 28		10 36	10 47	10 58	11 06	11 17
Chester Road	d	08 38	08 49		09 00		09 08	09 19		09 31	09 38	09 49	10 00		10 08	10 19	10 30		10 38	10 49	11 00	11 08	11 19
Wylde Green	d	08 40	08 51		09 02		09 10	09 21		09 33	09 40	09 51	10 02		10 10	10 21	10 32		10 40	10 51	11 02	11 10	11 21
Sutton Coldfield	d	08 43	08 54		09 05		09 13	09 24		09 36	09 43	09 54	10 05		10 13	10 24	10 35		10 43	10 54	11 05	11 13	11 24
Four Oaks	d	08 46	08 57		09a11		09 17	09 27		09a41	09 46	09 57	10a11		10 17	10 27	10a41		10 47	10 57	11a11	11 17	11 27
Butlers Lane	d	08 49	08 59				09 19	09 29			09 48	09 59			10 19	10 29			10 49	10 59		11 19	11 29
Blake Street	d	08 51	09 01				09 21	09 31			09 50	10 01			10 21	10 31			10 51	11 01		11 21	11 31
Shenstone	d	08 55					09 25				09 54				10 25				10 55			11 25	
Lichfield City	d	09a03	09 09				09a34	09 39			10a03	10 09			10a33	10 39			11a03	11 09		11a33	11 39
Lichfield Trent Valley	a		09 15					09 45				10 15				10 45				11 15			11 45

		LM	LM	LM	LM	LM	LM	LM	LM	LM	LM	LM	LM	XC ◇ D	LM	LM	LM	LM	LM	LM	LM	LM	LM
Bromsgrove	d		10 50							11 50								12 50					
Redditch	d				10 57			11 27				11 57				12 27				12 57			13 27
Alvechurch	d				11 02			11 32				12 02				12 32				13 02			13 32
Barnt Green	d				11 08			11 38				12 08				12 38				13 08			13 38
Longbridge	d	10 53		11 03	11 13	11 23	11 33	11 43	11 53		12 03	12 13	12 23		12 33	12 43	12 53		13 03	13 13	13 23	13 33	13 43
Northfield	d	10 55		11 05	11 15	11 25	11 35	11 45	11 55		12 05	12 15	12 25		12 35	12 45	12 55		13 05	13 15	13 25	13 35	13 45
Kings Norton	d	10 57		11 07	11 17	11 27	11 37	11 47	11 57		12 07	12 17	12 27		12 37	12 47	12 57		13 07	13 17	13 27	13 37	13 47
Bournville	d	11 00		11 10	11 20	11 30	11 40	11 50	12 00		12 10	12 20	12 30		12 40	12 50	13 00		13 10	13 20	13 30	13 40	13 50
Selly Oak	d	11 02		11 12	11 22	11 32	11 42	11 52	12 02		12 12	12 22	12 32		12 42	12 52	13 02		13 12	13 22	13 32	13 42	13 52
University	d	11 05	11 09	11 15	11 25	11 35	11 45	11 55	12 05	12 09	12 15	12 25	12 35	12 39	12 44	12 55	13 05	13 09	13 15	13 25	13 35	13 44	13 55
Five Ways	d	11 08		11 18	11 28	11 38	11 48	11 58	12 08		12 18	12 28	12 38		12 47	12 58	13 08		13 18	13 28	13 38	13 47	13 58
Birmingham New Street 12	a	11 13	11 23	11 23	11 33	11 43	11 53	12 03	12 13	12 23	12 23	12 34	12 43	12 46	12 53	13 03	13 13	13 18	13 23	13 33	13 43	13 53	14 03
	d	11 15		11 25	11 35	11 45	11 55	12 05	12 15		12 25	12 35	12 45		12 55	13 05	13 15		13 25	13 35	13 45	13 55	14 05
Duddeston	d	11 19				11 49			12 19				12 49				13 19				13 49		
Aston	d	11 22		11 30	11 42	11 52	12 00	12 11	12 22		12 30	12 41	12 52		13 00	13 11	13 22		13 30	13 42	13 52	14 00	14 11
Gravelly Hill	d	11 25		11 34	11 45	11 55	12 04	12 15	12 26		12 34	12 45	12 55		13 04	13 15	13 25		13 34	13 46	13 55	14 04	14 15
Erdington	d	11 28		11 36	11 47	11 58	12 06	12 17	12 28		12 36	12 47	12 58		13 06	13 17	13 28		13 36	13 48	13 58	14 06	14 17
Chester Road	d	11 30		11 38	11 49	12 00	12 08	12 19	12 30		12 38	12 49	13 00		13 08	13 19	13 30		13 38	13 50	14 00	14 08	14 19
Wylde Green	d	11 32		11 40	11 51	12 02	12 10	12 21	12 32		12 40	12 51	13 02		13 10	13 21	13 32		13 40	13 52	14 02	14 10	14 21
Sutton Coldfield	d	11 35		11 43	11 54	12 05	12 13	12 24	12 35		12 43	12 54	13 05		13 13	13 24	13 35		13 43	13 55	14 05	14 13	14 24
Four Oaks	d	11a41		11 47	11 57	12a11	12 17	12 27	12a41		12 47	12 57	13a11		13 17	13 27	13a41		13 47	13 58	14a11	14 17	14 27
Butlers Lane	d			11 49	11 59		12 19	12 29			12 49	12 59			13 19	13 29			13 49	14 00		14 19	14 29
Blake Street	d			11 51	12 01		12 21	12 31			12 51	13 01			13 21	13 31			13 51	14 02		14 21	14 31
Shenstone	d			11 55			12 25				12 55				13 25				13 55			14 25	
Lichfield City	d			12a03	12 09		12a33	12 39			13a03	13 09			13a33	13 39			14a03	14 10		14a33	14 39
Lichfield Trent Valley	a				12 15			12 45				13 15				13 45				14 15			14 45

For general notes see front of timetable
For details of catering facilities see Directory of Train Operators

A From 31 March
B From Gloucester (Table 57)
C From Gloucester to Nottingham (Table 57)
D To Nottingham (Table 57)

b Arr. 0709
c Arr. 0739

Table 69

Mondays to Fridays

Redditch and Longbridge → Birmingham → Lichfield

Network Diagram - see first page of Table 67

		LM	LM	LM	LM	LM	LM	LM	LM	LM	LM	LM	LM	LM	LM	LM	LM	LM	LM	LM	LM	LM
Bromsgrove	d		13 50							14 50						15 44						
Redditch	d				13 57			14 27				14 57			15 27				15 57			16 27
Alvechurch	d				14 02			14 32				15 02			15 32				16 02			16 32
Barnt Green	d				14 08			14 38				15 08			15 38				16 08			16 38
Longbridge	d	13 53		14 03	14 13	14 23	14 33	14 43	14 53		15 03	15 13	15 23	15 33	15 43		15 53	16 03	16 13	16 23	16 33	16 43
Northfield	d	13 55		14 05	14 15	14 25	14 35	14 45	14 55		15 05	15 15	15 25	15 35	15 45		15 55	16 05	16 15	16 25	16 35	16 45
Kings Norton	d	13 57		14 07	14 17	14 27	14 37	14 47	14 57		15 07	15 17	15 27	15 37	15 47		15 57	16 07	16 17	16 27	16 37	16 47
Bournville	d	14 00		14 10	14 20	14 30	14 40	14 50	15 00		15 10	15 20	15 30	15 40	15 50		16 00	16 10	16 20	16 30	16 40	16 50
Selly Oak	d	14 02		14 12	14 22	14 32	14 42	14 52	15 02		15 12	15 22	15 32	15 42	15 52		16 02	16 12	16 22	16 32	16 42	16 52
University	d	14 05	14 09	14 15	14 25	14 35	14 44	14 55	15 05	15 09	15 15	15 25	15 35	15 45	15 55	15 59	16 05	16 15	16 25	16 35	16 45	16 55
Five Ways	d	14 08		14 18	14 28	14 38	14 47	14 58	15 08		15 18	15 28	15 38	15 48	15 58		16 08	16 18	16 28	16 38	16 48	16 58
Birmingham New Street 12	a	14 13	14 23	14 23	14 33	14 43	14 53	15 03	15 13	15 21	15 23	15 33	15 43	15 53	16 03	16 09	16 13	16 23	16 33	16 43	16 53	17 03
	d	14 15		14 25	14 35	14 45	14 55	15 05	15 15		15 25	15 35	15 45	15 55	16 05		16 15	16 25	16 35	16 45	16 55	17 05
Duddeston	d	14 19				14 49			15 19				15 49				16 19			16 49		
Aston	d	14 22		14 30	14 41	14 52	15 00	15 11	15 22		15 30	15 41	15 52	16 00	16 11		16 22	16 31	16 41	16 52	17 01	17 12
Gravelly Hill	d	14 25		14 34	14 45	14 55	15 04	15 15	15 25		15 34	15 45	15 55	16 04	16 15		16 25	16 34	16 45	16 55	17 04	17 15
Erdington	d	14 28		14 36	14 47	14 58	15 06	15 17	15 28		15 36	15 47	15 58	16 06	16 17		16 28	16 36	16 47	16 58	17 07	17 17
Chester Road	d	14 30		14 38	14 49	15 00	15 08	15 19	15 30		15 38	15 49	16 00	16 08	16 19		16 30	16 38	16 49	17 00	17 09	17 19
Wylde Green	d	14 32		14 40	14 51	15 02	15 10	15 21	15 32		15 40	15 51	16 02	16 10	16 21		16 33	16 40	16 51	17 02	17 11	17 21
Sutton Coldfield	d	14 35		14 43	14 54	15 05	15 13	15 24	15 35		15 43	15 54	16 05	16 13	16 24		16 35	16 43	16 54	17 05	17 14	17 24
Four Oaks	d	14a41		14 47	14 57	15a11	15 17	15 27	15a41		15 47	15 57	16a11	16 17	16 27		16a41	16 46	16 57	17a11	17 17	17 28
Butlers Lane	d			14 49	14 59		15 19	15 29			15 49	15 59		16 19	16 29			16 48	16 59		17 19	17 30
Blake Street	d			14 51	15 01		15 21	15 31			15 51	16 01		16 21	16 31			16 51	17 01		17 21	17 32
Shenstone	d			14 55			15 25				15 55			16 25				16 55			17 25	17 36
Lichfield City	d			15a03	15 09		15a33	15 39			16a03	16 09		16a33	16 39			17a03	17 09		17 30	17 41
Lichfield Trent Valley	a				15 15			15 45				16 15			16 45				17 15		17 35	17 46

		LM	LM	LM	LM	LM	LM	LM	LM	LM	LM	LM	LM	XC ◇ A	LM	LM	LM	LM	LM	LM	LM	LM	LM
Bromsgrove	d	16 44								17 49							18 42						
Redditch	d				16 57			17 27				17 57				18 27				18 57			19 27
Alvechurch	d				17 02			17 32				18 02				18 32				19 02			19 32
Barnt Green	d	16 50			17 08			17 38				18 08				18 38	18 49			19 08			19 38
Longbridge	d		16 53	17 03	17 13	17 23	17 33	17 43	17 53		18 03	18 13	18 23		18 33	18 43		18 53	19 03	19 13	19 23	19 33	19 43
Northfield	d		16 55	17 05	17 15	17 25	17 35	17 45	17 55		18 05	18 15	18 25		18 35	18 45		18 55	19 05	19 15	19 25	19 35	19 45
Kings Norton	d		16 57	17 07	17 17	17 27	17 37	17 47	17 57		18 07	18 17	18 27		18 37	18 47		18 57	19 07	19 17	19 27	19 37	19 47
Bournville	d		17 00	17 10	17 20	17 30	17 40	17 50	18 00		18 10	18 20	18 30		18 40	18 50		19 00	19 10	19 20	19 30	19 40	19 50
Selly Oak	d		17 02	17 12	17 22	17 32	17 42	17 52	18 02		18 12	18 22	18 32		18 42	18 52		19 02	19 12	19 22	19 32	19 42	19 52
University	d	17 00	17 05	17 15	17 25	17 35	17 45	17 55	18 04	18 09	18 15	18 25	18 34	18 39	18 44	18 55	18 59	19 05	19 15	19 25	19 35	19 45	19 55
Five Ways	d		17 08	17 18	17 28	17 38	17 48	17 58	18 07		18 18	18 28	18 37		18 47	18 58		19 08	19 18	19 28	19 38	19 48	19 58
Birmingham New Street 12	a	17 14	17 13	17 23	17 34	17 43	17 53	18 03	18 13	18 21	18 23	18 33	18 43	18 45	18 53	19 03	19 12	19 13	19 23	19 33	19 43	19 53	20 03
	d		17 15	17 25	17 35	17 45	17 55	18 05	18 15		18 25	18 35	18 45		18 55	19 05		19 15		19 35			20 05
Duddeston	d		17 19			17 49			18 19		18 29		18 49		18 59			19 19		19 39			20 09
Aston	d		17 22	17 31	17 42	17 52	18 01	18 11	18 22		18 32	18 41	18 52		19 02	19 11		19 22		19 42			20 12
Gravelly Hill	d		17 25	17 34	17 45	17 55	18 04	18 14	18 25		18 35	18 45	18 55		19 05	19 15		19 25		19 45			20 15
Erdington	d		17 28	17 36	17 47	17 58	18 06	18 17	18 28		18 38	18 47	18 58		19 08	19 17		19 28		19 47			20 17
Chester Road	d		17 30	17 38	17 49	18 00	18 08	18 19	18 30		18 40	18 49	19 00		19 10	19 19		19 30		19 49			20 19
Wylde Green	d		17 32	17 40	17 51	18 02	18 10	18 21	18 32		18 42	18 51	19 02		19 12	19 21		19 32		19 51			20 21
Sutton Coldfield	d		17 35	17 43	17 54	18 05	18 14	18 24	18 35		18 45	18 54	19 05		19 15	19 24		19 35		19 54			20 24
Four Oaks	d		17a41	17 47	17 58	18a11	18 17	18 27	18a41		18 48	18 57	19a11		19 18	19 27		19a41		19 57			20 27
Butlers Lane	d			17 49	18 00		18 19	18 29			18 50	18 59			19 20	19 29				19 59			20 29
Blake Street	d			17 51	18 02		18 21	18 31			18 53	19 01			19 22	19 31				20 01			20 31
Shenstone	d			17 55	18 06		18 25				18 57				19 26					20 05			20 35
Lichfield City	d			18 00	18 11		18a33	18 39			19a03	19 09			19a33	19 39				20 10			20 40
Lichfield Trent Valley	a			18 05	18 16			18 45				19 15				19 45				20 15			20 45

		LM	LM	LM	LM	LM	LM	LM	LM	LM	LM	LM	LM	LM	XC ◇	LM	LM	LM	LM	LM	LM
Bromsgrove	d				20 10				20 59						22 20		22 28				
Redditch	d			19 57			20 27			20 57		21 27		21 57				22 27		22 57	
Alvechurch	d			20 02			20 32			21 02		21 32		22 02				22 32		23 02	
Barnt Green	d			20 08			20 38			21 08		21 38		22 08				22 38		23 08	
Longbridge	d	19 53	20 03	20 13		20 30	20 43	21 00		21 13	21 30	21 43	22 00	22 13		22 30		22 43	22 52	23 13	23 27
Northfield	d	19 55	20 05	20 15		20 32	20 45	21 02		21 15	21 32	21 45	22 02	22 15		22 32		22 45	22 54	23 15	23 29
Kings Norton	d	19 57	20 07	20 17		20 34	20 47	21 04		21 17	21 34	21 47	22 04	22 17		22 34		22 47	22 56	23 17	23 31
Bournville	d	20 00	20 10	20 20		20 37	20 50	21 07		21 20	21 37	21 50	22 07	22 20		22 37		22 50	22 59	23 20	23 34
Selly Oak	d	20 02	20 12	20 22		20 39	20 52	21 09		21 22	21 39	21 52	22 09	22 22		22 39		22 52	23 01	23 22	23 36
University	d	20 05	20 15	20 25	20 29	20 41	20 55	21 12	21 16	21 25	21 42	21 55	22 12	22 25		22 42	22 46	22 55	23 04	23 25	23 39
Five Ways	d	20 08	20 18	20 28		20 44	20 58	21 15		21 28	21 45	21 58	22 15	22 28		22 45		22 58	23 07	23 28	23 42
Birmingham New Street 12	a	20 13	20 23	20 33	20 44	20 50	21 03	21 20	21 27	21 33	21 50	22 04	22 20	22 33	22 48	22 50	22 57	23 03	23 12	23 34	23 47
	d			20 35			21 05			21 35		22 05		22 35		22 55			23 14		
Duddeston	d			20 39			21 09			21 39		22 09		22 39		22 59			23 18		
Aston	d			20 42			21 12			21 42		22 12		22 42		23 02			23 21		
Gravelly Hill	d			20 45			21 15			21 45		22 15		22 45		23 05			23 24		
Erdington	d			20 47			21 17			21 47		22 17		22 47		23 07			23 26		
Chester Road	d			20 49			21 19			21 49		22 19		22 49		23 09			23 28		
Wylde Green	d			20 51			21 21			21 51		22 21		22 51		23 11			23 30		
Sutton Coldfield	d			20 54			21 24			21 54		22 24		22 54		23 14			23 33		
Four Oaks	d			20 57			21 27			21 57		22 27		22 57		23 17			23 36		
Butlers Lane	d			20 59			21 29			21 59		22 29		22 59		23 19			23 38		
Blake Street	d			21 01			21 31			22 01		22 31		23 01		23a24			23 40		
Shenstone	d			21 05			21 35			22 05		22 35		23 05					23 44		
Lichfield City	d			21 10			21 40			22 10		22 40		23 10					23a53		
Lichfield Trent Valley	a			21 15			21 45			22 15		22 45		23 15							

For general notes see front of timetable
For details of catering facilities see
Directory of Train Operators

A To Nottingham (Table 57)

Table 69

Redditch and Longbridge → Birmingham → Lichfield

Network Diagram - see first page of Table 67

		LM	LM	LM	LM	LM	LM	LM	LM	LM	LM	LM	XC	LM	LM	LM	LM	LM	LM	LM	XC	LM	LM	LM	LM	LM
													A								B					
Bromsgrove	d								06 50				07 23				07 50				08 23				08 43	
Redditch	d						06 27				06 57				07 27				07 57				08 27			
Alvechurch	d						06 32				07 02				07 32				08 02				08 32			
Barnt Green	d						06 38				07 08				07 38				08 08				08 38			
Longbridge	d			06 13	06 23	06 33	06 43	06 53		07 03	07 13	07 23		07 33	07 43	07 53		08 03	08 13	08 23		08 33	08 43	08 53		09 03
Northfield	d			06 15	06 25	06 35	06 45	06 55		07 05	07 15	07 25		07 35	07 45	07 55		08 05	08 15	08 25		08 35	08 45	08 55		09 05
Kings Norton	d			06 17	06 27	06 37	06 47	06 57		07 07	07 17	07 27		07 37	07 47	07 57		08 07	08 17	08 27		08 37	08 47	08 57		09 07
Bournville	d			06 20	06 30	06 40	06 50	07 00		07 10	07 20	07 30		07 40	07 50	08 00		08 10	08 20	08 30		08 40	08 50	09 00		09 10
Selly Oak	d			06 22	06 32	06 42	06 52	07 02		07 12	07 22	07 32		07 42	07 52	08 02		08 12	08 22	08 32		08 42	08 52	09 02		09 12
University	d			06 25	06 35	06 45	06 55	07 05	07 09	07 15	07 25	07 35		07 45	07 55	08 05	08 09	08 15	08 25	08 35	08 39	08 45	08 55	09 05	08 59	09 15
Five Ways	d			06 28	06 38	06 48	06 58	07 08		07 18	07 28	07 38		07 48	07 58	08 08		08 18	08 28	08 38		08 48	08 58	09 08		09 18
Birmingham New Street 12	a			06 33	06 43	06 53	07 03	07 13	07 16	07 23	07 33	07 43	07 45	07 53	08 03	08 13	08 16	08 23	08 33	08 43	08 46	08 53	09 03	09 13	09 14	09 23
	d	05 57	06 25	06 35		06 55	07 05			07 25	07 35			07 55	08 05			08 24	08 35			08 55	09 05			09 25
Duddeston	d	06 01	06 29			06 59	07 10				07 40				08 10				08 40				09 10			
Aston	d	06 04	06 32			07 02	07 13			07 30	07 43			08 00	08 13			08 29	08 43			09 00	09 13			09 30
Gravelly Hill	d	06 07	06 35			07 05	07 16			07 33	07 46			08 03	08 16			08 32	08 46			09 03	09 16			09 33
Erdington	d	06 09	06 38	06 46		07 08	07 19			07 36	07 48			08 06	08 18			08 35	08 48			09 06	09 18			09 36
Chester Road	d	06 11	06 39	06 47		07 09	07 20			07 37	07 50			08 07	08 20			08 37	08 50			09 08	09 20			09 37
Wylde Green	d	06 13	06 41	06 49		07 11	07 22			07 39	07 52			08 09	08 22			08 39	08 52			09 10	09 22			09 39
Sutton Coldfield	d	06 16	06 44	06 52		07 14	07 25			07 42	07 55			08 12	08 25			08 42	08 55			09 13	09 25			09 42
Four Oaks	d	06 19	06 48	06 55		07 18	07 29			07 46	07 58			08 16	08 28			08 45	08 58			09 16	09 28			09 46
Butlers Lane	d	06 21	06 50	06 57		07 20	07 31			07 48	08 00			08 18	08 30			08 48	09 00			09 18	09 30			09 48
Blake Street	d	06 23	06 52	06 59		07 22	07 33			07 50	08 02			08 20	08 32			08 50	09 02			09 20	09 32			09 50
Shenstone	d	06 27	06 56			07 26	07 37			07 54	08 06			08 24	08 36			08 54	09 06			09 24	09 36			09 54
Lichfield City	d	06a37	07 01	07a09		07a33	07 42			08a03	08 11			08a33	08 41			09a03	09 11			09a33	09 41			10a03
Lichfield Trent Valley	a		07 06				07 46				08 16				08 46				09 16				09 46			

		LM		LM	XC	XC	LM	LM	LM	LM	LM	LM	LM	LM	LM	LM	LM	LM	LM	LM	LM	LM	LM	LM	LM	LM
					◇ C	◇ D																				
Bromsgrove	d				09 20	09 21				09 50							10 50							11 50		
Redditch	d	08 57						09 27				09 57			10 27				10 57			11 27				11 57
Alvechurch	d	09 02						09 32				10 02			10 32				11 02			11 32				12 02
Barnt Green	d	09 08						09 38				10 08			10 38				11 08			11 38				12 08
Longbridge	d	09 13		09 23			09 33	09 43	09 53		10 03	10 13	10 23	10 33	10 43	10 53		11 03	11 13	11 23	11 33	11 43	11 53		12 03	12 13
Northfield	d	09 15		09 25			09 35	09 45	09 55		10 05	10 15	10 25	10 35	10 45	10 55		11 05	11 15	11 25	11 35	11 45	11 55		12 05	12 15
Kings Norton	d	09 17		09 27			09 37	09 47	09 57		10 07	10 17	10 27	10 37	10 47	10 57		11 07	11 17	11 27	11 37	11 47	11 57		12 07	12 17
Bournville	d	09 20		09 30			09 40	09 50	10 00		10 10	10 20	10 30	10 40	10 50	11 00		11 10	11 20	11 30	11 40	11 50	12 00		12 10	12 20
Selly Oak	d	09 22		09 32			09 42	09 52	10 02		10 12	10 22	10 32	10 42	10 52	11 02		11 12	11 22	11 32	11 42	11 52	12 02		12 12	12 22
University	d	09 25		09 35			09 45	09 55	10 05	10 09	10 15	10 25	10 35	10 44	10 55	11 05	11 09	11 15	11 25	11 35	11 45	11 55	12 05	12 09	12 15	12 25
Five Ways	d	09 28		09 38			09 48	09 58	10 08		10 18	10 28	10 38	10 47	10 58	11 08		11 18	11 28	11 38	11 48	11 58	12 08		12 18	12 28
Birmingham New Street 12	a	09 33		09 43	09 45	09 45	09 53	10 03	10 13	10 21	10 23	10 33	10 43	10 53	11 02	11 13	11 21	11 23	11 33	11 43	11 53	12 03	12 13	12 21	12 23	12 33
	d	09 35					09 55	10 05			10 25	10 35		10 55	11 05			11 25	11 35		11 55	12 05			12 25	12 35
Duddeston	d	09 40						10 10				10 40			11 10				11 40			12 10				12 40
Aston	d	09 43					10 00	10 13			10 30	10 43		11 00	11 13			11 30	11 43		12 00	12 13			12 30	12 43
Gravelly Hill	d	09 46					10 03	10 16			10 33	10 46		11 03	11 16			11 33	11 46		12 03	12 16			12 33	12 46
Erdington	d	09 48					10 06	10 18			10 36	10 48		11 06	11 18			11 36	11 48		12 06	12 18			12 36	12 48
Chester Road	d	09 50					10 07	10 20			10 37	10 50		11 07	11 20			11 37	11 50		12 07	12 20			12 37	12 50
Wylde Green	d	09 52					10 09	10 22			10 39	10 52		11 09	11 22			11 39	11 52		12 09	12 22			12 39	12 52
Sutton Coldfield	d	09 55					10 12	10 25			10 42	10 55		11 12	11 25			11 42	11 55		12 12	12 25			12 42	12 55
Four Oaks	d	09 58					10 16	10 28			10 46	10 58		11 16	11 28			11 46	11 58		12 16	12 28			12 46	12 58
Butlers Lane	d	10 00					10 18	10 30			10 48	11 00		11 18	11 30			11 48	12 00		12 18	12 30			12 48	13 00
Blake Street	d	10 02					10 20	10 32			10 50	11 02		11 20	11 32			11 50	12 02		12 20	12 32			12 50	13 02
Shenstone	d	10 06					10 24	10 36			10 54	11 06		11 24	11 36			11 54	12 06		12 24	12 36			12 54	13 06
Lichfield City	d	10 11					10a33	10 41			11a03	11 11		11a33	11 41			12a03	12 11		12a33	12 41			13a03	13 11
Lichfield Trent Valley	a	10 16						10 46				11 16			11 46				12 16			12 46				13 16

		LM	XC	LM		LM	LM	LM	LM	LM	LM	LM	LM	LM	LM	LM	LM	LM	LM	LM	LM	LM	LM	LM	LM	LM
			◇ A																							
Bromsgrove	d							12 50							13 50							14 50				
Redditch	d					12 27				12 57			13 27				13 57			14 27				14 57		
Alvechurch	d					12 32				13 02			13 32				14 02			14 32				15 02		
Barnt Green	d					12 38				13 08			13 38				14 08			14 38				15 08		
Longbridge	d	12 23		12 33		12 43	12 53		13 03	13 13	13 23	13 33	13 43	13 53		14 03	14 13	14 23	14 33	14 43	14 53		15 03	15 13	15 23	15 33
Northfield	d	12 25		12 35		12 45	12 55		13 05	13 15	13 25	13 35	13 45	13 55		14 05	14 15	14 25	14 35	14 45	14 55		15 05	15 15	15 25	15 35
Kings Norton	d	12 27		12 37		12 47	12 57		13 07	13 17	13 27	13 37	13 47	13 57		14 07	14 17	14 27	14 37	14 47	14 57		15 07	15 17	15 27	15 37
Bournville	d	12 30		12 40		12 50	13 00		13 10	13 20	13 30	13 40	13 50	14 00		14 10	14 20	14 30	14 40	14 50	15 00		15 10	15 20	15 30	15 40
Selly Oak	d	12 32		12 42		12 52	13 02		13 12	13 22	13 32	13 42	13 52	14 02		14 12	14 22	14 32	14 42	14 52	15 02		15 12	15 22	15 32	15 42
University	d	12 35	12 39	12 44		12 55	13 05	13 09	13 15	13 25	13 35	13 45	13 55	14 05	14 09	14 15	14 25	14 35	14 44	14 55	15 05	15 09	15 15	15 25	15 35	15 45
Five Ways	d	12 38		12 47		12 58	13 08		13 18	13 28	13 38	13 48	13 58	14 08		14 18	14 28	14 38	14 47	14 58	15 08		15 18	15 28	15 38	15 48
Birmingham New Street 12	a	12 43	12 46	12 53		13 03	13 13	13 21	13 23	13 33	13 43	13 53	14 03	14 13	14 21	14 23	14 33	14 43	14 53	15 03	15 13	15 21	15 23	15 33	15 43	15 53
	d			12 55		13 05			13 25	13 35		13 55	14 05			14 25	14 35		14 55	15 05			15 25	15 35		15 55
Duddeston	d					13 10				13 40			14 10				14 40			15 10				15 40		
Aston	d			13 00		13 13			13 30	13 43		14 00	14 13			14 30	14 43		15 00	15 13			15 30	15 43		16 00
Gravelly Hill	d			13 03		13 16			13 33	13 46		14 03	14 16			14 33	14 46		15 03	15 16			15 33	15 46		16 03
Erdington	d			13 06		13 18			13 36	13 48		14 06	14 18			14 36	14 48		15 06	15 18			15 36	15 48		16 06
Chester Road	d			13 07		13 20			13 37	13 50		14 07	14 20			14 37	14 50		15 07	15 20			15 37	15 50		16 07
Wylde Green	d			13 09		13 22			13 39	13 52		14 09	14 22			14 39	14 52		15 09	15 22			15 39	15 52		16 09
Sutton Coldfield	d			13 12		13 25			13 42	13 55		14 12	14 25			14 42	14 55		15 12	15 25			15 42	15 55		16 12
Four Oaks	d			13 16		13 28			13 46	13 58		14 16	14 28			14 46	14 58		15 16	15 28			15 46	15 58		16 16
Butlers Lane	d			13 18		13 30			13 48	14 00		14 18	14 30			14 48	15 00		15 18	15 30			15 48	16 00		16 18
Blake Street	d			13 20		13 32			13 50	14 02		14 20	14 32			14 50	15 02		15 20	15 32			15 50	16 02		16 20
Shenstone	d			13 24		13 36			13 54	14 06		14 24	14 36			14 54	15 06		15 24	15 36			15 54	16 06		16 24
Lichfield City	d			13a33		13 41			14a03	14 11		14a33	14 41			15a03	15 11		15a33	15 41			16a03	16 11		16a33
Lichfield Trent Valley	a					13 46				14 16			14 46				15 16			15 46				16 16		

For general notes see front of timetable
For details of catering facilities see Directory of Train Operators

A To Nottingham (Table 57)
B From Gloucester to Nottingham (Table 57)
C From 2 February. To Nottingham (Table 57)
D Until 26 January. To Nottingham (Table 57)

Redditch and Longbridge → Birmingham → Lichfield

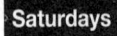

Network Diagram - see first page of Table 67

		LM	LM	LM	LM	LM		LM	LM	LM	LM	LM	LM	LM	LM	LM	LM	LM	LM	LM	LM	LM	XC ◇ A	LM	LM	LM
Bromsgrove	d			15 50								16 50							17 50							
Redditch	d	15 27				15 57				16 27				16 57			17 27				17 57				18 27	
Alvechurch	d	15 32				16 02				16 32				17 02			17 32				18 02				18 32	
Barnt Green	d	15 38				16 08				16 38				17 08			17 38				18 08				18 38	
Longbridge	d	15 43	15 53		16 03	16 13		16 23	16 33	16 43	16 53		17 03	17 13	17 23	17 33	17 43	17 53		18 03	18 13	18 23		18 33	18 43	18 53
Northfield	d	15 45	15 55		16 05	16 15		16 25	16 35	16 45	16 55		17 05	17 15	17 25	17 35	17 45	17 55		18 05	18 15	18 25		18 35	18 45	18 55
Kings Norton	d	15 47	15 57		16 07	16 17		16 27	16 37	16 47	16 57		17 07	17 17	17 27	17 37	17 47	17 57		18 07	18 17	18 27		18 37	18 47	18 57
Bournville	d	15 50	16 00		16 10	16 20		16 30	16 40	16 50	17 00		17 10	17 20	17 30	17 40	17 50	18 00		18 10	18 20	18 30		18 40	18 50	19 00
Selly Oak	d	15 52	16 02		16 12	16 22		16 32	16 42	16 52	17 02		17 12	17 22	17 32	17 42	17 52	18 02		18 12	18 22	18 32		18 42	18 52	19 02
University	d	15 55	16 05	16 09	16 15	16 25		16 35	16 44	16 55	17 05	17 09	17 15	17 25	17 35	17 45	17 55	18 04	18 09	18 14	18 25	18 35	18 39	18 44	18 55	19 05
Five Ways	d	15 58	16 08		16 18	16 28		16 38	16 47	16 58	17 08		17 18	17 28	17 38	17 48	17 58	18 07		18 17	18 28	18 38		18 47	18 58	19 08
Birmingham New Street 12	a	16 03	16 13	16 21	16 23	16 33		16 43	16 53	17 03	17 13	17 21	17 23	17 33	17 43	17 53	18 03	18 13	18 21	18 23	18 33	18 43	18 46	18 53	19 03	19 13
	d	16 05			16 25	16 35			16 55	17 05			17 25	17 35		17 55	18 05			18 25	18 35			18 55	19 05	
Duddeston	d	16 10				16 40				17 10				17 40			18 10				18 40				19 10	
Aston	d	16 13			16 30	16 43			17 00	17 13			17 30	17 43		18 00	18 13			18 30	18 43			19 00	19 13	
Gravelly Hill	d	16 16			16 33	16 46			17 03	17 16			17 33	17 46		18 03	18 16			18 33	18 46			19 03	19 16	
Erdington	d	16 18			16 36	16 48			17 06	17 18			17 36	17 48		18 06	18 18			18 36	18 48			19 06	19 18	
Chester Road	d	16 20			16 37	16 50			17 07	17 20			17 37	17 50		18 07	18 20			18 37	18 50			19 07	19 20	
Wylde Green	d	16 22			16 39	16 52			17 09	17 22			17 39	17 52		18 09	18 22			18 39	18 52			19 09	19 22	
Sutton Coldfield	d	16 25			16 42	16 55			17 12	17 25			17 42	17 55		18 12	18 25			18 42	18 55			19 12	19 25	
Four Oaks	d	16 28			16 46	16 58			17 16	17 28			17 46	17 58		18 16	18 28			18 46	18 58			19 16	19 28	
Butlers Lane	d	16 30			16 48	17 00			17 18	17 30			17 48	18 00		18 18	18 30			18 48	19 00			19 18	19 30	
Blake Street	d	16 32			16 50	17 02			17 20	17 32			17 50	18 02		18 20	18 32			18 50	19 02			19 20	19 32	
Shenstone	d	16 36			16 54	17 06			17 24	17 36			17 54	18 06		18 24	18 36			18 54	19 06			19 24	19 36	
Lichfield City	d	16 41			17a03	17 11			17a33	17 41			18a03	18 11		18a33	18 41			19a03	19 11			19a33	19 41	
Lichfield Trent Valley	a	16 46				17 16				17 46				18 16			18 46				19 16				19 46	

		LM	LM	LM	LM	LM	LM	LM	LM	LM	LM	LM	LM	LM	LM	LM	LM	LM	LM	LM	LM	LM	LM	LM		
Bromsgrove	d	18 50												21 00												
Redditch	d			18 57			19 27			19 57		20 27			20 57		21 27		21 57		22 27		22 57			
Alvechurch	d			19 02			19 32			20 02		20 32			21 02		21 32		22 02		22 32		23 02			
Barnt Green	d			19 08			19 38			20 08		20 38			21 08		21 38		22 08		22 38		23 08			
Longbridge	d		19 03	19 13	19 23	19 33	19 43	19 53	20 03	20 13	20 30	20 43	21 00		21 13	21 30	21 43	22 00	22 13	22 30	22 43	22 52	23 13	23 24		
Northfield	d		19 05	19 15	19 25	19 35	19 45	19 55	20 05	20 15	20 32	20 45	21 02		21 15	21 32	21 45	22 02	22 15	22 32	22 45	22 54	23 15	23 26		
Kings Norton	d		19 07	19 17	19 27	19 37	19 47	19 57	20 07	20 17	20 34	20 47	21 04		21 17	21 34	21 47	22 04	22 17	22 34	22 47	22 56	23 17	23 28		
Bournville	d		19 10	19 20	19 30	19 40	19 50	20 00	20 10	20 20	20 37	20 50	21 07		21 20	21 37	21 50	22 07	22 20	22 37	22 50	22 59	23 20	23 31		
Selly Oak	d		19 12	19 22	19 32	19 42	19 52	20 02	20 12	20 22	20 39	20 52	21 09		21 22	21 39	21 52	22 09	22 22	22 39	22 52	23 01	23 22	23 33		
University	d	19 09	19 15	19 25	19 35	19 45	19 55	20 05	20 15	20 25	20 42	20 55	21 12	21 16	21 25	21 42	21 55	22 12	22 25	22 42	22 55	23 04	23 25	23 36		
Five Ways	d		19 18	19 28	19 38	19 48	19 58	20 08	20 18	20 28	20 45	20 58	21 15		21 28	21 45	21 58	22 15	22 28	22 45	22 58	23 07	23 28	23 39		
Birmingham New Street 12	a	19 21	19 23	19 33	19 43	19 53	20 03	20 13	20 23	20 33	20 50	21 03	21 20	21 28	21 33	21 50	22 03	22 20	22 33	22 50	23 03	23 12	23 33	23 44		
	d			19 35			20 05			20 35		21 05			21 35		22 05		22 35		23 05	23 14				
Duddeston	d			19 39			20 09			20 39		21 09			21 39		22 09		22 39		23 09	23 18				
Aston	d			19 42			20 12			20 42		21 12			21 42		22 12		22 42		23 12	23 21				
Gravelly Hill	d			19 45			20 15			20 45		21 15			21 45		22 15		22 45		23 15	23 24				
Erdington	d			19 47			20 17			20 47		21 17			21 47		22 17		22 47		23 17	23 26				
Chester Road	d			19 49			20 19			20 49		21 19			21 49		22 19		22 49		23 19	23 28				
Wylde Green	d			19 51			20 21			20 51		21 21			21 51		22 21		22 51		23 21	23 30				
Sutton Coldfield	d			19 54			20 24			20 54		21 24			21 54		22 24		22 54		23 24	23 33				
Four Oaks	d			19 57			20 27			20 57		21 27			21 57		22 27		22 57		23 27	23 36				
Butlers Lane	d			19 59			20 29			20 59		21 29			21 59		22 29		22 59		23 29	23 38				
Blake Street	d			20 01			20 31			21 01		21 31			22 01		22 31		23 01		23a34	23 40				
Shenstone	d			20 05			20 35			21 05		21 35			22 05		22 35		23 05			23 44				
Lichfield City	d			20 10			20 40			21 10		21 40			22 10		22 40		23 10			23a53				
Lichfield Trent Valley	a			20 16			20 46			21 16		21 46			22 16		22 46		23 16							

Sundays

until 23 March

		LM	LM	LM		LM	LM	LM		LM	LM	LM		LM	LM	LM		LM	LM	LM		LM	LM	LM		LM
Bromsgrove	d																			15 09						16 51
Redditch	d			09 31		10 01	10 31	11 01		11 31	12 01	12 31		13 01	13 31	14 01		14 31	15 01			15 31	16 01	16 31		
Alvechurch	d			09 36		10 06	10 36	11 06		11 36	12 06	12 36		13 06	13 36	14 06		14 36	15 06			15 36	16 06	16 36		
Barnt Green	d			09 41		10 11	10 41	11 11		11 41	12 11	12 41		13 11	13 41	14 11		14 41	15 11			15 41	16 11	16 41		
Longbridge	d			09 46		10 16	10 46	11 16		11 46	12 16	12 46		13 16	13 46	14 16		14 46	15 16			15 46	16 16	16 46		
Northfield	d			09 48		10 18	10 48	11 18		11 48	12 18	12 48		13 18	13 48	14 18		14 48	15 18			15 48	16 18	16 48		
Kings Norton	d			09 51		10 21	10 51	11 21		11 51	12 21	12 51		13 21	13 51	14 21		14 51	15 21			15 51	16 21	16 51		
Bournville	d			09 53		10 23	10 53	11 23		11 53	12 23	12 53		13 23	13 53	14 23		14 53	15 23			15 53	16 23	16 53		
Selly Oak	d			09 55		10 25	10 55	11 25		11 55	12 25	12 55		13 25	13 55	14 25		14 55	15 25			15 55	16 25	16 55		
University	d			09 57		10 27	10 57	11 27		11 57	12 27	12 57		13 27	13 57	14 27		14 57	15 27			15 57	16 27	16 57		
Five Ways	d			10 01		10 31	11 01	11 31		12 01	12 31	13 01		13 31	14 01	14 31		15 01	15 31			16 01	16 31	17 01		
Birmingham New Street 12	a			10 06		10 36	11 06	11 36		12 06	12 36	13 06		13 36	14 06	14 36		15 06	15 36	15 40		16 06	16 36	17 06		17 17
	d	09 12	09 39	10 09		10 39	11 09	11 39		12 09	12 39	13 09		13 39	14 09	14 39		15 09	15 39			16 09	16 39	17 09		
Duddeston	d		09 43	10 13		10 43	11 13	11 43		12 13	12 43	13 13		13 43	14 13	14 43		15 13	15 43			16 13	16 43	17 13		
Aston	d		09 46	10 16		10 46	11 16	11 46		12 16	12 46	13 16		13 46	14 16	14 46		15 16	15 46			16 16	16 46	17 16		
Gravelly Hill	d		09 49	10 19		10 49	11 19	11 49		12 19	12 49	13 19		13 49	14 19	14 49		15 19	15 49			16 19	16 49	17 19		
Erdington	d		09 51	10 21		10 51	11 21	11 51		12 21	12 51	13 21		13 51	14 21	14 51		15 21	15 51			16 21	16 51	17 21		
Chester Road	d		09 53	10 23		10 53	11 23	11 53		12 23	12 53	13 23		13 53	14 23	14 53		15 23	15 53			16 23	16 53	17 23		
Wylde Green	d		09 55	10 25		10 55	11 25	11 55		12 25	12 55	13 25		13 55	14 25	14 55		15 25	15 55			16 25	16 55	17 25		
Sutton Coldfield	d	09 24	09 58	10 28		10 58	11 28	11 58		12 28	12 58	13 28		13 58	14 28	14 58		15 28	15 58			16 28	16 58	17 28		
Four Oaks	d	09 28	10 01	10 31		11 01	11 31	12 01		12 31	13 01	13 31		14 01	14 31	15 01		15 31	16 01			16 31	17 01	17 31		
Butlers Lane	d	09 30	10 03	10 33		11 03	11 33	12 03		12 33	13 03	13 33		14 03	14 33	15 03		15 33	16 03			16 33	17 03	17 33		
Blake Street	d	09 32	10 05	10 35		11 05	11 35	12 05		12 35	13 05	13 35		14 05	14 35	15 05		15 35	16 05			16 35	17 05	17 35		
Shenstone	d	09 36	10 09	10 39		11 09	11 39	12 09		12 39	13 09	13 39		14 09	14 39	15 09		15 39	16 09			16 39	17 09	17 39		
Lichfield City	d	09 41	10 14	10 44		11 14	11 44	12 14		12 44	13 14	13 44		14 14	14 44	15 14		15 44	16 14			16 44	17 14	17 44		
Lichfield Trent Valley	a	09 46	10 19	10 49		11 19	11 49	12 19		12 49	13 19	13 49		14 19	14 49	15 19		15 49	16 19			16 49	17 19	17 49		

For general notes see front of timetable
For details of catering facilities see
Directory of Train Operators

A To Nottingham (Table 57)

Table 69

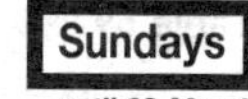

until 23 March

Redditch and Longbridge → Birmingham → Lichfield

Network Diagram - see first page of Table 67

		LM	LM	LM	LM	LM	LM	LM	LM	LM	LM	LM	LM	LM	LM	XC	LM	LM
Bromsgrove	d			17 51						20 13			21 08			22 20		
Redditch	d	17 01	17 31		18 01	18 31	19 01	19 31	20 01		20 31	21 01		21 31	22 01		22 31	23 01
Alvechurch	d	17 06	17 36		18 06	18 36	19 06	19 36	20 06		20 36	21 06		21 36	22 06		22 36	23 06
Barnt Green	d	17 11	17 41		18 11	18 41	19 11	19 41	20 11		20 41	21 11		21 41	22 11		22 41	23 11
Longbridge	d	17 16	17 46		18 16	18 46	19 16	19 46	20 16		20 46	21 16		21 46	22 16		22 46	23 16
Northfield	d	17 18	17 48		18 18	18 48	19 18	19 48	20 18		20 48	21 18		21 48	22 18		22 48	23 18
Kings Norton	d	17 21	17 51		18 21	18 51	19 21	19 51	20 21		20 51	21 21		21 51	22 21		22 51	23 21
Bournville	d	17 23	17 53		18 23	18 53	19 23	19 53	20 23		20 53	21 23		21 53	22 23		22 53	23 23
Selly Oak	d	17 25	17 55		18 25	18 55	19 25	19 55	20 25		20 55	21 25		21 55	22 25		22 55	23 25
University	d	17 27	17 57		18 27	18 57	19 27	19 57	20 27		20 57	21 27		21 57	22 27		22 57	23 27
Five Ways	d	17 31	18 01		18 31	19 01	19 31	20 01	20 31		21 01	21 31		22 01	22 31		23 01	23 31
Birmingham New Street 12	a	17 36	18 07	18 12	18 36	19 06	19 36	20 07	20 36	20 40	21 07	21 36	21 45	22 07	22 36	22 45	23 06	23 36
	d	17 39	18 09		18 39	19 09	19 39	20 09	20 39		21 09	21 39		22 09	22 39		23 09	
Duddeston	d	17 43	18 13		18 43	19 13	19 43	20 13	20 43		21 13	21 43		22 13	22 43		23 13	
Aston	d	17 46	18 16		18 46	19 16	19 46	20 16	20 46		21 16	21 46		22 16	22 46		23 16	
Gravelly Hill	d	17 49	18 19		18 49	19 19	19 49	20 19	20 49		21 19	21 49		22 19	22 49		23 19	
Erdington	d	17 51	18 21		18 51	19 21	19 51	20 21	20 51		21 21	21 51		22 21	22 51		23 21	
Chester Road	d	17 53	18 23		18 53	19 23	19 53	20 23	20 53		21 23	21 53		22 23	22 53		23 23	
Wylde Green	d	17 55	18 25		18 55	19 25	19 55	20 25	20 55		21 25	21 55		22 25	22 55		23 25	
Sutton Coldfield	d	17 58	18 28		18 58	19 28	19 58	20 28	20 58		21 28	21 58		22 28	22 58		23 28	
Four Oaks	d	18 01	18 31		19 01	19 31	20 01	20 31	21 01		21 31	22 01		22 31	23 01		23 31	
Butlers Lane	d	18 03	18 33		19 03	19 33	20 03	20 33	21 03		21 33	22 03		22 33	23 03		23 33	
Blake Street	d	18 05	18 35		19 05	19 35	20 05	20 35	21 05		21 35	22 05		22 35	23 05		23 35	
Shenstone	d	18 09	18 39		19 09	19 39	20 09	20 39	21 09		21 39	22 09		22 39	23 09		23 39	
Lichfield City	d	18 14	18 44		19 14	19 44	20 14	20 44	21 14		21 44	22 14		22 44	23 14		23 44	
Lichfield Trent Valley	a	18 19	18 49		19 19	19 49	20 19	20 49	21 19		21 49	22 19		22 49	23 19		23 49	

Sundays

from 30 March

		LM	LM 🚌	LM	LM	LM 🚌	LM	LM 🚌	LM	LM 🚌	LM	LM 🚌	LM	LM 🚌	LM	LM 🚌	LM	LM 🚌	LM	LM 🚌	LM	LM 🚌	LM
Bromsgrove	d																						
Redditch	d				09 31		10 01		10 31		11 01		11 31		12 01		12 31		13 01		13 31		14 01
Alvechurch	d				09 36		10 06		10 36		11 06		11 36		12 06		12 36		13 06		13 36		14 06
Barnt Green	d				09 41		10 11		10 41		11 11		11 41		12 11		12 41		13 11		13 41		14 11
Longbridge	d				09 46		10 16		10 46		11 16		11 46		12 16		12 46		13 16		13 46		14 16
Northfield	d				09 48		10 18		10 48		11 18		11 48		12 18		12 48		13 18		13 48		14 18
Kings Norton	d				09 51		10 21		10 51		11 21		11 51		12 21		12 51		13 21		13 51		14 21
Bournville	d				09 53		10 23		10 53		11 23		11 53		12 23		12 53		13 23		13 53		14 23
Selly Oak	d				09 55		10 25		10 55		11 25		11 55		12 25		12 55		13 25		13 55		14 25
University	d				09 57		10 27		10 57		11 27		11 57		12 27		12 57		13 27		13 57		14 27
Five Ways	d				10 01		10 31		11 01		11 31		12 01		12 31		13 01		13 31		14 01		14 31
Birmingham New Street 12	a				10 06		10 36		11 06		11 36		12 06		12 36		13 06		13 36		14 06		14 36
	d	09 12		09 39	10 09		10 39		11 09		11 39		12 09		12 39		13 09		13 39		14 09		14 39
Duddeston	d			09 43	10 13		10 43		11 13		11 43		12 13		12 43		13 13		13 43		14 13		14 43
Aston	d			09 46	10 16		10 46		11 16		11 46		12 16		12 46		13 16		13 46		14 16		14 46
Gravelly Hill	d			09 49	10 19		10 49		11 19		11 49		12 19		12 49		13 19		13 49		14 19		14 49
Erdington	d			09 51	10 21		10 51		11 21		11 51		12 21		12 51		13 21		13 51		14 21		14 51
Chester Road	d			09 53	10 23		10 53		11 23		11 53		12 23		12 53		13 23		13 53		14 23		14 53
Wylde Green	d			09 55	10 25		10 55		11 25		11 55		12 25		12 55		13 25		13 55		14 25		14 55
Sutton Coldfield	d	09 24		09 58	10 28		10 58		11 28		11 58		12 28		12 58		13 28		13 58		14 28		14 58
Four Oaks	d	09a27	09 35	10a01	10a31	10 38	11a01	11 08	11a31	11 38	12a01	12 08	12a31	12 38	13a01	13 08	13a31	13 38	14a01	14 08	14a31	14 38	15a01
Butlers Lane	d		09 38			10 41		11 11		11 41		12 11		12 41		13 11		13 41		14 11		14 41	
Blake Street	d		09 42			10 45		11 15		11 45		12 15		12 45		13 15		13 45		14 15		14 45	
Shenstone	d		09 49			10 52		11 22		11 52		12 22		12 52		13 22		13 52		14 22		14 52	
Lichfield City	d		09 59			11 02		11 32		12 02		12 32		13 02		13 32		14 02		14 32		15 02	
Lichfield Trent Valley	a		10 05			11 08		11 38		12 08		12 38		13 08		13 38		14 08		14 38		15 08	

		LM 🚌	LM	LM 🚌	LM	LM	LM 🚌	LM	LM 🚌	LM	LM 🚌	LM	LM	LM 🚌	LM	LM 🚌	LM	LM	LM 🚌	LM	LM 🚌	LM	LM 🚌
Bromsgrove	d					15 09							16 51					17 51					
Redditch	d		14 31		15 01			15 31		16 01		16 31			17 01		17 31			18 01		18 31	
Alvechurch	d		14 36		15 06			15 36		16 06		16 36			17 06		17 36			18 06		18 36	
Barnt Green	d		14 41		15 11			15 41		16 11		16 41			17 11		17 41			18 11		18 41	
Longbridge	d		14 46		15 16			15 46		16 16		16 46			17 16		17 46			18 16		18 46	
Northfield	d		14 48		15 18			15 48		16 18		16 48			17 18		17 48			18 18		18 48	
Kings Norton	d		14 51		15 21			15 51		16 21		16 51			17 21		17 51			18 21		18 51	
Bournville	d		14 53		15 23			15 53		16 23		16 53			17 23		17 53			18 23		18 53	
Selly Oak	d		14 55		15 25			15 55		16 25		16 55			17 25		17 55			18 25		18 55	
University	d		14 57		15 27			15 57		16 27		16 57			17 27		17 57			18 27		18 57	
Five Ways	d		15 01		15 31			16 01		16 31		17 01			17 31		18 01			18 31		19 01	
Birmingham New Street 12	a		15 06		15 36	15 40		16 06		16 36		17 06	17 17		17 36		18 07	18 12		18 36		19 06	
	d		15 09		15 39			16 09		16 39		17 09			17 39		18 09			18 39		19 09	
Duddeston	d		15 13		15 43			16 13		16 43		17 13			17 43		18 13			18 43		19 13	
Aston	d		15 16		15 46			16 16		16 46		17 16			17 46		18 16			18 46		19 16	
Gravelly Hill	d		15 19		15 49			16 19		16 49		17 19			17 49		18 19			18 49		19 19	
Erdington	d		15 21		15 51			16 21		16 51		17 21			17 51		18 21			18 51		19 21	
Chester Road	d		15 23		15 53			16 23		16 53		17 23			17 53		18 23			18 53		19 23	
Wylde Green	d		15 25		15 55			16 25		16 55		17 25			17 55		18 25			18 55		19 25	
Sutton Coldfield	d		15 28		15 58			16 28		16 58		17 28			17 58		18 28			18 58		19 28	
Four Oaks	d	15 08	15a31	15 38	16a01		16 08	16a32	16 38	17a01	17 08	17a31		17 38	18a01	18 08	18a31		18 38	19a01	19 08	19a31	19 38
Butlers Lane	d	15 11		15 41			16 11		16 41		17 11			17 41		18 11			18 41		19 11		19 41
Blake Street	d	15 15		15 45			16 15		16 45		17 15			17 45		18 15			18 45		19 15		19 45
Shenstone	d	15 22		15 52			16 22		16 52		17 22			17 52		18 22			18 52		19 22		19 52
Lichfield City	d	15 32		16 02			16 32		17 02		17 32			18 02		18 32			19 02		19 32		20 02
Lichfield Trent Valley	a	15 38		16 08			16 38		17 08		17 38			18 08		18 38			19 08		19 38		20 08

For general notes see front of timetable
For details of catering facilities see
Directory of Train Operators

Table 69

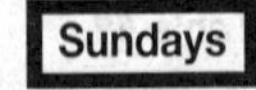

Sundays

from 30 March

Redditch and Longbridge → Birmingham → Lichfield

Network Diagram - see first page of Table 67

		LM	LM 🚌		LM	LM 🚌	LM	LM	LM 🚌	LM		LM 🚌	LM	LM	LM 🚌	LM	LM 🚌		LM	XC	LM 🚌	LM	LM	LM 🚌		
Bromsgrove	d							20 13						21 08						22 20						
Redditch	d	19 01			19 31		20 01			20 31			21 01			21 31			22 01			22 31	23 01			
Alvechurch	d	19 06			19 36		20 06			20 36			21 06			21 36			22 06			22 36	23 06			
Barnt Green	d	19 11			19 41		20 11			20 41			21 11			21 41			22 11			22 41	23 11			
Longbridge	d	19 16			19 46		20 16			20 46			21 16			21 46			22 16			22 46	23 16			
Northfield	d	19 18			19 48		20 18			20 48			21 18			21 48			22 18			22 48	23 18			
Kings Norton	d	19 21			19 51		20 21			20 51			21 21			21 51			22 21			22 51	23 21			
Bournville	d	19 23			19 53		20 23			20 53			21 23			21 53			22 23			22 53	23 23			
Selly Oak	d	19 25			19 55		20 25			20 55			21 25			21 55			22 25			22 55	23 25			
University	d	19 27			19 57		20 27			20 57			21 27			21 57			22 27			22 57	23 27			
Five Ways	d	19 31			20 01		20 31			21 01			21 31			22 01			22 31			23 01	23 31			
Birmingham New Street 12	a	19 36			20 07		20 36	20 40		21 07			21 36	21 45		22 07			22 36	22 45		23 06	23 36			
	d	19 39			20 09		20 39			21 09			21 39			22 09			22 39			23 09				
Duddeston	d	19 43			20 13		20 43			21 13			21 43			22 13			22 43			23 13				
Aston	d	19 46			20 16		20 46			21 16			21 46			22 16			22 46			23 16				
Gravelly Hill	d	19 49			20 19		20 49			21 19			21 49			22 19			22 49			23 19				
Erdington	d	19 51			20 21		20 51			21 21			21 51			22 21			22 51			23 21				
Chester Road	d	19 53			20 23		20 53			21 23			21 53			22 23			22 53			23 23				
Wylde Green	d	19 55			20 25		20 55			21 25			21 55			22 25			22 55			23 25				
Sutton Coldfield	d	19 58			20 28		20 58			21 28			21 58			22 28			22 58			23 28				
Four Oaks	d	20a01	20 08		20a30	20 38	21a01		21 08	21a30		21 38	22a01		22 08	22a31	22 38		23a01		23 08	23a31		23 38		
Butlers Lane	d		20 11			20 41			21 11			21 41			22 11		22 41				23 11			23 41		
Blake Street	d		20 15			20 45			21 15			21 45			22 15		22 45				23 15			23 45		
Shenstone	d		20 22			20 52			21 22			21 52			22 22		22 52				23 22			23 52		
Lichfield City	d		20 32			21 02			21 32			22 02			22 32		23 02				23 32			00 02		
Lichfield Trent Valley	a		20 38			21 08			21 38			22 08			22 38		23 08				23 38			00 08		

For general notes see front of timetable
For details of catering facilities see
Directory of Train Operators

Birmingham → Walsall, Rugeley and Stafford

Network Diagram - see first page of Table 67

Miles	Miles			LM MX	LM	LM [1]	LM	LM	LM	LM	LM A	LM	LM	LM B	LM	LM C	LM	LM	LM C	LM	LM C	LM
0	—	**Birmingham New Street [12]**	d	23p20	05 33		06 07	06 27		06 49		07 12	07 27		07 42	07 57	08 12		08 27	08 42	08 57	09 12
1½	—	Duddeston	d	23p24			06 11	06 32		06 53			07 31			08 01			08 31		09 01	
2¾	—	Aston	d	23p26			06 14	06 35		06 56			07 34			08 04			08 34		09 04	
3½	—	Witton	d	23p28			06 16	06 37		06 58			07 36			08 06			08 36		09 06	
4¼	—	Perry Barr	d	23p31			06 18	06 40		07 01			07 38			08 08			08 38		09 08	
5¾	—	Hamstead	d	23p34	05 41		06 21	06 43		07 04			07 41			08 11			08 41		09 11	
8½	—	Tame Bridge Parkway	d	23p38	05 45		06 26	06 47		07 09		07 23	07 45		07 54	08 15	08 23		08 45	08 53	09 15	09 23
9½	—	Bescot Stadium	d	23p41	05 48		06 29	06 49		07 11			07 47			08 17			08 47		09 17	
10¾	—	**Walsall**	a	23p45	05 55		06 33	06 55		07 17		07 30	07 55		08 05	08 25	08 30		08 55	09 05	09 25	09 30
—	0		d	23p46			06 34		07 04		07 30	07 30		08 03			08 30	08 44				09 30
—	6¾	**Wolverhampton [7]** [ferry]	a								07 45			08 20				08 59				
14	—	Bloxwich	d	23p53			06 41		07 12			07 37					08 37					09 37
14½	—	Bloxwich North	d	23p55			06 43		07 14			07 39					08 39					09 39
16¾	—	Landywood	d	23p59			06 47		07 18			07 43					08 43					09 43
18¾	—	Cannock	d	00 03			06 51		07 23			07 48					08 48					09 48
20¾	—	Hednesford	d	00a09			06 56		07a30			07 53					08 53					09 53
24¾	—	Rugeley Town	a				07 05					08 01					09 01					10 01
—	—		d				07 10					08 02					09 02					10 02
26¼	—	Rugeley Trent Valley	d			07 12	07 15					08b09					09c09					10e09
35½	—	**Stafford**	a			07 23	07 31					08 25					09 25					10 26

		LM	LM C	LM	LM C	LM [bus]	LM	LM	LM C	LM	LM C	LM	LM	LM C	LM	LM C	LM	LM	LM C	LM	LM C
Birmingham New Street [12]	d		09 27	09 42	09 57		10 12		10 27	10 42	10 57	11 12		11 27	11 42	11 57	12 12		12 27	12 42	12 57
Duddeston	d		09 31		10 01				10 31		11 01			11 31		12 01			12 31		13 01
Aston	d		09 34		10 04				10 34		11 04			11 34		12 04			12 34		13 04
Witton	d		09 36		10 06				10 36		11 06			11 36		12 06			12 36		13 06
Perry Barr	d		09 38		10 08				10 38		11 08			11 38		12 08			12 38		13 08
Hamstead	d		09 41		10 11				10 41		11 11			11 41		12 11			12 41		13 11
Tame Bridge Parkway	d		09 45	09 53	10 15		10 23		10 45	10 53	11 15	11 23		11 45	11 53	12 15	12 23		12 45	12 53	13 15
Bescot Stadium	d		09 47		10 17				10 47		11 17			11 47		12 17			12 47		13 17
Walsall	a		09 55	10 05	10 25		10 30		10 55	11 05	11 25	11 30		11 55	12 05	12 25	12 30		12 55	13 05	13 25
	d	09 44					10 30	10 44				11 30	11 44				12 30	12 44			
Wolverhampton [7] [ferry]	a	09 59						10 59					11 59					12 59			
Bloxwich	d						10 37					11 37					12 37				
Bloxwich North	d						10 39					11 39					12 39				
Landywood	d						10 43					11 43					12 43				
Cannock	d						10 48					11 48					12 48				
Hednesford	d						10 53					11 53					12 53				
Rugeley Town	a						11 01					12 01					13 01				
	d						11 02					12 02					13 02				
Rugeley Trent Valley	d					11 04	11f09					12a10					13g09				
Stafford	a					11 24	11 25										13 25				

		LM	LM	LM C	LM	LM C	LM [1] [bicycle]	LM	LM	LM C	LM	LM C	LM	LM	LM C	LM	LM C	LM	LM	LM C	LM	LM C
Birmingham New Street [12]	d	13 12		13 27	13 42	13 57		14 12		14 27	14 42	14 57	15 12		15 27	15 42	15 57	16 12		16 27	16 42	16 57
Duddeston	d			13 31		14 01				14 31		15 01			15 31		16 01			16 31		17 01
Aston	d			13 34		14 04				14 34		15 04			15 34		16 04			16 34		17 04
Witton	d			13 36		14 06				14 36		15 06			15 36		16 06			16 36		17 06
Perry Barr	d			13 38		14 08				14 38		15 08			15 38		16 08			16 38		17 08
Hamstead	d			13 41		14 11				14 41		15 11			15 41		16 11			16 41		17 11
Tame Bridge Parkway	d	13 23		13 45	13 53	14 15		14 23		14 45	14 53	15 15	15 23		15 45	15 53	16 15	16 23		16 45	16 53	17 15
Bescot Stadium	d			13 47		14 17				14 47		15 17			15 47		16 17			16 47		17 17
Walsall	a	13 30		13 55	14 05	14 25		14 30		14 55	15 05	15 25	15 30		15 55	16 05	16 25	16 30		16 55	17 00	17 25
	d	13 30	13 44					14 30	14 44				15 30	15 44				16 30	16 44		17 01	
Wolverhampton [7] [ferry]	a		13 59						14 59					15 59					16 59			
Bloxwich	d	13 37						14 37					15 37					16 37			17 08	
Bloxwich North	d	13 39						14 39					15 39					16 40			17 10	
Landywood	d	13 43						14 43					15 43					16 44			17 14	
Cannock	d	13 48						14 48					15 48					16 48			17 19	
Hednesford	d	13 53						14 53					15 53					16 54			17a28	
Rugeley Town	a	14 01						15 01					16 01					17 03				
	d	14 02						15 02					16 02					17 05				
Rugeley Trent Valley	d	14h09					14 33	15j09					16k09					17 09				
Stafford	a	14 25					14 43	15 25					16 25					17 25				

For general notes see front of timetable
For details of catering facilities see Directory of Train Operators

A To Shrewsbury (Table 74)

B From Hednesford
C From Birmingham International (Table 68)
b Arr. 0805
c Arr. 0905
e Arr. 1006

f Arr. 1105
g Arr. 1305
h Arr. 1405
j Arr. 1505
k Arr. 1605

Birmingham → Walsall, Rugeley and Stafford

Network Diagram - see first page of Table 67

		LM		LM	LM	LM	LM	LM		LM	LM	LM	LM	LM		LM	LM	LM	LM	LM	LM	LM	LM		
					A		A				A	🚌				[1]									
Birmingham New Street [12]	d	17 12			17 27	17 42	17 57	18 12			18 27		19 09			19 42	20 12		21 12		22 12		23 20		
Duddeston	d				17 31		18 01				18 31		19 13			19 46	20 16		21 16		22 16		23 24		
Aston	d				17 34		18 04				18 34		19 15			19 49	20 18		21 18		22 18		23 26		
Witton	d				17 36		18 06				18 36		19 17			19 51	20 20		21 20		22 20		23 28		
Perry Barr	d				17 38		18 08				18 38		19 20			19 53	20 23		21 23		22 23		23 31		
Hamstead	d				17 41		18 11				18 41		19 23			19 56	20 26		21 26		22 26		23 34		
Tame Bridge Parkway	d	17 23			17 45	17 53	18 15	18 23			18 45		19 27			20 00	20 30		21 30		22 30		23 38		
Bescot Stadium	d				17 47		18 17				18 47		19 30			20 02	20 33		21 33		22 33		23 41		
Walsall	a	17 30			17 55	18 00	18 25	18 30			18 55		19 34			20 10	20 37		21 37		22 37		23 45		
	d	17 30		17 44		18 02		18 32		18 44			19 35	19 44			20 38	21 00	21 38	22 15	22 38	23 20	23 46		
Wolverhampton [7] 🚉	a			17 59						18 59				19 59				21 13		22 32		23 34			
Bloxwich	d	17 37				18 10		18 40					19 42				20 45		21 45		22 45		23 53		
Bloxwich North	d	17 40				18 12		18 42					19 44				20 47		21 47		22 47		23 55		
Landywood	d	17 44				18 16		18 46					19 48				20 51		21 51		22 51		23 59		
Cannock	d	17 48				18 21		18 51					19 52				20 55		21 55		22 55		00 03		
Hednesford	d	17 54				18 26		18 56					20a02				21a01		22a01		23a03		00a09		
Rugeley Town	a	18 02				18 39		19 09																	
	d	18 03																							
Rugeley Trent Valley	d	18 07										19 05													
Stafford	a	18 25										19 32													

Saturdays

		LM	LM	LM	LM	LM	LM	LM	LM	LM	LM		LM	LM	LM	LM	LM	LM	LM	LM	LM	LM		LM	LM
					🚌			🚌									🚌							🚌	
Birmingham New Street [12]	d	23p20	06 06			06 40	07 12			07 27	07 57		08 12		08 27	08 42		08 57	09 12		09 27	09 42			09 57
Duddeston	d	23p24	06 10			06 44	07 16				08 01				08 31			09 01			09 31				10 01
Aston	d	23p26	06 12			06 47	07 19			07 33	08 04				08 34			09 04			09 34				10 04
Witton	d	23p28	06 14			06 49	07 21				08 06				08 36			09 06			09 36				10 06
Perry Barr	d	23p31	06 17			06 51	07 23			07 36	08 08				08 38			09 08			09 38				10 08
Hamstead	d	23p34	06 20			06 54	07 26			07 39	08 11				08 41			09 11			09 41				10 11
Tame Bridge Parkway	d	23p38	06 24			06 59	07 30			07 43	08 15		08 23		08 45	08 53		09 15	09 23		09 45	09 53			10 15
Bescot Stadium	d	23p41	06 27			07 02	07 32				08 17				08 47			09 17			09 47				10 17
Walsall	a	23p45	06 31			07 08	07 39			07 50	08 25		08 34		08 55	09 05		09 25	09 34		09 55	10 05			10 25
	d	23p46	06 32	06 42		07 09			07 44	07 51			08 34	08 44					09 34	09 44					
Wolverhampton [7] 🚉	a			06 57					07 59					08 59						09 59					
Bloxwich	d	23p53	06 39			07 16				07 58			08 41						09 41						
Bloxwich North	d	23p55	06 41			07 18				08 00			08 43						09 43						
Landywood	d	23p59	06 45			07 22				08 04			08 47						09 47						
Cannock	d	00 03	06 50			07 26				08 09			08 51						09 51						
Hednesford	d	00a09	06a56		07 01	07 31				08a15			08 56						09 56						
Rugeley Town	a				07 21	07 38							09 03						10 03						
	d				07 22	07 39		07 45					09 03				09 10		10 03					10 10	
Rugeley Trent Valley	d				07 33	07a45		07 56					09a12				09 21		10a12					10 21	
Stafford	a				07 53			08 16									09 41							10 41	

		LM	LM	LM	LM	LM	LM	LM	LM	LM	LM		LM	LM	LM	LM	LM	LM	LM	LM	LM	LM		LM	LM
		🚌					🚌							🚌						🚌		🚌			
Birmingham New Street [12]	d		10 12		10 27	10 42		10 57	11 12		11 27		11 42		11 57	12 12		12 27	12 42		12 57			13 12	
Duddeston	d				10 31			11 01			11 31				12 01			12 31			13 01				
Aston	d				10 34			11 04			11 34				12 04			12 34			13 04				
Witton	d				10 36			11 06			11 36				12 06			12 36			13 06				
Perry Barr	d				10 38			11 08			11 38				12 08			12 38			13 08				
Hamstead	d				10 43			11 11			11 41				12 11			12 41			13 11				
Tame Bridge Parkway	d		10 23		10 47	10 53		11 15	11 23		11 45		11 53		12 15	12 23		12 45	12 53		13 15			13 23	
Bescot Stadium	d				10 50			11 17			11 47				12 17			12 47			13 17				
Walsall	a		10 34		10 55	11 05		11 25	11 34		11 55		12 05		12 25	12 34		12 55	13 05		13 25			13 34	
	d		10 34	10 44					11 34	11 44						12 34	12 44							13 34	13 44
Wolverhampton [7] 🚉	a			10 59						11 59							12 59								13 59
Bloxwich	d		10 41						11 41							12 41								13 41	
Bloxwich North	d		10 43						11 43							12 43								13 43	
Landywood	d		10 47						11 47							12 47								13 47	
Cannock	d		10 51						11 51							12 51								13 51	
Hednesford	d		10 56						11 56							12 56								13 56	
Rugeley Town	a		11 03						12 03							13 03								14 03	
	d		11 03				11 10		12 03					12 10		13 03				13 10				14 03	
Rugeley Trent Valley	d	11 04	11a12				11 21		12a12					12 21		13a12				13 21		13 57		14a12	
Stafford	a	11 24					11 41							12 41						13 41		14 17			

For general notes see front of timetable
For details of catering facilities see
Directory of Train Operators

A From Birmingham International (Table 68)

Birmingham → Walsall, Rugeley and Stafford

Network Diagram - see first page of Table 67

		LM	LM	LM (bus)	LM	LM	LM	LM	LM	LM (bus)	LM		LM	LM	LM	LM	LM (bus)	LM	LM	LM	LM	LM		LM (bus)	LM
Birmingham New Street 12	d	13 27	13 42		13 57	14 12		14 27	14 42		14 57		15 12		15 27	15 42		15 57	16 12		16 27	16 42			16 57
Duddeston	d	13 31			14 01			14 31			15 01				15 31			16 01			16 31				17 01
Aston	d	13 34			14 04			14 34			15 04				15 34			16 04			16 34				17 04
Witton	d	13 36			14 06			14 36			15 06				15 36			16 06			16 36				17 06
Perry Barr	d	13 38			14 08			14 38			15 08				15 38			16 08			16 38				17 08
Hamstead	d	13 41			14 11			14 41			15 11				15 41			16 11			16 41				17 11
Tame Bridge Parkway	d	13 45	13 53		14 15	14 23		14 45	14 53		15 15		15 23		15 45	15 53		16 15	16 23		16 45	16 53			17 15
Bescot Stadium	d	13 47			14 17			14 47			15 17				15 47			16 17			16 47				17 17
Walsall	a	13 55	14 05		14 25	14 34		14 55	15 05		15 25		15 34		15 55	16 05		16 25	16 34		16 55	17 05			17 25
	d					14 34	14 44						15 34	15 44					16 34	16 44					
Wolverhampton 7 (train)	a						14 59							15 59						16 59					
Bloxwich	d					14 41							15 41						16 41						
Bloxwich North	d					14 43							15 43						16 43						
Landywood	d					14 47							15 47						16 47						
Cannock	d					14 51							15 51						16 51						
Hednesford	d					14 56							15 56						16 56						
Rugeley Town	a					15 03							16 03						17 02						
	d			14 10		15 03				15 10			16 03				16 10		17 03					17 10	
Rugeley Trent Valley	d			14 21		15a12				15 21			16a12				16 21		17a12					17 21	
Stafford	a			14 41						15 41							16 41							17 41	

		LM	LM	LM	LM (bus)	LM	LM	LM	LM	LM	LM (bus)		LM	LM	LM	LM	LM	LM	LM	LM	LM	LM	LM		
Birmingham New Street 12	d	17 12		17 27		17 42	17 57	18 12		18 27			18 57	19 12		19 42	20 12		21 12		22 12		23 20		
Duddeston	d			17 31			18 01			18 31			19 01	19 16		19 46	20 16		21 16		22 16		23 24		
Aston	d			17 34			18 04			18 34			19 04	19 18		19 48	20 18		21 18		22 18		23 26		
Witton	d			17 36			18 06			18 36			19 06	19 20		19 50	20 20		21 20		22 20		23 28		
Perry Barr	d			17 38			18 08			18 38			19 08	19 23		19 53	20 23		21 23		22 23		23 31		
Hamstead	d			17 41			18 11			18 41			19 11	19 26		19 56	20 26		21 26		22 26		23 34		
Tame Bridge Parkway	d	17 23		17 45		17 53	18 15	18 23		18 45			19 15	19 30		20 00	20 30		21 30		22 30		23 38		
Bescot Stadium	d			17 47			18 17			18 47			19 17	19 33		20 03	20 33		21 33		22 33		23 41		
Walsall	a	17 34		17 55		18 00	18 25	18 34		18 55			19 25	19 37		20 10	20 37		21 37		22 37		23 45		
	d	17 34	17 44			18 00		18 34	18 44					19 38	19 44		20 38	20 44	21 38	22 15	22 38	23 20	23 46		
Wolverhampton 7 (train)	a		17 59						18 59						19 59			20 59		22 32		23 39			
Bloxwich	d	17 41				18 07		18 41						19 45			20 45		21 45		22 45		23 53		
Bloxwich North	d	17 43				18 09		18 43						19 47			20 47		21 47		22 47		23 55		
Landywood	d	17 47				18 13		18 47						19 51			20 51		21 51		22 51		23 59		
Cannock	d	17 51				18 18		18 51						19 55			20 55		21 55		22 55		00 03		
Hednesford	d	17 56				18a25		18 56						20 00			21a01		22a01		23a01		00a09		
Rugeley Town	a	18 02						19 08						20 07											
	d	18 03			18 10									20 08											
Rugeley Trent Valley	d	18a12			18 21						19 07			20a14											
Stafford	a				18 41						19 27														

Sundays

		LM	LM	LM	LM	LM	LM	LM	LM	LM		LM	LM	LM	LM	LM	LM	LM	LM	LM		LM	LM	LM	LM
Birmingham New Street 12	d	23p20		09 42		10 12	10 42		11 12	11 42			12 12	12 42		13 12	13 42		14 12	14 42			15 12	15 42	
Duddeston	d	23p24		09 46			10 46			11 46				12 46			13 46			14 46				15 46	
Aston	d	23p26		09 49			10 49			11 49				12 49			13 49			14 49				15 49	
Witton	d	23p28		09 51			10 51			11 51				12 51			13 51			14 51				15 51	
Perry Barr	d	23p31		09 53			10 53			11 53				12 53			13 53			14 53				15 53	
Hamstead	d	23p34		09 56			10 56			11 56				12 56			13 56			14 56				15 56	
Tame Bridge Parkway	d	23p38		10 01		10 24	11 01		11 24	12 01			12 24	13 01		13 24	14 01		14 24	15 01			15 24	16 01	
Bescot Stadium	d	23p41		10 03			11 03			12 03				13 03			14 03			15 03				16 03	
Walsall	a	23p45		10 10		10 33	11 10		11 33	12 10			12 33	13 10		13 33	14 11		14 33	15 10			15 33	16 10	
	d	23p46	09 20		10 20	10 34		11 20	11 34			12 20	12 34		13 20	13 34		14 20	14 34			15 20	15 34		16 20
Wolverhampton 7 (train)	a		09 35		10 35			11 35				12 34			13 36			14 36				15 34			16 34
Bloxwich	d	23p53				10 41			11 41				12 41			13 41			14 41				15 41		
Bloxwich North	d	23p55				10 43			11 43				12 43			13 43			14 43				15 43		
Landywood	d	23p59				10 47			11 47				12 47			13 47			14 47				15 47		
Cannock	d	00 03				10 51			11 51				12 51			13 51			14 51				15 51		
Hednesford	d	00a09				10 56			11 56				12 56			13 56			14 56				15 56		
Rugeley Town	a					11 03			12 03				13 03			14 03			15 03				16 03		
	d					11 04			12 04				13 04			14 04			15 04				16 04		
Rugeley Trent Valley	d					11a07			12a07				13a07			14a07			15a07				16a07		
Stafford	a																								

		LM	LM	LM	LM	LM	LM	LM		LM	LM	LM	LM	LM	LM	LM	LM	LM	LM	LM	LM	LM	LM		
Birmingham New Street 12	d	16 12	16 42		17 12	17 42		18 11		18 42		19 12	19 42		20 12	20 42		21 12	21 42		22 12	22 42			
Duddeston	d		16 46			17 46				18 46			19 46			20 46			21 46			22 46			
Aston	d		16 49			17 49				18 49			19 49			20 49			21 49			22 49			
Witton	d		16 51			17 51				18 51			19 51			20 51			21 51			22 51			
Perry Barr	d		16 53			17 53				18 53			19 53			20 53			21 53			22 53			
Hamstead	d		16 56			17 56				18 56			19 56			20 56			21 56			22 56			
Tame Bridge Parkway	d	16 24	17 01		17 24	18 01		18 24		19 01		19 24	20 01		20 24	21 01		21 24	22 01		22 24	23 01			
Bescot Stadium	d		17 03			18 03				19 03			20 03			21 03			22 03			23 03			
Walsall	a	16 33	17 10		17 33	18 10		18 33		19 10		19 33	20 10		20 33	21 10		21 33	22 10		22 33	23 10			
	d	16 34		17 20	17 34		18 20	18 34			19 20	19 34		20 20	20 34		21 20	21 34		22 20	22 34		23 20		
Wolverhampton 7 (train)	a			17 34			18 34				19 34			20 34			21 34			22 34			23 37		
Bloxwich	d	16 41			17 41			18 41				19 41			20 41			21 41			22 41				
Bloxwich North	d	16 43			17 43			18 43				19 43			20 43			21 43			22 43				
Landywood	d	16 47			17 47			18 47				19 47			20 47			21 47			22 47				
Cannock	d	16 51			17 51			18 51				19 51			20 51			21 51			22 51				
Hednesford	d	16 56			17 56			18 56				19 56			20 56			21 56			22 56				
Rugeley Town	a	17 03			18 03			19 03				20 03			21 03			22 03			23 03				
	d	17 04			18 04			19 04				20 04			21 04			22 04			23 04				
Rugeley Trent Valley	d	17a07			18a07			19a07				20a07			21a07			22a07			23a07				
Stafford	a																								

For general notes see front of timetable
For details of catering facilities see Directory of Train Operators

Stafford, Rugeley and Walsall → Birmingham

Network Diagram - see first page of Table 67

Miles	Miles			LM	LM	LM	LM	LM	LM	LM	LM	LM	LM	LM	LM	LM	LM	LM	LM	LM	LM	LM	LM
											1 ◇				1								
									A		B		C	D			D						
0	—	**Stafford**	d												06 57	07 35					08 35		
9¼	—	Rugeley Trent Valley	d												07a06	07 46					08 46		
10¾	—	Rugeley Town	a													07 50					08 50		
—	—		d				06 23			06 45						07 50					08 50		
14¾	—	Hednesford	d		06 03		06 31			06 53		07 16	07 35			07 57			08 27		08 57		
16¾	—	Cannock	d		06 07		06 35			06 57		07 20	07 39			08 01			08 31		09 01		
18¾	—	Landywood	d		06 11		06 39			07 01		07 24				08 05			08 34		09 05		
21	—	Bloxwich North	d		06 15		06 44			07 05		07 28				08 09			08 39		09 09		
21½	—	Bloxwich	d		06 17		06 46			07 07		07 30				08 11			08 41		09 11		
—	0	**Wolverhampton** 7	d			06 38			06 56									08 23					09 25
24¾	6¾	**Walsall**	a		06 24	06 50	06 55		07 12	07 14		07 38	07 53			08 18		08 38	08 47		09 18		09 38
—	—		d	06 00	06 25			07 00		07 15	07 20	07 42	07 54	08 00		08 18	08 30		08 48	09 00	09 18	09 30	
26	—	Bescot Stadium	d	06 03	06 29			07 03			07 24			08 03			08 33			09 03		09 33	
27	—	Tame Bridge Parkway	d	06 06	06 32			07 06		07 21	07 27	07 47	08 00	08 06		08 23	08 36		08 53	09 06	09 23	09 36	
29¾	—	Hamstead	d	06 10	06 36			07 10			07 30			08 10			08 40			09 10		09 40	
31¼	—	Perry Barr	d	06 12	06 39			07 13			07 34			08 13			08 43			09 13		09 43	
32	—	Witton	d	06 14	06 42			07 15			07 36			08 15			08 45			09 16		09 45	
32¾	—	Aston	d	06 17	06 45			07 18			07 39			08 18			08 48			09 18		09 48	
34	—	Duddeston	d	06 19	06 48			07 20			07 42			08 20			08 50			09 21		09 50	
35½	—	**Birmingham New Street** 12	a	06 28	06 53			07 28		07 39	07 48	08 05	08 23	08 28		08 41	08 58		09 11	09 28	09 41	09 58	

		LM	LM	LM	LM	LM	LM	LM	LM	LM	LM	LM	LM	LM	LM	LM	LM	LM	LM	LM	LM	LM
														1								
					D			D		D			D			D			D		D	
														⚒								
Stafford	d			09 35					10 35					11 21	11 35							
Rugeley Trent Valley	d			09 46					10 46					11a32	11 46					12 46		
Rugeley Town	a			09 50					10 50						11 50					12 50		
	d			09 50					10 50						11 50					12 50		
Hednesford	d			09 57					10 57						11 57					12 57		
Cannock	d			10 01					11 01						12 01					13 01		
Landywood	d			10 05					11 05						12 05					13 05		
Bloxwich North	d			10 09					11 09						12 09					13 09		
Bloxwich	d			10 11					11 11						12 11					13 11		
Wolverhampton 7	d					10 25					11 25						12 25					13 25
Walsall	a			10 18		10 38			11 18		11 38				12 18		12 39			13 18		13 38
	d	09 42	10 00	10 18	10 30		10 42	11 00	11 18	11 30		11 42	12 00		12 18	12 30		12 42	13 00	13 18	13 30	
Bescot Stadium	d		10 03		10 33			11 03		11 33			12 03			12 33			13 03		13 33	
Tame Bridge Parkway	d	09 47	10 06	10 23	10 36		10 47	11 06	11 23	11 36		11 47	12 06		12 23	12 36		12 47	13 06	13 23	13 36	
Hamstead	d		10 10		10 40			11 10		11 40			12 10			12 40			13 10		13 40	
Perry Barr	d		10 13		10 43			11 13		11 43			12 13			12 43			13 13		13 43	
Witton	d		10 15		10 45			11 15		11 45			12 15			12 45			13 15		13 45	
Aston	d		10 18		10 48			11 18		11 47			12 18			12 47			13 18		13 48	
Duddeston	d		10 20		10 50			11 20		11 51			12 20			12 50			13 20		13 50	
Birmingham New Street 12	a	10 05	10 28	10 41	10 58		11 05	11 28	11 41	11 58		12 05	12 28		12 41	12 58		13 05	13 28	13 41	13 58	

		LM	LM	LM	LM	LM	LM	LM	LM	LM	LM	LM	LM	LM	LM	LM	LM	LM	LM	LM	LM	LM
			D	🚌		D			D		D			D					D		D	
Stafford	d			12 45	13 35					14 35					15 35					16 35		
Rugeley Trent Valley	d			13a05	13 46					14 46					15 46					16 46		
Rugeley Town	a				13 50					14 50					15 50					16 50		
	d				13 50					14 50					15 50					16 50		
Hednesford	d				13 57					14 57					15 57					16 57		
Cannock	d				14 01					15 01					16 01					17 01		
Landywood	d				14 05					15 05					16 05					17 05		
Bloxwich North	d				14 09					15 09					16 09					17 09		
Bloxwich	d				14 11					15 11					16 11					17 11		
Wolverhampton 7	d						14 25					15 25					16 25					17 25
Walsall	a				14 18		14 38			15 18		15 38			16 18		16 40			17 18		17 40
	d	13 42	14 00		14 18	14 30		14 42	15 00	15 18	15 30		15 42	16 00	16 18	16 30		16 42	17 00	17 18	17 30	
Bescot Stadium	d		14 03			14 33			15 03		15 33			16 03		16 33			17 03		17 33	
Tame Bridge Parkway	d	13 47	14 06		14 23	14 36		14 47	15 06	15 23	15 36		15 47	16 06	16 23	16 36		16 47	17 06	17 23	17 36	
Hamstead	d		14 10			14 40			15 10		15 40			16 10		16 40			17 10		17 40	
Perry Barr	d		14 13			14 43			15 13		15 43			16 13		16 43			17 13		17 43	
Witton	d		14 15			14 45			15 15		15 45			16 15		16 45			17 15		17 45	
Aston	d		14 18			14 48			15 18		15 48			16 18		16 48			17 18		17 48	
Duddeston	d		14 21			14 50			15 20		15 50			16 20		16 50			17 20		17 50	
Birmingham New Street 12	a	14 05	14 28		14 41	14 58		15 05	15 28	15 41	15 58		16 05	16 28	16 41	16 58		17 05	17 28	17 41	17 58	

For general notes see front of timetable
For details of catering facilities see Directory of Train Operators

A From Shrewsbury (Table 74)
B To Liverpool Lime Street (Table 65)
C To Wolverhampton (Table 68)
D To Birmingham International (Table 68)

Stafford, Rugeley and Walsall → Birmingham

Network Diagram - see first page of Table 67

		LM	LM	LM	LM	LM	LM	LM	LM	LM	LM	LM	LM	LM	LM	LM	LM	LM	LM
			A	1		A		A									B		
				(trolley)															(bus)
Stafford	d			17 20	17 35														20 22
Rugeley Trent Valley	d			17a29	17 46														20a50
Rugeley Town	a				17 50														
	d				17 50				19 00		19 29								
Hednesford	d	17 27			17 57				19 08		19 37	20 11		21 11		22 11		23 11	
Cannock	d	17 30			18 01				19 11		19 41	20 14		21 14		22 14		23 14	
Landywood	d	17 34			18 05				19 15		19 44	20 18		21 18		22 18		23 18	
Bloxwich North	d	17 38			18 09				19 19		19 48	20 22		21 22		22 22		23 22	
Bloxwich	d	17 40			18 11				19 21		19 50	20 24		21 24		22 24		23 24	
Wolverhampton 7	d						18 25			19 25			20 34		21 19		22 55		
Walsall	a	17 47			18 18		18 40		19 27	19 40	19 57	20 30	20 49	21 30	21 32	22 30	23 12	23 30	
	d	17 48	18 00		18 18	18 30		19 00	19 28		19 57	20 31		21 31		22 31		23 31	
Bescot Stadium	d		18 03			18 33		19 03	19 32		20 01	20 36		21 36		22 36			
Tame Bridge Parkway	d	17 53	18 06		18 23	18 36		19 06	19 35		20 04	20 39		21 39		22 39			
Hamstead	d		18 10			18 40		19 10	19 39		20 08	20 43		21 43		22 43			
Perry Barr	d		18 13			18 43		19 13	19 42		20 11	20 46		21 46		22 46			
Witton	d		18 15			18 45		19 15	19 44		20 13	20 48		21 48		22 48			
Aston	d		18 18			18 48		19 18	19 47		20 16	20 51		21 51		22 51			
Duddeston	d		18 20			18 50		19 20	19 50		20 19	20 54		21 54		22 54			
Birmingham New Street 12	a	18 11	18 30		18 41	18 58		19 28	19 56		20 28	21 02		21 59		22 59		23 55	

Saturdays

		LM	LM	LM	LM	LM	LM	LM	LM	LM	LM	LM	LM	LM	LM	LM	LM	LM	LM	LM	LM	LM	LM
					(bus)					(bus)	(bus)									(bus)			
Stafford	d				05 54					05 54	07 05									08 35			
Rugeley Trent Valley	d				06a19					06a19	07 31	07 47								09 01	09 13		
Rugeley Town	a										07 41	07 50								09 11	09 16		
	d					06 24						07 51									09 17		
Hednesford	d					06 32	07 05					07 59			08 21						09 25		
Cannock	d					06 35	07 09					08 02			08 25						09 29		
Landywood	d					06 39	07 12					08 06			08 28						09 33		
Bloxwich North	d					06 43	07 17					08 10			08 32						09 37		
Bloxwich	d					06 45	07 19					08 12			08 34						09 39		
Wolverhampton 7	d		06 08					07 25						08 25					09 25				
Walsall	a		06 22			06 52	07 25	07 38				08 18		08 40	08 41				09 40		09 46		
	d	05 58		06 32		06 53	07 31		08 02			08 19	08 30		08 47	09 00	09 15	09 30			09 47	10 00	10 16
Bescot Stadium	d	06 02		06 35		06 57	07 35		08 05				08 33			09 03		09 33				10 03	
Tame Bridge Parkway	d	06 04		06 38		07 00	07 37		08 08			08 24	08 36		08 52	09 06	09 20	09 36			09 52	10 06	10 21
Hamstead	d	06 08		06 41		07 04	07 41		08 11				08 40			09 10		09 40				10 10	
Perry Barr	d	06 11		06 44		07 07	07 44		08 14				08 43			09 13		09 43				10 13	
Witton	d	06 14		06 46		07 09	07 47		08 16				08 45			09 15		09 45				10 15	
Aston	d	06 16		06 48		07 12	07 50		08 19				08 48			09 18		09 48				10 18	
Duddeston	d	06 19		06 50		07 15	07 53		08 21				08 50			09 20		09 50				10 20	
Birmingham New Street 12	a	06 26		06 58		07 20	08 01		08 30			08 42	08 58		09 10	09 28	09 41	09 58			10 10	10 28	10 41

		LM	LM	LM	LM	LM	LM	LM	LM	LM	LM	LM	LM	LM	LM	LM	LM	LM	LM	LM	LM	LM	LM
				(bus)						(bus)						(bus)						(bus)	(bus)
Stafford	d			09 35						10 35						11 35						12 35	12 45
Rugeley Trent Valley	d			10 01	10 13					11 01	11 13					12 01	12 13					13 01	13a10
Rugeley Town	a			10 11	10 16					11 11	11 16					12 11	12 16					13 11	
	d				10 17						11 17						12 17						
Hednesford	d				10 25						11 25						12 25						
Cannock	d				10 29						11 29						12 29						
Landywood	d				10 33						11 33						12 33						
Bloxwich North	d				10 37						11 37						12 37						
Bloxwich	d				10 39						11 39						12 39						
Wolverhampton 7	d		10 25						11 25						12 25						13 25		
Walsall	a		10 40		10 46				11 40		11 46				12 40		12 46				13 40		
	d	10 30			10 47	11 00	11 18	11 30			11 47	12 00	12 18	12 30			12 47	13 00	13 18	13 30			
Bescot Stadium	d	10 33				11 03		11 33				12 03		12 33				13 03		13 33			
Tame Bridge Parkway	d	10 36			10 52	11 06	11 23	11 36			11 52	12 06	12 23	12 36			12 52	13 06	13 23	13 36			
Hamstead	d	10 40				11 10		11 40				12 10		12 40				13 10		13 40			
Perry Barr	d	10 43				11 13		11 43				12 13		12 43				13 13		13 43			
Witton	d	10 45				11 15		11 45				12 15		12 45				13 15		13 45			
Aston	d	10 48				11 18		11 48				12 18		12 48				13 18		13 48			
Duddeston	d	10 50				11 20		11 50				12 20		12 50				13 20		13 50			
Birmingham New Street 12	a	10 58			11 10	11 28	11 41	11 58			12 10	12 28	12 41	12 58			13 10	13 28	13 41	13 58			

For general notes see front of timetable
For details of catering facilities see Directory of Train Operators

A To Birmingham International (Table 68)
B From Shrewsbury (Table 74)

Table 70

Saturdays

Stafford, Rugeley and Walsall → Birmingham

Network Diagram - see first page of Table 67

		LM	LM		LM	LM	LM	LM 🚌	LM	LM		LM	LM	LM	LM 🚌	LM	LM		LM	LM	LM	LM 🚌	LM 🚌	LM		LM
Stafford	d							13 35							14 35							15 35	15 35			
Rugeley Trent Valley	d	13 13						14 01	14 13						15 01	15 13						16 01	16a00	16 13		
Rugeley Town	a	13 16						14 11	14 16						15 11	15 16						16 11		16 16		
	d	13 17							14 17							15 17								16 17		
Hednesford	d	13 25							14 25							15 25								16 25		
Cannock	d	13 29							14 29							15 29								16 29		
Landywood	d	13 33							14 33							15 33								16 33		
Bloxwich North	d	13 37							14 37							15 37								16 37		
Bloxwich	d	13 39							14 39							15 39								16 39		
Wolverhampton 7	d						14 25							15 25							16 25					
Walsall	a	13 46					14 40		14 46					15 40		15 46					16 40			16 46		
	d	13 47	14 00		14 18	14 30			14 47	15 00		15 18	15 30			15 47	16 00		16 18	16 30				16 47		17 00
Bescot Stadium	d		14 03			14 33				15 03			15 33				16 03			16 33						17 03
Tame Bridge Parkway	d	13 52	14 06		14 23	14 36			14 52	15 06		15 23	15 36			15 52	16 06		16 23	16 36				16 52		17 06
Hamstead	d		14 10			14 40				15 10			15 40				16 10			16 40						17 10
Perry Barr	d		14 13			14 43				15 13			15 43				16 13			16 43						17 13
Witton	d		14 15			14 45				15 15			15 45				16 15			16 45						17 15
Aston	d		14 18			14 48				15 18			15 48				16 18			16 48						17 18
Duddeston	d		14 20			14 50				15 20			15 50				16 20			16 50						17 20
Birmingham New Street 12	a	14 10	14 28		14 41	14 58			15 10	15 28		15 41	15 58			16 10	16 28		16 41	16 58				17 10		17 28

		LM	LM	LM	LM 🚌	LM	LM		LM	LM	LM 🚌	LM	LM	LM		LM	LM	LM	LM	LM	LM	LM A	LM	LM 🚌		
Stafford	d				16 35						17 35													19 52		
Rugeley Trent Valley	d				17 01	17 13					18 01	18 13						20 16						20a17		
Rugeley Town	a				17 11	17 16					18 11	18 16						20 19								
	d					17 17						18 17				19 30		20 20								
Hednesford	d					17 25						18 25				19 38		20 28		21 11	22 11		23 11			
Cannock	d					17 29						18 29				19 42		20 32		21 14	22 14		23 14			
Landywood	d					17 33						18 33				19 46		20 36		21 18	22 18		23 18			
Bloxwich North	d					17 37						18 37				19 50		20 40		21 22	22 22		23 22			
Bloxwich	d					17 39						18 39				19 52		20 42		21 24	22 24		23 24			
Wolverhampton 7	d			17 25						18 25				19 25			20 25		21 03			22 55				
Walsall	a			17 40		17 46				18 40		18 46		19 39		19 59	20 39	20 49	21 18	21 30	22 30	23 12	23 30			
	d	17 18	17 30			17 47	18 00		18 30			18 47	19 00			20 00		20 50		21 31	22 31		23 31			
Bescot Stadium	d		17 33				18 03		18 33				19 03			20 04		20 54		21 36	22 36					
Tame Bridge Parkway	d	17 23	17 36			17 52	18 06		18 36			18 52	19 06			20 07		20 57		21 39	22 39					
Hamstead	d		17 40				18 10		18 40				19 10			20 11		21 01		21 43	22 43					
Perry Barr	d		17 43				18 13		18 43				19 13			20 14		21 04		21 46	22 46					
Witton	d		17 45				18 15		18 45				19 15			20 17		21 07		21 48	22 48					
Aston	d		17 48				18 18		18 48				19 18			20 20		21 10		21 51	22 51					
Duddeston	d		17 50				18 20		18 50				19 20			20 23		21 13		21 54	22 54					
Birmingham New Street 12	a	17 41	17 58			18 10	18 28		18 58			19 10	19 28			20 28		21 18		21 59	22 59		23 55			

Sundays

		LM	LM	LM	LM	LM	LM		LM	LM	LM	CH B	LM	LM		LM	LM	LM	LM	LM	LM		LM	LM	LM	LM
Stafford	d																									
Rugeley Trent Valley	d				10 13				11 13				12 13				13 13			14 13				15 13		
Rugeley Town	a				10 16				11 16				12 16				13 16			14 16				15 16		
	d				10 17				11 17				12 17				13 17			14 17				15 17		
Hednesford	d				10 25				11 25				12 25				13 25			14 25				15 25		
Cannock	d				10 28				11 28				12 28				13 28			14 28				15 28		
Landywood	d				10 32				11 32				12 32				13 32			14 32				15 32		
Bloxwich North	d				10 36				11 36				12 36				13 36			14 36				15 36		
Bloxwich	d				10 38				11 38				12 38				13 38			14 38				15 38		
Wolverhampton 7	d	09 01	09 41			10 40				11 40		12 12		12 40				13 40			14 40				15 40	
Walsall	a	09 15	09 56		10 44	10 55			11 44	11 56			12 44	12 55			13 44	13 56		14 44	14 56			15 44	15 55	
	d			10 02	10 45		11 02		11 45		12 02		12 45			13 02	13 45		14 02	14 45			15 02	15 45		16 02
Bescot Stadium	d			10 06			11 06				12 06					13 06			14 06				15 06			16 06
Tame Bridge Parkway	d			10 08	10 51		11 08		11 51		12 08	12a26	12 51			13 08	13 51		14 08	14 51			15 08	15 51		16 08
Hamstead	d			10 12			11 12				12 12					13 12			14 12				15 12			16 12
Perry Barr	d			10 15			11 15				12 15					13 15			14 15				15 15			16 15
Witton	d			10 18			11 18				12 18					13 18			14 18				15 18			16 18
Aston	d			10 20			11 20				12 20					13 20			14 20				15 20			16 20
Duddeston	d			10 23			11 23				12 23					13 23			14 23				15 23			16 23
Birmingham New Street 12	a			10 30	11 06		11 30		12 06		12 30		13 06			13 30	14 06		14 30	15 06			15 30	16 06		16 30

For general notes see front of timetable
For details of catering facilities see
Directory of Train Operators

A From Shrewsbury (Table 74)
B Until 27 January.
To London Marylebone (Table 75)

Table 70

Sundays

Stafford, Rugeley and Walsall → Birmingham

Network Diagram - see first page of Table 67

		LM	LM	LM	LM		LM	LM	LM	LM	LM	LM		LM	LM	LM	LM	LM	LM	LM	LM	LM	LM	LM		
Stafford	d																									
Rugeley Trent Valley	d	16 13			17 13				18 13			19 13				20 13			21 13			22 13				
Rugeley Town	a	16 16			17 16				18 16			19 16				20 16			21 16			22 16				
	d	16 17			17 17				18 17			19 17				20 17			21 17			22 17				
Hednesford	d	16 25			17 25				18 25			19 25				20 25			21 25			22 25				
Cannock	d	16 28			17 28				18 28			19 28				20 28			21 28			22 28				
Landywood	d	16 32			17 32				18 32			19 32				20 32			21 32			22 32				
Bloxwich North	d	16 36			17 36				18 36			19 36				20 36			21 36			22 36				
Bloxwich	d	16 38			17 38				18 38			19 38				20 38			21 38			22 38				
Wolverhampton 7	d		16 40				17 40			18 40				19 40			20 40			21 40			22 40			
Walsall	a	16 44	16 55		17 44		17 55		18 44	18 55		19 44		19 55		20 44	20 55		21 44	21 55		22 44	22 55			
	d	16 45		17 02	17 45			18 02	18 45		19 02	19 45			20 02	20 45		21 02	21 45		22 02	22 45		23 02		
Bescot Stadium	d			17 06				18 06			19 06				20 06			21 06			22 06			23 06		
Tame Bridge Parkway	d	16 51		17 08	17 51			18 08	18 51		19 08	19 51			20 08	20 51		21 08	21 51		22 08	22 51		23 08		
Hamstead	d			17 12				18 12			19 12				20 12			21 12			22 12			23 12		
Perry Barr	d			17 15				18 15			19 15				20 15			21 15			22 15			23 15		
Witton	d			17 18				18 18			19 18				20 18			21 18			22 18			23 18		
Aston	d			17 20				18 20			19 20				20 20			21 20			22 20			23 20		
Duddeston	d			17 23				18 23			19 23				20 23			21 23			22 23			23 23		
Birmingham New Street 12	a	17 06		17 30	18 06			18 30	19 06		19 30	20 06			20 30	21 06		21 30	22 07		22 30	23 06		23 30		

For general notes see front of timetable
For details of catering facilities see Directory of Train Operators

Network Diagram for Tables 71, 72

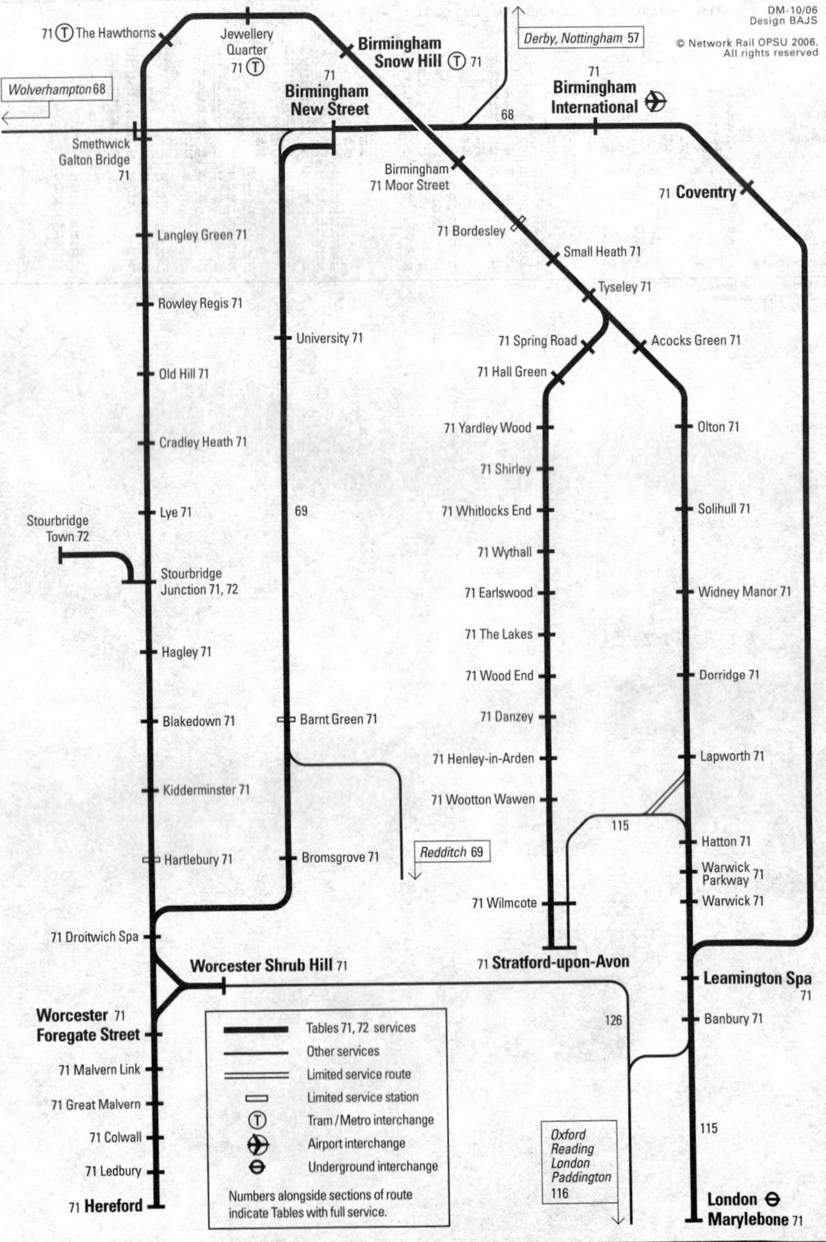
DM-10/06
Design BAJS
© Network Rail OPSU 2006.
All rights reserved
71 The Hawthorns
Jewellery Quarter 71
Birmingham Snow Hill 71
Derby, Nottingham 57
Wolverhampton 68
71 Birmingham New Street
71 Birmingham International
68
Smethwick Galton Bridge 71
Birmingham 71 Moor Street
71 Coventry
71 Bordesley
Small Heath 71
Tyseley 71
Langley Green 71
Rowley Regis 71
71 Spring Road
Acocks Green 71
University 71
71 Hall Green
Old Hill 71
71 Yardley Wood
Olton 71
Cradley Heath 71
71 Shirley
Lye 71
69
71 Whitlocks End
Solihull 71
Stourbridge Town 72
71 Wythall
Stourbridge Junction 71, 72
71 Earlswood
Widney Manor 71
71 The Lakes
Hagley 71
71 Wood End
Dorridge 71
Blakedown 71
Barnt Green 71
71 Danzey
71 Henley-in-Arden
Lapworth 71
Kidderminster 71
71 Wootton Wawen
115
Hatton 71
Hartlebury 71
Bromsgrove 71
Redditch 69
Warwick Parkway 71
71 Wilmcote
Warwick 71
71 Droitwich Spa
Worcester Shrub Hill 71
71 Stratford-upon-Avon
Leamington Spa 71
Worcester 71 Foregate Street
126
Banbury 71
71 Malvern Link
71 Great Malvern
71 Colwall
71 Ledbury
71 Hereford
Oxford Reading London Paddington 116
115
London Marylebone 71
Tables 71, 72 services
Other services
Limited service route
Limited service station
Tram / Metro interchange
Airport interchange
Underground interchange
Numbers alongside sections of route indicate Tables with full service.

Hereford, Worcester and Stourbridge → Birmingham → Leamington Spa, Marylebone and Stratford-upon-Avon

Network Diagram - See first page of Table 71

Miles	Miles	Miles			CH MX	CH	CH	LM	XC	CH	CH	LM	GW		LM	XC	LM	CH	LM	CH	XC	LM	CH		LM
									1 ◇				1 ◇			1 ◇				A	1 ◇		A		
						🛒	🛒		☕		🛒					☕				🛒	☕		🛒		
0	—	—	**Hereford** 7	d																					
13¾	—	—	Ledbury	a																					
—	—	—		d																					
18	—	—	Colwall	d																					
20¾	—	—	**Great Malvern**	a																					
—	—	—		d									05 31				05 50								
22	—	—	Malvern Link	d									05 34				05 53								
28¾	0	—	**Worcester Foregate Street** 7	a									05 41				06 01								
—	—	—		d									05 42				06 03								
29½	—	—	**Worcester Shrub Hill** 7	a									05 44												
—	—	—		d								05 30													
34¼	5½	—	Droitwich Spa	d								05 38					06 12								
40½	—	—	Bromsgrove	d													06 21								
44	—	—	Barnt Green	d																					
52	—	—	University	d													06 39								
—	11	—	Hartlebury	d																					
—	14¾	—	**Kidderminster**	d								05 48								06 09			06 30		
—	17¾	—	Blakedown	d																					
—	19½	—	Hagley	d																					
—	21½	—	**Stourbridge Junction** 2	d								05 57								06 17		06 24	06 39		
—	22¾	—	Lye	d								06 01										06 27			
—	24	—	Cradley Heath	d								06 04								06 24		06 31	06 44		
—	25½	—	Old Hill	d								06 08										06 35			
—	26¾	—	Rowley Regis	d								06 12								06 30		06 38	06 50		
—	28½	0	Langley Green	d								06 15										06 41			
—	29½	—	Smethwick Galton Bdg H.L. 7	d								06 18								06 35		06 45	06 56		
54½	—	6¼	**Birmingham New Street** 12	a													06 45								
—	—	—		d					06 03							06 33					07 03				
—	—	—	**Birmingham International** ✈	d					06 15												07 15				
—	—	—	**Coventry**	d					06 25												07 25				
—	30¼	—	The Hawthorns 🚊	d								06 21								06 38		06 47	06 58		
—	32¾	—	Jewellery Quarter 🚊	d								06 24										06 51			
—	33½	—	**Birmingham Snow Hill** 🚊	a								06 28								06 46		06 54	07 04		
—	—	—		d	23p30		05 43	05 58			06 14	06 29			06 33				06 43	06 50		06 56	07 13		07 19
—	34	—	**Birmingham Moor Street**	d	23p33		05 46	06 01			06 17	06 32			06 36				06 46	06 53		06 59	07 16		07 22
—	34¾	—	Bordesley	d																					
—	35¾	9¼	Small Heath	d				06 05							06 41				06 50			07 03			
—	36¾	10¼	Tyseley	d	23p37			06 07				06 36			06 42				06 52			07 05			
—	—	11¼	Acocks Green	d	23p40			06 10							06 45							07 08			07 28
—	—	12¼	Olton	d	23p43			06 13							06 48							07 11			07 30
—	—	14	Solihull	d	23p47		05 56	06 16			06 27				06 50					07 04		07 14	07 26		07 34
—	—	15½	Widney Manor	d	23p50			06 20							06 55							07 17			07 37
—	—	17½	Dorridge	d	23p54		06 01	06 24			06 32				07a02					07 09		07 21	07 31		07a42
—	—	20	Lapworth	d	23p58			06 28														07 25			
—	—	24¼	Hatton	d	00 03					06 31								07 03				07 31			
—	—	27	Warwick Parkway	d	00 08	05 40	06 12				06 44							07 09		07 21			07 43		
—	—	28¼	Warwick	d	00 11		06 15			06 38								07 13				07 37	07 46		
—	—	30¼	**Leamington Spa** 8	a	00 14	05 45	06 20		06 37	06 45	06 49					06 59		07 17		07 26	07 37	07 44	07 50		
—	—	—		d	00 15	05 45	06 20		06 38		06 49					07 00		07 18		07 26	07 38		07 50		
—	—	—	Banbury	d	00a38	06 03	06 38		06a54		07 07					07a18		07 36		07 44	07a54		08 08		
—	—	—	**London Marylebone** 10 ⊖	a		07 18	07 52				08 16							08 50		08 53			09 23		
—	37¾	—	Spring Road	d								06 39							06 55						
—	38¼	—	Hall Green	d								06 42							06 58						
—	39½	—	Yardley Wood	d								06 45							07 01						
—	40¾	—	Shirley	d								06 48							07 06						
—	41¾	—	Whitlocks End	d								06 51							07 09						
—	42¾	—	Wythall	d								06 53							07 11						
—	43¾	—	Earlswood (West Midlands)	d															07 14						
—	44½	—	The Lakes	d															07x16						
—	45¾	—	Wood End	d															07x18						
—	47½	—	Danzey	d															07x21						
—	50¼	—	Henley-in-Arden	d								07 03							07 26						
—	52¼	—	Wootton Wawen	d															07x28						
—	56	—	Wilmcote	d				06 44											07 34						
—	58¾	—	**Stratford-upon-Avon**	a				06 48				07 15							07 39						

For general notes see front of timetable
For details of catering facilities see Directory of Train Operators

A 🛒 from Birmingham Snow Hill

Hereford, Worcester and Stourbridge → Birmingham → Leamington Spa, Marylebone and Stratford-upon-Avon

Network Diagram - See first page of Table 71

		LM	LM	GW	LM	XC	CH	CH	LM	GW		LM	LM	XC	CH	LM	LM	GW	LM	LM		XC	XC	LM	LM
				1 ◇		1 ◇				1				1 ◇				1 ◇					1 ◇		
				A				B										C D				E			
				⊠		☕		☕						☕				⊠					☕		
Hereford 7	d			05 42														06 43							07 09
Ledbury	a			05 58														06 59							07 25
	d			06 00														07 00							07 26
Colwall	d			06 07														07 08							07 32
Great Malvern	a			06 12														07 14							07 37
	d			06 13									06 49				07 05	07 15							07 37
Malvern Link	d			06 17									06 51				07 08	07 19							07 40
Worcester Foregate Street 7	a			06 26									06 59				07 15	07 28							07 49
	d			06 28					06 45	06 52			06 59				07 16	07 29		07 33					07 49
Worcester Shrub Hill 7	a			06 31						06 54			07 03				07 18	07 32							07 52
	d	06 15	06 25										07 06			07 15	07 24								07 56
Droitwich Spa	d	06 23	06 33						06 54				07 14			07 23	07 34			07 42					08 05
Bromsgrove	d		06 42										07 23									07 50			
Barnt Green	d																								
University	d		06 59														07 59					08 09			08 29
Hartlebury	d	06 30							07 01							07 31									
Kidderminster	d	06 37						06 56	07 09			07 18			07 30	07 37				07 53					
Blakedown	d	06 42							07 14			07 24				07 42				07 58					
Hagley	d	06 45							07 18			07 28				07 46				08 02					
Stourbridge Junction 2	d	06 50						07 07	07 23			07 32			07 40	07 50			07 56	08 08				08 14	
Lye	d	06 53						07 11				07 35							07 59					08 17	
Cradley Heath	d	06 57						07 14	07 29			07 39			07 45	07 56			08 02	08 14				08 21	
Old Hill	d	07 01						07 18				07 43							08 06					08 25	
Rowley Regis	d	07 04						07 22	07 35			07 47			07 53	08 01			08 10	08 20				08 29	
Langley Green	d	07 07						07 25				07 50							08 13					08 32	
Smethwick Galton Bdg H.L. 7	d	07 11						07 29	07 40			07 53			07 59	08 06			08 16	08 25				08 35	
Birmingham New Street 12	a		07 07										07 45				08 09					08 16			08 37
	d					07 33								08 03									08 33		
Birmingham International ✈	d													08 15											
Coventry	d													08 25											
The Hawthorns 🚊	d	07 13						07 32	07 42			07 56			08 02	08 09			08 19	08 28				08 38	
Jewellery Quarter 🚊	d	07 17						07 36	07 46			07 59			08 06	08 12			08 22	08 31				08 41	
Birmingham Snow Hill 🚊	a	07 20						07 40	07 49			08 03			08 11	08 16			08 25	08 35				08 45	
	d	07 25			07 39			07 45	07 50			08 05			08 12	08 17			08 27	08 37				08 47	
Birmingham Moor Street	d	07 28			07 42			07 48	07 53			08 08			08 15	08 20			08 30	08 40				08 50	
Bordesley	d																								
Small Heath	d	07 32			07 46							08 12								08 44					
Tyseley	d	07 34			07 48				07 58			08 14								08 46					
Acocks Green	d								08 01							08 26				08 49					
Olton	d								08 03							08 28				08 52					
Solihull	d							07 58	08 07						08 25	08 32				08 55					
Widney Manor	d								08 10							08 35				08 58					
Dorridge	d							08 03	08a16						08 30	08a41				09a03					
Lapworth	d							08 07																	
Hatton	d						07 56	08 13																	
Warwick Parkway	d							08 19							08 41										
Warwick	d						08 05	08 23							08 44										
Leamington Spa 8	a					07 59	08 09	08 26						08 37	08 49								08 59		
	d					08 00	08 09	08 27						08 38	08 49								09 00		
Banbury	d					08a18	08 28	08 45						08a54	09 09								09a18		
London Marylebone 10 ⊖	a						09 53	09 59							10 25										
Spring Road	d	07 37			07 51							08 17							08 36					08 56	
Hall Green	d	07 40			07 54							08 20							08 39					08 59	
Yardley Wood	d	07 43			07 57							08 23							08 42					09 02	
Shirley	d	07 46			08a00							08a26							08 45					09a05	
Whitlocks End	d	07 49																	08 48						
Wythall	d	07 51																	08 50						
Earlswood (West Midlands)	d	07 54																	08 53						
The Lakes	d	07x56																	08x55						
Wood End	d	07x58																	08x57						
Danzey	d	08x01																	09x00						
Henley-in-Arden	d	08 06																	09 05						
Wootton Wawen	d	08x09																	09x08						
Wilmcote	d	08 14																	09 13						
Stratford-upon-Avon	a	08 20																	09 19						

For general notes see front of timetable
For details of catering facilities see Directory of Train Operators

A All Tuesdays to Fridays, also Mondays until 24 March from Abergavenny (Table 131)
B ☕ from Birmingham Snow Hill
C From Abergavenny (Table 131)
D **The Cathedrals Express**
E From Gloucester (Table 57)

Hereford, Worcester and Stourbridge → Birmingham → Leamington Spa, Marylebone and Stratford-upon-Avon

Network Diagram - See first page of Table 71

Station		XC	CH	LM	LM	XC	LM	GW	CH	LM	LM	LM	LM	XC	LM	GW	XC	CH	CH	LM	LM	XC	CH
		A				R 1		1 ◇						1 ◇		B	◇ C					R 1	
Hereford 7	d						07 35																
Ledbury	a						07 50																
	d						07 51																
Colwall	d						07 57																
Great Malvern	a						08 01																
	d						08 03								08 35	08 51							
Malvern Link	d						08 06								08 37	08 54							
Worcester Foregate Street 7	a						08 14								08 46	09 01							
	d				08 03		08 19	08 37							08 46	09 02							
Worcester Shrub Hill 7	a							08 40								09 04							
	d																						
Droitwich Spa	d				08 11		08b32								08 55								
Bromsgrove	d	08 23					08 41										09 21						
Barnt Green	d																						
University	d	08 39					08 59																
Hartlebury	d																						
Kidderminster	d		08 10		08 22							08 56									09 30		
Blakedown	d		08 15		08 27							09 01											
Hagley	d		08 18		08 30							09 04											
Stourbridge Junction 2	d		08 23		08 35					08 45	08 55	09 09	09 19							09 25	09 39		
Lye	d				08 38						08 58									09 28			
Cradley Heath	d		08 28		08 41					08 51	09 01	09 14	09 24							09 31	09 44		
Old Hill	d				08 45						09 05									09 35			
Rowley Regis	d		08 34		08 49					08 57	09 09	09 20	09 30							09 39	09 50		
Langley Green	d				08 52						09 12									09 42			
Smethwick Galton Bdg H.L. 7	d		08 40		08 55					09 02	09 15	09 25	09 35							09 45	09 55		
Birmingham New Street 12	a	08 46					09 07								09 43		09 45						
	d					09 03								09 33								10 03	
Birmingham International ✈	d					09 15																10 15	
Coventry	d					09 25																10 25	
The Hawthorns	d		08 42		08 58					09 05	09 18	09 28	09 38							09 48	09 58		
Jewellery Quarter	d		08 47		09 01					09 09	09 21	09 31	09 41							09 51	10 01		
Birmingham Snow Hill	a		08 51		09 05					09 15	09 25	09 36	09 45							09 55	10 05		
	d		08 52	08 57	09 07				09 12	09 17	09 27	09 37	09 47						09 52	09 57	10 07		10 12
Birmingham Moor Street	d		08 55	09 00	09 10				09 15	09 20	09 30	09 40	09 50						09 55	10 00	10 10		10 15
Bordesley	d																						
Small Heath	d				09 14							09 44									10 14		
Tyseley	d				09 16							09 46									10 16		
Acocks Green	d			09 06						09 26		09 49								10 06			
Olton	d			09 08						09 28		09 52								10 08			
Solihull	d		09 05	09 12					09 25	09 32		09 55							10 05	10 12			10 25
Widney Manor	d			09 15						09 35		09 58								10 15			
Dorridge	d		09 10	09a22					09 30	09a41		10a04							10 11	10a22			10 30
Lapworth	d								09 34														10 34
Hatton	d								09 40									10 00					10 40
Warwick Parkway	d		09 21						09 45										10 22				10 45
Warwick	d		09 24						09 49									10 06	10 25				10 49
Leamington Spa 8	a		09 29			09 37			09 53					09 59				10 10	10 29			10 37	10 53
	d		09 29			09 38			09 54					10 00				10 11	10 29			10 38	10 54
Banbury	d		09 47			09a54			10 12					10a18				10 29	10 47			10a54	11 13
London Marylebone 10 ⊖	a		10 59						11 30									11 56	12 00				12 30
Spring Road	d				09 19						09 36		09 56								10 19		
Hall Green	d				09 22						09 39		09 59								10 22		
Yardley Wood	d				09 25						09 42		10 02								10 25		
Shirley	d				09a28						09 45		10a05								10a28		
Whitlocks End	d										09 48												
Wythall	d										09 50												
Earlswood (West Midlands)	d										09 53												
The Lakes	d										09x55												
Wood End	d										09x57												
Danzey	d										10x00												
Henley-in-Arden	d										10 05												
Wootton Wawen	d										10x08												
Wilmcote	d										10 13												
Stratford-upon-Avon	a										10 21												

For general notes see front of timetable
For details of catering facilities see Directory of Train Operators

A From Gloucester to Nottingham (Table 57)
B To Westbury (Table 123)
C To Nottingham (Table 57)
b Arr. 0827

Hereford, Worcester and Stourbridge → Birmingham → Leamington Spa, Marylebone and Stratford-upon-Avon

Network Diagram - See first page of Table 71

		LM	LM	LM	GW	LM		XC	LM	CH	LM	EM	XC	CH	LM	LM		LM	LM	LM	GW	XC	CH	CH	LM
					[1] ◇			[1] ◇					[R] [1]								◇ A	[1] ◇			
								☕					☕									☕			
Hereford [7]	d			08 50														09 50							
Ledbury	a			09 06														10 06							
	d			09 07														10 07							
Colwall	d			09 13														10 13							
Great Malvern	a			09 18														10 18							
	d			09 18					09 35									10 18			10 43				
Malvern Link	d			09 21					09 37									10 21			10 46				
Worcester Foregate Street [7]	a			09 30					09 46									10 30			11 01				
	d	09 15		09 31	09 34				09 46						10 15			10 31			11 02				
Worcester Shrub Hill [7]	a				09 36																11 04				
	d																			10 47					
Droitwich Spa	d	09 24		09 40					09 55						10 24			10 40		10 55					
Bromsgrove	d			09 50														10 50							
Barnt Green	d																								
University	d			10 09														11 09							
Hartlebury	d																								
Kidderminster	d	09 36				09 56			10 06			10 26			10 36				10 56	11 06					
Blakedown	d	09 41							10 11			10 31								11 11					
Hagley	d	09 44							10 14			10 34								11 14					
Stourbridge Junction [2]	d	09 49	09 55			10b09			10 19		10 25	10 39			10 49	10 55			11c09	11 19					11 25
Lye	d		09 58								10 28					10 58									11 28
Cradley Heath	d	09 54	10 01			10 14			10 24		10 31	10 44			10 54	11 01			11 14	11 24					11 31
Old Hill	d		10 05								10 35					11 05									11 35
Rowley Regis	d	10 00	10 09			10 20			10 30		10 39	10 50			11 00	11 09			11 20	11 30					11 39
Langley Green	d		10 12								10 42					11 12									11 42
Smethwick Galton Bdg H.L. [7]	d	10 05	10 15			10 25			10 35		10 45	10 55			11 05	11 15			11 25	11 35					11 45
Birmingham New Street [12]	a			10 24														11 23							
	d							10 33					11 03									11 33			
Birmingham International ✈	d												11 15												
Coventry	d												11 25												
The Hawthorns 🚊	d	10 08	10 18			10 28			10 38		10 48	10 58			11 08	11 18			11 28	11 38					11 48
Jewellery Quarter 🚊	d	10 11	10 21			10 31			10 41		10 51	11 01			11 11	11 21			11 31	11 41					11 51
Birmingham Snow Hill 🚊	a	10 15	10 25			10 35			10 45		10 55	11 05			11 15	11 25			11 35	11 45					11 55
	d	10 17	10 27			10 37			10 47	10 52	10 57	11 07		11 12	11 17	11 27			11 37	11 47				11 52	11 57
Birmingham Moor Street	d	10 20	10 30			10 40			10 50	10 55	11 00	11 10		11 15	11 20	11 30			11 40	11 50				11 55	12 00
Bordesley	d																								
Small Heath	d					10 44						11 14							11 44						
Tyseley	d					10 46						11 16							11 46						
Acocks Green	d	10 26				10 49					11 06				11 26				11 49						12 06
Olton	d	10 28				10 52					11 08				11 28				11 52						12 08
Solihull	d	10 32				10 55				11 05	11 12			11 25	11 32				11 55					12 05	12 12
Widney Manor	d	10 35				10 58					11 15				11 35				11 58						12 15
Dorridge	d	10a41				11a04				11 10	11a21			11 31	11a41				12a04					12 10	12a22
Lapworth	d																								
Hatton	d																						11 59		
Warwick Parkway	d									11 21				11 41										12 21	
Warwick	d									11 24				11 45									12 05	12 24	
Leamington Spa [8]	a							10 59		11 29			11 37	11 51								11 59	12 07	12 29	
	d							11 00		11 29			11 38	11 52								12 00	12 08	12 29	
Banbury	d							11a18		11 47			11a54	12 09								12a18	12 28	12 47	
London Marylebone [10]	⊖ a									12 59				13 29									13 55	13 59	
Spring Road	d		10 36						10 56			11 19				11 36				11 56					
Hall Green	d		10 39						10 59			11 22				11 39				11 59					
Yardley Wood	d		10 42						11 02			11 25				11 42				12 02					
Shirley	d		10 45						11a05			11a28				11 45				12a05					
Whitlocks End	d		10 48													11 48									
Wythall	d		10 50													11 50									
Earlswood (West Midlands)	d		10 53													11 53									
The Lakes	d		10x55													11x55									
Wood End	d		10x57													11x57									
Danzey	d		11x00													12x00									
Henley-in-Arden	d		11 05													12 05									
Wootton Wawen	d		11x08													12x08									
Wilmcote	d		11 13													12 13									
Stratford-upon-Avon	a		11 21													12 21									

For general notes see front of timetable
For details of catering facilities see Directory of Train Operators

A To Brighton (Table 123)
b Arr. 1004
c Arr. 1104

Hereford, Worcester and Stourbridge → Birmingham → Leamington Spa, Marylebone and Stratford-upon-Avon

Network Diagram - See first page of Table 71

Station		LM	XC	CH	LM	GW	LM	LM	LM	XC	LM	CH	LM	LM	XC	CH	LM	LM	LM	GW	LM	LM	GW
			R 1			1 ◇				1 ◇					R 1					1 ◇			◇ A
			☕			🛒				☕					☕					🛒			
Hereford 7	d								10 50														
Ledbury	a								11 06														
	d								11 07														
Colwall	d								11 13														
Great Malvern	a								11 18														
	d					11 06			11 18		11 30								12 18				12 51
Malvern Link	d					11 10			11 21		11 32								12 21				12 54
Worcester Foregate Street 7	a					11 25			11 30		11 40								12 29				13 01
	d				11 15	11 26			11 31		11 41						12 15		12 31	12 40			13 02
Worcester Shrub Hill 7	a					11 29					11 43									12 43			13 04
	d										11 47											12 47	
Droitwich Spa	d				11 24				11 40		11 55						12 24		12 40			12 55	
Bromsgrove	d								11 50										12 50				
Barnt Green	d																						
University	d								12 09										13 09				
Hartlebury	d																						
Kidderminster	d	11 26			11 36			11 56			12 06			12 26			12 36				12 56	13 06	
Blakedown	d	11 31									12 11			12 31								13 11	
Hagley	d	11 34									12 14			12 34								13 14	
Stourbridge Junction 2	d	11 39			11 49		11 55	12b09			12 19		12 25	12 39			12 49	12 55			13c09	13 19	
Lye	d						11 58						12 28					12 58					
Cradley Heath	d	11 44			11 54		12 01	12 14			12 24		12 31	12 44			12 54	13 01			13 14	13 24	
Old Hill	d						12 05						12 35					13 05					
Rowley Regis	d	11 50			12 00		12 09	12 20			12 30		12 39	12 50			13 00	13 09			13 20	13 30	
Langley Green	d						12 12						12 42					13 12					
Smethwick Galton Bdg H.L. 7	d	11 55			12 05		12 15	12 25			12 35		12 45	12 55			13 05	13 15			13 25	13 35	
Birmingham New Street 12	a								12 23										13 18				
	d		12 03							12 33					13 03								
Birmingham International ✈	d		12 15												13 15								
Coventry	d		12 25												13 25								
The Hawthorns 🚊	d	11 58			12 08		12 18	12 28			12 38		12 48	12 58			13 08	13 18			13 28	13 38	
Jewellery Quarter 🚊	d	12 01			12 11		12 21	12 31			12 41		12 51	13 01			13 11	13 21			13 31	13 41	
Birmingham Snow Hill 🚊	a	12 05			12 15		12 25	12 35			12 45		12 55	13 05			13 15	13 25			13 35	13 45	
	d	12 07		12 12	12 17		12 27	12 37			12 47	12 52	12 57	13 07		13 12	13 17	13 27			13 37	13 47	
Birmingham Moor Street	d	12 10		12 15	12 20		12 30	12 40			12 50	12 55	13 00	13 10		13 15	13 20	13 30			13 40	13 50	
Bordesley	d																						
Small Heath	d	12 14						12 44						13 14							13 44		
Tyseley	d	12 16						12 46						13 16							13 46		
Acocks Green	d				12 26			12 49					13 06				13 26				13 49		
Olton	d				12 28			12 52					13 08				13 28				13 52		
Solihull	d			12 25	12 32			12 55				13 05	13 12			13 25	13 32				13 55		
Widney Manor	d				12 35			12 58					13 15				13 35				13 58		
Dorridge	d			12 31	12a41			13a04				13 10	13a21			13 31	13a41				14a04		
Lapworth	d			12 35																			
Hatton	d			12 41																			
Warwick Parkway	d			12 46								13 21				13 41							
Warwick	d			12 49								13 24				13 45							
Leamington Spa 8	a		12 37	12 53						12 59		13 29			13 37	13 50							
	d		12 38	12 54						13 00		13 29			13 38	13 50							
Banbury	d		12a54	13 12						13a18		13 47			13a54	14 08							
London Marylebone 10 ⊖	a			14 30								14 59				15 28							
Spring Road	d	12 19					12 36				12 56			13 19				13 36				13 56	
Hall Green	d	12 22					12 39				12 59			13 22				13 39				13 59	
Yardley Wood	d	12 25					12 42				13 02			13 25				13 42				14 02	
Shirley	d	12a28					12 45				13a05			13a28				13 45				14a05	
Whitlocks End	d						12 48											13 48					
Wythall	d						12 50											13 50					
Earlswood (West Midlands)	d						12 53											13 53					
The Lakes	d						12x55											13x55					
Wood End	d						12x57											13x57					
Danzey	d						13x00											14x00					
Henley-in-Arden	d						13 05											14 05					
Wootton Wawen	d						13x08											14x08					
Wilmcote	d						13 13											14 13					
Stratford-upon-Avon	a						13 21											14 21					

For general notes see front of timetable
For details of catering facilities see Directory of Train Operators

A To Weymouth (Table 123)
b Arr. 1204
c Arr. 1304

Hereford, Worcester and Stourbridge → Birmingham → Leamington Spa, Marylebone and Stratford-upon-Avon

Network Diagram - See first page of Table 71

		XC		CH	CH	LM	LM	XC	CH	LM	LM	LM		LM	LM	XC	CH	LM	LM	GW	XC	CH		LM	LM
		1 ◇ 🛒						R 1 🛒								1 ◇ 🛒				1 ◇ 🍴	1 ◇ 🛒				
Hereford 7	d													12 50						13 24					
Ledbury	a													13 06						13 40					
	d													13 07						13 42					
Colwall	d													13 13						13 49					
Great Malvern	a													13 18						13 53					
	d													13 18					13 38	13 54					
Malvern Link	d													13 21					13 40	13 58					
Worcester Foregate Street 7	a													13 30					13 48	14 08					
	d									13 15				13 31					13 49	14 09				14 15	
Worcester Shrub Hill 7	a																		13 51	14 12					
	d														13 47				13 57						
Droitwich Spa	d									13 24				13 40	13 55				14 07					14 24	
Bromsgrove	d													13 50											
Barnt Green	d																								
University	d													14 09											
Hartlebury	d																								
Kidderminster	d									13 36		13 56			14 06				14b26					14 36	
Blakedown	d														14 11				14 31						
Hagley	d														14 14				14 34						
Stourbridge Junction 2	d					13 25	13 37			13 49	13 55	14c09			14 19			14 25	14 39					14e49	14 55
Lye	d					13 28					13 58							14 28							14 58
Cradley Heath	d					13 31	13 43			13 54	14 01	14 14			14 24			14 31	14 44					14 54	15 01
Old Hill	d					13 35					14 05							14 35							15 05
Rowley Regis	d					13 39	13 49			14 00	14 09	14 20			14 30			14 39	14 50					15 00	15 09
Langley Green	d					13 42					14 12							14 42							15 12
Smethwick Galton Bdg H.L. 7	d					13 45	13 53			14 05	14 15	14 25			14 35			14 45	14 55					15 05	15 15
Birmingham New Street 12	a													14 23											
	d	13 33						14 03								14 33					15 03				
Birmingham International ✈	d							14 15													15 15				
Coventry	d							14 25													15 25				
The Hawthorns 🚊	d					13 48	13 56			14 08	14 18	14 28			14 38			14 48	14 58					15 08	15 18
Jewellery Quarter 🚊	d					13 51	13 59			14 11	14 21	14 31			14 41			14 51	15 01					15 11	15 21
Birmingham Snow Hill 🚊	a					13 56	14 03			14 15	14 25	14 35			14 45			14 55	15 05					15 15	15 25
	d				13 52	13 57	14 07		14 12	14 17	14 27	14 37			14 47		14 52	14 57	15 07			15 12		15 17	15 27
Birmingham Moor Street	d				13 55	14 00	14 10		14 15	14 20	14 30	14 40			14 50		14 55	15 00	15 10			15 15		15 20	15 30
Bordesley	d																								
Small Heath	d						14 14					14 44							15 14						
Tyseley	d						14 16					14 46							15 16						
Acocks Green	d					14 06				14 26		14 49						15 06						15 26	
Olton	d					14 08				14 28		14 52						15 08						15 28	
Solihull	d				14 05	14 12			14 25	14 32		14 55					15 05	15 12				15 25		15 32	
Widney Manor	d					14 15				14 35		14 58						15 15						15 35	
Dorridge	d				14 10	14a22			14 31	14a41		15a04					15 10	15a21				15 30		15a41	
Lapworth	d								14 35																
Hatton	d			13 57					14 41																
Warwick Parkway	d				14 21				14 46								15 21					15 41			
Warwick	d			14 03	14 24				14 49								15 24					15 44			
Leamington Spa 8	a	13 59		14 07	14 29			14 37	14 53							14 59	15 29				15 37	15 49			
	d	14 00		14 08	14 29			14 38	14 54							15 00	15 29				15 38	15 49			
Banbury	d	14a18		14 27	14 47			14a54	15 12							15a18	15 47				15a54	16 07			
London Marylebone 10 ⊖	a			15 53	16 00				16 31								17 01					17 31			
Spring Road	d						14 19				14 36				14 56				15 19						15 36
Hall Green	d						14 22				14 39				14 59				15 22						15 39
Yardley Wood	d						14 25				14 42				15 02				15 25						15 42
Shirley	d						14a28				14 45				15a05				15a28						15 45
Whitlocks End	d										14 48														15 48
Wythall	d										14 50														15 50
Earlswood (West Midlands)	d										14 53														15 53
The Lakes	d										14x55														15x55
Wood End	d										14x57														15x57
Danzey	d										15x00														16x00
Henley-in-Arden	d										15 05														16 05
Wootton Wawen	d										15x08														16x08
Wilmcote	d										15 13														16 13
Stratford-upon-Avon	a										15 21														16 21

For general notes see front of timetable
For details of catering facilities see Directory of Train Operators

b Arr. 1417
c Arr. 1404
e Arr. 1445

Hereford, Worcester and Stourbridge → Birmingham → Leamington Spa, Marylebone and Stratford-upon-Avon

Network Diagram - See first page of Table 71

		LM	LM	LM	XC	CH	CH	LM	GW	EM		XC	CH	EM	LM	LM	LM	XC	LM	CH		LM	LM	XC	CH
					1 ◇				1			R 1						R 1						R 1	
									A																
					☕							☕						☕						☕	
Hereford 7	d	13 50																							
Ledbury	a	14 06																							
	d	14 07																							
Colwall	d	14 13																							
Great Malvern	a	14 18																							
	d	14 18							14 51								15 14								
Malvern Link	d	14 21							14 54								15 17								
Worcester Foregate Street 7	a	14 30							15 01								15 24								
	d	14 31							15 02					15 15			15 25		15 39						
Worcester Shrub Hill 7	a								15 04										15 41						
	d			14 43															15 44						
Droitwich Spa	d	14 40		14b55										15 24			15 34		15 55						
Bromsgrove	d	14 50															15 44								
Barnt Green	d																								
University	d	15 09															15 59								
Hartlebury	d																								
Kidderminster	d		14 56	15 06						15 26				15 36		15 56			16 06				16 23		
Blakedown	d			15 11						15 31				15 41					16 11				16 28		
Hagley	d			15 14						15 34				15 44					16 14				16 31		
Stourbridge Junction 2	d		15c09	15 19				15 25		15 39				15 49	15 55	16e09			16 19			16 25	16 35		
Lye	d							15 28							15 58							16 28			
Cradley Heath	d		15 14	15 24				15 31		15 44				15 54	16 01	16 14			16 24			16 31	16 41		
Old Hill	d							15 35							16 05							16 35			
Rowley Regis	d		15 20	15 30				15 39		15 50				16 00	16 09	16 20			16 30			16 39	16 47		
Langley Green	d							15 42							16 12							16 42			
Smethwick Galton Bdg H.L. 7	d		15 25	15 35				15 45		15 55				16 05	16 15	16 25			16 35			16 45	16 52		
Birmingham New Street 12	a	15 21															16 09								
	d				15 33							16 03						16 33						17 03	
Birmingham International ✈	d											16 15												17 15	
Coventry	d											16 25												17 25	
The Hawthorns 🚊	d		15 28	15 38				15 48		15 58				16 08	16 18	16 28			16 38			16 48	16 54		
Jewellery Quarter 🚊	d		15 31	15 41				15 51		16 01				16 11	16 21	16 31			16 41			16 51	16 58		
Birmingham Snow Hill 🚊	a		15 35	15 45				15 55		16 05				16 15	16 25	16 35			16 45			16 55	17 01		
	d		15 37	15 47			15 52	15 57		16 07			16 12	16 17	16 27	16 37			16 47	16 52		16 57	17 02		17 10
Birmingham Moor Street	d		15 40	15 50			15 55	16 00		16 10			16 15	16 20	16 30	16 40			16 50	16 55		17 00	17 05		17 13
Bordesley	d																								
Small Heath	d		15 44							16 14						16 44			16 54						
Tyseley	d		15 46							16 16					16 34	16 46			16 56			17 04			
Acocks Green	d		15 49					16 06						16 26		16 49						17 07			
Olton	d		15 52					16 08						16 28		16 52						17 10			
Solihull	d		15 55				16 05	16 12					16 25	16 32		16 55				17 05		17 12			17 23
Widney Manor	d		15 58					16 15						16 35		16 58						17 16			17 26
Dorridge	d		16a04				16 10	16a21					16 30	16a41		17a04				17 10		17a22			17 30
Lapworth	d												16 34												17 34
Hatton	d					15 58							16 40												17 40
Warwick Parkway	d						16 21						16 45							17 20					17 45
Warwick	d					16 04	16 24						16 49							17 23					17 48
Leamington Spa 8	a				15 59	16 07	16 29					16 37	16 53					16 59		17 28				17 37	17 53
	d				16 00	16 08	16 29					16 38	16 54					17 00		17 28				17 38	17 53
Banbury	d				16a18	16 27	16 47					16a54	17 12					17a18		17 46				17a54	18 11
London Marylebone 10	⊖ a					17 55	18 04						18 33							19 08					19 33
Spring Road	d			15 56						16 19					16 37				16 59				17 11		
Hall Green	d			15 59						16 22					16 40				17 02				17 14		
Yardley Wood	d			16 02						16 25					16 43				17 05				17 17		
Shirley	d			16a05						16a28					16 46				17a08				17 20		
Whitlocks End	d														16 49								17 23		
Wythall	d														16 51								17 25		
Earlswood (West Midlands)	d														16 54										
The Lakes	d														16x56										
Wood End	d														16x58										
Danzey	d														17x01										
Henley-in-Arden	d														17 06								17 35		
Wootton Wawen	d														17x09										
Wilmcote	d														17 14										
Stratford-upon-Avon	a														17 22								17 49		

For general notes see front of timetable
For details of catering facilities see Directory of Train Operators

- **A** To Weymouth (Table 123)
- **b** Arr. 1450
- **c** Arr. 1504
- **e** Arr. 1604

Hereford, Worcester and Stourbridge → Birmingham → Leamington Spa, Marylebone and Stratford-upon-Avon

Network Diagram - See first page of Table 71

Station		GW	LM	LM	LM	LM	GW	CH		LM	LM	GW	LM	XC	CH	XC	LM	LM		CH	LM	GW	LM	LM	XC
		1 ◇					1 ◇					A		R 1		R 1						1 ◇			R 1 ◇
Hereford 7	d	15 19				15 38	15 19																	16 50	
Ledbury	a	15 35				15 53	15 35																	17 06	
	d	15 36				15 55	15 36																	17 07	
Colwall	d	15 43				16 01	15 43																	17 13	
Great Malvern	a	15 48				16 06	15 48																	17 18	
	d	15 51				16 10	15 51															17 06		17 18	
Malvern Link	d	15 55				16 13	15 55															17 10		17 21	
Worcester Foregate Street 7	a	16 04				16 22	16 04															17 19		17 30	
	d	16 06	16 07			16 24	16 06				16 34	17 02									17 14	17 21		17 31	
Worcester Shrub Hill 7	a	16 09					16 09				16 36	17 04										17 24			
	d			16 17							16 40														
Droitwich Spa	d		16 16	16 25		16 34					16 48										17 23			17 40	
Bromsgrove	d					16 44																		17 49	
Barnt Green	d					16 50																			
University	d					17 00																		18 09	
Hartlebury	d		16 23																		17 30				
Kidderminster	d		16 30	16 37						16 52	16 59							17 26			17 36				
Blakedown	d		16 35	16 43							17 04							17 31			17 41				
Hagley	d		16 39	16 47							17 08							17 34			17 44				
Stourbridge Junction 2	d		16 44	16 51	16 55					17 02	17 13						17 25	17 39			17 48		17 57		
Lye	d				16 58												17 28						18 00		
Cradley Heath	d		16 50	16 57	17 01					17 12	17 19						17 31	17 44			17 54		18 03		
Old Hill	d				17 05												17 35						18 07		
Rowley Regis	d		16 55	17 03	17 09					17 17	17 24						17 39	17 50			18 00		18 11		
Langley Green	d				17 12												17 42						18 14		
Smethwick Galton Bdg H.L. 7	d		17 00	17 08	17 15					17 22	17 29						17 45	17 55			18 05		18 17		
Birmingham New Street 12	a					17 14																		18 21	
	d													17 33		18 03									18 33
Birmingham International ✈	d															18 15									
Coventry	d															18 25									
The Hawthorns	d		17 03	17 10	17 18					17 25	17 32						17 48	17 58			18 08		18 20		
Jewellery Quarter	d		17 06	17 14	17 21					17 28	17 35						17 51	18 01			18 11		18 23		
Birmingham Snow Hill	a		17 09	17 17	17 25					17 32	17 38						17 55	18 05			18 15		18 26		
	d		17 15	17 22	17 27					17 34	17 42		17 47		17 52		17 57	18 07		18 12	18 22		18 27		
Birmingham Moor Street	d		17 18	17 25	17 30					17 37	17 45		17 50		17 55		18 00	18 10		18 15	18 25		18 30		
Bordesley	d																								
Small Heath	d		17 22							17 41	17 49		17 54				18 04	18 14					18 34		
Tyseley	d		17 24		17 34					17 45	17 51		17 56				18 06	18 16					18 36		
Acocks Green	d			17 31						17 48	17 54						18 09				18 31				
Olton	d			17 33						17 50	17 57						18 12				18 33				
Solihull	d			17 37						17 54	18 00				18 05		18 15			18 25	18 37				
Widney Manor	d			17 40						17 57	18 03						18 19				18 40				
Dorridge	d			17a46						18 01	18a08				18 12		18 23			18 30	18a47				
Lapworth	d									18 05							18 27			18 34					
Hatton	d							18 02		18 11							18 33			18 40					
Warwick Parkway	d									18 15					18 23		18 37			18 45					
Warwick	d							18 08		18 19					18 26		18 40			18 49					
Leamington Spa 8	a							18 12		18 24				17 59	18 30	18 37	18 47			18 53					18 59
	d							18 12						18 00	18 30	18 38				18 54					19 00
Banbury	d							18 32						18a18	18 48	18a54				19 12					19a18
London Marylebone 10 ⊖	a							19 57							20 06					20 35					
Spring Road	d		17 27		17 37								17 59					18 19					18 39		
Hall Green	d		17 30		17 40								18 02					18 22					18 42		
Yardley Wood	d		17 33		17 43								18 05					18 25					18 45		
Shirley	d		17a37		17 46								18 08					18a28					18 48		
Whitlocks End	d				17 49								18 11										18 51		
Wythall	d				17 51								18 13										18 53		
Earlswood (West Midlands)	d				17 54								18 16										18 56		
The Lakes	d				17x56								18x18										18x58		
Wood End	d				17x58								18x20										19x00		
Danzey	d				18x01								18x23										19x03		
Henley-in-Arden	d				18 06								18 28										19 08		
Wootton Wawen	d				18x09								18x30										19x10		
Wilmcote	d				18 14								18 36										19 16		
Stratford-upon-Avon	a				18 22								18 43										19 23		

For general notes see front of timetable
For details of catering facilities see Directory of Train Operators

A To Southampton (Table 123)

Hereford, Worcester and Stourbridge → Birmingham → Leamington Spa, Marylebone and Stratford-upon-Avon

Network Diagram - See first page of Table 71

		LM	XC	GW	EM	XC		CH	EM	LM	LM	EM	XC	EM	GW	GW		GW	LM	CH	CH	XC	CH	LM	LM
			R			R																R			
			1			1							1 ◇		1 ◇	1		1				1			
																A									
Hereford 7	d									17 40									18 52						
Ledbury	a									17 55									19 06						
	d									17 56									19 11						
Colwall	d									18 02									19 17						
Great Malvern	a									18 07									19 21						
	d			17 42						18 07						18 54			19 22						
Malvern Link	d			17 45						18 10									19 25						
Worcester Foregate Street 7	a			17 53						18 19						19 02			19 33						
	d			17 54	17 55					18 19		18 34			18 50	19 03		19 27	19 34						19 44
Worcester Shrub Hill 7	a			17 56						18 22					18 53	19 05		19 29	19 36						
	d									18 26				18 48					19 54						
Droitwich Spa	d				18 04					18 34		18 43		18 56					↪						19 53
Bromsgrove	d									18 42															
Barnt Green	d									18 49															
University	d									18 59															
Hartlebury	d													19 03											
Kidderminster	d	18 00			18 16				18 37			18 53		19 10											20b10
Blakedown	d	18 05							18 42			18 58		19 15											20 15
Hagley	d	18 09							18 46			19 02		19 19											20 19
Stourbridge Junction 2	d	18 13			18 25				18 51			19 09		19 24										19 54	20 24
Lye	d				18 28				18 54					19 27										19 57	20 27
Cradley Heath	d	18 19			18 31				18 57			19 15		19 30										20 00	20 30
Old Hill	d				18 35				19 01					19 34										20 04	20 34
Rowley Regis	d	18 25			18 39				19 05			19 21		19 38										20 08	20 38
Langley Green	d				18 42				19 08					19 41										20 11	20 41
Smethwick Galton Bdg H.L. 7	d	18 30			18 45				19 11			19 26		19 44										20 14	20 44
Birmingham New Street 12	a									19 12															
	d		18 33			19 03							19 33									20 03			
Birmingham International ✈	d					19 15																20 15			
Coventry	d					19 25																20 25			
The Hawthorns 🚋	d	18 33			18 48				19 14			19 29		19 47										20 17	20 47
Jewellery Quarter 🚋	d	18 36			18 51				19 17			19 32		19 50										20 20	20 50
Birmingham Snow Hill 🚋	a	18 41			18 55				19 20			19 35		19 53										20 23	20 53
	d	18 45			18 57			19 12	19 22		19 27	19 37		19 55									20 12	20 27	20 55
Birmingham Moor Street	d	18 48			19 00			19 15	19 25		19 30	19a39		19 58									20 15	20 30	20 58
Bordesley	d																								
Small Heath	d	18 52			19 04						19 34			20 02										20 34	21 02
Tyseley	d	18 54			19 06						19 36			20 04										20 36	21 04
Acocks Green	d	18 57							19 31					20 07											21 07
Olton	d	19 00							19 33					20 10											21 10
Solihull	d	19 03						19 25	19 37					20 13									20 25		21 13
Widney Manor	d	19 07						19 28	19 40					20 17									20 28		21 17
Dorridge	d	19 11						19 32	19a47					20a22									20 32		21a22
Lapworth	d	19 15						19 36															20 36		
Hatton	d	19 21						19 42												19 59	20 17		20 42		
Warwick Parkway	d							19 47												20 06			20 47		
Warwick	d	19 27						19 50												20 09	20 23		20 50		
Leamington Spa 8	a	19 32	18 59			19 37		19 54					19 59							20 14	20 33	20 38	20 54		
	d		19 00			19 38		19 54					20 00							20 14		20 38	20 54		
Banbury	d		19a18			19a54		20 11					20a18							20 32		20a54	21 12		
London Marylebone 10 ⊖	a							21 38												21 57			22 32		
Spring Road	d				19 09						19 39													20 39	
Hall Green	d				19 12						19 42													20 42	
Yardley Wood	d				19 15						19 45													20 45	
Shirley	d				19a18						19 48													20 48	
Whitlocks End	d										19 51													20 51	
Wythall	d										19 53													20 53	
Earlswood (West Midlands)	d										19 56													20 56	
The Lakes	d										19x58													20x58	
Wood End	d										20x00													21x00	
Danzey	d										20x03													21x03	
Henley-in-Arden	d										20 08													21 08	
Wootton Wawen	d										20x10													21x10	
Wilmcote	d										20 16													21 16	
Stratford-upon-Avon	a										20 23													21 23	

For general notes see front of timetable
For details of catering facilities see Directory of Train Operators

A To Weymouth (Table 123)
b Arr. 2003

Hereford, Worcester and Stourbridge → Birmingham → Leamington Spa, Marylebone and Stratford-upon-Avon

Network Diagram - See first page of Table 71

		LM	XC	LM		CH	LM	LM	GW	GW	CH	LM	LM	XC		LM	LM	GW	GW	CH	LM	CH		
																		FX	FO					
			1 ◇						1 ◇					◇				1 ◇	1 ◇					
										A														
									⊼									⊼	⊼					
Hereford 7	d			19 50												21 30					22 43			
Ledbury	a			20 08												21 46					22 58			
	d			20 17												21 47					22 59			
Colwall	d			20 23												21 53					23 05			
Great Malvern	a			20 28												21 58					23 10			
	d			20 28						20 51						21 58			22 32		23 10			
Malvern Link	d			20 31						20 54						22 01					23 13			
Worcester Foregate Street 7	a			20 40						21 04						22 10			22 42		23 20			
	d			20 42					20 58	21 05						22 10	22 17	22 35	22 44		23 20			
Worcester Shrub Hill 7	a	←							21 01	21 07							22 19	22 38	22 47		23 25			
	d	19 54						20 53					21 52				22 27							
Droitwich Spa	d	20 02		20 51				21 01					22 00			22 19	22 35							
Bromsgrove	d	20 10		20 59										22 20		22 28								
Barnt Green	d																							
University	d	20 29		21 16												22 46								
Hartlebury	d																							
Kidderminster	d							21 11					22 10				22 45							
Blakedown	d							21 16					22 15											
Hagley	d							21 20					22 19											
Stourbridge Junction 2	d						20 54	21 24				21 54	22 24				22 54							
Lye	d						20 57	21 27				21 57	22 27				22 57							
Cradley Heath	d						21 00	21 30				22 00	22 30				23 00							
Old Hill	d						21 04	21 34				22 04	22 34				23 04							
Rowley Regis	d						21 08	21 38				22 08	22 38				23 08							
Langley Green	d						21 11	21 41				22 11	22 41				23 11							
Smethwick Galton Bdg H.L. 7	d						21 14	21 44				22 14	22 44				23 14							
Birmingham New Street 12	a	20 44		21 27										22 48		22 57								
	d		21 03																					
Birmingham International ✈	d		21 15																					
Coventry	d		21 25																					
The Hawthorns	d						21 17	21 47				22 17	22 47				23 17							
Jewellery Quarter	d						21 20	21 50				22 20	22 50				23 20							
Birmingham Snow Hill	a						21 23	21 53				22 23					23 24							
	d					21 15	21 25	21 55			22 15	22 25					23 25					23 30		
Birmingham Moor Street	d					21 18	21 28	21 58			22 18	22 28	23 00				23 28					23 33		
Bordesley	d																							
Small Heath	d						21 32	22 02				22 32	23 04				23 32							
Tyseley	d						21 34	22 04			22 22	22 34	23 06				23 34					23 37		
Acocks Green	d							22 07			22 25		23 09									23 40		
Olton	d							22 10			22 28		23 11									23 43		
Solihull	d					21 27		22 13			22 32		23 15									23 47		
Widney Manor	d							22 17			22 35		23 18									23 50		
Dorridge	d					21 33		22a22			22 39		23a24									23 54		
Lapworth	d					21 37					22 43											23 58		
Hatton	d					21 42					22 48											00 03		
Warwick Parkway	d					21 47					22 53											00 08		
Warwick	d					21 50					22 56									23 21		00 11		
Leamington Spa 8	a		21 37			21 54					23 00									23 24		00 14		
	d		21 38			21 55					23 01									23 25		00 15		
Banbury	d		21a54			22 14					23a23									23a43		00a38		
London Marylebone 10 ⊖	a					23 53																		
Spring Road	d						21 37					22 37					23 37							
Hall Green	d						21 40					22 40					23 40							
Yardley Wood	d						21 43					22 43					23 43							
Shirley	d						21a46					22a46					23a46							
Whitlocks End	d																							
Wythall	d																							
Earlswood (West Midlands)	d																							
The Lakes	d																							
Wood End	d																							
Danzey	d																							
Henley-in-Arden	d																							
Wootton Wawen	d																							
Wilmcote	d																							
Stratford-upon-Avon	a																							

For general notes see front of timetable
For details of catering facilities see Directory of Train Operators

A To Gloucester (Table 57)

Table 71

Saturdays

Hereford, Worcester and Stourbridge → Birmingham → Leamington Spa, Marylebone and Stratford-upon-Avon

Network Diagram - See first page of Table 71

	CH	XC	CH	CH	LM	GW	XC	CH	LM		LM	LM	XC	XC	CH	CH	LM	GW	XC	LM	LM	LM	LM	LM
		1 ◇				1 ◇	1 ◇						1 ◇	A				1 ◇	1 ◇					
							☕						☕					☕	☕					
Hereford 7 d																								
Ledbury a																								
d																								
Colwall d																								
Great Malvern a																								
d						06 03						06 20						07 08						07 30
Malvern Link d						06 06						06 23						07 12						07 32
Worcester Foregate Street 7 a						06 13						06 30						07 21						07 40
d						06 19						06 31						07 23						07 43
Worcester Shrub Hill 7 a						06 21												07 26						
d					05 44						06 24						06 58			07 33				
Droitwich Spa d					05 52						06 32	06 40					07 06			07 40				07 52
Bromsgrove d												06 50		07 23						07 50				
Barnt Green d																								
University d												07 09								08 09				
Hartlebury d											06 39						07 13							
Kidderminster d					06 02			06 37			06 45					07 14	07 22					07 46		08 06
Blakedown d					06 07						06 50						07 27					07 51		08 11
Hagley d					06 11						06 54						07 30					07 54		08 14
Stourbridge Junction 2 d					06 15			06 45			07b02					07 22	07 35					07 59	08 05	08 19
Lye d					06 18						07 05						07 38						08 08	
Cradley Heath d					06 22			06 50			07 09					07 27	07 41					08 04	08 11	08 24
Old Hill d					06 26						07 13						07 45						08 15	
Rowley Regis d					06 29			06 56			07 16					07 33	07 49					08 10	08 19	08 30
Langley Green d					06 32						07 19						07 52						08 22	
Smethwick Galton Bdg H.L. 7 d					06 36			07 02			07 23					07 39	07 55					08 15	08 25	08 35
Birmingham New Street 12 a												07 16		07 45						08 16				
d		06 03					07 03						07 33						08 03					
Birmingham International ✈ d		06 15					07 15												08 15					
Coventry d		06 25					07 25												08 25					
The Hawthorns 🚊 d					06 38			07 04			07 25					07 41	07 58					08 18	08 28	08 38
Jewellery Quarter 🚊 d					06 42						07 29						08 01					08 21	08 31	08 41
Birmingham Snow Hill 🚊 a					06 46			07 10			07 32					07 47	08 05					08 25	08 35	08 45
d	23p30		06 12	06 37	06 51			07 12	07 20		07 35					07 52	08 07				08 17	08 27	08 37	08 47
Birmingham Moor Street d	23p33		06 15	06 40	06 54			07 15	07 23		07 38					07 55	08 10				08 20	08 30	08 40	08 50
Bordesley d																								
Small Heath d					06 58				07 27								08 14						08 44	
Tyseley d	23p37				07 00				07 29								08 16						08 46	
Acocks Green d	23p40				07 03						07 46										08 26		08 49	
Olton d	23p43				07 06						07 49										08 28		08 52	
Solihull d	23p47		06 25	06 50	07 09			07 25			07 52					08 04					08 32		08 55	
Widney Manor d	23p50				07 12						07 56										08 35		08 58	
Dorridge d	23p54		06 30	06 55	07a17			07 30			08a01					08 10					08a41		09a03	
Lapworth d	23p58							07 34																
Hatton d	00 03							07 40							07 56									
Warwick Parkway d	00 08		06 41	07 06				07 45								08 20								
Warwick d	00 11		06 44	07 09				07 50							08 03	08 23								
Leamington Spa 8 a	00 14	06 36	06 49	07 14			07 36	07 53					07 58		08 06	08 28			08 37					
d	00 15	06 38	06 49	07 14			07 38	07 54					08 00		08 08	08 29			08 38					
Banbury d	00a38	06a54	07 08	07 33			07a54	08 12					08a17		08 27	08 47			08a54					
London Marylebone 10 ⊖ a			08 29	08 47				09 30							09 55	10 01								
Spring Road d									07 32								08 19					08 36		08 56
Hall Green d									07 35								08 22					08 39		08 59
Yardley Wood d									07 38								08 25					08 42		09 02
Shirley d									07 41								08a28					08 45		09a05
Whitlocks End d									07 44													08 48		
Wythall d									07 46													08 50		
Earlswood (West Midlands) d									07 49													08 53		
The Lakes d									07x51													08x55		
Wood End d									07x53													08x57		
Danzey d									07x56													09x00		
Henley-in-Arden d									08 01													09 05		
Wootton Wawen d									08x04													09x08		
Wilmcote d									08 09													09 13		
Stratford-upon-Avon a									08 16													09 21		

For general notes see front of timetable
For details of catering facilities see Directory of Train Operators

A To Nottingham (Table 57)
b Arr. 0657

Table 71

Saturdays

Hereford, Worcester and Stourbridge → Birmingham → Leamington Spa, Marylebone and Stratford-upon-Avon

Network Diagram - See first page of Table 71

Station		GW	XC	CH	XC		LM	LM	XC	CH	LM	LM	GW	LM	LM	LM	XC	XC	XC	CH	CH	LM	LM	XC	CH
		1 ◇	1 ◇						1 ◇								1 ◇	◇	◇					1 ◇	
					A								B					C	D						
		☕	☕						☕								☕	🛒	🛒					☕	
Hereford 7	d	07 22										07 37													
Ledbury	a	07 38										07 53													
	d	07 40										07 54													
Colwall	d	07 47										08 00													
Great Malvern	a	07 51										08 04													
	d	07 52										08 06	08 25												
Malvern Link	d	07 56										08 09	08 28												
Worcester Foregate Street 7	a	08 06										08 17	08 35												
	d	08 07										08 19	08 36												
Worcester Shrub Hill 7	a	08 10										08 21	08 38												
	d										08 14	08 26													
Droitwich Spa	d										08 22	08 34													
Bromsgrove	d				08 23							08 43						09 20	09 21						
Barnt Green	d																								
University	d				08 39							08 59													
Hartlebury	d										08 29														
Kidderminster	d			08 13							08 36										09 03	09 16	09 26		
Blakedown	d										08 41										09 08		09 31		
Hagley	d										08 44										09 12		09 34		
Stourbridge Junction 2	d			08 26				08 35			08 49			08 55	09 09						09 15	09 25	09 39		
Lye	d							08 38						08 58								09 28			
Cradley Heath	d			08 31				08 41			08 54			09 01	09 14						09 21	09 31	09 44		
Old Hill	d							08 45						09 05								09 35			
Rowley Regis	d			08 37				08 49			09 00			09 09	09 20						09 26	09 39	09 50		
Langley Green	d							08 52						09 12											
Smethwick Galton Bdg H.L. 7	d			08 42				08 55			09 05			09 15	09 25						09 33	09 45	09 55		
Birmingham New Street 12	a				08 46							09 14						09 45	09 45						
	d		08 33						09 03								09 33							10 03	
Birmingham International ✈	d								09 15															10 15	
Coventry	d								09 25															10 25	
The Hawthorns 🚊	d			08 44				08 58			09 08			09 18	09 28						09 34	09 48	09 58		
Jewellery Quarter 🚊	d							09 01			09 11			09 21	09 31							09 51	10 01		
Birmingham Snow Hill 🚊	a			08 51				09 05			09 15			09 25	09 36						09 42	09 56	10 05		
	d			08 52			08 57	09 07		09 12	09 17			09 27	09 37	09 47					09 52	09 57	10 07		10 12
Birmingham Moor Street	d			08 55			09 00	09 10		09 15	09 20			09 30	09 40	09 50					09 55	10 00	10 10		10 15
Bordesley	d																								
Small Heath	d							09 14							09 44								10 14		
Tyseley	d							09 16							09 46								10 16		
Acocks Green	d						09 06				09 26				09 49										
Olton	d						09 08				09 28				09 52										
Solihull	d			09 06			09 12			09 25	09 32				09 55						10 05	10 12			10 25
Widney Manor	d			09 09			09 15				09 35				09 58							10 15			
Dorridge	d			09 13			09a21			09 31	09a41				10a04						10 12	10a22			10 31
Lapworth	d									09 35															10 35
Hatton	d																			09 56					10 41
Warwick Parkway	d			09 23						09 43											10 22				10 46
Warwick	d			09 27						09 46										10 04	10 26				10 49
Leamington Spa 8	a		08 58	09 31					09 37	09 50							09 58			10 07	10 29			10 37	10 53
	d		09 00	09 32					09 38	09 50							10 00			10 08	10 30			10 38	10 54
Banbury	d		09a17	09 50					09a54	10 10							10a17			10 28	10 48			10a54	11 12
London Marylebone 10 ⊖	a			11 00						11 31										11 56	11 59				12 30
Spring Road	d							09 19						09 36		09 56							10 19		
Hall Green	d							09 22						09 39		09 59							10 22		
Yardley Wood	d							09 25						09 42		10 02							10 25		
Shirley	d							09a28						09 45		10a05							10a28		
Whitlocks End	d													09 48											
Wythall	d													09 50											
Earlswood (West Midlands)	d													09 53											
The Lakes	d													09x55											
Wood End	d													09x57											
Danzey	d													10x00											
Henley-in-Arden	d													10 05											
Wootton Wawen	d													10x08											
Wilmcote	d													10 13											
Stratford-upon-Avon	a													10 21											

For general notes see front of timetable
For details of catering facilities see Directory of Train Operators

A From Gloucester to Nottingham (Table 57)
B To Westbury (Table 123)
C From 2 February. To Nottingham (Table 57)
D Until 26 January. To Nottingham (Table 57)

Hereford, Worcester and Stourbridge → Birmingham → Leamington Spa, Marylebone and Stratford-upon-Avon

Network Diagram - See first page of Table 71

Station		LM	GW 1 ◇ ☕	LM	EM	LM	EM	GW 1 ◇ ☕	XC 1 ◇ ☕	CH		LM	LM	XC 1 ◇ ☕	CH	LM	LM	LM	LM	EM	GW A	XC 1 ◇ ☕	CH	CH	LM
Hereford 7	d					08 50												09 50							
Ledbury	a					09 06												10 06							
	d					09 07												10 07							
Colwall	d					09 13												10 13							
Great Malvern	a					09 18												10 18							
	d		09 08			09 18		09 48										10 18			10 43				
Malvern Link	d		09 12			09 21		09 52										10 21			10 46				
Worcester Foregate Street 7	a		09 21			09 30		10 01										10 30			11 01				
	d	09 15	09 21			09 31		10 03								10 15		10 31			11 02				
Worcester Shrub Hill 7	a		09 26					10 06													11 04				
	d						09 47													10 47					
Droitwich Spa	d	09 24				09 40	09 55									10 24		10 40		10 55					
Bromsgrove	d					09 50												10 50							
Barnt Green	d																								
University	d					10 09												11 09							
Hartlebury	d																								
Kidderminster	d	09 36			09 56		10 06						10 26			10 36			10 56	11 06					
Blakedown	d	09 41					10 11						10 31							11 11					
Hagley	d	09 44					10 14						10 34							11 14					
Stourbridge Junction 2	d	09 49		09 55	10b09		10 19					10 25	10 39			10 49	10 55		11c09	11 19					11 25
Lye	d			09 58								10 28					10 58								11 28
Cradley Heath	d	09 54		10 01	10 14		10 24					10 31	10 44			10 54	11 01		11 14	11 24					11 31
Old Hill	d			10 05								10 35					11 05								11 35
Rowley Regis	d	10 00		10 09	10 20		10 30					10 39	10 50			11 00	11 09		11 20	11 30					11 39
Langley Green	d			10 12								10 42					11 12								11 42
Smethwick Galton Bdg H.L. 7	d	10 05		10 15	10 25		10 35					10 45	10 55			11 05	11 15		11 25	11 35					11 45
Birmingham New Street 12	a					10 21												11 21							
	d								10 33					11 03								11 33			
Birmingham International ✈	d													11 15											
Coventry	d													11 25											
The Hawthorns 🚋	d	10 08		10 18	10 28		10 38					10 48	10 58			11 08	11 18		11 28	11 38					11 48
Jewellery Quarter 🚋	d	10 11		10 21	10 31		10 41					10 51	11 01			11 11	11 21		11 31	11 41					11 51
Birmingham Snow Hill 🚋	a	10 15		10 25	10 35		10 45					10 56	11 05			11 15	11 25		11 35	11 45					11 55
	d	10 17		10 27	10 37		10 47			10 52		10 57	11 07		11 12	11 17	11 27		11 37	11 47				11 52	11 57
Birmingham Moor Street	d	10 20		10 30	10 40		10 50			10 55		11 00	11 10		11 15	11 20	11 30		11 40	11 50				11 55	12 00
Bordesley	d																								
Small Heath	d				10 44								11 14						11 44						
Tyseley	d				10 46								11 16						11 46						
Acocks Green	d	10 26			10 49							11 06				11 26			11 49						12 06
Olton	d	10 28			10 52							11 08				11 28			11 52						12 08
Solihull	d	10 32			10 55					11 05		11 12			11 25	11 32			11 55					12 05	12 12
Widney Manor	d	10 35			10 58							11 15				11 35			11 58						12 15
Dorridge	d	10a41			11a04					11 12		11a22			11 31	11a41			12a04					12 12	12a22
Lapworth	d																								
Hatton	d																						11 57		
Warwick Parkway	d									11 22					11 41									12 22	
Warwick	d									11 26					11 45								12 03	12 26	
Leamington Spa 8	a								10 58	11 30				11 37	11 49							11 58	12 07	12 29	
	d								11 00	11 31				11 38	11 49							12 00	12 07	12 30	
Banbury	d								11a17	11 49				11a54	12 07							12a17	12 27	12 49	
London Marylebone 10 ⊖	a									13 01					13 30								13 58	14 01	
Spring Road	d			10 36			10 56						11 19				11 36			11 56					
Hall Green	d			10 39			10 59						11 22				11 39			11 59					
Yardley Wood	d			10 42			11 02						11 25				11 42			12 02					
Shirley	d			10 45			11a05						11a28				11 45			12a05					
Whitlocks End	d			10 48													11 48								
Wythall	d			10 50													11 50								
Earlswood (West Midlands)	d			10 53													11 53								
The Lakes	d			10x55													11x55								
Wood End	d			10x57													11x57								
Danzey	d			11x00													12x00								
Henley-in-Arden	d			11 05													12 05								
Wootton Wawen	d			11x08													12x08								
Wilmcote	d			11 13													12 13								
Stratford-upon-Avon	a			11 21													12 21								

For general notes see front of timetable
For details of catering facilities see Directory of Train Operators

A To Brighton (Table 123)
b Arr. 1004
c Arr. 1104

Table 71

Saturdays

Hereford, Worcester and Stourbridge → Birmingham → Leamington Spa, Marylebone and Stratford-upon-Avon

Network Diagram - See first page of Table 71

		LM	XC	CH	LM	GW	LM	LM	LM	LM	GW	XC	CH	LM	LM		XC	CH	LM	LM	LM	LM	LM	GW	XC
			1 ◇			1 ◇					1 ◇	1 ◇					1 ◇							◇ A	1 ◇
			☕			☕					☕	☕					☕							Ħ	☕
Hereford 7	d								10 50												11 50				
Ledbury	a								11 05												12 06				
	d								11 07												12 07				
Colwall	d								11 13												12 13				
Great Malvern	a								11 18												12 18				
	d					11 05			11 18	11 30	11 45										12 18			12 51	
Malvern Link	d					11 09			11 21	11 32	11 49										12 21			12 54	
Worcester Foregate Street 7	a					11 20			11 31	11 40	11 58										12 30			13 01	
	d				11 15	11 22			11 31	11 41	12 00								12 15		12 31			13 02	
Worcester Shrub Hill 7	a					11 25				11 43	12 03													13 04	
	d									11 47													12 47		
Droitwich Spa	d				11 24				11 40	11 55									12 24		12 40		12 55		
Bromsgrove	d								11 50												12 50				
Barnt Green	d																								
University	d								12 09												13 09				
Hartlebury	d																								
Kidderminster	d	11 26			11 36			11 56		12 06					12 26				12 36			12 56	13 06		
Blakedown	d	11 31								12 11					12 31								13 11		
Hagley	d	11 34								12 14					12 34								13 14		
Stourbridge Junction 2	d	11 39			11 49		11 55	12b09		12 19				12 25	12 39				12 49	12 55		13c09	13 19		
Lye	d						11 58							12 28						12 58					
Cradley Heath	d	11 44			11 54		12 01	12 14		12 24				12 31	12 44				12 54	13 01		13 14	13 24		
Old Hill	d						12 05							12 35						13 05					
Rowley Regis	d	11 50			12 00		12 09	12 20		12 30				12 39	12 50				13 00	13 09		13 20	13 30		
Langley Green	d						12 12							12 42						13 12					
Smethwick Galton Bdg H.L. 7	d	11 55			12 05		12 15	12 25		12 35				12 45	12 55				13 05	13 15		13 25	13 35		
Birmingham New Street 12	a								12 21												13 21				
	d		12 03									12 33					13 03								13 33
Birmingham International ✈	d		12 15														13 15								
Coventry	d		12 25														13 25								
The Hawthorns 🚊	d	11 58			12 08		12 18	12 28		12 38				12 48	12 58				13 08	13 18		13 28	13 38		
Jewellery Quarter 🚊	d	12 01			12 11		12 21	12 31		12 41				12 51	13 01				13 11	13 21		13 31	13 41		
Birmingham Snow Hill 🚊	a	12 05			12 15		12 25	12 35		12 45				12 55	13 05				13 15	13 25		13 35	13 45		
	d	12 07		12 12	12 17		12 27	12 37		12 47			12 52	12 57	13 07			13 12	13 17	13 27		13 37	13 47		
Birmingham Moor Street	d	12 10		12 15	12 20		12 30	12 40		12 50			12 55	13 00	13 10			13 15	13 20	13 30		13 40	13 50		
Bordesley	d																								
Small Heath	d	12 14						12 44							13 14							13 44			
Tyseley	d	12 16						12 46							13 16							13 46			
Acocks Green	d				12 26			12 49						13 06					13 26			13 49			
Olton	d				12 28			12 52						13 08					13 28			13 52			
Solihull	d			12 25	12 32			12 55					13 05	13 12				13 25	13 32			13 55			
Widney Manor	d				12 35			12 58						13 15					13 35			13 58			
Dorridge	d			12 31	12a41			13a04					13 10	13a21				13 31	13a41			14a04			
Lapworth	d			12 35																					
Hatton	d			12 40																					
Warwick Parkway	d			12 45									13 21					13 41							
Warwick	d			12 48									13 24					13 45							
Leamington Spa 8	a		12 37	12 51								12 58	13 29				13 37	13 49							13 58
	d		12 38	12 52								13 00	13 29				13 38	13 49							14 00
Banbury	d		12a54	13 11								13a17	13 47				13a54	14 07							14a17
London Marylebone 10 ⊖	a			14 33									15 01					15 30							
Spring Road	d	12 19					12 36			12 56					13 19					13 36			13 56		
Hall Green	d	12 22					12 39			12 59					13 22					13 39			13 59		
Yardley Wood	d	12 25					12 42			13 02					13 25					13 42			14 02		
Shirley	d	12a28					12 45			13a05					13a28					13 45			14a05		
Whitlocks End	d						12 48													13 48					
Wythall	d						12 50													13 50					
Earlswood (West Midlands)	d						12 53													13 53					
The Lakes	d						12x55													13x55					
Wood End	d						12x57													13x57					
Danzey	d						13x00													14x00					
Henley-in-Arden	d						13 05													14 05					
Wootton Wawen	d						13x08													14x08					
Wilmcote	d						13 13													14 13					
Stratford-upon-Avon	a						13 21													14 21					

For general notes see front of timetable
For details of catering facilities see Directory of Train Operators

A Until 22 March to Weymouth,from 29 March to Westbury(Table 123)

b Arr. 1204

c Arr. 1304

Table 71

Saturdays

Hereford, Worcester and Stourbridge → Birmingham → Leamington Spa, Marylebone and Stratford-upon-Avon

Network Diagram - See first page of Table 71

		CH	CH	LM	LM	XC	CH	LM	GW	LM	LM	LM	LM	XC	CH	LM	LM	XC	CH	LM		GW	LM	LM	GW
						1 ◇			1 ◇					1 ◇				1 ◇				1 ◇			◇
																									A
						☕			☕					☕				☕				☕			
Hereford 7	d											12 50										13 20		13 50	
Ledbury	a											13 06										13 37		14 06	
	d											13 07										13 39		14 07	
Colwall	d											13 13										13 46		14 13	
Great Malvern	a											13 18										13 51		14 18	
	d											13 18	13 30									14 05		14 18	
Malvern Link	d											13 21	13 32									14 09		14 21	
Worcester Foregate Street 7	a											13 30	13 40									14 19		14 30	
	d							13 15	13 22			13 31	13 41							14 15		14 21		14 31	14 42
Worcester Shrub Hill 7	a								13 25				13 43									14 24			14 44
	d												13 47												
Droitwich Spa	d							13 24				13 40	13 55							14 24				14 40	
Bromsgrove	d											13 50												14 50	
Barnt Green	d																								
University	d											14 09												15 09	
Hartlebury	d																								
Kidderminster	d				13 26			13 36			13 56		14 06				14 26			14 36					
Blakedown	d				13 31								14 11				14 31								
Hagley	d				13 34								14 14				14 34								
Stourbridge Junction 2	d			13 25	13 39			13 49		13 55	14b09		14 19			14 25	14 39			14 49			14 55		
Lye	d			13 28						13 58						14 28							14 58		
Cradley Heath	d			13 31	13 44			13 54		14 01	14 14		14 24			14 31	14 44			14 54			15 01		
Old Hill	d			13 35						14 05						14 35							15 05		
Rowley Regis	d			13 39	13 50			14 00		14 09	14 20		14 30			14 39	14 50			15 00			15 09		
Langley Green	d			13 42						14 12						14 42							15 12		
Smethwick Galton Bdg H.L. 7	d			13 45	13 55			14 05		14 15	14 25		14 35			14 45	14 55			15 05			15 15		
Birmingham New Street 12	a											14 21												15 21	
	d					14 03								14 33				15 03							
Birmingham International ✈	d					14 15												15 15							
Coventry	d					14 25												15 25							
The Hawthorns 🚊	d			13 48	13 58			14 08		14 18	14 28		14 38			14 48	14 58			15 08			15 18		
Jewellery Quarter 🚊	d			13 51	14 01			14 11		14 21	14 31		14 41			14 51	15 01			15 11			15 21		
Birmingham Snow Hill 🚊	a			13 55	14 05			14 15		14 25	14 35		14 45			14 55	15 05			15 15			15 25		
	d		13 52	13 57	14 07		14 12	14 17		14 27	14 37		14 47		14 52	14 57	15 07		15 12	15 17			15 27		
Birmingham Moor Street	d		13 55	14 00	14 10		14 15	14 20		14 30	14 40		14 50		14 55	15 00	15 10		15 15	15 20			15 30		
Bordesley	d																								
Small Heath	d				14 14						14 44						15 14								
Tyseley	d				14 16						14 46						15 16								
Acocks Green	d			14 06				14 26			14 49					15 06				15 26					
Olton	d			14 08				14 28			14 52					15 08				15 28					
Solihull	d		14 05	14 12			14 25	14 32			14 55				15 05	15 12			15 25	15 32					
Widney Manor	d			14 15				14 35			14 58					15 15				15 35					
Dorridge	d		14 10	14a23			14 31	14a41			15a04				15 10	15a21			15 31	15a41					
Lapworth	d						14 35																		
Hatton	d	14 00					14 40																		
Warwick Parkway	d		14 21				14 45								15 21				15 41						
Warwick	d	14 05	14 24				14 48								15 24				15 45						
Leamington Spa 8	a	14 09	14 29			14 37	14 51							14 58	15 29			15 37	15 49						
	d	14 11	14 29			14 38	14 52							15 00	15 29			15 38	15 49						
Banbury	d	14 30	14 47			14a54	15 11							15a17	15 47			15a54	16 07						
London Marylebone 10 ⊖	a	15 58	16 01				16 33								16 59				17 28						
Spring Road	d				14 19					14 36			14 56				15 19						15 36		
Hall Green	d				14 22					14 39			14 59				15 22						15 39		
Yardley Wood	d				14 25					14 42			15 02				15 25						15 42		
Shirley	d				14a28					14 45			15a05				15a28						15 45		
Whitlocks End	d									14 48													15 48		
Wythall	d									14 50													15 50		
Earlswood (West Midlands)	d									14 53													15 53		
The Lakes	d									14x55													15x55		
Wood End	d									14x57													15x57		
Danzey	d									15x00													16x00		
Henley-in-Arden	d									15 05													16 05		
Wootton Wawen	d									15x08													16x08		
Wilmcote	d									15 13													16 13		
Stratford-upon-Avon	a									15 21													16 21		

For general notes see front of timetable
For details of catering facilities see Directory of Train Operators

A Until 22 March to Weymouth,from29 march to Westbury

b Arr. 1404

Table 71

Saturdays

Hereford, Worcester and Stourbridge → Birmingham → Leamington Spa, Marylebone and Stratford-upon-Avon

Network Diagram - See first page of Table 71

Station		LM	XC 1 ◇ ☕	LM	CH	CH	LM	LM	XC 1 ◇ ☕	CH	LM	LM	LM	LM	LM	GW 1 ◇ ☕	XC 1 ◇ ☕	CH	LM	LM	XC 1 ◇ ☕	CH	LM	LM	LM
Hereford 7	d													14 50		15 23									15 50
Ledbury	a													15 06		15 39									16 06
	d													15 07		15 40									16 07
Colwall	d													15 13		15 47									16 13
Great Malvern	a													15 18		15 52									16 18
	d													15 18	15 30	15 53									16 18
Malvern Link	d													15 21	15 32	15 57									16 21
Worcester Foregate Street 7	a													15 30	15 40	16 05									16 31
	d										15 15			15 31	15 41	16 06							16 13		16 31
Worcester Shrub Hill 7	a														15 43	16 11									
	d			14 47											15 47										
Droitwich Spa	d			14 55							15 24			15 40	15 55								16 22		16 40
Bromsgrove	d													15 50											16 50
Barnt Green	d																								
University	d													16 09											17 09
Hartlebury	d																						16 29		
Kidderminster	d	14 56		15 06				15 26			15 36		15 56		16 06					16 26			16 36		
Blakedown	d			15 11				15 31			15 41				16 11					16 31			16 41		
Hagley	d			15 14				15 34			15 44				16 14					16 34			16 44		
Stourbridge Junction 2	d	15b09		15 19			15 25	15 39			15 49	15 55	16c09		16 19				16 25	16 39			16 49	16 55	
Lye	d						15 28					15 58							16 28					16 58	
Cradley Heath	d	15 14		15 24			15 31	15 44			15 54	16 01	16 14		16 24				16 31	16 44			16 54	17 01	
Old Hill	d						15 35					16 05							16 35					17 05	
Rowley Regis	d	15 20		15 30			15 39	15 50			16 00	16 09	16 20		16 30				16 39	16 50			17 00	17 09	
Langley Green	d						15 42					16 12							16 42					17 12	
Smethwick Galton Bdg H.L. 7	d	15 25		15 35			15 45	15 55			16 05	16 15	16 25		16 35				16 45	16 55			17 05	17 15	
Birmingham New Street 12	a													16 21											17 21
	d		15 33						16 03								16 33				17 03				
Birmingham International ✈	d								16 15												17 15				
Coventry	d								16 25												17 25				
The Hawthorns 🚋	d	15 28		15 38			15 48	15 58			16 08	16 18	16 28		16 38				16 48	16 58			17 08	17 18	
Jewellery Quarter 🚋	d	15 31		15 41			15 51	16 01			16 11	16 21	16 31		16 41				16 51	17 01			17 11	17 21	
Birmingham Snow Hill 🚋	a	15 35		15 45			15 55	16 05			16 15	16 25	16 35		16 45				16 56	17 05			17 15	17 25	
	d	15 37		15 47		15 52	15 57	16 05		16 12	16 17	16 27	16 37		16 47			16 52	16 57	17 07		17 12	17 17	17 27	
Birmingham Moor Street	d	15 40		15 50		15 55	16 00	16 08		16 15	16 20	16 30	16 40		16 50			16 55	17 00	17 10		17 15	17 20	17 30	
Bordesley	d																								
Small Heath	d	15 44						16 12					16 44		16 54					17 14					
Tyseley	d	15 46						16 14				16 34	16 46		16 56				17 04	17 16				17 34	
Acocks Green	d	15 49					16 06				16 26		16 49						17 07				17 26		
Olton	d	15 52					16 08				16 28		16 52						17 10				17 28		
Solihull	d	15 55				16 05	16 12			16 25	16 32		16 55					17 06	17 13			17 25	17 32		
Widney Manor	d	15 58					16 15				16 35		16 58						17 16				17 35		
Dorridge	d	16a04				16 10	16a22			16 30	16a42		17a04					17 12	17a22			17 31	17a42		
Lapworth	d									16 34												17 35			
Hatton	d				15 58					16 40												17 41			
Warwick Parkway	d					16 21				16 45								17 22				17 46			
Warwick	d				16 04	16 24				16 49								17 26				17 49			
Leamington Spa 8	a		15 58		16 08	16 29			16 37	16 53							16 58	17 29			17 37	17 53			
	d		16 00		16 09	16 29			16 38	16 54							17 00	17 30			17 38	17 54			
Banbury	d		16a17		16 28	16 47			16a54	17 12							17a17	17 49			17a54	18 12			
London Marylebone 10 ⊖	a				17 57	18 00				18 32								19 02				19 30			
Spring Road	d			15 56				16 17				16 37			16 59					17 19				17 37	
Hall Green	d			15 59				16 20				16 40			17 02					17 22				17 40	
Yardley Wood	d			16 02				16 23				16 43			17 05					17 25				17 43	
Shirley	d			16a05				16a26				16 46			17a08					17 28				17a46	
Whitlocks End	d											16 49								17 31					
Wythall	d											16 51								17 33					
Earlswood (West Midlands)	d											16 54								17 36					
The Lakes	d											16x56								17x38					
Wood End	d											16x58								17x40					
Danzey	d											17x01								17x43					
Henley-in-Arden	d											17 06								17 48					
Wootton Wawen	d											17x09								17x51					
Wilmcote	d											17 14								17 56					
Stratford-upon-Avon	a											17 22								18 03					

For general notes see front of timetable
For details of catering facilities see Directory of Train Operators

b Arr. 1504
c Arr. 1604

Table 71

Saturdays

Hereford, Worcester and Stourbridge → Birmingham → Leamington Spa, Marylebone and Stratford-upon-Avon

Network Diagram - See first page of Table 71

		LM	LM		GW	XC	CH	CH	LM	LM	XC	CH	LM	GW	LM	LM	LM	LM	XC	XC	CH	LM	GW	LM	LM
						1 ◇					1 ◇			1 ◇					1 ◇	1 ◇			1 ◇		
					A																				
						☕					☕			☕					☕	☕			☕		
Hereford 7	d															16 50									17 50
Ledbury	a															17 06									18 06
	d															17 07									18 07
Colwall	d															17 13									18 13
Great Malvern	a															17 18									18 18
	d				16 43									17 08		17 18	17 30						18 08		18 18
Malvern Link	d				16 46									17 12		17 21	17 32						18 12		18 21
Worcester Foregate Street 7	a				17 01									17 21		17 30	17 40						18 21		18 30
	d				17 02								17 14	17 23		17 31	17 41						18 23		18 31
Worcester Shrub Hill 7	a				17 04									17 26			17 43						18 26		
	d		16 47														17 47					18 18			
Droitwich Spa	d		16 55										17 23			17 40	17 55					18 26			18 40
Bromsgrove	d															17 50									18 50
Barnt Green	d																								
University	d															18 09									19 09
Hartlebury	d												17 30												
Kidderminster	d	16 56	17 06							17 26			17 36				18 06					18 36			
Blakedown	d		17 11							17 31			17 41				18 11								
Hagley	d		17 14							17 34			17 44				18 14								
Stourbridge Junction 2	d	17b09	17 19						17 25	17 39			17 49		17 55		18 19	18 25				18 49		18 55	
Lye	d								17 28						17 58			18 28						18 58	
Cradley Heath	d	17 14	17 24						17 31	17 44			17 54		18 01		18 24	18 31				18 54		19 01	
Old Hill	d								17 35						18 05			18 35						19 05	
Rowley Regis	d	17 20	17 30						17 39	17 50			18 00		18 09		18 30	18 39				19 00		19 09	
Langley Green	d								17 42						18 12			18 42						19 12	
Smethwick Galton Bdg H.L. 7	d	17 25	17 35						17 45	17 55			18 05		18 15		18 35	18 45				19 05		19 15	
Birmingham New Street 12	a															18 21									19 21
	d					17 33					18 03								18 33	19 03					
Birmingham International ✈	d										18 15									19 15					
Coventry	d										18 25									19 25					
The Hawthorns 🚊	d	17 28	17 38						17 48	17 58			18 08		18 18		18 38	18 48				19 08		19 18	
Jewellery Quarter 🚊	d	17 31	17 41						17 51	18 01			18 11		18 21		18 41	18 51				19 11		19 21	
Birmingham Snow Hill 🚊	a	17 35	17 45						17 55	18 05			18 15		18 25		18 45	18 55				19 15		19 25	
	d	17 37	17 47					17 52	17 57	18 07		18 12	18 17		18 27		18 47	18 57			19 10	19 17		19 27	
Birmingham Moor Street	d	17 40	17 50					17 55	18 00	18 10		18 15	18 20		18 30		18 50	19 00			19 13	19 20		19 30	
Bordesley	d																								
Small Heath	d	17 44	17 54							18 14			18 24				18 54	19 04				19 24		19 34	
Tyseley	d	17 46	17 56							18 16			18 26				18 56	19 06				19 26		19 36	
Acocks Green	d	17 49							18 06				18 29				18 59					19 29			
Olton	d	17 52							18 08				18 32				19 02					19 32			
Solihull	d	17 55						18 06	18 12			18 25	18 35				19 05				19 23	19 35			
Widney Manor	d	17 58							18 15			18 28	18 38				19 08				19 26	19 39			
Dorridge	d	18a04						18 11	18a22			18 32	18a43				19a13				19 30	19a42			
Lapworth	d											18 36									19 34				
Hatton	d						17 56					18 42									19 40				
Warwick Parkway	d							18 22				18 46									19 44				
Warwick	d						18 04	18 25				18 48									19 47				
Leamington Spa 8	a					17 58	18 07	18 29			18 37	18 52							18 58	19 37	19 50				
	d					18 00	18 08	18 29			18 38	18 52							19 00	19 38	19 51				
Banbury	d					18a17	18 28	18 47			18a54	19 12							19a17	19a54	20 10				
London Marylebone 10 ⊖	a						19 56	20 01				20 37									21 36				
Spring Road	d		17 59							18 19					18 36			19 09						19 39	
Hall Green	d		18 02							18 22					18 39			19 12						19 42	
Yardley Wood	d		18 05							18 25					18 42			19 15						19 45	
Shirley	d		18 08							18a28					18 45			19a18						19 48	
Whitlocks End	d		18 11												18 48									19 51	
Wythall	d		18 13												18 50									19 53	
Earlswood (West Midlands)	d		18 16												18 53									19 56	
The Lakes	d		18x18												18x55									19x58	
Wood End	d		18x20												18x57									20x00	
Danzey	d		18x23												19x00									20x03	
Henley-in-Arden	d		18 28												19 05									20 08	
Wootton Wawen	d		18x30												19x08									20x10	
Wilmcote	d		18 36												19 13									20 16	
Stratford-upon-Avon	a		18 43												19 21									20 23	

For general notes see front of timetable
For details of catering facilities see Directory of Train Operators

A To Westbury (Table 123)
b Arr. 1704

Hereford, Worcester and Stourbridge → Birmingham → Leamington Spa, Marylebone and Stratford-upon-Avon

Network Diagram - See first page of Table 71

		LM	GW	LM	CH	XC	CH	LM	LM	XC	CH	LM	LM	LM	GW	CH	LM	LM	LM	XC	LM	EM	GW
			1 ◇			1 ◇				1 ◇					◇					◇			1
															A								
			🍴																				
Hereford 7	d			19 04									19 59						21 33				
Ledbury	a			19 19									20 14						21 48				
	d			19 20									20 15						21 49				
Colwall	d			19 26									20 21						21 55				
Great Malvern	a			19 31									20 25						22 00				
	d	18 30	18 45	19 31									20 26		21 18			21 30	22 00				22 40
Malvern Link	d	18 32	18 49	19 34									20 29		21 21			21 32	22 03				22 43
Worcester Foregate Street 7	a	18 40	19 00	19 41									20 37		21 28			21 41	22 12				22 50
	d	18 41	19 01	19 42					19 50				20 38		21 29			21 42	22 13				22 51
Worcester Shrub Hill 7	a	18 43	19 04	19 49									20 40		21 31			21 44	22 17				22 53
	d	18 47											20 44	20 52				21 52		22 22		22 48	
Droitwich Spa	d	18 55							19 59				20 52	21 00				22 00				22 56	
Bromsgrove	d												21 00										
Barnt Green	d																						
University	d												21 16										
Hartlebury	d	19 02																					
Kidderminster	d	19 10						19 40	20 10					21 11				22 10				23 06	
Blakedown	d	19 15						19 45	20 15					21 16				22 15				23 11	
Hagley	d	19 18						19 49	20 19					21 20				22 19				23 15	
Stourbridge Junction 2	d	19 24						19 54	20 24			20 54		21 24			21 54	22 24			22 54	23 19	
Lye	d	19 27						19 57	20 27			20 57		21 27			21 57	22 27			22 57		
Cradley Heath	d	19 30						20 00	20 30			21 00		21 30			22 00	22 30			23 00		
Old Hill	d	19 34						20 04	20 34			21 04		21 34			22 04	22 34			23 04		
Rowley Regis	d	19 38						20 08	20 38			21 08		21 38			22 08	22 38			23 08		
Langley Green	d	19 41						20 11	20 41			21 11		21 41			22 11	22 41			23 11		
Smethwick Galton Bdg H.L. 7	d	19 44						20 14	20 44			21 14		21 44			22 14	22 44			23 14		
Birmingham New Street 12	a												21 28							23 02			
	d					20 03				21 03													
Birmingham International ✈	d					20 15				21 15													
Coventry	d					20 25				21 25													
The Hawthorns 🚊	d	19 47						20 17	20 47			21 17		21 47			22 17	22 47			23 17		
Jewellery Quarter 🚊	d	19 50						20 20	20 50			21 20		21 50			22 20	22 50			23 20		
Birmingham Snow Hill 🚊	a	19 53						20 23	20 53			21 23		21 53			22 23	22 53			23 24	23 37	
	d	19 55					20 10	20 27	20 55		21 11	21 25		21 55		22 15	22 25	22 55			23 25	23 38	
Birmingham Moor Street	d	19 58					20 13	20 30	20 58		21 14	21 28		21 58		22 18	22 28	22 58			23 28	23 41	
Bordesley	d																						
Small Heath	d	20 02						20 34	21 02			21 32		22 02			22 32	23 02			23 32	23 45	
Tyseley	d	20 04						20 36	21 04			21 34		22 04		22 22	22 34	23 04			23 34	23 47	
Acocks Green	d	20 07							21 07					22 07		22 25		23 07				23 50	
Olton	d	20 10							21 10					22 10		22 28		23 10				23 53	
Solihull	d	20 13					20 23		21 13		21 23			22 13		22 32		23 13				23 56	
Widney Manor	d	20 17					20 26		21 17		21 26			22 17		22 35		23 17				23 59	
Dorridge	d	20a22					20 30		21a23		21 30			22a22		22 39		23a22				00 04	
Lapworth	d						20 34				21 34					22 43						00 08	
Hatton	d				20 10		20 40				21 40					22 48						00 14	
Warwick Parkway	d				20 16		20 45				21 44					22 53							
Warwick	d				20 19		20 48				21 47					22 56						00 19	
Leamington Spa 8	a				20 22	20 37	20 53			21 37	21 51					23 00						00 24	
	d				20 23	20 38	20 53			21 38	21 52					23 01							
Banbury	d				20 42	20a54	21 15			21a55	22 15					23a22							
London Marylebone 10 ⊖	a				22 21		22 40				23 46												
Spring Road	d							20 39				21 37					22 37				23 37		
Hall Green	d							20 42				21 40					22 40				23 40		
Yardley Wood	d							20 45				21 43					22 43				23 43		
Shirley	d							20 48				21a46					22a46				23a46		
Whitlocks End	d							20 51															
Wythall	d							20 53															
Earlswood (West Midlands)	d							20 56															
The Lakes	d							20x58															
Wood End	d							21x00															
Danzey	d							21x03															
Henley-in-Arden	d							21 08															
Wootton Wawen	d							21x10															
Wilmcote	d							21 16															
Stratford-upon-Avon	a							21 23															

For general notes see front of timetable
For details of catering facilities see Directory of Train Operators

A To Gloucester (Table 57)

Table 71

Sundays
until 27 January

Hereford, Worcester and Stourbridge → Birmingham → Leamington Spa, Marylebone and Stratford-upon-Avon

Network Diagram - See first page of Table 71

		LM	LM	XC	CH	GW	LM	CH	CH	XC	CH	LM	LM	XC	CH	LM	XC	CH	LM	LM	GW	LM
				1 ◇		1 ◇				1 ◇				1 ◇			1 ◇				1 ◇	
			🚌				🚌						🚌									🚌
				☕		🛒				☕				☕			☕				☕	
Hereford 7	d																					
Ledbury	a																					
	d																					
Colwall	d																					
Great Malvern	a																					
	d					09 01													10 02	10 56	11 08	
Malvern Link	d					09 04													10 04	10 58	11 11	
Worcester Foregate Street 7	a					09 11													10 12	11 06	11 18	
	d					09 13													10 13	11 20	11 19	
Worcester Shrub Hill 7	a					09 17													10 15	↳	11 22	
	d	22p48										09 21							10 21			
Droitwich Spa	d	22p56										09 32							10 29			
Bromsgrove	d																					
Barnt Green	d																					
University	d																					
Hartlebury	d																					
Kidderminster	d	23p06										09 42				10 08			10 39			
Blakedown	d	23p11										09 47				10 13						
Hagley	d	23p15										09 51				10 17			10 46			
Stourbridge Junction 2	d	23p19										09 55				10 22			10 52			
Lye	d															10 25						
Cradley Heath	d											10 01				10 29			10 58			
Old Hill	d															10 33						
Rowley Regis	d											10 06				10 36			11 03			
Langley Green	d															10 39						
Smethwick Galton Bdg H.L. 7	d											10 12				10 43			11 09			
Birmingham New Street 12	a																					
	d			09 03						09 48				10 33			11 03					
Birmingham International ✈	d			09 15						10 15				10 45			11 15					
Coventry	d			09 25						10 25				10 54			11 25					
The Hawthorns 🚋	d											10 15				10 45			11 12			
Jewellery Quarter 🚋	d											10 18				10 49			11 15			
Birmingham Snow Hill 🚋	a	23p37										10 20				10 52			11 17			
	d	23p38	08 25		09 10		09 25	09 40			10 10	10 22	10 25		10 40	10 53		11 10	11 19			11 25
Birmingham Moor Street	d	23p41			09 13			09 43			10 13	10a24			10 43	10 56		11 13	11a21			
Bordesley	d																					
Small Heath	d	23p45																				
Tyseley	d	23p47	08 46				09 46						10 46									11 46
Acocks Green	d	23p50														11 02						
Olton	d	23p53														11 04						
Solihull	d	23p56			09 22			09 52			10 22				10 52	11 08		11 22				
Widney Manor	d	23p59														11 11						
Dorridge	d	00 04			09 28			09 58			10 28				10 58	11a16		11 28				
Lapworth	d	00 08						10 02														
Hatton	d	00 14													11 05							
Warwick Parkway	d				09 39			10 10	10 21		10 38				11 10			11 38				
Warwick	d	00 19			09 42				10 24		10 41							11 41				
Leamington Spa 8	a	00 24		09 37	09 46			10 16	10 28	10 37	10 46			11 07	11 16		11 37	11 46				
	d			09 38	09 47			10 16	10 29	10 38	10 47			11 07	11 16		11 38	11 47				
Banbury	d			09a54	10 06			10 36	10 48	10a54	11 06			11a23	11 36		11a54	12 06				
London Marylebone 10 ⊖	a				11 23			12 00	12 16		12 22				13 00			13 22				
Spring Road	d		08 54				09 54						10 54									11 54
Hall Green	d		09 05				10 05						11 05									12 05
Yardley Wood	d		09 16				10 16						11 16									12 16
Shirley	d		09 27				10 27						11 27									12 27
Whitlocks End	d																					
Wythall	d		09 38				10 38						11 38									12 38
Earlswood (West Midlands)	d																					
The Lakes	d		09 49				10 49						11 49									12 49
Wood End	d																					
Danzey	d																					
Henley-in-Arden	d		10 05				11 05						12 05									13 05
Wootton Wawen	d																					
Wilmcote	d		10 21				11 21						12 21									13 21
Stratford-upon-Avon	a		10 36				11 36						12 36									13 36

For general notes see front of timetable
For details of catering facilities see Directory of Train Operators

Table 71

Sundays

until 27 January

Hereford, Worcester and Stourbridge → Birmingham → Leamington Spa, Marylebone and Stratford-upon-Avon

Network Diagram - See first page of Table 71

		XC	CH	LM	CH	XC		CH	LM	LM	XC	CH	LM		XC	CH	LM	GW	LM	XC		CH	LM	CH	XC
		1 ◇				**1** ◇				🚌	**1** ◇				**1** ◇			**1** ◇	🚌	**1** ◇					R **1**
		☕				☕					☕				☕			✕		☕					☕
Hereford 7	d																								
Ledbury	a																								
	d																								
Colwall	d																								
Great Malvern	a																								
	d																12 02	13 06							
Malvern Link	d																12 04	13 09							
Worcester Foregate Street 7	a								←								12 14	13 19							
	d								11 20								12 15	13 20							
Worcester Shrub Hill 7	a																12 17	13 24							
	d																12 21								
Droitwich Spa	d								11 29								12 29								
Bromsgrove	d																								
Barnt Green	d																								
University	d																								
Hartlebury	d																								
Kidderminster	d								11 39								12 39								
Blakedown	d																12 44								
Hagley	d								11 46								12 48								
Stourbridge Junction 2	d			11 22					11 52				12 22				12 52						13 22		
Lye	d			11 25									12 25										13 25		
Cradley Heath	d			11 29					11 58				12 29				12 58						13 29		
Old Hill	d			11 33									12 33										13 33		
Rowley Regis	d			11 36					12 03				12 36				13 03						13 36		
Langley Green	d			11 39									12 39										13 39		
Smethwick Galton Bdg H.L. 7	d			11 43					12 08				12 43				13 08						13 43		
Birmingham New Street 12	a																								
	d	11 33				12 03					12 33				13 03					13 33					14 03
Birmingham International ✈	d	11 45				12 15					12 45				13 15					13 45					14 15
Coventry	d	11 56				12 25					12 56				13 25					13 56					14 25
The Hawthorns 🚊	d			11 45					12 11				12 45				13 11						13 45		
Jewellery Quarter 🚊	d			11 49					12 14				12 49				13 14						13 49		
Birmingham Snow Hill 🚊	a			11 52					12 17				12 52				13 17						13 52		
	d		11 40	11 53				12 10	12 19	12 25		12 40	12 53			13 10	13 19		13 25			13 40	13 53		
Birmingham Moor Street	d		11 43	11 56				12 13	12a21			12 43	12 56			13 13	13a21					13 43	13 56		
Bordesley	d																								
Small Heath	d																								
Tyseley	d									12 46									13 46						
Acocks Green	d			12 02									13 02										14 02		
Olton	d			12 04									13 04										14 04		
Solihull	d		11 52	12 08				12 22				12 52	13 08			13 23						13 52	14 08		
Widney Manor	d			12 11									13 11										14 11		
Dorridge	d		11 58	12a16				12 28				12 58	13a16			13 29						13 58	14a17		
Lapworth	d		12 02																			14 02			
Hatton	d											13 05													
Warwick Parkway	d		12 10		12 21			12 38				13 10				13 39						14 10		14 21	
Warwick	d				12 24			12 41								13 42								14 24	
Leamington Spa 8	a	12 09	12 16		12 28	12 37		12 45			13 09	13 16			13 37	13 46				14 09		14 16		14 28	14 37
	d	12 09	12 16		12 29	12 38		12 46			13 09	13 16			13 38	13 47				14 09		14 16		14 29	14 38
Banbury	d	12a26	12 36		12 48	12a54		13 06			13a26	13 36			13a54	14 06				14a26		14 36		14 48	14a54
London Marylebone 10 ⊖	a		14 00		14 16			14 22				15 00				15 22						16 00		16 16	
Spring Road	d									12 54									13 54						
Hall Green	d									13 05									14 05						
Yardley Wood	d									13 16									14 16						
Shirley	d									13 27									14 27						
Whitlocks End	d																								
Wythall	d									13 38									14 38						
Earlswood (West Midlands)	d																								
The Lakes	d									13 49									14 49						
Wood End	d																								
Danzey	d																								
Henley-in-Arden	d									14 05									15 05						
Wootton Wawen	d																								
Wilmcote	d									14 21									15 21						
Stratford-upon-Avon	a									14 36									15 36						

For general notes see front of timetable
For details of catering facilities see
Directory of Train Operators

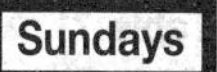

Sundays

until 27 January

Hereford, Worcester and Stourbridge → Birmingham → Leamington Spa, Marylebone and Stratford-upon-Avon

Network Diagram - See first page of Table 71

		CH	LM	GW	LM		XC	CH	LM	XC	CH	LM		LM	XC	LM	CH	LM	CH		XC	CH	LM	GW	LM
				1 ◇ ☕	🚌		1 ◇ ☕			R 1 ☕				🚌	1 ◇ ☕						R 1 ☕			1 ◇ ☕	🚌
Hereford 7	d			13 30																				14 30	
Ledbury	a			13 46																				14 46	
	d			13 48																				14 57	
Colwall	d			13 55																				15 04	
Great Malvern	a			13 59																				15 08	
	d			14 01												14 35								15 09	
Malvern Link	d			14 05												14 37								15 13	
Worcester Foregate Street 7	a			14 14												14 45								15 23	
	d		13 20	14 16								14 20				14 45							15 20	15 24	
Worcester Shrub Hill 7	a			14 19												14 48								15 27	
	d															14 51									
Droitwich Spa	d		13 29									14 29				14 59							15 29		
Bromsgrove	d															15 09									
Barnt Green	d																								
University	d																								
Hartlebury	d																								
Kidderminster	d		13 39									14 39											15 39		
Blakedown	d											14 44													
Hagley	d		13 46									14 48											15 46		
Stourbridge Junction 2	d		13 52						14 22			14 52						15 22					15 52		
Lye	d								14 25									15 25							
Cradley Heath	d		13 58						14 29			14 58						15 29					15 58		
Old Hill	d								14 33									15 33							
Rowley Regis	d		14 03						14 36			15 03						15 36					16 03		
Langley Green	d								14 39									15 39							
Smethwick Galton Bdg H.L. 7	d		14 08						14 43			15 08						15 43					16 08		
Birmingham New Street 12	a															15 40									
	d						14 33			15 03					15 33						16 03				
Birmingham International ✈	d						14 45			15 15					15 45						16 15				
Coventry	d						14 56			15 25					15 56						16 25				
The Hawthorns 🚋	d		14 11						14 45			15 11						15 45					16 11		
Jewellery Quarter 🚋	d		14 14						14 49			15 14						15 49					16 14		
Birmingham Snow Hill 🚋	a		14 17						14 52			15 17						15 52					16 17		
	d	14 10	14 19		14 25			14 40	14 53		15 10	15 19		15 25			15 40	15 53				16 10	16 19		16 25
Birmingham Moor Street	d	14 13	14a21					14 43	14 56		15 13	15a21					15 43	15 56				16 13	16a21		
Bordesley	d																								
Small Heath	d																								
Tyseley	d				14 46									15 46											16 46
Acocks Green	d								15 02									16 02							
Olton	d								15 04									16 04							
Solihull	d	14 22						14 52	15 08		15 22						15 52	16 08				16 22			
Widney Manor	d								15 11									16 11							
Dorridge	d	14 28						14 58	15a17		15 28						15 58	16a16				16 28			
Lapworth	d																16 02								
Hatton	d							15 05																	
Warwick Parkway	d	14 38						15 10			15 38						16 10		16 21			16 38			
Warwick	d	14 41									15 41								16 24			16 41			
Leamington Spa 8	a	14 46					15 09	15 16		15 37	15 46				16 09		16 16		16 28		16 37	16 46			
	d	14 47					15 09	15 16		15 38	15 47				16 09		16 16		16 29		16 38	16 47			
Banbury	d	15 06					15a26	15 36		15a54	16 06				16a26		16 36		16 48		16a54	17 06			
London Marylebone 10 ⊖	a	16 22						17 00			17 22						18 00		18 16			18 21			
Spring Road	d				14 54									15 54											16 54
Hall Green	d				15 05									16 05											17 05
Yardley Wood	d				15 16									16 16											17 16
Shirley	d				15 27									16 27											17 27
Whitlocks End	d																								
Wythall	d				15 38									16 38											17 38
Earlswood (West Midlands)	d																								
The Lakes	d				15 49									16 49											17 49
Wood End	d																								
Danzey	d																								
Henley-in-Arden	d				16 05									17 05											18 05
Wootton Wawen	d																								
Wilmcote	d				16 21									17 21											18 21
Stratford-upon-Avon	a				16 36									17 36											18 36

For general notes see front of timetable
For details of catering facilities see Directory of Train Operators

Table 71

Sundays

until 27 January

Hereford, Worcester and Stourbridge → Birmingham → Leamington Spa, Marylebone and Stratford-upon-Avon

Network Diagram - See first page of Table 71

		XC	CH	LM		LM	XC	CH	LM	LM	LM		XC	CH	LM	CH	XC	CH		LM	GW	LM	LM	XC	CH
		1 ◇					R 1						1 ◇				R 1				1 ◇			1 ◇	
											🚌												🚌		
		☕					☕						☕				☕				☕			☕	
Hereford 7	d									15 46											16 30				
Ledbury	a									16 02											16 46				
	d									16 02											16 47				
Colwall	d									16 09											16 55				
Great Malvern	a									16 14											17 00				
	d									16 15											17 00	17 16			
Malvern Link	d									16 18											17 04	17 19			
Worcester Foregate Street 7	a									16 26											17 20	17 27			
	d								16 20	16 26										17 20	17 21	17 27			
Worcester Shrub Hill 7	a									16 30											17 24	17 30			
	d			15 46						16 33												17 33			
Droitwich Spa	d			15 54					16 29	16 41										17 29		17 41			
Bromsgrove	d									16 51												17 51			
Barnt Green	d																								
University	d																								
Hartlebury	d																								
Kidderminster	d			16 04					16 39											17 39					
Blakedown	d																			17 44					
Hagley	d			16 11					16 46											17 48					
Stourbridge Junction 2	d			16 16		16 22			16 52						17 23					17 52					
Lye	d					16 25									17 26										
Cradley Heath	d					16 29			16 58						17 30					17 58					
Old Hill	d					16 33									17 34										
Rowley Regis	d					16 36			17 03						17 37					18 03					
Langley Green	d					16 39									17 40										
Smethwick Galton Bdg H.L. 7	d			16 29		16 43			17 08						17 44					18 08					
Birmingham New Street 12	a									17 17												18 12			
	d	16 33					17 03						17 33				18 03							18 33	
Birmingham International ✈	d	16 45					17 15						17 45				18 15							18 45	
Coventry	d	16 56					17 25						17 56				18 25							18 56	
The Hawthorns 🚋	d					16 45			17 11						17 46					18 11					
Jewellery Quarter 🚋	d					16 49			17 14						17 50					18 14					
Birmingham Snow Hill 🚋	a			16 35		16 52			17 17						17 53					18 17					
	d		16 40	16 45		16 53		17 10	17 19		17 25			17 40	17 54			18 10		18 19			18 25		18 40
Birmingham Moor Street	d		16 43	16a47		16 56		17 13	17a21					17 43	17 57			18 13		18a21					18 43
Bordesley	d																								
Small Heath	d																								
Tyseley	d										17 46												18 46		
Acocks Green	d					17 02									18 03										
Olton	d					17 04									18 05										
Solihull	d		16 52			17 08		17 22						17 52	18 09			18 22							18 52
Widney Manor	d					17 11									18 12										
Dorridge	d		16 58			17a17		17 28						17 58	18a17			18 28							18 58
Lapworth	d													18 02											
Hatton	d		17 05																						19 05
Warwick Parkway	d		17 10					17 38						18 10		18 21		18 38							19 10
Warwick	d							17 41								18 24		18 41							
Leamington Spa 8	a	17 09	17 16				17 37	17 46					18 09	18 16		18 28	18 37	18 46						19 09	19 15
	d	17 09	17 16				17 38	17 47					18 09	18 16		18 29	18 38	18 47						19 09	19 16
Banbury	d	17a26	17 36				17a54	18 06					18a26	18 36		18 48	18a54	19 06						19a26	19 35
London Marylebone 10 ⊖	a		19 00					19 22						20 00		20 16		20 21							21 00
Spring Road	d										17 54												18 54		
Hall Green	d										18 05												19 05		
Yardley Wood	d										18 16												19 16		
Shirley	d										18 27												19 27		
Whitlocks End	d																								
Wythall	d										18 38												19 38		
Earlswood (West Midlands)	d																								
The Lakes	d										18 49												19 49		
Wood End	d																								
Danzey	d																								
Henley-in-Arden	d										19 05												20 05		
Wootton Wawen	d																								
Wilmcote	d										19 21												20 21		
Stratford-upon-Avon	a										19 36												20 36		

For general notes see front of timetable
For details of catering facilities see Directory of Train Operators

Table 71

until 27 January

Hereford, Worcester and Stourbridge → Birmingham → Leamington Spa, Marylebone and Stratford-upon-Avon

Network Diagram - See first page of Table 71

Station	CH	XC		CH	LM	GW	XC	CH	LM		LM	GW	XC	CH	LM	LM		LM	GW	XC	LM	LM		
		R 1 ☕				1 ◇ ☕	R 1					1 ◇ ☕	1 ◇						1 ◇					
Hereford 7 d						18 30										20 05						22 40		
Ledbury a						18 46										20 20						22 56		
d						18 48										20 21						22 56		
Colwall d						18 55										20 27						23 03		
Great Malvern a						18 59										20 32						23 07		
d						19 08						20 08				20 32			21 05		22 05	23 08		
Malvern Link d						19 12						20 12				20 35			21 09		22 08	23 10		
Worcester Foregate Street 7 a						19 21						20 21				20 44			21 21		22 19	23 19		
d					18 20	19 23						20 23				20 44			21 23		22 20	23 22		
Worcester Shrub Hill 7 a						19 26						20 26				20 47			21 26		22 22	23 24		
d									19 31		19 56				20 33	20 50		21 17			22 26			
Droitwich Spa d					18 29				19 39		20 04				20 41	20 58		21 25			22 34			
Bromsgrove d											20 13					21 08				22 20				
Barnt Green d																								
University d																								
Hartlebury d																								
Kidderminster d					18 39				19 49						20 51			21b41			22 44			
Blakedown d																								
Hagley d					18 46				19 56						20 58			21 48			22 51			
Stourbridge Junction 2 d					18 52				20 01						21 02			21 52			22 55			
Lye d																								
Cradley Heath d					18 58				20 07						21 07			21 58			23 01			
Old Hill d																								
Rowley Regis d					19 03				20 12						21 13			22 03			23 06			
Langley Green d																								
Smethwick Galton Bdg H.L. 7 d					19 08				20 17						21 18			22 08			23 11			
Birmingham New Street 12 a											20 40					21 45				22 45				
d	18 53	19 03					20 03						21 03											
Birmingham International ✈ d		19 15					20 15						21 15											
Coventry d		19 25					20 25						21 25											
The Hawthorns 🚊 d					19 11				20 20						21 20			22 11			23 14			
Jewellery Quarter 🚊 d					19 14				20 23						21 24			22 14			23 17			
Birmingham Snow Hill 🚊 a					19 18				20 26						21 27			22 18			23 21			
d				19 15	19 20			20 15	20 27					21 15	21 27			22 18						
Birmingham Moor Street d				19 18	19a22			20 18	20a30					21 18	21a30			22a21						
Bordesley d																								
Small Heath d																								
Tyseley d																								
Acocks Green d																								
Olton d																								
Solihull d				19 27				20 27						21 27										
Widney Manor d				19 30				20 30						21 30										
Dorridge d				19 34				20 34						21 34										
Lapworth d																								
Hatton d																								
Warwick Parkway d				19 45				20 45						21 45										
Warwick d				19 48				20 48						21 48										
Leamington Spa 8 a		19 37		19 53			20 37	20 53					21 37	21 53										
d		19 38		19 53			20 38	20 53					21 38	21 53										
Banbury d	19 45	19a54		20 13			20a54	21 13					21a54	22 15										
London Marylebone 10 ⊖ a	21 08			21 50				22 50						23 53										
Spring Road d																								
Hall Green d																								
Yardley Wood d																								
Shirley d																								
Whitlocks End d																								
Wythall d																								
Earlswood (West Midlands) d																								
The Lakes d																								
Wood End d																								
Danzey d																								
Henley-in-Arden d																								
Wootton Wawen d																								
Wilmcote d																								
Stratford-upon-Avon a																								

For general notes see front of timetable
For details of catering facilities see Directory of Train Operators

b Arr. 2135

Table 71

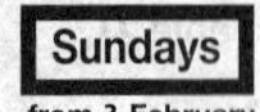

from 3 February

Hereford, Worcester and Stourbridge → Birmingham → Leamington Spa, Marylebone and Stratford-upon-Avon

Network Diagram - See first page of Table 71

		LM	LM	GW	LM	XC	CH	CH	LM	LM	XC	CH	LM		CH	CH	LM	LM	LM	XC	GW	LM	CH	LM	CH
				1 ◇		1 ◇					1 ◇									1 ◇	1 ◇				
															A	B									A
			bus		bus					bus							bus					bus			
				trolley		cup					cup									cup	cup				
Hereford 7	d																								
Ledbury	a																								
	d																								
Colwall	d																								
Great Malvern	a																								
	d			09 01														10 02	10 56		11 08				
Malvern Link	d			09 04														10 04	10 58		11 11				
Worcester Foregate Street 7	a			09 11														10 12	11 06		11 18				
	d			09 13														10 13	11 20		11 19				
Worcester Shrub Hill 7	a			09 17														10 15	⟶		11 21				
	d	22p48							09 21									10 21							
Droitwich Spa	d	22p56							09b32									10 29							
Bromsgrove	d																								
Barnt Green	d																								
University	d																								
Hartlebury	d																								
Kidderminster	d	23p06							09 42				10 08					10 39							
Blakedown	d	23p11							09 47				10 13												
Hagley	d	23p15							09 51				10 17					10 46							
Stourbridge Junction 2	d	23p19							09 55				10 22					10 52						11 22	
Lye	d												10 25											11 25	
Cradley Heath	d								10 01				10 29					10 58						11 29	
Old Hill	d												10 33											11 33	
Rowley Regis	d								10 06				10 36					11 03						11 36	
Langley Green	d												10 39											11 39	
Smethwick Galton Bdg H.L. 7	d								10 12				10 43					11 09						11 43	
Birmingham New Street 12	a																								
	d					09 03					09 48									11 03			11 15		
Birmingham International ✈	d					09 15					10 15									11 15			11 26		
Coventry	d					09 25					10 25									11 25			11 37		
The Hawthorns 🚋	d								10 15				10 45					11 12						11 45	
Jewellery Quarter 🚋	d								10 18				10 49					11 15						11 49	
Birmingham Snow Hill 🚋	a	23p37							10 20				10 52					11 17						11 52	
	d	23p38	08 25		09 25				10 22	10 25			10 54				11 00	11 19				11 25		11 53	
Birmingham Moor Street	d	23p41							10a24				10a56					11a21						11a55	
Bordesley	d																								
Small Heath	d	23p45																							
Tyseley	d	23p47	08 46		09 46					10 46												11 46			
Acocks Green	d	23p50															11 26								
Olton	d	23p53															11 32								
Solihull	d	23p56															11 43								
Widney Manor	d	23p59															11 54								
Dorridge	d	00 04															12a04								
Lapworth	d	00 08																							
Hatton	d	00 14																							
Warwick Parkway	d														10 58	10 58									11 58
Warwick	d	00 19													11 05	11 05									12 05
Leamington Spa 8	a	00 24				09 37					10 37				11 12	11 15				11 37			11 50		12 12
	d					09 38	09 47	10 13			10 38	10 47			11 13	11 16				11 38			11 52		12 13
Banbury	d					09a54	10 06	10 32			10a54	11 06			11 33	11 35				11a54			12 11		12 33
London Marylebone 10 ⊖	a						11 31	12 00				12 31			12 58	13 01							13 36		14 00
Spring Road	d		08 54		09 54					10 54												11 54			
Hall Green	d		09 05		10 05					11 05												12 05			
Yardley Wood	d		09 16		10 16					11 16												12 16			
Shirley	d		09 27		10 27					11 27												12 27			
Whitlocks End	d																								
Wythall	d		09 38		10 38					11 38												12 38			
Earlswood (West Midlands)	d																								
The Lakes	d		09 49		10 49					11 49												12 49			
Wood End	d																								
Danzey	d																								
Henley-in-Arden	d		10 05		11 05					12 05												13 05			
Wootton Wawen	d																								
Wilmcote	d		10 21		11 21					12 21												13 21			
Stratford-upon-Avon	a		10 36		11 36					12 36												13 36			

For general notes see front of timetable
For details of catering facilities see Directory of Train Operators

A From 30 March
B Until 23 March
b Arr. 0928

Table 71

Sundays
from 3 February

Hereford, Worcester and Stourbridge → Birmingham → Leamington Spa, Marylebone and Stratford-upon-Avon

Network Diagram - See first page of Table 71

		CH	LM	XC		LM	LM	CH	LM	CH	CH	LM	LM	XC	CH	GW	LM		LM	CH	LM	LM	XC	GW	LM
				1 ◇										1 ◇		1 ◇							R 1	1 ◇	
		A	🚌	☕			🚌			B	A	🚌		☕		🍴	🚌				🚌		☕	☕	🚌
Hereford 7	d																							13 30	
Ledbury	a																							13 46	
	d																							13 48	
Colwall	d																							13 55	
Great Malvern	a																							13 59	
	d												12 02			13 06								14 01	
Malvern Link	d												12 04			13 09								14 05	
Worcester Foregate Street 7	a					←							12 14			13 19								14 14	
	d					11 20							12 15			13 20						13 20		14 14	
Worcester Shrub Hill 7	a												12 17			13 24								14 18	
	d												12 21												
Droitwich Spa	d					11 29							12 29									13 29			
Bromsgrove	d																								
Barnt Green	d																								
University	d																								
Hartlebury	d																								
Kidderminster	d					11 39							12 39									13 39			
Blakedown	d												12 44												
Hagley	d					11 46							12 48									13 46			
Stourbridge Junction 2	d					11 52			12 22				12 52						13 22			13 52			
Lye	d								12 25										13 25						
Cradley Heath	d					11 58			12 29				12 58						13 29			13 58			
Old Hill	d								12 33										13 33						
Rowley Regis	d					12 03			12 36				13 03						13 36			14 03			
Langley Green	d								12 39										13 39						
Smethwick Galton Bdg H.L. 7	d					12 08			12 43				13 08						13 43			14 08			
Birmingham New Street 12	a																								
	d			12 03				12 15						13 03	13 15								14 03		
Birmingham International ✈	d			12 15				12 26						13 15	13 26								14 15		
Coventry	d			12 25				12 37						13 25	13 37								14 25		
The Hawthorns 🚊	d					12 11			12 45				13 11						13 45			14 11			
Jewellery Quarter 🚊	d					12 14			12 49				13 14						13 49			14 14			
Birmingham Snow Hill 🚊	a					12 17			12 52				13 17						13 52			14 17			
	d		12 00			12 19	12 25		12 53			13 00	13 19				13 25		13 53		14 00	14 19			14 25
Birmingham Moor Street	d					12a21			12a55				13a21						13a55			14a21			
Bordesley	d																								
Small Heath	d																								
Tyseley	d						12 46										13 46								14 46
Acocks Green	d		12 26									13 26									14 26				
Olton	d		12 32									13 32									14 32				
Solihull	d		12 43									13 43									14 43				
Widney Manor	d		12 54									13 54									14 54				
Dorridge	d		13a04									14a04									15a04				
Lapworth	d																								
Hatton	d																								
Warwick Parkway	d	11 58								12 58	12 58									13 58					
Warwick	d	12 05								13 05	13 05									14 05					
Leamington Spa 8	a	12 15		12 37				12 50		13 12	13 15			13 37	13 50					14 15			14 37		
	d	12 16		12 38				12 52		13 13	13 16			13 38	13 52					14 16			14 38		
Banbury	d	12 36		12a54				13 11		13 33	13 36			13a54	14 11					14 36			14a54		
London Marylebone 10	⊖ a	14 03						14 36		14 58	15 01				15 36					16 03					
Spring Road	d						12 54										13 54								14 54
Hall Green	d						13 05										14 05								15 05
Yardley Wood	d						13 16										14 16								15 16
Shirley	d						13 27										14 27								15 27
Whitlocks End	d																								
Wythall	d						13 38										14 38								15 38
Earlswood (West Midlands)	d																								
The Lakes	d						13 49										14 49								15 49
Wood End	d																								
Danzey	d																								
Henley-in-Arden	d						14 05										15 05								16 05
Wootton Wawen	d																								
Wilmcote	d						14 21										15 21								16 21
Stratford-upon-Avon	a						14 36										15 36								16 36

For general notes see front of timetable
For details of catering facilities see Directory of Train Operators

A Until 23 March
B From 30 March

Table 71

Sundays

from 3 February

Hereford, Worcester and Stourbridge → Birmingham → Leamington Spa, Marylebone and Stratford-upon-Avon

Network Diagram - See first page of Table 71

		CH	LM	CH	LM	LM	LM	XC		CH	LM	LM	CH	LM	LM	GW	LM	XC	CH	LM	LM		CH	LM	LM
					🚌		🚌	R 1 ☕						🚌		1 ◊ ☕	🚌	R 1 ☕						🚌	
Hereford 7	d															14 30									
Ledbury	a															14 46									
	d															14 57									
Colwall	d															15 04									
Great Malvern	a															15 08									
	d										14 35					15 09									
Malvern Link	d										14 37					15 13									
Worcester Foregate Street 7	a										14 45					15 23									
	d					14 20					14 45				15 20	15 24									16 20
Worcester Shrub Hill 7	a										14 48					15 27									
	d										14 51									15 46					
Droitwich Spa	d					14 29					14 59				15 29					15 54					16 29
Bromsgrove	d										15 09														
Barnt Green	d																								
University	d																								
Hartlebury	d																								
Kidderminster	d					14 39									15 39					16 04					16 39
Blakedown	d					14 44																			
Hagley	d					14 48									15 46					16 11					16 46
Stourbridge Junction 2	d		14 22			14 52						15 22			15 52					16 16	16 22				16 52
Lye	d		14 25									15 25									16 25				
Cradley Heath	d		14 29			14 58						15 29			15 58						16 29				16 58
Old Hill	d		14 33									15 33									16 33				
Rowley Regis	d		14 36			15 03						15 36			16 03						16 36				17 03
Langley Green	d		14 39									15 39									16 39				
Smethwick Galton Bdg H.L. 7	d		14 43			15 08						15 43			16 08					16 29	16 43				17 08
Birmingham New Street 12	a										15 40														
	d	14 15						15 03		15 15								16 03	16 15						
Birmingham International ✈	d	14 26						15 15		15 26								16 15	16 26						
Coventry	d	14 37						15 25		15 37								16 25	16 37						
The Hawthorns 🚊	d		14 45			15 11						15 45			16 11						16 45				17 11
Jewellery Quarter 🚊	d		14 49			15 14						15 49			16 14						16 49				17 14
Birmingham Snow Hill 🚊	a		14 52			15 17						15 52			16 17					16 35	16 52				17 17
	d		14 53		15 00	15 19	15 25					15 53		16 00	16 19		16 25			16 45	16 53			17 00	17 19
Birmingham Moor Street	d		14a55			15a21						15a55			16a21					16a47	16a55				17a21
Bordesley	d																								
Small Heath	d																								
Tyseley	d						15 46										16 46								
Acocks Green	d				15 26									16 26										17 26	
Olton	d				15 32									16 32										17 32	
Solihull	d				15 43									16 43										17 43	
Widney Manor	d				15 54									16 54										17 54	
Dorridge	d				16a04									17a04										18a04	
Lapworth	d																								
Hatton	d																								
Warwick Parkway	d			14 58									15 58										16 58		
Warwick	d			15 05									16 05										17 05		
Leamington Spa 8	a	14 50		15 15				15 37		15 50			16 15					16 37	16 50				17 15		
	d	14 52		15 16				15 38		15 52			16 16					16 38	16 52				17 16		
Banbury	d	15 11		15 36				15a54		16 11			16 36					16a54	17 11				17 36		
London Marylebone 10 ⊖	a	16 36		17 01						17 36			18 03						18 36				19 01		
Spring Road	d						15 54										16 54								
Hall Green	d						16 05										17 05								
Yardley Wood	d						16 16										17 16								
Shirley	d						16 27										17 27								
Whitlocks End	d																								
Wythall	d						16 38										17 38								
Earlswood (West Midlands)	d																								
The Lakes	d						16 49										17 49								
Wood End	d																								
Danzey	d																								
Henley-in-Arden	d						17 05										18 05								
Wootton Wawen	d																								
Wilmcote	d						17 21										18 21								
Stratford-upon-Avon	a						17 36										18 36								

For general notes see front of timetable
For details of catering facilities see Directory of Train Operators

Table 71

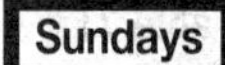
Sundays

from 3 February

Hereford, Worcester and Stourbridge → Birmingham → Leamington Spa, Marylebone and Stratford-upon-Avon

Network Diagram - See first page of Table 71

		XC	CH	CH	LM	GW	LM	LM	CH	LM	LM	XC	LM	LM	CH	XC	CH	XC	LM	GW	GW	CH	CH	CH
		R 1				1 ◇						R 1				1 ◇		R 1		1 ◇	1 ◇			
			A	B												A				B	B	A	B	A
							🚌			🚌				🚌										
		☕				☕						☕				☕		☕		☕	☕			
Hereford 7	d				15 46	16 30															18 30			
Ledbury	a				16 02	16 45															18 45			
	d				16 02	16 47															18 47			
Colwall	d				16 09	16 55															18 54			
Great Malvern	a				16 14	17 00															18 59			
	d				16 15	17 00							17 16							18 45	18 59			
Malvern Link	d				16 18	17 04							17 19							18 48	19 03			
Worcester Foregate Street 7	a				16 26	17 19							17 27							18 59	19 18			
	d				16 26	17 20					17 20		17 27						18 20	18 59	19 19			
Worcester Shrub Hill 7	a				16 30	17 23							17 30							19 03	19 22			
	d				16 33								17 33											
Droitwich Spa	d				16 41						17 29		17 41						18 29					
Bromsgrove	d				16 51								17 51											
Barnt Green	d																							
University	d																							
Hartlebury	d																							
Kidderminster	d										17 39								18 39					
Blakedown	d										17 44													
Hagley	d										17 48								18 46					
Stourbridge Junction 2	d							17 22			17 52								18 52					
Lye	d							17 25																
Cradley Heath	d							17 29			17 58								18 58					
Old Hill	d							17 33																
Rowley Regis	d							17 36			18 03								19 03					
Langley Green	d							17 39																
Smethwick Galton Bdg H.L. 7	d							17 43			18 08								19 08					
Birmingham New Street 12	a				17 17								18 12											
	d	17 03	17 15	17 15								18 03			18 15	18 33		19 03						19 15
Birmingham International ✈	d	17 15	17 26	17 26								18 15			18 26	18 46		19 15						19 26
Coventry	d	17 25	17 37	17 37								18 25			18 37	18 55		19 25						19 37
The Hawthorns 🚊	d							17 45			18 11								19 11					
Jewellery Quarter 🚊	d							17 49			18 14								19 14					
Birmingham Snow Hill 🚊	a							17 52			18 17								19 18					
	d						17 25	17 53		18 00	18 19			18 25					19 20					
Birmingham Moor Street	d							17a55			18a21								19a22					
Bordesley	d																							
Small Heath	d																							
Tyseley	d						17 46							18 46										
Acocks Green	d									18 26														
Olton	d									18 32														
Solihull	d									18 43														
Widney Manor	d									18 54														
Dorridge	d									19a04														
Lapworth	d																							
Hatton	d																							
Warwick Parkway	d								17 58								18 58					19 31	19 31	
Warwick	d								18 05								19 05					19 38	19 38	
Leamington Spa 8	a	17 37	17 50	17 51					18 15			18 37			18 50	19 07	19 15	19 37				19 42	19 47	19 51
	d	17 38	17 52	17 53					18 16			18 38			18 52	19 08	19 16	19 38				19 43	19 48	19 55
Banbury	d	17a54	18 11	18 12					18 36			18a54			19 11	19a24	19 36	19a54				20a03	20a08	20 14
London Marylebone 10	⊖ a		19 36	19 38					20 03						20 37		21 04							21 52
Spring Road	d						17 54							18 54										
Hall Green	d						18 05							19 05										
Yardley Wood	d						18 16							19 16										
Shirley	d						18 27							19 27										
Whitlocks End	d																							
Wythall	d						18 38							19 38										
Earlswood (West Midlands)	d																							
The Lakes	d						18 49							19 49										
Wood End	d																							
Danzey	d																							
Henley-in-Arden	d						19 05							20 05										
Wootton Wawen	d																							
Wilmcote	d						19 21							20 21										
Stratford-upon-Avon	a						19 36							20 36										

For general notes see front of timetable
For details of catering facilities see Directory of Train Operators

A Until 23 March
B From 30 March

Table 71

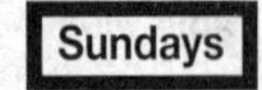

from 3 February

Hereford, Worcester and Stourbridge → Birmingham → Leamington Spa, Marylebone and Stratford-upon-Avon

Network Diagram - See first page of Table 71

		CH	GW	XC	EM	CH	CH	LM	GW	GW	XC	LM	CH	CH	LM	LM	GW	GW	CH	XC	EM	LM
			1 ◇	R 1					1 ◇	1 ◇	1 ◇						1 ◇	1 ◇				
		A	B ⊡						A ⊡	B ⊡							A ⚲	B ⚲				
Hereford 7	d		18 30												20 05							22 40
Ledbury	a		18 46												20 20							22 56
	d		18 48												20 21							22 56
Colwall	d		18 55												20 27							23 03
Great Malvern	a		18 59												20 32							23 07
	d		19 08						20 08	20 08					20 32		21 05	21 05			22 05	23 08
Malvern Link	d		19 12						20 12	20 12					20 35		21 09	21 09			22 08	23 10
Worcester Foregate Street 7	a		19 21						20 21	20 21					20 44		21 19	21 21			22 19	23 19
	d		19 21						20 22	20 23					20 44		21 20	21 23			22 20	23 22
Worcester Shrub Hill 7	a		19 25						20 24	20 26					20 47		21 23	21 26			22 22	23 24
	d				19 31			19 56				20 33			20 50	21 17					22 26	
Droitwich Spa	d				19 39			20 04				20 41			20 58	21 25					22 34	
Bromsgrove	d							20 13							21 08					22 20		
Barnt Green	d																					
University	d																					
Hartlebury	d																					
Kidderminster	d				19 49							20 51				21b41					22 44	
Blakedown	d																					
Hagley	d				19 56							20 58				21 48					22 51	
Stourbridge Junction 2	d				20 01							21 02				21 52					22 55	
Lye	d																					
Cradley Heath	d				20 07							21 07				21 58					23 01	
Old Hill	d																					
Rowley Regis	d				20 12							21 13				22 03					23 06	
Langley Green	d																					
Smethwick Galton Bdg H.L. 7	d				20 17							21 18				22 08					23 11	
Birmingham New Street 12	a							20 40							21 45					22 45		
	d	19 15		20 03			20 15				21 03			21 15								
Birmingham International ✈	d	19 26		20 15			20 26				21 15			21 26								
Coventry	d	19 37		20 25			20 37				21 25			21 37								
The Hawthorns 🚊	d				20 20							21 20				22 11					23 14	
Jewellery Quarter 🚊	d				20 23							21 24				22 14					23 17	
Birmingham Snow Hill 🚊	a				20 26							21 27				22 18					23 21	
	d				20 27							21 27				22 18						
Birmingham Moor Street	d				20a30							21a30				22a21						
Bordesley	d																					
Small Heath	d																					
Tyseley	d																					
Acocks Green	d																					
Olton	d																					
Solihull	d																					
Widney Manor	d																					
Dorridge	d																					
Lapworth	d																					
Hatton	d																					
Warwick Parkway	d					20 31							21 31						22 31			
Warwick	d					20 38							21 38						22s37			
Leamington Spa 8	a	19 53		20 37		20 42	20 50				21 37		21 42	21 50					22s41			
	d	19 55		20 38		20 43	20 55				21 38		21 43	21 55								
Banbury	d	20 14		20a54		21a03	21 14				21a54		22a03	22 16					23s02			
London Marylebone 10 ⊖	a	21 52					22 52							23 56								
Spring Road	d																					
Hall Green	d																					
Yardley Wood	d																					
Shirley	d																					
Whitlocks End	d																					
Wythall	d																					
Earlswood (West Midlands)	d																					
The Lakes	d																					
Wood End	d																					
Danzey	d																					
Henley-in-Arden	d																					
Wootton Wawen	d																					
Wilmcote	d																					
Stratford-upon-Avon	a																					

For general notes see front of timetable
For details of catering facilities see Directory of Train Operators

A From 30 March
B Until 23 March
b Arr. 2135

Stratford -upon-Avon, Marylebone and Leamington Spa → Birmingham → Stourbridge, Worcester and Hereford

Network Diagram - See first page of Table 71

Miles	Miles	Miles	Station		CH	LM	XC	LM	GW	CH	LM	LM	LM	GW	LM	LM	LM	GW	LM	LM	LM	CH	XC	LM	LM
					MX																				
									1									1 ◇					1 ◇		
							A							B											
—	0	—	**Stratford-upon-Avon**	d																06 31					06 54
—	2¾	—	Wilmcote	d																06 36					06 59
—	6½	—	Wootton Wawen	d																06x41					07x04
—	8¼	—	Henley-in-Arden	d																06 45					07 09
—	11¼	—	Danzey	d																06x49					07x13
—	13	—	Wood End	d																06x53					07x17
—	14¼	—	The Lakes	d																06x55					07x19
—	15	—	Earlswood (West Midlands)	d																06 57					07 22
—	16	—	Wythall	d																07 00					07 24
—	17	—	Whitlocks End	d																07 02					07 27
—	18	—	Shirley	d											06 35		06 52			07 05					07 30
—	19¼	—	Yardley Wood	d											06 38		06 55			07 08					07 33
—	20½	—	Hall Green	d											06 41		06 58			07 11					07 36
—	21	—	Spring Road	d											06 43		07 00			07 13					07 38
—	—	—	**London Marylebone 10**	⊖ d	22p10					08 00															
—	—	—	Banbury	d	23p29					09 34													06 53		
—	—	—	**Leamington Spa 8**	a	23p48					09 54													07 10		
—	—	0		d	23p48					09 54		05 48							06 30			06 55	07 11		
—	—	2	Warwick	d	23p53					09 59		05 52							06 34			06 58			
—	—	3¼	Warwick Parkway	d	23p56					10 02		05 55							06 37			07 01			
—	—	6	Hatton	d						10 07		06 00							06 42			07a07			
—	—	10½	Lapworth	d						10 11		06 06							06 48						
—	—	12¾	Dorridge	d	00 07					10 16	05 53	06 11							06 53		07 12				
—	—	14¾	Widney Manor	d							05 57	06 15							06 57		07 16				
—	—	16¼	Solihull	d	00 13					10 21	06 01	06 18							07 00		07 20				
—	—	18	Olton	d							06 04	06 22							07 04		07 23				
—	—	19	Acocks Green	d							06 07	06 24							07 06		07 26				
—	22	20	Tyseley	d							06 10	06 27			06 46		07 03		07 10	07 17	07 29				07 42
—	23	21	Small Heath	d							06 12	06 30			06 47		07 05		07 13	07 19	07 32				07 44
—	24	—	Bordesley	d																					
—	24¾	—	**Birmingham Moor Street**	d	00 24					10 33	06 16	06 35			06 51		07 09		07 19	07 23	07 36				07 48
—	25¼	—	**Birmingham Snow Hill**	🚋 a	00 31					10 40	06 19	06 37			06 54		07 12		07 21	07 27	07 38				07 52
—	—	—		d							06 20				06 55		07 15		07 23		07 39				07 53
—	26	—	Jewellery Quarter	🚋 d							06 22				06 58		07 17		07 25		07 42				07 55
—	28½	—	The Hawthorns	🚋 d							06 27				07 02		07 22		07 30		07 46				08 00
—	—	—	**Coventry**	a																			07 22		
—	—	—	**Birmingham International**	✈ a																			07 33		
—	—	24	**Birmingham New Street 12**	a																			07 45		
0	—	—		d			05 30						06 59			07 20								07 59	
—	29¼	29	Smethwick Galton Bdg H.L. 7	d							06 29				07 05		07 24		07 32		07 49				08 02
—	30½	30¼	Langley Green	d							06 32				07 08				07 35		07 52				
—	32¼	—	Rowley Regis	d							06 36				07 11		07 29		07 39		07 56				08 07
—	33½	—	Old Hill	d							06 39				07 14				07 42		07 59				
—	34¾	—	Cradley Heath	d							06 42				07 17		07 33		07 45		08 02				08 12
—	36¼	—	Lye	d							06 45				07 20				07 48		08 05				
—	37¼	—	**Stourbridge Junction 2**	d							06 49				07 24		07a39		07 52		08a09				08 17
—	39¼	—	Hagley	d							06 52				07 28				07 55						08 21
—	41	—	Blakedown	d							06 55				07 31				07 58						08 24
—	44¼	—	**Kidderminster**	d				06 00			07 00				07 36				08 03						08 29
—	47¾	—	Hartlebury	d											07 41				08 08						
2½	—	—	University	d									07 05			07 26								08 05	
10½	—	—	Barnt Green	d												07 42									
13	—	—	Bromsgrove	d									07 23			07 47								08 21	
19¼	53½	—	Droitwich Spa	d				06 10			07 12		07 33		07 49	07 57			08 17					08 31	08 40
25	—	—	**Worcester Shrub Hill 7**	a			06 10									08 05									
—	—	—		d		06 00			06 36					07 55		08 08		08 16							
25¾	58¾	—	**Worcester Foregate Street 7**	a		06 02		06 23	06 39		07 20		07 41	07 57	07 58	08 10		08 20	08 25					08 39	08 53
—	—	—		d		06 03							07 42	07 58		08 11			08 26					08 40	
32½	—	—	Malvern Link	d		06 12							07 52	08 09		08 19			08 36					08 50	
33¾	—	—	**Great Malvern**	a		06 15							07 54	08 13		08 22			08 39					08 52	
—	—	—		d		06 15							07 59											08 53	
36½	—	—	Colwall	d		06 20							08 05											08 58	
40¾	—	—	Ledbury	a		06 27							08 12											09 06	
—	—	—		d		06 28							08 12											09 08	
54½	—	—	**Hereford 7**	a		06 50							08 33											09 28	

For general notes see front of timetable
For details of catering facilities see Directory of Train Operators

A To Cardiff Central (Table 132)
B From Gloucester (Table 57)

Stratford -upon-Avon, Marylebone and Leamington Spa → Birmingham → Stourbridge, Worcester and Hereford

Network Diagram - See first page of Table 71

Station		LM	CH	XC	LM	LM	LM	GW	LM	CH	XC	LM	LM	LM	LM	LM	CH	XC	LM	LM	LM	CH	CH	XC	LM
				[1] ◇				[1]			[1] ◇							[1] ◇						[1] ◇	
			A																						
				☕							☕							☕						☕	
Stratford-upon-Avon	d				07 23								07 45							08 27					
Wilmcote	d												07 50							08 32					
Wootton Wawen	d												07x55							08x37					
Henley-in-Arden	d				07 34								07 59							08 41					
Danzey	d												08x04							08x45					
Wood End	d												08x08							08x49					
The Lakes	d												08x10							08x51					
Earlswood (West Midlands)	d				07 43								08 13							08 54					
Wythall	d				07 45								08 15							08 56					
Whitlocks End	d				07 48								08 18							08 59					
Shirley	d				07 52		08 09						08 21			08 38				09 02					09 22
Yardley Wood	d				07 55		08 12						08 24			08 41				09 05					09 25
Hall Green	d				07 58		08 15						08 27			08 44				09 08					09 28
Spring Road	d				08 00		08 17						08 29			08 46				09 10					09 30
London Marylebone [10] ⊖	d									06 45							06 50					07 20			
Banbury	d		07 02	07 25						07 59	07 53						08 05	08 25				08 35		08 53	
Leamington Spa [8]	a		07 22	07 41							08 10						08 23	08 41				08 53		09 10	
	d	07 07	07 22	07 43					07 47		08 11				08 03		08 24	08 43				08 53	09 04	09 11	
Warwick	d	07 11	07 26						07 51						08 07		08 28					08 57	09 07		
Warwick Parkway	d	07 15	07 30						07 55						08 11		08 32					09 01	09 10		
Hatton	d	07 20	07 34						08 00						08 16							09 07	09a16		
Lapworth	d	07 27							08 06						08 22							09 12			
Dorridge	d	07 33	07 43			07 58			08 11					08 20	08 29		08 43		08 46		09 09	09 16			
Widney Manor	d	07 37	07 47			08 01			08 14					08 24	08 32				08 50		09 13				
Solihull	d	07 41	07 51			08 05			08 18					08 28	08 36		08 48		08 53		09 16	09 21			
Olton	d	07 44	07 55			08 08			08 21					08 31	08 39				08 57		09 20				
Acocks Green	d	07 47				08 11			08 24					08 34	08 42				08 59		09 22				
Tyseley	d	07 50				08 14	08 20		08 28				08 32	08 37		08 49			09 02						09 33
Small Heath	d	07 53					08 23		08 31				08 34	08 40		08 51			09 05						09 35
Bordesley	d																								
Birmingham Moor Street	d	07 57	08 04		08 07	08 19	08 27		08 35				08 38	08 44	08 48	08 55	09 00		09 09	09 17	09 29	09 33			09 39
Birmingham Snow Hill 🚊	a	07 59	08 11		08 11	08 21	08 29		08 37				08 42	08 46	08 51	08 58	09 07		09 11	09 20	09 31	09 41			09 42
	d	08 03			08 13	08 23	08 33						08 43	08 53		09 03			09 13	09 23	09 33				09 43
Jewellery Quarter 🚊	d	08 05			08 15	08 25	08 35						08 45	08 55		09 05			09 15	09 25	09 35				09 45
The Hawthorns 🚊	d	08 10			08 20	08 30	08 40						08 50	09 00		09 10			09 20	09 30	09 40				09 50
Coventry	a										08 22													09 22	
Birmingham International ✈	a									08 40	08 33													09 33	
Birmingham New Street [12]	a			08 18							08 48							09 18						09 45	
	d											08 59													
Smethwick Galton Bdg H.L. [7]	d	08 12			08 22	08 32	08 42						08 52	09 02		09 12			09 22	09 32	09 42				09 52
Langley Green	d	08 15					08 45									09 15					09 45				
Rowley Regis	d	08 19			08 27	08 37	08 49						08 57	09 07		09 19			09 27	09 37	09 49				09 57
Old Hill	d	08 22					08 52									09 22					09 52				
Cradley Heath	d	08 25			08 32	08 42	08 55						09 02	09 12		09 25			09 32	09 42	09 55				10 02
Lye	d	08 28					08 58									09 28					09 58				
Stourbridge Junction [2]	d	08 32			08a38	08a49	09 02						09a08	09 17		09 32			09 39	09a48	10 02				10a08
Hagley	d	08 36					09 06							09 21							10 06				
Blakedown	d	08 39					09 09							09 24							10 09				
Kidderminster	d	08a45					09a15							09 29		09a42			09 48		10a15				
Hartlebury	d																		09 53						
University	d											09 05													
Barnt Green	d																								
Bromsgrove	d											09 21													
Droitwich Spa	d											09 31		09 40					10 01						
Worcester Shrub Hill [7]	a																		10 10						
	d							09 20																	
Worcester Foregate Street [7]	a							09 24				09 39		09 54											
	d											09 40													
Malvern Link	d											09 50													
Great Malvern	a											09 52													
	d											09 53													
Colwall	d											09 58													
Ledbury	a											10 06													
	d											10 08													
Hereford [7]	a											10 28													

For general notes see front of timetable
For details of catering facilities see Directory of Train Operators

A From High Wycombe (Table 115)

Stratford -upon-Avon, Marylebone and Leamington Spa → Birmingham → Stourbridge, Worcester and Hereford

Network Diagram - See first page of Table 71

		GW	GW	LM	LM	CH	XC	LM	LM	LM	LM	CH	XC	LM	GW	LM	LM	CH	CH	XC	LM	LM	LM	LM	CH
			1 ◇				1 ◇						1 ◇		1 ◇					1 ◇					
		A																							
Stratford-upon-Avon	d									09 27													10 27		
Wilmcote	d									09 32													10 32		
Wootton Wawen	d									09x37													10x37		
Henley-in-Arden	d									09 41													10 41		
Danzey	d									09x45													10x45		
Wood End	d									09x49													10x49		
The Lakes	d									09x51													10x51		
Earlswood (West Midlands)	d									09 54													10 54		
Wythall	d									09 56													10 56		
Whitlocks End	d									09 59													10 59		
Shirley	d							09 42		10 02				10 22							10 42		11 02		
Yardley Wood	d							09 45		10 05				10 25							10 45		11 05		
Hall Green	d							09 48		10 08				10 28							10 48		11 08		
Spring Road	d							09 50		10 10				10 30							10 50		11 10		
London Marylebone 10 ⊖	d					07 50						08 20						08 50	08 54						09 20
Banbury	d					08 56	09 25					09 35	09 53					09 56	10 14	10 25					10 35
Leamington Spa 8	a					09 14	09 41					09 53	10 10					10 14	10 33	10 41					10 54
	d					09 14	09 43					09 54	10 11					10 14	10 34	10 43					10 54
Warwick	d					09 19						09 58						10 19	10 38						10 59
Warwick Parkway	d					09 22						10 02						10 22							11 02
Hatton	d											10 07							10a45						
Lapworth	d											10 12													
Dorridge	d				09 28	09 33			09 46		10 09	10 17					10 28	10 33				10 46		11 09	11 13
Widney Manor	d				09 32				09 50		10 13						10 32					10 50		11 13	
Solihull	d				09 35	09 39			09 53		10 16	10 23					10 35	10 39				10 53		11 16	11 19
Olton	d				09 39				09 57		10 20						10 39					10 57		11 20	
Acocks Green	d				09 41				09 59		10 22						10 41					10 59		11 22	
Tyseley	d								10 02					10 33								11 02			
Small Heath	d								10 05					10 35								11 05			
Bordesley	d																								
Birmingham Moor Street	d				09 48	09 51		09 58	10 09	10 17	10 29	10 34		10 39			10 48	10 51			10 57	11 09	11 17	11 29	11 31
Birmingham Snow Hill	a				09 50	10 01		10 01	10 11	10 20	10 31	10 41		10 42			10 50	11 01			11 01	11 11	11 20	11 31	11 41
	d				09 53			10 03	10 13	10 23	10 33			10 43			10 53				11 03	11 13	11 23	11 33	
Jewellery Quarter	d				09 55			10 05	10 15	10 25	10 35			10 45			10 55				11 05	11 15	11 25	11 35	
The Hawthorns	d				10 00			10 10	10 20	10 30	10 40			10 50			11 00				11 10	11 20	11 30	11 40	
Coventry	a												10 22												
Birmingham International ✈	a												10 33												
Birmingham New Street 12	a						10 18						10 46							11 18					
	d			09 59												10 59									
Smethwick Galton Bdg H.L. 7	d				10 02			10 12	10 22	10 32	10 42			10 52			11 02				11 12	11 22	11 32	11 42	
Langley Green	d							10 15			10 45										11 15			11 45	
Rowley Regis	d				10 07			10 19	10 27	10 37	10 49			10 57			11 07				11 19	11 27	11 37	11 49	
Old Hill	d							10 22			10 52										11 22			11 52	
Cradley Heath	d				10 12			10 25	10 32	10 42	10 55			11 02			11 12				11 25	11 32	11 42	11 55	
Lye	d							10 28			10 58										11 28			11 58	
Stourbridge Junction 2	d				10 17			10 32	10 37	10a48	11 02			11a08			11 17				11 32	11 37	11a48	12 02	
Hagley	d				10 21						11 06						11 21							12 06	
Blakedown	d				10 24						11 09						11 24							12 09	
Kidderminster	d				10 29			10a42	10 48		11a15						11 29				11a42	11 48		12a15	
Hartlebury	d																								
University	d			10 05												11 05									
Barnt Green	d																								
Bromsgrove	d			10 21												11 21									
Droitwich Spa	d			10 31	10 40				11 00							11 31	11 40					12 00			
Worcester Shrub Hill 7	a				10 48																	12 09			
	d	10 14	10 23		10 52										11 12										
Worcester Foregate Street 7	a	10 16	10 26	10 39	10 54				11 08						11 16	11 39	11 49								
	d	10 17	10 27	10 40	10 55										11 16	11 40									
Malvern Link	d	10 26	10 35	10 50	11 03										11 25	11 50									
Great Malvern	a	10 30	10 42	10 52	11 06										11 29	11 55									
	d			10 53											11 29										
Colwall	d			10 58											11 34										
Ledbury	a			11 06											11 42										
	d			11 08											11 43										
Hereford 7	a			11 28											12 05										

For general notes see front of timetable
For details of catering facilities see Directory of Train Operators

A From Warminster (Table 123)

Stratford -upon-Avon, Marylebone and Leamington Spa → Birmingham → Stourbridge, Worcester and Hereford

Network Diagram - See first page of Table 71

		XC	LM	GW	GW	LM	LM	CH	XC	LM	LM	LM	LM	CH	XC	LM	LM	LM	CH	CH	XC	LM	GW	LM	LM
		R 1		◇ A	1 ◇				1 ◇						R 1						1 ◇		1 ◇		
Stratford-upon-Avon	d											11 27													12 27
Wilmcote	d											11 32													12 32
Wootton Wawen	d											11x37													12x37
Henley-in-Arden	d											11 41													12 41
Danzey	d											11x45													12x45
Wood End	d											11x49													12x49
The Lakes	d											11x51													12x51
Earlswood (West Midlands)	d											11 54													12 54
Wythall	d											11 56													12 56
Whitlocks End	d											11 59													12 59
Shirley	d		11 22							11 42		12 02				12 22						12 42			13 02
Yardley Wood	d		11 25							11 45		12 05				12 25						12 45			13 05
Hall Green	d		11 28							11 48		12 08				12 28						12 48			13 08
Spring Road	d		11 30							11 50		12 10				12 30						12 50			13 10
London Marylebone 10 ⊖	d							09 50						10 20					10 50	10 54					
Banbury	d	10 53						10 56	11 25					11 35	11 53				11 56	12 17	12 25				
Leamington Spa 8	a	11 10						11 14	11 41					11 54	12 10				12 14	12 37	12 41				
	d	11 11						11 14	11 43					11 54	12 11				12 15	12 38	12 43				
Warwick	d							11 19						11 59					12 19	12 42					
Warwick Parkway	d							11 22						12 02					12 23						
Hatton	d													12 07						12a49					
Lapworth	d													12 13											
Dorridge	d						11 28	11 33			11 46		12 09	12 17				12 28	12 34					12 46	
Widney Manor	d						11 32				11 50		12 13					12 32						12 50	
Solihull	d						11 35	11 39			11 53		12 16	12 23				12 35	12 39					12 53	
Olton	d						11 39				11 57		12 20					12 39						12 57	
Acocks Green	d						11 41				11 59		12 22					12 41						12 59	
Tyseley	d		11 33								12 02					12 33								13 02	
Small Heath	d		11 35								12 05					12 35								13 05	
Bordesley	d																								
Birmingham Moor Street	d		11 39				11 48	11 51		11 58	12 10	12 17	12 29	12 35		12 39		12 48	12 51			12 58		13 09	13 17
Birmingham Snow Hill	a		11 42				11 50	12 01			12 12	12 20	12 31	12 42		12 42		12 51	13 02			13 01		13 11	13 20
	d		11 43				11 53				12 13	12 23	12 33			12 43		12 53				13 03		13 13	13 23
Jewellery Quarter	d		11 45				11 55			12 05	12 15	12 25	12 35			12 45		12 55				13 05		13 15	13 25
The Hawthorns	d		11 50				12 00			12 10	12 20	12 30	12 40			12 50		13 00				13 10		13 20	13 30
Coventry	a	11 22													12 22										
Birmingham International ✈	a	11 33													12 33										
Birmingham New Street 12	a	11 45							12 18						12 45						13 18				
	d					11 59											12 59								
Smethwick Galton Bdg H.L. 7	d		11 52				12 02			12 12	12 22	12 32	12 42			12 52		13 02				13 12		13 22	13 32
Langley Green	d									12 15			12 45									13 15			
Rowley Regis	d		11 57				12 07			12 19	12 27	12 37	12 49			12 57		13 07				13 19		13 27	13 37
Old Hill	d									12 22			12 52									13 22			
Cradley Heath	d		12 02				12 12			12 25	12 32	12 42	12 55			13 02		13 12				13 25		13 32	13 42
Lye	d									12 28			12 58									13 28			
Stourbridge Junction 2	d		12a08				12 17			12 32	12 37	12a48	13 02			13a08		13 17				13a32		13 40	13a48
Hagley	d						12 21						13 06					13 21							
Blakedown	d						12 24						13 09					13 24							
Kidderminster	d						12 29			12a42	12 48		13a15					13 29						13 48	
Hartlebury	d																								
University	d					12 05											13 05								
Barnt Green	d																								
Bromsgrove	d					12 21											13 21								
Droitwich Spa	d					12 31	12 40				13 00						13 31	13 40						14 00	
Worcester Shrub Hill 7	a						12 48																	14 18	
	d			12 15	12 21		12 52																14 12		
Worcester Foregate Street 7	a			12 17	12 26	12 39	12 54				13 08						13 39	13 49					14 16		
	d			12 18		12 40	12 55										13 40						14 16		
Malvern Link	d			12 27		12 50	13 03										13 50						14 25		
Great Malvern	a			12 30		12 52	13 06										13 52						14 29		
	d					12 53											13 53						14 29		
Colwall	d					12 58											13 58						14 34		
Ledbury	a					13 06											14 06						14 42		
	d					13 08											14 08						14 43		
Hereford 7	a					13 28											14 28						15 05		

For general notes see front of timetable
For details of catering facilities see Directory of Train Operators

A From Weymouth (Table 123)

Stratford -upon-Avon, Marylebone and Leamington Spa → Birmingham → Stourbridge, Worcester and Hereford

Network Diagram - See first page of Table 71

Station		LM	CH	XC	LM	GW	LM	LM	CH	XC	LM	LM	LM	LM	CH	XC	LM	LM	LM	CH	CH	XC	LM	LM	LM
				R 1 ☕		◇ A				1 ◇ ☕						R 1 ☕						1 ◇ ☕			
Stratford-upon-Avon	d												13 27												14 27
Wilmcote	d												13 32												14 32
Wootton Wawen	d												13x37												14x37
Henley-in-Arden	d												13 41												14 41
Danzey	d												13x45												14x45
Wood End	d												13x49												14x49
The Lakes	d												13x51												14x51
Earlswood (West Midlands)	d												13 54												14 54
Wythall	d												13 56												14 56
Whitlocks End	d												13 59												14 59
Shirley	d				13 22						13 42		14 02				14 22						14 42		15 02
Yardley Wood	d				13 25						13 45		14 05				14 25						14 45		15 05
Hall Green	d				13 28						13 48		14 08				14 28						14 48		15 08
Spring Road	d				13 30						13 50		14 10				14 30						14 50		15 10
London Marylebone 10 ⊖	d		11 20						11 50						12 20					12 50	12 54				
Banbury	d		12 35	12 53					12 56	13 25					13 35	13 53				13 56	14 17	14 25			
Leamington Spa 8	a		12 54	13 10					13 14	13 41					13 54	14 10				14 14	14 37	14 41			
	d		12 54	13 11					13 14	13 43					13 54	14 11				14 15	14 38	14 43			
Warwick	d		12 59						13 19						13 59					14 19	14 42				
Warwick Parkway	d		13 02						13 22						14 02					14 23					
Hatton	d														14 07						14a49				
Lapworth	d														14 13										
Dorridge	d	13 09	13 13					13 28	13 33			13 46		14 09	14 17				14 28	14 34				14 46	
Widney Manor	d	13 13						13 32				13 50		14 13					14 32					14 50	
Solihull	d	13 16	13 21					13 35	13 39			13 53		14 16	14 23				14 35	14 39				14 53	
Olton	d	13 20						13 39				13 57		14 20					14 39					14 57	
Acocks Green	d	13 22						13 41				13 59		14 22					14 41					14 59	
Tyseley	d				13 33							14 02					14 33							15 02	
Small Heath	d				13 35							14 05					14 35							15 05	
Bordesley	d																								
Birmingham Moor Street	d	13 29	13 32		13 39			13 48	13 51		13 59	14 09	14 17	14 29	14 35		14 39		14 48	14 51			14 58	15 09	15 17
Birmingham Snow Hill 🚋	a	13 31	13 41		13 42			13 51	14 01		14 01	14 11	14 21	14 31	14 42		14 42		14 51	15 02			15 01	15 11	15 21
	d	13 33			13 43			13 53			14 03	14 13	14 23	14 33			14 43		14 53				15 03	15 13	15 23
Jewellery Quarter 🚋	d	13 35			13 45			13 55			14 05	14 15	14 25	14 35			14 45		14 55				15 05	15 15	15 25
The Hawthorns 🚋	d	13 40			13 50			14 00			14 10	14 20	14 30	14 40			14 50		15 00				15 10	15 20	15 30
Coventry	a			13 21												14 22									
Birmingham International ✈	a			13 33												14 33									
Birmingham New Street 12	a			13 45						14 18						14 45						15 18			
	d						13 59											14 59							
Smethwick Galton Bdg H.L. 7	d	13 42			13 52			14 02			14 12	14 22	14 32	14 42			14 52		15 02				15 12	15 22	15 32
Langley Green	d	13 45									14 15			14 45									15 15		
Rowley Regis	d	13 49			13 57			14 07			14 19	14 27	14 37	14 49			14 57		15 07				15 19	15 27	15 37
Old Hill	d	13 52									14 22			14 52									15 22		
Cradley Heath	d	13 55			14 02			14 12			14 25	14 32	14 42	14 55			15 02		15 12				15 25	15 32	15 42
Lye	d	13 58									14 28			14 58									15 28		
Stourbridge Junction 2	d	14 02			14a08			14 17			14 32	14 39	14a48	15 02			15a08		15 17				15 32	15 37	15a48
Hagley	d							14 21						15 06					15 21					15 41	
Blakedown	d							14 24						15 09					15 24					15 44	
Kidderminster	d	14a12						14 29			14a42	14 48		15a15					15 29				15a42	15 49	
Hartlebury	d																								
University	d						14 05											15 05							
Barnt Green	d																								
Bromsgrove	d						14 21											15 21							
Droitwich Spa	d						14 31	14 40				15 00						15 31	15 41					16 00	
Worcester Shrub Hill 7	a							14 48																16 08	
	d					14 23																			
Worcester Foregate Street 7	a					14 25	14 39					15 08						15 39	15 51						
	d					14 26	14 40											15 45							
Malvern Link	d					14 38	14 50											15 55							
Great Malvern	a					14 42	14 55											15 57							
	d																	16 05							
Colwall	d																	16 10							
Ledbury	a																	16 17							
	d																	16 18							
Hereford 7	a																	16 38							

For general notes see front of timetable
For details of catering facilities see Directory of Train Operators

A From Brighton (Table 123)

Stratford -upon-Avon, Marylebone and Leamington Spa → Birmingham → Stourbridge, Worcester and Hereford

Network Diagram - See first page of Table 71

		LM	CH	XC	LM	GW	LM	GW	LM	CH	XC	LM	LM	LM	XC	LM	LM	CH	XC	LM	LM	LM	CH	CH	XC
				R 1		1 ◇		A			R 1				◇ B				R 1						R 1 C
Stratford-upon-Avon	d															15 27									
Wilmcote	d															15 32									
Wootton Wawen	d															15x37									
Henley-in-Arden	d															15 41									
Danzey	d															15x45									
Wood End	d															15x49									
The Lakes	d															15x51									
Earlswood (West Midlands)	d															15 54									
Wythall	d															15 56									
Whitlocks End	d															15 59									
Shirley	d				15 22							15 42				16 02					16 22				
Yardley Wood	d				15 25							15 45				16 05					16 25				
Hall Green	d				15 28							15 48				16 08					16 28				
Spring Road	d				15 30							15 50				16 10					16 30				
London Marylebone 10 ⊖	d		13 20							13 50								14 20					14 50	14 54	
Banbury	d		14 35	14 53						14 56	15 25							15 35	15 53				15 56	16 17	16 25
Leamington Spa 8	a		14 54	15 10						15 14	15 41							15 54	16 10				16 14	16 37	16 41
	d		14 54	15 11						15 15	15 43							15 54	16 11				16 14	16 38	16 43
Warwick	d		14 59							15 19								15 59					16 19	16 42	
Warwick Parkway	d		15 02							15 23								16 02					16 22		
Hatton	d																	16 07						16a49	
Lapworth	d																	16 13							
Dorridge	d	15 09	15 13						15 28	15 34				15 46			16 09	16 17				16 27	16 33		
Widney Manor	d	15 13							15 32					15 50			16 13					16 31			
Solihull	d	15 16	15 21						15 35	15 39				15 53			16 16	16 23				16 34	16 39		
Olton	d	15 20							15 39					15 57			16 20					16 38			
Acocks Green	d	15 22							15 41					15 59			16 22					16 40			
Tyseley	d				15 33									16 02							16 33	16 43			
Small Heath	d				15 35									16 05							16 35				
Bordesley	d																								
Birmingham Moor Street	d	15 29	15 33		15 39				15 48	15 51		15 58		16 09		16 17	16 29	16 35			16 39	16 48	16 51		
Birmingham Snow Hill 🚊	a	15 31	15 41		15 42				15 51	16 01		16 01		16 11		16 21	16 31	16 42			16 42	16 51	17 01		
	d	15 33			15 43				15 53			16 03		16 13		16 23	16 33				16 43	16 53			
Jewellery Quarter 🚊	d	15 35			15 45				15 55			16 05		16 15		16 25	16 35				16 45	16 55			
The Hawthorns 🚊	d	15 40			15 50				16 00			16 10		16 20		16 30	16 40				16 50	17 00			
Coventry	a			15 22															16 22						
Birmingham International ✈	a			15 33															16 33						
Birmingham New Street 12	a			15 45							16 18								16 45						17 18
	d						15 59						16 19		16 30					16 59					
Smethwick Galton Bdg H.L. 7	d	15 42			15 52				16 02			16 12		16 22		16 32	16 43				16 52	17 02			
Langley Green	d	15 45										16 15					16 46								
Rowley Regis	d	15 49			15 57				16 07			16 19		16 28		16 38	16 49				16 58	17 07			
Old Hill	d	15 52										16 22					16 52								
Cradley Heath	d	15 55			16 02				16 12			16 25		16 33		16 43	16 56				17 03	17 12			
Lye	d	15 58										16 28					16 59								
Stourbridge Junction 2	d	16 02			16a08				16 17			16 32		16 39		16a49	17 02				17 10	17a18			
Hagley	d								16 21								17 06				17 14				
Blakedown	d								16 24								17 09				17 17				
Kidderminster	d	16a12							16 29			16a42		16 48			17a15				17 22				
Hartlebury	d																				17 27				
University	d						16 05						16 25		16 36					17 05					
Barnt Green	d																								
Bromsgrove	d						16 21								16a50					17 21					
Droitwich Spa	d						16 31		16 40				16 49	17 00						17 31	17 38				
Worcester Shrub Hill 7	a												17 00							17 38					
	d					16 09		16 40					17 08							17 42					
Worcester Foregate Street 7	a					16 13	16 39	16 42	16 49				17 10	17 09						17 44	17 47				
	d					16 13	16 40						17 12							17 46					
Malvern Link	d					16 22	16 50						17 21							17 56					
Great Malvern	a					16 29	16 52						17 24							17 58					
	d						16 53													18 08					
Colwall	d						16 58													18 13					
Ledbury	a						17 06													18 20					
	d						17 08													18 21					
Hereford 7	a						17 28													18 41					

For general notes see front of timetable
For details of catering facilities see Directory of Train Operators

A From Westbury (Table 123)
B From Nottingham to Cardiff Central (Table 57)
C To Derby (Table 57)

Stratford -upon-Avon, Marylebone and Leamington Spa → Birmingham → Stourbridge, Worcester and Hereford

Network Diagram - See first page of Table 71

Station		LM	LM	LM	XC	LM	GW	CH	XC	LM	LM	LM	LM	LM	CH	XC	LM	LM	LM	CH	CH	GW	LM	XC	XC
					◇ A 🍴		B		R 1 ☕						🍴	R 1 ☕				🍴		1		◇ C	R 1 ☕
Stratford-upon-Avon	d					16 27												17 27							
Wilmcote	d					16 32												17 32							
Wootton Wawen	d					16x37												17x37							
Henley-in-Arden	d					16 41												17 41							
Danzey	d					16x45												17x45							
Wood End	d					16x49												17x49							
The Lakes	d					16x51												17x51							
Earlswood (West Midlands)	d					16 54												17 54							
Wythall	d					16 56												17 56							
Whitlocks End	d					16 59												17 59							
Shirley	d	16 42				17 02							17 22				17 45	18 02							
Yardley Wood	d	16 45				17 05							17 25				17 48	18 05							
Hall Green	d	16 48				17 08							17 28				17 51	18 08							
Spring Road	d	16 50				17 10							17 30				17 53	18 10							
London Marylebone 10 ⊖	d							15 20							16 00					16 30	16 34				
Banbury	d							16 35	16 53						17 03	17 25				17 34	17 49				17 53
Leamington Spa 8	a							16 53	17 10						17 22	17 41				17 52	18 06				18 10
	d							16 54	17 11						17 22	17 43				17 52	18 07				18 11
Warwick	d							16 58												17 57					
Warwick Parkway	d							17 02							17 28					18 00	18 13				
Hatton	d																				18a19				
Lapworth	d																			18 09					
Dorridge	d			16 46				17 13			17 09			17 27	17 39				18 02	18 13					
Widney Manor	d			16 50							17 13			17 31					18 06						
Solihull	d			16 53				17 21			17 16			17 34	17 44				18 09	18 19					
Olton	d			16 57							17 20			17 38					18 13						
Acocks Green	d			16 59							17 22			17 40					18 15						
Tyseley	d	16 53		17 02									17 33	17 43					18 20						
Small Heath	d			17 05									17 35	17 46					18 22						
Bordesley	d																								
Birmingham Moor Street	d	16 58		17 09		17 17		17 33			17 29		17 39	17 50	17 59		18 00	18 17	18 26	18 30					
Birmingham Snow Hill 🚋	a	17 01		17 12		17 21		17 41			17 31		17 42	17 52	18 12		18 02	18 20	18 29	18 40					
	d	17 03		17 13		17 23					17 33		17 43	17 53			18 03	18 23							
Jewellery Quarter 🚋	d	17 05		17 15		17 25					17 35		17 45	17 55			18 05	18 25							
The Hawthorns 🚋	d	17 10		17 20		17 30					17 40		17 50	18 00			18 10	18 30							
Coventry	a								17 22																18 22
Birmingham International ✈	a								17 33																18 33
Birmingham New Street 12	a								17 45							18 18									18 45
	d		17 19		17 30					17 50		17 59											18 19	18 30	
Smethwick Galton Bdg H.L. 7	d	17 13		17 22		17 32					17 42		17 53	18 02			18 13	18 33							
Langley Green	d	17 16				17 35							17 56				18 16	18 36							
Rowley Regis	d	17 19		17 28		17 39					17 48		17 59	18 08			18 19	18 39							
Old Hill	d	17 22				17 42							18 02				18 22	18 42							
Cradley Heath	d	17 26		17 33		17 45					17 53		18 06	18 13			18 26	18 46							
Lye	d	17 29				17 48							18 09				18 29	18 49							
Stourbridge Junction 2	d	17 33		17 42		17a53					18 03		18 13	18 23			18 33	18 54							
Hagley	d	17 37		17 46							18 07		18 17	18 27			18 37	18 58							
Blakedown	d	17 40		17 49							18 10		18 20	18 30			18 40	19 01							
Kidderminster	d	17a45		17 54							18 15		18a26	18 35			18a46	19a06							
Hartlebury	d										18 20			18 40											
University	d		17 25		17 36							18 05													
Barnt Green	d																								
Bromsgrove	d		17 45		17a51							18 22											18 47	18a50	
Droitwich Spa	d		17 54	18 06						18 19	18 28	18 35		18 49									18 56		
Worcester Shrub Hill 7	a		18 05							18 29	18 38			18 57									19 11		
	d		18 08				18 28															19 11			
Worcester Foregate Street 7	a		18 11	18 14			18 30					18 44										19 15			
	d		18 11				18 31					18 44													
Malvern Link	d		18 20									18 54													
Great Malvern	a		18 23				18 40					18 57													
	d		18 23									18 57													
Colwall	d		18 29									19 02													
Ledbury	a		18 36									19 10													
	d		18 36									19 13													
Hereford 7	a		18 57									19 33													

For general notes see front of timetable
For details of catering facilities see Directory of Train Operators

A From Nottingham to Cardiff Central (Table 57). 🍴 to Newport (South Wales)

B From Warminster (Table 123)

C From Nottingham (Table 57)

Stratford -upon-Avon, Marylebone and Leamington Spa → Birmingham → Stourbridge, Worcester and Hereford

Network Diagram - See first page of Table 71

		XC	LM	LM	LM	CH	GW	LM	LM	GW	LM	LM	CH	XC	CH	LM	GW	LM	CH	XC	LM	CH	XC	LM	GW
		R 1					1 ◇							R 1			1 ◇			1 ◇			1 ◇		1 ◇
						A				B							C		A						
		🛒				🚌	🛒							🛒			🛒		🚌	🛒			🛒		🚌
Stratford-upon-Avon	d		17 58						18 26			18 50									19 27				
Wilmcote	d								18 31			18 55									19 32				
Wootton Wawen	d								18x36			19x00									19x37				
Henley-in-Arden	d		18 08						18 40			19 04									19 41				
Danzey	d								18x44												19x45				
Wood End	d								18x48												19x49				
The Lakes	d								18x50												19x51				
Earlswood (West Midlands)	d								18 53												19 54				
Wythall	d								18 55												19 56				
Whitlocks End	d								18 58												19 59				
Shirley	d		18 22		18 37				19 02			19 16				19 30					20 02				
Yardley Wood	d		18 25		18 40				19 05			19 19				19 33					20 05				
Hall Green	d		18 28		18 43				19 08			19 22				19 36					20 08				
Spring Road	d		18 30		18 45				19 10			19 24				19 38					20 10				
London Marylebone 10 ⊖	d					17 00							17 30		17 41				18 00			18 30			
Banbury	d	18 25				18 03							18 39	18 53	18 58				19 03	19 25		19 36	19 53		
Leamington Spa 8	a	18 41				18 23							18 58	19 10	19 15				19 21	19 41		19 54	20 10		
	d	18 43				18 23							18 58	19 11	19 16				19 21	19 43		19 54	20 11		
Warwick	d												19 03		19 20							19 59			
Warwick Parkway	d					18 29							19 06						19 27			20 02			
Hatton	d												19 11		19a27							20 07			
Lapworth	d												19 17									20 13			
Dorridge	d			18 23		18 40					18 58		19 21					19 31	19 38			20 17			
Widney Manor	d			18 27							19 02							19 35							
Solihull	d			18 30		18 45					19 06		19 27					19 38	19 43			20 23			
Olton	d			18 34							19 09							19 41							
Acocks Green	d			18 36							19 12							19 44							
Tyseley	d		18 33	18 39	18 48						19 16					19 41		19 47							
Small Heath	d		18 35	18 42							19 19					19 43		19 49							
Bordesley	d																								
Birmingham Moor Street	d		18 39	18 46	18 53	18 56			19 17		19 23	19 32	19 38			19 48		19 53	19 57		20 17	20 34			
Birmingham Snow Hill 🚋	a		18 42	18 48	18 55	19 01			19 19		19 25	19 35	19 47			19 50		19 56	20 01		20 20	20 44			
	d		18 43		18 57	19 10					19 27	19 36						19 57	20 10		20 21				
Jewellery Quarter 🚋	d		18 45		18 59						19 29	19 38						19 59			20 24				
The Hawthorns 🚋	d		18 50		19 04	19 16					19 34	19 43						20 04	20 16		20 28				
Coventry	a													19 22									20 22		
Birmingham International ✈	a													19 33									20 33		
Birmingham New Street 12	a	19 18												19 45						20 18			20 48		
	d							19 19																20 59	
Smethwick Galton Bdg H.L. 7	d		18 53		19 07	19 19					19 36	19 45						20 06	20 19		20 31				
Langley Green	d				19 10						19 39							20 09			20 34				
Rowley Regis	d		18 58		19 13	19 24					19 43	19 50						20 13	20 24		20 37				
Old Hill	d				19 16						19 46							20 16			20 40				
Cradley Heath	d		19 03		19 20	19 29					19 49	19 55						20 19	20 29		20 43				
Lye	d				19 23						19 52							20 22			20 46				
Stourbridge Junction 2	d		19 08		19a27	19 36					19 56	20a01						20 26	20 36		20a51				
Hagley	d		19 12								19 59							20 29							
Blakedown	d		19 15								20 02							20 32							
Kidderminster	d		19 20			19a48					20 07							20 37	20a50						
Hartlebury	d																								
University	d							19 25																21 05	
Barnt Green	d																								
Bromsgrove	d							19 40																21 21	
Droitwich Spa	d		19 31					19 50			20 19							20 50						21 31	
Worcester Shrub Hill 7	a							20 01			20 26							20 58						21 41	
	d						19 44	20 12		20 18							20 39							21 48	21 54
Worcester Foregate Street 7	a		19 40				19 48	20 14		20 20							20 42							21 50	21 57
	d						19 48	20 15		20 25							20 42							21 51	21 58
Malvern Link	d						19 57	20 24		20 34							20 52							22 00	22 10
Great Malvern	a						20 01	20 26		20 37							20 56							22 02	22 13
	d						20 01	20 27									20 56							22 03	
Colwall	d						20 07	20 32									21 02							22 08	
Ledbury	a						20 15	20 39									21 10							22 15	
	d						20 15	20 40									21 10							22 16	
Hereford 7	a						20 36	21 00									21 31							22 36	

For general notes see front of timetable
For details of catering facilities see Directory of Train Operators

A 🚌 to Birmingham Snow Hill
B From Warminster (Table 123)
C **The Cathedrals Express**

Stratford -upon-Avon, Marylebone and Leamington Spa → Birmingham → Stourbridge, Worcester and Hereford

Network Diagram - See first page of Table 71

		LM	CH	GW	XC	LM	CH	CH	XC	LM	LM	CH	LM	CH	XC	LM FO	LM FX	LM	CH	LM	CH	CH	CH FO
				1 ◇	1 ◇				1 ◇						1 ◇								
			A 🍴													B							
Stratford-upon-Avon	d					20 27																	
Wilmcote	d					20 32																	
Wootton Wawen	d					20x37																	
Henley-in-Arden	d					20 41																	
Danzey	d					20x45																	
Wood End	d					20x49																	
The Lakes	d					20x51																	
Earlswood (West Midlands)	d					20 54																	
Wythall	d					20 56																	
Whitlocks End	d					20 59																	
Shirley	d					21 02							21 56							22 54			
Yardley Wood	d					21 05							21 59							22 57			
Hall Green	d					21 08							22 02							23 00			
Spring Road	d					21 10							22 04							23 02			
London Marylebone 10 ⊖	d		19 00				19 30	19 33				20 00		20 30					21 00		21 30	22 10	23 54
Banbury	d		20 03		20 25		20 38	20 49	20 53			21 06		21 47	21 53				22 08		22 47	23 29	01 17
Leamington Spa 8	a		20 23		20 41		20 55	21 06	21 10			21 25		22 04	22 10				22 27		23 05	23 48	01 39
	d		20 23		20 43		20 56	21 07	21 11			21 25		22 05	22 11				22 27		23 06	23 48	
Warwick	d						21 00	21 12						22 10							23 10	23 53	
Warwick Parkway	d		20 29				21 04					21 31		22 14					22 32		23 14	23 56	
Hatton	d						21 09	21a19						22 19									
Lapworth	d						21 14							22 24									
Dorridge	d	20 28	20 40				21 19				21 31	21 42		22 29				22 30	22 43		23 25	00 07	
Widney Manor	d	20 32									21 35			22 32				22 37					
Solihull	d	20 35	20 45				21 25				21 38	21 47		22 36				22 40	22 49		23 30	00 13	
Olton	d	20 39									21 42			22 40				22 43					
Acocks Green	d	20 41									21 44			22 43				22 46					
Tyseley	d	20 44									21 47		22 07					22 50		23 05			
Small Heath	d	20 47									21 50		22 09					22 52		23 07			
Bordesley	d																						
Birmingham Moor Street	d	20 51	20 57			21 17	21 37				21 54	21 59	22 13	22 51				22 56	23 00	23 12	23 42	00 24	
Birmingham Snow Hill 🚋	a	20 54	21 03			21 20	21 47				21 56	22 04	22 16	22 58				22 59	23 05	23 15	23 49	00 31	
	d	20 55	21 05			21 21					21 57	22 10	22 17					23 00	23 15				
Jewellery Quarter 🚋	d	20 57				21 23					22 00		22 19					23 03	23 17				
The Hawthorns 🚋	d	21 02	21 11			21 28					22 04	22 16	22 24					23 07	23 22				
Coventry	a								21 22						22 22								
Birmingham International ✈	a								21 33						22 33								
Birmingham New Street 12	a				21 18				21 45						22 52								
	d									21 59						23 04	23 04						
Smethwick Galton Bdg H.L. 7	d	21 05	21 14			21 30					22 07	22 19	22 27					23 10	23 25				
Langley Green	d	21 08				21 33					22 10		22 30					23 13	23 28				
Rowley Regis	d	21 11	21 20			21 36					22 13	22 24	22 33					23 16	23 31				
Old Hill	d	21 14				21 39					22 16		22 36					23 19	23 34				
Cradley Heath	d	21 17	21 25			21 42					22 19	22 29	22 40					23 22	23 38				
Lye	d	21 20				21 45					22 22		22 43					23 25	23 41				
Stourbridge Junction 2	d	21 24	21 33			21a50					22 26	22 36	22a47					23 27	23a50				
Hagley	d	21 28									22 30							23 32					
Blakedown	d	21 31									22 33							23 35					
Kidderminster	d	21 36	21a49								22 38	22a50						23 40					
Hartlebury	d																						
University	d									22 05						23 10	23 10						
Barnt Green	d																						
Bromsgrove	d									22 21						23 23	23 23						
Droitwich Spa	d	21 47								22 31	22 49					23 32	23 32	23 52					
Worcester Shrub Hill 7	a	21 55								22 45	22 56					23 42	23 45	00 01					
	d	22 01		22 31							23 05												
Worcester Foregate Street 7	a	22 03		22 34							23 07												
	d			22 34							23 08												
Malvern Link	d			22 43							23 16												
Great Malvern	a			22 48							23 19												
	d																						
Colwall	d																						
Ledbury	a																						
	d																						
Hereford 7	a																						

For general notes see front of timetable
For details of catering facilities see Directory of Train Operators

A 🍴 to Birmingham Snow Hill
B To Gloucester (Table 57)

Stratford -upon-Avon, Marylebone and Leamington Spa → Birmingham → Stourbridge, Worcester and Hereford

Network Diagram - See first page of Table 71

		CH	CH	XC	LM	LM	LM	LM	LM	LM	GW	LM	LM	LM	CH	XC	LM	GW	XC	LM	LM		LM	LM	CH
																1 ◊		1 ◊	1 ◊						
				A																					
											⊡					⊡		⊡	⊡						
Stratford-upon-Avon	d													07 00							07 45				
Wilmcote	d													07 05							07 50				
Wootton Wawen	d													07x10							07x55				
Henley-in-Arden	d													07 14							07 59				
Danzey	d													07x19							08x04				
Wood End	d													07x22							08x08				
The Lakes	d													07x24							08x10				
Earlswood (West Midlands)	d													07 27							08 13				
Wythall	d													07 29							08 15				
Whitlocks End	d													07 32							08 18				
Shirley	d									07 05				07 35							08 21			08 38	
Yardley Wood	d									07 08				07 38							08 24			08 41	
Hall Green	d									07 11				07 41							08 27			08 44	
Spring Road	d									07 13				07 43							08 29			08 46	
London Marylebone 10	⊖ d	22p10	23p54																						06 27
Banbury	d	23p29	01 17												07 00	07 25			07 53						08 01
Leamington Spa 8	a	23p48	01 39												07 19	07 42			08 10						08 19
	d	23p48							06 28						07 19	07 43			08 11				07 55		08 20
Warwick	d	23p53							06 32						07 24								07 59		08 24
Warwick Parkway	d	23p56													07 27								08 03		08 28
Hatton	d								06 39														08 08		08 33
Lapworth	d								06 45														08 14		08 38
Dorridge	d	00 07							06 50				07 27		07 38		08 05						08 20		08 43
Widney Manor	d								06 53				07 31				08 08						08 24		08 46
Solihull	d	00 13							06 56				07 34		07 44		08 12						08 27		08 50
Olton	d								07 00				07 38				08 15						08 31		
Acocks Green	d								07 02				07 40				08 18						08 34		
Tyseley	d								07 05	07 17			07 43	07 46			08 21				08 32		08 37	08 49	
Small Heath	d								07 08	07 20			07 46	07 49							08 34		08 40	08 51	
Bordesley	d																								
Birmingham Moor Street	d	00 24				06 26		07 01	07 12	07 24			07 50	07 55	07 59		08 26				08 38		08 44	08 55	09 01
Birmingham Snow Hill	🚋 a	00 31				06 28		07 03	07 15	07 26			07 52	07 57	08 07		08 29				08 42		08 48	08 58	09 11
	d					06 29		07 05		07 30			07 53	08 03			08 30				08 43		08 53	09 03	
Jewellery Quarter	🚋 d							07 07		07 32			07 55	08 05			08 32				08 45		08 55	09 05	
The Hawthorns	🚋 d					06 34		07 12		07 37			08 00	08 10			08 37				08 50		09 00	09 10	
Coventry	a																		08 21						
Birmingham International	✈ a																		08 33						
Birmingham New Street 12	a															08 18			08 46						
	d			05 30			06 59					07 59								08 59					
Smethwick Galton Bdg H.L. 7	d					06 37		07 15		07 39			08 02	08 12			08 39				08 52		09 02	09 12	
Langley Green	d					06 40		07 18		07 42				08 15			08 42							09 15	
Rowley Regis	d					06 43		07 21		07 46			08 07	08 19			08 46				08 57		09 07	09 19	
Old Hill	d					06 46		07 24		07 49				08 22			08 49							09 22	
Cradley Heath	d					06 50		07 27		07 52			08 12	08 25			08 52				09 02		09 12	09 25	
Lye	d					06 53		07 30		07 55				08 28			08 55							09 28	
Stourbridge Junction 2	d					06 57		07 35		07a59			08 17	08a32			08a59				09a08		09 17	09 32	
Hagley	d					07 00		07 38					08 21										09 21		
Blakedown	d					07 03		07 41					08 24										09 24		
Kidderminster	d					07 08		07 46					08 29										09 29	09a42	
Hartlebury	d					07 13																			
University	d						07 05					08 05								09 05					
Barnt Green	d																								
Bromsgrove	d						07 23					08 21								09 21					
Droitwich Spa	d					07 22	07 32	07 58				08 31	08 40							09 31			09 40		
Worcester Shrub Hill 7	a			06 11		07 32	07 40																09 52		
	d				06 38		07 44				08 24							09 08							
Worcester Foregate Street 7	a				06 40		07 46	08 06			08 26	08 39	08 49					09 11		09 39					
	d				06 41		07 47	08 08			08 28	08 40						09 12		09 40					
Malvern Link	d				06 49		07 56	08 18				08 50						09 21		09 50					
Great Malvern	a				06 52		07 58	08 21			08 37	08 52						09 25		09 52					
	d				06 53		08 01					08 53								09 53					
Colwall	d				07 00		08 08					08 58								09 58					
Ledbury	a				07 07		08 14					09 06								10 06					
	d				07 07		08 14					09 08								10 08					
Hereford 7	a				07 28		08 35					09 28								10 28					

For general notes see front of timetable
For details of catering facilities see
Directory of Train Operators

A To Cardiff Central (Table 132)

Table 71

Stratford -upon-Avon, Marylebone and Leamington Spa → Birmingham → Stourbridge, Worcester and Hereford

Network Diagram - See first page of Table 71

		XC	LM	CH	XC	LM	LM	LM	GW	GW	LM	LM	CH	XC	LM	LM	LM	LM	CH	XC		GW	LM	LM	LM
		[1] ◇			[1] ◇					[1] ◇				[1] ◇						[1] ◇		[1] ◇			
									A																
		☕			☕					☕				☕						☕		☕			
Stratford-upon-Avon	d					08 27											09 27								
Wilmcote	d					08 32											09 32								
Wootton Wawen	d					08x37											09x37								
Henley-in-Arden	d					08 41											09 41								
Danzey	d					08x45											09x45								
Wood End	d					08x49											09x49								
The Lakes	d					08x51											09x51								
Earlswood (West Midlands)	d					08 54											09 54								
Wythall	d					08 56											09 56								
Whitlocks End	d					08 59											09 59								
Shirley	d					09 02		09 22							09 42		10 02						10 22		
Yardley Wood	d					09 05		09 25							09 45		10 05						10 25		
Hall Green	d					09 08		09 28							09 48		10 08						10 28		
Spring Road	d					09 10		09 30							09 50		10 10						10 30		
London Marylebone [10]	⊖ d												07 23						08 20						
Banbury	d	08 25		08 40	08 53								08 57	09 25					09 39	09 53					
Leamington Spa [8]	a	08 42		08 59	09 10								09 16	09 42					09 57	10 10					
	d	08 43		09 00	09 11								09 16	09 43					09 58	10 11					
Warwick	d			09 04									09 22						10 02						
Warwick Parkway	d			09 08									09 25						10 06						
Hatton	d			09a12																					
Lapworth	d																								
Dorridge	d		08 46				09 09					09 28	09 36			09 46		10 09	10 17						10 28
Widney Manor	d		08 50				09 13					09 32				09 50		10 13							10 32
Solihull	d		08 53				09 16					09 35	09 44			09 53		10 16	10 22						10 35
Olton	d		08 57				09 20					09 39				09 57		10 20							10 39
Acocks Green	d		08 59				09 22					09 41				09 59		10 22							10 41
Tyseley	d		09 02					09 33								10 02							10 33		
Small Heath	d		09 05					09 35								10 05							10 35		
Bordesley	d																								
Birmingham Moor Street	d		09 09			09 17	09 29	09 39				09 48	09 56		10 01	10 09	10 17	10 29	10 34				10 39		10 49
Birmingham Snow Hill	🚋 a		09 11			09 20	09 31	09 42				09 50	10 03		10 03	10 11	10 20	10 31	10 41				10 42		10 51
	d		09 13			09 23	09 33	09 43				09 53			10 03	10 13	10 23	10 33					10 43		10 53
Jewellery Quarter	🚋 d		09 15			09 25	09 35	09 45				09 55			10 05	10 15	10 25	10 35					10 45		10 55
The Hawthorns	🚋 d		09 20			09 30	09 40	09 50				10 00			10 10	10 20	10 30	10 40					10 50		11 00
Coventry	a				09 21															10 21					
Birmingham International	✈ a				09 33															10 33					
Birmingham New Street [12]	a	09 18			09 45									10 18						10 45					
	d										09 59													10 59	
Smethwick Galton Bdg H.L. [7]	d		09 22			09 32	09 42	09 52				10 02			10 12	10 22	10 32	10 42					10 52		11 02
Langley Green	d						09 45								10 15			10 45							
Rowley Regis	d		09 27			09 37	09 49	09 57				10 07			10 19	10 27	10 37	10 49					10 57		11 07
Old Hill	d						09 52								10 22			10 52							
Cradley Heath	d		09 32			09 42	09 55	10 02				10 12			10 25	10 32	10 42	10 55					11 02		11 12
Lye	d						09 58								10 28			10 58							
Stourbridge Junction [2]	d		09 39			09a48	10 02	10a08				10 17			10 32	10 37	10a48	11 02					11a08		11 17
Hagley	d						10 06					10 21						11 06							11 21
Blakedown	d						10 09					10 24						11 09							11 24
Kidderminster	d		09 48				10a15					10 29			10a42	10 48		11a15							11 29
Hartlebury	d																								
University	d										10 05													11 05	
Barnt Green	d																								
Bromsgrove	d										10 21													11 21	
Droitwich Spa	d		10 00								10 31	10 40				11 00								11 31	11 40
Worcester Shrub Hill [7]	a											10 48													11 48
	d								10 14	10 24		10 52										11 08			
Worcester Foregate Street [7]	a		10 08						10 16	10 26	10 39	10 54				11 11						11 11		11 39	
	d								10 17	10 28	10 40	10 55										11 12		11 40	
Malvern Link	d								10 26	10 36	10 50	11 03										11 21		11 50	
Great Malvern	a								10 28	10 39	10 52	11 06										11 24		11 52	
	d										10 53													11 53	
Colwall	d										10 58													11 58	
Ledbury	a										11 06													12 06	
	d										11 08													12 08	
Hereford [7]	a										11 28													12 28	

For general notes see front of timetable
For details of catering facilities see Directory of Train Operators

A From Warminster (Table 123)

Stratford -upon-Avon, Marylebone and Leamington Spa → Birmingham → Stourbridge, Worcester and Hereford

Network Diagram - See first page of Table 71

Station		CH	CH	XC 1 ◇	LM	LM	GW 1 ◇	LM	LM	LM	CH	XC 1 ◇	LM	GW ◇ A	LM	LM	CH	XC 1 ◇	LM		LM	LM	LM	CH	XC 1 ◇
Stratford-upon-Avon	d								10 27													11 27			
Wilmcote	d								10 32													11 32			
Wootton Wawen	d								10x37													11x37			
Henley-in-Arden	d								10 41													11 41			
Danzey	d								10x45													11x45			
Wood End	d								10x49													11x49			
The Lakes	d								10x51													11x51			
Earlswood (West Midlands)	d								10 54													11 54			
Wythall	d								10 56													11 56			
Whitlocks End	d								10 59													11 59			
Shirley	d				10 42				11 02				11 22						11 42			12 02			
Yardley Wood	d				10 45				11 05				11 25						11 45			12 05			
Hall Green	d				10 48				11 08				11 28						11 48			12 08			
Spring Road	d				10 50				11 10				11 30						11 50			12 10			
London Marylebone 10 ⊖	d	08 23	08 54								09 18						09 45							10 18	
Banbury	d	09 56	10 17	10 25							10 39	10 53					10 58	11 25						11 35	11 53
Leamington Spa 8	a	10 14	10 37	10 42							10 57	11 10					11 16	11 42						11 54	12 10
	d	10 15	10 38	10 43							10 58	11 11					11 16	11 43						11 54	12 11
Warwick	d	10 19	10 42								11 02						11 20							11 59	
Warwick Parkway	d	10 23									11 06						11 24							12 02	
Hatton	d	10 28	10a49																					12 07	
Lapworth	d	10 33																						12 13	
Dorridge	d	10 38				10 46		10 46		11 09	11 17					11 28	11 35				11 46		12 09	12 17	
Widney Manor	d					10 50		10 50		11 13						11 32					11 50		12 13		
Solihull	d	10 45				10 53		10 53		11 16	11 22					11 35	11 41				11 53		12 16	12 23	
Olton	d					10 57		10 57		11 20						11 39					11 57		12 20		
Acocks Green	d					10 59		10 59		11 22						11 41					11 59		12 22		
Tyseley	d					11 02		11 02					11 33								12 02				
Small Heath	d					11 05		11 05					11 35								12 05				
Bordesley	d																								
Birmingham Moor Street	d	10 56			10 58	11 09		11 09	11 17	11 29	11 34		11 39			11 48	11 52		11 57		12 09	12 17	12 29	12 35	
Birmingham Snow Hill	a	11 04			11 01	11 11		11 11	11 20	11 31	11 41		11 42			11 50	12 01		12 01		12 11	12 20	12 31	12 42	
	d				11 03	11 13		11 13	11 23	11 33			11 43			11 53			12 03		12 13	12 23	12 33		
Jewellery Quarter	d				11 05	11 15		11 15	11 25	11 35			11 45			11 55			12 05		12 15	12 25	12 35		
The Hawthorns	d				11 10	11 20		11 20	11 30	11 40			11 50			12 00			12 10		12 20	12 30	12 40		
Coventry	a											11 21													12 21
Birmingham International ✈	a											11 33													12 33
Birmingham New Street 12	a			11 18								11 45						12 18							12 45
	d														11 59										
Smethwick Galton Bdg H.L. 7	d				11 12	11 22		11 22	11 32	11 42			11 52			12 02			12 12		12 22	12 32	12 42		
Langley Green	d				11 15					11 45									12 15				12 45		
Rowley Regis	d				11 19	11 27		11 27	11 37	11 49			11 57			12 07			12 19		12 27	12 37	12 49		
Old Hill	d				11 22					11 52									12 22				12 52		
Cradley Heath	d				11 25	11 32		11 32	11 42	11 55			12 02			12 12			12 25		12 32	12 42	12 55		
Lye	d				11 28					11 58									12 28				12 58		
Stourbridge Junction 2	d				11 32	11 40		11 43	11a48	12 02			12a08			12 17			12 32		12 37	12a48	13 02		
Hagley	d									12 06						12 21							13 06		
Blakedown	d									12 09						12 24							13 09		
Kidderminster	d				11a43	11 49		11 52		12a15						12 29			12a42		12 48		13a15		
Hartlebury	d																								
University	d														12 05										
Barnt Green	d																								
Bromsgrove	d														12 21										
Droitwich Spa	d					12 01		12 04							12 31	12 40					13 00				
Worcester Shrub Hill 7	a															12 48									
	d						12 08							12 16		12 52									
Worcester Foregate Street 7	a					12 09	12 10	12 12						12 18	12 39	12 54					13 08				
	d						12 12							12 19	12 40	12 55									
Malvern Link	d													12 29	12 50	13 03									
Great Malvern	a						12 21							12 31	12 52	13 06									
	d						12 22								12 53										
Colwall	d						12 27								12 58										
Ledbury	a						12 34								13 06										
	d						12 37								13 08										
Hereford 7	a						12 53								13 28										

For general notes see front of timetable
For details of catering facilities see Directory of Train Operators

A From Weymouth (Table 123)

Table 71

Stratford -upon-Avon, Marylebone and Leamington Spa → Birmingham → Stourbridge, Worcester and Hereford

Network Diagram - See first page of Table 71

		GW 1 ◇	LM	LM	LM	CH	CH	XC 1 ◇	LM	LM	LM	LM	CH	XC 1 ◇	GW 1 ◇	LM	GW ◇ A	LM		LM	CH	XC 1 ◇	LM	LM	LM
Stratford-upon-Avon	d										12 27														13 27
Wilmcote	d										12 32														13 32
Wootton Wawen	d										12x37														13x37
Henley-in-Arden	d										12 41														13 41
Danzey	d										12x45														13x45
Wood End	d										12x49														13x49
The Lakes	d										12x51														13x51
Earlswood (West Midlands)	d										12 54														13 54
Wythall	d										12 56														13 56
Whitlocks End	d										12 59														13 59
Shirley	d		12 22						12 42		13 02					13 22							13 42		14 02
Yardley Wood	d		12 25						12 45		13 05					13 25							13 45		14 05
Hall Green	d		12 28						12 48		13 08					13 28							13 48		14 08
Spring Road	d		12 30						12 50		13 10					13 30							13 50		14 10
London Marylebone 10 ⊖	d					10 50	10 53						11 20								11 50				
Banbury	d					11 58	12 19	12 25					12 35	12 53							12 58	13 25			
Leamington Spa 8	a					12 17	12 38	12 42					12 54	13 10							13 17	13 42			
	d					12 17	12 39	12 43					12 54	13 11							13 17	13 43			
Warwick	d					12 22	12 43						12 59								13 22				
Warwick Parkway	d					12 25							13 02								13 25				
Hatton	d						12a49																		
Lapworth	d																								
Dorridge	d				12 28	12 36				12 46		13 09	13 13							13 28	13 36			13 46	
Widney Manor	d				12 32					12 50		13 13								13 32				13 50	
Solihull	d				12 35	12 42				12 53		13 16	13 20							13 35	13 42			13 53	
Olton	d				12 39					12 57		13 20								13 39				13 57	
Acocks Green	d				12 41					12 59		13 22								13 41				13 59	
Tyseley	d		12 33							13 02						13 33								14 02	
Small Heath	d		12 35							13 05						13 35								14 05	
Bordesley	d															13 38									
Birmingham Moor Street	d		12 39		12 48	12 53			12 57	13 09	13 17	13 29	13 32			13 41				13 48	13 53		13 58	14 09	14 17
Birmingham Snow Hill 🚋	a		12 42		12 50	13 01			13 01	13 11	13 20	13 31	13 41			13 43				13 50	14 01		14 01	14 11	14 21
	d		12 43		12 53				13 03	13 13	13 23	13 33				13 43				13 53			14 03	14 13	14 23
Jewellery Quarter 🚋	d		12 45		12 55				13 05	13 15	13 25	13 35				13 45				13 55			14 05	14 15	14 25
The Hawthorns 🚋	d		12 50		13 00				13 10	13 20	13 30	13 40				13 50				14 00			14 10	14 20	14 30
Coventry	a													13 21											
Birmingham International ✈	a													13 33											
Birmingham New Street 12	a							13 18						13 45								14 18			
	d			12 59														13 59							
Smethwick Galton Bdg H.L. 7	d		12 52		13 02				13 12	13 22	13 32	13 42				13 52				14 02			14 12	14 22	14 32
Langley Green	d								13 15			13 45											14 15		
Rowley Regis	d		12 57		13 07				13 19	13 27	13 37	13 49				13 57				14 07			14 19	14 27	14 37
Old Hill	d								13 22			13 52											14 22		
Cradley Heath	d		13 02		13 12				13 25	13 32	13 42	13 55				14 02				14 12			14 25	14 32	14 42
Lye	d								13 28			13 58											14 28		
Stourbridge Junction 2	d		13a08		13 17				13 32	13 39	13a48	14 02				14a09				14 17			14 32	14 39	14a48
Hagley	d				13 21							14 06								14 21					
Blakedown	d				13 24							14 09								14 24					
Kidderminster	d				13 29				13a42	13 48		14a15								14 29			14a42	14 48	
Hartlebury	d																								
University	d			13 05														14 05							
Barnt Green	d																								
Bromsgrove	d			13 21														14 21							
Droitwich Spa	d			13 31	13 40					14 00								14 31		14 40				15 00	
Worcester Shrub Hill 7	a				13 48															14 48					
	d	13 08													14 08		14 27			14 52					
Worcester Foregate Street 7	a	13 11		13 39						14 08					14 10		14 29	14 39		14 54				15 08	
	d			13 40											14 12			14 40		14 55					
Malvern Link	d			13 50														14 50		15 03					
Great Malvern	a			13 52											14 21			14 52		15 06					
	d			13 53											14 22			14 53							
Colwall	d			13 58											14 27			14 58							
Ledbury	a			14 06											14 34			15 06							
	d			14 08											14 37			15 08							
Hereford 7	a			14 28											14 53			15 28							

For general notes see front of timetable
For details of catering facilities see Directory of Train Operators

A From Brighton (Table 123)

Stratford -upon-Avon, Marylebone and Leamington Spa → Birmingham → Stourbridge, Worcester and Hereford

Network Diagram - See first page of Table 71

		LM	CH	XC	LM	LM	LM	CH	CH	XC	LM	LM	LM	LM	CH	XC	LM		GW	GW	LM	LM	CH	XC	LM
				1 ◇						1 ◇						1 ◇				1 ◇				1 ◇	
																			A						
				☕						☕						☕				☕				☕	
Stratford-upon-Avon	d												14 27												
Wilmcote	d												14 32												
Wootton Wawen	d												14x37												
Henley-in-Arden	d												14 41												
Danzey	d												14x45												
Wood End	d												14x49												
The Lakes	d												14x51												
Earlswood (West Midlands)	d												14 54												
Wythall	d												14 56												
Whitlocks End	d												14 59												
Shirley	d				14 22						14 42		15 02				15 22								15 42
Yardley Wood	d				14 25						14 45		15 05				15 25								15 45
Hall Green	d				14 28						14 48		15 08				15 28								15 48
Spring Road	d				14 30						14 50		15 10				15 30								15 50
London Marylebone 10	⊖ d		12 20					12 50	12 53						13 20								13 50		
Banbury	d		13 35	13 53				13 58	14 19	14 25					14 35	14 53							14 58	15 25	
Leamington Spa 8	a		13 54	14 10				14 17	14 38	14 42					14 54	15 10							15 17	15 42	
	d		13 54	14 11				14 17	14 39	14 43					14 54	15 11							15 17	15 43	
Warwick	d		13 59					14 22	14 43						14 59								15 22		
Warwick Parkway	d		14 02					14 25							15 02								15 25		
Hatton	d		14 07						14a49																
Lapworth	d		14 13																						
Dorridge	d	14 09	14 17				14 28	14 36				14 46		15 09	15 13							15 28	15 36		
Widney Manor	d	14 13					14 32					14 50		15 13								15 32			
Solihull	d	14 16	14 23				14 35	14 42				14 53		15 16	15 20							15 35	15 42		
Olton	d	14 20					14 39					14 57		15 20								15 39			
Acocks Green	d	14 22					14 41					14 59		15 22								15 41			
Tyseley	d				14 33							15 02					15 33								
Small Heath	d				14 35							15 05					15 35								
Bordesley	d																								
Birmingham Moor Street	d	14 29	14 34		14 40		14 48	14 54			14 57	15 09	15 17	15 29	15 33		15 39					15 48	15 54		15 57
Birmingham Snow Hill	🚋 a	14 31	14 42		14 42		14 50	15 01			15 01	15 11	15 21	15 31	15 41		15 42					15 51	16 01		16 01
	d	14 33			14 43		14 53				15 03	15 13	15 23	15 33			15 43					15 53			16 03
Jewellery Quarter	🚋 d	14 35			14 45		14 55				15 05	15 15	15 25	15 35			15 45					15 55			16 05
The Hawthorns	🚋 d	14 40			14 50		15 00				15 10	15 20	15 30	15 40			15 50					16 00			16 10
Coventry	a			14 21												15 21									
Birmingham International	✈ a			14 33												15 33									
Birmingham New Street 12	a			14 46						15 18						15 45								16 18	
	d					14 59															15 59				
Smethwick Galton Bdg H.L. 7	d	14 42			14 52		15 02				15 12	15 22	15 32	15 42			15 52					16 02			16 12
Langley Green	d	14 45									15 15			15 45											16 15
Rowley Regis	d	14 49			14 57		15 07				15 19	15 27	15 37	15 49			15 57					16 07			16 19
Old Hill	d	14 52									15 22			15 52											16 22
Cradley Heath	d	14 55			15 02		15 12				15 25	15 32	15 42	15 55			16 02					16 12			16 25
Lye	d	14 58									15 28			15 58											16 28
Stourbridge Junction 2	d	15 02			15a08		15 17				15 32	15 39	15a48	16 02			16a08					16 17			16 32
Hagley	d	15 06					15 21							16 06								16 21			
Blakedown	d	15 09					15 24							16 09								16 24			
Kidderminster	d	15a15					15 29				15a42	15 48		16a15								16 29			16a42
Hartlebury	d																								
University	d					15 05															16 05				
Barnt Green	d																								
Bromsgrove	d					15 21															16 21				
Droitwich Spa	d					15 31	15 40					16 00									16 31	16 40			
Worcester Shrub Hill 7	a						15 48															16 48			
	d																		16 14	16 23		16 52			
Worcester Foregate Street 7	a					15 39						16 08							16 16	16 26	16 39	16 54			
	d					15 40													16 17	16 27	16 40	16 55			
Malvern Link	d					15 50													16 26	16 36	16 50	17 03			
Great Malvern	a					15 52													16 28	16 39	16 52	17 06			
	d					15 53															16 53				
Colwall	d					15 58															16 58				
Ledbury	a					16 06															17 06				
	d					16 08															17 08				
Hereford 7	a					16 28															17 28				

For general notes see front of timetable
For details of catering facilities see Directory of Train Operators

A From Southampton Central (Table 123)

Table 71

Stratford -upon-Avon, Marylebone and Leamington Spa → Birmingham → Stourbridge, Worcester and Hereford

Network Diagram - See first page of Table 71

		LM	XC ◇ A	LM	LM	CH	XC 1 ◇ ☕	GW 1 ◇ ☕	LM	LM	LM	CH	CH	XC 1 ◇ ☕	LM	XC ◇ A		GW 1 ◇ ☕	LM	LM	LM	CH	XC 1 ◇ ☕	LM	LM
Stratford-upon-Avon	d			15 27																16 27					
Wilmcote	d			15 32																16 32					
Wootton Wawen	d			15x37																16x37					
Henley-in-Arden	d			15 41																16 41					
Danzey	d			15x45																16x45					
Wood End	d			15x49																16x49					
The Lakes	d			15x51																16x51					
Earlswood (West Midlands)	d			15 54																16 54					
Wythall	d			15 56																16 56					
Whitlocks End	d			15 59																16 59					
Shirley	d			16 02					16 22						16 42					17 02					17 22
Yardley Wood	d			16 05					16 25						16 45					17 05					17 25
Hall Green	d			16 08					16 28						16 48					17 08					17 28
Spring Road	d			16 10					16 30						16 50					17 10					17 30
London Marylebone 10 ⊖	d					14 20						14 50	14 53									15 20			
Banbury	d					15 35	15 53					15 58	16 19	16 25								16 35	16 53		
Leamington Spa 8	a					15 54	16 10					16 16	16 38	16 42								16 53	17 10		
	d					15 54	16 11					16 17	16 39	16 43								16 53	17 11		
Warwick	d					15 59						16 21	16 43									16 58			
Warwick Parkway	d					16 02						16 25										17 01			
Hatton	d					16 07							16a49									17 06			
Lapworth	d					16 13																17 12			
Dorridge	d	15 46			16 09	16 17					16 27	16 36							16 46		17 09	17 16			
Widney Manor	d	15 50			16 13						16 31								16 50		17 13				
Solihull	d	15 53			16 16	16 23					16 34	16 41							16 53		17 16	17 23			
Olton	d	15 57			16 20						16 38								16 57		17 20				
Acocks Green	d	15 59			16 22						16 40								16 59		17 22				
Tyseley	d	16 02							16 33		16 43				16 53				17 02						17 33
Small Heath	d	16 05							16 35										17 05						17 35
Bordesley	d																								
Birmingham Moor Street	d	16 09		16 17	16 29	16 34			16 39		16 48	16 53			16 57				17 09	17 17	17 29	17 34			17 39
Birmingham Snow Hill 🚊	a	16 12		16 21	16 32	16 41			16 42		16 51	17 02			17 01				17 12	17 21	17 31	17 41			17 42
	d	16 13		16 23	16 33				16 43		16 53				17 03				17 13	17 23	17 33				17 43
Jewellery Quarter 🚊	d	16 15		16 25	16 35				16 45		16 55				17 05				17 15	17 25	17 35				17 45
The Hawthorns 🚊	d	16 20		16 30	16 40				16 50		17 00				17 10				17 20	17 30	17 40				17 50
Coventry	a						16 21																17 21		
Birmingham International ✈	a						16 33																17 33		
Birmingham New Street 12	a						16 46							17 18									17 45		
	d		16 30							16 59						17 30								17 59	
Smethwick Galton Bdg H.L. 7	d	16 22		16 32	16 42				16 52		17 02				17 12				17 22	17 32	17 42				17 52
Langley Green	d				16 45										17 15						17 45				
Rowley Regis	d	16 27		16 37	16 49				16 57		17 07				17 19				17 27	17 37	17 49				17 57
Old Hill	d				16 52										17 22						17 52				
Cradley Heath	d	16 32		16 42	16 55				17 02		17 12				17 25				17 32	17 42	17 55				18 02
Lye	d				16 58										17 28						17 58				
Stourbridge Junction 2	d	16 39		16a48	17 02				17a08		17 17				17 32				17 37	17a48	18 02				18a08
Hagley	d				17 06						17 21								17 41		18 06				
Blakedown	d				17 09						17 24								17 44		18 09				
Kidderminster	d	16 48			17a15						17 29				17a42				17 49		18a15				
Hartlebury	d										17 34								17 54						
University	d		16 36							17 05						17 36								18 05	
Barnt Green	d																								
Bromsgrove	d		16a50							17 21						17a51								18 21	
Droitwich Spa	d	17 00								17 31	17 42								18 02					18 31	
Worcester Shrub Hill 7	a																		18 14					18 40	
	d							17 08										18 08						18 50	
Worcester Foregate Street 7	a	17 08						17 11		17 39	17 54							18 11						18 52	
	d							17 12		17 40	17 54							18 12						18 53	
Malvern Link	d							17 21		17 50	18 04							18 21						19 02	
Great Malvern	a							17 25		17 52	18 07							18 25						19 04	
	d									17 53														19 05	
Colwall	d									17 58														19 10	
Ledbury	a									18 06														19 17	
	d									18 08														19 22	
Hereford 7	a									18 28														19 42	

For general notes see front of timetable
For details of catering facilities see
Directory of Train Operators

A From Nottingham to Cardiff Central (Table 57)

Stratford -upon-Avon, Marylebone and Leamington Spa → Birmingham → Stourbridge, Worcester and Hereford

Network Diagram - See first page of Table 71

		LM	CH	XC	LM	XC	GW	LM	LM	CH	XC	LM	LM	CH	CH		XC	LM	LM	LM	CH	XC	LM	GW	LM
				1 ◇		◇ A	1 ◇				1 ◇						1 ◇					1 ◇		1 ◇	
Stratford-upon-Avon	d							17 27										18 07					18 46		
Wilmcote	d							17 32										18 12					18 51		
Wootton Wawen	d							17x37										18x17					18x56		
Henley-in-Arden	d							17 41										18 21					19 00		
Danzey	d							17x45										18x25					19x04		
Wood End	d							17x49										18x29					19x08		
The Lakes	d							17x51										18x31					19x10		
Earlswood (West Midlands)	d							17 54										18 34					19 12		
Wythall	d							17 56										18 36					19 15		
Whitlocks End	d							17 59										18 39					19 17		
Shirley	d							18 02				18 22						18 42					19 22		
Yardley Wood	d							18 05				18 25						18 45					19 25		
Hall Green	d							18 08				18 28						18 48					19 28		
Spring Road	d							18 10				18 30						18 50					19 30		
London Marylebone 10 ⊖	d		15 50							16 20				16 50	16 53						17 20				
Banbury	d		16 57	17 25						17 35	17 53			17 59	18 19		18 25				18 35	18 53			
Leamington Spa 8	a		17 16	17 42						17 54	18 10			18 18	18 38		18 42				18 54	19 10			
	d		17 16	17 43						17 54	18 11			18 18	18 39		18 43				18 54	19 11			
Warwick	d		17 21							17 59				18 23	18 43						18 59				
Warwick Parkway	d		17 24							18 02				18 26							19 02				
Hatton	d									18 07					18a49						19 07				
Lapworth	d									18 13											19 14				
Dorridge	d	17 27	17 35		17 46				18 09	18 17			18 28	18 37						19 00	19 18				19 28
Widney Manor	d	17 31			17 50				18 13				18 32							19 06					19 32
Solihull	d	17 34	17 41		17 53				18 16	18 23			18 35	18 43						19 09	19 24				19 35
Olton	d	17 38			17 57				18 20				18 39							19 12					19 39
Acocks Green	d	17 40			17 59				18 22				18 41							19 15					19 41
Tyseley	d	17 43			18 02							18 33	18 44					18 54		19 18			19 33		19 44
Small Heath	d				18 04							18 35	18 46					18 56		19 20			19 35		19 47
Bordesley	d																								
Birmingham Moor Street	d	17 48	17 53		18 08			18 17	18 28	18 34		18 40	18 50	18 55				19 00		19 24	19 34		19 39		19 51
Birmingham Snow Hill 🚊	a	17 51	18 01		18 11			18 20	18 31	18 41		18 43	18 53	19 03				19 03		19 27	19 41		19 42		19 53
	d	17 53			18 13			18 23	18 33				18 57							19 28					19 55
Jewellery Quarter 🚊	d	17 55			18 15			18 25	18 35				18 59							19 30					19 57
The Hawthorns 🚊	d	18 00			18 20			18 30	18 40				19 04							19 35					20 02
Coventry	a										18 21											19 21			
Birmingham International ✈	a										18 33											19 33			
Birmingham New Street 12	a			18 18							18 45						19 18					19 45			
	d					18 30													19 30						
Smethwick Galton Bdg H.L. 7	d	18 02			18 22			18 32	18 42				19 06							19 37					20 04
Langley Green	d	18 05			18 25				18 45				19 09							19 40					20 07
Rowley Regis	d	18 09			18 29			18 37	18 49				19 13							19 44					20 11
Old Hill	d	18 12			18 32				18 52				19 16							19 47					20 14
Cradley Heath	d	18 15			18 35			18 42	18 55				19 19							19 50					20 17
Lye	d	18 18			18 38				18 58				19 22							19 53					20 20
Stourbridge Junction 2	d	18 22			18a42			18 48	19 02				19 26							19 57					20 24
Hagley	d	18 25						18 51	19 06				19 29							20 00					20 27
Blakedown	d	18 28						18 54	19 09				19 32							20 03					20 30
Kidderminster	d	18 33						18 59	19a15				19 37							20 08					20 35
Hartlebury	d	18 38						19 04																	
University	d																		19 36						
Barnt Green	d																								
Bromsgrove	d					18a50													19 51						
Droitwich Spa	d	18 47						19 13					19 52						20 00	20 20					20 47
Worcester Shrub Hill 7	a	18 54											20 00						20 07	20 30					20 54
	d						19 16												20 11					20 43	20 58
Worcester Foregate Street 7	a						19 18	19 21											20 14					20 46	21 00
	d						19 20												20 14					20 47	21 01
Malvern Link	d						19 29												20 23					20 56	21 09
Great Malvern	a						19 32												20 26					20 59	21 12
	d						19 33												20 26					21 00	
Colwall	d						19 38												20 32					21 06	
Ledbury	a						19 45												20 40					21 13	
	d						19 46												20 40					21 15	
Hereford 7	a						20 02												21 00					21 32	

For general notes see front of timetable
For details of catering facilities see Directory of Train Operators

A From Nottingham (Table 57)

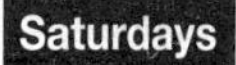

Stratford -upon-Avon, Marylebone and Leamington Spa → Birmingham → Stourbridge, Worcester and Hereford

Network Diagram - See first page of Table 71

Station		CH	XC 1 ◇ ☕	LM	CH	XC 1 ◇ ☕	LM	LM	CH	CH	XC 1 ◇	GW 1 ◇	CH	XC 1 ◇ ☕	LM	LM	LM	CH	XC 1 ◇	LM	CH	LM	CH
Stratford-upon-Avon	d			19 27											20 27								
Wilmcote	d			19 32											20 32								
Wootton Wawen	d			19x37											20x37								
Henley-in-Arden	d			19 41											20 41								
Danzey	d			19x45											20x45								
Wood End	d			19x49											20x49								
The Lakes	d			19x51											20x51								
Earlswood (West Midlands)	d			19 54											20 54								
Wythall	d			19 56											20 56								
Whitlocks End	d			19 59											20 59								
Shirley	d			20 02											21 02		21 56					22 54	
Yardley Wood	d			20 05											21 05		21 59					22 57	
Hall Green	d			20 08											21 08		22 02					23 00	
Spring Road	d			20 10											21 10		22 04					23 02	
London Marylebone 10 ⊖	d	17 50			18 20				18 50	18 53			19 20					20 00			20 50		21 40
Banbury	d	19 03	19 25		19 35	19 53			20 03	20 19	20 25		20 37	20 53				21 19	21 53		22 07		23 03
Leamington Spa 8	a	19 23	19 42		19 54	20 10			20 23	20 38	20 42		20 55	21 10				21 39	22 10		22 27		23 23
	d	19 23	19 43		19 54	20 11			20 23	20 39	20 43		20 55	21 11				21 39	22 11		22 28		23 24
Warwick	d	19 27			19 59				20 27	20 43			21 00					21 43			22 32		23 28
Warwick Parkway	d	19 31			20 02				20 31				21 03					21 47			22 35		23 31
Hatton	d				20 07					20a49			21 08										
Lapworth	d				20 13								21 14										
Dorridge	d	19 42			20 17			20 28	20 42				21 18			21 28		21 58		22 28	22 47		23 43
Widney Manor	d							20 32								21 32				22 32			23 46
Solihull	d	19 48			20 23			20 35	20 48				21 25			21 35		22 04		22 35	22 52		23 50
Olton	d							20 39								21 39				22 39			
Acocks Green	d							20 41								21 41				22 41			
Tyseley	d							20 44								21 44	22 07			22 44		23 05	
Small Heath	d							20 47								21 47	22 09			22 47		23 07	
Bordesley	d																						
Birmingham Moor Street	d	19 59		20 17	20 35			20 51	20 58				21 36		21 17	21 51	22 13	22 17		22 51	23 03	23 11	00 02
Birmingham Snow Hill 🚋	a	20 06		20 20	20 42			20 53	21 06				21 43		21 20	21 53	22 16	22 26		22 53	23 10	23 14	00 09
	d			20 21				20 55							21 21	21 55	22 18			22 56		23 15	
Jewellery Quarter 🚋	d			20 24				20 57							21 23	21 57	22 20			22 59		23 17	
The Hawthorns 🚋	d			20 28				21 02							21 28	22 02	22 25			23 03		23 22	
Coventry	a					20 21								21 21					22 21				
Birmingham International ✈	a					20 33								21 33					22 33				
Birmingham New Street 12	a		20 18			20 45					21 22			21 45					22 50				
	d						20 59																
Smethwick Galton Bdg H.L. 7	d			20 31				21 05							21 30	22 04	22 27			23 06		23 24	
Langley Green	d			20 34				21 08							21 33	22 07	22 30			23 09		23 27	
Rowley Regis	d			20 37				21 11							21 36	22 11	22 34			23 12		23 31	
Old Hill	d			20 40				21 14							21 39	22 14	22 37			23 15		23 34	
Cradley Heath	d			20 43				21 17							21 42	22 17	22 40			23 18		23 37	
Lye	d			20 46				21 20							21 45	22 20	22 43			23 21		23 40	
Stourbridge Junction 2	d			20a50				21 24							21a50	22 24	22a47			23 26		23a44	
Hagley	d							21 28								22 27				23 29			
Blakedown	d							21 31								22 30				23 32			
Kidderminster	d							21 36								22 35				23 37			
Hartlebury	d																						
University	d																						
Barnt Green	d																						
Bromsgrove	d						21 21																
Droitwich Spa	d						21 31	21 47								22 46				23 48			
Worcester Shrub Hill 7	a						21 38	21 55								22 55				23 56			
	d						21 46					22 05				22 57							
Worcester Foregate Street 7	a						21 49					22 08				23 00							
	d						21 49					22 08				23 00							
Malvern Link	d						21 58					22 17				23 09							
Great Malvern	a						22 01					22 21				23 12							
	d						22 01																
Colwall	d						22 07																
Ledbury	a						22 14																
	d						22 14																
Hereford 7	a						22 35																

For general notes see front of timetable
For details of catering facilities see Directory of Train Operators

Table 71

Sundays

until 27 January

Stratford -upon-Avon, Marylebone and Leamington Spa → Birmingham → Stourbridge, Worcester and Hereford

Network Diagram - See first page of Table 71

		CH	LM	LM	GW	LM	CH	LM	LM	CH	GW	LM	CH	XC	XC	LM	LM	GW	LM	CH	XC	LM
					1 ◇						1 ◇			A	1 ◇			1 ◇			1 ◇	
				🚌	☕				🚌		☕				☕		🚌	☕			☕	
Stratford-upon-Avon	d			08 05					09 05								10 05					
Wilmcote	d			08 16					09 16								10 16					
Wootton Wawen	d																					
Henley-in-Arden	d			08 27					09 27								10 27					
Danzey	d																					
Wood End	d																					
The Lakes	d			08 43					09 43								10 43					
Earlswood (West Midlands)	d																					
Wythall	d			08 54					09 54								10 54					
Whitlocks End	d																					
Shirley	d			09 05					10 05								11 05					
Yardley Wood	d			09 16					10 16								11 16					
Hall Green	d			09 27					10 27								11 27					
Spring Road	d			09 38					10 38								11 38					
London Marylebone 10 ⊖	d	21p40					08 00			09 11			09 15							10 15		
Banbury	d	23p03					09 34			10 33			10 36		10 53					11 38	11 53	
Leamington Spa 8	a	23p23					09 54						10 56		11 10					11 58	12 10	
	d	23p24					09 54						10 57		11 11					11 59	12 11	
Warwick	d	23p28					09 59						11 01							12 03		
Warwick Parkway	d	23p31					10 02						11 04							12 06		
Hatton	d						10 07													12 11		
Lapworth	d						10 11						11 13									
Dorridge	d	23p43					10 16	10 25					11 19			11 25				12 19		12 25
Widney Manor	d	23p46						10 29								11 29						12 29
Solihull	d	23p50					10 21	10 32					11 24			11 32				12 24		12 32
Olton	d							10 36								11 36						12 36
Acocks Green	d							10 38								11 38						12 38
Tyseley	d			09 46					10 46								11 46					
Small Heath	d																					
Bordesley	d																					
Birmingham Moor Street	d	00 02	09 26			10 13	10 33	10 45				11 13	11 34			11 45			12 13	12 35		12 45
Birmingham Snow Hill 🚋	a	00 09	09 28	10 06		10 15	10 40	10 47	11 06			11 15	11 41			11 47	12 06		12 15	12 43		12 47
	d		09 30			10 18		10 48				11 18				11 48			12 18			12 48
Jewellery Quarter 🚋	d		09 32			10 20		10 51				11 20				11 51			12 20			12 51
The Hawthorns 🚋	d		09 37			10 25		10 55				11 25				11 55			12 25			12 55
Coventry	a														11 23						12 23	
Birmingham International ✈	a														11 35						12 35	
Birmingham New Street 12	a									11 30					11 46						12 46	
	d													11 46								
Smethwick Galton Bdg H.L. 7	d		09 39			10 27		10 58				11 27				11 58			12 27			12 58
Langley Green	d							11 01								12 01						13 01
Rowley Regis	d		09 44			10 32		11 04				11 32				12 04			12 32			13 04
Old Hill	d							11 07								12 07						13 07
Cradley Heath	d		09 49			10 37		11 10				11 37				12 10			12 37			13 10
Lye	d							11 13								12 13						13 13
Stourbridge Junction 2	d		09 54			10 43		11a17				11 43				12a17			12 43			13a17
Hagley	d		09 58			10 46						11 47							12 46			
Blakedown	d											11 50							12 49			
Kidderminster	d		10 04			10 52						11 55							12 54			
Hartlebury	d																					
University	d																					
Barnt Green	d																					
Bromsgrove	d													12 05								
Droitwich Spa	d		10 15			11 04						12 06		12 13					13 06			
Worcester Shrub Hill 7	a		10 23			11 11						12 14		12 22					13 13			
	d		10 26		10 35	11 26					12 04							13 09	13 25			
Worcester Foregate Street 7	a		10 29		10 37	11 28					12 07							13 11	13 27			
	d		10 29		10 39	11 29					12 08							13 13	13 28			
Malvern Link	d		10 38		10 48	11 37					12 17							13 22	13 36			
Great Malvern	a		10 41		10 50	11 40					12 20							13 25	13 39			
	d										12 22							13 26				
Colwall	d										12 27							13 32				
Ledbury	a										12 34							13 39				
	d										12 37							13 48				
Hereford 7	a										12 54							14 04				

For general notes see front of timetable
For details of catering facilities see
Directory of Train Operators

A To Gloucester (Table 57)

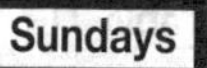

until 27 January

Stratford -upon-Avon, Marylebone and Leamington Spa → Birmingham → Stourbridge, Worcester and Hereford

Network Diagram - See first page of Table 71

		CH	XC	LM	LM	LM	CH	XC	LM	CH	XC	LM	GW	LM	CH	XC	LM	CH	XC	LM	LM	CH
			1 ◇ ☕	bus				R 1 ☕			1 ◇ ☕	bus	1 ◇ ☕			R 1 ☕			1 ◇ ☕	bus		
Stratford-upon-Avon	d			11 05								12 05								13 05		
Wilmcote	d			11 16								12 16								13 16		
Wootton Wawen	d																					
Henley-in-Arden	d			11 27								12 27								13 27		
Danzey	d																					
Wood End	d																					
The Lakes	d			11 43								12 43								13 43		
Earlswood (West Midlands)	d																					
Wythall	d			11 54								12 54								13 54		
Whitlocks End	d																					
Shirley	d			12 05								13 05								14 05		
Yardley Wood	d			12 16								13 16								14 16		
Hall Green	d			12 27								13 27								14 27		
Spring Road	d			12 38								13 38								14 38		
London Marylebone [10] ⊖	d	10 50					11 20			11 50					12 20			12 50				13 20
Banbury	d	12 02	12 25				12 41	12 53		13 05	13 25				13 43	13 53		14 02	14 25			14 41
Leamington Spa 8	a	12 22	12 41				13 01	13 10		13 25	13 41				14 02	14 10		14 22	14 41			15 01
	d	12 22	12 43				13 02	13 11		13 26	13 43				14 03	14 11		14 22	14 43			15 02
Warwick	d						13 06								14 07							15 06
Warwick Parkway	d	12 28					13 09			13 31					14 10			14 28				15 09
Hatton	d																					
Lapworth	d						13 18															15 18
Dorridge	d	12 39					13 23		13 25	13 43					14 22		14 25	14 39				15 23
Widney Manor	d								13 30								14 29					
Solihull	d	12 45					13 28		13 33	13 48					14 28		14 32	14 45				15 28
Olton	d								13 37								14 36					
Acocks Green	d								13 39								14 38					
Tyseley	d			12 46								13 46								14 46		
Small Heath	d																					
Bordesley	d																					
Birmingham Moor Street	d	12 56			13 15		13 39		13 46	13 59				14 13	14 39		14 45	14 56			15 13	15 39
Birmingham Snow Hill 🚊	a	13 03		13 06	13 17		13 46		13 48	14 06		14 06		14 15	14 47		14 47	15 03		15 06	15 15	15 46
	d				13 20				13 49					14 18			14 48				15 18	
Jewellery Quarter 🚊	d				13 22				13 52					14 20			14 51				15 20	
The Hawthorns 🚊	d				13 27				13 56					14 25			14 55				15 25	
Coventry	a		12 54					13 23			13 54					14 23			14 54			
Birmingham International ✈	a		13 04					13 35			14 04					14 35			15 04			
Birmingham New Street [12]	a		13 18					13 46			14 18					14 46			15 18			
	d					13 45																
Smethwick Galton Bdg H.L. 7	d				13 29				13 59					14 27			14 58				15 27	
Langley Green	d								14 02								15 01					
Rowley Regis	d				13 34				14 05					14 32			15 04				15 32	
Old Hill	d								14 08								15 07					
Cradley Heath	d				13 39				14 11					14 37			15 10				15 37	
Lye	d								14 14								15 13					
Stourbridge Junction 2	d				13 46				14a18					14 43			15a17				15 43	
Hagley	d				13 49									14 46							15 46	
Blakedown	d													14 49								
Kidderminster	d				13 55									14 54							15 52	
Hartlebury	d																					
University	d																					
Barnt Green	d																					
Bromsgrove	d					14 05																
Droitwich Spa	d				14 07	14 15								15 06							16 04	
Worcester Shrub Hill 7	a					14 22																
	d					14 28							15 08									
Worcester Foregate Street 7	a				14 20	14 30							15 10	15 14							16 12	
	d					14 31							15 12									
Malvern Link	d					14 39																
Great Malvern	a					14 42							15 21									
	d					14 43							15 22									
Colwall	d					14 48																
Ledbury	a					14 55							15 32									
	d					14 58							15 34									
Hereford 7	a					15 19							15 51									

For general notes see front of timetable
For details of catering facilities see Directory of Train Operators

Table 71

Sundays

until 27 January

Stratford -upon-Avon, Marylebone and Leamington Spa → Birmingham → Stourbridge, Worcester and Hereford

Network Diagram - See first page of Table 71

		XC	LM	CH	LM	CH	XC	LM	LM	CH	XC	LM	CH	XC	CH	GW	LM	LM	LM	CH	XC	LM
		R 1 ☕					1 ◇ ☕	🚌			R 1 ☕			1 ◇ ☕		1 ◇ ☕		🚌			R 1 ☕	
Stratford-upon-Avon	d							14 05										15 00				
Wilmcote	d							14 16										15 11				
Wootton Wawen	d																					
Henley-in-Arden	d							14 27										15 22				
Danzey	d																	15 33				
Wood End	d																					
The Lakes	d							14 43										15 44				
Earlswood (West Midlands)	d																					
Wythall	d							14 54										15 55				
Whitlocks End	d																					
Shirley	d							15 05										16 06				
Yardley Wood	d							15 16										16 17				
Hall Green	d							15 27										16 28				
Spring Road	d							15 38										16 39				
London Marylebone 10 ⊖	d			13 33		13 50				14 20			14 50		15 17					15 20		
Banbury	d	14 53		15 01		15 05	15 25			15 41	15 53		16 02	16 25	16 37					16 40	16 53	
Leamington Spa 8	a	15 10		15 21		15 25	15 41			16 01	16 10		16 22	16 41						17 01	17 10	
	d	15 11		15 21		15 26	15 43			16 02	16 11		16 22	16 43						17 01	17 11	
Warwick	d			15 25						16 06										17 06		
Warwick Parkway	d			15a34		15 31				16 09			16 28							17 09		
Hatton	d									16 14												
Lapworth	d																			17 18		
Dorridge	d		15 25			15 43				16 22		16 25	16 39							17 22		17 25
Widney Manor	d		15 30									16 30										17 30
Solihull	d		15 33			15 48				16 28		16 33	16 45							17 27		17 33
Olton	d		15 37									16 37										17 37
Acocks Green	d		15 39									16 39										17 39
Tyseley	d							15 46										16 47				
Small Heath	d																					
Bordesley	d																					
Birmingham Moor Street	d		15 46			15 59			16 13	16 39		16 46	16 56				17 02		17 13	17 39		17 46
Birmingham Snow Hill 🚊	a		15 48			16 06		16 06	16 15	16 46		16 48	16 59				17 04	17 07	17 16	17 46		17 48
	d		15 49						16 18			16 49					17 05		17 18			17 49
Jewellery Quarter 🚊	d		15 52						16 20			16 52							17 20			17 52
The Hawthorns 🚊	d		15 56						16 25			16 56							17 25			17 56
Coventry	a	15 23					15 54				16 23			16 54							17 23	
Birmingham International ✈	a	15 35					16 04				16 35			17 04							17 35	
Birmingham New Street 12	a	15 46					16 18				16 46			17 18	17 23						17 46	
	d				16 00																	
Smethwick Galton Bdg H.L. 7	d		15 59						16 27			16 59							17 27			17 59
Langley Green	d		16 02									17 02										18 02
Rowley Regis	d		16 05						16 32			17 05							17 32			18 05
Old Hill	d		16 08									17 08										18 08
Cradley Heath	d		16 11						16 37			17 11							17 37			18 11
Lye	d		16 14									17 14										18 14
Stourbridge Junction 2	d		16a18						16 43			17a18					17 28		17 43			18a19
Hagley	d								16 46								17 31		17 46			
Blakedown	d																					
Kidderminster	d								16 52								17 37		17 52			
Hartlebury	d																					
University	d																					
Barnt Green	d																					
Bromsgrove	d				16 21																	
Droitwich Spa	d				16 30				17 04								17 49		18 04			
Worcester Shrub Hill 7	a				16 41														18 11			
	d				16 45											17 09						
Worcester Foregate Street 7	a				16 47				17 12							17 12	18 02					
	d				16 48											17 13						
Malvern Link	d				16 57											17 22						
Great Malvern	a				17 02											17 25						
	d															17 27						
Colwall	d															17 32						
Ledbury	a															17 39						
	d															17 42						
Hereford 7	a															17 58						

For general notes see front of timetable
For details of catering facilities see Directory of Train Operators

Sundays
until 27 January

Stratford -upon-Avon, Marylebone and Leamington Spa → Birmingham → Stourbridge, Worcester and Hereford

Network Diagram - See first page of Table 71

		CH	LM	CH		XC	LM	GW	LM	CH	XC		LM	LM	CH	XC	GW	LM		CH	XC	CH	LM	CH	XC
						1 ◇ ☕	🚌	1 ◇ ☕			R 1 ☕			🚌		1 ◇ ☕	1 ◇ ☕				R 1 ☕		🚌		1 ◇ ☕
Stratford-upon-Avon	d						16 00							17 05									18 05		
Wilmcote	d						16 11							17 16									18 16		
Wootton Wawen	d																								
Henley-in-Arden	d						16 22							17 27									18 27		
Danzey	d						16 33																		
Wood End	d																								
The Lakes	d						16 44							17 43									18 43		
Earlswood (West Midlands)	d																								
Wythall	d						16 55							17 54									18 54		
Whitlocks End	d																								
Shirley	d						17 06							18 05									19 05		
Yardley Wood	d						17 17							18 16									19 16		
Hall Green	d						17 28							18 27									19 27		
Spring Road	d						17 39							18 38									19 38		
London Marylebone 10	⊖ d	15 33		15 50						16 20					16 57					17 20		17 35		17 57	
Banbury	d	17 01		17 05		17 25				17 41	17 53				18 09	18 25				18 41	18 53	19 01		19 09	19 25
Leamington Spa 8	a	17 20		17 25		17 41				18 01	18 10				18 29	18 41				19 01	19 10	19 21		19 29	19 42
	d	17 21		17 26		17 43				18 02	18 11				18 29	18 43				19 02	19 11	19 21		19 29	19 43
Warwick	d	17 25								18 06										19 06		19 25			
Warwick Parkway	d	17a34		17 31						18 09					18 35					19 09		19a34		19 35	
Hatton	d									18 14															
Lapworth	d																			19 18					
Dorridge	d			17 43						18 22					18 46					19 23				19 46	
Widney Manor	d									18 26										19 26					
Solihull	d			17 48						18 29					18 52					19 30				19 52	
Olton	d																								
Acocks Green	d																								
Tyseley	d						17 47							18 46									19 46		
Small Heath	d																								
Bordesley	d																								
Birmingham Moor Street	d			17 59					18 13	18 41					19 02			19 13		19 41				20 02	
Birmingham Snow Hill	🚋 a			18 07			18 07		18 15	18 49				19 06	19 10			19 15		19 48			20 06	20 10	
	d								18 18									19 18							
Jewellery Quarter	🚋 d								18 20									19 20							
The Hawthorns	🚋 d								18 25									19 25							
Coventry	a					17 54					18 23					18 54					19 23				19 54
Birmingham International	✈ a					18 04					18 35					19 04					19 35				20 04
Birmingham New Street 12	a					18 18					18 46					19 18					19 46				20 21
	d		18 00										19 00												
Smethwick Galton Bdg H.L. 7	d								18 27									19 27							
Langley Green	d																								
Rowley Regis	d								18 32									19 32							
Old Hill	d																								
Cradley Heath	d								18 37									19 37							
Lye	d																								
Stourbridge Junction 2	d								18 43									19 43							
Hagley	d								18 47									19 46							
Blakedown	d								18 50																
Kidderminster	d								18 55									19 52							
Hartlebury	d																								
University	d																								
Barnt Green	d																								
Bromsgrove	d		18 21										19 21												
Droitwich Spa	d		18 30						19 06				19 31					20 08							
Worcester Shrub Hill 7	a		18 38						19 14				19 41					20 15							
	d		18 41					19 10									20 10								
Worcester Foregate Street 7	a		18 44					19 12									20 12								
	d		18 44					19 14									20 14								
Malvern Link	d		18 53					19 22									20 22								
Great Malvern	a		18 56					19 26									20 26								
	d		18 57																						
Colwall	d		19 02																						
Ledbury	a		19 09																						
	d		19 09																						
Hereford 7	a		19 30																						

For general notes see front of timetable
For details of catering facilities see Directory of Train Operators

Table 71

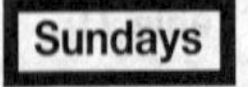

Sundays

until 27 January

Stratford -upon-Avon, Marylebone and Leamington Spa → Birmingham → Stourbridge, Worcester and Hereford

Network Diagram - See first page of Table 71

		CH	GW		LM	CH	XC	LM	LM	CH		GW	LM	CH	XC	CH	CH		XC	LM	CH	XC	CH		
			1 ◇				1 ◇		bus			1 ◇			1 ◇				1 ◇			1 ◇			
			catering				catering					catering													
Stratford-upon-Avon	d								19 05																
Wilmcote	d								19 16																
Wootton Wawen	d																								
Henley-in-Arden	d								19 27																
Danzey	d																								
Wood End	d																								
The Lakes	d								19 43																
Earlswood (West Midlands)	d																								
Wythall	d								19 54																
Whitlocks End	d																								
Shirley	d								20 05																
Yardley Wood	d								20 16																
Hall Green	d								20 27																
Spring Road	d								20 38																
London Marylebone 10 ⊖	d	18 17				18 20				18 57				19 22		19 57	20 20				20 50		21 40		
Banbury	d	19 36				19 41	19 53			20 09				20 44	20 53	21 09	21 41		21 53		22 10	22 53	23 01		
Leamington Spa 8	a					20 01	20 10			20 29				21 04	21 10	21 29	22 01		22 10		22 30	23 10	23 21		
	d					20 02	20 11			20 29				21 04	21 11	21 29	22 02		22 11		22 31	23 11	23 22		
Warwick	d					20 06								21 09			22 06				22 35		23 26		
Warwick Parkway	d					20 09				20 35				21 12		21 35	22 09				22 38		23 29		
Hatton	d																				22 43				
Lapworth	d																				22 48				
Dorridge	d					20 21				20 46				21 23		21 46	22 21				22 52		23 41		
Widney Manor	d					20 24								21 27							22 56				
Solihull	d					20 28				20 52				21 30		21 52	22 26				22 59		23 46		
Olton	d																								
Acocks Green	d																								
Tyseley	d								20 46																
Small Heath	d																								
Bordesley	d																								
Birmingham Moor Street	d				20 13	20 39				21 02			21 35	21 41		22 02	22 38			22 55	23 11		23 57		
Birmingham Snow Hill ⛴	a				20 15	20 46			21 06	21 10			21 37	21 48		22 10	22 45			22 57	23 18		00 04		
	d				20 18								21 45							23 00					
Jewellery Quarter ⛴	d				20 20								21 47							23 02					
The Hawthorns ⛴	d				20 25								21 52							23 07					
Coventry	a						20 23								21 23				22 23			23 27			
Birmingham International ✈	a						20 35								21 34				22 35			23 38			
Birmingham New Street 12	a	20 23					20 46								21 46				23 13			23 55			
	d							21 00																	
Smethwick Galton Bdg H.L. 7	d				20 27								21 54							23 09					
Langley Green	d																								
Rowley Regis	d				20 32								21 59							23 14					
Old Hill	d																								
Cradley Heath	d				20 37								22 03							23 19					
Lye	d																								
Stourbridge Junction 2	d				20 43								22 09							23 24					
Hagley	d				20 46								22 12							23 28					
Blakedown	d																								
Kidderminster	d				20 53								22 18							23 34					
Hartlebury	d																								
University	d																								
Barnt Green	d																								
Bromsgrove	d							21 21																	
Droitwich Spa	d				21 04			21 30					22 30							23 45					
Worcester Shrub Hill 7	a				21 14			21 37					22 37							23 53					
	d		21 11		21 29			21 40				22 08	22 41												
Worcester Foregate Street 7	a		21 13		21 31			21 42				22 11	22 43												
	d		21 15		21 32			21 43				22 12	22 44												
Malvern Link	d		21 24		21 40			21 52				22 21	22 52												
Great Malvern	a		21 27		21 43			21 54				22 23	22 55												
	d		21 28					21 55																	
Colwall	d		21 33					22 00																	
Ledbury	a		21 40					22 07																	
	d		21 43					22 08																	
Hereford 7	a		21 59					22 28																	

For general notes see front of timetable
For details of catering facilities see Directory of Train Operators

Table 71

Sundays

Stratford -upon-Avon, Marylebone and Leamington Spa → Birmingham → Stourbridge, Worcester and Hereford

from 3 February

Network Diagram - See first page of Table 71

		CH	LM	CH	LM	GW	LM	LM	LM	CH	CH		LM		LM	LM	XC	XC	LM	CH	CH	CH		XC	CH
						1◇								1◇				1◇						1◇	
																	A				B	C			B
					🚌			🚌					🚌			🚌									
						☕								☕				☕						☕	
Stratford-upon-Avon	d				08 05								09 05												
Wilmcote	d				08 16								09 16												
Wootton Wawen	d																								
Henley-in-Arden	d				08 27								09 27												
Danzey	d																								
Wood End	d																								
The Lakes	d				08 43								09 43												
Earlswood (West Midlands)	d																								
Wythall	d				08 54								09 54												
Whitlocks End	d																								
Shirley	d				09 05								10 05												
Yardley Wood	d				09 16								10 16												
Hall Green	d				09 27								10 27												
Spring Road	d				09 38								10 38												
London Marylebone 10 ⊖	d	21p40		08 00						09 00	09 20									10 00	10 10	10 20			10 22
Banbury	d	23p03		09 22						10 22	10 41							10 53		11 22	11 33	11 43		11 53	11 44
Leamington Spa 8	a	23p23		09 42						10 42	11 01							11 10		11 42	11 53	12 03		12 10	12 03
	d	23p24		09 44						10 44	11 02							11 11		11 44	11 54	12 04		12 11	12 04
Warwick	d	23p28									11 12										12 14	12 14			
Warwick Parkway	d	23p31									11a17										12a19	12a19			
Hatton	d																								
Lapworth	d																								
Dorridge	d	23p43						09 30								10 30									
Widney Manor	d	23p46						09 41								10 41									
Solihull	d	23p50						09 52								10 52									
Olton	d							10 03								11 03									
Acocks Green	d							10 09								11 09									
Tyseley	d				09 46								10 46												
Small Heath	d																								
Bordesley	d																								
Birmingham Moor Street	d	00 02	09 26				10 13		10 45						11 13				11 45						
Birmingham Snow Hill 🚋	a	00 09	09 28		10 06		10 15	10 34	10 47				11 06		11 15	11 34			11 47						
	d		09 30				10 18		10 48						11 18				11 48						
Jewellery Quarter 🚋	d		09 32				10 20		10 51						11 20				11 51						
The Hawthorns 🚋	d		09 37				10 25		10 55						11 25				11 55						
Coventry	a			09 57						10 57								11 23		12 02				12 23	12 18
Birmingham International ✈	a			10 08						11 08								11 35		12 13				12 35	12 30
Birmingham New Street 12	a			10 28						11 28								11 46		12 33				12 46	12 48
	d																11 46								
Smethwick Galton Bdg H.L. 7	d		09 39				10 27		10 58						11 27				11 58						
Langley Green	d								11 01										12 01						
Rowley Regis	d		09 44				10 32		11 04						11 32				12 04						
Old Hill	d								11 07										12 07						
Cradley Heath	d		09 49				10 37		11 10						11 37				12 10						
Lye	d								11 13										12 13						
Stourbridge Junction 2	d		09 54				10 43		11a17						11 43				12a17						
Hagley	d		09 58				10 46								11 47										
Blakedown	d														11 50										
Kidderminster	d		10 04				10 52								11 55										
Hartlebury	d																								
University	d																								
Barnt Green	d																								
Bromsgrove	d																12 05								
Droitwich Spa	d		10 15				11 04								12 06		12 13								
Worcester Shrub Hill 7	a		10 23				11 11								12 14		12 22								
	d		10 26			10 35	11 26							12 04											
Worcester Foregate Street 7	a		10 29			10 37	11 28							12 07											
	d		10 29			10 39	11 29							12 08											
Malvern Link	d		10 38			10 48	11 37							12 18											
Great Malvern	a		10 41			10 50	11 40							12 20											
	d													12 22											
Colwall	d													12 27											
Ledbury	a													12 34											
	d													12 37											
Hereford 7	a													12 54											

For general notes see front of timetable
For details of catering facilities see Directory of Train Operators

A To Gloucester (Table 57)
B Until 23 March
C From 30 March

Table 71

Sundays

from 3 February

Stratford -upon-Avon, Marylebone and Leamington Spa → Birmingham → Stourbridge, Worcester and Hereford

Network Diagram - See first page of Table 71

		LM	GW	LM	LM	LM	XC	CH	CH	LM	LM	LM	LM	XC	LM	CH	CH	LM	XC	GW	GW	LM	LM
			1 ◇				1 ◇							R 1					R 1	1 ◇	1 ◇		
							A	B												C	B		
		bus			bus					bus		bus						bus					bus
			catering				catering							catering					catering	catering	catering		
Stratford-upon-Avon	d	10 05								11 05								12 05					
Wilmcote	d	10 16								11 16								12 16					
Wootton Wawen	d																						
Henley-in-Arden	d	10 27								11 27								12 27					
Danzey	d																						
Wood End	d																						
The Lakes	d	10 43								11 43								12 43					
Earlswood (West Midlands)	d																						
Wythall	d	10 54								11 54								12 54					
Whitlocks End	d																						
Shirley	d	11 05								12 05								13 05					
Yardley Wood	d	11 16								12 16								13 16					
Hall Green	d	11 27								12 27								13 27					
Spring Road	d	11 38								12 38								13 38					
London Marylebone 10	⊖ d							11 00	11 20							12 00	12 20						
Banbury	d						12 25	12 29	12 41					12 53		13 22	13 45		13 53				
Leamington Spa 8	a						12 41	12 48	13 01					13 10		13 42	14 05		14 10				
	d						12 43	12 49	13 02					13 11		13 44	14 05		14 11				
Warwick	d								13 12								14 15						
Warwick Parkway	d								13a17								14a21						
Hatton	d																						
Lapworth	d																						
Dorridge	d				11 30							12 30											13 30
Widney Manor	d				11 41							12 41											13 41
Solihull	d				11 52							12 52											13 52
Olton	d				12 03							13 03											14 03
Acocks Green	d				12 09							13 09											14 09
Tyseley	d	11 46								12 46								13 46					
Small Heath	d																						
Bordesley	d																						
Birmingham Moor Street	d			12 13		12 45					13 15				13 45							14 13	
Birmingham Snow Hill	tram a	12 06		12 15	12 34	12 47				13 06	13 17	13 34			13 47			14 06				14 15	14 34
	d			12 18		12 48					13 20				13 48							14 18	
Jewellery Quarter	tram d			12 20		12 51					13 22				13 51							14 20	
The Hawthorns	tram d			12 25		12 55					13 27				13 55							14 25	
Coventry	a						13 02	13 02						13 23		14 02			14 23				
Birmingham International	✈ a						13 13	13 13						13 35		14 13			14 35				
Birmingham New Street 12	a						13 30	13 33						13 46		14 38			14 46				
	d												13 45										
Smethwick Galton Bdg H.L. 7	d			12 27		12 58					13 29				13 58							14 27	
Langley Green	d					13 01									14 01								
Rowley Regis	d			12 32		13 04					13 34				14 04							14 32	
Old Hill	d					13 07									14 07								
Cradley Heath	d			12 37		13 10					13 39				14 10							14 37	
Lye	d					13 13									14 13								
Stourbridge Junction 2	d			12 43		13a17					13 46				14a17							14 43	
Hagley	d			12 46							13 49											14 46	
Blakedown	d			12 49																		14 49	
Kidderminster	d			12 54							13 55											14 54	
Hartlebury	d																						
University	d																						
Barnt Green	d																						
Bromsgrove	d												14 05										
Droitwich Spa	d			13 06							14 07		14 15									15 06	
Worcester Shrub Hill 7	a			13 13									14 22										
	d		13 09	13 25									14 28							15 08	15 08		
Worcester Foregate Street 7	a		13 11	13 27							14 20		14 30							15 10	15 10	15 14	
	d		13 13	13 28									14 31							15 12	15 12		
Malvern Link	d		13 22	13 36									14 39										
Great Malvern	a		13 25	13 39									14 42							15 21	15 21		
	d		13 25										14 43							15 22			
Colwall	d		13 32										14 48										
Ledbury	a		13 39										14 55							15 32			
	d		13 48										14 58							15 34			
Hereford 7	a		14 04										15 19							15 50			

For general notes see front of timetable
For details of catering facilities see Directory of Train Operators

A Until 23 March. From Brighton (Table 51)

B From 30 March

C Until 23 March

Table 71

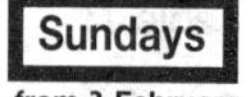

Sundays

from 3 February

Stratford -upon-Avon, Marylebone and Leamington Spa → Birmingham → Stourbridge, Worcester and Hereford

Network Diagram - See first page of Table 71

		LM	CH	CH	LM	XC	LM	LM	LM	LM	CH		CH	LM	XC	LM	LM	GW	GW	LM	GW	CH		LM	CH
						R 1									R 1			1 ◇	1 ◇		1 ◇				
																			A		B				
					bus	catering		bus						bus	catering		bus	catering	catering		catering				
Stratford-upon-Avon	d				13 05									14 05											
Wilmcote	d				13 16									14 16											
Wootton Wawen	d																								
Henley-in-Arden	d				13 27									14 27											
Danzey	d																								
Wood End	d																								
The Lakes	d				13 43									14 43											
Earlswood (West Midlands)	d																								
Wythall	d				13 54									14 54											
Whitlocks End	d																								
Shirley	d				14 05									15 05											
Yardley Wood	d				14 16									15 16											
Hall Green	d				14 27									15 27											
Spring Road	d				14 38									15 38											
London Marylebone 10 ⊖	d		13 00	13 20							14 00		14 20									15 00			15 20
Banbury	d		14 23	14 43		14 53					15 22		15 45		15 53							16 22			16 42
Leamington Spa 8	a		14 42	15 03		15 10					15 42		16 05		16 10							16 42			17 03
	d		14 44	15 03		15 11					15 44		16 05		16 11							16 44			17 03
Warwick	d			15 14									16 15												17 14
Warwick Parkway	d			15a19									16a21												17a19
Hatton	d																								
Lapworth	d																								
Dorridge	d							14 30									15 30								
Widney Manor	d							14 41									15 41								
Solihull	d							14 52									15 52								
Olton	d							15 03									16 03								
Acocks Green	d							15 09									16 09								
Tyseley	d				14 46									15 46											
Small Heath	d																								
Bordesley	d																								
Birmingham Moor Street	d	14 45					15 13		15 45							16 13				16 45				17 02	
Birmingham Snow Hill (tram)	a	14 47			15 06		15 15	15 34	15 47					16 06		16 15	16 34			16 47				17 04	
	d	14 48					15 18		15 48							16 18				16 48				17 05	
Jewellery Quarter (tram)	d	14 51					15 20		15 51							16 20				16 51					
The Hawthorns (tram)	d	14 55					15 25		15 55							16 25				16 55					
Coventry	a		15 02			15 23					16 02				16 23							17 02			
Birmingham International ✈	a		15 13			15 35					16 13				16 35							17 13			
Birmingham New Street 12	a		15 38			15 46					16 38				16 46							17 38			
	d									16 00															
Smethwick Galton Bdg H.L. 7	d	14 58					15 27		15 58							16 27				16 58					
Langley Green	d	15 01							16 01											17 01					
Rowley Regis	d	15 04					15 32		16 04							16 32				17 04					
Old Hill	d	15 07							16 07											17 07					
Cradley Heath	d	15 10					15 37		16 10							16 37				17 10					
Lye	d	15 13							16 13											17 13					
Stourbridge Junction 2	d	15a17					15 43		16a17							16 43				17a17				17 28	
Hagley	d						15 46									16 46								17 31	
Blakedown	d																								
Kidderminster	d						15 52									16 52								17 37	
Hartlebury	d																								
University	d																								
Barnt Green	d																								
Bromsgrove	d									16 21															
Droitwich Spa	d						16 04			16 30						17 04								17 49	
Worcester Shrub Hill 7	a									16 41															
	d									16 45								17 07	17 09		17 10				
Worcester Foregate Street 7	a						16 12			16 47						17 12		17 09	17 12		17 12			18 02	
	d									16 48								17 11	17 13		17 14				
Malvern Link	d									16 57								17 20	17 22		17 23				
Great Malvern	a									17 02								17 22	17 25		17 25				
	d																		17 27						
Colwall	d																		17 32						
Ledbury	a																		17 39						
	d																		17 42						
Hereford 7	a																		17 58						

For general notes see front of timetable
For details of catering facilities see Directory of Train Operators

A Until 23 March
B From 30 March

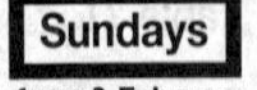

Sundays

from 3 February

Stratford -upon-Avon, Marylebone and Leamington Spa → Birmingham → Stourbridge, Worcester and Hereford

Network Diagram - See first page of Table 71

		LM	XC	LM	LM	LM	LM	CH	CH	LM	XC		GW	GW	LM	LM	LM	CH	CH	XC	LM	GW		GW	LM
			R 1								R 1		1 ◇ A	1 ◇ B						R 1		1 ◇ A		1 ◇ B	
		bus	coffee		bus					bus	coffee		coffee	coffee		bus				coffee	bus	coffee		coffee	
Stratford-upon-Avon	d	15 00								16 00											17 05				
Wilmcote	d	15 11								16 11											17 16				
Wootton Wawen	d																								
Henley-in-Arden	d	15 22								16 22											17 27				
Danzey	d	15 33								16 33															
Wood End	d																								
The Lakes	d	15 44								16 44											17 43				
Earlswood (West Midlands)	d																								
Wythall	d	15 55								16 55											17 54				
Whitlocks End	d																								
Shirley	d	16 06								17 06											18 05				
Yardley Wood	d	16 17								17 17											18 16				
Hall Green	d	16 28								17 28											18 27				
Spring Road	d	16 39								17 39											18 38				
London Marylebone 10 ⊖	d							16 00	16 20									17 00	17 20						
Banbury	d		16 53					17 22	17 45		17 53							18 23	18 43	18 53					
Leamington Spa 8	a		17 10					17 42	18 05		18 10							18 42	19 03	19 10					
	d		17 11					17 44	18 05		18 11							18 44	19 03	19 11					
Warwick	d								18 15										19 14						
Warwick Parkway	d								18a21										19a19						
Hatton	d																								
Lapworth	d																								
Dorridge	d				16 30											17 30									
Widney Manor	d				16 41											17 41									
Solihull	d				16 52											17 52									
Olton	d				17 03											18 03									
Acocks Green	d				17 09											18 09									
Tyseley	d	16 47								17 47											18 46				
Small Heath	d																								
Bordesley	d																								
Birmingham Moor Street	d			17 13		17 45									18 13										19 13
Birmingham Snow Hill ⛴	a	17 07		17 16	17 34	17 47				18 07					18 15	18 34					19 06				19 15
	d			17 18		17 48									18 18										19 18
Jewellery Quarter ⛴	d			17 20		17 51									18 20										19 20
The Hawthorns ⛴	d			17 25		17 55									18 25										19 25
Coventry	a		17 23					18 02			18 23							19 02		19 23					
Birmingham International ✈	a		17 35					18 13			18 35							19 13		19 35					
Birmingham New Street 12	a		17 46					18 33			18 46							19 33		19 46					
	d						18 00										19 00								
Smethwick Galton Bdg H.L. 7	d			17 27		17 58									18 27										19 27
Langley Green	d					18 01																			
Rowley Regis	d			17 32		18 04									18 32										19 32
Old Hill	d					18 07																			
Cradley Heath	d			17 37		18 10									18 37										19 37
Lye	d					18 13																			
Stourbridge Junction 2	d			17 43		18a18									18 43										19 43
Hagley	d			17 46											18 47										19 46
Blakedown	d														18 50										
Kidderminster	d			17 52											18 55										19 52
Hartlebury	d																								
University	d																								
Barnt Green	d																								
Bromsgrove	d						18 21										19 21								
Droitwich Spa	d			18 04			18 30								19 06		19 31								20 08
Worcester Shrub Hill 7	a			18 11			18 38								19 14		19 41								20 15
	d						18 41						19 06	19 10								20 09		20 10	
Worcester Foregate Street 7	a						18 44						19 09	19 12								20 11		20 12	
	d						18 44						19 09	19 14								20 13		20 14	
Malvern Link	d						18 53						19 19	19 22								20 22		20 22	
Great Malvern	a						18 56						19 22	19 26								20 25		20 25	
	d						18 57																		
Colwall	d						19 02																		
Ledbury	a						19 09																		
	d						19 09																		
Hereford 7	a						19 30																		

For general notes see front of timetable
For details of catering facilities see Directory of Train Operators

A From 30 March
B Until 23 March

Table 71

Sundays

from 3 February

Stratford -upon-Avon, Marylebone and Leamington Spa → Birmingham → Stourbridge, Worcester and Hereford

Network Diagram - See first page of Table 71

Station		CH	LM 🚌	CH	XC 1 ◇	GW 1 ◇ A ☕	GW 1 ◇ B ☕	LM A	LM B	LM	CH		LM 🚌	XC 1 ◇	GW 1 ◇ A ☕	GW 1 ◇ B ☕	LM	CH	XC 1 ◇	CH	LM	XC 1 ◇ C	CH		
Stratford-upon-Avon	d		18 05										19 05												
Wilmcote	d		18 16										19 16												
Wootton Wawen	d																								
Henley-in-Arden	d		18 27										19 27												
Danzey	d																								
Wood End	d																								
The Lakes	d		18 43										19 43												
Earlswood (West Midlands)	d																								
Wythall	d		18 54										19 54												
Whitlocks End	d																								
Shirley	d		19 05										20 05												
Yardley Wood	d		19 16										20 16												
Hall Green	d		19 27										20 27												
Spring Road	d		19 38										20 38												
London Marylebone 10 ⊖	d	18 00		18 20							19 20							20 20		21 00			21 40		
Banbury	d	19 22		19 45	19 53						20 45			20 53				21 43	21 53	22 22		22 53	23 05		
Leamington Spa 8	a	19 42		20 05	20 10						21 04			21 10				22 03	22 10	22 43		23 10	23 29		
	d	19 44		20 06	20 11						21 05			21 11				22 04	22 11			23 11			
Warwick	d			20 16							21 15							22 14							
Warwick Parkway	d			20a21							21a20							22a19							
Hatton	d																								
Lapworth	d																								
Dorridge	d																								
Widney Manor	d																								
Solihull	d																								
Olton	d																								
Acocks Green	d																								
Tyseley	d		19 46										20 46												
Small Heath	d																								
Bordesley	d																								
Birmingham Moor Street	d							20 13	20 13								21 35				22 55				
Birmingham Snow Hill 🚋	a		20 06					20 15	20 15				21 06				21 37				22 57				
	d							20 18	20 18								21 45				23 00				
Jewellery Quarter 🚋	d							20 20	20 20								21 47				23 02				
The Hawthorns 🚋	d							20 25	20 25								21 52				23 07				
Coventry	a	20 02			20 23									21 23					22 23			23 27			
Birmingham International ✈	a	20 13			20 35									21 35					22 35			23 38			
Birmingham New Street 12	a	20 33			20 46									21 46					23 13			23 55			
	d									21 00															
Smethwick Galton Bdg H.L. 7	d							20 27	20 27								21 54				23 09				
Langley Green	d																								
Rowley Regis	d							20 32	20 32								21 59				23 14				
Old Hill	d																								
Cradley Heath	d							20 37	20 37								22 03				23 19				
Lye	d																								
Stourbridge Junction 2	d							20 43	20 43								22 09				23 24				
Hagley	d							20 46	20 46								22 12				23 28				
Blakedown	d																								
Kidderminster	d							20 53	20 53								22 18				23 34				
Hartlebury	d																								
University	d																								
Barnt Green	d																								
Bromsgrove	d									21 21															
Droitwich Spa	d							21 04	21 04	21 30							22 30				23 45				
Worcester Shrub Hill 7	a							21 14	21 14	21 37							22 37				23 53				
	d					21 08	21 10	21 26	21 29	21 40					22 06	22 08	22 41								
Worcester Foregate Street 7	a					21 11	21 12	21 28	21 31	21 42					22 09	22 11	22 43								
	d						21 14	21 29	21 32	21 43					22 10	22 12	22 44								
Malvern Link	d						21 23	21 37	21 40	21 52					22 19	22 21	22 52								
Great Malvern	a						21 26	21 40	21 43	21 54					22 21	22 23	22 55								
	d						21 27			21 55															
Colwall	d						21 32			22 00															
Ledbury	a						21 39			22 07															
	d						21 42			22 08															
Hereford 7	a						21 58			22 28															

For general notes see front of timetable
For details of catering facilities see Directory of Train Operators

A From 30 March
B Until 23 March
C Until 23 March from Bournemouth (Table 51)

Table 72

Mondays to Saturdays

Stourbridge Junction — Stourbridge Town

Network Diagram - See first page of Table 71

Miles			LM	LM	LM	LM	LM	LM	LM	LM	LM	LM	LM	LM	LM	LM	LM	LM	LM	LM	LM	LM	LM	LM	LM	LM
0	Stourbridge Junction 2	d	06 07	06 37	06 50	07 03	07 16	07 29	07 42	07 56	08 09	08 24	08 37	08 50	09 07	09 24	09 37	09 54	10 07	10 24	10 37	10 54	11 07	11 24	11 37	11 54
¾	Stourbridge Town	a	06 10	06 40	06 53	07 06	07 19	07 32	07 45	07 59	08 12	08 27	08 40	08 53	09 10	09 27	09 40	09 57	10 10	10 27	10 40	10 57	11 10	11 27	11 40	11 57

		LM	LM	LM	LM	LM	LM	LM	LM	LM	LM	LM	LM	LM	LM	LM	LM	LM	LM	LM	LM	LM	LM	LM	LM	LM
Stourbridge Junction 2	d	12 07	12 24	12 37	12 54	13 07	13 24	13 37	13 54	14 07	14 24	14 37	14 54	15 11	15 24	15 37	15 52	16 05	16 18	16 31	16 44	16 57	17 10	17 23	17 35	17 48
Stourbridge Town	a	12 10	12 27	12 40	12 57	13 10	13 27	13 40	13 57	14 10	14 27	14 40	14 58	15 14	15 27	15 40	15 55	16 08	16 21	16 34	16 47	17 00	17 13	17 26	17 38	17 51

		LM	LM	LM	LM	LM	LM	LM	LM	LM	LM	LM	LM	LM	LM	LM	LM SO	LM SO	LM	LM	LM	LM	LM	LM	LM	
Stourbridge Junction 2	d	18 01	18 16	18 30	18 44	18 57	19 10	19 23	19 36	19 55	20 08	20 28	20 41	20 54	21 07	21 20	21 33	21 46	21 59	22 30	22 51	23 03	23 15	23 34	23 47	.....
Stourbridge Town	a	18 04	18 19	18 33	18 47	19 00	19 13	19 26	19 39	19 58	20 11	20 31	20 44	20 57	21 10	21 23	21 36	21 49	22 02	22 33	22 54	23 06	23 18	23 37	23 50	.

Mondays to Saturdays

Miles			LM	LM	LM	LM	LM	LM	LM	LM	LM	LM	LM	LM	LM	LM	LM	LM	LM	LM	LM	LM	LM	LM	LM	LM
0	Stourbridge Town	d	05 50	06 13	06 43	06 56	07 09	07 22	07 35	07 48	08 02	08 17	08 30	08 43	09 00	09 13	09 30	09 43	10 00	10 13	10 30	10 43	11 00	11 13	11 30	11 43
¾	Stourbridge Junction 2	a	05 53	06 16	06 46	06 59	07 12	07 25	07 38	07 51	08 05	08 20	08 33	08 46	09 03	09 16	09 33	09 46	10 03	10 16	10 33	10 46	11 03	11 16	11 33	11 46

		LM	LM	LM	LM	LM	LM	LM	LM	LM	LM	LM	LM	LM	LM	LM	LM	LM	LM	LM	LM	LM	LM	LM	LM	LM
Stourbridge Town	d	12 00	12 13	12 30	12 43	13 00	13 13	13 30	13 43	14 00	14 13	14 30	14 43	15 00	15 17	15 30	15 43	15 58	16 11	16 24	16 37	16 50	17 03	17 16	17 28	17 41
Stourbridge Junction 2	a	12 03	12 16	12 33	12 46	13 03	13 16	13 33	13 46	14 03	14 16	14 33	14 46	15 04	15 20	15 33	15 46	16 01	16 14	16 27	16 40	16 53	17 06	17 19	17 31	17 44

		LM	LM	LM	LM	LM	LM	LM	LM	LM	LM	LM	LM	LM	LM	LM	LM	LM SO	LM SO	LM	LM	LM	LM	LM	LM	
Stourbridge Town	d	17 54	18 07	18 22	18 36	18 50	19 03	19 16	19 29	19 42	20 01	20 15	20 34	20 47	21 00	21 13	21 26	21 39	21 52	22 16	22 44	22 57	23 09	23 21	23 40	.....
Stourbridge Junction 2	a	17 57	18 10	18 25	18 39	18 53	19 06	19 19	19 32	19 45	20 04	20 18	20 37	20 50	21 03	21 16	21 29	21 42	21 55	22 19	22 47	23 00	23 12	23 24	23 43	.

For general notes see front of timetable
For details of catering facilities see
Directory of Train Operators

No Sunday Service

Birmingham → Shrewsbury

Network Diagram - see first page of Table 67

Miles			AW	AW	AW	AW	LM		AW	LM	AW	LM	LM		AW	LM	CH	AW	LM		AW	LM	AW	LM	AW	LM
			MO	MX	MX	MO																				
									◇		◇				◇			◇			◇		◇		◇	
			A			B 🚌					C	D					E									
															🛒			🛒			🛒		🛒		🛒	
0	**Birmingham New Street**	d		23p33					06 33		07 17		07 57		08 33	08 57		09 33	09 57		10 33	10 57	11 33	11 57	12 33	12 57
8½	Coseley	d											08 09			09 09			10 09			11 09		12 09		13 09
13	**Wolverhampton** [7] ⛴	d	23p25	23p50	00 25	23p25	06 27		06 48	06 55	07 33	07 47	08 15		08 48	09 15	09 26	09 48	10 15		10 48	11 15	11 48	12 15	12 48	13 15
17	Bilbrook	d	23p32	23p57		23p45	06 33			07 01	07 39		08 22			09 22			10 22					12 22		13 22
17½	Codsall	d	23p34	23p59		23p50	06 36			07 03	07 42		08 24			09 24			10 24			11 24		12 24		13 24
20¾	Albrighton	d	23p39	00 04		00 05	06 41			07 08	07 46		08 29			09 29			10 29			11 29		12 29		13 29
22¼	Cosford	d	23p42	00 07		00 15	06 44			07 11	07 51		08 32			09 32	09 43		10 32			11 32		12 32		13 32
25½	Shifnal	d	23p47	00 12		00 25	06 50			07 16		08 01	08 37			09 37			10 37			11 37		12 37		13 37
28½	Telford Central	d	23p53	00 18	00 41	00 35	06 56		07 04	07 21	07 59	08 07	08 43		09 04	09 43	09 52	10 04	10 43		11 04	11 43	12 04	12 43	13 04	13 43
29½	Oakengates	d	23p55	00 20		00 45	06 59			07 23		08 10	08 46			09 46			10 46			11 46		12 46		13 46
32½	Wellington (Shropshire)	d	00 01	00 24	00 47	01 00	07 04		07 10	07 27	08 05	08 15	08 51		09 10	09 50		10 10	10 50		11 10	11 50	12 10	12 50	13 10	13 50
43	**Shrewsbury**	a	00 18	00 40	01 03	01 25	07 20		07 22	07 41	08 22	08 37	09 09		09 22	10 09	10 10	10 25	11 09		11 22	12 09	12 25	13 09	13 22	14 09

		AW		LM	AW	LM	AW	LM		AW	LM	LM	AW	LM		AW	LM	AW	LM	AW	LM	LM	AW	AW		
										R																
		◇			◇		◇						◇			◇		◇		◇			◇			
													C										G			
		🛒			🛒		🛒			🛒			🛒			🛒				🛒						
Birmingham New Street	d	13 33		13 57	14 33	14 57	15 33	15 57		16 33	16 57	17 24	17 33	17 57		18 33	18 57	19 33	19 57	20 33	20 57	21 57	22 33	23 33		
Coseley	d			14 09		15 09		16 09			17 09			18 09			19 09		20 09		21 09	22 09				
Wolverhampton [7] ⛴	d	13 48		14 15	14 48	15 15	15 48	16 15		16 48	17 15	17 48	17 48	18 15		18 48	19 15	19 48	20 15	20 50	21 17	22 16	22 48	23 50		
Bilbrook	d			14 22		15 22		16 22			17 22		17 58	18 22			19 22		20 22		21 23	22 23		23 57		
Codsall	d			14 24		15 24		16 24			17 24		18 01	18 24			19 24		20 24		21 26	22 25		23 59		
Albrighton	d			14 29		15 29		16 29			17 29		18 05	18 29			19 29		20 29		21 31	22 30		00 04		
Cosford	d			14 32		15 32		16 32			17 32	17 59		18 32			19 32		20 32		21 35	22 33		00 07		
Shifnal	d			14 37		15 37		16 37			17 37	18 04		18 37			19 37		20 37		21 40	22 39		00 12		
Telford Central	d	14 04		14 43	15 04	15 43	16 04	16 43		17 04	17 43	18 09	18 13	18 43		19 04	19 43	20 04	20 43	21 06	21 47	22 45	23 04	00 18		
Oakengates	d			14 46		15 46		16 46			17 46			18 46			19 46		20 46		21 49	22 48		00 20		
Wellington (Shropshire)	d	14 10		14 50	15 10	15 50	16 10	16 50		17 10	17 50	18 15	18 19	18 50		19 10	19 50	20 10	20 50	21 12	21 54	22 53	23 10	00 24		
Shrewsbury	a	14 25		15 09	15 22	16 09	16 25	17 09		17 22	18 09	18 30	18 35	19 09		19 22	20 09	20 25	21 09	21 27	22 09	23 06	23 25	00 40		

Saturdays

		AW	AW	AW		LM	AW	LM		AW	LM	AW		LM	AW	LM		AW	LM	AW		LM	AW	LM		AW
				◇			◇			◇		◇			◇			◇		◇			◇			◇
										🛒		🛒			🛒			🛒		🛒			🛒			🛒
Birmingham New Street	d	23p33		06 33			07 33	07 57		08 33	08 57	09 33		09 57	10 33	10 57		11 33	11 57	12 33		12 57	13 33	13 57		14 33
Coseley	d							08 09			09 09			10 09		11 09						13 09		14 09		
Wolverhampton [7] ⛴	d	23p50	00 25	06 48		07 15	07 48	08 15		08 48	09 15	09 48		10 15	10 48	11 15		11 48	12 15	12 48		13 15	13 48	14 15		14 48
Bilbrook	d	23p57				07 22		08 22			09 22			10 22		11 22			12 22			13 22		14 22		
Codsall	d	23p59				07 24		08 24			09 24			10 24		11 24			12 24			13 24		14 24		
Albrighton	d	00 04				07 29		08 29			09 29			10 29		11 29			12 29			13 29		14 29		
Cosford	d	00 07				07 32		08 32			09 32			10 32		11 32			12 32			13 32		14 32		
Shifnal	d	00 12				07 37		08 37			09 37			10 37		11 37			12 37			13 37		14 37		
Telford Central	d	00 18	00 41	07 04		07 43	08 04	08 43		09 04	09 43	10 04		10 43	11 04	11 43		12 04	12 43	13 04		13 43	14 04	14 43		15 04
Oakengates	d	00 20				07 46		08 46			09 46			10 46		11 46			12 46			13 46		14 46		
Wellington (Shropshire)	d	00 24	00 47	07 10		07 50	08 10	08 50		09 10	09 50	10 10		10 50	11 10	11 50		12 10	12 50	13 10		13 50	14 10	14 50		15 10
Shrewsbury	a	00 40	01 03	07 22		08 09	08 25	09 09		09 22	10 09	10 25		11 09	11 22	12 09		12 25	13 09	13 22		14 09	14 25	15 09		15 22

		LM	AW	LM		AW	LM	AW		LM	AW	LM		AW	LM	AW		LM	AW	LM		AW	AW			
						R																				
			◇					◇			◇			◇		◇			◇			◇				
																						H				
			🛒			🛒		🛒			🛒					🛒										
Birmingham New Street	d	14 57	15 33	15 57		16 33	16 57	17 33		17 57	18 33	18 57		19 33	19 57	20 33		20 57	21 33	21 57		22 33	23 33			
Coseley	d	15 09					17 09			18 09		19 09			20 09			21 09		22 09						
Wolverhampton [7] ⛴	d	15 15	15 48	16 15		16 48	17 15	17 48		18 15	18 48	19 15		19 48	20 15	20 48		21 15	21 48	22 15		22 48	23 50			
Bilbrook	d	15 22		16 22			17 22			18 22		19 22			20 22			21 22		22 22			23 57			
Codsall	d	15 24		16 24			17 24			18 24		19 24			20 24			21 24		22 24			23 59			
Albrighton	d	15 29		16 29			17 29			18 29		19 29			20 29			21 29		22 29			00 04			
Cosford	d	15 32		16 32			17 32			18 32		19 32			20 32			21 32		22 32			00 07			
Shifnal	d	15 37		16 37			17 37			18 37		19 37			20 37			21 37		22 37			00 12			
Telford Central	d	15 43	16 04	16 43		17 04	17 43	18 04		18 43	19 04	19 43		20 04	20 43	21 04		21 43	22 04	22 43		23 04	00 18			
Oakengates	d	15 46		16 46			17 46			18 46		19 46			20 46			21 46		22 46			00 20			
Wellington (Shropshire)	d	15 50	16 10	16 50		17 10	17 50	18 10		18 50	19 10	19 50		20 10	20 50	21 10		21 50	22 10	22 50		23 10	00 26			
Shrewsbury	a	16 09	16 25	17 09		17 22	18 09	18 25		19 09	19 22	20 09		20 25	21 09	21 22		22 09	22 25	23 09		23 25	00 40			

For general notes see front of timetable
For details of catering facilities see Directory of Train Operators

A Until 28 January and from 31 March
B 4 February to 24 March
C To Chester (Table 75)
D From Walsall (Table 68)
E From London Marylebone (Table 75)
G To Holyhead (Table 81)
H To Chester (Table 65)

Table 74

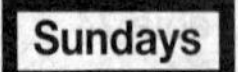

until 27 January and from 30 March

Birmingham → Shrewsbury

Network Diagram - see first page of Table 67

		AW	AW	AW	AW ◇ A		CH B	AW	AW ◇ 🚲	AW ◇ A		AW	AW ◇ C 🚲	AW ◇ A	CH B		AW	AW ◇ A 🚲	AW ◇ 🚲	CH B	AW	AW	AW ◇ D	AW		
Birmingham New Street	d	23p33		10 27	11 27		11 33	12 27	13 27	14 27		15 07	16 07	16 57	17 26		17 57	18 57	19 57	20 26	20 57	21 57	22 54			
Coseley	d																									
Wolverhampton 7	d	23p50	00 25	10 43	11 44		11 52	12 44	13 48	14 48		15 26	16 26	17 14	17 54		18 16	19 14	20 16	20 59	21 16	22 16	23 11	23 25		
Bilbrook	d	23p57		10 50	11 50			12 50				15 32					18 22	19 20			21 22	22 22		23 32		
Codsall	d	23p59		10 52	11 52			12 52				15 34					18 24	19 22			21 24	22 24		23 34		
Albrighton	d	00 04		10 57	11 57			12 57				15 39					18 29	19 27			21 29	22 29		23 39		
Cosford	d	00 07		11 00	12 00			13 00				15 42			18 05		18 32	19 30		21 10	21 32	22 32		23 42		
Shifnal	d	00 12		11 05	12 05			13 05				15 47					18 37	19 35			21 37	22 37		23 47		
Telford Central	d	00 18	00 41	11 11	12 11		12 18	13 11	14 04	15 04		15 53	16 42	17 30	18 13		18 43	19 41	20 32	21 18	21 43	22 43	23 28	23 53		
Oakengates	d	00 20		11 13	12 13			13 13		15 06		15 55	16 45	17 33			18 45	19 43			21 45	22 45		23 55		
Wellington (Shropshire)	d	00 26	00 48	11 19	12 19		12 26	13 19	14 11	15 12		16 01	16 50	17 38	18 20		18 51	19 47	20 39	21 25	21 51	22 51	23 34	00 01		
Shrewsbury	a	00 40	01 02	11 33	12 32		12 39	13 33	14 29	15 25		16 15	17 03	17 51	18 36		19 05	20 02	20 52	21 38	22 05	23 05	23 47	00 18		

Sundays

3 February to 23 March

		AW	AW	AW 🚌		AW 🚌	AW 🚌	AW 🚌		AW 🚌	AW 🚌	AW 🚌		AW 🚌	AW 🚌	AW 🚌		AW 🚌	AW 🚌	AW 🚌		AW 🚌	AW 🚌	AW 🚌		
Birmingham New Street	d	23p33																								
Coseley	d																									
Wolverhampton 7	d	23p50	00 25	10 24		11 24	12 12	13 10		13 56	15 08	15 43		16 18	18 03	18 50		19 30	20 03	21 16		22 20	22 16	23 25		
Bilbrook	d	23p57		10 44		11 44	12 32				15 28				18 23	19 10			20 23	21 36			22 36	23 45		
Codsall	d	23p59		10 49		11 49	12 37				15 33				18 28	19 15			20 28	21 41			22 41	23 50		
Albrighton	d	00 04		11 04		12 04	12 52				15 48				18 43	19 30			20 43	21 56			22 56	00 05		
Cosford	d	00 07		11 14		12 14	13 02				15 58				18 53	19 40			20 53	22 06			23 06	00 15		
Shifnal	d	00 12		11 24		12 24	13 12				16 08				19 03	19 50			21 03	22 16			23 16	00 25		
Telford Central	d	00 18	00 41	11 34		12 34	13 22	13 50		14 36	16 18	16 18		16 53	19 13	20 00		20 10	21 13	22 26		23 00	23 26	00 35		
Oakengates	d	00 20		11 44		12 44	13 32			14 46	16 28	16 28		17 03	19 23	20 10			21 23	22 36			23 36	00 45		
Wellington (Shropshire)	d	00 26	00 48	11 59		12 59	13 47	14 05		15 01	16 43	16 43		17 18	19 38	20 25		20 25	21 38	22 51		23 15	23 51	01 00		
Shrewsbury	a	00 40	01 02	12 24		13 24	14 12	14 30		15 26	17 08	17 08		17 43	20 03	20 50		20 50	22 03	23 16		23 40	00 16	01 25		

For general notes see front of timetable
For details of catering facilities see Directory of Train Operators

A To Chester (Table 75)
B Until 27 January. From London Marylebone (Table 71)
C To Aberystwyth (Table 75)
D To Holyhead (Table 81)

Shrewsbury → Birmingham

Network Diagram - see first page of Table 67

Mondays to Fridays

Miles	Station		AW MO A 🚌	AW MX ◇	AW	LM	AW	LM B	LM	AW ◇ C 🛒	LM	LM	AW ◇ 🛒	LM	AW ◇ 🛒	LM	AW ◇ 🛒	LM	AW ◇ 🛒	LM	AW ◇ 🛒	LM
0	**Shrewsbury**	d	22p50	23p31	05 24	05 30	05 54	06 05	06 48	07 12	07 37	07 47	08 22	08 42	09 22	09 35	10 22	10 35	11 22	11 35	12 22	12 35
10½	Wellington (Shropshire)	d	23p15	23p43	05 37	05 43	06 07	06 18	07 02	07 22	07 50	08 00	08 35	08 55	09 35	09 48	10 35	10 48	11 35	11 48	12 35	12 48
13¼	Oakengates	d	23p25	23p48		05 49		06 23		07 26		08 04		08 59		09 54		10 54		11 54		12 54
14¼	Telford Central	d	23p35	23p51	05 43	05 52	06 13	06 26	07 09	07 29	07 57	08 07	08 41	09 02	09 41	09 57	10 41	10 57	11 41	11 57	12 41	12 57
17½	Shifnal	d	23p45	23p56		05 57		06 32		07 34		08 12		09 07		10 02		11 02		12 02		13 02
20¾	Cosford	d	23p55	00 01		06 03		06 37		07 39		08 17		09 12		10 07		11 07		12 07		13 07
22¼	Albrighton	d	00 01	00 04		06 06		06 40		07 43		08 20		09 15		10 10		11 10		12 10		13 10
25½	Codsall	d	00 10	00 09		06 12		06 45		07 48		08 26		09 21		10 16		11 16		12 16		13 16
26	Bilbrook	d	00 15	00 11		06 14		06 47		07 51		08 28		09 23		10 18		11 18		12 18		
30	**Wolverhampton** [7]	a	00 35	00 23	06 00	06 22	06 30	06 55	07 27	07 58	08 19	08 35	08 58	09 30	09 58	10 27	10 58	11 27	11 58	12 27	12 58	13 27
34½	Coseley	a												09 35		10 33		11 33		12 33		13 33
43	**Birmingham New Street** [12]	a			06 18		06 48		07 48	08 18	08 36	08 55	09 18	09 51	10 18	10 48	11 18	11 48	12 18	12 48	13 18	13 48

Station		AW ◇ 🛒	LM	AW ◇ 🛒	LM	AW ◇ 🛒	LM	AW ◇ 🛒	LM	AW ◇ 🛒	LM	AW ◇ 🛒	LM	AW ◇ 🛒	LM	AW ◇ 🛒	LM B	AW	AW ◇
Shrewsbury	d	13 22	13 35	14 22	14 35	15 22	15 35	16 22	16 35	17 22	17 35	18 22	18 38	19 22	20 31	21 26	22 04	22 22	23 31
Wellington (Shropshire)	d	13 35	13 48	14 35	14 48	15 35	15 48	16 35	16 48	17 35	17 48	18 35	18 51	19 35	20 44	21 39	22 17	22 35	23 43
Oakengates	d		13 54		14 54		15 54		16 54		17 54		18 57		20 49		22 22		23 48
Telford Central	d	13 41	13 57	14 41	14 57	15 41	15 57	16 41	16 57	17 41	17 57	18 41	19 00	19 41	20 52	21 45	22 25	22 41	23 51
Shifnal	d		14 02		15 02		16 02		17 02		18 02		19 05		20 58		22 31		23 56
Cosford	d		14 07		15 07		16 07		17 07		18 07		19 10		21 03		22 36		00 01
Albrighton	d		14 10		15 10		16 10		17 10		18 10		19 13		21 06		22 39		00 04
Codsall	d		14 16		15 16		16 16		17 16		18 16		19 19		21 11		22 44		00 09
Bilbrook	d		14 18		15 18		16 18		17 18		18 18		19 21		21 13		22 46		00 11
Wolverhampton [7]	a	13 58	14 27	14 58	15 27	15 58	16 27	16 58	17 27	17 58	18 27	18 58	19 29	19 58	21 21	22 02	22 54	22 58	00 23
Coseley	a		14 33		15 33		16 33		17 33		18 33		19 35						
Birmingham New Street [12]	a	14 18	14 48	15 18	15 48	16 18	16 48	17 18	17 48	18 18	18 48	19 18	19 48	20 18	21 44	22 18		23 18	

Saturdays

Station		AW ◇	AW	AW	LM	AW ◇ C 🛒	LM	AW ◇ 🛒	LM	AW ◇ 🛒	LM	AW ◇ 🛒	LM	AW ◇ 🛒	LM	AW ◇ 🛒	LM	AW ◇ 🛒
Shrewsbury	d	23p31	05 24	06 22	06 40	07 12	07 40	08 22	08 40	09 22	09 41	10 22	10 40	11 22	11 40	12 22	12 40	13 22
Wellington (Shropshire)	d	23p43	05 37	06 35	06 53	07 22	07 53	08 35	08 53	09 35	09 55	10 35	10 53	11 35	11 53	12 35	12 53	13 35
Oakengates	d	23p48			06 59	07 26	07 59		08 59		10 00		10 59		11 59		12 59	
Telford Central	d	23p51	05 43	06 41	07 02	07 29	08 02	08 41	09 02	09 41	10 03	10 41	11 02	11 41	12 02	12 41	13 02	13 41
Shifnal	d	23p56			07 07	07 34	08 07		09 07		10 09		11 07		12 07		13 07	
Cosford	d	00 01			07 12	07 39	08 12		09 12		10 14		11 12		12 12		13 12	
Albrighton	d	00 04			07 15	07 43	08 15		09 15		10 17		11 15		12 15		13 15	
Codsall	d	00 09			07 21	07 48	08 21		09 21		10 22		11 21		12 21		13 21	
Bilbrook	d	00 11			07 23	07 51	08 23		09 23		10 24		11 23		12 23		13 23	
Wolverhampton [7]	a	00 23	06 00	06 58	07 31	07 58	08 31	08 58	09 31	09 58	10 31	10 58	11 31	11 58	12 31	12 58	13 31	13 58
Coseley	a						08 37		09 37		10 37		11 37		12 37		13 37	
Birmingham New Street [12]	a		06 18	07 18	07 51	08 18	08 51	09 18	09 51	10 18	10 51	11 18	11 51	12 18	12 51	13 18	13 51	14 18

Station		LM	AW ◇ 🛒	LM	AW ◇ 🛒	LM	AW ◇ 🛒	LM	AW ◇ 🛒	LM	AW ◇ 🛒	LM	AW ◇ 🛒	AW	LM	AW ◇ 🛒	LM B	AW	AW ◇
Shrewsbury	d	13 40	14 22	14 40	15 22	15 40	16 22	16 40	17 22	17 40	18 22	18 40	19 22	20 22	20 40	21 26	22 04	22 22	23 31
Wellington (Shropshire)	d	13 53	14 35	14 53	15 35	15 53	16 35	16 53	17 35	17 53	18 35	18 53	19 35	20 35	20 53	21 39	22 17	22 35	23 43
Oakengates	d	13 59		14 59		15 59		16 59		17 59		18 59			20 59		22 22		23 48
Telford Central	d	14 02	14 41	15 02	15 41	16 02	16 41	17 02	17 41	18 02	18 41	19 02	19 41	20 41	21 02	21 45	22 25	22 41	23 51
Shifnal	d	14 07		15 07		16 07		17 07		18 07		19 07			21 07		22 31		23 56
Cosford	d	14 12		15 12		16 12		17 12		18 12		19 12			21 12		22 36		00 01
Albrighton	d	14 15		15 15		16 15		17 15		18 15		19 15			21 15		22 39		00 04
Codsall	d	14 21		15 21		16 21		17 21		18 21		19 21			21 21		22 44		00 09
Bilbrook	d	14 23		15 23		16 23		17 23		18 23		19 23			21 23		22 46		00 11
Wolverhampton [7]	a	14 31	14 58	15 31	15 58	16 31	16 58	17 31	17 58	18 31	18 58	19 31	19 58	20 58	21 31	22 02	22 54	22 58	00 20
Coseley	a	14 37		15 37		16 37		17 37		18 37		19 37							
Birmingham New Street [12]	a	14 51	15 18	15 51	16 18	16 51	17 18	17 51	18 19	18 51	19 18	19 51	20 18	21 18	21 53	22 18		23 18	

For general notes see front of timetable
For details of catering facilities see Directory of Train Operators

A 4 February to 24 March
B To Walsall (Table 68)
C From Aberystwyth (Table 75)

Table 74

Sundays

until 27 January and from 30 March

Shrewsbury → Birmingham

Network Diagram - see first page of Table 67

		AW ◇	AW	AW	AW	CH A	AW ◇ B 🍴	AW	AW	AW ◇ 🍴	AW ◇ B	AW	AW ◇ C 🍴	CH A	AW ◇ B	AW ◇ C 🍴	AW ◇ B	AW ◇ D 🍴	AW B
Shrewsbury	d	23p31	08 41	09 41	10 50	11 30	12 08	12 53	13 42	14 24	15 25	16 28	17 26	17 53	18 27	19 25	20 25	21 20	22 29
Wellington (Shropshire)	d	23p43	08 54	09 54	11 04	11 44	12 22	13 07	13 55	14 38	15 38	16 41	17 40	18 07	18 40	19 39	20 38	21 34	22 42
Oakengates	d	23p48	09 00	10 00	11 10		12 27		14 01		15 44	16 47	17 46		18 46		20 44	21 40	22 48
Telford Central	d	23p51	09 03	10 03	11 13	11 50	12 30	13 13	14 04	14 44	15 47	16 50	17 49	18 13	18 49	19 45	20 47	21 43	22 51
Shifnal	d	23p56	09 08	10 08			12 35		14 09		15 52	16 55	17 54		18 54		20 52	21 48	22 56
Cosford	d	00 01	09 13	10 13		11 58	12 40		14 14		15 57	17 00	17 59	18 21	18 59		20 57	21 53	23 01
Albrighton	d	00 04	09 16	10 16			12 43		14 17		16 00	17 03	18 02		19 02		21 00	21 56	23 04
Codsall	d	00 09	09 21	10 21			12 49		14 22		16 05	17 08	18 07		19 07		21 05	22 01	23 09
Bilbrook	d	00 11	09 23	10 23			12 51		14 24		16 07	17 10	18 09		19 09		21 07	22 03	23 11
Wolverhampton 7	a	00 20	09 30	10 30	11 30	12 10	12 58	13 30	14 31	15 01	16 14	17 17	18 16	18 33	19 16	20 02	21 14	22 16	23 18
Coseley	a																		
Birmingham New Street 12	a		09 47	10 47	11 48		13 15	13 49	14 49	15 18	16 33	17 34	18 35	18 50	19 34	20 19	21 32	22 36	

Sundays

3 February to 23 March

		AW ◇	AW Bus	AW Bus	AW Bus	AW Bus	AW Bus	AW Bus	AW Bus	AW Bus	AW Bus	AW Bus	AW Bus	AW Bus	AW Bus	AW Bus	AW Bus
Shrewsbury	d	23p31	08 41	09 41	10 50	12 25	12 50	13 50	14 35	15 35	16 25	17 35	18 35	19 35	20 35	21 35	22 50
Wellington (Shropshire)	d	23p43	09 06	10 06	11 15	12 50	13 15	14 15	15 00	16 00	16 50	18 00	19 00	20 00	21 00	22 00	23 15
Oakengates	d	23p48	09 16	10 16	11 25	13 00		14 25		16 10	17 00	18 10	19 10		21 10	22 10	23 25
Telford Central	d	23p51	09 26	10 26	11 35	13 10	13 30	14 35	15 15	16 20	17 10	18 20	19 20	20 15	21 20	22 20	23 35
Shifnal	d	23p56	09 36	10 36		13 20		14 45		16 30	17 20	18 30	19 30		21 30	22 30	23 45
Cosford	d	00 01	09 46	10 46		13 30		14 55		16 40	17 30	18 40	19 40		21 40	22 40	23 55
Albrighton	d	00 04	09 51	10 51		13 35		15 00		16 45	17 35	18 45	19 45		21 45	22 45	00 01
Codsall	d	00 09	10 01	11 01		13 45		15 10		16 55	17 45	18 55	19 55		21 55	22 55	00 10
Bilbrook	d	00 11	10 06	11 06		13 50		15 15		17 00	17 50	19 00	20 00		22 00	23 00	00 15
Wolverhampton 7	a	00 20	10 26	11 26	12 10	14 10	14 05	15 35	15 50	17 20	18 10	19 20	20 20	20 50	22 20	23 20	00 35
Coseley	a																
Birmingham New Street 12	a																

For general notes see front of timetable
For details of catering facilities see Directory of Train Operators

A Until 27 January
B From Chester (Table 75)
C From Aberystwyth (Table 75)
D From Holyhead (Table 81)

Birmingham and Shrewsbury → Chester, Aberystwyth, Barmouth and Pwllheli

Network Diagram - see first page of Table 67

Miles	Miles	Miles			AW MX	AW	AW	AW	AW	AW	AW	AW	AW	AW	AW	AW	AW	AW	WS	AW	AW	AW		AW	AW
							◇			◇			◇	◇ A trolley	◇	◇	◇ trolley	◇ A trolley		◇	◇ trolley	◇ trolley		◇ A trolley	◇ trolley
—	—	—	London Euston 15 ⊖	d													06 36				07 40	08 40			09 40
—	—	—	London Marylebone 10 ⊖	d															06 45						
—	—	—	Banbury	d															07 59						
—	—	—	Birmingham International ✈	d												06 45	08 04		08 42		09 05	10 05			11 05
0	—	—	**Birmingham New Street 12**	d									06 33			07 17	08 33				09 33	10 33			11 33
—	—	—	Tame Bridge Parkway	d																					
12¾	—	—	**Wolverhampton 7**	d									06 48			07 33	08 48		09 26		09 48	10 48			11 48
22	—	—	Cosford	d												07 51			09 43						
28¼	—	—	Telford Central	d									07 04			07 59	09 04		09 52		10 04	11 04			12 04
32¼	—	—	Wellington (Shropshire)	d									07 10			08 05	09 10				10 10	11 10			12 10
42¾	—	—	**Shrewsbury**	a									07 22			08 22	09 22		10 10		10 25	11 22			12 25
—	—	—	Cardiff Central 7	d									05 10	05 10		05 35	07 20	07 20	07 50			09 20		09 20	09 50
—	—	—	Manchester Piccadilly 10	d												06 38	07 28					09 34			10 34
—	—	—	Crewe 10	d							04 54		05 55			07 27	08 08				09 27	10 17			11 26
—	—	0	**Shrewsbury**	d	23p31			05 20			06 10		07 28	07 30		08 28	09 28	09 30	10 12		10 26	11 28		11 30	12 26
—	—	17¾	Gobowen	d	23p51			05 39			06 29			07 49		08 47		09 49	10 31		10 46			11 49	12 46
—	—	20¾	Chirk	d	23p56			05 44			06 34			07 54		08 52		09 54	10 36		10 51			11 54	12 51
—	—	25	Ruabon	d	00 02			05 50			06 40			08 00		08 58		10 00	10 43		10 57			12 00	12 57
—	—	30	Wrexham General	d	00b17			05 57			06 47			08 07		09 05		10 07	10a49		11 03			12 07	13 03
—	—	42	**Chester**	a	00 35			06 16			07 09			08 28		09 27		10 28			11 21			12 28	13 26
62½	—	—	Welshpool	d									07 51				09 51					11 51			
76½	—	—	Newtown (Powys)	d									08 07				10 07					12 07			
82	—	—	Caersws	d									08 13				10 13					12 13			
103¾	—	—	**Machynlleth 4**	a									08 42				10 42					12 42			
—	0	—		d		04 35	05 30		06 30	06 49		08 10	08 45		09 05		10 45			11 00		12 45	12 56		
107¾	4	—	Dovey Junction 4	d		04 41	05c44		06 36	06 55		08 16	08 51		09 11		10 51			11 06		12 51	13 02		
116	—	—	Borth	d		04 52			06 47			08 27	09 02				11 02					13 02			
124¼	—	—	**Aberystwyth**	a		05 05			07 00			08 40	09 22				11 22					13 22			
—	9	—	Penhelig	d			05x52			07x04					09x20					11x15			13x11		
—	10	—	Aberdovey	d			05 56			07 07					09 23					11 18			13 14		
—	13½	—	Tywyn	d			06 02			07 15					09 30					11 26			13 22		
—	16	—	Tonfanau	d			06x06			07x19					09x34					11x30			13x26		
—	20	—	Llwyngwril	d			06x12			07x25					09x40					11x36			13x32		
—	22¾	—	Fairbourne	d			06 19			07 33					09 48					11 44			13 40		
—	23¾	—	Morfa Mawddach	d			06x21			07x35					09x50					11x46			13x42		
—	25½	—	**Barmouth**	a			06 30			07 40					09 56					11 52			13 48		
—	—	—		d			06 31			07 50					09 57					11 56			13 52		
—	26¾	—	Llanaber	d			06x35			07x53					10x00					11x59			13x55		
—	29¼	—	Talybont	d						07x57					10x04					12x03			13x59		
—	30¼	—	Dyffryn Ardudwy	d						07x59					10x06					12x05			14x01		
—	32½	—	Llanbedr	d						08x02					10x09					12x08			14x04		
—	33¼	—	Pensarn	d						08x04					10x11					12x10			14x06		
—	34	—	Llandanwg	d						08x05					10x12					12x11			14x07		
—	35¾	—	Harlech	d			06 51			08e32					10 21					12f24			14g30		
—	38½	—	Tygwyn	d						08x36					10x25					12x28			14x34		
—	39¼	—	Talsarnau	d						08x37					10x27					12x30			14x36		
—	40½	—	Llandecwyn	d						08x40					10x29					12x32			14x38		
—	41¼	—	Penrhyndeudraeth	d						08 43					10 32					12 35			14 41		
—	42½	—	Minffordd	d						08 46					10 36					12 39			14 45		
—	44½	—	Porthmadog	d			07 07			08 52					10 42					12 47			14 53		
—	49½	—	Criccieth	d						08 59					10 50					12 55			15 01		
—	54	—	Penychain	d			07x20			09x05					10x55					13x00			15x06		
—	55½	—	Abererch	d						09x08					10x58					13x03			15x09		
—	57½	—	**Pwllheli**	a			07 27			09 12					11 09					13 14			15 18		

For general notes see front of timetable
For details of catering facilities see Directory of Train Operators

A To Holyhead (Table 81)
b Arr. 0009
c Arr. 0536
e Arr. 0811
f Arr. 1217
g Arr. 1413

Birmingham and Shrewsbury → Chester, Aberystwyth, Barmouth and Pwllheli

Network Diagram - see first page of Table 67

		AW		AW	AW	AW		AW	AW	AW	AW	AW	AW	AW		AW	AW	AW	AW	AW	AW	AW	AW
												FO										FO	FX
										R							R						
		◇		◇	◇	◇		◇	◇		◇		◇	◇				◇	◇	◇			
				A				A			A			B			A		A				
		[trolley]		[trolley]	[trolley]	[trolley]		[trolley]	[trolley]	[trolley]	[trolley]		[trolley]	[trolley]			[trolley]		[trolley]	[trolley]			
London Euston 15 ⊖	d	10 40			11 40	12 40			13 40	14 40			15 40	16 40				17 30		18 40			
London Marylebone 10 ⊖	d																						
Banbury	d																						
Birmingham International ✈	d	12 05			13 05	14 05			15 05	16 05			17 05	18 05				19 05		20 05			
Birmingham New Street 12	d	12 33			13 33	14 33			15 33	16 33			17 33	18 33				19 33		20 33			
Tame Bridge Parkway	d																						
Wolverhampton 7	d	12 48			13 48	14 48			15 48	16 48			17 48	18 48				19 48		20 50			
Cosford	d																						
Telford Central	d	13 04			14 04	15 04			16 04	17 04			18 13	19 04				20 04		21 06			
Wellington (Shropshire)	d	13 10			14 10	15 10			16 10	17 10			18 19	19 10				20 10		21 12			
Shrewsbury	a	13 22			14 25	15 22			16 25	17 22			18 35	19 22				20 25		21 27			
Cardiff Central 7	d	11 20		11 20	11 50	13 20		13 20	13 50	15 20	15 20		15 50	17 20			17 20	17 50	19 34		20 10	20 53	20 53
Manchester Piccadilly 10	d	11 34			12 34	13 34			14 34	15 34			16 34	17 34				18 34	19 34		20 34	21 34	21 34
Crewe 10	d	12 18			13 26	14 18			15 26	16 18			17 27	18 18				19 26	20 18		21 18	21 18	22 18
Shrewsbury	d	13 28		13 30	14 26	15 28		15 30	16 26	17 28	17 30		18 36	19 28			19 30	20 26	21 38	21 47	22 26	23 31	23 31
Gobowen	d			13 49	14 46			15 49	16 46		17 49		18 55				19 49	20 47	21 57		22 46	23 51	23 51
Chirk	d			13 54	14 51			15 54	16 51		17 54		19 01				19 54	20 52	22 02		22 51	23 56	23 56
Ruabon	d			14 00	14 57			16 00	16 57		18 00		19 07				20 00	20 58	22 08		22 57	00 02	00 02
Wrexham General	d			14 07	15 03			16 07	17 03		18 07		19 13			19 38	20b13	21 04	22 15		23 06	00c15	00c17
Chester	a			14 28	15 22			16 28	17 22		18 25		19 34			19 55	20 31	21 23	22 32		23 26	00 35	00 35
Welshpool	d	13 51				15 51				17 51				19 51						22 10			
Newtown (Powys)	d	14 07				16 07				18 07				20 07						22 26			
Caersws	d	14 13				16 13				18 13				20 13						22 33			
Machynlleth 4	a	14 42				16 42				18 42				20 42						23 01			
	d	14 45	14 56			16 45	17 00			18 45		19 00		20 45	21 17					23 08			
Dovey Junction 4	d	14 51	15 02			16 51	17 06			18 51		19 06		20 51	21 23					23 15			
Borth	d	15 02				17 02				19 02				21 02						23 25			
Aberystwyth	a	15 22				17 22				19 22				21 22						23 43			
Penhelig	d		15x11				17x15					19x15			21x32								
Aberdovey	d		15 14				17 18					19 18			21 35								
Tywyn	d		15 22				17 26					19 26			21 41								
Tonfanau	d		15x26				17x30					19x30			21x45								
Llwyngwril	d		15x32				17x36					19x37			21x51								
Fairbourne	d		15 40				17 44					19 44			21 59								
Morfa Mawddach	d		15x42				17x46					19x47			22x01								
Barmouth	a		15 47				17 52					19 56			22 07								
	d		15 52				17 56								22 08								
Llanaber	d		15x55				17x59								22x11								
Talybont	d		15x58				18x03								22x14								
Dyffryn Ardudwy	d		16x00				18x05								22x16								
Llanbedr	d		16x04				18x08								22x20								
Pensarn	d		16x05				18x10								22x21								
Llandanwg	d		16x07				18x11								22x23								
Harlech	d		16e20				18f24								22 29								
Tygwyn	d		16x24				18x28								22x33								
Talsarnau	d		16x26				18x30								22x34								
Llandecwyn	d		16x28				18x32								22x37								
Penrhyndeudraeth	d		16 31				18 35								22 40								
Minffordd	d		16 35				18 39								22 43								
Porthmadog	d		16 42				18 46								22 48								
Criccieth	d		16 50				18 54								22 55								
Penychain	d		16x55				18x59								23x01								
Abererch	d		16x58				19x03								23x03								
Pwllheli	a		17 09				19 13								23 13								

For general notes see front of timetable
For details of catering facilities see Directory of Train Operators

A To Holyhead (Table 81)
B [trolley] to Aberystwyth
b Arr. 2006
c Arr. 0009
e Arr. 1612
f Arr. 1817

Table 75

until 22 March

Birmingham and Shrewsbury → Chester, Aberystwyth, Barmouth and Pwllheli

Network Diagram - see first page of Table 67

		AW	AW	AW	AW	AW	AW	AW	AW	AW	AW	AW	AW	AW	AW	AW	AW		AW	AW
				◇			◇		◇	◇	◇	◇	◇	◇	◇	◇	◇		◇	◇
										A				A					A	
										🛒			🛒	🛒		🛒	🛒		🛒	🛒
London Euston 15 ⊖	d												06 10			07 30	08 30			09 38
London Marylebone 10 ⊖	d																			
Banbury	d																			
Birmingham International ✈	d											06 50	07 57			08 57	09 57			10 57
Birmingham New Street 12	d								06 33			07 33	08 33			09 33	10 33			11 33
Tame Bridge Parkway	d																			
Wolverhampton 7	d								06 48			07 48	08 48			09 48	10 48			11 48
Cosford	d																			
Telford Central	d								07 04			08 04	09 04			10 04	11 04			12 04
Wellington (Shropshire)	d								07 10			08 10	09 10			10 10	11 10			12 10
Shrewsbury	a								07 22			08 25	09 22			10 25	11 22			12 25
Cardiff Central 7	d								05 10	05 10		05 35	07 20	07 20		07 50	09 20		09 20	09 50
Manchester Piccadilly 10	d											06 38	07 28			08 34	09 34			10 34
Crewe 10	d							04 54	05 55			07 27	08 08			09 27	10 17			11 26
Shrewsbury	d	23p31			05 20			06 10	07 28	07 30		08 28	09 28	09 30		10 26	11 28		11 30	12 26
Gobowen	d	23p51			05 39			06 29		07 49		08 47		09 49		10 46			11 49	12 46
Chirk	d	23p56			05 44			06 34		07 54		08 52		09 54		10 51			11 54	12 51
Ruabon	d	00 02			05 50			06 40		08 00		08 58		10 00		10 57			12 00	12 57
Wrexham General	d	00b15			05 57			06 47		08 07		09 05		10 07		11 03			12 07	13 03
Chester	a	00 35			06 16			07 09		08 28		09 27		10 28		11 27			12 25	13 26
Welshpool	d								07 51				09 51				11 51			
Newtown (Powys)	d								08 07				10 07				12 07			
Caersws	d								08 13				10 13				12 13			
Machynlleth 4	a								08 42				10 42				12 42			
	d		04 35	05 30		06 30	06 49		08 45		09 05		10 45		11 00		12 45	13 06		
Dovey Junction 4	d		04 41	05c44		06 36	06 55		08 51		09 11		10 51		11 06		12 51	13 02		
Borth	d		04 52			06 47			09 02				11 02				13 02			
Aberystwyth	a		05 05			07 00			09 22				11 22				13 22			
Penhelig	d			05x52			07x04				09x20				11x15			13x11		
Aberdovey	d			05 56			07 07				09 23				11 18			13 14		
Tywyn	d			06 02			07 15				09 30				11 26			13 22		
Tonfanau	d			06x06			07x19				09x34				11x30			13x26		
Llwyngwril	d			06x12			07x25				09x40				11x36			13x32		
Fairbourne	d			06 19			07 33				09 48				11 44			13 40		
Morfa Mawddach	d			06x21			07x35				09x50				11x46			13x42		
Barmouth	a			06 30			07 40				09 56				11 52			13 48		
	d			06 31			07 50				09 57				11 56			13 52		
Llanaber	d			06x35			07x53				10x00				11x59			13x55		
Talybont	d						07x57				10x04				12x03			13x59		
Dyffryn Ardudwy	d						07x59				10x06				12x05			14x01		
Llanbedr	d						08x02				10x09				12x08			14x04		
Pensarn	d						08x04				10x11				12x10			14x06		
Llandanwg	d						08x05				10x12				12x11			14x07		
Harlech	d			06 51			08e32				10 21				12f24			14g30		
Tygwyn	d						08x36				10x25				12x28			14x34		
Talsarnau	d						08x37				10x27				12x30			14x36		
Llandecwyn	d						08x40				10x29				12x32			14x38		
Penrhyndeudraeth	d						08 43				10 32				12 35			14 41		
Minffordd	d						08 46				10 36				12 39			14 45		
Porthmadog	d			07 07			08 52				10 42				12 47			14 53		
Criccieth	d						08 59				10 50				12 55			15 01		
Penychain	d			07x20			09x05				10x55				13x00			15x06		
Abererch	d						09x08				10x58				13x03			15x09		
Pwllheli	a			07 27			09 12				11 09				13 14			15 18		

For general notes see front of timetable
For details of catering facilities see Directory of Train Operators

- **A** To Holyhead (Table 81)
- **b** Arr. 0009
- **c** Arr. 0536
- **e** Arr. 0811
- **f** Arr. 1217
- **g** Arr. 1413

Table 75

Saturdays

until 22 March

Birmingham and Shrewsbury → Chester, Aberystwyth, Barmouth and Pwllheli

Network Diagram - see first page of Table 67

Station																									
		AW ◇ ⊼		AW ◇ A ⊼		AW ◇ ⊼	AW ◇ ⊼		AW ◇ A ⊼		AW ◇ ⊼	AW ◇ ⊼	AW ◇ A ⊼	AW ◇ ⊼		AW ◇ B ⊼		AW	AW ◇ A ⊼	AW ◇	AW ◇ ⊼	AW ◇ C ⊼	AW ◇	AW	
London Euston 15	⊖ d	10 38				11 38	12 38				13 38	14 38		15 38		16 38				17 38	18 38		18 57		
London Marylebone 10	⊖ d																								
Banbury	d																								
Birmingham International	✈ d	11 57				12 57	13 57				14 57	15 57		16 57		17 57				18 57	19 57		20 50		
Birmingham New Street 12	d	12 33				13 33	14 33				15 33	16 33		17 33		18 33				19 33	20 33		21 33		
Tame Bridge Parkway	d																								
Wolverhampton 7	🚌 d	12 48				13 48	14 48				15 48	16 48		17 48		18 48				19 48	20 48		21 48		
Cosford	d																								
Telford Central	d	13 04				14 04	15 04				16 04	17 04		18 04		19 04				20 04	21 04		22 04		
Wellington (Shropshire)	d	13 10				14 10	15 10				16 10	17 10		18 10		19 10				20 10	21 10		22 10		
Shrewsbury	a	13 22				14 25	15 22				16 25	17 22		18 25		19 22				20 25	21 22		22 25		
Cardiff Central 7	d	11 20		11 20		11 50	13 20		13 20		13 50	15 20	15 20	15 50		17 20			17 20	17 50	18 50	19 34	20 10	20 53	
Manchester Piccadilly 10	🚌 d	11 34				12 34	13 34				14 34	15 34		16 34		17 34				18 34	19 34		20 34	21 34	
Crewe 10	d	12 18				13 26	14 18				15 26	16 15		17 26		18 18				19 28	20 18		21 18	22 18	
Shrewsbury	d	13 28		13 30		14 26	15 28		15 30		16 26	17 28	17 30	18 26		19 28			19 30	20 26	21 28	21 38	22 26	23 31	
Gobowen	d			13 49		14 46			15 49		16 46		17 49	18 46					19 49	20 46		21 57	22 46	23 50	
Chirk	d			13 54		14 51			15 54		16 51		17 54	18 51					19 54	20 51		22 02	22 51	23 55	
Ruabon	d			14 00		14 57			16 00		16 57		18 00	18 57					20 00	20 57		22 08	22 57	00 01	
Wrexham General	d			14 07		15 03			16 07		17 03		18 07	19 03				19 46	20 07	21 03		22 15	23 06	00b12	
Chester	a			14 28		15 26			16 28		17 26		18 25	19 22				20 05	20 26	21 26		22 32	23 26	00 30	
Welshpool	d	13 51					15 51					17 51				19 51					21 51				
Newtown (Powys)	d	14 07					16 07					18 07				20 07					22 07				
Caersws	d	14 13					16 13					18 13				20 13					22 17				
Machynlleth 4	a	14 42					16 42					18 42				20 42					22 45				
	d	14 45	14 56				16 45	17 00				18 45				20 45	21 17				22 52				
Dovey Junction 4	d	14 51	15 02				16 51	17 06				18 51				20 51	21 23				22 59				
Borth	d	15 02					17 02					19 02				21 02					23 09				
Aberystwyth	a	15 22					17 22					19 22				21 22					23 30				
Penhelig	d		15x11					17x15									21x32								
Aberdovey	d		15 14					17 18									21 35								
Tywyn	d		15 22					17 26									21 41								
Tonfanau	d		15x26					17x30									21x45								
Llwyngwril	d		15x32					17x36									21x51								
Fairbourne	d		15 40					17 44									21 59								
Morfa Mawddach	d		15x42					17x46									22x01								
Barmouth	a		15 47					17 52									22 07								
	d		15 52					17 56									22 08								
Llanaber	d		15x55					17x59									22x11								
Talybont	d		15x58					18x03									22x14								
Dyffryn Ardudwy	d		16x00					18x05									22x16								
Llanbedr	d		16x04					18x08									22x20								
Pensarn	d		16x05					18x10									22x21								
Llandanwg	d		16x07					18x11									22x23								
Harlech	d		16c20					18e24									22 29								
Tygwyn	d		16x24					18x28									22x33								
Talsarnau	d		16x26					18x30									22x34								
Llandecwyn	d		16x28					18x32									22x37								
Penrhyndeudraeth	d		16 31					18 35									22 40								
Minffordd	d		16 35					18 39									22 43								
Porthmadog	d		16 42					18 46									22 48								
Criccieth	d		16 50					18 54									22 55								
Penychain	d		16x55					18x59									23x01								
Abererch	d		16x58					19x03									23x03								
Pwllheli	a		17 09					19 13									23 13								

For general notes see front of timetable
For details of catering facilities see Directory of Train Operators

A To Holyhead (Table 81)
B ⊼ to Aberystwyth
C To Llandudno Junction (Table 81)
b Arr. 0007
c Arr. 1612
e Arr. 1817

Table 75

from 29 March

Birmingham and Shrewsbury → Chester, Aberystwyth, Barmouth and Pwllheli

Network Diagram - see first page of Table 67

		AW	AW	AW ◇	AW	AW	AW ◇	AW	AW ◇	AW ◇ A	AW ◇	AW ◇	AW ◇ 🛒	AW A	AW ◇	AW ◇ 🛒	AW ◇ 🛒		AW A	AW ◇ 🛒
London Euston 15	⊖ d												06 10			07 30	08 30			09 38
London Marylebone 10	⊖ d																			
Banbury	d																			
Birmingham International	✈ d											06 50	07 57			08 57	09 57			10 57
Birmingham New Street 12	d								06 33			07 33	08 33			09 33	10 33			11 33
Tame Bridge Parkway	d																			
Wolverhampton 7	🚌 d								06 48			07 48	08 48			09 48	10 48			11 48
Cosford	d																			
Telford Central	d								07 04			08 04	09 04			10 04	11 04			12 04
Wellington (Shropshire)	d								07 10			08 10	09 10			10 10	11 10			12 10
Shrewsbury	a								07 22			08 25	09 22			10 25	11 22			12 25
Cardiff Central 7	d																			
Manchester Piccadilly 10	🚌 d											06 38	07 28			08 34	09 34			10 34
Crewe 10	d							04 54	05 55			07 27	08 08			09 27	10 17			11 26
Shrewsbury	d	23p31			05 20			06 10	07 28	07 30		08 28	09 28	09 30		10 26	11 28		11 30	12 26
Gobowen	d	23p51			05 39			06 29		07 49		08 47		09 49		10 46			11 49	12 46
Chirk	d	23p56			05 44			06 34		07 54		08 52		09 54		10 51			11 54	12 51
Ruabon	d	00 02			05 50			06 40		08 00		08 58		10 00		10 57			12 00	12 57
Wrexham General	d	00b15			05 57			06 47		08 07		09 05		10 07		11 03			12 07	13 03
Chester	a	00 35			06 16			07 09		08 28		09 27		10 28		11 27			12 25	13 26
Welshpool	d								07 51				09 51				11 51			
Newtown (Powys)	d								08 07				10 07				12 07			
Caersws	d								08 13				10 13				12 13			
Machynlleth 4	a								08 42				10 42				12 42			
	d		04 35	05 30		06 30	06 49		08 45		09 05		10 45		11 00		12 45	12 56		
Dovey Junction 4	d		04 41	05c44		06 36	06 55		08 51		09 11		10 51		11 06		12 51	13 02		
Borth	d		04 52			06 47			09 02				11 02				13 02			
Aberystwyth	a		05 05			07 00			09 22				11 22				13 22			
Penhelig	d			05x52			07x04				09x20				11x15			13x11		
Aberdovey	d			05 56			07 07				09 23				11 18			13 14		
Tywyn	d			06 02			07 15				09 30				11 26			13 22		
Tonfanau	d			06x06			07x19				09x34				11x30			13x26		
Llwyngwril	d			06x12			07x25				09x40				11x36			13x32		
Fairbourne	d			06 19			07 33				09 48				11 44			13 40		
Morfa Mawddach	d			06x21			07x35				09x50				11x46			13x42		
Barmouth	a			06 30			07 40				09 56				11 52			13 48		
	d			06 31			07 50				09 57				11 56			13 52		
Llanaber	d			06x35			07x53				10x00				11x59			13x55		
Talybont	d						07x57				10x04				12x03			13x59		
Dyffryn Ardudwy	d						07x59				10x06				12x05			14x01		
Llanbedr	d						08x02				10x09				12x08			14x04		
Pensarn	d						08x04				10x11				12x10			14x06		
Llandanwg	d						08x05				10x12				12x11			14x07		
Harlech	d			06 51			08e32				10 21				12f24			14g30		
Tygwyn	d						08x36				10x25				12x28			14x34		
Talsarnau	d						08x37				10x27				12x30			14x36		
Llandecwyn	d						08x40				10x29				12x32			14x38		
Penrhyndeudraeth	d						08 43				10 32				12 35			14 41		
Minffordd	d						08 46				10 36				12 39			14 45		
Porthmadog	d			07 07			08 52				10 42				12 47			14 53		
Criccieth	d						08 59				10 50				12 55			15 01		
Penychain	d			07x20			09x05				10x55				13x00			15x06		
Abererch	d						09x08				10x58				13x03			15x09		
Pwllheli	a			07 27			09 12				11 09				13 14			15 18		

For general notes see front of timetable
For details of catering facilities see Directory of Train Operators

A From Hereford (Table 131) to Holyhead (Table 81)
b Arr. 0009
c Arr. 0536
e Arr. 0811
f Arr. 1217
g Arr. 1413

Table 75

from 29 March

Birmingham and Shrewsbury → Chester, Aberystwyth, Barmouth and Pwllheli

Network Diagram - see first page of Table 67

		AW		AW	AW	AW		AW	AW	AW R	AW	AW	AW		AW	AW	AW	AW	AW	AW	AW
		◇			◇	◇			◇			◇	◇				◇	◇		◇	
				A				A			A		B			A			C		
		⌶			⌶	⌶			⌶	⌶		⌶	⌶					⌶			
London Euston 15	⊖ d	10 38			11 38	12 38			13 38	14 38		15 38	16 38				17 38	18 38		19 10	
London Marylebone 10	⊖ d																				
Banbury	d																				
Birmingham International	✈ d	11 57			12 57	13 57			14 57	15 57		16 57	17 57				18 57	19 57		20 50	
Birmingham New Street 12	d	12 33			13 33	14 33			15 33	16 33		17 33	18 33				19 33	20 33		21 33	
Tame Bridge Parkway	d																				
Wolverhampton 7	⛴ d	12 48			13 48	14 48			15 48	16 48		17 48	18 48				19 48	20 48		21 48	
Cosford	d																				
Telford Central	d	13 04			14 04	15 04			16 04	17 04		18 04	19 04				20 04	21 04		22 04	
Wellington (Shropshire)	d	13 10			14 10	15 10			16 10	17 10		18 10	19 10				20 10	21 10		22 10	
Shrewsbury	a	13 22			14 25	15 22			16 25	17 22		18 25	19 22				20 25	21 22		22 25	
Cardiff Central 7	d	08 09																			
Manchester Piccadilly 10	⛴ d	11 34			12 34	13 34			14 34	15 34		16 34	17 34				18 34	19 34		20 34	21 34
Crewe 10	d	12 18			13 26	14 18			15 26	16 15		17 26	18 18				19 28	20 18		21 18	22 18
Shrewsbury	d	13 28		13 30	14 26	15 28		15 30	16 26	17 28	17 30	18 26	19 28			19 30	20 26	21 28	21 38	22 26	23 31
Gobowen	d			13 49	14 46			15 49	16 46		17 49	18 46				19 49	20 46		21 57	22 46	23 50
Chirk	d			13 54	14 51			15 54	16 51		17 54	18 51				19 54	20 51		22 02	22 51	23 55
Ruabon	d			14 00	14 57			16 00	16 57		18 00	18 57				20 00	20 57		22 08	22 57	00 01
Wrexham General	d			14 07	15 03			16 07	17 03		18 07	19 03			19 46	20 07	21 03		22 15	23b06	00c12
Chester	a			14 28	15 26			16 28	17 26		18 25	19 22			20 05	20 26	21 26		22 32	23 26	00 30
Welshpool	d	13 51				15 51				17 51			19 51					21 51			
Newtown (Powys)	d	14 07				16 07				18 07			20 07					22 07			
Caersws	d	14 13				16 13				18 13			20 13					22 17			
Machynlleth 4	a	14 42				16 42				18 42			20 42					22 45			
	d	14 45	14 56			16 45	17 00			18 45			20 45	21 17				22 52			
Dovey Junction 4	d	14 51	15 02			16 51	17 06			18 51			20 51	21 23				22 59			
Borth	d	15 02				17 02				19 02			21 02					23 09			
Aberystwyth	a	15 22				17 22				19 22			21 22					23 30			
Penhelig	d		15x11				17x15							21x32							
Aberdovey	d		15 14				17 18							21 35							
Tywyn	d		15 22				17 26							21 41							
Tonfanau	d		15x26				17x30							21x45							
Llwyngwril	d		15x32				17x36							21x51							
Fairbourne	d		15 40				17 44							21 59							
Morfa Mawddach	d		15x42				17x46							22x01							
Barmouth	a		15 47				17 52							22 07							
	d		15 52				17 56							22 08							
Llanaber	d		15x55				17x59							22x11							
Talybont	d		15x58				18x03							22x14							
Dyffryn Ardudwy	d		16x00				18x05							22x16							
Llanbedr	d		16x04				18x08							22x20							
Pensarn	d		16x05				18x10							22x21							
Llandanwg	d		16x07				18x11							22x23							
Harlech	d		16e20				18f24							22 29							
Tygwyn	d		16x24				18x28							22x33							
Talsarnau	d		16x26				18x30							22x34							
Llandecwyn	d		16x28				18x32							22x37							
Penrhyndeudraeth	d		16 31				18 35							22 40							
Minffordd	d		16 35				18 39							22 43							
Porthmadog	d		16 42				18 46							22 48							
Criccieth	d		16 50				18 54							22 55							
Penychain	d		16x55				18x59							23x01							
Abererch	d		16x58				19x03							23x03							
Pwllheli	a		17 09				19 13							23 13							

For general notes see front of timetable
For details of catering facilities see Directory of Train Operators

- **A** From Hereford (Table 131) to Holyhead (Table 81)
- **B** ⌶ to Aberystwyth
- **C** From Hereford (Table 131) to Llandudno Junction (Table 81)
- **b** Arr. 2303
- **c** Arr. 0007
- **e** Arr. 1612
- **f** Arr. 1817

Table 75

until 27 January

Birmingham and Shrewsbury → Chester, Aberystwyth, Barmouth and Pwllheli

Network Diagram - see first page of Table 67

	AW	AW	AW		AW	WS	AW		AW	AW	AW		AW		AW		WS	AW	AW	AW	WS	AW		
																			R					
					◇				◇	◇	◇		◇		◇			◇		◇				
									A										A					
									[trolley]	[trolley]			[trolley]					[trolley]	[trolley]	[trolley]				
London Euston 15 ⊖ d					08 40					10 36	11 36		13 50		14 53		15b27	16 53		17 53	18b27			
London Marylebone 10 ⊖ d						09 11											15 17				18 17			
Banbury d						10 33											16 37				19 36			
Birmingham International ✈ d					10 46					12 46	13 46		15 36		16 26		16 55	18 26		19 26	19 55			
Birmingham New Street 12 d					11 27	11 33				13 27	14 27		16 07		16 57		17 26	18 57		19 57	20 26			
Tame Bridge Parkway d																								
Wolverhampton 7 d					11 44	11 52				13 48	14 48		16 26		17 14		17 54	19 14		20 16	20 59			
Cosford d					12 00												18 05	19 30			21 10			
Telford Central d					12 11	12 18				14 04	15 04		16 42		17 30		18 13	19 41		20 32	21 18			
Wellington (Shropshire) d					12 19	12 26				14 11	15 12		16 50		17 38		18 20	19 47		20 39	21 25			
Shrewsbury a					12 32	12 39				14 29	15 25		17 03		17 51		18 36	20 02		20 52	21 38			
Cardiff Central 7 d									11 35		12 35		14 35		15 35			16 35	18 35					
Manchester Piccadilly 10 d										12 33			15 49				16 37	18 37						
Crewe 10 d					10 50					13 23			16 32				17 22	19 20						
Shrewsbury d	23p31	10 16			12 34	12 45			13 52	14 40	15 36		17 18		17 53		18 37	20 14	20 46	21 00	21 39			
Gobowen d	23p50	10 35			12 53	13c11			14 12		15 57				18 12		18 57	20 33			21 59			
Chirk d	23p55	10 40			12 58	13 16			14 17		16 02				18 17		19 02	20 38			22 04			
Ruabon d	00 01	10 46			13 04	13 22			14 24		16 08				18 23		19 08	20 44			22 10			
Wrexham General d	00e12	10 53			13 11	13a28			14f41		16 14				18 30		19a14	20 51	21 16		22a16	22 35		
Chester a	00 30	11 11			13 29				14 59		16 33				18 48			21 09	21 34			22 54		
Welshpool d										15 02			17 43							21 26				
Newtown (Powys) d										15 18			17 59							21 42				
Caersws d										15 25			18 06							21 49				
Machynlleth 4 a										15 53			18 34							22 16				
d			11 30				14 30			16 10			18 36	18 40						22 19				
Dovey Junction 4 d			11 36				14 36			16 16			18 43	18 47						22 25				
Borth d			11 47				14 47			16 27			18 54							22 36				
Aberystwyth a			12 00				15 00			16 40			19 07							22 49				
Penhelig d														18x56										
Aberdovey d														18 59										
Tywyn d														19 06										
Tonfanau d														19x10										
Llwyngwril d														19x16										
Fairbourne d														19 24										
Morfa Mawddach d														19x26										
Barmouth a														19 33										
d														19 33										
Llanaber d														19x37										
Talybont d														19x41										
Dyffryn Ardudwy d														19x43										
Llanbedr d														19x47										
Pensarn d														19x49										
Llandanwg d														19x51										
Harlech d														19 57										
Tygwyn d														20x01										
Talsarnau d														20x03										
Llandecwyn d														20x05										
Penrhyndeudraeth d														20 08										
Minffordd d														20 12										
Porthmadog d														20 16										
Criccieth d														20 24										
Penychain d														20x30										
Abererch d														20x33										
Pwllheli a														20 42										

For general notes see front of timetable
For details of catering facilities see Directory of Train Operators

A To Holyhead (Table 81)
b Change at Birmingham New Street
c Arr. 1304
e Arr. 0007
f Arr. 1430

Table 75

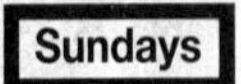

Sundays

3 February to 23 March

Birmingham and Shrewsbury → Chester, Aberystwyth, Barmouth and Pwllheli

Network Diagram - see first page of Table 67

		AW	AW	AW	AW	AW	AW ◇ A ✠	AW	AW	AW	AW ◇	AW	AW	AW R A ✠	AW	AW
London Euston 15 ⊖	d															
London Marylebone 10 ⊖	d															
Banbury	d															
Birmingham International ✈	d															
Birmingham New Street 12	d															
Tame Bridge Parkway	d															
Wolverhampton 7	d															
Cosford	d															
Telford Central	d															
Wellington (Shropshire)	d															
Shrewsbury	a															
Cardiff Central 7	d						11 35		12 35	14 35		15 35	16 35	18 35		
Manchester Piccadilly 10	d							12 33		15 49			18 37			
Crewe 10	d				10 50			13 23		16 32			19 20			
Shrewsbury	d	23p31	10 16		12 34		13 52	14 40	15 36	17 18		17 53	20 14	20 46	21 00	
Gobowen	d	23p50	10 35		12 53		14 12		15 55			18 12	20 33			
Chirk	d	23p55	10 40		12 58		14 17		16 00			18 17	20 38			
Ruabon	d	00 01	10 46		13 04		14 24		16 06			18 23	20 44			
Wrexham General	d	00b12	10 53		13 11		14c41		16 13			18 30	20 51	21 16		22 35
Chester	a	00 30	11 11		13 29		14 59		16 33			18 48	21 09	21 34		22 54
Welshpool	d							15 02		17 43					21 26	
Newtown (Powys)	d							15 18		17 59					21 42	
Caersws	d							15 25		18 06					21 49	
Machynlleth 4	a							15 53		18 34					22 16	
	d			11 30		14 30		16 10		18 36	18 40				22 19	
Dovey Junction 4	d			11 36		14 36		16 16		18 43	18 47				22 25	
Borth	d			11 47		14 47		16 27		18 54					22 36	
Aberystwyth	a			12 00		15 00		16 40		19 11					22 53	
Penhelig	d										18x56					
Aberdovey	d										18 59					
Tywyn	d										19 06					
Tonfanau	d										19x10					
Llwyngwril	d										19x16					
Fairbourne	d										19 24					
Morfa Mawddach	d										19x26					
Barmouth	a										19 33					
	d										19 33					
Llanaber	d										19x37					
Talybont	d										19x41					
Dyffryn Ardudwy	d										19x43					
Llanbedr	d										19x47					
Pensarn	d										19x49					
Llandanwg	d										19x51					
Harlech	d										19 57					
Tygwyn	d										20x01					
Talsarnau	d										20x03					
Llandecwyn	d										20x05					
Penrhyndeudraeth	d										20 08					
Minffordd	d										20 12					
Porthmadog	d										20 16					
Criccieth	d										20 24					
Penychain	d										20x30					
Abererch	d										20x33					
Pwllheli	a										20 42					

For general notes see front of timetable
For details of catering facilities see Directory of Train Operators

A To Holyhead (Table 81)
b Arr. 0007
c Arr. 1430

Table 75

Sundays
from 30 March

Birmingham and Shrewsbury → Chester, Aberystwyth, Barmouth and Pwllheli

Network Diagram - see first page of Table 67

		AW	AW	AW	AW	AW	AW	AW	AW	AW		AW	AW	AW	AW	AW
														R		
					◇			◇	◇	◇		◇	◇		◇	
							A							A		
								🛒		🛒			🛒	🛒	🛒	
London Euston 15	⊖ d				08 40			10 36	11 36	13 50		14 53	16 53		17 53	
London Marylebone 10	⊖ d															
Banbury	d															
Birmingham International	✈ d				10 46			12 46	13 46	15 36		16 26	18 26		19 26	
Birmingham New Street 12	d				11 27			13 27	14 27	16 07		16 57	18 57		19 57	
Tame Bridge Parkway	d															
Wolverhampton 7	🚌 d				11 44			13 48	14 48	16 26		17 14	19 14		20 16	
Cosford	d				12 00								19 30			
Telford Central	d				12 11			14 04	15 04	16 42		17 30	19 41		20 32	
Wellington (Shropshire)	d				12 19			14 11	15 12	16 50		17 38	19 47		20 39	
Shrewsbury	a				12 32			14 29	15 25	17 03		17 51	20 02		20 52	
Cardiff Central 7	d															
Manchester Piccadilly 10	🚌 d							12 33		15 40			18 37			
Crewe 10	d				10 50			13 23		16 32			19 20			
Shrewsbury	d	23p31	10 16		12 34		13 52	14 40	15 36	17 18		17 53	20 14	20 46	21 00	
Gobowen	d	23p50	10 35		12 53		14 12		15 57			18 12	20 33			
Chirk	d	23p55	10 40		12 58		14 17		16 02			18 17	20 38			
Ruabon	d	00 01	10 46		13 04		14 24		16 08			18 23	20 44			
Wrexham General	d	00b12	10 53		13 11		14c41		16 14			18 30	20 51	21 16		22 35
Chester	a	00 30	11 11		13 29		14 59		16 33			18 48	21 09	21 34		22 54
Welshpool	d							15 02		17 43					21 26	
Newtown (Powys)	d							15 18		17 59					21 42	
Caersws	d							15 25		18 06					21 49	
Machynlleth 4	a							15 53		18 34					22 16	
	d			11 30		14 30		16 10		18 36	18 40				22 19	
Dovey Junction 4	d			11 36		14 36		16 16		18 43	18 47				22 25	
Borth	d			11 47		14 47		16 27		18 54					22 36	
Aberystwyth	a			12 00		15 00		16 40		19 07					22 49	
Penhelig	d										18x56					
Aberdovey	d										18 59					
Tywyn	d										19 06					
Tonfanau	d										19x10					
Llwyngwril	d										19x16					
Fairbourne	d										19 24					
Morfa Mawddach	d										19x26					
Barmouth	a										19 33					
	d										19 33					
Llanaber	d										19x37					
Talybont	d										19x41					
Dyffryn Ardudwy	d										19x43					
Llanbedr	d										19x47					
Pensarn	d										19x49					
Llandanwg	d										19x51					
Harlech	d										19 57					
Tygwyn	d										20x01					
Talsarnau	d										20x03					
Llandecwyn	d										20x05					
Penrhyndeudraeth	d										20 08					
Minffordd	d										20 12					
Porthmadog	d										20 16					
Criccieth	d										20 24					
Penychain	d										20x30					
Abererch	d										20x33					
Pwllheli	a										20 42					

For general notes see front of timetable
For details of catering facilities see Directory of Train Operators

A To Holyhead (Table 81)
b Arr. 0007
c Arr. 1430

Pwllheli, Barmouth, Aberystwyth and Chester → Shrewsbury and Birmingham

Network Diagram - see first page of Table 67

Miles	Miles	Miles			AW MX	AW	AW	AW	AW	AW	AW	AW	AW	AW	AW	AW	AW	AW	AW	AW	AW	AW	AW
						◇		◇	◇	◇		◇	◇	◇	◇	◇	◇	◇	◇	◇	◇	◇	◇
									A			A				A				A			
								🛒	🛒	🛒		🛒	🛒		🛒	🛒	🛒	🛒	🛒	🛒	🛒	🛒	🛒
—	0	—	**Pwllheli**	d										06 10				07 34			09 36		
—	1¾	—	Abererch	d										06x14							09x40		
—	3¼	—	Penychain	d										06x16				07x40			09x42		
—	7¾	—	Criccieth	d										06 23				07 46			09 49		
—	12¾	—	Porthmadog	d										06 32				07 55			09 58		
—	15	—	Minffordd	d										06 36				07 59			10 02		
—	16¼	—	Penrhyndeudraeth	d										06 39				08 03			10 05		
—	17	—	Llandecwyn	d										06x42							10x08		
—	18¼	—	Talsarnau	d										06x44				08x07			10x10		
—	19	—	Tygwyn	d										06x46							10x12		
—	21½	—	Harlech	d										07b20				08c32			10e22		
—	23½	—	Llandanwg	d										07x25				08x37			10x27		
—	24¼	—	Pensarn	d										07x26				08x38			10x28		
—	25	—	Llanbedr	d										07x28				08x40			10x30		
—	27	—	Dyffryn Ardudwy	d										07x32				08x44			10x34		
—	28¼	—	Talybont	d										07x34				08x46			10x36		
—	30½	—	Llanaber	d										07x37				08x49			10x39		
—	32	—	**Barmouth**	a										07 41				08 53			10 43		
—	—	—		d							06 46			07 49				08 59			10 49		
—	33¾	—	Morfa Mawddach	d							06x50			07x54				09x04			10x54		
—	34¾	—	Fairbourne	d							06 53			07 56				09x06			10 56		
—	37¼	—	Llwyngwril	d							07x00			08x03				09x13			11x03		
—	41½	—	Tonfanau	d							07x06			08x09				09x19			11x09		
—	44¼	—	Tywyn	d							07f16			08 15				09g31			11h27		
—	47½	—	Aberdovey	d							07 22			08 21				09 37			11 33		
—	48½	—	Penhelig	d							07x24			08x24				09x40			11x35		
0	—	—	**Aberystwyth**	d	23p53			05 12					07 27				09 27	09 27				11 27	
8¼	—	—	Borth	d	00 05			05 25					07 39				09 39	09 39				11 39	
16½	53½	—	Dovey Junction 4	d	00 16			05 37			07 35		07 50	08 35			09 50	09 51			11 47	11 50	
20½	57½	—	**Machynlleth 4**	a	00 26			05 44			07 44		07 59	08 44			09 59	10 00			11 57	11 59	
—	—	—		d				05 45					08 02				10 02				12 02		
42¼	—	—	Caersws	d				06 17					08 33				10 33				12 33		
47¾	—	—	Newtown (Powys)	d				06 24					08 40				10 40				12 40		
61¾	—	—	Welshpool	d				06 39					08 55				10 55				12 55		
—	—	0	**Chester**	d		05 07	05 37		06 12	07 28		08 20			09 28	10 20			11 28	12 20			13 28
—	—	12	Wrexham General	d		05 24	05a57		06 28	07 44		08 37			09 44	10 37			11 44	12 37			13 44
—	—	17	Ruabon	d		05 30			06 35	07 51		08 44			09 51	10 43			11 51	12 43			13 51
—	—	21¼	Chirk	d		05 36			06 41	07 57		08 50			09 57	10 49			11 57	12 49			13 57
—	—	24¼	Gobowen	d		05 42			06 46	08 02		08 55			10 02	10 55			12 02	12 55			14 02
81½	—	42	**Shrewsbury**	a		06 07		07 05	07 07	08 22		09 16	09 21		10 22	11 15	11 21		12 22	13 15	13 21		14 22
—	—	—	Crewe 10	a		*07 05*			*08 25*	*09 25*			*10 25*		*11 25*								*15 24*
—	—	—	Manchester Piccadilly 10	⇌ a		*08 10*			*09 13*	*10 13*			*11 13*		*12 13*				*14 13*		*15 13*		*16 13*
—	—	—	Cardiff Central 7	a		08 29			09 18	*10 52*		11 20	*11 53*		*12 53*	13 21				15 20	*15 53*		*16 53*
—	—	—	**Shrewsbury**	d				07 12		08 22			09 22		10 22		11 22		12 22		13 22		14 22
92	—	—	Wellington (Shropshire)	d				07 22		08 35			09 35		10 35		11 35		12 35		13 35		14 35
96	—	—	Telford Central	d				07 29		08 41			09 41		10 41		11 41		12 41		13 41		14 41
122¾	—	—	Cosford	d				07 39															
111½	—	—	**Wolverhampton 7**	⇌ a				07 58		08 58			09 58		10 58		11 58		12 58		13 58		14 58
—	—	—	Tame Bridge Parkway	d																			
124¾	—	—	**Birmingham New Street 12**	a				08 18		09 18			10 18		11 18		12 18		13 18		14 18		15 18
—	—	—	Birmingham International	✈ a				*08 39*		*09 39*			*10 39*		*11 39*						*14 39*		*15 39*
—	—	—	Banbury	a																			
—	—	—	London Marylebone 10	⊖ a																			
—	—	—	London Euston 15	⊖ a				*10 03*		*11 00*			*12 00*		*13 00*						*16 00*		*17 00*

For general notes see front of timetable
For details of catering facilities see Directory of Train Operators

- **A** From Holyhead (Table 81)
- **b** Arr. 0650
- **c** Arr. 0813
- **e** Arr. 1016
- **f** Arr. 0710
- **g** Arr. 0925
- **h** Arr. 1114

Pwllheli, Barmouth, Aberystwyth and Chester → Shrewsbury and Birmingham

Network Diagram - see first page of Table 67

		AW	AW	AW	AW	AW	AW	AW	AW	AW		AW	AW	AW	AW	AW	AW	AW	AW	AW	AW	AW	AW
																						FO	
		◇ A 🍴	◇ 🍴	◇ 🍴	◇ 🍴	◇ A 🍴	◇ 🍴	◇ 🍴	◇ 🍴	◇ A 🍴		◇ 🍴	◇ 🍴				◇ A 🍴			◇	◇ A		
Pwllheli	d		11 32				13 32					15 32			17 32					20 00			
Abererch	d		11x36				13x36					15x36			17x36					20x04			
Penychain	d		11x38				13x38					15x38			17x38					20x06			
Criccieth	d		11 45				13 45					15 45			17 45					20 13			
Porthmadog	d		11 56				13 56					15 56			17 56					20 23			
Minffordd	d		12 00				14 00					16 00			18 00					20 27			
Penrhyndeudraeth	d		12 03				14 03					16 03			18 03					20 30			
Llandecwyn	d		12x06				14x06					16x06			18x06					20x33			
Talsarnau	d		12x08				14x08					16x08			18x08					20x35			
Tygwyn	d		12x10				14x10					16x11			18x10					20x37			
Harlech	d		12b25				14c30					16e20			18f25					20g46			
Llandanwg	d		12x30				14x35					16x25			18x30					20x51			
Pensarn	d		12x31				14x36					16x26			18x31					20x52			
Llanbedr	d		12x33				14x38					16x28			18x33					20x54			
Dyffryn Ardudwy	d		12x37				14x42					16x32			18x37					20x58			
Talybont	d		12x39				14x44					16x34			18x39					21x00			
Llanaber	d		12x42				14x47					16x37			18x42					21x03			
Barmouth	a		12 46				14 51					16 41			18 46					21 07			
	d		12 49				14 52					16 50			18 49					21 14		22 12	
Morfa Mawddach	d		12x54				14x57					16x55			18x54					21x19		22x17	
Fairbourne	d		12 56				14 59					16 57			18 56					21 21		22 19	
Llwyngwril	d		13x03				15x06					17x04			19x03					21x28		22x27	
Tonfanau	d		13x09				15x12					17x10			19x09					21x34		22x33	
Tywyn	d		13h23				15j23					17k27			19m26					21n46		22 38	
Aberdovey	d		13 29				15 29					17 33			19 32					21 52		22 44	
Penhelig	d		13x32				15x32					17x36			19x35					21x55		22x46	
Aberystwyth	d			13 27				15 27					17 27			19 27			21 36				23 53
Borth	d			13 39				15 39					17 39			19 39			21 48				00 05
Dovey Junction 4	d		13 41	13 50			15 41	15 50				17 46	17 50		19 46	19 50			21 59	22 07		22 58	00 16
Machynlleth 4	a		13 52	13 59			15 48	15 59				17 57	17 59		19 57	19 59			22 11	22 16		23 04	00 26
	d		14 02				16 02					18 02				20 02							
Caersws	d		14 33				16 33					18 33				20 33							
Newtown (Powys)	d		14 40				16 40					18 40				20 40							
Welshpool	d		14 55				16 55					18 55				20 55							
Chester	d	14 20			15 28	16 20			17 28	18 20				19 56			20 28	21 28			22 31		
Wrexham General	d	14 37			15 44	16 36			17 44	18 36				20 12			20 44	21 44			22 47		
Ruabon	d	14 43			15 51	16 43			17 51	18 43				20 19			20 51	21 51			22 54		
Chirk	d	14 49			15 57	16 49			17 57	18 49				20 25			20 57	21 57			23 00		
Gobowen	d	14 55			16 02	16 54			18 02	18 54				20 30			21 02	22 02			23 05		
Shrewsbury	a	15 15	15 21		16 22	17 15	17 21		18 22	19 15		19 21		20 55		21 21	21 23	22 22			23 26		
Crewe 10	a		*16 25*		*17 26*		*18 24*		*19 25*			*20 26*					*23 03*	*23 46*					
Manchester Piccadilly 10 🚢	a		*17 11*		*18 12*		*19 13*		*20 18*			*21 13*					*23 49*						
Cardiff Central 7	a	17 15	*17 54*		*19 01*	19 24	*19 54*		*21 01*	21 19		*21 57*					*00 17*	*01q22*					
Shrewsbury	d		15 22		16 22		17 22		18 22			19 22					21 26	22 22					
Wellington (Shropshire)	d		15 35		16 35		17 35		18 35			19 35					21 39	22 35					
Telford Central	d		15 41		16 41		17 41		18 41			19 41					21 45	22 41					
Cosford	d																						
Wolverhampton 7 🚢	a		15 58		16 58		17 58		18 58			19 58					22 02	22 58					
Tame Bridge Parkway	d																						
Birmingham New Street 12	a		16 18		17 18		18 18		19 18			20 18					22 18	23 18					
Birmingham International ✈	a		*16 39*		*17 39*		*18 39*		*19 39*			*20 39*					*22 52*	*00r21*					
Banbury	a																						
London Marylebone 10 ⊖	a																						
London Euston 15 ⊖	a		*18 00*		*19 03*		*20 00*		*21 04*			*22 04*					*01 02*						

For general notes see front of timetable
For details of catering facilities see Directory of Train Operators

A From Holyhead (Table 81)
b Arr. 1214
c Arr. 1414
e Arr. 1615
f Arr. 1814
g Arr. 2041
h Arr. 1316
j Arr. 1517
k Arr. 1715
m Arr. 1914
n Arr. 2139
q Saturday mornings arr. 0114
r Saturday mornings arr. 0022

Table 75

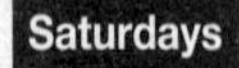

until 22 March

Pwllheli, Barmouth, Aberystwyth and Chester → Shrewsbury and Birmingham

Network Diagram - see first page of Table 67

		AW	AW	AW	AW ◇		AW ◇	AW ◇	AW	AW ◇		AW ◇	AW ◇	AW ◇	AW ◇		AW ◇	AW ◇	AW ◇	AW ◇		AW ◇	AW ◇	AW ◇	AW ◇
Pwllheli	d												06 10					07 34				09 36			
Abererch	d												06x14									09x40			
Penychain	d												06x16					07x40				09x42			
Criccieth	d												06 23					07 46				09 49			
Porthmadog	d												06 32					07 55				09 58			
Minffordd	d												06 36					07 59				10 02			
Penrhyndeudraeth	d												06 39					08 03				10 05			
Llandecwyn	d												06x42									10x08			
Talsarnau	d												06x44					08x07				10x10			
Tygwyn	d												06x46									10x12			
Harlech	d												07 20					08b32				10 22			
Llandanwg	d												07x25					08x37				10x27			
Pensarn	d												07x26					08x38				10x28			
Llanbedr	d												07x28					08x40				10x30			
Dyffryn Ardudwy	d												07x32					08x44				10x34			
Talybont	d												07x34					08x46				10x36			
Llanaber	d												07x37					08x49				10x39			
Barmouth	a												07 41					08 53				10 43			
	d								06 46				07 49					08 59				10 49			
Morfa Mawddach	d								06x50				07x54					09x04				10x54			
Fairbourne	d								06 53				07 56					09 06				10 56			
Llwyngwril	d								07x00				08x03					09x13				11x03			
Tonfanau	d								07x06				08x09					09x19				11x09			
Tywyn	d								07 16				08 15					09c31				11 27			
Aberdovey	d								07 22				08 21					09 37				11 33			
Penhelig	d								07x24				08x24					09x40				11x35			
Aberystwyth	d	23p53			05 12							07 27					09 27						11 27		
Borth	d	00 05			05 25							07 39					09 39						11 39		
Dovey Junction 4	d	00 16			05 37				07 35			07 50	08 35				09 50	09 51				11 47	11 50		
Machynlleth 4	a	00 26			05 44				07 44			07 59	08 44				09 59	10 00				11 57	11 59		
	d				05 45							08 02					10 02					12 02			
Caersws	d				06 17							08 33					10 33					12 33			
Newtown (Powys)	d				06 24							08 40					10 40					12 40			
Welshpool	d				06 39							08 55					10 55					12 55			
Chester	d		05 18	05 37			06 12	07 28		08 20				09 28	10 20				11 28	12 20				13 28	14 20
Wrexham General	d		05 34	05a55			06 29	07 44		08 37				09 44	10 37				11 44	12 37				13 44	14 37
Ruabon	d		05 41				06 35	07 51		08 44				09 51	10 43				11 51	12 43				13 51	14 43
Chirk	d		05 47				06 41	07 57		08 50				09 57	10 49				11 57	12 49				13 57	14 49
Gobowen	d		05 52				06 47	08 02		08 55				10 02	10 55				12 02	12 55				14 02	14 55
Shrewsbury	a		06 13		07 05		07 07	08 22		09 16		09 21		10 22	11 15		11 21		12 22	13 15		13 21		14 22	15 15
Crewe 10	a		07 05				08 28	09 28				10 28		11 28										15 28	
Manchester Piccadilly 10	a		08 00				09 12	10 13				11 13		12 13					14 13			15 13		16 13	
Cardiff Central 7	a		08 25				09 18	10 52		11 20		11 53		12 53	13 19					15 20		15 53		16 53	17 20
Shrewsbury	d		06 22		07 12			08 22				09 22		10 22			11 22		12 22			13 22		14 22	
Wellington (Shropshire)	d		06 35		07 22			08 35				09 35		10 35			11 35		12 35			13 35		14 35	
Telford Central	d		06 41		07 29			08 41				09 41		10 41			11 41		12 41			13 41		14 41	
Cosford	d				07 39																				
Wolverhampton 7	a		06 58		07 58			08 58				09 58		10 58			11 58		12 58			13 58		14 58	
Tame Bridge Parkway	d																								
Birmingham New Street 12	a		07 18		08 18			09 18				10 18		11 18			12 18		13 18			14 18		15 18	
Birmingham International	a		07 40		08 42			09 39				10 39		11 39								14 39		15 39	
Banbury	a																								
London Marylebone 10	⊖ a																								
London Euston 15	⊖ a		09 06		10 07			11 02				12 03		13 03								16 05		17 05	

For general notes see front of timetable
For details of catering facilities see
Directory of Train Operators

b arrives 0813
c arrives 0925

Table 75

until 22 March

Pwllheli, Barmouth, Aberystwyth and Chester → Shrewsbury and Birmingham

Network Diagram - see first page of Table 67

		AW ◇ ⊥	AW ◇ ⊥	AW ◇ ⊥	AW ◇ ⊥	AW ◇ ⊥	AW ◇ ⊥	AW ◇ ⊥	AW ◇ ⊥	AW ◇ ⊥	AW ◇ ⊥	AW	AW	AW	AW ◇ ⊥	AW	AW	AW ◇	AW ◇	AW
Pwllheli	d	11 32				13 32				15 32			17 32					20 00		
Abererch	d	11x36				13x36				15x36			17x36					20x04		
Penychain	d	11x38				13x38				15x38			17x38					20x06		
Criccieth	d	11 45				13 45				15 45			17 45					20 13		
Porthmadog	d	11 56				13 56				15 56			17 56					20 23		
Minffordd	d	12 00				14 00				16 00			18 00					20 27		
Penrhyndeudraeth	d	12 03				14 03				16 03			18 03					20 30		
Llandecwyn	d	12x06				14x06				16x06			18x06					20x33		
Talsarnau	d	12x08				14x08				16x08			18x08					20x35		
Tygwyn	d	12x10				14x10				16x11			18x10					20x37		
Harlech	d	12 25				14 30				16 20			18 25					20 46		
Llandanwg	d	12x30				14x35				16x25			18x30					20x51		
Pensarn	d	12x31				14x36				16x26			18x31					20x52		
Llanbedr	d	12x33				14x38				16x28			18x33					20x54		
Dyffryn Ardudwy	d	12x37				14x42				16x32			18x37					20x58		
Talybont	d	12x39				14x44				16x34			18x39					21x00		
Llanaber	d	12x42				14x47				16x37			18x42					21x03		
Barmouth	a	12 46				14 51				16 41			18 46					21 07		
	d	12 49				14 52				16 50			18 49					21 14		
Morfa Mawddach	d	12x54				14x57				16x55			18x54					21x19		
Fairbourne	d	12 56				14 59				16 57			18 56					21 21		
Llwyngwril	d	13x03				15x06				17x04			19x03					21x28		
Tonfanau	d	13x09				15x12				17x10			19x09					21x34		
Tywyn	d	13 23				15 23				17 27			19 26					21 46		
Aberdovey	d	13 29				15 29				17 33			19 32					21 52		
Penhelig	d	13x32				15x32				17x36			19x35					21x55		
Aberystwyth	d		13 27				15 27				17 27			19 27			21 36			23 40
Borth	d		13 39				15 39				17 39			19 39			21 48			23 52
Dovey Junction 4	d	13 41	13 50			15 41	15 50			17 46	17 50		19 46	19 50			21 59	22 07		00 03
Machynlleth 4	a	13 52	13 59			15 48	15 59			17 57	17 59		19 57	19 59			22 11	22 16		00 13
	d	14 02				16 02				18 02				20 02						
Caersws	d	14 33				16 33				18 33				20 33						
Newtown (Powys)	d	14 40				16 40				18 40				20 40						
Welshpool	d	14 55				16 55				18 55				20 55						
Chester	d			15 28	16 20			17 28	18 20			19 28			20 28	21 28			22 31	
Wrexham General	d			15 44	16 36			17 44	18 36			19 44			20 44	21 44			22 47	
Ruabon	d			15 51	16 43			17 51	18 43			19 51			20 51	21 51			22 54	
Chirk	d			15 57	16 49			17 57	18 49			19 57			20 57	21 57			23 00	
Gobowen	d			16 02	16 54			18 02	18 54			20 02			21 02	22 02			23 05	
Shrewsbury	a	15 21		16 22	17 15	17 21		18 22	19 15	19 21		20 22		21 21	21 23	22 22			23 26	
Crewe 10	a	*16 28*		*17 28*		*18 28*		*19 28*		*20 26*		*21 27*			*23 03*	*23 44*			*00 44*	
Manchester Piccadilly 10 ⛴	a	*17 13*		*18 10*		*19 16*		*20 13*		*21 13*		*22 13*			*23 50*					
Cardiff Central 7	a	*17 54*		*18 55*	19 22	*19 54*		*21 06*	21 20	*22 00*		*23 01*			*00 17*	*01 19*				
Shrewsbury	d	15 22		16 22		17 22		18 22		19 22		20 22			21 26	22 22				
Wellington (Shropshire)	d	15 35		16 35		17 35		18 35		19 35		20 35			21 39	22 35				
Telford Central	d	15 41		16 41		17 41		18 41		19 41		20 41			21 45	22 41				
Cosford	d																			
Wolverhampton 7 ⛴	a	15 58		16 58		17 58		18 58		19 58		20 58			22 02	22 58				
Tame Bridge Parkway	d																			
Birmingham New Street 12	a	16 18		17 18		18 19		19 18		20 18		21 18			22 18	23 18				
Birmingham International ✈	a	*16 39*		*17 39*		*18 44*		*19 42*		*20 42*		*21 42*			*23 04*	*00 21*				
Banbury	a																			
London Marylebone 10 ⊖	a																			
London Euston 15 ⊖	a	*18 03*		*19 03*		*20 16*		*21 42*		*22 46*		*23 43*								

For general notes see front of timetable
For details of catering facilities see Directory of Train Operators

Table 75

Saturdays

from 29 March

Pwllheli, Barmouth, Aberystwyth and Chester → Shrewsbury and Birmingham

Network Diagram - see first page of Table 67

		AW	AW	AW	AW ◇ 🛒	AW A	AW ◇ 🛒	AW	AW A	AW ◇ 🛒	AW ◇	AW ◇ 🛒	AW A	AW ◇ 🛒	AW ◇ 🛒	AW ◇ 🛒	AW A	AW ◇ 🛒	AW ◇ 🛒	AW ◇ 🛒	AW A
Pwllheli	d										06 10				07 34			09 36			
Abererch	d										06x14							09x40			
Penychain	d										06x16				07x40			09x42			
Criccieth	d										06 23				07 46			09 49			
Porthmadog	d										06 32				07 55			09 58			
Minffordd	d										06 36				07 59			10 02			
Penrhyndeudraeth	d										06 39				08 03			10 05			
Llandecwyn	d										06x42							10x08			
Talsarnau	d										06x44				08x07			10x10			
Tygwyn	d										06x46							10x12			
Harlech	d										07b20				08c32			10e22			
Llandanwg	d										07x25				08x37			10x27			
Pensarn	d										07x26				08x38			10x28			
Llanbedr	d										07x28				08x40			10x30			
Dyffryn Ardudwy	d										07x32				08x44			10x34			
Talybont	d										07x34				08x46			10x36			
Llanaber	d										07x37				08x49			10x39			
Barmouth	a										07 41				08 53			10 43			
	d							06 46			07 49				08 59			10 49			
Morfa Mawddach	d							06x50			07x54				09x04			10x54			
Fairbourne	d							06 53			07 56				09 06			10 56			
Llwyngwril	d							07x00			08x03				09x13			11x03			
Tonfanau	d							07x06			08x09				09x19			11x09			
Tywyn	d							07f16			08 15				09g31			11h27			
Aberdovey	d							07 22			08 21				09 37			11 33			
Penhelig	d							07x24			08x24				09x40			11x35			
Aberystwyth	d	23p53			05 12					07 27				09 27					11 27		
Borth	d	00 05			05 25					07 39				09 39					11 39		
Dovey Junction 4	d	00 16			05 37			07 35		07 50	08 35			09 50	09 51			11 47	11 50		
Machynlleth 4	a	00 26			05 44			07 44		07 59	08 44			09 59	10 00			11 57	11 59		
	d				05 45					08 02				10 02				12 02			
Caersws	d				06 17					08 33				10 33				12 33			
Newtown (Powys)	d				06 24					08 40				10 40				12 40			
Welshpool	d				06 39					08 55				10 55				12 55			
Chester	d		05 18	05 37		06 12	07 28		08 20			09 28	10 20			11 28	12 20			13 28	14 20
Wrexham General	d		05 34	05a55		06 29	07 44		08 37			09 44	10 37			11 44	12 37			13 44	14 37
Ruabon	d		05 41			06 35	07 51		08 44			09 51	10 43			11 51	12 43			13 51	14 43
Chirk	d		05 47			06 41	07 57		08 50			09 57	10 49			11 57	12 49			13 57	14 49
Gobowen	d		05 52			06 47	08 02		08 55			10 02	10 55			12 02	12 55			14 02	14 55
Shrewsbury	a		06 13		07 05	07 07	08 22		09 16	09 21		10 22	11 15	11 21		12 22	13 15	13 21		14 22	15 15
Crewe 10	a		07 05			08 28	09 28			10 27		11 28								15 28	
Manchester Piccadilly 10	a		08 00			09 12	10 13			11 13		12 13				14 13		15 13		16 13	
Cardiff Central 7	a																				
Shrewsbury	d		06 22		07 12		08 22			09 22		10 22		11 22		12 22		13 22		14 22	
Wellington (Shropshire)	d		06 35		07 22		08 35			09 35		10 35		11 35		12 35		13 35		14 35	
Telford Central	d		06 41		07 29		08 41			09 41		10 41		11 41		12 41		13 41		14 41	
Cosford	d				07 39																
Wolverhampton 7	a		06 58		07 58		08 58			09 58		10 58		11 58		12 58		13 58		14 58	
Tame Bridge Parkway	d																				
Birmingham New Street 12	a		07 18		08 18		09 18			10 18		11 18		12 18		13 18		14 18		15 18	
Birmingham International ✈	a		07 40		08 42		09 39			10 39		11 39						14 39		15 39	
Banbury	a																				
London Marylebone 10 ⊖	a																				
London Euston 15 ⊖	a		09 06		10 07		11 02			12 03		13 03						16 05		17 05	

For general notes see front of timetable
For details of catering facilities see Directory of Train Operators

A From Holyhead (Table 81) to Hereford (Table 131)
b Arr. 0650
c Arr. 0813
e Arr. 1016
f Arr. 0710
g Arr. 0925
h Arr. 1114

Table 75

Saturdays

from 29 March

Pwllheli, Barmouth, Aberystwyth and Chester → Shrewsbury and Birmingham

Network Diagram - see first page of Table 67

	AW	AW	AW		AW	AW	AW	AW		AW	AW	AW	AW		AW	AW	AW	AW	AW	AW	AW	AW		
	◇	◇	◇			◇	◇	◇			◇	◇					◇			◇	◇			
					A					A							B				B			
	🛒	🛒	🛒			🛒	🛒	🛒			🛒	🛒					🛒							
Pwllheli d	11 32					13 32					15 32				17 32					20 00				
Abererch d	11x36					13x36					15x36				17x36					20x04				
Penychain d	11x38					13x38					15x38				17x38					20x06				
Criccieth d	11 45					13 45					15 45				17 45					20 13				
Porthmadog d	11 56					13 56					15 56				17 56					20 23				
Minffordd d	12 00					14 00					16 00				18 00					20 27				
Penrhyndeudraeth d	12 03					14 03					16 03				18 03					20 30				
Llandecwyn d	12x06					14x06					16x06				18x06					20x33				
Talsarnau d	12x08					14x08					16x08				18x08					20x35				
Tygwyn d	12x10					14x10					16x11				18x10					20x37				
Harlech d	12b25					14c30					16e20				18f25					20g46				
Llandanwg d	12x30					14x35					16x25				18x30					20x51				
Pensarn d	12x31					14x36					16x26				18x31					20x52				
Llanbedr d	12x33					14x38					16x28				18x33					20x54				
Dyffryn Ardudwy d	12x37					14x42					16x32				18x37					20x58				
Talybont d	12x39					14x44					16x34				18x39					21x00				
Llanaber d	12x42					14x47					16x37				18x42					21x03				
Barmouth a	12 46					14 51					16 41				18 46					21 07				
d	12 49					14 52					16 50				18 49					21 14				
Morfa Mawddach d	12x54					14x57					16x55				18x54					21x19				
Fairbourne d	12 56					14 59					16 57				18 56					21 21				
Llwyngwril d	13x03					15x06					17x04				19x03					21x28				
Tonfanau d	13x09					15x12					17x10				19x09					21x34				
Tywyn d	13h23					15j23					17k27				19m26					21n46				
Aberdovey d	13 29					15 29					17 33				19 32					21 52				
Penhelig d	13x32					15x32					17x36				19x35					21x55				
Aberystwyth d		13 27					15 27					17 27				19 27			21 36			23 40		
Borth d		13 39					15 39					17 39				19 39			21 48			23 52		
Dovey Junction 4 d	13 41	13 50				15 41	15 50				17 46	17 50			19 46	19 50			21 59	22 07		00 03		
Machynlleth 4 a	13 52	13 59				15 48	15 59				17 57	17 59			19 57	19 59			22 11	22 16		00 13		
d	14 02					16 02					18 02					20 02								
Caersws d	14 33					16 33					18 33					20 33								
Newtown (Powys) d	14 40					16 40					18 40					20 40								
Welshpool d	14 55					16 55					18 55					20 55								
Chester d			15 28		16 20			17 28		18 20			19 28				20 28	21 28			22 31			
Wrexham General d			15 44		16 36			17 44		18 36			19 44				20 44	21 44			22 47			
Ruabon d			15 51		16 43			17 51		18 43			19 51				20 51	21 51			22 54			
Chirk d			15 57		16 49			17 57		18 49			19 57				20 57	21 57			23 00			
Gobowen d			16 02		16 54			18 02		18 54			20 02				21 02	22 02			23 05			
Shrewsbury a	15 21		16 22		17 15	17 21		18 22		19 15	19 21		20 22			21 21	21 23	22 22			23 26			
Crewe 10 a	*16 28*		*17 28*			*18 28*		*19 28*			*20 28*		*21 28*				*23 03*	*23 50*			*00 44*			
Manchester Piccadilly 10 ⛴ a	*17 13*		*18 10*			*19 16*		*20 13*			*21 13*		*22 13*				*23 50*							
Cardiff Central 7 a																		*01 19*						
Shrewsbury d	15 22		16 22			17 22		18 22			19 22		20 22				21 26	22 22			23 31			
Wellington (Shropshire) d	15 35		16 35			17 35		18 35			19 35		20 35				21 39	22 35			23 43			
Telford Central d	15 41		16 41			17 41		18 41			19 41		20 41				21 45	22 41			23 51			
Cosford d																					00 01			
Wolverhampton 7 ⛴ a	15 58		16 58			17 58		18 58			19 58		20 58				22 02	22 58			00 20			
Tame Bridge Parkway d																								
Birmingham New Street 12 a	16 18		17 18			18 19		19 18			20 18		21 18				22 18	23 18						
Birmingham International ✈ a	*16 39*		*17 39*			*18 44*		*19 42*			*20 42*		*21 42*				*23 04*	*00 21*						
Banbury a																								
London Marylebone 10 ⊖ a																								
London Euston 15 ⊖ a	*18 03*		*19 03*			*20 16*		*21 33*			*22 39*		*23 30*											

For general notes see front of timetable
For details of catering facilities see Directory of Train Operators

A From Holyhead (Table 81) to Hereford (Table 131)

B From Holyhead (Table 81)
b Arr. 1214
c Arr. 1414
e Arr. 1615
f Arr. 1814
g Arr. 2041

h Arr. 1316
j Arr. 1517
k Arr. 1715
m Arr. 1914
n Arr. 2139

Table 75

Sundays
until 27 January

Pwllheli, Barmouth, Aberystwyth and Chester → Shrewsbury and Birmingham

Network Diagram - see first page of Table 67

		AW	AW	AW	CH	AW	AW	AW	AW	AW	AW	WS	AW	AW	AW	AW	AW	AW	AW	AW	AW
						◇ 🚲	◇ A 🚲	◇ 🚲	◇	◇ 🚲	◇ 🚲		◇	◇ 🚲	R A 🚲	◇		◇ A 🚲			
Pwllheli	d									13 55											
Abererch	d									13x59											
Penychain	d									14x01											
Criccieth	d									14 08											
Porthmadog	d									14 20											
Minffordd	d									14 24											
Penrhyndeudraeth	d									14 28											
Llandecwyn	d									14x30											
Talsarnau	d									14x32											
Tygwyn	d									14x34											
Harlech	d									14 39											
Llandanwg	d									14x44											
Pensarn	d									14x46											
Llanbedr	d									14x48											
Dyffryn Ardudwy	d									14x51											
Talybont	d									14x53											
Llanaber	d									14x57											
Barmouth	a									15 00											
	d									15 02											
Morfa Mawddach	d									15x07											
Fairbourne	d									15 09											
Llwyngwril	d									15x16											
Tonfanau	d									15x22											
Tywyn	d									15 27											
Aberdovey	d									15 33											
Penhelig	d									15x36											
Aberystwyth	d	23p40						12 34			15 34			17 15			19 25				23 15
Borth	d	23p52						12 46			15 46			17 27			19 37				23 27
Dovey Junction 4	d	00 03						12 57		15 46	15 57			17 38			19 48				23 38
Machynlleth 4	a	00 13						13 04		15 53	16 06			17 45			19 56				23 46
	d							13 07		16 09				17 49							
Caersws	d							13 35		16 37				18 26							
Newtown (Powys)	d							13 42		16 44				18 33							
Welshpool	d							13 58		17 00				18 49							
Chester	d		08 08	09 53		11 12	12 20		14 24				17 30		19 07	19 28		20 24	21 31	22 03	
Wrexham General	d		08a26	10 10	10 50	11 28	12 37		14 44			17 13	17 47		19 23	19 44		20 40	21 48	22a21	
Ruabon	d			10 16	10 56	11 35	12 44		14 51			17 19	17 53		19 30	19 51		20 47	21 55		
Chirk	d			10 22	11 03	11 41	12 49		14 57			17 26	17 59		19 36	19 57		20 53	22 01		
Gobowen	d			10 28	11 08	11 46	12 55		15 02			17 31	18 05		19 41	20 02		20 58	22 07		
Shrewsbury	a			10 48	11 28	12 07	13 15	14 21	15 23	17 23		17 51	18 25	19 12	19 59	20 23		21 19	22 27		
Crewe 10	a					13 34	14 21	15 23	17 37	18 12			19 27	20 15		21 24			23 36		
Manchester Piccadilly 10	a					14 20	15 11	16 12	18 26				20 14			22 07					
Cardiff Central 7	a				13 54		15 31		18 16			20 17		21 21	22 28			00 29			
Shrewsbury	d				11 30	12 08		14 24	15 25	17 26		17 53	18 27	19 25		20 25		21 20	22 29		
Wellington (Shropshire)	d				11 44	12 22		14 38	15 38	17 40		18 07	18 40	19 39		20 38		21 34	22 42		
Telford Central	d				11 50	12 30		14 44	15 47	17 49		18 13	18 49	19 45		20 47		21 43	22 51		
Cosford	d				11 58	12 40			15 57	17 59		18 21	18 59			20 57		21 53	23 01		
Wolverhampton 7	a				12 10	12 58		15 01	16 14	18 16		18 33	19 16	20 02		21 14		22 16	23 18		
Tame Bridge Parkway	d				12 27																
Birmingham New Street 12	a					13 15		15 18	16 33	18 35		18 50	19 34	20 19		21 32		22 36			
Birmingham International	a					13 39		15 39	17 10			19 13	20 14	20 52		22 09		23 09			
Banbury	a				13 49							19 45									
London Marylebone 10	a				15 05							21 08									
London Euston 15	a					15 16		17 11	18 41			21b17	22 27			23 48		00 47			

For general notes see front of timetable
For details of catering facilities see Directory of Train Operators

A From Holyhead (Table 81)
b Change at Birmingham New Street

Table 75

3 February to 23 March

Pwllheli, Barmouth, Aberystwyth and Chester → Shrewsbury and Birmingham

Network Diagram - see first page of Table 67

		AW	AW	AW	AW	AW	AW	AW	AW	AW	AW	AW	AW	AW	AW	AW	AW	AW	AW
													R						
					◇	◇		◇	◇		◇			◇			◇		
						A							A			A			
						⚒			⚒				⚒						
Pwllheli	d								13 55										
Abererch	d								13x59										
Penychain	d								14x01										
Criccieth	d								14 08										
Porthmadog	d								14 20										
Minffordd	d								14 24										
Penrhyndeudraeth	d								14 28										
Llandecwyn	d								14x30										
Talsarnau	d								14x32										
Tygwyn	d								14x34										
Harlech	d								14 39										
Llandanwg	d								14x44										
Pensarn	d								14x46										
Llanbedr	d								14x48										
Dyffryn Ardudwy	d								14x51										
Talybont	d								14x53										
Llanaber	d								14x57										
Barmouth	a								15 00										
	d								15 02										
Morfa Mawddach	d								15x07										
Fairbourne	d								15 09										
Llwyngwril	d								15x16										
Tonfanau	d								15x22										
Tywyn	d								15 27										
Aberdovey	d								15 33										
Penhelig	d								15x36										
Aberystwyth	d	23p40					12 34			15 34		17 15			19 25				23 15
Borth	d	23p52					12 46			15 46		17 27			19 37				23 27
Dovey Junction 4	d	00 03					12 57		15 46	15 57		17 38			19 48				23 38
Machynlleth 4	a	00 13					13 04		15 53	16 06		17 45			19 56				23 46
	d						13 07			16 09		17 49							
Caersws	d						13 35			16 37		18 26							
Newtown (Powys)	d						13 42			16 44		18 33							
Welshpool	d						13 58			17 00		18 49							
Chester	d		08 08	09 53	11 15	12 20		14 24			17 30		19 07	19 28		20 24	21 31	22 03	
Wrexham General	d		08a26	10 10	11 31	12 37		14 44			17 47		19 23	19 44		20 40	21 48	22a21	
Ruabon	d			10 16	11 38	12 44		14 51			17 53		19 30	19 51		20 47	21 55		
Chirk	d			10 22	11 44	12 49		14 57			17 59		19 36	19 57		20 53	22 01		
Gobowen	d			10 28	11 49	12 55		15 02			18 05		19 41	20 02		20 58	22 07		
Shrewsbury	a			10 48	12 15	13 15	14 25	15 25		17 25	18 25	19 15	19 59	20 25		21 20	22 30		
Crewe 10	a				13 34	14 21	15 23	17 37		18 12	19 27	20 15		21 24			23 36		
Manchester Piccadilly 10	⛴ a				14 20	15 11	16 12	18 26			20 14			22 07					
Cardiff Central 7	a			13 54		15 31		18 18		20 17	21 21		22 28			00 29			
Shrewsbury	d																		
Wellington (Shropshire)	d																		
Telford Central	d																		
Cosford	d																		
Wolverhampton 7	⛴ a																		
Tame Bridge Parkway	d																		
Birmingham New Street 12	a																		
Birmingham International	✈ a																		
Banbury	a																		
London Marylebone 10	⊖ a																		
London Euston 15	⊖ a																		

For general notes see front of timetable
For details of catering facilities see Directory of Train Operators

A From Holyhead (Table 81)

Table 75

Sundays
from 30 March

Pwllheli, Barmouth, Aberystwyth and Chester → Shrewsbury and Birmingham

Network Diagram - see first page of Table 67

		AW	AW	AW	AW	AW	AW	AW	AW	AW	AW	AW	AW	AW	AW	AW	AW	AW	AW
					◇		◇	◇	◇	◇	◇	◇		◇		◇			
						A							A			B			
					⊼		⊼		⊼	⊼		⊼				⊼			
Pwllheli	d								13 55										
Abererch	d								13x59										
Penychain	d								14x01										
Criccieth	d								14 08										
Porthmadog	d								14 20										
Minffordd	d								14 24										
Penrhyndeudraeth	d								14 28										
Llandecwyn	d								14x30										
Talsarnau	d								14x32										
Tygwyn	d								14x34										
Harlech	d								14 39										
Llandanwg	d								14x44										
Pensarn	d								14x46										
Llanbedr	d								14x48										
Dyffryn Ardudwy	d								14x51										
Talybont	d								14x53										
Llanaber	d								14x57										
Barmouth	a								15 00										
	d								15 02										
Morfa Mawddach	d								15x07										
Fairbourne	d								15 09										
Llwyngwril	d								15x16										
Tonfanau	d								15x22										
Tywyn	d								15 27										
Aberdovey	d								15 33										
Penhelig	d								15x36										
Aberystwyth	d	23p40					12 34			15 34		17 15			19 25				23 15
Borth	d	23p52					12 46			15 46		17 27			19 37				23 27
Dovey Junction 4	d	00 03					12 57		15 46	15 57		17 38			19 48				23 38
Machynlleth 4	a	00 13					13 04		15 53	16 06		17 45			19 56				23 46
	d						13 07		16 09			17 49							
Caersws	d						13 35		16 37			18 26							
Newtown (Powys)	d						13 42		16 44			18 33							
Welshpool	d						13 58		17 00			18 49							
Chester	d		08 08	09 53	11 12	12 20		14 24			17 30		19 07	19 28		20 24	21 31	22 03	
Wrexham General	d		08a26	10 10	11 28	12 37		14 44			17 47		19 23	19 44		20 40	21 48	22a21	
Ruabon	d			10 16	11 35	12 44		14 51			17 53		19 30	19 51		20 47	21 55		
Chirk	d			10 22	11 41	12 49		14 57			17 59		19 36	19 57		20 53	22 01		
Gobowen	d			10 28	11 46	12 55		15 02			18 05		19 41	20 02		20 58	22 07		
Shrewsbury	a			10 48	12 07	13 15	14 21	15 23	17 23		18 25	19 12	19 59	20 23		21 19	22 27		
Crewe 10	a				*13 34*	*14 21*	*15 22*	*17 32*	*18 12*		*19 27*	*20 15*		*21 19*			*23 36*		
Manchester Piccadilly 10	a				*14 20*	*15 11*	*16 12*	*18 20*			*20 14*			*22 07*					
Cardiff Central 7	a							*21 30*											
Shrewsbury	d				12 08		14 24	15 25	17 26		18 27	19 25		20 25		21 20	22 29		
Wellington (Shropshire)	d				12 22		14 38	15 38	17 40		18 40	19 39		20 38		21 34	22 42		
Telford Central	d				12 30		14 44	15 47	17 49		18 49	19 45		20 47		21 43	22 51		
Cosford	d				12 40			15 57	17 59		18 59			20 57		21 53	23 01		
Wolverhampton 7	a				12 58		15 01	16 14	18 16		19 16	20 02		21 14		22 16	23 18		
Tame Bridge Parkway	d																		
Birmingham New Street 12	a				13 15		15 18	16 33	18 35		19 34	20 19		21 32		22 36			
Birmingham International	a				*13 39*		*15 39*	*17 09*	*19 13*		*20 14*	*20 52*		*22 09*		*23 09*			
Banbury	a																		
London Marylebone 10	a																		
London Euston 15	a				*15 16*		*17 11*	*18 41*	*21 17*		*22 27*			*23 58*		*00 57*			

For general notes see front of timetable
For details of catering facilities see Directory of Train Operators

A From Holyhead (Table 81) to Hereford (Table 131)
B From Holyhead (Table 81)

Network Diagram for Tables 78, 79, 84, 85, 86

DM-11/06(2)
Design BAJS

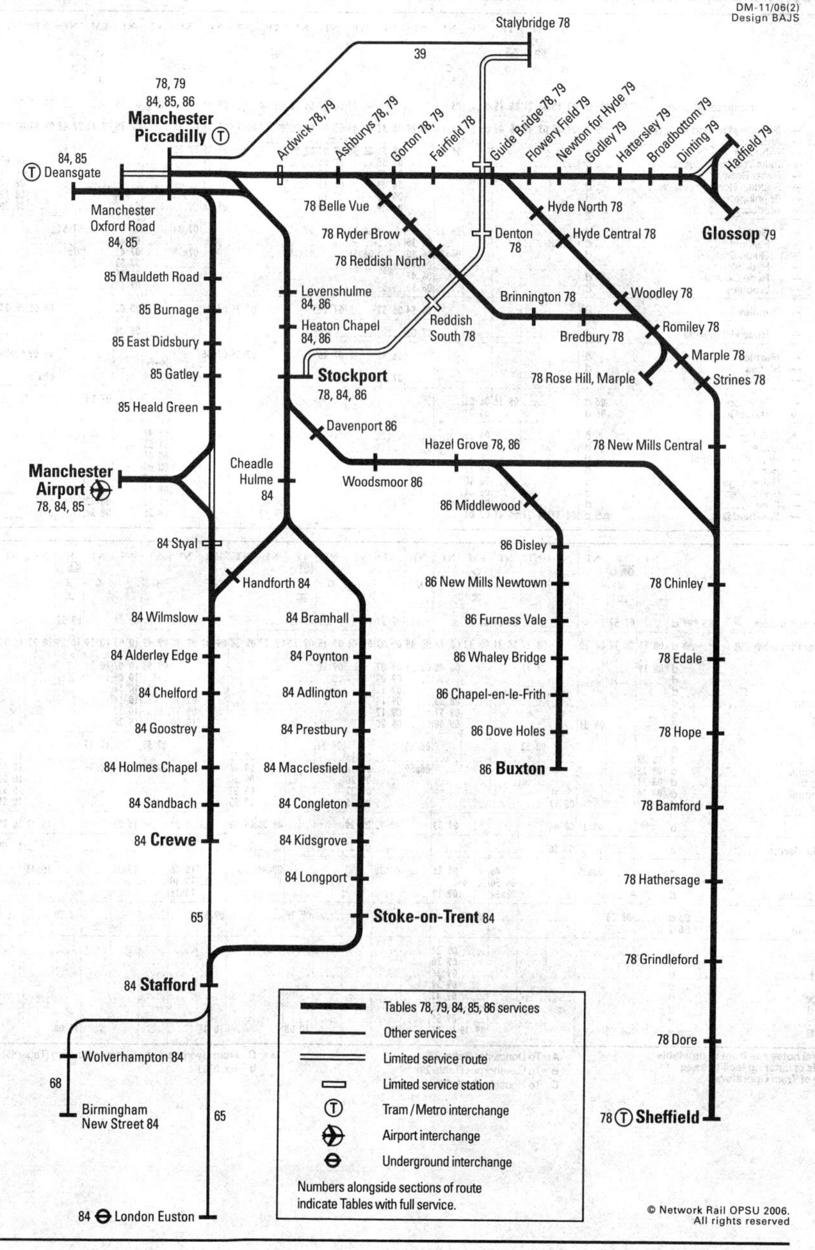

Stalybridge 78
39
78, 79
84, 85, 86
Manchester Piccadilly
84, 85
Deansgate
Manchester Oxford Road 84, 85
Ardwick 78, 79
Ashburys 78, 79
Gorton 78, 79
Fairfield 78
Guide Bridge 78, 79
Flowery Field 79
Newton for Hyde 79
Godley 79
Hattersley 79
Broadbottom 79
Dinting 79
Hadfield 79
Glossop 79
78 Belle Vue
78 Ryder Brow
78 Reddish North
Denton 78
Hyde North 78
Hyde Central 78
85 Mauldeth Road
85 Burnage
85 East Didsbury
85 Gatley
85 Heald Green
Levenshulme 84, 86
Heaton Chapel 84, 86
Reddish South 78
Brinnington 78
Bredbury 78
Woodley 78
Romiley 78
Marple 78
78 Rose Hill, Marple
Strines 78
Stockport 78, 84, 86
Davenport 86
Hazel Grove 78, 86
Woodsmoor 86
78 New Mills Central
Manchester Airport 78, 84, 85
Cheadle Hulme 84
86 Middlewood
84 Styal
86 Disley
Handforth 84
86 New Mills Newtown
78 Chinley
84 Wilmslow
84 Bramhall
86 Furness Vale
84 Alderley Edge
84 Poynton
86 Whaley Bridge
78 Edale
84 Chelford
84 Adlington
86 Chapel-en-le-Frith
84 Goostrey
84 Prestbury
86 Dove Holes
78 Hope
84 Holmes Chapel
84 Macclesfield
86 Buxton
84 Sandbach
84 Congleton
78 Bamford
84 Crewe
84 Kidsgrove
84 Longport
78 Hathersage
65
Stoke-on-Trent 84
78 Grindleford
84 Stafford
Wolverhampton 84
78 Dore
68
Birmingham New Street 84
65
78 Sheffield
84 London Euston
Tables 78, 79, 84, 85, 86 services
Other services
Limited service route
Limited service station
Tram / Metro interchange
Airport interchange
Underground interchange
Numbers alongside sections of route indicate Tables with full service.

Manchester Airport and Manchester → Romiley, Marple, Chinley and Sheffield

Network Diagram - see first page of Table 78

Miles	Miles	Miles		TP MO 1 ◇ A	TP MX 1 ◇ A	TP 1 ◇ B	NT	NT C	NT	NT	NT C	NT	NT C	TP 1 ◇ B ✠	NT	NT	NT C	NT	NT	EM ◇ D ✠	NT C	NT	NT	NT C
—	—	—	**Manchester Airport** 85 ✈ d	03 18	03 21	05 15		*05 47*			*06 19*	*06 23*	*06 28*	06 44		*06 47*			*07 05*			*07 22*	*07 34*	
0	0	—	**Manchester Piccadilly [10]** d	03 37	03 40	05 48	05 52	06 16	06 29	06 32	06 46	07 00	07 03	07 18	07 18	07 21	07 28		07 38	07 43	07 48	07 52	08 03	08 07
½	½	—	Ardwick d																					
1½	1½	—	Ashburys d					06 20		06 36	06 50	07 04	07 08			07 25	07 32				07 52		08 07	08 11
2¼	—	—	Belle Vue d							06 38		07 08				07 27							08 09	
2¾	—	—	Ryder Brow d							06 40		07 10				07 29							08 11	
3¾	—	—	Reddish North d							06 43		07 13				07 32							08 14	
5¼	—	—	Brinnington d							06 46		07 16				07 35							08 17	
6½	—	—	Bredbury d							06 49		07 19				07 38							08 20	
—	2½	—	Gorton d					06 22			06 52		07 11				07 34				07 54			08 13
—	3¼	—	Fairfield d						06 36										07 46					
—	4¾	—	Guide Bridge d					06a26	06 40		06a56		07a15				07a38		07 49		07a58			08a17
—	6¼	—	Hyde North d						06 44										07 53					
—	7¾	—	Hyde Central d						06 47										07 55					
—	9¼	—	Woodley d						06 50										07 58					
7½	10½	—	**Romiley** d						06 54	06 52		07 22			07 30	07 41			08 02			08 05	08 23	
—	12½	—	**Rose Hill Marple** a						07 00										08 08					
9	—	—	**Marple** d							06 56		07 26			07a35	07a46						08 09	08a28	
11¼	—	—	Strines d															←						
12¾	—	—	New Mills Central d							07a03		07b39						07 39				08a15		
—	—	—	Stockport 86 d			05 56	06 01					→		07 26						07 54				
—	—	0	Hazel Grove 86 d				06 08																	
16½	—	8½	**Chinley** d				06 19											07 47						
22	—	—	Edale d				06 28											07 55						
27¼	—	—	Hope (Derbyshire) d				06 34											08 01						
29	—	—	Bamford d				06 37											08 04						
30¾	—	—	Hathersage d				06 40											08 09						
32¼	—	—	Grindleford d				06 44											08 11						
37¾	—	—	Dore d				06 52							08 02				08 20		08 28				
42	—	—	**Sheffield [7]** a	04 37	04 31	06 48	07 01							08 10				08 28		08 34				

	NT	TP 1 ◇ B ✠	NT	NT	NT C	NT	EM ◇ D ✠	NT	NT C	NT	NT	NT C	TP 1 ◇ B ✠	NT	NT	EM ◇ D ✠	NT	NT C	NT	NT C	TP 1 ◇ B ✠	NT	NT	EM ◇ D ✠
Manchester Airport 85 ✈ d		07 52	*07 47*			*08 04*	*08 07*			*08 33*			08 52		*09 07*				*09 34*		09 52		*10 07*	
Manchester Piccadilly [10] d	08 15	08 17	08 20		08 27	08 31	08 42	08 44	08 49	09 03	09 06	09 15	09 20	09 22	09 36	09 42	09 46	09 49	10 03	10 19	10 20	10 22	10 36	10 42
Ardwick d																								
Ashburys d	08 19				08 31			08 48	08 53	09 07		09 20						09 53	10 07	10 23				
Belle Vue d										09 09									10 09					
Ryder Brow d										09 11									10 11					
Reddish North d								08 53		09 14							09 53		10 14					
Brinnington d								08 57		09 17							09 57		10 17					
Bredbury d			08 31					09 00		09 20							10 00		10 20					
Gorton d					08 33				08 55			09 22						09 55		10 25				
Fairfield d	08 22										09 13				09 43								10 43	
Guide Bridge d	08 25				08a37				08a59		09 16	09a26			09 46			09a59		10a29			10 46	
Hyde North d	08 31										09 20				09 50								10 50	
Hyde Central d	08 34			←							09 22				09 52								10 52	
Woodley d	08 37			08 37							09 25				09 55								10 55	
Romiley d	→		08 34	08 44				09 03		09 23	09 29			09 35	09 59		10 03		10 23			10 37	10 59	
Rose Hill Marple a				08 50							09 35				10 05								11 05	
Marple d			08a39			08 46		09 06		09a28				09a41			10 06		10a28			10a43		
Strines d						08 50											10 10							
New Mills Central d						08a54		09 13									10a15							
Stockport 86 d		08 26					08 53						09 28			09 55					10 28			10 55
Hazel Grove 86 d																								
Chinley d								09 22																
Edale d								09 30																
Hope (Derbyshire) d								09 36																
Bamford d								09 39																
Hathersage d								09 42																
Grindleford d								09 46																
Dore d								09 55																
Sheffield [7] a		09 09					09 35	10 05					10 08			10 35					11 08			11 35

For general notes see front of timetable
For details of catering facilities see Directory of Train Operators

A To Doncaster (Table 29)
B To Cleethorpes (Table 29)
C To Hadfield (Table 79)
D From Liverpool Lime Street to Norwich (Table 49)
b Arr. 0731

Manchester Airport and Manchester → Romiley, Marple, Chinley and Sheffield

Network Diagram - see first page of Table 78

	NT	NT A	NT	NT A	TP 1◇ B	NT	NT	EM ◇ C	NT	NT A	NT	NT A	TP 1◇ B	NT	NT	EM ◇ C	NT	NT A	NT	NT A	TP 1◇ B	NT	NT	EM ◇ C
Manchester Airport 85 ✈ d		10 15	10 34	10 47	10 52		11 07			11 15	11 34	11 47	11 52		12 07			12 15	12 34	12 47	12 52		13 07	
Manchester Piccadilly 10 d	10 46	10 49	11 03	11 19	11 20	11 22	11 36	11 42	11 46	11 49	12 03	12 19	12 20	12 22	12 36	12 42	12 46	12 49	13 03	13 19	13 20	13 22	13 36	13 42
Ardwick d																								
Ashburys d		10 53	11 07	11 23						11 53	12 07	12 23						12 53	13 07	13 23				
Belle Vue d			11 09								12 09								13 09					
Ryder Brow d			11 11								12 11								13 11					
Reddish North d	10 53		11 14						11 53		12 14						12 53		13 14					
Brinnington d	10 57		11 17						11 57		12 17						12 57		13 17					
Bredbury d	11 00		11 20						12 00		12 20						13 00		13 20					
Gorton d		10 55		11 25						11 55		12 25						12 55		13 25				
Fairfield d							11 43								12 43								13 43	
Guide Bridge d		10a59		11a29			11 46			11a59		12a29			12 46			12a59		13a29			13 46	
Hyde North d							11 50								12 50								13 50	
Hyde Central d							11 52								12 52								13 52	
Woodley d							11 55								12 55								13 55	
Romiley d	11 03		11 23			11 37	11 59		12 03		12 23			12 37	12 59		13 03		13 23			13 37	13 59	
Rose Hill Marple a							12 05								13 05								14 05	
Marple d	11 06		11a28			11a43			12 06		12a28			12a43			13 06		13a28			13a43		
Strines d									12 10															
New Mills Central d	11 12								12a15								13 12							
Stockport 86 d					11 27			11 55					12 28			12 55					13 28			13 55
Hazel Grove 86 d																								
Chinley d	11 19																13 19							
Edale d	11 28																13 28							
Hope (Derbyshire) d	11 34																13 34							
Bamford d	11 37																13 38							
Hathersage d	11 41																13 42							
Grindleford d	11 45																13 46							
Dore d	11 55																13 55							
Sheffield 7 a	12 04				12 08			12 35					13 08			13 35	14 04				14 08			14 35

	NT	NT A	NT	NT A	TP 1◇ B	NT	NT	EM ◇ D	NT	NT A	NT	NT A	TP 1◇ B	NT	NT	EM ◇ C	NT	NT A	NT	NT	NT A	TP 1◇ B	NT	NT A
Manchester Airport 85 ✈ d		13 15	13 34	13 47	13 52		14 07			14 15	14 34	14 47	14 52		15 07			15 15	15 34			15 52		16 07
Manchester Piccadilly 10 d	13 46	13 49	14 03	14 19	14 20	14 22	14 36	14 42	14 46	14 49	15 03	15 19	15 20	15 22	15 36	15 42	15 46	15 49	16 02	16 05	16 17	16 20	16 22	16 36
Ardwick d																								
Ashburys d		13 53	14 07	14 23						14 53	15 07	15 23						15 53	16 07	16 09	16 21			16 40
Belle Vue d			14 09								15 09								16 09					
Ryder Brow d			14 11								15 11								16 11					
Reddish North d	13 53		14 14						14 53		15 14						15 53		16 14					
Brinnington d	13 57		14 17						14 57		15 17						15 57		16 17					
Bredbury d	14 00		14 20						15 00		15 20						16 00		16 20					
Gorton d		13 55		14 25						14 55		15 25						15 55			16 23			16 42
Fairfield d							14 43								15 43					16 13				
Guide Bridge d		13a59		14a29			14 46			14a59		15a29			15 46			15a59		16 16	16a26			16a46
Hyde North d							14 50								15 50					16 20				
Hyde Central d							14 52								15 52					16 22				
Woodley d							14 55								15 55					16 25				
Romiley d	14 03		14 23			14 37	14 59		15 03		15 23			15 35	15 59		16 03		16 23	16 29			16 34	
Rose Hill Marple a							15 05								16 05					16 35				
Marple d	14 06		14a28			14a43			15 06		15a28			15a40			16 06		16a28				16a39	
Strines d	14 10																16 10							
New Mills Central d	14a15								15 12								16 14							
Stockport 86 d					14 28			14 55					15 28			15 51						16 28		
Hazel Grove 86 d																								
Chinley d									15 20								16 21							
Edale d									15 28								16 30							
Hope (Derbyshire) d									15 35								16 36							
Bamford d									15 38								16 39							
Hathersage d									15 41								16 43							
Grindleford d									15 46								16 46							
Dore d									15 54								16 54							
Sheffield 7 a					15 08			15 35	16 04				16 08			16 35	17 04					17 08		

For general notes see front of timetable
For details of catering facilities see Directory of Train Operators

- **A** To Hadfield (Table 79)
- **B** To Cleethorpes (Table 29)
- **C** From Liverpool Lime Street to Norwich (Table 49)
- **D** From Liverpool Lime Street (Table 49) to Nottingham

Manchester Airport and Manchester → Romiley, Marple, Chinley and Sheffield

Network Diagram - see first page of Table 78

		EM	NT	NT	NT	NT	NT	NT	TP	NT	NT	NT	NT	EM	NT	NT	NT	NT	TP	NT	NT	NT	EM	NT	NT
		◇ A			B			B	1 ◇ C				B	◇ D			B		1 ◇ C	B			◇ E		B
Manchester Airport 85	d				16 34				16 52			17 04				17 19	17 34		17 52			18 10			
Manchester Piccadilly 10	d	16 42	16 46	16 49	16 58	17 03	17 14	17 17	17 20		17 28	17 31	17 36	17 42	17 45	17 51	18 00	18 05	18 18	18 18	18 22	18 36	18 44	18 46	18 49
Ardwick	d					17 06												18 08							
Ashburys	d		16 50	16 53	17 02	17 08		17 21			17 32	17 35	17 40			17 56	18 04	18 10		18 22	18 26				18 53
Belle Vue	d		16 52			17 11										17 58									
Ryder Brow	d		16 54			17 13										18 00									
Reddish North	d		16 57				17 22				17 37					18 03					18 31			18 53	
Brinnington	d		17 00				17 25				17 40					18 06					18 34			18 57	
Bredbury	d		17 03			17 19	17 28				17 43					18 09					18 37			19 00	
Gorton	d				17 04			17 23					17 42				18 06			18 25					18 55
Fairfield	d			16 57								17 39						18 14				18 43			
Guide Bridge	d			17 00	17a08			17a27				17 42	17a46				18a10	18 17		18a29		18 46			18a59
Hyde North	d			17 04								17 46						18 21				18 50			
Hyde Central	d			17 06								17 48						18 24				18 52			
Woodley	d			17 09								17 51						18 27				18 55			
Romiley	d		17 06	17 13		17 22	17 31				17 46	17 55			17 59	18 12		18 30			18 40	18 59		19 03	
Rose Hill Marple	a			17 18								18 00						18 35				19 05			
Marple	d		17 10			17a27	17 35				17a51				18 04	18a16					18 44			19 06	
Strines	d						17 39			←					18 08						18 48				
New Mills Central	d		17a15				17 44			17 44					18 12						18a51			19 12	
Stockport 86	d	16 53					→		17 28					17 53					18 26				18 55		
Hazel Grove 86	d																								
Chinley	d	17 10							17 43	17 53					18a20									19 20	
Edale	d									18 02														19 28	
Hope (Derbyshire)	d									18 08														19 35	
Bamford	d									18 11														19 38	
Hathersage	d									18 14														19 41	
Grindleford	d									18 18														19 45	
Dore	d	17 30							18 06	18 25				18 33					19 02					19b55	
Sheffield 7	a	17 37							18 15	18 37				18 41					19 08				19 36	20 07	

		NT	TP	NT	NT	EM	NT	NT	TP	NT	EM	NT	NT	TP	NT	NT	TP	EM	NT	NT	NT	NT	TP	
			1 ◇ C	B		◇ D		B	1 ◇ C		◇ D		B	1 ◇ C	B		1 ◇	◇ D		B		G	1 ◇	
Manchester Airport 85	d	18 34	18 52	18 47		19 12		19 22	19 52		20 15		20 22	20 52	21 22	21 27	21 52			22 22	22 47		23 52	
Manchester Piccadilly 10	d	19 02	19 18	19 19	19 22	19 42	19 46	19 49	20 18	20 27	20 42	20 46	20 49	21 18	21 49	21 52	22 18	22 27	22 38	22 49	23 23	23 26	00 15	
Ardwick	d																							
Ashburys	d	19 08		19 23			19 50	19 53					20 53		21 53	21 56			22 42	22 53	23 27	23 30		
Belle Vue	d	19 10					19 52									21 58			22 44		23 29			
Ryder Brow	d	19 12					19 54									22 00			22 46		23 31			
Reddish North	d	19 15					19 57					20 53				22 03			22 49		23 34			
Brinnington	d	19 18					20 00					20 57				22 06			22 52		23 37			
Bredbury	d	19 21					20 03					21 00				22 09			22 55		23 40			
Gorton	d			19 25				19 55					20 55		21 55					22 55		23 32		
Fairfield	d									20 34														
Guide Bridge	d			19a29				19a59		20 39			20a59		21a59					22a59		23a36		
Hyde North	d									20 43														
Hyde Central	d									20 45														
Woodley	d									20 48														
Romiley	d	19 24			19 34		20 06			20 52		21 03				22 12			22 58		23 43			
Rose Hill Marple	a									20 57														
Marple	d	19a29			19a39		20 11					21 06				22 16			23 02		23 47			
Strines	d						20 15									22 20			23 06		23 51			
New Mills Central	d						20a20					21 12				22a26			23a10		23a56			
Stockport 86	d		19 26			19 55			20 26		20 55			21 26			22 26	22 38						
Hazel Grove 86	d																							
Chinley	d											21 20						22 53						
Edale	d											21 28						23 02						
Hope (Derbyshire)	d											21 35						23 08						
Bamford	d											21 38						23 11						
Hathersage	d											21 42						23 15						
Grindleford	d											21 46						23 22						
Dore	d											21 54						23 29						
Sheffield 7	a		20 08			20 39			21 08		21 34	22 03		22 09			23 13	23 35					01 13	

For general notes see front of timetable
For details of catering facilities see Directory of Train Operators

- **A** From Liverpool Lime Street to Norwich (Table 49)
- **B** To Hadfield (Table 79)
- **C** To Cleethorpes (Table 29)
- **D** From Liverpool Lime Street to Nottingham (Table 49)
- **E** From Liverpool Lime Street to Cambridge (Table 49)
- **G** To Glossop (Table 79)
- **b** Arr. 1952

Manchester Airport and Manchester → Romiley, Marple, Chinley and Sheffield

Network Diagram - see first page of Table 78

		TP 1◇ A	TP 1◇ B	NT	NT C	NT	NT C	NT	TP 1◇ B ⚲	NT C	NT	EM ◇ D	NT	NT C	NT	TP 1◇ B ⚲	NT C	NT	NT	EM ◇ D	NT	NT C
Manchester Airport 85 ✈	d	03 21	05 15		05 47		06 19	06 28	06 44	06 47		07 05			07 34	07 52			08 04	08 07		
Manchester Piccadilly 10	d	03 40	05 48	05 52	06 16	06 32	06 46	07 05	07 18	07 19	07 28	07 43	07 46	07 49	08 03	08 18	08 19	08 22	08 36	08 42	08 46	08 49
Ardwick	d																					
Ashburys	d				06 20	06 36	06 50	07 09		07 23				07 53	08 07		08 23					08 53
Belle Vue	d					06 38		07 11							08 09							
Ryder Brow	d					06 40		07 13							08 11							
Reddish North	d					06 43		07 16					07 53		08 14						08 53	
Brinnington	d					06 46		07 19					07 57		08 17						08 57	
Bredbury	d					06 49		07 22					08 00		08 20						09 00	
Gorton	d				06 22		06 52			07 25				07 55			08 25					08 55
Fairfield	d										07 35								08 43			
Guide Bridge	d				06a26		06a56			07a29	07 38			07a59			08a29		08 46			08a59
Hyde North	d										07 42								08 50			
Hyde Central	d										07 44								08 52			
Woodley	d										07 47								08 55			
Romiley	d					06 52		07 25			07 51		08 03		08 23			08 37	08 59		09 03	
Rose Hill Marple	a										07 57								09 05			
Marple	d					06 56		07a30					08 06		08a28			08a43			09 06	
Strines	d																				09 10	
New Mills Central	d					07 01							08 12								09 14	
Stockport 86	d		05 56	06 01					07 26			07 54				08 26				08 55		
Hazel Grove 86	d			06 08																		
Chinley	d			06 19		07 09							08 20								09 22	
Edale	d			06 28		07 19							08 29								09 30	
Hope (Derbyshire)	d			06 34		07 25							08 35								09 36	
Bamford	d			06 37		07 29							08 39								09 39	
Hathersage	d			06 40		07 33							08 41								09 43	
Grindleford	d			06 44		07 37							08 46								09 47	
Dore	d			06 52		07 48			08 02				08 55								09 55	
Sheffield 7	a	04 31	06 48	07 01		07 57			08 10			08 35	09 04			09 09				09 35	10 05	

		NT	NT C	TP 1◇ B ⚲	NT	NT	EM ◇ D	NT	NT C	NT	TP 1◇ B ⚲	NT C	NT	NT	EM ◇ D	NT	NT C	NT	TP 1◇ B ⚲	NT C	NT
Manchester Airport 85 ✈	d	08 33		08 52		09 07				09 34	09 52			10 07			10 15	10 34	10 52	10 47	
Manchester Piccadilly 10	d	09 03	09 16	09 18	09 22	09 36	09 42	09 46	09 49	10 03	10 18	10 19	10 22	10 36	10 42	10 46	10 49	11 03	11 18	11 19	11 22
Ardwick	d																				
Ashburys	d	09 07	09 20						09 53	10 07		10 23					10 53	11 07		11 23	
Belle Vue	d	09 09								10 09								11 09			
Ryder Brow	d	09 11								10 11								11 11			
Reddish North	d	09 14						09 53		10 14						10 53		11 14			
Brinnington	d	09 17						09 57		10 17						10 57		11 17			
Bredbury	d	09 20						10 00		10 20						11 00		11 20			
Gorton	d		09 22						09 55			10 25					10 55			11 25	
Fairfield	d					09 43								10 43							
Guide Bridge	d		09a26			09 46			09a59			10a29		10 46			10a59			11a29	
Hyde North	d					09 50								10 50							
Hyde Central	d					09 52								10 52							
Woodley	d					09 55								10 55							
Romiley	d	09 23			09 37	09 59		10 03		10 23			10 37	10 59		11 03		11 23			11 37
Rose Hill Marple	a					10 05								11 05							
Marple	d	09a28			09a43			10 06		10a28			10a43			11 06		11a28			11a43
Strines	d							10 10													
New Mills Central	d							10 14								11 12					
Stockport 86	d			09 26			09 55				10 26				10 55				11 26		
Hazel Grove 86	d																				
Chinley	d							10 21								11 19					
Edale	d							10 30								11 29					
Hope (Derbyshire)	d							10 36								11 35					
Bamford	d							10 39								11 39					
Hathersage	d							10 42								11 42					
Grindleford	d							10 46								11 47					
Dore	d							10 54								11 55					
Sheffield 7	a			10 08			10 35	11 03			11 08				11 35	12 04			12 08		

For general notes see front of timetable
For details of catering facilities see Directory of Train Operators

A To Doncaster (Table 29)
B To Cleethorpes (Table 29)
C To Hadfield (Table 79)
D From Liverpool Lime Street to Norwich (Table 49)

Manchester Airport and Manchester → Romiley, Marple, Chinley and Sheffield

Network Diagram - see first page of Table 78

		NT	EM ◇ A	NT		NT B	NT	TP 1 ◇ C	NT B	NT		NT	EM ◇ A	NT	NT B	NT		TP 1 ◇ C	NT B	NT	NT	EM ◇ A		NT	NT B
Manchester Airport	85 d	11 07				11 15	11 34	11 52	11 47			12 07			12 15	12 34		12 52	12 47		13 07				13 15
Manchester Piccadilly 10	d	11 36	11 42	11 46		11 49	12 03	12 18	12 19	12 22		12 36	12 42	12 46	12 49	13 03		13 18	13 19	13 22	13 36	13 42		13 46	13 49
Ardwick	d																								
Ashburys	d					11 53	12 07		12 23						12 53	13 07			13 23						13 53
Belle Vue	d						12 09									13 09									
Ryder Brow	d						12 11									13 11									
Reddish North	d			11 53			12 14							12 53		13 14								13 53	
Brinnington	d			11 57			12 17							12 57		13 17								13 57	
Bredbury	d			12 00			12 20							13 00		13 20								14 00	
Gorton	d					11 55			12 25						12 55				13 25						13 55
Fairfield	d	11 43										12 43									13 43				
Guide Bridge	d	11 46				11a59			12a29			12 46			12a59				13a29		13 46				13a59
Hyde North	d	11 50										12 50									13 50				
Hyde Central	d	11 52										12 52									13 52				
Woodley	d	11 55										12 55									13 55				
Romiley	d	11 59		12 03			12 23			12 37		12 59		13 03		13 23				13 37	13 59			14 03	
Rose Hill Marple	a	12 05										13 05									14 05				
Marple	d			12 06			12a28			12a43				13 06		13a28				13a43				14 06	
Strines	d			12 10																				14 10	
New Mills Central	d			12 14										13 12										14 14	
Stockport	86 d		11 55					12 26					12 55					13 26				13 55			
Hazel Grove	86 d																								
Chinley	d			12 21										13 19										14 21	
Edale	d			12 30										13 28										14 30	
Hope (Derbyshire)	d			12 36										13 34										14 36	
Bamford	d			12 39										13 38										14 39	
Hathersage	d			12 43										13 42										14 42	
Grindleford	d			12 46										13 46										14 46	
Dore	d			12 55										13 55										14 55	
Sheffield 7	a		12 35	13 04				13 08					13 35	14 04				14 08				14 35		15 03	

		NT	TP 1 ◇ C	NT B	NT	NT		EM ◇ D	NT	NT B	NT	TP 1 ◇ C		NT B	NT	NT	EM ◇ A	NT		NT B	NT	NT B	TP 1 ◇ C	NT	NT
Manchester Airport	85 d	13 34	13 52	13 47		14 07				14 15	14 34	14 52		14 47		15 07				15 15	15 34		15 52		16 07
Manchester Piccadilly 10	d	14 03	14 18	14 19	14 22	14 36		14 42	14 46	14 49	15 03	15 18		15 19	15 22	15 36	15 42	15 46		15 49	16 03	16 17	16 18	16 22	16 36
Ardwick	d																								
Ashburys	d	14 07		14 23						14 53	15 07			15 23						15 53	16 07	16 23			
Belle Vue	d	14 09									15 09										16 09				
Ryder Brow	d	14 11									15 11										16 11				
Reddish North	d	14 14							14 53		15 14							15 53			16 14				
Brinnington	d	14 17							14 57		15 17							15 57			16 17				
Bredbury	d	14 20							15 00		15 20							16 00			16 20				
Gorton	d			14 25						14 55				15 25						15 55		16 25			
Fairfield	d					14 43										15 43									16 43
Guide Bridge	d			14a29		14 46				14a59				15a29		15 46				15a59		16a29			16 46
Hyde North	d					14 50										15 50									16 50
Hyde Central	d					14 52										15 52									16 52
Woodley	d					14 55										15 55									16 55
Romiley	d	14 23			14 37	14 59			15 03		15 23				15 37	15 59		16 03			16 23			16 37	16 59
Rose Hill Marple	a					15 05										16 05									17 05
Marple	d	14a28			14a43				15 06		15a28				15a43			16 06			16a28			16a43	
Strines	d																	16 10							
New Mills Central	d								15 12									16 14							
Stockport	86 d		14 26					14 55				15 26					15 55						16 26		
Hazel Grove	86 d																								
Chinley	d								15 20									16 21							
Edale	d								15 29									16 30							
Hope (Derbyshire)	d								15 35									16 36							
Bamford	d								15 38									16 39							
Hathersage	d								15 42									16 43							
Grindleford	d								15 46									16 47							
Dore	d								15 54									16 54							
Sheffield 7	a		15 08					15 35	16 04			16 08					16 35	17 03					17 08		

For general notes see front of timetable
For details of catering facilities see Directory of Train Operators

A From Liverpool Lime Street to Norwich (Table 49)
B To Hadfield (Table 79)
C To Cleethorpes (Table 29)
D From Liverpool Lime Street to Nottingham (Table 49)

Table 78

Saturdays

Manchester Airport and Manchester → Romiley, Marple, Chinley and Sheffield

Network Diagram - see first page of Table 78

Station		EM ◇ A		NT	NT B	NT	NT B	TP 1 ◇ C		NT	NT	EM ◇ D	NT	NT B		NT	TP 1 ◇ C	NT B	NT	NT		EM ◇ D	NT	NT B	TP 1 ◇ C
Manchester Airport	85 ✈ d					16 34		16 52			17 04					17 34	17 52			18 10					18 52
Manchester Piccadilly 10	d	16 42		16 46	16 49	17 03	17 17	17 18		17 28	17 36	17 42	17 46	17 49		18 03	18 18	18 18	18 22	18 35		18 44	18 46	18 49	19 18
Ardwick	d																								
Ashburys	d				16 53	17 07	17 21							17 53		18 07		18 22						18 53	
Belle Vue	d					17 09										18 09									
Ryder Brow	d					17 11										18 11									
Reddish North	d			16 53		17 14							17 53			18 14							18 53		
Brinnington	d			16 57		17 17							17 57			18 17							18 57		
Bredbury	d			17 00		17 20							18 00			18 20							19 00		
Gorton	d				16 55		17 23							17 55				18 25						18 55	
Fairfield	d										17 43									18 43					
Guide Bridge	d				16a59		17a27				17 46			17a59				18a29		18 46				18a59	
Hyde North	d										17 50									18 50					
Hyde Central	d										17 52									18 52					
Woodley	d										17 55									18 55					
Romiley	d			17 03		17 23				17 41	17 59		18 03			18 23			18 37	18 59			19 03		
Rose Hill Marple	a										18 05									19 05					
Marple	d			17 06		17a28				17a45			18 06			18a28			18a43				19 06		
Strines	d												18 10												
New Mills Central	d			17 12									18 14										19 14		
Stockport	86 d	16 53						17 26				17 55					18 26					18 55			19 26
Hazel Grove	86 d																								
Chinley	d			17 19				17 43					18 21										19 22		
Edale	d			17 28									18 30										19 30		
Hope (Derbyshire)	d			17 35									18 36										19 36		
Bamford	d			17 38									18 39										19 39		
Hathersage	d			17 41									18 43										19 43		
Grindleford	d			17 46									18 47										19 47		
Dore	d	17 28		17 55				18 06					18 54				19 02						19 55		
Sheffield 7	a	17 37		18 04				18 12				18 35	19 04				19 08					19 35	20 04		20 08

Station		NT	EM ◇ E	NT		NT B	TP 1 ◇ C	NT	EM ◇ E	NT		NT B	TP 1 ◇ C	EM ◇ G	NT	NT B		TP 1 ◇	NT	NT B	NT H	NT J			
Manchester Airport	85 ✈ d		19 12			19 15	19 52		20 15			20 22	20 52	21 04	21 16	21 22		21 52		22 22	22 47				
Manchester Piccadilly 10	d	19 22	19 42	19 46		19 49	20 18	20 27	20 42	20 46		20 49	21 18	21 42	21 46	21 49		22 18	22 38	22 49	23 23	23 26			
Ardwick	d																								
Ashburys	d	19 26		19 51		19 53				20 50		20 53			21 50	21 53			22 42	22 53	23 27	23 30			
Belle Vue	d	19 28		19 53						20 52					21 52				22 44		23 29				
Ryder Brow	d	19 30		19 55						20 54					21 54				22 46		23 31				
Reddish North	d	19 33		19 58						20 57					21 57				22 49		23 34				
Brinnington	d	19 36		20 01						21 00					22 00				22 52		23 37				
Bredbury	d	19 39		20 04						21 03					22 03				22 55		23 40				
Gorton	d					19 55						20 55				21 55				22 55		23 32			
Fairfield	d							20 34																	
Guide Bridge	d					19a59		20 39				20a59				21a59				22a59		23a36			
Hyde North	d							20 43																	
Hyde Central	d							20 45																	
Woodley	d							20 48																	
Romiley	d	19 42		20 07				20 52		21 06					22 06				22 58		23 43				
Rose Hill Marple	a							20 57																	
Marple	d	19a47		20 11						21 10					22 10				23 02		23 47				
Strines	d			20 15											22 14				23 06		23 51				
New Mills Central	d			20a21						21 14					22a20				23a10		23a56				
Stockport	86 d		19 55				20 26		20 55				21 26	21 52				22 26							
Hazel Grove	86 d																								
Chinley	d									21 22															
Edale	d									21 30															
Hope (Derbyshire)	d									21 36															
Bamford	d									21 39															
Hathersage	d									21 43															
Grindleford	d									21 46															
Dore	d									21 54															
Sheffield 7	a		20 34				21 08		21 34	22 03			22 09	22 31				23 13							

For general notes see front of timetable
For details of catering facilities see Directory of Train Operators

- **A** From Liverpool Lime Street to Norwich (Table 49)
- **B** To Hadfield (Table 79)
- **C** To Cleethorpes (Table 29)
- **D** From Liverpool Lime Street to Cambridge (Table 49)
- **E** From Liverpool Lime Street to Nottingham (Table 49)
- **G** To Nottingham (Table 49)
- **H** From Manchester Oxford Road dep. 2319 (Table 84)
- **J** To Glossop (Table 79)

Table 78

Sundays
until 27 January

Manchester Airport and Manchester → Romiley, Marple, Chinley and Sheffield

Network Diagram - see first page of Table 78

	NT	TP 🚌	NT 🚌		NT A	NT	NT A		TP 🚌	NT 🚌	NT A		NT A	TP 🚌	NT A		EM 🚌	NT A	NT		TP 🚌	NT A	TP 🚌	EM 🚌
Manchester Airport 85 ✈ d	07 10	07 36			08 51		09 25		09 47				10 22	10 47	11 00		11 05	11 27			12 15	11 47		
Manchester Piccadilly 10 d	07 45	08 00			09 23	09 35	09 53		10 15		10 23		10 53	11 15	11 23		11 35	11 53	12 01			12 23	12 25	12 35
Ashburys d	07 49				09 27	09 39	09 57				10 27		10 57		11 27			11 57	12 05			12 27		
Belle Vue d	07 51					09 42													12 07					
Ryder Brow d	07 53					09 44													12 09					
Reddish North d	07 56					09 46													12 12					
Brinnington d	07 59					09 50													12 15					
Bredbury d	08 02					09 53													12 18					
Gorton d					09 29		09 59				10 29		10 59		11 29			11 59				12 29		
Guide Bridge d					09a33		10a03				10a33		11a03		11a33			12a03				12a33		
Romiley d	08 05					09 56													12 21					
Marple d	08 09					09 59													12 25					
Strines d	08 13					10 03													12 29					
New Mills Central d	08a18		08 25			10a09				10 15									12a34					
Stockport 86 d		08 25							10 40					11 40			12 00				12 35			13 00
Hazel Grove 86 d																								
Chinley d			08 45							10 35														
Edale d			09 05							10 55														
Hope (Derbyshire) d			09 19							11 09														
Bamford d			09 25							11 15														
Hathersage d			09 30							11 20														
Grindleford d			09 40							11 30														
Dore d			10 03							11 53														
Sheffield 7 a		09 45	10 15						12 00	12 05				13 00			13 25				13 55		13 55	14 25

	NT 🚌		NT A	TP 🚌	NT A		TP 🚌	EM 🚌	NT A		NT	TP 🚌	NT A		TP 🚌	EM 🚌	NT 🚌		NT A	TP 🚌	NT A		TP 🚌	EM 🚌
Manchester Airport 85 ✈ d			12 22	13 15	12 46			13b22	13 27			14 15	13 47						14 27	15 15	14 47			
Manchester Piccadilly 10 d			12 53		13 23		13 25	13 49	13 53		14 01		14 23		14 25	14 43			14 53		15 23		15 25	15 43
Ashburys d			12 57		13 27				13 57		14 05		14 27						14 57		15 27			
Belle Vue d											14 07													
Ryder Brow d											14 09													
Reddish North d											14 12													
Brinnington d											14 15													
Bredbury d											14 18													
Gorton d			12 59		13 29				13 59				14 29						14 59		15 29			
Guide Bridge d			13a03		13a33				14a03				14a33						15a03		15a33			
Romiley d											14 21													
Marple d											14 25													
Strines d											14 29													
New Mills Central d	12 40										14a34						14 40							
Stockport 86 d				13 35				14 05				14 35				15 00				15 35				16 00
Hazel Grove 86 d																								
Chinley d	13 00																15 00							
Edale d	13 20																15 20							
Hope (Derbyshire) d	13 34																15 34							
Bamford d	13 40																15 40							
Hathersage d	13 45																15 45							
Grindleford d	13 55																15 55							
Dore d	14 18																16 18							
Sheffield 7 a	14 30			14 55			14 55	15 30				15 55			15 55	16 25	16 30			16 55			16 55	17 20

	NT A	NT	TP 🚌		NT A	TP 🚌	EM 🚌		NT 🚌	NT A	TP 🚌		NT A	TP 🚌	EM 🚌		NT A	NT	TP 🚌		NT A	TP 🚌	EM 🚌	NT 🚌
Manchester Airport 85 ✈ d	15 27		16 15		15 47					16 27	17 15		16 47				17 27		18 15		17 47			
Manchester Piccadilly 10 d	15 53	16 07			16 23	16 25	16 43			16 53			17 23	17 25	17 43		17 53	18 01			18 23	18 25	18 42	
Ashburys d	15 57	16 11			16 27					16 57			17 27				17 57	18 05			18 27			
Belle Vue d		16 13																18 07						
Ryder Brow d		16 15																18 09						
Reddish North d		16 18																18 12						
Brinnington d		16 21																18 15						
Bredbury d		16 24																18 18						
Gorton d	15 59				16 29					16 59			17 29				17 59				18 29			
Guide Bridge d	16a03				16a33					17a03			17a33				18a03				18a33			
Romiley d		16 27																18 21						
Marple d		16 31																18 25						
Strines d		16 35																18 29						
New Mills Central d		16a40							16 45									18a34						18 40
Stockport 86 d			16 35				17 00				17 35				18 00				18 35				19 05	
Hazel Grove 86 d																								
Chinley d									17 05															19 00
Edale d									17 25															19 20
Hope (Derbyshire) d									17 39															19 34
Bamford d									17 45															19 40
Hathersage d									17 50															19 45
Grindleford d									18 00															19 55
Dore d									18 23															20 18
Sheffield 7 a			17 55			17 55	18 25		18 35		18 55			18 55	19 25				19 55			19 55	20 30	20 30

For general notes see front of timetable
For details of catering facilities see Directory of Train Operators

A To Hadfield (Table 79)
b Change at Manchester Piccadilly and Stockport

Manchester Airport and Manchester → Romiley, Marple, Chinley and Sheffield

Sundays
until 27 January

Network Diagram - see first page of Table 78

	NT		TP	NT	TP		EM	NT	NT		TP	EM	NT		NT	TP	NT		TP	EM	TP			
	A			A				A				B			A									
			🚌		🚌		🚌				🚌	🚌	🚌			🚌			🚌	🚌	🚌			
Manchester Airport 85 ✈ d	18 27		19 15	18 47				19 22			19 47	20b01			20 27	20 47	21 47		22 01		22 47			
Manchester Piccadilly 10 d	18 53			19 23	19 25		19 42	19 53	20 01		20 25	20 43			20 53	21 25	22 20		22 25		23 25			
Ashburys d	18 57			19 27				19 57	20 05						20 57		22 24							
Belle Vue d									20 07								22 26							
Ryder Brow d									20 09								22 28							
Reddish North d									20 12								22 31							
Brinnington d									20 15								22 34							
Bredbury d									20 18								22 37							
Gorton d	18 59			19 29				19 59							20 59									
Guide Bridge d	19a03			19a33				20a03							21a03									
Romiley d									20 21								22 40							
Marple d									20 25								22 44							
Strines d									20 29								22 48							
New Mills Central d									20a34				20 40				22a53							
Stockport 86 d			19 35				20 00				20 50	21 00				21 50			22 50	22 10	23 50			
Hazel Grove 86 d																								
Chinley d													21 00							22 50				
Edale d													21 20							23 10				
Hope (Derbyshire) d													21 34							23 24				
Bamford d													21 40							23 29				
Hathersage d													21 45							23 34				
Grindleford d													21 55							23 44				
Dore d													22 18							00 04				
Sheffield 7 a			20 55		20 55		21 25				22 10	22 25	22 30			23 10			00 10	00 19	01 10			

Sundays
from 3 February

	NT	TP	NT	NT	NT	NT		NT	TP	NT	NT	NT	NT		EM	NT	TP	NT	EM	NT		NT	TP	NT
		1 ◇							1 ◇						◇		1 ◇		◇				1 ◇	
		C	A		A	A		A	C	A	A		A		D	A	C	A	E	A			C	A
Manchester Airport 85 ✈ d	07 10	08 40	08 51		09 25	09 47		10 22	10 52	11 00	11c27		11 47		12 13	12 22	12 52		13 22	13e27			13 52	
Manchester Piccadilly 10 d	07 45	09 05	09 23	09 35	09 53	10 23		10 53	11 12	11 23	11 53	12 01	12 23		12 44	12 53	13 12	13 23	13 49	13 53		14 01	14 15	14 23
Ashburys d	07 49		09 27	09 39	09 57	10 27		10 57		11 27	11 57	12 05	12 27			12 57		13 27		13 57		14 05		14 27
Belle Vue d	07 51			09 42								12 07										14 07		
Ryder Brow d	07 53			09 44								12 09										14 09		
Reddish North d	07 56			09 46								12 12										14 12		
Brinnington d	07 59			09 50								12 15										14 15		
Bredbury d	08 02			09 53								12 18										14 18		
Gorton d			09 29		09 59	10 29		10 59		11 29	11 59		12 29			12 59		13 29		13 59				14 29
Guide Bridge d			09a33		10a03	10a33		11a03		11a33	12a03		12a33			13a03		13a33		14a03				14a33
Romiley d	08 05			09 56								12 21										14 21		
Marple d	08 09			09 59								12 25										14 25		
Strines d	08 13			10 03								12 29										14 29		
New Mills Central d	08 17			10 07								12 34										14 34		
Stockport 86 d		09 13							11 21						12 54		13 21		13 58			→	14 22	
Hazel Grove 86 d																								
Chinley d	08 24			10 14								12 42												
Edale d	08 33			10 23								12 51												
Hope (Derbyshire) d	08 39			10 29								12 57												
Bamford d	08 42			10 32								13 00												
Hathersage d	08 46			10 35								13 03												
Grindleford d	08 49			10 39								13 07												
Dore d	08 58			10 48								13 18												
Sheffield 7 a	09 05	09 54		10 56					12 03			13 25			13 37		14 06		14 37				15 03	

	NT	EM	NT	NT	TP		NT	NT	EM	NT	NT	TP		NT	NT	EM	NT	TP	NT		EM	NT	NT	TP
		◇			1 ◇				◇			1 ◇				◇		1 ◇			◇			1 ◇
		E	A	G	C		G	A	E	A		C		A		E	A	C	A		H	A		C
Manchester Airport 85 ✈ d		14 00	14c27		14 52			14 52	15 08	15c27		15 52				16 01	16c27	16 52	17 01		17 05	17c27		17 52
Manchester Piccadilly 10 d		14 43	14 53	15 08	15 15			15 23	15 43	15 53	16 07	16 15		16 23		16 43	16 53	17 15	17 23		17 43	17 53	18 01	18 15
Ashburys d			14 57					15 27		15 57	16 11			16 27			16 57		17 27			17 57	18 05	
Belle Vue d											16 13												18 07	
Ryder Brow d											16 15												18 09	
Reddish North d											16 18												18 12	
Brinnington d											16 21												18 15	
Bredbury d											16 24												18 18	
Gorton d			14 59					15 29		15 59				16 29			16 59		17 29			17 59		
Guide Bridge d			15a03					15a33		16a03				16a33			17a03		17a33			18a03		
Romiley d											16 27												18 21	
Marple d											16 31												18 25	
Strines d	←						←				16 35				←								18 29	
New Mills Central d	14 34										16 38				16 38								18 34	
Stockport 86 d		14 54		15 27	15 22		15 27		15 54		→	16 22				16 55		17 22			17 54		→	18 22
Hazel Grove 86 d				→			15 34																	
Chinley d	14 42						15 45								16 46									
Edale d	14 51						15 54								16 55									
Hope (Derbyshire) d	14 57						16 00								17 01									
Bamford d	15 00						16 03								17 04									
Hathersage d	15 03						16 06								17 07									
Grindleford d	15 07						16 10								17 11									
Dore d	15 15						16 21								17 24									
Sheffield 7 a	15 23	15 35			16 03		16 28		16 35			17 03			17 31	17 35		18 06			18 36			19 03

For general notes see front of timetable
For details of catering facilities see Directory of Train Operators

A To Hadfield (Table 79)
B To Nottingham (Table 49)
C To Cleethorpes (Table 29)
D To Norwich (Table 49)
E From Liverpool Lime Street to Norwich (Table 49)
G From 30 March
H From Liverpool Lime Street to Nottingham (Table 49)
b Change at Manchester Piccadilly and Stockport
c From 30 March dep. 5 minutes earlier
e Until 23 March only

Table 78

Sundays

from 3 February

Manchester Airport and Manchester → Romiley, Marple, Chinley and Sheffield

Network Diagram - see first page of Table 78

	NT	NT	EM	NT		TP	NT	EM	NT	NT	TP		NT	EM	NT	TP	EM	TP		EM	NT	TP		
			◇			1 ◇		◇			1 ◇			◇		1 ◇	◇	1 ◇		◇		1 ◇		
	A		B	A		C	A	D	A		C			D	A		D			D				
Manchester Airport 85 ✈ d			*18 01*	*18*b*27*		18 52		*19 05*	*19 22*		19 52			*20 01*	*20*b*27*	20 52		21 52				22 52		
Manchester Piccadilly 10 d	18 23		18 42	18 53		19 15	19 23	19 42	19 53	20 01	20 15			20 43	20 53	21 15	22 12	22 15			22 20	23 15		
Ashburys d	18 27			18 57			19 27		19 57	20 05					20 57						22 24			
Belle Vue d										20 07											22 26			
Ryder Brow d										20 09											22 28			
Reddish North d										20 12											22 31			
Brinnington d										20 15											22 34			
Bredbury d										20 18											22 37			
Gorton d	18 29			18 59			19 29		19 59						20 59									
Guide Bridge d	18a33			19a03			19a33		20a03						21a03									
Romiley d										20 21											22 40			
Marple d										20 25											22 44			
Strines d		←								20 29			←								22 48			
New Mills Central d		18 34								20 32			20 32							←	22a53			
Stockport 86 d			18 56			19 22		19 54		→	20 22			20 53		21 22	22 26 →	22 22		22 26		23 22		
Hazel Grove 86 d																								
Chinley d		18 42											20 42							22 43				
Edale d		18 50											20 50							22 51				
Hope (Derbyshire) d		18 56											20 56							22 57				
Bamford d		18 59											20 59							23 00				
Hathersage d		19 03											21 03							23 03				
Grindleford d		19 06											21 06							23 07				
Dore d		19 14											21 14							23 17				
Sheffield 7 a		19 21	19 35			20 04		20 35			21 06		21 23	21 38		22 06		23 06		23 23		00 09		

For general notes see front of timetable
For details of catering facilities see Directory of Train Operators

- **A** To Hadfield (Table 79)
- **B** From Liverpool Lime Street to Norwich (Table 49)
- **C** To Cleethorpes (Table 29)
- **D** From Liverpool Lime Street to Nottingham (Table 49)
- **b** From 30 March dep. 5 minutes earlier

Sheffield, Chinley, Marple and Romiley → Manchester and Manchester Airport

Network Diagram - see first page of Table 78

Miles	Miles	Miles			TP	TP	TP	TP	NT	NT	TP		NT	NT	NT	EM	NT	NT	NT		NT	NT	TP	NT	NT
						MO																			
					1 ◇	1 ◇	1 ◇	1 ◇			1 ◇					◇							1 ◇		
					A	B			C		D			C		E ✠		C				C	G ✠		
0	—	—	**Sheffield 7**	d	01 50	01 50	03 45	05 11			06 11					06 20							07 10		
4¾	—	—	Dore	d												06 27							07 16		
9¾	—	—	Grindleford	d												06 35									
11¼	—	—	Hathersage	d												06 39									
13	—	—	Bamford	d												06 43									
14¾	—	—	Hope (Derbyshire)	d												06 47									
20	—	—	Edale	d												06 55									
25½	—	0	**Chinley**	d												07 03									
—	—	8½	Hazel Grove	86 a																					
—	—	—	Stockport	86 a				05 53			06 53					07 23							07 55		
29¼	—	—	New Mills Central	d						06 21					06 42				07 14		07 29				
30¾	—	—	Strines	d						06 24					06 45				07 17		07 32				
33	—	—	**Marple**	d						06 28					06 49				07 21		07 35				07 49
—	0	—	**Rose Hill Marple**	d									06 33				07 04							07 40	
34¼	2	—	**Romiley**	d						06 31			06 38		06 52		07 09		07 24		07 39			07 45	07 52
—	3¼	—	Woodley	d									06 41				07 12							07 48	
—	4¾	—	Hyde Central	d									06 44				07 15							07 51	
—	6	—	Hyde North	d									06 47				07 18							07 55	
—	7¾	—	Guide Bridge	d					06 27				06 50	06 57			07 22	07 28				07 47		07 59	
—	9	—	Fairfield	d									06 53				07 25							08 02	
—	10	—	Gorton	d					06 30					07 00				07 31				07 50			
35½	—	—	Bredbury	d						06 34					06 55				07 27		07 42				07 55
36½	—	—	Brinnington	d						06 37					06 58				07 30		07 44				07 58
38¼	—	—	Reddish North	d						06 40					07 01				07 33		07 47				08 01
39¼	—	—	Ryder Brow	d						06 42					07 03				07 35						08 03
39½	—	—	Belle Vue	d						06 44					07 05				07 37						08 05
40½	11	—	Ashburys	d					06 33	06 47			06 57	07 03	07 08		07 28	07 34	07 40			07 54		08 06	08 09
41½	12	—	Ardwick	d														07 37							
42	12½	8¾	**Manchester Piccadilly 10**	a	02 42	02 54	04 40	06 04	06 42	06 53	07 05		07 06	07 12	07 15	07 35	07 36	07 42	07 47		08 00	08 03	08 08	08 13	08 16
—	—	—	**Manchester Airport**	85 ✈ a	03 06	03 14	05 01	06 34	*07 12*	*07 20*	07 35		*07 40*		*07 49*		*08 02*	*08 19*	*08 22*				08 33	*08 42*	

		NT	NT	NT	EM		NT	NT	NT	NT	TP	NT	NT		NT	NT	NT	EM	NT	NT	TP		NT	NT	NT
					◇						1 ◇							◇			1 ◇				
		C			E ✠		C				G ✠	C			C			E ✠	C		G ✠		C		
Sheffield 7	d			07 14	07 37						08 05							08 42			09 11				
Dore	d			07 21	07 45						08 11														
Grindleford	d			07 29																					
Hathersage	d			07 32																					
Bamford	d			07 36																					
Hope (Derbyshire)	d			07 39																					
Edale	d			07 47																					
Chinley	d			07 56	08 06						08 33														
Hazel Grove	86 a				08 19																				
Stockport	86 a				08 26						08 51							09 24			09 53				
New Mills Central	d			08 04					08 19								09 03								
Strines	d			08 07													09 06								
Marple	d		07 57	08 11					08 24	08 35			08 50				09 10			09 35				09 52	
Rose Hill Marple	d							08 13								08 59									09 55
Romiley	d		08 01	08 14				08 18	08 27	08 38			08 53			09 04	09 14			09 38				09 55	10 00
Woodley	d							08 21								09 09									10 03
Hyde Central	d							08 24								09 12									10 06
Hyde North	d							08 27								09 14									10 09
Guide Bridge	d	08 07					08 27	08 31				08 47			09 07	09 18			09 28				09 58		10 15
Fairfield	d							08 34								09 21									10 18
Gorton	d	08 10					08 30					08 50			09 10				09 31				10 01		
Bredbury	d		08 04						08 30	08 41			08 56				09 17			09 41					
Brinnington	d		08 06						08 33	08 44			08 59				09 20			09 44					
Reddish North	d		08 09						08 36	08 47			09 02				09 23			09 47					
Ryder Brow	d		08 12										09 04											10 03	
Belle Vue	d		08 14										09 06											10 04	
Ashburys	d	08 13	08 17				08 33	08 37	08 41			08 53	09 09		09 13				09 34				10 04	10 07	
Ardwick	d		08 20						08 44																
Manchester Piccadilly 10	a	08 19	08 26	08 34	08 36		08 42	08 45	08 49	08 57	09 01	09 02	09 15		09 21	09 31	09 34	09 36	09 42	09 57	10 03		10 12	10 15	10 28
Manchester Airport	85 ✈ a	*08 51*			*09 06*		*09 13*	*09 18*	*09 25*		09 33	*09 40*	*09 44*		*09 56*			*10 01*	*10 14*		10 33		*10 40*	*10 44*	

For general notes see front of timetable
For details of catering facilities see Directory of Train Operators

A All Tuesdays to Fridays, also Mondays from 4 February
B Until 28 January
C From Hadfield (Table 79)
D From Doncaster (Table 29)
E From Nottingham to Liverpool Lime Street (Table 49)
G From Cleethorpes (Table 29)

Sheffield, Chinley, Marple and Romiley → Manchester and Manchester Airport

Network Diagram - see first page of Table 78

	NT	EM ◇ A ⊥	NT B	NT	NT	NT		TP 1 ◇ C ⊥	NT B	NT	NT	EM ◇ D ⊥	NT B	NT		NT	NT	TP 1 ◇ C ⊥	NT B	NT	NT	EM ◇ A ⊥		NT B
Sheffield 7 d	09 14	09 42						10 11			10 14	10 42						11 11				11 42		
Dore d	09 21										10 21													
Grindleford d	09 29										10 29													
Hathersage d	09 32										10 32													
Bamford d	09 36										10 36													
Hope (Derbyshire) d	09 39										10 39													
Edale d	09 47										10 47													
Chinley d	09 55										10 55													
Hazel Grove 86 a																								
Stockport 86 a		10 24						10 53				11 24						11 53				12 24		
New Mills Central d	10 01										11 01										12 01			
Strines d	10 04																				12 04			
Marple d	10 07				10 35					10 52	11 07					11 35				11 52	12 07			
Rose Hill Marple d				10 30										11 30										
Romiley d	10 11			10 35	10 38	←				10 55	11 11			11 35		11 38	←			11 55	12 11			
Woodley d				10 38		10 38								11 38			11 38							
Hyde Central d				→		10 41								→			11 41							
Hyde North d						10 44											11 44							
Guide Bridge d			10 28			10 48			10 58				11 28				11 48		11 58					12 28
Fairfield d						10 51											11 51							
Gorton d			10 31						11 01				11 31						12 01					12 31
Bredbury d	10 14				10 41						11 14					11 41					12 14			
Brinnington d	10 16				10 44						11 16					11 44					12 16			
Reddish North d	10 19				10 47						11 19					11 47					12 19			
Ryder Brow d										11 03										12 03				
Belle Vue d										11 04										12 04				
Ashburys d			10 34						11 04	11 07			11 34						12 04	12 07				12 34
Ardwick d																								
Manchester Piccadilly 10 a	10 31	10 36	10 42		10 57	11 02		11 03	11 12	11 15	11 31	11 36	11 42			11 57	12 02	12 03	12 12	12 15	12 31	12 36		12 42
Manchester Airport 85 ✈ a		*11 01*	*11 14*					11 33	*11 40*	*11 44*		*12 01*	*12 14*					12 33	*12 40*	*12 51*		*13 01*		*13 14*

	NT	NT	NT	TP 1 ◇ C ⊥	NT B	NT	NT		EM ◇ A ⊥	NT B	NT	NT	NT	TP 1 ◇ C ⊥	NT B		NT	NT	EM ◇ A ⊥	NT B	NT	NT	NT	TP 1 ◇ C ⊥
Sheffield 7 d				12 11			12 14		12 42					13 11					13 42					14 11
Dore d							12 21																	
Grindleford d							12 28																	
Hathersage d							12 32																	
Bamford d							12 35																	
Hope (Derbyshire) d							12 39																	
Edale d							12 46																	
Chinley d							12 54																	
Hazel Grove 86 a																								
Stockport 86 a				12 53					13 24					13 53					14 24					14 53
New Mills Central d							13 01											14 01						
Strines d																		14 04						
Marple d		12 35				12 52	13 07					13 35					13 52	14 07				14 35		
Rose Hill Marple d	12 30										13 30										14 30			
Romiley d	12 35	12 38	←			12 55	13 11				13 35	13 38	←				13 55	14 11			14 35	14 38	←	
Woodley d	12 38		12 38								13 38		13 38								14 38		14 38	
Hyde Central d	→		12 41								→		13 41								→		14 41	
Hyde North d			12 44										13 44										14 44	
Guide Bridge d			12 48		12 58					13 28			13 48		13 58					14 28			14 48	
Fairfield d			12 51										13 51										14 51	
Gorton d					13 01					13 31					14 01					14 31				
Bredbury d		12 41					13 14					13 41						14 14				14 41		
Brinnington d		12 44					13 16					13 44						14 16				14 44		
Reddish North d		12 47					13 19					13 47						14 19				14 47		
Ryder Brow d						13 03											14 03							
Belle Vue d						13 04											14 04							
Ashburys d					13 04	13 07				13 34					14 04		14 07			14 34				
Ardwick d																								
Manchester Piccadilly 10 a		12 57	13 02	13 03	13 12	13 15	13 31		13 36	13 42		13 57	14 02	14 03	14 12		14 15	14 31	14 36	14 42		14 57	15 02	15 03
Manchester Airport 85 ✈ a				13 33	*13 40*	*13 44*			*14 01*	*14 14*				14 33	*14 40*		*14 44*		*15 01*	*15 14*				15 33

For general notes see front of timetable
For details of catering facilities see Directory of Train Operators

A From Norwich to Liverpool Lime Street (Table 49)
B From Hadfield (Table 79)
C From Cleethorpes (Table 29)
D From Cambridge to Liverpool Lime Street (Table 49)

Sheffield, Chinley, Marple and Romiley → Manchester and Manchester Airport

Network Diagram - see first page of Table 78

		NT A		NT	NT	EM ◇ B 🍴	NT A	NT	NT	NT		TP 1 ◇ C 🍴	NT	NT A	NT	NT	EM ◇ B 🍴	NT A		NT	TP 1 ◇ C 🍴	NT A	NT	NT	NT
Sheffield 7	d				14 14	14 42						15 11					15 42				16 11				
Dore	d				14 21																				
Grindleford	d				14 29																				
Hathersage	d				14 32																				
Bamford	d				14 36																				
Hope (Derbyshire)	d				14 39																				
Edale	d				14 47																				
Chinley	d				14 55																				
Hazel Grove	86 a																								
Stockport	86 a					15 24						15 53					16 24				16 53				
New Mills Central	d				15 01										15 47										
Strines	d														15 50										
Marple	d			14 52	15 07				15 35				15 47		15 53					16 36				16 45	
Rose Hill Marple	d							15 27								16 10							16 30		
Romiley	d			14 55	15 11			15 32	15 38	←			15 50		15 57	16 15				16 39			16 44	16 48	←
Woodley	d							15 38 →		15 38													16 47 →		16 47
Hyde Central	d									15 41															16 50
Hyde North	d									15 44															16 53
Guide Bridge	d	14 58					15 28			15 48				15 58				16 28				16 49			16 57
Fairfield	d									15 51															17 00
Gorton	d	15 01					15 31							16 01				16 31				16 52			
Bredbury	d				15 14				15 41						16 00	16 18								16 51	
Brinnington	d				15 16				15 44						16 02										
Reddish North	d				15 19				15 47						16 05	16 22								16 56	
Ryder Brow	d			15 03									15 58											16 58	
Belle Vue	d			15 04									15 59											17 00	
Ashburys	d	15 04		15 07			15 34						16 02	16 04				16 34				16 56		17 03	17 06
Ardwick	d																								
Manchester Piccadilly 10	a	15 12		15 15	15 31	15 36	15 42		15 57	16 01		16 03	16 10	16 12	16 16	16 32	16 35	16 42		16 54	17 03	17 04		17 10	17 14
Manchester Airport	85 ✈ a	*15 40*		*15 44*		*16 01*	*16 14*					16 33		*16 40*	*16 51*			*17 14*			17 39	*17 39*		*17 40*	*17 56*

		NT	NT A	EM ◇ B 🍴		NT	NT	NT A	NT	TP 1 ◇ C 🍴	NT D	NT		NT	NT A	EM ◇ B 🍴	NT	NT	NT A	TP 1 ◇ C 🍴		NT	NT A	NT	EM ◇ B 🍴
Sheffield 7	d	16 14		16 42						17 11				17 14		17 42				18 11					18 42
Dore	d	16 21												17 21											
Grindleford	d	16 29												17 29											
Hathersage	d	16 32												17 32											
Bamford	d	16 36												17 36											
Hope (Derbyshire)	d	16 39												17 39											
Edale	d	16 47												17 47											
Chinley	d	16 55												17 55						18 35				18 55	
Hazel Grove	86 a																								
Stockport	86 a			17 25						17 53						18 26				18 53					19 24
New Mills Central	d	17 01					17 21							18 01										19 01	
Strines	d													18 04										19 04	
Marple	d	17 06					17 26		17 34			17 58		18 08				18 25						19 07	
Rose Hill Marple	d					17 21											18 11					18 44			
Romiley	d	17 10					17 30		17 37					18 11			18 16	18 28				18 49		19 11	
Woodley	d																18 19								
Hyde Central	d																18 22								
Hyde North	d																18 25								
Guide Bridge	d		17 16					17 41			17 58				18 16		18 29		18 46				19 00		
Fairfield	d																18 32								
Gorton	d		17 19					17 44			18 02				18 20				18 49				19 03		
Bredbury	d								17 40					18 14				18 31				18 52		19 14	
Brinnington	d								17 43													18 54		19 16	
Reddish North	d								17 46													18 57		19 19	
Ryder Brow	d																					19 00			
Belle Vue	d																					19 01			
Ashburys	d		17 22					17 47	17 51		18 04				18 24				18 53				19 06		
Ardwick	d																								
Manchester Piccadilly 10	a	17 28	17 31	17 36		17 42	17 45	17 56	18 00	18 03	18 12	18 16		18 31	18 32	18 36	18 41	18 45	19 01	19 03		19 10	19 13	19 31	19 36
Manchester Airport	85 ✈ a			*18 05*			*18 14*			18 38	*18 42*	*18 46*					*19 09*	*19 14*		19 34		*19 40*	*19 52*		*20 05*

For general notes see front of timetable
For details of catering facilities see Directory of Train Operators

A From Hadfield (Table 79)
B From Norwich to Liverpool Lime Street (Table 49)
C From Cleethorpes (Table 29)
D From Hadfield (Table 49)

Sheffield, Chinley, Marple and Romiley → Manchester and Manchester Airport

Network Diagram - see first page of Table 78

		NT A	NT	NT	TP 1◇ B	NT A		NT	EM ◇ C	NT A	TP 1◇ B	NT	NT A	EM ◇ D		NT	NT	NT A	TP 1◇ B	NT	NT A	NT	NT
Sheffield 7	d				19 11			19 14	19 42		20 11			20 31			20 34		22 11			22 47	
Dore	d							19 22									20 42					22 54	
Grindleford	d							19 29									20 53					23 01	
Hathersage	d							19 32									20 57					23 05	
Bamford	d							19 36									21 00					23 08	
Hope (Derbyshire)	d							19 39									21 04					23 12	
Edale	d							19 47									21 11					23 19	
Chinley	d							19 55									21 19					23 27	
Hazel Grove	86 a																						
Stockport	86 a				19 52				20 26		20 53			21 17					22 53			23 46	
New Mills Central	d							20 01				20 30					21 30			22 30			23 30
Strines	d											20 33								22 33			23 33
Marple	d			19 36				20 07				20 36					21 36			22 36			23 36
Rose Hill Marple	d		19 15													21 10							
Romiley	d		19 20	19 39				20 11				20 40				21 15	21 40			22 40			23 40
Woodley	d		19 23													21 18							
Hyde Central	d		19 26													21 21							
Hyde North	d		19 29													21 24							
Guide Bridge	d	19 28	19 33			19 58				20 28			20 58			21 28		21 58			22 58		
Fairfield	d		19 36													21 31							
Gorton	d	19 31				20 01				20 31			21 01					22 01			23 01		
Bredbury	d			19 42				20 14				20 43					21 43			22 43			23 43
Brinnington	d			19 45				20 16				20 45					21 45			22 45			23 45
Reddish North	d			19 48				20 19				20 48					21 48			22 48			23 48
Ryder Brow	d			19 50								20 51					21 51			22 51			23 51
Belle Vue	d			19 52								20 52					21 52			22 52			23 52
Ashburys	d	19 34		19 55		20 04				20 34		20 55	21 04				21 55	22 04		22 55	23 04		23 55
Ardwick	d																						
Manchester Piccadilly 10	a	19 43	19 47	20 02	20 03	20 12		20 31	20 36	20 42	21 03	21 03	21 12	21 30		21 41	22 03	22 12	23 03	23 03	23 12	23 59	00 03
Manchester Airport	85 ✈ a	20 12	20 19		20 34	20 58		21 06	21 09	21 19	21 34	21 37	21 51			22 15	22 39	22 58	23 28		23 58		00 45

Saturdays

		TP 1◇	TP 1◇	TP 1◇	TP 1◇ E	NT A	EM ◇ G	NT A	NT	NT	NT	NT	TP 1◇ B		NT A	NT	EM ◇ G	NT A	NT	NT	TP 1◇ B	NT	NT A	NT	NT
Sheffield 7	d	01 50	03 45	05 11	06 11		06 20						07 10			07 14	07 36				08 05				08 14
Dore	d						06 27						07 16			07 22					08 11				08 21
Grindleford	d						06 35									07 29									08 29
Hathersage	d						06 39									07 32									08 32
Bamford	d						06 43									07 36									08 36
Hope (Derbyshire)	d						06 47									07 39									08 39
Edale	d						06 55									07 47									08 47
Chinley	d						07 03									07 55	08 03				08 32				08 55
Hazel Grove	86 a																								
Stockport	86 a			05 53	06 53		07 23						07 55				08 25				08 51				
New Mills Central	d								07 10							08 04									09 01
Strines	d								07 13							08 07									09 04
Marple	d								07 17		07 37					08 10				08 35				08 52	09 07
Rose Hill Marple	d									07 30									08 30						
Romiley	d								07 20	07 35	07 40	←				08 14			08 35	08 38		←		08 55	09 11
Woodley	d									07 38 →		07 38							08 38 →			08 38			
Hyde Central	d											07 41										08 41			
Hyde North	d											07 44										08 44			
Guide Bridge	d					06 58		07 28				07 48			07 58			08 28				08 48	08 58		
Fairfield	d											07 51										08 51			
Gorton	d					07 01		07 31							08 01			08 31					09 01		
Bredbury	d								07 23		07 43									08 41					09 14
Brinnington	d								07 26		07 46									08 44					09 16
Reddish North	d								07 29		07 49									08 47					09 19
Ryder Brow	d								07 31															09 03	
Belle Vue	d								07 33															09 04	
Ashburys	d					07 04		07 34	07 37						08 04			08 34					09 04	09 07	
Ardwick	d																								
Manchester Piccadilly 10	a	02 43	04 40	06 04	07 05	07 12	07 35	07 42	07 45		08 01	08 02	08 08		08 12	08 31	08 36	08 42		08 58	09 01	09 02	09 12	09 15	09 31
Manchester Airport	85 ✈ a	03 06	05 01	06 34	07 35	07 49	08 02		08 19				08 33		08 42		09 06	09 13			09 33	09 40		09 44	

For general notes see front of timetable
For details of catering facilities see Directory of Train Operators

A From Hadfield (Table 79)
B From Cleethorpes (Table 29)
C From Norwich to Liverpool Lime Street (Table 49)
D From Norwich (Table 49)
E From Doncaster (Table 29)
G From Nottingham to Liverpool Lime Street (Table 49)

Sheffield, Chinley, Marple and Romiley → Manchester and Manchester Airport

Network Diagram - see first page of Table 78

	EM	NT	NT		NT	NT	TP	NT	NT	NT	EM	NT	NT	NT	NT	TP		NT	NT	NT	EM	NT	NT	NT
	◇						[1] ◇				◇					[1] ◇					◇			
	A	B					C	B			D	B				C		B			E	B	G	
Sheffield [7] d	08 42						09 11			09 14	09 42					10 11				10 14	10 42			
Dore d										09 21										10 21				
Grindleford d										09 29										10 29				
Hathersage d										09 32										10 32				
Bamford d										09 36										10 36				
Hope (Derbyshire) d										09 39										10 39				
Edale d										09 47										10 47				
Chinley d										09 55										10 55				
Hazel Grove 86 a																								
Stockport 86 a	09 25						09 53				10 24					10 53					11 24		11d28	
New Mills Central d										10 01										11 01				
Strines d										10 04														
Marple d					09 35				09 52	10 07				10 35					10 52	11 07				
Rose Hill Marple d			09 30										10 30											11 30
Romiley d			09 35		09 38	←			09 55	10 11			10 35	10 38	←				10 55	11 11				11 35
Woodley d			09 38 →			09 38							10 38 →		10 38									11 38 →
Hyde Central d						09 41									10 41									
Hyde North d						09 44									10 44									
Guide Bridge d		09 28				09 48		09 58				10 28			10 48			10 58				11 28	11a42	
Fairfield d						09 51									10 51									
Gorton d		09 31						10 01				10 31						11 01				11 31		
Bredbury d					09 41					10 14				10 41						11 14				
Brinnington d					09 44					10 16				10 44						11 16				
Reddish North d					09 47					10 19				10 47						11 19				
Ryder Brow d									10 03										11 03					
Belle Vue d									10 04										11 04					
Ashburys d		09 34						10 04	10 07			10 34						11 04	11 07			11 34		
Ardwick d																								
Manchester Piccadilly [10] a	09 36	09 42			09 57	10 02	10 03	10 12	10 15	10 31	10 36	10 42		10 57	11 02	11 03		11 12	11 15	11 31	11 36	11 42		
Manchester Airport 85 a	*10 02*	*10 14*					10 33	*10 40*	*10 44*		*11 01*	*11 14*				11 33		*11 40*	*11 44*		*12 01*	*12 14*		

	NT	NT	TP	NT	NT	NT	EM		NT	NT	NT	NT	TP	NT	NT	NT	EM	NT	NT	NT		NT	TP	NT
			[1] ◇				◇						[1] ◇				◇						[1] ◇	
			C	B			D		B				C	B			D	B					C	B
Sheffield [7] d			11 11			11 14	11 42						12 11			12 14	12 42						13 11	
Dore d						11 21										12 21								
Grindleford d						11 29										12 29								
Hathersage d						11 32										12 32								
Bamford d						11 36										12 36								
Hope (Derbyshire) d						11 39										12 39								
Edale d						11 47										12 47								
Chinley d						11 55										12 55								
Hazel Grove 86 a																								
Stockport 86 a			11 53				12 24						12 53				13 24						13 53	
New Mills Central d						12 01										13 01								
Strines d						12 04																		
Marple d	11 35				11 52	12 07					12 35				12 52	13 07				13 35				
Rose Hill Marple d										12 30									13 30					
Romiley d	11 38	←			11 55	12 11				12 35	12 38	←			12 55	13 11			13 35	13 38		←		
Woodley d		11 38								12 38 →		12 38							13 38 →			13 38		
Hyde Central d		11 41										12 41										13 41		
Hyde North d		11 44										12 44										13 44		
Guide Bridge d		11 48		11 58					12 28			12 48		12 58				13 28				13 48		13 58
Fairfield d		11 51										12 51										13 51		
Gorton d				12 01					12 31					13 01				13 31						14 01
Bredbury d	11 41					12 14					12 41					13 14				13 41				
Brinnington d	11 44					12 16					12 44					13 16				13 44				
Reddish North d	11 47					12 19					12 47					13 19				13 47				
Ryder Brow d					12 03										13 03									
Belle Vue d					12 04										13 04									
Ashburys d				12 04	12 07				12 34					13 04	13 07			13 34						14 04
Ardwick d																								
Manchester Piccadilly [10] a	11 57	12 02	12 03	12 12	12 15	12 31	12 36		12 42		12 57	13 02	13 03	13 12	13 15	13 31	13 36	13 42		13 57		14 02	14 03	14 12
Manchester Airport 85 a			12 33	*12 40*	*12b51*		*13 01*		*13 14*				13 33	*13 40*	*13 44*		*14 01*	*14 14*					14 33	*14 40*

For general notes see front of timetable
For details of catering facilities see Directory of Train Operators

A From Nottingham to Liverpool Lime Street (Table 49)
B From Hadfield (Table 79)
C From Cleethorpes (Table 29)
D From Norwich to Liverpool Lime Street (Table 49)
E From Cambridge to Liverpool Lime Street (Table 49)
G To Stalybridge arr. 1149. Also stops at Reddish South 11x33 and Denton 11x37
b From 2 February arr. 1244

Sheffield, Chinley, Marple and Romiley → Manchester and Manchester Airport

Network Diagram - see first page of Table 78

	NT	NT	EM	NT	NT	NT	NT	TP	NT	NT	NT		EM	NT	NT	NT	NT	TP	NT	NT	NT	EM	NT	NT
			◇ A	B				1 ◇ C	B				◇ A	B				1 ◇ C	B			◇ A	B	
Sheffield 7 d		13 14	13 42					14 11			14 14		14 42					15 11			15 14	15 42		
Dore d		13 22									14 21										15 21			
Grindleford d		13 29									14 29										15 28			
Hathersage d		13 32									14 32										15 32			
Bamford d		13 36									14 36										15 35			
Hope (Derbyshire) d		13 40									14 39										15 39			
Edale d		13 49									14 47										15 46			
Chinley d		13 57									14 55										15 54			
Hazel Grove 86 a																								
Stockport 86 a			14 25					14 53					15 24					15 53				16 24		
New Mills Central d		14 04									15 01										16 01			
Strines d		14 07																			16 04			
Marple d	13 52	14 09				14 35				14 52	15 07					15 35				15 52	16 07			
Rose Hill Marple d					14 30										15 30									16 30
Romiley d	13 55	14 14			14 35	14 38	←			14 55	15 11				15 35	15 38	←			15 55	16 11			16 35
Woodley d					14 38 →		14 38								15 38 →		15 38							16 38 →
Hyde Central d							14 41										15 41							
Hyde North d							14 44										15 44							
Guide Bridge d				14 28			14 48		14 58					15 28			15 48		15 58				16 28	
Fairfield d							14 51										15 51							
Gorton d				14 31					15 01					15 31					16 01				16 31	
Bredbury d		14 17				14 41					15 14					15 41					16 14			
Brinnington d		14 19				14 44					15 16					15 44					16 16			
Reddish North d		14 22				14 47					15 19					15 47					16 19			
Ryder Brow d	14 03									15 03										16 03				
Belle Vue d	14 04									15 04										16 04				
Ashburys d	14 07			14 34					15 04	15 07				15 34					16 04	16 07			16 34	
Ardwick d																								
Manchester Piccadilly 10 a	14 15	14 34	14 36	14 42		14 57	15 02	15 03	15 12	15 15	15 31		15 36	15 42		15 57	16 02	16 03	16 12	16 15	16 32	16 37	16 42	
Manchester Airport 85 a	14 44		15 01	15 14				15 33	15 40	15 44			16 01	16 14				16 33	16 40	16b51			17 11	

	NT	NT		TP	NT	NT	NT	EM	NT	NT	NT	NT	TP	NT	NT		NT	EM	NT	NT	NT	NT	TP	NT
				1 ◇ C	B			◇ A	B				1 ◇ C	B				◇ A	B				1 ◇ C	B
Sheffield 7 d				16 11			16 14	16 42					17 11				17 14	17 42					18 11	
Dore d							16 21										17 21							
Grindleford d							16 29										17 29							
Hathersage d							16 32										17 32							
Bamford d							16 36										17 36							
Hope (Derbyshire) d							16 39										17 39							
Edale d							16 47										17 47							
Chinley d							16 55										17 55						18 35	
Hazel Grove 86 a																								
Stockport 86 a				16 53				17 24					17 53					18 26					18 52	
New Mills Central d							17 01										18 01							
Strines d																	18 04							
Marple d	16 36					16 50	17 07				17 35				17 52		18 07				18 35			
Rose Hill Marple d										17 30										18 30				
Romiley d	16 39	←				16 53	17 11			17 35	17 38	←			17 55		18 11			18 35	18 38	←		
Woodley d		16 38								17 38 →		17 38								18 38 →		18 38		
Hyde Central d		16 41										17 41										18 41		
Hyde North d		16 44										17 44										18 44		
Guide Bridge d		16 48			16 58				17 28			17 48		17 58					18 28			18 48		18 58
Fairfield d		16 51										17 51										18 51		
Gorton d					17 01				17 31					18 01					18 31					19 01
Bredbury d						16 56	17 14								17 58		18 14				18 41			
Brinnington d						16 59	17 16								18 01		18 16				18 44			
Reddish North d						17 02	17 19								18 04		18 19				18 47			
Ryder Brow d						17 04									18 06									
Belle Vue d						17 06									18 08									
Ashburys d					17 04	17 09			17 34					18 04	18 11				18 34					19 04
Ardwick d																								
Manchester Piccadilly 10 a	16 54	17 02		17 03	17 12	17 16	17 32	17 35	17 42		17 54	18 03	18 03	18 12	18 18		18 31	18 35	18 42		18 57	19 02	19 03	19 12
Manchester Airport 85 a				17 39	17 40	17 56		18 05	18 14		18 27		18 38	18 42	18 57				19 08			19 40	19 34	

For general notes see front of timetable
For details of catering facilities see Directory of Train Operators

A From Norwich to Liverpool Lime Street (Table 49)
B From Hadfield (Table 79)
C From Cleethorpes (Table 29)
b From 29 March arr. 1645

Table 78

Saturdays

Sheffield, Chinley, Marple and Romiley → Manchester and Manchester Airport

Network Diagram - see first page of Table 78

		NT	NT	EM ◇ A	NT B	NT	TP 1 ◇ C		NT B	NT	NT	EM ◇ D	TP 1 ◇ C	NT	NT B	EM ◇ A	NT	NT	NT B	NT	NT B	NT	NT
Sheffield 7	d		18 14	18 42			19 11				19 14	19 42	20 11			20 29		20 32				22 24	
Dore	d		18 21								19 21							20 41				22 31	
Grindleford	d		18 29								19 28							20 50				22 38	
Hathersage	d		18 32								19 32							20 54				22 41	
Bamford	d		18 36								19 35							20 57				22 45	
Hope (Derbyshire)	d		18 39								19 39							21 01				22 48	
Edale	d		18 47								19 46							21 08				22 56	
Chinley	d		18 55								19 54							21 16				23 04	
Hazel Grove	86 a																						
Stockport	86 a			19 24			19 53					20 25	20 53			21 11						23 21	
New Mills Central	d		19 01								20 01			20 30				21b30		22 30			23 23
Strines	d		19 04											20 33						22 33			23 26
Marple	d	18 52	19 07							19 59	20 06			20 36				21 36		22 36			23 29
Rose Hill Marple	d					19 15											21 10						
Romiley	d	18 55	19 11			19 20				20 02	20 09			20 40			21 15	21 40		22 40			23 33
Woodley	d					19 23											21 18						
Hyde Central	d					19 26											21 21						
Hyde North	d					19 29											21 24						
Guide Bridge	d				19 28	19 33			19 58						20 58		21 28		21 58		22 58		
Fairfield	d					19 36											21 31						
Gorton	d				19 31				20 01						21 01				22 01		23 01		
Bredbury	d		19 14							20 05	20 12			20 43				21 43		22 43			23 36
Brinnington	d		19 16							20 08	20 15			20 45				21 45		22 45			23 38
Reddish North	d		19 19							20 11	20 18			20 48				21 48		22 48			23 41
Ryder Brow	d	19 03								20 13				20 51				21 51		22 51			23 44
Belle Vue	d	19 04								20 15				20 52				21 52		22 52			23 45
Ashburys	d	19 07			19 34				20 04	20 18				20 55	21 04			21 55	22 04	22 55	23 04		23 48
Ardwick	d																						
Manchester Piccadilly 10	a	19 15	19 33	19 35	19 42	19 47	20 03		20 12	20 30	20 31	20 36	21 03	21 03	21 12	21 25	21 40	22 03	22 12	23 03	23 12	23 36	00 03
Manchester Airport	85 a	19 52		20 05	20 12	20 19	20 34		20 58		21 06	21 09	21 34	21 37	21 51	21 58	22 16	22 39	22 58		23 55		00 45

Sundays

until 27 January

		TP 🚌	NT 🚌	TP 🚌		NT B	NT	NT B		TP 🚌	NT B	NT B		EM E 🚌	NT 🚌	TP 🚌		NT B	NT B	NT		EM E 🚌	NT B	TP 🚌	TP 🚌
Sheffield 7	d	07 40	08 20	09 20						10 20				10 45	10 50	11 20						11 45		12 20	12 20
Dore	d		08 32												11 02										
Grindleford	d		08 55												11 25										
Hathersage	d		09 05												11 35										
Bamford	d		09 10												11 40										
Hope (Derbyshire)	d		09 16												11 46										
Edale	d		09 30												12 00										
Chinley	d		09 50												12 20										
Hazel Grove	86 a																								
Stockport	86 a													12 10								13 10		13 40	
New Mills Central	d		10a10				10 20								12a40					12 48					
Strines	d						10 23													12 51					
Marple	d						10 26													12 54					
Romiley	d						10 30													12 58					
Guide Bridge	d					10 32		11 02			11 32	12 02						12 32	13 02				13 32		
Gorton	d					10 35		11 05			11 35	12 05						12 35	13 05				13 35		
Bredbury	d						10 33													13 01					
Brinnington	d						10 35													13 03					
Reddish North	d						10 38													13 06					
Ryder Brow	d						10 41													13 09					
Belle Vue	d						10 42													13 10					
Ashburys	d					10 38	10 45	11 08			11 38	12 08						12 38	13 08	13 15			13 38		
Manchester Piccadilly 10	a	09 00		10 40		10 47	10 54	11 17		11 40	11 47	12 17		12 36		12 40		12 47	13 17	13 24		13 36	13 47		13 50
Manchester Airport	85 a	09 25		11 05			11 23	11 51		12 05	12 33	12 50				13 05		13 24		13 54			14 33	14 00	

		NT B		EM 🚌	NT B	NT 🚌		TP 🚌	TP 🚌	NT B		NT	EM 🚌	NT B		TP 🚌	TP 🚌	NT B		EM 🚌	NT B	NT 🚌		TP 🚌	TP 🚌
Sheffield 7	d			12 50		12 50		13 20	13 20				13 45			14 20	14 20			14 45		14 50		15 20	15 20
Dore	d					13 02																15 02			
Grindleford	d					13 25																15 25			
Hathersage	d					13 35																15 35			
Bamford	d					13 40																15 40			
Hope (Derbyshire)	d					13 46																15 46			
Edale	d					14 00																16 00			
Chinley	d					14 20																16 20			
Hazel Grove	86 a																								
Stockport	86 a			14 15				14 40					15 10			15 40				16 10				16 40	
New Mills Central	d					14a40						14 53										16a40			
Strines	d											14 56													
Marple	d											14 59													
Romiley	d											15 03													
Guide Bridge	d	14 02			14 32					15 02				15 32				16 02			16 32				
Gorton	d	14 05			14 35					15 05				15 35				16 05			16 35				
Bredbury	d											15 06													
Brinnington	d											15 08													
Reddish North	d											15 11													
Ryder Brow	d											15 14													
Belle Vue	d											15 15													
Ashburys	d	14 08			14 38					15 08		15 20		15 38				16 08			16 38				
Manchester Piccadilly 10	a	14 17		14 31	14 47				14 50	15 17		15 32	15 33	15 47			15 50	16 17		16 32	16 47				16 50
Manchester Airport	85 a	14 51			15 21			15 00		15 51		16 11		16 18		16 00		16 51			17 18			17 00	

For general notes see front of timetable
For details of catering facilities see Directory of Train Operators

- **A** From Norwich (Table 49)
- **B** From Hadfield (Table 79)
- **C** From Cleethorpes (Table 29)
- **D** From Norwich to Manchester Oxford Road (Table 49)
- **E** From Nottingham (Table 49)
- **b** Arr. 2125

Sundays until 27 January

Sheffield, Chinley, Marple and Romiley → Manchester and Manchester Airport

Network Diagram - see first page of Table 78

	NT A	NT	EM		NT A	TP	TP		NT A	EM	NT A		NT	TP	TP		NT A	NT	EM		NT A	TP	TP	NT A
Sheffield 7 d			15 45			16 20	16 20			16 45			16 50	17 20	17 20				17 55			18 20	18 20	
Dore d													17 02											
Grindleford d													17 25											
Hathersage d													17 35											
Bamford d													17 40											
Hope (Derbyshire) d													17 46											
Edale d													18 00											
Chinley d													18 20											
Hazel Grove 86 a																								
Stockport 86 a			17 10			17 40				18 10				18 40					19 15			19 40		
New Mills Central d		16 48											18a40					18 49						
Strines d		16 51																18 52						
Marple d		16 54																18 55						
Romiley d		16 58																18 59						
Guide Bridge d	17 02				17 32				18 02		18 32						19 02				19 32			20 02
Gorton d	17 05				17 35				18 05		18 35						19 05				19 35			20 05
Bredbury d		17 01																19 02						
Brinnington d		17 03																19 04						
Reddish North d		17 06																19 07						
Ryder Brow d		17 09																19 10						
Belle Vue d		17 10																19 11						
Ashburys d	17 08	17 13			17 38				18 08		18 38						19 08	19 16			19 38			20 08
Manchester Piccadilly 10 a	17 17	17 24	*17 36*		17 47		17 50		18 17	*18 36*	18 47				18 50		19 17	19 22	*19 33*		19 47		19 50	20 17
Manchester Airport 85 a		*17 51*			*18 18*	18 00			*18 52*		*19 18*			19 00				*19 51*			*20 18*	20 00		*20 52*

	EM		NT A	NT	TP		TP	NT A	NT		EM	TP	TP		NT A	EM	TP		TP	NT	NT			
Sheffield 7 d	18 45			18 50	19 20		19 20				19 45	20 20	20 20			20 50	21 30				22 00			
Dore d				19 02																	22 12			
Grindleford d				19 25																	22 35			
Hathersage d				19 35																	22 45			
Bamford d				19 40																	22 50			
Hope (Derbyshire) d				19 46																	22 56			
Edale d				20 00																	23 10			
Chinley d				20 20																	23 30			
Hazel Grove 86 a																								
Stockport 86 a	20 10				20 40						21 10	21 40				22 15	22 50		23d00		23 59			
New Mills Central d				20a40					20 49											23 02				
Strines d									20 52											23 05				
Marple d									20 55											23 09				
Romiley d									20 59											23 12				
Guide Bridge d			20 32					21 02							22 02									
Gorton d			20 35					21 05							22 05									
Bredbury d									21 02											23 15				
Brinnington d									21 04											23 18				
Reddish North d									21 07											23 21				
Ryder Brow d									21 10											23 23				
Belle Vue d									21 11											23 25				
Ashburys d			20 38					21 08	21 16						22 08					23 28				
Manchester Piccadilly 10 a	20 35		20 47				20 50	21 17	21 22		21 35		21 50		22 17	22 40	23 15			23 35	00 20			
Manchester Airport 85 a			*21 18*		21 00				*21 52*			22 00			*22 51*				23 20	*00 33*	*00 54*			

Sundays from 3 February

	TP 1 ◇	TP 1 ◇ B	NT A	NT	NT A		EM ◇ C	NT A	TP 1 ◇ D	NT A	EM ◇ C		NT A	NT	TP 1 ◇ E	NT	NT A		EM ◇ C	NT A	TP 1 ◇ D	NT A	EM ◇ C	NT A
Sheffield 7 d	07 55	09 13		09 30			10 26		11 13		11 40			11 43	12 13				12 40		13 13		13 39	
Dore d				09 37			10 32							11 50										
Grindleford d				09 45										11 59										
Hathersage d				09 49										12 03										
Bamford d				09 52										12 06										
Hope (Derbyshire) d				09 56										12 10										
Edale d				10 03										12 18										
Chinley d				10 11										12 26										
Hazel Grove 86 a																								
Stockport 86 a	08 36	09 58					11 18		11 58		12 23				12 56	←			13 24		14 02		14 21	
New Mills Central d				10 18										12 33		12 33								
Strines d				10 21										→		12 36								
Marple d				10 24												12 39								
Romiley d				10 28												12 43								
Guide Bridge d			10 32		11 02			11 32		12 02			12 32				13 02			13 32		14 02		14 32
Gorton d			10 35		11 05			11 35		12 05			12 35				13 05			13 35		14 05		14 35
Bredbury d				10 31												12 46								
Brinnington d				10 33												12 48								
Reddish North d				10 36												12 51								
Ryder Brow d				10 39												12 54								
Belle Vue d				10 40												12 55								
Ashburys d			10 38	10 45	11 08			11 38		12 08			12 38			13 02	13 08			13 38		14 08		14 38
Manchester Piccadilly 10 a	08 48	10 08	10 47	10 54	11 17		11 33	11 47	12 08	12 17	12 36		12 47		13 10	13 12	13 17		13 36	13 47	14 12	14 17	14 31	14 47
Manchester Airport 85 a	09 12	10 36		*11 23*	*11 51*		*12 11*		12 30	*12 50*	*13 12*		*13 24*		13 36		*13 54*		*14 14*	*14 33*	14 36	*14 51*	*15 11*	*15b21*

For general notes see front of timetable
For details of catering facilities see Directory of Train Operators

- **A** From Hadfield (Table 79)
- **B** From Meadowhall (Table 29)
- **C** From Nottingham to Liverpool Lime Street (Table 49)
- **D** From Doncaster (Table 29)
- **E** From Cleethorpes (Table 29)
- **b** Until 23 March arr. 3 minutes earlier

Table 78

Sundays
from 3 February

Sheffield, Chinley, Marple and Romiley → Manchester and Manchester Airport

Network Diagram - see first page of Table 78

		NT A		TP 1 ◇ B	NT C	EM ◇ D	NT C	TP 1 ◇ B		NT C	EM ◇ E	NT C	NT	TP 1 ◇ B		NT C	EM ◇ E	NT C	NT G	TP 1 ◇ B		NT C	EM ◇ D	NT C	NT
Sheffield 7	d	13 41		14 12		14 37		15 13			15 35		15 43	16 13			16 36		16 44	17 13			17 42		17 53
Dore	d	13 48											15 50						16 51						18 03
Grindleford	d	13 56											15 58						16 57						18 11
Hathersage	d	14 00											16 01						17 00						18 14
Bamford	d	14 03											16 05						17 04						18 18
Hope (Derbyshire)	d	14 07											16 09						17 08						18 22
Edale	d	14 15											16 17						17 16						18 30
Chinley	d	14 23											16 25						17 24						18 38
Hazel Grove	86 a																		17 36						
Stockport	86 a			15 01		15 22		16 03			16 19			16 56			17 22		17 47	17 55			18 24		
New Mills Central	d	14 30											16 32												18 45 →
Strines	d	14 33											16 35												
Marple	d	14 36											16 38												
Romiley	d	14 40											16 42												
Guide Bridge	d				15 02		15 32			16 02		16 32				17 02		17 32				18 02		18 32	
Gorton	d				15 05		15 35			16 05		16 35				17 05		17 35				18 05		18 35	
Bredbury	d	14 43											16 45												
Brinnington	d	14 45											16 47												
Reddish North	d	14 48											16 50												
Ryder Brow	d	14 51											16 53												
Belle Vue	d	14 52											16 54												
Ashburys	d	14 59			15 08		15 38			16 08		16 38	17 02			17 08		17 38				18 08		18 38	
Manchester Piccadilly 10	a	15 12		15 13	15 17	15 33	15 47	16 13		16 17	16 32	16 47	17 11	17 11		17 17	17 36	17 47	17 59	18 12		18 17	18 36	18 47	
Manchester Airport	85 a			15 36	15 51	16 11	16b33	16 36		16 51	17 12	17c21		17 36		17 51	18 11	18e18	18 33	18 36		18 52	19 12	19c21	

		TP 1 ◇ B	NT C	NT		EM ◇ E	NT C	TP 1 ◇ B	NT C	EM ◇ H		NT C	NT	TP 1 ◇ B	NT	NT C		EM ◇ H	TP 1 ◇ B	NT C	NT	NT			
Sheffield 7	d	18 13				18 35		19 13		19 35			19 42	20 13				20 35	21 19		21 56				
Dore	d												19 49								22 03				
Grindleford	d												19 55								22 12				
Hathersage	d												19 59								22 15				
Bamford	d												20 02								22 19				
Hope (Derbyshire)	d												20 07								22 23				
Edale	d												20 15								22 31				
Chinley	d												20 23								22 39				
Hazel Grove	86 a																								
Stockport	86 a	19 00		←		19 21		20 00		20 24				20 55	←			21 18	22 00		23 00				
New Mills Central	d			18 45									20 32 →		20 32							23 02			
Strines	d			18 48											20 35							23 05			
Marple	d			18 51											20 38							23 09			
Romiley	d			18 55											20 42							23 12			
Guide Bridge	d		19 02				19 32		20 02			20 32				21 02				22 02					
Gorton	d		19 05				19 35		20 05			20 35				21 05				22 05					
Bredbury	d			18 58											20 45							23 15			
Brinnington	d			19 00											20 47							23 18			
Reddish North	d			19 03											20 50							23 21			
Ryder Brow	d			19 06											20 53							23 23			
Belle Vue	d			19 07											20 54							23 25			
Ashburys	d		19 08	19 10			19 38		20 08			20 38			21 02	21 08				22 08		23 28			
Manchester Piccadilly 10	a	19 10	19 17	19 19		19 33	19 47	20 12	20 17	20 35		20 47		21 06	21 09	21 17		21 33	22 13	22 17	23 12	23 35			
Manchester Airport	85 a	19 36		19 51		20 12	20b33	20 36	20 52	21 12		21c21		21 36	21 36	21 52		22 11	22 36	22 51	23f54	00 33			

For general notes see front of timetable
For details of catering facilities see Directory of Train Operators

A Until 23 March
B From Cleethorpes (Table 29)
C From Hadfield (Table 79)
D From Norwich to Liverpool Lime Street (Table 49)
E From Nottingham to Liverpool Lime Street (Table 49)
G From 30 March
H From Norwich (Table 49)
b Until 23 March arr. 15 minutes earlier
c Until 23 March arr. 3 minutes earlier
e Until 23 March only
f Until 23 March arr. 2349

Manchester → Glossop and Hadfield

Network Diagram - see first page of Table 78

Mondays to Fridays

Miles	Miles	Station		NT	NT	NT	NT	NT	NT	NT	NT	NT	NT	NT		NT	NT	NT
0	—	**Manchester Piccadilly** 10	78 ⛴ d	06 16	06 46	07 03	07 28	07 48	08 07	08 27	08 49	09 15	09 49	10 19		15 19	15 49	16 17
½	—	Ardwick	78 d															
1½	—	Ashburys	78 d	06 20	06 50	07 08	07 32	07 52	08 11	08 31	08 53	09 20	09 53	10 23	and	15 23	15 53	16 21
2½	—	Gorton	78 d	06 22	06 52	07 11	07 34	07 54	08 13	08 33	08 55	09 22	09 55	10 25		15 25	15 55	16 23
4¾	—	Guide Bridge	78 d	06 26	06 56	07 15	07 38	07 58	08 17	08 37	08 59	09 27	09 59	10 29	every 30	15 29	15 59	16 26
6¾	—	Flowery Field	d	06 29	06 59	07 18	07 41	08 01	08 20	08 40	09 02	09 30	10 02	10 32		15 32	16 02	16 29
7½	—	Newton for Hyde	d	06 31	07 01	07 20	07 43	08 03	08 22	08 42	09 04	09 32	10 04	10 34	minutes	15 34	16 04	16 31
8½	—	Godley	d	06 33	07 03	07 22	07 45	08 05	08 24	08 44	09 06	09 34	10 06	10 36		15 36	16 06	16 33
9	—	Hattersley	d	06 35	07 05	07 24	07 47	08 07	08 26	08 46	09 08	09 36	10 08	10 38	until	15 38	16 08	16 35
10	—	Broadbottom	d	06 37	07 07	07 26	07 49	08 09	08 28	08 48	09 10	09 38	10 10	10 40		15 40	16 10	16 37
12¼	0	Dinting 3	d	06 45	07 15	07 35	07 55	08 15	08 34	08 54	09 16	09 45	10 16	10 46		15 46	16 16	16 42
13¼	—	**Glossop**	a	06 48	07b25	07b45	08b05	08b25	08b44	09b06	09 19	09 49	10 19	10 49		15 49	16 19	16 45
—	—		d	06 51							09 22	09 51	10 22	10 52		15 52	16 22	16 48
15	¾	**Hadfield**	a	06 57	07 17	07 37	07 57	08 18	08 38	08 57	09 28	09 57	10 28	10 58		15 58	16 28	16 56

Station		NT	NT	NT	NT	NT	NT	NT	NT	NT	NT	NT	NT	NT
Manchester Piccadilly 10	78 ⛴ d	16 36	16 58	17 17	17 36	18 00	18 18	18 49	19 19	19 49	20 49	21 49	22 49	23 26
Ardwick	78 d													
Ashburys	78 d	16 40	17 02	17 21	17 40	18 04	18 22	18 53	19 23	19 53	20 53	21 53	22 53	23 30
Gorton	78 d	16 42	17 04	17 23	17 42	18 06	18 25	18 55	19 25	19 55	20 55	21 55	22 55	23 32
Guide Bridge	78 d	16 46	17 08	17 27	17 46	18 10	18 29	18 59	19 29	19 59	20 59	21 59	22 59	23 36
Flowery Field	d	16 49	17 11	17 30	17 49	18 13	18 32	19 02	19 32	20 02	21 02	22 02	23 02	23 39
Newton for Hyde	d	16 51	17 13	17 32	17 51	18 15	18 34	19 04	19 34	20 04	21 04	22 04	23 04	23 41
Godley	d	16 53	17 15	17 34	17 53	18 17	18 36	19 06	19 36	20 06	21 06	22 06	23 06	23 43
Hattersley	d	16 55	17 17	17 36	17 55	18 19	18 38	19 08	19 38	20 08	21 08	22 08	23 08	23 45
Broadbottom	d	16 57	17 19	17 38	17 57	18 21	18 40	19 10	19 40	20 10	21 10	22 10	23 10	23 47
Dinting 3	d	17 04	17 26	17 44	18 04	18 26	18 46	19 16	19 45	20 16	21 16	22 16	23 16	23 53
Glossop	a	17 08	17 29	17 47	18 08	18 29	18 48	19 19	19 48	20 19	21 19	22 19	23 19	00b05
	d	17 10	17 32	17 50	18 10	18 32	18 52	19 22	19 51	20 22	21 22	22 22	23 22	
Hadfield	a	17 17	17 38	17 57	18 17	18 39	19 00	19 29	19 58	20 30	21 28	22 28	23 28	23 56

Saturdays

Station		NT	NT	NT	NT	NT	NT	NT	NT	NT		NT	NT	NT
Manchester Piccadilly 10	78 ⛴ d	06 16	06 46	07 19	07 49	08 19	08 49	09 16	09 49	10 19		15 19	15 49	16 17
Ashburys	78 d	06 20	06 50	07 23	07 53	08 23	08 53	09 20	09 53	10 23	and	15 23	15 53	16 23
Gorton	78 d	06 22	06 52	07 25	07 55	08 25	08 55	09 22	09 55	10 25		15 25	15 55	16 25
Guide Bridge	78 d	06 26	06 56	07 29	07 59	08 29	08 59	09 27	09 59	10 29	every 30	15 29	15 59	16 29
Flowery Field	d	06 29	06 59	07 32	08 02	08 32	09 02	09 30	10 02	10 32		15 32	16 02	16 32
Newton for Hyde	d	06 31	07 01	07 34	08 04	08 34	09 04	09 32	10 04	10 34	minutes	15 34	16 04	16 34
Godley	d	06 33	07 03	07 36	08 06	08 36	09 06	09 34	10 06	10 36		15 36	16 06	16 36
Hattersley	d	06 35	07 05	07 38	08 08	08 38	09 08	09 36	10 08	10 38	until	15 38	16 08	16 38
Broadbottom	d	06 37	07 07	07 40	08 10	08 40	09 10	09 38	10 10	10 40		15 40	16 10	16 40
Dinting 3	d	06 45	07 15	07 46	08 16	08 46	09 16	09 45	10 16	10 46		15 46	16 16	16 46
Glossop	a	06 48	07 18	07 49	08 19	08 49	09 19	09 49	10 19	10 49		15 49	16 19	16 49
	d	06 51	07 21	07 52	08 22	08 52	09 22	09 51	10 22	10 52		15 52	16 22	16 52
Hadfield	a	06 57	07 27	07 58	08 28	08 58	09 28	09 57	10 28	10 58		15 58	16 28	16 58

Station		NT	NT	NT	NT	NT	NT	NT	NT	NT	NT
Manchester Piccadilly 10	78 ⛴ d	16 49	17 17	17 49	18 18	18 49	19 49	20 49	21 49	22 49	23 26
Ashburys	78 d	16 53	17 21	17 53	18 22	18 53	19 53	20 53	21 53	22 53	23 30
Gorton	78 d	16 55	17 23	17 55	18 25	18 55	19 55	20 55	21 55	22 55	23 32
Guide Bridge	78 d	16 59	17 27	17 59	18 29	18 59	19 59	20 59	21 59	22 59	23 36
Flowery Field	d	17 02	17 30	18 02	18 32	19 02	20 02	21 02	22 02	23 02	23 39
Newton for Hyde	d	17 04	17 32	18 04	18 34	19 04	20 04	21 04	22 04	23 04	23 41
Godley	d	17 06	17 34	18 06	18 36	19 06	20 06	21 06	22 06	23 06	23 43
Hattersley	d	17 08	17 36	18 08	18 38	19 08	20 08	21 08	22 08	23 08	23 45
Broadbottom	d	17 10	17 38	18 10	18 40	19 10	20 10	21 10	22 10	23 10	23 47
Dinting 3	d	17 16	17 45	18 16	18 46	19 16	20 16	21 16	22 16	23 16	23 53
Glossop	a	17 19	17 48	18 19	18 49	19 19	20 19	21 19	22 19	23 19	00b05
	d	17 22	17 51	18 22	18 52	19 22	20 22	21 22	22 22	23 22	
Hadfield	a	17 28	17 57	18 28	18 58	19 28	20 30	21 28	22 28	23 28	23 56

Sundays

Station		NT	NT		NT	NT
Manchester Piccadilly 10	78 ⛴ d	09 23	09 53		19 53	20 53
Ashburys	78 d	09 27	09 57	and	19 57	20 57
Gorton	78 d	09 29	09 59		19 59	20 59
Guide Bridge	78 d	09 33	10 03	every 30	20 03	21 03
Flowery Field	d	09 36	10 06		20 06	21 06
Newton for Hyde	d	09 38	10 08	minutes	20 08	21 08
Godley	d	09 40	10 10		20 10	21 10
Hattersley	d	09 42	10 12	until	20 12	21 12
Broadbottom	d	09 44	10 14		20 14	21 14
Dinting 3	d	09 49	10 19		20 19	21 19
Glossop	a	09 53	10 23		20 23	21 23
	d	09 55	10 25		20 25	21 25
Hadfield	a	10 03	10 33		20 33	21 33

For general notes see front of timetable
For details of catering facilities see Directory of Train Operators

b Via Hadfield

Hadfield and Glossop → Manchester

Network Diagram - see first page of Table 78

Miles	Miles			NT	NT	NT	NT	NT	NT	NT	NT	NT	NT		NT	NT	NT
0	0	**Hadfield**	d	06 00	06 30	07 01	07 20	07 40	08 00	08 20	08 39	09 01	09 31		15 31	16 01	16 31
1¾	—	**Glossop**	a	06 05	06 35	07 06	07 25	07 45	08 05	08 25	08 44	09 06	09 36		15 36	16 06	
—	—		d	06 08	06 38	07 09	07 28	07 48	08 08	08 28	08 48	09 09	09 39	and	15 39	16 09	16b22
2¾	¾	Dinting 3	d	06 11	06 41	07 12	07 31	07 51	08 11	08 31	08 51	09 12	09 42		15 42	16 12	16 33
5	—	Broadbottom	d	06 15	06 45	07 16	07 35	07 55	08 15	08 35	08 55	09 16	09 46	every 30	15 46	16 16	16 37
6	—	Hattersley	d	06 18	06 48	07 19	07 38	07 58	08 18	08 38	08 58	09 19	09 49		15 49	16 19	16 40
6½	—	Godley	d	06 20	06 50	07 21	07 40	08 00	08 20	08 40	09 00	09 21	09 51	minutes	15 51	16 21	16 42
7½	—	Newton for Hyde	d	06 22	06 52	07 23	07 42	08 02	08 22	08 42	09 02	09 23	09 53		15 53	16 23	16 44
8¼	—	Flowery Field	d	06 24	06 54	07 25	07 44	08 04	08 24	08 44	09 04	09 25	09 55	until	15 55	16 25	16 46
10¼	—	Guide Bridge	78 a	06 27	06 57	07 28	07 47	08 07	08 27	08 47	09 07	09 28	09 58		15 58	16 28	16 49
12½	—	Gorton	78 a	06 30	07 00	07 31	07 50	08 10	08 30	08 50	09 10	09 31	10 01		16 01	16 31	16 52
13½	—	Ashburys	78 a	06 33	07 03	07 34	07 54	08 13	08 33	08 53	09 13	09 34	10 04		16 04	16 34	16 56
14½	—	Ardwick	78 a			07 37											
15	—	**Manchester Piccadilly 10**	78 ⛴ a	06 42	07 12	07 42	08 03	08 19	08 42	09 02	09 21	09 42	10 12		16 12	16 42	17 04

		NT	NT	NT	NT	NT	NT	NT	NT	NT	NT	NT	NT	NT A
Hadfield	d	16 59	17 20	17 45	17 59	18 28	18 42	19 01	19 31	20 01	20 31	21 31	22 31	23 59
Glossop	a							19 07	19 36	20 06	20 36	21 36	22 36	00 05
	d	16b48	17b10	17b32	17b50	18b10	18b32	19 09	19 39	20 09	20 39	21 39	22 39	
Dinting 3	d	17 01	17 22	17 47	18 01	18 30	18 44	19 12	19 42	20 12	20 42	21 42	22 42	
Broadbottom	d	17 05	17 26	17 51	18 05	18 34	18 48	19 16	19 46	20 16	20 46	21 46	22 46	
Hattersley	d	17 08	17 29		18 08	18 37	18 51	19 19	19 49	20 19	20 49	21 49	22 49	
Godley	d	17 10	17 31		18 10	18 39	18 53	19 21	19 51	20 21	20 51	21 51	22 51	
Newton for Hyde	d	17 12	17 33		18 12	18 41	18 55	19 23	19 53	20 23	20 53	21 53	22 53	
Flowery Field	d	17 14	17 35		18 14	18 43	18 57	19 25	19 55	20 25	20 55	21 55	22 55	
Guide Bridge	78 a	17 16	17 41	17 58	18 16	18 46	19 00	19 28	19 58	20 28	20 58	21 58	22 58	
Gorton	78 a	17 19	17 44	18 02	18 20	18 49	19 03	19 31	20 01	20 31	21 01	22 01	23 01	
Ashburys	78 a	17 22	17 47	18 04	18 24	18 53	19 06	19 34	20 04	20 34	21 04	22 04	23 04	
Ardwick	78 a													
Manchester Piccadilly 10	78 ⛴ a	17 31	17 56	18 12	18 32	19 01	19 13	19 43	20 12	20 42	21 12	22 12	23 12	

Saturdays

		NT	NT		NT	NT	NT	NT	NT	NT A
Hadfield	d	06 31	07 01		19 01	19 31	20 31	21 31	22 31	23 59
Glossop	a	06 36	07 06	and	19 06	19 36	20 36	21 36	22 36	00 05
	d	06 39	07 09		19 09	19 39	20 39	21 39	22 39	
Dinting 3	d	06 42	07 12	every 30	19 12	19 42	20 42	21 42	22 42	
Broadbottom	d	06 46	07 16		19 16	19 46	20 46	21 46	22 46	
Hattersley	d	06 49	07 19	minutes	19 19	19 49	20 49	21 49	22 49	
Godley	d	06 51	07 21		19 21	19 51	20 51	21 51	22 51	
Newton for Hyde	d	06 53	07 23	until	19 23	19 53	20 53	21 53	22 53	
Flowery Field	d	06 55	07 25		19 25	19 55	20 55	21 55	22 55	
Guide Bridge	78 a	06 58	07 28		19 28	19 58	20 58	21 58	22 58	
Gorton	78 a	07 01	07 31		19 31	20 01	21 01	22 01	23 01	
Ashburys	78 a	07 04	07 34		19 34	20 04	21 04	22 04	23 04	
Manchester Piccadilly 10	78 ⛴ a	07 12	07 42		19 42	20 12	21 12	22 12	23 12	

Sundays

		NT	NT		NT	NT
Hadfield	d	10 05	10 35		20 35	21 35
Glossop	a	10 10	10 40	and	20 40	21 40
	d	10 13	10 43		20 43	21 43
Dinting 3	d	10 16	10 46	every 30	20 46	21 46
Broadbottom	d	10 20	10 50		20 50	21 50
Hattersley	d	10 23	10 53	minutes	20 53	21 53
Godley	d	10 25	10 55		20 55	21 55
Newton for Hyde	d	10 27	10 57	until	20 57	21 57
Flowery Field	d	10 29	10 59		20 59	21 59
Guide Bridge	78 a	10 32	11 02		21 02	22 02
Gorton	78 a	10 35	11 05		21 05	22 05
Ashburys	78 a	10 38	11 08		21 08	22 08
Manchester Piccadilly 10	78 ⛴ a	10 47	11 17		21 17	22 17

For general notes see front of timetable
For details of catering facilities see Directory of Train Operators

A From Manchester Piccadilly dep. 2326
b Via Hadfield

Network Diagram for Tables 81, 102

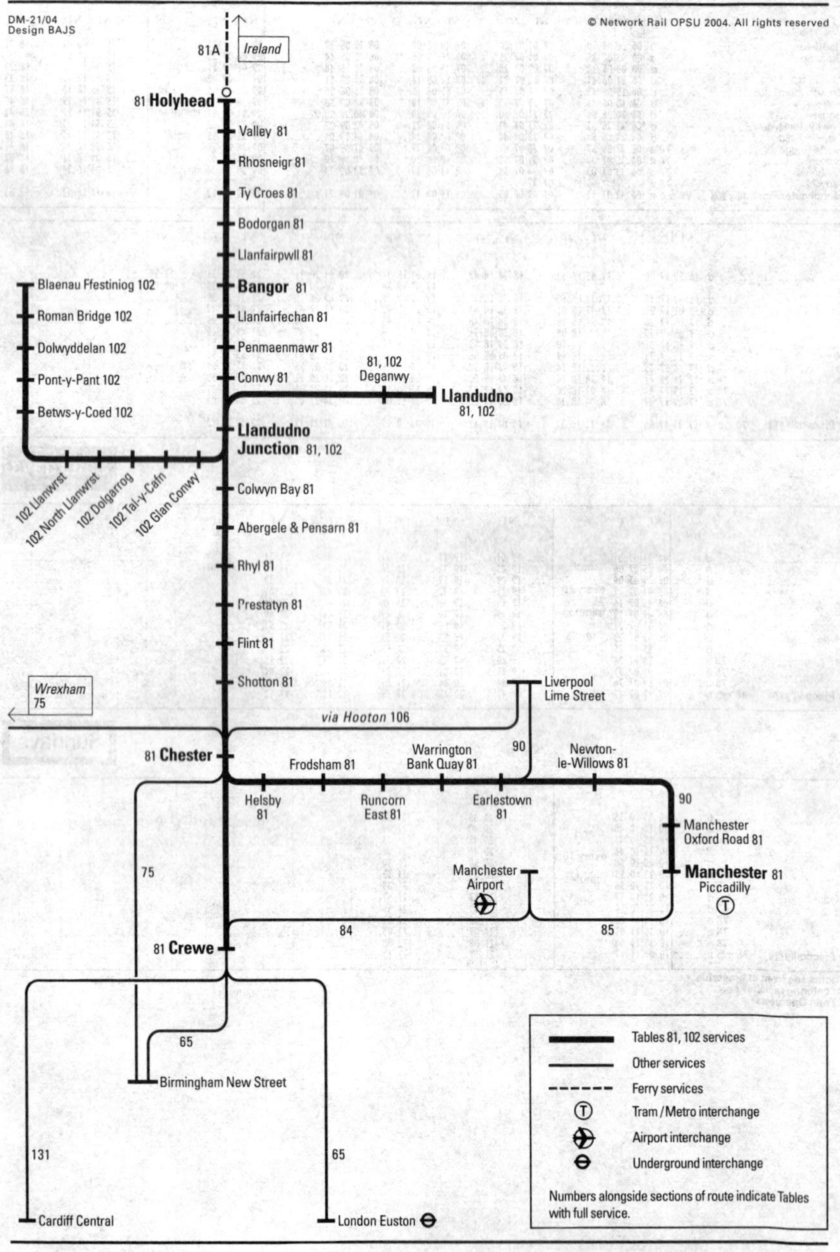

DM-21/04
Design BAJS
© Network Rail OPSU 2004. All rights reserved
81A
Ireland
81 Holyhead
Valley 81
Rhosneigr 81
Ty Croes 81
Bodorgan 81
Llanfairpwll 81
Bangor 81
Llanfairfechan 81
Penmaenmawr 81
Conwy 81
81, 102
Deganwy
Llandudno
81, 102
Llandudno Junction 81, 102
Blaenau Ffestiniog 102
Roman Bridge 102
Dolwyddelan 102
Pont-y-Pant 102
Betws-y-Coed 102
102 Llanrwst
102 North Llanrwst
102 Dolgarrog
102 Tal-y-Cafn
102 Glan Conwy
Colwyn Bay 81
Abergele & Pensarn 81
Rhyl 81
Prestatyn 81
Flint 81
Shotton 81
Wrexham
75
via Hooton 106
Liverpool
Lime Street
90
81 Chester
Frodsham 81
Warrington
Bank Quay 81
Newton-
le-Willows 81
Helsby
81
Runcorn
East 81
Earlestown
81
90
Manchester
Oxford Road 81
Manchester
Airport
Manchester 81
Piccadilly
75
84
85
81 Crewe
65
Birmingham New Street
131
65
Cardiff Central
London Euston
Tables 81, 102 services
Other services
Ferry services
Tram / Metro interchange
Airport interchange
Underground interchange
Numbers alongside sections of route indicate Tables with full service.

Crewe and Manchester → Chester and North Wales

Network Diagram - see first page of Table 81

Miles	Miles		AW	AW	NT	AW	AW	VT	AW	AW	AW	AW	AW	AW	AW	AW	NT	AW	AW	AW	AW	AW
			MO					1 ◇		◇	◇		◇		◇			◇	◇	◇		◇
			A		B												C	D				
										⊼	⊼		⊼		⊼				⊼	⊼		⊼
—	—	London Euston 15 ⊖ 65 d																		06 46	07 13	
—	—	Birmingham New Street 12 65 d						05 20	05 30			06 07		07 03		07 21				07 51	08 26	
—	—	Manchester Airport 84, 85 ✈ d								05 34			06 44	06 57			07 05		07b47	08 00		08b47
—	—	Cardiff Central 7 131 d										04 00			05 10					05 35		
0	—	**Crewe 10** d	00 30					06 18	06 35		07 03	07 33		08 03		08 33				09 03	09 33	
—	0	**Manchester Piccadilly 10** 90 d								06 00			07 16				07 39		08 16			09 16
—	½	**Manchester Oxford Road** 90 d								06 03			07 19				07 33		08 19			09 19
—	16¼	Newton-le-Willows 90 d								06 21			07 37						08 37			09 38
—	18	Earlestown 8 90 d								06 24			07 40						08 40			09 41
—	22	Warrington Bank Quay 90 d			06 00					06 33			07 48						08 49			09 50
—	27	Runcorn East d								06 40			07 55						08 56			09 57
—	30¼	Frodsham d								06 44			08 00						09 00			10 01
—	32¾	Helsby d			06a13					06 48			08 04						09 04			10 05
—	—	Liverpool Lime Street 10 106 d								05 58	06 28		07 28						08 28			09 28
21	40¼	**Chester** a	00 48					06 37	07 00	07 03	07 24	07 59	08 19	08 27	08 28	08 57	09 06		09 17	09 26	09 57	10 19
—	—	d	00 54					06 45		07 05	07 32		08 24		08 35				09 24	09 35		10 24
29	—	Shotton d								07 14			08 35						09 33			10 33
33½	—	Flint d	01 07					06 57		07 20	07 45		08 41		08 51				09 39	09 49		10 39
47½	—	Prestatyn d						07 10		07 33	07 58		08 54		09 04				09 52	10 02		10 52
51	—	Rhyl d	01 23					07 17		07 39	08 04		09 00		09 10				09 58	10 08		10 58
55¼	—	Abergele & Pensarn d								07 45			09 06						10 04			11 04
61½	—	Colwyn Bay d	01 34					07 28		07 53	08 15		09 14		09 21				10 12	10 19		11 12
65½	—	**Llandudno Junction** a	01 39					07 33		07 58	08 20		09 19		09 26				10 17	10 24		11 17
—	0	d	01 40	06 25		06 51	07 33	07 34		08 00	08 22		09 21		09 27			09 52	10 19	10 25		11 19
—	1¼	Deganwy d		06x28		06x54	07x36			08x04			09x25					09x55	10x23			11x23
—	3	**Llandudno** a		06 35		07 01	07 43			08 16			09 37					10 01	10 37			11 35
66½	—	Conwy d									08x25									10x28		
70¾	—	Penmaenmawr d									08x31									10x34		
73½	—	Llanfairfechan d									08x35									10x38		
80¾	—	**Bangor (Gwynedd)** a	01 56					07 49			08 43				09 43					10 46		
—	—	d	01 56					07 51			08 43				09 43					10 47		
84½	—	Llanfairpwll d									08x49									10x53		
93½	—	Bodorgan d									08x59									11x03		
96¼	—	Ty Croes d									09x04									11x07		
98	—	Rhosneigr d									09x07									11x10		
102	—	Valley d									09x12									11x16		
105½	—	**Holyhead** a	02 27					08 21			09 30				10 20					11 30		

	AW	AW	AW	AW	VT	AW	AW	AW	AW	AW	AW	AW	AW	AW	VT	AW	AW	AW	AW	AW	AW
		◇		◇	1 ◇	◇	◇		◇	◇		◇		◇	1 ◇	◇		◇		◇	
									D												
		⊼		⊼	⊠	⊼	⊼			⊼		⊼		⊼	⊓	⊼		⊼		⊼	
London Euston 15 ⊖ 65 d	07 46		08 17		09 00			09 17			09 46		10 15		11 28				11 46		12 17
Birmingham New Street 12 65 d	09 03		09 21				10 03	10 21			10 51		11 21		12 03		12 21		13 03		13 21
Manchester Airport 84, 85 ✈ d	09 00			09 34	10 00	09b47				10b47	11 00			11b47	12 00			12b47	13 00		
Cardiff Central 7 131 d	06 50	07 20			07 50						08 50	09 20			09 50				10 50	11 20	
Crewe 10 d	10 03		10 33		10 50		11 03	11 33			12 03		12 33		13 12	13 19	13 33		14 03		14 33
Manchester Piccadilly 10 90 d				10 03		10 16				11 16				12 16				13 16			
Manchester Oxford Road 90 d				10 06		10 19				11 19				12 19				13 19			
Newton-le-Willows 90 d				10 30		10 38				11 38				12 39				13 38			
Earlestown 8 90 d						10 41				11 41				12 41				13 41			
Warrington Bank Quay 90 d				10 40		10 50				11 50				12 50				13 50			
Runcorn East d						10 57				11 57				12 57				13 57			
Frodsham d						11 01				12 01				13 01				14 01			
Helsby d						11 05				12 05				13 05				14 05			
Liverpool Lime Street 10 106 d				09 58	10 28					11 28				12 28	12 28			13 28			
Chester a	10 27	10 28	10 57	11 05	11 17	11 22	11 29	11 59		12 19	12 27	12 28	12 59	13 20	13 32	13 43	13 57	14 20	14 27	14 28	14 57
d		10 35		11 07	11 19	11 24	11 35			12 24		12 35		13 22	13 34	13 44		14 25		14 35	
Shotton d						11 33				12 33						13 53		14 34			
Flint d		10 49		11 20		11 40	11 50			12 39		12 49			13 47	13 59		14 40		14 50	
Prestatyn d		11 02		11 33		11 54	12 04			12 52		13 02		13 47	14 00	14 13		14 53		15 03	
Rhyl d		11 08		11 39	11 48	12 00	12 10			12 58		13 08		13 53	14 06	14 19		14 59		15 09	
Abergele & Pensarn d						12 06				13 04						14 25		15 05			
Colwyn Bay d		11 19		11 50	12 01	12 14	12 20			13 12		13 19		14 04	14 17	14 33		15 13		15 20	
Llandudno Junction a		11 24		11 55	12 07	12 19	12 25			13 17		13 24		14 09	14 22	14 38		15 18		15 25	
d		11 25		11 56	12 09	12 20	12 27		12 52	13 19		13 25		14 11	14 24	14 39		15 20		15 26	
Deganwy d						12x24			12x55	13x23				14x14				15x24			
Llandudno a						12 35			13 01	13 35				14 27	14 44			15 36			
Conwy d							12x30					13x29								15x29	
Penmaenmawr d							12x36					13x35								15x35	
Llanfairfechan d							12x40					13x40								15x39	
Bangor (Gwynedd) a		11 41		12 12	12 26		12 48					13 48				14 55				15 47	
d		11 41		12 12	12 28		12 48					13 48				14 55				15 48	
Llanfairpwll d							12x54					13x54								15x55	
Bodorgan d							13x04					14x04								16x05	
Ty Croes d							13x09					14x09								16x09	
Rhosneigr d							13x12					14x12								16x12	
Valley d							13x17					14x17								16x18	
Holyhead a		12 20		12 47	13 03		13 30					14 30				15 30				16 30	

For general notes see front of timetable
For details of catering facilities see Directory of Train Operators

A 4 February to 24 March. From Shrewsbury (Table 131)
B To Ellesmere Port (Table 109)
C From Blackpool North (Table 82)
D From Blaenau Ffestiniog (Table 102)
b Change at Manchester Oxford Road

Crewe and Manchester → Chester and North Wales

Network Diagram - see first page of Table 81

	AW ◇ A	AW ◇ 🛒	NT B	AW ◇ 🛒	AW	AW ◇ 🛒	AW		AW ◇ 🛒	AW	AW ◇ 🛒	AW ◇ 🛒	AW	VT 1 ◇ ⊡	AW ◇ 🛒	AW ◇ 🛒	AW	AW ◇ 🛒	AW		AW ◇	AW	VT 1 ◇ ⊠
London Euston 15 ⊖ 65 d				12 46	13 17		13 46			14 17		14 46	15 17	15 49					16 17			16 49	17 21
Birmingham New Street 12 65 d				14 03	14 21		14 51			15 21		16 03		16 21			17 03		17 21			17 51	18 03
Manchester Airport 84, 85 ✈ d		13b47		14 00		14b47	15 00				15b47	16 00			16 47		17 00	17 04			17b47	18 00	
Cardiff Central 7 131 d				11 50			12 50		13 20			13 50				15 20						15 50	
Crewe 10 d				15 03	15 33		16 03			16 33		17 03	17 29	17 35			18 03		18 33			19 03	19 22
Manchester Piccadilly 10 90 ⛴ d		14 16				15 16					16 16				17 20			17 41			18 16		
Manchester Oxford Road 90 d		14 19				15 19					16 19				17 23			17 47			18 19		
Newton-le-Willows 90 d		14 38				15 38					16 37				17 42			18 05			18 37		
Earlestown 8 90 d		14 41	14 51			15 41					16 40				17 45			18 08			18 40		
Warrington Bank Quay 90 d		14 50	15 02			15 50					16 48				17 56			18 18			18 49		
Runcorn East d		14 57	15 10			15 56					16 55				18 03			18 25			18 56		
Frodsham d		15 01	15 15			16 01					17 00				18 07			18 29			19 00		
Helsby d		15 05	15a19			16 07					17 04				18 11			18 33			19 04		
Liverpool Lime Street 10 106 d		14 28				15 28					16 28	16 43		16 58	17 28	17 43		17 58			18 28		18 58
Chester a		15 19		15 26	15 57	16 19	16 27		16 28	16 57	17 19	17 26	17 53	17 58	18 24	18 25	18 29	18 48	18 57		19 17	19 25	19 49
d		15 24		15 35		16 24			16 35		17 24	17 35		18 00	18 24	18 35		18 50			19 24		19 51
Shotton d		15 33				16 33					17 33	17 44			18 33						19 33		
Flint d		15 39		15 49		16 39			16 49		17 39	17 50		18 13	18 39	18 51		19 03			19 39		
Prestatyn d		15 52		16 02		16 52			17 03		17 52	18 03		18 26	18 52	19 04		19 16			19 52		20 18
Rhyl d		15 58		16 08		16 58			17 09		17 58	18 09		18 33	18 58	19 10		19 22			19 58		20 25
Abergele & Pensarn d		16 04				17 04					18 04				19 04						20 04		
Colwyn Bay d		16 12		16 19		17 12			17 19		18 12	18 20		18 44	19 12	19 21		19 33			20 12		20 38
Llandudno Junction a		16 17		16 24		17 17			17 24		18 17	18 25		18 49	19 17	19 26		19 38			20 18		20 44
d	15 52	16 19		16 25		17 19			17 26		18 19	18 26		18 50	19 19	19 27		19 40			20 19		20 46
Deganwy d	15x55	16x23				17x23					18x23				19x23						20x23		
Llandudno a	16 01	16 35				17 35					18 35				19 37						20 35		
Conwy d				16x28					17x29			18x29				19x31							
Penmaenmawr d				16x34					17x35			18x35				19x37							
Llanfairfechan d				16x38					17x39			18x39				19x41							
Bangor (Gwynedd) a				16 46					17 47			18 47		19 05		19 49		19 56					21 03
d				16 47					17 48			18 48		19 07		19 49		20 00					21 05
Llanfairpwll d									17x54							19x55							
Bodorgan d									18x04							20x05							
Ty Croes d									18x08							20x10							
Rhosneigr d									18x11							20x13							
Valley d									18x17							20x18							
Holyhead a				17 20					18 30			19 20		19 41		20 30		20 46					21 40

	AW	AW	AW	AW ◇ A	AW R 🛒	AW	AW	AW	AW ◇	VT 1 ◇ ⊡		AW	AW	AW	AW ◇ 🛒	AW	AW	AW	AW ◇ C	AW	AW ◇
London Euston 15 ⊖ 65 d			18 08			18c17		18 45		19 38		19 46		20 17		20 46		21 10			
Birmingham New Street 12 65 d			18 51			19 21				20 03		20 21		21 03		21 21					22 33
Manchester Airport 84, 85 ✈ d		18b47					19b47						20b47				21b47			22 47	
Cardiff Central 7 131 d	16 50				17 20			17 50				18 50			19 34				20 53		
Crewe 10 d	19 38		20 03			20 33		21 03		21 29		21 47		22 17		22 45		23 11	23 51		00 02
Manchester Piccadilly 10 90 ⛴ d		19 16					20 16						21 16				22 16			23 20	
Manchester Oxford Road 90 d		19 19					20 19						21 19				22 19			23 23	
Newton-le-Willows 90 d		19 37					20 37						21 37				22 37			23 41	
Earlestown 8 90 d		19 40					20 40						21 40				22 40			23 44	
Warrington Bank Quay 90 d		19 48					20 48						21 49				22 48			23 52	
Runcorn East d		19 55					20 55						21 56				22 55			23 59	
Frodsham d		20 00					21 00						22 01				23 01			00 04	
Helsby d		20 04					21 04						22 05				23 04			00 08	
Liverpool Lime Street 10 106 d					19 28					20 58					21 28						23 28
Chester a	20 02	20 22	20 27		20 31	20 57	21 23	21 27		21 49		22 11	22 17	22 40	22 32	23 09	23 23	23 35	00 16	00 21	00 26
d					20 35					21 50					22 45						00 40
Shotton d					20 44										22 54						
Flint d					20 50					22 03					23 00						00 53
Prestatyn d					21 03					22 16					23 13						
Rhyl d					21 09					22 23					23 19						01 09
Abergele & Pensarn d					21 15										23 25						
Colwyn Bay d					21 23					22 34					23 33						01 20
Llandudno Junction a					21 28					22 39					23 38						01 25
d				20 58	21 30				21 33	22 40					23 40						01 26
Deganwy d				21x01					21x36												
Llandudno a				21 08					21 43												
Conwy d					21 33										23x43						
Penmaenmawr d					21x39										23x49						
Llanfairfechan d					21x43										23x53						
Bangor (Gwynedd) a					21 51					22 55					00 01						01 42
d					21 52					22 57					00 02						01 42
Llanfairpwll d					21x58										00x08						
Bodorgan d					22x08										00x18						
Ty Croes d					22x12										00x22						
Rhosneigr d					22x15										00x25						
Valley d					22x21										00x31						
Holyhead a					22 35					23 30					00 47						02 15

For general notes see front of timetable
For details of catering facilities see Directory of Train Operators

- **A** From Blaenau Ffestiniog (Table 102)
- **B** From Liverpool Lime Street (Table 90) to Ellesmere Port (Table 109)
- **C** From Carmarthen (Table 128)
- **b** Change at Manchester Oxford Road
- **c** Fridays dep. 1820

Table 81

Crewe and Manchester → Chester and North Wales

Network Diagram - see first page of Table 81

	AW	NT A	AW	AW	VT [1] ◇	AW ◇ 🛒	AW	AW ◇ 🛒	AW	AW ◇ 🛒	AW	AW ◇ B 🛒	AW ◇ C	AW	NT D	AW ◇ E	AW ◇ 🛒	AW ◇ 🛒	AW	AW ◇ 🛒	AW	AW ◇ B 🛒	AW C
London Euston [15] ⊖ 65 d																		05 31			07 15		
Birmingham New Street [12] 65 d					05 20		05 30		06b20					07 21					08 21				
Manchester Airport 84, 85 ✈ d						05 34				06 44	06 57				07 05		07c47	08 00		08c47	09 00		
Cardiff Central [7] 131 d									04e00			05§10	04f15					05e35			06e50	07§20	
Crewe [10] d					06 18		06 37	07 03	07 33		08 03			08 33				09 03	09 33		10 03		
Manchester Piccadilly [10] 90 ⛴ d						06 00				07 16					07 39		08 16			09 16			
Manchester Oxford Road 90 d						06 03				07 19					07 33		08 19			09 19			
Newton-le-Willows 90 d						06 21				07 37							08 37			09 38			
Earlestown [8] 90 d						06 24				07 40							08 40			09 41			
Warrington Bank Quay 90 d		06 00				06 33				07 48							08 49			09 50			
Runcorn East d						06 40				07 55							08 56			09 57			
Frodsham d						06 44				08 00							09 00			10 01			
Helsby d		06a13				06 48				08 04							09 04			10 05			
Liverpool Lime Street [10] 106 d						05 58		06 28		07 28							08 28			09 28			
Chester a					06 37	07 03	07 03	07 24	07 57	08 18	08 27	08§28		08 57	09 06		09 17	09 26	09 57	10 19	10 27	10§28	
d					06 45	07 05		07 32		08 24		08§35	08§35				09 21	09 35		10 24		10§35	10§35
Shotton d						07 14				08 35							09 33			10 33			
Flint d					06 57	07 20		07 45		08 41		08§51	08§51				09 39	09 49		10 39		10§51	10§51
Prestatyn d					07 10	07 33		07 58		08 54		09§04	09§04				09 52	10 02		10 52		11§04	11§04
Rhyl d					07 17	07 39		08 04		09 00		09§10	09§10				09 58	10 08		10 58		11§10	11§10
Abergele & Pensarn d						07 45				09 06							10 04			11 04			
Colwyn Bay d					07 28	07 53		08 15		09 14		09§21	09§21				10 12	10 19		11 12		11§21	11§21
Llandudno Junction a					07 33	07 58		08 20		09 19		09§26	09§26				10 17	10 24		11 17		11§26	11§26
d	06 25		06 51	07 33	07 34	08 00		08 22		09 21		09§27	09§27			09 52	10 19	10 25		11 19		11§27	11§27
Deganwy d	06x28		06x54	07x36		08x04				09x25						09x55	10x23			11x23			
Llandudno a	06 35		07 01	07 43		08 16				09 37						10 01	10 37			11 35			
Conwy d								08x25										10x28					
Penmaenmawr d								08x31										10x34					
Llanfairfechan d								08x35										10x38					
Bangor (Gwynedd) a					07 49			08 43				09§43	09§43					10 46				11§43	11§43
d					07 51			08 43				09§43	09§43					10 47				11§43	11§43
Llanfairpwll d								08x49										10x53					
Bodorgan d								08x59										11x03					
Ty Croes d								09x04										11x07					
Rhosneigr d								09x07										11x10					
Valley d								09x12										11x16					
Holyhead a					08 21			09 30				10§20	10§20					11 30				12§20	12§20

	AW	VT [1] ◇ 🍴	AW	AW ◇ 🛒	AW ◇ 🛒	AW	AW ◇ E	AW ◇ 🛒	AW B	AW ◇ 🛒	AW C	AW	AW ◇ 🛒	VT [1] ◇ 🍴	AW ◇ 🛒	AW	AW ◇ 🛒	AW	AW ◇ B 🛒	AW C	AW	AW ◇ E	AW ◇ 🛒
London Euston [15] ⊖ 65 d					08 17				09 17					10 17				11 17					
Birmingham New Street [12] 65 d	09 21				09 40	10 21			10 40			11 21		12 03		12 21		12 40			13 21		
Manchester Airport 84, 85 ✈ d		10 00						10c47	11 00				11c47	12 00			12c47	13 00					13c47
Cardiff Central [7] 131 d		07e50								09§20				09e50				10e50	11§20				
Crewe [10] d	10 33	10 44			11 03	11 33			12 03			12 33		13 13	13 15	13 33		14 03			14 33		
Manchester Piccadilly [10] 90 ⛴ d			10 03	10 16				11 16					12 16				13 16						14 16
Manchester Oxford Road 90 d			10 06	10 18				11 19					12 19				13 19						14 19
Newton-le-Willows 90 d			10 30	10 38				11 38					12 39				13 38						14 38
Earlestown [8] 90 d				10 41				11 41					12 41				13 41						14 41
Warrington Bank Quay 90 d			10 40	10 50				11 50					12 50				13 50						14 50
Runcorn East d				10 57				11 57					12 57				13 57						14 57
Frodsham d				11 01				12 01					13 01				14 01						15 01
Helsby d				11 05				12 05					13 05				14 05						15 05
Liverpool Lime Street [10] 106 d		10 28						11 28					12 28				13 28						14 28
Chester a	10 57	11 09	11 10	11 22	11 29	11 59		12 19	12 27	12§25		12 59	13 20	13 31	13 42	13 57	14 20	14 27	14§28		14 57		15 19
d		11 18		11 24	11 35			12 24		12§35	12§35		13 24	13 33	13 43		14 25		14§35	14§35			15 24
Shotton d				11 33				12 33							13 52		14 34						15 33
Flint d				11 39	11 50			12 39		12§49	12§49			13 46	13 58		14 40		14§50	14§50			15 39
Prestatyn d				11 52	12 04			12 52		13§02	13§02		13 47	13 59	14 12		14 53		15§03	15§03			15 52
Rhyl d		11 46		11 58	12 10			12 58		13§08	13§08		13 53	14 05	14 18		14 59		15§09	15§09			15 58
Abergele & Pensarn d				12 04				13 04							14 24		15 05						16 04
Colwyn Bay d		11 57		12 12	12 20			13 12		13§19	13§19		14 04	14 16	14 32		15 13		15§20	15§20			16 12
Llandudno Junction a		12 02		12 17	12 25			13 17		13§24	13§24		14 09	14 21	14 37		15 18		15§25	15§25			16 17
d		12 03		12 19	12 27		12 52	13 19		13§25	13§25		14 11	14 23	14 38		15 20		15§26	15§26		15 52	16 19
Deganwy d				12x23			12x55	13x23					14x14				15x24					15x55	16x23
Llandudno a				12 35			13 01	13 35					14 27	14 33			15 36					16 01	16 35
Conwy d					12x30					13x29	13x29								15x29	15x29			
Penmaenmawr d					12x36					13x35	13x35								15x35	15x35			
Llanfairfechan d					12x40					13x40	13x40								15x39	15x39			
Bangor (Gwynedd) a		12 18			12 48					13§48	13§48				14 54				15§47	15§47			
d		12 20			12 48					13§48	13§48				14 54				15§48	15§48			
Llanfairpwll d					12x54					13x54	13x54								15x54	15x54			
Bodorgan d					13x04					14x04	14x04								16x04	16x04			
Ty Croes d					13x09					14x09	14x09								16x08	16x08			
Rhosneigr d					13x12					14x12	14x12								16x11	16x11			
Valley d					13x17					14x17	14x17								16x17	16x17			
Holyhead a		12 53			13 30					14§30	14§30				15 30				16§30	16§30			

For general notes see front of timetable
For details of catering facilities see Directory of Train Operators

A To Ellesmere Port (Table 109)

B Until 22 March

C From 29 March. From Hereford (Table 131)

D From Blackpool North (Table 82)

E From Blaenau Ffestiniog (Table 102)

b Change at Stafford and Crewe

c Change at Manchester Oxford Road

e Until 22 March only

f By bus to Hereford (Table 131)

Crewe and Manchester → Chester and North Wales

Network Diagram - see first page of Table 81

		NT	AW	AW	AW	AW	AW	AW	AW	AW	AW	AW	VT	AW	AW	AW	AW	AW	AW	AW	AW	VT	AW	AW
			◇		◇		◇			◇	◇		1 ◇	◇		◇		◇		◇		1 ◇		
		A					B	C								B	C							
London Euston 15	⊖ 65 d		12 17			13 17					14 17				15 17						16 17			
Birmingham New Street 12	65 d		13 40	14 21		14 40			15 21		15 40	16 03	16 21		16 40				17 21		17 40	18 03	18 21	
Manchester Airport	84, 85 ✈ d		14 00		14b47	15 00				15b47	16 00			16 47	17 00			17 04		17b47	18 00			18b47
Cardiff Central 7	131 d		11c50			12c50	13 20				13c50					15 20					15c50		16c50	
Crewe 10	d		15 03	15 33		16 03			16 33		17 03	17 30	17 36		18 03				18 33		19 03	19 28	19 38	
Manchester Piccadilly 10	90 d				15 16					16 16				17 20				17 41		18 16				19 16
Manchester Oxford Road	90 d				15 19					16 19				17 26				17 47		18 19				19 19
Newton-le-Willows	90 d				15 38					16 38				17 45				18 04		18 37				19 37
Earlestown 8	90 d	14 51			15 41					16 41				17 47				18 07		18 40				19 40
Warrington Bank Quay	90 d	15 02			15 50					16 50				17 56				18 18		18 49				19 48
Runcorn East	d	15 10			15 57					16 57				18 03				18 25		18 56				19 55
Frodsham	d	15 15			16 01					17 01				18 07				18 29		19 00				20 00
Helsby	d	15a19			16 05					17 05				18 11				18 33		19 04				20 04
Liverpool Lime Street 10	106 d				15 28					16 28			16 58	17 28				17 58		18 28		18 58		
Chester	a		15 26	15 57	16 17	16 27	16 28		16 56	17 19	17 26	17 54	17 59	18 24	18 29	18 25		18 45	18 57	19 17	19 25	19 46	20 02	20 22
	d		15 35		16 24		16 35	16 35		17 24	17 35		18 00	18 24		18 35	18 35	18 50		19 24		19 48		
Shotton	d				16 33					17 33	17 44			18 33						19 33				
Flint	d		15 49		16 39		16 49	16 49		17 39	17 50		18 13	18 39		18 51	18 51	19 03		19 39				
Prestatyn	d		16 02		16 52		17 03	17 03		17 52	18 03		18 26	18 52		19 04	19 04	19 16		19 52		20 14		
Rhyl	d		16 08		16 58		17 09	17 09		17 58	18 09		18 33	18 58		19 10	19 10	19 22		19 58		20 20		
Abergele & Pensarn	d				17 04					18 04				19 04						20 04				
Colwyn Bay	d		16 19		17 12		17 19	17 19		18 12	18 20		18 44	19 12		19 21	19 21	19 33		20 12		20 32		
Llandudno Junction	a		16 24		17 17		17 24	17 24		18 17	18 25		18 49	19 17		19 26	19 26	19 38		20 18		20 37		
	d		16 25		17 19		17 26	17 26		18 19	18 26		18 50	19 19		19 27	19 27	19 40		20 19		20 38		
Deganwy	d				17x23					18x23				19x23						20x23				
Llandudno	a				17 35					18 35				19 37						20 35				
Conwy	d		16x28				17x29	17x29			18x29					19x31	19x31							
Penmaenmawr	d		16x34				17x35	17x35			18x35					19x37	19x37							
Llanfairfechan	d		16x38				17x39	17x39			18x39					19x41	19x41							
Bangor (Gwynedd)	a		16 46				17 47	17 47			18 47		19 05			19 49	19 49	19 56				20 55		
	d		16 47				17 48	17 48			18 48		19 07			19 49	19 49	20 00				20 57		
Llanfairpwll	d						17x54	17x54								19x55	19x55							
Bodorgan	d						18x04	18x04								20x05	20x05							
Ty Croes	d						18x08	18x08								20x10	20x10							
Rhosneigr	d						18x11	18x11								20x13	20x13							
Valley	d						18x17	18x17								20x18	20x18							
Holyhead	a		17 20				18 30	18 30			19 20		19 36			20 30	20 30	20 46				21 33		

		AW	AW	AW	AW	AW	AW	AW	AW	AW	AW	AW	AW	AW	AW	AW	AW	AW	AW	AW	AW	AW
		◇		◇				◇	◇				◇						◇	◇		◇
		D		B	C								B	C				🚌	E	C		
London Euston 15	⊖ 65 d		17 17						18 17	19 02		19e05			19f36							
Birmingham New Street 12	65 d		18 40			19 21				20 21					21 21							22 33
Manchester Airport	84, 85 ✈ d						19b47				20b47					21b47					22 47	
Cardiff Central 7	131 d			17 20					17c50	18c50			19 34						20 53			
Crewe 10	d		20 03			20 33			21 03	21 45		22 06			22 46		23 11		23 45	23 51		00 02
Manchester Piccadilly 10	90 d						20 16				21 16					22 16					23 20	
Manchester Oxford Road	90 d						20 20				21 19					22 19					23 23	
Newton-le-Willows	90 d						20 37				21 37					22 37					23 41	
Earlestown 8	90 d						20 40				21 40					22 40					23 44	
Warrington Bank Quay	90 d						20 48				21 49					22 48					23 52	
Runcorn East	d						20 55				21 56					22 55					23 59	
Frodsham	d						21 00				22 00					23 00					00 04	
Helsby	d						21 04				22 04					23 04					00 08	
Liverpool Lime Street 10	106 d			19 28	19 28				20 28				21 28	21 28								
Chester	a		20 27	20 26		20 57	21 23		21 27	22 09	22 17	22 30	22 32		23 10	23 23	23 34		00 10	00 16	00 21	00 24
	d			20 35	20 35				21 35				22 35	22 35								
Shotton	d			20 44	20 44				21 44				22 45	22 45								
Flint	d			20 50	20 50				21 50				22 51	22 51								
Prestatyn	d			21 03	21 03				22 03				23 05	23 05								
Rhyl	d			21 09	21 09				22 09				23 11	23 11								
Abergele & Pensarn	d			21 15	21 15								23 17	23 17								
Colwyn Bay	d			21 23	21 23				22 20				23 25	23 25								
Llandudno Junction	a			21 28	21 28				22 25				23 33	23 33								
	d	20 58		21 30	21 30			21 33	22 26									23 43				
Deganwy	d	21x01						21x36														
Llandudno	a	21 08						21 43														
Conwy	d			21 33	21 33													23 48				
Penmaenmawr	d			21x39	21x39													23 58				
Llanfairfechan	d			21x43	21x43													00 04				
Bangor (Gwynedd)	a			21 51	21 51				22 42									00 25				
	d			21 52	21 52				22 42									00 25				
Llanfairpwll	d			21x58	21x58				22x48									00 40				
Bodorgan	d			22x08	22x08				22x58									01 00				
Ty Croes	d			22x12	22x12				23x03									01 10				
Rhosneigr	d			22x15	22x15				23x06									01 20				
Valley	d			22x21	22x21				23x11									01 35				
Holyhead	a			22 35	22 35				23 30									01 45				

For general notes see front of timetable
For details of catering facilities see Directory of Train Operators

A From Liverpool Lime Street (Table 90) to Ellesmere Port (Table 109)
B Until 22 March
C From 29 March. From Hereford (Table 131)
D From Blaenau Ffestiniog (Table 102)
E Until 22 March. From Carmarthen (Table 128)
b Change at Manchester Oxford Road
c Until 22 March only
e From 29 March dep. 1917
f From 29 March dep. 1950

Sundays

until 23 March

Crewe and Manchester → Chester and North Wales

Network Diagram - see first page of Table 81

		AW	AW	AW ◇ 🛒	AW	AW	AW	AW	AW ◇ 🛒	AW	AW A 🚌	AW ◇ 🛒	AW	AW	AW	AW 🛒	AW ◇ 🛒
London Euston 15	⊖ 65 d												09 31	09 40			10 31
Birmingham New Street 12	65 d			09 03			09 30		10 03				11 30		12 03		12b18
Manchester Airport	84, 85 ✈ d				09 33	09 25						11 00	11 32			12 46	
Cardiff Central 7	131 d																
Crewe 10	d	08 55	09 25	10 05	10 25		10 55		11 15	11 55			12 35	12 55	13 25		13 55
Manchester Piccadilly 10	90 🚢 d					09 58						11 25				13 15	
Manchester Oxford Road	90 d					10 01						11 34				13 18	
Newton-le-Willows	90 d					10 19						11 52				13 36	
Earlestown 8	90 d					10 22						11 54				13 39	
Warrington Bank Quay	90 d					10 30						12 03				13 48	
Runcorn East	d					10 37						12 10				13 55	
Frodsham	d					10 42						12 14				13 59	
Helsby	d					10 46						12 18				14 03	
Liverpool Lime Street 10	106 d			09 28					10 28			11 28					13 28
Chester	a	09 20	09 50	10 28	10 50	10 58	11 20		11 36	12 20		12 30	13 00	13 20	13 50	14 15	14 15
	d			10 32					11 38			12 32					14 20
Shotton	d			10 41					11 47			12 41					14 29
Flint	d			10 47					11 53			12 47					14 35
Prestatyn	d			11 00					12 06			13 00					14 48
Rhyl	d			11 06					12 12			13 06					14 54
Abergele & Pensarn	d			11 12					12 18			13 12					
Colwyn Bay	d			11 20					12 26			13 20					15 05
Llandudno Junction	a			11 25					12 31			13 25					15 10
	d			11 27				11 45	12 33		13 15	13 27					15 11
Deganwy	d										13 18						
Llandudno	a										13 30						
Conwy	d							11x48				13x30					
Penmaenmawr	d							11x55				13x36					
Llanfairfechan	d							11x59				13x40					
Bangor (Gwynedd)	a			11 46				12 13	12 48			13 51					15 34
	d								12 49								
Llanfairpwll	d																
Bodorgan	d																
Ty Croes	d																
Rhosneigr	d																
Valley	d																
Holyhead	a								13 22								

		AW	AW ◇ B 🛒	AW	AW 🛒	AW A 🚌	AW ◇ 🛒	AW	AW ◇ 🛒	AW 🛒	AW ◇ 🛒	AW	AW A 🚌	AW ◇ 🛒	AW	AW	AW
London Euston 15	⊖ 65 d			11 40			12 40	13 40	13 55		14 50				15 50	15 58	
Birmingham New Street 12	65 d	13 03		13 30			14b18	15b18	16 03		16b18				17b18	17 30	
Manchester Airport	84, 85 ✈ d	13 26			14 27			15 25		16 01				17 01	17 24		18 01
Cardiff Central 7	131 d		11 35				12 35					14 35			15 35		
Crewe 10	d	14 25		14 55			15 55	16 30	17 05		17 40	17 55			18 30	18 55	
Manchester Piccadilly 10	90 🚢 d				14 57					16 29				17 32			18 32
Manchester Oxford Road	90 d				15 00					16 32				17 35			18 35
Newton-le-Willows	90 d				15 18					16 50				17 53			18 53
Earlestown 8	90 d				15 21					16 53				17 55			18 56
Warrington Bank Quay	90 d				15 29					17 01				18 05			19 04
Runcorn East	d				15 36					17 08				18 12			19 11
Frodsham	d				15 41					17 13				18 16			19 16
Helsby	d				15 45					17 17				18 20			19 20
Liverpool Lime Street 10	106 d		13 58				15 28		16 28		16 58			17 28			
Chester	a	14 50	14 59	15 20	16 01		16 17	16 54	17 29	17 30	18 01	18 20		18 32	18 55	19 20	19 34
	d		15 03				16 21		17 36		18 03			18 36			
Shotton	d		15 12						17 45					18 45			
Flint	d		15 18				16 34		17 51		18 16			18 51			
Prestatyn	d		15 32				16 47		18 04		18 29			19 04			
Rhyl	d		15 38				16 53		18 10		18 35			19 10			
Abergele & Pensarn	d		15 45						18 16		18 41			19 16			
Colwyn Bay	d		15 53				17 04		18 24		18 49			19 24			
Llandudno Junction	a		15 59				17 09		18 29		18 54			19 29			
	d		16 00			16 15	17 11		18 31		18 59		19 15	19 31			
Deganwy	d					16 18							19 18				
Llandudno	a					16 30							19 30				
Conwy	d		16x03											19x34			
Penmaenmawr	d		16x09											19x40			
Llanfairfechan	d		16x13											19x44			
Bangor (Gwynedd)	a		16 22				17 26		18 51		19 14			19 52			
	d		16 23				17 27				19 15			19 52			
Llanfairpwll	d										19x21						
Bodorgan	d										19x31						
Ty Croes	d										19x35						
Rhosneigr	d										19x38						
Valley	d										19x44						
Holyhead	a		16 58				18 02				20 00			20 25			

For general notes see front of timetable
For details of catering facilities see Directory of Train Operators

A From Blaenau Ffestiniog (Table 102)
B From Cardiff Central (Table 131)
b Change at Stafford and Crewe

Table 81

Sundays

until 23 March

Crewe and Manchester → Chester and North Wales

Network Diagram - see first page of Table 81

		VT	AW	AW	AW	AW	VT	AW	AW	AW	AW	AW	AW	AW	AW
		1 ◇		◇			1 ◇	R A (bike)			◇				◇ B
London Euston 15	⊖ 65 d	16 50	16 58	17 50		17 58				18 58		19 50			21b10
Birmingham New Street 12	65 d	18c18		19c18		19 30	20 03			20c18		21 40			22 54
Manchester Airport	84, 85 ✈ d			19 24	19 47				20 47		21 25		22e01	22f47	
Cardiff Central 7	131 d		16 35					18 35							20 35
Crewe 10	d	19 34	19 55	20 35		20 55	21 06			21 55	22 20	22 55			00 30
Manchester Piccadilly 10	90 ⛴ d				20 14				21 14				22 20	23 17	
Manchester Oxford Road	90 d				20 18				21 18				22 23	23 20	
Newton-le-Willows	90 d				20 36				21 36				22 44	23 38	
Earlestown 8	90 d				20 39				21 39				22 47	23 41	
Warrington Bank Quay	90 d				20 48				21 47				22 55	23 49	
Runcorn East	d				20 55				21 54				23 02	23 56	
Frodsham	d				20 59				21 59				23 07	00 01	
Helsby	d				21 03				22 03				23 11	00 05	
Liverpool Lime Street 10	106 d	18 58		19 58			20 28	20 58			21 28				23 28
Chester	a	19 52	20 20	20 56	21 17	21 20	21 33	21 34	22 17	22 20	22 41	23 19	23 25	00 18	00 48
	d	19 55		20 58			21 35	21 50			22 43				00 54
Shotton	d			21 07				21 59			22 52				01 07
Flint	d			21 13				22 05			22 58				
Prestatyn	d	20 18		21 26				22 20			23 11				01 23
Rhyl	d	20 24		21 32			22 04	22 28			23 17				
Abergele & Pensarn	d			21 38				22 35							
Colwyn Bay	d	20 35		21 46			22 17	22 43			23 28				01 34
Llandudno Junction	a	20 40		21 51			22 23	22 49			23 33				01 39
	d	20 42		21 53			22 25	22 50			23 34				01 40
Deganwy	d														
Llandudno	a														
Conwy	d			21x56				22x53							
Penmaenmawr	d			22x02				22x59							
Llanfairfechan	d			22x06				23x03							
Bangor (Gwynedd)	a	20 57		22 14			22 42	23 12			23 50				01 56
	d	20 58		22 14			22 44	23 12			23 50				01 56
Llanfairpwll	d							23x18							
Bodorgan	d							23x28							
Ty Croes	d							23x33							
Rhosneigr	d							23x36							
Valley	d							23x41							
Holyhead	a	21 26		22 50			23 14	23 51			00 26				02 27

Sundays

from 30 March

		AW	AW	AW	AW	AW	AW	AW	AW	AW	AW	AW	AW	AW	AW	AW	AW	AW	AW	AW
				◇ (bike)				C		◇ (bike)		C	D (bus)				C			C
London Euston 15	⊖ 65 d														09 31	09 40		10c10		
Birmingham New Street 12	65 d			09 03	09 18		09 30			10 03	10 18				11 30			12 18		
Manchester Airport	84, 85 ✈ d				09 33	08g51								10g22	11 25				12g00	
Cardiff Central 7	131 d																			
Crewe 10	d	08 55	09 25	10 05	10 25		10 55			11 15	11 55				12 35	12 55		13 25		
Manchester Piccadilly 10	90 ⛴ d					09h20								10h50					12h38	
Manchester Oxford Road	90 d					09h30								11h00					12h48	
Newton-le-Willows	90 d					09h55								11h25					13h13	
Earlestown 8	90 d					10h05								11h35					13h23	
Warrington Bank Quay	90 d					10 30								12 00					13 48	
Runcorn East	d					10 37								12 10					13 55	
Frodsham	d					10 42								12 14					13 59	
Helsby	d					10 46								12 18					14 03	
Liverpool Lime Street 10	106 d			09 28						10 28				11 28						
Chester	a	09 20	09 50	10 28	10 50	10 58	11 20			11 36	12 20			12 30	13 00	13 20		13 50	14 15	
	d			10 32						11 38				12 32						
Shotton	d			10 41						11 47				12 41						
Flint	d			10 47						11 53				12 47						
Prestatyn	d			11 00						12 06				13 00						
Rhyl	d			11 06						12 12				13 06						
Abergele & Pensarn	d			11 12						12 18				13 12						
Colwyn Bay	d			11 20						12 26				13 20						
Llandudno Junction	a			11 25						12 31				13 25						
	d			11 27				11 30	11 45	12 33		12 36	13 15	13 27			13 30			14 25
Deganwy	d							11x33				12x39	13 18				13x33			14x28
Llandudno	a							11 40				12 46	13 30				13 40			14 35
Conwy	d								11x48					13x30						
Penmaenmawr	d								11x55					13x36						
Llanfairfechan	d								11x59					13x40						
Bangor (Gwynedd)	a			11 46					12 13	12 48				13 51						
	d									12 49										
Llanfairpwll	d																			
Bodorgan	d																			
Ty Croes	d																			
Rhosneigr	d																			
Valley	d																			
Holyhead	a									13 22										

For general notes see front of timetable
For details of catering facilities see Directory of Train Operators

A From Milford Haven (Table 128)

B Until 27 January

C From 6 April

D From Blaenau Ffestiniog (Table 102)

b Change at Crewe

c Change at Stafford and Crewe

e Change at Manchester Oxford Road

f From 3 February dep. 2252

g Change at Manchester Piccadilly and Warrington Bank Quay. By bus from Manchester Piccadilly

h By bus

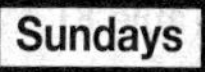

Sundays from 30 March

Crewe and Manchester → Chester and North Wales

Network Diagram - see first page of Table 81

	AW ◇ ⌶	AW	AW A	AW B	AW	AW	AW A	AW C bus	AW ◇ ⌶	AW	AW A	AW ◇ ⌶	AW	AW ◇ ⌶	AW	AW C bus	AW	AW	AW
London Euston 15 ⊖ 65 d	10 31	11b10			11 40				12 40	13 40		13 55		14 50				15 50	15 58
Birmingham New Street 12 65 d		13 18			13 30				14 18	15 18		15 30		16 18				17 18	17 30
Manchester Airport 84, 85 ✈ d		13 26				14c00				15 25			15e22				16e22	17 24	
Cardiff Central 7 131 d																			
Crewe 10 d	13 55	14 25			14 55				15 55	16 30		17 05		17 40	17 55			18 30	18 55
Manchester Piccadilly 10 90 ⛴ d						14f19							15f50				16f50		
Manchester Oxford Road 90 d						14f29							16f00				17f00		
Newton-le-Willows 90 d						14f54							16f25				17f25		
Earlestown 8 90 d						15f04							16f35				17f35		
Warrington Bank Quay 90 d						15 29							17 00				18 05		
Runcorn East d						15 36							17 08				18 12		
Frodsham d						15 41							17 13				18 16		
Helsby d						15 45							17 17				18 20		
Liverpool Lime Street 10 106 d	13 28			13 58					15 28			16 28		16 58			17 28		
Chester a	14 15	14 50			15 20	16 01			16 17	16 54		17 29	17 30	18 01	18 20		18 32	18 55	19 20
d	14 20			15 03					16 21			17 36		18 03			18 36		
Shotton d	14 29			15 12								17 45					18 45		
Flint d	14 35			15 18					16 34			17 51		18 16			18 51		
Prestatyn d	14 48			15 32					16 47			18 04		18 29			19 04		
Rhyl d	14 54			15 38					16 53			18 10		18 35			19 10		
Abergele & Pensarn d				15 45								18 16		18 41			19 16		
Colwyn Bay d	15 05			15 53					17 04			18 24		18 49			19 24		
Llandudno Junction a	15 10			15 59					17 09			18 29		18 54			19 29		
d	15 11		15 16	16 00			16 06	16 15	17 11		17 17	18 31		18 59		19 15	19 31		
Deganwy d			15x19				16x09	16 18			17x20					19 18			
Llandudno a			15 26				16 16	16 30			17 27					19 30			
Conwy d				16x03													19x34		
Penmaenmawr d				16x09													19x40		
Llanfairfechan d				16x13													19x44		
Bangor (Gwynedd) a	15 34			16 22					17 26			18 51		19 14			19 52		
d				16 23					17 27					19 15			19 52		
Llanfairpwll d														19x21					
Bodorgan d														19x31					
Ty Croes d														19x35					
Rhosneigr d														19x38					
Valley d														19x44					
Holyhead a				16 58					18 02					20 00			20 25		

	AW	VT 1 ◇ catering	AW	AW ◇	AW	AW	VT 1 ◇ catering	AW R B ⌶	AW	AW	AW ◇	AW	AW	AW	AW ◇	AW bus
London Euston 15 ⊖ 65 d		16 50	16 58	17 50		17 58				18 58		19 50			21g10	
Birmingham New Street 12 65 d		18 18		19 18		19 30	20 03			20 18		21 40			22 54	
Manchester Airport 84, 85 ✈ d	17e22			19 25	19e05				20e01		21 25		21e05	22e01		22 52
Cardiff Central 7 131 d																
Crewe 10 d		19 34	19 55	20 35		20 55	21 06			21 55	22 20	22 55			00 30	
Manchester Piccadilly 10 90 ⛴ d	17f50				19f35				20f35				21f45	22f35		23 20
Manchester Oxford Road 90 d	18f00				19f45				20f45				21f55	22f45		23 30
Newton-le-Willows 90 d	18f25				20f10				21f10				22f20	23f10		23 55
Earlestown 8 90 d	18f35				20f20				21f20				22f30	23f20		00 05
Warrington Bank Quay 90 d	19 04				20 48				21 48				22 55	23 49		00 20
Runcorn East d	19 11				20 55				21 55				23 02	23 56		00s35
Frodsham d	19 16				20 59				21 59				23 07	00 01		00s55
Helsby d	19 20				21 03				22 03				23 11	00 05		01s05
Liverpool Lime Street 10 106 d		18 58		19 58			20 28	20 58			21 28				23 28	
Chester a	19 34	19 52	20 20	20 56	21 17	21 20	21 33		22 17	22 20	22 41	23 19	23 25	00 18	00 48	01 20
d		19 55		20 58			21 35	21 50			22 43				00 54	
Shotton d				21 07				21 59			22 52					
Flint d				21 13				22 05			22 58				01 07	
Prestatyn d		20 18		21 26				22 20			23 11					
Rhyl d		20 24		21 32			22 04	22 28			23 17				01 23	
Abergele & Pensarn d				21 38				22 35								
Colwyn Bay d		20 35		21 46			22 17	22 43			23 28				01 34	
Llandudno Junction a		20 40		21 51			22 23	22 49			23 33				01 39	
d		20 42		21 53			22 25	22 50			23 34				01 40	
Deganwy d																
Llandudno a																
Conwy d				21x56				22x53								
Penmaenmawr d				22x02				22x59								
Llanfairfechan d				22x06				23x03								
Bangor (Gwynedd) a		20 57		22 14			22 42	23 12			23 50				01 56	
d		20 58		22 14			22 44	23 12			23 50				01 56	
Llanfairpwll d								23x18								
Bodorgan d								23x28								
Ty Croes d								23x33								
Rhosneigr d								23x36								
Valley d								23x41								
Holyhead a		21 26		22 50			23 14	23 51			00 26				02 27	

For general notes see front of timetable
For details of catering facilities see Directory of Train Operators

A From 6 April

B From Shrewsbury (Table 75)

C From Blaenau Ffestiniog (Table 102)

b Change at Stafford and Crewe

c Change at Manchester Oxford Road and Warrington Bank Quay. By bus from Manchester Oxford Road

e Change at Manchester Piccadilly and Warrington Bank Quay. By bus from Manchester Piccadilly

f By bus

g Change at Crewe

North Wales and Chester → Manchester and Crewe

Network Diagram - see first page of Table 81

Miles	Miles			VT [1] ◇	AW	AW	AW ◇ 🛒	AW	AW 🛒	AW	VT [1] ◇ ⊠	AW	NT A	AW 🛒		AW	AW ◇ 🛒	AW	AW	AW ◇ 🛒	VT [1] ◇ ☕	AW	AW ◇ 🛒	AW
0	—	**Holyhead**	d	02 15			04 27				05 32						06 00			06 15	06 45			
3½	—	Valley	d				04x33													06x21				
7½	—	Rhosneigr	d																	06x26				
9¼	—	Ty Croes	d																	06x30				
12	—	Bodorgan	d																	06x34				
21	—	Llanfairpwll	d				04x51													06x44				
24¾	—	**Bangor (Gwynedd)**	a	02 41			04 59				06 00						06 27			06 53	07 11			
—	—		d	02 42			05 00				06 01						06 28			06 59	07 12			
32¼	—	Llanfairfechan	d														06x37							
34¾	—	Penmaenmawr	d														06x41							
39	—	Conwy	d														06x48							
—	0	**Llandudno**	d									06 39						07 03					07 47	
—	1¾	Deganwy	d									06x43						07x07					07x51	
40	3	**Llandudno Junction**	a	02 59			05 17				06 19	06 48					06 51	07 12		07 16	07 29		07 55	
—	—		d	03 00		04 55	05 18			05 45	06 21						06 53			07 17	07 31		07 56	
44	—	Colwyn Bay	d			05 01	05 24			05 51	06 29						06 59			07 23	07 37		08 02	
50¼	—	Abergele & Pensarn	d			05 08				05 59							07 06			07 30			08 09	
54½	—	Rhyl	d			05 14	05 35			06 06	06 42						07 12			07 36	07 48		08 15	
58	—	Prestatyn	d			05 19	05 40			06 12							07 17			07 42	07 54		08 21	
72	—	Flint	d			05 33	05 54			06 27							07 31			07 55	08 07		08 34	
76¼	—	Shotton	d			05 39				06 34							07 37			08 01			08 40	
84¼	—	**Chester**	a	03 38		05 50	06 08			06 45	07 12						07 48			08 12	08 21		08 51	
—	0		d	03 40	04 55	05 51	06 12	06 30	06 50	07 00	07 15			07 27		07 30	07 53		08 00	08 20	08 22	08 30	08 54	09 00
—	—	Liverpool Lime Street [10]	106 a				06 58			07 58	08 13						08 43				09 28		09 58	
—	7½	Helsby	d						06 59				07 12	07 36			08 03						09 03	
—	10	Frodsham	d						07 03					07 40			08 07						09 07	
—	13¼	Runcorn East	d						07 08					07 45			08 13						09 12	
—	18¾	Warrington Bank Quay	90 a						07 15				07 27	07 52			08 20						09 19	
—	22¼	Earlestown [8]	90 a						07 23					08 01			08 28						09 27	
—	24	Newton-le-Willows	90 a						07 26					08 04			08 31						09 30	
—	39¾	**Manchester Oxford Road**	90 a						07 45					08 31			08 52						09 50	
—	40¼	**Manchester Piccadilly [10]**	90 a						07 54					08 40			09 02						09 58	
105½	—	**Crewe [10]**	a	03 59	05 19	06 14		06 55		07 24	07 38					07 55			08 24		08 45	08 55		09 24
—	—	Cardiff Central [7]	131 a	07 50	08 53		09 18	09 53								10 52				11 20		11 53		
—	—	Manchester Airport	84, 85 ✈ a						08b19	08 14				09b06			09b25		09 15				10b19	10 11
—	—	Birmingham New Street [12]	65 a	05 12	06 58	07c55		08 11			08 58					09 11					09e54	10 11		
—	—	London Euston [15]	⊖ 65 a		08 04	08 19		08 58			09 36								10 27		10 46			11 27

		AW ◇	AW ◇ 🛒	AW	AW ◇ 🛒		AW	AW ◇ 🛒	AW ◇ B	AW	AW ◇ 🛒	VT [1] ◇ ☕	AW ◇ 🛒	AW	AW ◇ 🛒	AW	AW ◇ 🛒		AW	AW ◇ 🛒	AW ◇ 🛒	AW ◇ B	AW	AW ◇ 🛒
Holyhead	d	07 15			08 10						09 28	09 50			10 30					11 40				12 35
Valley	d	07x21			08x16						09x34				10x36					11x46				
Rhosneigr	d	07x26			08x21						09x39									11x51				
Ty Croes	d	07x30			08x25						09x43									11x55				
Bodorgan	d	07x34			08x29						09x47									11x59				
Llanfairpwll	d	07x44			08x39						09x57				10x54					12x09				
Bangor (Gwynedd)	a	07 52			08 47						10 05	10 16			11 03					12 17				13 04
	d	08 01			09 04						10 07	10 18			11 03					12 19				13 04
Llanfairfechan	d	08x09			09x12						10x15				11x11					12x27				13x12
Penmaenmawr	d	08x13			09x16						10x19				11x15					12x31				13x16
Conwy	d	08x19			09x22						10x25				11x21					12x37				13x22
Llandudno	d		08 47					09 47	10 14				10 44				11 47				12 47	13 14		
Deganwy	d		08x51					09x51	10x18				10x48				11x51				12x51	13x18		
Llandudno Junction	a	08 22	08 55		09 25			09 55	10 22		10 28	10 34	10 52		11 25		11 55			12 40	12 55	13 22		13 26
	d	08 27	08 56		09 27			09 56			10 30	10 36	10 53		11 26		11 56			12 42	12 56			13 27
Colwyn Bay	d	08 33	09 02		09 33			10 02				10 42	10 59		11 32		12 02			12 48	13 02			13 33
Abergele & Pensarn	d		09 09					10 09					11 06				12 09				13 09			
Rhyl	d	08 43	09 15		09 43			10 15				10 53	11 12		11 43		12 15			12 58	13 15			13 44
Prestatyn	d	08 49	09 21		09 49			10 21				10 59	11 18		11 48		12 21			13 04	13 21			13 49
Flint	d	09 02	09 34		10 02			10 34				11 12	11 31		12 02		12 34			13 17	13 34			14 03
Shotton	d		09 40					10 40					11 37				12 40				13 40			
Chester	a	09 17	09 51		10 16			10 51			11 09	11 26	11 48		12 16		12 51			13 31	13 51			14 17
	d	09 19	09 54	10 00	10 20		10 29	10 54		11 00	11 14	11 28	11 50	12 00	12 20	12 29	12 54		13 00	13 33	13 54		14 00	14 20
Liverpool Lime Street [10]	106 a	10 28	10 58		11 28						11 58	12 28	12 58		13 28		13 58			14 28	14 58			15 28
Helsby	d		10 03					11 03					11 59				13 03				14 03			
Frodsham	d		10 07					11 07					12 03				13 07				14 07			
Runcorn East	d		10 12					11 12					12 08				13 12				14 12			
Warrington Bank Quay	90 a		10 19					11 19					12 17				13 19				14 20			
Earlestown [8]	90 a		10 27					11 27					12 28				13 28				14 27			
Newton-le-Willows	90 a		10 30					11 30					12 30				13 30				14 29			
Manchester Oxford Road	90 a		10 50					11 50					12 50				13 50				14 50			
Manchester Piccadilly [10]	90 a		10 58					11 58					12 58				13 58				14 58			
Crewe [10]	a	09 43		10 24			10 50			11 24	11 41	11 47		12 27		12 50			13 24	14 00			14 24	
Cardiff Central [7]	131 a	12 53			13 21		13 53					14 53			15 20	15 53				16 53				17 15
Manchester Airport	84, 85 ✈ a		11b19	11 11					12b19	12 11			13b19	13 11			14b19		14 11		15b19		15 11	
Birmingham New Street [12]	65 a	10 58					11c58					12 58				13 58			14 58	15 11			15 58	
London Euston [15]	⊖ 65 a	11 48		12 26			13 18			13 27		13 40		14 40					15 26				16 27	

For general notes see front of timetable
For details of catering facilities see Directory of Train Operators

A From Ellesmere Port (Table 109)
B To Blaenau Ffestiniog (Table 102)
b Change at Manchester Oxford Road
c Change at Crewe and Stafford
e Change at Tamworth

North Wales and Chester → Manchester and Crewe

Network Diagram - see first page of Table 81

		AW	AW ◇	AW	AW ◇	NT A	AW ◇	AW ◇		VT [1] ◇	AW ◇	AW	VT [1] ◇	AW ◇	NT B	AW	AW ◇	AW ◇ C	AW	AW ◇		AW ◇	AW	AW ◇
Holyhead	d				13 20		13 35			14 14				14 35						15 39				16 35
Valley	d						13x41													15x45				
Rhosneigr	d						13x46													15x50				
Ty Croes	d						13x50													15x54				
Bodorgan	d						13x54													15x58				
Llanfairpwll	d						14x04													16x08				
Bangor (Gwynedd)	a				13 47		14 12			14 42				15 02						16 16				17 02
	d				13 49		14 14			14 43				15 04						16 17				17 04
Llanfairfechan	d						14x22							15x12						16x25				17x12
Penmaenmawr	d						14x26							15x16						16x29				17x16
Conwy	d						14x32							15x22						16x35				17x22
Llandudno	d		13 47					14 35					15 08				15 47	16 14				16 47		
Deganwy	d		13x51					14x39									15x51	16x18				16x51		
Llandudno Junction	a		13 55		14 05		14 35	14 43		15 01			15 15	15 25			15 55	16 22		16 38		16 55		17 25
	d		13 56		14 07		14 37	14 44		15 03			15 17	15 27			15 56			16 40		16 56		17 27
Colwyn Bay	d		14 02		14 13		14 43	14 50					15 23	15 33			16 02			16 46		17 02		17 33
Abergele & Pensarn	d		14 09					14 57									16 09					17 09		
Rhyl	d		14 15		14 23		14 53	15 03					15 34	15 43			16 15			16 56		17 15		17 43
Prestatyn	d		14 21		14 29		14 59	15 09					15 40	15 49			16 21			17 02		17 21		17 49
Flint	d		14 34				15 12	15 22					15 53	16 02			16 34			17 15		17 34		18 02
Shotton	d		14 40					15 28									16 40					17 40		
Chester	a		14 51		14 57		15 27	15 39		15 45	←		16 06	16 16			16 51			17 29		17 51		18 16
	d	14 30	14 54	15 03	15 09		15 30	15 54		15 48	15 54	16 00	16 08	16 20		16 31	16 54		17 00	17 31		17 53	17 59	18 20
Liverpool Lime Street [10]	106 a				*15 58*			*16 28*					*16 58*	*17 28*			*17 58*			*18 28*		*18 58*		*19 28*
Helsby	d		15 03			15 29		→			16 03				16 27		17 03					18 02		
Frodsham	d		15 07			15 34					16 07				16 32		17 07					18 06		
Runcorn East	d		15 12			15 39					16 12				16 37		17 12					18 11		
Warrington Bank Quay	90 a		15 19		15 31	15 47					16 19				16 45		17 19					18 20		
Earlestown [8]	90 a		15 27		15 43	15 56					16 27				16 56		17 27					18 27		
Newton-le-Willows	90 a		15 30		15 46						16 30						17 30					18 30		
Manchester Oxford Road	90 a		15 50		16 13						16 50						17 51					18 51		
Manchester Piccadilly [10]	90 a		15 58		16 21						16 58						17 59					19 01		
Crewe [10]	a	14 55		15 28			15 55			16 11		16 24	16 38			16 59			17 24	17 56			18 24	
Cardiff Central [7]	131 a	*17 54*					*19 01*							*19 24*		*19 54*				*21 01*				*21 19*
Manchester Airport	84, 85 ✈ a		*16b19*	*16 11*	*16b40*						*17b19*	*17 15*					*18b27*		*18 15*	*18 54*		*19b26*		
Birmingham New Street [12]	65 a	*16 11*		*16 58*			*17 11*			*17 30*			*17c58*			*18 11*			*18 58*	*19 11*			*19c58*	
London Euston [15]	⊖ 65 a			*17 40*						*18 21*		*18 27*	*18 42*						*19 25*				*20 26*	

		AW	AW ◇	AW	AW ◇	AW ◇	AW	AW ◇	AW	AW	AW		AW	AW ◇	AW ◇	AW	AW	AW ◇ D	AW	AW	AW	AW		
Holyhead	d				17 27			18 35						19 35				20 35						
Valley	d				17x33			18x41						19x41										
Rhosneigr	d				17x38			18x46						19x46										
Ty Croes	d				17x42			18x50						19x50										
Bodorgan	d				17x46			18x54						19x54										
Llanfairpwll	d				17x56			19x04						20x04										
Bangor (Gwynedd)	a				18 04			19 12						20 12				21 02						
	d				18 06			19 14						20 14				21 03						
Llanfairfechan	d				18x14									20x22				21x11						
Penmaenmawr	d				18x18									20x26				21x15						
Conwy	d				18x24									20x32				21x21						
Llandudno	d		17 47			18 47				19 47					20 47	21 13			21 47					
Deganwy	d		17x51			18x51				19x51					20x51	21x17			21x51					
Llandudno Junction	a		17 55		18 27	18 55		19 30		19 55				20 35	20 55	21 21		21 24	21 57					
	d		17 56		18 29	18 56		19 32		19 56				20 37	20 56			21 26						
Colwyn Bay	d		18 02		18 35	19 02		19 38		20 02				20 43	21 02			21 32						
Abergele & Pensarn	d		18 09			19 09				20 09					21 09			21 39						
Rhyl	d		18 15		18 45	19 15		19 48		20 15				20 53	21 15			21 45						
Prestatyn	d		18 21		18 51	19 21		19 54		20 21				20 59	21 21			21 50						
Flint	d		18 34		19 04	19 34		20 07		20 34				21 12	21 34			22 04						
Shotton	d		18 40			19 40				20 40					21 40			22 10						
Chester	a		18 51		19 20	19 51		20 22		20 51				21 26	21 51			22 23						
	d	18 30	18 53	19 00	19 22	19 53	20 05	20 28	20 30		20 56		21 00	21 33	21 54		22 14			22 44	23 12	23 22		
Liverpool Lime Street [10]	106 a		*19 58*		*20 28*	*20 58*		*21 28*		*21 58*				*22 28*	*22 58*			*23 28*						
Helsby	d		19 02			20 02					21 05				22 03							23 31		
Frodsham	d		19 06			20 06					21 09				22 07							23 35		
Runcorn East	d		19 11			20 11					21 14				22 12							23 40		
Warrington Bank Quay	90 a		19 19			20 18					21 23				22 21							23 50		
Earlestown [8]	90 a		19 27			20 27					21 30				22 32							23 57		
Newton-le-Willows	90 a		19 30			20 30					21 33				22 34							23 59		
Manchester Oxford Road	90 a		19 50			20 51					21 54				22 55									
Manchester Piccadilly [10]	90 a		19 59			21 00					22 01				23 05							00 27		
Crewe [10]	a	18 56		19 24	19 44		20 29		20 55				21 24	21 57			22 38			23 07	23 39			
Cardiff Central [7]	131 a	*21 57*			*23 04*				*00 17*					*01e22*										
Manchester Airport	84, 85 ✈ a		*20b19*			*21b28*					*22 39*				*23 58*						*01 14*	*01 10*		
Birmingham New Street [12]	65 a	*20 11*			*20 58*		*22c04*	22 18	*22 30*				*22 38*	*23 11*										
London Euston [15]	⊖ 65 a				*21 51*		*23 05*		*23 14*				*00 09*											

For general notes see front of timetable
For details of catering facilities see Directory of Train Operators

A To Liverpool Lime Street (Table 90)
B From Ellesmere Port (Table 109) to Liverpool Lime Street (Table 90)
C To Blaenau Ffestiniog (Table 102)
D To Shrewsbury (Table 75)
b Change at Manchester Oxford Road
c Change at Crewe and Stafford
e Saturday mornings arr. 0114

Table 81

North Wales and Chester → Manchester and Crewe

Network Diagram - see first page of Table 81

		VT 1 ◇	AW	AW	AW ◇ A	AW B	AW	AW	AW	VT 1 ◇	AW	AW	AW	AW ◇	AW	AW	AW ◇ A	AW B	VT 1 ◇	AW	AW ◇	AW	AW ◇	AW ◇
Holyhead	d	02 15			04§27	04§27				05 35				06 00			06§15	06§15	06 45				07 15	
Valley	d				04x33	04x33											06x21	06x21					07x21	
Rhosneigr	d																06x26	06x26					07x26	
Ty Croes	d																06x30	06x30					07x30	
Bodorgan	d																06x34	06x34					07x34	
Llanfairpwll	d				04x51	04x51											06x44	06x44					07x44	
Bangor (Gwynedd)	a	02 41			04§59	04§59				06 03				06 27			06§53	06§53	07 11				07 52	
	d	02 42			05§00	05§00				06 04				06 30			06§59	06§59	07 12				08 01	
Llanfairfechan	d													06x38									08x09	
Penmaenmawr	d													06x43									08x13	
Conwy	d													06x49									08x19	
Llandudno	d										06 39				07 03						07 47			08 47
Deganwy	d										06x43				07x07						07x51			08x51
Llandudno Junction	a	02 59			05§17	05§17				06 22	06 48			06 53	07 12		07§16	07§16	07 29		07 55		08 22	08 55
	d	03 00		05 00	05§18	05§18			05 45	06 24				06 54			07§17	07§17	07 30		07 56		08 27	08 56
Colwyn Bay	d			05 06	05§24	05§24			05 51	06 32				07 00			07§23	07§23	07 37		08 02		08 33	09 02
Abergele & Pensarn	d			05 13					05 59					07 07			07§30	07§30			08 09			09 09
Rhyl	d			05 19	05§35	05§35			06 06	06 45				07 13			07§36	07§36	07 48		08 15		08 43	09 15
Prestatyn	d			05 24	05§40	05§40			06 12					07 19			07§42	07§42	07 53		08 21		08 49	09 21
Flint	d			05 38	05§54	05§54			06 27					07 32			07§55	07§55	08 06		08 34		09 02	09 34
Shotton	d			05 44					06 34					07 38			08§01	08§01			08 40			09 40
Chester	a	03 38		05 55	06§08	06§08			06 45	07 15				07 49			08§12	08§12	08 20		08 51		09 17	09 51
	d	03 40	04 55	06 00	06§12		06 30	06 50	06 56	07 18		07 27	07 30	07 53		08 00	08§20		08 22	08 30	08 54	09 00	09 19	09 54
Liverpool Lime Street 10	106 a				*06§58*	*06§58*			*07 58*	*08 28*				*08 58*					*09 28*		*09 58*		*10 28*	*10 58*
Helsby	d							06 59				07 36		08 03							09 03			10 03
Frodsham	d							07 03				07 40		08 07							09 07			10 07
Runcorn East	d							07 08				07 45		08 13							09 12			10 12
Warrington Bank Quay	90 a							07 15				07 52		08 20							09 19			10 19
Earlestown 8	90 a							07 23				08 01		08 28							09 27			10 27
Newton-le-Willows	90 a							07 26				08 04		08 31							09 30			10 30
Manchester Oxford Road	90 a							07 45				08 31		08 52							09 50			10 50
Manchester Piccadilly 10	90 a							07 54				08 40		09 02							09 58			10 58
Crewe 10	a	03 59	05 19	06 23			06 55		07 20	07 41			07 55			08 24			08 45	08 56		09 24	09 43	
Cardiff Central 7	131 a	*07b55*	*08b51*		09§18		*09b52*						*10b52*				11§20			*11b53*			*12b53*	
Manchester Airport	84, 85 a							*08c19*	*08 14*			*09c06*		*09c25*		*09 15*					*10c19*	*10 11*		*11c19*
Birmingham New Street 12	65 a	05 08	*06 58*	*07e56*			*08 10*		*08e58*	*09 10*			*09 10*			*09e58*				*10 11*			*10e58*	
London Euston 15	⊖ 65 a		*08 28*	*09 04*					*10 05*	*11 02*			*11 02*			*11 27*				*12 03*			*12 28*	

		AW		AW ◇ A	AW B	AW	AW ◇	AW ◇ C	AW	AW ◇	VT 1 ◇	AW ◇	AW	AW ◇ A	AW B	AW	AW ◇	AW	AW ◇	AW ◇	AW ◇ C	AW	AW ◇ A	AW B
Holyhead	d			08§25	08§25					09 28	09 50			10§30	10§30				11 40				12§35	12§35
Valley	d			08x31	08x31					09x34				10x36	10x36				11x46					
Rhosneigr	d			08x36	08x36					09x39									11x51					
Ty Croes	d			08x40	08x40					09x43									11x55					
Bodorgan	d			08x44	08x44					09x47									11x59					
Llanfairpwll	d			08x54	08x54					09x57				10x54	10x54				12x09					
Bangor (Gwynedd)	a			09§02	09§02					10 05	10 16			11§03	11§03				12 17				13§04	13§04
	d			09§04	09§04					10 07	10 18			11§03	11§03				12 19				13§04	13§04
Llanfairfechan	d			09x12	09x12					10x15				11x11	11x11				12x27				13x12	13x12
Penmaenmawr	d			09x16	09x16					10x19				11x15	11x15				12x31				13x16	13x16
Conwy	d			09x22	09x22					10x25				11x21	11x21				12x37				13x22	13x22
Llandudno	d						09 47	10 14				10 47					11 47			12 47	13 14			
Deganwy	d						09x51	10x18				10x51					11x51			12x51	13x18			
Llandudno Junction	a			09§25	09§25		09 55	10 22		10 28	10 34	10 55		11§25	11§25		11 55		12 40	12 55	13 22		13§26	13§26
	d			09§27	09§27		09 56			10 30	10 36	10 56		11§26	11§26		11 56		12 42	12 56			13§27	13§27
Colwyn Bay	d			09§33	09§33		10 02				10 42	11 02		11§32	11§32		12 02		12 48	13 02			13§33	13§33
Abergele & Pensarn	d						10 09					11 09					12 09			13 09				
Rhyl	d			09§43	09§43		10 15				10 53	11 15		11§43	11§43		12 15		12 58	13 15			13§44	13§44
Prestatyn	d			09§49	09§49		10 21				10 59	11 21		11§48	11§48		12 21		13 04	13 21			13§49	13§49
Flint	d			10§02	10§02		10 34				11 12	11 34		12§02	12§02		12 34		13 17	13 34			14§03	14§03
Shotton	d						10 40					11 40					12 40			13 40				
Chester	a			10§16	10§16		10 51			11 09	11 26	11 51		12§16	12§16		12 51		13 32	13 51			14§17	14§17
	d	10 00		10§20		10 29	10 54		11 00	11 14	11 28	11 54	12 00	12§20		12 29	12 54	13 00	13 33	13 54		14 00	14§20	
Liverpool Lime Street 10	106 a			*11§28*	*11§28*					*11 58*	*12 28*	*12 58*		*13§28*	*13§28*		*13 58*		*14 28*	*14 58*			*15§28*	*15§28*
Helsby	d						11 03					12 03					13 03			14 03				
Frodsham	d						11 07					12 07					13 07			14 07				
Runcorn East	d						11 12					12 12					13 12			14 12				
Warrington Bank Quay	90 a						11 19					12 19					13 19			14 19				
Earlestown 8	90 a						11 27					12 28					13 28			14 28				
Newton-le-Willows	90 a						11 30					12 30					13 30			14 30				
Manchester Oxford Road	90 a						11 50					12 50					13 50			14 50				
Manchester Piccadilly 10	90 a						11 58					12 58					13 58			14 58				
Crewe 10	a	10 24				10 50			11 24	11 43	11 50		12 24			12 50		13 24	14 00			14 24		
Cardiff Central 7	131 a			13§19		*13b53*					*14b53*			15§20		*15b53*			*16b53*				17§20	
Manchester Airport	84, 85 a	*11 11*						*12c19*	*12 11*			*13c19*	*13 11*				*14c19*	*14 11*		*15c19*		*15 11*		
Birmingham New Street 12	65 a	*11e58*				*12 11*				*12e58*	*13f11*		*13e58*			*14 11*		*14e58*	*15 11*			*15e58*		
London Euston 15	⊖ 65 a	*13 26*				*14 03*				*14 27*	*15 03*		*15 27*			*16 05*		*16 29*	*17 05*			*17 27*		

For general notes see front of timetable
For details of catering facilities see Directory of Train Operators

A Until 22 March
B From 29 March. To Hereford (Table 131)
C To Blaenau Ffestiniog (Table 102)
b Until 22 March only
c Change at Manchester Oxford Road
e Change at Crewe and Stafford
f From 29 March arr. 1324

Table 81

Saturdays

North Wales and Chester → Manchester and Crewe

Network Diagram - see first page of Table 81

		AW	AW	AW		AW	NT	AW	AW	VT	AW	AW	VT	AW	AW	NT	AW	AW	AW	AW	AW	AW	AW	AW
			◇					◇	◇	1 ◇	◇		1 ◇	◇				◇	◇		◇	◇		◇
							A							B	C	D			E					B
			🛒					🛒	🛒	🍴	🛒		🍴	🛒				🛒			🛒	🛒		🛒
Holyhead	d							13 35		14 13				14 35	14 35						15 39			16 35
Valley	d							13x41													15x45			
Rhosneigr	d							13x46													15x50			
Ty Croes	d							13x50													15x54			
Bodorgan	d							13x54													15x58			
Llanfairpwll	d							14x04													16x08			
Bangor (Gwynedd)	a							14 12		14 39				15 02	15 02						16 16			17 02
	d							14 14		14 41				15 04	15 04						16 17			17 04
Llanfairfechan	d							14x22						15x12	15x12						16x25			17x12
Penmaenmawr	d							14x26						15x16	15x16						16x29			17x16
Conwy	d							14x32						15x22	15x22						16x35			17x22
Llandudno	d		13 47						14 35				15 08					15 47	16 14			16 47		
Deganwy	d		13x51						14x39									15x51	16x18			16x51		
Llandudno Junction	a		13 55					14 35	14 43	14 57			15 15	15 25	15 25			15 55	16 22		16 38	16 55		17 25
	d		13 56					14 37	14 44	14 59			15 16	15 27	15 27			15 56			16 40	16 56		17 27
Colwyn Bay	d		14 02					14 43	14 50				15 23	15 33	15 33			16 02			16 46	17 02		17 33
Abergele & Pensarn	d		14 09						14 57									16 09				17 09		
Rhyl	d		14 15					14 53	15 03				15 34	15 43	15 43			16 15			16 56	17 15		17 43
Prestatyn	d		14 21					14 59	15 09				15 39	15 49	15 49			16 21			17 02	17 21		17 49
Flint	d		14 34					15 12	15 22				15 52	16 02	16 02			16 34			17 15	17 34		18 02
Shotton	d		14 40						15 28									16 40				17 40		
Chester	a		14 51					15 27	15 39	15 45	←		16 07	16 16	16 16			16 51			17 29	17 51		18 16
	d	14 30	14 53	15 03		15 09		15 30	15 54	15 48	15 54	16 00	16 12	16 20			16 31	16 54		17 00	17 31	17 53	18 00	18 20
Liverpool Lime Street 10	106 a		*15 58*						*16 28*				*16 58*	*17 28*	*17 28*			*17 58*			*18 28*	*18 58*		*19 28*
Helsby	d		15 02				15 29		→		16 03					16 27		17 03				18 02		
Frodsham	d		15 06				15 34				16 07					16 32		17 07				18 06		
Runcorn East	d		15 11				15 39				16 12					16 37		17 12				18 11		
Warrington Bank Quay	90 a		15 18			15 31	15 47				16 19					16 45		17 19				18 21		
Earlestown 8	90 a		15 28			15 44	15 56				16 28					16 56		17 27				18 27		
Newton-le-Willows	90 a		15 30			15 47					16 30							17 30				18 30		
Manchester Oxford Road	90 a		15 50			16 10					16 50							17 51				18 50		
Manchester Piccadilly 10	90 🚢 a		15 58			16 19					16 58							17 59				18 59		
Crewe 10	a	14 55		15 30				15 55		16 08		16 24	16 38				16 59			17 26	17 56		18 25	
Cardiff Central 7	131 a	*17b54*						*18b55*						19 22			*19b54*				*21c06*			21 20
Manchester Airport	84, 85 ✈ a	*16 11*	*16e19*			*16e40*					*17e19*	*17 15*						*18e27*		*18 15*		*19e19*	*19 16*	
Birmingham New Street 12	65 a	*16 11*		*16f58*				*17 11*		*17 24*			*17f58*				*18 11*			*18f58*	*19 11*		*19f58*	
London Euston 15	⊖ 65 a	*18 03*		*18 29*						*19 03*			*19 30*				*20 03*			*20 49*	*21g36*		*22 01*	

		AW	AW	AW	AW	AW	AW	AW	AW	AW	AW	AW	AW	AW	AW	AW	AW	AW	AW	AW	AW	AW
				◇		◇	◇		◇					◇	◇			◇				
		C						G										H				
				🛒		🛒			🛒													
Holyhead	d	16 35				17 35			18 35					19 35				20 35				
Valley	d					17x41			18x41					19x41								
Rhosneigr	d					17x46			18x46					19x46								
Ty Croes	d					17x50			18x50					19x50								
Bodorgan	d					17x54			18x54					19x54								
Llanfairpwll	d					18x04			19x04					20x04								
Bangor (Gwynedd)	a	17 02				18 12			19 12					20 12				21 02				
	d	17 04				18 14			19 14					20 14				21 03				
Llanfairfechan	d	17x12				18x22								20x22				21x11				
Penmaenmawr	d	17x16				18x26								20x26				21x15				
Conwy	d	17x22				18x32								20x32				21x21				
Llandudno	d			17 47			18 47				19 47				20 47	21 13			21 47			
Deganwy	d			17x51			18x51				19x51				20x51	21x17			21x51			
Llandudno Junction	a	17 25		17 55		18 35	18 55		19 30		19 55			20 35	20 55	21 21		21 24	21 57			
	d	17 27		17 56		18 37	18 56		19 32		19 56			20 37	20 56			21 26				
Colwyn Bay	d	17 33		18 02		18 43	19 02		19 38		20 02			20 43	21 02			21 32				
Abergele & Pensarn	d			18 09			19 09				20 09				21 09			21 39				
Rhyl	d	17 43		18 15		18 53	19 15		19 48		20 15			20 53	21 15			21 45				
Prestatyn	d	17 49		18 21		18 59	19 21		19 54		20 21			20 59	21 21			21 50				
Flint	d	18 02		18 34		19 12	19 34		20 07		20 34			21 12	21 34			22 04				
Shotton	d			18 40			19 40				20 40				21 40			22 10				
Chester	a	18 16		18 51		19 30	19 51		20 22		20 51			21 26	21 51			22 23				
	d		18 30	18 53	19 00	19 34	19 53	20 05	20 28	20 30		20 56	21 00	21 33	21 54		22 12			22 33	23 13	23 22
Liverpool Lime Street 10	106 a	*19 28*		*19 58*		*20 28*	*20 58*		*21 28*		*21 58*			*22 28*	*22 58*			*23 28*				
Helsby	d			19 02			20 02					21 05			22 03							23 31
Frodsham	d			19 06			20 06					21 09			22 07							23 35
Runcorn East	d			19 11			20 11					21 14			22 12							23 40
Warrington Bank Quay	90 a			19 19			20 18					21 23			22 19							23 50
Earlestown 8	90 a			19 28			20 27					21 30			22 27							23 57
Newton-le-Willows	90 a			19 30			20 30					21 33			22 30							23 59
Manchester Oxford Road	90 a			19 50			20 50					21 54			22 55							
Manchester Piccadilly 10	90 🚢 a			19 59			20 59					22 01			23 05							00 27
Crewe 10	a		18 56		19 24	19 59		20 29		20 55			21 24	21 57			22 36			22 56	23 40	
Cardiff Central 7	131 a	*22h35*	*22j00*			*23b01*				*00b17*				*01b19*								
Manchester Airport	84, 85 ✈ a			*20e19*			*21e19*					*22 39*			*23 55*							*00 57*
Birmingham New Street 12	65 a		*20 11*			*21 11*			*22 18*	*22 30*			*23 04*	*23 10*								
London Euston 15	⊖ 65 a		*22g42*			*23k36*		*23m49*														

For general notes see front of timetable
For details of catering facilities see Directory of Train Operators

- **A** To Liverpool Lime Street (Table 90)
- **B** Until 22 March
- **C** From 29 March. To Hereford (Table 131)
- **D** From Ellesmere Port (Table 109) to Liverpool Lime Street (Table 90)
- **E** To Blaenau Ffestiniog (Table 102)
- **G** From Wrexham General (Table 75)
- **H** To Shrewsbury (Table 75)
- **b** Until 22 March only
- **c** Until 22 March only. Until 26 January arr. 2101
- **e** Change at Manchester Oxford Road
- **f** Change at Crewe and Stafford
- **g** From 29 March arr. 8 minutes earlier
- **h** By bus from Hereford
- **j** Until 22 March. From 29 March arr. 2305; change at Crewe and Hereford. By bus from Hereford
- **k** From 29 March arr. 2326
- **m** Saturdays arr. 2334

Table 81

Sundays
until 23 March

North Wales and Chester → Manchester and Crewe

Network Diagram - see first page of Table 81

		AW	AW	AW	AW	AW	AW	AW	AW	AW	AW	AW	AW	AW	AW	AW	AW
											◇		◇		◇		
								A 🚌									
						🚲						🚲	🚲		🚲		🚲
Holyhead	d										09 56		10 35				
Valley	d										10x02						
Rhosneigr	d										10x07						
Ty Croes	d										10x11						
Bodorgan	d										10x15						
Llanfairpwll	d										10x25						
Bangor (Gwynedd)	a										10 33		11 02				
	d										10 34		11 04		11 56		
Llanfairfechan	d										10x42						
Penmaenmawr	d										10x46						
Conwy	d										10x52						
Llandudno	d							10 15									
Deganwy	d							10 25									
Llandudno Junction	a							10 35			10 56		11 21		12 12		
	d										10 57		11 22		12 14		
Colwyn Bay	d										11 03		11 28		12 20		
Abergele & Pensarn	d																
Rhyl	d										11 14		11 39		12 30		
Prestatyn	d										11 19		11 45		12 36		
Flint	d										11 33		11 59		12 49		
Shotton	d												12 05		12 55		
Chester	a										11 47		12 17		13 06		
	d	08 25	08 55	09 25	09 55	10 00	10 11		10 55	11 25	11 48	11 55	12 20	12 25	13 08	13 25	13 30
Liverpool Lime Street 10	106 a										12 58		13 28		13 58		
Helsby	d					10 09						12 04					13 39
Frodsham	d					10 13						12 08					13 43
Runcorn East	d					10 18						12 13					13 48
Warrington Bank Quay	90 a					10 28						12 22					13 57
Earlestown 8	90 a					10 37						12 30					14 08
Newton-le-Willows	90 a					10 40						12 33					14 11
Manchester Oxford Road	90 a					11 00						12 52					14 31
Manchester Piccadilly 10	90 ⛴ a					11 04						13 01					14 41
Crewe 10	a	08 50	09 20	09 50	10 20		10 36		11 20	11 50	12 11			12 49	13 31	13 49	
Cardiff Central 7	131 a						13 54						15 31	16 17			
Manchester Airport	84, 85 ✈ a			10 59		11 33					12 59	13 33				15 04	15b21
Birmingham New Street 12	65 a		10c30	11 11			11e58		12e58	13 11	13e58			14 11		15 08	
London Euston 15	⊖ 65 a		12 51	13e04	13 23		13 56		14 23		15 08			16 07	16 36		

		AW	AW	AW	VT	AW	AW	AW	AW	AW	AW	AW	AW	AW	AW	VT	AW
			◇		1 ◇		◇					◇				1 ◇	◇
				A 🚌									A 🚌				
			🚲		🍴		🚲					🚲				🍴	
Holyhead	d				13 14		13 31									15 57	
Valley	d																
Rhosneigr	d																
Ty Croes	d																
Bodorgan	d																
Llanfairpwll	d																
Bangor (Gwynedd)	a				13 40		13 57									16 23	
	d		12 52		13 41		13 58					15 42				16 24	16 32
Llanfairfechan	d		13x00														16x40
Penmaenmawr	d		13x04														16x44
Conwy	d		13x10														16x50
Llandudno	d			13 15									16 15				
Deganwy	d			13 25									16 25				
Llandudno Junction	a		13 13	13 35	13 58		14 15					15 58	16 35			16 41	16 52
	d		13 15		13 59		14 16					16 00				16 42	16 54
Colwyn Bay	d		13 21		14 06		14 22					16 06				16 49	17 00
Abergele & Pensarn	d		13 28														17 07
Rhyl	d		13 34		14 17		14 33					16 16				17 00	17 13
Prestatyn	d		13 39				14 38					16 22					17 19
Flint	d		13 53				14 52					16 35					17 32
Shotton	d		13 59														
Chester	a		14 10		14 44		15 05					16 49				17 27	17 46
	d	13 55	14 12		14 46	14 55	15 07	15 25	15 54	16 00	16 25	16 54		17 00	17 25	17 38	17 47
Liverpool Lime Street 10	106 a		14 58				15 58					17 58				18 28	18 58
Helsby	d								16 03								
Frodsham	d								16 07								
Runcorn East	d								16 12			17 09					
Warrington Bank Quay	90 a						15 28		16 21			17 17					18 07
Earlestown 8	90 a						15 36		16 29			17 25					18 20
Newton-le-Willows	90 a						15 39		16 31			17 28					18 23
Manchester Oxford Road	90 a						15 59		16 51			17 50					18 44
Manchester Piccadilly 10	90 ⛴ a						16 10		17 00			17 59					18 51
Crewe 10	a	14 20	14 37		15 06	15 20		15 49		16 24	16 49			17 24	17 50	17 57	
Cardiff Central 7	131 a				18f16			19 13			20 17						
Manchester Airport	84, 85 ✈ a						16g33	16 59	17g18			18g18					19 18
Birmingham New Street 12	65 a	15e58	16 11			16e58		17 11		17e58	18h11					19 04	
London Euston 15	⊖ 65 a	17 08				18 08				19 14				20 38			

For general notes see front of timetable
For details of catering facilities see Directory of Train Operators

A To Blaenau Ffestiniog (Table 102)
b From 3 February arr. 1518
c From 3 February arr. 1043
e Change at Crewe and Stafford
f From 3 February arr. 1818
g Change at Manchester Oxford Road
h Until 27 January only

Table 81

Sundays

until 23 March

North Wales and Chester → Manchester and Crewe

Network Diagram - see first page of Table 81

	AW	AW		AW	AW		AW	AW		AW	AW		AW	AW	AW	AW	AW	AW	AW	AW	AW		
				◇	R 🛒					A	◇ B 🛒					◇					◇		
Holyhead d				16 48	17 25					18 40	18 40										20 35		
Valley d				16x54																	20x41		
Rhosneigr d				16x59																	20x47		
Ty Croes d				17x03																	20x50		
Bodorgan d				17x07																	20x55		
Llanfairpwll d				17x17																	21x04		
Bangor (Gwynedd) a				17 25	17 52					19 07	19 07										21 13		
d				17 27	17 53					19 09	19 09					19 55					21 15		
Llanfairfechan d																20x03							
Penmaenmawr d																20x07							
Conwy d																20x13							
Llandudno d																							
Deganwy d																							
Llandudno Junction a				17 43	18 10					19 25	19 25					20 16					21 32		
d				17 46	18 11					19 27	19 27					20 18					21 33		
Colwyn Bay d				17 52	18 17					19 33	19 33					20 24					21 39		
Abergele & Pensarn d				17 59												20 31					21 46		
Rhyl d				18 05	18 28					19 43	19 43					20 37					21 52		
Prestatyn d				18 10	18 34					19 49	19 49					20 42					21 58		
Flint d				18 24	18 48					20 02	20 02					20 56					22 11		
Shotton d				18 30												21 02					22 17		
Chester a				18 41	19 03					20 16	20 16					21 13					22 28		
d	17 52	18 25		18 42	19 07		19 25	19 55			20 24		20 21	20 25	20 55	21 14	21 20	21 25	21 55	22 25	22 35		
Liverpool Lime Street [10] 106 a					*19 58*					*21 28*	*21 28*					*22 28*					*23 28*		
Helsby d													20 30				21 29				22 44		
Frodsham d													20 34				21 33				22 48		
Runcorn East d													20 39				21 38				22 53		
Warrington Bank Quay 90 a													20 48				21 48				23 01		
Earlestown [8] 90 a													20 56				21 56				23 10		
Newton-le-Willows 90 a													20 59				21 58				23 12		
Manchester Oxford Road 90 a													21 24				22 18				23 35		
Manchester Piccadilly [10] 90 🚌 a													21 34				22 27				23 41		
Crewe [10] a	18 16	18 49		19 05			19 49	20 20						20 49	21 19	21 40		21 49	22 19	22 50			
Cardiff Central [7] 131 a	*21 21*				22 28										*00 29*								
Manchester Airport 84, 85 ✈ a	*19 00*						*20 59*						*21b52*				*22b51*	*22 59*			*00 33*		
Birmingham New Street [12] 65 a	*19c58*			*20 11*			*21 08*	*21c56*			22 36			*22 17*				*23 17*	*23 45*				
London Euston [15] ⊖ 65 a	*21 14*			*22 23*				*23 25*															

Sundays

from 30 March

	AW	AW	AW	AW		AW	AW	AW	AW		AW	AW	AW	AW		AW	AW	AW	AW		AW	AW	AW
								C 🚌				◇		D		E		◇ 🛒	E				
Holyhead d												09 56		10 35									
Valley d												10x02											
Rhosneigr d												10x07											
Ty Croes d												10x11											
Bodorgan d												10x15											
Llanfairpwll d												10x25											
Bangor (Gwynedd) a												10 33		11 02									
d												10 34		11 04				11 56					
Llanfairfechan d												10x42											
Penmaenmawr d												10x46											
Conwy d												10x52											
Llandudno d								10 15								11 58			13 02				
Deganwy d								10 25								12x02			13x06				
Llandudno Junction a								10 35				10 56		11 21		12 08		12 12	13 12				
d												10 57		11 22				12 14					
Colwyn Bay d												11 03		11 28				12 20					
Abergele & Pensarn d																							
Rhyl d												11 14		11 39				12 30					
Prestatyn d												11 19		11 45				12 36					
Flint d												11 33		11 59				12 49					
Shotton d														12 05				12 55					
Chester a												11 47		12 17				13 06					
d	08 25	08 55	09 25	09 55		10 00	10 11		10 55		11 25	11 48	11 55				12 25	13 08			13 25	13 30	13 55
Liverpool Lime Street [10] 106 a												*12 58*		*13 28*				*13 58*					
Helsby d						10 09							12 04									13 39	
Frodsham d						10 13							12 08									13 43	
Runcorn East d						10 18							12 13									13 48	
Warrington Bank Quay 90 a						10 30							12 25									14 00	
Earlestown [8] 90 a						*10e55*							*12e55*									*14e25*	
Newton-le-Willows 90 a						*11e05*							*13e05*									*14e35*	
Manchester Oxford Road 90 a						*11e35*							*13e35*									*15e05*	
Manchester Piccadilly [10] 90 🚌 a						*11e45*							*13e45*									*15e15*	
Crewe [10] a	08 50	09 20	09 50	10 20			10 36		11 20		11 50	12 11					12 49	13 31			13 49		14 20
Cardiff Central [7] 131 a																							
Manchester Airport 84, 85 ✈ a			*10 59*			*12f30*						*12 59*	*14f33*								*15 04*	*15g33*	
Birmingham New Street [12] 65 a		*10 43*	*10 58*				*11 58*				*12 58*						*13 58*				*14 58*		
London Euston [15] ⊖ 65 a		*12 51*	*13c04*	*13 23*			*13 56*		*14 23*		*14c56*	*15 08*					*15c56*	*16 36*			*16c56*		*17 08*

For general notes see front of timetable
For details of catering facilities see Directory of Train Operators

A From 3 February. To Shrewsbury (Table 75)
B Until 27 January
C To Blaenau Ffestiniog (Table 102)
D To Hereford (Table 131)
E From 6 April
b Change at Manchester Oxford Road
c Change at Crewe and Stafford
e By bus
f Change at Warrington Bank Quay and Manchester Piccadilly. By bus to Manchester Piccadilly
g Change at Warrington Bank Quay and Manchester Oxford Road. By bus to Manchester Oxford Road

Sundays
from 30 March

North Wales and Chester → Manchester and Crewe

Network Diagram - see first page of Table 81

		AW ◇ ⊼	AW A 🚌	VT 1 ◇ ☕	AW B	AW	AW	AW B	AW	AW B	AW	AW	AW	AW ◇	AW A 🚌	AW	AW	VT 1 ◇ ☕	AW B	AW
Holyhead	d			13 14			13 31											15 57		
Valley	d																			
Rhosneigr	d																			
Ty Croes	d																			
Bodorgan	d																			
Llanfairpwll	d																			
Bangor (Gwynedd)	a			13 40			13 57											16 23		
	d	12 52		13 41			13 58							15 42				16 24		16 32
Llanfairfechan	d	13x00																		16x40
Penmaenmawr	d	13x04																		16x44
Conwy	d	13x10																		16x50
Llandudno	d		13 15		14\00			14\55		15\40					16 15				16\39	
Deganwy	d		13 25		14x04			14x59		15x44					16 25				16x43	
Llandudno Junction	a	13 13	13 35	13 58	14\10		14 15	15\05		15\50				15 58	16 35			16 41	16\49	16 52
	d	13 15		13 59			14 16							16 00				16 42		16 54
Colwyn Bay	d	13 21		14 06			14 22							16 06				16 49		17 00
Abergele & Pensarn	d	13 28																		17 07
Rhyl	d	13 34		14 17			14 33							16 16				17 00		17 13
Prestatyn	d	13 39					14 38							16 22						17 19
Flint	d	13 53					14 52							16 35						17 32
Shotton	d	13 59																		
Chester	a	14 10		14 44			15 05							16 49				17 27		17 46
	d	14 12		14 46		14 55	15 07		15 25		15 54	16 00	16 25	16 54		17 00	17 25	17 38		17 47
Liverpool Lime Street 10	106 a	*14 58*		*15 58*			*15 58*							*17 58*				*18 28*		*18 58*
Helsby	d										16 03									
Frodsham	d										16 07									
Runcorn East	d										16 12			17 09						
Warrington Bank Quay	90 a						15 33				16 25			17 16						18 06
Earlestown 8	90 a						*16b00*				*16b50*			*17b40*						*18b40*
Newton-le-Willows	90 a						*16b10*				*17b00*			*17b50*						*18b50*
Manchester Oxford Road	90 a						*16b40*				*17b30*			*18b20*						*19b20*
Manchester Piccadilly 10	90 a						*16b50*				*17b40*			*18b30*						*19b30*
Crewe 10	a	14 37		15 06		15 20			15 49			16 24	16 49			17 24	17 50	17 59		
Cardiff Central 7	131 a																			
Manchester Airport	84, 85 ✈ a			*16 59*			*17c21*		*16 59*		*18c33*			*18e52*						*19e51*
Birmingham New Street 12	65 a	*15 58*		*16 11*					*16 58*				*17 58*				*18 58*	*19 04*		
London Euston 15	⊖ 65 a	*17f56*		*18 08*		*18 08*			*18f51*			*19 14*	*19f53*			*20 38*		*20f53*		

		AW B	AW	AW	AW ◇	AW C	AW	AW	AW	AW ◇ ⊼	AW	AW	AW ◇	AW	AW	AW	AW	AW
Holyhead	d				16 48	17 25				18 40								20 35
Valley	d				16x54													20x41
Rhosneigr	d				16x59													20x47
Ty Croes	d				17x03													20x50
Bodorgan	d				17x07													20x55
Llanfairpwll	d				17x17													21x04
Bangor (Gwynedd)	a				17 25	17 52				19 07								21 13
	d				17 27	17 53				19 09			19 55					21 15
Llanfairfechan	d												20x03					
Penmaenmawr	d												20x07					
Conwy	d												20x13					
Llandudno	d	17\29																
Deganwy	d	17x33																
Llandudno Junction	a	17\39			17 43	18 10				19 25			20 16					21 32
	d				17 46	18 11				19 27			20 18					21 33
Colwyn Bay	d				17 52	18 17				19 33			20 24					21 39
Abergele & Pensarn	d				17 59								20 31					21 46
Rhyl	d				18 05	18 28				19 43			20 37					21 52
Prestatyn	d				18 10	18 34				19 49			20 42					21 58
Flint	d				18 24	18 48				20 02			20 56					22 11
Shotton	d				18 30								21 02					22 17
Chester	a				18 41	19 03				20 16			21 13					22 28
	d		17 52	18 25	18 42		19 25	19 55	20 21	20 24	20 25	20 55	21 14	21 20	21 25	21 55	22 25	22 35
Liverpool Lime Street 10	106 a					*19 58*				*21 28*			*22 28*					*23 28*
Helsby	d								20 30					21 29				22 44
Frodsham	d								20 34					21 33				22 48
Runcorn East	d								20 39					21 38				22 53
Warrington Bank Quay	90 a								20 50					21 50				23 05
Earlestown 8	90 a								*21b15*					*22b15*				*23b30*
Newton-le-Willows	90 a								*21b25*					*22b25*				*23b40*
Manchester Oxford Road	90 a								*21b55*					*22b55*				*00b10*
Manchester Piccadilly 10	90 a								*22b05*					*23b05*				*00b20*
Crewe 10	a		18 16	18 49	19 05		19 49	20 20			20 49	21 19	21 40		21 49	22 19	22 50	
Cardiff Central 7	131 a																	
Manchester Airport	84, 85 ✈ a		*19 00*				*20 59*		*22c33*					*23c33*	*22 59*			*00c54*
Birmingham New Street 12	65 a			*19 58*	*20 11*		*20 58*	*21f56*		*22 36*	*22 22*	*22 30*			*23 17*	*23 30*		
London Euston 15	⊖ 65 a		*21 14*	*21f57*	*22 23*		*23f00*	*23 25*										

For general notes see front of timetable
For details of catering facilities see Directory of Train Operators

- **A** To Blaenau Ffestiniog (Table 102)
- **B** From 6 April
- **C** To Hereford (Table 131)
- **b** By bus
- **c** Change at Warrington Bank Quay and Manchester Piccadilly. By bus to Manchester Piccadilly
- **e** Change at Warrington Bank Quay and Manchester Oxford Road. By bus to Manchester Oxford Road
- **f** Change at Crewe and Stafford

Holyhead — Dublin

Daily

	AW A				AW B				AW C				AW A				AW B				AW C					
Holyhead ⛴ d	02 40				08 55				12 00				14 10				15 30				17 15					
Dun Laoghaire ⛴ a					10 34												17 09									
Dublin Ferryport § ⛴ a	05 55								13 58				17 25								19 24					

Daily

	AW C				AW A				AW B				AW C				AW B				AW A					
Dublin Ferryport § ⛴ d	08 45				08 05								14 30								20 55					
Dun Laoghaire ⛴ d									11 10								18 00									
Holyhead ⛴ a	10 54				11 30				12 49				16 39				19 39				00 20					

For general notes see front of timetable
For details of catering facilities see Directory of Train Operators

§ Bus connections to/from city centre and railway stations

A Irish Ferries Cruise Ferry
B Stena Line High-Speed Sea Service
C Irish Ferries Fast Ferry

Network Diagram for Tables 82, 83

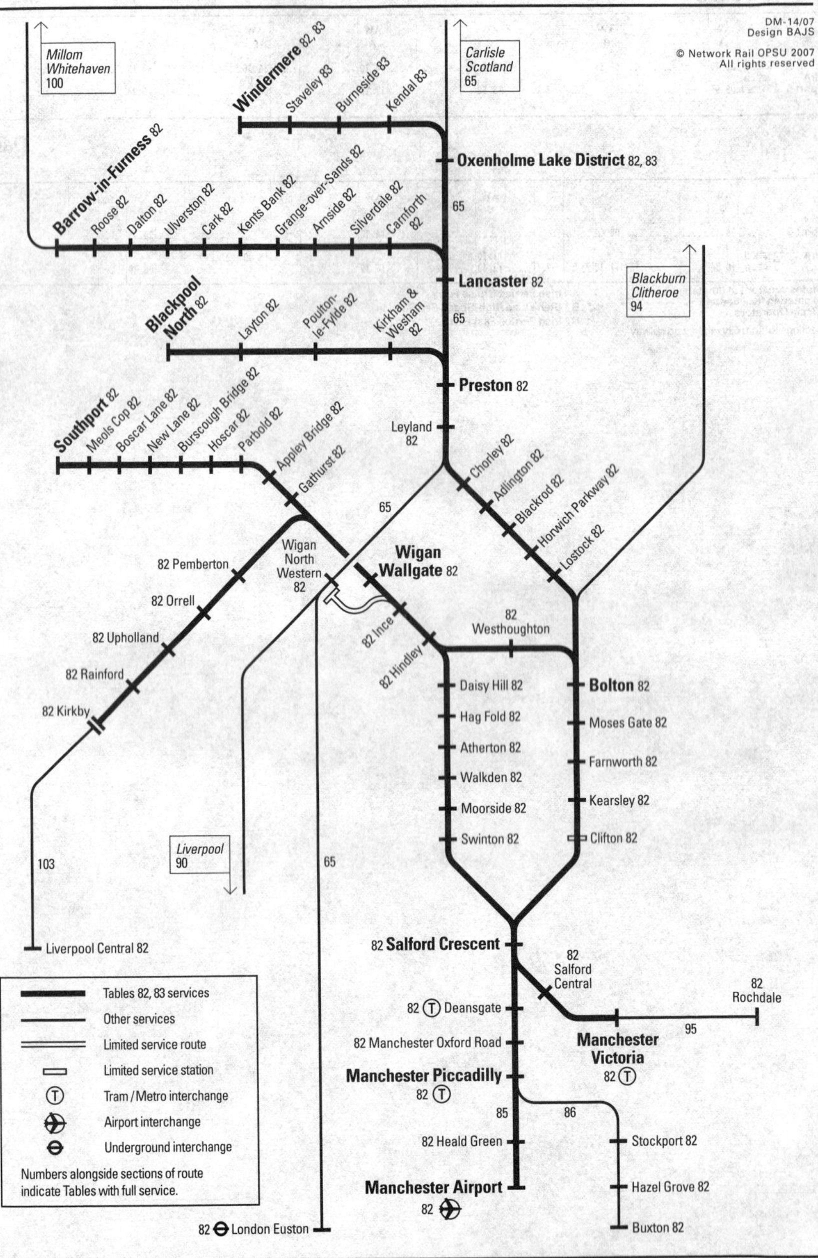

DM-14/07
Design BAJS
© Network Rail OPSU 2007
All rights reserved
Millom
Whitehaven
100
Carlisle
Scotland
65
Windermere 82, 83
Staveley 83
Burneside 83
Kendal 83
Oxenholme Lake District 82, 83
Barrow-in-Furness 82
Roose 82
Dalton 82
Ulverston 82
Cark 82
Kents Bank 82
Grange-over-Sands 82
Arnside 82
Silverdale 82
Carnforth 82
Lancaster 82
Blackburn
Clitheroe
94
Blackpool North 82
Layton 82
Poulton-le-Fylde 82
Kirkham & Wesham 82
Preston 82
Leyland 82
Southport 82
Meols Cop 82
Boscar Lane 82
New Lane 82
Burscough Bridge 82
Hoscar 82
Parbold 82
Appley Bridge 82
Gathurst 82
Chorley 82
Adlington 82
Blackrod 82
Horwich Parkway 82
Lostock 82
Wigan North Western 82
Wigan Wallgate 82
82 Pemberton
82 Orrell
82 Upholland
82 Rainford
82 Kirkby
82 Ince
82 Hindley
82 Westhoughton
Daisy Hill 82
Hag Fold 82
Atherton 82
Walkden 82
Moorside 82
Swinton 82
Bolton 82
Moses Gate 82
Farnworth 82
Kearsley 82
Clifton 82
Liverpool
90
103
Liverpool Central 82
82 Salford Crescent
82 Salford Central
82 Rochdale
95
82 Deansgate
82 Manchester Oxford Road
Manchester Victoria 82
Manchester Piccadilly 82
85
86
82 Heald Green
Stockport 82
Manchester Airport 82
Hazel Grove 82
Buxton 82
82 London Euston
Tables 82, 83 services
Other services
Limited service route
Limited service station
Tram / Metro interchange
Airport interchange
Underground interchange
Numbers alongside sections of route indicate Tables with full service.

Manchester → Bolton → Wigan, Kirkby, Southport, Preston, Barrow-in-Furness and Blackpool North

Network Diagram - see first page of Table 82

Miles	Miles	Miles	Miles	Miles			NT MX A	TP 1◇ B	TP MO 1◇ C	TP 1◇ B	TP MO 1◇ C	NT	VT 1◇ D	NT	TP 1◇	NT E		NT G	NT	NT	NT	TP 1◇	NT	NT E	NT
0	0	0	—	—	**Manchester Airport**	85 ✈ d		01 06	01 06	03 40	03 40		*04 34*		05 47							06 19			
1½	1½	1½	—	—	Heald Green	85 d									05 51							06 23			
—	—	—	—	—	Buxton	86 d																			
—	—	—	—	—	Hazel Grove	86 d																			
—	—	—	—	—	Stockport	84 d														06 17					
9¾	9¾	9¾	—	—	**Manchester Piccadilly 10**	d		01 25	01 25	03 55	03 55		04 58		06 05					06 29		06 44			
10¼	10¼	10¼	—	—	**Manchester Oxford Road**	d									06 10					06 32		06 48			
10½	10½	10½	—	—	Deansgate	d														06 34					
—	—	—	—	—	Rochdale	95 d																	*06 24*		
—	—	—	0	—	**Manchester Victoria**	d								06 00		06 26					06 35		06 51	07 00	
—	—	—	¾	—	Salford Central	d															06 38		06 54	07 03	
12	12	12	1¾	—	**Salford Crescent**	a								06 05	06 15	06 31				06 38	06 41	06 52	06 57	07 06	
—	—	—	—	—		d								06 06	06 15	06 31				06 38	06 42	06 53	06 57	07 06	
—	—	—	5¾	—	Swinton	d																			
—	—	—	6½	—	Moorside	d																			
—	—	—	8¼	—	Walkden	d																			
—	—	—	11¾	—	Atherton	d																			
—	—	—	13	—	Hag Fold	d																			
—	—	—	13¼	—	Daisy Hill	d																			
18	18	18	—	—	Kearsley	d															06 49				
18¾	18	18¾	—	—	Farnworth	d															06 51				
19¾	19¾	19¾	—	—	Moses Gate	d															06 54				
21	21	21	—	—	**Bolton**	a		01s39	01s39	04s09	04s09			06 16	06 25	06 44				06 48	06 57	07 03	07 07	07 18	
—	—	—	—	—		d								06 17	06 26					06 49	06 58	07 03	07 08		
—	—	25½	—	—	Westhoughton	d								06 24							07 05		07 15		
—	—	28	15¾	—	Hindley	d								06 28							07 09		07 19		
—	—	29½	17¼	0	Ince	d															07 12				
—	—	—	—	¾	Wigan North Western	a															07 19				
—	—	30½	18¼	—	**Wigan Wallgate**	a								06 33									07 24		
—	—	—	—	—		d								06 35					06 40				07 26		07 40
—	—	—	20	—	Pemberton	d								06 39											07 44
—	—	—	22	—	Orrell	d								06 43											07 48
—	—	—	23¼	—	Upholland	d								06 46											07 51
—	—	—	25¼	—	Rainford	d								06 50											07 55
—	—	—	30½	—	**Kirkby**	a								07 00											08 05
—	—	—	—	—	Liverpool Central 10	103 a								*07 31*											*08 31*
—	—	33¼	—	—	Gathurst	d													06 44				07 30		
—	—	35	—	—	Appley Bridge	d													06 48				07 34		
—	—	37¼	—	—	Parbold	d													06 52				07 38		
—	—	38¾	—	—	Hoscar	d													06 55						
—	—	40¼	—	—	Burscough Bridge	d													06 58				07 42		
—	—	41½	—	—	New Lane	d													07 00						
—	—	43½	—	—	Bescar Lane	d													07 04						
—	—	46¾	—	—	Meols Cop	d													07 09				07 50		
—	—	48	—	—	**Southport**	a													07 16				07 57		
24	24	—	—	—	Lostock	d									06 30					06 54					
26	26	—	—	—	Horwich Parkway	d									06 34					06 58					
27½	27½	—	—	—	Blackrod	d									06 37					07 01					
29½	29½	—	—	—	Adlington (Lancashire)	d									06 41					07 05					
33½	33½	—	—	—	Chorley	d									06 45					07 09		07 15			
37	37	—	—	—	Leyland	d	00 06								06 52					07 19					
41	41	—	—	—	**Preston 8**	a	00 15	02s10	02 10	04s41	04 41	05d24	05 54		06 59					07 26		07 26			
—	62	—	—	—	**Lancaster 6**	65 a						05 44	06 18		*07 34*							07 44			
—	—	—	—	—		d						05 45	06 20					07 15				07 45			
—	81	—	—	—	Oxenholme Lake District	65 a							06 34		*07 47*										
—	91	—	—	—	Windermere	83 a							*07 10*		*08b15*										
—	68	—	—	—	Carnforth	d						06 10						07a24				07 54			
—	71¾	—	—	—	Silverdale	d						06 15										08 00			
—	74	—	—	—	Arnside	d						06 20										08 04			
—	77¼	—	—	—	Grange-over-Sands	d						06 26										08 09			
—	79½	—	—	—	Kents Bank	d						06 29										08 13			
—	81½	—	—	—	Cark	d						06 33										08 17			
—	87½	—	—	—	Ulverston	d						06 42										08 25			
—	90¾	—	—	—	Dalton	d						06 50										08 34			
—	95	—	—	—	Roose	d						06 56										08 39			
—	96¾	—	—	—	**Barrow-in-Furness**	a						07 05										08 49			
48¾	—	—	—	—	Kirkham & Wesham	97 a							*06c54*		07 11					07 37		*07c47*			
55¼	—	—	—	—	Poulton-le-Fylde	97 a									07 21					07 46		*08c04*			
57¼	—	—	—	—	Layton	97 a									07 24					07 50					
58½	—	—	—	—	**Blackpool North**	97 a		02 34	*03e05*	05 05	*05e35*				07 31					07 56		*08c12*			

For general notes see front of timetable
For details of catering facilities see Directory of Train Operators

- **A** From Liverpool Lime Street (Table 90)
- **B** Not Mondays 4 February to 24 March
- **C** 4 February to 24 March
- **D** To Glasgow Central (Table 65)
- **E** To Clitheroe (Table 94)
- **G** To Leeds (Table 36)
- **b** Change at Preston and Oxenholme Lake District
- **c** Change at Preston
- **e** By bus

Manchester → Bolton → Wigan, Kirkby, Southport, Preston, Barrow-in-Furness and Blackpool North

Network Diagram - see first page of Table 82

	NT	TP 1 ◇	NT	NT		NT	NT	NT	NT	TP 1 ◇	NT	NT	NT	NT	TP 1 ◇		NT	NT	NT	NT	NT	NT	NT	TP 1 ◇
				A			B			C	D		E	G			E	A	H			H		J
Manchester Airport 85 d		06 47						07b02		07 22					07 47					08 07				08 27
Heald Green 85 d		06 51								07 26					07 51					08 11				08 31
Buxton 86 d		05 54						06 34							07 04						07 40			
Hazel Grove 86 d		06 27						07 10							07 40						08 14			
Stockport 84 d		06 42						07 19		07 24					07 49					08 03	08 21			08c27
Manchester Piccadilly 10 d		07 11						07 30		07 45					08 11					08 28	08 32			08 45
Manchester Oxford Road d		07 15						07 33		07 48					08 15					08 31	08 35			08 48
Deansgate d								07 35												08 33	08 37			08 50
Rochdale 95 d									07 06								07 35	07 52	08 05					
Manchester Victoria d	07 05		07 18	07 23		07 28			07 38				07 49	08 00			08 20	08 23	08 27				08 42	
Salford Central d	07 08		07 21	07 26		07 31			07 40				07 52	08 03			08 23	08 26	08 30				08 45	
Salford Crescent a	07 11	07 21	07 25	07 31		07 34		07 40	07 44	07 53			07 56	08 06	08 21		08 26	08 29	08 33	08 37	08 43		08 47	08 54
d	07 11	07 21	07 25	07 31		07 35		07 40	07 44	07 54			07 57	08 07	08 21		08 26	08 29	08 33	08 37	08 43		08 47	08 54
Swinton d	07 18												08 03						08 42					
Moorside d	07 20												08 06						08 44					
Walkden d	07 24					07 43							08 09						08 48					
Atherton d	07 29					07 49							08 15						08 53					
Hag Fold d	07 32												08 17						08 56			←		
Daisy Hill d	07 35					07 52							08 20						08 59			08 59		
Kearsley d									07 52										→				08 55	
Farnworth d									07 54														08 57	
Moses Gate d									07 56									08 37						
Bolton a		07 31	07 35	07 44				07 51	08 00	08 04				08 18	08 31		08 36	08 42		08 48	08 53		09 01	09 04
d		07 32	07 36					07 51	08 00	08 04					08 32		08 37			08 49	08 54		09 02	09 05
Westhoughton d			07 43						08 08											08 56			09 09	
Hindley d	07 39		07 47						08 12				08 25				08 47					09 03	09 13	
Ince d	07 42		07 50										08 28									09 06		
Wigan North Western a			07 55																					
Wigan Wallgate a	07 45					08 02			08 19				08 31				08 56			09 04		09 09	09 22	
d	07 47												08 32							09 05		09 11		
Pemberton d																						09 15		
Orrell d																						09 19		
Upholland d																						09 22		
Rainford d																						09 26		
Kirkby a																						09 34		
Liverpool Central 10 103 a			08e50																			10 01		
Gathurst d	07 51												08 37											
Appley Bridge d	07 55												08 40											
Parbold d	07 59												08 44											
Hoscar d	08 02																							
Burscough Bridge d	08 05												08 49							09 17				
New Lane d	08 07																							
Bescar Lane d	08 11																							
Meols Cop d	08 16												08 56											
Southport a	08 23												09 06							09 33				
Lostock d		07 36						07 56							08 36						08 59			
Horwich Parkway d		07 40						08 00							08 40						09 03			
Blackrod d		07 43						08 03													09 06			
Adlington (Lancashire) d		07 46						08 07													09 10			
Chorley d		07 50						08 12		08 16		←			08 47						09 15			09 17
Leyland d		07 58					08 17	08 20				08 20			08 56									
Preston 8 a		08 06					08 24	→		08 27		08 28			09 03						09 27			09 29
Lancaster 6 65 a										08 44		09 00			09 31						09 55			09 49
d										08 44	08 54													09 50
Oxenholme Lake District 65 a										08 58		09 17			09 45									10 10
Windermere 83 a										09 22					10f12									
Carnforth d											09 03													09 58
Silverdale d											09 09													
Arnside d											09 13													10 07
Grange-over-Sands d											09 19													10 12
Kents Bank d											09 23													
Cark d											09 27													
Ulverston d											09 35													10 25
Dalton d											09 43													
Roose d											09 49													
Barrow-in-Furness a											09 57													10 47
Kirkham & Wesham 97 a		08 15										08 38			09 22						09 38			
Poulton-le-Fylde 97 a		08 26					08 54					08 48			09 23						09 46			
Layton 97 a		08 30										08 52									09 50			
Blackpool North 97 a		08 36					08 51					08 59			09 33						09 57			

For general notes see front of timetable
For details of catering facilities see Directory of Train Operators

A To Blackburn (Table 94)
B From Liverpool Lime Street (Table 90)
C To Edinburgh (Table 65)
D To Carlisle via Whitehaven (Table 100)
E From Huddersfield (Table 39)
G To Clitheroe (Table 94)
H From Todmorden (Table 41)
J to Preston
b Change at Manchester Piccadilly
c Change at Manchester Oxford Road
e Liverpool Lime Street (Table 90)
f Change at Preston and Oxenholme Lake District

Manchester → Bolton → Wigan, Kirkby, Southport, Preston, Barrow-in-Furness and Blackpool North

Network Diagram - see first page of Table 82

	NT A	NT	NT B	NT C		TP 1 ◇ D ✠		NT	NT E	NT	NT	NT	NT	TP 1 ◇ G ✠	NT C		NT	NT B	NT H	NT	TP 1 ◇ ✠	NT	NT	NT
Manchester Airport 85 ✈ d						08 47				09 07				09 27							09 47		10 07	
Heald Green 85 d						08 37				08 56				09 31									09 56	
Buxton 86 d						07 57						08 36												
Hazel Grove 86 d						08 33						09 10									09 41			
Stockport 84 d						08 51				08 54		09 19		09b24							09 49		10b02	
Manchester Piccadilly 10 d						09 11				09 23		09 33		09 45							10 11		10 23	
Manchester Oxford Road d						09 15				09 26		09 36		09 48							10 15		10 26	
Deansgate d										09 28		09 38												
Rochdale 95 d		08 33						08 52			09 03						09 33					09 53		10 03
Manchester Victoria d		08 57	09 00					09 18			09 29		09 41				09 57	10 00				10 18		10 29
Salford Central d		09 00	09 03					09 21			09 32		09 44				10 00	10 03				10 21		10 32
Salford Crescent a		09 03	09 06			09 21		09 24		09 32	09 35	09 43	09 47	09 53			10 03	10 06			10 21	10 24	10 32	10 35
d		09 04	09 07			09 21		09 24		09 32	09 35	09 43	09 47	09 54			10 04	10 07			10 21	10 24	10 32	10 35
Swinton d		09 10									09 42						10 10							10 42
Moorside d											09 44													10 44
Walkden d		09 15									09 48						10 15							10 48
Atherton d		09 20									09 53						10 20							10 53
Hag Fold d											09 56													10 56
Daisy Hill d		09 24									09 59						10 24							10 59
Kearsley d													09 55											
Farnworth d													09 57											
Moses Gate d								09 32														10 32		
Bolton a			09 18			09 31		09 36		09 42		09 53	10 01	10 04				10 18			10 31	10 36	10 42	
d						09 32		09 36		09 43		09 54	10 02	10 05							10 32	10 36	10 43	
Westhoughton d										09 50			10 09										10 50	
Hindley d		09 28									10 03		10 13				10 28							11 03
Ince d											10 06													11 06
Wigan North Western a																								
Wigan Wallgate a		09 33						09 54		10 01	10 09		10 20				10 33					10 54	11 01	11 09
d		09 35								10 02	10 11						10 35						11 02	11 11
Pemberton d											10 15													11 15
Orrell d											10 19													11 19
Upholland d											10 22													11 22
Rainford d											10 26													11 26
Kirkby a											10 35													11 35
Liverpool Central 10 103 a											11 01													12 01
Gathurst d		09 39															10 39							
Appley Bridge d		09 43								10 09							10 43						11 09	
Parbold d		09 47								10 13							10 47						11 13	
Hoscar d																	10 50							
Burscough Bridge d		09 51								10 17							10 53						11 17	
New Lane d																	10 55							
Bescar Lane d																	10 59							
Meols Cop d		09 59															11 04							
Southport a		10 08								10 34							11 13						11 34	
Lostock d												09 59									10 36			
Horwich Parkway d						09 39						10 03									10 40			
Blackrod d												10 06												
Adlington (Lancashire) d												10 10												
Chorley d						09 46						10 15		10 17							10 47			
Leyland d	09 28			09 47		09 52									10 47						10 56			
Preston 8 a	09 38			09 54		09 58			10d10			10 27		10 27	10 54						11 03			
Lancaster 6 65 a	10 03						10 21		10 30					10 44							11 32			
d							10 23		10 30					10 45					11 02	11 11				
Oxenholme Lake District 65 a							10 44					11 11		11 03							11 46			
Windermere 83 a							11 01														12c14			
Carnforth d									10 40										11a11	11 20				
Silverdale d									10 45											11 26				
Arnside d									10 50											11 30				
Grange-over-Sands d									10 56											11 36				
Kents Bank d									10 59											11 40				
Cark d									11 03											11 44				
Ulverston d									11 12											11 52				
Dalton d									11 20											12 00				
Roose d									11 26											12 06				
Barrow-in-Furness a									11 33											12 16				
Kirkham & Wesham 97 a						10 21						10 38									11 21			
Poulton-le-Fylde 97 a						10 18						10 46									11 23			
Layton 97 a												10 50												
Blackpool North 97 a				10 21		10 28						10 57			11 21						11 32			

For general notes see front of timetable
For details of catering facilities see Directory of Train Operators

A From Liverpool Lime Street (Table 90) to Morecambe (Table 98)
B To Clitheroe (Table 94)
C From Liverpool Lime Street (Table 90)
D ✠ to Blackpool North
E To Carlisle via Whitehaven (Table 100)
G To Glasgow Central (Table 65)
H From Morecambe to Leeds (Table 36)
b Change at Manchester Oxford Road
c Change at Preston and Oxenholme Lake District

Manchester → Bolton → Wigan, Kirkby, Southport, Preston, Barrow-in-Furness and Blackpool North

Network Diagram - see first page of Table 82

		NT	NT	TP	NT	NT	NT	TP	NT	NT	NT	NT	NT	TP	NT	NT	NT	NT	NT	TP	NT	NT	NT
				1 ◇				1 ◇						1 ◇						1 ◇			
		A		B		C	D							E		C	D	G	H				
Manchester Airport	85 d			10 27				10 47		11 07				11 27						11 47		12 07	
Heald Green	85 d			10 31						*10 56*				11 31								*11 56*	
Buxton	86 d			*09 36*								10 37											
Hazel Grove	86 d			*10 12*				*10 41*				11 10								*11 41*			
Stockport	84 d	10 18		*10b25*				*10 49*		*11b02*		11 19		*11b25*						*11 49*		*12b02*	
Manchester Piccadilly 10	d	10 30		10 45				11 11		11 23		11 30		11 45						12 11		12 23	
Manchester Oxford Road	d	10 33		10 48				11 15		11 26		11 33		11 48						12 15		12 26	
Deansgate	d	10 35		10 50								11 35											
Rochdale	95 d				10 33				*10 50*		11 03				11 33						*11 50*		12 03
Manchester Victoria	d		10 41		10 57	11 00			11 18		11 29		11 41		11 57	12 00					12 18		12 29
Salford Central	d		10 44		11 00	11 03			11 21		11 32		11 44		12 00	12 03					12 21		12 32
Salford Crescent	a	10 40	10 47	10 53	11 03	11 06		11 21	11 24	11 32	11 35	11 40	11 47	11 53	12 03	12 06				12 21	12 24	12 32	12 35
	d	10 40	10 47	10 54	11 04	11 07		11 21	11 24	11 32	11 35	11 40	11 47	11 54	12 04	12 07				12 21	12 24	12 32	12 35
Swinton	d				11 10						11 42				12 10								12 42
Moorside	d										11 44												12 44
Walkden	d				11 15						11 48				12 15								12 48
Atherton	d				11 20						11 53				12 20								12 53
Hag Fold	d										11 56												12 56
Daisy Hill	d				11 24						11 59				12 24								12 59
Kearsley	d		10 55										11 55										
Farnworth	d		10 57										11 57										
Moses Gate	d								11 32												12 32		
Bolton	a	10 50	11 01	11 05		11 18		11 31	11 36	11 42		11 50	12 01	12 05		12 18				12 31	12 36	12 42	
	d	10 51	11 02	11 05				11 32	11 36	11 43		11 51	12 02	12 05						12 32	12 36	12 43	
Westhoughton	d		11 09							11 50			12 09									12 50	
Hindley	d		11 13		11 28						12 03		12 13		12 28								13 03
Ince	d										12 06												13 06
Wigan North Western	a																						
Wigan Wallgate	a		11 20		11 33				11 54	12 01	12 09		12 20		12 33						12 54	13 01	13 09
	d				11 35					12 02	12 11				12 35							13 02	13 11
Pemberton	d										12 15												13 15
Orrell	d										12 19												13 19
Upholland	d										12 22												13 22
Rainford	d										12 26												13 26
Kirkby	a										12 35												13 35
Liverpool Central 10	103 a										*13 01*												*14 01*
Gathurst	d				11 39										12 39								
Appley Bridge	d				11 43					12 09					12 43							13 09	
Parbold	d				11 47					12 13					12 47							13 13	
Hoscar	d				11 50																		
Burscough Bridge	d				11 53					12 17					12 51							13 17	
New Lane	d				11 55																		
Bescar Lane	d				11 59																		
Meols Cop	d				12 04										12 59								
Southport	a				12 14					12 34					13 08							13 34	
Lostock	d	10 56						11 36				11 56								12 36			
Horwich Parkway	d	11 00						11 40				12 00								12 40			
Blackrod	d	11 03										12 03											
Adlington (Lancashire)	d	11 07										12 07											
Chorley	d	11 12		11 17				11 47				12 12		12 17						12 47			
Leyland	d						11 46	11 56									12 47			12 56			
Preston 8	a	11 26		11 27			11 53	12 03				12 24		12 27			12 56			13 03			
Lancaster 6	65 a			11 44				*12 32*						12 44						*13 38*			
	d			11 45										12 45				13 12	13 15				
Oxenholme Lake District	65 a							*12 46*						12 59									
Windermere	83 a							*13 18*						*14 13*									
Carnforth	d			11 54														13 21	13a25				
Silverdale	d			12 00																			
Arnside	d			12 04																			
Grange-over-Sands	d			12 09														13 36					
Kents Bank	d			12 13																			
Cark	d			12 17																			
Ulverston	d			12 25														13 49					
Dalton	d			12 34																			
Roose	d			12 40																			
Barrow-in-Furness	a			12 49														14 07					
Kirkham & Wesham	97 a	11 35						*12 23*				12 35								*13 21*			
Poulton-le-Fylde	97 a	11 43		*11c52*				12 23				12 43								13 23			
Layton	97 a	11 47										12 47											
Blackpool North	97 a	11 54		*12c01*			12 20	12 32				12 54					13 21			13 32			

For general notes see front of timetable
For details of catering facilities see Directory of Train Operators

- **A** From Northwich (Table 88)
- **B** to Preston
- **C** To Clitheroe (Table 94)
- **D** From Liverpool Lime Street (Table 90)
- **E** To Edinburgh (Table 65)
- **G** To Carlisle via Whitehaven (Table 100)
- **H** From Morecambe to Leeds (Table 36)
- **b** Change at Manchester Oxford Road
- **c** Change at Preston

Manchester → Bolton → Wigan, Kirkby, Southport, Preston, Barrow-in-Furness and Blackpool North

Network Diagram - see first page of Table 82

		NT	NT	TP	NT		NT	NT	NT	TP	NT	NT	NT	NT	NT		TP	NT	NT	NT	TP	NT	NT	NT
				1 ◇						1 ◇							1 ◇				1 ◇			
				A			B	C	D	E							G		B	C				
				🛒						🛒							🛒				🛒			
Manchester Airport	85 ✈ d			12 27						12 47		13 07					13 27				13 47		14 07	
Heald Green	85 d			12 31								*12 56*					13 31						*13 56*	
Buxton	86 d	11 34												12 37										
Hazel Grove	86 d	12 10								*12 41*				13 10							*13 41*			
Stockport	84 d	12 19		*12b25*						*12 49*		*13 02*		13 19			*13b25*				*13 49*		*14b02*	
Manchester Piccadilly 10	🚌 d	12 30		12 45						13 11		13 23		13 30			13 45				14 11		14 23	
Manchester Oxford Road	d	12 33		12 48						13 15		13 26		13 33			13 48				14 15		14 26	
Deansgate	🚌 d	12 35		12 50										13 35										
Rochdale	95 d				12 33						*12 52*		13 03					13 33				*13 50*		14 03
Manchester Victoria	🚌 d		12 41		12 57		13 00				13 18		13 29		13 41			13 57	14 00			14 18		14 29
Salford Central	d		12 44		13 00		13 03				13 21		13 32		13 44			14 00	14 03			14 21		14 32
Salford Crescent	a	12 40	12 47	12 53	13 03		13 06			13 21	13 24	13 32	13 35	13 40	13 47		13 53	14 03	14 06		14 21	14 24	14 32	14 35
	d	12 40	12 47	12 54	13 04		13 07			13 21	13 24	13 32	13 35	13 40	13 47		13 54	14 04	14 07		14 21	14 24	14 32	14 35
Swinton	d				13 10								13 42					14 10						14 42
Moorside	d												13 44											14 44
Walkden	d				13 15								13 48					14 15						14 48
Atherton	d				13 20								13 53					14 20						14 53
Hag Fold	d												13 56											14 56
Daisy Hill	d				13 24								13 59					14 24						14 59
Kearsley	d		12 55												13 55									
Farnworth	d		12 57												13 57									
Moses Gate	d										13 32											14 32		
Bolton	a	12 50	13 01	13 05			13 18			13 31	13 36	13 42		13 50	14 01		14 05		14 18		14 31	14 36	14 42	
	d	12 51	13 02	13 05						13 32	13 36	13 43		13 51	14 02		14 05				14 32	14 36	14 43	
Westhoughton	d		13 09									13 50			14 09								14 50	
Hindley	d		13 13		13 28								14 03		14 13			14 28						15 03
Ince	d												14 06											15 06
Wigan North Western	a																							
Wigan Wallgate	a		13 20		13 33						13 54	14 01	14 09		14 20			14 33				14 54	15 01	15 09
	d				13 35							14 02	14 11					14 35					15 02	15 11
Pemberton	d												14 15											15 15
Orrell	d												14 19											15 19
Upholland	d												14 22											15 22
Rainford	d												14 26											15 26
Kirkby	a												14 35											15 35
Liverpool Central 10	103 a												*15 01*											*16 01*
Gathurst	d				13 39													14 39						
Appley Bridge	d				13 43							14 09						14 43					15 09	
Parbold	d				13 47							14 13						14 47					15 13	
Hoscar	d				13 50																			
Burscough Bridge	d				13 53							14 17						14 51					15 17	
New Lane	d				13 55																			
Bescar Lane	d				13 59																			
Meols Cop	d				14 04													14 59						
Southport	a				14 13							14 34						15 08					15 34	
Lostock	d	12 56								13 36				13 56							14 36			
Horwich Parkway	d	13 00								13 40				14 00							14 40			
Blackrod	d	13 03												14 03										
Adlington (Lancashire)	d	13 07												14 07										
Chorley	d	13 12		13 17						13 47				14 12			14 17				14 47			
Leyland	d							13 47		13 56										14 47	14 56			
Preston 8	a	13 24		13 27				13 54		14 01				14 24			14 27			14 54	15 03			
Lancaster 6	65 a			13 44						14 24							14 44				*15 38*			
	d			13 46					14 17	14 26							14 45							
Oxenholme Lake District	65 a			*14 08*						14 41							14 59							
Windermere	83 a									15 09							*16 10*							
Carnforth	d			13 55					14 27															
Silverdale	d								14 33															
Arnside	d			14 03					14 37															
Grange-over-Sands	d			14 09					14 43															
Kents Bank	d								14 47															
Cark	d								14 51															
Ulverston	d			14 21					14 59															
Dalton	d								15 07															
Roose	d								15 13															
Barrow-in-Furness	a			14 43					15 21															
Kirkham & Wesham	97 a	13 35								*14 21*				14 35							*15 21*			
Poulton-le-Fylde	97 a	13 43								14 23				14 43							15 23			
Layton	97 a	13 47												14 47										
Blackpool North	97 a	13 54						14 21		14 32				14 54						15 21	15 32			

For general notes see front of timetable
For details of catering facilities see Directory of Train Operators

- **A** 🛒 to Preston
- **B** To Clitheroe (Table 94)
- **C** From Liverpool Lime Street (Table 90)
- **D** To Sellafield (Table 100)
- **E** 🛒 to Blackpool North
- **G** To Edinburgh (Table 65)
- **b** Change at Manchester Oxford Road

Manchester → Bolton → Wigan, Kirkby, Southport, Preston, Barrow-in-Furness and Blackpool North

Network Diagram - see first page of Table 82

Station		NT	NT	TP 1 ◇ A	NT		NT B	NT C	TP 1 ◇	NT	NT	NT	NT	NT	NT D	TP 1 ◇ E		NT G	NT B	NT	NT	NT C	TP 1 ◇	NT B	NT
Manchester Airport	85 d			14 27					14 47		15 07					15 27							15 47		16 07
Heald Green	85 d			14 31							14 56					15 31									15 56
Buxton	86 d	13 34											14 37												
Hazel Grove	86 d	14 09							14 41				15 10										15 41		
Stockport	84 d	14 19		14b25					14 49		15b02		15 19			15b25							15 49		16b02
Manchester Piccadilly 10	d	14 30		14 45					15 11		15 23		15 30			15 45							16 11		16 23
Manchester Oxford Road	d	14 33		14 48					15 15		15 26		15 33			15 48							16 15		16 26
Deansgate	d	14 35		14 50									15 35												16 28
Rochdale	95 d				14 33					14 52		15 03							15 23	15 33				15 54	
Manchester Victoria	d		14 41		14 57		15 00			15 18		15 29		15 41					15 50	15 57	16 10			16 23	
Salford Central	d		14 44		15 00		15 03			15 21		15 32		15 44					15 53	16 00	16 13			16 26	
Salford Crescent	a	14 40	14 47	14 53	15 03		15 06		15 21	15 24	15 32	15 35	15 40	15 47		15 53			15 56	16 03	16 16		16 21	16 29	16 32
	d	14 40	14 47	14 54	15 04		15 07		15 21	15 24	15 32	15 35	15 40	15 47		15 54			15 57	16 04	16 16		16 21	16 30	16 32
Swinton	d				15 10							15 42								16 10					
Moorside	d											15 44													
Walkden	d				15 15							15 48								16 15					
Atherton	d				15 20							15 53								16 20					
Hag Fold	d											15 56													
Daisy Hill	d				15 24							15 59								16 24					
Kearsley	d		14 55											15 55											
Farnworth	d		14 57											15 57											
Moses Gate	d									15 32											16 24				
Bolton	a	14 50	15 01	15 05			15 18		15 31	15 36	15 42		15 50	16 01		16 05			16 08		16 28		16 31	16 42	16 43
	d	14 51	15 02	15 05					15 32	15 36	15 43		15 51	16 02		16 05					16 28		16 32		16 43
Westhoughton	d		15 09								15 50			16 09							16 36				16 50
Hindley	d		15 13		15 28							16 03		16 13						16 28	16 40				
Ince	d											16 06									16 43				
Wigan North Western	a																								
Wigan Wallgate	a		15 20		15 33					15 54	16 01	16 09		16 20						16 33	16 50				17 01
	d				15 35						16 02	16 11								16 35					17 02
Pemberton	d											16 15													
Orrell	d											16 19													
Upholland	d											16 22													
Rainford	d											16 26													
Kirkby	a											16 35													
Liverpool Central 10	103 a											17 01													
Gathurst	d				15 39						16 07									16 39					17 06
Appley Bridge	d				15 43						16 10									16 43					17 10
Parbold	d				15 47						16 14									16 47					17 14
Hoscar	d										16 17														
Burscough Bridge	d				15 51						16 20									16 51					17 18
New Lane	d										16 23														
Bescar Lane	d										16 26														
Meols Cop	d				15 59						16 31									16 59					17 26
Southport	a				16 08						16 41									17 08					17 35
Lostock	d	14 56							15 36				15 56										16 36		
Horwich Parkway	d	15 00							15 40				16 00										16 40		
Blackrod	d	15 03											16 03												
Adlington (Lancashire)	d	15 07											16 07												
Chorley	d	15 12		15 17					15 47				16 12			16 17							16 47		
Leyland	d							15 47	15 56													16 47	16 56		
Preston 8	a	15 24		15 27				15 54	16 03				16 24			16 27						16 54	17 04		
Lancaster 6	65 a			15 44					16 32							16 44						17 16	17 32		
	d			15 52											16 39	16 45		16 53				17 16			
Oxenholme Lake District	65 a								16 46							16 59									
Windermere	83 a															17 23									
Carnforth	d			16 01											16 49			17a03				17 26			
Silverdale	d			16 07											16 55							17 31			
Arnside	d			16 11											16 59							17 36			
Grange-over-Sands	d			16 16											17 05							17 44			
Kents Bank	d			16 20											17 09							17 47			
Cark	d			16 25											17 13							17 51			
Ulverston	d			16 33											17 22							18 00			
Dalton	d			16 41											17 30							18 08			
Roose	d			16 47											17 36							18 14			
Barrow-in-Furness	a			16 56											17 44							18 23			
Kirkham & Wesham	97 a	15 35							16 23				16 35										17 15		
Poulton-le-Fylde	97 a	15 43							16 23				16 43										17 25		
Layton	97 a	15 47											16 47										17 28		
Blackpool North	97 a	15 54						16 21	16 32				16 54										17 34		

For general notes see front of timetable
For details of catering facilities see Directory of Train Operators

A to Preston
B To Clitheroe (Table 94)
C From Liverpool Lime Street (Table 90)
D To Millom (Table 100)
E To Edinburgh (Table 65)
G From Morecambe to Skipton (Table 36)
b Change at Manchester Oxford Road

Manchester → Bolton → Wigan, Kirkby, Southport, Preston, Barrow-in-Furness and Blackpool North

Network Diagram - see first page of Table 82

Station			NT	NT	NT	TP	NT	NT	NT	NT	NT	NT	TP	NT	NT	NT	NT	NT	NT	NT	NT	TP
											BHX											
						1 ◇							1 ◇									1 ◇
						A		B		C	D		E			G	H	B			J	K
						🍴							🍴									🍴
Manchester Airport	85 ✈	d				16 27							16 47						17b04			17 32
Heald Green	85	d				16 31													16b56			
Buxton	86	d							15 47										16 36			
Hazel Grove	86	d		16 10					16 28				16 41						17 09			
Stockport	84	d		16 19		16c25			16 41				16 49		16 59				17 18			17 26
Manchester Piccadilly 10	🚇	d		16 30		16 44			16 52				17 11		17 15				17 32			17 50
Manchester Oxford Road		d		16 33		16 48			16 56				17 15		17 19				17 35			17 53
Deansgate	🚇	d		16 35					16 59						17 21				17 38			17 55
Rochdale	95	d	16 03				16 23				16 33			16 52			17 03					
Manchester Victoria	🚇	d	16 29		16 41		16 48			17 00	17 05	17 10		17 15		17 23	17 29			17 38	17 42	
Salford Central		d	16 32		16 44		16 51			17 03	17 08	17 13		17 18		17 26	17 32			17 41	17 45	
Salford Crescent		a	16 35	16 40	16 47		16 54		17 02	17 06		17 16		17 22	17 26	17 29	17 35		17 42	17 45	17 48	17 59
		d	16 35	16 40	16 47		16 54		17 03	17 07		17 16		17 23	17 26	17 30	17 36		17 42	17 46	17 49	18 00
Swinton		d	16 42				17 01							17 29								
Moorside		d	16 44				17 03							17 32								
Walkden		d	16 47				17 09							17 36						17 55		
Atherton		d	16 54				17 14					17 29		17 42						18 01		
Hag Fold		d	16 56				17 17							17 44								
Daisy Hill		d	16 59				17 20					17 33		17 47						18 05		
Kearsley		d			16 55												17 43				17 59	
Farnworth		d			16 57											17 38					18 01	
Moses Gate		d			16 59											17 41					18 03	
Bolton		a		16 50	17 02	17 05			17 13	17 18	17 22		17 30		17 36	17 44	17 49		17 53		18 07	18 10
		d		16 51	17 02	17 05			17 13		17 22		17 30		17 37	17 45			17 53		18 07	18 10
Westhoughton		d			17 10											17 52					18 15	
Hindley		d	17 03		17 17		17 24							17 52		17 56					18 19	
Ince		d	17 06				17 27							17 55		17 59						
Wigan North Western		a			17 26		17 36									18 07					18 27	
Wigan Wallgate		a	17 10									17 43		17 58						18 14		
		d	17 11									17 43		17 59						18 14		
Pemberton		d	17 15											18 03								
Orrell		d	17 19											18 07								
Upholland		d	17 22											18 11								
Rainford		d	17 26											18 14								
Kirkby		a	17 35											18 23								
Liverpool Central 10	103	a	18 01											18 46								
Gathurst		d										17 47								18 19		
Appley Bridge		d										17 51								18 23		
Parbold		d										17 56								18 27		
Hoscar		d																				
Burscough Bridge		d										18 01								18 32		
New Lane		d																				
Bescar Lane		d																				
Meols Cop		d										18 09								18 40		
Southport		a										18 18								18 49		
Lostock		d		16 56					17 18		17 27				17 42				17 58			18 15
Horwich Parkway		d		17 00					17 22						17 46				18 02			
Blackrod		d		17 03					17 25						17 49				18 05			
Adlington (Lancashire)		d		17 07					17 29						17 53				18 09			
Chorley		d		17 12		17 17			17 34		17 39		17 42		17 57				18 14			18 24
Leyland		d		17 19				17 25	17 40						18 04			18 09	18 20			
Preston 8		a		17 27		17 27		17 40	17 50		17 53		17 53		18 12			18 17	18 28			18 34
Lancaster 6	65	a				17 44					18 31		18 13									18 53
		d				17 45							18 14									18 54
Oxenholme Lake District	65	a				18 11			18 28		18 47		18 28						19 13			
Windermere	83	a											19 13									
Carnforth		d				17 53																19 03
Silverdale		d				17 59																19 09
Arnside		d				18 03																19 14
Grange-over-Sands		d				18 09																19 19
Kents Bank		d				18 13																19 23
Cark		d				18 17																19 28
Ulverston		d				18 25																19 36
Dalton		d				18 34																19 44
Roose		d				18 39																19 50
Barrow-in-Furness		a				18 50																19 59
Kirkham & Wesham	97	a		17 38							18 04		18 10		18 22				18 40			18 51
Poulton-le-Fylde	97	a		17 47		17e53					18 13		18 20		18 32				18 49			19 01
Layton	97	a		17 51									18 24		18 36				18 53			19 05
Blackpool North	97	a		17 58		18e03					18 22		18 30		18 43			18 48	19 00			19 09

For general notes see front of timetable
For details of catering facilities see Directory of Train Operators

- **A** 🍴 to Preston
- **B** From Liverpool Lime Street (Table 90)
- **C** To Clitheroe (Table 94)
- **D** From Stalybridge (Table 39)
- **E** Oxenholme Lake District portion continues to Glasgow Central (Table 65)
- **G** From Huddersfield (Table 39)
- **H** To Colne (Table 97)
- **J** Also stops at Clifton 1754
- **K** 🍴 to Blackpool North
- **b** Change at Manchester Piccadilly
- **c** Change at Manchester Oxford Road
- **e** Change at Preston

Manchester → Bolton → Wigan, Kirkby, Southport, Preston, Barrow-in-Furness and Blackpool North

Network Diagram - see first page of Table 82

		NT	NT	NT	TP		NT	NT	NT	NT	NT	NT	NT	NT	NT	TP		NT	TP	NT	NT	NT	NT	TP	NT
					1 ◇											1 ◇			1 ◇					1 ◇	
		A		B			C	D	A							E		B				A			B
					🛒											🛒			🛒						
Manchester Airport	85 ✈ d				17 47							18 10				18 27			18 47		18b52		19 12	19 27	
Heald Green	85 d				17 22							17 56				18 31					18b56			19 31	
Buxton	86 d											17 06	17 34								18 22				
Hazel Grove	86 d											17 40	18 10						18 22		18 55				
Stockport	84 d				17 39							17 56	18 19			18c26			18 39		19 05		19 06	19c24	
Manchester Piccadilly 10	🚇 d				18 11							18 26	18 31			18 45			19 11		19 26		19 33	19 44	
Manchester Oxford Road	d				18 15							18 29	18 34			18 48			19 15		19 29		19 37	19 47	
Deansgate	🚇 d				18 17							18 31	18 36			18 50			19 17		19 33			19 49	
Rochdale	95 d		17 33				17 52				18 03							18 23		18 32					19 23
Manchester Victoria	🚇 d		17 57	18 00			18 21				18 29				18 41			18 58		19 18					19 58
Salford Central	d		18 00	18 03			18 24				18 32				18 44			19 01		19 21					20 01
Salford Crescent	a		18 03	18 07	18 19		18 27				18 35	18 38	18 42		18 47	18 59		19 04	19 21	19 24	19 38		19 42	19 52	20 04
	d		18 04	18 07	18 21		18 28				18 35	18 39	18 42		18 47	19 01		19 05	19 21	19 25			19 42	19 53	20 05
Swinton	d		18 10								18 42									19 31					
Moorside	d		18 13								18 44									19 34					
Walkden	d		18 16								18 48									19 37					
Atherton	d		18 22								18 53									19 43					
Hag Fold	d		18 24								18 56			←						19 45					
Daisy Hill	d		18 27								18 59			18 59						19 48					
Kearsley	d										→				18 55										
Farnworth	d														18 57										
Moses Gate	d														19 00										
Bolton	a			18 19	18 32		18 44					18 49	18 50		19 03	19 11		19 17	19 31				19 52	20 03	20 17
	d				18 32							18 50	18 51		19 04	19 12			19 32				19 53	20 04	
Westhoughton	d											18 57			19 11								20 00		
Hindley	d		18 32											19 05	19 15					19 53			20 04		
Ince	d		18 35											19 08						19 56					
Wigan North Western	a																								
Wigan Wallgate	a		18 39									19 05		19 13	19 23					20 01			20 09		
	d		18 39									19 06											20 11		
Pemberton	d																								
Orrell	d																								
Upholland	d																								
Rainford	d																								
Kirkby	a																								
Liverpool Central 10	103 a																								
Gathurst	d		18 44									19 11											20 15		
Appley Bridge	d		18 47									19 14											20 19		
Parbold	d		18 51									19 18											20 23		
Hoscar	d											19 21													
Burscough Bridge	d		18 56									19 24											20 27		
New Lane	d											19 27													
Bescar Lane	d											19 30													
Meols Cop	d		19 03									19 35											20 35		
Southport	a		19 13									19 45											20 44		
Lostock	d				18 36								18 56			19 17			19 36						
Horwich Parkway	d				18 40								19 00						19 40						
Blackrod	d				18 43								19 03						19 43						
Adlington (Lancashire)	d												19 07						19 47						
Chorley	d				18 51								19 12			19 26			19 51					20 15	
Leyland	d	18 44			18 58				19 07				19 20						19 58			20 07			
Preston 8	a	18 54			19 05				19 17				19 27			19 44			20 05			20 17		20 26	
Lancaster 6	65 a				19 33								19 59			20 05			20 32					20 44	
	d							19 24		19 39						20 06								20 51	
Oxenholme Lake District	65 a				19 46								20 13			20 20								20e59	
Windermere	83 a				20f18																			21f24	
Carnforth	d							19a33		19 49														21 00	
Silverdale	d									19 54														21 06	
Arnside	d									19 59														21 10	
Grange-over-Sands	d									20 05														21 16	
Kents Bank	d									20 08														21 20	
Cark	d									20 12														21 24	
Ulverston	d									20 21														21 32	
Dalton	d									20 29														21 41	
Roose	d									20 35														21 46	
Barrow-in-Furness	a									20 42														21 56	
Kirkham & Wesham	97 a				19 16								19 37						20 15						
Poulton-le-Fylde	97 a	19 14			19 26								19 45						20 26			20 49			
Layton	97 a												19 49						20 30						
Blackpool North	97 a	19 23			19 35								19 57						20 36			20 56			

For general notes see front of timetable
For details of catering facilities see Directory of Train Operators

A From Liverpool Lime Street (Table 90)
B To Clitheroe (Table 94)
C To Blackburn (Table 94)
D From Morecambe to Leeds (Table 36)
E To Glasgow Central (Table 65)

b Change at Manchester Piccadilly
c Change at Manchester Oxford Road
e Change at Preston
f Change at Preston and Oxenholme Lake District

Manchester → Bolton → Wigan, Kirkby, Southport, Preston, Barrow-in-Furness and Blackpool North

Network Diagram - see first page of Table 82

Station		TP 1 ◇	NT	NT	NT	NT A	NT	TP 1 ◇	NT	NT	TP 1 ◇	NT B	TP 1 ◇ C	NT D	TP 1 ◇	NT	NT	NT	NT	NT B	TP 1 ◇	NT
Manchester Airport 85 ✈	d	19 47		20 15	20b22			20 47		21 16	21 27				21 47		21b52		22b22		22 47	
Heald Green 85	d			19 56	20b07					20 56	21 08						21b56		22b12		22 52	
Buxton 86	d	18 55			19 55												21 38					
Hazel Grove 86	d	19 31			20 31												22 14					
Stockport 84	d	19 40		19 57	20 40					21 10	21 17				21 39		22 23		22 38		22 39	
Manchester Piccadilly 10	d	20 11		20 32	20 52			21 11		21 35	21 43				22 11		22 35		22 49		23 11	
Manchester Oxford Road	d	20 15		20 35	20 54			21 15		21 38	21 46				22 15		22 38		22 52		23 15	
Deansgate	d	20 17		20 37	20 56			21 17		21 40	21 48				22 17		22 40		22 54		23 17	
Rochdale 95	d		19 52			20 02			20 52			21 02				21 52				22 02		
Manchester Victoria	d		20 21			20 58			21 21			21 58				22 34				23 08		23 18
Salford Central	d		20 24			21 01			21 24			22c01				22c37				23c11		23c21
Salford Crescent	a	20 20	20 28	20 41	21 00	21 04		21 20	21 27	21 44	21 51	22 04			22 21	22 40	22 44		23 00	23 14	23 21	23 25
	d	20 21	20 28	20 41	21 00	21 05		21 21	21 28	21 44	21 51	22 05			22 21	22 41	22 44		23 00	23 14	23 21	23 25
Swinton	d		20 34						21 34							22 47						23 32
Moorside	d		20 37						21 37							22 50						23 34
Walkden	d		20 40						21 40							22 53						23 38
Atherton	d		20 46						21 46							22 59						23 43
Hag Fold	d		20 48						21 48							23 01		←				23 46
Daisy Hill	d		20 51						21 51							23 04		23 04				23 49
Kearsley	d															↪			23 08			
Farnworth	d																		23 10			
Moses Gate	d																		23 12			
Bolton	a	20 31		20 51	21 16	21 17		21 31		21 54	22 02	22 16			22 31		22 54		23 16	23 26	23 31	
	d	20 32		20 52				21 32		21 55	22 02				22 32		22 55		23 16		23 32	
Westhoughton	d			20 59						22 02							23 02		23 24			
Hindley	d		20 56	21 03					21 56	22 06							23 06	23 10	23 28			23 53
Ince	d		20 59						21 59									23 13	23 31			23 56
Wigan North Western	a																					
Wigan Wallgate	a		21 05	21 10					22 05	22 11							23 11	23 18	23 36			00 03
	d			21 12						22 13							23 13					
Pemberton	d																					
Orrell	d																					
Upholland	d																					
Rainford	d																					
Kirkby	a																					
Liverpool Central 10 103	a																					
Gathurst	d			21 16						22 17							23 17					
Appley Bridge	d			21 20						22 21							23 21					
Parbold	d			21 24						22 25							23 25					
Hoscar	d			21 27																		
Burscough Bridge	d			21 30						22 29							23 29					
New Lane	d			21 32																		
Bescar Lane	d			21 36																		
Meols Cop	d			21 41						22 37							23 37					
Southport	a			21 49						22 45							23 46					
Lostock	d	20 36						21 36							22 36						23 36	
Horwich Parkway	d	20 40						21 40							22 40						23 40	
Blackrod	d	20 43						21 43							22 43						23 43	
Adlington (Lancashire)	d	20 47						21 47							22 47						23 47	
Chorley	d	20 51						21 51							22 51						23 51	
Leyland	d	20 58						21 58						22 54	22 58						23 58	
Preston 8	a	21 04					21d29	22 05			22 32			23 02	23 06						00 05	
Lancaster 6 65	a	21 34					21 49	22 38			22 49											
	d						21 49				22 50		22 57									
Oxenholme Lake District 65	a	21 48						22 51														
Windermere 83	a	22e12																				
Carnforth	d						21 59				22 58		23 25									
Silverdale	d						22 04				23 04											
Arnside	d						22 09				23 09		23 34									
Grange-over-Sands	d						22 15				23 14		23 40									
Kents Bank	d						22 18				23 18											
Cark	d						22 22				23 22											
Ulverston	d						22 31				23 30		23 53									
Dalton	d						22 39				23 39											
Roose	d						22 45				23 44											
Barrow-in-Furness	a						22 54				23 54		00 14									
Kirkham & Wesham 97	a	21 16						22 15			23f00			23 42	23 15						00 15	
Poulton-le-Fylde 97	a	21 26						22 26						23 52	23 26						00 26	
Layton 97	a	21 30						22 30							23 30						00 30	
Blackpool North 97	a	21 36						22 36						23 28	23 36						00 38	

For general notes see front of timetable
For details of catering facilities see Directory of Train Operators

A To Clitheroe (Table 94)
B To Blackburn (Table 94)
C From Windermere (Table 83). Also stops at Bare Lane 2302 and Morecambe 2306
D From Liverpool Lime Street (Table 90)

b Change at Manchester Piccadilly
c Fridays only
e Change at Preston and Oxenholme Lake District
f Change at Preston

Table 82

Saturdays

until 22 March

Manchester → Bolton → Wigan, Kirkby, Southport, Preston, Barrow-in-Furness and Blackpool North

Network Diagram - see first page of Table 82

		NT	TP	TP	VT	NT	TP	NT	NT	NT	NT	TP	NT	NT	NT	NT	TP	NT	NT	NT	NT	NT	NT	TP	NT
			1 ◇	1 ◇	1 ◇		1 ◇					1 ◇					1 ◇							1 ◇	
		A			B				C					C					D	E	A			G	H
Manchester Airport	85 ✈ d		01 06	03 40	*04 35*		05 47					06 19					06 47					07b02		07 22	
Heald Green	85 d						05 51					06 23					06 51							07 26	
Buxton	86 d																*05 54*					06 34			
Hazel Grove	86 d																*06 27*					07 10			
Stockport	84 d									06 17							*06 41*					07 19		*07 23*	
Manchester Piccadilly 10	d		01 25	03 55	05 10		06 05			06 29		06 44					07 11					07 30		07 45	
Manchester Oxford Road	d						06 10			06 32		06 48					07 15					07 33		07 48	
Deansgate	d									06 34												07 35			
Rochdale	95 d													*06 18*									*07 06*		
Manchester Victoria	d					06 00			06 26		06 35		06 51	07 00		07 05		07 18	07 23				07 37		
Salford Central	d										06 38		06 54	07 03		07 08		07 21	07 26				07 40		
Salford Crescent	a					06 05	06 15		06 31	06 38	06 41	06 53	06 57	07 06		07 11	07 21	07 25	07 31			07 40	07 44	07 53	
	d					06 06	06 15		06 31	06 38	06 42	06 54	06 57	07 06		07 11	07 21	07 25	07 31			07 40	07 44	07 54	
Swinton	d															07 18									
Moorside	d															07 20									
Walkden	d															07 24									
Atherton	d															07 29									
Hag Fold	d															07 32									
Daisy Hill	d															07 35									
Kearsley	d										06 49												07 52		
Farnworth	d										06 51												07 54		
Moses Gate	d										06 54												07 56		
Bolton	a		01s39	04s09		06 16	06 25		06 44	06 48	06 57	07 04	07 07	07 18			07 31	07 35	07 43			07 51	08 00	08 04	
	d					06 17	06 26			06 49	06 58	07 05	07 08				07 32	07 36				07 51	08 00	08 04	
Westhoughton	d					06 24					07 05		07 15					07 43					08 08		
Hindley	d					06 28					07 09		07 19			07 39		07 47					08 12		
Ince	d										07 12					07 42		07 50							
Wigan North Western	a																	07 54							
Wigan Wallgate	a					06 33					07 17		07 24			07 45							08 19		
	d					06 35		06 40					07 26		07 40	07 47									
Pemberton	d					06 39									07 44										
Orrell	d					06 43									07 48										
Upholland	d					06 46									07 51										
Rainford	d					06 50									07 55										
Kirkby	a					07 00									08 05										
Liverpool Central 10	103 a					*07 31*									*08 31*			08c50							
Gathurst	d							06 44					07 30			07 51									
Appley Bridge	d							06 48					07 34			07 55									
Parbold	d							06 52					07 38			07 59									
Hoscar	d							06 55								08 02									
Burscough Bridge	d							06 58					07 42			08 05									
New Lane	d							07 00								08 07									
Bescar Lane	d							07 04								08 11									
Meols Cop	d							07 09					07 50			08 16									
Southport	a							07 16					07 57			08 23									
Lostock	d						06 30			06 54							07 36					07 56			
Horwich Parkway	d						06 34			06 58							07 40					08 00			
Blackrod	d						06 37			07 01							07 43					08 03			
Adlington (Lancashire)	d						06 41			07 05							07 46					08 07			
Chorley	d						06 45			07 09		07 17					07 50					08 12		08 16	
Leyland	d	00 06					06 52			07 19							07 58				08 17	08 20			
Preston 8	a	00 15	02s18	04s41	05 47		06 59			07 26		07 27					08 05				08 24	⟶		08 27	
Lancaster 6	65 a				06 18		*07 33*					07 44												08 44	
	d				06 19							07 45								08 11				08 44	08 50
Oxenholme Lake District	65 a				06 33		*07 47*																	08 58	
Windermere	83 a				*07 19*		08e15																	*09 21*	
Carnforth	d											07 54								08a20					08 59
Silverdale	d											08 00													09 05
Arnside	d											08 04													09 09
Grange-over-Sands	d											08 09													09 15
Kents Bank	d											08 13													09 19
Cark	d											08 17													09 23
Ulverston	d											08 25													09 31
Dalton	d											08 34													09 39
Roose	d											08 39													09 45
Barrow-in-Furness	a											08 49													09 54
Kirkham & Wesham	97 a				06f54		07 11			07 37		07f49					08 15								
Poulton-le-Fylde	97 a						07 21			07 46		08f04					08 26				08 54				
Layton	97 a						07 24			07 50							08 30								
Blackpool North	97 a		02 46	05 07			07 31			07 56		08f12					08 36				08 51				

For general notes see front of timetable
For details of catering facilities see Directory of Train Operators

- **A** From Liverpool Lime Street (Table 90)
- **B** To Glasgow Central (from 2 February to Carlisle) (Table 65)
- **C** To Clitheroe (Table 94)
- **D** To Blackburn (Table 94)
- **E** To Leeds (Table 36)
- **G** To Edinburgh (from 2 February to Carlisle) (Table 65)
- **H** To Carlisle via Whitehaven (Table 100)
- **b** Change at Manchester Piccadilly
- **c** Liverpool Lime Street (Table 90)
- **e** Change at Preston and Oxenholme Lake District
- **f** Change at Preston

Table 82

Saturdays

until 22 March

Manchester → Bolton → Wigan, Kirkby, Southport, Preston, Barrow-in-Furness and Blackpool North

Network Diagram - see first page of Table 82

	NT		NT	NT	TP	NT	NT	NT	NT	NT	NT	NT	TP	NT	NT	NT	TP		NT	NT	NT	NT	NT	TP
					[1] ◇								[1] ◇				[1] ◇							[1] ◇
				A		B	C	D			D		E [trolley]		A	G	H [trolley]							J [trolley]
Manchester Airport 85 ✈ d					07 47				08 07				08 27				08 47			09 07				09 27
Heald Green 85 d					07 51				08 11				08 31				08 37			08 56				09 31
Buxton 86 d										07 36							07 57					08 37		
Hazel Grove 86 d					07 24				07 53	08 14							08 33					09 12		
Stockport 84 d					07 42				08 00	08 20			08b27				08 51			09b02		09 21		09b25
Manchester Piccadilly [10] d					08 11				08 28	08 31			08 45				09 11			09 23		09 33		09 45
Manchester Oxford Road d					08 15				08 31	08 35			08 48				09 15			09 26		09 36		09 48
Deansgate d									08 33	08 37			08 50							09 28		09 38		
Rochdale 95 d						07 35	07 52	08 05						08 33					08 52		09 03			
Manchester Victoria d			07 49	08 00		08 20	08 23	08 27				08 42		08 57	09 00				09 18		09 29		09 41	
Salford Central d			07 52	08 03		08 23	08 26	08 30				08 45		09 00	09 03				09 21		09 32		09 44	
Salford Crescent a			07 56	08 06	08 21	08 26	08 29	08 33	08 37	08 42		08 47	08 54	09 03	09 06		09 21		09 24	09 32	09 35	09 43	09 47	09 53
d			07 57	08 07	08 21	08 26	08 29	08 33	08 37	08 43		08 47	08 54	09 04	09 07		09 21		09 24	09 32	09 35	09 43	09 47	09 54
Swinton d			08 03					08 42						09 10							09 42			
Moorside d			08 06					08 44													09 44			
Walkden d			08 09					08 48						09 15							09 48			
Atherton d			08 15					08 53						09 20							09 53			
Hag Fold d			08 17					08 56			←										09 56			
Daisy Hill d			08 20					08 59			08 59			09 24							09 59			
Kearsley d								→				08 55											09 55	
Farnworth d												08 57											09 57	
Moses Gate d							08 37												09 32					
Bolton a				08 18	08 31	08 36	08 42		08 48	08 53		09 01	09 04		09 18		09 31		09 36	09 42		09 53	10 01	10 04
d					08 32	08 37			08 49	08 54		09 02	09 05				09 32		09 36	09 43		09 54	10 02	10 05
Westhoughton d									08 56			09 09								09 50			10 09	
Hindley d			08 25			08 47					09 03	09 13		09 28							10 03		10 13	
Ince d			08 28								09 06										10 06			
Wigan North Western a																								
Wigan Wallgate a			08 31			08 56			09 04		09 09	09 22		09 33					09 54	10 01	10 09		10 20	
d			08 32						09 05		09 11			09 35						10 02	10 11			
Pemberton d											09 15										10 15			
Orrell d											09 19										10 19			
Upholland d											09 22										10 22			
Rainford d											09 26										10 26			
Kirkby a											09 34										10 35			
Liverpool Central [10] 103 a											10 01										11 01			
Gathurst d			08 37											09 39										
Appley Bridge d			08 40											09 43						10 09				
Parbold d			08 44											09 47						10 13				
Hoscar d																								
Burscough Bridge d			08 49						09 17					09 51						10 17				
New Lane d																								
Bescar Lane d																								
Meols Cop d			08 56											09 59										
Southport a			09 06						09 33					10 08						10 34				
Lostock d					08 36					08 59							09 36					09 59		
Horwich Parkway d					08 40					09 03							09 40					10 03		
Blackrod d										09 06												10 06		
Adlington (Lancashire) d										09 10												10 10		
Chorley d	←				08 47					09 15			09 17				09 47					10 15		10 17
Leyland d	08 20				08 56											09 47	09 54							
Preston [8] a	08 28				09 03					09 28			09 30			09 54	10 01					10 27		10 27
Lancaster [6] 65 a	08c59				09 37					09 53			09 48					10 24						10 44
d													09 48					10 25						10 45
Oxenholme Lake District 65 a	09e16				09 50								10 08					10 43						11 03
Windermere 83 a					10f14													11 11						12 17
Carnforth d													09 57											
Silverdale d																								
Arnside d													10 05											
Grange-over-Sands d													10 11											
Kents Bank d																								
Cark d																								
Ulverston d													10 23											
Dalton d																								
Roose d																								
Barrow-in-Furness a													10 45											
Kirkham & Wesham 97 a	08 39				09 22					09 38							10 21					10 38		
Poulton-le-Fylde 97 a	08 48				09 23					09 46							10 21					10 46		
Layton 97 a	08 52									09 50												10 50		
Blackpool North 97 a	09 00				09 32					09 57						10 21	10 31					10 57		

For general notes see front of timetable
For details of catering facilities see Directory of Train Operators

- A To Clitheroe (Table 94)
- B From Huddersfield (Table 39)
- C To Blackburn (Table 94)
- D From Todmorden (Table 41)
- E [trolley] to Preston
- G From Liverpool Lime Street (Table 90)
- H [trolley] to Blackpool North
- J To Glasgow Central (from 2 February to Carlisle) (Table 65)
- b Change at Manchester Oxford Road
- c From 2 February arr. 0907
- e Until 26 January only
- f Change at Preston and Oxenholme Lake District

Manchester → Bolton → Wigan, Kirkby, Southport, Preston, Barrow-in-Furness and Blackpool North

Network Diagram - see first page of Table 82

	NT	NT	NT		NT	NT	TP	NT	NT	NT	NT	NT	TP	NT	NT	NT	TP	NT	NT	NT	NT	NT	TP	NT
							1 ◇						1 ◇				1 ◇						1 ◇	
	A		B		C	D					E		G		B	A							H	
							🛒						🛒				🛒						🛒	
Manchester Airport 85 ✈ d							09 47		10 07				10 27				10 47		11 07				11 27	
Heald Green 85 d									09 56				10 31						10 56				11 31	
Buxton 86 d													09 36								10 37			
Hazel Grove 86 d							09 40						10 12				10 41				11 10			
Stockport 84 d							09 48		10b02		10 18		10b25				10 49		11b02		11 19		11b25	
Manchester Piccadilly 10 🚇 d							10 11		10 23		10 30		10 45				11 11		11 23		11 30		11 45	
Manchester Oxford Road d							10 15		10 26		10 33		10 48				11 15		11 26		11 33		11 48	
Deansgate 🚇 d											10 35		10 50								11 35			
Rochdale 95 d		09 33						09 50		10 03				10 33				10 50		11 03				11 33
Manchester Victoria 🚇 d		09 57	10 00					10 18		10 29		10 38		10 57	11 00			11 18		11 29		11 41		11 57
Salford Central d		10 00	10 03					10 21		10 32		10 44		11 00	11 03			11 21		11 32		11 44		12 00
Salford Crescent a		10 03	10 06				10 21	10 24	10 32	10 35	10 40	10 47	10 53	11 03	11 06		11 21	11 24	11 32	11 35	11 40	11 47	11 53	12 03
d		10 04	10 07				10 21	10 24	10 32	10 35	10 40	10 47	10 54	11 04	11 07		11 21	11 24	11 32	11 35	11 40	11 47	11 54	12 04
Swinton d		10 10								10 42				11 10						11 42				12 10
Moorside d										10 44										11 44				
Walkden d		10 15								10 48				11 15						11 48				12 15
Atherton d		10 20								10 53				11 20						11 53				12 20
Hag Fold d										10 56										11 56				
Daisy Hill d		10 24								10 59				11 24						11 59				12 24
Kearsley d												10 55										11 55		
Farnworth d												10 57										11 57		
Moses Gate d								10 32										11 32						
Bolton a			10 18				10 31	10 36	10 42		10 51	11 01	11 05		11 18		11 31	11 36	11 42		11 50	12 01	12 05	
d							10 32	10 36	10 43		10 51	11 02	11 05				11 32	11 36	11 43		11 51	12 02	12 05	
Westhoughton d									10 50			11 09							11 50			12 09		
Hindley d		10 28								11 03		11 13		11 28						12 03		12 13		12 28
Ince d										11 06										12 06				
Wigan North Western a																								
Wigan Wallgate a		10 33						10 54	11 01	11 09		11 20		11 33				11 54	12 01	12 09		12 20		12 33
d		10 35							11 02	11 11				11 35					12 02	12 11				12 35
Pemberton d										11 15										12 15				
Orrell d										11 19										12 19				
Upholland d										11 22										12 22				
Rainford d										11 26										12 26				
Kirkby a										11 35										12 35				
Liverpool Central 10 103 a										12 01										13 01				
Gathurst d		10 39												11 39										12 39
Appley Bridge d		10 43							11 09					11 43					12 09					12 43
Parbold d		10 47							11 13					11 47					12 13					12 47
Hoscar d		10 50												11 50										
Burscough Bridge d		10 53							11 17					11 53					12 17					12 51
New Lane d		10 55												11 55										
Bescar Lane d		10 59												11 59										
Meols Cop d		11 04												12 04										12 59
Southport a		11 13							11 34					12 14					12 34					13 08
Lostock d							10 36				10 56						11 36				11 56			
Horwich Parkway d							10 40				11 00						11 40				12 00			
Blackrod d											11 03										12 03			
Adlington (Lancashire) d											11 07										12 07			
Chorley d							10 47				11 12		11 17				11 47				12 12		12 17	
Leyland d	10 47						10 56									11 46	11 56							
Preston 8 a	10 55						11 03				11 27		11 27			11 53	12 03				12 24		12 27	
Lancaster 6 65 a							11c40						11 44				12 34						12 44	
d					10 56	11 01							11 45										12 45	
Oxenholme Lake District 65 a							11c53										12 50						12 59	
Windermere 83 a							12e17										13 20						14 14	
Carnforth d					11a05	11 10							11 54											
Silverdale d													12 00											
Arnside d						11 19							12 04											
Grange-over-Sands d						11 25							12 09											
Kents Bank d													12 13											
Cark d													12 18											
Ulverston d						11 38							12 26											
Dalton d													12 34											
Roose d													12 40											
Barrow-in-Furness a						11 56							12 49											
Kirkham & Wesham 97 a							11 21				11 37						12 23				12 35			
Poulton-le-Fylde 97 a							11 23				11 45		11f52				12 23				12 43			
Layton 97 a											11 49										12 47			
Blackpool North 97 a	11 23						11 32				11 56		12f01			12 20	12 32				12 54			

For general notes see front of timetable
For details of catering facilities see Directory of Train Operators

A From Liverpool Lime Street (Table 90)
B To Clitheroe (Table 94)
C From Morecambe to Leeds (Table 36)
D To Carlisle via Whitehaven (Table 100)
E From Northwich (Table 88)
G 🛒 to Preston
H To Edinburgh (from 2 February to Carlisle) (Table 65)
b Change at Manchester Oxford Road
c Until 26 January only
e Until 26 January only, change at Preston and Oxenholme Lake District
f Change at Preston

Table 82

Saturdays
until 22 March

Manchester → Bolton → Wigan, Kirkby, Southport, Preston, Barrow-in-Furness and Blackpool North

Network Diagram - see first page of Table 82

	NT A	NT B	NT C	TP 1 ◇ ✠	NT		NT	NT	NT	NT	TP 1 ◇ D ✠	NT	NT B	NT E	NT C	TP 1 ◇ G ✠	TP 1 ◇ H ✠	NT	NT	NT	NT	NT	TP 1 ◇ J ✠
Manchester Airport 85 ✈ d				11 47			12 07				12 27					12 47	12 47		13 07				13 27
Heald Green 85 d							*11 56*				12 31								*12 56*				13 31
Buxton 86 d									11 34												12 37		
Hazel Grove 86 d				*11 41*					12 10							*12 41*	*12 41*				13 10		
Stockport 84 d				*11 49*			*12b02*		12 19		*12b25*					*12 49*	*12 49*		*13b02*		13 19		*13b25*
Manchester Piccadilly 10 🚇 d				12 11			12 23		12 30		12 45					13 11	13 11		13 23		13 30		13 45
Manchester Oxford Road d				12 15			12 26		12 33		12 48					13 15	13 15		13 26		13 33		13 48
Deansgate 🚇 d									12 35		12 50										13 35		
Rochdale 95 d					*11 50*			12 03				12 33						*12 52*		13 03			
Manchester Victoria 🚇 d		12 00			12 18			12 29		12 41		12 57	13 00					13 18		13 29		13 41	
Salford Central d		12 03			12 21			12 32		12 44		13 00	13 03					13 21		13 32		13 44	
Salford Crescent a		12 06		12 21	12 24		12 32	12 35	12 40	12 47	12 53	13 03	13 06			13 21	13 21	13 24	13 32	13 35	13 40	13 47	13 53
d		12 07		12 21	12 24		12 32	12 35	12 40	12 47	12 54	13 04	13 07			13 21	13 21	13 24	13 32	13 35	13 40	13 47	13 54
Swinton d								12 42				13 10								13 42			
Moorside d								12 44												13 44			
Walkden d								12 48				13 15								13 48			
Atherton d								12 53				13 20								13 53			
Hag Fold d								12 56												13 56			
Daisy Hill d								12 59				13 24								13 59			
Kearsley d										12 55												13 55	
Farnworth d										12 57												13 57	
Moses Gate d					12 32													13 32					
Bolton a		12 18		12 31	12 36		12 42		12 50	13 01	13 05		13 18			13 31	13 31	13 36	13 42		13 50	14 01	14 05
d				12 32	12 36		12 43		12 51	13 02	13 05					13 32	13 32	13 36	13 43		13 51	14 02	14 05
Westhoughton d							12 50			13 09									13 50			14 09	
Hindley d								13 03		13 13		13 28								14 03		14 13	
Ince d								13 06												14 06			
Wigan North Western a																							
Wigan Wallgate a					12 54		13 01	13 09		13 20		13 33						13 54	14 01	14 09		14 20	
d							13 02	13 11				13 35							14 02	14 11			
Pemberton d								13 15												14 15			
Orrell d								13 19												14 19			
Upholland d								13 22												14 22			
Rainford d								13 26												14 26			
Kirkby a								13 35												14 35			
Liverpool Central 10 103 a								*14 01*												*15 01*			
Gathurst d												13 39											
Appley Bridge d							13 09					13 43							14 09				
Parbold d							13 13					13 47							14 13				
Hoscar d												13 50											
Burscough Bridge d							13 17					13 53							14 17				
New Lane d												13 55											
Bescar Lane d												13 59											
Meols Cop d												14 04											
Southport a							13 34					14 13							14 34				
Lostock d				12 36					12 56							13 36	13 36				13 56		
Horwich Parkway d				12 40					13 00							13 40	13 40				14 00		
Blackrod d									13 03												14 03		
Adlington (Lancashire) d									13 07												14 07		
Chorley d				12 47					13 12		13 17					13 47	13 47				14 12		14 17
Leyland d			12 47	12 56											13 47	13 56	13 56						
Preston 8 a			12 56	13 03					13 25		13 27				13 54	14 01	14 01				14 24		14 27
Lancaster 6 65 a											13 44					14 24	*14 24*						14 44
d	13 09										13 45			14 18		14 25							14 45
Oxenholme Lake District 65 a											*14 07*					14 42	*14 42*						14 59
Windermere 83 a																15 01	*15 01*						
Carnforth d	13a19										13 54			14 28									
Silverdale d														14 34									
Arnside d											14 02			14 38									
Grange-over-Sands d											14 08			14 44									
Kents Bank d														14 48									
Cark d														14 52									
Ulverston d											14 20			15 01									
Dalton d														15 09									
Roose d														15 15									
Barrow-in-Furness a											14 42			15 23									
Kirkham & Wesham 97 a				*13 21*					13 35							*14 21*	*14 21*				14 35		
Poulton-le-Fylde 97 a				13 23					13 43							14 23	14 23				14 43		
Layton 97 a									13 47												14 47		
Blackpool North 97 a			13 21	13 32					13 54						14 21	14 32	14 32				14 54		

For general notes see front of timetable
For details of catering facilities see Directory of Train Operators

A From Morecambe to Leeds (Table 36)
B To Clitheroe (Table 94)
C From Liverpool Lime Street (Table 90)
D ✠ to Preston
E To Carlisle via Whitehaven (Table 100)
G Until 26 January. ✠ to Blackpool North
H From 2 February
J To Edinburgh (from 2 February to Carlisle) (Table 65)
b Change at Manchester Oxford Road

Table 82

Saturdays

until 22 March

Manchester → Bolton → Wigan, Kirkby, Southport, Preston, Barrow-in-Furness and Blackpool North

Network Diagram - see first page of Table 82

		NT	NT	NT	TP	NT	NT	NT		NT	NT	TP	NT	NT	NT	NT	TP	NT	NT	NT	NT	NT	TP	NT	NT
					1 ◇							1 ◇					1 ◇						1 ◇		
			A	B								C 🛒		A	D	B							E 🛒	A	
Manchester Airport	85 ✈ d				13 47		14 07					14 27					14 47		15 07				15 27		
Heald Green	85 d						*13 56*					14 31							*14 56*				15 31		
Buxton	86 d									13 34											14 37				
Hazel Grove	86 d				*13 41*					14 10							*14 41*				15 10				
Stockport	84 d				*13 49*		*14 02*			14 19		*14b25*					*14 49*		*15b02*		15 19		*15b24*		
Manchester Piccadilly 10	🚇 d				14 11		14 23			14 30		14 45					15 11		15 23		15 30		15 45		
Manchester Oxford Road	d				14 15		14 26			14 33		14 48					15 15		15 26		15 33		15 48		
Deansgate	🚇 d									14 35		14 50									15 35				
Rochdale	95 d	13 33				*13 50*		14 03					14 33					*14 52*		15 03				*15 23*	15 33
Manchester Victoria	🚇 d	13 57	14 00			14 18		14 29			14 41		14 57	15 00				15 18		15 29		15 41		15 50	15 57
Salford Central	d	14 00	14 03			14 21		14 32			14 44		15 00	15 03				15 21		15 32		15 44		15 53	16 00
Salford Crescent	a	14 03	14 06		14 21	14 24	14 32	14 35		14 40	14 47	14 53	15 03	15 06			15 21	15 24	15 32	15 35	15 40	15 47	15 53	15 56	16 03
	d	14 04	14 07		14 21	14 24	14 32	14 35		14 40	14 47	14 54	15 04	15 07			15 21	15 24	15 32	15 35	15 40	15 47	15 54	15 57	16 04
Swinton	d	14 10						14 42					15 10							15 42					16 10
Moorside	d							14 44												15 44					
Walkden	d	14 15						14 48					15 15							15 48					16 15
Atherton	d	14 20						14 53					15 20							15 53					16 20
Hag Fold	d							14 56												15 56					
Daisy Hill	d	14 24						14 59					15 24							15 59					16 24
Kearsley	d										14 55											15 55			
Farnworth	d										14 57											15 57			
Moses Gate	d					14 32												15 32							
Bolton	a		14 18		14 31	14 36	14 42			14 50	15 01	15 05		15 18			15 31	15 36	15 42		15 50	16 01	16 05	16 08	
	d				14 32	14 36	14 43			14 51	15 02	15 05					15 32	15 36	15 43		15 51	16 02	16 05		
Westhoughton	d						14 50				15 09								15 50			16 09			
Hindley	d	14 28						15 03			15 13		15 28							16 03		16 13			16 28
Ince	d							15 06												16 06					
Wigan North Western	a																								
Wigan Wallgate	a	14 33				14 54	15 01	15 09			15 20		15 33					15 54	16 01	16 09		16 20			16 33
	d	14 35					15 02	15 11					15 35						16 02	16 11					16 35
Pemberton	d							15 15												16 15					
Orrell	d							15 19												16 19					
Upholland	d							15 22												16 22					
Rainford	d							15 26												16 26					
Kirkby	a							15 35												16 35					
Liverpool Central 10	103 a							*16 01*												*17 01*					
Gathurst	d	14 39											15 39						16 07						16 39
Appley Bridge	d	14 43					15 09						15 43						16 10						16 43
Parbold	d	14 47					15 13						15 47						16 14						16 47
Hoscar	d																		16 17						
Burscough Bridge	d	14 51					15 17						15 51						16 20						16 51
New Lane	d																		16 23						
Bescar Lane	d																		16 26						
Meols Cop	d	14 59											15 59						16 31						16 59
Southport	a	15 08					15 34						16 08						16 41						17 08
Lostock	d				14 36					14 56							15 36				15 56				
Horwich Parkway	d				14 40					15 00							15 40				16 00				
Blackrod	d									15 03											16 03				
Adlington (Lancashire)	d									15 07											16 07				
Chorley	d				14 47					15 12		15 17					15 47				16 12		16 17		
Leyland	d			14 47	14 56											15 47	15 56								
Preston 8	a			14 54	15 04					15 25		15 27				15 54	16 03				16 25		16 27		
Lancaster 6	65 a				*15 39*							15 45					*16 38*						16 44		
	d											15 50			16 14								16 45		
Oxenholme Lake District	65 a				*15 52*												*16 52*						16 59		
Windermere	83 a				*16c17*																		*17 23*		
Carnforth	d											15 58			16 23										
Silverdale	d											16 04			16 29										
Arnside	d											16 08			16 33										
Grange-over-Sands	d											16 13			16 39										
Kents Bank	d											16 17			16 43										
Cark	d											16 22			16 47										
Ulverston	d											16 30			16 55										
Dalton	d											16 38			17 03										
Roose	d											16 44			17 09										
Barrow-in-Furness	a											16 53			17 17										
Kirkham & Wesham	97 a				*15 21*					15 35							*16 23*				16 35				
Poulton-le-Fylde	97 a				15 23					15 43							16 23				16 43				
Layton	97 a									15 47											16 47				
Blackpool North	97 a			15 21	15 32					15 54						16 21	16 32				16 54				

For general notes see front of timetable
For details of catering facilities see Directory of Train Operators

- **A** To Clitheroe (Table 94)
- **B** From Liverpool Lime Street (Table 90)
- **C** 🛒 to Preston
- **D** To Carlisle via Whitehaven (Table 100)
- **E** To Edinburgh (from 2 February to Carlisle) (Table 65)
- **b** Change at Manchester Oxford Road
- **c** Change at Preston and Oxenholme Lake District

Table 82

Saturdays
until 22 March

Manchester → Bolton → Wigan, Kirkby, Southport, Preston, Barrow-in-Furness and Blackpool North

Network Diagram - see first page of Table 82

		NT A	NT	NT B	TP 1 ◇ 🛒	NT C	NT	NT	NT	NT	TP 1 ◇ D 🛒	NT E	NT G	NT	NT C	TP 1 ◇ H 🛒	NT	NT	NT J	NT K	NT E	NT	NT
Manchester Airport	85 ✈ d				15 47		16 07				16 27					16 47						17b04	
Heald Green	85 d						*15 56*				16 31											*16b56*	
Buxton	86 d								15 34													16 36	
Hazel Grove	86 d				*15 41*				16 10							*16 41*						17 09	
Stockport	84 d				*15 49*		*15 59*		16 19		*16c25*			16 40		*16 49*		17 02				17 18	
Manchester Piccadilly 10	🚇 d				16 11		16 23		16 30		16 44			16 52		17 11		17 15				17 30	
Manchester Oxford Road	d				16 15		16 26		16 33		16 48			16 56		17 15		17 19				17 33	
Deansgate	🚇 d						16 28		16 35					16 59				17 21				17 35	
Rochdale	95 d					*15 54*		16 03					*16 23*				*16 52*			17 03			
Manchester Victoria	🚇 d		16 10			16 23		16 29		16 41			16 48		17 00		17 15		17 23	17 29			17 38
Salford Central	d		16 13			16 26		16 32		16 44			16 51		17 03		17 18		17 26	17 32			17 41
Salford Crescent	a		16 16		16 21	16 29	16 32	16 35	16 40	16 47			16 54	17 03	17 06		17 22	17 26	17 29	17 35		17 40	17 45
	d		16 16		16 21	16 30	16 32	16 35	16 40	16 47			16 54	17 03	17 07		17 23	17 26	17 29	17 36		17 40	17 46
Swinton	d							16 42					17 01				17 29						
Moorside	d							16 44					17 03				17 32						
Walkden	d							16 47					17 09				17 36						17 55
Atherton	d							16 54					17 14				17 42						18 01
Hag Fold	d							16 56					17 17				17 44						
Daisy Hill	d							16 59					17 20				17 47						18 05
Kearsley	d									16 55										17 43			
Farnworth	d									16 57									17 38				
Moses Gate	d		16 24							16 59									17 40				
Bolton	a		16 28		16 31	16 42	16 43		16 51	17 02	17 05			17 13	17 18	17 30		17 36	17 44	17 49		17 53	
	d		16 28		16 32		16 43		16 51	17 02	17 05			17 13		17 30		17 37	17 45			17 53	
Westhoughton	d		16 36				16 50			17 10									17 52				
Hindley	d		16 40					17 03		17 17			17 24				17 52		17 56				
Ince	d		16 43					17 06					17 27				17 55		17 59				
Wigan North Western	a									17 26													
Wigan Wallgate	a		16 50				17 01	17 10					17 36				17 58		18 06				18 14
	d						17 02	17 11					17 38				17 59						18 14
Pemberton	d							17 15									18 03						
Orrell	d							17 19									18 07						
Upholland	d							17 22									18 11						
Rainford	d							17 26									18 14						
Kirkby	a							17 35									18 23						
Liverpool Central 10	103 a							*18 01*									*18 46*						
Gathurst	d						17 06						17 42										18 19
Appley Bridge	d						17 10						17 46										18 23
Parbold	d						17 14						17 50										18 27
Hoscar	d																						
Burscough Bridge	d						17 18						17 54										18 32
New Lane	d																						
Bescar Lane	d																						
Meols Cop	d						17 26						18 02										18 40
Southport	a						17 35						18 09										18 49
Lostock	d				16 36				16 56					17 18				17 42				17 58	
Horwich Parkway	d				16 40				17 00					17 22				17 46				18 02	
Blackrod	d								17 03					17 25				17 49				18 05	
Adlington (Lancashire)	d								17 07					17 29				17 53				18 09	
Chorley	d				16 47				17 12		17 17			17 34		17 42		17 57				18 14	
Leyland	d			16 47	16 56				17 19			17 29		17 40				18 04			18 09	18 20	
Preston 8	a			16 54	17 04				17 27		17 27	17 40		17 50		17 53		18 12			18 17	18 29	
Lancaster 6	65 a			17 16	*17 40*						17 44					18 13					*18 39*		
	d	16 53		17 17							17 45					18 14							
Oxenholme Lake District	65 a				*17 53*						*18 09*					18 28					*18 52*		
Windermere	83 a															*19 02*							
Carnforth	d	17a02		17 26							17 53												
Silverdale	d			17 32							17 59												
Arnside	d			17 37							18 03												
Grange-over-Sands	d			17 43							18 09												
Kents Bank	d			17 46							18 13												
Cark	d			17 51							18 17												
Ulverston	d			17 59							18 25												
Dalton	d			18 07							18 34												
Roose	d			18 13							18 39												
Barrow-in-Furness	a			18 21							18 50												
Kirkham & Wesham	97 a				17 15				17 38							18 10		18 22				18 39	
Poulton-le-Fylde	97 a				17 25				17 47		*17e53*					18 20		18 32				18 48	
Layton	97 a				17 28				17 51							18 24		18 36				18 52	
Blackpool North	97 a				17 34				17 58		*18e03*					18 30		18 43			18 48	18 59	

For general notes see front of timetable
For details of catering facilities see Directory of Train Operators

A From Morecambe to Skipton (Table 36)
B From Liverpool Lime Street (Table 90) to Millom (Table 100)
C To Clitheroe (Table 94)
D 🛒 to Preston
E From Liverpool Lime Street (Table 90)
G From Stalybridge (Table 39)
H Oxenholme Lake District portion continues to Glasgow Central (from 2 February to Carlisle) (Table 65)
J From Huddersfield (Table 39)
K To Blackburn (Table 94)
b Change at Manchester Piccadilly
c Change at Manchester Oxford Road
e Change at Preston

Table 82

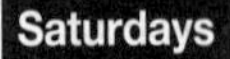

until 22 March

Manchester → Bolton → Wigan, Kirkby, Southport, Preston, Barrow-in-Furness and Blackpool North

Network Diagram - see first page of Table 82

	NT	TP	NT	NT	NT	NT	TP	NT	NT	NT	NT		NT	NT	NT	TP	NT	TP	NT	NT	NT	NT	TP	NT
		[1] ◇					[1] ◇									[1] ◇		[1] ◇					[1] ◇	
	A	B 🍴		C	D	E		G	D								C				D			C
Manchester Airport 85 ✈ d		17 32					17 47				18 10					18 27		18 47				19 12	19 27	
Heald Green 85 d							*17 22*				*17 56*					18 31						*18 56*	19 31	
Buxton 86 d													17 34							18 22				
Hazel Grove 86 d							*17 41*						18 10					*18 41*		18 55				
Stockport 84 d		*17 25*					*17 49*				*17 59*		18 19			*18 26*		*18 50*		19 05			*19 15*	
Manchester Piccadilly [10] 🚊 d		17 50					18 11				18 26		18 31			18 45		19 11		19 20		19 33	19 44	
Manchester Oxford Road d		17 54					18 15				18 29		18 36			18 47		19 15		19 23		19 37	19 48	
Deansgate 🚊 d		17 56					18 17				18 31		18 38			18 50		19 17		19 26			19 50	
Rochdale 95 d			17 33					*17 52*		18 03							*18 23*		*18 32*					*19 24*
Manchester Victoria 🚊 d	17 42		17 57	18 00				18 21		18 29					18 41		18 58		19 18					19 58
Salford Central d	17 45		18 00	18 03				18 24		18 32					18 44		19 01		19 21					20 01
Salford Crescent a	17 48	17 59	18 03	18 07			18 19	18 28		18 35	18 38		18 46		18 47	18 59	19 04	19 21	19 24	19 31		19 42	19 54	20 04
d	17 49	18 00	18 04	18 07			18 21	18 28		18 35	18 39		18 46		18 47	19 01	19 05	19 21	19 25			19 42	19 54	20 05
Swinton d			18 10							18 42									19 31					
Moorside d			18 13							18 44									19 34					
Walkden d			18 16							18 48									19 37					
Atherton d			18 22							18 53									19 43					
Hag Fold d			18 24							18 56				←					19 45					
Daisy Hill d			18 27							18 59				18 59					19 48					
Kearsley d	17 59									→					18 55									
Farnworth d	18 01														18 57									
Moses Gate d	18 03														19 00									
Bolton a	18 07	18 10		18 19			18 32	18 44			18 49		18 56		19 04	19 11	19 17	19 31				19 52	20 04	20 16
d	18 07	18 10					18 32				18 50		18 57		19 04	19 12		19 32				19 53	20 05	
Westhoughton d	18 15										18 57				19 11							20 00		
Hindley d	18 19		18 32											19 05	19 15				19 53			20 04		
Ince d			18 35											19 08					19 56					
Wigan North Western a																								
Wigan Wallgate a	18 26		18 42								19 05			19 13	19 24				20 01			20 09		
d											19 06											20 11		
Pemberton d																								
Orrell d																								
Upholland d																								
Rainford d																								
Kirkby a																								
Liverpool Central [10] 103 a																								
Gathurst d											19 11											20 15		
Appley Bridge d											19 14											20 19		
Parbold d											19 18											20 23		
Hoscar d											19 21													
Burscough Bridge d											19 24											20 27		
New Lane d											19 27													
Bescar Lane d											19 30													
Meols Cop d											19 35											20 35		
Southport a											19 45											20 44		
Lostock d		18 15					18 36						19 02					19 36						
Horwich Parkway d							18 40						19 06					19 40						
Blackrod d							18 43						19 09					19 43						
Adlington (Lancashire) d													19 12					19 47						
Chorley d		18 24					18 51						19 17			19 24		19 51					20 16	
Leyland d					18 44		18 58		19 07				19 23					19 58			20 07			
Preston [8] a		18 34			18 52		19 05		19 17				19 31			19 36		20 04			20 17		20 27	
Lancaster [6] 65 a		18 53							*19 39*							19 53							20 43	
d		18 54				19 19										19 55							20 43	
Oxenholme Lake District 65 a		*19 13*							*19 52*							*21b30*							*22b30*	
Windermere 83 a									*20c19*															
Carnforth d		19 03				19a31										20 04							20 54	
Silverdale d		19 09																					21 00	
Arnside d		19 14														20 12							21 04	
Grange-over-Sands d		19 19														20 18							21 10	
Kents Bank d		19 23																					21 14	
Cark d		19 28																					21 18	
Ulverston d		19 36														20 30							21 26	
Dalton d		19 44																					21 35	
Roose d		19 50																					21 40	
Barrow-in-Furness a		19 59														20 51							21 50	
Kirkham & Wesham 97 a							19 16						19 42					20 15						
Poulton-le-Fylde 97 a					19 10		19 26						19 51					20 26			*20 49*			
Layton 97 a													19 55					20 30						
Blackpool North 97 a					19 21		19 35						20 01					20 36			*20 56*			

For general notes see front of timetable
For details of catering facilities see Directory of Train Operators

- **A** Also stops at Clifton 1754
- **B** 🍴 to Preston
- **C** To Clitheroe (Table 94)
- **D** From Liverpool Lime Street (Table 90)
- **E** From Morecambe to Leeds (Table 36)
- **G** To Blackburn (Table 94)
- **b** By bus
- **c** Change at Preston and Oxenholme Lake District

Table 82

Saturdays

until 22 March

Manchester → Bolton → Wigan, Kirkby, Southport, Preston, Barrow-in-Furness and Blackpool North

Network Diagram - see first page of Table 82

	TP 1 ◇	TP 1 ◇	NT	NT	NT	NT	NT A	TP 1 ◇	NT	NT	TP 1 ◇	NT B	NT C	TP 1 ◇	NT	NT	NT	NT	NT B	TP 1 ◇ D	TP 1 ◇ E	NT
Manchester Airport 85 ✈ d		19 47			20 15	20b22		20 47		21 16	21 27			21 47		21b52		22b22		22 47	22 47	
Heald Green 85 d					19 57	20b07				20 56	21 08					21b56		22b12		22 51	22 51	
Buxton 86 d		18 55				19 55										21 38						
Hazel Grove 86 d		19 31				20 31										22 14						
Stockport 84 d		19 40			20 03	20 40				21 13	21 15			21 39		22 23		22 38		22 39	22 39	
Manchester Piccadilly 10 d		20 11			20 32	20 52		21 11		21 35	21 43			22 11		22 35		22 49		23 11	23 11	
Manchester Oxford Road d		20 15			20 35	20 54		21 15		21 38	21 46			22 15		22 38		22 52		23 15	23 15	
Deansgate d		20 17			20 37	20 56		21 17		21 40	21 48			22 17		22 40		22 54		23 17	23 17	
Rochdale 95 d				19 52			20 02		20 52			21 02			21 52				22 02			
Manchester Victoria d				20 21			20 58		21 21			21 58			22 34				23 08			23 18
Salford Central d				20 24			21 01		21 24			22 01			22 37				23 11			23 21
Salford Crescent a		20 20		20 28	20 41	21 00	21 04	21 20	21 27	21 44	21 51	22 04		22 20	22 40	22 44		23 00	23 13	23 21	23 21	23 25
d		20 21		20 28	20 41	21 00	21 05	21 21	21 28	21 44	21 54	22 05		22 21	22 41	22 44		23 00	23 14	23 21	23 21	23 25
Swinton d				20 34					21 34						22 47							23 32
Moorside d				20 37					21 37						22 50							23 34
Walkden d				20 40					21 40						22 53							23 38
Atherton d				20 46					21 46						22 59							23 43
Hag Fold d				20 48					21 48						23 01		←					23 46
Daisy Hill d				20 51					21 51						23 04		23 04					23 49
Kearsley d															→			23 08				
Farnworth d																		23 10				
Moses Gate d																		23 12				
Bolton a		20 31			20 51	21 16	21 17	21 31		21 54	22 05	22 16		22 31		22 54		23 16	23 27	23 31	23 31	
d		20 32			20 52			21 32		21 55	22 05			22 32		22 55		23 16		23 32	23 32	
Westhoughton d					20 59					22 02						23 02		23 24				
Hindley d				20 56	21 03				21 56	22 06						23 06	23 13	23 28				23 53
Ince d				20 59					21 59								23 16	23 31				23 56
Wigan North Western a																						
Wigan Wallgate a				21 05	21 10				22 05	22 11						23 11	23 21	23 36				00 03
d					21 12					22 13						23 13						
Pemberton d																						
Orrell d																						
Upholland d																						
Rainford d																						
Kirkby a																						
Liverpool Central 10 103 a																						
Gathurst d					21 16					22 17						23 17						
Appley Bridge d					21 20					22 21						23 21						
Parbold d					21 24					22 25						23 25						
Hoscar d					21 27																	
Burscough Bridge d					21 30					22 29						23 29						
New Lane d					21 32																	
Bescar Lane d					21 36																	
Meols Cop d					21 41					22 37						23 37						
Southport a					21 49					22 47						23 46						
Lostock d		20 36						21 36						22 36						23 36	23 36	
Horwich Parkway d		20 40						21 40						22 40						23 40	23 40	
Blackrod d		20 43						21 43						22 43						23 43	23 43	
Adlington (Lancashire) d		20 47						21 47						22 47						23 47	23 47	
Chorley d		20 51						21 51			22 17			22 51						23 51	23 51	
Leyland d		20 58						21 58					22 54	22 58						23 58	23 58	
Preston 8 a		21 04						22 05			22 32		23 02	23 05						00 06	00 06	
Lancaster 6 65 a		22c30									23c30											
d	21 43		22 45																			
Oxenholme Lake District 65 a																						
Windermere 83 a																						
Carnforth d	21 54		22 54																			
Silverdale d	22 00		23 00																			
Arnside d	22 04		23 04																			
Grange-over-Sands d	22 10		23 10																			
Kents Bank d	22 14		23 14																			
Cark d	22 18		23 18																			
Ulverston d	22 26		23 26																			
Dalton d	22 35		23 34																			
Roose d	22 40		23 40																			
Barrow-in-Furness a	22 50		23 50																			
Kirkham & Wesham 97 a		21 15						22 15			23 00		00 15	23 15						00 15	00c45	
Poulton-le-Fylde 97 a		21 26						22 26					00 26	23 26						00 26	01c05	
Layton 97 a		21 30						22 30					01c15	23 30						00 30	01c15	
Blackpool North 97 a		21 36						22 36					23 28	23 36						00 38	01c25	

For general notes see front of timetable
For details of catering facilities see Directory of Train Operators

A To Clitheroe (Table 94)
B To Blackburn (Table 94)
C From Liverpool Lime Street (Table 90)
D Until 26 January
E From 2 February
b Change at Manchester Piccadilly
c By bus

Table 82

Saturdays

from 29 March

Manchester → Bolton → Wigan, Kirkby, Southport, Preston, Barrow-in-Furness and Blackpool North

Network Diagram - see first page of Table 82

	NT	TP	TP	VT	TP	TP	NT	TP	NT	NT	NT	NT	TP		NT	NT	NT	NT	NT	NT	NT	TP	NT	NT
	A	■1 ◇	■1 ◇	■1 ◇ 🍴	🚌	■1		■1 ◇		B			■1 ◇			B			C	🚌	D	■1 ◇		E
Manchester Airport 85 ✈ d		01 06	03 40	*04 35*				05 47					06 19									06 47		
Heald Green 85 d								05 51					06 23									06 51		
Buxton 86 d																						*05 54*		
Hazel Grove 86 d																						*06 27*		
Stockport 84 d											06 17											*06 41*		
Manchester Piccadilly ■10 ⛴ d		01 25	03 55	05 10				06 05			06 29		06 44									07 11		
Manchester Oxford Road d								06 10			06 32		06 48									07 15		
Deansgate ⛴ d											06 34													
Rochdale 95 d																*06 18*								
Manchester Victoria ⛴ d							06 00			06 26		06 35			06 51	07 00		07 05					07 18	07 23
Salford Central d												06 38			06 54	07 03		07 08					07 21	07 26
Salford Crescent a							06 05	06 15		06 31	06 38	06 41	06 53		06 57	07 06		07 11				07 21	07 25	07 31
d							06 06	06 15		06 31	06 38	06 42	06 54		06 57	07 06		07 11				07 21	07 25	07 31
Swinton d																		07 18						
Moorside d																		07 20						
Walkden d																		07 24						
Atherton d																		07 29						
Hag Fold d																		07 32						
Daisy Hill d																		07 35						
Kearsley d												06 49												
Farnworth d												06 51												
Moses Gate d												06 54												
Bolton a		01s39	04s09				06 16	06 25		06 44	06 48	06 57	07 04		07 07	07 18						07 31	07 35	07 43
d							06 17	06 26			06 49	06 58	07 05		07 08							07 32	07 36	
Westhoughton d							06 24					07 05			07 15								07 43	
Hindley d							06 28					07 09			07 19			07 39					07 47	
Ince d												07 12						07 42					07 50	
Wigan North Western a																							07 54	
Wigan Wallgate a							06 33					07 17			07 24			07 45						
d							06 35		06 40						07 26		07 40	07 47						
Pemberton d							06 39										07 44							
Orrell d							06 43										07 48							
Upholland d							06 46										07 51							
Rainford d							06 50										07 55							
Kirkby a							07 00										08 05							
Liverpool Central ■10 103 a							*07 31*										*08 31*						08b50	
Gathurst d									06 44						07 30			07 51						
Appley Bridge d									06 48						07 34			07 55						
Parbold d									06 52						07 38			07 59						
Hoscar d									06 55									08 02						
Burscough Bridge d									06 58						07 42			08 05						
New Lane d									07 00									08 07						
Bescar Lane d									07 04									08 11						
Meols Cop d									07 09						07 50			08 16						
Southport a									07 16						07 57			08 23						
Lostock d								06 30			06 54											07 36		
Horwich Parkway d								06 34			06 58											07 40		
Blackrod d								06 37			07 01											07 43		
Adlington (Lancashire) d								06 41			07 05											07 46		
Chorley d								06 45			07 09		07 17									07 50		
Leyland d	00 06							06 52			07 19											07 58		
Preston ■8 a	00 15	02s18	04s41	06 03	06d55			06 59			07 26		07 27							08d00		08 05		
Lancaster ■6 65 a				*07c05*				*08c03*														*09c03*		
d						07 44													08 14		08 50			
Oxenholme Lake District 65 a				*07e25*				*08e25*														*09e25*		
Windermere 83 a				*07e47*				*08e47*														*09e47*		
Carnforth d					07a45	07 53													08a23	08a50	08 59			
Silverdale d						07 59															09 05			
Arnside d						08 03															09 09			
Grange-over-Sands d						08 08															09 15			
Kents Bank d						08 12															09 19			
Cark d						08 16															09 23			
Ulverston d						08 24															09 31			
Dalton d						08 33															09 39			
Roose d						08 38															09 45			
Barrow-in-Furness a						08 48															09 54			
Kirkham & Wesham 97 a				*06 54*				07 11			07 37		*07 49*									08 15		
Poulton-le-Fylde 97 a								07 21			07 46		*08 04*									08 26		
Layton 97 a								07 24			07 50											08 30		
Blackpool North 97 a		02 46	05 07					07 31			07 56		*08 12*									08 36		

For general notes see front of timetable
For details of catering facilities see Directory of Train Operators

A From Liverpool Lime Street (Table 90)
B To Clitheroe (Table 94)
C To Leeds (Table 36)
D To Carlisle via Whitehaven (Table 100)
E To Blackburn (Table 94)
b Liverpool Lime Street (Table 90)
c By bus
e Change at Preston and Lancaster. By bus to Lancaster

Table 82

Saturdays

from 29 March

Manchester → Bolton → Wigan, Kirkby, Southport, Preston, Barrow-in-Furness and Blackpool North

Network Diagram - see first page of Table 82

		NT	NT	NT	TP	NT	NT	TP	TP	TP	NT	NT	NT	NT	NT	NT	NT	TP	NT	NT	NT	TP	TP
					1 ◇				1	1 ◇								1 ◇				1 ◇	
		A					B	bus			C	D	E			E		trolley		B	A	trolley	bus
Manchester Airport	85 ✈ d		07b02		07 22					07 47				08 07				08 27				08 47	
Heald Green	85 d				07 26					07 51				08 11				08 31				08 37	
Buxton	86 d		06 34												07 36							07 57	
Hazel Grove	86 d		07 10							07 24				07 53	08 14							08 33	
Stockport	84 d		07 19		07 23					07 42				08 00	08 20			08c27				08 51	
Manchester Piccadilly 10	⛴ d		07 30		07 45					08 11				08 28	08 31			08 45				09 11	
Manchester Oxford Road	d		07 33		07 48					08 15				08 31	08 35			08 48				09 15	
Deansgate	⛴ d		07 35											08 33	08 37			08 50					
Rochdale	95 d			07 06							07 35	07 52	08 05						08 33				
Manchester Victoria	⛴ d			07 37		07 49	08 00				08 20	08 23	08 27				08 42		08 57	09 00			
Salford Central	d			07 40		07 52	08 03				08 23	08 26	08 30				08 45		09 00	09 03			
Salford Crescent	a		07 40	07 44	07 53	07 56	08 06			08 21	08 26	08 29	08 33	08 37	08 42		08 47	08 54	09 03	09 06		09 21	
	d		07 40	07 44	07 54	07 57	08 07			08 21	08 26	08 29	08 33	08 37	08 43		08 47	08 54	09 04	09 07		09 21	
Swinton	d					08 03							08 42						09 10				
Moorside	d					08 06							08 44										
Walkden	d					08 09							08 48						09 15				
Atherton	d					08 15							08 53						09 20				
Hag Fold	d					08 17							08 56			←							
Daisy Hill	d					08 20							08 59			08 59			09 24				
Kearsley	d			07 52									→				08 55						
Farnworth	d			07 54													08 57						
Moses Gate	d			07 56								08 37											
Bolton	a		07 51	08 00	08 04		08 18			08 31	08 36	08 42		08 48	08 53		09 01	09 04		09 18		09 31	
	d		07 51	08 00	08 04					08 32	08 37			08 49	08 54		09 02	09 05				09 32	
Westhoughton	d			08 08										08 56			09 09						
Hindley	d			08 12		08 25					08 47					09 03	09 13		09 28				
Ince	d					08 28										09 06							
Wigan North Western	a																						
Wigan Wallgate	a			08 19		08 31					08 56			09 04		09 09	09 22		09 33				
	d					08 32								09 05		09 11			09 35				
Pemberton	d															09 15							
Orrell	d															09 19							
Upholland	d															09 22							
Rainford	d															09 26							
Kirkby	a															09 34							
Liverpool Central 10	103 a															10 01							
Gathurst	d					08 37													09 39				
Appley Bridge	d					08 40													09 43				
Parbold	d					08 44													09 47				
Hoscar	d																						
Burscough Bridge	d					08 49								09 17					09 51				
New Lane	d																						
Bescar Lane	d																						
Meols Cop	d					08 56													09 59				
Southport	a					09 06								09 33					10 08				
Lostock	d		07 56							08 36					08 59							09 36	
Horwich Parkway	d		08 00							08 40					09 03							09 40	
Blackrod	d		08 03												09 06								
Adlington (Lancashire)	d		08 07												09 10								
Chorley	d		08 12		08 16					08 47					09 15			09 17				09 47	
Leyland	d	08 17	08 20							08 56											09 47	09 54	
Preston 8	a	08 24	08 28		08 29			08d55		09 03					09 28			09 30			09 54	10 00	10d10
Lancaster 6	65 a									10e03								10e45				11e03	
	d								09 48														
Oxenholme Lake District	65 a									10f25												11f25	
Windermere	83 a									10f47												11f47	
Carnforth	d							09a45	09 57														11a00
Silverdale	d																						
Arnside	d								10 05														
Grange-over-Sands	d								10 11														
Kents Bank	d																						
Cark	d																						
Ulverston	d								10 23														
Dalton	d																						
Roose	d																						
Barrow-in-Furness	a								10 46														
Kirkham & Wesham	97 a		08 39							09 22					09 38							10 21	
Poulton-le-Fylde	97 a	08 54	08 48							09 23					09 46							10 21	
Layton	97 a		08 52												09 50								
Blackpool North	97 a	08 51	09 00							09 32					09 57						10 21	10 31	

For general notes see front of timetable
For details of catering facilities see Directory of Train Operators

A From Liverpool Lime Street (Table 90)
B To Clitheroe (Table 94)
C From Huddersfield (Table 39)
D To Blackburn (Table 94)
E From Todmorden (Table 41)

b Change at Manchester Piccadilly
c Change at Manchester Oxford Road
e By bus
f Change at Preston and Lancaster. By bus to Lancaster

Table 82

Saturdays

from 29 March

Manchester → Bolton → Wigan, Kirkby, Southport, Preston, Barrow-in-Furness and Blackpool North

Network Diagram - see first page of Table 82

	NT	TP	NT	NT	NT	NT	NT	TP	NT	NT	NT	NT	NT	TP	NT	NT	NT	NT	NT	TP	NT	NT	NT
		1						1 ◇						1 ◇						1 ◇			
	A										B		C					D				C	B
									bus														
								cycle						cycle									
Manchester Airport 85 ✈ d				09 07				09 27						09 47		10 07				10 27			
Heald Green 85 d				*08 56*				09 31								*09 56*				10 31			
Buxton 86 d						08 37														*09 36*			
Hazel Grove 86 d						09 12								*09 40*						*10 12*			
Stockport 84 d				*09b02*		09 21		*09b25*						*09 48*		*10b02*		10 18		*10b25*			
Manchester Piccadilly 10 ⛴ d				09 23		09 33		09 45						10 11		10 23		10 30		10 45			
Manchester Oxford Road d				09 26		09 36		09 48						10 15		10 26		10 33		10 48			
Deansgate ⛴ d				09 28		09 38												10 35		10 50			
Rochdale 95 d			*08 52*		09 03							09 33			*09 50*		10 03				10 33		
Manchester Victoria ⛴ d			09 18		09 29		09 41					09 57	10 00		10 18		10 29		10 38		10 57	11 00	
Salford Central d			09 21		09 32		09 44					10 00	10 03		10 21		10 32		10 44		11 00	11 03	
Salford Crescent a			09 24	09 32	09 35	09 43	09 47	09 53				10 03	10 06	10 21	10 24	10 32	10 35	10 40	10 47	10 53	11 03	11 06	
d			09 24	09 32	09 35	09 43	09 47	09 54				10 04	10 07	10 21	10 24	10 32	10 35	10 40	10 47	10 54	11 04	11 07	
Swinton d					09 42							10 10					10 42				11 10		
Moorside d					09 44												10 44						
Walkden d					09 48							10 15					10 48				11 15		
Atherton d					09 53							10 20					10 53				11 20		
Hag Fold d					09 56												10 56						
Daisy Hill d					09 59							10 24					10 59				11 24		
Kearsley d							09 55												10 55				
Farnworth d							09 57												10 57				
Moses Gate d			09 32												10 32								
Bolton a			09 36	09 42		09 53	10 01	10 04					10 18	10 31	10 36	10 42		10 51	11 01	11 05		11 18	
d			09 36	09 43		09 54	10 02	10 05						10 32	10 36	10 43		10 51	11 02	11 05			
Westhoughton d				09 50			10 09									10 50			11 09				
Hindley d					10 03		10 13					10 28					11 03		11 13		11 28		
Ince d					10 06												11 06						
Wigan North Western a																							
Wigan Wallgate a			09 54	10 01	10 09		10 20					10 33			10 54	11 01	11 09		11 20		11 33		
d				10 02	10 11							10 35				11 02	11 11				11 35		
Pemberton d					10 15												11 15						
Orrell d					10 19												11 19						
Upholland d					10 22												11 22						
Rainford d					10 26												11 26						
Kirkby a					10 35												11 35						
Liverpool Central 10 103 a					*11 01*												*12 01*						
Gathurst d												10 39									11 39		
Appley Bridge d				10 09								10 43				11 09					11 43		
Parbold d				10 13								10 47				11 13					11 47		
Hoscar d												10 50									11 50		
Burscough Bridge d				10 17								10 53				11 17					11 53		
New Lane d												10 55									11 55		
Bescar Lane d												10 59									11 59		
Meols Cop d												11 04									12 04		
Southport a				10 34								11 13				11 34					12 14		
Lostock d						09 59								10 36				10 56					
Horwich Parkway d						10 03								10 40				11 00					
Blackrod d						10 06												11 03					
Adlington (Lancashire) d						10 10												11 07					
Chorley d						10 15		10 17						10 47				11 12		11 17			
Leyland d											10 47			10 56									11 46
Preston 8 a						10 27		10 29	10d55		10 55			11 03				11 27		11 27			11 53
Lancaster 6 65 a								*11c45*						*12c03*						*12c45*			
d	10 56	11 02								11 45													
Oxenholme Lake District 65 a														*12e25*									
Windermere 83 a														*12e47*									
Carnforth d	11a05	11 11							11a45	11 54													
Silverdale d										12 00													
Arnside d		11 20								12 05													
Grange-over-Sands d		11 25								12 11													
Kents Bank d										12 14													
Cark d										12 19													
Ulverston d		11 38								12 27													
Dalton d										12 35													
Roose d										12 41													
Barrow-in-Furness a		11 54								12 51													
Kirkham & Wesham 97 a						10 38								*11 21*				11 37					
Poulton-le-Fylde 97 a						10 46								11 23				11 45		*11 52*			
Layton 97 a						10 50												11 49					
Blackpool North 97 a						10 57					11 23			11 32				11 56		*12 01*			12 20

For general notes see front of timetable
For details of catering facilities see Directory of Train Operators

A From Morecambe to Leeds (Table 36)
B From Liverpool Lime Street (Table 90)
C To Clitheroe (Table 94)
D From Northwich (Table 88)

b Change at Manchester Oxford Road
c By bus
e Change at Preston and Lancaster. By bus to Lancaster

from 29 March

Manchester → Bolton → Wigan, Kirkby, Southport, Preston, Barrow-in-Furness and Blackpool North

Network Diagram - see first page of Table 82

	TP 1 ◇	NT	NT		NT	NT	NT	TP 1 ◇	NT	NT A	NT B	TP (bus)	TP 1	NT C	TP 1 ◇	NT	NT		NT	NT	NT	TP 1 ◇	NT (bus)	NT D
	trolley							trolley							trolley									
Manchester Airport 85 ✈ d	10 47		11 07					11 27							11 47		12 07					12 27		
Heald Green 85 d			10 56					11 31									11 56					12 31		
Buxton 86 d						10 37														11 34				
Hazel Grove 86 d	10 41					11 10									11 41					12 10				
Stockport 84 d	10 49		11b02			11 19		11b25							11 49		12b02			12 19		12b25		
Manchester Piccadilly 10 d	11 11		11 23			11 30		11 45							12 11		12 23			12 30		12 45		
Manchester Oxford Road d	11 15		11 26			11 33		11 48							12 15		12 26			12 33		12 48		
Deansgate d						11 35														12 35		12 50		
Rochdale 95 d		10 50			11 03				11 33							11 50			12 03					
Manchester Victoria d		11 18			11 29		11 41		11 57		12 00					12 18			12 29		12 41			
Salford Central d		11 21			11 32		11 44		12 00		12 03					12 21			12 32		12 44			
Salford Crescent a	11 21	11 24	11 32		11 35	11 40	11 47	11 53	12 03		12 06				12 21	12 24	12 32		12 35	12 40	12 47	12 53		
d	11 21	11 24	11 32		11 35	11 40	11 47	11 54	12 04		12 07				12 21	12 24	12 32		12 35	12 40	12 47	12 54		
Swinton d					11 42				12 10										12 42					
Moorside d					11 44														12 44					
Walkden d					11 48				12 15										12 48					
Atherton d					11 53				12 20										12 53					
Hag Fold d					11 56														12 56					
Daisy Hill d					11 59				12 24										12 59					
Kearsley d							11 55														12 55			
Farnworth d							11 57														12 57			
Moses Gate d		11 32														12 32								
Bolton a	11 31	11 36	11 42			11 50	12 01	12 05			12 18				12 31	12 36	12 42			12 50	13 01	13 05		
d	11 32	11 36	11 43			11 51	12 02	12 05							12 32	12 36	12 43			12 51	13 02	13 05		
Westhoughton d			11 50				12 09										12 50				13 09			
Hindley d					12 03		12 13		12 28										13 03		13 13			
Ince d					12 06														13 06					
Wigan North Western a																								
Wigan Wallgate a		11 54	12 01		12 09		12 20		12 33							12 54	13 01		13 09		13 20			
d			12 02		12 11				12 35								13 02		13 11					
Pemberton d					12 15														13 15					
Orrell d					12 19														13 19					
Upholland d					12 22														13 22					
Rainford d					12 26														13 26					
Kirkby a					12 35														13 35					
Liverpool Central 10 103 a					13 01														14 01					
Gathurst d									12 39															
Appley Bridge d			12 09						12 43								13 09							
Parbold d			12 13						12 47								13 13							
Hoscar d																								
Burscough Bridge d			12 17						12 51								13 17							
New Lane d																								
Bescar Lane d																								
Meols Cop d									12 59															
Southport a			12 34						13 08								13 34							
Lostock d	11 36					11 56									12 36					12 56				
Horwich Parkway d	11 40					12 00									12 40					13 00				
Blackrod d						12 03														13 03				
Adlington (Lancashire) d						12 07														13 07				
Chorley d	11 47					12 12		12 17							12 47					13 12		13 17		
Leyland d	11 56													12 47	12 56									
Preston 8 a	12 03					12 24		12 28				12d55		12 56	13 03					13 25		13 27	13d30	
Lancaster 6 65 a	13c03							13c45							14c03							14c45		
d										13 13			13 45											14 18
Oxenholme Lake District 65 a	13e25														14e25									
Windermere 83 a	13e47														14e47									
Carnforth d										13a23		13a45	13 53										14a20	14 28
Silverdale d													13 59											14 34
Arnside d													14 03											14 38
Grange-over-Sands d													14 08											14 44
Kents Bank d													14 12											14 48
Cark d													14 16											14 52
Ulverston d													14 24											15 01
Dalton d													14 32											15 09
Roose d													14 39											15 15
Barrow-in-Furness a													14 48											15 23
Kirkham & Wesham 97 a	12 23					12 35									13 21					13 35				
Poulton-le-Fylde 97 a	12 23					12 43									13 23					13 43				
Layton 97 a						12 47														13 47				
Blackpool North 97 a	12 32					12 54								13 21	13 32					13 54				

For general notes see front of timetable
For details of catering facilities see Directory of Train Operators

A From Morecambe to Leeds (Table 36)
B To Clitheroe (Table 94)
C From Liverpool Lime Street (Table 90)
D To Carlisle via Whitehaven (Table 100)

b Change at Manchester Oxford Road
c By bus
e Change at Preston and Lancaster. By bus to Lancaster

Table 82

Saturdays from 29 March

Manchester → Bolton → Wigan, Kirkby, Southport, Preston, Barrow-in-Furness and Blackpool North

Network Diagram - see first page of Table 82

Station			NT	NT	NT	TP	NT	NT	NT	NT	NT		TP	NT	NT	NT	TP	TP	TP	NT	NT	NT	NT	NT	NT	NT
						1 ◇							1 ◇					1	1 ◇							
				A	B										A	B										
																	bus								bus	
						trolley							trolley													
Manchester Airport	85 ✈	d				12 47		13 07					13 27						13 47		14 07					
Heald Green	85	d						*12 56*					13 31								*13 56*					
Buxton	86	d								12 37													13 34			
Hazel Grove	86	d				*12 41*				13 10									*13 41*				14 10			
Stockport	84	d				*12 49*		*13b02*		13 19			*13b25*						*13 49*		*14b02*		14 19			
Manchester Piccadilly 10		d				13 11		13 23		13 30			13 45						14 11		14 23		14 30			
Manchester Oxford Road		d				13 15		13 26		13 33			13 48						14 15		14 26		14 33			
Deansgate		d								13 35													14 35			
Rochdale	95	d	12 33				*12 52*		13 03					13 33						*13 50*		14 03				
Manchester Victoria		d	12 57	13 00			13 18		13 29		13 41			13 57	14 00					14 18		14 29		14 41		
Salford Central		d	13 00	13 03			13 21		13 32		13 44			14 00	14 03					14 21		14 32		14 44		
Salford Crescent		a	13 03	13 06		13 21	13 24	13 32	13 35	13 40	13 47		13 53	14 03	14 06				14 21	14 24	14 32	14 35	14 40	14 47		
		d	13 04	13 07		13 21	13 24	13 32	13 35	13 40	13 47		13 54	14 04	14 07				14 21	14 24	14 32	14 35	14 40	14 47		
Swinton		d	13 10						13 42					14 10								14 42				
Moorside		d							13 44													14 44				
Walkden		d	13 15						13 48					14 15								14 48				
Atherton		d	13 20						13 53					14 20								14 53				
Hag Fold		d							13 56													14 56				
Daisy Hill		d	13 24						13 59					14 24								14 59				
Kearsley		d									13 55													14 55		
Farnworth		d									13 57													14 57		
Moses Gate		d					13 32													14 32						
Bolton		a		13 18		13 31	13 36	13 42		13 50	14 01		14 05		14 18				14 31	14 36	14 42		14 50	15 01		
		d				13 32	13 36	13 43		13 51	14 02		14 05						14 32	14 36	14 43		14 51	15 02		
Westhoughton		d						13 50			14 09										14 50			15 09		
Hindley		d	13 28						14 03		14 13			14 28								15 03		15 13		
Ince		d							14 06													15 06				
Wigan North Western		a																								
Wigan Wallgate		a	13 33				13 54	14 01	14 09		14 20			14 33						14 54	15 01	15 09		15 20		
		d	13 35					14 02	14 11					14 35							15 02	15 11				
Pemberton		d							14 15													15 15				
Orrell		d							14 19													15 19				
Upholland		d							14 22													15 22				
Rainford		d							14 26													15 26				
Kirkby		a							14 35													15 35				
Liverpool Central 10	103	a							*15 01*													*16 01*				
Gathurst		d	13 39											14 39												
Appley Bridge		d	13 43					14 09						14 43							15 09					
Parbold		d	13 47					14 13						14 47							15 13					
Hoscar		d	13 50																							
Burscough Bridge		d	13 53					14 17						14 51							15 17					
New Lane		d	13 55																							
Bescar Lane		d	13 59																							
Meols Cop		d	14 04											14 59												
Southport		a	14 13					14 34						15 08							15 34					
Lostock		d				13 36				13 56									14 36				14 56			
Horwich Parkway		d				13 40				14 00									14 40				15 00			
Blackrod		d								14 03													15 03			
Adlington (Lancashire)		d								14 07													15 07			
Chorley		d				13 47				14 12			14 17						14 47				15 12			
Leyland		d			13 47	13 56										14 47			14 56							
Preston 8		a			13 54	14 01				14 24			14 31			14 54	14d55		15 04				15 25		15d25	
Lancaster 6	65	a				*15c03*							*15c45*						*16c03*							
		d																15 54								16 14
Oxenholme Lake District	65	a				*15e25*													*16e25*							
Windermere	83	a				*15e47*													*16e47*							
Carnforth		d															15a45	16 01							16a15	16 24
Silverdale		d																16 07								16 29
Arnside		d																16 11								16 34
Grange-over-Sands		d																16 16								16 40
Kents Bank		d																16 20								16 43
Cark		d																16 24								16 47
Ulverston		d																16 32								16 56
Dalton		d																16 41								17 04
Roose		d																16 46								17 10
Barrow-in-Furness		a																16 56								17 17
Kirkham & Wesham	97	a				*14 21*				14 35									*15 21*				15 35			
Poulton-le-Fylde	97	a				14 23				14 43									15 23				15 43			
Layton	97	a								14 47													15 47			
Blackpool North	97	a			14 21	14 32				14 54						15 21			15 32				15 54			

For general notes see front of timetable
For details of catering facilities see Directory of Train Operators

- **A** To Clitheroe (Table 94)
- **B** From Liverpool Lime Street (Table 90)
- **b** Change at Manchester Oxford Road
- **c** By bus
- **e** Change at Preston and Lancaster. By bus to Lancaster

Table 82

from 29 March

Manchester → Bolton → Wigan, Kirkby, Southport, Preston, Barrow-in-Furness and Blackpool North

Network Diagram - see first page of Table 82

Station		TP		NT	NT	NT	NT	TP	NT	NT	NT	NT	TP	TP	NT	TP		NT	NT	NT	TP	TP	NT	TP	NT
		1 ◇			A	B	C	1 ◇					🚌	1		1 ◇		A			🚌	1	B	1 ◇	A
		trolley														trolley								trolley	
Manchester Airport	85 ✈ d	14 27						14 47		15 07						15 27								15 47	
Heald Green	85 d	14 31								*14 56*						15 31									
Buxton	86 d											14 37													
Hazel Grove	86 d							*14 41*				15 10												*15 41*	
Stockport	84 d	*14b25*						*14 49*		*15b02*		15 19				*15b24*								*15 49*	
Manchester Piccadilly 10	⇌ d	14 45						15 11		15 23		15 30				15 45								16 11	
Manchester Oxford Road	d	14 48						15 15		15 26		15 33				15 48								16 15	
Deansgate	⇌ d	14 50										15 35													
Rochdale	95 d			14 33					*14 52*		15 03							*15 23*	15 33						*15 54*
Manchester Victoria	⇌ d			14 57	15 00				15 18		15 29				15 41			15 50	15 57	16 10					16 23
Salford Central	d			15 00	15 03				15 21		15 32				15 44			15 53	16 00	16 13					16 26
Salford Crescent	a	14 53		15 03	15 06			15 21	15 24	15 32	15 35	15 40			15 47	15 53		15 56	16 03	16 16				16 21	16 29
	d	14 54		15 04	15 07			15 21	15 24	15 32	15 35	15 40			15 47	15 54		15 57	16 04	16 16				16 21	16 30
Swinton	d			15 10							15 42								16 10						
Moorside	d										15 44														
Walkden	d			15 15							15 48								16 15						
Atherton	d			15 20							15 53								16 20						
Hag Fold	d										15 56														
Daisy Hill	d			15 24							15 59								16 24						
Kearsley	d														15 55										
Farnworth	d														15 57										
Moses Gate	d								15 32											16 24					
Bolton	a	15 05			15 18			15 31	15 36	15 42		15 50			16 01	16 05		16 08		16 28				16 31	16 42
	d	15 05						15 32	15 36	15 43		15 51			16 02	16 05				16 28				16 32	
Westhoughton	d									15 50					16 09					16 36					
Hindley	d			15 28							16 03				16 13				16 28	16 40					
Ince	d										16 06									16 43					
Wigan North Western	a																								
Wigan Wallgate	a			15 33					15 54	16 01	16 09				16 20				16 33	16 50					
	d			15 35						16 02	16 11								16 35						
Pemberton	d										16 15														
Orrell	d										16 19														
Upholland	d										16 22														
Rainford	d										16 26														
Kirkby	a										16 35														
Liverpool Central 10	103 a										*17 01*														
Gathurst	d			15 39						16 07									16 39						
Appley Bridge	d			15 43						16 10									16 43						
Parbold	d			15 47						16 14									16 47						
Hoscar	d									16 17															
Burscough Bridge	d			15 51						16 20									16 51						
New Lane	d									16 23															
Bescar Lane	d									16 26															
Meols Cop	d			15 59						16 31									16 59						
Southport	a			16 08						16 41									17 08						
Lostock	d							15 36				15 56												16 36	
Horwich Parkway	d							15 40				16 00												16 40	
Blackrod	d											16 03													
Adlington (Lancashire)	d											16 07													
Chorley	d	15 17						15 47				16 12				16 17								16 47	
Leyland	d					15 47		15 56															16 47	16 56	
Preston 8	a	15 27				15 54		16 03				16 25	16d25			16 29					16d55		16 56	17 04	
Lancaster 6	65 a	*16c45*						*17c03*								*17c45*								*18c03*	
	d						16 53							17 17								17 45			
Oxenholme Lake District	65 a							*17e25*																*18e25*	
Windermere	83 a							*17e47*																*18e47*	
Carnforth	d						17a02						17a15	17 26							17a45	17 53			
Silverdale	d													17 32								17 59			
Arnside	d													17 36								18 03			
Grange-over-Sands	d													17 41								18 09			
Kents Bank	d													17 45								18 13			
Cark	d													17 49								18 17			
Ulverston	d													17 57								18 25			
Dalton	d													18 05								18 34			
Roose	d													18 11								18 39			
Barrow-in-Furness	a													18 18								18 50			
Kirkham & Wesham	97 a							*16 23*				16 35												17 15	
Poulton-le-Fylde	97 a							16 23				16 43												17 25	
Layton	97 a											16 47												17 28	
Blackpool North	97 a					16 21		16 32				16 54												17 34	

For general notes see front of timetable
For details of catering facilities see Directory of Train Operators

A To Clitheroe (Table 94)
B From Liverpool Lime Street (Table 90)
C From Morecambe to Skipton (Table 36)
b Change at Manchester Oxford Road
c By bus
e Change at Preston and Lancaster. By bus to Lancaster

from 29 March

Manchester → Bolton → Wigan, Kirkby, Southport, Preston, Barrow-in-Furness and Blackpool North

Network Diagram - see first page of Table 82

		NT	NT	NT	NT	TP 1◇	NT	NT	NT	NT	TP 1◇	TP	TP 1	NT	NT	NT	NT	NT	NT	NT	NT	NT	TP 1◇
							A	B		C						D	E	A			G	H	
Manchester Airport	85 ✈ d	16 07				16 27					16 47								17b04				17 32
Heald Green	85 d	15 56				16 31													16b56				
Buxton	86 d			15 34															16 36				
Hazel Grove	86 d			16 10							16 41								17 09				
Stockport	84 d	15 59		16 19		16c25			16 40		16 49				17 02				17 18				17 25
Manchester Piccadilly 10	d	16 23		16 30		16 44			16 52		17 11				17 15				17 30				17 50
Manchester Oxford Road	d	16 26		16 33		16 48			16 56		17 15				17 19				17 33				17 54
Deansgate	d	16 28		16 35					16 59						17 21				17 35				17 56
Rochdale	95 d		16 03					16 23						16 52			17 03						
Manchester Victoria	d		16 29		16 41			16 48		17 00				17 15		17 23	17 29			17 38	17 42		
Salford Central	d		16 32		16 44			16 51		17 03				17 18		17 26	17 32			17 41	17 45		
Salford Crescent	a	16 32	16 35	16 40	16 47			16 54	17 03	17 06				17 22	17 26	17 29	17 35		17 40	17 45	17 48		17 59
	d	16 32	16 35	16 40	16 47			16 54	17 03	17 07				17 23	17 26	17 29	17 36		17 40	17 46	17 49		18 00
Swinton	d		16 42					17 01						17 29									
Moorside	d		16 44					17 03						17 32									
Walkden	d		16 47					17 09						17 36						17 55			
Atherton	d		16 54					17 14						17 42						18 01			
Hag Fold	d		16 56					17 17						17 44									
Daisy Hill	d		16 59					17 20						17 47						18 05			
Kearsley	d				16 55												17 43				17 59		
Farnworth	d				16 57											17 38					18 01		
Moses Gate	d				16 59											17 40					18 03		
Bolton	a	16 43		16 51	17 02	17 05			17 13	17 18	17 29				17 36	17 44	17 49		17 53		18 07		18 10
	d	16 43		16 51	17 02	17 05			17 13		17 30				17 37	17 45			17 53		18 07		18 10
Westhoughton	d	16 50			17 10											17 52					18 15		
Hindley	d		17 03		17 17			17 24						17 52		17 56					18 19		
Ince	d		17 06					17 27						17 55		17 59							
Wigan North Western	a				17 26																		
Wigan Wallgate	a	17 01	17 10					17 36						17 58		18 06				18 14	18 26		
	d	17 02	17 11					17 38						17 59						18 14			
Pemberton	d		17 15											18 03									
Orrell	d		17 19											18 07									
Upholland	d		17 22											18 11									
Rainford	d		17 26											18 14									
Kirkby	a		17 35											18 23									
Liverpool Central 10	103 a		18 01											18 46									
Gathurst	d	17 06						17 42												18 19			
Appley Bridge	d	17 10						17 46												18 23			
Parbold	d	17 14						17 50												18 27			
Hoscar	d																						
Burscough Bridge	d	17 18						17 54												18 32			
New Lane	d																						
Bescar Lane	d																						
Meols Cop	d	17 26						18 02												18 40			
Southport	a	17 35						18 09												18 49			
Lostock	d			16 56					17 18						17 42				17 58				18 15
Horwich Parkway	d			17 00					17 22						17 46				18 02				
Blackrod	d			17 03					17 25						17 49				18 05				
Adlington (Lancashire)	d			17 07					17 29						17 53				18 09				
Chorley	d			17 12		17 17			17 34		17 42				17 57				18 14				18 24
Leyland	d			17 19			17 29		17 40						18 04			18 09	18 20				
Preston 8	a			17 27		17 27	17 40		17 50		17 53	17d55			18 12			18 17	18 29				18 34
Lancaster 6	65 a						18e45				19e03												19e45
	d												18 54									19 19	
Oxenholme Lake District	65 a						19e30																
Windermere	83 a																						
Carnforth	d											18a45	19 03									19a31	
Silverdale	d												19 09										
Arnside	d												19 14										
Grange-over-Sands	d												19 19										
Kents Bank	d												19 23										
Cark	d												19 28										
Ulverston	d												19 36										
Dalton	d												19 44										
Roose	d												19 50										
Barrow-in-Furness	a												19 59										
Kirkham & Wesham	97 a			17 38							18 10				18 22				18 39				
Poulton-le-Fylde	97 a			17 47		17 53					18 20				18 32				18 48				
Layton	97 a			17 51							18 24				18 36				18 52				
Blackpool North	97 a			17 58		18 03					18 30				18 43			18 48	18 59				

For general notes see front of timetable
For details of catering facilities see Directory of Train Operators

A From Liverpool Lime Street (Table 90)
B From Stalybridge (Table 39)
C To Clitheroe (Table 94)
D From Huddersfield (Table 39)
E To Blackburn (Table 94)
G Also stops at Clifton 1754
H From Morecambe to Leeds (Table 36)
b Change at Manchester Piccadilly
c Change at Manchester Oxford Road
e By bus

Table 82

Saturdays from 29 March

Manchester → Bolton → Wigan, Kirkby, Southport, Preston, Barrow-in-Furness and Blackpool North

Network Diagram - see first page of Table 82

		NT	NT	NT	NT	TP	NT	NT	NT	NT	NT	NT	NT	TP		NT	TP	TP	TP	NT	NT	NT	NT	TP	NT
						1 ◇								1 ◇				1	1 ◇					1 ◇	
			A	B			C	B								A	(bus)					B			A
Manchester Airport	85 ✈ d					17 47				18 10				18 27					18 47				19 12	19 27	
Heald Green	85 d					*17 22*				*17 56*				18 31									*18 56*	19 31	
Buxton	86 d										17 34										18 22				
Hazel Grove	86 d					*17 41*					18 10								*18 41*		18 55				
Stockport	84 d					*17 49*				*17 59*	18 19			*18 26*					*18 50*		19 05			*19 15*	
Manchester Piccadilly 10	🚇 d					18 11				18 26	18 31			18 45					19 11		19 20		19 33	19 44	
Manchester Oxford Road	d					18 15				18 29	18 36			18 47					19 15		19 23		19 37	19 48	
Deansgate	🚇 d					18 17				18 31	18 38			18 50					19 17		19 26			19 50	
Rochdale	95 d	17 33					*17 52*		18 03							*18 23*				*18 32*					*19 24*
Manchester Victoria	🚇 d	17 57	18 00				18 21		18 29				18 41			18 58				19 18					19 58
Salford Central	d	18 00	18 03				18 24		18 32				18 44			19 01				19 21					20 01
Salford Crescent	a	18 03	18 07			18 19	18 28		18 35	18 38	18 46		18 47	18 59		19 04			19 21	19 24	19 31		19 42	19 54	20 04
	d	18 04	18 07			18 21	18 28		18 35	18 39	18 46		18 47	19 01		19 05			19 21	19 25			19 42	19 54	20 05
Swinton	d	18 10							18 42											19 31					
Moorside	d	18 13							18 44											19 34					
Walkden	d	18 16							18 48											19 37					
Atherton	d	18 22							18 53											19 43					
Hag Fold	d	18 24							18 56			←								19 45					
Daisy Hill	d	18 27							18 59			18 59								19 48					
Kearsley	d								→				18 55												
Farnworth	d												18 57												
Moses Gate	d												19 00												
Bolton	a		18 19			18 32	18 44			18 49	18 56		19 04	19 11		19 17			19 31				19 52	20 04	20 16
	d					18 32				18 50	18 57		19 04	19 12					19 32				19 53	20 05	
Westhoughton	d									18 57			19 11										20 00		
Hindley	d	18 32										19 05	19 15							19 53			20 04		
Ince	d	18 35										19 08								19 56					
Wigan North Western 10	a																								
Wigan Wallgate	a	18 42								19 05		19 13	19 24							20 01			20 09		
	d									19 06													20 11		
Pemberton	d																								
Orrell	d																								
Upholland	d																								
Rainford	d																								
Kirkby	a																								
Liverpool Central 10	103 a																								
Gathurst	d									19 11													20 15		
Appley Bridge	d									19 14													20 19		
Parbold	d									19 18													20 23		
Hoscar	d									19 21															
Burscough Bridge	d									19 24													20 27		
New Lane	d									19 27															
Bescar Lane	d									19 30															
Meols Cop	d									19 35													20 35		
Southport	a									19 45													20 44		
Lostock	d					18 36					19 02								19 36						
Horwich Parkway	d					18 40					19 06								19 40						
Blackrod	d					18 43					19 09								19 43						
Adlington (Lancashire)	d										19 12								19 47						
Chorley	d					18 51					19 17			19 24					19 51					20 16	
Leyland	d			18 44		18 58		19 07			19 23								19 58			20 07			
Preston 8	a			18 52	*18b55*	19 05		19 17			19 31			19 36			19d55		20 04			20 17		20 29	
Lancaster 6	65 a					*20c03*								*20c45*										*21c35*	
	d				19 55													20 43							
Oxenholme Lake District	65 a					*20e30*								*21c30*										*22c30*	
Windermere	83 a					*20e52*																			
Carnforth	d				20 04												20a45	20 54							
Silverdale	d																	21 00							
Arnside	d				20 13													21 04							
Grange-over-Sands	d				20 19													21 10							
Kents Bank	d																	21 14							
Cark	d																	21 18							
Ulverston	d				20 32													21 26							
Dalton	d																	21 35							
Roose	d																	21 40							
Barrow-in-Furness	a				20 52													21 50							
Kirkham & Wesham	97 a					19 16					19 42								20 15						
Poulton-le-Fylde	97 a			19 10		19 26					19 51								20 26			*20 49*			
Layton	97 a										19 55								20 30						
Blackpool North	97 a			19 21		19 35					20 01								20 36			*20 56*			

For general notes see front of timetable
For details of catering facilities see Directory of Train Operators

A To Clitheroe (Table 94)
B From Liverpool Lime Street (Table 90)
C To Blackburn (Table 94)

b Departure time. By bus
c By bus
e Change at Preston and Lancaster. By bus to Lancaster

Table 82

Manchester → Bolton → Wigan, Kirkby, Southport, Preston, Barrow-in-Furness and Blackpool North

Saturdays from 29 March

Network Diagram - see first page of Table 82

		TP ■1	TP ■1 ◇	NT	NT	NT		NT A	NT	TP ■1 ◇	NT	NT	TP ■1 ◇	NT B	NT C	TP ■1 ◇	NT	NT	NT	NT	NT B	TP ■1 ◇	NT		
Manchester Airport 85 ✈	d		19 47		20 15	20b22				20 47		21 16	21 27			21 47		21b52		22b22		22 47			
Heald Green 85	d				19 57	20b07						20 56	21 08					21b56		22b12		22 51			
Buxton 86	d		18 55			19 55												21 38							
Hazel Grove 86	d		19 31			20 31												22 14							
Stockport 84	d		19 40		20 03	20 40						21 13	21 15			21 39		22 23		22 38		22 39			
Manchester Piccadilly ■10	d		20 11		20 32	20 52				21 11		21 35	21 43			22 11		22 35		22 49		23 11			
Manchester Oxford Road	d		20 15		20 35	20 54				21 15		21 38	21 46			22 15		22 38		22 52		23 15			
Deansgate	d		20 17		20 37	20 56				21 17		21 40	21 48			22 17		22 40		22 54		23 17			
Rochdale 95	d			19 52				20 02			20 52			21 02			21 52				22 02				
Manchester Victoria	d			20 21				20 58			21 21			21 58			22 34				23 08		23 18		
Salford Central	d			20 24				21 01			21 24			22 01			22 37				23 11		23 21		
Salford Crescent	a		20 20	20 28	20 41	21 00		21 04		21 20	21 27	21 44	21 51	22 04		22 20	22 40	22 44		23 00	23 13	23 21	23 25		
	d		20 21	20 28	20 41	21 00		21 05		21 21	21 28	21 44	21 54	22 05		22 21	22 41	22 44		23 00	23 14	23 21	23 25		
Swinton	d			20 34							21 34						22 47						23 32		
Moorside	d			20 37							21 37						22 50						23 34		
Walkden	d			20 40							21 40						22 53						23 38		
Atherton	d			20 46							21 46						22 59						23 43		
Hag Fold	d			20 48							21 48						23 01		←				23 46		
Daisy Hill	d			20 51							21 51						23 04		23 04				23 49		
Kearsley	d																↪			23 08					
Farnworth	d																			23 10					
Moses Gate	d																			23 12					
Bolton	a		20 31		20 51	21 16		21 17		21 31		21 54	22 05	22 16		22 31		22 54		23 16	23 27	23 31			
	d		20 32		20 52					21 32		21 55	22 05			22 32		22 55		23 16		23 32			
Westhoughton	d				20 59							22 02						23 02		23 24					
Hindley	d			20 56	21 03						21 56	22 06						23 06	23 13	23 28			23 53		
Ince	d			20 59							21 59								23 16	23 31			23 56		
Wigan North Western	a																								
Wigan Wallgate	a			21 05	21 10						22 05	22 11						23 11	23 21	23 36			00 03		
	d				21 12							22 13						23 13							
Pemberton	d																								
Orrell	d																								
Upholland	d																								
Rainford	d																								
Kirkby	a																								
Liverpool Central ■10 103	a																								
Gathurst	d				21 16							22 17						23 17							
Appley Bridge	d				21 20							22 21						23 21							
Parbold	d				21 24							22 25						23 25							
Hoscar	d				21 27																				
Burscough Bridge	d				21 30							22 29						23 29							
New Lane	d				21 32																				
Bescar Lane	d				21 36																				
Meols Cop	d				21 41							22 37						23 37							
Southport	a				21 49							22 47						23 46							
Lostock	d		20 36							21 36						22 36						23 36			
Horwich Parkway	d		20 40							21 40						22 40						23 40			
Blackrod	d		20 43							21 43						22 43						23 43			
Adlington (Lancashire)	d		20 47							21 47						22 47						23 47			
Chorley	d		20 51							21 51			22 17			22 51						23 51			
Leyland	d		20 58							21 58					22 54	22 58						23 58			
Preston ■8	a	20c45	21 04						21c35	22 05			22 32		23 02	23 05						00 06			
Lancaster ■6 65	a		22e20										23e30												
	d	21 43							22 30																
Oxenholme Lake District 65	a																								
Windermere 83	a																								
Carnforth	d	21 54							22 39																
Silverdale	d	22 00							22 45																
Arnside	d	22 04							22 49																
Grange-over-Sands	d	22 10							22 55																
Kents Bank	d	22 14							22 59																
Cark	d	22 18							23 03																
Ulverston	d	22 26							23 11																
Dalton	d	22 35							23 19																
Roose	d	22 40							23 25																
Barrow-in-Furness	a	22 50							23 35																
Kirkham & Wesham 97	a		21 15							22 15			23 00			23 15						00 15			
Poulton-le-Fylde 97	a		21 26							22 26						23 26						00 26			
Layton 97	a		21 30							22 30						23 30						00 30			
Blackpool North 97	a		21 36							22 36					23 28	23 36						00 38			

For general notes see front of timetable
For details of catering facilities see Directory of Train Operators

A To Clitheroe (Table 94)
B To Blackburn (Table 94)
C From Liverpool Lime Street (Table 90)
b Change at Manchester Piccadilly
c Departure time. By bus
e By bus

Table 82

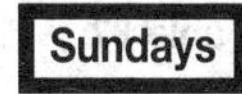

until 27 January

Manchester → Bolton → Wigan, Southport, Preston, Barrow-in-Furness and Blackpool North

Network Diagram - see first page of Table 82

		NT	TP	TP	TP	TP	TP	NT	NT	NT	NT	NT	TP	NT		NT	NT	TP	TP	NT	NT	NT	NT	TP	NT
						1 ◇	1 ◇						1 ◇					1 ◇	1 ◇					1 ◇	
		A						B	A			B					B			A			B		
			bus	bus	bus																				
Manchester Airport	85 d		01 10	03 10	05 45	*06 22*	07 36						08 47	*08b51*				09 47				*10b01*		10 47	*11b00*
Heald Green	85 d					*06 16*	*07 13*						*08 16*											*10 17*	
Buxton	86 d													08 25							09 25				10 25
Hazel Grove	86 d													08 59							09 59				10 59
Alderley Edge	84 d															09 10						10 10			
Stockport	84 d													09 11		09 29					10 11	10 29			11 11
Manchester Piccadilly 10	d		01 30	03 30	06 05	07 00	07 51						09 03	09 25		09 45		10 03			10 25	10 45		11 03	11 25
Manchester Oxford Road	d					07 03	07 54						09 06	09 29		09 48		10 06			10 29	10 48		11 06	11 29
Deansgate	d					07 05	07 56						09 08	09 31		09 50		10 08			10 31	10 50		11 08	11 31
Rochdale	95 d																						*10 18*		
Manchester Victoria	d							08 00		08 28	08 49	09 00					10 00						11 00		
Salford Crescent	a						08 00			08 33	08 54	09 04	09 11	09 34		09 54	10 04	10 11			10 34	10 54	11 04	11 11	11 35
	d						08 00			08 33	08 54	09 05	09 12	09 35		09 54	10 05	10 12			10 35	10 54	11 05	11 12	11 35
Bolton	a		01s55	03s55	06s30	07 20	08 10	08 13		08 43	09 04	09 15	09 22	09 45		10 04	10 15	10 22			10 45	11 04	11 15	11 22	11 45
	d						08 10			08 44	09 05		09 22	09 45		10 05		10 22			10 45	11 05		11 22	11 45
Westhoughton	d										09 12					10 12						11 12			
Hindley	d										09 16					10 16						11 16			
Wigan North Western	a																								
Wigan Wallgate	a										09 21					10 21						11 21			
	d										09 23					10 23						11 23			
Gathurst	d										09 27					10 27						11 27			
Appley Bridge	d										09 31					10 31						11 31			
Parbold	d										09 35					10 35						11 35			
Burscough Bridge	d										09 39					10 39						11 39			
Southport	a										09 56					10 56						11 56			
Lostock	d									08 49				09 50							10 50				11 50
Horwich Parkway	d									08 53				09 54							10 54				11 54
Blackrod	d									08 56				09 57							10 57				11 57
Adlington (Lancashire)	d									09 00				10 01							11 01				12 01
Chorley	d						08 22			09 04			09 34	10 06				10 34			11 06			11 34	12 06
Leyland	d	00 06			06s55		08 30		08 58	09 11				10 12						10 58	11 12				12 12
Preston 8	a	00 15	02s30	04s30	07s10		08 35		09 05	09 18			09 47	10 20				10 46	11d00	11 05	11 20			11 48	12 20
Lancaster 6	65 a																		11 15		*11 53*			*12 14*	*12 55*
	d																		11 16						
Oxenholme Lake District	65 a																				*12 07*			*12 31*	
Windermere	83 a																							*12 52*	
Carnforth	d																		11 24						
Silverdale	d																		11 30						
Arnside	d																		11 34						
Grange-over-Sands	d																		11 40						
Kents Bank	d																		11 43						
Cark	d																		11 48						
Ulverston	d																		11 56						
Dalton	d																		12 04						
Roose	d																		12 09						
Barrow-in-Furness	a																		12 18						
Kirkham & Wesham	97 a				07s30		08 57						09 57					10 57						11 57	
Poulton-le-Fylde	97 a				07s50		09 07		09 23	09 36			10 07	10 38				11 07		11 23	11 38			12 07	12 38
Blackpool North	97 a		03 10	05 10	08 05		09 16		09 34	09 45			10 16	10 47				11 16		11 34	11 47			12 16	12 47

For general notes see front of timetable
For details of catering facilities see Directory of Train Operators

A From Liverpool Lime Street (Table 90)
B To Clitheroe (Table 94)
b Change at Manchester Piccadilly

Table 82

Sundays

until 27 January

Manchester → Bolton → Wigan, Southport, Preston, Barrow-in-Furness and Blackpool North

Network Diagram - see first page of Table 82

	TP	NT	NT	TP	NT		NT	TP	NT	NT	TP	NT	TP	NT	NT	TP	NT	NT	TP		NT	NT	TP	NT
	1 ◇			1 ◇				1 ◇			1 ◇		1 ◇			1 ◇			1 ◇				1 ◇	
	A		B		C					B			A		B		C					B		
Manchester Airport 85 d	11 27			11 47					12b13		12 46		13 27	13b22		13 47			14 27				14 47	
Heald Green 85 d		11b17							12b16				13 17								14b18			
Buxton 86 d							11 20					12 20						13 25						14 25
Hazel Grove 86 d							11 56					12 54						13 59						14 59
Alderley Edge 84 d		11 10							12 10					13 10							14 10			
Stockport 84 d		11 29					12 08		12 29			13 08	13c24	13 29				14 11	14 22		14 27			15 11
Manchester Piccadilly 10 d	11 42	11 46		12 03			12 25		12 45		13 02	13 24	13 42	13 49		14 03		14 25	14 42		14 49		15 03	15 25
Manchester Oxford Road d	11 45	11 49		12 06			12 29		12 48		13 06	13 28	13 45	13 52		14 06		14 29	14 45		14 52		15 06	15 29
Deansgate d		11 51		12 08			12 31		12 50		13 08	13 30		13 54		14 08		14 31			14 54		15 08	15 31
Rochdale 95 d			11 18							12 18					13 20							14 18		
Manchester Victoria d			12 00							13 00					14 00							15 00		
Salford Crescent a		11 55	12 04	12 11			12 34		12 54	13 04	13 11	13 33		13 58	14 04	14 11		14 34			14 58	15 04	15 11	15 34
d		11 55	12 05	12 12			12 35		12 54	13 05	13 12	13 34		13 58	14 05	14 12		14 35			14 58	15 05	15 12	15 35
Bolton a	11 59	12 05	12 15	12 22			12 45		13 04	13 15	13 22	13 44	13 59	14 08	14 15	14 22		14 45	14 59		15 08	15 15	15 22	15 45
d	12 00	12 06		12 22			12 45		13 05		13 22	13 44	14 00	14 09		14 22		14 45	15 00		15 09		15 22	15 45
Westhoughton d		12 13							13 12					14 16							15 16			
Hindley d		12 17							13 16					14 22							15 23			
Wigan North Western a																								
Wigan Wallgate a		12 22							13 21					14 27							15 28			
d		12 24							13 23					14 29							15 30			
Gathurst d		12 28							13 27					14 33							15 34			
Appley Bridge d		12 32							13 31					14 37							15 38			
Parbold d		12 36							13 35					14 41							15 42			
Burscough Bridge d		12 40							13 39					14 45							15 46			
Southport a		12 56							13 56					15 02							16 03			
Lostock d							12 50					13 49						14 50						15 50
Horwich Parkway d							12 54					13 53						14 54						15 54
Blackrod d							12 57					13 56						14 57						15 57
Adlington (Lancashire) d							13 01					14 00						15 01						16 01
Chorley d				12 34			13 06				13 34	14 05				14 34		15 06					15 34	16 06
Leyland d					12 58		13 12					14 13					14 58	15 12						16 12
Preston 8 a	12 20			12 48	13 06		13 20	13d25			13 48	14 19	14 23			14 48	15 07	15 20	15 20				15 46	16 20
Lancaster 6 65 a	12 40			*13 20*			*13 54*	13 40				*14 53*	14 40			*15 21*		*15 55*	15 40				*16 20*	*16 53*
d	12 41							13 41					14 41						15 41					
Oxenholme Lake District 65 a	12 55			*13 34*			*14 09*					*15 08*	14 55			*15 34*							*16 33*	*17 08*
Windermere 83 a				*13e58*			*14e55*									*15e58*							*16e55*	
Carnforth d								13 49											15 49					
Silverdale d								13 55											15 55					
Arnside d								13 59											15 59					
Grange-over-Sands d								14 05											16 05					
Kents Bank d								14 08											16 08					
Cark d								14 13											16 13					
Ulverston d								14 21											16 21					
Dalton d								14 29											16 29					
Roose d								14 34											16 34					
Barrow-in-Furness a								14 44											16 44					
Kirkham & Wesham 97 a				12 57							13 57					14 57							15 57	
Poulton-le-Fylde 97 a				13 07	13 23		13 38				14 07	14 37				15 07	15 23	15 38					16 07	16 38
Blackpool North 97 a				13 16	13 34		13 47				14 16	14 47				15 16	15 34	15 47					16 16	16 47

For general notes see front of timetable
For details of catering facilities see Directory of Train Operators

A To Edinburgh (Table 65)
B To Clitheroe (Table 94)
C From Liverpool Lime Street (Table 90)
b Change at Manchester Piccadilly
c Change at Manchester Oxford Road
e Change at Preston and Oxenholme Lake District

Table 82

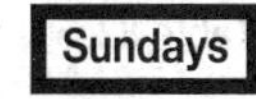

until 27 January

Manchester → Bolton → Wigan, Southport, Preston, Barrow-in-Furness and Blackpool North

Network Diagram - see first page of Table 82

		TP 1 ◇ A	NT	NT	NT B	TP 1 ◇	NT C	NT	TP 1 ◇	NT	NT D	NT B		TP 1 ◇	NT C	NT	TP 1 ◇ E	NT	NT B	TP 1 ◇	NT C	NT	TP 1 ◇	NT	NT D
Manchester Airport	85 d	15 27				15 47		16b01	16 27					16 47		17b01	17 27			17 47		18b01	18 27		
Heald Green	85 d			15b17						16b17										17 17					
Buxton	86 d							15 25								16 25						17 25			
Hazel Grove	86 d							15 59								16 59						17 59			
Alderley Edge	84 d			15 10						16 10								17 10						18 10	
Stockport	84 d	15c22		15 28				16 11	16 22	16 29						17 11	17c22	17 29				18 10	18c24	18 29	
Manchester Piccadilly 10	d	15 42		15 46		16 03		16 25	16 42	16 46				17 03		17 25	17 42	17 46		18 03		18 25	18 42	18 45	
Manchester Oxford Road	d	15 45		15 49		16 06		16 28	16 45	16 49				17 06		17 29	17 45	17 49		18 06		18 28	18 45	18 48	
Deansgate	d			15 51		16 08		16 30		16 51				17 08		17 31		17 51		18 08		18 30		18 50	
Rochdale	95 d				15 18							16 18							17 18						
Manchester Victoria	d				16 00							17 00							18 00						
Salford Crescent	a			15 55	16 04	16 11		16 34		16 55		17 04		17 12		17 34		17 55	18 04	18 11		18 34		18 54	
	d			15 55	16 05	16 12		16 34		16 55		17 05		17 12		17 35		17 55	18 05	18 12		18 34		18 54	
Bolton	a	15 59		16 05	16 15	16 22		16 45	16 59	17 05		17 15		17 22		17 45	17 59	18 05	18 15	18 22		18 45	18 59	19 04	
	d	16 00		16 06		16 22		16 45	17 00	17 06				17 22		17 45	18 00	18 06		18 22		18 45	19 00	19 05	
Westhoughton	d			16 13						17 13								18 13						19 12	
Hindley	d			16 17						17 17								18 17						19 16	
Wigan North Western	a																								
Wigan Wallgate	a			16 22						17 22								18 22						19 21	
	d			16 24						17 24								18 24						19 23	
Gathurst	d			16 28						17 28								18 28						19 27	
Appley Bridge	d			16 32						17 32								18 32						19 31	
Parbold	d			16 36						17 36								18 36						19 35	
Burscough Bridge	d			16 40						17 40								18 40						19 39	
Southport	a			16 57						17 57								18 57						19 57	
Lostock	d							16 50								17 50						18 50			
Horwich Parkway	d							16 54								17 54						18 54			
Blackrod	d							16 57								17 57						18 57			
Adlington (Lancashire)	d							17 01								18 01						19 01			
Chorley	d					16 34		17 05						17 34		18 06				18 34		19 05			
Leyland	d						16 57	17 12							17 58	18 12					18 58	19 12			
Preston 8	a	16 20				16 46	17 04	17 20	17 22					17 46	18 05	18 20	18 23			18 47	19 05	19 19	19 21		
Lancaster 6	65 a	16 40				17 21		17 53	17 40					18 20		18 53	18 40			19 20		19 56	19 40		
	d	16 41	16 45						17 41		18 04						18 41						19 41		20 15
Oxenholme Lake District	65 a	16 55				17 34								18 34		19 08	18 55			19 34			20 10		
Windermere	83 a					17e58								18e58						19e58					
Carnforth	d		16 55						17 49		18a12												19 49		20a24
Silverdale	d		17 01						17 55														19 55		
Arnside	d		17 07						17 59														19 59		
Grange-over-Sands	d		17 13						18 05														20 05		
Kents Bank	d		17 16						18 08														20 08		
Cark	d		17 21						18 13														20 13		
Ulverston	d		17 29						18 21														20 21		
Dalton	d		17 37						18 29														20 29		
Roose	d		17 43						18 34														20 34		
Barrow-in-Furness	a		17 51						18 44														20 44		
Kirkham & Wesham	97 a					16 57								17 57						18 57					
Poulton-le-Fylde	97 a					17 07	17 23	17 37						18 07	18 23	18 38	18f55			19 07	19 23	19 37	19f56		
Blackpool North	97 a					17 16	17 35	17 47						18 16	18 34	18 47	19f05			19 16	19 32	19 47	20f03		

For general notes see front of timetable
For details of catering facilities see Directory of Train Operators

- **A** To Edinburgh (Table 65)
- **B** To Clitheroe (Table 94)
- **C** From Liverpool Lime Street (Table 90)
- **D** From Morecambe to Leeds (Table 36)
- **E** To Glasgow Central (Table 65)
- **b** Change at Manchester Piccadilly
- **c** Change at Manchester Oxford Road
- **e** Change at Preston and Oxenholme Lake District
- **f** Change at Preston

Table 82

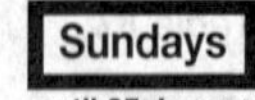

until 27 January

Manchester → Bolton → Wigan, Southport, Preston, Barrow-in-Furness and Blackpool North

Network Diagram - see first page of Table 82

		NT	TP 1◇	NT	NT	NT	TP 1◇	NT	NT	TP 1◇	NT	NT	TP 1◇	NT	NT	NT	TP 1◇	NT	NT	NT	NT	TP 1◇
		A				A		B				A				C					B	
Manchester Airport	85 ⇌ d		18 47	*19b01*	*19b05*		19 47			20 27			20 47		*21b05*		21 47		*22b01*			22 47
Heald Green	85 d		*18 17*				*19 17*						*20 17*				*21 17*					*22 17*
Buxton	86 d			18 25					19 25					20 25					*21c25*			
Hazel Grove	86 d			18 59					19 59					20 59					*21c59*			
Alderley Edge	84 d				19 10						20 10				21 10				22 10			
Stockport	84 d			19 10	19 29				20 10	*20 15*	20 29			21 10	21 29				22 29			
Manchester Piccadilly 10	⇌ d		19 03	19 26	19 45		20 03		20 25	20 42	20 46		21 03	21 25	21 45		22 03		22 45			23 03
Manchester Oxford Road	d		19 06	19 29	19 48		20 06		20 28	20 45	20 49		21 06	21 28	21 48		22 06		22 48			23 06
Deansgate	⇌ d		19 08	19 31	19 50		20 08		20 30		20 51		21 08	21 30	21 50		22 08		22 50			23 08
Rochdale	95 d	*18 18*				*19 18*						*20 18*				*21 18*				*21 23*		
Manchester Victoria	⇌ d	19 00				20 00						21 00				22 00				23 00		
Salford Crescent	a	19 04	19 11	19 34	19 54	20 04	20 11		20 34		20 55	21 04	21 11	21 34	21 54	22 04	22 12		22 54	23 04		23 11
	d	19 05	19 12	19 35	19 54	20 05	20 12		20 34		20 55	21 05	21 12	21 34	21 54	22 05	22 12		22 54			23 12
Bolton	a	19 15	19 22	19 45	20 04	20 15	20 22		20 45	20 59	21 05	21 15	21 22	21 45	22 04	22 15	22 22		23 04			23 22
	d		19 22	19 45	20 05		20 22		20 45	21 00	21 06		21 22	21 45	22 05		22 22		23 05			23 22
Westhoughton	d				20 12						21 13				22 12				23 12			
Hindley	d				20 16						21 17				22 16				23 16			
Wigan North Western	a																					
Wigan Wallgate	a				20 21						21 22				22 25				23 25			
	d				20 23						21 24											
Gathurst	d				20 27						21 28											
Appley Bridge	d				20 31						21 32											
Parbold	d				20 35						21 36											
Burscough Bridge	d				20 39						21 40											
Southport	a				20 56						21 57											
Lostock	d			19 50					20 50					21 50								
Horwich Parkway	d			19 54					20 54					21 54								
Blackrod	d			19 57					20 57					21 57								
Adlington (Lancashire)	d			20 01					21 01					22 01								
Chorley	d		19 34	20 06			20 34		21 05				21 34	22 05			22 34					23 34
Leyland	d			20 16				20 58	21 12					22 12							23 08	
Preston 8	a		19 48	20 20			20 47	21 05	21 20	21 21			21 48	22 20			22 45				23 15	23 46
Lancaster 6	65 a		*20 31*	*20 54*			*21 22*			21 40			*22 24*									
	d									21 41								23 00				
Oxenholme Lake District	65 a		*20e57*	*21 09*			*21 35*						*22 38*									
Windermere	83 a		*21e16*																			
Carnforth	d									21 49								23 09				
Silverdale	d									21 55								23 15				
Arnside	d									21 59								23 19				
Grange-over-Sands	d									22 05								23 25				
Kents Bank	d									22 08								23 29				
Cark	d									22 13								23 33				
Ulverston	d									22 21								23 41				
Dalton	d									22 29								23 49				
Roose	d									22 34								23 55				
Barrow-in-Furness	a									22 44								00 13				
Kirkham & Wesham	97 a		19 57				20 57						21 58				22 57					23 57
Poulton-le-Fylde	97 a		20 07	20 38			21 07	21 23	21 37				22 07	22 37			23 07				23 34	00 07
Blackpool North	97 a		20 16	20 47			21 16	21 34	21 47				22 16	22 47			23 16				23 43	00 16

For general notes see front of timetable
For details of catering facilities see Directory of Train Operators

- **A** To Clitheroe (Table 94)
- **B** From Liverpool Lime Street (Table 90)
- **C** To Blackburn (Table 94)
- **b** Change at Manchester Piccadilly
- **c** Change at Stockport
- **e** Change at Preston and Lancaster

Table 82

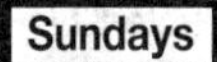

Sundays

Manchester → Bolton → Wigan, Southport, Preston, Barrow-in-Furness and Blackpool North

3 February to 23 March

Network Diagram - see first page of Table 82

	NT	TP	TP	TP	TP	TP	NT	NT	NT	NT	NT	TP	NT	NT	NT	TP	TP	NT	NT	NT	NT	TP	NT	TP
					1◇	1◇						1◇				1◇	1◇					1◇		1◇
	A						B	A			B				B			A			B			C
		bus	bus	bus																				trolley
Manchester Airport 85 d		01 10	03 10	05 45	*06b22*	07 36						08 47	*08c51*			09 47				*10c01*		10 47	*11c00*	11 27
Heald Green 85 d					*06 16*	*07 13*						*08 16*										*10 17*		
Buxton 86 d													08 25						09 25				10 25	
Hazel Grove 86 d													08 59						09 59				10 59	
Alderley Edge 84 d														09 10						10 10				
Stockport 84 d												*08 38*	09 11	09 29					10 11	10 29			11 11	
Manchester Piccadilly 10 d		01 30	03 30	06 05	07 00	07 51						09 03	09 25	09 45		10 03			10 25	10 45		11 03	11 25	11 42
Manchester Oxford Road d					07 03	07 54						09 06	09 29	09 48		10 06			10 29	10 48		11 06	11 29	11 45
Deansgate d					07 05	07 56						09 08	09 31	09 50		10 08			10 31	10 50		11 08	11 31	
Rochdale 95 d																					*10 18*			
Manchester Victoria d							08 00		08 28	08 49	09 00				10 00						11 00			
Salford Crescent a						08 00			08 33	08 54	09 04	09 11	09 34	09 54	10 04	10 11			10 34	10 54	11 04	11 11	11 35	
d						08 00			08 33	08 54	09 05	09 12	09 35	09 54	10 05	10 12			10 35	10 54	11 05	11 12	11 35	
Bolton a		01s55	03s55	06s30	07 20	08 10	08 13		08 43	09 04	09 15	09 22	09 45	10 04	10 15	10 22			10 45	11 04	11 15	11 22	11 45	11 59
d						08 10			08 44	09 05		09 22	09 45	10 05		10 22			10 45	11 05		11 22	11 45	12 00
Westhoughton d										09 12				10 12						11 12				
Hindley d										09 16				10 16						11 16				
Wigan North Western a																								
Wigan Wallgate a										09 21				10 21						11 21				
d										09 23				10 23						11 23				
Gathurst d										09 27				10 27						11 27				
Appley Bridge d										09 31				10 31						11 31				
Parbold d										09 35				10 35						11 35				
Burscough Bridge d										09 39				10 39						11 39				
Southport a										09 56				10 56						11 56				
Lostock d									08 49				09 50						10 50				11 50	
Horwich Parkway d									08 53				09 54						10 54				11 54	
Blackrod d									08 56				09 57						10 57				11 57	
Adlington (Lancashire) d									09 00				10 01						11 01				12 01	
Chorley d						08 22			09 04			09 34	10 06			10 34			11 06			11 34	12 06	
Leyland d	00 06			06s55		08 30		08 58	09 11				10 12					10 58	11 12				12 12	
Preston 8 a	00 15	02s30	04s30	07s10		08 36		09 05	09 18			09 47	10 22			10 46	11d00	11 05	11 21			11 48	→	12 20
Lancaster 6 65 a																	11 15		*11 53*			*12 14*		12 40
d																	11 16							12 41
Oxenholme Lake District 65 a																			*12 07*			*12 31*		12 55
Windermere 83 a																						*12 52*		
Carnforth d																	11 24							
Silverdale d																	11 30							
Arnside d																	11 34							
Grange-over-Sands d																	11 40							
Kents Bank d																	11 43							
Cark d																	11 48							
Ulverston d																	11 56							
Dalton d																	12 04							
Roose d																	12 09							
Barrow-in-Furness a																	12 18							
Kirkham & Wesham 97 a				07s30		*09e05*						*10f19*				*11b25*			*11g51*			*12b25*		
Poulton-le-Fylde 97 a				07s50		*09b45*			*10b15*			*10b45*	*11b15*			*11b45*		*12b05*	*12b15*			*12b45*		
Blackpool North 97 a		03 10	05 10	08 05				*09b55*	*10b30*			*11b00*	*11b30*					*11b55*	*12b30*			*13b00*		

For general notes see front of timetable
For details of catering facilities see Directory of Train Operators

A From Liverpool Lime Street (Table 90)
B To Clitheroe (Table 94)
C To Carlisle (Table 65)
b By bus
c Change at Manchester Piccadilly
e Until 24 February arr. 0925, by bus
f Until 24 February arr. 1025, by bus
g From 2 March only

Manchester → Bolton → Wigan, Southport, Preston, Barrow-in-Furness and Blackpool North

3 February to 23 March

Network Diagram - see first page of Table 82

	NT		NT	NT	NT	TP	NT	NT	TP	NT	NT	TP	NT	TP	NT	NT	NT	TP	NT	NT	TP	NT	NT	TP
						1 ◇			1 ◇			1 ◇		1 ◇				1 ◇			1 ◇			1 ◇
	A				B		C				B			D	A		B		C				B	
Manchester Airport 85 d				11b14		11 47				12b13		12 46	12b52	13 27		13b22		13 47		13b52	14 27			14 47
Heald Green 85 d				11b17						12b16				13 17								14b18		
Buxton 86 d								11 20					12 20							13 25				
Hazel Grove 86 d								11 56					12 54							13 59				
Alderley Edge 84 d				11 10						12 10						13 10						14 10		
Stockport 84 d				11 29				12 08		12 29		12 29	13 08	13c24		13 29				14 11	14 22	14 27		
Manchester Piccadilly 10 d				11 46		12 03		12 25		12 45		13 02	13 24	13 42		13 49		14 03		14 25	14 42	14 49		15 03
Manchester Oxford Road d				11 49		12 06		12 29		12 48		13 06	13 28	13 45		13 52		14 06		14 29	14 45	14 52		15 06
Deansgate d				11 51		12 08		12 31		12 50		13 08	13 30			13 54		14 08		14 31		14 54		15 08
Rochdale 95 d					11 18						12 18						13 20						14 18	
Manchester Victoria d					12 00						13 00						14 00						15 00	
Salford Crescent a				11 55	12 04	12 11		12 34		12 54	13 04	13 11	13 33			13 58	14 04	14 11		14 34		14 58	15 04	15 11
d				11 55	12 05	12 12		12 35		12 54	13 05	13 12	13 34			13 58	14 05	14 12		14 35		14 58	15 05	15 12
Bolton a				12 05	12 15	12 22		12 45		13 04	13 15	13 22	13 44	13 59		14 08	14 15	14 22		14 45	14 59	15 08	15 15	15 22
d				12 06		12 22		12 45		13 05		13 22	13 44	14 00		14 09		14 22		14 45	15 00	15 09		15 22
Westhoughton d				12 13						13 12						14 16						15 16		
Hindley d				12 17						13 16						14 22						15 23		
Wigan North Western a																								
Wigan Wallgate a				12 22						13 21						14 27						15 28		
d				12 24						13 23						14 29						15 30		
Gathurst d				12 28						13 27						14 33						15 34		
Appley Bridge d				12 32						13 31						14 37						15 38		
Parbold d				12 36						13 35						14 41						15 42		
Burscough Bridge d				12 40						13 39						14 45						15 46		
Southport a				12 56						13 56						15 02						16 03		
Lostock d								12 50					13 49							14 50				
Horwich Parkway d								12 54					13 53							14 54				
Blackrod d								12 57					13 56							14 57				
Adlington (Lancashire) d								13 01					14 00							15 01				
Chorley d			←			12 34		13 06				13 34	14 05					14 34		15 06				15 34
Leyland d			12 12				12 58	13 12					14 13						14 58	15 12				
Preston 8 a			12 24			12 48	13 06	13 20	13d25			13 49	14 19	14 23				14 49	15 07	15 20	15 20			15 46
Lancaster 6 65 a			12 55			13 20		13 54	13 40				14 53	14 40				15 21		15 55	15 40			16 20
d	12 45								13 41					14 41	14 47						15 41			
Oxenholme Lake District 65 a						13 34		14 09					15 08	14 55				15 34						16 33
Windermere 83 a						13e58		14e55										15e58						16e55
Carnforth d	12a54								13 49						14a55						15 49			
Silverdale d									13 55												15 55			
Arnside d									13 59												15 59			
Grange-over-Sands d									14 05												16 05			
Kents Bank d									14 08												16 08			
Cark d									14 13												16 13			
Ulverston d									14 21												16 21			
Dalton d									14 29												16 29			
Roose d									14 34												16 34			
Barrow-in-Furness a									14 44												16 44			
Kirkham & Wesham 97 a			12f51			13g25		13f51				14g25		14h51				15g25			15h51			16g25
Poulton-le-Fylde 97 a			13g15			13g45	14g05	14g15				14g45		15j15				15g45	16g05		16j15			16g45
Blackpool North 97 a			13g30				13g55	14g30				15g00		15j30					15g55		16j30			17g00

For general notes see front of timetable
For details of catering facilities see Directory of Train Operators

A 23 March. From Morecambe to Leeds (Table 36)
B To Clitheroe (Table 94)
C From Liverpool Lime Street (Table 90)
D To Carlisle (Table 65)
b Change at Manchester Piccadilly
c Change at Manchester Oxford Road
e Change at Preston and Oxenholme Lake District
f From 2 March only
g By bus
h From 2 March only. Change at Preston
j Change at Preston. By bus

Table 82

Sundays

3 February to 23 March

Manchester → Bolton → Wigan, Southport, Preston, Barrow-in-Furness and Blackpool North

Network Diagram - see first page of Table 82

		NT	TP 1 ◇ A	NT		NT	NT B	TP 1 ◇	NT C	NT	TP 1 ◇	NT	NT D	NT B	TP 1 ◇	NT C	NT	TP 1 ◇ A	NT	NT B	TP 1 ◇	NT C	NT	TP 1 ◇	NT
Manchester Airport	85 d	14b52	15 27					15 47		16b01	16 27				16 47		17b01	17 27			17 47		18b01	18 27	
Heald Green	85 d					15b17						16b17									17 17				
Buxton	86 d	14 25								15 25							16 25						17 25		
Hazel Grove	86 d	14 59								15 59							16 59						17 59		
Alderley Edge	84 d					15 10						16 10							17 10						18 10
Stockport	84 d	15 11	15c22			15 28				16 11	16 22	16 29					17 11	17c22	17 29				18 10	18c24	18 29
Manchester Piccadilly 10	d	15 25	15 42			15 46		16 03		16 25	16 42	16 46			17 03		17 25	17 42	17 46		18 03		18 25	18 42	18 45
Manchester Oxford Road	d	15 29	15 45			15 49		16 06		16 28	16 45	16 49			17 06		17 29	17 45	17 49		18 06		18 28	18 45	18 48
Deansgate	d	15 31				15 51		16 08		16 30		16 51			17 08		17 31		17 51		18 08		18 30		18 50
Rochdale	95 d						15 18							16 18						17 18					
Manchester Victoria	d						16 00							17 00						18 00					
Salford Crescent	a	15 34				15 55	16 04	16 11		16 34		16 55		17 04	17 12		17 34		17 55	18 04	18 11		18 34		18 54
	d	15 35				15 55	16 05	16 12		16 34		16 55		17 05	17 12		17 35		17 55	18 05	18 12		18 34		18 54
Bolton	a	15 45	15 59			16 05	16 15	16 22		16 45	16 59	17 05		17 15	17 22		17 45	17 59	18 05	18 15	18 22		18 45	18 59	19 04
	d	15 45	16 00			16 06		16 22		16 45	17 00	17 06			17 22		17 45	18 00	18 06		18 22		18 45	19 00	19 05
Westhoughton	d					16 13						17 13							18 13						19 12
Hindley	d					16 17						17 17							18 17						19 16
Wigan North Western	a																								
Wigan Wallgate	a					16 22						17 22							18 22						19 21
	d					16 24						17 24							18 24						19 23
Gathurst	d					16 28						17 28							18 28						19 27
Appley Bridge	d					16 32						17 32							18 32						19 31
Parbold	d					16 36						17 36							18 36						19 35
Burscough Bridge	d					16 40						17 40							18 40						19 39
Southport	a					16 57						17 57							18 57						19 57
Lostock	d	15 50								16 50							17 50						18 50		
Horwich Parkway	d	15 54								16 54							17 54						18 54		
Blackrod	d	15 57								16 57							17 57						18 57		
Adlington (Lancashire)	d	16 01								17 01							18 01						19 01		
Chorley	d	16 06						16 34		17 05					17 34		18 06				18 34		19 05		
Leyland	d	16 12							16 57	17 12						17 58	18 12					18 58	19 12		
Preston 8	a	16 20	16 20					16 46	17 04	17 20	17 22				17 46	18 05	18 20	18 23			18 47	19 05	19 20	19 21	
Lancaster 6	65 a	16 53	16 40							17 53	17 40				18 20		18 53	18 40			19 20			19 40	
	d		16 41	16 45							17 41		18 04					18 41						19 41	
Oxenholme Lake District	65 a	17 08	16 55												18 34	18 55	19 08	18 55			19 34				
Windermere	83 a		17 58												18e58						19e58				
Carnforth	d			16 55							17 49		18a12											19 49	
Silverdale	d			17 01							17 55													19 55	
Arnside	d			17 07							17 59													19 59	
Grange-over-Sands	d			17 13							18 05													20 05	
Kents Bank	d			17 16							18 08													20 08	
Cark	d			17 21							18 13													20 13	
Ulverston	d			17 29							18 21													20 21	
Dalton	d			17 37							18 29													20 29	
Roose	d			17 43							18 34													20 34	
Barrow-in-Furness	a			17 51							18 44													20 44	
Kirkham & Wesham	97 a		16f51					17g25			17f51				18g25			18f51			19g25			19f51	
Poulton-le-Fylde	97 a		17h15					17g45	18g05		18h15				18g45	19g05		19h15			19g45	20g05		20h15	
Blackpool North	97 a		17h30						17g55		18h30					18g55		19h30				19g55		20h30	

For general notes see front of timetable
For details of catering facilities see Directory of Train Operators

A To Carlisle (Table 65)

B To Clitheroe (Table 94)

C From Liverpool Lime Street (Table 90)

D From Morecambe to Leeds (Table 36)

b Change at Manchester Piccadilly

c Change at Manchester Oxford Road

e Change at Preston and Oxenholme Lake District

f From 2 March only. Change at Preston

g By bus

h Change at Preston. By bus

Table 82

Manchester → Bolton → Wigan, Southport, Preston, Barrow-in-Furness and Blackpool North

3 February to 23 March

Network Diagram - see first page of Table 82

		NT	NT	TP	NT	NT	NT	TP	NT	NT	TP	NT	NT	TP	NT	NT	NT	TP	NT	NT	NT	NT	TP
				1 ◇				1 ◇			1 ◇			1 ◇				1 ◇					1 ◇
		A	B				B		C				B				D					C	
Manchester Airport	85 d			18 47	19b01	19b05		19 47		19b52	20 27			20 47	20b52	21b05		21 47		22b01			22 47
Heald Green	85 d			18 17				19 17						20 17				21 17					22 17
Buxton	86 d				18 25					19 25					20 25					21c25			
Hazel Grove	86 d				18 59					19 59					20 59					21c59			
Alderley Edge	84 d					19 10						20 10				21 10				22 10			
Stockport	84 d				19 10	19 29				20 10	20 15	20 29			21 10	21 29				22 29			
Manchester Piccadilly 10	d			19 03	19 26	19 45		20 03		20 25	20 42	20 46		21 03	21 25	21 45		22 03		22 45			23 03
Manchester Oxford Road	d			19 06	19 29	19 48		20 06		20 28	20 45	20 49		21 06	21 28	21 48		22 06		22 48			23 06
Deansgate	d			19 08	19 31	19 50		20 08		20 30		20 51		21 08	21 30	21 50		22 08		22 50			23 08
Rochdale	95 d		18 18				19 18						20 18				21 18				21 23		
Manchester Victoria	d		19 00				20 00						21 00				22 00				23 00		
Salford Crescent	a		19 04	19 11	19 34	19 54	20 04	20 11		20 34		20 55	21 04	21 11	21 34	21 54	22 04	22 12		22 54	23 04		23 11
	d		19 05	19 12	19 35	19 54	20 05	20 12		20 34		20 55	21 05	21 12	21 34	21 54	22 05	22 12		22 54			23 12
Bolton	a		19 15	19 22	19 45	20 04	20 15	20 22		20 44	20 59	21 05	21 15	21 22	21 45	22 04	22 15	22 22		23 04			23 22
	d			19 22	19 45	20 05		20 22		20 45	21 00	21 06		21 22	21 45	22 05		22 22		23 05			23 22
Westhoughton	d					20 12						21 13				22 12				23 12			
Hindley	d					20 16						21 17				22 16				23 16			
Wigan North Western	a																						
Wigan Wallgate	a					20 21						21 22				22 25				23 25			
	d					20 23						21 24											
Gathurst	d					20 27						21 28											
Appley Bridge	d					20 31						21 32											
Parbold	d					20 35						21 36											
Burscough Bridge	d					20 39						21 40											
Southport	a					20 56						21 57											
Lostock	d				19 50					20 50					21 50								
Horwich Parkway	d				19 54					20 54					21 54								
Blackrod	d				19 57					20 57					21 57								
Adlington (Lancashire)	d				20 01					21 01					22 01								
Chorley	d			19 34	20 06			20 34		21 05				21 34	22 05			22 34					23 34
Leyland	d				20 14				20 58	21 12					22 12							23 08	
Preston 8	a			19 49	20 21			20 47	21 05	21 20	21 21			21 48	22 20			22 45				23 15	23 46
Lancaster 6	65 a			20 31				21 22			21 40			22 24									
	d	20 15									21 41								23 00				
Oxenholme Lake District	65 a			20e57				21 35			22 38			22 38									
Windermere	83 a			21e16																			
Carnforth	d	20a24									21 49								23 09				
Silverdale	d										21 55								23 15				
Arnside	d										21 59								23 19				
Grange-over-Sands	d										22 05								23 25				
Kents Bank	d										22 08								23 29				
Cark	d										22 13								23 33				
Ulverston	d										22 21								23 41				
Dalton	d										22 29								23 49				
Roose	d										22 34								23 55				
Barrow-in-Furness	a										22 44								00 13				
Kirkham & Wesham	97 a			20f25	20g51			21f25						22f25				23f30					00f30
Poulton-le-Fylde	97 a			20f45	21f15			21f45	22f05		22h15			22f45	23f15			23f50					00f50
Blackpool North	97 a			21f00	21f30				21f55		22h30			23f00	23f30							00f05	01f05

For general notes see front of timetable
For details of catering facilities see Directory of Train Operators

A From Morecambe to Leeds (Table 36)
B To Clitheroe (Table 94)
C From Liverpool Lime Street (Table 90)
D To Blackburn (Table 94)
b Change at Manchester Piccadilly
c Change at Stockport
e Change at Preston and Lancaster
f By bus
g From 2 March only
h Change at Preston. By bus

Table 82

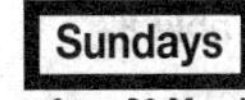

from 30 March

Manchester → Bolton → Wigan, Southport, Preston, Barrow-in-Furness and Blackpool North

Network Diagram - see first page of Table 82

	NT A	TP (bus)	TP (bus)	TP (bus)	TP 1 ◇	TP 1 ◇	NT B	NT A	NT	NT	NT B	TP 1 ◇	TP (bus)	TP 1	NT	NT	NT B	TP 1 ◇	NT A	NT	NT C	NT	NT B	TP 1 ◇
Manchester Airport 85 d		01 10	03 10	05 45	*06 22*	07 36						08 47			*08b51*			09 47				*10b01*		10 47
Heald Green 85 d					*06 16*	*07 13*						*08 16*												*10 17*
Buxton 86 d															08 25					09 25				
Hazel Grove 86 d															08 59					09 59				
Alderley Edge 84 d																09 10						10 10		
Stockport 84 d												*08 38*			09 11	09 29				10 11		10 29		
Manchester Piccadilly 10 d		01 30	03 30	06 05	07 00	07 51						09 03			09 25	09 45		10 03		10 25		10 45		11 03
Manchester Oxford Road d					07 03	07 54						09 06			09 29	09 48		10 06		10 29		10 48		11 06
Deansgate d					07 05	07 56						09 08			09 31	09 50		10 08		10 31		10 50		11 08
Rochdale 95 d																							*10 18*	
Manchester Victoria d							08 00		08 28	08 49	09 00						10 00						11 00	
Salford Crescent a						08 00			08 33	08 54	09 04	09 11			09 34	09 54	10 04	10 11		10 34		10 54	11 04	11 11
d						08 00			08 33	08 54	09 05	09 12			09 35	09 54	10 05	10 12		10 35		10 54	11 05	11 12
Bolton a		01s55	03s55	06s30	07 20	08 10	08 13		08 43	09 04	09 15	09 22			09 45	10 04	10 15	10 22		10 45		11 04	11 15	11 22
d						08 10			08 44	09 05		09 22			09 45	10 05		10 22		10 45		11 05		11 22
Westhoughton d										09 12						10 12						11 12		
Hindley d										09 16						10 16						11 16		
Wigan North Western a																								
Wigan Wallgate a										09 21						10 21						11 21		
d										09 23						10 23						11 23		
Gathurst d										09 27						10 27						11 27		
Appley Bridge d										09 31						10 31						11 31		
Parbold d										09 35						10 35						11 35		
Burscough Bridge d										09 39						10 39						11 39		
Southport a										09 56						10 56						11 56		
Lostock d									08 49						09 50					10 50				
Horwich Parkway d									08 53						09 54					10 54				
Blackrod d									08 56						09 57					10 57				
Adlington (Lancashire) d									09 00						10 01					11 01				
Chorley d						08 22			09 04			09 34			10 06			10 34		11 06				11 34
Leyland d	00 06			06s55		08 30		08 58	09 11						10 12				10 58	11 12				
Preston 8 a	00 15	02s30	04s30	07s10		08 35		09 05	09 18			09 47	10d00		10 20			10 46	11 05	11 20				11 48
Lancaster 6 65 a																		*11c47*		*12c40*				
d														11 00							12 45			
Oxenholme Lake District 65 a															*12c05*			*12e11*						*13c05*
Windermere 83 a																		*12e33*						*13f26*
Carnforth d													10a50	11 08							12a54			
Silverdale d														11 14										
Arnside d														11 18										
Grange-over-Sands d														11 24										
Kents Bank d														11 27										
Cark d														11 32										
Ulverston d														11 40										
Dalton d														11 48										
Roose d														11 53										
Barrow-in-Furness a														12 01										
Kirkham & Wesham 97 a				07s30		08 57						09 57						10 57		*11 51*				11 57
Poulton-le-Fylde 97 a				07s50		09 07		09 23	09 36			10 07			10 38			11 07	11 23	11 38				12 07
Blackpool North 97 a		03 10	05 10	08 05		09 16		09 34	09 45			10 16			10 47			11 16	11 34	11 47				12 16

For general notes see front of timetable
For details of catering facilities see Directory of Train Operators

- **A** From Liverpool Lime Street (Table 90)
- **B** To Clitheroe (Table 94)
- **C** From Morecambe to Leeds (Table 36)
- **b** Change at Manchester Piccadilly
- **c** By bus
- **e** Change at Preston and Lancaster. By bus to Lancaster
- **f** Change at Preston and Oxenholme Lake District. By bus to Oxenholme Lake District

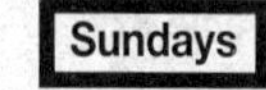

from 30 March

Manchester → Bolton → Wigan, Southport, Preston, Barrow-in-Furness and Blackpool North

Network Diagram - see first page of Table 82

		NT		NT	NT	TP	NT	NT	TP	TP	NT	NT	NT	TP	NT	NT	NT	TP	NT	NT	TP	TP	NT	NT	NT
						1 ◊				1				1 ◊				1 ◊				1			
					A		B		bus	C		A	D				A		B		bus	C		A	
Manchester Airport	85 d	11b00		11b14		11 47					12b13			12 46	12b52	13b22		13 47		13b52			14b16		
Heald Green	85 d			11b17							12b16					13b17							14b18		
Buxton	86 d	10 25						11 20							12 20					13 25					
Hazel Grove	86 d	10 59						11 56							12 54					13 59					
Alderley Edge	84 d			11 10							12 10					13 10							14 10		
Stockport	84 d	11 11		11 29		11 31		12 08			12 29			12 37	13 08	13 29				14 11			14 28		
Manchester Piccadilly 10	d	11 25		11 46		12 03		12 25			12 45			13 02	13 24	13 49		14 03		14 25			14 46		
Manchester Oxford Road	d	11 29		11 49		12 06		12 29			12 48			13 06	13 28	13 52		14 06		14 29			14 49		
Deansgate	d	11 31		11 51		12 08		12 31			12 50			13 08	13 30	13 54		14 08		14 31			14 51		
Rochdale	95 d				11 18							12 18					13 20							14 18	
Manchester Victoria	d				12 00							13 00					14 00							15 00	
Salford Crescent	a	11 35		11 55	12 04	12 11		12 34			12 54	13 04		13 11	13 33	13 58	14 04	14 11		14 34			14 55	15 04	
	d	11 35		11 55	12 05	12 12		12 35			12 54	13 05		13 12	13 34	13 58	14 05	14 12		14 35			14 55	15 05	
Bolton	a	11 45		12 05	12 15	12 22		12 45			13 04	13 15		13 22	13 44	14 08	14 15	14 22		14 45			15 05	15 15	
	d	11 45		12 06		12 22		12 45			13 05			13 22	13 44	14 09		14 22		14 45			15 06		
Westhoughton	d			12 13							13 12					14 16							15 13		
Hindley	d			12 17							13 16					14 22							15 17		
Wigan North Western	a																								
Wigan Wallgate	a			12 22							13 21					14 27							15 22		
	d			12 24							13 23					14 29							15 24		
Gathurst	d			12 28							13 27					14 33							15 28		
Appley Bridge	d			12 32							13 31					14 37							15 32		
Parbold	d			12 36							13 35					14 41							15 36		
Burscough Bridge	d			12 40							13 39					14 45							15 40		
Southport	a			12 56							13 56					15 02							15 57		
Lostock	d	11 50						12 50							13 49					14 50					
Horwich Parkway	d	11 54						12 54							13 53					14 54					
Blackrod	d	11 57						12 57							13 56					14 57					
Adlington (Lancashire)	d	12 01						13 01							14 00					15 01					
Chorley	d	12 06				12 34		13 06						13 34	14 05			14 34		15 06					
Leyland	d	12 12					12 58	13 12							14 13				14 58	15 12					
Preston 8	a	12 20				12 48	13 06	13 20	13d27					13 48	14 19			14 48	15 07	15 20	15d27				
Lancaster 6	65 a					13c47								14c47				15c47		16c20					
	d									14 15			14 47									16 15			16 45
Oxenholme Lake District	65 a	14c05				14e11								15c05	16c05			16e11							
Windermere	83 a					14e33								15f29				16e33							
Carnforth	d								14a17	14 23			14a55								16a17	16 23			16 55
Silverdale	d									14 29												16 29			17 01
Arnside	d									14 33												16 33			17 07
Grange-over-Sands	d									14 39												16 39			17 13
Kents Bank	d									14 42												16 42			17 16
Cark	d									14 47												16 47			17 21
Ulverston	d									14 55												16 55			17 29
Dalton	d									15 03												17 03			17 37
Roose	d									15 08												17 08			17 43
Barrow-in-Furness	a									15 16												17 16			17 51
Kirkham & Wesham	97 a	12 51				12 57		13 51						13 57	14 51			14 57		15 51					
Poulton-le-Fylde	97 a	12 38				13 07	13 23	13 38						14 07	14 37			15 07	15 23	15 38					
Blackpool North	97 a	12 47				13 16	13 34	13 47						14 16	14 47			15 16	15 34	15 47					

For general notes see front of timetable
For details of catering facilities see Directory of Train Operators

- **A** To Clitheroe (Table 94)
- **B** From Liverpool Lime Street (Table 90)
- **C** From Windermere (Table 83)
- **D** From Morecambe to Leeds (Table 36)
- **b** Change at Manchester Piccadilly
- **c** By bus
- **e** Change at Preston and Lancaster. By bus to Lancaster
- **f** Change at Preston and Oxenholme Lake District. By bus to Oxenholme Lake District

Table 82

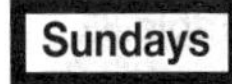

Sundays

from 30 March

Manchester → Bolton → Wigan, Southport, Preston, Barrow-in-Furness and Blackpool North

Network Diagram - see first page of Table 82

	TP	NT	NT	NT	TP	NT	NT	NT	TP	TP	NT	NT	TP	NT	NT	NT	NT	TP	NT	NT	TP	TP	NT
	1 ◇			A	1 ◇	B	C		Bus	1 D		A	1 ◇	C			A	1 ◇	C		Bus	1 E	
Manchester Airport 85 d	14 47	14b52	15b14		15 47			16b01			16b14		16 47		17b01	17b05		17 47		18b01			
Heald Green 85 d			15b17								16b17							17 17					
Buxton 86 d		14 25						15 25							16 25					17 25			
Hazel Grove 86 d		14 59						15 59							16 59					17 59			
Alderley Edge 84 d			15 10								16 10					17 10							18 10
Stockport 84 d		15 11	15 28					16 11			16 29				17 10	17 29				18 10			18 29
Manchester Piccadilly 10 d	15 03	15 25	15 46		16 03			16 25			16 46		17 03		17 25	17 46		18 03		18 25			18 45
Manchester Oxford Road d	15 06	15 29	15 49		16 06			16 28			16 49		17 06		17 29	17 49		18 06		18 28			18 48
Deansgate d	15 08	15 31	15 51		16 08			16 30			16 51		17 08		17 31	17 51		18 08		18 30			18 50
Rochdale 95 d				15 18								16 18					17 18						
Manchester Victoria d				16 00								17 00					18 00						
Salford Crescent a	15 11	15 34	15 55	16 04	16 11			16 34			16 55	17 04	17 12		17 34	17 55	18 04	18 11		18 34			18 54
d	15 12	15 35	15 55	16 05	16 12			16 34			16 55	17 05	17 12		17 35	17 55	18 05	18 12		18 34			18 54
Bolton a	15 22	15 45	16 05	16 15	16 22			16 45			17 05	17 15	17 22		17 45	18 05	18 15	18 22		18 45			19 04
d	15 22	15 45	16 06		16 22			16 45			17 06		17 22		17 45	18 06		18 22		18 45			19 05
Westhoughton d			16 13								17 13					18 13							19 12
Hindley d			16 17								17 17					18 17							19 16
Wigan North Western a																							
Wigan Wallgate a			16 22								17 22					18 22							19 21
d			16 24								17 24					18 24							19 23
Gathurst d			16 28								17 28					18 28							19 27
Appley Bridge d			16 32								17 32					18 32							19 31
Parbold d			16 36								17 36					18 36							19 35
Burscough Bridge d			16 40								17 40					18 40							19 39
Southport a			16 57								17 57					18 57							19 57
Lostock d		15 50						16 50							17 50					18 50			
Horwich Parkway d		15 54						16 54							17 54					18 54			
Blackrod d		15 57						16 57							17 57					18 57			
Adlington (Lancashire) d		16 01						17 01							18 01					19 01			
Chorley d	15 34	16 06			16 34			17 05					17 34		18 06			18 34		19 05			
Leyland d		16 12					16 57	17 12						17 58	18 12				18 58	19 12			
Preston 8 a	15 46	16 20			16 46		17 04	17 20	17d27				17 46	18 05	18 20			18 47	19 05	19 19	19d27		
Lancaster 6 65 a	16c47				17c47		18c10						18c47		19c20			19c47		20c20			
d						18 04				18 15												20 20	
Oxenholme Lake District 65 a	17c05				18e11		18c55						19c05		20c05			20e11		21c05			
Windermere 83 a	17f26				18e33								19f30					20e33					
Carnforth d						18a12			18a17	18 23											20a17	20 28	
Silverdale d										18 29												20 34	
Arnside d										18 33												20 38	
Grange-over-Sands d										18 39												20 44	
Kents Bank d										18 42												20 47	
Cark d										18 47												20 52	
Ulverston d										18 55												21 00	
Dalton d										19 03												21 08	
Roose d										19 08												21 13	
Barrow-in-Furness a										19 16												21 21	
Kirkham & Wesham 97 a	15 57	16 51			16 57			17 51					17 57		18 51			18 57		19 51			
Poulton-le-Fylde 97 a	16 07	16 38			17 07		17 23	17 37					18 07	18 23	18 38			19 07	19 23	19 37			
Blackpool North 97 a	16 16	16 47			17 16		17 35	17 47					18 16	18 34	18 47			19 16	19 32	19 47			

For general notes see front of timetable
For details of catering facilities see Directory of Train Operators

A To Clitheroe (Table 94)

B From Morecambe to Leeds (Table 36)

C From Liverpool Lime Street (Table 90)

D From Windermere (Table 83)

E From Windermere (Table 65)

b Change at Manchester Piccadilly

c By bus

e Change at Preston and Lancaster. By bus to Lancaster

f Change at Preston and Oxenholme Lake District. By bus to Oxenholme Lake District

Table 82

Sundays from 30 March

Manchester → Bolton → Wigan, Southport, Preston, Barrow-in-Furness and Blackpool North

Network Diagram - see first page of Table 82

	NT	TP	NT	NT	NT	NT	TP	TP	NT	NT	NT	NT	NT	TP	NT	NT	NT	TP	NT	NT	NT	TP
		1 ◇					1 ◇	1						1 ◇				1 ◇				1 ◇
	A		B			A			C				A				D				C	
Manchester Airport 85 ✈ d		18 47		19b01	19b05		19 47				19b52	20b01		20 47	20b52	21b05		21 47	22b01			22 47
Heald Green 85 d		18 17					19 17							20 17				21 17				22 17
Buxton 86 d				18 25							19 25				20 25				21c25			
Hazel Grove 86 d				18 59							19 59				20 59				21c59			
Alderley Edge 84 d					19 10							20 10				21 10			22 10			
Stockport 84 d				19 10	19 29						20 10	20 29			21 10	21 29			22 29			
Manchester Piccadilly 10 ✈ d		19 03		19 26	19 45		20 03				20 25	20 46		21 03	21 25	21 45		22 03	22 45			23 03
Manchester Oxford Road d		19 06		19 29	19 48		20 06				20 28	20 49		21 06	21 28	21 48		22 06	22 48			23 06
Deansgate ✈ d		19 08		19 31	19 50		20 08				20 30	20 51		21 08	21 30	21 50		22 08	22 50			23 08
Rochdale 95 d	18 18					19 18							20 18				21 18			21 23		
Manchester Victoria ✈ d	19 00					20 00							21 00				22 00			23 00		
Salford Crescent a	19 04	19 11		19 34	19 54	20 04	20 11				20 34	20 55	21 04	21 11	21 34	21 54	22 04	22 12	22 54	23 04		23 11
d	19 05	19 12		19 35	19 54	20 05	20 12				20 34	20 55	21 05	21 12	21 34	21 54	22 05	22 12	22 54			23 12
Bolton a	19 15	19 22		19 45	20 04	20 15	20 22				20 45	21 05	21 15	21 22	21 45	22 04	22 15	22 22	23 04			23 22
d		19 22		19 45	20 05		20 22				20 45	21 06		21 22	21 45	22 05		22 22	23 05			23 22
Westhoughton d					20 12							21 13				22 12			23 12			
Hindley d					20 16							21 17				22 16			23 16			
Wigan North Western a																						
Wigan Wallgate a					20 21							21 22				22 25			23 25			
d					20 23							21 24										
Gathurst d					20 27							21 28										
Appley Bridge d					20 31							21 32										
Parbold d					20 35							21 36										
Burscough Bridge d					20 39							21 40										
Southport a					20 56							21 57										
Lostock d				19 50							20 50				21 50							
Horwich Parkway d				19 54							20 54				21 54							
Blackrod d				19 57							20 57				21 57							
Adlington (Lancashire) d				20 01							21 01				22 01							
Chorley d		19 34		20 06			20 34				21 05			21 34	22 05			22 34				23 34
Leyland d				20 16					20 58		21 12				22 12						23 08	
Preston 8 a		19 48		20 20			20 47	20e55	21 05	21e15	21 20			21 48	22 20			22 45			23 15	23 46
Lancaster 6 65 a		20f50		21f20			21f40		22f05					23f05								
d			20 15					21 50		23 00												
Oxenholme Lake District 65 a		21f35		22f05					22f50					23f50								
Windermere 83 a																						
Carnforth d			20 24					21 58		23 09												
Silverdale d								22 04		23 15												
Arnside d								22 09		23 19												
Grange-over-Sands d								22 15		23 25												
Kents Bank d								22 18		23 29												
Cark d								22 23		23 33												
Ulverston d								22 31		23 41												
Dalton d								22 39		23 49												
Roose d								22 44		23 55												
Barrow-in-Furness a								22 52		00 13												
Kirkham & Wesham 97 a		19 57		20g51			20 57							21 58				22 57				23 57
Poulton-le-Fylde 97 a		20 07		20 38			21 07		21 23		21 37			22 07	22 37			23 07			23 34	00 07
Blackpool North 97 a		20 16		20 47			21 16		21 34		21 47			22 16	22 47			23 16			23 43	00 16

For general notes see front of timetable
For details of catering facilities see Directory of Train Operators

A To Clitheroe (Table 94)
B From Morecambe to Leeds (Table 36)
C From Liverpool Lime Street (Table 90)
D To Blackburn (Table 94)
b Change at Manchester Piccadilly
c Change at Stockport
e Departure time. By bus
f By bus
g 4 May arr. 2045

Blackpool, Barrow-in-Furness, Preston, Southport, Kirkby and Wigan → Bolton → Manchester

Network Diagram - see first page of Table 82

Miles	Miles	Miles	Miles	Miles			TP	TP	TP	TP	TP	TP	TP	TP	NT	TP	TP	NT	NT	NT	NT	NT	TP	NT	NT
								MO		MO			MO			MX	MO								
							[1] ◇	[1] ◇	[1] ◇	[1] ◇	[1] ◇	[1] ◇	[1] ◇	[1] ◇		[1] ◇	[1] ◇						[1] ◇		
							A	B	A	B	C		D					E		G		H	(bicycle)	J	
0	—	—	—	—	**Blackpool North**	97 d	01 43	01b15	03 53	03b25		04c45		05 19		05e30	05e30			06 09			06 34		
1¼	—	—	—	—	Layton	97 d								05c09						06 13			06 37		
3¼	—	—	—	—	Poulton-le-Fylde	97 d								05 25		05e36	05e36			06 17			06 41		
9¾	—	—	—	—	Kirkham & Wesham	97 d								05c22						06 25			06 51		
—	0	—	—	—	**Barrow-in-Furness**	d					04 20		04 20			05 00	05 15								
—	1¾	—	—	—	Roose	d																			
—	6	—	—	—	Dalton	d																			
—	9¼	—	—	—	Ulverston	d					04 35		04 36			05 15	05 30								
—	15¼	—	—	—	Cark	d																			
—	17¼	—	—	—	Kents Bank	d																			
—	19½	—	—	—	Grange-over-Sands	d					04 48		04 49			05 28	05 43								
—	22¾	—	—	—	Arnside	d					04 55		04 55			05 34	05 49								
—	25	—	—	—	Silverdale	d																			
—	28¾	—	—	—	Carnforth	d					05 05		05f15			05 43	05 58								
—	—	—	—	—	Windermere	83 d																			
—	—	—	—	—	Oxenholme Lake District	65 d																			
—	34¾	—	—	—	**Lancaster [6]**	65 a					05 14		05 22			05 53	06 08								
—	—	—	—	—		d							05 24			05 53	06 08						06 33		
17½	55¾	—	—	—	**Preston [8]**	d	02u08	02 08	04u18	04 18		05 17	05a42	05 50		06 28	06 28			06 39			07 03		
21½	59¾	—	—	—	Leyland	d														06 44			07 08		
26	64¼	—	—	—	Chorley	d						05 26				06 37	06 37			06 51			07 15		
29	67¼	—	—	—	Adlington (Lancashire)	d														06 56					
31	69¼	—	—	—	Blackrod	d														06 59			07 21		
32½	70¾	—	—	—	Horwich Parkway	d										06 45	06 45			07 03			07 24		
34½	72¾	—	—	—	Lostock	d						05 34				06 48	06 48			07 07			07 27		
—	—	0	—	—	**Southport**	d															06 35				06 59
—	—	1¼	—	—	Meols Cop	d															06 40				07 04
—	—	4½	—	—	Bescar Lane	d																			
—	—	6½	—	—	New Lane	d																			
—	—	7¾	—	—	Burscough Bridge	d															06 48				07 13
—	—	9¼	—	—	Hoscar	d																			
—	—	10¾	—	—	Parbold	d															06 53				07 18
—	—	13	—	—	Appley Bridge	d															06 57				07 22
—	—	14¾	—	—	Gathurst	d															07 00				07 26
—	—	—	—	—	Liverpool Central [10]	103 d																			
—	—	—	0	—	**Kirkby**	d																			
—	—	—	5¼	—	Rainford	d																			
—	—	—	7¼	—	Upholland	d																			
—	—	—	8½	—	Orrell	d																			
—	—	—	10½	—	Pemberton	d																			
—	—	17½	12¼	—	**Wigan Wallgate**	a															07 05				07 31
—	—	—	—	—		d									06 08				06 45		07 06			07 13	07 32
—	—	—	—	0	Wigan North Western	d								06 13											
—	—	18½	13¼	¾	Ince	d									06 11				06 48					07 16	
—	—	20	14¾	—	Hindley	d								06 19	06 14				06 51					07 19	
—	—	22½	—	—	Westhoughton	d								06 23							07 14				
37½	75¾	27	—	—	**Bolton**	a						05 39		06 29		06 52	06 52			07 12	07 22		07 33		
—	—	—	—	—		d	02u37	02u37	04u48	04u48		05 40		06 31		06 54	06 54	06 58		07 13	07 23	07 30	07 33		
38¼	76½	27¾	—	—	Moses Gate	d												07 01							
39¾	78	29¼	—	—	Farnworth	d												07 03							
40½	78¾	30	—	—	Kearsley	d												07 05							
—	—	—	17¼	—	Daisy Hill	d									06 18				06 55					07 23	07 40
—	—	—	17½	—	Hag Fold	d									06 21				06 58					07 26	
—	—	—	18¾	—	Atherton	d									06 24				07 01					07 29	07 44
—	—	—	22¼	—	Walkden	d									06 29				07 06					07 34	
—	—	—	24	—	Moorside	d									06 33				07 10					07 38	
—	—	—	24¾	—	Swinton	d									06 35				07 12					07 40	
46½	84¾	36	28¾	—	**Salford Crescent**	a								06 43	06 46	07 06	07 06	07 17	07 19	07 26	07 35	07 42	07 45	07 47	07 59
—	—	—	—	—		d								06 43	06 46	07 06	07 06	07 17	07 19	07 26	07 36	07 43	07 46	07 47	07 59
—	—	—	29¾	—	Salford Central	d									06 49			07 20	07 22			07 46		07 50	08 02
—	—	—	30½	—	**Manchester Victoria**	(ferry) a									06 54			07 25	07 28			07 51		07 55	08 07
—	—	—	—	—	Rochdale	95 a									07 38				08 06						08 25
48	86¼	37½	—	—	Deansgate	(ferry) a								06 49						07 29	07 39				
48¼	86½	37¾	—	—	**Manchester Oxford Road**	a								06 51		07 12	07 12			07 32	07 41		07 50		
48¾	87	38¼	—	—	**Manchester Piccadilly [10]**	(ferry) a	02 53	02 53				05 57		06 56		07 15	07 15			07 36	07 45		07 54		
—	—	—	—	—	Stockport	84 a						06 24		07 26		07 37	07 37			07 46	08 07		08 24		
—	—	—	—	—	Hazel Grove	86 a						07 01		07 44		07 54	07 54			08 13					
—	—	—	—	—	Buxton	86 a						07 45				08 33	08 33								
57	95¼	46½	—	—	Heald Green	85 a						06 21		07 27		07 32	07 32						08 11		
58½	96¾	48	—	—	**Manchester Airport**	85 (plane) a	03 09	03 09	05 22	05 22		06 14		07 15		07 40	07 40				08 02		08 19		

For general notes see front of timetable
For details of catering facilities see Directory of Train Operators

A Not Mondays 4 February to 24 March
B 4 February to 24 March
C Not Mondays 28 January to 24 March. To Windermere (Table 83)
D 28 January to 24 March
E From Blackburn (Table 94). Also stops at Clifton 0709
G To Chester (Table 88)
H From Colne (Table 97)
J To Stalybridge (Table 39)
b By bus
e Change at Preston
f Arr. 0505

Blackpool, Barrow-in-Furness, Preston, Southport, Kirkby and Wigan → Bolton → Manchester

Network Diagram - see first page of Table 82

	NT	NT	NT	NT	NT	NT	TP	TP	NT	NT	NT	NT	NT	NT	TP	NT	NT	TP	NT	NT	NT	NT	NT	NT
									BHX															
							1 ◇	1 ◇							1 ◇			1 ◇						
		A	B		C	D	E	E					B					E	G				C	B
Blackpool North 97 d					06 57		07 03		07 16						07 41						08 09			
Layton 97 d							07 06								07 44						08 12			
Poulton-le-Fylde 97 d					07 03		07 11		07 23						07 48						08 16			
Kirkham & Wesham 97 d		07 04					07 21		07 32						07 58						08 25		08b28	
Barrow-in-Furness d								06 15										07 01					07 17	
Roose d								06 19															07 21	
Dalton d								06 25										07 10					07 27	
Ulverston d								06 34										07 18					07 36	
Cark d								06 42										07 26					07 44	
Kents Bank d								06 46															07 48	
Grange-over-Sands d								06 50										07 33					07 52	
Arnside d								06 56										07 39					07 58	
Silverdale d								07 01										07 43					08 03	
Carnforth d						06 43		07 08										07 51					08 10	
Windermere 83 d												*06c20*												
Oxenholme Lake District 65 d					*06e22*							*06f47*												
Lancaster 6 65 a						06 53		07 15										07 58					08 19	
d					*06g38*			07 16				*07 23*						07 59					08 19	
Preston 8 d		07 20			07 25		07 40		07 46			07 50			08 12			08 34			08 38		08 50	
Leyland d		07 25			07a30							07 55									08 43		08a55	
Chorley d		07 33					07 50		07 57			08 03			08 22			08 44			08 51			
Adlington (Lancashire) d		07 38										08 08									08 56			
Blackrod d		07 42										08 11									09 00			
Horwich Parkway d		07 46										08 15						08 52			09 03			
Lostock d		07 49							08 05			08 19									09 07			
Southport d										07 27										08 09		08 35		
Meols Cop d										07 32										08 14		08 40		
Bescar Lane d																				08 19				
New Lane d																				08 23				
Burscough Bridge d										07 41										08 25		08 48		
Hoscar d																				08 29				
Parbold d										07 46										08 32		08 53		
Appley Bridge d										07 50										08 36		08 57		
Gathurst d										07 54										08 39		09 00		
Liverpool Central 10 103 d				*06 50*							07h04						*07 50*							
Kirkby d				07 16													08 16							
Rainford d				07 23													08 23							
Upholland d				07 27													08 27							
Orrell d				07 31													08 31							
Pemberton d				07 34													08 34							
Wigan Wallgate a				07 39						07 59							08 40			08 44		09 05		
d				07 43						08 00				08 13		08 32				08 45		09 07		
Wigan North Western d	07 26										07 56													
Ince d	07 29			07 46										08 16										
Hindley d	07 33			07 49							08 01			08 19		08 37				08 50				
Westhoughton d	07 37										08 06					08 41						09 15		
Bolton a	07 45	07 54					08 02		08 10		08 14	08 24			08 33	08 49		08 58			09 12	09 23		
d	07 46	07 55	08 00				08 04		08 11		08 15	08 24	08 30		08 34	08 50		08 59	09 01		09 12	09 23		09 30
Moses Gate d	07 49										08 18								09 04					
Farnworth d	07 51										08 20					08 53								
Kearsley d	07 53										08 22					08 55								
Daisy Hill d				07 53						08 08				08 23						08 54				
Hag Fold d				07 56										08 26						08 57				
Atherton d				07 59						08 13				08 29						09 00				
Walkden d				08 04										08 34						09 05				
Moorside d				08 08										08 38						09 09				
Swinton d				08 10										08 40						09 11				
Salford Crescent a	08 03	08 07	08 13	08 18						08 28	08 32	08 37	08 42	08 46		09 06		09 11	09 16	09 19	09 25	09 36		09 42
d	08 03	08 07	08 13	08 18						08 28	08 32	08 37	08 42	08 46		09 07		09 11	09 16	09 19	09 25	09 36		09 42
Salford Central d	08 06		08 16	08 21					08 24	08 31	08 35		08 45	08 49		09 09			09 19	09 24				09 45
Manchester Victoria ⇌ a	08 13		08 21	08 25					08 30	08 37	08 40		08 50	08 54		09 14			09 25	09 27				09 50
Rochdale 95 a	*08 38*			08 55							*09 08*			09 25		*09 38*				09 55				
Deansgate ⇌ a		08 11										08 41						09 15			09 29	09 40		
Manchester Oxford Road a		08 14					08 20					08 43			08 49			09 16			09 31	09 42		
Manchester Piccadilly 10 ⇌ a		08 19					08 25					08 47			08 53			09 20			09 35	09 45		
Stockport 84 a		08 30					*08 53*					*09 08*			*09 13*			*09 42*			09 46	*10 12*		
Hazel Grove 86 a		*08 49*										*09 16*			*09 29*						09 55	*10 29*		
Buxton 86 a		*09 26*										*09 56*									10 33			
Heald Green 85 a		*08j51*													*09 18*			09 31						
Manchester Airport 85 ✈ a							08 42					09 06			09 13			09 40				10 01		

For general notes see front of timetable
For details of catering facilities see Directory of Train Operators

A From St Annes-on-the-Sea (Table 97) to Greenbank (Table 88)
B From Clitheroe (Table 94)
C To Liverpool Lime Street (Table 90)
D From Skipton (Table 36)
E Trolley from Preston
G From Blackburn (Table 94)
b Change at Preston
c Change at Oxenholme Lake District and Preston. By bus to Oxenholme Lake District Mondays 28 January to 24 March
e Not Mondays 28 January to 24 March
f Mondays 28 January to 24 March dep. 0708
g Mondays 28 January to 24 March dep. 0658
h Liverpool Lime Street (Table 90)
j Change at Manchester Piccadilly

Blackpool, Barrow-in-Furness, Preston, Southport, Kirkby and Wigan → Bolton → Manchester

Network Diagram - see first page of Table 82

		TP	NT	NT	NT	TP	NT	NT	NT	NT	NT	NT	NT	TP	NT	NT	NT	TP	NT	NT	NT	NT	NT	NT	TP
		1 ◇				1 ◇								1 ◇				1 ◇							1 ◇
				A		B	C					D	E			G		H					D	E	
		🍴				🍴								🍴				🍴							🍴
Blackpool North	97 d	08 41								09 11		09 25		09 38							10 11		10 25		10 41
Layton	97 d									09 14											10 14				
Poulton-le-Fylde	97 d	08 47								09 18				09 44							10 18				10 47
Kirkham & Wesham	97 d									09 27								*10b19*			10 27				
Barrow-in-Furness	d			07 58														09 15							
Roose	d			08 02														09 19							
Dalton	d			08 08														09 25							
Ulverston	d			08 17														09 34							
Cark	d			08 25														09 42							
Kents Bank	d			08 29														09 46							
Grange-over-Sands	d			08 33														09 50							
Arnside	d			08 39														09 56							
Silverdale	d			08 43														10 01							
Carnforth	d			08 51												09 55		10 08							
Windermere	83 d	*07c24*				*08 20*												*09e28*							
Oxenholme Lake District	65 d	*07 53*				08 59												*09 54*							*10 13*
Lancaster 6	65 a			08 59		09 14										10 04		10 15							
	d	*08 29*		09 00		09 14								*09 29*				10 16			*10 09*				*10 29*
Preston 8	d	09 08		09a25		09 38				09 41		09 50		10 08				10 38			10 41		10 50		11 08
Leyland	d	09 13										09a55		10 13									10a55		11 13
Chorley	d	09 19				09 47				09 51				10 19				10 47			10 51				11 19
Adlington (Lancashire)	d									09 56											10 56				
Blackrod	d									10 00											11 00				
Horwich Parkway	d	09 27								10 03				10 27							11 03				11 27
Lostock	d	09 30								10 07				10 30							11 07				11 30
Southport	d							09 10			09 38								10 15			10 38			
Meols Cop	d							09 15											10 20						
Bescar Lane	d							09 20																	
New Lane	d							09 24																	
Burscough Bridge	d							09 26			09 50								10 28			10 50			
Hoscar	d							09 30																	
Parbold	d							09 33			09 55								10 33			10 55			
Appley Bridge	d							09 37			09 59								10 37			10 59			
Gathurst	d							09 40											10 40						
Liverpool Central 10	103 d														*09 20*										
Kirkby	d														09 51										
Rainford	d														09 58										
Upholland	d														10 02										
Orrell	d														10 06										
Pemberton	d														10 09										
Wigan Wallgate	a							09 45			10 05				10 14				10 45			11 05			
	d		09 16		09 32			09 47	09 52		10 07				10 16		10 32		10 47	10 52		11 07			
Wigan North Western	d																								
Ince	d		09 19												10 19										
Hindley	d		09 22		09 37			09 52							10 22		10 37		10 52						
Westhoughton	d				09 41						10 15						10 41					11 15			
Bolton	a	09 34			09 49	09 58			10 06	10 12	10 23			10 34			10 49	10 58		11 06	11 12	11 23			11 34
	d	09 36			09 50	09 59	10 01		10 07	10 12	10 23		10 30	10 36			10 50	10 59		11 07	11 12	11 23		11 30	11 36
Moses Gate	d								10 10											11 10					
Farnworth	d				09 53												10 53								
Kearsley	d				09 55												10 55								
Daisy Hill	d		09 26					09 56							10 26				10 56						
Hag Fold	d		09 29												10 29										
Atherton	d		09 32					10 00							10 32				11 00						
Walkden	d		09 37					10 05							10 37				11 05						
Moorside	d		09 41												10 41										
Swinton	d		09 43					10 10							10 43				11 10						
Salford Crescent	a	09 48	09 50		10 06	10 10	10 13	10 17	10 22	10 25	10 36		10 43	10 48	10 50		11 06	11 11	11 17	11 21	11 25	11 36		11 42	11 48
	d	09 48	09 50		10 07	10 10	10 13	10 17	10 22	10 25	10 36		10 43	10 48	10 50		11 07	11 11	11 17	11 22	11 25	11 36		11 43	11 48
Salford Central	d		09 53		10 09		10 16	10 20	10 24				10 45		10 53		11 09		11 20	11 24				11 45	
Manchester Victoria	🚋 a		10 00		10 14		10 21	10 24	10 32				10 50		11 00		11 14		11 24	11 29				11 50	
Rochdale	95 a		10 25		*10 38*			10 55	*11 08*						11 25		*11 38*		11 55	*12 08*					
Deansgate	🚋 a									10 29								11 15			11 29				
Manchester Oxford Road	a	09 53				10 16				10 31	10 41			10 53				11 16			11 31	11 41			11 53
Manchester Piccadilly 10	🚋 a	09 57				10 20				10 35	10 45			10 57				11 20			11 35	11 45			11 57
Stockport	84 a	*10 28*				*10 42*				10 46	*11 12*			*11 27*				*11 42*			11 46	*12 12*			*12 28*
Hazel Grove	86 a									10 55	*11 29*										11 55	*12 29*			
Buxton	86 a									11 30											12 33				
Heald Green	85 a	10 11				10 32								11 12				11 32							12 12
Manchester Airport	85 ✈ a	10 19				10 40					11 01			11 19				11 40				12 01			12 19

For general notes see front of timetable
For details of catering facilities see Directory of Train Operators

A From Maryport (Table 100)
B From Glasgow Central (Table 65)
C From Blackburn (Table 94)
D To Liverpool Lime Street (Table 90)
E From Clitheroe (Table 94)
G From Leeds to Morecambe (Table 36)
H 🍴 from Preston
b Change at Preston
c Change at Oxenholme Lake District and Preston
e Change at Oxenholme Lake District and Lancaster

Blackpool, Barrow-in-Furness, Preston, Southport, Kirkby and Wigan → Bolton → Manchester

Network Diagram - see first page of Table 82

		NT	NT	NT	TP	NT	NT	NT	NT	NT	NT	TP	NT	NT	NT	TP	NT	NT	NT	NT	NT	NT	TP	NT	NT
					1 ◇							1 ◇				1 ◇							1 ◇		
			A		B					C	D			E		G					C	D			
					⊼							⊼				⊼							⊼		
Blackpool North	97 d							11 11		11 25		11 41							12 11		12 25		12 41		
Layton	97 d							11 14											12 14						
Poulton-le-Fylde	97 d							11 18				11 47							12 18				12 47		
Kirkham & Wesham	97 d				11b19			11 27								12b19			12 27						
Barrow-in-Furness	d		09 57													11 18									
Roose	d		10 01																						
Dalton	d		10 07													11 27									
Ulverston	d		10 16													11 34									
Cark	d		10 24													11 42									
Kents Bank	d		10 28																						
Grange-over-Sands	d		10 32													11 49									
Arnside	d		10 38													11 55									
Silverdale	d		10 43													12 01									
Carnforth	d		10 50											11 52		12c10									
Windermere	83 d				10 18																		11e30		
Oxenholme Lake District	65 d				10f46																		12 13		
Lancaster 6	65 a		11 00		11 04									12 01		12 17									
	d				11f05							11 29				12 18			12 12				12 29		
Preston 8	d				11 38			11 41		11 50		12 08				12 38			12 41		12 50		13 08		
Leyland	d									11a55		12 13									12a55		13 13		
Chorley	d				11 47			11 51				12 19				12 47			12 51				13 19		
Adlington (Lancashire)	d							11 56											12 56						
Blackrod	d							12 00											13 00						
Horwich Parkway	d							12 03											13 03				13 27		
Lostock	d							12 07				12 30							13 07				13 30		
Southport	d					11 10			11 38								12 15			12 38					
Meols Cop	d					11 15											12 20								
Bescar Lane	d					11 20																			
New Lane	d					11 24																			
Burscough Bridge	d					11 26			11 50								12 28			12 50					
Hoscar	d					11 30																			
Parbold	d					11 33			11 55								12 33			12 55					
Appley Bridge	d					11 37			11 59								12 37			12 59					
Gathurst	d					11 40											12 40								
Liverpool Central 10	103 d	10 20											11 20											12 20	
Kirkby	d	10 51											11 51											12 51	
Rainford	d	10 58											11 58											12 58	
Upholland	d	11 02											12 02											13 02	
Orrell	d	11 06											12 06											13 06	
Pemberton	d	11 09											12 09											13 09	
Wigan Wallgate	a	11 14				11 45			12 05				12 14				12 45			13 05				13 14	
	d	11 16		11 32		11 47	11 52		12 07				12 16		12 32		12 47	12 52		13 07				13 16	13 32
Wigan North Western	d																								
Ince	d	11 19											12 19											13 19	
Hindley	d	11 22		11 37		11 52							12 22		12 37		12 52							13 22	13 37
Westhoughton	d			11 41					12 15						12 41					13 15					13 41
Bolton	a			11 49	11 58		12 06	12 12	12 23			12 35			12 49	12 58		13 06	13 12	13 23			13 34		13 49
	d			11 50	11 59		12 07	12 12	12 23		12 30	12 36			12 50	12 59		13 07	13 12	13 23		13 30	13 36		13 50
Moses Gate	d						12 10											13 10							
Farnworth	d			11 53											12 53										13 53
Kearsley	d			11 55											12 55										13 55
Daisy Hill	d	11 26				11 56							12 26				12 56							13 26	
Hag Fold	d	11 29											12 29											13 29	
Atherton	d	11 32				12 00							12 32				13 00							13 32	
Walkden	d	11 37				12 05							12 37				13 05							13 37	
Moorside	d	11 41											12 41											13 41	
Swinton	d	11 43				12 10							12 43				13 10							13 43	
Salford Crescent	a	11 50		12 06	12 11	12 17	12 21	12 25	12 36		12 42	12 48	12 50		13 06	13 11	13 17	13 21	13 25	13 36		13 42	13 48	13 50	14 06
	d	11 50		12 07	12 11	12 17	12 22	12 25	12 36		12 43	12 48	12 50		13 07	13 11	13 17	13 22	13 25	13 36		13 43	13 48	13 50	14 07
Salford Central	d	11 53		12 09		12 20	12 24				12 45		12 53		13 09		13 20	13 24				13 45		13 53	14 09
Manchester Victoria	⇌ a	12 00		12 14		12 24	12 29				12 50		13 00		13 14		13 24	13 30				13 50		14 00	14 14
Rochdale	95 a	12 25		12 38		12 55	13 08						13 25		13 38		13 55	14 08						14 25	14 38
Deansgate	⇌ a							12 29								13 15			13 29						
Manchester Oxford Road	a				12 16			12 31	12 41			12 53				13 16			13 31	13 41			13 53		
Manchester Piccadilly 10	⇌ a				12 20			12 35	12 45			12 57				13 20			13 35	13 45			13 57		
Stockport	84 a				12 42			12 46	13 12			13 28				13 42			13 46	14 12			14 28		
Hazel Grove	86 a							12 55	13 29										13 55	14 29					
Buxton	86 a							13 30											14 33						
Heald Green	85 a				12 32							13 12				13 32							14 12		
Manchester Airport	85 ✈ a				12 40				13 01			13 19				13 40				14 01			14 19		

For general notes see front of timetable
For details of catering facilities see Directory of Train Operators

A From Millom (Table 100)
B From Glasgow Central and from Edinburgh (Table 65)
C To Liverpool Lime Street (Table 90)
D From Clitheroe (Table 94)
E From Leeds to Morecambe (Table 36)
G ⊼ from Preston
b Change at Preston
c Arr. 1207
e Change at Oxenholme Lake District and Preston
f By changing at Preston, passengers may depart Oxenholme Lake District at 1053, Lancaster at 1110

Blackpool, Barrow-in-Furness, Preston, Southport, Kirkby and Wigan → Bolton → Manchester

Network Diagram - see first page of Table 82

Station		TP 1 ◇ A	NT B	NT	NT	NT	NT	NT C	NT D	TP 1 ◇	NT	NT	NT	TP 1 ◇ E	NT	NT	NT	NT	NT C	NT D	TP 1 ◇	NT	NT	TP 1 ◇ A	TP 1 ◇ A
Blackpool North	97 d					13 11		13 25		13 41							14 11		14 21		14 41				
Layton	97 d					13 14											14 14								
Poulton-le-Fylde	97 d					13 18				13 47							14 18				14 47				
Kirkham & Wesham	97 d	13b19				13 27								14b19			14 27							15b19	
Barrow-in-Furness	d		12 06									12 56													14 10
Roose	d											13 00													
Dalton	d											13 06													
Ulverston	d		12 22									13 14													14 26
Cark	d											13 22													
Kents Bank	d											13 26													
Grange-over-Sands	d		12 35									13 30													14 39
Arnside	d		12 41									13 36													14 45
Silverdale	d											13 41													
Carnforth	d		12 53									13 50													14 55
Windermere	83 d	12 21												13 24										14 18	
Oxenholme Lake District	65 d	12c40								13 13				13e49			13 59							14f37	
Lancaster 6	65 a	12 58	13 05									14 00		14 05										14 54	15 03
	d	12c59								13 29				14 06							14 29			15 16	
Preston 8	d	13 38				13 41		13 50		14 08				14 38			14 41		14 46		15 08			15 38	
Leyland	d							13a55		14 13									14a51		15 13				
Chorley	d	13 47				13 51				14 19				14 47			14 51				15 19			15 47	
Adlington (Lancashire)	d					13 56											14 56								
Blackrod	d					14 00											15 00								
Horwich Parkway	d					14 03				14 27							15 03				15 27				
Lostock	d					14 07				14 30							15 07				15 30				
Southport	d			13 10			13 38								14 15			14 38							
Meols Cop	d			13 15											14 20										
Bescar Lane	d			13 20																					
New Lane	d			13 24																					
Burscough Bridge	d			13 26			13 50								14 28			14 50							
Hoscar	d			13 30																					
Parbold	d			13 33			13 55								14 33			14 55							
Appley Bridge	d			13 37			13 59								14 37			14 59							
Gathurst	d			13 40											14 40										
Liverpool Central 10	103 d										13 20											14 20			
Kirkby	d										13 51											14 51			
Rainford	d										13 58											14 58			
Upholland	d										14 02											15 02			
Orrell	d										14 06											15 06			
Pemberton	d										14 09											15 09			
Wigan Wallgate	a			13 45			14 05				14 14				14 45			15 05				15 14			
	d			13 47	13 52		14 07				14 16		14 32		14 47	14 52		15 07				15 16	15 32		
Wigan North Western	d																								
Ince	d										14 19											15 19			
Hindley	d			13 52							14 22		14 37		14 52							15 22	15 37		
Westhoughton	d						14 15						14 41					15 15					15 41		
Bolton	a	13 58			14 06	14 12	14 23			14 34			14 49	14 58		15 06	15 12	15 23			15 34		15 49	15 58	
	d	13 59			14 07	14 12	14 23		14 30	14 36			14 50	14 59		15 07	15 12	15 23		15 30	15 36		15 50	15 59	
Moses Gate	d				14 10											15 10									
Farnworth	d												14 53										15 53		
Kearsley	d												14 55										15 55		
Daisy Hill	d			13 56							14 26				14 56							15 26			
Hag Fold	d										14 29											15 29			
Atherton	d			14 00							14 32				15 00							15 32			
Walkden	d			14 05							14 37				15 05							15 37			
Moorside	d										14 41											15 41			
Swinton	d			14 10							14 43				15 10							15 43			
Salford Crescent	a	14 11		14 17	14 21	14 25	14 36		14 42	14 48	14 50		15 06	15 11	15 17	15 21	15 25	15 36		15 42	15 48	15 50	16 06	16 11	
	d	14 11		14 17	14 22	14 25	14 36		14 43	14 48	14 50		15 07	15 11	15 17	15 22	15 25	15 36		15 43	15 48	15 50	16 07	16 11	
Salford Central	d			14 20	14 24				14 45		14 53		15 09		15 20	15 24				15 45		15 53	16 10		
Manchester Victoria	a			14 24	14 32				14 50		15 00		15 14		15 24	15 30				15 50		15 59	16 14		
Rochdale	95 a			14 55	15 08						15 25		15 38		15 55	16 08						16 25	16 38		
Deansgate	a	14 15				14 29											15 29							16 15	
Manchester Oxford Road	a	14 16				14 31	14 41			14 53				15 16			15 31	15 41			15 53			16 16	
Manchester Piccadilly 10	a	14 20				14 35	14 45			14 57				15 20			15 35	15 45			15 57			16 20	
Stockport	84 a	14 42				14 46	15 12			15 28				15 42			15 46	16 12			16 28			16 42	
Hazel Grove	86 a					14 55	15 28										15 56	16 29							
Buxton	86 a					15 30	16 06										16 41								
Heald Green	85 a	14 32								15 12				15 32							16 11			16 49	
Manchester Airport	85 a	14 40					15 01			15 19				15 40				16 01			16 19			16 40	

For general notes see front of timetable
For details of catering facilities see Directory of Train Operators

A ⚯ from Preston
B From Carlisle via Whitehaven (Table 100)
C To Liverpool Lime Street (Table 90)
D From Clitheroe (Table 94)
E From Edinburgh (Table 65)
b Change at Preston
c By changing at Preston, passengers may depart Oxenholme Lake District at 1253, Lancaster at 1309
e By changing at Preston, passengers may depart at 1359
f By changing at Preston, passengers may depart at 1453

Blackpool, Barrow-in-Furness, Preston, Southport, Kirkby and Wigan → Bolton → Manchester

Network Diagram - see first page of Table 82

		NT	NT	NT	NT	NT	TP	NT	NT	NT	NT	TP	NT	NT	NT	NT	NT	NT	NT	NT	TP	NT	NT	TP	NT
							1 ◇					1 ◇									1 ◇			1 ◇	
					A	B			C		D	E						B	A			G		H	A
							𝌀					𝌀									𝌀			𝌀	
Blackpool North	97 d			15 11		15 25	15 41							16 10				16 25			16 38				
Layton	97 d			15 14										16 13							16 41				
Poulton-le-Fylde	97 d			15 18			15 47							16 17							16 45				
Kirkham & Wesham	97 d			15 27										16 26							16 56				
Barrow-in-Furness	d																					15 28		16 21	
Roose	d																					15 32			
Dalton	d																					15 38			
Ulverston	d																					15 47		16 37	
Cark	d																					15 55			
Kents Bank	d																					15 59			
Grange-over-Sands	d																					16 03		16 50	
Arnside	d																					16 09		16 56	
Silverdale	d																					16 14			
Carnforth	d								15 26													16 22		17 06	
Windermere	83 d											*15 21*												*16b28*	
Oxenholme Lake District	65 d			*14 53*			*15 12*					15 47												*16 53*	
Lancaster 6	65 a								15 38			16 02										16 33		17 14	
	d			*15 08*			*15 28*					16c03		*16 09*							*16 29*			17 15	
Preston 8	d			15 41		15 50	16 08					16 38		16 38				16 50			17 08			17 35	
Leyland	d					15a55	16 13							16 44				16a55			17 13				
Chorley	d			15 51			16 19					16 47		16 51							17 19			17 44	
Adlington (Lancashire)	d			15 56										16 56							17 23				
Blackrod	d			16 00										16 59											
Horwich Parkway	d			16 03			16 27							17 03							17 28				
Lostock	d			16 07			16 30							17 06							17 31			17 52	
Southport	d	15 10								15 51			16 16				16 43								
Meols Cop	d	15 15											16 21												
Bescar Lane	d	15 20																							
New Lane	d	15 24																							
Burscough Bridge	d	15 26								16 03			16 29				16 55								
Hoscar	d	15 30																							
Parbold	d	15 33								16 08			16 34				17 00								
Appley Bridge	d	15 37								16 12			16 38				17 04								
Gathurst	d	15 40								16 15			16 41												
Liverpool Central 10	103 d							*15 20*								*16 05*									
Kirkby	d							15 51								16 38									
Rainford	d							15 58								16 45									
Upholland	d							16 02								16 49									
Orrell	d							16 06								16 52									
Pemberton	d							16 09								16 55									
Wigan Wallgate	a	15 45						16 14		16 20			16 46			17 01	17 10								
	d	15 47	15 52					16 16		16 21	16 32		16 47		16 58	17 06	17 12								
Wigan North Western	d																						17 31		
Ince	d							16 19							17 01	17 09							17 33		
Hindley	d	15 52						16 22			16 37		16 52		17 04	17 13							17 37		
Westhoughton	d									16 30	16 41				17 09								17 41		
Bolton	a		16 07	16 12			16 34			16 40	16 49	16 58		17 11	17 17		17 27				17 36		17 50	17 59	
	d		16 10	16 12	16 20		16 36			16 43	16 50	16 59		17 12	17 18		17 27		17 30		17 36		17 50	17 59	18 03
Moses Gate	d				16 23														17 34						
Farnworth	d										16 53												17 53		
Kearsley	d										16 55									←			17 55		
Daisy Hill	d	15 56						16 26					16 56			17 17 →				17 17					
Hag Fold	d							16 29												17 20					
Atherton	d	16 00						16 32					17 00							17 22					
Walkden	d	16 05						16 37					17 06							17 28					
Moorside	d							16 41												17 31					
Swinton	d	16 10						16 43					17 10							17 34					
Salford Crescent	a	16 17	16 22	16 25	16 34		16 48	16 50		16 55	17 06	17 11	17 18	17 24	17 30		17 40			17 45	17 48		18 07	18 11	18 14
	d	16 17	16 22	16 25	16 35		16 48	16 50		16 56	17 07	17 12	17 18	17 25	17 31		17 40			17 45	17 48		18 07	18 11	18 14
Salford Central	d	16 20	16 25		16 37			16 55			17 09		17 23		17 33				17 45	17 48			18 09		18 16
Manchester Victoria	⇌ a	16 25	16 30		16 42			16 59			17 14		17 27		17 40				17 51	17 54			18 15		18 23
Rochdale	95 a	16 55			*17 08*			17 25					17 55		*18 08*					*18 32*					
Deansgate	⇌ a			16 29						16 59				17 28										18 15	
Manchester Oxford Road	a			16 32			16 53			17 01		17 16		17 30			17 45				17 55			18 17	
Manchester Piccadilly 10	⇌ a			16 35			16 57			17 06		17 20		17 35			17 49				17 57			18 20	
Stockport	84 a			16 45						17 19		*17 42*		17 47			*18 12*				*18 26*			*18 42*	
Hazel Grove	86 a			16 53						17 27				17 56			*18 27*								
Buxton	86 a			17 30						18 07				18 30			*19 08*								
Heald Green	85 a						17 12					*17 49*									18 12			18 35	
Manchester Airport	85 ✈ a			*17e14*			17 19					17 40					18 05				18 19			18 42	

For general notes see front of timetable
For details of catering facilities see Directory of Train Operators

A From Clitheroe (Table 94)

B To Liverpool Lime Street (Table 90)

C From Leeds to Morecambe (Table 36)

D To Huddersfield (Table 39)

E From Glasgow Central (Table 65)

G From Carlisle via Whitehaven (Table 100)

H 𝌀 from Preston

b Change at Oxenholme Lake District and Lancaster

c By changing at Preston, passengers may depart at 1609

e Change at Manchester Piccadilly

Table 82

Mondays to Fridays

Blackpool, Barrow-in-Furness, Preston, Southport, Kirkby and Wigan → Bolton → Manchester

Network Diagram - see first page of Table 82

		NT	NT	NT	NT	NT	NT	TP	NT	TP	NT	TP	NT	NT	NT	NT	NT	NT	NT	NT	TP	TP	NT	NT	NT
								1 ◇		1 ◇		1 ◇									1 ◇	1 ◇			
						A						B	C			A	C	D	E				G		
Blackpool North	97 d			17 10				17 38						18 11		18 25					18 38				19 10
Layton	97 d			17 13				17 41						18 14											19 13
Poulton-le-Fylde	97 d			17 17				17 45						18 18							18 44				19 17
Kirkham & Wesham	97 d			17 26				17 56				18b19		18 27											19 26
Barrow-in-Furness	d									17 06									17 43						
Roose	d																		17 47						
Dalton	d									17 15									17 53						
Ulverston	d									17 24									18 01						
Cark	d									17 32									18 09						
Kents Bank	d																		18 13						
Grange-over-Sands	d									17 39									18 17						
Arnside	d									17 45									18 23						
Silverdale	d																		18 28						
Carnforth	d									17 55								18 31	18 34						
Windermere	83 d											17 27										18 09			
Oxenholme Lake District	65 d							*17 13*				17c53		*18 00*								18 38			*18 51*
Lancaster 6	65 a									18 04		18 09						18 43	18 44			18 55			
	d							*17 29*				18 16										18 55			*19 08*
Preston 8	d			17 40		17 50		18 08				18 38		18 41		18 50					19 03	19 14			19 39
Leyland	d			17 45		17a55		18 13								18a55					19 08				19 44
Chorley	d			17 51				18 19				18 47		18 51							19 15				19 51
Adlington (Lancashire)	d			17 56										18 56											19 56
Blackrod	d			18 00										19 00											20 00
Horwich Parkway	d			18 03				18 27						19 03							19 22				20 03
Lostock	d			18 07				18 30						19 07							19 25				20 07
Southport	d	17 14			17 42										18 28									19 16	
Meols Cop	d	17 19			17 47										18 33									19 21	
Bescar Lane	d	17 24													18 38										
New Lane	d	17 28													18 42										
Burscough Bridge	d	17 30			17 55										18 44									19 29	
Hoscar	d	17 34													18 48										
Parbold	d	17 37			18 00										18 51									19 34	
Appley Bridge	d	17 41			18 04										18 55									19 38	
Gathurst	d	17 44													18 58									19 41	
Liverpool Central 10	103 d		*17 05*																	*18 20*					
Kirkby	d		17 41																	18 43					
Rainford	d		17 48																	18 50					
Upholland	d		17 52																	18 54					
Orrell	d		17 55																	18 58					
Pemberton	d		17 58																	19 01					
Wigan Wallgate	a	17 49	18 04		18 10										19 04					19 09				19 46	
	d	17 50	18 05		18 12										19 05					19 11				19 48	
Wigan North Western	d								18 18		18 31														
Ince	d		18 08						18 21		18 34									19 14					
Hindley	d	17 55	18 12						18 25		18 38				19 10					19 17				19 53	
Westhoughton	d				18 21				18 29						19 15										
Bolton	a			18 13	18 29			18 34	18 39			18 58		19 12	19 23						19 30	19 45			20 12
	d			18 13	18 29			18 36	18 40			18 59	19 02	19 12	19 23		19 30				19 33	19 46	20 00		20 12
Moses Gate	d								18 43																
Farnworth	d																								
Kearsley	d						←																		
Daisy Hill	d	18 00	18 16 →				18 16				18 42									19 21				19 57	
Hag Fold	d						18 19													19 24					
Atherton	d	18 04					18 21				18 46									19 27				20 01	
Walkden	d	18 09					18 27				18 51									19 32				20 06	
Moorside	d						18 30													19 36					
Swinton	d	18 14					18 33				18 56									19 38				20 11	
Salford Crescent	a	18 21		18 26	18 41		18 43	18 48	18 54		19 05	19 11	19 13	19 25	19 36		19 42			19 44	19 49		20 13	20 18	20 25
	d	18 22		18 26	18 41		18 43	18 48	18 55		19 05	19 11	19 14	19 25	19 36		19 43			19 44	19 49		20 13	20 18	20 25
Salford Central	d	18 24					18 46		18 57		19 08		19 16				19 45			19 47			20 17	20 21	
Manchester Victoria	⇌ a	18 29					18 54		19 01		19 14		19 23				19 50			19 53			20 22	20 26	
Rochdale	95 a	*19 05*							*19 38*											*20 38*					
Deansgate	⇌ a													19 29							19 53				20 29
Manchester Oxford Road	a			18 33	18 47			18 55				19 16		19 33	19 41						19 54	20 00			20 31
Manchester Piccadilly 10	⇌ a			18 38	18 51			18 59				19 20		19 36	19 46						19 57	20 04			20 34
Stockport	84 a			18 48	*19 15*			*19 25*				*19 42*		19 47	*20 15*							*20 26*			20 44
Hazel Grove	86 a			18 56										19 55											20 52
Buxton	86 a			19 36										20 36											21 30
Heald Green	85 a			*19e07*				19 12				19 31									20 12	20 18			*21e01*
Manchester Airport	85 ✈ a				19 09			19 19				19 40			20 05						20 19	20 26			*21e06*

For general notes see front of timetable
For details of catering facilities see Directory of Train Operators

- **A** To Liverpool Lime Street (Table 90)
- **B** From Edinburgh (Table 65)
- **C** From Clitheroe (Table 94)
- **D** From Leeds to Morecambe (Table 36)
- **E** From Sellafield (Table 100)
- **G** From Blackburn (Table 94)
- **b** Change at Preston
- **c** By changing at Preston, passengers may depart at 1800
- **e** Change at Manchester Piccadilly

Blackpool, Barrow-in-Furness, Preston, Southport, Kirkby and Wigan → Bolton → Manchester

Network Diagram - see first page of Table 82

	NT	NT	NT	TP	NT	NT	TP	TP	NT	NT	NT	TP	NT	NT	NT	TP	NT	NT	VT	NT	NT	NT	TP
				1 ◇			1 ◇	1 ◇				1 ◇				1 ◇			1 ◇				1 ◇
		A	B			A	C			B				B	D			A	E	B			
							🍴												☕				
Blackpool North 97 d		19 25		19 42								20 53				21 53		22 03					23 13
Layton 97 d				19 45								20 56				21 56							23 16
Poulton-le-Fylde 97 d				19 49								21 00				22 00							23 20
Kirkham & Wesham 97 d				19 59								21 10				22 10							23 30
Barrow-in-Furness d								19 10														21 45	
Roose d								19 14														21 49	
Dalton d								19 21														21 55	
Ulverston d								19 29														22 04	
Cark d								19 37														22 12	
Kents Bank d								19 41														22 16	
Grange-over-Sands d								19 45														22 20	
Arnside d								19 51														22 26	
Silverdale d								19 57														22 31	
Carnforth d								20 07														22 38	
Windermere 83 d						*19b18*										*20b27*			*21 28*			*22 16*	
Oxenholme Lake District 65 d						*19 44*	19 55					*20 07*				*20 52*			22 27			*22 36*	
Lancaster 6 65 a							20 10	20 15											22 42			22 49	
d						*20 01*	20 11	20 17				*20 23*				*21 07*			22 44			23 01	
Preston 8 d		19 50		20 11		20 27	20 32	20 38				21 24				22 22		22 27	23 23			23 29	23 42
Leyland d		19a55				20a32		20 43				21 29				22 27		22a32					23 47
Chorley d				20 21			20 42	20 49				21 35				22 35							23 54
Adlington (Lancashire) d								20 54				21 40				22 39							23 58
Blackrod d								20 57				21 43				22 43							00 02
Horwich Parkway d								21 01				21 47				22 46							00 05
Lostock d								21 04				21 50				22 49							00 08
Southport d	19 34								20 34				21 34				22 29				23 10		
Meols Cop d	19 39								20 39				21 39				22 34				23 15		
Bescar Lane d																	22 39						
New Lane d																	22 43						
Burscough Bridge d	19 47								20 47				21 47				22 45				23 23		
Hoscar d																	22 49						
Parbold d	19 52								20 52				21 52				22 52				23 28		
Appley Bridge d	19 56								20 56				21 56				22 56				23 32		
Gathurst d	19 59								20 59				21 59				22 59				23 35		
Liverpool Central 10 103 d																							
Kirkby d																							
Rainford d																							
Upholland d																							
Orrell d																							
Pemberton d																							
Wigan Wallgate a	20 04								21 04				22 04				23 04				23 43		
d	20 05				20 18				21 05		21 18		22 05		22 16		23 05						
Wigan North Western d																							
Ince d					20 21						21 21				22 19								
Hindley d	20 10				20 24				21 10		21 24		22 10		22 22		23 10						
Westhoughton d	20 15								21 15				22 15				23 15						
Bolton a	20 23			20 32			20 53	21 08	21 23			21 54	22 23			22 53	23 23					23 51	00 12
d	20 23		20 30	20 34			20 54	21 09	21 23	21 30		21 56	22 23	22 33		22 55	23 23			23 40		23 51	00 13
Moses Gate d																							
Farnworth d																							
Kearsley d																							
Daisy Hill d					20 28						21 28				22 26								
Hag Fold d					20 31						21 31				22 29								
Atherton d					20 34						21 34				22 32								
Walkden d					20 39						21 39				22 37								
Moorside d					20 43						21 43				22 41								
Swinton d					20 45						21 45				22 43								
Salford Crescent a	20 36		20 42	20 46	20 52		21 06	21 21	21 36	21 42	21 52	22 08	22 36	22 46	22 51	23 07	23 36			23 52			
d	20 36		20 43	20 47	20 52		21 06	21 22	21 36	21 43	21 52	22 09	22 36	22 46	22 52	23 09	23 36			23 53			
Salford Central d			20 45		20 56					21 45	21 56		22c39		22c55								
Manchester Victoria 🚋 a			20 50		21 00					21 50	22 00		22 44		23 00					00 01		00 09	
Rochdale 95 a					*21 38*						*22 38*				*23 38*								
Deansgate 🚋 a				20 53					21 40			22 13		22 50		23 15							
Manchester Oxford Road a	20 41			20 54			21 11	21 26	21 41			22 14		22 52		23 19	23 41						
Manchester Piccadilly 10 🚋 a	20 45			20 58			21 14	21 30	21 46			22 18		22 56		23 30	23 46		00 16				00 29
Stockport 84 a	*21 14*			*21 26*			*21 34*		21 59			22e37		23 06		23e50							
Hazel Grove 86 a									22 06					23 14									
Buxton 86 a									22 46					23 54									
Heald Green 85 a				21 12			21 30	21 44				22 31				23 47							00 40
Manchester Airport 85 ✈ a	21 09			21 19			21 37	21 51				22 39		23f28		23 58							00 45

For general notes see front of timetable
For details of catering facilities see Directory of Train Operators

- **A** To Liverpool Lime Street (Table 90)
- **B** From Clitheroe (Table 94)
- **C** From Edinburgh (Table 65)
- **D** To Huddersfield (Table 39)
- **E** From Glasgow Central (Table 65)
- **b** Change at Oxenholme Lake District and Preston
- **c** Fridays only
- **e** Change at Manchester Oxford Road
- **f** Change at Manchester Piccadilly

Table 82

Blackpool, Barrow-in-Furness, Preston, Southport, Kirkby and Wigan → Bolton → Manchester

until 22 March

Network Diagram - see first page of Table 82

		TP	TP	TP	TP	TP	TP	NT	NT	NT	NT	NT		TP	NT	NT	NT	NT	NT	NT	TP	TP	NT	NT	NT
		1◇	1◇	1◇	1◇	1◇	1◇							1◇							1◇	1◇			
				A				B		C		D					E	G	H		J	J			K
																					✠	✠			
Blackpool North	97 d	01 43	03 50		04 43	05 19	05b30			06 08				06 34				06 57			07 03				
Layton	97 d					05 09				06 12				06 37				07 00			07 07				
Poulton-le-Fylde	97 d					05 25	05b36			06 16				06 41				07 04			07 11				
Kirkham & Wesham	97 d					05 22				06 24				06 51			07 04	07 13			07 20				
Barrow-in-Furness	d			04 15			05 15															06 15			
Roose	d																					06 19			
Dalton	d																					06 25			
Ulverston	d			04 30			05 30															06 34			
Cark	d																					06 42			
Kents Bank	d																					06 46			
Grange-over-Sands	d			04 43			05 43															06 50			
Arnside	d			04 50			05 49															06 56			
Silverdale	d																					07 01			
Carnforth	d			05c02			05 58															07 08			07 42
Windermere	83 d																							06e35	
Oxenholme Lake District	65 d																							07 08	
Lancaster 6	65 a			05 11			06 08															07 15			07 53
	d					05 20	06 08							06 25								07 16		07 24	
Preston 8	d	02u08	04u16		05 17	05 48	06 28			06 37				07 03			07 20	07 25			07 40			07 50	
Leyland	d									06 42				07 08			07 25	07a30						07 55	
Chorley	d				05 26		06 37			06 50				07 15			07 33				07 49			08 03	
Adlington (Lancashire)	d									06 55							07 38							08 08	
Blackrod	d									06 58				07 21			07 42							08 11	
Horwich Parkway	d						06 45			07 02				07 24			07 46							08 15	
Lostock	d				05 34		06 48			07 06				07 27			07 49							08 19	
Southport	d										06 35														
Meols Cop	d										06 40														
Bescar Lane	d																								
New Lane	d																								
Burscough Bridge	d										06 48														
Hoscar	d																								
Parbold	d										06 53														
Appley Bridge	d										06 57														
Gathurst	d										07 00														
Liverpool Central 10	103 d																			06 50			07f04		
Kirkby	d																			07 16					
Rainford	d																			07 23					
Upholland	d																			07 27					
Orrell	d																			07 31					
Pemberton	d																			07 34					
Wigan Wallgate	a										07 05									07 39					
	d								06 45		07 06				07 13	07 27				07 43					
Wigan North Western	d					06 13																	07 56		
Ince	d								06 48						07 16	07 30				07 46					
Hindley	d					06 18			06 51						07 19	07 34				07 49			08 01		
Westhoughton	d					06 22					07 14					07 38							08 06		
Bolton	a				05 39	06 29	06 52			07 11	07 22			07 32		07 46	07 55				08 02		08 14	08 24	
	d	02u43	04u43		05 40	06 31	06 54	06 58		07 12	07 23	07 30		07 33		07 47	07 55		08 00		08 04		08 15	08 24	
Moses Gate	d							07 01								07 50							08 18		
Farnworth	d							07 03								07 52							08 20		
Kearsley	d							07 05								07 54							08 22		
Daisy Hill	d								06 55						07 23					07 53					
Hag Fold	d								06 58						07 26					07 56					
Atherton	d								07 01						07 29					07 59					
Walkden	d								07 06						07 34					08 04					
Moorside	d								07 10						07 38					08 08					
Swinton	d								07 12						07 40					08 10					
Salford Crescent	a					06 43	07 06	07 17	07 18	07 25	07 35	07 42		07 45	07 47	08 04	08 07		08 13	08 18			08 32	08 37	
	d					06 43	07 06	07 17	07 18	07 26	07 36	07 43		07 46	07 47	08 04	08 07		08 13	08 18			08 32	08 37	
Salford Central	d							07 21	07 23			07 45			07 49	08 07			08 16	08 21			08 35		
Manchester Victoria	🚋 a							07 25	07 27			07 51			07 56	08 14			08 21	08 25			08 41		
Rochdale	95 a								08 06			08 33				08 38				08 55			09 08		
Deansgate	🚋 a					06 49				07 29	07 39						08 12							08 41	
Manchester Oxford Road	a					06 51	07 12			07 32	07 41			07 50			08 14				08 20			08 43	
Manchester Piccadilly 10	🚋 a	02 58			05 57	06 56	07 15			07 36	07 45			07 54			08 20				08 25			08 47	
Stockport	84 a				06 25	07 26	07 37			07 48	08 02			08 25			08 29				08 53			09 08	
Hazel Grove	86 a				07 07	07 44	07 54			08 13				08 51										09 16	
Buxton	86 a				07 45		08 33							09 27										09 53	
Heald Green	85 a				06 21	07 27	07 32							08 11			08g51								
Manchester Airport	85 ✈ a	03 13	05 21		06 14	07 15	07 40				08 02			08 19							08 42			09 06	

For general notes see front of timetable
For details of catering facilities see Directory of Train Operators

A To Windermere (Table 83)
B From Blackburn (Table 94). Also stops at Clifton 0709
C To Chester (Table 88)
D From Blackburn (Table 94)
E From St Annes-on-the-Sea (Table 97) to Greenbank (Table 88)
G To Liverpool Lime Street (Table 90)
H From Clitheroe (Table 94)
J ✠ from Preston
K From Leeds (Table 36)
b Change at Preston
c Arr. 0459
e Change at Oxenholme Lake District and Preston
f Liverpool Lime Street (Table 90)
g Change at Manchester Piccadilly

Table 82

until 22 March

Blackpool, Barrow-in-Furness, Preston, Southport, Kirkby and Wigan → Bolton → Manchester

Network Diagram - see first page of Table 82

	NT		NT	TP	NT	NT	TP	NT	NT	NT	NT	NT	NT		TP	NT	NT	NT	TP	NT	NT	NT	NT	NT
				1 ◇			1 ◇								1 ◇				1 ◇					
	A						B	C				D	A				E		G	C				
				🍴			🍴												🍴					
Blackpool North 97 d				07 41						08 09					08 41								09 11	
Layton 97 d				07 44						08 12													09 14	
Poulton-le-Fylde 97 d				07 48						08 16					08 47								09 18	
Kirkham & Wesham 97 d				07 58						08 25		*08 28*											09 27	
Barrow-in-Furness d							07 05										07 58							
Roose d																	08 02							
Dalton d							07 14										08 08							
Ulverston d							07 22										08 17							
Cark d							07 30										08 25							
Kents Bank d																	08 29							
Grange-over-Sands d							07 37										08 33							
Arnside d							07 43										08 39							
Silverdale d							07 47										08 43							
Carnforth d							07 55										08 51							
Windermere 83 d															*07b24*				*08 28*					
Oxenholme Lake District 65 d															*08 07*				08 59				*08c53*	
Lancaster 6 65 a							08 02										09 02		09 14					
d							08 03								*08 27*				09 14				*09c09*	
Preston 8 d				08 12			08 34			08 38		08 50			09 08				09 38				09 41	
Leyland d										08 43		08a55			09 13									
Chorley d				08 22			08 44			08 51					09 19				09 47				09 51	
Adlington (Lancashire) d										08 56													09 56	
Blackrod d										09 00													10 00	
Horwich Parkway d							08 52			09 03					09 27								10 03	
Lostock d										09 07					09 30								10 07	
Southport d			07 41						08 09		08 35										09 10			09 38
Meols Cop d			07 46						08 14		08 40										09 15			
Bescar Lane d									08 19												09 20			
New Lane d									08 23												09 24			
Burscough Bridge d			07 54						08 25		08 48										09 26			09 50
Hoscar d									08 29												09 30			
Parbold d			07 59						08 32		08 53										09 33			09 55
Appley Bridge d			08 03						08 36		08 57										09 37			09 59
Gathurst d			08 06						08 39		09 00										09 40			
Liverpool Central 10 103 d						*07 50*																		
Kirkby d						08 16																		
Rainford d						08 23																		
Upholland d						08 27																		
Orrell d						08 31																		
Pemberton d						08 34																		
Wigan Wallgate a			08 11			08 40			08 44		09 05										09 45			10 05
d			08 13		08 32				08 45		09 07					09 16		09 32			09 47	09 52		10 07
Wigan North Western d																								
Ince d			08 16													09 19								
Hindley d			08 19		08 37				08 50							09 22		09 37			09 52			
Westhoughton d					08 41						09 15							09 41						10 15
Bolton a				08 33	08 49		08 58			09 12	09 23				09 34			09 49	09 58			10 06	10 12	10 23
d	08 30			08 34	08 50		08 59	09 01		09 12	09 23		09 30		09 36			09 50	09 59	10 01		10 07	10 12	10 23
Moses Gate d								09 04														10 10		
Farnworth d					08 53													09 53						
Kearsley d					08 55													09 55						
Daisy Hill d			08 23						08 54							09 26					09 56			
Hag Fold d			08 26						08 57							09 29								
Atherton d			08 29						09 00							09 32					10 00			
Walkden d			08 34						09 05							09 37					10 05			
Moorside d			08 38						09 09							09 41								
Swinton d			08 40						09 11							09 43					10 10			
Salford Crescent a	08 42		08 50		09 06		09 11	09 16	09 20	09 25	09 36		09 42		09 48	09 50		10 06	10 11	10 13	10 17	10 22	10 25	10 36
d	08 42		08 50		09 07		09 11	09 16	09 20	09 25	09 36		09 42		09 48	09 50		10 07	10 11	10 13	10 17	10 22	10 25	10 36
Salford Central d	08 45		08 53		09 09			09 19	09 23				09 45			09 53		10 09		10 16	10 20	10 24		
Manchester Victoria ⇌ a	08 50		09 00		09 14			09 25	09 26				09 50			10 00		10 14		10 21	10 24	10 32		
Rochdale 95 a			09 25		*09 38*				09 55							10 25		*10 38*			10 55	*11 08*		
Deansgate ⇌ a							09 15			09 29													10 29	
Manchester Oxford Road a				08 49			09 16			09 31	09 41				09 53				10 16				10 31	10 41
Manchester Piccadilly 10 ⇌ a				08 53			09 20			09 35	09 45				09 57				10 20				10 35	10 45
Stockport 84 a				*09 13*			*09 39*			09 49	*10 12*				*10 26*				*10 39*				10 49	*11 05*
Hazel Grove 86 a				*09 32*						09 57	*10 29*												10 57	*11 29*
Buxton 86 a										10 36													11 33	
Heald Green 85 a				*09 18*			09 31								10 11				10 32					
Manchester Airport 85 ✈ a				09 13			09 40				10 02				10 19				10 40					11 01

For general notes see front of timetable
For details of catering facilities see Directory of Train Operators

- **A** From Clitheroe (Table 94)
- **B** 🍴 from Preston
- **C** From Blackburn (Table 94)
- **D** To Liverpool Lime Street (Table 90)
- **E** From Maryport (Table 100)
- **G** From Glasgow Central (from 2 February from Carlisle) (Table 65)
- **b** Change at Oxenholme Lake District and Preston
- **c** Until 26 January only

Table 82

Saturdays

until 22 March

Blackpool, Barrow-in-Furness, Preston, Southport, Kirkby and Wigan → Bolton → Manchester

Network Diagram - see first page of Table 82

Station	NT	NT	TP		NT	NT	NT	TP	NT	NT	NT	NT	NT	NT	TP		NT	NT	NT	TP	NT	NT	NT	NT
			1 ◇					1 ◇							1 ◇					1 ◇				
	A	B			C			D					A	B				E		G				
			(trolley)					(trolley)							(trolley)					(trolley)				
Blackpool North 97 d	09 25		09 40								10 11		10 25		10 41								11 11	
Layton 97 d											10 14												11 14	
Poulton-le-Fylde 97 d			09 46								10 18				10 47								11 18	
Kirkham & Wesham 97 d								10b19			10 27									11b19			11 27	
Barrow-in-Furness d								09 15										09 58						
Roose d								09 19										10 02						
Dalton d								09 25										10 08						
Ulverston d								09 34										10 16						
Cark d								09 42										10 24						
Kents Bank d								09 46										10 28						
Grange-over-Sands d								09 50										10 32						
Arnside d								09 56										10 38						
Silverdale d								10 01										10 43						
Carnforth d					09 53			10 08										10 50						
Windermere 83 d								09c26												10 18				
Oxenholme Lake District 65 d			09 11					09 54							10 06					10 54				
Lancaster 6 65 a					10 04			10 15										11 01		11 10				
d			09 27					10 16			10 09				10 22					11 10			11 10	
Preston 8 d	09 50		10 08					10 38			10 41		10 50		11 08					11 38			11 41	
Leyland d	09a55		10 13										10a55		11 13									
Chorley d			10 19					10 47			10 51				11 19					11 47			11 51	
Adlington (Lancashire) d											10 56												11 56	
Blackrod d											11 00												12 00	
Horwich Parkway d			10 27								11 03				11 27								12 03	
Lostock d			10 30								11 07				11 30								12 07	
Southport d									10 15			10 38									11 10			11 38
Meols Cop d									10 20												11 15			
Bescar Lane d																					11 20			
New Lane d																					11 24			
Burscough Bridge d									10 28			10 50									11 26			11 50
Hoscar d																					11 30			
Parbold d									10 33			10 55									11 33			11 55
Appley Bridge d									10 37			10 59									11 37			11 59
Gathurst d									10 40												11 40			
Liverpool Central 10 103 d						09 20											10 20							
Kirkby d						09 51											10 51							
Rainford d						09 58											10 58							
Upholland d						10 02											11 02							
Orrell d						10 06											11 06							
Pemberton d						10 09											11 09							
Wigan Wallgate a						10 14			10 45			11 05					11 14				11 45			12 05
d						10 16	10 32		10 47	10 52		11 07					11 16		11 32		11 47	11 52		12 07
Wigan North Western d																								
Ince d						10 19											11 19							
Hindley d						10 22	10 37		10 52								11 22		11 37		11 52			
Westhoughton d							10 41					11 15							11 41					12 15
Bolton a			10 34				10 49	10 58		11 06	11 12	11 23			11 34				11 49	11 58		12 06	12 12	12 23
d		10 30	10 36				10 50	10 59		11 07	11 12	11 23		11 30	11 36				11 50	11 59		12 07	12 12	12 23
Moses Gate d										11 10												12 10		
Farnworth d							10 53												11 53					
Kearsley d							10 55												11 55					
Daisy Hill d						10 26			10 56								11 26				11 56			
Hag Fold d						10 29											11 29							
Atherton d						10 32			11 00								11 32				12 00			
Walkden d						10 37			11 05								11 37				12 05			
Moorside d						10 41											11 41							
Swinton d						10 43			11 10								11 43				12 10			
Salford Crescent a		10 43	10 48			10 50	11 06	11 11	11 17	11 21	11 25	11 36		11 43	11 48		11 50		12 06	12 11	12 17	12 21	12 25	12 36
d		10 43	10 48			10 50	11 07	11 11	11 17	11 22	11 25	11 36		11 43	11 48		11 50		12 07	12 11	12 17	12 22	12 25	12 36
Salford Central d		10 45				10 53	11 10		11 20	11 24				11 45			11 53		12 09		12 20	12 24		
Manchester Victoria (tram) a		10 50				11 00	11 14		11 24	11 29				11 51			12 00		12 14		12 24	12 29		
Rochdale 95 a						11 25	11 38		11 55	12 08							12 25		12 38		12 55	13 08		
Deansgate (tram) a								11 15			11 29												12 29	
Manchester Oxford Road a			10 53					11 16			11 31	11 41			11 53					12 16			12 31	12 41
Manchester Piccadilly 10 (tram) a			10 57					11 20			11 35	11 45			11 57					12 20			12 35	12 45
Stockport 84 a			11 26					11 39			11 49	12 05			12 26					12 39			12 49	13 05
Hazel Grove 86 a											11 57	12 29											12 57	13 29
Buxton 86 a											12 36												13 33	
Heald Green 85 a			11 12					11 32							12 12					12 32				
Manchester Airport 85 (air) a			11 19					11 40				12 01			12 19					12 40				13 01

For general notes see front of timetable
For details of catering facilities see Directory of Train Operators

A To Liverpool Lime Street (Table 90)
B From Clitheroe (Table 94)
C From Leeds to Morecambe (Table 36)
D (trolley) from Preston
E From Millom (Table 100)
G From Glasgow Central and from Edinburgh (from 2 February from Carlisle) (Table 65)
b Change at Preston
c Change at Oxenholme Lake District and Lancaster

until 22 March

Blackpool, Barrow-in-Furness, Preston, Southport, Kirkby and Wigan → Bolton → Manchester

Network Diagram - see first page of Table 82

		NT	NT	NT	TP	NT	NT	TP	NT	NT	NT	NT	NT	NT	TP	NT	NT	TP	NT	NT	NT	NT	NT
					1 ◇			1 ◇							1 ◇			1 ◇					
		A	B	C				D					A	C				D					A
					⊼			⊼							⊼			⊼					
Blackpool North	97 d	11 25			11 41						12 11		12 25		12 41						13 11		13 25
Layton	97 d										12 14										13 14		
Poulton-le-Fylde	97 d				11 47						12 18				12 47						13 18		
Kirkham & Wesham	97 d							12b19			12 27							13b19			13 27		
Barrow-in-Furness	d							11 18															
Roose	d																						
Dalton	d							11 27															
Ulverston	d							11 35															
Cark	d							11 43															
Kents Bank	d																						
Grange-over-Sands	d							11 50															
Arnside	d							11 56															
Silverdale	d							12 01															
Carnforth	d		11 55					12 08															
Windermere	83 d														11c30			12 23					
Oxenholme Lake District	65 d														12e11			12f42			12 53		
Lancaster 6	65 a		12 04					12 16										13 02					
	d							12 16			12 11				12g16			13f04			13 09		
Preston 8	d	11 50			12 08			12 38			12 41		12 50		13 08			13 38			13 41		13 50
Leyland	d	11a55			12 13								12a55		13 13								13a55
Chorley	d				12 19			12 47			12 51				13 19			13 47			13 51		
Adlington (Lancashire)	d										12 56										13 56		
Blackrod	d										13 00										14 00		
Horwich Parkway	d				12 27						13 03				13 27						14 03		
Lostock	d				12 30						13 07				13 30						14 07		
Southport	d								12 15			12 38							13 10			13 38	
Meols Cop	d								12 20										13 15				
Bescar Lane	d																		13 20				
New Lane	d																		13 24				
Burscough Bridge	d								12 28			12 50							13 26			13 50	
Hoscar	d																		13 30				
Parbold	d								12 33			12 55							13 33			13 55	
Appley Bridge	d								12 37			12 59							13 37			13 59	
Gathurst	d								12 40										13 40				
Liverpool Central 10	103 d					11 20										12 20							
Kirkby	d					11 51										12 51							
Rainford	d					11 58										12 58							
Upholland	d					12 02										13 02							
Orrell	d					12 06										13 06							
Pemberton	d					12 09										13 09							
Wigan Wallgate	a					12 14			12 45			13 05				13 14			13 45			14 05	
	d					12 16	12 32		12 47	12 52		13 07				13 16	13 32		13 47	13 52		14 07	
Wigan North Western	d																						
Ince	d					12 19										13 19							
Hindley	d					12 22	12 37		12 52							13 22	13 37		13 52				
Westhoughton	d						12 41					13 15					13 41					14 15	
Bolton	a				12 35		12 49	12 58		13 06	13 12	13 23			13 34		13 49	13 58		14 06	14 12	14 23	
	d			12 30	12 36		12 50	12 59		13 07	13 12	13 23		13 30	13 36		13 50	13 59		14 07	14 12	14 23	
Moses Gate	d									13 10										14 10			
Farnworth	d						12 53										13 53						
Kearsley	d						12 55										13 55						
Daisy Hill	d					12 26			12 56							13 26			13 56				
Hag Fold	d					12 29										13 29							
Atherton	d					12 32			13 00							13 32			14 00				
Walkden	d					12 37			13 05							13 37			14 05				
Moorside	d					12 41										13 41							
Swinton	d					12 43			13 10							13 43			14 10				
Salford Crescent	a			12 43	12 48	12 50	13 06	13 11	13 17	13 21	13 25	13 36		13 42	13 48	13 50	14 06	14 11	14 17	14 21	14 25	14 36	
	d			12 43	12 49	12 50	13 07	13 11	13 17	13 22	13 25	13 36		13 43	13 48	13 50	14 07	14 11	14 17	14 22	14 25	14 36	
Salford Central	d			12 45		12 53	13 09		13 20	13 24				13 45		13 53	14 09		14 20	14 25			
Manchester Victoria	⇌ a			12 50		13 00	13 14		13 24	13 30				13 50		14 00	14 14		14 24	14 32			
Rochdale	95 a					13 25	13 38		13 55	14 08						14 25	14 38		14 55	15 08			
Deansgate	⇌ a							13 15			13 29							14 15			14 29		
Manchester Oxford Road	a				12 53			13 16			13 31	13 41			13 53			14 16			14 31	14 41	
Manchester Piccadilly 10	⇌ a				12 57			13 20			13 35	13 45			13 57			14 20			14 35	14 45	
Stockport	84 a				13 26			13 39			13 49	14 05			14 26			14 39			14 49	15 05	
Hazel Grove	86 a										13 57	14 29									14 57	15 29	
Buxton	86 a										14 36										15 33		
Heald Green	85 a				13 12			13 32							14 12			14 32					
Manchester Airport	85 ✈ a				13 19			13 40				14 01			14 19			14 40				15 01	

For general notes see front of timetable
For details of catering facilities see Directory of Train Operators

A To Liverpool Lime Street (Table 90)
B From Leeds to Morecambe (Table 36)
C From Clitheroe (Table 94)
D ⊼ from Preston
b Change at Preston
c Until 26 January only. Change at Oxenholme Lake District and Preston
e Until 26 January only
f By changing at Preston, passengers may depart Oxenholme Lake District at 1253, Lancaster at 1309
g Until 26 January dep. 1227

Table 82

until 22 March

Blackpool, Barrow-in-Furness, Preston, Southport, Kirkby and Wigan → Bolton → Manchester

Network Diagram - see first page of Table 82

	NT A	TP 1◇ ⚲	NT	NT	NT	TP 1◇ B ⚲	NT		NT	NT	NT	NT C	NT A	TP 1◇	NT	NT	TP 1◇ D ⚲	TP 1◇ D ⚲	NT		NT	NT	NT A	NT C
Blackpool North 97 d		13 41								14 11		14 25		14 41								15 11		15 25
Layton 97 d										14 14												15 14		
Poulton-le-Fylde 97 d		13 47								14 18				14 47								15 18		
Kirkham & Wesham 97 d						14b19				14 27							15b19					15 27		
Barrow-in-Furness d				12 56														14 10						
Roose d				13 00																				
Dalton d				13 06																				
Ulverston d				13 15														14 26						
Cark d				13 23																				
Kents Bank d				13 27																				
Grange-over-Sands d				13 31														14 39						
Arnside d				13 37														14 45						
Silverdale d				13 42																				
Carnforth d				13 49														14 55						
Windermere 83 d						13 25											14 18							
Oxenholme Lake District 65 d		13 11				13c50				13 58							14e37					14 53		
Lancaster 6 65 a				13 59		14 07											14 54	15 03						
d		13 27				14 17											15 16					15 09		
Preston 8 d		14 08				14 38				14 41		14 50		15 08			15 38					15 41		15 50
Leyland d		14 13										14a55		15 13										15a55
Chorley d		14 19				14 47				14 51				15 19			15 47					15 51		
Adlington (Lancashire) d										14 56												15 56		
Blackrod d										15 00												16 00		
Horwich Parkway d		14 27								15 03				15 27								16 03		
Lostock d		14 30								15 07				15 30								16 07		
Southport d							14 15				14 38								15 10					
Meols Cop d							14 20												15 15					
Bescar Lane d																			15 20					
New Lane d																			15 24					
Burscough Bridge d							14 28				14 50								15 26					
Hoscar d																			15 30					
Parbold d							14 33				14 55								15 33					
Appley Bridge d							14 37				14 59								15 37					
Gathurst d							14 40												15 40					
Liverpool Central 10 103 d			13 20												14 20									
Kirkby d			13 51												14 51									
Rainford d			13 58												14 58									
Upholland d			14 02												15 02									
Orrell d			14 06												15 06									
Pemberton d			14 09												15 09									
Wigan Wallgate a			14 14				14 45				15 05				15 14				15 45					
d			14 16		14 32		14 47		14 52		15 07				15 16	15 32			15 47		15 52			
Wigan North Western d																								
Ince d			14 19												15 19									
Hindley d			14 22		14 37		14 52								15 22	15 37			15 52					
Westhoughton d					14 41						15 15					15 41								
Bolton a		14 34			14 49	14 58			15 06	15 12	15 23			15 34		15 49	15 58				16 07	16 12		
d	14 30	14 36			14 50	14 59			15 07	15 12	15 23		15 30	15 36		15 50	15 59				16 10	16 13	16 20	
Moses Gate d									15 10														16 23	
Farnworth d					14 53											15 53								
Kearsley d					14 55											15 55								
Daisy Hill d			14 26				14 56								15 26				15 56					
Hag Fold d			14 29												15 29									
Atherton d			14 32				15 00								15 32				16 00					
Walkden d			14 37				15 05								15 37				16 05					
Moorside d			14 41												15 41									
Swinton d			14 43				15 10								15 43				16 10					
Salford Crescent a	14 43	14 48	14 50		15 06	15 11	15 17		15 21	15 25	15 36		15 42	15 48	15 50	16 06	16 11		16 17		16 22	16 25	16 34	
d	14 43	14 48	14 50		15 07	15 11	15 17		15 22	15 25	15 36		15 43	15 48	15 50	16 07	16 11		16 17		16 22	16 25	16 35	
Salford Central d	14 45		14 53		15 09		15 20		15 24				15 45		15 53	16 10			16 20		16 25		16 37	
Manchester Victoria ⇌ a	14 50		15 00		15 14		15 24		15 30				15 50		15 59	16 14			16 25		16 30		16 42	
Rochdale 95 a			15 25		15 38		15 55		16 08						16 25	16 38			16 55				17 08	
Deansgate ⇌ a										15 29							16 15					16 29		
Manchester Oxford Road a		14 53				15 16				15 31	15 41			15 53			16 16					16 32		
Manchester Piccadilly 10 ⇌ a		14 57				15 20				15 35	15 45			15 57			16 20					16 36		
Stockport 84 a		15 26				15 39				15 49	16 05			16 26			16 39					16 46		
Hazel Grove 86 a										15 57	16 29											16 54		
Buxton 86 a										16 36												17 30		
Heald Green 85 a		15 12				15 32								16 11			16 49							
Manchester Airport 85 ✈ a		15 19				15 40					16 01			16 19			16 40					17f11		

For general notes see front of timetable
For details of catering facilities see Directory of Train Operators

A From Clitheroe (Table 94)
B From Edinburgh (from 2 February from Carlisle) (Table 65)
C To Liverpool Lime Street (Table 90)
D ⚲ from Preston

b Change at Preston
c By changing at Preston, passengers may depart at 1358
e By changing at Preston, passengers may depart at 1453
f Change at Manchester Piccadilly

Table 82

Blackpool, Barrow-in-Furness, Preston, Southport, Kirkby and Wigan → Bolton → Manchester

Saturdays

until 22 March

Network Diagram - see first page of Table 82

		TP 1 ◇	NT	NT	NT	NT	TP 1 ◇	NT	NT	NT		NT	NT	NT	NT	NT	NT	TP 1 ◇	NT	TP 1 ◇	NT	NT		NT	NT
					A		B ⫟					C			D	E				G ⫟	E				
Blackpool North	97 d	15 41							16 10						16 25			16 38							17 10
Layton	97 d								16 13									16 41							17 13
Poulton-le-Fylde	97 d	15 47							16 17									16 45							17 17
Kirkham & Wesham	97 d								16 26									16 56							17 26
Barrow-in-Furness	d											15 28								16 21					
Roose	d											15 32													
Dalton	d											15 38													
Ulverston	d											15 47								16 37					
Cark	d											15 55													
Kents Bank	d											15 59													
Grange-over-Sands	d											16 03								16 50					
Arnside	d											16 09								16 56					
Silverdale	d											16 14													
Carnforth	d				15 26							16 20								17 06					
Windermere	83 d						*15 22*													*16b22*					
Oxenholme Lake District	65 d	*15 11*					15 47													*16 48*					
Lancaster 6	65 a				15 38		16 02					16 32								17 14					
	d	*15 27*					16c03		*16 10*											17 15					
Preston 8	d	16 08					16 38		16 38						16 50			17 08		17 35					17 39
Leyland	d	16 13							16 44						16a55			17 13							17 45
Chorley	d	16 19					16 47		16 51									17 19		17 44					17 51
Adlington (Lancashire)	d								16 56									17 23							17 56
Blackrod	d								16 59																18 00
Horwich Parkway	d	16 27							17 03									17 28							18 03
Lostock	d	16 30							17 06									17 31		17 52					18 07
Southport	d			15 51				16 16						16 43								17 14			
Meols Cop	d							16 21														17 19			
Bescar Lane	d																					17 24			
New Lane	d																					17 28			
Burscough Bridge	d			16 03				16 29						16 55								17 30			
Hoscar	d																					17 34			
Parbold	d			16 08				16 34						17 00								17 37			
Appley Bridge	d			16 12				16 38						17 04								17 41			
Gathurst	d			16 15				16 41														17 44			
Liverpool Central 10	103 d		*15 20*										*16 05*											*17 05*	
Kirkby	d		15 51										16 38											17 41	
Rainford	d		15 58										16 45											17 48	
Upholland	d		16 02										16 49											17 52	
Orrell	d		16 06										16 52											17 55	
Pemberton	d		16 09										16 55											17 58	
Wigan Wallgate	a		16 14	16 20				16 46					17 01	17 10								17 49		18 04	
	d		16 16	16 21		16 32		16 47		16 58			17 06	17 12					17 31			17 50		18 05	
Wigan North Western	d																								
Ince	d		16 19							17 01			17 09						17 33					18 08	
Hindley	d		16 22			16 37		16 52		17 04			17 13						17 37			17 55		18 12	
Westhoughton	d			16 30		16 41				17 09									17 41						
Bolton	a	16 34		16 40		16 49	16 58		17 11	17 17				17 27				17 36	17 50	17 59					18 11
	d	16 36		16 43		16 50	16 59		17 12	17 18				17 27		17 30		17 36	17 50	17 59	18 03				18 12
Moses Gate	d															17 34									
Farnworth	d					16 53													17 53						
Kearsley	d					16 55											⟵		17 55						
Daisy Hill	d		16 26					16 56					17 17 ⟶				17 17					18 00		18 16 ⟶	
Hag Fold	d		16 29														17 20								
Atherton	d		16 32					17 00									17 22					18 04			
Walkden	d		16 37					17 06									17 28					18 09			
Moorside	d		16 41														17 31								
Swinton	d		16 43					17 10									17 34					18 14			
Salford Crescent	a	16 48	16 50	16 55		17 06	17 11	17 18	17 24	17 30				17 40			17 45	17 48	18 06	18 11	18 14	18 21			18 24
	d	16 48	16 50	16 56		17 07	17 11	17 18	17 25	17 31				17 40			17 45	17 48	18 07	18 11	18 14	18 22			18 25
Salford Central	d		16 55			17 09		17 21		17 33						17 45	17 48		18 09		18 17	18 24			
Manchester Victoria	⇌ a		16 59			17 14		17 24		17 40						17 51	17 54		18 15		18 23	18 29			
Rochdale	95 a		17 25					17 55		*18 08*							*18 32*					*19 05*			
Deansgate	⇌ a			16 59					17 28											18 15					
Manchester Oxford Road	a	16 53		17 01			17 16		17 30					17 45				17 55		18 17					18 34
Manchester Piccadilly 10	⇌ a	16 57		17 06			17 20		17 35					17 49				17 57		18 20					18 38
Stockport	84 a			17 19			*17 40*		17 51					*18 12*				*18 26*		*18 39*					18 50
Hazel Grove	86 a			17 27					17 59					*18 29*											18 57
Buxton	86 a			18 07					18 37																19 37
Heald Green	85 a	17 12					*17 49*											18 14		18 35					*19e07*
Manchester Airport	85 ✈ a	17 19					17 40							18 05				18 19		18 42					

For general notes see front of timetable
For details of catering facilities see Directory of Train Operators

A From Leeds to Morecambe (Table 36)

B From Glasgow Central (from 2 February from Carlisle) (Table 65)

C From Carlisle via Whitehaven (Table 100)

D To Liverpool Lime Street (Table 90)

E From Clitheroe (Table 94)

G ⫟ from Preston

b Change at Oxenholme Lake District and Lancaster

c By changing at Preston, passengers may depart at 1610

e Change at Manchester Piccadilly

Table 82

until 22 March

Blackpool, Barrow-in-Furness, Preston, Southport, Kirkby and Wigan → Bolton → Manchester

Network Diagram - see first page of Table 82

	NT	NT A	NT	TP 1 ◇	NT	TP 1 ◇	NT	TP 1 ◇ B ⚲	NT C	NT	NT		NT A	NT C	NT	TP 1 ◇	NT D	TP 1 ◇	NT E	NT	NT	NT	NT G	NT A
Blackpool North 97 d				17 38						18 11			18 25			18 42					19 10			19 25
Layton 97 d				17 41						18 14											19 13			
Poulton-le-Fylde 97 d				17 45						18 18						18 48					19 17			
Kirkham & Wesham 97 d				17 56				18b19		18 27											19 26			
Barrow-in-Furness d						17 06																	18 14	
Roose d																							18 18	
Dalton d						17 15																	18 24	
Ulverston d						17 24																	18 32	
Cark d						17 32																	18 40	
Kents Bank d																							18 44	
Grange-over-Sands d						17 39																	18 48	
Arnside d						17 45																	18 54	
Silverdale d																							18 59	
Carnforth d						17 55											18 30						19 07	
Windermere 83 d								17 27										18 10						
Oxenholme Lake District 65 d				17 11				17c53		18 00						18 11		18 33			18 51			
Lancaster 6 65 a						18 05		18 09									18 42	18 49					19 17	
d				17 27				18 16								18 27		18 51			19 07		19 18	
Preston 8 d		17 50		18 08				18 38		18 41			18 50			19 06		19 14			19 38		19a43	19 50
Leyland d		17a55		18 13									18a55			19 11					19 44			19a55
Chorley d				18 19				18 47		18 51						19 19		19 23			19 51			
Adlington (Lancashire) d										18 56											19 56			
Blackrod d										19 00											19 59			
Horwich Parkway d				18 27						19 03						19 25					20 03			
Lostock d				18 30						19 07						19 28					20 06			
Southport d	17 42										18 28									19 16		19 34		
Meols Cop d	17 47										18 33									19 21		19 39		
Bescar Lane d											18 38													
New Lane d											18 42													
Burscough Bridge d	17 55										18 44									19 29		19 47		
Hoscar d											18 48													
Parbold d	18 00										18 51									19 34		19 52		
Appley Bridge d	18 04										18 55									19 38		19 56		
Gathurst d											18 58									19 41		19 59		
Liverpool Central 10 103 d															18 20									
Kirkby d															18 43									
Rainford d															18 50									
Upholland d															18 54									
Orrell d															18 58									
Pemberton d															19 01									
Wigan Wallgate a	18 10										19 03				19 09					19 46		20 04		
d	18 12				18 18						19 05				19 11					19 48		20 05		
Wigan North Western d							18 31																	
Ince d					18 21		18 34								19 14									
Hindley d					18 25		18 38				19 10				19 17					19 53		20 10		
Westhoughton d	18 21				18 29						19 15											20 15		
Bolton a	18 29			18 34	18 39			18 58		19 12	19 23					19 34		19 37			20 11	20 23		
d	18 29			18 36	18 40			18 59	19 02	19 12	19 23			19 30		19 34		19 39	20 00		20 12	20 23		
Moses Gate d					18 43																			
Farnworth d																								
Kearsley d			←																					
Daisy Hill d			18 16				18 42								19 21					19 57				
Hag Fold d			18 19												19 24									
Atherton d			18 21				18 46								19 27					20 01				
Walkden d			18 27				18 51								19 32					20 06				
Moorside d			18 30												19 36									
Swinton d			18 33				18 56								19 38					20 11				
Salford Crescent a	18 41		18 43	18 48	18 54		19 05	19 11	19 13	19 25	19 36			19 42	19 44	19 49		19 52	20 13	20 18	20 24	20 36		
d	18 41		18 43	18 48	18 55		19 05	19 11	19 14	19 25	19 36			19 43	19 44	19 49		19 52	20 13	20 18	20 25	20 36		
Salford Central d			18 46		18 57		19 08		19 16					19 45	19 47				20 16	20 21				
Manchester Victoria ⇌ a			18 54		19 01		19 14		19 23					19 50	19 53				20 22	20 26				
Rochdale 95 a							19 45								20 38									
Deansgate ⇌ a										19 29						19 53					20 28			
Manchester Oxford Road a	18 47			18 54				19 16		19 33	19 43					19 54		19 58			20 30	20 41		
Manchester Piccadilly 10 ⇌ a	18 51			18 59				19 20		19 36	19 47					19 58		20 04			20 34	20 45		
Stockport 84 a	19 15			19 26				19 42		19 47	20 05							20 24			20 44	21 10		
Hazel Grove 86 a										19 55											20 52			
Buxton 86 a										20 34											21 31			
Heald Green 85 a				19 12				19 32								20 12		20 18			21e01			
Manchester Airport 85 ✈ a	19 08			19 19				19 40			20 05					20 19		20 26			21e06	21 09		

For general notes see front of timetable
For details of catering facilities see Directory of Train Operators

A To Liverpool Lime Street (Table 90)

B From Edinburgh (from 2 February from Carlisle) (Table 65)

C From Clitheroe (Table 94)

D From Leeds to Morecambe (Table 36)

E From Blackburn (Table 94)

G From Carlisle via Whitehaven (Table 100)

b Change at Preston

c By changing at Preston, passengers may depart at 1800

e Change at Manchester Piccadilly

Table 82

Saturdays

until 22 March

Blackpool, Barrow-in-Furness, Preston, Southport, Kirkby and Wigan → Bolton → Manchester

Network Diagram - see first page of Table 82

		TP 1◇	NT A	NT B	NT	TP 1◇ C ✠	TP 1◇	NT	NT B	NT	TP 1◇	NT	NT B	NT D	NT	TP 1◇	NT	NT A	NT B	NT	TP 1◇
Blackpool North	97 d	19 42									20 53					21 52		22 03			23 13
Layton	97 d	19 45									20 56					21 56					23 16
Poulton-le-Fylde	97 d	19 49									21 00					22 00					23 20
Kirkham & Wesham	97 d	19 59									21 10					22 09					23 30
Barrow-in-Furness	d						19 15								21 30						
Roose	d						19 19								21 34						
Dalton	d						19 26								21 40						
Ulverston	d						19 33								21 49						
Cark	d						19 41								21 57						
Kents Bank	d						19 46								22 01						
Grange-over-Sands	d						19 50								22 05						
Arnside	d						19 56								22 11						
Silverdale	d						20 01								22 16						
Carnforth	d						20 08								22 23						
Windermere	83 d					19 28										20b24					
Oxenholme Lake District	65 d	19 12				19 55					20c04					20e51					
Lancaster 6	65 a					20 10	20 16								22 35						
	d	19 28				20 11	20 16				20 21					21 20					
Preston 8	d	20 11	20 27			20 32	20 37				21 23					22 21		22 28			23 42
Leyland	d		20a32				20 42				21 28					22 26		22a32			23 47
Chorley	d	20 21				20 42	20 48				21 34					22 34					23 54
Adlington (Lancashire)	d						20 53				21 39					22 38					23 58
Blackrod	d						20 56				21 42					22 42					00 02
Horwich Parkway	d						21 00				21 46					22 45					00 05
Lostock	d						21 03				21 49					22 48					00 08
Southport	d							20 34				21 34					22 29			23 10	
Meols Cop	d							20 39				21 39					22 34			23 15	
Bescar Lane	d																22 39				
New Lane	d																22 43				
Burscough Bridge	d							20 47				21 47					22 45			23 23	
Hoscar	d																22 49				
Parbold	d							20 52				21 52					22 52			23 28	
Appley Bridge	d							20 56				21 56					22 56			23 32	
Gathurst	d							20 59				21 59					22 59			23 35	
Liverpool Central 10	103 d																				
Kirkby	d																				
Rainford	d																				
Upholland	d																				
Orrell	d																				
Pemberton	d																				
Wigan Wallgate	a							21 04				22 04					23 04			23 43	
	d				20 18			21 05		21 18		22 05		22 16			23 05				
Wigan North Western	d																				
Ince	d				20 21					21 21				22 19							
Hindley	d				20 24			21 10		21 24		22 10		22 22			23 10				
Westhoughton	d							21 15				22 15					23 15				
Bolton	a	20 32				20 53	21 07	21 23			21 53	22 23				22 52	23 23				00 12
	d	20 34		20 36		20 54	21 09	21 23	21 30		21 54	22 23	22 33			22 53	23 23		23 40		00 13
Moses Gate	d																				
Farnworth	d																				
Kearsley	d																				
Daisy Hill	d				20 28					21 28				22 26							
Hag Fold	d				20 31					21 31				22 29							
Atherton	d				20 34					21 34				22 32							
Walkden	d				20 39					21 39				22 37							
Moorside	d				20 43					21 43				22 41							
Swinton	d				20 45					21 45				22 43							
Salford Crescent	a	20 46		20 48	20 52	21 06	21 21	21 36	21 42	21 52	22 06	22 36	22 46	22 51		23 05	23 36		23 53		
	d	20 47		20 49	20 52	21 06	21 22	21 36	21 43	21 52	22 07	22 36	22 46	22 52		23 05	23 36		23 53		
Salford Central	d			20 51	20 56				21 45	21 56		22 39		22 55							
Manchester Victoria	⇌ a			20 56	21 00				21 50	22 00		22 44		23 00					23 59		
Rochdale	95 a				21 38				22 39			23 08		00 02							
Deansgate	⇌ a	20 53						21 40			22 13		22 50			23 15					
Manchester Oxford Road	a	20 54				21 11	21 26	21 41			22 14		22 52			23 17	23 41				
Manchester Piccadilly 10	⇌ a	20 58				21 14	21 30	21 46			22 18		22 56			23 30	23 46				00 29
Stockport	84 a	21 26				21 34	21 52	21 56			22 42		23 06			23f50					
Hazel Grove	86 a							22 05					23 14								
Buxton	86 a							22 44					23 54								
Heald Green	85 a	21 12				21 30	21 42				22 31					23 47					00 40
Manchester Airport	85 ✈ a	21 19				21 37	21 51				22 39					23 55					00 45

For general notes see front of timetable
For details of catering facilities see Directory of Train Operators

A To Liverpool Lime Street (Table 90)

B From Clitheroe (Table 94)

C From Edinburgh (from 2 February from Carlisle) (Table 65)

D To Huddersfield (from 2 February to Greenfield) (Table 39)

b Until 26 January change at Lancaster and Preston. From 2 February change at Oxenholme Lake District and Preston

c Until 26 January dep. 2008

e Until 26 January dep. 2046

f Change at Manchester Oxford Road

Table 82

from 29 March

Blackpool, Barrow-in-Furness, Preston, Southport, Kirkby and Wigan → Bolton → Manchester

Network Diagram - see first page of Table 82

		TP 1◇	TP 1◇	TP 1◇	TP 1◇	TP 1	TP (bus)	TP 1◇	NT A	NT		NT B	NT	NT C	TP 1◇	NT	NT	NT D	NT E	NT G		NT	TP 1◇ (trolley)	NT	NT
Blackpool North 97	d	01 43	03 50	04 43	05 19			05 30				06 08			06 34				06 57				07 03		
Layton 97	d				05 09							06 12			06 37				07 00				07 07		
Poulton-le-Fylde 97	d				05 25			05 36				06 16			06 41				07 04				07 11		
Kirkham & Wesham 97	d				05 22							06 24			06 51			07 04	07 13				07 20		
Barrow-in-Furness	d					04 50																			
Roose	d																								
Dalton	d																								
Ulverston	d					05 05																			
Cark	d																								
Kents Bank	d																								
Grange-over-Sands	d					05 18																			
Arnside	d					05 25																			
Silverdale	d																								
Carnforth	d					05 35	05 40																		
Windermere 83	d																								
Oxenholme Lake District 65	d																						05b55		
Lancaster 6 65	a					05 45																			
	d														05b45								06b40		
Preston 8	d	02u08	04u16	05 17	05 48		06a25	06 28				06 37			07 03			07 20	07 25				07 40		07 50
Leyland	d											06 42			07 08			07 25	07a30						07 55
Chorley	d			05 26				06 37				06 50			07 15			07 33					07 49		08 03
Adlington (Lancashire)	d											06 55						07 38							08 08
Blackrod	d											06 58			07 21			07 42							08 11
Horwich Parkway	d							06 45				07 02			07 24			07 46							08 15
Lostock	d			05 34				06 48				07 06			07 27			07 49							08 19
Southport	d												06 35												
Meols Cop	d												06 40												
Bescar Lane	d																								
New Lane	d																								
Burscough Bridge	d												06 48												
Hoscar	d																								
Parbold	d												06 53												
Appley Bridge	d												06 57												
Gathurst	d												07 00												
Liverpool Central 10 103	d																					06 50		07c04	
Kirkby	d																					07 16			
Rainford	d																					07 23			
Upholland	d																					07 27			
Orrell	d																					07 31			
Pemberton	d																					07 34			
Wigan Wallgate	a												07 05									07 39			
	d									06 45			07 06			07 13	07 27					07 43			
Wigan North Western	d				06 13																			07 56	
Ince	d									06 48						07 16	07 30					07 46			
Hindley	d				06 18					06 51						07 19	07 34					07 49		08 01	
Westhoughton	d				06 22								07 14				07 38							08 06	
Bolton	a			05 39	06 29			06 52				07 11	07 22		07 32		07 46	07 55					08 02	08 14	08 24
	d	02u43	04u43	05 40	06 31			06 54	06 58			07 12	07 23	07 30	07 33		07 47	07 55		08 00			08 04	08 15	08 24
Moses Gate	d								07 01								07 50							08 18	
Farnworth	d								07 03								07 52							08 20	
Kearsley	d								07 05								07 54							08 22	
Daisy Hill	d									06 55						07 23						07 53			
Hag Fold	d									06 58						07 26						07 56			
Atherton	d									07 01						07 29						07 59			
Walkden	d									07 06						07 34						08 04			
Moorside	d									07 10						07 38						08 08			
Swinton	d									07 12						07 40						08 10			
Salford Crescent	a				06 43			07 06	07 17	07 18		07 25	07 35	07 42	07 45	07 47	08 04	08 07		08 13		08 18		08 32	08 37
	d				06 43			07 06	07 17	07 18		07 26	07 36	07 43	07 46	07 47	08 04	08 07		08 13		08 18		08 32	08 37
Salford Central	d								07 21	07 23				07 45		07 49	08 07			08 16		08 21		08 35	
Manchester Victoria ⇌	a								07 25	07 27				07 51		07 56	08 14			08 21		08 25		08 41	
Rochdale 95	a									08 06				08 33			08 38					08 55		09 08	
Deansgate ⇌	a				06 49							07 29	07 39					08 12							08 41
Manchester Oxford Road	a				06 51			07 12				07 32	07 41		07 50			08 14					08 20		08 43
Manchester Piccadilly 10 ⇌	a	02 58		05 57	06 56			07 15				07 36	07 45		07 54			08 20					08 25		08 47
Stockport 84	a			06 25	07 26			07 37				07 48	08 02		08 25			08 29					08 53		09 08
Hazel Grove 86	a			07 07	07 44			07 54				08 13			08 51										09 16
Buxton 86	a			07 45				08 33							09 27										09 53
Heald Green 85	a			06 21	07 27			07 32							08 11			08e51							
Manchester Airport 85 ✈	a	03 13	05 21	06 14	07 15			07 40					08 02		08 19								08 42		09 06

For general notes see front of timetable
For details of catering facilities see Directory of Train Operators

A From Blackburn (Table 94). Also stops at Clifton 0709

B To Chester (Table 88)

C From Blackburn (Table 94)

D From St Annes-on-the-Sea (Table 97) to Greenbank (Table 88)

E To Liverpool Lime Street (Table 90)

G From Clitheroe (Table 94)

b By bus

c Liverpool Lime Street (Table 90)

e Change at Manchester Piccadilly

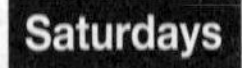

from 29 March

Blackpool, Barrow-in-Furness, Preston, Southport, Kirkby and Wigan → Bolton → Manchester

Network Diagram - see first page of Table 82

	TP	TP	NT	NT	TP	NT	NT		TP	NT	NT	NT	NT	NT	NT	TP	TP		NT	TP	NT	NT	TP	NT
	1	bus	A		1 ◇ trolley				1 ◇ trolley	B				C	D	1	bus		A	1 ◇			1 ◇ trolley	B
Blackpool North 97 d					07 41							08 09								08 41				
Layton 97 d					07 44							08 12												
Poulton-le-Fylde 97 d					07 48							08 16								08 47				
Kirkham & Wesham 97 d					07 58							08 25			08 28									
Barrow-in-Furness d	06 00															07 05								
Roose d	06 04																							
Dalton d	06 10															07 14								
Ulverston d	06 18															07 23								
Cark d	06 26															07 31								
Kents Bank d	06 30																							
Grange-over-Sands d	06 34															07 38								
Arnside d	06 40															07 44								
Silverdale d	06 45															07 48								
Carnforth d	06 52	07 05												07 42		07 56	08 05							
Windermere 83 d									06b51														07b51	
Oxenholme Lake District 65 d									07b12														08b12	
Lancaster 6 65 a	07 02													07 53		08 06								
d									07c35			07c40											08c35	
Preston 8 d		07a55			08 12				08 34			08 38			08 50		08a55			09 08			09 38	
Leyland d												08 43			08a55					09 13				
Chorley d					08 22				08 44			08 51								09 19			09 47	
Adlington (Lancashire) d												08 56												
Blackrod d												09 00												
Horwich Parkway d									08 52			09 03								09 27				
Lostock d												09 07								09 30				
Southport d				07 41							08 09		08 35											
Meols Cop d				07 46							08 14		08 40											
Bescar Lane d											08 19													
New Lane d											08 23													
Burscough Bridge d				07 54							08 25		08 48											
Hoscar d											08 29													
Parbold d				07 59							08 32		08 53											
Appley Bridge d				08 03							08 36		08 57											
Gathurst d				08 06							08 39		09 00											
Liverpool Central 10 103 d							07 50																	
Kirkby d							08 16																	
Rainford d							08 23																	
Upholland d							08 27																	
Orrell d							08 31																	
Pemberton d							08 34																	
Wigan Wallgate a				08 11			08 40				08 44		09 05											
d				08 13		08 32					08 45		09 07								09 16	09 32		
Wigan North Western d																								
Ince d				08 16																	09 19			
Hindley d				08 19		08 37					08 50										09 22	09 37		
Westhoughton d						08 41							09 15									09 41		
Bolton a					08 33	08 49			08 58			09 12	09 23							09 34		09 49	09 58	
d			08 30		08 34	08 50			08 59	09 01		09 12	09 23						09 30	09 36		09 50	09 59	10 01
Moses Gate d										09 04														
Farnworth d						08 53																09 53		
Kearsley d						08 55																09 55		
Daisy Hill d				08 23							08 54										09 26			
Hag Fold d				08 26							08 57										09 29			
Atherton d				08 29							09 00										09 32			
Walkden d				08 34							09 05										09 37			
Moorside d				08 38							09 09										09 41			
Swinton d				08 40							09 11										09 43			
Salford Crescent a			08 42	08 50		09 06			09 11	09 16	09 20	09 25	09 36						09 42	09 48	09 50	10 06	10 11	10 13
d			08 42	08 50		09 07			09 11	09 16	09 20	09 25	09 36						09 42	09 48	09 50	10 07	10 11	10 13
Salford Central d			08 45	08 53		09 09				09 19	09 23								09 45		09 53	10 09		10 16
Manchester Victoria ⇌ a			08 50	09 00		09 14				09 25	09 26								09 50		10 00	10 14		10 21
Rochdale 95 a				09 25		09 38					09 55										10 25	10 38		
Deansgate ⇌ a									09 15			09 29												
Manchester Oxford Road a					08 49				09 16			09 31	09 41							09 53			10 16	
Manchester Piccadilly 10 ⇌ a					08 53				09 20			09 35	09 45							09 57			10 20	
Stockport 84 a					09 13				09 39			09 49	10 12							10 26			10 39	
Hazel Grove 86 a					09 32							09 57	10 29											
Buxton 86 a												10 36												
Heald Green 85 a					09 18				09 31											10 11			10 32	
Manchester Airport 85 ✈ a					09 13				09 40				10 02							10 19			10 40	

For general notes see front of timetable
For details of catering facilities see Directory of Train Operators

- **A** From Clitheroe (Table 94)
- **B** From Blackburn (Table 94)
- **C** From Leeds (Table 36)
- **D** To Liverpool Lime Street (Table 90)
- **b** Change at Lancaster and Preston. By bus from Lancaster
- **c** By bus

Saturdays

from 29 March

Blackpool, Barrow-in-Furness, Preston, Southport, Kirkby and Wigan → Bolton → Manchester

Network Diagram - see first page of Table 82

		NT	NT	NT	NT	NT	NT	NT	NT	TP	NT	NT	TP	NT	NT	NT	NT	NT	NT	TP	TP	NT	TP
										1 ◇			1 ◇							1			1 ◇
						A	B		C									A	D			C	
								🚌		🛒			🛒								🚌		🛒
Blackpool North	97 d			09 11		09 25				09 40						10 11		10 25					10 41
Layton	97 d			09 14												10 14							
Poulton-le-Fylde	97 d			09 18						09 46						10 18							10 47
Kirkham & Wesham	97 d			09 27									*10 19*			10 27							
Barrow-in-Furness	d						07 58													09 05			
Roose	d						08 02													09 09			
Dalton	d						08 08													09 16			
Ulverston	d						08 17													09 24			
Cark	d						08 25													09 32			
Kents Bank	d						08 29													09 37			
Grange-over-Sands	d						08 33													09 41			
Arnside	d						08 39													09 47			
Silverdale	d						08 43													09 51			
Carnforth	d						08 51	09 00											09 53	09 59	10 05		
Windermere	83 d												*08b51*										
Oxenholme Lake District	65 d												*09b12*										
Lancaster 6	65 a						09 02												10 04	10 09			
	d												*09c35*										
Preston 8	d			09 41		09 50		09a50		10 08			10 38			10 41		10 50			10a55		11 08
Leyland	d					09a55				10 13								10a55					11 13
Chorley	d			09 51						10 19			10 47			10 51							11 19
Adlington (Lancashire)	d			09 56												10 56							
Blackrod	d			10 00												11 00							
Horwich Parkway	d			10 03						10 27						11 03							11 27
Lostock	d			10 07						10 30						11 07							11 30
Southport	d	09 10			09 38									10 15			10 38						
Meols Cop	d	09 15												10 20									
Bescar Lane	d	09 20																					
New Lane	d	09 24																					
Burscough Bridge	d	09 26			09 50									10 28			10 50						
Hoscar	d	09 30																					
Parbold	d	09 33			09 55									10 33			10 55						
Appley Bridge	d	09 37			09 59									10 37			10 59						
Gathurst	d	09 40												10 40									
Liverpool Central 10	103 d										*09 20*												
Kirkby	d										09 51												
Rainford	d										09 58												
Upholland	d										10 02												
Orrell	d										10 06												
Pemberton	d										10 09												
Wigan Wallgate	a	09 45			10 05						10 14			10 45			11 05						
	d	09 47	09 52		10 07						10 16	10 32		10 47	10 52		11 07						
Wigan North Western	d																						
Ince	d										10 19												
Hindley	d	09 52									10 22	10 37		10 52									
Westhoughton	d				10 15							10 41					11 15						
Bolton	a		10 06	10 12	10 23					10 34		10 49	10 58		11 06	11 12	11 23						11 34
	d		10 07	10 12	10 23				10 30	10 36		10 50	10 59		11 07	11 12	11 23					11 30	11 36
Moses Gate	d		10 10												11 10								
Farnworth	d											10 53											
Kearsley	d											10 55											
Daisy Hill	d	09 56									10 26			10 56									
Hag Fold	d										10 29												
Atherton	d	10 00									10 32			11 00									
Walkden	d	10 05									10 37			11 05									
Moorside	d										10 41												
Swinton	d	10 10									10 43			11 10									
Salford Crescent	a	10 17	10 22	10 25	10 36				10 43	10 48	10 50	11 06	11 11	11 17	11 21	11 25	11 36					11 43	11 48
	d	10 17	10 22	10 25	10 36				10 43	10 48	10 50	11 07	11 11	11 17	11 22	11 25	11 36					11 43	11 48
Salford Central	d	10 20	10 24						10 45		10 53	11 10		11 20	11 24							11 45	
Manchester Victoria	⇌ a	10 24	10 32						10 50		11 00	11 14		11 24	11 29							11 51	
Rochdale	95 a	10 55	*11 08*								11 25	*11 38*		11 55	*12 08*								
Deansgate	⇌ a			10 29									11 15			11 29							
Manchester Oxford Road	a			10 31	10 41					10 53			11 16			11 31	11 41						11 53
Manchester Piccadilly 10	⇌ a			10 35	10 45					10 57			11 20			11 35	11 45						11 57
Stockport	84 a			10 49	*11 05*					*11 26*			*11 39*			11 49	*12 05*						*12 26*
Hazel Grove	86 a			10 57	*11 29*											11 57	*12 29*						
Buxton	86 a			11 33												12 36							
Heald Green	85 a									11 12			11 32										12 12
Manchester Airport	85 ✈ a				11 01					11 19			11 40				12 01						12 19

For general notes see front of timetable
For details of catering facilities see Directory of Train Operators

- **A** To Liverpool Lime Street (Table 90)
- **B** From Maryport (Table 100)
- **C** From Clitheroe (Table 94)
- **D** From Leeds to Morecambe (Table 36)
- **b** Change at Lancaster and Preston. By bus from Lancaster
- **c** By bus

Table 82

Saturdays

from 29 March

Blackpool, Barrow-in-Furness, Preston, Southport, Kirkby and Wigan → Bolton → Manchester

Network Diagram - see first page of Table 82

	NT	NT	TP		NT	NT	NT	NT	NT	NT	NT	NT	TP		NT	NT	TP	NT	NT	NT	NT	NT	NT	TP
			1 ◇										1 ◇				1 ◇							1
									A	B	🚌	C										A	D	
			⚲										⚲				⚲							
Blackpool North 97 d							11 11		11 25				11 41							12 11		12 25		
Layton 97 d							11 14													12 14				
Poulton-le-Fylde 97 d							11 18						11 47							12 18				
Kirkham & Wesham 97 d			*11 19*				11 27										*12 19*			12 27				
Barrow-in-Furness d										09 58														11 09
Roose d										10 02														
Dalton d										10 08														11 18
Ulverston d										10 16														11 26
Cark d										10 24														11 34
Kents Bank d										10 28														
Grange-over-Sands d										10 32														11 41
Arnside d										10 38														11 47
Silverdale d										10 43														11 52
Carnforth d										10 50	11 00												11 55	11 59
Windermere 83 d			*09b51*														*10b51*							
Oxenholme Lake District 65 d			*10b12*														*11b12*							
Lancaster 6 65 a										11 01													12 04	12 09
d			*10c35*														*11c35*							
Preston 8 d			11 38				11 41		11 50		11a50		12 08				12 38			12 41		12 50		
Leyland d									11a55				12 13									12a55		
Chorley d			11 47				11 51						12 19				12 47			12 51				
Adlington (Lancashire) d							11 56													12 56				
Blackrod d							12 00													13 00				
Horwich Parkway d							12 03						12 27							13 03				
Lostock d							12 07						12 30							13 07				
Southport d					11 10			11 38										12 15			12 38			
Meols Cop d					11 15													12 20						
Bescar Lane d					11 20																			
New Lane d					11 24																			
Burscough Bridge d					11 26			11 50										12 28			12 50			
Hoscar d					11 30																			
Parbold d					11 33			11 55										12 33			12 55			
Appley Bridge d					11 37			11 59										12 37			12 59			
Gathurst d					11 40													12 40						
Liverpool Central 10 103 d	*10 20*														*11 20*									
Kirkby d	10 51														11 51									
Rainford d	10 58														11 58									
Upholland d	11 02														12 02									
Orrell d	11 06														12 06									
Pemberton d	11 09														12 09									
Wigan Wallgate a	11 14				11 45			12 05							12 14			12 45			13 05			
d	11 16	11 32			11 47	11 52		12 07							12 16	12 32		12 47	12 52		13 07			
Wigan North Western d																								
Ince d	11 19														12 19									
Hindley d	11 22	11 37			11 52										12 22	12 37		12 52						
Westhoughton d		11 41						12 15								12 41					13 15			
Bolton a		11 49	11 58			12 06	12 12	12 23					12 35			12 49	12 58		13 06	13 12	13 23			
d		11 50	11 59			12 07	12 12	12 23				12 30	12 36			12 50	12 59		13 07	13 12	13 23			
Moses Gate d						12 10													13 10					
Farnworth d		11 53														12 53								
Kearsley d		11 55														12 55								
Daisy Hill d	11 26				11 56										12 26			12 56						
Hag Fold d	11 29														12 29									
Atherton d	11 32				12 00										12 32			13 00						
Walkden d	11 37				12 05										12 37			13 05						
Moorside d	11 41														12 41									
Swinton d	11 43				12 10										12 43			13 10						
Salford Crescent a	11 50	12 06	12 11		12 17	12 21	12 25	12 36				12 43	12 48		12 50	13 06	13 11	13 17	13 21	13 25	13 36			
d	11 50	12 07	12 11		12 17	12 22	12 25	12 36				12 43	12 49		12 50	13 07	13 11	13 17	13 22	13 25	13 36			
Salford Central d	11 53	12 09			12 20	12 24						12 45			12 53	13 09		13 20	13 24					
Manchester Victoria ⇌ a	12 00	12 14			12 24	12 29						12 50			13 00	13 14		13 24	13 30					
Rochdale 95 a	12 25	*12 38*			12 55	*13 08*									13 25	*13 38*		13 55	*14 08*					
Deansgate ⇌ a							12 29										13 15			13 29				
Manchester Oxford Road a			12 16				12 31	12 41					12 53				13 16			13 31	13 41			
Manchester Piccadilly 10 ⇌ a			12 20				12 35	12 45					12 57				13 20			13 35	13 45			
Stockport 84 a			*12 39*				12 49	*13 05*					*13 26*				*13 39*			13 49	*14 05*			
Hazel Grove 86 a							12 57	*13 29*												13 57	*14 29*			
Buxton 86 a							13 33													14 36				
Heald Green 85 a			12 32										13 12				13 32							
Manchester Airport 85 ✈ a			12 40					13 01					13 19				13 40				14 01			

For general notes see front of timetable
For details of catering facilities see Directory of Train Operators

A To Liverpool Lime Street (Table 90)
B From Millom (Table 100)
C From Clitheroe (Table 94)
D From Leeds to Morecambe (Table 36)

b Change at Lancaster and Preston. By bus from Lancaster
c By bus

Table 82

Saturdays

from 29 March

Blackpool, Barrow-in-Furness, Preston, Southport, Kirkby and Wigan → Bolton → Manchester

Network Diagram - see first page of Table 82

		TP		NT	TP	NT	NT	TP	NT	NT	NT	NT		NT	NT	TP	NT	NT	TP	NT	NT	NT		NT	NT
				A	1 ◇			1 ◇						B	A	1 ◇			1 ◇						B
		🚌			🍴			🍴								🍴			🍴						
Blackpool North	97 d				12 41						13 11			13 25		13 41						14 11			14 25
Layton	97 d										13 14											14 14			
Poulton-le-Fylde	97 d				12 47						13 18					13 47						14 18			
Kirkham & Wesham	97 d							*13 19*			13 27								*14 19*			14 27			
Barrow-in-Furness	d																								
Roose	d																								
Dalton	d																								
Ulverston	d																								
Cark	d																								
Kents Bank	d																								
Grange-over-Sands	d																								
Arnside	d																								
Silverdale	d																								
Carnforth	d	12 05																							
Windermere	83 d							*11b51*											*12b51*						
Oxenholme Lake District	65 d				*11c45*			*12b12*											*13b12*						
Lancaster 6	65 a																								
	d							*12c35*											*13c35*						
Preston 8	d	12a55			13 08			13 38			13 41			13 50		14 08			14 38			14 41			14 50
Leyland	d				13 13									13a55		14 13									14a55
Chorley	d				13 19			13 47			13 51					14 19			14 47			14 51			
Adlington (Lancashire)	d										13 56											14 56			
Blackrod	d										14 00											15 00			
Horwich Parkway	d				13 27						14 03					14 27						15 03			
Lostock	d				13 30						14 07					14 30						15 07			
Southport	d								13 10			13 38								14 15				14 38	
Meols Cop	d								13 15											14 20					
Bescar Lane	d								13 20																
New Lane	d								13 24																
Burscough Bridge	d								13 26			13 50								14 28				14 50	
Hoscar	d								13 30																
Parbold	d								13 33			13 55								14 33				14 55	
Appley Bridge	d								13 37			13 59								14 37				14 59	
Gathurst	d								13 40											14 40					
Liverpool Central 10	103 d					*12 20*											*13 20*								
Kirkby	d					12 51											13 51								
Rainford	d					12 58											13 58								
Upholland	d					13 02											14 02								
Orrell	d					13 06											14 06								
Pemberton	d					13 09											14 09								
Wigan Wallgate	a					13 14			13 45			14 05					14 14			14 45				15 05	
	d					13 16	13 32		13 47	13 52		14 07					14 16	14 32		14 47	14 52			15 07	
Wigan North Western	d																								
Ince	d					13 19											14 19								
Hindley	d					13 22	13 37		13 52								14 22	14 37		14 52					
Westhoughton	d						13 41					14 15						14 41						15 15	
Bolton	a				13 34		13 49	13 58		14 06	14 12	14 23				14 34		14 49	14 58		15 06	15 12		15 23	
	d			13 30	13 36		13 50	13 59		14 07	14 12	14 23			14 30	14 36		14 50	14 59		15 07	15 12		15 23	
Moses Gate	d									14 10											15 10				
Farnworth	d						13 53											14 53							
Kearsley	d						13 55											14 55							
Daisy Hill	d					13 26			13 56								14 26			14 56					
Hag Fold	d					13 29											14 29								
Atherton	d					13 32			14 00								14 32			15 00					
Walkden	d					13 37			14 05								14 37			15 05					
Moorside	d					13 41											14 41								
Swinton	d					13 43			14 10								14 43			15 10					
Salford Crescent	a			13 42	13 48	13 50	14 06	14 11	14 17	14 21	14 25	14 36			14 43	14 48	14 50	15 06	15 11	15 17	15 21	15 25		15 36	
	d			13 43	13 48	13 50	14 07	14 11	14 17	14 22	14 25	14 36			14 43	14 48	14 50	15 07	15 11	15 17	15 22	15 25		15 36	
Salford Central	d			13 45		13 53	14 09		14 20	14 25					14 45		14 53	15 09		15 20	15 24				
Manchester Victoria	🚋 a			13 50		14 00	14 14		14 24	14 32					14 50		15 00	15 14		15 24	15 30				
Rochdale	95 a					14 25	*14 38*		14 55	*15 08*							15 25	*15 38*		15 55	*16 08*				
Deansgate	🚋 a							14 15			14 29											15 29			
Manchester Oxford Road	a				13 53			14 16			14 31	14 41				14 53			15 16			15 31		15 41	
Manchester Piccadilly 10	🚋 a				13 57			14 20			14 35	14 45				14 57			15 20			15 35		15 45	
Stockport	84 a				*14 26*			*14 39*			14 49	*15 05*				*15 26*			*15 39*			15 49		*16 05*	
Hazel Grove	86 a										14 57	*15 29*										15 57		*16 29*	
Buxton	86 a										15 33											16 36			
Heald Green	85 a				14 12			14 32								15 12			15 32						
Manchester Airport	85 ✈ a				14 19			14 40				15 01				15 19			15 40					16 01	

For general notes see front of timetable
For details of catering facilities see Directory of Train Operators

A From Clitheroe (Table 94)
B To Liverpool Lime Street (Table 90)

b Change at Lancaster and Preston. By bus from Lancaster
c By bus

Table 82

Saturdays

from 29 March

Blackpool, Barrow-in-Furness, Preston, Southport, Kirkby and Wigan → Bolton → Manchester

Network Diagram - see first page of Table 82

Station		NT	NT	NT	TP	NT	NT	TP	NT	NT		NT	NT	NT	TP	TP	TP	NT	NT	NT		TP	NT	NT	NT
					1 ◇			1 ◇							1		1 ◇					1 ◇			
		A	(bus)	B				(trolley)					B	C		(bus)						(trolley)	D		
Blackpool North	97 d				14 41							15 11		15 25			15 41								16 10
Layton	97 d											15 14													16 13
Poulton-le-Fylde	97 d				14 47							15 18					15 47								16 17
Kirkham & Wesham	97 d							*15 19*				15 27													16 26
Barrow-in-Furness	d	12 56													14 10										
Roose	d	13 00																							
Dalton	d	13 07																							
Ulverston	d	13 15													14 26										
Cark	d	13 23																							
Kents Bank	d	13 28																							
Grange-over-Sands	d	13 32													14 39										
Arnside	d	13 38													14 45										
Silverdale	d	13 42																							
Carnforth	d	13 50	14 00												14 55	15 05							15 26		
Windermere	83 d							*13b51*														*14b51*			
Oxenholme Lake District	65 d				*13c45*			*14b12*														*15b12*			
Lancaster 6	65 a	14 00													15 05								15 38		
	d							*14c35*														*15c35*			
Preston 8	d		14a50		15 08			15 38				15 41		15 50		15a55	16 08					16 38			16 38
Leyland	d				15 13									15a55			16 13								16 44
Chorley	d				15 19			15 47				15 51					16 19					16 47			16 51
Adlington (Lancashire)	d											15 56													16 56
Blackrod	d											16 00													16 59
Horwich Parkway	d				15 27							16 03					16 27								17 03
Lostock	d				15 30							16 07					16 30								17 06
Southport	d								15 10										15 51					16 16	
Meols Cop	d								15 15															16 21	
Bescar Lane	d								15 20																
New Lane	d								15 24																
Burscough Bridge	d								15 26										16 03					16 29	
Hoscar	d								15 30																
Parbold	d								15 33										16 08					16 34	
Appley Bridge	d								15 37										16 12					16 38	
Gathurst	d								15 40										16 15					16 41	
Liverpool Central 10	103 d					*14 20*												*15 20*							
Kirkby	d					14 51												15 51							
Rainford	d					14 58												15 58							
Upholland	d					15 02												16 02							
Orrell	d					15 06												16 06							
Pemberton	d					15 09												16 09							
Wigan Wallgate	a					15 14			15 45									16 14	16 20					16 46	
	d					15 16	15 32		15 47	15 52								16 16	16 21	16 32				16 47	
Wigan North Western	d																								
Ince	d					15 19												16 19							
Hindley	d					15 22	15 37		15 52									16 22		16 37				16 52	
Westhoughton	d						15 41												16 30	16 41					
Bolton	a				15 34		15 49	15 58		16 07		16 12					16 34		16 40	16 49		16 58			17 11
	d			15 30	15 36		15 50	15 59		16 10		16 13	16 20				16 36		16 43	16 50		16 59			17 12
Moses Gate	d												16 23												
Farnworth	d						15 53													16 53					
Kearsley	d						15 55													16 55					
Daisy Hill	d					15 26			15 56									16 26						16 56	
Hag Fold	d					15 29												16 29							
Atherton	d					15 32			16 00									16 32						17 00	
Walkden	d					15 37			16 05									16 37						17 06	
Moorside	d					15 41												16 41							
Swinton	d					15 43			16 10									16 43						17 10	
Salford Crescent	a			15 42	15 48	15 50	16 06	16 11	16 17	16 22		16 25	16 34				16 48	16 50	16 55	17 06		17 11		17 18	17 24
	d			15 43	15 48	15 50	16 07	16 11	16 17	16 22		16 25	16 35				16 48	16 50	16 56	17 07		17 11		17 18	17 25
Salford Central	d			15 45		15 53	16 10		16 20	16 25			16 37					16 55		17 09				17 21	
Manchester Victoria	(tram) a			15 50		15 59	16 14		16 25	16 30			16 42					16 59		17 14				17 24	
Rochdale	95 a					16 25	*16 38*		16 55				*17 08*					17 25						17 55	
Deansgate	(tram) a							16 15				16 29							16 59						17 28
Manchester Oxford Road	a				15 53			16 16				16 32					16 53		17 01			17 16			17 30
Manchester Piccadilly 10	(tram) a				15 57			16 20				16 36					16 57		17 06			17 20			17 35
Stockport	84 a				*16 26*			*16 39*				16 46							17 19			*17 40*			17 51
Hazel Grove	86 a											16 54							17 27						17 59
Buxton	86 a											17 30							18 07						18 37
Heald Green	85 a				16 11			*16 49*									17 12					*17 49*			
Manchester Airport	85 (air) a				16 19			16 40				*17e11*					17 19					17 40			

For general notes see front of timetable
For details of catering facilities see Directory of Train Operators

A

B From Clitheroe (Table 94)
C To Liverpool Lime Street (Table 90)
D From Leeds to Morecambe (Table 36)

b Change at Lancaster and Preston. By bus from Lancaster
c By bus
e Change at Manchester Piccadilly

Table 82

Saturdays

from 29 March

Blackpool, Barrow-in-Furness, Preston, Southport, Kirkby and Wigan → Bolton → Manchester

Network Diagram - see first page of Table 82

	NT	NT	NT	NT	NT	NT	TP		NT	NT	NT	TP	NT	NT	NT	NT	NT		NT	TP	TP	NT	TP	NT
				A	B		1 ◇		C	🚌		1 ◇ trolley	B						A	1	🚌		1 ◇	
Blackpool North 97 d				16 25			16 38									17 10							17 38	
Layton 97 d							16 41									17 13							17 41	
Poulton-le-Fylde 97 d							16 45									17 17							17 45	
Kirkham & Wesham 97 d							16 56									17 26							17 56	
Barrow-in-Furness d									15 28											16 10				
Roose d									15 32															
Dalton d									15 38															
Ulverston d									15 47											16 26				
Cark d									15 55															
Kents Bank d									15 59															
Grange-over-Sands d									16 03											16 39				
Arnside d									16 09											16 45				
Silverdale d									16 14															
Carnforth d									16 23	16 30										16 56	17 05			
Windermere 83 d												15b51												
Oxenholme Lake District 65 d												16b12												
Lancaster 6 65 a									16 34											17 06				
d												16c35												
Preston 8 d				16 50			17 08			17a20		17 35				17 39			17 50		17a55		18 08	
Leyland d				16a55			17 13									17 45			17a55				18 13	
Chorley d							17 19					17 44				17 51							18 19	
Adlington (Lancashire) d							17 23									17 56								
Blackrod d																18 00								
Horwich Parkway d							17 28									18 03							18 27	
Lostock d							17 31					17 52				18 07							18 30	
Southport d			16 43											17 14			17 42							
Meols Cop d														17 19			17 47							
Bescar Lane d														17 24										
New Lane d														17 28										
Burscough Bridge d			16 55											17 30			17 55							
Hoscar d														17 34										
Parbold d			17 00											17 37			18 00							
Appley Bridge d			17 04											17 41			18 04							
Gathurst d														17 44										
Liverpool Central 10 103 d		*16 05*													*17 05*									
Kirkby d		16 38													17 41									
Rainford d		16 45													17 48									
Upholland d		16 49													17 52									
Orrell d		16 52													17 55									
Pemberton d		16 55													17 58									
Wigan Wallgate a		17 01	17 10											17 49	18 04		18 10							
d	16 58	17 06	17 12								17 31			17 50	18 05		18 12							18 18
Wigan North Western d																								
Ince d	17 01	17 09									17 33				18 08									18 21
Hindley d	17 04	17 13									17 37			17 55	18 12									18 25
Westhoughton d	17 09										17 41						18 21							18 29
Bolton a	17 17		17 27				17 36				17 50	17 59				18 11	18 29						18 34	18 39
d	17 18		17 27		17 30		17 36				17 50	17 59	18 03			18 12	18 29						18 36	18 40
Moses Gate d					17 34																			18 43
Farnworth d											17 53													
Kearsley d						←					17 55											←		
Daisy Hill d		17 17 →				17 17								18 00	18 16 →							18 16		
Hag Fold d						17 20																18 19		
Atherton d						17 22								18 04								18 21		
Walkden d						17 28								18 09								18 27		
Moorside d						17 31																18 30		
Swinton d						17 34								18 14								18 33		
Salford Crescent a	17 30		17 40			17 45	17 48				18 06	18 11	18 14	18 21		18 24	18 41					18 43	18 48	18 54
d	17 31		17 40			17 45	17 48				18 07	18 11	18 14	18 22		18 25	18 41					18 43	18 48	18 55
Salford Central d	17 33				17 45	17 48					18 09		18 17	18 24								18 46		18 57
Manchester Victoria 🚊 a	17 40				17 51	17 54					18 15		18 23	18 29								18 54		19 01
Rochdale 95 a	*18 08*					*18 32*								*19 05*										
Deansgate 🚊 a												18 15												
Manchester Oxford Road a			17 45				17 55					18 17				18 34	18 47						18 54	
Manchester Piccadilly 10 🚊 a			17 49				17 57					18 20				18 38	18 51						18 59	
Stockport 84 a			*18 12*				*18 26*					*18 39*				18 50	*19 15*						*19 26*	
Hazel Grove 86 a			*18 29*													18 57								
Buxton 86 a																19 37								
Heald Green 85 a							18 14					18 35				*19e07*							19 12	
Manchester Airport 85 ✈ a			18 05				18 19					18 42					19 08						19 19	

For general notes see front of timetable
For details of catering facilities see Directory of Train Operators

A To Liverpool Lime Street (Table 90)
B From Clitheroe (Table 94)
C From Carlisle via Whitehaven (Table 100)

b Change at Lancaster and Preston. By bus from Lancaster
c By bus
e Change at Manchester Piccadilly

from 29 March

Blackpool, Barrow-in-Furness, Preston, Southport, Kirkby and Wigan → Bolton → Manchester

Network Diagram - see first page of Table 82

		NT	TP 1◇	NT	NT	NT		NT	TP 1	TP	NT	NT	TP 1◇	TP 1◇	NT	NT		NT	NT	NT	NT	TP 1◇	NT	NT	NT
				A				B	C		A				D				E		B		G	B	A
Blackpool North	97 d				18 11			18 25					18 42					19 10			19 25	19 42			
Layton	97 d				18 14													19 13				19 45			
Poulton-le-Fylde	97 d				18 18								18 48					19 17				19 49			
Kirkham & Wesham	97 d		18 19		18 27													19 26				19 59			
Barrow-in-Furness	d								17 06														18 14		
Roose	d																						18 18		
Dalton	d								17 15														18 24		
Ulverston	d								17 24														18 32		
Cark	d								17 32														18 40		
Kents Bank	d																						18 44		
Grange-over-Sands	d								17 39														18 48		
Arnside	d								17 45														18 54		
Silverdale	d																						18 59		
Carnforth	d								17 55	18 05									18 30				19 07		
Windermere	83 d		16b51															17b51							
Oxenholme Lake District	65 d		17b12										17c45					18b12						18c40	
Lancaster 6	65 a								18 05										18 42				19 19		
	d		17c35															18c35						19c25	
Preston 8	d		18 38		18 41			18 50		18a55			19 06	19 14				19 38			19 50	20 11	20e15	20 27	
Leyland	d							18a55					19 11					19 44			19a55			20a32	
Chorley	d		18 47		18 51								19 19	19 23				19 51				20 21			
Adlington (Lancashire)	d				18 56													19 56							
Blackrod	d				19 00													19 59							
Horwich Parkway	d				19 03								19 25					20 03							
Lostock	d				19 07								19 28					20 06							
Southport	d					18 28										19 16				19 34					
Meols Cop	d					18 33										19 21				19 39					
Bescar Lane	d					18 38																			
New Lane	d					18 42																			
Burscough Bridge	d					18 44										19 29				19 47					
Hoscar	d					18 48																			
Parbold	d					18 51										19 34				19 52					
Appley Bridge	d					18 55										19 38				19 56					
Gathurst	d					18 58										19 41				19 59					
Liverpool Central 10	103 d											18 20													
Kirkby	d											18 43													
Rainford	d											18 50													
Upholland	d											18 54													
Orrell	d											18 58													
Pemberton	d											19 01													
Wigan Wallgate	a					19 03						19 09				19 46				20 04					
	d					19 05						19 11				19 48				20 05					
Wigan North Western	d	18 31																							
Ince	d	18 34										19 14													
Hindley	d	18 38				19 10						19 17				19 53				20 10					
Westhoughton	d					19 15														20 15					
Bolton	a		18 58		19 12	19 23							19 34	19 37				20 11		20 23		20 32			
	d		18 59	19 02	19 12	19 23					19 30		19 34	19 39	20 00			20 12		20 23		20 34			20 36
Moses Gate	d																								
Farnworth	d																								
Kearsley	d																								
Daisy Hill	d	18 42										19 21				19 57									
Hag Fold	d											19 24													
Atherton	d	18 46										19 27				20 01									
Walkden	d	18 51										19 32				20 06									
Moorside	d											19 36													
Swinton	d	18 56										19 38				20 11									
Salford Crescent	a	19 05	19 11	19 13	19 25	19 36					19 42	19 44	19 49	19 52	20 13	20 18		20 24		20 36		20 46			20 48
	d	19 05	19 11	19 14	19 25	19 36					19 43	19 44	19 49	19 52	20 13	20 18		20 25		20 36		20 47			20 49
Salford Central	d	19 08		19 16							19 45	19 47			20 16	20 21									20 51
Manchester Victoria	a	19 14		19 23							19 50	19 53			20 22	20 26									20 56
Rochdale	95 a	19 45										20 38													
Deansgate	a				19 29								19 53					20 28				20 53			
Manchester Oxford Road	a		19 16		19 33	19 43							19 54	19 58				20 30		20 41		20 54			
Manchester Piccadilly 10	a		19 20		19 36	19 47							19 58	20 04				20 34		20 45		20 58			
Stockport	84 a		19 42		19 47	20 05								20 24				20 44		21 10		21 26			
Hazel Grove	86 a				19 55													20 52							
Buxton	86 a				20 34													21 31							
Heald Green	85 a		19 32										20 12	20 18				21f01				21 12			
Manchester Airport	85 a		19 40			20 05							20 19	20 26				21f06		21 09		21 19			

For general notes see front of timetable
For details of catering facilities see Directory of Train Operators

A From Clitheroe (Table 94)
B To Liverpool Lime Street (Table 90)
C To Windermere (Table 83)
D From Blackburn (Table 94)
E From Leeds to Morecambe (Table 36)
G From Carlisle via Whitehaven (Table 100)

b Change at Lancaster and Preston. By bus from Lancaster
c By bus
e Arrival time. By bus
f Change at Manchester Piccadilly

Table 82

from 29 March

Blackpool, Barrow-in-Furness, Preston, Southport, Kirkby and Wigan → Bolton → Manchester

Network Diagram - see first page of Table 82

	NT	TP 1 ◇	TP 1 ◇	TP 1 A	TP (bus)	NT	NT B	NT	TP 1 ◇	NT	NT B	NT C	TP 1 ◇	NT	NT D	NT	NT B	NT	TP 1 ◇
Blackpool North 97 d									20 53				21 52		22 03				23 13
Layton 97 d									20 56				21 56						23 16
Poulton-le-Fylde 97 d									21 00				22 00						23 20
Kirkham & Wesham 97 d									21 10				22 09						23 30
Barrow-in-Furness d				19 09												21 15			
Roose d				19 13												21 19			
Dalton d				19 20												21 25			
Ulverston d				19 28												21 34			
Cark d				19 36												21 42			
Kents Bank d				19 40												21 46			
Grange-over-Sands d				19 44												21 50			
Arnside d				19 50												21 56			
Silverdale d				19 54												22 01			
Carnforth d				20 01	20 15											22 08			
Windermere 83 d									19b45										
Oxenholme Lake District 65 d									20b06				20c41						
Lancaster 6 65 a				20 11												22 20			
d									20c30				21c26						
Preston 8 d		20 32	20 37		21a05				21 23				22 21		22 28				23 42
Leyland d			20 42						21 28				22 26		22a32				23 47
Chorley d		20 42	20 48						21 34				22 34						23 54
Adlington (Lancashire) d			20 53						21 39				22 38						23 58
Blackrod d			20 56						21 42				22 42						00 02
Horwich Parkway d			21 00						21 46				22 45						00 05
Lostock d			21 03						21 49				22 48						00 08
Southport d						20 34				21 34				22 29				23 10	
Meols Cop d						20 39				21 39				22 34				23 15	
Bescar Lane d														22 39					
New Lane d														22 43					
Burscough Bridge d						20 47				21 47				22 45				23 23	
Hoscar d														22 49					
Parbold d						20 52				21 52				22 52				23 28	
Appley Bridge d						20 56				21 56				22 56				23 32	
Gathurst d						20 59				21 59				22 59				23 35	
Liverpool Central 10 103 d																			
Kirkby d																			
Rainford d																			
Upholland d																			
Orrell d																			
Pemberton d																			
Wigan Wallgate a						21 04				22 04				23 04				23 43	
d	20 18					21 05		21 18		22 05		22 16		23 05					
Wigan North Western d																			
Ince d	20 21							21 21				22 19							
Hindley d	20 24					21 10		21 24		22 10		22 22		23 10					
Westhoughton d						21 15				22 15				23 15					
Bolton a		20 53	21 07			21 23			21 53	22 23			22 52	23 23					00 12
d		20 54	21 09			21 23	21 30		21 54	22 23	22 33		22 53	23 23			23 40		00 13
Moses Gate d																			
Farnworth d																			
Kearsley d																			
Daisy Hill d	20 28							21 28				22 26							
Hag Fold d	20 31							21 31				22 29							
Atherton d	20 34							21 34				22 32							
Walkden d	20 39							21 39				22 37							
Moorside d	20 43							21 43				22 41							
Swinton d	20 45							21 45				22 43							
Salford Crescent a	20 52	21 06	21 21			21 36	21 42	21 52	22 06	22 36	22 46	22 51	23 05	23 36			23 53		
d	20 52	21 06	21 22			21 36	21 43	21 52	22 07	22 36	22 46	22 52	23 05	23 36			23 53		
Salford Central d	20 56						21 45	21 56		22 39		22 55							
Manchester Victoria (connecting rail) a	21 00						21 50	22 00		22 44		23 00					23 59		
Rochdale 95 a	*21 38*						*22 39*			*23 08*		*00 02*							
Deansgate (connecting rail) a						21 40			22 13		22 50		23 15						
Manchester Oxford Road a		21 11	21 26			21 41			22 14		22 52		23 17	23 41					
Manchester Piccadilly 10 (connecting rail) a		21 16	21 30			21 46			22 18		22 56		23 30	23 46					00 29
Stockport 84 a		*21 40*	*21 52*			21 56			*22 42*		23 06		*23e50*						
Hazel Grove 86 a						22 05					23 14								
Buxton 86 a						22 44					23 54								
Heald Green 85 a		21 30	21 42						22 31				23 47						00 40
Manchester Airport 85 (airport) a		21 37	21 51						22 39				23 55						00 45

For general notes see front of timetable
For details of catering facilities see Directory of Train Operators

A To Windermere (Table 83)
B From Clitheroe (Table 94)
C To Huddersfield (Table 39)
D To Liverpool Lime Street (Table 90)

b Change at Lancaster and Preston. By bus from Lancaster
c By bus
e Change at Manchester Oxford Road

Table 82

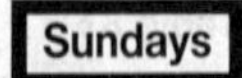
Sundays

until 27 January

Blackpool, Barrow-in-Furness, Preston, Southport and Wigan → Bolton → Manchester

Network Diagram - see first page of Table 82

	TP	TP	TP	TP	TP	TP	NT	NT	NT	NT	TP	NT	NT	NT	TP	NT	NT	NT		NT	TP	TP	NT	NT
	🚌	🚌	🚌	1 ◇	1 ◇	1 ◇		A	B		1 ◇		C		1 ◇		A	C			1 ◇	1 ◇		C
Blackpool North 97 d	01 00	03 20	05 20			08 02		08 17		08 28	09 02			09 28	10 02		10 17			10 28		11 02		
Poulton-le-Fylde 97 d						08 08		08 23		08 34	09 08			09 34	10 08		10 23			10 34		11 08		
Kirkham & Wesham 97 d						08 17					09 17				10 17							11 17		
Barrow-in-Furness d																					09 58			
Roose d																					10 03			
Dalton d																					10 09			
Ulverston d																					10 17			
Cark d																					10 25			
Kents Bank d																					10 29			
Grange-over-Sands d																					10 33			
Arnside d																					10 39			
Silverdale d																					10 44			
Carnforth d																					10 50			
Windermere 83 d																								
Oxenholme Lake District 65 d																								
Lancaster 6 65 a																					10 57			
d															*09b00*						10 58			
Preston 8 d	01u40	04u00	06u00			08 30		08 42		08 53	09 30			09 53	10 30		10 42			10 53	11a17	11 30		
Leyland d								08a47		08 59				09 59			10a47			10 59				
Chorley d						08 40				09 06	09 40			10 06	10 40					11 06		11 40		
Adlington (Lancashire) d										09 10				10 10						11 10				
Blackrod d										09 14				10 14						11 14				
Horwich Parkway d										09 17				10 17						11 17				
Lostock d										09 21				10 21						11 21				
Southport d												09 13				10 13							11 13	
Burscough Bridge d												09 25				10 25							11 25	
Parbold d												09 30				10 30							11 30	
Appley Bridge d												09 34				10 34							11 34	
Gathurst d												09 37				10 37							11 37	
Wigan Wallgate a												09 42				10 42							11 42	
d							08 43					09 43				10 43							11 43	
Wigan North Western d																								
Hindley d							08 48					09 48				10 48							11 48	
Westhoughton d							08 53					09 53				10 53							11 53	
Bolton a						08 51	09 01			09 26	09 51	10 01		10 26	10 51	11 01				11 26		11 51	12 01	
d	02u15	04u35	06u35	06 59	07 45	08 53	09 01		09 16	09 26	09 53	10 01	10 16	10 26	10 53	11 01		11 16		11 26		11 53	12 01	12 16
Salford Crescent a						09 05	09 14		09 29	09 39	10 05	10 14	10 29	10 39	11 05	11 14		11 29		11 39		12 05	12 14	12 29
d						09 06	09 14		09 29	09 39	10 06	10 14	10 29	10 39	11 06	11 14		11 29		11 39		12 06	12 14	12 29
Manchester Victoria 🚊 a									09 35				10 35					11 35						12 35
Rochdale a									*10 34*				*11 34*					*12 34*						*13 34*
Deansgate 🚊 a						09 09	09 18			09 43	10 09	10 18		10 43	11 09	11 18				11 46		12 09	12 18	
Manchester Oxford Road a						09 11	09 20			09 45	10 11	10 21		10 45	11 11	11 20				11 49		12 11	12 20	
Manchester Piccadilly 10 🚊 a				07 14	08 00	09 15	09 24			09 49	10 15	10 25		10 49	11 15	11 24				11 52		12 15	12 24	
Stockport 84 a				*08b25*	*09 05*		09 38			10 07		10 38		11 07		11 38				12 07			12 37	
Alderley Edge 84 a							09 57					10 59				11 58							12 58	
Hazel Grove 86 a					*09 13*					10 15				11 15						12 15				
Buxton 86 a					*09 53*					10 55				11 55						12 55				
Heald Green 85 a				*08 04*			*10c04*					*11c05*				*12c04*							*13c05*	
Manchester Airport 85 ✈ a	03 00	05 20	07 20	07 32	08 17	09 33	*09c51*				10 33	*10c51*		*11c23*	11 33	*11c51*						12 33	*12c50*	

For general notes see front of timetable
For details of catering facilities see Directory of Train Operators

A To Liverpool Lime Street (Table 90)
B From Blackburn (Table 94)
C From Clitheroe (Table 94)

b By bus
c Change at Manchester Piccadilly

Table 82

Sundays
until 27 January

Blackpool, Barrow-in-Furness, Preston, Southport and Wigan → Bolton → Manchester

Network Diagram - see first page of Table 82

		NT	TP	NT	NT	NT	NT	TP	TP	NT	NT	NT	TP	TP	NT	NT		NT	NT	NT	TP	TP	NT	NT	NT
			1 ◇					1 ◇	1 ◇				1 ◇	1 ◇							1 ◇	1 ◇			
					A	B					B		C	C		A			B					B	
Blackpool North	97 d	11 28	12 02		12 17		12 28		13 02			13 28	13 57			14 17				14 28		15 02			15 28
Poulton-le-Fylde	97 d	11 34	12 08		12 23		12 34		13 08			13 34	14 03			14 23				14 34		15 08			15 34
Kirkham & Wesham	97 d		12 17						13 17				14 12									15 17			
Barrow-in-Furness	d							12 00										13 30			14 00				
Roose	d							12 05										13 34			14 05				
Dalton	d							12 11										13 40			14 11				
Ulverston	d							12 19										13 48			14 19				
Cark	d							12 27										13 57			14 27				
Kents Bank	d							12 31										14 01			14 31				
Grange-over-Sands	d							12 35										14 05			14 35				
Arnside	d							12 41										14 11			14 41				
Silverdale	d							12 46										14 16			14 46				
Carnforth	d							12 52										14 23			14 53				
Windermere	83 d													*12 59*											*14b15*
Oxenholme Lake District	65 d		*10c45*						*12 32*			*12 53*		13 45											*14 53*
Lancaster 6	65 a							12 59						14 01				14 34			15 00				
	d		*11 43*					13 00				*13 09*		14 01		*14 07*					15 02				*15 09*
Preston 8	d	11 53	12 30		12 42		12 54	13a19	13 30			13 53		14 30		14 42				14 53	15 23	15 30			15 53
Leyland	d	11 59			12a47		12 59					13 59				14a47				14 59					15 59
Chorley	d	12 06	12 40				13 06		13 40			14 06		14 40						15 06		15 40			16 06
Adlington (Lancashire)	d	12 10					13 10					14 10								15 10					16 10
Blackrod	d	12 14					13 14					14 14								15 14					16 14
Horwich Parkway	d	12 17					13 17					14 17								15 17					16 17
Lostock	d	12 21					13 21					14 21								15 21					16 21
Southport	d			12 13						13 13					14 13								15 13		
Burscough Bridge	d			12 25						13 25					14 25								15 25		
Parbold	d			12 30						13 30					14 30								15 30		
Appley Bridge	d			12 34						13 34					14 34								15 34		
Gathurst	d			12 37						13 37					14 37								15 37		
Wigan Wallgate	a			12 42						13 42					14 42								15 42		
	d			12 43						13 43					14 43								15 43		
Wigan North Western	d																								
Hindley	d			12 48						13 48					14 48								15 48		
Westhoughton	d			12 53						13 53					14 53								15 53		
Bolton	a	12 26	12 52	13 01			13 26		13 52	14 01		14 26		14 52	15 01					15 26	15 41	15 52	16 01		16 26
	d	12 26	12 53	13 01		13 16	13 26		13 53	14 01	14 16	14 26		14 53	15 01				15 16	15 26	15 42	15 53	16 01	16 16	16 26
Salford Crescent	a	12 39	13 05	13 14		13 29	13 39		14 05	14 14	14 29	14 39		15 05	15 14				15 29	15 39		16 05	16 14	16 29	16 39
	d	12 39	13 06	13 14		13 29	13 39		14 06	14 14	14 29	14 39		15 06	15 14				15 29	15 39		16 06	16 14	16 29	16 39
Manchester Victoria	a					13 35					14 35								15 35					16 35	
Rochdale	a					*14 34*					*15 34*								*16 34*					*17 34*	
Deansgate	a	12 43	13 09	13 18			13 43		14 09	14 18		14 43		15 09	15 18					15 43		16 09	16 18		16 43
Manchester Oxford Road	a	12 46	13 11	13 20			13 46		14 11	14 20		14 46		15 11	15 20					15 45	15 56	16 11	16 20		16 45
Manchester Piccadilly 10	a	12 49	13 15	13 24			13 49		14 15	14 24		14 49		15 15	15 24					15 49	16 01	16 15	16 24		16 49
Stockport	84 a	13 07		13 39			14 07			14 38		15 07			15 36					16 04	*16 31*		16 37		17 04
Alderley Edge	84 a			13 58						14 59					15 58								16 58		
Hazel Grove	86 a	13 15					14 15					15 15								16 12					17 15
Buxton	86 a	13 55					14 55					15 56								16 53					17 55
Heald Green	85 a			*14e07*						*15e04*					*16e04*								*17e05*		
Manchester Airport	85 ✈ a	*13e24*	13 33	*13e54*					14 33	*14e51*		*15e21*		15 33	*15e51*						16 18	16 33	*16e51*		

For general notes see front of timetable
For details of catering facilities see Directory of Train Operators

- **A** To Liverpool Lime Street (Table 90)
- **B** From Clitheroe (Table 94)
- **C** From Edinburgh (Table 65)
- **b** Change at Oxenholme Lake District and Preston
- **c** Change at Lancaster and Preston. By bus to Lancaster
- **e** Change at Manchester Piccadilly

Table 82

Sundays
until 27 January

Blackpool, Barrow-in-Furness, Preston, Southport and Wigan → Bolton → Manchester

Network Diagram - see first page of Table 82

		TP	TP	NT	NT	NT	NT	NT	TP	TP	NT	NT	NT	NT	TP	TP	NT	NT	NT	NT	TP	TP	NT	NT
		1 ◇	1 ◇						1 ◇	1 ◇					1 ◇	1 ◇					1 ◇	1 ◇		
		A			B	C		D				B	C		E			B	C					C
		🍴													🍴									
Blackpool North	97 d		16 02		16 17		16 28		16b45	17 02		17 17		17 25	17b45	18 02		18 17		18 28		19 02		
Poulton-le-Fylde	97 d		16 08		16 23		16 34		16b51	17 08		17 23		17 32	17b51	18 08		18 23		18 34		19 08		
Kirkham & Wesham	97 d		16 17							17 17				17 41		18 17						19 17		
Barrow-in-Furness	d								16 00												18 00			
Roose	d								16 05												18 05			
Dalton	d								16 11												18 11			
Ulverston	d								16 19												18 19			
Cark	d								16 27												18 27			
Kents Bank	d								16 31												18 31			
Grange-over-Sands	d								16 35												18 35			
Arnside	d								16 41												18 41			
Silverdale	d								16 46												18 46			
Carnforth	d							16 38	16 53												18 53			
Windermere	83 d	*14 59*							*16c02*						*16 59*						*18c02*			
Oxenholme Lake District	65 d	15 41							*16 26*			*16 53*			17 45			*17 55*			*18 24*			
Lancaster 6	65 a	15 57						16 47	17 00						18 01						19 00			
	d	15 57	*16 04*						17 02			*17 09*			18 01			*18 10*			19 02			
Preston 8	d	16 20	16 30		16 42		16 53		17 23	17 30		17 42		17 53	18 23	18 30		18 42		18 53	19 23	19 30		
Leyland	d				16a47		16 59					17a47		17 59				18a47		18 59				
Chorley	d		16 40				17 06			17 40				18 06		18 40				19 06		19 40		
Adlington (Lancashire)	d						17 10							18 10						19 10				
Blackrod	d						17 14							18 14						19 14				
Horwich Parkway	d						17 17							18 17						19 17				
Lostock	d						17 21							18 21						19 21				
Southport	d			16 13							17 13						18 13						19 13	
Burscough Bridge	d			16 25							17 25						18 25						19 25	
Parbold	d			16 30							17 30						18 30						19 30	
Appley Bridge	d			16 34							17 34						18 34						19 34	
Gathurst	d			16 37							17 37						18 37						19 37	
Wigan Wallgate	a			16 42							17 42						18 42						19 42	
	d			16 43							17 43						18 43						19 43	
Wigan North Western	d																							
Hindley	d			16 48							17 48						18 48						19 48	
Westhoughton	d			16 53							17 53						18 53						19 53	
Bolton	a	16 42	16 51	17 01			17 26		17 41	17 52	18 01			18 26	18 42	18 52	19 01			19 26	19 41	19 51	20 01	
	d	16 42	16 53	17 01		17 16	17 26		17 42	17 53	18 01		18 16	18 26	18 42	18 53	19 01		19 16	19 26	19 42	19 53	20 01	20 16
Salford Crescent	a		17 05	17 14		17 29	17 39			18 05	18 14		18 29	18 39		19 05	19 14		19 29	19 39		20 05	20 14	20 29
	d		17 06	17 14		17 29	17 39			18 06	18 14		18 29	18 39		19 06	19 14		19 29	19 39		20 06	20 14	20 29
Manchester Victoria 🚊	a					17 35							18 35						19 35					20 35
Rochdale	a					*18 34*							*19 34*						*20 34*					*21 34*
Deansgate 🚊	a		17 09	17 18			17 43			18 09	18 18			18 43		19 09	19 18			19 43		20 09	20 18	
Manchester Oxford Road	a	16 57	17 11	17 20			17 45		17 57	18 11	18 20			18 46	18 57	19 11	19 20			19 45	19 56	20 11	20 20	
Manchester Piccadilly 10 🚊	a	17 01	17 15	17 24			17 49		18 01	18 15	18 24			18 49	19 01	19 15	19 24			19 49	20 01	20 15	20 24	
Stockport	84 a	*17 31*		17 37			18 04		*18 31*		18 38			19 04	*19 32*		19 38			20 04	*20 31*		20 38	
Alderley Edge	84 a			17 58							18 58						19 58						20 58	
Hazel Grove	86 a						18 13							19 13						20 13				
Buxton	86 a						18 53							19 53						20 53				
Heald Green	85 a			*18e04*							*19e04*						*20e04*						*21e05*	
Manchester Airport	85 ✈ a	17 18	17 33	*17e51*					18 18	18 33	*18e52*				19 18	19 33	*19e51*				20 18	20 33	*20e52*	

For general notes see front of timetable
For details of catering facilities see Directory of Train Operators

- **A** From Glasgow Central (Table 65)
- **B** To Liverpool Lime Street (Table 90)
- **C** From Clitheroe (Table 94)
- **D** From Leeds to Morecambe (Table 36)
- **E** From Edinburgh (Table 65)
- **b** Change at Preston
- **c** Change at Oxenholme Lake District and Lancaster
- **e** Change at Manchester Piccadilly

Table 82

Sundays

until 27 January

Blackpool, Barrow-in-Furness, Preston, Southport and Wigan → Bolton → Manchester

Network Diagram - see first page of Table 82

		NT	NT	TP	TP	NT	NT	NT	NT	NT	TP	NT	NT	NT	NT	TP	TP	TP	NT	NT	NT	VT	TP
				1 ◇	1 ◇						1 ◇					1 ◇	1 ◇	1 ◇				1 ◇	1 ◇
		A		B			C	D						D						C	D	E	
Blackpool North	97 d		19 28		20 02		20 17		20 28		21 02				21 28			22 02		22 17			23 02
Poulton-le-Fylde	97 d		19 34		20 08		20 23		20 34		21 08				21 34			22 08		22 23			23 08
Kirkham & Wesham	97 d				20 17						21 17							22 17					23 17
Barrow-in-Furness	d												19 57			20 50							
Roose	d												20 01			20 55							
Dalton	d												20 07			21 01							
Ulverston	d												20 15			21 09							
Cark	d												20 23			21 17							
Kents Bank	d												20 27			21 21							
Grange-over-Sands	d												20 31			21 25							
Arnside	d												20 37			21 31							
Silverdale	d												20 42			21 36							
Carnforth	d	18 57											20 50			21 43							
Windermere	83 d			*19 02*											*20b02*		21 20						
Oxenholme Lake District	65 d		*18 58*	19 45			*19 52*								*20 58*		21 40					22 09	
Lancaster 6	65 a	19 11		20 01									21 00			21 51	21 56					22 25	
	d		*19 16*	20 01			*20 08*								*21 14*	22 02						22 26	
Preston 8	d		19 53	20 23	20 30		20 42		20 53		21 30				21 53	22 23		22 30		22 42		23 01	23 30
Leyland	d		19 59				20a47		20 59						21 59					22a47			23 35
Chorley	d		20 06		20 40				21 06		21 40				22 06			22 40					23 43
Adlington (Lancashire)	d		20 10						21 10						22 10								23 47
Blackrod	d		20 14						21 14						22 14								23 50
Horwich Parkway	d		20 17						21 17						22 17								23 53
Lostock	d		20 21						21 21						22 21								23 57
Southport	d					20 13						21 13							22 13				
Burscough Bridge	d					20 25						21 25							22 25				
Parbold	d					20 30						21 30							22 30				
Appley Bridge	d					20 34						21 34							22 34				
Gathurst	d					20 37						21 37							22 37				
Wigan Wallgate	a					20 42						21 42							22 42				
	d					20 43						21 43							22 43				
Wigan North Western	d																						
Hindley	d					20 48						21 48							22 48				
Westhoughton	d					20 53						21 53							22 53				
Bolton	a		20 26	20 42	20 51	21 01			21 26		21 51	22 01			22 26	22 41		22 51	23 01			23s37	00 01
	d		20 26	20 42	20 53	21 01		21 16	21 26		21 53	22 01		22 16	22 26	22 42		22 53	23 01		23 16		00 02
Salford Crescent	a		20 39		21 05	21 14		21 29	21 39		22 05	22 14		22 29	22 39			23 05	23 14		23 29		
	d		20 39		21 06	21 14		21 29	21 39	21 50	22 06	22 14		22 29	22 39			23 06	23 14		23 29		
Manchester Victoria ⇌	a							21 35		21 54				22 35							23 35		
Rochdale	a									*22 34*				*23 58*									
Deansgate ⇌	a		20 43		21 09	21 18			21 43		22 09	22 18			22 43			23 09	23 18				
Manchester Oxford Road	a		20 45	20 57	21 12	21 20			21 45		22 11	22 20			22 45	22 56		23 12	23 21				
Manchester Piccadilly 10 ⇌	a		20 49	21 01	21 15	21 24			21 49		22 15	22 24			22 49	23 01		23 15	23 25			23 59	00 17
Stockport	84 a		21 04			21 36			22 04			22 37			23 03				23 38				
Alderley Edge	84 a					21 58						22 58							00 01				
Hazel Grove	86 a		21 13						22 13						23 11								
Buxton	86 a		21 53						22 53						23 51								
Heald Green	85 a					*22c04*									*23c19*								
Manchester Airport	85 ✈ a			21 18	21 33	*21c52*					22 33	*22c51*				23 18		23 33	*23c49*				00 33

For general notes see front of timetable
For details of catering facilities see Directory of Train Operators

- **A** From Leeds to Morecambe (Table 36)
- **B** From Edinburgh (Table 65)
- **C** To Liverpool Lime Street (Table 90)
- **D** From Clitheroe (Table 94)
- **E** From Glasgow Central (Table 65)
- **b** Change at Oxenholme Lake District and Preston
- **c** Change at Manchester Piccadilly

Table 82

Sundays

3 February to 23 March

Blackpool, Barrow-in-Furness, Preston, Southport and Wigan → Bolton → Manchester

Network Diagram - see first page of Table 82

Station		TP	TP	TP	TP	TP	TP	NT	NT	NT	NT	TP	NT	NT	NT	TP	NT	NT	NT	NT	NT	TP	TP	NT	NT
					1 ◇	1 ◇	1 ◇					1 ◇				1 ◇						1 ◇	1 ◇		
									A	B				C				D	A	C					C
		(bus)	(bus)	(bus)																					
Blackpool North	97 d	01 00	03 20	05 20			07b20		07b50			08b20			08b45	09b20			09b50				10b20		
Poulton-le-Fylde	97 d						07b35				08b00	08b35			09b00	09b35					10b00		10b35		
Kirkham & Wesham	97 d						07b55					08b55				10c05							10b55		
Barrow-in-Furness	d																					09 58			
Roose	d																					10 03			
Dalton	d																					10 09			
Ulverston	d																					10 17			
Cark	d																					10 25			
Kents Bank	d																					10 29			
Grange-over-Sands	d																					10 33			
Arnside	d																					10 39			
Silverdale	d																					10 44			
Carnforth	d																	10 30				10 50			
Windermere	83 d																								
Oxenholme Lake District	65 d																								
Lancaster 6	65 a																	10 39				10 57			
	d															09b00						10 58			
Preston 8	d	01u40	04u00	06u00			08 30		08 42		08 53	09 30			09 53	10 30			10 42		10 53	11a17	11 30		
Leyland	d								08a47		08 59				09 59				10a47		10 59				
Chorley	d						08 40				09 06	09 40			10 06	10 40					11 06		11 40		
Adlington (Lancashire)	d										09 10				10 10						11 10				
Blackrod	d										09 14				10 14						11 14				
Horwich Parkway	d										09 17				10 17						11 17				
Lostock	d										09 21				10 21						11 21				
Southport	d												09 13				10 13							11 13	
Burscough Bridge	d												09 25				10 25							11 25	
Parbold	d												09 30				10 30							11 30	
Appley Bridge	d												09 34				10 34							11 34	
Gathurst	d												09 37				10 37							11 37	
Wigan Wallgate	a												09 42				10 42							11 42	
	d							08 43					09 43				10 43							11 43	
Wigan North Western	d																								
Hindley	d							08 48					09 48				10 48							11 48	
Westhoughton	d							08 53					09 53				10 53							11 53	
Bolton	a						08 51	09 01			09 26	09 51	10 01		10 26	10 51	11 01				11 26		11 51	12 01	
	d	02u15	04u35	06u35	06 59	07 45	08 53	09 01		09 16	09 26	09 53	10 01	10 16	10 26	10 53	11 01			11 16	11 26		11 53	12 01	12 16
Salford Crescent	a						09 05	09 14		09 29	09 39	10 05	10 14	10 29	10 39	11 05	11 14			11 29	11 39		12 05	12 14	12 29
	d						09 06	09 14		09 29	09 39	10 06	10 14	10 29	10 39	11 06	11 14			11 29	11 39		12 06	12 14	12 29
Manchester Victoria (tram)	a									09 35				10 35						11 35					12 35
Rochdale	a									10 34				11 34						12 34					13 34
Deansgate (tram)	a						09 09	09 18			09 43	10 09	10 18		10 43	11 09	11 18				11 46		12 09	12 18	
Manchester Oxford Road	a						09 11	09 20			09 45	10 11	10 21		10 45	11 11	11 20				11 49		12 11	12 20	
Manchester Piccadilly 10 (tram)	a				07 14	08 00	09 15	09 24			09 49	10 15	10 25		10 49	11 15	11 24				11 52		12 15	12 24	
Stockport	84 a					09 05		09 38			10 07		10 38		11 07		11 38				12 07			12 37	
Alderley Edge	84 a							09 57					10 59				11 58							12 58	
Hazel Grove	86 a					09 13					10 15				11 15						12 15				
Buxton	86 a					09 53					10 55				11 55						12 55				
Heald Green	85 a				08 04			10e04					11e05				12e04							13e05	
Manchester Airport	85 ✈ a	03 00	05 20	07 20	07 32	08 17	09 33	09e51				10 33	10e51		11e23	11 33	11e51				12e30		12 33	12e50	

For general notes see front of timetable
For details of catering facilities see Directory of Train Operators

- **A** To Liverpool Lime Street (Table 90)
- **B** From Blackburn (Table 94)
- **C** From Clitheroe (Table 94)
- **D** 23 March. From Leeds to Morecambe (Table 36)
- **b** By bus
- **c** Until 24 February dep. 0955, by bus
- **e** Change at Manchester Piccadilly

Table 82

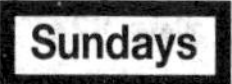

Sundays

3 February to 23 March

Blackpool, Barrow-in-Furness, Preston, Southport and Wigan → Bolton → Manchester

Network Diagram - see first page of Table 82

	NT	TP 1 ◇	NT	NT A	NT B	NT C	NT	TP 1 ◇	TP 1 ◇		NT	NT C	NT	TP 1 ◇ D ⚒	TP 1 ◇	NT	NT B	NT	NT C	NT	TP 1 ◇	TP 1 ◇	NT	NT C
Blackpool North 97 d	10b45	11b20			11b50				12b20				12b45		13b20		13b50					14b20		
Poulton-le-Fylde 97 d	11b00	11b35					12b00		12b35				13b00		13b35					14b00		14b35		
Kirkham & Wesham 97 d		11b55							12b55					13c51	13b55						14c51	14b55		
Barrow-in-Furness d								12 00										13 30			14 00			
Roose d								12 05										13 34			14 05			
Dalton d								12 11										13 40			14 11			
Ulverston d								12 19										13 48			14 19			
Cark d								12 27										13 57			14 27			
Kents Bank d								12 31										14 01			14 31			
Grange-over-Sands d								12 35										14 05			14 35			
Arnside d								12 41										14 11			14 41			
Silverdale d								12 46										14 16			14 46			
Carnforth d				12 34				12 52										14 23			14 53			
Windermere 83 d														12 59										
Oxenholme Lake District 65 d		10e45							12 32					13 44										
Lancaster 6 65 a				12 42				12 59						14 01				14 34			15 00			
d		11 43						13 00						14 01			14 07				15 02			
Preston 8 d	11 53	12 30			12 42		12 53	13a19	13 30				13 53	14 23	14 30		14 42			14 53	15 23	15 30		
Leyland d	11 59				12a47		12 59						13 59				14a47			14 59				
Chorley d	12 06	12 40					13 06		13 40				14 06		14 40					15 06		15 40		
Adlington (Lancashire) d	12 10						13 10						14 10							15 10				
Blackrod d	12 14						13 14						14 14							15 14				
Horwich Parkway d	12 17						13 17						14 17							15 17				
Lostock d	12 21						13 21						14 21							15 21				
Southport d			12 13								13 13					14 13							15 13	
Burscough Bridge d			12 25								13 25					14 25							15 25	
Parbold d			12 30								13 30					14 30							15 30	
Appley Bridge d			12 34								13 34					14 34							15 34	
Gathurst d			12 37								13 37					14 37							15 37	
Wigan Wallgate a			12 42								13 42					14 42							15 42	
d			12 43								13 43					14 43							15 43	
Wigan North Western d																								
Hindley d			12 48								13 48					14 48							15 48	
Westhoughton d			12 53								13 53					14 53							15 53	
Bolton a	12 26	12 52	13 01				13 26		13 52		14 01		14 26	14 42	14 52	15 01				15 26	15 41	15 53	16 01	
d	12 26	12 53	13 01			13 16	13 26		13 53		14 01	14 16	14 26	14 42	14 53	15 01			15 16	15 26	15 42	15 53	16 01	16 16
Salford Crescent a	12 39	13 05	13 14			13 29	13 39		14 05		14 14	14 29	14 39		15 05	15 14			15 29	15 39		16 05	16 14	16 29
d	12 39	13 06	13 14			13 29	13 39		14 06		14 14	14 29	14 39		15 06	15 14			15 29	15 39		16 06	16 14	16 29
Manchester Victoria 🚊 a						13 35						14 35							15 35					16 35
Rochdale a						14 34						15 34							16 34					17 34
Deansgate 🚊 a	12 43	13 09	13 18				13 43		14 09		14 18		14 43		15 09	15 18				15 43		16 09	16 18	
Manchester Oxford Road a	12 46	13 11	13 20				13 46		14 11		14 20		14 46	14 57	15 11	15 20				15 45	15 56	16 11	16 20	
Manchester Piccadilly 10 🚊 a	12 49	13 15	13 24				13 49		14 15		14 24		14 49	15 00	15 15	15 24				15 49	16 01	16 15	16 24	
Stockport 84 a	13 07		13 39				14 07				14 38		15 07	15 22		15 36				16 04	16 22		16 37	
Alderley Edge 84 a			13 58								14 59					15 58							16 58	
Hazel Grove 86 a	13 15						14 15						15 15							16 12				
Buxton 86 a	13 55						14 55						15 56							16 53				
Heald Green 85 a			14f07								15f04					16f04							17f05	
Manchester Airport 85 ✈ a	13f24	13 33	13f54						14 33		14f51			15 18	15 33	15f51					16 18	16 33	16f51	

For general notes see front of timetable
For details of catering facilities see Directory of Train Operators

A 23 March. From Leeds to Morecambe (Table 36)
B To Liverpool Lime Street (Table 90)
C From Clitheroe (Table 94)
D From Carlisle (Table 65)

b By bus
c From 2 March only. Change at Preston
e Change at Lancaster and Preston. By bus to Lancaster
f Change at Manchester Piccadilly

Table 82

Blackpool, Barrow-in-Furness, Preston, Southport and Wigan → Bolton → Manchester

3 February to 23 March

Network Diagram - see first page of Table 82

		NT	TP	TP	NT	NT	NT	NT	NT	TP	TP	NT	NT	NT	NT	TP	TP	NT	NT	NT	NT	TP	NT	TP	NT
			1 ◇	1 ◇						1 ◇	1 ◇					1 ◇	1 ◇					1 ◇		1 ◇	
			A			B	C	D					B	D		A			B	D			C		
Blackpool North	97 d	14b45		15b20		15b50					16b20		16b50				17b20		17b50					18b20	
Poulton-le-Fylde	97 d	15b00		15b35					16b00		16b35		16b45		17b00		17b35		17b45		18b00			18b35	
Kirkham & Wesham	97 d		15c51	15b55						16c51	16b55					17c51	17b55					18c51		18b55	
Barrow-in-Furness	d									16 00												18 00			
Roose	d									16 05												18 05			
Dalton	d									16 11												18 11			
Ulverston	d									16 19												18 19			
Cark	d									16 27												18 27			
Kents Bank	d									16 31												18 31			
Grange-over-Sands	d									16 35												18 35			
Arnside	d									16 41												18 41			
Silverdale	d									16 46												18 46			
Carnforth	d						16 38			16 53												18 53	18 57		
Windermere	83 d	14e15	14 59							16f02						16 59						18f02			
Oxenholme Lake District	65 d	14 53	15 41							16 26			16 53			17 44			17 55			18 24			
Lancaster 6	65 a		15 57				16 47			17 00						18 01						19 00	19 11		
	d	15 09	15 57							17 02			17 09			18 01			18 10			19 02			
Preston 8	d	15 53	16 20	16 30		16 42			16 53	17 23	17 30		17 42		17 53	18 23	18 30		18 42		18 53	19 23		19 30	
Leyland	d	15 59				16a47			16 59				17a47		17 59				18a47		18 59				
Chorley	d	16 06		16 40					17 06		17 40				18 06		18 40				19 06			19 40	
Adlington (Lancashire)	d	16 10							17 10						18 10						19 10				
Blackrod	d	16 14							17 14						18 14						19 14				
Horwich Parkway	d	16 17							17 17						18 17						19 17				
Lostock	d	16 21							17 21						18 21						19 21				
Southport	d				16 13							17 13						18 13							19 13
Burscough Bridge	d				16 25							17 25						18 25							19 25
Parbold	d				16 30							17 30						18 30							19 30
Appley Bridge	d				16 34							17 34						18 34							19 34
Gathurst	d				16 37							17 37						18 37							19 37
Wigan Wallgate	a				16 42							17 42						18 42							19 42
	d				16 43							17 43						18 43							19 43
Wigan North Western	d																								
Hindley	d				16 48							17 48						18 48							19 48
Westhoughton	d				16 53							17 53						18 53							19 53
Bolton	a	16 26	16 42	16 51	17 01				17 26	17 41	17 52	18 01			18 26	18 42	18 52	19 01			19 26	19 41		19 51	20 01
	d	16 26	16 42	16 53	17 01			17 16	17 26	17 42	17 53	18 01		18 16	18 26	18 42	18 53	19 01		19 16	19 26	19 42		19 53	20 01
Salford Crescent	a	16 39		17 05	17 14			17 29	17 39		18 05	18 14		18 29	18 39		19 05	19 14		19 29	19 39			20 05	20 14
	d	16 39		17 06	17 14			17 29	17 39		18 06	18 14		18 29	18 39		19 06	19 14		19 29	19 39			20 06	20 14
Manchester Victoria 🚋	a							17 35						18 35						19 35					
Rochdale	a							18 34						19 34						20 34					
Deansgate 🚋	a	16 43		17 09	17 18				17 43		18 09	18 18			18 43		19 09	19 18			19 43			20 09	20 18
Manchester Oxford Road	a	16 45	16 57	17 11	17 20				17 45	17 57	18 11	18 20			18 46	18 57	19 11	19 20			19 45	19 56		20 11	20 20
Manchester Piccadilly 10 🚋	a	16 49	17 01	17 15	17 24				17 49	18 01	18 15	18 24			18 49	19 01	19 15	19 24			19 49	20 01		20 15	20 24
Stockport	84 a	17 04	17 22		17 37				18 04	18 22		18 38			19 04	19 22		19 38			20 04	20 22			20 38
Alderley Edge	84 a				17 58							18 58						19 58							20 58
Hazel Grove	86 a	17 15							18 13						19 13						20 13				
Buxton	86 a	17 55							18 53						19 53						20 53				
Heald Green	85 a				18g04							19g04						20g04							21g05
Manchester Airport	85 ✈ a		17 18	17 33	17g51					18 18	18 33	18g52				19 18	19 33	19g51				20 18		20 33	20g52

For general notes see front of timetable
For details of catering facilities see Directory of Train Operators

A From Carlisle (Table 65)
B To Liverpool Lime Street (Table 90)
C From Leeds to Morecambe (Table 36)
D From Clitheroe (Table 94)
b By bus
c From 2 March only. Change at Preston
e Change at Oxenholme Lake District and Preston
f Change at Oxenholme Lake District and Lancaster
g Change at Manchester Piccadilly

Table 82

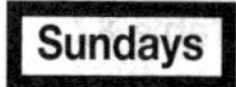

Blackpool, Barrow-in-Furness, Preston, Southport and Wigan → Bolton → Manchester

Sundays

3 February to 23 March

Network Diagram - see first page of Table 82

	NT	NT	TP	TP	NT	NT	NT	NT	NT	NT	TP	NT	NT	NT	TP	TP	TP	NT	NT	NT	VT	TP
			1 ◇	1 ◇							1 ◇				1 ◇	1 ◇	1 ◇				1 ◇	1 ◇
	A		B			C		A					A						C	A	D	
Blackpool North 97 d		18b45		19b20		19b50					20b20			20b45			21b20		21b50			22b20
Poulton-le-Fylde 97 d		19b00		19b35					20b00		20b35			21b00			21b35					22b35
Kirkham & Wesham 97 d			19c51	19b55							20b55				21c51		21b55					22b55
Barrow-in-Furness d							19 57								20 50							
Roose d							20 01								20 55							
Dalton d							20 07								21 01							
Ulverston d							20 15								21 09							
Cark d							20 23								21 17							
Kents Bank d							20 27								21 21							
Grange-over-Sands d							20 31								21 25							
Arnside d							20 37								21 31							
Silverdale d							20 42								21 36							
Carnforth d							20 50								21 43							
Windermere 83 d			19 02											20e02		21 20						
Oxenholme Lake District 65 d			19 44			19 52								20 58		21 40					22 09	
Lancaster 6 65 a			20 01				21 00								21 51	21 56					22 25	
d			20 01			20 08								21 14	22 02						22 26	
Preston 8 d		19 53	20 23	20 30		20 42			20 53		21 30			21 53	22 23		22 30		22 42		23 01	23 30
Leyland d		19 59				20a47			20 59					21 59					22a47			23 35
Chorley d		20 06		20 40					21 06		21 40			22 06			22 40					23 43
Adlington (Lancashire) d		20 10							21 10					22 10								23 47
Blackrod d		20 14							21 14					22 14								23 50
Horwich Parkway d		20 17							21 17					22 17								23 53
Lostock d		20 21							21 21					22 21								23 57
Southport d					20 13							21 13						22 13				
Burscough Bridge d					20 25							21 25						22 25				
Parbold d					20 30							21 30						22 30				
Appley Bridge d					20 34							21 34						22 34				
Gathurst d					20 37							21 37						22 37				
Wigan Wallgate a					20 42							21 42						22 42				
d					20 43							21 43						22 43				
Wigan North Western d																						
Hindley d					20 48							21 48						22 48				
Westhoughton d					20 53							21 53						22 53				
Bolton a		20 26	20 42	20 51	21 01				21 26		21 51	22 01		22 26	22 41		22 51	23 01			23s37	00 01
d	20 16	20 26	20 42	20 53	21 01			21 16	21 26		21 53	22 01	22 16	22 26	22 42		22 53	23 01		23 16		00 02
Salford Crescent a	20 29	20 39		21 05	21 14			21 29	21 39		22 05	22 14	22 29	22 39			23 05	23 14		23 29		
d	20 29	20 39		21 06	21 14			21 29	21 39	21 50	22 06	22 14	22 29	22 39			23 06	23 14		23 29		
Manchester Victoria a	20 35							21 35		21 54			22 35							23 35		
Rochdale a	21 34									22 34			23 58									
Deansgate a		20 43		21 09	21 18				21 43		22 09	22 18		22 43			23 09	23 18				
Manchester Oxford Road a		20 45	20 57	21 12	21 20				21 45		22 11	22 20		22 45	22 56		23 12	23 21				
Manchester Piccadilly 10 a		20 49	21 01	21 15	21 24				21 49		22 15	22 24		22 49	23 01		23 15	23 25			23 59	00 17
Stockport 84 a		21 04	21 22		21 36				22 04			22 37		23 03	23 20			23 38				
Alderley Edge 84 a					21 58							22 58						00 01				
Hazel Grove 86 a		21 13							22 13					23 11								
Buxton 86 a		21 53							22 53					23 51								
Heald Green 85 a					22f04									23f19								
Manchester Airport 85 ✈ a			21 18	21 33	21f52						22 33	22f51			23 18		23 33	23f49				00 33

For general notes see front of timetable
For details of catering facilities see Directory of Train Operators

A From Clitheroe (Table 94)
B From Carlisle (Table 65)
C To Liverpool Lime Street (Table 90)
D From Lockerbie (Table 65)
b By bus
c From 2 March only. Change at Preston
e Change at Oxenholme Lake District and Preston
f Change at Manchester Piccadilly

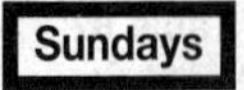

from 30 March

Blackpool, Barrow-in-Furness, Preston, Southport and Wigan → Bolton → Manchester

Network Diagram - see first page of Table 82

		TP	TP	TP	TP	TP	TP	NT	NT	NT	NT	TP	NT	NT	NT	TP	NT	NT	NT	NT	TP	NT	TP	TP	NT
					1 ◇	1 ◇	1 ◇		A	B		1 ◇		C		1 ◇		A	C		1 ◇	D	1		
		bus	bus	bus																				bus	
Blackpool North	97 d	01 00	03 20	05 20			08 02		08 17		08 28	09 02			09 28	10 02		10 17		10 28	11 02				
Poulton-le-Fylde	97 d						08 08		08 23		08 34	09 08			09 34	10 08		10 23		10 34	11 08				
Kirkham & Wesham	97 d						08 17					09 17				10 17					11 17				
Barrow-in-Furness	d																						09 40		
Roose	d																						09 44		
Dalton	d																						09 50		
Ulverston	d																						09 59		
Cark	d																						10 07		
Kents Bank	d																						10 11		
Grange-over-Sands	d																						10 15		
Arnside	d																						10 21		
Silverdale	d																						10 25		
Carnforth	d																					10 30	10 35	10 50	
Windermere	83 d																								
Oxenholme Lake District	65 d																								
Lancaster 6	65 a																					10 39	10 45		
	d															*09b00*					*10b25*				
Preston 8	d	01u40	04u00	06u00			08 30		08 42		08 53	09 30			09 53	10 30		10 42		10 53	11 30			11a40	
Leyland	d								08a47		08 59				09 59			10a47		10 59					
Chorley	d						08 40				09 06	09 40			10 06	10 40				11 06	11 40				
Adlington (Lancashire)	d										09 10				10 10					11 10					
Blackrod	d										09 14				10 14					11 14					
Horwich Parkway	d										09 17				10 17					11 17					
Lostock	d										09 21				10 21					11 21					
Southport	d												09 13				10 13								11 13
Burscough Bridge	d												09 25				10 25								11 25
Parbold	d												09 30				10 30								11 30
Appley Bridge	d												09 34				10 34								11 34
Gathurst	d												09 37				10 37								11 37
Wigan Wallgate	a												09 42				10 42								11 42
	d							08 43					09 43				10 43								11 43
Wigan North Western	d																								
Hindley	d							08 48					09 48				10 48								11 48
Westhoughton	d							08 53					09 53				10 53								11 53
Bolton	a						08 51	09 01			09 26	09 51	10 01		10 26	10 51	11 01			11 26	11 51				12 01
	d	02u15	04u35	06u35	06 59	07 45	08 53	09 01		09 16	09 26	09 53	10 01	10 16	10 26	10 53	11 01		11 16	11 26	11 53				12 01
Salford Crescent	a						09 05	09 14		09 29	09 39	10 05	10 14	10 29	10 39	11 05	11 14		11 29	11 39	12 05				12 14
	d						09 06	09 14		09 29	09 39	10 06	10 14	10 29	10 39	11 06	11 14		11 29	11 39	12 06				12 14
Manchester Victoria (tram)	a									09 35				10 35					11 35						
Rochdale	a									*10 34*				*11 34*					*12 34*						
Deansgate (tram)	a						09 09	09 18			09 43	10 09	10 18		10 43	11 09	11 18			11 46	12 09				12 18
Manchester Oxford Road	a						09 11	09 20			09 45	10 11	10 21		10 45	11 11	11 20			11 49	12 11				12 20
Manchester Piccadilly 10 (tram)	a				07 14	08 00	09 15	09 24			09 49	10 15	10 25		10 49	11 15	11 24			11 52	12 15				12 24
Stockport	84 a					*09 05*		09 38			10 07		10 38		11 07		11 38			12 07					12 37
Alderley Edge	84 a							09 57					10 59				11 58								12 58
Hazel Grove	86 a					*09 13*					10 15				11 15					12 15					
Buxton	86 a					*09 53*					10 55				11 55					12 55					
Heald Green	85 a				*08 04*			*10c04*					*11c05*				*12c04*								*13c05*
Manchester Airport	85 ✈ a	03 00	05 20	07 20	07 32	08 17	09 33	*09c51*				10 33	*10c51*		*11c23*	11 33	*11c51*			*12c30*	12 33				*12c50*

For general notes see front of timetable
For details of catering facilities see Directory of Train Operators

A To Liverpool Lime Street (Table 90)
B From Blackburn (Table 94)
C From Clitheroe (Table 94)
D From Leeds to Morecambe (Table 36)

b By bus
c Change at Manchester Piccadilly

Blackpool, Barrow-in-Furness, Preston, Southport and Wigan → Bolton → Manchester

Sundays

from 30 March

Network Diagram - see first page of Table 82

		NT	NT	TP	NT	TP	TP	NT	NT	NT	TP	NT	NT	NT	NT	TP	NT	TP	TP	NT	NT	NT	TP	NT	NT
				1 ◇		1					1 ◇					1 ◇		1					1 ◇		
		A				B	🚌	C	A				D	A				B	🚌	C	A				
Blackpool North	97 d		11 28	12 02				12 17		12 28	13 02				13 28	14 02				14 17		14 28	15 02		
Poulton-le-Fylde	97 d		11 34	12 08				12 23		12 34	13 08				13 34	14 08				14 23		14 34	15 08		
Kirkham & Wesham	97 d			12 17							13 17					14 17							15 17		
Barrow-in-Furness	d					10 50												12 50							13 30
Roose	d					10 54												12 54							13 34
Dalton	d					11 00												13 00							13 40
Ulverston	d					11 09												13 09							13 48
Cark	d					11 17												13 17							13 57
Kents Bank	d					11 21												13 21							14 01
Grange-over-Sands	d					11 25												13 25							14 05
Arnside	d					11 31												13 31							14 11
Silverdale	d					11 35												13 35							14 16
Carnforth	d					11 42	11 50						12 34					13 42	13 50						14 23
Windermere	83 d																						*13b33*		
Oxenholme Lake District	65 d			*10c15*							*11c15*					*12c15*							*13b54*		
Lancaster 6	65 a					11 52							12 42					13 52							14 34
	d			*11c00*							*12c00*					*13c25*							*14c25*		
Preston 8	d		11 53	12 30			12a40	12 42		12 54	13 30				13 53	14 30			14a40	14 42		14 53	15 30		*15e50*
Leyland	d		11 59					12a47		12 59					13 59					14a47		14 59			
Chorley	d		12 06	12 40						13 06	13 40				14 06	14 40						15 06	15 40		
Adlington (Lancashire)	d		12 10							13 10					14 10							15 10			
Blackrod	d		12 14							13 14					14 14							15 14			
Horwich Parkway	d		12 17							13 17					14 17							15 17			
Lostock	d		12 21							13 21					14 21							15 21			
Southport	d				12 13							13 13					14 13							15 13	
Burscough Bridge	d				12 25							13 25					14 25							15 25	
Parbold	d				12 30							13 30					14 30							15 30	
Appley Bridge	d				12 34							13 34					14 34							15 34	
Gathurst	d				12 37							13 37					14 37							15 37	
Wigan Wallgate	a				12 42							13 42					14 42							15 42	
	d				12 43							13 43					14 43							15 43	
Wigan North Western	d																								
Hindley	d				12 48							13 48					14 48							15 48	
Westhoughton	d				12 53							13 53					14 53							15 53	
Bolton	a		12 26	12 52	13 01					13 26	13 52	14 01			14 26	14 52	15 01					15 26	15 52	16 01	
	d	12 16	12 26	12 53	13 01				13 16	13 26	13 53	14 01		14 16	14 26	14 53	15 01				15 16	15 26	15 53	16 01	
Salford Crescent	a	12 29	12 39	13 05	13 14				13 29	13 39	14 05	14 14		14 29	14 39	15 05	15 14				15 29	15 39	16 05	16 14	
	d	12 29	12 39	13 06	13 14				13 29	13 39	14 06	14 14		14 29	14 39	15 06	15 14				15 29	15 39	16 06	16 14	
Manchester Victoria	🚋 a	12 35							13 35					14 35							15 35				
Rochdale	a	*13 34*							*14 34*					*15 34*							*16 34*				
Deansgate	🚋 a		12 43	13 09	13 18					13 43	14 09	14 18			14 43	15 09	15 18					15 43	16 09	16 18	
Manchester Oxford Road	a		12 46	13 11	13 20					13 46	14 11	14 20			14 46	15 11	15 20					15 45	16 11	16 20	
Manchester Piccadilly 10	🚋 a		12 49	13 15	13 24					13 49	14 15	14 24			14 49	15 15	15 24					15 49	16 15	16 24	
Stockport	84 a		13 07		13 39					14 07		14 38			15 07		15 36					16 04		16 37	
Alderley Edge	84 a				13 58							14 59					15 58							16 58	
Hazel Grove	86 a		13 15							14 15					15 15							16 12			
Buxton	86 a		13 55							14 55					15 56							16 53			
Heald Green	85 a				*14f07*							*15f04*					*16f04*							*17f05*	
Manchester Airport	85 ✈ a		*13f24*	13 33	*13f54*						14 33	*14f51*			*15f21*	15 33	*15f51*						16 33	*16f51*	

For general notes see front of timetable
For details of catering facilities see Directory of Train Operators

A From Clitheroe (Table 94)
B To Windermere (Table 83)
C To Liverpool Lime Street (Table 90)
D From Leeds to Morecambe (Table 36)

b Change at Lancaster and Preston. By bus from Lancaster
c By bus
e Arrival time. By bus
f Change at Manchester Piccadilly

Table 82

Sundays

from 30 March

Blackpool, Barrow-in-Furness, Preston, Southport and Wigan → Bolton → Manchester

Network Diagram - see first page of Table 82

	NT	NT	TP	NT	TP	TP	NT	NT	NT	TP	NT	NT	NT	NT	NT	TP	NT	TP	TP	NT	NT	NT	TP	NT
			1 ◇		1					1 ◇						1 ◇		1					1 ◇	
	A				B	Bus	C	A				C	A		D			B	Bus	C	A			
Blackpool North 97 d		15 28	16 02				16 17		16 28	17 02		17 17		17 25		18 02				18 17		18 28	19 02	
Poulton-le-Fylde 97 d		15 34	16 08				16 23		16 34	17 08		17 23		17 32		18 08				18 23		18 34	19 08	
Kirkham & Wesham 97 d			16 17							17 17				17 41		18 17							19 17	
Barrow-in-Furness d					14 50													16 50						
Roose d					14 54													16 54						
Dalton d					15 00													17 00						
Ulverston d					15 09													17 09						
Cark d					15 17													17 17						
Kents Bank d					15 21													17 21						
Grange-over-Sands d					15 25													17 25						
Arnside d					15 31													17 31						
Silverdale d					15 35													17 35						
Carnforth d					15 42	15 50									16 38			17 42	17 50					
Windermere 83 d									14b40	15c35												16b40	17c33	
Oxenholme Lake District 65 d			14e15						15e40	15c54						16e40						17e40	17c54	
Lancaster 6 65 a					15 52										16 47			17 52						
d			15e25						15e55	16e25						17e25							18e25	
Preston 8 d		15 53	16 30			16a40	16 42		16 53	17 30		17 42		17 53		18 30			18a40	18 42		18 53	19 30	
Leyland d		15 59					16a47		16 59			17a47		17 59						18a47		18 59		
Chorley d		16 06	16 40						17 06	17 40				18 06		18 40						19 06	19 40	
Adlington (Lancashire) d		16 10							17 10					18 10								19 10		
Blackrod d		16 14							17 14					18 14								19 14		
Horwich Parkway d		16 17							17 17					18 17								19 17		
Lostock d		16 21							17 21					18 21								19 21		
Southport d				16 13							17 13						18 13							19 13
Burscough Bridge d				16 25							17 25						18 25							19 25
Parbold d				16 30							17 30						18 30							19 30
Appley Bridge d				16 34							17 34						18 34							19 34
Gathurst d				16 37							17 37						18 37							19 37
Wigan Wallgate a				16 42							17 42						18 42							19 42
d				16 43							17 43						18 43							19 43
Wigan North Western d																								
Hindley d				16 48							17 48						18 48							19 48
Westhoughton d				16 53							17 53						18 53							19 53
Bolton a		16 26	16 51	17 01					17 26	17 52	18 01			18 26		18 52	19 01					19 26	19 52	20 01
d	16 16	16 26	16 53	17 01				17 16	17 26	17 53	18 01		18 16	18 26		18 53	19 01				19 16	19 26	19 53	20 01
Salford Crescent a	16 29	16 39	17 05	17 14				17 29	17 39	18 05	18 14		18 29	18 39		19 05	19 14				19 29	19 39	20 05	20 14
d	16 29	16 39	17 06	17 14				17 29	17 39	18 06	18 14		18 29	18 39		19 06	19 14				19 29	19 39	20 06	20 14
Manchester Victoria ⇌ a	16 35							17 35					18 35								19 35			
Rochdale a	*17 34*							*18 34*					*19 34*								*20 34*			
Deansgate ⇌ a		16 43	17 09	17 18					17 43	18 09	18 18			18 43		19 09	19 18					19 43	20 09	20 18
Manchester Oxford Road a		16 45	17 11	17 20					17 45	18 11	18 20			18 46		19 11	19 20					19 45	20 11	20 20
Manchester Piccadilly 10 ⇌ a		16 49	17 15	17 24					17 49	18 15	18 24			18 49		19 15	19 24					19 49	20 15	20 24
Stockport 84 a		17 04		17 37					18 04		18 38			19 04			19 38					20 04		20 38
Alderley Edge 84 a				17 58							18 58						19 58							20 58
Hazel Grove 86 a		17 15							18 13					19 15								20 13		
Buxton 86 a		17 55							18 53					19 53								20 53		
Heald Green 85 a				*18f04*							*19f04*						*20f04*							*21f05*
Manchester Airport 85 ✈ a		*17f21*	17 33	*17f51*						18 33	*18f58*			*19f21*		19 33	*19f51*						20 33	*20f52*

For general notes see front of timetable
For details of catering facilities see Directory of Train Operators

A From Clitheroe (Table 94)
B To Windermere (Table 83)
C To Liverpool Lime Street (Table 90)
D From Leeds to Morecambe (Table 36)
b Change at Oxenholme Lake District and Preston. By bus from Oxenholme Lake District
c Change at Lancaster and Preston. By bus from Lancaster
e By bus
f Change at Manchester Piccadilly

Table 82

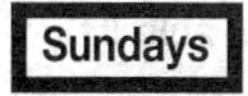

from 30 March

Blackpool, Barrow-in-Furness, Preston, Southport and Wigan → Bolton → Manchester

Network Diagram - see first page of Table 82

	NT	NT	NT	TP	NT	TP	TP	NT	NT	NT	NT	TP	NT	NT	NT	NT	TP	NT	NT	NT	TP	VT	TP
				1 ◇		1						1 ◇					1 ◇				1	1 ◇	1 ◇
	A		B			C	bus	D	A					A					D	A		E	
Blackpool North 97 d		19 28		20 02				20 17		20 28		21 02			21 28		22 02		22 17				23 02
Poulton-le-Fylde 97 d		19 34		20 08				20 23		20 34		21 08			21 34		22 08		22 23				23 08
Kirkham & Wesham 97 d				20 17								21 17					22 17						23 17
Barrow-in-Furness d						18 50										19 57					20 30		
Roose d						18 54										20 01					20 34		
Dalton d						19 00										20 07					20 40		
Ulverston d						19 09										20 15					20 49		
Cark d						19 17										20 23					20 57		
Kents Bank d						19 21										20 27					21 01		
Grange-over-Sands d						19 25										20 31					21 05		
Arnside d						19 31										20 37					21 11		
Silverdale d						19 35										20 42					21 15		
Carnforth d			18 57			19 42	19 50									20 50					21 22		
Windermere 83 d										*18b40*		*19c40*					*20c40*						
Oxenholme Lake District 65 d				*18e45*						*19e40*		*19c59*					*21c01*					*21e15*	*21e40*
Lancaster 6 65 a			19 11			19 52										21 00					21 32		
d				*19e30*								*20e25*					*21e40*					*22e00*	*22e25*
Preston 8 d		19 53		20 30			20a40	20 42		20 53		21 30			21 53		22 30		22 42		*22f50*	23 01	23 30
Leyland d		19 59						20a47		20 59					21 59				22a47				23 35
Chorley d		20 06		20 40						21 06		21 40			22 06		22 40						23 43
Adlington (Lancashire) d		20 10								21 10					22 10								23 47
Blackrod d		20 14								21 14					22 14								23 50
Horwich Parkway d		20 17								21 17					22 17								23 53
Lostock d		20 21								21 21					22 21								23 57
Southport d					20 13								21 13					22 13					
Burscough Bridge d					20 25								21 25					22 25					
Parbold d					20 30								21 30					22 30					
Appley Bridge d					20 34								21 34					22 34					
Gathurst d					20 37								21 37					22 37					
Wigan Wallgate a					20 42								21 42					22 42					
d					20 43								21 43					22 43					
Wigan North Western d																							
Hindley d					20 48								21 48					22 48					
Westhoughton d					20 53								21 53					22 53					
Bolton a		20 26		20 51	21 01					21 26		21 52	22 01		22 26		22 51	23 01				23s37	00 01
d	20 16	20 26		20 53	21 01				21 16	21 26		21 53	22 01	22 16	22 26		22 53	23 01		23 16			00 02
Salford Crescent a	20 29	20 39		21 05	21 14				21 29	21 39		22 05	22 14	22 29	22 39		23 05	23 14		23 29			
d	20 29	20 39		21 06	21 14				21 29	21 39	21 50	22 06	22 14	22 29	22 39		23 06	23 14		23 29			
Manchester Victoria ⇌ a	20 35								21 35		21 54			22 35						23 35			
Rochdale a	*21 34*										*22 34*			*23 58*									
Deansgate ⇌ a		20 43		21 09	21 18					21 43		22 09	22 18		22 43		23 09	23 18					
Manchester Oxford Road a		20 45		21 12	21 20					21 45		22 11	22 20		22 45		23 12	23 21					
Manchester Piccadilly 10 ⇌ a		20 49		21 15	21 24					21 49		22 15	22 24		22 49		23 15	23 25				23 59	00 17
Stockport 84 a		21 04			21 36					22 04			22 37		23 03			23 38					
Alderley Edge 84 a					21 58								22 58					23 58					
Hazel Grove 86 a		21 13								22 13					23 11								
Buxton 86 a		21 53								22 53					23 51								
Heald Green 85 a					*22g04*										*23g19*								
Manchester Airport 85 ✈ a		*21g21*		21 33	*21g52*							22 33	*22g51*		*23g26*		23 33	*23g54*					00 33

For general notes see front of timetable
For details of catering facilities see Directory of Train Operators

A From Clitheroe (Table 94)
B From Leeds to Morecambe (Table 36)
C To Windermere (Table 83)
D To Liverpool Lime Street (Table 90)
E From Glasgow Central (Table 65)
b Change at Oxenholme Lake District and Preston. By bus from Oxenholme Lake District
c Change at Lancaster and Preston. By bus from Lancaster
e By bus
f Arrival time. By bus
g Change at Manchester Piccadilly

Oxenholme: Lake District → Windermere

Network Diagram - see first page of Table 82

Mondays to Fridays

Miles			TP 1◇ A	TP 1	TP 1	TP 1	TP 1	TP 1◇ B	TP 1	TP 1◇ C	TP 1	TP 1◇ B	TP 1	TP 1	TP 1	TP 1◇ D	TP 1	TP 1	TP 1
0	**Oxenholme Lake District**	d	05 53	06 51	07 56	09 06	09 53	10 44	11 55	12 57	13 54	14 51	15 51	17 04	17 48	18 52	19 59	21 05	21 53
2¼	Kendal	d	05 57	06 55	08 00	09 10	09 57	10 48	11 59	13 01	13 58	14 55	15 55	17 08	17 52	18 56	20 03	21 09	21 57
4	Burneside	d	⌇	06x58	08x03		10x00		12x02	13x04	14x01		15x58	17x11		18x59	20x06	21x12	22x00
6½	Staveley	d	⌇	07x03	08x08		10x05		12x07	13x09	14x06		16x03	17x16		19x04	20x11	21x17	22x05
10	**Windermere**	a	06 12	07 10	08 15	09 22	10 12	11 01	12 14	13 18	14 13	15 09	16 10	17 23	18 04	19 13	20 18	21 24	22 12

Saturdays until 22 March

		TP 1◇ E	TP 1	TP 1	TP 1	TP 1	TP 1◇ B	TP 1	TP 1◇ C	TP 1	TP 1◇ G	TP 1	TP 1	TP 1	TP 1◇ D	TP 1
Oxenholme Lake District	d	06 04	07 00	07 56	09 05	09 55	10 50	11 58	12 59	13 55	14 43	15 58	17 04	17 48	18 40	20 00
Kendal	d	06 08	07 04	08 00	09 09	09 59	10 54	12 02	13 03	13 59	14 47	16 02	17 08	17 52	18 44	20 04
Burneside	d		07x07	08x03		10x02	10x57	12x05	13x06	14x02		16x05	17x11		18x48	20x07
Staveley	d		07x12	08x08		10x07	11x02	12x10	13x11	14x07		16x10	17x16		18x53	20x12
Windermere	a	06 25	07 19	08 15	09 21	10 14	11 11	12 17	13 20	14 14	15 01	16 17	17 23	18 04	19 02	20 19

Saturdays from 29 March

		TP 1 D	TP 1 D	TP 1 D	TP 1 D	TP 1 D	TP 1 D	TP 1 D	TP 1 D	TP 1 D	TP 1 D	TP 1 D	TP 1 D	TP 1 E	TP 1	TP 1 E
Oxenholme Lake District	d	06 26	07 26	08 26	09 26	10 26	11 26	12 26	13 26	14 26	15 26	16 26	17 26	18 26	19 20	20 31
Kendal	d	06 30	07 30	08 30	09 30	10 30	11 30	12 30	13 30	14 30	15 30	16 30	17 30	18 30	19 24	20 35
Burneside	d	06x33	07x33	08x33	09x33	10x33	11x33	12x33	13x33	14x33	15x33	16x33	17x33	18x33	19x27	20x38
Staveley	d	06x38	07x38	08x38	09x38	10x38	11x38	12x38	13x38	14x38	15x38	16x38	17x38	18x38	19x32	20x43
Windermere	a	06 47	07 47	08 47	09 47	10 47	11 47	12 47	13 47	14 47	15 47	16 47	17 47	18 47	19 39	20 52

Sundays until 23 March

		TP 1◇ C	TP 1	TP 1	TP 1	TP 1	TP 1	TP 1	TP 1	TP 1 D
Oxenholme Lake District	d	12 31	13 39	14 39	15 39	16 39	17 39	18 39	19 39	20 58
Kendal	d	12 35	13 43	14 43	15 43	16 43	17 43	18 43	19 43	21 02
Burneside	d	12x39	13x46		15x46		17x46	18x46	19x46	
Staveley	d	12x44	13x51		15x51		17x51	18x51	19x51	
Windermere	a	12 52	13 58	14 55	15 58	16 55	17 58	18 58	19 58	21 16

Sundays from 30 March

		TP 1 E	TP 1	TP 1 E	TP 1	TP 1 E	TP 1	TP 1 E	TP 1	TP 1 E
Oxenholme Lake District	d	12 12	13 10	14 12	15 10	16 12	17 10	18 12	19 10	20 12
Kendal	d	12 16	13 14	14 16	15 14	16 16	17 14	18 16	19 14	20 16
Burneside	d	12x19		14x19	15x17	16x19		18x19	19x17	20x19
Staveley	d	12x24		14x24	15x22	16x24		18x24	19x22	20x24
Windermere	a	12 33	13 26	14 33	15 29	16 33	17 26	18 33	19 30	20 33

For general notes see front of timetable
For details of catering facilities see Directory of Train Operators

A All Tuesdays to Fridays, also Mondays until 21 January and from 31 March. From Barrow-in-Furness (Table 82)
B From Manchester Airport (Table 82)
C From Preston (Table 65)
D From Lancaster (Table 65)
E From Barrow-in-Furness (Table 82)
G Until 26 January from Manchester Airport (Table 82). From 2 February from Preston (Table 65)

Windermere → Oxenholme: Lake District

Network Diagram - see first page of Table 82

Miles	Miles			TP	TP MO	TP	TP	TP	TP	TP	TP	TP	TP	TP	TP	TP	TP	TP	TP	TP	TP
				1		1	1	1	1◇	1	1◇	1	1◇	1	1	1	1◇	1	1	1	1◇
				A	B (bus)				C		D		D				D				E
—	0	**Windermere**	d	06§20	06§20	07 24	08 20	09 28	10 18	11 30	12 21	13 24	14 18	15 21	16 28	17 27	18 09	19 18	20 27	21 28	22 16
—	3½	Staveley	d	06x25	06x30	07x29	08x25	09x33		11x35		13x29		15x26	16x33		18x15	19x23	20x32	21x33	22x21
—	6	Burneside	d	06x30	06x40	07x34	08x30	09x38		11x40		13x34		15x31	16x38		18x20	19x28	20x37	21x38	22x26
—	7¾	Kendal	d	06§34	06§50	07 38	08 34	09 42	10 29	11 44	12 32	13 38	14 29	15 35	16 42	17 38	18 23	19 32	20 41	21 42	22 30
—	10	**Oxenholme Lake District**	a	06§40	07§00	07 44	08 40	09 48	10 35	11 50	12 38	13 44	14 35	15 41	16 48	17 44	18 29	19 38	20 47	21 48	22 36

Saturdays

until 22 March

		TP	TP	TP	TP	TP	TP	TP	TP	TP	TP	TP	TP	TP	TP	TP
		1	1	1	1	1◇	1	1◇	1	1◇	1	1	1	1◇	1	1
						C		D		D				D		G
Windermere	d	06 35	07 24	08 28	09 26	10 18	11 30	12 23	13 25	14 18	15 22	16 22	17 27	18 10	19 28	20 24
Staveley	d	06x40	07x29	08x33	09x31		11x35		13x30		15x27	16 27		18x16	19x33	20x29
Burneside	d	06x45	07x34	08x38	09x36		11x40		13x35		15x32	16x32		18x21	19x38	20x34
Kendal	d	06 49	07 38	08 42	09 40	10 29	11 44	12 34	13 39	14 29	15 36	16x36	17 38	18 24	19 42	20 38
Oxenholme Lake District	a	06 55	07 44	08 48	09 46	10 35	11 50	12 40	13 45	14 35	15 42	16 42	17 44	18 30	19 48	20 44

Saturdays

from 29 March

		TP	TP	TP	TP	TP	TP	TP	TP	TP	TP	TP	TP	TP	TP	TP
		1	1	1	1	1	1	1	1	1	1	1	1	1	1	1
		G	G	G	G	G	G	G	G	G	G	G	G		G	G
Windermere	d	06 51	07 51	08 51	09 51	10 51	11 51	12 51	13 51	14 51	15 51	16 51	17 51	18 51	19 45	20 56
Staveley	d	06x56	07x56	08x56	09x56	10x56	11x56	12x56	13x56	14x56	15x56	16x56	17x56	18x56	19x50	21x01
Burneside	d	07x01	08x01	09x01	10x01	11x01	12x01	13x01	14x01	15x01	16x01	17x01	18x01	19x01	19x55	21x06
Kendal	d	07 05	08 05	09 05	10 05	11 05	12 05	13 05	14 05	15 05	16 05	17 05	18 05	19 05	19 59	21 10
Oxenholme Lake District	a	07 11	08 11	09 11	10 11	11 11	12 11	13 11	14 11	15 11	16 11	17 11	18 11	19 11	20 05	21 16

Sundays

until 23 March

		TP	TP	TP	TP	TP	TP	TP	TP	TP
		1	1	1	1	1	1	1	1	1◇
									G	D
Windermere	d	12 59	14 15	14 59	16 02	16 59	18 02	19 02	20 02	21 20
Staveley	d	13x04	14x20	15x04		17x04		19x07		21x25
Burneside	d	13x09	14x25	15x09		17x09		19x12		21x30
Kendal	d	13 13	14 29	15 13	16 13	17 13	18 13	19 16	20 13	21 34
Oxenholme Lake District	a	13 19	14 35	15 19	16 19	17 19	18 19	19 22	20 19	21 40

Sundays

from 30 March

		TP	TP	TP	TP	TP	TP	TP	TP	TP
		1	1	1	1	1	1	1	1	1
			H		H		H		H	G
Windermere	d	12 40	13 33	14 40	15 35	16 40	17 33	18 40	19 40	20 40
Staveley	d	12x45	13x38	14x45		16x45	17x38	18x45		20x45
Burneside	d	12x50	13x43	14x50		16x50	17x43	18x50		20x50
Kendal	d	12 54	13 47	14 54	15 46	16 54	17 47	18 54	19 51	20 54
Oxenholme Lake District	a	13 00	13 53	15 00	15 52	17 00	17 53	19 00	19 57	21 00

For general notes see front of timetable
For details of catering facilities see Directory of Train Operators

- **A** All Tuesdays to Fridays, also Mondays until 21 January and from 31 March
- **B** 28 January to 24 March
- **C** To Preston (Table 65)
- **D** To Manchester Airport (Table 82)
- **E** To Barrow-in-Furness (Table 82) via Morecambe (Table 98)
- **G** To Lancaster (Table 65)
- **H** To Barrow-in-Furness (Table 82)

Stoke-on-Trent and Crewe → Manchester Airport, Stockport and Manchester

Network Diagram - see first page of Table 78

Miles	Miles	Miles		NT	NT	TP	NT	NT	NT	TP	AW	NT	NT	NT	NT	NT	NT	EM	XC	NT	NT	NT	AW	NT
				MX	MX	1 ◇				1 ◇								◇	1 ◇				◇	
				A		B	C	D		E		G		A			H	J		G			K	L
—	—	—	London Euston 15 ⊖ 65 d																					
—	—	—	Birmingham New Street 12 68 d								05 20					05 30			06 03					
—	—	—	Wolverhampton 7 68 d								05 38					05 49			06 21					
—	—	—	Stafford 65, 68 d								05 52					06 05			06 34					
0	—	—	**Stoke-on-Trent** 50, 68 d																06 52 →			06 55		
3	—	—	Longport 50 d																			06 59		
6¼	—	—	Kidsgrove 50 d																			07 04		
—	0	—	**Crewe 10** 65 d		00 50				06 03		06 27					06 35					07 00		07 09	
—	4¾	—	Sandbach d						06 10							06 42					07 07			
—	8½	—	Holmes Chapel d						06 14							06 46					07 11			
—	10½	—	Goostrey d						06 17							06 49					07 14			
—	14¼	—	Chelford d						06 22							06 54					07 19			
—	17¼	—	Alderley Edge d						06 26						06 49	06 58					07 23			
—	19	0	**Wilmslow** d						06 29						06 52	07 01					07 26		07 30	
—	—	2	Styal d																					
—	—	4¼	**Manchester Airport** a		01 14										07 02									
—	20½	—	Handforth d						06 32							07 04					07 29			
11¾	—	—	Congleton d																			07 12		
19¾	—	—	**Macclesfield** a																			07 19		
—	—	—	d										06 45									07 20		
22½	—	—	Prestbury d										06 49									07 24		
24½	—	—	Adlington (Cheshire) d										06 52									07 27		
26½	—	—	Poynton d										06 56									07 31		
28	—	—	Bramhall d										06 58									07 34		
29½	22¾	—	Cheadle Hulme d						06 37				07 00			07 09					07 34	07 37		
31¾	25	—	**Stockport** a						06 42				07 06			07 14					07 39	07 42	07 46	
—	—	—	d	00 01		05 53	06 17	06 36	06 42	06 53		07 02	07 06	07 11		07 15	07 19	07 24		07 30	07 39	07 44	07 47 →	07 49
31¾	26½	—	Heaton Chapel d						06 46			07 06	07 10							07 33	07 43			
34¾	28	—	Levenshulme d						06 49			07 09	07 13							07 36	07 46			
37¾	31	—	**Manchester Piccadilly 10** a	00 13	01 35	06 04	06 27	06 47	06 56	07 05	07 13	07 17	07 22	07 25	07 28	07 28	07 30	07 35		07 45	07 55	07 57		08 00
—	—	—	d				06 29										07 30	07 35						08 00
38½	31½	—	**Manchester Oxford Road** a				06 31										07 33	07 38						08 03
38¾	32	—	Deansgate a				06 34										07 35							08 15

	XC	TP	AW	NT	NT	NT	NT	XC	NT	NT	NT	NT	NT	NT	EM	NT	NT	VT	NT	NT	NT	NT	XC	TP
														BHX										
	1 ◇	1 ◇	◇					1 ◇							◇			1 ◇					1 ◇	1 ◇
		N	K	G		G	A		G			H			J				G		D	A		N
London Euston 15 ⊖ 65 d																		06 20						
Birmingham New Street 12 68 d								06 30		06 07								07b10		06c30			07 18	
Wolverhampton 7 68 d								07 06		06 39										07c06			07 39	
Stafford 65, 68 d	←							07 18		07 00										07 25			07 54	
Stoke-on-Trent 50, 68 d	06 52				07 13			07 36					07 40					08 04					08 13	
Longport 50 d					07 20																			
Kidsgrove 50 d					07 25								07 48											
Crewe 10 65 d	07 15									07 33	07 43									08 00				
Sandbach d										07 40	07 50									08 07				
Holmes Chapel d										07 45	07 55									08 11				
Goostrey d										07 48										08 14				
Chelford d										07 52										08 19				
Alderley Edge d										07 56	08 04			08 09						08 23				
Wilmslow d	07 33									08 00	08 07			08 12						08 26				
Styal d																←								
Manchester Airport a											08 14					08 14								
Handforth d										08 03	→									08 29				
Congleton d					07 32			07 49					07 55										08 25	
Macclesfield a					07 39			07 56					08 02					08 20					08 32	
d					07 40			07 57					08 03				08 08	08 20					08 33	
Prestbury d					07 44												08 13							
Adlington (Cheshire) d					07 47												08 16							
Poynton d					07 50												08 19							
Bramhall d					07 53								08 10				08 22							
Cheadle Hulme d					07 55					08 09			08 14	08 18			08 24			08 34				
Stockport a			←		08 03			08 09		08 13			08 19	08 24			08 29	08s35		08 41			08 46	
d		07 55	07 47	08 01	08 03	←	08 10	08 10	08 15	08 15		08 21	08 20	08 24	08 27		08 29		08 37	08 41	08 42	08 46	08 46	08 51
Heaton Chapel d				08 05		08 05				08 18							08 33		08 41	08 45				
Levenshulme d				→		08 08				08 21							08 36		08 44	08 48				
Manchester Piccadilly 10 a	08 02	08 08	08 10		08 15	08 19	08 24	08 27	08 26	08 31		08 31	08 34	08 39	08 36	08 42	08 44	08 48	08 53	08 56	08 56	08 59	09 02	09 01
d												08 32			08 37					08 56				
Manchester Oxford Road a												08 35			08 40					08 58				
Deansgate a												08 37								09 03				

For general notes see front of timetable
For details of catering facilities see Directory of Train Operators

- **A** From Chester (Table 88)
- **B** From Sheffield to Manchester Airport (Table 78)
- **C** To Blackpool North (Table 82)
- **D** From Buxton (Table 86)
- **E** From Doncaster to Manchester Airport (Table 29)
- **G** From Hazel Grove (Table 86)
- **H** From Buxton (Table 86) to Blackpool North (Table 82)
- **J** From Nottingham to Liverpool Lime Street (Table 49)
- **K** From Cardiff Central (Table 131)
- **L** From Buxton (Table 86) to Liverpool Lime Street (Table 89)
- **N** From Cleethorpes to Manchester Airport (Table 29)
- **b** Change at Tamworth
- **c** Change at Stafford and Crewe

Stoke-on-Trent and Crewe → Manchester Airport, Stockport and Manchester

Network Diagram - see first page of Table 78

	AW	NT	XC	VT	NT	NT	NT	EM	NT	VT	NT		NT	XC	TP	AW	NT	XC	VT	NT	NT	NT	EM	NT
	◇		1 ◇	1 ◇				◇		1 ◇				1 ◇	1 ◇	◇		1 ◇	1 ◇				◇	
	A		B			C	D	E					G	H	J	K		L			N	Q	U	
	🛒		☕	⊠				🛒		⊠				☕	🛒	🛒		☕	⊠				🛒	
London Euston 15 ⊖ 65 d				07 03					*06 46*	07 35						*07 13*			08 05					
Birmingham New Street 12 68 d	*07 03*		07 48						*07 21*					08 18		*08 03*		08 48						*08 26*
Wolverhampton 7 68 ⛴ d	*07 21*		08 06						*07 44*					08 39		*08 21*		09 06						*08 44*
Stafford 65, 68 d	*07 34*		08 18						*08 01*					08 54		*08 47*		09 18						*09 01*
Stoke-on-Trent 50, 68 d			08 36	08 41						09 06				09 13				09 36	09 41					
Longport 50 d																								
Kidsgrove 50 d																								
Crewe 10 65 d	08 27								08 40		09 00					09 27								09 38
Sandbach d									08 47		09 07													09 45
Holmes Chapel d									08 51		09 11													09 49
Goostrey d											09 14													
Chelford d											09 19													
Alderley Edge d					08 57				09 00		09 23									09 53				09 58
Wilmslow d	08 45				09 00				09 03		09 26					09 44				09 56				10 01
Styal d																								
Manchester Airport ✈ a									09 15															10 11
Handforth d					09 03						09 29									09 59				
Congleton d																								
Macclesfield a			08 52	08 57										09 31				09 52	09 57					
d		08 41	08 53	08 57										09 32			09 41	09 53	09 57					
Prestbury d		08 45															09 45							
Adlington (Cheshire) d		08 48															09 48							
Poynton d		08 52															09 52							
Bramhall d		08 54															09 54							
Cheadle Hulme d		08 56			09 09						09 34						09 56			10 04				
Stockport a	08 53	09 01	09 05	09s12	09 14					09s34	09 39			09 46		09 54	10 01	10 05	10s12	10 09				
d	08 54	09 02	09 06		09 14	09 19	09 20	09 24			09 39		09 49	09 46	09 53	09 56	10 02	10 06		10 11	10 18	10 21	10 25	
Heaton Chapel d		09 05				09 23					09 43						10 05			10 15				
Levenshulme d		09 08				09 26					09 46						10 08			10 18				
Manchester Piccadilly 10 ⛴ a	09 13	09 18	09 20	09 25	09 27	09 32	09 32	09 36	09 41	09 46	09 54		10 01	10 02	10 03	10 13	10 18	10 20	10 24	10 28	10 29	10 33	10 36	10 39
d		09 19				09 33		09 37									10 19				10 30		10 37	
Manchester Oxford Road a		09 21				09 36		09 40									10 21				10 32		10 40	
Deansgate ⛴ a		09 26				09 38											10 26				10 35			

	VT	NT	NT	XC	TP	AW	NT	XC	VT	NT	NT	NT	EM	NT	VT	NT	NT	XC	TP	AW	NT	XC	VT	NT
	1 ◇			1 ◇	1 ◇	◇		1 ◇	1 ◇				◇		1 ◇			1 ◇	1 ◇	◇		1 ◇	1 ◇	
			G	V	J	K		X			C	D	Y				G	Z	J	AA		BB		
	⊠			☕	🛒	🛒		☕	⊠				🛒		⊠			☕	🛒	🛒		☕	⊠	
London Euston 15 ⊖ 65 d	08 35	*07 46*				*08 17*			09 05						09 35	*09 00*				*09 17*			10 05	
Birmingham New Street 12 68 d		*08 51*		09 18		*09 03*		09 48						*09 21*		*09 51*		10 18		*10 03*		10 48		
Wolverhampton 7 68 ⛴ d		*09 10*		09 39		*09 21*		10 06						*09 44*		*10 10*		10 39		*10 21*		11 06		
Stafford 65, 68 d		*09 24*				*09 47*		10 18						*10 01*		*10 24*				*10 47*		11 18		
Stoke-on-Trent 50, 68 d	10 06			10 13				10 36	10 41						11 06			11 13				11 36	11 41	
Longport 50 d																								
Kidsgrove 50 d																								
Crewe 10 65 d		10 00				10 27								10 38		11 00				11 27				
Sandbach d		10 07												10 45		11 07								
Holmes Chapel d		10 11												10 49		11 11								
Goostrey d		10 14														11 14								
Chelford d		10 19														11 19								
Alderley Edge d		10 23								10 53				10 58		11 23								11 53
Wilmslow d		10 26				10 45				10 56				11 01		11 26				11 44				11 56
Styal d																								
Manchester Airport ✈ a														11 11										
Handforth d		10 29								10 59						11 29								11 59
Congleton d				10 25																				
Macclesfield a				10 32				10 52	10 57									11 31				11 52	11 57	
d				10 33			10 41	10 53	10 57									11 32			11 41	11 53	11 57	
Prestbury d							10 45														11 45			
Adlington (Cheshire) d							10 48														11 48			
Poynton d							10 52														11 52			
Bramhall d							10 54														11 54			
Cheadle Hulme d		10 34					10 56			11 04						11 34					11 56			12 04
Stockport a	10s34	10 39		10 46		10 53	11 01	11 05	11s12	11 09					11s34	11 39		11 46		11 53	12 01	12 05	12s12	12 09
d		10 39	10 49	10 46	10 53	10 57	11 02	11 06		11 11	11 19	11 17	11 25			11 39	11 49	11 46	11 53	11 56	12 02	12 06		12 11
Heaton Chapel d		10 43					11 05			11 15						11 43					12 05			12 15
Levenshulme d		10 46					11 08			11 18						11 46					12 08			12 18
Manchester Piccadilly 10 ⛴ a	10 46	10 54	11 01	11 02	11 03	11 13	11 18	11 20	11 24	11 28	11 29	11 32	11 36	11 39	11 46	11 54	12 01	12 02	12 03	12 13	12 18	12 20	12 24	12 28
d							11 19				11 30		11 37								12 19			
Manchester Oxford Road a							11 21				11 32		11 40								12 21			
Deansgate ⛴ a							11 26				11 35										12 26			

For general notes see front of timetable
For details of catering facilities see Directory of Train Operators

- **A** From Cardiff Central (Table 131)
- **B** From Southampton Central (Table 51)
- **C** From Buxton (Table 86) to Blackpool North (Table 82)
- **D** From Chester (Table 88)
- **E** From Nottingham to Liverpool Lime Street (Table 49)
- **G** From Hazel Grove (Table 86)
- **H** From Gatwick Airport (Table 51)
- **J** From Cleethorpes to Manchester Airport (Table 29)
- **K** From Carmarthen (Table 128)
- **L** From Derby (Table 57)
- **N** From Northwich (Table 88) to Blackpool North (Table 82)
- **Q** From Buxton (Table 86)
- **U** From Norwich to Liverpool Lime Street (Table 49)
- **V** From Exeter St Davids (Table 51)
- **X** From Bournemouth (Table 51)
- **Y** From Cambridge to Liverpool Lime Street (Table 49)
- **Z** From Reading (Table 51)
- **AA** From Milford Haven (Table 128)
- **BB** From Birmingham International (Table 65)

Stoke-on-Trent and Crewe → Manchester Airport, Stockport and Manchester

Network Diagram - see first page of Table 78

	NT	NT	EM	NT	VT	NT	VT	NT	XC	TP	AW	NT	XC	VT	NT	NT	NT	EM	NT	VT		NT	NT	XC
									R				R											
			◇		1 ◇		1 ◇		1	1 ◇	◇		1	1 ◇				◇		1 ◇				1 ◇
	A	B	C					D	E	G	H		J			A	B	C					D	K
			🛒		⊠		⊠		🍴	🛒	🛒		🍴	🍴				🛒		🍴				🍴
London Euston [15] ⊖ 65 d					10 35	09 46	09b38				10 15			11 05						11 35		10 46		
Birmingham New Street [12] 68 d				10 21		10 51	11 03		11 18				11 48						11 21			11 51		12 18
Wolverhampton [7] 68 🚋 d				10 44		11 10	11 21		11 39				11 44						11 44			12 10		12 39
Stafford 65, 68 d				11 01		11 24					11 45		12 18						12 01			12 24		
Stoke-on-Trent 50, 68 d					12 06				12 13				12 36	12 41						13 06				13 13
Longport 50 d																								
Kidsgrove 50 d																								
Crewe [10] 65 d				11 38		12 00	12 08				12 27								12 38			13 00		
Sandbach d				11 45		12 07													12 45			13 07		
Holmes Chapel d				11 49		12 11													12 49			13 11		
Goostrey d						12 14																13 14		
Chelford d						12 19																13 19		
Alderley Edge d				11 58		12 23									12 53				12 58			13 23		
Wilmslow d				12 01		12 26	12 28				12 45				12 56				13 01			13 26		
Styal d																								
Manchester Airport ✈ a				12 11															13 11					
Handforth d						12 29									12 59							13 29		
Congleton d									12 25															
Macclesfield a									12 32				12 52	12 57										13 31
d									12 33			12 41	12 53	12 57										13 32
Prestbury d												12 45												
Adlington (Cheshire) d												12 48												
Poynton d												12 52												
Bramhall d												12 54												
Cheadle Hulme d						12 34						12 56			13 04							13 34		
Stockport a					12s34	12 39	12s41		12 46		12 53	13 01	13 05	13s12	13 09					13s34		13 39		13 46
d	12 19	12 17	12 25			12 39		12 49	12 46	12 53	12 57	13 02	13 06		13 11	13 19	13 17	13 25				13 39	13 49	13 46
Heaton Chapel d						12 43						13 05			13 15							13 43		
Levenshulme d						12 46						13 08			13 18							13 46		
Manchester Piccadilly [10] 🚋 a	12 29	12 32	12 36	12 39	12 46	12 54	12 55	13 01	13 02	13 03	13 13	13 18	13 20	13 24	13 28	13 27	13 32	13 36	13 39	13 46		13 54	14 01	14 02
d	12 30		12 37									13 19				13 30		13 37						
Manchester Oxford Road a	12 32		12 40									13 21				13 32		13 40						
Deansgate 🚋 a	12 35											13 26				13 35								

	TP	AW	NT	XC	VT	NT	NT	NT	EM	NT	VT	NT	NT	XC	TP	AW	NT	XC	VT	NT	NT	NT	EM	NT
														R				R						
	1 ◇	◇		1 ◇	1 ◇				◇		1 ◇			1	1 ◇	◇		1	1 ◇				◇	
	G	L		N			A	B	C				D	Q	G	H		J			A	B	C	
	🛒	🛒		🍴	🍴				🛒		🍴			🍴	🛒	🛒		🍴	🍴				🛒	
London Euston [15] ⊖ 65 d		11 28			12 05						12 35	11 46				12 17			13 05					
Birmingham New Street [12] 68 d		12 03		12 48						12 21		12 51		13 18		13 03		13 48						13 21
Wolverhampton [7] 68 🚋 d		12 21		13 06						12 44		13 10		13 39		13 21		14 06						13 44
Stafford 65, 68 d		12 48		13 18						13 01		13 24				13 47		14 18						14 01
Stoke-on-Trent 50, 68 d				13 36	13 41						14 06			14 13				14 36	14 41					
Longport 50 d																								
Kidsgrove 50 d																								
Crewe [10] 65 d		13 27								13 38		14 00				14 27								14 38
Sandbach d										13 45		14 07												14 45
Holmes Chapel d										13 49		14 11												14 49
Goostrey d												14 14												
Chelford d												14 19												
Alderley Edge d						13 53				13 58		14 23								14 53				14 58
Wilmslow d		13 44				13 56				14 01		14 26				14 45				14 56				15 01
Styal d																								
Manchester Airport ✈ a										14 11														15 11
Handforth d						13 59						14 29								14 59				
Congleton d														14 25										
Macclesfield a				13 52	13 57									14 32				14 52	14 57					
d			13 41	13 53	13 57									14 33			14 41	14 53	14 57					
Prestbury d			13 45														14 45							
Adlington (Cheshire) d			13 48														14 48							
Poynton d			13 52														14 52							
Bramhall d			13 54														14 54							
Cheadle Hulme d			13 56			14 04						14 34					14 56			15 04				
Stockport a		13 53	14 01	14 05	14s12	14 11					14s34	14 39		14 46		14 53	15 01	15 05	15s12	15 09				
d	13 53	13 57	14 02	14 06		14 11	14 19	14 17	14 25			14 39	14 49	14 46	14 53	14 56	15 02	15 06		15 11	15 19	15 17	15 25	
Heaton Chapel d			14 05			14 15						14 43					15 05			15 15				
Levenshulme d			14 08			14 18						14 46					15 08			15 18				
Manchester Piccadilly [10] 🚋 a	14 03	14 13	14 18	14 20	14 24	14 28	14 27	14 32	14 36	14 39	14 46	14 54	15 01	15 02	15 03	15 13	15 18	15 20	15 24	15 28	15 27	15 32	15 36	15 39
d			14 19				14 30		14 37								15 19				15 30		15 37	
Manchester Oxford Road a			14 21				14 32		14 40								15 21				15 32		15 40	
Deansgate 🚋 a			14 26				14 35										15 26				15 35			

For general notes see front of timetable
For details of catering facilities see Directory of Train Operators

- **A** From Buxton (Table 86) to Blackpool North (Table 82)
- **B** From Chester (Table 88)
- **C** From Norwich to Liverpool Lime Street (Table 49)
- **D** From Hazel Grove (Table 86)
- **E** From Plymouth (Table 51)
- **G** From Cleethorpes to Manchester Airport (Table 29)
- **H** From Milford Haven (Table 128)
- **J** From Bournemouth (Table 51)
- **K** From Reading (Table 51)
- **L** From Carmarthen (Table 128)
- **N** From Birmingham International (Table 65)
- **Q** From Penzance (Table 135)
- **b** By changing at Crewe, passengers may depart at 0946

Stoke-on-Trent and Crewe → Manchester Airport, Stockport and Manchester

Network Diagram - see first page of Table 78

	VT	NT	NT	XC	TP	AW	NT	XC	VT	NT	NT	NT	EM	NT	VT	NT	NT	NT	NT	NT	XC	TP	NT	AW
	1 ◇			1 ◇	1 ◇	◇		1 ◇	1 ◇				◇		1 ◇						R 1	1 ◇		◇
			A	B	C	D		E			G	H	J				K			A	L	C	H	N
	☕			☕	🛒	🛒		☕	☕				🛒		☕						☕	🛒		🛒
London Euston 15 ⊖ 65 d	13 35	12 46				13 17			14 05						14 35				13 46					14 17
Birmingham New Street 12 68 d		13 51		14 18		14 03		14 48						14 21					14 51		15 18			15 03
Wolverhampton 7 68 ⛴ d		14 10		14 39		14 21		15 06						14 44					15 10		15 39			15 21
Stafford 65, 68 d		14 24				14 47		15 18						15 01					15 24					15 47
Stoke-on-Trent 50, 68 d	15 06			15 13				15 36	15 41						16 06						16 13			
Longport 50 d																								
Kidsgrove 50 d																								
Crewe 10 65 d		15 00				15 27								15 38					16 00					16 27
Sandbach d		15 07												15 45					16 07					
Holmes Chapel d		15 11												15 49					16 11					
Goostrey d		15 14																	16 14					
Chelford d		15 19																	16 19					
Alderley Edge d		15 23								15 53				15 58					16 23					
Wilmslow d		15 26				15 45				15 56				16 01					16 26					16 45
Styal d																								
Manchester Airport ✈ a														16 11										
Handforth d		15 29								15 59									16 29					
Congleton d																					16 25			
Macclesfield a				15 31				15 52	15 57												16 32			
d				15 32			15 41	15 53	15 57							16 11					16 33			
Prestbury d							15 45									16 15								
Adlington (Cheshire) d							15 48									16 18								
Poynton d							15 52									16 22								
Bramhall d							15 54									16 24								
Cheadle Hulme d		15 34					15 56			16 04						16 26			16 34					
Stockport a	15s34	15 39		15 46		15 53	16 01	16 05	16s12	16 09					16s34	16 31			16 40		16 46			16 53
d		15 39	15 49	15 46	15 53	15 57	16 02	16 06		16 11	16 19	16 17	16 25			16 35	16 41	←	16 43	16 49	16 46	16 53	16 56	16 55
Heaton Chapel d		15 43					16 05			16 15						16 38		16 38						
Levenshulme d		15 46					16 08			16 18						→		16 41						
Manchester Piccadilly 10 ⛴ a	15 46	15 54	16 01	16 02	16 03	16 13	16 18	16 20	16 24	16 28	16 27	16 32	16 35	16 41	16 46		16 50	16 54	16 54	17 01	17 02	17 03	17 09	17 11
d							16 19				16 30		16 37				16 52	16 56						
Manchester Oxford Road a							16 21				16 32		16 39				16 55	16 58						
Deansgate ⛴ a							16 26				16 35						16 58	17 03						

	NT	XC	VT	NT	NT	NT	EM		NT	NT	VT	NT	XC	NT	TP	AW	NT	XC	VT	NT	NT	NT	EM	NT
		R 1	1 ◇				◇				1 ◇		R 1		1 ◇	R		1 ◇	1 ◇				◇	
	Q	U			H	V	J						B	X	C	D		E		A	V	H	J	
		☕	☕				🛒				⊠		☕		🛒	🛒		☕	☕				🛒	
London Euston 15 ⊖ 65 d			15 05						14 46		15 35					15 17			16 05					
Birmingham New Street 12 68 d		15 48							15 21			15 51	16 18			16 03		16 48						16 21
Wolverhampton 7 68 ⛴ d		15 44							15 44			16 10	16 39			16 21		17 06						16 44
Stafford 65, 68 d		16 18							16 01			16 24				16 47		17 18						17 01
Stoke-on-Trent 50, 68 d		16 36	16 41								17 06		17 13					17 36	17 41					
Longport 50 d																								
Kidsgrove 50 d																								
Crewe 10 65 d									16 42			17 00				17 27								17 38
Sandbach d									16 49			17 07												17 45
Holmes Chapel d									16 53			17 11												17 49
Goostrey d												17 14												17 52
Chelford d												17 19												17 57
Alderley Edge d				16 53					17 02			17 23												18 01
Wilmslow d				16 56					17 05			17 26				17 46								18 04
Styal d																								18 07
Manchester Airport ✈ a									17 15															18 15
Handforth d				16 59								17 29												
Congleton d													17 25											
Macclesfield a		16 52	16 57								17 21		17 32					17 52	17 57					
d		16 53	16 57							17 11	17 22		17 33				17 41	17 53	17 57					
Prestbury d										17 15							17 45							
Adlington (Cheshire) d										17 18							17 48							
Poynton d										17 22							17 52							
Bramhall d										17 24							17 54							
Cheadle Hulme d				17 04						17 26		17 34					17 57							
Stockport a		17 05	17s12	17 10						17 31	17s35	17 38	17 46			17 54	18 02	18 05	18s11					
d	16 59	17 06		17 11	17 16	17 18	17 26			17 32		17 39	17 46	17 49	17 53	17 56	18 02	18 06		18 15	18 19	18 17	18 26	
Heaton Chapel d	17 03			17 15	17 19							17 43					18 05							
Levenshulme d	17 06			17 18	17 22							17 46					18 08							
Manchester Piccadilly 10 ⛴ a	17 15	17 20	17 24	17 28	17 31	17 31	17 36		17 41	17 44	17 49	17 54	18 02	18 02	18 03	18 12	18 20	18 20	18 25	18 26	18 29	18 32	18 36	18 40
d	17 15					17 32	17 37														18 31		18 37	
Manchester Oxford Road a	17 17					17 34	17 39														18 33		18 39	
Deansgate ⛴ a	17 21					17 37															18 36			

For general notes see front of timetable
For details of catering facilities see Directory of Train Operators

- **A** From Hazel Grove (Table 86)
- **B** From Reading (Table 51)
- **C** From Cleethorpes to Manchester Airport (Table 29)
- **D** From Carmarthen (Table 128)
- **E** From Birmingham International (Table 65)
- **G** From Hazel Grove (Table 86) to Blackpool North (Table 82)
- **H** From Chester (Table 88)
- **J** From Norwich to Liverpool Lime Street (Table 49)
- **K** From Buxton (Table 86) to Preston (Table 82)
- **L** From Penzance (Table 135)
- **N** From Milford Haven (Table 128)
- **Q** To Blackpool North (Table 82)
- **U** From Bournemouth (Table 51)
- **V** From Buxton (Table 86) to Blackpool North (Table 82)
- **X** From Buxton (Table 86)

Stoke-on-Trent and Crewe → Manchester Airport, Stockport and Manchester

Network Diagram - see first page of Table 78

		NT	NT	VT	NT	NT	XC	NT	TP	AW	NT	XC	VT	NT	VT	NT	NT	EM	NT	VT	NT	NT	XC	TP	AW
							[R]			[R]		[R]											[R]		[R]
				[1] ◇			[1]		[1] ◇			[1]	[1] ◇		[1] ◇			◇		[1] ◇			[1]	[1] ◇	
		A					B		C	D	E	G		E		H		J			K		L	C	N
				⊏P			⊏P		⊤	⊤		⊏P	⊏P		⊏P			⊤		⊠			⊏P	⊤	⊤
London Euston [15]	⊖ 65 d			16 35		*15 49*		*16 17*				16b46	16 49		17 05					17 35					*17 21*
Birmingham New Street [12]	68 d					*16 51*	17 18	*17 03*				17 48	*17 21*									*17 51*	18 18		*18 03*
Wolverhampton [7]	68 ⛴ d					*17 10*	17 39					18 06	*17 44*									*18 10*	18 39		*18 21*
Stafford	65, 68 d					*17 27*		*17 47*				18 18	*18 11*									*18 27*			*18 50*
Stoke-on-Trent	50, 68 d			18 06			18 13					18 36			18 41					19 07			19 13		
Longport	50 d																								
Kidsgrove	50 d																								
Crewe [10]	65 d					18 00		18 19		18 27			18 42									19 00			19 27
Sandbach	d					18 07		18 26														19 07			
Holmes Chapel	d					18 11		18 30														19 11			
Goostrey	d					18 14																19 14			
Chelford	d					18 19																19 19			
Alderley Edge	d					18 23		18 39														19 23			
Wilmslow	d					18 26		18 44		18 45			18 58									19 26			19 46
Styal	d																←								
Manchester Airport	✈ a							18 54									18 54								
Handforth	d					18 29		→														19 29			
Congleton	d						18 25																		
Macclesfield	a			18 21			18 32					18 52			18 57					19 22			19 31		
	d		18 12	18 21			18 33					18 53			18 57				19 09	19 23			19 32		
Prestbury	d		18 16																19 14						
Adlington (Cheshire)	d		18 19																19 17						
Poynton	d		18 23																19 20						
Bramhall	d		18 25																19 23						
Cheadle Hulme	d		18 28			18 34													19 25			19 34			
Stockport	a		18 32	18s35		18 39	18 46			18 53		19 05	19s09		19s12				19 30	19s36		19 39	19 46		19 53
	d	18 31	18 33		←	18 39	18 46		18 53	18 56	19 05	19 06		←		19 10		19 24	19 30		19 40	19 40	19 46	19 53	19 57
Heaton Chapel	d		18 36		18 36	18 43					19 09			19 09		19 14						19 43			
Levenshulme	d		→		18 39	18 46					→			19 12		19 17						19 46			
Manchester Piccadilly [10]	⛴ a	18 42		18 49	18 52	18 56	19 02		19 03	19 13		19 20	19 21	19 24	19 24	19 28	19 29	19 36	19 43	19 50	19 54	19 57	20 02	20 03	20 18
	d													19 26				19 37							
Manchester Oxford Road	a													19 28				19 40							
Deansgate	⛴ a													19 31											

		VT	NT	VT	NT	NT	NT	VT	EM	VT	NT	NT	NT	XC	TP	VT	AW	NT	NT	VT	NT	EM	XC	NT	VT
																FO									
														[R]			[R]						[R]		
		[1] ◇		[1] ◇				[1] ◇	◇	[1] ◇				[1]	[1] ◇	[1] ◇				[1] ◇		◇	[1]		[1] ◇
						H			J			Q		B	C		D		H			U	G		
		⊠		⊠				⊏P		⊠				⊏P	⊤	⊏P	⊤			⊏P					⊏P
London Euston [15]	⊖ 65 d	17 48		18 05				17c10		18 35						18 20	*18e17*			19 05			*18f45*		19 35
Birmingham New Street [12]	68 d							18 43			*18 51*			19 18		*19 03*	*19 03*						20 03	*19 21*	
Wolverhampton [7]	68 ⛴ d							19 06			*19 10*			19 39		*19 21*	*19 21*						20 21	*19 44*	
Stafford	65, 68 d							19 27			*19 24*					19 52	*19e45*						20 34	*20 01*	20 57
Stoke-on-Trent	50, 68 d		19 19	19 39				19 45		20 06				20 13						20 40					
Longport	50 d																								
Kidsgrove	50 d		19 27																						
Crewe [10]	65 d	19 35									20 00					20 16	20 28						20 56	21 00	
Sandbach	d										20 07													21 07	
Holmes Chapel	d										20 11													21 11	
Goostrey	d										20 14													21 14	
Chelford	d										20 19													21 19	
Alderley Edge	d										20 23													21 23	
Wilmslow	d	19 51					19 51				20 26					20 33	20 45				20 50		21 16	21 26	21 31
Styal	d																								
Manchester Airport	✈ a						20 02														21 02				
Handforth	d										20 29													21 29	
Congleton	d		19 34											20 25											
Macclesfield	a		19 41	19 57				20 01		20 23				20 32						20 57					
	d		19 42	19 57				20 01		20 23				20 33				20 42		20 57					
Prestbury	d		19 46															20 46							
Adlington (Cheshire)	d		19 49															20 49							
Poynton	d		19 53															20 53							
Bramhall	d		19 55															20 55							
Cheadle Hulme	d		19 57								20 34							20 57						21 34	
Stockport	a	20s02	20 03	20s12				20 16		20s36	20 39			20 46		20s44	20 53	21 02		21s12			21 25	21 39	21s42
	d		20 03		←	20 10		20 17	20 26		20 39	20 40	←	20 46	20 53		20 57	21 03	21 10			21 17	21 26	21 39	
Heaton Chapel	d		20 06		20 06						20 43		20 43					21 06						21 43	
Levenshulme	d		→		20 09						→		20 46					21 09						21 46	
Manchester Piccadilly [10]	⛴ a	20 14		20 20	20 23	20 28	20 31	20 35	20 36	20 51		20 52	20 54	21 02	21 03	21 04	21 13	21 18	21 24	21 24	21 28	21 30	21 48	21 54	21 54
	d								20 37			20 52						21 19						21 54	
Manchester Oxford Road	a								20 39			20 54						21 21						21 56	
Deansgate	⛴ a											20 56						21 26						22 01	

For general notes see front of timetable
For details of catering facilities see Directory of Train Operators

A From Hazel Grove (Table 86)
B From Plymouth (Table 51)
C From Cleethorpes to Manchester Airport (Table 29)
D From Milford Haven (Table 128)
E From Buxton (Table 86) to Salford Crescent (Table 82)
G From Bournemouth (Table 51)
H From Chester (Table 88)
J From Norwich to Liverpool Lime Street (Table 49)
K From Buxton (Table 86)
L From Brighton (Table 51)
N From Carmarthen (Table 128)
Q From Buxton (Table 86) to Bolton (Table 82)
U From Norwich (Table 49)
b Change at Stafford
c By changing at Stafford, passengers may depart at 1745
e Mondays to Thursdays only
f Change at Crewe

Stoke-on-Trent and Crewe → Manchester Airport, Stockport and Manchester

Network Diagram - see first page of Table 78

Mondays to Fridays

		XC	AW	NT	VT	NT	NT	XC	NT	NT	NT	XC	TP	NT	VT	NT	AW	NT	NT	NT	NT	XC	VT		
																				FX	FO				
		1 ◇	◇		1 ◇			1 ◇				1 ◇	1 ◇		1 ◇		◇					1 ◇	1 ◇		
		A	B			C		D	E	G		H	J				K	L	N			Q			
London Euston 15	⊖ 65 d				20 05						19 46	20b17			21 05		20 46					21b10	22 05		
Birmingham New Street 12	68 d	20 18						20 48			20 21	21 18					21 21					22 18	23c10		
Wolverhampton 7	68 d	20 39						21 11			20 44	21 39					21 44					22 39			
Stafford	65, 68 d							21 24			21 01	21 54					22 01					22 54			
Stoke-on-Trent	50, 68 d	21 13			21 39			21 46				22 13			22 44										
Longport	50 d																								
Kidsgrove	50 d																								
Crewe 10	65 d		21 27								22 00						23 05			23 08	23 08				
Sandbach	d										22 07									23 15	23 15				
Holmes Chapel	d										22 11									23 19	23 19				
Goostrey	d										22 14									23 22	23 22				
Chelford	d										22 19									23 27	23 27				
Alderley Edge	d										22 23									23 31	23 31				
Wilmslow	d		21 46				21 55				22 26					22 52	23 23			23 34	23 34				
Styal	d																								
Manchester Airport	a						22 07									23 02									
Handforth	d										22 29									23 36	23 36				
Congleton	d											22 25													
Macclesfield	a	21 28			21 57			22 02				22 32			23 00										
	d	21 32		21 42	21 58			22 03				22 33		22 42	23 00										
Prestbury	d			21 46										22 46											
Adlington (Cheshire)	d			21 49										22 49											
Poynton	d			21 53										22 53											
Bramhall	d			21 55										22 55											
Cheadle Hulme	d			21 57							22 34			22 57						23 42	23 42				
Stockport	a	21 46	21 53	22 02	22s12			22 15			22 39	22 46		23 02	23s15		23 33			23 48	23 48		00s58		
	d	21 46	21 57	22 03		22 13		22 16	22 23	22 38	22 39	22 46	22 53	23 03			23 34	23 40	23 46	23 48	23 48				
Heaton Chapel	d			22 06							22 43			23 06							23 52				
Levenshulme	d			22 09							22 46			23 09							23 55				
Manchester Piccadilly 10	a	22 02	22 12	22 19	22 24	22 26	22 31	22 32	22 33	22 47	22 52	23 02	23 03	23 19	23 29	23 31	23 49	23 52	23 59	00 01	00 03	00 07	01 10		
	d			22 19					22 35	22 49	22 54														
Manchester Oxford Road	a			22 21					22 37	22 51	22 56														
Deansgate	a			22 26					22 40	22 54	23 00														

Saturdays

		NT	NT	TP	NT	NT	NT	TP	AW	NT		NT	NT	NT	EM	NT	NT	NT	NT	AW		XC	TP	NT	NT
				1 ◇				1 ◇							◇					◇		1 ◇	1 ◇		
		C		U	V	L		X		C				Y	Z		AA			BB			J	AA	C
London Euston 15	⊖ 65 d																								
Birmingham New Street 12	68 d												05 30									06 20			
Wolverhampton 7	68 d												05 49									06 40			
Stafford	65, 68 d												06 05									06 54			
Stoke-on-Trent	50, 68 d															06 45						07 13			
Longport	50 d															06 49									
Kidsgrove	50 d															06 54									
Crewe 10	65 d		00 50						06 20				06 35						07 00	07 15					
Sandbach	d												06 42						07 07						
Holmes Chapel	d												06 46						07 11						
Goostrey	d												06 49						07 14						
Chelford	d												06 54						07 19						
Alderley Edge	d											06 49	06 58						07 23						
Wilmslow	d											06 52	07 01						07 26	07 33					
Styal	d																								
Manchester Airport	a		01 14									07 02													
Handforth	d												07 04						07 29						
Congleton	d															07 02						07 25			
Macclesfield	a															07 09						07 32			
	d															07 10						07 33			
Prestbury	d															07 14									
Adlington (Cheshire)	d															07 17									
Poynton	d															07 20									
Bramhall	d															07 23									
Cheadle Hulme	d												07 09			07 25			07 34						
Stockport	a												07 13			07 30			07 39	07 42		07 46			
	d	00 01		05 53	06 17	06 36	06 41	06 53		07 13			07 13	07 19	07 23	07 30	07 32	←	07 39	07 42		07 46	07 55	08 00	08 10
Heaton Chapel	d						06 45						07 18			07 34		07 34	07 43					08 05	
Levenshulme	d						06 48						07 21			→		07 37	07 46					08 08	
Manchester Piccadilly 10	a	00 13	01 35	06 04	06 27	06 46	06 54	07 05	07 07	07 25		07 28	07 28	07 30	07 35		07 42	07 45	07 55	08 00		08 02	08 08	08 14	08 24
	d				06 29									07 30	07 35										
Manchester Oxford Road	a				06 31									07 33	07 38										
Deansgate	a				06 34									07 35											

For general notes see front of timetable
For details of catering facilities see Directory of Train Operators

- **A** From Guildford (Table 51)
- **B** From Carmarthen (Table 128)
- **C** From Chester (Table 88)
- **D** From Bristol Temple Meads (Table 51)
- **E** From Buxton (Table 86) to Southport (Table 82)
- **G** To Wigan Wallgate (Table 82)
- **H** From Plymouth (Table 51)
- **J** From Cleethorpes to Manchester Airport (Table 29)
- **K** From Swansea (Fridays from Milford Haven) (Table 128)
- **L** From Buxton (Table 86)
- **N** From Sheffield (Table 78)
- **Q** From Bournemouth (Table 51)
- **U** From Sheffield to Manchester Airport (Table 78)
- **V** To Blackpool North (Table 82)
- **X** From Doncaster to Manchester Airport (Table 29)
- **Y** From Buxton (Table 86) to Blackpool North (Table 82)
- **Z** From Nottingham to Liverpool Lime Street (Table 49)
- **AA** From Hazel Grove (Table 86)
- **BB** From Cardiff Central (from 29 March from Hereford) (Table 131)
- **b** Change at Stafford
- **c** Change at Tamworth

Table 84

Stoke-on-Trent and Crewe → Manchester Airport, Stockport and Manchester

Network Diagram - see first page of Table 78

	NT	NT	EM	NT	NT	NT	NT		NT	NT	XC	TP	AW	NT	NT	NT	NT		EM	NT	VT	NT	NT	XC
			◇								1 ◇	1 ◇	◇						◇		1 ◇			1 ◇
		A	B			C			D	E		G	H			E	A		B				C	J
London Euston 15 ⊖ 65 d																					06 30	*05 31*		
Birmingham New Street 12 68 d	*06b20*										07 20		*07 03*							*07 21*				08 20
Wolverhampton 7 68 d	*06b40*										07 40		*07 21*							*07 44*				08 40
Stafford 65, 68 d	*07 00*										07 54		*07 33*							*08 02*		*08 18*		08 54
Stoke-on-Trent 50, 68 d											08 13										09 05			09 13
Longport 50 d																								
Kidsgrove 50 d																								
Crewe 10 65 d	07 33				07 43		08 00						08 30							08 40		09 00		
Sandbach d	07 40				07 50		08 07													08 47		09 07		
Holmes Chapel d	07 45				07 55		08 11													08 51		09 11		
Goostrey d	07 48						08 14															09 14		
Chelford d	07 52						08 19															09 19		
Alderley Edge d	07 56				08 04		08 23								08 57					09 00		09 23		
Wilmslow d	08 00				08 07		08 26						08 48		09 00					09 03		09 26		
Styal d																								
Manchester Airport ✈ a					08 14															09 15				
Handforth d	08 03						08 29								09 03							09 29		
Congleton d											08 25													
Macclesfield a											08 32										09 19			09 29
d				08 09							08 33			08 41							09 21			09 30
Prestbury d				08 14										08 45										
Adlington (Cheshire) d				08 17										08 48										
Poynton d				08 20										08 52										
Bramhall d				08 23										08 54										
Cheadle Hulme d	08 09			08 25			08 34							08 56	09 08							09 34		
Stockport a	08 13			08 30			08 41				08 46		08 56	09 01	09 13						09s34	09 39		09 46
d	08 14	08 20	08 27	08 30		08 35	08 41		08 42	08 46	08 46	08 51	08 57	09 02	09 13	09 16	09 21		09 25			09 39	09 48	09 46
Heaton Chapel d	08 18						08 45							09 05	09 17								09 51	
Levenshulme d	08 21						08 48							09 08	09 20								09 54	
Manchester Piccadilly 10 a	08 28	08 29	08 36	08 41	08 42	08 44	08 55		08 56	08 59	09 02	09 01	09 12	09 18	09 28	09 31	09 32		09 36	09 40	09 48	09 54	10 01	10 02
d		08 31	08 37				08 56							09 19			09 33		09 37					
Manchester Oxford Road a		08 33	08 40				08 58							09 21			09 36		09 40					
Deansgate a		08 37					09 03							09 26			09 38							

	TP	AW	NT	NT	VT		NT	NT	EM	NT	VT	NT	NT	XC	TP		AW	NT	NT	VT	NT	NT	EM	NT
	1 ◇	◇			1 ◇				◇		1 ◇			1 ◇	1 ◇		◇			1 ◇			◇	
	G	K					L	D	N				C	Q	G		K				A	E	U	
London Euston 15 ⊖ 65 d					07 06						07 52	*07 15*								08 10				
Birmingham New Street 12 68 d		*08 03*			08 48					*08 21*				09 20			*09 03*			09 48				*09 21*
Wolverhampton 7 68 d		*08 21*			09 09					*08 44*				09 40			*09 21*			10 09				*09 44*
Stafford 65, 68 d					09 26					*09 02*		*09 16*		09 54						10 26				*10 02*
Stoke-on-Trent 50, 68 d					09 45						10 06			10 13						10 44				
Longport 50 d																								
Kidsgrove 50 d																								
Crewe 10 65 d		09 30								09 38		10 00					10 30							10 38
Sandbach d										09 45		10 07												10 45
Holmes Chapel d										09 49		10 11												10 49
Goostrey d												10 14												
Chelford d												10 19												
Alderley Edge d				09 53						09 58		10 23							10 53					10 58
Wilmslow d		09 48		09 56						10 01		10 26					10 48		10 56					11 01
Styal d																								
Manchester Airport ✈ a										10 11														11 11
Handforth d				09 59								10 29							10 59					
Congleton d														10 25										
Macclesfield a					09 59						10 21			10 32						10 58				
d			09 41		10 01						10 22			10 33				10 41		11 00				
Prestbury d			09 45															10 45						
Adlington (Cheshire) d			09 48															10 48						
Poynton d			09 52															10 52						
Bramhall d			09 54															10 54						
Cheadle Hulme d			09 56	10 04								10 34						10 56	11 04					
Stockport a		09 58	10 01	10 09	10 13						10s34	10 39		10 46			10 58	11 01	11 09	11 13				
d	09 53	09 59	10 02	10 09	10 15		10 18	10 21	10 25			10 39	10 49	10 46	10 53		10 59	11 02	11 09	11 15	11 19	11 17	11 25	
Heaton Chapel d			10 05	10 13								10 43						11 05	11 13					
Levenshulme d			10 08	10 16								10 46						11 08	11 16					
Manchester Piccadilly 10 a	10 03	10 13	10 18	10 22	10 28		10 29	10 32	10 36	10 39	10 48	10 54	11 00	11 02	11 03		11 13	11 18	11 24	11 28	11 29	11 32	11 36	11 39
d			10 19				10 30		10 37									11 19			11 30		11 37	
Manchester Oxford Road a			10 21				10 32		10 40									11 21			11 32		11 40	
Deansgate a			10 26				10 35											11 26			11 35			

For general notes see front of timetable
For details of catering facilities see Directory of Train Operators

- **A** From Buxton (Table 86) to Blackpool North (Table 82)
- **B** From Nottingham to Liverpool Lime Street (Table 49)
- **C** From Hazel Grove (Table 86)
- **D** From Buxton (Table 86)
- **E** From Chester (Table 88)
- **G** From Cleethorpes to Manchester Airport (Table 29)
- **H** From Cardiff Central (from 29 March from Hereford) (Table 131)
- **J** From Gatwick Airport (Table 51)
- **K** Until 22 March from Carmarthen (Table 128). From 29 March from Hereford (Table 131)
- **L** From Northwich (Table 88) to Blackpool North (Table 82)
- **N** From Norwich to Liverpool Lime Street (Table 49)
- **Q** From Exeter St Davids (Table 51)
- **U** From Cambridge to Liverpool Lime Street (Table 49)
- **b** Change at Stafford and Crewe

Table 84

Saturdays

Stoke-on-Trent and Crewe → Manchester Airport, Stockport and Manchester

Network Diagram - see first page of Table 78

		VT	NT	NT		XC	TP	AW	NT	NT	VT	NT	NT	EM		NT	VT	NT	NT	XC	TP	AW	NT	NT	NT
		1 ◇				1 ◇	1 ◇	◇			1 ◇			◇			1 ◇			1 ◇	1 ◇	◇			
				A		B	C	D				E	G	H					A	J	C	D			E
		🍴				🍴	🛒	🛒			🍴						🍴			🍴	🛒	🛒			
London Euston [15]	⊖ 65 d	08 53	*08 17*								09 10						09 53	*09 17*							
Birmingham New Street [12]	68 d		*09 40*			10 20		*10 03*			10 48					*10 21*		*10 40*		11 20		*11 03*			
Wolverhampton [7]	68 ⛴ d					10 40		*10 21*			11 09					*10 44*				11 40		*11 21*			
Stafford	65, 68 d		*10 19*			10 54					11 26					*11 02*		*11 21*		11 54					
Stoke-on-Trent	50, 68 d	11 06				11 13					11 44						12 06			12 13					
Longport	50 d																								
Kidsgrove	50 d																								
Crewe [10]	65 d		11 00					11 30								11 38		12 00				12 30			
Sandbach	d		11 07													11 45		12 07							
Holmes Chapel	d		11 11													11 49		12 11							
Goostrey	d		11 14															12 14							
Chelford	d		11 19															12 19							
Alderley Edge	d		11 23							11 53						11 58		12 23						12 53	
Wilmslow	d		11 26					11 48		11 56						12 01		12 26				12 48		12 56	
Styal	d																								
Manchester Airport	✈ a															12 11									
Handforth	d		11 29							11 59								12 29						12 59	
Congleton	d																			12 25					
Macclesfield	a	11 21				11 29					11 59						12 21			12 32					
	d	11 22				11 30			11 41		12 00						12 22			12 33			12 41		
Prestbury	d								11 45														12 45		
Adlington (Cheshire)	d								11 48														12 48		
Poynton	d								11 52														12 52		
Bramhall	d								11 54														12 54		
Cheadle Hulme	d		11 34						11 56	12 04								12 34					12 56	13 04	
Stockport	a	11s34	11 39			11 46		11 58	12 01	12 09	12 13						12s34	12 39		12 46		12 58	13 01	13 09	
	d		11 39	11 49		11 46	11 53	11 59	12 02	12 09	12 15	12 19	12 17	12 25				12 39	12 49	12 46	12 53	12 59	13 02	13 09	13 19
Heaton Chapel	d		11 43						12 05	12 13								12 43					13 05	13 13	
Levenshulme	d		11 46						12 08	12 16								12 46					13 08	13 16	
Manchester Piccadilly [10]	⛴ a	11 48	11 54	12 00		12 02	12 03	12 13	12 18	12 24	12 28	12 29	12 32	12 36		12 39	12 48	12 54	13 00	13 02	13 03	13 13	13 18	13 24	13 27
	d								12 19			12 30		12 37									13 19		13 30
Manchester Oxford Road	a								12 21			12 33		12 40									13 21		13 32
Deansgate	⛴ a								12 26			12 35											13 26		13 35

		VT		NT	EM	NT	VT	NT	NT	XC	TP	AW		NT	NT	NT	VT	NT	EM	NT	VT	NT		NT	XC
		1 ◇			◇		1 ◇			1 ◇	1 ◇	◇					1 ◇		◇		1 ◇				1 ◇
				G	H				A	B	C	K				E		G	H					A	L
		🍴					🍴			🍴	🛒	🛒					🍴				🍴				🍴
London Euston [15]	⊖ 65 d	10 10					10 53	*10 17*									11 10				11 53	*11 17*			
Birmingham New Street [12]	68 d	11 48				*11 21*		*11 40*		12 20		*12 03*					12 48			*12 21*		*12 40*			13 20
Wolverhampton [7]	68 ⛴ d	12 09				*11 44*				12 40		*12 21*					13 09			*12 44*					13 40
Stafford	65, 68 d	12 26				*12 02*		*12 19*		12 54							13 26			*13 02*		*13 19*			13 54
Stoke-on-Trent	50, 68 d	12 44					13 06			13 13							13 44				14 06				14 13
Longport	50 d																								
Kidsgrove	50 d																								
Crewe [10]	65 d					12 38		13 00				13 30								13 38		14 00			
Sandbach	d					12 45		13 07												13 45		14 07			
Holmes Chapel	d					12 49		13 11												13 49		14 11			
Goostrey	d							13 14														14 14			
Chelford	d							13 19														14 19			
Alderley Edge	d					12 58		13 23							13 53					13 58		14 23			
Wilmslow	d					13 01		13 26				13 48			13 56					14 01		14 26			
Styal	d																								
Manchester Airport	✈ a					13 11														14 11					
Handforth	d							13 29							13 59							14 29			
Congleton	d																								14 25
Macclesfield	a	12 59					13 21			13 29							13 59				14 21				14 32
	d	13 00					13 22			13 30				13 41			14 00				14 22				14 33
Prestbury	d													13 45											
Adlington (Cheshire)	d													13 48											
Poynton	d													13 52											
Bramhall	d													13 54											
Cheadle Hulme	d							13 34						13 56	14 04							14 34			
Stockport	a	13 13					13s34	13 39		13 46		13 58		14 01	14 09		14 13				14s34	14 39			14 46
	d	13 15		13 17	13 25			13 39	13 49	13 46	13 53	13 59		14 02	14 09	14 19	14 15	14 17	14 25			14 39		14 49	14 46
Heaton Chapel	d							13 43						14 05	14 13							14 43			
Levenshulme	d							13 46						14 08	14 16							14 46			
Manchester Piccadilly [10]	⛴ a	13 28		13 32	13 36	13 39	13 48	13 54	14 00	14 02	14 03	14 13		14 18	14 24	14 27	14 28	14 32	14 36	14 39	14 48	14 54		15 00	15 02
	d				13 37									14 19		14 30			14 37						
Manchester Oxford Road	a				13 40									14 21		14 32			14 40						
Deansgate	⛴ a													14 26		14 35									

For general notes see front of timetable
For details of catering facilities see Directory of Train Operators

- **A** From Hazel Grove (Table 86)
- **B** From Bournemouth (Table 51)
- **C** From Cleethorpes to Manchester Airport (Table 29)
- **D** Until 22 March from Milford Haven (Table 128). From 29 March from Hereford (Table 131)
- **E** From Buxton (Table 86) to Blackpool North (Table 82)
- **G** From Chester (Table 88)
- **H** From Norwich to Liverpool Lime Street (Table 49)
- **J** From Plymouth (Table 51)
- **K** Until 22 March from Carmarthen (Table 128). From 29 March from Hereford (Table 131)
- **L** From Penzance (Table 135)

Table 84

Stoke-on-Trent and Crewe → Manchester Airport, Stockport and Manchester

Network Diagram - see first page of Table 78

	TP 1◇ A	AW ◇ B	NT	NT	NT C	VT 1◇	NT D	EM ◇ E	NT		VT 1◇	NT	NT G	XC 1◇ H	TP 1◇ A	AW ◇ J	NT	NT	NT C		VT 1◇	NT D	EM ◇ E	NT
London Euston 15 ⊖ 65 d						12 10					12 53	12 17									13 10			
Birmingham New Street 12 68 d		13 03				13 48			13 21			13 40		14 20		14b03					14 48			
Wolverhampton 7 68 d		13 21				14 09			13 44					14 40		14b21					15 09			
Stafford 65, 68 d						14 26			14 02			14 19		14 54							15 26			
Stoke-on-Trent 50, 68 d						14 44					15 06			15 13							15 44			
Longport 50 d																								
Kidsgrove 50 d																								
Crewe 10 65 d		14 30							14 38			15 00				15 30								
Sandbach d									14 45			15 07												
Holmes Chapel d									14 49			15 11												
Goostrey d												15 14												
Chelford d												15 19												
Alderley Edge d				14 53					14 58			15 23						15 53						
Wilmslow d		14 48		14 56					15 01			15 26				15 48		15 56						
Styal d																								
Manchester Airport ✈ a									15 11															
Handforth d				14 59								15 29						15 59						
Congleton d																								
Macclesfield a						14 59					15 21			15 29							15 59			
d			14 41			15 00					15 22			15 30			15 41				16 00			16 11
Prestbury d			14 45														15 45							16 15
Adlington (Cheshire) d			14 48														15 48							16 18
Poynton d			14 52														15 52							16 22
Bramhall d			14 54														15 54							16 24
Cheadle Hulme d			14 56	15 04								15 34					15 56	16 04						16 26
Stockport a		14 58	15 01	15 09		15 13					15s34	15 39		15 46		15 58	16 01	16 09			16 13			16 31
d	14 53	14 59	15 02	15 09	15 19	15 15	15 17	15 24				15 39	15 49	15 46	15 53	15 59	16 02	16 09	16 19		16 15	16 17	16 25	16 35
Heaton Chapel d			15 05	15 13								15 43					16 05	16 13						16 38
Levenshulme d			15 08	15 16								15 46					16 08	16 16						→
Manchester Piccadilly 10 a	15 03	15 13	15 18	15 24	15 27	15 28	15 32	15 36	15 39		15 48	15 54	16 00	16 02	16 03	16 13	16 18	16 24	16 27		16 28	16 32	16 37	
d			15 19		15 30			15 37											16 30				16 37	
Manchester Oxford Road a			15 21		15 32			15 40											16 32				16 40	
Deansgate a			15 26		15 35														16 35					

	NT	VT 1◇	NT K	NT	NT	NT G	XC 1◇ L		TP 1◇ A	AW ◇ B	NT N	NT	VT 1◇	NT C	NT D	EM ◇ E	NT		NT	VT 1◇	NT	NT G	XC 1◇ H	TP 1◇ A
London Euston 15 ⊖ 65 d		13 53		13 17									14 10							14 53	14 17			
Birmingham New Street 12 68 d	14 21			14 40			15 20			15 03			15 48				15 21				15 40		16 20	
Wolverhampton 7 68 d	14 44						15 40			15 21			16 09				15 44						16 40	
Stafford 65, 68 d	15 02			15 19			15 54						16 26				16 02				16 19		16 54	
Stoke-on-Trent 50, 68 d		16 06					16 13						16 44							17 06			17 13	
Longport 50 d																								
Kidsgrove 50 d																								
Crewe 10 65 d	15 38			16 00						16 30							16 42				17 00			
Sandbach d	15 45			16 07													16 49				17 07			
Holmes Chapel d	15 49			16 11													16 53				17 11			
Goostrey d				16 14																	17 14			
Chelford d				16 19																	17 19			
Alderley Edge d	15 58			16 23								16 53					17 02				17 23			
Wilmslow d	16 01			16 26						16 48		16 56					17 05				17 26			
Styal d																								
Manchester Airport ✈ a	16 11																17 15							
Handforth d				16 29								16 59									17 29			
Congleton d							16 25																	
Macclesfield a		16 21					16 33						16 59							17 21			17 29	
d		16 22					16 33						17 00						17 11	17 22			17 30	
Prestbury d																			17 15					
Adlington (Cheshire) d																			17 18					
Poynton d																			17 22					
Bramhall d																			17 24					
Cheadle Hulme d				16 34								17 04							17 26		17 34			
Stockport a		16s34		16 40			16 46			16 58		17 09	17 13						17 31	17s34	17 39		17 46	
d			16 40	16 43	←	16 49	16 46		16 53	16 59	17 02	17 09	17 15	17 18	17 16	17 25			17 32		17 39	17 49	17 46	17 53
Heaton Chapel d					16 38						17 06	17 13			17 19						17 43			
Levenshulme d					16 41						17 09	17 16			17 22						17 46			
Manchester Piccadilly 10 a	16 41	16 48	16 50	16 54	16 54	17 00	17 02		17 03	17 13	17 15	17 23	17 28	17 28	17 31	17 35	17 41		17 44	17 48	17 54	18 01	18 02	18 03
d			16 52		16 56						17 15			17 30		17 37								
Manchester Oxford Road a			16 55		16 58						17 18			17 32		17 39								
Deansgate a			16 58		17 03						17 21			17 35										

For general notes see front of timetable
For details of catering facilities see Directory of Train Operators

A From Cleethorpes to Manchester Airport (Table 29)
B Until 22 March from Milford Haven (Table 128). From 29 March from Hereford (Table 131)
C From Buxton (Table 86) to Blackpool North (Table 82)
D From Chester (Table 88)
E From Norwich to Liverpool Lime Street (Table 49)
G From Hazel Grove (Table 86)
H From Bournemouth (Table 51)
J Until 22 March from Carmarthen (Table 128). From 29 March from Hereford (Table 131)
K To Preston (Table 82)
L From Penzance (Table 135)
N To Blackpool North (Table 82)
b Until 22 March only

Stoke-on-Trent and Crewe → Manchester Airport, Stockport and Manchester

Network Diagram - see first page of Table 78

		AW	VT	NT	NT	EM		NT	NT	VT	NT	NT	XC	TP	AW	NT		NT	VT	EM	NT	NT	VT	NT	NT
		R	1 ◇			◇				1 ◇			1 ◇	1 ◇	R				1 ◇	◇			1 ◇		
		A		B	C	D						E	G	H	J	K		C		L				N	
London Euston 15	⊖ 65 d		15 10							15 53	*15 17*								16 10				16 53		*16 17*
Birmingham New Street 12	68 d	*16 03*	16 48					*16 21*			*16 40*		17 20		*17 03*				17 48		*17 21*				*17 40*
Wolverhampton 7	68 ⛴ d	*16 21*	17 09					*16 44*					17 40		*17 21*				18 09		*17 44*				
Stafford	65, 68 d		17 26					*17 02*			*17 19*		17 54						18 26		*18 02*				*18 19*
Stoke-on-Trent	50, 68 d		17 44							18 06			18 13						18 44				19 06		
Longport	50 d																								
Kidsgrove	50 d																								
Crewe 10	65 d	17 30						17 38			18 00				18 30						18 42				19 00
Sandbach	d							17 45			18 07										18 49				19 07
Holmes Chapel	d							17 50			18 11										18 53				19 11
Goostrey	d							17 53			18 14														19 14
Chelford	d							17 57			18 19														19 19
Alderley Edge	d							18 01			18 23										19 02				19 23
Wilmslow	d	17 48						18 04			18 26				18 48						19 05				19 26
Styal	d							18 08																	
Manchester Airport	✈ a							18 15													19 16				
Handforth	d										18 29														19 29
Congleton	d												18 25												
Macclesfield	a		17 59							18 21			18 32						18 59				19 21		
	d		18 00						18 12	18 22			18 33						19 00			19 09	19 22		
Prestbury	d								18 16													19 14			
Adlington (Cheshire)	d								18 19													19 17			
Poynton	d								18 23													19 20			
Bramhall	d								18 25													19 23			
Cheadle Hulme	d								18 28		18 34											19 25			19 34
Stockport	a	17 58	18 13						18 32	18s34	18 39		18 46		18 58				19 13			19 30	19s34		19 39
	d	17 59	18 15	18 19	18 17	18 26			18 32		18 39	18 50	18 46	18 53	18 59	19 05		19 10	19 15	19 24		19 30		19 40	19 39
Heaton Chapel	d				18 23						18 43					19 09		19 14							19 43
Levenshulme	d				18 26						18 46					19 12		19 17							19 46
Manchester Piccadilly 10	⛴ a	18 10	18 28	18 30	18 32	18 35		18 40	18 43	18 48	18 54	19 00	19 02	19 03	19 16	19 19		19 28	19 28	19 35	19 41	19 43	19 48	19 51	19 57
	d			18 31		18 37										19 20					19 41				
Manchester Oxford Road	a			18 34		18 39										19 22					19 46				
Deansgate	⛴ a			18 38												19 25									

		XC	TP	AW		NT	NT	VT	NT	EM	VT	NT	NT	XC		TP	AW	AW	NT	NT	EM	VT	NT	VT	NT
		1 ◇	1 ◇	R				1 ◇		◇	1 ◇			1 ◇		1 ◇	R	R			◇	1 ◇		1 ◇	
		Q	H	A			C			L		U		G		H	V	X		C	L				
London Euston 15	⊖ 65 d							17 10			17 53		*17 17*									18 10		18 53	*18 17*
Birmingham New Street 12	68 d	18 20		*18 03*				18 48					*18 40*	19 20			*19 03*	*19 03*				19 48			*19 21*
Wolverhampton 7	68 ⛴ d	18 40		*18 20*				19 09					*18 44*	19 40			*19 21*	*19 21*				20 09			*19 44*
Stafford	65, 68 d	18 54						19 26					*19 19*	19 54			*19 33*	*19 33*				20 26			*20 15*
Stoke-on-Trent	50, 68 d	19 13				19 19		19 44			20 06			20 13								20 44		21 06	
Longport	50 d																								
Kidsgrove	50 d					19 27																			
Crewe 10	65 d			19 30									20 00				20 26	20 29							21 00
Sandbach	d												20 07												21 07
Holmes Chapel	d												20 11												21 11
Goostrey	d												20 14												21 14
Chelford	d												20 19												21 19
Alderley Edge	d												20 23												21 23
Wilmslow	d			19 48					19 51				20 26				20 45	20 48					20 50		21 26
Styal	d																								
Manchester Airport	✈ a								20 02														21 02		
Handforth	d												20 29												21 29
Congleton	d					19 34								20 25											
Macclesfield	a	19 29				19 41		19 59			20 21			20 32								20 59		21 21	
	d	19 30				19 42		20 00			20 22			20 33					20 42			21 00		21 22	
Prestbury	d					19 46													20 46						
Adlington (Cheshire)	d					19 49													20 49						
Poynton	d					19 52													20 53						
Bramhall	d					19 55													20 55						
Cheadle Hulme	d					19 57							20 34						20 57						21 34
Stockport	a	19 46		19 59		20 02		20 13			20s34		20 39	20 46			20 56	20 59	21 02			21 13		21s34	21 39
	d	19 46	19 53	19 59		20 03	20 10	20 15		20 25		20 40	20 39	20 46		20 53	20 56	20 59	21 03	21 10	21 13	21 15			21 39
Heaton Chapel	d					20 06							20 43						21 06						21 43
Levenshulme	d					20 09							20 46						21 09						21 46
Manchester Piccadilly 10	⛴ a	20 02	20 03	20 13		20 17	20 24	20 28	20 31	20 36	20 48	20 52	20 54	21 02		21 03	21 13	21 13	21 19	21 24	21 25	21 28	21 31	21 51	21 53
	d									20 37		20 52													21 54
Manchester Oxford Road	a									20 39		20 54													21 56
Deansgate	⛴ a											20 56													22 01

For general notes see front of timetable
For details of catering facilities see Directory of Train Operators

- **A** Until 22 March from Carmarthen (Table 128). From 29 March from Hereford (Table 131)
- **B** From Buxton (Table 86) to Blackpool North (Table 82)
- **C** From Chester (Table 88)
- **D** From Norwich to Liverpool Lime Street (Table 49)
- **E** From Hazel Grove (Table 86)
- **G** From Plymouth (Table 51)
- **H** From Cleethorpes to Manchester Airport (Table 29)
- **J** Until 22 March from Milford Haven (Table 128). From 29 March from Hereford (Table 131)
- **K** From Buxton (Table 86) to Salford Crescent (Table 82)
- **L** From Norwich (Table 49)
- **N** From Buxton (Table 86)
- **Q** From Bournemouth (Table 51)
- **U** From Buxton (Table 86) to Bolton (Table 82)
- **V** Until 22 March. From Milford Haven (Table 128)
- **X** From 29 March. From Hereford (Table 131)

Stoke-on-Trent and Crewe → Manchester Airport, Stockport and Manchester

Saturdays

Network Diagram - see first page of Table 78

		XC 1◇ A	AW ◇ B	NT	VT 1◇	NT C	NT	NT D	VT 1◇	NT E	NT	XC 1◇ G	NT	NT	NT H	AW ◇ J	VT 1◇	NT K	XC 1◇ A	NT
London Euston 15	⊖ 65 d				18b57				19c20		*19e05*					*19f36*	20g00			
Birmingham New Street 12	68 d	20 20			20 48						*20 21*	21 20				*21 21*	*21 21*		22 20	
Wolverhampton 7	68 ⛴ d	20 40			21 10						*20 44*	21 40				*21 44*	*21 44*		22 40	
Stafford	65, 68 d	20 54			21 26						*21 15*	21 54				*22 17*	22 49		22 54	
Stoke-on-Trent	50, 68 d	21 13			21 45				22 03			22 13					23 08			
Longport	50 d																			
Kidsgrove	50 d																			
Crewe 10	65 d		21 27								22 00					23 04				23 08
Sandbach	d										22 07									23 15
Holmes Chapel	d										22 11									23 19
Goostrey	d										22 14									23 22
Chelford	d										22 19									23 27
Alderley Edge	d										22 23									23 31
Wilmslow	d		21 46				21 55				22 26			22 55		23 23				23 34
Styal	d																			
Manchester Airport	✈ a						22 05							23 05						
Handforth	d										22 29									23 36
Congleton	d											22 25								
Macclesfield	a	21 29			22 00				22 17			22 32					23 23		23s30	
	d	21 30		21 42	22 01				22 19			22 33	22 42				23 24			
Prestbury	d			21 46									22 46							
Adlington (Cheshire)	d			21 49									22 49							
Poynton	d			21 53									22 53							
Bramhall	d			21 55									22 55							
Cheadle Hulme	d			21 57							22 34		22 57							23 42
Stockport	a	21 46	21 57	22 02	22 12				22s32		22 39	22 46	23 02			23 33	23s37		23s46	23 48
	d	21 46	21 57	22 03	22 13	22 13		22 23		22 38	22 39	22 46	23 03		23 22	23 33		23 40		23 48
Heaton Chapel	d			22 06							22 43		23 06							23 52
Levenshulme	d			22 09							22 46		23 09							23 55
Manchester Piccadilly 10	⛴ a	22 02	22 13	22 19	22 25	22 26	22 31	22 33	22 45	22 47	22 52	23 02	23 19	23 34	23 36	23 50	23 51	23 52	00 02	00 03
	d							22 35		22 49	22 54									
Manchester Oxford Road	a							22 37		22 51	22 56									
Deansgate	⛴ a							22 40		22 54	23 00									

Sundays

until 23 March

		NT C	TP 1◇ L	NT N	NT Q	TP 1◇ U	NT N	NT Q	XC 1◇	NT	NT N	EM ◇ V	NT Q	XC 1◇	TP 1◇ X	AW Y	NT N	VT 1◇	EM ◇ Z	NT Q	XC 1◇ AA	TP 1◇ BB	NT N	VT 1◇	NT
London Euston 15	⊖ 65 d																	08 40						09 36	
Birmingham New Street 12	68 d								09 18	*09 03*				10 18		*10 03*		10 48			11 18			11 48	*11 03*
Wolverhampton 7	68 ⛴ d								09 38	*09 21*				10 38		*10 21*		11 10			11 38			12 10	*11 21*
Stafford	65, 68 d								09 53	*09 35*				10 53		*10 03*					11 53				
Stoke-on-Trent	50, 68 d								10 12					11 12				11 43			12 12			12 41	
Longport	50 d																								
Kidsgrove	50 d																								
Crewe 10	65 d									10 25						11 31									12 27
Sandbach	d									10 32															12 34
Holmes Chapel	d									10 36															12 38
Goostrey	d									10 39															
Chelford	d									10 44															
Alderley Edge	d				09 10			10 10		10 48			11 10							12 10					12 47
Wilmslow	d				09 12			10 12		10 51			11 13			11 51				12 12					12 50
Styal	d																								
Manchester Airport	✈ a									10 59															12 59
Handforth	d				09 17			10 17					11 17							12 17					
Congleton	d																								
Macclesfield	a								10 27					11 27				11 58			12 27			12 56	
	d								10 29					11 29				11 59			12 29			12 57	
Prestbury	d																								
Adlington (Cheshire)	d																								
Poynton	d																								
Bramhall	d																								
Cheadle Hulme	d				09 23			10 23					11 23							12 23					
Stockport	a				09 28			10 28	10 41				11 28	11 41		12 01		12 15		12 28	12 41			13 10	
	d	00 01	08{38	09 11	09 29	09{58	10 11	10 29	10 43		11 11	11{22	11 29	11 43	11{59	12 02	12 08	12 16	12 24	12 29	12 43	13{00	13 08	13 11	
Heaton Chapel	d		{	09 15	09 33	{	10 15	10 33			11 15	{	11 33		{		12 11			12 33		{	13 12		
Levenshulme	d		{	09 18	09 36	{	10 18	10 36			11 18	{	11 36		{		12 14			12 36		{	13 15		
Manchester Piccadilly 10	⛴ a	00 13	08{48	09 24	09 43	10{08	10 24	10 42	10 57	11 21	11 24	11{33	11 44	11 57	12{08	12 16	12 24	12 30	12 36	12 42	12 57	13{10	13 23	13 23	13 28
	d			09 25	09 45		10 25	10 45			11 25	11{37	11 46				12 25		12 37	12 45			13 24		
Manchester Oxford Road	a			09 27	09 47		10 27	10 47			11 27	11{39	11 48				12 27		12 39	12 47			13 26		
Deansgate	⛴ a			09 31	09 50		10 31	10 50			11 31		11 51				12 31			12 50			13 30		

For general notes see front of timetable
For details of catering facilities see Directory of Train Operators

- **A** From Bournemouth (Table 51)
- **B** Until 22 March from Carmarthen (Table 128). From 29 March from Hereford (Table 131)
- **C** From Chester (Table 88)
- **D** From Buxton (Table 86) to Southport (Table 82)
- **E** To Wigan Wallgate (Table 82)
- **G** From Plymouth (Table 51)
- **H** From Sheffield (Table 78)
- **J** Until 22 March from Milford Haven (Table 128). From 29 March from Hereford (Table 131)
- **K** From Buxton (Table 86)
- **L** From 3 February. From Sheffield to Manchester Airport (Table 78)
- **N** From Buxton (Table 86) to Blackpool North (from 3 February to Preston) (Table 82)
- **Q** To Southport (Table 82)
- **U** From 3 February. From Meadowhall to Manchester Airport (Table 29)
- **V** From 3 February. From Nottingham to Liverpool Lime Street (Table 49)
- **X** From 3 February. From Doncaster to Manchester Airport (Table 29)
- **Y** From Shrewsbury (Table 131)
- **Z** Until 27 January to Liverpool Lime Street (Table 89). From 3 February from Nottingham to Liverpool Lime Street (Table 49)
- **AA** From Bristol Temple Meads (Table 51)
- **BB** From 3 February. From Cleethorpes to Manchester Airport (Table 29)
- **b** From 29 March dep. 1910
- **c** From 29 March dep. 1925
- **e** From 29 March dep. 1917
- **f** From 29 March dep. 1950
- **g** From 29 March dep. 2012

Sundays

until 23 March

Stoke-on-Trent and Crewe → Manchester Airport, Stockport and Manchester

Network Diagram - see first page of Table 78

Station		EM		VT	NT	XC	TP	AW	NT	VT	EM	VT	NT	XC	AW	TP	NT	NT	VT	EM	NT	VT	XC	AW	TP
																							R		
		◇		1 ◇		1 ◇	1 ◇			1 ◇	◇	1 ◇		1 ◇	◇	1 ◇			1 ◇	◇		1 ◇	1	◇	1 ◇
		A			B	C	D	E	G		A		B	H	J	K		G		L	B		N	Q	K
				☕		☕				☕		☕		☕	🛒				☕			☕	☕	🛒	
London Euston 15	⊖ 65 d			10 10				*10 31*		10 36		11 10							11 36			12 10		*11 40*	
Birmingham New Street 12	68 d					12 18		*12b18*		12 48				13 18	*13 03*				13 48				14 18	*14 03*	
Wolverhampton 7	68 ⛴ d					12 38		*12b38*		13 10				13 38	*13 21*				14 10				14 38	*14 21*	
Stafford	65, 68 d			12 40		12 53		*13 01*				13 40		13 53									14 53	*14 09*	
Stoke-on-Trent	50, 68 d			13 00		13 12				13 44		14 00		14 12					14 44			14 57	15 12		
Longport	50 d																								
Kidsgrove	50 d																								
Crewe 10	65 d							13 35							14 21		14 27							15 25	
Sandbach	d																14 34								
Holmes Chapel	d																14 38								
Goostrey	d																14 41								
Chelford	d																14 46								
Alderley Edge	d				13 10								14 10				14 50				15 10				
Wilmslow	d				13 12			13 55					14 12		14 44		14 53				15 12			15 45	
Styal	d																								
Manchester Airport	✈ a																15 04								
Handforth	d				13 17								14 17								15 17				
Congleton	d																								
Macclesfield	a			13 14		13 27				13 59		14 14		14 27					14 58			15 12	15 27		
	d			13 16		13 29				14 00		14 16		14 29					15 00			15 13	15 29		
Prestbury	d																								
Adlington (Cheshire)	d																								
Poynton	d																								
Bramhall	d																								
Cheadle Hulme	d				13 23								14 21								15 23				
Stockport	a			13s30	13 28	13 41		14 05		14 13		14s30	14 26	14 41	14 55				15 13		15 28	15s30	15 41	15 55	
	d	13 24			13 29	13 43	14 02	14 06	14 11	14 14	14 22		14 27	14 43	14 55	15 01		15 11	15 14	15 22	15 28		15 43	15 56	16 04
Heaton Chapel	d				13 33				14 15				14 31					15 15			15 33				
Levenshulme	d				13 36				14 18				14 34					15 18			15 36				
Manchester Piccadilly 10	⛴ a	13 36		13 44	13 47	13 57	14 12	14 20	14 24	14 26	14 31	14 44	14 47	14 57	15 11	15 13	15 21	15 24	15 27	15 33	15 44	15 46	15 57	16 12	16 13
	d	13 37			13 49				14 25		14 37		14 49					15 25		15 37	15 46				
Manchester Oxford Road	a	13 39			13 51				14 27		14 39		14 51					15 27		15 39	15 48				
Deansgate	⛴ a				13 54				14 31				14 54					15 31			15 51				

Station		NT	VT	EM		NT	VT	XC	TP	NT	NT	NT	VT	EM	NT	VT	XC	TP	NT	AW	VT	EM	NT	VT	XC
								R									R								R
			1 ◇	◇			1 ◇	1	1 ◇				1 ◇	◇		1 ◇	1	1 ◇		◇	1 ◇	◇		1 ◇	1
		G		A		B		U	K			G		A	B		N	K	G	Q		L	B		V
			☕				☕	☕					☕			☕	☕			🛒	☕			☕	☕
London Euston 15	⊖ 65 d		12 36				13 10				*12 40*		13 50			14 36				*14 50*	14 53			15 36	
Birmingham New Street 12	68 d		14 48					15 18			*15 03*		15 51				16 18			*16b18*	16 48				17 18
Wolverhampton 7	68 ⛴ d		15 10					15 38			*15 21*		16 13				16 38			*16b38*	17 10				17 38
Stafford	65, 68 d							15 53			*15 20*						16 53			*17 01*					17 53
Stoke-on-Trent	50, 68 d		15 45				15 59	16 12		16 19			16 45			17 00	17 12				17 44			17 59	18 12
Longport	50 d									16 23															
Kidsgrove	50 d									16 27															
Crewe 10	65 d										16 27									17 39					
Sandbach	d										16 34														
Holmes Chapel	d										16 38														
Goostrey	d																								
Chelford	d																								
Alderley Edge	d					16 10					16 47				17 10								18 10		
Wilmslow	d					16 12					16 50				17 12					17 59			18 12		
Styal	d																								
Manchester Airport	✈ a										16 59														
Handforth	d					16 17									17 17								18 17		
Congleton	d									16 34															
Macclesfield	a		15 59				16 14	16 27		16 41			17 00			17 15	17 27				17 59			18 14	18 27
	d		16 01				16 15	16 29		16 41			17 01			17 16	17 29				18 00			18 15	18 29
Prestbury	d									16 45															
Adlington (Cheshire)	d									16 48															
Poynton	d									16 52															
Bramhall	d									16 54															
Cheadle Hulme	d					16 23				16 56					17 23								18 23		
Stockport	a		16 14			16 28	16s30	16 41		17 01			17 13		17 28	17s30	17 41			18 11	18 14		18 28	18s30	18 41
	d	16 11	16 15	16 22		16 29		16 43	16 56	17 03		17 11	17 14	17 22	17 29		17 43	17 56	18 10	18 12	18 15	18 24	18 29		18 43
Heaton Chapel	d	16 14				16 33						17 15			17 33				18 14				18 33		
Levenshulme	d	16 17				16 36						17 18			17 36				18 17				18 36		
Manchester Piccadilly 10	⛴ a	16 24	16 27	16 32		16 44	16 44	16 57	17 11	17 14	17 23	17 24	17 27	17 36	17 44	17 44	17 57	18 12	18 24	18 26	18 27	18 36	18 43	18 45	18 57
	d	16 25		16 37		16 46						17 25		17 37	17 46				18 25			18 37	18 45		
Manchester Oxford Road	a	16 27		16 39		16 48						17 27		17 39	17 48				18 27			18 38	18 47		
Deansgate	⛴ a	16 30				16 51						17 31			17 51				18 30				18 50		

For general notes see front of timetable
For details of catering facilities see Directory of Train Operators

- **A** Until 27 January to Liverpool Lime Street (Table 89). From 3 February from Nottingham to Liverpool Lime Street (Table 49)
- **B** To Southport (Table 82)
- **C** From Southampton Central (Table 51)
- **D** From 3 February. From Doncaster to Manchester Airport (Table 29)
- **E** From Shrewsbury (Table 131)
- **G** From Buxton (Table 86) to Blackpool North (from 3 February to Preston) (Table 82)
- **H** From Plymouth (Table 51)
- **J** From Cardiff Central (Table 131)
- **K** From 3 February. From Cleethorpes to Manchester Airport (Table 29)
- **L** Until 27 January to Liverpool Lime Street (Table 89). From 3 February from Norwich to Liverpool Lime Street (Table 49)
- **N** From Bournemouth (Table 51)
- **Q** From Carmarthen (Table 128)
- **U** Until 27 January from Penzance (Table 135). From 3 February from Plymouth (Table 51)
- **V** From Penzance (Table 135)
- **b** Change at Stafford and Crewe

Table 84

Sundays
until 23 March

Stoke-on-Trent and Crewe → Manchester Airport, Stockport and Manchester

Network Diagram - see first page of Table 78

	TP	NT	NT	VT	EM		NT	VT	XC	TP	AW	NT	NT	VT	EM	EM	NT	VT	XC	TP	NT	NT	VT	EM
	1 ◇			1 ◇	◇			1 ◇	R 1	1 ◇	R			1 ◇		◇		1 ◇	R 1	1 ◇			1 ◇	◇
	A		B		C		D		E	A	G		B		H	J	D		K	A		B		J
London Euston 15 ⊖ 65 d				15 53				16 36			*15 58*			16 53				17 36			*16 58*		17 53	
Birmingham New Street 12 68 d		*17 03*		17 48					18 18		*18 03*			18 48					19 18		*19 03*		19 48	
Wolverhampton 7 68 d		*17 21*		18 10					18 38		*18 21*			19 10					19 38		*19 21*		20 10	
Stafford 65, 68 d									18 53		*18 07*								19 53		*19 34*			
Stoke-on-Trent 50, 68 d				18 44				18 59	19 12			19 20		19 45				19 59	20 12				20 45	
Longport 50 d												19 24												
Kidsgrove 50 d												19 28												
Crewe 10 65 d		18 27									19 29										20 27			
Sandbach d		18 34																			20 34			
Holmes Chapel d		18 38																			20 38			
Goostrey d																								
Chelford d																								
Alderley Edge d		18 47					19 10										20 10				20 47			
Wilmslow d		18 50					19 12				19 49						20 12				20 50			
Styal d																								
Manchester Airport a		19 00																			20 59			
Handforth d							19 17										20 17							
Congleton d												19 35												
Macclesfield a				18 59				19 14	19 27			19 42		19 59				20 14	20 27				21 00	
d				19 00				19 15	19 29			19 42		20 01				20 15	20 29				21 01	
Prestbury d												19 46												
Adlington (Cheshire) d												19 49												
Poynton d												19 53												
Bramhall d												19 55												
Cheadle Hulme d							19 23					19 58					20 23							
Stockport a				19 13			19 28	19s30	19 41		19 59	20 03		20 14			20 28	20s30	20 41				21 13	
d	19 00		19 10	19 14	19 22		19 29		19 43	20 00	20 00	20 04	20 10	20 15	20 10	20 25	20 29		20 43	20 55		21 10	21 14	21 19
Heaton Chapel d			19 14				19 33						20 14				20 33					21 14		
Levenshulme d			19 17				19 36						20 17				20 36					21 17		
Manchester Piccadilly 10 a	19 10	19 21	19 24	19 26	19 33		19 43	19 44	19 57	20 12	20 14	20 15	20 24	20 26	20 35	20 35	20 44	20 44	20 57	21 06	21 20	21 24	21 26	21 33
d			19 26		19 37		19 45						20 25				20 46					21 25		
Manchester Oxford Road a			19 27		19 39		19 47						20 27				20 48					21 27		
Deansgate a			19 31				19 50						20 30				20 51					21 30		

	EM	NT	VT	XC	AW	TP	NT	VT	EM	NT	VT	XC	NT	NT	NT	VT	NT	XC	VT	NT	VT	VT
			1 ◇	R 1	R	1 ◇		1 ◇			1 ◇	1 ◇				1 ◇		1 ◇	1 ◇		1 ◇	1 ◇
	H	L		E	G	A	N		H	L		K		Q			N	E		H		
London Euston 15 ⊖ 65 d			18 36		*17 58*			18 53			19 36				*18 58*	19 53			20 10		21 10	21 40
Birmingham New Street 12 68 d				20 18	*20 03*			20 48				21 18			*20b18*	21 48		22 18				
Wolverhampton 7 68 d				20 38	*20 22*			21 10				21 38			*20b38*	22 10		22 38				
Stafford 65, 68 d				20 53	*20 38*						21 43	21 53			*21 22*			22 53	22 58		23 50	00 14
Stoke-on-Trent 50, 68 d			21 00	21 12				21 45			22 03	22 12	22 15			22 41			23 18			
Longport 50 d													22 19									
Kidsgrove 50 d													22 23									
Crewe 10 65 d					21 25										22 25							
Sandbach d															22 32							
Holmes Chapel d															22 36							
Goostrey d															22 39							
Chelford d															22 44							
Alderley Edge d		21 10								22 10					22 48							
Wilmslow d		21 13			21 45					22 12					22 51						00s33	
Styal d																						
Manchester Airport a															22 59							
Handforth d		21 17								22 17												
Congleton d													22 30									
Macclesfield a			21 15	21 27				22 00			22 17	22 27	22 37			22 56		23s27	23 32			
d			21 16	21 29				22 01			22 19	22 29	22 37			22 57			23 34			
Prestbury d													22 41									
Adlington (Cheshire) d													22 44									
Poynton d													22 48									
Bramhall d													22 50									
Cheadle Hulme d		21 23								22 23			22 53									
Stockport a		21 28	21s30	21 41	21 56			22 14		22 28	22s30	22 41	22 57			23 11		23s41	23s47		00s43	01s04
d	21 10	21 29		21 43	21 56	22 01	22 10	22 15	22 15	22 29		22 43	22 58	23 01		23 12	23 10			23 59		
Heaton Chapel d		21 33					22 14			22 33							23 14					
Levenshulme d		21 36					22 17			22 36							23 17					
Manchester Piccadilly 10 a	21 35	21 42	21 44	21 57	22 07	22 13	22 27	22 27	22 40	22 42	22 42	22 57	23 09	23 12	23 22	23 26	23 27	23 57	23 59	00 20	00 55	01 16
d		21 45								22 45												
Manchester Oxford Road a		21 47								22 47												
Deansgate a		21 50								22 50												

For general notes see front of timetable
For details of catering facilities see Directory of Train Operators

- **A** From 3 February. From Cleethorpes to Manchester Airport (Table 29)
- **B** From Buxton (Table 86) to Blackpool North (from 3 February to Preston) (Table 82)
- **C** Until 27 January to Liverpool Lime Street (Table 89). From 3 February from Nottingham to Liverpool Lime Street (Table 49)
- **D** To Southport (Table 82)
- **E** From Bournemouth (Table 51)
- **G** From Milford Haven (Table 128)
- **H** Until 27 January. From Sheffield (Table 78)
- **J** From 3 February. From Norwich (Table 49)
- **K** From Plymouth (Table 51)
- **L** To Wigan Wallgate (Table 82)
- **N** From Buxton (Table 86)
- **Q** From 3 February. From Sheffield (Table 78)
- **b** Change at Stafford and Crewe

Table 84

Sundays

from 30 March

Stoke-on-Trent and Crewe → Manchester Airport, Stockport and Manchester

Network Diagram - see first page of Table 78

	NT	TP	NT	NT	TP	NT	NT	NT	XC	NT	NT	EM	NT		NT	NT	XC	TP	AW	NT	VT	EM	NT	NT
		1◇			1◇				1◇			◇					1◇	1◇			1◇	◇		
	A	B	C	D	E	C		D			C	G	D			D		H	J	C		G	D	
									🍴								🍴				🍴			
London Euston 15 ⊖ 65 d																					08 40			
Birmingham New Street 12 68 d									09 18								10 18				10 48			
Wolverhampton 7 68 ⛴ d									09 38								10 38				11 10			
Stafford 65, 68 d									09 53								10 53				11 26			
Stoke-on-Trent 50, 68 d																								
Longport 50 d																								
Kidsgrove 50 d																								
Crewe 10 65 d									10 16	10 25							11 16		11 31					
Sandbach d										10 32														
Holmes Chapel d										10 36														
Goostrey d										10 39														
Chelford d										10 44														
Alderley Edge d				09 10				10 10		10 48			11 10										12 10	
Wilmslow d				09 12				10 12	10 33	10 51			11 13				11 33		11 51		12 06		12 12	
Styal d																								
Manchester Airport ✈ a										10 59														
Handforth d				09 17				10 17					11 17										12 17	
Congleton d																								
Macclesfield a																								
d							10 07								11 16									12 22
Prestbury d																								
Adlington (Cheshire) d																								
Poynton d																								
Bramhall d																								
Cheadle Hulme d				09 23				10 23					11 23										12 23	
Stockport a				09 28			10 22	10 28	10 41				11 28		11 31		11 41		12 01		12 15		12 28	12 36
d	00 01	08 38	09 11	09 29	09 58	10 11	10 23	10 29	10 43		11 11	11 22	11 29		11 31	←	11 43	11 59	12 02	12 08	12 16	12 24	12 29	12 37
Heaton Chapel d			09 15	09 33		10 15		10 33			11 15		11 33			11 33				12 11			12 33	
Levenshulme d			09 18	09 36		10 18		10 36			11 18		→			11 36				12 14			12 36	
Manchester Piccadilly 10 ⛴ a	00 13	08 48	09 24	09 43	10 08	10 24	10 32	10 42	10 57	11 21	11 24	11 33			11 41	11 44	11 57	12 08	12 16	12 24	12 30	12 36	12 42	12 48
d			09 25	09 45		10 25		10 45			11 25	11 37				11 46				12 25		12 37	12 45	
Manchester Oxford Road a			09 27	09 47		10 27		10 47			11 27	11 39				11 48				12 27		12 39	12 47	
Deansgate ⛴ a			09 31	09 50		10 31		10 50			11 31					11 51				12 31			12 50	

	VT	VT	XC	NT	TP		NT	VT	NT	EM	NT	VT	NT	VT	VT	XC	NT	TP	AW		NT	VT	NT	EM
			1◇		1◇			1◇		◇		1◇				1◇		1◇				1◇		◇
			K		L		C			G	D		D			N		H	J		C			G
	🚌	🚌	🍴					🍴				🍴		🚌	🚌	🍴						🍴		
London Euston 15 ⊖ 65 d				*08b40*				09 36				10 10							*10 31*			10 36		
Birmingham New Street 12 68 d			11 18					11 48								12 18						12 48		
Wolverhampton 7 68 ⛴ d			11 38					12 10								12 38						13 10		
Stafford 65, 68 d	11 35		11 53					12 26				12 40			12 50	12 53			*13 01*			13 29		
Stoke-on-Trent 50, 68 d	12 05														13 20									
Longport 50 d																								
Kidsgrove 50 d																								
Crewe 10 65 d			12 16	12 27												13 16			13 35					
Sandbach d				12 34																				
Holmes Chapel d				12 38																				
Goostrey d																								
Chelford d																								
Alderley Edge d				12 47							13 10													
Wilmslow d		12 30	12 33	12 50				13 02			13 12	13 18		13 30		13 33			13 55			14 06		
Styal d									←															
Manchester Airport ✈ a				12 59					12 59															
Handforth d				→							13 17													
Congleton d																								
Macclesfield a	12 55	13 00												14 00	14 10									
d																	13 31						14 05	
Prestbury d																								
Adlington (Cheshire) d																								
Poynton d																								
Bramhall d																								
Cheadle Hulme d											13 23													
Stockport a			12 41					13 10			13 28	13s30				13 41	13 45		14 05			14 13	14 19	
d			12 43		13 00		13 08	13 11		13 24	13 29		←			13 43	13 46	14 02	14 06		14 11	14 14	14 19	14 22
Heaton Chapel d							13 12				13 33		13 33								14 15			
Levenshulme d							13 15				→		13 36								14 18			
Manchester Piccadilly 10 ⛴ a			12 57		13 10		13 23	13 23	13 28	13 36		13 44	13 47			13 57	13 58	14 12	14 20		14 24	14 26	14 30	14 31
d							13 24			13 37			13 49								14 25			14 37
Manchester Oxford Road a							13 26			13 39			13 51								14 27			14 39
Deansgate ⛴ a							13 30						13 54								14 31			

For general notes see front of timetable
For details of catering facilities see Directory of Train Operators

A From Chester (Table 88)
B From Sheffield to Manchester Airport (Table 78)
C From Buxton (Table 86) to Blackpool North (Table 82)
D To Southport (Table 82)
E From Meadowhall to Manchester Airport (Table 29)
G From Nottingham to Liverpool Lime Street (Table 49)
H From Doncaster to Manchester Airport (Table 29)
J From Shrewsbury (Table 131)
K From Bristol Temple Meads (Table 51)
L From Cleethorpes to Manchester Airport (Table 29)
N From Oxford (Table 51)
b Change at Stafford and Crewe

Table 84

Sundays

from 30 March

Stoke-on-Trent and Crewe → Manchester Airport, Stockport and Manchester

Network Diagram - see first page of Table 78

	NT	VT	VT	VT	XC	AW	TP	NT	NT	VT	NT		EM	NT	VT	VT	VT	XC	AW	TP	NT	VT	NT	EM
		1 ◇			1 ◇		1 ◇			1 ◇			◇		1 ◇			R 1		1 ◇		1 ◇		◇
	A				B	C	D		E				G	A				H	C	D	E			J
		buffet	bus	bus	buffet					buffet					buffet	bus	bus	buffet				buffet		
London Euston 15 ⊖ 65 d		11 10						*11b10*		11 36					12 10							12 36		
Birmingham New Street 12 68 d					13 18					13 48								14 18				14 48		
Wolverhampton 7 68 ⛴ d					13 38					14 10								14 38				15 10		
Stafford 65, 68 d		13 40		13 50	13 53					14 28					14 40		14 50	14 53				15 29		
Stoke-on-Trent 50, 68 d				14 20													15 20							
Longport 50 d																								
Kidsgrove 50 d																								
Crewe 10 65 d					14 16	14 21		14 27										15 16	15 25					
Sandbach d								14 34																
Holmes Chapel d								14 38																
Goostrey d								14 41																
Chelford d								14 46																
Alderley Edge d	14 10							14 50						15 10										
Wilmslow d	14 12	14 18	14 30		14 33	14 44		14 53		15 05				15 12	15 18	15 30		15 33	15 45			16 06		
Styal d																								
Manchester Airport ✈ a								15 04																
Handforth d	14 17													15 17										
Congleton d																								
Macclesfield a			15 00	15 10												16 00	16 10							
d											15 05												16 05	
Prestbury d																								
Adlington (Cheshire) d																								
Poynton d																								
Bramhall d																								
Cheadle Hulme d	14 21													15 23										
Stockport a	14 26	14s30			14 41	14 55				15 13	15 18			15 28	15s30			15 41	15 55			16 14	16 19	
d	14 28				14 43	14 55	15 01		15 11	15 14	15 19		15 22	15 28				15 43	15 56	16 04	16 11	16 15	16 19	16 22
Heaton Chapel d	14 32								15 15					15 33							16 14			
Levenshulme d	14 35								15 18					15 36							16 17			
Manchester Piccadilly 10 ⛴ a	14 44	14 44			14 57	15 11	15 13	15 21	15 24	15 27	15 30		15 33	15 44	15 46			15 57	16 12	16 13	16 24	16 27	16 31	16 32
d	14 46								15 25				15 37	15 46							16 25			16 37
Manchester Oxford Road a	14 48								15 27				15 39	15 48							16 27			16 39
Deansgate ⛴ a	14 51								15 31					15 51							16 30			

	NT	VT	VT		VT	XC	TP	NT	NT	VT	NT	NT	EM	NT	VT	VT	VT		XC	NT	TP	AW	NT	VT
		1 ◇				R 1	1 ◇			1 ◇			◇		1 ◇				R 1		1 ◇	◇		1 ◇
	A					K	D		E				J	A					H	L	D	C	E	
		buffet	bus		bus	buffet				buffet	bus				buffet	bus	bus		buffet			trolley		buffet
London Euston 15 ⊖ 65 d		13 10						*13b10*		13 50					14 36							*14 50*		14 53
Birmingham New Street 12 68 d						15 18				15 51									16 18					16 48
Wolverhampton 7 68 ⛴ d						15 38				16 13									16 38					17 10
Stafford 65, 68 d		15 42			15 50	15 53				16 30					16 42		16 50		16 53			*17 01*		17 29
Stoke-on-Trent 50, 68 d					16 20						15 52						17 20							
Longport 50 d																								
Kidsgrove 50 d											16 14													
Crewe 10 65 d						16 16		16 27											17 16			17 35		
Sandbach d								16 34																
Holmes Chapel d								16 38																
Goostrey d																								
Chelford d																								
Alderley Edge d	16 10							16 47						17 10										
Wilmslow d	16 12	16 18	16 30			16 33		16 50		17 04				17 12	17 18	17 30			17 33			17 55		18 05
Styal d																								
Manchester Airport ✈ a								16 59																
Handforth d	16 17													17 17										
Congleton d											16 28													
Macclesfield a			17 00		17 10						16 50					18 00	18 10							
d												16 58												
Prestbury d												17 02												
Adlington (Cheshire) d												17 05												
Poynton d												17 09												
Bramhall d												17 11												
Cheadle Hulme d	16 23											17 13		17 23										
Stockport a	16 28	16s30				16 41				17 13		17 18		17 28	17s30				17 41			18 06		18 14
d	16 29					16 43	16 56		17 10	17 14		17 19	17 22	17 29					17 43	17 47	17 56	18 06	18 10	18 15
Heaton Chapel d	16 33								17 15					17 33									18 14	
Levenshulme d	16 36								17 18					17 36									18 17	
Manchester Piccadilly 10 ⛴ a	16 44	16 44				16 57	17 11	17 23	17 24	17 27		17 28	17 36	17 44	17 44				17 57	17 59	18 12	18 20	18 24	18 27
d	16 46								17 25				17 37	17 46									18 25	
Manchester Oxford Road a	16 48								17 27				17 39	17 48									18 27	
Deansgate ⛴ a	16 51								17 31					17 51									18 30	

For general notes see front of timetable
For details of catering facilities see Directory of Train Operators

A To Southport (Table 82)

B From Plymouth (Table 51)
C From Hereford (Table 131)
D From Cleethorpes to Manchester Airport (Table 29)
E From Buxton (Table 86) to Blackpool North (Table 82)
G From Norwich to Liverpool Lime Street (Table 49)

H From Oxford (Table 51)
J From Nottingham to Liverpool Lime Street (Table 49)
K From Penzance (Table 135)
L From Sheffield (Table 78)
b Change at Stafford and Crewe

Table 84

Sundays

from 30 March

Stoke-on-Trent and Crewe → Manchester Airport, Stockport and Manchester

Network Diagram - see first page of Table 78

		NT	EM	NT	VT	VT	VT	XC	TP	NT		NT	VT	NT	EM	NT	VT	NT	VT	VT	XC	TP	AW	NT	VT
			◇		1 ◇			R 1	1 ◇				1 ◇		◇		1 ◇				R 1	1 ◇			1 ◇
			A	B				C	D			E			G	B					H	D	J	E	
						bus	bus											bus	bus	bus					
					☕			☕					☕				☕				☕				☕
London Euston [15] ⊖ 65	d				15 36					15b36			15 53				16 36						16b36		16c53
Birmingham New Street [12] 68	d							17 18					17 48								18 18				18 48
Wolverhampton [7] 68 ⛴	d							17 38					18 10								18 38				19 10
Stafford 65, 68	d				17 42		17 50	17 53					18 29				18 42			18 50	18 53				19 29
Stoke-on-Trent 50, 68	d						18 20											18 52		19 20					
Longport 50	d																								
Kidsgrove 50	d																	19 14							
Crewe [10] 65	d							18 16		18 27											19 16		19 29		
Sandbach	d									18 34															
Holmes Chapel	d									18 38															
Goostrey	d																								
Chelford	d																								
Alderley Edge	d			18 10						18 47						19 10									
Wilmslow	d			18 12	18 18	18 30		18 33		18 50			19 05			19 12	19 18		19 30		19 33		19 49		20 04
Styal	d																								
Manchester Airport ✈	a									19 00															
Handforth	d			18 17												19 17									
Congleton	d																	19 28							
Macclesfield	a					19 00	19 10											19 50	20 00	20 10					
	d	18 05												19 05											
Prestbury	d																								
Adlington (Cheshire)	d																								
Poynton	d																								
Bramhall	d																								
Cheadle Hulme	d			18 23												19 23									
Stockport	a	18 18		18 28	18s30			18 41					19 13	19 18		19 28	19s30				19 41		19 59		20 14
	d	18 19	18 24	18 29				18 43	19 00			19 10	19 14	19 19	19 22	19 29					19 43	20 00	20 00	20 10	20 15
Heaton Chapel	d			18 33								19 14				19 33								20 14	
Levenshulme	d			18 36								19 17				19 36								20 17	
Manchester Piccadilly [10] ⛴	a	18 30	18 36	18 43	18 45			18 57	19 10	19 21		19 24	19 26	19 30	19 33	19 43	19 44				19 57	20 12	20 14	20 24	20 26
	d		18 37	18 45								19 26			19 37	19 45								20 25	
Manchester Oxford Road	a		18 38	18 47								19 27			19 39	19 47								20 27	
Deansgate ⛴	a			18 50								19 31				19 50								20 30	

		NT		EM	NT	VT	VT	VT	XC	TP	NT	NT	VT	NT	EM	NT		VT	VT	VT	XC	AW	TP	NT	VT
				◇		1 ◇			R 1	1 ◇			1 ◇		◇			1 ◇			R 1		1 ◇		1 ◇
				K	B				L	D		E			K	N					H	J	D	Q	
							bus	bus											bus	bus					
						☕			☕				☕					☕							☕
London Euston [15] ⊖ 65	d					17 36					17b36		17 53					18 36							18c53
Birmingham New Street [12] 68	d					*19 03*			19 18				19 48					*20 03*			20 18				20 48
Wolverhampton [7] 68 ⛴	d					*19 21*			19 38				20 10					*20 22*			20 38				21 10
Stafford 65, 68	d					19 42		19 50	19 53				20 30					20 43		20 50	20 53				21 30
Stoke-on-Trent 50, 68	d							20 20												21 20					
Longport 50	d																								
Kidsgrove 50	d																								
Crewe [10] 65	d								20 16		20 27										21 16	21 23			
Sandbach	d										20 34														
Holmes Chapel	d										20 38														
Goostrey	d																								
Chelford	d																								
Alderley Edge	d				20 10						20 47					21 10									
Wilmslow	d				20 12	20 18	20 30		20 33		20 50		21 04			21 13		21 18	21 30		21 33	21 43			22 04
Styal	d																								
Manchester Airport ✈	a										20 59														
Handforth	d				20 17											21 17									
Congleton	d																								
Macclesfield	a						21 00	21 10											22 00	22 10					
	d	19 58												21 05											
Prestbury	d	20 02																							
Adlington (Cheshire)	d	20 05																							
Poynton	d	20 09																							
Bramhall	d	20 11																							
Cheadle Hulme	d	20 13			20 23											21 23									
Stockport	a	20 18			20 28	20s30			20 41				21 13	21 18		21 28		21s30			21 41	21 54			22 14
	d	20 19		20 25	20 29				20 43	20 55		21 10	21 14	21 19	21 19	21 29					21 43	21 54	22 01	22 10	22 15
Heaton Chapel	d				20 33							21 14				21 33								22 14	
Levenshulme	d				20 36							21 17				21 36								22 17	
Manchester Piccadilly [10] ⛴	a	20 28		20 35	20 44	20 44			20 57	21 06	21 20	21 24	21 26	21 33	21 33	21 42		21 44			21 57	22 07	22 13	22 27	22 27
	d				20 46							21 25				21 45									
Manchester Oxford Road	a				20 48							21 27				21 47									
Deansgate ⛴	a				20 51							21 30				21 50									

For general notes see front of timetable
For details of catering facilities see Directory of Train Operators

- **A** From Norwich to Liverpool Lime Street (Table 49)
- **B** To Southport (Table 82)
- **C** From Penzance (Table 135)
- **D** From Cleethorpes to Manchester Airport (Table 29)
- **E** From Buxton (Table 86) to Blackpool North (Table 82)
- **G** From Nottingham to Liverpool Lime Street (Table 49)
- **H** From Oxford (Table 51)
- **J** From Hereford (Table 131)
- **K** From Norwich (Table 49)
- **L** From Plymouth (Table 51)
- **N** To Wigan Wallgate (Table 82)
- **Q** From Buxton (Table 86)
- **b** Change at Stafford and Crewe
- **c** By changing at Stafford, passengers may depart 5 minutes later

Table 84

from 30 March

Stoke-on-Trent and Crewe → Manchester Airport, Stockport and Manchester

Network Diagram - see first page of Table 78

		NT	NT	VT	NT	VT	VT	XC		NT	NT	NT	VT	NT	NT	VT	VT	XC	VT	VT	VT	VT	VT		
				1 ◇				1 ◇					1 ◇					1 ◇	1 ◇			1 ◇	1 ◇		
			A					B				C			D			E							
					bus	bus	bus									bus	bus			bus	bus				
				catering									catering						catering			catering	catering		
London Euston 15	⊖ 65 d			19 36							19b36		19 53					19c58	20 10			21 10	21 40		
Birmingham New Street 12	68 d							21 18					21 48					22 18							
Wolverhampton 7	68 ⛴ d							21 38					22 10					22 38							
Stafford	65, 68 d			21 43			21 50	21 53					22 26				22 35	22 53	22 58		23 10	23 50	00 14		
Stoke-on-Trent	50, 68 d				21 35		22 20										23 05				23 40				
Longport	50 d																								
Kidsgrove	50 d				21 54																				
Crewe 10	65 d							22 16			22 25							23 20							
Sandbach	d										22 32														
Holmes Chapel	d										22 36														
Goostrey	d										22 39														
Chelford	d										22 44														
Alderley Edge	d		22 10								22 48														
Wilmslow	d		22 12	22 18		22 30		22 33			22 51		23 00			23 10		23 37	23 42	23 50		00s33			
Styal	d													←											
Manchester Airport	✈ a										22 59			22 59											
Handforth	d		22 17								→														
Congleton	d				22 08																				
Macclesfield	a				22 30	23 00	23 10									23 40	23 55			00 20	00 30	01e15			
	d	22 05								22 37															
Prestbury	d									22 41															
Adlington (Cheshire)	d									22 44															
Poynton	d									22 48															
Bramhall	d									22 50															
Cheadle Hulme	d		22 23							22 53															
Stockport	a	22 18	22 28	22s30				22 41		22 57			23 09					23s41	23s50			00s43	01s04		
	d	22 19	22 29					22 43		22 58		23 01	23 10		23 10										
Heaton Chapel	d		22 33												23 14										
Levenshulme	d		22 36												23 17										
Manchester Piccadilly 10	⛴ a	22 32	22 42	22 42				22 57		23 09		23 12	23 21	23 23	23 27			23 57	00 04			00 55	01 16		
	d		22 45																						
Manchester Oxford Road	a		22 47																						
Deansgate	⛴ a		22 50																						

For general notes see front of timetable
For details of catering facilities see Directory of Train Operators

A To Wigan Wallgate (Table 82)
B From Plymouth (Table 51)
C From Sheffield (Table 78)
D From Buxton (Table 86)
E From Oxford (Table 51)

b Change at Stafford and Crewe
c Change at Crewe
e Monday morning. By bus from Wilmslow (depart 0045)

Manchester, Stockport and Manchester Airport → Crewe and Stoke-on-Trent

Network Diagram - see first page of Table 78

Miles	Miles	Miles			VT	NT	NT	TP	NT	NT	VT	NT	VT	NT	NT	VT	NT	AW	NT	NT	VT	NT		XC	NT
					[1] ◇			[1] ◇			[1] ◇		[1] ◇			[1] ◇		◇			[1] ◇			[1] ◇	
								A		B			C				D	E	G			H		J	
					⊠						⊠		⊠			⊠		⫧			⊠			☕	
0	0	—	Deansgate	d																					
½	½	—	**Manchester Oxford Road**	d																					
1	1	—	**Manchester Piccadilly** [10]	a																					
—	—	—		d	05 20	05 26	05 42	05 48		05 52	06 02	06 13	06 17	06 22	06 32	06 35	06 35	06 38	06 41		06 45	06 51		06 54	07 02
4	4	—	Levenshulme	d			05 48					06 18							06 47						07 07
5½	5½	—	Heaton Chapel	d			05 51					06 21							06 50						07 10
7	7	—	**Stockport**	a			05 54	05 56		06 01		06 25	06 24	06 34			06 46	06 48	06 53			07 01			07 14
—	—	—		d	05u31		05 55				06u11	06 25	06 25	06 34		06u44		06 48			06u53				07 14
9¼	9¼	—	Cheadle Hulme	d			05 59					06 29		06 38											07 20
9¾	—	—	Bramhall	d										06 41											
12¼	—	—	Poynton	d										06 44											
14¼	—	—	Adlington (Cheshire)	d										06 48											
16¼	—	—	Prestbury	d										06 51											
19	—	—	**Macclesfield**	a							06 22		06 37	06 55							07 08				
—	—	—		d					06 04		06 24		06 38	06 57							07 09				
27	—	—	Congleton	d					06 11					07 04										07 21	
—	11½	—	Handforth	d			06 03					06 33								←					07 24
—	—	0	**Manchester Airport**	d		05 53									06 57					06 57					
—	—	2¼	Styal	d											→										
—	13	4	**Wilmslow**	d	05 39	06 00	06 05					06 36				06 51		06 56		07 04					07 27
—	14¾	—	Alderley Edge	d		06a05	06 08					06 39								07 07					07 30
—	17¾	—	Chelford	d			06 12					06 43													07 34
—	21½	—	Goostrey	d			06 17					06 47													07 39
—	23½	—	Holmes Chapel	d			06 20					06 50								07 15					07 42
—	27¼	—	Sandbach	d			06 24					06 55								07 19					07 46
—	32	—	**Crewe** [10]	65 a	05 56		06 40					07 07				07 10		07 16		07 31					07 57
32½	—	—	Kidsgrove	50 a					06 17					07 10											
35¾	—	—	Longport	50 a										07 14											
38¾	—	—	**Stoke-on-Trent**	50, 68 a					06 27		06 39		06 54	07 19							07 24			07 32	
—	—	—	Stafford	68 a	06 16		*07 24*						07 13			*07 43*				*08 20*				07 53	
—	—	—	Wolverhampton [7]	68 a	*06 41*		*07 48*						07 32			*08 05*				*08 37*				08 12	*08 48*
—	—	—	Birmingham New Street [12]	68 a	*06 58*		*08 11*				*07b36*		07 55			*08 30*				*08 58*				08 30	*09 11*
—	—	—	London Euston [15]	⊖ 65 a	08 04		*08 58*				08 27	*09c14*	09e44			09 01				*09 36*	09 07				

		VT	VT	TP	NT	XC	NT	AW	NT	NT	NT	NT	NT	EM	VT	NT	XC	NT	NT		NT	VT	TP	NT	XC
		[1] ◇	[1] ◇	[1] ◇		[R] [1]		◇						◇	[1] ◇		[1] ◇					[1] ◇	[1] ◇		[1] ◇
				A	G	K	G	L				H	N	Q		G	U	G					A	V	X
		⊠	⊠	⫧		☕		⫧						⫧	⊠		☕					⊠	⫧		☕
Deansgate	d												07 29											08 12	
Manchester Oxford Road	d												07 33	07 39										08 15	
Manchester Piccadilly [10]	a												07 36	07 41										08 19	
	d	07 05	07 15	07 18	07 22	07 24		07 28	07 29	07 33	07 34	07 37	07 39	07 43	07 45	07 51	07 54		07 58		08 03	08 15	08 17	08 20	08 24
Levenshulme	d				07 28		←		07 34							07 56		←			08 09				
Heaton Chapel	d				07 31		07 31		07 37							07 59		07 59			08 12				
Stockport	a			07 26	→	07 33	07 34	07 37	07 41	07 43		07 47	07 46	07 52		→	08 01	08 03	08 07		08 15		08 24	08 30	08 32
	d	07u14	07u23			07 33		07 37	07 41	07 43					07u55		08 03		08 08		08 16	08u24			08 33
Cheadle Hulme	d								07 45	07 47									08 12		08 20				
Bramhall	d								07 48												08 23				
Poynton	d								07 51												08 26				
Adlington (Cheshire)	d								07 55												08 29				
Prestbury	d								07 58												08 32				
Macclesfield	a		07 36			07 46			08 03						08 07		08 15				08 37				08 46
	d		07 37			07 47									08 07		08 16								08 47
Congleton	d					07 55											08 24								
Handforth	d									07 51									08 16						
Manchester Airport	d										08 00														
Styal	d										08 04														
Wilmslow	d							07 46		07 54	08 07								08 18			08 33			
Alderley Edge	d									08a00	08 10								08 21						
Chelford	d										08 14														
Goostrey	d										08 19														
Holmes Chapel	d										08 22								08 29						
Sandbach	d										08 26								08 34						
Crewe [10]	65 a							08 06			08 37								08 45			08 51			
Kidsgrove	50 a																								
Longport	50 a																								
Stoke-on-Trent	50, 68 a		07 52			08 07									08 22		08 38								09 03
Stafford	68 a					08 25		*08 45*									08 55		*09 21*			09 12			09 25
Wolverhampton [7]	68 a					08 41		*09 06*									09 12					*09 36*			09 41
Birmingham New Street [12]	68 a					08 58		*09 30*									09 30		*09 58*						09 58
London Euston [15]	⊖ 65 a	09 11	09 45					*10 27*			*10 46*				10 09							10 50			

For general notes see front of timetable
For details of catering facilities see Directory of Train Operators

- **A** From Manchester Airport to Cleethorpes (Table 29)
- **B** To Sheffield (Table 78)
- **C** ☕ to Wolverhampton, ⊠ from Wolverhampton
- **D** To Chester (Table 88)
- **E** To Milford Haven (Table 128)
- **G** To Hazel Grove (Table 86)
- **H** To Buxton (Table 86)
- **J** To Reading (Table 51)
- **K** To Bournemouth (Table 51)
- **L** To Carmarthen (Table 128)
- **N** From Blackpool North (Table 82) to Chester (Table 88)
- **Q** From Liverpool Lime Street to Norwich (Table 49)
- **U** To Brighton (Table 51)
- **V** From St Annes-on-the-Sea (Table 97) to Greenbank (Table 88)
- **X** To Plymouth (Table 51)
- **b** Change at Tamworth
- **c** Change at Crewe and Stafford
- **e** By changing at Stafford, passengers may arrive at 0858

Manchester, Stockport and Manchester Airport → Crewe and Stoke-on-Trent

Network Diagram - see first page of Table 78

Station		NT	NT	AW	NT	EM	VT	NT	XC	NT	NT	NT	NT	VT	TP	XC		NT	NT	NT	AW	NT	EM	NT	VT
		A		◇ B		◇ C	1 ◇		1 ◇ D		A		E	1 ◇	1 ◇ G	R 1 H		J			◇ K	L	◇ C		1 ◇
Deansgate	d																		09 24			09 29			
Manchester Oxford Road	d					08 38													09 27			09 33	09 38		
Manchester Piccadilly 10	a					08 42													09 29			09 35	09 40		
	d	08 29	08 32	08 34	08 34	08 42	08 45	08 51	08 54		08 59	09 03	09 06	09 15	09 20	09 24		09 24	09 30	09 33	09 34	09 37	09 42		09 45
Levenshulme	d	08 34						08 56		←			09 12						09 36						
Heaton Chapel	d	08 37						08 59		08 59			09 15						09 39						
Stockport	a	08 41	08 41	08 44		08 53		→	09 01	09 03	09 08	09 13	09 19		09 28	09 32		09 34	09 42		09 42	09 46	09 51		
	d		08 41	08 44			08u55		09 03	09 05		09 13		09u23		09 33			09 43		09 42				09u54
Cheadle Hulme	d		08 45							09 11		09 17							09 47						
Bramhall	d		08 48																09 50						
Poynton	d		08 51																09 53						
Adlington (Cheshire)	d		08 55																09 56						
Prestbury	d		08 58																09 59						
Macclesfield	a		09 03				09 08		09 15							09 46			10 04						10 07
	d						09 08		09 16							09 47									10 07
Congleton	d								09 24																
Handforth	d									09 15		09 21												←	
Manchester Airport	d				09 00															10 00 →				10 00	
Styal	d																								
Wilmslow	d			08 52	09 07					09 18		09 24									09 54			10 06	
Alderley Edge	d				09 10					09a23		09 27												10 09	
Chelford	d											09 31													
Goostrey	d											09 35													
Holmes Chapel	d				09 18							09 38												10 17	
Sandbach	d				09 22							09 43												10 22	
Crewe 10	65 a			09 16	09 33							09 54									10 15			10 33	
Kidsgrove	50 a																								
Longport	50 a																								
Stoke-on-Trent	50, 68 a						09 24		09 38					09 48		10 03									10 23
Stafford	68 a				*10 10*											10 25					*10 45*			*11 10*	
Wolverhampton 7	68 a				*10 36*				10 12			*10 47*				10 41					*11 07*			*11b41*	
Birmingham New Street 12	68 a				*10 58*				10 30			*11 11*				10 58					*11 30*			*11b58*	
London Euston 15	⊖ 65 a			*11 27*	*11 48*		11 09							11 28							*12 26*			*12 48*	12 07

Station		NT	XC	NT	NT	VT	TP	XC	NT	NT	NT	AW	NT		EM	NT	VT	NT	XC	NT	NT	NT	VT	TP	XC
			1 ◇ D		E	1 ◇	1 ◇ G	1 ◇ N	J			◇ B	L		◇ C		1 ◇		1 ◇ D			E	1 ◇	1 ◇ G	R 1 H
Deansgate	d									10 24			10 29												
Manchester Oxford Road	d									10 27			10 33		10 38										
Manchester Piccadilly 10	a									10 29			10 35		10 41										
	d	09 51	09 54	10 03	10 06	10 15	10 20	10 24	10 24	10 30	10 33	10 34	10 37		10 42		10 45	10 51	10 54		11 03	11 06	11 15	11 20	11 24
Levenshulme	d	09 56			10 12					10 36								10 56		←		11 12			
Heaton Chapel	d	09 59			10 15					10 39								10 59		10 59		11 15			
Stockport	a	10 03	10 03	10 12	10 18		10 28	10 32	10 34	10 42		10 42	10 46		10 51			→	11 02	11 03	11 12	11 18		11 27	11 32
	d	10 05	10 03	10 13		10u24		10 33		10 43		10 42					10u54		11 03	11 05	11 13		11u23		11 33
Cheadle Hulme	d	10 11		10 17						10 47										11 11	11 17				
Bramhall	d									10 50															
Poynton	d									10 53															
Adlington (Cheshire)	d									10 56															
Prestbury	d									10 59															
Macclesfield	a		10 15					10 46		11 04							11 07		11 15						11 46
	d		10 16					10 47									11 07		11 16						11 47
Congleton	d																		11 24						
Handforth	d	10 15		10 21												←				11 15	11 21				
Manchester Airport	d										11 00 →					11 00									
Styal	d																								
Wilmslow	d	10 18		10 24								10 54				11 06				11 18	11 24				
Alderley Edge	d	10a23		10 27												11 09				11a23	11 27				
Chelford	d			10 31																	11 31				
Goostrey	d			10 36																	11 36				
Holmes Chapel	d			10 39												11 17					11 39				
Sandbach	d			10 43												11 22					11 43				
Crewe 10	65 a			10 54								11 16				11 33					11 54				
Kidsgrove	50 a																								
Longport	50 a																								
Stoke-on-Trent	50, 68 a		10 38			10 48		11 03									11 23		11 38				11 48		12 03
Stafford	68 a			*11 45*				11 25								*12 10*					*12 46*				12 25
Wolverhampton 7	68 a		11 12	*12 06*				11 41								*12 36*			12 12		*12 48*				12 41
Birmingham New Street 12	68 a		11 30	*12 11*				11 58								*12 58*			12 30		*13 11*				12 58
London Euston 15	⊖ 65 a					12 26						*13 27*				*13 40*	13 09						13 28		

For general notes see front of timetable
For details of catering facilities see Directory of Train Operators

- **A** To Buxton (Table 86)
- **B** To Milford Haven (Table 128)
- **C** From Liverpool Lime Street to Norwich (Table 49)
- **D** To Reading (Table 51)
- **E** To Hazel Grove (Table 86)
- **G** From Manchester Airport to Cleethorpes (Table 29)
- **H** To Bournemouth (Table 51)
- **J** To Chester (Table 88)
- **K** To Carmarthen (Table 128)
- **L** From Blackpool North (Table 82) to Buxton (Table 86)
- **N** To Plymouth (Table 51)
- **b** Change at Crewe and Stafford

Manchester, Stockport and Manchester Airport → Crewe and Stoke-on-Trent

Network Diagram - see first page of Table 78

		NT	NT	NT	AW	NT	EM	NT	VT	NT		XC	NT	NT	NT	VT	TP	XC	NT	NT	NT	AW	NT	EM	NT
					◇		◇		1◇			1◇				1◇	1◇	R 1				R		◇	
		A			B	C	D					E			G		H	J	A			K	C	D	
					🛒		🛒		☕			☕				☕	🛒	☕				🛒		🛒	
Deansgate 🚊	d		11 24			11 29														12 24			12 29		
Manchester Oxford Road	d		11 27			11 33	11 38													12 27			12 33	12 38	
Manchester Piccadilly 10 🚊	a		11 29			11 35	11 40													12 29			12 35	12 40	
	d	11 24	11 30	11 33	11 34	11 37	11 42		11 45	11 51		11 54		12 03	12 06	12 15	12 20	12 24	12 24	12 30	12 33	12 34	12 37	12 42	
Levenshulme	d		11 36							11 56			←		12 12					12 36					
Heaton Chapel	d		11 39							11 59			11 59		12 15					12 39					
Stockport	a	11 34	11 42		11 42	11 46	11 51			→		12 02	12 03	12 12	12 18		12 28	12 32	12 34	12 42		12 42	12 46	12 51	
	d		11 43		11 42				11u54			12 03	12 05	12 13		12u24		12 33		12 43		12 42			
Cheadle Hulme	d		11 47										12 11	12 17						12 47					
Bramhall	d		11 50																	12 50					
Poynton	d		11 53																	12 53					
Adlington (Cheshire)	d		11 56																	12 56					
Prestbury	d		11 59																	12 59					
Macclesfield	a		12 04						12 07			12 15						12 46		13 04					
	d								12 07			12 16						12 47							
Congleton	d																								
Handforth	d							←					12 15	12 21											←
Manchester Airport ✈	d			12 00 →				12 00													13 00 →				13 00
Styal	d																								
Wilmslow	d				11 54			12 06					12 18	12 24								12 54			13 06
Alderley Edge	d							12 09					12a23	12 27											13 09
Chelford	d													12 31											
Goostrey	d													12 36											
Holmes Chapel	d							12 17						12 39											13 17
Sandbach	d							12 22						12 43											13 22
Crewe 10	65 a				12 15			12 33						12 54								13 15			13 33
Kidsgrove	50 a																								
Longport	50 a																								
Stoke-on-Trent	50, 68 a								12 23			12 38				12 48		13 03							
Stafford	68 a							*13 10*										13 25				*13 45*			*14 10*
Wolverhampton 7	68 🚊 a							*13 36*				13 12						13 41				*14 06*			*14 36*
Birmingham New Street 12	68 a							*13 58*				13 30						13 58				*14 30*			*14 58*
London Euston 15	⊖ 65 a							*14 40*	14 04							14 26						*15 26*			*15 48*

		VT	NT	XC	NT	NT	NT		VT	TP	XC	NT	NT	NT	AW	NT	EM	NT	VT	NT	XC	NT	NT	VT	NT
		1◇		1◇					1◇	1◇	1◇				R		◇		1◇		1◇			1◇	
				L			G			H	N	A			B	C	D				E				G
		☕		☕					☕	🛒	☕				🛒		🛒		☕		☕			☕	
Deansgate 🚊	d												13 24			13 29									
Manchester Oxford Road	d												13 27			13 33	13 38								
Manchester Piccadilly 10 🚊	a												13 29			13 35	13 40								
	d	12 45	12 51	12 54		13 03	13 06		13 15	13 20	13 24	13 24	13 30	13 33	13 34	13 37	13 42		13 45	13 51	13 54		14 03	14 05	14 06
Levenshulme	d		12 56		←		13 12						13 36							13 56		←			14 12
Heaton Chapel	d		12 59		12 59		13 15						13 39							13 59		13 59			14 15
Stockport	a		→	13 01	13 03	13 12	13 18			13 28	13 32	13 34	13 42		13 42	13 46	13 51			→	14 02	14 03	14 12	14 15	14 18
	d	12u54		13 03	13 05	13 13			13u24		13 33		13 43		13 42				13u54		14 03	14 05	14 13	14 15	
Cheadle Hulme	d				13 11	13 17							13 47									14 11	14 20		
Bramhall	d												13 50												
Poynton	d												13 53												
Adlington (Cheshire)	d												13 56												
Prestbury	d												13 59												
Macclesfield	a	13 07		13 15							13 46		14 04						14 07		14 15				
	d	13 07		13 16							13 47								14 07		14 16				
Congleton	d			13 24																					
Handforth	d				13 15	13 21												←				14 15	14 24		
Manchester Airport ✈	d													14 00 →				14 00					→		
Styal	d																								
Wilmslow	d				13 18	13 24									13 54			14 06				14 18		14 25	
Alderley Edge	d				13a23	13 27												14 09				14a23			
Chelford	d					13 31																			
Goostrey	d					13 36																			
Holmes Chapel	d					13 39												14 17							
Sandbach	d					13 43												14 22							
Crewe 10	65 a					13 54									14 15			14 33						14 42	
Kidsgrove	50 a																								
Longport	50 a																								
Stoke-on-Trent	50, 68 a	13 23		13 38					13 48		14 03								14 23		14 38				
Stafford	68 a										14 25				*14 45*									*15 10*	
Wolverhampton 7	68 🚊 a			14 12		*14 47*					14 41				*15 06*						15 12			*15 36*	
Birmingham New Street 12	68 a			14 30		*15 11*					14 58				*15 30*						15 30			*15b54*	
London Euston 15	⊖ 65 a	15 08							15 28						*16 27*			*16 48*	16 07					17c22	

For general notes see front of timetable
For details of catering facilities see Directory of Train Operators

A To Chester (Table 88)
B To Carmarthen (Table 128)
C From Blackpool North (Table 82) to Buxton (Table 86)
D From Liverpool Lime Street to Norwich (Table 49)
E To Reading (Table 51)
G To Hazel Grove (Table 86)
H From Manchester Airport to Cleethorpes (Table 29)
J To Penzance (Table 135)
K To Milford Haven (Table 128)
L To Guildford (Table 51)
N To Bournemouth (Table 51)
b Change at Tamworth
c By changing at Crewe, passengers may arrive at 1648

Manchester, Stockport and Manchester Airport → Crewe and Stoke-on-Trent

Network Diagram - see first page of Table 78

	NT	VT	TP		XC	NT	NT	NT	AW	NT	EM	NT	VT	NT	XC	NT	NT	NT	VT	TP	XC	NT		NT
					R				R						R						R			
		1 ◇	1 ◇		1						◇		1 ◇		1				1 ◇	1 ◇	1			
			A		B	C			D	E	G				H			J		A	K	C		
Deansgate d							14 24			14 29														15 24
Manchester Oxford Road d							14 27			14 33	14 38													15 27
Manchester Piccadilly 10 a							14 29			14 35	14 40													15 29
d		14 15	14 20		14 24	14 24	14 30	14 33	14 34	14 37	14 42		14 45	14 51	14 54		15 03	15 06	15 15	15 20	15 24	15 24		15 30
Levenshulme d							14 36							14 56		←		15 11						15 36
Heaton Chapel d							14 39							14 59		14 59		15 14						15 39
Stockport a			14 28		14 32	14 34	14 42		14 42	14 46	14 51			→	15 01	15 03	15 12	15 18		15 28	15 32	15 34		15 42
d		14u24			14 33		14 43		14 42				14u54		15 03	15 05	15 13		15u24		15 33			15 43
Cheadle Hulme d							14 47									15 11	15 17							15 47
Bramhall d							14 50																	15 50
Poynton d							14 53																	15 53
Adlington (Cheshire) d							14 56																	15 56
Prestbury d							14 59																	15 59
Macclesfield a					14 46		15 04						15 07		15 15						15 46			16 04
d					14 47								15 07		15 16						15 47			
Congleton d	←														15 24									
Handforth d	14 24											←				15 15	15 21							
Manchester Airport d								15 00 →				15 00												
Styal d																								
Wilmslow d	14 26								14 54			15 06				15 18	15 24							
Alderley Edge d	14 29											15 09				15a23	15 27							
Chelford d	14 33																15 31							
Goostrey d	14 38																15 36							
Holmes Chapel d	14 41											15 17					15 39							
Sandbach d	14 45											15 22					15 43							
Crewe 10 65 a	14 57								15 16			15 33					15 54							
Kidsgrove 50 a																								
Longport 50 a																								
Stoke-on-Trent 50, 68 a		14 48			15 03								15 23		15 38				15 48		16 03			
Stafford 68 a	*15 45*				15 25							*16 10*									16 25			
Wolverhampton 7 68 a	*15 48*				15 41							*16 36*			16 12		*16 48*				16 41			
Birmingham New Street 12 68 a	*16 11*				15 58							*16 58*			16 30		*17 11*				16 58			
London Euston 15 ⊖ 65 a		16 28							*17 40*			*17 47*	17 08						17 27					

	NT	AW	NT	NT	NT	EM	NT	VT	NT	XC	NT	NT	NT	VT	TP	XC	NT	NT		NT	AW	NT	NT	EM
		R								R											R			
						◇		1 ◇		1				1 ◇	1 ◇	1 ◇								◇
		L	N		J	Q	J			U			V		A	X	C				D	E		Q
Deansgate d			15 29															16 24				16 29		
Manchester Oxford Road d			15 33			15 38												16 27				16 33		16 38
Manchester Piccadilly 10 a			15 35			15 40												16 29				16 35		16 40
d	15 33	15 34	15 37		15 40	15 42		15 45	15 51	15 54		16 03	16 06	16 15	16 20	16 24	16 24	16 30		16 33	16 34	16 37	16 37	16 42
Levenshulme d					15 46		←		15 56		←		16 12					16 36					16 42	
Heaton Chapel d					15 49		15 49		15 59		15 59		16 15					16 39					16 45	
Stockport a		15 42	15 46		→	15 50	15 52		→	16 02	16 03	16 12	16 18		16 28	16 32	16 34	16 42			16 42	16 45	16 49	16 51
d		15 42						15u54		16 03	16 05	16 13		16u24		16 33		16 43			16 42		16 51	
Cheadle Hulme d											16 11	16 17						16 47					16 55	
Bramhall d																		16 50						
Poynton d																		16 53						
Adlington (Cheshire) d																		16 56						
Prestbury d																		16 59						
Macclesfield a								16 07		16 15						16 46		17 04						
d								16 07		16 16						16 47								
Congleton d																								
Handforth d				←							16 15	16 21											16 59	
Manchester Airport d	16 00 →			16 00																17 00 →				
Styal d																								
Wilmslow d		15 54		16 06							16 18	16 24									16 54		17 02	
Alderley Edge d				16 09							16a23	16 27											17a08	
Chelford d				16 13								16 31												
Goostrey d				16 18								16 36												
Holmes Chapel d				16 21								16 39												
Sandbach d				16 25								16 43												
Crewe 10 65 a		16 15		16 36								16 54									17 16			
Kidsgrove 50 a																								
Longport 50 a																								
Stoke-on-Trent 50, 68 a								16 23		16 38				16 48		17 03								
Stafford 68 a		*16 45*		*17 10*								*17 45*				17 25								
Wolverhampton 7 68 a		*17 05*		*17b41*						17 12		*17 48*				17 41								
Birmingham New Street 12 68 a		*17 30*		*17b58*						17 30		*18 11*				17 58								
London Euston 15 ⊖ 65 a		*18 21*		*18 42*				18 07						18 28							*19 25*			

For general notes see front of timetable
For details of catering facilities see Directory of Train Operators

A From Manchester Airport to Cleethorpes (Table 29)
B To Penzance (Table 135)
C To Chester (Table 88)
D To Milford Haven (Table 128)
E From Blackpool North (Table 82) to Buxton (Table 86)
G From Liverpool Lime Street to Nottingham (Table 49)
H To Brighton (Table 51)
J To Buxton (Table 86)
K To Bournemouth (Table 51)
L To Carmarthen (Table 128)
N From Blackpool North (Table 82) to Hazel Grove (Table 86)
Q From Liverpool Lime Street to Norwich (Table 49)
U To Reading (Table 51)
V To Hazel Grove (Table 86)
X To Plymouth (Table 51)
b Change at Crewe and Stafford

Manchester, Stockport and Manchester Airport → Crewe and Stoke-on-Trent

Network Diagram - see first page of Table 78

	NT	NT	VT	NT	NT	XC	NT	NT	NT	VT	NT	TP	XC	NT	NT		NT	NT	AW	NT	NT	NT	EM	NT
			[1] ◇			[R] [1]				[1] ◇		[1] ◇	[R] [1]						[R]				◇	
		A		A	B	C			D			E	G	B	A				H		J		K	
			buffet			buffet				buffet		trolley	buffet						trolley				trolley	
Deansgate d									16 59		17 10						17 24				17 28			
Manchester Oxford Road d									17 03		17 13						17 27				17 32		17 38	
Manchester Piccadilly [10] a									17 06		17 15						17 29				17 35		17 40	
d		16 44	16 45		16 51	16 54	16 58	17 04	17 07	17 15	17 17	17 20	17 24	17 24	17 27		17 31	17 33	17 34		17 37	17 39	17 42	
Levenshulme d		16 51		←				17 09	17 13								17 37			←		17 44		←
Heaton Chapel d		16 54		16 54				17 12	17 16								17 40			17 40		17 47		17 47
Stockport a		→		16 58	17 00	17 02	17 07	17 16	17 19		17 28	17 28	17 32	17 34	17 37		→		17 42	17 43	17 47	→	17 50	17 51
d			16u54			17 03	17 07	17 16		17u23	17 30		17 33						17 42	17 44				17 51
Cheadle Hulme d							17 12	17 19			17 35									17 49				17 55
Bramhall d							17 15													17 52				
Poynton d							17 18													17 55				
Adlington (Cheshire) d							17 22																	
Prestbury d							17 25													18 00				
Macclesfield a			17 08			17 15	17 30						17 46							18 05				
d			17 08			17 16							17 47											
Congleton d						17 24																		
Handforth d	←							17 23																18 00
Manchester Airport ✈ d	17 00																	18 00 →						
Styal d																								
Wilmslow d	17 06							17 26			17 41								17 51					18 03
Alderley Edge d	17 09							17 29			17 45													18a09
Chelford d								17 33																
Goostrey d								17 37																
Holmes Chapel d	17 17							17 40																
Sandbach d	17 22							17 45			17 56													
Crewe [10] 65 a	17 33							17 56			18 07								18 15					
Kidsgrove 50 a																								
Longport 50 a																								
Stoke-on-Trent 50, 68 a			17 24			17 38				17 49			18 03											
Stafford 68 a	*18 11*												18 25						*18 45*					
Wolverhampton [7] 68 a	*18 36*					18 12		*18 48*					18 41						*19 05*					
Birmingham New Street [12] 68 a	*18 58*					18 30		*19 11*					18 58						*19 30*					
London Euston [15] ⊖ 65 a	*19 50*		19 11							19 28									*20 26*					

	VT	NT	NT	NT	XC	NT	NT	NT	VT	TP	XC	NT		NT	AW	NT	NT	NT	EM	VT	NT	XC	NT	NT
	[1] ◇				[1] ◇				[1] ◇	[1] ◇	[1] ◇				◇				◇	[1] ◇		[1] ◇		
		A		B	C			L		E	N	B			Q			J	U					
	buffet				buffet				buffet	trolley	buffet				trolley				trolley	buffet		buffet		
Deansgate d																								
Manchester Oxford Road d																		18 35	18 40					
Manchester Piccadilly [10] a																		18 38	18 43					
d	17 45	17 50		17 53	17 54	17 57	18 03	18 06	18 15	18 18	18 24	18 24		18 30	18 34		18 36	18 39	18 44	18 45	18 51	18 54		19 03
Levenshulme d						18 02		18 12						18 36		←					18 56		←	19 08
Heaton Chapel d						18 05		18 15						18 39		18 39					18 59		18 59	19 11
Stockport a		17 59		18 04	18 02	18 09	18 12	18 18		18 26	18 32	18 34		→	18 42	18 43		18 48	18 54		→	19 02	19 03	19 15
d	17u55				18 03	18 09	18 13		18u24		18 33				18 42	18 43				18u54		19 03	19 03	19 15
Cheadle Hulme d						18 13	18 17									18 47							19 11	19 19
Bramhall d						18 16										18 50								
Poynton d						18 19										18 53								
Adlington (Cheshire) d						18 23										18 56								
Prestbury d						18 26										18 59								
Macclesfield a	18 08				18 15	18 30					18 46					19 04				19 05		19 15		
d	18 08				18 16	18 39					18 47									19 07		19 16		
Congleton d					18 24	18 46																19 24		
Handforth d			←				18 21																19 15	19 23
Manchester Airport ✈ d			18 00														19 01							
Styal d			18 07																					
Wilmslow d			18 11				18 24								18 54		19 07						19 18	19 26
Alderley Edge d			18 14				18 27										19a15						19a24	19 29
Chelford d			18 18				18 31																	19 33
Goostrey d			18 22				18 36																	19 38
Holmes Chapel d			18 25				18 39																	19 41
Sandbach d			18 30				18 43																	19 45
Crewe [10] 65 a			18 41				18 54								19 15									19 56
Kidsgrove 50 a						18 52																		
Longport 50 a						18 57																		
Stoke-on-Trent 50, 68 a	18 24				18 38	19 02			18 50		19 03									19 24		19 38		
Stafford 68 a			*19 10*								19 25				*19 47*							19 57		*20 44*
Wolverhampton [7] 68 a			*19b41*		19 12		*19 48*				19 41				*20 06*							20 12		*20 48*
Birmingham New Street [12] 68 a			*19b58*		19 30		*20 11*				19 58				*20 30*							20 35		*21 11*
London Euston [15] ⊖ 65 a	20 07		*20 48*						20 33						*21 51*					21 07				

For general notes see front of timetable
For details of catering facilities see Directory of Train Operators

- **A** To Hazel Grove (Table 86)
- **B** To Chester (Table 88)
- **C** To Gatwick Airport (Table 51)
- **D** From Southport (Table 82) to Buxton (Table 86)
- **E** From Manchester Airport to Cleethorpes (Table 29)
- **G** To Bournemouth (Table 51)
- **H** To Milford Haven (Table 128)
- **J** From Blackpool North (Table 82) to Buxton (Table 86)
- **K** From Liverpool Lime Street to Nottingham (Table 49)
- **L** To Buxton (Table 86)
- **N** To Plymouth (Table 51)
- **Q** To Carmarthen (Table 128)
- **U** From Liverpool Lime Street to Cambridge (Table 49)
- **b** Change at Crewe and Stafford

Manchester, Stockport and Manchester Airport → Crewe and Stoke-on-Trent

Network Diagram - see first page of Table 78

	VT	TP	XC	NT	NT	NT	AW	NT	EM		NT	XC	NT	VT	TP	XC	NT	NT	AW	NT	EM	NT	VT	NT
	1 ◇	1 ◇	1 ◇				◇		◇			1 ◇		1 ◇	1 ◇	1 ◇			◇		◇		1 ◇	
		A	B	C			D	E	G						A		C		D	E	G			
Deansgate d								19 29												20 29				
Manchester Oxford Road d								19 33	19 38											20 32	20 38			
Manchester Piccadilly 10 a								19 36	19 42											20 34	20 40			
d	19 15	19 18	19 24	19 24	19 30	19 30	19 34	19 37	19 42			19 54	20 03	20 15	20 18	20 24	20 24	20 27	20 34	20 36	20 42	20 44	20 45	
Levenshulme d						19 36							20 08					20 32						
Heaton Chapel d						19 39							20 11					20 35						
Stockport a		19 25	19 32	19 34		19 42	19 42	19 47	19 53			20 01	20 15		20 26	20 32	20 34	20 39	20 46	20 44	20 51			
d	19u24		19 33			19 43	19 43					20 03	20 15	20u24		20 33		20 40	20 46				20u54	
Cheadle Hulme d						19 47							20 19					20 44						
Bramhall d						19 50												20 47						
Poynton d						19 53												20 50						
Adlington (Cheshire) d						19 56												20 53						
Prestbury d						19 59												20 56						
Macclesfield a	19 36		19 46			20 04						20 15		20 36		20 46		21 01						
d	19 37		19 47									20 16		20 37		20 47								
Congleton d												20 24												
Handforth d											←		20 23											←
Manchester Airport d					19 56 →						19 56											21 10 →		21 10
Styal d																								
Wilmslow d							19 54				20a06		20 26						20 54				21 05	21a19
Alderley Edge d													20 29											
Chelford d													20 33											
Goostrey d													20 37											
Holmes Chapel d													20 40											
Sandbach d													20 45											
Crewe 10 65 a							20 16						20 56						21 14				21 28	
Kidsgrove 50 a																								
Longport 50 a																								
Stoke-on-Trent 50, 68 a	19 52		20 03									20 38		20 52		21 03							21 51	
Stafford 68 a			20 25				20 59					20 56				21 25			21 45					
Wolverhampton 7 68 a			20 41				21b41					21 12				21 41			22 08					
Birmingham New Street 12 68 a			20 58				22b04					21 35				22 04			22 30				22c54	
London Euston 15 ⊖ 65 a	21 36						23 05							22 52									00 09	

	NT	TP	NT	NT	AW	NT		NT	XC	NT	NT	TP	NT	EM	AW	NT	NT	NT	NT	NT	NT	NT		
		1 ◇			◇				1 ◇			1 ◇		◇										
		A	C		D	H						J	C	G	K			L		C				
Deansgate d						21 40				21 59						22 31		22 50	23 00			23 31		
Manchester Oxford Road d						21 43				22 01				22 23		22 33		22 53	23 02		23 07	23 33		
Manchester Piccadilly 10 a						21 46				22 04				22 25		22 36		22 56	23 05		23 09	23 36		
d	21 03	21 18	21 24	21 28	21 34	21 49		21 52	21 54	22 05		22 18	22 24	22 27	22 34	22 36	22 46	22 58	23 06	23 09	23 11	23 37		
Levenshulme d	21 08			21 33						22 10						22 42			23 11			23 42		
Heaton Chapel d	21 11			21 36						22 13						22 45			23 14			23 45		
Stockport a	21 14	21 26	21 34	21 40	21 46	21 59			22 01	22 16		22 26	22 33	22 37	22 42	22 49		23 06	23 18	23 19	23 21	23 50		
d	21 15			21 40	21 46				22 03	22 16					22 42	22 49			23 18		23 21	23 50		
Cheadle Hulme d	21 19			21 44						22 20						22 53			23 22		23 25	23 54		
Bramhall d				21 47												22 56					23 28			
Poynton d				21 50												22 59					23 31			
Adlington (Cheshire) d				21 54												23 02					23 35			
Prestbury d				21 57												23 05					23 38			
Macclesfield a				22 02					22 15							23 10					23 44			
d									22 16															
Congleton d									22 24															
Handforth d	21 23									22 24	←								23 26			23 58		
Manchester Airport d								22 18 →			22 18						23 12							
Styal d																								
Wilmslow d	21 26				21 54					22 27	22a29				22 50		23a22		23 29			00 01		
Alderley Edge d	21 29									22 30									23a34			00 04		
Chelford d	21 33									22 34												00 08		
Goostrey d	21 37									22 38												00 12		
Holmes Chapel d	21 40									22 41												00 15		
Sandbach d	21 45									22 46												00 20		
Crewe 10 65 a	21 56				22 16					22 58					23 11							00 31		
Kidsgrove 50 a																								
Longport 50 a																								
Stoke-on-Trent 50, 68 a									22 38															
Stafford 68 a	22 35								22 56															
Wolverhampton 7 68 a	22 48								23 12															
Birmingham New Street 12 68 a	23 11								23 47															
London Euston 15 ⊖ 65 a																								

For general notes see front of timetable
For details of catering facilities see Directory of Train Operators

A From Manchester Airport to Cleethorpes (Table 29)
B To Southampton Central (Table 51)
C To Chester (Table 88)
D To Cardiff Central (Table 131)
E From Blackpool North (Table 82) to Buxton (Table 86)
G From Liverpool Lime Street to Nottingham (Table 49)
H From Southport (Table 82) to Buxton (Table 86)
J From Manchester Airport to Sheffield (Table 78)
K To Shrewsbury (Table 131)
L From Clitheroe (Table 94) to Buxton (Table 86)
b Change at Crewe and Stafford
c Change at Tamworth

Manchester, Stockport and Manchester Airport → Crewe and Stoke-on-Trent

Network Diagram - see first page of Table 78

		VT	NT	TP	NT	NT	VT	NT	VT	NT	NT	AW	NT	VT	NT	VT	NT	NT	TP	NT	XC	NT	AW	NT	NT
		1 ◇		1 ◇			1 ◇		1 ◇			◇		1 ◇		1 ◇			1 ◇		1 ◇		◇		
				A		B					C	D			E		G		A	G	H	G	J		
Deansgate	d																								
Manchester Oxford Road	d																								
Manchester Piccadilly 10	a																								
	d	05 05	05 26	05 48		05 52	06 03	06 13	06 21	06 32	06 35	06 38		06 40	06 50	06 55	07 00	07 04	07 18	07 22	07 24		07 28	07 28	07 33
Levenshulme	d							06 18									07 05	07 09		07 28		←		07 33	
Heaton Chapel	d							06 21									07 08	07 12		07 31		07 31		07 36	
Stockport	a			05 56		06 01		06 25	06 28		06 45	06 47			07 00	07 03	07 12	07 16	07 26	→	07 32	07 34	07 37	07 40	07 43
	d	05u15					06u12	06 25	06 30			06 48		06u49		07 04		07 16			07 33		07 37	07 40	07 43
Cheadle Hulme	d							06 29										07 20						07 44	07 47
Bramhall	d																							07 47	
Poynton	d																							07 50	
Adlington (Cheshire)	d																							07 54	
Prestbury	d																							07 57	
Macclesfield	a						06 24		06 41					07 04		07 16					07 45			08 02	
	d				06 02		06 25		06 43					07 05		07 17					07 46				
Congleton	d				06 09																				
Handforth	d							06 33					←					07 24							07 51
Manchester Airport	d		05 53							06 57 →			06 57												
Styal	d																								
Wilmslow	d	05 23	06 01					06 36				06 55	07 04					07 27					07 46		07 54
Alderley Edge	d		06a06					06 39					07 07					07 30							08a00
Chelford	d							06 43										07 34							
Goostrey	d							06 47										07 39							
Holmes Chapel	d							06 50					07 15					07 42							
Sandbach	d							06 55					07 19					07 46							
Crewe 10	65 a	05 41						07 04				07 16	07 31					07 57					08 06		
Kidsgrove	50 a				06 15																				
Longport	50 a																								
Stoke-on-Trent	50, 68 a				06 25		06 40		06 58					07 20		07 32					08 02				
Stafford	68 a	06 08						07 44	07 18			07 47									08 25		08 43		
Wolverhampton 7	68 a	06 41						08 07	07 35			08b41				08 11		08 47			08 41		09 05		
Birmingham New Street 12	68 a	06 58						08 27	07 56			08b58				08 30		09 10			08 58		09 24		
London Euston 15	⊖ 65 a	08 28					09 15		09 38			10 05	10 32	09 56		10 07							11 02		

		NT	NT	NT	VT	EM	NT	VT		NT	NT	NT	TP	NT	XC	NT	NT	AW	NT	VT	EM	NT	VT	NT	NT
					1 ◇	◇		1 ◇					1 ◇		1 ◇			◇		1 ◇	◇		1 ◇		
			E	K		L	G			G			A	N	Q		E	D			L			E	
Deansgate	d			07 29										08 12											
Manchester Oxford Road	d			07 33		07 39								08 18							08 38				
Manchester Piccadilly 10	a			07 36		07 41								08 20							08 42				
	d	07 34	07 37	07 39	07 43	07 43	07 51	07 55			07 58	08 03	08 18	08 22	08 24	08 27	08 29	08 34	08 34	08 40	08 42	08 51	08 54	08 59	09 03
Levenshulme	d						07 56			←	08 04						08 36					08 56			
Heaton Chapel	d						07 59			07 59	08 07						08 39					08 59			
Stockport	a		07 47	07 48		07 54	→	08 02		08 03	08 10	08 12	08 25	08 29	08 32	08 37	08 43	08 43			08 53	09 03	09 02	09 08	09 13
	d				07u53			08 04			08 10	08 14			08 33	08 37		08 44		08u49		09 03	09 04		09 13
Cheadle Hulme	d										08 15	08 18				08 41						09 07			09 17
Bramhall	d											08 21				08 44									
Poynton	d											08 24				08 47									
Adlington (Cheshire)	d											08 27				08 51									
Prestbury	d											08 30				08 54									
Macclesfield	a				08 04			08 15				08 35			08 45	08 59				09 04			09 18		
	d				08 05			08 17							08 46					09 05			09 20		
Congleton	d														08 54										
Handforth	d										08 19											09 11			09 21
Manchester Airport	d	08 00																	09 00						
Styal	d	08 04																							
Wilmslow	d	08 07									08 21							08 52	09 07			09 14			09 24
Alderley Edge	d	08 10									08 24								09 10			09a19			09 27
Chelford	d										08 28														09 31
Goostrey	d										08 33														09 35
Holmes Chapel	d	08 19									08 36								09 18						09 38
Sandbach	d	08 23									08 40								09 22						09 43
Crewe 10	65 a	08 34									08 51							09 16	09 33						09 54
Kidsgrove	50 a																								
Longport	50 a																								
Stoke-on-Trent	50, 68 a				08 20			08 37							09 06					09 20			09 37		
Stafford	68 a	09 08									09 43				09 25				10 11						10 43
Wolverhampton 7	68 a	09b41						09 11			09 47				09 41				10b41				10 11		10 48
Birmingham New Street 12	68 a	09b58						09 30			10 11				09 58			10 24	10b58				10 30		11 11
London Euston 15	⊖ 65 a	11 27			10 41			11 09										12 03	12 28	11 40			12 13		

For general notes see front of timetable
For details of catering facilities see Directory of Train Operators

- **A** From Manchester Airport to Cleethorpes (Table 29)
- **B** To Sheffield (Table 78)
- **C** To Chester (Table 88)
- **D** Until 22 March to Milford Haven (Table 128). From 29 March to Hereford (Table 131)
- **E** To Buxton (Table 86)
- **G** To Hazel Grove (Table 86)
- **H** To Bournemouth (Table 51)
- **J** Until 22 March to Carmarthen (Table 128). From 29 March to Hereford (Table 131)
- **K** From Blackpool North (Table 82) to Chester (Table 88)
- **L** From Liverpool Lime Street to Norwich (Table 49)
- **N** From St Annes-on-the-Sea (Table 97) to Greenbank (Table 88)
- **Q** To Plymouth (Table 51)
- **b** Change at Crewe and Stafford

Table 84

Saturdays

Manchester, Stockport and Manchester Airport → Crewe and Stoke-on-Trent

Network Diagram - see first page of Table 78

	NT A	TP 1◇ B	XC 1◇ C	NT D	NT	NT	AW ◇ E	NT G	VT 1◇	EM ◇ H	NT	NT	VT 1◇	NT	NT A		TP 1◇ B	XC 1◇ J	NT D	NT	NT	AW ◇ K	NT G	VT 1◇
Deansgate d					09 24			09 29												10 24			10 29	
Manchester Oxford Road d					09 27			09 33		09 38										10 27			10 33	
Manchester Piccadilly 10 a					09 29			09 35		09 40										10 29			10 35	
d	09 10	09 18	09 24	09 24	09 30	09 33	09 34	09 37	09 40	09 42		09 49	09 54	10 03	10 06		10 18	10 24	10 24	10 30	10 33	10 34	10 37	10 40
Levenshulme d	09 15							09 42				09 54			10 12								10 42	
Heaton Chapel d	09 18							09 45				09 57			10 15								10 45	
Stockport a	09 22	09 26	09 32	09 34	09 39		09 42	09 49		09 55		10 01	10 01	10 12	10 18		10 26	10 32	10 34	10 39		10 42	10 49	
d			09 33		09 40		09 42		09u49			10 01	10 03	10 13				10 33		10 40		10 43		10u49
Cheadle Hulme d					09 44							10 05		10 17						10 44				
Bramhall d					09 47															10 47				
Poynton d					09 50															10 50				
Adlington (Cheshire) d					09 53															10 53				
Prestbury d					09 56															10 56				
Macclesfield a			09 46		10 01				10 04				10 18					10 45		11 01				11 04
d			09 46						10 05				10 20					10 46						11 05
Congleton d																		10 54						
Handforth d											←	10 09		10 21										
Manchester Airport ✈ d						10 00 →					10 00										11 00 →			
Styal d																								
Wilmslow d							09 51				10 06	10 12		10 24								10 51		
Alderley Edge d											10 09	10a17		10 27										
Chelford d														10 31										
Goostrey d														10 36										
Holmes Chapel d											10 17			10 39										
Sandbach d											10 22			10 43										
Crewe 10 65 a							10 15				10 33			10 54								11 16		
Kidsgrove 50 a																								
Longport 50 a																								
Stoke-on-Trent 50, 68 a			10 03						10 20				10 37					11 06						11 20
Stafford 68 a			10 25								*11 11*			*11 43*				11 25						
Wolverhampton 7 68 a			10 41								*11b41*		11 11	*11 48*				11 41						
Birmingham New Street 12 68 a			10 58				*11 24*				*11b58*		11 30	*12 11*				11 58				*12 24*		
London Euston 15 ⊖ 65 a							*13 03*		12 42		*13 26*		13 09									*14 03*		13 41

	EM ◇ H	NT	NT	VT 1◇	NT	NT A	TP 1◇ B	XC 1◇ C	NT D	NT	NT	AW ◇ E	NT G	VT 1◇	EM ◇ H	NT	NT	VT 1◇	NT	NT A	TP 1◇ B	XC 1◇ L	NT D	NT
Deansgate d										11 24			11 29											12 24
Manchester Oxford Road d	10 38									11 27			11 33		11 38									12 27
Manchester Piccadilly 10 a	10 40									11 29			11 35		11 40									12 29
d	10 42		10 51	10 58	11 03	11 06	11 18	11 24	11 24	11 30	11 33	11 34	11 37	11 40	11 42		11 51	11 58	12 03	12 06	12 18	12 24	12 24	12 30
Levenshulme d			10 56			11 12							11 42				11 56			12 12				
Heaton Chapel d			10 59			11 15							11 45				11 59			12 15				
Stockport a	10 52		11 03	11 05	11 12	11 18	11 26	11 32	11 34	11 39		11 42	11 49		11 52		12 03	12 05	12 12	12 18	12 26	12 32	12 34	12 39
d			11 03	11 07	11 13			11 33		11 40		11 42		11u49			12 03	12 07	12 13			12 33		12 40
Cheadle Hulme d			11 07		11 17					11 44							12 07		12 17					12 44
Bramhall d										11 47														12 47
Poynton d										11 50														12 50
Adlington (Cheshire) d										11 53														12 53
Prestbury d										11 56														12 56
Macclesfield a				11 19				11 45		12 01				12 04				12 19				12 45		13 01
d				11 20				11 46						12 05				12 20				12 46		
Congleton d																						12 54		
Handforth d		←	11 11		11 21											←	12 11		12 21					
Manchester Airport ✈ d		11 00									12 00 →					12 00								
Styal d																								
Wilmslow d		11 06	11 14		11 24							11 51				12 06	12 14		12 24					
Alderley Edge d		11 09	11a19		11 27											12 09	12a19		12 27					
Chelford d					11 31														12 31					
Goostrey d					11 36														12 36					
Holmes Chapel d		11 17			11 39											12 17			12 39					
Sandbach d		11 22			11 43											12 22			12 43					
Crewe 10 65 a		11 33			11 54							12 15				12 33			12 54					
Kidsgrove 50 a																								
Longport 50 a																								
Stoke-on-Trent 50, 68 a				11 37				12 03						12 20				12 37				13 06		
Stafford 68 a		*12 11*			*12 43*			12 25								*13 11*			*13 43*			13 25		
Wolverhampton 7 68 a		*12b41*		12 11	*12c48*			12 41								*13b41*		13 11	*13 48*			13 41		
Birmingham New Street 12 68 a		*12b58*		12 30	*13c11*			12 58				*13 24*				*13b58*		13 30	*14 11*			13 58		
London Euston 15 ⊖ 65 a		*14 27*		14 12								*15 03*		14 43		*15 27*		15 09						

For general notes see front of timetable
For details of catering facilities see Directory of Train Operators

A To Hazel Grove (Table 86)
B From Manchester Airport to Cleethorpes (Table 29)
C To Bournemouth (Table 51)
D To Chester (Table 88)
E Until 22 March to Carmarthen (Table 128). From 29 March to Hereford (Table 131)
G From Blackpool North (Table 82) to Buxton (Table 86)
H From Liverpool Lime Street to Norwich (Table 49)
J To Plymouth (Table 51)
K Until 22 March to Milford Haven (Table 128). From 29 March to Hereford (Table 131)
L To Penzance (Table 135)
b Change at Crewe and Stafford
c From 29 March arr. Wolverhampton 1305, Birmingham New Street 1324

Table 84

Manchester, Stockport and Manchester Airport → Crewe and Stoke-on-Trent

Network Diagram - see first page of Table 78

		NT		AW	NT	VT	EM	NT	NT	VT	NT	NT	TP	XC	NT	NT	NT	AW	NT	VT	EM	NT	NT	VT	NT
				R		1 ◇	◇			1 ◇			1 ◇	1 ◇				R		1 ◇	◇			1 ◇	
				A	B		C					D	E	G	H			J	B		C				
				⚲		⊏				⊏			⚲	⊏				⚲		⊏				⊏	
Deansgate	d				12 29											13 24			13 29						
Manchester Oxford Road	d				12 33		12 38									13 27			13 33		13 38				
Manchester Piccadilly 10	a				12 35		12 40									13 29			13 35		13 40				
	d	12 33		12 34	12 37	12 40	12 42		12 51	12 58	13 03	13 06	13 18	13 24	13 24	13 30	13 33	13 34	13 37	13 40	13 42		13 51	13 58	14 03
Levenshulme	d				12 42				12 56			13 12							13 42				13 56		
Heaton Chapel	d				12 45				12 59			13 15							13 45				13 59		
Stockport	a			12 42	12 49		12 52		13 03	13 05	13 12	13 18	13 26	13 32	13 34	13 39		13 42	13 49		13 52		14 03	14 05	14 12
	d			12 42		12u49			13 03	13 07	13 13			13 33		13 40		13 42		13u49			14 03	14 07	14 13
Cheadle Hulme	d								13 07		13 17					13 44							14 07		14 17
Bramhall	d															13 47									
Poynton	d															13 50									
Adlington (Cheshire)	d															13 53									
Prestbury	d															13 56									
Macclesfield	a					13 04				13 19				13 45		14 01				14 04				14 19	
	d					13 05				13 20				13 46						14 05				14 20	
Congleton	d																								
Handforth	d							←	13 11		13 21											←	14 11		14 21
Manchester Airport	d	13 00 →						13 00									14 00 →					14 00			
Styal	d																								
Wilmslow	d			12 51				13 06	13 14		13 24							13 54				14 06	14 14		14 24
Alderley Edge	d							13 09	13a19		13 27											14 09	14a19		14 27
Chelford	d										13 31														14 31
Goostrey	d										13 36														14 36
Holmes Chapel	d							13 17			13 39											14 17			14 39
Sandbach	d							13 22			13 43											14 22			14 43
Crewe 10	65 a			13 15				13 33			13 54							14 15				14 33			14 54
Kidsgrove	50 a																								
Longport	50 a																								
Stoke-on-Trent	50, 68 a					13 20				13 37				14 03						14 20				14 37	
Stafford	68 a							*14 13*			*14 43*			14 25								*15 11*			*15 43*
Wolverhampton 7	68 a							*14b41*		14 11	*14 48*			14 41								*15b41*		15 11	*15 46*
Birmingham New Street 12	68 a			*14 24*				*14b58*		14 30	*15 11*			14 58				*15 24*				*15b58*		15 30	*16 11*
London Euston 15	⊖ 65 a			*16 05*		15 40		*16 29*		16 10								*17 05*		16 42		*17 27*		17 10	

		NT	TP	XC	NT	NT	NT	AW	NT	VT		EM	NT	NT	VT	NT	NT	TP	XC	NT	NT	NT	AW	NT	VT
			1 ◇	1 ◇				R		1 ◇		◇			1 ◇			1 ◇	1 ◇				R		1 ◇
		D	E	K	H			A	B			L					D	E	G	H			J	B	
			⚲	⊏				⚲		⊏					⊏			⚲	⊏				⚲		⊏
Deansgate	d					14 24			14 29												15 24			15 29	
Manchester Oxford Road	d					14 27			14 33			14 38									15 27			15 33	
Manchester Piccadilly 10	a					14 29			14 35			14 40									15 29			15 35	
	d	14 06	14 18	14 24	14 24	14 30	14 33	14 34	14 37	14 40		14 42		14 51	14 58	15 03	15 06	15 18	15 24	15 24	15 30	15 33	15 34	15 37	15 40
Levenshulme	d	14 12							14 42					14 56			15 12							15 42	
Heaton Chapel	d	14 15							14 45					14 59			15 15							15 45	
Stockport	a	14 18	14 26	14 32	14 34	14 39		14 42	14 49			14 52		15 03	15 05	15 12	15 18	15 26	15 32	15 34	15 39		15 42	15 49	
	d			14 33		14 40		14 42		14u49				15 03	15 07	15 13			15 33		15 40		15 42		15u49
Cheadle Hulme	d					14 44								15 07		15 17					15 44				
Bramhall	d					14 47															15 47				
Poynton	d					14 50															15 50				
Adlington (Cheshire)	d					14 53															15 53				
Prestbury	d					14 56															15 56				
Macclesfield	a			14 45		15 01				15 04					15 19				15 45		16 01				16 04
	d			14 46						15 05					15 20				15 46						16 05
Congleton	d			14 54																					
Handforth	d												←	15 11		15 21									
Manchester Airport	d						15 00 →						15 00									16 00 →			
Styal	d																								
Wilmslow	d							14 51					15 06	15 14		15 24							15 51		
Alderley Edge	d												15 09	15a19		15 27									
Chelford	d															15 31									
Goostrey	d															15 36									
Holmes Chapel	d												15 17			15 39									
Sandbach	d												15 22			15 43									
Crewe 10	65 a							15 15					15 33			15 54							16 14		
Kidsgrove	50 a																								
Longport	50 a																								
Stoke-on-Trent	50, 68 a			15 06						15 20					15 37				16 03						16 20
Stafford	68 a			15 25									*16 07*			*16 44*			16 24						
Wolverhampton 7	68 a			15 41									*16b41*		16 11	*16 48*			16 41						
Birmingham New Street 12	68 a			15 58				*16 24*					*16b58*		16 30	*17 11*			16 58				*17 24*		
London Euston 15	⊖ 65 a							*18 03*		17 40			*18 29*		18 10								*19 03*		18 44

For general notes see front of timetable
For details of catering facilities see Directory of Train Operators

- **A** Until 22 March to Milford Haven (Table 128). From 29 March to Hereford (Table 131)
- **B** From Blackpool North (Table 82) to Buxton (Table 86)
- **C** From Liverpool Lime Street to Norwich (Table 49)
- **D** To Hazel Grove (Table 86)
- **E** From Manchester Airport to Cleethorpes (Table 29)
- **G** To Bournemouth (Table 51)
- **H** To Chester (Table 88)
- **J** Until 22 March to Carmarthen (Table 128). From 29 March to Hereford (Table 131)
- **K** To Penzance (Table 135)
- **L** From Liverpool Lime Street to Nottingham (Table 49)
- **b** Change at Crewe and Stafford

Manchester, Stockport and Manchester Airport → Crewe and Stoke-on-Trent

Network Diagram - see first page of Table 78

	EM	NT	NT	VT	NT	NT	TP	XC	NT	NT	NT	AW	NT	VT	EM	NT	NT		VT	NT	NT	NT	TP	XC
	◇			1◇			1◇	1◇				R		1◇	◇				1◇				1◇	1◇
	A					B	C	D	E			G	H		A						J	B	C	K
Deansgate d										16 24			16 29								16 59			
Manchester Oxford Road d	15 38									16 27			16 33		16 38						17 03			
Manchester Piccadilly a	15 40									16 29			16 36		16 41						17 06			
d	15 42		15 51	15 58	16 03	16 06	16 18	16 24	16 24	16 30	16 33	16 34	16 37	16 40	16 42		16 49		16 58	17 02	17 07	17 07	17 18	17 24
Levenshulme d			15 56			16 12											16 54			17 08		17 16		
Heaton Chapel d			15 59			16 15											16 57			17 11		17 19		
Stockport a	15 53		16 03	16 05	16 12	16 18	16 26	16 32	16 34	16 39		16 42	16 46		16 52		17 01		17 05	17 15	17 19	17 22	17 26	17 32
d			16 03	16 07	16 13			16 33		16 40		16 43		16u49			17 03		17 07	17 15				17 33
Cheadle Hulme d			16 07		16 17					16 44							17 07			17 19				
Bramhall d										16 47														
Poynton d										16 50														
Adlington (Cheshire) d										16 53														
Prestbury d										16 56														
Macclesfield a				16 19				16 45		17 01				17 04					17 19					17 45
d				16 20				16 46						17 05					17 20					17 46
Congleton d								16 54																
Handforth d		←	16 11		16 21											←	17 11			17 23				
Manchester Airport d		16 00									17 00 →					17 00								
Styal d																								
Wilmslow d		16 06	16 14		16 24							16 51				17 06	17 14			17 26				
Alderley Edge d		16 09	16a19		16 27											17 09	17a19			17 29				
Chelford d		16 13			16 31															17 33				
Goostrey d		16 18			16 36															17 37				
Holmes Chapel d		16 21			16 39											17 17				17 40				
Sandbach d		16 25			16 43											17 22				17 45				
Crewe 65 a		16 36			16 54							17 16				17 33				17 56				
Kidsgrove 50 a																								
Longport 50 a																								
Stoke-on-Trent 50, 68 a				16 37				17 06						17 20					17 37					18 03
Stafford 68 a		17 11			17 43			17 25								18 11				18 43				18 25
Wolverhampton 68 a		17b41		17 11	17 48			17 41								18b41			18 11	18 48				18 41
Birmingham New Street 68 a		17b58		17 30	18 11			17 58				18 24				18b58			18 30	19 11				18 58
London Euston ⊖ 65 a		19 30		19 10								20 03		19 42		20 49			20 16					

	NT	NT	NT	AW	NT	VT	NT	EM	NT	NT	NT	VT	NT	NT	NT	TP	XC	NT	NT	AW	NT	NT	VT	NT
				R		1◇		◇				1◇				1◇	1◇			◇			1◇	
	E			L	H		H	N							B	C	D	E		Q		H		H
Deansgate d		17 24			17 28																			
Manchester Oxford Road d		17 27			17 32			17 38														18 35		
Manchester Piccadilly a		17 29			17 35			17 40														18 38		
d	17 24	17 31	17 33	17 34	17 37	17 40		17 42		17 49	17 52	17 58		18 03	18 06	18 18	18 24	18 24	18 30	18 34	18 36	18 39	18 40	
Levenshulme d					17 45		←			17 54					18 12							18 45		←
Heaton Chapel d					17 48		17 48			17 57					18 15							18 48		18 48
Stockport a	17 33	17 40		17 42	→		17 51	17 54		18 01	18 04	18 05	←	18 12	18 18	18 26	18 32	18 34	18 39	18 42		→		18 50
d		17 40		17 42		17u49				18 01	18 07	18 07	18 07	18 13			18 33		18 40	18 43			18u49	
Cheadle Hulme d		17 44								18 05	→		18 13	18 17					18 44					
Bramhall d		17 47											18 16						18 47					
Poynton d		17 50											18 19						18 50					
Adlington (Cheshire) d		17 53											18 23						18 53					
Prestbury d		17 56											18 26						18 56					
Macclesfield a		18 01				18 04						18 18	18 30				18 45		19 01				19 04	
d						18 05						18 20	18 31				18 46						19 05	
Congleton d													18 38				18 54							
Handforth d									←	18 09				18 21										
Manchester Airport d			18 00 →						18 00												19 02			
Styal d									18 07															
Wilmslow d				17 51					18 11	18 13				18 24						18 51	19 11			
Alderley Edge d									18 14	18a20				18 27							19a18			
Chelford d														18 31										
Goostrey d														18 35										
Holmes Chapel d									18 22					18 38										
Sandbach d									18 26					18 43										
Crewe 65 a				18 15					18 37					18 54						19 15				
Kidsgrove 50 a													18 44											
Longport 50 a													18 48											
Stoke-on-Trent 50, 68 a						18 20						18 37	18 53				19 06						19 20	
Stafford 68 a									19 06					19 44			19 25			19 50				
Wolverhampton 68 a									19b41			19 11		19 48			19 41			20b41				
Birmingham New Street 68 a									19b58			19 30		20 11			19 58			20b58				
London Euston ⊖ 65 a				21c36		21 20			22 01			21e42								22f42			22g34	

For general notes see front of timetable
For details of catering facilities see Directory of Train Operators

- **A** From Liverpool Lime Street to Norwich (Table 49)
- **B** To Hazel Grove (Table 86)
- **C** From Manchester Airport to Cleethorpes (Table 29)
- **D** To Plymouth (Table 51)
- **E** To Chester (Table 88)
- **G** Until 22 March to Milford Haven (Table 128). From 29 March to Hereford (Table 131)
- **H** From Blackpool North (Table 82) to Buxton (Table 86)
- **J** From Southport (Table 82) to Buxton (Table 86)
- **K** To Bournemouth (Table 51)
- **L** Until 22 March to Haverfordwest (Table 128). From 29 March to Hereford (Table 131)
- **N** From Liverpool Lime Street to Cambridge (Table 49)
- **Q** Until 22 March to Carmarthen (Table 128). From 29 March to Hereford (Table 131)
- **b** Change at Crewe and Stafford
- **c** From 29 March arr. 2128
- **e** From 29 March arr. 2133
- **f** From 29 March arr. 2234
- **g** From 29 March arr. 2228

Table 84

Saturdays

Manchester, Stockport and Manchester Airport → Crewe and Stoke-on-Trent

Network Diagram - see first page of Table 78

	EM	NT	VT		NT	TP	XC	NT	NT	NT	AW	NT	EM	NT	VT	NT	VT	TP	NT	NT	AW	NT	EM	NT
	◇		1◇			1◇	1◇				◇		◇		1◇		1◇	1◇			◇		◇	
	A					B	C	D			E	G	H					B	D		E	G	H	
Deansgate d												19 29										20 28		
Manchester Oxford Road d	18 39											19 33	19 38									20 32	20 38	
Manchester Piccadilly 10 a	18 42											19 36	19 42									20 34	20 40	
d	18 44	18 49	18 58		19 03	19 18	19 24	19 24	19 30	19 30	19 34	19 37	19 42		19 58	20 03	20 17	20 18	20 24	20 27	20 34	20 36	20 42	20 44
Levenshulme d		18 54			19 08					19 36						20 08				20 32				
Heaton Chapel d		18 57			19 11					19 39						20 11				20 35				
Stockport a	18 54	19 01	19 05		19 15	19 26	19 32	19 33		19 42	19 42	19 47	19 53		20 05	20 14	20 24	20 26	20 34	20 39	20 46	20 44	20 51	
d		19 01	19 07		19 15		19 33			19 43	19 42				20 07	20 15	20 26			20 40	20 46			
Cheadle Hulme d		19 04			19 19					19 47						20 19				20 44				
Bramhall d										19 50										20 47				
Poynton d										19 53										20 50				
Adlington (Cheshire) d										19 56										20 53				
Prestbury d										19 59										20 56				
Macclesfield a			19 18				19 45			20 04					20 18		20 39			21 01				
d			19 20				19 46								20 20		20 40							
Congleton d							19 54																	
Handforth d		19 08			19 23									←		20 23								
Manchester Airport d									19 56 →					19 56										21 10
Styal d																								
Wilmslow d		19 13			19 26						19 54			20a06		20 26					20 54			21a19
Alderley Edge d		19a20			19 29											20 29								
Chelford d					19 33											20 33								
Goostrey d					19 37											20 37								
Holmes Chapel d					19 40											20 40								
Sandbach d					19 45											20 45								
Crewe 10 65 a					19 56						20 15					20 56					21 14			
Kidsgrove 50 a																								
Longport 50 a																								
Stoke-on-Trent 50, 68 a			19 37				20 06								20 34		20 56							
Stafford 68 a					*20 43*		20 25										21 17				*21 51*			
Wolverhampton 7 68 a			20 11		*20 48*		20 41								21 11		21 35				*22 09*			
Birmingham New Street 12 68 a			20 30		*21 11*		20 58								21 30		21 56				*22 30*			
London Euston 15 ⊖ 65 a			22b46								*23c36*				23e43		00 16							

	XC	NT	TP	NT	NT	AW	EM	NT	NT	NT	NT	TP	NT	AW	NT	NT	NT	NT	NT	NT	NT	NT		
	1◇		1◇			◇	◇					1◇												
			B	D		E	J	K				L	D	N			Q		D		U			
Deansgate d								21 40									22 50	23 00				23 31		
Manchester Oxford Road d								21 43									22 53	23 02		23 10	23 19	23 33		
Manchester Piccadilly 10 a								21 46									22 56	23 05		23 12	23 21	23 36		
d	20 54	20 58	21 18	21 24	21 28	21 34	21 42	21 49	21 55	22 04		22 18	22 24	22 34	22 38	22 46	22 57	23 06	23 09	23 14		23 37		
Levenshulme d		21 03			21 33					22 09					22 44			23 11				23 42		
Heaton Chapel d		21 06			21 36					22 12					22 47			23 14				23 45		
Stockport a	21 03	21 10	21 26	21 34	21 40	21 45	21 52	21 56		22 15		22 26	22 34	22 42	22 50		23 06	23 18	23 18	23 22		23 50		
d	21 04	21 15			21 40	21 45				22 16				22 42	22 51			23 18		23 23		23 50		
Cheadle Hulme d		21 19			21 44					22 20					22 55			23 22		23 27		23 55		
Bramhall d					21 47										22 58					23 30				
Poynton d					21 50										23 01					23 33				
Adlington (Cheshire) d					21 54										23 04					23 36				
Prestbury d					21 57										23 07					23 39				
Macclesfield a	21 16				22 02										23 12					23 44				
d	21 17																							
Congleton d	21 25																							
Handforth d		21 23								22 24	←							23 26				23 59		
Manchester Airport d									22 25 →		22 25					23 12								
Styal d																								
Wilmslow d		21 26				21 54				22 27	22a35			22 51		23a22		23 29				00 02		
Alderley Edge d		21 29								22 30								23 32				00a07		
Chelford d		21 33								22 34								23 36						
Goostrey d		21 37								22 38								23 40						
Holmes Chapel d		21 40								22 41								23 43						
Sandbach d		21 45								22 46								23 48						
Crewe 10 65 a		21 56				22 14				22 57				23 11				23 59						
Kidsgrove 50 a																								
Longport 50 a																								
Stoke-on-Trent 50, 68 a	21 39																							
Stafford 68 a	21 57	*22 32*																						
Wolverhampton 7 68 a	22 13	*22 48*																						
Birmingham New Street 12 68 a	22 37	*23 10*																						
London Euston 15 ⊖ 65 a																								

For general notes see front of timetable
For details of catering facilities see Directory of Train Operators

A From Liverpool Lime Street to Cambridge (Table 49)
B From Manchester Airport to Cleethorpes (Table 29)
C To Southampton Central (Table 51)
D To Chester (Table 88)
E To Cardiff Central (from 29 March to Hereford) (Table 131)
G From Blackpool North (Table 82) to Buxton (Table 86)
H From Liverpool Lime Street to Nottingham (Table 49)
J To Nottingham (Table 49)
K From Southport (Table 82) to Buxton (Table 86)
L From Manchester Airport to Sheffield (Table 78)
N To Shrewsbury (Table 131)
Q From Clitheroe (Table 94) to Buxton (Table 86)
U To New Mills Central (Table 78)
b From 29 March arr. 2239
c From 29 March arr. 2326
e From 29 March arr. 2330

Table 84

Sundays

until 23 March

Manchester, Stockport and Manchester Airport → Crewe and Stoke-on-Trent

Network Diagram - see first page of Table 78

		TP	XC	NT	VT	TP		NT	XC	NT	VT	VT		NT	TP	XC	NT	VT		VT	NT	NT	TP	TP	XC
			1◇		1◇	1◇			1◇		1◇	1◇				1◇		1◇		1◇			1◇		1◇
		A	B	C		D			E	G				H	A	J	K				H		D	A	E
		🚌	☕		☕				☕		☕	☕			🚌	☕		☕		☕				🚌	☕
Deansgate	d									09 18				09 43			10 18				10 43				
Manchester Oxford Road	d									09 21				09 46			10 21				10 46				
Manchester Piccadilly 10	a									09 24				09 49			10 25				10 49				
	d	08 00	08 08	08 53	09 00	09 05		09 14	09 24	09 26	09 44	09 53		09 56	10 15	10 24	10 26	10 44		10 53	10 56	11 07	11 12	11 15	11 24
Levenshulme	d			08 58						09 31				10 01			10 31				11 01				
Heaton Chapel	d			09 01						09 34				10 04			10 34				11 04				
Stockport	a	08 25		09 05		09 13			09 31	09 38		10 00		10 07	10 40	10 32	10 38			11 00	11 07		11 20	11 40	11 31
	d				09u10				09 33	09 38	09u53	10 02				10 33	10 38	10u52		11 02					11 33
Cheadle Hulme	d									09 41							10 43								
Bramhall	d																								
Poynton	d																								
Adlington (Cheshire)	d																								
Prestbury	d																								
Macclesfield	a								09 45		10 04	10 13				10 45		11 04		11 13					11 45
	d								09 46		10 06	10 15				10 46		11 05		11 15					11 46
Congleton	d																								
Handforth	d									09 47							10 48								
Manchester Airport ✈	d							09 33														11 32			
Styal	d																								
Wilmslow	d		08 24		09 19			09 41		09 49							10 50					11 40			
Alderley Edge	d							09 44		09a57							10a59					11 43			
Chelford	d																								
Goostrey	d																								
Holmes Chapel	d							09 52														11 51			
Sandbach	d							09 56														11 55			
Crewe 10	65 a		08 43		09 36			10 07														12 06			
Kidsgrove	50 a																								
Longport	50 a																								
Stoke-on-Trent	50, 68 a		09 04						10 02		10 20	10 29				11 02		11 20		11 29					12 02
Stafford	68 a		09 24		10 06			*10 54*	10 24		10 40					11 24						*12 42*			12 24
Wolverhampton 7	68 🚢 a		09 40					*11b40*	10 40			11 05				11 40				12 05		*13 02*			12 40
Birmingham New Street 12	68 a		09 58					*11b58*	10 58			11 26				11 58				12 26		*13 21*			12 58
London Euston 15	⊖ 65 a		*12c00*		12 51			*13 23*			13 04	13 29						14 00		14 29		*15 08*			

		NT		EM	VT	VT	NT	XC		NT	AW	EM	EM	VT		VT	NT	NT	TP	XC		NT	VT	EM	VT
					1◇	1◇		R 1			R		◇	1◇		1◇			1◇	R 1			1◇	◇	1◇
		K		A			H	L		K	N	A	Q				H		D	E		K		U	
				🚌	☕	☕		☕			🛒	🚌		☕		☕				☕			☕		☕
Deansgate	d	11 18					11 46			12 18							12 43					13 18			
Manchester Oxford Road	d	11 21					11 50			12 21							12 46					13 21		13 41	
Manchester Piccadilly 10	a	11 24					11 52			12 24							12 49					13 24		13 44	
	d	11 26		11 35	11 44	11 53	11 56	12 08		12 26	12 33	12 35	12 44	12 45		12 53	12 56	13 08	13 12	13 24		13 28	13 45	13 49	13 53
Levenshulme	d	11 31					12 01			12 31							13 01					13 33			
Heaton Chapel	d	11 34					12 04			12 34							13 04					13 36			
Stockport	a	11 38		12 00		12 00	12 07	12 16		12 37	12 41	13 00	12 53			13 01	13 07		13 21	13 32		13 39		13 58	14 02
	d	11 38			11u52	12 02		12 22		12 38	12 42			12u56		13 02				13 33		13 40	13u55		14 03
Cheadle Hulme	d	11 42								12 42												13 44			
Bramhall	d																								
Poynton	d																								
Adlington (Cheshire)	d																								
Prestbury	d																								
Macclesfield	a				12 04	12 13		12 34						13 07		13 14				13 45			14 07		14 15
	d				12 05	12 15		12 35						13 09		13 15				13 46			14 08		14 16
Congleton	d																								
Handforth	d	11 47								12 47												13 48			
Manchester Airport ✈	d																	13 26							
Styal	d																								
Wilmslow	d	11 50								12 50	12 54							13 33				13 51			
Alderley Edge	d	11a58								12a58								13 36				13a58			
Chelford	d																								
Goostrey	d																								
Holmes Chapel	d																	13 44							
Sandbach	d																	13 48							
Crewe 10	65 a										13 18							13 59							
Kidsgrove	50 a																								
Longport	50 a																								
Stoke-on-Trent	50, 68 a				12 20	12 29		12 56						13 23		13 30				14 04			14 23		14 31
Stafford	68 a							13 24			*13 57*							*14 31*		14 24					
Wolverhampton 7	68 🚢 a					13 05		13 40			*14b40*					14 05		*14 49*		14 40					15 04
Birmingham New Street 12	68 a					13 26		13 58			*14b58*					14 26		*15 08*		14 58					15 26
London Euston 15	⊖ 65 a				14 56	15 16					*16 07*			15 56		16 16		*17 08*					16 56		17 11

For general notes see front of timetable
For details of catering facilities see Directory of Train Operators

- **A** Until 27 January. To Sheffield (Table 78)
- **B** To Paignton (from 3 February to Plymouth) (Table 51)
- **C** To Buxton (Table 86)
- **D** From 3 February. From Manchester Airport to Cleethorpes (Table 29)
- **E** To Bournemouth (Table 51)
- **G** From Wigan Wallgate (Table 82)
- **H** From Blackpool North (from 3 February from Preston) (Table 82) to Buxton (Table 86)
- **J** To Plymouth (Table 51)
- **K** From Southport (Table 82)
- **L** To Penzance (Table 135)
- **N** To Milford Haven (Table 128)
- **Q** From 3 February. To Norwich (Table 49)
- **U** Until 27 January from Liverpool Lime Street (Table 89). From 3 February from Liverpool Lime Street to Norwich (Table 49)
- **b** Change at Crewe and Stafford
- **c** Change at Stafford

Table 84

Sundays

until 23 March

Manchester, Stockport and Manchester Airport → Crewe and Stoke-on-Trent

Network Diagram - see first page of Table 78

	NT	TP	XC	NT	AW	EM	VT	VT	NT	NT	NT	TP	XC	NT	EM	VT	AW	VT	NT	TP
		1 ◇	R 1		R	◇	1 ◇	1 ◇				1 ◇	R 1		◇	1 ◇	R	1 ◇		1 ◇
	A	B	C	D	E	G			A			B	H	D	G		J		A	B
Deansgate d	13 43			14 18					14 43					15 18					15 43	
Manchester Oxford Road d	13 46			14 21		14 39			14 46					15 21	15 39				15 46	
Manchester Piccadilly 10 a	13 49			14 24		14 41			14 49					15 24	15 41				15 49	
d	13 56	14 15	14 24	14 26	14 34	14 43	14 45	14 53	14 56	15 01	15 05	15 15	15 24	15 26	15 43	15 45	15 49	15 53	15 53	16 15
Levenshulme d	14 01			14 32					15 01					15 31					15 58	
Heaton Chapel d	14 04			14 35					15 04					15 34					16 01	
Stockport a	14 07	14 22	14 32	14 38	14 42	14 51		15 01	15 07	15 10		15 22	15 32	15 36	15 52		15 58	16 01	16 04	16 22
d			14 33	14 39	14 42		14u55	15 02		15 11			15 33	15 38		15u55	15 58	16 02		
Cheadle Hulme d				14 43						15 15				15 44						
Bramhall d										15 18										
Poynton d										15 21										
Adlington (Cheshire) d										15 24										
Prestbury d										15 27										
Macclesfield a			14 45				15 07	15 14		15 31			15 45			16 06		16 14		
d			14 46				15 08	15 15		15 31			15 46			16 08		16 15		
Congleton d										15 38										
Handforth d				14 48										15 49						
Manchester Airport ✈ d											15 25									
Styal d																				
Wilmslow d				14 51	14 55						15 33			15 52			16 06			
Alderley Edge d				14a59							15 36			15a58						
Chelford d																				
Goostrey d																				
Holmes Chapel d											15 44									
Sandbach d											15 47									
Crewe 10 65 a					15 17						15 58						16 30			
Kidsgrove 50 a										15 44										
Longport 50 a										15 49										
Stoke-on-Trent 50, 68 a			15 03				15 23	15 30		15 54			16 03			16 22		16 30		
Stafford 68 a			15 24		*15 54*						*16 36*		16 24				*17 06*			
Wolverhampton 7 68 a			15 40		*16b40*			16 04			*16 54*		16 40				*17c40*	17 04		
Birmingham New Street 12 68 a			15 58		*16b58*			16 26			*17 11*		16 58				*17b58*	17 26		
London Euston 15 ⊖ 65 a					*18 08*		17 56	18 11			*19 14*					18 51	*19 33*	19 17		

	XC	NT	AW	EM	VT	VT	NT	NT	TP	XC	NT	EM	VT	VT	NT	NT	TP	XC	NT	AW	EM
	R 1		R	◇	1 ◇	1 ◇			1 ◇	R 1		◇	1 ◇	1 ◇			1 ◇	R 1		R	◇
	K	D	L	G			A		B	H	D	N			A		B	K	D	J	Q
Deansgate d		16 18					16 43				17 18				17 43				18 18		
Manchester Oxford Road d		16 21		16 39			16 46				17 21	17 39			17 46				18 21		18 39
Manchester Piccadilly 10 a		16 24		16 41			16 49				17 24	17 41			17 49				18 24		18 41
d	16 24	16 26	16 37	16 43	16 45	16 53	16 53	17 06	17 15	17 24	17 26	17 43	17 45	17 53	17 53	17 59	18 15	18 24	18 26	18 37	18 42
Levenshulme d		16 31					16 58				17 31				17 58				18 31		
Heaton Chapel d		16 34					17 01				17 34				18 01				18 34		
Stockport a	16 31	16 37	16 45	16 52		17 01	17 04		17 22	17 31	17 37	17 52		18 00	18 04	18 08	18 22	18 31	18 38	18 45	18 52
d	16 33	16 38	16 45		16u55	17 02				17 33	17 38		17u55	18 02		18 08		18 33	18 38	18 45	
Cheadle Hulme d		16 42									17 42					18 12			18 42		
Bramhall d																18 15					
Poynton d																18 18					
Adlington (Cheshire) d																18 22					
Prestbury d																18 25					
Macclesfield a	16 45				17 06	17 13				17 45			18 06	18 13		18 28		18 45			
d	16 46				17 08	17 15				17 46			18 08	18 15		18 29		18 46			
Congleton d																18 36					
Handforth d		16 47									17 47								18 47		
Manchester Airport ✈ d								17 24													
Styal d																					
Wilmslow d		16 50	16 54					17 31			17 49								18 50	18 55	
Alderley Edge d		16a58						17 34			17a58								18a58		
Chelford d								17 39													
Goostrey d								17 44													
Holmes Chapel d								17 47													
Sandbach d								17 51													
Crewe 10 65 a			17 17					18 01												19 18	
Kidsgrove 50 a																18 42					
Longport 50 a																18 46					
Stoke-on-Trent 50, 68 a	17 02				17 22	17 29				18 02			18 22	18 29		18 52		19 02			
Stafford 68 a	17 24		*18 30*					*18 53*		18 24								19 24		*19 54*	
Wolverhampton 7 68 a	17 40		*18 48*			18 04		*18 51*		18 40				19 04				19 40		*20b40*	
Birmingham New Street 12 68 a	17 58		*19 04*			18 26		*19 14*		18 58				19 26				19 58		*20b58*	
London Euston 15 ⊖ 65 a			*20 38*		19 53	20 11		*21 14*					20 53	21 17						*22 23*	

For general notes see front of timetable
For details of catering facilities see Directory of Train Operators

- **A** From Blackpool North (from 3 February from Preston) (Table 82) to Buxton (Table 86)
- **B** From 3 February. From Manchester Airport to Cleethorpes (Table 29)
- **C** To Penzance (Table 135)
- **D** From Southport (Table 82)
- **E** To Pembroke Dock and to Milford Haven (Table 128)
- **G** Until 27 January from Liverpool Lime Street (Table 89). From 3 February from Liverpool Lime Street to Norwich (Table 49)
- **H** To Bournemouth (Table 51)
- **J** To Cardiff Central (Table 131)
- **K** To Plymouth (Table 51)
- **L** To Milford Haven (Table 128)
- **N** Until 27 January from Liverpool Lime Street (Table 89). From 3 February from Liverpool Lime Street to Nottingham (Table 49)
- **Q** From 3 February. From Liverpool Lime Street to Norwich (Table 49)
- **b** Change at Crewe and Stafford
- **c** Change at Crewe and Stafford. From 3 February arr. 1741

Manchester, Stockport and Manchester Airport → Crewe and Stoke-on-Trent

Sundays

until 23 March

Network Diagram - see first page of Table 78

	EM		VT	VT	NT	NT	TP		XC	NT	EM	VT	NT		VT	NT	TP	VT	TP		NT	EM	AW	NT
	◇		1 ◇	1 ◇			1 ◇		1 ◇		◇	1 ◇			1 ◇		1 ◇	1 ◇				◇	◇	
	A				B		C		D	E	G		B			B	C		H		E	G	J	B
			☕	☕								☕			☕			☕	🚌					
Deansgate d					18 43					19 18			19 43								20 18			20 43
Manchester Oxford Road d	18 39				18 46					19 21	19 39		19 46								20 21	20 39		20 46
Manchester Piccadilly 10 a	18 41				18 49					19 24	19 41		19 49								20 24	20 41		20 49
d	18 42		18 45	18 53	18 53	19 06	19 15		19 24	19 26	19 42	19 45	19 53		19 55		20 15	20 23	20 25		20 26	20 43	20 46	20 53
Levenshulme d					18 58					19 31			19 58			←					20 31			20 58
Heaton Chapel d					19 01					19 34			20 01			20 01					20 34			21 01
Stockport a	18 57			19 00	19 04		19 22		19 32	19 38	19 52		→		20 03	20 04	20 22	20 31	20 50		20 38	20 52	20 54	→
d			18u55	19 02					19 33	19 38		19u55			20 04			20 32			20 38		20 54	
Cheadle Hulme d										19 42											20 42			
Bramhall d																								
Poynton d																								
Adlington (Cheshire) d																								
Prestbury d																								
Macclesfield a			19 06	19 13					19 45			20 07			20 16			20 44						
d			19 08	19 15					19 46			20 08			20 17			20 45						
Congleton d																								
Handforth d										19 47											20 47			
Manchester Airport d						19 24																		
Styal d																								
Wilmslow d						19 32				19 50											20 50		21 02	
Alderley Edge d						19 35				19a58											20a58			
Chelford d																								
Goostrey d																								
Holmes Chapel d						19 43																		
Sandbach d						19 48																		
Crewe 10 65 a						19 59																	21 23	
Kidsgrove 50 a																								
Longport 50 a																								
Stoke-on-Trent 50, 68 a			19 22	19 29					20 03			20 23			20 32			21 00						
Stafford 68 a						20 58			20 24						20 51			21 19						
Wolverhampton 7 68 a				20 04		20b52			20 40						21 08			21 35						
Birmingham New Street 12 68 a				20 26		21b15			20 58						21 32			21 56						
London Euston 15 ⊖ 65 a			21 57	22 27		23 25						23 00						23 48						

	XC	NT	NT		NT	TP	TP	NT	NT		XC	NT	EM	TP	TP		NT	AW	NT	TP	TP	NT		
	1 ◇					1 ◇					1 ◇		◇	1 ◇						1 ◇				
		B				K	H	E	B			B	G	K	H		E	L	B	K	H	E		
							🚌								🚌						🚌			
Deansgate d								21 18	21 43								22 18		22 43			23 18		
Manchester Oxford Road d								21 21	21 46				22 08				22 22		22 46			23 21		
Manchester Piccadilly 10 a								21 24	21 49				22 10				22 24		22 49			23 25		
d	20 55		20 58		21 06	21 15	21 25	21 26	21 53		21 55		22 12	22 15	22 25		22 26	22 46	22 51	23 15	23 25	23 26		
Levenshulme d		←						21 31	21 58			←					22 31		22 56			23 31		
Heaton Chapel d		21 01						21 34	22 01			22 01					22 34		22 59			23 34		
Stockport a	21 03	21 04	21 07			21 22	21 50	21 36	→		22 03	22 04	22 21	22 22	22 50		22 37	22 54	23 03	23 20	23 50	23 38		
d	21 04		21 08					21 38			22 04						22 38	22 54				23 38		
Cheadle Hulme d			21 12					21 42									22 42					23 44		
Bramhall d			21 15																					
Poynton d			21 18																					
Adlington (Cheshire) d			21 22																					
Prestbury d			21 25																					
Macclesfield a	21 16		21 28								22 16													
d	21 17		21 29								22 17													
Congleton d			21 36																					
Handforth d								21 47									22 47					23 49		
Manchester Airport d					21 25																			
Styal d																								
Wilmslow d					21 32			21 50									22 50	23 02				23 52		
Alderley Edge d					21 35			21a58									22a58					00a01		
Chelford d																								
Goostrey d																								
Holmes Chapel d					21 43																			
Sandbach d					21 48																			
Crewe 10 65 a					21 59													23 24						
Kidsgrove 50 a			21 42																					
Longport 50 a			21 46																					
Stoke-on-Trent 50, 68 a	21 34		21 51								22 34													
Stafford 68 a	21 52				22 39						22 52													
Wolverhampton 7 68 a	22 09				22 54						23 09													
Birmingham New Street 12 68 a	22 30				23 17						23 30													
London Euston 15 ⊖ 65 a																								

For general notes see front of timetable
For details of catering facilities see Directory of Train Operators

- **A** Until 27 January. From Liverpool Lime Street (Table 89)
- **B** From Blackpool North (from 3 February from Preston) (Table 82) to Buxton (Table 86)
- **C** From 3 February. From Manchester Airport to Cleethorpes (Table 29)
- **D** To Southampton Central (Table 51)
- **E** From Southport (Table 82)
- **G** Until 27 January from Liverpool Lime Street (Table 89). From 3 February from Liverpool Lime Street to Nottingham (Table 49)
- **H** Until 27 January. To Sheffield (Table 78)
- **J** To Cardiff Central (Table 131)
- **K** From 3 February. From Manchester Airport to Sheffield (Table 78)
- **L** To Shrewsbury (Table 131)
- **b** From 3 February arr. Wolverhampton 2135, Birmingham New Street 2156, change at Crewe and Stafford

Table 84

Sundays
from 30 March

Manchester, Stockport and Manchester Airport → Crewe and Stoke-on-Trent

Network Diagram - see first page of Table 78

	XC 1◇ A ☕	NT B	VT 1◇ ☕	TP 1◇ C	NT	NT	XC 1◇ D ☕	NT		NT E	VT 🚌	VT 🚌	VT 1◇ ☕	VT 1◇ ☕	NT G	NT	XC 1◇ H ☕		VT 🚌	VT 🚌	NT J	VT 1◇ ☕	VT 1◇ ☕	NT G
Deansgate d										09 18					09 43						10 18			10 43
Manchester Oxford Road d										09 21					09 46						10 21			10 46
Manchester Piccadilly 10 a										09 24					09 49						10 25			10 49
d	08 08	08 53	09 00	09 05	09 14	09 17	09 24			09 26			09 44	09 53	09 56	10 15	10 24				10 26	10 44	10 53	10 56
Levenshulme d		08 58								09 31					10 01						10 31			11 01
Heaton Chapel d		09 01								09 34					10 04						10 34			11 04
Stockport a		09 05		09 13		09 27	09 32			09 38				10 00	10 07	10 24	10 32				10 38		11 00	11 07
d			09u10			09 28	09 33			09 38			09u53	10 02		10 25	10 33				10 38	10u52	11 02	
Cheadle Hulme d										09 41											10 43			
Bramhall d																								
Poynton d																								
Adlington (Cheshire) d																								
Prestbury d																								
Macclesfield a						09 40										10 37								
d											09 10	09 20							10 10	10 20				
Congleton d																								
Handforth d								←		09 47											10 48			
Manchester Airport d					09 33 →			09 33																
Styal d																								
Wilmslow d	08 24		09 19				09 41	09 41		09 49		09a50	10 01	10 10			10 41			10a50	10 50	11 00	11 10	
Alderley Edge d								09 44		09a57											10a59			
Chelford d																								
Goostrey d																								
Holmes Chapel d								09 52																
Sandbach d								09 56																
Crewe 10 65 a	08 43		09 36				09 59	10 07									10 59							
Kidsgrove 50 a																								
Longport 50 a																								
Stoke-on-Trent 50, 68 a											10 00								11 00					
Stafford 68 a	09 18		10 06				10 21	*10 54*			10 30		10 40	10 47			11 21		11 30			11 38	11 47	
Wolverhampton 7 68 a	09 40						10 40							11 05			11 40						12 05	
Birmingham New Street 12 68 a	09 58						10 58							11 26			11 58						12 26	
London Euston 15 ⊖ 65 a	*12b00*		12 51					*13 23*					13 04	13c29								14 00	14c29	

	NT	TP 1◇ C	NT	XC 1◇ D ☕		VT 🚌	VT 🚌	NT J	VT 1◇ ☕	VT 1◇ ☕	NT G	XC R 1 K ☕	NT J		VT 🚌	VT 🚌	NT	AW R L	EM ◇ N	VT 1◇ ☕	VT 1◇ ☕	NT G		NT
Deansgate d								11 18			11 46		12 18									12 43		
Manchester Oxford Road d								11 21			11 50		12 21									12 46		
Manchester Piccadilly 10 a								11 24			11 52		12 24									12 49		
d	11 07	11 12	11 15	11 24				11 26	11 44	11 53	11 56	12 08	12 26				12 29	12 33	12 44	12 45	12 53	12 56		13 04
Levenshulme d								11 31			12 01		12 31									13 01		
Heaton Chapel d								11 34			12 04		12 34									13 04		
Stockport a		11 20	11 24	11 31				11 38		12 00	12 07	12 16	12 37				12 38	12 42	12 53		13 01	13 07		13 14
d			11 25	11 33				11 38	11u52	12 02		12 22	12 38				12 39	12 44		12u56	13 02			13 15
Cheadle Hulme d								11 42					12 42											
Bramhall d																								
Poynton d																								
Adlington (Cheshire) d																								
Prestbury d																								
Macclesfield a			11 37														12 55							13 27
d						11 10	11 20								12 10	12 20								
Congleton d																								
Handforth d								11 47					12 47											
Manchester Airport d	11 25																							
Styal d																								
Wilmslow d	11 33			11 41			11a50	11 50	12 01	12 10		12 30	12 50			12a50		12 54		13 04	13 11			
Alderley Edge d	11 36							11a58					12a58											
Chelford d																								
Goostrey d																								
Holmes Chapel d	11 44																							
Sandbach d	11 48																							
Crewe 10 65 a	11 59			12 01								12 53						13 19						
Kidsgrove 50 a																								
Longport 50 a																								
Stoke-on-Trent 50, 68 a						12 00									13 00									
Stafford 68 a	*12 42*			12 23		12 30			12 37	12 47		13 21			13 30					13 41	13 46			
Wolverhampton 7 68 a	*12 48*			12 40					*13 02*	13 05		13 40									14 05			
Birmingham New Street 12 68 a	*13 11*			12 58					*13 21*	13 26		13 58									14 26			
London Euston 15 ⊖ 65 a	*15 08*								14 56	15e16										15 56	16f16			

For general notes see front of timetable
For details of catering facilities see Directory of Train Operators

- **A** To Paignton (Table 51)
- **B** To Buxton (Table 86)
- **C** From Manchester Airport to Cleethorpes (Table 29)
- **D** To Oxford (Table 51)
- **E** From Wigan Wallgate (Table 82)
- **G** From Blackpool North (Table 82) to Buxton (Table 86)
- **H** To Plymouth (Table 51)
- **J** From Southport (Table 82)
- **K** To Penzance (Table 135)
- **L** To Hereford (Table 131)
- **N** To Norwich (Table 49)
- **b** Change at Stafford
- **c** By changing at Stafford, passengers may arrive 6 minutes earlier
- **e** By changing at Stafford, passengers may arrive at 1508
- **f** By changing at Stafford, passengers may arrive at 1607

Table 84

Sundays

Manchester, Stockport and Manchester Airport → Crewe and Stoke-on-Trent

from 30 March

Network Diagram - see first page of Table 78

		NT	TP	XC	VT	VT	NT	VT	EM		VT	NT	NT	TP	XC	VT	VT	NT		AW	EM	VT	VT	NT	NT
			■1 ◇	R ■1				■1 ◇	◇		■1 ◇			■1 ◇	R ■1					R	◇	■1 ◇	■1 ◇		
			A	B			C		D			E		A	G			C		H	D			E	
				☕	bus	bus		☕			☕				☕	bus	bus					☕	☕		
Deansgate	d						13 18					13 43						14 18						14 43	
Manchester Oxford Road	d						13 21		13 41			13 46						14 21			14 39			14 46	
Manchester Piccadilly 10	a						13 24		13 44			13 49						14 24			14 41			14 49	
	d	13 08	13 12	13 24			13 28	13 45	13 49		13 53	13 56	14 08	14 15	14 24			14 26		14 34	14 43	14 45	14 53	14 56	15 02
Levenshulme	d						13 33					14 01						14 32						15 01	
Heaton Chapel	d						13 36					14 04						14 35						15 04	
Stockport	a		13 21	13 32			13 39		13 58		14 02	14 07	14 17	14 22	14 32			14 38		14 42	14 51		15 01	15 07	15 11
	d			13 33			13 40	13u55			14 03		14 18		14 33			14 39		14 42		14u55	15 02		15 12
Cheadle Hulme	d						13 44											14 43							15 16
Bramhall	d																								15 19
Poynton	d																								15 22
Adlington (Cheshire)	d																								15 25
Prestbury	d																								15 28
Macclesfield	a												14 32												15 32
	d				13 10	13 20										14 10	14 20								
Congleton	d																								
Handforth	d						13 48											14 48							
Manchester Airport	d	13 26																							
Styal	d																								
Wilmslow	d	13 33		13 41		13a50	13 51	14 03			14 11				14 41		14a50	14 51		14 55		15 03	15 10		
Alderley Edge	d	13 36					13a58											14a59							
Chelford	d																								
Goostrey	d																								
Holmes Chapel	d	13 44																							
Sandbach	d	13 48																							
Crewe 10	65 a	13 59		14 01											15 00					15 17					
Kidsgrove	50 a																								
Longport	50 a																								
Stoke-on-Trent	50, 68 a				14 00											15 00									
Stafford	68 a	*14 31*		14 22	14 30			14 40			14 47				15 21	15 30						15 40	15 47		
Wolverhampton 7	68 a	*14 49*		14 40							15 04				15 40								16 04		
Birmingham New Street 12	68 a	*15 08*		14 58							15 26				15 58								16 26		
London Euston 15	⊖ 65 a	*16b56*						16 56			17 11											17 56	18 11		

		NT	NT	TP	XC		VT	VT	NT	NT	AW	EM	VT	VT		NT	NT	TP	XC	VT	VT	NT	AW		EM
				■1 ◇	R ■1						R	◇	■1 ◇	■1 ◇				■1 ◇	R ■1				R		◇
			J	A	B					C	H	D				E		A	K			C	H		D
					☕		bus	bus	bus				☕	☕					☕	bus	bus				
Deansgate	d									15 18						15 43						16 18			
Manchester Oxford Road	d									15 21		15 39				15 46						16 21			16 39
Manchester Piccadilly 10	a									15 24		15 41				15 49						16 24			16 41
	d	15 05	15 08	15 15	15 24					15 26	15 40	15 43	15 45	15 53		15 53	16 02	16 15	16 24			16 26	16 37		16 43
Levenshulme	d									15 31						15 58						16 31			
Heaton Chapel	d									15 34						16 01						16 34			
Stockport	a		15 17	15 22	15 32					15 36	15 48	15 52		16 01		16 04	16 11	16 22	16 31			16 37	16 45		16 52
	d				15 33					15 38	15 49		15u55	16 02			16 12		16 33			16 38	16 45		
Cheadle Hulme	d									15 44												16 42			
Bramhall	d																								
Poynton	d																								
Adlington (Cheshire)	d																								
Prestbury	d																								
Macclesfield	a																16 24								
	d						15 10	15 20	15 40											16 10	16 20				
Congleton	d								15 59																
Handforth	d									15 49												16 47			
Manchester Airport	d	15 25																							
Styal	d																								
Wilmslow	d	15 33			15 41			15a50		15 52	15 56		16 03	16 13					16 41		16a50	16 50	16 54		
Alderley Edge	d	15 36								15a58												16a58			
Chelford	d																								
Goostrey	d																								
Holmes Chapel	d	15 44																							
Sandbach	d	15 47																							
Crewe 10	65 a	15 58			16 01						16 26								16 59				17 17		
Kidsgrove	50 a								16 13																
Longport	50 a																								
Stoke-on-Trent	50, 68 a						16 00		16 39											17 00					
Stafford	68 a	*16 36*			16 23		16 30						16 39	16 46					17 21	17 30					
Wolverhampton 7	68 a	*16 54*			16 40									17 04					17 40						
Birmingham New Street 12	68 a	*17 11*			16 58									17 26					17 58						
London Euston 15	⊖ 65 a	*18b51*											18 51	19 17											

For general notes see front of timetable
For details of catering facilities see Directory of Train Operators

A From Manchester Airport to Cleethorpes (Table 29)
B To Oxford (Table 51)
C From Southport (Table 82)
D From Liverpool Lime Street to Norwich (Table 49)
E From Blackpool North (Table 82) to Buxton (Table 86)
G To Penzance (Table 135)
H To Hereford (Table 131)
J To Sheffield (Table 78)
K To Plymouth (Table 51)
b Change at Crewe and Stafford

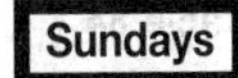

from 30 March

Manchester, Stockport and Manchester Airport → Crewe and Stoke-on-Trent

Network Diagram - see first page of Table 78

	VT	VT	NT	NT	NT	TP	XC	NT		VT	VT	EM	NT	VT	VT	NT	NT		TP	XC	VT	VT	NT	NT
	1 ◇	1 ◇				1 ◇	R 1					◇		1 ◇	1 ◇				1 ◇	R 1				
			A			B	C	D				E				A			B	G				D
	☕	☕					☕			🚌	🚌			☕	☕					☕	🚌	🚌	🚌	
Deansgate d			16 43					17 18								17 43								18 18
Manchester Oxford Road d			16 46					17 21				17 39				17 46								18 21
Manchester Piccadilly 10 a			16 49					17 24				17 41				17 49								18 24
d	16 45	16 53	16 53	17 02	17 06	17 15	17 24	17 26				17 43		17 45	17 53	17 53	18 02		18 15	18 24				18 26
Levenshulme d			16 58					17 31								17 58								18 31
Heaton Chapel d			17 01					17 34								18 01								18 34
Stockport a		17 01	17 04	17 11		17 22	17 31	17 37				17 52			18 00	18 04	18 11		18 22	18 31				18 38
d	16u55	17 02		17 12			17 33	17 38						17u55	18 02		18 12			18 33				18 38
Cheadle Hulme d								17 42									18 16							18 42
Bramhall d																	18 19							
Poynton d																	18 22							
Adlington (Cheshire) d																	18 25							
Prestbury d																	18 28							
Macclesfield a				17 24													18 32							
d										17 10	17 20										18 10	18 20	18 40	
Congleton d																							18 59	
Handforth d								17 47																18 47
Manchester Airport d					17 24																			
Styal d																								
Wilmslow d	17 03	17 12			17 32		17 41	17 49			17a50			18 03	18 12					18 41		18a50		18 50
Alderley Edge d					17 35			17a58																18a58
Chelford d					17 40								←											
Goostrey d					17 51 →								17 51											
Holmes Chapel d													17 54											
Sandbach d													17 58											
Crewe 10 65 a							17 59						18 07							18 59				
Kidsgrove 50 a																							19 13	
Longport 50 a																								
Stoke-on-Trent 50, 68 a										18 00											19 00		19 39	
Stafford 68 a	17 39	17 47					18 21			18 30			*18 53*	18 40	18 47					19 21	19 30			
Wolverhampton 7 68 a		18 04					18 40						*19 40*		19 04					19 40				
Birmingham New Street 12 68 a		18 26					18 58						*19 58*		19 26					19 58				
London Euston 15 ⊖ 65 a	19 53	20 11											*21 14*	20 53	21 17									

	AW	EM	VT	VT		NT	NT	NT	TP	XC	VT	VT	NT		EM	VT	NT	VT	VT	VT	NT	TP		VT
	R	◇	1 ◇	1 ◇					1 ◇	1 ◇					◇	1 ◇		1 ◇				1 ◇		1 ◇
	H	J				A			B	C			D		E		A					B		
			☕	☕							🚌	🚌				☕		☕	🚌	🚌				☕
Deansgate d						18 43							19 18				19 43							
Manchester Oxford Road d		18 39				18 46							19 21		19 39		19 46							
Manchester Piccadilly 10 a		18 41				18 49							19 24		19 41		19 49							
d	18 37	18 42	18 45	18 53		18 53	19 02	19 06	19 15	19 24			19 26		19 42	19 45	19 53	19 55			20 02	20 15		20 23
Levenshulme d						18 58							19 31				19 58							
Heaton Chapel d						19 01							19 34				20 01							
Stockport a	18 45	18 52		19 00		19 04	19 11		19 22	19 31			19 38		19 52		20 04	20 03			20 11	20 22		20 31
d	18 45		18u55	19 02			19 12			19 33			19 38			19u55		20 04			20 12			20 32
Cheadle Hulme d													19 42											
Bramhall d																								
Poynton d																								
Adlington (Cheshire) d																								
Prestbury d																								
Macclesfield a							19 24														20 24			
d											19 10	19 20							19 50	20 00				
Congleton d																								
Handforth d													19 47											
Manchester Airport d								19 25																
Styal d																								
Wilmslow d	18 55		19 03	19 12				19 32		19 41		19a50	19 50			20 03		20 13		20a30				20 40
Alderley Edge d								19 35					19a58											
Chelford d																								
Goostrey d																								
Holmes Chapel d								19 43																
Sandbach d								19 48																
Crewe 10 65 a	19 18							19 59		20 00														
Kidsgrove 50 a																								
Longport 50 a																								
Stoke-on-Trent 50, 68 a											20 00								20 40					
Stafford 68 a			19 40	19 47				*20 58*		20 22	20 30					20 40		20 51	21 10					21 19
Wolverhampton 7 68 a				20 04				*20 52*		20 40								21 08						21 35
Birmingham New Street 12 68 a				20 26				*21 15*		20 58								21 32						21 56
London Euston 15 ⊖ 65 a			21 57	22 27				*23 25*								23 00		23b25						23 58

For general notes see front of timetable
For details of catering facilities see Directory of Train Operators

- **A** From Blackpool North (Table 82) to Buxton (Table 86)
- **B** From Manchester Airport to Cleethorpes (Table 29)
- **C** To Oxford (Table 51)
- **D** From Southport (Table 82)
- **E** From Liverpool Lime Street to Nottingham (Table 49)
- **G** To Plymouth (Table 51)
- **H** To Shrewsbury (Table 131)
- **J** From Liverpool Lime Street to Norwich (Table 49)
- **b** Change at Stafford

Sundays

from 30 March

Manchester, Stockport and Manchester Airport → Crewe and Stoke-on-Trent

Network Diagram - see first page of Table 78

		NT	EM	AW	NT	XC	NT	NT	TP		NT	NT	NT	XC	NT	EM	TP	NT		AW	NT	TP	NT		
			◇	◇		1 ◇			1 ◇					1 ◇		◇	1 ◇					1 ◇			
		A	B	C	D				E		🚌	A	D			B	E	A		G	D	E	A		
Deansgate	🚢 d	20 18			20 43							21 18	21 43					22 18			22 43		23 18		
Manchester Oxford Road	d	20 21	20 39		20 46							21 21	21 46			22 08		22 22			22 46		23 21		
Manchester Piccadilly 10	🚢 a	20 24	20 41		20 49							21 24	21 49			22 10		22 24			22 49		23 25		
	d	20 26	20 43	20 46	20 53	20 55	21 02	21 06	21 15			21 26	21 53	21 55	22 02	22 12	22 15	22 26		22 46	22 51	23 15	23 26		
Levenshulme	d	20 31			20 58							21 31	21 58					22 31			22 56		23 32		
Heaton Chapel	d	20 34			21 01							21 34	22 01					22 34			22 59		23 35		
Stockport	a	20 38	20 52	20 54	21 04	21 03	21 11		21 22			21 36	22 04	22 03	22 12	22 21	22 22	22 37		22 54	23 03	23 20	23 38		
	d	20 38		20 54		21 04	21 12					21 38		22 04	22 13			22 38		22 54			23 39		
Cheadle Hulme	d	20 42					21 16					21 42						22 42					23 43		
Bramhall	d						21 19																		
Poynton	d						21 22																		
Adlington (Cheshire)	d						21 25																		
Prestbury	d						21 28																		
Macclesfield	a						21 32								22 25										
	d										21 40														
Congleton	d										21 59														
Handforth	d	20 47										21 47						22 47					23 47		
Manchester Airport	✈ d							21 25																	
Styal	d																								
Wilmslow	d	20 50		21 02		21 12		21 32				21 50		22 12				22 50		23 02			23 50		
Alderley Edge	d	20a58						21 35				21a58						22a58					23a58		
Chelford	d																								
Goostrey	d																								
Holmes Chapel	d							21 43																	
Sandbach	d							21 48																	
Crewe 10	65 a			21 25		21 31		21 59						22 31						23 24					
Kidsgrove	50 a										22 13														
Longport	50 a																								
Stoke-on-Trent	50, 68 a										22 39														
Stafford	68 a					21 52		22 39						22 52											
Wolverhampton 7	68 🚢 a					22 09		22 54						23 09											
Birmingham New Street 12	68 a					22 30		23 17						23 30											
London Euston 15	⊖ 65 a																								

For general notes see front of timetable
For details of catering facilities see Directory of Train Operators

A From Southport (Table 82)
B From Liverpool Lime Street to Nottingham (Table 49)
C To Hereford (Table 131)
D From Blackpool North (Table 82) to Buxton (Table 86)
E From Manchester Airport to Sheffield (Table 78)
G To Shrewsbury (Table 131)

Manchester → Manchester Airport

Network Diagram - see first page of Table 78

Miles			TP	TP	TP	TP	TP	TP	TP	TP	TP	NT	TP	TP	TP	TP	NT	TP	NT	TP	TP	NT	TP	TP	NT
			MO	MX	MO	MX		MX	MO	MO					MX	MO									
			1◇	1◇	1◇	1◇	1◇	1◇	1◇	1◇	1◇		1◇	1◇	1◇	1◇		1◇		1◇	1◇		1◇	1◇	
			A	B	C	D	E	B	A	G	H	J	K	H	B	A	L	N	J	H	K		H	B	J
—	Deansgate	d																						06 49	
—	Manchester Oxford Road	d																						06 52	07 00
—	Manchester Piccadilly 10	a																						06 56	07 03
0		d	00 17	00 30	00 35	00 54	02 50	02 55	02 55	02 58	04 00	04 15	04 44	05 00	05u05	05u05	05 26	05 59	06 03	06 07	06 12	06 32	06 53	06 57	07 04
3½	Mauldeth Road	d															05 33				06 19	06 39			
4½	Burnage	d															05 35				06 21	06 41			
5½	East Didsbury	d															05 37			06 15		06 43			
6¾	Gatley	d															05 39			06 18		06 45			
8¼	Heald Green	d		00 40													05 42			06 21		06 48			
9¾	Manchester Airport	a	00 33	00 45	00 54	01 10	03 06	03 09	03 09	03 14	04 15	04 30	05 01	05 19	05 22	05 22	05 47	06 14	06 19	06 29	06 34	06 53	07 12	07 15	07 20
—	Wilmslow	84 a															06 00					07 04			
—	Crewe 10	84 a															*06 40*					07 31			

		TP	TP	TP	NT	NT	TP	TP	NT	TP	TP	TP	NT	NT	TP	TP	NT	TP	TP	TP	NT	NT	TP	TP	NT
		1◇	1◇	1◇			1◇	1◇		1◇	1◇	1◇			1◇	1◇		1◇	1◇	1◇			1◇	1◇	
		Q	U	H		V	B	H	J	X	Y	C		N	B	Z	J	X	U	Z		V	C	B	J
				🛒			🛒	🛒		🛒	🛒	🛒			🛒	🛒		🛒	🛒	🛒			🛒	🛒	
Deansgate	d					07 39								08 41					09 15			09 40			
Manchester Oxford Road	d		07 13			07 43	07 52		08 03		08 20			08 45	08 50		08 59		09 17			09 43		09 55	09 59
Manchester Piccadilly 10	a		07 15			07 45	07 54		08 06		08 25			08 47	08 53		09 02		09 20			09 45		09 57	10 02
	d	07 08	07 17	07 30	07 34	07 47	07 55	08 03	08 07	08 14	08 25	08 30	08 34	08 49	08 54	08 55	09 03	09 08	09 21	09 27	09 33	09 47	09 53	09 59	10 03
Mauldeth Road	d	07 17			07 42			08 10					08 41					09 17			09 40				
Burnage	d	07 19			07 44		08 03						08 43					09 19			09 42				
East Didsbury	d	07 22			07 46		08 05				08 34		08 45		09 02		09 12				09 44				10 12
Gatley	d	07 24			07 49		08 08						08 48				09 15				09 46				10 15
Heald Green	d	07 27	07 32		07 52		08 11			08 25			08 51				09 18		09 32		09 49			10 12	10 18
Manchester Airport	a	07 35	07 40	07 49	07 57	08 02	08 19	08 22	08 25	08 33	08 42	08 51	08 57	09 06	09 13	09 18	09 25	09 33	09 40	09 44	09 56	10 01	10 14	10 19	10 25
Wilmslow	84 a				08 07								09 07								10 06				
Crewe 10	84 a				08 37								09 33								10 33				

		TP	TP	TP	NT		NT	TP	TP	NT	TP	TP	TP	NT	NT	TP	TP	NT	TP	TP	TP	NT	NT	TP	TP
		1◇	1◇	1◇				1◇	1◇		1◇	1◇	1◇			1◇	1◇		1◇	1◇	1◇			1◇	1◇
		X	AA	D			V	H	B	J	X	U	C		V	D	B	J	X	BB	C		V	D	B
		🛒	🛒	🛒				🛒	🛒		🛒	🛒	🛒			🛒	🛒		🛒	🛒	🛒			🛒	🛒
Deansgate	d											11 15													
Manchester Oxford Road	d		10 18				10 43		10 55	10 59		11 18			11 43		11 55	11 59		12 18			12 43		12 55
Manchester Piccadilly 10	a		10 20				10 45		10 57	11 02		11 20			11 45		11 57	12 02		12 20			12 45		12 57
	d	10 08	10 22	10 27	10 33		10 47	10 53	10 59	11 03	11 08	11 22	11 27	11 33	11 47	11 53	11 59	12 03	12 08	12 22	12 27	12 33	12 47	12 53	12 59
Mauldeth Road	d	10 17			10 40						11 17			11 40					12 17			12 40			
Burnage	d	10 19			10 42						11 19			11 42					12 19			12 42			
East Didsbury	d				10 44					11 12				11 44				12 12				12 44			
Gatley	d				10 46					11 15				11 46				12 15				12 46			
Heald Green	d		10 32		10 49				11 12	11 18		11 32		11 49			12 12	12 18		12 32		12 49			13 12
Manchester Airport	a	10 33	10 40	10 44	10 56		11 01	11 14	11 19	11 25	11 33	11 40	11 44	11 56	12 01	12 14	12 19	12 25	12 33	12 40	12 51	12 56	13 01	13 14	13 19
Wilmslow	84 a				11 06									12 06								13 06			
Crewe 10	84 a				11 33									12 33								13 33			

		NT	TP	TP	TP	NT	NT	TP	TP	NT	TP	TP	TP	NT	NT	TP	TP	NT	TP	TP	TP	NT	NT	TP	TP
			1◇	1◇	1◇			1◇	1◇		1◇	1◇	1◇			1◇	1◇		1◇	1◇	1◇			1◇	1◇
		J	X	U	C		V	D	B	J	X	CC	C		V	D	B	J	X	DD	C		V	D	B
			🛒	🛒	🛒			🛒	🛒		🛒	🛒	🛒			🛒	🛒		🛒	🛒	🛒			🛒	🛒
Deansgate	d			13 15								14 15													
Manchester Oxford Road	d	12 59		13 18			13 43		13 55	13 59		14 18			14 43		14 55	14 59		15 18			15 43		15 55
Manchester Piccadilly 10	a	13 02		13 20			13 45		13 57	14 02		14 20			14 45		14 57	15 02		15 20			15 45		15 57
	d	13 03	13 08	13 22	13 27	13 33	13 47	13 53	13 59	14 03	14 08	14 22	14 27	14 33	14 47	14 53	14 59	15 03	15 08	15 22	15 27	15 33	15 47	15 53	15 59
Mauldeth Road	d		13 17			13 40					14 17			14 40					15 17			15 40			
Burnage	d		13 19			13 42					14 19			14 42					15 19			15 42			
East Didsbury	d	13 12				13 44				14 12				14 44				15 12				15 44			
Gatley	d	13 15				13 46				14 15				14 46				15 15				15 46			
Heald Green	d	13 18		13 32		13 49			14 12	14 18		14 32		14 49			15 12	15 18		15 32		15 49			16 12
Manchester Airport	a	13 25	13 33	13 40	13 44	13 56	14 01	14 14	14 19	14 25	14 33	14 40	14 44	14 56	15 01	15 14	15 19	15 25	15 33	15 40	15 44	15 56	16 01	16 14	16 19
Wilmslow	84 a					14 06								15 06								16 06			
Crewe 10	84 a					14 33								15 33								16 36			

		NT	TP	TP	TP	NT	TP	TP	NT	TP	TP	NT	NT	TP	TP	NT	TP	TP	TP	NT	NT	TP	TP	NT	TP
			1◇	1◇	1◇		1◇	1◇		1◇	1◇			1◇	1◇		1◇	1◇	1◇			1◇	1◇		1◇
		J	X	EE	C		D	B	J	X	AA		V	D	B	J	X	U	C	L	V	D	B	J	X
			🛒	🛒	🛒		🛒	🛒		🛒	🛒			🛒	🛒		🛒	🛒	🛒			🛒			
Deansgate	d			16 15														18 15							
Manchester Oxford Road	d	15 59		16 18				16 55	16 59		17 18		17 46		17 55	17 59		18 18			18 49		18 55	19 01	
Manchester Piccadilly 10	a	16 01		16 20				16 57	17 02		17 20		17 49		17 57	18 04		18 20			18 51		18 59	19 05	
	d	16 03	16 08	16 22	16 27	16 33	16 53	16 59	17 03	17 14	17 22	17 33	17 50	17 58	17 59	18 05	18 08	18 22	18 27	18 36	18 53	18 55	18 59	19 06	19 08
Mauldeth Road	d		16 17			16 40			17 10	17 21		17 40					18 17			18 43					19 17
Burnage	d		16 19			16 42			17 13	17 24		17 42					18 19			18 45					19 19
East Didsbury	d	16 12				16 44		17 06		17 26		17 44				18 15	18 22			18 47					19 22
Gatley	d	16 15				16 46		17 09		17 29		17 46				18 18	18 24			18 49					19 24
Heald Green	d	16 18			16 38	16 49		17 12		17 32		17 49			18 12	18 21	18 27	18 35	18 40	18 52		19 07	19 12		19 27
Manchester Airport	a	16 25	16 33	16 40	16 51	16 56	17 14	17 19	17 25	17 39	17 40	17 56	18 05	18 14	18 19	18 27	18 38	18 42	18 46	18 57	19 09	19 14	19 19	19 26	19 34
Wilmslow	84 a					17 06						18 11								19 07					
Crewe 10	84 a					17 33						18 41								*19 56*					

For general notes see front of timetable
For details of catering facilities see Directory of Train Operators

- **A** From Blackpool North (4 February to 24 March from Preston) (Table 82)
- **B** From Blackpool North (Table 82)
- **C** From Middlesbrough (Table 39)
- **D** From Newcastle (Table 39)
- **E** All Tuesdays to Fridays, also Mondays from 4 February. From Sheffield (Table 78)
- **G** Until 28 January. From Sheffield (Table 78)
- **H** From York (Table 39)
- **J** From Liverpool Lime Street (Table 90)
- **K** From Sheffield (Table 78)
- **L** To Alderley Edge (Table 84)
- **N** From Preston (Table 82)
- **Q** From Doncaster (Table 29)
- **U** From Barrow-in-Furness (Table 82)
- **V** From Southport (Table 82)
- **X** From Cleethorpes (Table 29)
- **Y** From Barrow-in-Furness and from Blackpool North (Table 82)
- **Z** From Scarborough (Table 39)
- **AA** From Glasgow Central (Table 65)
- **BB** From Glasgow Central and from Edinburgh (Table 65)
- **CC** From Windermere (Table 83)
- **DD** From Edinburgh (Table 65)
- **EE** From Windermere (Table 83) and from Barrow-in-Furness (Table 82)

Manchester → Manchester Airport

Network Diagram - see first page of Table 78

Mondays to Fridays

		TP 1◇ A 🍴	NT	NT B	TP 1◇ C	TP 1◇ D	TP 1◇ E	TP 1◇ G	TP 1◇ H	NT	NT B	TP 1◇ D	NT J	TP 1◇ G	TP 1◇ A 🍴	TP 1◇ K	TP 1◇ C	NT	TP 1◇ D	TP 1◇ H	NT	TP 1◇ G	TP 1◇ D
Deansgate	d					19 53						20 53							22 13				23 15
Manchester Oxford Road	d	19 17		19 43		19 55	20 00				20 42	20 55	21 01		21 12	21 28			22 16				23 26
Manchester Piccadilly 10	a	19 20		19 46		19 57	20 04				20 45	20 58	21 05		21 14	21 30			22 18				23 30
	d	19 21	19 30	19 47	19 53	19 59	20 05	20 08	20 38	20 44	20 47	20 59	21 06	21 08	21 16	21 32	21 38	21 52	22 21	22 38	22 46	23 08	23 30
Mauldeth Road	d		19 37					20 17		20 51				21 17				22 00			22 53		23 36
Burnage	d		19 39					20 19		20 53				21 19				22 02			22 55		23 39
East Didsbury	d		19 41					20 22		20 55				21 22				22 04			22 57		23 41
Gatley	d		19 44					20 24		20 58				21 24				22 06			22 59		23 43
Heald Green	d	19 32	19 47			20 12	20 18	20 27		21 01		21 12		21 27	21 30	21 44		22 09	22 31		23 02		23 47
Manchester Airport ✈	a	19 40	19 52	20 05	20 12	20 19	20 26	20 34	20 58	21 06	21 09	21 19	21 28	21 34	21 37	21 51	21 58	22 15	22 39	22 58	23 09	23 28	23 58
Wilmslow	84 a		20 06							21 19								22 29			23 22		
Crewe 10	84 a		*20 56*							*21 56*								*23 11*			*00 31*		

Saturdays

		TP 1◇ D	TP 1◇ C	TP 1◇ L	TP 1◇ D	TP 1◇ N	NT J	TP 1◇ L	TP 1◇ N	TP 1◇ D	NT Q	TP 1◇ U	NT J	TP 1◇ N		TP 1◇ L	NT	TP 1◇ N	TP 1◇ D	NT J	TP 1◇ V	TP 1◇ X	TP 1◇ N	NT	NT B
Deansgate	d																		06 49						07 39
Manchester Oxford Road	d																		06 52	07 00		07 13			07 43
Manchester Piccadilly 10	a																		06 56	07 03		07 15			07 45
	d	00 30	00 54	02 50	03 00	04 00	04 15	04 44	04 59	05u01	05 26	05 59	06 03	06 07		06 12	06 32	06 53	06 57	07 04	07 08	07 17	07 30	07 34	07 47
Mauldeth Road	d										05 33					06 19	06 39				07 17			07 42	
Burnage	d										05 35					06 21	06 41				07 19			07 44	
East Didsbury	d										05 37			06 17			06 43				07 22			07 46	
Gatley	d										05 39			06 19			06 45				07 24			07 49	
Heald Green	d	00 40									05 42			06 21			06 48				07 27	07 32		07 52	
Manchester Airport ✈	a	00 45	01 10	03 06	03 13	04 15	04 30	05 01	05 19	05 21	05 47	06 14	06 19	06 29		06 34	06 53	07 12	07 15	07 20	07 35	07 40	07 49	07 57	08 02
Wilmslow	84 a										06 01						07 04							08 07	
Crewe 10	84 a										*07 04*						07 31							08 34	

		TP 1◇ D	TP 1◇ N	NT J	TP 1◇ G 🍴	TP 1◇ Y 🍴		TP 1◇ H	NT	NT U	TP 1◇ D 🍴	TP 1◇ Z	NT J	TP 1◇ G 🍴	TP 1◇ X 🍴	TP 1◇ Z	NT	NT B	TP 1◇ H 🍴	TP 1◇ D		NT J	TP 1◇ G 🍴	TP 1◇ AA 🍴	TP 1◇ C 🍴
Deansgate	d									08 41					09 15										
Manchester Oxford Road	d	07 52		08 03		08 21				08 45	08 50		08 59		09 17			09 43		09 55		09 59		10 18	
Manchester Piccadilly 10	a	07 54		08 06		08 25				08 47	08 53		09 02		09 20			09 45		09 57		10 02		10 20	
	d	07 56	08 03	08 07	08 14	08 25		08 30	08 34	08 49	08 54	08 55	09 03	09 08	09 21	09 27	09 33	09 47	09 53	09 59		10 03	10 08	10 22	10 27
Mauldeth Road	d		08 10						08 41					09 17			09 40						10 17		
Burnage	d	08 03							08 43					09 19			09 42						10 19		
East Didsbury	d	08 05				08 34			08 45		09 02		09 12				09 44					10 12			
Gatley	d	08 08							08 48				09 15				09 46					10 15			
Heald Green	d	08 11			08 25				08 51				09 18		09 31		09 49			10 12		10 18		10 32	
Manchester Airport ✈	a	08 19	08 22	08 25	08 33	08 42		08 51	08 57	09 06	09 13	09 18	09 25	09 33	09 40	09 44	09 56	10 02	10 14	10 19		10 25	10 33	10 40	10 44
Wilmslow	84 a								09 07								10 06								
Crewe 10	84 a								09 33								10 33								

		NT	NT B	TP 1◇ N 🍴	TP 1◇ D 🍴	NT J	TP 1◇ G 🍴	TP 1◇ X 🍴	TP 1◇ H 🍴	NT	NT B	TP 1◇ C		TP 1◇ D 🍴	NT J	TP 1◇ G 🍴	TP 1◇ BB 🍴	TP 1◇ H 🍴	NT	NT B	TP 1◇ C 🍴	TP 1◇ D 🍴	NT J	TP 1◇ G 🍴	TP 1◇ X 🍴
Deansgate	d							11 15																	13 15
Manchester Oxford Road	d		10 43		10 55	10 59		11 18			11 43			11 55	11 59		12 18			12 43		12 55	12 59		13 18
Manchester Piccadilly 10	a		10 45		10 57	11 02		11 20			11 45			11 57	12 02		12 20			12 45		12 57	13 02		13 20
	d	10 33	10 47	10 53	10 59	11 03	11 08	11 22	11 27	11 33	11 47	11 53		11 59	12 03	12 08	12 22	12 27	12 33	12 47	12 53	12 59	13 03	13 08	13 22
Mauldeth Road	d	10 40					11 17			11 40						12 17			12 40					13 17	
Burnage	d	10 42					11 19			11 42						12 19			12 42					13 19	
East Didsbury	d	10 44				11 12				11 44					12 12				12 44				13 12		
Gatley	d	10 46				11 15				11 46					12 15				12 46				13 15		
Heald Green	d	10 49			11 12	11 18		11 32		11 49				12 12	12 18		12 32		12 49			13 12	13 18		13 32
Manchester Airport ✈	a	10 56	11 01	11 14	11 19	11 25	11 33	11 40	11 44	11 56	12 01	12 14		12 19	12 25	12 33	12 40	12b51	12 56	13 01	13 14	13 19	13 25	13 33	13 40
Wilmslow	84 a	11 06								12 06									13 06						
Crewe 10	84 a	11 33								12 33									13 33						

For general notes see front of timetable
For details of catering facilities see Directory of Train Operators

- **A** From Edinburgh (Table 65)
- **B** From Southport (Table 82)
- **C** From Newcastle (Table 39)
- **D** From Blackpool North (Table 82)
- **E** From Windermere (Table 82)
- **G** From Cleethorpes (Table 29)
- **H** From Middlesbrough (Table 39)
- **J** From Liverpool Lime Street (Table 90)
- **K** From Barrow-in-Furness (Table 82)
- **L** From Sheffield (Table 78)
- **N** From York (Table 39)
- **Q** To Alderley Edge (Table 84)
- **U** From Preston (Table 82)
- **V** From Doncaster (Table 29)
- **X** From Barrow-in-Furness (from 29 March from Preston) (Table 82)
- **Y** From Blackpool North (Table 82). Until 22 March also conveys portion from Barrow-in-Furness
- **Z** From Scarborough (Table 39)
- **AA** Until 26 January from Glasgow Central (Table 65). 2 February to 22 March from Carlisle (Table 65). From 29 March from Preston (Table 82)
- **BB** Until 26 January from Glasgow Central and from Edinburgh (Table 65). 2 February to 22 March from Carlisle (Table 65). From 29 March from Preston (Table 82)
- **b** From 2 February arr. 1244

Table 85

Manchester → Manchester Airport

Network Diagram - see first page of Table 78

		TP 1◇ A ⊼	NT	NT B		TP 1◇ C ⊼	TP 1◇ D ⊼	NT E	TP 1◇ G ⊼	TP 1◇ H ⊼	TP 1◇ A ⊼	NT	NT B	TP 1◇ C ⊼	TP 1◇ D ⊼	NT E	TP 1◇ G ⊼	TP 1◇ J ⊼		TP 1◇ A ⊼	NT	NT B	TP 1◇ C ⊼	TP 1◇ D	NT E
Deansgate	d									14 15															
Manchester Oxford Road	d			13 43			13 55	13 59		14 18			14 43		14 55	14 59		15 18				15 43		15 55	15 59
Manchester Piccadilly 10	a			13 45			13 57	14 02		14 20			14 45		14 57	15 02		15 20				15 45		15 57	16 01
	d	13 27	13 33	13 47		13 53	13 59	14 03	14 08	14 22	14 27	14 33	14 47	14 53	14 59	15 03	15 08	15 22		15 27	15 33	15 47	15 53	15 59	16 03
Mauldeth Road	d		13 40						14 17			14 40					15 17				15 40				
Burnage	d		13 42						14 19			14 42					15 19				15 42				
East Didsbury	d		13 44					14 12				14 44				15 12					15 44				16 12
Gatley	d		13 46					14 15				14 46				15 15					15 46				16 15
Heald Green	d		13 49				14 12	14 18		14 32		14 49			15 12	15 18		15 32			15 49			16 12	16 18
Manchester Airport	a	13 44	13 56	14 01		14 14	14 19	14 25	14 33	14 40	14 44	14 56	15 01	15 14	15 19	15 25	15 33	15 40		15 44	15 56	16 01	16 14	16 19	16 25
Wilmslow	84 a		14 06									15 06									16 06				
Crewe 10	84 a		14 33									15 33									16 36				

		TP 1◇ G ⊼	TP 1◇ K ⊼	TP 1◇ A ⊼	NT	TP 1◇ C ⊼	TP 1◇ D	NT E	TP 1◇ G ⊼	TP 1◇ L ⊼		NT	NT B	TP 1◇ C ⊼	TP 1◇ D	NT E	TP 1◇ G ⊼	TP 1◇ N ⊼	TP 1◇ A ⊼	NT Q	NT B	TP 1◇ C ⊼	TP 1◇ D	NT E	TP 1◇ G
Deansgate	d		16 15															18 15							
Manchester Oxford Road	d		16 18				16 55	16 59		17 18			17 46		17 55	17 59		18 18			18 49		18 55	19 01	
Manchester Piccadilly 10	a		16 20				16 57	17 02		17 20			17 49		17 57	18 04		18 20			18 51		18 59	19 05	
	d	16 08	16 22	16 27	16 33	16 53	16 59	17 03	17 14	17 22		17 33	17 50	17 58	17 59	18 05	18 08	18 22	18 27	18 36	18 53	18 55	18 59	19 06	19 08
Mauldeth Road	d	16 17			16 40			17 10	17 21			17 40					18 17			18 43					19 17
Burnage	d	16 19			16 42			17 13	17 24			17 42					18 19			18 45					19 19
East Didsbury	d				16 44		17 06		17 26			17 44				18 15	18 22			18 47					19 22
Gatley	d				16 46		17 09		17 29			17 46				18 18	18 24			18 49					19 24
Heald Green	d			16 38	16 49		17 12		17 32			17 49			18 14	18 21	18 27	18 35	18 40	18 52		19 07	19 12		19 27
Manchester Airport	a	16 33	16 40	16b51	16 56	17 11	17 19	17 25	17 39	17 40		17 56	18 05	18 14	18 19	18 27	18 38	18 42	18 46	18 57	19 08	19 14	19 19	19 26	19 34
Wilmslow	84 a				17 06							18 10								19 11					
Crewe 10	84 a				17 33							18 37								*19 56*					

		TP 1◇ J ⊼		NT	NT B	TP 1◇ C	TP 1◇ D	TP 1◇ H	TP 1◇ G	TP 1◇ A	NT	NT B	TP 1◇ D	NT E	TP 1◇ G	TP 1◇ J ⊼	TP 1◇ N	TP 1◇ C	NT	TP 1◇ D	TP 1◇ A	NT	TP 1◇ D		
Deansgate	d						19 53						20 53							22 13			23 15		
Manchester Oxford Road	d	19 17			19 43		19 55	19 59				20 42	20 55	21 01		21 12	21 28			22 16			23 26		
Manchester Piccadilly 10	a	19 20			19 47		19 58	20 04				20 45	20 58	21 05		21 14	21 30			22 18			23 30		
	d	19 21		19 30	19 47	19 53	19 59	20 05	20 08	20 38	20 44	20 47	20 59	21 06	21 08	21 16	21 32	21 38	21 55	22 21	22 38	22 46	23 30		
Mauldeth Road	d			19 37					20 17		20 51				21 17				22 02			22 53	23 37		
Burnage	d			19 39					20 19		20 53				21 19				22 04			22 55	23 39		
East Didsbury	d			19 41					20 22		20 55				21 22				22 06			22 57	23 42		
Gatley	d			19 44					20 24		20 58				21 24				22 08			22 59	23 44		
Heald Green	d	19 32		19 47			20 12	20 18	20 27		21 01		21 12		21 27	21 31	21 42		22 11	22 31		23 02	23 47		
Manchester Airport	a	19 40		19 52	20 05	20 12	20 19	20 26	20 34	20 58	21 06	21 09	21 19	21 28	21 34	21 37	21 51	21 58	22 16	22 39	22 58	23 08	23 55		
Wilmslow	84 a			20 06							21 19								22 35			23 22			
Crewe 10	84 a			*20 56*							*21 56*								*23 11*			*23 59*			

Sundays

until 27 January

		TP 1◇ D	TP 1◇ A	TP D 🚌	TP 1◇ U	TP D 🚌	TP 1◇ U	NT	TP 1◇ U	NT	TP D 🚌	TP 1◇ V	TP 1◇ U	NT	TP 1◇ V	TP 1◇ U		TP X 🚌	NT	TP 1◇ D	NT E	TP 1◇ U	NT	TP 1◇ D	NT E
Deansgate	d																			09 09				10 09	
Manchester Oxford Road	d																			09 12	09 31			10 12	10 31
Manchester Piccadilly 10	a																			09 15	09 34			10 15	10 34
	d	00 30	00 38	02u40	04 05	05u00	05 20	05 27	06 37	06 45	07u00	07 16	07 41	07 48	08 02	08 50		09 00	09 14	09 18	09 35	09 39	09 48	10 18	10 35
Mauldeth Road	d							05 34		06 52				07 55									09 55		
Burnage	d							05 36		06 54				07 57									09 57		
East Didsbury	d							05 38		06 56				07 59									09 59		
Gatley	d							05 40		06 58				08 01									10 01		
Heald Green	d	00 40						05 43		07 01				08 04									10 04		
Manchester Airport	a	00 45	00 57	03 00	04 21	05 20	05 36	05 51	06 53	07 08	07 20	07 32	07 58	08 11	08 17	09 05		09 25	09 29	09 33	09 51	09 58	10 11	10 33	10 51
Wilmslow	84 a																		09 40						
Crewe 10	84 a																		10 07						

For general notes see front of timetable
For details of catering facilities see Directory of Train Operators

- **A** From Middlesbrough (Table 39)
- **B** From Southport (Table 82)
- **C** From Newcastle (Table 39)
- **D** From Blackpool North (Table 82)
- **E** From Liverpool Lime Street (Table 90)
- **G** From Cleethorpes (Table 29)
- **H** Until 22 March from Windermere (Table 83). From 29 March from Preston (Table 82)
- **J** Until 26 January from Edinburgh (Table 65). 2 February to 22 March from Carlisle (Table 65). From 29 March from Preston (Table 82)
- **K** Until 22 March from Windermere (Table 83) and fro m Barrow-in-Furness (Table 82). From 29 March from Preston (Table 82)
- **L** Until 26 January from Glasgow Central (Table 65). 2 February to 22 March from Carlisle (Table 65). From 29 March from Preston (Table 82)
- **N** From Barrow-in-Furness (from 29 March from Preston) (Table 82)
- **Q** To Alderley Edge (Table 84)
- **U** From York (Table 39)
- **V** From Bolton (Table 82)
- **X** From Sheffield (Table 78)
- **b** From 29 March arr. 1645

Table 85

Sundays

until 27 January

Manchester → Manchester Airport

Network Diagram - see first page of Table 78

		TP 1 ◇ A	TP B Bus	NT	NT	TP 1 ◇ C	NT D	TP 1 ◇ E	TP B Bus	NT	TP 1 ◇ C	NT D	TP 1 ◇ G	TP B Bus	NT	NT	TP 1 ◇ C	NT D	TP 1 ◇ H	NT	TP 1 ◇ C	NT D	TP 1 ◇ G	NT
Deansgate	d					11 09					12 09						13 09				14 09			
Manchester Oxford Road	d					11 12	11 31				12 12	12 31					13 12	13 31			14 12	14 30		
Manchester Piccadilly 10	a					11 15	11 35				12 15	12 35					13 15	13 35			14 15	14 32		
	d	10 39	10 40	10 49	11 07	11 18	11 35	11 39	11 40	11 48	12 18	12 35	12 39	12 40	12 49	13 08	13 18	13 39	13 41	13 51	14 16	14 34	14 39	14 48
Mauldeth Road	d			10 56						11 55					12 56					13 57				14 55
Burnage	d			10 58						11 57					12 58					13 59				14 57
East Didsbury	d			11 00						11 59					13 00					14 01				14 59
Gatley	d			11 02						12 01					13 02					14 04				15 01
Heald Green	d			11 05						12 04					13 05					14 07				15 04
Manchester Airport	a	11 04	11 05	11 12	11 23	11 33	11 51	11 58	12 05	12 11	12 33	12 50	12 58	13 05	13 12	13 24	13 33	13 54	13 58	14 14	14 33	14 51	14 58	15 11
Wilmslow	84 a				11 39											13 32								
Crewe 10	84 a				12 06											13 59								

		NT	TP 1 ◇ J Trolley	NT D	TP 1 ◇ H	NT	TP 1 ◇ K	TP 1 ◇ C	NT D	TP 1 ◇ H	NT	TP 1 ◇ L Trolley	NT	TP 1 ◇ C	NT D	TP 1 ◇ H	NT	TP 1 ◇ K	TP 1 ◇ C	NT D	TP 1 ◇ H	NT	TP 1 ◇ N Trolley
Deansgate	d		15 09					16 09						17 09					18 09				
Manchester Oxford Road	d		15 12	15 32			15 58	16 12	16 31			16 58		17 12	17 31			17 58	18 12	18 31			18 58
Manchester Piccadilly 10	a		15 15	15 34			16 01	16 15	16 35			17 01		17 15	17 35			18 01	18 15	18 33			19 01
	d	15 05	15 16	15 36	15 39	15 48	16 02	16 16	16 35	16 39	16 49	17 02	17 06	17 16	17 35	17 39	17 48	18 02	18 16	18 35	18 39	18 48	19 02
Mauldeth Road	d					15 55					16 56						17 55					18 55	
Burnage	d					15 57					16 58						17 57					18 57	
East Didsbury	d					15 59					17 00						17 59					18 59	
Gatley	d					16 01					17 02						18 01					19 01	
Heald Green	d					16 04					17 05						18 04					19 04	
Manchester Airport	a	15 21	15 33	15 51	15 58	16 11	16 18	16 33	16 51	16 58	17 12	17 18	17 21	17 33	17 51	17 58	18 11	18 18	18 33	18 52	18 58	19 12	19 18
Wilmslow	84 a	15 32											17 31										
Crewe 10	84 a	15 58											18 01										

		NT	TP 1 ◇ C	NT D	TP 1 ◇ H	NT	TP 1 ◇ K	TP 1 ◇ C	NT D	TP 1 ◇ H	NT	TP 1 ◇ N Trolley	NT	TP 1 ◇ C	NT D	NT	TP 1 ◇ C	NT D	TP 1 ◇ G	TP 1 ◇ Q	NT	TP 1 ◇ C	NT D
Deansgate	d		19 09					20 09						21 09			22 09					23 09	
Manchester Oxford Road	d		19 12	19 31			19 58	20 12	20 31			20 58		21 12	21 31		22 12	22 31		22 58		23 12	23 31
Manchester Piccadilly 10	a		19 15	19 35			20 01	20 15	20 33			21 01		21 15	21 34		22 15	22 33		23 01		23 15	23 33
	d	19 06	19 16	19 35	19 39	19 48	20 02	20 16	20 35	20 39	20 49	21 02	21 06	21 16	21 35	21 48	22 16	22 35	22 39	23 02	23 03	23 16	23 35
Mauldeth Road	d					19 55					20 56					21 55					23 10		
Burnage	d					19 57					20 58					21 57					23 12		
East Didsbury	d					19 59					21 00					21 59					23 14		
Gatley	d					20 01					21 02					22 01					23 16		
Heald Green	d					20 04					21 05					22 04					23 19		
Manchester Airport	a	19 21	19 33	19 51	19 58	20 12	20 18	20 33	20 52	20 58	21 12	21 18	21 21	21 33	21 52	22 11	22 33	22 49	22 58	23 18	23 26	23 33	23 49
Wilmslow	84 a	19 32											21 32										
Crewe 10	84 a	19 59											21 59										

Sundays

3 February to 23 March

		TP 1 ◇ C	TP 1 ◇ U	TP C Bus	TP C Bus	TP A Bus	NT	NT	TP A Bus	TP C Bus	TP 1 ◇ V	NT	TP 1 ◇ V	TP X Bus	TP 1 ◇ B	NT	TP 1 ◇ Y	NT D	TP X Bus	NT	TP 1 ◇ Y
Deansgate	d																09 09				10 09
Manchester Oxford Road	d																09 12	09 31			10 12
Manchester Piccadilly 10	a																09 15	09 34			10 15
	d	00 30	01 01	02u40	05u00	05 20	05 27	06 45	06 55	07u00	07 16	07 48	08 02	08 10	08 55	09 14	09 18	09 35	09 35	09 48	10 18
Mauldeth Road	d						05 34	06 52				07 55								09 55	
Burnage	d						05 36	06 54				07 57								09 57	
East Didsbury	d						05 38	06 56				07 59								09 59	
Gatley	d						05 40	06 58				08 01								10 01	
Heald Green	d	00 40					05 43	07 01				08 04								10 04	
Manchester Airport	a	00 45	01 16	03 00	05 20	05 45	05 51	07 08	07 20	07 20	07 32	08 11	08 17	08 35	09 12	09 29	09 33	09 51	10 00	10 11	10 33
Wilmslow	84 a															09 40					
Crewe 10	84 a															10 07					

For general notes see front of timetable
For details of catering facilities see Directory of Train Operators

- **A** From York (Table 39)
- **B** From Sheffield (Table 78)
- **C** From Blackpool North (Table 82)
- **D** From Liverpool Lime Street (Table 90)
- **E** From Scarborough (Table 39)
- **G** From Middlesbrough (Table 39)
- **H** From Newcastle (Table 39)
- **J** From Edinburgh (Table 65) and from Blackpool North (Table 82)
- **K** From Barrow-in-Furness (Table 82)
- **L** From Glasgow Central (Table 65)
- **N** From Edinburgh (Table 65)
- **Q** From Windermere (Table 83) and from Barrow-in-Furness (Table 82)
- **U** From Huddersfield (Table 39)
- **V** From Bolton (Table 82)
- **X** From Leeds (Table 39)
- **Y** From Preston (Table 82)

Table 85

Sundays

3 February to 23 March

Manchester → Manchester Airport

Network Diagram - see first page of Table 78

	TP [1] ◇ A	NT B	TP [1] ◇ C	NT	NT	TP [1] ◇ D	NT B	TP [1] ◇ E	NT	TP [1] ◇ G	TP [1] ◇ D	NT B	TP [1] ◇ H	NT	NT	TP [1] ◇ D	TP [1] ◇ J	NT B	TP [1] ◇ K
Deansgate d						11 09					12 09					13 09			
Manchester Oxford Road d		10 31				11 12	11 31				12 12	12 31				13 12		13 31	
Manchester Piccadilly [10] a		10 34				11 15	11 35				12 15	12 35				13 15		13 35	
d	10 20	10 35	10 39	10 49	11 07	11 18	11 35	11 39	11 48	12 13	12 18	12 35	12 39	12 49	13 08	13 18	13 20	13 39	13 41
Mauldeth Road d				10 56					11 55					12 56					
Burnage d				10 58					11 57					12 58					
East Didsbury d				11 00					11 59					13 00					
Gatley d				11 02					12 01					13 02					
Heald Green d				11 05					12 04					13 05					
Manchester Airport a	10 36	10 51	11 04	11 12	11 23	11 33	11 51	11 58	12 11	12 30	12 33	12 50	12 58	13 12	13 24	13 33	13 36	13 54	13 58
Wilmslow 84 a					11 39										13 32				
Crewe [10] 84 a					12 06										13 59				

	NT	TP [1] ◇ D	TP [1] ◇ G	NT B	TP [1] ◇ H	NT	TP [1] ◇ L 🚲	NT	TP [1] ◇ D	TP [1] ◇ J	NT B	TP [1] ◇ K	NT	TP [1] ◇ N	TP [1] ◇ D	TP [1] ◇ J	NT B	TP [1] ◇ K	NT	TP [1] ◇ L 🚲
Deansgate d		14 09							15 09						16 09					
Manchester Oxford Road d		14 12		14 30			14 58		15 12		15 32			15 58	16 12		16 31			16 58
Manchester Piccadilly [10] a		14 15		14 32			15 00		15 15		15 34			16 01	16 15		16 35			17 01
d	13 51	14 16	14 20	14 34	14 39	14 48	15 02	15 05	15 16	15 20	15 36	15 39	15 48	16 02	16 16	16 20	16 35	16 39	16 49	17 02
Mauldeth Road d	13 57					14 55							15 55						16 56	
Burnage d	13 59					14 57							15 57						16 58	
East Didsbury d	14 01					14 59							15 59						17 00	
Gatley d	14 04					15 01							16 01						17 02	
Heald Green d	14 07					15 04							16 04						17 05	
Manchester Airport a	14 14	14 33	14 36	14 51	14 58	15 11	15 18	15 21	15 33	15 36	15 51	15 58	16 11	16 18	16 33	16 36	16 51	16 58	17 12	17 18
Wilmslow 84 a								15 32												
Crewe [10] 84 a								15 58												

	NT	TP [1] ◇ D	TP [1] ◇ J	NT B	TP [1] ◇ K	NT	TP [1] ◇ N	TP [1] ◇ D	TP [1] ◇ J	NT B	TP [1] ◇ K	NT	TP [1] ◇ L 🚲	NT	TP [1] ◇ D	TP [1] ◇ J	NT B	TP [1] ◇ K	NT
Deansgate d		17 09						18 09							19 09				
Manchester Oxford Road d		17 12		17 31			17 58	18 12		18 31			18 58		19 12		19 31		
Manchester Piccadilly [10] a		17 15		17 35			18 01	18 15		18 33			19 01		19 15		19 35		
d	17 06	17 16	17 20	17 35	17 39	17 48	18 02	18 16	18 20	18 35	18 39	18 48	19 02	19 06	19 16	19 20	19 35	19 39	19 48
Mauldeth Road d						17 55						18 55							19 55
Burnage d						17 57						18 57							19 57
East Didsbury d						17 59						18 59							19 59
Gatley d						18 01						19 01							20 01
Heald Green d						18 04						19 04							20 04
Manchester Airport a	17 21	17 33	17 36	17 51	17 58	18 11	18 18	18 33	18 36	18 52	18 58	19 12	19 18	19 21	19 33	19 36	19 51	19 58	20 12
Wilmslow 84 a	17 31													19 32					
Crewe [10] 84 a	18 01													19 59					

	TP [1] ◇ N	TP [1] ◇ D	TP [1] ◇ J	NT B	TP [1] ◇ K	NT	TP [1] ◇ L 🚲	NT	TP [1] ◇ D	TP [1] ◇ J	NT B	NT	TP [1] ◇ D	TP [1] ◇ J	NT B	TP [1] ◇ H	TP [1] ◇ Q	NT	TP [1] ◇ D	NT B
Deansgate d		20 09							21 09				22 09						23 09	
Manchester Oxford Road d	19 58	20 12		20 31			20 58		21 12		21 31		22 12		22 31		22 58		23 12	23 31
Manchester Piccadilly [10] a	20 01	20 15		20 33			21 01		21 15		21 34		22 15		22 33		23 01		23 15	23 33
d	20 02	20 16	20 20	20 35	20 39	20 49	21 02	21 06	21 16	21 20	21 35	21 48	22 16	22 20	22 35	22 39	23 02	23 03	23 16	23 35
Mauldeth Road d						20 56						21 55						23 10		
Burnage d						20 58						21 57						23 12		
East Didsbury d						21 00						21 59						23 14		
Gatley d						21 02						22 01						23 16		
Heald Green d						21 05						22 04						23 19		
Manchester Airport a	20 18	20 33	20 36	20 52	20 58	21 12	21 18	21 21	21 33	21 36	21 52	22 11	22 33	22 36	22 51	22 58	23 18	23 26	23 33	23 49
Wilmslow 84 a								21 32												
Crewe [10] 84 a								21 59												

For general notes see front of timetable
For details of catering facilities see Directory of Train Operators

A From Meadowhall (Table 29)
B From Liverpool Lime Street (Table 90)
C From York (Table 39)
D From Preston (Table 82)
E From Scarborough (Table 39)
G From Doncaster (Table 29)
H From Middlesbrough (Table 39)
J From Cleethorpes (Table 29)
K From Newcastle (Table 39)
L From Carlisle (Table 65)
N From Barrow-in-Furness (Table 82)
Q From Windermere (Table 83) and from Barrow-in-Furness (Table 82)

Table 85

Sundays

from 30 March

Manchester → Manchester Airport

Network Diagram - see first page of Table 78

		TP	TP	TP	TP	TP	TP	NT	TP	NT	TP	TP	TP	NT	TP	TP	TP	NT	TP	NT	TP	NT	TP	TP	NT
		1◇	1◇		1◇		1◇		1◇			1◇	1◇		1◇	1◇	1◇		1◇		1◇		1◇	1◇	
		A	B	A 🚌	C	A 🚌	C		C		A 🚌	D	C		D	C	E		A	G	C		A	H	G
Deansgate	d																		09 09				10 09		
Manchester Oxford Road	d																		09 12	09 31			10 12		10 31
Manchester Piccadilly 10	a																		09 15	09 34			10 15		10 34
	d	00 30	00 38	02u40	04 05	05u00	05 20	05 27	06 37	06 45	07u00	07 16	07 41	07 48	08 02	08 50	08 55	09 14	09 18	09 35	09 39	09 48	10 18	10 20	10 35
Mauldeth Road	d							05 34		06 52				07 55								09 55			
Burnage	d							05 36		06 54				07 57								09 57			
East Didsbury	d							05 38		06 56				07 59								09 59			
Gatley	d							05 40		06 58				08 01								10 01			
Heald Green	d	00 40						05 43		07 01				08 04								10 04			
Manchester Airport	a	00 45	00 57	03 00	04 21	05 20	05 36	05 51	06 53	07 08	07 20	07 32	07 58	08 11	08 17	09 05	09 12	09 29	09 33	09 51	09 58	10 11	10 33	10 36	10 51
Wilmslow	84 a																	09 40							
Crewe 10	84 a																	10 07							

		TP		NT	NT	TP	NT	TP	NT	TP	TP	NT	TP	NT	NT	TP	TP	NT	TP	NT	TP	TP	NT	TP	NT
		1◇				1◇		1◇		1◇	1◇		1◇			1◇	1◇		1◇		1◇	1◇		1◇	
		C				A	G	J		K	A	G	B			A	L	G	N		A	K	G	B	
Deansgate	d					11 09					12 09					13 09					14 09				
Manchester Oxford Road	d					11 12	11 30				12 12	12 31				13 12		13 31			14 12		14 31		
Manchester Piccadilly 10	a					11 15	11 34				12 15	12 35				13 15		13 35			14 15		14 33		
	d	10 39		10 49	11 07	11 18	11 34	11 39	11 48	12 13	12 18	12 35	12 39	12 49	13 08	13 18	13 20	13 39	13 41	13 51	14 16	14 20	14 35	14 39	14 48
Mauldeth Road	d			10 56					11 55					12 56						13 57					14 55
Burnage	d			10 58					11 57					12 58						13 59					14 57
East Didsbury	d			11 00					11 59					13 00						14 01					14 59
Gatley	d			11 02					12 01					13 02						14 04					15 01
Heald Green	d			11 05					12 04					13 05						14 07					15 04
Manchester Airport	a	11 04		11 12	11 23	11 33	11 51	11 58	12 11	12 30	12 33	12 50	12 58	13 12	13 24	13 33	13 36	13 54	13 58	14 14	14 33	14 36	14 51	14 58	15 11
Wilmslow	84 a				11 32										13 32										
Crewe 10	84 a				11 59										13 59										

		NT	TP	TP		NT	TP	NT	TP	TP	NT	TP	NT	NT	TP	TP	NT	TP	NT	TP	TP	NT	TP	NT	NT
			1◇	1◇			1◇		1◇	1◇		1◇			1◇	1◇		1◇		1◇	1◇		1◇		
			A	L		G	N		A	L	G	N			A	L	G	N		A	L	G	N		
Deansgate	d		15 09						16 09						17 09					18 09					
Manchester Oxford Road	d		15 12			15 31			16 12		16 31				17 12		17 31			18 12		18 29			
Manchester Piccadilly 10	a		15 15			15 34			16 15		16 35				17 15		17 35			18 15		18 33			
	d	15 05	15 16	15 20		15 35	15 39	15 48	16 16	16 20	16 35	16 39	16 49	17 06	17 16	17 20	17 35	17 39	17 48	18 16	18 20	18 33	18 39	18 48	19 06
Mauldeth Road	d							15 55					16 56						17 55					18 55	
Burnage	d							15 57					16 58						17 57					18 57	
East Didsbury	d							15 59					17 00						17 59					18 59	
Gatley	d							16 01					17 02						18 01					19 01	
Heald Green	d							16 04					17 05						18 04					19 04	
Manchester Airport	a	15 21	15 33	15 36		15 51	15 58	16 11	16 33	16 36	16 51	16 58	17 12	17 21	17 33	17 36	17 51	17 58	18 11	18 33	18 36	18 52	18 58	19 12	19 21
Wilmslow	84 a	15 32												17 32											19 32
Crewe 10	84 a	15 58												18b07											19 59

		TP	TP	NT	TP	NT	TP	TP	NT	TP	NT	NT	TP	TP	NT	NT	TP	TP	NT	TP	NT	TP	NT		
		1◇	1◇		1◇		1◇	1◇		1◇			1◇	1◇			1◇	1◇		1◇		1◇			
		A	L	G	N		A	L	G	N			A	L	G		A	L	G	B		A	G		
Deansgate	d	19 09					20 09						21 09				22 09					23 09			
Manchester Oxford Road	d	19 12		19 31			20 12		20 31				21 12		21 31		22 12		22 32			23 12	23 34		
Manchester Piccadilly 10	a	19 15		19 34			20 15		20 33				21 15		21 34		22 15		22 34			23 15	23 38		
	d	19 16	19 20	19 35	19 39	19 48	20 16	20 20	20 35	20 39	20 49	21 06	21 16	21 20	21 34	21 48	22 16	22 20	22 37	22 39	23 03	23 16	23 38		
Mauldeth Road	d					19 55					20 56					21 55					23 10				
Burnage	d					19 57					20 58					21 57					23 12				
East Didsbury	d					19 59					21 00					21 59					23 14				
Gatley	d					20 01					21 02					22 01					23 16				
Heald Green	d					20 04					21 05					22 04					23 19				
Manchester Airport	a	19 33	19 36	19 51	19 58	20 12	20 33	20 36	20 52	20 58	21 12	21 21	21 33	21 36	21 52	22 11	22 33	22 36	22 51	22 58	23 26	23 33	23 54		
Wilmslow	84 a											21 32													
Crewe 10	84 a											21 59													

For general notes see front of timetable
For details of catering facilities see Directory of Train Operators

A From Blackpool North (Table 82)
B From Middlesbrough (Table 39)
C From York (Table 39)
D From Bolton (Table 82)
E From Sheffield (Table 78)
G From Liverpool Lime Street (Table 89)
H From Meadowhall (Table 29)
J From Scarborough (Table 39)
K From Doncaster (Table 29)
L From Cleethorpes (Table 29)
N From Newcastle (Table 39)
b By changing at Wilmslow, passengers may arrive at 1759

Manchester Airport → Manchester

Network Diagram - see first page of Table 78

Miles			NT	TP	NT	TP	TP	TP	TP	TP	TP	NT	TP	TP	TP	TP	TP	NT	TP	TP	TP	NT		TP	NT
			MO		MX		MX	MO	MX	MO															
				1◇		1◇	1◇	1◇	1◇	1◇	1◇		1◇	1◇	1◇	1◇	1◇		1◇	1◇	1◇			1◇	
				A		B	C	D	D	C	A	E	G	H	J	K	C	E	G	J	L	N		Q	E
																	🛒		🛒		🛒			🛒	
—	Crewe 10	84 d			00 50																	*06 03*			
—	Wilmslow	84 d																				06 52			
0	**Manchester Airport** ✈	d	00 09	01 06	01 17	01 22	03 17	03 18	03 21	03 22	03 40	04 34	05 15	05 34	05 47	06 19	06 23	06 28	06 44	06 47	07 02	07 05		07 22	07 26
1½	Heald Green	d													05 51	06 23		06 32		06 51		07 09		07 26	
4	Gatley	d																06 35		06 54		07 12			07 32
5¼	East Didsbury	d																06 38		06 56		07 14			07 35
6¼	Burnage	d																06 40		06 59		07 16		07 30	
7¼	Mauldeth Road	d																06 43		07 01		07 18		07 33	
9¾	**Manchester Piccadilly 10**	a	00 23	01 19	01 35	01 36	03 31	03 33	03 36	03 36	03 53	04 47	05 32	05 48	06 02	06 35	06 39	06 51	07 02	07 09	07 19	07 28		07 42	07 47
—		d													06 05	06 44		06 52		07 11				07 45	07 49
—	**Manchester Oxford Road**	a													06 07	06 46		06 54		07 15				07 47	07 51
—	Deansgate	a																							

		TP	TP	TP	TP	NT	NT	TP	NT	TP	TP	TP	TP	NT	NT	TP	NT	TP	TP	TP	TP		NT	NT	TP
		1◇	1◇	1◇	1◇			1◇		1◇	1◇	1◇	1◇			1◇		1◇	1◇	1◇	1◇				1◇
		C	J	G	L	U		K	E	C	V	G	L	U		X	E	C	J	G	L		U		K
		🛒		🛒	🛒			🛒		🛒	🛒	🛒	🛒			🛒		🛒	🛒	🛒	🛒				🛒
Crewe 10	84 d						07 43								08 40									09 38	
Wilmslow	84 d						08 07								09 03									10 01	
Manchester Airport ✈	d	07 34	07 47	07 52	08 04	08 07	08 18	08 27	08 30	08 33	08 47	08 52	09 04	09 07	09 18	09 27	09 31	09 34	09 47	09 52	10 04		10 07	10 15	10 27
Heald Green	d		07 51	07 56		08 11	08 21	08 31		08 37		08 56			09 21	09 31				09 56				10 18	10 31
Gatley	d			07 59		08 14	08 24					08 59			09 24					09 59				10 21	
East Didsbury	d			08 01		08 17	08 27				08 53				09 27				09 53					10 24	
Burnage	d		07 55				08 29				08 56				09 29				09 56					10 26	
Mauldeth Road	d		07 58				08 31				08 58				09 31				09 58					10 28	
Manchester Piccadilly 10	a	07 48	08 10	08 11	08 19	08 26	08 42	08 44	08 49	08 49	09 10	09 11	09 19	09 22	09 41	09 42	09 48	09 48	10 10	10 11	10 19		10 21	10 39	10 42
	d		08 11			08 28		08 45	08 50		09 11			09 23		09 45	09 49		10 11				10 23		10 45
Manchester Oxford Road	a		08 14			08 30		08 47	08 52		09 14			09 25		09 47	09 51		10 14				10 25		10 47
Deansgate	a					08 33		08 50						09 28											10 50

		NT	TP	TP	TP	TP	NT	NT	TP	NT	TP	TP	TP	TP	NT	NT	TP	NT	TP	TP		TP	TP	NT	NT
			1◇	1◇	1◇	1◇			1◇		1◇	1◇	1◇	1◇			1◇		1◇	1◇		1◇	1◇		
		E	C	J	G	L	U		Q	E	C	J	G	L	U		K	E	C	V		G	L	U	
			🛒	🛒	🛒	🛒			🛒		🛒	🛒	🛒	🛒			🛒		🛒	🛒		🛒	🛒		
Crewe 10	84 d							10 38								11 38									12 38
Wilmslow	84 d							11 01								12 01									13 01
Manchester Airport ✈	d	10 31	10 34	10 47	10 52	11 04	11 07	11 15	11 27	11 31	11 34	11 47	11 52	12 04	12 07	12 15	12 27	12 31	12 34	12 47		12 52	13 04	13 07	13 15
Heald Green	d				10 56			11 18	11 31				11 56			12 18	12 31					12 56			13 18
Gatley	d				10 59			11 21					11 59			12 21						12 59			13 21
East Didsbury	d			10 53				11 24				11 53				12 24				12 53					13 24
Burnage	d			10 56				11 26				11 56				12 26				12 56					13 26
Mauldeth Road	d			10 58				11 28				11 58				12 28				12 58					13 28
Manchester Piccadilly 10	a	10 48	10 48	11 09	11 11	11 19	11 21	11 39	11 42	11 48	11 48	12 09	12 11	12 19	12 21	12 39	12 42	12 48	12 48	13 09		13 11	13 19	13 21	13 39
	d	10 49		11 11			11 23		11 45	11 49		12 11			12 23		12 45	12 49		13 11				13 23	
Manchester Oxford Road	a	10 51		11 13			11 25		11 47	11 51		12 13			12 25		12 47	12 51		13 13				13 25	
Deansgate	a																12 50								

		TP	NT	TP	TP	TP	TP	NT	NT	TP	NT	TP	TP	TP	TP	NT	NT	TP	NT		TP	TP	TP	TP	NT
		1◇		1◇	1◇	1◇	1◇			1◇		1◇	1◇	1◇	1◇			1◇			1◇	1◇	1◇	1◇	
		Q	E	C	J	G	B	U		K	E	C	J	G	L	U		Q	E		H	J	G	H	U
		🛒		🛒	🛒	🛒	🛒			🛒		🛒	🛒	🛒	🛒			🛒			🛒	🛒	🛒	🛒	
Crewe 10	84 d								13 38								14 38								
Wilmslow	84 d								14 01								15 01								
Manchester Airport ✈	d	13 27	13 31	13 34	13 47	13 52	14 04	14 07	14 15	14 27	14 31	14 34	14 47	14 52	15 04	15 07	15 15	15 27	15 31		15 34	15 47	15 52	16 04	16 07
Heald Green	d	13 31				13 56			14 18	14 31				14 56			15 18	15 31					15 56		
Gatley	d					13 59			14 21					14 59			15 21						15 59		
East Didsbury	d				13 53				14 24				14 53				15 24					15 53			
Burnage	d				13 56				14 26				14 56				15 26					15 56			
Mauldeth Road	d				13 58				14 28				14 58				15 28					15 58			
Manchester Piccadilly 10	a	13 42	13 48	13 48	14 09	14 11	14 19	14 21	14 39	14 42	14 48	14 48	15 09	15 11	15 19	15 21	15 39	15 42	15 48		15 48	16 09	16 11	16 19	16 21
	d	13 45	13 49		14 11			14 23		14 45	14 49		15 11			15 23		15 45	15 49			16 11			16 23
Manchester Oxford Road	a	13 47	13 51		14 13			14 25		14 47	14 51		15 13			15 25		15 47	15 51			16 13			16 25
Deansgate	a									14 50															16 28

		NT	TP	NT	TP	TP	TP	TP	NT	NT	TP	TP	TP	TP	NT	NT	TP	NT		TP	TP	TP	NT	NT	TP
			1◇		1◇	1◇	1◇	1◇			1◇	1◇	1◇	1◇			1◇			1◇	1◇	1◇			1◇
			K	E	C	Y	G	L		E	Z	C	J	G	U		X	E		C	J	G		U	L
			🛒		🛒	🛒	🛒	🛒			🛒	🛒	🛒	🛒			🛒				🛒				
Crewe 10	84 d	15 38							16 42							17 38							18 19		
Wilmslow	84 d	16 01							17 05							18 04							18 44		
Manchester Airport ✈	d	16 15	16 27	16 31	16 34	16 47	16 52	17 04	17 19	17 29	17 32	17 34	17 47	17 52	18 10	18 18	18 27	18 31		18 34	18 47	18 52	19 04	19 12	19 22
Heald Green	d	16 18	16 31				16 56		17 22					17 56		18 22	18 31					18 56	19 07		
Gatley	d	16 21					16 59		17 25					17 59		18 25						18 59	19 10		
East Didsbury	d	16 24				16 53			17 28				17 53			18 27					18 53		19 13		
Burnage	d	16 26				16 56			17 30				17 56			18 29					18 56		19 15		
Mauldeth Road	d	16 28				16 58			17 32				17 58			18 31					18 58		19 17		
Manchester Piccadilly 10	a	16 41	16 42	16 47	16 48	17 10	17 11	17 19	17 41	17 44	17 47	17 49	18 09	18 11	18 24	18 40	18 43	18 48		18 49	19 09	19 11	19 29	19 31	19 38
	d		16 44	16 48		17 11				17 45	17 50		18 11		18 26		18 45	18 49			19 11			19 33	
Manchester Oxford Road	a		16 46	16 50		17 13				17 47	17 52		18 13		18 28		18 47	18 51			19 13			19 36	
Deansgate	a										17 55		18 17		18 31		18 50				19 17				

For general notes see front of timetable
For details of catering facilities see Directory of Train Operators

- **A** To Blackpool North (Mondays 4 February to 24 March to Preston) (Table 82)
- **B** To York (Table 39)
- **C** To Middlesbrough (Table 39)
- **D** To Doncaster (Table 29)
- **E** To Liverpool Lime Street (Table 90)
- **G** To Cleethorpes (Table 29)
- **H** To Scarborough (Table 39)
- **J** To Blackpool North (Table 82)
- **K** To Barrow-in-Furness (Table 82)
- **L** To Newcastle (Table 39)
- **N** From Alderley Edge (Table 84)
- **Q** To Edinburgh (Table 65)
- **U** To Southport (Table 82)
- **V** To Windermere (Table 83) and to Blackpool North (Table 82)
- **X** To Glasgow Central (Table 65)
- **Y** To Glasgow Central (Table 65) and to Blackpool North (Table 82)
- **Z** To Barrow-in-Furness and to Blackpool North (Table 82)

Manchester Airport → Manchester

Network Diagram - see first page of Table 78

Mondays to Fridays

		TP	NT	TP	TP	NT	NT	TP	TP	TP	NT	NT	TP	TP	NT	TP	TP	NT	TP	TP	NT	TP	TP
		1◇ A	B	1◇ C	1◇ D		E	1◇ G	1◇ C	1◇ D		E	1◇ H	1◇ A	B	1◇ C	1◇ J		1◇ K	1◇ C		1◇ K	1◇ J
Crewe 10	84 d					*19 27*					*20 28*							*21 27*			*22 00*		
Wilmslow	84 d					19 51					20 50							21 55			22 52		
Manchester Airport ✈	d	19 27	19 30	19 47	19 52	20 04	20 15	20 22	20 47	20 52	21 04	21 16	21 22	21 27	21 30	21 47	21 52	22 08	22 22	22 47	23 04	23 22	23 52
Heald Green	d	19 31			19 56	20 07				20 56	21 08						21 56	22 12		22 52	23 07		
Gatley	d				19 59	20 10				20 59	21 11						21 59	22 15		22 55	23 10		
East Didsbury	d			19 53		20 13			20 53		21 13					21 53		22 17		22 57	23 13		
Burnage	d			19 56		20 15			20 56		21 15					21 56		22 19		23 00	23 15		
Mauldeth Road	d			19 58		20 17			20 58		21 17					21 58		22 21		23 02	23 17		
Manchester Piccadilly 10	a	19 41	19 47	20 09	20 11	20 31	20 30	20 38	21 09	21 11	21 28	21 33	21 38	21 42	21 47	22 10	22 15	22 31	22 38	23 09	23 31	23 38	00 08
	d	19 44	19 48	20 11			20 32		21 11			21 35		21 43	21 47	22 11				23 11			
Manchester Oxford Road	a	19 46	19 50	20 13			20 34		21 13			21 37		21 45	21 49	22 14				23 15			
Deansgate	a	19 49		20 17			20 37		21 17			21 40		21 48		22 17				23 17			

Saturdays

		TP	NT	TP	TP	TP	TP	NT	TP	TP	TP	TP		TP	NT	TP	TP	TP	NT	TP	NT	TP	TP	TP	TP
		1◇ C		1◇ K	1◇ L	1◇ N	1◇ C	B	1◇ D	1◇ G	1◇ C	1◇ Q		1◇ L ⚒	B	1◇ D ⚒	1◇ C	1◇ H ⚒	U	1◇ VX ⚒	B	1◇ L ⚒	1◇ C	1◇ D ⚒	1◇ H ⚒
Crewe 10	84 d		00 50																						
Wilmslow	84 d																		06 52						
Manchester Airport ✈	d	01 06	01 17	01 22	03 17	03 21	03 40	04 35	05 15	05 34	05 47	06 19		06 23	06 28	06 44	06 47	07 02	07 05	07 22	07 26	07 34	07 47	07 52	08 04
Heald Green	d										05 51	06 23			06 32		06 51		07 09	07 26			07 51	07 56	
Gatley	d														06 35		06 54		07 12		07 32			07 59	
East Didsbury	d														06 38		06 56		07 14		07 35			08 01	
Burnage	d														06 40		06 59		07 16	07 30			07 55		
Mauldeth Road	d														06 43		07 01		07 18	07 33			07 58		
Manchester Piccadilly 10	a	01 22	01 35	01 36	03 31	03 36	03 53	04 49	05 32	05 48	06 02	06 36		06 40	06 51	07 03	07 09	07 19	07 28	07 42	07 47	07 48	08 10	08 11	08 19
	d										06 05	06 44			06 52		07 11			07 45	07 49		08 11		
Manchester Oxford Road	a										06 07	06 46			06 54		07 15			07 47	07 51		08 14		
Deansgate	a																								

		NT		NT	TP	NT	TP	TP	TP	TP	NT	NT	TP	NT		TP	TP	TP	TP	NT	NT	TP	NT	TP	TP
		E			1◇ Q ⚒	B	1◇ L ⚒	1◇ Y ⚒	1◇ D ⚒	1◇ H ⚒	E		1◇ Z ⚒	B		1◇ L ⚒	1◇ C ⚒	1◇ D ⚒	1◇ H	E		1◇ Q ⚒	B	1◇ L ⚒	1◇ C ⚒
Crewe 10	84 d			07 43								08 40									09 38				
Wilmslow	84 d			08 07								09 03									10 01				
Manchester Airport ✈	d	08 07		08 18	08 27	08 30	08 33	08 47	08 52	09 04	09 07	09 18	09 27	09 31		09 34	09 47	09 52	10 04	10 07	10 15	10 27	10 31	10 34	10 47
Heald Green	d	08 11		08 21	08 31		08 37		08 56			09 21	09 31					09 56			10 18	10 31			
Gatley	d	08 14		08 24					08 59			09 24						09 59			10 21				
East Didsbury	d			08 27				08 53				09 27					09 53				10 24				10 53
Burnage	d			08 29				08 56				09 29					09 56				10 26				10 56
Mauldeth Road	d			08 31				08 58				09 31					09 58				10 28				10 58
Manchester Piccadilly 10	a	08 27		08 42	08 44	08 49	08 49	09 10	09 11	09 21	09 22	09 40	09 42	09 47		09 48	10 10	10 11	10 19	10 21	10 39	10 42	10 48	10 48	11 09
	d	08 28			08 45	08 50		09 11			09 23		09 45	09 49			10 11			10 23		10 45	10 49		11 11
Manchester Oxford Road	a	08 31			08 47	08 52		09 14			09 25		09 47	09 51			10 14			10 25		10 47	10 51		11 13
Deansgate	a	08 33			08 50						09 28											10 50			

		TP	TP	NT		NT	TP	NT	TP	TP	TP	TP	NT	NT	TP	NT		TP	TP	TP	TP	NT	NT	TP	NT
		1◇ D ⚒	1◇ H ⚒	E			1◇ V ⚒	B	1◇ L ⚒	1◇ C ⚒	1◇ D ⚒	1◇ H ⚒	E		1◇ Q ⚒	B		1◇ L ⚒	1◇ AA ⚒	1◇ D ⚒	1◇ H ⚒	E		1◇ V ⚒	B
Crewe 10	84 d					10 38								11 38									12 38		
Wilmslow	84 d					11 01								12 01									13 01		
Manchester Airport ✈	d	10 52	11 04	11 07		11 15	11 27	11 31	11 34	11 47	11 52	12 04	12 07	12 15	12 27	12 31		12 34	12 47	12 52	13 04	13 07	13 15	13 27	13 31
Heald Green	d	10 56				11 18	11 31				11 56			12 18	12 31					12 56			13 18	13 31	
Gatley	d	10 59				11 21					11 59			12 21						12 59			13 21		
East Didsbury	d					11 24				11 53				12 24					12 53				13 24		
Burnage	d					11 26				11 56				12 26					12 56				13 26		
Mauldeth Road	d					11 28				11 58				12 28					12 58				13 28		
Manchester Piccadilly 10	a	11 11	11 19	11 21		11 39	11 42	11 48	11 48	12 09	12 11	12 19	12 21	12 39	12 42	12 48		12 48	13 09	13 11	13 19	13 21	13 39	13 42	13 48
	d			11 23			11 45	11 49		12 11			12 23		12 45	12 49			13 11			13 23		13 45	13 49
Manchester Oxford Road	a			11 25			11 47	11 51		12 13			12 25		12 47	12 51			13 13			13 25		13 47	13 51
Deansgate	a														12 50										

		TP	TP	TP	TP	NT		NT	TP	NT	TP	TP	TP	TP	NT	NT	TP	NT		TP	TP	TP	TP	NT	NT
		1◇ L ⚒	1◇ C	1◇ D ⚒	1◇ K ⚒	E			1◇ Q ⚒	B	1◇ L	1◇ C	1◇ D ⚒	1◇ H ⚒	E		1◇ V ⚒	B		1◇ G ⚒	1◇ C ⚒	1◇ D ⚒	1◇ G	E	
Crewe 10	84 d							13 38								14 38									15 38
Wilmslow	84 d							14 01								15 01									16 01
Manchester Airport ✈	d	13 34	13 47	13 52	14 04	14 07		14 15	14 27	14 31	14 34	14 47	14 52	15 04	15 07	15 15	15 27	15 31		15 34	15 47	15 52	16 04	16 07	16 15
Heald Green	d			13 56				14 18	14 31				14 56			15 18	15 31					15 56			16 18
Gatley	d			13 59				14 21					14 59			15 21						15 59			16 21
East Didsbury	d		13 53					14 24				14 53				15 24					15 53				16 24
Burnage	d		13 56					14 26				14 56				15 26					15 56				16 26
Mauldeth Road	d		13 58					14 28				14 58				15 28					15 58				16 28
Manchester Piccadilly 10	a	13 48	14 09	14 11	14 19	14 21		14 39	14 42	14 48	14 48	15 09	15 11	15 19	15 21	15 39	15 42	15 48		15 48	16 09	16 11	16 19	16 21	16 41
	d		14 11			14 23			14 45	14 49		15 11			15 23		15 45	15 49			16 11			16 23	
Manchester Oxford Road	a		14 13			14 25			14 47	14 51		15 13			15 25		15 47	15 51			16 13			16 25	
Deansgate	a								14 50															16 28	

For general notes see front of timetable
For details of catering facilities see Directory of Train Operators

- **A** To Barrow-in-Furness (Table 82)
- **B** To Liverpool Lime Street (Table 90)
- **C** To Blackpool North (Table 82)
- **D** To Cleethorpes (Table 29)
- **E** To Southport (Table 82)
- **G** To Scarborough (Table 39)
- **H** To Newcastle (Table 39)
- **J** To Sheffield (Table 78)
- **K** To York (Table 39)
- **L** To Middlesbrough (Table 39)
- **N** To Doncaster (Table 29)
- **Q** To Barrow-in-Furness (from 29 March to Preston) (Table 82)
- **U** From Alderley Edge (Table 84)
- **V** Until 26 January to Edinburgh, 2 February to 22 March to Carlisle (Table 65). From 29 March to Preston (Table 82)
- **X** ⚒ until 22 March
- **Y** To Blackpool North (Table 82). Until 22 March also conveys portion to Windermere (Table 83)
- **Z** Until 26 January to Glasgow Central, 2 February to 22 March to Carlisle (Table 65). From 29 March to Preston (Table 82)
- **AA** To Blackpool North (Table 82). Until 26 January also conveys portion to Windermere (Table 83)

Table 85

Saturdays

Manchester Airport → Manchester

Network Diagram - see first page of Table 78

		TP	NT	TP	TP	TP	TP	NT		NT	TP	TP	TP	TP	NT	NT	TP	NT	TP	TP		TP	NT	TP	NT
		1◇		1◇	1◇	1◇	1◇				1◇	1◇	1◇	1◇			1◇		1◇	1◇		1◇		1◇	
		A	B	C	D	E	G			B	A	C	H	E	J		A	B	C	H		E	J	G	
		🛒			🛒	🛒					🛒			🛒											
Crewe 10	84 d							16 42								17 38									18 42
Wilmslow	84 d							17 05								18 04									19 05
Manchester Airport ✈	d	16 27	16 31	16 34	16 47	16 52	17 04	17 19		17 29	17 32	17 34	17 47	17 52	18 10	18 18	18 27	18 31	18 34	18 47		18 52	19 12	19 15	19 20
Heald Green	d	16 31				16 56		17 22						17 56		18 22	18 31					18 56			19 23
Gatley	d					16 59		17 25						17 59		18 25						18 59			19 26
East Didsbury	d				16 53			17 28					17 53			18 27				18 53					19 29
Burnage	d				16 56			17 30					17 55			18 29				18 56					19 31
Mauldeth Road	d				16 58			17 32					17 58			18 31				18 58					19 33
Manchester Piccadilly 10	a	16 42	16 47	16 48	17 10	17 11	17 19	17 41		17 44	17 47	17 49	18 09	18 11	18 24	18 40	18 43	18 48	18 52	19 09		19 11	19 31	19 38	19 41
	d	16 44	16 48		17 11					17 45	17 50		18 11		18 26		18 45	18 49		19 11			19 33		19 41
Manchester Oxford Road	a	16 46	16 50		17 13					17 47	17 52		18 13		18 28		18 47	18 51		19 13			19 35		19 46
Deansgate	a										17 55		18 17		18 31		18 50			19 17					

		TP	NT	TP	TP	NT	NT	TP	TP	TP		NT	NT	TP	TP	NT	TP	TP	NT	TP	TP	NT	TP		
		1◇		1◇	1◇			1◇	1◇	1◇				1◇	1◇		1◇	1◇		1◇	1◇		1◇		
		A	B	H	E		J	K	H	E			J	L	N	B	H	Q		L	U		V		
Crewe 10	84 d					*19 00*						*20b26*							*21 27*			*22 00*			
Wilmslow	84 d					19 51						20 50							21 55			22 55			
Manchester Airport ✈	d	19 27	19 30	19 47	19 52	20 04	20 15	20 22	20 47	20 52		21 04	21 16	21 22	21 27	21 30	21 47	21 52	22 08	22 22	22 47	23 07	23 22		
Heald Green	d	19 31			19 57	20 07				20 56		21 08						21 56	22 12		22 51	23 10			
Gatley	d				20 00	20 10				20 59		21 11						21 59	22 15		22 54	23 13			
East Didsbury	d			19 53		20 13			20 53			21 13					21 53		22 17		22 56	23 16			
Burnage	d			19 56		20 15			20 56			21 15					21 56		22 19		22 59	23 18			
Mauldeth Road	d			19 58		20 17			20 58			21 17					21 58		22 21		23 01	23 20			
Manchester Piccadilly 10	a	19 42	19 48	20 09	20 11	20 31	20 30	20 38	21 09	21 11		21 31	21 33	21 37	21 42	21 48	22 10	22 15	22 31	22 38	23 09	23 34	23 38		
	d	19 44	19 49	20 11			20 32		21 11				21 35		21 43	21 49	22 11				23 11				
Manchester Oxford Road	a	19 47	19 51	20 13			20 34		21 13				21 37		21 45	21 52	22 14				23 13				
Deansgate	a	19 50		20 17			20 37		21 17				21 40		21 48		22 17				23 17				

Sundays

until 27 January

		TP	TP	TP	TP	TP	NT		TP	NT	TP	TP	NT	TP		TP	NT	TP	TP	NT	NT		TP	TP	NT
			1◇		1◇				1◇		1◇	1◇		1◇		1◇		1◇	1◇				1◇	1◇	
		H	L	H	L	H			C		G	H		C		H	B	G	H	B			C	H	B
		🚌		🚌		🚌																			
Crewe 10	84 d																								
Wilmslow	84 d																								
Manchester Airport ✈	d	01 10	01 22	03 10	04 42	05 45	06 13		06 22	07 10	07 22	07 36	08 13	08 22		08 47	08 51	09 25	09 47	10 01	10 14		10 22	10 47	11 00
Heald Green	d						06 16			07 13			08 16								10 17				
Gatley	d						06 19			07 16			08 19								10 20				
East Didsbury	d						06 22			07 19			08 22								10 23				
Burnage	d						06 24			07 21			08 24								10 25				
Mauldeth Road	d						06 26			07 23			08 26								10 27				
Manchester Piccadilly 10	a	01 30	01 36	03 30	04 56	06 05	06 37		06 38	07 33	07 37	07 50	08 37	08 37		09 02	09 10	09 41	10 01	10 16	10 37		10 38	11 01	11 13
	d											07 51				09 03	09 16		10 03	10 16				11 03	11 16
Manchester Oxford Road	a											07 53				09 06	09 18		10 05	10 20				11 05	11 19
Deansgate	a											07 56				09 08			10 08					11 08	

		NT	NT	TP	TP	TP		NT	NT	TP	TP	NT	NT		NT	TP	TP	TP	NT	NT		TP	TP	TP	NT
				1◇	1◇	1◇				1◇	1◇					1◇	1◇	1◇				1◇	1◇	1◇	
				G	X	H		B		C	H	B				G	X	H	B			G	Y	H	B
					🛒												🛒								
Crewe 10	84 d	10 25											12 27												
Wilmslow	84 d	10 51											12 50												
Manchester Airport ✈	d	11 05	11 14	11 22	11 27	11 47		12 00	12 13	12 22	12 46	13 00	13 05		13 14	13 22	13 27	13 47	14 00	14 16		14 22	14 27	14 47	15 00
Heald Green	d		11 17						12 16						13 17					14 18					
Gatley	d		11 20						12 19						13 20					14 21					
East Didsbury	d		11 23						12 22						13 23					14 25					
Burnage	d		11 25					12 07				13 07							14 07						
Mauldeth Road	d		11 27					12 10				13 10							14 10						
Manchester Piccadilly 10	a	11 21	11 36	11 38	11 41	12 01		12 17	12 31	12 37	13 00	13 17	13 28		13 32	13 38	13 41	14 02	14 17	14 35		14 38	14 41	15 01	15 16
	d				11 42	12 03		12 17			13 02	13 17					13 42	14 03	14 17				14 42	15 03	15 16
Manchester Oxford Road	a				11 44	12 05		12 20			13 04	13 20					13 44	14 05	14 20				14 44	15 05	15 20
Deansgate	a					12 08					13 08							14 08						15 08	

For general notes see front of timetable
For details of catering facilities see Directory of Train Operators

- **A** To Barrow-in-Furness (from 29 March to Preston) (Table 82)
- **B** To Liverpool Lime Street (Table 90)
- **C** To Middlesbrough (Table 39)
- **D** To Blackpool North (Table 82). Until 26 January also conveys portion to Glasgow Central (Table 65). 2 February to 22 March also conveys portion to Carlisle (Table 65)
- **E** To Cleethorpes (Table 29)
- **G** To Newcastle (Table 39)
- **H** To Blackpool North (Table 82)
- **J** To Southport (Table 82)
- **K** To Scarborough (Table 39)
- **L** To York (Table 39)
- **N** To Preston (Table 82)
- **Q** To Sheffield (Table 78)
- **U** To Blackpool North (2 February to 22 March to Preston) (Table 82)
- **V** Until 26 January and from 29 March to York (Table 39)
- **X** To Edinburgh (Table 65)
- **Y** To Barrow-in-Furness (Table 82)
- **b** From 29 March dep. 2000

Table 85

Sundays until 27 January

Manchester Airport → Manchester

Network Diagram - see first page of Table 78

		NT	NT	TP 1◇ A	TP 1◇ B		TP 1◇ C	NT D	NT	TP 1◇ E	TP 1◇ G	TP 1◇ C		NT D	NT	NT	TP 1◇ A	TP 1◇ H	TP 1◇ C		NT D	NT	TP 1◇ E	TP 1◇ G	TP 1◇ C
Crewe 10	84 d	14 27													16 27										
Wilmslow	84 d	14 53													16 50										
Manchester Airport	✈ d	15 08	15 14	15 17	15 27		15 47	16 01	16 14	16 22	16 27	16 47		17 01	17 05	17 14	17 22	17 27	17 47		18 01	18 14	18 22	18 27	18 47
Heald Green	d		15 17						16 17							17 17						18 17			
Gatley	d		15 20						16 20							17 20						18 20			
East Didsbury	d		15 23						16 23							17 23						18 23			
Burnage	d		15 25						16 25							17 25						18 25			
Mauldeth Road	d		15 27						16 27							17 27						18 27			
Manchester Piccadilly 10	a	15 21	15 36	15 39	15 41		16 01	16 15	16 35	16 38	16 41	17 00		17 14	17 23	17 39	17 38	17 41	18 00		18 14	18 36	18 39	18 41	19 00
	d				15 42		16 03	16 16			16 42	17 03		17 16				17 42	18 03		18 16			18 42	19 03
Manchester Oxford Road	a				15 45		16 05	16 18			16 44	17 05		17 18				17 45	18 05		18 18			18 44	19 05
Deansgate	a						16 08					17 08							18 08						19 08

		NT D	NT	NT		TP 1◇ A	TP 1◇ C	NT D	NT	TP 1◇ J	TP 1◇ G		TP 1◇ C	NT D	NT	NT	TP 1◇ K	TP 1◇ C	NT D	NT	TP 1◇ C	NT	TP 1◇ K		
Crewe 10	84 d		18 27												20 27							22 25			
Wilmslow	84 d		18 50												20 50							22 51			
Manchester Airport	✈ d	19 01	19 05	19 14		19 22	19 47	20 01	20 14	20 22	20 27		20 47	21 01	21 05	21 14	21 22	21 47	22 01	22 14	22 47	23 05	23 22		
Heald Green	d			19 17					20 17							21 17				22 17					
Gatley	d			19 20					20 20							21 20				22 20					
East Didsbury	d			19 23					20 23							21 23				22 23					
Burnage	d			19 25					20 25							21 25				22 25					
Mauldeth Road	d			19 27					20 27							21 27				22 27					
Manchester Piccadilly 10	a	19 15	19 21	19 37		19 38	20 00	20 16	20 37	20 38	20 41		21 00	21 16	21 20	21 37	21 38	22 00	22 14	22 37	23 00	23 22	23 36		
	d	19 16					20 03	20 16			20 42		21 03	21 16				22 03	22 16		23 03				
Manchester Oxford Road	a	19 19					20 05	20 20			20 44		21 05	21 20				22 05	22 18		23 05				
Deansgate	a						20 08						21 08					22 08			23 08				

Sundays 3 February to 23 March

		TP C	TP K	TP C	TP K	TP C	NT	TP L	NT	TP 1◇ N	TP 1◇ E	NT	TP 1◇ Q	TP 1◇ N	NT D	TP 1◇ A	TP 1◇ N	NT D	NT	TP 1◇ E	TP 1◇ N	TP 1◇ Q	NT D	NT	NT
Crewe 10	84 d																							10 25	
Wilmslow	84 d																							10 51	
Manchester Airport	✈ d	01 10	01 35	03 10	04 45	05 45	06 13	06 22	07 10	07 36	07 41	08 13	08 40	08 47	08 51	09 25	09 47	10 01	10 14	10 22	10 47	10 52	11 00	11 05	11 14
Heald Green	d						06 16		07 13			08 16							10 17						11 17
Gatley	d						06 19		07 16			08 19							10 20						11 20
East Didsbury	d						06 22		07 19			08 22							10 23						11 23
Burnage	d						06 24		07 21			08 24							10 25						11 25
Mauldeth Road	d						06 26		07 23			08 26							10 27						11 27
Manchester Piccadilly 10	a	01 30	02 00	03 30	05 05	06 05	06 37	06 42	07 33	07 50	07 54	08 37	08 54	09 02	09 10	09 41	10 01	10 16	10 37	10 38	11 01	11 06	11 13	11 21	11 36
	d									07 51				09 03	09 16		10 03	10 16			11 03		11 16		
Manchester Oxford Road	a									07 53				09 06	09 18		10 05	10 20			11 05		11 19		
Deansgate	a									07 56				09 08			10 08				11 08				

		TP 1◇ A	TP 1◇ U	TP 1◇ N	NT D	NT	TP 1◇ E	TP 1◇ N	TP 1◇ Q	NT D	NT	NT	TP 1◇ A	TP 1◇ U	TP 1◇ N	TP 1◇ Q	NT D	NT	TP 1◇ A	TP 1◇ G	TP 1◇ N	TP 1◇ Q	NT D	NT	NT
Crewe 10	84 d										12 27													14 27	
Wilmslow	84 d										12 50													14 53	
Manchester Airport	✈ d	11 22	11 27	11 47	12 00	12 13	12 22	12 46	12 52	13 00	13 05	13 14	13 22	13 27	13 47	13 52	14 00	14 16	14 22	14 27	14 47	14 52	15 00	15 08	15 14
Heald Green	d					12 16						13 17						14 18							15 17
Gatley	d					12 19						13 20						14 21							15 20
East Didsbury	d					12 22						13 23						14 25							15 23
Burnage	d				12 07					13 07							14 07								15 25
Mauldeth Road	d				12 10					13 10							14 10								15 27
Manchester Piccadilly 10	a	11 38	11 41	12 01	12 17	12 31	12 37	13 00	13 07	13 17	13 28	13 32	13 38	13 41	14 02	14 09	14 17	14 35	14 38	14 41	15 01	15 09	15 16	15 21	15 36
	d		11 42	12 03	12 17			13 02		13 17				13 42	14 03		14 17			14 42	15 03		15 16		
Manchester Oxford Road	a		11 44	12 05	12 20			13 04		13 20				13 44	14 05		14 20			14 44	15 05		15 20		
Deansgate	a			12 08				13 08							14 08						15 08				

For general notes see front of timetable
For details of catering facilities see Directory of Train Operators

A To Newcastle (Table 39)
B To Edinburgh (Table 65)
C To Blackpool North (Table 82)
D To Liverpool Lime Street (Table 90)
E To Middlesbrough (Table 39)
G To Barrow-in-Furness (Table 82)
H To Glasgow Central (Table 65)
J To Scarborough (Table 39)
K To York (Table 39)
L To Leeds (Table 39)
N To Preston (Table 82)
Q To Cleethorpes (Table 29)
U To Carlisle (Table 65)

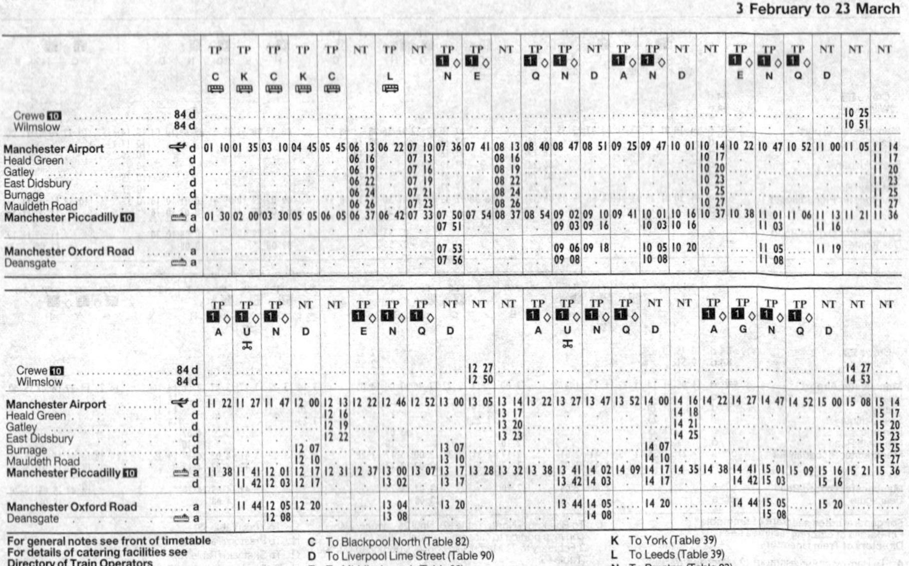

Table 85

Sundays

3 February to 23 March

Manchester Airport → Manchester

Network Diagram - see first page of Table 78

		TP	TP	TP	TP	NT	NT	TP	TP	TP	TP	NT	NT	NT	TP	TP	TP	TP	NT	NT	TP	TP	TP	TP	NT
		1 ◇	1 ◇	1 ◇	1 ◇			1 ◇	1 ◇	1 ◇	1 ◇				1 ◇	1 ◇	1 ◇	1 ◇			1 ◇	1 ◇	1 ◇	1 ◇	
		A	B	C	D	E		G	H	C	D	E			A	B	C	D	E		G	H	C	D	E
			trolley													trolley									
Crewe 10	84 d												16 27												
Wilmslow	84 d												16 50												
Manchester Airport	✈ d	15 22	15 27	15 47	15 52	16 01	16 14	16 22	16 27	16 47	16 52	17 01	17 05	17 14	17 22	17 27	17 47	17 52	18 01	18 14	18 22	18 27	18 47	18 52	19 01
Heald Green	d						16 17							17 17						18 17					
Gatley	d						16 20							17 20						18 20					
East Didsbury	d						16 23							17 23						18 23					
Burnage	d						16 25							17 25						18 25					
Mauldeth Road	d						16 27							17 27						18 27					
Manchester Piccadilly 10	a	15 39	15 41	16 01	16 10	16 15	16 35	16 38	16 41	17 00	17 08	17 14	17 23	17 39	17 38	17 41	18 00	18 09	18 14	18 36	18 39	18 41	19 00	19 07	19 15
	d		15 42	16 03		16 16			16 42	17 03		17 16				17 42	18 03		18 16			18 42	19 03		19 16
Manchester Oxford Road	a		15 45	16 05		16 18			16 44	17 05		17 18				17 45	18 05		18 18			18 44	19 05		19 19
Deansgate	a			16 08						17 08							18 08						19 08		

		NT	NT	TP	TP	TP	NT	NT	TP	TP	TP	TP	NT	NT	NT	TP	TP	TP	NT	NT	TP	TP	NT	TP	
				1 ◇	1 ◇	1 ◇			1 ◇	1 ◇	1 ◇	1 ◇				1 ◇	1 ◇	1 ◇			1 ◇	1 ◇		1 ◇	
				A	C	D	E		J	H	C	K	E			L	C	K	E		C	K		L	
Crewe 10	84 d	18 27												20 27									22 25		
Wilmslow	84 d	18 50												20 50									22 51		
Manchester Airport	✈ d	19 05	19 14	19 22	19 47	19 52	20 01	20 14	20 22	20 27	20 47	20 52	21 01	21 05	21 14	21 22	21 47	21 52	22 01	22 14	22 47	22 52	23 05	23 22	
Heald Green	d		19 17					20 17							21 17					22 17					
Gatley	d		19 20					20 20							21 20					22 20					
East Didsbury	d		19 23					20 23							21 23					22 23					
Burnage	d		19 25					20 25							21 25					22 25					
Mauldeth Road	d		19 27					20 27							21 27					22 27					
Manchester Piccadilly 10	a	19 21	19 37	19 38	20 00	20 06	20 16	20 37	20 38	20 41	21 00	21 10	21 16	21 20	21 37	21 38	22 00	22 10	22 14	22 37	23 00	23 06	23 22	23 36	
	d				20 03		20 16			20 42	21 03		21 16				22 03		22 16		23 03				
Manchester Oxford Road	a				20 05		20 20			20 44	21 05		21 20				22 05		22 18		23 05				
Deansgate	a				20 08						21 08						22 08				23 08				

Sundays

from 30 March

		TP	TP	TP	TP	TP	NT	TP	NT	TP	TP	NT		TP	TP	TP	NT	TP	TP	NT	NT	TP	TP	TP	NT
			1 ◇		1 ◇			1 ◇		1 ◇	1 ◇			1 ◇	1 ◇	1 ◇		1 ◇	1 ◇			1 ◇	1 ◇	1 ◇	
		N	L	N	L	N		G		A	N			G	D	N	Q	A	N	Q		G	N	D	Q
		bus		bus		bus																			
Crewe 10	84 d																								
Wilmslow	84 d																								
Manchester Airport	✈ d	01 10	01 22	03 10	04 42	05 45	06 13	06 22	07 10	07 22	07 36	08 13		08 22	08 40	08 47	08 51	09 25	09 47	10 01	10 14	10 22	10 47	10 52	11 00
Heald Green	d						06 16		07 13			08 16									10 17				
Gatley	d						06 19		07 16			08 19									10 20				
East Didsbury	d						06 22		07 19			08 22									10 23				
Burnage	d						06 24		07 21			08 24									10 25				
Mauldeth Road	d						06 26		07 23			08 26									10 27				
Manchester Piccadilly 10	a	01 30	01 36	03 30	04 56	06 05	06 37	06 38	07 33	07 37	07 50	08 37		08 37	08 54	09 02	09 10	09 41	10 01	10 16	10 37	10 38	11 01	11 06	11 13
	d										07 51					09 03	09 16		10 03	10 16			11 03		11 16
Manchester Oxford Road	a										07 53					09 06	09 18		10 05	10 20			11 05		11 19
Deansgate	a										07 56					09 08			10 08				11 08		

		NT		NT	TP	TP	NT	NT	TP	TP	TP	NT	NT	NT		TP	TP	TP	NT	NT	TP	TP	TP	NT	NT
					1 ◇	1 ◇			1 ◇	1 ◇	1 ◇					1 ◇	1 ◇	1 ◇			1 ◇	1 ◇	1 ◇		
					A	N	Q		G	N	D	Q				A	N	D	Q		A	N	D	Q	
Crewe 10	84 d	10 25											12 27												14 27
Wilmslow	84 d	10 51											12 50												14 53
Manchester Airport	✈ d	11 05		11 14	11 22	11 47	12 00	12 13	12 22	12 46	12 52	13 00	13 05	13 14		13 22	13 47	13 52	14 00	14 16	14 22	14 47	14 52	15 00	15 08
Heald Green	d			11 17				12 16						13 17						14 18					
Gatley	d			11 20				12 19						13 20						14 21					
East Didsbury	d			11 23				12 22						13 23						14 25					
Burnage	d			11 25			12 07					13 07							14 07						
Mauldeth Road	d			11 27			12 10					13 10							14 10						
Manchester Piccadilly 10	a	11 21		11 36	11 38	12 01	12 17	12 31	12 37	13 00	13 07	13 17	13 28	13 32		13 38	14 02	14 09	14 17	14 35	14 38	15 01	15 09	15 16	15 21
	d					12 03	12 17			13 02		13 17					14 03		14 17			15 03		15 16	
Manchester Oxford Road	a					12 05	12 22			13 04		13 21					14 05		14 20			15 05		15 20	
Deansgate	a					12 08				13 08							14 08					15 08			

		NT	TP	TP		TP	NT	NT	TP	TP	TP	NT	NT	NT	TP	TP		TP	NT	NT	TP	TP	TP	NT	NT
			1 ◇	1 ◇		1 ◇			1 ◇	1 ◇	1 ◇				1 ◇	1 ◇		1 ◇			1 ◇	1 ◇	1 ◇		
			A	N		D	Q		G	N	D	Q			A	N		D	Q		G	N	D	Q	
Crewe 10	84 d												16 27												18 27
Wilmslow	84 d												16 50												18 50
Manchester Airport	✈ d	15 14	15 22	15 47		15 52	16 01	16 14	16 22	16 47	16 52	17 01	17 05	17 14	17 22	17 47		17 52	18 01	18 14	18 22	18 47	18 52	19 01	19 05
Heald Green	d	15 17						16 17						17 17						18 17					
Gatley	d	15 20						16 20						17 20						18 20					
East Didsbury	d	15 23						16 23						17 23						18 23					
Burnage	d	15 25						16 25						17 25						18 25					
Mauldeth Road	d	15 27						16 27						17 27						18 27					
Manchester Piccadilly 10	a	15 36	15 39	16 01		16 10	16 15	16 35	16 38	17 00	17 08	17 14	17 23	17 39	17 38	18 00		18 09	18 14	18 36	18 39	19 00	19 07	19 15	19 21
	d			16 03			16 16			17 03		17 16				18 03			18 16			19 03		19 16	
Manchester Oxford Road	a			16 05			16 18			17 05		17 18				18 05			18 18			19 05		19 19	
Deansgate	a			16 08						17 08						18 08						19 08			

For general notes see front of timetable
For details of catering facilities see Directory of Train Operators

A To Newcastle (Table 39)
B To Carlisle (Table 65)
C To Preston (Table 82)
D To Cleethorpes (Table 29)
E To Liverpool Lime Street (Table 90)
G To Middlesbrough (Table 39)
H To Barrow-in-Furness (Table 82)
J To Scarborough (Table 39)
K To Sheffield (Table 78)
L To York (Table 39)
N To Blackpool North (Table 82)
Q To Liverpool Lime Street (Table 89)

Table 85

Sundays

from 30 March

Manchester Airport → Manchester

Network Diagram - see first page of Table 78

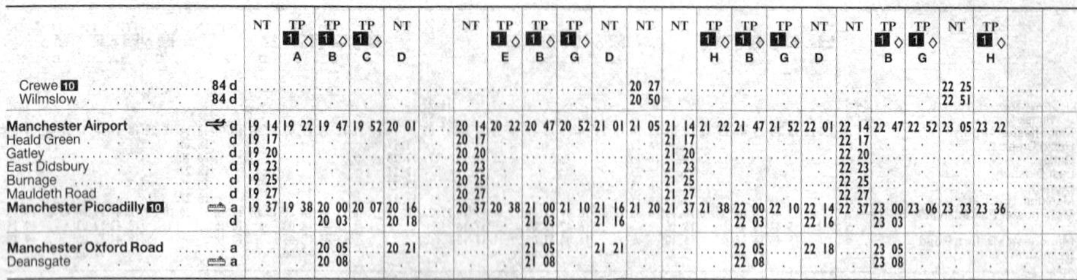

		NT	TP 1◇ A	TP 1◇ B	TP 1◇ C	NT D		NT	TP 1◇ E	TP 1◇ B	TP 1◇ G	NT D	NT	NT	TP 1◇ H	TP 1◇ B	TP 1◇ G	NT D	NT	TP 1◇ B	TP 1◇ G	NT	TP 1◇ H		
Crewe 10	84 d												20 27									22 25			
Wilmslow	84 d												20 50									22 51			
Manchester Airport ✈	d	19 14	19 22	19 47	19 52	20 01		20 14	20 22	20 47	20 52	21 01	21 05	21 14	21 22	21 47	21 52	22 01	22 14	22 47	22 52	23 05	23 22		
Heald Green	d	19 17						20 17						21 17					22 17						
Gatley	d	19 20						20 20						21 20					22 20						
East Didsbury	d	19 23						20 23						21 23					22 23						
Burnage	d	19 25						20 25						21 25					22 25						
Mauldeth Road	d	19 27						20 27						21 27					22 27						
Manchester Piccadilly 10	a	19 37	19 38	20 00	20 07	20 16		20 37	20 38	21 00	21 10	21 16	21 20	21 37	21 38	22 00	22 10	22 14	22 37	23 00	23 06	23 23	23 36		
	d			20 03		20 18				21 03		21 16				22 03		22 16		23 03					
Manchester Oxford Road	a			20 05		20 21				21 05		21 21				22 05		22 18		23 05					
Deansgate	a			20 08						21 08						22 08				23 08					

For general notes see front of timetable
For details of catering facilities see Directory of Train Operators

- **A** To Newcastle (Table 39)
- **B** To Blackpool North (Table 82)
- **C** To Cleethorpes (Table 29)
- **D** To Liverpool Lime Street (Table 89)
- **E** To Scarborough (Table 39)
- **G** To Sheffield (Table 78)
- **H** To York (Table 39)

Manchester → Hazel Grove and Buxton

Network Diagram - see first page of Table 78

Miles			NT A	NT	NT	NT	NT	NT	NT	NT	NT	NT B	NT	NT B	NT	NT B	NT	NT B	NT	NT B
—	Deansgate	d				*06 49*		*07 29*	*08 12*	*08 41*		09 29	*09 40*	10 29	*10*b*31*	11 29	*11*b*31*	12 29	*12*b*31*	13 29
—	Manchester Oxford Road	d				*07 07*	*07 13*	*07 39*	*08 15*	*08 45*	*08 50*	09 33	*09 43*	10 33	*10 43*	11 33	*11 43*	12 33	*12 43*	13 33
0	**Manchester Piccadilly** 10	84 d	05 52	06 41	06 51	07 22	07 37	07 51	08 29	08 59	09 06	09 37	10 06	10 37	11 06	11 37	12 06	12 37	13 06	13 37
3	Levenshulme	84 d		06 47		07 28		07 56	08 34		09 12		10 12		11 12		12 12		13 12	
4½	Heaton Chapel	84 d		06 50		07 31		07 59	08 37		09 15		10 15		11 15		12 15		13 15	
6	**Stockport**	84 d	06 01	06 54	07 01	07 35	07 47	08 03	08 41	09 08	09 19	09 47	10 19	10 47	11 19	11 47	12 19	12 47	13 19	13 47
7	Davenport	d		06 57		07 38		08 07	08 45	09 12	09 22	09 50	10 22	10 50	11 22	11 50	12 22	12 50	13 22	13 50
7¾	Woodsmoor	d		06 59		07 40		08 09	08 47	09 14	09 24	09 52	10 24	10 52	11 24	11 52	12 24	12 52	13 24	13 52
8¾	**Hazel Grove**	a	06 08	07 01	07 07	07 44	07 54	08 13	08 49	09 16	09 29	09 55	10 29	10 55	11 29	11 55	12 29	12 55	13 29	13 55
—		d			07 08		07 54		08 49	09 18		09 55		10 55		11 55		12 55		13 55
11	Middlewood	d					07 59					09 59				11 59				13 59
12½	Disley	d			07 15		08 03		08 56	09 26		10 03		11 02		12 03		13 02		14 03
14¼	New Mills Newtown	d			07 18		08 06		08 59	09 29		10 06		11 05		12 06		13 05		14 06
15¼	Furness Vale	d			07 20		08 08		09 02	09 31		10 09		11 07		12 09		13 07		14 09
16¼	Whaley Bridge	d			07 24		08 12		09 05	09 35		10 12		11 11		12 12		13 11		14 12
20½	Chapel-en-le-Frith	d			07 31		08 19		09 13	09 42		10 20		11 18		12 20		13 18		14 20
22¾	Dove Holes	d			07 36		08 24					10 25				12 25				14 25
25¾	**Buxton**	a			07 45		08 33		09 26	09 56		10 33		11 30		12 33		13 30		14 33

		NT	NT B	NT	NT B	NT	NT	NT B	NT	NT C	NT	NT B	NT	NT	NT B	NT B	NT B	NT C	NT D
Deansgate	d	*13*b*31*	14 29	*14*b*31*	15 29		*15*b*31*	16 29		16 59	*17 10*	17 28			*18 15*	19 29	20 29	21 40	22 50
Manchester Oxford Road	d	*13 43*	14 33	*14 43*	15 33		*15 43*	16 33		17 03	*17 13*	17 32	*17 38*	*17 46*	18 35	19 33	20 32	21 43	22 53
Manchester Piccadilly 10	84 d	14 06	14 37	15 06	15 37	15 40	16 06	16 37	16 44	17 07	17 27	17 37	17 50	18 06	18 39	19 37	20 36	21 49	22 58
Levenshulme	84 d	14 12		15 11		15 46	16 12		16 51	17 13				18 12					
Heaton Chapel	84 d	14 15		15 14		15 49	16 15		16 54	17 16				18 15					
Stockport	84 d	14 19	14 47	15 18	15 47	15 55	16 19	16 46	16 58	17 19	17 37	17 48	17 59	18 19	18 48	19 47	20 45	21 59	23 07
Davenport	d	14 22	14 50	15 22	15 50	15 58	16 22	16 49	17 02	17 23	17 41	17 51	18 03	18 22	18 52	19 50	20 48	22 02	23 10
Woodsmoor	d	14 24	14 52	15 24	15 52	16 00	16 24	16 51	17 04	17 25	17 43	17 53	18 05	18 24	18 54	19 52	20 50	22 04	23 12
Hazel Grove	a	14 29	14 55	15 28	15 56	16 03	16 29	16 53	17 07	17 27	17 47	17 56	18 09	18 27	18 56	19 55	20 52	22 06	23 14
	d		14 55	15 28		16 03		16 54		17 27		17 56		18 27	18 56	19 55	20 52	22 07	23 15
Middlewood	d			15 32		16 07				17 32				18 32	19 01	19 59	20 56	22 11	23 19
Disley	d		15 02	15 36		16 11		17 01		17 36		18 03		18 36	19 05	20 03	21 00	22 15	23 23
New Mills Newtown	d		15 05	15 39		16 14		17 04		17 39		18 06		18 39	19 08	20 06	21 03	22 18	23 26
Furness Vale	d		15 07	15 42		16 17		17 06		17 41				18 41	19 10	20 09	21 06	22 21	23 29
Whaley Bridge	d		15 11	15 45		16 20		17 10		17 45		18 10		18 45	19 14	20 12	21 09	22 24	23 32
Chapel-en-le-Frith	d		15 18	15 53		16 28		17 17		17 52		18 18		18 52	19 21	20 20	21 17	22 32	23 40
Dove Holes	d			15 58		16 33				17 57				18 57	19 26	20 25	21 22	22 37	23 45
Buxton	a		15 30	16 06		16 41		17 30		18 07		18 30		19 08	19 36	20 36	21 30	22 46	23 54

Saturdays

		NT A	NT	NT	NT	NT	NT	NT	NT	NT	NT B	NT	NT B	NT	NT B	NT	NT B	NT
Deansgate	d				*06 49*		*07 29*	*07 39*	*08 41*		09 29	*09*b*31*	10 29	*10*b*31*	11 29	*11*b*31*	12 29	*12*b*31*
Manchester Oxford Road	d				*07 07*	*07 13*	*07 39*	*08 07*	*08 45*	*08 50*	09 33	*09 43*	10 33	*10 43*	11 33	*11 43*	12 33	*12 43*
Manchester Piccadilly 10	84 d	05 52	06 50	07 00	07 22	07 37	07 51	08 29	08 59	09 10	09 37	10 06	10 37	11 06	11 37	12 06	12 37	13 06
Levenshulme	84 d			07 05	07 28		07 56	08 36		09 15	09 42	10 12	10 42	11 12	11 42	12 12	12 42	13 12
Heaton Chapel	84 d			07 08	07 31		07 59	08 39		09 18	09 45	10 15	10 45	11 15	11 45	12 15	12 45	13 15
Stockport	84 d	06 01	07 01	07 12	07 35	07 47	08 03	08 43	09 08	09 22	09 49	10 19	10 49	11 19	11 49	12 19	12 49	13 19
Davenport	d			07 16	07 38		08 07	08 47	09 12	09 26	09 53	10 22	10 53	11 22	11 53	12 22	12 53	13 22
Woodsmoor	d			07 18	07 40		08 09	08 49	09 14	09 28	09 55	10 24	10 55	11 24	11 55	12 24	12 55	13 24
Hazel Grove	a	06 08	07 07	07 22	07 44	07 54	08 13	08 51	09 16	09 32	09 57	10 29	10 57	11 29	11 57	12 29	12 57	13 29
	d		07 08			07 54		08 51	09 16		09 57		10 57		11 57		12 57	
Middlewood	d					07 59					10 02				12 02			
Disley	d		07 15			08 03		08 58	09 23		10 06		11 04		12 06		13 04	
New Mills Newtown	d		07 18			08 06		09 01	09 26		10 09		11 07		12 09		13 07	
Furness Vale	d		07 20			08 08		09 04	09 29		10 11		11 10		12 11		13 10	
Whaley Bridge	d		07 24			08 12		09 07	09 32		10 15		11 13		12 15		13 13	
Chapel-en-le-Frith	d		07 31			08 19		09 15	09 40		10 22		11 21		12 22		13 21	
Dove Holes	d		07 36			08 24					10 27				12 27			
Buxton	a		07 45			08 33		09 27	09 53		10 36		11 33		12 36		13 33	

		NT B	NT	NT B	NT	NT B	NT	NT B	NT C	NT	NT B	NT	NT B	NT B	NT B	NT C	NT D
Deansgate	d	13 29	*13*b*31*	14 29	*14*b*31*	15 29	*15*b*31*	16 29	16 59	*16*b*31*	17 28		*18 15*	19 29	20 28	21 40	22 50
Manchester Oxford Road	d	13 33	*13 43*	14 33	*14 43*	15 33	*15 43*	16 33	17 03	*16 55*	17 32	*17 46*	18 35	19 33	20 32	21 43	22 53
Manchester Piccadilly 10	84 d	13 37	14 06	14 37	15 06	15 37	16 06	16 37	17 07	17 07	17 37	18 06	18 39	19 37	20 36	21 49	22 57
Levenshulme	84 d	13 42	14 12	14 42	15 12	15 42	16 12			17 16	17 45	18 12	18 45				
Heaton Chapel	84 d	13 45	14 15	14 45	15 15	15 45	16 15			17 19	17 48	18 15	18 48				
Stockport	84 d	13 49	14 19	14 49	15 19	15 49	16 19	16 46	17 19	17 23	17 51	18 19	18 50	19 48	20 45	21 57	23 07
Davenport	d	13 53	14 22	14 53	15 22	15 53	16 22	16 49	17 23	17 27	17 54	18 22	18 53	19 50	20 48	22 00	23 10
Woodsmoor	d	13 55	14 24	14 55	15 24	15 55	16 24	16 51	17 25	17 29	17 56	18 24	18 55	19 52	20 50	22 02	23 12
Hazel Grove	a	13 57	14 29	14 57	15 29	15 57	16 29	16 54	17 27	17 32	17 59	18 29	18 57	19 55	20 52	22 05	23 14
	d	13 57		14 57		15 57		16 54	17 27		17 59		18 58	19 56	20 52	22 05	23 15
Middlewood	d	14 02				16 02			17 32		18 03		19 02	19 59	20 56	22 09	23 19
Disley	d	14 06		15 04		16 06		17 01	17 36		18 07		19 06	20 03	21 00	22 13	23 23
New Mills Newtown	d	14 09		15 07		16 09		17 04	17 39		18 10		19 09	20 06	21 03	22 16	23 26
Furness Vale	d	14 11		15 10		16 11		17 06	17 41				19 12	20 10	21 06	22 19	23 29
Whaley Bridge	d	14 15		15 13		16 15		17 10	17 45		18 15		19 15	20 12	21 09	22 22	23 32
Chapel-en-le-Frith	d	14 22		15 21		16 22		17 17	17 52		18 22		19 23	20 21	21 17	22 30	23 40
Dove Holes	d	14 27				16 27			17 57		18 27		19 28	20 26	21 22	22 35	23 45
Buxton	a	14 36		15 33		16 36		17 30	18 07		18 37		19 37	20 34	21 31	22 44	23 54

For general notes see front of timetable
For details of catering facilities see Directory of Train Operators

A To Sheffield (Table 78)
B From Blackpool North (Table 82)
C From Southport (Table 82)
D From Clitheroe (Table 94)

b Change at Manchester Oxford Road and Manchester Piccadilly

Sundays

Manchester → Hazel Grove and Buxton

Network Diagram - see first page of Table 78

		NT	NT	NT	NT	NT	NT	NT	NT	NT	NT	NT	NT	NT	NT	NT	NT
			A	A	A	A	A	A	B	A	A	A	A	A	A	A	A
Deansgate	d		09 43	10 43	11 46	12 43	13 43	14 43		15 43	16 43	17 43	18 43	19 43	20 43	21 43	22 43
Manchester Oxford Road	d		09 46	10 46	11 50	12 46	13 46	14 46		15 46	16 46	17 46	18 46	19 46	20 46	21 46	22 46
Manchester Piccadilly 10	84 d	08 53	09 56	10 56	11 56	12 56	13 56	14 56	15 08	15 53	16 53	17 53	18 53	19 53	20 53	21 53	22 51
Levenshulme	84 d	08 58	10 01	11 01	12 01	13 01	14 01	15 01		15 58	16 58	17 58	18 58	19 58	20 58	21 58	22 56
Heaton Chapel	84 d	09 01	10 04	11 04	12 04	13 04	14 04	15 04		16 01	17 01	18 01	19 01	20 01	21 01	22 01	22 59
Stockport	84 d	09 05	10 08	11 08	12 08	13 08	14 08	15 08	15 27	16 05	17 05	18 05	19 05	20 05	21 05	22 05	23 03
Davenport	d	09 09	10 11	11 11	12 11	13 11	14 11	15 11		16 08	17 09	18 09	19 09	20 09	21 09	22 09	23 07
Woodsmoor	d	09 11	10 13	11 13	12 13	13 13	14 13	15 13		16 10	17 11	18 11	19 11	20 11	21 11	22 11	23 09
Hazel Grove	a	09 13	10 15	11 15	12 15	13 15	14 15	15 15	15 34	16 12	17 15	18 13	19 13	20 13	21 13	22 13	23 11
	d	09 13	10 16	11 16	12 16	13 16	14 16	15 16		16 13	17 15	18 13	19 13	20 13	21 13	22 13	23 11
Middlewood	d	09 18	10 20	11 20	12 20	13 20	14 20	15 20		16 17	17 20	18 18	19 18	20 18	21 18	22 18	23 16
Disley	d	09 22	10 24	11 24	12 24	13 24	14 24	15 24		16 21	17 24	18 22	19 22	20 22	21 22	22 22	23 20
New Mills Newtown	d	09 25	10 27	11 27	12 27	13 27	14 27	15 27		16 24	17 27	18 25	19 25	20 25	21 25	22 25	23 23
Furness Vale	d	09 27	10 30	11 30	12 30	13 30	14 30	15 30		16 27	17 29	18 27	19 27	20 27	21 27	22 27	23 25
Whaley Bridge	d	09 31	10 33	11 33	12 33	13 33	14 33	15 33		16 30	17 33	18 31	19 31	20 31	21 31	22 31	23 29
Chapel-en-le-Frith	d	09 38	10 41	11 41	12 41	13 41	14 41	15 41		16 38	17 40	18 38	19 38	20 38	21 38	22 38	23 36
Dove Holes	d	09 43	10 46	11 46	12 46	13 46	14 46	15 46		16 43	17 45	18 43	19 43	20 43	21 43	22 43	23 41
Buxton	a	09 53	10 55	11 55	12 55	13 55	14 55	15 56		16 53	17 55	18 53	19 53	20 53	21 53	22 53	23 51

For general notes see front of timetable
For details of catering facilities see Directory of Train Operators

A From Blackpool North (3 February to 23 March from Preston) (Table 82)

B From 30 March.
To Sheffield (Table 78)

Buxton and Hazel Grove → Manchester

Network Diagram - see first page of Table 78

Miles			NT	NT	NT	NT		NT	NT	NT	NT		EM ◇	NT	NT	NT		NT	NT	NT	NT		NT	NT	NT
					A			B			A		C			A					A			A	
0	**Buxton**	d	05 54		06 34			07 04			07 40				07 57	08 36			09 36		10 37			11 34	
3	Dove Holes	d			06 40			07 10							08 03	08 42			09 42					11 40	
5¼	Chapel-en-le-Frith	d	06 02		06 44			07 14			07 49				08 07	08 46			09 46		10 45			11 44	
9½	Whaley Bridge	d	06 08		06 49			07 19			07 55				08 12	08 51			09 51		10 51			11 49	
10½	Furness Vale	d	06 11		06 52			07 22							08 15	08 54			09 54		10 54			11 52	
11½	New Mills Newtown	d	06 14		06 55			07 25			08 00				08 18	08 57			09 57		10 57			11 55	
13¼	Disley	d	06 17		06 59			07 29			08 04				08 22	09 01			10 01		11 00			11 59	
14¾	Middlewood	d			07 02			07 32							08 25				10 04					12 02	
17	**Hazel Grove**	a	06 27		07 10			07 40			08 13				08 33	09 09			10 12		11 10			12 10	
—		d	06 27	06 53	07 10	07 20		07 40	07 53	08 06	08 14		08 19	08 29	08 33	09 10		09 41	10 12	10 41	11 10		11 41	12 10	12 41
18	Woodsmoor	d	06 29	06 55	07 12	07 22		07 42	07 55	08 08				08 31	08 35	09 12		09 43	10 14	10 43	11 12		11 43	12 12	12 43
18¾	Davenport	d	06 31	06 57	07 14	07 24		07 44	07 57	08 10				08 33	08 37	09 14		09 45	10 16	10 45	11 14		11 45	12 14	12 45
19¾	**Stockport**	84 a	06 36	07 02	07 19	07 29		07 49	08 00	08 14	08 21		08 26	08 37	08 41	09 19		09 49	10 21	10 49	11 18		11 49	12 18	12 49
21¼	Heaton Chapel	84 a		07 06		07 33			08 05					08 41		09 23									
22¾	Levenshulme	84 a		07 09		07 36			08 08					08 44		09 26									
25¾	**Manchester Piccadilly** 10	84 a	06 47	07 17	07 30	07 45		08 00	08 19	08 26	08 31		08 36	08 53	08 56	09 32		10 01	10 33	11 01	11 29		12 01	12 29	13 01
—	Manchester Oxford Road	a	*07 09*		07 33			08 03			08 35		08 40		*09 09*	09 36		*10 14*	*10 47*	*11 13*	11 32		*12 13*	12 32	*13 13*
—	Deansgate	a			07 35			08 15			08 37		*08 50*		*09 26*	09 38		*10 26*	*10 50*	*11 26*	11 35		*12 26*	12 35	*13 26*

		NT	NT	NT		NT	NT	NT	NT		NT	NT	NT	NT		NT	NT	NT	NT	NT	NT	NT	NT
		A		A			A		A		D		A				A		E		G	H	
Buxton	d	12 37		13 34			14 37				15 47		16 36	17 06			17 34		18 22	18 55	19 55	21 38	22 55
Dove Holes	d			13 40							15 53						17 40			19 01	20 01	21 44	23 01
Chapel-en-le-Frith	d	12 45		13 44			14 45				15 57		16 44	17 14			17 44		18 30	19 05	20 05	21 48	23 05
Whaley Bridge	d	12 51		13 49			14 51				16 02		16 50	17 20			17 49		18 36	19 10	20 10	21 53	23 10
Furness Vale	d	12 54		13 52			14 54				16 05		16 53	17 23			17 52		18 39	19 13	20 13	21 56	23 13
New Mills Newtown	d	12 57		13 55			14 57				16 08		16 56	17 26			17 55		18 42	19 16	20 16	21 59	23 16
Disley	d	13 00		13 59			15 00				16 12		16 59	17 29			17 59		18 45	19 20	20 20	22 03	23 20
Middlewood	d			14 02							16 15						18 02			19 23	20 23	22 06	23 23
Hazel Grove	a	13 10		14 09			15 10				16 26		17 09	17 39			18 10		18 55	19 31	20 31	22 14	23 31
	d	13 10	13 41	14 09		14 41	15 10	15 41	16 10		16 28	16 41	17 09	17 40		18 07	18 10	18 22	18 55	19 31	20 31	22 14	23 31
Woodsmoor	d	13 12	13 43	14 11		14 43	15 12	15 43	16 12		16 30	16 43	17 11	17 42		18 09	18 12	18 24	18 57	19 33	20 33	22 16	23 33
Davenport	d	13 14	13 45	14 13		14 45	15 14	15 45	16 14		16 32	16 45	17 13	17 44		18 11	18 14	18 26	18 59	19 35	20 35	22 18	23 35
Stockport	84 a	13 18	13 49	14 17		14 49	15 18	15 49	16 18		16 40	16 49	17 17	17 49		18 14	18 18	18 30	19 04	19 40	20 40	22 23	23 39
Heaton Chapel	84 a																		19 09				
Levenshulme	84 a																		19 12				
Manchester Piccadilly 10	84 a	13 27	14 01	14 27		15 01	15 27	16 01	16 27		16 50	17 01	17 31	18 02		18 26	18 29	18 42	19 24	19 54	20 52	22 33	23 52
Manchester Oxford Road	a	13 32	*14 13*	14 32		*15 13*	15 32	*16 13*	16 32		16 55	*17 13*	17 34	*18 18*		*18 39*	18 33	*19 09*	19 28	*20 09*	20 54	22 37	
Deansgate	a	13 35	*14 26*	14 35		*15 26*	15 35	*16 26*	16 35		16 58	*17 21*	17 37	*18 31*		*18 50*	18 36	*19 17*	19 31	*20 17*	20 56	22 40	

Saturdays

		NT	NT		NT	NT		NT	NT		NT	NT		NT	NT		NT	NT		NT	NT		NT	NT	NT
			A					A				A						A			A			A	
Buxton	d	05 54	06 34					07 36			07 57	08 37			09 36			10 37			11 34			12 37	
Dove Holes	d		06 40					07 42			08 03	08 43			09 42						11 40				
Chapel-en-le-Frith	d	06 02	06 44					07 46			08 07	08 47			09 46			10 45			11 44			12 45	
Whaley Bridge	d	06 08	06 49					07 51			08 12	08 52			09 51			10 51			11 49			12 51	
Furness Vale	d	06 11	06 52					07 54			08 15	08 55			09 54			10 54			11 52			12 54	
New Mills Newtown	d	06 14	06 55					07 57			08 18	08 58			09 57			10 57			11 55			12 57	
Disley	d	06 17	06 59					08 01			08 22	09 02			10 01			11 00			11 59			13 00	
Middlewood	d		07 02					08 06			08 25				10 04						12 02				
Hazel Grove	a	06 27	07 10					08 13			08 33	09 11			10 12			11 10			12 10			13 10	
	d	06 27	07 10		07 24	07 53		08 14	08 25		08 33	09 12		09 40	10 12		10 41	11 10		11 41	12 10		12 41	13 10	13 41
Woodsmoor	d	06 29	07 12		07 26	07 55			08 27		08 35	09 14		09 42	10 14		10 43	11 12		11 43	12 12		12 43	13 12	13 43
Davenport	d	06 31	07 14		07 28	07 57			08 29		08 37	09 16		09 44	10 16		10 45	11 14		11 45	12 14		12 45	13 14	13 45
Stockport	84 a	06 35	07 17		07 32	08 00		08 20	08 34		08 42	09 20		09 48	10 21		10 49	11 18		11 49	12 18		12 49	13 18	13 49
Heaton Chapel	84 a					08 05								09 51											
Levenshulme	84 a					08 08								09 54											
Manchester Piccadilly 10	84 a	06 46	07 30		07 42	08 14		08 29	08 44		08 56	09 32		10 01	10 32		11 00	11 29		12 00	12 29		13 00	13 27	14 00
Manchester Oxford Road	a	*07 09*	07 33		*08 09*	*08 31*		08 33	*08 58*		*09 09*	09 36		*10 14*	*10 47*		*11 13*	11 32		*12 13*	12 33		*13 13*	13 32	*14 13*
Deansgate	a	*07 35*	07 35			*08 33*		08 37	*09 03*		*09 26*	09 38		*10 26*	*10 50*		*11 26*	11 35		*12 26*	12 35		*13 26*	13 35	*14 26*

		NT		NT	NT		NT	NT		NT	NT		NT	NT		NT	NT		NT	NT		NT	NT
		A			A			A			A			A			E			G		H	
Buxton	d	13 34			14 37			15 34			16 36			17 34			18 22		18 55	19 55		21 38	22 55
Dove Holes	d	13 40						15 40						17 40					19 01	20 01		21 44	23 01
Chapel-en-le-Frith	d	13 44			14 45			15 44			16 44			17 44			18 30		19 05	20 05		21 48	23 05
Whaley Bridge	d	13 49			14 51			15 49			16 50			17 49			18 36		19 10	20 10		21 53	23 10
Furness Vale	d	13 52			14 54			15 52			16 53			17 52			18 39		19 13	20 13		21 56	23 13
New Mills Newtown	d	13 55			14 57			15 55			16 56			17 55			18 42		19 16	20 16		21 59	23 16
Disley	d	13 59			15 00			15 59			16 59			17 59			18 45		19 20	20 20		22 03	23 20
Middlewood	d	14 02						16 02						18 02					19 23	20 23		22 06	23 23
Hazel Grove	a	14 10			15 10			16 10			17 09			18 10			18 55		19 31	20 31		22 14	23 31
	d	14 10		14 41	15 10		15 41	16 10		16 41	17 09		17 41	18 10		18 41	18 55		19 31	20 31		22 14	23 31
Woodsmoor	d	14 12		14 43	15 12		15 43	16 12		16 43	17 11		17 43	18 12		18 43	18 57		19 33	20 33		22 16	23 33
Davenport	d	14 14		14 45	15 14		15 45	16 14		16 45	17 13		17 45	18 14		18 45	18 59		19 35	20 35		22 18	23 35
Stockport	84 a	14 18		14 49	15 18		15 49	16 18		16 49	17 17		17 49	18 18		18 50	19 04		19 40	20 40		22 23	23 40
Heaton Chapel	84 a																19 09						
Levenshulme	84 a																19 12						
Manchester Piccadilly 10	84 a	14 27		15 00	15 27		16 00	16 27		17 00	17 28		18 01	18 30		19 00	19 19		19 51	20 52		22 33	23 52
Manchester Oxford Road	a	14 32		*15 13*	15 32		*16 13*	16 32		*17 13*	17 32		*18 13*	18 34		*19 13*	19 22		*20 09*	20 54		22 37	
Deansgate	a	14 35		*15 26*	15 35		*16 28*	16 35		*17 21*	17 35		*18 17*	18 38		*19 17*	19 25		*20 17*	20 56		22 40	

For general notes see front of timetable
For details of catering facilities see Directory of Train Operators

- **A** To Blackpool North (Table 82)
- **B** To Liverpool Lime Street (Table 89)
- **C** From Nottingham to Liverpool Lime Street (Table 49)
- **D** To Preston (Table 82)
- **E** To Salford Crescent (Table 82)
- **G** To Bolton (Table 82)
- **H** To Southport (Table 82)

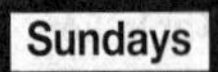

Buxton and Hazel Grove → Manchester

Network Diagram - see first page of Table 78

		NT	NT	NT	NT	NT	NT	NT	NT	NT	NT	NT	NT	NT	NT	NT	NT
		A	A	A	A	A	A	A	A	A	B	A	A	A	A		
Buxton	d	08 25	09 25	10 25	11 20	12 20	13 25	14 25	15 25	16 25		17 25	18 25	19 25	20 25	21 25	22 25
Dove Holes	d	08 31	09 31	10 31	11 26	12 26	13 31	14 31	15 31	16 31		17 31	18 31	19 31	20 31	21 31	22 31
Chapel-en-le-Frith	d	08 35	09 35	10 35	11 30	12 30	13 35	14 35	15 35	16 35		17 35	18 35	19 35	20 35	21 35	22 35
Whaley Bridge	d	08 40	09 40	10 40	11 35	12 35	13 40	14 40	15 40	16 40		17 40	18 40	19 40	20 40	21 40	22 40
Furness Vale	d	08 43	09 43	10 43	11 38	12 38	13 43	14 43	15 43	16 43		17 43	18 43	19 43	20 43	21 43	22 43
New Mills Newtown	d	08 46	09 46	10 46	11 41	12 41	13 46	14 46	15 46	16 46		17 46	18 46	19 46	20 46	21 46	22 46
Disley	d	08 50	09 50	10 50	11 45	12 45	13 50	14 50	15 50	16 50		17 50	18 50	19 50	20 50	21 50	22 50
Middlewood	d	08 53	09 53	10 53	11 48	12 48	13 53	14 53	15 53	16 53		17 53	18 53	19 53	20 53	21 53	22 53
Hazel Grove	a	08 59	09 59	10 59	11 55	12 54	13 59	14 59	15 59	16 59		17 59	18 59	19 59	20 59	21 59	22 59
	d	08 59	09 59	10 59	11 56	12 54	13 59	14 59	15 59	16 59	17 36	17 59	18 59	19 59	20 59	21 59	22 59
Woodsmoor	d	09 01	10 01	11 01	11 58	12 56	14 01	15 01	16 01	17 01		18 01	19 01	20 01	21 01	22 01	23 01
Davenport	d	09 03	10 03	11 03	12 00	12 58	14 03	15 03	16 03	17 03		18 03	19 03	20 03	21 03	22 03	23 03
Stockport	84 a	09 10	10 11	11 11	12 07	13 08	14 10	15 10	16 10	17 10	17 47	18 10	19 10	20 10	21 10	22 10	23 10
Heaton Chapel	84 a	09 15	10 15	11 15	12 11	13 12	14 15	15 15	16 14	17 15		18 14	19 14	20 14	21 14	22 14	23 14
Levenshulme	84 a	09 18	10 18	11 18	12 14	13 15	14 18	15 18	16 17	17 18		18 17	19 17	20 17	21 17	22 17	23 17
Manchester Piccadilly 10	84 ⇌ a	09 24	10 24	11 24	12 24	13 23	14 24	15 24	16 24	17 24	17 59	18 24	19 24	20 24	21 24	22 27	23 27
Manchester Oxford Road	a	09 27	10 27	11 27	12 27	13 26	14 27	15 27	16 27	17 27	*18 18*	18 27	19 27	20 27	21 27	*22 47*	
Deansgate	⇌ a	09 31	10 31	11 31	12 31	13 30	14 31	15 31	16 30	17 31		18 30	19 31	20 30	21 30	*22 50*	

For general notes see front of timetable
For details of catering facilities see
Directory of Train Operators

A To Blackpool North (3 February to 23 March to Preston) (Table 82)

B From 30 March.
From Sheffield (Table 78)

Network Diagram for Tables 88, 89, 90, 91

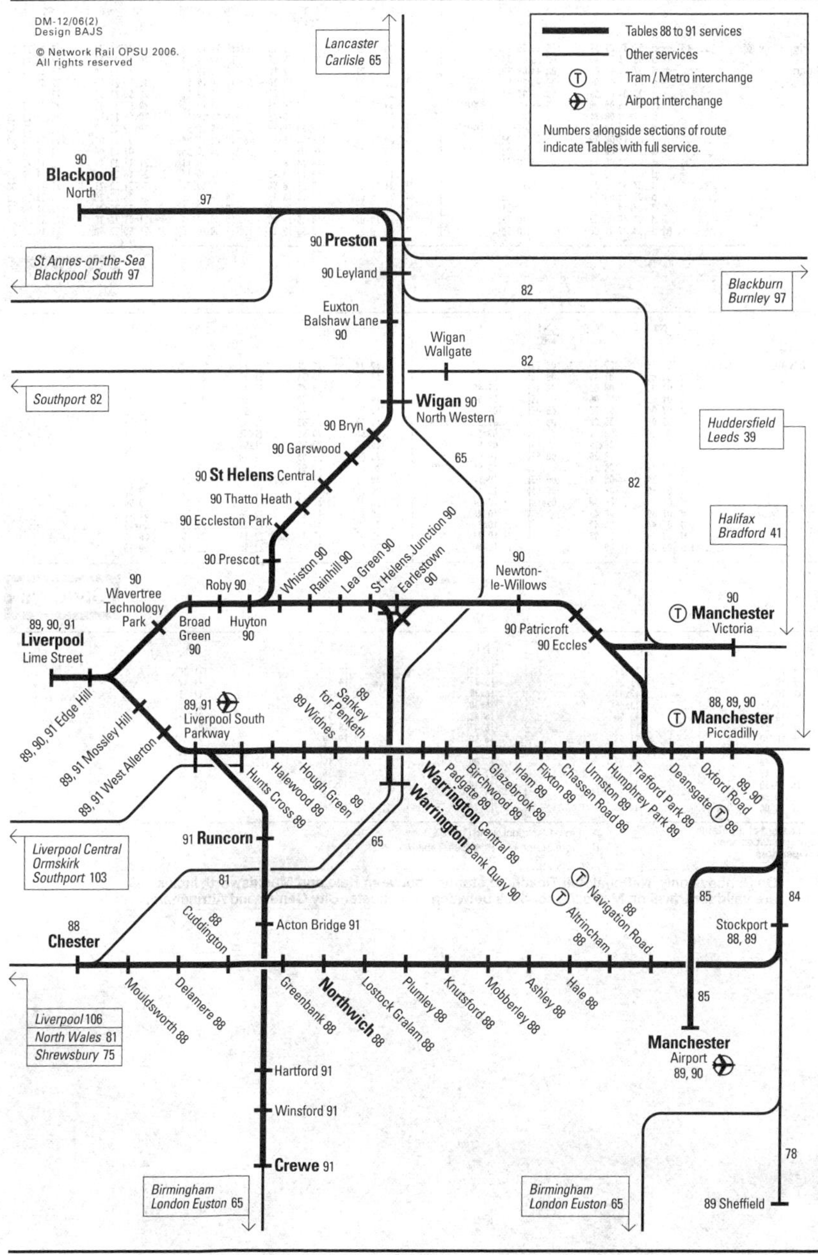
DM-12/06(2)
Design BAJS
© Network Rail OPSU 2006.
All rights reserved
Tables 88 to 91 services
Other services
Tram / Metro interchange
Airport interchange
Numbers alongside sections of route indicate Tables with full service.
Lancaster
Carlisle 65
90
Blackpool
North
97
90 Preston
St Annes-on-the-Sea
Blackpool South 97
90 Leyland
Blackburn
Burnley 97
82
Euxton
Balshaw Lane
90
Wigan
Wallgate
82
Southport 82
Wigan 90
North Western
90 Bryn
90 Garswood
65
Huddersfield
Leeds 39
90 St Helens Central
90 Thatto Heath
82
90 Eccleston Park
Halifax
Bradford 41
90 Prescot
Whiston 90
Rainhill 90
Lea Green 90
St Helens Junction 90
Earlestown 90
90
Newton-
le-Willows
90
Wavertree
Technology
Park
Roby 90
Broad
Green
90
Huyton
90
90 Patricroft
90 Eccles
90
Manchester
Victoria
89, 90, 91
Liverpool
Lime Street
89, 90, 91 Edge Hill
89, 91 Mossley Hill
89, 91 West Allerton
89, 91
Liverpool South
Parkway
89 Widnes
89
Sankey
for Penketh
88, 89, 90
Manchester
Piccadilly
Hunts Cross 89
Halewood 89
Hough Green 89
Warrington Central 89
Warrington Bank Quay 90
Padgate 89
Birchwood 89
Glazebrook 89
Irlam 89
Flixton 89
Chassen Road 89
Urmston 89
Humphrey Park 89
Trafford Park 89
Deansgate 89
Oxford Road 89, 90
Liverpool Central
Ormskirk
Southport 103
91 Runcorn
65
81
88
Cuddington
Navigation Road 88
Altrincham 88
85
84
Stockport
88, 89
88
Chester
Acton Bridge 91
Liverpool 106
North Wales 81
Shrewsbury 75
Mouldsworth 88
Delamere 88
Greenbank 88
Northwich 88
Lostock Gralam 88
Plumley 88
Knutsford 88
Mobberley 88
Ashley 88
Hale 88
85
Manchester
Airport
89, 90
Hartford 91
Winsford 91
Crewe 91
78
Birmingham
London Euston 65
Birmingham
London Euston 65
89 Sheffield

Manchester → Northwich and Chester

Network Diagram - see first page of Table 88

Mondays to Fridays

Miles			NT	NT A	NT B	NT		NT	NT	NT	NT	NT	NT	NT	NT	NT	NT
½	**Manchester Piccadilly** 10	81, 84 d	06 35	07 39	08 20	09 24		16 24	16 51	17 24	17 53	18 24	19 24	20 24	21 24	22 24	23 09
6½	**Stockport**	84 d	06 46	07 49	08 30	09 34		16 34	17 01	17 34	18 05	18 34	19 34	20 34	21 34	22 34	23 21
14¾	Navigation Road	d	07 01	08 03	08 44	09 48		16 48	17 21	17 48	18 18	18 48	19 48	20 48	21 48	22 48	23 35
15¼	**Altrincham**	a	07 03	08 05	08 46	09 50	and	16 50	17 23	17 50	18 20	18 50	19 50	20 50	21 50	22 50	23 37
—		d	07 04	08 05	08 46	09 51		16 51	17 24	17 51	18 21	18 51	19 51	20 50	21 51	22 51	23 37
16	Hale	d	07 06	08 08	08 49	09 53	every	16 53	17 26	17 53	18 23	18 53	19 53	20 53	21 53	22 53	23 40
17¾	Ashley	d	07x09	08x11		09x56		16x56	17x29	17x56	18x26	18x56	19x56	20x56	21x56	22x56	23x43
18½	Mobberley	d	07x12	08x15		09x59	hour	16x59	17x32	17x59	18x29	18x59	19x59	20x59	21x59	22x59	23x46
22¼	Knutsford	d	07 17	08 20	08 57	10 04		17 04	17 37	18 04	18 34	19 04	20 04	21 03	22 04	23 04	23 50
24¾	Plumley	d	07 21	08 24		10 08	until	17 08	17 41	18 08	18 38	19 08	20 08	21 07	22 08	23 08	23 54
26¼	Lostock Gralam	d	07 24	08 28	09 03	10 11		17 11	17 45	18 11	18 42	19 11	20 11	21 11	22 11	23 11	23 58
28¼	**Northwich**	d	07 30	08 33	09 06	10 17		17 17	17 50	18 17	18 45	19 17	20 17	21 16	22 17	23 17	00 03
30	Greenbank	d	07 34	08 38	09a15	10 21		17 21	17 55	18 21	18 50	19 21	20 21	21 21	22 21	23 21	00 08
32¾	Cuddington	d	07 39	08 43		10 26		17 26	18 00	18 26	18 55	19 26	20 26	21 26	22 26	23 26	00 13
35¾	Delamere	d	07x44	08x47		10x31		17x31	18x05	18x31	19x00	19x31	20x31	21x30	22x31	23x31	00x17
38¾	Mouldsworth	d	07 48	08 52		10 35		17 35	18 09	18 35	19 08	19 35	20 35	21 35	22 35	23 35	00 22
45¼	**Chester**	81 a	08 02	09 06		10 50		17 50	18 22	18 50	19 22	19 50	20 50	21 50	22 50	23 50	00 35

Saturdays

		NT	NT A	NT B	NT		NT	NT	NT	NT	NT
Manchester Piccadilly 10	81, 84 d	06 35	07 39	08 22	09 24		19 24	20 24	21 24	22 24	23 09
Stockport	84 d	06 46	07 49	08 30	09 34		19 34	20 34	21 34	22 34	23 19
Navigation Road	d	07 01	08 03	08 43	09 48		19 48	20 48	21 48	22 48	23 33
Altrincham	a	07 03	08 05	08 45	09 50	and	19 50	20 50	21 50	22 50	23 35
	d	07 04	08 05	08 46	09 51		19 51	20 50	21 51	22 51	23 35
Hale	d	07 06	08 08	08 48	09 53	every	19 53	20 53	21 53	22 53	23 38
Ashley	d	07x09	08x11		09x56		19x56	20x56	21x56	22x56	23x41
Mobberley	d	07x12	08x15		09x59	hour	19x59	20x59	21x59	22x59	23x44
Knutsford	d	07 17	08 20	08 57	10 04		20 04	21 03	22 04	23 04	23 48
Plumley	d	07 21	08 24		10 08	until	20 08	21 07	22 08	23 08	23 52
Lostock Gralam	d	07 24	08 28	09 03	10 11		20 11	21 11	22 11	23 11	23 56
Northwich	d	07 30	08 33	09 06	10 17		20 17	21 16	22 17	23 17	00 02
Greenbank	d	07 34	08 38	09a14	10 21		20 21	21 21	22 21	23 21	00 06
Cuddington	d	07 39	08 43		10 26		20 26	21 26	22 26	23 26	00 11
Delamere	d	07x44	08x47		10x31		20x31	21x30	22x31	23x31	00x15
Mouldsworth	d	07 48	08 52		10 35		20 35	21 35	22 35	23 35	00 20
Chester	81 a	08 02	09 06		10 50		20 50	21 49	22 50	23 50	00 33

Sundays

		NT	NT	NT	NT	NT
Altrincham	d	10 10	13 37	16 30	18 40	21 30
Hale	d	10 12	13 39	16 32	18 42	21 32
Ashley	d	10x15	13x42	16x35	18x45	21x35
Mobberley	d	10x18	13x45	16x38	18x48	21x38
Knutsford	d	10 23	13 50	16 43	18 53	21 43
Plumley	d	10 27	13 54	16 47	18 57	21 47
Lostock Gralam	d	10 30	13 57	16 50	19 00	21 50
Northwich	d	10 36	14 03	16 56	19 06	21 56
Greenbank	d	10 40	14 07	17 00	19 10	22 00
Cuddington	d	10 45	14 12	17 05	19 15	22 05
Delamere	d	10x50	14x17	17x10	19x20	22x10
Mouldsworth	d	10 54	14 21	17 15	19 24	22 14
Chester	a	11 06	14 33	17 26	19 36	22 26

For general notes see front of timetable
For details of catering facilities see Directory of Train Operators

A From Blackpool North (Table 82)
B From St Annes-on-the-Sea (Table 97)

On Sundays only, National Rail Tickets to stations between Hale and Mouldsworth inclusive are valid for travel on Metrolink services between Manchester City Centre and Altrincham.

Chester and Northwich → Manchester

Network Diagram - see first page of Table 88

Mondays to Fridays

Miles	Station		NT	NT	NT	NT	NT	NT A	NT		NT	NT	NT	NT	NT	NT	NT	NT	NT
0	**Chester**	81 d	05 57		06 54	07 30	08 05		10 05		15 05	15 49	16 00	17 05	17 56	18 56	19 56	20 59	22 45
6½	Mouldsworth	d	06 08		07 05	07 41	08 16		10 16		15 16		16 11	17 16	18 07	19 07	20 07	21 10	22 56
9¼	Delamere	d	06x13		07x10	07x46	08x21		10x21		15x21		16x16	17x21	18x12	19x12	20x12	21x15	23x01
12¾	Cuddington	d	06 17		07 15	07 50	08 25		10 25	and	15 25	16 06	16 20	17 25	18 16	19 16	20 16	21 19	23 05
15¼	Greenbank	d	06 22		07 20	07 55	08 30		10 30		15 30	16 10	16 25	17 30	18 21	19 21	20 21	21 24	23 10
17	**Northwich**	d	06 27	06 50	07 25	08 00	08 35	09 33	10 35	every	15 35	16 15	16 30	17 35	18 26	19 26	20 26	21 29	23 15
18½	Lostock Gralam	d	06 30	06 53	07 28	08 03	08 38	09 36	10 38		15 38	16 19	16 33	17 38	18 29	19 29	20 29	21 32	23 18
20½	Plumley	d	06 33	06 56	07 32	08 07	08 41	09 39	10 41	hour	15 41		16 36	17 41	18 32	19 32	20 32	21 35	23 21
23	Knutsford	d	06 38	07 01	07 37	08 12	08 46	09 44	10 46		15 46	16 26	16 41	17 46	18 37	19 37	20 37	21 40	23 26
26¾	Mobberley	d	06x42	07x05	07x41	08x16	08x50	09x48	10x50	until	15x50		16x45	17x50	18x41	19x41	20x41	21x44	23x30
27½	Ashley	d	06x46	07x09	07x45	08x20	08x54	09x52	10x54		15x54		16x49	17x54	18x45	19x45	20x45	21x48	23x34
29¼	Hale	d	06 49	07 12	07 48	08 23	08 57	09 55	10 57		15 57	16 34	16 52	17 57	18 48	19 48	20 48	21 51	23 37
30	**Altrincham**	⇌ a	06 53	07 16	07 53	08 27	09 01	09 59	11 01		16 01	16 38	16 56	18 01	18 52	19 52	20 52	21 55	23 41
—		d	06 54	07 17	07 53	08 28	09 02	10 00	11 02		16 02	16 38	16 57	18 02	18 53	19 53	20 53	21 56	23 42
30½	Navigation Road	⇌ d	06 56	07 19	07 55	08 30	09 04	10 02	11 04		16 04	16 41	16 59	18 04	18 55	19 55	20 55	21 58	23 44
38¾	**Stockport**	84 a	07 09	07 35	08 10	08 45	09 20	10 16	11 17		16 17	16 56	17 14	18 17	19 09	20 09	21 09	22 12	23 59
44¾	**Manchester Piccadilly** 10	81, 84 ⇌ a	07 25	07 57	08 24	08 59	09 32	10 29	11 32		16 32	17 09	17 31	18 32	19 28	20 28	21 24	22 26	00 13

Saturdays

Station		NT	NT	NT	NT	NT A	NT		NT	NT	NT	NT	NT	NT	NT	NT
Chester	81 d	05 55	06 53	07 30	08 04		10 05		15 05	16 00	17 05	17 56	18 58	19 56	20 59	22 45
Mouldsworth	d	06 06	07 04	07 41	08 15		10 16		15 16	16 11	17 16	18 07	19 09	20 07	21 10	22 56
Delamere	d	06x11	07x09	07x46	08x20		10x21		15x21	16x16	17x21	18x12	19x14	20x12	21x15	23x01
Cuddington	d	06 15	07 14	07 50	08 24		10 25	and	15 25	16 20	17 25	18 16	19 18	20 16	21 19	23 05
Greenbank	d	06 20	07 19	07 55	08 29		10 30		15 30	16 25	17 30	18 21	19 23	20 21	21 24	23 10
Northwich	d	06 25	07 24	08 00	08 34	09 33	10 35	every	15 35	16 30	17 35	18 26	19 28	20 26	21 29	23 15
Lostock Gralam	d	06 28	07 27	08 03	08 37	09 36	10 38		15 38	16 33	17 38	18 29	19 31	20 29	21 32	23 18
Plumley	d	06 31	07 31	08 07	08 40	09 39	10 41	hour	15 41	16 36	17 41	18 32	19 34	20 32	21 35	23 21
Knutsford	d	06 36	07 36	08 12	08 45	09 44	10 46		15 46	16 41	17 46	18 37	19 39	20 37	21 40	23 26
Mobberley	d	06x40	07x40	08x16	08x49	09x48	10x50	until	15x50	16x45	17x50	18x41	19x43	20x41	21x44	23x30
Ashley	d	06x44	07x44	08x20	08x53	09x52	10x54		15x54	16x49	17x54	18x45	19x47	20x45	21x48	23x34
Hale	d	06 47	07 47	08 23	08 56	09 55	10 57		15 57	16 52	17 57	18 48	19 50	20 48	21 51	23 37
Altrincham	⇌ a	06 51	07 52	08 27	09 00	09 59	11 01		16 01	16 56	18 01	18 52	19 54	20 52	21 55	23 41
	d	06 52	07 52	08 28	09 01	10 00	11 02		16 02	16 57	18 02	18 53	19 55	20 53	21 56	23 42
Navigation Road	⇌ d	06 54	07 54	08 30	09 03	10 02	11 04		16 04	16 59	18 04	18 55	19 57	20 55	21 58	23 44
Stockport	84 a	07 07	08 09	08 46	09 16	10 16	11 17		16 17	17 14	18 17	19 10	20 10	21 09	22 12	23 59
Manchester Piccadilly 10	81, 84 ⇌ a	07 25	08 24	08 59	09 31	10 29	11 32		16 32	17 31	18 32	19 28	20 24	21 24	22 26	00 13

Sundays

Station		NT	NT	NT	NT	NT
Chester	d	08 48	12 00	15 20	17 31	20 10
Mouldsworth	d	08 59	12 13	15 31	17 42	20 21
Delamere	d	09x04	12x17	15x36	17x47	20x26
Cuddington	d	09 08	12 22	15 40	17 51	20 30
Greenbank	d	09 13	12 26	15 45	17 56	20 35
Northwich	d	09 18	12 31	15 50	18 01	20 40
Lostock Gralam	d	09 21	12 34	15 53	18 04	20 43
Plumley	d	09 24	12 38	15 56	18 07	20 46
Knutsford	d	09 29	12 43	16 01	18 12	20 51
Mobberley	d	09x33	12x47	16x05	18x16	20x55
Ashley	d	09x37	12x50	16x09	18x20	20x59
Hale	d	09 40	12 53	16 12	18 23	21 02
Altrincham	⇌ a	09 44	12 58	16 16	18 27	21 06

For general notes see front of timetable
For details of catering facilities see Directory of Train Operators

A To Blackpool North (Table 82)

On Sundays only, National Rail Tickets from stations between Mouldsworth and Hale inclusive are valid for travel on Metrolink services between Altrincham and Manchester City Centre.

Liverpool → Warrington Central → Manchester and Manchester Airport

Network Diagram - see first page of Table 88

Miles	Station		NT	NT	NT	NT	NT	TP	NT	EM	NT	NT	NT	TP	NT	EM	NT	NT	NT	NT	TP
																		BHX			
								1 ◇ A		◇ B				1 ◇ C		◇ B					1 ◇ C
0	**Liverpool Lime Street** 10	90, 91 d	03b38	05 18		05 50	06 14	06 18	06 21	06 47		06 50	07 14	07 15	07 21	07 47	07 50		08 14		08 22
1¾	Edge Hill	90, 91 d				05 54						06 54					07 54				
3¾	Mossley Hill	91 d				05 59			06 29			06 59			07 29		07 59				
4½	West Allerton	91 d				06 01						07 01					08 01				
—	Liverpool Central 10	103 d										*06c43*			*06 58*	*07 28*	*07c43*				
5½	**Liverpool South Parkway** 7	91, 103 d				06 04			06 32			07 04			07 32		08 04				
7¼	Hunts Cross	103 d				06 08						07 08				08 02	08 08				
8¾	Halewood	d				06 10						07 10					08 10				
10½	Hough Green	d				06 14			06 40			07 14			07 39		08 14				
12¼	Widnes	d				06 18			06 43	07 07		07 18		07 32		08 08	08 18				
16	Sankey for Penketh	d				06 23						07 23					08 23				
18½	**Warrington Central**	a				06 30		06 41	06 50	07 15		07 30		07 39	07 48	08 16	08 27			←	08 43
—		d			06 08			06 42	06 51	07 15	07 22			07 39	07 49	08 16	08 28 →			08 28	08 44
20¼	Padgate	d			06 11				06 55		07 25				07 52					08 31	
21¾	Birchwood	d			06 14			06 47	06 58	07 20	07 28			07 44	07 55	08 21				08 34	08 49
24¼	Glazebrook	d			06 19						07 33				08 00						
25¾	Irlam	d			06 22				07 04		07 36			07 49	08 03			08 32		08 40	
28	Flixton	d			06 26				07 08		07 40				08 07			08 36		08 44	
28½	Chassen Road	d			06 28				07 10		07 42				08 09			08 38			
29	Urmston	d			06 30				07 12		07 44				08 11			08 40		08 47	
30¼	Humphrey Park	d			06 32						07 46				08 14			08 42			
31	Trafford Park	d			06 35				07 15		07 49				08 17			08 45			
34	Deansgate	84, 85 a			06 43				07 25		07 56				08 25			08 52		08 59	
34½	**Manchester Oxford Road**	84, 85 a			06 47		06 58	07 02	07 30	07 37	08 01		08 01	08 04	08 29	08 38		08 57	08 58	09 04	09 06
35	**Manchester Piccadilly** 10	78, 84, 85 a	04 14	06 03	*06 56*		07 03	07 10		07 41			08 06	08 10		08 42			09 02		09 10
—	Stockport	84 a	*05 54*	*06 24*			*07 26*	*07 33*		07 52			*08 24*	*08 30*		08 53					*09 28*
—	Sheffield 7	78 a	*06 48*				*08 10*			08 34			*09 09*			09 35					*10 08*
44¾	**Manchester Airport**	85 a	04 30	06 19	*07 15*		07 20	*07e40*		*08e02*			08 25	*08 42*		*09e06*			09 25		*09 40*

Station		NT	EM	NT	NT	NT	TP	NT	EM	NT	NT	NT	TP	NT	EM	NT	NT	NT	TP	NT
			◇ B				1 ◇ C		◇ B				1 ◇ C		◇ B				1 ◇ C	
Liverpool Lime Street 10	90, 91 d	08 29	08 52	08 55	09 14		09 22	09 29	09 52	09 55	10 14		10 22	10 29	10 52	10 55	11 14		11 22	11 29
Edge Hill	90, 91 d			08 59						09 59						10 59				
Mossley Hill	91 d	08 37		09 04				09 37		10 04				10 37		11 04				11 37
West Allerton	91 d			09 06						10 06						11 06				
Liverpool Central 10	103 d	*08 13*		*08c43*				*09 13*		*09c43*				*10 13*		*10c43*				*11 13*
Liverpool South Parkway 7	91, 103 d	08 40		09 09				09 40		10 09				10 40		11 09				11 40
Hunts Cross	103 d			09 13						10 13						11 13				
Halewood	d			09 16						10 16						11 16				
Hough Green	d	08 47		09 20				09 47		10 20				10 47		11 20				11 47
Widnes	d	08 50	09 09	09 23				09 50	10 09	10 23				10 50	11 09	11 23				11 50
Sankey for Penketh	d			09 28						10 28						11 28				
Warrington Central	a	08 58	09 17	09 33		←	09 43	09 58	10 17	10 33		←	10 43	10 58	11 17	11 33		←	11 43	11 58
	d	08 59	09 17	09 34 →		09 34	09 44	09 59	10 17	10 34 →		10 34	10 44	10 59	11 17	11 34 →		11 34	11 44	11 59
Padgate	d					09 37						10 37						11 37		
Birchwood	d	09 03				09 40	09 49	10 03				10 40	10 49	11 03				11 40	11 49	12 03
Glazebrook	d							10 08												12 08
Irlam	d	09 09				09 46		10 11				10 46		11 09				11 46		12 11
Flixton	d	09 13						10 15						11 13						12 15
Chassen Road	d							10 17												12 17
Urmston	d	09 16				09 51		10 19				10 51		11 16				11 51		12 19
Humphrey Park	d	09 19												11 19						
Trafford Park	d	09 21												11 21						
Deansgate	84, 85 a	09 31				10 01		10 31				11 01		11 31				12 01		12 31
Manchester Oxford Road	84, 85 a	09 35	09 38		09 58	10 05	10 06	10 35	10 38		10 57	11 05	11 06	11 35	11 38		11 57	12 05	12 06	12 35
Manchester Piccadilly 10	78, 84, 85 a		09 40		10 02		10 10		10 41		11 02		11 10		11 40		12 02		12 10	
Stockport	84 a		09 51				*10 28*		10 51				*11 27*		11 51				*12 28*	
Sheffield 7	78 a		10 35				*11 08*		11 35				*12 08*		12 35				*13 08*	
Manchester Airport	85 a		*10e01*		10 25		*10 40*		*11e01*		11 25		*11 40*		*12e01*		12 25		*12 40*	

For general notes see front of timetable
For details of catering facilities see Directory of Train Operators

- **A** To Scarborough and to Newcastle (Table 39)
- **B** To Norwich (Table 49)
- **C** To Scarborough (Table 39)
- **b** Mondays from 31 March dep. 0330
- **c** Change at Hunts Cross
- **e** Change at Manchester Oxford Road

Liverpool → Warrington Central → Manchester and Manchester Airport

Network Diagram - see first page of Table 88

Station		EM ◇ A	NT		NT	NT	TP 1 ◇ B	NT	EM ◇ A	NT		NT	NT	TP 1 ◇ B	NT	EM ◇ C	NT		NT	NT	TP 1 ◇ B	NT	EM ◇ A
Liverpool Lime Street 10	90, 91 d	11 52	11 55		12 14		12 22	12 29	12 52	12 55		13 14		13 22	13 29	13 52	13 55		14 14		14 22	14 29	14 52
Edge Hill	90, 91 d		11 59							12 59							13 59						
Mossley Hill	91 d		12 04					12 37		13 04					13 37		14 04					14 37	
West Allerton	91 d		12 06							13 06							14 06						
Liverpool Central 10	103 d		*11b43*					*12 13*		*12b43*					*13 13*		*13b43*					*14 13*	
Liverpool South Parkway 7	91, 103 ✈ d		12 09					12 40		13 09					13 40		14 09					14 40	
Hunts Cross	103 d		12 13							13 13							14 13						
Halewood	d		12 16							13 16							14 16						
Hough Green	d		12 20					12 47		13 20					13 47		14 20					14 47	
Widnes	d	12 09	12 23					12 50	13 09	13 23					13 50	14 09	14 23					14 50	15 09
Sankey for Penketh	d		12 28							13 28							14 28						
Warrington Central	a	12 17	12 33			←	12 43	12 58	13 17	13 33			←	13 43	13 58	14 17	14 33			←	14 43	14 58	15 17
	d	12 17	12 34 →			12 34	12 44	12 59	13 17	13 34 →			13 34	13 44	13 59	14 17	14 34 →			14 34	14 44	14 59	15 17
Padgate	d					12 37							13 37							14 37			
Birchwood	d					12 40	12 49	13 03					13 40	13 49	14 03					14 40	14 49	15 03	
Glazebrook	d														14 08								
Irlam	d					12 46		13 09					13 46		14 11					14 46		15 09	
Flixton	d							13 13							14 15							15 13	
Chassen Road	d														14 17								
Urmston	d					12 51		13 16					13 51		14 19					14 51		15 16	
Humphrey Park	d							13 19														15 19	
Trafford Park	d							13 21														15 21	
Deansgate	84, 85 ⛴ a					13 01		13 31					14 01		14 31					15 01		15 31	
Manchester Oxford Road	84, 85 a	12 38			12 57	13 05	13 06	13 35	13 38			13 57	14 05	14 06	14 35	14 38			14 57	15 05	15 06	15 35	15 38
Manchester Piccadilly 10	78, 84, 85 ⛴ a	12 40			13 02		13 10		13 40			14 02		14 10		14 40			15 02		15 10		15 40
Stockport	84 a	12 51					*13 28*		13 51					*14 28*		14 51					*15 28*		15 50
Sheffield 7	78 ⛴ a	13 35					*14 08*		14 35					*15 08*		15 35					*16 08*		16 35
Manchester Airport	85 ✈ a	*13c01*			13 25		*13 40*		*14c01*			14 25		*14 40*		*15c01*			15 25		*15 40*		*16c01*

Station		NT	NT	NT		TP 1 ◇ D	NT	EM ◇ A	NT	NT	NT		TP 1 ◇ B	NT	EM ◇ C	NT	NT	NT		TP 1 ◇ B	NT	EM ◇ E	NT
Liverpool Lime Street 10	90, 91 d	14 55	15 14			15 22	15 29	15 52	15 55	16 14			16 22	16 28	16 52	16 55	17 09			17 22	17 25	17 52	17 55
Edge Hill	90, 91 d	14 59							15 59							16 59					17 29		17 59
Mossley Hill	91 d	15 04					15 37		16 04					16 36		17 04					17 34		18 04
West Allerton	91 d	15 06							16 06							17 06					17 36		18 06
Liverpool Central 10	103 d	*14b43*					*15 13*		*15b43*					*16 13*		*16b43*					*17b13*		*17b43*
Liverpool South Parkway 7	91, 103 ✈ d	15 09					15 40		16 09					16 39		17 09					17 39		18 09
Hunts Cross	103 d	15 13							16 13							17 13					17 43		18 13
Halewood	d	15 16							16 16							17 15					17 45		18 15
Hough Green	d	15 20					15 47		16 20					16 46		17 19					17 49		18 19
Widnes	d	15 23					15 50	16 09	16 23					16 49	17 09	17 23					17 53	18 09	18 23
Sankey for Penketh	d	15 28							16 28							17 28					17 58		18 28
Warrington Central	a	15 33		←		15 43	15 58	16 17	16 33		←		16 43	16 57	17 17	17 33		←		17 43	18 03	18 17	18 33
	d	15 34 →		15 34		15 44	15 59	16 17	16 34 →		16 34		16 44	16 58	17 17	17 33 →		17 33		17 44	18 03	18 17	18 33 →
Padgate	d			15 37							16 37							17 36					
Birchwood	d			15 40		15 49	16 03				16 40		16 49	17 02				17 39		17 49	18 08		
Glazebrook	d						16 08							17 07									
Irlam	d			15 46			16 11				16 46			17 10				17 45			18 14		
Flixton	d						16 15				16 50			17 14				17 49					
Chassen Road	d						16 17														18 18		
Urmston	d			15 51			16 19				16 53			17 17				17 52			18 20		
Humphrey Park	d													17 20							18 23		
Trafford Park	d													17 22									
Deansgate	84, 85 ⛴ a			16 01			16 31				17 03							18 01					
Manchester Oxford Road	84, 85 a		15 57	16 05		16 06	16 35	16 37		16 57	17 06		17 06	17 35	17 36		17 58	18 05		18 06	18 34	18 38	
Manchester Piccadilly 10	78, 84, 85 ⛴ a		16 01			16 10		16 40		17 02			17 10		17 40		18 04			18 10		18 43	
Stockport	84 a					*16 28*		16 51		*17c19*			*17 28*		17 50		*18 26*			*18 32*		18 54	
Sheffield 7	78 ⛴ a					*17 08*		17 37					*18 15*		18 41		*19 08*					19 36	
Manchester Airport	85 ✈ a		16 25			*16 40*		*17e14*		17 25			*17 40*		*18e05*		18 27			*18 42*		*19e09*	

For general notes see front of timetable
For details of catering facilities see Directory of Train Operators

- **A** To Norwich (Table 49)
- **B** To Scarborough (Table 39)
- **C** To Nottingham (Table 49)
- **D** To Middlesbrough (Table 39)
- **E** To Cambridge (Table 49)
- **b** Change at Hunts Cross
- **c** Change at Manchester Oxford Road
- **e** Change at Manchester Piccadilly

Liverpool → Warrington Central → Manchester and Manchester Airport

Network Diagram - see first page of Table 88

			NT	NT	TP 1 ◇ A	NT	EM ◇ B	NT	TP 1 ◇ C	NT	EM ◇ B	NT	NT	TP 1 ◇ C	NT	EM ◇ B	NT	TP 1 ◇ C	NT
Liverpool Lime Street 10	90, 91	d	18 14		18 22	18 25	18 52	18 55	19 22		19 52	19 55	20 14	20 22	20 55	21 35	21 55	22 30	23 35
Edge Hill	90, 91	d				18 29		18 59				19 59			20 59		21 59		23 39
Mossley Hill	91	d				18 34		19 04				20 04			21 04		22 04		23 43
West Allerton	91	d				18 36		19 06				20 06			21 06		22 06		23 46
Liverpool Central 10	103	d				18b13		18b43				19b43			20b43		21b43		23b28
Liverpool South Parkway 7	91, 103 ✈	d				18 39		19 09				20 09			21 09		22 09		23 49
Hunts Cross	103	d				18 43		19 13				20 13			21 13		22 13		23 52
Halewood		d				18 45		19 15				20 15			21 15		22 15		23 55
Hough Green		d				18 49		19 19				20 19			21 19		22 19		23 59
Widnes		d				18 53	19 09	19 23			20 09	20 23			21 23	21 53	22 23		00 03
Sankey for Penketh		d				18 58		19 28				20 28			21 28		22 28		00 07
Warrington Central		a		←	18 43	19 03	19 17	19 35	19 43		20 17	20 35		20 43	21 33	22 01	22 33	22 52	00 13
		d		18 33	18 44	19 03	19 17		19 44	19 52	20 17			20 44	21 33	22 01	22 33	22 52	00 13
Padgate		d				19 06				19 55					21 36		22 36		
Birchwood		d		18 38	18 49	19 09			19 49	19 58				20 49	21 39		22 39	22 57	
Glazebrook		d				19 14				20 03					21 44		22 44		
Irlam		d		18 44		19 17				20 06					21 47		22 47		
Flixton		d		18 48						20 10					21 51		22 51		
Chassen Road		d								20 12					21 53		22 53		
Urmston		d		18 51		19 22				20 14					21 55		22 55		
Humphrey Park		d								20 17					21 58		22 58		
Trafford Park		d		18 54						20 19					22 00		23 00		
Deansgate	84, 85 ⛴	a				19 32				20 31					22 07		23 07		
Manchester Oxford Road	84, 85	a	18 59	19 04	19 05	19 35	19 37		20 06	20 34	20 38		20 59	21 06	22 12	22 22	23 12	23 13	
Manchester Piccadilly 10	78, 84, 85 ⛴	a	19 05		19 10		19 42		20 10		20 40		21 05	21 10		22 25		23 17	00 36
Stockport	84	a	19 25		19 32		19 53		20 32		20 51		21 26	21 34		22 37		23 50	
Sheffield 7	78 ⛴	a	20 08				20 39				21 34		22 09	23 13		23 35		01 13	
Manchester Airport	85 ✈	a	19 26		19 40		20c05		20 58		21e19		21 28	21c37		22e58		23 58	01 10

Saturdays

			NT	NT	NT	NT	TP 1 ◇ A	NT	EM ◇ D	NT	NT	TP 1 ◇ A	NT	EM ◇ D	NT	NT	NT	TP 1 ◇ A	NT	EM ◇ D
Liverpool Lime Street 10	90, 91	d	03 38	05 18	05 50	06 10	06 18	06 21	06 47	06 50	07 14	07 18	07 21	07 47	07 50	08 14		08 21	08 29	08 52
Edge Hill	90, 91	d			05 54					06 54					07 54					
Mossley Hill	91	d			05 59			06 29		06 59			07 29		07 59				08 37	
West Allerton	91	d			06 01					07 01					08 01					
Liverpool Central 10	103	d								06b43			06 58	07 28	07b43				08 13	
Liverpool South Parkway 7	91, 103 ✈	d			06 04			06 32		07 04			07 32		08 04				08 40	
Hunts Cross	103	d			06 08					07 08				08 02	08 08					
Halewood		d			06 10					07 10					08 10					
Hough Green		d			06 14			06 40		07 14			07 39		08 14				08 47	
Widnes		d			06 18			06 43	07 07	07 18		07 36		08 08	08 18				08 50	09 09
Sankey for Penketh		d			06 23					07 23					08 23					
Warrington Central		a			06 30		06 41	06 51	07 15	07 30		07 43	07 48	08 16	08 28		←	08 43	08 58	09 17
		d					06 42	06 51	07 15			07 43	07 49	08 16	08 28 →		08 28	08 44	08 59	09 17
Padgate		d						06 55					07 52				08 31			
Birchwood		d					06 47	06 58	07 20			07 48	07 55	08 21			08 34	08 49	09 03	
Glazebrook		d											08 00							
Irlam		d						07 04				07 53	08 04				08 40		09 09	
Flixton		d						07 08					08 07				08 44		09 13	
Chassen Road		d						07 10					08 09							
Urmston		d						07 12					08 11				08 47		09 16	
Humphrey Park		d											08 14				08 50		09 19	
Trafford Park		d						07 15					08 17				08 52		09 21	
Deansgate	84, 85 ⛴	a						07 25					08 25				09 00		09 31	
Manchester Oxford Road	84, 85	a				06 57	07 02	07 30	07 37		08 00	08 06	08 29	08 38		08 58	09 05	09 06	09 35	09 38
Manchester Piccadilly 10	78, 84, 85 ⛴	a	04 14	06 03		07 03	07 10		07 41		08 06	08 10		08 42		09 02		09 10		09 40
Stockport	84	a	05 56	06 25		07 26	07 32		07 54		08 25	08 29		08 53		09 26		09 32		09 55
Sheffield 7	78 ⛴	a	06 48	07 57		08 10			08 35		09 09			09 35		10 08				10 35
Manchester Airport	85 ✈	a	04 30	06 19		07 20	07c40		08c02		08 25	08 42		09c06		09 25		09 40		10c02

For general notes see front of timetable
For details of catering facilities see Directory of Train Operators

A To Scarborough (Table 39)
B To Nottingham (Table 49)
C To York (Table 39)
D To Norwich (Table 49)

b Change at Hunts Cross
c Change at Manchester Oxford Road
e Change at Manchester Piccadilly

Table 89

Liverpool → Warrington Central → Manchester and Manchester Airport

Network Diagram - see first page of Table 88

Station		NT	NT	NT	TP	NT	EM	NT	NT	NT	TP	NT	EM	NT	NT	NT	TP	NT	EM
					1 ◇		◇				1 ◇		◇				1 ◇		◇
					A		B				A		B				A		B
					🛒						🛒						🛒		
Liverpool Lime Street 10	90, 91 d	08 55	09 14		09 22	09 29	09 52	09 55	10 14		10 22	10 29	10 52	10 55	11 14		11 22	11 29	11 52
Edge Hill	90, 91 d	08 59						09 59						10 59					
Mossley Hill	91 d	09 04				09 37		10 04				10 37		11 04				11 37	
West Allerton	91 d	09 06						10 06						11 06					
Liverpool Central 10	103 d	08b43				09 13		09b43				10 13		10b43				11 13	
Liverpool South Parkway 7	91, 103 ✈ d	09 09				09 40		10 09				10 40		11 09				11 40	
Hunts Cross	103 d	09 13						10 13						11 13					
Halewood	d	09 16						10 16						11 16					
Hough Green	d	09 20				09 47		10 20				10 47		11 20				11 47	
Widnes	d	09 23				09 50	10 09	10 23				10 50	11 09	11 23				11 50	12 09
Sankey for Penketh	d	09 28						10 28						11 28					
Warrington Central	a	09 33		←	09 43	09 58	10 17	10 33		←	10 43	10 58	11 17	11 33		←	11 43	11 58	12 17
	d	09 34		09 34	09 44	09 59	10 17	10 34		10 34	10 44	10 59	11 17	11 34		11 34	11 44	11 59	12 17
Padgate	d	→		09 37				→		10 37				→		11 37			
Birchwood	d			09 40	09 49	10 03				10 40	10 49	11 03				11 40	11 49	12 03	
Glazebrook	d					10 08												12 08	
Irlam	d			09 46		10 11				10 46		11 09				11 46		12 11	
Flixton	d					10 15						11 13						12 15	
Chassen Road	d					10 17												12 17	
Urmston	d			09 51		10 19				10 51		11 16				11 51		12 19	
Humphrey Park	d											11 19							
Trafford Park	d											11 21							
Deansgate	84, 85 ⛴ a			10 01		10 31				11 01		11 31				12 01		12 31	
Manchester Oxford Road	84, 85 a		09 58	10 05	10 06	10 35	10 37		10 57	11 05	11 06	11 35	11 37		11 57	12 05	12 06	12 35	12 37
Manchester Piccadilly 10	78, 84, 85 ⛴ a		10 02		10 10		10 40		11 02		11 10		11 40		12 02		12 10		12 40
Stockport	84 a		10 26		10 32		10 52		11 26		11 32		11 52		12 26		12 32		12 52
Sheffield 7	78 ⛴ a		11 08				11 35		12 08				12 35		13 08				13 35
Manchester Airport	85 ✈ a		10 25		10 40		11c01		11 25		11 40		12c01		12 25		12 40		13c01

Station		NT	NT	NT	TP	NT	EM	NT	NT	NT	TP	NT	EM	NT	NT	NT	TP	NT	EM
					1 ◇		◇				1 ◇		◇				1 ◇		◇
					A		B				A		C				A		B
					🛒						🛒						🛒		
Liverpool Lime Street 10	90, 91 d	11 55	12 14		12 22	12 29	12 52	12 55	13 14		13 22	13 29	13 52	13 55	14 14		14 22	14 28	14 52
Edge Hill	90, 91 d	11 59						12 59						13 59					
Mossley Hill	91 d	12 04				12 37		13 04				13 37		14 04				14 37	
West Allerton	91 d	12 06						13 06						14 06					
Liverpool Central 10	103 d	11b43				12 13		12b43				13 13		13b43				14 13	
Liverpool South Parkway 7	91, 103 ✈ d	12 09				12 40		13 09				13 40		14 09				14 40	
Hunts Cross	103 d	12 13						13 13						14 13					
Halewood	d	12 16						13 16						14 16					
Hough Green	d	12 20				12 47		13 20				13 47		14 20				14 47	
Widnes	d	12 23				12 50	13 09	13 23				13 50	14 09	14 23				14 50	15 09
Sankey for Penketh	d	12 28						13 28						14 28					
Warrington Central	a	12 33		←	12 43	12 58	13 17	13 33		←	13 43	13 58	14 17	14 33		←	14 43	14 58	15 17
	d	12 34		12 34	12 44	12 59	13 17	13 34		13 34	13 44	13 59	14 17	14 34		14 34	14 44	14 59	15 17
Padgate	d	→		12 37				→		13 37				→		14 37			
Birchwood	d			12 40	12 49	13 03				13 40	13 49	14 03				14 40	14 49	15 03	
Glazebrook	d											14 08							
Irlam	d			12 46		13 09				13 46		14 11				14 46		15 09	
Flixton	d					13 13						14 15						15 13	
Chassen Road	d											14 17							
Urmston	d			12 51		13 16				13 51		14 19				14 51		15 16	
Humphrey Park	d					13 19												15 19	
Trafford Park	d					13 21												15 21	
Deansgate	84, 85 ⛴ a			13 01		13 31				14 01		14 31				15 01		15 31	
Manchester Oxford Road	84, 85 a		12 57	13 05	13 06	13 35	13 37		13 57	14 05	14 06	14 35	14 37		14 57	15 05	15 06	15 35	15 37
Manchester Piccadilly 10	78, 84, 85 ⛴ a		13 02		13 10		13 40		14 02		14 10		14 40		15 02		15 10		15 40
Stockport	84 a		13 26		13 32		13 52		14 26		14 32		14 52		15 26		15 32		15 53
Sheffield 7	78 ⛴ a		14 08				14 35		15 08				15 35		16 08				16 35
Manchester Airport	85 ✈ a		13 25		13 40		14c01		14 25		14 40		15c01		15 25		15 40		16c01

Station		NT	NT	NT	TP	NT	EM	NT	NT	NT	TP	NT	EM	NT	NT	NT	TP	NT	EM
					1 ◇		◇				1 ◇		◇				1 ◇		◇
					D		B				A		E				A		E
Liverpool Lime Street 10	90, 91 d	14 55	15 14		15 22	15 29	15 52	15 55	16 14		16 22	16 28	16 52	16 55	17 09		17 22	17 25	17 52
Edge Hill	90, 91 d	14 59						15 59						16 59				17 29	
Mossley Hill	91 d	15 04				15 37		16 04				16 36		17 04				17 34	
West Allerton	91 d	15 06						16 06						17 06				17 36	
Liverpool Central 10	103 d	14b43				15 13		15b43				16 13		16b43				17b13	
Liverpool South Parkway 7	91, 103 ✈ d	15 09				15 40		16 09				16 39		17 09				17 39	
Hunts Cross	103 d	15 13						16 13						17 13				17 43	
Halewood	d	15 16						16 16						17 15				17 45	
Hough Green	d	15 20				15 47		16 20				16 46		17 19				17 49	
Widnes	d	15 23				15 50	16 09	16 23				16 49	17 09	17 23				17 53	18 09
Sankey for Penketh	d	15 28						16 28						17 28				17 58	
Warrington Central	a	15 33		←	15 43	15 58	16 17	16 33		←	16 43	16 57	17 17	17 33		←	17 43	18 03	18 17
	d	15 34		15 34	15 44	15 59	16 17	16 34		16 34	16 44	16 58	17 17	17 33		17 33	17 44	18 03	18 17
Padgate	d	→		15 37				→		16 37				→		17 36			
Birchwood	d			15 40	15 49	16 03				16 40	16 49	17 02				17 39	17 49	18 08	
Glazebrook	d					16 08						17 07							
Irlam	d			15 46		16 11				16 46		17 10				17 45		18 14	
Flixton	d					16 15				16 50		17 14				17 49			
Chassen Road	d					16 17												18 18	
Urmston	d			15 51		16 19				16 53		17 17				17 52		18 20	
Humphrey Park	d											17 20						18 23	
Trafford Park	d											17 22							
Deansgate	84, 85 ⛴ a			16 01		16 31				17 03						18 01			
Manchester Oxford Road	84, 85 a		15 57	16 05	16 06	16 35	16 37		16 57	17 06	17 07	17 35	17 38		17 58	18 05	18 06	18 34	18 39
Manchester Piccadilly 10	78, 84, 85 ⛴ a		16 01		16 10		16 41		17 02		17 10		17 40		18 04		18 10		18 42
Stockport	84 a		16 26		16 32		16 52		17c19		17 32		17 54		18 26		18 32		18 54
Sheffield 7	78 ⛴ a		17 08				17 37		18 12				18 35		19 08				19 35
Manchester Airport	85 ✈ a		16 25		16 40		17e11		17 25		17 40		18e05		18 27		18 42		19e08

For general notes see front of timetable
For details of catering facilities see Directory of Train Operators

- **A** To Scarborough (Table 39)
- **B** To Norwich (Table 49)
- **C** To Nottingham (Table 49)
- **D** To Middlesbrough (Table 39)
- **E** To Cambridge (Table 49)
- **b** Change at Hunts Cross
- **c** Change at Manchester Oxford Road
- **e** Change at Manchester Piccadilly

Table 89

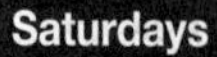

Saturdays

Liverpool → Warrington Central → Manchester and Manchester Airport

Network Diagram - see first page of Table 88

		NT	NT	NT	TP	NT	EM	NT	TP	NT	EM	NT	NT	TP	NT	NT	TP	NT
					1 ◇		◇		1 ◇		◇			1 ◇			1 ◇	
					A		B		C		B			C			D	
Liverpool Lime Street 10	90, 91 d	17 55	18 14		18 22	18 25	18 52	18 55	19 22		19 52	19 55	20 14	20 22	20 55	21 55	22 30	23 33
Edge Hill	90, 91 d	17 59				18 29		18 59				19 59			20 59	21 59		23 37
Mossley Hill	91 d	18 04				18 34		19 04				20 04			21 04	22 04		23 41
West Allerton	91 d	18 06				18 36		19 06				20 06			21 06	22 06		23 44
Liverpool Central 10	103 d	17b43				18b13		18b43				19b43			20b43	21b43		23b13
Liverpool South Parkway 7	91, 103 ✈ d	18 09				18 39		19 09				20 09			21 09	22 09		23 47
Hunts Cross	103 d	18 13				18 43		19 13				20 13			21 13	22 13		23 50
Halewood	d	18 15				18 45		19 15				20 15			21 15	22 15		23 53
Hough Green	d	18 19				18 49		19 19				20 19			21 19	22 19		23 57
Widnes	d	18 23				18 53	19 09	19 23			20 09	20 23			21 23	22 23		00 01
Sankey for Penketh	d	18 28				18 58		19 28				20 28			21 28	22 28		00 05
Warrington Central	a	18 33		←	18 43	19 03	19 17	19 35	19 43		20 17	20 35		20 43	21 33	22 33	22 52	00 11
	d	18 33 →		18 33	18 44	19 03	19 17		19 44	19 52	20 17			20 44	21 33	22 33	22 52	00 11
Padgate	d					19 06				19 55					21 36	22 36		
Birchwood	d			18 38	18 49	19 09			19 49	19 58				20 49	21 39	22 39	22 57	
Glazebrook	d					19 14				20 03					21 44	22 44		
Irlam	d			18 44		19 17				20 06					21 47	22 47		
Flixton	d			18 48						20 10					21 51	22 51		
Chassen Road	d									20 12					21 53	22 53		
Urmston	d			18 51		19 22				20 14					21 55	22 55		
Humphrey Park	d									20 17					21 58	22 58		
Trafford Park	d			18 54						20 19					22 00	23 00		
Deansgate	84, 85 🚋 a					19 32				20 31					22 07	23 07		
Manchester Oxford Road	84, 85 a		18 59	19 04	19 05	19 35	19 38		20 05	20 34	20 37		20 58	21 06	22 12	23 12	23 13	
Manchester Piccadilly 10	78, 84, 85 🚋 a		19 05		19 10		19 42		20 10		20 40		21 05	21 10	22 56		23 17	00 34
Stockport	84 a		19 26		19 32		19 53		20 34		20 51		21 26	21 34	23 06		23 50	
Sheffield 7	78 🚋 a		20 08				20 34				21 34		22 09	22 31				
Manchester Airport	85 ✈ a		19 26		19 40		20c05		20 58		21c09		21 28	21c37			23 55	01e16

Sundays

until 23 March

		TP	NT	NT	TP	NT	NT	NT	NT	TP	NT	NT	NT	EM	EM	NT	TP	NT	EM	EM	NT	TP
		1 ◇			1 ◇					1 ◇				◇	◇		1 ◇		◇	◇		1 ◇
		E			A					A				G	H		A		G	H		J
Liverpool Lime Street 10	90, 91 d	08 22	08 30	08 57	09 22	09 30	09 57	10 30	10 57	11 22	11 30	12 00	12 30	12 52	12 52	13 00	13 22	13 30	13 52	13 52	14 00	14 22
Mossley Hill	91 d			09 05			10 05		11 05			12 08				13 08					14 08	
West Allerton	91 d			09 07			10 07		11 07			12 10				13 10					14 10	
Liverpool Central 10	103 d			08b43			09b43		10b43			11b43				12b43					13b43	
Liverpool South Parkway 7	91, 103 ✈ d			09 10			10 10		11 10			12 13				13 13					14 13	
Hunts Cross	103 d			09 14			10 14		11 14			12 17				13 17					14 17	
Halewood	d			09 16			10 16		11 16			12 19				13 19					14 19	
Hough Green	d			09 20			10 20		11 20			12 23				13 23					14 23	
Widnes	d			09 24			10 24		11 24			12 27		13 10	13 10	13 27			14 10	14 10	14 27	
Warrington Central	a	08 43		09 32	09 44		10 32		11 32	11 43		12 35		13 17	13 17	13 35	13 43		14 17	14 17	14 35	14 43
	d	08 44		09 32	09 45		10 32		11 32	11 44		12 35		13 18	13 18	13 35	13 44		14 18	14 18	14 35	14 44
Birchwood	d	08 49		09 37	09 50		10 37		11 37	11 49		12 40				13 40	13 49				14 40	14 49
Irlam	d			09 43			10 43		11 43			12 46				13 46					14 46	
Urmston	d			09 48			10 48		11 48			12 51				13 51					14 51	
Deansgate	84, 85 🚋 a			09 58			10 58		11 58			13 01				14 01					15 01	
Manchester Oxford Road	84, 85 a	09 06	09 27	10 02	10 06	10 27	11 03	11 27	12 02	12 04	12 31	13 05	13 30	13 36	13 36	14 05	14 06	14 27	14 36	14 36	15 05	15 06
Manchester Piccadilly 10	78, 84, 85 🚋 a	09 10	09 34		10 10	10 34	11 15	11 35		12 10	12 35	13 15	13 35	13 44	13 44		14 10	14 32	14 41	14 41		15 10
Stockport	84 a	09 31	10 00	10 38	10 32	11 00	11 38	12 00		12 37	13 01	13 39		13 58	13 58		14 32		14 51	14 51		15 32
Sheffield 7	78 🚋 a	10f56	12g00			12h03		13f25		13j37	14f06			15k30	14 37		15g55		16k25	15 35		16g55
Manchester Airport	85 ✈ a	09c33	09 51		10c33	10 51	11 33	11 51		12c33	12 50	13 33	13 54	14m33	14m33		14c33	14 51	15m21	15m18		15c33

		NT	EM	EM	NT	TP	NT	EM	EM	NT	TP	NT	EM	EM	NT	TP	NT	EM	EM	NT	TP
			◇	◇		1 ◇		◇	◇		1 ◇		◇	◇		1 ◇		◇	◇		1 ◇
			G	H		A		G	H		C		G	K		A		H	G		A
Liverpool Lime Street 10	90, 91 d	14 30	14 52	14 52	15 00	15 22	15 30	15 52	15 52	16 00	16 22	16 30	16 52	16 52	17 00	17 22	17 30	17 52	17 52	18 00	18 22
Mossley Hill	91 d				15 08					16 08					17 08					18 08	
West Allerton	91 d				15 10					16 10					17 10					18 10	
Liverpool Central 10	103 d				14b43					15b43					16b43					17b43	
Liverpool South Parkway 7	91, 103 ✈ d				15 13					16 13					17 13					18 13	
Hunts Cross	103 d				15 17					16 17					17 17					18 17	
Halewood	d				15 19					16 19					17 19					18 19	
Hough Green	d				15 23					16 23					17 23					18 23	
Widnes	d		15 10	15 10	15 27			16 10	16 10	16 27			17 10	17 10	17 27			18 10	18 10	18 27	
Warrington Central	a		15 17	15 17	15 35	15 43		16 17	16 17	16 35	16 43		17 17	17 17	17 35	17 43		18 17	18 17	18 35	18 43
	d		15 18	15 18	15 35	15 44		16 18	16 18	16 35	16 44		17 18	17 18	17 35	17 44		18 18	18 18	18 35	18 44
Birchwood	d				15 40	15 49				16 40	16 49				17 40	17 49				18 40	18 49
Irlam	d				15 46					16 46					17 46					18 46	
Urmston	d				15 51					16 51					17 51					18 51	
Deansgate	84, 85 🚋 a				16 01					17 01					18 01					19 01	
Manchester Oxford Road	84, 85 a	15 29	15 36	15 36	16 05	16 06	16 27	16 38	16 38	17 05	17 06	17 30	17 36	17 36	18 05	18 06	18 27	18 36	18 36	19 05	19 06
Manchester Piccadilly 10	78, 84, 85 🚋 a	15 34	15 41	15 41		16 10	16 35	16 41	16 41		17 10	17 35	17 41	17 41		18 10	18 33	18 41	18 41		19 10
Stockport	84 a		15 52	15 52		16 31		16 52	16 52		17 31		17 52	17 52		18 31		18 52	18 57		19 32
Sheffield 7	78 🚋 a		17k20	16 35		17g55		18k25	17 35		18g55		19k25	18 36		19g55		19 35	20k30		20g55
Manchester Airport	85 ✈ a	15 51	16m18	16m18		16c33	16 51	17m18	17m18		17c33	17 51	18m18	18m18		18c33	18 52	19m18	19m18		19c33

For general notes see front of timetable
For details of catering facilities see Directory of Train Operators

- **A** To Scarborough (Table 39)
- **B** To Nottingham (Table 49)
- **C** To York (Table 39)
- **D** To York (2 February to 22 March to Huddersfield) (Table 39)
- **E** To Newcastle (Table 39)
- **G** Until 27 January
- **H** From 3 February. To Norwich (Table 49)
- **J** To Hull (Table 39)
- **K** From 3 February. To Nottingham (Table 49)
- **b** Change at Hunts Cross
- **c** Change at Manchester Oxford Road
- **e** 2 February to 22 March only
- **f** From 3 February only
- **g** Until 27 January only. By bus
- **h** Until 27 January arr. 1300, by bus
- **j** Until 27 January arr. 1425, by bus
- **k** By bus
- **m** Change at Manchester Piccadilly

Table 89

Sundays

until 23 March

Liverpool → Warrington Central → Manchester and Manchester Airport

Network Diagram - see first page of Table 88

		NT	EM ◇ A	EM ◇ B	NT	TP 1 ◇ C	NT	EM ◇ A	EM ◇ B	NT	TP 1 ◇ D	NT	NT	EM ◇ A	EM ◇ B	NT	TP 1 ◇ C	NT	NT	NT	NT		
Liverpool Lime Street 10	90, 91 d	18 30	18 52	18 52	19 00	19 22	19 30	19 52	19 52	20 00	20 22	20 30	21 00	21 22	21 22	21 30	21 52	22 00	22 27	22 30			
Mossley Hill	91 d				19 08					20 08			21 08					22 08	22 35				
West Allerton	91 d				19 10					20 10			21 10					22 10	22 37				
Liverpool Central 10	103 d				18b43					19b43			20b43					21b43	22b13				
Liverpool South Parkway 7	91, 103 ✈ d				19 13					20 13			21 13					22 13	22 40				
Hunts Cross	103 d				19 17					20 17			21 17					22 17	22 44				
Halewood	d				19 19					20 19			21 19					22 19	22 46				
Hough Green	d				19 23					20 23			21 23					22 23	22 50				
Widnes	d		19 10	19 10	19 27			20 10	20 10	20 27			21 27	21 40	21 40			22 27	22 54				
Warrington Central	a		19 17	19 17	19 35	19 43		20 17	20 17	20 35	20 43		21 35	21 47	21 47		22 14	22 35	23 02		←		
	d		19 18	19 18	19 35	19 44		20 18	20 18	20 35	20 44		21 35	21 47	21 47		22 15	22 35	23 02		23 02		
Birchwood	d				19 40	19 49				20 40	20 49		21 40				22 20	22 40	→		23 07		
Irlam	d				19 46					20 46			21 46					22 46			23 13		
Urmston	d				19 51					20 51			21 51					22 51			23 18		
Deansgate	84, 85 🚢 a				20 01					21 01			22 01					23 01			23 28		
Manchester Oxford Road	84, 85 a	19 28	19 36	19 36	20 05	20 06	20 28	20 39	20 39	21 05	21 06	21 28	22 05	22 06	22 06	22 27	22 36	23 05		23 27	23 32		
Manchester Piccadilly 10	78, 84, 85 🚢 a	19 35	19 41	19 41		20 10	20 33	20 41	20 41		21 10	21 34		22 10	22 10	22 33	22 40	23 15		23 33	23 41		
Stockport	84 a		19 52	19 52		20 31		20 52	20 52		21 36	22 03		22 21	22 21	22 54	23 03	23 38					
Sheffield 7	78 🚢 a		21c25	20 35		22e10		22c25	21 38		23e10	23f06		00c10	23 23		00g09						
Manchester Airport	85 ✈ a	19 51	20h18	20h18		20j33	20 52	21h18	21h18		21j33	21 52		22j33	22j33	22 51	23 18	23 33		23 49	00k33		

Sundays

from 30 March

		TP 1 ◇ D	NT	NT		TP 1 ◇ E	NT	NT		NT	NT	TP 1 ◇ E		NT	NT	NT		EM ◇ G	NT	TP 1 ◇ E		NT	EM ◇ G
Liverpool Lime Street 10	90, 91 d	08 22	08 43	08 57		09 22	09 43	09 57		10 43	10 57	11 22		11 43	12 00	12 43		12 52	13 00	13 22		13 43	13 52
Mossley Hill	91 d			09 05				10 05			11 05				12 08				13 08				
West Allerton	91 d			09 07				10 07			11 07				12 10				13 10				
Liverpool Central 10	103 d			08b43				09b43			10b43				11b43				12b43				
Liverpool South Parkway 7	91, 103 ✈ d			09 10				10 10			11 10				12 13				13 13				
Hunts Cross	103 d			09 14				10 14			11 14				12 17				13 17				
Halewood	d			09 16				10 16			11 16				12 19				13 19				
Hough Green	d			09 20				10 20			11 20				12 23				13 23				
Widnes	d			09 24				10 24			11 24				12 27			13 10	13 27				14 10
Warrington Central	a	08 43		09 32		09 44		10 32			11 32	11 43			12 35			13 17	13 35	13 43			14 17
	d	08 44		09 32		09 45		10 32			11 32	11 44			12 35			13 18	13 35	13 44			14 18
Birchwood	d	08 49		09 37		09 50		10 37			11 37	11 49			12 40				13 40	13 49			
Irlam	d			09 43				10 43			11 43				12 46				13 46				
Urmston	d			09 48				10 48			11 48				12 51				13 51				
Deansgate	84, 85 🚢 a			09 58				10 58			11 58				13 01				14 01				
Manchester Oxford Road	84, 85 a	09 06	09 28	10 02		10 06	10 30	11 03		11 30	12 02	12 04		12 31	13 05	13 30		13 36	14 05	14 06		14 25	14 36
Manchester Piccadilly 10	78, 84, 85 🚢 a	09 10	09 34			10 10	10 34	11 15		11 34		12 10		12 35	13 15	13 35		13 44		14 10		14 33	14 41
Stockport	84 a	09 32	10 00			10 32	11 00	11 38		12 00		12 37		13 01	13 39			13 58		14 32			14 51
Sheffield 7	78 🚢 a	10 56				12 03	12 03			13 25		13 37		14 03				14 37					15 35
Manchester Airport	85 ✈ a	09j33	09 51			10j33	10 51	11 33		11 51		12j33		12 50	13 33	13 54				14j33		14 51	15h21

		NT	TP 1 ◇ H	NT		EM ◇ G	NT	TP 1 ◇ E		NT	EM ◇ G	NT		TP 1 ◇ C	NT	EM ◇ J		NT	TP 1 ◇ E	NT		EM ◇ G	NT
Liverpool Lime Street 10	90, 91 d	14 00	14 22	14 43		14 52	15 00	15 22		15 43	15 52	16 00		16 22	16 43	16 52		17 00	17 22	17 43		17 52	18 00
Mossley Hill	91 d	14 08					15 08					16 08						17 08					18 08
West Allerton	91 d	14 10					15 10					16 10						17 10					18 10
Liverpool Central 10	103 d	13b43					14b43					15b43						16b43					17b43
Liverpool South Parkway 7	91, 103 ✈ d	14 13					15 13					16 13						17 13					18 13
Hunts Cross	103 d	14 17					15 17					16 17						17 17					18 17
Halewood	d	14 19					15 19					16 19						17 19					18 19
Hough Green	d	14 23					15 23					16 23						17 23					18 23
Widnes	d	14 27				15 10	15 27				16 10	16 27				17 10		17 27				18 10	18 27
Warrington Central	a	14 35	14 43			15 17	15 35	15 43			16 17	16 35		16 43		17 17		17 35	17 43			18 17	18 35
	d	14 35	14 44			15 18	15 35	15 44			16 18	16 35		16 44		17 18		17 35	17 44			18 18	18 35
Birchwood	d	14 40	14 49				15 40	15 49				16 40		16 49				17 40	17 49				18 40
Irlam	d	14 46					15 46					16 46						17 46					18 46
Urmston	d	14 51					15 51					16 51						17 51					18 51
Deansgate	84, 85 🚢 a	15 01					16 01					17 01						18 01					19 01
Manchester Oxford Road	84, 85 a	15 05	15 06	15 25		15 36	16 05	16 06		16 27	16 38	17 05		17 06	17 25	17 36		18 05	18 06	18 25		18 36	19 05
Manchester Piccadilly 10	78, 84, 85 🚢 a		15 10	15 34		15 41		16 10		16 35	16 41			17 10	17 35	17 41			18 10	18 33		18 41	
Stockport	84 a		15 32			15 52		16 31			16 52			17 31		17 52			18 31			18 52	
Sheffield 7	78 🚢 a					16 35					17 35					18 36						19 35	
Manchester Airport	85 ✈ a		15j33	15 51				16j33		16 51	17h21			17j33	17 51				18j33	18 52		19h21	

For general notes see front of timetable
For details of catering facilities see Directory of Train Operators

- **A** Until 27 January
- **B** From 3 February. To Nottingham (Table 49)
- **C** To York (Table 39)
- **D** To Newcastle (Table 39)
- **E** To Scarborough (Table 39)
- **G** To Norwich (Table 49)
- **H** To Hull (Table 39)
- **J** To Nottingham (Table 49)
- **b** Change at Hunts Cross
- **c** By bus
- **e** Until 27 January only. By bus
- **f** From 3 February only
- **g** Until 27 January arr 0110, by bus
- **h** Change at Manchester Piccadilly
- **j** Change at Manchester Oxford Road
- **k** Change at Manchester Oxford Road and Manchester Piccadilly

Table 89

Sundays

from 30 March

Liverpool → Warrington Central → Manchester and Manchester Airport

Network Diagram - see first page of Table 88

		TP 1 ◇ A	NT	EM ◇ B		NT	TP 1 ◇ C	NT		EM ◇ B	NT	TP 1 ◇ D		NT	NT	EM ◇ B	NT	TP 1 ◇ C	NT	NT	NT
Liverpool Lime Street 10	90, 91 d	18 22	18 43	18 52		19 00	19 22	19 43		19 52	20 00	20 22		20 43	21 00	21 22	21 43	21 52	22 00	22 27	22 43
Mossley Hill	91 d					19 08					20 08				21 08				22 08	22 35	
West Allerton	91 d					19 10					20 10				21 10				22 10	22 37	
Liverpool Central 10	103 d					18b43					19b43				20b43				21b43	22b13	
Liverpool South Parkway 7	91, 103 ✈ d					19 13					20 13				21 13				22 13	22 40	
Hunts Cross	103 d					19 17					20 17				21 17				22 17	22 44	
Halewood	d					19 19					20 19				21 19				22 19	22 46	
Hough Green	d					19 23					20 23				21 23				22 23	22 50	
Widnes	d			19 10		19 27				20 10	20 27				21 27	21 40			22 27	22 54	
Warrington Central	a	18 43		19 17		19 35	19 43			20 17	20 35	20 43			21 35	21 47		22 14	22 35	23 02	
	d	18 44		19 18		19 35	19 44			20 18	20 35	20 44			21 35	21 47		22 15	22 35	23 02	
Birchwood	d	18 49				19 40	19 49				20 40	20 49			21 40			22 20	22 40	23 07	
Irlam	d					19 46					20 46				21 46				22 46	23 13	
Urmston	d					19 51					20 51				21 51				22 51	23 18	
Deansgate	84, 85 ⛴ a					20 01					21 01				22 01				23 01	23 28	
Manchester Oxford Road	84, 85 a	19 06	19 29	19 36		20 05	20 06	20 26		20 39	21 05	21 06		21 30	22 05	22 06	22 29	22 36	23 05	23 32	23 34
Manchester Piccadilly 10	78, 84, 85 ⛴ a	19 10	19 34	19 41			20 10	20 33		20 41		21 10		21 34		22 10	22 34	22 40	23 15		23 38
Stockport	84 a	19 31		19 52			20 31			20 52		21 36		22 03		22 21	22 54	23 03	23 38		
Sheffield 7	78 ⛴ a			20 35						21 38				23 06		23 23		00 09			
Manchester Airport	85 ✈ a	19c33	19 51				20c33	20 52		21e21		21c33		21 52		22c33	22 51	23 26	23 33		23 54

For general notes see front of timetable
For details of catering facilities see Directory of Train Operators

A To Scarborough (Table 39)
B To Nottingham (Table 49)
C To York (Table 39)
D To Newcastle (Table 39)

b Change at Hunts Cross
c Change at Manchester Oxford Road
e Change at Manchester Piccadilly

Manchester Airport and Manchester → Warrington Central → Liverpool

Network Diagram - see first page of Table 88

Miles	Station	NT	NT	NT	NT	NT	NT	TP 1 ◇		NT	EM ◇ A	NT	NT	NT	NT B	TP 1 ◇ C		NT B	EM ◇ A	NT	NT	NT
0	**Manchester Airport** 85 ✈ d	04 34			05 47	06 19	06 28				07b02		07 26		07b34				08b07		08 30	
—	Sheffield 7 78 🚊 d						05 11				06 20								07 37			
—	Stockport 84 d					06 17		06 42			07 24				07 49				08 27			
9¾	**Manchester Piccadilly** 10 78, 84, 85 🚊 d	04 49			06 05	06 44	06 52	07 07			07 35		07 49		08 00	08 07		←	08 37		08 50	
10¼	**Manchester Oxford Road** 84, 85 d				06 24	06 53	06 56	07 10			07 38	07 41	07 52		08 13 →	08 10		08 13	08 41	08 43	08 55	
10¾	Deansgate 84, 85 🚊 d				06 26													08 15		08 45		
13¾	Trafford Park d				06 31							07 47						08 20				
14½	Humphrey Park d				06 33																	
15¾	Urmston d				06 35	07 00						07 51						08 24		08 52		
16¼	Chassen Road d				06 37													08 26				
16¾	Flixton d				06 40							07 54						08 28				
19	Irlam d				06 44	07 05						07 58						08 32		08 57		
20¼	Glazebrook d				06 47							08 01						08 35				
23	Birchwood d				06 51	07 11		07 24				08 05				08 24		08 40		09 02		
24½	Padgate d				06 54							08 08						08 43				
26¼	**Warrington Central** a				06 58	07 19		07 29			07 54	08 12		←		08 29		08 46	08 57	09 07		←
—	d		06 03	06 37	06 58			07 29		07 40	07 54	08 12 →		08 12		08 29		08 47	08 57	09 08 →		09 08
28¾	Sankey for Penketh d		06 07	06 41	07 02					07 44				08 16								09 12
32½	Widnes d		06 12	06 46	07 08					07 49	08 02			08 22				08 55	09 05			09 17
34¼	Hough Green d		06 16	06 50	07 11					07 53	08 06			08 25				08 58				09 21
36½	Halewood d		06 20	06 54	07 15					07 57				08 29								09 25
37½	Hunts Cross 89 d		06 23	06 57	07 18					08 00	08s11			08 32								09 28
39¼	**Liverpool South Parkway** 7 91, 103 ✈ a		06 28	07 02	07 24					08 03				08 37				09 07				09 33
—	Liverpool Central 10 103 a		06 53	07 23	07 53					08c23	08 38			09 08				09 38				09c53
40¼	West Allerton 91 a		06 31	07 05	07 27					08 06				08 40				09 10				09 36
41	Mossley Hill 91 a		06 34	07 07	07 30					08 09				08 42				09 13				09 39
43	Edge Hill 90, 91 a		06 39	07 13	07 37					08 14				08 47								09 45
44¾	**Liverpool Lime Street** 10 90, 91 a	05 30	06 46	07 19	07 44		07 47	07 57		08 21	08 29		08 42	08 55		08 57		09 24	09 29		09 42	09 51

Station	TP 1 ◇ E	NT	EM ◇ A	NT		NT	NT	TP 1 ◇ G	NT	EM ◇ H	NT	NT		NT	TP 1 ◇ G	NT	EM ◇ J	NT	NT	NT		TP 1 ◇ G
Manchester Airport 85 ✈ d	08 33		09b07			09 31		09 34		10b07		10 31			10 34		11b07		11 31			11 34
Sheffield 7 78 🚊 d			08 42							09 42							10 42					
Stockport 84 d	08 42		09 24					09 39		10 25					10 39		11 25					11 39
Manchester Piccadilly 10 78, 84, 85 🚊 d	09 07		09 37			09 49		10 07		10 37		10 49			11 07		11 37		11 49			12 07
Manchester Oxford Road 84, 85 d	09 10	09 13	09 41	09 43		09 52		10 10	10 13	10 41	10 43	10 52			11 10	11 13	11 41	11 43	11 52			12 10
Deansgate 84, 85 🚊 d		09 15		09 45					10 15		10 45					11 15		11 45				
Trafford Park d		09 20														11 20						
Humphrey Park d		09 22														11 22						
Urmston d		09 24		09 52					10 21		10 52					11 24		11 52				
Chassen Road d									10 23													
Flixton d		09 27							10 26							11 27						
Irlam d		09 31		09 57					10 30		10 57					11 31		11 57				
Glazebrook d									10 33													
Birchwood d	09 24	09 37		10 02				10 24	10 37		11 02				11 24	11 37		12 02				12 24
Padgate d		09 40							10 40							11 40						
Warrington Central a	09 29	09 43	09 57	10 07			←	10 28	10 44	10 57	11 07			←	11 28	11 43	11 57	12 07		←		12 28
d	09 29	09 44	09 57	10 08 →			10 08	10 29	10 44	10 57	11 08 →			11 08	11 29	11 44	11 57	12 08 →		12 08		12 29
Sankey for Penketh d							10 12							11 12						12 12		
Widnes d		09 52	10 05				10 17		10 52	11 05				11 17		11 52	12 05			12 17		
Hough Green d		09 55					10 21		10 55					11 21		11 55				12 21		
Halewood d							10 25							11 25						12 25		
Hunts Cross 89 d							10 28							11 28						12 28		
Liverpool South Parkway 7 91, 103 ✈ a		10 04					10 33		11 04					11 33		12 04				12 33		
Liverpool Central 10 103 a		10 38					10c53		11 38					11c53		12 38				12c53		
West Allerton 91 a							10 36							11 36						12 36		
Mossley Hill 91 a		10 08					10 39		11 08					11 39		12 08				12 39		
Edge Hill 90, 91 a							10 45							11 45						12 45		
Liverpool Lime Street 10 90, 91 a	09 57	10 20	10 29			10 39	10 51	10 57	11 20	11 29		11 39		11 51	11 57	12 20	12 29		12 39	12 51		12 57

Station	NT	EM ◇ H	NT	NT	NT	TP 1 ◇ G	NT		EM ◇ H	NT	NT	NT	TP 1 ◇ G	NT	EM ◇ H		NT	NT	NT	TP 1 ◇ G	NT	EM ◇ H
Manchester Airport 85 ✈ d		12b07		12 31		12 34			13b07		13 31		13 34		14b07			14 31		14 34		15b07
Sheffield 7 78 🚊 d		11 42							12 42						13 42							14 42
Stockport 84 d		12 25				12 39			13 25				13 39		14 25					14 39		15 25
Manchester Piccadilly 10 78, 84, 85 🚊 d		12 37		12 49		13 07			13 37		13 49		14 07		14 37			14 49		15 07		15 37
Manchester Oxford Road 84, 85 d	12 13	12 41	12 43	12 52		13 10	13 13		13 41	13 43	13 52		14 10	14 13	14 41		14 43	14 52		15 10	15 13	15 41
Deansgate 84, 85 🚊 d	12 15		12 45				13 15			13 45				14 15			14 45				15 15	
Trafford Park d							13 20														15 20	
Humphrey Park d							13 22														15 22	
Urmston d	12 21		12 52				13 24			13 52				14 21			14 52				15 24	
Chassen Road d	12 23													14 23								
Flixton d	12 26						13 27							14 26							15 27	
Irlam d	12 30		12 57				13 31			13 57				14 30			14 57				15 31	
Glazebrook d	12 33													14 33								
Birchwood d	12 37		13 02			13 24	13 37			14 02			14 24	14 37			15 02			15 24	15 37	
Padgate d	12 40						13 40							14 40							15 40	
Warrington Central a	12 44	12 57	13 07		←	13 28	13 43		13 57	14 07		←	14 28	14 44	14 57		15 07		←	15 28	15 44	15 57
d	12 44	12 57	13 08 →		13 08	13 29	13 44		13 57	14 08 →		14 08	14 29	14 44	14 57		15 08 →		15 08	15 29	15 44	15 57
Sankey for Penketh d					13 12							14 12							15 12			
Widnes d	12 52	13 05			13 17		13 52		14 05			14 17		14 52	15 05				15 17		15 52	16 05
Hough Green d	12 55				13 21		13 55					14 21		14 55					15 21		15 55	
Halewood d					13 25							14 25							15 25		15 59	
Hunts Cross 89 d					13 28							14 28							15 28			
Liverpool South Parkway 7 91, 103 ✈ a	13 04				13 33		14 04					14 33		15 04					15 33		16 06	
Liverpool Central 10 103 a	13 38				13c53		14 38					14c53		15 38					15c53		16 38	
West Allerton 91 a					13 36							14 36							15 36			
Mossley Hill 91 a	13 08				13 39		14 08					14 39		15 08					15 39		16 10	
Edge Hill 90, 91 a					13 45							14 45							15 45			
Liverpool Lime Street 10 90, 91 a	13 20	13 29		13 39	13 51	13 57	14 20		14 29		14 39	14 51	14 57	15 20	15 29			15 39	15 51	15 57	16 22	16 27

For general notes see front of timetable
For details of catering facilities see Directory of Train Operators

- **A** From Nottingham (Table 49)
- **B** From Buxton (Table 86)
- **C** From Hull (Table 39)
- **E** From Newcastle (Table 39)
- **G** From Scarborough (Table 39)
- **H** From Norwich (Table 49)
- **J** From Cambridge (Table 49)
- **b** Change at Manchester Piccadilly
- **c** Change at Hunts Cross

Manchester Airport and Manchester → Warrington Central → Liverpool

Network Diagram - see first page of Table 88

		NT	NT	NT		TP 1 ◇ A (trolley)	NT	EM ◇ B (trolley)	NT	NT	NT	TP 1 ◇ A (trolley)		NT	EM ◇ B (trolley)	NT	NT	TP 1 ◇ A (trolley)	NT	NT		EM ◇ B (trolley)	NT
Manchester Airport	85 ✈ d		15 31			*15 34*		*16b07*		16 31		*16 34*			*17b04*		17 29	*17 34*				*18b10*	
Sheffield 7	78 🚌 d							15 42							16 42							17 42	
Stockport	84 d					*15 39*		16 25				*16 43*			17 26			*17 39*				18 26	
Manchester Piccadilly 10	78, 84, 85 🚌 d	*15 30*	15 49			16 07		16 37		16 48		17 07			17 37		17 45	18 07				18 37	
Manchester Oxford Road	84, 85 d	15 43	15 52			16 10	16 13	16 41	16 43	16 52		17 10		17 13	17 41	17 43	17 49	18 10		18 13		18 41	
Deansgate	84, 85 🚌 d	15 45					16 15		16 45					17 15		17 45				18 15			
Trafford Park	d								16 50					17 20		17 50				18 20			
Humphrey Park	d													17 22		17 52				18 22			
Urmston	d	15 52					16 21		16 54					17 25		17 55				18 24			
Chassen Road	d						16 23							17 27		17 57				18 26			
Flixton	d						16 26		16 57					17 29		17 59				18 29			
Irlam	d	15 57					16 30		17 01					17 33	17 51	18 03				18 33			
Glazebrook	d						16 33							17 36		18 06							
Birchwood	d	16 02				16 24	16 37		17 06			17 24		17 41	17 57	18 11		18 24		18 38			
Padgate	d						16 40		17 09					17 44		18 14							
Warrington Central	a	16 07		←		16 28	16 44	16 57	17 13		←	17 28		17 47	18 02	18 18		18 28		18 43		18 57	
	d	16 08 →		16 08		16 29	16 44	16 57	17 13 →		17 13	17 29		17 48	18 02	18 18		18 29		18 44		18 57	
Sankey for Penketh	d			16 12							17 17			17 52						18 48			
Widnes	d			16 17			16 52	17 05			17 23			17 57	18 10					18 53		19 05	
Hough Green	d			16 21			16 55				17 26			18 01		18 28				18 57			
Halewood	d			16 25							17 30			18 05						19 01			
Hunts Cross	89 d			16 28							17 33	17 40		18 08		18 33				19 04		19 12	
Liverpool South Parkway 7	91, 103 ✈ a			16 33			17 04				17 39			18 14		18 40				19 09			
Liverpool Central 10	103 a			*16c53*			*17 38*					*18 08*		*18 38*		*19 08*						*19 38*	
West Allerton	91 a			16 36							17 42			18 17		18 43			←	19 13			←
Mossley Hill	91 a			16 39			17 08				17 44			18 20		18 45 →			18 45	19 15 →			19 15
Edge Hill	90, 91 a			16 45							17 50			18 25					18 51				19 25
Liverpool Lime Street 10	90, 91 a		16 39	16 51		16 57	17 24	17 27		17 38	17 58	18 00		18 32	18 32		18 40	18 57	18 59			19 29	19 32

		NT	NT	TP 1 ◇ A	NT	EM ◇ B (trolley)	NT	NT		TP 1 ◇ A	NT	NT	EM ◇ B	NT	TP 1 ◇ A	NT	NT	NT	TP 1 ◇ A	NT	NT		
Manchester Airport	85 ✈ d		18 31	*18 34*		*19e12*		19 30					*20e15*		*20 22*		*21e16*	21 30			*22 47*		
Sheffield 7	78 🚌 d					18 42							19 42				*20 11*	*20 31*					
Stockport	84 d			*18 39*		19 24				*19 40*			20 26		*20 40*		*21 10*	*21 17*	*21 39*		*22 39*		
Manchester Piccadilly 10	78, 84, 85 🚌 d		18 49	19 07		19 37		19 48		20 07			20 37		21 07		21 39	21 47	22 07		*23 20*		
Manchester Oxford Road	84, 85 d	18 43	18 52	19 10		19 41	19 43	19 52		20 10			20 41	20 43	21 10		21 43	21 50	22 10		23 27		
Deansgate	84, 85 🚌 d	18 45					19 45							20 45			21 45				23 29		
Trafford Park	d	18 50					19 50							20 50			21 50				23 34		
Humphrey Park	d	18 52					19 52							20 52			21 52				23 36		
Urmston	d	18 55					19 55							20 54			21 54				23 38		
Chassen Road	d	18 57					19 57							20 56			21 56				23 40		
Flixton	d	18 59					19 59							20 59			21 59				23 43		
Irlam	d	19 03					20 03							21 03			22 03				23 47		
Glazebrook	d	19 06					20 06							21 06			22 06				23 50		
Birchwood	d	19 11		19 24			20 11			20 24				21 10	21 24		22 10		22 24		23 54		
Padgate	d	19 14					20 14							21 13			22 13				23 57		
Warrington Central	a	19 20		19 28		19 57	20 17			20 28			20 57	21 20	21 28		22 20		22 29		00 01		
	d			19 29	19 40	19 57	20 18			20 29		20 40	20 57		21 29	21 40			22 29	22 40	00 01		
Sankey for Penketh	d				19 44							20 44				21 44				22 44	00 05		
Widnes	d				19 49	20 05						20 49	21 05			21 49				22 49	00 11		
Hough Green	d				19 53		20 27					20 53				21 53				22 53	00 14		
Halewood	d				19 57							20 57				21 57				22 57			
Hunts Cross	89 d				20 00		20 32					21 00				22 00				23 00	00 19		
Liverpool South Parkway 7	91, 103 ✈ a				20 03		20 38					21 03				22 03				23 03			
Liverpool Central 10	103 a				*20c23*		*21 08*					*21c23*				*22c23*				*23c23*			
West Allerton	91 a				20 06		20 41				←	21 06				22 06				23 06			
Mossley Hill	91 a				20 09		20 43 →				20 43	21 09				22 09				23 09			
Edge Hill	90, 91 a				20 14							21 14				22 14				23 14			
Liverpool Lime Street 10	90, 91 a		19 38	19 57	20 21	20 29		20 38		20 55	20 59	21 21	21 29		21 55	22 22		22 41	22 55	23 21	00 37		

For general notes see front of timetable
For details of catering facilities see Directory of Train Operators

A From Scarborough (Table 39)
B From Norwich (Table 49)
b Change at Manchester Piccadilly
c Change at Hunts Cross
e Change at Manchester Oxford Road

Manchester Airport and Manchester → Warrington Central → Liverpool

Network Diagram - see first page of Table 88

	NT	NT	NT	NT	NT		TP	NT	EM	NT	NT		NT	TP	NT	EM	NT		NT	NT	TP	NT
							1 ◇		◇					1 ◇		◇					1 ◇	
									A					B		A					C	
Manchester Airport 85 ✈ d	04 35			05 47	06 28				07b02		07 26			07 34		08b07			08 30		08 33	
Sheffield 7 78 d	03 45				05 11				06 20							07 36						
Stockport 84 d					06 17		06 41		07 23					07 39		08 27					08 42	
Manchester Piccadilly 10 78, 84, 85 d	04 50			06 05	06 52		07 07		07 35		07 49			08 07		08 37			08 50		09 07	
Manchester Oxford Road 84, 85 d				06 29	06 56		07 10		07 38	07 41	07 52			08 10	08 13	08 41	08 43		08 55		09 10	09 13
Deansgate 84, 85 d				06 31											08 15		08 45					09 15
Trafford Park d				06 36						07 47					08 20							09 20
Humphrey Park d				06 38																		09 22
Urmston d				06 40						07 51					08 24		08 52					09 24
Chassen Road d				06 42											08 26							
Flixton d				06 45						07 54					08 28							09 27
Irlam d				06 49						07 58					08 32		08 57					09 31
Glazebrook d				06 52						08 01					08 35							
Birchwood d				06 56			07 24			08 05				08 24	08 40		09 02				09 24	09 37
Padgate d				06 59						08 08					08 43							09 40
Warrington Central a				07 03			07 29		07 54	08 12			←	08 29	08 46	08 57	09 07			←	09 29	09 43
d		06 03	06 37	07 03			07 29	07 40	07 54	08 12			08 12	08 29	08 47	08 57	09 08			09 08	09 29	09 44
Sankey for Penketh d		06 07	06 41	07 07				07 44		→			08 16				→			09 12		
Widnes d		06 12	06 46	07 13				07 49	08 02				08 22		08 55	09 05				09 17		09 52
Hough Green d		06 16	06 50	07 16				07 53	08 06				08 25		08 58					09 21		09 55
Halewood d		06 20	06 54	07 20				07 57					08 29							09 25		
Hunts Cross 89 d		06 23	06 57	07 23				08 00	08s11				08 32							09 28		
Liverpool South Parkway 7 91, 103 ✈ a		06 28	07 02	07 29				08 03					08 37		09 07					09 33		10 04
Liverpool Central 10 103 a		06 53	07 23	07 53				08c23	08 38				09 08		09 38					09c53		10 38
West Allerton 91 a		06 31	07 05	07 32				08 06					08 40		09 10					09 36		
Mossley Hill 91 a		06 34	07 07	07 35				08 09					08 42		09 13					09 39		10 08
Edge Hill 90, 91 a		06 39	07 13	07 40				08 14					08 47							09 45		
Liverpool Lime Street 10 90, 91 a	05 29	06 46	07 19	07 47	07 48		07 57	08 21	08 29		08 42		08 55	08 57	09 24	09 27			09 42	09 51	09 57	10 20

	EM	NT	NT		NT	TP	NT	EM	NT		NT	NT	TP	NT	EM		NT	NT	NT	TP	NT	EM
	◇					1 ◇		◇					1 ◇		◇					1 ◇		◇
	A					D		E					D		G					D		E
Manchester Airport 85 ✈ d	09b07		09 31			09 34		10b07			10 31		10 34		11b07			11 31		11 34		12b07
Sheffield 7 78 d	08 42							09 42							10 42							11 42
Stockport 84 d	09 25					09 39		10 25					10 39		11 25					11 39		12 25
Manchester Piccadilly 10 78, 84, 85 d	09 37		09 49			10 07		10 37			10 49		11 07		11 37			11 49		12 07		12 37
Manchester Oxford Road 84, 85 d	09 41	09 43	09 52			10 10	10 13	10 41	10 43		10 52		11 10	11 13	11 41		11 43	11 52		12 10	12 13	12 41
Deansgate 84, 85 d		09 45					10 15		10 45					11 15			11 45				12 15	
Trafford Park d														11 20								
Humphrey Park d														11 22								
Urmston d		09 52					10 21		10 52					11 24			11 52				12 21	
Chassen Road d							10 23														12 23	
Flixton d							10 26							11 27							12 26	
Irlam d		09 57					10 30		10 57					11 31			11 57				12 30	
Glazebrook d							10 33														12 33	
Birchwood d		10 02				10 24	10 37		11 02				11 24	11 37			12 02			12 24	12 37	
Padgate d							10 40							11 40							12 40	
Warrington Central a	09 57	10 07			←	10 28	10 44	10 57	11 07			←	11 28	11 43	11 57		12 07		←	12 28	12 44	12 57
d	09 57	10 08			10 08	10 29	10 44	10 57	11 08			11 08	11 29	11 44	11 57		12 08		12 08	12 29	12 44	12 57
Sankey for Penketh d		→			10 12				→			11 12					→		12 12			
Widnes d	10 05				10 17		10 52	11 05				11 17		11 52	12 05				12 17		12 52	13 05
Hough Green d					10 21		10 55					11 21		11 55					12 21		12 55	
Halewood d					10 25							11 25							12 25			
Hunts Cross 89 d					10 28							11 28							12 28			
Liverpool South Parkway 7 91, 103 ✈ a					10 33		11 04					11 33		12 04					12 33		13 04	
Liverpool Central 10 103 a					10c53		11 38					11c53		12 38					12c53		13 38	
West Allerton 91 a					10 36							11 36							12 36			
Mossley Hill 91 a					10 39		11 08					11 39		12 08					12 39		13 08	
Edge Hill 90, 91 a					10 45							11 45							12 45			
Liverpool Lime Street 10 90, 91 a	10 27		10 39		10 51	10 57	11 20	11 29			11 39	11 51	11 57	12 20	12 29			12 39	12 51	12 57	13 20	13 27

For general notes see front of timetable
For details of catering facilities see Directory of Train Operators

A From Nottingham (Table 49)
B From Hull (Table 39)
C From Newcastle (Table 39)
D From Scarborough (Table 39)
E From Norwich (Table 49)
G From Cambridge (Table 49)
b Change at Manchester Piccadilly
c Change at Hunts Cross

Table 89

Manchester Airport and Manchester → Warrington Central → Liverpool

Network Diagram - see first page of Table 88

	NT		NT	NT	TP	NT	EM		NT	NT	NT	TP	NT		EM	NT	NT	NT	TP		NT	EM
					1 ◇ A		◇ B					1 ◇ A			◇ B				1 ◇ A			◇ B
Manchester Airport 85 ✈ d			12 31		12 34		13b07			13 31		13 34			14b07		14 31		14 34			15b07
Sheffield 7 78 d							12 42								13 42				13 42			14 42
Stockport 84 d					12 39		13 25					13 39			14 25				14 39			15 24
Manchester Piccadilly 10 78, 84, 85 d			12 49		13 07		13 37			13 49		14 07			14 37		14 49		15 07			15 37
Manchester Oxford Road 84, 85 d	12 43		12 52		13 10	13 13	13 41		13 43	13 52		14 10	14 13		14 41	14 43	14 52		15 10		15 13	15 41
Deansgate 84, 85 d	12 45					13 15			13 45				14 15			14 45					15 15	
Trafford Park d						13 20															15 20	
Humphrey Park d						13 22															15 22	
Urmston d	12 52					13 24			13 52				14 21			14 52					15 24	
Chassen Road d													14 23									
Flixton d						13 27							14 26								15 27	
Irlam d	12 57					13 31			13 57				14 30			14 57					15 31	
Glazebrook d													14 33									
Birchwood d	13 02				13 24	13 37			14 02			14 24	14 37			15 02			15 24		15 37	
Padgate d						13 40							14 40								15 40	
Warrington Central a	13 07			←	13 28	13 43	13 57		14 07		←	14 28	14 44		14 57	15 07		←	15 28		15 44	15 57
d	13 08 →			13 08	13 29	13 44	13 57		14 08 →		14 08	14 29	14 44		14 57	15 08 →		15 08	15 29		15 44	15 57
Sankey for Penketh d				13 12							14 12							15 12				
Widnes d				13 17		13 52	14 05				14 17		14 52		15 05			15 17			15 52	16 05
Hough Green d				13 21		13 55					14 21		14 55					15 21			15 55	
Halewood d				13 25							14 25							15 25			15 59	
Hunts Cross d				13 28							14 28							15 28				
Liverpool South Parkway 7 91, 103 ✈ a				13 33		14 04					14 33		15 04					15 33			16 06	
Liverpool Central 10 103 a				13c53		14 38					14c53		15 38					15c53			16 38	
West Allerton 91 a				13 36							14 36							15 36				
Mossley Hill 91 a				13 39		14 08					14 39		15 08					15 39			16 10	
Edge Hill 90, 91 a				13 45							14 45							15 45				
Liverpool Lime Street 10 90, 91 a			13 39	13 51	13 57	14 20	14 27			14 39	14 51	14 57	15 19		15 25		15 39	15 51	15 57		16 22	16 29

	NT	NT	NT	TP	NT		EM	NT	NT	NT	TP		NT	EM	NT	NT	NT		TP	NT	NT	EM
				1 ◇ A			◇ B				1 ◇ A			◇ B					1 ◇ A			◇ B
Manchester Airport 85 ✈ d		15 31		15 34			16b07		16 31		16 34			17b04			17 29		17 34			18b10
Sheffield 7 78 d							15 42							16 42								17 42
Stockport 84 d				15 39			16 25				16 43			17 25					17 39			18 26
Manchester Piccadilly 10 78, 84, 85 d		15 49		16 07			16 37		16 48		17 07			17 37			17 45		18 07			18 37
Manchester Oxford Road 84, 85 d	15 43	15 52		16 10	16 13		16 41	16 43	16 52		17 10		17 13	17 41		17 43	17 49		18 10		18 13	18 41
Deansgate 84, 85 d	15 45				16 15			16 45					17 15			17 45					18 15	
Trafford Park d								16 50					17 20			17 50					18 20	
Humphrey Park d													17 22			17 52					18 22	
Urmston d	15 52				16 21			16 54					17 25			17 55					18 24	
Chassen Road d					16 23								17 27			17 57					18 26	
Flixton d					16 26			16 57					17 29			17 59					18 29	
Irlam d	15 57				16 30			17 01					17 33	17 51		18 03					18 33	
Glazebrook d					16 33								17 36			18 06						
Birchwood d	16 02			16 24	16 37			17 06			17 24		17 41	17 57		18 11			18 24		18 38	
Padgate d					16 40			17 09					17 44			18 14						
Warrington Central a	16 07		←	16 28	16 44		16 57	17 13		←	17 28		17 47	18 02		18 18			18 28		18 43	18 57
d	16 08 →		16 08	16 29	16 44		16 57	17 13 →		17 13	17 29		17 48	18 02		18 18			18 29		18 44	18 57
Sankey for Penketh d			16 12							17 17			17 52								18 48	
Widnes d			16 17		16 52		17 05			17 23			17 57	18 10							18 53	19 05
Hough Green d			16 21		16 55					17 26			18 01			18 28					18 57	
Halewood d			16 25							17 30			18 05								19 01	
Hunts Cross 89 d			16 28							17 33	17 40		18 08			18 33					19 04	19 12
Liverpool South Parkway 7 91, 103 ✈ a			16 33		17 04					17 39			18 14			18 38					19 09	
Liverpool Central 10 103 a			16c53		17 38						18 08		18 38			19 08						19 38
West Allerton 91 a			16 36							17 42			18 17		←	18 43				←	19 13	
Mossley Hill 91 a			16 39		17 08					17 44			18 20 →		18 20	18 45 →				18 45	19 15	
Edge Hill 90, 91 a			16 45							17 50					18 27					18 51	19 21	
Liverpool Lime Street 10 90, 91 a		16 39	16 51	16 57	17 24		17 29		17 38	17 58	18 00			18 32	18 35		18 40		18 57	18 59	19 28	19 29

	NT	NT	TP		NT	NT	NT	TP	NT		NT	NT	TP	NT	NT		NT	TP	NT	NT		
			1 ◇ A					1 ◇ A					1 ◇ A					1 ◇ A				
Manchester Airport 85 ✈ d		18 31	18 34			19 12	19 30					20 15	20 22		21e16		21 30			22 47		
Sheffield 7 78 d							18 42						19 42		20 29							
Stockport 84 d			18 39			19 05	19 24	19 40					20 40		21 15			21 39		22 39		
Manchester Piccadilly 10 78, 84, 85 d		18 49	19 07			19 33	19 49	20 07				20 32	21 07		21 42		21 49	22 07		23 11		
Manchester Oxford Road 84, 85 d	18 43	18 52	19 10			19 43	19 52	20 10				20 43	21 10		21 45		21 52	22 10		23 20		
Deansgate 84, 85 d	18 45					19 45						20 45			21 47					23 22		
Trafford Park d	18 50					19 50						20 50			21 52					23 27		
Humphrey Park d	18 52					19 52						20 52			21 54					23 29		
Urmston d	18 55					19 55						20 54			21 57					23 31		
Chassen Road d	18 57					19 57						20 56			21 59					23 33		
Flixton d	18 59					19 59						20 59			22 01					23 36		
Irlam d	19 03					20 03						21 03			22 05					23 40		
Glazebrook d	19 06					20 06						21 06			22 08					23 43		
Birchwood d	19 11		19 24			20 11		20 24				21 10	21 24		22 13			22 24		23 47		
Padgate d	19 14					20 14						21 13			22 16					23 50		
Warrington Central a	19 20		19 28			20 17		20 28				21 20	21 28		22 21			22 28		23 54		
d			19 29		19 40	20 18		20 29			20 40		21 29	21 40				22 29	22 40	23 54		
Sankey for Penketh d					19 44						20 44			21 44					22 44	23 58		
Widnes d					19 49						20 49			21 49					22 49	00 04		
Hough Green d					19 53	20 27					20 53			21 53					22 53	00 07		
Halewood d					19 57						20 57			21 57					22 57			
Hunts Cross 89 d					20 00	20 32					21 00			22 00					23 00	00 12		
Liverpool South Parkway 7 91, 103 ✈ a					20 03	20 38					21 03			22 03					23 03			
Liverpool Central 10 103 a					20c23	21 08					21c23			22c23					23c23			
West Allerton 91 a					20 06	20 41			←		21 06			22 06					23 06			
Mossley Hill 91 a					20 09	20 43 →			20 43		21 09			22 09					23 09			
Edge Hill 90, 91 a					20 14						21 14			22 14					23 14			
Liverpool Lime Street 10 90, 91 a		19 38	19 57		20 21		20 38	20 55	20 57		21 21		21 55	22 22			22 41	22 55	23 21	00 31		

For general notes see front of timetable
For details of catering facilities see Directory of Train Operators

A From Scarborough (Table 39)
B From Norwich (Table 49)
b Change at Manchester Piccadilly
c Change at Hunts Cross
e Change at Manchester Oxford Road

Table 89

Sundays

until 23 March

Manchester Airport and Manchester → Warrington Central → Liverpool

Network Diagram - see first page of Table 88

	NT	NT	NT	TP	NT	NT	NT		NT	EM	TP	NT	NT	EM	EM		TP	NT	NT	EM	EM	TP
				1 ◇						◇	1 ◇			◇	◇		1 ◇			◇	◇	1 ◇
				A						B	C			D	B		E			D	B	G
Manchester Airport 85 ✈ d	07 36	08 47	08 51	09b47		10 01	10 47		11 00	11c05	11b47		12 00				12b46		13 00			13b47
Sheffield 7 78 🚌 d			07e55						09f30	10 26	10g20			10h45	11 40		11g20			11h45	12 40	12g20
Stockport 84 d			08j38	09 29			10 29		10 43	11 22	11 43			12 24	12 24		12 43			13 24	13 24	13 43
Manchester Piccadilly 10 78, 84, 85 🚌 d	07 51	09 03	09 16	10 07		10 16	11 03		11 16	11 37	12 07		12 17	12 37	12 37		13 07		13 17	13 37	13 37	14 07
Manchester Oxford Road 84, 85 d	08 01	09 15	09 20	10 10	10 13	10 20	11 15		11 20	11 40	12 10	12 15	12 20	12 40	12 40		13 10	13 15	13 20	13 40	13 40	14 10
Deansgate 84, 85 🚌 d	08 03	09 17			10 15		11 17					12 17						13 17				
Urmston d	08 09	09 23			10 21		11 23					12 23						13 23				
Irlam d	08 14	09 28			10 26		11 28					12 28						13 28				
Birchwood d	08 20	09 34		10 24	10 32		11 34				12 24	12 34					13 24	13 34				14 24
Warrington Central a	08 25	09 39		10 28	10 37		11 39			11 56	12 28	12 39		12 56	12 56		13 28	13 39		13 56	13 56	14 28
d	08 39	09 39		10 29	10 39		11 39			11 57	12 29	12 39		12 57	12 57		13 29	13 39		13 57	13 57	14 29
Widnes d	08 47	09 47			10 47		11 47			12 05		12 47		13 05	13 05			13 47		14 05	14 05	
Hough Green d	08 51	09 51			10 51		11 51					12 51						13 51				
Halewood d	08 55	09 55			10 55		11 55					12 55						13 55				
Hunts Cross 89 d	08 58	09 58			10 58		11 58					12 58						13 58				
Liverpool South Parkway 7 91, 103 ✈ a	09 03	10 03			11 03		12 03					13 03						14 03				
Liverpool Central 10 103 a	09k23	10k23			11k23		12k23					13k23						14k23				
West Allerton 91 a	09 06	10 06			11 06		12 06					13 06						14 06				
Mossley Hill 91 a	09 09	10 09			11 09		12 09					13 09						14 09				
Liverpool Lime Street 10 90, 91 a	09 20	10 20	10 22	10 58	11 20	11 21	12 20		12 21	12 29	12 57	13 20	13 21	13 31	13 31		13 57	14 20	14 21	14 28	14 28	14 57

	NT	NT	EM		EM	TP	NT	NT	EM	EM	TP		NT	NT	EM	EM	TP	NT	NT		EM	EM
			◇		◇	1 ◇			◇	◇	1 ◇				◇	◇	1 ◇				◇	◇
			D		B	E			D	H	J				D	B	E				D	B
Manchester Airport 85 ✈ d		14 00				14b47		15 00	15c08	15c08	15b47			16 01			16b47		17 01		17c05	17c05
Sheffield 7 78 🚌 d			12h50		13 39	13g20			13h45	14 37	14g20				14h45	15 35	15g20				15h45	16 36
Stockport 84 d			14 22		14 22	14 43			15 22	15 22	15 43				16 22	16 22	16 43				17 22	17 22
Manchester Piccadilly 10 78, 84, 85 🚌 d		14 17	14 37		14 37	15 07		15 16	15 37	15 37	16 07			16 16	16 37	16 37	17 07		17 16		17 37	17 37
Manchester Oxford Road 84, 85 d	14 15	14 20	14 40		14 40	15 10	15 15	15 20	15 40	15 40	16 10		16 15	16 20	16 40	16 40	17 10	17 15	17 20		17 40	17 40
Deansgate 84, 85 🚌 d	14 17						15 17						16 17					17 17				
Urmston d	14 23						15 23						16 23					17 23				
Irlam d	14 28						15 28						16 28					17 28				
Birchwood d	14 34					15 24	15 34				16 24		16 34				17 24	17 34				
Warrington Central a	14 39		14 56		14 56	15 28	15 39		15 56	15 56	16 28		16 39		16 56	16 56	17 28	17 39			17 56	17 56
d	14 39		14 57		14 57	15 29	15 39		15 57	15 57	16 29		16 39		16 57	16 57	17 29	17 39			17 57	17 57
Widnes d	14 47		15 05		15 05		15 47		16 05	16 05			16 47		17 05	17 05		17 47			18 05	18 05
Hough Green d	14 51						15 51						16 51					17 51				
Halewood d	14 55						15 55						16 55					17 55				
Hunts Cross 89 d	14 58						15 58						16 58					17 58				
Liverpool South Parkway 7 91, 103 ✈ a	15 03						16 03						17 03					18 03				
Liverpool Central 10 103 a	15k23						16k23						17k23					18k23				
West Allerton 91 a	15 06						16 06						17 06					18 06				
Mossley Hill 91 a	15 09						16 09						17 09					18 09				
Liverpool Lime Street 10 90, 91 a	15 20	15 21	15 28		15 28	15 57	16 20	16 21	16 29	16 29	16 57		17 20	17 21	17 29	17 29	17 57	18 20	18 21		18 29	18 29

	TP	NT	NT	EM	EM	TP	NT		NT	EM	EM	TP	NT	NT	TP	NT	NT	TP	NT	NT		
	1 ◇			◇	◇	1 ◇				◇	◇	1 ◇			1 ◇			1 ◇				
	J			D	H	E				D	B	J			E			C				
Manchester Airport 85 ✈ d	17b47		18 01			18b47			19 01	19c05	19c05	19b47		20 01	20b47		21 01	21b47		22 01		
Sheffield 7 78 🚌 d	16g20			16h45	17 42	17g20				17h55	18 35	18g20			19m35		20j13	20n35				
Stockport 84 d	17 43			18 24	18 24	18 43				19 22	19 22	19 43			20 43		20j55	21 43				
Manchester Piccadilly 10 78, 84, 85 🚌 d	18 07		18 16	18 37	18 37	19 07			19 16	19 37	19 37	20 07		20 16	21 07		21 16	22 07		22 16		
Manchester Oxford Road 84, 85 d	18 10	18 15	18 20	18 40	18 40	19 11	19 15		19 20	19 40	19 40	20 10	20 15	20 20	21 10	21 15	21 20	22 10	22 15	22 19		
Deansgate 84, 85 🚌 d		18 17					19 17						20 17			21 17			22 17			
Urmston d		18 23					19 23						20 23			21 23			22 23			
Irlam d		18 28					19 28						20 28			21 28			22 28			
Birchwood d	18 24	18 34				19 24	19 34					20 24	20 34		21 24	21 34		22 24	22 34			
Warrington Central a	18 28	18 39		18 57	18 57	19 29	19 39			19 56	19 56	20 28	20 39		21 28	21 39		22 28	22 39			
d	18 29	18 39		18 57	18 57	19 29	19 39			19 56	19 56	20 29	20 39		21 29	21 39		22 29	22 39			
Widnes d		18 47		19 05	19 05		19 47			20 05	20 05		20 47			21 47			22 47			
Hough Green d		18 51					19 51						20 51			21 51			22 51			
Halewood d		18 55					19 55						20 55			21 55			22 55			
Hunts Cross 89 d		18 58					19 58						20 58			21 58			22 58			
Liverpool South Parkway 7 91, 103 ✈ a		19 03					20 03						21 03			22 03			23 03			
Liverpool Central 10 103 a		19k23					20k23						21k23			22k23			23k23			
West Allerton 91 a		19 06					20 06						21 06			22 06			23 06			
Mossley Hill 91 a		19 09					20 09						21 09			22 09			23 09			
Liverpool Lime Street 10 90, 91 a	18 57	19 20	19 21	19 29	19 29	19 57	20 20		20 21	20 29	20 29	20 57	21 20	21 21	21 57	22 20	22 21	23 00	23 20	23 21		

For general notes see front of timetable
For details of catering facilities see Directory of Train Operators

- **A** From Leeds (Table 39)
- **B** From 3 February. From Nottingham (Table 49)
- **C** From Newcastle (Table 39)
- **D** Until 27 January
- **E** From Scarborough (Table 39)
- **G** From York (Table 39)
- **H** From 3 February. From Norwich (Table 49)
- **J** From Middlesbrough (Table 39)
- **b** Change at Manchester Oxford Road
- **c** Change at Manchester Piccadilly
- **e** Until 27 January dep. 0740, by bus
- **f** Until 27 January dep. 0920, by bus
- **g** Until 27 January only. By bus
- **h** By bus
- **j** From 3 February only
- **k** Change at Hunts Cross
- **m** Until 27 January dep. 1920, by bus
- **n** Until 27 January dep. 1945, by bus

Table 89

Sundays

from 30 March

Manchester Airport and Manchester → Warrington Central → Liverpool

Network Diagram - see first page of Table 88

		NT	NT	NT		TP 1 ◇ A	NT	NT		NT	NT	EM ◇ B		TP 1 ◇ C	NT	NT		EM ◇ B	TP 1 ◇ D	NT		NT	EM ◇ B
Manchester Airport	85 ✈ d	07 36	08 47	08 51		09b47		10 01		10 47	11 00	11c05		11b47		12 00			12b46			13 00	
Sheffield 7	78 d			07 55							09 30	10 26						11 40					12 40
Stockport	84 d			08 38		09 29				10 29	10 43	11 22		11 43				12 24	12 43				13 24
Manchester Piccadilly 10	78, 84, 85 d	07 51	09 03	09 16		10 07		10 16		11 03	11 16	11 37		12 07		12 17		12 37	13 07			13 17	13 37
Manchester Oxford Road	84, 85 d	08 01	09 15	09 20		10 10	10 13	10 22		11 15	11 21	11 40		12 10	12 15	12 23		12 40	13 10	13 15		13 23	13 40
Deansgate	84, 85 d	08 03	09 17				10 15			11 17					12 17					13 17			
Urmston	d	08 09	09 23				10 21			11 23					12 23					13 23			
Irlam	d	08 14	09 28				10 26			11 28					12 28					13 28			
Birchwood	d	08 20	09 34			10 24	10 32			11 34				12 24	12 34				13 24	13 34			
Warrington Central	a	08 25	09 39			10 28	10 37			11 39		11 56		12 28	12 39			12 56	13 28	13 39			13 56
	d	08 39	09 39			10 29	10 39			11 39		11 57		12 29	12 39			12 57	13 29	13 39			13 57
Widnes	d	08 47	09 47				10 47			11 47		12 05			12 47			13 05		13 47			14 05
Hough Green	d	08 51	09 51				10 51			11 51					12 51					13 51			
Halewood	d	08 55	09 55				10 55			11 55					12 55					13 55			
Hunts Cross	89 d	08 58	09 58				10 58			11 58					12 58					13 58			
Liverpool South Parkway 7	91, 103 ✈ a	09 03	10 03				11 03			12 03					13 03					14 03			
Liverpool Central 10	103 a	09e23	10e23				11e23			12e23					13e23					14e23			
West Allerton	91 a	09 06	10 06				11 06			12 06					13 06					14 06			
Mossley Hill	91 a	09 09	10 09				11 09			12 09					13 09					14 09			
Liverpool Lime Street 10	90, 91 a	09 20	10 20	10 23		10 58	11 20	11 24		12 20	12 22	12 29		12 57	13 20	13 21		13 31	13 57	14 20		14 22	14 28

		TP 1 ◇ E	NT	NT		EM ◇ B	TP 1 ◇ D	NT		NT	EM ◇ G	TP 1 ◇ H		NT	NT	EM ◇ B		TP 1 ◇ D	NT	NT		EM ◇ B	TP 1 ◇ H
Manchester Airport	85 ✈ d	13b47		14 00			14b47			15 00	15c08	15b47			16 01			16b47		17 01		17c05	17b47
Sheffield 7	78 d					13 39					14 37					15 35						16 36	
Stockport	84 d	13 43		13 46		14 22	14 43				15 22	15 43				16 22		16 43				17 22	17 43
Manchester Piccadilly 10	78, 84, 85 d	14 07		14 17		14 37	15 07			15 16	15 37	16 07			16 16	16 37		17 07		17 16		17 37	18 07
Manchester Oxford Road	84, 85 d	14 10	14 15	14 21		14 40	15 10	15 15		15 23	15 40	16 10		16 15	16 23	16 40		17 10	17 15	17 23		17 40	18 10
Deansgate	84, 85 d		14 17					15 17						16 17					17 17				
Urmston	d		14 23					15 23						16 23					17 23				
Irlam	d		14 28					15 28						16 28					17 28				
Birchwood	d	14 24	14 34				15 24	15 34				16 24		16 34				17 24	17 34				18 24
Warrington Central	a	14 28	14 39			14 56	15 28	15 39			15 56	16 28		16 39		16 56		17 28	17 39			17 56	18 28
	d	14 29	14 39			14 57	15 29	15 39			15 57	16 29		16 39		16 57		17 29	17 39			17 57	18 29
Widnes	d		14 47			15 05		15 47			16 05			16 47		17 05			17 47			18 05	
Hough Green	d		14 51					15 51						16 51					17 51				
Halewood	d		14 55					15 55						16 55					17 55				
Hunts Cross	89 d		14 58					15 58						16 58					17 58				
Liverpool South Parkway 7	91, 103 ✈ a		15 03					16 03						17 03					18 03				
Liverpool Central 10	103 a		15e23					16e23						17e23					18e23				
West Allerton	91 a		15 06					16 06						17 06					18 06				
Mossley Hill	91 a		15 09					16 09						17 09					18 09				
Liverpool Lime Street 10	90, 91 a	14 57	15 20	15 26		15 28	15 57	16 20		16 26	16 29	16 57		17 20	17 23	17 29		17 57	18 20	18 23		18 29	18 57

		NT	NT	EM ◇ G		TP 1 ◇ D	NT	NT		EM ◇ B	TP 1 ◇ H	NT		NT	TP 1 ◇ D	NT		NT	TP 1 ◇ C	NT	NT		
Manchester Airport	85 ✈ d		18 01			18b47		19 01		19c05	19b47			20 01	20b47			21 01	21b47		22 01		
Sheffield 7	78 d		16 44	17 42						18 35					19 35			20 13	20 35				
Stockport	84 d		17 47	18 24		18 43				19 22	19 43				20 43			20 55	21 43				
Manchester Piccadilly 10	78, 84, 85 d		18 16	18 37		19 07		19 16		19 37	20 07			20 18	21 07			21 16	22 07		22 16		
Manchester Oxford Road	84, 85 d	18 15	18 23	18 40		19 11	19 15	19 23		19 40	20 10	20 15		20 23	21 10	21 15		21 23	22 10	22 15	22 19		
Deansgate	84, 85 d	18 17					19 17					20 17				21 17				22 17			
Urmston	d	18 23					19 23					20 23				21 23				22 23			
Irlam	d	18 28					19 28					20 28				21 28				22 28			
Birchwood	d	18 34				19 24	19 34				20 24	20 34			21 24	21 34			22 24	22 34			
Warrington Central	a	18 39		18 57		19 29	19 39			19 56	20 28	20 39			21 28	21 39			22 28	22 39			
	d	18 39		18 57		19 29	19 39			19 56	20 29	20 39			21 29	21 39			22 29	22 39			
Widnes	d	18 47		19 05			19 47			20 05		20 47				21 47				22 47			
Hough Green	d	18 51					19 51					20 51				21 51				22 51			
Halewood	d	18 55					19 55					20 55				21 55				22 55			
Hunts Cross	89 d	18 58					19 58					20 58				21 58				22 58			
Liverpool South Parkway 7	91, 103 ✈ a	19 03					20 03					21 03				22 03				23 03			
Liverpool Central 10	103 a	19e23					20e23					21e23				22e23				23e23			
West Allerton	91 a	19 06					20 06					21 06				22 06				23 06			
Mossley Hill	91 a	19 09					20 09					21 09				22 09				23 09			
Liverpool Lime Street 10	90, 91 a	19 20	19 28	19 29		19 57	20 20	20 26		20 29	20 57	21 20		21 27	21 57	22 20		22 25	23 00	23 20	23 23		

For general notes see front of timetable
For details of catering facilities see Directory of Train Operators

A From Leeds (Table 39)
B From Nottingham (Table 49)
C From Newcastle (Table 39)
D From Scarborough (Table 39)
E From York (Table 39)
G From Norwich (Table 49)
H From Middlesbrough (Table 39)
b Change at Manchester Oxford Road
c Change at Manchester Piccadilly
e Change at Hunts Cross

Liverpool and St Helens → Newton-le-Willows, Wigan, Preston and Manchester

Network Diagram - see first page of Table 88

Miles	Miles	Miles	Miles	Station			NT	NT	NT	NT	NT	NT	NT	NT	NT	AW	NT	NT	NT	NT	AW	NT	NT	AW	NT	NT
															B	C			B		C		D	◇ E		
0	0	0	—	**Liverpool Lime Street 10**	89, 91	d	03b38	05 18	05 34	05 47	06 04	06 14	06 18	06 34	06 39		07 04	07 14	07 18	07 30		07 34	07 47		08 04	08 14
1¾	1¾	1¾	—	Edge Hill	89, 91	d				05 51			06 22	06 38					07 22				07 51			
2½	2½	2½	—	Wavertree Technology Park		d			05 40	05 54	06 09	06 19	06 24	06 40	06 45		07 10	07 19	07 24			07 40	07 53		08 10	08 19
3½	3½	3½	—	Broad Green		d			05 43	05 57	06 12		06 27	06 43	06 48		07 13		07 27			07 43	07 56		08 13	
5	5	5	—	Roby		d			05 46	06 01	06 16		06 31	06 46	06 51		07 16		07 31			07 46	08 00		08 16	
5½	5½	5½	—	Huyton		d			05 49	06 03	06 18		06 33	06 49	06 53		07 18		07 33	07 39		07 49	08 02		08 19	
—	7¾	—	—	Prescot		d			05 53		06 22			06 53			07 23					07 53			08 23	
—	8¾	—	—	Eccleston Park		d			05 56		06 25			06 56			07 25					07 56			08 26	
—	9¾	—	—	Thatto Heath		d			05 58		06 27			06 58			07 28					07 58			08 28	
—	11¼	—	—	**St Helens Central**		a			06 02		06 31			07 02			07 31			07 47		08 02			08 32	
—	—	—	—			d			06 02		06 31			07 02			07 32			07 48		08 02			08 32	
—	15	—	—	Garswood		d			06 09		06 38			07 09			07 39					08 09			08 39	
—	16¼	—	—	Bryn		d			06 12		06 41			07 12			07 42					08 12			08 42	
7½	—	7½	—	Whiston		d				06 06			06 36		06 57				07 36				08 05			
9	—	9	—	Rainhill		d				06 09			06 39		07 00				07 39				08 08			
10¾	—	10¾	—	Lea Green		d				06 13			06 43		07 03			07 29	07 43				08 12			
12	—	12	—	**St Helens Junction**		d		05 32		06 16		06 30	06 46		07 06			07 32	07 46				08 15			08 30
—	—	—	—	Warrington Bank Quay		d									*07 48*	07 16					07 54		*08 48*	08 21		
14¾	—	14¾	—	Earlestown 8		d				06 20			06 51		07 11	07 23			07 50		08 01		08 19	08 29		
—	—	—	—	Warrington Bank Quay		a							07 02													
16¼	—	16¼	0	**Newton-le-Willows**		d		05 38		06 23		06 38			07 14	07 26		07 38	07 53		08 04		08 22	08 32		08 36
—	20	23¼	—	**Wigan North Western**		a			06 23		06 52			07 23			07 53			08 01		08 23			08 53	
—	—	—	—		65	d											07 56			08 02						
—	28¼	31½	—	Euxton Balshaw Lane		d														08 12						
—	31	34¼	—	Leyland	82	a														08 17						
—	35	38¼	—	**Preston 8**	65, 82	a					*07 17*									08 24					*09 14*	
—	52½	—	—	Blackpool North	97	a					*07c56*									08 51					*09c57*	
26¾	—	—	10½	Patricroft		d				06 35									08 05				08 34			
27¾	—	—	11½	Eccles		d				06 38					07 26				08 08				08 37			
31¾	—	—	—	**Manchester Victoria**		a				06 50					07 37		08e40		08 18				08 48			
—	—	—	15¾	**Manchester Oxford Road**		a						06 58				07 45		08 01			08 31			08 52		08 58
—	—	—	16¼	**Manchester Piccadilly 10**		a	04 14	06 03				07 03				07 54		08 06			08 40			09 02		09 02
—	—	—	26	**Manchester Airport**	85	a	04 30	06 19				07 20						08 25								09 25

Station			NT	NT	NT	NT	AW	NT	NT	NT	NT	NT	NT	AW	NT	NT	NT	NT	NT	NT	NT	AW	NT		NT	NT
				G		D	◇ H						D	◇ H						D		◇ H				
Liverpool Lime Street 10	89, 91	d	08 18	08 28	08 34	08 48		08 57	09 04	09 14	09 18	09 34	09 48		09 57	10 04	10 14	10 18	10 34	10 48	10 57		11 04		11 14	11 18
Edge Hill	89, 91	d	08 22			08 52					09 22		09 52					10 22		10 52						11 22
Wavertree Technology Park		d	08 24		08 40	08 54			09 10	09 19	09 24	09 40	09 54			10 10	10 19	10 24	10 40	10 54			11 10		11 19	11 24
Broad Green		d	08 27		08 43	08 57			09 13		09 27	09 43	09 57			10 13		10 27	10 43	10 57			11 13			11 27
Roby		d	08 31		08 46	09 01			09 16		09 31	09 46	10 01			10 16		10 31	10 46	11 01			11 16			11 31
Huyton		d	08 33	08 37	08 49	09 03		09 08	09 19		09 33	09 49	10 03		10 08	10 19		10 33	10 49	11 03	11 07		11 19			11 33
Prescot		d			08 53				09 23			09 53				10 23			10 53				11 23			
Eccleston Park		d			08 56				09 25			09 56				10 26			10 56				11 26			
Thatto Heath		d			08 58				09 28			09 58				10 28			10 58				11 28			
St Helens Central		a		08 45	09 02			09 16	09 31			10 02			10 16	10 32			11 02		11 16		11 32			
		d		08 53	09 02			09 17	09 32			10 02			10 17	10 32			11 02		11 16		11 32			
Garswood		d			09 09				09 39			10 09				10 39			11 09				11 39			
Bryn		d			09 12				09 42			10 12				10 42			11 12				11 42			
Whiston		d	08 36			09 06					09 36		10 06					10 36		11 06						11 36
Rainhill		d	08 39			09 09					09 39		10 09					10 39		11 09						11 39
Lea Green		d	08 43			09 13					09 43		10 13					10 43		11 13						11 43
St Helens Junction		d	08 46			09 16				09 30	09 46		10 16				10 30	10 46		11 16					11 30	11 46
Warrington Bank Quay		d					09 20							10 20								11 20				
Earlestown 8		d	08 51			09 20	09 28				09 51		10 20	10 28				10 51		11 20		11 28				11 51
Warrington Bank Quay		a	09 02			*09 49*					10 02		*10 49*					11 02		*11 49*						12 02
Newton-le-Willows		d				09 23	09 31			09 36			10 23	10 31			10 36			11 23		11 31			11 36	
Wigan North Western		a		09 12	09 23			09 30	09 53			10 23			10 31	10 53			11 23		11 30		11 53			
	65	d		09 13				09 31							10 31						11 30					
Euxton Balshaw Lane		d		09 23				09 42							10 42						11 41					
Leyland	82	a		09 28				09 47							10 47						11 46					
Preston 8	65, 82	a		09 38				09 54	*10 14*						10 54	*11 15*					11 53		*12 15*			
Blackpool North	97	a						10 21	*10c57*						11 21	*11c54*					12 20		*12c54*			
Patricroft		d				09 35							10 35							11 35						
Eccles		d				09 38							10 38							11 38						
Manchester Victoria		a				09 48							10 48							11 48						
Manchester Oxford Road		a					09 50			09 58				10 50			10 57					11 50			11 57	
Manchester Piccadilly 10		a					09 58			10 02				10 58			11 02					11 58			12 02	
Manchester Airport	85	a								10 25							11 25								12 25	

For general notes see front of timetable
For details of catering facilities see Directory of Train Operators

- **B** To Huddersfield (Table 39)
- **C** From Chester (Table 81)
- **D** To Stalybridge (Table 39)
- **E** From Holyhead (Table 81)
- **G** To Morecambe (Table 98)
- **H** From Llandudno (Table 81)
- **b** Mondays from 31 March dep. 0330
- **c** Change at Wigan North Western and Preston
- **e** Via Bolton (Table 82)

Liverpool and St Helens → Newton-le-Willows, Wigan, Preston and Manchester

Network Diagram - see first page of Table 88

		NT	NT	AW	NT	NT	NT	NT	NT	NT	AW	NT	NT	NT	NT	NT	NT	AW	NT	NT	NT	NT	NT	NT	AW
			A	◇ B						A	◇ B						A	◇ B				C		A	◇ B
Liverpool Lime Street 10	89, 91 d	11 34	11 48		11 57	12 04	12 14	12 18	12 34	12 48		12 57	13 04	13 14	13 18	13 34	13 48		13 57	14 04	14 14	14 18	14 34	14 48	
Edge Hill	89, 91 d		11 52					12 22		12 52					13 22		13 52					14 22		14 52	
Wavertree Technology Park	d	11 40	11 54			12 10	12 19	12 24	12 40	12 54			13 10	13 19	13 24	13 40	13 54			14 10	14 19	14 24	14 40	14 54	
Broad Green	d	11 43	11 57			12 13		12 27	12 43	12 57			13 13		13 27	13 43	13 57			14 13		14 27	14 43	14 57	
Roby	d	11 46	12 01			12 16		12 31	12 46	13 01			13 16		13 31	13 46	14 01			14 16		14 31	14 46	15 01	
Huyton	d	11 49	12 03		12 08	12 19		12 33	12 49	13 03		13 08	13 18		13 33	13 49	14 03		14 08	14 19		14 33	14 49	15 03	
Prescot	d	11 53				12 23			12 53				13 23			13 53				14 23			14 53		
Eccleston Park	d	11 56				12 26			12 56				13 25			13 56				14 26			14 56		
Thatto Heath	d	11 58				12 28			12 58				13 28			13 58				14 28			14 58		
St Helens Central	a	12 02			12 16	12 32			13 02			13 16	13 31			14 02			14 16	14 32			15 02		
	d	12 02			12 17	12 32			13 02			13 17	13 32			14 02			14 17	14 32			15 02		
Garswood	d	12 09				12 39			13 09				13 39			14 09				14 39			15 09		
Bryn	d	12 12				12 42			13 12				13 42			14 12				14 42			15 12		
Whiston	d		12 06					12 36		13 06					13 36		14 06					14 36		15 06	
Rainhill	d		12 09					12 39		13 09					13 39		14 09					14 39		15 09	
Lea Green	d		12 13					12 43		13 13					13 43		14 13					14 43		15 13	
St Helens Junction	d		12 16				12 30	12 46		13 16				13 30	13 46		14 16				14 30	14 46		15 16	
Warrington Bank Quay	d			12 20							13 20							14 20							15 20
Earlestown 8	d		12 20	12 28				12 51		13 20	13 28				13 51		14 20	14 27				14 51		15 20	15 28
Warrington Bank Quay	a		*12 49*					13 02		*13 49*					14 02		*14 49*					15 02		*15 50*	
Newton-le-Willows	d		12 23	12 31			12 36			13 23	13 31			13 36			14 23	14 30			14 36			15 23	15 31
Wigan North Western	a	12 23			12 31	12 53			13 23			13 31	13 53			14 23			14 31	14 53			15 23		
	65 d				12 31							13 31							14 31						
Euxton Balshaw Lane	d				12 42							13 42							14 42						
Leyland	82 a				12 47							13 47							14 47						
Preston 8	65, 82 a				12 56	*13 15*						13 54	*14 15*						14 54	*15 15*					
Blackpool North	97 a				13 21	*13b54*						14 21	*14b54*						15 21	*15b54*					
Patricroft	d		12 35							13 35							14 35							15 35	
Eccles	d		12 38							13 38							14 38							15 38	
Manchester Victoria	a		12 48							13 48							14 48							15 48	
Manchester Oxford Road	a			12 50			12 57				13 50			13 57				14 50			14 57				15 50
Manchester Piccadilly 10	a			12 58			13 02				13 58			14 02				14 58			15 02				15 58
Manchester Airport	85 a						13 25							14 25							15 25				

		NT	NT	NT	AW	NT	NT	NT	AW	NT	NT	NT	NT	NT	NT	NT	AW	NT	NT	NT	NT	NT	NT	NT	NT
					◇ D			E	◇ B	G			E			E	◇ B			H			J		
Liverpool Lime Street 10	89, 91 d	14 57	15 04	15 14		15 18	15 34	15 48		15 57	16 04	16 14	16 18	16 30	16 34	16 48		17 02	17 09	17 12	17 20	17 25	17 35	17 45	17 50
Edge Hill	89, 91 d					15 22		15 52					16 22			16 52				17 16			17 39		17 54
Wavertree Technology Park	d		15 10	15 19		15 24	15 40	15 54			16 10	16 19	16 24		16 40	16 54		17 08	17 14	17 18		17 30	17 41	17 50	17 56
Broad Green	d		15 13			15 27	15 43	15 57			16 13		16 27		16 43	16 57		17 11		17 21		17 33	17 44	17 53	17 59
Roby	d		15 16			15 31	15 46	16 01			16 16		16 31		16 46	17 01		17 14		17 25		17 37	17 48		18 03
Huyton	d	15 08	15 19			15 33	15 49	16 03		16 08	16 19		16 33	16 39	16 49	17 03		17 16	17 20	17 27	17 30	17 39	17 50	17 58	18 05
Prescot	d		15 23				15 53				16 23				16 53			17 21				17 44		18 02	
Eccleston Park	d		15 26				15 56				16 26				16 56			17 23				17 46		18 05	
Thatto Heath	d		15 28				15 58				16 28				16 58			17 26				17 49		18 07	
St Helens Central	a	15 16	15 32				16 02			16 16	16 32			16 47	17 02			17 29			17 39	17 52		18 11	
	d	15 17	15 32				16 02			16 17	16 32			16 52	17 02			17 30			17 39	17 53		18 11	
Garswood	d		15 39				16 09				16 39				17 09			17 37				18 00		18 18	
Bryn	d		15 42				16 12				16 42				17 12			17 40				18 03		18 21	
Whiston	d					15 36		16 06					16 36			17 06				17 30			17 53		18 09
Rainhill	d					15 39		16 09					16 39			17 09				17 33			17 56		18 12
Lea Green	d					15 43		16 13					16 43			17 13			17 27	17 37			18 00		18 15
St Helens Junction	d			15 30		15 46		16 16				16 30	16 46			17 16			17 30	17 40			18 03		18 18
Warrington Bank Quay	d				15 33				16 20								17 20								
Earlestown 8	d				15 44	15 51		16 20	16 27				16 50			17 20	17 27			17 44			18 07		18 23
Warrington Bank Quay	a					16 02		*16 48*								*17 55*				*18 17*					*18 48*
Newton-le-Willows	d			15 36	15 47			16 23	16 30			16 36	16 53			17 23	17 30		17 36	17 47			18 10		18 26
Wigan North Western	a	15 31	15 53				16 23			16 31	16 53			17 09	17 23			17 50			17 54	18 13		18 28	
	65 d	15 31								16 31				17 10							17 54			18 28	
Euxton Balshaw Lane	d	15 42								16 42				17 20							18 05			18 39	
Leyland	82 a	15 47								16 47				17 25							18 09			18 44	
Preston 8	65, 82 a	15 54	*16 15*							16 54	*17 15*			17 40				*18 15*			18 17			18 54	
Blackpool North	97 a	16 21	*16b54*							*17 34*	*17b58*			*18 22*							18 48			19 23	
Patricroft	d							16 35					17 05			17 35				17 59			18 22		
Eccles	d							16 38					17 08			17 38				18 02			18 25		
Manchester Victoria	a							16 48					17 21			17 49				18 12			18 40		18 51
Manchester Oxford Road	a			15 57	16 13				16 50			16 57					17 51		17 58						
Manchester Piccadilly 10	a			16 01	16 21				16 58			17 02					17 59		18 04						
Manchester Airport	85 a			16 25								17 25							18 27						

For general notes see front of timetable
For details of catering facilities see Directory of Train Operators

- **A** To Stalybridge (Table 39)
- **B** From Llandudno (Table 81)
- **C** To Ellesmere Port (Table 109)
- **D** From Holyhead (Table 81)
- **E** To Huddersfield (Table 39)
- **G** To Barrow-in-Furness (Table 82)
- **H** To Rochdale (Table 95)
- **J** To Todmorden (Table 41)
- **b** Change at Wigan North Western and Preston

Liverpool and St Helens → Newton-le-Willows, Wigan, Preston and Manchester

Network Diagram - see first page of Table 88

Mondays to Fridays

Station		AW ◇ A 🛒	NT	NT	NT	NT	NT	AW ◇ A 🛒	NT	NT	AW ◇ A	NT	NT	NT	AW B	NT	NT	AW ◇ A	NT	NT	NT	NT	AW B
Liverpool Lime Street 10	89, 91 d		18 04	18 14	18 18	18 34	18 48		19 04	19 18		19 48	20 14	20 18		20 48	21 18		21 48	22 18	23 05	23 18	
Edge Hill	89, 91 d				18 22		18 52			19 22		19 52		20 22		20 52	21 22		21 52	22 22	23 09	23 22	
Wavertree Technology Park	d		18 10	18 19	18 24	18 40	18 54		19 10	19 24		19 54	20 19	20 24		20 54	21 24		21 54	22 24	23 11	23 24	
Broad Green	d		18 13		18 27	18 43	18 57		19 13	19 27		19 57		20 27		20 57	21 27		21 57	22 27	23 14	23 27	
Roby	d		18 16		18 31	18 46	19 01		19 16	19 31		20 01		20 31		21 01	21 31		22 01	22 31	23 17	23 31	
Huyton	d		18 19		18 33	18 49	19 03		19 19	19 33		20 03		20 33		21 03	21 33		22 03	22 33	23 20	23 33	
Prescot	d		18 23			18 53			19 23			20 08				21 08			22 08		23 24		
Eccleston Park	d		18 26			18 56			19 26			20 10				21 10			22 10		23 27		
Thatto Heath	d		18 28			18 58			19 28			20 13				21 13			22 13		23 29		
St Helens Central	a		18 32			19 02			19 32			20 16				21 16			22 16		23 33		
	d		18 32			19 02			19 32			20 17				21 17			22 17		23 34		
Garswood	d		18 39			19 09			19 39			20 24				21 24			22 24		23 41		
Bryn	d		18 42			19 12			19 42			20 27				21 27			22 27		23 44		
Whiston	d				18 36		19 06			19 36				20 36			21 36			22 36		23 36	
Rainhill	d			18 28	18 39		19 09			19 39				20 39			21 39			22 39		23 39	
Lea Green	d				18 43		19 13			19 43				20 43			21 43			22 43		23 43	
St Helens Junction	d			18 32	18 46		19 16			19 46			20 30	20 46			21 46			22 46		23 46	
Warrington Bank Quay	d	18 20						19 20			20 20				21 23			22 21					23 50
Earlestown 8	d	18 27			18 51		19 20	19 27		19 50	20 27			20 50	21 30		21 50	22 32		22 50		23 50	23 57
Warrington Bank Quay	a				19 02		*19 48*			*20 48*				*21 49*			*22 48*			*23 52*			
Newton-le-Willows	d	18 30		18 38			19 23	19 30		19 53	20 30		20 36	20 53	21 33		21 53	22 35		22 53		23 53	23 59
Wigan North Western	a		18 51			19 23			19 51			20 40				21 37			22 37		23 51		
	65 d		18 51						19 51										22 38		23 51		
Euxton Balshaw Lane	d		19 02						20 02										22 49		00 01		
Leyland	82 a		19 07						20 07										22 54		00 06		
Preston 8	65, 82 a		19 17			*20 13*			20 17			*21 15*				*22 21*			23 02		00 15		
Blackpool North	97 a		*19 57*						*20 56*			*21b56*							23 28				
Patricroft	d						19 35			20 05				21 05			22 05			23 05		00 05	
Eccles	d						19 38			20 08				21 08			22 08			23 08		00 08	
Manchester Victoria	🚢 a						19 50			20 20				21 20			22 21			23 22		00 20	
Manchester Oxford Road	a	18 51		18 59				19 50			20 51		20 59		21 54			22 55					
Manchester Piccadilly 10	🚢 a	19 01		19 05				19 59			21 00		21 05		22 01			23 05					00 27
Manchester Airport	85 ✈ a			19 26									21 28										

Saturdays

Station		NT	NT	NT	NT	NT	NT	NT	NT	NT C	AW B 🛒	NT	NT	NT C	NT	AW B 🛒	NT		NT D	AW ◇ E 🛒	NT	NT	NT	NT	NT D
Liverpool Lime Street 10	89, 91 d	03 38	05 18	05 34	05 47	06 04	06 10	06 18	06 34	06 39		07 04	07 14	07 18	07 30		07 34		07 47		08 04	08 14	08 19	08 34	08 48
Edge Hill	89, 91 d				05 51			06 22	06 38					07 22					07 51				08 22		08 52
Wavertree Technology Park	d			05 40	05 54	06 09	06 15	06 24	06 40	06 45		07 10	07 19	07 24			07 40		07 53		08 10	08 19	08 25	08 40	08 54
Broad Green	d			05 43	05 57	06 12		06 27	06 43	06 48		07 13		07 27			07 43		07 56		08 13		08 27	08 43	08 57
Roby	d			05 46	06 01	06 16		06 31	06 46	06 51		07 16		07 31			07 46		08 00		08 16		08 31	08 46	09 01
Huyton	d			05 49	06 03	06 18		06 33	06 49	06 53		07 18		07 33	07 39		07 49		08 02		08 19		08 33	08 49	09 03
Prescot	d			05 53		06 22			06 53			07 23					07 53				08 23			08 53	
Eccleston Park	d			05 56		06 25			06 56			07 25					07 56				08 26			08 56	
Thatto Heath	d			05 58		06 27			06 58			07 28					07 58				08 28			08 58	
St Helens Central	a			06 02		06 31			07 02			07 32			07 47		08 02				08 32			09 02	
	d			06 02		06 31			07 02			07 32			07 48		08 02				08 32			09 02	
Garswood	d			06 09		06 38			07 09			07 39					08 09				08 39			09 09	
Bryn	d			06 12		06 41			07 12			07 42					08 12				08 42			09 12	
Whiston	d				06 06			06 36		06 57				07 36					08 05				08 36		09 06
Rainhill	d				06 09			06 39		07 00				07 39					08 08				08 39		09 09
Lea Green	d				06 13			06 43		07 03			07 29	07 43					08 12				08 43		09 13
St Helens Junction	d		05 32		06 16		06 28	06 46		07 06			07 32	07 46					08 15			08 30	08 46		09 16
Warrington Bank Quay	d										07 16					07 54				08 21					
Earlestown 8	d				06 20			06 51		07 11	07 23			07 50		08 01			08 19	08 29			08 51		09 20
Warrington Bank Quay	a							07 02		*07 48*									*08 48*				09 02		*09 49*
Newton-le-Willows	d		05 38		06 23		06 32			07 14	07 26		07 38	07 53		08 04			08 22	08 32		08 36			09 23
Wigan North Western	a			06 23		06 52			07 23			07 53			08 01		08 23				08 53			09 23	
	65 d											07 56			08 02										
Euxton Balshaw Lane	d														08 12										
Leyland	82 a														08 17										
Preston 8	65, 82 a					*07 18*									08 24						*09c20*				
Blackpool North	97 a					*07b56*									08 51						*09e57*				
Patricroft	d				06 35									08 05					08 34						09 35
Eccles	d				06 38					07 26				08 08					08 37						09 38
Manchester Victoria	🚢 a				06 50					07 38		08f41		08 22					08 48						09 48
Manchester Oxford Road	a						06 57				07 45		08 00			08 31				08 52		08 58			
Manchester Piccadilly 10	🚢 a	04 14	06 03				07 03				07 54		08 06			08 40				09 02		09 02			
Manchester Airport	85 ✈ a	05 30	06 19				07 20						08 25									09 25			

For general notes see front of timetable
For details of catering facilities see Directory of Train Operators

A From Llandudno (Table 81)
B From Chester (Table 81)
C To Huddersfield (Table 39)
D To Stalybridge (Table 39)
E From Holyhead (Table 81)
b Change at Wigan North Western and Preston
c From 29 March arr. 5 minutes later
e Change at Wigan North Western and Preston. From 29 March arr. 1002
f Via Bolton (Table 82)

Table 90

Saturdays

Liverpool and St Helens → Newton-le-Willows, Wigan, Preston and Manchester

Network Diagram - see first page of Table 88

Station		AW ◇ A	NT	NT	NT	NT	NT	NT B	AW ◇ A	NT	NT	NT		NT	NT	NT B	AW ◇ A	NT	NT	NT	NT	NT	NT B	AW ◇ A	NT
Liverpool Lime Street 10	89, 91 d		08 57	09 04	09 14	09 18	09 34	09 48		09 57	10 04	10 14		10 18	10 34	10 48		10 57	11 04	11 14	11 18	11 34	11 48		11 57
Edge Hill	89, 91 d					09 22		09 52						10 22		10 52					11 22		11 52		
Wavertree Technology Park	d			09 10	09 19	09 24	09 40	09 54			10 10	10 19		10 24	10 40	10 54			11 10	11 19	11 24	11 40	11 54		
Broad Green	d			09 13		09 27	09 43	09 57			10 13			10 27	10 43	10 57			11 13		11 27	11 43	11 57		
Roby	d			09 16		09 31	09 46	10 01			10 16			10 31	10 46	11 01			11 16		11 31	11 46	12 01		
Huyton	d		09 08	09 19		09 33	09 49	10 03		10 08	10 19			10 33	10 49	11 03		11 07	11 19		11 33	11 49	12 03		12 08
Prescot	d			09 23			09 53				10 23				10 53				11 23			11 53			
Eccleston Park	d			09 25			09 56				10 26				10 56				11 26			11 56			
Thatto Heath	d			09 28			09 58				10 28				10 58				11 28			11 58			
St Helens Central	a		09 16	09 31			10 02			10 16	10 32				11 02			11 16	11 32			12 02			12 16
	d		09 17	09 32			10 02			10 17	10 32				11 02			11 16	11 32			12 02			12 17
Garswood	d			09 39			10 09				10 39				11 09				11 39			12 09			
Bryn	d			09 42			10 12				10 42				11 12				11 42			12 12			
Whiston	d					09 36		10 06						10 36		11 06					11 36		12 06		
Rainhill	d					09 39		10 09						10 39		11 09					11 39		12 09		
Lea Green	d					09 43		10 13						10 43		11 13					11 43		12 13		
St Helens Junction	d				09 30	09 46		10 16				10 30		10 46		11 16				11 30	11 46		12 16		
Warrington Bank Quay	d	09 20							10 20								11 20							12 20	
Earlestown 8	d	09 28				09 51		10 20	10 27					10 51		11 20	11 27				11 51		12 20	12 28	
Warrington Bank Quay	a					10 02		*10 49*						11 02		*11 49*					12 02		*12 49*		
Newton-le-Willows	d	09 31			09 36			10 23	10 30			10 36				11 23	11 30			11 36			12 23	12 31	
Wigan North Western	a		09 30	09 53			10 23			10 31	10 53				11 23			11 30	11 53			12 23			12 31
	65 d		09 31							10 31								11 30							12 31
Euxton Balshaw Lane	d		09 42							10 42								11 41							12 42
Leyland	82 a		09 47							10 47								11 46							12 47
Preston 8	65, 82 a		09 54	*10 26*						10 55	*11b22*							11 53	*12 24*						12 56
Blackpool North	97 a		10 21							11 23	*12c01*							12 20	*13c01*						13 21
Patricroft	d							10 35								11 35							12 35		
Eccles	d							10 38								11 38							12 38		
Manchester Victoria	a							10 48								11 48							12 48		
Manchester Oxford Road	a	09 50			09 58				10 50			10 57					11 50			11 57				12 50	
Manchester Piccadilly 10	a	09 58			10 02				10 58			11 02					11 58			12 02				12 58	
Manchester Airport	85 ✈ a				10 25							11 25								12 25					

Station		NT	NT	NT	NT	NT B	AW ◇ A		NT	NT	NT	NT	NT	NT B	AW ◇ A	NT	NT	NT	NT C	NT	NT B	AW ◇ A	NT	NT	NT
Liverpool Lime Street 10	89, 91 d	12 04	12 14	12 18	12 34	12 48			12 57	13 04	13 14	13 18	13 34	13 48		13 57	14 04	14 14	14 18	14 34	14 48		14 57	15 04	15 14
Edge Hill	89, 91 d			12 22		12 52						13 22		13 52					14 22		14 52				
Wavertree Technology Park	d	12 10	12 19	12 24	12 40	12 54				13 10	13 19	13 24	13 40	13 54			14 10	14 19	14 24	14 40	14 54			15 10	15 19
Broad Green	d	12 13		12 27	12 43	12 57				13 13		13 27	13 43	13 57			14 13		14 27	14 43	14 57			15 13	
Roby	d	12 16		12 31	12 46	13 01				13 17		13 31	13 46	14 01			14 16		14 31	14 46	15 01			15 16	
Huyton	d	12 19		12 33	12 49	13 03			13 08	13 19		13 33	13 49	14 03		14 08	14 19		14 33	14 49	15 03		15 08	15 19	
Prescot	d	12 23			12 53					13 23			13 53				14 23			14 53				15 23	
Eccleston Park	d	12 26			12 56					13 26			13 56				14 26			14 56				15 26	
Thatto Heath	d	12 28			12 58					13 28			13 58				14 28			14 58				15 28	
St Helens Central	a	12 32			13 02				13 16	13 32			14 02			14 16	14 31			15 02			15 16	15 32	
	d	12 32			13 02				13 17	13 32			14 02			14 17	14 32			15 02			15 17	15 32	
Garswood	d	12 39			13 09					13 39			14 09				14 39			15 09				15 39	
Bryn	d	12 42			13 12					13 42			14 12				14 42			15 12				15 42	
Whiston	d			12 36		13 06						13 36		14 06					14 36		15 06				
Rainhill	d			12 39		13 09						13 39		14 09					14 39		15 09				
Lea Green	d			12 43		13 13						13 43		14 13					14 43		15 13				
St Helens Junction	d		12 30	12 46		13 16					13 30	13 46		14 16				14 30	14 46		15 16				15 30
Warrington Bank Quay	d						13 20								14 20							15 20			
Earlestown 8	d			12 51		13 20	13 28					13 51		14 20	14 28				14 51		15 20	15 28			
Warrington Bank Quay	a			13 02		*13 49*						14 02		*14 49*					15 02		*15 49*				
Newton-le-Willows	d		12 36			13 23	13 31				13 36			14 23	14 31			14 36			15 23	15 31			15 36
Wigan North Western	a	12 53			13 23				13 31	13 53			14 23			14 31	14 53			15 23			15 31	15 53	
	65 d								13 31							14 31							15 31		
Euxton Balshaw Lane	d								13 42							14 42							15 42		
Leyland	82 a								13 47							14 47							15 47		
Preston 8	65, 82 a	*13 26*							13 54	*14e23*						14 54	*15f22*						15 54	*16b22*	
Blackpool North	97 a	*14c00*							14 21	*15g01*						15 21	*16c01*						16 21	*17c01*	
Patricroft	d					13 35								14 35							15 35				
Eccles	d					13 38								14 38							15 38				
Manchester Victoria	a					13 48								14 48							15 48				
Manchester Oxford Road	a		12 57				13 50				13 57				14 50			14 57				15 50			15 57
Manchester Piccadilly 10	a		13 02				13 58				14 02				14 58			15 02				15 58			16 01
Manchester Airport	85 ✈ a		13 25								14 25							15 25							16 25

For general notes see front of timetable
For details of catering facilities see Directory of Train Operators

- **A** From Llandudno (Table 81)
- **B** To Stalybridge (Table 39)
- **C** To Ellesmere Port (Table 109)
- **b** From 29 March arr. 3 minutes later
- **c** Change at Wigan North Western and Preston
- **e** From 29 March arr. 5 minutes later
- **f** From 29 March arr. 4 minutes later
- **g** Until 22 March only. Change at Wigan North We stern and Preston

Table 90

Liverpool and St Helens → Newton-le-Willows, Wigan, Preston and Manchester

Network Diagram - see first page of Table 88

		AW		NT	NT	NT	AW	NT	NT	NT	NT	NT	NT	NT	NT	AW	NT	NT	NT		NT	NT	NT	NT	NT
		A				B	◇ C	D	E			G			B	◇ C			H				J		
Liverpool Lime Street [10]	89, 91 d			15 18	15 34	15 48		15 57	15 57	16 04	16 14	16 18	16 30	16 34	16 48		17 02	17 09	17 12		17 20	17 25	17 35	17 45	17 48
Edge Hill	89, 91 d			15 22		15 52						16 22			16 52				17 16				17 39		17 52
Wavertree Technology Park	d			15 24	15 40	15 54				16 10	16 19	16 24		16 40	16 54		17 08	17 14	17 18			17 30	17 41	17 50	17 54
Broad Green	d			15 27	15 43	15 57				16 13		16 27		16 43	16 57		17 11		17 21			17 33	17 44	17 53	17 57
Roby	d			15 31	15 46	16 01				16 16		16 31		16 46	17 01		17 14		17 25			17 37	17 48		18 01
Huyton	d			15 33	15 49	16 03		16 08	16 08	16 19		16 33	16 39	16 49	17 03		17 16	17 20	17 27		17 30	17 39	17 50	17 57	18 03
Prescot	d				15 53					16 23				16 53			17 21					17 44		18 02	
Eccleston Park	d				15 56					16 26				16 56			17 23					17 46		18 04	
Thatto Heath	d				15 58					16 28				16 58			17 26					17 49		18 07	
St Helens Central	a				16 02			16 16	16 16	16 32			16 47	17 02			17 29				17 39	17 52		18 10	
	d				16 02			16 17	16 17	16 32			16 55	17 02			17 30				17 39	17 53		18 11	
Garswood	d				16 09					16 39				17 09			17 37					18 00		18 18	
Bryn	d				16 12					16 42				17 12			17 40					18 03		18 21	
Whiston	d			15 36		16 06						16 36			17 06				17 30				17 53		18 06
Rainhill	d			15 39		16 09						16 39			17 09				17 33				17 56		18 09
Lea Green	d			15 43		16 13						16 43			17 13			17 27	17 37				18 00		18 13
St Helens Junction	d			15 46		16 16					16 30	16 46			17 16			17 30	17 40				18 03		18 16
Warrington Bank Quay	d	15 33					16 20									17 20									
Earlestown [8]	d	15 44		15 51		16 20	16 28					16 50			17 20	17 27			17 44				18 07		18 20
Warrington Bank Quay	a			16 02		*16 49*									*17 55*	*17 55*			*18 17*						*18 48*
Newton-le-Willows	d	15 47				16 23	16 31				16 36	16 53			17 23	17 30		17 36	17 47				18 10		18 23
Wigan North Western	a				16 23			16 31	16 31	16 53			17 11	17 23			17 50				17 54	18 13		18 28	
	65 d							16 31	16 31				17 12								17 54			18 28	
Euxton Balshaw Lane	d							16 42	16 42				17 24								18 05			18 39	
Leyland	82 a							16 47	16 47				17 29								18 09			18 44	
Preston [8]	65, 82 a							16 54	16 56	*17b23*			17 40								18 17	*18b39*		18 52	
Blackpool North	97 a							*17 34*	*17 34*	*18c03*			*18 30*								18 48			19 21	
Patricroft	d					16 35						17 05			17 35				17 59				18 22		
Eccles	d					16 38						17 08			17 38				18 02				18 25		
Manchester Victoria	a					16 48						17 21			17 49				18 12				18 40		18 46
Manchester Oxford Road	a	16 10					16 50				16 57					17 51		17 58							
Manchester Piccadilly [10]	a	16 19					16 58				17 02					17 59		18 04							
Manchester Airport	85 a										17 25							18 27							

		AW	NT	NT	NT	NT	NT	AW	NT	NT	AW	NT	NT	NT	AW	NT	NT	AW	NT	NT	NT	NT	AW		
		◇ C						◇ C			◇ C				A			◇ C					A		
Liverpool Lime Street [10]	89, 91 d		18 04	18 14	18 18	18 34	18 48		19 04	19 18		19 48	20 14	20 18		20 48	21 18		21 48	22 18	23 05	23 18			
Edge Hill	89, 91 d				18 22		18 52			19 22		19 52		20 22		20 52	21 22		21 52	22 22	23 09	23 22			
Wavertree Technology Park	d		18 10	18 19	18 24	18 40	18 54		19 10	19 24		19 54	20 19	20 24		20 54	21 24		21 54	22 24	23 11	23 24			
Broad Green	d		18 13		18 27	18 43	18 57		19 13	19 27		19 57		20 27		20 57	21 27		21 57	22 27	23 14	23 27			
Roby	d		18 16		18 31	18 47	19 01		19 16	19 31		20 01		20 31		21 01	21 31		22 01	22 31	23 17	23 31			
Huyton	d		18 19		18 33	18 49	19 03		19 19	19 33		20 03		20 33		21 03	21 33		22 03	22 33	23 20	23 33			
Prescot	d		18 23			18 53			19 23			20 08				21 08			22 08		23 24				
Eccleston Park	d		18 25			18 56			19 26			20 10				21 10			22 10		23 27				
Thatto Heath	d		18 28			18 58			19 28			20 13				21 13			22 13		23 29				
St Helens Central	a		18 31			19 02			19 32			20 16				21 16			22 16		23 33				
	d		18 32			19 02			19 32			20 17				21 17			22 17		23 34				
Garswood	d		18 39			19 09			19 39			20 24				21 24			22 24		23 41				
Bryn	d		18 42			19 12			19 42			20 27				21 27			22 27		23 44				
Whiston	d				18 36		19 06			19 36				20 36			21 36			22 36		23 36			
Rainhill	d			18 28	18 39		19 09			19 39				20 39			21 39			22 39		23 39			
Lea Green	d				18 43		19 13			19 43				20 43			21 43			22 43		23 43			
St Helens Junction	d			18 32	18 46		19 16			19 46			20 30	20 46			21 46			22 46		23 46			
Warrington Bank Quay	d	18 21						19 20			20 20				21 23			22 20					23 50		
Earlestown [8]	d	18 27			18 51		19 20	19 28		19 50	20 27			20 50	21 30		21 50	22 27		22 50		23 50	23 57		
Warrington Bank Quay	a				19 02		*19 48*			*20 48*				*21 48*			*22 48*			*23 52*					
Newton-le-Willows	d	18 30		18 38			19 23	19 31		19 53	20 30		20 36	20 53	21 33		21 53	22 30		22 53		23 53	23 59		
Wigan North Western	a		18 51			19 23			19 51			20 40				21 37			22 37		23 51				
	65 d		18 51						19 51										22 38		23 51				
Euxton Balshaw Lane	d		19 02						20 02										22 49		00 01				
Leyland	82 a		19 07						20 07										22 54		00 06				
Preston [8]	65, 82 a		19 17						20 17			*21 24*				*22 24*			23 02		00 15				
Blackpool North	97 a		*20 01*						*20 56*			*21c56*							23 28						
Patricroft	d						19 35			20 05				21 05			22 05			23 05		00 05			
Eccles	d						19 38			20 08				21 08			22 08			23 08		00 08			
Manchester Victoria	a						19 50			20 20				21 20			22 21			23 22		00 20			
Manchester Oxford Road	a	18 50		18 59				19 50			20 50		20 58		21 54			22 55							
Manchester Piccadilly [10]	a	18 59		19 05				19 59			20 59		21 05		22 01			23 05					00 27		
Manchester Airport	85 a			19 26									21 28												

For general notes see front of timetable
For details of catering facilities see Directory of Train Operators

- **A** From Chester (Table 81)
- **B** To Stalybridge (Table 39)
- **C** From Llandudno (Table 81)
- **D** Until 22 March. To Millom (Table 100)
- **E** From 29 March
- **G** To Huddersfield (Table 39)
- **H** To Rochdale (Table 95)
- **J** To Todmorden (Table 41)
- **b** From 29 March arr. 5 minutes later
- **c** Change at Wigan North Western and Preston

Table 90

Sundays

until 23 March

Liverpool and St Helens → Newton-le-Willows, Wigan, Preston and Manchester

Network Diagram - see first page of Table 88

		NT	NT	NT	NT	NT	AW	NT	NT	NT	NT	NT	AW	NT	NT	NT	NT	NT
		A	B				C 🛒	A	B				C 🛒	A	B			
Liverpool Lime Street 10	89, 91 d	08 00	08 00	08 30	09 00	09 30		10 00	10 00	10 30	11 00	11 30		12 00	12 00	12 30	13 00	13 30
Wavertree Technology Park	d	08 06	08 06	08 36	09 06	09 36		10 06	10 06	10 36	11 06	11 36		12 06	12 06	12 36	13 06	13 36
Broad Green	d	08 09	08 09	08 39	09 09	09 39		10 09	10 09	10 39	11 09	11 39		12 09	12 09	12 39	13 09	13 39
Roby	d	08 12	08 12	08 42	09 12	09 42		10 12	10 12	10 42	11 12	11 42		12 12	12 12	12 42	13 12	13 42
Huyton	d	08 14	08 14	08 45	09 14	09 45		10 14	10 14	10 45	11 14	11 45		12 14	12 14	12 45	13 14	13 45
Prescot	d	08 19	08 19		09 19			10 19	10 19		11 19			12 19	12 19		13 19	
Thatto Heath	d	08 22	08 22		09 22			10 22	10 22		11 22			12 22	12 22		13 22	
St Helens Central	a	08 26	08 26		09 26			10 26	10 26		11 26			12 26	12 26		13 26	
	d	08 26	08 26		09 26			10 26	10 26		11 26			12 26	12 26		13 26	
Garswood	d	08 33	08 33		09 33			10 33	10 33		11 33			12 33	12 33		13 33	
Whiston	d			08 48		09 48				10 48		11 48				12 48		13 48
Rainhill	d			08 51		09 51				10 51		11 51				12 51		13 51
Lea Green	d			08 55		09 55				10 55		11 55				12 55		13 55
St Helens Junction	d			08 58		09 58				10 58		11 58				12 58		13 58
Warrington Bank Quay	d						10 30						12 23					
Earlestown 8	d			09 02		10 02	10 38			11 02		12 02	12 31			13 02		14 02
Warrington Bank Quay	a					*10 30*				*12 02*						*13 47*		
Newton-le-Willows	d			09 05		10 05	10 41			11 05		12 05	12 33			13 05		14 05
Wigan North Western	a	08 41	08 41		09 44			10 41	10 41		11 44			12 42	12 42		13 44	
	65 d	08 42	08 42					10 42	10 42					12 42	12 42			
Euxton Balshaw Lane	d	08 53	08 53					10 53	10 53					12 53	12 53			
Leyland	82 a	08 58	08 58					10 58	10 58					12 58	12 58			
Preston 8	65, 82 a	09 05	09 05		*10 40*			11 05	11 05		*12 39*			13 06	13 06		*14 08*	
Blackpool North	97 a	09 34	*09b55*					11 34	*11b55*					13 34	*13b55*			
Eccles	d			09 18		10 18				11 18		12 18				13 18		14 18
Manchester Oxford Road	a			09 27		10 27	11 00			11 27		12 31	12 52			13 30		14 27
Manchester Piccadilly 10	a			09 34		10 34	11 04			11 35		12 35	13 01			13 35		14 32
Manchester Airport	85 a			09 51		10 51				11 51		12 50				13 54		14 51

		AW	NT	NT	NT	AW	NT	NT	AW	NT	NT	NT	AW	NT	NT	NT	AW
		C 🛒	A	B		◇ D 🛒			C	A	B		◇ E 🛒	A	B		◇ E
Liverpool Lime Street 10	89, 91 d		14 00	14 00	14 30		15 00	15 30		16 00	16 00	16 30		17 00	17 00	17 30	
Wavertree Technology Park	d		14 06	14 06	14 36		15 06	15 36		16 06	16 06	16 36		17 06	17 06	17 36	
Broad Green	d		14 09	14 09	14 39		15 09	15 39		16 09	16 09	16 39		17 09	17 09	17 39	
Roby	d		14 12	14 12	14 42		15 12	15 42		16 12	16 12	16 42		17 12	17 12	17 42	
Huyton	d		14 14	14 14	14 45		15 14	15 45		16 14	16 14	16 45		17 14	17 14	17 45	
Prescot	d		14 19	14 19			15 19			16 19	16 19			17 19	17 19		
Thatto Heath	d		14 22	14 22			15 22			16 22	16 22			17 22	17 22		
St Helens Central	a		14 26	14 26			15 26			16 26	16 26			17 26	17 26		
	d		14 26	14 26			15 26			16 26	16 26			17 26	17 26		
Garswood	d		14 33	14 33			15 33			16 33	16 33			17 33	17 33		
Whiston	d				14 48			15 48				16 48				17 48	
Rainhill	d				14 51			15 51				16 51				17 51	
Lea Green	d				14 55			15 55				16 55				17 55	
St Helens Junction	d				14 58			15 58				16 58				17 58	
Warrington Bank Quay	d	13 58				15 28			16 21				17 17				18 08
Earlestown 8	d	14 08			15 02	15 36		16 02	16 29			17 02	17 25			18 02	18 20
Warrington Bank Quay	a				*15 29*			*17 01*				*18 03*				*19 04*	
Newton-le-Willows	d	14 11			15 05	15 39		16 05	16 32			17 05	17 28			18 05	18 23
Wigan North Western	a		14 42	14 42			15 44			16 41	16 41			17 41	17 41		
	65 d		14 42	14 42						16 42	16 42			17 42	17 42		
Euxton Balshaw Lane	d		14 53	14 53						16 52	16 52			17 53	17 53		
Leyland	82 a		14 58	14 58						16 57	16 57			17 58	17 58		
Preston 8	65, 82 a		15 07	15 07			*16 03*			17 04	17 04			18 05	18 05		
Blackpool North	97 a		15 34	*15b55*						17 35	*17b55*			18 34	*18b55*		
Eccles	d				15 18			16 18				17 18				18 18	
Manchester Oxford Road	a	14 31			15 29	15 59		16 27	16 51			17 30	17 50			18 27	18 44
Manchester Piccadilly 10	a	14 41			15 34	16 10		16 35	17 00			17 35	17 59			18 33	18 51
Manchester Airport	85 a				15 51			16 51				17 51				18 52	

For general notes see front of timetable
For details of catering facilities see Directory of Train Operators

A Until 27 January
B From 3 February
C From Chester (Table 81)
D From Holyhead (Table 81)
E From Bangor (Gwynedd) (Table 81)
b By bus

Liverpool and St Helens → Newton-le-Willows, Wigan, Preston and Manchester

Sundays
until 23 March

Network Diagram - see first page of Table 88

	NT	NT	NT	NT	NT	NT	NT	AW	NT	NT	AW	NT	NT	NT	NT	AW	NT
	A	B				A	B	C			C		A	B		◇ D	
Liverpool Lime Street 10 89, 91 d	18 00	18 00	18 30	19 00	19 30	20 00	20 00		20 30	21 00		21 30	22 00	22 00	22 30		23 00
Wavertree Technology Park d	18 06	18 06	18 36	19 06	19 36	20 06	20 06		20 36	21 06		21 36	22 06	22 06	22 36		23 06
Broad Green d	18 09	18 09	18 39	19 09	19 39	20 09	20 09		20 39	21 09		21 39	22 09	22 09	22 39		23 09
Roby d	18 12	18 12	18 42	19 12	19 42	20 12	20 12		20 42	21 12		21 42	22 12	22 12	22 42		23 12
Huyton d	18 14	18 14	18 45	19 14	19 45	20 14	20 14		20 45	21 14		21 45	22 14	22 14	22 45		23 14
Prescot d	18 19	18 19		19 19		20 19	20 19			21 19			22 19	22 19			23 19
Thatto Heath d	18 22	18 22		19 22		20 22	20 22			21 22			22 22	22 22			23 22
St Helens Central a	18 26	18 26		19 26		20 26	20 26			21 26			22 26	22 26			23 26
d	18 26	18 26		19 26		20 26	20 26			21 26			22 26	22 26			23 26
Garswood d	18 33	18 33		19 33		20 33	20 33			21 33			22 33	22 33			23 33
Whiston d			18 48		19 48				20 48			21 48			22 48		
Rainhill d			18 51		19 51				20 51			21 51			22 51		
Lea Green d			18 55		19 55				20 55			21 55			22 55		
St Helens Junction d			18 58		19 58				20 58			21 58			22 58		
Warrington Bank Quay d								20 49			21 48					23 02	
Earlestown 8 d			19 02		20 02			20 56	21 02		21 56	22 02			23 02	23 10	
Warrington Bank Quay a					*20 47*				*21 47*			*22 55*			*23 49*		
Newton-le-Willows d			19 05		20 05			20 59	21 05		21 59	22 05			23 05	23 13	
Wigan North Western a	18 41	18 41		19 44		20 41	20 41			21 44			22 41	22 41			23 50
65 d	18 42	18 42				20 42	20 42						22 42	22 42			
Euxton Balshaw Lane d	18 53	18 53				20 53	20 53						23 03	23 03			
Leyland 82 a	18 58	18 58				20 58	20 58						23 08	23 08			
Preston 8 65, 82 a	19 05	19 05		*20 11*		21 05	21 05			*22 08*			23 15	23 15			*00 27*
Blackpool North 97 a	19 32	*19b55*				21 34	*21b55*						23 43	*00b05*			
Eccles d			19 18		20 18				21 18			22 18			23 18		
Manchester Oxford Road a			19 28		20 28			21 24	21 28		22 18	22 27			23 27	23 35	
Manchester Piccadilly 10 a			19 35		20 33			21 34	21 34		22 27	22 33			23 33	23 41	
Manchester Airport 85 ✈ a			19 51		20 52				21 52			22 51			23 49		

Sundays
from 30 March

	NT	NT (bus)	NT	NT (bus)	NT	AW (bus)	NT (bus)	NT	NT (bus)	NT	AW (bus)	NT (bus)	NT	AW (bus)	NT (bus)	NT	NT (bus)	NT	AW (bus)	AW (bus)	NT (bus)
Liverpool Lime Street 10 89, 91 d	08 00	08 30	09 00	09 30	10 00		10 30	11 00	11 30	12 00		12 30	13 00		13 30	14 00	14 30	15 00			15 30
Wavertree Technology Park d	08 06	08 45	09 06	09 45	10 06		10 45	11 06	11 45	12 06		12 45	13 06		13 45	14 06	14 45	15 06			15 45
Broad Green d	08 09	08 53	09 09	09 53	10 09		10 53	11 09	11 53	12 09		12 53	13 09		13 53	14 09	14 53	15 09			15 53
Roby d	08 12	09 00	09 12	10 00	10 12		11 00	11 12	12 00	12 12		13 00	13 12		14 00	14 12	15 00	15 12			16 00
Huyton d	08 14	09 05	09 14	10 05	10 14		11 05	11 14	12 05	12 14		13 05	13 14		14 05	14 14	15 05	15 14			16 05
Prescot d	08 19		09 19		10 19			11 19		12 19			13 19			14 19		15 19			
Thatto Heath d	08 22		09 22		10 22			11 22		12 22			13 22			14 22		15 22			
St Helens Central a	08 26		09 26		10 26			11 26		12 26			13 26			14 26		15 26			
d	08 26		09 26		10 26			11 26		12 26			13 26			14 26		15 26			
Garswood d	08 33		09 33		10 33			11 33		12 33			13 33			14 33		15 33			
Whiston d		09 15		10 15			11 15		12 15			13 15			14 15		15 15				16 15
Rainhill d		09 25		10 25			11 25		12 25			13 25			14 25		15 25				16 25
Lea Green d		09 33		10 33			11 33		12 33			13 33			14 33		15 33				16 33
St Helens Junction d		09 40		10 40			11 40		12 40			13 40			14 40		15 40				16 40
Warrington Bank Quay d						10 40					12 40			14 10					15 45	16 35	
Earlestown 8 d		09 52		10 52		10 55	11 52		12 52		12 55	13 52		14 25	14 52		15 52		16 00	16 50	16 52
Warrington Bank Quay a		*10b20*		*11b50*					*13b38*						*15b19*		*16b50*				*17b50*
Newton-le-Willows d		10 00		11 00		11 05	12 00		13 00		13 05	14 00		14 35	15 00		16 00		16 10	17 00	17 00
Wigan North Western a	08 41		09 44		10 41			11 44		12 42			13 44			14 42		15 44			
65 d	08 42				10 42					12 42						14 42					
Euxton Balshaw Lane d	08 53				10 53					12 53						14 53					
Leyland 82 a	08 58				10 58					12 58						14 58					
Preston 8 65, 82 a	09 05		*10 40*		11 05			*12 39*		13 06			*14 07*			15 07		*16 05*			
Blackpool North 97 a	09 34		*11c16*		11 34			*13c16*		13 34			*14c47*			15 34		*16c47*			
Eccles d		10 25		11 25			12 25		13 25			14 25			15 25		16 25				17 25
Manchester Oxford Road a		10 40		11 40		11 35	12 40		13 40		13 35	14 40		15 05	15 40		16 40		16 40	17 30	17 40
Manchester Piccadilly 10 a						11 45					13 45			15 15					16 50	17 40	
Manchester Airport 85 ✈ a																					

For general notes see front of timetable
For details of catering facilities see Directory of Train Operators

A Until 27 January
B From 3 February
C From Chester (Table 81)
D From Holyhead (Table 81)
b By bus
c Change at Wigan North Western and Preston

Table 90

Sundays

from 30 March

Liverpool and St Helens → Newton-le-Willows, Wigan, Preston and Manchester

Network Diagram - see first page of Table 88

		NT	AW 🚌	NT 🚌	NT	AW 🚌		NT 🚌	NT	NT 🚌	NT	NT 🚌	NT		AW 🚌	NT 🚌	NT	AW 🚌	NT 🚌	NT	AW 🚌	NT 🚌	NT		
Liverpool Lime Street 10	89, 91 d	16 00		16 30	17 00			17 30	18 00	18 30	19 00	19 30	20 00			20 30	21 00		21 30	22 00		22 30	23 00		
Wavertree Technology Park	d	16 06		16 45	17 06			17 45	18 06	18 45	19 06	19 45	20 06			20 45	21 06		21 45	22 06		22 45	23 06		
Broad Green	d	16 09		16 53	17 09			17 53	18 09	18 53	19 09	19 53	20 09			20 53	21 09		21 53	22 09		22 53	23 09		
Roby	d	16 12		17 00	17 12			18 00	18 12	19 00	19 12	20 00	20 12			21 00	21 12		22 00	22 12		23 00	23 12		
Huyton	d	16 14		17 05	17 14			18 05	18 14	19 05	19 14	20 05	20 14			21 05	21 14		22 05	22 14		23 05	23 14		
Prescot	d	16 19			17 19				18 19		19 19		20 19				21 19			22 19			23 19		
Thatto Heath	d	16 22			17 22				18 22		19 22		20 22				21 22			22 22			23 22		
St Helens Central	a	16 26			17 26				18 26		19 26		20 26				21 26			22 26			23 26		
	d	16 26			17 26				18 26		19 26		20 26				21 26			22 26			23 26		
Garswood	d	16 33			17 33				18 33		19 33		20 33				21 33			22 33			23 33		
Whiston	d			17 15				18 15		19 15		20 15				21 15			22 15			23 15			
Rainhill	d			17 25				18 25		19 25		20 25				21 25			22 25			23 25			
Lea Green	d			17 33				18 33		19 33		20 33				21 33			22 33			23 33			
St Helens Junction	d			17 40				18 40		19 40		20 40				21 40			22 40			23 40			
Warrington Bank Quay	d		17 25			18 25									21 00			22 00			23 15				
Earlestown 8	d		17 40	17 52		18 40		18 52		19 52		20 52			21 15	21 52		22 15	22 52		23 30	23 52			
Warrington Bank Quay	a			18b50						20b35		21b35				22b45			23b35			00b20			
Newton-le-Willows	d		17 50	18 00		18 50		19 00		20 00		21 00			21 25	22 00		22 25	23 00		23 40	00 01			
Wigan North Western	a	16 41			17 41				18 41		19 44		20 41				21 44			22 41			23 50		
	65 d	16 42			17 42				18 42				20 42							22 42					
Euxton Balshaw Lane	d	16 52			17 53				18 53				20 53							23 03					
Leyland	82 a	16 57			17 58				18 58				20 58							23 08					
Preston 8	65, 82 a	17 04			18 05				19 05		20 17		21 05				22 05			23 15			00 27		
Blackpool North	97 a	17 35			18 34				19 32		21c16		21 34				22e47			23 43					
Eccles	d			18 25				19 25		20 25		21 25				22 25			23 25			00 25			
Manchester Oxford Road	a		18 20	18 40		19 20		19 40		20 40		21 40			21 55	22 40		22 55	23 40		00 10	00 40			
Manchester Piccadilly 10	a		18 30			19 30									22 05			23 05			00 20				
Manchester Airport	85 ✈ a																								

For general notes see front of timetable
For details of catering facilities see Directory of Train Operators

b By bus

c Change at Wigan North Western and Preston. 4 May arr. 2103

e Change at Wigan North Western and Preston

Manchester, Preston, Wigan and Newton-le-Willows → St Helens and Liverpool

Network Diagram - see first page of Table 88

Miles	Miles	Miles	Miles			NT	NT	NT	NT	AW ◇ A	NT	NT	NT	NT	NT	NT	NT	NT	AW ◇ A	NT B	NT	NT	NT C	NT	AW ◇ A
—	—	—	0	**Manchester Airport** 85 ✈	d	04 34								06 28							07 26				
—	—	—	9¾	**Manchester Piccadilly** 10	d	04 49				06 00				06 52					07 16		07 49				08 16
—	—	—	10¼	**Manchester Oxford Road**	d					06 03				06 56					07 19		07 52				08 19
0	—	—	—	**Manchester Victoria**	d			05 45			06 07					07 10				07 31		07b18	08 01		
4	—	—	14½	Eccles	d						06 14					07 17				07 38			08 08		
5	—	—	15½	Patricroft	d						06 17					07 20				07 41			08 11		
—	—	—	—	Blackpool North 97	d							*05c30*			*06c09*			06 57						*07c03*	
—	0	0	—	**Preston** 8 65, 82	d							*06 15*			*06 51*			07 25				*07 29*		*07 43*	
—	4	4	—	Leyland 82	d													07 30							
—	6¾	6¾	—	Euxton Balshaw Lane	d													07 35							
—	15	15	—	**Wigan North Western** 65	a													07 44				07 55			
—	—	—	—		d				06 08			06 39	06 45		07 09		07 29	07 45				07 59		08 29	
15½	—	22	26	**Newton-le-Willows**	d			06 04		06 21	06 29		07 01	07 14		07 32			07 37	07 53	08 10		08 23		08 37
—	—	—	—	Warrington Bank Quay	d											*07 16*							*07 54*		
17	—	23½	27½	Earlestown 8	d			06 06		06 24	06 31		07 03			07 34			07 40	07 55			08 26		08 40
—	—	—	—	Warrington Bank Quay	a					06 32									07 48						08 48
19¾	—	26¼	30¼	**St Helens Junction**	d			06 11			06 36		07 08	07 19		07 39				08 00	08 15		08 31		
21	—	27½	31½	Lea Green	d			06 14			06 39		07 11			07 42				08 03	08 18		08 34		
22¾	—	29¼	33¼	Rainhill	d			06 18			06 43		07 15	07 25		07 46				08 07	08 22		08 38		
24¼	—	30¾	34¾	Whiston	d			06 21			06 46		07 18			07 49				08 10	08 25		08 41		
—	18¾	—	—	Bryn	d				06 16			06 47			07 17		07 37					08 07		08 37	
—	20	—	—	Garswood	d				06 20			06 50			07 20		07 40	07 54				08 10		08 41	
—	23¾	—	—	**St Helens Central**	a				06 27			06 57			07 27		07 47	08 01				08 17		08 47	
—	—	—	—		d		05 57		06 27			06 57			07 27		07 47	08 01				08 17		08 48	
—	25¼	—	—	Thatto Heath	d		06 01		06 31			07 01			07 31		07 51					08 21		08 51	
—	26¼	—	—	Eccleston Park	d		06 03		06 33			07 03			07 33		07 53					08 23		08 54	
—	27¼	—	—	Prescot	d		06 05		06 35			07 05			07 35		07 55	08 07				08 25		08 56	
26¼	29½	32¾	36¾	Huyton	d		06 10	06 25	06 40		06 50	07 10	07 22	07 30	07 40	07 53	08 00	08 11		08 15		08 30	08 45	09 00	
26¾	30	33¼	37¼	Roby	d		06 12	06 27	06 42		06 52	07 12	07 24		07 42	07 55	08 02			08 17		08 32	08 47	09 02	
28¼	31½	34¾	38¾	Broad Green	d		06 15	06 30	06 45		06 55	07 15	07 27		07 45	07 58	08 05	08 15		08 20		08 35	08 50	09 05	
29¼	32½	35¾	39¾	Wavertree Technology Park	d		06 18	06 33	06 48		06 58	07 18	07 30	07 36	07 48	08 01	08 08			08 23	08 32	08 38	08 53	09 08	
30	33¼	36½	40½	Edge Hill 89, 91	d			06 36			07 01		07 33			08 04				08 26			08 56		
31¾	35	38¼	42¼	**Liverpool Lime Street** 10 89, 91	a	05 30	06 29	06 44	06 59		07 10	07 29	07 42	07 47	07 59	08 13	08 19	08 27		08 35	08 42	08 50	09 05	09 19	

		NT D	NT	NT	NT E	NT B	NT	AW ◇ A	NT	NT	NT	NT	NT D	NT	AW ◇ G	AW ◇ A	NT	NT	NT	NT	NT D	NT		AW ◇ A	NT
Manchester Airport 85 ✈	d		08 30							09 31								10 31							
Manchester Piccadilly 10	d		08 50					09 16		09 49					10 03	10 16		10 49						11 16	
Manchester Oxford Road	d		08 55					09 19		09 52					10 06	10 19		10 52						11 19	
Manchester Victoria	d	08 40				09 01							10 01								11 01				
Eccles	d					09 08							10 08								11 08				
Patricroft	d					09 11							10 11								11 11				
Blackpool North 97	d			*07c41*	08 09						*08c41*	09 25							*09c38*	10 25					
Preston 8 65, 82	d			*08 29*	08 50						*09 29*	09 50							*10 28*	10 50					
Leyland 82	d				08 55							09 55								10 55					
Euxton Balshaw Lane	d				09 00							10 00								11 00					
Wigan North Western 65	a				09 10							10 10								11 11					
	d			08 59	09 11		09 29				09 59	10 11		10 29					10 59	11 11		11 29			
Newton-le-Willows	d		09 13			09 23		09 38		10 10			10 23		10 30	10 38		11 10			11 23			11 38	
Warrington Bank Quay	d	*08 21*							09 48								10 48								11 48
Earlestown 8	d	08 56				09 26		09 41	09 56				10 26			10 41	10 56				11 26			11 41	11 56
Warrington Bank Quay	a							09 49							10 39	10 49								11 49	
St Helens Junction	d	09 01	09 18			09 31			10 01	10 15			10 31				11 01	11 15			11 31				12 01
Lea Green	d	09 04				09 34			10 04				10 34				11 04				11 34				12 04
Rainhill	d	09 08				09 38			10 08				10 38				11 08				11 38				12 08
Whiston	d	09 11				09 41			10 11				10 41				11 11				11 41				12 11
Bryn	d			09 07			09 37				10 07			10 37					11 07			11 37			
Garswood	d			09 11			09 41				10 11			10 41					11 11			11 41			
St Helens Central	a			09 17	09 26		09 47				10 17	10 26		10 47					11 18	11 26		11 47			
	d			09 18	09 27		09 48				10 18	10 27		10 48					11 18	11 27		11 48			
Thatto Heath	d			09 21			09 51				10 21			10 51					11 21			11 51			
Eccleston Park	d			09 24			09 54				10 24			10 54					11 24			11 54			
Prescot	d			09 26			09 56				10 26			10 56					11 26			11 56			
Huyton	d	09 15		09 30	09 37	09 45	10 00		10 15		10 30	10 37	10 45	11 00			11 15		11 30	11 37	11 45	12 00			12 15
Roby	d	09 17		09 32		09 47	10 02		10 17		10 32		10 47	11 02			11 17		11 32		11 47	12 02			12 17
Broad Green	d	09 20		09 35		09 50	10 05		10 20		10 35		10 50	11 05			11 20		11 35		11 50	12 05			12 20
Wavertree Technology Park	d	09 23	09 30	09 38		09 53	10 08		10 23	10 27	10 38		10 53	11 08			11 23	11 27	11 38		11 53	12 08			12 23
Edge Hill 89, 91	d	09 26				09 56			10 26				10 56				11 26				11 56				12 26
Liverpool Lime Street 10 89, 91	a	09 39	09 42	09 49	09 53	10 05	10 19		10 35	10 39	10 49	10 52	11 05	11 19			11 35	11 39	11 49	11 52	12 05	12 19			12 35

For general notes see front of timetable
For details of catering facilities see
Directory of Train Operators

- **A** To Llandudno (Table 81)
- **B** From Huddersfield (Table 39)
- **C** From Todmorden (Table 41)
- **D** From Stalybridge (Table 39)
- **E** From Barrow-in-Furness (Table 82)
- **G** To Holyhead (Table 81)
- **b** Via Bolton (Table 82)
- **c** Change at Preston and Wigan North Western

Manchester, Preston, Wigan and Newton-le-Willows → St Helens and Liverpool

Network Diagram - see first page of Table 88

	NT	NT	NT	NT	NT	AW	NT	NT	NT	NT	NT	NT	AW	NT	NT	NT	NT	NT	NT	AW	NT	NT	NT	NT
				A		◇ B					A		◇ B					A		◇ B				
Manchester Airport 85 ✈ d	11 31							12 31							13 31							14 31		
Manchester Piccadilly 10 d	11 49					12 16		12 49					13 16		13 49					14 16		14 49		
Manchester Oxford Road d	11 52					12 19		12 52					13 19		13 52					14 19		14 52		
Manchester Victoria d				12 01							13 01							14 01						
Eccles d				12 08							13 08							14 08						
Patricroft d				12 11							13 11							14 11						
Blackpool North 97 d		10b41	11 25						11b41	12 25						12b41	13 25						13b41	14 21
Preston 8 65, 82 d		11 29	11 50		11 56				12 32	12 50						13 29	13 50						14 30	14 46
Leyland 82 d			11 55							12 55							13 55							14 51
Euxton Balshaw Lane d			12 00							13 00							14 00							14 56
Wigan North Western 65 a			12 10							13 10							14 11							15 09
d		11 59	12 11		12 29				12 59	13 11		13 29				13 59	14 11		14 29				14 59	15 11
Newton-le-Willows d	12 10			12 23		12 39		13 10			13 23		13 38		14 10			14 23		14 38		15 10		
Warrington Bank Quay d							12 48							13 48							14 48			
Earlestown 8 d				12 26		12 41	12 56				13 26		13 41	13 56				14 26		14 41	14 56			
Warrington Bank Quay a						12 49							13 49							14 49				
St Helens Junction d	12 15			12 31			13 01	13 15			13 31			14 01	14 15			14 31			15 01	15 15		
Lea Green d				12 34			13 04				13 34			14 04				14 34			15 04			
Rainhill d				12 38			13 08				13 38			14 08				14 38			15 08			
Whiston d				12 41			13 11				13 41			14 11				14 41			15 11			
Bryn d		12 07			12 37				13 07			13 37				14 07			14 37				15 07	
Garswood d		12 11			12 41				13 11			13 41				14 11			14 41				15 11	
St Helens Central a		12 18	12 26		12 47				13 17	13 27		13 47				14 17	14 26		14 47				15 17	15 26
d		12 18	12 27		12 48				13 18	13 27		13 48				14 18	14 27		14 48				15 18	15 27
Thatto Heath d		12 21			12 51				13 21			13 51				14 21			14 51				15 21	
Eccleston Park d		12 24			12 54				13 24			13 54				14 24			14 54				15 24	
Prescot d		12 26			12 56				13 26			13 56				14 26			14 56				15 26	
Huyton d		12 30	12 37	12 45	13 00		13 15		13 30	13 37	13 45	14 00		14 15		14 30	14 37	14 45	15 00		15 15		15 30	15 37
Roby d		12 32		12 47	13 02		13 17		13 32		13 47	14 02		14 17		14 32		14 47	15 02		15 17		15 32	
Broad Green d		12 35		12 50	13 05		13 20		13 35		13 50	14 05		14 20		14 35		14 50	15 05		15 20		15 35	
Wavertree Technology Park d	12 27	12 38		12 53	13 08		13 23	13 27	13 38		13 53	14 08		14 23	14 27	14 38		14 53	15 08		15 23	15 27	15 38	
Edge Hill 89, 91 d				12 56			13 26				13 56			14 26				14 56			15 26			
Liverpool Lime Street 10 89, 91 a	12 39	12 49	12 52	13 05	13 19		13 35	13 39	13 49	13 52	14 05	14 19		14 35	14 39	14 49	14 52	15 05	15 19		15 35	15 39	15 49	15 52

	NT	NT	AW	NT	NT	NT	NT	NT	NT	AW	NT	NT	NT	NT	NT	NT	AW	NT	AW	NT	NT	NT	NT	NT
	A		◇ B	C				A		◇ B	D				E		◇ B		◇ G					
Manchester Airport 85 ✈ d					15 31							16 31								17 29				
Manchester Piccadilly 10 d			15 16		15 49					16 16		16 48					17 20		17 41	17 45				
Manchester Oxford Road d			15 19		15 52					16 19		16 52					17 23		17 47	17 49				
Manchester Victoria d	15 01							16 01							17 01								18 01	
Eccles d	15 08							16 08							17 08					17 56			18 08	
Patricroft d	15 11							16 11							17 11								18 11	
Blackpool North 97 d						14b41	15 25						15b41	16 25							16b38	17 10		
Preston 8 65, 82 d		14 49				15 29	15 50						16 29	16 50							17 29	17 50		
Leyland 82 d							15 55							16 55								17 55		
Euxton Balshaw Lane d							16 00							17 00								18 00		
Wigan North Western 65 a							16 10							17 09								18 11		
d		15 29				15 59	16 11		16 29				16 59	17 11		17 29		17 42			17 59	18 11		18 29
Newton-le-Willows d	15 23		15 38		16 10			16 23		16 37		17 10			17 23		17 42	17 53	18 05	18 10			18 23	
Warrington Bank Quay d				15 48							16 48							17 20						
Earlestown 8 d	15 26		15 41	15 56				16 26		16 40	16 56				17 26		17 45	17 56	18 08				18 26	
Warrington Bank Quay a			15 50							16 48							17 55		18 17					
St Helens Junction d	15 31			16 01	16 15			16 31			17 01	17 15			17 31			18 01		18 15			18 31	
Lea Green d	15 34			16 04				16 34			17 04				17 34			18 04		18 18			18 34	
Rainhill d	15 38			16 08				16 38			17 08				17 38			18 08		18 22			18 38	
Whiston d	15 41			16 11				16 41			17 11				17 41			18 11					18 41	
Bryn d		15 37				16 07			16 37				17 07			17 37					18 07			18 37
Garswood d		15 41				16 11			16 41				17 11			17 41					18 11			18 41
St Helens Central a		15 47				16 17	16 26		16 47				17 18	17 27		17 47					18 17	18 27		18 47
d		15 48				16 18	16 27		16 48				17 18	17 27		17 48					18 18	18 27		18 48
Thatto Heath d		15 51				16 21			16 51				17 21			17 51					18 21			18 51
Eccleston Park d		15 54				16 24			16 54				17 24			17 54					18 24			18 54
Prescot d		15 56				16 26			16 56				17 26			17 56					18 26			18 56
Huyton d	15 45	16 00		16 15		16 30	16 37	16 44	17 00		17 14		17 30	17 37	17 45	18 00		18 14			18 30	18 37	18 45	19 00
Roby d	15 47	16 02		16 17		16 32		16 46	17 02		17 16		17 32		17 47	18 02		18 16			18 32		18 47	19 02
Broad Green d	15 50	16 05		16 20		16 35		16 50	17 05		17 20		17 35		17 50	18 05		18 20			18 35		18 50	19 05
Wavertree Technology Park d	15 53	16 08		16 23	16 27	16 38		16 53	17 08		17 23	17 27	17 38		17 53	18 08		18 23		18 30	18 38		18 53	19 08
Edge Hill 89, 91 d	15 56			16 26				16 56	17 11				17 41		17 56			18 26					18 56	
Liverpool Lime Street 10 89, 91 a	16 05	16 19		16 35	16 39	16 49	16 53	17 04	17 19		17 33	17 38	17 49	17 53	18 05	18 19		18 34		18 40	18 49	18 55	19 05	19 19

For general notes see front of timetable
For details of catering facilities see Directory of Train Operators

A From Stalybridge (Table 39)
B To Llandudno (Table 81)
C From Helsby (Table 81)
D From Ellesmere Port (Table 109)
E From Rochdale (Table 95)
G To Holyhead (Table 81)
b Change at Preston and Wigan North Western

Manchester, Preston, Wigan and Newton-le-Willows → St Helens and Liverpool

Network Diagram - see first page of Table 88

	AW	NT	NT	NT	NT	NT	AW	NT	NT	NT	NT	AW	NT	NT	AW	NT	NT	NT	NT	AW	NT	AW		
	◇ A						B					B			B					B		B		
Manchester Airport 85 ✈ d			18 31						19 30								21 30							
Manchester Piccadilly [10] ⛴ d	18 16		18 49				19 16		19 48			20 16			21 16		21 47			22 16		23 20		
Manchester Oxford Road d	18 19		18 52				19 19		19 52			20 19			21 19		21 50			22 19		23 23		
Manchester Victoria ⛴ d		18 31			19 01						20 01			21 01				22 01			23 11			
Eccles d		18 38			19 08						20 08			21 08				22 08			23 18			
Patricroft d		18 41			19 11						20 11			21 11				22 11			23 21			
Blackpool North 97 d				18 25		*18b38*				19 25			*19 42*			*20b53*			22 03					
Preston [8] 65, 82 d				18 50		*19 10*				19 50			20 27			*21 29*			22 27					
Leyland 82 d				18 55						19 55			20 32						22 32					
Euxton Balshaw Lane d				19 00						20 00			20 37						22 37					
Wigan North Western 65 a				19 10						20 11			20 46						22 47					
d				19 11		19 29				20 11			20 47			21 47			22 47					
Newton-le-Willows d	18 37	18 53	19 10		19 23		19 37		20 10		20 23	20 37		21 23	21 37		22 10	22 23		22 37	23 33	23 41		
Warrington Bank Quay d		*18 20*						19 48						*20 20*				*21 23*						
Earlestown [8] d	18 40	18 56			19 26		19 40	19 56			20 26	20 40		21 26	21 40			22 26		22 40	23 35	23 44		
Warrington Bank Quay a	18 48						19 48					20 48			21 49					22 48		23 52		
St Helens Junction d		19 01	19 15		19 31			20 01	20 15		20 31			21 31			22 15	22 31			23 40			
Lea Green d		19 04			19 34			20 04			20 34			21 34				22 34			23 43			
Rainhill d		19 08			19 38			20 08			20 38			21 38				22 38			23 47			
Whiston d		19 11			19 41			20 11			20 41			21 41				22 41			23 50			
Bryn d						19 37							20 55			21 55			22 55					
Garswood d						19 41							20 58			21 58			22 58					
St Helens Central a				19 26		19 48				20 27			21 05			22 05			23 05					
d				19 27		19 48				20 27			21 05			22 05			23 05					
Thatto Heath d						19 51							21 09			22 09			23 09					
Eccleston Park d						19 54							21 11			22 11			23 11					
Prescot d						19 56							21 13			22 13			23 13					
Huyton d		19 15		19 37	19 45	20 00		20 15		20 37	20 45		21 18	21 45		22 18		22 45	23 18		23 54			
Roby d		19 17			19 47	20 02		20 17			20 47		21 20	21 47		22 20		22 47	23 20		23 56			
Broad Green d		19 20			19 50	20 05		20 20			20 50		21 23	21 50		22 23		22 50	23 23		23 59			
Wavertree Technology Park d		19 23	19 27		19 53	20 08		20 23	20 27		20 53		21 26	21 53		22 26	22 27	22 53	23 26		00 02			
Edge Hill 89, 91 d		19 26			19 56			20 26			20 56		21 29	21 56		22 29		22 56	23 29		00 05			
Liverpool Lime Street [10] 89, 91 a		19 35	19 38	19 52	20 05	20 19		20 35	20 38	20 52	21 05		21 38	22 05		22 38	22 41	23 05	23 38		00 14			

Saturdays

	NT	NT	NT	NT	AW	NT	NT	NT	NT	NT	NT	NT	NT	AW	NT	NT		NT	NT	NT	AW	NT	NT	NT
					◇ A ✠									◇ A ✠					C		◇ A ✠			
Manchester Airport 85 ✈ d	04 35								06 28							07 26							08 30	
Manchester Piccadilly [10] ⛴ d	04 50				06 00				06 52					07 16		07 49					08 16		08 50	
Manchester Oxford Road d					06 03				06 56					07 19		07 52					08 19		08 55	
Manchester Victoria ⛴ d			05 45			06 07					07 10				07 31			07c18	08 01			08 40		
Eccles d						06 14					07 17				07 38				08 08					
Patricroft d						06 17					07 20				07 41				08 11					
Blackpool North 97 d				*04b43*			*05b30*			*06b08*			06 57							*07b03*				*07b41*
Preston [8] 65, 82 d				*05 40*			*06 15*			*06 45*			07 25							*07 44*				*08 29*
Leyland 82 d													07 30											
Euxton Balshaw Lane d													07 35											
Wigan North Western 65 a													07 44					07 54						
d				06 08			06 39	06 45		07 09		07 29	07 45					07 59		08 29				08 59
Newton-le-Willows d			06 04		06 21	06 29		07 01	07 14		07 32			07 37	07 53	08 10			08 23		08 37		09 13	
Warrington Bank Quay d											*07 16*								*07 54*			*08 21*		
Earlestown [8] d			06 06		06 24	06 31		07 03			07 34			07 40	07 55				08 26		08 40	08 56		
Warrington Bank Quay a					06 32									07 48							08 48			
St Helens Junction d			06 11			06 36		07 08	07 19		07 39				08 00	08 15			08 31			09 01	09 18	
Lea Green d			06 14			06 39		07 11			07 42				08 03	08 18			08 34			09 04		
Rainhill d			06 18			06 43		07 15	07 25		07 46				08 07	08 22			08 38			09 08		
Whiston d			06 21			06 46		07 18			07 49				08 10	08 25			08 41			09 11		
Bryn d				06 16			06 47			07 17		07 37						08 07		08 37				09 07
Garswood d				06 20			06 50			07 20		07 40	07 54					08 10		08 41				09 11
St Helens Central a				06 26			06 57			07 27		07 47	08 01					08 17		08 47				09 17
d		05 57		06 27			06 57			07 27		07 47	08 01					08 17		08 48				09 18
Thatto Heath d		06 01		06 31			07 01			07 31		07 51						08 20		08 51				09 21
Eccleston Park d		06 03		06 33			07 03			07 33		07 53						08 23		08 54				09 24
Prescot d		06 05		06 35			07 05			07 35		07 55	08 07					08 25		08 56				09 26
Huyton d		06 10	06 25	06 40		06 50	07 10	07 22	07 30	07 40	07 53	08 00	08 11		08 15			08 30	08 45	09 00		09 15		09 30
Roby d		06 12	06 27	06 42		06 52	07 12	07 24		07 42	07 55	08 02			08 17			08 32	08 47	09 02		09 17		09 32
Broad Green d		06 15	06 30	06 45		06 55	07 15	07 27		07 45	07 58	08 05	08 15		08 20			08 36	08 50	09 05		09 20		09 35
Wavertree Technology Park d		06 18	06 33	06 48		06 58	07 18	07 30	07 36	07 48	08 01	08 08			08 23	08 32		08 39	08 53	09 08		09 23	09 30	09 38
Edge Hill 89, 91 d			06 36			07 01		07 33			08 04				08 26				08 56			09 26		
Liverpool Lime Street [10] 89, 91 a	05 29	06 29	06 44	06 59		07 10	07 29	07 43	07 48	07 59	08 13	08 19	08 26		08 35	08 42		08 50	09 05	09 20		09 39	09 42	09 49

For general notes see front of timetable
For details of catering facilities see Directory of Train Operators

A To Llandudno (Table 81)
B To Chester (Table 81)
C From Todmorden (Table 41)
b Change at Preston and Wigan North Western
c Via Bolton (Table 82)

Table 90

Saturdays

Manchester, Preston, Wigan and Newton-le-Willows → St Helens and Liverpool

Network Diagram - see first page of Table 88

		NT	NT	NT	AW	NT	NT	NT	NT	NT	NT	AW		AW	NT	NT	NT	NT	NT	NT	AW	NT	NT	NT	NT
			A		◇ B					C		D		◇ B					C		◇ B				
Manchester Airport	85 d						09 31									10 31							11 31		
Manchester Piccadilly 10	d				09 16		09 49					10 03		10 16		10 49					11 16		11 49		
Manchester Oxford Road	d				09 19		09 52					10 06		10 18		10 52					11 19		11 52		
Manchester Victoria	d		09 01							10 01									11 01						
Eccles	d		09 08							10 08									11 08						
Patricroft	d		09 11							10 11									11 11						
Blackpool North	97 d	*08 09*						08b41	09 25								09b40	10 25						10c41	11 25
Preston 8	65, 82 d	08 50						*09 29*	09 50								*10 29*	10 50						11c28	11 50
Leyland	82 d	08 55							09 55									10 55							11 55
Euxton Balshaw Lane	d	09 00							10 00									11 00							12 00
Wigan North Western	65 a	09 10							10 09									11 11							12 09
	d	09 11		09 29				09 59	10 11		10 29						10 59	11 11		11 29				11 59	12 11
Newton-le-Willows	d		09 23		09 38		10 10			10 23		10 30		10 38		11 10			11 23		11 38		12 10		
Warrington Bank Quay	d					09 48									10 48							11 48			
Earlestown 8	d		09 26		09 41	09 56				10 26				10 41	10 56				11 26		11 41	11 56			
Warrington Bank Quay	a				09 49							10 39		10 49							11 49				
St Helens Junction	d		09 31			10 01	10 15			10 31					11 01	11 15			11 31			12 01	12 15		
Lea Green	d		09 34			10 04				10 34					11 04				11 34			12 04			
Rainhill	d		09 38			10 08				10 38					11 08				11 38			12 08			
Whiston	d		09 41			10 11				10 41					11 11				11 41			12 11			
Bryn	d			09 37				10 07			10 37						11 07			11 37				12 07	
Garswood	d			09 41				10 11			10 41						11 11			11 41				12 11	
St Helens Central	a	09 26		09 47				10 17	10 26		10 48						11 18	11 26		11 47				12 18	12 26
	d	09 27		09 48				10 18	10 27		10 48						11 18	11 27		11 48				12 18	12 27
Thatto Heath	d			09 51				10 21			10 51						11 21			11 51				12 21	
Eccleston Park	d			09 54				10 24			10 54						11 24			11 54				12 24	
Prescot	d			09 56				10 26			10 56						11 26			11 56				12 26	
Huyton	d	09 37	09 45	10 00		10 15		10 30	10 37	10 45	11 00				11 15		11 30	11 37	11 45	12 00		12 15		12 30	12 37
Roby	d		09 47	10 02		10 17		10 32		10 47	11 02				11 17		11 32		11 47	12 02		12 17		12 32	
Broad Green	d		09 50	10 05		10 20		10 35		10 50	11 05				11 20		11 35		11 50	12 05		12 20		12 35	
Wavertree Technology Park	d		09 53	10 08		10 23	10 27	10 38		10 53	11 08				11 23	11 27	11 38		11 53	12 08		12 23	12 27	12 38	
Edge Hill	89, 91 d		09 56			10 26				10 56					11 26				11 56			12 26			
Liverpool Lime Street 10	89, 91 a	09 52	10 05	10 20		10 35	10 39	10 49	10 52	11 05	11 19				11 35	11 39	11 49	11 52	12 05	12 19		12 35	12 39	12 49	12 52

		NT	NT	AW	NT	NT	NT		NT	NT	NT	AW	NT	NT	NT	NT	NT	NT	AW	NT	NT	NT	NT	NT	NT
		C		◇ B						C		◇ B					C		◇ B					C	
Manchester Airport	85 d					12 31								13 31							14 31				
Manchester Piccadilly 10	d			12 16		12 49						13 16		13 49					14 16		14 49				
Manchester Oxford Road	d			12 19		12 52						13 19		13 52					14 19		14 52				
Manchester Victoria	d	12 01								13 01							14 01							15 01	
Eccles	d	12 08								13 08							14 08							15 08	
Patricroft	d	12 11								13 11							14 11							15 11	
Blackpool North	97 d						11b41		12 25						12b41	13 25						13b41	14 25		
Preston 8	65, 82 d						12e29		12 50						*13 29*	13 50						*14 29*	14 50		
Leyland	82 d								12 55							13 55							14 55		
Euxton Balshaw Lane	d								13 00							14 00							15 00		
Wigan North Western	65 a								13 09							14 11							15 10		
	d		12 29				12 59		13 11		13 29				13 59	14 11		14 29				14 59	15 11		15 29
Newton-le-Willows	d	12 23		12 39		13 10				13 23		13 38		14 10			14 23		14 38		15 10			15 23	
Warrington Bank Quay	d				12 48								13 48							14 48					
Earlestown 8	d	12 26		12 41	12 56					13 26		13 41	13 56				14 26		14 41	14 56				15 26	
Warrington Bank Quay	a			12 49								13 49							14 49						
St Helens Junction	d	12 31			13 01	13 15				13 31			14 01	14 15			14 31			15 01	15 15			15 31	
Lea Green	d	12 34			13 04					13 34			14 04				14 34			15 04				15 34	
Rainhill	d	12 38			13 08					13 38			14 08				14 38			15 08				15 38	
Whiston	d	12 41			13 11					13 41			14 11				14 41			15 11				15 41	
Bryn	d		12 37				13 07				13 37				14 07			14 37				15 07			15 37
Garswood	d		12 41				13 11				13 41				14 11			14 41				15 11			15 41
St Helens Central	a		12 47				13 17		13 26		13 47				14 17	14 26		14 47				15 17	15 26		15 47
	d		12 48				13 18		13 27		13 48				14 18	14 27		14 48				15 18	15 27		15 48
Thatto Heath	d		12 51				13 21				13 51				14 21			14 51				15 21			15 51
Eccleston Park	d		12 54				13 24				13 54				14 24			14 54				15 24			15 54
Prescot	d		12 56				13 26				13 56				14 26			14 56				15 26			15 56
Huyton	d	12 45	13 00		13 15		13 30		13 37	13 45	14 00		14 15		14 30	14 37	14 45	15 00		15 15		15 30	15 37	15 45	16 00
Roby	d	12 47	13 02		13 17		13 32			13 47	14 02		14 17		14 32		14 47	15 02		15 17		15 32		15 47	16 02
Broad Green	d	12 50	13 05		13 20		13 35			13 50	14 05		14 20		14 35		14 50	15 05		15 20		15 35		15 50	16 05
Wavertree Technology Park	d	12 53	13 08		13 23	13 27	13 38			13 53	14 08		14 23	14 28	14 38		14 53	15 08		15 23	15 28	15 38		15 53	16 08
Edge Hill	89, 91 d	12 56			13 26					13 56			14 26				14 56			15 26				15 56	
Liverpool Lime Street 10	89, 91 a	13 05	13 19		13 35	13 39	13 49		13 52	14 05	14 19		14 35	14 39	14 49	14 52	15 05	15 19		15 35	15 39	15 49	15 52	16 05	16 19

For general notes see front of timetable
For details of catering facilities see Directory of Train Operators

A From Huddersfield (Table 39)
B To Llandudno (Table 81)
C From Stalybridge (Table 39)
D To Chester (Table 81)

b Change at Preston and Wigan North Western
c Until 22 March only
e From 29 March dep. 1227

Manchester, Preston, Wigan and Newton-le-Willows → St Helens and Liverpool

Network Diagram - see first page of Table 88

	AW ◇ A		NT B	NT	NT	NT	NT C	NT	AW ◇ A	NT D	NT	NT	NT	NT E	NT	AW ◇ A	NT	AW ◇ G		NT	NT	NT	NT C	NT
Manchester Airport 85 ✈ d				15 31							16 31									17 29				
Manchester Piccadilly [10] d	15 16			15 49					16 16		16 48					17 20		17 41		17 45				
Manchester Oxford Road d	15 19			15 52					16 19		16 52					17 26		17 47		17 49				
Manchester Victoria d							16 01							17 01									18 01	
Eccles d							16 08							17 08						17 56			18 08	
Patricroft d							16 11							17 11									18 11	
Blackpool North 97 d					*14b41*	15 25						*15b41*	16 25				*16b38*					*17 10*		
Preston [8] 65, 82 d					*15 29*	15 50						*16 29*	16 50				*17 24*					17 50		
Leyland 82 d						15 55							16 55									17 55		
Euxton Balshaw Lane d						16 00							17 00									18 00		
Wigan North Western 65 a						16 10							17 09									18 11		
d					15 59	16 11		16 29				16 59	17 11		17 29		17 42				17 59	18 11		18 29
Newton-le-Willows d	15 38			16 10			16 23		16 38		17 10			17 23		17 45	17 53	18 04		18 10			18 23	
Warrington Bank Quay d			15 48							16 48							*17 20*							
Earlestown [8] d	15 41		15 56				16 26		16 41	16 56				17 26		17 47	17 56	18 07					18 26	
Warrington Bank Quay a	15 49								16 49							17 55		18 17						
St Helens Junction d			16 01	16 15			16 31			17 01	17 15			17 31			18 01			18 15			18 31	
Lea Green d			16 04				16 34			17 04				17 34			18 04			18 18			18 34	
Rainhill d			16 08				16 38			17 08				17 38			18 08			18 22			18 38	
Whiston d			16 11				16 41			17 11				17 41			18 11						18 41	
Bryn d					16 07			16 37				17 07			17 37						18 07			18 37
Garswood d					16 11			16 41				17 11			17 41						18 11			18 41
St Helens Central a					16 17	16 26		16 47				17 17	17 26		17 47						18 17	18 27		18 47
d					16 18	16 27		16 48				17 18	17 27		17 48						18 18	18 27		18 48
Thatto Heath d					16 21			16 51				17 21			17 51						18 21			18 51
Eccleston Park d					16 24			16 54				17 24			17 54						18 24			18 54
Prescot d					16 26			16 56				17 26			17 56						18 26			18 56
Huyton d			16 15		16 30	16 37	16 44	17 00		17 14		17 30	17 37	17 45	18 00		18 14				18 30	18 37	18 45	19 00
Roby d			16 17		16 32		16 46	17 02		17 16		17 32		17 47	18 02		18 16				18 32		18 47	19 02
Broad Green d			16 20		16 35		16 50	17 05		17 20		17 35		17 50	18 05		18 20				18 35		18 50	19 05
Wavertree Technology Park d			16 23	16 28	16 38		16 53	17 08		17 23	17 27	17 38		17 53	18 08		18 23			18 30	18 38		18 53	19 08
Edge Hill 89, 91 d			16 26				16 56	17 11				17 41		17 56			18 26						18 56	
Liverpool Lime Street [10] 89, 91 a			16 35	16 39	16 49	16 54	17 04	17 19		17 33	17 38	17 49	17 53	18 05	18 19		18 34			18 40	18 49	18 55	19 05	19 17

	AW ◇ A	NT	NT	NT	NT C	NT	AW H	NT	NT	NT	NT	AW H	NT	NT	AW H	NT	NT	NT	NT	AW H	NT	AW H		
Manchester Airport 85 ✈ d			18 31						19 30								21 30							
Manchester Piccadilly [10] d	18 16		18 49				19 16		19 49			20 16			21 16		21 49			22 16		23 20		
Manchester Oxford Road d	18 19		18 52				19 19		19 52			20 20			21 19		21 52			22 19		23 23		
Manchester Victoria d		18 31			19 01						20 01			21 01				22 01			23 11			
Eccles d		18 38			19 08						20 08			21 08				22 08			23 18			
Patricroft d		18 41			19 11						20 11			21 11				22 11			23 21			
Blackpool North 97 d				18 25						19 25			*19 42*			*20b53*			22 03					
Preston [8] 65, 82 d				18 50						19 50			20 27			*21 28*			22 28					
Leyland 82 d				18 55						19 55			20 32						22 32					
Euxton Balshaw Lane d				19 00						20 00			20 37						22 36					
Wigan North Western 65 a				19 10						20 10			20 47						22 47					
d				19 11		19 29				20 11			20 48			21 47			22 47					
Newton-le-Willows d	18 37	18 53	19 10		19 23		19 37		20 10		20 23	20 37		21 23	21 37		22 10	22 23		22 37	23 33	23 41		
Warrington Bank Quay d		*18 21*						19 48						*20 20*				*21 23*			*22 20*			
Earlestown [8] d	18 40	18 56			19 26		19 40	19 56			20 26	20 40		21 26	21 40			22 26		22 40	23 35	23 44		
Warrington Bank Quay a	18 48						19 48					20 48			21 48					22 48		23 52		
St Helens Junction d		19 01	19 15		19 31			20 01	20 15		20 31			21 31			22 15	22 31			23 40			
Lea Green d		19 04			19 34			20 04			20 34			21 34				22 34			23 43			
Rainhill d		19 08			19 38			20 08			20 38			21 38				22 38			23 47			
Whiston d		19 11			19 41			20 11			20 41			21 41				22 41			23 50			
Bryn d						19 37							20 55			21 55			22 55					
Garswood d						19 41							20 59			21 58			22 58					
St Helens Central a				19 26		19 48				20 26			21 05			22 05			23 05					
d				19 27		19 48				20 27			21 06			22 05			23 05					
Thatto Heath d						19 51							21 09			22 09			23 09					
Eccleston Park d						19 54							21 11			22 11			23 11					
Prescot d						19 56							21 13			22 13			23 13					
Huyton d		19 15		19 37	19 45	20 00		20 15		20 37	20 45		21 18	21 45		22 18		22 45	23 18		23 54			
Roby d		19 17			19 47	20 02		20 17			20 47		21 20	21 47		22 20		22 47	23 20		23 56			
Broad Green d		19 20			19 50	20 05		20 20			20 50		21 23	21 50		22 23		22 50	23 23		23 59			
Wavertree Technology Park d		19 23	19 27		19 53	20 08		20 23	20 27		20 53		21 26	21 53		22 26	22 30	22 53	23 26		00 02			
Edge Hill 89, 91 d		19 26			19 56			20 26			20 56		21 29	21 56		22 29		22 56	23 29		00 05			
Liverpool Lime Street [10] 89, 91 a		19 35	19 38	19 52	20 05	20 19		20 35	20 38	20 52	21 05		21 39	22 05		22 38	22 41	23 05	23 38		00 14			

For general notes see front of timetable
For details of catering facilities see Directory of Train Operators

- **A** To Llandudno (Table 81)
- **B** From Helsby (Table 81)
- **C** From Stalybridge (Table 39)
- **D** From Ellesmere Port (Table 109)
- **E** From Rochdale (Table 95)
- **G** To Holyhead (Table 81)
- **H** To Chester (Table 81)
- **b** Change at Preston and Wigan North Western

Table 90

Sundays

until 23 March

Manchester, Preston, Wigan and Newton-le-Willows → St Helens and Liverpool

Network Diagram - see first page of Table 88

		NT	NT	NT	NT	NT	NT	AW	NT	NT	NT	NT	AW	NT	NT	NT	NT	AW
				A	B			C		B	A		◇ D			A	B	C
Manchester Airport	85 d					08 51			10 01			11 00			12 00			
Manchester Piccadilly 10	d					09 16		09 58	10 16			11 16			12 17			13 15
Manchester Oxford Road	d		08b17			09 20		10 01	10 20			11 20	11 34		12 20			13 18
Eccles	d		08 27			09 27			10 27			11 27			12 27			
Blackpool North	97 d			*07c50*	08 17					10 17	*09c50*					*11c50*	12 17	
Preston 8	65, 82 d			08 42	08 42					10 42	10 42			*11 25*		12 42	12 42	
Leyland	82 d			08 47	08 47					10 47	10 47					12 47	12 47	
Euxton Balshaw Lane	d			08 52	08 52					10 52	10 52					12 52	12 52	
Wigan North Western	65 a			09 01	09 01					11 00	11 01					13 01	13 01	
	d	08 01		09 01	09 01		10 01			11 00	11 01			12 01		13 01	13 01	
Newton-le-Willows	d		08 40			09 40		10 19	10 40			11 40	11 52		12 40			13 36
Warrington Bank Quay	d											*10 30*			*12 23*			
Earlestown 8	d		08 42			09 42		10 22	10 42			11 42	11 54		12 42			13 39
Warrington Bank Quay	a							10 30					12 02					13 47
St Helens Junction	d		08 47			09 47			10 47			11 47			12 47			
Lea Green	d		08 50			09 50			10 50			11 50			12 50			
Rainhill	d		08 54			09 54			10 54			11 54			12 54			
Whiston	d		08 57			09 57			10 57			11 57			12 57			
Garswood	d	08 11		09 11	09 11		10 11			11 11	11 11			12 11		13 11	13 11	
St Helens Central	a	08 18		09 18	09 18		10 18			11 18	11 18			12 18		13 17	13 17	
	d	08 18		09 18	09 18		10 18			11 18	11 18			12 18		13 18	13 18	
Thatto Heath	d	08 22		09 22	09 22		10 22			11 22	11 22			12 22		13 22	13 22	
Prescot	d	08 26		09 26	09 26		10 26			11 26	11 26			12 26		13 26	13 26	
Huyton	d	08 30	09 00	09 30	09 30	10 00	10 30		11 00	11 30	11 30	12 00		12 30	13 00	13 30	13 30	
Roby	d	08 32	09 02	09 32	09 32	10 02	10 32		11 02	11 32	11 32	12 02		12 32	13 02	13 32	13 32	
Broad Green	d	08 36	09 06	09 36	09 36	10 06	10 36		11 06	11 36	11 36	12 06		12 36	13 06	13 36	13 36	
Wavertree Technology Park	d	08 39	09 09	09 39	09 39	10 09	10 39		11 09	11 39	11 39	12 09		12 39	13 09	13 39	13 39	
Liverpool Lime Street 10	89, 91 a	08 49	09 26	09 49	09 49	10 22	10 49		11 21	11 49	11 49	12 21		12 49	13 21	13 50	13 50	

		NT	NT	NT	NT	NT	AW	NT	NT	NT	NT	NT	AW	NT	NT	NT	AW
					A	B	C				A	B	C		A	B	◇ E
Manchester Airport	85 d	13 00		14 00				15 00		16 01				17 01			
Manchester Piccadilly 10	d	13 17		14 17			14 57	15 16		16 16			16 29	17 16			17 32
Manchester Oxford Road	d	13 20		14 20			15 00	15 20		16 20			16 32	17 20			17 35
Eccles	d	13 27		14 27				15 27		16 27				17 27			
Blackpool North	97 d				*13c50*	14 17					*15c50*	16 17			*16c50*	17 17	
Preston 8	65, 82 d		*13 29*		14 42	14 42			*15 28*		16 42	16 42			17 42	17 42	
Leyland	82 d				14 47	14 47					16 47	16 47			17 47	17 47	
Euxton Balshaw Lane	d				14 52	14 52					16 52	16 52			17 52	17 52	
Wigan North Western	65 a				15 00	15 00					17 00	17 00			18 00	18 00	
	d		14 01		15 01	15 01			16 01		17 01	17 01			18 01	18 01	
Newton-le-Willows	d	13 40		14 40			15 18	15 40		16 40			16 50	17 40			17 53
Warrington Bank Quay	d			*13 58*						*16 21*				*17 17*			
Earlestown 8	d	13 42		14 42			15 21	15 42		16 42			16 53	17 42			17 55
Warrington Bank Quay	a						15 29						17 01				18 03
St Helens Junction	d	13 47		14 47				15 47		16 47				17 47			
Lea Green	d	13 50		14 50				15 50		16 50				17 50			
Rainhill	d	13 54		14 54				15 54		16 54				17 54			
Whiston	d	13 57		14 57				15 57		16 57				17 57			
Garswood	d		14 11		15 11	15 11			16 11		17 11	17 11			18 11	18 11	
St Helens Central	a		14 18		15 17	15 17			16 18		17 18	17 18			18 18	18 18	
	d		14 18		15 18	15 18			16 18		17 18	17 18			18 18	18 18	
Thatto Heath	d		14 22		15 22	15 22			16 22		17 22	17 22			18 22	18 22	
Prescot	d		14 26		15 26	15 26			16 26		17 26	17 26			18 26	18 26	
Huyton	d	14 00	14 30	15 00	15 30	15 30		16 00	16 30	17 00	17 30	17 30		18 00	18 30	18 30	
Roby	d	14 02	14 32	15 02	15 32	15 32		16 02	16 32	17 02	17 32	17 32		18 02	18 32	18 32	
Broad Green	d	14 06	14 36	15 06	15 36	15 36		16 06	16 36	17 06	17 36	17 36		18 06	18 36	18 36	
Wavertree Technology Park	d	14 09	14 39	15 09	15 39	15 39		16 09	16 39	17 09	17 39	17 39		18 09	18 39	18 39	
Liverpool Lime Street 10	89, 91 a	14 21	14 49	15 21	15 49	15 49		16 21	16 49	17 21	17 49	17 49		18 21	18 49	18 49	

For general notes see front of timetable
For details of catering facilities see Directory of Train Operators

A From 3 February
B Until 27 January
C To Chester (Table 81)
D To Bangor (Gwynedd) (Table 81)
E To Holyhead (Table 81)
b Manchester Victoria
c By bus

Table 90

Sundays

until 23 March

Manchester, Preston, Wigan and Newton-le-Willows → St Helens and Liverpool

Network Diagram - see first page of Table 88

		NT	NT A	NT B	AW C	NT	NT	AW C	NT	NT A	NT B	AW C	NT	NT	NT	NT A	NT B	AW C	AW C
Manchester Airport	85 ✈ d	18 01				19 01			20 01				21 01		22 01				
Manchester Piccadilly 10	d	18 16			18 32	19 16		20 14	20 16			21 14	21 16		22 16			22 20	23 17
Manchester Oxford Road	d	18 20			18 35	19 20		20 18	20 20			21 18	21 20		22 19			22 23	23 20
Eccles	d	18 27				19 27			20 27				21 27		22 26				
Blackpool North	97 d		*17b50*	18 17						*19b50*	20 17					*21b50*	22 17		
Preston 8	65, 82 d		18 42	18 42			*19c35*			20 42	20 42			*21 34*		22 42	22 42		
Leyland	82 d		18 47	18 47						20 47	20 47					22 47	22 47		
Euxton Balshaw Lane	d		18 52	18 52						20 52	20 52					22 52	22 52		
Wigan North Western	65 a		19 00	19 00						21 01	21 01					23 11	23 11		
	d		19 01	19 01			20 01			21 01	21 01			22 01		23 11	23 11		
Newton-le-Willows	d	18 40			18 53	19 40		20 36	20 40			21 36	21 40		22 39			22 44	23 38
Warrington Bank Quay	d	*18 08*													*21 48*				
Earlestown 8	d	18 42			18 56	19 42		20 39	20 42			21 39	21 42		22 42			22 47	23 41
Warrington Bank Quay	a				19 04			20 47				21 47	*20 49*					22 55	23 49
St Helens Junction	d	18 47				19 47			20 47				21 47		22 46				
Lea Green	d	18 50				19 50			20 50				21 50		22 49				
Rainhill	d	18 54				19 54			20 54				21 54		22 53				
Whiston	d	18 57				19 57			20 57				21 57		22 56				
Garswood	d		19 11	19 11			20 11			21 11	21 11			22 11		23 21	23 21		
St Helens Central	a		19 18	19 18			20 18			21 18	21 18			22 18		23 28	23 28		
	d		19 18	19 18			20 18			21 18	21 18			22 18		23 28	23 28		
Thatto Heath	d		19 22	19 22			20 22			21 22	21 22			22 22		23 32	23 32		
Prescot	d		19 26	19 26			20 26			21 26	21 26			22 26		23 36	23 36		
Huyton	d	19 00	19 30	19 30		20 00	20 30		21 00	21 30	21 30		22 00	22 30	23 00	23 40	23 40		
Roby	d	19 02	19 32	19 32		20 02	20 32		21 02	21 32	21 32		22 02	22 32	23 02	23 42	23 42		
Broad Green	d	19 06	19 36	19 36		20 06	20 36		21 06	21 36	21 36		22 06	22 36	23 06	23 45	23 45		
Wavertree Technology Park	d	19 09	19 39	19 39		20 09	20 39		21 09	21 39	21 39		22 09	22 39	23 09	23 48	23 48		
Liverpool Lime Street 10	89, 91 a	19 21	19 49	19 49		20 21	20 49		21 21	21 49	21 49		22 21	22 49	23 21	23 59	23 59		

Sundays

from 30 March

		NT	NT	NT 🚌	NT	NT 🚌	AW 🚌	NT	NT 🚌	AW 🚌	NT	NT 🚌	NT	NT 🚌	AW 🚌	NT	NT 🚌	NT	NT 🚌	AW 🚌	NT	NT 🚌	AW 🚌
Manchester Airport	85 ✈ d																						
Manchester Piccadilly 10	d						09 20			10 50					12 38					14 19			15 50
Manchester Oxford Road	d			08e00		09 00	09 30		10 00	11 00		11 00		12 00	12 48		13 00		14 00	14 29		15 00	16 00
Eccles	d			08 15		09 15			10 15			11 15		12 15			13 15		14 15			15 15	
Blackpool North	97 d		08 17					10 17			*10f28*		12 17			*12f28*		14 17			*14f28*		
Preston 8	65, 82 d		08 42					10 42			*11 25*		12 42			*13 08*		14 42			*15 27*		
Leyland	82 d		08 47					10 47					12 47					14 47					
Euxton Balshaw Lane	d		08 52					10 52					12 52					14 52					
Wigan North Western	65 a		09 01					11 01					13 01					15 00					
	d	08 01	09 01		10 01			11 01			12 01		13 01			14 01		15 01			16 01		
Newton-le-Willows	d			08 40		09 40	09 55		10 40	11 25		11 40		12 40	13 13		13 40		14 40	14 54		15 40	16 25
Warrington Bank Quay	d											*10b40*					*12b40*		*14b10*				
Earlestown 8	d			08 48		09 48	10 05		10 48	11 35		11 48		12 48	13 23		13 48		14 48	15 04		15 48	16 35
Warrington Bank Quay	a						10 20			11 50					13 38					15 19			16 50
St Helens Junction	d			09 00		10 00			11 00			12 00		13 00			14 00		15 00			16 00	
Lea Green	d			09 07		10 07			11 07			12 07		13 07			14 07		15 07			16 07	
Rainhill	d			09 15		10 15			11 15			12 15		13 15			14 15		15 15			16 15	
Whiston	d			09 25		10 25			11 25			12 25		13 25			14 25		15 25			16 25	
Garswood	d	08 11	09 11		10 11			11 11			12 11		13 11			14 11		15 11			16 11		
St Helens Central	a	08 18	09 18		10 18			11 18			12 18		13 17			14 18		15 17			16 18		
	d	08 18	09 18		10 18			11 18			12 18		13 18			14 18		15 18			16 18		
Thatto Heath	d	08 22	09 22		10 22			11 22			12 22		13 22			14 22		15 22			16 22		
Prescot	d	08 26	09 26		10 26			11 26			12 26		13 26			14 26		15 26			16 26		
Huyton	d	08 30	09 30	09 35	10 30	10 35		11 30	11 35		12 30	12 35	13 30	13 35		14 30	14 35	15 30	15 35		16 30	16 35	
Roby	d	08 32	09 32	09 39	10 32	10 39		11 32	11 39		12 32	12 39	13 32	13 39		14 32	14 39	15 32	15 39		16 32	16 39	
Broad Green	d	08 36	09 36	09 47	10 36	10 47		11 36	11 47		12 36	12 47	13 36	13 47		14 36	14 47	15 36	15 47		16 36	16 47	
Wavertree Technology Park	d	08 39	09 39	09 55	10 39	10 55		11 39	11 55		12 39	12 55	13 39	13 55		14 39	14 55	15 39	15 55		16 39	16 55	
Liverpool Lime Street 10	89, 91 a	08 49	09 49	10 10	10 49	11 10		11 49	12 10		12 49	13 10	13 50	14 10		14 49	15 10	15 49	16 10		16 49	17 10	

For general notes see front of timetable
For details of catering facilities see Directory of Train Operators

A From 3 February
B Until 27 January
C To Chester (Table 81)
b By bus
c From 3 February dep. 1900
e Manchester Victoria
f Change at Preston and Wigan North Western

Table 90

from 30 March

Manchester, Preston, Wigan and Newton-le-Willows → St Helens and Liverpool

Network Diagram - see first page of Table 88

		NT	NT	AW	NT	NT	AW	NT		NT	NT	NT	AW	NT	NT	AW	NT	NT	AW	NT	NT	AW	AW		
																							A		
			bus	bus		bus	bus			bus		bus	bus		bus	bus		bus	bus		bus	bus	bus		
Manchester Airport 85 ✈	d																								
Manchester Piccadilly [10] ⛴	d			16 50			17 50						19 35			20 35			21 45			22 35	23 20		
Manchester Oxford Road	d		16 00	17 00		17 00	18 00			18 00		19 00	19 45		20 00	20 45		21 00	21 55		22 00	22 45	23 30		
Eccles	d		16 15			17 15				18 15		19 15			20 15			21 15			22 15				
Blackpool North 97	d	16 17			17 17			18 17			*18b28*			20 17			*20b28*			22 17					
Preston [8] 65, 82	d	16 42			17 42			18 42			*19 29*			20 42			*21 34*			22 42					
Leyland 82	d	16 47			17 47			18 47						20 47						22 47					
Euxton Balshaw Lane	d	16 52			17 52			18 52						20 52						22 52					
Wigan North Western 65	a	17 00			18 00			19 00						21 01						23 11					
	d	17 01			18 01			19 01			20 01			21 01			22 01			23 11					
Newton-le-Willows	d		16 40	17 25		17 40	18 25			18 40		19 40	20 10		20 40	21 10		21 40	22 20		22 40	23 10	23 55		
Warrington Bank Quay	d		*15c45*			*17c25*				*18c25*								*21c00*			*22c40*				
Earlestown [8]	d		16 48	17 35		17 48	18 35			18 48		19 48	20 20		20 48	21 20		21 48	22 30		22 48	23 20	00 05		
Warrington Bank Quay	a			17 50			18 50						20 35			21 35			22 45			23 35	00 20		
St Helens Junction	d		17 00			18 00				19 00		20 00			21 00			22 00			23 00				
Lea Green	d		17 07			18 07				19 07		20 07			21 07			22 07			23 07				
Rainhill	d		17 15			18 15				19 15		20 15			21 15			22 15			23 15				
Whiston	d		17 25			18 25				19 25		20 25			21 25			22 25			23 25				
Garswood	d	17 11			18 11			19 11			20 11			21 11			22 11			23 21					
St Helens Central	a	17 18			18 18			19 18			20 18			21 18			22 18			23 28					
	d	17 18			18 18			19 18			20 18			21 18			22 18			23 28					
Thatto Heath	d	17 22			18 22			19 22			20 22			21 22			22 22			23 32					
Prescot	d	17 26			18 26			19 26			20 26			21 26			22 26			23 36					
Huyton	d	17 30	17 35		18 30	18 35		19 30		19 35	20 30	20 35		21 30	21 35		22 30	22 35		23 40	23 35				
Roby	d	17 32	17 39		18 32	18 39		19 32		19 39	20 32	20 39		21 32	21 39		22 32	22 39		23 42	23 39				
Broad Green	d	17 36	17 47		18 36	18 47		19 36		19 47	20 36	20 47		21 36	21 47		22 36	22 47		23 45	23 47				
Wavertree Technology Park	d	17 39	17 55		18 39	18 55		19 39		19 55	20 39	20 55		21 39	21 55		22 39	22 55		23 48	23 55				
Liverpool Lime Street [10] 89, 91	a	17 49	18 10		18 49	19 10		19 49		20 10	20 49	21 10		21 49	22 10		22 49	23 10		23 59	00 10				

For general notes see front of timetable
For details of catering facilities see Directory of Train Operators

A To Chester (Table 81)
b Change at Preston and Wigan North Western
c By bus

Liverpool → Runcorn and Crewe

Network Diagram - see first page of Table 88

Miles			VT	NT	NT	VT	LM	NT	VT	LM	NT	LM	NT	VT	LM	NT	LM	NT	VT	LM
			1 ◇			1 ◇	1 ◇		1 ◇	1 ◇		1 ◇		1 ◇	1 ◇		1 ◇		1 ◇	1 ◇
				A	B			A			B		B			B		B		
			⊠			⊠	⚲		⊠	⚲		⚲		⊠	⚲		⚲		⊠	⚲
0	**Liverpool Lime Street** 10	90 d	05 44	05 50	06 21	06 27	06 35	06 50	07 07	07 18	07 21	07 40	07 50	08 15	08 19	08 29	08 40	08 55	09 15	09 19
1¾	Edge Hill	90 d		05 54				06 54					07 54					08 59		
3¾	Mossley Hill	d		05 59	06 29			06 59			07 29		07 59			08 37		09 04		
4½	West Allerton	d		06 01				07 01					08 01					09 06		
5½	**Liverpool South Parkway** 7 ✈	a		06 04	06 32		06 45	07 04			07 32	07 49	08 04			08 40	08 49	09 09		
—		d					06 45					07 50					08 50			
13	**Runcorn**	a	05 59			06 42	06 53			07 34		07 57		08 30	08 34		08 57		09 30	09 34
—		d	06 00			06 43	06 53		07u22	07 35		07 58		08 31	08 35		08 58		09 31	09 35
21	Acton Bridge	d					07 00										09 05			
23¾	Hartford	d					07 05					08 08					09 10			
28	Winsford	d					07 09					08 12								
35½	**Crewe** 10	65 a	06 20			07 02	07 20			07 54		08 23			08 59		09 23		09 50	09 58
—	Birmingham New Street 12	65 a	*07b55*				08 29			08 58		09 30			09 58		10 30			10 58
—	London Euston ⊖	65 a	08 19			08 58	*09b14*		09 17			*10c27*		10 35			*11c27*		11 48	

		NT	LM	NT	VT	LM	NT	LM	NT	VT	LM	NT	LM	NT	VT	NT	LM	NT	VT
			1 ◇		1 ◇	1		1 ◇		1 ◇	1 ◇		1 ◇		1 ◇		1 ◇		1 ◇
		B		B			B		B			B		B		B		B	
			⚲		⊠	⚲		⚲		⊏	⚲		⚲		⊏		⚲		⊏
Liverpool Lime Street 10	90 d	09 29	09 40	09 55	10 15	10 19	10 29	10 40	10 55	11 15	11 19	11 29	11 40	11 55	12 15	12 29	12 40	12 55	13 15
Edge Hill	90 d			09 59					10 59					11 59				12 59	
Mossley Hill	d	09 37		10 04			10 37		11 04			11 37		12 04		12 37		13 04	
West Allerton	d			10 06					11 06					12 06				13 06	
Liverpool South Parkway 7 ✈	a	09 40	09 49	10 09			10 40	10 49	11 09			11 40	11 49	12 09		12 40	12 49	13 09	
	d		09 50					10 50					11 50				12 50		
Runcorn	a		09 57		10 30	10 34		10 57		11 30	11 35		11 57		12 30		12 57		13 30
	d		09 58		10 31	10 35		10 58		11 31	11 35		11 58		12 31		12 58		13 31
Acton Bridge	d																13 05		
Hartford	d		10 08			10 46		11 09					12 08				13 10		
Winsford	d		10 12					11 13					12 12						
Crewe 10	65 a		10 23		10 50	10 58		11 23		11 50	11 58		12 24		12 50		13 23		13 50
Birmingham New Street 12	65 a		11 30			*11b58*		12 30			12 58		13 30		*13b58*		14 30		
London Euston ⊖	65 a		*12c26*		12 48	13 18		*13c27*		13 47			*14c40*		14 49		*15c26*		15 48

		LM	NT	LM	NT	VT	NT	LM	NT	VT	LM	NT	LM	NT	VT	NT	LM	NT	VT	LM
		1 ◇		1 ◇		1 ◇		1 ◇		1 ◇	1 ◇		1 ◇		1 ◇		1 ◇		1 ◇	1 ◇
			B		B		B		B			B		B		B		B		
		⚲		⚲		⊏		⚲		⊏	⚲		⚲		⊏		⚲		⊏	⚲
Liverpool Lime Street 10	90 d	13 19	13 29	13 40	13 55	14 15	14 29	14 40	14 55	15 15	15 19	15 29	15 40	15 55	16 15	16 28	16 40	16 55	17 15	17 18
Edge Hill	90 d				13 59				14 59					15 59				16 59		
Mossley Hill	d		13 37		14 04		14 37		15 04			15 37		16 04		16 36		17 04		
West Allerton	d				14 06				15 06					16 06				17 06		
Liverpool South Parkway 7 ✈	a		13 40	13 49	14 09		14 40	14 49	15 09			15 40	15 49	16 09		16 39	16 49	17 09		17 27
	d			13 50				14 50					15 50				16 50			17 28
Runcorn	a	13 35		13 57		14 30		14 57		15 30	15 35		15 57		16 30		16 57		17 30	17 36
	d	13 35		13 58		14 31		14 58		15 31	15 35		15 58		16 31		16 58		17 31	17 36
Acton Bridge	d																17 04			
Hartford	d			14 08				15 08					16 08				17 09			
Winsford	d			14 12				15 12					16 12							
Crewe 10	65 a	13 58		14 23		14 50		15 23		15 50	15 58		16 23		16 50		17 23		17 51	17 58
Birmingham New Street 12	65 a	14 58		15 30		*15b58*		16 30			16 58		17 30		*17b58*		18 30			18 58
London Euston ⊖	65 a			*16c27*		16 48		*17c40*		17 47	*18c21*		*18c27*		18 50		*19c25*		19 50	

		NT	LM	NT	VT	NT	LM	NT	LM	LM	VT	NT	LM	NT	LM	NT	LM	NT
			1 ◇		1 ◇		1 ◇		1 ◇	1 ◇	1 ◇		1 ◇		1 ◇		1	
		B		B		B		A				A		B		B		C
			⚲		⊏		⚲		⚲	⚲	⊏		⚲		⚲			
Liverpool Lime Street 10	90 d	17 25	17 37	17 55	18 15	18 25	18 40	18 55	19 19	19 40	19 49	19 55	20 40	20 55	21 40	21 55	23 20	23 35
Edge Hill	90 d	17 29		17 59		18 29		18 59				19 59		20 59		21 59		23 39
Mossley Hill	d	17 34		18 04		18 34		19 04				20 04		21 04	21 48	22 04		23 43
West Allerton	d	17 36		18 06		18 36		19 06				20 06		21 06		22 06		23 46
Liverpool South Parkway 7 ✈	a	17 39	17 46	18 09		18 39	18 49	19 09		19 49		20 09	20 49	21 09	21 51	22 09	23 30	23 49
	d		17 47				18 50			19 50			20 50		21 51		23 30	
Runcorn	a		17 54		18 30		18 57		19 34	19 57	20 04		20 57		21 59		23 38	
	d		17 56		18 31		18 58		19 35	19 58	20 05		20 58		21 59		23 38	
Acton Bridge	d		18 03				19 07										23 46	
Hartford	d		18 08				19 12			20 08			21 08		22 09		23 50	
Winsford	d		18 12							20 12			21 12		22 14		23 55	
Crewe 10	65 a		18 23		18 50		19 25		19 58	20 22	20 31		21 23		22 24		00 11	
Birmingham New Street 12	65 a		19 30		*19b58*		20 30		20 58	21 30	*22b04*		22 30		23 30			
London Euston ⊖	65 a		*20c26*		20 48		*21b51*				23 05		*00c09*					

For general notes see front of timetable
For details of catering facilities see Directory of Train Operators

A To Warrington Central (Table 89)
B To Manchester Oxford Road (Table 89)
C To Manchester Piccadilly (Table 89)

b Change at Stafford
c Change at Crewe

Table 91

Liverpool → Runcorn and Crewe

Saturdays

Network Diagram - see first page of Table 88

		NT A	VT 1◇	NT B	LM 1◇	NT A	VT 1◇	NT B	LM 1◇	NT B	VT 1◇	NT B	LM 1◇	NT B	VT 1◇	NT B	LM 1◇	NT B	VT 1◇	NT B	LM 1◇	NT B
Liverpool Lime Street 10	90 d	05 50	06 07	06 21	06 33	06 50	07 12	07 21	07 39	07 50	08 12	08 29	08 38	08 55	09 15	09 29	09 37	09 55	10 15	10 29	10 37	10 55
Edge Hill	90 d	05 54				06 54				07 54				08 59				09 59				10 59
Mossley Hill	d	05 59		06 29	06 40	06 59		07 29		07 59		08 37		09 04		09 37		10 04		10 37		11 04
West Allerton	d	06 01				07 01				08 01				09 06				10 06				11 06
Liverpool South Parkway 7 ✈	a	06 04		06 32	06 44	07 04		07 32	07 48	08 04		08 40	08 47	09 09		09 40	09 47	10 09		10 40	10 47	11 09
	d				06 45				07 49				08 47				09 47				10 47	
Runcorn	a		06 22		06 52		07 27		07 56		08 27		08 55		09 30		09 55		10 30		10 55	
	d		06 24		06 53		07 28		07 57		08 28		08 55		09 31		09 55		10 31		10 55	
Acton Bridge	d				07 02								09 02									
Hartford	d				07 07				08 06				09 07				10 05				11 05	
Winsford	d				07 11				08 10								10 09				11 09	
Crewe 10	65 a		06 43		07 23		07 48		08 21		08 47		09 21		09 50		10 21		10 50		11 21	
Birmingham New Street 12	65 a		07b56		08 27		09 10		09c27		09b58		10e27		10b58		11e27		11b58		12e27	
London Euston ⊖	65 a		09 29				10 32		11b02		11 27		12f03		12 28		13f03		13 26		14f03	

		VT 1◇	NT B	LM 1◇	NT B	VT 1◇	NT B	LM 1◇	NT B	VT 1◇	NT B	LM 1◇	NT B	VT 1◇	NT B	LM 1◇	NT B	VT 1◇	NT B	LM 1◇	NT B	VT 1◇
Liverpool Lime Street 10	90 d	11 15	11 29	11 37	11 55	12 15	12 29	12 37	12 55	13 15	13 29	13 37	13 55	14 15	14 28	14 37	14 55	15 10	15 29	15 37	15 55	16 15
Edge Hill	90 d				11 59				12 59				13 59				14 59				15 59	
Mossley Hill	d		11 37		12 04		12 37		13 04		13 37		14 04		14 37		15 04		15 37		16 04	
West Allerton	d				12 06				13 06				14 06				15 06				16 06	
Liverpool South Parkway 7 ✈	a		11 40	11 46	12 09		12 40	12 47	13 09		13 40	13 47	14 09		14 40	14 47	15 09		15 40	15 47	16 09	
	d			11 47				12 47				13 47				14 47				15 47		
Runcorn	a	11 30		11 54		12 30		12 55		13 30		13 55		14 30		14 55		15 25		15 55		16 30
	d	11 31		11 55		12 31		12 55		13 31		13 55		14 31		14 55		15 26		15 55		16 31
Acton Bridge	d							13 02														
Hartford	d			12 05				13 07				14 05				15 05				16 05		
Winsford	d			12 09								14 09				15 09				16 09		
Crewe 10	65 a	11 50		12 21		12 50		13 21		13 51		14 21		14 50		15 21		15 45		16 21		16 50
Birmingham New Street 12	65 a	12b58		13e27		13b58		14e27		14b58		15e27		15b58		16e27		16b58		17e27		17b58
London Euston ⊖	65 a	14 27		15f03		15 27		16f05		16 29		17f05		17 27		18f03		18 29		19f03		19 30

		NT B	LM 1◇	NT B	VT 1◇	NT B	LM 1◇	NT B	VT 1◇	NT B	LM 1◇	NT A	LM 1◇	NT A	VT 1◇	LM 1	NT B	LM 1◇	NT B	NT C
Liverpool Lime Street 10	90 d	16 28	16 37	16 55	17 15	17 25	17 37	17 55	18 10	18 25	18 40	18 55	19 37	19 55	20 10	20 40	20 55	21 16	21 55	23 33
Edge Hill	90 d			16 59		17 29		17 59		18 29		18 59		19 59			20 59		21 59	23 37
Mossley Hill	d	16 36		17 04		17 34	17 45	18 04		18 34		19 04		20 04			21 04		22 04	23 41
West Allerton	d			17 06		17 36		18 06		18 36		19 06		20 06			21 06		22 06	23 44
Liverpool South Parkway 7 ✈	a	16 39	16 47	17 09		17 39	17 47	18 09		18 39	18 49	19 09	19 47	20 09		20 49	21 09	21 25	22 09	23 47
	d		16 47				17 47				18 50		19 47			20 50		21 26		
Runcorn	a		16 55		17 30		17 55		18 25		18 57		19 55		20 25	20 57		21 33		
	d		16 55		17 31		17 55		18 26		18 58		19 55		20 26	20 58		21 34		
Acton Bridge	d		17 02								19 05									
Hartford	d		17 07				18 05				19 09		20 05			21 07		21 44		
Winsford	d						18 11						20 09			21 11		21 48		
Crewe 10	65 a		17 21		17 50		18 21		18 45		19 22		20 21		20 45	21 24		21 58		
Birmingham New Street 12	65 a		18e27		18b58		19 27		19b58		20 30		21 27		22 30			23 04		
London Euston ⊖	65 a		20f03		20 49		21g36		22 01		22h42		23j36		23k49					

Sundays

		NT B	VT 1◇	NT B	VT 1◇	NT B	LM 1◇	VT 1◇	NT B	VT 1◇	NT B	LM 1◇	VT 1◇	NT B	VT 1◇	NT B	LM 1◇	VT 1◇
Liverpool Lime Street 10	d	08 57	09 53	09 57	10 53	10 57	11 35	11 56	12 00	12 56	13 00	13 26	13 56	14 00	14 56	15 00	15 31	15 56
Mossley Hill	d	09 05		10 05		11 05			12 08		13 08			14 08		15 08		
West Allerton	d	09 07		10 07		11 07			12 10		13 10			14 10		15 10		
Liverpool South Parkway 7 ✈	a	09 10		10 10		11 10	11 44		12 13		13 13	13 35		14 13		15 13	15 40	
	d						11 45					13 36					15 41	
Runcorn	a		10 08		11 08		11 52	12 13		13 13		13 44	14 13		15 13		15 48	16 13
	d		10 09		11 09		11 53	12 14		13 14		13 44	14 14		15 14		15 49	16 14
Hartford	d						12 03					13 54						
Winsford	d						12 07					13 58						
Crewe 10	65 a		10 29		11 28		12 17	12 33		13 33		14 08	14 33		15 33		16 08	16 33
Birmingham New Street 12	65 a		11b58		12b58		13 21	13b58		14b58		15 08	15b58		16b58		17 14	17b58
London Euston ⊖	65 a		13 23		14 23		15b08	15 08		16 07		16m56	17 08		18 08		18m51	19 14

For general notes see front of timetable
For details of catering facilities see Directory of Train Operators

- **A** To Warrington Central (Table 89)
- **B** To Manchester Oxford Road (Table 89)
- **C** To Manchester Piccadilly (Table 89)

- **b** Change at Stafford
- **c** By changing at Stafford, passengers may arrive at 0924
- **e** By changing at Crewe, passengers may arrive 3 minutes earlier
- **f** Change at Crewe
- **g** Change at Crewe. From 29 March arr. 2128
- **h** Change at Stafford. From 29 March arr. 2234
- **j** Change at Crewe. From 29 March arr. 2326
- **k** From 29 March arr. 2334
- **m** From 30 March only. Change at Stafford

Table 91

Sundays

Liverpool → Runcorn and Crewe

Network Diagram - see first page of Table 88

		NT	NT	LM	VT	NT	VT	NT	LM	VT	NT	NT	LM	NT	NT
				1 ◇	1 ◇		1 ◇		1 ◇	1 ◇			1 ◇		
		A	A			A		A			A	A		A	A
					⊡		⊡			⊡					
Liverpool Lime Street 10	d	16 00	17 00	17 25	17 56	18 00	18 56	19 00	19 30	19 56	20 00	21 00	21 47	22 00	22 27
Mossley Hill	d	16 08	17 08	.	.	18 08	.	19 08	.	.	20 08	21 08	.	22 08	22 35
West Allerton	d	16 10	17 10	.	.	18 10	.	19 10	.	.	20 10	21 10	.	22 10	22 37
Liverpool South Parkway 7 ✈	a	16 13	17 13	17 35	.	18 13	.	19 13	19 39	.	20 13	21 13	21 56	22 13	22 40
	d	.	.	17 35	.	.	.	.	19 39	.	.	.	21 57	.	.
Runcorn	a	.	.	17 42	18 13	.	19 13	.	19 47	20 13	.	.	22 04	.	.
	d	.	.	17 43	18 14	.	19 14	.	19 47	20 14	.	.	22 05	.	.
Hartford	d	.	.	17 52	.	.	.	.	.	.	.	.	22 15	.	.
Winsford	d	.	.	17 57	.	.	.	.	.	.	.	.	22 19	.	.
Crewe 10	65 a	.	.	18 07	18 33	.	19 33	.	20 07	20 33	.	.	22 40	.	.
Birmingham New Street 12	65 a	.	.	19 04	19b58	.	20b58	.	21 08	21b56	.	.	23 45	.	.
London Euston ⊖	65 a	.	.	20c53	21 14	.	22 23	.	23c00	23 25	.	.	.	.	.

For general notes see front of timetable
For details of catering facilities see Directory of Train Operators

A To Manchester Oxford Road (Table 89)
b Change at Stafford
c From 30 March only. Change at Stafford

Table 91

Mondays to Fridays

Crewe and Runcorn → Liverpool

Network Diagram - see first page of Table 88

Miles		NT A	LM 1 🛒	NT A		LM 1 🛒	NT B	LM 1 ◇ 🛒		NT A	LM 1 C 🛒	NT B		LM 1 ◇ 🛒	NT D	LM 1 ◇ E 🛒		VT 1 ◇ ⊠	NT B	LM 1 C 🛒		NT B	LM 1 ◇ 🛒	VT 1 ◇ ⊠
—	London Euston ⊖ 65 d															06b46		07 13					07b46	08 17
—	Birmingham New Street 12 65 d					05 30		06 07			06c30			07 21		07 51		08 03		08 26			08 51	09 03
0	**Crewe 10** 65 d		06 12			06 47		07 23			07 47			08 24		08 52		09 08		09 24			09 47	10 08
7½	Winsford d		06 19					07 30			07 54			08 31						09 31				
11¾	Hartford d		06 24					07 35			07 59			08 36						09 36				
14½	Acton Bridge d		06 28					07 39			08 03													
22½	**Runcorn** a		06 35			07 03		07 47			08 10			08 45		09 08		09 25		09 45			10 03	10 25
—	d		06 36			07 03		07 47			08 11			08 45		09 08		09 25		09 45			10 03	10 25
30	**Liverpool South Parkway 7** ✈ a		06 44					07 53						08 53						09 53				
—	d	06 28	06 45	07 02			07 24	07 53		08 03		08 37		08 53	09 07				09 33	09 53		10 04		
31	West Allerton d	06 31		07 05			07 27			08 06		08 40			09 10				09 36					
31¾	Mossley Hill d	06 34	06 47	07 07			07 30			08 09		08 42			09 13				09 39			10 08		
33¾	Edge Hill 90 d	06 39		07 13			07 37			08 14		08 47							09 45					
35½	**Liverpool Lime Street 10** 90 a	06 46	07 01	07 19		07 27	07 44	08 11		08 21	08 35	08 55		09 09	09 24	09 31		09 47	09 51	10 09		10 20	10 26	10 47

	NT B	LM 1 ◇ 🛒		NT B	LM 1 ◇ 🛒	VT 1 ◇ ⊠		NT B	LM 1 ◇ 🛒	NT B		VT 1 ◇ ⊠	NT B	LM 1 ◇ 🛒		NT B	LM 1 ◇ 🛒	VT 1 ◇ ☕		NT B	LM 1 ◇ 🛒	NT B		VT 1 ◇ ☕
London Euston ⊖ 65 d					08b46	09 17						10 15					10b46	11 17			11b28			12 17
Birmingham New Street 12 65 d		09 21			09 51	10 03			10 21			11 03		11 21			11 51	12 03			12 21			13 03
Crewe 10 65 d		10 24			10 47	11 08			11 24			12 08		12 24			12 48	13 10			13 24			14 08
Winsford d									11 31												13 31			
Hartford d		10 34							11 36					12 34							13 36			
Acton Bridge d		10 38												12 38										
Runcorn a		10 45			11 03	11 25			11 45			12 25		12 45			13 03	13 26			13 45			14 25
d		10 46			11 03	11 25			11 45			12 25		12 46			13 03	13 26			13 45			14 25
Liverpool South Parkway 7 ✈ a		10 53							11 53					12 53							13 53			
d	10 33	10 53		11 04				11 33	11 53	12 04			12 33	12 53		13 04				13 33	13 53	14 04		
West Allerton d	10 36							11 36					12 36							13 36				
Mossley Hill d	10 39			11 08				11 39		12 08			12 39			13 08				13 39		14 08		
Edge Hill 90 d	10 45							11 45					12 45							13 45				
Liverpool Lime Street 10 90 a	10 51	11 09		11 20	11 26	11 47		11 51	12 09	12 20		12 47	12 51	13 09		13 20	13 26	13 49		13 51	14 09	14 20		14 47

	NT B	LM 1 ◇ 🛒	NT B		LM 1 ◇ 🛒	VT 1 ◇ ☕	NT B		LM 1 ◇ 🛒	NT B	VT 1 ◇ ☕		NT B	LM 1 ◇ 🛒	NT B		LM 1 ◇ 🛒	VT 1 ◇ ⊠	NT B		LM 1 ◇ 🛒	NT B	VT 1 ◇ ☕	NT B
London Euston ⊖ 65 d					12b46	13 17					14 17						14b46	15 17					16 17	
Birmingham New Street 12 65 d		13 21			13 51	14 03			14 21		15 03			15 21			15 51	16 03			16 21		17 03	
Crewe 10 65 d		14 24			14 47	15 08			15 24		16 08			16 24			16 47	17 08			17 24		18 08	
Winsford d		14 31							15 31												17 31			
Hartford d		14 36							15 36					16 34							17 36			
Acton Bridge d														16 38										
Runcorn a		14 45			15 03	15 25			15 45		16 25			16 45			17 03	17 25			17 45		18 25	
d		14 45			15 03	15 25			15 45		16 25			16 46			17 03	17 25			17 45		18 25	
Liverpool South Parkway 7 ✈ a		14 53							15 53					16 53							17 53			
d	14 33	14 53	15 04				15 33		15 53	16 06			16 33	16 53	17 04				17 39		17 53	18 14		18 40
West Allerton d	14 36						15 36						16 36						17 42			18 17		18 43
Mossley Hill d	14 39		15 08				15 39			16 10			16 39		17 08				17 44			18 20		18 45
Edge Hill 90 d	14 45						15 45						16 45						17 50			18 25		18 51
Liverpool Lime Street 10 90 a	14 51	15 09	15 20		15 26	15 48	15 51		16 09	16 22	16 48		16 51	17 09	17 24		17 26	17 47	17 58		18 09	18 32	18 47	18 59

	LM 1 ◇ 🛒		LM 1 ◇ 🛒	NT B	VT 1 ◇ ⊠		LM 1 ◇ 🛒	NT A	VT 1 ◇ ⊠		NT B	LM 1 ◇ 🛒	NT A		VT 1 ◇ ☕	LM 1 ◇ 🛒	NT A		VT 1 ◇ ☕	LM 1 ◇ 🛒	NT A	VT 1 ◇ ☕		
London Euston ⊖ 65 d			16c46		17 17		17c21		18 17			18e20			19 17				20 17			21 10		
Birmingham New Street 12 65 d	17 21		17 51		18 03		18 21		19c03			19 21			20 03	20 21			21c03	21 21				
Crewe 10 65 d	18 24		18 49		19 08		19 31		20 08			20 24			21 04	21 24			22 08	22 24		23 02		
Winsford d	18 31						19 39					20 31				21 31				22 31				
Hartford d	18 36						19 44					20 36				21 36				22 36				
Acton Bridge d																								
Runcorn a	18 45		19 05		19 25		19 53		20 25			20 45			21 21	21 45			22 25	22 45		23 19		
d	18 45		19 05		19 25		19 54		20 25			20 45			21 21	21 45			22 25	22 45		23 19		
Liverpool South Parkway 7 ✈ a	18 53						20 01					20 53				21 53				22 54				
d	18 53			19 09			20 02	20 03			20 38	20 53	21 03			21 53	22 03			22 54	23 03			
West Allerton d				19 13				20 06			20 41		21 06				22 06				23 06			
Mossley Hill d				19 15				20 09			20 43		21 09				22 09				23 09			
Edge Hill 90 d				19 25				20 14					21 14				22 14				23 14			
Liverpool Lime Street 10 90 a	19 09		19 29	19 32	19 45		20 18	20 21	20 47		20 59	21 09	21 21		21 45	22 09	22 22		22 47	23 12	23 21	23 47		

For general notes see front of timetable
For details of catering facilities see Directory of Train Operators

- A From Warrington Central (Table 89)
- B From Manchester Oxford Road (Table 89)
- C From Northampton (Table 68)
- D From Buxton (Table 86)
- E From Walsall (Table 70)
- b Change at Crewe
- c Change at Stafford
- e Fridays only. Change at Crewe

Table 91

Crewe and Runcorn → Liverpool

Network Diagram - see first page of Table 88

	NT	LM	NT	NT	LM	NT		NT	LM	NT	VT	NT	LM		NT	VT	NT	LM	NT	VT		NT	LM	NT
		1			1◇				1◇		1◇		1◇			1◇		1◇		1◇			1◇	
	A		A	B		A		B		B		B			B		B		B			B		B
											☕					☕				☕				
London Euston ⊖ 65 d											05 31					07 15				08 17				
Birmingham New Street 12 65 d					06b07				07 21				08 21					09 21		*09 40*			10 21	
Crewe 10 65 d		06 13			07 22				08 24		08 49		09 24			09 52		10 24		10 52			11 24	
Winsford d		06 20			07 29				08 31				09 31										11 31	
Hartford d		06 25			07 34				08 36				09 36					10 34					11 36	
Acton Bridge d		06 29			07 38													10 38						
Runcorn a		06 36			07 46				08 46		09 04		09 45			10 09		10 45		11 08			11 45	
d		06 37			07 46				08 46		09 04		09 46			10 09		10 46		11 10			11 46	
Liverpool South Parkway 7 ✈ a		06 45			07 54				08 56				09 54					10 54					11 54	
d	06 28	06 45	07 02	07 29	07 54	08 03		08 37	08 56	09 07		09 33	09 54		10 04		10 33	10 54	11 04			11 33	11 54	12 04
West Allerton d	06 31		07 05	07 32		08 06		08 40		09 10		09 36					10 36					11 36		
Mossley Hill d	06 34	06 48	07 07	07 35		08 09		08 42		09 13		09 39			10 08		10 39		11 08			11 39		12 08
Edge Hill 90 d	06 39		07 13	07 40		08 14		08 47				09 45					10 45					11 45		
Liverpool Lime Street 10 90 a	06 46	07 02	07 19	07 47	08 10	08 21		08 55	09 10	09 24	09 31	09 51	10 09		10 20	10 31	10 51	11 09	11 20	11 31		11 51	12 09	12 20

	VT	NT	LM	NT	VT		NT	LM	NT	VT	NT	LM		NT	VT	NT	LM	NT	VT		NT	LM	NT	VT
	1◇		1◇		1◇			1◇		1◇		1◇			1◇		1◇		1◇			1◇		1◇
		B		B			B		B		B			B		B		B			B		B	
	☕				☕					☕					☕				☕					☕
London Euston ⊖ 65 d	09 17				10 17					11 17					12 17				13 17					14 17
Birmingham New Street 12 65 d	*10 40*		11 21		*11 40*			12 21		*12 40*		13 21			*13 40*		14 21		*14 40*			15 21		*15 40*
Crewe 10 65 d	11 52		12 24		12 51			13 24		13 52		14 24			14 52		15 24		15 52			16 24		16 52
Winsford d								13 31				14 31					15 31							
Hartford d			12 34					13 36				14 36					15 36					16 34		
Acton Bridge d			12 38																			16 38		
Runcorn a	12 09		12 46		13 08			13 45		14 08		14 45			15 09		15 45		16 09			16 46		17 09
d	12 10		12 46		13 09			13 46		14 09		14 46			15 10		15 46		16 10			16 46		17 10
Liverpool South Parkway 7 ✈ a			12 54					13 54				14 54					15 54					16 54		
d		12 33	12 54	13 04			13 33	13 54	14 04		14 33	14 54		15 04		15 33	15 54	16 06			16 33	16 54	17 04	
West Allerton d		12 36					13 36				14 36					15 36					16 36			
Mossley Hill d		12 39		13 08			13 39		14 08		14 39			15 08		15 39		16 10			16 39		17 08	
Edge Hill 90 d		12 45					13 45				14 45					15 45					16 45			
Liverpool Lime Street 10 90 a	12 31	12 51	13 09	13 20	13 30		13 51	14 09	14 20	14 32	14 51	15 09		15 19	15 31	15 51	16 09	16 22	16 33		16 51	17 09	17 24	17 30

	NT	LM	VT	NT		NT	LM	NT	VT	LM	NT		VT	NT	LM	NT	VT	NT		VT	VT	NT		
		1◇	1◇				1◇		1◇	1◇			1◇		1◇		1◇			1◇	1◇			
	B			B		B		B			A			B		A		A				A		
			☕						☕				☕				☕			☕	☕			
London Euston ⊖ 65 d			15 17						16 17				17 17				18 17			19c05	19e36			
Birmingham New Street 12 65 d		16 21	*16 40*				17 21		*17 40*	18 21			*18 40*		19 21					*20 21*	*21f21*			
Crewe 10 65 d		17 24	17 52				18 24		18 52	19 24			19 52		20 24		20 52			21 52	22 39			
Winsford d		17 31								19 31					20 31									
Hartford d		17 36					18 34			19 36					20 36									
Acton Bridge d																								
Runcorn a		17 45	18 09				18 43		19 08	19 45			20 08		20 45		21 08			22 08	22 54			
d		17 46	18 10				18 46		19 09	19 46			20 09		20 46		21 09			22 09	22 55			
Liverpool South Parkway 7 ✈ a		17 53					18 54			19 54					20 54									
d	17 39	17 53		18 14		18 38	18 54	19 09		19 54	20 03			20 38	20 54	21 03		22 03				23 03		
West Allerton d	17 42			18 17		18 43		19 13			20 06			20 41		21 06		22 06				23 06		
Mossley Hill d	17 44			18 20		18 45	18 57	19 15			20 09			20 43		21 09		22 09				23 09		
Edge Hill 90 d	17 50			18 27		18 51		19 21			20 14					21 14		22 14				23 14		
Liverpool Lime Street 10 90 a	17 58	18 09	18 28	18 35		18 59	19 09	19 28	19 32	20 09	20 21		20 30	20 57	21 09	21 21	21 27	22 22		22 27	23 15	23 21		

Sundays

	NT	NT		LM	NT		NT	LM		VT	NT		NT	LM		NT	VT		NT	VT		LM	NT	VT
				1◇				1◇		1◇				1◇			1◇			1◇		1◇		1◇
	B	B			B		B				B		B			B			B				B	
										☕							☕			☕				☕
London Euston ⊖ 65 d								*09f31*		09 40				*11f31*			11 40			12 40		*13f40*		13 55
Birmingham New Street 12 65 d				09 30				11 30						13 30						*14f18*		15 30		
Crewe 10 65 d				10 26				12 28		12 40				14 31			14 42			15 44		16 28		16 45
Winsford d				10 33										14 38										
Hartford d				10 38										14 43										
Runcorn a				10 47				12 45		12 55				14 52			15 00			16 00		16 44		17 01
d				10 48				12 45		12 56				14 53			15 01			16 01		16 45		17 02
Liverpool South Parkway 7 ✈ a				10 54				12 54						15 01								16 52		
d	09 03	10 03		10 55	11 03		12 03	12 54			13 03		14 03	15 01		15 03			16 03			16 53	17 03	
West Allerton d	09 06	10 06			11 06		12 06				13 06		14 06			15 06			16 06				17 06	
Mossley Hill d	09 09	10 09			11 09		12 09				13 09		14 09			15 09			16 09				17 09	
Liverpool Lime Street 10 a	09 20	10 21		11 13	11 20		12 20	13 11		13 18	13 20		14 20	15 18		15 20	15 26		16 20	16 24		17 09	17 20	17 27

For general notes see front of timetable
For details of catering facilities see Directory of Train Operators

A From Warrington Central (Table 89)
B From Manchester Oxford Road (Table 89)
b By changing at Stafford, passengers may depart at 0620
c From 29 March dep. 1917
e From 29 March dep. 1950
f Change at Stafford

Table 91

Sundays

Crewe and Runcorn → Liverpool

Network Diagram - see first page of Table 88

		NT	LM	NT	VT	NT	VT	LM	NT	VT	NT	VT	NT	VT	VT
			1 ◇		1 ◇		1 ◇	1 ◇		1 ◇		1 ◇		1 ◇	1 ◇
		A		A		A			A		A		A		
					⊡		⊡			⊡		⊡		⊡	⊡
London Euston	⊖ 65 d		15b50		15 58		16 58	17b50		17 58		18 58		19 58	20 40
Birmingham New Street 12	65 d		17 30				18b18	19 30				20b18		21 40	22b18
Crewe 10	65 d		18 29		18 42		19 44	20 28		20 46		21 44		22 52	23 45
Winsford	d		18 36					20 35							
Hartford	d		18 41					20 40							
Runcorn	a		18 50		18 58		20 00	20 49		21 02		21 59		23 07	00 01
	d		18 51		18 59		20 01	20 50		21 03		22 00		23 08	00 02
Liverpool South Parkway 7	✈ a		18 58					21 00							
	d	18 03	19 00	19 03		20 03		21 00	21 03		22 03		23 03		
West Allerton	d	18 06		19 06		20 06			21 06		22 06		23 06		
Mossley Hill	d	18 09		19 09		20 09			21 09		22 09		23 09		
Liverpool Lime Street 10	a	18 20	19 13	19 20	19 26	20 20	20 24	21 15	21 20	21 25	22 20	22 24	23 20	23 35	00 39

For general notes see front of timetable
For details of catering facilities see Directory of Train Operators

A From Manchester Oxford Road (Table 89)
b Change at Stafford

Network Diagram for Tables 94, 95

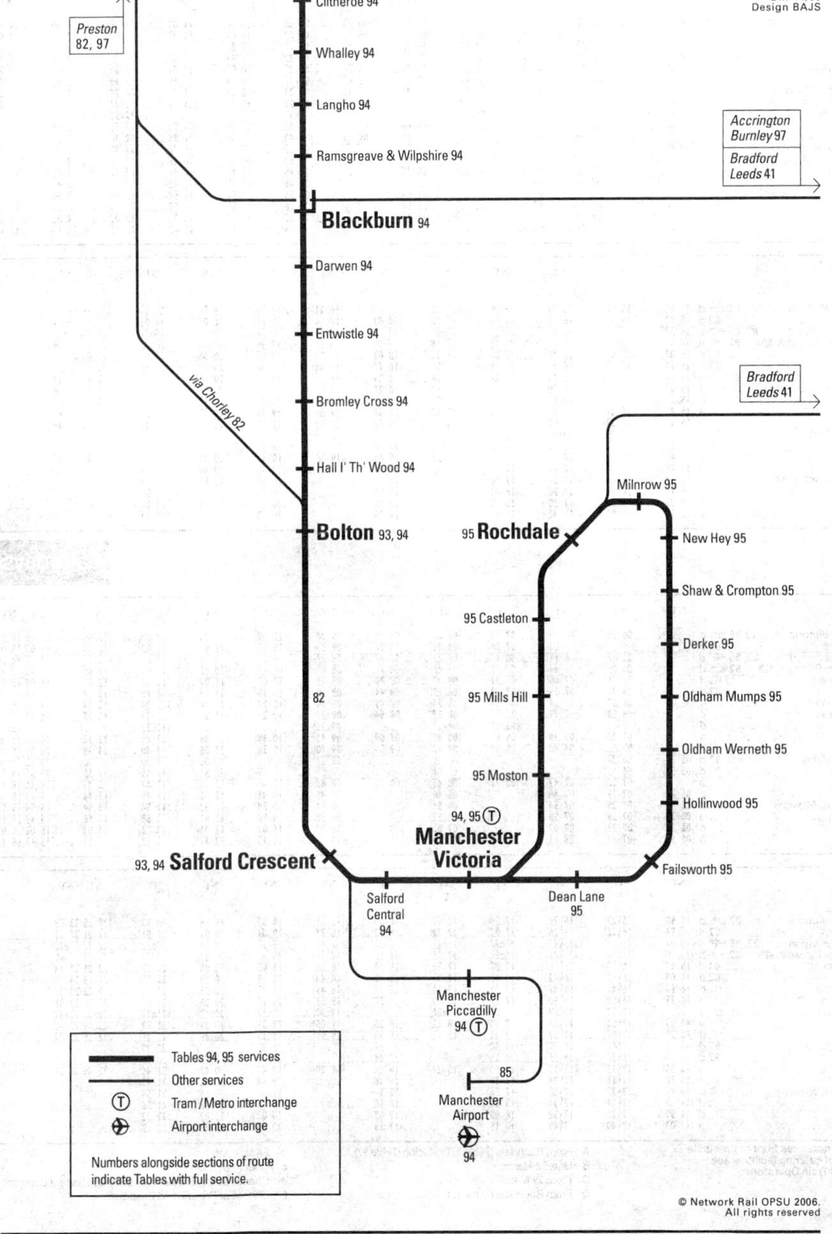
DM-11/06
Design BAJS
Preston
82, 97
Clitheroe 94
Whalley 94
Langho 94
Ramsgreave & Wilpshire 94
Accrington
Burnley 97
Bradford
Leeds 41
Blackburn 94
Darwen 94
Entwistle 94
via Chorley 82
Bromley Cross 94
Hall I' Th' Wood 94
Bradford
Leeds 41
Milnrow 95
Bolton 93, 94
95 Rochdale
New Hey 95
Shaw & Crompton 95
95 Castleton
Derker 95
82
95 Mills Hill
Oldham Mumps 95
Oldham Werneth 95
95 Moston
Hollinwood 95
94, 95 T
Manchester
Victoria
93, 94 Salford Crescent
Failsworth 95
Salford
Central
94
Dean Lane
95
Manchester
Piccadilly
94 T
Tables 94, 95 services
Other services
Tram / Metro interchange
Airport interchange
85
Manchester
Airport
94
Numbers alongside sections of route
indicate Tables with full service.

Manchester and Bolton → Blackburn → Clitheroe

Network Diagram - see first page of Table 94

Miles		NT	NT	NT	NT	NT	NT	NT	NT	NT	NT	NT	NT
0	**Manchester Victoria** 82 d		06 26	07 00	07 23	08 00	08 23	09 00	10 00	11 00	12 00	13 00	14 00
¾	Salford Central 82 d			07 03	07 26	08 03	08 26	09 03	10 03	11 03	12 03	13 03	14 03
—	Manchester Airport 82, 85 d		*05 47*	*06 19*	*06 47*	*07 22*	*07 47*	*08 27*	*09 27*	*10 27*	*11 27*	*12 27*	*13 27*
—	Manchester Piccadilly [10] 82 d		*06 05*	*06 44*	*07 11*	*07 45*	*08 11*	*08 45*	*09 45*	*10 45*	*11 45*	*12 45*	*13 45*
1¾	Salford Crescent 82 d		06 31	07 06	07 31	08 07	08 29	09 07	10 07	11 07	12 07	13 07	14 07
10¾	**Bolton** 82 d		06 45	07 19	07 44	08 19	08 44	09 19	10 19	11 19	12 19	13 19	14 19
12½	Hall I' Th' Wood d		06 50	07 24	07 49	08 24	08 49	09 24	10 24	11 24	12 24	13 24	14 24
13½	Bromley Cross d		06 53	07 27	07 54	08 27	08 54	09 27	10 27	11 27	12 27	13 27	14 27
16½	Entwistle d				08x01	08x33		09x33			12x33		
20¼	Darwen a		07 05	07 39	08 09	08 40	09 09	09 40	10 38	11 38	12 40	13 38	14 38
—	d		07 08	07 40	08 09	08 40	09 09	09 40	10 38	11 38	12 40	13 38	14 38
—	Blackpool North 97 d	*05 30*	*06 28*			*07 30*		*08 29*	*09 30*	*10 30*	*11 30*	*12 30*	*13 30*
—	Preston [8] 97 d	*05 55*	*06 54*			*08 01*		*08 54*	*09 55*	*10 55*	*11 55*	*12 55*	*13 55*
24½	**Blackburn** a		07 18	07 47	08 23	08 47	09 21	09 48	10 46	11 46	12 47	13 46	14 46
—	d	06 25	07 19	07 48		08 48		09 48	10 48	11 48	12 48	13 48	14 48
27¼	Ramsgreave & Wilpshire d	06 31	07 25	07 54		08 54		09 54	10 54	11 54	12 54	13 54	14 54
29¾	Langho d	06 35	07 29	07 58		08 58		09 58	10 58	11 58	12 58	13 58	14 58
31¾	Whalley d	06 39	07 33	08 02		09 02		10 02	11 02	12 02	13 02	14 02	15 02
34¼	**Clitheroe** a	06 50	07 44	08 13		09 13		10 13	11 13	12 13	13 13	14 13	15 13

	NT	NT	NT	NT	NT A	NT	NT	NT	NT	NT	NT	NT
Manchester Victoria 82 d	15 00	15 50	16 23	17 00	17 29	18 00	18 21	18 58	19 58	20 58	21 58	23 08
Salford Central 82 d	15 03	15 53	16 26	17 03	17 32	18 03	18 24	19 01	20 01	21 01	22b01	23b11
Manchester Airport 82, 85 d	*14 27*	*15 07*	*15 47*	*16c27*	*16c47*	*17 32*	*17 47*	*18 27*	*19 27*	*20e22*	*21 27*	*22e22*
Manchester Piccadilly [10] 82 d	*14 45*	*15 30*	*16 11*	*16 52*	*17 15*	*17 50*	*18 11*	*18 45*	*19 44*	*20 52*	*21 43*	*22 49*
Salford Crescent 82 d	15 07	15 57	16 30	17 07	17 36	18 07	18 28	19 05	20 05	21 05	22 05	23 14
Bolton 82 d	15 19	16 09	16 42	17 19	17 51	18 19	18 44	19 18	20 18	21 18	22 18	23 28
Hall I' Th' Wood d	15 24	16 14	16 47	17 24	17 56	18 24	18 49	19 23	20 23	21 23	22 23	23 33
Bromley Cross d	15 27	16 17	16 50	17 27	17 59	18 27	18 53	19 26	20 26	21 26	22 26	23 36
Entwistle d	15x33		16x57		18x06		19x00	19x32	20x32	21x32	22x32	23x42
Darwen a	15 40	16 29	17 03	17 38	18 12	18 38	19 06	19 39	20 39	21 39	22 39	23 49
d	15 40	16 29	17 07	17 42	18 12	18 38	19 09	19 39	20 39	21 39	22 39	23 49
Blackpool North 97 d	*14 30*	*15 30*	*15f41*	*16 30*		*17 19*		*18 30*		*20 28*		
Preston [8] 97 d	*14 55*	*15 55*	*16 31*	*16 55*		*17 44*		*18 55*		*20 54*		
Blackburn a	15 47	16 36	17 15	17 50	18 22	18 48	19 20	19 47	20 47	21 46	22 49	23 59
d	15 48	16 38	17 15	17 50		18 48		19 48	20 48	21 48		
Ramsgreave & Wilpshire d	15 54	16 44	17 21	17 56		18 54		19 54	20 54	21 54		
Langho d	15 58	16 48	17 26	18 01		18 58		19 58	20 58	21 58		
Whalley d	16 02	16 52	17 30	18 05		19 02		20 02	21 02	22 02		
Clitheroe a	16 13	17 03	17 40	18 15		19 13		20 13	21 13	22 13		

Saturdays

	NT	NT	NT	NT	NT	NT	NT	NT	NT	NT	NT	NT	NT
Manchester Victoria 82 d		06 26	07 00	07 23	08 00	08 23	09 00	10 00	11 00	12 00	13 00	14 00	15 00
Salford Central 82 d			07 03	07 26	08 03	08 26	09 03	10 03	11 03	12 03	13 03	14 03	15 03
Manchester Airport 82, 85 d		*05 47*	*06 19*	*06 47*	*07 22*	*07 47*	*08 27*	*09 27*	*10 27*	*11 27*	*12 27*	*13 27*	*14 27*
Manchester Piccadilly [10] 82 d		*06 05*	*06 44*	*07 11*	*07 45*	*08 11*	*08 45*	*09 45*	*10 45*	*11 45*	*12 45*	*13 45*	*14 45*
Salford Crescent 82 d		06 31	07 06	07 31	08 07	08 29	09 07	10 07	11 07	12 07	13 07	14 07	15 07
Bolton 82 d		06 45	07 19	07 44	08 19	08 44	09 19	10 19	11 19	12 19	13 19	14 19	15 19
Hall I' Th' Wood d		06 50	07 24	07 49	08 24	08 49	09 24	10 24	11 24	12 24	13 24	14 24	15 24
Bromley Cross d		06 53	07 27	07 54	08 27	08 54	09 27	10 27	11 27	12 27	13 27	14 27	15 27
Entwistle d				08x01	08x33		09x33			12x33			15x33
Darwen a		07 05	07 39	08 09	08 40	09 09	09 40	10 38	11 38	12 40	13 38	14 38	15 40
d		07 08	07 40	08 09	08 40	09 09	09 40	10 38	11 38	12 40	13 38	14 38	15 40
Blackpool North 97 d	*05 30*	*06 27*			*07 30*		*08 27*	*09 30*	*10 30*	*11 30*	*12 30*	*13 30*	*14 30*
Preston [8] 97 d	*05 55*	*06 55*			*08 01*		*08 52*	*09 55*	*10 55*	*11 55*	*12 55*	*13 55*	*14 55*
Blackburn a		07 18	07 47	08 21	08 47	09 21	09 48	10 46	11 46	12 47	13 46	14 46	15 47
d	06 25	07 19	07 48		08 48		09 48	10 48	11 46	12 48	13 48	14 48	15 48
Ramsgreave & Wilpshire d	06 31	07 25	07 54		08 54		09 54	10 54	11 52	12 54	13 54	14 54	15 54
Langho d	06 35	07 29	07 58		08 58		09 58	10 58	11 57	12 58	13 58	14 58	15 58
Whalley d	06 39	07 33	08 02		09 02		10 02	11 02	12 01	13 02	14 02	15 02	16 02
Clitheroe a	06 50	07 44	08 13		09 13		10 13	11 13	12 11	13 13	14 13	15 13	16 13

	NT	NT B	NT C	NT	NT D	NT	NT	NT	NT	NT	NT	NT
Manchester Victoria 82 d	15 50	16 23	16 23	17 00	17 29	18 00	18 21	18 58	19 58	20 58	21 58	23 08
Salford Central 82 d	15 53	16 26	16 26	17 03	17 32	18 03	18 24	19 01	20 01	21 01	22 01	23 11
Manchester Airport 82, 85 d	*15 07*	*15 47*	*15 47*	*16c27*	*16c47*	*17 32*	*17 47*	*18 27*	*19 27*	*20e22*	*21 27*	*22e22*
Manchester Piccadilly [10] 82 d	*15 30*	*16 11*	*16 11*	*16c52*	*17 15*	*17 50*	*18 11*	*18 45*	*19 44*	*20 52*	*21 43*	*22 49*
Salford Crescent 82 d	15 57	16 30	16 30	17 07	17 36	18 07	18 28	19 05	20 05	21 05	22 05	23 14
Bolton 82 d	16 09	16 42	16 42	17 19	17 51	18 19	18 44	19 18	20 18	21 18	22 18	23 28
Hall I' Th' Wood d	16 14	16 47	16 47	17 24	17 56	18 24	18 49	19 23	20 23	21 23	22 23	23 33
Bromley Cross d	16 17	16 50	16 50	17 27	17 59	18 27	18 53	19 26	20 26	21 26	22 26	23 36
Entwistle d		16x57	16x57		18x06		19x00	19x32	20x32	21x32	22x32	23x42
Darwen a	16 29	17 03	17 03	17 38	18 12	18 38	19 06	19 39	20 39	21 39	22 39	23 49
d	16 29	17 07	17 07	17 42	18 12	18 38	19 09	19 39	20 39	21 39	22 39	23 49
Blackpool North 97 d	*15 30*	*15f41*	*16 30*	*16 30*		*17 19*		*18 30*		*20 30*		
Preston [8] 97 d	*15 55*	*16 31*	*16 55*	*16 55*		*17 44*		*18 56*		*20 55*		
Blackburn a	16 36	17 15	17 15	17 50	18 24	18 48	19 20	19 47	20 47	21 46	22 49	23 59
d	16 38	17 15	17 24	17 50		18 48		19 48	20 48	21 48		
Ramsgreave & Wilpshire d	16 44	17 21	17 30	17 56		18 54		19 54	20 54	21 54		
Langho d	16 48	17 26	17 34	18 01		18 58		19 58	20 58	21 58		
Whalley d	16 52	17 30	17 38	18 05		19 02		20 02	21 02	22 02		
Clitheroe a	17 03	17 40	17 49	18 15		19 13		20 13	21 13	22 13		

For general notes see front of timetable
For details of catering facilities see Directory of Train Operators

- **A** From Rochdale (Table 95) to Colne (Table 97)
- **B** Until 22 March
- **C** From 29 March
- **D** From Rochdale (Table 95)
- **b** Fridays only
- **c** Change at Bolton
- **e** Change at Manchester Piccadilly and Salford Crescent
- **f** Change at Preston and Blackburn

Table 94

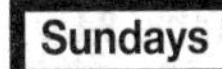

Manchester and Bolton → Blackburn → Clitheroe

Network Diagram - see first page of Table 94

Station		NT	NT A	NT	NT	NT	NT	NT	NT	NT	NT	NT	NT	NT	NT	NT	NT
Manchester Victoria	82 d	08 00		09 00	10 00	11 00	12 00	13 00	14 00	15 00	16 00	17 00	18 00	19 00	20 00	21 00	22 00
Manchester Airport	82, 85 d																
Manchester Piccadilly 10	82 d																
Salford Crescent	82 d			09 05	10 05	11 05	12 05	13 05	14 05	15 05	16 05	17 05	18 05	19 05	20 05	21 05	22 05
Bolton	82 d	08 13		09 18	10 18	11 18	12 18	13 18	14 18	15 18	16 18	17 18	18 18	19 18	20 18	21 18	22 18
Hall I' Th' Wood	d			09 23		11 23		13 23		15 23		17 23		19 23		21 23	
Bromley Cross	d	08 20		09 26	10 24	11 26	12 24	13 26	14 24	15 26	16 24	17 26	18 24	19 26	20 24	21 26	22 24
Entwistle	d				10x31		12x31		14x31		16x31		18x31		20x31		22x31
Darwen	a	08 31		09 37	10 37	11 37	12 37	13 37	14 37	15 37	16 37	17 37	18 37	19 37	20 37	21 37	22 37
	d	08 31		09 37	10 37	11 37	12 37	13 37	14 37	15 37	16 37	17 37	18 37	19 37	20 37	21 37	22 37
Blackpool North	97 d		08 42														
Preston 8	97 d		09 10														
Blackburn	a	08 39	09 29	09 46	10 45	11 45	12 45	13 45	14 45	15 45	16 45	17 44	18 45	19 45	20 45	21 45	22 47
	d	08 43	09 30	09 55	10 50	11 45	12 45	13 45	14 45	15 45	16 45	17 45	18 45	19 45	20 45	21 45	
Ramsgreave & Wilpshire	d	08 49	09 36	10 01	10 56	11 51	12 51	13 51	14 51	15 51	16 51	17 51	18 51	19 51	20 51	21 51	
Langho	d	08 54	09 41	10 05	11 00	11 56	12 56	13 56	14 56	15 56	16 56	17 56	18 56	19 56	20 56	21 56	
Whalley	d	08 58	09 46	10 09	11 04	12 00	13 00	14 00	15 00	16 00	17 00	18 00	19 00	20 00	21 00	22 00	
Clitheroe	a	09 08	09 52	10 20	11 15	12 10	13 10	14 10	15 10	16 10	17 10	18 10	19 10	20 10	21 10	22 10	

For general notes see front of timetable
For details of catering facilities see
Directory of Train Operators

A 23 March and 4 May.
To Carlisle (Table 36)

For Sunday connections from Manchester Airport and Manchester Piccadilly, please see Table 82. For Sunday connections from Blackpool North and Preston, please see Table 97.

Clitheroe → Blackburn → Bolton and Manchester

Network Diagram - see first page of Table 94

Miles	Station		NT	NT A	NT	NT	NT B	NT	NT	NT	NT	NT	NT	NT
0	**Clitheroe**	d			07 08	07 35	07 56		08 26		09 36	10 36	11 36	12 36
2¼	Whalley	d			07 14	07 41	08 02		08 32		09 42	10 42	11 42	12 42
4½	Langho	d			07 18	07 45	08 06		08 36		09 46	10 46	11 46	12 46
7	Ramsgreave & Wilpshire	d			07 23	07 50	08 11		08 41		09 51	10 51	11 51	12 51
9¾	**Blackburn**	a			07 29	07 57	08 19		08 47		09 58	10 57	11 57	12 57
—		d	06 30	07 00	07 30	08 00	08 19	08 30	09 00	09 30	10 00	11 00	12 00	13 00
—	Preston 8	97 a			*08 17*	*08 33*	08 43		*09 34*		*10 32*	*11 34*	*12 32*	*13 32*
—	Blackpool North	97 a			*08b51*	*09 04*	*09 33*		*10 02*		*11 02*	*12 01*	*13 00*	*13 59*
14	Darwen	a	06 37	07 07	07 37	08 07		08 37	09 07	09 37	10 07	11 07	12 07	13 07
—		d	06 37	07 07	07 40	08 10		08 41	09 10	09 41	10 07	11 07	12 07	13 07
17¾	Entwistle	d	06x44		07x47						10x14		12x14	
20¾	Bromley Cross	d	06 50	07 18	07 52	08 21		08 52	09 21	09 52	10 19	11 19	12 19	13 19
21¾	Hall I' Th' Wood	d	06 52	07 23	07 55	08 24		08 55	09 24	09 55	10 22	11c24	12 22	13 22
23¼	**Bolton**	82 a	06 57	07 29	08 00	08 29		09 00	09 29	10 00	10 29	11 29	12 29	13 29
32½	Salford Crescent	82 a	07 17	07 42	08 13	08 42		09 16	09 42	10 13	10 43	11 42	12 42	13 42
—	Manchester Piccadilly 10	82 ⇌ a	*07 36*	*08 19*	*08 47*	*08e53*		*09 35*	*09 57*	*10 35*	*10 57*	*11 57*	*12 57*	*13 57*
—	Manchester Airport	82, 85 ✈ a	*08 02*	*08e42*	*09 06*	*09e13*		*10 01*	*10 19*	*11 01*	*11 19*	*12 19*	*13 19*	*14 19*
33½	Salford Central	82 a	07 20	07 46	08 16	08 45		09 18	09 45	10 16	10 45	11 45	12 45	13 45
34¼	**Manchester Victoria**	82 ⇌ a	07 25	07 51	08 21	08 50		09 25	09 50	10 21	10 50	11 50	12 50	13 50

Station		NT	NT	NT	NT	NT	NT	NT	NT	NT	NT	NT C	NT
Clitheroe	d	13 36	14 36	15 26	16 36	17 12	18 08	18 36		19 36	20 36	21 36	22 46
Whalley	d	13 42	14 42	15 32	16 42	17 18	18 14	18 42		19 42	20 42	21 42	22 52
Langho	d	13 46	14 46	15 36	16 46	17 23	18 18	18 46		19 46	20 46	21 46	22 56
Ramsgreave & Wilpshire	d	13 51	14 51	15 41	16 51	17 27	18 23	18 51		19 51	20 51	21 51	23 01
Blackburn	a	13 57	14 57	15 47	16 57	17 34	18 30	18 57		19 57	20 57	22 00	23 10
	d	14 00	15 00	15 50	16 58	17 34	18 31	19 00	19 30	20 00	21 00	22 00	23 10
Preston 8	97 a	*14 32*	*15 32*	*16 33*	*17 34*	*18 07*	*19 10*	*19 36*		*20 31*	*21 31*	22 51	23 53
Blackpool North	97 a	*15 00*	*16 00*	*17 00*	*18 03*	*18b48*	*19b57*	*20 03*		*20 56*	*21 56*	23b28	00b38
Darwen	a	14 07	15 07	15 57	17 06	17 42	18 38	19 07	19 37	20 07	21 07	22 07	23 18
	d	14 07	15 07	15 57	17 06	17 42	18 41	19 07	19 40	20 07	21 07	22 07	23 18
Entwistle	d		15x14		17x13	17x49		19x14		20x14	21x14	22x14	23x25
Bromley Cross	d	14 19	15 19	16 08	17 18	17 54	18 52	19 19	19 51	20 19	21 19	22 19	23 30
Hall I' Th' Wood	d	14 22	15 22	16c14	17f23	17 58	18 55	19 22	19 53	20 22	21 22	22 22	23 34
Bolton	82 a	14 29	15 29	16 19	17 30	18 03	19 00	19 29	19 58	20 29	21 29	22 29	23 39
Salford Crescent	82 a	14 42	15 42	16 34	*17 48*	18 14	19 13	19 42	20 13	20 42	21 42	22 46	23 52
Manchester Piccadilly 10	82 ⇌ a	*14 57*	*15 57*	*16 57*	*17 57*	*18 38*	*19 36*	*19 57*	*20 34*	*20 58*	*22 18*	22 56	00e29
Manchester Airport	82, 85 ✈ a	*15 19*	*16 19*	*17 19*	*18 19*	*19 09*	*20 05*	*20 19*	*21g06*	*21 19*	*22 39*	*23 28*	00e45
Salford Central	82 a	14 45	15 45	16 37	17 45	18 16	19 16	19 45	20 16	20 45	21 45		
Manchester Victoria	82 ⇌ a	14 50	15 50	16 42	17 51	18 23	19 23	19 50	20 22	20 50	21 50		00 01

Saturdays

Station		NT	NT	NT	NT	NT D	NT	NT	NT	NT	NT	NT	NT
Clitheroe	d			07 08	07 35	07 56		08 26		09 36	10 36	11 36	12 36
Whalley	d			07 14	07 41	08 02		08 32		09 42	10 42	11 42	12 42
Langho	d			07 18	07 45	08 06		08 36		09 46	10 46	11 46	12 46
Ramsgreave & Wilpshire	d			07 23	07 50	08 11		08 41		09 51	10 51	11 51	12 51
Blackburn	a			07 29	07 57	08 19		08 47		09 57	10 57	11 57	12 57
	d	06 30	07 00	07 30	08 00	08 19	08 30	09 00	09 30	10 00	11 00	12 00	13 00
Preston 8	97 a			*08 17*	*08 33*	08 43		*09 33*		*10 32*	*11 34*	*12 32*	*13 32*
Blackpool North	97 a			*08b51*	*09 03*	*09 32*		*10 02*		*11 03*	*12 01*	*13 01*	*14 00*
Darwen	a	06 37	07 07	07 37	08 07		08 37	09 07	09 37	10 07	11 07	12 07	13 07
	d	06 37	07 07	07 40	08 10		08 41	09 10	09 41	10 07	11 07	12 07	13 07
Entwistle	d	06x44		07x47						10x14		12x14	
Bromley Cross	d	06 50	07 18	07 52	08 21		08 52	09 21	09 52	10 19	11 19	12 19	13 19
Hall I' Th' Wood	d	06 52	07 23	07 55	08 24		08 55	09 24	09 55	10 22	11 22	12 22	13 22
Bolton	82 a	06 57	07 29	08 00	08 29		09 00	09 29	10 00	10 29	11 29	12 29	13 29
Salford Crescent	82 a	07 17	07 42	08 13	08 42		09 16	09 42	10 13	10 43	11 43	12 43	13 42
Manchester Piccadilly 10	82 ⇌ a	*07 36*	*08 20*	*08 47*	*08e53*		*09 35*	*09 57*	*10 35*	*10 57*	*11 57*	*12 57*	*13 57*
Manchester Airport	82, 85 ✈ a	*08 02*	*08e42*	*09 06*	*09e13*		*10 02*	*10 19*	*11 01*	*11 19*	*12 19*	*13 19*	*14 19*
Salford Central	82 a	07 20	07 45	08 16	08 45		09 19	09 45	10 16	10 45	11 45	12 45	13 45
Manchester Victoria	82 ⇌ a	07 25	07 51	08 21	08 50		09 25	09 50	10 21	10 50	11 51	12 50	13 50

Station		NT	NT	NT	NT	NT	NT	NT	NT	NT	NT	NT C	NT
Clitheroe	d	13 36	14 36	15 26	16 36	17 12	18 08	18 36		19 42	20 36	21 36	22 46
Whalley	d	13 42	14 42	15 32	16 42	17 18	18 14	18 42		19 48	20 42	21 42	22 52
Langho	d	13 46	14 46	15 36	16 46	17 23	18 18	18 46		19 52	20 46	21 46	22 56
Ramsgreave & Wilpshire	d	13 51	14 51	15 41	16 51	17 27	18 23	18 51		19 57	20 51	21 51	23 01
Blackburn	a	13 57	14 57	15 47	16 57	17 34	18 29	18 57		20 03	20 57	22 00	23 10
	d	14 00	15 00	15 50	16 58	17 34	18 30	19 00	19 30	20 06	21 00	22 00	23 10
Preston 8	97 a	*14 32*	*15 32*	*16 33*	*17 34*	*18 07*	*19 12*	*19 35*		*20 31*	*21 31*	*22 51*	*23 53*
Blackpool North	97 a	*15 01*	*16 01*	*17 01*	*18 03*	*18b48*	*20b01*	*20 07*		*20 56*	*21 56*	23b28	00h38
Darwen	a	14 07	15 07	15 57	17 06	17 42	18 37	19 07	19 37	20 13	21 07	22 07	23 18
	d	14 07	15 07	15 57	17 06	17 42	18 41	19 07	19 40	20 13	21 07	22 07	23 18
Entwistle	d		15x14		17x13	17x49		19x14		20x21	21x14	22x14	23x25
Bromley Cross	d	14 19	15 19	16 08	17 18	17 54	18 52	19 19	19 51	20 25	21 19	22 19	23 30
Hall I' Th' Wood	d	14 22	15 22	16j14	17f23	17 58	18 55	19 22	19 53	20 28	21 22	22 22	23 34
Bolton	82 a	14 29	15 29	16 19	17 30	18 03	19 00	19 29	19 58	20 35	21 29	22 29	23 39
Salford Crescent	82 a	14 43	15 42	16 34	*17 48*	18 14	19 13	19 42	20 13	20 48	21 42	22 46	23 53
Manchester Piccadilly 10	82 ⇌ a	*14 57*	*15 57*	*16 57*	*17 57*	*18 38*	*19 36*	*19 58*	*20 34*	*21 14*	*22 18*	22 56	*00e29*
Manchester Airport	82, 85 ✈ a	*15 19*	*16 19*	*17 19*	*18 19*	*19 08*	*20 05*	*20 19*	*21g06*	*21 37*	*22 39*	*23 55*	*00e45*
Salford Central	82 a	14 45	15 45	16 37	17 45	18 17	19 16	19 45	20 16	20 51	21 45		
Manchester Victoria	82 ⇌ a	14 50	15 50	16 42	17 51	18 23	19 23	19 50	20 22	20 56	21 50		23 59

For general notes see front of timetable
For details of catering facilities see Directory of Train Operators

A From Colne (Table 97)
B To Morecambe (Table 98)
C To Buxton (Table 86)
D Until 22 March to Morecambe (Table 98)
b Change at Blackburn and Preston
c Arr. 3 minutes earlier
e Change at Bolton
f Arr. 1719
g Change at Salford Crescent and Manchester Piccadilly
h Change at Blackburn and Preston, 2 February to 22 March arr. 0125, by bus from Preston
j Arr. 1611

Table 94

Sundays

Clitheroe → Blackburn → Bolton and Manchester

Network Diagram - see first page of Table 94

	NT	NT	NT	NT	NT	NT	NT	NT	NT	NT	NT	NT	NT A ⚲	NT	NT	NT
Clitheroe d		09 17	10 27	11 24	12 24	13 24	14 24	15 24	16 24	17 24	18 24	19 24	19 47	20 24	21 24	22 24
Whalley d		09 23	10 33	11 30	12 30	13 30	14 30	15 30	16 30	17 30	18 30	19 30	19 55	20 30	21 30	22 30
Langho d		09 27	10 37	11 34	12 34	13 34	14 34	15 34	16 34	17 34	18 34	19 34	20 00	20 34	21 34	22 34
Ramsgreave & Wilpshire d		09 32	10 42	11 39	12 39	13 39	14 39	15 39	16 39	17 39	18 39	19 39	20 05	20 39	21 39	22 39
Blackburn a		09 38	10 48	11 45	12 45	13 45	14 45	15 45	16 45	17 45	18 45	19 45	20 14	20 45	21 45	22 45
d	08 48	09 48	10 48	11 48	12 48	13 48	14 48	15 48	16 48	17 48	18 48	19 48	20 14	20 48	21 48	22 48
Preston 8 97 a													20 34			
Blackpool North 97 a													21 03			
Darwen a	08 55	09 55	10 55	11 55	12 55	13 55	14 55	15 55	16 55	17 55	18 55	19 55		20 55	21 55	22 55
d	08 55	09 55	10 55	11 55	12 55	13 55	14 55	15 55	16 55	17 55	18 55	19 55		20 55	21 55	22 55
Entwistle d		10x02		12x02		14x02		16x02		18x02		20x02			22x02	
Bromley Cross d	09 06	10 08	11 06	12 08	13 06	14 08	15 06	16 08	17 06	18 08	19 06	20 08		21 06	22 08	23 06
Hall I' Th' Wood d	09 09		11 09		13 09		15 09		17 09		19 09			21 09		23 09
Bolton 82 a	09 14	10 14	11 16	12 14	13 14	14 14	15 14	16 14	17 14	18 14	19 14	20 14		21 14	22 14	23 15
Salford Crescent 82 a	09 29	10 29	11 29	12 29	13 29	14 29	15 29	16 29	17 29	18 29	19 29	20 29		21 29	22 29	23 29
Manchester Piccadilly 10 82 ⛴ a																
Manchester Airport 82, 85 ✈ a																
Manchester Victoria 82 ⛴ a	09 35	10 35	11 35	12 35	13 35	14 35	15 35	16 35	17 35	18 35	19 35	20 35		21 35	22 35	23 35

For general notes see front of timetable
For details of catering facilities see
Directory of Train Operators

A 23 March and 4 May.
From Carlisle (Table 36)

For Sunday connections to Preston and Blackpool North, please see Table 97. For Sunday connections to Manchester Piccadilly and Manchester Airport, please see Table 82.

Manchester → Oldham and Rochdale

Network Diagram - see first page of Table 94

Miles	Miles			NT A	NT SX B	NT SO B	NT	NT B	NT	NT	NT B	NT	NT	NT B	NT	NT SX C	NT	NT	NT B	NT		NT D	NT	NT	NT B
—	—	Liverpool Lime Street 10	90 d							05 47			06b39	06 39						07 18					07 47
—	—	Bolton	82 d										06 58		07 30	07 33			07c46	08 00				08b11	08 15
—	—	Salford Crescent	82 d							06b46			07e19		07f47	07 59		07g47	08c03	08 18		08 18		08b28	08 32
—	—	Salford Central	82 d							06b49			07e22		07f50	08 02		07g49	08c06	08 21		08 21		08b31	08 35
0	0	**Manchester Victoria**	d	05 54	06 18	06 24	06 45	06 49		07 07	07 18	07 25	07 42	07 47	08 00	08 09		08 12	08 19	08 30		08 33		08 42	08 54
—	4	Moston	d		06 25			06 55			07 25			07 53					08 25			08 40			
—	5¾	Mills Hill	d		06 30			07 00			07 30			07 58					08 30			08 44			
—	8¾	Castleton	d		06 35			07 05			07 35			08 03					08 35			08 49			
2½	—	Dean Lane	d				06 51			07 13			07 48					08 18						08 48	
3½	—	Failsworth	d				06 54			07 16			07 51					08 21						08 51	
4½	—	Hollinwood	d				06 56			07 18			07 54					08 24						08 54	
6¼	—	Oldham Werneth	d				07 01			07 23			07 58					08 28						08 58	
7½	—	**Oldham Mumps**	d				07 04			07 26		07 39	08 02		08 14			08 32		08 44				09 02	
8	—	Derker	d				07 07			07 29			08 04					08 34						09 04	
10	—	Shaw & Crompton	a				07 11		←	07 35		07 44	08 11		08 19		←	08 41		08 49			←	09 11	
—	—		d				07 11		07 11			07 44			08 19		08 19			08 49			08 49		
11¾	—	New Hey	d				→		07 14			07 47			→		08 23			→			08 52		
12¾	—	Milnrow	d						07 17			07 50					08 25						08 55		
14¾	10¼	**Rochdale**	a	06 08	06 38	06 38		07 08	07 25		07 38	07 57		08 06		08 25	08 33		08 38			08 55	09 03		09 08

		NT	NT E	NT	NT	NT B	NT	NT C	NT	NT	NT B	NT	NT G	NT	NT	NT B		NT	NT C	NT	NT	NT B	NT	NT D	NT
Liverpool Lime Street 10	90 d										08 48											09 48			
Bolton	82 d	08 30				08 50	09 01					09 30				09 50		10 01			10 07		10 30		
Salford Crescent	82 d	08h46	08j46			09 07	09 16	09c19				09 42	09 50			10 07		10 17	10 17		10 22		10 43	10 50	
Salford Central	82 d	08h49	08j49			09 09	09 19	09c24				09 45	09 53			10 09		10 20	10 20		10 24		10 45	10 53	
Manchester Victoria	d	09 00	09 03		09 15	09 24	09 30	09 33		09 45	09 54	10 00	10 03		10 15	10 24		10 30	10 33		10 45	10 54	11 00	11 03	
Moston	d		09 09					09 40					10 10						10 40					11 10	
Mills Hill	d		09 13					09 44					10 14						10 44					11 14	
Castleton	d		09 18					09 49					10 19						10 49					11 19	
Dean Lane	d				09 22					09 52					10 22						10 52				
Failsworth	d				09 25					09 55					10 25						10 55				
Hollinwood	d				09 27					09 57					10 27						10 57				
Oldham Werneth	d				09 32					10 02					10 32						11 02				
Oldham Mumps	d	09 14			09 35		09 44			10 05		10 14			10 35			10 44			11 05		11 14		
Derker	d				09 38					10 08					10 38						11 08				
Shaw & Crompton	a	09 19		←	09 44		09 49		←	10 14		10 19		←	10 44			10 49		←	11 14		11 19		←
	d	09 19		09 19			09 49		09 49			10 19		10 19				10 49		10 49			11 19		11 19
New Hey	d	→		09 23			→		09 53			→		10 23				→		10 53			→		11 23
Milnrow	d			09 25					09 55					10 25						10 55					11 25
Rochdale	a		09 25	09 33		09 38		09 55	10 03		10 08		10 25	10 33		10 38			10 55	11 03		11 08		11 25	11 33

		NT	NT B	NT	NT C	NT	NT	NT B	NT	NT D	NT	NT		NT B	NT	NT C	NT	NT	NT B	NT	NT D	NT	NT	NT B	NT
Liverpool Lime Street 10	90 d							10 48											11 48						
Bolton	82 d		10 50	10k59	10 59		11 07		11 30					11 50	11k59	11 59		12 07		12 30				12 50	12k59
Salford Crescent	82 d		11 07	11 17	11 17		11 22		11 43	11 50				12 07	12 17	12 17		12 22		12 43	12 50			13 07	13 17
Salford Central	82 d		11c09	11 20	11 20		11 24		11 45	11 53				12 09	12 20	12 20		12 24		12 45	12 53			13 09	13 20
Manchester Victoria	d	11 15	11 24	11 30	11 33		11 45	11 54	12 00	12 03		12 15		12 24	12 30	12 33		12 45	12 54	13 00	13 03		13 15	13 24	13 30
Moston	d				11 40					12 10						12 40					13 10				
Mills Hill	d				11 44					12 14						12 44					13 14				
Castleton	d				11 49					12 19						12 49					13 19				
Dean Lane	d	11 22					11 52					12 22						12 52					13 22		
Failsworth	d	11 25					11 55					12 25						12 55					13 25		
Hollinwood	d	11 27					11 57					12 27						12 57					13 27		
Oldham Werneth	d	11 32					12 02					12 32						13 02					13 32		
Oldham Mumps	d	11 35		11 44			12 05		12 14			12 35			12 44			13 05		13 14			13 35		13 44
Derker	d	11 38					12 08					12 38						13 08					13 38		
Shaw & Crompton	a	11 44		11 49		←	12 14		12 19		←	12 44			12 49		←	13 14		13 19		←	13 44		13 49
	d			11 49		11 49			12 19		12 19				12 49		12 49			13 19		13 19			13 49
New Hey	d			→		11 53			→		12 23				→		12 53			→		13 23			→
Milnrow	d					11 55					12 25						12 55					13 25			
Rochdale	a		11 38		11 55	12 03		12 08		12 25	12 33			12 38		12 55	13 03		13 08		13 25	13 33		13 38	

		NT C	NT	NT	NT B	NT	NT D	NT		NT	NT B	NT	NT C	NT	NT	NT B	NT	NT D	NT	NT	NT B	NT	NT C	NT	NT
Liverpool Lime Street 10	90 d				12 48											13 48									
Bolton	82 d	12 59		13 07		13 30					13 50	13k59	13 59		14 07		14 30				14 50	14k59	14 59		15 07
Salford Crescent	82 d	13 17		13 22		13 43	13 50				14 07	14 17	14 17		14 22		14 43	14 50			15 07	15 17	15 17		15 22
Salford Central	82 d	13 20		13 24		13 45	13 53				14 09	14 20	14 20		14c24		14 45	14 53			15 09	15 20	15 20		15 24
Manchester Victoria	d	13 33		13 45	13 54	14 00	14 03			14 15	14 24	14 30	14 33		14 45	14 54	15 00	15 03		15 15	15 24	15 30	15 33		15 45
Moston	d	13 40					14 10						14 40					15 10					15 40		
Mills Hill	d	13 44					14 14						14 44					15 14					15 44		
Castleton	d	13 49					14 19						14 49					15 19					15 49		
Dean Lane	d			13 52						14 22					14 52					15 22					15 52
Failsworth	d			13 55						14 25					14 55					15 25					15 55
Hollinwood	d			13 57						14 27					14 57					15 27					15 57
Oldham Werneth	d			14 02						14 32					15 02					15 32					16 02
Oldham Mumps	d			14 05		14 14				14 35		14 44			15 05		15 14			15 35		15 44			16 05
Derker	d			14 08						14 38					15 08					15 38					16 08
Shaw & Crompton	a		←	14 14		14 19		←		14 44		14 49		←	15 14		15 19		←	15 44		15 49		←	16 14
	d		13 49			14 19		14 19				14 49		14 49			15 19		15 19			15 49		15 49	
New Hey	d		13 53			→		14 23				→		14 53			→		15 23			→		15 53	
Milnrow	d		13 55					14 25						14 55					15 25					15 55	
Rochdale	a	13 55	14 03		14 08		14 25	14 33			14 38		14 55	15 03		15 08		15 25	15 33		15 38		15 55	16 03	

For general notes see front of timetable
For details of catering facilities see Directory of Train Operators

A To Selby (Saturdays to Leeds) (Table 41)
B To Leeds (Table 41)
C From Southport (Table 82)
D From Kirkby (Table 82)
E From Wigan Wallgate (Saturdays from Southport) (Table 82)
G From Wigan Wallgate (Table 82)
b Mondays to Fridays only
c Saturdays dep. 1 minute later
e Saturdays dep. Salford Crescent 0718, Salford Central 0723
f Saturdays dep. Salford Crescent 0743, Salford Central 0745
g Saturdays only
h Saturdays dep. Salford Crescent 0842, Salford Central 0845
j Saturdays dep. Salford Crescent 0850, Salford Central 0853
k Change at Salford Crescent and Manchester Victoria

Manchester → Oldham and Rochdale

Network Diagram - see first page of Table 94

		NT A	NT	NT B	NT	NT	NT A	NT	NT C	NT	NT	NT A	NT	NT B	NT	NT	NT A	NT	NT C	NT	NT	NT A	NT
Liverpool Lime Street 10	90 d	14 48										15 48						16 18					16 48
Bolton	82 d		15 30				15 50	15b59	15 59		16 10	16 20						16c50	16 59		17 18		17 30
Salford Crescent	82 d		15 43	15 50			16 07	16 17	16 17		16 22	16 35		16 50				17c07	17 18		17 31		17 45
Salford Central	82 d		15 45	15 53			16 10	16 20	16 20		16 25	16 37		16 55				17c09	17e23		17 33		17 48
Manchester Victoria	d	15 54	16 00	16 03		16 15	16 24	16 30	16 33		16 45	16 54	17 00	17 03		17 10	17 18	17 30	17 33		17 45	17 49	18 00
Moston	d			16 10					16 40					17 10			17 25		17 40			17 55	
Mills Hill	d			16 14					16 44					17 14			17 30		17 44			18 00	
Castleton	d			16 19					16 49					17 19			17 35		17 49			18 05	
Dean Lane	d					16 22					16 52					17 15					17 52		
Failsworth	d					16 25					16 55					17 18					17 55		
Hollinwood	d					16 27					16 57					17 21					17 57		
Oldham Werneth	d					16 32					17 02					17 25					18 02		
Oldham Mumps	d		16 14			16 35		16 44			17 05		17 14			17 29		17 44			18 05		18 14
Derker	d					16 38					17 08					17 31					18 08		
Shaw & Crompton	a		16 19		←	16 44		16 49		←	17 14		17 19		←	17 38		17 49		←	18 14		18 19
	d		16 19 →		16 19			16 49 →		16 49			17 19 →		17 19			17 49 →		17 49			18 19 →
New Hey	d				16 23					16 53					17 23					17 53			
Milnrow	d				16 25					16 55					17 25					17 55			
Rochdale	a	16 08		16 25	16 33		16 38		16 55	17 03		17 08		17 25	17 33		17 38		17 55	18 03		18 08	

		NT	NT	NT A	NT	NT D	NT	NT	NT SX A	NT SO A	NT	NT	NT A	NT	NT	NT A	NT	NT	NT SX A	NT	NT SO A	NT SX A	NT
Liverpool Lime Street 10	90 d	17 12				17 35		17e50				18 48			19 18			20 18			21 18	21 18	
Bolton	82 d				18 03			18 40				19 30			20f30	20g34		21 30			22 23	22b33	22b33
Salford Crescent	82 d				18 14	18 22		18 55		19 05		19 44			20f43	20 52		21 43	21 52		22 36	22 52	22 52
Salford Central	82 d				18h16	18 24		18 57		19 08		19 47			20f45	20 56		21 45	21 56		22 39	22j55	22k55
Manchester Victoria	d	18 13		18 19	18 30	18 47		19 07	19 18	19 26		20 07	20 19		21 00	21 19		22 00	22 19		22 49	23 19	23 21
Moston	d			18 25		18 53			19 25	19 32			20 25			21 25			22 25		22 55	23 25	
Mills Hill	d	18 21		18 30		18 57			19 30	19 37			20 30			21 30			22 30		23 00	23 30	
Castleton	d	18 27		18 35		19 02			19 35	19 42			20 35			21 35			22 35		23 05	23 35	
Dean Lane	d				18 37			19 13				20 13			21 06			22 06					23 28
Failsworth	d				18 40			19 16				20 16			21 09			22 09					23 31
Hollinwood	d				18 42			19 19				20 19			21 12			22 12					23 33
Oldham Werneth	d				18 47			19 23				20 23			21 16			22 16					23 38
Oldham Mumps	d				18 50			19 27				20 27			21 20			22 20					23 41
Derker	d				18 53			19 29				20 29			21 22			22 22					23 44
Shaw & Crompton	a		←		18 56		←	19 33			←	20 33		←	21 26		←	22 26		←			23 47
	d		18 19		18 56 →		18 56	19 36 →			19 36	20 33 →		20 33	21 26 →		21 26	22 26 →		22 26			23 47
New Hey	d		18 23				19 00				19 39			20 36			21 29			22 29			23 51
Milnrow	d		18 25				19 02				19 42			20 39			21 32			22 32			23 53
Rochdale	a	18 32	18 33	18 38		19 05	19 13		19 38	19 45	19m49		20 38	20 46		21 38	21 39		22 38	22 39	23 08	23 38	00 02

Sundays

		NT A	NT	NT A		NT A	NT	NT A	NT	NT
Liverpool Lime Street 10	90 d									
Bolton	82 d			09 16		20 16		21b26		22 16
Salford Crescent	82 d			09 29	and at	20 29		21 50		22 29
Manchester Victoria	d	09 14	09 35	10 15		21 15	21 35	22 15	22 35	23 20
Moston	d	09 21		10 21	the same	21 21		22 21		
Mills Hill	d	09 25		10 25		21 25		22 25		
Castleton	d	09 30		10 30	minutes	21 30		22 30		
Dean Lane	d		09 41		past		21 41		22 41	23 26
Failsworth	d		09 44				21 44		22 44	23 29
Hollinwood	d		09 47		each		21 47		22 47	23 31
Oldham Werneth	d		09 51				21 51		22 51	23 36
Oldham Mumps	d		09 55		hour until		21 55		22 55	23 39
Derker	d		09 57				21 57		22 57	23 42
Shaw & Crompton	a		10 01				22 01		23 01	23 45
	d		10 01				22 01		23 01	23 45
New Hey	d		10 04				22 04		23 04	23 49
Milnrow	d		10 07				22 07		23 07	23 51
Rochdale	a	09 34	10 13	10 34		21 34	22 13	22 34	23 13	23 58

For general notes see front of timetable
For details of catering facilities see Directory of Train Operators

A To Leeds (Table 41)
B From Kirkby (Table 82)
C From Southport (Table 82)
D To Todmorden (Table 41)
b Change at Salford Crescent and Manchester Victoria
c Saturdays dep. Bolton 1659, Salford Crescent 1718, Salford Central 1721
e Saturdays dep. 2 minutes earlier
f Saturdays dep. Bolton 2000, Salford Crescent 2018, Salford Central 2021
g Saturdays dep. 2 minutes later
h Saturdays dep. 1 minute later
j Fridays only
k Fridays and Saturdays only
m Saturdays arr. 1956

Table 95 — Mondays to Saturdays

Rochdale and Oldham → Manchester

Network Diagram - see first page of Table 94

Miles	Miles	Station		NT	NT	NT	NT	NT	NT	NT	NT	NT	NT	NT	NT	NT		NT	NT	NT	NT	NT	NT	NT	NT
					SX																				
					A			A			B		A			C			A			D		A	
0	0	**Rochdale**	d	06 18	06 24		06 58	07 06		07 29	07 35		07 52		07 59	08 05			08 24		08 32	08 33		08 52	
2	—	Milnrow	d	06 22			07 02			07 33					08 03						08 36				
3	—	New Hey	d	06 24			07 04			07 35					08 05						08 38				
4¾	—	Shaw & Crompton	a	06 28		←	07 08		←	07 39		←			08 13			←			08 42		←		
—	—		d	06 28		06 28	07 08		07 08	07 39		07 39		07 56	08 13			08 13		08 26	08 42		08 42		08 56
6¾	—	Derker	d	→		06 32	→		07 12	→				08 00	→					08 30	→				09 00
7¼	—	**Oldham Mumps**	d			06 35			07 15			07 44		08 02				08 18		08 32			08 47		09 02
8½	—	Oldham Werneth	d			06 38			07 18					08 05						08 35					09 05
10¼	—	Hollinwood	d			06 41			07 21					08 08						08 38					09 08
11¼	—	Failsworth	d			06 43			07 23					08 11						08 41					09 11
12¼	—	Dean Lane	d			06 46			07 26					08 13						08 43					09 13
—	1½	Castleton	d		06 27			07 09			07 38		07 55			08 08			08 27			08 36			
—	4¼	Mills Hill	d		06 32			07 14			07 42		08 00			08 12			08 32			08 40			
—	6¼	Moston	d		06 35			07 17			07 45		08 03			08 15			08 35			08 43			
14¾	10¼	**Manchester Victoria**	a		06 46	06 55		07 29	07 34		07 57	08 01	08 16	08 24		08 25		08 40	08 46	08 53		08 54	09 05	09 09	09 23
—	—	Salford Central	82 a		06 54	07 03		07 40	07 52			08 23	08 26	08 45		08 30				09 03		09 00		09 21	09 32
—	—	Salford Crescent	82 a		06 57	07 06		07 44	07 56			08 26	08 29	08 47		08 33				09 06		09 03		09 24	09 35
—	—	Bolton	82 a		07 07	07 18		08 00	08 18			08 36	08 42	09 01		08 53						09b18		09 36	09c53
—	—	Liverpool Lime Street 10	90 a			08 13					09 05					09b39						10b05			

Station		NT	NT	NT	NT	NT	NT	NT		NT	NT	NT	NT	NT	NT	NT	NT	NT	NT	NT	NT	NT		NT	NT
											SO	SX					SX	SO							
			E		G			D			A	A			E		A	A			D			A	
Rochdale	d	09 02	09 03		09 23		09 32	09 33			09 50	09 53		10 02	10 03		10 23	10 24		10 32	10 33			10 50	
Milnrow	d	09 06					09 36							10 06						10 36					
New Hey	d	09 08					09 38							10 08						10 38					
Shaw & Crompton	a	09 12		←			09 42			←				10 12		←				10 42		←			
	d	09 12		09 12		09 26	09 42			09 42			09 56	10 12		10 12			10 26	10 42		10 42			10 56
Derker	d	→				09 30	→						10 00	→					10 30	→					11 00
Oldham Mumps	d			09 17		09 32				09 47			10 02			10 17			10 32			10 47			11 02
Oldham Werneth	d					09 35							10 05						10 35						11 05
Hollinwood	d					09 38							10 08						10 38						11 08
Failsworth	d					09 41							10 11						10 41						11 11
Dean Lane	d					09 43							10 13						10 43						11 13
Castleton	d		09 06					09 36							10 06						10 36				
Mills Hill	d		09 10					09 40							10 10						10 40				
Moston	d		09 13					09 43							10 13						10 43				
Manchester Victoria	a		09 24	09 35	09 40	09 53		09 55		10 05	10 10	10 10	10 23		10 25	10 35	10 40	10 41	10 53		10 54	11 05		11 10	11 23
Salford Central	82 a		09 32	09 44		10 03		10 00			10 21	10 21	10 32		10 32	10e44			11 03		11 00			11 21	11 32
Salford Crescent	82 a		09 35	09 47		10 06		10 03			10 24	10 24	10 35		10 35	10e47			11 06		11 03			11 24	11 35
Bolton	82 a		09 53	10 01				10b18			10 36	10 36	10f50		10g50	11e01					11b18			11 36	11c50
Liverpool Lime Street 10	90 a							11b05													12b05				

Station		NT	NT	NT	NT	NT	NT	NT	NT	NT	NT	NT	NT	NT		NT	NT	NT	NT	NT	NT	NT	NT	NT	NT
			E		A			D		A			E			A			D		A			E	
Rochdale	d	11 02	11 03		11 23		11 32	11 33		11 50		12 02	12 03			12 23		12 32	12 33		12 52		13 02	13 03	
Milnrow	d	11 06					11 36					12 06						12 36					13 06		
New Hey	d	11 08					11 38					12 08						12 38					13 08		
Shaw & Crompton	a	11 12		←			11 42		←			12 12		←				12 42		←			13 12		←
	d	11 12		11 12		11 26	11 42		11 42		11 56	12 12		12 12			12 26	12 42		12 42		12 56	13 12		13 12
Derker	d	→				11 30	→				12 00	→					12 30	→				13 00	→		
Oldham Mumps	d			11 17		11 32			11 47		12 02			12 17			12 32			12 47		13 02			13 17
Oldham Werneth	d					11 35					12 05						12 35					13 05			
Hollinwood	d					11 38					12 08						12 38					13 08			
Failsworth	d					11 41					12 11						12 41					13 11			
Dean Lane	d					11 43					12 13						12 43					13 13			
Castleton	d		11 06					11 36					12 06						12 36					13 06	
Mills Hill	d		11 10					11 40					12 10						12 40					13 10	
Moston	d		11 13					11 43					12 13						12 43					13 13	
Manchester Victoria	a		11 25	11 35	11 40	11 53		11 54	12 05	12 09	12 23		12 24	12 35		12 40	12 53		12 54	13 05	13 09	13 23		13 24	13 35
Salford Central	82 a		11 32	11 44		12 03		12 00		12 21	12 32		12 32	12 44			13 03		13 00		13 21	13 32		13 32	13 44
Salford Crescent	82 a		11 35	11 47		12 06		12 03		12 24	12 35		12 35	12 47			13 06		13 03		13 24	13 35		13 35	13 47
Bolton	82 a		11 50	12 01				12b18		12 36	12c50		12 50	13 01					13b18		13 36	13c50		13 50	14 01
Liverpool Lime Street 10	90 a							13b05											14b05						

Station		NT	NT	NT	NT	NT		NT	NT	NT	NT	NT	NT	NT	NT	NT	NT	NT	NT	NT		NT	NT	NT	NT
		A			D			A			E		A			D		A				E		A	
Rochdale	d	13 23		13 32	13 33			13 50		14 02	14 03		14 23		14 32	14 33		14 52		15 02		15 03		15 23	
Milnrow	d			13 36						14 06					14 36					15 06					
New Hey	d			13 38						14 08					14 38					15 08					
Shaw & Crompton	a			13 42		←				14 12		←			14 42		←			15 12			←		
	d		13 26	13 42		13 42			13 56	14 12		14 12		14 26	14 42		14 42		14 56	15 12			15 12		15 26
Derker	d		13 30	→					14 00	→				14 30	→				15 00	→					15 30
Oldham Mumps	d		13 32			13 47			14 02			14 17		14 32			14 47		15 02				15 17		15 32
Oldham Werneth	d		13 35						14 05					14 35					15 05						15 35
Hollinwood	d		13 38						14 08					14 38					15 08						15 38
Failsworth	d		13 41						14 11					14 41					15 11						15 41
Dean Lane	d		13 43						14 13					14 43					15 13						15 43
Castleton	d				13 36						14 06					14 36						15 06			
Mills Hill	d				13 40						14 10					14 40						15 10			
Moston	d				13 43						14 13					14 43						15 13			
Manchester Victoria	a	13 40	13 53		13 55	14 06		14 09	14 23		14 25	14 35	14 40	14 53		14 55	15 05	15 09	15 23			15 26	15 35	15 40	15 53
Salford Central	82 a		14 03		14 00			14 21	14 32		14 32	14 44		15 03		15 00		15 21	15 32			15 32	15 44	15 53	
Salford Crescent	82 a		14 06		14 03			14 24	14 35		14 35	14 47		15 06		15 03		15 24	15 35			15 35	15 47	15 56	
Bolton	82 a				14b18			14 36	14c50		14 50	15 01				15b18		15 36	15c50			15 50	16 01	16 08	
Liverpool Lime Street 10	90 a				15b05											16b05									

For general notes see front of timetable
For details of catering facilities see Directory of Train Operators

- **A** From Leeds (Table 41)
- **B** From Todmorden (Table 41)
- **C** From Todmorden (Table 41) to Kirkby (Table 82)
- **D** To Southport (Table 82)
- **E** To Kirkby (Table 82)
- **G** From Selby (Saturdays from Leeds) (Table 41)
- **b** Change at Manchester Victoria
- **c** Change at Manchester Victoria and Salford Crescent
- **e** Saturdays arr. Salford Central 1100, Salford Crescent 1103, Bolton 1118
- **f** Change at Manchester Victoria and Salford Crescent. Saturdays arr. 1 minute later
- **g** Saturdays arr. 1 minute later

Rochdale and Oldham → Manchester

Network Diagram - see first page of Table 94

		NT	NT A	NT	NT B	NT	NT	NT C	NT	NT B	NT	NT		NT	NT	NT B	NT	NT	NT D	NT	NT B	NT	NT E	NT	NT
Rochdale	d	15 32	15 33		15 54		16 02	16 03		16 23		16 32		16 33		16 52		17 02	17 03		17 23	17 32	17 33		
Milnrow	d	15 36					16 06					16 36						17 06				17 36			←
New Hey	d	15 38					16 08					16 38						17 08				17 38			17 38
Shaw & Crompton	a	15 42		←			16 12		←			16 42			←			17 12		←		→			17 42
	d	15 42 →		15 42		15 56	16 12 →		16 12		16 26	16 42 →			16 42		16 56	17 12 →		17 12				17 26	17 42
Derker	d					16 00					16 30						17 00							17 30	
Oldham Mumps	d			15 47		16 02			16 17		16 32				16 47		17 02			17 17				17 32	17 47
Oldham Werneth	d					16 05					16 35						17 05							17 35	
Hollinwood	d					16 08					16 38						17 08							17 38	
Failsworth	d					16 11					16 41						17 11							17 41	
Dean Lane	d					16 13					16 43						17 13							17 43	
Castleton	d		15 36					16 06						16 36					17 06				17 36		
Mills Hill	d		15 40					16 10						16 40					17 10				17 40		
Moston	d		15 43					16 13						16 43					17 13				17 43		
Manchester Victoria	a		15 55	16 04	16 10	16 23		16 27	16 35	16 40	16 52			16 57	17 05	17 10	17 24		17 26	17 35	17 40		17 53	17 54	18 05
Salford Central	82 a		16 00	16 13	16 26	16 32		16 32	16 44	16 51	17 03			17b08	17b13	17 18	17c41		17 32	17 45			18 00	18 03	
Salford Crescent	82 a		16 03	16 16	16 29	16 35		16 35	16 47	16 54	17 06				17b16	17 22	17c45		17 35	17 48			18 03	18 07	
Bolton	82 a		16 28	16 28	16 42	16e50		16f50	17 02	17g13	17 18			17b22	17h36	17 44			17 49	18 07				18 19	
Liverpool Lime Street 10	90 a		17j04											18 05										19 05	

		NT B	NT	NT		NT G	NT	NT B	NT	NT	NT SX B	NT SO B	NT B	NT	NT B	NT	NT B	NT	NT B	NT	NT B	NT	NT B		
Rochdale	d	17 52		18 02		18 03		18 23		18 32	18 52	18 54	19 23	19 24	19 52	20 02	20 52	21 02	21 52	22 02	22 52	23 02	23 52		
Milnrow	d			18 06						18 36				19 28		20 06		21 06		22 06		23 06			
New Hey	d			18 08						18 38				19 30		20 08		21 08		22 08		23 08			
Shaw & Crompton	a			18 12			←			18 42				19 34		20 12		21 12		22 12		23 12			
	d		17 56	18 12 →			18 12		18 26	18 42				19 34		20 12		21 12		22 12		23 12			
Derker	d		18 00						18 30					19 38		20 16		21 16		22 16		23 16			
Oldham Mumps	d		18 02				18 17		18 32	18 47				19 41		20 19		21 19		22 19		23 19			
Oldham Werneth	d		18 05						18 35					19 44		20 22		21 22		22 22		23 22			
Hollinwood	d		18 08						18 38					19 47		20 25		21 25		22 25		23 25			
Failsworth	d		18 11						18 41					19 49		20 27		21 27		22 27		23 27			
Dean Lane	d		18 13						18 43					19 52		20 30		21 30		22 30		23 30			
Castleton	d					18 06					18 55	18 57			19 55		20 55		21 55		22 55				
Mills Hill	d					18 10					19 00	19 02			20 00		21 00		22 00		23 00				
Moston	d					18 13					19 03	19 05			20 03		21 03		22 03		23 03				
Manchester Victoria	a	18 10	18 23			18 24	18 35	18 41	18 55	19 05	19 14	19 15	19 40	20 01	20 14	20 39	21 14	21 39	22 14	22 39	23 14	23 38	00 08		
Salford Central	82 a	18 24	18 32			18 32	18 44	19 01		19 21			20 01		20 24	21 01	21 24	22k01	22k37	23k11					
Salford Crescent	82 a	18f27	18 35			18 35	18 47	19 04		19 24			20 04		20 28	21 04	21 27	22 04	22 40	23m14					
Bolton	82 a	18 44	18n50			18q50	19f03	19 17		19g52			20m17		20g51	21 17	21g54	22 16	23g16	23m26					
Liverpool Lime Street 10	90 a					19j35			20 05				21 05			22 05		23 05		00 14					

Sundays

		NT	NT B		NT B	NT		NT B	NT		NT B	NT		NT B		NT	NT B			NT B	NT	NT H		
Rochdale	d	09 23	09 41		10 18	10 23		11 18	11 23		12 18	12 23		13 20		13 23	14 18	and at the same minutes past each hour until		21 18	21 23	22 51		
Milnrow	d	09 27				10 27			11 27			12 27				13 27					21 27			
New Hey	d	09 29				10 29			11 29			12 29				13 29					21 29			
Shaw & Crompton	a	09 33				10 33			11 33			12 33				13 33					21 33			
	d	09 33				10 33			11 33			12 33				13 33					21 33			
Derker	d	09 37				10 37			11 37			12 37				13 37					21 37			
Oldham Mumps	d	09 40				10 40			11 40			12 40				13 40					21 40			
Oldham Werneth	d	09 43				10 43			11 43			12 43				13 43					21 43			
Hollinwood	d	09 46				10 46			11 46			12 46				13 46					21 46			
Failsworth	d	09 48				10 48			11 48			12 48				13 48					21 48			
Dean Lane	d	09 51				10 51			11 51			12 51				13 51					21 51			
Castleton	d		09 44		10 21			11 21			12 21			13 23			14 21			21 21		22 54		
Mills Hill	d		09 49		10 26			11 26			12 26			13 28			14 26			21 26		22 59		
Moston	d		09 52		10 29			11 29			12 29			13 31			14 29			21 29		23 02		
Manchester Victoria	a	09 59	10 01		10 39	10 59		11 38	11 59		12 38	12 59		13 40		13 59	14 38			21 38	21 59	23 11		
Salford Crescent	82 a				11 04			12 04			13 04			14 04			15 04			22 04	23 04			
Bolton	82 a				11 15			12 15			13 15			14 15			15 15			22 15	23g22			
Liverpool Lime Street 10	90 a																							

For general notes see front of timetable
For details of catering facilities see Directory of Train Operators

A To Southport (Table 82)
B From Leeds (Table 41)
C To Kirkby (Table 82)
D Mondays to Fridays to Colne (Table 97). Saturdays to Blackburn (Table 94)
E To Southport (Saturdays to Wigan Wallgate) (Table 82)
G To Wigan Wallgate (Table 82)
H From York (Table 41)
b Mondays to Fridays only
c Saturdays only
e Change at Manchester Victoria and Salford Crescent. Saturdays arr. 1 minute later
f Saturdays arr. 1 minute later
g Change at Manchester Victoria and Salford Crescent
h Mondays to Fridays only. Change at Manchester Victoria and Salford Crescent
j Change at Manchester Victoria
k Fridays and Saturdays only
m Saturdays arr. 1 minute earlier
n Change at Manchester Victoria and Salford Crescent. Saturdays arr. 1856
q Saturdays arr. 1856

Network Diagram for Tables 97, 98, 99, 100

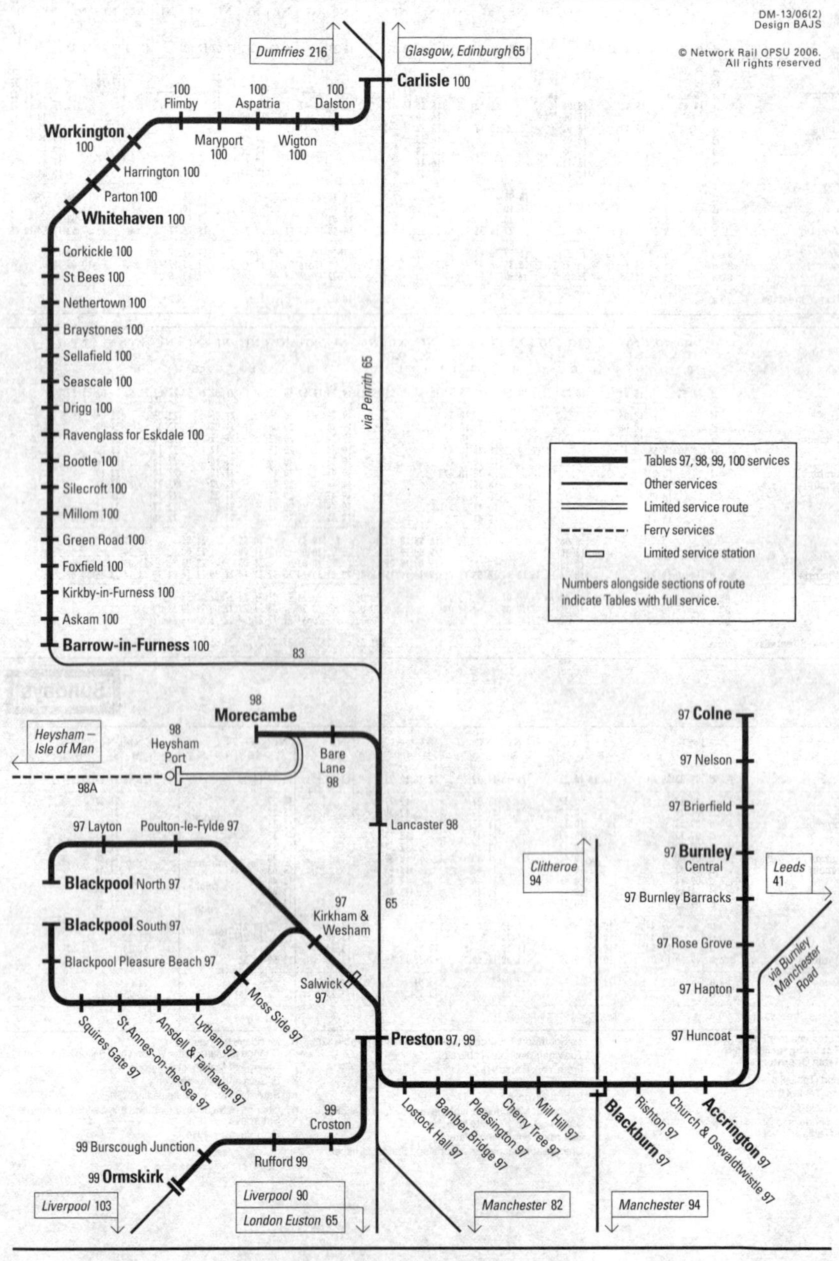

DM-13/06(2)
Design BAJS
© Network Rail OPSU 2006. All rights reserved
Dumfries 216
Glasgow, Edinburgh 65
Carlisle 100
100 Flimby
100 Aspatria
100 Dalston
Maryport 100
Wigton 100
Workington 100
Harrington 100
Parton 100
Whitehaven 100
Corkickle 100
St Bees 100
Nethertown 100
Braystones 100
Sellafield 100
Seascale 100
Drigg 100
Ravenglass for Eskdale 100
Bootle 100
Silecroft 100
Millom 100
Green Road 100
Foxfield 100
Kirkby-in-Furness 100
Askam 100
Barrow-in-Furness 100
83
via Penrith 65
Tables 97, 98, 99, 100 services
Other services
Limited service route
Ferry services
Limited service station
Numbers alongside sections of route indicate Tables with full service.
98 Morecambe
Heysham – Isle of Man
98 Heysham Port
98A
Bare Lane 98
Lancaster 98
97 Layton
Poulton-le-Fylde 97
Blackpool North 97
Blackpool South 97
Blackpool Pleasure Beach 97
97 Kirkham & Wesham
65
Salwick 97
Moss Side 97
Squires Gate 97
St Annes-on-the-Sea 97
Ansdell & Fairhaven 97
Lytham 97
Preston 97, 99
99 Croston
Rufford 99
99 Burscough Junction
99 Ormskirk
Liverpool 103
Liverpool 90
London Euston 65
Manchester 82
Manchester 94
Clitheroe 94
Lostock Hall 97
Bamber Bridge 97
Pleasington 97
Cherry Tree 97
Mill Hill 97
Blackburn 97
Rishton 97
Church & Oswaldtwistle 97
Accrington 97
97 Colne
97 Nelson
97 Brierfield
97 Burnley Central
97 Burnley Barracks
97 Rose Grove
97 Hapton
97 Huncoat
Leeds 41
via Burnley Manchester Road

Blackpool → Preston → Blackburn, Accrington, Burnley and Colne

Network Diagram - see first page of Table 97

Miles	Miles			TP MO A (bus)	TP MO A (bus)	NT	NT B	NT MO A	NT B	TP 1 ◇ C	NT D	NT	NT E	NT	NT D	NT	TP 1 ◇ C (trolley)	NT G	NT H	TP 1 ◇ C	NT BHX J		NT D	NT	TP 1 ◇ C (trolley)
—	0	**Blackpool North**	d	01 15	03 25		04 45		05 06	05 19	05 30		06 09		06 28		06 34		06 57	07 03	07 16		07 30		07 41
—	1¼	Layton	d						05 09				06 13				06 37			07 06					07 44
—	3¼	Poulton-le-Fylde	d						05 13	05 25	05 36		06 17		06 34		06 41		07 03	07 11	07 23		07 36		07 48
0	—	**Blackpool South**	d											05 50										07 23	
½	—	Blackpool Pleasure Beach	d											05 52										07 25	
1¾	—	Squires Gate	d											05 55										07 27	
3¼	—	St Annes-on-the-Sea	d											05 58				06 36						07 31	
5¼	—	Ansdell & Fairhaven	d											06 02				06 40						07 34	
6½	—	Lytham	d											06 05				06 43						07 37	
9	—	Moss Side	d											06 10				06 48						07 42	
12¼	9¾	Kirkham & Wesham	d						05 22				06 25	06 16			06 51	07b04		07 21	07 32			07 49	07 58
14¾	12¼	Salwick	d															07 08							
20	17½	**Preston 8**	a	01 55	04 05		05 08		05 33	05 43	05 54		06 36	06 28	06 52		07 02	07 18	07 23	07 31	07 45		07 54	07 59	08 08
—	—		d			04 43	05 16	05 16			05 55	06 10		06 42	06 54								07 55	08 01	
22¾	—	Lostock Hall	d									06 15		06 47										08 06	
24	—	Bamber Bridge	d									06 18		06 50										08 09	
29	—	Pleasington	d									06 26		06 58										08 17	
30	—	Cherry Tree	d									06 29		07 01										08 20	
30¾	—	Mill Hill (Lancashire)	d									06 31		07 03										08 22	
32	—	**Blackburn**	a			04 59	05 32	05 32			06 11	06 34		07 06	07 10								08 11	08 25	
—	—	Clitheroe 94	a								*06 50*				*07 44*									*09 13*	
—	—	Manchester Victoria 94 (bus)	d													←							*07 00*		
—	—	**Blackburn**	d			05 00	05 33	05 33			06 11	06 35		07 15 →	07 11	07 15							08 11	08 26	
35¾	—	Rishton	d				05 38	05 38								07 20								08 31	
37½	—	Church & Oswaldtwistle	d				05 41	05 41								07 23								08 34	
38¼	—	**Accrington**	d			05 07	05 44	05 44			06 19	06 42			07 18	07 26							08 19	08 37	
40	—	Huncoat	d				05 48	05 48								07 30									
41½	—	Hapton	d				05 51	05 51								07 33									
43	—	Rose Grove	d				05 54	05 54								07 36								08 44	
—	—	Burnley Manchester Road 41	a								06 27				07 27								08 27		
—	—	Leeds 10 41	a								07 37				08 39								09 39		
44	—	Burnley Barracks	d													07 39									
44½	—	**Burnley Central**	d			05 17	05 59	05 59				06 52				07 42								08 48	
46¾	—	Brierfield	d				06 03	06 03				06 57				07 46								08 53	
48	—	Nelson	d				06 06	06 06				07 00				07 49								08 56	
50	—	**Colne**	a			05 32	06 16	06 16				07 09				07 59								09 05	

		NT K	NT	NT D	NT	TP 1 ◇ C (trolley)	NT	NT K	NT H	NT D	TP 1 ◇ C (trolley)	NT	NT K	NT H	NT D	TP 1 ◇ C (trolley)	NT	NT K		NT H	NT D	TP 1 ◇ C (trolley)	NT	NT K	NT H
Blackpool North	d	08 09		08 29		08 41		09 11	09 25	09 30	09 38		10 11	10 25	10 30	10 41		11 11		11 25	11 30	11 41		12 11	12 25
Layton	d	08 12						09 14					10 14					11 14						12 14	
Poulton-le-Fylde	d	08 16		08 35		08 47		09 18		09 36	09 44		10 18		10 36	10 47		11 18			11 36	11 47		12 18	
Blackpool South	d						08 58					09 53					10 53						11 53		
Blackpool Pleasure Beach	d						09 00					09 55					10 55						11 55		
Squires Gate	d						09 02					09 57					10 57						11 57		
St Annes-on-the-Sea	d		08 10				09 06					10 01					11 01						12 01		
Ansdell & Fairhaven	d		08 13				09 09					10 04					11 04						12 04		
Lytham	d		08 16				09 12					10 07					11 07						12 07		
Moss Side	d		08 21				09 17					10 12					11 12						12 12		
Kirkham & Wesham	d	08 25	08 28				09 24	09 27				10 19	10 27				11 19	11 27					12 19	12 27	
Salwick	d		08 33																						
Preston 8	a	08 36	08 41	08 53		09 05	09 34	09 39	09 48	09 54	10 02	10 30	10 38	10 48	10 54	11 05	11 29	11 38		11 48	11 54	12 05	12 29	12 38	12 48
	d		08 42	08 54			09 36			09 55		10 31			10 55		11 31				11 55		12 31		
Lostock Hall	d		08 48				09 41					10 36					11 36						12 36		
Bamber Bridge	d		08 51				09 44					10 39					11 39						12 39		
Pleasington	d		08 58				09 52					10 47					11 47						12 47		
Cherry Tree	d		09 01				09 55					10 50					11 50						12 50		
Mill Hill (Lancashire)	d		09 04				09 57					10 52					11 52						12 52		
Blackburn	a		09 07	09 11			10 00			10 11		10 56			11 11		11 55				12 11		12 55		
Clitheroe 94	a			*10 13*						*11 13*					*12 13*						*13 13*				
Manchester Victoria 94 (bus)	d			*08 00*	←		*09 00*					*10 00*					*11 00*						*12 00*		
Blackburn	d		09 15 →	09 11	09 15		10 01			10 11		10 57			11 11		11 57				12 11		12 57		
Rishton	d				09 20		10 06					11 02					12 02						13 02		
Church & Oswaldtwistle	d				09 23		10 09					11 05					12 05						13 05		
Accrington	d			09 19	09 26		10 12			10 19		11 08			11 19		12 08				12 19		13 08		
Huncoat	d				09 31							11 13					12 13						13 13		
Hapton	d				09 34							11 16					12 16						13 16		
Rose Grove	d				09 37		10 19					11 19					12 19						13 19		
Burnley Manchester Road 41	a			09 27						10 27					11 27						12 27				
Leeds 10 41	a			10 37						11 39					12 39						13 37				
Burnley Barracks	d				09 40		10 22					11 22					12 22						13 22		
Burnley Central	d				09 42		10 24					11 24					12 24						13 24		
Brierfield	d				09 47		10 29					11 29					12 29						13 29		
Nelson	d				09 50		10 32					11 32					12 32						13 32		
Colne	a				09 59		10 41					11 41					12 41						13 41		

For general notes see front of timetable
For details of catering facilities see Directory of Train Operators

A 4 February to 24 March
B All Tuesdays to Fridays, also Mondays until 28 January and from 31 March
C To Manchester Airport (Table 82)
D To York (Table 41)
E To Chester (Table 88)
G To Greenbank (Table 88)
H To Liverpool Lime Street (Table 90)
J To Manchester Victoria (Table 82)
K To Buxton (Table 86)
b Arr. 0654

For connections to and from London Euston, please refer to Table 65

Blackpool → Preston → Blackburn, Accrington, Burnley and Colne

Network Diagram - see first page of Table 97

	NT A	TP 1◇ B ✠	NT	NT C	NT D	NT A	TP 1◇ B ✠	NT	NT E	NT D	NT A	TP 1◇ B ✠	NT	NT C		NT D	NT A	TP 1◇ B ✠	NT	NT C	NT D	NT A	TP 1◇ B ✠	NT
Blackpool North d	12 30	12 41		13 11	13 25	13 30	13 41		14 11	14 21	14 30	14 41		15 11		15 25	15 30	15 41		16 10	16 25	16 30	16 38	
Layton d				13 14					14 14					15 14						16 13			16 41	
Poulton-le-Fylde d	12 36	12 47		13 18		13 36	13 47		14 18		14 36	14 47		15 18			15 36	15 47		16 17		16 36	16 45	
Blackpool South d			12 53					13 53					14 53						15 53					16 53
Blackpool Pleasure Beach d			12 55					13 55					14 55						15 55					16 55
Squires Gate d			12 57					13 57					14 57						15 57					16 57
St Annes-on-the-Sea d			13 01					14 01					15 01						16 01					17 01
Ansdell & Fairhaven d			13 04					14 04					15 04						16 04					17 04
Lytham d			13 07					14 07					15 07						16 07					17 07
Moss Side d			13 12					14 12					15 12						16 12					17 12
Kirkham & Wesham d			13 19	13 27				14 19	14 27				15 19	15 27					16 19	16 26			16 56	17 19
Salwick d																			16 24					
Preston 8 a	12 53	13 05	13 29	13 38	13 48	13 54	14 05	14 29	14 38	14 44	14 54	15 05	15 29	15 38		15 48	15 54	16 05	16 31	16 37	16 48	16 54	17 06	17 29
d	12 55		13 31			13 55		14 31			14 55		15 31				15 55		16 31			16 55		17 31
Lostock Hall d			13 36					14 36					15 36						16 36					17 36
Bamber Bridge d			13 39					14 39					15 39						16 39					17 39
Pleasington d			13 47					14 47					15 47						16 47					17 47
Cherry Tree d			13 50					14 50					15 50						16 50					17 50
Mill Hill (Lancashire) d			13 52					14 52					15 52						16 52					17 52
Blackburn a	13 11		13 55			14 11		14 55			15 11		15 55				16 11		16 57			17 11		17 55
Clitheroe 94 a	*14 13*					*15 13*					*16 13*						*17 03*		*17 40*			*18 15*		
Manchester Victoria 94 ⛴ d			*13 00*					*14 00*					*15 00*						*15 50*					*17 00*
Blackburn d	13 11		13 57			14 11		14 57			15 11		15 57				16 11		16 57			17 11		17 57
Rishton d			14 02					15 02					16 02						17 02					18 02
Church & Oswaldtwistle d			14 05					15 05					16 05						17 05					18 05
Accrington d	13 19		14 08			14 19		15 08			15 19		16 08				16 19		17 08			17 19		18 08
Huncoat d			14 13					15 13					16 13						17 13					18 13
Hapton d			14 16					15 16					16 16						17 16					18 16
Rose Grove d			14 19					15 19					16 19						17 19					18 19
Burnley Manchester Road 41 a	13 27					14 27					15 27						16 27					17 27		
Leeds 10 41 a	14 39					15 37					16 37						17 37					18 37		
Burnley Barracks d			14 22					15 22					16 22						17 22					18 22
Burnley Central d			14 24					15 24					16 24						17 24					18a24
Brierfield d			14 29					15 29					16 29						17 29					
Nelson d			14 32					15 32					16 32						17 32					
Colne a			14 41					15 41					16 41						17 41					

	NT C	NT A	TP 1◇ B	NT G	NT	NT C	NT D	NT A	TP 1◇ B	NT	NT C	NT D	TP 1◇ B	NT	NT A	TP 1◇ B	NT	TP 1◇ B	NT D	NT	TP 1◇ B	NT		
Blackpool North d	17 10	17 19	17 38			18 11	18 25	18 30	18 38		19 10	19 25	19 42		20 28	20 53		21 53	22 03		23 13			
Layton d	17 13		17 41			18 14					19 13		19 45			20 56		21 56			23 16			
Poulton-le-Fylde d	17 17	17 25	17 45			18 18		18 36	18 44		19 17		19 49		20 34	21 00		22 00			23 20			
Blackpool South d					17 53					18 50				19 51			21 01			22 00		23 30		
Blackpool Pleasure Beach d					17 55					18 52				19 53			21 03			22 02		23 32		
Squires Gate d					17 57					18 54				19 55			21 05			22 04		23 34		
St Annes-on-the-Sea d					18 01					18 58				19 59			21 09			22 08		23 38		
Ansdell & Fairhaven d					18 04					19 01				20 02			21 12			22 11		23 41		
Lytham d					18 07					19 04				20 05			21 15			22 14		23 44		
Moss Side d					18 12					19 09				20 10			21 20			22 19		23 49		
Kirkham & Wesham d	17 26		17 56		18 19	18 27				19 16	19 26		19 59	20 17		21 10	21 27	22 10		22 25	23 30	23 56		
Salwick d																								
Preston 8 a	17 37	17 43	18 06		18 29	18 40	18 49	18 54	19 02	19 28	19 37	19 49	20 09	20 31	20 52	21 20	21 37	22 20	22 26	22 36	23 40	00 08		
d		17 44			18 37			18 55						20 31	20 54		21 40			22 38				
Lostock Hall d		17 50			18 42									20 36			21 45			22 43				
Bamber Bridge d		17 54			18 45									20 39			21 48			22 46				
Pleasington d		18 01			18 53									20 47			21 56			22 54				
Cherry Tree d		18 05			18 56									20 50			21 59			22 57				
Mill Hill (Lancashire) d		18 08			18 58									20 52			22 01			22 59				
Blackburn a		18 11			19 01			19 11						20 56	21 10		22 04			23 02				
Clitheroe 94 a		*19 13*						*20 13*							*22 13*									
Manchester Victoria 94 ⛴ d				17 29	*18 00*			*18 00*						*19 58*			*20 58*			*21 58*				
Blackburn d		18 11		18 23	19 15			19 11						20 57	21 11		22 08			23 03				
Rishton d				18 28	19 20									21 02			22 13			23 08				
Church & Oswaldtwistle d				18 31	19 23									21 05			22 16			23 11				
Accrington d		18 19		18 34	19 26			19 19						21 08	21 18		22 19			23 14				
Huncoat d				18 39	19 30									21 13			22 24			23 18				
Hapton d				18 42	19 33									21 16			22 27			23 21				
Rose Grove d				18 45	19 36									21 19			22 30			23 24				
Burnley Manchester Road 41 a		18 27						19 27							21 27									
Leeds 10 41 a		19 37						20 37							22 38									
Burnley Barracks d				18 48	19 39									21 22			22 33			23 27				
Burnley Central d				18 50	19 42									21 24			22 35			23 30				
Brierfield d				18 55	19 46									21 29			22 40			23 34				
Nelson d				18 58	19 49									21 32			22 43			23 37				
Colne a				19 05	19 59									21 41			22 52			23 47				

For general notes see front of timetable
For details of catering facilities see Directory of Train Operators

- **A** To York (Table 41)
- **B** To Manchester Airport (Table 82)
- **C** To Buxton (Table 86)
- **D** To Liverpool Lime Street (Table 90)
- **E** To Hazel Grove (Table 86)
- **G** From Rochdale (Table 95)

For connections to and from London Euston, please refer to Table 65

Table 97

Saturdays

Blackpool → Preston → Blackburn, Accrington, Burnley and Colne

Network Diagram - see first page of Table 97

		NT	NT	NT	TP 1◇ A	NT B	NT	NT C	NT		NT B	NT	TP 1◇ A	NT D	NT E	TP 1◇ A	NT B	NT		TP 1◇ A	NT G	NT	NT B	NT	TP 1◇ A
Blackpool North	d		04 43	05 06	05 19	05 30		06 08			06 27		06 34		06 57	07 03	07 30			07 41	08 09		08 27		08 41
Layton	d			05 09				06 12					06 37		07 00	07 07				07 44	08 12				
Poulton-le-Fylde	d			05 13	05 25	05 36		06 16			06 33		06 41		07 04	07 11	07 36			07 48	08 16		08 33		08 47
Blackpool South	d								05 50									07 23							
Blackpool Pleasure Beach	d								05 52									07 25							
Squires Gate	d								05 55									07 27							
St Annes-on-the-Sea	d								05 58					06 36				07 31				08 10			
Ansdell & Fairhaven	d								06 02					06 40				07 34				08 13			
Lytham	d								06 05					06 43				07 37				08 16			
Moss Side	d								06 10					06 48				07 42				08 21			
Kirkham & Wesham	d			05 22				06 24	06 16				06 51	07b04	07 13	07 20		07 49		07 58	08 25	08 28			
Salwick	d													07 08								08 33			
Preston 8	a		05 08	05 33	05 43	05 54		06 35	06 26		06 54		07 01	07 18	07 23	07 31	07 54	07 59		08 08	08 36	08 41	08 51		09 05
	d	04 43	05 22			05 55	06 10		06 42		06 55						07 55	08 01				08 42	08 52		
Lostock Hall	d						06 15		06 47									08 06				08 48			
Bamber Bridge	d						06 18		06 50									08 09				08 51			
Pleasington	d						06 26		06 58									08 17				08 58			
Cherry Tree	d						06 29		07 01									08 20				09 01			
Mill Hill (Lancashire)	d						06 31		07 03									08 22				09 04			
Blackburn	a	04 59	05 38			06 11	06 34		07 06		07 11						08 11	08 25				09 07	09 11		
Clitheroe 94	a					*06 50*					*07 44*							*09 13*					*10 13*		
Manchester Victoria 94 🚌	d											←					*07 00*	*07 23*				*08 00*	*08 00*	←	
Blackburn	d	05 00	05 39			06 11	06 35		07 15 →		07 11	07 15					08 11	08 26				09 15 →	09 11	09 15	
Rishton	d		05 44									07 20						08 31						09 20	
Church & Oswaldtwistle	d		05 47									07 23						08 34						09 23	
Accrington	d	05 07	05 50			06 19	06 42				07 19	07 26					08 19	08 37					09 19	09 26	
Huncoat	d		05 54									07 30												09 31	
Hapton	d		05 57									07 33												09 34	
Rose Grove	d		06 00									07 36						08 44						09 37	
Burnley Manchester Road 41	a					06 27					07 27						08 27						09 27		
Leeds 10 41	a					07 37					08 37						09 39						10 37		
Burnley Barracks	d											07 39												09 40	
Burnley Central	d	05 17	06 05				06 52					07 42						08 48						09 42	
Brierfield	d		06 09				06 57					07 46						08 53						09 47	
Nelson	d		06 12				07 00					07 49						08 56						09 50	
Colne	a	05 32	06 22				07 09					07 59						09 05						09 59	

		NT	NT G	NT E	NT B		TP 1◇ A	NT	NT G	NT E	NT B	TP 1◇ A	NT	NT G		NT E	NT B	TP 1◇ A	NT	NT G	NT E	NT B	TP 1◇ A		NT
Blackpool North	d		09 11	09 25	09 30		09 40		10 11	10 25	10 30	10 41		11 11		11 25	11 30	11 41		12 11	12 25	12 30	12 41		
Layton	d		09 14						10 14					11 14						12 14					
Poulton-le-Fylde	d		09 18		09 36		09 46		10 18		10 36	10 47		11 18			11 36	11 47		12 18		12 36	12 47		
Blackpool South	d	08 58						09 53					10 53						11 53						12 53
Blackpool Pleasure Beach	d	09 00						09 55					10 55						11 55						12 55
Squires Gate	d	09 02						09 57					10 57						11 57						12 57
St Annes-on-the-Sea	d	09 06						10 01					11 01						12 01						13 01
Ansdell & Fairhaven	d	09 09						10 04					11 04						12 04						13 04
Lytham	d	09 12						10 07					11 07						12 07						13 07
Moss Side	d	09 17						10 12					11 12						12 12						13 12
Kirkham & Wesham	d	09 24	09 27					10 19	10 27				11 19	11 27					12 19	12 27					13 19
Salwick	d																								
Preston 8	a	09 34	09 39	09 48	09 54		10 04	10 30	10 38	10 48	10 54	11 05	11 29	11 38		11 48	11 54	12 05	12 29	12 38	12 48	12 54	13 05		13 29
	d	09 36			09 55			10 31			10 55		11 31				11 55		12 31			12 55			13 31
Lostock Hall	d	09 41						10 36					11 36						12 36						13 36
Bamber Bridge	d	09 44						10 39					11 39						12 39						13 39
Pleasington	d	09 52						10 47					11 47						12 47						13 47
Cherry Tree	d	09 55						10 50					11 50						12 50						13 50
Mill Hill (Lancashire)	d	09 57						10 52					11 52						12 52						13 52
Blackburn	a	10 00			10 11			10 56			11 11		11 55				12 11		12 55			13 11			13 55
Clitheroe 94	a				*11 13*						*12 11*						*13 13*					*14 13*			
Manchester Victoria 94 🚌	d	*09 00*						*10 00*					*11 00*						*12 00*						*13 00*
Blackburn	d	10 01			10 11			10 57			11 11		11 57				12 11		12 57			13 11			13 57
Rishton	d	10 06						11 02					12 02						13 02						14 02
Church & Oswaldtwistle	d	10 09						11 05					12 05						13 05						14 05
Accrington	d	10 12			10 19			11 08			11 19		12 08				12 19		13 08			13 19			14 08
Huncoat	d							11 13					12 13						13 13						14 13
Hapton	d							11 16					12 16						13 16						14 16
Rose Grove	d	10 19						11 19					12 19						13 19						14 19
Burnley Manchester Road 41	a				10 27						11 27						12 27					13 27			
Leeds 10 41	a				11 39						12 38						13 37					14 39			
Burnley Barracks	d	10 22						11 22					12 22						13 22						14 22
Burnley Central	d	10 24						11 24					12 24						13 24						14 24
Brierfield	d	10 29						11 29					12 29						13 29						14 29
Nelson	d	10 32						11 32					12 32						13 32						14 32
Colne	a	10 41						11 41					12 41						13 41						14 41

For general notes see front of timetable
For details of catering facilities see Directory of Train Operators

A To Manchester Airport (Table 82)
B To York (Table 41)
C To Chester (Table 88)
D To Greenbank (Table 88)
E To Liverpool Lime Street (Table 90)
G To Buxton (Table 86)
b Arr. 0654

For connections to and from London Euston, please refer to Table 65

Blackpool → Preston → Blackburn, Accrington, Burnley and Colne

Network Diagram - see first page of Table 97

		NT	NT	NT	TP	NT	NT	NT	NT		TP	NT	NT	NT	NT	TP	NT	NT		NT	NT	TP	NT	NT	NT
					1 ◇						1 ◇					1 ◇						1 ◇			
		A	B	C	D		A	B	C		D		A	B	C	D		A		B	C	D		A	C
Blackpool North	d	13 11	13 25	13 30	13 41		14 11	14 25	14 30		14 41		15 11	15 25	15 30	15 41		16 10		16 25	16 30	16 38		17 10	17 19
Layton	d	13 14					14 14						15 14					16 13				16 41		17 13	
Poulton-le-Fylde	d	13 18		13 36	13 47		14 18		14 36		14 47		15 18		15 36	15 47		16 17			16 36	16 45		17 17	17 25
Blackpool South	d					13 53						14 53					15 53						16 53		
Blackpool Pleasure Beach	d					13 55						14 55					15 55						16 55		
Squires Gate	d					13 57						14 57					15 57						16 57		
St Annes-on-the-Sea	d					14 01						15 01					16 01						17 01		
Ansdell & Fairhaven	d					14 04						15 04					16 04						17 04		
Lytham	d					14 07						15 07					16 07						17 07		
Moss Side	d					14 12						15 12					16 12						17 12		
Kirkham & Wesham	d	13 27				14 19	14 27					15 19	15 27				16 19	16 26				16 56	17 19	17 26	
Salwick	d																16 24								
Preston 8	a	13 38	13 48	13 54	14 05	14 29	14 38	14 48	14 54		15 05	15 29	15 38	15 48	15 54	16 05	16 31	16 37		16 48	16 54	17 06	17 29	17 37	17 43
	d			13 55		14 31			14 55			15 31			15 55		16 31				16 55		17 31		17 44
Lostock Hall	d					14 36						15 36					16 36						17 36		17 50
Bamber Bridge	d					14 39						15 39					16 39						17 39		17 54
Pleasington	d					14 47						15 47					16 47						17 47		18 01
Cherry Tree	d					14 50						15 50					16 50						17 50		18 05
Mill Hill (Lancashire)	d					14 52						15 52					16 52						17 52		18 08
Blackburn	a			14 11		14 55			15 11			15 55			16 11		16 57				17 11		17 55		18 11
Clitheroe 94	a			*15 13*					*16 13*						*17 03*		*17b40*				*18c15*				*19 13*
Manchester Victoria 94	d					*14 00*						*15 00*					*15 50*						*17 00*		
Blackburn	d			14 11		14 57			15 11			15 57			16 11		16 57				17 11		17 57		18 11
Rishton	d					15 02						16 02					17 02						18 02		
Church & Oswaldtwistle	d					15 05						16 05					17 05						18 05		
Accrington	d			14 19		15 08			15 19			16 08			16 19		17 08				17 19		18 08		18 19
Huncoat	d					15 13						16 13					17 13						18 13		
Hapton	d					15 16						16 16					17 16						18 16		
Rose Grove	d					15 19						16 19					17 19						18 19		
Burnley Manchester Road 41	a			14 27					15 27						16 27						17 27				18 27
Leeds 10 41	a			15 37					16 37						17 37						18 37				19 37
Burnley Barracks	d					15 22						16 22					17 22						18 22		
Burnley Central	d					15 24						16 24					17 24						18 24		
Brierfield	d					15 29						16 29					17 29						18 29		
Nelson	d					15 32						16 32					17 32						18 32		
Colne	a					15 41						16 41					17 41						18 41		

		TP	NT	NT	NT		NT	TP	NT	NT	NT	TP	NT	NT		TP	NT	TP	NT	NT	NT	TP	NT		
		1 ◇						1 ◇				1 ◇				1 ◇		1 ◇			bus	1 ◇			
		D		A	B		C	D		A	B	D		C		D		D	B			D			
Blackpool North	d	17 38		18 11	18 25		18 30	18 42		19 10	19 25	19 42		20 30		20 53		21 52	22 03			23 13			
Layton	d	17 41		18 14						19 13		19 45				20 56		21 56				23 16			
Poulton-le-Fylde	d	17 45		18 18			18 36	18 48		19 17		19 49		20 37		21 00		22 00				23 20			
Blackpool South	d		17 53						18 50				19 51				20 53			22 00			23 30		
Blackpool Pleasure Beach	d		17 55						18 52				19 53				20 55			22 02			23 32		
Squires Gate	d		17 57						18 54				19 55				20 57			22 04			23 34		
St Annes-on-the-Sea	d		18 01						18 58				19 59				21 01			22 08			23 38		
Ansdell & Fairhaven	d		18 04						19 01				20 02				21 04			22 11			23 41		
Lytham	d		18 07						19 04				20 05				21 07			22 14			23 44		
Moss Side	d		18 12						19 09				20 10				21 12			22 19			23 49		
Kirkham & Wesham	d	17 56	18 19	18 27					19 16	19 26		19 59	20 17			21 10	21 19	22 09		22 25		23 30	23 56		
Salwick	d																								
Preston 8	a	18 06	18 29	18 39	18 49		18 54	19 06	19 28	19 37	19 49	20 09	20 31	20 54		21 20	21 29	22 20	22 26	22 36		23 40	00 08		
	d		18 31				18 56						20 31	20 55			21 31			22 38					
Lostock Hall	d		18 36										20 36				21 36			22 43					
Bamber Bridge	d		18 39										20 39				21 39			22 46					
Pleasington	d		18 47										20 47				21 47			22 54					
Cherry Tree	d		18 50										20 50				21 50			22 57					
Mill Hill (Lancashire)	d		18 52										20 52				21 52			22 59					
Blackburn	a		18 55				19 12						20 56	21 11			21 55			23 04					
Clitheroe 94	a						*20 13*							*22 13*											
Manchester Victoria 94	d		*18 00*										*19 58*				*20 58*				*21 58*				
Blackburn	d		18 57				19 13						20 57	21 11			22 00				23 10				
Rishton	d		19 02										21 02				22 05				23 20				
Church & Oswaldtwistle	d		19 05										21 05				22 08				23 32				
Accrington	d		19 08				19 20						21 08	21 19			22 11				23 36				
Huncoat	d		19 13										21 13				22 16				23 42				
Hapton	d		19 16										21 16				22 19				23 48				
Rose Grove	d		19 19										21 19				22 22				23 54				
Burnley Manchester Road 41	a						19 29							21 27											
Leeds 10 41	a						20 40							22 37											
Burnley Barracks	d		19 22										21 22				22 25				23 58				
Burnley Central	d		19 24										21 24				22 27				00 03				
Brierfield	d		19 29										21 29				22 32				00 11				
Nelson	d		19 32										21 32				22 35				00 16				
Colne	a		19 41										21 41				22 44				00 24				

For general notes see front of timetable
For details of catering facilities see Directory of Train Operators

A To Buxton (Table 86)
B To Liverpool Lime Street (Table 90)
C To York (Table 41)
D To Manchester Airport (Table 82)

b Until 22 March only
c From 29 March arr. 1749

For connections to and from London Euston, please refer to Table 65

Table 97

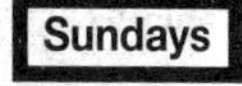

Blackpool → Preston → Blackburn, Accrington, Burnley and Colne

until 27 January

Network Diagram - see first page of Table 97

	NT	TP 1◇ A	NT B	NT C	TP 1◇ A	NT C	NT	TP 1◇ A	NT B	NT C	TP 1◇ A	NT	NT C	NT	TP 1◇ A	NT B	NT C	TP 1◇ A	NT
Blackpool North d		08 02	08 17	08 28	09 02	09 28		10 02	10 17	10 28	11 02	11 12	11 28		12 02	12 17	12 28	13 02	13 12
Poulton-le-Fylde d		08 08	08 23	08 34	09 08	09 34		10 08	10 23	10 34	11 08	11 18	11 34		12 08	12 23	12 34	13 08	13 18
Kirkham & Wesham d		08 17			09 17			10 17			11 17				12 17			13 17	
Preston 8 a		08 28	08 40	08 52	09 28	09 52		10 28	10 40	10 52	11 28	11 36	11 52		12 28	12 40	12 51	13 28	13 36
d	08 01						10 10					11 38		12 05					13 38
Lostock Hall d	08 06						10 15							12 11					
Bamber Bridge d	08 09						10 18							12 14					
Pleasington d							10 26							12 21					
Cherry Tree d							10 29							12 24					
Mill Hill (Lancashire) d							10 31							12 27					
Blackburn a	08 20						10 34					11 54		12 30					13 54
Clitheroe 94 a	09 08						11 15							13 10					
Manchester Victoria 94 🚌 d							09 00					11 00							13 00
Blackburn d	08 21						10 35					11 55		12 30					13 55
Rishton d							10 40							12 35					
Church & Oswaldtwistle d							10 43							12 38					
Accrington d	08 28						10 46					12 02		12 41					14 02
Huncoat d							10 50							12 46					
Hapton d							10 53							12 49					
Rose Grove d	08 35						10 56							12 52					
Burnley Barracks d							10 59							12 55					
Burnley Central d	08 40						11 02					12a14		12 57					14a14
Leeds 41 a												13b52							15b52
Brierfield d	08 44						11 06							13 02					
Nelson d	08 47						11 09							13 05					
Colne a	08 57						11 19							13 14					

	NT C	NT	TP 1◇ A	NT B	NT C	TP 1◇ A	NT	NT C	NT	TP 1◇ A	NT B	NT C	NT	TP 1◇ A	NT B	NT C	NT	NT	TP 1◇ A
Blackpool North d	13 28		13 57	14 17	14 28	15 02	15 12	15 28		16 02	16 17	16 28	16 45	17 02	17 17	17 25	17 45		18 02
Poulton-le-Fylde d	13 34		14 03	14 23	14 34	15 08	15 18	15 34		16 08	16 23	16 34	16 51	17 08	17 23	17 32	17 51		18 08
Kirkham & Wesham d			14 12			15 17				16 17				17 17		17 41			18 17
Preston 8 a	13 52		14 24	14 40	14 52	15 28	15 36	15 52		16 28	16 40	16 52	17 09	17 29	17 40	17 52	18 09		18 28
d		14 07					15 38		16 05				17 11				18 11	18 15	
Lostock Hall d		14 13							16 11									18 24	
Bamber Bridge d		14 16							16 14									18 29	
Pleasington d		14 23							16 21									18 41	
Cherry Tree d		14 26							16 24									18 44	
Mill Hill (Lancashire) d		14 29							16 27									18 48	
Blackburn a		14 32					15 54		16 30				17 27				18 27	18 51	
Clitheroe 94 a		15 10							17 10				18 10				19 10	20 10	
Manchester Victoria 94 🚌 d							15 00						16 00				17 00	18 00	
Blackburn d		14 32					15 55		16 30				17 28				18 28	18 52	
Rishton d		14 37							16 35									18 57	
Church & Oswaldtwistle d		14 40							16 38									19 00	
Accrington d		14 43					16 02		16 41				17 38				18 35	19 03	
Huncoat d		14 48							16 46									19 07	
Hapton d		14 51							16 49									19 10	
Rose Grove d		14 54							16 52								18 42	19 13	
Burnley Barracks d		14 57							16 55									19 17	
Burnley Central d		14 59					16a14		16 57				17a52				18a47	19 19	
Leeds 41 a							17b52						19b21				20b22		
Brierfield d		15 04							17 02									19 24	
Nelson d		15 07							17 05									19 27	
Colne a		15 16							17 14									19 36	

	NT B	NT C	TP 1◇ A	NT	NT C	NT	TP 1◇ A	NT B	NT C	TP 1◇ A	NT	NT C	NT	TP 1◇ A	NT B	TP 1◇ A
Blackpool North d	18 17	18 28	19 02	19 12	19 28		20 02	20 17	20 28	21 02	21 12	21 28		22 02	22 17	23 02
Poulton-le-Fylde d	18 23	18 34	19 08	19 18	19 34		20 08	20 23	20 34	21 08	21 18	21 34		22 08	22 23	23 08
Kirkham & Wesham d			19 17				20 17			21 17				22 17		23 17
Preston 8 a	18 40	18 52	19 28	19 36	19 52		20 28	20 40	20 52	21 28	21 36	21 52		22 28	22 40	23 28
d				19 38		20 05					21 38		22 03			
Lostock Hall d						20 11							22 09			
Bamber Bridge d						20 14							22 12			
Pleasington d						20 21							22 19			
Cherry Tree d						20 24							22 22			
Mill Hill (Lancashire) d						20 27							22 25			
Blackburn a				19 54		20 30					21 54		22 28			
Clitheroe 94 a						21 10										
Manchester Victoria 94 🚌 d				19 00							21 00					
Blackburn d				19 55		20 30					21 55		22 28			
Rishton d						20 35							22 33			
Church & Oswaldtwistle d						20 38							22 36			
Accrington d				20 02		20 41					22 02		22 39			
Huncoat d						20 46							22 44			
Hapton d						20 49							22 47			
Rose Grove d						20 52							22 50			
Burnley Barracks d						20 55							22 53			
Burnley Central d				20a14		20 57					22a14		22 55			
Leeds 41 a				21b54							23b52					
Brierfield d						21 02							23 00			
Nelson d						21 05							23 03			
Colne a						21 14							23 12			

For general notes see front of timetable
For details of catering facilities see Directory of Train Operators

A To Manchester Airport (Table 82)
B To Liverpool Lime Street (Table 90)
C To Buxton (Table 86)

b Change at Burnley Central and Hebden Bridge. By bus to Hebden Bridge

For connections to and from London Euston, please refer to Table 65

Table 97

Sundays

3 to 24 February

Blackpool → Preston → Blackburn, Accrington, Burnley and Colne

Network Diagram - see first page of Table 97

		NT	TP	NT	NT	NT	TP	NT	NT	TP	NT	NT	NT	TP	NT	NT	NT	NT	TP	NT	NT	NT	TP	NT	NT
																A									A
			🚌	🚌	🚌	🚌	🚌	🚌		🚌	🚌	🚌	🚌	🚌	🚌		🚌		🚌	🚌	🚌	🚌	🚌	🚌	
Blackpool North	d		07 20	07 45	07 50	←	08 20	08 45		09 20	09 45	09 50	←	10 20	10 30		10 45		11 20	11 45	11 50	←	12 20	12 30	
Poulton-le-Fylde	d		07 35	08 00		08 00	08 35	09 00		09 35	10 00		10 00	10 35	10 45		11 00		11 35	12 00		12 00	12 35	12 45	
Kirkham & Wesham	d		07 55	→			08 55			09 55	→			10 55					11 55	→			12 55		
Preston 8	a		08 20		08 30	08 40	09 20	09 40		10 20		10 30	10 40	11 20	11 25		11 40		12 20		12 30	12 40	13 20	13 25	
	d	08 01							10 10							11 37		12 05							13 37
Lostock Hall	d	08 06							10 15									12 11							
Bamber Bridge	d	08 09							10 18									12 14							
Pleasington	d								10 26									12 21							
Cherry Tree	d								10 29									12 24							
Mill Hill (Lancashire)	d								10 31									12 27							
Blackburn	a	08 20							10 34							11 53		12 30							13 53
Clitheroe 94	a	*09 08*							*11 15*									*13 10*							
Manchester Victoria 94 🚌	d								*09 00*							*11 00*									*13 00*
Blackburn	d	08 21							10 35							11 53		12 30							13 53
Rishton	d								10 40									12 35							
Church & Oswaldtwistle	d								10 43									12 38							
Accrington	d	08 28							10 46							12 01		12 41							14 01
Huncoat	d								10 50									12 46							
Hapton	d								10 53									12 49							
Rose Grove	d	08 35							10 56									12 52							
Burnley Manchester Road 41	a															12 09									14 09
Leeds 41	a															13 21									15 21
Burnley Barracks	d								10 59									12 55							
Burnley Central	d	08 40							11 02									12 57							
Brierfield	d	08 44							11 06									13 02							
Nelson	d	08 47							11 09									13 05							
Colne	a	08 57							11 19									13 14							

		NT	NT	TP	NT	NT	NT	TP	NT	NT	NT	NT	TP	NT	NT	NT	TP	NT	NT	NT	NT	NT	NT	TP	NT
										A											A				
		🚌		🚌	🚌	🚌	🚌	🚌	🚌		🚌		🚌	🚌	🚌	🚌	🚌	🚌	🚌	🚌		🚌		🚌	🚌
Blackpool North	d	12 45		13 20	13 45	13 50	←	14 20	14 30		14 45		15 20	15 45	15 50	←	16 20	16 30	16 45	16 50		←		17 20	17 30
Poulton-le-Fylde	d	13 00		13 35	14 00		14 00	14 35	14 45		15 00		15 35	16 00		16 00	16 35	16 45	17 00			17 00		17 35	17 45
Kirkham & Wesham	d			13 55	→			14 55					15 55	→			16 55		→					17 55	
Preston 8	a	13 40		14 20		14 30	14 40	15 20	15 25		15 40		16 20		16 30	16 40	17 20	17 25		17 30		17 40		18 20	18 25
	d		14 07							15 37		16 05									17 37		18 05		
Lostock Hall	d		14 13									16 11											18 12		
Bamber Bridge	d		14 16									16 14											18 15		
Pleasington	d		14 23									16 21											18 23		
Cherry Tree	d		14 26									16 24											18 26		
Mill Hill (Lancashire)	d		14 29									16 27											18 28		
Blackburn	a		14 32							15 53		16 30									17 53		18 31		
Clitheroe 94	a		*15 10*									*17 10*											*19 10*		
Manchester Victoria 94 🚌	d									*15 00*											*17 00*				
Blackburn	d		14 32							15 53		16 30									17 53		18 32		
Rishton	d		14 37									16 35											18 37		
Church & Oswaldtwistle	d		14 40									16 38											18 40		
Accrington	d		14 43							16 01		16 41									18 01		18 43		
Huncoat	d		14 48									16 46											18 47		
Hapton	d		14 51									16 49											18 50		
Rose Grove	d		14 54									16 52											18 53		
Burnley Manchester Road 41	a									16 09											18 09				
Leeds 41	a									17 21											19 21				
Burnley Barracks	d		14 57									16 55											18 57		
Burnley Central	d		14 59									16 57											18 59		
Brierfield	d		15 04									17 02											19 04		
Nelson	d		15 07									17 05											19 07		
Colne	a		15 16									17 14											19 16		

For general notes see front of timetable
For details of catering facilities see Directory of Train Operators

A To York (Table 41)

For connections to and from London Euston, please refer to Table 65

Table 97

Blackpool → Preston → Blackburn, Accrington, Burnley and Colne

Sundays
3 to 24 February

Network Diagram - see first page of Table 97

	NT	NT	NT A	NT	TP	NT	NT A	NT	NT	TP	NT	NT	NT	TP	NT	NT	NT	NT	TP	NT	TP	TP
	🚌	🚌		🚌	🚌	🚌		🚌		🚌	🚌	🚌	🚌	🚌	🚌		🚌		🚌	🚌	🚌	🚌
Blackpool North d	17 45	17 50		←	18 20	18 30		18 45		19 20	19 45	19 50	←	20 20	20 30		20 45		21 20	21 50	22 20	23 05
Poulton-le-Fylde d	18 00			18 00	18 35	18 45		19 00		19 35	20 00		20 00	20 35	20 45		21 00		21 35		22 35	23 20
Kirkham & Wesham d	→				18 55					19 55	→			20 55					21 55		22 55	23 40
Preston [8] a		18 30		18 40	19 20	19 25		19 40		20 20		20 30	20 40	21 20	21 25		21 40		22 20	22 30	23 20	00 05
d			18 37				19 37		20 05							21 37		22 03				
Lostock Hall d									20 11									22 09				
Bamber Bridge d									20 14									22 12				
Pleasington d									20 21									22 19				
Cherry Tree d									20 24									22 22				
Mill Hill (Lancashire) d									20 27									22 25				
Blackburn a			18 53				19 53		20 30							21 53		22 28				
Clitheroe 94 a			*20 10*						*21 10*													
Manchester Victoria 94 🚌 d			*18 00*				*19 00*									*21 00*						
Blackburn d			18 53				19 53		20 30							21 53		22 28				
Rishton d									20 35									22 33				
Church & Oswaldtwistle d									20 38									22 36				
Accrington d			19 01				20 01		20 41							22 01		22 39				
Huncoat d									20 46									22 44				
Hapton d									20 49									22 47				
Rose Grove d									20 52									22 50				
Burnley Manchester Road 41 a			19 09				20 09									22 09						
Leeds 41 a			20 22				21 21									23 21						
Burnley Barracks d									20 55									22 53				
Burnley Central d									20 57									22 55				
Brierfield d									21 02									23 00				
Nelson d									21 05									23 03				
Colne a									21 14									23 12				

Sundays
2 to 23 March

	NT	TP	NT	NT	NT	NT B	TP	NT	NT	TP	NT	NT	NT	NT	TP	NT	NT A	NT	NT	TP
		🚌	🚌	🚌	🚌	(catering)	🚌	🚌		🚌		🚌	🚌	🚌	🚌	🚌		🚌		🚌
Blackpool North d		07 20	07 45	07 50	←	08 42	08 20	08 45		09 20		09 45	09 50	←	10 20	10 30		10 45		11 20
Poulton-le-Fylde d		07 35	08 00		08 00	08 48	08 35	09 00		09 35		10 00		10 00	10 35	10 45		11 00		11 35
Blackpool South d			→								09 36	→							11 25	
Blackpool Pleasure Beach d											09 38								11 27	
Squires Gate d											09 40								11 29	
St Annes-on-the-Sea d											09 44								11 33	
Ansdell & Fairhaven d											09 47								11 36	
Lytham d											09 50								11 39	
Moss Side d											09 55								11 44	
Kirkham & Wesham d		07 55				08 57	08 55			09 55	10 05				10 55				11 51	11 55
Preston [8] a		08 20		08 30	08 40	09 08	09 20	09 40		10 20	10 17		10 30	10 40	11 20	11 25		11 40	12 01	12 20
d	08 01					09 10			10 10								11 37		12 05	
Lostock Hall d	08 06					09 15			10 15										12 11	
Bamber Bridge d	08 09					09 18			10 18										12 14	
Pleasington d									10 26										12 21	
Cherry Tree d									10 29										12 24	
Mill Hill (Lancashire) d									10 31										12 27	
Blackburn a	08 20					09 29			10 34								11 53		12 30	
Clitheroe 94 a	*09 08*					09 52			*11 15*										*13 10*	
Manchester Victoria 94 🚌 d									*09 00*								*11 00*			
Blackburn d	08 21								10 35								11 53		12 30	
Rishton d									10 40										12 35	
Church & Oswaldtwistle d									10 43										12 38	
Accrington d	08 28								10 46								12 01		12 41	
Huncoat d									10 50										12 46	
Hapton d									10 53										12 49	
Rose Grove d	08 35								10 56										12 52	
Burnley Manchester Road 41 a																	12 09			
Leeds [10] 41 a																	13 21			
Burnley Barracks d									10 59										12 55	
Burnley Central d	08 40								11 02										12 57	
Brierfield d	08 44								11 06										13 02	
Nelson d	08 47								11 09										13 05	
Colne a	08 57								11 19										13 14	

For general notes see front of timetable
For details of catering facilities see Directory of Train Operators

A To York (Table 41)
B 23 March. To Carlisle (Table 36)

For connections to and from London Euston, please refer to Table 65

A special service will operate on Easter Day Sunday 23 March. Details will be advertised locally.

Table 97

Sundays

2 to 23 March

Blackpool → Preston → Blackburn, Accrington, Burnley and Colne

Network Diagram - see first page of Table 97

		NT	NT	NT	NT	TP	NT	NT A	NT	NT	TP	NT	NT	NT	NT	TP	NT	NT A	NT	NT
		🚌	🚌	🚌		🚌	🚌		🚌		🚌	🚌	🚌	🚌		🚌	🚌		🚌	
Blackpool North	d	11 45	11 50	←		12 20	12 30		12 45		13 20	13 45	13 50	←		14 20	14 30		14 45	
Poulton-le-Fylde	d	12 00		12 00		12 35	12 45		13 00		13 35	14 00		14 00		14 35	14 45		15 00	
Blackpool South	d	→			12 25					13 25		→			14 25					15 25
Blackpool Pleasure Beach	d				12 27					13 27					14 27					15 27
Squires Gate	d				12 29					13 29					14 29					15 29
St Annes-on-the-Sea	d				12 33					13 33					14 33					15 33
Ansdell & Fairhaven	d				12 36					13 36					14 36					15 36
Lytham	d				12 39					13 39					14 39					15 39
Moss Side	d				12 44					13 44					14 44					15 44
Kirkham & Wesham	d				12 51	12 55				13 51	13 55				14 51	14 55				15 51
Preston [8]	a		12 30	12 40	13 02	13 20	13 25		13 40	14 01	14 20		14 30	14 40	15 02	15 20	15 25		15 40	16 01
	d							13 37		14 05								15 37		16 05
Lostock Hall	d									14 11										16 11
Bamber Bridge	d									14 14										16 14
Pleasington	d									14 21										16 21
Cherry Tree	d									14 24										16 24
Mill Hill (Lancashire)	d									14 27										16 27
Blackburn	a							13 53		14 30								15 53		16 30
Clitheroe 94	a									*15 10*										*17 10*
Manchester Victoria 94 🚌	d							*13 00*										*15 00*		
Blackburn	d							13 53		14 30								15 53		16 30
Rishton	d									14 35										16 35
Church & Oswaldtwistle	d									14 38										16 38
Accrington	d							14 01		14 41								16 01		16 41
Huncoat	d									14 46										16 46
Hapton	d									14 49										16 49
Rose Grove	d									14 52										16 52
Burnley Manchester Road 41	a							14 09										16 09		
Leeds [10] 41	a							15 21										17 21		
Burnley Barracks	d									14 55										16 55
Burnley Central	d									14 57										16 57
Brierfield	d									15 02										17 02
Nelson	d									15 05										17 05
Colne	a									15 14										17 14

		TP	NT	NT	NT	NT	TP	NT	NT	NT	NT A	NT	NT	TP	NT	NT	NT	NT A	NT	NT	TP
		🚌	🚌	🚌	🚌		🚌	🚌	🚌	🚌		🚌		🚌	🚌	🚌	🚌		🚌		🚌
Blackpool North	d	15 20	15 45	15 50	←		16 20	16 30	16 45	16 50		←		17 20	17 30	17 45	17 50		←		18 20
Poulton-le-Fylde	d	15 35	16 00		16 00		16 35	16 45	17 00			17 00		17 35	17 45	18 00			18 00		18 35
Blackpool South	d		→			16 25			→				17 25			→				18 25	
Blackpool Pleasure Beach	d					16 27							17 27							18 27	
Squires Gate	d					16 29							17 29							18 29	
St Annes-on-the-Sea	d					16 33							17 33							18 33	
Ansdell & Fairhaven	d					16 36							17 36							18 36	
Lytham	d					16 39							17 39							18 39	
Moss Side	d					16 44							17 44							18 44	
Kirkham & Wesham	d	15 55				16 51	16 55						17 51	17 55						18 51	18 55
Preston [8]	a	16 20		16 30	16 40	17 02	17 20	17 25		17 30		17 40	18 01	18 20	18 25		18 30		18 40	19 02	19 20
	d										17 37		18 05					18 37			
Lostock Hall	d												18 11								
Bamber Bridge	d												18 14								
Pleasington	d												18 21								
Cherry Tree	d												18 24								
Mill Hill (Lancashire)	d												18 27								
Blackburn	a										17 53		18 30					18 53			
Clitheroe 94	a												*19 10*					*20 10*			
Manchester Victoria 94 🚌	d										*17 00*							*18 00*			
Blackburn	d										17 53		18 30					18 53			
Rishton	d												18 35								
Church & Oswaldtwistle	d												18 38								
Accrington	d										18 01		18 41					19 01			
Huncoat	d												18 46								
Hapton	d												18 49								
Rose Grove	d												18 52								
Burnley Manchester Road 41	a										18 09							19 09			
Leeds [10] 41	a										19 21							20 22			
Burnley Barracks	d												18 55								
Burnley Central	d												18 57								
Brierfield	d												19 02								
Nelson	d												19 05								
Colne	a												19 14								

For general notes see front of timetable
For details of catering facilities see Directory of Train Operators

A To York (Table 41)

For connections to and from London Euston, please refer to Table 65

A special service will operate on Easter Day Sunday 23 March. Details will be advertised locally.

Blackpool → Preston → Blackburn, Accrington, Burnley and Colne

Sundays

2 to 23 March

Network Diagram - see first page of Table 97

		NT	NT	NT	NT	TP	NT	NT	NT	NT	TP	NT	NT	NT	NT	TP	NT	TP	TP
			A																
		🚌		🚌		🚌	🚌	🚌	🚌		🚌	🚌		🚌		🚌	🚌	🚌	🚌
Blackpool North	d	18 30		18 45		19 20	19 45	19 50	←		20 20	20 30		20 45		21 20	21 50	22 20	23 05
Poulton-le-Fylde	d	18 45		19 00		19 35	20 00 →		20 00		20 35	20 45		21 00		21 35		22 35	23 20
Blackpool South	d				19 25					20 25					21 25				
Blackpool Pleasure Beach	d				19 27					20 27					21 27				
Squires Gate	d				19 29					20 29					21 29				
St Annes-on-the-Sea	d				19 33					20 33					21 33				
Ansdell & Fairhaven	d				19 36					20 36					21 36				
Lytham	d				19 39					20 39					21 39				
Moss Side	d				19 44					20 44					21 44				
Kirkham & Wesham	d				19 51	19 55				20 51	20 55				21 51	21 55		22 55	23 40
Preston 8	a	19 25		19 40	20 01	20 20		20 30	20 40	21 01	21 20	21 25		21 40	22 01	22 20	22 30	23 20	00 05
	d		19 37		20 05					21 02			21 37		22 03				
Lostock Hall	d				20 11					21 08					22 09				
Bamber Bridge	d				20 14					21 11					22 12				
Pleasington	d				20 21					21 18					22 19				
Cherry Tree	d				20 24					21 21					22 22				
Mill Hill (Lancashire)	d				20 27					21 24					22 25				
Blackburn	a		19 53		20 30					21 27			21 53		22 28				
Clitheroe 94	a				*21 10*					*22 10*									
Manchester Victoria 94 🚢	d		*19 00*							*20 00*			*21 00*						
Blackburn	d		19 53		20 30					21 29			21 53		22 28				
Rishton	d				20 35					21 34					22 33				
Church & Oswaldtwistle	d				20 38					21 37					22 36				
Accrington	d		20 01		20 41					21 40			22 01		22 39				
Huncoat	d				20 46					21 44					22 44				
Hapton	d				20 49					21 47					22 47				
Rose Grove	d				20 52					21 50					22 50				
Burnley Manchester Road 41	a		20 09										22 09						
Leeds 10 41	a		21 21										23 21						
Burnley Barracks	d				20 55					21 53					22 53				
Burnley Central	d				20 57					21a58					22 55				
Brierfield	d				21 02										23 00				
Nelson	d				21 05										23 03				
Colne	a				21 14										23 12				

Sundays

from 30 March

		NT	NT	TP	NT	NT	NT	TP	NT	NT	NT	TP	NT	NT	TP	NT	NT	NT	TP	NT	NT	NT
				1 ◇				1 ◇				1 ◇			1 ◇				1 ◇			
				B	C	D	E	B	D			B	C	D	B	A	D		B	C	D	
		🚌					🍴															
Blackpool North	d			08 02	08 17	08 28	08 42	09 02	09 28			10 02	10 17	10 28	11 02	11 12	11 28		12 02	12 17	12 28	
Poulton-le-Fylde	d			08 08	08 23	08 34	08 48	09 08	09 34			10 08	10 23	10 34	11 08	11 18	11 34		12 08	12 23	12 34	
Blackpool South	d										09 36							11 25				12 25
Blackpool Pleasure Beach	d										09 38							11 27				12 27
Squires Gate	d										09 40							11 29				12 29
St Annes-on-the-Sea	d										09 44							11 33				12 33
Ansdell & Fairhaven	d										09 47							11 36				12 36
Lytham	d										09 50							11 39				12 39
Moss Side	d										09 55							11 44				12 44
Kirkham & Wesham	d			08 17			08 57	09 17			10 05	10 17			11 17			11 51	12 17			12 51
Preston 8	a			08 28	08 40	08 52	09 08	09 28	09 52		10 17	10 28	10 40	10 52	11 28	11 35	11 52	12 01	12 28	12 40	12 51	13 02
	d		08 01				09 10			10 10						11 37		12 05				
Lostock Hall	d		08 06				09 15			10 15								12 11				
Bamber Bridge	d		08 09				09 18			10 18								12 14				
Pleasington	d									10 26								12 21				
Cherry Tree	d									10 29								12 24				
Mill Hill (Lancashire)	d									10 31								12 27				
Blackburn	a		08 20				09 29			10 34						11 53		12 30				
Clitheroe 94	a		*09 08*				09 52			*11 15*								*13 10*				
Manchester Victoria 94 🚢	d									*09 00*						*11 00*						
Blackburn	d	23p10	08 21							10 35						11 53		12 30				
Rishton	d	23p20								10 40								12 35				
Church & Oswaldtwistle	d	23p32								10 43								12 38				
Accrington	d	23p36	08 28							10 46						12 01		12 41				
Huncoat	d	23p42								10 50								12 46				
Hapton	d	23p48								10 53								12 49				
Rose Grove	d	23p54	08 35							10 56								12 52				
Burnley Manchester Road 41	a															12 09						
Leeds 10 41	a															13 21						
Burnley Barracks	d	23p58								10 59								12 55				
Burnley Central	d	00 03	08 40							11 02								12 57				
Brierfield	d	00 11	08 44							11 06								13 02				
Nelson	d	00 16	08 47							11 09								13 05				
Colne	a	00 24	08 57							11 19								13 14				

For general notes see front of timetable
For details of catering facilities see Directory of Train Operators

A To York (Table 41)
B To Manchester Airport (Table 82)
C To Liverpool Lime Street (Table 90)
D To Buxton (Table 86)
E 4 May. To Carlisle (Table 36)

A special service will operate on Easter Day Sunday 23 March. Details will be advertised locally.

For connections to and from London Euston, please refer to Table 65

Table 97

from 30 March

Blackpool → Preston → Blackburn, Accrington, Burnley and Colne

Network Diagram - see first page of Table 97

		TP 1 ◇ A	NT B	NT C	NT	TP 1 ◇ A		NT D	NT C	NT	TP 1 ◇ A	NT B	NT C		NT	TP 1 ◇ A	NT D	NT C	NT	TP 1 ◇ A		NT B	NT D	NT C	NT
Blackpool North	d	13 02	13 12	13 28		14 02		14 17	14 28		15 02	15 12	15 28			16 02	16 17	16 28		17 02		17 10	17 17	17 25	
Poulton-le-Fylde	d	13 08	13 18	13 34		14 08		14 23	14 34		15 08	15 18	15 34			16 08	16 23	16 34		17 08		17 16	17 23	17 32	
Blackpool South	d				13 25					14 25					15 25				16 25						17 25
Blackpool Pleasure Beach	d				13 27					14 27					15 27				16 27						17 27
Squires Gate	d				13 29					14 29					15 29				16 29						17 29
St Annes-on-the-Sea	d				13 33					14 33					15 33				16 33						17 33
Ansdell & Fairhaven	d				13 36					14 36					15 36				16 36						17 36
Lytham	d				13 39					14 39					15 39				16 39						17 39
Moss Side	d				13 44					14 44					15 44				16 44						17 44
Kirkham & Wesham	d	13 17			13 51	14 17				14 51	15 17				15 51	16 17			16 51	17 17				17 41	17 51
Preston 8	a	13 28	13 35	13 52	14 01	14 28		14 40	14 52	15 02	15 28	15 35	15 52		16 01	16 28	16 40	16 52	17 02	17 29		17 35	17 40	17 52	18 01
	d		13 37		14 05							15 37			16 05							17 37			18 05
Lostock Hall	d				14 11										16 11										18 11
Bamber Bridge	d				14 14										16 14										18 14
Pleasington	d				14 21										16 21										18 21
Cherry Tree	d				14 24										16 24										18 24
Mill Hill (Lancashire)	d				14 27										16 27										18 27
Blackburn	a		13 53		14 30							15 53			16 30							17 53			18 30
Clitheroe 94	a				*15 10*										*17 10*										*19 10*
Manchester Victoria 94 🚌	d		*13 00*									*15 00*										*17 00*			
Blackburn	d		13 53		14 30							15 53			16 30							17 53			18 30
Rishton	d				14 35										16 35										18 35
Church & Oswaldtwistle	d				14 38										16 38										18 38
Accrington	d		14 01		14 41							16 01			16 41							18 01			18 41
Huncoat	d				14 46										16 46										18 46
Hapton	d				14 49										16 49										18 49
Rose Grove	d				14 52										16 52										18 52
Burnley Manchester Road 41	a		14 09									16 09										18 09			
Leeds 10 41	a		15 21									17 21										19 21			
Burnley Barracks	d				14 55										16 55										18 55
Burnley Central	d				14 57										16 57										18 57
Brierfield	d				15 02										17 02										19 02
Nelson	d				15 05										17 05										19 05
Colne	a				15 14										17 14										19 14

		TP 1 ◇ A	NT B	NT D	NT C		NT	TP 1 ◇ A	NT B	NT C	NT	TP 1 ◇ A		NT D	NT C	NT	TP 1 ◇ A	NT	NT C	NT	TP 1 ◇ A	NT D	TP 1 ◇ A		
Blackpool North	d	18 02	18 10	18 17	18 28			19 02	19 12	19 28		20 02		20 17	20 28		21 02	21 12	21 28		22 02	22 17	23 02		
Poulton-le-Fylde	d	18 08	18 16	18 23	18 34			19 08	19 18	19 34		20 08		20 23	20 34		21 08	21 18	21 34		22 08	22 23	23 08		
Blackpool South	d						18 25				19 25					20 25				21 25					
Blackpool Pleasure Beach	d						18 27				19 27					20 27				21 27					
Squires Gate	d						18 29				19 29					20 29				21 29					
St Annes-on-the-Sea	d						18 33				19 33					20 33				21 33					
Ansdell & Fairhaven	d						18 36				19 36					20 36				21 36					
Lytham	d						18 39				19 39					20 39				21 39					
Moss Side	d						18 44				19 44					20 44				21 44					
Kirkham & Wesham	d	18 17					18 51	19 17			19 51	20 17				20 51	21 17			21 51	22 17		23 17		
Preston 8	a	18 28	18 35	18 40	18 52		19 02	19 28	19 35	19 52	20 01	20 28		20 40	20 52	21 01	21 28	21 35	21 52	22 01	22 28	22 40	23 28		
	d		18 37						19 37		20 05					21 02		21 37		22 03					
Lostock Hall	d										20 11					21 08				22 09					
Bamber Bridge	d										20 14					21 11				22 12					
Pleasington	d										20 21					21 18				22 19					
Cherry Tree	d										20 24					21 21				22 22					
Mill Hill (Lancashire)	d										20 27					21 24				22 25					
Blackburn	a		18 53						19 53		20 30					21 27		21 53		22 28					
Clitheroe 94	a		*20 10*								*21 10*					*22 10*									
Manchester Victoria 94 🚌	d		*18 00*						*19 00*							*20 00*		*21 00*							
Blackburn	d		18 53						19 53		20 30					21 29		21 53		22 28					
Rishton	d										20 35					21 34				22 33					
Church & Oswaldtwistle	d										20 38					21 37				22 36					
Accrington	d		19 01						20 01		20 41					21 40		22 01		22 39					
Huncoat	d										20 46					21 44				22 44					
Hapton	d										20 49					21 47				22 47					
Rose Grove	d										20 52					21 50				22 50					
Burnley Manchester Road 41	a		19 09						20 09									22 09							
Leeds 10 41	a		20 22						21 21									23 21							
Burnley Barracks	d										20 55					21 53				22 53					
Burnley Central	d										20 57					21a58				22 55					
Brierfield	d										21 02									23 00					
Nelson	d										21 05									23 03					
Colne	a										21 14									23 12					

For general notes see front of timetable
For details of catering facilities see Directory of Train Operators

A To Manchester Airport (Table 82)
B To York (Table 41)
C To Buxton (Table 86)
D To Liverpool Lime Street (Table 90)

For connections to and from London Euston, please refer to Table 65

Table 97

Mondays to Fridays

Colne, Burnley, Accrington and Blackburn → Preston → Blackpool

Network Diagram - see first page of Table 97

Miles	Miles			TP MX 1 ◇ A	TP MO B	TP MO B	TP MO B	NT	TP 1 ◇ A	NT C	NT	NT	NT	TP 1 ◇ A		NT	NT D	NT E	NT G	NT H	TP 1 ◇ A	NT	NT E	NT G	NT D
0	—	**Colne**	d					05 36			06 19					07 12						08 00			
2	—	Nelson	d					05 41			06 24					07 17						08 05			
3¼	—	Brierfield	d					05 44			06 27					07 20						08 08			
5½	—	**Burnley Central**	d					05 49			06 32					07 25						08 13			
6	—	Burnley Barracks	d								06 34											08 15			
—	—	Leeds 10	41 d										06 03						06 51					07 51	
—	—	Burnley Manchester Road	41 d										07 08						07 57					08 57	
7	—	Rose Grove	d					05 53			06 37					07 29						08 18			
8½	—	Hapton	d								06 40					07 32						08 21			
10	—	Huncoat	d								06 43					07 35						08 24			
11¾	—	Accrington	d					06 00			06 47		07 17			07 40			08 06			08 29		09 06	
12½	—	Church & Oswaldtwistle	d					06 03			06 50					07 42						08 31			
14¼	—	Rishton	d					06 06			06 53					07 45						08 34			
18	—	**Blackburn**	a					06 11			06 58		07 25			07 51			08 14			08 41		09 14	
—	—	Manchester Victoria	94 a					*07 25*			07 51		*08 21*			*08 50*			*09 25*			*09 50*		*10 21*	
—	—	Clitheroe	94 d													*07 08*			*07 35*	07 56				*08 26*	
—	—	**Blackburn**	d					06 11				07 09	07 25			07 52			08 15	08 19		08 42		09 15	
19¼	—	Mill Hill (Lancashire)	d					06 14				07 12				07 55				08 22		08 45			
20	—	Cherry Tree	d					06 16				07 14				07 57						08 47			
21	—	Pleasington	d					06 19				07 16				07 59						08 49			
26	—	Bamber Bridge	d					06 26				07 23	07 35			08 06				08 31		08 56			
27¼	—	Lostock Hall	d					06 28				07 26	07 38			08 09				08 33		08 59			
30	—	**Preston 8**	a					06 36				07 34	07 46			08 17			08 33	08 43		09 11		09 34	
—	—		d	00 06	00 05	02 25	04 55	06 45	07 02	07 28		07 36	07 48	08 06		08 18	08 26	08 29	08 34		09 06	09 12	09 29	09 35	09 56
35¼	5¼	Salwick	d									07 43													
37¾	7¾	Kirkham & Wesham	d	00 16	00 30			06 54	07 11	07 38		07 49		08 16		08 28		08 39				09 24	09 38		
41	—	Moss Side	d																			09 30			
43½	—	Lytham	d					07 04				07 59				08 38						09 34			
44¾	—	Ansdell & Fairhaven	d					07 07				08 02				08 41						09 37			
46¾	—	St Annes-on-the-Sea	d					07 11				08a07				08 45						09 41			
48¼	—	Squires Gate	d					07 14								08 48						09 45			
49½	—	Blackpool Pleasure Beach	d					07 17								08 51						09 47			
50	—	**Blackpool South**	a					07 21								08 55						09 51			
—	14¼	Poulton-le-Fylde	d	00 26	00 50				07 21	07 46			08 04	08 26				08 48	08 54		09 23		09 46	09 53	
—	16¼	Layton	d	00 30					07 24	07 50				08 30				08 52					09 50		
—	17½	**Blackpool North**	a	00 38	01 05	03 05	05 35		07 31	07 56			08 12	08 36			08 51	08 59	09 04		09 33		09 57	10 02	10 21

		TP 1 ◇ A	NT	NT E		NT J	NT D	TP 1 ◇ A	NT	NT K	NT G	NT D	TP 1 ◇ A	NT	NT E	NT G		NT D	TP 1 ◇ A	NT	NT E	NT G	NT D	TP 1 ◇ A	NT
Colne	d		09 07						10 00					11 00						12 00					13 00
Nelson	d		09 12						10 05					11 05						12 05					13 05
Brierfield	d		09 15						10 08					11 08						12 08					13 08
Burnley Central	d		09 20						10 13					11 13						12 13					13 13
Burnley Barracks	d								10 15					11 15						12 15					13 15
Leeds 10	41 d					08 51					09 51					10 51						11 51			
Burnley Manchester Road	41 d					09 57					10 57					11 57						12 57			
Rose Grove	d		09 24						10 18					11 18						12 18					13 18
Hapton	d		09 27						10 21					11 21						12 21					13 21
Huncoat	d		09 30						10 24					11 24						12 24					13 24
Accrington	d		09 35			10 05			10 29		11 06			11 29		12 06				12 29		13 06			13 29
Church & Oswaldtwistle	d		09 37						10 31					11 31						12 31					13 31
Rishton	d		09 40						10 34					11 34						12 34					13 34
Blackburn	a		09 46			10 13			10 40		11 14			11 39		12 14				12 39		13 14			13 39
Manchester Victoria	94 a		*10 50*						*11 50*					*12 50*						*13 50*					*14 50*
Clitheroe	94 d					*09 36*					*10 36*					*11 36*						*12 36*			
Blackburn	d		09 46			10 14			10 42		11 15			11 42		12 15				12 42		13 15			13 42
Mill Hill (Lancashire)	d		09 49						10 45					11 45						12 45					13 45
Cherry Tree	d		09 51						10 47					11 47						12 47					13 47
Pleasington	d		09 53						10 49					11 49						12 49					13 49
Bamber Bridge	d		10 00						10 56					11 56						12 56					13 56
Lostock Hall	d		10 03						10 59					11 59						12 59					13 59
Preston 8	a		10 11			10 32			11 10		11 34			12 12		12 32				13 12		13 32			14 12
	d	10 01	10 12	10 29		10 33	10 56	11 06	11 12	11 26	11 36	11 55	12 06	12 12	12 26	12 34		12 56	13 06	13 12	13 26	13 34	13 56	14 06	14 12
Salwick	d													12 19											
Kirkham & Wesham	d		10 21	10 38					11 21	11 35				12 23	12 35					13 21	13 35				14 21
Moss Side	d		10 27						11 27					12 29						13 27					14 27
Lytham	d		10 31						11 31					12 33						13 31					14 31
Ansdell & Fairhaven	d		10 34						11 34					12 36						13 34					14 34
St Annes-on-the-Sea	d		10 38						11 38					12 40						13 38					14 38
Squires Gate	d		10 42						11 42					12 44						13 42					14 42
Blackpool Pleasure Beach	d		10 44						11 44					12 46						13 44					14 44
Blackpool South	a		10 49						11 50					12 51						13 49					14 49
Poulton-le-Fylde	d	10 18		10 46		10 52		11 23		11 43	11 52		12 23		12 43	12 52			13 23		13 43	13 52		14 23	
Layton	d			10 50						11 47					12 47						13 47				
Blackpool North	a	10 28		10 57		11 02	11 21	11 32		11 54	12 01	12 20	12 32		12 54	13 00		13 21	13 32		13 54	13 59	14 21	14 32	

For general notes see front of timetable
For details of catering facilities see Directory of Train Operators

- **A** From Manchester Airport (Table 82)
- **B** 4 February to 24 March
- **C** From Stockport (Table 84)
- **D** From Liverpool Lime Street (Table 90)
- **E** From Buxton (Table 86)
- **G** From York (Table 41)
- **H** To Morecambe (Table 98)
- **J** From Selby (Table 41)
- **K** From Northwich (Table 88)

For connections to and from London Euston, please refer to Table 65

Colne, Burnley, Accrington and Blackburn → Preston → Blackpool

Network Diagram - see first page of Table 97

		NT	NT	NT	TP	NT		NT	NT	NT	TP	NT	NT	NT	TP	NT	NT	NT		NT	TP	NT	NT	NT	NT
					1 ◇						1 ◇				1 ◇					BHX	1 ◇				
		A	B	C	D			A	B	C	D		A	B	D		E	B		G	D		H	C	A
					🛒						🛒				🛒						🛒				
Colne	d					14 00						15 00				16 00						17 00			
Nelson	d					14 05						15 05				16 05						17 05			
Brierfield	d					14 08						15 08				16 08						17 08			
Burnley Central	d					14 13						15 13				16 13						17 13			
Burnley Barracks	d					14 15						15 15				16 15						17 15			
Leeds 10	41 d		12 51						13 51					14 51				15 51							
Burnley Manchester Road	41 d		13 57						14 57					15 57				16 58							
Rose Grove	d					14 18						15 18				16 18						17 18			
Hapton	d					14 21						15 21				16 21						17 21			
Huncoat	d					14 24						15 24				16 24						17 24			
Accrington	d		14 06			14 29			15 06			15 29		16 06		16 29		17 06				17 29			
Church & Oswaldtwistle	d					14 31						15 31				16 31						17 31			
Rishton	d					14 34						15 34				16 34						17 34			
Blackburn	a		14 14			14 39			15 14			15 39		16 14		16 39		17 14				17 39			
Manchester Victoria	94 🚌 a					*15 50*						*16 42*				*17 51*		*18 23*							
Clitheroe	94 d		*13 36*						*14 36*					*15 26*				*16 36*				*17 12*			
Blackburn	d		14 15			14 42			15 15			15 42		16 15		16 42		17 15				17 42			
Mill Hill (Lancashire)	d					14 45						15 45				16 45						17 45			
Cherry Tree	d					14 47						15 47				16 47						17 47			
Pleasington	d					14 49						15 49				16 49						17 49			
Bamber Bridge	d					14 56						15 56				16 56						17 56			
Lostock Hall	d					14 59						15 59				16 59						17 59			
Preston 8	a		14 32			15 10			15 32			16 12		16 33		17 11		17 34				18 07			
	d	14 26	14 34	14 56	15 06	15 12		15 26	15 34	15 56	16 06	16 12	16 26	16 34	17 06	17 12	17 28	17 36		17 54	18 01	18 08	18 13	18 18	18 30
Salwick	d											16 19													
Kirkham & Wesham	d	14 35				15 21		15 35				16 23	16 35		17 15	17 21	17 38			18 04	18 10	18 19	18 22		18 40
Moss Side	d					15 27						16 29				17 27						18 25			
Lytham	d					15 31						16 33				17 31						18 29			
Ansdell & Fairhaven	d					15 34						16 36				17 34						18 32			
St Annes-on-the-Sea	d					15 38						16 40				17 38						18 36			
Squires Gate	d					15 42						16 44				17 42						18 40			
Blackpool Pleasure Beach	d					15 44						16 46				17 44						18 42			
Blackpool South	a					15 49						16 51				17 49						18 47			
Poulton-le-Fylde	d	14 43	14 52		15 23			15 43	15 52		16 23		16 43	16 52	17 25		17 47	17 53		18 13	18 20		18 32		18 49
Layton	d	14 47						15 47					16 47		17 28		17 51				18 24		18 36		18 53
Blackpool North	a	14 54	15 00	15 21	15 32			15 54	16 00	16 21	16 32		16 54	17 00	17 34		17 58	18 03		18 22	18 30		18 43	18 48	19 00

		NT	TP	NT	TP	NT	NT	NT		NT	TP	NT	NT	TP	NT	NT	NT	TP	NT	NT	TP	TP	NT		
			1 ◇		1 ◇						1 ◇			1 ◇				1 ◇			1 ◇	1 ◇			
		B	D	C	D		A			B	D		B	D		B		D		C	D				
			🛒																						
Colne	d					18 00						19 12			20 05				21 44				22 56		
Nelson	d					18 05						19 17			20 10				21 49				23 01		
Brierfield	d					18 08						19 20			20 13				21 52				23 04		
Burnley Central	d					18 13		18 28				19 25			20 18				21 57				23 09		
Burnley Barracks	d					18 15						19 27			20 20				21 59				23 11		
Leeds 10	41 d	16 51								17 51			18 51			19 51									
Burnley Manchester Road	41 d	17 57								18 58			19 57			20 57									
Rose Grove	d					18 18						19 30			20 23				22 02				23 14		
Hapton	d					18 21						19 33			20 26				22 05						
Huncoat	d					18 24						19 36			20 29				22 08						
Accrington	d	18 06				18 29		18 37		19 07		19 41	20 06		20 34	21 06			22 13				23 21		
Church & Oswaldtwistle	d					18 31						19 43			20 36				22 15						
Rishton	d					18 34						19 46			20 39				22 18						
Blackburn	a	18 14				18 39		18 45		19 15		19 52	20 14		20 44	21 14			22 23				23 29		
Manchester Victoria	94 🚌 a	*19 23*						*19 50*		*20 22*		*20 50*			*21 50*				*00 01*						
Clitheroe	94 d					*18 08*				*18 36*			*19 36*			*20 36*			*21 36*				*22 46*		
Blackburn	d	18 15				18 42				19 16		19 54	20 14		20 47	21 14			22 24				23 30		
Mill Hill (Lancashire)	d					18 45						19 57			20 50				22 27				23 33		
Cherry Tree	d					18 47						19 59			20 52				22 29						
Pleasington	d					18 49						20 01			20 54				22 31						
Bamber Bridge	d					18 56						20 08			21 01				22 38				23 41		
Lostock Hall	d					18 59						20 11			21 04				22 41				23 43		
Preston 8	a	18 34				19 10				19 36		20 20	20 31		21 13	21 31			22 51				23 53		
	d	18 35	18 42	18 57	19 06	19 12	19 27			19 37	20 06	20 21	20 33	21 06	21 15	21 33	21 45	22 06	22 51	23 03	23 06	23 33			
Salwick	d																								
Kirkham & Wesham	d		18 51		19 16	19 21	19 37				20 16	20 30		21 16	21b28		21 55	22 16	23 00		23 16	23 42			
Moss Side	d					19 27						20 36			21 34				23 06						
Lytham	d					19 31						20 40			21 38				23 10						
Ansdell & Fairhaven	d					19 34						20 43			21 41				23 13						
St Annes-on-the-Sea	d					19 38						20 47			21 45				23 17						
Squires Gate	d					19 42						20 51			21 49				23 21						
Blackpool Pleasure Beach	d					19 44						20 53			21 51				23 23						
Blackpool South	a					19 49						20 58			21 56				23 28						
Poulton-le-Fylde	d	18 54	19 01	19 14	19 26		19 45			19 54	20 26		20 49	21 26		21 49	22 03	22 26			23 26	23 52			
Layton	d		19 05				19 49				20 30			21 30			22 07	22 30			23 30				
Blackpool North	a	19 03	19 09	19 23	19 35		19 57			20 03	20 36		20 56	21 36		21 56	22 12	22 36		23 28	23 36	23 59			

For general notes see front of timetable
For details of catering facilities see Directory of Train Operators

- **A** From Buxton (Table 86)
- **B** From York (Table 41)
- **C** From Liverpool Lime Street (Table 90)
- **D** From Manchester Airport (Table 82)
- **E** From Hazel Grove (Table 86)
- **G** From Stalybridge (Table 39)
- **H** From Stockport (Table 84)
- **b** Arr. 2124

For connections to and from London Euston, please refer to Table 65

Table 97

Colne, Burnley, Accrington and Blackburn → Preston → Blackpool

Network Diagram - see first page of Table 97

Station			TP	NT	TP	NT	NT	NT	TP	NT	NT	NT	NT	NT	TP	NT	NT	NT	NT	TP	NT	NT
			1 ◇		1 ◇				1 ◇						1 ◇					1 ◇		
			A		A	B			A		C	D	E	G	A		D	E	C	A		D
																				♿		
Colne		d		05 43			06 30			07 12						08 00					09 07	
Nelson		d		05 48			06 35			07 17						08 05					09 12	
Brierfield		d		05 51			06 38			07 20						08 08					09 15	
Burnley Central		d		05 56			06 43			07 25						08 13					09 20	
Burnley Barracks		d														08 15						
Leeds 10	41	d						06 03					06 51					07 51				
Burnley Manchester Road	41	d						07 09					07 57					08 57				
Rose Grove		d		06 00			06 47			07 29						08 18					09 24	
Hapton		d					06 50			07 32						08 21					09 27	
Huncoat		d					06 53			07 35						08 24					09 30	
Accrington		d		06 07			06 58	07 17		07 40			08 06			08 29		09 06			09 35	
Church & Oswaldtwistle		d		06 10			07 00			07 42						08 31					09 37	
Rishton		d		06 13			07 03			07 45						08 34					09 40	
Blackburn		a		06 18			07 08	07 25		07 51			08 14			08 41		09 14			09 46	
Manchester Victoria	94 🚌	a		*07 25*				*08 21*		*08 50*			*09 25*			*09 50*		*10 21*			*10 50*	
Clitheroe	94	d								*07 08*			*07 35*	07 56				*08 26*				
Blackburn		d		06 18			07 09	07 26		07 52			08 15	08 19		08 42		09 15			09 46	
Mill Hill (Lancashire)		d		06 21			07 12			07 55				08 22		08 45					09 49	
Cherry Tree		d		06 23			07 14			07 57						08 47					09 51	
Pleasington		d		06 26			07 16			07 59						08 49					09 53	
Bamber Bridge		d		06 33			07 23	07 36		08 06				08 31		08 56					10 00	
Lostock Hall		d		06 35			07 26	07 39		08 09				08 33		08 59					10 03	
Preston 8		a		06 43			07 34	07 47		08 17			08 33	08 43		09 11		09 33			10 11	
		d	00 06	06 45	07 02	07 28	07 38	07 48	08 06	08 18	08 26	08 29	08 34		09 06	09 12	09 29	09 34	09 56	10 04	10 12	10 29
Salwick		d					07 45															
Kirkham & Wesham		d	00 16	06 54	07 11	07 38	07 49		08 16	08 28		08 39				09 24	09 38				10 21	10 38
Moss Side		d														09 30					10 27	
Lytham		d		07 04			07 59			08 38						09 34					10 31	
Ansdell & Fairhaven		d		07 07			08 02			08 41						09 37					10 34	
St Annes-on-the-Sea		d		07 11			08a07			08 45						09 41					10 38	
Squires Gate		d		07 14						08 48						09 45					10 42	
Blackpool Pleasure Beach		d		07 17						08 51						09 47					10 44	
Blackpool South		a		07 21						08 55						09 51					10 49	
Poulton-le-Fylde		d	00 26		07 21	07 46		08 04	08 26			08 48	08 54		09 23		09 46	09 54		10 21		10 46
Layton		d	00 30		07 24	07 50			08 30			08 52					09 50					10 50
Blackpool North		a	00 38		07 31	07 56		08 12	08 36		08 51	09 00	09 03		09 32		09 57	10 02	10 21	10 31		10 57

Station			NT	NT	TP	NT	NT	NT	NT	TP	NT	NT	NT	NT	TP	NT	NT	NT	NT	TP	NT
					1 ◇					1 ◇					1 ◇					1 ◇	
			E	C	A		H	E	C	A		D	E	C	A		D	E	C	A	
					♿					♿					♿					♿	
Colne		d				10 00					11 00					12 00					13 00
Nelson		d				10 05					11 05					12 05					13 05
Brierfield		d				10 08					11 08					12 08					13 08
Burnley Central		d				10 13					11 13					12 13					13 13
Burnley Barracks		d				10 15					11 15					12 15					13 15
Leeds 10	41	d	08 51					09 51					10 51					11 51			
Burnley Manchester Road	41	d	09 58					10 57					11 57					12 57			
Rose Grove		d				10 18					11 18					12 18					13 18
Hapton		d				10 21					11 21					12 21					13 21
Huncoat		d				10 24					11 24					12 24					13 24
Accrington		d	10 07			10 29		11 06			11 29		12 06			12 29		13 06			13 29
Church & Oswaldtwistle		d				10 31					11 31					12 31					13 31
Rishton		d				10 34					11 34					12 34					13 34
Blackburn		a	10 15			10 40		11 14			11 39		12 14			12 39		13 14			13 39
Manchester Victoria	94 🚌	a				*11 51*					*12 50*					*13 50*					*14 50*
Clitheroe	94	d	*09 36*					*10 36*					*11 36*					*12 36*			
Blackburn		d	10 15			10 42		11 15			11 42		12 15			12 42		13 15			13 42
Mill Hill (Lancashire)		d				10 45					11 45					12 45					13 45
Cherry Tree		d				10 47					11 47					12 47					13 47
Pleasington		d				10 49					11 49					12 49					13 49
Bamber Bridge		d				10 56					11 56					12 56					13 56
Lostock Hall		d				10 59					11 59					12 59					13 59
Preston 8		a	10 32			11 10		11 34			12 12		12 32			13 12		13 32			14 12
		d	10 33	10 56	11 06	11 12	11 27	11 36	11 55	12 06	12 12	12 26	12 34	12 56	13 06	13 12	13 26	13 34	13 56	14 06	14 12
Salwick		d									12 19										
Kirkham & Wesham		d				11 21	11 37				12 23	12 35				13 21	13 35				14 21
Moss Side		d				11 27					12 29					13 27					14 27
Lytham		d				11 31					12 33					13 31					14 31
Ansdell & Fairhaven		d				11 34					12 36					13 34					14 34
St Annes-on-the-Sea		d				11 38					12 40					13 38					14 38
Squires Gate		d				11 42					12 44					13 42					14 42
Blackpool Pleasure Beach		d				11 44					12 46					13 44					14 44
Blackpool South		a				11 50					12 51					13 49					14 49
Poulton-le-Fylde		d	10 53		11 23		11 45	11 52		12 23		12 43	12 52		13 23		13 43	13 52		14 23	
Layton		d					11 49					12 47					13 47				
Blackpool North		a	11 03	11 23	11 32		11 56	12 01	12 20	12 32		12 54	13 01	13 21	13 32		13 54	14 00	14 21	14 32	

For general notes see front of timetable
For details of catering facilities see Directory of Train Operators

- **A** From Manchester Airport (Table 82)
- **B** From Stockport (Table 84)
- **C** From Liverpool Lime Street (Table 90)
- **D** From Buxton (Table 86)
- **E** From York (Table 41)
- **G** Until 22 March to Morecambe (Table 98)
- **H** From Northwich (Table 88)

For connections to and from London Euston, please refer to Table 65

Table 97

Saturdays

Colne, Burnley, Accrington and Blackburn → Preston → Blackpool

Network Diagram - see first page of Table 97

Station		NT A	NT B	NT C	TP 1 ◇ D	NT	NT A	NT B	NT C	TP 1 ◇ D	NT	NT A	NT B	TP 1 ◇ D (trolley)	NT	NT A	NT B	TP 1 ◇ D (trolley)	NT	NT E	NT C
Colne	d					14 00					15 00				16 00				17 00		
Nelson	d					14 05					15 05				16 05				17 05		
Brierfield	d					14 08					15 08				16 08				17 08		
Burnley Central	d					14 13					15 13				16 13				17 13		
Burnley Barracks	d					14 15					15 15				16 15				17 15		
Leeds 10	41 d		12 51					13 51					14 51				15 51				
Burnley Manchester Road	41 d		13 57					14 57					15 57				16 58				
Rose Grove	d					14 18					15 18				16 18				17 18		
Hapton	d					14 21					15 21				16 21				17 21		
Huncoat	d					14 24					15 24				16 24				17 24		
Accrington	d		14 06			14 29		15 06			15 29		16 06		16 29		17 06		17 29		
Church & Oswaldtwistle	d					14 31					15 31				16 31				17 31		
Rishton	d					14 34					15 34				16 34				17 34		
Blackburn	a		14 14			14 39		15 14			15 42		16 14		16 39		17 14		17 39		
Manchester Victoria	94 (tram) a					*15 50*					*16 42*				*17 51*		*18 23*				
Clitheroe	94 d		*13 36*					*14 36*					*15 26*				*16 36*		*17 12*		
Blackburn	d		14 15			14 42		15 15			15 42		16 15		16 42		17 15		17 42		
Mill Hill (Lancashire)	d					14 45					15 45				16 45				17 45		
Cherry Tree	d					14 47					15 47				16 47				17 47		
Pleasington	d					14 49					15 49				16 49				17 49		
Bamber Bridge	d					14 56					15 56				16 56				17 56		
Lostock Hall	d					14 59					15 59				16 59				17 59		
Preston 8	a		14 32			15 10		15 32			16 12		16 33		17 11		17 34		18 07		
	d	14 26	14 34	14 56	15 06	15 12	15 26	15 34	15 56	16 06	16 12	16 26	16 34	17 06	17 12	17 28	17 36	18 01	18 08	18 14	18 18
Salwick	d										16 19										
Kirkham & Wesham	d	14 35				15 21	15 35				16 23	16 35		17 15	17 21	17 38		18 10	18 19	18 22	
Moss Side	d					15 27					16 29				17 27				18 25		
Lytham	d					15 31					16 33				17 31				18 29		
Ansdell & Fairhaven	d					15 34					16 36				17 34				18 32		
St Annes-on-the-Sea	d					15 38					16 40				17 38				18 36		
Squires Gate	d					15 42					16 44				17 42				18 40		
Blackpool Pleasure Beach	d					15 44					16 46				17 44				18 42		
Blackpool South	a					15 49					16 51				17 49				18 47		
Poulton-le-Fylde	d	14 43	14 52		15 23		15 43	15 52		16 23		16 43	16 52	17 25		17 47	17 53	18 20		18 32	
Layton	d	14 47					15 47					16 47		17 28		17 51		18 24		18 36	
Blackpool North	a	14 54	15 01	15 21	15 32		15 54	16 01	16 21	16 32		16 54	17 01	17 34		17 58	18 03	18 30		18 43	18 48

Station		NT A	NT B	NT C	TP 1 ◇ D	NT	NT A	NT B	TP 1 ◇ D	NT	NT B	TP 1 ◇ D	NT	NT B	TP 1 ◇ D	NT	NT C	TP 1 ◇ D	NT
Colne	d					18 00				19 00			20 00			21 44			22 56
Nelson	d					18 05				19 05			20 05			21 49			23 01
Brierfield	d					18 08				19 08			20 08			21 52			23 04
Burnley Central	d					18 13				19 13			20 13			21 57			23 09
Burnley Barracks	d					18 15				19 15			20 15			21 59			23 11
Leeds 10	41 d		16 51					17 51			18 51			19 51					
Burnley Manchester Road	41 d		17 57					18 57			19 57			20 57					
Rose Grove	d					18 18				19 18			20 18			22 02			23 14
Hapton	d					18 21				19 21			20 21			22 05			
Huncoat	d					18 24				19 24			20 24			22 08			
Accrington	d		18 06			18 29		19 06		19 29	20 06		20 29	21 06		22 13			23 21
Church & Oswaldtwistle	d					18 31				19 31			20 31			22 15			
Rishton	d					18 34				19 34			20 34			22 18			
Blackburn	a		18 14			18 39		19 14		19 44	20 14		20 39	21 14		22 23			23 29
Manchester Victoria	94 (tram) a		*19 23*			*19 50*		*20 22*		*20 56*			*21 50*			*23 59*			
Clitheroe	94 d					*18 08*		*18 36*			*19 42*			*20 36*		*21 36*			*22 46*
Blackburn	d		18 15			18 42		19 15		19 44	20 14		20 42	21 14		22 24			23 30
Mill Hill (Lancashire)	d					18 45				19 47			20 45			22 27			23 33
Cherry Tree	d					18 47				19 49			20 47			22 29			
Pleasington	d					18 49				19 52			20 49			22 31			
Bamber Bridge	d					18 56				19 58			20 56			22 38			23 41
Lostock Hall	d					18 59				19 59			20 59			22 41			23 43
Preston 8	a		18 34			19 12		19 35		20 11	20 31		21 13	21 31		22 51			23 53
	d	18 30	18 35	18 53	19 06	19 12	19 33	19 39	20 06	20 12	20 33	21 06	21 15	21 33	22 06	22 51	23 03	23 06	
Salwick	d																		
Kirkham & Wesham	d	18 40			19 16	19 21	19 42		20 16	20 21		21 16	21 24		22 16	23 00		23 16	
Moss Side	d					19 27				20 27			21 30			23 06			
Lytham	d					19 31				20 31			21 34			23 10			
Ansdell & Fairhaven	d					19 34				20 34			21 37			23 13			
St Annes-on-the-Sea	d					19 38				20 38			21 41			23 17			
Squires Gate	d					19 42				20 42			21 45			23 21			
Blackpool Pleasure Beach	d					19 44				20 44			21 47			23 23			
Blackpool South	a					19 49				20 49			21 52			23 28			
Poulton-le-Fylde	d	18 48	18 55	19 10	19 26		19 51	19 58	20 26		20 49	21 26		21 49	22 26			23 26	
Layton	d	18 52					19 55		20 30			21 30			22 30			23 30	
Blackpool North	a	18 59	19 04	19 21	19 35		20 01	20 07	20 36		20 56	21 36		21 56	22 36		23 28	23 36	

For general notes see front of timetable
For details of catering facilities see Directory of Train Operators

A From Buxton (Table 86)
B From York (Table 41)
C From Liverpool Lime Street (Table 90)
D From Manchester Airport (Table 82)
E From Stockport (Table 84)

For connections to and from London Euston, please refer to Table 65

Table 97

Sundays

until 27 January

Colne, Burnley, Accrington and Blackburn → Preston → Blackpool

Network Diagram - see first page of Table 97

		TP 1◇ A	TP 1◇ B	NT C	NT D	TP 1◇ B	NT	NT E	TP 1◇ B	NT C	NT	NT E	TP 1◇ B	NT E	NT	TP 1◇ B	NT C	NT	NT E	TP 1◇ B
Colne	d						09 01								11 35					
Nelson	d						09 06								11 40					
Brierfield	d						09 09								11 43					
Leeds 41	d										*09b02*							*11b02*		
Burnley Central	d						09 14				10 37				11 48			12 37		
Burnley Barracks	d						09 16								11 50					
Rose Grove	d						09 19								11 53					
Hapton	d						09 22								11 56					
Huncoat	d						09 25								11 59					
Accrington	d						09 30				10 47				12 04			12 47		
Church & Oswaldtwistle	d						09 32								12 06					
Rishton	d						09 35								12 09					
Blackburn	a						09 42				10 55				12 14			12 55		
Manchester Victoria 94	a						*10 35*				*12 35*				*13 35*			*14 35*		
Clitheroe 94	d						*09 17*				*10 27*				*11 24*			*12 24*		
Blackburn	d						09 43				10 56				12 15			12 56		
Mill Hill (Lancashire)	d						09 46								12 18					
Cherry Tree	d						09 48								12 20					
Pleasington	d						09 50								12 22					
Bamber Bridge	d						09 57								12 29					
Lostock Hall	d						10 00								12 32					
Preston 8	a						10 10				11 13				12 42			13 13		
	d	00 06	08 48	09 07	09 20	09 48		10 21	10 48	11 07	11 14	11 21	11 48	12 21		12 48	13 07	13 14	13 21	13 48
Kirkham & Wesham	d	00 16	08 58			09 58			10 58				11 58			12 58				13 58
Poulton-le-Fylde	d	00 26	09 07	09 23	09 36	10 07		10 38	11 07	11 23	11 31	11 38	12 07	12 38		13 07	13 23	13 31	13 38	14 07
Blackpool North	a	00 38	09 16	09 34	09 45	10 16		10 47	11 16	11 34	11 38	11 47	12 16	12 47		13 16	13 34	13 38	13 47	14 16

		NT E	NT	TP 1◇ B	NT C	NT	NT E	TP 1◇ B	NT E	NT	TP 1◇ B	NT C	NT	NT E	TP 1◇ B	NT C	NT E	NT	NT	TP 1◇ B
Colne	d		13 35							15 35								17 28		
Nelson	d		13 40							15 40								17 33		
Brierfield	d		13 43							15 43								17 36		
Leeds 41	d					*13b02*							*15b02*						*16b35*	
Burnley Central	d		13 48			14 37				15 48			16 37					17 41	18 00	
Burnley Barracks	d		13 50							15 50								17 43		
Rose Grove	d		13 53							15 53								17 46		
Hapton	d		13 56							15 56								17 49		
Huncoat	d		13 59							15 59								17 52		
Accrington	d		14 04			14 47				16 04			16 47					17 57	18 10	
Church & Oswaldtwistle	d		14 06							16 06								17 59		
Rishton	d		14 09							16 09								18 02		
Blackburn	a		14 14			14 55				16 14			16 55					18 07	18 18	
Manchester Victoria 94	a		*15 35*			*16 35*				*17 35*			*18 35*						*19 35*	
Clitheroe 94	d		*13 24*			*14 24*				*15 24*			*16 24*					*17 24*		
Blackburn	d		14 15			14 56				16 15			16 56					18 08	18 19	
Mill Hill (Lancashire)	d		14 18							16 18								18 11		
Cherry Tree	d		14 20							16 20								18 13		
Pleasington	d		14 22							16 22								18 15		
Bamber Bridge	d		14 29							16 29								18 22		
Lostock Hall	d		14 32							16 32								18 25		
Preston 8	a		14 42			15 13				16 42			17 13					18 35	18 37	
	d	14 21		14 48	15 07	15 14	15 21	15 48	16 21		16 48	17 07	17 14	17 21	17 48	18 07	18 21		18 38	18 48
Kirkham & Wesham	d			14 58				15 58			16 58				17 58					18 58
Poulton-le-Fylde	d	14 37		15 07	15 23	15 31	15 38	16 07	16 38		17 07	17 23	17 31	17 37	18 07	18 23	18 38		18 55	19 07
Blackpool North	a	14 47		15 16	15 34	15 38	15 47	16 16	16 47		17 16	17 35	17 38	17 47	18 16	18 34	18 47		19 05	19 16

		NT C	NT E	NT	TP 1◇ B	NT E	TP 1◇ B	NT	NT C	NT	NT E	TP 1◇ B	NT E	NT	TP 1◇ B	NT C	TP 1◇ B
Colne	d							19 40						21 29			
Nelson	d							19 45						21 34			
Brierfield	d							19 48						21 37			
Leeds 41	d			*17b35*						*19b02*							
Burnley Central	d			19 00				19 53		20 37				21 42			
Burnley Barracks	d							19 55						21 44			
Rose Grove	d			19 04				19 58						21 47			
Hapton	d							20 01						21 50			
Huncoat	d							20 04						21 53			
Accrington	d			19 12				20 09		20 47				21 57			
Church & Oswaldtwistle	d							20 11						22 00			
Rishton	d							20 14						22 03			
Blackburn	a			19 20				20 19		20 55				22 08			
Manchester Victoria 94	a			*20 35*				*21 35*		*22 35*				*23 35*			
Clitheroe 94	d			*18 24*				*19 24*		*20 24*				*21 24*			
Blackburn	d			19 20				20 20		20 56				22 09			
Mill Hill (Lancashire)	d							20 23						22 12			
Cherry Tree	d							20 25						22 14			
Pleasington	d							20 27						22 16			
Bamber Bridge	d							20 34						22 23			
Lostock Hall	d							20 37						22 26			
Preston 8	a			19 38				20 53		21 13				22 36			
	d	19 07	19 21	19 39	19 48	20 21	20 48		21 07	21 14	21 21	21 48	22 21		22 48	23 17	23 48
Kirkham & Wesham	d				19 58		20 58					21 58			22 58		23 58
Poulton-le-Fylde	d	19 23	19 37	19 56	20 07	20 38	21 07		21 23	21 31	21 37	22 07	22 37		23 07	23 34	00 07
Blackpool North	a	19 32	19 47	20 03	20 16	20 47	21 16		21 34	21 38	21 47	22 16	22 47		23 16	23 43	00 16

For general notes see front of timetable
For details of catering facilities see Directory of Train Operators

- **A** From Manchester Airport (Table 82). Also stops at Layton 0030
- **B** From Manchester Airport (Table 82)
- **C** From Liverpool Lime Street (Table 90)
- **D** From Manchester Victoria (Table 82)
- **E** From Buxton (Table 86)
- **b** Change at Hebden Bridge and Burnley Central. By bus from Hebden Bridge

For connections to and from London Euston, please refer to Table 65

Table 97

Sundays

3 to 24 February

Colne, Burnley, Accrington and Blackburn → Preston → Blackpool

Network Diagram - see first page of Table 97

		TP A	TP	NT	TP	NT	TP	NT	NT	TP	NT	TP	NT B	NT	NT	TP	NT	NT		TP	NT B	NT	TP	NT	NT
Colne	d							09 01										11 35							
Nelson	d							09 06										11 40							
Brierfield	d							09 09										11 43							
Burnley Central	d							09 14										11 48							
Burnley Barracks	d							09 16										11 50							
Leeds	41 d												09 35								11 35				
Burnley Manchester Road	41 d												10 41								12 39				
Rose Grove	d							09 19										11 53							
Hapton	d							09 22										11 56							
Huncoat	d							09 25										11 59							
Accrington	d							09 30					10 50					12 04			12 47				
Church & Oswaldtwistle	d							09 32										12 06							
Rishton	d							09 35										12 09							
Blackburn	a							09 42					10 58					12 14			12 55				
Manchester Victoria	94 a							*10 35*					*12 35*					*13 35*			*14 35*				
Clitheroe	94 d							*09 17*					*10 27*					*11 24*			*12 24*				
Blackburn	d							09 43					10 58					12 15			12 56				
Mill Hill (Lancashire)	d							09 46										12 18							
Cherry Tree	d							09 48										12 20							
Pleasington	d							09 50										12 22							
Bamber Bridge	d							09 57										12 29							
Lostock Hall	d							10 00										12 32							
Preston 8	a							10 10					11 15					12 42			13 13				
	d	00 20	09 00	09 15	←	09 35	10 00		10 35	11 00	11 15	←		11 25	11 35	12 00	12 35			13 00		13 15	←	13 25	13 35
Kirkham & Wesham	d	00 45	09 25				10 25			11 25						12 25				13 25					
Poulton-le-Fylde	d	01 05	09 45		09 45	10 15	10 45		11 15	11 45		11 45		12 05	12 15	12 45	13 15			13 45			13 45	14 05	14 15
Blackpool North	a	01 25	→	09 55	10 00	10 30	11 00		11 30	→	11 55	12 00		12 20	12 30	13 00	13 30			→		13 55	14 00	14 20	14 30

		TP	NT	NT	TP	NT B	NT	TP	NT	NT	TP	NT	NT	TP		NT B	NT	TP	NT	NT	TP	NT B	NT	TP	NT
Colne	d			13 35									15 35												
Nelson	d			13 40									15 40												
Brierfield	d			13 43									15 43												
Burnley Central	d			13 48									15 48												
Burnley Barracks	d			13 50									15 50												
Leeds	41 d					13 35										15 35						16 35			
Burnley Manchester Road	41 d					14 39										16 39						17 39			
Rose Grove	d			13 53									15 53												
Hapton	d			13 56									15 56												
Huncoat	d			13 59									15 59												
Accrington	d			14 04		14 47							16 04			16 47						17 47			
Church & Oswaldtwistle	d			14 06									16 06												
Rishton	d			14 09									16 09												
Blackburn	a			14 14		14 55							16 14			16 55						17 55			
Manchester Victoria	94 a			*15 35*		*16 35*							*17 35*			*18 35*									
Clitheroe	94 d			*13 24*		*14 24*							*15 24*			*16 24*						*17 24*			
Blackburn	d			14 15		14 56							16 15			16 56						17 56			
Mill Hill (Lancashire)	d			14 18									16 18												
Cherry Tree	d			14 20									16 20												
Pleasington	d			14 22									16 22												
Bamber Bridge	d			14 29									16 29												
Lostock Hall	d			14 32									16 32												
Preston 8	a			14 42		15 13							16 42			17 13						18 13			
	d	14 00	14 35		15 00		15 15	←	15 25	15 35	16 00	16 35		17 00			17 15	←	17 25	17 35	18 00		18 15	←	18 25
Kirkham & Wesham	d	14 25			15 25						16 25			17 25							18 25				
Poulton-le-Fylde	d	14 45	15 15		15 45			15 45	16 05	16 15	16 45	17 15		17 45				17 45	18 05	18 15	18 45			18 45	19 05
Blackpool North	a	15 00	15 30		→		15 55	16 00	16 20	16 30	17 00	17 30		→			17 55	18 00	18 20	18 30	→		18 55	19 00	19 20

For general notes see front of timetable
For details of catering facilities see Directory of Train Operators

A Also stops at Layton 01 15
B From York (Table 41)

For connections to and from London Euston, please refer to Table 65

Table 97

Sundays
3 to 24 February

Colne, Burnley, Accrington and Blackburn → Preston → Blackpool

Network Diagram - see first page of Table 97

		NT	NT	TP	NT	NT	TP	NT	NT	TP	NT	NT	TP	NT	NT	TP	NT	NT	TP	NT	NT	TP	NT		
					A									A											
		Bus		Bus		Bus	Bus	Bus	Bus	Bus		Bus	Bus		Bus	Bus	Bus	Bus	Bus	Bus		Bus	Bus		
Colne	d		17 28								19 21										21 29				
Nelson	d		17 33								19 26										21 34				
Brierfield	d		17 36								19 29										21 37				
Burnley Central	d		17 41								19 34										21 42				
Burnley Barracks	d		17 43								19 36										21 44				
Leeds 41	d				17 35									19 35											
Burnley Manchester Road 41	d				18 39									20 39											
Rose Grove	d		17 46								19 39										21 47				
Hapton	d		17 49								19 42										21 50				
Huncoat	d		17 52								19 45										21 53				
Accrington	d		17 57		18 47						19 50			20 47							21 57				
Church & Oswaldtwistle	d		17 59								19 52										22 00				
Rishton	d		18 02								19 55										22 03				
Blackburn	a		18 07		18 55						20 00			20 55							22 08				
Manchester Victoria 94	a		*19 35*		*20 35*						*21 35*			*22 35*							*23 35*				
Clitheroe 94	d				*18 24*						*19 24*			*20 24*							*21 24*				
Blackburn	d		18 08		18 56						20 01			20 56							22 09				
Mill Hill (Lancashire)	d		18 11								20 04										22 12				
Cherry Tree	d		18 13								20 06										22 14				
Pleasington	d		18 15								20 08										22 16				
Bamber Bridge	d		18 22								20 15										22 23				
Lostock Hall	d		18 25								20 18										22 26				
Preston 8	a		18 35		19 13						20 28			21 13							22 36				
	d	18 35		19 00		19 15		19 25	19 35	20 00		20 35	21 00		21 15		21 25	21 35	22 00	22 35		23 05	23 25		
Kirkham & Wesham	d			19 25			←			20 25			21 25			←			22 25			23 30			
Poulton-le-Fylde	d	19 15		19 45			19 45	20 05	20 15	20 45		21 15	21 45			21 45	22 05	22 15	22 45	23 15		23 50			
Blackpool North	a	19 30		→		19 55	20 00	20 20	20 30	21 00		21 30	→		21 55	22 00	22 20	22 30	23 00	23 30		00 05	00 05		

Sundays
2 to 23 March

		TP	NT	TP	NT		TP	NT	TP	NT		NT	TP	NT	TP		NT	NT	NT	NT		TP	NT	NT	TP
		B															A								
		Bus		Bus	Bus		Bus	Bus	Bus			Bus	Bus	Bus	Bus			Bus	Bus			Bus	Bus		Bus
Colne	d									09 01														11 35	
Nelson	d									09 06														11 40	
Brierfield	d									09 09														11 43	
Burnley Central	d									09 14														11 48	
Burnley Barracks	d									09 16														11 50	
Leeds 10 41	d																09 35								
Burnley Manchester Road 41	d																10 41								
Rose Grove	d									09 19														11 53	
Hapton	d									09 22														11 56	
Huncoat	d									09 25														11 59	
Accrington	d									09 30							10 50							12 04	
Church & Oswaldtwistle	d									09 32														12 06	
Rishton	d									09 35														12 09	
Blackburn	a									09 42							10 58							12 14	
Manchester Victoria 94	a									*10 35*							*12 35*							*13 35*	
Clitheroe 94	d									*09 17*							*10 27*							*11 24*	
Blackburn	d									09 43							10 58							12 15	
Mill Hill (Lancashire)	d									09 46														12 18	
Cherry Tree	d									09 48														12 20	
Pleasington	d									09 50														12 22	
Bamber Bridge	d									09 57														12 29	
Lostock Hall	d									10 00														12 32	
Preston 8	a									10 08							11 15							12 40	
	d	00 20	08 56	09 00	09 15			09 35	10 00	10 10		10 35	11 00	11 15				11 25	11 35	11 42		12 00	12 35	12 42	13 00
Kirkham & Wesham	d	00 45	09 05	09 25					10 25	10 19			11 25							11 51		12 25		12 51	13 25
Moss Side	d		09 11							10 25										11 57				12 57	
Lytham	d		09 15							10 29										12 01				13 01	
Ansdell & Fairhaven	d		09 18							10 32										12 04				13 04	
St Annes-on-the-Sea	d		09 22							10 36										12 08				13 08	
Squires Gate	d		09 26							10 40										12 12				13 12	
Blackpool Pleasure Beach	d		09 28							10 42										12 14				13 14	
Blackpool South	a		09 33				←			10 47					←					12 19				13 19	
Poulton-le-Fylde	d	01 05		09 45			09 45	10 15	10 45			11 15	11 45		11 45			12 05	12 15			12 45	13 15		13 45
Blackpool North	a	01 25		→	09 55		10 00	10 30	11 00			11 30	→	11 55	12 00			12 20	12 30			13 00	13 30		→

For general notes see front of timetable
For details of catering facilities see Directory of Train Operators

A From York (Table 41)
B Also stops at Layton 01 15

For connections to and from London Euston, please refer to Table 65

A special service will operate on Easter Day Sunday 23 March. Details will be advertised locally.

Table 97

Sundays

2 to 23 March

Colne, Burnley, Accrington and Blackburn → Preston → Blackpool

Network Diagram - see first page of Table 97

		NT	NT		TP	NT	NT	NT		TP	NT	NT	TP		NT	NT	TP	NT		NT	NT	TP	NT		NT
		A													A										
			🚌		🚌	🚌	🚌			🚌	🚌		🚌			🚌	🚌	🚌		🚌		🚌	🚌		
Colne	d											13 35													15 35
Nelson	d											13 40													15 40
Brierfield	d											13 43													15 43
Burnley Central	d											13 48													15 48
Burnley Barracks	d											13 50													15 50
Leeds 10	41 d	11 35													13 35										
Burnley Manchester Road	41 d	12 39													14 39										
Rose Grove	d											13 53													15 53
Hapton	d											13 56													15 56
Huncoat	d											13 59													15 59
Accrington	d	12 47										14 04			14 47										16 04
Church & Oswaldtwistle	d											14 06													16 06
Rishton	d											14 09													16 09
Blackburn	a	12 55										14 14			14 55										16 14
Manchester Victoria	94 ⛴ a	*14 35*										*15 35*			*16 35*										*17 35*
Clitheroe	94 d	*12 24*										*13 24*			*14 24*										*15 24*
Blackburn	d	12 56										14 15			14 56										16 15
Mill Hill (Lancashire)	d											14 18													16 18
Cherry Tree	d											14 20													16 20
Pleasington	d											14 22													16 22
Bamber Bridge	d											14 29													16 29
Lostock Hall	d											14 32													16 32
Preston 8	a	13 13										14 40			15 13										16 40
	d		13 15			13 25	13 35	13 42		14 00	14 35	14 42	15 00			15 15		15 25		15 35	15 42	16 00	16 35		16 42
Kirkham & Wesham	d							13 51		14 25		14 51	15 25								15 51	16 25			16 51
Moss Side	d							13 57				14 57									15 57				16 57
Lytham	d							14 01				15 01									16 01				17 01
Ansdell & Fairhaven	d							14 04				15 04									16 04				17 04
St Annes-on-the-Sea	d							14 08				15 08									16 08				17 08
Squires Gate	d							14 12				15 12									16 12				17 12
Blackpool Pleasure Beach	d							14 14				15 14									16 14				17 14
Blackpool South	a				←			14 19				15 19					←				16 19				17 19
Poulton-le-Fylde	d				13 45	14 05	14 15			14 45	15 15		15 45				15 45	16 05		16 15		16 45	17 15		
Blackpool North	a		13 55		14 00	14 20	14 30			15 00	15 30		→			15 55	16 00	16 20		16 30		17 00	17 30		

		TP	NT	NT	TP		NT	NT	NT	TP		NT	NT	TP	NT		NT	NT	TP	NT		NT	TP	NT	NT
			A									A								A					
		🚌		🚌	🚌		🚌	🚌		🚌			🚌	🚌	🚌		🚌		🚌			🚌	🚌	🚌	🚌
Colne	d																	17 28							
Nelson	d																	17 33							
Brierfield	d																	17 36							
Burnley Central	d																	17 41							
Burnley Barracks	d																	17 43							
Leeds 10	41 d		15 35									16 35								17 35					
Burnley Manchester Road	41 d		16 39									17 39								18 39					
Rose Grove	d																	17 46							
Hapton	d																	17 49							
Huncoat	d																	17 52							
Accrington	d		16 47									17 47						17 57		18 47					
Church & Oswaldtwistle	d																	17 59							
Rishton	d																	18 02							
Blackburn	a		16 55									17 55						18 07		18 55					
Manchester Victoria	94 ⛴ a		*18 35*															*19 35*		*20 35*					
Clitheroe	94 d		*16 24*									*17 24*								*18 24*					
Blackburn	d		16 56									17 56						18 08		18 56					
Mill Hill (Lancashire)	d																	18 11							
Cherry Tree	d																	18 13							
Pleasington	d																	18 15							
Bamber Bridge	d																	18 22							
Lostock Hall	d																	18 25							
Preston 8	a		17 13									18 13						18 33		19 13					
	d	17 00		17 15			17 25	17 35	17 42	18 00			18 15		18 25		18 35	18 42	19 00			19 15		19 25	19 35
Kirkham & Wesham	d	17 25							17 51	18 25								18 51	19 25						
Moss Side	d								17 57									18 57							
Lytham	d								18 01									19 01							
Ansdell & Fairhaven	d								18 04									19 04							
St Annes-on-the-Sea	d								18 08									19 08							
Squires Gate	d								18 12									19 12							
Blackpool Pleasure Beach	d								18 14									19 14							
Blackpool South	a				←				18 19					←				19 19					←		
Poulton-le-Fylde	d	17 45			17 45		18 05	18 15		18 45				18 45	19 05		19 15		19 45				19 45	20 05	20 15
Blackpool North	a	→		17 55	18 00		18 20	18 30		→			18 55	19 00	19 20		19 30		→			19 55	20 00	20 20	20 30

For general notes see front of timetable
For details of catering facilities see Directory of Train Operators

A From York (Table 41)

For connections to and from London Euston, please refer to Table 65

A special service will operate on Easter Day Sunday 23 March. Details will be advertised locally.

Table 97

Colne, Burnley, Accrington and Blackburn → Preston → Blackpool

Sundays

2 to 23 March

Network Diagram - see first page of Table 97

		NT	TP Bus	NT Bus	NT	NT A	TP Bus	NT B	NT Bus	TP Bus	NT Bus	NT Bus	TP Bus	NT Bus	NT	TP Bus	NT Bus
Colne	d				19 21										21 29		
Nelson	d				19 26										21 34		
Brierfield	d				19 29										21 37		
Burnley Central	d				19 34										21 42		
Burnley Barracks	d				19 36										21 44		
Leeds 10 41	d							19 35									
Burnley Manchester Road 41	d							20 39									
Rose Grove	d				19 39										21 47		
Hapton	d				19 42										21 50		
Huncoat	d				19 45										21 53		
Accrington	d				19 50			20 47							21 57		
Church & Oswaldtwistle	d				19 52										22 00		
Rishton	d				19 55										22 03		
Blackburn	a				20 00			20 55							22 08		
Manchester Victoria 94	a				*21 35*			*22 35*							*23 35*		
Clitheroe 94	d				*19 24*	19 47		*20 24*							*21 24*		
Blackburn	d				20 01	20 14		20 56							22 09		
Mill Hill (Lancashire)	d				20 04										22 12		
Cherry Tree	d				20 06										22 14		
Pleasington	d				20 08										22 16		
Bamber Bridge	d				20 15	20 24									22 23		
Lostock Hall	d				20 18	20 26									22 26		
Preston 8	a				20 26	20 34		21 13							22 36		
	d	19 42	20 00	20 35	20 42	20 36	21 00		21 15		21 25	21 35	22 00	22 35		23 05	23 25
Kirkham & Wesham	d	19 51	20 25		20 51	20 46	21 25						22 25			23 30	
Moss Side	d	19 57			20 57												
Lytham	d	20 01			21 01												
Ansdell & Fairhaven	d	20 04			21 04												
St Annes-on-the-Sea	d	20 08			21 08												
Squires Gate	d	20 12			21 12												
Blackpool Pleasure Beach	d	20 14			21 14												
Blackpool South	a	20 19			21 19					←							
Poulton-le-Fylde	d		20 45	21 15		20 54	21 45			21 45	22 05	22 15	22 45	23 15		23 50	
Blackpool North	a		21 00	21 30		21 03	→		21 55	22 00	22 20	22 30	23 00	23 30		00 05	00 05

Sundays

from 30 March

		TP 1◇ C	TP 1◇ D	NT	NT E	NT G	TP 1◇ D	NT	NT H	TP 1◇ D	NT E	NT B	NT H	NT	TP 1◇ D	NT H	NT	TP 1◇ D	NT E	NT B	NT H	NT
Colne	d							09 01									11 35					
Nelson	d							09 06									11 40					
Brierfield	d							09 09									11 43					
Burnley Central	d							09 14									11 48					
Burnley Barracks	d							09 16									11 50					
Leeds 10 41	d											09 35								11 35		
Burnley Manchester Road 41	d											10 41								12 39		
Rose Grove	d							09 19									11 53					
Hapton	d							09 22									11 56					
Huncoat	d							09 25									11 59					
Accrington	d							09 30				10 50					12 04			12 47		
Church & Oswaldtwistle	d							09 32									12 06					
Rishton	d							09 35									12 09					
Blackburn	a							09 42				10 58					12 14			12 55		
Manchester Victoria 94	a							*10 35*				*12 35*					*13 35*			*14 35*		
Clitheroe 94	d							*09 17*				*10 27*					*11 24*			*12 24*		
Blackburn	d							09 43				10 58					12 15			12 56		
Mill Hill (Lancashire)	d							09 46									12 18					
Cherry Tree	d							09 48									12 20					
Pleasington	d							09 50									12 22					
Bamber Bridge	d							09 57									12 29					
Lostock Hall	d							10 00									12 32					
Preston 8	a							10 08				11 15					12 40			13 13		
	d	00 06	08 48	08 56	09 07	09 20	09 48	10 10	10 21	10 48	11 07	11 17	11 21	11 42	11 48	12 21	12 42	12 48	13 07	13 14	13 21	13 42
Kirkham & Wesham	d	00 16	08 58	09 05			09 58	10 19		10 58				11 51	11 58		12 51	12 58				13 51
Moss Side	d			09 11				10 25						11 57			12 57					13 57
Lytham	d			09 15				10 29						12 01			13 01					14 01
Ansdell & Fairhaven	d			09 18				10 32						12 04			13 04					14 04
St Annes-on-the-Sea	d			09 22				10 36						12 08			13 08					14 08
Squires Gate	d			09 26				10 40						12 12			13 12					14 12
Blackpool Pleasure Beach	d			09 28				10 42						12 14			13 14					14 14
Blackpool South	a			09 33				10 47						12 19			13 19					14 19
Poulton-le-Fylde	d	00 26	09 07		09 23	09 36	10 07		10 38	11 07	11 23	11 33	11 38		12 07	12 38		13 07	13 23	13 31	13 38	
Blackpool North	a	00 38	09 16		09 34	09 45	10 16		10 47	11 16	11 34	11 40	11 47		12 16	12 47		13 16	13 34	13 39	13 47	

For general notes see front of timetable
For details of catering facilities see Directory of Train Operators

A 23 March. From Carlisle (Table 36)
B From York (Table 41)
C From Manchester Airport (Table 82). Also stops at Layton 0030
D From Manchester Airport (Table 82)
E From Liverpool Lime Street (Table 90)
G From Manchester Victoria (Table 82)
H From Buxton (Table 86)

A special service will operate on Easter Day Sunday 23 March. Details will be advertised locally.

For connections to and from London Euston, please refer to Table 65

Table 97

Sundays

from 30 March

Colne, Burnley, Accrington and Blackburn → Preston → Blackpool

Network Diagram - see first page of Table 97

		TP 1 ◇ A	NT B	NT	TP 1 ◇ A	NT C		NT D	NT B	NT	TP 1 ◇ A	NT B	NT		TP 1 ◇ A	NT C	NT D	NT B	NT	TP 1 ◇ A		NT C	NT D	NT B	NT
Colne	d			13 35									15 35												17 28
Nelson	d			13 40									15 40												17 33
Brierfield	d			13 43									15 43												17 36
Burnley Central	d			13 48									15 48												17 41
Burnley Barracks	d			13 50									15 50												17 43
Leeds 10	41 d							13 35									15 35						16 35		
Burnley Manchester Road	41 d							14 39									16 39						17 39		
Rose Grove	d			13 53									15 53												17 46
Hapton	d			13 56									15 56												17 49
Huncoat	d			13 59									15 59												17 52
Accrington	d			14 04				14 47					16 04				16 47						17 47		17 57
Church & Oswaldtwistle	d			14 06									16 06												17 59
Rishton	d			14 09									16 09												18 02
Blackburn	a			14 14				14 55					16 14				16 55						17 55		18 07
Manchester Victoria	94 🚌 a			*15 35*				*16 35*					*17 35*				*18 35*								*19 35*
Clitheroe	94 d			*13 24*				*14 24*					*15 24*				*16 24*						*17 24*		
Blackburn	d			14 15				14 56					16 15				16 56						17 56		18 08
Mill Hill (Lancashire)	d			14 18									16 18												18 11
Cherry Tree	d			14 20									16 20												18 13
Pleasington	d			14 22									16 22												18 15
Bamber Bridge	d			14 29									16 29												18 22
Lostock Hall	d			14 32									16 32												18 25
Preston 8	a			14 40				15 13					16 40				17 13						18 13		18 33
	d	13 48	14 21	14 42	14 48	15 07		15 14	15 21	15 42	15 48	16 21	16 42		16 48	17 07	17 14	17 21	17 42	17 48		18 07	18 14	18 21	18 42
Kirkham & Wesham	d	13 58		14 51	14 58					15 51	15 58		16 51		16 58				17 51	17 58					18 51
Moss Side	d			14 57						15 57			16 57						17 57						18 57
Lytham	d			15 01						16 01			17 01						18 01						19 01
Ansdell & Fairhaven	d			15 04						16 04			17 04						18 04						19 04
St Annes-on-the-Sea	d			15 08						16 08			17 08						18 08						19 08
Squires Gate	d			15 12						16 12			17 12						18 12						19 12
Blackpool Pleasure Beach	d			15 14						16 14			17 14						18 14						19 14
Blackpool South	a			15 19						16 19			17 19						18 19						19 19
Poulton-le-Fylde	d	14 07	14 37		15 07	15 23		15 32	15 38		16 07	16 38			17 07	17 23	17 31	17 37		18 07		18 23	18 31	18 38	
Blackpool North	a	14 16	14 47		15 16	15 34		15 40	15 47		16 16	16 47			17 16	17 35	17 38	17 47		18 16		18 34	18 38	18 47	

		TP 1 ◇ A	NT C	NT D	NT B		NT	TP 1 ◇ A	NT B	NT	NT E 🚌	NT		TP 1 ◇ A	NT C	NT D	NT B	TP 1 ◇ A	NT B	NT	TP 1 ◇ A	NT C	TP 1 ◇ A		
Colne	d									19 21										21 29					
Nelson	d									19 26										21 34					
Brierfield	d									19 29										21 37					
Burnley Central	d									19 34										21 42					
Burnley Barracks	d									19 36										21 44					
Leeds 10	41 d			17 35												19 35									
Burnley Manchester Road	41 d			18 39												20 39									
Rose Grove	d									19 39										21 47					
Hapton	d									19 42										21 50					
Huncoat	d									19 45										21 53					
Accrington	d			18 47						19 50						20 47				21 57					
Church & Oswaldtwistle	d									19 52										22 00					
Rishton	d									19 55										22 03					
Blackburn	a			18 55						20 00						20 55				22 08					
Manchester Victoria	94 🚌 a			*20 35*						*21 35*						*22 35*				*23 35*					
Clitheroe	94 d			*18 24*						*19 24*	19 47					*20 24*				*21 24*					
Blackburn	d			18 56						20 01	20 14					20 56				22 09					
Mill Hill (Lancashire)	d									20 04										22 12					
Cherry Tree	d									20 06										22 14					
Pleasington	d									20 08										22 16					
Bamber Bridge	d									20 15	20 24									22 23					
Lostock Hall	d									20 18	20 26									22 26					
Preston 8	a			19 13						20 26	20 34	←				21 13				22 36					
	d	18 48	19 07	19 14	19 21		19 42	19 48	20 21	20 42	20 36	20 42		20 48	21 07	21 14	21 21	21 48	22 21		22 48	23 17	23 48		
Kirkham & Wesham	d	18 58					19 51	19 58		→	20 46	20 51		20 58				21 58			22 58		23 58		
Moss Side	d						19 57					20 57													
Lytham	d						20 01					21 01													
Ansdell & Fairhaven	d						20 04					21 04													
St Annes-on-the-Sea	d						20 08					21 08													
Squires Gate	d						20 12					21 12													
Blackpool Pleasure Beach	d						20 14					21 14													
Blackpool South	a						20 19					21 19													
Poulton-le-Fylde	d	19 07	19 23	19 31	19 37			20 07	20 38		20 54			21 07	21 23	21 31	21 37	22 07	22 37		23 07	23 34	00 07		
Blackpool North	a	19 16	19 32	19 38	19 47			20 16	20 47		21 03			21 16	21 34	21 38	21 47	22 16	22 47		23 16	23 43	00 16		

For general notes see front of timetable
For details of catering facilities see Directory of Train Operators

A From Manchester Airport (Table 82)
B From Buxton (Table 86)
C From Liverpool Lime Street (Table 90)
D From York (Table 41)
E 4 May. From Carlisle (Table 36)

For connections to and from London Euston, please refer to Table 65

Table 98

Mondays to Fridays

Lancaster → Morecambe and Heysham

Network Diagram - see first page of Table 97

Miles			NT	NT	NT	NT	NT	NT	NT	NT	NT	NT	NT	NT	NT	NT	NT	NT	NT	NT	NT	NT	NT	NT	NT	TP
							A	B	C			C				C					C					1 ◇ D
0	**Lancaster** 3	.. 82 d	06 28	07 10	07 49	08 19	09 07	10 03	10 10	11 14	12 03	12 10	13 22	14 40	15 24	16 02	16 49	17 23	18 04	18 37	18 45	19 15	20 14	21 07	21 45	22 57
2½	Bare Lane	. d	06 34	07 16	07 55	08 25	09 13	10 10	10 16	11 20	12 09	12 16	13 28	14 46	15 30	16 08	16 55	17 28	18 10	18 43	18 51	19 21	20 20	21 13	21 51	23 02
4¼	**Morecambe**	..... a	06 38	07 20	08 00	08 29	09 21	10 17	10 22	11 25	12 13	12 21	13 32	14 50	15 36	16 13	16 59	17 34	18 15	18 48	18 57	19 26	20 24	21 17	21 55	23 06
—		d									12 17		13 36													
8½	**Heysham Port**	.. a									12 31		13 50													

Saturdays
until 22 March

		NT	NT	NT	NT	NT	NT		NT	NT	NT	NT	NT	NT		NT	NT	NT	NT	NT	NT	NT	NT	NT	NT	NT
					A				C			C					C					C				🚌
Lancaster 6	.. 82 d	07 10	07 49	08 19	09 07	09 16	10 00		10 10	11 06	12 00	12 14	13 20	14 35		15 24	16 02	16 49	17 23	17 58	18 33	18 45	19 10	20 14	20 56	21 25
Bare Lane	. d	07 16	07 55	08 25	09 13	09 22	10 06		10 16	11 12	12 06	12 20	13 26	14 41		15 30	16 08	16 55	17 29	18 04	18 39	18 51	19 16	20 20	21 02	21 35
Morecambe	..... a	07 20	07 59	08 29	09 21	09 27	10 12		10 22	11 16	12 10	12 25	13 30	14 47		15 36	16 13	16 59	17 34	18 10	18 44	18 57	19 22	20 24	21 06	21 45
	d										12 14		13 34													
Heysham Port	.. a										12 28		13 48													

Saturdays
from 29 March

		NT	NT	NT	NT	NT	NT		NT	NT	NT	NT	NT	NT		NT	NT	NT	NT	NT	NT	NT	NT	NT	NT	NT
							C			C						C					C				🚌	🚌
Lancaster 6	.. 82 d	07 14	07 49	08 19	09 16	10 00	10 13		11 14	12 00	12 14	13 20	14 35	15 24		16 02	16 44	17 23	17 58	18 33	18 45	19 10	20 10	20 56	21 25	22 45
Bare Lane	. d	07 20	07 55	08 25	09 22	10 06	10 20		11 20	12 06	12 20	13 26	14 41	15 30		16 08	16 50	17 29	18 04	18 39	18 51	19 16	20 16	21 02	21 35	22 55
Morecambe	..... a	07 24	07 59	08 29	09 27	10 12	10 25		11 25	12 10	12 25	13 30	14 47	15 36		16 13	16 55	17 34	18 10	18 44	18 57	19 22	20 20	21 06	21 45	23 05
	d									12 14		13 34														
Heysham Port	.. a									12 28		13 48														

Sundays

		NT	NT	NT	NT	NT	NT	NT	NT
		E	G	E	G		C	C	
Lancaster 6	.. 82 d	10 45	12 11	12 48	14 09	15 00	16 50	19 14	21 46
Bare Lane	. d	10 51	12 17	12 54	14 15	15 06	16 56	19 20	21 51
Morecambe	..... a	10 55	12 21	12 59	14 19	15 10	17 00	19 24	21 55
	d								
Heysham Port	.. a								

For general notes see front of timetable
For details of catering facilities see Directory of Train Operators

A From Clitheroe (Table 94)
B From Liverpool Lime Street (Table 90)
C From Leeds (Table 36)
D From Windermere (Table 83) to Barrow-in-Furness (Table 82)
E From 23 March.
From Leeds (Table 36)
G From 23 March

Heysham and Morecambe → Lancaster

Network Diagram - see first page of Table 97

Mondays to Fridays

Miles			NT	NT	NT	NT	NT	NT	NT	NT	NT	NT	NT	NT	NT	NT	NT	NT	NT	NT	NT	NT	NT	NT	NT	NT	TP
																											[1] ◇
								A		B		B					C					B					D
0	Heysham Port	d	.....	.....	.....	.....	.....	.....	.....	.....	.....	.....	12 48	13 53	.....	.....	.....	.....	.....	.....	.....	.....	.....	.....	.....	.....	.....
4¼	Morecambe	a	.	.	.	.	.	.	.	.	.	.	12 58	14 03	.	.	.	.	.	.	.	.	.	.	.	.	.
—		d	06 13	06 55	07 34	08 05	08 33	09 25	10 22	10 45	11 33	12 44	13 02	14 07	15 08	15 40	16 38	17 09	17 48	18 20	18 52	19 05	19 39	20 29	21 28	22 25	23 10
6	Bare Lane	d	06 17	06 59	07 38	08 09	08 37	09 29	10 26	10 49	11 37	12 48	13 09	14 14	15 12	15 44	16 42	17 13	17 52	18 24	18 56	19 09	19 43	20 33	21 32	22 29	23a14
8½	Lancaster [3]	82 a	06 23	07 06	07 44	08 15	08 43	09 34	10 35	10 56	11 43	12 53	13 16	14 20	15 18	15 52	16 48	17 20	17 59	18 30	19 04	19 18	19 49	20 40	21 39	22 36	.....

Saturdays until 22 March

		NT	NT	NT	NT	NT	NT	NT	NT		NT	NT	NT	NT	NT	NT	NT	NT	NT	NT	NT	NT	NT	NT	NT	NT
									B			B					C					B			A	🚌
Heysham Port	d	.....	.....	.....	.....	.....	.....	.....	.....	.....	.....	.....	12 44	14 01	.....	.....	.....	.....	.....	.....	.....	.....	.....	.....	.....	.....
Morecambe	a	.	.	.	.	.	.	.	.	.	.	.	12 54	14 11	.	.	.	.	.	.	.	.	.	.	.	.
	d	06 55	07 34	08 05	08 33	09 30	09 48	10 22	10 36	.....	11 23	12 47	12 58	14 15	15 08	15 40	16 38	17 09	17 40	18 20	18 52	19 00	19 39	20 29	21 10	22 05
Bare Lane	d	06 59	07 38	08 09	08 37	09 34	09 52	10 26	10 40	.	11 27	12 51	13 05	14 22	15 12	15 44	16 42	17 13	17 44	18 24	18 56	19 05	19 43	20 33	21 14	22 15
Lancaster [6]	82 a	07 06	07 44	08 15	08 43	09 43	09 59	10 35	10 47	.....	11 33	12 58	13 14	14 28	15 18	15 52	16 49	17 20	17 51	18 30	19 04	19 13	19 49	20 40	21 20	22 25

Saturdays from 29 March

		NT	NT	NT	NT	NT	NT		NT	NT	NT	NT	NT	NT		NT	NT	NT	NT	NT	NT	NT	NT	NT	NT	NT
									B		B						C					B				🚌
Heysham Port	d	.....	.....	.....	.....	.....	.....	.....	.....	.....	.....	12 36	14 05	.....	.....	.....	.....	.....	.....	.....	.....	.....	.....	.....	.....	.....
Morecambe	a	.	.	.	.	.	.	.	.	.	.	12 46	14 15	.	.	.	.	.	.	.	.	.	.	.	.	.
	d	06 55	07 32	08 02	08 33	09 30	10 22	.....	10 40	11 27	12 47	12 50	14 19	15 08	.....	15 40	16 38	17 09	17 40	18 12	18 52	19 00	19 39	20 29	21 10	22 05
Bare Lane	d	06 59	07 36	08 06	08 37	09 34	10 26	.	10 44	11 31	12 51	12 57	14 26	15 12	.	15 44	16 42	17 13	17 44	18 16	18 56	19 05	19 43	20 33	21 14	22 15
Lancaster [6]	82 a	07 06	07 42	08 12	08 43	09 43	10 35	.....	10 51	11 37	12 58	13 06	14 33	15 18	.....	15 52	16 49	17 20	17 51	18 23	19 04	19 13	19 49	20 40	21 20	22 25

Sundays

		NT	NT	NT	NT	NT	NT	NT	NT
		E	G	E	G		B	B	
Heysham Port	d	.....	.....	.....	.....	.....	.....	.....	.....
Morecambe	a	.	.	.	.	.	.	.	.
	d	11 19	12 26	13 11	14 28	15 21	17 45	20 00	22 19
Bare Lane	d	11 23	12 30	13 15	14 32	15 25	17 49	20 04	22 23
Lancaster [6]	82 a	11 29	12 36	13 21	14 38	15 31	17 56	20 11	22 29

For general notes see front of timetable
For details of catering facilities see Directory of Train Operators

A To Preston (Table 65)
B To Leeds (Table 36)
C To Skipton (Table 36)
D From Windermere (Table 83) to Barrow-in-Furness (Table 82)
E From 23 March
G From 23 March. To Leeds (Table 36)

To and from The Isle of Man via Heysham and Liverpool

Mondays to Fridays

One Class only on ship

		VT ℝ A	NT	NT	VT ℝ B	VT MX ℝ C	VT ℝ D	VT ThX ℝ E	VT ThFX ℝ G
London Euston 15	65 d								
Birmingham New Street 12	65 d								
Crewe 10	65 d								
Manchester Piccadilly 10	82, 89 d								
Preston 10	82 d								
Lancaster 8	98 d		12 03	13 22					
Morecambe	98 d		12 17	13 36					
Heysham Port	a		12 31	13 50					
Liverpool Lime Street	a	11 15							
Liverpool Landing Stage	⛴ d						19 00	19 00	19 00
Heysham Port	⛴ d				14 15	14 15			
Douglas (Isle of Man)	⛴ a	13 45			17 45	16 45	21 30	21 30	21 30

Saturdays

until 26 January

One Class only on ship

		NT	NT	VT ℝ H
London Euston 15	65 d			
Birmingham New Street 12	65 d			
Crewe 10	65 d			
Manchester Piccadilly 10	82, 89 d			
Preston 10	82 d			
Lancaster 8	98 d	12 00	13 20	
Morecambe	98 d	12 14	13 34	
Heysham Port	a	12 28	13 48	
Liverpool Lime Street	a			
Liverpool Landing Stage	⛴ d			
Heysham Port	⛴ d			14 15
Douglas (Isle of Man)	⛴ a			17 45

Saturdays

2 February to 22 March

One Class only on ship

		VT ℝ J	NT	NT	VT ℝ K	VT ℝ L	VT ℝ J
London Euston 15	65 d						
Birmingham New Street 12	65 d						
Crewe 10	65 d						
Manchester Piccadilly 10	82, 89 d						
Preston 10	82 d						
Lancaster 8	98 d		12 00	13 20			
Morecambe	98 d		12 14	13 34			
Heysham Port	a		12 28	13 48			
Liverpool Lime Street	a						
Liverpool Landing Stage	⛴ d	11 15				19 00	21 15
Heysham Port	⛴ d				14 15		
Douglas (Isle of Man)	⛴ a	13 45			17 45	21 30	23 45

For general notes see front of timetable
For details of catering facilities see Directory of Train Operators

A From 25 March
B Until 22 February and from 10 March
C 26 February to 7 March, also operates 3 March
D 24 to 28 March
E 31 March to 25 April and from 5 May
G 28 to 30 April
H Until 29 December
J 22 March
K From 8 March
L 1 to 15 March

Reservations: Customers, including all children, must obtain an advance reservation for the ship. This can be obtained free of charge from stations, appointed Agents or direct from The Isle of Man Steam Packet Company Offices in Douglas, Isle of Man.Customers without a reservation may not be able to travel if the ship is fully reserved.

Customers travelling via Liverpool should allow a minimum of 45 minutes for the transfer to and from the ship. Bus transfers between Liverpool Lime Street and the Landing Stage are available free of charge for customers with through rail tickets.

A special service will operate to and from Liverpool Birkenhead on Saturdays and Sundays during December, January and February. For details please contact the Isle of Man Steam Ship Packet Company.

Table 98A **SHIPPING SERVICES**

To and from The Isle of Man via Heysham and Liverpool

Saturdays

from 29 March

One Class only on ship

		VT R	NT	NT	VT R	VT R A	VT R B
London Euston [15]	65 d	.	.	.	.	.	.
Birmingham New Street [12]	65 d	.	.	.	.	.	.
Crewe [10]	65 d	.	.	.	.	.	.
Manchester Piccadilly [10]	82, 89 ⛴ d	.	.	.	.	.	.
Preston [10]	82 d	.	.	.	.	.	.
Lancaster [8]	98 d	.	12 00	13 20	.	.	.
Morecambe	98 d	.	12 14	13 34	.	.	.
Heysham Port	a	.	12 28	13 48	.	.	.
Liverpool Lime Street	a	.	.	.	.	.	.
Liverpool Landing Stage	⛴ d	11 15	.	.	.	19 00	21 15
Heysham Port	⛴ d	.	.	.	14 15	.	.
Douglas (Isle of Man)	⛴ a	13 45	.	.	17 45	21 30	23 45

Sundays

until 27 January

One Class only on ship

London Euston [15]	65 d	.
Birmingham New Street [12]	65 d	.
Crewe [10]	65 d	.
Manchester Piccadilly [10]	82, 89 ⛴ d	.
Preston [10]	82 d	.
Lancaster [8]	98 d	.
Morecambe	98 d	.
Heysham Port	a	.
Liverpool Lime Street	a	.
Liverpool Landing Stage	⛴ d	.
Heysham Port	⛴ d	.
Douglas (Isle of Man)	⛴ a	.

Sundays

3 February to 23 March

One Class only on ship

		VT R C	VT R D	VT R D
London Euston [15]	65 d	.	.	.
Birmingham New Street [12]	65 d	.	.	.
Crewe [10]	65 d	.	.	.
Manchester Piccadilly [10]	82, 89 ⛴ d	.	.	.
Preston [10]	82 d	.	.	.
Lancaster [8]	98 d	.	.	.
Morecambe	98 d	.	.	.
Heysham Port	a	.	.	.
Liverpool Lime Street	a	.	.	.
Liverpool Landing Stage	⛴ d	13 30	.	18 30
Heysham Port	⛴ d	.	14 15	.
Douglas (Isle of Man)	⛴ a	16 30	17 45	21 00

For general notes see front of timetable
For details of catering facilities see Directory of Train Operators

A 29 March, 12 and 26 April, 3 and 10 May
B 5 and 19 April, 17 May
C 2 March
D From 9 March

Reservations: Customers, including all children, must obtain an advance reservation for the ship. This can be obtained free of charge from stations, appointed Agents or direct from The Isle of Man Steam Packet Company Offices in Douglas, Isle of Man.Customers without a reservation may not be able to travel if the ship is fully reserved.

Customers travelling via Liverpool should allow a minimum of 45 minutes for the transfer to and from the ship. Bus transfers between Liverpool Lime Street and the Landing Stage are available free of charge for customers with through rail tickets.

A special service will operate to and from Liverpool Birkenhead on Saturdays and Sundays during December, January and February. For details please contact the Isle of Man Steam Ship Packet Company.

Table 98A **SHIPPING SERVICES**

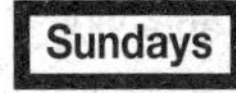

from 30 March

One Class only on ship

To and from The Isle of Man via Heysham and Liverpool

		VT R	VT R A
London Euston 15	65 d	.	.
Birmingham New Street 12	65 d	.	.
Crewe 10	65 d	.	.
Manchester Piccadilly 10	82, 89 d	.	.
Preston 10	82 d	.	.
Lancaster 8	98 d	.	.
Morecambe	98 d	.	.
Heysham Port	a	.	.
Liverpool Lime Street	a	.	.
Liverpool Landing Stage	d	.	19 00
Heysham Port	d	14 15	
Douglas (Isle of Man)	a	17 45	21 30

For general notes see front of timetable
For details of catering facilities see Directory of Train Operators

A Until 11 May

Reservations: Customers, including all children, must obtain an advance reservation for the ship. This can be obtained free of charge from stations, appointed Agents or direct from The Isle of Man Steam Packet Company Offices in Douglas, Isle of Man.Customers without a reservation may not be able to travel if the ship is fully reserved.

Customers travelling via Liverpool should allow a minimum of 45 minutes for the transfer to and from the ship. Bus transfers between Liverpool Lime Street and the Landing Stage are available free of charge for customers with through rail tickets.

A special service will operate to and from Liverpool Birkenhead on Saturdays and Sundays during December, January and February. For details please contact the Isle of Man Steam Ship Packet Company.

To and from The Isle of Man via Heysham and Liverpool

One Class only on ship

		VT R A	VT MX R B	VT R C	NT	NT	VT R D	VT ThX R E	VT ThFX R G
Douglas (Isle of Man)	⛴ d	07 30	08 45	08 45			15 00	15 00	15 00
Heysham Port	⛴ a		11 15	12 15					
Liverpool Landing Stage	⛴ a	10 00					17 30	17 30	17 30
Liverpool Lime Street	d								
Heysham Port	d				12 48	13 53			
Morecambe	98 a				12 58	14 03			
Lancaster 8	98 a				13 16	14 20			
Preston 10	82 a								
Manchester Piccadilly 10	82, 89 ⛴ a								
Crewe 10	65 a								
Birmingham New Street 12	65 a								
London Euston 15	65 a								

Saturdays

until 26 January

One Class only on ship

		VT R H	NT	NT
Douglas (Isle of Man)	⛴ d	08 45		
Heysham Port	⛴ a	12 15		
Liverpool Landing Stage	⛴ a			
Liverpool Lime Street	d			
Heysham Port	d		12 44	14 01
Morecambe	98 a		12 54	14 11
Lancaster 8	98 a		13 14	14 28
Preston 10	82 a			
Manchester Piccadilly 10	82, 89 ⛴ a			
Crewe 10	65 a			
Birmingham New Street 12	65 a			
London Euston 15	65 a			

Saturdays

2 February to 22 March

One Class only on ship

		VT R J	VT R K	VT R L	NT	NT	VT R N
Douglas (Isle of Man)	⛴ d	07 30	08 00	08 45			17 45
Heysham Port	⛴ a			12 15			
Liverpool Landing Stage	⛴ a	10 00	10 30				20 15
Liverpool Lime Street	d						
Heysham Port	d				12 44	14 01	
Morecambe	98 a				12 54	14 11	
Lancaster 8	98 a				13 14	14 28	
Preston 10	82 a						
Manchester Piccadilly 10	82, 89 ⛴ a						
Crewe 10	65 a						
Birmingham New Street 12	65 a						
London Euston 15	65 a						

For general notes see front of timetable
For details of catering facilities see Directory of Train Operators

A From 25 March
B 26 February to 7 March, also operates 3 March
C Until 22 February and from 10 March
D 24 to 28 March
E 31 March to 25 April and from 5 May
G 28 to 30 April
H Until 29 December
J From 15 March
K 1 and 8 March
L From 8 March
N 22 March

Reservations: Customers, including all children, must obtain an advance reservation for the ship. This can be obtained free of charge from stations, appointed Agents or direct from The Isle of Man Steam Packet Company Offices in Douglas, Isle of Man.Customers without a reservation may not be able to travel if the ship is fully reserved.

Customers travelling via Liverpool should allow a minimum of 45 minutes for the transfer to and from the ship. Bus transfers between Liverpool Lime Street and the Landing Stage are available free of charge for customers with through rail tickets.

A special service will operate to and from Liverpool Birkenhead on Saturdays and Sundays during December, January and February. For details please contact the Isle of Man Steam Ship Packet Company.

Table 98A

SHIPPING SERVICES

To and from The Isle of Man via Heysham and Liverpool

Saturdays
from 29 March

One Class only on ship

		VT R	VT R	NT	NT	VT R A	VT R B
Douglas (Isle of Man)	⛴ d	07 30	08 45			15 00	17 45
Heysham Port	⛴ a		12 15				
Liverpool Landing Stage	⛴ a	10 00				17 30	20 15
Liverpool Lime Street	d						
Heysham Port	d			12 36	14 05		
Morecambe	98 a			12 46	14 15		
Lancaster 8	98 a			13 06	14 33		
Preston 10	82 a						
Manchester Piccadilly 10	82, 89 ⛴ a						
Crewe 10	65 a						
Birmingham New Street 12	65 a						
London Euston 15	65 a						

Sundays
until 27 January

One Class only on ship

Douglas (Isle of Man)	⛴ d
Heysham Port	⛴ a
Liverpool Landing Stage	⛴ a
Liverpool Lime Street	d
Heysham Port	d
Morecambe	98 a
Lancaster 8	98 a
Preston 10	82 a
Manchester Piccadilly 10	82, 89 ⛴ a
Crewe 10	65 a
Birmingham New Street 12	65 a
London Euston 15	65 a

Sundays
3 February to 23 March

One Class only on ship

		VT R C	VT R C
Douglas (Isle of Man)	⛴ d	08 45	15 00
Heysham Port	⛴ a	12 15	
Liverpool Landing Stage	⛴ a		17 30
Liverpool Lime Street	d		
Heysham Port	d		
Morecambe	98 a		
Lancaster 8	98 a		
Preston 10	82 a		
Manchester Piccadilly 10	82, 89 ⛴ a		
Crewe 10	65 a		
Birmingham New Street 12	65 a		
London Euston 15	65 a		

For general notes see front of timetable
For details of catering facilities see Directory of Train Operators

A 29 March, 12 and 26 April, 3 and 10 May
B 5 and 19 April, 17 May
C From 9 March

Reservations: Customers, including all children, must obtain an advance reservation for the ship. This can be obtained free of charge from stations, appointed Agents or direct from The Isle of Man Steam Packet Company Offices in Douglas, Isle of Man.Customers without a reservation may not be able to travel if the ship is fully reserved.

Customers travelling via Liverpool should allow a minimum of 45 minutes for the transfer to and from the ship. Bus transfers between Liverpool Lime Street and the Landing Stage are available free of charge for customers with through rail tickets.

A special service will operate to and from Liverpool Birkenhead on Saturdays and Sundays during December, January and February. For details please contact the Isle of Man Steam Ship Packet Company.

SHIPPING SERVICES

Sundays
from 30 March

To and from The Isle of Man via Heysham and Liverpool

One Class only on ship

		VT ℝ	VT ℝ
Douglas (Isle of Man)	⛴ d	08 45	15 00
Heysham Port	⛴ a	12 15	
Liverpool Landing Stage	⛴ a		17 30
Liverpool Lime Street	d		
Heysham Port	d		
Morecambe	98 a		
Lancaster 8	98 a		
Preston 10	82 a		
Manchester Piccadilly 10	82, 89 ⛴ a		
Crewe 10	65 a		
Birmingham New Street 12	65 a		
London Euston 15	65 a		

For general notes see front of timetable
For details of catering facilities see Directory of Train Operators

Reservations: Customers, including all children, must obtain an advance reservation for the ship. This can be obtained free of charge from stations, appointed Agents or direct from The Isle of Man Steam Packet Company Offices in Douglas, Isle of Man.Customers without a reservation may not be able to travel if the ship is fully reserved.

Customers travelling via Liverpool should allow a minimum of 45 minutes for the transfer to and from the ship. Bus transfers between Liverpool Lime Street and the Landing Stage are available free of charge for customers with through rail tickets.

A special service will operate to and from Liverpool Birkenhead on Saturdays and Sundays during December, January and February. For details please contact the Isle of Man Steam Ship Packet Company.

Ormskirk — Preston

Network Diagram - see first page of Table 97

Miles			NT	NT	NT	NT	NT	NT	NT	NT	NT	NT	NT	NT
—	Liverpool Central 10	103 d	*06 10*	*07 40*	*08 55*	*10 10*	*11 40*	*12 55*	*14 25*	*15 55*	*17 10*	*18 25*	*19 40*	*21 40*
0	**Ormskirk**	d	07 15	08 22	09 35	10 50	12 23	13 38	15 04	16 32	17 51	19 02	20 19	22 17
2½	Burscough Junction	d	07 19	08 26	09 39	10 54	12 27	13 42	15 08	16 36	17 55	19 06	20 23	22 21
5½	Rufford	d	07 23	08 30	09 43	10 58	12 31	13 46	15 12	16 40	17 59	19 10	20 27	22 25
8	Croston	d	07 28	08 35	09 48	11 03	12 36	13 51	15 17	16 45	18 04	19 15	20 32	22 30
15	**Preston** 3	a	07 44	08 51	10 05	11 19	12 52	14 07	15 39	17 01	18 21	19 34	20 49	22 46

Mondays to Saturdays

Miles			NT	NT	NT	NT	NT	NT	NT	NT	NT	NT	NT	NT
0	**Preston** 3	d	06 28	07 48	09 02	10 12	11 26	13 02	14 26	15 45	17 06	18 25	19 39	21 36
7	Croston	d	06 39	07 59	09 14	10 23	11 37	13 13	14 37	15 57	17 17	18 36	19 50	21 48
9½	Rufford	d	06 44	08 03	09 18	10 28	11 42	13 18	14 42	16 01	17 22	18 41	19 55	21 52
12½	Burscough Junction	d	06 49	08 08	09 23	10 33	11 47	13 23	14 47	16 06	17 27	18 46	20 00	21 57
15	**Ormskirk**	a	06 58	08 15	09 30	10 42	11 56	13 30	14 56	16 15	17 36	18 54	20 09	22 06
—	Liverpool Central 10	103 a	*07 35*	*08 50*	*10 05*	*11 20*	*12 35*	*14 05*	*15 35*	*16 50*	*18 20*	*19 35*	*20 50*	*22 50*

For general notes see front of timetable
For details of catering facilities see
Directory of Train Operators

No Sunday Service

Barrow-in-Furness → Whitehaven and Carlisle

Network Diagram - see first page of Table 97

Miles			NT	NT	NT	NT	NT		NT	NT	NT A	NT	NT		NT	NT	NT	NT	NT	NT	NT	NT	NT	NT		
—	Lancaster 3	82 d								08 54	10 30		*11 45*		13 12	*13 46*	14 17		*15 52*	16 39			*17 45*	*19 39*		
0	**Barrow-in-Furness**	d		05 56	06 47				08 46	09 58	11 35		13 00		14 09	14 53	15 30		17 12	17 58			19 10	21 19		
6	Askam	d		06 06	06 57				08 56	10 08	11 45		13 10		14 19	15 03	15 40		17 22	18 08			19 20	21 29		
9¼	Kirkby-in-Furness	d		06x10	07x01				09x00	10x12	11x49		13x14			15x07	15x44		17x26	18x12			19x24	21x33		
11¼	Foxfield	d		06x14	07x05				09x03	10x16	11x52		13x17			15x10	15x47		17x29	18x16			19x27	21x36		
13½	Green Road	d		06x17	07x08					10x19	11x56		13x21			15x14	15x51		17x33	18x19			19x31	21x40		
16	Millom	a		06 24	07 15				09 15	10 26	12 02		13 30		14 33	15 20	15 57		17 39	18 29			19 40	21 49		
—		d		06 25	07 16					10 26	12 02				14 33	15 20	15 58		17 39							
19	Silecroft	d		06x30	07x21					10x31	12x07					15x25	16x02		17x44							
24½	Bootle	d		06x37	07x28					10x37	12x13					15x31	16x09		17x50							
29¼	Ravenglass for Eskdale	d		06 43	07 34					10 43	12 19				14 48	15 37	16 15		17 56							
31	Drigg	d		06x47	07x37					10x46	12x22					15x40	16x18		17x59							
33¼	Seascale	d		06x50	07x41					10x49	12x25					15x43	16x21		18x02							
35	Sellafield	d		06 58	07 48					10 55	12 31				14 56	15 49	16a31		18 08							
37	Braystones	d		07x02	07x51										15x00				18x12							
38¼	Nethertown	d		07x04	07x54										15x02				18x14							
41½	St Bees	d		07 09	07 58					11 05	12 40				15 07	15 59			18 19							
44¾	Corkickle	d		07x14	08x03					11x10	12x45				15x12	16x04			18x24							
45¾	**Whitehaven**	a		07 17	08 07					11 13	12 48				15 15	16 06			18 27							
—		d	06 34	07 22	08 08	08 59	09 49			11 14	12 49	14 03			15 17	16 08		16 54	18 29		19 19	19 50				
47	Parton	d	06x38	07x25	08x12	09x02	09x52			11x18	12x53	14x06			15x20	16x11		16x57	18x32		19x22	19x53				
50½	Harrington	d	06x46	07x33	08x20	09x10	10x00			11x26	13x01	14x14			15x28	16x19		17x05	18x40		19x30	20x01				
52¼	**Workington**	d	06 51	07 40	08 26	09 16	10 06			11 32	13 07	14 21			15 35	16 26		17 12	18 47		19 37	20 08				
56	Flimby	d	06x56	07x44	08x31		10x11			11x37	13x12	14x25			15x39	16x30		17x16	18x51		19x41	20x12				
58	Maryport	d	06 59	07 48	08 34	09 24	10 14			11 40	13 15	14 29			15 43	16 34		17 20	18 55		19 45	20 16				
65½	Aspatria	d	07x09	07x57	08x44	09x33	10x24			11x50	13x25	14x38			15x52	16x43		17x29	19x04		19x54	20x25				
71¾	Wigton	d	07 19	08 07	08 54	09 43	10 34			12 00	13 35	14 48			16 02	16 53		17 39	19 14		20 04	20 35				
81¼	Dalston	d	07x27	08x16	09x02	09x52	10x42			12x08	13x43	14x57			16x11	17x02		17x48	19x23		20x13	20x44				
85¼	**Carlisle 3**	a	07 43	08 31	09 17	10 07	10 58			12 22	13 57	15 12			16 26	17 17		18 03	19 38		20 28	20 59				

Saturdays

until 22 March

		NT	NT	NT	NT		NT	NT	NT	NT		NT	NT	NT	NT		NT	NT	NT	NT	NT B	NT	NT	NT		
Lancaster 6	82 d									08 50		*09 48*	11 01	*11 45*				14 18	16 14		17 17		*17 45*	*19 55*		
Barrow-in-Furness	d			05 57	07 34				08 47	09 58		11 09	11 58	12 58	13 55			15 25	17 19		18 24		19 10	21 19		
Askam	d			06 07	07 44				08 57	10 08		11 19	12 08	13 08	14 05			15 35	17 29		18 34		19 20	21 29		
Kirkby-in-Furness	d			06x11	07x48				09x01	10x12			12x12	13x12	14x09			15x39	17x33		18x38		19x24	21x33		
Foxfield	d			06x14	07x51				09x04	10x15			12x15	13x15	14x12			15x42	17x36		18x41		19x27	21x36		
Green Road	d			06x18	07x55					10x19			12x19	13x19	14x16			15x46	17x40		18x45		19x31	21x40		
Millom	a			06 24	08 01				09 16	10 25		11 36	12 25	13 25	14 22			15 52	17 46		18 54		19 40	21 49		
	d			06 25	08 01					10 26			12 25	13 25	14 22			15 53	17 47							
Silecroft	d			06x30	08x06					10x30			12x30		14x27			15x57	17x51							
Bootle	d			06x37	08x12					10x37			12x36	13x35	14x33			16x04	17x58							
Ravenglass for Eskdale	d			06 43	08 18					10 43			12 42	13 41	14 39			16 10	18 04							
Drigg	d			06x47	08x21					10x46			12x45		14x42			16x13	18x07							
Seascale	d			06x50	08x24					10x49			12x48	13x47	14x45			16x16	18x10							
Sellafield	d			06 56	08 30					10 55			12 54	13 51	14 51			16 22	18 16							
Braystones	d			07x00	08x34													16x25	18x19							
Nethertown	d			07x02	08x36													16x28	18x22							
St Bees	d			07 07	08 41					11 04			13 03	14 02	15 00			16 32	18 26							
Corkickle	d			07x12	08x46					11x09			13x08	14x07	15x05			16x37	18x31							
Whitehaven	a			07 15	08 52					11 12			13 11	14 10	15 08			16 41	18 35							
	d	05 54	06 37	07 17			08 57	09 47		11 13			13 12	14 11	15 09		16 04	16 42	18 36	19 15		19 50				
Parton	d	05x57	06x41	07x20			09x00	09x50		11x17			13x16	14x15	15x13		16x07	16x46	18x40	19x18		19x53				
Harrington	d	06x05	06x49	07x28			09x08	09x58		11x25			13x24	14x23	15x21		16x15	16x54	18x48	19x26		20x01				
Workington	d	06 12	06 55	07 35			09 15	10 05		11 31			13 30	14 29	15 27		16 22	17 00	18 54	19 33		20 08				
Flimby	d	06x16	07x00	07x39			09x19	10x09		11x36			13x35	14x34	15x32		16x26	17x05	18x59	19x37		20x12				
Maryport	d	06 20	07 03	07 43			09 23	10 13		11 39			13 38	14 37	15 35		16 30	17 08	19 02	19 41		20 16				
Aspatria	d	06x29	07x13	07x52			09x32	10x22		11x49			13x48	14x47	15x45		16x39	17x18	19x12	19x50		20x25				
Wigton	d	06 39	07 23	08 02			09 42	10 32		11 59			13 58	14 57	15 55		16 49	17 28	19 22	20 00		20 35				
Dalston	d	06x48	07x31	08x11			09x51	10x41		12x07			14x06	15x05	16x03		16x58	17x36	19x30	20x09		20x44				
Carlisle 8	a	07 03	07 46	08 25			10 05	10 56		12 22			14 21	15 19	16 18		17 12	17 51	19 46	20 24		20 59				

For general notes see front of timetable
For details of catering facilities see Directory of Train Operators

A From Preston (Table 65)
B From Liverpool Lime Street (Table 65)

Barrow-in-Furness → Whitehaven and Carlisle

Saturdays
from 29 March

Network Diagram - see first page of Table 97

		NT	NT	NT	NT	NT	NT	NT	NT	NT	NT	NT	NT	NT	NT	NT	NT	NT	NT	NT	NT
Lancaster 6	82 d								08 50	09 48	11 02	11 45			14 18	15 54		17 17		17 45	19 55
Barrow-in-Furness	d			05 57	07 34			08 47	09 58	11 05	12 14	12 58	13 55		15 25	17 22		18 24		19 10	21 19
Askam	d			06 07	07 44			08 57	10 08	11 15	12 24	13 08	14 05		15 35	17 32		18 34		19 20	21 29
Kirkby-in-Furness	d			06x11	07x48			09x01	10x12		12x28	13x12	14x09		15x39	17x36		18x38		19x24	21x33
Foxfield	d			06x14	07x51			09x04	10x15		12x31	13x15	14x12		15x42	17x39		18x41		19x27	21x36
Green Road	d			06x18	07x55				10x19		12x35	13x19	14x16		15x46	17x43		18x45		19x31	21x40
Millom	a			06 24	08 01			09 16	10 25	11 32	12 41	13 25	14 22		15 52	17 49		18 54		19 40	21 49
	d			06 25	08 01				10 26		12 41	13 25	14 22		15 53	17 50					
Silecroft	d			06x30	08x06				10x30		12x46		14x27		15x57	17x54					
Bootle	d			06x37	08x12				10x37		12x52	13x35	14x33		16x04	18x01					
Ravenglass for Eskdale	d			06 43	08 18				10 43		12 58	13 41	14 39		16 10	18 07					
Drigg	d			06x47	08x21				10x46		13x01		14x42		16x13	18x10					
Seascale	d			06x50	08x24				10x49		13x04	13x47	14x45		16x16	18x13					
Sellafield	d			06 56	08 30				10 55		13 10	13 51	14 51		16 22	18 19					
Braystones	d			07x00	08x34										16x25						
Nethertown	d			07x02	08x36										16x28						
St Bees	d			07 07	08 41				11 04		13 19	14 02	15 00		16 32	18 28					
Corkickle	d			07x12	08x46				11x09		13x24	14x07	15x05		16x37	18x33					
Whitehaven	a			07 15	08 52				11 12		13 27	14 10	15 08		16 41	18 37					
	d	05 54	06 37	07 17		08 57	09 47		11 13		13 28	14 11	15 09	16 04	16 42	18 37	19 15		19 50		
Parton	d	05x57	06x41	07x20		09x00	09x50		11x17		13x32	14x15	15x13	16x07	16x46	18x41	19x18		19x53		
Harrington	d	06x05	06x49	07x28		09x08	09x58		11x25		13x40	14x23	15x21	16x15	16x54	18x49	19x26		20x01		
Workington	d	06 12	06 55	07 35		09 15	10 05		11 31		13 46	14 29	15 27	16 22	17 00	18 55	19 33		20 08		
Flimby	d	06x16	07x00	07x39		09x19	10x09		11x36		13x51	14x34	15x32	16x26	17x05	19x00	19x37		20x12		
Maryport	d	06 20	07 03	07 43		09 23	10 13		11 39		13 54	14 37	15 35	16 30	17 08	19 03	19 41		20 16		
Aspatria	d	06x29	07x13	07x52		09x32	10x22		11x49		14x04	14x47	15x45	16x39	17x18	19x13	19x50		20x25		
Wigton	d	06 39	07 23	08 02		09 42	10 32		11 59		14 14	14 57	15 55	16 49	17 28	19 23	20 00		20 35		
Dalston	d	06x48	07x31	08x11		09x51	10x41		12x07		14x22	15x05	16x03	16x58	17x36	19x31	20x09		20x44		
Carlisle 8	a	07 03	07 46	08 25		10 05	10 56		12 22		14 37	15 19	16 18	17 12	17 51	19 46	20 24		20 59		

Sundays

		NT	NT	NT
Whitehaven	d	12 50	16 10	20 15
Parton	d	12x53	16x13	20x18
Harrington	d	13x01	16x21	20x26
Workington	d	13 07	16 27	20 32
Flimby	d	13x11	16x31	20x36
Maryport	d	13 15	16 35	20 40
Aspatria	d	13x24	16x44	20x49
Wigton	d	13 34	16 54	20 59
Dalston	d	13x43	17x03	21x08
Carlisle 8	a	13 57	17 17	21 22

For general notes see front of timetable
For details of catering facilities see Directory of Train Operators

No Sunday Service Whitehaven to Barrow-in-Furness

Carlisle and Whitehaven → Barrow-in-Furness

Network Diagram - see first page of Table 97

Miles			NT	NT	NT	NT	NT	NT	NT	NT	NT	NT	NT	NT	NT	NT	NT	NT	NT	NT	NT	NT	NT	NT	NT
				A															B					FO	
0	**Carlisle** 3	d					07 46	08 35	09 27	10 14	11 44		12 41	14 18		15 40	16 33	17 27	18 04		18 36	20 09		20 50	21 53
4	Dalston	d					07x54	08x43	09x35	10x22	11x52		12x49	14x26		15x48	16x41	17x35	18x12		18x44	20x17		20x58	22x01
11½	Wigton	d					08 03	08 52	09 44	10 31	12 01		12 58	14 35		15 57	16 50	17 44	18 21		18 53	20 26		21 07	22 10
19¾	Aspatria	d					08x13	09x02	09x54	10x41	12x11		13x08	14x45		16x07	17x00	17x54	18x31		19x03	20x36		21x17	22x20
27¼	Maryport	d		06 04			08 23	09 12	10 04	10 51	12 21		13 18	14 55		16 17	17 10	18 04	18 41		19 13	20 46		21 27	22 30
29¼	Flimby	d		06x07			08x26	09x15	10x07	10x54	12x24		13x21	14x58		16x20	17x13	18x07	18x44		19x16	20x49		21x30	22x33
33	**Workington**	d		06 15			08 35	09 24	10b17	11 03	12 33		13 30	15 07		16 29	17 22	18 16	18 53		19 25	20 58		21 39	22 42
34¾	Harrington	d		06x18			08x38	09x27	10x20	11x06	12x36		13x33	15x10		16x32	17x25	18x19	18x56		19x28	21x01		21x42	22x45
38¼	Parton	d		06x27			08x47	09x36	10x29	11x15	12x46		13x42	15x19		16x41	17x34	18x28	19x05		19x37	21x10		21x51	22x54
39½	**Whitehaven**	a		06 33			08 56	09 45	10 35	11 21	12 54		13 48	15 25		16 50	17 40	18 35	19 14		19 46	21 19		22 00	23 02
—		d		06 35	07 23				10 36	11 24			13 49	15 26			17 41	18 36							
40½	Corkickle	d		06x37	07x25				10x38	11x26			13x51	15x28			17x43	18x38							
44	St Bees	d		06 42	07 30				10 44	11 32			13 58	15 34			17 49	18 43							
47	Nethertown	d		06x46						11x36			14x02				17x53								
48¼	Braystones	d		06x49						11x38			14x05				17x55								
50¼	Sellafield	d		06 55	07 41				10 54	11 45			14 11	15c54	16 40		18 03	18 54							
52	Seascale	d		06x58	07x44				10x57	11x48			14x14	15x57	16x43		18x06	18x57							
54¼	Drigg	d		07x01	07x47				11x00	11x51			14x17	16x00	16x46		18x09	19x00							
56	Ravenglass for Eskdale	d		07 04	07 50				11 04	11 54			14 20	16 04	16 49		18 12	19 03							
60¾	Bootle	d		07x10	07x56				11x10	12x00			14x26	16x09	16x55		18x18	19x09							
66¼	Silecroft	d		07x16	08x02				11x16	12x06			14x32	16x16	17x01		18x24	19x15							
69¼	Millom	a		07 23	08 09				11 23	12 13			14 39	16 23	17 08		18 31	19 22							
—		d	06 08	07 23	08 10	09 24			11 24	12 14		13 56	14 40	16 24	17 09		18 32	19 22		19 55			21 55		
71¾	Green Road	d	06x12	07x27	08x14	09x28				12x18		14x00	14x44	16x28	17x13		18x36	19x26		19x59			21x59		
73¾	Foxfield	d	06x15	07x31	08x17	09x31			11x31	12x21		14x03	14x47	16x31	17x16		18x39	19x30		20x02			22x02		
76	Kirkby-in-Furness	d	06x19	07x35	08x21	09x35			11x35	12x25		14x07	14x51	16x36	17x20		18x43	19x34		20x06			22x06		
79¼	Askam	d	06 24	07 40	08 26	09 40			11 40	12 30		14 12	14 56	16 41	17 25		18 48	19 39		20 11			22 11		
85¼	**Barrow-in-Furness**	a	06 39	07 56	08 42	09 55			11 56	12 46		14 28	15 16	16 57	17 41		19 04	19 55		20 27			22 27		
—	Lancaster 3	82 a	*07 58*	08 59	*10 15*	11 00			13 05	*14 00*			16 33	*18 04*	18 44		*20 15*			*22 49*					

Saturdays

until 22 March

		NT	NT	NT	NT	NT	NT	NT		NT	NT	NT	NT	NT	NT	NT	NT	NT	NT	NT	NT	NT	NT	NT	
																A			B						
Carlisle 8	d					07 28	08 15	08 39			10 14	11 11	12 41	13 46	14 28	15 45	16 33	17 34	17 57		18 36	20 09		21 45	
Dalston	d					07x36	08x23	08x47			10x22	11x19	12x49	13x54	14x36	15x53	16x41	17x42	18x05		18x44	20x17		21x53	
Wigton	d					07 45	08 32	08 56			10 31	11 28	12 58	14 03	14 45	16 02	16 50	17 51	18 14		18 53	20 26		22 02	
Aspatria	d					07x55	08x42	09x06			10x41	11x38	13x08	14x13	14x55	16x12	17x00	18x01	18x25		19x03	20x36		22x12	
Maryport	d		06 04			08 05	08 52	09 16			10 51	11 48	13 18	14 23	15 05	16 22	17 10	18 11	18 35		19 13	20 46		22 22	
Flimby	d		06x07			08x08	08x55				10x54	11x51	13x21	14x26	15x08	16x25	17x13	18x14	18x39		19x16	20x49		22x25	
Workington	d		06 15			08 17	09 04	09 28			11 03	12 00	13 30	14 35	15 17	16 34	17 22	18 23	18 47		19 25	20 58		22 34	
Harrington	d		06x19			08x20	09x07	09x31			11x06	12x03	13x33	14x38	15x20	16x37	17x25	18x26	18x51		19x28	21x01		22x37	
Parton	d		06x27			08x29	09x16	09x40			11x15	12x12	13x42	14x47	15x29	16x46	17x34	18x35	19x00		19x37	21x10		22x46	
Whitehaven	a		06 33			08 38	09 25	09 46			11 21	12 18	13 48	14 56	15 35	16 52	17 40	18 41	19 09		19 46	21 19		22 55	
	d		06 35					09 47			11 24	12 19	13 49		15 36	16 53	17 41	18 43							
Corkickle	d		06x37					09x49			11x26	12x21	13x51		15x38	16x55	17x43	18x45							
St Bees	d		06 42					09x55			11 32	12 27	14e02		15 44	17x01	17 49	18 50							
Nethertown	d		06x46								11x36		14x06		15x48		17x53								
Braystones	d		06x49								11x38		14x09		15x50		17x55								
Sellafield	d		06 55					10 05			11 45	12 38	14 15		15 56	17 11	18 03	19 01							
Seascale	d		06x58					10x08			11x48	12x41	14x18		15x59	17x14	18x06	19x04							
Drigg	d		07x01					10x11			11x51	12x44	14x21		16x02	17x17	18x09	19x07							
Ravenglass for Eskdale	d		07 04					10 15			11 54	12 47	14 24		16 06	17 21	18 12	19 10							
Bootle	d		07x10					10x20			12x00	12x53	14x30		16x11	17x26	18x18	19x16							
Silecroft	d		07x16					10x27			12x06	12x59	14x36		16x18	17x33	18x24	19x22							
Millom	a		07 23					10 34			12 13	13 06	14 43		16 25	17 40	18 31	19 29							
	d	06 15	07 23	08 10	09 25			10 34		11 47	12 14	13 07	14 44		16 25	17 40	18 32	19 29		19 55			21 55		
Green Road	d	06x19	07x27	08x14	09x29					11x51	12x18	13 11	14x48		16x29	17x44	18x36	19x33		19x59			21x59		
Foxfield	d	06x22	07x31	08x17	09x32			10x41		11x54	12x21	13x14	14x51		16x32	17x47	18x39	19x37		20x02			22x02		
Kirkby-in-Furness	d	06x26	07x35	08x21	09x36					11x58	12x25	13x18	14x55		16x36	17x51	18x43	19x41		20x06			22x06		
Askam	d	06 31	07 40	08 26	09 41			10 49		12 03	12 30	13 23	15 00		16 41	17 56	18 48	19 46		20 11			22 11		
Barrow-in-Furness	a	06 47	07 56	08 42	09 56			11 06		12 19	12 46	13 39	15 16		16 57	18 14	19 04	20 02		20 27			22 27		
Lancaster 6	82 a	*08 02*	09 02	*10 15*	11 01			*12 16*			*13 59*	*15 03*	16 32		*18 05*	19 17	*20 16*			*22 35*					

For general notes see front of timetable
For details of catering facilities see Directory of Train Operators

A To Preston (Table 65)
B From Newcastle (Table 48)
b Arr. 1014
c Arr. 1544
e Arr. 1357

Saturdays
from 29 March

Carlisle and Whitehaven → Barrow-in-Furness

Network Diagram - see first page of Table 97

		NT	NT	NT	NT	NT	NT	NT		NT	NT	NT	NT	NT	NT	NT	NT	NT	NT A	NT	NT	NT	NT	NT
Carlisle 8	d					07 28	08 15	08 35			10 14	11 11	12 45	13 46	14 45	15 45	16 33	17 34	17 57		18 36	20 09		21 45
Dalston	d					07x36	08x23	08x43			10x22	11x19	12x53	13x54	14x53	15x53	16x41	17x42	18x05		18x44	20x17		21x53
Wigton	d					07 45	08 32	08 52			10 31	11 28	13 02	14 03	15 02	16 02	16 50	17 51	18 14		18 53	20 26		22 02
Aspatria	d					07x55	08x42	09x02			10x41	11x38	13x12	14x13	15x12	16x12	17x00	18x01	18x25		19x03	20x36		22x12
Maryport	d		06 04			08 05	08 52	09 12			10 51	11 48	13 22	14 23	15 22	16 22	17 10	18 11	18 35		19 13	20 46		22 22
Flimby	d		06x07			08x08	08x55				10x54	11x51	13x25	14x26	15x25	16x25	17x13	18x14	18x39		19x16	20x49		22x25
Workington	d		06 15			08 17	09 04	09 24			11 03	12 00	13 34	14 35	15 34	16 34	17 22	18 23	18 47		19 25	20 58		22 34
Harrington	d		06x19			08x20	09x07	09x27			11x06	12x03	13x37	14x38	15x37	16x37	17x25	18x26	18x51		19x28	21x01		22x37
Parton	d		06x27			08x29	09x16	09x36			11x15	12x12	13x46	14x47	15x46	16x46	17x34	18x35	19x00		19x37	21x10		22x46
Whitehaven	a		06 33			08 38	09 25	09 42			11 21	12 18	13 52	14 56	15 52	16 52	17 40	18 41	19 09		19 46	21 19		22 55
	d		06 35					09 43			11 24	12 19	13 53		15 53	16 53	17 41	18 43						
Corkickle	d		06x37					09x45			11x26	12x21	13x55		15x55	16x55	17x43	18x45						
St Bees	d		06 42					09x51			11 32	12 27	14 02		16 01	17x01	17 49	18 50						
Nethertown	d		06x46								11x36		14x06		16x05		17x53							
Braystones	d		06x49								11x38		14x09		16x07		17x55							
Sellafield	d		06 55					10 01			11 45	12 38	14 15		16 13	17 11	18 03	19 01						
Seascale	d		06x58					10x04			11x48	12x41	14x18		16x16	17x14	18x06	19x04						
Drigg	d		07x01					10x07			11x51	12x44	14x21		16x19	17x17	18x09	19x07						
Ravenglass for Eskdale	d		07 04					10 11			11 54	12 47	14 24		16 23	17 21	18 12	19 10						
Bootle	d		07x10					10x16			12x00	12x53	14x30		16x28	17x26	18x18	19x16						
Silecroft	d		07x16					10x23			12x06	12x59	14x36		16x35	17x33	18x24	19x22						
Millom	a		07 23					10 30			12 13	13 06	14 43		16 42	17 40	18 31	19 29						
	d	06 15	07 23	08 10	09 25			10 30		11 37	12 14	13 07	14 44		16 42	17 40	18 32	19 29		19 55			21 55	
Green Road	d	06x19	07x27	08x14	09x29					11x41	12x18	13 11	14x48		16x46	17x44	18x36	19x33		19x59			21x59	
Foxfield	d	06x22	07x31	08x17	09x32			10x37		11x44	12x21	13x14	14x51		16x49	17x47	18x39	19x37		20x02			22x02	
Kirkby-in-Furness	d	06x26	07x35	08x21	09x36					11x48	12x25	13x18	14x55		16x53	17x51	18x43	19x41		20x06			22x06	
Askam	d	06 31	07 40	08 26	09 41			10 45		11 53	12 30	13 23	15 00		16 58	17 56	18 48	19 46		20 11			22 11	
Barrow-in-Furness	a	06 47	07 56	08 42	09 56			11 02		12 09	12 46	13 39	15 16		17 14	18 14	19 04	20 02		20 27			22 27	
Lancaster 6	82 a	*08 06*	09 02	*10 09*	11 01			*12 09*			*14 00*	*15 05*	16 34			19 19	*20 11*			*22 20*				

Sundays

		NT	NT	NT
Carlisle 8	d	14 47	18 56	21 42
Dalston	d	14x55	19x04	21x50
Wigton	d	15 04	19 13	21 59
Aspatria	d	15x14	19x23	22x09
Maryport	d	15 24	19 33	22 19
Flimby	d	15x27	19x36	22x22
Workington	d	15 36	19 45	22 31
Harrington	d	15x39	19x48	22x34
Parton	d	15x48	19x57	22x43
Whitehaven	a	15 57	20 06	22 52

For general notes see front of timetable
For details of catering facilities see
Directory of Train Operators

A From Newcastle (Table 48)

No Sunday Service Whitehaven to Barrow-in-Furness

Network Diagram for Tables 101, 103, 106, 109

DM-14/06(2)
Design BAJS

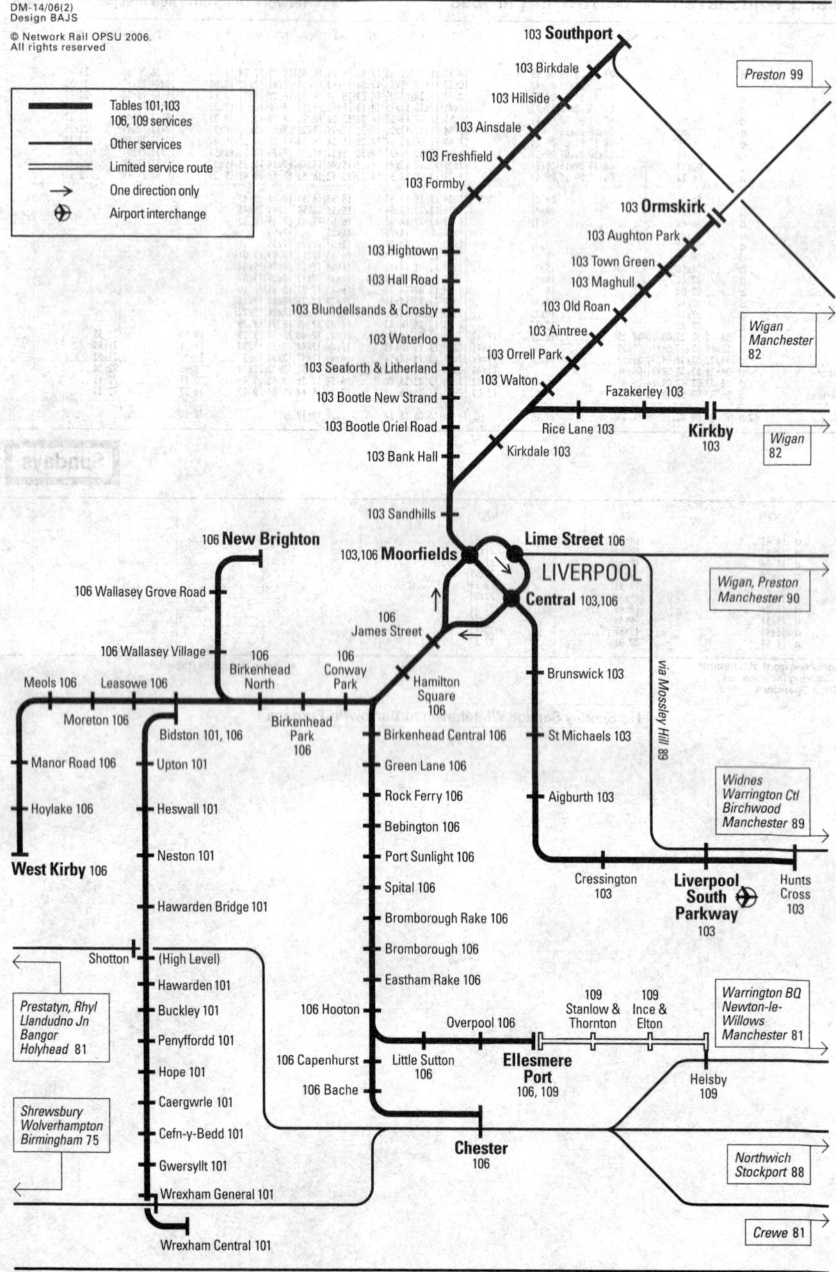

Wrexham → Bidston

Network Diagram - see first page of Table 101

Miles			AW	AW	AW	AW	AW	AW	AW	AW	AW	AW	AW	AW	AW	AW	AW
				BHX		BHX		BHX		BHX		BHX		BHX		SO	SX
0	**Wrexham Central**	d		07 30	08 32	09 32	10 32	11 32	12 32	13 32	14 32	15 32	16 32	17 45	19 46	21 45	21 57
½	**Wrexham General**	a		07 32	08 34	09 34	10 34	11 34	12 34	13 34	14 34	15 34	16 34	17 47	19 48	21 47	21 59
—		d	06 33	07 32	08 34	09 34	10 34	11 34	12 34	13 34	14 34	15 34	16 34	17 47	19 48	21 47	21 59
2¼	Gwersyllt	d	06x37	07 36	08x38	09x38	10x38	11x38	12x38	13x38	14x38	15x38	16x38	17 51	19x52	21x51	22x03
4	Cefn-y-Bedd	d	06x42	07 41	08x43	09x43	10x43	11x43	12x43	13x43	14x43	15x43	16x43	17 56	19x57	21x56	22x08
4¾	Caergwrle	d	06x44	07 43	08x45	09x45	10x45	11x45	12x45	13x45	14x45	15x45	16x45	17 58	19x59	21x58	22x10
5¼	Hope (Flintshire)	d	06x46	07 45	08x47	09x47	10x47	11x47	12x47	13x47	14x47	15x47	16x47	18 00	20x01	22x00	22x12
7¼	Penyffordd	d	06x50	07 49	08x51	09x51	10x51	11x51	12x51	13x51	14x51	15x51	16x51	18 04	20x05	22x04	22x16
8½	Buckley	d	06x53	07 52	08x54	09x54	10x54	11x54	12x54	13x54	14x54	15x54	16x54	18 07	20x08	22x07	22x19
10½	Hawarden	d	06x57	07 56	08x58	09x58	10x58	11x58	12x58	13x58	14x58	15x58	16x58	18 11	20x12	22x11	22x23
12¾	Shotton High Level	d	07 01	08 01	09 02	10 02	11 02	12 02	13 02	14 02	15 02	16 02	17 02	18 15	20 16	22 15	22 27
13¼	Hawarden Bridge	d	07x03	08x03									17x04				
18¾	Neston	d	07x12	08 12	09x12	10x12	11x12	12x12	13x12	14x12	15x12	16x12	17x12	18 25	20x26	22x25	22x37
21¼	Heswall	d	07x17	08 17	09x17	10x17	11x17	12x17	13x17	14x17	15x17	16x17	17x17	18 30	20x31	22x30	22x42
25½	Upton	d	07x23	08 23	09x23	10x23	11x23	12x23	13x23	14x23	15x23	16x23	17x23	18 36	20x37	22x36	22x48
27½	**Bidston**	a	07 29	08 29	09 29	10 29	11 29	12 29	13 29	14 29	15 29	16 29	17 29	18 44	20 43	22 42	22 54
—	Liverpool Lime Street 10	106 a	*07 53*	*08 53*	*09 53*	*10 53*	*11 53*	*12 53*	*13 53*	*14 53*	*15 53*	*16 53*	*17 53*	*19 08*	*21 33*	*23 33*	*23 33*

Sundays

		AW	AW	AW	AW	AW	AW
Wrexham Central	d		11 13	13 43	16 13	18 43	21 13
Wrexham General	a		11 15	13 45	16 15	18 45	21 15
	d	08 46	11 16	13 46	16 17	18 46	21 16
Gwersyllt	d	08x50	11x20	13x50	16x20	18x50	21x20
Cefn-y-Bedd	d	08x55	11x25	13x55	16x25	18x55	21x25
Caergwrle	d	08x57	11x27	13x57	16x27	18x57	21x27
Hope (Flintshire)	d	08x59	11x29	13x59	16x29	18x59	21x29
Penyffordd	d	09x03	11x33	14x03	16x33	19x03	21x33
Buckley	d	09x06	11x36	14x06	16x36	19x06	21x36
Hawarden	d	09x10	11x40	14x10	16x40	19x10	21x40
Shotton High Level	d	09 14	11 44	14 14	16 44	19 14	21 44
Hawarden Bridge	d						
Neston	d	09x24	11x54	14x24	16x54	19x24	21x54
Heswall	d	09x29	11x59	14x29	16x59	19x29	21x59
Upton	d	09x35	12x05	14x35	17x05	19x35	22x05
Bidston	a	09 41	12 11	14 41	17 11	19 41	22 11
Liverpool Lime Street 10	106 a	*10 03*	*12 33*	*15 03*	*17 33*	*20 03*	*22 33*

For general notes see front of timetable
For details of catering facilities see Directory of Train Operators

Bidston → Wrexham

Network Diagram - see first page of Table 101

Miles			AW BHX	AW	AW BHX		AW	AW BHX	AW		AW BHX	AW	AW BHX		AW	AW BHX	AW		AW BHX	AW SO	AW SX	AW SO	AW SX		
—	Liverpool Lime Street 10	106 d		06 53	08 08		09 08	10 08	11 08		12 08	13 08	14 08		15 08	16 08	17 23		18 23	20 03	20 33	22 03	22 33		
0	**Bidston**	d		07 31	08 31		09 32	10 32	11 32		12 32	13 32	14 32		15 32	16 31	17 45		18 46	20 45	20 56	22 45	22 56		
2	Upton	d		07 35	08x35		09x36	10x36	11x36		12x36	13x36	14x36		15x36	16x35	17 49		18x50	20x49	21x00	22x49	23x00		
6¼	Heswall	d		07 42	08x42		09x43	10x43	11x43		12x43	13x43	14x43		15x43	16x42	17 56		18x57	20x56	21x07	22x56	23x07		
8¾	Neston	d		07 47	08x47		09x48	10x48	11x48		12x48	13x48	14x48		15x48	16x47	18 01		19x02	21x01	21x12	23x01	23x12		
14¼	Hawarden Bridge	d		07x55	08x55											16x55	18x09								
14¾	Shotton High Level	d		07 57	08 57		09 57	10 57	11 57		12 57	13 57	14 57		15 57	16 57	18 11		19 11	21 10	21 21	23 11	23 22		
17½	Hawarden	d		08 02	09x02		10x02	11x02	12x02		13x02	14x02	15x02		16x02	17x02	18 16		19x16	21x15	21x26	23x16	23x27		
19	Buckley	d		08 07	09x07		10x07	11x07	12x07		13x07	14x07	15x07		16x07	17x07	18 21		19x21	21x20	21x31	23x21	23x32		
20¼	Penyffordd	d		08 10	09x10		10x10	11x10	12x10		13x10	14x10	15x10		16x10	17x10	18 24		19x24	21x23	21x34	23x24	23x35		
22¼	Hope (Flintshire)	d		08 14	09x14		10x14	11x14	12x14		13x14	14x14	15x14		16x14	17x14	18 28		19x28	21x27	21x38	23x28	23x39		
22¾	Caergwrle	d		08 16	09x16		10x16	11x16	12x16		13x16	14x16	15x16		16x16	17x16	18 30		19x30	21x29	21x40	23x30	23x41		
23½	Cefn-y-Bedd	d		08 18	09x18		10x18	11x18	12x18		13x18	14x18	15x18		16x18	17x18	18 32		19x32	21x31	21x42	23x32	23x43		
25¼	Gwersyllt	d		08 22	09x22		10x22	11x22	12x22		13x22	14x22	15x22		16x22	17x22	18 36		19x36	21x35	21x46	23 36	23 47		
27	**Wrexham General**	a		08 27	09 27		10 27	11 27	12 27		13 27	14 27	15 27		16 27	17 27	18 41		19 41	21 40	21 51	23 41	23 52		
—		d	07 10	08 27	09 27		10 27	11 27	12 27		13 27	14 27	15 27		16 27	17 27	18 41		19 41	21 40	21 51				
27½	**Wrexham Central**	a	07 13	08 32	09 30		10 30	11 30	12 30		13 30	14 30	15 30		16 30	17 30	18 44		19 44	21 43	21 54				

Sundays

		AW			AW			AW			AW			AW			AW								
Liverpool Lime Street 10	106 d	09 33			12 03			14 33			17 03			19 33			22 03								
Bidston	d	09 57			12 27			14 57			17 27			19 57			22 27								
Upton	d	10x01			12x31			15x01			17x31			20x01			22x31								
Heswall	d	10x08			12x38			15x08			17x38			20x08			22x38								
Neston	d	10x13			12x43			15x13			17x43			20x13			22x43								
Hawarden Bridge	d																								
Shotton High Level	d	10 22			12 52			15 22			17 52			20 22			22 52								
Hawarden	d	10x27			12x57			15x27			17x57			20x27			22x57								
Buckley	d	10x32			13x02			15x32			18x02			20x32			23x02								
Penyffordd	d	10x35			13x05			15x35			18x05			20x35			23x05								
Hope (Flintshire)	d	10x39			13x09			15x39			18x09			20x39			23x09								
Caergwrle	d	10x41			13x11			15x41			18x11			20x41			23x11								
Cefn-y-Bedd	d	10x43			13x13			15x43			18x13			20x43			23x13								
Gwersyllt	d	10x47			13x17			15x47			18x17			20x47			23x17								
Wrexham General	a	10 52			13 22			15 52			18 22			20 52			23 22								
	d	10 53			13 23			15 53			18 23			20 53											
Wrexham Central	a	10 56			13 26			15 56			18 26			20 56											

For general notes see front of timetable
For details of catering facilities see
Directory of Train Operators

Llandudno → Blaenau Ffestiniog

Network Diagram - see first page of Table 81

Miles			AW ◇	AW ◇	AW ◇	AW ◇	AW ◇	AW ◇
0	**Llandudno**	81 d		07 03	10 14	13 14	16 14	18 47
1¾	Deganwy	81 d		07 07	10x18	13x18	16x18	18 51
—	Crewe 10	81 d		06 18	09 03	12b03	15 03	17c35
—	Chester	81 d		06 45	09 35	12 35	15 35	18 00
—	Rhyl	81 d		07 17	10 08	13 08	16 08	18 33
—	Bangor (Gwynedd)	81 d	05 00	07 12	10 07	13 04	15 04	18c06
3	**Llandudno Junction**	81 d	05 35	07 39	10 33	13 33	16 33	19 00
5	Glan Conwy	d		07x42	10x36	13x36	16x36	19x03
8½	Tal-y-Cafn	d		07 47	10 41	13 41	16 41	19 08
11½	Dolgarrog	d		07x52	10x46	13x46	16x46	19x13
14½	North Llanrwst	d		07x59	10x52	13x52	16x52	19x19
15	Llanrwst	d	05 53	08 01	10 54	13 54	16 54	19 21
18½	Betws-y-Coed	d	05 59	08 07	11 00	14 00	17 00	19 27
22¾	Pont-y-Pant	d		08x15	11x08	14x08	17x08	19x35
24¼	Dolwyddelan	d		08x18	11x11	14x11	17x11	19x38
26	Roman Bridge	d		08x22	11x15	14x15	17x15	19x42
31	**Blaenau Ffestiniog**	a	06 27	08 37	11 30	14 30	17 30	19 57

Sundays

		AW 🚌	AW 🚌	AW 🚌
Llandudno	81 d	10 15	13 15	16 15
Deganwy	81 d	10 25	13 25	16 25
Crewe 10	81 d		11b55	14b25
Chester	81 d		12 32	15 03
Rhyl	81 d		13 06	15 38
Bangor (Gwynedd)	81 d		12 52	15 42
Llandudno Junction	81 d	10 40	13 40	16 40
Glan Conwy	d	10 43	13 43	16 43
Tal-y-Cafn	d	10 48	13 48	16 48
Dolgarrog	d	10 53	13 53	16 53
North Llanrwst	d	10 58	13 58	16 58
Llanrwst	d	11 01	14 01	17 01
Betws-y-Coed	d	11 10	14 10	17 10
Pont-y-Pant	d	11 20	14 20	17 20
Dolwyddelan	d	11 25	14 25	17 25
Roman Bridge	d	11 32	14 32	17 32
Blaenau Ffestiniog	a	11 45	14 45	17 45

For general notes see front of timetable
For details of catering facilities see Directory of Train Operators

b Change at Chester and Llandudno Junction
c Saturdays dep. Crewe 1736, Bangor (Gwynedd) 1814

Blaenau Ffestiniog → Llandudno

Network Diagram - see first page of Table 81

Miles			AW ◇	AW ◇	AW ◇	AW ◇	AW ◇	AW ◇
—	**Blaenau Ffestiniog**	d	06 30	08 54	11 54	14 54	17 54	20 00
—	Roman Bridge	d	06x40	09x04	12x04	15x04	18x04	20x10
6¾	Dolwyddelan	d	06x43	09x07	12x07	15x07	18x07	20x13
8¼	Pont-y-Pant	d	06x46	09x10	12x10	15x10	18x10	20x16
12½	Betws-y-Coed	d	06 56	09 20	12 20	15 20	18 20	20 26
16	Llanrwst	d	07 02	09 26	12 26	15 26	18 26	20 32
16½	North Llanrwst	d	07x03	09x27	12x27	15x27	18x27	20x33
19¼	Dolgarrog	d	07x09	09x33	12x33	15x33	18x33	20x39
22½	Tal-y-Cafn	d	07x14	09x39	12x39	15x39	18x39	20x45
26	Glan Conwy	d	07x20	09x45	12x45	15x45	18x45	20x51
28	**Llandudno Junction**	81 a	07 26	09 50	12 50	15 50	18 51	20 56
—	Bangor (Gwynedd)	81 a	*07 49*	*10 46*	*13 48*	*16 46*	*19 49*	*21 51*
—	Rhyl	81 a	*07 47*	*10 15*	*13 15*	*16 15*	*19 15*	*21b44*
—	Chester	81 a	*08 21*	*10 51*	*13 51*	*16 51*	*19 51*	*22b23*
—	Crewe 10	81 a	*08 45*	*11c24*	*14c24*	*17e24*	*20c29*	*23f07*
29¼	Deganwy	81 a	*07 36*	09x55	12x55	15x55	*19 23*	21x01
31	**Llandudno**	81 a	*07 43*	10 01	13 01	16 01	*19 37*	21 08

Sundays

		AW (bus)	AW (bus)	AW (bus)
Blaenau Ffestiniog	d	12 00	15 00	18 00
Roman Bridge	d	12 10	15 10	18 10
Dolwyddelan	d	12 15	15 15	18 15
Pont-y-Pant	d	12 19	15 19	18 19
Betws-y-Coed	d	12 30	15 30	18 30
Llanrwst	d	12 40	15 40	18 40
North Llanrwst	d	12 45	15 45	18 43
Dolgarrog	d	12 50	15 50	18 48
Tal-y-Cafn	d	12 55	15 55	18 55
Glan Conwy	d	13 05	16 05	19 05
Llandudno Junction	81 a	13 15	16 15	19 15
Bangor (Gwynedd)	81 a	*13 51*	*17 26*	*19 52*
Rhyl	81 a	*14 15*	*16 58*	*19 43*
Chester	81 a	*14 44*	*17 27*	*20 16*
Crewe 10	81 a	*15 06*	*17 57*	*20c49*
Deganwy	81 a	13 18	16 18	19 18
Llandudno	81 a	13 30	16 30	19 30

For general notes see front of timetable
For details of catering facilities see Directory of Train Operators

b Saturdays arr. Rhyl 2150, Chester 2227
c Change at Llandudno Junction and Chester
e Change at Llandudno Junction and Chester. Saturdays arr. 1726
f Change at Llandudno Junction and Chester. Saturdays arr. 2256

Merseyrail

These notes apply to Tables 103 and 106

Christmas and New Year Holiday 2007/8

Monday 24 December	—	A normal weekday service will operate with an early finish
Tuesday 25 December	—	No service
Wednesday 26 December	—	No service
Thursday 27 December	—	A normal Saturday service will operate
Friday 28 December	—	A normal Saturday service will operate
Saturday 29 December	—	A normal Saturday service will operate
Sunday 30 December	—	A normal Sunday service will operate
Monday 31 December	—	A normal Saturday service will operate with an early finish
Tuesday 1 January	—	A normal Sunday service will operate

Easter

Friday 21 March	—	A normal Saturday service will operate
Monday 24 March	—	A normal Saturday service will operate

May Day

Monday 5 May	—	A normal Saturday service will operate

Hunts Cross and Liverpool → Kirkby, Ormskirk and Southport

Network Diagram - see first page of Table 101

Miles	Miles	Miles			ME	ME	ME	ME		ME	ME	ME	ME		ME	ME	ME	ME			ME	ME	ME	ME
0	—	—	**Hunts Cross**	89 d						06 06		06 21				06 36		06 51					07 06	
1½	—	—	**Liverpool South Parkway** 7	89 ✈ d						06 09		06 24				06 39		06 54					07 09	
2½	—	—	Cressington	d						06 12		06 27				06 42		06 57					07 12	
3¼	—	—	Aigburth	d						06 14		06 29				06 44		06 59					07 14	
4½	—	—	St Michaels	d						06 16		06 31				06 46		07 01					07 16	
5¾	—	—	Brunswick	d						06 19		06 34				06 49		07 04					07 19	
7¼	—	—	**Liverpool Central** 10	a						06 23		06 38				06 53		07 08					07 23	
—	0	0		d		05 55	06 08	06 10		06 23	06 25	06 38	06 40		06 50	06 53	06 55	07 08			07 10	07 20	07 23	07 25
7¾	½	½	**Moorfields** 10	d		05 57	06 10	06 12		06 25	06 27	06 40	06 42		06 52	06 55	06 57	07 10			07 12	07 22	07 25	07 27
9¼	2	2	Sandhills	d	05 59	06 01	06 14	06 16		06 29	06 31	06 44	06 46		06 56	06 59	07 01	07 14			07 16	07 26	07 29	07 31
—	3	3	Kirkdale	d		06 04		06 19			06 34		06 49		06 59		07 04				07 19	07 29		07 34
—	—	4¼	Rice Lane	d		06 07					06 37				07 02							07 32		
—	—	5¾	Fazakerley	d		06 10					06 40				07 03							07 34		
—	—	7½	**Kirkby**	a		06 13					06 43				07 08							07 38		
—	4¼	—	Walton (Merseyside)	d				06 22					06 52				07 07				07 22			07 37
—	4½	—	Orrell Park	d				06 23					06 53				07 08				07 23			07 38
—	5½	—	Aintree	d				06 26					06 56				07 11				07 26			07 41
—	6¼	—	Old Roan	d				06 28					06 58				07 13				07 28			07 43
—	8	—	Maghull	d				06 31					07 01				07 16				07 31			07 46
—	10½	—	Town Green	d				06 35					07 05				07 20				07 35			07 50
—	11½	—	Aughton Park	d				06 37					07 07				07 22				07 37			07 52
—	12¾	—	**Ormskirk**	a				06 42					07 12				07 27				07 42			07 57
10	—	—	Bank Hall	d	06 01		06 16			06 31		06 46				07 01		07 16					07 31	
10¾	—	—	Bootle Oriel Road	d	06 03		06 18			06 33		06 48				07 03		07 18					07 33	
11	—	—	Bootle New Strand	d	06 05		06 20			06 35		06 50				07 05		07 20					07 35	
12	—	—	Seaforth & Litherland	d	06 07		06 22			06 37		06 52				07 07		07 22					07 37	
13¼	—	—	Waterloo (Merseyside)	d	06 09		06 24			06 39		06 54				07 09		07 24					07 39	
14¼	—	—	Blundellsands & Crosby	d	06 12		06 27			06 42		06 57				07 12		07 27					07 42	
15	—	—	Hall Road	d	06 14		06 29			06 44		06 59				07 14		07 29					07 44	
17	—	—	Hightown	d	06 17		06 32			06 47		07 02				07 17		07 32					07 47	
19	—	—	Formby	d	06 21		06 36			06 51		07 06				07 21		07 36					07 51	
20	—	—	Freshfield	d	06 23		06 38			06 53		07 08				07 23		07 38					07 53	
22¾	—	—	Ainsdale	d	06 27		06 42			06 57		07 12				07 27		07 42					07 57	
24½	—	—	Hillside	d	06 30		06 45			07 00		07 15				07 30		07 45					08 00	
25¼	—	—	Birkdale	d	06 32		06 47			07 02		07 17				07 32		07 47					08 02	
26¼	—	—	**Southport**	a	06 37		06 52			07 07		07 22				07 37		07 52					08 07	

		ME	ME	ME	ME	ME	ME	ME	ME	and at the same minutes past each hour until		ME	ME	ME SX	ME		ME	ME	ME	ME		ME	ME
Hunts Cross	89 d		07 21			07 36			07 51			16 51					17 06			17 21			
Liverpool South Parkway 7	89 ✈ d		07 24			07 39			07 54			16 54					17 09			17 24			
Cressington	d		07 27			07 42			07 57			16 57					17 12			17 27			
Aigburth	d		07 29			07 44			07 59			16 59					17 14			17 29			
St Michaels	d		07 31			07 46			08 01			17 01					17 16			17 31			
Brunswick	d		07 34			07 49			08 04			17 04					17 19			17 34			
Liverpool Central 10	a		07 38			07 53			08 08			17 08					17 23			17 38			
	d	07 35	07 38	07 40	07 50	07 53	07 55	08 05	08 08			17 08	17 10	17 13	17 20		17 23	17 25	17 35	17 38		17 40	17 50
Moorfields 10	d	07 37	07 40	07 42	07 52	07 55	07 57	08 07	08 10			17 10	17 12	17 15	17 22		17 25	17 27	17 37	17 40		17 42	17 52
Sandhills	d	07 41	07 44	07 46	07 56	07 59	08 01	08 11	08 14			17 14	17 16	17 19	17 26		17 29	17 31	17 41	17 44		17 46	17 56
Kirkdale	d	07 44		07 49	07 59		08 04	08 14					17 19		17 29			17 34	17 44			17 49	17 59
Rice Lane	d	07 47			08 02			08 17							17 32				17 47				18 02
Fazakerley	d	07 49			08 04			08 19							17 34				17 49				18 04
Kirkby	a	07 53			08 08			08 23							17 38				17 53				18 08
Walton (Merseyside)	d			07 52			08 07						17 22					17 37				17 52	
Orrell Park	d			07 53			08 08						17 23					17 38				17 53	
Aintree	d			07 56			08 11						17 26					17 41				17 56	
Old Roan	d			07 58			08 13						17 28					17 43				17 58	
Maghull	d			08 01			08 16						17 31					17 46				18 01	
Town Green	d			08 05			08 20						17 35					17 50				18 05	
Aughton Park	d			08 07			08 22						17 37					17 52				18 07	
Ormskirk	a			08 12			08 27						17 42					17 57				18 12	
Bank Hall	d		07 46			08 01			08 16			17 16		17 21			17 31			17 46			
Bootle Oriel Road	d		07 48			08 03			08 18			17 18		17 23			17 33			17 48			
Bootle New Strand	d		07 50			08 05			08 20			17 20		17 25			17 35			17 50			
Seaforth & Litherland	d		07 52			08 07			08 22			17 22		17 27			17 37			17 52			
Waterloo (Merseyside)	d		07 54			08 09			08 24			17 24		17 29			17 39			17 54			
Blundellsands & Crosby	d		07 57			08 12			08 27			17 27		17 32			17 42			17 57			
Hall Road	d		07 59			08 14			08 29			17 29		17 34			17 44			17 59			
Hightown	d		08 02			08 17			08 32			17 32		17 37			17 47			18 02			
Formby	d		08 06			08 21			08 36			17 36		17 41			17 51			18 06			
Freshfield	d		08 08			08 23			08 38			17 38		17 43			17 53			18 08			
Ainsdale	d		08 12			08 27			08 42			17 42		17 47			17 57			18 12			
Hillside	d		08 15			08 30			08 45			17 45		17 50			18 00			18 15			
Birkdale	d		08 17			08 32			08 47			17 47		17 52			18 02			18 17			
Southport	a		08 22			08 37			08 52			17 52		17 57			18 07			18 22			

For general notes see front of timetable
For details of catering facilities see Directory of Train Operators

Hunts Cross and Liverpool → Kirkby, Ormskirk and Southport

Network Diagram - see first page of Table 101

		ME	ME	ME	ME	ME	ME	ME	ME	ME	ME	ME	ME	ME	ME	ME	ME	ME	ME	ME
Hunts Cross 89	d	17 36			17 51			18 06			18 21			18 36			18 51		19 06	
Liverpool South Parkway 7 89 ✈	d	17 39			17 54			18 09			18 24			18 39			18 54		19 09	
Cressington	d	17 42			17 57			18 12			18 27			18 42			18 57		19 12	
Aigburth	d	17 44			17 59			18 14			18 29			18 44			18 59		19 14	
St Michaels	d	17 46			18 01			18 16			18 31			18 46			19 01		19 16	
Brunswick	d	17 49			18 04			18 19			18 34			18 49			19 04		19 19	
Liverpool Central 10	a	17 53			18 08			18 23			18 38			18 53			19 08		19 23	
	d	17 53	17 55	18 05	18 08	18 10	18 20	18 23	18 25	18 35	18 38	18 40	18 50	18 53	18 55	19 05	19 08	19 10	19 23	19 25
Moorfields 10	d	17 55	17 57	18 07	18 10	18 12	18 22	18 25	18 27	18 37	18 40	18 42	18 52	18 55	18 57	19 07	19 10	19 12	19 25	19 27
Sandhills	d	17 59	18 01	18 11	18 14	18 16	18 26	18 29	18 31	18 41	18 44	18 46	18 56	18 59	19 01	19 11	19 14	19 16	19 29	19 31
Kirkdale	d		18 04	18 14		18 19	18 29		18 34	18 44		18 49	18 59		19 04	19 14		19 19		19 34
Rice Lane	d			18 17			18 32			18 47			19 02			19 17				19 37
Fazakerley	d			18 19			18 34			18 49			19 04			19 19				19 40
Kirkby	a			18 23			18 38			18 53			19 08			19 23				19 43
Walton (Merseyside)	d		18 07			18 22			18 37			18 52			19 07			19 22		
Orrell Park	d		18 08			18 23			18 38			18 53			19 08			19 23		
Aintree	d		18 11			18 26			18 41			18 56			19 11			19 26		
Old Roan	d		18 13			18 28			18 43			18 58			19 13			19 28		
Maghull	d		18 16			18 31			18 46			19 01			19 16			19 31		
Town Green	d		18 20			18 35			18 50			19 05			19 20			19 35		
Aughton Park	d		18 22			18 37			18 52			19 07			19 22			19 37		
Ormskirk	a		18 27			18 42			18 57			19 12			19 27			19 42		
Bank Hall	d	18 01			18 16			18 31			18 46			19 01			19 16		19 31	
Bootle Oriel Road	d	18 03			18 18			18 33			18 48			19 03			19 18		19 33	
Bootle New Strand	d	18 05			18 20			18 35			18 50			19 05			19 20		19 35	
Seaforth & Litherland	d	18 07			18 22			18 37			18 52			19 07			19 22		19 37	
Waterloo (Merseyside)	d	18 09			18 24			18 39			18 54			19 09			19 24		19 39	
Blundellsands & Crosby	d	18 12			18 27			18 42			18 57			19 12			19 27		19 42	
Hall Road	d	18 14			18 29			18 44			18 59			19 14			19 29		19 44	
Hightown	d	18 17			18 32			18 47			19 02			19 17			19 32		19 47	
Formby	d	18 21			18 36			18 51			19 06			19 21			19 36		19 51	
Freshfield	d	18 23			18 38			18 53			19 08			19 23			19 38		19 53	
Ainsdale	d	18 27			18 42			18 57			19 12			19 27			19 42		19 57	
Hillside	d	18 30			18 45			19 00			19 15			19 30			19 45		20 00	
Birkdale	d	18 32			18 47			19 02			19 17			19 32			19 47		20 02	
Southport	a	18 37			18 52			19 07			19 22			19 37			19 52		20 07	

		ME	ME	ME	ME		ME	ME	ME	ME	ME	ME	ME	ME
Hunts Cross 89	d	19 21		19 36				22 51		23 06		23 21		
Liverpool South Parkway 7 89 ✈	d	19 24		19 39				22 54		23 09		23 24		
Cressington	d	19 27		19 42				22 57		23 12		23 27		
Aigburth	d	19 29		19 44				22 59		23 14		23 29		
St Michaels	d	19 31		19 46				23 01		23 16		23 31		
Brunswick	d	19 34		19 49				23 04		23 19		23 34		
Liverpool Central 10	a	19 38		19 53				23 08		23 23		23 38		
	d	19 38	19 40	19 53	19 55		22 55	23 08	23 10	23 23	23 25	23 38	23 40	23 55
Moorfields 10	d	19 40	19 42	19 55	19 57		22 57	23 10	23 12	23 25	23 27	23 40	23 42	23 57
Sandhills	d	19 44	19 46	19 59	20 01		23 01	23 14	23 16	23 29	23 31	23 44	23 46	00 01
Kirkdale	d		19 49		20 04		23 04		23 19		23 34		23 49	00 04
Rice Lane	d				20 07	and at	23 07				23 37			00 07
Fazakerley	d				20 10	the same	23 10				23 40			00 10
Kirkby	a				20 13		23 13				23 43			00 13
Walton (Merseyside)	d		19 52			minutes			23 22				23 52	
Orrell Park	d		19 53						23 23				23 53	
Aintree	d		19 56			past			23 26				23 56	
Old Roan	d		19 58						23 28				23 58	
Maghull	d		20 01			each			23 31				00 01	
Town Green	d		20 05						23 35				00 05	
Aughton Park	d		20 07			hour until			23 37				00 07	
Ormskirk	a		20 12						23 42				00 12	
Bank Hall	d	19 46		20 01				23 16		23 31		23 46		
Bootle Oriel Road	d	19 48		20 03				23 18		23 33		23 48		
Bootle New Strand	d	19 50		20 05				23 20		23 35		23 50		
Seaforth & Litherland	d	19 52		20 07				23 22		23 37		23 52		
Waterloo (Merseyside)	d	19 54		20 09				23 24		23 39		23 54		
Blundellsands & Crosby	d	19 57		20 12				23 27		23 42		23 57		
Hall Road	d	19 59		20 14				23 29		23 44		23 59		
Hightown	d	20 02		20 17				23 32		23 47		00 02		
Formby	d	20 06		20 21				23 36		23 51		00 06		
Freshfield	d	20 08		20 23				23 38		23 53		00 08		
Ainsdale	d	20 12		20 27				23 42		23 57		00 12		
Hillside	d	20 15		20 30				23 45		23 59		00 15		
Birkdale	d	20 17		20 32				23 47		00 02		00 17		
Southport	a	20 22		20 37				23 52		00 07		00 22		

For general notes see front of timetable
For details of catering facilities see Directory of Train Operators

Table 103

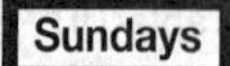

Hunts Cross and Liverpool → Kirkby, Ormskirk and Southport

Network Diagram - see first page of Table 101

		ME	ME	ME	ME	ME	ME	ME	ME	ME	ME	ME	ME		ME	ME	ME	ME	ME	ME	ME	ME
Hunts Cross 89	d			08b06			08 36			09 06			09 36	and at the same minutes past each hour until	22 36			23 06				
Liverpool South Parkway 7 89 ✈	d			08 09			08 39			09 09			09 39		22 39			23 09				
Cressington	d			08 12			08 42			09 12			09 42		22 42			23 12				
Aigburth	d			08 14			08 44			09 14			09 44		22 44			23 14				
St Michaels	d			08 16			08 46			09 16			09 46		22 46			23 16				
Brunswick	d			08 19			08 49			09 19			09 49		22 49			23 19				
Liverpool Central 10	a			08 23			08 53			09 23			09 53		22 53			23 23				
	d	08 08	08 10	08 23	08 25	08 40	08 53	08 55	09 10	09 23	09 25	09 40	09 53		22 53	22 55	23 10	23 23	23 25	23 38	23 40	23 55
Moorfields 10	d	08 10	08 12	08 25	08 27	08 42	08 55	08 57	09 12	09 25	09 27	09 42	09 55		22 55	22 57	23 12	23 25	23 27	23 40	23 42	23 57
Sandhills	d	08 14	08 16	08 29	08 31	08 46	08 59	09 01	09 16	09 29	09 31	09 46	09 59		22 59	23 01	23 16	23 29	23 31	23 44	23 46	00 01
Kirkdale	d		08 19		08 34	08 49		09 04	09 19		09 34	09 49				23 04	23 19		23 34		23 49	00 04
Rice Lane	d				08 37			09 07			09 37					23 07			23 37			00 07
Fazakerley	d				08 40			09 10			09 40					23 10			23 40			00 10
Kirkby	a				08 43			09 13			09 43					23 13			23 43			00 13
Walton (Merseyside)	d		08 22			08 52			09 22			09 52					23 22				23 52	
Orrell Park	d		08 23			08 53			09 23			09 53					23 23				23 53	
Aintree	d		08 26			08 56			09 26			09 56					23 26				23 56	
Old Roan	d		08 28			08 58			09 28			09 58					23 28				23 58	
Maghull	d		08 31			09 01			09 31			10 01					23 31				00 01	
Town Green	d		08 35			09 05			09 35			10 05					23 35				00 05	
Aughton Park	d		08 37			09 07			09 37			10 07					23 37				00 07	
Ormskirk	a		08 42			09 12			09 42			10 12					23 42				00 12	
Bank Hall	d	08 16		08 31			09 01			09 31			10 01		23 01			23 31		23 46		
Bootle Oriel Road	d	08 18		08 33			09 03			09 33			10 03		23 03			23 33		23 48		
Bootle New Strand	d	08 20		08 35			09 05			09 35			10 05		23 05			23 35		23 50		
Seaforth & Litherland	d	08 22		08 37			09 07			09 37			10 07		23 07			23 37		23 52		
Waterloo (Merseyside)	d	08 24		08 39			09 09			09 39			10 09		23 09			23 39		23 54		
Blundellsands & Crosby	d	08 27		08 42			09 12			09 42			10 12		23 12			23 42		23 57		
Hall Road	d	08 29		08 44			09 14			09 44			10 14		23 14			23 44		23 59		
Hightown	d	08 32		08 47			09 17			09 47			10 17		23 17			23 47		00 02		
Formby	d	08 36		08 51			09 21			09 51			10 21		23 21			23 51		00 06		
Freshfield	d	08 38		08 53			09 23			09 53			10 23		23 23			23 53		00 08		
Ainsdale	d	08 42		08 57			09 27			09 57			10 27		23 27			23 57		00 12		
Hillside	d	08 45		09 00			09 30			10 00			10 30		23 30			23 59		00 15		
Birkdale	d	08 47		09 02			09 32			10 02			10 32		23 32			00 02		00 17		
Southport	a	08 52		09 07			09 37			10 07			10 37		23 37			00 07		00 22		

For general notes see front of timetable
For details of catering facilities see Directory of Train Operators

b Until 27 January and from 30 March only

Southport, Ormskirk and Kirkby → Liverpool and Hunts Cross

Network Diagram - see first page of Table 101

Miles	Miles	Miles			ME	ME	ME	ME	ME	ME	ME	ME	ME	ME	ME	ME	ME	ME	ME	ME	ME	ME	ME
0	—	—	**Southport**	d				05 43		05 58		06 13		06 28		06 43			06 58			07 13	
1	—	—	Birkdale	d				05 47		06 02		06 17		06 32		06 47			07 02			07 17	
2	—	—	Hillside	d				05 49		06 04		06 19		06 34		06 49			07 04			07 19	
3½	—	—	Ainsdale	d				05 52		06 07		06 22		06 37		06 52			07 07			07 22	
6¼	—	—	Freshfield	d				05 56		06 11		06 26		06 41		06 56			07 11			07 26	
7¼	—	—	Formby	d				05 58		06 13		06 28		06 43		06 58			07 13			07 28	
9¼	—	—	Hightown	d				06 02		06 17		06 32		06 47		07 02			07 17			07 32	
11¼	—	—	Hall Road	d				06 05		06 20		06 35		06 50		07 05			07 20			07 35	
12	—	—	Blundellsands & Crosby	d				06 07		06 22		06 37		06 52		07 07			07 22			07 37	
13	—	—	Waterloo (Merseyside)	d				06 10		06 25		06 40		06 55		07 10			07 25			07 40	
14¼	—	—	Seaforth & Litherland	d				06 12		06 27		06 42		06 57		07 12			07 27			07 42	
15¼	—	—	Bootle New Strand	d				06 15		06 30		06 45		07 00		07 15			07 30			07 45	
15½	—	—	Bootle Oriel Road	d				06 16		06 31		06 46		07 01		07 16			07 31			07 46	
16¼	—	—	Bank Hall	d				06 18		06 33		06 48		07 03		07 18			07 33			07 48	
—	0	—	**Ormskirk**	d			05 50				06 20				06 50			07 05			07 20		
—	1¼	—	Aughton Park	d			05 53				06 23				06 53			07 08			07 23		
—	2¼	—	Town Green	d			05 55				06 25				06 55			07 10			07 25		
—	4¾	—	Maghull	d			06 00				06 30				07 00			07 15			07 30		
—	6½	—	Old Roan	d			06 03				06 33				07 03			07 18			07 33		
—	7¼	—	Aintree	d			06 05				06 35				07 05			07 20			07 35		
—	8¼	—	Orrell Park	d			06 07				06 37				07 07			07 22			07 37		
—	8½	—	Walton (Merseyside)	d			06 09				06 39				07 09			07 24			07 39		
—	—	0	**Kirkby**	d	05 48				06 18				06 48				07 13			07 28			07 43
—	—	1¾	Fazakerley	d	05 51				06 21				06 51				07 16			07 31			07 46
—	—	3¼	Rice Lane	d	05 54				06 24				06 54				07 19			07 34			07 49
—	9¾	4½	Kirkdale	d	05 57		06 12		06 27		06 42		06 57		07 12		07 22	07 27		07 37	07 42		07 52
17	10¾	5½	Sandhills	d	06 00	06 07	06 14	06 22	06 30	06 37	06 44	06 52	07 00	07 07	07 14	07 22	07 25	07 29	07 37	07 40	07 44	07 52	07 55
18½	12¼	7	**Moorfields 10**	d	06 03	06 10	06 18	06 26	06 33	06 40	06 48	06 55	07 03	07 10	07 18	07 25	07 28	07 33	07 40	07 43	07 48	07 55	07 58
19	12¾	7½	**Liverpool Central 10**	a	06 06	06 13	06 20	06 28	06 36	06 43	06 50	06 58	07 06	07 13	07 20	07 28	07 31	07 35	07 43	07 46	07 50	07 58	08 01
—	—	—		d		06 13		06 28		06 43		06 58		07 13		07 28			07 43			07 58	
20½	—	—	Brunswick	d		06 17		06 32		06 47		07 02		07 17		07 32			07 47			08 02	
21¾	—	—	St Michaels	d		06 19		06 34		06 49		07 04		07 19		07 34			07 49			08 04	
23	—	—	Aigburth	d		06 22		06 37		06 52		07 07		07 22		07 37			07 52			08 07	
23¾	—	—	Cressington	d		06 24		06 39		06 54		07 09		07 24		07 39			07 54			08 09	
24¾	—	—	**Liverpool South Parkway 7**	89 ✈ d		06 26		06 41		06 56		07 11		07 26		07 41			07 56			08 11	
26¼	—	—	**Hunts Cross**	89 a		06 31		06 46		07 01		07 16		07 31		07 46			08 01			08 16	

		ME	ME	ME	ME	ME	ME	ME SX	ME	ME	ME	ME SX	ME	ME	ME	ME	ME	ME	ME	ME	ME
Southport	d		07 28			07 43		07 48		07 58		08 03		08 13			08 28			08 43	
Birkdale	d		07 32			07 47		07 52		08 02		08 07		08 17			08 32			08 47	
Hillside	d		07 34			07 49		07 54		08 04		08 09		08 19			08 34			08 49	
Ainsdale	d		07 37			07 52		07 57		08 07		08 12		08 22			08 37			08 52	
Freshfield	d		07 41			07 56		08 01		08 11		08 16		08 26			08 41			08 56	
Formby	d		07 43			07 58		08 03		08 13		08 18		08 28			08 43			08 58	
Hightown	d		07 47			08 02		08 07		08 17		08 22		08 32			08 47			09 02	
Hall Road	d		07 50			08 05		08 10		08 20		08 25		08 35			08 50			09 05	
Blundellsands & Crosby	d		07 52			08 07		08 12		08 22		08 27		08 37			08 52			09 07	
Waterloo (Merseyside)	d		07 55			08 10		08 15		08 25		08 30		08 40			08 55			09 10	
Seaforth & Litherland	d		07 57			08 12		08 17		08 27		08 32		08 42			08 57			09 12	
Bootle New Strand	d		08 00			08 15		08 20		08 30		08 35		08 45			09 00			09 15	
Bootle Oriel Road	d		08 01			08 16		08 21		08 31		08 36		08 46			09 01			09 16	
Bank Hall	d		08 03			08 18		08 23		08 33		08 38		08 48			09 03			09 18	
Ormskirk	d	07 35			07 50				08 05				08 20			08 35			08 50		
Aughton Park	d	07 38			07 53				08 08				08 23			08 38			08 53		
Town Green	d	07 40			07 55				08 10				08 25			08 40			08 55		
Maghull	d	07 45			08 00				08 15				08 30			08 45			09 00		
Old Roan	d	07 48			08 03				08 18				08 33			08 48			09 03		
Aintree	d	07 50			08 05				08 20				08 35			08 50			09 05		
Orrell Park	d	07 52			08 07				08 22				08 37			08 52			09 07		
Walton (Merseyside)	d	07 54			08 09				08 24				08 39			08 54			09 09		
Kirkby	d			07 58			08 13				08 28				08 43			08 58			09 13
Fazakerley	d			08 01			08 16				08 31				08 46			09 01			09 16
Rice Lane	d			08 04			08 19				08 34				08 49			09 04			09 19
Kirkdale	d	07 57		08 07	08 12		08 22		08 27		08 37		08 42		08 52	08 57		09 07	09 12		09 22
Sandhills	d	07 59	08 07	08 10	08 14	08 22	08 25	08 27	08 29	08 37	08 40	08 42	08 44	08 52	08 55	08 59	09 07	09 10	09 14	09 22	09 25
Moorfields 10	d	08 03	08 10	08 13	08 18	08 25	08 28	08 31	08 33	08 40	08 43	08 46	08 48	08 55	08 58	09 03	09 10	09 13	09 18	09 25	09 28
Liverpool Central 10	a	08 05	08 13	08 16	08 20	08 28	08 31	08 33	08 35	08 43	08 46	08 48	08 50	08 58	09 01	09 05	09 13	09 16	09 20	09 28	09 31
	d		08 13			08 28				08 43				08 58			09 13			09 28	
Brunswick	d		08 17			08 32				08 47				09 02			09 17			09 32	
St Michaels	d		08 19			08 34				08 49				09 04			09 19			09 34	
Aigburth	d		08 22			08 37				08 52				09 07			09 22			09 37	
Cressington	d		08 24			08 39				08 54				09 09			09 24			09 39	
Liverpool South Parkway 7	89 ✈ d		08 26			08 41				08 56				09 11			09 26			09 41	
Hunts Cross	89 a		08 31			08 46				09 01				09 16			09 31			09 46	

For general notes see front of timetable
For details of catering facilities see Directory of Train Operators

Table 103

Mondays to Saturdays

Southport, Ormskirk and Kirkby → Liverpool and Hunts Cross

Network Diagram - see first page of Table 101

		ME	ME	ME	ME	ME		ME	ME	ME	ME	ME	ME	ME	ME	ME	ME	ME	ME	ME
Southport	d		08 58			09 13	and at the same minutes past each hour until	18 13			18 28			18 43			18 58			19 13
Birkdale	d		09 02			09 17		18 17			18 32			18 47			19 02			19 17
Hillside	d		09 04			09 19		18 19			18 34			18 49			19 04			19 19
Ainsdale	d		09 07			09 22		18 22			18 37			18 52			19 07			19 22
Freshfield	d		09 11			09 26		18 26			18 41			18 56			19 11			19 26
Formby	d		09 13			09 28		18 28			18 43			18 58			19 13			19 28
Hightown	d		09 17			09 32		18 32			18 47			19 02			19 17			19 32
Hall Road	d		09 20			09 35		18 35			18 50			19 05			19 20			19 35
Blundellsands & Crosby	d		09 22			09 37		18 37			18 52			19 07			19 22			19 37
Waterloo (Merseyside)	d		09 25			09 40		18 40			18 55			19 10			19 25			19 40
Seaforth & Litherland	d		09 27			09 42		18 42			18 57			19 12			19 27			19 42
Bootle New Strand	d		09 30			09 45		18 45			19 00			19 15			19 30			19 45
Bootle Oriel Road	d		09 31			09 46		18 46			19 01			19 16			19 31			19 46
Bank Hall	d		09 33			09 48		18 48			19 03			19 18			19 33			19 48
Ormskirk	d	09 05			09 20					18 35			18 50			19 05			19 20	
Aughton Park	d	09 08			09 23					18 38			18 53			19 08			19 23	
Town Green	d	09 10			09 25					18 40			18 55			19 10			19 25	
Maghull	d	09 15			09 30					18 45			19 00			19 15			19 30	
Old Roan	d	09 18			09 33					18 48			19 03			19 18			19 33	
Aintree	d	09 20			09 35					18 50			19 05			19 20			19 35	
Orrell Park	d	09 22			09 37					18 52			19 07			19 22			19 37	
Walton (Merseyside)	d	09 24			09 39					18 54			19 09			19 24			19 39	
Kirkby	d			09 28					18 43			18 58			19 13			19 28		
Fazakerley	d			09 31					18 46			19 01			19 16			19 31		
Rice Lane	d			09 34					18 49			19 04			19 19			19 34		
Kirkdale	d	09 27		09 37	09 42				18 52	18 57		19 07	19 12		19 22	19 27		19 37	19 42	
Sandhills	d	09 29	09 37	09 40	09 44	09 52		18 52	18 55	18 59	19 07	19 10	19 14	19 22	19 25	19 29	19 37	19 40	19 44	19 52
Moorfields 10	d	09 33	09 40	09 43	09 48	09 55		18 55	18 58	19 03	19 10	19 13	19 18	19 25	19 28	19 33	19 40	19 43	19 48	19 55
Liverpool Central 10	a	09 35	09 43	09 46	09 50	09 58		18 58	19 01	19 05	19 13	19 16	19 20	19 28	19 31	19 35	19 43	19 46	19 50	19 58
	d		09 43			09 58		18 58			19 13			19 28			19 43			19 58
Brunswick	d		09 47			10 02		19 02			19 17			19 32			19 47			20 02
St Michaels	d		09 49			10 04		19 04			19 19			19 34			19 49			20 04
Aigburth	d		09 52			10 07		19 07			19 22			19 37			19 52			20 07
Cressington	d		09 54			10 09		19 09			19 24			19 39			19 54			20 09
Liverpool South Parkway 7	89 d		09 56			10 11		19 11			19 26			19 41			19 56			20 11
Hunts Cross	89 a		10 01			10 16		19 16			19 31			19 46			20 01			20 17

		ME	ME	ME	ME	ME	ME		ME	ME	ME	ME	ME	ME	ME	ME	ME	ME	ME
Southport	d		19 28		19 43		19 58	and at the same minutes past each hour until	21 58		22 13		22 28		22 43		22 58		23 16
Birkdale	d		19 32		19 47		20 02		22 02		22 17		22 32		22 47		23 02		23 20
Hillside	d		19 34		19 49		20 04		22 04		22 19		22 34		22 49		23 04		23 22
Ainsdale	d		19 37		19 52		20 07		22 07		22 22		22 37		22 52		23 07		23 25
Freshfield	d		19 41		19 56		20 11		22 11		22 26		22 41		22 56		23 11		23 29
Formby	d		19 43		19 58		20 13		22 13		22 28		22 43		22 58		23 13		23 31
Hightown	d		19 47		20 02		20 17		22 17		22 32		22 47		23 02		23 17		23 35
Hall Road	d		19 50		20 05		20 20		22 20		22 35		22 50		23 05		23 20		23 38
Blundellsands & Crosby	d		19 52		20 07		20 22		22 22		22 37		22 52		23 07		23 22		23 40
Waterloo (Merseyside)	d		19 55		20 10		20 25		22 25		22 40		22 55		23 10		23 25		23 43
Seaforth & Litherland	d		19 57		20 12		20 27		22 27		22 42		22 57		23 12		23 27		23 45
Bootle New Strand	d		20 00		20 15		20 30		22 30		22 45		23 00		23 15		23 30		23 48
Bootle Oriel Road	d		20 01		20 16		20 31		22 31		22 46		23 01		23 16		23 31		23 49
Bank Hall	d		20 03		20 18		20 33		22 33		22 48		23 03		23 18		23 33		23 51
Ormskirk	d			19 50						22 20				22 50				23 20	
Aughton Park	d			19 53						22 23				22 53				23 23	
Town Green	d			19 55						22 25				22 55				23 25	
Maghull	d			20 00						22 30				23 00				23 30	
Old Roan	d			20 03						22 33				23 03				23 33	
Aintree	d			20 05						22 35				23 05				23 35	
Orrell Park	d			20 07						22 37				23 07				23 37	
Walton (Merseyside)	d			20 09						22 39				23 09				23 39	
Kirkby	d	19 48				20 18						22 48				23 18			
Fazakerley	d	19 51				20 21						22 51				23 21			
Rice Lane	d	19 54				20 24						22 54				23 24			
Kirkdale	d	19 57		20 12		20 27				22 42		22 57		23 12		23 27		23 42	
Sandhills	d	20 00	20 07	20 14	20 22	20 30	20 37		22 37	22 44	22 52	23 00	23 07	23 14	23 22	23 30	23 37	23 44	23 55
Moorfields 10	d	20 03	20 10	20 18	20 25	20 33	20 40		22 40	22 48	22 55	23 03	23 10	23 18	23 25	23 33	23 40	23 48	23 58
Liverpool Central 10	a	20 06	20 13	20 20	20 28	20 36	20 43		22 43	22 50	22 58	23 06	23 13	23 20	23 28	23 36	23 43	23 50	00 01
	d		20 13		20 28		20 43		22 43		22 58		23 13		23 28		23 43		
Brunswick	d		20 17		20 32		20 47		22 47		23 02		23 17		23 32		23 47		
St Michaels	d		20 19		20 34		20 49		22 49		23 04		23 19		23 34		23 49		
Aigburth	d		20 22		20 37		20 52		22 52		23 07		23 22		23 37		23 52		
Cressington	d		20 24		20 39		20 54		22 54		23 09		23 24		23 39		23 54		
Liverpool South Parkway 7	89 d		20 26		20 41		20 56		22 56		23 11		23 26		23 41		23 56		
Hunts Cross	89 a		20 31		20 46		21 01		23 01		23 18		23 32		23 46		00 01		

For general notes see front of timetable
For details of catering facilities see Directory of Train Operators

Table 103

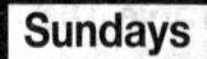

Southport, Ormskirk and Kirkby → Liverpool and Hunts Cross

Network Diagram - see first page of Table 101

		ME		ME	ME	ME	ME	ME	ME			ME	ME		ME	ME		ME					
Southport	d				07 58			08 28							22 58			23 16					
Birkdale	d				08 02			08 32							23 02			23 20					
Hillside	d				08 04			08 34							23 04			23 22					
Ainsdale	d				08 07			08 37							23 07			23 25					
Freshfield	d				08 11			08 41							23 11			23 29					
Formby	d				08 13			08 43							23 13			23 31					
Hightown	d				08 17			08 47							23 17			23 35					
Hall Road	d				08 20			08 50							23 20			23 38					
Blundellsands & Crosby	d				08 22			08 52							23 22			23 40					
Waterloo (Merseyside)	d				08 25			08 55							23 25			23 43					
Seaforth & Litherland	d				08 27			08 57							23 27			23 45					
Bootle New Strand	d				08 30			09 00							23 30			23 48					
Bootle Oriel Road	d				08 31			09 01							23 31			23 49					
Bank Hall	d				08 33			09 03		and at					23 33			23 51					
Ormskirk	d					08 20			08 50	the same		22 50				23 20							
Aughton Park	d					08 23			08 53			22 53				23 23							
Town Green	d					08 25			08 55	minutes		22 55				23 25							
Maghull	d					08 30			09 00			23 00				23 30							
Old Roan	d					08 33			09 03	past		23 03				23 33							
Aintree	d					08 35			09 05			23 05				23 35							
Orrell Park	d					08 37			09 07	each		23 07				23 37							
Walton (Merseyside)	d					08 39			09 09			23 09				23 39							
Kirkby	d			08 18			08 48			hour until			23 18										
Fazakerley	d			08 21			08 51						23 21										
Rice Lane	d			08 24			08 54						23 24										
Kirkdale	d			08 27		08 42	08 57		09 12			23 12	23 27			23 42							
Sandhills	d			08 30	08 37	08 44	09 00	09 07	09 14			23 14	23 30		23 37	23 44		23 55					
Moorfields 10	d			08 33	08 40	08 48	09 03	09 10	09 18			23 18	23 33		23 40	23 48		23 58					
Liverpool Central 10	a			08 36	08 43	08 50	09 06	09 13	09 20			23 20	23 36		23 43	23 50		00 01					
	d	08 13			08 43			09 13							23 43								
Brunswick	d	08 17			08 47			09 17							23 47								
St Michaels	d	08 19			08 49			09 19							23 49								
Aigburth	d	08 22			08 52			09 22							23 52								
Cressington	d	08 24			08 54			09 24							23 54								
Liverpool South Parkway 7 89 ✈	d	08 26			08 56			09 26							23 56								
Hunts Cross 89	a	08 31			09 01			09 31							00 01								

For general notes see front of timetable
For details of catering facilities see Directory of Train Operators

Liverpool and Birkenhead → New Brighton, West Kirby, Ellesmere Port and Chester

Network Diagram - see first page of Table 101

Miles	Miles	Miles	Miles			ME	ME	ME	ME	ME	ME	ME	ME	ME	ME	ME	ME	ME	ME	ME	ME	ME	ME	ME	ME
0	—	0	0	**Moorfields** 10	d	05 46	05 56	06 11	06 16	06 21	06 26	06 41	06 46	06 51	06 56	07 11	07 16	07 21	07 26	07 31	07 36	07 41	07 46	07 51	07 56
½	—	½	½	**Liverpool Lime Street** 10	d	05 48	05 58	06 13	06 18	06 23	06 28	06 43	06 48	06 53	06 58	07 13	07 18	07 23	07 28	07 33	07 38	07 43	07 48	07 53	07 58
1	—	1	1	**Liverpool Central** 10	d	05 50	06 00	06 15	06 20	06 25	06 30	06 45	06 50	06 55	07 00	07 15	07 20	07 25	07 30	07 35	07 40	07 45	07 50	07 55	08 00
1½	—	1½	1½	James Street	d	05 52	06 02	06 17	06 22	06 27	06 32	06 47	06 52	06 57	07 02	07 17	07 22	07 27	07 32	07 37	07 42	07 47	07 52	07 57	08 02
2¾	—	2¾	2¾	Hamilton Square	d	05 55	06 05	06 20	06 25	06 30	06 35	06 50	06 55	07 00	07 05	07 20	07 25	07 30	07 35	07 40	07 45	07 50	07 55	08 00	08 05
—	—	3¼	3¼	Conway Park	d				06 27	06 32			06 57	07 02			07 27	07 32		07 42	07 47		07 57	08 02	
—	—	4	4	Birkenhead Park	d				06 29	06 34			06 59	07 04			07 29	07 34		07 44	07 49		07 59	08 04	
—	—	4¾	4¾	Birkenhead North	d				06 32	06 37			07 02	07 07			07 32	07 37		07 47	07 42		08 02	08 07	
—	—	—	6¼	Wallasey Village	d				06 37				07 07				07 37			07 52			08 07		
—	—	—	6½	Wallasey Grove Road	d				06 38				07 08				07 38			07 53			08 08		
—	—	—	7¾	**New Brighton**	a				06 43				07 13				07 43			07 58			08 13		
—	—	5¼	—	Bidston	d					06 40				07 10				07 40			07 55			08 10	
—	—	6½	—	Leasowe	d					06 42				07 12				07 42			07 57			08 12	
—	—	7	—	Moreton (Merseyside)	d					06 44				07 14				07 44			07 59			08 14	
—	—	8¼	—	Meols	d					06 48				07 18				07 48			08 03			08 18	
—	—	9½	—	Manor Road	d					06 50				07 20				07 50			08 05			08 20	
—	—	10	—	Hoylake	d					06 52				07 22				07 52			08 07			08 22	
—	—	11¼	—	**West Kirby**	a					06 57				07 27				07 57			08 12			08 27	
3	—	—	—	Birkenhead Central	d	05 57	06 07	06 22			06 37	06 52			07 07	07 22			07 37			07 52			08 07
3¾	—	—	—	Green Lane	d	05 59	06 09	06 24			06 39	06 54			07 09	07 24			07 39			07 54			08 09
4½	—	—	—	Rock Ferry	d	06 02	06 12	06 27			06 42	06 57			07 12	07 27			07 42			07 57			08 12
5½	—	—	—	Bebington	d	06 04	06 14	06 29			06 44	06 59			07 14	07 29			07 44			07 59			08 14
6½	—	—	—	Port Sunlight	d	06 06	06 16	06 31			06 46	07 01			07 16	07 31			07 46			08 01			08 16
7	—	—	—	Spital	d	06 08	06 18	06 33			06 48	07 03			07 18	07 33			07 48			08 03			08 18
7¾	—	—	—	Bromborough Rake	d	06 10	06 20	06 35			06 50	07 05			07 20	07 35			07 50			08 05			08 20
8½	—	—	—	Bromborough	d	06 12	06 22	06 37			06 52	07 07			07 22	07 37			07 52			08 07			08 22
9	—	—	—	Eastham Rake	d	06 15	06 25	06 40			06 55	07 10			07 25	07 40			07 55			08 10			08 25
10	0	—	—	Hooton	d	06 17	06 27	06 42			06 57	07 12			07 27	07 42			07 57			08 12			08 27
—	1½	—	—	Little Sutton	d	06 21		06 46				07 16				07 46						08 16			
—	2½	—	—	Overpool	d	06 23		06 48				07 18				07 48						08 18			
—	4	—	—	**Ellesmere Port**	a	06 27		06 52				07 22				07 52						08 22			
13	—	—	—	Capenhurst	d		06 32				07 02				07 32				08 02						08 32
16¾	—	—	—	Bache	d		06 37				07 07				07 37				08 07						08 37
18¾	—	—	—	**Chester**	a		06 41				07 11				07 41				08 11						08 41

		ME	ME SX	ME	ME	ME	ME SX	ME	ME	ME	ME SX	ME	ME	ME	ME SX	ME	ME	ME	ME SX	ME	ME	ME	ME SX
Moorfields 10	d	08 01	08 03	08 06	08 11	08 16	08 18	08 21	08 26	08 31	08 33	08 36	08 41	08 46	08 48	08 51	08 56	09 01	09 03	09 06	09 11	09 16	09 18
Liverpool Lime Street 10	d	08 03	08 05	08 08	08 13	08 18	08 20	08 23	08 28	08 33	08 35	08 38	08 43	08 48	08 50	08 53	08 58	09 03	09 05	09 08	09 13	09 18	09 20
Liverpool Central 10	d	08 05	08a07	08 10	08 15	08 20	08a22	08 25	08 30	08 35	08a37	08 40	08 45	08 50	08a52	08 55	09 00	09 05	09a07	09 10	09 15	09 20	09a22
James Street	d	08 07		08 12	08 17	08 22		08 27	08 32	08 37		08 42	08 47	08 52		08 57	09 02	09 07		09 12	09 17	09 22	
Hamilton Square	d	08 10		08 15	08 20	08 25		08 30	08 35	08 40		08 45	08 50	08 55		09 00	09 05	09 10		09 15	09 20	09 25	
Conway Park	d	08 12		08 17		08 27		08 32		08 42		08 47		08 57		09 02		09 12		09 17		09 27	
Birkenhead Park	d	08 14		08 19		08 29		08 34		08 44		08 49		08 59		09 04		09 14		09 19		09 29	
Birkenhead North	d	08 17		08 22		08 32		08 37		08 47		08 52		09 02		09 07		09 17		09 22		09 32	
Wallasey Village	d	08 22				08 37				08 52				09 07				09 22				09 37	
Wallasey Grove Road	d	08 23				08 38				08 53				09 08				09 23				09 38	
New Brighton	a	08 28				08 43				08 58				09 13				09 28				09 43	
Bidston	d			08 25				08 40				08 55				09 10				09 25			
Leasowe	d			08 27				08 42				08 57				09 12				09 27			
Moreton (Merseyside)	d			08 29				08 44				08 59				09 14				09 29			
Meols	d			08 33				08 48				09 03				09 18				09 33			
Manor Road	d			08 35				08 50				09 05				09 20				09 35			
Hoylake	d			08 37				08 52				09 07				09 22				09 37			
West Kirby	a			08 42				08 57				09 12				09 27				09 42			
Birkenhead Central	d				08 22				08 37				08 52				09 07				09 22		
Green Lane	d				08 24				08 39				08 54				09 09				09 24		
Rock Ferry	d				08 27				08 42				08 57				09 12				09 27		
Bebington	d				08 29				08 44				08 59				09 14				09 29		
Port Sunlight	d				08 31				08 46				09 01				09 16				09 31		
Spital	d				08 33				08 48				09 03				09 18				09 33		
Bromborough Rake	d				08 35				08 50				09 05				09 20				09 35		
Bromborough	d				08 37				08 52				09 07				09 22				09 37		
Eastham Rake	d				08 40				08 55				09 10				09 25				09 40		
Hooton	d				08 42				08 57				09 12				09 27				09 42		
Little Sutton	d				08 46								09 16								09 46		
Overpool	d				08 48								09 18								09 48		
Ellesmere Port	a				08 52								09 22								09 52		
Capenhurst	d								09 02								09 32						
Bache	d								09 07								09 37						
Chester	a								09 11								09 41						

For general notes see front of timetable
For details of catering facilities see
Directory of Train Operators

Liverpool and Birkenhead → New Brighton, West Kirby, Ellesmere Port and Chester

Network Diagram - see first page of Table 101

			ME	ME	ME	ME	ME	ME	ME	ME	ME	ME	ME	ME			ME	ME	ME	ME	ME	ME	ME	ME	ME
Moorfields 10	d		09 21	09 26	09 31	09 36	09 41	09 46	09 51	09 56	10 01	10 06	10 11	10 16	and at the same minutes past each hour until		15 16	15 21	15 26	15 31	15 36	15 41	15 46	15 51	15 56
Liverpool Lime Street 10	d		09 23	09 28	09 33	09 38	09 43	09 48	09 53	09 58	10 03	10 08	10 13	10 18			15 18	15 23	15 28	15 33	15 38	15 43	15 48	15 53	15 58
Liverpool Central 10	d		09 25	09 30	09 35	09 40	09 45	09 50	09 55	10 00	10 05	10 10	10 15	10 20			15 20	15 25	15 30	15 35	15 40	15 45	15 50	15 55	16 00
James Street	d		09 27	09 32	09 37	09 42	09 47	09 52	09 57	10 02	10 07	10 12	10 17	10 22			15 22	15 27	15 32	15 37	15 42	15 47	15 52	15 57	16 02
Hamilton Square	d		09 30	09 35	09 40	09 45	09 50	09 55	10 00	10 05	10 10	10 15	10 20	10 25			15 25	15 30	15 35	15 40	15 45	15 50	15 55	16 00	16 05
Conway Park	d		09 32		09 42	09 47		09 57	10 02		10 12	10 17		10 27			15 27	15 32		15 42	15 47		15 57	16 02	
Birkenhead Park	d		09 34		09 44	09 49		09 59	10 04		10 14	10 19		10 29			15 29	15 34		15 44	15 49		15 59	16 04	
Birkenhead North	d		09 37		09 47	09 52		10 02	10 07		10 17	10 22		10 32			15 32	15 37		15 47	15 52		16 02	16 07	
Wallasey Village	d				09 52			10 07			10 22			10 37			15 37			15 52			16 07		
Wallasey Grove Road	d				09 53			10 08			10 23			10 38			15 38			15 53			16 08		
New Brighton	a				09 58			10 13			10 28			10 43			15 43			15 58			16 13		
Bidston	d		09 40			09 55			10 10			10 25						15 40			15 55			16 10	
Leasowe	d		09 42			09 57			10 12			10 27						15 42			15 57			16 12	
Moreton (Merseyside)	d		09 44			09 59			10 14			10 29						15 44			15 59			16 14	
Meols	d		09 48			10 03			10 18			10 33						15 48			16 03			16 18	
Manor Road	d		09 50			10 05			10 20			10 35						15 50			16 05			16 20	
Hoylake	d		09 52			10 07			10 22			10 37						15 52			16 07			16 22	
West Kirby	a		09 57			10 12			10 27			10 42						15 57			16 12			16 27	
Birkenhead Central	d			09 37			09 52			10 07			10 22						15 37			15 52			16 07
Green Lane	d			09 39			09 54			10 09			10 24						15 39			15 54			16 09
Rock Ferry	d			09 42			09 57			10 12			10 27						15 42			15 57			16 12
Bebington	d			09 44			09 59			10 14			10 29						15 44			15 59			16 14
Port Sunlight	d			09 46			10 01			10 16			10 31						15 46			16 01			16 16
Spital	d			09 48			10 03			10 18			10 33						15 48			16 03			16 18
Bromborough Rake	d			09 50			10 05			10 20			10 35						15 50			16 05			16 20
Bromborough	d			09 52			10 07			10 22			10 37						15 52			16 07			16 22
Eastham Rake	d			09 55			10 10			10 25			10 40						15 55			16 10			16 25
Hooton	d			09 57			10 12			10 27			10 42						15 57			16 12			16 27
Little Sutton	d						10 16						10 46									16 16			
Overpool	d						10 18						10 48									16 18			
Ellesmere Port	a						10 22						10 52									16 22			
Capenhurst	d			10 02						10 32									16 02						16 32
Bache	d			10 07						10 37									16 07						16 37
Chester	a			10 11						10 41									16 11						16 41

		ME	ME SX	ME	ME	ME		ME SX	ME	ME	ME	ME SX	ME	ME SX	ME SO	ME	ME SX	ME	ME		ME	ME SX	ME	ME SX	ME SO	ME
Moorfields 10	d	16 01	16 03	16 06	16 11	16 16		16 18	16 21	16 26	16 31	16 33	16 36	16 41	16 41	16 46	16 48	16 51	16 56		17 01	17 03	17 06	17 11	17 11	17 16
Liverpool Lime Street 10	d	16 03	16 05	16 08	16 13	16 18		16 20	16 23	16 28	16 33	16 35	16 38	16 43	16 43	16 48	16 50	16 53	16 58		17 03	17 05	17 08	17 13	17 13	17 18
Liverpool Central 10	d	16 05	16 07	16 10	16 15	16 20		16 22	16 25	16 30	16 35	16 37	16 40	16 45	16 45	16 50	16 52	16 55	17 00		17 05	17 07	17 10	17 15	17 15	17 20
James Street	d	16 07	16 09	16 12	16 17	16 22		16 24	16 27	16 32	16 37	16 39	16 42	16 47	16 47	16 52	16 54	16 57	17 02		17 07	17 09	17 12	17 17	17 17	17 22
Hamilton Square	d	16 10	16 12	16 15	16 20	16 25		16 27	16 30	16 35	16 40	16 42	16 45	16 50	16 50	16 55	16 57	17 00	17 05		17 10	17 12	17 15	17 20	17 20	17 25
Conway Park	d	16 12		16 17		16 27			16 32		16 42		16 47			16 57		17 02			17 12		17 17			17 27
Birkenhead Park	d	16 14		16 19		16 29			16 34		16 44		16 49			16 59		17 04			17 14		17 19			17 29
Birkenhead North	d	16 17		16 22		16 32			16 37		16 47		16 52			17 02		17 07			17 17		17 22			17 32
Wallasey Village	d	16 22				16 37					16 52					17 07					17 22					17 37
Wallasey Grove Road	d	16 23				16 38					16 53					17 08					17 23					17 38
New Brighton	a	16 28				16 43					16 58					17 13					17 28					17 43
Bidston	d			16 25					16 40				16 55					17 10					17 25			
Leasowe	d			16 27					16 42				16 57					17 12					17 27			
Moreton (Merseyside)	d			16 29					16 44				16 59					17 14					17 29			
Meols	d			16 33					16 48				17 03					17 18					17 33			
Manor Road	d			16 35					16 50				17 05					17 20					17 35			
Hoylake	d			16 37					16 52				17 07					17 22					17 37			
West Kirby	a			16 42					16 57				17 12					17 27					17 42			
Birkenhead Central	d		16 15		16 22			16 30		16 37		16 45		16 52	16 52		17 00		17 07			17 15		17 22	17 22	
Green Lane	d		16 17		16 24			16 32		16 39		16 47		16 54	16 54		17 02		17 09			17 17		17 24	17 24	
Rock Ferry	d		16 20		16 27			16 34		16 42		16 49		16 57	16 57		17 04		17 12			17 19		17 27	17 27	
Bebington	d		16 22		16 29			16 37		16 44		16 52		16 59	16 59		17 07		17 14			17 22		17 29	17 29	
Port Sunlight	d		16 24		16 31			16 39		16 46		16 54		17 01	17 01		17 09		17 16			17 24		17 31	17 31	
Spital	d		16 26		16 33			16 41		16 48		16 56		17 03	17 03		17 11		17 18			17 26		17 33	17 33	
Bromborough Rake	d		16 28		16 35			16 43		16 50		16 58		17 05	17 05		17 13		17 20			17 28		17 35	17 35	
Bromborough	d		16 30		16 37			16 45		16 52		17 00		17 07	17 07		17 15		17 22			17 30		17 37	17 37	
Eastham Rake	d		16 33		16 40			16 47		16 55		17 02		17 10	17 10		17 17		17 25			17 32		17 40	17 40	
Hooton	d		16a35		16 42			16a49		16 57		17 04		17 12	17 12		17 19		17 27			17 34		17 42	17 42	
Little Sutton	d				16 46							17 09			17 16		17 24					17 39			17 46	
Overpool	d				16 48							17 11			17 18		17 26					17 41			17 48	
Ellesmere Port	a				16 52							17 14			17 22		17 29					17 44			17 52	
Capenhurst	d									17 02				17 17					17 32					17 47		
Bache	d									17 07				17 22					17 37					17 52		
Chester	a									17 11				17 26					17 41					17 56		

For general notes see front of timetable
For details of catering facilities see
Directory of Train Operators

Table 106

Mondays to Saturdays

Liverpool and Birkenhead → New Brighton, West Kirby, Ellesmere Port and Chester

Network Diagram - see first page of Table 101

		ME SX	ME	ME	ME	ME SX	ME	ME SX	ME SO		ME	ME SX	ME	ME	ME	ME	ME	ME	ME	ME	ME	ME		ME	ME	ME
Moorfields 10	d	17 18	17 21	17 26	17 31	17 33	17 36	17 41	17 41		17 46	17 48	17 51	17 56	18 01	18 06	18 11	18 16	18 21	18 26	18 31	18 36		18 41	18 46	18 51
Liverpool Lime Street 10	d	17 20	17 23	17 28	17 33	17 35	17 38	17 43	17 43		17 48	17 50	17 53	17 58	18 03	18 08	18 13	18 18	18 23	18 28	18 33	18 38		18 43	18 48	18 53
Liverpool Central 10	d	17 22	17 25	17 30	17 35	17 37	17 40	17 45	17 45		17 50	17 52	17 55	18 00	18 05	18 10	18 15	18 20	18 25	18 30	18 35	18 40		18 45	18 50	18 55
James Street	d	17 24	17 27	17 32	17 37	17 39	17 42	17 47	17 47		17 52	17 54	17 57	18 02	18 07	18 12	18 17	18 22	18 27	18 32	18 37	18 42		18 47	18 52	18 57
Hamilton Square	d	17 27	17 30	17 35	17 40	17 42	17 45	17 50	17 50		17 55	17 57	18 00	18 05	18 10	18 15	18 20	18 25	18 30	18 35	18 40	18 45		18 50	18 55	19 00
Conway Park	d		17 32		17 42		17 47				17 57		18 02		18 12	18 17		18 27	18 32		18 42	18 47			18 57	19 02
Birkenhead Park	d		17 34		17 44		17 49				17 59		18 04		18 14	18 19		18 29	18 34		18 44	18 49			18 59	19 04
Birkenhead North	d		17 37		17 47		17 52				18 02		18 07		18 17	18 22		18 32	18 37		18 47	18 52			19 02	19 07
Wallasey Village	d				17 52						18 07				18 22			18 37			18 52				19 07	
Wallasey Grove Road	d				17 53						18 08				18 23			18 38			18 53				19 08	
New Brighton	a				17 58						18 13				18 28			18 43			18 58				19 13	
Bidston	d		17 40				17 55						18 10			18 25			18 40			18 55				19 10
Leasowe	d		17 42				17 57						18 12			18 27			18 42			18 57				19 12
Moreton (Merseyside)	d		17 44				17 59						18 14			18 29			18 44			18 59				19 14
Meols	d		17 48				18 03						18 18			18 33			18 48			19 03				19 18
Manor Road	d		17 50				18 05						18 20			18 35			18 50			19 05				19 20
Hoylake	d		17 52				18 07						18 22			18 37			18 52			19 07				19 22
West Kirby	a		17 57				18 12						18 27			18 42			18 57			19 12				19 27
Birkenhead Central	d	17 30		17 37		17 45		17 52	17 52			18 00		18 07			18 22			18 37				18 52		
Green Lane	d	17 32		17 39		17 47		17 54	17 54			18 02		18 09			18 24			18 39				18 54		
Rock Ferry	d	17 34		17 42		17 49		17 57	17 57			18 04		18 12			18 27			18 42				18 57		
Bebington	d	17 37		17 44		17 52		17 59	17 59			18 07		18 14			18 29			18 44				18 59		
Port Sunlight	d	17 39		17 46		17 54		18 01	18 01			18 09		18 16			18 31			18 46				19 01		
Spital	d	17 41		17 48		17 56		18 03	18 03			18 11		18 18			18 33			18 48				19 03		
Bromborough Rake	d	17 43		17 50		17 58		18 05	18 05			18 13		18 20			18 35			18 50				19 05		
Bromborough	d	17 45		17 52		18 00		18 07	18 07			18 15		18 22			18 37			18 52				19 07		
Eastham Rake	d	17 47		17 55		18 02		18 10	18 10			18 17		18 25			18 40			18 55				19 10		
Hooton	d	17 49		17 57		18 04		18 12	18 12			18 19		18 27			18 42			18 57				19 12		
Little Sutton	d	17 54				18 09			18 16			18 24					18 46							19 16		
Overpool	d	17 56				18 11			18 18			18 26					18 48							19 18		
Ellesmere Port	a	17 59				18 14			18 22			18 29					18 52							19 22		
Capenhurst	d			18 02				18 17						18 32						19 02						
Bache	d			18 07				18 22						18 37						19 07						
Chester	a			18 11				18 26						18 41						19 11						

		ME	ME	ME		ME	ME	ME	ME	ME	ME	ME	ME			ME	ME	ME	ME	ME	ME	ME	ME		
Moorfields 10	d	18 56	19 01	19 06		19 11	19 16	19 26	19 31	19 41	19 46	19 56	20 01	and at the same minutes past each hour until		23 01	23 11	23 16	23 26	23 31	23 41	23 46	23 56		
Liverpool Lime Street 10	d	18 58	19 03	19 08		19 13	19 18	19 28	19 33	19 43	19 48	19 58	20 03			23 03	23 13	23 18	23 28	23 33	23 43	23 48	23 58		
Liverpool Central 10	d	19 00	19 05	19 10		19 15	19 20	19 30	19 35	19 45	19 50	20 00	20 05			23 05	23 15	23 20	23 30	23 35	23 45	23 50	23 59		
James Street	d	19 02	19 07	19 12		19 17	19 22	19 32	19 37	19 47	19 52	20 02	20 07			23 07	23 17	23 22	23 32	23 37	23 47	23 52	00 02		
Hamilton Square	d	19 05	19 10	19 15		19 20	19 25	19 35	19 40	19 50	19 55	20 05	20 10			23 10	23 20	23 25	23 35	23 40	23 50	23 55	00a05		
Conway Park	d		19 12	19 17			19 27		19 42		19 57		20 12			23 12		23 27		23 42		23 57			
Birkenhead Park	d		19 14	19 19			19 29		19 44		19 59		20 14			23 14		23 29		23 44		23 59			
Birkenhead North	d		19 17	19 22			19 32		19 47		20 02		20 17			23 17		23 32		23 47		00 02			
Wallasey Village	d		19 22				19 37				20 07							23 37				00 07			
Wallasey Grove Road	d		19 23				19 38				20 08							23 38				00 08			
New Brighton	a		19 28				19 43				20 13							23 43				00 13			
Bidston	d			19 25					19 50				20 20			23 20				23 50					
Leasowe	d			19 27					19 52				20 22			23 22				23 52					
Moreton (Merseyside)	d			19 29					19 54				20 24			23 24				23 54					
Meols	d			19 33					19 58				20 28			23 28				23 58					
Manor Road	d			19 35					20 00				20 30			23 30				23 59					
Hoylake	d			19 37					20 02				20 32			23 32				00 02					
West Kirby	a			19 42					20 07				20 37			23 37				00 07					
Birkenhead Central	d	19 07				19 22		19 37		19 52		20 07					23 22		23 37		23 52				
Green Lane	d	19 09				19 24		19 39		19 54		20 09					23 24		23 39		23 54				
Rock Ferry	d	19 12				19 27		19 42		19 57		20 12					23 27		23 42		23 57				
Bebington	d	19 14				19 29		19 44		19 59		20 14					23 29		23 44		23 59				
Port Sunlight	d	19 16				19 31		19 46		20 01		20 16					23 31		23 46		00 01				
Spital	d	19 18				19 33		19 48		20 03		20 18					23 33		23 48		00 03				
Bromborough Rake	d	19 20				19 35		19 50		20 05		20 20					23 35		23 50		00 05				
Bromborough	d	19 22				19 37		19 52		20 07		20 22					23 37		23 52		00 07				
Eastham Rake	d	19 25				19 40		19 55		20 10		20 25					23 40		23 55		00 10				
Hooton	d	19 27				19 42		19 57		20 12		20 27					23 42		23 57		00 12				
Little Sutton	d					19 46				20 16							23 46				00 16				
Overpool	d					19 48				20 18							23 48				00 18				
Ellesmere Port	a					19 52				20 22							23 52				00 22				
Capenhurst	d	19 32						20 02				20 32							00 02						
Bache	d	19 37						20 07				20 37							00 07						
Chester	a	19 41						20 11				20 41							00 11						

For general notes see front of timetable
For details of catering facilities see Directory of Train Operators

Table 106

Liverpool and Birkenhead → New Brighton, West Kirby, Ellesmere Port and Chester

Network Diagram - see first page of Table 101

		ME	ME		ME	ME	ME	ME	ME	ME	ME	ME			ME	ME	ME	ME	ME		ME	ME	ME		
Moorfields 10	d	07 56	08 01		08 11	08 16	08 26	08 31	08 41	08 46	08 56	09 01			23 01	23 11	23 16	23 26	23 31		23 41	23 46	23 56		
Liverpool Lime Street 10	d	07 58	08 03		08 13	08 18	08 28	08 33	08 43	08 48	08 58	09 03			23 03	23 13	23 18	23 28	23 33		23 43	23 48	23 58		
Liverpool Central 10	d	06 00	08 05		08 15	08 20	08 30	08 35	08 45	08 50	09 00	09 05			23 05	23 15	23 20	23 30	23 35		23 45	23 50	23 59		
James Street	d	08 02	08 07		08 17	08 22	08 32	08 37	08 47	08 52	09 02	09 07			23 07	23 17	23 22	23 32	23 37		23 47	23 52	00 02		
Hamilton Square	d	08 05	08 10		08 20	08 25	08 35	08 40	08 50	08 55	09 05	09 10			23 10	23 20	23 25	23 35	23 40		23 50	23 55	00a05		
Conway Park	d		08 12			08 27		08 42		08 57		09 12			23 12		23 27		23 42			23 57			
Birkenhead Park	d		08 14			08 29		08 44		08 59		09 14			23 14		23 29		23 44			23 59			
Birkenhead North	d		08 17			08 32		08 47		09 02		09 17			23 17		23 32		23 47			00 02			
Wallasey Village	d					08 37				09 07							23 37					00 07			
Wallasey Grove Road	d					08 38				09 08							23 38					00 08			
New Brighton	a					08 43				09 13			and at				23 43					00 13			
Bidston	d		08 20					08 50				09 20			23 20				23 50						
Leasowe	d		08 22					08 52				09 22	the same		23 22				23 52						
Moreton (Merseyside)	d		08 24					08 54				09 24			23 24				23 54						
Meols	d		08 28					08 58				09 26	minutes		23 26				23 58						
Manor Road	d		08 30					09 00				09 30			23 30				23 59						
Hoylake	d		08 32					09 02				09 32	past		23 32				00 02						
West Kirby	a		08 37					09 07				09 37	each		23 37				00 07						
Birkenhead Central	d	08 07			08 22		08 37		08 52		09 07					23 22		23 37			23 52				
Green Lane	d	08 09			08 24		08 39		08 54		09 09		hour until			23 24		23 39			23 54				
Rock Ferry	d	08 12			08 27		08 42		08 57		09 12					23 27		23 42			23 57				
Bebington	d	08 14			08 29		08 44		08 59		09 14					23 29		23 44			23 59				
Port Sunlight	d	08 16			08 31		08 46		09 01		09 16					23 31		23 46			00 01				
Spital	d	08 18			08 33		08 48		09 03		09 18					23 33		23 48			00 03				
Bromborough Rake	d	08 20			08 35		08 50		09 05		09 20					23 35		23 50			00 05				
Bromborough	d	08 22			08 37		08 52		09 07		09 22					23 37		23 52			00 07				
Eastham Rake	d	08 25			08 40		08 55		09 10		09 25					23 40		23 55			00 10				
Hooton	d	08 27			08 42		08 57		09 12		09 27					23 42		23 57			00 12				
Little Sutton	d				08 46				09 16							23 46					00 16				
Overpool	d				08 48				09 18							23 48					00 18				
Ellesmere Port	a				08 52				09 22							23 52					00 22				
Capenhurst	d	08 32					09 02				09 32							00 02							
Bache	d	08 37					09 07				09 37							00 07							
Chester	a	08 41					09 11				09 41							00 11							

For general notes see front of timetable
For details of catering facilities see Directory of Train Operators

Chester, Ellesmere Port, West Kirby and New Brighton → Birkenhead and Liverpool

Network Diagram - see first page of Table 101

Miles	Miles	Miles	Miles			ME	ME	ME	ME	ME	ME	ME	ME	ME	ME	ME	ME	ME		ME	ME	ME	ME	ME	ME	ME
0	—	—	—	**Chester**	d									06 15				06 45							07 15	
1½	—	—	—	Bache	d									06 18				06 48							07 18	
5¼	—	—	—	Capenhurst	d									06 24				06 54							07 24	
—	0	—	—	**Ellesmere Port**	d						06 04				06 34							07 04				
—	1½	—	—	Overpool	d						06 07				06 37							07 07				
—	2½	—	—	Little Sutton	d						06 09				06 39							07 09				
8¼	4	—	—	Hooton	d		05 44			05 59	06 14			06 29	06 44			06 59				07 14			07 29	
9¼	—	—	—	Eastham Rake	d		05 46			06 01	06 16			06 31	06 46			07 01				07 16			07 31	
9¾	—	—	—	Bromborough	d		05 48			06 03	06 18			06 33	06 48			07 03				07 18			07 33	
10½	—	—	—	Bromborough Rake	d		05 50			06 05	06 20			06 35	06 50			07 05				07 20			07 35	
11¼	—	—	—	Spital	d		05 52			06 07	06 22			06 37	06 52			07 07				07 22			07 37	
11¾	—	—	—	Port Sunlight	d		05 54			06 09	06 24			06 39	06 54			07 09				07 24			07 39	
12¾	—	—	—	Bebington	d		05 56			06 11	06 26			06 41	06 56			07 11				07 26			07 41	
13¾	—	—	—	Rock Ferry	d	05 44	05 59			06 14	06 29			06 44	06 59			07 14				07 29			07 44	
14½	—	—	—	Green Lane	d	05 47	06 02			06 17	06 32			06 47	07 02			07 17				07 32			07 47	
15	—	—	—	Birkenhead Central	d	05 49	06 04			06 19	06 34			06 49	07 04			07 19				07 34			07 49	
—	—	0	—	**West Kirby**	d				05 51				06 21				06 51				07 06			07 21		
—	—	1	—	Hoylake	d				05 54				06 24				06 54				07 09			07 24		
—	—	1¾	—	Manor Road	d				05 56				06 26				06 56				07 11			07 26		
—	—	3	—	Meols	d				05 58				06 28				06 58				07 13			07 28		
—	—	4¼	—	Moreton (Merseyside)	d				06 01				06 31				07 01				07 16			07 31		
—	—	4¾	—	Leasowe	d				06 03				06 33				07 03				07 18			07 33		
—	—	5¾	—	Bidston	d				06 06				06 36				07 06				07 21			07 36		
—	—	—	0	**New Brighton**	d			05 53				06 23				06 53				07 08			07 23			07 38
—	—	—	1¼	Wallasey Grove Road	d			05 57				06 27				06 57				07 12			07 27			07 42
—	—	—	1½	Wallasey Village	d			05 59				06 29				06 59				07 14			07 29			07 44
—	—	6½	3	Birkenhead North	d			06 04	06 09			06 34	06 39			07 04	07 09			07 19	07 24		07 34	07 39		07 49
—	—	7¼	3¾	Birkenhead Park	d			06 06	06 11			06 36	06 41			07 06	07 11			07 21	07 26		07 36	07 41		07 51
—	—	8¼	4½	Conway Park	d			06 09	06 14			06 39	06 44			07 09	07 14			07 24	07 29		07 39	07 44		07 54
15½	—	8¾	5	Hamilton Square	d	05 51	06 06	06 11	06 16	06 21	06 36	06 41	06 46	06 51	07 06	07 11	07 16	07 21		07 26	07 31	07 36	07 41	07 46	07 51	07 56
16¾	—	9¾	6¼	James Street	d	05 54	06 09	06 14	06 19	06 24	06 39	06 44	06 49	06 54	07 09	07 14	07 19	07 24		07 29	07 34	07 39	07 44	07 49	07 54	07 59
17¼	—	10¼	7¼	**Moorfields** 10	a	05 56	06 11	06 16	06 21	06 26	06 41	06 46	06 51	06 56	07 11	07 16	07 21	07 26		07 31	07 36	07 41	07 46	07 51	07 56	08 01
17¾	—	10¾	8¼	**Liverpool Lime Street** 10	a	05 58	06 13	06 18	06 23	06 28	06 43	06 48	06 53	06 58	07 13	07 18	07 23	07 28		07 33	07 38	07 43	07 48	07 53	07 58	08 03
18½	—	11¼	8¾	**Liverpool Central** 10	a	06 00	06 15	06 20	06 25	06 30	06 45	06 50	06 55	07 00	07 15	07 20	07 25	07 30		07 35	07 40	07 45	07 50	07 55	08 00	08 05

		ME SX	ME	ME SO	ME SX	ME	ME SX	ME	ME		ME	ME SX	ME	ME SO	ME SX	ME	ME SX	ME	ME	ME	ME SX	ME	ME		ME	ME SX
Chester	d				07 30				07 45						08 00				08 15							
Bache	d				07 33				07 48						08 03				08 18							
Capenhurst	d				07 39				07 54						08 09				08 24							
Ellesmere Port	d	07 27		07 34			07 42					07 57		08 04			08 12						08 34			
Overpool	d	07 30		07 37			07 45					08 00		08 07			08 15						08 37			
Little Sutton	d	07 32		07 39			07 47					08 02		08 09			08 17						08 39			
Hooton	d	07 36		07 44	07 44		07 51		07 59			08 06		08 14	08 14		08 21		08 29		08 36		08 44			08 51
Eastham Rake	d	07 38		07 46	07 46		07 53		08 01			08 08		08 16	08 16		08 23		08 31		08 38		08 46			08 53
Bromborough	d	07 41		07 48	07 48		07 56		08 03			08 11		08 18	08 18		08 26		08 33		08 41		08 48			08 56
Bromborough Rake	d	07 43		07 50	07 50		07 58		08 05			08 13		08 20	08 20		08 28		08 35		08 43		08 50			08 58
Spital	d	07 45		07 52	07 52		08 00		08 07			08 15		08 22	08 22		08 30		08 37		08 45		08 52			09 00
Port Sunlight	d	07 47		07 54	07 54		08 02		08 09			08 17		08 24	08 24		08 32		08 39		08 47		08 54			09 02
Bebington	d	07 49		07 56	07 56		08 04		08 11			08 19		08 26	08 26		08 34		08 41		08 49		08 56			09 04
Rock Ferry	d	07 52		07 59	07 59		08 07		08 14			08 22		08 29	08 29		08 37		08 44		08 52		08 59			09 07
Green Lane	d	07 54		08 02	08 02		08 09		08 17			08 24		08 32	08 32		08 39		08 47		08 54		09 02			09 09
Birkenhead Central	d	07 57		08 04	08 04		08 12		08 19			08 27		08 34	08 34		08 42		08 49		08 57		09 04			09 12
West Kirby	d		07 36					07 51					08 06					08 21				08 36				
Hoylake	d		07 39					07 54					08 09					08 24				08 39				
Manor Road	d		07 41					07 56					08 11					08 26				08 41				
Meols	d		07 43					07 58					08 13					08 28				08 43				
Moreton (Merseyside)	d		07 46					08 01					08 16					08 31				08 46				
Leasowe	d		07 48					08 03					08 18					08 33				08 48				
Bidston	d		07 51					08 06					08 21					08 36				08 51				
New Brighton	d					07 53					08 08					08 23				08 38					08 53	
Wallasey Grove Road	d					07 57					08 12					08 27				08 42					08 57	
Wallasey Village	d					07 59					08 14					08 29				08 44					08 59	
Birkenhead North	d		07 54			08 04		08 09			08 19		08 24			08 34		08 39		08 49		08 54			09 04	
Birkenhead Park	d		07 56			08 06		08 11			08 21		08 26			08 36		08 41		08 51		08 56			09 06	
Conway Park	d		07 59			08 09		08 14			08 24		08 29			08 39		08 44		08 54		08 59			09 09	
Hamilton Square	d	07 59	08 01	08 06	08 06	08 11	08 14	08 16	08 21		08 26	08 29	08 31	08 36	08 36	08 41	08 44	08 46	08 51	08 56	08 59	09 01	09 06		09 11	09 14
James Street	d	08 02	08 04	08 09	08 09	08 14	08 17	08 19	08 24		08 29	08 32	08 34	08 39	08 39	08 44	08 47	08 49	08 54	08 59	09 02	09 04	09 09		09 14	09 17
Moorfields 10	a	08 03	08 06	08 11	08 11	08 16	08 18	08 21	08 26		08 31	08 33	08 36	08 41	08 41	08 46	08 48	08 51	08 56	09 01	09 03	09 06	09 11		09 16	09 18
Liverpool Lime Street 10	a	08 05	08 08	08 13	08 13	08 18	08 20	08 23	08 28		08 33	08 35	08 38	08 43	08 43	08 48	08 50	08 53	08 58	09 03	09 05	09 08	09 13		09 18	09 20
Liverpool Central 10	a	08 07	08 10	08 15	08 15	08 20	08 22	08 25	08 30		08 35	08 37	08 40	08 45	08 45	08 50	08 52	08 55	09 00	09 05	09 07	09 10	09 15		09 20	09 22

For general notes see front of timetable
For details of catering facilities see
Directory of Train Operators

Table 106

Mondays to Saturdays

Chester, Ellesmere Port, West Kirby and New Brighton → Birkenhead and Liverpool

Network Diagram - see first page of Table 101

			ME	ME	ME	ME	ME	ME	ME	ME	ME	ME	ME	ME	and at the same minutes past each hour until	ME		ME	ME	ME	ME	ME	ME	ME	ME
Chester	d			08 45						09 15									17 45						18 15
Bache	d			08 48						09 18									17 48						18 18
Capenhurst	d			08 54						09 24									17 54						18 24
Ellesmere Port	d						09 04						09 34									18 04			
Overpool	d						09 07						09 37									18 07			
Little Sutton	d						09 09						09 39									18 09			
Hooton	d			08 59			09 14			09 29			09 44						17 59			18 14			18 29
Eastham Rake	d			09 01			09 16			09 31			09 46						18 01			18 16			18 31
Bromborough	d			09 03			09 18			09 33			09 48						18 03			18 18			18 33
Bromborough Rake	d			09 05			09 20			09 35			09 50						18 05			18 20			18 35
Spital	d			09 07			09 22			09 37			09 52						18 07			18 22			18 37
Port Sunlight	d			09 09			09 24			09 39			09 54						18 09			18 24			18 39
Bebington	d			09 11			09 26			09 41			09 56						18 11			18 26			18 41
Rock Ferry	d			09 14			09 29			09 44			09 59						18 14			18 29			18 44
Green Lane	d			09 17			09 32			09 47			10 02						18 17			18 32			18 47
Birkenhead Central	d			09 19			09 34			09 49			10 04						18 19			18 34			18 49
West Kirby	d		08 51			09 06			09 21			09 36						17 51			18 06			18 21	
Hoylake	d		08 54			09 09			09 24			09 39						17 54			18 09			18 24	
Manor Road	d		08 56			09 11			09 26			09 41						17 56			18 11			18 26	
Meols	d		08 58			09 13			09 28			09 43						17 58			18 13			18 28	
Moreton (Merseyside)	d		09 01			09 16			09 31			09 46						18 01			18 16			18 31	
Leasowe	d		09 03			09 18			09 33			09 48						18 03			18 18			18 33	
Bidston	d		09 06			09 21			09 36			09 51						18 06			18 21			18 36	
New Brighton	d				09 08			09 23			09 38			09 53		17 53				18 08			18 23		
Wallasey Grove Road	d				09 12			09 27			09 42			09 57		17 57				18 12			18 27		
Wallasey Village	d				09 14			09 29			09 44			09 59		17 59				18 14			18 29		
Birkenhead North	d		09 09		09 19	09 24		09 34	09 39		09 49	09 54		10 04		18 04		18 09		18 19	18 24		18 34	18 39	
Birkenhead Park	d		09 11		09 21	09 26		09 36	09 41		09 51	09 56		10 06		18 06		18 11		18 21	18 26		18 36	18 41	
Conway Park	d		09 14		09 24	09 29		09 39	09 44		09 54	09 59		10 09		18 09		18 14		18 24	18 29		18 39	18 44	
Hamilton Square	d		09 16	09 21	09 26	09 31	09 36	09 41	09 46	09 51	09 56	10 01	10 06	10 11		18 11		18 16	18 21	18 26	18 31	18 36	18 41	18 46	18 51
James Street	d		09 19	09 24	09 29	09 34	09 39	09 44	09 49	09 54	09 59	10 04	10 09	10 14		18 14		18 19	18 24	18 29	18 34	18 39	18 44	18 49	18 54
Moorfields 10	a		09 21	09 26	09 31	09 36	09 41	09 46	09 51	09 56	10 01	10 06	10 11	10 16		18 16		18 21	18 26	18 31	18 36	18 41	18 46	18 51	18 56
Liverpool Lime Street 10	a		09 23	09 28	09 33	09 38	09 43	09 48	09 53	09 58	10 03	10 08	10 13	10 18		18 18		18 23	18 28	18 33	18 38	18 43	18 48	18 53	18 58
Liverpool Central 10	a		09 25	09 30	09 35	09 40	09 45	09 50	09 55	10 00	10 05	10 10	10 15	10 20		18 20		18 25	18 30	18 35	18 40	18 45	18 50	18 55	19 00

		ME	ME	ME		ME	ME	ME	ME	ME	ME	ME	ME	and at the same minutes past each hour until		ME	ME	ME	ME	ME	ME	ME	ME		
Chester	d						18 45				19 15							22 45				23 15	23 45		
Bache	d						18 48				19 18							22 48				23 18	23 48		
Capenhurst	d						18 54				19 24							22 54				23 24	23 54		
Ellesmere Port	d			18 34					19 04				19 34			22 34				23 04					
Overpool	d			18 37					19 07				19 37			22 37				23 07					
Little Sutton	d			18 39					19 09				19 39			22 39				23 09					
Hooton	d			18 44			18 59		19 14		19 29		19 44			22 44		22 59		23 14		23 29	23a59		
Eastham Rake	d			18 46			19 01		19 16		19 31		19 46			22 46		23 01		23 16		23 31			
Bromborough	d			18 48			19 03		19 18		19 33		19 48			22 48		23 03		23 18		23 33			
Bromborough Rake	d			18 50			19 05		19 20		19 35		19 50			22 50		23 05		23 20		23 35			
Spital	d			18 52			19 07		19 22		19 37		19 52			22 52		23 07		23 22		23 37			
Port Sunlight	d			18 54			19 09		19 24		19 39		19 54			22 54		23 09		23 24		23 39			
Bebington	d			18 56			19 11		19 26		19 41		19 56			22 56		23 11		23 26		23 41			
Rock Ferry	d			18 59			19 14		19 29		19 44		19 59			22 59		23 14		23 29		23 44			
Green Lane	d			19 02			19 17		19 32		19 47		20 02			23 02		23 17		23 32		23 47			
Birkenhead Central	d			19 04			19 19		19 34		19 49		20 04			23 04		23 19		23 34		23 49			
West Kirby	d		18 36					19 01				19 31							23 01						
Hoylake	d		18 39					19 04				19 34							23 04						
Manor Road	d		18 41					19 06				19 36							23 06						
Meols	d		18 43					19 08				19 38							23 08						
Moreton (Merseyside)	d		18 46					19 11				19 41							23 11						
Leasowe	d		18 48					19 13				19 43							23 13						
Bidston	d		18 51					19 16				19 46							23 16						
New Brighton	d	18 38				18 53				19 23							22 53				23 23				
Wallasey Grove Road	d	18 42				18 57				19 27							22 57				23 27				
Wallasey Village	d	18 44				18 59				19 29							22 59				23 29				
Birkenhead North	d	18 49	18 54			19 04		19 19		19 34		19 49					23 04		23 19		23 34				
Birkenhead Park	d	18 51	18 56			19 06		19 21		19 36		19 51					23 06		23 21		23 36				
Conway Park	d	18 54	18 59			19 09		19 24		19 39		19 54					23 09		23 24		23 39				
Hamilton Square	d	18 56	19 01	19 06		19 11	19 21	19 26	19 36	19 41	19 51	19 56	20 06			23 06	23 11	23 21	23 26	23 36	23 41	23 51			
James Street	d	18 59	19 04	19 09		19 14	19 24	19 29	19 39	19 44	19 54	19 59	20 09			23 09	23 14	23 24	23 29	23 39	23 44	23 54			
Moorfields 10	a	19 01	19 06	19 11		19 16	19 26	19 31	19 41	19 46	19 56	20 01	20 11			23 11	23 16	23 26	23 31	23 41	23 46	23 56			
Liverpool Lime Street 10	a	19 03	19 08	19 13		19 18	19 28	19 33	19 43	19 48	19 58	20 03	20 13			23 13	23 18	23 28	23 33	23 43	23 48	23 58			
Liverpool Central 10	a	19 05	19 10	19 15		19 20	19 30	19 35	19 45	19 50	20 00	20 05	20 15			23 15	23 20	23 30	23 35	23 45	23 50	23 59			

For general notes see front of timetable
For details of catering facilities see Directory of Train Operators

Table 106

Chester, Ellesmere Port, West Kirby and New Brighton → Birkenhead and Liverpool

Network Diagram - see first page of Table 101

		ME	ME	ME	ME	ME	ME	ME	ME	ME	ME	ME		ME	ME	ME	ME	ME	ME	ME	ME
Chester	d					07 45				08 15						22 45				23 15	23 45
Bache	d					07 48				08 18						22 48				23 18	23 48
Capenhurst	d					07 54				08 24						22 54				23 24	23 54
Ellesmere Port	d							08 04				08 34		22 34				23 04			
Overpool	d							08 07				08 37		22 37				23 07			
Little Sutton	d							08 09				08 39		22 39				23 09			
Hooton	d			07 44		07 59		08 14		08 29		08 44		22 44		22 59		23 14		23 29	23a59
Eastham Rake	d			07 46		08 01		08 16		08 31		08 46		22 46		23 01		23 16		23 31	
Bromborough	d			07 48		08 03		08 18		08 33		08 48		22 48		23 03		23 18		23 33	
Bromborough Rake	d			07 50		08 05		08 20		08 35		08 50		22 50		23 05		23 20		23 35	
Spital	d			07 52		08 07		08 22		08 37		08 52		22 52		23 07		23 22		23 37	
Port Sunlight	d			07 54		08 09		08 24		08 39		08 54	and at	22 54		23 09		23 24		23 39	
Bebington	d			07 56		08 11		08 26		08 41		08 56		22 56		23 11		23 26		23 41	
Rock Ferry	d	07 44	07 49	07 59		08 14		08 29		08 44		08 59	the same	22 59		23 14		23 29		23 44	
Green Lane	d	07 47	07 52	08 02		08 17		08 32		08 47		09 02		23 02		23 17		23 32		23 47	
Birkenhead Central	d	07 49	07 54	08 04		08 19		08 34		08 49		09 04	minutes	23 04		23 19		23 34		23 49	
West Kirby	d						08 01				08 31		past				23 01				
Hoylake	d						08 04				08 34						23 04				
Manor Road	d						08 06				08 36		each				23 06				
Meols	d						08 08				08 38						23 08				
Moreton (Merseyside)	d						08 11				08 41		hour until				23 11				
Leasowe	d						08 13				08 43						23 13				
Bidston	d						08 16				08 46						23 16				
New Brighton	d				07 53				08 23						22 53				23 23		
Wallasey Grove Road	d				07 57				08 27						22 57				23 27		
Wallasey Village	d				07 59				08 29						22 59				23 29		
Birkenhead North	d				08 04		08 19		08 34		08 49				23 04		23 19		23 34		
Birkenhead Park	d				08 06		08 21		08 36		08 51				23 06		23 21		23 36		
Conway Park	d				08 09		08 24		08 39		08 54				23 09		23 24		23 39		
Hamilton Square	d	07 51	07 56	08 06	08 11	08 21	08 26	08 36	08 41	08 51	08 56	09 06		23 06	23 11	23 21	23 26	23 36	23 41	23 51	
James Street	d	07 54	07 59	08 09	08 14	08 24	08 29	08 39	08 44	08 54	08 59	09 09		23 09	23 14	23 24	23 29	23 39	23 44	23 54	
Moorfields 10	a	07 56	08 01	08 11	08 16	08 26	08 31	08 41	08 46	08 56	09 01	09 11		23 11	23 16	23 26	23 31	23 41	23 46	23 56	
Liverpool Lime Street 10	a	07 58	08 03	08 13	08 18	08 28	08 33	08 43	08 48	08 58	09 03	09 13		23 13	23 18	23 28	23 33	23 43	23 48	23 58	
Liverpool Central 10	a	08 00	08 05	08 15	08 20	08 30	08 35	08 45	08 50	09 00	09 05	09 15		23 15	23 20	23 30	23 35	23 45	23 50	23 59	

For general notes see front of timetable
For details of catering facilities see
Directory of Train Operators

Helsby — Ellesmere Port

Mondays to Saturdays

Network Diagram - see first page of Table 101

Miles			NT	NT	NT A	NT
—	Warrington Bank Quay	81 d	06 00		15 02	
0	**Helsby**	d	06 14	06 46	15 30	16 03
2	Ince & Elton	d	06 17	06 49	15 33	16 06
2¾	Stanlow & Thornton	d	06 19	06 51	15 35	16 08
5¼	**Ellesmere Port**	a	06 27	06 57	15 41	16 14
—	Hooton	106 a	06 44	07 14	16 14	16 44
—	Liverpool Lime Street	106 a	07 13	07 43	16 43	17 13

Mondays to Saturdays

Miles			NT	NT SX	NT SO	NT	NT B
—	Liverpool Lime Street	106 d	05 48	06 13	06 13	14 43	15 13
—	Hooton	106 d	06 17	06 42	06 42	15 12	15 42
0	**Ellesmere Port**	d	06 32	07 02	07 02	15 47	16 17
2½	Stanlow & Thornton	d	06 36	07 06	07 06	15 51	16 21
3¼	Ince & Elton	d	06 39	07 09	07 09	15 54	16 24
5¼	**Helsby**	a	06 42	07 12	07 12	15 57	16 27
—	Warrington Bank Quay	81 a	07 15	07 27	07 52	16 19	16 45

For general notes see front of timetable
For details of catering facilities see
Directory of Train Operators

A From Liverpool Lime Street (Table 90)
B To Liverpool Lime Street (Table 90)

No Sunday Service

Network Diagram for Tables 114, 115

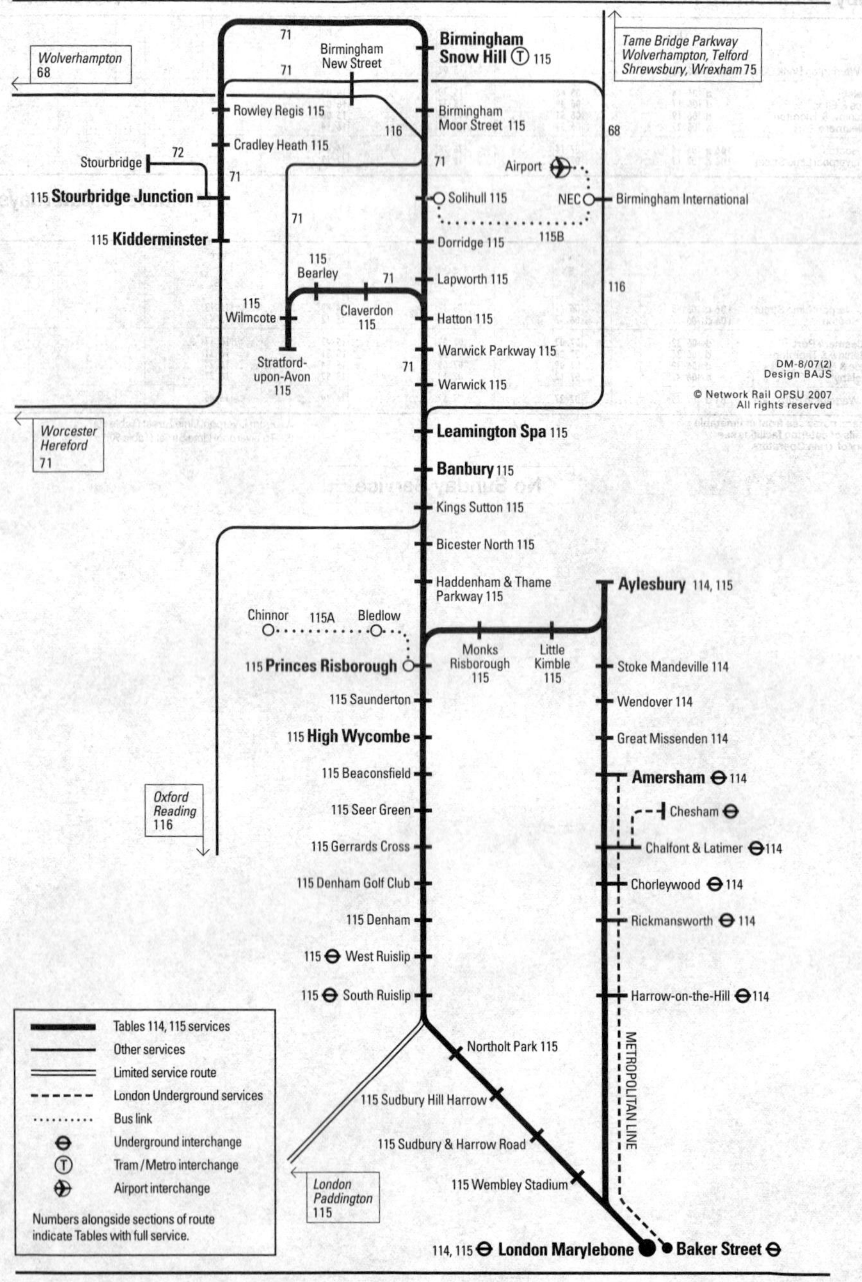

Birmingham Snow Hill 115
Wolverhampton 68
Birmingham New Street
Tame Bridge Parkway
Wolverhampton, Telford
Shrewsbury, Wrexham 75
Rowley Regis 115
Birmingham Moor Street 115
Cradley Heath 115
Stourbridge
115 Stourbridge Junction
Airport
Solihull 115
NEC
Birmingham International
115 Kidderminster
Dorridge 115
115B
115 Bearley
Lapworth 115
115 Wilmcote
Claverdon 115
Hatton 115
Warwick Parkway 115
Stratford-upon-Avon 115
Warwick 115
DM-8/07(2)
Design BAJS
© Network Rail OPSU 2007
All rights reserved
Worcester
Hereford
71
Leamington Spa 115
Banbury 115
Kings Sutton 115
Bicester North 115
Haddenham & Thame Parkway 115
Aylesbury 114, 115
Chinnor
115A
Bledlow
115 Princes Risborough
Monks Risborough 115
Little Kimble 115
Stoke Mandeville 114
115 Saunderton
Wendover 114
115 High Wycombe
Great Missenden 114
115 Beaconsfield
Amersham 114
Oxford
Reading
116
115 Seer Green
Chesham
115 Gerrards Cross
Chalfont & Latimer 114
115 Denham Golf Club
Chorleywood 114
115 Denham
Rickmansworth 114
115 West Ruislip
115 South Ruislip
Harrow-on-the-Hill 114
Tables 114, 115 services
Other services
Limited service route
London Underground services
Bus link
Underground interchange
Tram / Metro interchange
Airport interchange
Numbers alongside sections of route indicate Tables with full service.
Northolt Park 115
115 Sudbury Hill Harrow
METROPOLITAN LINE
115 Sudbury & Harrow Road
115 Wembley Stadium
London Paddington 115
114, 115 London Marylebone
Baker Street

London → Amersham and Aylesbury

Network Diagram - See first page of Table 114

Mondays to Fridays

Miles	Station		CH	CH MX	CH	CH	CH	CH	CH	CH	CH	CH	CH	CH	CH	CH	CH	CH	CH	CH	CH	CH	CH	CH	CH
0	**London Marylebone** 10	⊖ d	23p27	23p57	06 35	07 07	07 29	07 56	08 27	09 00	09 27	09 57	10 27	10 57	11 27	11 57	12 27	12 57	13 27	13 57	14 27	14 57	15 27	15 57
9	Harrow-on-the-Hill 3 §	⊖ d	23p39	00 09	06 47	07 19	07 41	08 08	08 39	09 12	09 39	10 09	10 39	11 09	11 39	12 09	12 39	13 09	13 39	14 09	14 39	15 09	15 39	16 09
17	Rickmansworth §	⊖ d	23p49	00 19	06 58	07 29	07 51	08 18	08 49	09 22	09 49	10 19	10 49	11 19	11 49	12 20	12 49	13 19	13 49	14 19	14 49	15 19	15 49	16 19
19¼	Chorleywood §	⊖ d	23p54	00 24	07 02	07 34	07 56	08 23	08 54	09 27	09 54	10 24	10 54	11 24	11 54	12 24	12 54	13 24	13 54	14 24	14 54	15 24	15 54	16 24
21½	Chalfont & Latimer §	⊖ d	23p58	00 28	07 06	07 38	08 00	08 27	08 58	09 31	09 58	10 28	10 58	11 28	11 58	12 28	12 58	13 28	13 58	14 28	14 58	15 28	15 58	16 28
23½	**Amersham** §	⊖ d	00 02	00 32	07 10	07 42	08 04	08 31	09 02	09 35	10 02	10 32	11 02	11 32	12 02	12 32	13 02	13 32	14 02	14 32	15 02	15 32	16 02	16 32
28¾	Great Missenden	d	00 08	00 38	07 17	07 48	08 10	08 37	09 08	09 41	10 08	10 38	11 08	11 38	12 08	12 39	13 08	13 38	14 08	14 38	15 08	15 38	16 08	16 38
33¼	Wendover	d	00 14	00 44	07 23	07 54	08 16	08 43	09 14	09 47	10 14	10 44	11 14	11 44	12 14	12 45	13 14	13 44	14 14	14 44	15 14	15 44	16 14	16 44
35¼	Stoke Mandeville	d	00 18	00 48	07 27	07 58	08 20	08 47	09 18	09 51	10 18	10 48	11 18	11 48	12 18	12 49	13 18	13 48	14 18	14 48	15 18	15 48	16 18	16 48
37¾	**Aylesbury**	a	00 26	00 56	07 34	08 06	08 28	08 55	09 26	09 59	10 26	10 56	11 26	11 56	12 26	12 56	13 26	13 56	14 26	14 56	15 26	15 56	16 26	16 56

Station		CH	CH	CH	CH	CH	CH	CH	CH	CH	CH	CH	CH	CH	CH	CH	CH	CH	CH	CH	CH	CH
London Marylebone 10	⊖ d	16 25	16 42	16 56	17 16	17 27	17 50	18 06	18 23	18 40	18 57	19 15	19 27	19 57	20 27	20 57	21 27	21 57	22 27	22 57	23 27	23 57
Harrow-on-the-Hill 3 §	⊖ d	16 37		17 08		17 39		18 18		18 52	19 09		19 39	20 09	20 39	21 09	21 39	22 09	22 39	23 09	23 39	00 09
Rickmansworth §	⊖ d			17 18		17 50							19 50	20 19	20 49	21 19	21 49	22 19	22 49	23 19	23 49	00 19
Chorleywood §	⊖ d	16 51		17 23		17 54		18 32		19 06	19 23		19 54	20 24	20 54	21 24	21 54	22 24	22 54	23 24	23 54	00 24
Chalfont & Latimer §	⊖ d	16 55		17 27		18 00		18 36		19 10	19 27		19 58	20 28	20 58	21 28	21 58	22 28	22 58	23 28	23 58	00 28
Amersham §	⊖ d	16 59	17 12	17 31		18 04	18 20	18 41		19 15	19 31		20 02	20 32	21 02	21 32	22 02	22 32	23 02	23 32	00 02	00 32
Great Missenden	d	17 05	17 19	17 37	17 51	18 10	18 26	18 47	18 59	19 21	19 37	19 51	20 09	20 38	21 08	21 38	22 08	22 38	23 08	23 38	00 08	00 38
Wendover	d	17 11	17 25	17 43	17 57	18 16	18 32	18 53	19 05	19 27	19 43	19 57	20 15	20 44	21 14	21 44	22 14	22 44	23 14	23 44	00 14	00 44
Stoke Mandeville	d	17 15	17 29	17 47	18 01	18 20	18 36	18 57	19 09	19 31	19 47	20 01	20 19	20 48	21 18	21 48	22 18	22 48	23 18	23 48	00 18	00 48
Aylesbury	a	17 23	17 39	17 55	18 12	18 26	18 47	19 05	19 19	19 39	19 55	20 13	20 26	20 56	21 26	21 56	22 26	22 56	23 26	23 56	00 26	00 56

Saturdays

Station		CH	CH	CH	CH	CH	CH	CH	CH	CH	CH	CH	CH	CH	CH	CH	CH	CH
London Marylebone 10	⊖ d	23p27	23p57		07 27	07 57	08 27	08 57	09 27	09 57	10 27	10 57	11 27	11 57	12 27	12 57	13 27	13 57
Harrow-on-the-Hill 3 §	⊖ d	23p39	00 09		07 39	08 09	08 39	09 09	09 39	10 09	10 39	11 09	11 39	12 09	12 39	13 09	13 39	14 09
Rickmansworth §	⊖ d	23p49	00 19		07 49	08 19	08 49	09 19	09 49	10 19	10 49	11 19	11 49	12 19	12 49	13 19	13 49	14 19
Chorleywood §	⊖ d	23p54	00 24		07 54	08 24	08 54	09 24	09 54	10 24	10 54	11 24	11 54	12 24	12 54	13 24	13 54	14 24
Chalfont & Latimer §	⊖ d	23p58	00 28		07 58	08 28	08 58	09 28	09 58	10 28	10 58	11 28	11 58	12 28	12 58	13 28	13 58	14 28
Amersham §	⊖ d	00 02	00 32	07 05	08 02	08 32	09 02	09 32	10 02	10 32	11 02	11 32	12 02	12 32	13 02	13 32	14 02	14 32
Great Missenden	d	00 08	00 38	07 11	08 08	08 38	09 08	09 38	10 08	10 38	11 08	11 38	12 08	12 38	13 08	13 38	14 08	14 38
Wendover	d	00 14	00 44	07 17	08 14	08 44	09 14	09 44	10 14	10 44	11 14	11 44	12 14	12 44	13 14	13 44	14 14	14 44
Stoke Mandeville	d	00 18	00 48	07 21	08 18	08 48	09 18	09 48	10 18	10 48	11 18	11 48	12 18	12 48	13 18	13 48	14 18	14 48
Aylesbury	a	00 26	00 56	07 29	08 26	08 56	09 26	09 56	10 26	10 56	11 26	11 56	12 26	12 56	13 26	13 56	14 26	14 56

Station		CH	CH	CH	CH	CH	CH	CH	CH	CH	CH	CH	CH	CH	CH	CH	CH
London Marylebone 10	⊖ d	14 27	14 57	15 27	15 57	16 27	16 57	17 27	17 57	18 27	18 57	19 27	19 57	20 57	21 57	22 57	23 57
Harrow-on-the-Hill 3 §	⊖ d	14 39	15 09	15 39	16 09	16 39	17 09	17 39	18 09	18 39	19 09	19 39	20 09	21 09	22 09	23 09	00 09
Rickmansworth §	⊖ d	14 49	15 19	15 49	16 19	16 49	17 19	17 49	18 19	18 49	19 19	19 49	20 19	21 19	22 19	23 19	00 19
Chorleywood §	⊖ d	14 54	15 24	15 54	16 24	16 54	17 24	17 54	18 24	18 54	19 24	19 54	20 24	21 24	22 24	23 24	00 24
Chalfont & Latimer §	⊖ d	14 58	15 28	15 58	16 28	16 58	17 28	17 58	18 28	18 58	19 28	19 58	20 28	21 28	22 28	23 28	00 28
Amersham §	⊖ d	15 02	15 32	16 02	16 32	17 02	17 32	18 02	18 32	19 02	19 32	20 02	20 32	21 32	22 32	23 32	00 32
Great Missenden	d	15 08	15 38	16 08	16 38	17 08	17 38	18 08	18 38	19 08	19 38	20 08	20 38	21 38	22 38	23 38	00 38
Wendover	d	15 14	15 44	16 14	16 44	17 14	17 44	18 14	18 44	19 14	19 44	20 14	20 44	21 44	22 44	23 44	00 44
Stoke Mandeville	d	15 18	15 48	16 18	16 48	17 18	17 48	18 18	18 48	19 18	19 48	20 18	20 48	21 48	22 48	23 48	00 48
Aylesbury	a	15 26	15 56	16 26	16 56	17 26	17 56	18 26	18 56	19 26	19 56	20 26	20 56	21 56	22 56	23 56	00 56

Sundays

Station		CH	CH	CH	CH	CH	CH	CH	CH	CH	CH	CH	CH	CH
London Marylebone 10	⊖ d		23p57		08 27	09 27	10 27	11 27	12 27	13 27	14 27		15 27	
Harrow-on-the-Hill 3 §	⊖ d		00 09		08 39	09 39	10 39	11 39	12 39	13 39	14 39		15 39	
Rickmansworth §	⊖ d		00 19		08 50	09 50	10 49	11 49	12 49	13 49	14 49		15 49	
Chorleywood §	⊖ d		00 24		08 54	09 54	10 54	11 54	12 54	13 54	14 54		15 54	
Chalfont & Latimer §	⊖ d		00 28		08 58	09 58	10 58	11 58	12 58	13 58	14 58		15 58	
Amersham §	⊖ d	00 02	00 32	08 32	09 02	10 02	11 02	12 02	13 02	14 02	15 02	15 32	16 02	16 32
Great Missenden	d	00 08	00 38	08 38	09 09	10 09	11 08	12 08	13 08	14 08	15 08	15 38	16 08	16 38
Wendover	d	00 14	00 44	08 44	09 15	10 15	11 14	12 14	13 14	14 14	15 14	15 44	16 14	16 44
Stoke Mandeville	d	00 18	00 48	08 48	09 19	10 19	11 18	12 18	13 18	14 18	15 18	15 48	16 18	16 48
Aylesbury	a	00 26	00 56	08 56	09 26	10 26	11 26	12 26	13 26	14 26	15 26	15 56	16 26	16 56

Station		CH	CH	CH	CH	CH	CH	CH	CH	CH	CH	CH	CH	CH
London Marylebone 10	⊖ d	16 27		17 27		18 27		19 27		20 27		21 27	22 27	23 27
Harrow-on-the-Hill 3 §	⊖ d	16 39		17 39		18 39		19 39		20 39		21 39	22 39	23 39
Rickmansworth §	⊖ d	16 49		17 49		18 49		19 49		20 49		21 49	22 49	23 49
Chorleywood §	⊖ d	16 54		17 54		18 54		19 54		20 54		21 54	22 54	23 54
Chalfont & Latimer §	⊖ d	16 58		17 58		18 58		19 58		20 58		21 58	22 58	23 58
Amersham §	⊖ d	17 02	17 32	18 02	18 32	19 02	19 32	20 02	20 32	21 02	21 32	22 02	23 02	00 02
Great Missenden	d	17 08	17 38	18 08	18 38	19 08	19 38	20 08	20 38	21 08	21 38	22 08	23 08	00 08
Wendover	d	17 14	17 44	18 14	18 44	19 14	19 44	20 14	20 44	21 14	21 44	22 14	23 14	00 14
Stoke Mandeville	d	17 18	17 48	18 18	18 48	19 18	19 48	20 18	20 48	21 18	21 48	22 18	23 18	00 18
Aylesbury	a	17 26	17 56	18 26	18 56	19 26	19 56	20 26	20 56	21 26	21 56	22 26	23 26	00 26

For general notes see front of timetable
For details of catering facilities see Directory of Train Operators

§ London Underground Limited (Metropolitan Line) services operate between Harrow-on-the-Hill, Rickmansworth, Chorleywood, Chalfont & Latimer and Amersham

Aylesbury and Amersham → London

Network Diagram - See first page of Table 114

Mondays to Fridays

Miles			CH	CH	CH	CH	CH	CH	CH	CH	CH	CH	CH	CH	CH	CH	CH	CH	CH	CH	CH	CH
0	**Aylesbury**	d	05 31	06 06	06 26	06 43	06 57	07 16	07 30	07 50	08 06	08 25	08 39	09 06	09 37	10 05	10 35	11 05	11 35	12 05	12 35	13 05
2¼	Stoke Mandeville	d	05 35	06 10	06 30	06 47	07 01	07 20	07 34	07 54	08 10	08 29	08 43	09 10	09 41	10 09	10 39	11 09	11 39	12 09	12 39	13 09
4¼	Wendover	d	05 39	06 14	06 34	06 51	07 05	07 24	07 38	07 58	08 14	08 33	08 47	09 14	09 45	10 13	10 43	11 13	11 43	12 13	12 43	13 13
9	Great Missenden	d	05 45	06 20	06 40	06 57	07 11	07 30	07 44	08 04	08 20	08 39	08 53	09 20	09 51	10 19	10 49	11 19	11 49	12 19	12 49	13 19
14¼	**Amersham §**	⊖ d	05 52	06 27	06 47		07 18	07 38	07 51	08 12	08 27		09 00	09 27	09 58	10 26	10 56	11 26	11 56	12 26	12 56	13 26
16¼	Chalfont & Latimer §	⊖ d		06 32	06 51		07 22		07 55		08 31		09 04	09 31	10 02	10 30	11 00	11 30	12 00	12 30	13 00	13 30
18¼	Chorleywood §	⊖ d		06 36	06 54		07 25		07 58		08 34		09 07	09 34	10 05	10 33	11 03	11 33	12 03	12 33	13 03	13 33
20¾	Rickmansworth §	⊖ d			06 59				08 03				09 12	09 39	10 10	10 38	11 08	11 38	12 08	12 38	13 08	13 38
28¾	Harrow-on-the-Hill [3] §	⊖ d	06 10	06 50	07 10		07 39		08 14		08 48		09 23	09 50	10 21	10 49	11 19	11 49	12 19	12 49	13 19	13 49
37¾	**London Marylebone [10]**	⊖ a	06 26	07 04	07 25	07 37	07 55	08 14	08 29	08 44	09 05	09 20	09 38	10 05	10 37	11 05	11 35	12 05	12 34	13 05	13 35	14 04

		CH	CH	CH	CH	CH	CH	CH	CH	CH	CH	CH	CH	CH	CH	CH	CH	CH	CH	CH
Aylesbury	d	13 35	14 05	14 35	15 05	15 35	16 05	16 35	17 05	17 35	17 55	18 26	18 45	19 15	19 35	20 05	20 35	21 05	21 35	22 35
Stoke Mandeville	d	13 39	14 09	14 39	15 09	15 39	16 09	16 39	17 09	17 39	17 59	18 30	18 49	19 19	19 39	20 09	20 39	21 09	21 39	22 39
Wendover	d	13 43	14 13	14 43	15 13	15 43	16 13	16 43	17 13	17 43	18 03	18 34	18 53	19 23	19 43	20 13	20 43	21 13	21 43	22 43
Great Missenden	d	13 49	14 19	14 49	15 19	15 49	16 19	16 49	17 19	17 49	18 09	18 40	18 59	19 29	19 49	20 19	20 49	21 19	21 49	22 49
Amersham §	⊖ d	13 56	14 26	14 56	15 26	15 56	16 26	16 56	17 26	17 56	18 16	18 47	19 06	19 36	19 56	20 26	20 56	21 26	21 56	22 56
Chalfont & Latimer §	⊖ d	14 00	14 30	15 00	15 30	16 00	16 30	17 00	17 30	18 00	18 20	18 51	19 10	19 40	20 00	20 30	21 00	21 30	22 00	23 00
Chorleywood §	⊖ d	14 03	14 33	15 03	15 33	16 03	16 33	17 03	17 33	18 03	18 23	18 54	19 13	19 43	20 03	20 33	21 03	21 33	22 03	23 03
Rickmansworth §	⊖ d	14 08	14 38	15 08	15 38	16 08	16 38	17 08	17 38	18 08	18 28	18 59	19 18	19 48	20 08	20 38	21 08	21 38	22 08	23 08
Harrow-on-the-Hill [3] §	⊖ d	14 19	14 49	15 19	15 49	16 19	16 49	17 19	17 49	18 19	18 39	19 10	19 29	19 59	20 19	20 49	21 19	21 49	22 19	23 19
London Marylebone [10]	⊖ a	14 34	15 05	15 34	16 05	16 35	17 05	17 35	18 05	18 35	18 55	19 26	19 45	20 15	20 35	21 05	21 34	22 05	22 35	23 35

Saturdays

		CH	CH	CH	CH	CH	CH	CH	CH	CH	CH	CH	CH	CH	CH	CH	CH	CH
Aylesbury	d	06 05	06 35	07 05	07 35	08 05	08 35	09 05	09 35	10 05	10 35	11 05	11 35	12 05	12 35	13 05	13 35	14 05
Stoke Mandeville	d	06 09	06 39	07 09	07 39	08 09	08 39	09 09	09 39	10 09	10 39	11 09	11 39	12 09	12 39	13 09	13 39	14 09
Wendover	d	06 13	06 43	07 13	07 43	08 13	08 43	09 13	09 43	10 13	10 43	11 13	11 43	12 13	12 43	13 13	13 43	14 13
Great Missenden	d	06 19	06 49	07 19	07 49	08 19	08 49	09 19	09 49	10 19	10 49	11 19	11 49	12 19	12 49	13 19	13 49	14 19
Amersham §	⊖ d	06 26	06a58	07 26	07 56	08 26	08 56	09 26	09 56	10 26	10 56	11 26	11 56	12 26	12 56	13 26	13 56	14 26
Chalfont & Latimer §	⊖ d	06 30		07 30	08 00	08 30	09 00	09 30	10 00	10 30	11 00	11 30	12 00	12 30	13 00	13 30	14 00	14 30
Chorleywood §	⊖ d	06 33		07 33	08 03	08 33	09 03	09 33	10 03	10 33	11 03	11 33	12 03	12 33	13 03	13 33	14 03	14 33
Rickmansworth §	⊖ d	06 38		07 38	08 08	08 38	09 08	09 38	10 08	10 38	11 08	11 38	12 08	12 38	13 08	13 38	14 08	14 38
Harrow-on-the-Hill [3] §	⊖ d	06 49		07 49	08 19	08 49	09 19	09 49	10 19	10 49	11 19	11 49	12 19	12 49	13 19	13 49	14 19	14 49
London Marylebone [10]	⊖ a	07 04		08 04	08 34	09 04	09 34	10 05	10 35	11 04	11 35	12 04	12 35	13 05	13 35	14 05	14 35	15 05

		CH	CH	CH	CH	CH	CH	CH	CH	CH	CH	CH	CH	CH	CH
Aylesbury	d	14 35	15 05	15 35	16 05	16 35	17 05	17 35	18 05	18 35	19 05	20 05	21 05	22 05	23 20
Stoke Mandeville	d	14 39	15 09	15 39	16 09	16 39	17 09	17 39	18 09	18 39	19 09	20 09	21 09	22 09	23 24
Wendover	d	14 43	15 13	15 43	16 13	16 43	17 13	17 43	18 13	18 43	19 13	20 13	21 13	22 13	23 28
Great Missenden	d	14 49	15 19	15 49	16 19	16 49	17 19	17 49	18 19	18 49	19 19	20 19	21 19	22 19	23 34
Amersham §	⊖ d	14 56	15 26	15 56	16 26	16 56	17 26	17 56	18 26	18 56	19 26	20 26	21 26	22 26	23a43
Chalfont & Latimer §	⊖ d	15 00	15 30	16 00	16 30	17 00	17 30	18 00	18 30	19 00	19 30	20 30	21 30	22 30	
Chorleywood §	⊖ d	15 03	15 33	16 03	16 33	17 03	17 33	18 03	18 33	19 03	19 33	20 33	21 33	22 33	
Rickmansworth §	⊖ d	15 08	15 38	16 08	16 38	17 08	17 38	18 08	18 38	19 08	19 38	20 38	21 38	22 38	
Harrow-on-the-Hill [3] §	⊖ d	15 19	15 49	16 19	16 49	17 19	17 49	18 19	18 49	19 19	19 49	20 49	21 49	22 49	
London Marylebone [10]	⊖ a	15 34	16 05	16 35	17 04	17 35	18 05	18 35	19 05	19 35	20 04	21 04	22 05	23 04	

Sundays

		CH	CH	CH	CH	CH	CH	CH A	CH B	CH	CH C	CH D	CH B	CH	CH	CH	CH C	CH E
Aylesbury	d	07 35	08 35	09 05	10 05	11 05	12 05	13⌇05	13⌇05	14 05	15⌇05	15⌇05	15⌇05	15 35	16 05	16 35	17⌇05	17⌇05
Stoke Mandeville	d	07 39	08 39	09 09	10 09	11 09	12 09	13⌇09	13⌇09	14 09	15⌇09	15⌇09	15⌇09	15 39	16 09	16 39	17⌇09	17⌇09
Wendover	d	07 43	08 43	09 13	10 13	11 13	12 13	13⌇13	13⌇13	14 13	15⌇13	15⌇13	15⌇13	15 43	16 13	16 43	17⌇13	17⌇13
Great Missenden	d	07 49	08 49	09 19	10 19	11 19	12 19	13⌇19	13⌇19	14 19	15⌇19	15⌇19	15⌇19	15 49	16 19	16 49	17⌇19	17⌇19
Amersham §	⊖ d	07 56	08 56	09 26	10 26	11 26	12 26	13⌇26	13⌇26	14 26	15⌇26	15⌇26	15⌇26	15a58	16 26	16a58	17⌇26	17⌇26
Chalfont & Latimer §	⊖ d	08 00	09 00	09 30	10 30	11 30	12 30	13⌇30	13⌇30	14 30	15⌇30	15⌇30	15⌇30		16 30		17⌇30	17⌇30
Chorleywood §	⊖ d	08 03	09 03	09 33	10 33	11 33	12 33	13⌇33	13⌇33	14 33	15⌇33	15⌇33	15⌇33		16 33		17⌇33	17⌇33
Rickmansworth §	⊖ d	08 08	09 08	09 38	10 38	11 38	12 38	13⌇38	13⌇38	14 38	15⌇38	15⌇38	15⌇38		16 38		17⌇38	17⌇38
Harrow-on-the-Hill [3] §	⊖ d	08 19	09 19	09 49	10 49	11 49	12 49	13⌇49	13⌇49	14 49	15⌇49	15⌇49	15⌇49		16 49		17⌇49	17⌇49
London Marylebone [10]	⊖ a	08 34	09 34	10 04	11 04	12 05	13 04	14⌇05	14⌇06	15 04	16⌇05	16⌇06	16⌇07		17 04		18⌇05	18⌇07

		CH	CH	CH	CH C	CH E	CH	CH C	CH E	CH	CH	CH	CH	CH
Aylesbury	d	17 35	18 05	18 35	19⌇05	19⌇05	19 35	20⌇05	20⌇05	20 35	21 05	21 35	22 05	22 35
Stoke Mandeville	d	17 39	18 09	18 39	19⌇09	19⌇09	19 39	20⌇09	20⌇09	20 39	21 09	21 39	22 09	22 39
Wendover	d	17 43	18 13	18 43	19⌇13	19⌇13	19 43	20⌇13	20⌇13	20 43	21 13	21 43	22 13	22 43
Great Missenden	d	17 49	18 19	18 49	19⌇19	19⌇19	19 49	20⌇19	20⌇19	20 49	21 19	21 49	22 19	22 49
Amersham §	⊖ d	17a58	18 26	18a58	19⌇26	19⌇26	19a58	20⌇26	20⌇26	20a58	21 26	21a58	22a28	22 56
Chalfont & Latimer §	⊖ d		18 30		19⌇30	19⌇30		20⌇30	20⌇30		21 30			23 00
Chorleywood §	⊖ d		18 33		19⌇33	19⌇33		20⌇33	20⌇33		21 33			23 03
Rickmansworth §	⊖ d		18 38		19⌇38	19⌇38		20⌇38	20⌇38		21 38			23 08
Harrow-on-the-Hill [3] §	⊖ d		18 49		19⌇49	19⌇49		20⌇49	20⌇49		21 49			23 19
London Marylebone [10]	⊖ a		19 05		20⌇04	20⌇06		21⌇04	21⌇07		22 04			23 34

For general notes see front of timetable
For details of catering facilities see Directory of Train Operators

§ London Underground Limited (Metropolitan Line) services operate between Harrow-on-the-Hill, Rickmansworth, Chorleywood, Chalfont & Latimer and Amersham

A Until 27 January and from 30 March
B 3 February to 23 March
C Until 27 January
D From 30 March
E From 3 February

London → High Wycombe, Aylesbury, Banbury, Stratford-upon-Avon, Birmingham Snow Hill and Kidderminster

Network Diagram - See first page of Table 114

Miles	Miles	Miles			CH MX	CH MO A	CH MO B	CH MX	CH MX	CH MX	CH MO	CH MO	CH MX	LM C	CH	CH	CH	CH	CH	CH	CH	CH	CH	CH	CH
0	—	—	**London Marylebone 10**	⊖ d	22p10	22p45	22p45	23p10	23p30	23p54	23p45		00 10				06 00	06 27		06 50	06 54	07 20	07 23	07 26	
—	—	0	**London Paddington 15**	⊖ d																					
6½	—	—	Wembley Stadium	d		22p54	22p54	23p19	23p39		23p54		00 19				06 09	06 36			07 03		07 32	07 35	
8	—	—	Sudbury & Harrow Road	d																					
8¾	—	—	Sudbury Hill Harrow	d																				07 39	
9¾	—	—	Northolt Park	d		22p59	22p59		23p44		00 01		00 24				06 14	06 41						07 42	
11½	—	—	South Ruislip §	⊖ d		23p03	23p03		23p48		00 03		00 28				06 18	06 45						07 45	
13¼	—	12	West Ruislip 3 §	⊖ d		23p06	23p06		23p51		00 06		00 31					06 48			07 12			07 49	
16	—	—	Denham	d		23p11	23p11		23p56		00 11		00 36				06 24	06 53			07 17			07 53	
17	—	—	Denham Golf Club	d		23p13	23p13		23p58		00 13		00 38					06 55						07 56	
18¾	—	—	Gerrards Cross 1	d	22p31	23p16	23p16	23p33	00 01	00 15	00 16		00 41				06 28	06 58			07 21		07 46	07 59	
21¼	—	—	Seer Green	d			23p21		00 06		00 21		00 46				06 33				07 26		07 50		
23	—	—	Beaconsfield	d	22p37	23p22	23p24	23p39	00 09	00 21	00 24		00 49				06 36	07 04			07 29		07 54	08 05	
27¾	—	—	**High Wycombe 1**	d	22p43	23p29	23p30	23p45	00 15	00 28	00 30		00 55			06 10	06 42	07a14		07 20	07a38	07 50	08 00	08a15	
32¾	—	—	Saunderton	d		23p35	23p37		00 22	00 34	00 37		01 02			06 16	06 49						08 07		
36	0	—	**Princes Risborough 2**	d	22p54	23p41	23p43	23p56	00 27	00 41	00 43	00 48	01 07			06 21	06 55		07 08	07 31		08 00	08 12		08 18
—	1½	—	Monks Risborough	d					00 31			00 51	01 11						07 11						08 21
—	3	—	Little Kimble	d					00 34			00 55	01 14						07 15						08 25
—	7½	—	**Aylesbury**	a					00 48			01 05	01 28						07 25						08 36
41¾	—	—	Haddenham & Thame Parkway	d	23p01	23p48	23p50	00 03		00 47	00 50					06 28	07 02			07 37		08 06			
54¾	—	—	**Bicester North 3**	a	23p12	00 01	00 02	00 16		00 59	01 03					06 42	07 15			07 48		08 18	08 28		
—	—	—		d	23p12	00 02	00 04	00 16		01 00	01 03					06 43	07 15			07 49		08 19	08 28		
65¼	—	—	Kings Sutton	d		00 14	00 16	00 30								06 56	07 29						08 39		
68¾	—	—	**Banbury**	d	23p29	00a23	00a25	00a42		01a21	01a23					07 02	07a37			08 05		08 35	08a50		
88¾	—	0	**Leamington Spa 8**	d	23p48										06 55	07 22				08 24		08 53			
90¾	—	2	Warwick	d	23p53										06 58	07 26				08 28		08 57			
92	—	3¼	Warwick Parkway	d	23p56										07 01	07 30				08 32		09 01			
94¾	—	6	Hatton	d											07 07	07 34						09 07			
—	—	7¾	Claverdon	d										06x36	07 12										
—	—	10	Bearley	d										06x40	07 17										
—	—	11½	Wilmcote	d										06 44	07 20										
—	—	15¼	**Stratford-upon-Avon**	a										06 48	07 30										
99	—	—	Lapworth	a																		09 12			
101½	—	—	Dorridge	a	00 07											07 42				08 42		09 16			
104¾	—	—	Solihull	a	00 12											07 50				08 48		09 20			
111¼	—	—	**Birmingham Moor Street**	a	00 23											08 03				08 59		09 32			
112	—	—	**Birmingham Snow Hill**	a	00 31											08 11				09 07		09 41			
—	—	—	Rowley Regis	a																					
—	—	—	Cradley Heath	a																					
—	—	—	**Stourbridge Junction 2**	a																					
—	—	—	**Kidderminster**	a																					

		CH	CH	CH	CH	CH	CH	CH	CH	CH	CH	CH	CH	CH	CH	CH	CH		CH	CH	CH	CH	CH	CH	CH
London Marylebone 10	⊖ d		07 50	07 53	08 00	08 20	08 24		08 31	08 50	08 54	09 04	09 20		09 24	09 30	09 50		09 54	10 00	10 20		10 24	10 30	10 50
London Paddington 15	⊖ d																								
Wembley Stadium	d				08 09				08 40			09 13				09 40				10 09				10 39	
Sudbury & Harrow Road	d																								
Sudbury Hill Harrow	d				08 13				08 44							09 44								10 43	
Northolt Park	d						08 37									09 46				10 14				10 46	
South Ruislip §	⊖ d				08 18							09 21								10 18					
West Ruislip 3 §	⊖ d				08 21				08 51							09 51								10 51	
Denham	d				08 26				08 55			09 26				09 56				10 24				10 56	
Denham Golf Club	d								08 58							09 58								10 58	
Gerrards Cross 1	d			08 14	08 30		08 47		09 01			09 31			09 45	10 01			10 15	10 28			10 45	11 01	
Seer Green	d			08 19	08 35		08 51					09 35				10 06				10 33				11 06	
Beaconsfield	d			08 22	08 38		08 54		09 07			09 39			09 51	10 09			10 21	10 36			10 51	11 09	
High Wycombe 1	d		08 20	08 29	08a47	08 50	09 01		09a16	09 20	09 25	09a48	09 50		09 58	10a19	10 20		10 28	10a45	10 50		10 58	11a18	
Saunderton	d			08 35			09 07								10 04								11 04		
Princes Risborough 2	d			08 41		09 01	09 13	09 17			09 35		10 01	10 06	10a13				10 37		11 01	11 06	11 10		
Monks Risborough	d							09 20						10 09								11 09			
Little Kimble	d							09 24						10 13								11 13			
Aylesbury	a							09 35						10 24								11 24			
Haddenham & Thame Parkway	d			08 48		09 07	09 19				09 42		10 07						10 44		11 07		11 16		
Bicester North 3	a			09 06		09 18	09 36				09 55		10 18						11 01		11 18		11 34		11 38
	d					09 19					09 55		10 19								11 19				11 39
Kings Sutton	d										10 08														
Banbury	d		08 56			09 35				09 56	10 14		10 35				10 56				11 35				11 56
Leamington Spa 8	d	09 04	09 14			09 54				10 14	10 34		10 54				11 14				11 54				12 15
Warwick	d	09 07	09 19			09 58				10 19	10 38		10 59				11 19				11 59				12 19
Warwick Parkway	d	09 10	09 22			10 02				10 22			11 02				11 22				12 02				12 23
Hatton	d	09 16				10 07					10 45										12 07				
Claverdon	d	09 21																							
Bearley	d										10 53														
Wilmcote	d										10 57														
Stratford-upon-Avon	a	09 37									11 08														
Lapworth	a					10 12															12 13				
Dorridge	a		09 33			10 16				10 33			11 13				11 33				12 17				12 33
Solihull	a		09 38			10 22				10 38			11 18				11 38				12 22				12 39
Birmingham Moor Street	a		09 50			10 33				10 51			11 30				11 50				12 34				12 51
Birmingham Snow Hill	a		10 01			10 41				11 01			11 41				12 01				12 42				13 02
Rowley Regis	a																								
Cradley Heath	a																								
Stourbridge Junction 2	a																								
Kidderminster	a																								

For general notes see front of timetable
For details of catering facilities see Directory of Train Operators

§ London Underground Limited (Central Line) also operate services between South Ruislip and West Ruislip at frequent intervals

A From 31 March
B Until 24 March
C From Birmingham Snow Hill (Table 71)

London → High Wycombe, Aylesbury, Banbury, Stratford-upon-Avon, Birmingham Snow Hill and Kidderminster

Network Diagram - See first page of Table 114

Station		CH	CH	CH	CH	CH	CH	CH	CH	CH	CH	CH	CH	CH	CH	CH	CH	CH	CH	CH	CH	CH	CH	CH	CH
London Marylebone 10	⊖ d	10 54	11 00	11 20			11 30	11 50	11 54	12 00	12 20		12 24	12 30	12 50	12 54	13 00	13 20		13 24	13 30	13 50	13 54	14 00	14 20
London Paddington 15	⊖ d					11 12																			
Wembley Stadium	d		11 09				11 39			12 09				12 39			13 09				13 39			14 09	
Sudbury & Harrow Road	d																								
Sudbury Hill Harrow	d						11 43							12 43							13 43				
Northolt Park	d		11 14				11 46			12 14				12 46			13 14				13 46			14 14	
South Ruislip §	⊖ d		11 18							12 18							13 18							14 18	
West Ruislip 3 §	⊖ d						11 51							12 51							13 51				
Denham	d		11 24				11 56			12 24				12 56			13 24				13 56			14 24	
Denham Golf Club	d						11 58							12 58							13 58				
Gerrards Cross 1	d	11 15	11 28			11 45	12 01		12 15	12 28			12 45	13 01		13 15	13 28			13 45	14 01		14 15	14 28	
Seer Green	d		11 33				12 06			12 33				13 06			13 33				14 06			14 33	
Beaconsfield	d	11 21	11 36			11 51	12 09		12 21	12 36			12 51	13 09		13 21	13 36			13 51	14 09		14 21	14 36	
High Wycombe 1	d	11 28	11a45	11 50		11 58	12a18		12 28	12a45	12 50		12 58	13a18		13 28	13a45	13 50		13 58	14a18		14 28	14a45	14 50
Saunderton	d					12 04							13 04							14 04					
Princes Risborough 2	d	11 38		12 01	12 06	12a13			12 37		13 00	13 06	13 10			13 38		14 01	14 08	14a13			14 38		15 01
Monks Risborough	d				12 09							13 09							14 11						
Little Kimble	d				12 13							13 13							14 15						
Aylesbury	a				12 24							13 24							14 26						
Haddenham & Thame Parkway	d	11 45		12 07					12 44		13 06		13 16			13 45		14 07					14 45		15 07
Bicester North 3	a	11 58		12 18				12 39	13 01		13 18		13 34		13 39	13 58		14 18				14 39	15 01		15 18
	d	11 59		12 19				12 39			13 19				13 39	13 59		14 19				14 39			15 19
Kings Sutton	d	12 12														14 12									
Banbury	d	12 17		12 35				12 56			13 35				13 56	14 17		14 35				14 56			15 35
Leamington Spa 8	d	12 38		12 54				13 14			13 54				14 15	14 38		14 54				15 15			15 54
Warwick	d	12 42		12 59				13 19			13 59				14 19	14 42		14 59				15 19			15 59
Warwick Parkway	d			13 02				13 22			14 02				14 23			15 02				15 23			16 02
Hatton	d	12 49									14 07					14 49									16 07
Claverdon	d	12 54																							
Bearley	d	12 59														14 57									
Wilmcote	d																								
Stratford-upon-Avon	a	13 11														15 09									
Lapworth	a										14 13														16 13
Dorridge	a			13 13				13 33			14 17				14 33			15 13				15 33			16 17
Solihull	a			13 20				13 38			14 22				14 39			15 20				15 39			16 22
Birmingham Moor Street	a			13 31				13 50			14 34				14 51			15 33				15 50			16 34
Birmingham Snow Hill	a			13 41				14 01			14 42				15 02			15 41				16 01			16 42
Rowley Regis	a																								
Cradley Heath	a																								
Stourbridge Junction 2	a																								
Kidderminster	a																								

Station		CH	CH	CH	CH	CH	CH	CH	CH		CH	CH	CH	CH	CH	CH	CH	CH	CH	CH	CH	CH	CH	CH	CH
																								A	
														(trolley)					(trolley)					(trolley)	
London Marylebone 10	⊖ d		14 24	14 30	14 50	14 54	15 00	15 20			15 24	15 30	15 42	16 00	16 03	16 06	16 13	16 17	16 30		16 34	16 38	16 48	17 00	17 03
London Paddington 15	⊖ d																								
Wembley Stadium	d			14 39			15 09					15 39						16 26				16 47			
Sudbury & Harrow Road	d																	16 29							
Sudbury Hill Harrow	d			14 43								15 43						16 32							
Northolt Park	d			14 46			15 14					15 46						16 35				16 52			
South Ruislip §	⊖ d						15 18									16 21						16 56			
West Ruislip 3 §	⊖ d			14 51								15 51					16 30						17 05		
Denham	d			14 56			15 24					15 56					16 34					17 02			
Denham Golf Club	d			14 58													16 36								
Gerrards Cross 1	d		14 45	15 01		15 15	15 28				15 48	16 00	16 03			16 29	16 40	16a48				17 06	17 11		
Seer Green	d			15 06			15 33				15 53						16 44					17 11			
Beaconsfield	d		14 51	15 09		15 21	15 36				15 56	16 06	16 09			16 35	16 48					17 14	17 18		
High Wycombe 1	d		14 58	15a18		15 28	15a45	15 50			16 02	16a15	16 17		16 32	16 41	16a57				17 04	17 20	17a27		17 33
Saunderton	d		15 04								16 09					16 48									
Princes Risborough 2	d	15 06	15 10			15 38		16 00	16 05		16a21		16 26		16 43	16a57				17 00	17 14	17a33			17 44
Monks Risborough	d	15 09							16 08											17 03					
Little Kimble	d	15 13							16 12											17 07					
Aylesbury	a	15 24							16 23											17 18					
Haddenham & Thame Parkway	d		15 16			15 45		16 07					16 33		16 49						17 21				17 50
Bicester North 3	a		15 34		15 38	15 58		16 18					16 50		17 00						17 32				18 01
	d				15 39	15 59		16 19							17 01						17 32				18 01
Kings Sutton	d					16 12									17 12										18 14
Banbury	d				15 56	16 17		16 35						17 03	17a25				17 34		17 49			18 03	18a24
Leamington Spa 8	d				16 14	16 38		16 54						17 22					17 52		18 07			18 23	
Warwick	d				16 19	16 42		16 58											17 57						
Warwick Parkway	d				16 22			17 02						17 28					18 00		18 13			18 29	
Hatton	d					16 49															18 19				
Claverdon	d					16 54																			
Bearley	d					16 59																			
Wilmcote	d					17 02															18 30				
Stratford-upon-Avon	a					17 12															18 40				
Lapworth	a																		18 09						
Dorridge	a				16 33			17 12						17 38					18 13					18 39	
Solihull	a				16 38			17 20						17 44					18 18					18 45	
Birmingham Moor Street	a				16 50			17 32						17 58					18 29					18 56	
Birmingham Snow Hill	a				17 01			17 41						18 12					18 40					19 01	
Rowley Regis	a																							19 24	
Cradley Heath	a																							19 29	
Stourbridge Junction 2	a																							19 35	
Kidderminster	a																							19 48	

For general notes see front of timetable
For details of catering facilities see Directory of Train Operators

§ London Underground Limited (Central Line) also operate services between South Ruislip and West Ruislip at frequent intervals

A (trolley) to Birmingham Snow Hill

London → High Wycombe, Aylesbury, Banbury, Stratford-upon-Avon, Birmingham Snow Hill and Kidderminster

Network Diagram - See first page of Table 114

		CH	CH	CH	CH	CH	CH	CH	CH	CH	CH	CH A	CH	CH	CH	CH	CH	CH	CH	CH	CH	CH	CH A	CH	CH
London Marylebone 10	⊖ d		17 06	17 09	17 20	17 30	17 33	17 36	17 41	17 45	17 53	18 00	18 03	18 09		18 12	18 15	18 19	18 30	18 33	18 36	18 47	19 00	19 03	19 07
London Paddington 15	⊖ d																								
Wembley Stadium	d		17 15	17 18					17 50	17 54							18 24	18 28			18 45				
Sudbury & Harrow Road	d			17 21														18 31							
Sudbury Hill Harrow	d							17 48									18 28								
Northolt Park	d		17 20				17 46				18 06							18 35				19 00			
South Ruislip §	⊖ d			17 27					17 58								18 33				18 53				19 22
West Ruislip 3 §	⊖ d		17 26					17 54								18 29					18 56				
Denham	d		17 30				17 53										18 39				19 00				
Denham Golf Club	d			17 34												18 34									
Gerrards Cross 1	d		17 34		17 41			18a04		18 08				18 30			18 43	18a49			19 05	19 10			19 30
Seer Green	d			17 40			18 00			18 12						18 40					19 09				19 34
Beaconsfield	d		17 40		17 47		18 04			18 16	18 21					18 43	18 49			18 58	19 12	19 16			19 38
High Wycombe 1	d		17 47	17a52	17 53		18a13		18 15	18 22	18a29			18 41		18 50	18a59			19 04	19 18	19 22		19 33	19 44
Saunderton	d		17 53							18 29						18 56						19 29			19 51
Princes Risborough 2	d	17 48	17 59		18a07				18 25	18 34			18 42	18 50	18 54	19a05				19 14	19 28	19 34		19 43	19a59
Monks Risborough	d	17 51								18 38												19 39			
Little Kimble	d	17 55								18 41												19 44			
Aylesbury	a	18 06								18 56					19 10						19 49	19 59			
Haddenham & Thame Parkway	d		18 05			18 12			18 31				18 48	18 59						19 21				19 50	
Bicester North 3	a		18 22			18 24			18 42				19 03	19 15					19 20	19 39				20 03	
	d					18 24			18 42										19 21					20 03	
Kings Sutton	d																							20 15	
Banbury	d					18 39			18 58			19 03							19 36				20 03	20a26	
Leamington Spa 8	d					18 58			19 16			19 21							19 54				20 23		
Warwick	d					19 03			19 20										19 59						
Warwick Parkway	d					19 06						19 27							20 02				20 29		
Hatton	d					19 11			19 27										20 07						
Claverdon	d								19 33																
Bearley	d																								
Wilmcote	d																								
Stratford-upon-Avon	a								19 51																
Lapworth	a					19 17													20 13						
Dorridge	a					19 21						19 37							20 17				20 39		
Solihull	a					19 27						19 43							20 23				20 45		
Birmingham Moor Street	a					19 38						19 56							20 33				20 57		
Birmingham Snow Hill	a					19 47						20 01							20 44				21 03		
Rowley Regis	a											20 24											21 19		
Cradley Heath	a											20 29											21 25		
Stourbridge Junction 2	a											20 35											21 32		
Kidderminster	a											20 50											21 49		

		CH	CH	CH	CH	CH	CH	CH	CH	CH	CH	CH	CH	CH	CH	CH	CH	CH	CH	CH	CH	CH FX	CH FO		
London Marylebone 10	⊖ d	19 11	19 30	19 33	19 36	19 40	20 00	20 06	20 10	20 30	20 33	21 00	21 06	21 10	21 30	21 40	22 10	22 20	22 40	23 10	23 30	23 54	23 54		
London Paddington 15	⊖ d																								
Wembley Stadium	d	19 20				19 49			20 19		20 42			21 19		21 49		22 29	22 49	23 19	23 39				
Sudbury & Harrow Road	d	19 23									20 45														
Sudbury Hill Harrow	d	19 26									20 48														
Northolt Park	d	19 29				19 54			20 24					21 24				22 34			23 44				
South Ruislip §	⊖ d					19 58					20 53					21 57			22 57		23 48				
West Ruislip 3 §	⊖ d	19 34				20 01			20 30					21 30				22 40			23 51				
Denham	d	19 38				20 06			20 34		20 58			21 34		22 02		22 44	23 02		23 56				
Denham Golf Club	d	19 40							20 36					21 36				22 46			23 58				
Gerrards Cross 1	d	19 44			19 57	20 10		20 27	20 40		21 03		21 27	21 40		22 07	22 31	22 50	23 07	23 33	00 01	00 15	00 15		
Seer Green	d					20 14			20 44		21 07			21 44		22 11		22 54	23 11		00 06				
Beaconsfield	d			19 57	20 03	20 18		20 33	20 47		21 11		21 33	21 47		22 15	22 37	22 57	23 15	23 39	00 09	00 21	00 21		
High Wycombe 1	d	19a58		20 04	20 10	20a27		20 40	20 54	21 00	21 17		21 40	21 54	22 00	22 21	22 43	23 04	23 21	23 45	00 15	00 28	00 28		
Saunderton	d								21 00				21 46			22 27		23 10			00 22	00 34	00 34		
Princes Risborough 2	d			20 15	20 20			20 49	21 06	21 11	21a30		21 57	22a10	22 11	22 36	22 54	23 19	23 31	23 56	00 27	00 41	00 41		
Monks Risborough	d								21 09				22 01					23 22			00 31				
Little Kimble	d								21 13				22 05					23 26			00 34				
Aylesbury	a								21 27				22 19			22 54		23 38			00 48				
Haddenham & Thame Parkway	d		20 11	20 21	20 27			20 56		21 17		21 41			22 17		23 01		23 38	00 03		00 47	00 47		
Bicester North 3	a		20 22	20 32	20 43		20 50	21 13		21 28		21 52			22 28		23 12		23 51	00 16		00 59	01 00		
	d		20 22	20 32			20 50			21 28		21 52			22 28		23 12		23 52	00 16		01 00	01 00		
Kings Sutton	d									21 41					22 41					00 30					
Banbury	d		20 38	20 49			21 06			21 47		22 08			22 47		23 29		00a12	00a42		01a21	01 17		
Leamington Spa 8	d		20 56	21 07			21 25			22 05		22 27			23 06		23 48						01a39		
Warwick	d		21 00	21 12						22 10					23 10		23 53								
Warwick Parkway	d		21 04				21 31			22 14		22 32			23 14		23 56								
Hatton	d		21 09	21 19						22 19															
Claverdon	d			21 24																					
Bearley	d			21 29																					
Wilmcote	d			21 33																					
Stratford-upon-Avon	a			21 43																					
Lapworth	a		21 14							22 24															
Dorridge	a		21 18				21 41			22 28		22 43			23 24		00 07								
Solihull	a		21 24				21 47			22 35		22 49			23 30		00 12								
Birmingham Moor Street	a		21 36				21 58			22 50		23 00			23 41		00 23								
Birmingham Snow Hill	a		21 47				22 04			22 58		23 05			23 51		00 31								
Rowley Regis	a						22 24					23 31													
Cradley Heath	a						22 29					23 37													
Stourbridge Junction 2	a						22 35					23 50													
Kidderminster	a						22 50																		

For general notes see front of timetable
For details of catering facilities see Directory of Train Operators

§ London Underground Limited (Central Line) also operate services between South Ruislip and West Ruislip at frequent intervals

A to Birmingham Snow Hill

London → High Wycombe, Aylesbury, Banbury, Stratford-upon-Avon, Birmingham Snow Hill and Kidderminster

Network Diagram - See first page of Table 114

Station		CH	CH	CH	CH	CH	CH	CH	CH	CH		CH	CH	CH	CH	CH	CH	CH	CH	CH		CH	CH	CH	CH
London Marylebone 10	⊖ d	22p10	23p10	23p30	23p54	00 10		06 27				07 23		08 20	08 23		08 54	09 18		09 24		09 45	10 00	10 18	10 24
London Paddington 15	⊖ d																								
Wembley Stadium	d		23p19	23p39		00 19		06 36				07 32			08 32					09 33			10 09		10 33
Sudbury & Harrow Road	d																								
Sudbury Hill Harrow	d																								
Northolt Park	d			23p44		00 24		06 41				07 37			08 37					09 38			10 14		10 38
South Ruislip §	⊖ d			23p48		00 28		06 45				07 41			08 41					09 42			10 18		
West Ruislip 3 §	⊖ d			23p51		00 31		06 48				07 44			08 44					09 45					10 44
Denham	d			23p56		00 36		06 53				07 49			08 49					09 50			10 24		10 48
Denham Golf Club	d			23p58		00 38		06 55				07 51			08 51					09 52					10 50
Gerrards Cross 1	d	22p31	23p33	00 01	00 15	00 41		06 59				07 54		08 41	08 54		09 15	09 39		09 55			10 28		10 54
Seer Green	d			00 06		00 46		07 03				07 59			08 59					10 00			10 33		10 58
Beaconsfield	d	22p37	23p39	00 09	00 21	00 49		07 07				08 02		08 47	09 02		09 21	09 45		10 03			10 36		11 01
High Wycombe 1	d	22p43	23p45	00 15	00 28	00 55	06 12	07 13				08 08		08 53	09 08		09 28	09 51		10a12		10 15	10a45	10 48	11a11
Saunderton	d			00 22	00 34	01 02	06 18	07 21				08 15			09 15			09 58						10 54	
Princes Risborough 2	d	22p54	23p56	00 27	00 41	01 07	06 24	07 26	07 30			08 22	08 30	09 04	09 21	09 26	09 38	10 04	10 11					11 01	
Monks Risborough	d			00 31		01 11			07 33				08 33			09 29			10 14						
Little Kimble	d			00 34		01 14			07 37				08 37			09 33			10 18						
Aylesbury	a			00 48		01 28			07 47				08 47			09 43			10 28						
Haddenham & Thame Parkway	d	23p01	00 03		00 47		06 31	07 33				08 28		09 11	09 28		09 45	10 11				10 30		11 07	
Bicester North 3	a	23p12	00 16		01 00		06 42	07 44				08 39		09 22	09 39		09 58	10 22				10 41		11 18	
	d	23p12	00 16		01 00		06 42	07 44				08 40		09 22	09 39		09 59	10 22				10 41		11 19	
Kings Sutton	d		00 30				06 53					08 52					10 10								
Banbury	d	23p29	00a42		01 17		07 00	08 01		08 40		08 57		09 39	09 56		10 17	10 39				10 58		11 35	
Leamington Spa 8	d	23p48			01a39		07 19	08 20		09 00		09 16		09 58	10 15		10 38	10 58				11 16		11 54	
Warwick	d	23p53					07 24	08 24		09 04		09 22		10 02	10 19		10 42	11 02				11 20		11 59	
Warwick Parkway	d	23p56					07 27	08 28		09 08		09 25		10 06	10 23			11 06				11 24		12 02	
Hatton	d							08 33		09 12					10 28		10 49							12 07	
Claverdon	d																10 54								
Bearley	d																10 59								
Wilmcote	d																11 02								
Stratford-upon-Avon	a									09 35							11 12								
Lapworth	a							08 38							10 33									12 13	
Dorridge	a	00 07					07 38	08 42				09 36		10 16	10 37			11 16				11 34		12 17	
Solihull	a	00 12					07 43	08 49				09 43		10 22	10 45			11 22				11 40		12 22	
Birmingham Moor Street	a	00 23					07 58	09 00				09 55		10 33	10 55			11 33				11 51		12 34	
Birmingham Snow Hill	a	00 31					08 07	09 11				10 03		10 41	11 04			11 41				12 01		12 42	
Rowley Regis	a																								
Cradley Heath	a																								
Stourbridge Junction 2	a																								
Kidderminster	a																								

Station		CH	CH	CH	CH	CH	CH	CH		CH	CH	CH	CH	CH	CH	CH	CH	CH		CH	CH	CH	CH	CH	CH
London Marylebone 10	⊖ d	10 50		10 53	11 00	11 20	11 24	11 50			11 53	12 20	12 23	12 50		12 53	13 20	13 23		13 50		13 53	14 20	14 23	14 50
London Paddington 15	⊖ d																								
Wembley Stadium	d				11 09		11 33				12 02		12 32					13 32				14 02		14 32	
Sudbury & Harrow Road	d																								
Sudbury Hill Harrow	d																								
Northolt Park	d				11 14		11 38						12 37					13 37						14 37	
South Ruislip §	⊖ d				11 18		11 42						12 41					13 41						14 41	
West Ruislip 3 §	⊖ d						11 45						12 44					13 44						14 44	
Denham	d				11 24		11 50						12 49					13 49						14 49	
Denham Golf Club	d						11 52						12 51					13 51						14 51	
Gerrards Cross 1	d			11 14	11 28		11 55				12 16		12 54			13 14		13 54				14 16		14 54	
Seer Green	d				11 33		12 00						12 59					13 59						14 59	
Beaconsfield	d			11 20	11 36		12 03				12 22		13 02			13 20		14 02				14 22		15 02	
High Wycombe 1	d			11 27	11a45	11 50	12a12				12 28	12 50	13a11			13 27	13 50	14a11				14 28	14 50	15a11	
Saunderton	d			11 33							12 35					13 33						14 35			
Princes Risborough 2	d		11 08	11 40		12 01				12 11	12 41	13 01			13 05	13 40	14 01				14 05	14 41	15 01		
Monks Risborough	d		11 11							12 14					13 08						14 08				
Little Kimble	d		11 15							12 18					13 12						14 12				
Aylesbury	a		11 25							12 28					13 22						14 22				
Haddenham & Thame Parkway	d			11 46		12 07					12 48	13 07				13 46	14 07					14 48	15 07		
Bicester North 3	a	11 41		11 59		12 18		12 41			13 04	13 18		13 41		13 59	14 18			14 41		15 04	15 18		15 41
	d	11 42		12 00		12 19		12 42				13 19		13 42		14 00	14 19			14 42			15 19		15 42
Kings Sutton	d			12 11												14 11									
Banbury	d	11 58		12 19		12 35		12 58				13 35		13 58		14 19	14 35			14 58			15 35		15 58
Leamington Spa 8	d	12 17		12 39		12 54		13 17				13 54		14 17		14 39	14 54			15 17			15 54		16 17
Warwick	d	12 22		12 43		12 59		13 22				13 59		14 22		14 43	14 59			15 22			15 59		16 21
Warwick Parkway	d	12 25				13 02		13 25				14 02		14 25			15 02			15 25			16 02		16 25
Hatton	d			12 49								14 07				14 49							16 07		
Claverdon	d																								
Bearley	d			12 58																					
Wilmcote	d			13 01												15 00									
Stratford-upon-Avon	a			13 11												15 10									
Lapworth	a											14 13											16 13		
Dorridge	a	12 36				13 13		13 36				14 17		14 36			15 13			15 36			16 17		16 35
Solihull	a	12 41				13 19		13 41				14 22		14 41			15 19			15 41			16 22		16 41
Birmingham Moor Street	a	12 52				13 32		13 52				14 34		14 53			15 32			15 53			16 33		16 53
Birmingham Snow Hill	a	13 01				13 41		14 01				14 42		15 01			15 41			16 01			16 41		17 02
Rowley Regis	a																								
Cradley Heath	a																								
Stourbridge Junction 2	a																								
Kidderminster	a																								

For general notes see front of timetable
For details of catering facilities see Directory of Train Operators

§ London Underground Limited (Central Line) also operate services between South Ruislip and West Ruislip at frequent intervals

London → High Wycombe, Aylesbury, Banbury, Stratford-upon-Avon, Birmingham Snow Hill and Kidderminster

Network Diagram - See first page of Table 114

		CH	CH	CH	CH	CH		CH	CH	CH	CH	CH	CH	CH	CH	CH		CH	CH	CH	CH	CH	CH	CH	CH
London Marylebone 10	⊖ d		14 53	15 00	15 20	15 24		15 50		15 53	16 00	16 20	16 24	16 50		16 53		17 00	17 20	17 24	17 50		17 53	18 00	18 15
London Paddington 15	⊖ d																								
Wembley Stadium	d			15 09		15 33					16 09		16 33					17 09		17 33				18 09	
Sudbury & Harrow Road	d																								
Sudbury Hill Harrow	d																								
Northolt Park	d			15 14		15 38					16 14		16 38					17 14		17 38				18 14	
South Ruislip §	⊖ d			15 18							16 18		16 42					17 18						18 18	
West Ruislip 3 §	⊖ d					15 44							16 45							17 44					
Denham	d			15 24		15 48					16 24		16 50					17 24		17 48				18 24	
Denham Golf Club	d					15 50							16 52							17 50					
Gerrards Cross 1	d		15 14	15 28		15 54				16 14	16 28		16 55			17 14		17 28		17 54			18 14	18 28	
Seer Green	d			15 33		15 58					16 33		17 00					17 33		17 58				18 33	
Beaconsfield	d		15 20	15 36		16 01				16 20	16 36		17 03			17 20		17 36		18 01			18 20	18 36	
High Wycombe 1	d		15 27	15a45	15 50	16a11				16 27	16a45	16 50	17a12			17 27		17a45	17 50	18a11			18 27	18a45	18 47
Saunderton	d		15 33							16 33						17 33							18 33		
Princes Risborough 2	d	15 05	15 40		16 01				16 05	16 40		17 01			17 05	17 40			18 01			18 05	18 40		18 56
Monks Risborough	d	15 08							16 08						17 08							18 08			
Little Kimble	d	15 12							16 12						17 12							18 12			
Aylesbury	a	15 22							16 22						17 22							18 22			19 14
Haddenham & Thame Parkway	d		15 46		16 07					16 46		17 07				17 46			18 07				18 46		
Bicester North 3	a		15 59		16 18			16 41		17 02		17 18		17 42		17 59			18 18		18 46		19 02		
	d		16 00		16 19			16 42				17 19		17 42		18 00			18 19		18 46				
Kings Sutton	d		16 11													18 11									
Banbury	d		16 19		16 35			16 57				17 35		17 59		18 19			18 35		19 03				
Leamington Spa 8	d		16 39		16 53			17 16				17 54		18 18		18 39			18 54		19 23				
Warwick	d		16 43		16 58			17 21				17 59		18 23		18 43			18 59		19 27				
Warwick Parkway	d				17 01			17 24				18 02		18 26					19 02		19 31				
Hatton	d		16 49		17 06							18 07				18 49			19 07						
Claverdon	d		16 54													18 54									
Bearley	d		16 59													18 59									
Wilmcote	d															19 03									
Stratford-upon-Avon	a		17 11													19 13									
Lapworth	a				17 12							18 13							19 14						
Dorridge	a				17 16			17 35				18 17		18 37					19 18		19 42				
Solihull	a				17 22			17 40				18 22		18 42					19 23		19 48				
Birmingham Moor Street	a				17 33			17 52				18 33		18 54					19 33		19 58				
Birmingham Snow Hill	a				17 41			18 01				18 41		19 03					19 41		20 06				
Rowley Regis	a																								
Cradley Heath	a																								
Stourbridge Junction 2	a																								
Kidderminster	a																								

		CH	CH	CH		CH	CH	CH	CH	CH	CH	CH	CH	CH		CH	CH	CH	CH	CH	CH	CH	CH		
London Marylebone 10	⊖ d	18 20	18 24	18 50			18 53	19 00	19 20		19 30	20 00	20 05	20 40		20 50	21 15	21 40	22 10	22 45	23 10	23 14	23 45		
London Paddington 15	⊖ d																								
Wembley Stadium	d		18 33					19 09			19 39		20 14				21 24		22 19	22 54	23 19	23 23	23 54		
Sudbury & Harrow Road	d																								
Sudbury Hill Harrow	d																								
Northolt Park	d		18 38					19 14			19 44		20 19				21 29		22 24			23 28			
South Ruislip §	⊖ d							19 18					20 23				21 33		22 28			23 32			
West Ruislip 3 §	⊖ d		18 44								19 50		20 26				21 36		22 31			23 35			
Denham	d		18 48					19 24			19 54		20 31				21 41		22 36			23 40			
Denham Golf Club	d		18 50								19 56		20 33				21 43		22 38			23 42			
Gerrards Cross 1	d		18 54				19 14	19 28			20 00		20 36	21 02			21 46	22 02	22 41	23 08	23 33	23 45	00 08		
Seer Green	d		18 58					19 33			20 04		20 41				21 51		22 46			23 50			
Beaconsfield	d		19 01				19 20	19 36			20 07		20 44	21 08			21 54	22 08	22 49	23 14	23 39	23 53	00 14		
High Wycombe 1	d	18 50	19a11				19 27	19 42	19 50		20 14	20 30	20 50	21 14		21 22	22 00	22 14	22 55	23 20	23 45	00 01	00 20		
Saunderton	d						19 33				20 20			21 21			22 07		23 02			00 06			
Princes Risborough 2	d	19 01				19 05	19 40	19 53	20 01	20 05	20 27	20 41	21 00	21 27		21 31	22 14	22 25	23 07	23 32	23 56	00 12	00 32		
Monks Risborough	d					19 08				20 08	20 30			21 30			22 17		23 11			00 16			
Little Kimble	d					19 12				20 12	20 34			21 34			22 21		23 14			00 19			
Aylesbury	a					19 22		20 12		20 22	20 46		21 19	21 47			22 33		23 28			00 32			
Haddenham & Thame Parkway	d	19 07					19 46		20 07			20 48				21 38		22 32		23 38	00 03		00 38		
Bicester North 3	a	19 18		19 46			19 59		20 18			21 01				21 51		22 45		23 51	00 16		00 51		
	d	19 19		19 46			20 00		20 19			21 01				21 51		22 46		23 52	00 16		00 52		
Kings Sutton	d						20 11		20 30											00 03			01 03		
Banbury	d	19 35		20 03			20 19		20 37			21 19				22 07		23 03		00a14	00a36		01a14		
Leamington Spa 8	d	19 54		20 23			20 39		20 55			21 39				22 28		23 24							
Warwick	d	19 59		20 27			20 43		21 00			21 43				22 32		23 28							
Warwick Parkway	d	20 02		20 31					21 03			21 47				22 35		23 31							
Hatton	d	20 07					20 49		21 08																
Claverdon	d						20 54																		
Bearley	d																								
Wilmcote	d																								
Stratford-upon-Avon	a						21 10																		
Lapworth	a	20 13							21 14																
Dorridge	a	20 17		20 42					21 18			21 58				22 46		23 42							
Solihull	a	20 22		20 47					21 24			22 03				22 52		23 49							
Birmingham Moor Street	a	20 34		20 58					21 35			22 16				23 02		00 01							
Birmingham Snow Hill	a	20 42		21 06					21 43			22 26				23 10		00 09							
Rowley Regis	a																								
Cradley Heath	a																								
Stourbridge Junction 2	a																								
Kidderminster	a																								

For general notes see front of timetable
For details of catering facilities see Directory of Train Operators

§ London Underground Limited (Central Line) also operate services between South Ruislip and West Ruislip at frequent intervals

Table 115

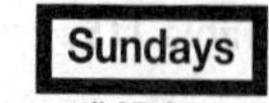

Sundays

London → High Wycombe, Aylesbury, Banbury, Stratford-upon-Avon, Birmingham Snow Hill and Kidderminster

until 27 January

Network Diagram - See first page of Table 114

Station		CH	CH	CH	CH		CH	CH	CH	CH		CH	CH	CH	CH		CH	CH	CH	CH		CH	CH	CH	CH ⌶
London Marylebone 10 ⊖	d	21p40	22p45	23p10	23p14		23p45	00 10	07 35			08 00	08 54	09 15	09 54		10 15	10 50	10 54	11 20		11 50	11 54	12 20	12 33
London Paddington 15 ⊖	d																								
Wembley Stadium	d		22p54	23p19	23p23		23p54	00 19	07 44			08 09	09 03		10 03				11 03				12 03		12 42
Sudbury & Harrow Road	d																								
Sudbury Hill Harrow	d																								
Northolt Park	d				23p28			00 24	07 49			08 14	09 08		10 08				11 08				12 08		
South Ruislip § ⊖	d				23p32			00 28	07 53			08 18	09 12		10 12				11 12				12 12		
West Ruislip 3 § ⊖	d				23p35			00 31	07 56			08 21	09 15		10 15				11 15				12 15		
Denham	d				23p40			00 36	08 01			08 26	09 20		10 20				11 20				12 20		
Denham Golf Club	d				23p42			00 38	08 03				09 22						11 22						
Gerrards Cross 1	d	22p02	23p08	23p33	23p45		00 08	00 41	08 06			08 30	09 25	09 36	10 24		10 36		11 25	11 41			12 24	12 41	12 56
Seer Green	d				23p50			00 46	08 11			08 34	09 30		10 28				11 30				12 28		
Beaconsfield	d	22p08	23p14	23p39	23p53		00 14	00 49	08 14			08 38	09 33	09 42	10 32		10 42		11 33	11 47			12 32	12 47	13 02
High Wycombe 1	d	22p14	23p20	23p45	00 01		00 20	00 55	08 20			08 44	09 39	09 49	10 38		10 49		11 39	11 54			12 38	12 54	13 08
Saunderton	d				00 06			01 02	08 27			08 51	09 46		10 45				11 46				12 45		
Princes Risborough 2	d	22p25	23p32	23p56	00 12		00 32	01 07	08 33	08 38		08 57	09 51	09 59	10 50		10 59		11 51	12 04			12 50	13 04	13 18
Monks Risborough	d				00 16			01 11		08 41			09 55		10 54				11 55				12 54		
Little Kimble	d				00 19			01 14		08 45			09 58		10 57				11 58				12 57		
Aylesbury	a				00 32			01 28		08 56			10 12		11 11				12 12				13 11		
Haddenham & Thame Parkway	d	22p32	23p38	00 03			00 38		08 40			09 04		10 06			11 06			12 11				13 11	13 25
Bicester North 3	a	22p45	23p51	00 16			00 51		08 53			09 17		10 19			11 19	11 45		12 24		12 45		13 24	13 41
	d	22p46	23p52	00 16			00 52		08 54			09 17		10 20			11 20	11 45		12 25		12 45		13 25	
Kings Sutton	d		00 03				01 03		09 07								11 33							13 38	
Banbury	d	23p03	00a14	00a36			01a14		09a15			09 34		10 36			11 38	12 02		12 41		13 05		13 43	
Leamington Spa 8	d	23p24										09 54		10 57			11 59	12 22		13 02		13 26		14 03	
Warwick	d	23p28										09 59		11 01			12 03			13 06				14 07	
Warwick Parkway	d	23p31										10 02		11 04			12 06	12 28		13 09		13 31		14 10	
Hatton	d											10 07					12 11								
Claverdon	d																								
Bearley	d																								
Wilmcote	d																								
Stratford-upon-Avon	a																								
Lapworth	a											10 11		11 13						13 18					
Dorridge	a	23p42										10 16		11 18			12 19	12 39		13 22		13 42		14 21	
Solihull	a	23p49										10 21		11 23			12 24	12 44		13 27		13 48		14 28	
Birmingham Moor Street	a	00 01										10 32		11 33			12 35	12 55		13 38		13 58		14 39	
Birmingham Snow Hill	a	00 09										10 40		11 41			12 43	13 03		13 46		14 06		14 47	
Rowley Regis	a																								
Cradley Heath	a																								
Stourbridge Junction 2	a																								
Kidderminster	a																								

Station		CH	CH		CH	CH	CH	CH		CH	CH ⌶	CH	CH		CH	CH	CH	CH		CH	CH ⌶	CH	CH		CH
London Marylebone 10 ⊖	d	12 50	12 54		13 20	13 33	13 50	13 54		14 20	14 33	14 50	14 54		15 20	15 33	15 50	15 54		16 20	16 35	16 57	17 00		17 20
London Paddington 15 ⊖	d																								
Wembley Stadium	d		13 03			13 42		14 03			14 42		15 03			15 42		16 03			16 44		17 09		
Sudbury & Harrow Road	d																								
Sudbury Hill Harrow	d																								
Northolt Park	d		13 08					14 08					15 08					16 08					17 14		
South Ruislip § ⊖	d		13 12					14 12					15 12					16 12					17 18		
West Ruislip 3 § ⊖	d		13 15					14 15					15 15					16 15					17 21		
Denham	d		13 20					14 20					15 20					16 20					17 26		
Denham Golf Club	d		13 22										15 22										17 28		
Gerrards Cross 1	d		13 25		13 41	13 56		14 24		14 41	14 56		15 25		15 41	15 56		16 24		16 41	16 58		17 31		17 41
Seer Green	d		13 30					14 28					15 30					16 28					17 36		
Beaconsfield	d		13 33		13 47	14 02		14 32		14 47	15 02		15 33		15 47	16 02		16 32		16 47	17 04		17 39		17 47
High Wycombe 1	d		13 39		13 54	14 08		14 38		14 54	15 08		15 39		15 54	16 08		16 38		16 54	17 10		17 45		17 54
Saunderton	d		13 46					14 45					15 46					16 45					17 52		
Princes Risborough 2	d		13 51		14 04	14 19		14 50		15 04	15 18		15 51		16 04	16 19		16 50		17 04	17 20		17 57		18 04
Monks Risborough	d		13 55					14 54					15 55					16 54					18 01		
Little Kimble	d		13 58					14 57					15 58					16 57					18 04		
Aylesbury	a		14 12					15 11					16 12					17 11					18 18		
Haddenham & Thame Parkway	d				14 11	14 26				15 11	15 25				16 11	16 26				17 11	17 27				18 11
Bicester North 3	a	13 45			14 24	14 39	14 45			15 24	15 41	15 45			16 24	16 39	16 45			17 24	17 43	17 52			18 24
	d	13 45			14 25	14 39	14 45			15 25		15 45			16 25	16 39	16 45			17 25		17 52			18 25
Kings Sutton	d					14 55										16 55									
Banbury	d	14 02			14 41	15 01	15 05			15 41		16 02			16 40	17 01	17 05			17 41		18 09			18 41
Leamington Spa 8	d	14 22			15 02	15 21	15 26			16 02		16 22			17 01	17 21	17 26			18 02		18 29			19 02
Warwick	d				15 06	15 25				16 06					17 06	17 25				18 06					19 06
Warwick Parkway	d	14 28			15 09	15a34	15 31			16 09		16 28			17 09	17a34	17 31			18 09		18 35			19 09
Hatton	d									16 14										18 14					
Claverdon	d																								
Bearley	d																								
Wilmcote	d																								
Stratford-upon-Avon	a																								
Lapworth	a				15 18										17 18										19 18
Dorridge	a	14 39			15 22		15 42			16 22		16 39			17 22		17 42			18 22		18 46			19 22
Solihull	a	14 44			15 27		15 48			16 27		16 44			17 27		17 48			18 29		18 51			19 29
Birmingham Moor Street	a	14 55			15 38		15 58			16 38		16 55			17 38		17 59			18 40		19 01			19 40
Birmingham Snow Hill	a	15 03			15 46		16 06			16 46		16 59			17 46		18 07			18 49		19 10			19 48
Rowley Regis	a																								
Cradley Heath	a																								
Stourbridge Junction 2	a																								
Kidderminster	a																								

For general notes see front of timetable
For details of catering facilities see Directory of Train Operators

§ London Underground Limited (Central Line) also operate services between South Ruislip and West Ruislip at frequent intervals

Table 115

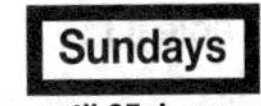

until 27 January

London → High Wycombe, Aylesbury, Banbury, Stratford-upon-Avon, Birmingham Snow Hill and Kidderminster

Network Diagram - See first page of Table 114

		CH	CH	CH	CH		CH	CH	CH	CH		CH	CH	CH	CH		CH	CH	CH	CH	CH	CH	CH		
London Marylebone 10	⊖ d	17 35	17 57	18 00	18 20		18 35	18 57	19 00	19 22		19 35	19 57	20 00	20 20		20 50	21 10	21 40	22 10	22 45		23 45		
London Paddington 15	⊖ d																								
Wembley Stadium	d	17 44		18 09			18 44		19 09			19 44		20 09				21 19		22 19	22 54		23 54		
Sudbury & Harrow Road	d																								
Sudbury Hill Harrow	d																								
Northolt Park	d			18 14					19 14					20 14				21 24		22 24	22 59		00 01		
South Ruislip §	⊖ d			18 18					19 18					20 18				21 28		22 28	23 03		00 03		
West Ruislip 3 §	⊖ d			18 21					19 21					20 21				21 31		22 31	23 06		00 06		
Denham	d			18 26					19 26					20 26				21 36		22 36	23 11		00 11		
Denham Golf Club	d								19 28									21 38			23 13		00 13		
Gerrards Cross 1	d	17 58		18 30	18 41		18 58		19 31	19 43		19 58		20 30	20 41		21 11	21 41	22 01	22 40	23 16		00 16		
Seer Green	d			18 34					19 36					20 34				21 46		22 44	23 21		00 21		
Beaconsfield	d	18 04		18 38	18 47		19 04		19 39	19 49		20 04		20 38	20 47		21 17	21 49	22 07	22 48	23 24		00 24		
High Wycombe 1	d	18 10		18 44	18 54		19 10		19 45	19 56		20 10		20 44	20 54		21 24	21 55	22 14	22 54	23 30		00 30		
Saunderton	d			18 51					19 52					20 51				22 01		23 00	23 37		00 37		
Princes Risborough 2	d	18 21		18 56	19 04		19 20		19 57	20 07		20 21		20 56	21 04		21 34	22 07	22 24	23 05	23 43	23 49	00 43		
Monks Risborough	d			19 00					20 01					21 00				22 10		23 09		23 52			
Little Kimble	d			19 03					20 04					21 03				22 14		23 12		23 56			
Aylesbury	a			19 17					20 18					21 17				22 28		23 26		00 07			
Haddenham & Thame Parkway	d	18 28			19 11		19 27			20 14		20 28			21 11		21 41		22 31		23 50		00 50		
Bicester North 3	a	18 41	18 52		19 24		19 40	19 52		20 27		20 41	20 52		21 24		21 54		22 44		00 02		01 03		
	d	18 41	18 52		19 25		19 40	19 52		20 27		20 41	20 52		21 25		21 55		22 45		00 04		01 03		
Kings Sutton	d	18 55										20 55									00 16				
Banbury	d	19 01	19 09		19 41		20a02	20 09		20 44		21a04	21 09		21 41		22 10		23 01		00a25		01a23		
Leamington Spa 8	d	19 21	19 29		20 02			20 29		21 04			21 29		22 02		22 31		23 22						
Warwick	d	19 25			20 06					21 09					22 06		22 35		23 26						
Warwick Parkway	d	19a34	19 35		20 09			20 35		21 12			21 35		22 09		22 38		23 29						
Hatton	d																22 43								
Claverdon	d																								
Bearley	d																								
Wilmcote	d																								
Stratford-upon-Avon	a																								
Lapworth	a																22 48								
Dorridge	a		19 46		20 20			20 46		21 23			21 46		22 20		22 52		23 40						
Solihull	a		19 51		20 28			20 51		21 30			21 51		22 26		22 59		23 46						
Birmingham Moor Street	a		20 01		20 38			21 01		21 40			22 01		22 37		23 10		23 56						
Birmingham Snow Hill	a		20 10		20 46			21 10		21 48			22 10		22 45		23 18		00 04						
Rowley Regis	a																								
Cradley Heath	a																								
Stourbridge Junction 2	a																								
Kidderminster	a																								

Sundays

3 February to 23 March

		CH	CH	CH		CH	CH	CH		CH	CH	CH A		CH	CH A	CH		CH	CH A	CH		CH A	CH	CH	CH
London Marylebone 10	⊖ d	21p40	22p45	23p10		23p14	23p45	00 10		07 35		08 00		08 40	09 00	09 20		09 40	10 00	10 10		10 22	10 40	11 20	11 40
London Paddington 15	⊖ d																								
Wembley Stadium	d		22p54	23p19		23p23	23p54	00 19		07 44				08 49				09 49					10 49		11 49
Sudbury & Harrow Road	d																								
Sudbury Hill Harrow	d																								
Northolt Park	d					23p28		00 24		07 49				08 54				09 54					10 54		11 54
South Ruislip §	⊖ d					23p32		00 28		07 53				08 58				09 58					10 58		11 58
West Ruislip 3 §	⊖ d					23p35		00 31		07 56				09 01				10 01					11 01		12 01
Denham	d					23p40		00 36		08 01				09 06				10 06					11 06		12 06
Denham Golf Club	d					23p42		00 38		08 03				09 08									11 08		
Gerrards Cross 1	d	22p02	23p08	23p33		23p45	00 08	00 41		08 06		08 21		09 11	09 21	09 41		10 10	10 21	10 31		10 44	11 11	11 41	12 10
Seer Green	d					23p50		00 46		08 11								10 14							12 14
Beaconsfield	d	22p08	23p14	23p39		23p53	00 14	00 49		08 14		08 27		09 17	09 27	09 47		10 18	10 27	10 37		10 50	11 17	11 47	12 18
High Wycombe 1	d	22p14	23p20	23p45		00 01	00 20	00 55		08 20		08 34		09 24	09 34	09 54		10 24	10 34	10 44		10 56	11 24	11 54	12 24
Saunderton	d					00 06		01 02		08 27				09 30				10 31					11 30		12 31
Princes Risborough 2	d	22p25	23p32	23p56		00 12	00 32	01 07		08 33	08 38	08 44		09 35	09 44	10 04		10 36	10 44	10 54		11 07	11 35	12 04	12 36
Monks Risborough	d					00 16		01 11			08 41			09 39				10 40					11 39		12 40
Little Kimble	d					00 19		01 14			08 45			09 42				10 43					11 42		12 43
Aylesbury	a					00 32		01 28			08 56			09 56				10 57					11 56		12 57
Haddenham & Thame Parkway	d	22p32	23p38	00 03			00 38			08 40		08 51			09 51	10 11			10 51	11 01		11 13		12 11	
Bicester North 3	a	22p45	23p51	00 16			00 51			08 53		09 04			10 04	10 24			11 04	11 14		11 26		12 24	
	d	22p46	23p52	00 16			00 52			08 54		09 05			10 05	10 25			11 05	11 15		11 27		12 25	
Kings Sutton	d		00 03				01 03			09 07										11 28					
Banbury	d	23p03	00a14	00a36			01a14			09a12		09 22			10 22	10 41			11 22	11 33		11 44		12 41	
Leamington Spa 8	d	23p24										09a42			10a42	11 02			11a42	11 54		12a03		13 02	
Warwick	d	23p28														11 12				12 14				13 12	
Warwick Parkway	d	23p31														11a17				12a19				13a17	
Hatton	d																								
Claverdon	d																								
Bearley	d																								
Wilmcote	d																								
Stratford-upon-Avon	a																								
Lapworth	a																								
Dorridge	a	23p42																							
Solihull	a	23p49																							
Birmingham Moor Street	a	00 01																							
Birmingham Snow Hill	a	00 09																							
Rowley Regis	a																								
Cradley Heath	a																								
Stourbridge Junction 2	a																								
Kidderminster	a																								

For general notes see front of timetable
For details of catering facilities see Directory of Train Operators

§ London Underground Limited (Central Line) also operate services between South Ruislip and West Ruislip at frequent intervals

A To Birmingham New Street (Table 71)

Table 115

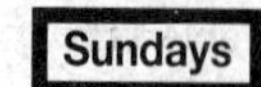

London → High Wycombe, Aylesbury, Banbury, Stratford-upon-Avon, Birmingham Snow Hill and Kidderminster

3 February to 23 March

Network Diagram - See first page of Table 114

Station		CH A		CH	CH	CH A		CH	CH	CH A		CH	CH	CH A		CH	CH	CH A		CH	CH	CH A		CH	CH
London Marylebone [10]	⊖ d	12 00		12 20	12 40	13 00		13 20	13 40	14 00		14 20	14 40	15 00		15 20	15 40	16 00		16 20	16 40	17 00		17 20	17 40
London Paddington [15]	⊖ d																								
Wembley Stadium	d			12 29	12 49			13 29	13 49			14 29	14 49			15 29	15 49			16 29	16 49			17 29	17 49
Sudbury & Harrow Road	d																								
Sudbury Hill Harrow	d																								
Northolt Park	d				12 54				13 54				14 54				15 54				16 54				17 54
South Ruislip §	⊖ d				12 58				13 58				14 58				15 58				16 58				17 58
West Ruislip [3] §	⊖ d				13 01				14 01				15 01				16 01				17 01				18 01
Denham	d				13 06				14 06				15 06				16 06				17 06				18 06
Denham Golf Club	d				13 08								15 08								17 08				
Gerrards Cross [1]	d	12 21		12 43	13 11	13 21		13 43	14 10	14 21		14 43	15 11	15 21		15 43	16 10	16 21		16 43	17 11	17 21		17 43	18 10
Seer Green	d								14 14								16 14								18 14
Beaconsfield	d	12 27		12 49	13 17	13 27		13 49	14 18	14 27		14 49	15 17	15 27		15 49	16 18	16 27		16 49	17 17	17 27		17 49	18 18
High Wycombe [1]	d	12 34		12 55	13 24	13 34		13 55	14 24	14 34		14 55	15 24	15 34		15 55	16 24	16 34		16 55	17 24	17 34		17 55	18 24
Saunderton	d				13 30				14 31				15 30				16 31				17 30				18 31
Princes Risborough [2]	d	12 44		13 06	13 35	13 44		14 06	14 36	14 44		15 06	15 35	15 44		16 06	16 36	16 44		17 06	17 35	17 44		18 06	18 36
Monks Risborough	d				13 39				14 40				15 39				16 40				17 39				18 40
Little Kimble	d				13 42				14 43				15 42				16 43				17 42				18 43
Aylesbury	a				13 56				14 57				15 56				16 57				17 56				18 57
Haddenham & Thame Parkway	d	12 51		13 13		13 51		14 13		14 51		15 13		15 51		16 13		16 51		17 13		17 51		18 13	
Bicester North [3]	a	13 04		13 26		14 04		14 26		15 04		15 26		16 04		16 26		17 04		17 26		18 04		18 26	
	d	13 05		13 26		14 05		14 26		15 05		15 26		16 05		16 26		17 05		17 26		18 05		18 26	
Kings Sutton	d			13 39								15 39								17 39					
Banbury	d	13 22		13 45		14 23		14 43		15 22		15 45		16 22		16 42		17 22		17 45		18 23		18 43	
Leamington Spa [8]	d	13a42		14 05		14a42		15 03		15a42		16 05		16a42		17 03		17a42		18 05		18a42		19 03	
Warwick	d			14 15				15 14				16 15				17 14				18 15				19 14	
Warwick Parkway	d			14a21				15a19				16a21				17a19				18a21				19a19	
Hatton	d																								
Claverdon	d																								
Bearley	d																								
Wilmcote	d																								
Stratford-upon-Avon	a																								
Lapworth	a																								
Dorridge	a																								
Solihull	a																								
Birmingham Moor Street	a																								
Birmingham Snow Hill	a																								
Rowley Regis	a																								
Cradley Heath	a																								
Stourbridge Junction [2]	a																								
Kidderminster	a																								

Station		CH A	CH	CH		CH	CH	CH		CH	CH	CH		CH	CH	CH		CH	CH	CH		CH			
London Marylebone [10]	⊖ d	18 00	18 20	18 40		19 00	19 20	19 40		20 00	20 20	20 40		21 00	21 20	21 40		22 10	22 45			23 45			
London Paddington [15]	⊖ d																								
Wembley Stadium	d		18 29	18 49			19 29	19 49				20 49			21 29			22 19	22 54			23 54			
Sudbury & Harrow Road	d																								
Sudbury Hill Harrow	d																								
Northolt Park	d			18 54				19 54				20 54						22 24	22 59			00 01			
South Ruislip §	⊖ d			18 58				19 58				20 58			21 37			22 28	23 03			00 03			
West Ruislip [3] §	⊖ d			19 01				20 01				21 01						22 31	23 06			00 06			
Denham	d			19 06				20 06				21 06			21 42			22 36	23 11			00 11			
Denham Golf Club	d			19 08								21 08							23 13			00 13			
Gerrards Cross [1]	d	18 21	18 43	19 11		19 21	19 43	20 10		20 21	20 41	21 11		21 21	21 47	22 01		22 40	23 16			00 16			
Seer Green	d							20 14										22 44	23 21			00 21			
Beaconsfield	d	18 27	18 49	19 17		19 27	19 49	20 18		20 27	20 47	21 17		21 27	21 53	22 07		22 48	23 24			00 24			
High Wycombe [1]	d	18 34	18 55	19 24		19 34	19 55	20 24		20 34	20 54	21 23		21 34	21 59	22 14		22 54	23 30			00 30			
Saunderton	d			19 30				20 31				21 30			22 05			23 00	23 37			00 37			
Princes Risborough [2]	d	18 44	19 06	19 35		19 44	20 07	20 36		20 44	21 04	21 35		21 44	22 10	22 24		23 05	23 43	23 49		00 43			
Monks Risborough	d			19 39				20 40				21 39			22 14			23 09		23 52					
Little Kimble	d			19 42				20 43				21 42			22 17			23 12		23 56					
Aylesbury	a			19 56				20 57				21 56			22 29			23 26		00 07					
Haddenham & Thame Parkway	d	18 51	19 13			19 51	20 14			20 51	21 11			21 51		22 31			23 50			00 50			
Bicester North [3]	a	19 04	19 26			20 04	20 27			21 04	21 24			22 04		22 44			00 02			01 03			
	d	19 05	19 26			20 05	20 28			21 05	21 25			22 05		22 45			00 04			01 03			
Kings Sutton	d		19 39								21 38								00 16						
Banbury	d	19 22	19 45			20a22	20 45			21a23	21 43			22 22		23 05			00a25			01a23			
Leamington Spa [8]	d	19a42	20 06				21 05				22 04			22a43		23a29									
Warwick	d		20 16				21 15				22 14														
Warwick Parkway	d		20a21				21a20				22a19														
Hatton	d																								
Claverdon	d																								
Bearley	d																								
Wilmcote	d																								
Stratford-upon-Avon	a																								
Lapworth	a																								
Dorridge	a																								
Solihull	a																								
Birmingham Moor Street	a																								
Birmingham Snow Hill	a																								
Rowley Regis	a																								
Cradley Heath	a																								
Stourbridge Junction [2]	a																								
Kidderminster	a																								

For general notes see front of timetable
For details of catering facilities see Directory of Train Operators

§ London Underground Limited (Central Line) also operate services between South Ruislip and West Ruislip at frequent intervals

A To Birmingham New Street (Table 71)

Table 115

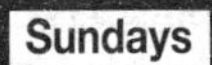

from 30 March

London → High Wycombe, Aylesbury, Banbury, Stratford-upon-Avon, Birmingham Snow Hill and Kidderminster

Network Diagram - See first page of Table 114

		CH	CH	CH	CH	CH	CH	CH	CH	CH	CH	CH	CH	CH	CH	CH	CH	CH	CH	CH
										A		A			A			A		
London Marylebone 10	⊖ d	21p40	22p45	23p10	23p14	23p45	00 10	07 35		08 00	08 40	09 00	09 20	09 40	10 00	10 20	10 40	11 00	11 20	11 40
London Paddington 15	⊖ d																			
Wembley Stadium	d		22p54	23p19	23p23	23p54	00 19	07 44			08 49			09 49			10 49			11 49
Sudbury & Harrow Road	d																			
Sudbury Hill Harrow	d																			
Northolt Park	d				23p28		00 24	07 49			08 54			09 54			10 54			11 54
South Ruislip §	⊖ d				23p32		00 28	07 53			08 58			09 58			10 58			11 58
West Ruislip 3 §	⊖ d				23p35		00 31	07 56			09 01			10 01			11 01			12 01
Denham	d				23p40		00 36	08 01			09 06			10 06			11 06			12 06
Denham Golf Club	d				23p42		00 38	08 03			09 08						11 08			
Gerrards Cross 1	d	22p02	23p08	23p33	23p45	00 08	00 41	08 06		08 21	09 11	09 21	09 41	10 10	10 21	10 41	11 11	11 21	11 41	12 10
Seer Green	d				23p50		00 46	08 11						10 14						12 14
Beaconsfield	d	22p08	23p14	23p39	23p53	00 14	00 49	08 14		08 27	09 17	09 27	09 47	10 18	10 27	10 47	11 17	11 27	11 47	12 18
High Wycombe 1	d	22p14	23p20	23p45	00 01	00 20	00 55	08 20		08 34	09 24	09 34	09 54	10 24	10 34	10 54	11 24	11 34	11 54	12 24
Saunderton	d				00 06		01 02	08 27			09 30			10 31			11 30			12 31
Princes Risborough 2	d	22p25	23p32	23p56	00 12	00 32	01 07	08 33	08 38	08 44	09 35	09 44	10 04	10 36	10 44	11 04	11 35	11 44	12 04	12 36
Monks Risborough	d				00 16		01 11		08 41		09 39			10 40			11 39			12 40
Little Kimble	d				00 19		01 14		08 45		09 42			10 43			11 42			12 43
Aylesbury	a				00 32		01 28		08 56		09 56			10 57			11 56			12 57
Haddenham & Thame Parkway	d	22p32	23p38	00 03		00 38		08 40		08 51		09 51	10 11		10 51	11 11		11 51	12 11	
Bicester North 3	a	22p45	23p51	00 16		00 51		08 53		09 04		10 04	10 24		11 04	11 24		12 04	12 24	
	d	22p46	23p52	00 16		00 52		08 54		09 05		10 05	10 25		11 05	11 25		12 05	12 25	
Kings Sutton	d		00 03			01 03		09 07								11 38				
Banbury	d	23p03	00a14	00a36		01a14		09a12		09 22		10 22	10 41		11 22	11 43		12 29	12 41	
Leamington Spa 8	d	23p24								09a42		10a42	11 02		11a42	12 04		12a48	13 02	
Warwick	d	23p28											11 12			12 14			13 12	
Warwick Parkway	d	23p31											11a17			12a19			13a17	
Hatton	d																			
Claverdon	d																			
Bearley	d																			
Wilmcote	d																			
Stratford-upon-Avon	a																			
Lapworth	a																			
Dorridge	a	23p42																		
Solihull	a	23p49																		
Birmingham Moor Street	a	00 01																		
Birmingham Snow Hill	🚋 a	00 09																		
Rowley Regis	a																			
Cradley Heath	a																			
Stourbridge Junction 2	a																			
Kidderminster	a																			

		CH	CH	CH	CH	CH	CH	CH	CH	CH	CH	CH	CH	CH	CH	CH	CH	CH	CH
		A			A			A			A			A			A		
London Marylebone 10	⊖ d	12 00	12 20	12 40	13 00	13 20	13 40	14 00	14 20	14 40	15 00	15 20	15 40	16 00	16 20	16 40	17 00	17 20	17 40
London Paddington 15	⊖ d																		
Wembley Stadium	d		12 29	12 49		13 29	13 49		14 29	14 49		15 29	15 49		16 29	16 49		17 29	17 49
Sudbury & Harrow Road	d																		
Sudbury Hill Harrow	d																		
Northolt Park	d			12 54			13 54			14 54			15 54			16 54			17 54
South Ruislip §	⊖ d			12 58			13 58			14 58			15 58			16 58			17 58
West Ruislip 3 §	⊖ d			13 01			14 01			15 01			16 01			17 01			18 01
Denham	d			13 06			14 06			15 06			16 06			17 06			18 06
Denham Golf Club	d			13 08						15 08						17 08			
Gerrards Cross 1	d	12 21	12 43	13 11	13 21	13 43	14 10	14 21	14 43	15 11	15 21	15 43	16 10	16 21	16 43	17 11	17 21	17 43	18 10
Seer Green	d						14 14						16 14						18 14
Beaconsfield	d	12 27	12 49	13 17	13 27	13 49	14 18	14 27	14 49	15 17	15 27	15 49	16 18	16 27	16 49	17 17	17 27	17 49	18 18
High Wycombe 1	d	12 34	12 55	13 24	13 34	13 55	14 24	14 34	14 55	15 24	15 34	15 55	16 24	16 34	16 55	17 24	17 34	17 55	18 24
Saunderton	d			13 30			14 31			15 30			16 31			17 30			18 31
Princes Risborough 2	d	12 44	13 06	13 35	13 44	14 06	14 36	14 44	15 06	15 35	15 44	16 06	16 36	16 44	17 06	17 35	17 44	18 06	18 36
Monks Risborough	d			13 39			14 40			15 39			16 40			17 39			18 40
Little Kimble	d			13 42			14 43			15 42			16 43			17 42			18 43
Aylesbury	a			13 56			14 57			15 56			16 57			17 56			18 57
Haddenham & Thame Parkway	d	12 51	13 13		13 51	14 13		14 51	15 13		15 51	16 13		16 51	17 13		17 51	18 13	
Bicester North 3	a	13 04	13 26		14 04	14 26		15 04	15 26		16 04	16 26		17 04	17 26		18 04	18 26	
	d	13 05	13 26		14 05	14 26		15 05	15 26		16 05	16 26		17 05	17 26		18 05	18 26	
Kings Sutton	d		13 39						15 39						17 39				
Banbury	d	13 22	13 45		14 23	14 43		15 22	15 45		16 22	16 42		17 22	17 45		18 23	18 43	
Leamington Spa 8	d	13a42	14 05		14a42	15 03		15a42	16 05		16a42	17 03		17a42	18 05		18a42	19 03	
Warwick	d		14 15			15 14			16 15			17 14			18 15			19 14	
Warwick Parkway	d		14a21			15a19			16a21			17a19			18a21			19a19	
Hatton	d																		
Claverdon	d																		
Bearley	d																		
Wilmcote	d																		
Stratford-upon-Avon	a																		
Lapworth	a																		
Dorridge	a																		
Solihull	a																		
Birmingham Moor Street	a																		
Birmingham Snow Hill	🚋 a																		
Rowley Regis	a																		
Cradley Heath	a																		
Stourbridge Junction 2	a																		
Kidderminster	a																		

For general notes see front of timetable
For details of catering facilities see Directory of Train Operators

§ London Underground Limited (Central Line) also operate services between South Ruislip and West Ruislip at frequent intervals

A To Birmingham New Street (Table 71)

Table 115

from 30 March

London → High Wycombe, Aylesbury, Banbury, Stratford-upon-Avon, Birmingham Snow Hill and Kidderminster

Network Diagram - See first page of Table 114

		CH A	CH	CH		CH	CH	CH		CH	CH	CH		CH	CH	CH		CH	CH	CH		CH			
London Marylebone [10]	⊖ d	18 00	18 20	18 40		19 00	19 20	19 40		20 00	20 20	20 40		21 00	21 20	21 40		22 10	22 45			23 45			
London Paddington [15]	⊖ d																								
Wembley Stadium	d		18 29	18 49			19 29	19 49				20 49			21 29			22 19	22 54			23 54			
Sudbury & Harrow Road	d																								
Sudbury Hill Harrow	d																								
Northolt Park	d			18 54				19 54				20 54						22 24	22 59			00 01			
South Ruislip §	⊖ d			18 58				19 58				20 58			21 37			22 28	23 03			00 03			
West Ruislip [3] §	⊖ d			19 01				20 01				21 01						22 31	23 06			00 06			
Denham	d			19 06				20 06				21 06			21 42			22 36	23 11			00 11			
Denham Golf Club	d			19 08								21 08							23 13			00 13			
Gerrards Cross [1]	d	18 21	18 43	19 11		19 21	19 43	20 10		20 21	20 41	21 11		21 21	21 47	22 01		22 40	23 16			00 16			
Seer Green	d							20 14										22 44				00 21			
Beaconsfield	d	18 27	18 49	19 17		19 27	19 49	20 18		20 27	20 47	21 17		21 27	21 53	22 07		22 48	23 22			00 24			
High Wycombe [1]	d	18 34	18 55	19 24		19 34	19 55	20 24		20 34	20 54	21 23		21 34	21 59	22 14		22 54	23 29			00 30			
Saunderton	d			19 30				20 31				21 30			22 05			23 00	23 35			00 37			
Princes Risborough [2]	d	18 44	19 06	19 35		19 44	20 07	20 36		20 44	21 04	21 35		21 44	22 10	22 24		23 05	23 41	23 47		00 43			
Monks Risborough	d			19 39				20 40				21 39			22 14			23 09		23 50					
Little Kimble	d			19 42				20 43				21 42			22 17			23 12		23 54					
Aylesbury	a			19 56				20 57				21 56			22 29			23 26		00 05					
Haddenham & Thame Parkway	d	18 51	19 13			19 51	20 14			20 51	21 11			21 51		22 31			23 48			00 50			
Bicester North [3]	a	19 04	19 26			20 04	20 27			21 04	21 24			22 04		22 44			00 01			01 03			
	d	19 05	19 26			20 05	20 28			21 05	21 25			22 05		22 45			00 02			01 03			
Kings Sutton	d		19 39								21 38								00 14						
Banbury	d	19 22	19 45			20a22	20 45			21a23	21 43			22 22		23 05			00a23			01a23			
Leamington Spa [8]	d	19a42	20 06				21 05				22 04			22a43		23a29									
Warwick	d		20 16				21 15				22 14														
Warwick Parkway	d		20a21				21a20				22a19														
Hatton	d																								
Claverdon	d																								
Bearley	d																								
Wilmcote	d																								
Stratford-upon-Avon	a																								
Lapworth	a																								
Dorridge	a																								
Solihull	a																								
Birmingham Moor Street	a																								
Birmingham Snow Hill	🚌 a																								
Rowley Regis	a																								
Cradley Heath	a																								
Stourbridge Junction [2]	a																								
Kidderminster	a																								

For general notes see front of timetable
For details of catering facilities see Directory of Train Operators

§ London Underground Limited (Central Line) also operate services between South Ruislip and West Ruislip at frequent intervals

A To Birmingham New Street (Table 71)

Kidderminster, Birmingham Snow Hill, Stratford-upon-Avon, Banbury, Aylesbury and High Wycombe → London

Network Diagram - See first page of Table 114

Miles	Miles	Miles			CH	CH	CH	CH	CH	CH	CH	CH	CH	CH		CH	LM	CH	CH	CH	CH	CH	CH	CH	CH
										🛒				🛒									🛒		
—	—	—	**Kidderminster**	d																					
—	—	—	**Stourbridge Junction 2**	d																					
—	—	—	Cradley Heath	d																					
—	—	—	Rowley Regis	d																					
0	—	—	**Birmingham Snow Hill** 🚌	d										05 43			05 58						06 14		
¾	—	—	**Birmingham Moor Street**	d										05 46			06 01						06 17		
7¼	—	—	Solihull	d										05 56			06 16						06 27		
10½	—	—	Dorridge	d										06 01			06 24						06 32		
13	—	—	Lapworth	d													06 28								
—	—	0	**Stratford-upon-Avon**	d												06 10									
—	—	2¾	Wilmcote	d												06 14	06a44								
—	—	4¼	Bearley	d												06 20									
—	—	7½	Claverdon	d												06 25	06x36								
17¼	—	9¼	Hatton	d												06 31									
20	—	12	Warwick Parkway	d						05 40				06 12									06 44		
21¼	—	13¼	Warwick	d										06 15		06 38									
23¼	—	15¼	**Leamington Spa 8**	d						05 45				06 20		06a45							06 49		
43¼	—	—	**Banbury**	d			05 24			06 03				06 38					06 25			06 53	07 07		
46¾	—	—	Kings Sutton	d			05 28												06 29						
57¼	—	—	**Bicester North 3**	a			05 40			06 18				06 53					06 41			07 07			
—	—	—		d			05 40			06 18				06 54					06 42		06 59	07 12			
70¼	—	—	Haddenham & Thame Parkway	d			05 53			06 29									06 55		07 12	07 24			
—	0	—	**Aylesbury**	d	05 05	05 35			05 59		06 25		06 35												
—	4½	—	Little Kimble	d	05 13				06 07				06 43												
—	6	—	Monks Risborough	d	05 17				06 11				06 47												
76	7½	—	**Princes Risborough 2**	d	05 20	05 48	06 02		06 14	06 36	06 39		06 50						07 02		07 19				
79¼	—	—	Saunderton	d	05 25				06 19				06 55								07 24				
84¼	—	—	**High Wycombe 1**	d	05 32	05 58	06 12	06 19	06 26		06 50	06 55	07 02					07 08	07 13	07 21	07 30			07 45	07 50
89	—	—	Beaconsfield	d	05 38	06 04	06 18	06 25	06 32		06 56	07 01	07 08					07 14	07 19	07 27	07 37				07 56
90¾	—	—	Seer Green	d	05 41	06 07			06 35				07 12							07 30					
93¼	—	—	Gerrards Cross 1	d	05 45	06 12	06 24	06 30	06 40		07 01	07 07	07 16					07 20		07 34	07 42			07 54	08 02
95	—	—	Denham Golf Club	d	05 48			06 33				07 10													
96	—	—	Denham	d	05 51	06 16			06 44			07 12								07 38					08 06
98¾	—	0	West Ruislip 8 §	⊖ d	05 55			06 38	06 48			07 17						07b35							
100½	—	—	South Ruislip §	⊖ d	05 59			06 42			07 09									07 44					08 12
102¼	—	—	Northolt Park	d	06 02			06 46	06 54			07 22						07 41						08 04	
103¼	—	—	Sudbury Hill Harrow	d				06 48										07 43							
104	—	—	Sudbury & Harrow Road	d				06 51										07 46							
105½	—	—	Wembley Stadium	d	06 07		06 37	06 53	06 59			07 27								07 51				08 09	08 19
—	—	12	**London Paddington 15**	⊖ a																					
112	—	—	**London Marylebone 10**	⊖ a	06 21	06 39	06 50	07 07	07 12	07 18	07 29	07 40	07 44	07 52				08 01	07 48	08 04	08 07	08 10	08 16	08 25	08 32

		CH	CH		CH	CH	CH	CH	CH	CH	CH	CH	CH	CH		CH	CH	CH	CH	CH	CH	CH	CH	CH	CH
							A 🛒					A 🛒						A 🛒							
Kidderminster	d						06 09					06 30						06 56				07 30			
Stourbridge Junction 2	d						06 17					06 39						07 07				07 40			
Cradley Heath	d						06 24					06 44						07 14				07 45			
Rowley Regis	d						06 30					06 50						07 22				07 53			
Birmingham Snow Hill 🚌	d						06 50					07 13						07 45				08 12			
Birmingham Moor Street	d						06 53					07 16						07 48				08 15			
Solihull	d						07 04					07 26						07 58				08 25			
Dorridge	d						07 09					07 31						08 03				08 30			
Lapworth	d																	08 07							
Stratford-upon-Avon	d					06 46											07 36								
Wilmcote	d																07 40								
Bearley	d																07 46								
Claverdon	d																07 51								
Hatton	d					07 03											07 56	08 13							
Warwick Parkway	d					07 09	07 21					07 43						08 19				08 41			
Warwick	d					07 13						07 46					08 05	08 23				08 44			
Leamington Spa 8	d					07 18	07 26					07 50					08 09	08 27				08 49			
Banbury	d		07 21			07 36	07 44				07 50	08 08					08 28	08 45				09 09	09 15		
Kings Sutton	d																08 33								
Bicester North 3	a		07 35			07 51					08 04	08 24					08 46	08 59					09 30		
	d		07 35			07 51					08 04	08 24					08 47	08 59			09 11		09 30		
Haddenham & Thame Parkway	d		07 47			08 03					08 16	08 36					08 58	09 11			09 24		09 42		
Aylesbury	d	07 29			07 44			07 55						08 35		08 45								09 41	
Little Kimble	d	07 37						08 03								08 53								09 49	
Monks Risborough	d	07 41						08 07								08 57								09 53	
Princes Risborough 2	d	07 44	07 53		07 58			08a13			08 22			08 49		09a03	09 06				09 31		09 49	09a59	
Saunderton	d				08 03						08 29										09 36				
High Wycombe 1	d	07 55			08 10					08 25	08 36		08 54	09 00			09 16			09 35	09 42	09 46	09 59		
Beaconsfield	d	08 01			08 16					08 31	08 42		09 00	09 06			09 22			09 41	09 49				
Seer Green	d	08 05								08 34				09 09						09 44					
Gerrards Cross 1	d				08 21				08 16	08 38	08 47		09 05	09 13			09 27		09 40	09 48	09 54				10 03
Denham Golf Club	d								08 19				09 08												10 06
Denham	d								08 21	08 42			09 11						09 44						10 08
West Ruislip 8 §	⊖ d	08 14							08c33				09e21						09 45						10 12
South Ruislip §	⊖ d									08 48			09 24						09 48						
Northolt Park	d								08 38					09 23					09 52						
Sudbury Hill Harrow	d								08 41				09 29												
Sudbury & Harrow Road	d								08 43				09 31												
Wembley Stadium	d		08 25							08 55	09 00		09 34							10 03					
London Paddington 15	⊖ a																								10 43
London Marylebone 10	⊖ a	08 35	08 38		08 47	08 50	08 53		09 02	09 09	09 16	09 23	09 49	09 41			09 53	09 59	10 13	10 17	10 21	10 25	10 36		

For general notes see front of timetable
For details of catering facilities see Directory of Train Operators

§ London Underground Limited (Central Line) also operate services between South Ruislip and West Ruislip at frequent intervals

A 🛒 from Birmingham Snow Hill
b Arr. 0727
c Arr. 0825
e Arr. 0914

Kidderminster, Birmingham Snow Hill, Stratford-upon-Avon, Banbury, Aylesbury and High Wycombe → London

Network Diagram - See first page of Table 114

		CH	CH		CH	CH	CH	CH	CH	CH	CH	CH	CH	CH		CH	CH	CH	CH	CH	CH	CH	CH	CH	CH
Kidderminster	d				08 10																				
Stourbridge Junction 2	d				08 23																				
Cradley Heath	d				08 28																				
Rowley Regis	d				08 34																				
Birmingham Snow Hill	d				08 52			09 12				09 52				10 12				10 52			11 12		
Birmingham Moor Street	d				08 55			09 15				09 55				10 15				10 55			11 15		
Solihull	d				09 05			09 25				10 05				10 25				11 05			11 25		
Dorridge	d				09 10			09 30				10 11				10 30				11 10			11 31		
Lapworth	d							09 34								10 34									
Stratford-upon-Avon	d										09 41														
Wilmcote	d										09 45														
Bearley	d										09 51														
Claverdon	d																								
Hatton	d							09 40			10 00					10 40									
Warwick Parkway	d				09 21			09 45				10 22				10 45				11 21			11 41		
Warwick	d				09 24			09 49			10 06	10 25				10 49				11 24			11 45		
Leamington Spa 8	d				09 29			09 54			10 11	10 29				10 54				11 29			11 52		
Banbury	d				09 47			10 12			10 29	10 47				11 13				11 47			12 09		
Kings Sutton	d										10 34														
Bicester North 3	a				10 03			10 28			10 46	11 03				11 28				12 03			12 24		
	d		09 47		10 04			10 28			10 46	11 04		11 12		11 28			11 44	12 04			12 24		
Haddenham & Thame Parkway	d		10 00					10 40			10 59			11 25		11 40			11 57				12 36		
Aylesbury	d								10 38								11 38							12 38	
Little Kimble	d								10 46								11 46							12 46	
Monks Risborough	d								10 50								11 50							12 50	
Princes Risborough 2	d		10 06				10 33	10 47	10a56		11 06			11 32		11 47	11a56		12 05			12 33	12 43	12a56	
Saunderton	d						10 38							11 37								12 38			
High Wycombe 1	d	10 04	10 18			10 32	10 44	10 57		11 02	11 16		11 32	11 43		11 57		12 02	12 15		12 32	12 44	12 53		13 02
Beaconsfield	d	10 10	10 24			10 38	10 51			11 08	11 22		11 38	11 50				12 08	12 21		12 38	12 50			13 08
Seer Green	d	10 13				10 41				11 11			11 41					12 11			12 41				13 11
Gerrards Cross 1	d	10 17	10 29			10 45	10 56			11 15	11 27		11 45	11 55				12 15	12 26		12 45	12 56			13 15
Denham Golf Club	d					10 48							11 48								12 48				
Denham	d	10 21				10 50				11 19			11 50					12 19			12 50				13 20
West Ruislip 3 §	⊖ d					10 55							11 55								12 55				
South Ruislip §	⊖ d	10 27								11 25								12 25							13 26
Northolt Park	d	10 30				11 00				11 28			12 00					12 28			13 00				13 29
Sudbury Hill Harrow	d	10 33								11 31								12 31							13 32
Sudbury & Harrow Road	d																								
Wembley Stadium	d	10 37				11 05				11 35			12 05					12 35			13 05				13 36
London Paddington 15	⊖ a																								
London Marylebone 10	⊖ a	10 50	10 55		10 59	11 19	11 22	11 30		11 48	11 56	12 00	12 18	12 21		12 30		12 48	12 51	12 59	13 18	13 21	13 29		13 49

		CH	CH		CH	CH	CH	CH	CH	CH	CH	CH	CH	CH		CH	CH	CH	CH	CH	CH	CH	CH	CH	CH
Kidderminster	d																								
Stourbridge Junction 2	d																								
Cradley Heath	d																								
Rowley Regis	d																								
Birmingham Snow Hill	d		11 52				12 12				12 52			13 12					13 52			14 12			
Birmingham Moor Street	d		11 55				12 15				12 55			13 15					13 55			14 15			
Solihull	d		12 05				12 25				13 05			13 25					14 05			14 25			
Dorridge	d		12 10				12 31				13 10			13 31					14 10			14 31			
Lapworth	d						12 35															14 35			
Stratford-upon-Avon	d	11 40																13 39							
Wilmcote	d																								
Bearley	d	11 48																							
Claverdon	d																	13 50							
Hatton	d	11 59					12 41											13 57				14 41			
Warwick Parkway	d		12 21				12 46				13 21			13 41					14 21			14 46			
Warwick	d	12 05	12 24				12 49				13 24			13 45				14 03	14 24			14 49			
Leamington Spa 8	d	12 08	12 29				12 54				13 29			13 50				14 08	14 29			14 54			
Banbury	d	12 28	12 47				13 12				13 47			14 08				14 27	14 47			15 12			
Kings Sutton	d	12 33																14 32							
Bicester North 3	a	12 45	13 03				13 28				14 03			14 23				14 44	15 03			15 28			
	d	12 45	13 04			13 13	13 28			13 44	14 04			14 24				14 44	15 04		15 13	15 28			15 44
Haddenham & Thame Parkway	d	12 58				13 26	13 40			13 57				14 35				14 57			15 26	15 40			15 57
Aylesbury	d							13 42								14 38							15 38		
Little Kimble	d							13 50								14 46							15 46		
Monks Risborough	d							13 54								14 50							15 50		
Princes Risborough 2	d	13 06				13 33	13 47	14a00		14 05			14 36	14 43		14a56		15 06			15 33	15 47	15a56		16 05
Saunderton	d					13 38							14 41								15 38				
High Wycombe 1	d	13 17			13 32	13 44	13 57		14 02	14 15		14 32	14 47	14 53			15 02	15 16		15 32	15 44	15 57		16 02	16 15
Beaconsfield	d	13 23			13 38	13 51			14 08	14 21		14 38	14 54				15 08	15 22		15 38	15 51			16 08	16 21
Seer Green	d				13 41				14 11			14 41					15 11			15 41				16 11	
Gerrards Cross 1	d	13 28			13 45	13 56			14 15	14 26		14 45	14 59				15 15	15 27		15 45	15 56			16 15	16 26
Denham Golf Club	d				13 48							14 48								15 48					
Denham	d				13 50				14 19			14 50					15 19			15 50				16 20	
West Ruislip 3 §	⊖ d				13 55							14 55								15 55					
South Ruislip §	⊖ d								14 25								15 25							16 26	
Northolt Park	d				14 00				14 28			15 00					15 28			16 00				16 29	
Sudbury Hill Harrow	d								14 31								15 31							16 32	
Sudbury & Harrow Road	d																								
Wembley Stadium	d				14 05				14 35			15 05					15 35			16 05				16 36	
London Paddington 15	⊖ a																								
London Marylebone 10	⊖ a	13 55	13 59		14 18	14 21	14 30		14 48	14 51	14 59	15 18	15 24	15 28			15 48	15 53	16 00	16 18	16 22	16 31		16 49	16 53

For general notes see front of timetable
For details of catering facilities see Directory of Train Operators

§ London Underground Limited (Central Line) also operate services between South Ruislip and West Ruislip at frequent intervals

Table 115

Mondays to Fridays

Kidderminster, Birmingham Snow Hill, Stratford-upon-Avon, Banbury, Aylesbury and High Wycombe → London

Network Diagram - See first page of Table 114

Station		CH	CH	CH	CH	CH	CH	CH	CH	CH	CH	CH	CH	CH	CH	CH	CH	CH	CH	CH	CH	CH	CH
Kidderminster	d																						
Stourbridge Junction [2]	d																						
Cradley Heath	d																						
Rowley Regis	d																						
Birmingham Snow Hill	d	14 52			15 12					15 52				16 12					16 52			17 10	
Birmingham Moor Street	d	14 55			15 15					15 55				16 15					16 55			17 13	
Solihull	d	15 05			15 25					16 05				16 25					17 05			17 23	
Dorridge	d	15 10			15 30					16 10				16 30					17 10			17 30	
Lapworth	d													16 34								17 34	
Stratford-upon-Avon	d								15 41														
Wilmcote	d																						
Bearley	d								15 49														
Claverdon	d																						
Hatton	d								15 58					16 40								17 40	
Warwick Parkway	d	15 21			15 41					16 21				16 45					17 20			17 45	
Warwick	d	15 24			15 44				16 04	16 24				16 49					17 23			17 48	
Leamington Spa [8]	d	15 29			15 49				16 08	16 29				16 54					17 28			17 53	
Banbury	d	15 47			16 07				16 27	16 47				17 12					17 46		17 51	18 11	
Kings Sutton	d								16 32												17 56		
Bicester North [3]	a	16 03			16 23				16 44	17 03				17 28					18 02		18 08	18 27	
	d	16 04			16 23				16 45	17 04		17 17		17 28					18 03		18 08	18 27	
Haddenham & Thame Parkway	d				16 35				16 59			17 30		17 40					18 14		18 21	18 39	
Aylesbury	d					16 39							17 21					18 09					
Little Kimble	d					16 47							17 29					18 17					
Monks Risborough	d					16 51							17 33					18 21					
Princes Risborough [2]	d			16 36	16 44	16a57			17 06			17 37	17a42	17 47		17 55	18 15	18a28			18 30	18 46	
Saunderton	d			16 40					17 12			17 42									18 35		
High Wycombe [1]	d		16 33	16 47	16 54			17 04	17 19	17 26	17 36	17 48		17 57	18 01	18 06	18 25		18 30	18 35	18 41	18 56	19 07
Beaconsfield	d		16 39	16 53				17 10	17 25		17 42	17 55			18 07	18 12	18 31			18 41	18 47		19 13
Seer Green	d		16 42					17 13			17 45				18 10						18 51		19 16
Gerrards Cross [1]	d		16 46	16 59			17 10	17 17	17 30		17 49	18 00			18 14	18 17	18 36			18 46	18 55		19 20
Denham Golf Club	d		16 49				17 13									18 20							19 23
Denham	d		16 51				17 15	17 21			17 53					18 23				18 50			19 25
West Ruislip [3] §	⊖ d		16 56					17 25			17 57				18 21					18 55			
South Ruislip §	⊖ d						17 21									18 28							19 31
Northolt Park	d		17 01					17 31			18 03					18 32				19 00			19 35
Sudbury Hill Harrow	d							17 33							18 27								19 37
Sudbury & Harrow Road	d																						
Wembley Stadium	d		17 06				17 28	17 37			18 08				18 31					19 05			19 41
London Paddington [15]	⊖ a																						
London Marylebone [10]	⊖ a	17 01	17 21	17 25	17 31		17 42	17 51	17 55	18 04	18 24	18 27		18 33	18 45	18 49	19 01		19 08	19 18	19 21	19 33	19 54

Station		CH	CH	CH	CH	CH	CH	CH	CH	CH	CH	CH	CH	CH	CH	CH	CH	CH [1]	CH	CH	CH		
Kidderminster	d																						
Stourbridge Junction [2]	d																						
Cradley Heath	d																						
Rowley Regis	d																						
Birmingham Snow Hill	d		17 52				18 12					19 12				20 12			21 15				
Birmingham Moor Street	d		17 55				18 15					19 15				20 15			21 18				
Solihull	d		18 05				18 25					19 25				20 25			21 27				
Dorridge	d		18 12				18 30					19 32				20 32			21 33				
Lapworth	d						18 34					19 36				20 36			21 37				
Stratford-upon-Avon	d	17 42												19 43	20 00						23 00		
Wilmcote	d	17 46													20 04								
Bearley	d	17 52																					
Claverdon	d	17 57												19 54									
Hatton	d	18 02					18 40					19 42		19 59	20 17	20 42			21 42				
Warwick Parkway	d		18 23				18 45					19 47		20 06		20 47			21 47				
Warwick	d	18 08	18 26				18 49					19 50		20 09	20 23	20 50			21 50		23 21		
Leamington Spa [8]	d	18 12	18 30				18 54					19 54		20 14	20a33	20 54			21 55		23 25		
Banbury	d	18 32	18 48				19 12					20 11		20 32		21 12			22 14		23a43		
Kings Sutton	d						19 17							20 37					22 19				
Bicester North [3]	a	18 47	19 04				19 30					20 26		20 50		21 27			22 32				
	d	18 48	19 04			19 20	19 30		19 50	20 03		20 26		20 50		21 27			22 32				
Haddenham & Thame Parkway	d	19 02				19 33	19 42		20 03			20 37		21 02		21 39			22 45				
Aylesbury	d				19 13						20 16						21 37			23 00			
Little Kimble	d										20 24						21 45			23 08			
Monks Risborough	d				19 24						20 28						21 49			23 12			
Princes Risborough [2]	d	19 09		19 25	19a32	19 40	19 49		20 11		20a34	20 44		21 09		21 46	21 52		22 53	23 15			
Saunderton	d					19 45						20 50					21 57		22 58				
High Wycombe [1]	d	19 19	19 28	19 36		19 51	19 59	20 06	20 21	20 27		20 58	21 05	21 19		21 56	22 06		23 05	23 25			
Beaconsfield	d	19 25		19 42		19 58		20 12	20 27			21 04	21 11	21 25			22 12		23 11	23 31			
Seer Green	d			19 45				20 15					21 14				22 15		23 14				
Gerrards Cross [1]	d	19 31		19 49		20 03		20 19	20 32			21 10	21 18	21 31			22 19		23 18	23 37			
Denham Golf Club	d							20 22					21 21				22 22		23 21				
Denham	d			19 53				20 24					21 23				22 25		23 24				
West Ruislip [3] §	⊖ d			19 57				20 29					21 28				22 29		23 28				
South Ruislip §	⊖ d							20 32					21 31				22 33		23 32				
Northolt Park	d			20 03				20 36					21 35				22 36		23 35				
Sudbury Hill Harrow	d																						
Sudbury & Harrow Road	d																						
Wembley Stadium	d			20 08				20 41		20 49		21 23	21 40			22 18	22 41	23 00	23 40	23 50			
London Paddington [15]	⊖ a																						
London Marylebone [10]	⊖ a	19 57	20 06	20 21		20 28	20 35	20 54	20 58	21 02		21 38	21 53	21 57		22 32	22 55	23 13	23 53	00 04			

For general notes see front of timetable
For details of catering facilities see Directory of Train Operators

§ London Underground Limited (Central Line) also operate services between South Ruislip and West Ruislip at frequent intervals

Table 115

Saturdays

Kidderminster, Birmingham Snow Hill, Stratford-upon-Avon, Banbury, Aylesbury and High Wycombe → London

Network Diagram - See first page of Table 114

		CH	CH	CH	CH	CH		CH	CH	CH	CH	CH		CH	CH	CH	CH	CH		CH	CH	CH	CH	CH	CH
Kidderminster	d										06 37				07 14							08 13			
Stourbridge Junction 2	d										06 45				07 22							08 26			
Cradley Heath	d										06 50				07 27							08 31			
Rowley Regis	d										06 56				07 33							08 37			
Birmingham Snow Hill	d							06 12	06 37		07 12				07 52		08 12					08 52		09 12	
Birmingham Moor Street	d							06 15	06 40		07 15				07 55		08 15					08 55		09 15	
Solihull	d							06 25	06 50		07 25				08 04		08 25					09 06		09 25	
Dorridge	d							06 30	06 55		07 30				08 10		08 31					09 13		09 31	
Lapworth	d										07 34						08 35							09 35	
Stratford-upon-Avon	d													07 35											
Wilmcote	d																								
Bearley	d																								
Claverdon	d													07 47											
Hatton	d										07 40			07b56			08 40								
Warwick Parkway	d							06 41	07 06		07 45				08 20		08 45					09 23		09 43	
Warwick	d							06 44	07 09		07 50			08 03	08 23		08 48					09 27		09 46	
Leamington Spa 8	d							06 49	07 14		07 54			08 08	08 29		08 52					09 32		09 50	
Banbury	d			06 05	06 34			07 08	07 33		08 12			08 27	08 47		09 12				09 28	09 50		10 10	
Kings Sutton	d			06 09										08 32							09 32				
Bicester North 3	a			06 21	06 49			07 23	07 48		08 28			08 45			09 27				09 44			10 26	
	d			06 22	06 49			07 24	07 49		08 28			08 45			09 28				09 46			10 26	
Haddenham & Thame Parkway	d			06 35	07 01			07 35	08 00		08 40			08 58			09 41				09 59			10 39	
Aylesbury	d	05 15	05 56			06 56				07 56						09 06				09 46					10 38
Little Kimble	d	05 23	06 04			07 04				08 04						09 14				09 54					10 46
Monks Risborough	d	05 27	06 08			07 08				08 08						09 18				09 58					10 50
Princes Risborough 2	d	05 30	06 11	06 43		07 11		07 43		08 11	08 47			09 06		09 21	09 49			10a04	10 08			10 47	10a59
Saunderton	d	05 35	06 16			07 16				08 16						09 26					10 13				
High Wycombe 1	d	05 42	06 23	06 53		07 23		07 53		08 23	08 57	09 04		09 17		09c39	09 59	10 04			10 20		10 34	10 57	
Beaconsfield	d	05 48	06 29	06 59		07 29		07 59		08 29		09 10		09 23		09 45		10 10			10 26		10 40		
Seer Green	d	05 51	06 32			07 32				08 32		09 13				09 48		10 13					10 43		
Gerrards Cross 1	d	05 55	06 36	07 05		07 36		08 04		08 36		09 17		09 28		09 52		10 17			10 31		10 47		
Denham Golf Club	d	05 58	06 39			07 39				08 39						09 55							10 50		
Denham	d	06 01	06 42			07 42				08 42		09 21				09 58		10 21					10 52		
West Ruislip 3 §	⊖ d	06 05	06 46			07 46				08 46						10 02							10 57		
South Ruislip §	⊖ d	06 09	06 50			07 50				08 50		09 27						10 27							
Northolt Park	d	06 12	06 53			07 53				08 53		09 30				10 07		10 30					11 02		
Sudbury Hill Harrow	d																								
Sudbury & Harrow Road	d																								
Wembley Stadium	d	06 17	06 58	07 18		07 58				08 58		09 35				10 12		10 35					11 07		
London Paddington 15	⊖ a																								
London Marylebone 10	⊖ a	06 31	07 11	07 31	07 47	08 11		08 29	08 47	09 12	09 30	09 50		09 55	10 01	10 26	10 32	10 49			10 56	11 00	11 20	11 31	

		CH		CH	CH	CH	CH	CH		CH	CH	CH	CH	CH		CH	CH	CH	CH	CH		CH	CH	CH	CH
Kidderminster	d				09 03																				
Stourbridge Junction 2	d				09 15																				
Cradley Heath	d				09 21																				
Rowley Regis	d				09 26																				
Birmingham Snow Hill	d				09 52		10 12					10 52		11 12				11 52		12 12				12 52	
Birmingham Moor Street	d				09 55		10 15					10 55		11 15				11 55		12 15				12 55	
Solihull	d				10 05		10 25					11 05		11 25				12 05		12 25				13 05	
Dorridge	d				10 12		10 31					11 12		11 31				12 12		12 31				13 10	
Lapworth	d						10 35													12 35					
Stratford-upon-Avon	d			09 36													11 38								
Wilmcote	d			09 40													11 42								
Bearley	d			09 46													11 48								
Claverdon	d			09 51																					
Hatton	d			09 56			10 41										11 57			12 40					
Warwick Parkway	d				10 22		10 46					11 22		11 41				12 22		12 45				13 21	
Warwick	d			10 04	10 26		10 49					11 26		11 45			12 03	12 26		12 48				13 24	
Leamington Spa 8	d			10 08	10 30		10 54					11 31		11 49			12 07	12 30		12 52				13 29	
Banbury	d			10 28	10 48		11 12				11 29	11 49		12 07			12 27	12 49		13 11				13 47	
Kings Sutton	d										11 33						12 32								
Bicester North 3	a			10 44	11 04		11 28				11 46	12 05		12 23			12 45	13 04		13 27				14 03	
	d			10 44	11 04		11 28				11 46	12 05		12 24			12 45	13 04		13 28			13 47	14 04	
Haddenham & Thame Parkway	d			10 57			11 40				11 59			12 35			12 58			13 41			14 00		
Aylesbury	d							11 38								12 38						13 38			
Little Kimble	d							11 46								12 46						13 46			
Monks Risborough	d							11 50								12 50						13 50			
Princes Risborough 2	d			11 05			11 47	11a56			12 08			12 43		12a56	13 06			13 49		13a56	14 06		
Saunderton	d			11 10							12 13						13 11						14 12		
High Wycombe 1	d	11 04		11 17		11 34	11 57			12 04	12 19		12 38	12 53			13 18		13 38	13 59			14 18		14 38
Beaconsfield	d	11 10		11 23		11 40				12 10	12 25		12 44				13 24		13 44				14 25		14 44
Seer Green	d	11 13				11 43				12 13			12 47						13 47						14 47
Gerrards Cross 1	d	11 17		11 28		11 47				12 17	12 31		12 51				13 30		13 51				14 30		14 51
Denham Golf Club	d					11 50							12 55						13 55						14 55
Denham	d	11 21				11 52				12 21			12 57						13 57						14 57
West Ruislip 3 §	⊖ d					11 57							13 01						14 01						15 01
South Ruislip §	⊖ d	11 27								12 27			13 05						14 05						15 05
Northolt Park	d	11 30				12 02				12 30			13 08						14 08						15 08
Sudbury Hill Harrow	d																								
Sudbury & Harrow Road	d																								
Wembley Stadium	d	11 35				12 07				12 35			13 13				13 43		14 13				14 43		15 13
London Paddington 15	⊖ a																								
London Marylebone 10	⊖ a	11 48		11 56	11 59	12 20	12 30			12 48	12 58	13 01	13 27	13 30			13 58	14 01	14 28	14 33			14 58	15 01	15 27

For general notes see front of timetable
For details of catering facilities see Directory of Train Operators

b Arr. 0752
c Arr. 0934

§ London Underground Limited (Central Line) also operate services between South Ruislip and West Ruislip at frequent intervals

Table 115

Kidderminster, Birmingham Snow Hill, Stratford-upon-Avon, Banbury, Aylesbury and High Wycombe → London

Network Diagram - See first page of Table 114

		CH	CH	CH		CH	CH	CH	CH	CH		CH	CH	CH	CH	CH		CH	CH	CH	CH	CH		CH	CH
Kidderminster	d																								
Stourbridge Junction 2	d																								
Cradley Heath	d																								
Rowley Regis	d																								
Birmingham Snow Hill	d	13 12				13 52		14 12					14 52		15 12					15 52		16 12			
Birmingham Moor Street	d	13 15				13 55		14 15					14 55		15 15					15 55		16 15			
Solihull	d	13 25				14 05		14 25					15 05		15 25					16 05		16 25			
Dorridge	d	13 31				14 10		14 31					15 10		15 31					16 10		16 30			
Lapworth	d							14 35														16 34			
Stratford-upon-Avon	d			13 40															15 39						
Wilmcote	d																		15 43						
Bearley	d																								
Claverdon	d																		15 52						
Hatton	d			14 00				14 40											15 58			16 40			
Warwick Parkway	d	13 41				14 21		14 45					15 21		15 41					16 21		16 45			
Warwick	d	13 45		14 05		14 24		14 48					15 24		15 45				16 04	16 24		16 49			
Leamington Spa 8	d	13 49		14 11		14 29		14 52					15 29		15 49				16 09	16 29		16 54			
Banbury	d	14 07		14 30		14 47		15 11					15 47		16 07				16 28	16 47		17 12			
Kings Sutton	d			14 35															16 33						
Bicester North 3	a	14 23		14 47		15 03		15 27					16 03		16 23				16 46	17 03		17 28			
	d	14 24		14 47		15 04		15 28				15 47	16 04		16 24				16 46	17 04		17 28			
Haddenham & Thame Parkway	d	14 35		15 00				15 41				16 00			16 35				16 59			17 40			
Aylesbury	d		14 38						15 38							16 38								17 38	
Little Kimble	d		14 46						15 46							16 46								17 46	
Monks Risborough	d		14 50						15 50							16 50								17 50	
Princes Risborough 2	d	14 43	14a56	15 07				15 49	15a56			16 06			16 43	16a56			17 06			17 46		17a56	
Saunderton	d			15 14								16 12							17 13						
High Wycombe 1	d	14 53		15 20			15 38	15 59		16 04		16 18		16 34	16 53			17 04	17 19		17 34	17 56			18 04
Beaconsfield	d			15 26			15 44			16 10		16 25		16 40				17 10	17 25		17 40				18 10
Seer Green	d						15 47			16 13				16 43				17 13			17 43				18 13
Gerrards Cross 1	d			15 32			15 51			16 17		16 30		16 47				17 17	17 31		17 47				18 17
Denham Golf Club	d						15 55							16 50							17 50				
Denham	d						15 57			16 21				16 52				17 21			17 52				18 21
West Ruislip 3 §	⊖ d						16 01							16 57							17 57				
South Ruislip §	⊖ d						16 05			16 27								17 27							18 27
Northolt Park	d						16 08			16 30				17 02				17 30			18 02				18 30
Sudbury Hill Harrow	d																								
Sudbury & Harrow Road	d																								
Wembley Stadium	d			15 45			16 13			16 35				17 07				17 35			18 07				18 35
London Paddington 15	⊖ a																								
London Marylebone 10	⊖ a	15 30		15 58		16 01	16 27	16 33		16 48		16 55	16 59	17 20	17 28			17 48	17 57	18 00	18 20	18 32			18 48

		CH	CH	CH	CH	CH		CH	CH	CH	CH	CH		CH	CH	CH	CH	CH		CH	CH	CH			
Kidderminster	d																								
Stourbridge Junction 2	d																								
Cradley Heath	d																								
Rowley Regis	d																								
Birmingham Snow Hill	d		16 52		17 12					17 52				18 12		19 10		20 10				21 11			
Birmingham Moor Street	d		16 55		17 15					17 55				18 15		19 13		20 13				21 14			
Solihull	d		17 06		17 25					18 06				18 25		19 23		20 23				21 23			
Dorridge	d		17 12		17 31					18 11				18 32		19 30		20 30				21 30			
Lapworth	d				17 35									18 36		19 34		20 34				21 34			
Stratford-upon-Avon	d								17 36								19 53			21 15					
Wilmcote	d								17 40																
Bearley	d								17 46								20 01								
Claverdon	d								17 51																
Hatton	d				17 41				17 56					18 42		19 40	20 10	20 40		21a33		21 40			
Warwick Parkway	d		17 22		17 46					18 22				18 46		19 44	20 16	20 45				21 44			
Warwick	d		17 26		17 49				18 04	18 25				18 48		19 47	20 19	20 48				21 47			
Leamington Spa 8	d		17 30		17 54				18 08	18 29				18 52		19 51	20 23	20 53				21 52			
Banbury	d		17 49		18 12				18 28	18 47				19 12		20 10	20 42	21 15				22b15			
Kings Sutton	d								18 32							20 15						22 20			
Bicester North 3	a		18 04		18 28				18 45	19 03				19 28		20 28	20 59	21 29				22 32			
	d	17 47	18 04		18 28				18 46	19 04				19 28	19 59	20 29	21 00	21 30				22 32			
Haddenham & Thame Parkway	d	18 00			18 40				18 59					19 41	20 12	20 42	21 13	21 43				22 45			
Aylesbury	d					18 38						19 27									21 55				
Little Kimble	d					18 46						19 35									22 03				
Monks Risborough	d					18 50						19 39									22 07				
Princes Risborough 2	d	18 06			18 47	18a56			19 06			19a45		19 50	20 19	20 49	21 21	21 52			22 10	22 54			
Saunderton	d	18 11							19 12						20 25		21 26				22 15				
High Wycombe 1	d	18 17	18 28	18 34	18 57			19 04	19 19	19 28	19 34			20 00	20 31	20 59	21 32	22 02			22c30	23 04			
Beaconsfield	d	18 24		18 40				19 10	19 25		19 40			20 06	20 38	21 06	21 39	22 08			22 36	23 10			
Seer Green	d			18 43				19 13			19 43				20 41		21 42				22 39				
Gerrards Cross 1	d	18 29		18 47				19 17	19 30		19 47			20 12	20 45	21 11	21 46	22 13			22 43	23 16			
Denham Golf Club	d			18 50							19 50				20 48		21 49				22 46				
Denham	d			18 52				19 21			19 52				20 50		21 51				22 49	23 20			
West Ruislip 3 §	⊖ d			18 57							19 57				20 55		21 56				22 53				
South Ruislip §	⊖ d							19 27			20 00				20 58		21 59				22 57	23 25			
Northolt Park	d			19 02				19 30			20 04				21 02		22 03				23 00				
Sudbury Hill Harrow	d																								
Sudbury & Harrow Road	d																								
Wembley Stadium	d			19 07				19 35			20 09				21 07		22 08	22 27			23 05	23 32			
London Paddington 15	⊖ a																								
London Marylebone 10	⊖ a	18 57	19 02	19 20	19 30			19 48	19 56	20 01	20 22			20 37	21 20	21 36	22 21	22 40			23 19	23 46			

For general notes see front of timetable
For details of catering facilities see
Directory of Train Operators

§ London Underground Limited (Central Line) also operate services between South Ruislip and West Ruislip at frequent intervals

b Arr. 2212

c Arr. 2221

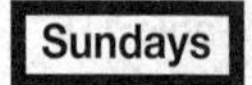

until 27 January

Kidderminster, Birmingham Snow Hill, Stratford-upon-Avon, Banbury, Aylesbury and High Wycombe → London

Network Diagram - See first page of Table 114

		CH	CH	CH 🚲	CH 🚲	CH	CH	CH	CH	CH	CH	CH	CH	CH	CH 🚲	CH	CH	CH
Kidderminster	d																	
Stourbridge Junction 2	d																	
Cradley Heath	d																	
Rowley Regis	d																	
Birmingham Snow Hill	d							09 10		09 40		10 10		10 40		11 10		11 40
Birmingham Moor Street	d							09 13		09 43		10 13		10 43		11 13		11 43
Solihull	d							09 22		09 52		10 22		10 52		11 22		11 52
Dorridge	d							09 28		09 58		10 28		10 58		11 28		11 58
Lapworth	d									10 02								12 02
Stratford-upon-Avon	d																	
Wilmcote	d																	
Bearley	d																	
Claverdon	d																	
Hatton	d													11 05				
Warwick Parkway	d							09 39		10 10	10 21	10 38		11 10		11 38		12 10
Warwick	d							09 42			10 24	10 41				11 41		
Leamington Spa 8	d							09 47		10 16	10 29	10 47		11 16		11 47		12 16
Banbury	d				09 00		09 47	10 06		10 36	10 48	11 06		11 36		12 06		12 36
Kings Sutton	d				09 04						10 53							
Bicester North 3	a				09 17		10 01	10 22		10 51	11 06	11 22		11 51		12 22		12 51
	d			08 24	09 17		10 02	10 22		10 52	11 06	11 22		11 52	12 11	12 22		12 52
Haddenham & Thame Parkway	d			08 37	09 30		10 15			11 05	11 19			12 05	12 24			13 05
Aylesbury	d	07 27	08 18			09 30			10 28				11 30				12 28	
Little Kimble	d	07 35	08 26			09 38			10 36				11 38				12 36	
Monks Risborough	d	07 39	08 30			09 42			10 40				11 42				12 40	
Princes Risborough 2	d	07 42	08 33	08 44	09 37	09 45	10 23		10 43	11 13	11 28		11 45	12 13	12 31		12 43	13 13
Saunderton	d	07 47		08 49		09 50			10 48				11 50				12 48	
High Wycombe 1	d	07 54	08 43	08 55	09 47	09 57	10 33		10 55	11 23	11 38		11 57	12 23	12 41		12 55	13 23
Beaconsfield	d	08 00	08 49	09 02	09 53	10 03	10 39		11 01	11 29	11 44		12 03	12 29	12 47		13 01	13 29
Seer Green	d	08 03		09 05		10 06			11 04				12 06				13 04	
Gerrards Cross 1	d	08 07	08 55	09 09	09 59	10 10	10 45		11 08	11 35	11 49		12 10	12 35	12 52		13 08	13 35
Denham Golf Club	d	08 10				10 13							12 13					
Denham	d	08 13		09 13		10 16			11 12				12 16				13 12	
West Ruislip 3 §	⊖ d	08 17		09 17		10 20			11 16				12 20				13 16	
South Ruislip §	⊖ d	08 21		09 21		10 24			11 20				12 24				13 20	
Northolt Park	d	08 24		09 24		10 27			11 24				12 27				13 24	
Sudbury Hill Harrow	d																	
Sudbury & Harrow Road	d																	
Wembley Stadium	d	08 29		09 29		10 32			11 29		12 03		12 32		13 06		13 29	
London Paddington 15	⊖ a																	
London Marylebone 10	⊖ a	08 42	09 20	09 43	10 27	10 47	11 10	11 23	11 42	12 00	12 16	12 22	12 47	13 00	13 19	13 22	13 42	14 00

		CH	CH	CH	CH	CH 🚲	CH	CH	CH	CH	CH	CH	CH	CH 🚲	CH	CH	CH
Kidderminster	d																
Stourbridge Junction 2	d																
Cradley Heath	d																
Rowley Regis	d																
Birmingham Snow Hill	d		12 10		12 40		13 10		13 40		14 10		14 40		15 10		15 40
Birmingham Moor Street	d		12 13		12 43		13 13		13 43		14 13		14 43		15 13		15 43
Solihull	d		12 22		12 52		13 23		13 52		14 22		14 52		15 22		15 52
Dorridge	d		12 28		12 58		13 29		13 58		14 28		14 58		15 28		15 58
Lapworth	d								14 02								16 02
Stratford-upon-Avon	d																
Wilmcote	d																
Bearley	d																
Claverdon	d																
Hatton	d				13 05								15 05				
Warwick Parkway	d	12 21	12 38		13 10		13 39		14 10	14 21	14 38		15 10		15 38		16 10
Warwick	d	12 24	12 41				13 42			14 24	14 41				15 41		
Leamington Spa 8	d	12 29	12 46		13 16		13 47		14 16	14 29	14 47		15 16		15 47		16 16
Banbury	d	12 48	13 06		13 36		14 06		14 36	14 48	15 06		15 36		16 06		16 36
Kings Sutton	d	12 53								14 53							
Bicester North 3	a	13 06	13 22		13 51		14 22		14 51	15 06	15 22		15 51		16 22		16 51
	d	13 06	13 22		13 52	14 11	14 22		14 52	15 06	15 22		15 52	16 11	16 22		16 52
Haddenham & Thame Parkway	d	13 19			14 05	14 24			15 05	15 19			16 05	16 24			17 05
Aylesbury	d			13 30				14 28				15 30				16 28	
Little Kimble	d			13 38				14 36				15 38				16 36	
Monks Risborough	d			13 42				14 40				15 42				16 40	
Princes Risborough 2	d	13 28		13 45	14 13	14 31		14 43	15 13	15 28		15 45	16 13	16 31		16 43	17 13
Saunderton	d			13 50				14 48				15 50				16 48	
High Wycombe 1	d	13 38		13 57	14 23	14 41		14 55	15 23	15 38		15 57	16 23	16 41		16 55	17 23
Beaconsfield	d	13 44		14 03	14 29	14 47		15 01	15 29	15 44		16 03	16 29	16 47		17 01	17 29
Seer Green	d			14 06				15 04				16 06				17 04	
Gerrards Cross 1	d	13 49		14 10	14 35	14 52		15 08	15 35	15 49		16 10	16 35	16 52		17 08	17 35
Denham Golf Club	d			14 13								16 13					
Denham	d			14 16				15 12				16 16				17 12	
West Ruislip 3 §	⊖ d			14 20				15 16				16 20				17 16	
South Ruislip §	⊖ d			14 24				15 20				16 24				17 20	
Northolt Park	d			14 27				15 24				16 27				17 24	
Sudbury Hill Harrow	d																
Sudbury & Harrow Road	d																
Wembley Stadium	d	14 03		14 32		15 06		15 29		16 03		16 32		17 06		17 29	
London Paddington 15	⊖ a																
London Marylebone 10	⊖ a	14 16	14 22	14 47	15 00	15 19	15 22	15 42	16 00	16 16	16 22	16 47	17 00	17 19	17 22	17 42	18 00

For general notes see front of timetable
For details of catering facilities see
Directory of Train Operators

§ London Underground Limited (Central Line) also operate services between South Ruislip and West Ruislip at frequent intervals

Table 115

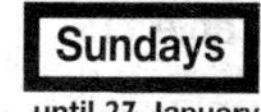

until 27 January

Kidderminster, Birmingham Snow Hill, Stratford-upon-Avon, Banbury, Aylesbury and High Wycombe → London

Network Diagram - See first page of Table 114

		CH	CH	CH	CH	CH 🚲	CH	CH	CH	CH	CH	CH	CH	CH	CH	CH	CH
Kidderminster	d																
Stourbridge Junction 2	d																
Cradley Heath	d																
Rowley Regis	d																
Birmingham Snow Hill	d		16 10		16 40		17 10		17 40		18 10		18 40	19 15	20 15		21 15
Birmingham Moor Street	d		16 13		16 43		17 13		17 43		18 13		18 43	19 18	20 18		21 18
Solihull	d		16 22		16 52		17 22		17 52		18 22		18 52	19 27	20 27		21 27
Dorridge	d		16 28		16 58		17 28		17 58		18 28		18 58	19 34	20 34		21 34
Lapworth	d								18 02								
Stratford-upon-Avon	d																
Wilmcote	d																
Bearley	d																
Claverdon	d																
Hatton	d				17 05								19 05				
Warwick Parkway	d	16 21	16 38		17 10		17 38		18 10	18 21	18 38		19 10	19 45	20 45		21 45
Warwick	d	16 24	16 41				17 41			18 24	18 41			19 48	20 48		21 48
Leamington Spa 8	d	16 29	16 47		17 16		17 47		18 16	18 29	18 47		19 16	19 53	20 53		21 53
Banbury	d	16 48	17 06		17 36		18 06		18 36	18 48	19 06		19 35	20 13	21 13		22b15
Kings Sutton	d	16 53								18 53							22 20
Bicester North 3	a	17 06	17 22		17 51		18 22		18 51	19 06	19 22		19 51	20 29	21 29		22 33
	d	17 06	17 22		17 52	18 11	18 22		18 52	19 06	19 22		19 52	20 29	21 29		22 33
Haddenham & Thame Parkway	d	17 19			18 05	18 24			19 05	19 19			20 05	20 42	21 42		22 46
Aylesbury	d			17 30				18 28				19 30				22 32	
Little Kimble	d			17 38				18 36				19 38				22 40	
Monks Risborough	d			17 42				18 40				19 42				22 44	
Princes Risborough 2	d	17 28		17 45	18 13	18 31		18 43	19 13	19 28		19 45	20 13	20 50	21 50	22a50	22 54
Saunderton	d			17 50				18 48				19 50		20 55	21 55		22 59
High Wycombe 1	d	17 38		17 57	18 23	18 41		18 55	19 23	19 38		19 57	20 23	21 02	22 02		23 06
Beaconsfield	d	17 44		18 03	18 29	18 47		19 01	19 29	19 44		20 03	20 29	21 08	22 08		23 12
Seer Green	d			18 06				19 04				20 06		21 11			23 15
Gerrards Cross 1	d	17 49		18 10	18 35	18 52		19 08	19 34	19 49		20 10	20 35	21 15	22 14		23 19
Denham Golf Club	d			18 13								20 13			22 17		
Denham	d			18 16				19 12				20 16		21 19	22 19		23 23
West Ruislip 3 §	⊖ d			18 20				19 16				20 20		21 24	22 23		23 28
South Ruislip §	⊖ d			18 24				19 20				20 24		21 27	22 27		23 31
Northolt Park	d			18 27				19 24				20 27		21 31	22 31		23 35
Sudbury Hill Harrow	d																
Sudbury & Harrow Road	d																
Wembley Stadium	d	18 03		18 32		19 06		19 29		20 03		20 32		21 36	22 36		23 40
London Paddington 15	⊖ a																
London Marylebone 10	⊖ a	18 16	18 21	18 47	19 00	19 19	19 22	19 42	20 00	20 16	20 21	20 48	21 00	21 50	22 50		23 53

Sundays

3 February to 23 March

		CH	CH	CH 🚲	CH	CH 🚲	CH	CH	CH	CH	CH	CH	CH	CH	CH A	CH	CH	CH A	CH	CH	CH A	CH
Kidderminster	d																					
Stourbridge Junction 2	d																					
Cradley Heath	d																					
Rowley Regis	d																					
Birmingham Snow Hill	d																					
Birmingham Moor Street	d																					
Solihull	d																					
Dorridge	d																					
Lapworth	d																					
Stratford-upon-Avon	d																					
Wilmcote	d																					
Bearley	d																					
Claverdon	d																					
Hatton	d																					
Warwick Parkway	d												10 58			11 58			12 58			13 58
Warwick	d												11 05			12 05			13 05			14 05
Leamington Spa 8	d								09 47	10 13		10 47	11 16		11 52	12 16		12 52	13 16		13 52	14 16
Banbury	d					09 00	09 36		10 06	10 32		11 06	11 35		12 11	12 36		13 11	13 36		14 11	14 36
Kings Sutton	d					09 04				10 38						12 41						14 42
Bicester North 3	a					09 17	09 50		10 22	10 50		11 22	11 51		12 27	12 53		13 27	13 52		14 27	14 53
	d			08 24		09 17	09 51		10 22	10 50		11 22	11 52		12 27	12 54		13 27	13 52		14 27	14 54
Haddenham & Thame Parkway	d			08 37		09 30	10 04		10 35	11 03		11 35	12 05		12 40	13 07		13 40	14 05		14 40	15 07
Aylesbury	d	07 27	08 18		09 05			10 05			11 05			12 05			13 05			14 05		
Little Kimble	d	07 35	08 26		09 13			10 13			11 13			12 13			13 13			14 13		
Monks Risborough	d	07 39	08 30		09 17			10 17			11 17			12 17			13 17			14 17		
Princes Risborough 2	d	07 42	08 33	08 44	09 20	09 37	10 12	10 20	10 43	11 12	11 20	11 43	12 13	12 20	12 48	13 15	13 20	13 48	14 13	14 20	14 48	15 15
Saunderton	d	07 47		08 49	09 25			10 25			11 25			12 25			13 25			14 25		
High Wycombe 1	d	07 54	08 43	08 55	09 32	09 47	10 22	10 32	10 54	11 22	11 32	11 54	12 23	12 32	12 59	13 25	13 32	13 59	14 23	14 32	14 59	15 25
Beaconsfield	d	08 00	08 49	09 02	09 38	09 53	10 28	10 38	11 00	11 28	11 38	12 00	12 29	12 38	13 05	13 31	13 38	14 05	14 29	14 38	15 05	15 31
Seer Green	d	08 03		09 05				10 41						12 41						14 41		
Gerrards Cross 1	d	08 07	08 55	09 09	09 43	09 59	10 34	10 45	11 06	11 33	11 43	12 06	12 34	12 45	13 11	13 37	13 43	14 11	14 35	14 45	15 11	15 37
Denham Golf Club	d	08 10			09 47						11 47						13 47					
Denham	d	08 13		09 13	09 49			10 49			11 49			12 49			13 49			14 49		
West Ruislip 3 §	⊖ d	08 17		09 17	09 53			10 53			11 53			12 53			13 53			14 53		
South Ruislip §	⊖ d	08 21		09 21	09 57			10 57			11 57			12 57			13 57			14 57		
Northolt Park	d	08 24		09 24	10 00			11 01			12 00			13 01			14 00			15 01		
Sudbury Hill Harrow	d																					
Sudbury & Harrow Road	d																					
Wembley Stadium	d	08 29		09 29	10 05			11 06		11 46	12 05		12 48	13 06		13 50	14 05		14 48	15 06		15 50
London Paddington 15	⊖ a																					
London Marylebone 10	⊖ a	08 42	09 20	09 43	10 19	10 27	10 59	11 19	11 31	12 00	12 19	12 31	13 01	13 19	13 36	14 03	14 19	14 36	15 01	15 19	15 36	16 03

For general notes see front of timetable
For details of catering facilities see Directory of Train Operators

§ London Underground Limited (Central Line) also operate services between South Ruislip and West Ruislip at frequent intervals

A From Birmingham New Street (Table 71)
b Arr. 2212

Table 115

Kidderminster, Birmingham Snow Hill, Stratford-upon-Avon, Banbury, Aylesbury and High Wycombe → London

Sundays

3 February to 23 March

Network Diagram - See first page of Table 114

		CH	CH A	CH	CH	CH A		CH	CH	CH A	CH	CH	CH A		CH	CH	CH A	CH	CH A	CH A	CH	CH A	CH		
Kidderminster	d																								
Stourbridge Junction 2	d																								
Cradley Heath	d																								
Rowley Regis	d																								
Birmingham Snow Hill ⛴	d																								
Birmingham Moor Street	d																								
Solihull	d																								
Dorridge	d																								
Lapworth	d																								
Stratford-upon-Avon	d																								
Wilmcote	d																								
Bearley	d																								
Claverdon	d																								
Hatton	d																								
Warwick Parkway	d			14 58				15 58			16 58				17 58			18 58					22 31		
Warwick	d			15 05				16 05			17 05				18 05			19 05					22s37		
Leamington Spa 8	d		14 52	15 16		15 52		16 16		16 52	17 16		17 52		18 16		18 52	19 16	19 55	20 55		21 55	22s41		
Banbury	d		15 11	15 36		16 11		16 36		17 11	17 36		18 11		18 36		19 11	19 36	20 14	21 14		22 16	23s02		
Kings Sutton	d							16 42							18 41							22 21			
Bicester North 3	a		15 27	15 52		16 27		16 53		17 27	17 52		18 27		18 53		19 27	19 52	20 30	21 30		22 34	23s17		
	d		15 27	15 52		16 27		16 54		17 27	17 52		18 27		18 54		19 27	19 52	20 31	21 31		22 35			
Haddenham & Thame Parkway	d		15 40	16 05		16 40		17 07		17 40	18 05		18 40		19 07		19 40	20 05	20 44	21 44		22 48	23s31		
Aylesbury	d	15 05			16 05				17 05			18 05				19 05					22 32				
Little Kimble	d	15 13			16 13				17 13			18 13				19 13					22 40				
Monks Risborough	d	15 17			16 17				17 17			18 17				19 17					22 44				
Princes Risborough 2	d	15 20	15 48	16 13	16 20	16 48		17 15	17 20	17 48	18 13	18 20	18 48		19 15	19 20	19 48	20 13	20 52	21 52	22a50	22 55	23s40		
Saunderton	d	15 25			16 25				17 25			18 25				19 25			20 57	21 57		23 01			
High Wycombe 1	d	15 32	15 59	16 23	16 32	16 59		17 25	17 32	17 59	18 23	18 32	18 59		19 25	19 32	19 59	20 23	21 04	22 04		23 07	23a51		
Beaconsfield	d	15 38	16 05	16 29	16 38	17 05		17 31	17 38	18 05	18 29	18 38	19 05		19 31	19 38	20 05	20 29	21 10	22 10		23 14			
Seer Green	d				16 41							18 41							21 13			23 17			
Gerrards Cross 1	d	15 43	16 11	16 35	16 45	17 11		17 37	17 43	18 11	18 35	18 45	19 11		19 36	19 43	20 11	20 34	21 17	22 15		23 21			
Denham Golf Club	d	15 47							17 47							19 47				22 18					
Denham	d	15 49			16 49				17 49			18 49				19 49		20 38	21 21	22 21		23 25			
West Ruislip 3 §	⊖ d	15 53			16 53				17 53			18 53				19 53			21 25	22 25		23 29			
South Ruislip §	⊖ d	15 57			16 57				17 57			18 57				19 57		20 44	21 29	22 29		23 33			
Northolt Park	d	16 00			17 01				18 00			19 01				20 00			21 32	22 32		23 36			
Sudbury Hill Harrow	d																								
Sudbury & Harrow Road	d																								
Wembley Stadium	d	16 05		16 48	17 06			17 50	18 05		18 48	19 06			19 50	20 05		20 51	21 37	22 37		23 41			
London Paddington 15	⊖ a																								
London Marylebone 10	⊖ a	16 19	16 36	17 01	17 19	17 36		18 03	18 19	18 36	19 01	19 19	19 36		20 03	20 19	20 37	21 04	21 52	22 52		23 56			

Sundays

from 30 March

		CH	CH	CH 🛒	CH	CH 🛒	CH		CH	CH	CH	CH	CH	CH		CH	CH A	CH	CH	CH A	CH		CH	CH A	CH
Kidderminster	d																								
Stourbridge Junction 2	d																								
Cradley Heath	d																								
Rowley Regis	d																								
Birmingham Snow Hill ⛴	d																								
Birmingham Moor Street	d																								
Solihull	d																								
Dorridge	d																								
Lapworth	d																								
Stratford-upon-Avon	d																								
Wilmcote	d																								
Bearley	d																								
Claverdon	d																								
Hatton	d																								
Warwick Parkway	d													10 58				11 58			12 58				13 58
Warwick	d													11 05				12 05			13 05				14 05
Leamington Spa 8	d									09 47	10 13		10 47	11 13			11 52	12 13		12 52	13 13			13 52	14 16
Banbury	d					09 00	09 36			10 06	10 32		11 06	11 33			12 11	12 33		13 11	13 33			14 11	14 36
Kings Sutton	d					09 04					10 37							12 38							14 41
Bicester North 3	a					09 17	09 50			10 22	10 50		11 22	11 49			12 27	12 50		13 27	13 49			14 27	14 53
	d			08 24		09 17	09 51			10 22	10 50		11 22	11 49			12 27	12 51		13 27	13 49			14 27	14 54
Haddenham & Thame Parkway	d			08 37		09 30	10 04			10 35	11 03		11 35	12 02			12 40	13 04		13 40	14 02			14 40	15 07
Aylesbury	d	07 27	08 18		09 05				10 05			11 05				12 05			13 05				14 05		
Little Kimble	d	07 35	08 26		09 13				10 13			11 13				12 13			13 13				14 13		
Monks Risborough	d	07 39	08 30		09 17				10 17			11 17				12 17			13 17				14 17		
Princes Risborough 2	d	07 42	08 33	08 44	09 20	09 37	10 12		10 20	10 43	11 12	11 20	11 43	12 10		12 20	12 48	13 12	13 20	13 48	14 10		14 20	14 48	15 15
Saunderton	d	07 47		08 49	09 25				10 25			11 25				12 25			13 25				14 25		
High Wycombe 1	d	07 54	08 43	08 55	09 32	09 47	10 22		10 32	10 54	11 22	11 32	11 54	12 20		12 32	12 59	13 22	13 32	13 59	14 20		14 32	14 59	15 25
Beaconsfield	d	08 00	08 49	09 02	09 38	09 53	10 28		10 38	11 00	11 28	11 38	12 00	12 26		12 38	13 05	13 28	13 38	14 05	14 26		14 38	15 05	15 31
Seer Green	d	08 03		09 05					10 41							12 41							14 41		
Gerrards Cross 1	d	08 07	08 55	09 09	09 43	09 59	10 34		10 45	11 06	11 33	11 43	12 06	12 32		12 45	13 11	13 34	13 43	14 11	14 32		14 45	15 11	15 37
Denham Golf Club	d	08 10			09 47							11 47							13 47						
Denham	d	08 13		09 13	09 49				10 49			11 49				12 49			13 49				14 49		
West Ruislip 3 §	⊖ d	08 17		09 17	09 53				10 53			11 53				12 53			13 53				14 53		
South Ruislip §	⊖ d	08 21		09 21	09 57				10 57			11 57				12 57			13 57				14 57		
Northolt Park	d	08 24		09 24	10 00				11 01			12 00				13 01			14 00				15 01		
Sudbury Hill Harrow	d																								
Sudbury & Harrow Road	d																								
Wembley Stadium	d	08 29		09 29	10 05				11 06		11 46	12 05		12 45		13 06		13 47	14 05		14 45		15 06		15 50
London Paddington 15	⊖ a																								
London Marylebone 10	⊖ a	08 42	09 20	09 43	10 19	10 27	10 59		11 19	11 31	12 00	12 19	12 31	12 58		13 19	13 36	14 00	14 19	14 36	14 58		15 19	15 36	16 03

For general notes see front of timetable
For details of catering facilities see Directory of Train Operators

§ London Underground Limited (Central Line) also operate services between South Ruislip and West Ruislip at frequent intervals

A From Birmingham New Street (Table 71)

Table 115

from 30 March

Kidderminster, Birmingham Snow Hill, Stratford-upon-Avon, Banbury, Aylesbury and High Wycombe → London

Network Diagram - See first page of Table 114

	CH	CH A	CH	CH	CH A		CH	CH	CH A	CH	CH	CH A		CH	CH	CH A	CH	CH A	CH A	CH	CH A	CH		
Kidderminster d																								
Stourbridge Junction 2 d																								
Cradley Heath d																								
Rowley Regis d																								
Birmingham Snow Hill d																								
Birmingham Moor Street d																								
Solihull d																								
Dorridge d																								
Lapworth d																								
Stratford-upon-Avon d																								
Wilmcote d																								
Bearley d																								
Claverdon d																								
Hatton d																								
Warwick Parkway d			14 58				15 58			16 58				17 58			18 58					22 31		
Warwick d			15 05				16 05			17 05				18 05			19 05					22s37		
Leamington Spa 8 d		14 52	15 16		15 52		16 16		16 52	17 16		17 53		18 16		18 52	19 16	19 55	20 55		21 55	22s41		
Banbury d		15 11	15 36		16 11		16 36		17 11	17 36		18 12		18 36		19 11	19 36	20 14	21 14		22 16	23s02		
Kings Sutton d							16 41							18 41							22 21			
Bicester North 3 a		15 27	15 52		16 27		16 53		17 27	17 52		18 28		18 53		19 27	19 52	20 30	21 30		22 34	23s17		
d		15 27	15 52		16 27		16 54		17 27	17 52		18 28		18 54		19 27	19 52	20 31	21 31		22 35			
Haddenham & Thame Parkway d		15 40	16 05		16 40		17 07		17 40	18 05		18 41		19 07		19 40	20 05	20 44	21 44		22 48	23s31		
Aylesbury d	15 05			16 05				17 05			18 05				19 05					22 32				
Little Kimble d	15 13			16 13				17 13			18 13				19 13					22 40				
Monks Risborough d	15 17			16 17				17 17			18 17				19 17					22 44				
Princes Risborough 2 d	15 20	15 48	16 13	16 20	16 48		17 15	17 20	17 48	18 13	18 20	18 49		19 15	19 20	19 48	20 13	20 52	21 52	22a50	22 55	23s40		
Saunderton d	15 25			16 25				17 25			18 25				19 25			20 57	21 57		23 01			
High Wycombe 1 d	15 32	15 59	16 23	16 32	16 59		17 25	17 32	17 59	18 23	18 32	19 00		19 25	19 32	19 59	20 23	21 04	22 04		23 07	23a51		
Beaconsfield d	15 38	16 05	16 29	16 38	17 05		17 31	17 38	18 05	18 29	18 38	19 06		19 31	19 38	20 05	20 29	21 10	22 10		23 14			
Seer Green d				16 41							18 41							21 13			23 17			
Gerrards Cross 1 d	15 43	16 11	16 35	16 45	17 11		17 37	17 43	18 11	18 35	18 45	19 12		19 36	19 43	20 11	20 34	21 17	22 15		23 21			
Denham Golf Club d	15 47							17 47							19 47				22 18					
Denham d	15 49			16 49				17 49			18 49				19 49		20 38	21 21	22 21		23 25			
West Ruislip 3 § ⊖ d	15 53			16 53				17 53			18 53				19 53			21 25	22 25		23 29			
South Ruislip § ⊖ d	15 57			16 57				17 57			18 57				19 57		20 44	21 29	22 29		23 33			
Northolt Park d	16 00			17 01				18 00			19 01				20 00			21 32	22 32		23 36			
Sudbury Hill Harrow d																								
Sudbury & Harrow Road d																								
Wembley Stadium d	16 05		16 48	17 06			17 50	18 05		18 48	19 06			19 50	20 05		20 51	21 37	22 37		23 41			
London Paddington 15 ⊖ a																								
London Marylebone 10 ⊖ a	16 19	16 36	17 01	17 19	17 36		18 03	18 19	18 36	19 01	19 19	19 38		20 03	20 19	20 37	21 04	21 52	22 52		23 56			

For general notes see front of timetable
For details of catering facilities see Directory of Train Operators

§ London Underground Limited (Central Line) also operate services between South Ruislip and West Ruislip at frequent intervals

A From Birmingham New Street (Table 71)

Table 115A

Mondays to Fridays

Chinnor — Princes Risborough

Bus Service

		CH	CH	CH	CH	CH	CH	CH	CH	CH	CH	CH	CH	CH
Chinnor, Lower Road	d	06 12	06 40	07 34	08 00	09 07	09 36	17 00	17 29	18 22	18 57	19 27	20 29	21 04
Chinnor, Estover Way	d	06 14	06 42	07 36	08 02	09 09	09 38	17 02	17 31	18 24	18 59	19 29	20 31	21 06
Chinnor, The Wheatsheaf	d	06 15	06 43	07 37	08 03	09 10	09 39	17 03	17 32	18 25	19 00	19 30	20 32	21 07
Chinnor, The Red Lion	d	06 18	06 46	07 40	08 06	09 13	09 42	17a06	17a35	18a28	19a03	19a33	20a35	21a10
Bledlow, Village Hall	d	06 21	06 49	07 43	08 09	09 16	09 45							
Princes Risborough	a	06 28	06 56	07 50	08 16	09 23	09 52							

Mondays to Fridays

		CH	CH	CH	CH	CH	CH	CH	CH	CH	CH	CH	CH	CH
Princes Risborough	d							16 50	17 19	18 12	18 47	19 17	20 19	20 54
Bledlow, Village Hall	d							16 57	17 26	18 19	18 54	19 24	20 26	21 01
Chinnor, Lower Road	d	06 12	06 40	07 34	08 00	09 07	09 36	17 00	17 29	18 22	18 57	19 27	20 29	21 04
Chinnor, Estover Way	d	06 14	06 42	07 36	08 02	09 09	09 38	17 02	17 31	18 24	18 59	19 29	20 31	21 06
Chinnor, The Wheatsheaf	d	06 15	06 43	07 37	08 03	09 10	09 39	17 03	17 32	18 25	19 00	19 30	20 32	21 07
Chinnor, The Red Lion	a	06 18	06 46	07 40	08 06	09 13	09 42	17 06	17 35	18 28	19 03	19 33	20 35	21 10

For general notes see front of timetable
For details of catering facilities see Directory of Train Operators

NO SATURDAY OR SUNDAY SERVICE

Solihull → Birmingham International Airport

Bus Service

	CH	CH	CH		CH	CH	CH		CH	CH	CH		CH	CH	CH		CH	CH	CH		CH	CH	CH		CH
Solihull d	05 50	06 20	06 50		07 20	07 50	08 20		08 50	09 20	09 50		10 20	10 50	11 20		11 50	12 20	12 50		13 20	13 50	14 20		14 50
Birmingham Nec (Bus) d	06 07	06 37	07 07		07 44	08 14	08 44		09 14	09 44	10 14		10 44	11 14	11 44		12 14	12 44	13 14		13 44	14 14	14 44		15 14
Birmingham Airport (Bus) a	06 09	06 39	07 09		07 46	08 16	08 46		09 16	09 46	10 16		10 46	11 16	11 46		12 16	12 46	13 16		13 46	14 16	14 46		15 16

	CH	CH	CH		CH	CH	CH		CH	CH	CH		CH	CH	CH		CH	CH	CH		CH	CH			
Solihull d	15 20	15 50	16 20		16 50	17 15	17 45		18 15	18 48	19 18		19 48	20 18	20 48		21 18	21 48	22 18		22 48	23 18			
Birmingham Nec (Bus) d	15 44	16 14	16 44		17 14	17 39	18 05		18 35	19 05	19 35		20 05	20 35	21 05		21 35	22 05	22 35		23 05	23 35			
Birmingham Airport (Bus) a	15 46	16 16	16 46		17 16	17 41	18 07		18 37	19 07	19 37		20 07	20 37	21 07		21 37	22 07	22 37		23 07	23 37			

Saturdays

	CH	CH	CH		CH	CH	CH		CH	CH	CH		CH	CH	CH		CH	CH	CH		CH	CH	CH		CH
Solihull d	05 50	06 20	06 50		07 20	07 50	08 20		08 50	09 20	09 50		10 20	10 50	11 20		11 50	12 20	12 50		13 20	13 50	14 20		14 50
Birmingham Nec (Bus) d	06 07	06 37	07 07		07 44	08 14	08 44		09 14	09 44	10 14		10 44	11 14	11 44		12 14	12 44	13 14		13 44	14 14	14 44		15 14
Birmingham Airport (Bus) a	06 09	06 39	07 09		07 46	08 16	08 46		09 16	09 46	10 16		10 46	11 16	11 46		12 16	12 46	13 16		13 46	14 16	14 46		15 16

	CH	CH	CH		CH	CH	CH		CH	CH	CH		CH	CH	CH		CH	CH	CH		CH	CH			
Solihull d	15 20	15 50	16 20		16 50	17 15	17 45		18 15	18 48	19 18		19 48	20 18	20 48		21 18	21 48	22 18		22 48	23 18			
Birmingham Nec (Bus) d	15 44	16 14	16 44		17 14	17 39	18 09		18 39	19 05	19 35		20 05	20 35	21 05		21 35	22 05	22 35		23 05	23 35			
Birmingham Airport (Bus) a	15 46	16 16	16 46		17 16	17 41	18 11		18 41	19 07	19 37		20 07	20 37	21 07		21 37	22 07	22 37		23 07	23 37			

Sundays

	CH		CH		CH		CH		CH		CH		CH		CH		CH		CH		CH		CH		CH
Solihull d	09 48		10 18		10 48		11 18		11 48		12 18		12 48		13 18		13 48		14 18		14 48		15 18		15 48
Birmingham Nec (Bus) d	10 05		10 35		11 05		11 35		12 05		12 35		13 05		13 35		14 05		14 35		15 05		15 35		16 05
Birmingham Airport (Bus) a	10 07		10 37		11 07		11 37		12 07		12 37		13 07		13 37		14 07		14 37		15 07		15 37		16 07

	CH		CH		CH		CH		CH		CH		CH		CH		CH	CH	CH	CH	CH	CH	CH		
Solihull d	16 18		16 48		17 18		17 48		18 18		18 48		19 18		19 48		20 18	20 48	21 18	21 48	22 18	22 48	23 18		
Birmingham Nec (Bus) d	16 35		17 05		17 35		18 05		18 35		19 05		19 35		20 05		20 35	21 05	21 35	22 05	22 35	23 05	23 35		
Birmingham Airport (Bus) a	16 37		17 07		17 37		18 07		18 37		19 07		19 37		20 07		20 37	21 07	21 37	22 07	22 37	23 07	23 37		

For general notes see front of timetable
For details of catering facilities see Directory of Train Operators

Birmingham International Airport → Solihull

Bus Service

	CH	CH		CH	CH		CH	CH		CH	CH		CH	CH		CH	CH		CH	CH		CH	CH		CH
Birmingham Airport (Bus) .. d	06 12	06 42	.....	07 06	07 39	.....	08 12	08 42	.....	09 12	09 42	.....	10 12	10 42	.....	11 12	11 42	.....	12 12	12 42	.....	13 12	13 42	.....	14 12
Birmingham Nec (Bus) . . d	06 14	06 44	.	07 10	07 43	.	08 16	08 46	.	09 16	09 46	.	10 16	10 46	.	11 16	11 46	.	12 16	12 46	.	13 16	13 46	.	14 16
Solihull .... a	06 31	07 01	.....	07 30	08 03	.....	08 37	09 07	.....	09 37	10 07	.....	10 37	11 07	.....	11 37	12 07	.....	12 37	13 07	.....	13 37	14 07	.....	14 37

	CH	CH		CH	CH		CH	CH		CH	CH		CH	CH		CH	CH		CH	CH	CH	CH	CH		
Birmingham Airport (Bus) .. d	14 42	15 12	.....	15 42	16 12	.....	16 42	17 12	.....	17 42	18 12	.....	18 42	19 19	.....	19 49	20 19	.....	20 49	21 19	21 49	22 19	22 49	.....	.....
Birmingham Nec (Bus) . . d	14 46	15 16	.	15 46	16 16	.	16 46	17 16	.	17 46	18 16	.	18 46	19 21	.	19 51	20 21	.	20 51	21 21	21 51	22 21	22 51	.	.
Solihull .... a	15 07	15 37	.....	16 07	16 37	.....	17 07	17 37	.....	18 07	18 37	.....	19 07	19 40	.....	20 10	20 40	.....	21 10	21 40	22 10	22 40	23 10	.....	.....

Saturdays

	CH	CH		CH	CH		CH	CH		CH	CH		CH	CH		CH	CH		CH	CH		CH	CH		CH
Birmingham Airport (Bus) .. d	05 41	06 12	.....	06 42	07 06	.....	07 39	08 12	.....	08 42	09 12	.....	09 42	10 12	.....	10 42	11 12	.....	11 42	12 12	.....	12 42	13 12	.....	13 42
Birmingham Nec (Bus) . . d	05 43	06 14	.	06 44	07 10	.	07 43	08 16	.	08 46	09 16	.	09 46	10 16	.	10 46	11 16	.	11 46	12 16	.	12 46	13 16	.	13 46
Solihull .... a	06 00	06 31	.....	07 01	07 30	.....	08 03	08 37	.....	09 07	09 37	.....	10 07	10 37	.....	11 07	11 37	.....	12 07	12 37	.....	13 07	13 37	.....	14 07

	CH	CH		CH	CH		CH	CH		CH	CH		CH	CH		CH	CH	CH	CH	CH	CH	CH	CH		
Birmingham Airport (Bus) .. d	14 12	14 42	.....	15 12	15 42	.....	16 12	16 42	.....	17 12	17 42	.....	18 12	18 42	.....	19 19	19 49	20 19	21 19	21 49	22 19	22 49	22 49	.....	.....
Birmingham Nec (Bus) . . d	14 16	14 46	.	15 16	15 46	.	16 16	16 46	.	17 16	17 46	.	18 16	18 46	.	19 21	19 51	20 21	21 21	21 51	22 21	22 51	22 51	.	.
Solihull .... a	14 37	15 07	.....	15 37	16 07	.....	16 37	17 07	.....	17 37	18 07	.....	18 37	19 07	.....	19 40	20 10	20 40	21 40	22 10	22 40	23 10	23 10	.....	.....

Sundays

	CH		CH		CH		CH		CH		CH		CH		CH		CH		CH		CH		CH		CH
Birmingham Airport (Bus) .. d	10 19	.....	10 49	.....	11 19	.....	11 49	.....	12 19	.....	12 49	.....	13 19	.....	13 49	.....	14 19	.....	14 49	.....	15 19	.....	15 49	.....	16 19
Birmingham Nec (Bus) . . d	10 21	.	10 51	.	11 21	.	11 51	.	12 21	.	12 51	.	13 21	.	13 51	.	14 21	.	14 51	.	15 21	.	15 51	.	16 21
Solihull .... a	10 40	.....	11 10	.....	11 40	.....	12 10	.....	12 40	.....	13 10	.....	13 40	.....	14 10	.....	14 40	.....	15 10	.....	15 40	.....	16 10	.....	16 40

	CH		CH		CH		CH		CH		CH		CH		CH		CH		CH		CH	CH	CH		
Birmingham Airport (Bus) .. d	16 49	.....	17 19	.....	17 49	.....	18 19	.....	18 49	.....	19 19	.....	19 49	.....	20 19	.....	20 49	.....	21 19	.....	21 49	22 19	22 49	.....	.....
Birmingham Nec (Bus) . . d	16 51	.	17 21	.	17 51	.	18 21	.	18 51	.	19 21	.	19 51	.	20 21	.	20 51	.	21 21	.	21 51	22 21	22 51	.	.
Solihull .... a	17 10	.....	17 40	.....	18 10	.....	18 40	.....	19 10	.....	19 40	.....	20 10	.....	20 40	.....	21 10	.....	21 40	.....	22 10	22 40	23 10	.....	.....

For general notes see front of timetable
For details of catering facilities see
Directory of Train Operators

Network Diagram for Tables 116, 117, 118, 119, 120, 121, 122, 126

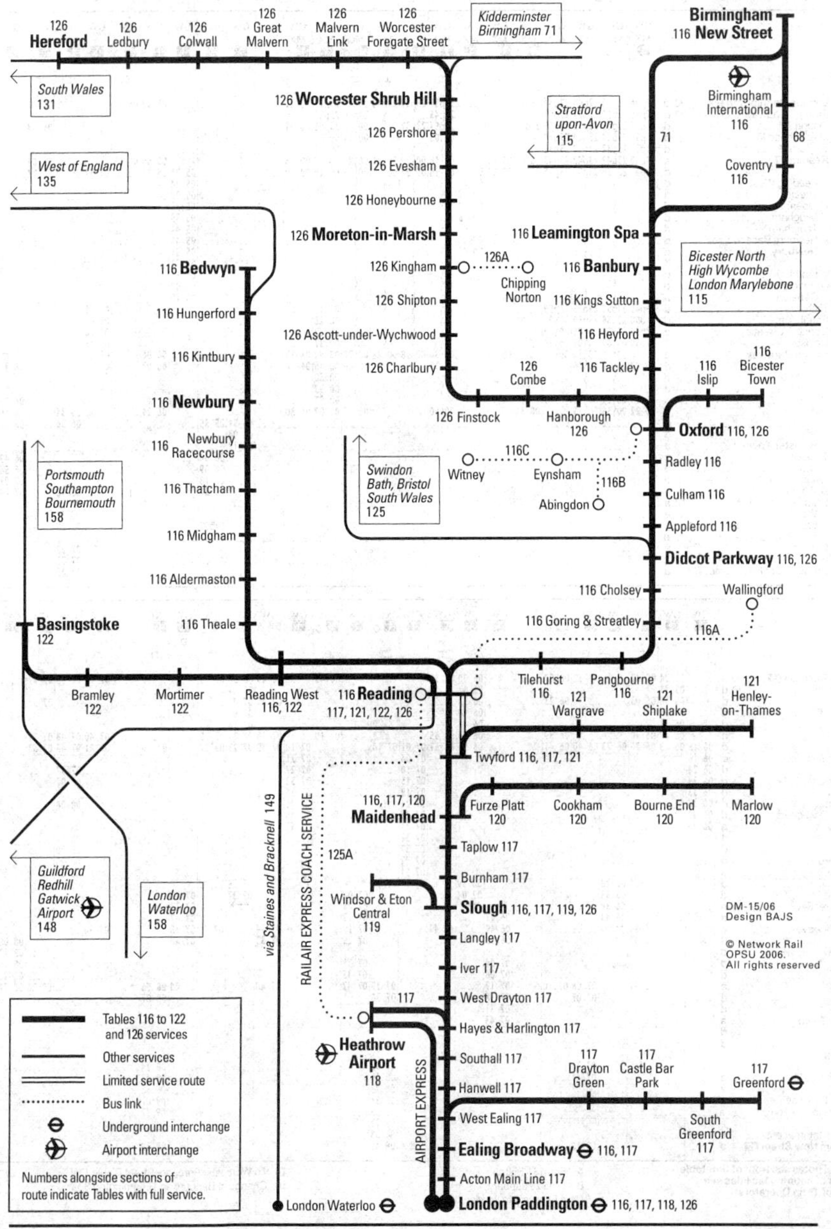

126 Hereford
126 Ledbury
126 Colwall
126 Great Malvern
126 Malvern Link
126 Worcester Foregate Street
Kidderminster Birmingham 71
Birmingham 116 New Street
South Wales 131
126 Worcester Shrub Hill
126 Pershore
126 Evesham
126 Honeybourne
126 Moreton-in-Marsh
126 Kingham
126A
Chipping Norton
126 Shipton
126 Ascott-under-Wychwood
126 Charlbury
126 Combe
126 Finstock
Hanborough 126
West of England 135
Stratford upon-Avon 115
Birmingham International 116
71
68
Coventry 116
116 Leamington Spa
116 Banbury
116 Kings Sutton
116 Heyford
116 Tackley
Bicester North High Wycombe London Marylebone 115
116 Islip
116 Bicester Town
Oxford 116, 126
116C
Witney
Eynsham
116B
Abingdon
Radley 116
Culham 116
Appleford 116
Didcot Parkway 116, 126
116 Cholsey
116 Goring & Streatley
Wallingford
116A
116 Bedwyn
116 Hungerford
116 Kintbury
116 Newbury
116 Newbury Racecourse
116 Thatcham
116 Midgham
116 Aldermaston
116 Theale
Portsmouth Southampton Bournemouth 158
Swindon Bath, Bristol South Wales 125
Basingstoke 122
Bramley 122
Mortimer 122
Reading West 116, 122
116 Reading 117, 121, 122, 126
Tilehurst 116
Pangbourne 116
121 Wargrave
121 Shiplake
121 Henley-on-Thames
Twyford 116, 117, 121
116, 117, 120 Maidenhead
Furze Platt 120
Cookham 120
Bourne End 120
Marlow 120
Taplow 117
Burnham 117
125A
Windsor & Eton Central 119
Slough 116, 117, 119, 126
Langley 117
Iver 117
West Drayton 117
117
Hayes & Harlington 117
Heathrow Airport 118
Southall 117
Hanwell 117
West Ealing 117
Ealing Broadway 116, 117
Acton Main Line 117
London Paddington 116, 117, 118, 126
117 Drayton Green
117 Castle Bar Park
117 Greenford
South Greenford 117
Guildford Redhill Gatwick Airport 148
London Waterloo 158
via Staines and Bracknell 149
RAILAIR EXPRESS COACH SERVICE
AIRPORT EXPRESS
London Waterloo
Tables 116 to 122 and 126 services
Other services
Limited service route
Bus link
Underground interchange
Airport interchange
Numbers alongside sections of route indicate Tables with full service.
DM-15/06 Design BAJS
© Network Rail OPSU 2006. All rights reserved

London and Reading → Bedwyn, Oxford, Bicester, Banbury and Birmingham

Network Diagram - see first page of Table 116

Miles	Miles			GW	GW	GW	GW	GW	GW	GW	GW	GW	GW	GW	GW	GW		GW	GW	GW	GW	GW	GW	XC	GW	GW
				MX	MO	MO	MO	MX	MX	MX	MO	MO	MO	MO	MX	MX										
				1				1 ◇	1 ◇	1	1 ◇	1 ◇	1 ◇	1 ◇	1	1 ◇		1	1	1	1 ◇	1 ◇	1	1 ◇	1 ◇	1
							A				B	A	B	C												
									🛒		🛒	☕	☕	🛒								☕		☕	🛒	
0	—	**London Paddington** 15 ⊖	d	22p46	22p44	22p44	22p44	23p21	23p30		23p37	23p37	23p45	23p42	23p29	00 21					05 22	05 27			05 30	
5¾	—	Ealing Broadway ⊖	d	22p55	22p51	22p51	22p51				23p45			23p50	23p36											
18½	—	Slough 3	d	23p14	23p16	23p15	23p15	23p43			23p57	23p57		00 03	23p55	00 41									05 49	
24¼	—	Maidenhead 3	d	23p25	23p24	23p24	23p24				00 05			00 11	00 03											
31	—	Twyford 3	d	23p33	23p32	23p32	23p32								00 11											
36	—	**Reading** 7	a	23p40	23p42	23p42	23p43	00 01	00 05		00 18	00 20	00 21	00 24	00 18	00 58					05 50	05 55			06 04	
—	0		d	23p41	23p50	23p50	23p55	00 01	00 06	00 15	00 18	00 22	00 21	00 25	00 19	00 59				05 21	05 51		05 57	06 10	06 07	
—	1	Reading West	d							00s21										05 24						
—	5¼	Theale	d							00s27										05 30						
—	8¾	Aldermaston	d							00s32										05 35						
—	10¾	Midgham	d							00s36										05 39						
—	13½	Thatcham	d							00s41										05 44						
—	16½	Newbury Racecourse	d							00s45										05 48						
—	17	**Newbury**	a							00 49										05 51						
—	—		d																	05 51						
—	22½	Kintbury	d																	05 57						
—	25½	Hungerford	d																	06 02						
—	30½	**Bedwyn**	a																	06 10						
38¾	—	Tilehurst	d	23p45	23p55	23p55	23p59								00 23								06 01			
41½	—	Pangbourne	d	23p50	23p59	23p59	00 04								00 28								06 06			
44¾	—	Goring & Streatley	d	23p54	00 05	00 05	00 09								00 32								06 10			
48½	—	Cholsey	d	23p59	00 09	00 09	00 14								00 37								06 15			
53¼	—	**Didcot Parkway**	a	00 06	00 16	00 16	00 21		00 24		00 34	00s38	00s38	00 39	00 44	01 15					06 06		06 21		06 22	⟵
—	—		d	00 07	00 16	00 16					00 35			00 40	00 45	01 16					06 07		06 24 ⟶			06 24
55¼	—	Appleford	d												00 50											
56¼	—	Culham	d												00 53											
58½	—	Radley	d	00 15	00 25	00 25									00 57											06 32
63½	—	**Oxford**	a	00 22	00 35	00 35		00 34			00 50			00 55	01 07	01 30					06 21			06 34		06 40
—	0		d															05 51	05 55					06 36		06 40
—	5¾	Islip	d															06 04								
—	11¾	**Bicester Town**	a															06 17								
72½	—	Tackley	d																06 04							06 49
75¼	—	Heyford	d																06 09							06 54
82¾	—	Kings Sutton	d																06 18							07 03
86¼	—	**Banbury**	a																06 24					06 52		07 09
106¼	—	Leamington Spa 3	a																					07 10		
—	—	Warwick	a																					*07 26*		
—	—	Warwick Parkway	a																*07b09*					*07 30*		
—	—	Stratford-upon-Avon	a																							
115¾	—	Coventry	a																					07 22		
126½	—	Birmingham International	a																					07 33		
135	—	**Birmingham New Street** 12	a																					07 45		

		GW	GW	GW	GW	XC	GW		GW	GW	GW	GW	XC	GW	GW	GW	GW	GW	GW	GW	XC		GW	GW	GW	GW
		1	1	1 ◇	1	1 ◇	1 ◇		1	1	1 ◇	1	1 ◇	1	1 ◇	1	1 ◇	1	1 ◇	1	1 ◇		1 ◇	1	1 ◇	1
																		D		D						
				🛒		☕					🛒		☕		☕				🛒		☕		☕			
London Paddington 15 ⊖	d		05 24	05 42			06 07			06 00	06 30				06 45		06 48	06 30	07 00				07 15	07 18	07 21	
Ealing Broadway ⊖	d		05 31							06 07								06 37								
Slough 3	d		05 58	06 03			06 23			06 33							07 04	07 01							07 37	
Maidenhead 3	d		06 05							06 40								07 09								
Twyford 3	d		06 13							06 48								07 16								
Reading 7	a		06 19	06 20	⟵		06 39			06 54	06 55				07 10		07 18	07 23	07 25				07 40	07 48	07 51	
	d	06 15	06 23	06 20	06 23	06 40	06 41			06 55	06 57	07 01	07 10			07 18	07 20	07 23	07 27		07 40		07 41	07 48	07 53	
Reading West	d	06 18	⟶									07 04				07 21										
Theale	d	06 24										07 10				07 27								07 57		
Aldermaston	d	06 29										07 15				07 32								08 02		
Midgham	d	06 33										07 19				07 36										
Thatcham	d	06 38										07 24				07 41								08 08		
Newbury Racecourse	d	06 42										07 28				07 45										
Newbury	a	06 46										07 31				07 52								08 14		
	d											07 31												08 14		
Kintbury	d											07 37												08 20		
Hungerford	d											07 42												08 25		
Bedwyn	a											07 51												08 33		
Tilehurst	d				06 28					06 59				⟵				07 28		⟵						
Pangbourne	d				06 33					07 04				07 04				07 32		07 32						
Goring & Streatley	d				06 38				⟵	⟶				07 08				⟶		07 37						
Cholsey	d				06 43				06 43					07 13						07 42						
Didcot Parkway	a			06 36	⟶				06 49		07 11			07 19			07 34		07 41	07 48			07 56			
	d			06 37					06 58					07 25			07 35			07 48						08 08
Appleford	d																									08 13
Culham	d								07 04					07 31												08 16
Radley	d								07 08					07 35												08 20
Oxford	a			06 52		07 06	07 10		07 17				07 35	07 42			07 48			08 00	08 06				08 20	08 27
	d					07 07			07 18				07 36								08 07					
Islip	d								07 31																	
Bicester Town	a								07 43																	
Tackley	d																									
Heyford	d																									
Kings Sutton	d																									
Banbury	a					07 24							07 52								08 24					
Leamington Spa 3	a					07 41							08 10								08 41					
Warwick	a					*08 07*							*08 28*								*08 56*					
Warwick Parkway	a					*08 11*							*08 31*								*09 01*					
Stratford-upon-Avon	a																				*09 37*					
Coventry	a												08 22													
Birmingham International	a												08 33													
Birmingham New Street 12	a					08 18							08 48								09 18					

For general notes see front of timetable
For details of catering facilities see Directory of Train Operators

A From 31 March
B Until 28 January
C 4 February to 24 March

D To Worcester Foregate Street (Table 126)
b Change at Banbury and Leamington Spa

London and Reading → Bedwyn, Oxford, Bicester, Banbury and Birmingham

Network Diagram - see first page of Table 116

		GW 1	GW 1◇ A ⊠	XC 1◇ ☕	GW 1◇ A ⊠	GW 1	GW 1	GW 1	GW 1◇ 🛒	GW 1◇ 🛒	GW 1	GW 1◇ 🛒		GW 1	XC 1◇ ☕	GW 1	GW 1◇ 🛒	GW 1◇ 🛒	GW 1◇	GW 1	GW 1	GW 1◇ 🛒	XC 1◇ ☕	GW 1	GW 1◇ ☕	GW 1
London Paddington 15 ⊖	d	07 00	07 30		07 45				07 48	07 51	07 30	08 00					08 15	08 18	08 21		08 00	08 30			08 45	
Ealing Broadway ⊖	d	07 07									07 37										08 07					
Slough 3	d	07 33								08 07	08 03								08 37		08 33					
Maidenhead 3	d	07 40									08 10										08 40					
Twyford 3	d	07 48									08 18										08 48					
Reading 7	a	07 54	07 57		08 10				08 15	08 21	08 24	08 26					08 40	08 45	08 51		08 54	08 57			09 10	
	d	07 55		08 10				08 11	08 16	08 23	08 25	08 27			08 40		08 41	08 47	08 53	08 54	08 55	08 57	09 10			09 11
Reading West	d							08 14																		09 14
Theale	d							08 20										08 55		09 02						09 20
Aldermaston	d							08 25												09 07						09 25
Midgham	d							08 29																		09 29
Thatcham	d							08 34										09 04		09 13						09 34
Newbury Racecourse	d							08 38																		09 38
Newbury	a							08 41										09 10		09 21						09 43
	d							08 41										09 10								
Kintbury	d							08 48																		
Hungerford	d							08 53										09a20								
Bedwyn	a							09 01																		
Tilehurst	d	07 59									08 29					←					08 59			←		
Pangbourne	d	08 04					←				08 34					08 34					09 04			09 04		
Goring & Streatley	d	08 08					08 08				→					08 38					→			09 08		
Cholsey	d	→					08 13									08 43								09 13		
Didcot Parkway	a						08 19		08 31			08 42				08 49	08 56					09 12		09 19		
	d						08 25									08 55								09 25		
Appleford	d															09 00										
Culham	d															09 03										
Radley	d						08 33									09 07										
Oxford	a			08 34			08 41			08 47					09 06	09 14			09 24				09 34	09 39		
	d			08 36		08 39								08 53	09 07								09 36			
Islip	d					08 52																				
Bicester Town	a					09 04																				
Tackley	d													09 02												
Heyford	d													09 06												
Kings Sutton	d													09 15												
Banbury	a			08 52										09 21	09 24								09 52			
Leamington Spa 8	a			09 10										*09 53*	09 41								10 10			
Warwick	a													*09 58*	*09 58*								*10 38*			
Warwick Parkway	a													*10 01*	*10 06*											
Stratford-upon-Avon	a																						*11 08*			
Coventry	a			09 22																			10 22			
Birmingham International	a			09 33																			10 33			
Birmingham New Street 12	a			09 45											10 18								10 46			

		GW 1◇ 🛒	GW 1		GW 1◇ 🛒	GW 1◇ ☕	XC 1◇ ☕	GW 1	GW 1◇ ☕	GW 1	GW 1◇	GW 1	GW 1◇ ☕	GW 1	XC R 1 ☕	GW 1◇ ⊠	GW 1		GW 1◇ 🛒	GW 1◇ 🛒	GW 1	GW 1◇ B 🛒	GW 1◇ C ⊠	XC 1◇ ☕	GW 1	GW 1◇ 🛒
London Paddington 15 ⊖	d	08 51	08 30		09 00	09 05			09 15	09 18	09 21	09 00	09 30			09 45			09 48	09 51	09 30	10 00	10 05			10 15
Ealing Broadway ⊖	d		08 37									09 07									09 37					
Slough 3	d	09 07	09 03								09 37	09 31								10 07	10 01					
Maidenhead 3	d		09 10									09 38									10 08					
Twyford 3	d		09 18									09 46									10 16					
Reading 7	a	09 21	09 24		09 26	09 31			09 40	09 48	09 51	09 52	09 57			10 10			10 15	10 21	10 22	10 26	10 31			10 40
	d	09 23	09 25				09 40		09 41	09 48	09 53	09 53	09 57		10 10		10 11		10 16	10 23	10 23			10 40		10 41
Reading West	d																10 14									
Theale	d									09 56							10 20									
Aldermaston	d																10 25									
Midgham	d																10 29									
Thatcham	d									10 04							10 34									
Newbury Racecourse	d																10 38									
Newbury	a									10 10							10 43									
	d									10 11																
Kintbury	d									10 17																
Hungerford	d									10 22																
Bedwyn	a									10 30																
Tilehurst	d		09 29									09 57		←							10 27					
Pangbourne	d		09 34									10 02		10 02							10 32					
Goring & Streatley	d		09 38					←				→		10 06							10 36				←	
Cholsey	d		09 43					09 43						10 11							10 41				10 41	
Didcot Parkway	a		→					09 49	09 56				10 12	10 17					10 31		→				10 47	10 56
	d							09 55						10 18											10 55	
Appleford	d																								11 00	
Culham	d							10 00																		
Radley	d							10 04																	11 04	
Oxford	a	09 47					10 06	10 13			10 18			10 30	10 34					10 47				11 06	11 13	
	d						10 07								10 36									11 07		
Islip	d																									
Bicester Town	a																									
Tackley	d																									
Heyford	d																									
Kings Sutton	d																									
Banbury	a						10 24								10 52									11 24		
Leamington Spa 8	a						10 41								11 10									11 41		
Warwick	a						*10 58*																	*11 58*		
Warwick Parkway	a						*11 02*																	*12 02*		
Stratford-upon-Avon	a																									
Coventry	a														11 22											
Birmingham International	a														11 33											
Birmingham New Street 12	a						11 18								11 45									12 18		

For general notes see front of timetable
For details of catering facilities see Directory of Train Operators

A The St David
B The Torbay Express
C The Cornish Riviera

London and Reading → Bedwyn, Oxford, Bicester, Banbury and Birmingham

Network Diagram - see first page of Table 116

		GW	GW	GW	GW	GW	XC	GW	GW	GW	GW	GW	GW	XC	GW	GW	GW	GW	GW	GW	GW	XC	GW	GW
		1	1◇	1	1◇	1	R 1	1◇	1	1◇	1	1◇	1◇	1◇	1	1◇	1	1◇	1	1◇	1	R 1	1◇	1
													A											
					🛒		☕	☒		🛒		🛒	☒	☕		🛒				🛒		☕	☒	
London Paddington 15 ⊖	d	10 18	10 21	10 00	10 30			10 45		10 51	10 30	11 00	11 05			11 15	11 18	11 21	11 00	11 30			11 45	
Ealing Broadway ⊖	d			10 07							10 37								11 07					
Slough 3	d		10 37	10 31						11 07	11 01							11 37	11 31					
Maidenhead 3	d			10 38							11 08								11 38					
Twyford 3	d			10 46							11 16								11 46					
Reading 7	a	10 48	10 51	10 52	10 57			11 10		11 21	11 22	11 26	11 31			11 40	11 48	11 51	11 52	11 56			12 10	
	d	10 48	10 53	10 53	10 57		11 10		11 11	11 23	11 23			11 40		11 41	11 48	11 53	11 53	11 56		12 10		12 11
Reading West	d								11 14															12 14
Theale	d	10 56							11 20								11 56							12 20
Aldermaston	d								11 25															12 25
Midgham	d								11 29															12 29
Thatcham	d	11 04							11 34								12 04							12 34
Newbury Racecourse	d								11 38															12 38
Newbury	a	11 10							11 43								12 10							12 43
	d	11 11															12 11							
Kintbury	d	11 17															12 17							
Hungerford	d	11 22															12 22							
Bedwyn	a	11 30															12 30							
Tilehurst	d			10 57		←					11 27								11 57		←			
Pangbourne	d			11 02 →		11 02					11 32								12 02 →		12 02			
Goring & Streatley	d					11 06					11 36				←						12 06			
Cholsey	d					11 11					11 41 →				11 41						12 11			
Didcot Parkway	a				11 12	11 17									11 47	11 56				12 12	12 17			
	d					11 18									11 55						12 18			
Appleford	d																							
Culham	d														12 00									
Radley	d														12 04									
Oxford	a		11 18			11 30	11 34			11 47				12 06	12 13			12 18			12 30	12 34		
	d						11 36							12 07								12 36		
Islip	d																							
Bicester Town	a																							
Tackley	d																							
Heyford	d																							
Kings Sutton	d																							
Banbury	a						11 52							12 24								12 52		
Leamington Spa 8	a						12 10							12 41								13 10		
Warwick	a						*12 41*							*12 58*										
Warwick Parkway	a													*13 02*										
Stratford-upon-Avon	a						*13 11*																	
Coventry	a						12 22															13 21		
Birmingham International	a						12 33															13 33		
Birmingham New Street 12	a						12 45							13 18								13 45		

		GW	GW	GW	GW	GW	XC	GW	GW	GW	GW	GW	GW	GW	GW	GW	XC	GW	GW	GW	GW	GW	GW	XC	GW
		1◇	1◇	1	1◇	1◇	1◇	1	1◇	1◇	1◇	1	1◇	1	1	1	R 1	1◇	1	1◇	1	1◇	1◇	1◇	1
		B				C																			
		🛒	🛒		☕	✕	☕		☕	🛒			☕				☕	☒				🛒	☕	☕	
London Paddington 15 ⊖	d	11 48	11 51	11 30	12 00	12 05			12 15	12 18	12 21	12 00	12 30					12 45		12 51	12 30	13 00	13 05		
Ealing Broadway ⊖	d			11 37								12 07									12 37				
Slough 3	d		12 07	12 01							12 37	12 31								13 07	13 01				
Maidenhead 3	d			12 08								12 38									13 08				
Twyford 3	d			12 16								12 46									13 16				
Reading 7	a	12 15	12 21	12 22	12 26	12 31			12 40	12 45	12 51	12 52	12 57					13 10		13 21	13 22	13 26	13 31		
	d	12 16	12 23	12 23			12 40		12 41	12 47	12 53	12 53	12 57				13 10		13 11	13 23	13 23			13 40	
Reading West	d																		13 14						
Theale	d									12 55									13 20						
Aldermaston	d																		13 25						
Midgham	d																		13 29						
Thatcham	d									13 04									13 34						
Newbury Racecourse	d																		13 38						
Newbury	a									13 10									13 43						
	d									13 10															
Kintbury	d																								
Hungerford	d									13 20															
Bedwyn	a									13 29															
Tilehurst	d			12 27								12 57				←					13 27				
Pangbourne	d			12 32								13 02 →				13 02					13 32				
Goring & Streatley	d			12 36				←								13 06					13 36				←
Cholsey	d			12 41 →				12 41								13 11					13 41 →				13 41
Didcot Parkway	a	12 31						12 47	12 56				13 12			13 17									13 47
	d							12 55								13 18									13 55
Appleford	d							13 00																	
Culham	d																								14 00
Radley	d							13 04																	14 04
Oxford	a		12 47				13 06	13 13			13 18					13 30	13 34			13 47				14 06	14 13
	d						13 07							13 22	13 26		13 36							14 07	
Islip	d														13 39										
Bicester Town	a														13 52										
Tackley	d													13 31											
Heyford	d													13 35											
Kings Sutton	d													13 43											
Banbury	a						13 24							13 49			13 52							14 24	
Leamington Spa 8	a						13 41							*14 14*			14 10							14 41	
Warwick	a						*13 58*							*14 19*			*14 41*							*14 58*	
Warwick Parkway	a						*14 02*							*14 22*										*15 02*	
Stratford-upon-Avon	a													*15 09*			*15 09*								
Coventry	a																14 22								
Birmingham International	a																14 33								
Birmingham New Street 12	a						14 18										14 45							15 18	

For general notes see front of timetable
For details of catering facilities see Directory of Train Operators

A The Mayflower
B The Cheltenham Spa Express
C The Royal Duchy

London and Reading → Bedwyn, Oxford, Bicester, Banbury and Birmingham

Network Diagram - see first page of Table 116

		GW	GW	GW		GW	GW	GW	XC	GW	GW	GW	GW	GW	GW	GW	XC	GW		GW	GW	GW	GW	GW	GW	XC
									R								R									R
		1 ◇	1	1 ◇		1	1 ◇	1	1	1 ◇	1	1 ◇	1 ◇	1	1 ◇	1 ◇	1	1		1 ◇	1	1 ◇	1	1 ◇	1	1
																								A		
		🛒					🛒		🍴	🍴		🛒	🛒		🛒	☒	🍴			🛒				🍴		🍴
London Paddington 15 ⊖	d	13 15	13 18	13 21		13 00	13 30			13 45		13 48	13 51	13 30	14 00	14 05				14 15	14 18	14 21	14 00	14 30		
Ealing Broadway ⊖	d					13 07								13 37									14 07			
Slough 3	d			13 37		13 31							14 07	14 01									14 31			
Maidenhead 3	d					13 38								14 08									14 38			
Twyford 3	d					13 46								14 16									14 46			
Reading 7	a	13 40	13 48	13 51		13 52	13 57			14 10		14 15	14 21	14 22	14 26	14 31				14 40	14 48	14 51	14 52	14 57		
	d	13 41	13 48	13 53		13 53	13 57		14 10		14 11	14 16	14 23	14 23			14 40			14 41	14 48	14 53	14 53	14 57		15 10
Reading West	d										14 14															
Theale	d		13 56								14 20										14 56					
Aldermaston	d										14 25															
Midgham	d										14 29															
Thatcham	d		14 04								14 34										15 04					
Newbury Racecourse	d										14 38															
Newbury	a		14 10								14 43										15 10					
	d		14 11																		15 11					
Kintbury	d		14 17																		15 17					
Hungerford	d		14 22																		15 22					
Bedwyn	a		14 30																		15 30					
Tilehurst	d					13 57		←						14 27									14 57		←	
Pangbourne	d					14 02		14 02						14 32									15 02		15 02	
Goring & Streatley	d					→		14 06						14 36				←					→		15 06	
Cholsey	d							14 11						14 41				14 41							15 11	
Didcot Parkway	a	13 56					14 12	14 17				14 31		→				14 47		14 56				15 12	15 17	
	d							14 18										14 55							15 18	
Appleford	d																	15 00								
Culham	d																									
Radley	d																	15 04								
Oxford	a			14 18				14 30	14 34				14 47				15 06	15 13				15 18			15 30	15 34
	d								14 36								15 07									15 36
Islip	d																									
Bicester Town	a																									
Tackley	d																									
Heyford	d																									
Kings Sutton	d																									
Banbury	a								14 52								15 24									15 52
Leamington Spa 8	a								15 10								15 41									16 10
Warwick	a																*15 58*									*16 41*
Warwick Parkway	a																*16 02*									
Stratford-upon-Avon	a																									*17 12*
Coventry	a								15 22																	16 22
Birmingham International	a								15 33																	16 33
Birmingham New Street 12	a								15 45								16 18									16 45

		GW	GW	GW	GW	GW	GW	XC	GW		GW	GW	GW	GW	GW	GW	GW	GW	XC	GW	GW	GW	GW		GW	GW
								R											R							
		1 ◇	1	1 ◇	1	1 ◇	1 ◇	1	1		1 ◇	1	1 ◇	1	1 ◇	1	1	1	1	1 ◇	1	1 ◇	1		1 ◇	1 ◇
								B							A											
		🍴				🛒	🍴	🍴			🛒				🛒				🍴	🛒		🛒			🛒	🛒
London Paddington 15 ⊖	d	14 45		14 51	14 30	15 00	15 05				15 15	15 18	15 21	15 00	15 30					15 45		15 48	15 30		15 51	16 00
Ealing Broadway ⊖	d				14 37									15 07									15 37			
Slough 3	d			15 07	15 01								15 37	15 31									15 55		16 07	
Maidenhead 3	d				15 08									15 38									16 03			
Twyford 3	d				15 16									15 46									16 11			
Reading 7	a	15 10		15 21	15 22	15 26	15 31				15 40	15 48	15 51	15 52	15 57					16 10		16 15	16 17		16 21	16 26
	d		15 11	15 23	15 23			15 40			15 41	15 48	15 53	15 53	15 57				16 10		16 11	16 16	16 19		16 23	
Reading West	d		15 14																		16 14					
Theale	d		15 20									15 56									16 20					
Aldermaston	d		15 25																		16 25					
Midgham	d		15 29																		16 29					
Thatcham	d		15 34									16 04									16 34					
Newbury Racecourse	d		15 38																		16 38					
Newbury	a		15 43									16 10									16 43					
	d											16 11														
Kintbury	d											16 17														
Hungerford	d											16 22														
Bedwyn	a											16 30														
Tilehurst	d				15 27									15 57				←					16 23			
Pangbourne	d				15 32									16 02				16 02					16 28			
Goring & Streatley	d				15 36				←					→				16 06					16 32			
Cholsey	d				15 41				15 41									16 11					16 37			
Didcot Parkway	a				→				15 47		15 56				16 12			16 17				16 31	→			
	d								15 55									16 18								
Appleford	d																									
Culham	d								16 00																	
Radley	d								16 04																	
Oxford	a			15 47				16 06	16 13				16 18					16 30	16 34						16 47	
	d							16 07								16 22	16 28		16 36							
Islip	d																16 41									
Bicester Town	a																16 53									
Tackley	d															16 31										
Heyford	d															16 35										
Kings Sutton	d															16 44										
Banbury	a							16 24								16 49			16 52							
Leamington Spa 8	a							16 41								*17 22*			17 10							
Warwick	a							*16 58*																		
Warwick Parkway	a							*17 01*								*17 27*			*17 27*							
Stratford-upon-Avon	a																									
Coventry	a																		17 22							
Birmingham International	a																		17 33							
Birmingham New Street 12	a							17 18											17 45							

For general notes see front of timetable
For details of catering facilities see Directory of Train Operators

A To Weston-super-Mare (Table 134)
B To Derby (Table 57)

London and Reading → Bedwyn, Oxford, Bicester, Banbury and Birmingham

Network Diagram - see first page of Table 116

Station		GW	GW	XC	GW	GW	GW	GW	GW	GW	GW	XC	GW
				R								R	
		1 ◇	1	1	1 ◇	1	1	1 ◇	1	1 ◇	1 ◇	1	1
										A			
		☕		☕	☕					☕	🛒	☕	
London Paddington 15	⊖ d	16 05			16 15		16 18	16 21	16 00	16 30	16 33		
Ealing Broadway	⊖ d								16 07				
Slough 3	d							16 37	16 30		16u48		
Maidenhead 3	d								16 38				
Twyford 3	d								16 46				
Reading 7	a	16 31			16 40		16 48	16 51	16 52	16 56	17 03		
	d			16 40	16 41		16 48	16 53	16 54	16 57	17 04	17 10	
Reading West	d												
Theale	d						16 56						
Aldermaston	d						17 02						
Midgham	d												
Thatcham	d						17 08						
Newbury Racecourse	d												
Newbury	a						17 15				17 19		
	d					17 05	17 25				17 20		
Kintbury	d					17 12	→						
Hungerford	d					17 17					17a29		
Bedwyn	a					17 25							
Tilehurst	d								16 58				←
Pangbourne	d								17 03				17 03
Goring & Streatley	d		←						→				17 07
Cholsey	d		16 37										17 12
Didcot Parkway	a		16 43		16 56			17 08		17 12			17 18
	d		16 44					17 09					17 24
Appleford	d		16 49										
Culham	d												17 29
Radley	d		16 54										17 33
Oxford	a		17 02	17 06				17 23				17 34	17 41
	d			17 07								17 36	17 42
Islip	d												
Bicester Town	a												
Tackley	d												17 52
Heyford	d												17 56
Kings Sutton	d												18 07
Banbury	a			17 24								17 52	18 13
Leamington Spa 8	a			17 41								18 10	
Warwick	a			*17 56*									
Warwick Parkway	a			*18 00*								*18 28*	
Stratford-upon-Avon	a			*18 40*									
Coventry	a											18 22	
Birmingham International	a											18 33	
Birmingham New Street 12	a			18 18								18 45	

Station		GW	GW	GW	GW	GW	GW	GW	GW	GW	GW	XC	GW
												R	
		1 ◇	1	1	1	1 ◇	1	1 ◇	1	1 ◇	1 ◇	1	1 ◇
											B		
		🛒						☕		☕	🛒	☕	☕
London Paddington 15	⊖ d	16 45				16 51	16 30	17 00		17 03	17 06		17 15
Ealing Broadway	⊖ d						16 37						
Slough 3	d						16 57						
Maidenhead 3	d						17 04						
Twyford 3	d						17 12				17 28		
Reading 7	a	17 10				17 16	17 19	17 25		17 30	17 35		17 40
	d	17 11		17 11		17 18	17 20	17 27		17 32	17 37	17 40	17 41
Reading West	d			17 14									
Theale	d			17 20							17 45		
Aldermaston	d			17 25									
Midgham	d			17 29									
Thatcham	d			17 34							17 54		
Newbury Racecourse	d			17 38									
Newbury	a		←	17 43						17 46	17 59		
	d		17 25								18 01		
Kintbury	d		17 31								18 08		
Hungerford	d		17 36								18 14		
Bedwyn	a		17 44								18 21		
Tilehurst	d						17 25		←				
Pangbourne	d						17 29		17 29				
Goring & Streatley	d						→		17 34				
Cholsey	d								17 39				
Didcot Parkway	a	17 26				17 32		17 41	17 45				17 56
	d					17 34			17 45				
Appleford	d												
Culham	d								17 51				
Radley	d								17 55				
Oxford	a					17 47			18 02			18 06	
	d				17 46							18 07	
Islip	d				17 59								
Bicester Town	a				18 12								
Tackley	d												
Heyford	d												
Kings Sutton	d												
Banbury	a											18 24	
Leamington Spa 8	a											18 41	
Warwick	a											*19 03*	
Warwick Parkway	a											*19 06*	
Stratford-upon-Avon	a												
Coventry	a												
Birmingham International	a												
Birmingham New Street 12	a											19 18	

Station		GW	GW	GW	GW	XC	GW	GW	GW	GW	GW	GW	GW
						R							
		1 ◇	1	1 ◇	1 ◇	1	1	1 ◇	1	1	1 ◇	1 ◇	1 ◇
				A									
		☕		🛒	☕	☕		🛒			🛒		🛒
London Paddington 15	⊖ d	17 21	17 18	17 30	17 33			17 45			17 48	17 36	17 51
Ealing Broadway	⊖ d												
Slough 3	d												
Maidenhead 3	d		17 40									17 59	
Twyford 3	d		17 48									18 08	
Reading 7	a	17 49	17 54	17 55	18 00			18 10			18 15	18 15	18 20
	d	17 50	17 56	17 57	18 02	18 10				18 11	18 16	18 17	18 21
Reading West	d									18 14			
Theale	d									18 20			
Aldermaston	d									18 25			
Midgham	d									18 29			
Thatcham	d									18 34			
Newbury Racecourse	d									18 38			
Newbury	a				18 16					18 43			
	d								18 22				
Kintbury	d								18 29				
Hungerford	d								18 34				
Bedwyn	a								18 41				
Tilehurst	d		18 01				←					18 24	
Pangbourne	d		18 05				18 05					18 28	
Goring & Streatley	d		→				18 10					18 33	
Cholsey	d						18 15					→	
Didcot Parkway	a			18 11			18 21				18 31		
	d						18 25						
Appleford	d												
Culham	d												
Radley	d												
Oxford	a	18 15				18 34	18 39						18 47
	d					18 36							
Islip	d												
Bicester Town	a												
Tackley	d												
Heyford	d												
Kings Sutton	d												
Banbury	a					18 52							
Leamington Spa 8	a					19 10							
Warwick	a					*19b20*							
Warwick Parkway	a					*19 26*							
Stratford-upon-Avon	a					*19b51*							
Coventry	a					19 22							
Birmingham International	a					19 33							
Birmingham New Street 12	a					19 45							

Station		GW	GW	GW	GW	GW	XC	GW	GW	GW	GW	GW
		1 ◇	1 ◇	1	1 ◇	1 ◇	1 ◇	1	1	1 ◇	1 ◇	1 ◇
		C			D	E				G	H	
		🛒			✕	🛒	☕			☕	☕	
London Paddington 15	⊖ d	18 00		17 30	18 03	18 06				18 15	18 21	18 18
Ealing Broadway	⊖ d			17 37								
Slough 3	d			18 03								
Maidenhead 3	d			18 12								18 40
Twyford 3	d			18 20		18 27						18 48
Reading 7	a	18 25		18 26	18 30	18 35				18 40	18 49	18 54
	d	18 27		18 28		18 36	18 40			18 41	18 50	18 56
Reading West	d											
Theale	d					18 45						
Aldermaston	d											
Midgham	d											
Thatcham	d					18 54						
Newbury Racecourse	d											
Newbury	a					19 00						
	d					19 01						
Kintbury	d					19 09						
Hungerford	d					19 15						
Bedwyn	a					19 23						
Tilehurst	d			18 33								19 00
Pangbourne	d		←	18 38								19 05
Goring & Streatley	d		18 33	18 42					←			→
Cholsey	d		18 38	18 47					18 47			
Didcot Parkway	a	18 41	18 44	→					18 53	18 56		
	d		18 45						18 54			
Appleford	d								19 00			
Culham	d											
Radley	d		18 53						19 05			
Oxford	a		19 00				19 06		19 12		19 17	
	d						19 07	19 10	19 14			
Islip	d							19 23				
Bicester Town	a							19 36				
Tackley	d								19 23			
Heyford	d								19 28			
Kings Sutton	d								19 39			
Banbury	a						19 24		19 45			
Leamington Spa 8	a						19 41					
Warwick	a						*19 58*		*21 00*			
Warwick Parkway	a						*20 02*					
Stratford-upon-Avon	a								*21 43*			
Coventry	a											
Birmingham International	a											
Birmingham New Street 12	a						20 18					

For general notes see front of timetable
For details of catering facilities see Directory of Train Operators

A To Taunton (Table 134)
B To Westbury (Table 135)
C **The Bristolian**
D **The Golden Hind**
E To Frome (Table 123)
G **The Red Dragon**
H **The Cathedrals Express**
b Change at Banbury

London and Reading → Bedwyn, Oxford, Bicester, Banbury and Birmingham

Network Diagram - see first page of Table 116

		GW	GW	XC	GW	GW	GW	GW	GW	GW		GW	GW	GW	GW	XC	GW	GW	GW	GW	GW	GW	GW	GW		XC
		1 ◇	1 ◇	1 ◇	1 ◇	1 ◇	1	1	1 ◇	1 ◇		1 ◇	1 ◇	1	1	1 ◇	1 ◇	1	1 ◇	1	1 ◇	1 ◇	1	1		1 ◇
		A																								
		⊥	⊡P	⊡P		⊥			⊥				⊥		✕				⊥		⊥	⊥				
London Paddington 15 ⊖	d	18 30	18 36			18 45			18 48	18 33		18 51	19 00	18 30	19 03				19 15		19 21	19 30	19 14			
Ealing Broadway ⊖	d													18 37												
Slough 3	d											19 07		19 03							19 37		19 41			
Maidenhead 3	d									18 53				19 12									19 50			
Twyford 3	d									19 03				19 20									19 58			
Reading 7	a	18 55	19 02			19 10			19 15	19 10		19 21	19 26	19 26	19 31				19 40		19 51	19 57	20 05			
	d	18 57	19 03	19 10				19 12	19 16	19 17		19 23	19 27	19 28	19 32	19 40			19 41	19 42	19 53					20 10
Reading West	d							19 15												19 45						
Theale	d							19 21												19 51						
Aldermaston	d							19 27												19 56						
Midgham	d							19 30												20 00						
Thatcham	d							19 35												20 05						
Newbury Racecourse	d							19 40												20 09						
Newbury	a		19 18					19 43							19 48					20 16						
	d		19 19				19 24													20 32						
Kintbury	d						19 30													20 38						
Hungerford	d		19a28				19 35													20 43						
Bedwyn	a						19 43													20 51						
Tilehurst	d				←					19 24				19 32												
Pangbourne	d				19 05					19 30				19 37			←	←								
Goring & Streatley	d				19 09					19 35				19 41			19 35	19 41								
Cholsey	d				19 14					→				→			19 41	19 46								
Didcot Parkway	a	19 11			19 20				19 31				19 42				19 48	19 52	19 56					←		
	d				19 25												19 55	20 08 →						20 08		
Appleford	d				19 31																					
Culham	d				19 33																					
Radley	d				19 37												20 03							20 16		
Oxford	a			19 34	19 45							19 50				20 06	20 12				20 19			20 24		20 34
	d			19 36												20 07										20 36
Islip	d																									
Bicester Town	a																									
Tackley	d																									
Heyford	d																									
Kings Sutton	d																									
Banbury	a			19 52												20 24										20 52
Leamington Spa 8	a			20 10												20 41										21 10
Warwick	a															*21 00*										
Warwick Parkway	a			*20 28*												*21 03*										*21 30*
Stratford-upon-Avon	a															*21 43*										
Coventry	a			20 22																						21 22
Birmingham International	a			20 33																						21 33
Birmingham New Street 12	a			20 48												21 18										21 45

		GW	GW	GW	GW	GW	GW	GW	GW	GW	GW	GW	GW	XC		GW	GW	GW	GW	GW	GW	GW	GW	GW	GW	GW
		1	1 ◇	1 ◇	1	1 ◇	1 ◇	1	1 ◇	1	1 ◇	1	1 ◇	1 ◇		1 ◇	1	1 ◇	1	1 ◇	1 ◇	1	1	1 ◇	1	1 ◇
		B																								
			⊡P	⊥			⊡P		⊥				⊥			⊥				⊡P				⊡P		
London Paddington 15 ⊖	d		19 45	19 48	19 17	19 51	20 00		20 15		20 19	20 00	20 35			20 45		20 51	20 30	21 15	21 21	21 00		21 45	21 30	21 48
Ealing Broadway ⊖	d				19 25							20 07							20 37			21 07			21 37	
Slough 3	d				19 44	20 07					20 36	20 31						21 07	21 01		21 37	21 31			21 55	22 05
Maidenhead 3	d				19 56							20 38							21 08			21 38			22 02	
Twyford 3	d				20 04							20 46							21 16			21 46			22 10	
Reading 7	a		20 10	20 15	20 15	20 21	20 26		20 40		20 52	20 52	21 00			21 10		21 21	21 22	21 40	21 51	21 52		22 10	22 17	22 21
	d		20 11	20 16	20 18	20 23	20 27		20 41	20 44	20 53	20 53		21 10		21 12		21 22	21 28	21 41	21 53	21 58	22 00	22 12	22 26 →	22 21
Reading West	d									20 47													22 03			
Theale	d									20 53													22 09			
Aldermaston	d									20 58													22 14			
Midgham	d									21 02													22 18			
Thatcham	d									21 07													22 23			
Newbury Racecourse	d									21 11													22 27			
Newbury	a		20 26							21 14													22 30			
	d									21 23													22 30			
Kintbury	d									21 29													22 37			
Hungerford	d									21 34													22 42			
Bedwyn	a									21 42													22 50			
Tilehurst	d				20 22							20 57							21 32			22 02				
Pangbourne	d				20 27							21 02							21 37			22 07				
Goring & Streatley	d				20 31			←				21 06							21 41			22 11				
Cholsey	d				20 36			20 36				21 11							21 46			22 16				
Didcot Parkway	a			20 31	→		20 42	20 42	20 56			21 17				21 26			21 53	22 00		22 23		22 31		
	d							20 43				21 18							21 54			22 24				
Appleford	d							20 48											21 59							
Culham	d							20 51											22 02							
Radley	d							20 55											22 06							
Oxford	a					20 47		21 02			21 16	21 30		21 34				21 50	22 13		22 20	22 36				22 50
	d	20 39												21 36			21 39									
Islip	d																									
Bicester Town	a																									
Tackley	d	20 48															21 48									
Heyford	d	20 52															21 52									
Kings Sutton	d	21 01															22 01									
Banbury	a	21 07												21 52			22 07									
Leamington Spa 8	a	*22 04*												22 10			*23 05*									
Warwick	a	*22 10*															*23 10*									
Warwick Parkway	a	*22 13*												*22 32*			*23 13*									
Stratford-upon-Avon	a																									
Coventry	a													22 22												
Birmingham International	a													22 33												
Birmingham New Street 12	a													22 52												

For general notes see front of timetable
For details of catering facilities see Directory of Train Operators

A To Weston-super-Mare (Table 134)
B From Bicester Town

London and Reading → Bedwyn, Oxford, Bicester, Banbury and Birmingham

Network Diagram - see first page of Table 116

		GW	GW	GW FO	GW FO		GW FX	GW FO	GW FO	GW FX	GW	GW FX	GW FX	GW FO	GW FX	GW FO	GW FX	GW	GW FO		GW FX	GW FO	GW FX	GW		
		1	1	1 ◇	1		1 ◇	1 ◇	1	1	1	1 ◇	1	1 ◇	1 ◇	1 ◇	1 ◇	1	1 ◇		1 ◇	1 ◇	1 ◇	1		
														A												
				🍴			🍴							🛒	🛒							🛒	🛒			
London Paddington 15 ⊖	d			22 15	21 59		22 15	22 21		21 57		22 21		22 45	22 45	22 51	22 48	22 46	23 21		23 21	23 30	23 30	23 29		
Ealing Broadway ⊖	d				22 06					22 04								22 55						23 36		
Slough 3	d				22 23			22 39		22 33		22 43				23 09	23 07	23 14	23 39		23 43			23 55		
Maidenhead 3	d				22 32					22 41								23 25						00 03		
Twyford 3	d				22 40					22 48								23 33						00 11		
Reading 7	a		←	22 40	22 46		22 48	22 55		22 56		23 02		23 10	23 18	23 25	23 34	23 40	23 55		00 01	00 01	00 05	00 18		
	d		22 26	22 41	22 48		22 49	22 55		22 56	23 00	23 02		23 11	23 18	23 25	23 35	23 41	23 55		00 01	00 02	00 06	00 19		
Reading West	d										23 03															
Theale	d										23 09															
Aldermaston	d										23 14															
Midgham	d										23 18															
Thatcham	d										23 23															
Newbury Racecourse	d										23 27															
Newbury	a										23 30															
	d										23 30															
Kintbury	d										23 37															
Hungerford	d										23 42															
Bedwyn	a										23 50															
Tilehurst	d		22 32		22 52					23 01								23 45						00 23		
Pangbourne	d		22 36		22 57				←	23 05			←					23 50						00 28		
Goring & Streatley	d		22 41		23 01 →				23 01	23 10 →			23 10					23 54						00 32		
Cholsey	d		22 46						23 06				23 15					23 59						00 37		
Didcot Parkway	a		22 53	23 00			23 07		23 12				23 21	23 30	23 37			00 06				00 20	00 24	00 44		
	d		22 53						23 16				23 24					00 07						00 45		
Appleford	d		22 59																					00 50		
Culham	d		23 01																					00 53		
Radley	d		23 05															00 15						00 57		
Oxford	a		23 13					23 25	23 31			23 33	23 41			23 51	00 09	00 22	00 28		00 34			01 07		
	d	22 56																								
Islip	d																									
Bicester Town	a																									
Tackley	d	23 05																								
Heyford	d	23 10																								
Kings Sutton	d	23 19																								
Banbury	a	23 25																								
Leamington Spa 8	a																									
Warwick	a																									
Warwick Parkway	a																									
Stratford-upon-Avon	a																									
Coventry	a																									
Birmingham International	a																									
Birmingham New Street 12	a																									

For general notes see front of timetable
For details of catering facilities see
Directory of Train Operators

A 🛒 to Reading

Table 116

Saturdays

until 26 January

London and Reading → Bedwyn, Oxford, Bicester, Banbury and Birmingham

Network Diagram - see first page of Table 116

	GW 1	GW 1◇ 🚌	GW 1	GW 1	GW 1◇	GW 1	GW 1	GW 1	GW 1◇	GW 1	GW 1	GW 1	GW 1◇ 🚌		GW 1	XC 1◇ ☕	GW 1	GW 1	GW 1◇	GW 1◇ ☕	GW 1	XC 1◇ ☕	GW 1	GW 1	GW 1◇ ☕
London Paddington 15 ⊖ d	22p46	23p30		23p29	00 21				05 12				05 42		05 25		05 45		06 21	06 30				06 15	06 51
Ealing Broadway ⊖ d	22p55			23p36											05 32		05 52							06 22	
Slough 3 d	23p14			23p55	00 41				05 29				05 57		05 51		06 18							06 48	07 07
Maidenhead 3 d	23p25			00 03											06 03		06 29							06 59	
Twyford 3 d	23p33			00 11											06 10		06 37							07 07	
Reading 7 a	23p40	00 01		00 18	00 58				05 46				06 13		06 17		06 43		06 51	06 55				07 13	07 21
d	23p41	00 02	00 15	00 19	00 59	05 11		05 41	05 48	05 48	06 11		06 14		06 19	06 40	06 48	06 48	06 52	06 55		07 10	07 11	07 16	07 23
Reading West d			00s17			05 14		05 44			06 14												07 14		
Theale d			00s23			05 20		05 50			06 20							06 56					07 20		
Aldermaston d			00s28			05 25		05 55			06 25												07 25		
Midgham d			00s32			05 29		05 59			06 29												07 29		
Thatcham d			00s37			05 34		06 04			06 34							07 04					07 34		
Newbury Racecourse d			00s41			05 38		06 08			06 38												07 38		
Newbury a			00 45			05 41		06 11			06 42							07 10					07 42		
d						05 41		06 11										07 10							
Kintbury d						05 47		06 17										07 16							
Hungerford d						05 52		06 22										07 21							
Bedwyn a						06 01		06 31										07 30							
Tilehurst d	23p45			00 23						05 52					06 24		06 53							07 20	
Pangbourne d	23p50			00 28						05 57					06 28		06 57				←			07 25	
Goring & Streatley d	23p54			00 32						06 01					06 33		07 02				07 02			07 29	
Cholsey d	23p59			00 37						06 06					06 38		→				07 07			07 34	
Didcot Parkway a	00 06	00 20		00 44	01 15				06 02	06 12			06 28		06 44					07 11	07 15			→	
d	00 07			00 45	01 16				06 03	06 13			06 29		06 44						07 15				
Appleford d				00 50						06 18					06 50										
Culham d				00 53						06 21															
Radley d	00 15			00 57						06 25					06 55										
Oxford a	00 22			01 07	01 30				06 17	06 32			06 45		07 03	07 06			07 17		07 28	07 34			07 48
d							06 16					06 44				07 07						07 36			
Islip d												06 57													
Bicester Town a												07 10													
Tackley d							06 25																		
Heyford d							06 29																		
Kings Sutton d							06 37																		
Banbury a							06 44									07 24						07 52			
Leamington Spa 8 a							*07 19*									07 42						08 10			
Warwick a							*07 23*									*07 59*						*08 24*			
Warwick Parkway a							*07 27*									*08 03*						*08 27*			
Stratford-upon-Avon a																									
Coventry a																						08 21			
Birmingham International a																						08 33			
Birmingham New Street 12 a																08 18						08 46			

	GW 1◇ ☕	GW 1	GW 1	XC 1◇ ☕		GW 1	GW 1◇	GW 1	GW 1◇ ☕	GW 1	XC 1◇ ☕	GW 1	GW 1◇ ☕	GW 1	GW 1	GW 1◇ ☕	GW 1◇ ☕	XC 1◇ ☕		GW 1	GW 1◇ ☕	GW 1	GW 1◇ ☕	GW 1◇	GW 1
London Paddington 15 ⊖ d	07 00						07 21	07 00	07 30				07 45		07 30	07 51	08 00				08 15		08 18	08 21	08 00
Ealing Broadway ⊖ d								07 07							07 37										08 07
Slough 3 d								07 31							08 01	08 07									08 31
Maidenhead 3 d								07 38							08 08										08 38
Twyford 3 d								07 46							08 16										08 46
Reading 7 a	07 26						07 51	07 52	07 56				08 10		08 21	08 21	08 26				08 40		08 45	08 51	08 52
d				07 40		07 48	07 51	07 53	07 57		08 10			08 11	08 23	08 23		08 40			08 41		08 49	08 53	08 53
Reading West d														08 14											
Theale d						07 56								08 20									08 58		
Aldermaston d														08 25											
Midgham d														08 29											
Thatcham d						08 04								08 34									09 06		
Newbury Racecourse d														08 38											
Newbury a						08 10								08 42									09 11		
d						08 10																08 58	09 12		
Kintbury d						08 16																09 04			
Hungerford d						08 21																09 09	09 21		
Bedwyn a						08 30																09 18	09 27		
Tilehurst d								07 57				←			08 27										08 57
Pangbourne d								08 02				08 02			08 32										09 02
Goring & Streatley d			←					→				08 06			08 36					←					→
Cholsey d			07 34									08 11			08 41					08 41					
Didcot Parkway a			07 40						08 11			08 17			→					08 47	08 56				
d			07 41									08 25								08 55					
Appleford d																				09 03					
Culham d			07 46																						
Radley d			07 50																	09 07					
Oxford a			08 00	08 03			08 16				08 34	08 39				08 47		09 06		09 15				09 20	
d		07 53		08 04						08 24	08 36							09 07							
Islip d										08 37															
Bicester Town a										08 50															
Tackley d		08 02																							
Heyford d		08 06																							
Kings Sutton d		08 14																							
Banbury a		08 21		08 21							08 52							09 24							
Leamington Spa 8 a		*08 59*		08 42							09 10							09 42							
Warwick a		*09 04*		*09 04*							*09b21*							*10 02*							
Warwick Parkway a		*09 07*		*09 07*							*09b25*							*10 05*							
Stratford-upon-Avon a		*09 35*		*09 35*																					
Coventry a											09 21														
Birmingham International a											09 33														
Birmingham New Street 12 a				09 18							09 45							10 18							

For general notes see front of timetable
For details of catering facilities see Directory of Train Operators

b Change at Banbury

Table 116

Saturdays

until 26 January

London and Reading → Bedwyn, Oxford, Bicester, Banbury and Birmingham

Network Diagram - see first page of Table 116

		GW	GW	XC	GW	GW	GW	GW	GW	GW		XC	GW	GW	GW	GW	GW	GW	GW	GW	XC	GW	GW	GW		GW
		1◇ ☕	1	1◇ ☕	1◇ ☕	1	1	1◇ ☕	1◇ ☕	1◇ ☕		1◇ ☕	1	1	1	1	1◇	1	1◇ ☕	1	1◇ ☕	1◇ ☕	1	1		1◇ ☕
London Paddington 15 ⊖	d	08 30			08 45		08 30	08 51	09 00	09 05					09 18	09 00	09 21		09 30			09 45		09 30		09 51
Ealing Broadway ⊖	d						08 37									09 07								09 37		
Slough 3	d						09 01	09 07								09 31								10 01		10 07
Maidenhead 3	d						09 08									09 38								10 08		
Twyford 3	d						09 16									09 46								10 16		
Reading 7	a	08 56			09 10		09 21	09 21	09 26	09 31					09 48	09 52	09 52		09 57			10 10		10 21		10 21
	d	08 57		09 10		09 11	09 23	09 23				09 40			09 48	09 53	09 54		09 57		10 10		10 11	10 23		10 23
Reading West	d					09 14																	10 14			
Theale	d					09 20									09 56								10 20			
Aldermaston	d					09 25																	10 25			
Midgham	d					09 29																	10 29			
Thatcham	d					09 34									10 04								10 34			
Newbury Racecourse	d					09 38																	10 38			
Newbury	a					09 43									10 10								10 43			
	d														10 11											
Kintbury	d														10 17											
Hungerford	d														10 22											
Bedwyn	a														10 31											
Tilehurst	d		←				09 27									09 57								10 27		
Pangbourne	d		09 02				09 32									10 02				←				10 32		
Goring & Streatley	d		09 06				09 36						←			10 06				10 06				10 36		
Cholsey	d		09 11				09 41						09 41			→				10 11				10 41		
Didcot Parkway	a	09 12	09 17				→						09 47						10 12	10 17				→		
	d		09 18										09 55							10 18						
Appleford	d												10 00													
Culham	d																									
Radley	d												10 04													
Oxford	a		09 31	09 34				09 47				10 06	10 13				10 18			10 30	10 34					10 47
	d			09 36								10 07		10 16				10 24			10 36					
Islip	d																	10 37								
Bicester Town	a																	10 50								
Tackley	d													10 25												
Heyford	d													10 29												
Kings Sutton	d													10 39												
Banbury	a			09 52								10 24		10 46							10 52					
Leamington Spa 8	a			10 10								10 42									11 10					
Warwick	a			*10 41*								*11 02*									*11b20*					
Warwick Parkway	a											*11 05*									*11b23*					
Stratford-upon-Avon	a			*11 12*																						
Coventry	a			10 21																	11 21					
Birmingham International	a			10 33																	11 33					
Birmingham New Street 12	a			10 45								11 18									11 45					

		GW	GW	XC	GW	GW	GW	GW	GW	GW	GW	XC	GW	GW		GW	GW	GW	GW	XC	GW	GW	GW	GW	GW	GW
		1◇ ☕	1◇ ☕	1◇ ☕	1	1◇ ☕	1	1	1◇	1◇ ☕	1	1◇ ☕	1◇ ☕	1		1	1◇ ☕	1◇ ☕	1◇ ☕	1◇ ☕	1	1	1	1◇	1	1◇ ☕
London Paddington 15 ⊖	d	10 00	10 05			10 15	10 18	10 00	10 21	10 30			10 45			10 30	10 51	11 00	11 05			11 18		11 21	11 00	11 30
Ealing Broadway ⊖	d							10 07								10 37									11 07	
Slough 3	d							10 30								11 01	11 07								11 31	
Maidenhead 3	d							10 38								11 08									11 38	
Twyford 3	d							10 46								11 16									11 46	
Reading 7	a	10 26	10 31			10 40	10 47	10 52	10 52	10 57			11 10			11 21	11 21	11 26	11 31			11 47		11 51	11 52	11 56
	d			10 40		10 41	10 49	10 53	10 54	10 57		11 10		11 11		11 23	11 23			11 40		11 49		11 53	11 53	11 57
Reading West	d													11 14												
Theale	d						10 57							11 20								11 57				
Aldermaston	d													11 25												
Midgham	d													11 29												
Thatcham	d						11 05							11 34								12 06				
Newbury Racecourse	d													11 38												
Newbury	a						11 11							11 43								12 11				
	d						11 11															12 11				
Kintbury	d						11 17															12 18				
Hungerford	d						11 22															12 23				
Bedwyn	a						11 31															12 32				
Tilehurst	d							10 57								11 27									11 57	
Pangbourne	d							11 02			←					11 32									12 02	
Goring & Streatley	d				←			11 06			11 06					11 36					←				→	
Cholsey	d				10 41			→			11 11					11 41					11 41					
Didcot Parkway	a				10 47	10 56				11 12	11 17					→					11 47					12 12
	d				10 55						11 18										11 55					
Appleford	d				11 00																12 00					
Culham	d																									
Radley	d				11 04																12 04					
Oxford	a			11 06	11 13				11 19		11 30	11 34					11 47			12 06	12 13			12 17		
	d			11 07								11 36								12 07			12 16			
Islip	d																									
Bicester Town	a																									
Tackley	d																						12 25			
Heyford	d																						12 29			
Kings Sutton	d																						12 37			
Banbury	a			11 24								11 52								12 24			12 44			
Leamington Spa 8	a			11 42								12 10								12 42						
Warwick	a			*11 58*								*12b21*								*12 58*						
Warwick Parkway	a			*12 02*								*12b25*								*13 02*						
Stratford-upon-Avon	a											*13 11*														
Coventry	a											12 21														
Birmingham International	a											12 33														
Birmingham New Street 12	a			12 18								12 45								13 18						

For general notes see front of timetable
For details of catering facilities see
Directory of Train Operators

b Change at Banbury

Table 116

Saturdays

until 26 January

London and Reading → Bedwyn, Oxford, Bicester, Banbury and Birmingham

Network Diagram - see first page of Table 116

		GW	XC	GW	GW		GW	GW	GW	GW	XC	GW	GW	GW	GW	GW	GW	GW	GW		XC	GW	GW	GW	GW	GW
		1	1 ◇ ☕	1 ◇ ☕	1		1	1 ◇ ☕	1 ◇ ☕	1 ◇ ☕	1 ◇ ☕	1	1 ◇ ☕	1 ◇ ☕	1	1 ◇	1 ◇ ☕	1	1		1 ◇ ☕	1 ◇ ☕	1	1 ◇	1	1 ◇ ☕
London Paddington 15	⊖ d			11 45			11 30	11 51	12 00	12 05			12 15	12 18	12 00	12 21	12 30					12 45		12 51	12 30	13 00
Ealing Broadway	⊖ d						11 37								12 07										12 37	
Slough 3	d						12 01	12 07						12 34	12 31										13 01	
Maidenhead 3	d						12 08								12 38										13 08	
Twyford 3	d						12 16								12 46										13 16	
Reading 7	a			12 10			12 21	12 21	12 26	12 31			12 40	12 48	12 52	12 53	12 58					13 10		13 21	13 21	13 26
	d		12 10		12 11		12 23	12 23			12 40		12 41	12 49	12 53	12 55	12 58				13 10		13 11	13 22	13 23	
Reading West	d				12 14																		13 14			
Theale	d				12 20									12 58									13 20			
Aldermaston	d				12 25																		13 25			
Midgham	d				12 29																		13 29			
Thatcham	d				12 34									13 06									13 34			
Newbury Racecourse	d				12 38																		13 38			
Newbury	a				12 43									13 12									13 43			
	d													13 12												
Kintbury	d																									
Hungerford	d													13a21												
Bedwyn	a																									
Tilehurst	d	←					12 27								12 57										13 27	
Pangbourne	d	12 02					12 32								13 02				←						13 32	
Goring & Streatley	d	12 06					12 36					←			13 06				13 06						13 36	
Cholsey	d	12 11					12 41					12 41			→				13 11						13 41	
Didcot Parkway	a	12 17					→					12 47	12 56				13 14		13 17						→	
	d	12 18										12 55							13 18							
Appleford	d											13 00														
Culham	d																									
Radley	d											13 04														
Oxford	a	12 30	12 34					12 47			13 06	13 13				13 19			13 30		13 34			13 47		
	d		12 35								13 07							13 24			13 36					
Islip	d																	13 37								
Bicester Town	a																	13 50								
Tackley	d																									
Heyford	d																									
Kings Sutton	d																									
Banbury	a		12 52								13 24										13 52					
Leamington Spa 8	a		13 10								13 42										14 10					
Warwick	a		13b21								13 58										14b21					
Warwick Parkway	a		13b25								14 02										14b25					
Stratford-upon-Avon	a																				15 10					
Coventry	a		13 21																		14 21					
Birmingham International	a		13 33																		14 33					
Birmingham New Street 12	a		13 45								14 18										14 46					

		GW	XC	GW	GW	GW	GW	GW	GW	GW		XC	GW	GW	GW	GW	GW	XC	GW	GW	GW	GW	GW	GW		GW
		1 ◇ ☕	1 ◇ ☕	1	1	1	1 ◇	1	1 ◇ ☕	1		1 ◇ ☕	1 ◇ ☕	1	1	1 ◇ ☕	1 ◇ ☕	1 ◇ ☕	1	1 ◇ ☕	1	1 ◇	1	1 ◇ ☕		1
London Paddington 15	⊖ d	13 05			13 18		13 21	13 00	13 30				13 45		13 30	13 51	14 00			14 15	14 18	14 21	14 00	14 30		
Ealing Broadway	⊖ d							13 07							13 37								14 07			
Slough 3	d							13 31							14 01	14 07							14 31			
Maidenhead 3	d							13 38							14 08								14 38			
Twyford 3	d							13 46							14 16								14 46			
Reading 7	a	13 31			13 47		13 51	13 52	13 55				14 10		14 21	14 21	14 26			14 40	14 47	14 51	14 52	14 56		
	d		13 40		13 49		13 52	13 53	13 57			14 10		14 11	14 23	14 23		14 40		14 41	14 49	14 53	14 53	14 57		
Reading West	d													14 14												
Theale	d				13 57									14 20							14 57					
Aldermaston	d													14 25												
Midgham	d													14 29												
Thatcham	d				14 06									14 34							15 05					
Newbury Racecourse	d													14 38												
Newbury	a				14 11									14 43							15 11					
	d				14 11																15 11					
Kintbury	d				14 18																15 17					
Hungerford	d				14 23																15 22					
Bedwyn	a				14 32																15 31					
Tilehurst	d							13 57		←					14 27								14 57			
Pangbourne	d							14 02		14 02					14 32								15 02			
Goring & Streatley	d			←				→		14 06					14 36				←				→			
Cholsey	d			13 41						14 11					14 41				14 41							
Didcot Parkway	a			13 47					14 11	14 17					→				14 47	14 56				15 12		
	d			13 55						14 18									14 55							
Appleford	d			14 00															15 00							
Culham	d																									
Radley	d			14 04															15 04							
Oxford	a		14 06	14 13			14 17			14 30		14 34				14 47		15 06	15 13			15 17				
	d		14 07			14 16						14 36						15 07								15 24
Islip	d																									15 37
Bicester Town	a																									15 50
Tackley	d					14 25																				
Heyford	d					14 29																				
Kings Sutton	d					14 37																				
Banbury	a		14 24			14 44						14 52						15 24								
Leamington Spa 8	a		14 42									15 10						15 42								
Warwick	a		14 58									15b21						15 58								
Warwick Parkway	a		15 02									15b25						16 02								
Stratford-upon-Avon	a																									
Coventry	a											15 21														
Birmingham International	a											15 33														
Birmingham New Street 12	a		15 18									15 45						16 18								

For general notes see front of timetable
For details of catering facilities see Directory of Train Operators

b Change at Banbury

Table 116

Saturdays

until 26 January

London and Reading → Bedwyn, Oxford, Bicester, Banbury and Birmingham

Network Diagram - see first page of Table 116

		GW	XC	GW	GW	GW	GW	GW	XC	GW	GW	GW	GW	GW		GW	GW	XC	GW	GW	GW	GW	GW	GW	XC	GW
		1	1 ◇ ☕	1 ◇ ☕	1	1	1 ◇ ☕	1 ◇ ☕	1 ◇ ☕	1	1	1	1 ◇	1		1 ◇ ☕	1	1 ◇ ☕	1 ◇ ☕	1	1	1 ◇ ☕	1 ◇ ☕	1 ◇ ☕	1 ◇ ☕	1
London Paddington 15 ⊖	d			14 45		14 30	14 51	15 00			15 18		15 21	15 00		15 30			15 45		15 30	15 51	16 00	16 05		
Ealing Broadway ⊖	d					14 37								15 07							15 37					
Slough 3	d					15 01	15 07							15 31							16 01	16 07				
Maidenhead 3	d					15 08								15 38							16 08					
Twyford 3	d					15 16								15 46							16 16					
Reading 7	a			15 10		15 21	15 21	15 26			15 47		15 51	15 52		15 56			16 10		16 21	16 21	16 26	16 31		
	d		15 10		15 11	15 23	15 23		15 40		15 49		15 53	15 53		15 57		16 10		16 11	16 23	16 23			16 40	
Reading West	d				15 14															16 14						
Theale	d				15 20						15 57									16 20						
Aldermaston	d				15 25															16 25						
Midgham	d				15 29															16 29						
Thatcham	d				15 34						16 05									16 34						
Newbury Racecourse	d				15 38															16 38						
Newbury	a				15 43						16 11									16 43						
	d										16 11															
Kintbury	d										16 17															
Hungerford	d										16 22															
Bedwyn	a										16 31															
Tilehurst	d	←				15 27								15 57			←				16 27					
Pangbourne	d	15 02				15 32								16 02			16 02				16 32					
Goring & Streatley	d	15 06				15 36				←				→			16 06				16 36					←
Cholsey	d	15 11				15 41				15 41							16 11				16 41					16 41
Didcot Parkway	a	15 17				→				15 47						16 12	16 17				→					16 47
	d	15 18								15 55							16 18									16 55
Appleford	d									16 00																17 00
Culham	d																									
Radley	d									16 04																17 04
Oxford	a	15 30	15 34				15 47		16 06	16 13			16 17				16 30	16 34				16 47			17 06	17 13
	d		15 36						16 07			16 16						16 36							17 07	
Islip	d																									
Bicester Town	a																									
Tackley	d											16 25														
Heyford	d											16 29														
Kings Sutton	d											16 37														
Banbury	a		15 52						16 24			16 44						16 52							17 24	
Leamington Spa 8	a		16 10						16 42									17 10							17 42	
Warwick	a		*16b21*						*16 57*									*17b20*							*17 58*	
Warwick Parkway	a		*16b24*						*17 01*									*17b24*							*18 02*	
Stratford-upon-Avon	a		*17 11*																							
Coventry	a		16 21															17 21								
Birmingham International	a		16 33															17 33								
Birmingham New Street 12	a		16 46						17 18									17 45							18 18	

		GW	GW	GW	GW		GW	GW	GW	XC	GW	GW	GW	GW	GW	GW	XC	GW	GW		GW	GW	GW	GW	GW	XC
		1 ◇ ☕	1	1 ◇	1		1 ◇ ☕	1	1	1 ◇ ☕	1 ◇ ☕	1	1	1 ◇ ☕	1 ◇ ☕	1 ◇ ☕	1 ◇ ☕	1	1		1	1 ◇	1	1 ◇ ☕	1	1 ◇ ☕
London Paddington 15 ⊖	d	16 15	16 18	16 21	16 00		16 30				16 45		16 30	16 51	17 00	17 05			17 18			17 21	17 00	17 30		
Ealing Broadway ⊖	d				16 07								16 37										17 07			
Slough 3	d				16 31								17 01	17 07									17 31			
Maidenhead 3	d				16 38								17 08										17 38			
Twyford 3	d				16 46								17 16										17 46			
Reading 7	a	16 40	16 47	16 51	16 52		16 56				17 10		17 21	17 21	17 26	17 31			17 47			17 51	17 52	17 56		
	d	16 41	16 49	16 53	16 53		16 57			17 10		17 11	17 23	17 23			17 40		17 49			17 53	17 53	17 56		18 10
Reading West	d											17 14														
Theale	d		16 57									17 20							17 57							
Aldermaston	d											17 25														
Midgham	d											17 29														
Thatcham	d		17 05									17 34							18 05							
Newbury Racecourse	d											17 38														
Newbury	a		17 11									17 43							18 11							
	d		17 11																18 11							
Kintbury	d		17 17																18 17							
Hungerford	d		17 22																18 22							
Bedwyn	a		17 31																18 31							
Tilehurst	d				16 57				←				17 27										17 57		←	
Pangbourne	d				17 02				17 02				17 32										18 02		18 02	
Goring & Streatley	d				→				17 06				17 36					←					→		18 06	
Cholsey	d								17 11				17 41					17 41							18 11	
Didcot Parkway	a	16 56					17 12		17 17				→					17 47						18 12	18 17	
	d								17 18									17 55							18 18	
Appleford	d																	18 00								
Culham	d																									
Radley	d																	18 04								
Oxford	a			17 17					17 30	17 34				17 47			18 06	18 13				18 17			18 30	18 34
	d							17 24		17 36							18 07				18 16					18 36
Islip	d							17 37																		
Bicester Town	a							17 50																		
Tackley	d																				18 25					
Heyford	d																				18 29					
Kings Sutton	d																				18 37					
Banbury	a									17 52							18 24				18 44					18 52
Leamington Spa 8	a									18 10							18 42									19 10
Warwick	a									*18 22*							*18 58*									*19 27*
Warwick Parkway	a									*18 26*							*19 02*									*19 31*
Stratford-upon-Avon	a									*19 13*																
Coventry	a									18 21																19 21
Birmingham International	a									18 33																19 33
Birmingham New Street 12	a									18 45							19 18									19 45

For general notes see front of timetable
For details of catering facilities see
Directory of Train Operators

b Change at Banbury

London and Reading → Bedwyn, Oxford, Bicester, Banbury and Birmingham

Saturdays

until 26 January

Network Diagram - see first page of Table 116

		GW	GW	GW	GW	GW	GW	XC	GW	GW		GW	GW	GW	GW	GW	GW	XC	GW	GW	GW	GW	GW	GW		XC
		1	1 ◇ ☕	1	1 ◇	1 ◇ ☕	1 ◇ ☕	1 ◇ ☕	1	1 ◇ ☕		1	1	1 ◇ ☕	1	1 ◇ ☕	1	1 ◇ ☕	1 ◇ ☕	1	1 ◇	1 ◇ ☕	1 ◇ ☕	1		1 ◇
London Paddington 15 ⊖	d		17 45	17 30	17 51	18 00	18 05			18 15		18 18		18 21	18 00	18 30			18 45	18 30	18 51	19 00	19 05			
Ealing Broadway ⊖	d			17 37											18 07					18 37						
Slough 3	d			18 01										18 37	18 31					19 01						
Maidenhead 3	d			18 08											18 38					19 08						
Twyford 3	d			18 16											18 46					19 16						
Reading 7	a		18 11	18 21	18 21	18 26	18 31			18 40		18 47		18 51	18 52	18 56			19 11	19 21	19 21	19 26	19 31			
	d	18 11		18 23	18 23			18 40		18 41		18 49		18 53	18 53	18 57		19 10		19 23	19 23		19 32			19 40
Reading West	d	18 14																								
Theale	d	18 20										18 57														
Aldermaston	d	18 25																								
Midgham	d	18 29																								
Thatcham	d	18 34										19 05														
Newbury Racecourse	d	18 38																								
Newbury	a	18 43										19 11											19 47			
	d											19 11														
Kintbury	d											19 17														
Hungerford	d											19 22														
Bedwyn	a											19 31														
Tilehurst	d			18 27											18 57		←			19 27						
Pangbourne	d			18 32											19 02 →		19 02			19 32						
Goring & Streatley	d			18 36					←								19 06			19 36						
Cholsey	d			18 41 →					18 41								19 11			19 41 →						
Didcot Parkway	a								18 47	18 56						19 12	19 17									
	d								18 55								19 18									
Appleford	d								19 00																	
Culham	d																									
Radley	d								19 04																	
Oxford	a				18 47			19 06	19 13					19 18			19 30	19 34			19 47					20 06
	d							19 07					19 16					19 36						19 56		20 07
Islip	d																									
Bicester Town	a																									
Tackley	d												19 25											20 05		
Heyford	d												19 29											20 09		
Kings Sutton	d												19 37											20 17		
Banbury	a							19 24					19 44					19 52						20 24		20 24
Leamington Spa 8	a							19 42										20 10						*20 55*		20 42
Warwick	a							*19 58*										*20 27*						*20 59*		*20 59*
Warwick Parkway	a							*20 02*										*20 31*						*21 03*		*21 03*
Stratford-upon-Avon	a																	*21 10*								
Coventry	a																	20 21								
Birmingham International	a																	20 33								
Birmingham New Street 12	a							20 18										20 45								21 22

		GW	GW	GW	GW	GW	GW	GW	XC	GW	GW	GW	GW	GW		GW	GW	GW	GW	GW	GW	GW	GW	GW	XC	GW
		1	1 ◇ ☕	1	1 ◇	1	1 ◇ ☕	1	1 ◇ ☕	1 ◇ ☕	1	1 ◇	1 ◇ ☕	1 ◇ ☕		1	1	1 ◇ ☕	1	1	1	1 ◇	1 ◇ ☕	1	1 ◇	1 ◇ ☕
London Paddington 15 ⊖	d		19 15		19 21	19 00	19 30			19 45	19 30	19 51	20 00	20 05				20 15			20 00	20 21	20 30			20 45
Ealing Broadway ⊖	d					19 07					19 37										20 07					
Slough 3	d					19 31					20 01	20 07									20 31					
Maidenhead 3	d					19 38					20 08										20 38					
Twyford 3	d					19 46					20 16										20 46					
Reading 7	a		19 40		19 51	19 52	19 56			20 10	20 21	20 21	20 27	20 32				20 40			20 52	20 51	20 56			21 10
	d		19 41	19 49	19 52	19 53	19 57		20 10		20 23	20 23	20 27	20 32				20 41		20 49	20 53	20 52	20 57		21 10	
Reading West	d			19 52																20 52						
Theale	d			19 58																20 58						
Aldermaston	d			20 03																21 03						
Midgham	d			20 07																21 07						
Thatcham	d			20 12																21 12						
Newbury Racecourse	d			20 16																21 16						
Newbury	a			20 19										20 46						21 19						
	d			20 19																21 33						
Kintbury	d			20 25																21 39						
Hungerford	d			20 30																21 44						
Bedwyn	a			20 39																21 53						
Tilehurst	d					19 57		←			20 27						←				20 57					
Pangbourne	d					20 02 →		20 02			20 32 →						20 32				21 02			←		
Goring & Streatley	d	←						20 06									20 36				21 06 →			21 06		
Cholsey	d	19 41						20 11									20 41							21 11		
Didcot Parkway	a	19 47	19 55				20 11	20 17					20 42				20 47	20 56					21 12	21 17		
	d	19 58						20 18									20 55							21 18		
Appleford	d	20 04															21 00									
Culham	d																									
Radley	d	20 08															21 04									
Oxford	a	20 16			20 20			20 30	20 34			20 47					21 13					21 19		21 30	21 34	
	d								20 36							20 49			21 20						21 36	
Islip	d															21 02										
Bicester Town	a															21 15										
Tackley	d																		21 29							
Heyford	d																		21 33							
Kings Sutton	d																		21 41							
Banbury	a								20 52										21 48						21 52	
Leamington Spa 8	a								21 10																22 10	
Warwick	a								*21 43*																*22 31*	
Warwick Parkway	a								*21 47*																*22 35*	
Stratford-upon-Avon	a																									
Coventry	a								21 21																22 21	
Birmingham International	a								21 33																22 33	
Birmingham New Street 12	a								21 45																22 50	

For general notes see front of timetable
For details of catering facilities see Directory of Train Operators

Table 116

Saturdays

until 26 January

London and Reading → Bedwyn, Oxford, Bicester, Banbury and Birmingham

Network Diagram - see first page of Table 116

		GW 1	GW 1 ◇	GW 1	GW 1	GW 1 ◇	GW 1	GW 1 ◇ ☕	GW 1	GW 1 ◇	GW 1 ◇	GW 1 ◇ ☕	GW 1 ◇	GW 🚌	GW 🚌	GW 1	GW 1 ◇	GW 🚌	GW 1	GW 1 ◇ ☕	GW 1 ◇	GW 1
London Paddington 15 ⊖	d	20 30	20 51			21 21	21 00	21 30		21 51	22 00	22 30	22 32				23 00		22 45	23 30	23 33	23 20
Ealing Broadway ⊖	d	20 37					21 07												22 54			23 27
Slough 3	d	21 01	21 08				21 31			22 08			22 50				23 17		23 20		23 50	23 53
Maidenhead 3	d	21 08					21 38												23 29			00 05
Twyford 3	d	21 16					21 46												23 36			00 12
Reading 7	a	21 21	21 25			21 51	21 52	21 56		22 23	22 27	22 55	23 06				23 33		23 43	23 59	00 07	00 19
	d	21 23	21 26		21 49	21 52	21 53	21 57		22 23	22 27	22 57	23 07			23 11	23 34		23 48	23 59	00 08	00 19
Reading West	d				21 52											23 14						
Theale	d				21 58											23 20						
Aldermaston	d				22 04											23 25						
Midgham	d				22 07											23 29						
Thatcham	d				22 12											23 34						
Newbury Racecourse	d				22 17											23 38						
Newbury	a				22 19											23 41						
	d				22 19											23 41						
Kintbury	d				22 26											23 47						
Hungerford	d				22 31											23 52						
Bedwyn	a				22 39											00 02						
Tilehurst	d	21 27		←			21 57		←										23 52			00 24
Pangbourne	d	21 32 →		21 32			22 02 →		22 02										23 57			
Goring & Streatley	d			21 36					22 06										00 01			00 31
Cholsey	d			21 41					22 11										00 06			00 36
Didcot Parkway	a		21 42	21 47		22 08		22 12	22 17		22 42	23 16	23 24				23 51		00 13	00 16	00 25	00 43
	d		21 43	21 52		22 08			22 18						23 31			23 58				
Appleford	d			21 58																		
Culham	d																					
Radley	d			22 02																		
Oxford	a		21 55	22 10		22 20			22 30	22 46					23 56			00 23				
	d													23 37								
Islip	d																					
Bicester Town	a																					
Tackley	d													23s57								
Heyford	d													00s12								
Kings Sutton	d													00b27								
Banbury	a													00 37								
Leamington Spa 8	a																					
Warwick	a																					
Warwick Parkway	a																					
Stratford-upon-Avon	a																					
Coventry	a																					
Birmingham International	a																					
Birmingham New Street 12	a																					

For general notes see front of timetable
For details of catering facilities see Directory of Train Operators

b Kings Sutton V. Square. Stops to set down only

Table 116

Saturdays

2 February to 22 March

London and Reading → Bedwyn, Oxford, Bicester, Banbury and Birmingham

Network Diagram - see first page of Table 116

		GW 1	GW 1◇ 🛒	GW 1	GW 1	GW 1◇	GW 1	GW 1	GW 1	GW 1◇	GW 1	GW 1	GW 1	GW 1◇	GW 1		XC 1◇ ☕	GW 1	GW 1	GW 1◇	GW 1	XC 1◇ ☕	GW 1	GW 1	GW 1◇ ☕	GW 1
London Paddington 15 ⊖	d	22p46	23p30		23p29	00 21				05 12				05 42	05 25			05 45		06 21				06 15	06 51	
Ealing Broadway ⊖	d	22p55			23p36										05 32			05 52						06 22		
Slough 3	d	23p14			23p55	00 41				05 29				05 57	05 51			06 18						06 48	07 07	
Maidenhead 3	d	23p25			00 03										06 03			06 29						06 59		
Twyford 3	d	23p33			00 11										06 10			06 37						07 07		
Reading 7	a	23p40	00 01		00 18	00 58				05 46				06 13	06 17			06 43		06 51				07 13	07 21	
	d	23p41	00 02	00 15	00 19	00 59	05 11		05 41	05 48	05 48	06 11		06 14	06 19		06 40	06 48	06 49	06 52		07 10	07 11	07 16	07 23	
Reading West	d			00s17			05 14		05 44			06 14											07 14			
Theale	d			00s23			05 20		05 50			06 20							06 57				07 20			
Aldermaston	d			00s28			05 25		05 55			06 25											07 25			
Midgham	d			00s32			05 29		05 59			06 29											07 29			
Thatcham	d			00s37			05 34		06 04			06 34							07 05				07 34			
Newbury Racecourse	d			00s41			05 38		06 08			06 38											07 38			
Newbury	a			00 45			05 41		06 11			06 42							07 11				07 42			
	d						05 41		06 11										07 11							
Kintbury	d						05 47		06 17										07 17							
Hungerford	d						05 52		06 22										07 22							
Bedwyn	a						06 01		06 31										07 31							
Tilehurst	d	23p45			00 23						05 52				06 24			06 53						07 20		
Pangbourne	d	23p50			00 28						05 57				06 28			06 57			←			07 25		
Goring & Streatley	d	23p54			00 32						06 01				06 33			07 02 →			07 02			07 29		
Cholsey	d	23p59			00 37						06 06				06 38						07 07			07 34 →		
Didcot Parkway	a	00 06	00 20		00 44	01 15				06 02	06 12			06 28	06 44						07 15					
	d	00 07			00 45	01 16				06 03	06 13			06 29	06 44						07 15					
Appleford	d				00 50						06 18				06 50											
Culham	d				00 53						06 21															
Radley	d	00 15			00 57						06 25				06 55											
Oxford	a	00 22			01 07	01 30				06 17	06 32			06 45	07 03		07 06			07 17	07 28	07 34			07 48	
	d							06 16					06 44				07 07					07 36				07 53
Islip	d												06 57													
Bicester Town	a												07 10													
Tackley	d							06 25																		08 02
Heyford	d							06 29																		08 06
Kings Sutton	d							06 37																		08 14
Banbury	a							06 44									07 24					07 52				08 21
Leamington Spa 8	a							*07 19*									07 42					08 10				*08 59*
Warwick	a							*07 23*									*07 59*					*08 24*				*09 04*
Warwick Parkway	a							*07 27*									*08 03*					*08 27*				*09 07*
Stratford-upon-Avon	a																									*09 35*
Coventry	a																					08 21				
Birmingham International	a																					08 33				
Birmingham New Street 12	a																08 18					08 46				

		GW 1	XC 1◇ ☕	GW 1◇ ☕	GW 1◇	GW 1	GW 1◇ ☕		GW 1	XC 1◇ ☕	GW 1	GW 1	GW 1	GW 1◇ ☕	XC 1◇ ☕	GW 1	GW 1	GW 1◇ ☕	GW 1◇	GW 1	GW 1◇ ☕	XC 1◇ ☕		GW 1	GW 1	GW 1◇ ☕
London Paddington 15 ⊖	d			07 15	07 21	07 00	07 30						07 30	07 51				08 18	08 21	08 00	08 42				08 30	08 51
Ealing Broadway ⊖	d					07 07							07 37							08 07					08 37	
Slough 3	d					07 31							08 01	08 07						08 31					09 01	09 07
Maidenhead 3	d					07 38							08 08							08 38					09 08	
Twyford 3	d					07 46							08 16							08 46					09 16	
Reading 7	a			07 40	07 51	07 52	07 57						08 21	08 21				08 45	08 52	08 52	09 07				09 21	09 21
	d		07 40		07 51	07 53				08 10		08 11	08 23	08 23	08 40			08 49	08 53	08 53		09 10		09 11	09 23	09 23
Reading West	d											08 14												09 14		
Theale	d											08 20						08 58						09 20		
Aldermaston	d											08 25												09 25		
Midgham	d											08 29												09 29		
Thatcham	d											08 34						09 07						09 34		
Newbury Racecourse	d											08 38												09 38		
Newbury	a											08 42						09 12						09 43		
	d																08 58	09 13								
Kintbury	d																09 04									
Hungerford	d																09 09	09a22								
Bedwyn	a																09 18									
Tilehurst	d					07 57							08 27							08 57					09 27	
Pangbourne	d					08 02					←		08 32							09 02					09 32	
Goring & Streatley	d	←				08 06 →					08 06		08 36			←				09 06					09 36	
Cholsey	d	07 34									08 11		08 41 →			08 41				09 11					09 41 →	
Didcot Parkway	a	07 40									08 17					08 47				09 17						
	d	07 41									08 25					08 55				09 18						
Appleford	d															09 03										
Culham	d	07 46																								
Radley	d	07 50														09 07										
Oxford	a	08 00	08 03		08 16					08 34	08 39			08 47	09 06	09 15			09 20	09 31		09 34				09 47
	d		08 04						08 24	08 36					09 07							09 36				
Islip	d								08 37																	
Bicester Town	a								08 50																	
Tackley	d																									
Heyford	d																									
Kings Sutton	d																									
Banbury	a		08 21							08 52					09 24							09 52				
Leamington Spa 8	a		08 42							09 10					09 42							10 10				
Warwick	a		*09 04*							*09b21*					*10 02*							*10 41*				
Warwick Parkway	a		*09 07*							*09b25*					*10 05*											
Stratford-upon-Avon	a		*09 35*																			*11 12*				
Coventry	a									09 21												10 21				
Birmingham International	a									09 33												10 33				
Birmingham New Street 12	a		09 18							09 45					10 18							10 45				

For general notes see front of timetable
For details of catering facilities see Directory of Train Operators

b Change at Banbury

Table 116

London and Reading → Bedwyn, Oxford, Bicester, Banbury and Birmingham

2 February to 22 March

Network Diagram - see first page of Table 116

		GW 1◇ ☕	XC 1◇ ☕	GW 1	GW 1	GW 1	GW 1	GW 1◇	GW 1	GW 1	XC 1◇ ☕	GW 1	GW 1	GW 1◇ ☕		GW 1◇ ☕	XC 1◇ ☕	GW 1◇ ☕	GW 1	GW 1	GW 1	GW 1◇	GW 1◇ ☕	GW 1	XC 1◇ ☕	GW 1
London Paddington 15 ⊖	d	09 05				09 18	09 00	09 21					09 30	09 51		10 05		10 15		10 18	10 00	10 21	10 42			
Ealing Broadway ⊖	d						09 07						09 37								10 07					
Slough 3	d						09 31						10 01	10 07							10 30					
Maidenhead 3	d						09 38						10 08								10 38					
Twyford 3	d						09 46						10 16								10 46					
Reading 7	a	09 31				09 48	09 52	09 52					10 21	10 21		10 31		10 40		10 47	10 52	10 53	11 07			
	d		09 40			09 48	09 53	09 54			10 10	10 11	10 23	10 23			10 40			10 49	10 53	10 55			11 10	11 11
Reading West	d											10 14														11 14
Theale	d					09 56						10 20								10 57						11 20
Aldermaston	d											10 25														11 25
Midgham	d											10 29														11 29
Thatcham	d					10 04						10 34								11 05						11 34
Newbury Racecourse	d											10 38														11 38
Newbury	a					10 10						10 43								11 11						11 43
	d					10 11														11 11						
Kintbury	d					10 17														11 17						
Hungerford	d					10 22														11 22						
Bedwyn	a					10 31														11 31						
Tilehurst	d						09 57						10 27								10 57					
Pangbourne	d						10 02			←			10 32								11 02			←		
Goring & Streatley	d			←			10 06			10 06			10 36						←		11 06			11 06		
Cholsey	d			09 41			→			10 11			10 41						10 41		→			11 11		
Didcot Parkway	a			09 47						10 17			→						10 47					11 17		
	d			09 55						10 18									10 55					11 18		
Appleford	d			10 00															11 00							
Culham	d																									
Radley	d			10 04															11 04							
Oxford	a		10 06	10 13				10 18		10 30	10 34			10 47			11 06		11 13			11 19		11 30	11 34	
	d		10 07		10 16				10 24		10 36						11 07								11 36	
Islip	d								10 37																	
Bicester Town	a								10 50																	
Tackley	d				10 25																					
Heyford	d				10 29																					
Kings Sutton	d				10 39																					
Banbury	a		10 24		10 46						10 52						11 24								11 52	
Leamington Spa 8	a		10 42								11 10						11 42								12 10	
Warwick	a		*11 02*								*11b20*						*11 58*								*12b21*	
Warwick Parkway	a		*11 05*								*11b23*						*12 02*								*12b25*	
Stratford-upon-Avon	a																								*13 11*	
Coventry	a										11 21														12 21	
Birmingham International	a										11 33														12 33	
Birmingham New Street 12	a		11 18								11 45						12 18								12 45	

		GW 1	GW 1◇ ☕	GW 1◇ ☕	XC 1◇ ☕	GW 1◇ ☕		GW 1	GW 1	GW 1	GW 1◇	GW 1	GW 1◇ ☕	XC 1◇ ☕	GW 1	GW 1	GW 1◇ ☕	GW 1◇ ☕	XC 1◇ ☕	GW 1◇ ☕	GW 1		GW 1◇ ☕	GW 1	GW 1◇	GW 1◇ ☕
London Paddington 15 ⊖	d	10 30	10 51	11 05		11 15			11 18		11 21	11 00	11 42			11 30	11 51	12 05		12 15			12 18	12 00	12 21	12 42
Ealing Broadway ⊖	d	10 37										11 07				11 37								12 07		
Slough 3	d	11 01	11 07									11 31				12 01	12 07						12 34	12 31		
Maidenhead 3	d	11 08										11 38				12 08								12 38		
Twyford 3	d	11 16										11 46				12 16								12 46		
Reading 7	a	11 21	11 21	11 31		11 40			11 47		11 52	11 52	12 07			12 21	12 21	12 31		12 40			12 48	12 52	12 53	13 07
	d	11 23	11 23		11 40				11 49		11 53	11 53		12 10	12 11	12 23	12 23		12 40				12 50	12 53	12 55	
Reading West	d														12 14											
Theale	d								11 57						12 20								12 59			
Aldermaston	d														12 25											
Midgham	d														12 29											
Thatcham	d								12 05						12 34								13 07			
Newbury Racecourse	d														12 38											
Newbury	a								12 11						12 43								13 13			
	d								12 11														13 14			
Kintbury	d								12 17																	
Hungerford	d								12 22														13a22			
Bedwyn	a								12 31																	
Tilehurst	d	11 27										11 57				12 27								12 57		
Pangbourne	d	11 32										12 02				12 32								13 02		
Goring & Streatley	d	11 36						←				12 06				12 36					←			13 06		
Cholsey	d	11 41						11 41				12 11				12 41					12 41			→		
Didcot Parkway	a	→						11 47				12 17				→					12 47					
	d							11 55				12 18									12 55					
Appleford	d							12 00													13 00					
Culham	d																									
Radley	d							12 04													13 04					
Oxford	a		11 47		12 06			12 13			12 17	12 30		12 34			12 47		13 06		13 13				13 19	
	d				12 07					12 16				12 35					13 07							
Islip	d																									
Bicester Town	a																									
Tackley	d									12 25																
Heyford	d									12 29																
Kings Sutton	d									12 37																
Banbury	a				12 24					12 44				12 52					13 24							
Leamington Spa 8	a				12 42									13 10					13 42							
Warwick	a				*12 58*									*13b21*					*13 58*							
Warwick Parkway	a				*13 02*									*13b25*					*14 02*							
Stratford-upon-Avon	a																									
Coventry	a													13 21												
Birmingham International	a													13 33												
Birmingham New Street 12	a				13 18									13 45					14 18							

For general notes see front of timetable
For details of catering facilities see
Directory of Train Operators

b Change at Banbury

Table 116

Saturdays

2 February to 22 March

London and Reading → Bedwyn, Oxford, Bicester, Banbury and Birmingham

Network Diagram - see first page of Table 116

		GW 1	GW 1	XC 1◇ ☕	GW 1	GW 1◇	GW 1	GW 1◇ ☕	XC 1◇ ☕	GW 1◇ ☕	GW 1	GW 1	GW 1		GW 1◇	GW 1	GW 1◇ ☕	XC 1◇ ☕	GW 1	GW 1	GW 1◇ ☕	XC 1◇ ☕	GW 1◇ ☕	GW 1	GW 1	GW 1◇
London Paddington 15	⊖ d					12 51	12 30	13 05		13 15		13 18			13 21	13 00	13 42			13 30	13 51		14 15		14 18	14 21
Ealing Broadway	⊖ d						12 37									13 07				13 37						
Slough 3	d						13 01									13 31				14 01	14 07					
Maidenhead 3	d						13 08									13 38				14 08						
Twyford 3	d						13 16									13 46				14 16						
Reading 7	a					13 21	13 21	13 31		13 41		13 47			13 52	13 52	14 07			14 21	14 21		14 40		14 47	14 52
	d			13 10	13 11	13 22	13 23		13 40			13 49			13 53	13 53		14 10	14 11	14 23	14 23	14 40			14 49	14 53
Reading West	d				13 14														14 14							
Theale	d				13 20							13 57							14 20						14 57	
Aldermaston	d				13 25														14 25							
Midgham	d				13 29														14 29							
Thatcham	d				13 34							14 05							14 34						15 05	
Newbury Racecourse	d				13 38														14 38							
Newbury	a				13 43							14 11							14 43						15 11	
	d											14 11													15 11	
Kintbury	d											14 17													15 17	
Hungerford	d											14 22													15 22	
Bedwyn	a											14 31													15 31	
Tilehurst	d						13 27									13 57				14 27						
Pangbourne	d		←				13 32									14 02				14 32						
Goring & Streatley	d		13 06				13 36				←					14 06				14 36				←		
Cholsey	d		13 11				13 41				13 41					14 11				14 41				14 41		
Didcot Parkway	a		13 17				→				13 47					14 17				→				14 47		
	d		13 18								13 55					14 18								14 55		
Appleford	d										14 00													15 00		
Culham	d																									
Radley	d										14 04													15 04		
Oxford	a		13 30	13 34		13 47			14 06		14 13				14 17	14 30		14 34			14 47	15 06		15 13		15 17
	d	13 24		13 36					14 07				14 16					14 36				15 07				
Islip	d	13 37																								
Bicester Town	a	13 50																								
Tackley	d												14 25													
Heyford	d												14 29													
Kings Sutton	d												14 37													
Banbury	a			13 52					14 24				14 44					14 52				15 24				
Leamington Spa 8	a			14 10					14 42									15 10				15 42				
Warwick	a			*14b21*					*14 58*									*15b21*				*15 58*				
Warwick Parkway	a			*14b25*					*15 02*									*15b25*				*16 02*				
Stratford-upon-Avon	a			*15 10*																						
Coventry	a			14 21														15 21								
Birmingham International	a			14 33														15 33								
Birmingham New Street 12	a			14 46					15 18									15 45				16 18				

		GW 1	GW 1	XC 1◇ ☕	GW 1		GW 1	GW 1◇ ☕	XC 1◇ ☕	GW 1◇ ☕	GW 1	GW 1	GW 1	GW 1◇	GW 1	GW 1◇ ☕	XC 1◇ ☕	GW 1	GW 1	GW 1◇ ☕		GW 1◇ ☕	XC 1◇ ☕	GW 1◇ ☕	GW 1	GW 1
London Paddington 15	⊖ d		14 00				14 30	14 51		15 15		15 18		15 21	15 00	15 42			15 30	15 51		16 05		16 15		16 18
Ealing Broadway	⊖ d		14 07				14 37								15 07				15 37							
Slough 3	d		14 31				15 01	15 07							15 31				16 01	16 07						
Maidenhead 3	d		14 38				15 08								15 38				16 08							
Twyford 3	d		14 46				15 16								15 46				16 16							
Reading 7	a		14 52				15 21	15 21		15 40		15 47		15 52	15 52	16 07			16 21	16 21		16 31		16 40		16 47
	d		14 53	15 10	15 11		15 23	15 23	15 40			15 49		15 53	15 53		16 10	16 11	16 23	16 23			16 40			16 49
Reading West	d				15 14													16 14								
Theale	d				15 20							15 57						16 20								16 57
Aldermaston	d				15 25													16 25								
Midgham	d				15 29													16 29								
Thatcham	d				15 34							16 05						16 34								17 05
Newbury Racecourse	d				15 38													16 38								
Newbury	a				15 43							16 11						16 43								17 11
	d											16 11														17 11
Kintbury	d											16 17														17 17
Hungerford	d											16 22														17 22
Bedwyn	a											16 31														17 31
Tilehurst	d		14 57				15 27								15 57				16 27							
Pangbourne	d		15 02				15 32								16 02				16 32							
Goring & Streatley	d		15 06				15 36				←				16 06				16 36						←	
Cholsey	d		15 11				15 41				15 41				16 11				16 41						16 41	
Didcot Parkway	a		15 17				→				15 47				16 17				→						16 47	
	d		15 18								15 55				16 18										16 55	
Appleford	d										16 00														17 00	
Culham	d																									
Radley	d										16 04														17 04	
Oxford	a		15 30	15 34				15 47	16 06		16 13			16 17	16 30		16 34			16 47			17 06		17 13	
	d	15 24		15 36					16 07				16 16				16 36						17 07			
Islip	d	15 37																								
Bicester Town	a	15 50																								
Tackley	d												16 25													
Heyford	d												16 29													
Kings Sutton	d												16 37													
Banbury	a			15 52					16 24				16 44				16 52						17 24			
Leamington Spa 8	a			16 10					16 42								17 10						17 42			
Warwick	a			*16b21*					*16 57*								*17b20*						*17 58*			
Warwick Parkway	a			*16b24*					*17 01*								*17b24*						*18 02*			
Stratford-upon-Avon	a			*17 11*																						
Coventry	a			16 21													17 21									
Birmingham International	a			16 33													17 33									
Birmingham New Street 12	a			16 46					17 18								17 45						18 18			

For general notes see front of timetable
For details of catering facilities see
Directory of Train Operators

b Change at Banbury

London and Reading → Bedwyn, Oxford, Bicester, Banbury and Birmingham

2 February to 22 March

Network Diagram - see first page of Table 116

		GW	GW	GW	XC	GW	GW	GW	XC	GW	GW	GW	GW	GW	GW	GW	XC	GW	GW	GW	GW	XC	GW	GW	GW
		1 ◇	1	1	1 ◇ ☕	1	1	1 ◇ ☕	1 ◇ ☕	1 ◇ ☕	1	1	1	1 ◇	1	1 ◇ ☕	1 ◇ ☕	1	1	1 ◇	1 ◇ ☕	1 ◇ ☕	1 ◇ ☕	1	1
London Paddington 15 ⊖	d	16 21		16 00			16 30	16 51		17 15		17 18		17 21	17 00	17 30			17 30	17 51	18 05		18 15		
Ealing Broadway ⊖	d			16 07			16 37								17 07				17 37						
Slough 3	d			16 31			17 01	17 07							17 31				18 01						
Maidenhead 3	d			16 38			17 08								17 38				18 08						
Twyford 3	d			16 46			17 16								17 46				18 16						
Reading 7	a	16 52		16 52			17 21	17 21		17 40		17 47		17 52	17 52	17 57			18 21	18 21	18 31		18 40		
	d	16 53		16 53	17 10	17 11	17 23	17 23	17 40			17 49		17 53	17 53		18 10	18 11	18 23	18 23		18 40			
Reading West	d					17 14												18 14							
Theale	d					17 20						17 57						18 20							
Aldermaston	d					17 25												18 25							
Midgham	d					17 29												18 29							
Thatcham	d					17 34						18 05						18 34							
Newbury Racecourse	d					17 38												18 38							
Newbury	a					17 43						18 11						18 43							
	d											18 11													
Kintbury	d											18 17													
Hungerford	d											18 22													
Bedwyn	a											18 31													
Tilehurst	d			16 57			17 27								17 57				18 27						
Pangbourne	d			17 02			17 32								18 02				18 32						
Goring & Streatley	d			17 06			17 36				←				18 06				18 36					←	
Cholsey	d			17 11			17 41				17 41				18 11				18 41					18 41	
Didcot Parkway	a			17 17			→				17 47				18 17				→					18 47	
	d			17 18							17 55				18 18									18 55	
Appleford	d										18 00													19 00	
Culham	d																								
Radley	d										18 04													19 04	
Oxford	a	17 17		17 30	17 34			17 47	18 06		18 13			18 17	18 30		18 34			18 47		19 06		19 13	
	d		17 24		17 36				18 07				18 16				18 36					19 07			19 16
Islip	d		17 37																						
Bicester Town	a		17 50																						
Tackley	d												18 25												19 25
Heyford	d												18 29												19 29
Kings Sutton	d												18 37												19 37
Banbury	a				17 52				18 24				18 44				18 52					19 24			19 44
Leamington Spa 8	a				18 10				18 42								19 10					19 42			
Warwick	a				*18 22*				*18 58*				*19 27*				*19 27*					*19 58*			
Warwick Parkway	a				*18 26*				*19 02*				*19 30*				*19 31*					*20 02*			
Stratford-upon-Avon	a				*19 13*																				
Coventry	a				18 21												19 21								
Birmingham International	a				18 33												19 33								
Birmingham New Street 12	a				18 45				19 18								19 45					20 18			

		GW	GW	GW	XC	GW	GW	GW	GW	XC	GW	GW	GW	GW	GW	XC	GW	GW	GW	GW	GW	GW	GW	GW
		1 ◇ ☕	1	1 ◇ ☕	1 ◇ ☕	1	1 ◇	1 ◇ ☕	1	1 ◇	1 ◇ ☕	1	1	1 ◇	1	1 ◇	1 ◇	1	1	1 ◇ ☕	1 ◇ ☕	1	1 ◇	1
London Paddington 15 ⊖	d	18 21	18 00	18 30		18 30	18 51	19 05			19 15			19 21	19 00		19 51		19 30	20 05	20 15		20 21	20 00
Ealing Broadway ⊖	d		18 07			18 37									19 07				19 37					20 07
Slough 3	d	18 37	18 31			19 01									19 31		20 07		20 01					20 31
Maidenhead 3	d		18 38			19 08									19 38				20 08					20 38
Twyford 3	d		18 46			19 16									19 46				20 16					20 46
Reading 7	a	18 51	18 52	18 57		19 21	19 21	19 31			19 40			19 51	19 52		20 21		20 21	20 30	20 40		20 51	20 52
	d	18 53	18 53		19 10	19 23	19 23	19 32		19 40			19 49	19 52	19 53	20 10	20 23		20 23	20 32			20 52	20 53
Reading West	d												19 52											
Theale	d												19 58											
Aldermaston	d												20 03											
Midgham	d												20 07											
Thatcham	d												20 12											
Newbury Racecourse	d												20 16											
Newbury	a							19 47					20 19							20 46				
	d												20 19											
Kintbury	d												20 25											
Hungerford	d												20 30											
Bedwyn	a												20 39											
Tilehurst	d		18 57			19 27									19 57				20 27					20 57
Pangbourne	d		19 02			19 32									20 02				20 32					21 02
Goring & Streatley	d		19 06			19 36						←			20 06				20 36					21 06
Cholsey	d		19 11			19 41						19 41			20 11				20 41					21 11
Didcot Parkway	a		19 17			→						19 47			20 17				20 47					21 17
	d		19 18									19 58			20 18				20 55					21 18
Appleford	d											20 04							21 00					
Culham	d																							
Radley	d											20 08							21 04					
Oxford	a	19 18	19 30		19 34		19 47			20 06		20 16		20 20	20 30	20 34	20 47		21 13				21 19	21 30
	d				19 36				19 56	20 07						20 36		20 49				21 20		
Islip	d																	21 02						
Bicester Town	a																	21 15						
Tackley	d								20 05													21 29		
Heyford	d								20 09													21 33		
Kings Sutton	d								20 17													21 41		
Banbury	a				19 52				20 24	20 24						20 52						21 48		
Leamington Spa 8	a				20 10				*20 55*	20 42						21 10								
Warwick	a				*20 27*				*20 59*	*20 59*						*21 43*								
Warwick Parkway	a				*20 31*				*21 03*	*21 03*						*21 47*								
Stratford-upon-Avon	a				*21 10*																			
Coventry	a				20 21											21 21								
Birmingham International	a				20 33											21 33								
Birmingham New Street 12	a				20 45					21 22						21 45								

For general notes see front of timetable
For details of catering facilities see
Directory of Train Operators

Table 116

Saturdays

2 February to 22 March

London and Reading → Bedwyn, Oxford, Bicester, Banbury and Birmingham

Network Diagram - see first page of Table 116

		GW	XC	GW	GW	GW	GW	GW	GW	GW	GW	GW	GW	GW	GW	GW	GW	GW	GW	GW	GW	GW	GW
		1 ◇	1 ◇	1	1 ◇	1	1 ◇	1 ◇	1	1 ◇	1 ◇	1 ◇	1	1 ◇	1 ◇	🚌	🚌	1	1 ◇	🚌	1	1 ◇	1
		🛒					🛒			🛒				🛒									
London Paddington 15 ⊖	d	20 30		20 30	20 51		21 15	21 21	21 00	21 30	21 51	22 15	22 00	22 30	22 32				23 00		22 45	23 33	23 20
Ealing Broadway ⊖	d			20 37					21 07				22 07								22 54		23 27
Slough 3	d			21 01	21 08				21 31		22 08		22 31		22 50				23 17		23 20	23 50	23 53
Maidenhead 3	d			21 08					21 38				22 38								23 29		00 05
Twyford 3	d			21 16					21 46				22 46								23 36		00 12
Reading 7	a	20 55		21 21	21 25		21 40	21 51	21 52	21 57	22 23	22 40	22 52	22 55	23 06				23 33		23 43	00 07	00 19
	d		21 10	21 23	21 26			21 52	21 53		22 23		22 53		23 07			23 11	23 34		23 48	00 08	00 19
Reading West	d																	23 14					
Theale	d																	23 20					
Aldermaston	d																	23 25					
Midgham	d																	23 29					
Thatcham	d																	23 34					
Newbury Racecourse	d																	23 38					
Newbury	a																	23 41					
	d																	23 41					
Kintbury	d																	23 47					
Hungerford	d																	23 52					
Bedwyn	a																	00 02					
Tilehurst	d			21 27		←			21 57				22 57								23 52		00 24
Pangbourne	d			21 32		21 32			22 02				23 02								23 57		
Goring & Streatley	d			→		21 36			22 06				23 06								00 01		00 31
Cholsey	d					21 41			22 11				23 11								00 06		00 36
Didcot Parkway	a				21 42	21 47		22 08	22 17				23 17		23 24				23 51		00 13	00 25	00 43
	d				21 43	21 52		22 08	22 18				23 18				23 31			23 58			
Appleford	d					21 58																	
Culham	d																						
Radley	d					22 02																	
Oxford	a		21 34		21 55	22 10		22 20	22 30		22 46		23 31				23 56			00 23			
	d		21 36													23 37							
Islip	d																						
Bicester Town	a																						
Tackley	d															23s57							
Heyford	d															00s12							
Kings Sutton	d															00b27							
Banbury	a		21 52													00 37							
Leamington Spa 8	a		22 10																				
Warwick	a		22 31																				
Warwick Parkway	a		22 35																				
Stratford-upon-Avon	a																						
Coventry	a		22 21																				
Birmingham International	a		22 33																				
Birmingham New Street 12	a		22 50																				

For general notes see front of timetable
For details of catering facilities see Directory of Train Operators

b Kings Sutton V. Square. Stops to set down only

London and Reading → Bedwyn, Oxford, Bicester, Banbury and Birmingham

Saturdays

from 29 March

Network Diagram - see first page of Table 116

		GW	GW	GW	GW	GW	GW	GW	GW	GW	GW	GW	GW	GW	GW	XC	GW	GW	GW	GW	GW	XC	GW	GW	GW	GW
		1	1 ◊	1	1	1 ◊	1	1	1	1 ◊	1	1	1	1 ◊	1	1 ◊	1	1	1 ◊	1 ◊	1	1 ◊	1 ◊	1	1	1 ◊
			🚌													☕				☕		☕	☕			☕
London Paddington 15 ⊖	d	22p46	23p30		23p29	00 21				05 12				05 42	05 25		05 45		06 21	06 30			06 45		06 15	06 51
Ealing Broadway ⊖	d	22p55			23p36										05 32		05 52								06 22	
Slough 3	d	23p14			23p55	00 41				05 29				05 57	05 51		06 18								06 48	07 07
Maidenhead 3	d	23p25			00 03										06 03		06 29								06 59	
Twyford 3	d	23p33			00 11										06 10		06 37								07 07	
Reading 7	a	23p40	00 01		00 18	00 58				05 46				06 13	06 17		06 43		06 51	06 55			07 10		07 13	07 21
	d	23p41	00 02	00 15	00 19	00 59	05 11		05 41	05 48	05 48	06 11		06 14	06 19	06 40	06 48	06 48	06 52	06 55		07 10	07 11	07 11	07 16	07 23
Reading West	d			00s17			05 14		05 44			06 14												07 14		
Theale	d			00s23			05 20		05 50			06 20						06 56						07 20		
Aldermaston	d			00s28			05 25		05 55			06 25												07 25		
Midgham	d			00s32			05 29		05 59			06 29												07 29		
Thatcham	d			00s37			05 34		06 04			06 34						07 04						07 34		
Newbury Racecourse	d			00s41			05 38		06 08			06 38												07 38		
Newbury	a			00 45			05 41		06 11			06 42						07 10						07 42		
	d						05 41		06 11									07 10								
Kintbury	d						05 47		06 17									07 16								
Hungerford	d						05 52		06 22									07 21								
Bedwyn	a						06 01		06 31									07 30								
Tilehurst	d	23p45			00 23						05 52				06 24		06 53								07 20	
Pangbourne	d	23p50			00 28						05 57				06 28		06 57				←				07 25	
Goring & Streatley	d	23p54			00 32						06 01				06 33		07 02				07 02				07 29	
Cholsey	d	23p59			00 37						06 06				06 38		→				07 07				07 34	
Didcot Parkway	a	00 06	00 20		00 44	01 15				06 02	06 12			06 28	06 44					07 11	07 15		07 26		→	
	d	00 07			00 45	01 16				06 03	06 13			06 29	06 44						07 15					
Appleford	d				00 50						06 18				06 50											
Culham	d				00 53						06 21															
Radley	d	00 15			00 57						06 25				06 55											
Oxford	a	00 22			01 07	01 30				06 17	06 32			06 42	07 03	07 06			07 17		07 28	07 34				07 48
	d							06 16					06 44			07 07						07 36				
Islip	d												06 57													
Bicester Town	a												07 10													
Tackley	d							06 25																		
Heyford	d							06 29																		
Kings Sutton	d							06 37																		
Banbury	a							06 44								07 24						07 52				
Leamington Spa 8	a							*07 19*								07 42						08 10				
Warwick	a							*07 23*								*07 59*						*08 24*				
Warwick Parkway	a							*07 27*								*08 03*						*08 20*				
Stratford-upon-Avon	a																									
Coventry	a																					08 21				
Birmingham International	a																					08 33				
Birmingham New Street 12	a															08 18						08 46				

		GW	GW	GW	XC	GW	GW	GW	GW	GW	XC	GW	GW	GW	GW	GW	GW	XC	GW	GW	GW	GW	GW	GW	GW	XC
		1 ◊	1	1	1 ◊	1	1 ◊	1	1 ◊	1	1 ◊	1	1 ◊	1	1	1 ◊	1 ◊	1 ◊	1	1	1 ◊	1 ◊	1	1 ◊	1	1 ◊
		☕			☕				☕		☕		☕			☕	☕	☕			☕			☕		☕
London Paddington 15 ⊖	d	07 00					07 21	07 00	07 30				07 45		07 30	07 51	08 00				08 18	08 21	08 00	08 30		
Ealing Broadway ⊖	d							07 07							07 37								08 07			
Slough 3	d							07 31							08 01	08 07							08 31			
Maidenhead 3	d							07 38							08 08								08 38			
Twyford 3	d							07 46							08 16								08 46			
Reading 7	a	07 26					07 51	07 52	07 56				08 10		08 21	08 21	08 26				08 45	08 51	08 52	08 56		
	d				07 40	07 48	07 51	07 53	07 57		08 10		08 11	08 11	08 23	08 23		08 40			08 49	08 53	08 53	08 57		09 10
Reading West	d													08 14												
Theale	d					07 56								08 20							08 58					
Aldermaston	d													08 25												
Midgham	d													08 29												
Thatcham	d					08 04								08 34							09 06					
Newbury Racecourse	d													08 38												
Newbury	a					08 10								08 42							09 11					
	d					08 10														08 58	09 12					
Kintbury	d					08 16														09 04						
Hungerford	d					08 21														09 09	09 21					
Bedwyn	a					08 30														09 18	09 27					
Tilehurst	d							07 57				←			08 27								08 57		←	
Pangbourne	d							08 02				08 02			08 32								09 02		09 02	
Goring & Streatley	d			←				→				08 06			08 36				←				→		09 06	
Cholsey	d			07 34								08 11			08 41				08 41						09 11	
Didcot Parkway	a			07 40					08 11			08 17	08 26		→				08 47					09 12	09 17	
	d			07 41								08 25							08 55						09 18	
Appleford	d																		09 03							
Culham	d			07 46																						
Radley	d			07 50															09 07							
Oxford	a			08 00	08 03		08 16				08 34	08 39				08 47		09 06	09 15			09 20			09 31	09 34
	d		07 53		08 04					08 24	08 36							09 07								09 36
Islip	d									08 37																
Bicester Town	a									08 50																
Tackley	d		08 02																							
Heyford	d		08 06																							
Kings Sutton	d		08 14																							
Banbury	a		08 21		08 21						08 52							09 24								09 52
Leamington Spa 8	a		*08 59*		08 42						09 10							09 42								10 10
Warwick	a		*09 04*		*09 04*						*09b21*							*10 02*								*10 41*
Warwick Parkway	a		*09 07*		*09 07*						*09b25*							*10 05*								
Stratford-upon-Avon	a		*09 35*		*09 35*																					*11 12*
Coventry	a										09 21															10 21
Birmingham International	a										09 33															10 33
Birmingham New Street 12	a				09 18						09 45							10 18								10 45

For general notes see front of timetable
For details of catering facilities see Directory of Train Operators

b Change at Banbury

London and Reading → Bedwyn, Oxford, Bicester, Banbury and Birmingham

Saturdays
from 29 March

Network Diagram - see first page of Table 116

		GW 1◇ ☕	GW 1	GW 1	GW 1◇ ☕	GW 1◇ ☕	GW 1◇ ☕	XC 1◇ ☕	GW 1	GW 1	GW 1	GW 1	GW 1◇	GW 1	GW 1◇ ☕	GW 1	XC 1◇ ☕	GW 1◇ ☕	GW 1	GW 1	GW 1◇ ☕	GW 1◇ ☕	GW 1◇ ☕	XC 1◇ ☕	GW 1	GW 1
London Paddington 15 ⊖	d	08 45		08 30	08 51	09 00	09 05				09 18	09 00	09 21		09 30			09 45		09 30	09 51	10 00	10 05			10 18
Ealing Broadway ⊖	d			08 37								09 07								09 37						
Slough 3	d			09 01	09 07							09 31								10 01	10 07					
Maidenhead 3	d			09 08								09 38								10 08						
Twyford 3	d			09 16								09 46								10 16						
Reading 7	a	09 10		09 21	09 21	09 26	09 31				09 48	09 52	09 52		09 57			10 10		10 21	10 21	10 26	10 31			10 47
	d	09 11	09 11	09 23	09 23			09 40			09 48	09 53	09 54		09 57		10 10	10 11	10 11	10 23	10 23			10 40		10 49
Reading West	d		09 14																10 14							
Theale	d		09 20								09 56								10 20							10 57
Aldermaston	d		09 25																10 25							
Midgham	d		09 29																10 29							
Thatcham	d		09 34								10 04								10 34							11 05
Newbury Racecourse	d		09 38																10 38							
Newbury	a		09 43								10 10								10 43							11 11
	d										10 11															11 11
Kintbury	d										10 17															11 17
Hungerford	d										10 22															11 22
Bedwyn	a										10 31															11 31
Tilehurst	d			09 27								09 57								10 27						
Pangbourne	d			09 32								10 02				←				10 32						
Goring & Streatley	d			09 36					←			10 06				10 06				10 36					←	
Cholsey	d			09 41					09 41			→				10 11				10 41					10 41	
Didcot Parkway	a	09 26		→					09 47						10 12	10 17		10 26		→					10 47	
	d								09 55							10 18									10 55	
Appleford	d								10 00																11 00	
Culham	d																									
Radley	d								10 04																11 04	
Oxford	a				09 47			10 06	10 13				10 18			10 30	10 34				10 47			11 06	11 13	
	d							10 07		10 16				10 24			10 36							11 07		
Islip	d													10 37												
Bicester Town	a													10 50												
Tackley	d									10 25																
Heyford	d									10 29																
Kings Sutton	d									10 39																
Banbury	a							10 24		10 46							10 52							11 24		
Leamington Spa 8	a							10 42									11 10							11 42		
Warwick	a							11 02									11b20							11 58		
Warwick Parkway	a							11 06									11b23							12 02		
Stratford-upon-Avon	a																									
Coventry	a																11 21									
Birmingham International	a																11 33									
Birmingham New Street 12	a							11 18									11 45							12 18		

		GW 1	GW 1◇	GW 1◇ ☕	GW 1	XC 1◇ ☕	GW 1◇ ☕	GW 1	GW 1	GW 1◇ ☕	GW 1◇ ☕	GW 1◇ ☕	XC 1◇ ☕	GW 1	GW 1	GW 1	GW 1◇	GW 1	GW 1◇ ☕	GW 1	XC 1◇ ☕	GW 1◇ ☕	GW 1	GW 1	GW 1◇ ☕	GW 1◇ ☕
London Paddington 15 ⊖	d	10 00	10 21	10 30			10 45		10 30	10 51	11 00	11 05			11 18		11 21	11 00	11 30			11 45		11 30	11 51	12 00
Ealing Broadway ⊖	d	10 07							10 37									11 07						11 37		
Slough 3	d	10 30							11 01	11 07								11 31						12 01	12 07	
Maidenhead 3	d	10 38							11 08									11 38						12 08		
Twyford 3	d	10 46							11 16									11 46						12 16		
Reading 7	a	10 52	10 52	10 57			11 10		11 21	11 21	11 26	11 31			11 47		11 51	11 52	11 56			12 10		12 21	12 21	12 26
	d	10 53	10 54	10 57		11 10	11 11	11 11	11 23	11 23			11 40		11 49		11 53	11 53	11 57		12 10	12 11	12 11	12 23	12 23	
Reading West	d							11 14															12 14			
Theale	d							11 20							11 57								12 20			
Aldermaston	d							11 25															12 25			
Midgham	d							11 29															12 29			
Thatcham	d							11 34							12 06								12 34			
Newbury Racecourse	d							11 38															12 38			
Newbury	a							11 43							12 11								12 43			
	d														12 11											
Kintbury	d														12 18											
Hungerford	d														12 23											
Bedwyn	a														12 32											
Tilehurst	d	10 57							11 27									11 57		←				12 27		
Pangbourne	d	11 02			←				11 32									12 02		12 02				12 32		
Goring & Streatley	d	11 06			11 06				11 36					←				→		12 06				12 36		
Cholsey	d	→			11 11				11 41					11 41						12 11				12 41		
Didcot Parkway	a			11 12	11 17		11 26		→					11 47					12 12	12 17		12 26		→		
	d				11 18									11 55						12 18						
Appleford	d													12 00												
Culham	d																									
Radley	d													12 04												
Oxford	a		11 19		11 30	11 34				11 47			12 06	12 13			12 17			12 30	12 34				12 47	
	d					11 36							12 07			12 16					12 35					
Islip	d																									
Bicester Town	a																									
Tackley	d															12 25										
Heyford	d															12 29										
Kings Sutton	d															12 37										
Banbury	a					11 52							12 24			12 44					12 52					
Leamington Spa 8	a					12 10							12 42								13 10					
Warwick	a					12b21							12 58								13b21					
Warwick Parkway	a					12 25							13 02								13b25					
Stratford-upon-Avon	a					13 11																				
Coventry	a					12 21															13 21					
Birmingham International	a					12 33															13 33					
Birmingham New Street 12	a					12 45							13 18								13 45					

For general notes see front of timetable
For details of catering facilities see
Directory of Train Operators

b Change at Banbury

London and Reading → Bedwyn, Oxford, Bicester, Banbury and Birmingham

Network Diagram - see first page of Table 116

		GW	XC	GW	GW	GW	GW	GW	GW	XC	GW	GW	GW	GW	GW	GW	XC	GW	GW	GW	GW	GW	GW	GW	XC	GW
		1 ◇	1 ◇	1	1	1 ◇	1 ◇	1	1	1 ◇	1 ◇	1	1 ◇	1	1 ◇	1 ◇	1 ◇	1	1	1	1 ◇	1	1 ◇	1	1 ◇	1 ◇
		☕	☕				☕			☕	☕				☕	☕	☕						☕		☕	☕
London Paddington 15 ⊖	d	12 05			12 00	12 21	12 30				12 45		12 51	12 30	13 00	13 05			13 18		13 21	13 00	13 30			13 45
Ealing Broadway ⊖	d				12 07									12 37								13 07				
Slough 3	d				12 31									13 01								13 31				
Maidenhead 3	d				12 38									13 08								13 38				
Twyford 3	d				12 46									13 16								13 46				
Reading 7	a	12 31			12 52	12 53	12 58				13 10		13 21	13 21	13 26	13 31			13 47		13 51	13 52	13 55			14 11
	d		12 40		12 53	12 55	12 58			13 10	13 11	13 11	13 22	13 23			13 40		13 49		13 52	13 53	13 57		14 10	14 11
Reading West	d											13 14														
Theale	d											13 20							13 57							
Aldermaston	d											13 25														
Midgham	d											13 29														
Thatcham	d											13 34							14 06							
Newbury Racecourse	d											13 38														
Newbury	a											13 43							14 11							
	d																		14 11							
Kintbury	d																		14 18							
Hungerford	d																		14 23							
Bedwyn	a																		14 32							
Tilehurst	d				12 57									13 27								13 57		←		
Pangbourne	d				13 02				←					13 32								14 02 →		14 02		
Goring & Streatley	d			←	13 06 →				13 06					13 36				←						14 06		
Cholsey	d			12 41					13 11					13 41 →				13 41						14 11		
Didcot Parkway	a			12 47			13 14		13 17		13 26							13 47					14 11	14 17		14 26
	d			12 55					13 18									13 55						14 18		
Appleford	d			13 00														14 00								
Culham	d																									
Radley	d			13 04														14 04								
Oxford	a		13 06	13 13		13 19			13 30	13 34			13 47				14 06	14 13			14 17			14 30	14 34	
	d		13 07					13 24		13 36							14 07			14 16					14 36	
Islip	d							13 37																		
Bicester Town	a							13 50																		
Tackley	d																			14 25						
Heyford	d																			14 29						
Kings Sutton	d																			14 37						
Banbury	a		13 24							13 52							14 24			14 44					14 52	
Leamington Spa 8	a		13 42							14 10							14 42								15 10	
Warwick	a		*13 58*							*14b21*							*14 58*								*15b21*	
Warwick Parkway	a		*14 02*							*14b25*							*15 02*								*15 25*	
Stratford-upon-Avon	a									*15 10*																
Coventry	a									14 21															15 21	
Birmingham International	a									14 33															15 33	
Birmingham New Street 12	a		14 18							14 46							15 18								15 45	

		GW	GW	GW	GW	GW	XC	GW	GW	GW	GW	GW	GW	GW	XC	GW	GW	GW	GW	GW	XC	GW	GW	GW	GW	GW
		1	1	1 ◇	1 ◇	1 ◇	1 ◇	1	1	1 ◇	1	1 ◇	1	1	1 ◇	1 ◇	1	1	1 ◇	1 ◇	1 ◇	1	1	1	1 ◇	1
				☕	☕	☕	☕					☕			☕	☕			☕	☕	☕					
London Paddington 15 ⊖	d		13 30	13 51	14 00	14 05			14 18	14 21	14 00	14 30				14 45		14 30	14 51	15 00			15 18		15 21	15 00
Ealing Broadway ⊖	d		13 37								14 07							14 37								15 07
Slough 3	d		14 01	14 07							14 31							15 01	15 07							15 31
Maidenhead 3	d		14 08								14 38							15 08								15 38
Twyford 3	d		14 16								14 46							15 16								15 46
Reading 7	a		14 21	14 21	14 26	14 31			14 47	14 51	14 52	14 56				15 10		15 21	15 21	15 26			15 47		15 51	15 52
	d	14 11	14 23	14 23			14 40		14 49	14 53	14 53	14 57			15 10	15 11	15 11	15 23	15 23		15 40		15 49		15 53	15 53
Reading West	d	14 14															15 14									
Theale	d	14 20							14 57								15 20						15 57			
Aldermaston	d	14 25															15 25									
Midgham	d	14 29															15 29									
Thatcham	d	14 34							15 05								15 34						16 05			
Newbury Racecourse	d	14 38															15 38									
Newbury	a	14 43							15 11								15 43						16 11			
	d								15 11														16 11			
Kintbury	d								15 17														16 17			
Hungerford	d								15 22														16 22			
Bedwyn	a								15 31														16 31			
Tilehurst	d		14 27								14 57			←				15 27								15 57
Pangbourne	d		14 32								15 02 →			15 02				15 32								16 02 →
Goring & Streatley	d		14 36					←						15 06				15 36				←				
Cholsey	d		14 41 →					14 41						15 11				15 41 →				15 41				
Didcot Parkway	a							14 47				15 12		15 17		15 26						15 47				
	d							14 55						15 18								15 55				
Appleford	d							15 00														16 00				
Culham	d																									
Radley	d							15 04														16 04				
Oxford	a			14 47			15 06	15 13		15 17				15 30	15 34				15 47		16 06	16 13			16 17	
	d						15 07						15 24		15 36						16 07			16 16		
Islip	d												15 37													
Bicester Town	a												15 50													
Tackley	d																							16 25		
Heyford	d																							16 29		
Kings Sutton	d																							16 37		
Banbury	a						15 24								15 52						16 24			16 44		
Leamington Spa 8	a						15 42								16 10						16 42					
Warwick	a						*15 58*								*16b21*						*16 57*					
Warwick Parkway	a						*16 02*								*16b24*						*17 01*					
Stratford-upon-Avon	a														*17 11*											
Coventry	a														16 21											
Birmingham International	a														16 33											
Birmingham New Street 12	a						16 18								16 46						17 18					

For general notes see front of timetable
For details of catering facilities see
Directory of Train Operators

b Change at Banbury

Table 116

Saturdays

from 29 March

London and Reading → Bedwyn, Oxford, Bicester, Banbury and Birmingham

Network Diagram - see first page of Table 116

		GW	GW	XC	GW	GW	GW	GW	GW	GW	XC	GW	GW	GW	GW	GW	GW	GW	XC	GW	GW	GW	GW	GW	GW	XC
		1 ◇ ☕	1	1 ◇ ☕	1 ◇ ☕	1	1	1 ◇ ☕	1 ◇ ☕	1 ◇ ☕	1 ◇ ☕	1	1	1 ◇	1	1 ◇ ☕	1	1	1 ◇ ☕	1	1 ◇ ☕	1	1 ◇ ☕	1 ◇ ☕	1 ◇ ☕	1 ◇ ☕
London Paddington 15	⊖ d	15 30			15 45		15 30	15 51	16 00	16 05			16 18	16 21	16 00	16 30					16 45	16 30	16 51	17 00	17 05	
Ealing Broadway	⊖ d						15 37								16 07							16 37				
Slough 3	d						16 01	16 07							16 31							17 01	17 07			
Maidenhead 3	d						16 08								16 38							17 08				
Twyford 3	d						16 16								16 46							17 16				
Reading 7	a	15 56			16 11		16 21	16 21	16 26	16 31			16 47	16 51	16 52	16 56					17 11	17 21	17 21	17 26	17 31	
	d	15 57		16 10	16 11	16 11	16 23	16 23			16 40		16 49	16 53	16 53	16 57			17 10	17 11		17 23	17 23			17 40
Reading West	d					16 14														17 14						
Theale	d					16 20							16 57							17 20						
Aldermaston	d					16 25														17 25						
Midgham	d					16 29														17 29						
Thatcham	d					16 34							17 05							17 34						
Newbury Racecourse	d					16 38														17 38						
Newbury	a					16 43							17 11							17 43						
	d												17 11													
Kintbury	d												17 17													
Hungerford	d												17 22													
Bedwyn	a												17 31													
Tilehurst	d		←				16 27								16 57			←				17 27				
Pangbourne	d		16 02				16 32								17 02			17 02				17 32				
Goring & Streatley	d		16 06				16 36					←			→			17 06				17 36				
Cholsey	d		16 11				16 41					16 41						17 11				17 41				
Didcot Parkway	a	16 12	16 17		16 26		→					16 47				17 12		17 17				→				
	d		16 18									16 55						17 18								
Appleford	d											17 00														
Culham	d																									
Radley	d											17 04														
Oxford	a		16 30	16 34				16 47			17 06	17 13		17 17				17 30	17 34				17 47			18 06
	d			16 36							17 07						17 24		17 36							18 07
Islip	d																17 37									
Bicester Town	a																17 50									
Tackley	d																									
Heyford	d																									
Kings Sutton	d																									
Banbury	a			16 52							17 24								17 52							18 24
Leamington Spa 8	a			17 10							17 42								18 10							18 42
Warwick	a			17b20							17 58								18 22							18 58
Warwick Parkway	a			17b24							18 02								18 24							19 02
Stratford-upon-Avon	a																		19 13							
Coventry	a			17 21															18 21							
Birmingham International	a			17 33															18 33							
Birmingham New Street 12	a			17 45							18 18								18 45							19 18

		GW	GW	GW	GW	GW	GW	GW	XC	GW	GW	GW	GW	GW	GW	XC	GW	GW	GW	GW	GW	GW	GW	XC	GW	GW
		1	1	1	1 ◇	1	1 ◇ ☕	1	1 ◇ ☕	1	1 ◇ ☕	1	1 ◇	1 ◇ ☕	1 ◇ ☕	1 ◇ ☕	1	1	1	1 ◇ ☕	1	1 ◇ ☕	1	1 ◇ ☕	1 ◇ ☕	1
London Paddington 15	⊖ d		17 18		17 21	17 00	17 30				17 45	17 30	17 51	18 00	18 05			18 18		18 21	18 00	18 30			18 45	18 30
Ealing Broadway	⊖ d					17 07						17 37									18 07					18 37
Slough 3	d					17 31						18 01								18 37	18 31					19 01
Maidenhead 3	d					17 38						18 08									18 38					19 08
Twyford 3	d					17 46						18 16									18 46					19 16
Reading 7	a		17 47		17 51	17 52	17 56				18 11	18 21	18 21	18 26	18 31			18 47		18 51	18 52	18 56			19 11	19 21
	d		17 49		17 53	17 53	17 56		18 10	18 11		18 23	18 23			18 40		18 49		18 53	18 53	18 57		19 10		19 23
Reading West	d									18 14																
Theale	d		17 57							18 20								18 57								
Aldermaston	d									18 25																
Midgham	d									18 29																
Thatcham	d		18 05							18 34								19 05								
Newbury Racecourse	d									18 38																
Newbury	a		18 11							18 43								19 11								
	d		18 11															19 11								
Kintbury	d		18 17															19 17								
Hungerford	d		18 22															19 22								
Bedwyn	a		18 31															19 31								
Tilehurst	d					17 57		←				18 27									18 57		←			19 27
Pangbourne	d					18 02		18 02				18 32									19 02		19 02			19 32
Goring & Streatley	d	←				→		18 06				18 36					←				→		19 06			19 36
Cholsey	d	17 41						18 11				18 41					18 41						19 11			19 41
Didcot Parkway	a	17 47					18 12	18 17				→					18 47					19 12	19 17			→
	d	17 55						18 18									18 55						19 18			
Appleford	d	18 00															19 00									
Culham	d																									
Radley	d	18 04															19 04									
Oxford	a	18 13			18 17			18 30	18 34				18 47			19 06	19 13			19 18			19 30	19 34		
	d			18 16					18 36							19 07			19 16					19 36		
Islip	d																									
Bicester Town	a																									
Tackley	d			18 25															19 25							
Heyford	d			18 29															19 29							
Kings Sutton	d			18 37															19 37							
Banbury	a			18 44					18 52							19 24			19 44					19 52		
Leamington Spa 8	a								19 10							19 42								20 10		
Warwick	a								19 27							19 58								20 27		
Warwick Parkway	a								19 31							20 02								20 31		
Stratford-upon-Avon	a																							21 10		
Coventry	a								19 21															20 21		
Birmingham International	a								19 33															20 33		
Birmingham New Street 12	a								19 45							20 18								20 45		

b Change at Banbury

For general notes see front of timetable
For details of catering facilities see
Directory of Train Operators

Table 116

Saturdays
from 29 March

London and Reading → Bedwyn, Oxford, Bicester, Banbury and Birmingham

Network Diagram - see first page of Table 116

		GW	GW	GW	GW	XC	GW	GW	GW	GW	GW	GW	GW	XC	GW	GW	GW	GW	GW	GW	GW	GW	GW	GW	GW	GW
		1 ◇	1 ◇ ☕	1 ◇ ☕	1	1 ◇	1	1 ◇ ☕	1	1 ◇	1	1 ◇ ☕	1	1 ◇ ☕	1 ◇ ☕	1	1 ◇	1 ◇ ☕	1 ◇ ☕	1	1	1	1	1 ◇	1	1 ◇ ☕
London Paddington 15 ⊖	d	18 51	19 00	19 05				19 15		19 21	19 00	19 30			19 45	19 30	19 51	20 00	20 05					20 21	20 00	20 30
Ealing Broadway ⊖	d										19 07					19 37									20 07	
Slough 3	d										19 31					20 01	20 07								20 31	
Maidenhead 3	d										19 38					20 08									20 38	
Twyford 3	d										19 46					20 16									20 46	
Reading 7	a	19 21	19 26	19 31				19 40		19 51	19 52	19 56			20 10	20 21	20 21	20 27	20 32					20 51	20 52	20 55
	d	19 23		19 32		19 40		19 41	19 49	19 52	19 53	19 57		20 10		20 23	20 23	20 27	20 33				20 49	20 52	20 53	20 57
Reading West	d								19 52														20 52			
Theale	d								19 58														20 58			
Aldermaston	d								20 03														21 03			
Midgham	d								20 07														21 07			
Thatcham	d								20 12														21 12			
Newbury Racecourse	d								20 16														21 16			
Newbury	a			19 47					20 19										20 48				21 19			
	d								20 19														21 33			
Kintbury	d								20 25														21 39			
Hungerford	d								20 30														21 44			
Bedwyn	a								20 39														21 53			
Tilehurst	d										19 57		←			20 27					←				20 57	
Pangbourne	d										20 02 →		20 02			20 32 →					20 32				21 02	
Goring & Streatley	d						←						20 06								20 36				21 06 →	
Cholsey	d						19 41						20 11								20 41					
Didcot Parkway	a						19 47	19 55				20 11	20 17					20 42			20 47					21 11
	d						19 58						20 18								20 55					
Appleford	d						20 04														21 00					
Culham	d																									
Radley	d						20 08														21 04					
Oxford	a	19 47				20 06	20 16			20 20			20 30	20 34			20 47				21 13			21 19		
	d				19 56	20 07								20 36						20 49		21 20				
Islip	d																			21 02						
Bicester Town	a																			21 15						
Tackley	d				20 05																	21 29				
Heyford	d				20 09																	21 33				
Kings Sutton	d				20 17																	21 41				
Banbury	a				20 24	20 24								20 52								21 48				
Leamington Spa 8	a				*20 55*	20 42								21 10												
Warwick	a				*20 59*	*20 59*								*21 43*												
Warwick Parkway	a				*21 03*	*21 03*								*21 47*												
Stratford-upon-Avon	a																									
Coventry	a													21 21												
Birmingham International	a													21 33												
Birmingham New Street 12	a					21 22								21 45												

		GW	XC	GW	GW	GW	GW	GW	GW	GW	GW	GW	GW	GW	GW	GW	GW	GW	GW	GW	GW	GW	GW	GW	GW
		1	1 ◇	1 ◇ ☕	1	1 ◇	1	1	1 ◇	1	1 ◇ ☕	1	1 ◇	1 ◇	1 ◇ ☕	1 ◇	🚌	🚌	1	1 ◇	🚌	1	1 ◇ ☕	1 ◇	1
London Paddington 15 ⊖	d			20 45	20 30	20 51			21 21	21 00	21 30		21 51	22 00	22 30	22 32				23 00		22 45	23 30	23 33	23 20
Ealing Broadway ⊖	d				20 37					21 07												22 54			23 27
Slough 3	d				21 01	21 08				21 31			22 08			22 50				23 17		23 20		23 50	23 53
Maidenhead 3	d				21 08					21 38												23 29			00 05
Twyford 3	d				21 16					21 46												23 36			00 12
Reading 7	a			21 10	21 21	21 25			21 51	21 52	21 56		22 23	22 27	22 55	23 06				23 33		23 43	23 59	00 07	00 19
	d		21 10	21 11	21 23	21 26		21 49	21 52	21 53	21 57		22 23	22 27	22 57	23 07			23 11	23 34		23 48	23 59	00 08	00 19
Reading West	d							21 52											23 14						
Theale	d							21 58											23 20						
Aldermaston	d							22 04											23 25						
Midgham	d							22 07											23 29						
Thatcham	d							22 12											23 34						
Newbury Racecourse	d							22 17											23 38						
Newbury	a							22 19											23 41						
	d							22 19											23 41						
Kintbury	d							22 26											23 47						
Hungerford	d							22 31											23 52						
Bedwyn	a							22 39											00 02						
Tilehurst	d				21 27		←			21 57		←										23 52			00 24
Pangbourne	d	←			21 32 →		21 32			22 02 →		22 02										23 57			
Goring & Streatley	d	21 06					21 36					22 06										00 01			00 31
Cholsey	d	21 11					21 41					22 11										00 06			00 36
Didcot Parkway	a	21 17		21 30		21 42	21 47		22 08		22 12	22 17		22 42	23 16	23 24				23 51		00 13	00 16	00 25	00 43
	d	21 18				21 43	21 52		22 08			22 18						23 31			23 58				
Appleford	d						21 58																		
Culham	d																								
Radley	d						22 02																		
Oxford	a	21 30	21 34			21 55	22 10		22 20			22 30	22 46					23 56			00 23				
	d		21 36														23 37								
Islip	d																								
Bicester Town	a																								
Tackley	d																23s57								
Heyford	d																00s12								
Kings Sutton	d																00b27								
Banbury	a		21 52														00 37								
Leamington Spa 8	a		22 10																						
Warwick	a		*22 31*																						
Warwick Parkway	a		*22 35*																						
Stratford-upon-Avon	a																								
Coventry	a		22 21																						
Birmingham International	a		22 33																						
Birmingham New Street 12	a		22 50																						

For general notes see front of timetable
For details of catering facilities see Directory of Train Operators

b Kings Sutton V. Square.
Stops to set down only

until 27 January

London and Reading → Bedwyn, Oxford, Bicester, Banbury and Birmingham

Network Diagram - see first page of Table 116

		GW	GW	GW	GW	GW	GW	GW	GW	GW	GW	GW	GW	GW	GW	GW	GW	GW	GW	GW	GW	GW	GW	GW	XC	GW
		1		1 ◇		1	1					1 ◇	1 ◇		1 ◇	1	1 ◇	1 ◇	1 ◇		1 ◇		1	1 ◇	1 ◇	1 ◇
													A													
			🚌		🚌			🚌																		
												☕	☕		☕		☕	🍴	☕		☕			☕	☕	☕
London Paddington 15 ⊖	d	22p45		23p33			23p20				07 43	08 00	08 03		08 33		08 37	08 42	08 57	08 44	09 07		09 22	09 30		09 35
Ealing Broadway ⊖	d	22p54					23p27				07 50									08 51						
Slough 3	d	23p20		23p50			23p53				08 14		08 25					09 01		09 15			09 39			09 53
Maidenhead 3	d	23p29					00 05				08 23		08 33							09 24			09 46			
Twyford 3	d	23p36					00 12				08 31									09 32						
Reading 7	a	23p43		00 07			00 19				08 37	08 42	08 46	←	09 11		09 16	09 21	09 31	09 39	09 41	←	09 59	10 06		10 13
	d	23p48		00 08		00 15	00 19		08 14	08 34	08 50	08 43	08 46	08 50	09 11	09 14	09 17	09 21	09 32	09 46	09 41	09 46	10 03		10 10	10 13
Reading West	d					00s18				08 37	→									→			10 06			
Theale	d					00s24			08 22	08 43						09 22							10 12			
Aldermaston	d					00s29				08 48													10 17			
Midgham	d					00s33				08 52													10 21			
Thatcham	d					00s38			08 30	08 57						09 30							10 26			
Newbury Racecourse	d					00s42										09 35							10 30			
Newbury	a					00 46			08 36	09 02						09 37			09 47				10 34			
	d									09 03						09 37										
Kintbury	d									09 09						09 44										
Hungerford	d									09 14						09 49										
Bedwyn	a									09 22						09 56										
Tilehurst	d	23p52					00 24							08 55								09 50				
Pangbourne	d	23p57												08 59								09 54				
Goring & Streatley	d	00 01					00 31							09 04								10 00				
Cholsey	d	00 06					00 36							09 10								10 05				
Didcot Parkway	a	00 13		00 25			00 43					08 58	09 00	09 14	09 28		09 33	09 37			09 58	10 11				10 29
	d		00 18		00 30			00 49					09 00	09 14				09 37				10 11				10 30
Appleford	d							00s59														10 17				
Culham	d							01s09																		
Radley	d		00s33					01s19						09 24								10 22				
Oxford	a		00 48		00 55			01 34					09 14	09 31				09 51				10 29			10 34	10 42
	d																								10 36	
Islip	d																									
Bicester Town	a																									
Tackley	d																									
Heyford	d																									
Kings Sutton	d																									
Banbury	a																								10 52	
Leamington Spa 8	a																								11 10	
Warwick	a																								*12 02*	
Warwick Parkway	a																								*12 05*	
Stratford-upon-Avon	a																									
Coventry	a																								11 23	
Birmingham International	a																								11 35	
Birmingham New Street 12	a																								11 46	

For general notes see front of timetable
For details of catering facilities see Directory of Train Operators

A To Great Malvern (Table 126)

Table 116

Sundays

until 27 January

London and Reading → Bedwyn, Oxford, Bicester, Banbury and Birmingham

Network Diagram - see first page of Table 116

		GW	GW	GW	GW	XC	GW	GW	GW	GW	XC	GW	GW	GW	GW	XC	GW	GW	GW	GW	XC	GW	GW	GW	GW	XC
		1 ◇		1	1 ◇	1 ◇	1 ◇	1 ◇	1 ◇		1 ◇	1 ◇		1 ◇	1	R 1	1 ◇	1 ◇	1 ◇		1 ◇	1 ◇		1	1 ◇	R 1
												A														
		☕			☕	☕	☕	☕	☕		☕	☕		☕		☕	☕	🍴	☕		☕	☕			☕	☕
London Paddington 15 ⊖	d	09 57	09 44	10 22	10 27		10 37	10 42	10 57	10 44		11 07		11 18	11 22		11 37	11 42	11 57	11 44		12 07		12 22	12 27	
Ealing Broadway ⊖	d		09 51							10 51										11 51						
Slough 3	d		10 15	10 39				10 58		11 15					11 39			12 00		12 15				12 39		
Maidenhead 3	d		10 24	10 46						11 24					11 46					12 24				12 46		
Twyford 3	d		10 32							11 32										12 32						
Reading 7	a	10 31	10 38	10 59	11 02		11 11	11 19	11 31	11 37		11 42	⟵	11 52	11 59		12 11	12 17	12 31	12 38		12 41	⟵	12 59	13 02	
	d		10 43	11 03	11 04	11 10		11 20		11 43 ⟶	11 39	11 42	11 43		12 03	12 10		12 23	12 32	12 43 ⟶	12 40	12 42	12 43	13 03	13 05	13 10
Reading West	d														12 06											
Theale	d			11 11											12 12									13 11		
Aldermaston	d														12 17											
Midgham	d														12 21											
Thatcham	d			11 19											12 26									13 19		
Newbury Racecourse	d														12 30											
Newbury	a			11 25											12 34				12 47					13 25		
	d			11 25																				13 25		
Kintbury	d			11 31																				13 31		
Hungerford	d			11 36																				13 36		
Bedwyn	a			11 44																				13 44		
Tilehurst	d		10 47										11 47										12 47			
Pangbourne	d		10 51										11 51										12 51			
Goring & Streatley	d		10 57										11 57										12 57			
Cholsey	d		11 02										12 02										13 02			
Didcot Parkway	a		11 08		11 19			11 35				11 57	12 08					12 38				12 57	13 08		13 19	
	d		11 08					11 36					12 08					12 39					13 08			
Appleford	d																						13 15			
Culham	d																									
Radley	d		11 17										12 17										13 20			
Oxford	a		11 25			11 35		11 49			12 04		12 27			12 35		12 51			13 04		13 27			13 35
	d					11 36					12 06					12 36					13 06					13 36
Islip	d																									
Bicester Town	a																									
Tackley	d																									
Heyford	d																									
Kings Sutton	d																									
Banbury	a					11 52					12 24					12 52					13 24					13 52
Leamington Spa 8	a					12 10					12 41					13 10					13 41					14 10
Warwick	a										*13 05*										*14 06*					
Warwick Parkway	a					*12 28*					*13 09*					*13 31*					*14 10*					*14 28*
Stratford-upon-Avon	a																									
Coventry	a					12 23					12 54					13 23					13 54					14 23
Birmingham International	a					12 35					13 04					13 35					14 04					14 35
Birmingham New Street 12	a					12 46					13 18					13 46					14 18					14 46

		GW	GW	GW		GW	XC	GW	GW	GW	XC	GW	GW	GW	GW	XC	GW	GW	GW	GW	XC	GW	GW	GW	GW	XC
		1 ◇	1 ◇	1 ◇			1 ◇	1 ◇		1	R 1	1 ◇	1 ◇	1 ◇		1 ◇	1 ◇		1	1 ◇	R 1	1 ◇	1 ◇	1 ◇		1 ◇
		☕	☕	☕			☕	☕			☕	☕	☕	☕		☕	☕			☕	☕	☕	☕	☕		☕
London Paddington 15 ⊖	d	12 37	12 42	12 57		12 44		13 07		13 22		13 37	13 42	13 57	13 44		14 07		14 22	14 27		14 37	14 42	14 57	14 44	
Ealing Broadway ⊖	d					12 51									13 51										14 51	
Slough 3	d		12 58			13 15				13 39			13 58		14 15				14 39				14 58		15 15	
Maidenhead 3	d					13 24				13 46					14 24				14 46						15 24	
Twyford 3	d					13 32									14 32										15 32	
Reading 7	a	13 11	13 20	13 31		13 38		13 41	⟵	13 59		14 11	14 19	14 31	14 38		14 41	⟵	14 59	15 02		15 11	15 19	15 31	15 38	
	d		13 20			13 43 ⟶	13 40	13 42	13 43	14 03	14 10		14 20	14 34	14 43 ⟶	14 40	14 42	14 43	15 03	15 05	15 10		15 20		15 43 ⟶	15 40
Reading West	d									14 06																
Theale	d									14 12									15 11							
Aldermaston	d									14 17																
Midgham	d									14 21																
Thatcham	d									14 26									15 19							
Newbury Racecourse	d									14 30																
Newbury	a									14 34				14 50					15 25							
	d																		15 25							
Kintbury	d																		15 31							
Hungerford	d																		15 36							
Bedwyn	a																		15 44							
Tilehurst	d								13 47									14 47								
Pangbourne	d								13 51									14 51								
Goring & Streatley	d								13 57									14 57								
Cholsey	d								14 02									15 02								
Didcot Parkway	a		13 36					13 57	14 08				14 35				14 57	15 08		15 19			15 35			
	d		13 37						14 08				14 36					15 08					15 36			
Appleford	d																	15 15								
Culham	d																									
Radley	d								14 17									15 20								
Oxford	a		13 49				14 04		14 25		14 35		14 49			15 04		15 27			15 35		15 48			16 04
	d						14 06				14 36					15 06					15 36					16 06
Islip	d																									
Bicester Town	a																									
Tackley	d																									
Heyford	d																									
Kings Sutton	d																									
Banbury	a						14 24				14 52					15 24					15 52					16 24
Leamington Spa 8	a						14 41				15 10					15 41					16 10					16 41
Warwick	a						*15 05*				*15 25*					*16 05*										*17 05*
Warwick Parkway	a						*15 09*				*15 34*					*16 09*					*16 28*					*17 09*
Stratford-upon-Avon	a																									
Coventry	a						14 54				15 23					15 54					16 23					16 54
Birmingham International	a						15 04				15 35					16 04					16 35					17 04
Birmingham New Street 12	a						15 18				15 46					16 18					16 46					17 18

For general notes see front of timetable
For details of catering facilities see Directory of Train Operators

A To Weston-super-Mare (Table 134)

Table 116

London and Reading → Bedwyn, Oxford, Bicester, Banbury and Birmingham

Sundays

until 27 January

Network Diagram - see first page of Table 116

		GW	GW	GW	XC	GW	GW	GW	GW	XC	GW	GW	GW	GW	XC	GW	GW	GW	GW	XC	GW	GW	GW	GW	XC	GW
		1 ◇		1	R 1	1 ◇	1 ◇	1 ◇		1 ◇	1 ◇		1	1 ◇	R 1	1 ◇	1 ◇	1 ◇		1 ◇	1 ◇		1 ◇	1	R 1	1 ◇
		A																			B					
		☕			☕	☕	☕	☕		☕	☕			☕	☕	☕	☕	☕		☕	☕		☕		☕	☕
London Paddington 15 ⊖	d	15 07		15 22		15 37	15 42	15 57	15 44		16 07		16 22	16 27		16 37	16 42	16 57	16 44		17 07		17 12	17 22		17 37
Ealing Broadway ⊖	d								15 51										16 51							
Slough 3	d			15 39			15 58		16 15				16 39				16 58		17 15					17 39		
Maidenhead 3	d			15 46					16 24				16 46						17 24					17 46		
Twyford 3	d								16 32										17 32							
Reading 7	a	15 41	←	15 59		16 12	16 19	16 31	16 38		16 41	←	16 59	17 02		17 12	17 19	17 31	17 38		17 41	←	17 46	17 59		18 12
	d	15 42	15 43	16 03	16 10		16 20	16 32	16 43 →	16 40	16 42	16 43	17 03	17 05	17 10		17 20		17 43 →	17 40	17 42	17 43		18 03	18 10	
Reading West	d			16 06																						
Theale	d			16 12									17 11											18 11		
Aldermaston	d			16 17																				18 16		
Midgham	d			16 21																				18 20		
Thatcham	d			16 26									17 19											18 25		
Newbury Racecourse	d			16 30																				18 29		
Newbury	a			16 36				16 47					17 25											18 39		
	d												17 25													
Kintbury	d												17 31													
Hungerford	d												17 36													
Bedwyn	a												17 44													
Tilehurst	d		15 47									16 47										17 47				
Pangbourne	d		15 51									16 51										17 51				
Goring & Streatley	d		15 57									16 57										17 57				
Cholsey	d		16 02									17 02										18 02				
Didcot Parkway	a	15 57	16 08				16 35				16 57	17 08		17 19			17 35				17 57	18 08				
	d		16 08				16 36					17 08					17 36					18 08				
Appleford	d																					18 15				
Culham	d																									
Radley	d		16 17									17 17										18 20				
Oxford	a		16 25		16 35		16 49			17 04		17 25			17 36		17 49			18 04		18 27			18 34	
	d				16 36					17 06					17 36					18 06					18 36	
Islip	d																									
Bicester Town	a																									
Tackley	d																									
Heyford	d																									
Kings Sutton	d																									
Banbury	a				16 52					17 24					17 52					18 24					18 52	
Leamington Spa 8	a				17 10					17 41					18 10					18 41					19 10	
Warwick	a				*17 24*					*18 05*										*19 05*					*19 25*	
Warwick Parkway	a				*17 34*					*18 09*					*18 35*					*19 09*					*19 34*	
Stratford-upon-Avon	a																									
Coventry	a				17 23					17 54					18 23					18 54					19 23	
Birmingham International	a				17 35					18 04					18 35					19 04					19 35	
Birmingham New Street 12	a				17 46					18 18					18 46					19 18					19 46	

		GW	GW	GW	XC	GW	GW	GW	GW	XC	GW	GW	GW	GW	GW	GW	GW	XC	GW	GW	GW	GW	GW	GW	GW	GW
		1 ◇	1 ◇		1 ◇	1 ◇		1	1 ◇	1 ◇	1 ◇	1 ◇	1 ◇		1 ◇		1	1 ◇	1 ◇	1 ◇	1 ◇		1 ◇		1 ◇	1
		☕	☕		☕	☕			☕	☕	☕	☕	☕		☕			☕	☕	☕	☕		☕		☕	
London Paddington 15 ⊖	d	17 42	17 57	17 44		18 07		18 22	18 27		18 37	18 42	18 57	18 44	19 07		19 22		19 37	19 42	19 57	19 44	20 07		20 27	20 15
Ealing Broadway ⊖	d			17 51										18 51								19 51				20 22
Slough 3	d	17 58		18 15				18 39				18 58		19 15			19 39			19 57		20 15				20 46
Maidenhead 3	d			18 24				18 47						19 24			19 46					20 24				20 55
Twyford 3	d			18 32										19 32								20 32				21 02
Reading 7	a	18 19	18 31	18 38		18 41	←	18 59	19 04		19 11	19 20	19 31	19 38	19 41	←	19 59		20 12	20 17	20 31	20 38	20 41	←	21 04	21 09
	d	18 20	18 33	18 43 →	18 40	18 42	18 43	19 03	19 05	19 10		19 20		19 43 →	19 42	19 43	20 03	20 10		20 20	20 34	20 43 →	20 42	20 43	21 06	21 09
Reading West	d																20 06									
Theale	d							19 11									20 12									21 17
Aldermaston	d																20 17									
Midgham	d																20 21									
Thatcham	d							19 19									20 26									21 26
Newbury Racecourse	d																20 30									
Newbury	a		18 50					19 25									20 34				20 50					21 31
	d							19 25																		21 31
Kintbury	d							19 31																		21 38
Hungerford	d							19 36																		21 43
Bedwyn	a							19 44																		21 50
Tilehurst	d						18 47									19 47								20 47		
Pangbourne	d						18 51									19 51								20 51		
Goring & Streatley	d						18 57									19 57								20 57		
Cholsey	d						19 02									20 02								21 02		
Didcot Parkway	a	18 35				18 57	19 08		19 19			19 36			19 57	20 08				20 35			20 57	21 08	21 20	
	d	18 36					19 08					19 36				20 08				20 35				21 08		
Appleford	d																									
Culham	d																									
Radley	d						19 17									20 17								21 17		
Oxford	a	18 49			19 04		19 25			19 35		19 50				20 25		20 35		20 47				21 25		
	d				19 06					19 36								20 36								
Islip	d																									
Bicester Town	a																									
Tackley	d																									
Heyford	d																									
Kings Sutton	d																									
Banbury	a				19 24					19 52								20 52								
Leamington Spa 8	a				19 42					20 10								21 10								
Warwick	a				*20 05*					*21 08*								*22 05*								
Warwick Parkway	a				*20 09*					*20 35*								*21 35*								
Stratford-upon-Avon	a																									
Coventry	a				19 54					20 23								21 23								
Birmingham International	a				20 04					20 35								21 34								
Birmingham New Street 12	a				20 21					20 46								21 46								

For general notes see front of timetable
For details of catering facilities see Directory of Train Operators

A To Taunton (Table 134)
B To Weston-super-Mare (Table 134)

Table 116

Sundays until 27 January

London and Reading → Bedwyn, Oxford, Bicester, Banbury and Birmingham

Network Diagram - see first page of Table 116

		XC 1◇	GW 1◇	GW 1◇ H	GW 1◇ P	GW	GW 1◇ A	GW	GW	XC 1◇	GW 1◇	GW 1◇ B P	GW	GW 1◇ P	GW	GW	GW 1◇ P	GW Bus	GW 1◇ H	GW	GW 1◇ P	GW	GW 1◇ H	GW 1◇ P		
London Paddington 15 ⊖	d		20 37	20 42	20 57	20 44	21 07		21 15		21 37	21 42	21 44	22 07		22 15	22 37		22 42	22 44	23 07		23 37	23 45		
Ealing Broadway ⊖	d					20 51			21 22				21 52			22 24				22 51			23 45			
Slough 3	d			20 58		21 15			21 46			21 59	22 16			22 47			23 00	23 16			23 57			
Maidenhead 3	d					21 24			21 55			22 08	22 26			22 55				23 24			00 05			
Twyford 3	d					21 32			22 02				22 33			23 04				23 32						
Reading 7	a		21 13	21 20	21 31	21 38	21 41	←	22 09		22 13	22 20	22 40	22 43	←	23 10	23 14		23 18	23 42	23 46	←	00 18	00 21		
	d	21 10		21 22		21 46	21 42	21 46	22 09	22 10		22 20	22 47	22 43	22 47	23 12	23 14		23 19	23 50	23 46	23 50	00 18	00 21		
Reading West	d					→							→			23 17				→						
Theale	d								22 17							23 23										
Aldermaston	d															23 28										
Midgham	d															23 32										
Thatcham	d								22 26							23 37										
Newbury Racecourse	d															23 41										
Newbury	a								22 32							23 45										
	d																									
Kintbury	d																									
Hungerford	d																									
Bedwyn	a																									
Tilehurst	d							21 50							22 51							23 55				
Pangbourne	d							21 55							22 56							23 59				
Goring & Streatley	d							22 00							23 01							00 05				
Cholsey	d							22 05							23 06							00 09				
Didcot Parkway	a			21 37			21 59	22 11				22 37		22 59	23 12		23 30		23 34		00s02	00 16	00 34	00s38		
	d			21 38				22 12				22 38			23 13				23 35			00 16	00 35			
Appleford	d																									
Culham	d																									
Radley	d							22 19							23 21							00 25				
Oxford	a	21 35		21 50				22 27		22 34		22 50			23 29				23 47			00 35	00 50			
	d	21 36								22 36								23 37								
Islip	d																									
Bicester Town	a																									
Tackley	d																	23s57								
Heyford	d																	00s12								
Kings Sutton	d																	00b27								
Banbury	a	21 52								22 52								00 37								
Leamington Spa 8	a	22 10								23 10																
Warwick	a	22 34								23 25																
Warwick Parkway	a	22 38								23 29																
Stratford-upon-Avon	a																									
Coventry	a	22 23								23 27																
Birmingham International	a	22 35								23 38																
Birmingham New Street 12	a	23 13								23 55																

For general notes see front of timetable
For details of catering facilities see Directory of Train Operators

A To Weston-super-Mare (Table 134)
B To Worcester Shrub Hill (Table 126)

b Kings Sutton V. Square.
s Stops to set down only

Sundays

3 February to 23 March

London and Reading → Bedwyn, Oxford, Bicester, Banbury and Birmingham

Network Diagram - see first page of Table 116

	GW	GW	GW	GW	GW	GW	GW		GW	GW	GW	GW	GW	GW	GW		GW	GW	GW	GW	GW	XC	GW		GW
	1		1 ◇			1				1 ◇		1 ◇		1 ◇	1		1 ◇	1 ◇		1 ◇	1 ◇	1 ◇	1 ◇		1
												A									A		A		
		🚌		🚌	🚌		🚌			☕		☕		☕			🛒	☕		☕	☕	☕	☕		
London Paddington 15 ⊖ d	22p45		23p33			23p20				08 00	07 43	08 03		08 30			08 42	09 00	08 44	09 03	09 30				09 33
Ealing Broadway ⊖ d	22p54					23p27					07 52								08 51						
Slough 3 d	23p20		23p50			23p53					08 16	08 25					09 01		09 15		09 52				09 56
Maidenhead 3 d	23p29					00 05					08 25	08 32							09 24						10 03
Twyford 3 d	23p36					00 12					08 33								09 32						
Reading 7 a	23p43		00 07			00 19				08 36	08 39	08 44	←	09 03			09 20	09 37	09 39	09 42	10 07				10 13
d	23p48		00 08		00 15	00 19			08 14		08 47	08 44	08 47		09 13		09 22	09 37	09 43		10 09	10 10			10 16
Reading West d					00s23				08 17		→														10 19
Theale d					00s38				08 23						09 22										10 25
Aldermaston d					00s44				08 28																10 30
Midgham d					00s52				08 32																10 34
Thatcham d					00s59				08 37						09 30										10 39
Newbury Racecourse d					01s09										09 35										10 43
Newbury a					01 19				08 43						09 37			09 53							10 47
d									08 59						09 37										
Kintbury d									09 05						09 44										
Hungerford d									09 10						09 49										
Bedwyn a									09 17						09 56										
Tilehurst d	23p52					00 24							08 52						09 47						
Pangbourne d	23p57												08 57						09 52						
Goring & Streatley d	00 01					00 31							09 01						09 57						
Cholsey d	00 06					00 36							09 07						10 02						
Didcot Parkway a	00 13		00 25			00 43						08 59	09 11				09 37		10 08		10 27		←		
d		00 18		00 30			00 49					09 05	09 11				09 38		10 09		10 28 →		10 28		
Appleford d							00s59												10 15						
Culham d							01s09																		
Radley d		00s33					01s19						09 21						10 20						
Oxford a		00 48		00 55			01 34					09 15	09 30				09 51		10 27			10 35	10 40		
d																						10 36			
Islip d																									
Bicester Town a																									
Tackley d																									
Heyford d																									
Kings Sutton d																									
Banbury a																						10 52			
Leamington Spa 8 a																						11 10			
Warwick a																						*12 13*			
Warwick Parkway a																						*12 19*			
Stratford-upon-Avon a																									
Coventry a																						11 23			
Birmingham International a																						11 35			
Birmingham New Street 12 a																						11 46			

For general notes see front of timetable
For details of catering facilities see Directory of Train Operators

A To Great Malvern (Table 126)

Sundays

London and Reading → Bedwyn, Oxford, Bicester, Banbury and Birmingham

3 February to 23 March

Network Diagram - see first page of Table 116

		GW	GW	GW	XC	GW	GW	GW	XC	GW	GW	GW	XC	GW	GW	GW	GW	GW	XC	GW	GW	GW	GW
		1 ◇ ☕		1 ◇ ☕	1 ◇ ☕	1	1 ◇ ☕	1 ◇ ☕	1 ◇ ☕		1 ◇ ☕	1 ◇ ☕	R 1 ☕	1	1 ◇ 🍴	1 ◇ ☕		1 ◇ ☕	R 1 ☕	1	1 ◇ ☕	1 ◇ ☕	
London Paddington 15 ⊖	d	10 00	09 44	10 03		10 33	10 42	11 00		10 44	11 03	11 30		11 33	11 42	12 00	11 44	12 03		12 33	12 42	13 00	12 44
Ealing Broadway ⊖	d		09 51							10 51							11 51						12 51
Slough 3	d		10 15			10 52	11 01			11 15				11 54	12 00		12 15			12 52	13 01		13 15
Maidenhead 3	d		10 24			11 00				11 24				12 01			12 24			12 59			13 24
Twyford 3	d		10 32							11 32							12 32						13 32
Reading 7	a	10 37	10 39	10 42		11 13	11 19	11 39		11 39	11 44	12 03		12 13	12 19	12 37	12 39	12 42		13 13	13 19	13 37	13 39
	d		10 40		11 10	11 16	11 20		11 40	11 43			12 10	12 16	12 22	12 37	12 43		13 10	13 16	13 21		13 43
Reading West	d													12 19									
Theale	d					11 24								12 25						13 24			
Aldermaston	d													12 30									
Midgham	d													12 34									
Thatcham	d					11 32								12 39						13 32			
Newbury Racecourse	d													12 43									
Newbury	a					11 38								12 47		12 53				13 38			
	d					11 38														13 38			
Kintbury	d					11 44														13 44			
Hungerford	d					11 49														13 49			
Bedwyn	a					11 57														13 57			
Tilehurst	d		10 44							11 47							12 47						13 47
Pangbourne	d		10 49							11 52							12 52						13 52
Goring & Streatley	d		10 54							11 57							12 57						13 57
Cholsey	d		10 59							12 02							13 02						14 02
Didcot Parkway	a		11 05				11 35			12 08					12 37		13 08				13 35		14 08
	d		11 06				11 36			12 09					12 38		13 09				13 37		14 09
Appleford	d																13 15						
Culham	d																						
Radley	d		11 14							12 17							13 20						14 17
Oxford	a		11 22		11 35		11 50		12 02	12 25			12 35		12 50		13 27		13 34		13 49		14 25
	d				11 36				12 07				12 36						13 36				
Islip	d																						
Bicester Town	a																						
Tackley	d																						
Heyford	d																						
Kings Sutton	d																						
Banbury	a				11 52				12 24				12 52						13 52				
Leamington Spa 8	a				12 10				12 41				13 10						14 10				
Warwick	a								*13 11*				*14 15*						*15 13*				
Warwick Parkway	a								*13 17*				*14 21*						*15 19*				
Stratford-upon-Avon	a																						
Coventry	a				12 23				13 02				13 23						14 23				
Birmingham International	a				12 35				13 13				13 35						14 35				
Birmingham New Street 12	a				12 46				13 30				13 46						14 46				

		GW	XC	GW	GW	GW	GW	GW	XC	GW	GW	GW	GW	GW	XC	GW	GW	GW	GW	GW	XC	GW	GW
		1 ◇ ☕	R 1 ☕	1	1 ◇ ☕	1 ◇ ☕		1 ◇ ☕	R 1 ☕	1	1 ◇ ☕	1 ◇ ☕		1 ◇ ☕	R 1 ☕	1	1 ◇ ☕	1 ◇ ☕		1 ◇ ☕	R 1 ☕	1	1 ◇ ☕
London Paddington 15 ⊖	d	13 03		13 33	13 42	14 00	13 44	14 03		14 33	14 42	15 00	14 44	15 03		15 33	15 42	16 00	15 44	16 03		16 33	16 42
Ealing Broadway ⊖	d						13 51						14 51						15 51				
Slough 3	d			13 52	14 01		14 15			14 52	15 01		15 15			15 52	16 01		16 15			16 52	17 01
Maidenhead 3	d			13 59			14 24			14 59			15 24			16 01			16 24			16 59	
Twyford 3	d						14 32						15 32						16 32				
Reading 7	a	13 42		14 13	14 19	14 37	14 39	14 42		15 13	15 19	15 37	15 39	15 42		16 13	16 19	16 37	16 39	16 42		17 13	17 19
	d		14 10	14 16	14 20	14 37	14 43		15 10	15 16	15 20		15 43		16 10	16 16	16 20	16 37	16 43		17 10	17 16	17 20
Reading West	d			14 19												16 19							
Theale	d			14 25						15 24						16 25						17 24	
Aldermaston	d			14 30												16 30							
Midgham	d			14 34												16 34							
Thatcham	d			14 39						15 32						16 39						17 32	
Newbury Racecourse	d			14 43												16 43							
Newbury	a			14 47		14 53				15 38						16 47		16 53				17 38	
	d									15 38												17 38	
Kintbury	d									15 44												17 44	
Hungerford	d									15 49												17 49	
Bedwyn	a									15 57												17 57	
Tilehurst	d						14 47						15 47						16 47				
Pangbourne	d						14 52						15 52						16 52				
Goring & Streatley	d						14 57						15 57						16 57				
Cholsey	d						15 02						16 02						17 02				
Didcot Parkway	a				14 35		15 08				15 35		16 08				16 35		17 09				17 35
	d				14 36		15 09				15 35		16 09				16 36		17 09				17 36
Appleford	d						15 15																
Culham	d																						
Radley	d						15 20						16 17						17 17				
Oxford	a		14 35		14 50		15 27		15 35		15 48		16 25		16 35		16 50		17 24		17 35		17 49
	d		14 36						15 36						16 36						17 36		
Islip	d																						
Bicester Town	a																						
Tackley	d																						
Heyford	d																						
Kings Sutton	d																						
Banbury	a		14 52						15 52						16 52						17 52		
Leamington Spa 8	a		15 10						16 10						17 10						18 10		
Warwick	a		*16 15*						*17 13*						*18 15*						*19 13*		
Warwick Parkway	a		*16 21*						*17 19*						*18 21*						*19 19*		
Stratford-upon-Avon	a																						
Coventry	a		15 23						16 23						17 23						18 23		
Birmingham International	a		15 35						16 35						17 35						18 35		
Birmingham New Street 12	a		15 46						16 46						17 46						18 46		

For general notes see front of timetable
For details of catering facilities see Directory of Train Operators

Sundays

3 February to 23 March

London and Reading → Bedwyn, Oxford, Bicester, Banbury and Birmingham

Network Diagram - see first page of Table 116

		GW	GW	GW	GW	XC	GW	GW	GW	GW	GW	GW	XC	GW	GW	GW	GW	GW	XC	GW	GW	GW	GW
		1 ◇ ☕		1 ◇ ☕	1 ◇ ☕	R 1 ☕	1	1 ◇ ☕	1 ◇ ☕	1		1 ◇ ☕	1 ◇ ☕	1	1 ◇ ☕	1 ◇ ☕		1 ◇ ☕	1 ◇ ☕	1	1 ◇ ☕	1 ◇ ☕	
London Paddington 15 ⊖	d	17 00	16 44	17 03	17 30		17 33	17 42	18 00		17 44	18 03		18 33	18 42	19 00	18 44	19 03		19 33	19 42	20 00	19 44
Ealing Broadway ⊖	d		16 51								17 51						18 51						19 51
Slough 3	d		17 15				17 54	18 00			18 15			18 52	19 00		19 15			19 52	19 59		20 15
Maidenhead 3	d		17 24				18 01				18 24			18 59			19 24			19 59			20 24
Twyford 3	d		17 32								18 32						19 32						20 32
Reading 7	a	17 37	17 39	17 42	18 04		18 13	18 19	18 37		18 39	18 42		19 13	19 19	19 37	19 39	19 42		20 13	20 20	20 37	20 39
	d		17 43			18 10	18 16	18 20	18 37		18 43		19 10	19 16	19 20		19 43		20 10	20 16	20 20	20 37	20 43
Reading West	d						18 19													20 19			
Theale	d						18 25			←				19 24						20 25			
Aldermaston	d						18 30 →			18 30										20 30			
Midgham	d									18 34										20 34			
Thatcham	d									18 39				19 32						20 39			
Newbury Racecourse	d									18b56										20 43			
Newbury	a								18 53	18 58				19 38						20 47		20 53	
	d													19 38									
Kintbury	d													19 44									
Hungerford	d													19 49									
Bedwyn	a													19 57									
Tilehurst	d		17 47								18 47						19 47						20 47
Pangbourne	d		17 52								18 52						19 52						20 52
Goring & Streatley	d		17 57								18 57						19 57						20 57
Cholsey	d		18 02								19 02						20 02						21 02
Didcot Parkway	a		18 08					18 35			19 08				19 35		20 08				20 35		21 08
	d		18 09					18 36			19 09				19 36		20 09				20 35		21 09
Appleford	d		18 15																				
Culham	d																						
Radley	d		18 20								19 17						20 17						21 17
Oxford	a		18 27			18 35		18 49			19 25		19 35		19 49		20 25		20 35		20 47		21 25
	d					18 36							19 36						20 36				
Islip	d																						
Bicester Town	a																						
Tackley	d																						
Heyford	d																						
Kings Sutton	d																						
Banbury	a					18 52							19 52						20 52				
Leamington Spa 8	a					19 10							20 10						21 10				
Warwick	a					*20 15*							*21 15*						*22 13*				
Warwick Parkway	a					*20 21*							*21 20*						*22 19*				
Stratford-upon-Avon	a																						
Coventry	a					19 23							20 23						21 23				
Birmingham International	a					19 35							20 35						21 35				
Birmingham New Street 12	a					19 46							20 46						21 46				

		GW	XC	GW	GW	GW	GW	GW	GW	XC	GW	GW	GW	GW	GW	GW	GW	GW	GW	GW	GW	GW
		1 ◇ ☕	1 ◇	1	1 ◇ 🛒	1 ◇ ☕		1 ◇ ☕	1 ◇ ☕	1 ◇		1 ◇ A ☕			1 ◇ ☕	🚌	1 ◇ 🛒		🚌		1 ◇ ☕	1 ◇ 🛒
London Paddington 15 ⊖	d	20 03		20 15	20 42	21 00	20 44	21 03	21 33		21 15	21 42	21 45	22 15	22 37		22 42			22 44	23 37	23 42
Ealing Broadway ⊖	d			20 24			20 51				21 24		21 52	22 24						22 51		23 50
Slough 3	d			20 47	21 01		21 15				21 47	21 59	22 16	22 47			23 01			23 15		00 03
Maidenhead 3	d			20 56			21 24				21 56	22 06	22 26	22 56						23 24		00 11
Twyford 3	d			21 04			21 32				22 04		22 33	23 04						23 32		
Reading 7	a	20 41		21 10	21 20	21 37	21 39	21 41	22 06		22 13	22 18	22 40	23 10	23 13		23 18	←		23 43	00 13	00 24
	d		21 10	21 11	21 22		21 46			22 10	22 15	22 19	22 47	23 21 →			23 19	23 21		23 50		00 25
Reading West	d																					
Theale	d			21 19							22 25							23 29				
Aldermaston	d																	23 34				
Midgham	d																	23 38				
Thatcham	d			21 27							22 34							23 43				
Newbury Racecourse	d																	23 47				
Newbury	a			21 33							22 40							23 50				
	d			21 33																		
Kintbury	d			21 39																		
Hungerford	d			21 44																		
Bedwyn	a			21 52																		
Tilehurst	d						21 50						22 51							23 55		
Pangbourne	d						21 55						22 55							00 01		
Goring & Streatley	d						22 00						23 01							00 05		
Cholsey	d						22 05						23 06							00 10		
Didcot Parkway	a				21 36		22 11					22 35	23 12				23 35			00 16		00 39
	d				21 37		22 12					22 39	23 12				23 35		23 57	00 17		00 40
Appleford	d																					
Culham	d																					
Radley	d						22 19						23 21						00s12	00 25		
Oxford	a		21 35		21 50		22 27			22 34		22 50	23 29				23 48		00 27	00 35		00 55
	d		21 36							22 36						23 37						
Islip	d																					
Bicester Town	a																					
Tackley	d															23s57						
Heyford	d															00s12						
Kings Sutton	d															00c27						
Banbury	a		21 52							22 52						00 37						
Leamington Spa 8	a		22 10							23 10												
Warwick	a																					
Warwick Parkway	a																					
Stratford-upon-Avon	a																					
Coventry	a		22 23							23 27												
Birmingham International	a		22 35							23 38												
Birmingham New Street 12	a		23 13							23 55												

For general notes see front of timetable
For details of catering facilities see Directory of Train Operators

A To Worcester Shrub Hill (Table 126)
b Arr. 1846
c Kings Sutton V. Square. Stops to set down only

Table 116

Sundays

from 30 March

London and Reading → Bedwyn, Oxford, Bicester, Banbury and Birmingham

Network Diagram - see first page of Table 116

Station		GW	GW	GW	GW	GW	GW	GW	GW	GW	GW	GW	GW	GW	GW	GW	GW	GW	GW	XC	GW	XC	XC	GW	XC	GW
		1	bus	1 ◇	bus	bus	1	bus			1 ◇		1 ◇		1	1 ◇		1 ◇		1 ◇		1 ◇	bus	1 ◇	1 ◇	1
																				A					B	
											catering		catering			catering		catering		catering		catering		catering	catering	
London Paddington 15 ⊖	d	22p45		23p33			23p20				08 00	07 43	08 03			09 00	08 44	09 03						09 30		09 42
Ealing Broadway ⊖	d	22p54					23p27					07 52					08 51									
Slough 3	d	23p20		23p50			23p53					08 16					09 15									10 00
Maidenhead 3	d	23p29					00 05					08 25					09 24									10 07
Twyford 3	d	23p36					00 12					08 33					09 32									
Reading 7	a	23p43		00 07			00 19				08 36	08 39	08 41			09 36	09 39	09 42	←					10 06		10 19
	d	23p48		00 08		00 15	00 19		08 14	08 34	08 37	08 42	08 42		09 13		09 43	09 42	09 43	09 46				10 07	10 10	10 23
Reading West	d					00s23				08 37							→									10 26
Theale	d					00s38			08 22	08 43					09 22											10 31
Aldermaston	d					00s44				08 48																10 37
Midgham	d					00s52				08 52																10 41
Thatcham	d					00s59			08 30	08 57					09 30											10 45
Newbury Racecourse	d					01s09									09 35											10 49
Newbury	a					01 19			08 37	09 03					09 37											10 57
	d									09 03					09 37											
Kintbury	d									09 09					09 44											
Hungerford	d									09 14					09 49											
Bedwyn	a									09 22					09 56											
Tilehurst	d	23p52					00 24					08 46		←					09 47		←					
Pangbourne	d	23p57										08 51		08 51					09 52		09 52					
Goring & Streatley	d	00 01					00 31					→		08 55					→		09 57					
Cholsey	d	00 06					00 36							09 01							10 02					
Didcot Parkway	a	00 13		00 25			00 43				08 52		08 57	09 07				09 57		10 05	10 09			10 22	10 35	
	d		00 18		00 30			00 49															10 15			
Appleford	d							00s59																		
Culham	d							01s09																		
Radley	d		00s33					01s19																		
Oxford	a		00 48		00 55			01 34															10 45			
	d																					10 36				
Islip	d																									
Bicester Town	a																									
Tackley	d																									
Heyford	d																									
Kings Sutton	d																									
Banbury	a																					10 52				
Leamington Spa 8	a																					11 10				
Warwick	a																					*12 13*				
Warwick Parkway	a																					*12 19*				
Stratford-upon-Avon	a																									
Coventry	a																					11 23				
Birmingham International	a																					11 35				
Birmingham New Street 12	a																					11 46				

For general notes see front of timetable
For details of catering facilities see
Directory of Train Operators

A From Brighton (Table 148)
B From Southampton Central (Table 158)

Table 116

Sundays

from 30 March

London and Reading → Bedwyn, Oxford, Bicester, Banbury and Birmingham

Network Diagram - see first page of Table 116

		GW	GW	XC	GW	GW	GW	XC	XC	GW	GW	XC	GW	GW	GW	GW	XC	GW	XC	GW	GW	XC	GW	GW	GW	XC
		1 ◇		🚌	1 ◇ A		1 ◇	1 ◇ B	1 ◇	1		🚌	1 ◇	1 ◇		1 ◇	1 ◇ B	1 ◇	R 1	1		🚌	1 ◇		1 ◇	1 ◇ B
		☕			☕		☕	☕	☕				☕	☕		☕	☕	☕	☕				☕		☕	☕
London Paddington 15 ⊖	d	10 00	09 44		10 03		10 30			10 42	10 44		11 00	11 03		11 30		11 37		11 42	11 44		12 03		12 30	
Ealing Broadway ⊖	d		09 51								10 51										11 51					
Slough 3	d		10 15							11 00	11 15									12 00	12 15					
Maidenhead 3	d		10 24							11 07	11 24									12 08	12 24					
Twyford 3	d		10 32								11 32										12 32					
Reading 7	a	10 35	10 39		10 42	←	11 06			11 19	11 39		11 37	11 42	←	12 06		12 11		12 19	12 39		12 42	←	13 06	
	d		10 43 →		10 42	10 43	11 07	11 10		11 23	11 43 →			11 42	11 43	12 07	12 10			12 23	12 43 →		12 42	12 43	13 07	13 10
Reading West	d																			12 26						
Theale	d									11 31										12 32						
Aldermaston	d																			12 37						
Midgham	d																			12 41						
Thatcham	d									11 39										12 46						
Newbury Racecourse	d																			12 50						
Newbury	a									11 45										12 58						
	d									11 45																
Kintbury	d									11 51																
Hungerford	d									11 56																
Bedwyn	a									12 04																
Tilehurst	d					10 47									11 47									12 47		
Pangbourne	d					10 52									11 52									12 52		
Goring & Streatley	d					10 57									11 57									12 57		
Cholsey	d					11 02									12 02									13 02		
Didcot Parkway	a				10 57	11 09	11 22	11 35						11 57	12 09	12 22	12 35						12 57	13 09	13 22	13 35
	d			10 45								11 45										12 45				
Appleford	d																									
Culham	d																									
Radley	d																									
Oxford	a			11 15								12 15										13 15				
	d								11 36										12 36							
Islip	d																									
Bicester Town	a																									
Tackley	d																									
Heyford	d																									
Kings Sutton	d																									
Banbury	a								11 52										12 52							
Leamington Spa 8	a								12 10										13 10							
Warwick	a								*13 11*										*14 15*							
Warwick Parkway	a								*13 17*										*14 21*							
Stratford-upon-Avon	a																									
Coventry	a								12 23										13 23							
Birmingham International	a								12 35										13 35							
Birmingham New Street 12	a								12 46										13 46							

		XC	GW	GW		GW	XC	GW	GW	GW	GW	XC	XC	GW	GW	XC	GW	GW	GW	XC	GW	XC	GW	GW	XC	GW
		R 1	1	1 ◇			🚌	1 ◇		1 ◇	1 ◇	1 ◇ B	R 1	1		🚌	1 ◇		1 ◇	1 ◇ B	1 ◇	R 1	1		🚌	1 ◇ C
		☕		☕				☕		☕	☕	☕	☕				☕		☕	☕	☕	☕				☕
London Paddington 15 ⊖	d		12 42	13 00		12 44		13 03		13 30	13 37			13 42	13 44		14 03		14 30		14 37		14 42	14 44		15 03
Ealing Broadway ⊖	d					12 51									13 51									14 51		
Slough 3	d		13 00			13 15								14 00	14 15								15 00	15 15		
Maidenhead 3	d		13 07			13 24								14 07	14 24								15 08	15 24		
Twyford 3	d					13 32									14 32									15 32		
Reading 7	a		13 19	13 37		13 39		13 42	←	14 06	14 10			14 19	14 39		14 42	←	15 06		15 12		15 19	15 39		15 42
	d		13 23			13 43 →		13 42	13 43	14 07	14 10	14 10		14 23	14 43 →		14 42	14 43	15 07	15 10			15 23	15 43 →		15 42
Reading West	d													14 26												
Theale	d		13 31											14 32									15 31			
Aldermaston	d													14 37												
Midgham	d													14 41												
Thatcham	d		13 39											14 46									15 39			
Newbury Racecourse	d													14 50												
Newbury	a		13 45								14 27			14 54									15 45			
	d		13 45																				15 45			
Kintbury	d		13 51																				15 51			
Hungerford	d		13 56																				15 56			
Bedwyn	a		14 04																				16 04			
Tilehurst	d								13 47									14 47								
Pangbourne	d								13 52									14 52								
Goring & Streatley	d								13 57									14 57								
Cholsey	d								14 02									15 02								
Didcot Parkway	a							13 57	14 09	14 22		14 35					14 57	15 09	15 22	15 35						15 58
	d						13 45									14 45									15 45	
Appleford	d																									
Culham	d																									
Radley	d																									
Oxford	a						14 15									15 15									16 15	
	d	13 36											14 36									15 36				
Islip	d																									
Bicester Town	a																									
Tackley	d																									
Heyford	d																									
Kings Sutton	d																									
Banbury	a	13 52											14 53									15 52				
Leamington Spa 8	a	14 10											15 10									16 10				
Warwick	a	*15 13*											*16 15*									*17 13*				
Warwick Parkway	a	*15 19*											*16 21*									*17 19*				
Stratford-upon-Avon	a																									
Coventry	a	14 23											15 23									16 23				
Birmingham International	a	14 35											15 35									16 35				
Birmingham New Street 12	a	14 46											15 46									16 46				

For general notes see front of timetable
For details of catering facilities see Directory of Train Operators

A To Weston-super-Mare (Table 134)
B From Bournemouth (Table 158)
C To Taunton (Table 134)

Sundays

from 30 March

London and Reading → Bedwyn, Oxford, Bicester, Banbury and Birmingham

Network Diagram - see first page of Table 116

		GW	GW	XC	GW	XC	GW	GW	XC	GW	GW	GW	XC	GW	XC	GW	GW	XC	GW	GW	GW	GW	XC	XC	GW	GW
			1◇	1◇	1◇	R 1	1			1◇		1◇	1◇	1◇	R 1	1			1◇		1◇	1◇	1◇	R 1	1	1◇
				A					🚌				A					🚌	B				A			
			☕	☕	☕	☕				☕		☕	☕	☕	☕				☕		☕	☕	☕	☕		☕
London Paddington 15 ⊖	d		15 30		15 37		15 42	15 44		16 03		16 30		16 37		16 42	16 44		17 03		17 30	17 33			17 42	18 00
Ealing Broadway ⊖	d							15 51									16 51									
Slough 3	d						16 00	16 15								17 00	17 15								18 00	
Maidenhead 3	d						16 07	16 24								17 07	17 24								18 07	
Twyford 3	d							16 32									17 32									
Reading 7	a	←	16 06		16 11		16 19	16 39		16 42	←	17 06		17 13		17 19	17 39		17 42	←	18 06	18 11			18 19	18 36
	d	15 43	16 07	16 10	16 12		16 23	16 43		16 42	16 43	17 07	17 10			17 23	17 43		17 42	17 43	18 07	18 12	18 10		18 23	
Reading West	d						16 26	→									→								18 26	
Theale	d						16 32									17 31									18 32	
Aldermaston	d						16 37																		18 37	
Midgham	d						16 41																		18 41	
Thatcham	d						16 46									17 39									18 46	
Newbury Racecourse	d						16 50																		18 50	
Newbury	a				16 30		16 58									17 45									18 58	
	d															17 45										
Kintbury	d															17 51										
Hungerford	d															17 56										
Bedwyn	a															18 04										
Tilehurst	d	15 47									16 47									17 47						
Pangbourne	d	15 52									16 52									17 52						
Goring & Streatley	d	15 57									16 57									17 57						
Cholsey	d	16 02									17 02									18 02						
Didcot Parkway	a	16 09	16 22	16 35						16 57	17 09	17 22	17 35						17 57	18 09	18 22	18 27	18 35			
	d								16 45									17 45								
Appleford	d																									
Culham	d																									
Radley	d																									
Oxford	a								17 15									18 15								
	d					16 36									17 36									18 36		
Islip	d																									
Bicester Town	a																									
Tackley	d																									
Heyford	d																									
Kings Sutton	d																									
Banbury	a					16 52									17 52									18 52		
Leamington Spa 8	a					17 10									18 10									19 10		
Warwick	a					*18 15*									*19 13*									*20 15*		
Warwick Parkway	a					*18 21*									*19 19*									*20 21*		
Stratford-upon-Avon	a																									
Coventry	a					17 23									18 23									19 23		
Birmingham International	a					17 35									18 35									19 35		
Birmingham New Street 12	a					17 46									18 46									19 46		

		XC	GW	GW	GW	GW	XC	XC	GW	GW	GW	GW	XC	GW	GW	GW	XC	XC	GW	GW	GW	XC	GW	GW	GW	XC
				1◇		1◇	1◇	1◇	1	1◇	1◇			1◇		1◇	1◇	1◇	1	1◇			1◇		1◇	1◇
		🚌					A						🚌				A					🚌				A
				☕		☕	☕			☕	☕			☕		☕	☕			☕			☕		☕	
London Paddington 15 ⊖	d		17 44	18 03		18 30			18 37	18 42	19 00	18 44		19 03		19 30			19 42	20 00	19 44		20 03		20 30	
Ealing Broadway ⊖	d		17 51									18 51									19 51					
Slough 3	d		18 15						18 55	19 02		19 15							20 00		20 15					
Maidenhead 3	d		18 24						19 02			19 24							20 07		20 24					
Twyford 3	d		18 32									19 32									20 32					
Reading 7	a		18 39	18 43		19 07			19 14	19 20	19 36	19 39		19 42	←	20 06			20 19	20 37	20 39		20 42	←	21 06	
	d		18 43	18 43		19 07	19 10		19 16	19 21	19 38	19 43		19 42	19 43	20 07	20 10		20 23	20 37	20 43		20 42	20 43	21 06	21 10
Reading West	d											→							20 26		→					
Theale	d								19 24										20 32							
Aldermaston	d																		20 37							
Midgham	d																		20 41							
Thatcham	d								19 32										20 46							
Newbury Racecourse	d																		20 50							
Newbury	a								19 38		19 54								20 54	20 59						
	d								19 38																	
Kintbury	d								19 44																	
Hungerford	d								19 49																	
Bedwyn	a								19 57																	
Tilehurst	d		18 47		←										19 47									20 47		
Pangbourne	d		18 52		18 52										19 52									20 52		
Goring & Streatley	d		→		18 57										19 57									20 57		
Cholsey	d				19 02										20 02									21 02		
Didcot Parkway	a			18 57	19 09	19 22	19 35			19 35				19 57	20 09	20 22	20 34						21 00	21 09	21 22	21 35
	d	18 45											19 45									20 45				
Appleford	d																									
Culham	d																									
Radley	d																									
Oxford	a	19 15											20 15									21 15				
	d							19 36										20 36								
Islip	d																									
Bicester Town	a																									
Tackley	d																									
Heyford	d																									
Kings Sutton	d																									
Banbury	a							19 52										20 52								
Leamington Spa 8	a							20 10										21 10								
Warwick	a							*21 15*										*22 13*								
Warwick Parkway	a							*21 20*										*22 19*								
Stratford-upon-Avon	a																									
Coventry	a							20 23										21 23								
Birmingham International	a							20 35										21 35								
Birmingham New Street 12	a							20 46										21 46								

For general notes see front of timetable
For details of catering facilities see Directory of Train Operators

A From Bournemouth (Table 158)
B To Weston-super-Mare (Table 134)

Table 116

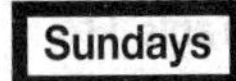

from 30 March

London and Reading → Bedwyn, Oxford, Bicester, Banbury and Birmingham

Network Diagram - see first page of Table 116

		XC	GW	GW	GW	XC	GW	GW	GW	XC	XC	GW	GW	XC	GW	GW	GW	GW	GW	GW	GW	GW	GW	GW		
		1 ◇	1	1 ◇			1 ◇		1 ◇	1 ◇	1 ◇				1 ◇			1 ◇				1 ◇		1 ◇		
							A			B																
						🚌								🚌					🚌		🚌					
				☕			☕		☕						☕			☕				☕		☕		
London Paddington 15 ⊖	d		20 15	21 00	20 44		21 03		21 30			21 15	21 45		22 03		22 15	22 37		22 44		23 03		23 37		
Ealing Broadway ⊖	d		20 24		20 51							21 24	21 52				22 24			22 51						
Slough 3	d		20 47		21 15							21 47	22 16				22 47			23 15				23 57		
Maidenhead 3	d		20 56		21 24							21 56	22 25				22 56			23 24						
Twyford 3	d		21 04		21 32							22 04	22 33				23 04			23 32						
Reading 7	a		21 10	21 37	21 39		21 41	←	22 06			22 13	22 39		22 42	←	23 10	23 13		23 43		23 50	←	00 20		
	d		21 11		21 46		21 42	21 46	22 07	22 10		22 15	22 47		22 43	22 47	23 14	23 15		23 55		23 50	23 55	00 22		
Reading West	d				↪								↪							↪						
Theale	d		21 19									22 25					23 22									
Aldermaston	d																23 27									
Midgham	d																23 31									
Thatcham	d		21 27									22 34					23 36									
Newbury Racecourse	d																23 40									
Newbury	a		21 33									22 42					23 43									
	d		21 33																							
Kintbury	d		21 39																							
Hungerford	d		21 44																							
Bedwyn	a		21 52																							
Tilehurst	d							21 50								22 51							23 59			
Pangbourne	d							21 55								22 55							00 04			
Goring & Streatley	d							22 00								23 01							00 09			
Cholsey	d							22 05								23 06							00 14			
Didcot Parkway	a						22 00	22 12	22 23	22 35					22 59	23 13		23 34				00s06	00 21	00s38		
	d					21 45								22 45							23 57					
Appleford	d																									
Culham	d																									
Radley	d																				00s12					
Oxford	a					22 15								23 15							00 27					
	d	21 36									22 36								23 37							
Islip	d																									
Bicester Town	a																									
Tackley	d																		23s57							
Heyford	d																		00s12							
Kings Sutton	d																		00b27							
Banbury	a	21 52									22 52								00 37							
Leamington Spa 8	a	22 10									23 10															
Warwick	a																									
Warwick Parkway	a																									
Stratford-upon-Avon	a																									
Coventry	a	22 23									23 27															
Birmingham International	a	22 35									23 38															
Birmingham New Street 12	a	23 13									23 55															

For general notes see front of timetable
For details of catering facilities see Directory of Train Operators

A To Weston-super-Mare (Table 134)
B From Bournemouth (Table 158)

b Kings Sutton V. Square. Stops to set down only

Birmingham, Banbury, Bicester, Oxford and Bedwyn → Reading and London

Network Diagram - see first page of Table 116

Miles	Miles			GW MO 1 A	GW MO 1 B	GW MO 1 C	GW MO 1◇ B	GW MO 1◇ C	GW MX 1◇	GW MO	GW MX 1	GW 1	GW 1	GW 1◇	GW 1	GW 1◇	GW 1	GW 1◇	GW 1◇	GW 1	GW 1◇	GW 1◇	GW 1	GW 1	GW 1◇
0	—	**Birmingham New Street** 12	d																						
8½	—	Birmingham International	d																						
19¼	—	Coventry	d																						
—	—	Stratford-upon-Avon	d																						
—	—	Warwick Parkway	d																						
—	—	Warwick	d																						
28¾	—	Leamington Spa 3	d																						
48¾	—	**Banbury**	d								23p50														
52¼	—	Kings Sutton	d								23p55														
59¾	—	Heyford	d								00 04														
62½	—	Tackley	d								00 08														
—	0	**Bicester Town**	d																						
—	6	Islip	d																						
71½	11¾	**Oxford**	a								00 18														
—	—		d		22p58	22p58	23p44	23p44	23p55		00 20	04 00	05 06			05 50	05 58		06 03					06 15	06 30
76½	—	Radley	d		23p04	23p04							05 12			05 56								06 21	
78¾	—	Culham	d																					06 25	
79¾	—	Appleford	d																					06 28	
81¾	—	**Didcot Parkway**	a		23p13	23p13	23p56	23p56	00 07		00 31	04 12	05 19			06 03	06 09		06 14					06 32	06 42
—	—		d	23p14	23p14	23p14	23p57	23p57	00 08		00 33	04 12	05 20	05 41		06 04	06 10	06 13	06 16		06 29			06 38	06 43
86½	—	Cholsey	d	23p20	23p20	23p20					00 39	04 18	05 26				06 16	06 20		←		←		06 44	
90½	—	Goring & Streatley	d	23p25	23p25	23p25					00 44	04 23	05 31				06 21	06 26		06 21		06 26		06 49	
93½	—	Pangbourne	d	23p30	23p30	23p30					00 48	04 28	05 35				→	→		06 25		06 32		→	
96¼	—	Tilehurst	d	23p34	23p35	23p35					00 53	04 32	05 40							06 30		06 37			
—	0	**Bedwyn**	d																				06 03		
—	5	Hungerford	d																				06 09		
—	8	Kintbury	d																				06 13		
—	13½	**Newbury**	a																				06 20		
—	—		d							23p50					05 41								06 25		
—	14	Newbury Racecourse	d							23p52					05 43										
—	17	Thatcham	d							23p56					05 47								06 30		
—	19¾	Midgham	d							00 01					05 52										
—	21¾	Aldermaston	d							00 05					05 56										
—	25¾	Theale	d							00 10					06 01								06 38		
—	29½	Reading West	d							00 20					06 08								06 46		
99	30½	**Reading** 7	a	23p39	23p39	23p40	00 13	00 14	00 22	00 24	00 58	04 38	05 44	05 57	06 12	06 20			06 30	06 36	06 43	06 43	06 49		06 57
—	—		d	23p40	23p41	23p41	00 14	00 15	00 24		01 00	04 40	05 45	05 57		06 22			06 32	06 36	06 45	06 46	06 50		06 59
104	—	Twyford 3	a	23p48	23p48	23p48	00 20	00 21			01 06	04 46	05 51			06 29				06 42		06 54			
110¾	—	Maidenhead 3	a	23p56	23p56	23p56	00 27	00 28			01 14	04 54	05 58						06 42	06 50		07 03	07 01		
116½	—	Slough 3	a	00 05	00 05	00 05	00 34	00 40	00 41		01 22	05 02	06 10	06 11		06 40			06 50	07 07	06 58				
129¼	—	Ealing Broadway	⊖ a	00 27	00 27	00 27	00 55	00 57			01 39	05 30	06 33							07 32					
135	—	**London Paddington** 15	⊖ a	00 40	00 40	00 40	01 01	01 05	01 02		01 48	05 41	06 44	06 30		07 00			07 08	07 40	07 16	07 27	07 24		07 29

		GW 1◇		GW 1◇	GW 1	GW 1	GW 1◇	GW 1◇	GW 1	GW 1	GW 1◇	GW 1	GW 1◇	GW 1	GW 1◇	GW 1	XC 1◇	GW 1◇ D	GW 1◇	GW 1	GW 1	GW 1	GW 1◇	GW 1◇	GW 1◇
Birmingham New Street 12	d																06 03								
Birmingham International	d																06 15								
Coventry	d																06 25								
Stratford-upon-Avon	d																								
Warwick Parkway	d								05 40								06 12								
Warwick	d																06 15								
Leamington Spa 8	d								05 45								06 38								
Banbury	d								06 08							06 31	06 55								
Kings Sutton	d								06 13							06 36									
Heyford	d								06 22							06 45									
Tackley	d								06 26							06 49									
Bicester Town	d									06 24															
Islip	d									06 36															
Oxford	a								06 36	06 50						07 00	07 14								
	d								06 38		06 57					07 02	07 15					07 21		07 30	
Radley	d								06 44							07 08						07 27			
Culham	d								06 48							07 12						07 31			
Appleford	d								06 51							07 15						07 34			
Didcot Parkway	a								06 55		07 09					07 19					←	07 39		07 42	
	d	06 46		06 46			07 00		07 02		07 10			07 20	07 20	07 30			07 30		07 30	07 46	07 44	07 43	
Cholsey	d			06 52	←				07 08			←		07 26		→					07 36	→			
Goring & Streatley	d			06 58	06 49				07 13			07 13		07 32							07 41				
Pangbourne	d			07 04	06 54				→			07 17		07 38							07 45				
Tilehurst	d			07 09	06 58							07 22		07 43							07 50				
Bedwyn	d					06 23												06 51							
Hungerford	d					06 29		06 42										06 58							
Kintbury	d					06 33												07 04							
Newbury	a					06 40		06 51										07 11							
	d					06 40		06 52										07 13		07 18					07 42
Newbury Racecourse	d					06 42														07 20					
Thatcham	d					06 47		06 59										07 19		07 25					
Midgham	d					06 51														07 29					
Aldermaston	d					06 55														07 33					
Theale	d					07 00		07 08										07 28		07 38					
Reading West	d					07 07												07 38		07 45					
Reading 7	a	07 02			07 05	07 12	07 14	07 18			07 25	07 29			07 35		07 39	07 41	07 44	07 49	07 54		07 58	08 01	08 07
	d	07 03			07 07		07 16	07 19			07 26	07 30	07 31		07 37			07 43	07 46		07 57		08 00	08 03	08 09
Twyford 3	a				07 13							07 36									08 04				
Maidenhead 3	a			07 25	07 21							07 45		07 59							08 12				
Slough 3	a				07 34							07 55									08 19				
Ealing Broadway	⊖ a				07 58							08 19													
London Paddington 15	⊖ a	07 32		07 46	08 09		07 42	07 51			07 58	08 30	08 01	08 21	08 06			08 09	08 14		08 42		08 30	08 32	08 38

For general notes see front of timetable
For details of catering facilities see Directory of Train Operators

A From 31 March
B 4 February to 24 March
C Until 28 January
D From Frome (Table 123)

Birmingham, Banbury, Bicester, Oxford and Bedwyn → Reading and London

Network Diagram - see first page of Table 116

		GW		GW	XC	GW	GW	GW	GW	GW	GW	GW	GW	GW	GW	XC	GW	GW	GW	GW	GW	GW	GW	GW	GW
		1		1◇	1◇	1◇	1	1	1◇	1	1	1	1◇	1◇	1◇	1◇	1◇	1	1◇	1	1	1◇	1	1◇	1
						A											A B					C			
				Ŧ	⊡	Ŧ			⊠				Ŧ	Ŧ		⊡	⊠		⊡			✕		Ŧ	
Birmingham New Street 12	d				06 33											07 03									
Birmingham International	d															07 15									
Coventry	d															07 25									
Stratford-upon-Avon	d				*06 10*											*06 46*									
Warwick Parkway	d				*06 44*											*07 21*									
Warwick	d				*06 38*											*07 13*									
Leamington Spa 8	d				07 00											07 38									
Banbury	d				07 19							07 28				07 55									
Kings Sutton	d											07 33													
Heyford	d											07 42													
Tackley	d											07 46													
Bicester Town	d																				07 57				
Islip	d																				08 09				
Oxford	a				07 41							07 56				08 14					08 23				
	d				07 43				07 52			07 58			08 07	08 15				08 21					
Radley	d											08 04								08 27					
Culham	d											08 08													
Appleford	d											08 11													
Didcot Parkway	a	←										08 16			08 19					08 36					
	d	07 46		07 54		08 01						08 17	08 17		08 20		08 30			08 37		08 47		08 53	
Cholsey	d	07 53										08 23								08 43			←		
Goring & Streatley	d	07 59						←				08 29						←		08 48			08 48		
Pangbourne	d	08 05						08 05				08 34						08 34		→			08 52		
Tilehurst	d	→						08 10				→						08 39					08 57		
Bedwyn	d										07 57														
Hungerford	d										08 03														
Kintbury	d										08 07														
Newbury	a										08 14														
	d						07 48			07 57									08 33						08 40
Newbury Racecourse	d						07 50			07 59															08 42
Thatcham	d						07 54			08 03															08 46
Midgham	d						07 59			08 08															08 51
Aldermaston	d						08 03			08 12															08 55
Theale	d						08 08			08 17															09 00
Reading West	d						08 15			08 23															09 07
Reading 7	a			08 12	08 13	08 15	08 19	08 17	08 22	08 27			08 32		08 35	08 39	08 44	08 44	08 52			09 01	09 02	09 06	09 12
	d			08 14		08 17		08 19	08 24				08 34	08 35	08 37		08 45	08 48	08 54			09 02	09 04	09 09	
Twyford 3	a							08 25										08 54					09 10		
Maidenhead 3	a							08 33										09 02					09 18		
Slough 3	a																						09 25		
Ealing Broadway	⊖ a																						09 49		
London Paddington 15	⊖ a			08 41		08 44		08 57	08 51				09 06	09 00	09 09		09 15	09 27	09 22			09 29	10 00	09 38	

		XC		GW	GW	GW	GW	GW	GW	GW	XC	GW	GW	GW	GW	GW	GW	GW	GW	XC	GW	GW	GW	GW	GW
		1◇		1◇	1◇	1	1◇	1	1◇	1◇	1◇	1◇	1	1◇	1	1	1◇	1◇	1◇	1◇	1	1	1◇	1	1◇
				D					E																
		⊡		⊠	⊠		Ŧ		✕		⊡	⊡		Ŧ			Ŧ	Ŧ	Ŧ	⊡			Ŧ		⊠
Birmingham New Street 12	d	07 33									08 03									08 33					
Birmingham International	d										08 15														
Coventry	d										08 25														
Stratford-upon-Avon	d										*07 36*														
Warwick Parkway	d	*07 43*									*08 19*									*08 41*					
Warwick	d	*07 46*									*08 23*									*08 44*					
Leamington Spa 8	d	08 00									08 38									09 00					
Banbury	d	08 19									08 55									09 19				09 38	
Kings Sutton	d																							09 43	
Heyford	d																							09 52	
Tackley	d																							09 56	
Bicester Town	d															09 07									
Islip	d															09 19									
Oxford	a	08 41									09 14					09 32				09 41				10 06	
	d	08 43		08 50				08 55		09 06	09 15				09 20		09 38			09 43		09 55	10 00		
Radley	d														09 26										
Culham	d														09 30										
Appleford	d																								
Didcot Parkway	a							09 06		09 18					09 35							10 06			
	d				09 00			09 07		09 19		09 29			09 37			09 53				10 07			10 17
Cholsey	d							09 13							09 43							10 13			
Goring & Streatley	d							09 18							09 48							10 18			
Pangbourne	d							09 22							09 52							→			
Tilehurst	d							09 27							09 57										
Bedwyn	d					08 40															09 37				
Hungerford	d					08 46															09 43				
Kintbury	d					08 50															09 47				
Newbury	a					08 57															09 54				
	d					08 57							09 23								09 54				
Newbury Racecourse	d												09 26												
Thatcham	d					09 02							09 30								09 59				
Midgham	d												09 35												
Aldermaston	d												09 39												
Theale	d					09 10							09 44								10 07				
Reading West	d												09 51												
Reading 7	a	09 13		09 14	09 14	09 20		09 33		09 35	09 39	09 44	09 55		10 02		10 03	10 09		10 13	10 16		10 24		10 32
	d			09 15	09 16	09 22	09 28	09 34	09 35	09 38		09 45		09 58	10 04		10 04	10 10	10 11		10 18		10 25		10 33
Twyford 3	a							09 40							10 10										
Maidenhead 3	a							09 48							10 18										
Slough 3	a							09 55		09 51					10 25		10 17						10 38		
Ealing Broadway	⊖ a							10 19							10 49										
London Paddington 15	⊖ a			09 47	09 44	09 53	09 59	10 30	10 02	10 09		10 15		10 27	11 00		10 36	10 39	10 44		10 52		10 59		11 02

For general notes see front of timetable
For details of catering facilities see Directory of Train Operators

A From Weston-super-Mare (Table 134)
B **The Bristolian**
C **The Red Dragon**
D **The Cathedrals Express**
E **The Golden Hind**

Birmingham, Banbury, Bicester, Oxford and Bedwyn → Reading and London

Network Diagram - see first page of Table 116

		GW		XC	GW	GW	GW	GW	GW	GW	GW	XC	GW	GW	GW	GW	GW	GW	XC	GW	GW	GW	GW	GW	GW
		1		R 1 ☕	1◇ 🛒	1	1	1◇ ⊠	1◇	1◇ ⊠	1	1◇ ☕	1◇ ☕	1	1	1◇	1◇ ☕	1	R 1 ☕	1◇ 🛒	1	1	1◇ ⊠	1◇ 🛒	1◇ ☕
Birmingham New Street 12	d			09 03								09 33							10 03						
Birmingham International	d			09 15															10 15						
Coventry	d			09 25															10 25						
Stratford-upon-Avon	d																		09 41						
Warwick Parkway	d			09 21								09b45							10 22						
Warwick	d			09 24								09b49							10 25						
Leamington Spa 8	d			09 38								10 00							10 38						
Banbury	d			09 55								10 19							10 55						
Kings Sutton	d																								
Heyford	d																								
Tackley	d																								
Bicester Town	d																								
Islip	d																								
Oxford	a			10 14								10 41							11 14						
	d			10 15			10 21		10 30			10 43			10 55	11 00			11 15			11 21		11 30	
Radley	d						10 27															11 27			
Culham	d																					11 31			
Appleford	d						10 32																		
Didcot Parkway	a						10 36								11 06							11 36			
	d				10 29		10 37			10 47	←				11 07		11 17			11 29		11 37			11 47
Cholsey	d	←					10 43				10 43				11 13			←				11 43			
Goring & Streatley	d	10 18					→				10 48				11 18			11 18				→			
Pangbourne	d	10 22									10 52				→			11 22							
Tilehurst	d	10 27									10 57							11 27							
Bedwyn	d													10 37											
Hungerford	d													10 43											
Kintbury	d													10 47											
Newbury	a													10 54											
	d					10 13								10 54							11 13				
Newbury Racecourse	d					10 15															11 15				
Thatcham	d					10 19								10 59							11 19				
Midgham	d					10 24															11 24				
Aldermaston	d					10 28															11 28				
Theale	d					10 33								11 07							11 33				
Reading West	d					10 40															11 40				
Reading 7	a	10 32		10 39	10 44	10 45			10 55	11 01	11 02	11 08		11 17		11 25	11 32	11 32	11 39	11 44	11 45			11 55	12 01
	d	10 34			10 45			10 52	10 56	11 03	11 04		11 11	11 18		11 26	11 33	11 34		11 45			11 53	11 56	12 03
Twyford 3	a	10 40									11 10							11 40							
Maidenhead 3	a	10 48									11 18							11 48							
Slough 3	a	10 55							11 09		11 25							11 55						12 09	
Ealing Broadway	⊖ a	11 19									11 49							12 19							
London Paddington 15	⊖ a	11 30			11 15			11 23	11 29	11 32	12 00		11 42	11 52		11 58	12 02	12 30		12 15			12 23	12 29	12 32

		GW		GW	GW	XC	GW	GW	GW	GW	GW	XC	GW	GW	GW	GW	GW	GW	GW	XC	GW	GW	GW	GW	GW
		1		1◇ 🛒	1◇ 🛒	1◇ ☕	1	1	1◇	1◇ 🛒	1	R 1 ☕	1◇ 🛒	1	1	1◇	1◇ ☕	1	1◇ ☕	1◇ ☕	1	1 A ☕	1◇ 🛒	1	1◇ ☕
Birmingham New Street 12	d					10 33						11 03								11 33					
Birmingham International	d											11 15													
Coventry	d											11 25													
Stratford-upon-Avon	d																							11 40	
Warwick Parkway	d					10b45						11 21								11 41					
Warwick	d					10b49						11 24								11 45				12 05	
Leamington Spa 8	d					11 00						11 38								12 00				12 08	
Banbury	d					11 19						11 55								12 19				12 38	
Kings Sutton	d																							12 43	
Heyford	d																							12 52	
Tackley	d																							12 56	
Bicester Town	d																								
Islip	d																								
Oxford	a					11 41						12 14								12 41				13 06	
	d					11 43		11 55	12 00			12 15			12 21	12 30				12 43	12 55		13 00		
Radley	d														12 27										
Culham	d																								
Appleford	d														12 32										
Didcot Parkway	a							12 06							12 36						13 06				
	d	←		11 53				12 07		12 17			12 29		12 37		12 47	←			13 07				13 17
Cholsey	d	11 43						12 13			←				12 43			12 43			13 13				
Goring & Streatley	d	11 48						12 18			12 18				→			12 48			13 18				
Pangbourne	d	11 52						→			12 22							12 52			→				
Tilehurst	d	11 57									12 27							12 57							
Bedwyn	d						11 37																		
Hungerford	d						11 43																		
Kintbury	d						11 47																		
Newbury	a						11 54																		
	d						11 54							12 13											
Newbury Racecourse	d													12 15											
Thatcham	d						11 59							12 19											
Midgham	d													12 24											
Aldermaston	d													12 28											
Theale	d						12 07							12 33											
Reading West	d													12 40											
Reading 7	a	12 02		12 07		12 13	12 16		12 25	12 32	12 32	12 39	12 44	12 45		12 54	13 01	13 02		13 13			13 25		13 32
	d	12 04		12 09	12 11		12 18		12 27	12 33	12 34		12 45			12 55	13 03	13 04	13 11			13 19	13 27		13 33
Twyford 3	a	12 10									12 40							13 10							
Maidenhead 3	a	12 18									12 48							13 18							
Slough 3	a	12 25							12 40		12 55					13 08		13 25					13 40		
Ealing Broadway	⊖ a	12 49									13 19							13 49							
London Paddington 15	⊖ a	13 00		12 39	12 42		12 52		12 59	13 02	13 30		13 15			13 26	13 29	14 00	13 42			13 45	13 58		14 02

For general notes see front of timetable
For details of catering facilities see
Directory of Train Operators

A The Cornish Riviera
b Change at Banbury

Birmingham, Banbury, Bicester, Oxford and Bedwyn → Reading and London

Network Diagram - see first page of Table 116

		GW	XC	GW	GW	GW	GW	GW	GW	GW	GW	GW	XC	GW	GW	GW	GW	GW	XC	GW	GW	GW	GW	GW
		1	R 1	1◇	1	1	1	1◇	1◇ A	1	1◇	1◇	1◇	1◇	1	1◇	1◇	1	R 1	1	1◇	1	1	1
			🍴	🛒					⊠		🛒	🛒	🍴	🛒		🛒	🛒		🍴		🛒			✕
Birmingham New Street 12	d		12 03										12 33						13 03					
Birmingham International	d		12 15																13 15					
Coventry	d		12 25																13 25					
Stratford-upon-Avon	d																							
Warwick Parkway	d		12 21										12b46						13 21					
Warwick	d		12 24										12b49						13 24					
Leamington Spa 8	d		12 38										13 00						13 38					
Banbury	d		12 55										13 19						13 55					
Kings Sutton	d																							
Heyford	d																							
Tackley	d																							
Bicester Town	d																						13 55	
Islip	d																						14 07	
Oxford	a		13 14										13 41						14 14				14 22	
	d		13 15				13 21	13 30					13 43		13 55	14 00			14 15			14 21		
Radley	d						13 27															14 27		
Culham	d						13 31																	
Appleford	d																					14 32		
Didcot Parkway	a						13 36								14 06							14 36		
	d			13 29			13 37		13 47	←	13 53				14 07		14 17	←			14 29	14 37		
Cholsey	d	←					13 43			13 43					14 13							14 43		
Goring & Streatley	d	13 18					→			13 48					14 18			14 18				→		
Pangbourne	d	13 22								13 52					→			14 22						
Tilehurst	d	13 27								13 57								14 27						
Bedwyn	d					13 07								13 32										
Hungerford	d					13 13								13 39										
Kintbury	d					13 17																		
Newbury	a					13 24								13 48										
	d				13 13	13 24								13 49						14 13				
Newbury Racecourse	d				13 15															14 15				
Thatcham	d				13 19	13 29								13 55						14 19				
Midgham	d				13 24															14 24				
Aldermaston	d				13 28															14 28				
Theale	d				13 33	13 42								14 03						14 33				
Reading West	d				13 40															14 40				
Reading 7	a	13 32	13 39	13 44	13 45	13 50		13 55	14 01	14 02	14 07		14 13	14 15		14 25	14 32	14 32	14 39	14 44	14 44			
	d	13 34		13 45		13 51		13 56	14 03	14 04	14 09	14 11		14 18		14 27	14 33	14 34			14 45			14 52
Twyford 3	a	13 40								14 10								14 40						
Maidenhead 3	a	13 48								14 18								14 48						
Slough 3	a	13 55						14 09		14 25						14 40		14 55						
Ealing Broadway	⊖ a	14 19								14 49								15 19						
London Paddington 15	⊖ a	14 30		14 15		14 22		14 29	14 32	15 00	14 39	14 42		14 49		14 59	15 02	15 30			15 15			15 23

		GW	GW	GW	GW	XC	GW	GW	GW	GW	GW	XC	GW	GW	GW	GW	GW	GW	GW	GW	GW	XC	GW	GW
		1◇	1◇	1	1◇	1◇	1	1	1◇	1◇	1	R 1	1◇	1	1	1◇	1◇	1	1◇	1	1◇ B	1◇	1◇	1
			🍴		🛒	🍴			🛒	🛒		🍴	🍴			⊠			🍴		🛒	🍴	🍴	
Birmingham New Street 12	d					13 33						14 03										14 33		
Birmingham International	d											14 15												
Coventry	d											14 25												
Stratford-upon-Avon	d											13 39												
Warwick Parkway	d					13 41						14 21										14b46		
Warwick	d					13 45						14 24										14b49		
Leamington Spa 8	d					14 00						14 38										15 00		
Banbury	d					14 19						14 55						15 02				15 19		
Kings Sutton	d																	15 07						
Heyford	d																	15 16						
Tackley	d																	15 20						
Bicester Town	d																							
Islip	d																							
Oxford	a					14 41						15 14						15 31				15 41		
	d	14 30				14 43		14 55	15 00			15 15			15 21		15 30					15 43		
Radley	d														15 27									
Culham	d														15 31									
Appleford	d																							
Didcot Parkway	a							15 06							15 36									
	d		14 47	←				15 07		15 17			15 29		15 37				15 47	←	15 53			
Cholsey	d			14 43				15 13			←				15 43					15 43				
Goring & Streatley	d			14 48				15 18			15 18				→					15 48				
Pangbourne	d			14 52				→			15 22									15 52				
Tilehurst	d			14 57							15 27									15 57				
Bedwyn	d						14 37																	15 37
Hungerford	d						14 43																	15 43
Kintbury	d						14 47																	15 47
Newbury	a						14 54																	15 54
	d						14 54							15 13										15 54
Newbury Racecourse	d													15 15										
Thatcham	d						14 59							15 19										15 59
Midgham	d													15 24										
Aldermaston	d													15 28										
Theale	d						15 07							15 33										16 07
Reading West	d													15 40										
Reading 7	a	14 55	15 01	15 02		15 13	15 16		15 25	15 32	15 32	15 39	15 44	15 45			15 55		16 01	16 02	16 07	16 11		16 17
	d	14 57	15 03	15 04	15 11		15 18		15 27	15 33	15 34		15 45			15 53	15 56		16 03	16 04	16 09		16 14	16 18
Twyford 3	a			15 10							15 40									16 10				
Maidenhead 3	a			15 18							15 48									16 18				
Slough 3	a	15 10		15 25					15 40		15 55						16 09			16 25				
Ealing Broadway	⊖ a			15 49							16 19									16 49				
London Paddington 15	⊖ a	15 28	15 30	16 00	15 42		15 52		15 59	16 02	16 30		16 15			16 22	16 27		16 30	17 00	16 39		16 44	16 52

For general notes see front of timetable
For details of catering facilities see Directory of Train Operators

A **The St David**
B **The Cheltenham Spa Express**
b Change at Banbury

Birmingham, Banbury, Bicester, Oxford and Bedwyn → Reading and London

Network Diagram - see first page of Table 116

		GW		GW	GW	GW	XC	GW	GW	GW	GW	GW	GW	GW	GW	XC	GW	GW	GW	GW	GW	GW	XC	GW	GW
																							R		
		1		1◊	1◊	1	1◊	1◊	1	1	1◊	1◊	1◊	1	1◊	1◊	1◊	1	1	1◊	1◊	1	1	1◊	1
											A														
				[trolley]	[buffet]		[buffet]	[trolley]			[buffet]		[buffet]		[trolley]	[buffet]	[trolley]				[trolley]		[buffet]	[trolley]	
Birmingham New Street 12	d						15 03									15 33							16 03		
Birmingham International	d						15 15																16 15		
Coventry	d						15 25																16 25		
Stratford-upon-Avon	d																						*15 41*		
Warwick Parkway	d						*15 21*									*15 41*							*16 21*		
Warwick	d						*15 24*									*15 44*							*16 24*		
Leamington Spa 8	d						15 38									16 00							16 38		
Banbury	d						15 55									16 19							16 55		
Kings Sutton	d																								
Heyford	d																								
Tackley	d																								
Bicester Town	d																								
Islip	d																								
Oxford	a						16 14									16 41							17 14		
	d	15 55		16 00			16 15			16 21		16 30				16 43			16 53	17 00			17 15		
Radley	d									16 27									16 59						
Culham	d																								
Appleford	d									16 32															
Didcot Parkway	a	16 06								16 36									17 06						
	d	16 07			16 17			16 29		16 37			16 47	←					17 07		17 17	←		17 29	
Cholsey	d	16 13				←				16 43				16 43					17 13			17 13			
Goring & Streatley	d	16 18				16 18				→				16 48					→			17 18			
Pangbourne	d	→				16 22								16 52								17 22			
Tilehurst	d					16 27								16 57								17 27			
Bedwyn	d																	16 44							
Hungerford	d																16 39	16 50							
Kintbury	d																	16 54							
Newbury	a																16 48	17 01							
	d								16 13								16 49								17 16
Newbury Racecourse	d								16 15																17 18
Thatcham	d								16 19								16 55								17 22
Midgham	d								16 24																17 27
Aldermaston	d								16 28																17 31
Theale	d								16 33								17 03								17 36
Reading West	d								16 40																17 42
Reading 7	a			16 25	16 32	16 32	16 39	16 44	16 45			16 55	17 01	17 02		17 13	17 17			17 25	17 32	17 32	17 39	17 44	17 45
	d			16 27	16 33	16 34		16 45			16 53	16 56	17 03	17 04	17 11		17 18			17 27	17 33	17 34		17 45	
Twyford 3	a					16 40								17 10								17 40			
Maidenhead 3	a					16 48								17 18								17 48			
Slough 3	a			16 40		16 55						17 09		17 25			17 31			17 40		17 55			
Ealing Broadway	⊖ a					17 19								17 49								18 19			
London Paddington 15	⊖ a			16 59	17 02	17 30		17 15			17 22	17 27	17 30	18 00	17 42		17 53			17 58	18 02	18 30		18 15	

		GW		GW	GW	GW	GW	GW	XC	GW	GW	GW	GW	GW	GW	XC	GW	GW	GW	GW	GW	GW	GW	GW	XC
									R							R									R
		1◊		1◊	1	1	1◊	1◊	1	1◊	1	1	1◊	1◊	1	1	1◊	1	1	1◊	1◊	1◊	1	1◊	1
		B																		C					
		[restaurant]		[buffet]			[buffet]	[trolley]	[buffet]	[trolley]				[trolley]		[buffet]	[buffet]			[buffet]		[buffet]		[trolley]	[buffet]
Birmingham New Street 12	d								16 33							17 03									17 33
Birmingham International	d															17 15									
Coventry	d															17 25									
Stratford-upon-Avon	d											*15 41*													
Warwick Parkway	d								*16b45*			*16 45*				*17 20*									*17b45*
Warwick	d								*16b49*			*16 49*				*17 23*									*17b48*
Leamington Spa 8	d								17 00			*16 54*				17 38									18 00
Banbury	d								17 19			17 22				17 55									18 19
Kings Sutton	d											17 27													
Heyford	d											17 36													
Tackley	d											17 40													
Bicester Town	d					16 56																			
Islip	d					17 08																			
Oxford	a					17 22			17 41			17 50				18 14									18 41
	d				17 21		17 38		17 43			17 51	18 00			18 15			18 21		18 30				18 43
Radley	d				17 27							17 57							18 27						
Culham	d				17 31														18 31						
Appleford	d											18 02													
Didcot Parkway	a				17 36							18 06							18 36						
	d				17 37			17 53				18 07		18 17	←		18 29		18 37			18 47	←		
Cholsey	d				17 43							18 13			18 13				18 43				18 43		
Goring & Streatley	d				17 48							→			18 18				→				18 48		
Pangbourne	d				17 52										18 22								18 52		
Tilehurst	d				17 57										18 27								18 57		
Bedwyn	d										17 37							17 56							
Hungerford	d										17 43							18 02							
Kintbury	d										17 47							18 06							
Newbury	a										17 54							18 13							
	d										17 54							18 13							
Newbury Racecourse	d																	18 15							
Thatcham	d										17 59							18 19							
Midgham	d																	18 24							
Aldermaston	d										18 04							18 28							
Theale	d										18 09							18 33							
Reading West	d																	18 40							
Reading 7	a				18 02		18 03	18 07	18 11		18 22		18 25	18 32	18 32	18 39	18 44	18 45			18 55	19 01	19 02		19 13
	d	17 52		17 58	18 04		18 04	18 09		18 15	18 22		18 27	18 33	18 34		18 46			18 53	18 56	19 03	19 04	19 11	
Twyford 3	a				18 10										18 40								19 10		
Maidenhead 3	a				18 18										18 48								19 18		
Slough 3	a				18 25								18 40		18 55						19 09		19 25		
Ealing Broadway	⊖ a				18 49										19 19								19 49		
London Paddington 15	⊖ a	18 22		18 27	19 00		18 31	18 39		18 45	18 53		18 58	19 02	19 30		19 15			19 24	19 29	19 32	20 00	19 42	

For general notes see front of timetable
For details of catering facilities see Directory of Train Operators

A The Torbay Express
B The Mayflower
C The Royal Duchy

b Change at Banbury

Birmingham, Banbury, Bicester, Oxford and Bedwyn → Reading and London

Network Diagram - see first page of Table 116

		GW	GW	GW	GW	GW	GW	GW	XC	GW	GW	GW	GW	GW	GW	XC	GW	GW	GW	GW	GW	GW	GW	XC
		[1]	[1]	[1]	[1]◇ 🛒	[1]	[1]◇ 🛒	[1]	[R] [1] ☕	[1]◇ 🛒	[1]	[1]◇	[1]◇ ☕	[1]	[1]◇ ☕	[R] [1] ☕	[1]◇ 🛒	[1]	[1]	[1]◇	[1]	[1]◇ A 🛒	[1] B	[R] [1] ☕
Birmingham New Street [12]	d								18 03							18 33								19 03
Birmingham International	d								18 15															19 15
Coventry	d								18 25															19 25
Stratford-upon-Avon	d								17 42															
Warwick Parkway	d								18 23							18b45								18 45
Warwick	d								18 26							18b49								18 49
Leamington Spa [8]	d								18 38							19 00								19 38
Banbury	d								18 55			19 01				19 19								19 55
Kings Sutton	d											19 06												
Heyford	d											19 15												
Tackley	d											19 19												
Bicester Town	d	18 19																					19 40	
Islip	d	18 31																					19 52	
Oxford	a	18 46							19 14			19 28				19 41							20 06	20 14
	d			18 55	19 00				19 15		19 21	19 30				19 43			19 55	20 00				20 15
Radley	d										19 27													
Culham	d																							
Appleford	d										19 32													
Didcot Parkway	a			19 06							19 36								20 06					
	d			19 07			19 17			19 29	19 37		19 47	←			19 53		20 07					
Cholsey	d			19 13				←			19 43			19 43					20 13		←			
Goring & Streatley	d			19 18				19 18			→			19 48					20 18		20 18			
Pangbourne	d			→				19 22						19 52					→		20 22			
Tilehurst	d							19 27						19 57							20 27			
Bedwyn	d					19 03																19 46		
Hungerford	d					19 09																19 52		
Kintbury	d					19 13																19 58		
Newbury	a					19 20																20 05		
	d		18 54												19 46			19 51				20 06		
Newbury Racecourse	d																	19 53						
Thatcham	d		18 59															19 57				20 12		
Midgham	d																	20 02						
Aldermaston	d																	20 06						
Theale	d		19 07															20 11				20 20		
Reading West	d																	20 18						
Reading [7]	a		19 16		19 26		19 32	19 32	19 39	19 44		19 54	20 01	20 02	20 07	20 09	20 12	20 21		20 25	20 32	20 33		20 39
	d		19 18		19 27		19 33	19 34		19 45		19 54	20 03	20 04	20 10		20 14			20 26	20 34	20 35		
Twyford [3]	a							19 40						20 10							20 40			
Maidenhead [3]	a							19 48						20 18							20 48			
Slough [3]	a				19 40			19 55				20 09		20 25							20 55			
Ealing Broadway	⊖ a							20 19						20 49							21 19			
London Paddington [15]	⊖ a		19 52		19 59		20 02	20 30		20 15		20 28	20 30	21 00	20 39		20 44			20 57	21 30	21 02		

		GW	GW	GW	GW	GW	GW	GW	GW	XC	GW	GW	GW	XC	GW	GW	GW	GW	GW FO	GW FX	GW FO	GW FX	GW	GW
		[1]	[1]◇ ☕	[1]	[1]◇ ⊠	[1]◇ 🛒	[1]	[1]◇ ☕	[1]	[1]◇ ☕	[1]	[1]◇	[1]	[R] [1]	[1]◇ 🛒	[1]	[1]◇ 🛒	[1]	[1]◇	[1]◇	[1]◇ 🛒	[1]◇ ☕ 🛒	[1]	[1]
Birmingham New Street [12]	d									19 33				20 03										
Birmingham International	d													20 15										
Coventry	d													20 25										
Stratford-upon-Avon	d													19 43										20c00
Warwick Parkway	d									19b47				20 06										20 47
Warwick	d									19b50				20 09										20 50
Leamington Spa [8]	d									20 00				20 38										20 54
Banbury	d						20 05			20 19				20 55										21 35
Kings Sutton	d						20 10																	21 40
Heyford	d						20 19																	21 49
Tackley	d						20 23																	21 53
Bicester Town	d																							
Islip	d																							
Oxford	a						20 33			20 41				21 14										22 03
	d			20 20		20 30				20 43	20 53	21 00		21 15				21 20	21 38	21 38			21 53	
Radley	d			20 26														21 26					21 59	
Culham	d			20 30														21 30						
Appleford	d										21 01													
Didcot Parkway	a			20 36							21 06							21 36					22 06	
	d		20 29	20 37				20 47	←		21 07		←		21 29			21 37			21 51	21 51	22 07	
Cholsey	d			20 43					20 43		21 13		21 13					21 43					22 13	
Goring & Streatley	d			→					20 48		→		21 18					21 48					22 18	
Pangbourne	d								20 53				21 22					21 53					22 23	
Tilehurst	d								20 57				21 27					21 57					22 27	
Bedwyn	d	19 56														20 58								
Hungerford	d	20 02														21 04								
Kintbury	d	20 06														21 08								
Newbury	a	20 13														21 15								
	d	20 13														21 15	21 42							
Newbury Racecourse	d	20 15														21 17								
Thatcham	d	20 19														21 21								
Midgham	d	20 24														21 26								
Aldermaston	d	20 28														21 30								
Theale	d	20 33														21 35								
Reading West	d	20 40														21 42								
Reading [7]	a	20 43	20 44			20 55		21 01	21 03	21 06		21 24	21 32	21 39	21 44	21 46	22 00	22 03	22 10	22 10	22 15	22 15	22 34	
	d		20 45		20 53	20 56		21 03				21 26	21 34		21 46		22 01		22 11	22 11	22 17	22 17	22 50	
Twyford [3]	a												21 40										→	
Maidenhead [3]	a												21 47											
Slough [3]	a					21 09						21 38	21 59						22 24	22 28				
Ealing Broadway	⊖ a												22 20											
London Paddington [15]	⊖ a		21 15		21 22	21 27		21 30				21 58	22 30		22 15		22 30		22 42	22 52	22 45	22 56		

For general notes see front of timetable
For details of catering facilities see Directory of Train Operators

A From Westbury (Table 135)
B To Banbury
b Change at Banbury
c Change at Warwick and Banbury

Birmingham, Banbury, Bicester, Oxford and Bedwyn → Reading and London

Network Diagram - see first page of Table 116

		XC		GW	GW	GW	GW	GW	GW	GW	GW	GW	GW	GW	GW	GW	GW	GW	GW	GW	GW	CH	GW		
					FO	FX		FO	FX	FO	FX	FO	FX							FX	FO				
		1 ◇		1	1 ◇	1 ◇	1	1 ◇	1 ◇	1 ◇	1 ◇	1 ◇	1 ◇	1	1	1 ◇	1	1	1 ◇	1 ◇	1 ◇		1		
																			A						
					[trolley]	[restaurant] [trolley]		[restaurant]	[restaurant]			[trolley]	[restaurant] [trolley]						[trolley]		[trolley]				
Birmingham New Street 12	d	21 03																							
Birmingham International	d	21 15																							
Coventry	d	21 25																							
Stratford-upon-Avon	d																					23 00			
Warwick Parkway	d													21 47								22b53			
Warwick	d													21 50								23 21			
Leamington Spa 8	d	21 38												21 55								23 25			
Banbury	d	21 55												22 19								23 44	23 50		
Kings Sutton	d													22 24									23 55		
Heyford	d													22 33									00 04		
Tackley	d													22 37									00 08		
Bicester Town	d																								
Islip	d																								
Oxford	a	22 14												22 47								00 18	00 18		
	d	22 15			22 21	22 21				22 34	22 34				22 55	23 05				23 55	23 59		00 20		
Radley	d														23 01										
Culham	d														23 05										
Appleford	d														23 08										
Didcot Parkway	a									22 46	22 46				23 12	23 17	←			00 07	00 11		00 31		
	d									22 47	22 47	22 47	22 47		23 21 →	23 18	23 21		23 32	00 08	00 12		00 33		
Cholsey	d																23 27						00 39		
Goring & Streatley	d																23 32						00 44		
Pangbourne	d																23 36						00 48		
Tilehurst	d																23 41						00 53		
Bedwyn	d			21 54														23 00							
Hungerford	d			22 00														23 06							
Kintbury	d			22 04														23 10							
Newbury	a			22 11														23 17							
	d			22 11														23 17							
Newbury Racecourse	d			22 13														23 19							
Thatcham	d			22 18														23 23							
Midgham	d			22 22														23 28							
Aldermaston	d			22 26														23 32							
Theale	d			22 31														23 37							
Reading West	d			22 38														23 44							
Reading 7	a	22 39		22 42	22 45	22 45	←			23 02	23 02	23 06	23 06			23 33	23 46	23 49	23 52	00 22	00 26		00 58		
	d				22 47	22 47	22 50	22 55	22 55	23 04	23 04	23 07	23 07			23 35			23 53	00 24	00 27		01 00		
Twyford 3	a						22 56																01 06		
Maidenhead 3	a						23 04																01 14		
Slough 3	a				23 00	23 04	23 17			23 17	23 21					23 52				00 41	00 40		01 22		
Ealing Broadway	⊖ a						23 50																01 39		
London Paddington 15	⊖ a				23 22	23 25	23 59	23 29	23 36	23 36	23 41	23 42	23 50			00 22			00 32	01 02	00 58		01 48		

For general notes see front of timetable
For details of catering facilities see Directory of Train Operators

A From Taunton (Table 134).
[trolley] to Reading

b Change at Leamington Spa

Table 116

Saturdays

until 26 January

Birmingham, Banbury, Bicester, Oxford and Bedwyn → Reading and London

Network Diagram - see first page of Table 116

		GW	GW	GW	GW	GW	GW	GW	GW	GW	GW	GW	GW	GW	GW	GW	GW	XC	GW	GW	GW	GW	GW	GW	GW
		1 ◇	1	1	1	1	1 ◇	1	1	1 ◇	1	1 ◇	1	1	1 ◇	1 ◇	1	1 ◇	1	1 ◇	1	1	1 ◇	1 ◇	1
		🛒					☕					☕				☕				☕				☕	
Birmingham New Street 12	d																	06 03							
Birmingham International	d																	06 15							
Coventry	d																	06 25							
Stratford-upon-Avon	d																								
Warwick Parkway	d																								
Warwick	d																								
Leamington Spa 8	d																	06 38							
Banbury	d		23p50															06 55				07 02			
Kings Sutton	d		23p55																			07 07			
Heyford	d		00 04																			07 16			
Tackley	d		00 08																			07 20			
Bicester Town	d																								
Islip	d																								
Oxford	a		00 18															07 14				07 30			
	d	23p59	00 20	04 00	05 21	05 55			06 21	06 30				06 55	07 00			07 15			07 21		07 37		
Radley	d				05 27				06 27												07 27				
Culham	d				05 31																07 31				
Appleford	d								06 32																
Didcot Parkway	a	00 11	00 31	04 11	05 37	06 06			06 36					07 06							07 37				
	d	00 12	00 33	04 12	05 38	06 07	06 29		06 37		←	06 59		07 07		07 17				07 30	07 38			08 00	
Cholsey	d		00 39		05 44	06 13			06 43		06 43			07 13			←				07 44				
Goring & Streatley	d		00 44		05 49	06 18			→		06 48			07 18			07 18				07 49				
Pangbourne	d		00 48		05 53	06 22					06 53			→			07 22				07 53				
Tilehurst	d		00 53		05 58	06 27					06 57						07 27				07 58				
Bedwyn	d							06 07					06 37												07 37
Hungerford	d							06 13					06 43												07 43
Kintbury	d							06 17					06 47												07 47
Newbury	a							06 24					06 54												07 54
	d							06 24					06 54						07 13						07 54
Newbury Racecourse	d							06 26											07 15						
Thatcham	d							06 30					06 59						07 19						07 59
Midgham	d							06 35											07 24						
Aldermaston	d							06 39											07 28						
Theale	d							06 44					07 07						07 33						08 07
Reading West	d																		07 40						
Reading 7	a	00 26	00 58	04 29	06 03	06 32	06 43	06 52		06 56	07 03	07 14	07 20		07 25	07 32	07 32	07 44	07 44	07 44	08 03		08 08	08 14	08 16
	d	00 27	01 00	04 40	06 04	06 34	06 45	06 53		06 57	07 04	07 15	07 21		07 26	07 33	07 34			07 46	08 04		08 09	08 16	08 18
Twyford 3	a		01 06	04 46	06 10	06 40					07 10						07 40				08 10				
Maidenhead 3	a		01 14	04 54	06 18	06 48					07 18						07 48				08 18				
Slough 3	a	00 40	01 22	05 01	06 25	06 55				07 12	07 25				07 39		07 55				08 25				
Ealing Broadway	⊖ a		01 39	05 19	06 49	07 19					07 49						08 19				08 49				
London Paddington 15	⊖ a	00 58	01 48	05 30	06 58	07 31	07 14	07 25		07 31	07 58	07 45	07 53		07 57	08 01	08 28			08 14	08 58		08 40	08 45	08 52

For general notes see front of timetable
For details of catering facilities see
Directory of Train Operators

Saturdays

until 26 January

Birmingham, Banbury, Bicester, Oxford and Bedwyn → Reading and London

Network Diagram - see first page of Table 116

		GW		GW	GW	GW	GW	XC	GW	GW	GW	GW	GW	GW	GW	XC	GW	GW	GW	GW	GW	GW	GW	XC	GW
		1		1 ◇	1	1 ◇	1	1 ◇	1	1 ◇	1	1 ◇	1 ◇	1	1 ◇	1 ◇	1 ◇	1	1	1 ◇	1 ◇	1	1 ◇	1 ◇	1 ◇
																	A								
						☕		☕		☕			☕		☕	☕	☕			☕	☕		☕	☕	☕
Birmingham New Street 12	d							07 03								07 33								08 03	
Birmingham International	d							07 15																08 15	
Coventry	d							07 25																08 25	
Stratford-upon-Avon	d																							07 35	
Warwick Parkway	d							*07 06*								*07 41*								*08 20*	
Warwick	d							*07 09*								*07 45*								*08 23*	
Leamington Spa 8	d							07 38								08 00								08 38	
Banbury	d							07 55								08 19								08 55	
Kings Sutton	d																								
Heyford	d																								
Tackley	d																								
Bicester Town	d				07 41																				
Islip	d				07 53																				
Oxford	a				08 08			08 14								08 41								09 14	
	d	07 55		08 00				08 15			08 21	08 30				08 43			08 55	09 00				09 15	
Radley	d										08 27								09 01						
Culham	d																								
Appleford	d										08 32														
Didcot Parkway	a	08 06									08 36								09 09						
	d	08 07				08 17				08 30	08 37		08 47	←	08 52		09 00		09 09		09 17	←			09 29
Cholsey	d	08 13					←				08 43			08 43					09 15			09 15			
Goring & Streatley	d	08 18					08 18				→			08 48					→			09 20			
Pangbourne	d	→					08 22							08 53								09 25			
Tilehurst	d						08 27							08 57								09 29			
Bedwyn	d																	08 37							
Hungerford	d																	08 43							
Kintbury	d																	08 47							
Newbury	a																	08 54							
	d								08 13									08 54							
Newbury Racecourse	d								08 15																
Thatcham	d								08 19									08 59							
Midgham	d								08 24																
Aldermaston	d								08 28																
Theale	d								08 33									09 07							
Reading West	d								08 40																
Reading 7	a			08 24		08 32	08 32	08 39	08 44	08 44		08 56	09 02	09 03	09 07	09 13	09 14	09 17		09 26	09 33	09 35		09 39	09 44
	d			08 25		08 33	08 34			08 46		08 57	09 04	09 04	09 08		09 16	09 19		09 28	09 34	09 35	09 38		09 45
Twyford 3	a						08 40							09 10								09 41			
Maidenhead 3	a						08 48							09 18								09 49			
Slough 3	a						08 55							09 25						09 41		09 57			
Ealing Broadway	⊖ a						09 19							09 49								10 20			
London Paddington 15	⊖ a			08 56		09 06	09 28			09 15		09 28	09 30	09 58	09 36		09 44	09 51		09 58	10 06	10 29	10 10		10 14

		GW	GW	GW		GW	GW	GW	XC	GW	GW	GW	GW	GW	GW	GW	GW	XC	GW	GW	GW	GW	GW	GW	XC
		1	1	1 ◇		1	1 ◇	1	1 ◇	1	1	1	1 ◇	1	1 ◇	1	1 ◇	1 ◇	1	1 ◇	1 ◇	1 ◇	1	1 ◇	1 ◇
							☕		☕				☕		☕		☕	☕		☕	☕	☕		☕	☕
Birmingham New Street 12	d								08 33									09 03							09 33
Birmingham International	d																	09 15							
Coventry	d																	09 25							
Stratford-upon-Avon	d																								
Warwick Parkway	d								*08 45*									09b23							*09 43*
Warwick	d								*08 48*									09b27							*09 46*
Leamington Spa 8	d								09 00									09 38							10 00
Banbury	d					09 02			09 19									09 55							10 19
Kings Sutton	d					09 07																			
Heyford	d					09 16																			
Tackley	d					09 20																			
Bicester Town	d										09 19														
Islip	d										09 31														
Oxford	a					09 30			09 41		09 46							10 14							10 41
	d		09 20	09 30					09 43			09 52	09 57					10 15					10 21		10 43
Radley	d		09 26																				10 27		
Culham	d		09 30																						
Appleford	d																						10 32		
Didcot Parkway	a		09 35									10 03											10 36		
	d		09 37				09 47	←				10 04			10 17		10 22			10 29			10 37		
Cholsey	d		09 43					09 43				10 10		←									10 43		
Goring & Streatley	d		→					09 48				10 15		10 15									10 48		
Pangbourne	d							09 52				→		10 20									10 53		
Tilehurst	d							09 57						10 24									10 57		
Bedwyn	d									09 37															
Hungerford	d									09 43															
Kintbury	d									09 47															
Newbury	a									09 54															
	d	09 23								09 54									10 13						
Newbury Racecourse	d	09 26																	10 15						
Thatcham	d	09 30								09 59									10 19						
Midgham	d	09 35																	10 24						
Aldermaston	d	09 39																	10 28						
Theale	d	09 44								10 07									10 33						
Reading West	d	09 51																	10 40						
Reading 7	a	09 55		09 55			10 01	10 02	10 13	10 16			10 21	10 30	10 32	←	10 37	10 39	10 45	10 45			11 03		11 13
	d			09 56			10 03	10 04		10 18			10 23	10 34	10 33	10 34	10 38			10 45	10 52	11 01	11 04	11 11	
Twyford 3	a							10 10						→		10 40							11 10		
Maidenhead 3	a							10 18								10 48							11 18		
Slough 3	a							10 25					10 36			10 55							11 25		
Ealing Broadway	⊖ a							10 49								11 19							11 49		
London Paddington 15	⊖ a			10 27			10 31	10 58		10 52			10 54		10 59	11 28	11 07			11 15	11 22	11 31	11 58	11 42	

For general notes see front of timetable
For details of catering facilities see
Directory of Train Operators

A From Taunton (Table 134)
b Change at Banbury

Birmingham, Banbury, Bicester, Oxford and Bedwyn → Reading and London

Network Diagram - see first page of Table 116

	GW 1	GW 1	GW 1◇ 🍴	GW 1	XC 1◇ 🍴		GW 1◇ 🍴	GW 1	GW 1	GW 1	GW 1◇ 🍴	GW 1	XC 1◇ 🍴	GW 1	GW 1	GW 1	GW 1◇ 🍴	GW 1	XC 1◇ 🍴	GW 1◇ 🍴	GW 1	GW 1◇ 🍴	GW 1	GW 1◇ 🍴
Birmingham New Street 12 d					10 03								10 33						11 03					
Birmingham International d					10 15														11 15					
Coventry d					10 25														11 25					
Stratford-upon-Avon d					*09 36*																			
Warwick Parkway d					*10 22*								*10b46*						*11 22*					
Warwick d					*10 26*								*10b49*						*11 26*					
Leamington Spa 8 d					10 38								11 00						11 38					
Banbury d					10 55					11 02			11 19						11 55					
Kings Sutton d										11 07														
Heyford d										11 16														
Tackley d										11 20														
Bicester Town d															11 19									
Islip d															11 31									
Oxford a					11 14					11 30			11 41		11 46				12 14					
Oxford d		10 52	11 00		11 15				11 21				11 43			11 55	12 00		12 15				12 21	
Radley d									11 27														12 27	
Culham d									11 31															
Appleford d																							12 32	
Didcot Parkway a		11 04							11 37							12 06							12 36	
Didcot Parkway d		11 05					11 29		11 37		11 47					12 08				12 29		12 22	12 37	
Cholsey d		11 11		←					11 43			←				12 14		←					12 43 →	
Goring & Streatley d		11 16 →		11 16					11 48 →			11 48				12 19 →		12 19						
Pangbourne d				11 20								11 53						12 24						
Tilehurst d				11 25								11 57						12 28						
Bedwyn d	10 37													11 37										
Hungerford d	10 43													11 43										
Kintbury d	10 47													11 47										
Newbury a	10 54													11 54										
Newbury d	10 54							11 13						11 54							12 13			
Newbury Racecourse d								11 15													12 15			
Thatcham d	10 59							11 19						11 59							12 19			
Midgham d								11 24													12 24			
Aldermaston d								11 28													12 28			
Theale d	11 07							11 33						12 07							12 33			
Reading West d								11 40													12 40			
Reading 7 a	11 17		11 25	11 30	11 39		11 44	11 45			12 02	12 03	12 13	12 16			12 25	12 34	12 39	12 44	12 45	12 36		
Reading d	11 18		11 26	11 34			11 45				12 03	12 04		12 18			12 27	12 34		12 45		12 38		12 54
Twyford 3 a				11 40								12 10						12 40						
Maidenhead 3 a				11 48								12 18						12 48						
Slough 3 a			11 40	11 55								12 25					12 40	12 56						
Ealing Broadway ⊖ a				12 19								12 49						13 19						
London Paddington 15 ⊖ a	11 52		11 58	12 28			12 15				12 32	12 58		12 52			12 58	13 29		13 15		13 06		13 23

	GW 1◇	GW 1◇ 🍴	GW 1	GW 1◇ 🍴	XC 1◇ 🍴	GW 1◇ 🍴	GW 1		GW 1◇ 🍴	GW 1	XC 1◇ 🍴	GW 1	GW 1	GW 1	GW 1◇	GW 1	GW 1◇ 🍴	GW 1	XC 1◇ 🍴	GW 1◇ 🍴	GW 1	GW 1◇ 🍴	GW 1	GW 1◇ 🍴
Birmingham New Street 12 d					11 33						12 03								12 33					
Birmingham International d											12 15													
Coventry d											12 25													
Stratford-upon-Avon d											*11 38*													
Warwick Parkway d					*11 41*						*12 22*								*12 45*					
Warwick d					*11 45*						*12 26*								*12 48*					
Leamington Spa 8 d					12 00						12 38								13 00					
Banbury d					12 19						12 55					13 02			13 19					
Kings Sutton d																13 07								
Heyford d																13 16								
Tackley d																13 20								
Bicester Town d																								
Islip d																								
Oxford a					12 41						13 14					13 30			13 41					
Oxford d	12 30				12 43		12 52		13 00		13 15			13 21	13 30				13 43		13 55	14 00		
Radley d														13 27										
Culham d														13 31										
Appleford d																								
Didcot Parkway a							13 03							13 37							14 06			
Didcot Parkway d		12 47	←				13 04							13 38			13 47	←			14 08			14 22
Cholsey d			12 43				13 10			←				13 44 →				13 44			14 14		←	
Goring & Streatley d			12 48				13 15 →			13 15								13 49			14 19 →		14 19	
Pangbourne d			12 53							13 20								13 53					14 23	
Tilehurst d			12 57							13 24								13 58					14 28	
Bedwyn d													13 07							13 33				
Hungerford d													13 13							13 40				
Kintbury d													13 17											
Newbury a													13 24							13 49				
Newbury d												13 13	13 29							13 50				
Newbury Racecourse d												13 15												
Thatcham d												13 19	13 34							13 56				
Midgham d												13 24												
Aldermaston d												13 28												
Theale d												13 33	13 42							14 05				
Reading West d												13 40												
Reading 7 a	12 58	13 01	13 03		13 13				13 27	13 30	13 39	13 45	13 50		13 55		14 01	14 03	14 13	14 19		14 25	14 33	14 36
Reading d	12 58	13 02	13 04	13 11		13 23			13 28	13 34			13 51		13 56		14 03	14 04		14 19		14 27	14 34	14 38
Twyford 3 a			13 10							13 40								14 10					14 40	
Maidenhead 3 a			13 18							13 48								14 18					14 48	
Slough 3 a			13 25						13 41	13 55								14 25				14 40	14 55	
Ealing Broadway ⊖ a			13 49							14 19								14 49					15 19	
London Paddington 15 ⊖ a	13 29	13 36	13 58	13 42		13 51			13 59	14 28			14 25		14 27		14 30	14 58		14 46		14 58	15 28	15 06

For general notes see front of timetable
For details of catering facilities see Directory of Train Operators

b Change at Banbury

Table 116

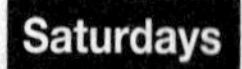

until 26 January

Birmingham, Banbury, Bicester, Oxford and Bedwyn → Reading and London

Network Diagram - see first page of Table 116

		XC	GW	GW	GW	GW	GW	GW	GW	GW	XC	GW	GW	GW	GW	GW	XC	GW	GW	GW	GW	GW	GW	GW
		1◇ ☕	1◇ ☕	1	1	1 ☕	1◇	1◇ ☕	1	1◇ ☕	1◇ ☕	1	1	1	1◇ ☕	1	1◇ ☕	1◇ ☕	1	1	1	1◇ ☕	1◇ ☕	1
Birmingham New Street 12	d	13 03									13 33						14 03							
Birmingham International	d	13 15															14 15							
Coventry	d	13 25															14 25							
Stratford-upon-Avon	d																13 40							
Warwick Parkway	d	13 21									13 41						14 21							
Warwick	d	13 24									13 45						14 24							
Leamington Spa 8	d	13 38									14 00						14 38							
Banbury	d	13 55									14 19						14 55				15 02			
Kings Sutton	d																				15 07			
Heyford	d																				15 16			
Tackley	d																				15 20			
Bicester Town	d												14 19											
Islip	d												14 31											
Oxford	a	14 14									14 41		14 46				15 14				15 31			
	d	14 15			14 21		14 30				14 43			14 55	15 00		15 15			15 21				
Radley	d				14 27															15 27				
Culham	d																			15 31				
Appleford	d				14 32																			
Didcot Parkway	a				14 36									15 06						15 37				
	d		14 29		14 37			14 47	←					15 08				15 29		15 38			15 47	
Cholsey	d				14 43				14 43					15 14		←				15 44				←
Goring & Streatley	d				→				14 48					15 19		15 19				15 49				15 49
Pangbourne	d								14 53					→		15 24				→				15 53
Tilehurst	d								14 57							15 28								15 58
Bedwyn	d											14 37												
Hungerford	d											14 43												
Kintbury	d											14 47												
Newbury	a											14 54												
	d			14 13								14 54							15 13					
Newbury Racecourse	d			14 15															15 15					
Thatcham	d			14 19								14 59							15 19					
Midgham	d			14 24															15 24					
Aldermaston	d			14 28															15 28					
Theale	d			14 33								15 07							15 33					
Reading West	d			14 40															15 40					
Reading 7	a	14 39	14 44	14 45			14 57	15 01	15 03		15 13	15 16			15 25	15 34	15 39	15 44	15 45				16 01	16 03
	d		14 45			14 52	14 57	15 03	15 04	15 11		15 18			15 27	15 35		15 46				15 52	16 03	16 04
Twyford 3	a								15 10							15 41								16 10
Maidenhead 3	a								15 18							15 49								16 18
Slough 3	a								15 25						15 40	15 56								16 25
Ealing Broadway	⊖ a								15 49							16 19								16 49
London Paddington 15	⊖ a		15 15			15 23	15 28	15 31	15 58	15 42		15 52			15 58	16 29		16 15				16 22	16 30	16 58

		XC	GW	GW	GW	GW	GW	XC	GW	GW	GW	GW	GW	XC	GW	GW	GW	GW	GW	GW	XC	GW	GW	GW
		1◇ ☕	1	1	1◇ ☕	1	1◇ ☕	1◇ ☕	1◇ ☕	1	1◇ ☕	1	1◇ ☕	1◇ ☕	1	1	1◇	1	1◇ ☕	1	1◇ ☕	1	1◇ ☕	1
Birmingham New Street 12	d	14 33						15 03						15 33							16 03			
Birmingham International	d							15 15													16 15			
Coventry	d							15 25													16 25			
Stratford-upon-Avon	d																				15 39			
Warwick Parkway	d	14 45						15 21						15 41							16 21			
Warwick	d	14 48						15 24						15 45							16 24			
Leamington Spa 8	d	15 00						15 38						16 00							16 38			
Banbury	d	15 19						15 55						16 19							16 55			
Kings Sutton	d																							
Heyford	d																							
Tackley	d																							
Bicester Town	d														16 19									
Islip	d														16 31									
Oxford	a	15 41						16 14						16 41	16 46						17 14			
	d	15 43		15 55	16 00			16 15				16 21		16 43		16 51	17 00				17 15			17 21
Radley	d											16 27												17 27
Culham	d																							17 31
Appleford	d											16 32												
Didcot Parkway	a			16 06								16 36				17 02								17 37
	d			16 08			16 22		16 29			16 37				17 03							17 29	17 37
Cholsey	d			16 14		←						16 43				17 09		←						17 43
Goring & Streatley	d			16 19		16 19						16 48				17 14		17 14						→
Pangbourne	d			→		16 24						16 53				→		17 18						
Tilehurst	d					16 28						16 57						17 23						
Bedwyn	d		15 37																16 48			16 55		
Hungerford	d		15 43																16 55			17 01		
Kintbury	d		15 47																			17 05		
Newbury	a		15 54																17 04			17 12		
	d		15 54							16 13									17 05			17 12		
Newbury Racecourse	d									16 15												17 14		
Thatcham	d		15 59							16 19									17 12			17 18		
Midgham	d									16 24												17 23		
Aldermaston	d									16 28												17 27		
Theale	d		16 07							16 33									17 21			17 32		
Reading West	d									16 40												17 39		
Reading 7	a	16 13	16 16		16 26	16 34	16 36	16 39	16 44	16 45		17 03		17 13			17 24	17 28	17 30	←	17 39	17 43	17 44	
	d		16 18		16 27	16 35	16 38		16 45		16 52	17 04	17 11				17 25	17 34	17 32	17 34			17 45	
Twyford 3	a					16 41						17 10						→		17 40				
Maidenhead 3	a					16 49						17 18								17 48				
Slough 3	a				16 40	16 56						17 25					17 40		17 45	17 55				
Ealing Broadway	⊖ a					17 19						17 49								18 19				
London Paddington 15	⊖ a		16 52		16 58	17 29	17 06		17 15		17 23	17 58	17 42				17 59		18 07	18 28			18 15	

For general notes see front of timetable
For details of catering facilities see
Directory of Train Operators

Table 116

Birmingham, Banbury, Bicester, Oxford and Bedwyn → Reading and London

Network Diagram - see first page of Table 116

		GW 1◇ ☕	GW 1◇	GW 1	GW 1◇ ☕	GW 1	XC 1◇ ☕	GW 1	GW 1	GW 1◇ ☕	GW 1	GW 1◇ ☕	XC 1◇ ☕	GW 1◇ ☕	GW 1	GW 1	GW 1◇	GW 1◇ ☕	GW 1	GW 1◇ ☕	XC 1◇ ☕	GW 1	GW 1	GW 1
Birmingham New Street 12	d						16 33						17 03								17 33			
Birmingham International	d												17 15											
Coventry	d												17 25											
Stratford-upon-Avon	d																							
Warwick Parkway	d						16b45						17 22								17b46			
Warwick	d						16b49						17 26								17b49			
Leamington Spa 8	d						17 00						17 38								18 00			
Banbury	d			17 02			17 19						17 55								18 19			
Kings Sutton	d			17 07																				
Heyford	d			17 16																				
Tackley	d			17 20																				
Bicester Town	d																						18 19	
Islip	d																						18 31	
Oxford	a			17 30			17 41						18 14								18 41		18 46	
	d		17 30				17 43		17 55	18 00			18 15			18 21	18 30				18 43			18 55
Radley	d															18 27								
Culham	d																							
Appleford	d															18 32								
Didcot Parkway	a								18 06							18 36								19 06
	d				17 47	←			18 08			18 22		18 29		18 37		18 47	←					19 08
Cholsey	d					17 43			18 14		←					18 43			18 43					19 14
Goring & Streatley	d					17 48			18 19		18 19					→			18 48					19 19
Pangbourne	d					17 53			→		18 24								18 52					→
Tilehurst	d					17 57					18 28								18 57					
Bedwyn	d							17 37														18 37		
Hungerford	d							17 43														18 43		
Kintbury	d							17 47														18 47		
Newbury	a							17 54														18 54		
	d							17 54							18 13							18 54		
Newbury Racecourse	d														18 15									
Thatcham	d							17 59							18 19							18 59		
Midgham	d														18 24									
Aldermaston	d														18 28									
Theale	d							18 07							18 33							19 07		
Reading West	d														18 40									
Reading 7	a		17 57		18 01	18 03	18 13	18 16		18 25	18 34	18 36	18 39	18 44	18 45		18 56	19 01	19 02		19 13	19 16		
	d	17 55	17 57		18 03	18 04		18 18		18 27	18 34	18 38		18 45			18 57	19 03	19 04	19 11		19 18		
Twyford 3	a					18 10					18 40								19 10					
Maidenhead 3	a					18 18					18 48								19 18					
Slough 3	a					18 25				18 40	18 56								19 25					
Ealing Broadway	⊖ a					18 49					19 19								19 49					
London Paddington 15	⊖ a	18 23	18 28		18 31	18 58		18 52		18 58	19 28	19 06		19 15			19 28	19 31	19 58	19 42		19 52		

		GW 1◇ ☕	GW 1	XC 1◇ ☕	GW 1◇ ☕	GW 1	GW 1◇ ☕	GW 1	GW 1◇	GW 1	GW 1◇ ☕	GW 1	XC 1◇ ☕	GW 1	GW 1	GW 1◇ ☕	GW 1	XC 1◇ ☕	GW 1◇ ☕	GW 1◇ ☕	GW 1	GW 1◇	GW 1	GW 1◇ ☕
Birmingham New Street 12	d			18 03									18 33					19 03						
Birmingham International	d			18 15														19 15						
Coventry	d			18 25														19 25						
Stratford-upon-Avon	d			17 36																				
Warwick Parkway	d			18 22									18 46											
Warwick	d			18 25									18 48											
Leamington Spa 8	d			18 38									19 00					19 38						
Banbury	d			18 55						19 01			19 19					19 55					20 02	
Kings Sutton	d									19 06													20 07	
Heyford	d									19 15													20 16	
Tackley	d									19 19													20 20	
Bicester Town	d																							
Islip	d																							
Oxford	a			19 14						19 32			19 41					20 14					20 30	
	d	19 00		19 15				19 21	19 30				19 43		19 55	20 09		20 15			20 20	20 30		
Radley	d							19 27													20 26			
Culham	d							19 31																
Appleford	d																				20 32			
Didcot Parkway	a							19 37							20 06						20 36			
	d				19 29			19 37			19 47	←			20 08				20 22	20 29	20 37			
Cholsey	d		←					19 43				19 43			20 14		←				20 43			
Goring & Streatley	d		19 19					→				19 48			20 19		20 19				→			
Pangbourne	d		19 24									19 53			→		20 24							
Tilehurst	d		19 28									19 57					20 28							
Bedwyn	d													19 37										
Hungerford	d													19 43										
Kintbury	d													19 47										
Newbury	a													19 54										
	d					19 13	19 32							19 54										
Newbury Racecourse	d					19 15								19 56										
Thatcham	d					19 19								20 00										
Midgham	d					19 24								20 05										
Aldermaston	d					19 28								20 09										
Theale	d					19 33								20 14										
Reading West	d					19 40								20 21										
Reading 7	a	19 25	19 34	19 39	19 44	19 45	19 50		19 55		20 01	20 03	20 13	20 24		20 33	20 34	20 39	20 38	20 44		20 54		
	d	19 27	19 34		19 45		19 52		19 56		20 03	20 04				20 34	20 34		20 39	20 45		20 54		20 59
Twyford 3	a		19 40									20 10					20 40							
Maidenhead 3	a		19 48									20 18					20 48							
Slough 3	a	19 40	19 55									20 25				20 47	20 55							
Ealing Broadway	⊖ a		20 19									20 49					21 19							
London Paddington 15	⊖ a	19 58	20 28		20 15		20 21		20 27		20 31	20 58				21 06	21 28		21 09	21 15		21 25		21 28

For general notes see front of timetable
For details of catering facilities see
Directory of Train Operators

b Change at Banbury

until 26 January

Birmingham, Banbury, Bicester, Oxford and Bedwyn → Reading and London

Network Diagram - see first page of Table 116

		GW 1	GW 1◇	GW 1	GW 1	GW 1◇	GW 1	GW 1	GW 1	XC 1◇	GW 1◇	GW 1◇	GW 1◇	GW 1	GW 1◇	GW 1	XC 1◇	GW 1	GW 1◇	GW 1	GW 1	GW 1◇	GW 1
			☕			☕					☕		☕									A	
Birmingham New Street 12	d									20 03							21 03						
Birmingham International	d									20 15							21 15						
Coventry	d									20 25							21 25						
Stratford-upon-Avon	d									*19 53*													
Warwick Parkway	d						*19 44*			*20 16*							*20 45*						
Warwick	d						*19 47*			*20 19*							*20 48*						
Leamington Spa 8	d						*19 51*			20 38							21 38						
Banbury	d						20 38			20 55							21 55			22 02			
Kings Sutton	d						20 43													22 07			
Heyford	d						20 52													22 16			
Tackley	d						20 56													22 20			
Bicester Town	d																						
Islip	d																						
Oxford	a						21 06			21 14							22 14			22 30			
	d				20 53	21 00				21 15		21 30		21 53	22 08		22 15		22 30				23 09
Radley	d				20 59									21 59									23 15
Culham	d																						23 20
Appleford	d																						23 23
Didcot Parkway	a				21 06									22 06									23 27
	d	←	20 47		21 07			←			21 34			22 08		←						23 32	23 36
Cholsey	d	20 43			21 13 →			21 13						22 14 →		22 14							23 42
Goring & Streatley	d	20 48						21 18								22 19							23 47
Pangbourne	d	20 52						21 22								22 24							23 51
Tilehurst	d	20 57						21 27								22 28							23 56
Bedwyn	d								20 48									22 00			23 00		
Hungerford	d								20 54									22 06			23 06		
Kintbury	d								20 58									22 10			23 10		
Newbury	a								21 05									22 17			23 17		
	d								21 05									22 17			23 17		
Newbury Racecourse	d								21 07									22 19			23 19		
Thatcham	d								21 11									22 23			23 23		
Midgham	d								21 16									22 28			23 28		
Aldermaston	d								21 20									22 32			23 32		
Theale	d								21 25									22 37			23 37		
Reading West	d								21 32									22 44			23 44		
Reading 7	a	21 02	21 03	←		21 24		21 32	21 36	21 39	21 48	21 53			22 32	22 34	22 39	22 49	22 53		23 49	23 52	00 01
	d	21 09 →	21 05	21 09		21 25		21 34			21 50	21 54	22 00		22 33	22 35			22 56			23 53	00 05
Twyford 3	a			21 15				21 40								22 41							00 11
Maidenhead 3	a			21 23				21 48								22 49							00 18
Slough 3	a			21 35		21 38		21 55				22 09			22 48	22 57							00 30
Ealing Broadway	⊖ a			21 58				22 19								23 19							00 53
London Paddington 15	⊖ a		21 36	22 08		21 58		22 28			22 16	22 28	22 31		23 07	23 28			23 29			00 32	01 02

For general notes see front of timetable
For details of catering facilities see Directory of Train Operators

A From Taunton (Table 134)

Table 116

Saturdays

2 February to 22 March

Birmingham, Banbury, Bicester, Oxford and Bedwyn → Reading and London

Network Diagram - see first page of Table 116

		GW 1◇ 🛏	GW 1	GW 1	GW 1	GW 1	GW 1	GW 1	GW 1◇	GW 1		GW 1	GW 1	GW 1◇	GW 1◇ ☕	GW 1	XC 1◇	GW 1	GW 1	GW 1		GW 1◇	GW 1	GW 1	GW 1◇
Birmingham New Street 12	d																06 03								
Birmingham International	d																06 15								
Coventry	d																06 25								
Stratford-upon-Avon	d																								
Warwick Parkway	d																								
Warwick	d																								
Leamington Spa 8	d																06 38								
Banbury	d		23p50														06 55			07 02					
Kings Sutton	d		23p55																	07 07					
Heyford	d		00 04																	07 16					
Tackley	d		00 08																	07 20					
Bicester Town	d																								
Islip	d																								
Oxford	a		00 18														07 14			07 30					
	d	23p59	00 20	04 00	05 21	05 55		06 21	06 30				06 55	07 00			07 15		07 21			07 37		07 55	08 00
Radley	d				05 27			06 27											07 27						
Culham	d				05 31														07 31						
Appleford	d							06 32																	
Didcot Parkway	a	00 11	00 31	04 11	05 37	06 06		06 36					07 06						07 37					08 06	
	d	00 12	00 33	04 12	05 38	06 07		06 37		←			07 07						07 38					08 07	
Cholsey	d		00 39		05 44	06 13		06 43		06 43			07 13			←			07 44					08 13	
Goring & Streatley	d		00 44		05 49	06 18		→		06 48			07 18			07 18			07 49					08 18	
Pangbourne	d		00 48		05 53	06 22				06 53			→			07 22			07 53					→	
Tilehurst	d		00 53		05 58	06 27				06 57						07 27			07 58						
Bedwyn	d						06 07					06 37											07 37		
Hungerford	d						06 13					06 43											07 43		
Kintbury	d						06 17					06 47											07 47		
Newbury	a						06 24					06 54											07 54		
	d						06 24					06 54						07 13					07 54		
Newbury Racecourse	d						06 26											07 15							
Thatcham	d						06 30					06 59						07 19					07 59		
Midgham	d						06 35											07 24							
Aldermaston	d						06 39											07 28							
Theale	d						06 44					07 07						07 33					08 07		
Reading West	d																	07 40							
Reading 7	a	00 26	00 58	04 29	06 03	06 32	06 52		06 56	07 03		07 20		07 25		07 32	07 44	07 44	08 03			08 08	08 16		08 24
	d	00 27	01 00	04 40	06 04	06 34	06 53		06 57	07 04		07 21		07 26	07 29	07 34			08 04			08 09	08 18		08 25
Twyford 3	a		01 06	04 46	06 10	06 40				07 10						07 40			08 10						
Maidenhead 3	a		01 14	04 54	06 18	06 48				07 18						07 48			08 18						
Slough 3	a	00 40	01 22	05 01	06 25	06 55			07 12	07 25				07 39		07 55			08 25						
Ealing Broadway	⊖ a		01 39	05 19	06 49	07 19				07 49						08 19			08 49						
London Paddington 15	⊖ a	00 58	01 48	05 30	06 58	07 31	07 25		07 31	07 58		07 53		07 57	07 58	08 28			08 58			08 40	08 52		08 56

		GW 1◇ ☕	GW 1	GW 1	XC 1◇ ☕	GW 1	GW 1	GW 1◇		GW 1	XC 1◇ ☕	GW 1	GW 1	GW 1◇ ☕	GW 1◇ ☕	GW 1	GW 1◇ ☕	XC 1◇ ☕		GW 1	GW 1	GW 1◇	GW 1◇ ☕	GW 1	GW 1
Birmingham New Street 12	d				07 03						07 33							08 03							
Birmingham International	d				07 15													08 15							
Coventry	d				07 25													08 25							
Stratford-upon-Avon	d																	*07 35*							
Warwick Parkway	d				*07 06*						*07 41*							*08 20*							
Warwick	d				*07 09*						*07 45*							*08 23*							
Leamington Spa 8	d				07 38						08 00							08 38							
Banbury	d				07 55						08 19							08 55						09 02	
Kings Sutton	d																							09 07	
Heyford	d																							09 16	
Tackley	d																							09 20	
Bicester Town	d		07 41																						
Islip	d		07 53																						
Oxford	a		08 08		08 14						08 41							09 14						09 30	
	d				08 15		08 21	08 30			08 43		08 55	09 00				09 15		09 20		09 30			
Radley	d						08 27						09 01							09 26					
Culham	d																			09 30					
Appleford	d						08 32																		
Didcot Parkway	a						08 36						09 09							09 35					
	d						08 37			←			09 09			←				09 37					←
Cholsey	d			←			08 43			08 43			09 15			09 15				09 43					09 43
Goring & Streatley	d			08 18			→			08 48			→			09 20				→					09 48
Pangbourne	d			08 22						08 53						09 25									09 52
Tilehurst	d			08 27						08 57						09 29									09 57
Bedwyn	d											08 37													
Hungerford	d											08 43													
Kintbury	d											08 47													
Newbury	a											08 54													
	d					08 13						08 54									09 23				
Newbury Racecourse	d					08 15															09 26				
Thatcham	d					08 19						08 59									09 30				
Midgham	d					08 24															09 35				
Aldermaston	d					08 28															09 39				
Theale	d					08 33						09 07									09 44				
Reading West	d					08 40															09 51				
Reading 7	a			08 32	08 39	08 44		08 56		09 03	09 13	09 17		09 26		09 35		09 39			09 55	09 55			10 02
	d	08 29		08 34				08 57		09 04		09 19		09 28	09 29	09 35	09 38					09 56	09 59		10 04
Twyford 3	a			08 40						09 10						09 41									10 10
Maidenhead 3	a			08 48						09 18						09 49									10 18
Slough 3	a			08 55						09 25				09 41		09 57									10 25
Ealing Broadway	⊖ a			09 19						09 49						10 20									10 49
London Paddington 15	⊖ a	08 58		09 28				09 28		09 58		09 51		09 58	10 01	10 29	10 06					10 27	10 27		10 58

For general notes see front of timetable
For details of catering facilities see Directory of Train Operators

Table 116

Saturdays

2 February to 22 March

Birmingham, Banbury, Bicester, Oxford and Bedwyn → Reading and London

Network Diagram - see first page of Table 116

		XC 1◇ ☕	GW 1	GW 1	GW 1	GW 1◇ ☕		GW 1	XC 1◇ ☕	GW 1	GW 1◇ ☕	GW 1◇ ☕	GW 1	XC 1◇ ☕	GW 1	GW 1		GW 1◇ ☕	GW 1	XC 1◇ ☕	GW 1	GW 1	GW 1	XC 1◇ ☕	GW 1
Birmingham New Street 12	d	08 33							09 03					09 33						10 03				10 33	
Birmingham International	d								09 15											10 15					
Coventry	d								09 25											10 25					
Stratford-upon-Avon	d																			*09 36*					
Warwick Parkway	d	*08 45*							*09b23*					*09 43*						*10 22*				*10b46*	
Warwick	d	*08 48*							*09b27*					*09 46*						*10 26*				*10b49*	
Leamington Spa 8	d	09 00							09 38					10 00						10 38				11 00	
Banbury	d	09 19							09 55					10 19						10 55			11 02	11 19	
Kings Sutton	d																						11 07		
Heyford	d																						11 16		
Tackley	d																						11 20		
Bicester Town	d			09 19																					
Islip	d			09 31																					
Oxford	a	09 41		09 46					10 14					10 41						11 14			11 30	11 41	
	d	09 43			09 52	09 57			10 15				10 21	10 43		10 52		11 00		11 15		11 21		11 43	
Radley	d												10 27									11 27			
Culham	d																					11 31			
Appleford	d												10 32												
Didcot Parkway	a				10 03								10 36			11 04						11 37			
	d				10 04								10 37			11 05						11 37			
Cholsey	d				10 10			←					10 43			11 11			←			11 43			
Goring & Streatley	d				10 15			10 15					10 48			11 16			11 16			11 48			
Pangbourne	d				→			10 20					10 53			→			11 20			11 53			
Tilehurst	d							10 24					10 57						11 25			11 57			
Bedwyn	d		09 37												10 37										11 37
Hungerford	d		09 43												10 43										11 43
Kintbury	d		09 47												10 47										11 47
Newbury	a		09 54												10 54										11 54
	d		09 54							10 13					10 54						11 13				11 54
Newbury Racecourse	d									10 15											11 15				
Thatcham	d		09 59							10 19					10 59						11 19				11 59
Midgham	d									10 24											11 24				
Aldermaston	d									10 28											11 28				
Theale	d		10 07							10 33					11 07						11 33				12 07
Reading West	d									10 40											11 40				
Reading 7	a	10 13	10 16			10 21		10 30	10 39	10 45			11 03	11 13	11 17			11 25	11 30	11 39	11 45	12 03		12 13	12 16
	d		10 18			10 23		10 34			10 52	10 59	11 04		11 18			11 26	11 34			12 04			12 18
Twyford 3	a							10 40					11 10						11 40			12 10			
Maidenhead 3	a							10 48					11 18						11 48			12 18			
Slough 3	a					10 36		10 55					11 25					11 40	11 55			12 25			
Ealing Broadway	⊖ a							11 19					11 49						12 19			12 49			
London Paddington 15	⊖ a		10 52			10 54		11 28			11 22	11 28	11 58		11 52			11 58	12 28			12 58			12 52

		GW 1	GW 1	GW 1◇ ☕		GW 1◇ ☕	GW 1	XC 1◇ ☕	GW 1	GW 1	GW 1◇ ☕	GW 1◇	GW 1	XC 1◇ ☕		GW 1◇ ☕	GW 1	GW 1◇ ☕	GW 1◇ ☕	GW 1	XC 1◇ ☕	GW 1	GW 1	GW 1	GW 1◇
Birmingham New Street 12	d							11 03						11 33							12 03				
Birmingham International	d							11 15													12 15				
Coventry	d							11 25													12 25				
Stratford-upon-Avon	d																				*11 38*				
Warwick Parkway	d							*11 22*						*11 41*							*12 22*				
Warwick	d							*11 26*						*11 45*							*12 26*				
Leamington Spa 8	d							11 38						12 00							12 38				
Banbury	d							11 55						12 19							12 55				
Kings Sutton	d																								
Heyford	d																								
Tackley	d																								
Bicester Town	d	11 19																							
Islip	d	11 31																							
Oxford	a	11 46						12 14						12 41							13 14				
	d		11 55	12 00				12 15		12 21		12 30		12 43			12 52	13 00			13 15			13 21	13 30
Radley	d									12 27														13 27	
Culham	d																							13 31	
Appleford	d									12 32															
Didcot Parkway	a		12 06							12 36							13 03							13 37	
	d		12 08							12 37			←				13 04							13 38	
Cholsey	d		12 14				←			12 43			12 43				13 10			←				13 44	
Goring & Streatley	d		12 19				12 19			→			12 48				13 15			13 15				→	
Pangbourne	d		→				12 24						12 53				→			13 20					
Tilehurst	d						12 28						12 57							13 24					
Bedwyn	d																						13 07		
Hungerford	d																						13 13		
Kintbury	d																						13 17		
Newbury	a																						13 24		
	d								12 13													13 13	13 29		
Newbury Racecourse	d								12 15													13 15			
Thatcham	d								12 19													13 19	13 34		
Midgham	d								12 24													13 24			
Aldermaston	d								12 28													13 28			
Theale	d								12 33													13 33	13 42		
Reading West	d								12 40													13 40			
Reading 7	a			12 25			12 34	12 39	12 45			12 58	13 03	13 13				13 27		13 30	13 39	13 45	13 50		13 55
	d			12 27		12 29	12 34				12 54	12 58	13 04			13 23		13 28	13 29	13 34			13 51		13 56
Twyford 3	a						12 40						13 10							13 40					
Maidenhead 3	a						12 48						13 18							13 48					
Slough 3	a			12 40			12 56						13 25					13 41		13 55					
Ealing Broadway	⊖ a						13 19						13 49							14 19					
London Paddington 15	⊖ a			12 58		12 59	13 29				13 23	13 29	13 58			13 51		13 59	13 58	14 28			14 25		14 27

For general notes see front of timetable
For details of catering facilities see Directory of Train Operators

b Change at Banbury

Table 116

Birmingham, Banbury, Bicester, Oxford and Bedwyn → Reading and London

2 February to 22 March

Network Diagram - see first page of Table 116

		GW 1◇ ☕	GW 1	GW 1	XC 1◇ ☕	GW 1◇ ☕	GW 1	GW 1◇ ☕	GW 1◇ ☕	GW 1	XC 1◇ ☕	GW 1	GW 1	GW 1 ☕	GW 1◇	GW 1	XC 1◇ ☕	GW 1	GW 1	GW 1	GW 1◇ ☕	GW 1◇ ☕
Birmingham New Street 12	d				12 33						13 03						13 33					
Birmingham International	d										13 15											
Coventry	d										13 25											
Stratford-upon-Avon	d																					
Warwick Parkway	d				*12 45*						*13 21*						*13 41*					
Warwick	d				*12 48*						*13 24*						*13 45*					
Leamington Spa 8	d				13 00						13 38						14 00					
Banbury	d		13 02		13 19						13 55						14 19					
Kings Sutton	d		13 07																			
Heyford	d		13 16																			
Tackley	d		13 20																			
Bicester Town	d																		14 19			
Islip	d																		14 31			
Oxford	a		13 30		13 41						14 14						14 41		14 46			
	d				13 43		13 55	14 00			14 15		14 21		14 30		14 43			14 55	15 00	
Radley	d												14 27									
Culham	d																					
Appleford	d												14 32									
Didcot Parkway	a						14 06						14 36							15 06		
	d			←			14 08						14 37			←				15 08		
Cholsey	d			13 44			14 14			←			14 43 →			14 43				15 14		
Goring & Streatley	d			13 49			14 19 →			14 19						14 48				15 19 →		
Pangbourne	d			13 53						14 23						14 53						
Tilehurst	d			13 58						14 28						14 57						
Bedwyn	d					13 39												14 37				
Hungerford	d					13 46												14 43				
Kintbury	d																	14 47				
Newbury	a					13 55												14 54				
	d					13 56						14 13						14 54				
Newbury Racecourse	d											14 15										
Thatcham	d					14 02						14 19						14 59				
Midgham	d											14 24										
Aldermaston	d											14 28										
Theale	d					14 11						14 33						15 07				
Reading West	d											14 40										
Reading 7	a			14 03	14 13	14 22		14 25		14 33	14 39	14 45			14 57	15 03	15 13	15 16			15 25	
	d	13 59		14 04		14 22		14 27	14 33	14 34				14 52	14 57	15 04		15 18			15 27	15 29
Twyford 3	a			14 10						14 40						15 10						
Maidenhead 3	a			14 18						14 48						15 18						
Slough 3	a			14 25				14 40		14 55						15 25					15 40	
Ealing Broadway ⊖	a			14 49						15 19						15 49						
London Paddington 15 ⊖	a	14 26		14 58		14 52		14 58	15 03	15 28				15 23	15 28	15 58		15 52			15 58	15 59

		GW 1	XC 1◇ ☕	GW 1	GW 1◇ ☕	GW 1	GW 1	XC 1◇ ☕	GW 1	GW 1	GW 1◇ ☕	GW 1◇ ☕	GW 1	XC 1◇ ☕	GW 1	GW 1◇ ☕	GW 1	XC 1◇ ☕	GW 1	GW 1	GW 1◇	GW 1◇ ☕	GW 1◇ ☕
Birmingham New Street 12	d		14 03					14 33						15 03				15 33					
Birmingham International	d		14 15											15 15									
Coventry	d		14 25											15 25									
Stratford-upon-Avon	d		*13 40*																				
Warwick Parkway	d		*14 21*					*14 45*						*15 21*				*15 41*					
Warwick	d		*14 24*					*14 48*						*15 24*				*15 45*					
Leamington Spa 8	d		14 38					15 00						15 38				16 00					
Banbury	d		14 55				15 02	15 19						15 55				16 19					
Kings Sutton	d						15 07																
Heyford	d						15 16																
Tackley	d						15 20																
Bicester Town	d																		16 19				
Islip	d																		16 31				
Oxford	a		15 14				15 31	15 41						16 14				16 41	16 46				
	d		15 15			15 21		15 43		15 55	16 00			16 15			16 21	16 43		16 51	17 00		
Radley	d					15 27											16 27						
Culham	d					15 31																	
Appleford	d																16 32						
Didcot Parkway	a					15 37				16 06							16 36			17 02			
	d					15 38				16 08							16 37			17 03			
Cholsey	d	←				15 44				16 14			←				16 43			17 09			
Goring & Streatley	d	15 19				15 49				16 19 →			16 19				16 48			17 14 →			
Pangbourne	d	15 24				15 53							16 24				16 53						
Tilehurst	d	15 28				15 58							16 28				16 57						
Bedwyn	d								15 37														
Hungerford	d								15 43													16 51	
Kintbury	d								15 47														
Newbury	a								15 54													17 00	
	d			15 13					15 54						16 13							17 01	
Newbury Racecourse	d			15 15											16 15								
Thatcham	d			15 19					15 59						16 19							17 07	
Midgham	d			15 24											16 24								
Aldermaston	d			15 28											16 28								
Theale	d			15 33					16 07						16 33							17 16	
Reading West	d			15 40											16 40								
Reading 7	a	15 34	15 39	15 45		16 03		16 13	16 16		16 26		16 34	16 39	16 45		17 03	17 13			17 24	17 26	
	d	15 35			15 52	16 04			16 18		16 27	16 29	16 35			16 52	17 04				17 25	17 27	17 29
Twyford 3	a	15 41				16 10							16 41				17 10						
Maidenhead 3	a	15 49				16 18							16 49				17 18						
Slough 3	a	15 56				16 25					16 40		16 56				17 25				17 40	17 40	
Ealing Broadway ⊖	a	16 19				16 49							17 19				17 49						
London Paddington 15 ⊖	a	16 29			16 22	16 58			16 52		16 58	16 59	17 29			17 23	17 58				17 59	18 03	17 59

For general notes see front of timetable
For details of catering facilities see Directory of Train Operators

Birmingham, Banbury, Bicester, Oxford and Bedwyn → Reading and London

2 February to 22 March

Network Diagram - see first page of Table 116

		GW	GW	XC	GW	GW	GW	GW	GW	GW	XC	GW	GW	GW	GW	GW	XC	GW	GW	XC	GW	GW	GW
		1	1	1◇ ☕	1	1◇	1◇ ☕	1	1	1	1◇ ☕	1	1	1◇ ☕	1◇ ☕	1	1◇ ☕	1	1	1◇ ☕	1	1	1
Birmingham New Street 12	d			16 03							16 33						17 03			17 33			
Birmingham International	d			16 15													17 15						
Coventry	d			16 25													17 25						
Stratford-upon-Avon	d			15 39																			
Warwick Parkway	d			16 21							16b45						17 22			17b46			
Warwick	d			16 24							16b49						17 26			17b49			
Leamington Spa 8	d			16 38							17 00						17 38			18 00			
Banbury	d			16 55				17 02			17 19						17 55			18 19			
Kings Sutton	d							17 07															
Heyford	d							17 16															
Tackley	d							17 20															
Bicester Town	d																					18 19	
Islip	d																					18 31	
Oxford	a			17 14				17 30			17 41						18 14			18 41		18 46	
	d			17 15	17 21	17 30					17 43		17 55		18 00		18 15		18 21	18 43			18 55
Radley	d				17 27														18 27				
Culham	d				17 31																		
Appleford	d																		18 32				
Didcot Parkway	a				17 37								18 06						18 36				19 06
	d				17 37				←				18 08						18 37				19 08
Cholsey	d		←		17 43				17 43				18 14			←			18 43				19 14
Goring & Streatley	d		17 14		→				17 48				18 19			18 19			18 48				19 19
Pangbourne	d		17 18						17 53				→			18 24			18 52				→
Tilehurst	d		17 23						17 57							18 28			18 57				
Bedwyn	d	17 00										17 37									18 37		
Hungerford	d	17 06										17 43									18 43		
Kintbury	d	17 10										17 47									18 47		
Newbury	a	17 18										17 54									18 54		
	d									17 39		17 54						18 13			18 54		
Newbury Racecourse	d									17 41								18 15					
Thatcham	d									17 45		17 59						18 19			18 59		
Midgham	d									17 50								18 24					
Aldermaston	d									17 54								18 28					
Theale	d									17 59		18 07						18 33			19 07		
Reading West	d									18 06								18 40					
Reading 7	a		17 28	17 39		17 57			18 03	18 10	18 13	18 16			18 25	18 34	18 39	18 45	19 02	19 13	19 16		
	d		17 34			17 57	17 59		18 04			18 18		18 29	18 27	18 34			19 04		19 18		
Twyford 3	a		17 40						18 10							18 40			19 10				
Maidenhead 3	a		17 48						18 18							18 48			19 18				
Slough 3	a		17 55						18 25						18 40	18 56			19 25				
Ealing Broadway	⊖ a		18 19						18 49							19 19			19 49				
London Paddington 15	⊖ a		18 28			18 28	18 26		18 58			18 52		18 59	18 58	19 28			19 58		19 52		

		GW	GW	GW	XC	GW	GW	GW	GW	GW	GW	XC	GW	GW	GW	GW	XC	GW	GW	GW	GW	GW	GW
		1◇ ☕	1◇ ☕	1	1◇ ☕	1	1◇ ☕	1	1◇	1	1	1◇ ☕	1	1	1◇ ☕	1	1◇ ☕	1	1◇	1◇ ☕	1	1◇ ☕	1
Birmingham New Street 12	d				18 03							18 33					19 03						
Birmingham International	d				18 15												19 15						
Coventry	d				18 25												19 25						
Stratford-upon-Avon	d				17 36																		
Warwick Parkway	d				18 22							18 46											
Warwick	d				18 25							18 48											
Leamington Spa 8	d				18 38							19 00					19 38						
Banbury	d				18 55					19 01		19 19					19 55				20 02		
Kings Sutton	d									19 06											20 07		
Heyford	d									19 15											20 16		
Tackley	d									19 19											20 20		
Bicester Town	d																						
Islip	d																						
Oxford	a				19 14					19 32		19 41					20 14				20 30		
	d	19 00			19 15			19 21	19 30			19 43		19 55	20 09		20 15	20 20	20 30				
Radley	d							19 27										20 26					
Culham	d							19 31															
Appleford	d																	20 32					
Didcot Parkway	a							19 37						20 06				20 36					
	d							19 37			←			20 08				20 37					←
Cholsey	d			←				19 43			19 43			20 14		←		20 43					20 43
Goring & Streatley	d			19 19				→			19 48			20 19		20 19		→					20 48
Pangbourne	d			19 24							19 53			→		20 24							20 52
Tilehurst	d			19 28							19 57					20 28							20 57
Bedwyn	d												19 37										
Hungerford	d												19 43										
Kintbury	d												19 47										
Newbury	a												19 54										
	d					19 13	19 32						19 54										
Newbury Racecourse	d					19 15							19 56										
Thatcham	d					19 19							20 00										
Midgham	d					19 24							20 05										
Aldermaston	d					19 28							20 09										
Theale	d					19 33							20 14										
Reading West	d					19 40							20 21										
Reading 7	a	19 25		19 34	19 39	19 45	19 50		19 54		20 03	20 13	20 24		20 33	20 34	20 39		20 54				21 02
	d	19 27	19 29	19 34			19 52		19 56		20 04				20 34	20 34			20 55	20 59		21 08	21 09
Twyford 3	a			19 40							20 10					20 40							21 15
Maidenhead 3	a			19 48							20 18					20 48							21 23
Slough 3	a	19 40		19 55							20 25				20 47	20 55			21 10				21 35
Ealing Broadway	⊖ a			20 19							20 49					21 19							21 58
London Paddington 15	⊖ a	19 58	19 58	20 28			20 21		20 27		20 58				21 06	21 28			21 29	21 26		21 36	22 08

For general notes see front of timetable
For details of catering facilities see
Directory of Train Operators

b Change at Banbury

Table 116

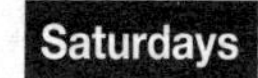

Birmingham, Banbury, Bicester, Oxford and Bedwyn → Reading and London

2 February to 22 March

Network Diagram - see first page of Table 116

Station		GW 1	GW 1 ◇ ☕	GW 1		GW 1	GW 1	XC 1 ◇	GW 1 ◇	GW 1 ◇ ☕	GW 1 ◇ ☕	GW 1	GW 1 ◇	GW 1		GW 1	XC 1 ◇	GW 1 ◇	GW 1 ◇ ☕	GW 1	GW 1	GW 1 ◇	GW 1
Birmingham New Street 12	d							20 03									21 03						
Birmingham International	d							20 15									21 15						
Coventry	d							20 25									21 25						
Stratford-upon-Avon	d							*19 53*															
Warwick Parkway	d			*19 44*				*20 16*									*20 45*						
Warwick	d			*19 47*				*20 19*									*20 48*						
Leamington Spa 8	d			*19 51*				20 38									21 38						
Banbury	d			20 38				20 55									21 55			22 02			
Kings Sutton	d			20 43																22 07			
Heyford	d			20 52																22 16			
Tackley	d			20 56																22 20			
Bicester Town	d																						
Islip	d																						
Oxford	a			21 06				21 14									22 14			22 30			
	d	20 53	21 00					21 15	21 30			21 53	22 08				22 15	22 30					23 09
Radley	d	20 59										21 59											23 15
Culham	d																						23 20
Appleford	d																						23 23
Didcot Parkway	a	21 06										22 06											23 27
	d	21 07				←						22 08		←									23 36
Cholsey	d	21 13				21 13						22 14		22 14									23 42
Goring & Streatley	d	→				21 18						→		22 19									23 47
Pangbourne	d					21 22								22 24									23 51
Tilehurst	d					21 27								22 28									23 56
Bedwyn	d						20 48									21 44					23 00		
Hungerford	d						20 54									21 50					23 06		
Kintbury	d						20 58									21 54					23 10		
Newbury	a						21 05									22 01					23 17		
	d						21 05									22 01					23 17		
Newbury Racecourse	d						21 07									22 03					23 19		
Thatcham	d						21 11									22 07					23 23		
Midgham	d						21 16									22 12					23 28		
Aldermaston	d						21 20									22 16					23 32		
Theale	d						21 25									22 21					23 37		
Reading West	d						21 32									22 31					23 44		
Reading 7	a		21 24			21 32	21 36	21 39	21 53				22 32	22 34		22 34	22 39	22 53			23 49		00 01
	d		21 25			21 34			21 54	21 59	21 59		22 33	22 35				22 56	22 59			23 57	00 05
Twyford 3	a					21 40								22 41									00 11
Maidenhead 3	a					21 48								22 49									00 18
Slough 3	a		21 38			21 55			22 09				22 48	22 57									00 30
Ealing Broadway	⊖ a					22 19								23 19									00 53
London Paddington 15	⊖ a		21 58			22 28			22 28	22 25	22 27		23 07	23 28				23 29	23 26			00 37	01 02

For general notes see front of timetable
For details of catering facilities see Directory of Train Operators

Table 116

from 29 March

Birmingham, Banbury, Bicester, Oxford and Bedwyn → Reading and London

Network Diagram - see first page of Table 116

		GW	GW	GW	GW	GW	GW	GW	GW	GW	GW	GW	GW	GW	GW	GW	XC	GW	GW	GW	GW	GW	GW	GW	GW
		1 ◇	1	1	1	1	1 ◇	1	1	1 ◇	1	1	1	1 ◇	1 ◇	1	1 ◇	1	1 ◇	1	1	1 ◇	1 ◇	1	1
		🛏					☕							☕					☕				☕		
Birmingham New Street 12	d																06 03								
Birmingham International	d																06 15								
Coventry	d																06 25								
Stratford-upon-Avon	d																								
Warwick Parkway	d																								
Warwick	d																								
Leamington Spa 8	d																06 38								
Banbury	d		23p50														06 55				07 02				
Kings Sutton	d		23p55																		07 07				
Heyford	d		00 04																		07 16				
Tackley	d		00 08																		07 20				
Bicester Town	d																								
Islip	d																								
Oxford	a		00 18														07 14				07 30				
	d	23p59	00 20	04 00	05 21	05 55			06 21	06 30			06 55		07 00		07 15			07 21		07 37			07 55
Radley	d				05 27				06 27											07 27					
Culham	d				05 31															07 31					
Appleford	d								06 32																
Didcot Parkway	a	00 11	00 31	04 11	05 37	06 06			06 36				07 06							07 37					08 06
	d	00 12	00 33	04 12	05 38	06 07	06 29		06 37		←		07 07			←			07 30	07 38			08 00		08 07
Cholsey	d		00 39		05 44	06 13			06 43 →		06 43		07 13							07 44					08 13
Goring & Streatley	d		00 44		05 49	06 18					06 48		07 18 →			07 18				07 49					08 18 →
Pangbourne	d		00 48		05 53	06 22					06 53					07 22				07 53					
Tilehurst	d		00 53		05 58	06 27					06 57					07 27				07 58					
Bedwyn	d							06 07				06 37												07 37	
Hungerford	d							06 13				06 43												07 43	
Kintbury	d							06 17				06 47												07 47	
Newbury	a							06 24				06 54												07 54	
	d							06 24				06 54						07 13						07 54	
Newbury Racecourse	d							06 26										07 15							
Thatcham	d							06 30				06 59						07 19						07 59	
Midgham	d							06 35										07 24							
Aldermaston	d							06 39										07 28							
Theale	d							06 44				07 07						07 33						08 07	
Reading West	d																	07 40							
Reading 7	a	00 26	00 58	04 29	06 03	06 32	06 43	06 52		06 56	07 03	07 20			07 25	07 32	07 44	07 44	07 44	08 03		08 08	08 14	08 16	
	d	00 27	01 00	04 40	06 04	06 34	06 45	06 53		06 57	07 04	07 21		07 22	07 26	07 34			07 46	08 04		08 09	08 16	08 18	
Twyford 3	a		01 06	04 46	06 10	06 40					07 10					07 40				08 10					
Maidenhead 3	a		01 14	04 54	06 18	06 48					07 18					07 48				08 18					
Slough 3	a	00 40	01 22	05 01	06 25	06 55				07 12	07 25				07 39	07 55				08 25					
Ealing Broadway	⊖ a		01 39	05 19	06 49	07 19					07 49					08 19				08 49					
London Paddington 15	⊖ a	00 58	01 48	05 30	06 58	07 31	07 14	07 25		07 31	07 58	07 53		07 56	07 57	08 28			08 14	08 58		08 40	08 45	08 52	

For general notes see front of timetable
For details of catering facilities see
Directory of Train Operators

Birmingham, Banbury, Bicester, Oxford and Bedwyn → Reading and London

Saturdays
from 29 March

Network Diagram - see first page of Table 116

		GW	GW	GW	XC	GW	GW	GW	GW	GW	GW	XC	GW	GW	GW	GW	GW	GW	GW	XC	GW	GW	GW	GW	GW
		1 ◇	1	1	1 ◇	1	1 ◇	1 ◇	1	1 ◇	1	1 ◇	1 ◇	1 ◇	1	1	1 ◇	1	1 ◇	1 ◇	1 ◇	1 ◇	1	1	1 ◇
													A												
					☕		☕	☕				☕	☕	☕			☕		☕	☕	☕	☕			
Birmingham New Street 12	d				07 03							07 33								08 03					
Birmingham International	d				07 15															08 15					
Coventry	d				07 25															08 25					
Stratford-upon-Avon	d																			*07 35*					
Warwick Parkway	d				*07 06*							*07 41*								*08 20*					
Warwick	d				*07 09*							*07 45*								*08 23*					
Leamington Spa 8	d				07 38							08 00								08 38					
Banbury	d				07 55							08 19								08 55					
Kings Sutton	d																								
Heyford	d																								
Tackley	d																								
Bicester Town	d		07 41																						
Islip	d		07 53																						
Oxford	a		08 08		08 14							08 41								09 14					
	d	08 00			08 15				08 21	08 30		08 43				08 55	09 00			09 15				09 20	09 30
Radley	d								08 27							09 01								09 26	
Culham	d																							09 30	
Appleford	d								08 32																
Didcot Parkway	a								08 36							09 09								09 35	
	d						08 30	08 36	08 37		←		09 00	09 00		09 09		←			09 29	09 34		09 37	
Cholsey	d			←					08 43 →		08 43					09 15 →		09 15						09 43 →	
Goring & Streatley	d			08 18							08 48							09 20							
Pangbourne	d			08 22							08 53							09 25							
Tilehurst	d			08 27							08 57							09 29							
Bedwyn	d														08 37										
Hungerford	d														08 43										
Kintbury	d														08 47										
Newbury	a														08 54										
	d					08 13									08 54								09 23		
Newbury Racecourse	d					08 15																	09 26		
Thatcham	d					08 19									08 59								09 30		
Midgham	d					08 24																	09 35		
Aldermaston	d					08 28																	09 39		
Theale	d					08 33									09 07								09 44		
Reading West	d					08 40																	09 51		
Reading 7	a	08 24		08 32	08 39	08 44	08 44	08 50		08 56	09 03	09 13	09 14	09 14	09 17		09 26	09 35		09 39	09 44	09 48	09 55		09 55
	d	08 25		08 34			08 46	08 52		08 57	09 04		09 16	09 16	09 19		09 28	09 35	09 38		09 45	09 50			09 56
Twyford 3	a			08 40							09 10							09 41							
Maidenhead 3	a			08 48							09 18							09 49							
Slough 3	a			08 55							09 25						09 41	09 57							
Ealing Broadway	⊖ a			09 19							09 49							10 20							
London Paddington 15	⊖ a	08 56		09 28			09 15	09 19		09 28	09 58		09 44	09 44	09 51		09 58	10 29	10 06		10 14	10 16			10 27

		GW	GW	XC	GW	GW	GW	GW	GW	GW	XC	GW	GW	GW	GW	GW	XC	GW	GW	GW	GW	XC	GW	GW	GW
		1	1	1 ◇	1	1	1	1 ◇	1 ◇	1	1 ◇	1	1 ◇	1 ◇	1	1 ◇	1 ◇	1	1	1 ◇	1	1 ◇	1 ◇	1 ◇	1
				☕				☕	☕		☕		☕	☕		☕	☕			☕		☕	☕	☕	
Birmingham New Street 12	d			08 33							09 03						09 33					10 03			
Birmingham International	d										09 15											10 15			
Coventry	d										09 25											10 25			
Stratford-upon-Avon	d																					*09 36*			
Warwick Parkway	d			*08 45*							*09b23*						*09 43*					*10 22*			
Warwick	d			*08 48*							*09b27*						*09 46*					*10 26*			
Leamington Spa 8	d			09 00							09 38						10 00					10 38			
Banbury	d	09 02		09 19							09 55						10 19					10 55			
Kings Sutton	d	09 07																							
Heyford	d	09 16																							
Tackley	d	09 20																							
Bicester Town	d					09 19																			
Islip	d					09 31																			
Oxford	a	09 30		09 41		09 46					10 14						10 41					11 14			
	d			09 43			09 52		09 57		10 15				10 21		10 43		10 52	11 00		11 15			
Radley	d														10 27										
Culham	d																								
Appleford	d														10 32										
Didcot Parkway	a						10 03								10 36				11 04						
	d		←				10 04	10 04					10 29		10 37				11 05					11 29	
Cholsey	d		09 43				10 10			←					10 43				11 11		←				
Goring & Streatley	d		09 48				10 15 →			10 15					10 48				11 16 →		11 16				
Pangbourne	d		09 52							10 20					10 53						11 20				
Tilehurst	d		09 57							10 24					10 57						11 25				
Bedwyn	d				09 37													10 37							
Hungerford	d				09 43													10 43							
Kintbury	d				09 47													10 47							
Newbury	a				09 54													10 54							
	d				09 54							10 13						10 54							11 13
Newbury Racecourse	d											10 15													11 15
Thatcham	d				09 59							10 19						10 59							11 19
Midgham	d											10 24													11 24
Aldermaston	d											10 28													11 28
Theale	d				10 07							10 33						11 07							11 33
Reading West	d											10 40													11 40
Reading 7	a		10 02	10 13	10 16			10 19	10 21	10 30	10 39	10 45	10 45		11 03		11 13	11 17		11 25	11 30	11 39		11 44	11 45
	d		10 04		10 18			10 21	10 23	10 34			10 45	10 52	11 04	11 11		11 18		11 26	11 34		11 45	11 45	
Twyford 3	a		10 10							10 40					11 10						11 40				
Maidenhead 3	a		10 18							10 48					11 18						11 48				
Slough 3	a		10 25						10 36	10 55					11 25					11 40	11 55				
Ealing Broadway	⊖ a		10 49							11 19					11 49						12 19				
London Paddington 15	⊖ a		10 58		10 52			10 57	10 54	11 28			11 15	11 22	11 58	11 42		11 52		11 58	12 28		12 12	12 15	

For general notes see front of timetable
For details of catering facilities see Directory of Train Operators

A From Taunton (Table 134)
b Change at Banbury

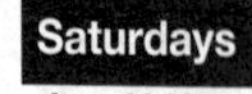

Birmingham, Banbury, Bicester, Oxford and Bedwyn → Reading and London

from 29 March

Network Diagram - see first page of Table 116

		GW	GW	XC	GW	GW		GW	GW	GW	XC	GW	GW	GW	GW	GW	GW	GW	GW	XC	GW	GW	GW	GW	XC
		1	1	1 ◇ ☕	1	1		1	1 ◇ ☕	1	1 ◇ ☕	1 ◇ ☕	1	1 ◇ ☕	1	1 ◇ ☕	1 ◇	1	1 ◇ ☕	1 ◇ ☕	1 ◇ ☕	1	1 ◇ ☕	1	1 ◇ ☕
Birmingham New Street 12	d			10 33							11 03									11 33					12 03
Birmingham International	d										11 15														12 15
Coventry	d										11 25														12 25
Stratford-upon-Avon	d																								11 38
Warwick Parkway	d			10b46							11 22									11 41					12 22
Warwick	d			10b49							11 26									11 45					12 26
Leamington Spa 8	d			11 00							11 38									12 00					12 38
Banbury	d		11 02	11 19							11 55									12 19					12 55
Kings Sutton	d		11 07																						
Heyford	d		11 16																						
Tackley	d		11 20																						
Bicester Town	d					11 19																			
Islip	d					11 31																			
Oxford	a		11 30	11 41		11 46					12 14									12 41					13 14
	d	11 21		11 43				11 55	12 00		12 15				12 21		12 30			12 43		12 52	13 00		13 15
Radley	d	11 27													12 27										
Culham	d	11 31																							
Appleford	d														12 32										
Didcot Parkway	a	11 37						12 06							12 36							13 03			
	d	11 37						12 08				12 29		12 33	12 37			←				13 04			
Cholsey	d	11 43						12 14		←					12 43			12 43				13 10		←	
Goring & Streatley	d	11 48						12 19		12 19					→			12 48				13 15		13 15	
Pangbourne	d	11 53						→		12 24								12 53				→		13 20	
Tilehurst	d	11 57								12 28								12 57						13 24	
Bedwyn	d				11 37																				
Hungerford	d				11 43																				
Kintbury	d				11 47																				
Newbury	a				11 54																				
	d				11 54								12 13												
Newbury Racecourse	d												12 15												
Thatcham	d				11 59								12 19												
Midgham	d												12 24												
Aldermaston	d												12 28												
Theale	d				12 07								12 33												
Reading West	d												12 40												
Reading 7	a	12 03		12 13	12 16				12 25	12 34	12 39	12 44	12 45	12 48			12 58	13 03		13 13			13 27	13 30	13 39
	d	12 04			12 18				12 27	12 34		12 45		12 49		12 54	12 58	13 04	13 11		13 23		13 28	13 34	
Twyford 3	a	12 10								12 40								13 10						13 40	
Maidenhead 3	a	12 18								12 48								13 18						13 48	
Slough 3	a	12 25							12 40	12 56								13 25					13 41	13 55	
Ealing Broadway	⊖ a	12 49								13 19								13 49						14 19	
London Paddington 15	⊖ a	12 58			12 52				12 58	13 29		13 15		13 16		13 23	13 29	13 58	13 42		13 51		13 59	14 28	

		GW	GW	GW	GW	GW	GW	XC	GW	GW	GW	GW	XC	GW	GW	GW	GW	GW	GW	GW	GW	XC	GW	GW	GW
		1	1	1	1 ◇	1	1	1 ◇ ☕	1 ◇ ☕	1	1 ◇ ☕	1	1 ◇ ☕	1 ◇ ☕	1	1 ◇ ☕	1	1 ☕	1 ◇	1	1 ◇ ☕	1 ◇ ☕	1	1	1
Birmingham New Street 12	d							12 33					13 03									13 33			
Birmingham International	d												13 15												
Coventry	d												13 25												
Stratford-upon-Avon	d																								
Warwick Parkway	d							12 45					13 21									13 41			
Warwick	d							12 48					13 24									13 45			
Leamington Spa 8	d							13 00					13 38									14 00			
Banbury	d					13 02		13 19					13 55									14 19			
Kings Sutton	d					13 07																			
Heyford	d					13 16																			
Tackley	d					13 20																			
Bicester Town	d																							14 19	
Islip	d																							14 31	
Oxford	a					13 30		13 41					14 14									14 41		14 46	
	d			13 21	13 30			13 43		13 55	14 00		14 15				14 21		14 30			14 43			14 55
Radley	d			13 27													14 27								
Culham	d			13 31																					
Appleford	d																14 32								
Didcot Parkway	a			13 37						14 06							14 36								15 06
	d			13 38			←			14 08				14 29		14 33	14 37			←					15 08
Cholsey	d			13 44			13 44			14 14		←					14 43			14 43					15 14
Goring & Streatley	d			→			13 49			14 19		14 19					→			14 48					15 19
Pangbourne	d						13 53			→		14 23								14 53					→
Tilehurst	d						13 58					14 28								14 57					
Bedwyn	d		13 07						13 33														14 37		
Hungerford	d		13 13						13 40														14 43		
Kintbury	d		13 17																				14 47		
Newbury	a		13 24						13 49														14 54		
	d	13 13	13 29						13 50						14 13								14 54		
Newbury Racecourse	d	13 15													14 15										
Thatcham	d	13 19	13 34						13 56						14 19								14 59		
Midgham	d	13 24													14 24										
Aldermaston	d	13 28													14 28										
Theale	d	13 33	13 42						14 05						14 33								15 07		
Reading West	d	13 40													14 40										
Reading 7	a	13 45	13 50		13 55		14 03	14 13	14 19		14 25	14 33	14 39	14 44	14 45	14 48			14 57	15 03		15 13	15 16		
	d		13 51		13 56		14 04		14 19		14 27	14 34		14 45		14 49		14 52	14 57	15 04	15 11		15 18		
Twyford 3	a						14 10					14 40								15 10					
Maidenhead 3	a						14 18					14 48								15 18					
Slough 3	a						14 25				14 40	14 55								15 25					
Ealing Broadway	⊖ a						14 49					15 19								15 49					
London Paddington 15	⊖ a		14 25		14 27		14 58		14 46		14 58	15 28		15 15		15 17		15 23	15 28	15 58	15 42		15 52		

For general notes see front of timetable
For details of catering facilities see
Directory of Train Operators

b Change at Banbury

Table 116

Saturdays

from 29 March

Birmingham, Banbury, Bicester, Oxford and Bedwyn → Reading and London

Network Diagram - see first page of Table 116

		GW 1◇ ☕	GW 1	XC 1◇ ☕	GW 1◇ ☕	GW 1	GW 1◇ ☕	GW 1◇ ☕	GW 1	GW 1	XC 1◇ ☕	GW 1	GW 1	GW 1◇ ☕	GW 1	XC 1◇ ☕	GW 1◇ ☕	GW 1	GW 1◇ ☕	GW 1	GW 1◇ ☕	XC 1◇ ☕	GW 1	GW 1	GW 1◇
Birmingham New Street 12	d			14 03							14 33					15 03						15 33			
Birmingham International	d			14 15												15 15									
Coventry	d			14 25												15 25									
Stratford-upon-Avon	d			*13 40*																					
Warwick Parkway	d			*14 21*							*14 45*					*15 21*						*15 41*			
Warwick	d			*14 24*							*14 48*					*15 24*						*15 45*			
Leamington Spa 8	d			14 38							15 00					15 38						16 00			
Banbury	d			14 55						15 02	15 19					15 55						16 19			
Kings Sutton	d									15 07															
Heyford	d									15 16															
Tackley	d									15 20															
Bicester Town	d																						16 19		
Islip	d																						16 31		
Oxford	a			15 14						15 31	15 41					16 14						16 41	16 46		
	d	15 00		15 15					15 21		15 43		15 55	16 00		16 15				16 21		16 43		16 51	17 00
Radley	d								15 27											16 27					
Culham	d								15 31																
Appleford	d																			16 32					
Didcot Parkway	a								15 37				16 06							16 36				17 02	
	d				15 29		15 33		15 38				16 08				16 29			16 37				17 03	
Cholsey	d		←						15 44				16 14		←					16 43				17 09	
Goring & Streatley	d		15 19						15 49				16 19		16 19					16 48				17 14	
Pangbourne	d		15 24						15 53				→		16 24					16 53				→	
Tilehurst	d		15 28						15 58						16 28					16 57					
Bedwyn	d											15 37													
Hungerford	d											15 43													
Kintbury	d											15 47													
Newbury	a											15 54													
	d					15 13						15 54						16 13							
Newbury Racecourse	d					15 15												16 15							
Thatcham	d					15 19						15 59						16 19							
Midgham	d					15 24												16 24							
Aldermaston	d					15 28												16 28							
Theale	d					15 33						16 07						16 33							
Reading West	d					15 40												16 40							
Reading 7	a	15 25	15 34	15 39	15 44	15 45	15 48		16 03		16 13	16 16		16 26	16 34	16 39	16 44	16 45		17 03		17 13			17 24
	d	15 27	15 35		15 46		15 49	15 56	16 04			16 18		16 27	16 35		16 45		17 01	17 04	17 11				17 25
Twyford 3	a		15 41						16 10						16 41					17 10					
Maidenhead 3	a		15 49						16 18						16 49					17 18					
Slough 3	a	15 40	15 56						16 25					16 40	16 56					17 25					17 40
Ealing Broadway	⊖ a		16 19						16 49						17 19					17 49					
London Paddington 15	⊖ a	15 58	16 29		16 15		16 17	16 25	16 58			16 52		16 58	17 29		17 15		17 29	17 58	17 42				17 59

		GW 1	XC 1◇ ☕	GW 1	GW 1◇ ☕	GW 1◇ ☕	GW 1◇ ☕	GW 1	GW 1◇	GW 1	GW 1	GW 1◇ ☕	XC 1◇ ☕	GW 1	GW 1	GW 1◇ ☕	GW 1	XC 1◇ ☕	GW 1◇ ☕	GW 1	GW 1◇ ☕	GW 1	GW 1◇ ☕	XC 1◇ ☕	GW 1
Birmingham New Street 12	d		16 03										16 33					17 03						17 33	
Birmingham International	d		16 15															17 15							
Coventry	d		16 25															17 25							
Stratford-upon-Avon	d		*15 39*																						
Warwick Parkway	d		*16 21*										*16b45*					*17 22*						*17b46*	
Warwick	d		*16 24*										*16b49*					*17 26*						*17b49*	
Leamington Spa 8	d		16 38										17 00					17 38						18 00	
Banbury	d		16 55							17 02			17 19					17 55						18 19	
Kings Sutton	d									17 07															
Heyford	d									17 16															
Tackley	d									17 20															
Bicester Town	d																								
Islip	d																								
Oxford	a		17 14							17 30			17 41					18 14						18 41	
	d		17 15					17 21	17 30				17 43		17 55	18 00		18 15				18 21		18 43	
Radley	d							17 27														18 27			
Culham	d							17 31																	
Appleford	d																					18 32			
Didcot Parkway	a							17 37							18 06							18 36			
	d				17 29	17 33		17 37			←				18 08				18 29		18 33	18 37			
Cholsey	d	←						17 43			17 43				18 14		←					18 43			
Goring & Streatley	d	17 14						→			17 48				18 19		18 19					18 48			
Pangbourne	d	17 18									17 53				→		18 24					18 52			
Tilehurst	d	17 23									17 57						18 28					18 57			
Bedwyn	d			16 55			17 08							17 37											18 37
Hungerford	d			17 01			17 15							17 43											18 43
Kintbury	d			17 05										17 47											18 47
Newbury	a			17 12			17 24							17 54											18 54
	d			17 12			17 25							17 54						18 13					18 54
Newbury Racecourse	d			17 14																18 15					
Thatcham	d			17 18			17 32							17 59						18 19					18 59
Midgham	d			17 23																18 24					
Aldermaston	d			17 27																18 28					
Theale	d			17 32			17 41							18 07						18 33					19 07
Reading West	d			17 39																18 40					
Reading 7	a	17 28	17 39	17 43	17 44	17 48	17 50		17 57		18 03		18 13	18 16		18 25	18 34	18 39	18 44	18 45	18 48	19 02		19 13	19 16
	d	17 34			17 45	17 49	17 52		17 57		18 04	18 08		18 18		18 27	18 34		18 45		18 50	19 04	19 11		19 18
Twyford 3	a	17 40									18 10						18 40					19 10			
Maidenhead 3	a	17 48									18 18						18 48					19 18			
Slough 3	a	17 55					18 05				18 25					18 40	18 56					19 25			
Ealing Broadway	⊖ a	18 19									18 49						19 19					19 49			
London Paddington 15	⊖ a	18 28			18 15	18 16	18 23		18 28		18 58	18 38		18 52		18 58	19 28		19 15		19 17	19 58	19 42		19 52

For general notes see front of timetable
For details of catering facilities see
Directory of Train Operators

b Change at Banbury

Table 116

Saturdays

from 29 March

Birmingham, Banbury, Bicester, Oxford and Bedwyn → Reading and London

Network Diagram - see first page of Table 116

		GW	GW	GW	GW	XC	GW	GW	GW	GW	GW	GW	GW	XC	GW	GW	GW	GW	GW	XC	GW	GW	GW	GW	GW
		1	1	1 ◇	1	1 ◇	1 ◇	1	1 ◇	1	1 ◇	1	1	1 ◇	1	1 ◇	1	1 ◇	1	1 ◇	1 ◇	1 ◇	1	1 ◇	1
				☕		☕	☕		☕					☕		☕		☕		☕	☕	☕			
Birmingham New Street 12	d					18 03								18 33						19 03					
Birmingham International	d					18 15														19 15					
Coventry	d					18 25														19 25					
Stratford-upon-Avon	d					*17 36*																			
Warwick Parkway	d					*18 22*								*18 46*											
Warwick	d					*18 25*								*18 48*											
Leamington Spa 8	d					18 38								19 00						19 38					
Banbury	d					18 55						19 01		19 19						19 55					20 02
Kings Sutton	d											19 06													20 07
Heyford	d											19 15													20 16
Tackley	d											19 19													20 20
Bicester Town	d	18 19																							
Islip	d	18 31																							
Oxford	a	18 46				19 14						19 32		19 41						20 14					20 30
	d		18 55	19 00		19 15				19 21	19 30			19 43			19 55	20 09		20 15			20 20	20 30	
Radley	d									19 27													20 26		
Culham	d									19 31															
Appleford	d																						20 32		
Didcot Parkway	a		19 06							19 37							20 06						20 36		
	d		19 08				19 29		19 33	19 37			←				20 08				20 29	20 33	20 37		
Cholsey	d		19 14		←					19 43			19 43				20 14		←				20 43		
Goring & Streatley	d		19 19		19 19					→			19 48				20 19		20 19				→		
Pangbourne	d		→		19 24								19 53				→		20 24						
Tilehurst	d				19 28								19 57						20 28						
Bedwyn	d														19 37										
Hungerford	d														19 43										
Kintbury	d														19 47										
Newbury	a														19 54										
	d							19 13							19 54	20 10									
Newbury Racecourse	d							19 15							19 56										
Thatcham	d							19 19							20 00										
Midgham	d							19 24							20 05										
Aldermaston	d							19 28							20 09										
Theale	d							19 33							20 14										
Reading West	d							19 40							20 21										
Reading 7	a			19 25	19 34	19 39	19 44	19 45	19 48		19 54		20 03	20 13	20 24	20 27		20 33	20 34	20 39	20 44	20 48		20 54	
	d			19 27	19 34		19 45		19 49		19 56		20 04			20 29		20 34	20 34		20 45	20 49		20 55	
Twyford 3	a				19 40								20 10						20 40						
Maidenhead 3	a				19 48								20 18						20 48						
Slough 3	a			19 40	19 55								20 25					20 47	20 55					21 10	
Ealing Broadway	⊖ a				20 19								20 49						21 19						
London Paddington 15	⊖ a			19 58	20 28		20 15		20 16		20 27		20 58			20 58		21 06	21 28		21 15	21 16		21 29	

		GW	GW	GW	GW	GW	GW	GW	XC	GW	GW	GW	GW	GW	GW	XC	GW	GW	GW	GW	GW	GW	GW
		1	1	1 ◇	1 ◇	1	1	1	1 ◇	1 ◇	1 ◇	1 ◇	1	1 ◇	1	1 ◇	1 ◇	1	1 ◇	1	1	1 ◇	1
																						A	
				☕	☕					☕	☕						☕						
Birmingham New Street 12	d								20 03							21 03							
Birmingham International	d								20 15							21 15							
Coventry	d								20 25							21 25							
Stratford-upon-Avon	d								*19 53*														
Warwick Parkway	d					*19 44*			*20 16*							*20 45*							
Warwick	d					*19 47*			*20 19*							*20 48*							
Leamington Spa 8	d					*19 51*			20 38							21 38							
Banbury	d					20 38			20 55							21 55				22 02			
Kings Sutton	d					20 43														22 07			
Heyford	d					20 52														22 16			
Tackley	d					20 56														22 20			
Bicester Town	d																						
Islip	d																						
Oxford	a					21 06			21 14							22 14				22 30			
	d		20 53	21 00					21 15			21 30	21 53	22 08		22 15			22 30				23 09
Radley	d		20 59										21 59										23 15
Culham	d																						23 20
Appleford	d																						23 23
Didcot Parkway	a		21 06										22 06										23 27
	d	←	21 07				←			21 29	21 34		22 08		←							23 32	23 36
Cholsey	d	20 43	21 13				21 13						22 14		22 14								23 42
Goring & Streatley	d	20 48	→				21 18						→		22 19								23 47
Pangbourne	d	20 52					21 22								22 24								23 51
Tilehurst	d	20 57					21 27								22 28								23 56
Bedwyn	d							20 48										22 00			23 00		
Hungerford	d							20 54										22 06			23 06		
Kintbury	d							20 58										22 10			23 10		
Newbury	a							21 05										22 17			23 17		
	d							21 05										22 17			23 17		
Newbury Racecourse	d							21 07										22 19			23 19		
Thatcham	d							21 11										22 23			23 23		
Midgham	d							21 16										22 28			23 28		
Aldermaston	d							21 20										22 32			23 32		
Theale	d							21 25										22 37			23 37		
Reading West	d							21 32										22 44			23 44		
Reading 7	a	21 02		21 24			21 32	21 36	21 39	21 44	21 48	21 53		22 32	22 34	22 39		22 49	22 53		23 49	23 52	00 01
	d	21 09		21 25	21 31		21 34			21 48	21 50	21 54		22 33	22 35		22 49		22 56			23 53	00 05
Twyford 3	a	21 15					21 40								22 41								00 11
Maidenhead 3	a	21 23					21 48								22 49								00 18
Slough 3	a	21 35		21 38			21 55					22 09		22 48	22 57								00 30
Ealing Broadway	⊖ a	21 58					22 19								23 19								00 53
London Paddington 15	⊖ a	22 08		21 58	21 59		22 28			22 16	22 16	22 28		23 07	23 28		23 16		23 29			00 32	01 02

For general notes see front of timetable
For details of catering facilities see Directory of Train Operators

A From Taunton (Table 134)

Table 116

Sundays

until 27 January

Birmingham, Banbury, Bicester, Oxford and Bedwyn → Reading and London

Network Diagram - see first page of Table 116

		GW	GW	GW	GW	GW	GW	GW	GW	GW	GW	GW	GW	GW	GW	GW	GW	XC	GW	GW	GW	GW	GW	GW	GW
		1	1		1	1 ◇	1 ◇	1 ◇	1 ◇	1	1	1 ◇	1 ◇	1 ◇	1	1 ◇	1	1 ◇	1	1 ◇	1 ◇	1 ◇	1	1	1 ◇
				[bus]																					
			[trolley]			[buffet]	[trolley]	[buffet]	[buffet]			[trolley]	[buffet]	[buffet]		[buffet]		[buffet]		[trolley]	[buffet]	[buffet]			[buffet]
Birmingham New Street 12	d																	09 03							
Birmingham International	d																	09 15							
Coventry	d																	09 25							
Stratford-upon-Avon	d																								
Warwick Parkway	d																								
Warwick	d																								
Leamington Spa 8	d																	09 38							
Banbury	d																	09 55							
Kings Sutton	d																								
Heyford	d																								
Tackley	d																								
Bicester Town	d																								
Islip	d																								
Oxford	a																	10 14							
	d	23p09		07 45							09 05	09 38					10 05	10 15		10 38				11 05	
Radley	d	23p15									09 11						10 11							11 11	
Culham	d	23p20																							
Appleford	d	23p23															10 16								
Didcot Parkway	a	23p27		08 10							09 20	09 49					10 20			10 49				11 20	
	d	23p36	07 45		08 21	08 39	08 50	09 09			09 21	09 50	10 00				10 21		←	10 50	10 58			11 21	
Cholsey	d	23p42			08 27						09 27						10 27 →		10 27					11 27 →	
Goring & Streatley	d	23p47	07 52		08 32						09 32								10 32						
Pangbourne	d	23p51			08 37						09 37								10 37						
Tilehurst	d	23p56			08 42						09 42								10 42						
Bedwyn	d														09 47								10 54		
Hungerford	d														09 53								11 00		
Kintbury	d														09 56								11 04		
Newbury	a														10 04								11 11		
	d									09 05					10 04	10 17							11 11		
Newbury Racecourse	d									09 07					10 06										
Thatcham	d									09 11					10 10								11 16		
Midgham	d									09 16					10 15										
Aldermaston	d									09 20					10 19										
Theale	d									09 24					10 23								11 23		
Reading West	d																								
Reading 7	a	00 01	08 02		08 46	08 55	09 05	09 25		09 35	09 46	10 05	10 13		10 32	10 37		10 44	10 46	11 06	11 13		11 34		
	d	00 05	08 03		08 48	08 55	09 05	09 26	09 34	09 42	09 48	10 05	10 16	10 31	10 36	10 39			10 46	11 07	11 15	11 27	11 35		11 41
Twyford 3	a	00 11			08 54						09 54								10 54						
Maidenhead 3	a	00 18			09 01					09 54	10 01				10 48				11 01				11 47		
Slough 3	a	00 30	08 21		09 09		09 24			10 01	10 09	10 26			10 55				11 09	11 26			11 56		
Ealing Broadway	⊖ a	00 53			09 32						10 32								11 32						
London Paddington 15	⊖ a	01 02	08 44		09 40	09 35	09 43	10 03	10 16	10 23	10 40	10 45	10 54	11 07	11 16	11 21			11 40	11 46	11 55	12 08	12 16		12 22

For general notes see front of timetable
For details of catering facilities see Directory of Train Operators

Sundays

until 27 January

Birmingham, Banbury, Bicester, Oxford and Bedwyn → Reading and London

Network Diagram - see first page of Table 116

		XC		GW	GW	GW	GW	GW	XC	GW	GW	GW	XC	GW	GW	GW	GW	XC	GW	GW	GW	GW	XC	GW	GW
		1◇		1	1◇	1	1◇	1◇	1◇	1	1◇	1	1◇	1	1◇	1◇	1◇	1◇	1◇	1	1◇	1	1◇	1	1◇
		☕			☕		🍽	☕	☕		☕		☕		☕	☕	☕	☕	☕		☕		☕		🍽
Birmingham New Street 12	d	09 48							10 33				11 03					11 33					12 03		
Birmingham International	d	10 15							10 45				11 15					11 45					12 15		
Coventry	d	10 25							10 54				11 25					11 56					12 25		
Stratford-upon-Avon	d																								
Warwick Parkway	d	*10 21*							*10 38*				*11 10*					*11 38*					*12 21*		
Warwick	d	*10 24*							*10 41*									*11 41*					*12 24*		
Leamington Spa 8	d	10 38							11 07				11 38					12 09					12 38		
Banbury	d	10 55							11 23				11 55					12 26					12 55		
Kings Sutton	d																								
Heyford	d																								
Tackley	d																								
Bicester Town	d																								
Islip	d																								
Oxford	a	11 14							11 43				12 14					12 53					13 14		
	d	11 15					11 38		11 45	12 05			12 15				12 50	12 55				13 05	13 15		13 38
Radley	d									12 11												13 11			
Culham	d																								
Appleford	d									12 16															
Didcot Parkway	a						11 50			12 20							13 01					13 20			13 49
	d			←			11 51	11 58		12 21				←	12 58		13 03					13 21		←	13 50
Cholsey	d			11 27						12 27 →				12 27								13 27 →		13 27	
Goring & Streatley	d			11 32										12 32										13 32	
Pangbourne	d			11 37										12 37										13 37	
Tilehurst	d			11 42										12 42										13 42	
Bedwyn	d																			12 54					
Hungerford	d																			13 00					
Kintbury	d																			13 04					
Newbury	a																			13 11					
	d				11 29							12 05								13 11	13 25				
Newbury Racecourse	d											12 07													
Thatcham	d											12 11								13 16					
Midgham	d											12 16													
Aldermaston	d											12 20													
Theale	d											12 24								13 23					
Reading West	d											12 32													
Reading 7	a	11 44		11 46	11 48	←	12 06	12 13	12 15			12 35	12 44	12 46	13 13		13 20	13 28		13 33	13 42		13 44	13 46	14 04
	d			11 52 →	11 50	11 52	12 07	12 15			12 29	12 36		12 47	13 15	13 20	13 22		13 29	13 35	13 43			13 46	14 06
Twyford 3	a					11 59								12 55										13 55	
Maidenhead 3	a					12 06						12 48		13 02						13 47				14 02	
Slough 3	a					12 14	12 28					12 57		13 10			13 47			13 55				14 10	14 25
Ealing Broadway	⊖ a					12 35								13 32										14 32	
London Paddington 15	⊖ a				12 28	12 44	12 46	12 55			13 07	13 16		13 40	13 55	13 59	14 08		14 10	14 16	14 22			14 40	14 44

		GW	XC	GW		GW	GW	GW	XC	GW	GW	GW	GW	XC	GW	GW	GW	GW	XC	GW	GW	GW	XC	GW	GW
		1◇	1◇	1		1◇	1	1◇	1◇	1	1◇	1◇	1◇	1◇	1	1◇	1	1◇	R 1	1	1◇	1◇	1◇	1	1◇
		☕	☕			☕		☕	☕		🍽	☕	☕	☕		☕		☕	☕		☕	☕	☕		☕
Birmingham New Street 12	d		12 33						13 03					13 33					14 03				14 33		
Birmingham International	d		12 45						13 15					13 45					14 15				14 45		
Coventry	d		12 56						13 25					13 56					14 25				14 56		
Stratford-upon-Avon	d																								
Warwick Parkway	d		*12 38*						*13 10*					*13 39*					*14 21*				*14 38*		
Warwick	d		*12 41*											*13 42*					*14 24*				*14 41*		
Leamington Spa 8	d		13 09						13 38					14 09					14 38				15 09		
Banbury	d		13 26						13 55					14 26					14 55				15 26		
Kings Sutton	d																								
Heyford	d																								
Tackley	d																								
Bicester Town	d																								
Islip	d																								
Oxford	a		13 45						14 14					14 45					15 14				15 53		
	d		13 47	14 05					14 15		14 38			14 47	15 05				15 15			15 48	15 55	16 05	
Radley	d			14 11											15 11									16 11	
Culham	d																								
Appleford	d			14 16																				16 16	
Didcot Parkway	a			14 20							14 49				15 20							16 01		16 20	
	d	13 58		14 21						←	14 50	14 58			15 21					←	15 58	16 01		16 21	
Cholsey	d			14 27 →						14 27					15 27 →					15 27				16 27 →	
Goring & Streatley	d									14 32										15 32					
Pangbourne	d									14 37										15 37					
Tilehurst	d									14 42										15 42					
Bedwyn	d																14 54								
Hungerford	d																15 00								
Kintbury	d																15 04								
Newbury	a																15 11								
	d						14 05										15 11								
Newbury Racecourse	d						14 07																		
Thatcham	d						14 11										15 16								
Midgham	d						14 16																		
Aldermaston	d						14 20																		
Theale	d						14 24										15 23								
Reading West	d						14 32																		
Reading 7	a	14 14	14 22				14 33		14 44	14 46	15 04	15 14		15 22			15 34		15 44	15 46	16 14	16 18	16 28		
	d	14 15				14 29	14 36	14 39		14 46	15 05	15 15	15 20			15 29	15 35	15 38		15 46	16 15	16 21			16 29
Twyford 3	a									14 55										15 55					
Maidenhead 3	a						14 48			15 02							15 47			16 02					
Slough 3	a						14 56			15 10	15 23						15 56			16 12		16 45			
Ealing Broadway	⊖ a									15 32										16 32					
London Paddington 15	⊖ a	14 54				15 08	15 15	15 22		15 40	15 43	15 57	15 59			16 08	16 16	16 21		16 42	16 54	17 07			17 11

For general notes see front of timetable
For details of catering facilities see Directory of Train Operators

Table 116

Sundays

until 27 January

Birmingham, Banbury, Bicester, Oxford and Bedwyn → Reading and London

Network Diagram - see first page of Table 116

		GW	XC	GW	GW	GW		GW	GW	XC	GW	GW	GW	GW	XC	GW	GW	GW	XC	GW	GW	GW	GW	XC	GW
			R												R									R	
		1	1	1	1◇	1◇		1◇	1◇	1◇	1	1◇	1	1◇	1	1	1◇	1◇	1◇	1	1◇	1	1◇	1	1
			☕		☕	☕		☕	☕	☕		☕		☕	☕		☕	☕	☕		☕		☕	☕	
Birmingham New Street 12	d		15 03							15 33					16 03				16 33					17 03	
Birmingham International	d		15 15							15 45					16 15				16 45					17 15	
Coventry	d		15 25							15 56					16 25				16 56					17 25	
Stratford-upon-Avon	d																								
Warwick Parkway	d		*15 10*							*15 38*					*16 21*				*16 38*					*17 10*	
Warwick	d									*15 41*					*16 24*				*16 41*						
Leamington Spa 8	d		15 38							16 09					16 38				17 09					17 38	
Banbury	d		15 55							16 26					16 55				17 26					17 55	
Kings Sutton	d																								
Heyford	d																								
Tackley	d																								
Bicester Town	d																								
Islip	d																								
Oxford	a		16 14							16 53					17 14				17 53					18 14	
	d		16 15						16 50	16 55	17 05				17 15			17 50	17 55	18 05				18 15	
Radley	d										17 11									18 11					
Culham	d																								
Appleford	d																			18 16					
Didcot Parkway	a								17 01		17 20							18 01		18 20					
	d			←		16 58			17 03		17 21					←	17 58	18 03		18 21					←
Cholsey	d			16 27							17 27					17 27				18 27					18 27
Goring & Streatley	d			16 32							→					17 32				→					18 32
Pangbourne	d			16 37												17 37									18 37
Tilehurst	d			16 42												17 42									18 41
Bedwyn	d												16 54												
Hungerford	d												17 00												
Kintbury	d												17 04												
Newbury	a												17 11												
	d	16 05			16 30								17 11									18 05			
Newbury Racecourse	d	16 07																				18 07			
Thatcham	d	16 11											17 16									18 11			
Midgham	d	16 16																				18 16			
Aldermaston	d	16 20																				18 20			
Theale	d	16 24											17 23									18 24			
Reading West	d	16 32																				18 32			
Reading 7	a	16 35	16 44	16 46	16 48	17 14			17 18	17 28			17 34		17 44	17 46	18 15	18 18	18 28			18 35		18 44	18 46
	d	16 36		16 46	16 52	17 15		17 21	17 24			17 29	17 35	17 42		17 46	18 15	18 21			18 29	18 36	18 44		18 46
Twyford 3	a			16 55												17 55									18 55
Maidenhead 3	a	16 48		17 02									17 47			18 02						18 48			19 02
Slough 3	a	16 56		17 12					17 48				17 56			18 12		18 45				18 56			19 12
Ealing Broadway	⊖ a			17 33												18 33									19 33
London Paddington 15	⊖ a	17 15		17 42	17 36	17 54		17 59	18 08			18 10	18 16	18 27		18 42	18 54	19 08			19 10	19 15	19 24		19 42

		GW	GW	GW	XC	GW	GW	GW		GW	GW	XC	GW	GW	GW	GW	GW	XC	GW	GW	GW	XC	GW	GW	GW
												R										R			
		1◇	1◇	1◇	1◇	1◇	1◇	1		1	1◇	1	1◇	1	1◇	1◇	1◇	1◇	1	1◇	1	1	1◇	1	1◇
					A																				
		☕	☕	☕	☕	☕	☕				☕	☕	☕		☕	☕	☕	☕		☕		☕	☕		☕
Birmingham New Street 12	d				17 33							18 03						18 33				19 03			
Birmingham International	d				17 45							18 15						18 45				19 15			
Coventry	d				17 56							18 25						18 56				19 25			
Stratford-upon-Avon	d																								
Warwick Parkway	d				*17 38*							*18 21*						*18 38*				*19 10*			
Warwick	d				*17 41*							*18 24*						*18 41*							
Leamington Spa 8	d				18 09							18 38						19 09				19 38			
Banbury	d				18 26							18 55						19 26				19 55			
Kings Sutton	d																								
Heyford	d																								
Tackley	d																								
Bicester Town	d																								
Islip	d																								
Oxford	a				18 45							19 14						19 53				20 14			
	d			18 41	18 47					19 05		19 15					19 50	19 55			20 05	20 15			
Radley	d									19 11											20 11				
Culham	d																								
Appleford	d																								
Didcot Parkway	a			18 52						19 20							20 01				20 20				
	d			18 52		18 59				19 21				←		19 58	20 03				20 21			←	
Cholsey	d									19 27				19 27							20 27			20 27	
Goring & Streatley	d									→				19 32							→			20 32	
Pangbourne	d													19 37										20 37	
Tilehurst	d													19 42										20 42	
Bedwyn	d							18 54																	
Hungerford	d							19 00																	
Kintbury	d							19 04																	
Newbury	a							19 11																	
	d	18 35						19 11											20 05	20 23					
Newbury Racecourse	d																		20 07						
Thatcham	d							19 16											20 11						
Midgham	d																		20 16						
Aldermaston	d																		20 20						
Theale	d							19 23											20 24						
Reading West	d																		20 32						
Reading 7	a	18 53		19 06	19 11	19 14		19 34				19 44		19 46		20 14	20 18	20 19	20 34	20 40		20 44		20 46	
	d	18 54	19 00	19 06		19 15	19 20	19 35			19 38		19 45	19 46	19 58	20 15	20 22		20 34	20 40			20 45	20 48	20 58
Twyford 3	a													19 55										20 57	
Maidenhead 3	a							19 47						20 02					20 48					21 04	
Slough 3	a			19 31				19 56						20 12			20 45		20 56					21 14	
Ealing Broadway	⊖ a													20 33										21 36	
London Paddington 15	⊖ a	19 34	19 41	19 52		19 58	20 00	20 16			20 21		20 24	20 42	20 40	20 55	21 08		21 16	21 24			21 26	21 44	21 40

For general notes see front of timetable
For details of catering facilities see Directory of Train Operators

A To Brighton (Table 51)

Table 116

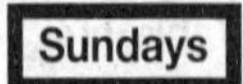

until 27 January

Birmingham, Banbury, Bicester, Oxford and Bedwyn → Reading and London

Network Diagram - see first page of Table 116

		GW	GW	GW	GW	GW	GW	XC	GW	GW	GW	GW	GW	GW	GW	GW	XC	GW	GW	GW	GW	GW	GW
		1 ◇ ☕	1 ◇ ☕	1 ◇ ☕		1	1 ◇ ☕	R 1	1	1 ◇		1 ◇ ☕		1 ◇ ☕	1 ◇ ☕	1	1 ◇		1 ◇ 🍴	1 ◇ ☕	1	1 ◇ 🍴	
Birmingham New Street 12	d							20 03									21 03						
Birmingham International	d							20 15									21 15						
Coventry	d							20 25									21 25						
Stratford-upon-Avon	d																						
Warwick Parkway	d							19 45									20 45						
Warwick	d							19 48									20 48						
Leamington Spa 8	d							20 38									21 38						
Banbury	d							20 55									21 55						
Kings Sutton	d																						
Heyford	d																						
Tackley	d																						
Bicester Town	d																						
Islip	d																						
Oxford	a							21 14									22 14						
	d			20 50		21 05		21 15				21 50				22 05	22 15		22 40		22 58	23 44	
Radley	d					21 11										22 11					23 04		
Culham	d																						
Appleford	d																						
Didcot Parkway	a			21 02		21 20						22 01				22 20			22 52		23 13	23 56	
	d		20 58	21 03		21 21			←	22 01		22 03				22 21			22 53		23 14	23 57	
Cholsey	d					21 27			21 27							22 27					23 20		
Goring & Streatley	d					→			21 32							22 32					23 25		
Pangbourne	d								21 36							22 36					23 30		
Tilehurst	d								21 41							22 41					23 35		
Bedwyn	d				20 30													22 10					
Hungerford	d				20 36													22 16					
Kintbury	d				20 39													22 20					
Newbury	a				20 47													22 27					
	d				20 59						21 47			22 08				22 28					23 50
Newbury Racecourse	d										21 49												23 52
Thatcham	d				21 04						21 53							22 33					23 56
Midgham	d										21 58												00 01
Aldermaston	d										22 02												00 05
Theale	d				21 12						22 06							22 40					00 10
Reading West	d										22 14												00 20
Reading 7	a		21 16	21 19	21 23			21 44	21 46	22 16	22 17	22 19	←	22 29		22 45	22 49	22 50	23 06		23 40	00 14	00 24
	d	21 12	21 17	21 19	21 24		21 35		21 46	22 17	22 24	22 19	22 24	22 30	22 35	22 52			23 06	23 27	23 41	00 15	
Twyford 3	a				21 30				21 53		→		22 30			22 58					23 48	00 21	
Maidenhead 3	a				21 37				22 00				22 38			23 05					23 56	00 28	
Slough 3	a			21 41	21 48				22 10			22 42	22 47			23 15			23 29		00 05	00 40	
Ealing Broadway	⊖ a				22 10				22 31				23 09			23 39					00 27	00 57	
London Paddington 15	⊖ a	21 53	21 59	22 03	22 18		22 23		22 40	23 01		23 05	23 18	23 23	23 26	23 49			23 51	00 17	00 40	01 05	

For general notes see front of timetable
For details of catering facilities see Directory of Train Operators

Table 116

Birmingham, Banbury, Bicester, Oxford and Bedwyn → Reading and London

3 February to 23 March

Network Diagram - see first page of Table 116

		GW	GW	GW	GW	GW	GW	GW	GW	GW	GW	GW	GW
		1	1	🚌	1	1 ◇	1 ◇	1	1	1 ◇	1	1	1 ◇
			🛒			☕	🛒			🛒			☕
Birmingham New Street 12	d												
Birmingham International	d												
Coventry	d												
Stratford-upon-Avon	d												
Warwick Parkway	d												
Warwick	d												
Leamington Spa 8	d												
Banbury	d												
Kings Sutton	d												
Heyford	d												
Tackley	d												
Bicester Town	d												
Islip	d												
Oxford	a												
	d	23p09		07 45					09 05	09 38		10 05	
Radley	d	23p15							09 11			10 11	
Culham	d	23p20											
Appleford	d	23p23										10 16	
Didcot Parkway	a	23p27		08 10					09 20	09 49		10 20	
	d	23p36	07 45		08 21		08 50		09 21	09 50		10 21	
Cholsey	d	23p42			08 27				09 27			10 27 →	
Goring & Streatley	d	23p47	07 53		08 32				09 32				
Pangbourne	d	23p51			08 37				09 37				
Tilehurst	d	23p56			08 42				09 42				
Bedwyn	d										09 36		
Hungerford	d										09 42		
Kintbury	d										09 45		
Newbury	a										09 53		
	d							08 55			09 54		
Newbury Racecourse	d							08 57			09 56		
Thatcham	d							09 01			10 01		
Midgham	d							09 06			10 05		
Aldermaston	d							09 10			10 09		
Theale	d							09 15			10 13		
Reading West	d										10 21		
Reading 7	a	00 01	08 03		08 47		09 05	09 23	09 46	10 04	10 24		
	d	00 05	08 04		08 52	09 01	09 06	09 25	09 52	10 06	10 25		10 31
Twyford 3	a	00 11			08 58				09 58				
Maidenhead 3	a	00 18			09 05			09 36	10 05		10 36		
Slough 3	a	00 30	08 24		09 18		09 25	09 44	10 18	10 23	10 44		
Ealing Broadway	⊖ a	00 53			09 40				10 39				
London Paddington 15	⊖ a	01 02	08 49		09 48	09 39	09 50	10 04	10 49	10 51	11 04		11 13

		GW	XC	GW	GW	GW	GW	GW	XC	GW	GW	GW	GW
		1 ◇	1 ◇	1	1 ◇	1	1 ◇	1	1 ◇	1	1 ◇	1	1 ◇
		☕	☕		🛒		☕		☕		☕		☕
Birmingham New Street 12	d		09 03						09 48				
Birmingham International	d		09 15						10 15				
Coventry	d		09 25						10 25				
Stratford-upon-Avon	d												
Warwick Parkway	d												
Warwick	d												
Leamington Spa 8	d		09 38						10 38				
Banbury	d		09 55						10 55				
Kings Sutton	d												
Heyford	d												
Tackley	d												
Bicester Town	d												
Islip	d												
Oxford	a		10 14						11 14				
	d		10 15		10 38			11 05	11 15				
Radley	d							11 11					
Culham	d												
Appleford	d												
Didcot Parkway	a				10 49			11 20					
	d			←	10 50			11 21		←			
Cholsey	d			10 27				11 27 →		11 27			
Goring & Streatley	d			10 32						11 32			
Pangbourne	d			10 37						11 37			
Tilehurst	d			10 42						11 42			
Bedwyn	d					10 36							
Hungerford	d					10 42							
Kintbury	d					10 45							
Newbury	a					10 53							
	d	10 20				10 54					11 29		
Newbury Racecourse	d												
Thatcham	d					10 59							
Midgham	d												
Aldermaston	d												
Theale	d					11 06							
Reading West	d												
Reading 7	a	10 38	10 44	10 48	11 04	11 17			11 44	11 48	11 49	←	
	d	10 39		10 52	11 06	11 19	11 25			11 52 →	11 50	11 52	12 09
Twyford 3	a			10 58								11 58	
Maidenhead 3	a			11 05		11 30						12 05	
Slough 3	a			11 18	11 23	11 42						12 18	
Ealing Broadway	⊖ a			11 39								12 39	
London Paddington 15	⊖ a	11 21		11 49	11 51	12 04	12 06				12 33	12 49	12 57

For general notes see front of timetable
For details of catering facilities see Directory of Train Operators

Table 116

Sundays

Birmingham, Banbury, Bicester, Oxford and Bedwyn → Reading and London

3 February to 23 March

Network Diagram - see first page of Table 116

		GW		GW	GW	GW	XC	GW	GW	GW	GW	GW	GW	GW	XC	GW	GW	GW	GW	GW	GW	XC	GW	GW	GW
		■1 ◇ 🛒		■1	■1	■1 ◇ ☕	■1 ◇ ☕	■1	■1 ◇ ☕	■1	■1 ◇ ☕	■1	■1 ◇ ☕	■1	■1 ◇ ☕	■1	■1 ◇ ☕	■1 ◇ 🛒	■1	■1	■1 ◇ ☕	■1 ◇ ☕	■1	■1 ◇ ☕	■1 ◇ 🛒
Birmingham New Street 12	d						11 03								12 03							13 03			
Birmingham International	d						11 15								12 15							13 15			
Coventry	d						11 25								12 25							13 25			
Stratford-upon-Avon	d																								
Warwick Parkway	d						*10 58*								*11 58*							*12 58*			
Warwick	d						*11 05*								*12 05*							*13 05*			
Leamington Spa 8	d						11 38								12 38							13 38			
Banbury	d						11 55								12 55							13 55			
Kings Sutton	d																								
Heyford	d																								
Tackley	d																								
Bicester Town	d																								
Islip	d																								
Oxford	a						12 14								13 14							14 14			
	d	11 50			12 05		12 15				12 50			13 05	13 15			13 50		14 05		14 15			14 38
Radley	d				12 11									13 11						14 11					
Culham	d																								
Appleford	d				12 16															14 16					
Didcot Parkway	a	12 02			12 20						13 02			13 20				14 01		14 20					14 49
	d	12 03			12 21			←			13 03			13 21		←		14 02		14 21			←		14 50
Cholsey	d				12 27 →			12 27						13 27 →		13 27				14 27 →			14 27		
Goring & Streatley	d							12 32								13 32							14 32		
Pangbourne	d							12 37								13 37							14 37		
Tilehurst	d							12 42								13 42							14 42		
Bedwyn	d									12 30															
Hungerford	d									12 36															
Kintbury	d									12 40															
Newbury	a									12 47															
	d			11 54						12 54			13 25						13 54						
Newbury Racecourse	d			11 56															13 56						
Thatcham	d			12 00						12 59									14 00						
Midgham	d			12 05															14 05						
Aldermaston	d			12 09															14 09						
Theale	d			12 13						13 07									14 13						
Reading West	d			12 21															14 21						
Reading 7	a	12 19		12 24			12 44	12 46		13 18	13 20	←	13 42		13 44	13 48		14 18	14 24			14 44	14 48		15 04
	d	12 21		12 25		12 43		12 52	13 10	13 24 →	13 21	13 24	13 43			13 52	14 10	14 20	14 25		14 35		14 52	15 10	15 10
Twyford 3	a							12 58								13 58							14 58		
Maidenhead 3	a			12 36				13 05				13 36				14 05			14 36				15 05		
Slough 3	a	12 35		12 44				13 18			13 37	13 43				14 18		14 35	14 44				15 18		15 34
Ealing Broadway	⊖ a							13 39								14 39							15 39		
London Paddington 15	⊖ a	13 00		13 04		13 25		13 49	13 52		13 57	14 04	14 22			14 49	14 53	14 57	15 04		15 22		15 49	15 53	15 56

		GW	GW	GW		XC	GW	GW	GW	GW	GW	XC	GW	GW	GW	GW	GW	GW	GW	GW	XC	GW	GW	GW	GW
		■1	■1	■1 ◇ ☕		R ■1 ☕	■1	■1 ◇ ☕	■1 ◇ ☕	■1	■1	R ■1 ☕	■1	■1 ◇ ☕	■1	■1 ◇ ☕	■1 ◇ ☕	■1	■1	■1 ◇ ☕	R ■1 ☕	■1 ◇ ☕	■1	■1 ◇ ☕	■1 ◇ ☕
Birmingham New Street 12	d					14 03						15 03									16 03				
Birmingham International	d					14 15						15 15									16 15				
Coventry	d					14 25						15 25									16 25				
Stratford-upon-Avon	d																								
Warwick Parkway	d					*13 58*						*14 58*									*15 58*				
Warwick	d					*14 05*						*15 05*									*16 05*				
Leamington Spa 8	d					14 38						15 38									16 38				
Banbury	d					14 55						15 55									16 55				
Kings Sutton	d																								
Heyford	d																								
Tackley	d																								
Bicester Town	d																								
Islip	d																								
Oxford	a					15 14						16 14									17 14				
	d		15 05			15 15			15 50		16 05	16 15					16 48		17 05		17 15				17 50
Radley	d		15 11								16 11								17 11						
Culham	d																								
Appleford	d										16 16														
Didcot Parkway	a		15 20						16 02		16 20						17 00		17 20						18 02
	d		15 21				←		16 03		16 21		←				17 01		17 21				←		18 03
Cholsey	d		15 27 →				15 27				16 27 →		16 27						17 27 →				17 27		
Goring & Streatley	d						15 32						16 32										17 32		
Pangbourne	d						15 37						16 37										17 37		
Tilehurst	d						15 42						16 42										17 42		
Bedwyn	d	14 30																16 30							
Hungerford	d	14 36																16 36							
Kintbury	d	14 39																16 39							
Newbury	a	14 47																16 47							
	d	14 54								15 54				16 28				16 54							
Newbury Racecourse	d									15 56															
Thatcham	d	14 59								16 00								16 59							
Midgham	d									16 05															
Aldermaston	d									16 09															
Theale	d	15 06								16 13								17 06							
Reading West	d									16 21															
Reading 7	a	15 18				15 44	15 48		16 17	16 24		16 44	16 46	16 47	←		17 15	17 17			17 44		17 46		18 17
	d	15 21		15 38			15 52	16 10	16 20	16 25			16 52 →	16 48	16 52	17 10	17 17	17 24		17 38		17 45	17 52	18 09	18 20
Twyford 3	a						15 58								16 58								17 58		
Maidenhead 3	a	15 33					16 06			16 36					17 06			17 36					18 06		
Slough 3	a	15 40					16 18		16 34	16 44					17 18		17 32	17 43					18 18		18 35
Ealing Broadway	⊖ a						16 39								17 39								18 39		
London Paddington 15	⊖ a	16 04		16 21			16 49	16 52	17 01	17 04				17 37	17 49	17 57	17 58	18 04		18 21		18 31	18 49	18 52	18 59

For general notes see front of timetable
For details of catering facilities see Directory of Train Operators

Table 116

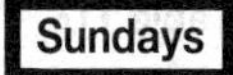

Birmingham, Banbury, Bicester, Oxford and Bedwyn → Reading and London

3 February to 23 March

Network Diagram - see first page of Table 116

		GW	GW	GW	XC	GW		GW	GW	GW	GW	GW	GW	GW	GW	XC	GW	GW	XC	GW	GW	GW	GW	XC	GW
		1	1	1◇ ☕	R 1 ☕	1		1◇ ☕	1◇ ☕	1◇ ☕	1◇ ☕	1	1	1◇ ☕	1◇ ☕	R 1 ☕	1	1◇ ☕	1◇ ☕	1◇ ☕	1	1◇ ☕	1	R 1 ☕	1◇ ☕
Birmingham New Street 12	d				17 03											18 03			18 33					19 03	
Birmingham International	d				17 15											18 15			18 46					19 15	
Coventry	d				17 25											18 25			18 55					19 25	
Stratford-upon-Avon	d																								
Warwick Parkway	d				*16 58*											*17 58*								*18 58*	
Warwick	d				*17 05*											*18 05*								*19 05*	
Leamington Spa 8	d				17 38											18 38			19 08					19 38	
Banbury	d				17 55											18 55			19 25					19 55	
Kings Sutton	d																								
Heyford	d																								
Tackley	d																								
Bicester Town	d																								
Islip	d																								
Oxford	a				18 14											19 14			19 44					20 14	
	d		18 05		18 15						18 50		19 05			19 16			19 46	19 51			20 05	20 15	
Radley	d		18 11										19 11										20 11		
Culham	d																								
Appleford	d		18 16																						
Didcot Parkway	a		18 20								19 02		19 20							20 03			20 20		
	d		18 21			←					19 03		19 21				←			20 04			20 21		
Cholsey	d		18 27			18 27							19 27				19 27						20 27		
Goring & Streatley	d		→			18 32							→				19 32						→		
Pangbourne	d					18 37											19 37								
Tilehurst	d					18 42											19 42								
Bedwyn	d											18 47													
Hungerford	d											18 53													
Kintbury	d											18 56													
Newbury	a											19 04													
	d	17 54						18 35				19 04									19 54	20 20			
Newbury Racecourse	d	17 56																			19 56				
Thatcham	d	18 00										19 09									20 00				
Midgham	d	18 05																			20 05				
Aldermaston	d	18 09																			20 09				
Theale	d	18 13										19 16									20 13				
Reading West	d	18 21																			20 21				
Reading 7	a	18 24			18 44	18 48		18 53			19 19	19 26				19 44	19 48		20 11	20 18	20 24	20 42		20 44	
	d	18 25		18 29		18 52		18 54	19 02	19 10	19 21	19 26		19 33	19 38		19 52	20 10		20 19	20 25	20 42			20 50
Twyford 3	a					18 58											19 58								
Maidenhead 3	a	18 36				19 06						19 37					20 06				20 36				
Slough 3	a	18 44				19 18					19 36	19 44					20 18			20 34	20 43				
Ealing Broadway	⊖ a					19 39											20 39								
London Paddington 15	⊖ a	19 04		19 25		19 49		19 35	19 54	20 01	20 02	20 08		20 26	20 28		20 49	20 51		21 00	21 05	21 24			21 32

		GW	GW	GW	GW	GW	GW	XC	GW	GW	GW	GW	GW	GW	XC	GW	GW	GW	GW	GW	GW	GW	GW
		1	1◇ ☕	1◇ ☕	1◇ ☕		1	R 1	1	1◇ ☕	1◇ ☕		1◇ ☕	1	1◇	1◇ ☕	1		1◇ trolley	1◇ ☕	1	1◇ trolley	
Birmingham New Street 12	d							20 03							21 03								
Birmingham International	d							20 15							21 15								
Coventry	d							20 25							21 25								
Stratford-upon-Avon	d																						
Warwick Parkway	d							*19 31*							*20 31*								
Warwick	d							*19 38*							*20 38*								
Leamington Spa 8	d							20 38							21 38								
Banbury	d							20 55							21 55								
Kings Sutton	d																						
Heyford	d																						
Tackley	d																						
Bicester Town	d																						
Islip	d																						
Oxford	a							21 14							22 14								
	d				20 50		21 05	21 15			21 50			22 05	22 15				22 40		22 58	23 44	
Radley	d						21 11							22 11							23 04		
Culham	d																						
Appleford	d																						
Didcot Parkway	a				21 02		21 20				22 02			22 20					22 52		23 13	23 56	
	d	←			21 03		21 21		←		22 03			22 21					22 53		23 14	23 57	
Cholsey	d	20 27					21 27		21 27					22 27							23 20		
Goring & Streatley	d	20 32					→		21 32					22 32							23 25		
Pangbourne	d	20 37							21 36					22 36							23 30		
Tilehurst	d	20 42							21 41					22 41							23 35		
Bedwyn	d					20 30												22 10					
Hungerford	d					20 36												22 16					
Kintbury	d					20 40												22 20					
Newbury	a					20 47												22 27					
	d					21 00						21 53	22 07					22 36					23 50
Newbury Racecourse	d											21 55											23 52
Thatcham	d					21 05						21 59						22 41					23 56
Midgham	d											22 04											00 01
Aldermaston	d											22 08											00 05
Theale	d					21 12						22 12						22 48					00 10
Reading West	d											22 23											00 20
Reading 7	a	20 48			21 18	21 22		21 44	21 45		22 18	22 26	22 31	22 45	22 49		←	22 58	23 07		23 39	00 13	00 24
	d	20 52	21 10	21 14	21 19	21 22			21 46	22 10	22 18	22 27	22 32	22 53		22 50	22 53		23 07	23 27	23 41	00 14	
Twyford 3	a	20 58				21 29			21 52			22 33		→			22 59				23 48	00 20	
Maidenhead 3	a	21 05				21 35			21 59			22 40					23 06				23 56	00 27	
Slough 3	a	21 18			21 36	21 47			22 09		22 36	22 50					23 16		23 26		00 05	00 34	
Ealing Broadway	⊖ a	21 39				22 07			22 30			23 12					23 39				00 27	00 55	
London Paddington 15	⊖ a	21 49	21 51	21 59	22 00	22 16			22 39	22 49	23 00	23 22	23 24			23 32	23 48		23 51	00 27	00 40	01 07	

For general notes see front of timetable
For details of catering facilities see Directory of Train Operators

Table 116

Sundays

from 30 March

Birmingham, Banbury, Bicester, Oxford and Bedwyn → Reading and London

Network Diagram - see first page of Table 116

		GW	GW	GW	GW	GW	GW	GW	GW	GW	GW	XC	GW	XC	GW	GW	XC	GW	GW	GW	XC	XC	GW	GW	XC
		1	1		1	1 ◊	1	1 ◊	1	1 ◊	1		1 ◊	1 ◊	1	1 ◊	1 ◊	1	1 ◊	1		1 ◊	1	1 ◊	1 ◊
																	A								A
				bus								bus									bus				
			bike			cafe		cafe		cafe			cafe	cafe		cafe	cafe		cafe			cafe		cafe	cafe
Birmingham New Street 12	d													09 03								09 48			
Birmingham International	d													09 15								10 15			
Coventry	d													09 25								10 25			
Stratford-upon-Avon	d																								
Warwick Parkway	d																								
Warwick	d																								
Leamington Spa 8	d													09 38								10 38			
Banbury	d													09 55								10 55			
Kings Sutton	d																								
Heyford	d																								
Tackley	d																								
Bicester Town	d																								
Islip	d																								
Oxford	a													10 19								11 19			
	d	23p09		07 45								09 30									10 30				
Radley	d	23p15																							
Culham	d	23p20																							
Appleford	d	23p23																							
Didcot Parkway	a	23p27		08 10								10 00									11 00				
	d	23p36	07 45		08 21	08 38		09 19	09 21	09 58			10 12		10 21		10 25		10 58				11 21	11 29	11 25
Cholsey	d	23p42			08 27				09 27						10 27			←					11 27		
Goring & Streatley	d	23p47	07 53		08 32				09 32						10 32			10 32					11 32		
Pangbourne	d	23p51			08 37				09 37						→			10 37					→		
Tilehurst	d	23p56			08 42				09 42									10 42							
Bedwyn	d										09 35									10 45					
Hungerford	d										09 41									10 51					
Kintbury	d										09 44									10 55					
Newbury	a										09 52									11 02					
	d						08 55				09 52									11 02					
Newbury Racecourse	d						08 57				09 54														
Thatcham	d						09 01				09 59									11 07					
Midgham	d						09 06				10 03														
Aldermaston	d						09 10				10 07														
Theale	d						09 15				10 11									11 15					
Reading West	d										10 20														
Reading 7	a	00 01	08 03		08 47	08 54	09 23	09 35	09 46	10 14	10 23		10 29				10 44	10 48	11 13	11 23				11 43	11 44
	d	00 05	08 04		08 52	08 55	09 24	09 36	09 52	10 15	10 24		10 30			10 41		10 52	11 15	11 24				11 45	
Twyford 3	a	00 11			08 58				09 58									10 58							
Maidenhead 3	a	00 18			09 05		09 35		10 05		10 35							11 05		11 35					
Slough 3	a	00 30	08 22		09 18		09 43		10 18		10 43							11 18		11 43					
Ealing Broadway	⊖ a	00 53			09 39				10 39									11 39							
London Paddington 15	⊖ a	01 02	08 42		09 49	09 39	10 03	10 22	10 49	11 04	11 03		11 12			11 27		11 49	11 56	12 03				12 22	

For general notes see front of timetable
For details of catering facilities see
Directory of Train Operators

A To Bournemouth (Table 158)

Table 116

Sundays

from 30 March

Birmingham, Banbury, Bicester, Oxford and Bedwyn → Reading and London

Network Diagram - see first page of Table 116

		GW	GW	GW	GW	GW	GW	XC	XC	GW	XC	GW	GW	GW	GW	XC	XC	GW	GW	XC	GW	GW	GW	GW	GW
		1	1◇	1	1◇	1◇	1		1◇	1	1◇	1◇	1	1◇	1		1◇	1	1◇	1◇	1	1◇	1	1◇	1
											A									A					
			☕		☕	☕		🚌	☕		☕	☕		☕		🚌	☕		☕	☕		☕		☕	
Birmingham New Street 12	d								11 03								12 03								
Birmingham International	d								11 15								12 15								
Coventry	d								11 25								12 25								
Stratford-upon-Avon	d																								
Warwick Parkway	d								*10 58*								*11 58*								
Warwick	d								*11 05*								*12 05*								
Leamington Spa 8	d								11 38								12 38								
Banbury	d								11 55								12 55								
Kings Sutton	d																								
Heyford	d																								
Tackley	d																								
Bicester Town	d																								
Islip	d																								
Oxford	a								12 19								13 19								
	d							11 30								12 30									
Radley	d																								
Culham	d																								
Appleford	d																								
Didcot Parkway	a							12 00								13 00									
	d		11 34			11 58				12 21	12 25	12 29		12 58				13 21		13 25		13 35		13 58	
Cholsey	d	←								12 27			←					13 27			←				
Goring & Streatley	d	11 32								12 32			12 32					13 32			13 32				
Pangbourne	d	11 37								→			12 37					→			13 37				
Tilehurst	d	11 42											12 42								13 42				
Bedwyn	d														12 45										
Hungerford	d														12 51										
Kintbury	d														12 55										
Newbury	a														13 02										
	d						11 54								13 02										13 54
Newbury Racecourse	d						11 56																		13 56
Thatcham	d						12 00								13 07										14 00
Midgham	d						12 05																		14 05
Aldermaston	d						12 09																		14 09
Theale	d						12 13								13 15										14 13
Reading West	d						12 21																		14 21
Reading 7	a	11 48	11 50	←		12 14	12 24				12 42	12 44	12 48	13 14	13 23					13 44	13 48	13 49	←	14 14	14 24
	d	11 52	11 51	11 52	11 57	12 15	12 25					12 44	12 52	13 15	13 24				13 41		13 52	13 51	13 52	14 15	14 25
Twyford 3	a	→		11 58									12 58								→		13 58		
Maidenhead 3	a			12 05			12 36						13 05		13 35								14 05		14 36
Slough 3	a			12 18			12 44						13 18		13 43								14 18		14 44
Ealing Broadway	⊖ a			12 39									13 39										14 39		
London Paddington 15	⊖ a		12 33	12 49	12 42	12 59	13 04					13 26	13 49	13 55	14 04				14 22			14 30	14 49	15 03	15 04

		XC	XC	GW	XC	GW	GW	GW	GW	GW	XC	XC	GW	XC	GW	GW	GW	GW	GW	XC	XC	GW	XC	GW	GW
			1◇	1	1◇	1◇	1◇	1	1◇	1		R 1	1	1◇	1◇	1◇	1	1◇	1		R 1	1	1◇	1◇	1
					A									A									A		
		🚌	☕		☕	☕	☕		☕		🚌	☕		☕	☕	☕		☕		🚌	☕		☕	☕	
Birmingham New Street 12	d		13 03									14 03									15 03				
Birmingham International	d		13 15									14 15									15 15				
Coventry	d		13 25									14 25									15 25				
Stratford-upon-Avon	d																								
Warwick Parkway	d		*12 58*									*13 58*									*14 58*				
Warwick	d		*13 05*									*14 05*									*15 05*				
Leamington Spa 8	d		13 38									14 38									15 38				
Banbury	d		13 55									14 55									15 55				
Kings Sutton	d																								
Heyford	d																								
Tackley	d																								
Bicester Town	d																								
Islip	d																								
Oxford	a		14 19									15 19									16 19				
	d	13 30									14 30									15 30					
Radley	d																								
Culham	d																								
Appleford	d																								
Didcot Parkway	a	14 00									15 00									16 00					
	d			14 21	14 25	14 29			14 58				15 21	15 25	15 29			15 58				16 21	16 25	16 29	
Cholsey	d			14 27				←					15 27				←					16 27			←
Goring & Streatley	d			14 32				14 32					15 32				15 32					16 32			16 32
Pangbourne	d			→				14 37					→				15 37					→			16 37
Tilehurst	d							14 42									15 42								16 42
Bedwyn	d									14 45															
Hungerford	d									14 51															
Kintbury	d									14 55															
Newbury	a									15 02															
	d									15 02									15 54						
Newbury Racecourse	d																		15 56						
Thatcham	d									15 07									16 00						
Midgham	d																		16 05						
Aldermaston	d																		16 09						
Theale	d									15 15									16 13						
Reading West	d																		16 21						
Reading 7	a				14 44	14 44		14 48	15 13	15 23				15 43	15 44		15 48	16 13	16 24				16 44	16 44	16 46
	d					14 45	14 50	14 52	15 15	15 24					15 45	15 49	15 52	16 15	16 25					16 45	16 52
Twyford 3	a							14 58									15 58								16 58
Maidenhead 3	a							15 05		15 35							16 06		16 36						17 06
Slough 3	a							15 18		15 43							16 18		16 44						17 18
Ealing Broadway	⊖ a							15 39									16 39								17 39
London Paddington 15	⊖ a					15 23	15 32	15 49	15 56	16 03					16 23	16 31	16 49	16 53	17 04					17 22	17 49

For general notes see front of timetable
For details of catering facilities see
Directory of Train Operators

A To Bournemouth (Table 158)

Table 116

Sundays

from 30 March

Birmingham, Banbury, Bicester, Oxford and Bedwyn → Reading and London

Network Diagram - see first page of Table 116

		GW	GW	XC	GW	XC	GW	GW	XC	GW	GW	GW	GW	GW	GW	XC	XC	GW	XC	GW	GW	GW	GW	GW	GW
		1 ◇	1		1 ◇	R 1	1	1 ◇	1 ◇ A	1	1 ◇	1	1 ◇	1 ◇	1		R 1	1	1 ◇ A	1 ◇	1	1 ◇	1	1 ◇	1
				🚌												🚌									
		☕			☕	☕		☕	☕		☕		☕	☕			☕		☕	☕		☕		☕	
Birmingham New Street 12	d					16 03											17 03								
Birmingham International	d					16 15											17 15								
Coventry	d					16 25											17 25								
Stratford-upon-Avon	d																								
Warwick Parkway	d					*15 58*											*16 58*								
Warwick	d					*16 05*											*17 05*								
Leamington Spa 8	d					16 38											17 38								
Banbury	d					16 55											17 55								
Kings Sutton	d																								
Heyford	d																								
Tackley	d																								
Bicester Town	d																								
Islip	d																								
Oxford	a					17 19											18 19								
	d			16 30												17 30									
Radley	d																								
Culham	d																								
Appleford	d																								
Didcot Parkway	a			17 00												18 00									
	d	16 58					17 21	17 29	17 25	←	17 35			17 58				18 21	18 25	18 30	←	18 35		18 45	
Cholsey	d						17 27											18 27							
Goring & Streatley	d						17 32 →			17 32								18 32 →			18 32				
Pangbourne	d									17 37											18 37				
Tilehurst	d									17 42											18 42				
Bedwyn	d		16 36																						18 36
Hungerford	d		16 42																						18 42
Kintbury	d		16 45																						18 45
Newbury	a		16 53																						18 53
	d		16 53		17 02										17 54										18 54
Newbury Racecourse	d														17 56										
Thatcham	d		16 59												18 00										18 59
Midgham	d														18 05										
Aldermaston	d														18 09										
Theale	d		17 06												18 13										19 06
Reading West	d														18 21										
Reading 7	a	17 13	17 17		17 23			17 43	17 44	17 46	17 50	←		18 14	18 24				18 44	18 44	18 48	18 50	←	18 59	19 20
	d	17 15	17 21		17 25			17 44		17 52 →	17 51	17 52	17 55	18 15	18 25					18 44	18 52 →	18 51	18 52	19 01	19 21
Twyford 3	a											17 58											18 58		
Maidenhead 3	a		17 32									18 06			18 36								19 06		19 32
Slough 3	a		17 40									18 18			18 44								19 20	19 16	19 40
Ealing Broadway	⊖ a											18 39											19 42		
London Paddington 15	⊖ a	17 52	18 03		18 09			18 21			18 35	18 49	18 39	18 56	19 04					19 23		19 30	19 50	19 39	20 03

		XC	GW	GW	XC	GW	XC	GW	GW	GW	GW	GW	GW	GW	XC	XC	GW	GW	XC	GW	GW	GW	GW	GW	GW
			1 ◇	1 ◇	R 1	1	1 ◇ A	1 ◇	1	1 ◇	1	1 ◇	1 ◇	1		R 1	1	1 ◇	1 ◇ A	1	1 ◇	1	1 ◇		1 ◇
		🚌													🚌										
			☕	☕	☕			☕		☕		☕	☕			☕		☕			☕		☕		☕
Birmingham New Street 12	d				18 03											19 03									
Birmingham International	d				18 15											19 15									
Coventry	d				18 25											19 25									
Stratford-upon-Avon	d																								
Warwick Parkway	d				*17 58*											*18 58*									
Warwick	d				*18 05*											*19 05*									
Leamington Spa 8	d				18 38											19 38									
Banbury	d				18 55											19 55									
Kings Sutton	d																								
Heyford	d																								
Tackley	d																								
Bicester Town	d																								
Islip	d																								
Oxford	a				19 19											20 19									
	d	18 30													19 30										
Radley	d																								
Culham	d																								
Appleford	d																								
Didcot Parkway	a	19 00													20 00										
	d		19 04			19 21	19 25	19 30	←	19 34			19 58				20 21		20 25	←	20 34				
Cholsey	d					19 27											20 28								
Goring & Streatley	d					19 32 →			19 32								20 33 →			20 33					
Pangbourne	d								19 37											20 38					
Tilehurst	d								19 42											20 43					
Bedwyn	d																							20 30	
Hungerford	d																							20 36	
Kintbury	d																							20 39	
Newbury	a																							20 47	
	d			19 05										19 54										20 47	20 54
Newbury Racecourse	d													19 56											
Thatcham	d													20 00										20 52	
Midgham	d													20 05											
Aldermaston	d													20 09											
Theale	d													20 13										20 59	
Reading West	d													20 21											
Reading 7	a		19 20	19 25			19 44	19 44	19 48	19 49	←		20 13	20 24					20 44	20 48	20 49	←		21 08	21 14
	d		19 21	19 25				19 44	19 52 →	19 50	19 52	19 54	20 15	20 25				20 43		20 52 →	20 49	20 52	21 03	21 08	21 14
Twyford 3	a										19 58											20 58		21 15	
Maidenhead 3	a										20 06			20 36								21 05		21 21	
Slough 3	a										20 18			20 43								21 22	21 18	21 37	
Ealing Broadway	⊖ a										20 39											21 43		21 58	
London Paddington 15	⊖ a		20 03	20 09				20 23		20 29	20 49	20 39	20 56	21 05				21 25			21 29	21 52	21 44	22 07	21 59

For general notes see front of timetable
For details of catering facilities see Directory of Train Operators

A To Bournemouth (Table 158)

Sundays
from 30 March

Birmingham, Banbury, Bicester, Oxford and Bedwyn → Reading and London

Network Diagram - see first page of Table 116

		GW	XC	XC	GW	GW	XC	GW	GW	GW	GW	XC	XC	GW	GW	XC	GW	XC	GW	GW	GW	XC	GW
		1 ◇		R 1	1 ◇	1	1 ◇	1	1 ◇	1 ◇			1 ◇	1 ◇	1	1 ◇			1 ◇	1 ◇	1	1 ◇	
							A									A						B	
			🚌									🚌						🚌					
		☕			☕				☕	☕				☕					☕	☕			
Birmingham New Street 12	d			20 03									21 03										
Birmingham International	d			20 15									21 15										
Coventry	d			20 25									21 25										
Stratford-upon-Avon	d																						
Warwick Parkway	d			*19 31*									*20 31*										
Warwick	d			*19 38*									*20 38*										
Leamington Spa 8	d			20 38									21 38										
Banbury	d			20 55									21 55										
Kings Sutton	d																						
Heyford	d																						
Tackley	d																						
Bicester Town	d																						
Islip	d																						
Oxford	a			21 19									22 19										
	d		20 30									21 30						22 30					
Radley	d																						
Culham	d																						
Appleford	d																						
Didcot Parkway	a		21 00									22 00						23 00					
	d	20 58				21 20	21 25		21 30	22 00					22 21	22 25			23 05		23 14	23 25	
Cholsey	d					21 26		←							22 27						23 20		
Goring & Streatley	d					21 31		21 31							22 32						23 25		
Pangbourne	d					↳		21 36							22 36						23 30		
Tilehurst	d							21 41							22 41						23 34		
Bedwyn	d																22 20						
Hungerford	d																22 26						
Kintbury	d																22 30						
Newbury	a																22 37						
	d										21 53			22 26			22 38						23 50
Newbury Racecourse	d										21 55												23 52
Thatcham	d										21 59						22 43						23 56
Midgham	d										22 04												00 01
Aldermaston	d										22 08												00 05
Theale	d										22 12						22 50						00 10
Reading West	d										22 23												00 20
Reading 7	a	21 17					21 44	21 45	21 52	22 14	22 26			22 43	22 45	22 49	23 00		23 20		23 39	23 45	00 24
	d	21 18			21 22			21 46	21 54	22 16	22 27			22 44	22 52				23 22	23 29	23 40		
Twyford 3	a							21 52			22 33				22 58						23 48		
Maidenhead 3	a							21 59			22 40				23 05						23 56		
Slough 3	a							22 11			22 50				23 15						00 05		
Ealing Broadway	⊖ a							22 39			23 12				23 39						00 27		
London Paddington 15	⊖ a	22 05			22 17			22 48	22 30	23 07	23 22			23 30	23 49				00 10	00 11	00 40		

For general notes see front of timetable
For details of catering facilities see Directory of Train Operators

A To Southampton Central (Table 158)
B To Gatwick Airport (Table 148)

Table 116A

Mondays to Saturdays

Reading — Wallingford
Bus Service

		GW MX	GW SX	GW	GW	GW	GW	GW	GW	GW	GW	GW	GW	GW	GW	GW	GW	GW	GW FSO
Reading	d	00 35	07 27	08 27	09 25	10 25	11 25	12 25	13 25	14 25	15 25	16 35	17 35	18 35	19 35	20 35	21 35	22 35	23 35
Wallingford Market Place	a	01 10	07 59	08 59	09 58	10 58	11 58	12 58	13 58	14 58	15 58	17 10	18 10	19 10	20 10	21 10	22 10	23 10	00 10

Sundays

		GW	GW	GW	GW	GW	GW	GW	GW	GW
Reading	d	00 35	11 25	13 25	15 25	17 25	19 25	21 25	23 25	23 35
Wallingford Market Place	a	01 10	11 58	13 58	15 58	17 58	19 58	21 58	23 58	00 10

Mondays to Saturdays

		GW SX	GW SX	GW	GW	GW	GW	GW	GW	GW	GW	GW	GW	GW	GW	GW	GW	GW	GW	GW FSO
Wallingford Market Place	d	06 07	06 47	07 40	08 40	09 40	10 40	11 40	12 40	13 40	14 40	15 50	16 50	17 50	18 50	19 50	20 50	21 50	22 50	23 50
Reading	a	06 40	07 25	08 20	09 18	10 18	11 18	12 18	13 18	14 18	15 18	16 28	17 28	18 28	19 28	20 28	21 28	22 28	23 28	00 28

Sundays

		GW	GW	GW	GW	GW	GW	GW	GW
Wallingford Market Place	d	10 40	12 40	14 40	16 40	18 40	20 40	22 40	23 50
Reading	a	11 18	13 18	15 18	17 18	19 18	21 18	23 18	00 28

For general notes see front of timetable
For details of catering facilities see
Directory of Train Operators

Table 116B

Mondays to Fridays

Oxford → Abingdon
Bus Service

		GW	GW	GW	GW	GW	GW	GW	GW	GW	GW	GW	GW	GW	GW	GW	GW	GW	GW	GW	GW	GW
Oxford	d	06 30	06 50	07 10	07 30	07 47	07 55	08 10	08 25	08 40	08 55	09 13	09 23	09 43	10 03	10 23	10 43	11 03	11 23	11 43	12 03	12 23
Abingdon High Street	a	07 00	07 20	07 40	08 00	08 17	08 25	08 40	08 55	09 10	09 25	09 43	09 53	10 13	10 33	10 53	11 13	11 33	11 53	12 13	12 33	12 53

		GW	GW	GW	GW	GW	GW	GW	GW	GW	GW	GW	GW	GW	GW	GW	GW	GW	GW	GW	GW	GW
																						FO
Oxford	d	12 43	13 03	13 23	13 43	14 03	14 23	14 43	15 03	15 23	15 43	16 03	16 23	16 38	16 53	17 08	17 23	17 38	17 53	18 13	18 30	18 40
Abingdon High Street	a	13 13	13 33	13 53	14 13	14 33	14 53	15 13	15 33	15 53	16 13	16 33	16 53	17 08	17 23	17 38	17 53	18 08	18 23	18 43	19 00	19 10

		GW	GW	GW	GW	GW	GW	GW	GW	GW	GW	GW	GW	GW	GW	GW	GW	GW	GW	GW	GW	GW
		FX	FO		FO	FX	FO	FX	FO		FO	FX	FX									
Oxford	d	18 50	18 55	19 10	19 25	19 30	19 40	19 50	19 55	20 10	20 25	20 30	20 50	21 10	21 30	21 50	22 10	22 30	22 50	23 10	23 30	23 50
Abingdon High Street	a	19 20	19 25	19 40	19 55	20 00	20 10	20 20	20 25	20 40	20 55	21 00	21 20	21 40	22 00	22 20	22 40	23 00	23 20	23 40	23 59	00 20

Saturdays

		GW	GW	GW	GW	GW	GW	GW	GW	GW	GW	GW	GW	GW	GW	GW	GW	GW	GW	GW
Oxford	d	06 50	07 10	07 30	07 50	08 10	08 30	08 50	09 03	09 23	09 43	10 03	10 23	10 43	11 03	11 23	11 43	12 03	12 23	12 43
Abingdon High Street	a	07 20	07 40	08 00	08 20	08 40	09 00	09 20	09 33	09 53	10 13	10 33	10 53	11 13	11 33	11 53	12 13	12 33	12 53	13 13

		GW	GW	GW	GW	GW	GW	GW	GW	GW	GW	GW	GW	GW	GW	GW	GW	GW	GW	GW
Oxford	d	13 03	13 23	13 43	14 03	14 23	14 43	15 03	15 23	15 43	16 03	16 23	16 43	17 03	17 23	17 43	18 03	18 26	18 40	18 55
Abingdon High Street	a	13 33	13 53	14 13	14 33	14 53	15 13	15 33	15 53	16 13	16 33	16 53	17 13	17 33	17 53	18 13	18 33	18 56	19 10	19 25

		GW	GW	GW	GW	GW	GW	GW	GW	GW	GW	GW	GW	GW	GW	GW	GW	GW
Oxford	d	19 10	19 25	19 40	19 55	20 10	20 25	20 40	20 55	21 10	21 30	21 50	22 10	22 30	22 50	23 10	23 30	23 50
Abingdon High Street	a	19 40	19 55	20 10	20 25	20 40	20 55	21 10	21 25	21 40	22 00	22 20	22 40	23 00	23 20	23 40	23 59	00 20

Sundays

		GW	GW	GW	GW	GW	GW	GW	GW	GW	GW	GW	GW	GW	GW	GW	GW	GW
Oxford	d	08 00	08 20	08 40	09 00	09 20	09 40	10 10	10 40	11 10	11 40	12 10	12 40	13 10	13 40	14 10	14 40	15 10
Abingdon High Street	a	08 30	08 50	09 10	09 30	09 50	10 10	10 40	11 10	11 40	12 10	12 40	13 10	13 40	14 10	14 40	15 10	15 40

		GW	GW	GW	GW	GW	GW	GW	GW	GW	GW	GW	GW	GW	GW	GW	GW	GW
Oxford	d	15 40	16 10	16 40	17 10	17 40	18 10	18 40	19 10	19 40	20 10	20 40	21 10	21 40	22 10	22 40	23 10	23 50
Abingdon High Street	a	16 10	16 40	17 10	17 40	18 10	18 40	19 10	19 40	20 10	20 40	21 10	21 40	22 10	22 40	23 10	23 40	00 20

For general notes see front of timetable
For details of catering facilities see
Directory of Train Operators

Table 116B

Mondays to Fridays

Abingdon → Oxford

Bus Service

		GW	GW	GW	GW	GW	GW	GW		GW	GW	GW	GW	GW	GW	GW		GW	GW	GW	GW	GW	GW	GW		GW
Abingdon High Street	d	05 50	06 10	06 30	06 50	07 10	07 30	07 45	.....	08 00	08 15	08 30	08 45	09 00	09 15	09 30	.....	09 50	10 10	10 30	10 50	11 10	11 30	11 50	.....	12 10
Oxford	a	06 20	06 40	07 00	07 20	07 40	08 00	08 15	.	08 30	08 45	09 00	09 15	09 30	09 45	10 00	.	10 20	10 40	11 00	11 20	11 40	12 00	12 20	.	12 40

		GW	GW	GW	GW	GW	GW	GW		GW	GW	GW	GW	GW	GW	GW		GW	GW	GW	GW	GW	GW	GW		GW FO
Abingdon High Street	d	12 30	12 50	13 10	13 30	13 50	14 10	14 30	.....	14 50	15 10	15 30	15 50	16 10	16 30	16 50	.....	17 05	17 20	17 35	17 50	18 05	18 25	18 40	.....	18 55
Oxford	a	13 00	13 20	13 40	14 00	14 20	14 40	15 00	.	15 20	15 40	16 00	16 20	16 40	17 00	17 20	.	17 35	17 50	18 05	18 20	18 35	18 55	19 10	.	19 25

		GW FX	GW FO	GW FX	GW FO	GW	GW FO	GW FX		GW FO	GW FX	GW FO	GW	GW FO	GW FX	GW FO	GW FX	GW FO	GW	GW	GW	GW	GW	GW	
Abingdon High Street	d	19 00	19 10	19 20	19 25	19 40	19 55	20 00	.....	20 10	20 20	20 25	20 40	20 55	21 00	21 10	21 20	21 25	21 40	22 00	22 20	22 40	23 00	23 20	.....
Oxford	a	19 30	19 40	19 50	19 55	20 10	20 25	20 30	.	20 40	20 50	20 55	21 10	21 25	21 30	21 40	21 50	21 55	22 10	22 30	22 50	23 10	23 30	23 50	

Saturdays

		GW	GW	GW		GW	GW	GW		GW	GW	GW		GW	GW	GW		GW	GW	GW		GW	GW	GW		GW
Abingdon High Street	d	06 20	06 40	07 00	.....	07 20	07 40	08 00	.....	08 20	08 30	08 50	.....	09 10	09 30	09 50	.....	10 10	10 30	10 50	.....	11 10	11 30	11 50	.....	12 10
Oxford	a	06 50	07 10	07 30	.	07 50	08 10	08 30	.	08 50	09 00	09 20	.	09 40	10 00	10 20	.	10 40	11 00	11 20	.	11 40	12 00	12 20	.	12 40

		GW	GW	GW		GW	GW	GW		GW	GW	GW		GW	GW	GW		GW	GW	GW		GW	GW	GW		GW
Abingdon High Street	d	12 30	12 50	13 10	.....	13 30	13 50	14 10	.....	14 30	14 50	15 10	.....	15 30	15 50	16 10	.....	16 30	16 50	17 10	.....	17 30	17 50	18 10	.....	18 25
Oxford	a	13 00	13 20	13 40	.	14 00	14 20	14 40	.	15 00	15 20	15 40	.	16 00	16 20	16 40	.	17 00	17 20	17 40	.	18 00	18 20	18 40	.	18 53

		GW	GW	GW		GW	GW	GW		GW	GW	GW		GW	GW	GW		GW	GW	GW		GW	GW	GW	
Abingdon High Street	d	18 40	18 55	19 10	.....	19 25	19 40	19 55	.....	20 10	20 25	20 40	.....	20 55	21 10	21 25	.....	21 40	22 00	22 20	.....	22 40	23 00	23 20	.....
Oxford	a	19 08	19 23	19 38	.	19 53	20 08	20 23	.	20 38	20 53	21 08	.	21 23	21 38	21 53	.	22 10	22 30	22 50	.	23 10	23 30	23 50	

Sundays

		GW	GW		GW	GW		GW	GW		GW	GW		GW	GW		GW	GW		GW	GW		GW	GW		GW
Abingdon High Street	d	07 30	07 50	.....	08 10	08 30	.....	08 50	09 10	.....	09 40	10 10	.....	10 40	11 10	.....	11 40	12 10	.....	12 40	13 10	.....	13 40	14 10	.....	14 40
Oxford	a	08 00	08 20	.	08 40	09 00	.	09 20	09 40	.	10 10	10 40	.	11 10	11 40	.	12 10	12 40	.	13 10	13 40	.	14 10	14 40	.	15 10

		GW	GW		GW	GW		GW	GW		GW	GW		GW	GW		GW	GW		GW	GW		GW	GW	
Abingdon High Street	d	15 10	15 40	.....	16 10	16 40	.....	17 10	17 40	.....	18 10	18 40	.....	19 10	19 40	.....	20 10	20 40	.....	21 10	21 40	.....	22 10	22 40	.....
Oxford	a	15 40	16 10	.	16 40	17 10	.	17 40	18 10	.	18 40	19 10	.	19 40	20 10	.	20 40	21 10	.	21 40	22 10	.	22 40	23 10	

For general notes see front of timetable
For details of catering facilities see
Directory of Train Operators

Oxford → Eynsham → Witney

Bus Service

		GW MX	GW MO	GW MFO	GW	GW	GW	GW	GW	GW	GW	GW	GW	GW	GW	GW	GW	GW	GW	GW	GW	GW
Oxford	d	23p47	23p52	00 47	05 59	06 54	07 14	07 19	07 39	07 59	08 19	08 39	08 59	09 14	09 29	09 44	09 59	10 14	10 29	10 44	10 59	11 14
Eynsham Church	a	00 01	00 08	01 00	06 14	07 09	07 29	07 36	07 57	08 17	08 37	08 57	09 17	09 32	09 47	10 02	10 17	10 32	10 47	11 02	11 17	11 32
Witney Market Place	a	00 12	00 24	01 12	06 27	07 21	07 41	07 51	08 14	08 34	08 54	09 14	09 34	09 49	10 04	10 19	10 34	10 49	11 04	11 19	11 34	11 49

		GW	GW	GW	GW	GW	GW	GW	GW	GW	GW	GW	GW	GW	GW	GW	GW	GW	GW	GW	GW	GW
Oxford	d	11 29	11 44	11 59	12 14	12 29	12 44	12 59	13 14	13 29	13 44	13 59	14 14	14 29	14 44	14 59	15 14	15 29	15 44	15 59	16 14	16 29
Eynsham Church	a	11 47	12 02	12 17	12 32	12 47	13 02	13 17	13 32	13 47	14 02	14 17	14 32	14 47	15 02	15 17	15 32	15 47	16 02	16 17	16 32	16 47
Witney Market Place	a	12 04	12 19	12 34	12 49	13 04	13 19	13 34	13 49	14 04	14 19	14 34	14 49	15 04	15 19	15 34	15 49	16 04	16 19	16 34	16 49	17 04

		GW	GW	GW	GW	GW	GW	GW	GW	GW	GW	GW	GW	GW	GW	GW	GW	GW	GW	GW	GW	GW
Oxford	d	16 39	16 49	16 59	17 09	17 19	17 29	17 39	17 49	17 59	18 12	18 27	18 47	19 22	19 57	20 37	20 52	21 17	21 57	22 27	23 07	23 47
Eynsham Church	a	17 03	17 14	17 24	17 34	17 44	17 54	18 04	18 14	18 24	18 35	18 45	19 05	19 37	20 10	20 50	21 05	21 30	22 10	22 40	23 20	00 01
Witney Market Place	a	17 22	17 35	17 43	17 53	18 03	18 13	18 23	18 33	18 43	18 52	19 02	19 22	19 52	20 22	21 02	21 17	21 42	22 22	22 52	23 32	00 12

Saturdays

		GW	GW	GW	GW	GW	GW	GW	GW	GW	GW	GW	GW	GW	GW	GW	GW	GW	GW	GW	GW
Oxford	d	23p47	00 17	00 47	01 47	06 35	07 22	07 52	08 17	08 38	08 59	09 14	09 29	09 44	09 59	10 14	10 29	10 44	10 59	11 14	11 29
Eynsham Church	a	00 01	00 30	01 00	02 00	06 50	07 37	08 07	08 33	08 55	09 16	09 32	09 47	10 02	10 17	10 32	10 47	11 02	11 17	11 32	11 47
Witney Market Place	a	00 12	00 42	01 12	02 12	07 02	07 49	08 19	08 48	09 10	09 31	09 49	10 04	10 19	10 32	10 49	11 04	11 19	11 32	11 49	12 04

		GW	GW	GW	GW	GW	GW	GW	GW	GW	GW	GW	GW	GW	GW	GW	GW	GW	GW	GW	GW
Oxford	d	11 44	11 59	12 14	12 29	12 44	12 59	13 14	13 29	13 44	13 59	14 14	14 29	14 44	14 59	15 14	15 29	15 44	15 59	16 14	16 29
Eynsham Church	a	12 02	12 17	12 32	12 47	13 02	13 17	13 32	13 47	14 02	14 17	14 32	14 47	15 02	15 17	15 32	15 47	16 02	16 17	16 32	16 47
Witney Market Place	a	12 19	12 32	12 49	13 04	13 19	13 32	13 49	14 04	14 19	14 32	14 49	15 04	15 19	15 32	15 49	16 04	16 19	16 32	16 49	17 04

		GW	GW	GW	GW	GW	GW	GW	GW	GW	GW	GW	GW	GW	GW	GW	GW	GW	GW
Oxford	d	16 44	16 59	17 14	17 29	17 44	17 54	18 09	18 29	18 47	19 22	19 57	20 37	20 52	21 17	21 57	22 27	23 07	23 47
Eynsham Church	a	17 02	17 17	17 32	17 47	17 52	18 02	18 17	18 39	18 55	19 37	20 10	20 50	21 05	21 30	22 10	22 40	23 20	23 59
Witney Market Place	a	17 19	17 32	17 49	18 04	18 19	18 29	18 44	19 04	19 22	19 52	20 22	21 02	21 17	21 42	22 22	22 52	23 32	00 12

Sundays

		GW	GW	GW	GW	GW	GW	GW	GW	GW	GW	GW	GW	GW	GW	GW
Oxford	d	00 17	00 47	01 17	01 47	08 22	09 22	10 22	11 22	11 52	12 22	12 52	13 22	13 52	14 22
Eynsham Church	a	00 30	01 00	01 30	02 00	08 38	09 38	10 38	11 38	12 08	12 38	13 08	13 38	14 08	14 38
Witney Market Place	a	00 42	01 12	01 42	02 12	08 54	09 54	10 54	11 54	12 24	12 54	13 24	13 54	14 24	14 54

		GW	GW	GW	GW	GW	GW	GW	GW	GW	GW	GW	GW	GW	GW	GW	GW
Oxford	d	14 52	15 22	15 52	16 22	16 52	17 22	17 52	18 22	18 52	19 22	20 22	21 22	22 22	23 12	23 47	23 52
Eynsham Church	a	15 08	15 38	16 08	16 38	17 08	17 38	18 08	18 38	19 08	19 38	20 38	21 38	22 38	23 28	23 59	00 08
Witney Market Place	a	15 24	15 54	16 24	16 54	17 24	17 54	18 24	18 54	19 24	19 54	20 54	21 54	22 54	23 44	00 12	00 24

For general notes see front of timetable
For details of catering facilities see Directory of Train Operators

Table 116C

Mondays to Fridays

Witney → Eynsham → Oxford
Bus Service

	GW	GW	GW	GW		GW	GW	GW	GW		GW	GW	GW	GW		GW	GW	GW	GW		GW	GW	GW	GW		GW
Witney Market Place ... d	05 20	06 12	06 28	06 44	.....	06 59	07 14	07 24	07 34	.....	07 44	07 54	08 05	08 25	.....	08 40	08 55	09 10	09 25	.....	09 40	09 55	10 10	10 25	.....	10 40
Eynsham Witney Road d	05 29	06 26	06 42	06 58	.	07 13	07 28	07 38	07 48	.	07 58	08 08	08 19	08 39	.	08 54	09 09	09 24	09 39	.	09 54	10 09	10 24	10 39	.	10 54
Oxford .... a	05 50	06 50	07 10	07 30	.....	07 45	08 10	08 20	08 30	.....	08 40	08 50	09 11	09 21	.....	09 32	09 37	09 52	10 07	.....	10 22	10 37	10 52	11 07	.....	11 22

	GW	GW	GW	GW		GW	GW	GW	GW		GW	GW	GW	GW		GW	GW	GW	GW		GW	GW	GW	GW		GW
Witney Market Place ... d	10 55	11 10	11 25	11 40	.....	11 55	12 10	12 25	12 40	.....	12 55	13 10	13 25	13 40	.....	13 55	14 10	14 25	14 40	.....	14 55	15 10	15 25	15 40	.....	16 00
Eynsham Witney Road d	11 09	11 24	11 39	11 54	.	12 09	12 24	12 39	12 54	.	13 09	13 24	13 39	13 54	.	14 09	14 24	14 39	14 54	.	15 09	15 24	15 39	15 54	.	16 14
Oxford .... a	11 37	11 52	12 07	12 22	.....	12 37	12 52	13 07	13 22	.....	13 37	13 52	14 07	14 22	.....	14 37	14 52	15 07	15 22	.....	15 37	15 52	16 07	16 22	.....	16 42

	GW	GW	GW	GW		GW	GW	GW	GW		GW	GW	GW	GW FX		GW FO	GW	GW	GW		GW	GW	GW	GW		
Witney Market Place ... d	16 10	16 30	16 50	17 10	.....	17 21	17 34	17 56	18 22	.....	18 52	19 00	19 35	20 04	.....	20 12	20 34	20 40	21 04	.....	21 44	22 24	23 04	23 34	.....	.....
Eynsham Witney Road d	16 24	16 44	17 04	17 24	.	17 35	17 48	18 10	18 38	.	19 08	19 16	19 50	20 19	.	20 28	20 49	20 55	21 18	.	21 58	22 38	23 18	23 48	.	.
Oxford .... a	16 52	17 12	17 32	17 52	.....	18 03	18 16	18 38	19 03	.....	19 33	19 41	20 11	20 40	.....	20 53	21 10	21 19	21 40	.....	22 20	23 00	23 40	00 10	.....	.....

Saturdays

	GW	GW		GW	GW		GW	GW		GW	GW		GW	GW		GW	GW		GW	GW		GW	GW		GW	GW
Witney Market Place ... d	05 52	06 42	.....	07 12	07 32	.....	07 53	08 10	.....	08 25	08 40	.....	08 55	09 10	.....	09 25	09 40	.....	09 55	10 10	.....	10 25	10 40	.....	10 55	11 10
Eynsham Witney Road d	06 01	06 51	.	07 21	07 45	.	08 07	08 24	.	08 39	08 54	.	09 09	09 24	.	09 39	09 54	.	10 09	10 24	.	10 39	10 54	.	11 09	11 24
Oxford .... a	06 25	07 15	.....	07 45	08 09	.....	08 31	08 52	.....	09 07	09 22	.....	09 37	09 52	.....	10 07	10 22	.....	10 37	10 52	.....	11 07	11 22	.....	11 37	11 52

	GW	GW		GW	GW		GW	GW		GW	GW		GW	GW		GW	GW		GW	GW		GW	GW		GW	GW
Witney Market Place ... d	11 25	11 40	.....	11 55	12 10	.....	12 25	12 40	.....	12 55	13 10	.....	13 25	13 40	.....	13 55	14 10	.....	14 25	14 40	.....	14 55	15 10	.....	15 25	15 40
Eynsham Witney Road d	11 39	11 54	.	12 09	12 24	.	12 39	12 54	.	13 09	13 24	.	13 39	13 54	.	14 09	14 24	.	14 39	14 54	.	15 09	15 24	.	15 39	15 54
Oxford .... a	12 07	12 22	.....	12 37	12 52	.....	13 07	13 22	.....	13 37	13 52	.....	14 07	14 22	.....	14 37	14 52	.....	15 07	15 22	.....	15 37	15 52	.....	16 07	16 22

	GW	GW		GW	GW		GW	GW		GW	GW		GW	GW		GW	GW	GW	GW	GW	GW	GW	GW	GW		
Witney Market Place ... d	15 55	16 10	.....	16 25	16 40	.....	16 55	17 15	.....	17 35	17 58	.....	18 25	18 52	.....	19 00	19 38	20 12	20 40	21 04	21 44	22 24	23 04	23 34	.....	.....
Eynsham Witney Road d	16 09	16 24	.	16 39	16 54	.	17 09	17 29	.	17 49	18 12	.	18 41	19 08	.	19 16	19 54	20 29	20 55	21 18	21 58	22 38	23 18	23 48	.	.
Oxford .... a	16 37	16 52	.....	17 07	17 22	.....	17 37	17 57	.....	18 17	18 40	.....	19 06	19 33	.....	19 41	20 19	20 53	21 19	21 40	22 20	23 00	23 40	00 10	.....	.....

Sundays

	GW	GW	GW	GW	GW	GW	GW	GW	GW	GW	GW	GW	GW	GW	GW	GW	GW	GW	GW	GW	GW	GW	GW	GW	GW	
Witney Market Place ... d	07 35	08 35	09 35	10 35	11 05	11 35	12 05	12 35	13 05	13 35	14 05	14 35	15 05	15 35	16 05	16 35	17 05	17 35	18 05	18 35	19 35	20 35	21 35	22 35	23 34	.....
Eynsham Witney Road d	07 51	08 51	09 51	10 51	11 21	11 51	12 21	12 51	13 21	13 51	14 21	14 51	15 21	15 51	16 21	16 51	17 21	17 51	18 21	18 51	19 51	20 51	21 51	22 51	23 48	.
Oxford .... a	08 08	09 08	10 08	11 08	11 38	12 08	12 38	13 08	13 38	14 08	14 38	15 08	15 38	16 08	16 38	17 08	17 38	18 08	18 38	19 08	20 08	21 08	22 08	23 08	00 10	.....

For general notes see front of timetable
For details of catering facilities see
Directory of Train Operators

Table 117

London → Greenford and Reading
(Local services only)

Mondays to Fridays
until Wednesday 26 March

Network Diagram - see first page of Table 116

Miles	Miles	Miles			GW MO 1 A	GW MO 1 B	GW MX 1 ◇	GW MO 1 A	GW MO 1 B	GW MX 1	GW MX 1	GW MO 1 ◇ A ⊼	GW MO 1 ◇ B ⊼	GW MX 1	GW MO 1 A	GW MO 1 B	GW MX 1	GW MX 1 ◇	GW MO 1		GW MX 1	GW 1	GW 1	HC	HC
0	0	0	**London Paddington 15** ⊖	d	23p15	23p15	23p21				23p29	23p37	23p42	23p48	23p53	23p53		00 21	00 34		00 34	01 34	03 34	04 42	05 13
4¼	4¼	4¼	Acton Main Line	d										23p54											
5¾	5¾	5¾	**Ealing Broadway** ⊖	d	23p23	23p24					23p36	23p45	23p50	23p57	00 01	00 01			00 41		00 41	01 41	03 41	04 50	05 21
6½	6½	6½	West Ealing	d										23p59											
—	7¼	—	Drayton Green	d																					
—	7½	—	Castle Bar Park	d																					
—	8¼	—	South Greenford	d																					
—	9¼	—	**Greenford** ⊖	a																					
7¼	—	7¼	Hanwell	d										00 02											
9	—	9	Southall	d	23p28	23p29		←	←					00 06	00 06	00 06			00 46		00 46	01 46	03 47	04 54	05 25
10¾	—	10¾	Hayes & Harlington	d	23p32	23p33		23p32	23p33		23p44			00 10	00 10	00 10			00 50		00 50	01 50	03 51	04 58	05 29
—	—	14¾	**Heathrow Terminals 1-2-3** ✈	a	→	→																		05 04	05 35
—	—	16½	**Heathrow Terminal 4** ✈	a													←								
13¼	—	—	West Drayton	d				23p37	23p37					00 14	00 14	00 14	00 14		00 55		00 55	01 55	03 55		
14¾	—	—	Iver	d										→			00 17								
16¼	—	—	Langley	d				23p41	23p42						00 19	00 19	00 20		00 59		00 59				
18½	—	—	**Slough 3**	a			23p42	23p46	23p47		23p55	23p55	00 02		00 24	00 24	00 26	00 40	01 05		01 05	02 04	04 04		
—	—	—		d			23p43	23p47	23p47		23p55	23p57	00 03		00 24	00 24	00 27	00 41	01 05		01 05	02 04	04 05		
21	—	—	Burnham	d				23p51	23p51						00 28	00 28	00 31		01 09		01 09				
22½	—	—	Taplow	d												00 32	00 34				01 12				
24¼	—	—	**Maidenhead 3**	d				23p56	23p56		00 03	00 05	00 11		00 33	00 36	00 38		01 13		01 16	02 12	04 12		
31	—	—	**Twyford 3**	d				00 04	00 04	00 07	00 11				00 41	00 44	00 46		01 22		01 24	02 19	04 20		
36	—	—	**Reading 7**	a			00 01	00 10	00 10	00 17	00 18	00 18	00 24		00 48	00 50	00 53	00 58	01 32		01 33	02 28	04 28		
—	—	—	Oxford	a			00 34		*00b55*		01 07	00 50	00 55					01 30					*06 21*		

		GW 1 C	GW 1 ◇ ⊼	HC	GW 1 ◇ ⊼	GW 1 C	GW 1	GW 1 ◇ ⊼	GW 1	GW 1	GW 1	HC	GW 1 ◇		GW 1	GW 1	GW 1	GW 1	GW 1 D	HC	GW 1	GW 1 ◇	GW 1 D	GW 1	GW 1
London Paddington 15 ⊖	d	05 24	05 30	05 33	05 42		05 44	05 48		05 55	06 00	06 03	06 07				06 15	06 25	06 30	06 33	06 45	06 48			06 55
Acton Main Line	d									06 01								06 31							07 01
Ealing Broadway ⊖	d	05 31		05 41			05 51			06 04	06 07	06 11					06 22	06 34	06 37	06 41	06 52				07 04
West Ealing	d			05 43						06 06		06 13						06 36		06 43					07 06
Drayton Green	d									06 09								06 39							07 09
Castle Bar Park	d									06 10								06 40							07 10
South Greenford	d									06 13								06 43							07 13
Greenford ⊖	a									06 19								06 49							07 19
Hanwell	d			05 46					←			06 16								06 46				←	
Southall	d	05 37		05 49		←	05 56		05 56		06 13	06 19				←	06 27			06 49	06 57			06 57	
Hayes & Harlington	d	05 42		05 53		05 42	→		06 00		06 17	06 23				06 17	06 31		06 45	06 53	→			07 01	
Heathrow Terminals 1-2-3 ✈	a	→		06 01							→	06 31								07 01					
Heathrow Terminal 4 ✈	a																								
West Drayton	d					05 46			06 05							06 21	06 36		06 49					07 06	
Iver	d					05 49										06 24			06 52						
Langley	d					05 52										06 27			06 55						
Slough 3	a		05 47		06 03	05 57		06 05	06 13				06 22			06 32	06 44		07 00			07 03		07 14	
	d		05 49		06 03	05 58		06 06	06 13				06 23			06 33	06 44		07 01			07 04		07 14	
Burnham	d								06 17						←		06 48							07 18	
Taplow	d								06 21						06 21		06 52						←	07 22	
Maidenhead 3	d					06 05			→						06 25	06 40	06 56		07 09				07 09	07 26	
Twyford 3	d					06 13									06 32	06 48	07 03		→				07 16	07 33	
Reading 7	a		06 04		06 20	06 19		06 20					06 39		06 40	06 54	07 12					07 18	07 23	07 42	
Oxford	a				06 52	07 17		*07 06*					07 10		*07 35*	07 42						07 48	08 00		

		GW 1	HC	GW 1	GW 1 ◇	GW 1	GW 1		GW 1	GW 1	HC	GW 1	GW 1 ◇ ⊼	GW 1	GW 1	GW 1	GW 1	HC	GW 1	GW 1 ◇	GW 1	GW 1	GW 1		GW 1
London Paddington 15 ⊖	d	07 00	07 03	07 15	07 21				07 25	07 30	07 33	07 45	07 51			07 55	08 00	08 03	08 15	08 21			08 25		08 30
Acton Main Line	d								07 31							08 01							08 31		
Ealing Broadway ⊖	d	07 07	07 11	07 22					07 34	07 37	07 41	07 52				08 04	08 07	08 11	08 22				08 34		08 37
West Ealing	d		07 13						07 36		07 43					08 06		08 13					08 36		
Drayton Green	d								07 39							08 09							08 39		
Castle Bar Park	d								07 40							08 10							08 40		
South Greenford	d								07 43							08 13							08 43		
Greenford ⊖	a								07 49							08 19							08 49		
Hanwell	d		07 16				←				07 46				←			08 16				←			
Southall	d	07 13	07 19	07 27			07 27			07 43	07 49	07 57			07 57		08 13	08 19	08 27			08 27			08 43
Hayes & Harlington	d	07 17	07 23	→			07 31			07 47	07 53	→			08 01		08 17	08 23	→			08 31			08 47
Heathrow Terminals 1-2-3 ✈	a		07 31								08 01							08 31							
Heathrow Terminal 4 ✈	a																								
West Drayton	d	07 21					07 36			07 51					08 06		08 21					08 36			08 51
Iver	d	07 24								07 54							08 24								08 54
Langley	d	07 27								07 57							08 27								08 57
Slough 3	a	07 32			07 37		07 44			08 02			08 06		08 14		08 32			08 37		08 44			09 02
	d	07 33			07 37		07 44			08 03			08 07		08 14		08 33			08 37		08 44			09 03
Burnham	d						07 48								08 18							08 48			
Taplow	d					←	07 52							←	08 22						←	08 52			
Maidenhead 3	d	07 40				07 40	07 56			08 10				08 10	08 26		08 40				08 40	08 56			09 10
Twyford 3	d	→				07 48	08 03			→				08 18	08 33		→				08 48	09 03			→
Reading 7	a				07 51	07 54	08 12						08 21	08 24	08 42					08 51	08 54	09 12			
Oxford	a				08 20	08 41							08 47	09 14						09 24	09 39				

For general notes see front of timetable
For details of catering facilities see Directory of Train Operators

For fast services between London Paddington and Reading see Table 116

A Until 28 January
B From 4 February
C To Bicester Town (Table 116)
D To Worcester Foregate Street (Table 126)
b 4 February arr. 0050

Table 117

Mondays to Fridays

until Wednesday 26 March

London → Greenford and Reading

(Local services only)

Network Diagram - see first page of Table 116

		HC	GW 1	GW 1	GW 1 ◇ ⊼	GW 1	GW 1	GW 1	GW 1	GW 1	HC	GW 1	GW 1 ◇	GW 1	GW 1	GW 1		GW 1	HC	GW 1	GW 1 ◇ ⊼	GW 1	GW 1	GW 1	GW 1
London Paddington 15	⊖ d	08 33	08 40	08 45	08 51				08 55	09 00	09 03	09 15	09 21			09 25		09 30	09 33	09 45	09 51			09 55	10 00
Acton Main Line	d								09 01							09 31								10 01	
Ealing Broadway	⊖ d	08 41	08 47	08 52					09 04	09 07	09 11	09 22				09 34		09 37	09 41	09 52				10 04	10 07
West Ealing	d	08 43		08 55					09 06		09 13					09 36			09 43					10 06	
Drayton Green	d								09 09							09 39								10 09	
Castle Bar Park	d								09 10							09 40								10 10	
South Greenford	d								09 13							09 43								10 13	
Greenford	⊖ a								09 19							09 49								10 19	
Hanwell	d	08 46		08 57				←			09 16				←				09 46				←		
Southall	d	08 49	08 52	09 01				09 01			09 19	09 27			09 27				09 49	09 57			09 57		
Hayes & Harlington	d	08 53	08 56	→				09 05		09 15	09 23	→			09 31			09 45	09 53	→			10 01		10 15
Heathrow Terminals 1-2-3	✈ a	09 01									09 31								10 01						
Heathrow Terminal 4	✈ a																								
West Drayton	d							09 09		09 19					09 36			09 49					10 06		10 19
Iver	d							09 12		09 22								09 52							10 22
Langley	d							09 15		09 25								09 55							10 25
Slough 3	a		09 06		09 06			09 20		09 30			09 37		09 44			10 00			10 06		10 14		10 30
	d		09 06		09 07			09 21		09 31			09 37		09 44			10 01			10 07		10 14		10 31
Burnham	d		09 10				←								09 48								10 18		
Taplow	d		09 14			←	09 14							←	09 52							←	10 22		
Maidenhead 3	d		→			09 10	09 18	09 28		09 38				09 38	09 56			10 08				10 08	10 26		10 38
Twyford 3	d					09 18	09 25	09a35		→				09 46	10 03			→				10 16	10 33		→
Reading 7	a				09 21	09 24	09 33						09 51	09 52	10 12						10 21	10 22	10 42		
Oxford	a				09 47	10 13	*10 06*						10 18	10 30							10 47	11 13			

		HC	GW 1	GW 1 ◇	GW 1	GW 1	GW 1	GW 1	HC	GW 1		GW 1 ◇ ⊼	GW 1	GW 1	GW 1	GW 1	HC	GW 1	GW 1 ◇	GW 1	GW 1	GW 1	GW 1	HC	GW 1
London Paddington 15	⊖ d	10 03	10 15	10 21			10 25	10 30	10 33	10 45		10 51			10 55	11 00	11 03	11 15	11 21			11 25	11 30	11 33	11 45
Acton Main Line	d						10 31								11 01							11 31			
Ealing Broadway	⊖ d	10 11	10 22				10 34	10 37	10 41	10 52					11 04	11 07	11 11	11 22				11 34	11 37	11 41	11 52
West Ealing	d	10 13					10 36		10 43						11 06		11 13					11 36		11 43	
Drayton Green	d						10 39								11 09							11 39			
Castle Bar Park	d						10 40								11 10							11 40			
South Greenford	d						10 43								11 13							11 43			
Greenford	⊖ a						10 49								11 19							11 49			
Hanwell	d	10 16				←			10 46					←			11 16				←			11 46	
Southall	d	10 19	10 27			10 27			10 49	10 57				10 57			11 19	11 27			11 27			11 49	11 57
Hayes & Harlington	d	10 23	→			10 31		10 45	10 53	→				11 01		11 15	11 23	→			11 31		11 45	11 53	→
Heathrow Terminals 1-2-3	✈ a	10 31							11 01								11 31							12 01	
Heathrow Terminal 4	✈ a																								
West Drayton	d					10 36		10 49						11 06		11 19					11 36		11 49		
Iver	d							10 52								11 22							11 52		
Langley	d							10 55								11 25							11 55		
Slough 3	a			10 37		10 44		11 00				11 06		11 14		11 30			11 37		11 44		12 00		
	d			10 37		10 44		11 01				11 07		11 14		11 31			11 37		11 44		12 01		
Burnham	d					10 48								11 18							11 48				
Taplow	d				←	10 52							←	11 22						←	11 52				
Maidenhead 3	d				10 38	10 56		11 08					11 08	11 26		11 38				11 38	11 56		12 08		
Twyford 3	d				10 46	11 03		→					11 16	11 33		→				11 46	12 03		→		
Reading 7	a			10 51	10 52	11 12						11 21	11 22	11 42					11 51	11 52	12 12				
Oxford	a			11 18	11 30							11 47	12 13						12 18	12 30					

		GW 1 ◇ ⊼	GW 1	GW 1		GW 1	GW 1	HC	GW 1	GW 1 ◇	GW 1	GW 1	GW 1	GW 1	HC	GW 1	GW 1 ◇	GW 1	GW 1	GW 1		GW 1	HC	GW 1	GW 1 ◇
London Paddington 15	⊖ d	11 51				11 55	12 00	12 03	12 15	12 21			12 25	12 30	12 33	12 45	12 51			12 55		13 00	13 03	13 15	13 21
Acton Main Line	d					12 01							12 31							13 01					
Ealing Broadway	⊖ d					12 04	12 07	12 11	12 22				12 34	12 37	12 41	12 52				13 04		13 07	13 11	13 22	
West Ealing	d					12 06		12 13					12 36		12 43					13 06			13 13		
Drayton Green	d					12 09							12 39							13 09					
Castle Bar Park	d					12 10							12 40							13 10					
South Greenford	d					12 13							12 43							13 13					
Greenford	⊖ a					12 19							12 49							13 19					
Hanwell	d			←				12 16				←			12 46				←				13 16		
Southall	d			11 57				12 19	12 27			12 27			12 49	12 57			12 57				13 19	13 27	
Hayes & Harlington	d			12 01			12 15	12 23	→			12 31		12 45	12 53	→			13 01			13 15	13 23	→	
Heathrow Terminals 1-2-3	✈ a							12 31							13 01								13 31		
Heathrow Terminal 4	✈ a																								
West Drayton	d			12 06			12 19					12 36		12 49					13 06			13 19			
Iver	d						12 22							12 52								13 22			
Langley	d						12 25							12 55								13 25			
Slough 3	a	12 06		12 14			12 30			12 37		12 44		13 00			13 06		13 14			13 30			13 37
	d	12 07		12 14			12 31			12 37		12 44		13 01			13 07		13 14			13 31			13 37
Burnham	d			12 18								12 48							13 18						
Taplow	d		←	12 22							←	12 52						←	13 22						
Maidenhead 3	d		12 08	12 26			12 38				12 38	12 56		13 08				13 08	13 26			13 38			
Twyford 3	d		12 16	12 33			→				12 46	13 03		→				13 16	13 33			→			
Reading 7	a	12 21	12 22	12 42						12 51	12 52	13 12					13 21	13 22	13 42						13 51
Oxford	a	12 47	13 13							13 18	13 30						13 47	14 13							14 18

For general notes see front of timetable
For details of catering facilities see Directory of Train Operators

For fast services between London Paddington and Reading see Table 116

until Wednesday 26 March

London → Greenford and Reading

(Local services only)

Network Diagram - see first page of Table 116

		GW	GW	GW	GW	HC	GW	GW	GW	GW	GW	GW	HC	GW		GW	GW	HC	GW	GW	GW	GW	GW	GW	HC
		1	1	1	1		1	1 ◇	1	1	1	1		1		1	1		1	1 ◇	1	1	1	1	
								🚲																	
London Paddington 15	⊖ d			13 25	13 30	13 33	13 45	13 51			13 55	14 00	14 03	14 15		14 25	14 30	14 33	14 45	14 51			14 55	15 00	15 03
Acton Main Line	d			13 31							14 01					14 31							15 01		
Ealing Broadway	⊖ d			13 34	13 37	13 41	13 52				14 04	14 07	14 11	14 22		14 34	14 37	14 41	14 52				15 04	15 07	15 11
West Ealing	d			13 36		13 43					14 06		14 13			14 36		14 43					15 06		15 13
Drayton Green	d			13 39							14 09					14 39							15 09		
Castle Bar Park	d			13 40							14 10					14 40							15 10		
South Greenford	d			13 43							14 13					14 43							15 13		
Greenford	⊖ a			13 49							14 19					14 49							15 19		
Hanwell	d		←			13 46				←			14 16					14 46				←			15 16
Southall	d		13 27			13 49	13 57			13 57			14 19	14 27				14 49	14 57			14 57			15 19
Hayes & Harlington	d		13 31		13 45	13 53	→			14 01		14 15	14 23	14 31			14 45	14 53	→			15 01		15 15	15 23
Heathrow Terminals 1-2-3	✈ a					14 01							14 31					15 01							15 31
Heathrow Terminal 4	✈ a																								
West Drayton	d		13 36		13 49					14 06		14 19		14 36			14 49					15 06		15 19	
Iver	d				13 52							14 22					14 52							15 22	
Langley	d				13 55							14 25					14 55							15 25	
Slough 3	a		13 44		14 00			14 06		14 14		14 30		14 44			15 00			15 06		15 14		15 30	
	d		13 44		14 01			14 07		14 14		14 31		14 44			15 01			15 07		15 14		15 31	
Burnham	d		13 48							14 18				14 48								15 18			
Taplow	d	←	13 52						←	14 22				14 52							←	15 22			
Maidenhead 3	d	13 38	13 56		14 08				14 08	14 26		14 38		14 56			15 08				15 08	15 26		15 38	
Twyford 3	d	13 46	14 03		→				14 16	14 33		14 46		15 03			→				15 16	15 33		→	
Reading 7	a	13 52	14 12					14 21	14 22	14 42		14 52		15 12						15 21	15 22	15 42			
Oxford	a	14 30						14 47	15 13	*15 18*		15 30								15 47	16 13				

		GW	GW	GW	GW	GW	GW	HC		GW	GW	GW	GW	GW	HC	GW	GW	GW	GW	GW	GW	GW	GW	HC	GW
		1	1 ◇	1	1	1	1			1	1 ◇	1	1	1		1	1 ◇	1	1	1	1 ◇	1	1		1
														A				A							
											🚲										🚲				
London Paddington 15	⊖ d	15 15	15 21			15 25	15 30	15 33		15 45	15 51		15 55	16 00	16 03	16 15	16 21		16 25	16 30	16 33			16 33	16 45
Acton Main Line	d					15 31							16 01						16 31						
Ealing Broadway	⊖ d	15 22				15 34	15 37	15 41		15 52			16 04	16 07	16 11	16 22			16 34	16 37				16 41	16 52
West Ealing	d					15 36		15 43					16 06		16 13				16 36					16 43	
Drayton Green	d					15 39							16 09						16 39						
Castle Bar Park	d					15 40							16 10						16 40						
South Greenford	d					15 43							16 13						16 43						
Greenford	⊖ a					15 49							16 19						16 49						
Hanwell	d							15 46							16 16								←	16 46	
Southall	d	15 27			←			15 49		15 57		←		16 13	16 19	16 27				16 43		←	16 43	16 49	16 57
Hayes & Harlington	d	15 31			15 31		15 45	15 53		16 01		16 01		16 17	16 23	16 31				→		16 31	16 47	16 53	17 01
Heathrow Terminals 1-2-3	✈ a	→						16 01		→					16 31	→								17 01	
Heathrow Terminal 4	✈ a																								
West Drayton	d				15 36							16 06		16 22								16 36			17 06
Iver	d				15 39							16 10										16 40			17 09
Langley	d				15 42							16 13										16 43			→
Slough 3	a		15 37		15 47		15 54				16 06	16 18		16 30			16 37					16 48	16 56		
	d		15 37		15 47		15 55				16 07	16 19		16 30			16 37				16u48	16 49	16 57		
Burnham	d				15 51							16 23										16 53			
Taplow	d			←	15 55							16 26						←				16 56			
Maidenhead 3	d			15 38	15 59		16 03					16 30		16 38				16 38				17 00	17 04		
Twyford 3	d			15 46	16 07		16 11					16 38		→				16 46				17 08	17 12		
Reading 7	a		15 51	15 52	16 14		16 17				16 21	16 45					16 51	16 52			17 03	17 15	17 19		
Oxford	a		16 18	16 30			17 02				16 47						17 23	17 43			*17 34*	*18 06*	18 02		

		GW		GW	HC	GW	GW	GW	GW	GW	GW	GW	GW	GW	GW	HC	GW	GW		GW	GW	GW	GW	GW	HC
		1		1		1 ◇	1	1	1	1	1	1	1	1	1		1 ◇	1		1	1	1	1	1	
						B			C				C		A					A	D				
						🚲																			
London Paddington 15	⊖ d	16 55		17 00	17 03	17 06			17 14	17 17	17 18			17 25	17 30	17 33	17 36				17 44	17 47	17 55	18 00	18 03
Acton Main Line	d	17 01												17 31									18 01		
Ealing Broadway	⊖ d	17 04		17 07	17 11					17 25				17 34	17 37	17 41						17 55	18 04	18 07	18 11
West Ealing	d	17 06			17 13									17 36		17 43							18 06		18 13
Drayton Green	d	17 09												17 39									18 09		
Castle Bar Park	d	17 10												17 40									18 10		
South Greenford	d	17 13												17 43									18 13		
Greenford	⊖ a	17 19												17 49									18 19		
Hanwell	d				17 16											17 46									18 16
Southall	d			17 13	17 19					17 30					17 43	17 49						18 00		18 13	18 19
Hayes & Harlington	d			17 17	17 23					17 34					17 47	17 53						18 04		18 17	18 23
Heathrow Terminals 1-2-3	✈ a				17 31											18 01									18 31
Heathrow Terminal 4	✈ a																			←					
West Drayton	d			17 21			←	←		17 39					17 51			←		17 51		18 09		18 21	
Iver	d			17 24			17 09	17 24		17 43					→			17 43		17 54				18 24	
Langley	d			→			17 12	17 27		→								17 46		17 57		18 14		→	
Slough 3	a						17 17	17 32	17 36				←					17 51		18 02	18 06	→			
	d						17 17	17 33	17 37				17 37					17 52		18 03	18 07				
Burnham	d						17 21	17 37	→			←						17 56		18 07					
Taplow	d						17 25	17 40				17 40						17 59							
Maidenhead 3	d						17 29	→			17 40	17 44	17 48				17 59	18 03		18 12	18a14				
Twyford 3	d					17 28	17 37				17 48	17 52	17a58				18 08	18 12		18 20					
Reading 7	a					17 35	17 43				17 54	17 59					18 15	18 18		18 26					
Oxford	a						*18 15*				18 39	*18 34*					19 00	*19 06*		19 12					

For general notes see front of timetable
For details of catering facilities see Directory of Train Operators

For fast services between London Paddington and Reading see Table 116

A To Banbury (Table 116)
B To Westbury (Table 135)
C To Henley-on-Thames (Table 121)
D To Bourne End (Table 120)

Table 117

London → Greenford and Reading

(Local services only)

Mondays to Fridays

until Wednesday 26 March

Network Diagram - see first page of Table 116

Station		GW 1 ◇ A ⚒	GW 1	GW 1	GW 1 B	GW 1	GW 1 ◇	GW 1	GW 1 B	GW 1	GW 1	GW 1 ◇		GW 1	GW 1	HC	GW 1 C	GW 1	GW 1 ◇	GW 1	GW 1	GW 1	HC	GW 1 B	GW 1
London Paddington 15 ⊖	d	18 06			18 14	18 17	18 18			18 25	18 30	18 33				18 33	18 44	18 47	18 51	18 55		19 00	19 03	19 06	
Acton Main Line	d									18 31										19 01					
Ealing Broadway ⊖	d					18 25				18 34	18 37					18 41		18 55		19 04		19 07	19 11		
West Ealing	d									18 36						18 43				19 06			19 13		
Drayton Green	d									18 39										19 09					
Castle Bar Park	d									18 40										19 10					
South Greenford	d									18 43										19 13					
Greenford ⊖	a									18 49										19 19					
Hanwell	d															18 46							19 16		
Southall	d					18 30					18 43					18 49		19 00				19 13	19 19		←
Hayes & Harlington	d					18 34					18 47					18 53		19 04 →				19 17	19 23		19 04
Heathrow Terminals 1-2-3 ✈	a															19 01							19 31		
Heathrow Terminal 4 ✈	a													←	←										
West Drayton	d			←		18 39 →					18 51 →			18 39	18 51							19 22 →			19 09
Iver	d		←	18 24											18 54										
Langley	d		18 14	18 27										18 44	18 57										19 14
Slough 3	a		18 19	18 32	18 36				←					18 49	19 02		19 06		19 06						19 19
	d		18 20	18 33	18 37 →				18 37					18 50	19 03		19 07		19 07						19 20
Burnham	d		18 24	18 37				←						18 54	19 07										19 24
Taplow	d		18 27	18 40 →				18 40						18 57							←				19 27
Maidenhead 3	d		18 31				18 40	18 44	18 48			18 53		19 01	19 12 →		19a14				19 12			19 27	19 31
Twyford 3	d	18 27	18 39				18 48	18 52	18a58			19 03		19 09							19 20			19a35	19 40
Reading 7	a	18 35	18 46				18 54	18 59				19 10		19 16					19 21		19 26				19 46
Oxford	a	19 17					19 45	19 34				20 12							19 50		20 24				

Station		GW 1	GW 1	GW 1	GW 1 ◇ ⚒	GW 1		GW 1	GW 1	GW 1	HC	GW 1	GW 1 ◇	GW 1	GW 1	GW 1	GW 1	HC	GW 1	GW 1 ◇	GW 1	GW 1		GW 1	HC
London Paddington 15 ⊖	d		19 15	19 18	19 21				19 25	19 30	19 33	19 45	19 51			19 55	20 00	20 03	20 15	20 19		20 25		20 30	20 33
Acton Main Line	d								19 31							20 01						20 31			
Ealing Broadway ⊖	d			19 25					19 34	19 37	19 41	19 52				20 04	20 07	20 11	20 22			20 34		20 37	20 41
West Ealing	d								19 36		19 43					20 06		20 13				20 36			20 43
Drayton Green	d								19 39							20 09						20 39			
Castle Bar Park	d								19 40							20 10						20 40			
South Greenford	d								19 43							20 13						20 43			
Greenford ⊖	a								19 49							20 19						20 49			
Hanwell	d							←			19 46							20 16			←				20 46
Southall	d			19 31				19 31		19 43	19 49	19 57			←			20 19	20 27 →		20 27				20 49
Hayes & Harlington	d			→				19 35		19 47	19 53	20 01			20 01		20 15	20 23			20 31			20 45	20 53
Heathrow Terminals 1-2-3 ✈	a										20 01	→						20 31							21 01
Heathrow Terminal 4 ✈	a	←																							
West Drayton	d	19 22								19 51					20 06		20 19				20 36			20 49	
Iver	d	19 25								19 54					20 09		20 22							20 52	
Langley	d	19 28								19 57					20 12		20 25							20 55	
Slough 3	a	19 33			19 37			19 44		20 02			20 06		20 17		20 30			20 35	20 44			21 00	
	d	19 34			19 37			19 45		20 03			20 07		20 17		20 31			20 36	20 44			21 01	
Burnham	d	19 38						19 49		20 07					20 21						20 48				
Taplow	d					←		19 52						←	20 25						20 52				
Maidenhead 3	d	19 44 →	19 40			19 44		19 56		20 12 →				20 12	20 29		20 38				20 56			21 08 →	
Twyford 3	d		19 48			19 51		20 04						20 19	20 36		20 46				21 03				
Reading 7	a		19 55		19 51	19 58		20 12					20 21	20 26	20 43		20 52			20 52	21 12				
Oxford	a		20 44		20 19	20 34							20 49	21 07			21 30			21 16					

Station		GW 1	GW 1 ◇	GW 1	GW 1	GW 1	GW 1	HC	GW 1	GW 1 ◇	GW 1	GW 1	GW 1	GW 1	HC	GW FX 1		GW FO 1	GW 1 ◇	GW FX 1	GW FO 1	GW FX 1	GW FO 1	GW FX 1	HC
London Paddington 15 ⊖	d	20 45	20 51			20 55	21 00	21 03	21 15	21 21			21 25	21 30	21 33	21 45		21 45	21 48			21 57	21 59		22 03
Acton Main Line	d					21 01							21 31							←					
Ealing Broadway ⊖	d	20 52				21 04	21 07	21 11	21 22				21 34	21 37	21 41	21 52		21 52		21 52		22 04	22 06		22 11
West Ealing	d					21 06		21 13					21 36		21 43	→									22 13
Drayton Green	d					21 09							21 39												
Castle Bar Park	d					21 10							21 40												
South Greenford	d					21 13							21 43												
Greenford ⊖	a					21 19							21 49												
Hanwell	d				←			21 16				←			21 46										22 16
Southall	d	20 57			20 57			21 19	21 27			21 27			21 49			21 57		21 57	←	22 09			22 19
Hayes & Harlington	d	→			21 01		21 15	21 23	→			21 31		21 45	21 53			22 01		22 01	22 01	22 13	22 13		22 23
Heathrow Terminals 1-2-3 ✈	a							21 31							22 01			→							22 31
Heathrow Terminal 4 ✈	a																							←	
West Drayton	d				21 06		21 19					21 36								22 06	22 06	22 19 →		22 19	
Iver	d						21 22													22 09	22 09			22 22	
Langley	d						21 25													22 12	22 12			22 25	
Slough 3	a		21 06		21 14		21 30			21 37		21 44		21 54					22 04	22 17	22 17		22 23	22 30	
	d		21 07		21 14		21 31			21 37		21 44		21 55					22 05	22 17	22 17		22 23	22 33	
Burnham	d				21 18							21 48								22 21	22 21				
Taplow	d			←	21 22						←	21 52								22 25	22 25				
Maidenhead 3	d			21 08	21 26		21 38 →				21 38	21 56		22 02						22 29	22 29		22 32	22 41 →	
Twyford 3	d			21 16	21 33						21 46	22 03		22 10						22 36	22 36		22 40		
Reading 7	a		21 21	21 22	21 42					21 51	21 52	22 12		22 17					22 21	22 45	22 45		22 46		
Oxford	a		21 50	22 13						22 20	22 36			23 13					22 50				23 31		

For general notes see front of timetable
For details of catering facilities see Directory of Train Operators

For fast services between London Paddington and Reading see Table 116

A To Frome (Table 123)
B To Henley-on-Thames (Table 121)
C To Bourne End (Table 120)

London → Greenford and Reading

(Local services only)

Mondays to Fridays

until Wednesday 26 March

Network Diagram - see first page of Table 116

Station		GW	GW	GW	GW	GW	GW	GW	GW	HC		GW	GW	GW	GW	GW	GW	HC	GW	GW	GW	GW	GW		
		FX	FO	FO	FX	FX	FX	FX	FO				FX	FO	FX				FO		FX				
		1	1	1 ◇	1	1	1 ◇	1	1			1	1 ◇	1 ◇	1 ◇	1	1		1 ◇	1	1 ◇	1	1		
London Paddington 15 ⊖	d	22 14	22 14	22 21			22 21			22 33		22 46	22 48	22 51			22 59	23 03	23 21		23 21	23 29	23 48		
Acton Main Line	d											22 52				←							23 54		
Ealing Broadway ⊖	d	22 21	22 21							22 41		22 55				22 55	23 06	23 11				23 36	23 57		
West Ealing	d									22 43		→						23 13					23 59		
Drayton Green	d																								
Castle Bar Park	d																								
South Greenford	d																								
Greenford ⊖	a																								
Hanwell	d				←					22 46								23 16					00 02		
Southall	d	22 26	22 26		22 26				←	22 49							23 13	23 19					00 06		
Hayes & Harlington	d	→	22 30		22 30				22 30	22 53						23 03	23 17	23 23				23 44	00 10		
Heathrow Terminals 1-2-3 ✈	a		→							23 01								23 31							
Heathrow Terminal 4 ✈	a																	23 38							
West Drayton	d								22 35								23 24						00 14		
Iver	d								22 38								23 27						00 17		
Langley	d								22 41								23 30						00 20		
Slough 3	a			22 38	22 40		22 43	←	22 47				23 06	23 08	←	23 13	23 34		23 38		23 42	23 55	00 26		
	d			22 39	22 45		22 43	22 45	22 47				23 07	23 09	23 07	23 14	23 34		23 39		23 43	23 55	00 27		
Burnham	d				→			22 49	22 51				→			23 18							00 31		
Taplow	d					←		22 53	22 55							23 21				←			00 34		
Maidenhead 3	d					22 41		22 57	22 59							23 25	23 42			23 42		00 03	00 38		
Twyford 3	d					22 48		23 04	23 06							23 33	→			23 49		00 11	00 46		
Reading 7	a			22 55		22 56	23 02	23 12	23 14					23 25	23 34	23 40			23 55	23 57	00 01	00 18	00 53		
Oxford	a			23 25		23 41	23 33							23 51	00 09	00 22			00 28	*01 07*	00 34	01 07			

Mondays to Fridays

from Thursday 27 March

Station		GW	GW	GW	GW	GW	GW	GW	GW	GW	GW	GW	GW	GW	HC	HC	GW	GW	HC	GW	GW	GW	GW	GW	GW
		MO	MX	MO	MX	MX	MX	MO	MX	MX	MO	MX													
		1	1 ◇	1	1	1	1	1	1	1 ◇	1	1	1	1			1	1 ◇		1 ◇	1	1	1 ◇	1	1
																	A				A				
																		⊥		⊥			⊥		
London Paddington 15 ⊖	d	23p15	23p21			23p29	23p48	23p53		00 21	00 34	00 34	01 34	03 34	04 42	05 13	05 24	05 30	05 33	05 42		05 44	05 48		05 55
Acton Main Line	d						23p54																		06 01
Ealing Broadway ⊖	d	23p24				23p36	23p57	00 01			00 41	00 41	01 41	03 41	04 50	05 21	05 31		05 41			05 51			06 04
West Ealing	d						23p59												05 43						06 06
Drayton Green	d																								06 09
Castle Bar Park	d																								06 10
South Greenford	d																								06 13
Greenford ⊖	a																								06 19
Hanwell	d						00 02												05 46					←	
Southall	d	23p29		←			00 06	00 06			00 46	00 46	01 46	03 47	04 54	05 25	05 37		05 49		←	05 56		05 56	
Hayes & Harlington	d	23p33		23p33		23p44	00 10	00 10			00 50	00 50	01 50	03 51	04 58	05 29	05 42		05 53		05 42	→		06 00	
Heathrow Terminals 1-2-3 ✈	a	→													05 04	05 35	→		05 59						
Heathrow Terminal 4 ✈	a														05 10	05 41			06 05						
Heathrow Terminal 5 ✈	a								←						*05b32*	*05b46*			*06b16*						
West Drayton	d			23p37			00 14	00 14	00 14		00 55	00 55	01 55	03 55							05 46			06 05	
Iver	d						→		00 17												05 49				
Langley	d			23p42				00 19	00 20		00 59	00 59									05 52				
Slough 3	a		23p42	23p47		23p55		00 24	00 26	00 40	01 05	01 05	02 04	04 04				05 47		06 03	05 57		06 05	06 13	
	d		23p43	23p47		23p55		00 24	00 27	00 41	01 05	01 05	02 04	04 05				05 49		06 03	05 58		06 06	06 13	
Burnham	d			23p51				00 28	00 31		01 09	01 09												06 17	
Taplow	d							00 32	00 34			01 12												06 21	
Maidenhead 3	d			23p56		00 03		00 36	00 38		01 13	01 16	02 12	04 12							06 05			→	
Twyford 3	d			00 04	00 07	00 11		00 44	00 46		01 22	01 24	02 19	04 20							06 13				
Reading 7	a		00 01	00 10	00 17	00 18		00 50	00 53	00 58	01 32	01 33	02 28	04 28				06 04		06 20	06 19		06 20		
Oxford	a		00 34	*00c55*		01 07				01 30				*06 21*						06 52	07 17		*07 06*		

For general notes see front of timetable
For details of catering facilities see Directory of Train Operators

For fast services between London Paddington and Reading see Table 116

A To Bicester Town (Table 116)
b Change at Heathrow Terminals 1-2-3
c 31 March only

Table 117

Mondays to Fridays

from Thursday 27 March

London → Greenford and Reading

(Local services only)

Network Diagram - see first page of Table 116

		GW 1	HC	GW 1 ◇	GW 1	GW 1	GW 1	GW 1	GW 1 A	HC	GW 1	GW 1 ◇	GW 1 A	GW 1	GW 1	GW 1	HC	GW 1	GW 1 ◇	GW 1	GW 1	GW 1	GW 1	HC	GW 1
London Paddington 15 ⊖	d	06 00	06 03	06 07			06 15	06 25	06 30	06 33	06 45	06 48			06 55	07 00	07 03	07 15	07 21			07 25	07 30	07 33	07 45
Acton Main Line	d							06 31							07 01							07 31			
Ealing Broadway ⊖	d	06 07	06 11				06 22	06 34	06 37	06 41	06 52				07 04	07 07	07 11	07 22				07 34	07 37	07 41	07 52
West Ealing	d		06 13					06 36		06 43					07 06		07 13					07 36		07 43	
Drayton Green	d							06 39							07 09							07 39			
Castle Bar Park	d							06 40							07 10							07 40			
South Greenford	d							06 43							07 13							07 43			
Greenford ⊖	a							06 49							07 19							07 49			
Hanwell	d		06 16							06 46				←			07 16				←			07 46	
Southall	d	06 13	06 19			←	06 27			06 49	06 57			06 57		07 13	07 19	07 27			07 27		07 43	07 49	07 57
Hayes & Harlington	d	06 17	06 23			06 17	06 31		06 45	06 53	→			07 01		07 17	07 23	→			07 31		07 47	07 53	→
Heathrow Terminals 1-2-3 ✈	a	→	06 29							06 59							07 29							07 59	
Heathrow Terminal 4 ✈	a		06 35							07 05							07 35							08 05	
Heathrow Terminal 5 ✈	a		*06*b*46*							*07*b*16*							*07*b*46*							*08*b*16*	
West Drayton	d					06 21	06 36		06 49					07 06		07 21					07 36		07 51		
Iver	d					06 24			06 52							07 24							07 54		
Langley	d					06 27			06 55							07 27							07 57		
Slough 3	a			06 22		06 32	06 44		07 00			07 03		07 14		07 32			07 37		07 44		08 02		
	d			06 23		06 33	06 44		07 01			07 04		07 14		07 33			07 37		07 44		08 03		
Burnham	d				←		06 48							07 18							07 48				
Taplow	d				06 21		06 52						←	07 22						←	07 52				
Maidenhead 3	d				06 25	06 40	06 56		07 09				07 09	07 26		07 40				07 40	07 56		08 10		
Twyford 3	d				06 32	06 48	07 03		→				07 16	07 33		→				07 48	08 03		→		
Reading 7	a			06 39	06 40	06 54	07 12					07 18	07 23	07 42					07 51	07 54	08 12				
Oxford	a			07 10	*07 35*	07 42						07 48	08 00						08 20	08 41					

		GW 1 ◇ 🍴	GW 1	GW 1		GW 1	GW 1	HC	GW 1	GW 1 ◇	GW 1	GW 1	GW 1	GW 1	HC	GW 1	GW 1	GW 1 ◇ 🍴	GW 1	GW 1	GW 1	GW 1	GW 1	HC	GW 1
London Paddington 15 ⊖	d	07 51				07 55	08 00	08 03	08 15	08 21			08 25	08 30	08 33	08 40	08 45	08 51				08 55	09 00	09 03	09 15
Acton Main Line	d					08 01							08 31									09 01			
Ealing Broadway ⊖	d					08 04	08 07	08 11	08 22				08 34	08 37	08 41	08 47	08 52					09 04	09 07	09 11	09 22
West Ealing	d					08 06		08 13					08 36		08 43		08 55					09 06		09 13	
Drayton Green	d					08 09							08 39									09 09			
Castle Bar Park	d					08 10							08 40									09 10			
South Greenford	d					08 13							08 43									09 13			
Greenford ⊖	a					08 19							08 49									09 19			
Hanwell	d			←				08 16				←			08 46		08 57				←			09 16	
Southall	d			07 57			08 13	08 19	08 27			08 27		08 43	08 49	08 52	09 01				09 01			09 19	09 27
Hayes & Harlington	d			08 01			08 17	08 23	→			08 31		08 47	08 53	08 56	→				09 05		09 15	09 23	→
Heathrow Terminals 1-2-3 ✈	a							08 29							08 59									09 29	
Heathrow Terminal 4 ✈	a							08 35							09 05									09 35	
Heathrow Terminal 5 ✈	a							*08*b*46*							*09*b*16*									*09*b*46*	
West Drayton	d			08 06			08 21					08 36		08 51							09 09		09 19		
Iver	d						08 24							08 54							09 12		09 22		
Langley	d						08 27							08 57							09 15		09 25		
Slough 3	a	08 06		08 14			08 32			08 37		08 44		09 02		09 06		09 06			09 20		09 30		
	d	08 07		08 14			08 33			08 37		08 44		09 03		09 06		09 07			09 21		09 31		
Burnham	d			08 18								08 48				09 10				←					
Taplow	d		←	08 22							←	08 52				09 14			←	09 14					
Maidenhead 3	d		08 10	08 26			08 40				08 40	08 56		09 10		→			09 10	09 18	09 28		09 38		
Twyford 3	d		08 18	08 33			→				08 48	09 03		→					09 18	09 25	09a35		→		
Reading 7	a	08 21	08 24	08 42						08 51	08 54	09 12						09 21	09 24	09 33					
Oxford	a	08 47	09 14							09 24	09 39							09 47	10 13	*10 06*					

		GW 1 ◇	GW 1	GW 1	GW 1	GW 1	HC	GW 1	GW 1 ◇ 🍴	GW 1	GW 1	GW 1	GW 1	HC	GW 1	GW 1 ◇	GW 1	GW 1	GW 1	GW 1	HC	GW 1	GW 1 ◇ 🍴	GW 1	GW 1
London Paddington 15 ⊖	d	09 21			09 25	09 30	09 33	09 45	09 51			09 55	10 00	10 03	10 15	10 21			10 25	10 30	10 33	10 45	10 51		
Acton Main Line	d				09 31							10 01							10 31						
Ealing Broadway ⊖	d				09 34	09 37	09 41	09 52				10 04	10 07	10 11	10 22				10 34	10 37	10 41	10 52			
West Ealing	d				09 36		09 43					10 06		10 13					10 36		10 43				
Drayton Green	d				09 39							10 09							10 39						
Castle Bar Park	d				09 40							10 10							10 40						
South Greenford	d				09 43							10 13							10 43						
Greenford ⊖	a				09 49							10 19							10 49						
Hanwell	d			←			09 46				←			10 16				←			10 46				←
Southall	d			09 27			09 49	09 57			09 57			10 19	10 27			10 27			10 49	10 57			10 57
Hayes & Harlington	d			09 31		09 45	09 53	→			10 01		10 15	10 23	→			10 31		10 45	10 53	→			11 01
Heathrow Terminals 1-2-3 ✈	a						09 59							10 29							10 59				
Heathrow Terminal 4 ✈	a						10 05							10 35							11 05				
Heathrow Terminal 5 ✈	a						*10*b*16*							*10*b*46*							*11*b*16*				
West Drayton	d			09 36		09 49					10 06		10 19					10 36		10 49					11 06
Iver	d					09 52							10 22							10 52					
Langley	d					09 55							10 25							10 55					
Slough 3	a	09 37		09 44		10 00			10 06		10 14		10 30			10 37		10 44		11 00			11 06		11 14
	d	09 37		09 44		10 01			10 07		10 14		10 31			10 37		10 44		11 01			11 07		11 14
Burnham	d			09 48							10 18							10 48							11 18
Taplow	d		←	09 52						←	10 22						←	10 52						←	11 22
Maidenhead 3	d		09 38	09 56		10 08				10 08	10 26		10 38				10 38	10 56		11 08				11 08	11 26
Twyford 3	d		09 46	10 03		→				10 16	10 33		→				10 46	11 03		→				11 16	11 33
Reading 7	a	09 51	09 52	10 12					10 21	10 22	10 42					10 51	10 52	11 12					11 21	11 22	11 42
Oxford	a	10 18	10 30						10 47	11 13						11 18	11 30						11 47	12 13	

For general notes see front of timetable
For details of catering facilities see Directory of Train Operators

For fast services between London Paddington and Reading see Table 116

A To Worcester Foregate Street (Table 126)
b Change at Heathrow Terminals 1-2-3

from Thursday 27 March

London → Greenford and Reading

(Local services only)

Network Diagram - see first page of Table 116

		GW 1	GW 1	HC	GW 1	GW 1 ◇	GW 1	GW 1		GW 1	GW 1	HC	GW 1	GW 1 ◇	GW 1	GW 1	GW 1	GW 1	HC	GW 1	GW 1 ◇	GW 1	GW 1	GW 1	GW 1
London Paddington 15	⊖ d	10 55	11 00	11 03	11 15	11 21	.	.	.	11 25	11 30	11 33	11 45	11 51	.	.	11 55	12 00	12 03	12 15	12 21	.	.	12 25	12 30
Acton Main Line	d	11 01	.	.	.	.	.	.	.	11 31	.	.	.	.	.	.	12 01	.	.	.	.	.	.	12 31	.
Ealing Broadway	⊖ d	11 04	11 07	11 11	11 22	.	.	.	.	11 34	11 37	11 41	11 52	.	.	.	12 04	12 07	12 11	12 22	.	.	.	12 34	12 37
West Ealing	d	11 06	.	11 13	.	.	.	.	.	11 36	.	11 43	.	.	.	.	12 06	.	12 13	.	.	.	.	12 36	.
Drayton Green	d	11 09	.	.	.	.	.	.	.	11 39	.	.	.	.	.	.	12 09	.	.	.	.	.	.	12 39	.
Castle Bar Park	d	11 10	.	.	.	.	.	.	.	11 40	.	.	.	.	.	.	12 10	.	.	.	.	.	.	12 40	.
South Greenford	d	11 13	.	.	.	.	.	.	.	11 43	.	.	.	.	.	.	12 13	.	.	.	.	.	.	12 43	.
Greenford	⊖ a	11 19	.	.	.	.	.	.	.	11 49	.	.	.	.	.	.	12 19	.	.	.	.	.	.	12 49	.
Hanwell	d	.	.	11 16	.	.	.	←	.	.	.	11 46	.	.	.	←	.	.	12 16	.	.	.	←	.	.
Southall	d	.	.	11 19	11 27	.	.	11 27	.	.	.	11 49	11 57	.	.	11 57	.	.	12 19	12 27	.	.	12 27	.	.
Hayes & Harlington	d	.	11 15	11 23	→	.	.	11 31	.	.	11 45	11 53	→	.	.	12 01	.	12 15	12 23	→	.	.	12 31	.	12 45
Heathrow Terminals 1-2-3	✈ a	.	.	11 29	.	.	.	.	.	.	.	11 59	.	.	.	.	.	.	12 29	.	.	.	.	.	.
Heathrow Terminal 4	✈ a	.	.	11 35	.	.	.	.	.	.	.	12 05	.	.	.	.	.	.	12 35	.	.	.	.	.	.
Heathrow Terminal 5	✈ a	.	.	*11b46*	.	.	.	.	.	.	.	*12b16*	.	.	.	.	.	.	*12b46*	.	.	.	.	.	.
West Drayton	d	.	11 19	.	.	.	.	11 36	.	.	11 49	.	.	.	.	12 06	.	12 19	.	.	.	.	12 36	.	12 49
Iver	d	.	11 22	.	.	.	.	.	.	.	11 52	.	.	.	.	.	.	12 22	.	.	.	.	.	.	12 52
Langley	d	.	11 25	.	.	.	.	.	.	.	11 55	.	.	.	.	.	.	12 25	.	.	.	.	.	.	12 55
Slough 3	a	.	11 30	.	.	11 37	.	11 44	.	.	12 00	.	.	12 06	.	12 14	.	12 30	.	.	12 37	.	12 44	.	13 00
	d	.	11 31	.	.	11 37	.	11 44	.	.	12 01	.	.	12 07	.	12 14	.	12 31	.	.	12 37	.	12 44	.	13 01
Burnham	d	.	.	.	.	.	.	11 48	.	.	.	.	.	.	.	12 18	.	.	.	.	.	.	12 48	.	.
Taplow	d	.	.	.	.	.	←	11 52	.	.	.	.	.	.	←	12 22	.	.	.	.	.	←	12 52	.	.
Maidenhead 3	d	.	11 38	.	.	.	11 38	11 56	.	.	12 08	.	.	.	12 08	12 26	.	12 38	.	.	.	12 38	12 56	.	13 08
Twyford 3	d	.	→	.	.	.	11 46	12 03	.	.	→	.	.	.	12 16	12 33	.	→	.	.	.	12 46	13 03	.	→
Reading 7	a	.	.	.	.	11 51	11 52	12 12	.	.	.	.	.	12 21	12 22	12 42	.	.	.	.	12 51	12 52	13 12	.	.
Oxford	a	.	.	.	.	12 18	12 30	.	.	.	.	.	.	12 47	13 13	.	.	.	.	.	13 18	13 30	.	.	.

		HC	GW 1	GW 1 ◇	GW 1	GW 1	GW 1	GW 1	HC	GW 1	GW 1 ◇	GW 1	GW 1	GW 1	GW 1	HC	GW 1	GW 1 ◇	GW 1	GW 1	GW 1	GW 1	HC	GW 1	GW 1
London Paddington 15	⊖ d	12 33	12 45	12 51	.	.	12 55	13 00	13 03	13 15	13 21	.	.	13 25	13 30	13 33	13 45	13 51	.	.	13 55	14 00	14 03	14 15	14 25
Acton Main Line	d	.	.	.	.	.	13 01	.	.	.	.	.	.	13 31	.	.	.	.	.	.	14 01	.	.	.	14 31
Ealing Broadway	⊖ d	12 41	12 52	.	.	.	13 04	13 07	13 11	13 22	.	.	.	13 34	13 37	13 41	13 52	.	.	.	14 04	14 07	14 11	14 22	14 34
West Ealing	d	12 43	.	.	.	.	13 06	.	13 13	.	.	.	.	13 36	.	13 43	.	.	.	.	14 06	.	14 13	.	14 36
Drayton Green	d	.	.	.	.	.	13 09	.	.	.	.	.	.	13 39	.	.	.	.	.	.	14 09	.	.	.	14 39
Castle Bar Park	d	.	.	.	.	.	13 10	.	.	.	.	.	.	13 40	.	.	.	.	.	.	14 10	.	.	.	14 40
South Greenford	d	.	.	.	.	.	13 13	.	.	.	.	.	.	13 43	.	.	.	.	.	.	14 13	.	.	.	14 43
Greenford	⊖ a	.	.	.	.	.	13 19	.	.	.	.	.	.	13 49	.	.	.	.	.	.	14 19	.	.	.	14 49
Hanwell	d	12 46	.	.	.	←	.	.	13 16	.	.	.	←	.	.	13 46	.	.	.	←	.	.	14 16	.	.
Southall	d	12 49	12 57	.	.	12 57	.	.	13 19	13 27	.	.	13 27	.	.	13 49	13 57	.	.	13 57	.	.	14 19	14 27	.
Hayes & Harlington	d	12 53	→	.	.	13 01	.	13 15	13 23	→	.	.	13 31	.	13 45	13 53	→	.	.	14 01	.	14 15	14 23	14 31	.
Heathrow Terminals 1-2-3	✈ a	12 59	.	.	.	.	.	.	13 29	.	.	.	.	.	.	13 59	.	.	.	.	.	.	14 29	.	.
Heathrow Terminal 4	✈ a	13 05	.	.	.	.	.	.	13 35	.	.	.	.	.	.	14 05	.	.	.	.	.	.	14 35	.	.
Heathrow Terminal 5	✈ a	*13b16*	.	.	.	.	.	.	*13b46*	.	.	.	.	.	.	*14b16*	.	.	.	.	.	.	*14b46*	.	.
West Drayton	d	.	.	.	.	13 06	.	13 19	.	.	.	.	13 36	.	13 49	.	.	.	.	14 06	.	14 19	.	14 36	.
Iver	d	.	.	.	.	.	.	13 22	.	.	.	.	.	.	13 52	.	.	.	.	.	.	14 22	.	.	.
Langley	d	.	.	.	.	.	.	13 25	.	.	.	.	.	.	13 55	.	.	.	.	.	.	14 25	.	.	.
Slough 3	a	.	.	13 06	.	13 14	.	13 30	.	.	13 37	.	13 44	.	14 00	.	.	14 06	.	14 14	.	14 30	.	14 44	.
	d	.	.	13 07	.	13 14	.	13 31	.	.	13 37	.	13 44	.	14 01	.	.	14 07	.	14 14	.	14 31	.	14 44	.
Burnham	d	.	.	.	.	13 18	.	.	.	.	.	.	13 48	.	.	.	.	.	.	14 18	.	.	.	14 48	.
Taplow	d	.	.	.	←	13 22	.	.	.	.	.	←	13 52	.	.	.	.	.	←	14 22	.	.	.	14 52	.
Maidenhead 3	d	.	.	.	13 08	13 26	.	13 38	.	.	.	13 38	13 56	.	14 08	.	.	.	14 08	14 26	.	14 38	.	14 56	.
Twyford 3	d	.	.	.	13 16	13 33	.	→	.	.	.	13 46	14 03	.	→	.	.	.	14 16	14 33	.	14 46	.	15 03	.
Reading 7	a	.	.	13 21	13 22	13 42	.	.	.	.	13 51	13 52	14 12	.	.	.	.	14 21	14 22	14 42	.	14 52	.	15 12	.
Oxford	a	.	.	13 47	14 13	.	.	.	.	.	14 18	14 30	.	.	.	.	.	14 47	15 13	*15 18*	.	15 30	.	.	.

		GW 1	HC	GW 1	GW 1 ◇	GW 1	GW 1	GW 1	GW 1	HC	GW 1	GW 1 ◇		GW 1	GW 1	GW 1	GW 1	HC	GW 1	GW 1 ◇	GW 1	GW 1	GW 1 A	HC	GW 1
London Paddington 15	⊖ d	14 30	14 33	14 45	14 51	.	.	14 55	15 00	15 03	15 15	15 21	.	.	.	15 25	15 30	15 33	15 45	15 51	.	15 55	16 00	16 03	16 15
Acton Main Line	d	.	.	.	.	.	.	15 01	.	.	.	.	.	.	.	15 31	.	.	.	.	.	16 01	.	.	.
Ealing Broadway	⊖ d	14 37	14 41	14 52	.	.	.	15 04	15 07	15 11	15 22	.	.	.	.	15 34	15 37	15 41	15 52	.	.	16 04	16 07	16 11	16 22
West Ealing	d	.	14 43	.	.	.	.	15 06	.	15 13	.	.	.	.	.	15 36	.	15 43	.	.	.	16 06	.	16 13	.
Drayton Green	d	.	.	.	.	.	.	15 09	.	.	.	.	.	.	.	15 39	.	.	.	.	.	16 09	.	.	.
Castle Bar Park	d	.	.	.	.	.	.	15 10	.	.	.	.	.	.	.	15 40	.	.	.	.	.	16 10	.	.	.
South Greenford	d	.	.	.	.	.	.	15 13	.	.	.	.	.	.	.	15 43	.	.	.	.	.	16 13	.	.	.
Greenford	⊖ a	.	.	.	.	.	.	15 19	.	.	.	.	.	.	.	15 49	.	.	.	.	.	16 19	.	.	.
Hanwell	d	.	14 46	.	.	.	←	.	.	15 16	.	.	.	.	.	.	.	15 46	.	.	.	.	.	16 16	.
Southall	d	.	14 49	14 57	.	.	14 57	.	.	15 19	15 27	.	.	.	←	.	.	15 49	15 57	.	←	.	16 13	16 19	16 27
Hayes & Harlington	d	14 45	14 53	→	.	.	15 01	.	15 15	15 23	15 31	.	.	.	15 31	.	15 45	15 53	16 01	.	16 01	.	16 17	16 23	16 31
Heathrow Terminals 1-2-3	✈ a	.	14 59	.	.	.	.	.	.	15 29	→	.	.	.	.	.	.	15 59	→	.	.	.	.	16 29	→
Heathrow Terminal 4	✈ a	.	15 05	.	.	.	.	.	.	15 35	.	.	.	.	.	.	.	16 05	.	.	.	.	.	16 35	.
Heathrow Terminal 5	✈ a	.	*15b16*	.	.	.	.	.	.	*15b46*	.	.	.	.	.	.	.	*16b16*	.	.	.	.	.	*16b46*	.
West Drayton	d	14 49	.	.	.	.	15 06	.	15 19	.	.	.	.	.	15 36	.	.	.	.	.	16 06	.	16 22	.	.
Iver	d	14 52	.	.	.	.	.	.	15 22	.	.	.	.	.	15 39	.	.	.	.	.	16 10	.	.	.	.
Langley	d	14 55	.	.	.	.	.	.	15 25	.	.	.	.	.	15 42	.	.	.	.	.	16 13	.	.	.	.
Slough 3	a	15 00	.	.	15 06	.	15 14	.	15 30	.	.	15 37	.	.	15 47	.	15 54	.	.	16 06	16 18	.	16 30	.	.
	d	15 01	.	.	15 07	.	15 14	.	15 31	.	.	15 37	.	.	15 47	.	15 55	.	.	16 07	16 19	.	16 30	.	.
Burnham	d	.	.	.	.	.	15 18	.	.	.	.	.	.	.	15 51	.	.	.	.	.	16 23	.	.	.	.
Taplow	d	.	.	.	.	←	15 22	.	.	.	.	.	.	←	15 55	.	.	.	.	.	16 26	.	.	.	.
Maidenhead 3	d	15 08	.	.	.	15 08	15 26	.	15 38	.	.	.	.	15 38	15 59	.	16 03	.	.	.	16 30	.	16 38	.	.
Twyford 3	d	→	.	.	.	15 16	15 33	.	→	.	.	.	.	15 46	16 07	.	16 11	.	.	.	16 38	.	→	.	.
Reading 7	a	.	.	.	15 21	15 22	15 42	.	.	.	.	15 51	.	15 52	16 14	.	16 17	.	.	16 21	16 45	.	.	.	.
Oxford	a	.	.	.	15 47	16 13	.	.	.	.	.	16 18	.	16 30	.	.	17 02	.	.	16 47	.	.	.	.	.

For general notes see front of timetable
For details of catering facilities see Directory of Train Operators

For fast services between London Paddington and Reading see Table 116

A To Banbury (Table 116)
b Change at Heathrow Terminals 1-2-3

Table 117

Mondays to Fridays
from Thursday 27 March

London → Greenford and Reading

(Local services only)

Network Diagram - see first page of Table 116

		GW	GW	GW	GW	GW	GW	GW	HC	GW	GW	GW	HC	GW	GW	GW	GW	GW	GW	GW	GW	GW	GW	HC	GW
		1 ◇	1	1	1	1 ◇	1	1		1	1	1		1 ◇	1	1	1	1	1	1	1	1	1		1 ◇
			A											B			C				C		A		
						⊥								⊥											
London Paddington 15	⊖ d	16 21		16 25	16 30	16 33			16 33	16 45	16 55	17 00	17 03	17 06			17 14	17 17	17 18			17 25	17 30	17 33	17 36
Acton Main Line	d			16 31							17 01											17 31			
Ealing Broadway	⊖ d			16 34	16 37				16 41	16 52	17 04	17 07	17 11					17 25				17 34	17 37	17 41	
West Ealing	d			16 36					16 43		17 06		17 13									17 36		17 43	
Drayton Green	d			16 39							17 09											17 39			
Castle Bar Park	d			16 40							17 10											17 40			
South Greenford	d			16 43							17 13											17 43			
Greenford	⊖ a			16 49							17 19											17 49			
Hanwell	d							←	16 46				17 16											17 46	
Southall	d				16 43		←	16 43	16 49	16 57		17 13	17 19					17 30					17 43	17 49	
Hayes & Harlington	d				→		16 31	16 47	16 53	17 01		17 17	17 23					17 34					17 47	17 53	
Heathrow Terminals 1-2-3	✈ a								16 59				17 29											17 59	
Heathrow Terminal 4	✈ a								17 05				17 35											18 05	
Heathrow Terminal 5	✈ a								17b16				17b46											18b16	
West Drayton	d						16 36			17 06		17 21			←	←		17 39					17 51		
Iver	d						16 40			17 09		17 24			17 09	17 24		17 43					→		
Langley	d						16 43			→		→			17 12	17 27		→							
Slough 3	a	16 37					16 48	16 56							17 17	17 32	17 36				←				
	d	16 37				16u48	16 49	16 57							17 17	17 33	17 37				17 37				
Burnham	d						16 53								17 21	17 37	→			←					
Taplow	d		←				16 56								17 25	17 40				17 40					
Maidenhead 3	d		16 38				17 00	17 04							17 29	→			17 40	17 44	17 48				17 59
Twyford 3	d		16 46				17 08	17 12						17 28	17 37				17 48	17 52	17a58				18 08
Reading 7	a	16 51	16 52			17 03	17 15	17 19						17 35	17 43				17 54	17 59					18 15
Oxford	a	17 23	17 43			*17 34*	*18 06*	18 02							*18 15*				18 39	*18 34*					19 00

		GW	GW	GW	GW	GW	GW	HC	GW	GW	GW	GW	GW	GW	GW	GW		GW	GW	GW	GW	GW	HC	GW	GW
		1	1	1	1	1	1		1 ◇	1	1	1	1	1 ◇	1	1		1	1	1 ◇	1	1		1	1
			A	D					E			C				C								D	
									⊥																
London Paddington 15	⊖ d			17 44	17 47	17 55	18 00	18 03	18 06			18 14	18 17	18 18				18 25	18 30	18 33			18 33	18 44	18 47
Acton Main Line	d					18 01												18 31							
Ealing Broadway	⊖ d				17 55	18 04	18 07	18 11					18 25					18 34	18 37				18 41		18 55
West Ealing	d					18 06		18 13										18 36					18 43		
Drayton Green	d					18 09												18 39							
Castle Bar Park	d					18 10												18 40							
South Greenford	d					18 13												18 43							
Greenford	⊖ a					18 19												18 49							
Hanwell	d							18 16															18 46		
Southall	d				18 00		18 13	18 19					18 30						18 43				18 49		19 00
Hayes & Harlington	d				18 04		18 17	18 23					18 34						18 47				18 53		19 04
Heathrow Terminals 1-2-3	✈ a							18 29															18 59		→
Heathrow Terminal 4	✈ a							18 35															19 05		
Heathrow Terminal 5	✈ a		←					18b46													←	←	19b16		
West Drayton	d	←	17 51		18 09		18 21				←		18 39						18 51		18 39	18 51			
Iver	d	17 43	17 54				18 24			←	18 24		→						→			18 54			
Langley	d	17 46	17 57		18 14		→			18 14	18 27										18 44	18 57			
Slough 3	a	17 51	18 02	18 06	→					18 19	18 32	18 36				←					18 49	19 02		19 06	
	d	17 52	18 03	18 07						18 20	18 33	18 37				18 37					18 50	19 03		19 07	
Burnham	d	17 56	18 07							18 24	18 37	→			←						18 54	19 07			
Taplow	d	17 59								18 27	18 40				18 40						18 57				
Maidenhead 3	d	18 03	18 12	18a14						18 31	→			18 40	18 44	18 48				18 53	19 01	19 12		19a14	
Twyford 3	d	18 12	18 20						18 27	18 39				18 48	18 52	18a58				19 03	19 09	→			
Reading 7	a	18 18	18 26						18 35	18 46				18 54	18 59					19 10	19 16				
Oxford	a	*19 06*	19 12						*19 17*					19 45	*19 34*					20 12					

		GW	GW	GW	GW	HC	GW	GW	GW	GW	GW	GW	GW	GW	GW	HC	GW	GW	GW	GW	GW	GW	HC	GW	GW
		1 ◇	1	1	1		1	1	1	1	1 ◇	1	1	1	1		1	1 ◇	1	1	1	1		1	1 ◇
							C																		
											⊥														
London Paddington 15	⊖ d	18 51	18 55		19 00	19 03	19 06			19 18	19 21			19 25	19 30	19 33	19 45	19 51			19 55	20 00	20 03	20 15	20 19
Acton Main Line	d		19 01											19 31							20 01				
Ealing Broadway	⊖ d		19 04		19 07	19 11				19 25				19 34	19 37	19 41	19 52				20 04	20 07	20 11	20 22	
West Ealing	d		19 06			19 13								19 36		19 43					20 06		20 13		
Drayton Green	d		19 09											19 39							20 09				
Castle Bar Park	d		19 10											19 40							20 10				
South Greenford	d		19 13											19 43							20 13				
Greenford	⊖ a		19 19											19 49							20 19				
Hanwell	d					19 16							←			19 46							20 16		
Southall	d				19 13	19 19		←		19 31			19 31		19 43	19 49	19 57			←			20 19	20 27	
Hayes & Harlington	d				19 17	19 23		19 04		→			19 35		19 47	19 53	20 01			20 01		20 15	20 23	→	
Heathrow Terminals 1-2-3	✈ a					19 29										19 59	→						20 29		
Heathrow Terminal 4	✈ a					19 35										20 05							20 35		
Heathrow Terminal 5	✈ a					19b46			←							20b16							20b46		
West Drayton	d				19 22			19 09	19 22						19 51					20 06		20 19			
Iver	d				→				19 25						19 54					20 09		20 22			
Langley	d							19 14	19 28						19 57					20 12		20 25			
Slough 3	a	19 06						19 19	19 33		19 37		19 44		20 02			20 06		20 17		20 30			20 35
	d	19 07						19 20	19 34		19 37		19 45		20 03			20 07		20 17		20 31			20 36
Burnham	d							19 24	19 38				19 49		20 07					20 21					
Taplow	d			←				19 27				←	19 52						←	20 25					
Maidenhead 3	d			19 12			19 27	19 31	19 44			19 44	19 56		20 12				20 12	20 29		20 38			
Twyford 3	d			19 20			19a35	19 40	→			19 51	20 04		→				20 19	20 36		20 46			
Reading 7	a	19 21		19 26				19 46			19 51	19 58	20 12					20 21	20 26	20 43		20 52			20 52
Oxford	a	19 50		20 24							20 19	*20 34*						20 49	21 07			21 30			21 16

For general notes see front of timetable
For details of catering facilities see Directory of Train Operators

For fast services between London Paddington and Reading see Table 116

A To Banbury (Table 116)
B To Westbury (Table 135)
C To Henley-on-Thames (Table 121)
D To Bourne End (Table 120)
E To Frome (Table 123)
b Change at Heathrow Terminals 1-2-3

Table 117

Mondays to Fridays

from Thursday 27 March

London → Greenford and Reading
(Local services only)

Network Diagram - see first page of Table 116

		GW	GW	GW	HC	GW	GW	GW	GW	GW	GW	HC	GW	GW	GW	GW	GW	GW	HC	GW	GW	GW	GW	GW	GW
																							FX	FO	FX
		1	1	1		1	1 ◇	1	1	1	1		1	1 ◇	1	1	1	1		1	1 ◇	1	1	1	1
London Paddington 15 ⊖	d		20 25	20 30	20 33	20 45	20 51			20 55	21 00	21 03	21 15	21 21			21 25	21 30	21 33	21 45	21 48		21 57	21 59	
Acton Main Line	d		20 31							21 01							21 31								
Ealing Broadway ⊖	d		20 34	20 37	20 41	20 52				21 04	21 07	21 11	21 22				21 34	21 37	21 41	21 52			22 04	22 06	
West Ealing	d		20 36		20 43					21 06		21 13					21 36		21 43						
Drayton Green	d		20 39							21 09							21 39								
Castle Bar Park	d		20 40							21 10							21 40								
South Greenford	d		20 43							21 13							21 43								
Greenford ⊖	a		20 49							21 19							21 49								
Hanwell	d	←			20 46				←			21 16				←			21 46						
Southall	d	20 27			20 49	20 57			20 57			21 19	21 27			21 27			21 49	21 57		←	22 09		
Hayes & Harlington	d	20 31		20 45	20 53	→			21 01		21 15	21 23	→			21 31		21 45	21 53	22 01		22 01	22 13	22 13	
Heathrow Terminals 1-2-3 ✈	a				20 59							21 29							21 59	→					
Heathrow Terminal 4 ✈	a				21 05							21 35							22 05						
Heathrow Terminal 5 ✈	a				21b16							21b46							22b16						←
West Drayton	d	20 36		20 49					21 06		21 19					21 36						22 06	22 19		22 19
Iver	d			20 52							21 22											22 09	→		22 22
Langley	d			20 55							21 25											22 12			22 25
Slough 3	a	20 44		21 00			21 06		21 14		21 30			21 37		21 44		21 54			22 04	22 17		22 23	22 30
	d	20 44		21 01			21 07		21 14		21 31			21 37		21 44		21 55			22 05	22 17		22 23	22 33
Burnham	d	20 48							21 18							21 48						22 21			
Taplow	d	20 52						←	21 22						←	21 52						22 25			
Maidenhead 3	d	20 56		21 08				21 08	21 26		21 38				21 38	21 56		22 02				22 29		22 32	22 41
Twyford 3	d	21 03		→				21 16	21 33		→				21 46	22 03		22 10				22 36		22 40	→
Reading 7	a	21 12					21 21	21 22	21 42					21 51	21 52	22 12		22 17			22 21	22 45		22 46	
Oxford	a						21 50	22 13						22 20	22 36			23 13			22 50			23 31	

		HC	GW	GW	GW	GW	GW	GW	GW	GW	HC	GW	GW	GW	GW	GW	GW	HC	GW	GW	GW	GW	GW		
			FX	FO	FO	FX	FX	FX	FX	FO			FX	FO	FX				FO		FX				
			1	1	1 ◇	1	1	1 ◇	1	1		1	1 ◇	1 ◇	1 ◇	1	1		1 ◇	1	1 ◇	1	1		
London Paddington 15 ⊖	d	22 03	22 14	22 14	22 21			22 21			22 33	22 46	22 48	22 51			22 59	23 03	23 21		23 21	23 29	23 48		
Acton Main Line	d											22 52				←							23 54		
Ealing Broadway ⊖	d	22 11	22 21	22 21							22 41	22 55				22 55	23 06	23 11				23 36	23 57		
West Ealing	d	22 13									22 43	→						23 13					23 59		
Drayton Green	d																								
Castle Bar Park	d																								
South Greenford	d																								
Greenford ⊖	a																								
Hanwell	d	22 16				←					22 46							23 16					00 02		
Southall	d	22 19	22 26	22 26		22 26				←	22 49						23 13	23 19					00 06		
Hayes & Harlington	d	22 23	→	22 30		22 30				22 30	22 53					23 03	23 17	23 23				23 44	00 10		
Heathrow Terminals 1-2-3 ✈	a	22 29		→							22 59							23 29							
Heathrow Terminal 4 ✈	a	22 35									23 05							23 35							
Heathrow Terminal 5 ✈	a	22b46									23b16							23b46							
West Drayton	d									22 35							23 24						00 14		
Iver	d									22 38							23 27						00 17		
Langley	d									22 41							23 30						00 20		
Slough 3	a				22 38	22 40		22 43	←	22 47			23 06	23 08	←	23 13	23 34		23 38		23 42	23 55	00 26		
	d				22 39	22 45		22 43	22 45	22 47			23 07	23 09	23 07	23 14	23 34		23 39		23 43	23 55	00 27		
Burnham	d					→			22 49	22 51			→			23 18							00 31		
Taplow	d						←		22 53	22 55						23 21				←			00 34		
Maidenhead 3	d						22 41		22 57	22 59						23 25	23 42			23 42		00 03	00 38		
Twyford 3	d						22 48		23 04	23 06						23 33	→			23 49		00 11	00 46		
Reading 7	a				22 55		22 56	23 02	23 12	23 14				23 25	23 34	23 40			23 55	23 57	00 01	00 18	00 53		
Oxford	a				23 25		23 41	23 33						23 51	00 09	00 22			00 28	*01 07*	00 34	01 07			

Saturdays

until 22 March

		GW	GW	GW	GW	GW	GW	GW	HC	GW	HC	GW	HC	GW	GW	HC	GW	GW	GW	HC	GW	GW	GW	GW	GW
		1	1	1	1 ◇	1	1	1		1 ◇		1		1	1		1	1	1		1	1 ◇	1	1	1
London Paddington 15 ⊖	d		23p29	23p48	00 21	00 34	01 44	03 34	04 42	05 12	05 16	05 25	05 33	05 45	05 55	06 03	06 15	06 25	06 30	06 33	06 45	06 51			06 55
Acton Main Line	d			23p54											06 01			06 31							07 01
Ealing Broadway ⊖	d		23p36	23p57		00 41	01 51	03 41	04 50		05 24	05 32	05 41	05 52	06 04	06 11	06 22	06 34	06 37	06 41	06 52				07 04
West Ealing	d			23p59									05 43		06 06	06 13		06 36		06 43					07 06
Drayton Green	d														06 09			06 39							07 09
Castle Bar Park	d														06 10			06 40							07 10
South Greenford	d														06 13			06 43							07 13
Greenford ⊖	a														06 19			06 49							07 19
Hanwell	d			00 02									05 46			06 16				06 46				←	
Southall	d			00 06		00 46	01 56	03 46	04 54			05 37	05 49	05 57		06 19	06 27		06 42	06 49	06 57			06 57	
Hayes & Harlington	d		23p44	00 10		00 50	02 00	03 50	04 58		05 30	05 41	05 53	06 02		06 23	06 32		06 47	06 53	→			07 02	
Heathrow Terminals 1-2-3 ✈	a								05 04		05 36		06 01			06 31				07 01					
Heathrow Terminal 4 ✈	a																								
West Drayton	d			00 14		00 55	02 05	03 55						06 06			06 36		06 51					07 06	
Iver	d			00 17										06 09			06 39								
Langley	d			00 20		00 59								06 12			06 42								
Slough 3	a		23p55	00 26	00 40	01 04	02 13	04 03		05 29		05 51		06 17			06 47		06 58			07 06		07 14	
	d		23p55	00 27	00 41	01 05	02 13	04 03		05 29		05 51		06 18			06 48		06 59			07 07		07 14	
Burnham	d			00 31		01 09						05 55		06 22			06 52		07 03				←	07 18	
Taplow	d			00 34		01 12						05 59		06 25			06 55		07 06				07 06	07 22	
Maidenhead 3	d		00 03	00 38		01 16	02 21	04 11				06 03		06 29			06 59		→				07 10	07 26	
Twyford 3	d	00 07	00 11	00 46		01 24	02 29	04 19				06 10		06 37			07 07						07 18	07 33	
Reading 7	a	00 17	00 18	00 53	00 58	01 33	02 36	04 28		05 46		06 17		06 43			07 13					07 21	07 25	07 41	
Oxford	a		01 07		01 30					06 17		07 03		07 28			08 00					07 52	*08 03*	*08 16*	

For general notes see front of timetable
For details of catering facilities see Directory of Train Operators

For fast services between London Paddington and Reading see Table 116

b Change at Heathrow Terminals 1-2-3

Table 117

Saturdays

until 22 March

London → Greenford and Reading

(Local services only)

Network Diagram - see first page of Table 116

Station		GW 1	HC	GW	GW 1	GW 1	GW 1	HC	GW 1	GW 1 ◇ ☕	GW 1	GW 1	GW 1	HC	GW 1	GW 1	GW 1	HC	GW 1	GW 1 ◇ ☕	GW 1	GW 1	GW 1	HC	GW 1
London Paddington 15 ⊖	d	07 00	07 03	07 12	07 15	07 25	07 30	07 33	07 45	07 51		07 55	08 00	08 03	08 15	08 25	08 30	08 33	08 45	08 51		08 55	09 00	09 03	09 15
Acton Main Line	d					07 31						08 01				08 31						09 01			
Ealing Broadway ⊖	d	07 07	07 11		07 22	07 34	07 37	07 41	07 52			08 04	08 07	08 11	08 22	08 34	08 37	08 41	08 52			09 04	09 07	09 11	09 22
West Ealing	d		07 13			07 36		07 43				08 06		08 13		08 36		08 43				09 06		09 13	
Drayton Green	d					07 39						08 09				08 39						09 09			
Castle Bar Park	d					07 40						08 10				08 40						09 10			
South Greenford	d					07 43						08 13				08 43						09 13			
Greenford ⊖	a					07 49						08 19				08 49						09 19			
Hanwell	d		07 16					07 46			←			08 16				08 46			←			09 16	
Southall	d		07 19		07 27			07 49	07 57		07 57			08 19	08 27			08 49	08 57		08 57			09 19	09 27
Hayes & Harlington	d	07 15	07 23		07 32		07 45	07 53	→		08 02		08 14	08 23	08 32		08 45	08 53	→		09 02		09 15	09 23	09 32
Heathrow Terminals 1-2-3 ✈	a		07 31					08 01						08 31				09 01						09 31	
Heathrow Terminal 4 ✈	a																								
West Drayton	d	07 20			07 36		07 50				08 06		08 20		08 36		08 50				09 06		09 20		09 36
Iver	d	07 23					07 53						08 23				08 53						09 23		
Langley	d	07 26					07 56						08 26				08 56						09 26		
Slough 3	a	07 30		07 34	07 44		08 00			08 06	08 14		08 30		08 44		09 00			09 06	09 14		09 30		09 44
	d	07 31		07 36	07 45		08 01			08 07	08 14		08 31		08 45		09 01			09 07	09 14		09 31		09 45
Burnham	d				07 49						08 18				08 49						09 18				09 49
Taplow	d				07 52						08 22				08 52						09 22				09 52
Maidenhead 3	d	07 38			07 56		08 08				08 26		08 38		08 56		09 08				09 26		09 38		09 56
Twyford 3	d	07 46			08 04		08 16				08 33		08 46		09 04		09 16				09 33		09 46		10 04
Reading 7	a	07 52			08 11		08 21			08 21	08 41		08 52		09 11		09 21			09 21	09 41		09 52		10 11
Oxford	a	08 39		08 07			09 15			08 51	*09 20*		09 31				10 13			09 51	*10 18*		10 30		

Station		GW 1	GW 1	HC		GW 1	GW 1 ◇ ☕	GW 1	GW 1	GW 1	HC	GW 1	GW 1	GW 1	HC	GW 1	GW 1 ◇ ☕	GW 1	GW 1	GW 1	HC	GW 1	GW 1	GW 1	HC
London Paddington 15 ⊖	d	09 25	09 30	09 33		09 45	09 51		09 55	10 00	10 03	10 15	10 25	10 30	10 33	10 45	10 51		10 55	11 00	11 03	11 15	11 25	11 30	11 33
Acton Main Line	d	09 31							10 01				10 31						11 01				11 31		
Ealing Broadway ⊖	d	09 34	09 37	09 41		09 52			10 04	10 07	10 11	10 22	10 34	10 37	10 41	10 52			11 04	11 07	11 11	11 22	11 34	11 37	11 41
West Ealing	d	09 36		09 43					10 06		10 13		10 36		10 43				11 06		11 13		11 36		11 43
Drayton Green	d	09 39							10 09				10 39						11 09				11 39		
Castle Bar Park	d	09 40							10 10				10 40						11 10				11 40		
South Greenford	d	09 43							10 13				10 43						11 13				11 43		
Greenford ⊖	a	09 49							10 19				10 49						11 19				11 49		
Hanwell	d			09 46				←			10 16				10 46			←			11 16				11 46
Southall	d			09 49		09 57		09 57			10 19	10 27			10 49	10 57		10 57			11 19	11 27			11 49
Hayes & Harlington	d		09 45	09 53		→		10 02		10 14	10 23	10 32		10 45	10 53	→		11 02		11 15	11 23	11 32		11 45	11 53
Heathrow Terminals 1-2-3 ✈	a			10 01							10 31				11 01						11 31				12 01
Heathrow Terminal 4 ✈	a																								
West Drayton	d		09 50					10 06		10 20		10 36		10 50				11 06		11 20		11 36		11 50	
Iver	d		09 53							10 23				10 53						11 23				11 53	
Langley	d		09 56							10 26				10 56						11 26				11 56	
Slough 3	a		10 00				10 06	10 14		10 30		10 44		11 00			11 06	11 14		11 30		11 44		12 00	
	d		10 01				10 07	10 14		10 30		10 45		11 01			11 07	11 14		11 31		11 45		12 01	
Burnham	d							10 18				10 49						11 18				11 49			
Taplow	d							10 22				10 52						11 22				11 52			
Maidenhead 3	d		10 08					10 26		10 38		10 56		11 08				11 26		11 38		11 56		12 08	
Twyford 3	d		10 16					10 33		10 46		11 04		11 16				11 33		11 46		12 04		12 16	
Reading 7	a		10 21				10 21	10 41		10 52		11 11		11 21			11 21	11 41		11 52		12 11		12 21	
Oxford	a		11 13				10 51	*11 19*		11 30				12 13			11 51	*12 17*		12 30				13 13	

Station		GW 1	GW 1 ◇ ☕	GW 1	GW 1	GW 1	HC	GW 1	GW 1 ◇ ☕	GW 1	GW 1	GW 1	GW 1	HC	GW 1	GW 1	GW 1	HC	GW 1	GW 1	GW 1	HC	GW 1	GW 1 ◇ ☕	GW 1
London Paddington 15 ⊖	d	11 45	11 51		11 55	12 00	12 03	12 15	12 18			12 25	12 30	12 33	12 45	12 55	13 00	13 03	13 15	13 25	13 30	13 33	13 45	13 51	
Acton Main Line	d				12 01							12 31				13 01				13 31					
Ealing Broadway ⊖	d	11 52			12 04	12 07	12 11	12 22				12 34	12 37	12 41	12 52	13 04	13 07	13 11	13 22	13 34	13 37	13 41	13 52		
West Ealing	d				12 06		12 13					12 36		12 43		13 06		13 13		13 36		13 43			
Drayton Green	d				12 09							12 39				13 09				13 39					
Castle Bar Park	d				12 10							12 40				13 10				13 40					
South Greenford	d				12 13							12 43				13 13				13 43					
Greenford ⊖	a				12 19							12 49				13 19				13 49					
Hanwell	d			←			12 16				←			12 46				13 16				13 46			←
Southall	d	11 57		11 57			12 19	12 27			12 27			12 49	12 57			13 19	13 27			13 49	13 57		13 57
Hayes & Harlington	d	→		12 02		12 15	12 23	→			12 32		12 45	12 53	13 02		13 15	13 23	13 32		13 45	13 53	→		14 02
Heathrow Terminals 1-2-3 ✈	a						12 31							13 01				13 31				14 01			
Heathrow Terminal 4 ✈	a																								
West Drayton	d			12 06		12 20					12 36		12 50		13 06		13 20		13 36		13 50				14 06
Iver	d					12 23							12 53				13 23				13 53				
Langley	d					12 26							12 56				13 26				13 56				
Slough 3	a		12 06	12 14		12 30			12 33		12 44		13 00		13 14		13 30		13 44		14 00			14 06	14 14
	d		12 07	12 14		12 31			12 34		12 45		13 01		13 14		13 31		13 45		14 01			14 07	14 14
Burnham	d			12 18							12 49				13 18				13 49						14 18
Taplow	d			12 22						←	12 52				13 22				13 52						14 22
Maidenhead 3	d			12 26		12 38				12 38	12 56		13 08		13 26		13 38		13 56		14 08				14 26
Twyford 3	d			12 33		→				12 46	13 04		13 16		13 33		13 46		14 04		14 16				14 33
Reading 7	a		12 21	12 41					12 48	12 52	13 11		13 21		13 41		13 52		14 11		14 21			14 21	14 41
Oxford	a		12 51						*13 19*	13 30	*13 47*		14 13		*14 17*		14 30				15 13			14 51	*15 17*

For general notes see front of timetable
For details of catering facilities see
Directory of Train Operators

For fast services between London Paddington and
Reading see Table 116

Table 117

until 22 March

London → Greenford and Reading

(Local services only)

Network Diagram - see first page of Table 116

		GW 1	GW 1	HC	GW 1	GW 1	GW 1	HC		GW 1	GW 1 ◇	GW 1	GW 1	GW 1	HC	GW 1	GW 1	GW 1	HC	GW 1	GW 1 ◇	GW 1	GW 1	GW 1	HC
London Paddington 15	⊖ d	13 55	14 00	14 03	14 15	14 25	14 30	14 33		14 45	14 51		14 55	15 00	15 03	15 15	15 25	15 30	15 33	15 45	15 51		15 55	16 00	16 03
Acton Main Line	d	14 01				14 31							15 01				15 31						16 01		
Ealing Broadway	⊖ d	14 04	14 07	14 11	14 22	14 34	14 37	14 41		14 52			15 04	15 07	15 11	15 22	15 34	15 37	15 41	15 52			16 04	16 07	16 11
West Ealing	d	14 06		14 13		14 36		14 43					15 06		15 13		15 36		15 43				16 06		16 13
Drayton Green	d	14 09				14 39							15 09				15 39						16 09		
Castle Bar Park	d	14 10				14 40							15 10				15 40						16 10		
South Greenford	d	14 13				14 43							15 13				15 43						16 13		
Greenford	⊖ a	14 19				14 49							15 19				15 49						16 19		
Hanwell	d			14 16				14 46				←			15 16				15 46			←			16 16
Southall	d			14 19	14 27			14 49		14 57		14 57			15 19	15 27			15 49	15 57		15 57			16 19
Hayes & Harlington	d		14 15	14 23	14 32		14 45	14 53		→		15 02		15 15	15 23	15 32		15 45	15 53	→		16 02		16 15	16 23
Heathrow Terminals 1-2-3	✈ a			14 31				15 01							15 31				16 01						16 31
Heathrow Terminal 4	✈ a																								
West Drayton	d		14 20		14 36		14 50					15 06		15 20		15 36		15 50				16 06		16 20	
Iver	d		14 23				14 53							15 23				15 53						16 23	
Langley	d		14 26				14 56							15 26				15 56						16 26	
Slough 3	a		14 30		14 44		15 00				15 06	15 14		15 30		15 44		16 00			16 06	16 14		16 30	
	d		14 31		14 45		15 01				15 07	15 14		15 31		15 45		16 01			16 07	16 14		16 31	
Burnham	d				14 49							15 18				15 49						16 18			
Taplow	d				14 52							15 22				15 52						16 22			
Maidenhead 3	d		14 38		14 56		15 08					15 26		15 38		15 56		16 08				16 26		16 38	
Twyford 3	d		14 46		15 04		15 16					15 33		15 46		16 04		16 16				16 33		16 46	
Reading 7	a		14 52		15 11		15 21				15 21	15 41		15 52		16 11		16 21			16 21	16 41		16 52	
Oxford	a		15 30				16 13				15 47	*16 17*		16 30				17 13			16 51	*17 17*		17 30	

		GW 1	GW 1	GW 1	HC	GW 1	GW 1 ◇	GW 1	GW 1	GW 1	HC	GW 1	GW 1	GW 1	HC	GW 1	GW 1	GW 1	HC	GW 1	GW 1 ◇	GW 1	GW 1	GW 1	GW 1
London Paddington 15	⊖ d	16 15	16 25	16 30	16 33	16 45	16 51		16 55	17 00	17 03	17 15	17 25	17 30	17 33	17 45	17 55	18 00	18 03	18 15	18 21			18 25	18 30
Acton Main Line	d		16 31						17 01				17 31				18 01							18 31	
Ealing Broadway	⊖ d	16 22	16 34	16 37	16 41	16 52			17 04	17 07	17 11	17 22	17 34	17 37	17 41	17 52	18 04	18 07	18 11	18 22				18 34	18 37
West Ealing	d		16 36		16 43				17 06		17 13		17 36		17 43		18 06		18 13					18 36	
Drayton Green	d		16 39						17 09				17 39				18 09							18 39	
Castle Bar Park	d		16 40						17 10				17 40				18 10							18 40	
South Greenford	d		16 43						17 13				17 43				18 13							18 43	
Greenford	⊖ a		16 49						17 19				17 49				18 19							18 49	
Hanwell	d				16 46			←			17 16				17 46				18 16				←		
Southall	d	16 27			16 49	16 57		16 57			17 19	17 27			17 49	17 57			18 19	18 27			18 27		
Hayes & Harlington	d	16 32		16 45	16 53	→		17 02		17 15	17 23	17 32		17 45	17 53	18 02		18 15	18 23	→			18 32		18 45
Heathrow Terminals 1-2-3	✈ a				17 01						17 31				18 01				18 31						
Heathrow Terminal 4	✈ a																								
West Drayton	d	16 36		16 50				17 06		17 20		17 36		17 50		18 06		18 20					18 36		18 50
Iver	d			16 53						17 23				17 53				18 23							18 53
Langley	d			16 56						17 26				17 56				18 26							18 56
Slough 3	a	16 44		17 00			17 06	17 14		17 30		17 44		18 00		18 14		18 30			18 36		18 44		19 00
	d	16 45		17 01			17 07	17 14		17 31		17 45		18 01		18 14		18 31			18 37		18 45		19 01
Burnham	d	16 49						17 18				17 49				18 18							18 49		
Taplow	d	16 52						17 22				17 52				18 22						←	18 52		
Maidenhead 3	d	16 56		17 08				17 26		17 38		17 56		18 08		18 26		18 38 →				18 38	18 56		19 08
Twyford 3	d	17 04		17 16				17 33		17 46		18 04		18 16		18 33						18 46	19 04		19 16
Reading 7	a	17 11		17 21			17 21	17 41		17 52		18 11		18 21		18 41					18 51	18 52	19 11		19 21
Oxford	a			18 13			17 51	*18 17*		18 30		*18 47*		19 13							19 18	19 30	*19 47*		20 16

		HC	GW 1	GW 1	GW 1	HC	GW 1	GW 1	GW 1	HC	GW 1	GW 1 ◇	GW 1	GW 1	GW 1	HC	GW 1	GW 1	GW 1	GW 1	HC	GW 1	GW 1 ◇	GW 1	GW 1
London Paddington 15	⊖ d	18 33	18 45	18 55	19 00	19 03	19 15	19 25	19 30	19 33	19 45	19 51		19 55	20 00	20 03	20 15		20 25	20 30	20 33	20 47	20 51		20 55
Acton Main Line	d			19 01				19 31						20 01					20 31						21 01
Ealing Broadway	⊖ d	18 41	18 52	19 04	19 07	19 11	19 22	19 34	19 37	19 41	19 52			20 04	20 07	20 11	20 22		20 34	20 37	20 41	20 54			21 04
West Ealing	d	18 43		19 06		19 13		19 36		19 43				20 06		20 13			20 36		20 43				21 06
Drayton Green	d			19 09				19 39						20 09					20 39						21 09
Castle Bar Park	d			19 10				19 40						20 10					20 40						21 10
South Greenford	d			19 13				19 43						20 13					20 43						21 13
Greenford	⊖ a			19 19				19 49						20 19					20 49						21 19
Hanwell	d	18 46				19 16				19 46			←			20 16		←			20 46			←	
Southall	d	18 49	18 57			19 19	19 27			19 49	19 57		19 57			20 19	20 27	20 27			20 49	20 59		20 59	
Hayes & Harlington	d	18 53	19 02		19 15	19 23	19 32		19 45	19 53	→		20 02		20 15	20 23	→	20 31		20 45	20 53	→		21 04	
Heathrow Terminals 1-2-3	✈ a	19 01				19 31				20 01						20 31					21 01				
Heathrow Terminal 4	✈ a																								
West Drayton	d		19 06		19 20		19 36		19 50				20 06		20 20			20 36		20 50				21 08	
Iver	d				19 23				19 53						20 23					20 53					
Langley	d				19 26				19 56						20 26					20 56					
Slough 3	a		19 14		19 30		19 44		20 00			20 07	20 14		20 30			20 44		21 00			21 07	21 15	
	d		19 14		19 31		19 45		20 01			20 07	20 14		20 31			20 44		21 01			21 08	21 16	
Burnham	d		19 18				19 49						20 18					20 48						21 20	
Taplow	d		19 22				19 52						20 22					20 52						21 23	
Maidenhead 3	d		19 26		19 38		19 56		20 08				20 26		20 38			20 56		21 08				21 27	
Twyford 3	d		19 33		19 46		20 04		20 16				20 33		20 46			21 03		21 16				21 35	
Reading 7	a		19 41		19 52		20 11		20 21			20 21	20 41		20 52			21 11		21 21			21 25	21 43	
Oxford	a		*20 20*		20 30				21 13			20 47			21 30					22 10			21 55	*22 20*	

For general notes see front of timetable
For details of catering facilities see Directory of Train Operators

For fast services between London Paddington and Reading see Table 116

Table 117

London → Greenford and Reading
(Local services only)

Saturdays
until 22 March

Network Diagram - see first page of Table 116

		GW 1	HC	GW 1	GW 1	HC	GW 1	GW 1 ◇	GW 1	GW 1 A	HC	GW 1	GW 1 ◇	GW 1	HC	GW 1 B	GW 1 ◇	GW 1 B	HC	GW 1 B	GW 1 ◇	GW 1 B	GW 1
London Paddington 15	⊖ d	21 00	21 03	21 15	21 25	21 33	21 45	21 51		22 00	22 03	22 20	22 32		22 33	22 45	23 00		23 03	23 20	23 33		23 45
Acton Main Line	d				21 31											22 51							23 51
Ealing Broadway	⊖ d	21 07	21 11	21 22	21 34	21 41	21 52			22 07	22 11	22 27			22 41	22 54			23 11	23 27			23 54
West Ealing	d		21 13		21 36	21 43					22 13				22 43				23 13				23 56
Drayton Green	d				21 39																		
Castle Bar Park	d				21 40																		
South Greenford	d				21 43																		
Greenford	⊖ a				21 49																		
Hanwell	d		21 16			21 46					22 16				22 46				23 16				23 59
Southall	d		21 19	21 27		21 49	21 57		←		22 19	22 32		←	22 49	22 59		←	23 19	23 32		←	00 02
Hayes & Harlington	d	21 15	21 23	21 31		21 53	22 01		22 01	22 15	22 23	22 36		22 36	22 53	23 03		23 03	23 23	23 36		23 36	00 06
Heathrow Terminals 1-2-3	✈ a		21 31			22 01	→				22 31	→			23 01	→			23 31	→			
Heathrow Terminal 4	✈ a																		23 38				
West Drayton	d	21 20		21 36					22 06	22 20				22 41				23 07				23 41	00 11
Iver	d	21 23							22 09	22 23				22 44				23 10				23 44	00 14
Langley	d	21 26							22 12	22 26				22 47				23 13				23 47	00 17
Slough 3	a	21 30		21 44				22 07	22 17	22 30			22 49	22 52			23 16	23 18			23 49	23 52	00 22
	d	21 31		21 44				22 08	22 17	22 31			22 50	22 52			23 17	23 20			23 50	23 53	00 22
Burnham	d			21 48					22 21					22 56				23 24				23 57	00 26
Taplow	d			21 52					22 25					23 00								00 01	
Maidenhead 3	d	21 38		21 56					22 29	22 38				23 04				23 29				00 05	00 31
Twyford 3	d	21 46		22 03					22 36	22 46				23 11				23 36				00 12	00 39
Reading 7	a	21 52		22 11				22 23	22 43	22 52			23 06	23 19			23 33	23 43			00 07	00 19	00 46
Oxford	a	22 30						22 51	23b31	23 31			23c56	00e23			00c23	00c48			00c55	01c34	

Saturdays
from 29 March

		GW 1	GW 1	GW 1	GW 1 ◇	GW 1	GW 1	GW 1	HC	GW 1 ◇	HC	GW 1	HC	GW 1	GW 1	HC	GW 1	GW 1	GW 1	HC	GW 1		GW 1 ◇ ☕	GW 1	GW 1
London Paddington 15	⊖ d		23p29	23p48	00 21	00 34	01 44	03 34	04 42	05 12	05 16	05 25	05 33	05 45	05 55	06 03	06 15	06 25	06 30	06 33	06 45		06 51		
Acton Main Line	d			23p54											06 01			06 31							
Ealing Broadway	⊖ d		23p36	23p57		00 41	01 51	03 41	04 50		05 24	05 32	05 41	05 52	06 04	06 11	06 22	06 34	06 37	06 41	06 52				
West Ealing	d			23p59									05 43		06 06	06 13		06 36		06 43					
Drayton Green	d														06 09			06 39							
Castle Bar Park	d														06 10			06 40							
South Greenford	d														06 13			06 43							
Greenford	⊖ a														06 19			06 49							
Hanwell	d			00 02									05 46			06 16				06 46					←
Southall	d			00 06		00 46	01 56	03 46	04 54			05 37	05 49	05 57		06 19	06 27		06 42	06 49	06 57				06 57
Hayes & Harlington	d		23p44	00 10		00 50	02 00	03 50	04 58		05 30	05 41	05 53	06 02		06 23	06 32		06 47	06 53	→				07 02
Heathrow Terminals 1-2-3	✈ a								05 04		05 36		05 59			06 29				06 59					
Heathrow Terminal 4	✈ a								05 10		05 42		06 05			06 35				07 05					
Heathrow Terminal 5	✈ a								05f32		05f46		06f16			06f46				07f16					
West Drayton	d			00 14		00 55	02 05	03 55						06 06			06 36		06 51						07 06
Iver	d			00 17										06 09			06 39								
Langley	d			00 20		00 59								06 12			06 42								
Slough 3	a		23p55	00 26	00 40	01 04	02 13	04 03		05 29		05 51		06 17			06 47		06 58				07 06		07 14
	d		23p55	00 27	00 41	01 05	02 13	04 03		05 29		05 51		06 18			06 48		06 59				07 07		07 14
Burnham	d			00 31		01 09						05 55		06 22			06 52		07 03					←	07 18
Taplow	d			00 34		01 12						05 59		06 25			06 55		07 06					07 06	07 22
Maidenhead 3	d		00 03	00 38		01 16	02 21	04 11				06 03		06 29			06 59		→					07 10	07 26
Twyford 3	d	00 07	00 11	00 46		01 24	02 29	04 19				06 10		06 37			07 07							07 18	07 33
Reading 7	a	00 17	00 18	00 53	00 58	01 33	02 36	04 28		05 46		06 17		06 43			07 13						07 21	07 25	07 41
Oxford	a		01 07		01 30					06 17		07 03		07 28			08 00						07 48	08 03	08 16

		GW 1	GW 1	HC	GW 1	GW 1	GW 1	HC	GW 1	GW 1 ◇ ☕	GW 1	GW 1	GW 1	HC	GW 1	GW 1	GW 1	HC	GW 1	GW 1 ◇ ☕		GW 1	GW 1	GW 1	HC
London Paddington 15	⊖ d	06 55	07 00	07 03	07 15	07 25	07 30	07 33	07 45	07 51		07 55	08 00	08 03	08 15	08 25	08 30	08 33	08 45	08 51			08 55	09 00	09 03
Acton Main Line	d	07 01				07 31						08 01				08 31							09 01		
Ealing Broadway	⊖ d	07 04	07 07	07 11	07 22	07 34	07 37	07 41	07 52			08 04	08 07	08 11	08 22	08 34	08 37	08 41	08 52				09 04	09 07	09 11
West Ealing	d	07 06		07 13		07 36		07 43				08 06		08 13		08 36		08 43					09 06		09 13
Drayton Green	d	07 09				07 39						08 09				08 39							09 09		
Castle Bar Park	d	07 10				07 40						08 10				08 40							09 10		
South Greenford	d	07 13				07 43						08 13				08 43							09 13		
Greenford	⊖ a	07 19				07 49						08 19				08 49							09 19		
Hanwell	d			07 16				07 46			←			08 16				08 46				←			09 16
Southall	d			07 19	07 27			07 49	07 57		07 57			08 19	08 27			08 49	08 57			08 57			09 19
Hayes & Harlington	d		07 15	07 23	07 32		07 45	07 53	→		08 02		08 14	08 23	08 32		08 45	08 53	→			09 02		09 15	09 23
Heathrow Terminals 1-2-3	✈ a			07 29				07 59						08 29				08 59							09 29
Heathrow Terminal 4	✈ a			07 35				08 05						08 35				09 05							09 35
Heathrow Terminal 5	✈ a			07f46				08f16						08f46				09f16							09f46
West Drayton	d		07 20		07 36		07 50				08 06		08 20		08 36		08 50					09 06		09 20	
Iver	d		07 23				07 53						08 23				08 53							09 23	
Langley	d		07 26				07 56						08 26				08 56							09 26	
Slough 3	a		07 30		07 44		08 00			08 06	08 14		08 30		08 44		09 00			09 06		09 14		09 30	
	d		07 31		07 45		08 01			08 07	08 14		08 31		08 45		09 01			09 07		09 14		09 31	
Burnham	d				07 49						08 18				08 49							09 18			
Taplow	d				07 52						08 22				08 52							09 22			
Maidenhead 3	d		07 38		07 56		08 08				08 26		08 38		08 56		09 08					09 26		09 38	
Twyford 3	d		07 46		08 04		08 16				08 33		08 46		09 04		09 16					09 33		09 46	
Reading 7	a		07 52		08 11		08 21			08 21	08 41		08 52		09 11		09 21			09 21		09 41		09 52	
Oxford	a		08 39				09 15			08 47	09 20		09 31				10 13			09 47		10 18		10 30	

For general notes see front of timetable
For details of catering facilities see Directory of Train Operators

For fast services between London Paddington and Reading see Table 116

A From 2 February
B To Didcot Parkway (Table 116)
b Until 26 January arr. 2356, change at Reading and Didcot Parkway, by bus from Didcot Parkway
c Change at Didcot Parkway. By bus
e Change at Reading and Didcot Parkway. By bus from Didcot Parkway
f Change at Heathrow Terminals 1-2-3

Table 117

Saturdays

from 29 March

London → Greenford and Reading

(Local services only)

Network Diagram - see first page of Table 116

		GW 1	GW 1	GW 1	HC	GW 1	GW 1◇	GW 1	GW 1	GW 1	HC	GW 1	GW 1	GW 1	HC	GW 1	GW 1◇	GW 1	GW 1		GW 1	HC	GW 1	GW 1	GW 1
London Paddington 15 ⊖	d	09 15	09 25	09 30	09 33	09 45	09 51		09 55	10 00	10 03	10 15	10 25	10 30	10 33	10 45	10 51		10 55		11 00	11 03	11 15	11 25	11 30
Acton Main Line	d		09 31						10 01				10 31						11 01					11 31	
Ealing Broadway ⊖	d	09 22	09 34	09 37	09 41	09 52			10 04	10 07	10 11	10 22	10 34	10 37	10 41	10 52			11 04		11 07	11 11	11 22	11 34	11 37
West Ealing	d		09 36		09 43				10 06		10 13		10 36		10 43				11 06			11 13		11 36	
Drayton Green	d		09 39						10 09				10 39						11 09					11 39	
Castle Bar Park	d		09 40						10 10				10 40						11 10					11 40	
South Greenford	d		09 43						10 13				10 43						11 13					11 43	
Greenford ⊖	a		09 49						10 19				10 49						11 19					11 49	
Hanwell	d				09 46			←			10 16				10 46			←				11 16			
Southall	d	09 27			09 49	09 57		09 57			10 19	10 27			10 49	10 57		10 57				11 19	11 27		
Hayes & Harlington	d	09 32		09 45	09 53	→		10 02		10 14	10 23	10 32		10 45	10 53	→		11 02			11 15	11 23	11 32		11 45
Heathrow Terminals 1-2-3 ✈	a				09 59						10 29				10 59							11 29			
Heathrow Terminal 4 ✈	a				10 05						10 35				11 05							11 35			
Heathrow Terminal 5 ✈	a				*10b16*						*10b46*				*11b16*							*11b46*			
West Drayton	d	09 36		09 50				10 06		10 20		10 36		10 50				11 06			11 20		11 36		11 50
Iver	d			09 53						10 23				10 53							11 23				11 53
Langley	d			09 56						10 26				10 56							11 26				11 56
Slough 3	a	09 44		10 00			10 06	10 14		10 30		10 44		11 00			11 06	11 14			11 30		11 44		12 00
	d	09 45		10 01			10 07	10 14		10 30		10 45		11 01			11 07	11 14			11 31		11 45		12 01
Burnham	d	09 49						10 18				10 49						11 18					11 49		
Taplow	d	09 52						10 22				10 52						11 22					11 52		
Maidenhead 3	d	09 56		10 08				10 26		10 38		10 56		11 08				11 26			11 38		11 56		12 08
Twyford 3	d	10 04		10 16				10 33		10 46		11 04		11 16				11 33			11 46		12 04		12 16
Reading 7	a	10 11		10 21			10 21	10 41		10 52		11 11		11 21			11 21	11 41			11 52		12 11		12 21
Oxford	a			11 13			10 47	*11 19*		11 30				12 13			11 47	*12 17*			12 30				13 13

		HC	GW 1	GW 1◇	GW 1	GW 1	GW 1	HC	GW 1	GW 1	GW 1	HC	GW 1	GW 1	GW 1	HC	GW 1	GW 1		GW 1	HC	GW 1	GW 1◇	GW 1	GW 1
London Paddington 15 ⊖	d	11 33	11 45	11 51		11 55	12 00	12 03	12 15	12 25	12 30	12 33	12 45	12 55	13 00	13 03	13 15	13 25		13 30	13 33	13 45	13 51		13 55
Acton Main Line	d					12 01				12 31				13 01				13 31							14 01
Ealing Broadway ⊖	d	11 41	11 52			12 04	12 07	12 11	12 22	12 34	12 37	12 41	12 52	13 04	13 07	13 11	13 22	13 34		13 37	13 41	13 52			14 04
West Ealing	d	11 43				12 06		12 13		12 36		12 43		13 06		13 13		13 36			13 43				14 06
Drayton Green	d					12 09				12 39				13 09				13 39							14 09
Castle Bar Park	d					12 10				12 40				13 10				13 40							14 10
South Greenford	d					12 13				12 43				13 13				13 43							14 13
Greenford ⊖	a					12 19				12 49				13 19				13 49							14 19
Hanwell	d	11 46			←			12 16				12 46				13 16					13 46			←	
Southall	d	11 49	11 57		11 57			12 19	12 27			12 49	12 57			13 19	13 27				13 49	13 57		13 57	
Hayes & Harlington	d	11 53	→		12 02		12 15	12 23	12 32		12 45	12 53	13 02		13 15	13 23	13 32			13 45	13 53	→		14 02	
Heathrow Terminals 1-2-3 ✈	a	11 59						12 29				12 59				13 29					13 59				
Heathrow Terminal 4 ✈	a	12 05						12 35				13 05				13 35					14 05				
Heathrow Terminal 5 ✈	a	*12b16*						*12b46*				*13b16*				*13b46*					*14b16*				
West Drayton	d				12 06		12 20		12 36		12 50		13 06		13 20		13 36			13 50				14 06	
Iver	d						12 23				12 53				13 23					13 53					
Langley	d						12 26				12 56				13 26					13 56					
Slough 3	a			12 06	12 14		12 30		12 44		13 00		13 14		13 30		13 44			14 00			14 06	14 14	
	d			12 07	12 14		12 31		12 45		13 01		13 14		13 31		13 45			14 01			14 07	14 14	
Burnham	d				12 18				12 49				13 18				13 49							14 18	
Taplow	d				12 22				12 52				13 22				13 52							14 22	
Maidenhead 3	d				12 26		12 38		12 56		13 08		13 26		13 38		13 56			14 08				14 26	
Twyford 3	d				12 33		12 46		13 04		13 16		13 33		13 46		14 04			14 16				14 33	
Reading 7	a			12 21	12 41		12 52		13 11		13 21		13 41		13 52		14 11			14 21			14 21	14 41	
Oxford	a			12 47	*13 19*		13 30		*13 47*		14 13		*14 17*		14 30					15 13			14 47	*15 17*	

		GW 1	HC	GW 1	GW 1	GW 1	HC	GW 1	GW 1◇	GW 1	GW 1	GW 1	HC	GW 1	GW 1	GW 1	HC		GW 1	GW 1◇	GW 1	GW 1	GW 1	HC	GW 1
London Paddington 15 ⊖	d	14 00	14 03	14 15	14 25	14 30	14 33	14 45	14 51		14 55	15 00	15 03	15 15	15 25	15 30	15 33		15 45	15 51		15 55	16 00	16 03	16 15
Acton Main Line	d				14 31						15 01				15 31							16 01			
Ealing Broadway ⊖	d	14 07	14 11	14 22	14 34	14 37	14 41	14 52			15 04	15 07	15 11	15 22	15 34	15 37	15 41		15 52			16 04	16 07	16 11	16 22
West Ealing	d		14 13		14 36		14 43				15 06		15 13		15 36		15 43					16 06		16 13	
Drayton Green	d				14 39						15 09				15 39							16 09			
Castle Bar Park	d				14 40						15 10				15 40							16 10			
South Greenford	d				14 43						15 13				15 43							16 13			
Greenford ⊖	a				14 49						15 19				15 49							16 19			
Hanwell	d		14 16				14 46			←			15 16				15 46				←			16 16	
Southall	d		14 19	14 27			14 49	14 57		14 57			15 19	15 27			15 49		15 57		15 57			16 19	16 27
Hayes & Harlington	d	14 15	14 23	14 32		14 45	14 53	→		15 02		15 15	15 23	15 32		15 45	15 53		→		16 02		16 15	16 23	16 32
Heathrow Terminals 1-2-3 ✈	a		14 29				14 59						15 29				15 59							16 29	
Heathrow Terminal 4 ✈	a		14 35				15 05						15 35				16 05							16 35	
Heathrow Terminal 5 ✈	a		*14b46*				*15b16*						*15b46*				*16b16*							*16b46*	
West Drayton	d	14 20		14 36		14 50				15 06		15 20		15 36		15 50					16 06		16 20		16 36
Iver	d	14 23				14 53						15 23				15 53							16 23		
Langley	d	14 26				14 56						15 26				15 56							16 26		
Slough 3	a	14 30		14 44		15 00			15 06	15 14		15 30		15 44		16 00				16 06	16 14		16 30		16 44
	d	14 31		14 45		15 01			15 07	15 14		15 31		15 45		16 01				16 07	16 14		16 31		16 45
Burnham	d			14 49						15 18				15 49							16 18				16 49
Taplow	d			14 52						15 22				15 52							16 22				16 52
Maidenhead 3	d	14 38		14 56		15 08				15 26		15 38		15 56		16 08					16 26		16 38		16 56
Twyford 3	d	14 46		15 04		15 16				15 33		15 46		16 04		16 16					16 33		16 46		17 04
Reading 7	a	14 52		15 11		15 21			15 21	15 41		15 52		16 11		16 21				16 21	16 41		16 52		17 11
Oxford	a	15 30				16 13			15 47	*16 17*		16 30				17 13				16 47	*17 17*		17 30		

For general notes see front of timetable
For details of catering facilities see Directory of Train Operators

For fast services between London Paddington and Reading see Table 116

b Change at Heathrow Terminals 1-2-3

Table 117

Saturdays from 29 March

London → Greenford and Reading

(Local services only)

Network Diagram - see first page of Table 116

	GW 1	GW 1	HC	GW 1	GW 1 ◇	GW 1	GW 1	GW 1	HC	GW 1	GW 1	GW 1	HC	GW 1	GW 1		GW 1	HC	GW 1	GW 1 ◇	GW 1	GW 1	GW 1	GW 1
London Paddington 15 ⊖ d	16 25	16 30	16 33	16 45	16 51		16 55	17 00	17 03	17 15	17 25	17 30	17 33	17 45	17 55		18 00	18 03	18 15	18 21			18 25	18 30
Acton Main Line d	16 31						17 01				17 31				18 01								18 31	
Ealing Broadway ⊖ d	16 34	16 37	16 41	16 52			17 04	17 07	17 11	17 22	17 34	17 37	17 41	17 52	18 04		18 07	18 11	18 22				18 34	18 37
West Ealing d	16 36		16 43				17 06		17 13		17 36		17 43		18 06			18 13					18 36	
Drayton Green d	16 39						17 09				17 39				18 09								18 39	
Castle Bar Park d	16 40						17 10				17 40				18 10								18 40	
South Greenford d	16 43						17 13				17 43				18 13								18 43	
Greenford ⊖ a	16 49						17 19				17 49				18 19								18 49	
Hanwell d			16 46			←			17 16				17 46					18 16				←		
Southall d			16 49	16 57		16 57			17 19	17 27			17 49	17 57				18 19	18 27			18 27		
Hayes & Harlington d		16 45	16 53	→		17 02		17 15	17 23	17 32		17 45	17 53	18 02			18 15	18 23	→			18 32		18 45
Heathrow Terminals 1-2-3 ✈ a			16 59						17 29				17 59					18 29						
Heathrow Terminal 4 ✈ a			17 05						17 35				18 05					18 35						
Heathrow Terminal 5 ✈ a			*17b16*						*17b46*				*18b16*					*18b46*						
West Drayton d		16 50				17 06		17 20		17 36		17 50		18 06			18 20					18 36		18 50
Iver d		16 53						17 23				17 53					18 23							18 53
Langley d		16 56						17 26				17 56					18 26							18 56
Slough 3 a		17 00			17 06	17 14		17 30		17 44		18 00		18 14			18 30			18 36		18 44		19 00
Slough 3 d		17 01			17 07	17 14		17 31		17 45		18 01		18 14			18 31			18 37		18 45		19 01
Burnham d						17 18				17 49				18 18								18 49		
Taplow d						17 22				17 52				18 22							←	18 52		
Maidenhead 3 d		17 08				17 26		17 38		17 56		18 08		18 26			18 38 →				18 38	18 56		19 08
Twyford 3 d		17 16				17 33		17 46		18 04		18 16		18 33							18 46	19 04		19 16
Reading 7 a		17 21			17 21	17 41		17 52		18 11		18 21		18 41						18 51	18 52	19 11		19 21
Oxford a		18 13			17 47	*18 17*		18 30		*18 47*		19 13								19 18	19 30	*19 47*		20 16

	HC	GW 1	GW 1	GW 1	HC	GW 1	GW 1	GW 1	HC	GW 1	GW 1 ◇	GW 1	GW 1	GW 1		HC	GW 1	GW 1	GW 1	GW 1	HC	GW 1	GW 1 ◇	GW 1
London Paddington 15 ⊖ d	18 33	18 45	18 55	19 00	19 03	19 15	19 25	19 30	19 33	19 45	19 51		19 55	20 00		20 03	20 15		20 25	20 30	20 33	20 47	20 51	
Acton Main Line d			19 01				19 31						20 01						20 31					
Ealing Broadway ⊖ d	18 41	18 52	19 04	19 07	19 11	19 22	19 34	19 37	19 41	19 52			20 04	20 07		20 11	20 22		20 34	20 37	20 41	20 54		
West Ealing d	18 43		19 06		19 13		19 36		19 43				20 06			20 13			20 36		20 43			
Drayton Green d			19 09				19 39						20 09						20 39					
Castle Bar Park d			19 10				19 40						20 10						20 40					
South Greenford d			19 13				19 43						20 13						20 43					
Greenford ⊖ a			19 19				19 49						20 19						20 49					
Hanwell d	18 46				19 16				19 46			←				20 16		←			20 46			←
Southall d	18 49	18 57			19 19	19 27			19 49	19 57		19 57				20 19	20 27	20 27			20 49	20 59		20 59
Hayes & Harlington d	18 53	19 02		19 15	19 23	19 32		19 45	19 53	→		20 02		20 15		20 23	→	20 31		20 45	20 53	→		21 04
Heathrow Terminals 1-2-3 ✈ a	18 59				19 29				19 59							20 29					20 59			
Heathrow Terminal 4 ✈ a	19 05				19 35				20 05							20 35					21 05			
Heathrow Terminal 5 ✈ a	*19b16*				*19b46*				*20b16*							*20b46*					*21b16*			
West Drayton d		19 06		19 20		19 36		19 50				20 06		20 20				20 36		20 50				21 08
Iver d				19 23				19 53						20 23						20 53				
Langley d				19 26				19 56						20 26						20 56				
Slough 3 a		19 14		19 30		19 44		20 00			20 07	20 14		20 30				20 44		21 00			21 07	21 15
Slough 3 d		19 14		19 31		19 45		20 01			20 07	20 14		20 31				20 44		21 01			21 08	21 16
Burnham d		19 18				19 49						20 18						20 48						21 20
Taplow d		19 22				19 52						20 22						20 52						21 23
Maidenhead 3 d		19 26		19 38		19 56		20 08				20 26		20 38				20 56		21 08				21 27
Twyford 3 d		19 33		19 46		20 04		20 16				20 33		20 46				21 03		21 16				21 35
Reading 7 a		19 41		19 52		20 11		20 21			20 21	20 41		20 52				21 11		21 21			21 25	21 43
Oxford a		*20 20*		20 30				21 13			20 47			21 30						22 10			21 55	*22 20*

	GW 1	GW 1	HC	GW 1	GW 1	HC	GW 1	GW 1 ◇	GW 1	HC	GW 1	GW 1 ◇	GW 1	HC	GW 1 A	GW 1 ◇	GW 1 A	HC	GW 1 A	GW 1 ◇	GW 1 A	GW 1		
London Paddington 15 ⊖ d	20 55	21 00	21 03	21 15	21 25	21 33	21 45	21 51		22 03	22 20	22 32		22 33	22 45	23 00		23 03	23 20	23 33		23 45		
Acton Main Line d	21 01				21 31										22 51							23 51		
Ealing Broadway ⊖ d	21 04	21 07	21 11	21 22	21 34	21 41	21 52			22 11	22 27			22 41	22 54			23 11	23 27			23 54		
West Ealing d	21 06		21 13		21 36	21 43				22 13				22 43				23 13				23 56		
Drayton Green d	21 09				21 39																			
Castle Bar Park d	21 10				21 40																			
South Greenford d	21 13				21 43																			
Greenford ⊖ a	21 19				21 49																			
Hanwell d			21 16			21 46				22 16				22 46				23 16				23 59		
Southall d			21 19	21 27		21 49	21 57		←	22 19	22 32		←	22 49	22 59		←	23 19	23 32		←	00 02		
Hayes & Harlington d		21 15	21 23	21 31		21 53	22 01		22 01	22 23	22 36		22 36	22 53	23 03		23 03	23 23	23 36		23 36	00 06		
Heathrow Terminals 1-2-3 ✈ a			21 29			21 59	→			22 29	→			22 59	→			23 29	→					
Heathrow Terminal 4 ✈ a			21 35			22 05				22 35				23 05				23 35						
Heathrow Terminal 5 ✈ a			*21b46*			*22b16*				*22b46*				*23b16*				*23b46*						
West Drayton d		21 20		21 36					22 06				22 41				23 07				23 41	00 11		
Iver d		21 23							22 09				22 44				23 10				23 44	00 14		
Langley d		21 26							22 12				22 47				23 13				23 47	00 17		
Slough 3 a		21 30		21 44				22 07	22 17			22 49	22 52			23 16	23 18			23 49	23 52	00 22		
Slough 3 d		21 31		21 44				22 08	22 17			22 50	22 52			23 17	23 20			23 50	23 53	00 22		
Burnham d				21 48					22 21				22 56				23 24				23 57	00 26		
Taplow d				21 52					22 25				23 00								00 01			
Maidenhead 3 d		21 38		21 56					22 29				23 04				23 29				00 05	00 31		
Twyford 3 d		21 46		22 03					22 36				23 11				23 36				00 12	00 39		
Reading 7 a		21 52		22 11				22 23	22 43			23 06	23 19			23 33	23 43			00 07	00 19	00 46		
Oxford a		22 30						22 46	*23c56*			*23e56*	*00c23*			*00e23*	*00e48*			*00e55*	*01e34*			

For general notes see front of timetable
For details of catering facilities see Directory of Train Operators

For fast services between London Paddington and Reading see Table 116

A To Didcot Parkway (Table 116)
b Change at Heathrow Terminals 1-2-3
c Change at Reading and Didcot Parkway. By bus from Didcot Parkway
e Change at Didcot Parkway. By bus

Table 117

Sundays

until 27 January

London → Greenford and Reading

(Local services only)

Network Diagram - see first page of Table 116

		GW	GW	GW	GW	GW	HC	HC	GW	HC	GW	GW	HC	GW	GW	GW	HC	GW	GW	GW	GW	HC	GW
		1	1	1	1	1			1			1 ◇		1	1 ◇			1	1	1	1 ◇		
		A										B ☕			🍴						☕		
London Paddington 15	⊖ d	23p20	23p45	00 05	00 30	01 00	05 12	06 12	06 43	07 12	07 43	08 03	08 12	08 16	08 42	08 44	09 07	09 15	09 22		09 35	09 37	09 44
Acton Main Line	d		23p51																				
Ealing Broadway	⊖ d	23p27	23p54	00 12	00 37	01 07	05 20	06 20	06 50	07 20	07 50		08 20	08 23		08 51	09 15	09 22				09 45	09 51
West Ealing	d																						
Drayton Green	d																						
Castle Bar Park	d																						
South Greenford	d																						
Greenford	⊖ a																						
Hanwell	d																						
Southall	d	23p32	23p59	00 17	00 42	01 12	05 24	06 24	06 55	07 24	07 55		08 24	08 29		08 56	09 19	09 27		←		09 49	09 56
Hayes & Harlington	d	23p36	00 03	00 21	00 46	01 16	05 28	06 28	06 59	07 28	07 58		08 28	08 33		09 00	09 23	09 31		09 31		09 53	09 59
Heathrow Terminals 1-2-3	✈ a						05 34	06 34		07 34			08 34				09 31	→				10 01	
Heathrow Terminal 4	✈ a																						
West Drayton	d	23p41	00 07	00 26	00 51				07 04		08 04			08 37		09 05				09 36			10 05
Iver	d	23p44	00 10	00 29																			
Langley	d	23p47	00 13	00 32	00 55				07 08		08 09			08 42		09 10				09 40			10 10
Slough 3	a	23p52	00 18	00 37	01 00	01 26			07 12		08 14	08 24		08 46	09 01	09 15			09 38	09 47	09 52		10 15
	d	23p53	00 19	00 37	01 01	01 26			07 14		08 14	08 25		08 47	09 01	09 15			09 39	09 47	09 53		10 15
Burnham	d	23p57	00 23	00 41					07 18		08 18					09 19							10 19
Taplow	d	00 01		00 45																			
Maidenhead 3	d	00 05	00 28	00 49	01 08	01 34			07 25		08 23	08 33		08 54		09 24			09 46	09 55			10 24
Twyford 3	d	00 12	00 35	00 56	01 16	01 41			07 33		08 31			09 02		09 32				10 02			10 32
Reading 7	a	00 19	00 42	01 04	01 22	01 49			07 40		08 37	08 46		09 08	09 21	09 39			09 59	10 11	10 13		10 38
Oxford	a	*01b34*									09 31	09 14			09 51	10 29			*10 34*	*11 25*	10 42		11 25

		HC	GW	GW	GW	HC	GW	GW	HC	GW	GW	GW	HC	GW	GW	HC	GW	GW	GW	HC	GW	GW	HC
			1	1	1		1 ◇			1	1	1		1 ◇			1	1	1		1 ◇		
							☕							🍴							☕		
London Paddington 15	⊖ d	10 07	10 15	10 22		10 37	10 42	10 44	11 07	11 15	11 22		11 37	11 42	11 44	12 07	12 15	12 22		12 37	12 42	12 44	13 07
Acton Main Line	d																						
Ealing Broadway	⊖ d	10 15	10 22			10 45		10 51	11 15	11 22			11 45		11 51	12 15	12 22			12 45		12 51	13 15
West Ealing	d																						
Drayton Green	d																						
Castle Bar Park	d																						
South Greenford	d																						
Greenford	⊖ a																						
Hanwell	d																						
Southall	d	10 19	10 27		←	10 49		10 56	11 19	11 27		←	11 49		11 56	12 19	12 27		←	12 49		12 56	13 19
Hayes & Harlington	d	10 23	10 31		10 31	10 53		10 59	11 23	11 31		11 31	11 53		11 59	12 23	12 31		12 31	12 53		12 59	13 23
Heathrow Terminals 1-2-3	✈ a	10 31	→			11 01			11 31	→			12 01			12 31	→			13 01			13 31
Heathrow Terminal 4	✈ a																						
West Drayton	d				10 36			11 05				11 36			12 05				12 36			13 05	
Iver	d																						
Langley	d				10 40			11 10				11 40			12 10				12 40			13 10	
Slough 3	a			10 38	10 45		10 57	11 15			11 38	11 45		11 59	12 15			12 38	12 45		12 57	13 15	
	d			10 39	10 46		10 58	11 15			11 39	11 46		12 00	12 15			12 39	12 46		12 58	13 15	
Burnham	d							11 19							12 19							13 19	
Taplow	d																						
Maidenhead 3	d			10 46	10 53			11 24			11 46	11 53			12 24			12 46	12 53			13 24	
Twyford 3	d				11 01			11 32				12 01			12 32				13 01			13 32	
Reading 7	a			10 59	11 07		11 19	11 37			11 59	12 07		12 17	12 38			12 59	13 07		13 20	13 38	
Oxford	a			*11 35*			11 49	12 27			*12 35*			12 51	13 27			*13 35*			13 49	14 25	

		GW	GW	GW	HC	GW	GW	HC	GW	GW	GW	HC	GW	GW	HC	GW	GW	GW	HC	GW	GW	HC	GW
		1	1	1		1 ◇			1	1	1		1 ◇			1	1	1		1 ◇			1
						☕							☕							☕			
London Paddington 15	⊖ d	13 15	13 22		13 37	13 42	13 44	14 07	14 15	14 22		14 37	14 42	14 44	15 07	15 15	15 22		15 37	15 42	15 44	16 07	16 15
Acton Main Line	d																						
Ealing Broadway	⊖ d	13 22			13 45		13 51	14 15	14 22			14 45		14 51	15 15	15 22			15 45		15 51	16 15	16 22
West Ealing	d																						
Drayton Green	d																						
Castle Bar Park	d																						
South Greenford	d																						
Greenford	⊖ a																						
Hanwell	d																						
Southall	d	13 27		←	13 49		13 56	14 19	14 27		←	14 49		14 56	15 19	15 27		←	15 49		15 56	16 19	16 27
Hayes & Harlington	d	13 31		13 31	13 53		13 59	14 23	14 31		14 31	14 53		14 59	15 23	15 31		15 31	15 53		15 59	16 23	16 31
Heathrow Terminals 1-2-3	✈ a	→			14 01			14 31	→			15 01			15 31	→			16 01			16 31	→
Heathrow Terminal 4	✈ a																						
West Drayton	d			13 36			14 05				14 36			15 05				15 36			16 05		
Iver	d																						
Langley	d			13 40			14 10				14 40			15 10				15 40			16 10		
Slough 3	a		13 38	13 45		13 57	14 15			14 38	14 45		14 57	15 15			15 38	15 45		15 57	16 15		
	d		13 39	13 46		13 58	14 15			14 39	14 47		14 58	15 15			15 39	15 46		15 58	16 15		
Burnham	d						14 19							15 19				15 50			16 19		
Taplow	d																						
Maidenhead 3	d		13 46	13 53			14 24			14 46	14 54			15 24			15 46	15 55			16 24		
Twyford 3	d			14 01			14 32				15 02			15 32				16 03			16 32		
Reading 7	a		13 59	14 08		14 19	14 38			14 59	15 08		15 19	15 38			15 59	16 09		16 19	16 38		
Oxford	a		*14 35*			14 49	15 27			*15 35*			15 48	16 25			*16 35*			16 49	17 25		

For general notes see front of timetable
For details of catering facilities see Directory of Train Operators

For fast services between London Paddington and Reading see Table 116

A To Didcot Parkway (Table 116)
B To Great Malvern (Table 126)
b Change at Didcot Parkway. By bus

Table 117

Sundays

London → Greenford and Reading

(Local services only)

until 27 January

Network Diagram - see first page of Table 116

		GW	GW	HC	GW	GW	HC	GW	GW	GW	HC		GW	GW	HC	GW	GW	GW	HC	GW	GW	HC		GW	GW
		1	1		1 ◇			1	1	1			1 ◇			1	1	1		1 ◇				1	1
London Paddington 15 ⊖	d	16 22		16 37	16 42	16 44	17 07	17 15	17 22		17 37		17 42	17 44	18 07	18 15	18 22		18 37	18 42	18 44	19 07		19 15	19 22
Acton Main Line	d																								
Ealing Broadway ⊖	d			16 45		16 51	17 15	17 22			17 45			17 51	18 15	18 22			18 45		18 51	19 15		19 22	
West Ealing	d																								
Drayton Green	d																								
Castle Bar Park	d																								
South Greenford	d																								
Greenford ⊖	a																								
Hanwell	d																								
Southall	d		←	16 49		16 56	17 19	17 27		←	17 49			17 56	18 19	18 27		←	18 49		18 56	19 19		19 27	
Hayes & Harlington	d		16 31	16 53		16 59	17 23	17 31		17 31	17 53			17 59	18 23	18 31		18 31	18 53		18 59	19 23		19 31	
Heathrow Terminals 1-2-3 ✈	a			17 01			17 31	→			18 01				18 31	→			19 01			19 31		→	
Heathrow Terminal 4 ✈	a																								
West Drayton	d		16 36			17 05				17 36				18 05				18 36			19 05				
Iver	d																								
Langley	d		16 40			17 10				17 40				18 10				18 40			19 10				
Slough 3	a	16 38	16 45		16 57	17 15			17 38	17 45			17 57	18 15			18 38	18 45		18 57	19 15				19 38
	d	16 39	16 46		16 58	17 15			17 39	17 46			17 58	18 15			18 39	18 46		18 58	19 15				19 39
Burnham	d		16 50			17 19				17 50				18 19				18 50			19 19				
Taplow	d																								
Maidenhead 3	d	16 46	16 55			17 24			17 46	17 55				18 24			18 47	18 55			19 24				19 46
Twyford 3	d		17 03			17 32				18 03				18 32				19 03			19 32				
Reading 7	a	16 59	17 09		17 19	17 38			17 59	18 09			18 19	18 38			18 59	19 09		19 20	19 38				19 59
Oxford	a	*17 36*			17 49	18 27			*18 34*				18 49	19 25			*19 35*			19 50	20 25				*20 35*

		GW	HC	GW	GW	HC	GW	HC	GW	GW	HC		GW	GW	GW	HC	GW	GW	GW	HC	GW	GW	GW		
		1		1 ◇			1		1 ◇					1 ◇				1 ◇			1	1 ◇	1		
							A						B	C			B								
London Paddington 15 ⊖	d		19 37	19 42	19 44	20 07	20 15	20 37	20 42	20 44	21 07		21 15	21 42	21 44	22 12	22 15	22 42	22 44	23 12	23 15	23 37	23 53		
Acton Main Line	d																								
Ealing Broadway ⊖	d		19 45		19 51	20 15	20 22	20 45		20 51	21 15		21 22		21 52	22 20	22 24		22 51	23 20	23 23	23 45	00 01		
West Ealing	d																								
Drayton Green	d																								
Castle Bar Park	d																								
South Greenford	d																								
Greenford ⊖	a																								
Hanwell	d																								
Southall	d	←	19 49		19 56	20 19	20 27	20 49		20 56	21 19		21 27		21 57	22 24	22 29		22 56	23 24	23 28		00 06		
Hayes & Harlington	d	19 31	19 53		19 59	20 23	20 31	20 53		20 59	21 23		21 31		22 00	22 28	22 33		22 59	23 28	23 32		00 10		
Heathrow Terminals 1-2-3 ✈	a		20 01			20 31		21 01			21 31					22 34				23 34					
Heathrow Terminal 4 ✈	a																			23 41					
West Drayton	d	19 36			20 05		20 36			21 05			21 36		22 06		22 36		23 05		23 37		00 14		
Iver	d																								
Langley	d	19 40			20 10		20 40			21 10			21 40		22 11		22 42		23 11		23 41		00 19		
Slough 3	a	19 45		19 57	20 15		20 45		20 57	21 15			21 45	21 59	22 16		22 47	22 59	23 15		23 46	23 55	00 24		
	d	19 46		19 57	20 15		20 46		20 58	21 15			21 46	21 59	22 16		22 47	23 00	23 16		23 47	23 57	00 24		
Burnham	d	19 50			20 19		20 50			21 19			21 50		22 20		22 51		23 19		23 51		00 28		
Taplow	d																								
Maidenhead 3	d	19 55			20 24		20 55			21 24			21 55	22 08	22 28		22 55		23 24		23 56	00 05	00 33		
Twyford 3	d	20 02			20 32		21 02			21 32			22 02		22 35		23 04		23 32		00 04		00 41		
Reading 7	a	20 09		20 17	20 38		21 09		21 20	21 38			22 09	22 20	22 42		23 10	23 18	23 42		00 10	00 18	00 48		
Oxford	a			20 48	21 25				21 50	22 27				22 50	23 29			23 47	00 35			00 50			

Sundays

3 February to 23 March

		GW	GW	GW	GW	GW	HC	HC	GW	HC		GW	GW	HC	GW	GW	GW	HC	GW	GW		GW	GW	HC	GW
		1	1	1	1	1			1				1 ◇		1	1 ◇			1	1 ◇		1			1
		D											E												
London Paddington 15 ⊖	d	23p20	23p45	00 05	00 30	01 00	05 12	06 12	06 45	07 12		07 43	08 03	08 12	08 16	08 42	08 44	09 12	09 15	09 30		09 33	09 44	10 12	10 15
Acton Main Line	d		23p51	00 12																					
Ealing Broadway ⊖	d	23p27	23p54		00 37	01 07	05 20	06 20	06 52	07 20		07 52		08 20	08 24		08 51	09 20	09 24				09 51	10 20	10 24
West Ealing	d																								
Drayton Green	d																								
Castle Bar Park	d																								
South Greenford	d																								
Greenford ⊖	a																								
Hanwell	d																								
Southall	d	23p32	23p59	00 17	00 42	01 12	05 24	06 24	06 57	07 24		07 57		08 24			08 56	09 24	09 29				09 56	10 24	10 29
Hayes & Harlington	d	23p36	00 03	00 21	00 46	01 16	05 28	06 28	07 01	07 28		08 01		08 28	08 32		09 00	09 28	09 33				10 00	10 28	10 33
Heathrow Terminals 1-2-3 ✈	a						05 34	06 34		07 34				08 34				09 34						10 34	
Heathrow Terminal 4 ✈	a																								
West Drayton	d	23p41	00 07	00 26	00 51				07 06			08 06			08 37		09 05		09 37				10 05		10 37
Iver	d	23p44	00 10	00 29																					
Langley	d	23p47	00 13	00 32	00 55				07 10			08 11			08 41		09 10		09 42				10 10		10 42
Slough 3	a	23p52	00 18	00 37	01 00	01 26			07 15			08 16	08 24		08 46	09 00	09 15		09 47	09 51		09 55	10 15		10 47
	d	23p53	00 19	00 37	01 01	01 26			07 16			08 16	08 25		08 47	09 01	09 15		09 47	09 52		09 56	10 15		10 47
Burnham	d	23p57	00 23	00 41					07 20			08 20					09 19						10 19		
Taplow	d	00 01		00 45																					
Maidenhead 3	d	00 05	00 28	00 49	01 08	01 34			07 25			08 25	08 32		08 54		09 24		09 55			10 03	10 24		10 55
Twyford 3	d	00 12	00 35	00 56	01 16	01 41			07 33			08 33			09 02		09 32		10 03				10 32		11 03
Reading 7	a	00 19	00 42	01 04	01 22	01 49			07 39			08 39	08 44		09 09	09 20	09 39		10 09	10 07		10 13	10 39		11 09
Oxford	a	*01b34*										09 30	09 15			09 51	10 27			10 40		*11 22*	11 22		

For general notes see front of timetable
For details of catering facilities see Directory of Train Operators

For fast services between London Paddington and Reading see Table 116

- **A** To Bedwyn (Table 116)
- **B** To Newbury (Table 116)
- **C** To Worcester Shrub Hill (Table 126)
- **D** To Didcot Parkway (Table 116)
- **E** To Great Malvern (Table 126)
- **b** Change at Didcot Parkway. By bus

London → Greenford and Reading

(Local services only)

Sundays

3 February to 23 March

Network Diagram - see first page of Table 116

	GW 1	GW 1◇ ☕	GW	HC	GW 1	GW 1	GW 1◇ 🛒		GW	HC	GW 1	GW 1	GW 1◇ ☕	GW	HC	GW 1	GW 1		GW 1◇ ☕	GW	HC	GW 1	GW 1	GW 1◇ ☕
London Paddington 15 ⊖ d	10 33	10 42	10 44	11 12	11 15	11 33	11 42		11 44	12 12	12 15	12 33	12 42	12 44	13 12	13 15	13 33		13 42	13 44	14 12	14 15	14 33	14 42
Acton Main Line d																								
Ealing Broadway ⊖ d			10 51	11 20	11 24				11 51	12 20	12 24			12 51	13 20	13 24				13 51	14 20	14 24		
West Ealing d																								
Drayton Green d																								
Castle Bar Park d																								
South Greenford d																								
Greenford ⊖ a																								
Hanwell d																								
Southall d			10 56	11 24	11 29				11 56	12 24	12 29			12 56	13 24	13 29				13 56	14 24	14 29		
Hayes & Harlington d			11 00	11 28	11 33				12 00	12 28	12 33			13 00	13 28	13 33				14 00	14 28	14 33		
Heathrow Terminals 1-2-3 ✈ a				11 34						12 34					13 34						14 34			
Heathrow Terminal 4 ✈ a																								
West Drayton d			11 05		11 37				12 05		12 37			13 05		13 37				14 05		14 37		
Iver d																								
Langley d			11 10		11 42				12 10		12 42			13 10		13 42				14 10		14 42		
Slough 3 a	10 52	11 00	11 15		11 47	11 53	12 00		12 15		12 47	12 52	13 00	13 15		13 47	13 52		14 00	14 15		14 47	14 52	15 00
Slough d	10 52	11 01	11 15		11 47	11 54	12 00		12 15		12 47	12 52	13 01	13 15		13 47	13 52		14 01	14 15		14 47	14 52	15 01
Burnham d			11 19						12 19					13 19						14 19				
Taplow d																								
Maidenhead 3 d	11 00		11 24		11 55	12 01			12 24		12 55	12 59		13 24		13 55	13 59			14 24		14 55	14 59	
Twyford 3 d			11 32		12 03				12 32		13 03			13 32		14 03				14 32		15 03		
Reading 7 a	11 13	11 19	11 39		12 09	12 13	12 19		12 39		13 09	13 13	13 19	13 39		14 09	14 13		14 19	14 39		15 09	15 13	15 19
Oxford a		11 50	12 25				12 50		13 27				13 49	14 25					14 50	15 27				15 48

	GW	HC	GW 1	GW 1	GW 1◇ ☕		GW	HC	GW 1	GW 1	GW 1◇ ☕	GW	HC	GW 1	GW 1		GW 1◇ ☕	GW	HC	GW 1	GW 1	GW 1◇ ☕	GW	HC
London Paddington 15 ⊖ d	14 44	15 12	15 15	15 33	15 42		15 44	16 12	16 15	16 33	16 42	16 44	17 12	17 15	17 33		17 42	17 44	18 12	18 15	18 33	18 42	18 44	19 12
Acton Main Line d																								
Ealing Broadway ⊖ d	14 51	15 20	15 24				15 51	16 20	16 24			16 51	17 20	17 24				17 51	18 20	18 24			18 51	19 20
West Ealing d																								
Drayton Green d																								
Castle Bar Park d																								
South Greenford d																								
Greenford ⊖ a																								
Hanwell d																								
Southall d	14 56	15 24	15 29				15 56	16 24	16 29			16 56	17 24	17 29				17 56	18 24	18 29			18 56	19 24
Hayes & Harlington d	15 00	15 28	15 33				16 00	16 28	16 33			17 00	17 28	17 33				18 00	18 28	18 33			19 00	19 28
Heathrow Terminals 1-2-3 ✈ a		15 34						16 34					17 34						18 34					19 34
Heathrow Terminal 4 ✈ a																								
West Drayton d	15 05		15 37				16 05		16 37			17 05		17 37				18 05		18 37			19 05	
Iver d																								
Langley d	15 10		15 42				16 10		16 42			17 10		17 42				18 10		18 42			19 10	
Slough 3 a	15 15		15 47	15 52	16 00		16 15		16 47	16 52	17 00	17 15		17 47	17 54		17 59	18 15		18 47	18 52	19 00	19 15	
Slough d	15 15		15 47	15 52	16 01		16 15		16 47	16 52	17 01	17 15		17 47	17 54		18 00	18 15		18 47	18 52	19 00	19 15	
Burnham d	15 19		15 51				16 19		16 51			17 19		17 51				18 19		18 51			19 19	
Taplow d																								
Maidenhead 3 d	15 24		15 56	16 01			16 24		16 56	16 59		17 24		17 56	18 01			18 24		18 56	18 59		19 24	
Twyford 3 d	15 32		16 04				16 32		17 04			17 32		18 04				18 32		19 04			19 32	
Reading 7 a	15 39		16 10	16 13	16 19		16 39		17 10	17 13	17 19	17 39		18 10	18 13		18 19	18 39		19 10	19 13	19 19	19 39	
Oxford a	16 25				16 50		17 24				17 49	18 27					18 49	19 25				19 49	20 25	

	GW 1	GW 1	GW 1◇ ☕		GW	HC	GW 1 A	GW 1◇ 🛒	GW	HC	GW B	GW 1◇ C ☕	GW		HC	GW B	GW 1◇ 🛒	GW	HC	GW 1	GW 1◇ 🛒	GW 1		
London Paddington 15 ⊖ d	19 15	19 33	19 42		19 44	20 12	20 15	20 42	20 44	21 12	21 15	21 42	21 45		22 12	22 15	22 42	22 44	23 12	23 15	23 42	23 53		
Acton Main Line d																								
Ealing Broadway ⊖ d	19 24				19 51	20 20	20 24		20 51	21 20	21 24		21 52		22 20	22 24		22 51	23 20	23 24	23 50	00 01		
West Ealing d																								
Drayton Green d																								
Castle Bar Park d																								
South Greenford d																								
Greenford ⊖ a																								
Hanwell d																								
Southall d	19 29				19 56	20 24	20 29		20 56	21 24	21 29		21 57		22 24	22 29		22 56	23 24	23 29		00 06		
Hayes & Harlington d	19 33				20 00	20 28	20 33		21 00	21 28	21 33		22 00		22 28	22 33		23 00	23 28	23 33		00 10		
Heathrow Terminals 1-2-3 ✈ a						20 34				21 34					22 34				23 34					
Heathrow Terminal 4 ✈ a																			23 41					
West Drayton d	19 37				20 05		20 37		21 05		21 37		22 06			22 37		23 05		23 37		00 14		
Iver d																								
Langley d	19 42				20 10		20 42		21 10		21 42		22 11			22 42		23 10		23 42		00 19		
Slough 3 a	19 47	19 52	19 59		20 15		20 47	21 00	21 15		21 47	21 59	22 16			22 47	22 59	23 15		23 47	00 02	00 24		
Slough d	19 47	19 52	19 59		20 15		20 47	21 01	21 15		21 47	21 59	22 16			22 47	23 01	23 15		23 47	00 03	00 24		
Burnham d	19 51				20 19		20 51		21 19		21 51		22 20			22 51		23 19		23 51		00 28		
Taplow d																						00 32		
Maidenhead 3 d	19 56	19 59			20 24		20 56		21 24		21 56	22 06	22 26			22 56		23 24		23 56	00 11	00 36		
Twyford 3 d	20 04				20 32		21 04		21 32		22 04		22 33			23 04		23 32		00 04		00 44		
Reading 7 a	20 10	20 13	20 20		20 39		21 10	21 19	21 39		22 13	22 18	22 40			23 10	23 18	23 43		00 10	00 24	00 50		
Oxford a			20 47		21 25			21 50	22 27			22 50	23 29				23 48	00 35			00 55			

For general notes see front of timetable
For details of catering facilities see Directory of Train Operators

For fast services between London Paddington and Reading see Table 116

- **A** To Bedwyn (Table 116)
- **B** To Newbury (Table 116)
- **C** To Worcester Shrub Hill (Table 126)

Table 117

Sundays

from 30 March

London → Greenford and Reading
(Local services only)

Network Diagram - see first page of Table 116

		GW	GW	GW	GW	GW	HC	HC	GW	HC	GW	HC	GW	GW	HC	GW	GW	GW	HC	GW	GW	GW	HC	GW	GW
		1	1	1	1	1			1				1			1	1			1	1			1	1
		A									A			A				A				A			
London Paddington 15	⊖ d	23p20	23p45	00 05	00 30	01 00	05 12	06 12	06 45	07 12	07 43	08 12	08 16	08 44	09 12	09 15	09 42	09 44	10 12	10 15	10 42	10 44	11 12	11 15	11 42
Acton Main Line	d		23p51	00 12																					
Ealing Broadway	⊖ d	23p27	23p54		00 37	01 07	05 20	06 20	06 52	07 20	07 52	08 20	08 24	08 51	09 20	09 24		09 51	10 20	10 24		10 51	11 20	11 24	
West Ealing	d																								
Drayton Green	d																								
Castle Bar Park	d																								
South Greenford	d																								
Greenford	⊖ a																								
Hanwell	d																								
Southall	d	23p32	23p59	00 17	00 42	01 12	05 24	06 24	06 57	07 24	07 57	08 24		08 56	09 24	09 29		09 56	10 24	10 29		10 56	11 24	11 29	
Hayes & Harlington	d	23p36	00 03	00 21	00 46	01 16	05 28	06 28	07 01	07 28	08 01	08 28	08 32	09 00	09 28	09 33		10 00	10 28	10 33		11 00	11 28	11 33	
Heathrow Terminals 1-2-3	✈ a						05 34	06 34		07 34		08 34			09 34				10 34				11 34		
Heathrow Terminal 4	✈ a						05 40	06 40		07 40		08 40			09 40				10 40				11 40		
Heathrow Terminal 5	✈ a						05b47	06b50		07b50		08b50			09b50				10b50				11b50		
West Drayton	d	23p41	00 07	00 26	00 51				07 06		08 06		08 37	09 05		09 37		10 05		10 37		11 05		11 37	
Iver	d	23p44	00 10	00 29																					
Langley	d	23p47	00 13	00 32	00 55				07 10		08 11		08 41	09 10		09 42		10 10		10 42		11 10		11 42	
Slough 3	a	23p52	00 18	00 37	01 00	01 26			07 15		08 16		08 46	09 15		09 47	09 59	10 15		10 47	11 00	11 15		11 47	12 00
	d	23p53	00 19	00 37	01 01	01 26			07 16		08 16		08 47	09 15		09 47	10 00	10 15		10 47	11 00	11 15		11 47	12 00
Burnham	d	23p57	00 23	00 41					07 20		08 20			09 19				10 19				11 19			
Taplow	d	00 01		00 45																					
Maidenhead 3	d	00 05	00 28	00 49	01 08	01 34			07 25		08 25		08 54	09 24		09 55	10 07	10 24		10 55	11 07	11 24		11 55	12 08
Twyford 3	d	00 12	00 35	00 56	01 16	01 41			07 33		08 33		09 02	09 32		10 03		10 32		11 03		11 32		12 03	
Reading 7	a	00 19	00 42	01 04	01 23	01 49			07 39		08 39		09 09	09 39		10 09	10 19	10 39		11 09	11 19	11 39		12 09	12 19
Oxford	a	01c34											10e45	10c45			12e15	12c15			13e15	13c15			14e15

		GW	HC	GW	GW	GW	HC	GW	GW	GW	HC	GW	GW	GW	HC	GW	GW	GW	HC	GW	GW	GW	HC	GW	GW
				1	1			1	1			1	1			1	1			1	1			1	1
		A				A				A				A				A				A			
London Paddington 15	⊖ d	11 44	12 12	12 15	12 42	12 44	13 12	13 15	13 42	13 44	14 12	14 15	14 42	14 44	15 12	15 15	15 42	15 44	16 12	16 15	16 42	16 44	17 12	17 15	17 42
Acton Main Line	d																								
Ealing Broadway	⊖ d	11 51	12 20	12 24		12 51	13 20	13 24		13 51	14 20	14 24		14 51	15 20	15 24		15 51	16 20	16 24		16 51	17 20	17 24	
West Ealing	d																								
Drayton Green	d																								
Castle Bar Park	d																								
South Greenford	d																								
Greenford	⊖ a																								
Hanwell	d																								
Southall	d	11 56	12 24	12 29		12 56	13 24	13 29		13 56	14 24	14 29		14 56	15 24	15 29		15 56	16 24	16 29		16 56	17 24	17 29	
Hayes & Harlington	d	12 00	12 28	12 33		13 00	13 28	13 33		14 00	14 28	14 33		15 00	15 28	15 33		16 00	16 28	16 33		17 00	17 28	17 33	
Heathrow Terminals 1-2-3	✈ a		12 34				13 34				14 34				15 34				16 34				17 34		
Heathrow Terminal 4	✈ a		12 40				13 40				14 40				15 40				16 40				17 40		
Heathrow Terminal 5	✈ a		12b50				13b50				14b50				15b50				16b50				17b50		
West Drayton	d	12 05		12 37		13 05		13 37		14 05		14 37		15 05		15 37		16 05		16 37		17 05		17 37	
Iver	d																								
Langley	d	12 10		12 42		13 10		13 42		14 10		14 42		15 10		15 42		16 10		16 42		17 10		17 42	
Slough 3	a	12 15		12 47	13 00	13 15		13 47	14 00	14 15		14 47	15 00	15 15		15 47	16 00	16 15		16 47	17 00	17 15		17 47	17 59
	d	12 15		12 47	13 00	13 15		13 47	14 00	14 15		14 47	15 00	15 15		15 47	16 00	16 15		16 47	17 00	17 15		17 47	18 00
Burnham	d	12 19				13 19				14 19				15 19		15 51		16 19		16 51		17 19		17 51	
Taplow	d																								
Maidenhead 3	d	12 24		12 55	13 07	13 24		13 55	14 07	14 24		14 55	15 08	15 24		15 56	16 07	16 24		16 56	17 07	17 24		17 56	18 07
Twyford 3	d	12 32		13 03		13 32		14 03		14 32		15 03		15 32		16 04		16 32		17 04		17 32		18 04	
Reading 7	a	12 39		13 09	13 19	13 39		14 09	14 19	14 39		15 09	15 19	15 39		16 10	16 19	16 39		17 10	17 19	17 39		18 10	18 19
Oxford	a	14c15			15e15	15c15			16e15	16c15			17e15	17c15			18e15	18c15			19e15	19c15			20e15

		GW	HC	GW	GW	GW	GW	HC	GW	GW	GW	HC	GW	GW	HC	GW	GW	HC	GW	GW	HC	GW	GW	GW	
				1	1	1 ◇			1	1			1									1	1 ◇	1	
		A					A				A		B	A		C	A		C	A					
London Paddington 15	⊖ d	17 44	18 12	18 15	18 37	18 42	18 44	19 12	19 15	19 42	19 44	20 12	20 15	20 44	21 12	21 15	21 45	22 12	22 15	22 44	23 12	23 15	23 37	23 53	
Acton Main Line	d																								
Ealing Broadway	⊖ d	17 51	18 20	18 24			18 51	19 20	19 24		19 51	20 20	20 24	20 51	21 20	21 24	21 52	22 20	22 24	22 51	23 20	23 24		00 01	
West Ealing	d																								
Drayton Green	d																								
Castle Bar Park	d																								
South Greenford	d																								
Greenford	⊖ a																								
Hanwell	d																								
Southall	d	17 56	18 24	18 29			18 56	19 24	19 29		19 56	20 24	20 29	20 56	21 24	21 29	21 57	22 24	22 29	22 56	23 24	23 29		00 06	
Hayes & Harlington	d	18 00	18 28	18 33			19 00	19 28	19 33		20 00	20 28	20 33	21 00	21 28	21 33	22 00	22 28	22 33	23 00	23 28	23 33		00 10	
Heathrow Terminals 1-2-3	✈ a		18 34					19 34				20 34			21 34			22 34			23 34				
Heathrow Terminal 4	✈ a		18 40					19 40				20 40			21 40			22 40			23 40				
Heathrow Terminal 5	✈ a		18b50					19b50				20b50			21b50			22b50			23b50				
West Drayton	d	18 05		18 37			19 05		19 37		20 05		20 37	21 05		21 37	22 06		22 37	23 05		23 37		00 14	
Iver	d																								
Langley	d	18 10		18 42			19 10		19 42		20 10		20 42	21 10		21 42	22 11		22 42	23 10		23 42		00 19	
Slough 3	a	18 15		18 47	18 54	19 02	19 15		19 47	20 00	20 15		20 47	21 15		21 47	22 16		22 47	23 15		23 47	23 56	00 24	
	d	18 15		18 47	18 55	19 02	19 15		19 47	20 00	20 15		20 47	21 15		21 47	22 16		22 47	23 15		23 47	23 57	00 24	
Burnham	d	18 19		18 51			19 19		19 51		20 19		20 51	21 19		21 51	22 20		22 51	23 19		23 51		00 28	
Taplow	d																							00 32	
Maidenhead 3	d	18 24		18 56	19 02		19 24		19 56	20 07	20 24		20 56	21 24		21 56	22 28		22 56	23 24		23 56		00 36	
Twyford 3	d	18 32		19 04			19 32		20 04		20 32		21 04	21 32		22 04	22 35		23 04	23 32		00 04		00 44	
Reading 7	a	18 39		19 10	19 14	19 19	19 39		20 10	20 19	20 39		21 10	21 39		22 13	22 42		23 10	23 43		00 10	00 20	00 50	
Oxford	a	20c15			21e15		21c15			22e15	22c15		23e15	23c15		00e27	00c27			00e55					

For general notes see front of timetable
For details of catering facilities see Directory of Train Operators

For fast services between London Paddington and Reading see Table 116

A To Didcot Parkway (Table 116)
B To Bedwyn (Table 116)
C To Newbury (Table 116)
b Change at Heathrow Terminals 1-2-3
c Change at Didcot Parkway. By bus
e Change at Reading and Didcot Parkway. By bus from Didcot Parkway

Table 117

Mondays to Fridays
until Wednesday 26 March

Reading and Greenford → London
(Local services only)

Network Diagram - see first page of Table 116

Miles	Miles	Miles			GW MX 1	GW MO 1 A	GW MX 1	GW MO 1 B	HC	GW MO 1	GW MO 1◇ bus	GW MO 1◇ bus	GW MX 1◇	GW MO 1◇ bus	GW MO 1◇ bus	GW MO 1	GW MX 1	GW FO 1◇ bus	GW FX 1◇	GW MX 1 C	GW 1	GW 1	GW 1	HC	GW 1
—	—	—	Oxford	d						22p58	23p44	23p44	23p55				23b05	00 01	00 06	00 20			04 00		
0	—	—	**Reading 7**	d	23p16	23p19		23p24		23p41	00 14	00 15	00 24			00 24	00 15	00 29	00 38	01 00	02 24	03 54	04 40		05 16
5	—	—	**Twyford 3**	d	23p22	23p25		23p30		23p48	00 20	00 21				00 30	00 21			01 06	02 30	04 00	04 46		05 23
11¾	—	—	**Maidenhead 3**	d	23p30	23p33		23p38		23p56	00 28	00 29				00 38	00 29			01 14	02 38	04 08	04 54		05 31
13½	—	—	Taplow	d	23p33												00 33								05 34
15	—	—	Burnham	d	23p37	23p37		23p42		00 01							00 36								05 38
17½	—	—	**Slough 3**	a	23p42	23p42	←	23p47		00 05	00 34	00 40	00 41			00 46	00 42	00 42	00 55	01 22	02 46	04 16	05 02		05 42
—	—	—		d	23p42	23p42	23p42	23p47		00 06	00 35	00 41	00 42			00 47	00 42	00 43	00 56	01 23	02 47	04 17	05 04		05 43
19¾	—	—	Langley	d	→	23p46	23p46	23p51		00 10						00 51	00 46						05 09		05 47
21¼	—	—	Iver	d			23p49																05 13		05 50
22¾	—	—	West Drayton	d		23p50	23p52	23p57		00 14						00 55	00 51				02 53	04 23	05 16		05 53
—	—	0	**Heathrow Terminal 4** ✈	d					00 01																
—	—	1¾	**Heathrow Terminals 1-2-3** ✈	d					00 06					←										05 22	
25¼	—	5¾	Hayes & Harlington	d		23p56	23p57	00 02	00 12	00 19	00 48	00 50		00 50		01 00	00 55			01 32	02 58	04 28	05 21	05 28	05 57
27	—	7½	Southall	d		23p59	23p59	00 04	00 15	00 22		→				01 04	01 00				03 02	04 32	05 25	05 31	06 01
28¾	—	9¼	Hanwell	d																				05 34	
—	0	—	**Greenford** ⊖	d																					
—	1	—	South Greenford	d																					
—	1¾	—	Castle Bar Park	d																					
—	2	—	Drayton Green	d																					
29½	2¾	10	West Ealing	d											←									05 37	
30¼	3½	11	**Ealing Broadway** ⊖	d		00 04	00 07	00 10	00 20	00 27	00 55			00 57	00 55	01 09	01 05			01 39	03 07	04 37	05 30	05 39	06 07
31¾	5	12¼	Acton Main Line	d							→												05 34		06 10
36	9¼	16½	**London Paddington 15** ⊖	a		00 12	00 16	00 20	00 29	00 40			01 02	01 05	01 07	01 18	01 13	01 00	01 16	01 48	03 16	04 46	05 41	05 48	06 18

		GW 1	HC	GW 1	GW 1	GW 1◇ bus	GW 1	GW 1	HC	GW 1	GW 1	GW 1	GW 1◇	GW 1	GW 1	GW 1◇ cup	GW 1	GW 1	GW 1	GW 1◇ cup	GW 1	GW 1◇	GW 1	HC	GW 1◇
Oxford	d				05 06	*05c06*							05 50			06 03			05 58	*06c03*					
Reading 7	d	05 33		05 39	05 45	05 57				06 05	06 14	06 15	06 22			06 32		06 32	06 36	06 45		06 46	06 50		←
Twyford 3	d	05a39		05 45	05 51					06 11	06a20	06 21	06 29					06 38	06 43			06 55			06 55
Maidenhead 3	d			05 53	05 59					06 19		06 29			←	06 43		06 46	06e53			→	07 02		07 04
Taplow	d				06 02					06 23		06 33			06 33				→						
Burnham	d				06 06					06 26		→			06 36			06 50							
Slough 3	a			06 00	06 10	06 11				06 31			06 40		06 41	06 50		06 55		06 58					
	d			06 01	06 11	06 12				06 31			06 40		06 41	06 51		06 55		06 59					
Langley	d				06 15					06 35					06 45			06 59							
Iver	d				06 18										06 48		←	07 03							
West Drayton	d				06 21					06 40					06 51		06 51	07 06							
Heathrow Terminal 4 ✈	d														→			→							
Heathrow Terminals 1-2-3 ✈	d		05 56				←		06 26					←										06 56	
Hayes & Harlington	d		06 03	06 10	06 25		06 25		06 33	06 44				06 44			06 56							07 03	
Southall	d		06 06	06 13	→		06 29		06 36	→				06 48			07 00							07 06	
Hanwell	d		06 09						06 39															07 09	
Greenford ⊖	d							06 25													06 55				
South Greenford	d							06 28													06 58				
Castle Bar Park	d							06 31													07 01				
Drayton Green	d							06 33													07 03				
West Ealing	d		06 12					06 36	06 42												07 06			07 12	
Ealing Broadway ⊖	d		06 14	06 19			06 34	06 39	06 44					06 53			07 05				07 09			07 14	
Acton Main Line	d						06 37	06 42													07 12				
London Paddington 15 ⊖	a		06 24	06 30		06 30	06 44	06 50	06 54				07 00	07 02		07 08	07 13			07 16	07 21		07 24	07 24	07 27

		GW 1	GW 1	GW 1	GW 1	HC	GW 1	GW 1	GW 1 D	GW 1	GW 1	GW 1 E	GW 1	HC	GW 1 C	GW 1	GW 1 D	GW 1 C	GW 1	GW 1	GW 1	GW 1	HC	GW 1	GW 1 E
Oxford	d							06 15							06 38	*06 57*				07 02	*07 15*			*07 30*	
Reading 7	d			06 58			07 02	07 07							07 30	07 41				07 57	08 06			08 12	
Twyford 3	d		←	07 04			07 08	07 13	07 23						07 37	07 47	07 56			08 04	08a12			08 18	
Maidenhead 3	d		06 53	07 12			07 16	07 21	07 31			07 42			07 46	07 55	08 04			08 12				08 26	08 42
Taplow	d		06 58					07 25								07 59								08 30	
Burnham	d		07 02				07 21	07 29							07 51	08 02								08 33	
Slough 3	a		07 07	07 19			07 26	07 34				07 49			07 55	08 07				08 19				08 38	08 49
	d		07 08	07 20			07 26	07 34				07 50			07 56	08 07				08 20				08 38	08 49
Langley	d		07 12				07 30	07 39			←				08 00	08 12			←					08 43	
Iver	d	←	07 15					07 42		←	07 42					08 15		←	08 15					08 46	
West Drayton	d	07 06	07 19				07 36	→		07 36	07 45				08 05	→		08 05	08 18					08 49	
Heathrow Terminal 4 ✈	d						→								→										
Heathrow Terminals 1-2-3 ✈	d					07 26								07 56									08 26		
Hayes & Harlington	d	07 10	07 23			07 33				07 40	07 50			08 03				08 10	08 23				08 33	08 54	
Southall	d	07 14	07 27			07 36				07 44	07 54			08 06				08 14	08 27				08 36	08 58	
Hanwell	d					07 39								08 09									08 39		
Greenford ⊖	d				07 25								07 55									08 25			
South Greenford	d				07 28								07 58									08 28			
Castle Bar Park	d				07 31								08 01									08 31			
Drayton Green	d				07 33								08 03									08 33			
West Ealing	d				07 36	07 42							08 06	08 12								08 36	08 42		
Ealing Broadway ⊖	d	07 19	07 32		07 39	07 44				07 49	07 59		08 09	08 14				08 19	08 32			08 39	08 44	09 03	
Acton Main Line	d				07 42								08 12									08 42			
London Paddington 15 ⊖	a	07 30	07 40	07 44	07 50	07 54			07 54	08 00	08 09	08 13	08 20	08 24			08 27	08 30	08 40	08 42		08 50	08 54	09 11	09 15

For general notes see front of timetable
For details of catering facilities see Directory of Train Operators

For fast services between Reading and London Paddington see Table 116

- **A** Until 28 January
- **B** From 4 February
- **C** From Banbury (Table 116)
- **D** From Henley-on-Thames (Table 121)
- **E** From Bourne End (Table 120)
- **b** Tuesdays to Fridays
- **c** Change at Didcot Parkway
- **e** Arr. 0650

Table 117

Mondays to Fridays

until Wednesday 26 March

Reading and Greenford → London

(Local services only)

Network Diagram - see first page of Table 116

	GW 1	HC	GW 1	GW 1	GW 1	GW 1	HC	GW 1	GW 1	GW 1	GW 1 ◇	GW 1	GW 1	HC	GW 1	GW 1	GW 1 ◇ ⊥	GW 1	GW 1	HC	GW 1	GW 1	GW 1 ◇ ⊥	GW 1
Oxford d			*07 52*	07 58				08 21		08 55	09 06					*09 15*	09 38				09 20		10 00	
Reading 7 d			08 31	08 48				09 04	09 19	09 34	09 38				←	09 49	10 04				10 04	10 19	10 25	
Twyford 3 d			08 37	08 55				09 10	09 25	09 40					09 40	09 55					10 10	10 25		
Maidenhead 3 d			08 45	09 03				09 18	09 33	→					09 48	10 03					10 18	10 33		
Taplow d			08 49						09 37							10 07						→		
Burnham d			08 52						09 40							10 10								
Slough 3 a			08 57					09 25	09 45		09 51				09 55	10 15	10 17				10 25		10 38	
d			08 57		←			09 26	09 45		09 52				09 56	10 15	10 18				10 26		10 39	
Langley d			09 01		09 01			09 30							10 00						10 30			
Iver d			→		09 04			09 33							10 03						10 33			←
West Drayton d					09 07			09 36	09 52						10 06	10 22					10 36			10 36
Heathrow Terminal 4 ✈ d																					→			
Heathrow Terminals 1-2-3 ✈ d		08 56					09 26					←		09 56				←		10 26				
Hayes & Harlington d		09 03			09 12		09 33	09 40	09 56			09 56		10 03	10 10	10 26		10 26		10 33				10 40
Southall d		09 06			09 15		09 36	09 44	→					10 06	10 14	→				10 36				10 44
Hanwell d		09 09					09 39							10 09						10 39				
Greenford ⊖ d	08 55					09 25							09 53						10 25					
South Greenford d	08 58					09 28							09 56						10 28					
Castle Bar Park d	09 01					09 31							09 59						10 31					
Drayton Green d	09 03					09 33							10 01						10 33					
West Ealing d	09 06	09 12				09 37	09 42						10 04	10 12					10 36	10 42				
Ealing Broadway ⊖ d	09 09	09 14			09 20	09 40	09 44	09 49				10 03	10 07	10 14	10 19			10 33	10 39	10 44				10 49
Acton Main Line d	09 12					09 43							10 10						10 44					
London Paddington 15 ⊖ a	09 20	09 24		09 27	09 29	09 51	09 54	10 00			10 09	10 12	10 22	10 24	10 30		10 36	10 42	10 51	10 54			10 59	11 00

	GW 1	GW 1	HC	GW 1	GW 1	GW 1 ◇	GW 1	GW 1	GW 1	HC	GW 1	GW 1	GW 1	HC	GW 1	GW 1	GW 1 ◇ ⊥	GW 1	GW 1	GW 1	HC	GW 1	GW 1	GW 1 ◇
Oxford d				09 55	*10 15*	10 30					10 21	*10 43*			10 55	*11 15*	11 30					11 21		12 00
Reading 7 d				10 34	10 49	10 56					11 04	11 19			11 34	11 49	11 56					12 04	12 19	12 27
Twyford 3 d	←			10 40	10 55			←			11 10	11 25			11 40	11 55			←			12 10	12 25	
Maidenhead 3 d	10 33			10 48	11 03			11 03			11 18	11 33			11 48	12 03			12 03			12 18	12 33	
Taplow d	10 37				→			11 07				11 37				→			12 07				→	
Burnham d	10 40							11 10				11 40							12 10					
Slough 3 a	10 45			10 55		11 09		11 15			11 25	11 45			11 55		12 09		12 15			12 25		12 40
d	10 45			10 56		11 10		11 15			11 26	11 45			11 56		12 10		12 15			12 26		12 41
Langley d				11 00							11 30				12 00							12 30		
Iver d				11 03			←				11 33				12 03			←				12 33		
West Drayton d	10 52			11 06			11 06	11 22			11 36	11 52			12 06			12 06	12 22			12 36		
Heathrow Terminal 4 ✈ d				→											→							→		
Heathrow Terminals 1-2-3 ✈ d			10 56							11 26				11 56							12 26			
Hayes & Harlington d	10 56		11 03				11 10	11 26		11 33	11 40	11 56		12 03				12 10	12 26		12 33			
Southall d			11 06				11 14			11 36	11 44			12 06				12 14			12 36			
Hanwell d			11 09							11 39				12 09							12 39			
Greenford ⊖ d		10 53							11 23				11 53							12 23				
South Greenford d		10 56							11 26				11 56							12 26				
Castle Bar Park d		10 59							11 29				11 59							12 29				
Drayton Green d		11 01							11 31				12 01							12 31				
West Ealing d		11 04	11 12						11 34	11 42			12 04	12 12						12 34	12 42			
Ealing Broadway ⊖ d	11 03	11 07	11 14				11 19	11 33	11 37	11 44	11 49	12 03	12 07	12 14				12 19	12 33	12 37	12 44			
Acton Main Line d		11 10							11 40				12 10							12 40				
London Paddington 15 ⊖ a	11 12	11 18	11 24			11 29	11 30	11 42	11 48	11 54	12 00	12 12	12 18	12 24			12 29	12 30	12 42	12 48	12 54			12 59

	GW 1	GW 1	GW 1	HC	GW 1	GW 1	GW 1 ◇	GW 1	GW 1	GW 1	HC	GW 1	GW 1	GW 1 ◇ ⊥	GW 1	GW 1	GW 1	HC	GW 1	GW 1	GW 1 ◇	GW 1	GW 1	GW 1
Oxford d					11 55	*12 15*	12 30					12 21		13 00					12 55	*13 15*	13 30			
Reading 7 d					12 34	12 49	12 55					13 04	13 19	13 27					13 34	13 49	13 56			
Twyford 3 d		←			12 40	12 55			←			13 10	13 25			←			13 40	13 55			←	
Maidenhead 3 d		12 33			12 48	13 03			13 03			13 18	13 33			13 33			13 48	14 03			14 03	
Taplow d		12 37				→			13 07				→			13 37				→			14 07	
Burnham d		12 40							13 10							13 40							14 10	
Slough 3 a		12 45			12 55		13 08		13 15			13 25		13 40		13 45			13 55		14 09		14 15	
d		12 45			12 56		13 09		13 15			13 26		13 41		13 45			13 56		14 10		14 15	
Langley d					13 00							13 30							14 00					
Iver d	←				13 03			←				13 33			←				14 03			←		
West Drayton d	12 36	12 52			13 06			13 06	13 22			13 36			13 36	13 52			14 06			14 06	14 22	
Heathrow Terminal 4 ✈ d					→							→							→					
Heathrow Terminals 1-2-3 ✈ d				12 56							13 26							13 56						
Hayes & Harlington d	12 40	12 56		13 03				13 10	13 26		13 33				13 40	13 56		14 03				14 10	14 26	
Southall d	12 44			13 06				13 14			13 36				13 44			14 06				14 14		
Hanwell d				13 09							13 39							14 09						
Greenford ⊖ d			12 53							13 23							13 53							14 23
South Greenford d			12 56							13 26							13 56							14 26
Castle Bar Park d			12 59							13 29							13 59							14 29
Drayton Green d			13 01							13 31							14 01							14 31
West Ealing d			13 04	13 12						13 34	13 42						14 04	14 12						14 34
Ealing Broadway ⊖ d	12 49	13 03	13 07	13 14				13 19	13 33	13 37	13 44				13 49	14 03	14 07	14 14				14 19	14 33	14 37
Acton Main Line d			13 10							13 40							14 10							14 40
London Paddington 15 ⊖ a	13 00	13 12	13 18	13 24			13 26	13 30	13 42	13 48	13 54			13 58	14 00	14 12	14 18	14 24			14 29	14 30	14 42	14 48

For general notes see front of timetable
For details of catering facilities see Directory of Train Operators

For fast services between Reading and London Paddington see Table 116

Reading and Greenford → London

(Local services only)

Network Diagram - see first page of Table 116

		HC	GW	GW	GW	GW	GW	GW	HC	GW	GW	GW	GW	GW	GW	HC	GW	GW	GW	GW	GW	GW	HC	GW	GW
			1	1	1◇ 🚲	1	1	1		1	1	1◇	1	1	1		1	1	1◇ 🚲	1	1	1		1	1
Oxford	d		13 21		14 00					13 55	*14 15*	14 30					14 21		15 00					14 55	*15 15*
Reading 7	d		14 04	14 19	14 27					14 34	14 49	14 57					15 04	15 19	15 27					15 34	15 49
Twyford 3	d		14 10	14 25			←			14 40	14 55			←			15 10	15 25			←			15 40	15 55
Maidenhead 3	d		14 18	14 33			14 33			14 48	15 03			15 03			15 18	15 33			15 33			15 48	16 03
Taplow	d			→			14 37				→			15 07				→			15 37				→
Burnham	d						14 40							15 10							15 40				
Slough 3	a		14 25		14 40		14 45			14 55		15 10		15 15			15 25		15 40		15 45			15 55	
	d		14 26		14 41		14 45			14 56		15 11		15 15			15 26		15 41		15 45			15 56	
Langley	d		14 30							15 00							15 30							16 00	
Iver	d		14 33			←				15 03			←				15 33			←				16 03	
West Drayton	d		14 36			14 36	14 52			15 06			15 06	15 22			15 36			15 36	15 52			16 06	
Heathrow Terminal 4	d		→							→							→							→	
Heathrow Terminals 1-2-3	d	14 26							14 56							15 26							15 56		
Hayes & Harlington	d	14 33				14 40	14 56		15 03				15 10	15 26		15 33				15 40	15 56		16 03		
Southall	d	14 36				14 44			15 06				15 14			15 36				15 44			16 06		
Hanwell	d	14 39							15 09							15 39							16 09		
Greenford	⊖ d							14 53							15 23							15 53			
South Greenford	d							14 56							15 26							15 56			
Castle Bar Park	d							14 59							15 29							15 59			
Drayton Green	d							15 01							15 31							16 01			
West Ealing	d	14 42						15 04	15 12						15 34	15 42						16 04	16 12		
Ealing Broadway	⊖ d	14 44				14 49	15 03	15 07	15 14				15 19	15 33	15 37	15 44				15 49	16 03	16 07	16 14		
Acton Main Line	d							15 10							15 40							16 10			
London Paddington 15	⊖ a	14 54			14 59	15 00	15 12	15 18	15 24			15 28	15 30	15 42	15 48	15 54			15 59	16 00	16 12	16 18	16 24		

		GW	GW	GW	GW	HC	GW	GW	GW	GW	GW	GW	HC	GW	GW	GW	GW	GW	GW	GW	GW	HC	GW	GW	GW
		1◇	1	1	1		1	1	1◇ 🚲	1	1	1		1	1	1◇	1	1	1	1	1◇ 🚲		1	1◇	1
Oxford	d	15 30					15 21	*15 43*	16 00					15 55	*16 15*	16 30				16 21				17 00	
Reading 7	d	15 56					16 04	16 19	16 27					16 34	16 49	16 56				17 04	17 18		17 19	17 27	
Twyford 3	d			←			16 10	16 25			←			16 40	16 55			←		17 10			17 25		
Maidenhead 3	d			16 03			16 18	16 33			16 33			16 48	17 03			17 03		17 18			17 33		
Taplow	d			16 07				→			16 37				→			17 07					→		
Burnham	d			16 10							16 40							17 10							
Slough 3	a	16 09		16 15			16 25		16 40		16 45			16 55		17 09		17 15		17 25	17 31			17 40	
	d	16 10		16 15			16 26		16 41		16 45			16 56		17 10		17 15		17 26	17 32			17 41	
Langley	d						16 30							17 00						17 30					
Iver	d		←				16 33			←				17 03			←			17 33					←
West Drayton	d		16 06	16 22			16 36			16 36	16 52			17 06			17 06	17 22		17 36					17 36
Heathrow Terminal 4	d						→							→						→					
Heathrow Terminals 1-2-3	d					16 26							16 56									17 26			
Hayes & Harlington	d		16 10	16 26		16 33				16 40	16 56		17 03				17 10	17 26				17 33			17 40
Southall	d		16 14			16 36				16 44			17 06				17 14					17 36			17 44
Hanwell	d					16 39							17 09									17 39			
Greenford	⊖ d				16 23							16 53							17 23						
South Greenford	d				16 26							16 56							17 26						
Castle Bar Park	d				16 29							16 59							17 29						
Drayton Green	d				16 31							17 01							17 31						
West Ealing	d				16 34	16 42						17 04	17 12						17 34			17 42			
Ealing Broadway	⊖ d		16 19	16 33	16 37	16 44				16 49	17 03	17 07	17 14				17 19	17 33	17 37			17 44			17 49
Acton Main Line	d				16 40							17 10							17 40						
London Paddington 15	⊖ a	16 27	16 30	16 42	16 48	16 54			16 59	17 00	17 12	17 19	17 24			17 27	17 30	17 42	17 48		17 53	17 54		17 58	18 00

		GW	GW	HC	GW	GW	GW	HC	GW	GW	GW	GW	GW	GW	HC	GW	GW	GW	GW	GW	GW	HC	GW	GW	GW
		1	1		1	1	1		1	1	1◇	1	1	1		1 A	1	1◇	1 A	1	1		1	1	1◇ 🚲
Oxford	d				16 53	*17 15*			17 21	*17 43*	18 00					17 51	*18 15*	18 30					18 21		19 00
Reading 7	d				17 34	17 49			18 04	18 19	18 27					18 34	18 49	18 56					19 04	19 19	19 27
Twyford 3	d	←			17 40	17 55			18 10	18 25			←			18 40	18 55			←			19 10	19 25	
Maidenhead 3	d	17 33			17 48	18 03			18 18	18 33			18 33			18 48	19 03			19 03			19 18	19 33	
Taplow	d	17 37				18 07				→			18 37				→			19 07				→	
Burnham	d	17 40				18 10							18 40							19 10					
Slough 3	a	17 45			17 55	18 15			18 25		18 40		18 45			18 55		19 09		19 15			19 25		19 40
	d	17 45			17 56	18 15			18 26		18 41		18 45			18 56		19 10		19 15			19 26		19 41
Langley	d				18 00				18 30							19 00							19 30		
Iver	d				18 03				18 33			←				19 03			←				19 33		
West Drayton	d	17 52			18 06	18 22			18 36			18 36	18 52			19 06			19 06	19 22			19 36		
Heathrow Terminal 4	d								→							→							→		
Heathrow Terminals 1-2-3	d			17 56				18 26							18 56							19 26			
Hayes & Harlington	d	17 56		18 03	18 10	18 26		18 33				18 40	18 56		19 03				19 10	19 26		19 33			
Southall	d			18 06	18 14			18 36				18 44			19 06				19 14			19 36			
Hanwell	d			18 09				18 39							19 09							19 39			
Greenford	⊖ d		17 53				18 23							18 53							19 23				
South Greenford	d		17 56				18 26							18 56							19 26				
Castle Bar Park	d		17 59				18 29							18 59							19 29				
Drayton Green	d		18 01				18 31							19 01							19 31				
West Ealing	d		18 04	18 12			18 34	18 42						19 04	19 12						19 34	19 42			
Ealing Broadway	⊖ d	18 03	18 07	18 14	18 19	18 33	18 37	18 44				18 49	19 03	19 07	19 14				19 19	19 33	19 37	19 44			
Acton Main Line	d		18 10				18 40							19 10							19 40				
London Paddington 15	⊖ a	18 12	18 18	18 24	18 30	18 42	18 50	18 54			18 58	19 00	19 12	19 18	19 24			19 29	19 30	19 42	19 48	19 54			19 59

For general notes see front of timetable
For details of catering facilities see Directory of Train Operators

For fast services between Reading and London Paddington see Table 116

A From Banbury (Table 116)

Table 117

Mondays to Fridays

until Wednesday 26 March

Reading and Greenford → London

(Local services only)

Network Diagram - see first page of Table 116

	GW	GW	GW	HC	GW	GW	GW	GW	GW	GW	HC	GW	GW	GW	HC	GW	GW	GW	GW	GW	GW	HC	GW	GW
	1	1	1		1	1	1 ◇	1	1	1		1	1	1		1	1	1 ◇ 🍴	1	1	1		1	1 ◇
Oxford d					18 55	*19 15*	19 30					19 21	*19 43*			19 55	*20 15*	20 30					*20 43*	21 00
Reading 7 d					19 34	19 49	19 54					20 04	20 19			20 34	20 46	20 56					21 20	21 26
Twyford 3 d		←			19 40	19 55			←			20 10	20 25			20 40	20 52			←			21 26	
Maidenhead 3 d		19 33			19 48	20 03			20 03			20 18	20 33			20 48	21 00			21 00			→	
Taplow d		19 37				→			20 07				20 37				→			21 03				
Burnham d		19 40							20 10				20 40							21 07				
Slough 3 a		19 45			19 55		20 09		20 15			20 25	20 45			20 55		21 09		21 11				21 38
d		19 45			19 56		20 10		20 15			20 26	20 45			20 56		21 10		21 12				21 39
Langley d					20 00							20 30				21 00				21 16				
Iver d	←				20 03			←				20 33				21 03			←	21 19				
West Drayton d	19 36	19 52			20 06			20 06	20 22			20 36	20 52			21 06			21 06	21 22				
Heathrow Terminal 4 ✈ d					→											→								
Heathrow Terminals 1-2-3 ✈ d				19 56							20 26				20 56							21 26		
Hayes & Harlington d	19 40	19 56		20 03				20 10	20 26		20 33	20 40	20 56		21 03				21 10	21 26		21 33		
Southall d	19 44			20 06				20 14			20 36	20 44			21 06				21 14			21 36		
Hanwell d				20 09							20 39				21 09							21 39		
Greenford ⊖ d			19 53							20 23				20 53							21 23			
South Greenford d			19 56							20 26				20 56							21 26			
Castle Bar Park d			19 59							20 29				20 59							21 29			
Drayton Green d			20 01							20 31				21 01							21 31			
West Ealing d			20 04	20 12						20 34	20 42			21 04	21 12						21 34	21 42		
Ealing Broadway ⊖ d	19 49	20 03	20 07	20 14				20 19	20 33	20 37	20 44	20 49	21 03	21 07	21 14				21 19	21 33	21 37	21 44		
Acton Main Line d			20 10							20 41				21 10							21 40			
London Paddington 15 ⊖ a	20 00	20 12	20 18	20 24			20 28	20 30	20 42	20 48	20 54	21 00	21 12	21 18	21 24			21 27	21 30	21 42	21 48	21 54		21 58

	GW	GW	HC	GW	GW	GW	GW	GW	HC	GW	GW	GW	HC	GW	GW	GW	GW	GW	HC	GW	GW	GW
					FX	FO	FX	FX		FX	FO	FO		FX			FO	FX				
	1	1		1	1	1 ◇	1	1 ◇		1	1	1 ◇ 🍴		1 ◇ 🍴	1	1	1 ◇	1 ◇		1	1	1 ◇
Oxford d				20 53	*21 15*	21 38		21 38			*21 20*	22 21		22 21	21 53		22 34	22 34				23 05
Reading 7 d	←			21 34	22 00	22 11		22 11			22 16	22 47		22 47	22 50		23 04	23 04			23 16	23 35
Twyford 3 d	21 26			21 40	22 06		←				22 22				22 56	←					23 22	
Maidenhead 3 d	21 34			21 48	22 14		22 14				22 30				23 04	23 04					23 30	
Taplow d				21 51	→		22 17				22 33				→	23 08					23 33	
Burnham d				21 55			22 21				22 37					23 11					23 37	
Slough 3 a	21 41			21 59		22 24	22 26	22 28		←	22 42	23 00		23 04		23 17	23 17	23 21		←	23 42	23 52
d	21 42			22 00		22 25	22 36	22 29		22 36	22 42	23 01		23 05		23 27	23 18	23 22		23 27	23 42	23 53
Langley d	21 46			22 04			→			22 40	22 46					→				23 31	23 46	
Iver d	21 49			22 07						22 43	22 49									23 34	23 49	
West Drayton d	21 52			22 10						22 46	22 52									23 37	23 52	
Heathrow Terminal 4 ✈ d																						
Heathrow Terminals 1-2-3 ✈ d			21 56						22 26				22 56						23 26			
Hayes & Harlington d	21 56		22 03	22 14					22 33	22 50	22 57		23 03						23 33	23 41	23 57	
Southall d	22 00		22 06						22 36	22 55	23 00		23 06						23 36	23 46	23 59	
Hanwell d			22 09						22 39				23 09						23 39			
Greenford ⊖ d		21 53																				
South Greenford d		21 56																				
Castle Bar Park d		21 59																				
Drayton Green d		22 01																				
West Ealing d		22 06	22 12						22 42				23 12						23 42			
Ealing Broadway ⊖ d	22 05	22 09	22 14	22 21					22 44	23 00	23 05		23 14						23 44	23 51	00 07	
Acton Main Line d		22 12																				
London Paddington 15 ⊖ a	22 14	22 19	22 24	22 30		22 42		22 52	22 54	23 08	23 15	23 22	23 24	23 25			23 36	23 41	23 54	23 59	00 16	00 22

For general notes see front of timetable
For details of catering facilities see Directory of Train Operators

For fast services between Reading and London Paddington see Table 116

Table 117

Mondays to Fridays

from Thursday 27 March

Reading and Greenford → London

(Local services only)

Network Diagram - see first page of Table 116

		GW	GW	HC	GW	GW	GW	GW	GW	GW	GW	GW	GW	GW	GW	GW	HC	HC	GW	GW	GW	GW	GW	HC	GW
		MX	MO		MO	FO	FX	MX	MO	MX	MX														
		1	1		1	1 ◇	1 ◇	1 ◇	1	1	1	1	1	1	1	1	1	1	1	1	1 ◇	1	1	1	1
					A						B														
Oxford	d					00 01	00 06	23p55	22b58	23c05	00 20			04 00						05 06	05e06				
Reading 7	d	23p16	23p24		23p40	00 29	00 38	00 24	00 24	00 24	01 00	02 24	03 54	04 40	05 16	05 33			05 39	05 45	05 57				06 05
Twyford 3	d	23p22	23p30		23p48				00 30	00 30	01 06	02 30	04 00	04 46	05 23	05a42			05 45	05 51					06 11
Maidenhead 3	d	23p30	23p38		23p56				00 38	00 41	01 14	02 38	04 08	04 54	05 31				05 53	05 59					06 19
Taplow	d	23p33								00 44					05 34					06 02					06 23
Burnham	d	23p37	23p42		00 01					00 48					05 38					06 06					06 26
Slough 3	a	23p42	23p47		00 05	00 42	00 55	00 41	00 46	00 53	01 22	02 46	04 16	05 02	05 42				06 00	06 10	06 11				06 31
	d	23p42	23p47		00 06	00 43	00 56	00 42	00 47	00 54	01 23	02 47	04 17	05 04	05 43				06 01	06 11	06 12				06 31
Langley	d	23p46	23p51		00 10				00 51	00 58				05 09	05 47					06 15					06 35
Iver	d	23p49												05 13	05 50					06 18					
West Drayton	d	23p52	23p57		00 14				00 55	01 02		02 53	04 23	05 16	05 53					06 21					06 40
Heathrow Terminal 5	d			23f53													05g07	05g42						06g12	
Heathrow Terminal 4	d			00 01													05 23	05 51						06 21	
Heathrow Terminals 1-2-3	d			00 06													05 29	05 56				←		06 26	
Hayes & Harlington	d	23p57	00 02	00 12	00 19				01 00	01 07	01 32	02 58	04 28	05 21	05 57		05 34	06 03	06 10	06 25		06 25		06 33	06 44
Southall	d	23p59	00 04	00 15	00 22				01 04	01 11		03 02	04 32	05 25	06 01		05 38	06 06	06 13	→		06 29		06 36	→
Hanwell	d																05 41	06 09						06 39	
Greenford	⊖ d																						06 25		
South Greenford	d																						06 28		
Castle Bar Park	d																						06 31		
Drayton Green	d																						06 33		
West Ealing	d																05 43	06 12					06 36	06 42	
Ealing Broadway	⊖ d	00 07	00 10	00 20	00 27				01 09	01 16	01 39	03 07	04 37	05 30	06 07		05 46	06 14	06 19			06 34	06 39	06 44	
Acton Main Line	d													05 34	06 10							06 37	06 42		
London Paddington 15	⊖ a	00 16	00 20	00 29	00 40	01 00	01 16	01 02	01 18	01 24	01 48	03 16	04 46	05 41	06 18		05 57	06 24	06 30		06 30	06 44	06 50	06 54	

		GW		GW	GW	GW	GW	GW	GW	GW	GW	GW	GW	GW	GW	HC	GW	GW	GW	GW	GW	HC	GW	GW	GW
		1		1	1 ◇	1	1	1 ◇	1	1	1	1 ◇	1	1 ◇	1	1	1 ◇	1	1	1	1	1	1	1	1
																									C
Oxford	d				05 50			06 03			05 58	06e03												06 15	
Reading 7	d	06 14		06 15	06 22			06 32		06 32	06 36	06 45		06 46	06 50		←			06 58			07 02	07 07	
Twyford 3	d	06a20		06 21	06 29					06 38	06 43			06 55			06 55		←	07 04			07 08	07 13	07 23
Maidenhead 3	d			06 29			←	06 43		06 46	06h53			→	07 02		07 04		06 53	07 12			07 16	07 21	07 31
Taplow	d			06 33			06 33				→								06 58					07 25	
Burnham	d			→			06 36			06 50									07 02				07 21	07 29	
Slough 3	a				06 40		06 41	06 50		06 55		06 58							07 07	07 19			07 26	07 34	
	d				06 40		06 41	06 51		06 55		06 59							07 08	07 20			07 26	07 34	
Langley	d						06 45			06 59									07 12				07 30	07 39	
Iver	d						06 48		←	07 03								←	07 15					07 42	
West Drayton	d						06 51		06 51	07 06								07 06	07 19				07 36	→	
Heathrow Terminal 5	d						→			→						06g42						07g12	→		
Heathrow Terminal 4	d															06 51						07 21			
Heathrow Terminals 1-2-3	d					←										06 56						07 26			
Hayes & Harlington	d					06 44			06 56							07 03		07 10	07 23			07 33			
Southall	d					06 48			07 00							07 06		07 14	07 27			07 36			
Hanwell	d															07 09						07 39			
Greenford	⊖ d												06 55								07 25				
South Greenford	d												06 58								07 28				
Castle Bar Park	d												07 01								07 31				
Drayton Green	d												07 03								07 33				
West Ealing	d												07 06			07 12					07 36	07 42			
Ealing Broadway	⊖ d					06 53			07 05				07 09			07 14		07 19	07 32		07 39	07 44			
Acton Main Line	d												07 12								07 42				
London Paddington 15	⊖ a				07 00	07 02		07 08	07 13			07 16	07 21		07 24	07 24	07 27	07 30	07 40	07 44	07 50	07 54			07 54

For general notes see front of timetable
For details of catering facilities see Directory of Train Operators

For fast services between Reading and London Paddington see Table 116

A From Didcot Parkway (Table 116)

B From Banbury (Table 116)

C From Henley-on-Thames (Table 121)

b Mondays. Mondays from 7 April dep. 2230, by bus to Didcot Parkway

c Tuesdays to Fridays

e Change at Didcot Parkway

f Change at Heathrow Terminals 1-2-3. Sundays dep. 2357

g Change at Heathrow Terminals 1-2-3

h Arr. 0650

from Thursday 27 March

Reading and Greenford → London

(Local services only)

Network Diagram - see first page of Table 116

		GW 1	GW 1	GW 1 A		GW 1	HC 1	GW 1 B	GW 1	GW 1 C	GW 1 B	GW 1	GW 1	GW 1	GW 1	HC 1	GW 1	GW 1 A	GW 1	HC 1	GW 1	GW 1	GW 1	GW 1	HC 1
Oxford	d							06 38	06 57				07 02	07 15			07 30				07 52	07 58			
Reading 7	d							07 30	07 41				07 57	08 06			08 12				08 31	08 48			
Twyford 3	d							07 37	07 47	07 56			08 04	08a14			08 18				08 37	08 55			
Maidenhead 3	d			07 42				07 46	07 55	08 04			08 12				08 26	08 42			08 45	09 03			
Taplow	d								07 59								08 30				08 49				
Burnham	d							07 51	08 02								08 33				08 52				
Slough 3	a			07 49				07 55	08 07				08 19				08 38	08 49			08 57				
	d			07 50				07 56	08 07				08 20				08 38	08 50			08 57		←		
Langley	d		←					08 00	08 12			←					08 43				09 01		09 01		
Iver	d	←	07 42						08 15		←	08 15					08 46				→		09 04		
West Drayton	d	07 36	07 45					08 05	→		08 05	08 18					08 49						09 07		
Heathrow Terminal 5	d						07b42	→								08b12				08b42					09b12
Heathrow Terminal 4	d						07 51									08 21				08 51					09 21
Heathrow Terminals 1-2-3	d						07 56									08 26				08 56					09 26
Hayes & Harlington	d	07 40	07 50				08 03				08 10	08 23				08 33	08 54			09 03			09 12		09 33
Southall	d	07 44	07 54				08 06				08 14	08 27				08 36	08 58			09 06			09 15		09 36
Hanwell	d						08 09									08 39				09 09					09 39
Greenford	d					07 55									08 25				08 55					09 25	
South Greenford	d					07 58									08 28				08 58					09 28	
Castle Bar Park	d					08 01									08 31				09 01					09 31	
Drayton Green	d					08 03									08 33				09 03					09 33	
West Ealing	d					08 06	08 12								08 36	08 42			09 06	09 12				09 37	09 42
Ealing Broadway	d	07 49	07 59			08 09	08 14				08 19	08 32			08 39	08 44	09 03		09 09	09 14			09 20	09 40	09 44
Acton Main Line	d					08 12									08 42				09 12					09 43	
London Paddington 15	a	08 00	08 09	08 13		08 20	08 24			08 27	08 30	08 40	08 42		08 50	08 54	09 11	09 15	09 20	09 24		09 27	09 29	09 51	09 54

		GW 1	GW 1	GW 1	GW 1 ◇	GW 1		GW 1	HC 1	GW 1	GW 1	GW 1 ◇	GW 1	GW 1	HC 1	GW 1	GW 1	GW 1 ◇	GW 1	GW 1	GW 1	HC 1	GW 1	GW 1	GW 1 ◇
Oxford	d	08 21		08 55	09 06						09 15	09 38				09 20		10 00					09 55	10 15	10 30
Reading 7	d	09 04	09 19	09 34	09 38					←	09 49	10 04				10 04	10 19	10 25					10 34	10 49	10 56
Twyford 3	d	09 10	09 25	09 40						09 40	09 55					10 10	10 25			←			10 40	10 55	
Maidenhead 3	d	09 18	09 33	→						09 48	10 03					10 18	10 33			10 33			10 48	11 03	
Taplow	d		09 37								10 07						→			10 37				→	
Burnham	d		09 40								10 10									10 40					
Slough 3	a	09 25	09 45		09 51					09 55	10 15	10 17				10 25		10 38		10 45			10 55		11 09
	d	09 26	09 45		09 52					09 56	10 15	10 18				10 26		10 39		10 45			10 56		11 10
Langley	d	09 30								10 00						10 30							11 00		
Iver	d	09 33								10 03						10 33			←				11 03		
West Drayton	d	09 36	09 52							10 06	10 22					10 36			10 36	10 52			11 06		
Heathrow Terminal 5	d								09b42						10b12	→						10b42	→		
Heathrow Terminal 4	d								09 51						10 21							10 51			
Heathrow Terminals 1-2-3	d					←			09 56				←		10 26							10 56			
Hayes & Harlington	d	09 40	09 56			09 56			10 03	10 10	10 26		10 26		10 33				10 40	10 56		11 03			
Southall	d	09 44	→						10 06	10 14	→				10 36				10 44			11 06			
Hanwell	d								10 09						10 39							11 09			
Greenford	d							09 53						10 25							10 53				
South Greenford	d							09 56						10 28							10 56				
Castle Bar Park	d							09 59						10 31							10 59				
Drayton Green	d							10 01						10 33							11 01				
West Ealing	d							10 04	10 12					10 36	10 42						11 04	11 12			
Ealing Broadway	d	09 49				10 03		10 07	10 14	10 19			10 33	10 39	10 44				10 49	11 03	11 07	11 14			
Acton Main Line	d							10 10						10 44							11 10				
London Paddington 15	a	10 00			10 09	10 12		10 21	10 24	10 30		10 36	10 42	10 51	10 54			10 59	11 00	11 12	11 18	11 24			11 29

		GW 1	GW 1	GW 1	HC 1	GW 1	GW 1	GW 1		HC 1	GW 1	GW 1	GW 1 ◇	GW 1	GW 1	GW 1	HC 1	GW 1	GW 1	GW 1 ◇	GW 1	GW 1	GW 1	HC 1	GW 1
Oxford	d					10 21	10 43				10 55	11 15	11 30					11 21		12 00					11 55
Reading 7	d					11 04	11 19				11 34	11 49	11 56					12 04	12 19	12 27					12 34
Twyford 3	d		←			11 10	11 25				11 40	11 55			←			12 10	12 25			←			12 40
Maidenhead 3	d		11 03			11 18	11 33				11 48	12 03			12 03			12 18	12 33			12 33			12 48
Taplow	d		11 07				11 37					→			12 07				→			12 37			
Burnham	d		11 10				11 40								12 10							12 40			
Slough 3	a		11 15			11 25	11 45				11 55		12 09		12 15			12 25		12 40		12 45			12 55
	d		11 15			11 26	11 45				11 56		12 10		12 15			12 26		12 41		12 45			12 56
Langley	d					11 30					12 00							12 30							13 00
Iver	d	←				11 33					12 03			←				12 33			←				13 03
West Drayton	d	11 06	11 22			11 36	11 52				12 06			12 06	12 22			12 36			12 36	12 52			13 06
Heathrow Terminal 5	d				11b12					11b42	→						12b12	→						12b42	→
Heathrow Terminal 4	d				11 21					11 51							12 21							12 51	
Heathrow Terminals 1-2-3	d				11 26					11 56							12 26							12 56	
Hayes & Harlington	d	11 10	11 26		11 33	11 40	11 56			12 03				12 10	12 26		12 33				12 40	12 56		13 03	
Southall	d	11 14			11 36	11 44				12 06				12 14			12 36				12 44			13 06	
Hanwell	d				11 39					12 09							12 39							13 09	
Greenford	d			11 23				11 53								12 23							12 53		
South Greenford	d			11 26				11 56								12 26							12 56		
Castle Bar Park	d			11 29				11 59								12 29							12 59		
Drayton Green	d			11 31				12 01								12 31							13 01		
West Ealing	d			11 34	11 42			12 04		12 12						12 34	12 42						13 04	13 12	
Ealing Broadway	d	11 19	11 33	11 37	11 44	11 49	12 03	12 07		12 14				12 19	12 33	12 37	12 44				12 49	13 03	13 07	13 14	
Acton Main Line	d			11 40				12 10								12 40							13 10		
London Paddington 15	a	11 30	11 42	11 48	11 54	12 00	12 12	12 18		12 24			12 29	12 30	12 42	12 48	12 54			12 59	13 00	13 12	13 18	13 24	

For general notes see front of timetable
For details of catering facilities see Directory of Train Operators

For fast services between Reading and London Paddington see Table 116

A From Bourne End (Table 120)
B From Banbury (Table 116)
C From Henley-on-Thames (Table 121)

b Change at Heathrow Terminals 1-2-3

Table 117

Mondays to Fridays

from Thursday 27 March

Reading and Greenford → London

(Local services only)

Network Diagram - see first page of Table 116

		GW 1	GW 1 ◇	GW 1	GW 1	GW 1	HC 1	GW 1	GW 1	GW 1 ◇ 🍴	GW 1	GW 1	GW 1	HC 1	GW 1	GW 1	GW 1 ◇	GW 1	GW 1	GW 1	HC 1	GW 1	GW 1	GW 1 ◇ 🍴
Oxford	d	*12 15*	12 30					12 21		13 00					12 55	*13 15*	13 30					13 21		14 00
Reading 7	d	12 49	12 55					13 04	13 19	13 27					13 34	13 49	13 56					14 04	14 19	14 27
Twyford 3	d	12 55			←			13 10	13 25			←			13 40	13 55			←			14 10	14 25	
Maidenhead 3	d	13 03			13 03			13 18	13 33			13 33			13 48	14 03			14 03			14 18	14 33	
Taplow	d	→			13 07				→			13 37				→			14 07				→	
Burnham	d				13 10							13 40							14 10					
Slough 3	a		13 08		13 15			13 25		13 40		13 45			13 55		14 09		14 15			14 25		14 40
	d		13 09		13 15			13 26		13 41		13 45			13 56		14 10		14 15			14 26		14 41
Langley	d							13 30							14 00							14 30		
Iver	d			←				13 33			←				14 03			←				14 33		
West Drayton	d			13 06	13 22			13 36			13 36	13 52			14 06			14 06	14 22			14 36		
Heathrow Terminal 5 ✈	d						13b12	→						13b42	→						14b12	→		
Heathrow Terminal 4 ✈	d						13 21							13 51							14 21			
Heathrow Terminals 1-2-3 ✈	d						13 26							13 56							14 26			
Hayes & Harlington	d			13 10	13 26		13 33				13 40	13 56		14 03				14 10	14 26		14 33			
Southall	d			13 14			13 36				13 44			14 06				14 14			14 36			
Hanwell	d						13 39							14 09							14 39			
Greenford ⊖	d					13 23							13 53							14 23				
South Greenford	d					13 26							13 56							14 26				
Castle Bar Park	d					13 29							13 59							14 29				
Drayton Green	d					13 31							14 01							14 31				
West Ealing	d					13 34	13 42						14 04	14 12						14 34	14 42			
Ealing Broadway ⊖	d			13 19	13 33	13 37	13 44				13 49	14 03	14 07	14 14				14 19	14 33	14 37	14 44			
Acton Main Line	d					13 40							14 10							14 40				
London Paddington 15 ⊖	a		13 26	13 30	13 42	13 48	13 54			13 58	14 00	14 12	14 18	14 24			14 29	14 30	14 42	14 48	14 54			14 59

		GW 1	GW 1	GW 1	HC 1	GW 1	GW 1	GW 1 ◇	GW 1	GW 1	GW 1	HC 1	GW 1	GW 1	GW 1 ◇ 🍴	GW 1	GW 1	GW 1	HC 1	GW 1	GW 1	GW 1 ◇	GW 1	GW 1
Oxford	d					13 55	*14 15*	14 30					14 21		15 00					14 55	*15 15*	15 30		
Reading 7	d					14 34	14 49	14 57					15 04	15 19	15 27					15 34	15 49	15 56		
Twyford 3	d		←			14 40	14 55			←			15 10	15 25			←			15 40	15 55			←
Maidenhead 3	d		14 33			14 48	15 03			15 03			15 18	15 33			15 33			15 48	16 03			16 03
Taplow	d		14 37				→			15 07				→			15 37				→			16 07
Burnham	d		14 40							15 10							15 40							16 10
Slough 3	a		14 45			14 55		15 10		15 15			15 25		15 40		15 45			15 55		16 09		16 15
	d		14 45			14 56		15 11		15 15			15 26		15 41		15 45			15 56		16 10		16 15
Langley	d					15 00							15 30							16 00				
Iver	d	←				15 03			←				15 33			←				16 03			←	
West Drayton	d	14 36	14 52			15 06			15 06	15 22			15 36			15 36	15 52			16 06			16 06	16 22
Heathrow Terminal 5 ✈	d				14b42	→						15b12	→						15b42	→				
Heathrow Terminal 4 ✈	d				14 51							15 21							15 51					
Heathrow Terminals 1-2-3 ✈	d				14 56							15 26							15 56					
Hayes & Harlington	d	14 40	14 56		15 03				15 10	15 26		15 33				15 40	15 56		16 03				16 10	16 26
Southall	d	14 44			15 06				15 14			15 36				15 44			16 06				16 14	
Hanwell	d				15 09							15 39							16 09					
Greenford ⊖	d			14 53							15 23							15 53						
South Greenford	d			14 56							15 26							15 56						
Castle Bar Park	d			14 59							15 29							15 59						
Drayton Green	d			15 01							15 31							16 01						
West Ealing	d			15 04	15 12						15 34	15 42						16 04	16 12					
Ealing Broadway ⊖	d	14 49	15 03	15 07	15 14				15 19	15 33	15 37	15 44				15 49	16 03	16 07	16 14				16 19	16 33
Acton Main Line	d			15 10							15 40							16 10						
London Paddington 15 ⊖	a	15 00	15 12	15 18	15 24			15 28	15 30	15 42	15 48	15 54			15 59	16 00	16 12	16 18	16 24			16 27	16 30	16 42

		GW 1	HC 1	GW 1	GW 1	GW 1 ◇ 🍴	GW 1	GW 1	GW 1	HC 1	GW 1	GW 1	GW 1 ◇	GW 1	GW 1	GW 1	GW 1	GW 1 ◇ 🍴	HC 1	GW 1	GW 1 ◇	GW 1	GW 1	GW 1
Oxford	d			15 21	*15 43*	16 00					15 55	*16 15*	16 30				16 21				17 00			
Reading 7	d			16 04	16 19	16 27					16 34	16 49	16 56				17 04	17 18		17 19	17 27			
Twyford 3	d			16 10	16 25			←			16 40	16 55			←		17 10			17 25			←	
Maidenhead 3	d			16 18	16 33			16 33			16 48	17 03			17 03		17 18			17 33			17 33	
Taplow	d				→			16 37				→			17 07					→			17 37	
Burnham	d							16 40							17 10								17 40	
Slough 3	a			16 25		16 40		16 45			16 55		17 09		17 15		17 25	17 31			17 40		17 45	
	d			16 26		16 41		16 45			16 56		17 10		17 15		17 26	17 32			17 41		17 45	
Langley	d			16 30							17 00						17 30							
Iver	d			16 33			←				17 03			←			17 33					←		
West Drayton	d			16 36			16 36	16 52			17 06			17 06	17 22		17 36					17 36	17 52	
Heathrow Terminal 5 ✈	d		16b12	→						16b42	→						→		17b12					
Heathrow Terminal 4 ✈	d		16 21							16 51									17 21					
Heathrow Terminals 1-2-3 ✈	d		16 26							16 56									17 26					
Hayes & Harlington	d		16 33				16 40	16 56		17 03				17 10	17 26				17 33			17 40	17 56	
Southall	d		16 36				16 44			17 06				17 14					17 36			17 44		
Hanwell	d		16 39							17 09									17 39					
Greenford ⊖	d	16 23							16 53							17 23								17 53
South Greenford	d	16 26							16 56							17 26								17 56
Castle Bar Park	d	16 29							16 59							17 29								17 59
Drayton Green	d	16 31							17 01							17 31								18 01
West Ealing	d	16 34	16 42						17 04	17 12						17 34			17 42					18 04
Ealing Broadway ⊖	d	16 37	16 44				16 49	17 03	17 07	17 14				17 19	17 33	17 37			17 44			17 49	18 03	18 07
Acton Main Line	d	16 40							17 10							17 40								18 10
London Paddington 15 ⊖	a	16 48	16 54			16 59	17 00	17 12	17 19	17 24			17 27	17 30	17 42	17 48		17 53	17 54		17 58	18 00	18 12	18 18

For general notes see front of timetable
For details of catering facilities see Directory of Train Operators

For fast services between Reading and London Paddington see Table 116

b Change at Heathrow Terminals 1-2-3

from Thursday 27 March

Reading and Greenford → London

(Local services only)

Network Diagram - see first page of Table 116

	HC	GW	GW	GW	HC	GW	GW	GW	GW	GW	GW	HC	GW	GW	GW		GW	GW	GW	HC	GW	GW	GW	GW
	1	1	1	1	1	1	1	1 ◇	1	1	1	1	1	1	1 ◇		1	1	1	1	1	1	1 ◇	1
													A				A						[trolley]	
Oxford d		16 53	*17 15*			17 21	*17 43*	18 00					17 51	*18 15*	18 30						18 21		19 00	
Reading 7 d		17 34	17 49			18 04	18 19	18 27					18 34	18 49	18 56						19 04	19 19	19 27	
Twyford 3 d		17 40	17 55			18 10	18 25			⟵			18 40	18 55				⟵			19 10	19 25		
Maidenhead 3 d		17 48	18 03			18 18	18 33			18 33			18 48	19 03				19 03			19 18	19 33		
Taplow d			18 07				⟶			18 37				⟶				19 07				⟶		
Burnham d			18 10							18 40								19 10						
Slough 3 a		17 55	18 15			18 25		18 40		18 45			18 55		19 09			19 15			19 25		19 40	
d		17 56	18 15			18 26		18 41		18 45			18 56		19 10			19 15			19 26		19 41	
Langley d		18 00				18 30							19 00								19 30			
Iver d		18 03				18 33			⟵				19 03				⟵				19 33			⟵
West Drayton d		18 06	18 22			18 36			18 36	18 52			19 06				19 06	19 22			19 36			19 36
Heathrow Terminal 5 ✈ d	*17b42*				*18b12*	⟶						*18b42*	⟶							*19b12*	⟶			
Heathrow Terminal 4 ✈ d	17 51				18 21							18 51								19 21				
Heathrow Terminals 1-2-3 ✈ d	17 56				18 26							18 56								19 26				
Hayes & Harlington d	18 03	18 10	18 26		18 33				18 40	18 56		19 03					19 10	19 26		19 33				19 40
Southall d	18 06	18 14			18 36				18 44			19 06					19 14			19 36				19 44
Hanwell d	18 09				18 39							19 09								19 39				
Greenford ⊖ d				18 23							18 53								19 23					
South Greenford d				18 26							18 56								19 26					
Castle Bar Park d				18 29							18 59								19 29					
Drayton Green d				18 31							19 01								19 31					
West Ealing d	18 12			18 34	18 42						19 04	19 12							19 34	19 42				
Ealing Broadway ⊖ d	18 14	18 19	18 33	18 37	18 44				18 49	19 03	19 07	19 14					19 19	19 33	19 37	19 44				19 49
Acton Main Line d				18 40							19 10								19 40					
London Paddington 15 ⊖ a	18 24	18 30	18 42	18 50	18 54			18 58	19 00	19 12	19 18	19 24			19 29		19 30	19 42	19 48	19 54			19 59	20 00

	GW	GW	HC	GW	GW	GW	GW	GW	GW	HC	GW	GW	GW	HC	GW	GW	GW		GW	GW	GW	HC	GW	GW
	1	1	1	1	1	1 ◇	1	1	1	1	1	1	1	1	1	1	1 ◇		1	1	1	1	1	1 ◇
																	[trolley]							
Oxford d				18 55	*19 15*	19 30					19 21	*19 43*			19 55	*20 15*	20 30						*20 43*	21 00
Reading 7 d				19 34	19 49	19 54					20 04	20 19			20 34	20 46	20 56						21 20	21 26
Twyford 3 d	⟵			19 40	19 55			⟵			20 10	20 25			20 40	20 52				⟵			21 26	
Maidenhead 3 d	19 33			19 48	20 03			20 03			20 18	20 33			20 48	21 00				21 00			⟶	
Taplow d	19 37				⟶			20 07				20 37				⟶				21 03				
Burnham d	19 40							20 10				20 40								21 07				
Slough 3 a	19 45			19 55		20 09		20 15			20 25	20 45			20 55		21 09			21 11				21 38
d	19 45			19 56		20 10		20 15			20 26	20 45			20 56		21 10			21 12				21 39
Langley d				20 00							20 30				21 00					21 16				
Iver d				20 03			⟵				20 33				21 03				⟵	21 19				
West Drayton d	19 52			20 06			20 06	20 22			20 36	20 52			21 06				21 06	21 22				
Heathrow Terminal 5 ✈ d			*19b42*	⟶						*20b12*				*20b42*	⟶							*21b12*		
Heathrow Terminal 4 ✈ d			19 51							20 21				20 51								21 21		
Heathrow Terminals 1-2-3 ✈ d			19 56							20 26				20 56								21 26		
Hayes & Harlington d	19 56		20 03				20 10	20 26		20 33	20 40	20 56		21 03					21 10	21 26		21 33		
Southall d			20 06				20 14			20 36	20 44			21 06					21 14			21 36		
Hanwell d			20 09							20 39				21 09								21 39		
Greenford ⊖ d		19 53							20 23				20 53								21 23			
South Greenford d		19 56							20 26				20 56								21 26			
Castle Bar Park d		19 59							20 29				20 59								21 29			
Drayton Green d		20 01							20 31				21 01								21 31			
West Ealing d		20 04	20 12						20 34	20 42			21 04	21 12							21 34	21 42		
Ealing Broadway ⊖ d	20 03	20 07	20 14				20 19	20 33	20 37	20 44	20 49	21 03	21 07	21 14					21 19	21 33	21 37	21 44		
Acton Main Line d		20 10							20 41				21 10								21 40			
London Paddington 15 ⊖ a	20 12	20 18	20 24			20 28	20 30	20 42	20 48	20 54	21 00	21 12	21 18	21 24			21 27		21 30	21 42	21 48	21 54		21 58

	GW	GW	HC	GW	GW	GW	GW	GW	HC	GW	GW	GW	HC	GW	GW	GW	GW	GW	HC	GW	GW	GW
					FX	FO	FX	FX		FX	FO	FO		FX			FO	FX				
	1	1	1	1	1	1 ◇	1	1 ◇	1	1	1	1 ◇	1	1 ◇	1	1	1 ◇	1 ◇	1	1	1	1 ◇
												[trolley]		[restaurant] [trolley]								
Oxford d				20 53	*21 15*	21 38		21 38			*21 20*	22 21		22 21	21 53		22 34	22 34				23 05
Reading 7 d	⟵			21 34	22 00	22 11		22 11			22 16	22 47		22 47	22 50		23 04	23 04			23 16	23 35
Twyford 3 d	21 26			21 40	22 06		⟵				22 22				22 56	⟵					23 22	
Maidenhead 3 d	21 34			21 48	22 14		22 14				22 30				23 04	23 04					23 30	
Taplow d				21 51	⟶		22 17				22 33				⟶	23 08					23 33	
Burnham d				21 55			22 21				22 37					23 11					23 37	
Slough 3 a	21 41			21 59		22 24	22 26	22 28		⟵	22 42	23 00		23 04		23 17	23 17	23 21		⟵	23 42	23 52
d	21 42			22 00		22 25	22 36	22 29		22 36	22 42	23 01		23 05		23 27	23 18	23 22		23 27	23 42	23 53
Langley d	21 46			22 04			⟶			22 40	22 46					⟶				23 31	23 46	
Iver d	21 49			22 07						22 43	22 49									23 34	23 49	
West Drayton d	21 52			22 10						22 46	22 52									23 37	23 52	
Heathrow Terminal 5 ✈ d			*21b42*						*22b12*				*22b42*						*23b12*			
Heathrow Terminal 4 ✈ d			21 51						22 21				22 51						23 21			
Heathrow Terminals 1-2-3 ✈ d			21 56						22 26				22 56						23 26			
Hayes & Harlington d	21 56		22 03	22 14					22 33	22 50	22 57		23 03						23 33	23 41	23 57	
Southall d	22 00		22 06						22 36	22 55	23 00		23 06						23 36	23 46	23 59	
Hanwell d			22 09						22 39				23 09						23 39			
Greenford ⊖ d		21 53																				
South Greenford d		21 56																				
Castle Bar Park d		21 59																				
Drayton Green d		22 01																				
West Ealing d		22 06	22 12						22 42				23 12						23 42			
Ealing Broadway ⊖ d	22 05	22 09	22 14	22 21					22 44	23 00	23 05		23 14						23 44	23 51	00 07	
Acton Main Line d		22 12																				
London Paddington 15 ⊖ a	22 14	22 19	22 24	22 30		22 42		22 52	22 54	23 08	23 15	23 22	23 24	23 25			23 36	23 41	23 54	23 59	00 16	00 22

For general notes see front of timetable
For details of catering facilities see Directory of Train Operators

For fast services between Reading and London Paddington see Table 116

A From Banbury (Table 116)
b Change at Heathrow Terminals 1-2-3

Table 117

Saturdays

until 22 March

Reading and Greenford → London

(Local services only)

Network Diagram - see first page of Table 116

		GW	HC	GW	GW	GW	GW	GW	HC	GW	HC	GW	GW	GW	HC	GW	GW		GW	HC	GW	GW	GW	GW	GW
		1		1◇	1	1	1	1		1		1	1	1		1	1		1		1	1	1◇	1	1
				⚲		A																			
Oxford	d			00 01	23b05	00 20		04 00								05 21					05 55		06 30		
Reading 7	d	23p16		00 29	00 24	01 00	04 10	04 40		05 10		05 34	05 49			06 04	06 19				06 34	06 49	06 57		
Twyford 3	d	23p22			00 30	01 06	04 16	04 46		05 16		05 40	05 55			06 10	06 25				06 40	06 56		←	
Maidenhead 3	d	23p30			00 38	01 14	04 24	04 54		05 24		05 48	06 03			06 18	06 33				06 48	07 04 →		07 04	
Taplow	d	23p33			00 42					05 28		05 52	06 07				06 37							07 07	
Burnham	d	23p37			00 45					05 31		05 55	06 10				06 40							07 11	
Slough 3	a	23p42		00 42	00 49	01 22	04 31	05 01		05 36		06 00	06 15			06 25	06 45				06 55		07 12	07 15	
	d	23p42		00 43	00 49	01 23	04 32	05 02		05 36		06 01	06 15			06 26	06 45				06 56		07 12	07 16	
Langley	d	23p46			00 53					05 40						06 30					07 00				
Iver	d	23p49								05 43						06 33					07 03				
West Drayton	d	23p52			00 59		04 38			05 45			06 22			06 36	06 52				07 06			07 22	
Heathrow Terminal 4 ✈	d		00 01																						
Heathrow Terminals 1-2-3 ✈	d		00 06						05 22		05 56				06 26					06 56					
Hayes & Harlington	d	23p57	00 12		01 03	01 32	04 43	05 11	05 28	05 51	06 03	06 10	06 26		06 33	06 40	06 56			07 03	07 10			07 27	
Southall	d	23p59	00 15		01 07		04 46	05 14	05 31	05 54	06 06	06 13			06 37	06 44				07 06	07 14				
Hanwell	d								05 34		06 09				06 40					07 09					
Greenford ⊖	d													06 23					06 53						07 23
South Greenford	d													06 26					06 56						07 26
Castle Bar Park	d													06 29					06 59						07 29
Drayton Green	d													06 31					07 01						07 31
West Ealing	d								05 37		06 12			06 34	06 42				07 04	07 12					07 34
Ealing Broadway ⊖	d	00 07	00 20		01 12	01 39	04 51	05 19	05 39	05 59	06 14	06 19	06 33	06 37	06 46	06 49	07 03		07 07	07 14	07 20			07 33	07 37
Acton Main Line	d							05 23		06 03			06 36	06 40					07 10						07 40
London Paddington 15 ⊖	a	00 16	00 29	01 00	01 22	01 48	05 00	05 30	05 48	06 10	06 24	06 28	06 44	06 48	06 54	06 58	07 12		07 18	07 24	07 31		07 31	07 42	07 48

		HC	GW	GW	GW	GW	GW	GW	HC	GW	GW	GW		HC	GW	GW	GW	HC	GW	GW	GW	HC	GW	GW	GW
			1	1	1◇	1	1	1		1	1	1			1	1	1		1	1	1		1◇	1	1
Oxford	d		06 21		07 00					06 55					07 21	*07 37*			07 55	*08 15*			08 30	08 21	*08 30*
Reading 7	d		07 04	07 19	07 26					07 34	07 49				08 04	08 19			08 34	08 49			08 59	09 04	09 19
Twyford 3	d		07 10	07 25			←			07 40	07 55				08 10	08 25			08 40	08 55				09 10	09 25
Maidenhead 3	d		07 18	07 33 →			07 33			07 48	08 03				08 18	08 33			08 48	09 03				09 18	09 33 →
Taplow	d						07 37				08 07					08 37				09 07					
Burnham	d						07 40				08 10					08 40				09 10					
Slough 3	a		07 25		07 39		07 45			07 55	08 15				08 25	08 45			08 55	09 15			09c15	09 25	
	d		07 26		07 40		07 45			07 56	08 15				08 26	08 45			08 56	09 15			09c16	09 26	
Langley	d		07 30							08 00					08 30				09 00					09 30	
Iver	d		07 33			←				08 03					08 33				09 03					09 33	
West Drayton	d		07 36 →			07 36	07 52			08 06	08 22				08 36	08 52			09 06					09 36	
Heathrow Terminal 4 ✈	d																								
Heathrow Terminals 1-2-3 ✈	d	07 26							07 56					08 26				08 56				09 26			
Hayes & Harlington	d	07 33				07 40	07 56		08 03	08 10	08 26			08 33	08 40	08 56		09 03	09 10	09 24		09 33		09 40	
Southall	d	07 36				07 44			08 06	08 14				08 36	08 44			09 06	09 14			09 36		09 44	
Hanwell	d	07 39							08 09					08 39				09 09				09 39			
Greenford ⊖	d							07 53				08 23					08 53				09 23				
South Greenford	d							07 56				08 26					08 56				09 26				
Castle Bar Park	d							07 59				08 29					08 59				09 29				
Drayton Green	d							08 01				08 31					09 01				09 31				
West Ealing	d	07 42						08 04	08 12			08 34		08 42			09 04	09 12			09 34	09 42			
Ealing Broadway ⊖	d	07 44				07 49	08 03	08 07	08 14	08 19	08 33	08 37		08 44	08 49	09 03	09 07	09 14	09 19	09 31	09 37	09 44		09 49	
Acton Main Line	d							08 10				08 40					09 10				09 40				
London Paddington 15 ⊖	a	07 54			07 57	07 58	08 12	08 18	08 24	08 28	08 42	08 48		08 54	08 58	09 12	09 18	09 24	09 28	09 40	09 48	09 54	09 36	09 58	

		GW	GW	GW	HC	GW	GW		GW	GW	GW	GW	GW	HC	GW	GW	GW	HC	GW	GW	GW	GW	HC	GW	GW
		1◇	1	1		1	1		1	1◇	1	1	1◇		1	1	1		1	1◇	1	1		1	1
		⊡											⊡												
Oxford	d	09 00				08 55	*09 15*			09 30	09 20	*09 30*	09 57						09 52	10 30	*10 15*			10 21	
Reading 7	d	09 28				09 35	09 49			09 58	10 04	10 19	10 23						10 34	10 59	10 49			11 04	11 19
Twyford 3	d		←			09 42	09 55				10 10	10 25				←			10 40		10 55			11 10	11 25
Maidenhead 3	d		09 33			09 50	10 03				10 18	10 33 →				10 33			10 48		11 03			11 18	11 33 →
Taplow	d		09 37				10 07									10 37					11 07				
Burnham	d		09 40				10 10									10 40					11 10				
Slough 3	a	09 41	09 45			09 57	10 15			10c14	10 25		10 36			10 45			10 55	11c15	11 15			11 25	
	d	09 41	09 45			09 57	10 15			10c15	10 26		10 36			10 45			10 56	11c16	11 15			11 26	
Langley	d					10 01					10 30								11 00					11 30	
Iver	d					10 04					10 33				←				11 03					11 33	
West Drayton	d		09 52			10 07	10 22				10 36 →				10 36	10 52			11 06		11 22			11 36	
Heathrow Terminal 4 ✈	d																								
Heathrow Terminals 1-2-3 ✈	d				09 56									10 26				10 56					11 26		
Hayes & Harlington	d		09 56		10 03	10 12	10 26							10 33	10 40	10 56		11 03	11 10		11 26		11 33	11 40	
Southall	d				10 06	10 15								10 36	10 44			11 06	11 14				11 36	11 44	
Hanwell	d				10 09									10 39				11 09					11 39		
Greenford ⊖	d			09 53					10 23								10 53					11 23			
South Greenford	d			09 56					10 26								10 56					11 26			
Castle Bar Park	d			09 59					10 29								10 59					11 29			
Drayton Green	d			10 01					10 31								11 01					11 31			
West Ealing	d			10 04	10 12				10 34					10 42			11 04	11 12				11 34	11 42		
Ealing Broadway ⊖	d		10 03	10 07	10 14	10 20	10 33		10 37					10 44	10 49	11 03	11 07	11 14	11 19		11 33	11 37	11 44	11 49	
Acton Main Line	d			10 10					10 40								11 10					11 40			
London Paddington 15 ⊖	a	09 58	10 12	10 18	10 24	10 29	10 42		10 48	10 36			10 54	10 54	10 58	11 12	11 18	11 24	11 28	11 36	11 42	11 48	11 54	11 58	

For general notes see front of timetable
For details of catering facilities see Directory of Train Operators

For fast services between Reading and London Paddington see Table 116

A From Banbury (Table 116)
b Saturdays
c From 2 February

Saturdays

until 22 March

Reading and Greenford → London

(Local services only)

Network Diagram - see first page of Table 116

		GW 1◇ ☕		GW 1	GW 1	HC	GW 1	GW 1	GW 1	HC	GW 1◇	GW 1	GW 1	GW 1◇ ☕	GW 1	GW 1	HC	GW 1	GW 1		GW 1◇	GW 1	HC	GW 1	GW 1
Oxford	d	11 00					10 52	*11 15*			11 30	11 21		12 00				11 55	*12 15*		12 30			12 21	*12 30*
Reading 7	d	11 26					11 34	11 49			12 05	12 04	12 19	12 27				12 34	12 49		12 59			13 04	13 19
Twyford 3	d			←			11 40	11 55				12 10	12 25		←			12 41	12 55					13 10	13 25
Maidenhead 3	d			11 33			11 48	12 03				12 18	12 33		12 33			12 49	13 03					13 18	13 33
Taplow	d			11 37				12 07					→		12 37				13 07						→
Burnham	d			11 40				12 10							12 40				13 10						
Slough 3	a	11 40		11 45			11 55	12 15			12b21	12 25		12 40	12 45			12 56	13 15		13b15			13 25	
	d	11 41		11 45			11 56	12 15			12b22	12 26		12 41	12 45			12 56	13 15		13b16			13 26	
Langley	d						12 00					12 30						13 00						13 30	
Iver	d						12 03					12 33						13 03						13 33	
West Drayton	d			11 52			12 06	12 22				12 36			12 52			13 06						13 36	
Heathrow Terminal 4 ✈	d																								
Heathrow Terminals 1-2-3 ✈	d					11 56				12 26							12 56						13 26		
Hayes & Harlington	d			11 56		12 03	12 10	12 26		12 33		12 40			12 56		13 03	13 11	13 24				13 33	13 40	
Southall	d					12 06	12 14			12 36		12 44					13 06	13 14					13 36	13 44	
Hanwell	d					12 09				12 39							13 09						13 39		
Greenford ⊖	d				11 53				12 23							12 53						13 23			
South Greenford	d				11 56				12 26							12 56						13 26			
Castle Bar Park	d				11 59				12 29							12 59						13 29			
Drayton Green	d				12 01				12 31							13 01						13 31			
West Ealing	d				12 04	12 12			12 34	12 42						13 04	13 12					13 34	13 42		
Ealing Broadway ⊖	d			12 03	12 07	12 14	12 19	12 33	12 37	12 44		12 49			13 03	13 07	13 14	13 20	13 31			13 37	13 44	13 49	
Acton Main Line	d				12 10				12 40							13 10						13 40			
London Paddington 15 ⊖	a	11 58		12 12	12 18	12 24	12 28	12 42	12 48	12 54	12 42	12 58		12 58	13 12	13 18	13 24	13 29	13 40		13 36	13 48	13 54	13 58	

		GW 1◇ ☕	GW 1	GW 1	HC	GW 1	GW 1	GW 1◇	GW 1	GW 1	HC	GW 1	GW 1◇ ☕	GW 1		GW 1	GW 1	HC	GW 1	GW 1	GW 1◇	GW 1	HC	GW 1	GW 1
Oxford	d	13 00				12 52	*13 15*	13 30		13 21			14 00						13 55	*14 15*	14 30			14 21	*14 30*
Reading 7	d	13 28				13 34	13 49	13 59		14 04		14 19	14 27						14 34	14 49	15c01			15 04	15 19
Twyford 3	d		←			13 40	13 55			14 10		14 25				←			14 40	14 55				15 10	15 25
Maidenhead 3	d		13 33			13 48	14 03			14 18		14 33				14 33			14 48	15 03				15 18	15 33
Taplow	d		13 37				14 07					→				14 37				15 07					→
Burnham	d		13 40				14 10									14 40				15 10					
Slough 3	a	13 41	13 45			13 55	14 15	14b15		14 25			14 40			14 45			14 55	15 15	15b18			15 25	
	d	13 42	13 45			13 56	14 15	14b16		14 26			14 41			14 45			14 56	15 15	15b18			15 26	
Langley	d					14 00				14 30									15 00					15 30	
Iver	d					14 03				14 33				←					15 03					15 33	
West Drayton	d		13 52			14 06	14 22			14 36				14 36		14 52			15 06	15 22				15 36	
Heathrow Terminal 4 ✈	d									→															
Heathrow Terminals 1-2-3 ✈	d				13 56						14 26							14 56					15 26		
Hayes & Harlington	d		13 56		14 03	14 10	14 26				14 33			14 40		14 56		15 03	15 10	15 26			15 33	15 40	
Southall	d				14 06	14 14					14 36			14 44				15 06	15 14				15 36	15 44	
Hanwell	d				14 09						14 39							15 09					15 39		
Greenford ⊖	d			13 53					14 23								14 53					15 23			
South Greenford	d			13 56					14 26								14 56					15 26			
Castle Bar Park	d			13 59					14 29								14 59					15 29			
Drayton Green	d			14 01					14 31								15 01					15 31			
West Ealing	d			14 04	14 12				14 34		14 42						15 04	15 12				15 34	15 42		
Ealing Broadway ⊖	d		14 03	14 07	14 14	14 19	14 33		14 37		14 44			14 49		15 03	15 07	15 14	15 19	15 33		15 37	15 44	15 49	
Acton Main Line	d			14 10					14 40								15 10					15 40			
London Paddington 15 ⊖	a	13 59	14 12	14 18	14 24	14 28	14 42	14 36	14 48		14 54		14 58	14 58		15 12	15 18	15 24	15 28	15 42	15e39	15 48	15 54	15 58	

		GW 1◇ ☕	GW 1	GW 1	HC	GW 1	GW 1	GW 1◇	GW 1		HC	GW 1	GW 1	GW 1◇ ☕	GW 1	GW 1	HC	GW 1	GW 1	GW 1◇	GW 1	HC	GW 1	GW 1	GW 1◇
Oxford	d	15 00				14 55	*15 15*	15 30				15 21		16 00				15 55	*16 15*	16 30			16 21		17 00
Reading 7	d	15 27				15 35	15 49	15f59				16 04	16 19	16 27				16 35	16 49	16g59			17 04	17 19	17 25
Twyford 3	d		←			15 41	15 55					16 10	16 25		←			16 41	16 55				17 10	17 25	
Maidenhead 3	d		15 33			15 49	16 03					16 18	16 33		16 33			16 49	17 03				17 18	17 33	
Taplow	d		15 37				16 07						→		16 37				17 07					→	
Burnham	d		15 40				16 10								16 40				17 10						
Slough 3	a	15 40	15 45			15 56	16 15	16b15				16 25		16 40	16 45			16 56	17 15	17b15			17 25		17 40
	d	15 41	15 45			15 57	16 15	16b16				16 26		16 41	16 45			16 57	17 15	17b16			17 26		17 41
Langley	d					16 01						16 30						17 01					17 30		
Iver	d					16 04						16 33						17 04					17 33		
West Drayton	d		15 52			16 07	16 22					16 36			16 52			17 07	17 22				17 36		
Heathrow Terminal 4 ✈	d																								
Heathrow Terminals 1-2-3 ✈	d				15 56						16 26						16 56					17 26			
Hayes & Harlington	d		15 56		16 03	16 11	16 26				16 33	16 40			16 56		17 03	17 11	17 26			17 33	17 40		
Southall	d				16 06	16 15					16 36	16 44					17 06	17 15				17 36	17 44		
Hanwell	d				16 09						16 39						17 09					17 39			
Greenford ⊖	d			15 53					16 23							16 53					17 23				
South Greenford	d			15 56					16 26							16 56					17 26				
Castle Bar Park	d			15 59					16 29							16 59					17 29				
Drayton Green	d			16 01					16 31							17 01					17 31				
West Ealing	d			16 04	16 12				16 34		16 42					17 04	17 12				17 34	17 42			
Ealing Broadway ⊖	d		16 03	16 07	16 14	16 20	16 33		16 37		16 44	16 49			17 03	17 07	17 14	17 20	17 33		17 37	17 44	17 49		
Acton Main Line	d			16 10					16 40							17 10					17 40				
London Paddington 15 ⊖	a	15 58	16 12	16 18	16 24	16 29	16 42	16h36	16 48		16 54	16 58		16 58	17 12	17 18	17 24	17 29	17 42	17j36	17 48	17 54	17 58		17 59

For general notes see front of timetable
For details of catering facilities see Directory of Train Operators

For fast services between Reading and London Paddington see Table 116

b From 2 February
c Until 26 January dep. 1457
e Until 26 January arr. 1528
f Until 26 January dep. 1556
g Until 26 January dep. 1656
h Until 26 January arr. 1627
j Until 26 January arr. 1727

Table 117

Reading and Greenford → London
(Local services only)

Saturdays
until 22 March

Network Diagram - see first page of Table 116

		GW	GW	GW		GW	HC	GW	GW	GW	GW	HC	GW	GW	GW	GW	GW	HC	GW	GW	GW		HC	GW	GW
		1 ◇	1 ◇	1		1		1	1	1 ◇	1		1	1	1 ◇	1	1		1	1	1			1	1
		A ☕	B ☕												☕										
Oxford	d	16 43						16 51	*17 15*	17 30			17 21	*17 30*	18 00				17 55	*18 15*				18 21	
Reading 7	d	17 27	17 32					17 34	17 49	17b59			18 04	18 19	18 27				18 34	18 49				19 04	19 19
Twyford 3	d			←				17 40	17 55				18 10	18 25		←			18 41	18 55				19 10	19 25
Maidenhead 3	d			17 33				17 48	18 03				18 18	18 33		18 33			18 49	19 03				19 18	19 33
Taplow	d			17 37					18 07					→		18 37				19 07					→
Burnham	d			17 40					18 10							18 40				19 10					
Slough 3	a	17 40	17 45	17 45				17 55	18 15	18c15			18 25		18 40	18 45			18 56	19 15				19 25	
	d	17 41	17 45	17 45				17 56	18 15	18c16			18 26		18 41	18 45			18 56	19 15				19 26	
Langley	d							18 00					18 30						19 00					19 30	
Iver	d							18 03					18 33						19 03					19 33	
West Drayton	d							18 06	18 22				18 36			18 52			19 06	19 22				19 36	
Heathrow Terminal 4	d																								
Heathrow Terminals 1-2-3	d						17 56					18 26						18 56					19 26		
Hayes & Harlington	d			17 54			18 03	18 10	18 26			18 33	18 40			18 56		19 03	19 11	19 26			19 33	19 40	
Southall	d						18 06	18 14				18 36	18 44					19 06	19 14				19 36	19 44	
Hanwell	d						18 09					18 39						19 09					19 39		
Greenford	d					17 53					18 23						18 53				19 23				
South Greenford	d					17 56					18 26						18 56				19 26				
Castle Bar Park	d					17 59					18 29						18 59				19 29				
Drayton Green	d					18 01					18 31						19 01				19 31				
West Ealing	d					18 04	18 12				18 34	18 42					19 04	19 12			19 34		19 42		
Ealing Broadway	d			18 01		18 07	18 14	18 19	18 33		18 37	18 44	18 49			19 03	19 07	19 14	19 19	19 33	19 37		19 44	19 49	
Acton Main Line	d					18 10					18 40						19 10				19 40				
London Paddington 15	a	18 03	18 07	18 10		18 18	18 24	18 28	18 42	18e36	18 48	18 54	18 58		18 58	19 12	19 18	19 24	19 28	19 42	19 48		19 54	19 58	

		GW	GW	GW	HC	GW	GW	GW	GW	HC	GW	GW	GW	GW	GW	HC		GW	GW	GW	GW	GW	HC	GW	GW
		1 ◇	1	1		1	1	1 ◇	1		1	1	1 ◇	1	1			1	1	1 ◇	1	1		1	1 ◇
		☕											☕							A					☕
Oxford	d	19 00				18 55	*19 15*	19 30			19 21	*19 30*	20 09					19 55	*20 15*	20 30				20 20	21 00
Reading 7	d	19 27				19 34	19 49	19f59			20 04	20 19	20 34					20 34	20 49	20 59				21 09	21 25
Twyford 3	d		←			19 40	19 55				20 10	20 25						20 40	20 55		←			21 15	
Maidenhead 3	d		19 33			19 48	20 03				20 18	20 33						20 48	21 03		21 03			21 23	
Taplow	d		19 37				20 07					20 37							→		21 07			21 27	
Burnham	d		19 40				20 10					20 40									21 10			21 30	
Slough 3	a	19 40	19 45			19 55	20 15	20c15			20 25	20 45	20 47					20 55		21 15	21 15			21 35	21 38
	d	19 41	19 45			19 56	20 15	20c16			20 26	20 45	20 48					20 56		21 16	21 15			21 35	21 39
Langley	d					20 00					20 30							21 00						21 39	
Iver	d					20 03					20 33							21 03						21 42	
West Drayton	d		19 52			20 06	20 22				20 36	20 52						21 06			21 22			21 45	
Heathrow Terminal 4	d																							→	
Heathrow Terminals 1-2-3	d				19 56					20 26				←		20 56							21 26		
Hayes & Harlington	d		19 56		20 03	20 10	20 26			20 33	20 40	20 56		20 56		21 03		21 10			21 26		21 33		
Southall	d				20 06	20 14				20 36	20 44	→				21 06		21 14					21 36		
Hanwell	d				20 09					20 39						21 09							21 39		
Greenford	d			19 53					20 23						20 53							21 23			
South Greenford	d			19 56					20 26						20 56							21 26			
Castle Bar Park	d			19 59					20 29						20 59							21 29			
Drayton Green	d			20 01					20 31						21 01							21 31			
West Ealing	d			20 04	20 12				20 34	20 42					21 04	21 12						21 34	21 42		
Ealing Broadway	d		20 01	20 07	20 14	20 19	20 33		20 37	20 44	20 49			21 03	21 07	21 14		21 19			21 33	21 37	21 44		
Acton Main Line	d			20 10					20 40						21 10							21 40			
London Paddington 15	a	19 58	20 12	20 18	20 24	20 28	20 42	20g36	20 48	20 54	20 58		21 06	21 12	21 18	21 24		21 28		21 36	21 42	21 48	21 54		21 58

		GW	GW	HC	GW	GW	GW	GW	HC	GW	GW		GW	HC	GW	GW	HC	GW	GW	GW	GW	GW	GW		
		1	1		1	1	1 ◇	1		1	1 ◇		1		1	1		1 ◇	1	1 ◇	1	1 ◇	1		
Oxford	d				20 53		21 30				22 08				21 53			22 30	*22 30*	23 00		23 00	23 09		
Reading 7	d				21 34	21 44	21 54			22 16	22 33				22 35	22 45		23h03	23 16	23 29		23 29	00 05		
Twyford 3	d				21 40	21 50		←		22 22					22 42	22 52			23 23				00 11		
Maidenhead 3	d				21 48	21 58		21 58		22 30					22 50	23 00			23 32				00 19		
Taplow	d					→		22 02		22 34						23 04			23 35				00 22		
Burnham	d							22 05		22 37						23 07			23 39				00 26		
Slough 3	a				21 55		22 09	22 10		22 42	22 48				22 57	23 12		23c20	23 43	23 48		23 48	00 30		
	d				21 56		22 09	22 10		22 42	22 49				22 57	23 12		23c21	23 44	23 49		23 49	00 31		
Langley	d							22 14		22 46						23 16			23 48				00 35		
Iver	d	←						22 17		22 49			←			23 19			23 51		←		00 38		
West Drayton	d	21 45						22 20		22 52			22 52			23 22			23 54		23 54		00 41		
Heathrow Terminal 4	d									→									→						
Heathrow Terminals 1-2-3	d			21 56					22 26					22 56			23 26								
Hayes & Harlington	d	21 50		22 03	22 06			22 25	22 33				22 57	23 03	23 06	23 27	23 33				23 58		00 45		
Southall	d	21 53		22 06	22 10			22 28	22 36				23 00	23 06	23 10	23 30	23 36				00 02		00 49		
Hanwell	d			22 09					22 39					23 09			23 39								
Greenford	d		21 53																						
South Greenford	d		21 56																						
Castle Bar Park	d		21 59																						
Drayton Green	d		22 01																						
West Ealing	d		22 04	22 12					22 42					23 12			23 42								
Ealing Broadway	d	21 58	22 07	22 14	22 19			22 33	22 44				23 05	23 14	23 19	23 35	23 44				00 07		00 54		
Acton Main Line	d		22 10																						
London Paddington 15	a	22 08	22 18	22 24	22 28		22 28	22 42	22 54		23 07		23 14	23 24	23 28	23 44	23 54	23j41		00 09	00 16	00 09	01 02		

Station symbols: Greenford, Ealing Broadway and London Paddington ⊖ (Underground interchange); Heathrow Terminal 4 and Heathrow Terminals 1-2-3 ✈ (airport).

For general notes see front of timetable
For details of catering facilities see Directory of Train Operators

For fast services between Reading and London Paddington see Table 116

- **A** From 2 February
- **B** Until 26 January
- **b** Until 26 January dep. 1757
- **e** Until 26 January arr. 1828
- **f** Until 26 January dep. 1956
- **g** Until 26 January arr. 2027
- **h** Until 26 January dep. 2256
- **j** Until 26 January arr. 2329

Table 117

Saturdays

from 29 March

Reading and Greenford → London

(Local services only)

Network Diagram - see first page of Table 116

		GW 1	HC 1	GW 1◇	GW 1	GW 1	GW 1	GW 1	HC 1	GW 1	HC 1	GW 1	GW 1	GW 1	HC 1	GW 1	GW 1	GW 1	HC 1	GW 1	GW 1	GW 1◇	GW 1	GW 1	HC 1
						A		B																	
Oxford	d			00p01	23b05	00 20		04 00								05 21				05 55		06 30			
Reading 7	d	23p16		00 29	00 24	01 00	04 10	04 40		05 10		05 34	05 49			06 04	06 19			06 34	06 49	06 57			
Twyford 3	d	23p22			00 30	01 06	04 16	04 46		05 16		05 40	05 55			06 10	06 25			06 40	06 56		←		
Maidenhead 3	d	23p30			00 38	01 14	04 24	04 54		05 24		05 48	06 03			06 18	06 33			06 48	07 04		07 04		
Taplow	d	23p33			00 42					05 28			06 07				06 37				→		07 07		
Burnham	d	23p37			00 45					05 31			06 10				06 40						07 11		
Slough 3	a	23p42		00 42	00 49	01 22	04 31	05 01		05 36		05 55	06 15			06 25	06 45			06 55		07 12	07 15		
	d	23p42		00 43	00 49	01 23	04 32	05 02		05 36		05 56	06 15			06 26	06 45			06 56		07 12	07 16		
Langley	d	23p46			00 53					05 40		06 00				06 30				07 00					
Iver	d	23p49								05 43		06 03				06 33				07 03					
West Drayton	d	23p52			00 59		04 38			05 45		06 06	06 22			06 36	06 52			07 06			07 22		
Heathrow Terminal 5	d		23c53						05c07		05c42				06c12				06c42						07c12
Heathrow Terminal 4	d		00 01						05 23		05 51				06 21				06 51						07 21
Heathrow Terminals 1-2-3	d		00 06						05 29		05 56				06 26				06 56						07 26
Hayes & Harlington	d	23p57	00 12		01 03	01 32	04 43	05 11	05 34	05 51	06 03	06 10	06 26		06 33	06 40	06 56		07 03	07 10			07 27		07 33
Southall	d	23p59	00 15		01 07		04 46	05 14	05 38	05 54	06 06	06 14			06 36	06 44			07 06	07 14					07 36
Hanwell	d								05 41		06 09				06 39				07 09						07 39
Greenford	⊖ d													06 23				06 53						07 23	
South Greenford	d													06 26				06 56						07 26	
Castle Bar Park	d													06 29				06 59						07 29	
Drayton Green	d													06 31				07 01						07 31	
West Ealing	d								05 43		06 12			06 34	06 42			07 04	07 12					07 34	07 42
Ealing Broadway	⊖ d	00 07	00 20		01 12	01 39	04 51	05 19	05 46	05 59	06 14	06 19	06 33	06 37	06 44	06 49	07 03	07 07	07 14	07 20			07 33	07 37	07 44
Acton Main Line	d							05 23		06 03			06 36	06 40				07 10						07 40	
London Paddington 15	⊖ a	00 16	00 29	01 00	01 22	01 48	05 00	05 30	05 57	06 10	06 24	06 28	06 44	06 48	06 54	06 58	07 12	07 18	07 24	07 31		07 31	07 42	07 48	07 54

		GW 1	GW 1	GW 1◇	GW 1	GW 1	GW 1	HC 1	GW 1	GW 1	GW 1	HC 1	GW 1	GW 1	GW 1	HC 1	GW 1	GW 1	GW 1	HC 1	GW 1	GW 1	GW 1◇	GW 1	GW 1
Oxford	d	06 21		07 00					06 55				07 21	*07 37*			07 55	*08 15*			08 21	*08 30*	09 00		
Reading 7	d	07 04	07 19	07 26					07 34	07 49			08 04	08 19			08 34	08 49			09 04	09 19	09 28		
Twyford 3	d	07 10	07 25			←			07 40	07 55			08 10	08 25			08 40	08 55			09 10	09 25		←	
Maidenhead 3	d	07 18	07 33			07 33			07 48	08 03			08 18	08 33			08 48	09 03			09 18	09 33		09 33	
Taplow	d		→			07 37				08 07				08 37				09 07				→		09 37	
Burnham	d					07 40				08 10				08 40				09 10						09 40	
Slough 3	a	07 25		07 39		07 45			07 55	08 15			08 25	08 45			08 55	09 15			09 25		09 41	09 45	
	d	07 26		07 40		07 45			07 56	08 15			08 26	08 45			08 56	09 15			09 26		09 41	09 45	
Langley	d	07 30							08 00				08 30				09 00				09 30				
Iver	d	07 33			←				08 03				08 33				09 03				09 33				
West Drayton	d	07 36			07 36	07 52			08 06	08 22			08 36	08 52			09 06	09 22			09 36			09 52	
Heathrow Terminal 5	d	→						07c42				08c12				08c42				09c12					
Heathrow Terminal 4	d							07 51				08 21				08 51				09 21					
Heathrow Terminals 1-2-3	d							07 56				08 26				08 56				09 26					
Hayes & Harlington	d				07 40	07 56		08 03	08 10	08 26		08 33	08 40	08 56		09 03	09 10	09 26		09 33	09 40			09 56	
Southall	d				07 44			08 06	08 14			08 36	08 44			09 06	09 14			09 36	09 44				
Hanwell	d							08 09				08 39				09 09				09 39					
Greenford	⊖ d						07 53				08 23				08 53				09 23						09 53
South Greenford	d						07 56				08 26				08 56				09 26						09 56
Castle Bar Park	d						07 59				08 29				08 59				09 29						09 59
Drayton Green	d						08 01				08 31				09 01				09 31						10 01
West Ealing	d						08 04	08 12			08 34	08 42			09 04	09 12			09 34	09 42					10 04
Ealing Broadway	⊖ d				07 49	08 03	08 07	08 14	08 19	08 33	08 37	08 44	08 49	09 03	09 07	09 14	09 19	09 33	09 37	09 44	09 49			10 03	10 07
Acton Main Line	d						08 10				08 40				09 10				09 40						10 10
London Paddington 15	⊖ a			07 57	07 58	08 12	08 18	08 24	08 28	08 42	08 48	08 54	08 58	09 12	09 18	09 24	09 28	09 42	09 48	09 54	09 58		09 58	10 12	10 18

		HC 1	GW 1	GW 1	GW 1	GW 1	GW 1	GW 1◇	HC 1	GW 1	GW 1	GW 1	HC 1	GW 1	GW 1	GW 1	HC 1	GW 1	GW 1	GW 1◇	GW 1	GW 1	HC 1	GW 1	GW 1
Oxford	d		08 55	*09 15*		09 20	*09 30*	09 57						09 52	*10 15*			10 21		11 00				10 52	*11 15*
Reading 7	d		09 35	09 49		10 04	10 19	10 23						10 34	10 49			11 04	11 19	11 26				11 34	11 49
Twyford 3	d		09 42	09 55		10 10	10 25				←			10 40	10 55			11 10	11 25		←			11 40	11 55
Maidenhead 3	d		09 50	10 03		10 18	10 33				10 33			10 48	11 03			11 18	11 33		11 33			11 48	12 03
Taplow	d			10 07			→				10 37				11 07				→		11 37				12 07
Burnham	d			10 10							10 40				11 10						11 40				12 10
Slough 3	a		09 57	10 15		10 25		10 36			10 45			10 55	11 15			11 25		11 40	11 45			11 55	12 15
	d		09 57	10 15		10 26		10 36			10 45			10 56	11 15			11 26		11 41	11 45			11 56	12 15
Langley	d		10 01			10 30								11 00				11 30						12 00	
Iver	d		10 04			10 33				←				11 03				11 33						12 03	
West Drayton	d		10 07	10 22		10 36				10 36	10 52			11 06	11 22			11 36			11 52			12 06	12 22
Heathrow Terminal 5	d	09c42				→			10c12				10c42				11c12						11c42		
Heathrow Terminal 4	d	09 51							10 21				10 51				11 21						11 51		
Heathrow Terminals 1-2-3	d	09 56							10 26				10 56				11 26						11 56		
Hayes & Harlington	d	10 03	10 12	10 26					10 33	10 40	10 56		11 03	11 10	11 26		11 33	11 40			11 56		12 03	12 10	12 26
Southall	d	10 06	10 15						10 36	10 44			11 06	11 14			11 36	11 44					12 06	12 14	
Hanwell	d	10 09							10 39				11 09				11 39						12 09		
Greenford	⊖ d				10 23							10 53				11 23						11 53			
South Greenford	d				10 26							10 56				11 26						11 56			
Castle Bar Park	d				10 29							10 59				11 29						11 59			
Drayton Green	d				10 31							11 01				11 31						12 01			
West Ealing	d	10 12			10 34				10 42			11 04	11 12			11 34	11 42					12 04	12 12		
Ealing Broadway	⊖ d	10 14	10 20	10 33	10 37				10 44	10 49	11 03	11 07	11 14	11 19	11 33	11 37	11 44	11 49			12 03	12 07	12 14	12 19	12 33
Acton Main Line	d				10 40							11 10				11 40						12 10			
London Paddington 15	⊖ a	10 24	10 29	10 42	10 48			10 54	10 54	10 58	11 12	11 18	11 24	11 28	11 42	11 48	11 54	11 58		11 58	12 12	12 18	12 24	12 28	12 42

For general notes see front of timetable
For details of catering facilities see Directory of Train Operators

For fast services between Reading and London Paddington see Table 116

A From Banbury (Table 116)
B Also stops at Didcot Parkway 0412
b Saturdays
c Change at Heathrow Terminals 1-2-3

Table 117

Saturdays

from 29 March

Reading and Greenford → London

(Local services only)

Network Diagram - see first page of Table 116

	GW 1	HC 1	GW 1	GW 1	GW 1 ◇ ☕	GW 1	GW 1	HC 1	GW 1	GW 1	GW 1	HC 1	GW 1	GW 1	GW 1 ◇ ☕	GW 1	GW 1	HC 1	GW 1	GW 1	GW 1	GW 1	HC 1	GW 1
Oxford d			11 21		12 00				11 55	*12 15*			12 21	*12 30*	13 00				12 52	*13 15*		13 21		
Reading [7] d			12 04	12 19	12 27				12 34	12 49			13 04	13 19	13 28				13 34	13 49		14 04		14 19
Twyford [3] d			12 10	12 25		←			12 41	12 55			13 10	13 25		←			13 40	13 55		14 10		14 25
Maidenhead [3] d			12 18	12 33		12 33			12 49	13 03			13 18	13 33		13 33			13 48	14 03		14 18		14 33
Taplow d				→		12 37				13 07				→		13 37				14 07				→
Burnham d						12 40				13 10						13 40				14 10				
Slough [3] a			12 25		12 40	12 45			12 56	13 15			13 25		13 41	13 45			13 55	14 15		14 25		
d			12 26		12 41	12 45			12 56	13 15			13 26		13 42	13 45			13 56	14 15		14 26		
Langley d			12 30						13 00				13 30						14 00			14 30		
Iver d			12 33						13 03				13 33						14 03			14 33		
West Drayton d			12 36			12 52			13 06	13 22			13 36			13 52			14 06	14 22		14 36		
Heathrow Terminal 5 ✈ d		*12b12*						*12b42*				*13b12*						*13b42*				→	*14b12*	
Heathrow Terminal 4 ✈ d		12 21						12 51				13 21						13 51					14 21	
Heathrow Terminals 1-2-3 ✈ d		12 26						12 56				13 26						13 56					14 26	
Hayes & Harlington d		12 33	12 40			12 56		13 03	13 11	13 26		13 33	13 40			13 56		14 03	14 10	14 26			14 33	
Southall d		12 36	12 44					13 06	13 14			13 36	13 44					14 06	14 14				14 36	
Hanwell d		12 39						13 09				13 39						14 09					14 39	
Greenford ⊖ d	12 23						12 53				13 23						13 53				14 23			
South Greenford d	12 26						12 56				13 26						13 56				14 26			
Castle Bar Park d	12 29						12 59				13 29						13 59				14 29			
Drayton Green d	12 31						13 01				13 31						14 01				14 31			
West Ealing d	12 34	12 42					13 04	13 12			13 34	13 42					14 04	14 12			14 34		14 42	
Ealing Broadway ⊖ d	12 37	12 44	12 49			13 03	13 07	13 14	13 20	13 33	13 37	13 44	13 49			14 03	14 07	14 14	14 19	14 33	14 37		14 44	
Acton Main Line d	12 40						13 10				13 40						14 10				14 40			
London Paddington [15] ⊖ a	12 48	12 54	12 58		12 58	13 12	13 18	13 24	13 29	13 42	13 48	13 54	13 58		13 59	14 12	14 18	14 24	14 28	14 42	14 48		14 54	

	GW 1 ◇ ☕	GW 1	GW 1	GW 1	HC 1	GW 1	GW 1	GW 1	HC 1	GW 1	GW 1	GW 1 ◇ ☕	GW 1	GW 1	HC 1	GW 1	GW 1	GW 1	HC 1	GW 1	GW 1	GW 1 ◇ ☕	GW 1	GW 1
Oxford d	14 00					13 55	*14 15*			14 21	*14 30*	15 00				14 55	*15 15*			15 21		16 00		
Reading [7] d	14 27					14 34	14 49			15 04	15 19	15 27				15 35	15 49			16 04	16 19	16 27		
Twyford [3] d			←			14 40	14 55			15 10	15 25		←			15 41	15 55			16 10	16 25		←	
Maidenhead [3] d			14 33			14 48	15 03			15 18	15 33		15 33			15 49	16 03			16 18	16 33		16 33	
Taplow d			14 37				15 07				→		15 37				16 07				→		16 37	
Burnham d			14 40				15 10						15 40				16 10						16 40	
Slough [3] a	14 40		14 45			14 55	15 15			15 25		15 40	15 45			15 56	16 15			16 25		16 40	16 45	
d	14 41		14 45			14 56	15 15			15 26		15 41	15 45			15 57	16 15			16 26		16 41	16 45	
Langley d						15 00				15 30						16 01				16 30				
Iver d		←				15 03				15 33						16 04				16 33				
West Drayton d		14 36	14 52			15 06	15 22			15 36			15 52			16 07	16 22			16 36			16 52	
Heathrow Terminal 5 ✈ d					*14b42*				*15b12*						*15b42*				*16b12*					
Heathrow Terminal 4 ✈ d					14 51				15 21						15 51				16 21					
Heathrow Terminals 1-2-3 ✈ d					14 56				15 26						15 56				16 26					
Hayes & Harlington d		14 40	14 56		15 03	15 10	15 26		15 33	15 40			15 56		16 03	16 11	16 26		16 33	16 40			16 56	
Southall d		14 44			15 06	15 14			15 36	15 44					16 06	16 15			16 36	16 44				
Hanwell d					15 09				15 39						16 09				16 39					
Greenford ⊖ d				14 53				15 23						15 53				16 23						16 53
South Greenford d				14 56				15 26						15 56				16 26						16 56
Castle Bar Park d				14 59				15 29						15 59				16 29						16 59
Drayton Green d				15 01				15 31						16 01				16 31						17 01
West Ealing d				15 04	15 12			15 34	15 42					16 04	16 12			16 34	16 42					17 04
Ealing Broadway ⊖ d		14 49	15 03	15 07	15 14	15 19	15 31	15 37	15 44	15 49			16 03	16 07	16 14	16 20	16 33	16 37	16 44	16 49			17 03	17 07
Acton Main Line d				15 10				15 40						16 10				16 40						17 10
London Paddington [15] ⊖ a	14 58	14 58	15 12	15 18	15 24	15 28	15 42	15 48	15 54	15 58		15 58	16 12	16 18	16 24	16 29	16 42	16 48	16 54	16 58		16 58	17 12	17 18

	HC 1	GW 1	GW 1	GW 1	HC 1	GW 1	GW 1	GW 1 ◇	GW 1	GW 1	GW 1	GW 1	GW 1 ◇ ☕	HC 1	GW 1	GW 1	GW 1	HC 1	GW 1	GW 1	GW 1 ◇ ☕	GW 1	GW 1	HC 1
Oxford d		15 55	*16 15*			16 21		17 00			16 51	*17 15*							17 21	*17 30*	18 00			
Reading [7] d		16 35	16 49			17 04	17 19	17 25			17 34	17 49	17 52						18 04	18 19	18 27			
Twyford [3] d		16 41	16 55			17 10	17 25		←		17 40	17 55				←			18 10	18 25		←		
Maidenhead [3] d		16 49	17 03			17 18	17 33		17 33		17 48	18 03				18 03			18 18	18 33		18 33		
Taplow d			17 07				→		17 37			→				18 07				→		18 37		
Burnham d			17 10						17 40							18 10						18 40		
Slough [3] a		16 56	17 15			17 25		17 40	17 45		17 55		18 05			18 15			18 25		18 40	18 45		
d		16 57	17 15			17 26		17 41	17 45		17 56		18 05			18 15			18 26		18 41	18 45		
Langley d		17 01				17 30					18 00								18 30					
Iver d		17 04				17 33					18 03				←				18 33					
West Drayton d		17 07	17 22			17 36			17 52		18 06				18 06	18 22			18 36			18 52		
Heathrow Terminal 5 ✈ d	*16b42*				*17b12*						→			*17b42*				*18b12*						*18b42*
Heathrow Terminal 4 ✈ d	16 51				17 21									17 51				18 21						18 51
Heathrow Terminals 1-2-3 ✈ d	16 56				17 26									17 56				18 26						18 56
Hayes & Harlington d	17 03	17 11	17 26		17 33	17 40			17 56					18 03	18 10	18 26		18 33	18 40			18 56		19 03
Southall d	17 06	17 15			17 36	17 44								18 06	18 14			18 36	18 44					19 06
Hanwell d	17 09				17 39									18 09				18 39						19 09
Greenford ⊖ d				17 23						17 53							18 23						18 53	
South Greenford d				17 26						17 56							18 26						18 56	
Castle Bar Park d				17 29						17 59							18 29						18 59	
Drayton Green d				17 31						18 01							18 31						19 01	
West Ealing d	17 12			17 34	17 42					18 04				18 12			18 34	18 42					19 04	19 12
Ealing Broadway ⊖ d	17 14	17 20	17 33	17 37	17 44	17 49			18 03	18 07				18 14	18 19	18 33	18 37	18 44	18 49			19 03	19 07	19 14
Acton Main Line d				17 40						18 10							18 40						19 10	
London Paddington [15] ⊖ a	17 24	17 29	17 42	17 48	17 54	17 58		17 59	18 12	18 18			18 23	18 24	18 28	18 42	18 48	18 54	18 58		18 58	19 12	19 18	19 24

For general notes see front of timetable
For details of catering facilities see Directory of Train Operators

For fast services between Reading and London Paddington see Table 116

b Change at Heathrow Terminals 1-2-3

Table 117

Saturdays

from 29 March

Reading and Greenford → London

(Local services only)

Network Diagram - see first page of Table 116

		GW 1	GW 1	GW 1	HC 1	GW 1	GW 1	GW 1◇ ☕	GW 1	GW 1	HC 1	GW 1	GW 1	GW 1	HC 1	GW 1	GW 1	GW 1◇ ☕	GW 1	GW 1	HC 1	GW 1	GW 1	GW 1◇	GW 1
Oxford	d	17 55	*18 15*			18 21		19 00				18 55	*19 15*			19 21	*19 30*	20 09				19 55	*20 15*	20 30	
Reading 7	d	18 34	18 49			19 04	19 19	19 27				19 34	19 49			20 04	20 19	20 34				20 34	20 49	20 55	
Twyford 3	d	18 41	18 55			19 10	19 25		←			19 40	19 55			20 10	20 25					20 40	20 55		←
Maidenhead 3	d	18 49	19 03			19 18	19 33		19 33			19 48	20 03			20 18	20 33					20 48	21 03		21 03
Taplow	d		19 07				→		19 37				20 07				20 37						→		21 07
Burnham	d		19 10						19 40				20 10				20 40								21 10
Slough 3	a	18 56	19 15			19 25		19 40	19 45			19 55	20 15			20 25	20 45	20 47				20 55		21 10	21 15
	d	18 56	19 15			19 26		19 41	19 45			19 56	20 15			20 26	20 45	20 48				20 56		21 11	21 15
Langley	d	19 00				19 30						20 00				20 30						21 00			
Iver	d	19 03				19 33						20 03				20 33						21 03			
West Drayton	d	19 06	19 22			19 36			19 52			20 06	20 22			20 36	20 52					21 06			21 22
Heathrow Terminal 5 ✈	d				*19b12*						*19b42*				*20b12*						*20b42*				
Heathrow Terminal 4 ✈	d				19 21						19 51				20 21						20 51				
Heathrow Terminals 1-2-3 ✈	d				19 26						19 56				20 26				←		20 56				
Hayes & Harlington	d	19 11	19 26		19 33	19 40			19 56		20 03	20 10	20 26		20 33	20 40	20 56		20 56		21 03	21 10			21 26
Southall	d	19 14			19 36	19 44					20 06	20 14			20 36	20 44	→				21 06	21 14			
Hanwell	d				19 39						20 09				20 39						21 09				
Greenford ⊖	d			19 23						19 53				20 23						20 53					
South Greenford	d			19 26						19 56				20 26						20 56					
Castle Bar Park	d			19 29						19 59				20 29						20 59					
Drayton Green	d			19 31						20 01				20 31						21 01					
West Ealing	d			19 34	19 42					20 04	20 12			20 34	20 42					21 04	21 12				
Ealing Broadway ⊖	d	19 19	19 33	19 37	19 44	19 49			20 03	20 07	20 14	20 19	20 33	20 37	20 44	20 49			21 03	21 07	21 14	21 19			21 33
Acton Main Line	d			19 40						20 10				20 40						21 10					
London Paddington 15 ⊖	a	19 28	19 42	19 48	19 54	19 58		19 58	20 12	20 18	20 24	20 28	20 42	20 48	20 54	20 58		21 06	21 12	21 18	21 24	21 28		21 29	21 42

		GW 1	HC 1	GW 1	GW 1◇ ☕	GW 1	GW 1	HC 1	GW 1	GW 1	GW 1◇	GW 1	HC 1	GW 1	GW 1◇	GW 1	HC 1	GW 1	GW 1	HC 1	GW 1	GW 1◇	GW 1	GW 1
Oxford	d			20 20	21 00				20 53		21 30				22 08			21 53			*22 30*	23 00		23 09
Reading 7	d			21 09	21 25				21 34	21 44	21 54			22 16	22 33			22 35	22 45		23 16	23 29		00 05
Twyford 3	d			21 15					21 40	21 50		←		22 22				22 42	22 52		23 23			00 11
Maidenhead 3	d			21 23					21 48	21 58		21 58		22 30				22 50	23 00		23 32			00 19
Taplow	d			21 27						→		22 02		22 34					23 04		23 35			00 22
Burnham	d			21 30								22 05		22 37					23 07		23 39			00 26
Slough 3	a			21 35	21 38				21 55		22 09	22 10		22 42	22 48			22 57	23 12		23 43	23 48		00 30
	d			21 35	21 39				21 56		22 09	22 10		22 42	22 49			22 57	23 12		23 44	23 49		00 31
Langley	d			21 39								22 14		22 46					23 16		23 48			00 35
Iver	d			21 42		←						22 17		22 49		←			23 19		23 51		←	00 38
West Drayton	d			21 45		21 45						22 20		22 52		22 52			23 22		23 54		23 54	00 41
Heathrow Terminal 5 ✈	d		*21b12*	→				*21b42*					*22b12*	→			*22b42*			*23b12*	→			
Heathrow Terminal 4 ✈	d		21 21					21 51					22 21				22 51			23 21				
Heathrow Terminals 1-2-3 ✈	d		21 26					21 56					22 26				22 56			23 26				
Hayes & Harlington	d		21 33			21 50		22 03	22 06			22 25	22 33			22 57	23 03	23 06	23 27	23 33			23 58	00 45
Southall	d		21 36			21 53		22 06	22 10			22 28	22 36			23 00	23 06	23 10	23 30	23 36			00 02	00 49
Hanwell	d		21 39					22 09					22 39				23 09			23 39				
Greenford ⊖	d	21 23					21 53																	
South Greenford	d	21 26					21 56																	
Castle Bar Park	d	21 29					21 59																	
Drayton Green	d	21 31					22 01																	
West Ealing	d	21 34	21 42				22 04	22 12					22 42				23 12			23 42				
Ealing Broadway ⊖	d	21 37	21 44			21 58	22 07	22 14	22 19			22 33	22 44			23 05	23 14	23 19	23 35	23 44			00 07	00 54
Acton Main Line	d	21 40					22 10																	
London Paddington 15 ⊖	a	21 48	21 54		21 58	22 08	22 18	22 24	22 28		22 28	22 42	22 54		23 07	23 14	23 24	23 28	23 44	23 54		00 09	00 16	01 02

Sundays

until 27 January

		GW 1	HC	GW 1	HC	GW 1	HC		GW 1	HC	GW 1 🚌	GW 1	GW 1 A	GW 1◇ 🚌		HC	GW 1	GW 1	HC	GW 1	GW 1		GW 1◇ 🚌	HC	GW 1
Oxford	d			23p09									*07c45*				*07e45*				09 05		09 38		
Reading 7	d	23p16		00 05		06 22			07 22		08 03	08 22	08 48	09 05			09 18	09 30		09 42	09 48		10 05		10 18
Twyford 3	d	23p23		00 11		06 28			07 28			08 28	08 54				09 24	09a36			09 54				10 25
Maidenhead 3	d	23p32		00 19		06 36			07 36			08 36	09 02				09 32			09 54	10 02				10f33
Taplow	d	23p35		00 22																					
Burnham	d	23p39		00 26		06 40			07 40			08 40					09 36								10 37
Slough 3	a	23p43		00 30		06 45			07 45		08 21	08 45	09 09	09 24			09 41			10 01	10 09		10 26		10 42
	d	23p44		00 31		06 45			07 45		08 21	08 45	09 11	09 25			09 41			10 01	10 11		10 27		10 42
Langley	d	23p48		00 35		06 49			07 49			08 49	09 15				09 45				10 15				10 46
Iver	d	23p51		00 38																					
West Drayton	d	23p54		00 41		06 54			07 54			08 53	09 19				09 49				10 19				10 50
Heathrow Terminal 4 ✈	d		00 01																						
Heathrow Terminals 1-2-3 ✈	d		00 06		06 13		07 13			08 13						09 26			09 56					10 26	
Hayes & Harlington	d	23p58	00 12	00 45	06 18	07 01	07 18		08 01	08 18		09 01	09 24			09 32	09 55		10 02		10 24			10 32	10 56
Southall	d	00 02	00 15	00 49	06 22	07 05	07 22		08 05	08 22		09 05	09 27			09 35	09 58		10 05		10 27			10 35	10 59
Hanwell	d																								
Greenford ⊖	d																								
South Greenford	d																								
Castle Bar Park	d																								
Drayton Green	d																								
West Ealing	d																								
Ealing Broadway ⊖	d	00 07	00 20	00 54	06 27	07 10	07 27		08 10	08 27		09 10	09 32			09 40	10 03		10 10		10 32			10 40	11 04
Acton Main Line	d																								
London Paddington 15 ⊖	a	00 16	00 29	01 02	06 35	07 18	07 35		08 18	08 35	08 44	09 19	09 40	09 43		09 49	10 11		10 19	10 23	10 40		10 45	10 49	11 12

For general notes see front of timetable
For details of catering facilities see Directory of Train Operators

For fast services between Reading and London Paddington see Table 116

A From Didcot Parkway (Table 116)
b Change at Heathrow Terminals 1-2-3
c Change at Didcot Parkway. By bus
e Change at Didcot Parkway and Reading. By bus to Didcot Parkway
f Arr. 1030

Sundays

until 27 January

Reading and Greenford → London

(Local services only)

Network Diagram - see first page of Table 116

		GW	HC	GW	GW	HC		GW	GW	HC	GW	GW	HC		GW	GW	HC	GW	HC	GW		GW	GW	GW	HC
		1		1	1 ◇ ⌶			1	1		1	1 ◇ ⌶			1	1		1		1		1 ◇ ⎍	1	1	
Oxford	d			10 05	10 38						11 05	11 38				*11 45*		12 05		*12 15*		12 50		*12 55*	
Reading 7	d	10 36		10 46	11 07			11 18	11 35		11 52	12 07			12 18	12 36		12 47		13 18		13 22		13 35	
Twyford 3	d			10 54				11 24			11 59				12 24			12 55		13 24					
Maidenhead 3	d	10 48		11 02				11 32	11 47		12 07				12 32	12 48		13 03		13 32				13 47	
Taplow	d																								
Burnham	d							11 36							12 36					13 36					
Slough 3	a	10 55		11 09	11 26			11 41	11 56		12 14	12 28			12 41	12 57		13 10		13 41		13 47		13 55	
	d	10 55		11 11	11 27			11 41	11 56		12 14	12 29			12 41	12 57		13 11		13 41		13 47		13 55	
Langley	d			11 15				11 45			12 18				12 45			13 15		13 45					
Iver	d																								
West Drayton	d			11 19				11 49			12 23				12 49			13 19		13 49					
Heathrow Terminal 4 ✈	d																								
Heathrow Terminals 1-2-3 ✈	d		10 56			11 26				11 56			12 26				12 56		13 26				←		13 56
Hayes & Harlington	d		11 02	11 24		11 32		11 55		12 02	12 27		12 32		12 55		13 02	13 24	13 32	13 55			13 55		14 02
Southall	d		11 05	11 27		11 35		11 58		12 05	12 31		12 35		12 58		13 05	13 27	13 35	→			13 58		14 05
Hanwell	d																								
Greenford ⊖	d																								
South Greenford	d																								
Castle Bar Park	d																								
Drayton Green	d																								
West Ealing	d																								
Ealing Broadway ⊖	d		11 10	11 32		11 40		12 03		12 10	12 36		12 40		13 03		13 10	13 32	13 40				14 03		14 10
Acton Main Line	d																								
London Paddington 15 ⊖	a	11 16	11 19	11 40	11 46	11 49		12 12	12 16	12 19	12 44	12 46	12 49		13 11	13 16	13 19	13 40	13 49			14 08	14 11	14 16	14 19

		GW	GW	HC	GW		GW	HC	GW	GW	HC	GW		GW	HC	GW	HC	GW	GW		GW	GW	HC	GW	HC
		1	1 ◇ ⌶		1		1		1	1 ◇ ⌶		1		1		1		1	1 ◇ ⎍		1	1		1	
Oxford	d	13 05	13 38				*13 47*		14 05	14 38				*14 47*		15 05		*15 15*	15 48			*15 55*		16 05	
Reading 7	d	13 46	14 06		14 18		14 36		14 46	15 05		15 18		15 35		15 46		16 18	16 21			16 36		16 46	
Twyford 3	d	13 55			14 24				14 55			15 24				15 55		16 24						16 55	
Maidenhead 3	d	14 03			14 32		14 48		15 03			15 32		15 47		16 03		16 32				16 48		17 03	
Taplow	d																								
Burnham	d				14 36							15 36				16 07		16 36						17 07	
Slough 3	a	14 10	14 25		14 41		14 56		15 10	15 23		15 41		15 56		16 12		16 41	16 45			16 56		17 12	
	d	14 11	14 26		14 41		14 56		15 11	15 23		15 41		15 56		16 12		16 41	16 45			16 56		17 12	
Langley	d	14 15			14 45				15 15			15 45				16 16		16 45						17 16	
Iver	d																								
West Drayton	d	14 19			14 49				15 19			15 49				16 21		16 49						17 21	
Heathrow Terminal 4 ✈	d																								
Heathrow Terminals 1-2-3 ✈	d			14 26				14 56			15 26				15 56		16 26				←		16 56		17 26
Hayes & Harlington	d	14 24		14 32	14 55			15 02	15 24		15 32	15 55			16 02	16 25	16 32	16 55			16 55		17 02	17 25	17 32
Southall	d	14 27		14 35	14 58			15 05	15 27		15 35	15 58			16 05	16 29	16 35	→			16 58		17 05	17 29	17 35
Hanwell	d																								
Greenford ⊖	d																								
South Greenford	d																								
Castle Bar Park	d																								
Drayton Green	d																								
West Ealing	d																								
Ealing Broadway ⊖	d	14 32		14 40	15 03			15 10	15 32		15 40	16 03			16 10	16 34	16 40				17 03		17 10	17 34	17 40
Acton Main Line	d																								
London Paddington 15 ⊖	a	14 40	14 44	14 49	15 11		15 15	15 19	15 40	15 43	15 49	16 11		16 16	16 19	16 42	16 49		17 07		17 11	17 15	17 19	17 42	17 49

		GW	GW	GW		GW	HC	GW	HC	GW	GW		GW	GW	HC	GW	HC	GW		GW	GW	HC	GW	HC	GW
		1	1 ◇ ⎍	1		1		1		1	1 ◇ ⎍		1	1		1		1 ◇ ⎍		1	1		1		1
Oxford	d	*16 15*	16 50			*16 55*		17 05		*17 15*	17 50			*17 55*		18 05		18 41		*18 47*			19 05		*19 15*
Reading 7	d	17 18	17 24			17 35		17 46		18 18	18 21			18 36		18 46		19 06		19 18	19 35		19 46		20 18
Twyford 3	d	17 24						17 55		18 24						18 55				19 24			19 55		20 24
Maidenhead 3	d	17 32				17 47		18 03		18 32				18 48		19 03				19 32	19 47		20 03		20 32
Taplow	d																								
Burnham	d	17 36						18 07		18 36						19 07				19 36			20 07		20 36
Slough 3	a	17 41	17 48			17 56		18 12		18 41	18 45			18 56		19 12		19 31		19 41	19 56		20 12		20 41
	d	17 41	17 48			17 56		18 12		18 41	18 45			18 56		19 12		19 31		19 41	19 56		20 12		20 41
Langley	d	17 45						18 16		18 45						19 16				19 45			20 16		20 45
Iver	d																								
West Drayton	d	17 49						18 21		18 49						19 21				19 49			20 21		20 49
Heathrow Terminal 4 ✈	d																								
Heathrow Terminals 1-2-3 ✈	d			←			17 56		18 26				←		18 56		19 26					19 56		20 26	
Hayes & Harlington	d	17 55		17 55			18 02	18 25	18 32	18 55			18 55		19 02	19 25	19 32			19 55		20 02	20 25	20 32	20 55
Southall	d	→		17 58			18 05	18 29	18 35	→			18 58		19 05	19 29	19 35			19 58		20 05	20 29	20 35	→
Hanwell	d																								
Greenford ⊖	d																								
South Greenford	d																								
Castle Bar Park	d																								
Drayton Green	d																								
West Ealing	d																								
Ealing Broadway ⊖	d			18 03			18 10	18 34	18 40				19 03		19 10	19 34	19 40			20 03		20 10	20 34	20 40	
Acton Main Line	d																								
London Paddington 15 ⊖	a		18 08	18 11		18 16	18 19	18 42	18 49		19 08		19 11	19 15	19 19	19 42	19 49	19 52		20 11	20 16	20 19	20 42	20 49	

For general notes see front of timetable
For details of catering facilities see Directory of Train Operators

For fast services between Reading and London Paddington see Table 116

Sundays

until 27 January

Reading and Greenford → London

(Local services only)

Network Diagram - see first page of Table 116

		GW 1◇ ☕	GW 1		GW 1	HC	GW 1	HC	GW 1◇ ☕	GW A		HC	GW 1	GW 1◇ ☕	GW B	HC	GW 1		GW 1◇ 🛒	GW 1	GW 1	GW 1◇ 🛒	GW 1◇ 🛒		
Oxford	d	19 50			*19 55*		20 05		20 50	*20 15*			21 05	21 50	*21 15*		22 05		*22 15*		22 58	23 00	23 44		
Reading 7	d	20 22			20 34		20 48		21 19	21 24			21 46	22 19	22 24		22 52		23 07	23 19	23 41	23 29	00 15		
Twyford 3	d						20 57			21 30			21 53		22 30		22 58			23 25	23 48		00 21		
Maidenhead 3	d				20 49		21 05			21 38			22 01		22 38		23 06			23 33	23 56		00 29		
Taplow	d																								
Burnham	d						21 09			21 42			22 05		22 43		23 10			23 37	00 01				
Slough 3	a	20 45			20 56		21 14		21 41	21 48			22 10	22 42	22 47		23 15		23 30	23 42	00 05	23 48	00 40		
	d	20 45			20 57		21 15		21 41	21 50			22 10	22 43	22 48		23 15		23 31	23 42	00 06	23 49	00 41		
Langley	d						21 19			21 54			22 14		22 52		23 19			23 46	00 10				
Iver	d																								
West Drayton	d						21 23			21 59			22 19		22 56		23 24			23 50	00 14				
Heathrow Terminal 4 ✈	d																								
Heathrow Terminals 1-2-3 ✈	d		←			20 56		21 26				22 13				23 13									
Hayes & Harlington	d		20 55			21 02	21 28	21 32		22 03		22 18	22 23		23 01	23 18	23 31			23 56	00 19		00 50		
Southall	d		20 58			21 05	21 31	21 35				22 22	22 27		23 05	23 22	23 35			23 59	00 22				
Hanwell	d																								
Greenford ⊖	d																								
South Greenford	d																								
Castle Bar Park	d																								
Drayton Green	d																								
West Ealing	d																								
Ealing Broadway ⊖	d		21 03			21 10	21 36	21 40		22 10		22 27	22 32		23 10	23 27	23 40			00 04	00 27		00 57		
Acton Main Line	d																								
London Paddington 15 ⊖	a	21 08	21 11		21 16	21 19	21 44	21 49	22 03	22 18		22 35	22 40	23 05	23 18	23 35	23 49		23 53	00 12	00 40	00 09	01 05		

Sundays

3 February to 23 March

		GW 1	HC	GW 1	HC		GW 1	HC	GW 1	HC		GW 1 🛒	GW 1	HC	GW 1 C		GW 1◇ 🛒	GW 1	GW 1	GW 1		GW 1	HC	GW 1	GW 1◇ 🛒
Oxford	d			23p09											*07b45*			*07c45*						09 05	09 38
Reading 7	d	23p16		00 05			06 22		07 22			08 04	08 22		08 47		09 06	09 18	09 25	09 30				09 52	10 06
Twyford 3	d	23p23		00 11			06 28		07 28				08 28		08 53			09 25		09a36				09 58	
Maidenhead 3	d	23p32		00 19			06 36		07 36				08 36		09 01			09e36	09 37					10 06	
Taplow	d	23p35		00 22																		←			
Burnham	d	23p39		00 26			06 40		07 40				08 40					09 40				09 40			
Slough 3	a	23p43		00 30			06 48		07 48			08 24	08 48		09 08		09 25	→	09 44			09 48		10 18	10 23
	d	23p44		00 31			06 48		07 48			08 24	08 48		09 08		09 26		09 44			09 48		10 18	10 23
Langley	d	23p48		00 35			06 52		07 52				08 52		09 12							09 52		10 22	
Iver	d	23p51		00 38																					
West Drayton	d	23p54		00 41			06 57		07 57				08 57		09 17							09 57		10 27	
Heathrow Terminal 4 ✈	d		00 01																						
Heathrow Terminals 1-2-3 ✈	d		00 06		06 13			07 13		08 13				09 13									10 13		
Hayes & Harlington	d	23p58	00 12	00 45	06 18		07 01	07 18	08 01	08 18			09 01	09 18	09 21							10 01	10 18	10 31	
Southall	d	00 02	00 15	00 49	06 22		07 05	07 22	08 05	08 22			09 05	09 22	09 25							10 05	10 22	10 35	
Hanwell	d																								
Greenford ⊖	d																								
South Greenford	d																								
Castle Bar Park	d																								
Drayton Green	d																								
West Ealing	d																								
Ealing Broadway ⊖	d	00 07	00 20	00 54	06 27		07 10	07 27	08 10	08 27			09 10	09 27	09 30							10 10	10 27	10 40	
Acton Main Line	d																								
London Paddington 15 ⊖	a	00 16	00 29	01 02	06 35		07 18	07 35	08 20	08 35		08 49	09 20	09 35	09 31		09 50		10 04			10 20	10 35	10 49	10 51

		GW 1	GW 1		GW 1	HC	GW 1	GW 1◇ 🛒		GW 1	GW 1	HC	GW 1		GW 1	GW 1◇ 🛒	GW 1	GW 1		HC	GW 1	GW 1	GW 1◇ ☕		GW 1
Oxford	d						10 05	10 38					11 05		*11 15*	11 50					12 05	*12 15*	12 50		
Reading 7	d	10 18	10 25				10 52	11 06		11 19	11 22		11 52		12 18	12 21	12 25				12 52	13 18	13 21		13 24
Twyford 3	d	10 24					10 58				11 28		11 58		12 24			←			12 58	13 24			
Maidenhead 3	d	10f36	10 37				11 06			11 31	11 36		12 06		12g36		12 37	12 36			13 06	13h36			13 36
Taplow	d				←										→							→			
Burnham	d	10 40			10 40						11 40							12 40							
Slough 3	a	→	10 44		10 48		11 18	11 23		11 42	11 48		12 18			12 35	12 44	12 48			13 18		13 37		13 43
	d		10 44		10 49		11 18	11 23		11 43	11 48		12 18			12 36	12 44	12 48			13 18		13 38		13 44
Langley	d				10 53		11 22				11 52		12 22					12 52			13 22				
Iver	d																								
West Drayton	d				10 57		11 27				11 57		12 27					12 57			13 27				
Heathrow Terminal 4 ✈	d																								
Heathrow Terminals 1-2-3 ✈	d					11 13						12 13								13 13					
Hayes & Harlington	d				11 01	11 18	11 31				12 01	12 18	12 31					13 01		13 18	13 31				
Southall	d				11 05	11 22	11 35				12 05	12 22	12 35					13 05		13 22	13 35				
Hanwell	d																								
Greenford ⊖	d																								
South Greenford	d																								
Castle Bar Park	d																								
Drayton Green	d																								
West Ealing	d																								
Ealing Broadway ⊖	d				11 10	11 27	11 40				12 10	12 27	12 40					13 10		13 27	13 40				
Acton Main Line	d																								
London Paddington 15 ⊖	a		11 04		11 20	11 35	11 49	11 51		12 04	12 20	12 35	12 49			13 00	13 04	13 18		13 35	13 49		13 57		14 04

For general notes see front of timetable
For details of catering facilities see Directory of Train Operators

For fast services between Reading and London Paddington see Table 116

A From Bedwyn (Table 116)
B From Newbury (Table 116)
C From Didcot Parkway (Table 116)
b Change at Didcot Parkway. By bus
c Change at Didcot Parkway and Reading. By bus to Didcot Parkway
e Arr. 0930
f Arr. 1030
g Arr. 1230
h Arr. 1330

Table 117

Reading and Greenford → London

(Local services only)

3 February to 23 March

Network Diagram - see first page of Table 116

Station		GW 1	HC	GW 1	GW 1	GW 1 ◇	GW 1	GW 1	HC	GW 1	GW 1 ◇	GW 1	GW 1	GW 1	HC	GW 1	GW 1	GW 1 ◇	GW 1	GW 1	HC
Oxford	d			13 05	*13 15*	13 50				14 05	14 38					15 05	*15 15*	15 50			
Reading 7	d			13 52	14 18	14 20	14 25			14 52	15 10	15 18	15 21			15 52	16 18	16 20	16 25		
Twyford 3	d	←		13 58	14 24			←		14 58		15 24		←		15 58	16 24			←	
Maidenhead 3	d	13 36		14 06	14b36 →		14 37	14 36		15 06		15c36 →	15 33	15 36		16 06	16e36 →		16 37	16 36	
Taplow	d																				
Burnham	d	13 40						14 40						15 40		16 11				16 40	
Slough 3	a	13 48		14 18		14 35	14 44	14 48		15 18	15 34		15 40	15 48		16 18		16 34	16 44	16 48	
	d	13 48		14 18		14 36	14 44	14 48		15 18	15 34		15 41	15 48		16 18		16 35	16 44	16 48	
Langley	d	13 52		14 22				14 52		15 22				15 52		16 22				16 52	
Iver	d																				
West Drayton	d	13 57		14 27				14 57		15 27				15 57		16 27				16 57	
Heathrow Terminal 4	d																				
Heathrow Terminals 1-2-3	d		14 13						15 13						16 13						17 13
Hayes & Harlington	d	14 01	14 18	14 31				15 01	15 18	15 31				16 01	16 18	16 31				17 01	17 18
Southall	d	14 05	14 22	14 35				15 05	15 22	15 35				16 05	16 22	16 35				17 05	17 22
Hanwell	d																				
Greenford ⊖	d																				
South Greenford	d																				
Castle Bar Park	d																				
Drayton Green	d																				
West Ealing	d																				
Ealing Broadway ⊖	d	14 10	14 27	14 40				15 10	15 27	15 40				16 10	16 27	16 40				17 10	17 27
Acton Main Line	d																				
London Paddington 15 ⊖	a	14 18	14 35	14 49		14 57	15 04	15 20	15 35	15 49	15 56		16 04	16 20	16 35	16 49		17 01	17 04	17 20	17 35

Station		GW 1	GW 1 ◇	GW 1	GW 1	GW 1	HC	GW 1	GW 1	GW 1 ◇	GW 1	GW 1	HC	GW 1	GW 1	GW 1 ◇	GW 1	GW 1	HC	GW 1
Oxford	d	16 05	16 48	*16 15*				17 05	*17 15*	17 50				18 05	*18 15*	18 50				19 05
Reading 7	d	16 52	17 17	17 18	17 24			17 52	18 18	18 20	18 25			18 52	19 18	19 21	19 26			19 52
Twyford 3	d	16 58		17 24				17 58	18 24			←		18 58	19 24			←		19 58
Maidenhead 3	d	17 06		17f36	17 36			18 06	18g36 →		18 37	18 36		19 06	19h36 →		19 38	19 36		20 06
Taplow	d					←														
Burnham	d	17 11		17 41		17 41		18 11				18 41		19 11				19 41		20 11
Slough 3	a	17 18	17 32	→	17 43	17 48		18 18		18 35	18 44	18 48		19 18		19 36	19 44	19 48		20 18
	d	17 18	17 33		17 44	17 48		18 18		18 36	18 44	18 48		19 18		19 36	19 44	19 48		20 18
Langley	d	17 22				17 52		18 22				18 52		19 22				19 52		20 22
Iver	d																			
West Drayton	d	17 27				17 57		18 27				18 57		19 27				19 57		20 27
Heathrow Terminal 4	d																			
Heathrow Terminals 1-2-3	d						18 13						19 13						20 13	
Hayes & Harlington	d	17 31				18 01	18 18	18 31				19 01	19 18	19 31				20 01	20 18	20 31
Southall	d	17 35				18 05	18 22	18 35				19 05	19 22	19 35				20 05	20 22	20 35
Hanwell	d																			
Greenford ⊖	d																			
South Greenford	d																			
Castle Bar Park	d																			
Drayton Green	d																			
West Ealing	d																			
Ealing Broadway ⊖	d	17 40				18 10	18 27	18 40				19 10	19 27	19 40				20 10	20 27	20 40
Acton Main Line	d																			
London Paddington 15 ⊖	a	17 49	17 58		18 04	18 20	18 35	18 49		18 59	19 04	19 20	19 35	19 49		20 02	20 08	20 20	20 35	20 49

Station		GW 1	GW 1 ◇	GW 1	GW 1	HC	GW 1	GW 1 ◇	GW A	HC	GW 1	GW 1 ◇	GW B	HC	GW 1	GW 1 ◇	GW 1	GW 1	GW 1 ◇
Oxford	d	*19 46*	19 51				20 05	20 50	*20 15*		21 05	21 50			22 05	22 40		22 58	23 44
Reading 7	d	20 18	20 19	20 25			20 52	21 19	21 22		21 46	22 18	22 27		22 53	23 07	23 24	23 41	00 14
Twyford 3	d	20 24			←		20 58		21 29		21 52		22 33		22 59		23 30	23 48	00 20
Maidenhead 3	d	20j36 →		20 37	20 36		21 06		21 36		22 00		22 41		23 07		23 38	23 56	00 28
Taplow	d																		
Burnham	d				20 40		21 10		21 42		22 04		22 45		23 11		23 42	00 01	
Slough 3	a		20 34	20 43	20 48		21 18	21 36	21 47		22 09	22 36	22 50		23 16	23 26	23 47	00 05	00 34
	d		20 34	20 43	20 48		21 18	21 36	21 48		22 09	22 36	22 50		23 16	23 26	23 47	00 06	00 35
Langley	d				20 52		21 22		21 52		22 13		22 54		23 20		23 51	00 10	
Iver	d																		
West Drayton	d				20 57		21 27		21 56		22 18		22 59		23 25		23 57	00 14	
Heathrow Terminal 4	d																		
Heathrow Terminals 1-2-3	d					21 13				22 13				23 13					
Hayes & Harlington	d				21 01	21 18	21 31		22 01	22 18	22 22		23 03	23 18	23 31		00 02	00 19	00 48
Southall	d				21 05	21 22	21 35			22 22	22 26		23 07	23 22	23 35		00 04	00 22	
Hanwell	d																		
Greenford ⊖	d																		
South Greenford	d																		
Castle Bar Park	d																		
Drayton Green	d																		
West Ealing	d																		
Ealing Broadway ⊖	d				21 10	21 27	21 40		22 08	22 27	22 31		23 12	23 27	23 40		00 10	00 27	00 55
Acton Main Line	d																		
London Paddington 15 ⊖	a		21 00	21 05	21 20	21 35	21 49	22 00	22 16	22 35	22 39	23 00	23 22	23 35	23 48	23 51	00 20	00 40	01 07

For general notes see front of timetable
For details of catering facilities see Directory of Train Operators

For fast services between Reading and London Paddington see Table 116

A From Bedwyn (Table 116)
B From Newbury (Table 116)
b Arr. 1430
c Arr. 1530
e Arr. 1630
f Arr. 1730
g Arr. 1830
h Arr. 1930
j Arr. 2030

Table 117

Sundays

from 30 March

Reading and Greenford → London

(Local services only)

Network Diagram - see first page of Table 116

		GW 1	HC	GW 1	HC	GW 1	HC	GW 1	HC		GW 1	GW 1	HC	GW 1	GW 1	GW 1	GW 1	GW 1		HC	GW 1	GW 1	GW 1	GW 1	HC
														A							A				
Oxford	d			23p09										07b45	07c45										
Reading 7	d	23p16		00 05		06 22		07 22			08 04	08 22		08 52	09 18	09 24	09 30				09 52	10 18	10 24		
Twyford 3	d	23p23		00 11		06 28		07 28				08 28		08 58	09 24		09a36				09 58	10 24			
Maidenhead 3	d	23p32		00 19		06 36		07 36				08 36		09 06	09e36	09 36					10 06	10f36	10 36		
Taplow	d	23p35		00 22														←						←	
Burnham	d	23p39		00 26		06 40		07 40				08 40			09 40			09 40				10 40		10 40	
Slough 3	a	23p43		00 30		06 48		07 48			08 22	08 48		09 18	→	09 43		09 46			10 18	→	10 43	10 49	
	d	23p44		00 31		06 48		07 48			08 22	08 48		09 18		09 43		09 46			10 18		10 43	10 50	
Langley	d	23p48		00 35		06 52		07 52				08 52		09 22				09 50			10 22			10 54	
Iver	d	23p51		00 38																					
West Drayton	d	23p54		00 41		06 57		07 57				08 57		09 27				09 55			10 27			10 58	
Heathrow Terminal 5	d		23g53		06h03		07h03		08h03				09h03							10h03					11h03
Heathrow Terminal 4	d		00 01		06 07		07 07		08 07				09 07							10 07					11 07
Heathrow Terminals 1-2-3	d		00 06		06 13		07 13		08 13				09 13							10 13					11 13
Hayes & Harlington	d	23p58	00 12	00 45	06 18	07 01	07 18	08 01	08 18			09 01	09 18	09 31				10 00		10 18	10 31			11 03	11 18
Southall	d	00 02	00 15	00 49	06 22	07 05	07 22	08 05	08 22			09 05	09 22	09 35				10 04		10 22	10 35			11 06	11 22
Hanwell	d																								
Greenford	⊖ d																								
South Greenford	d																								
Castle Bar Park	d																								
Drayton Green	d																								
West Ealing	d																								
Ealing Broadway	⊖ d	00 07	00 20	00 54	06 27	07 10	07 27	08 10	08 27			09 10	09 27	09 40				10 09		10 27	10 40			11 11	11 27
Acton Main Line	d																								
London Paddington 15	⊖ a	00 16	00 29	01 02	06 35	07 18	07 35	08 20	08 35		08 42	09 20	09 35	09 49		10 03		10 18		10 35	10 49		11 03	11 21	11 35

		GW 1	GW 1	GW 1	GW 1		HC	GW 1	GW 1	GW 1	GW 1	HC	GW 1	GW 1		GW 1	GW 1	HC	GW 1	GW 1	GW 1	GW 1	HC		GW 1
		A						A					A						A						A
Oxford	d	09b30	09c30					10b30	10c30				11b30	11c30					12b30	12c30					13b30
Reading 7	d	10 52	11 18	11 24				11 52	12 18	12 25			12 52	13 18		13 24			13 52	14 18	14 25				14 52
Twyford 3	d	10 58	11 24					11 58	12 24				12 58	13 24					13 58	14 24					14 58
Maidenhead 3	d	11 06	11j36	11 36				12 06	12k36	12 37			13 06	13m36		13 36			14 06	14n36	14 37				15 06
Taplow	d				←						←						←					←			
Burnham	d		11 40		11 40				12 40		12 40			13 40			13 40			14 40		14 40			
Slough 3	a	11 18	→	11 43	11 48			12 18	→	12 44	12 48		13 18	→		13 43	13 48		14 18	→	14 44	14 48			15 18
	d	11 18		11 43	11 48			12 18		12 44	12 48		13 18			13 43	13 48		14 18		14 44	14 48			15 18
Langley	d	11 22			11 52			12 22			12 52		13 22				13 52		14 22			14 52			15 22
Iver	d																								
West Drayton	d	11 27			11 57			12 27			12 57		13 27				13 57		14 27			14 57			15 27
Heathrow Terminal 5	d						12h03					13h03						14h03					15h03		
Heathrow Terminal 4	d						12 07					13 07						14 07					15 07		
Heathrow Terminals 1-2-3	d						12 13					13 13						14 13					15 13		
Hayes & Harlington	d	11 31			12 01		12 18	12 31			13 01	13 18	13 31				14 01	14 18	14 31			15 01	15 18		15 31
Southall	d	11 35			12 05		12 22	12 35			13 05	13 22	13 35				14 05	14 22	14 35			15 05	15 22		15 35
Hanwell	d																								
Greenford	⊖ d																								
South Greenford	d																								
Castle Bar Park	d																								
Drayton Green	d																								
West Ealing	d																								
Ealing Broadway	⊖ d	11 40			12 10		12 27	12 40			13 10	13 27	13 40				14 10	14 27	14 40			15 10	15 27		15 40
Acton Main Line	d																								
London Paddington 15	⊖ a	11 49		12 03	12 20		12 35	12 49		13 04	13 18	13 35	13 49			14 04	14 18	14 35	14 49		15 04	15 20	15 35		15 49

		GW 1	GW 1	GW 1	HC	GW 1	GW 1	GW 1	GW 1		HC	GW 1	GW 1	GW 1	GW 1	HC	GW 1	GW 1		GW 1	GW 1	GW 1	HC	GW 1 ◇	GW 1
						A						A					A					A			A
Oxford	d	13c30				14b30	14c30					15b30	15c30				16b30	16c30				17b30			
Reading 7	d	15 18	15 24			15 52	16 18	16 25				16 52	17 18	17 21			17 52	18 18		18 25		18 52		19 01	
Twyford 3	d	15 24				15 58	16 24					16 58	17 24		←		17 58	18 24				18 58			←
Maidenhead 3	d	15q36	15 36			16 06	16r36	16 37				17 06	17t36	17 33	17 36		18 06	18v36		18 37		19 06			19 06
Taplow	d			←					←				→								←	→			
Burnham	d	15 40		15 40		16 11	16 41		16 41			17 11			17 41		18 11	18 41			18 41				19 11
Slough 3	a	→	15 43	15 48		16 18	→	16 44	16 48			17 18		17 40	17 48		18 18	→		18 44	18 48			19 16	19 20
	d		15 43	15 48		16 18		16 44	16 48			17 18		17 40	17 48		18 18			18 44	18 48			19 16	19 21
Langley	d			15 52		16 22			16 52			17 22			17 52		18 22				18 52				19 25
Iver	d																								
West Drayton	d			15 57		16 27			16 57			17 27			17 57		18 27				18 57				19 29
Heathrow Terminal 5	d				16h03						17h03					18h03							19h03		
Heathrow Terminal 4	d				16 07						17 07					18 07							19 07		
Heathrow Terminals 1-2-3	d				16 13						17 13					18 13							19 13		
Hayes & Harlington	d			16 01	16 18	16 31			17 01		17 18	17 31			18 01	18 18	18 31				19 01		19 18		19 34
Southall	d			16 05	16 22	16 35			17 05		17 22	17 35			18 05	18 22	18 35				19 05		19 22		19 37
Hanwell	d																								
Greenford	⊖ d																								
South Greenford	d																								
Castle Bar Park	d																								
Drayton Green	d																								
West Ealing	d																								
Ealing Broadway	⊖ d			16 10	16 27	16 40			17 10		17 27	17 40			18 10	18 27	18 40				19 10		19 27		19 42
Acton Main Line	d																								
London Paddington 15	⊖ a		16 03	16 20	16 35	16 49		17 04	17 18		17 35	17 49		18 03	18 20	18 35	18 49			19 04	19 20		19 35	19 39	19 50

For general notes see front of timetable
For details of catering facilities see Directory of Train Operators

For fast services between Reading and London Paddington see Table 116

A From Didcot Parkway (Table 116)

b Change at Didcot Parkway. By bus

c Change at Didcot Parkway and Reading. By bus to Didcot Parkway

e Arr. 0930

f Arr. 1030

g Sundays. Change at Heathrow Terminals 1-2-3

h Change at Heathrow Terminals 1-2-3

j Arr. 1130

k Arr. 1230

m Arr. 1330

n Arr. 1430

q Arr. 1530

r Arr. 1630

t Arr. 1730

v Arr. 1830

Table 117

Sundays

from 30 March

Reading and Greenford → London
(Local services only)

Network Diagram - see first page of Table 116

		GW	GW	GW	HC		GW	GW	GW	GW	GW	HC	GW	GW		GW	HC	GW	GW	HC	GW	GW	GW		
		1	1	1			1	1	1	1	1		1 ◇	1				1			1	1	1		
							A				A			A		B		A	C		A		A		
													☕												
Oxford	d	17b30					18c30	18b30			19c30					19b30		20c30	20b30		21c30	21b30	22c30		
Reading 7	d	19 18	19 21				19 52	20 18	20 25		20 52		21 10			21 24		21 46	22 27		22 52	23 24	23 40		
Twyford 3	d	19 24		←			19 58	20 24			20 58			←		21 30		21 52	22 33		22 58	23 30	23 48		
Maidenhead 3	d	19e36	19 33	19 36			20 06	20f36	20 37		21 06			21 06		21 38		22 00	22 41		23 06	23 38	23 56		
Taplow	d	→								←	→														
Burnham	d			19 41			20 11	20 40		20 40				21 10		21 42		22 04	22 45		23 10	23 42	00 01		
Slough 3	a		19 40	19 48			20 18	→	20 43	20 48			21 24	21 18		21 47		22 11	22 50		23 15	23 47	00 05		
	d		19 40	19 48			20 18		20 43	20 48			21 25	21 18		21 47		22 13	22 50		23 15	23 47	00 06		
Langley	d			19 52			20 22			20 52				21 22		21 51		22 17	22 54		23 19	23 51	00 10		
Iver	d																								
West Drayton	d			19 57			20 27			20 57				21 27		21 56		22 22	22 59		23 24	23 57	00 14		
Heathrow Terminal 5 ✈	d				20g03							21g03					22g03			23g03					
Heathrow Terminal 4 ✈	d				20 07							21 07					22 07			23 07					
Heathrow Terminals 1-2-3 ✈	d				20 13							21 13					22 13			23 13					
Hayes & Harlington	d			20 01	20 18		20 31			21 01		21 18		21 31		22 01	22 18	22 31	23 03	23 18	23 31	00 02	00 19		
Southall	d			20 05	20 22		20 35			21 05		21 22		21 35		22 05	22 22	22 35	23 07	23 22	23 35	00 04	00 22		
Hanwell	d																								
Greenford ⊖	d																								
South Greenford	d																								
Castle Bar Park	d																								
Drayton Green	d																								
West Ealing	d																								
Ealing Broadway ⊖	d			20 10	20 27		20 40			21 10		21 27		21 40		22 10	22 27	22 40	23 12	23 27	23 40	00 10	00 27		
Acton Main Line	d																								
London Paddington 15 ⊖	a		20 03	20 20	20 35		20 49		21 05	21 20		21 35	21 53	21 48		22 18	22 35	22 48	23 22	23 35	23 49	00 20	00 40		

For general notes see front of timetable
For details of catering facilities see Directory of Train Operators

For fast services between Reading and London Paddington see Table 116

A From Didcot Parkway (Table 116)
B From Bedwyn (Table 116)
C From Newbury (Table 116)
b Change at Didcot Parkway and Reading. By bus to Didcot Parkway
c Change at Didcot Parkway. By bus
e Arr. 1930
f Arr. 2030
g Change at Heathrow Terminals 1-2-3

Table 118

London → Heathrow Airport

Mondays to Fridays

until 26 March

Network Diagram - see first page of Table 116

Miles			HX 1	HX 1	HX 1	HX 1		HX 1	HX 1	HX 1	HX 1		HX 1	HX 1	HX 1	HX 1		HX 1	HX 1	HX 1	HX 1		HX 1	HX 1	HX 1
0	London Paddington 15	⊖ d	05 10	05 25	05 40	05 55	.....	06 10	06 25	06 40	06 55	.....	07 10	07 25	07 40	07 55	.....	08 10	08 25	08 40	08 55	.....	09 10	09 25	09 40
14¾	Heathrow Terminals 1-2-3	✈ a	05 26	05 40	05 55	06 10	.	06 25	06 40	06 55	07 10	.	07 25	07 40	07 55	08 10	.	08 25	08 40	08 55	09 10	.....	09 25	09 40	09 55
16½	Heathrow Terminal 4	✈ a	05 33	05 48	06 03	06 18	.....	06 33	06 48	07 03	07 18	.....	07 33	07 48	08 03	08 18	.....	08 33	08 48	09 03	09 18	.....	09 33	09 48	10 03

		HX 1	HX 1	HX 1		HX 1	HX 1	HX 1	HX 1		HX 1	HX 1	HX 1	HX 1		HX 1	HX 1	HX 1	HX 1		HX 1	HX 1	HX 1	HX 1	HX 1
London Paddington 15	⊖ d	09 55	10 10	10 25	.....	10 40	10 55	11 10	11 25	.....	11 40	11 55	12 10	12 25	.....	12 40	12 55	13 10	13 25	.....	13 40	13 55	14 10	14 25	14 40
Heathrow Terminals 1-2-3	✈ a	10 10	10 25	10 40	.	10 55	11 10	11 25	11 40	.	11 55	12 10	12 25	12 40	.	12 55	13 10	13 25	13 40	.	13 55	14 10	14 25	14 40	14 55
Heathrow Terminal 4	✈ a	10 18	10 33	10 48	.	11 03	11 18	11 33	11 48	.....	12 03	12 18	12 33	12 48	.....	13 03	13 18	13 33	13 48	.....	14 03	14 18	14 33	14 48	15 03

		HX 1		HX 1	HX 1	HX 1	HX 1		HX 1	HX 1	HX 1	HX 1		HX 1	HX 1	HX 1	HX 1		HX 1	HX 1	HX 1	HX 1		HX 1	HX 1
London Paddington 15	⊖ d	14 55	.....	15 10	15 25	15 40	15 55	.....	16 10	16 25	16 40	16 55	.....	17 10	17 25	17 40	17 55	.....	18 10	18 25	18 40	18 55	.....	19 10	19 25
Heathrow Terminals 1-2-3	✈ a	15 10	.	15 25	15 40	15 55	16 10	.	16 25	16 40	16 55	17 10	.	17 25	17 40	17 55	18 10	.	18 25	18 40	18 55	19 10	.	19 25	19 40
Heathrow Terminal 4	✈ a	15 18	.....	15 33	15 48	16 03	16 18	.....	16 33	16 48	17 03	17 18	.....	17 33	17 48	18 03	18 18	.....	18 33	18 48	19 03	19 18	.....	19 33	19 48

		HX 1	HX 1	HX 1	HX 1		HX 1	HX 1	HX 1	HX 1		HX 1	HX 1	HX 1	HX 1		HX 1	HX 1	HX 1	HX 1					
London Paddington 15	⊖ d	19 40	19 55	20 10	20 25	.....	20 40	20 55	21 10	21 25	.....	21 40	21 55	22 10	22 25	.....	22 40	22 55	23 10	23 25	.....	.....	.....	.....	.....
Heathrow Terminals 1-2-3	✈ a	19 55	20 10	20 25	20 40	.	20 55	21 10	21 25	21 40	.	21 55	22 10	22 25	22 40	..	22 55	23 10	23 25	23 40	.	.	.	.	.
Heathrow Terminal 4	✈ a	20 03	20 18	20 33	20 48	.	21 03	21 18	21 33	21 48	.	22 03	22 18	22 33	22 48	.....	23 03	23 18	23 33	23 48	.....	.....	.....	.....	.....

Mondays to Fridays

from 27 March

		HX 1	HX 1	HX 1		HX 1	HX 1	HX 1		HX 1	HX 1	HX 1		HX 1	HX 1	HX 1		HX 1	HX 1	HX 1		HX 1	HX 1	HX 1	HX 1
London Paddington 15	⊖ d	05 10	05 25	05 40	.....	05 55	06 10	06 25	.....	06 40	06 55	07 10	.....	07 25	07 40	07 55	.....	08 10	08 25	08 40	.....	08 55	09 10	09 25	09 40
Heathrow Terminals 1-2-3	✈ a	05 26	05 40	05 55	.	06 10	06 25	06 40	.	06 55	07 10	07 25	.	07 40	07 55	08 10	.	08 25	08 40	08 55	.	09 10	09 25	09 40	09 55
Heathrow Terminal 4	✈ a	*05 41*	*05 48*	*06 05*	.....	*06 18*	*06 35*	*06 48*	.....	*07 05*	*07 18*	*07 35*	.....	*07 48*	*08 05*	*08 18*	.....	*08 35*	*08 48*	*09 05*	.....	*09 18*	*09 35*	*09 48*	*10 05*
Heathrow Terminal 5	✈ a	05 32	05 46	06 01	.	06 16	06 31	06 46	.	07 01	07 16	07 31	.	07 46	08 01	08 16	.	08 31	08 46	09 01	.	09 16	09 31	09 46	10 01

		HX 1		HX 1	HX 1	HX 1		HX 1	HX 1	HX 1		HX 1	HX 1	HX 1		HX 1	HX 1	HX 1		HX 1	HX 1	HX 1		HX 1	HX 1
London Paddington 15	⊖ d	09 55	.....	10 10	10 25	10 40	.....	10 55	11 10	11 25	.....	11 40	11 55	12 10	.....	12 25	12 40	12 55	.....	13 10	13 25	13 40	.....	13 55	14 10
Heathrow Terminals 1-2-3	✈ a	10 10	.....	10 25	10 40	10 55	.	11 10	11 25	11 40	.	11 55	12 10	12 25	.	12 40	12 55	13 10	.	13 25	13 40	13 55	.	14 10	14 25
Heathrow Terminal 4	✈ a	*10 18*	.....	*10 35*	*10 48*	*11 05*	.....	*11 18*	*11 35*	*11 48*	.....	*12 05*	*12 18*	*12 35*	.....	*12 48*	*13 05*	*13 18*	.....	*13 35*	*13 48*	*14 05*	.....	*14 18*	*14 35*
Heathrow Terminal 5	✈ a	10 16	.	10 31	10 46	11 01	.	11 16	11 31	11 46	.	12 01	12 16	12 31	.	12 46	13 01	13 16	.	13 31	13 46	14 01	.	14 16	14 31

		HX 1	HX 1	HX 1		HX 1	HX 1	HX 1		HX 1	HX 1	HX 1		HX 1	HX 1	HX 1		HX 1	HX 1	HX 1		HX 1	HX 1	HX 1	HX 1
London Paddington 15	⊖ d	14 25	14 40	14 55	.....	15 10	15 25	15 40	.....	15 55	16 10	16 25	.....	16 40	16 55	17 10	.....	17 25	17 40	17 55	.....	18 10	18 25	18 40	18 55
Heathrow Terminals 1-2-3	✈ a	14 40	14 55	15 10	.	15 25	15 40	15 55	.	16 10	16 25	16 40	.	16 55	17 10	17 25	.	17 40	17 55	18 10	.	18 25	18 40	18 55	19 10
Heathrow Terminal 4	✈ a	*14 48*	*15 05*	*15 18*	.....	*15 35*	*15 48*	*16 05*	.....	*16 18*	*16 35*	*16 48*	.....	*17 05*	*17 18*	*17 35*	.....	*17 48*	*18 05*	*18 18*	.....	*18 35*	*18 48*	*19 05*	*19 18*
Heathrow Terminal 5	✈ a	14 46	15 01	15 16	.	15 31	15 46	16 01	.	16 16	16 31	16 46	.	17 01	17 16	17 31	.	17 46	18 01	18 16	.	18 31	18 46	19 01	19 16

		HX 1		HX 1	HX 1	HX 1		HX 1	HX 1	HX 1		HX 1	HX 1	HX 1		HX 1	HX 1	HX 1	HX 1	HX 1	HX 1	HX 1	HX 1		
London Paddington 15	⊖ d	19 10	.....	19 25	19 40	19 55	.....	20 10	20 25	20 40	.....	20 55	21 10	21 25	.....	21 40	21 55	22 10	22 25	22 40	22 55	23 10	23 25	.....	.....
Heathrow Terminals 1-2-3	✈ a	19 25	.....	19 40	19 55	20 10	.	20 25	20 40	20 55	.	21 10	21 25	21 40	.	21 55	22 10	22 25	22 40	22 55	23 10	23 25	23 40	.	.
Heathrow Terminal 4	✈ a	*19 35*	.....	*19 48*	*20 05*	*20 18*	.....	*20 35*	*20 48*	*21 05*	.....	*21 18*	*21 35*	*21 48*	.....	*22 05*	*22 18*	*22 35*	*22 48*	*23 05*	*23 18*	*23 35*	*23 48*	.....	.....
Heathrow Terminal 5	✈ a	19 31	.	19 46	20 01	20 16	.	20 31	20 46	21 01	.	21 16	21 31	21 46	.	22 01	22 16	22 31	22 46	23 01	23 16	23 31	23 46	.	.

Saturdays

until 22 March

		HX 1	HX 1	HX 1		HX 1	HX 1	HX 1		HX 1	HX 1	HX 1		HX 1	HX 1	HX 1		HX 1	HX 1	HX 1		HX 1	HX 1	HX 1	HX 1
London Paddington 15	⊖ d	05 10	05 25	05 40	.....	05 55	06 10	06 25	.....	06 40	06 55	07 10	.....	07 25	07 40	07 55	.....	08 10	08 25	08 40	.....	08 55	09 10	09 25	09 40
Heathrow Terminals 1-2-3	✈ a	05 26	05 40	05 55	.	06 10	06 25	06 40	.	06 55	07 10	07 25	.	07 40	07 55	08 10	.	08 25	08 40	08 55	.	09 10	09 25	09 40	09 55
Heathrow Terminal 4	✈ a	05 33	05 48	06 03	.....	06 18	06 33	06 48	.....	07 03	07 18	07 33	.....	07 48	08 03	08 18	.....	08 33	08 48	09 03	.....	09 18	09 33	09 48	10 03

		HX 1		HX 1	HX 1	HX 1		HX 1	HX 1	HX 1		HX 1	HX 1	HX 1		HX 1	HX 1	HX 1		HX 1	HX 1	HX 1		HX 1	HX 1
London Paddington 15	⊖ d	09 55	.....	10 10	10 25	10 40	.....	10 55	11 10	11 25	.....	11 40	11 55	12 10	.....	12 25	12 40	12 55	.....	13 10	13 25	13 40	.....	13 55	14 10
Heathrow Terminals 1-2-3	✈ a	10 10	.	10 25	10 40	10 55	.	11 10	11 25	11 40	.	11 55	12 10	12 25	.	12 40	12 55	13 10	.	13 25	13 40	13 55	.	14 10	14 25
Heathrow Terminal 4	✈ a	10 18	.....	10 33	10 48	11 03	.....	11 18	11 33	11 48	.....	12 03	12 18	12 33	.....	12 48	13 03	13 18	.....	13 33	13 48	14 03	.....	14 18	14 33

		HX 1	HX 1	HX 1		HX 1	HX 1	HX 1		HX 1	HX 1	HX 1		HX 1	HX 1	HX 1		HX 1	HX 1	HX 1		HX 1	HX 1	HX 1	HX 1
London Paddington 15	⊖ d	14 25	14 40	14 55	.....	15 10	15 25	15 40	.....	15 55	16 10	16 25	.....	16 40	16 55	17 10	.....	17 25	17 40	17 55	.....	18 10	18 25	18 40	18 55
Heathrow Terminals 1-2-3	✈ a	14 40	14 55	15 10	.	15 25	15 40	15 55	.	16 10	16 25	16 40	.	16 55	17 10	17 25	.	17 40	17 55	18 10	.	18 25	18 40	18 55	19 10
Heathrow Terminal 4	✈ a	14 48	15 03	15 18	.....	15 33	15 48	16 03	.....	16 18	16 33	16 48	.....	17 03	17 18	17 33	.....	17 48	18 03	18 18	.....	18 33	18 48	19 03	19 18

For general notes see front of timetable
For details of catering facilities see
Directory of Train Operators

Table 118

Saturdays

until 22 March

London → Heathrow Airport

Network Diagram - see first page of Table 116

	HX 1		HX 1	HX 1	HX 1		HX 1	HX 1	HX 1		HX 1	HX 1	HX 1		HX 1	HX 1	HX 1	HX 1	HX 1	HX 1	HX 1	HX 1		
London Paddington 15 ⊖ d	19 10		19 25	19 40	19 55		20 10	20 25	20 40		20 55	21 10	21 25		21 40	21 55	22 10	22 25	22 40	22 55	23 10	23 25		
Heathrow Terminals 1-2-3 ✈ a	19 25		19 40	19 55	20 10		20 25	20 40	20 55		21 10	21 25	21 40		21 55	22 10	22 25	22 40	22 55	23 10	23 25	23 40		
Heathrow Terminal 4 ✈ a	19 33		19 48	20 03	20 18		20 33	20 48	21 03		21 18	21 33	21 48		22 03	22 18	22 33	22 48	23 03	23 18	23 33	23 48		

Saturdays

from 29 March

	HX 1	HX 1	HX 1		HX 1	HX 1	HX 1		HX 1	HX 1	HX 1		HX 1	HX 1	HX 1		HX 1	HX 1	HX 1		HX 1	HX 1	HX 1	HX 1
London Paddington 15 ⊖ d	05 10	05 25	05 40		05 55	06 10	06 25		06 40	06 55	07 10		07 25	07 40	07 55		08 10	08 25	08 40		08 55	09 10	09 25	09 40
Heathrow Terminals 1-2-3 ✈ a	05 26	05 40	05 55		06 10	06 25	06 40		06 55	07 10	07 25		07 40	07 55	08 10		08 25	08 40	08 55		09 10	09 25	09 40	09 55
Heathrow Terminal 4 ✈ a	05 42	05 48	06 05		06 18	06 35	06 48		07 05	07 18	07 35		07 48	08 05	08 18		08 35	08 48	09 05		09 18	09 35	09 48	10 05
Heathrow Terminal 5 ✈ a	05 32	05 46	06 01		06 16	06 31	06 46		07 01	07 16	07 31		07 46	08 01	08 16		08 31	08 46	09 01		09 16	09 31	09 46	10 01

	HX 1		HX 1	HX 1	HX 1		HX 1	HX 1	HX 1		HX 1	HX 1	HX 1		HX 1	HX 1	HX 1		HX 1	HX 1	HX 1		HX 1	HX 1
London Paddington 15 ⊖ d	09 55		10 10	10 25	10 40		10 55	11 10	11 25		11 40	11 55	12 10		12 25	12 40	12 55		13 10	13 25	13 40		13 55	14 10
Heathrow Terminals 1-2-3 ✈ a	10 10		10 25	10 40	10 55		11 10	11 25	11 40		11 55	12 10	12 25		12 40	12 55	13 10		13 25	13 40	13 55		14 10	14 25
Heathrow Terminal 4 ✈ a	10 18		10 35	10 48	11 05		11 18	11 35	11 48		12 05	12 18	12 35		12 48	13 05	13 18		13 35	13 48	14 05		14 18	14 35
Heathrow Terminal 5 ✈ a	10 16		10 31	10 46	11 01		11 16	11 31	11 46		12 01	12 16	12 31		12 46	13 01	13 16		13 31	13 46	14 01		14 16	14 31

	HX 1	HX 1	HX 1		HX 1	HX 1	HX 1		HX 1	HX 1	HX 1		HX 1	HX 1	HX 1		HX 1	HX 1	HX 1		HX 1	HX 1	HX 1	HX 1
London Paddington 15 ⊖ d	14 25	14 40	14 55		15 10	15 25	15 40		15 55	16 10	16 25		16 40	16 55	17 10		17 25	17 40	17 55		18 10	18 25	18 40	18 55
Heathrow Terminals 1-2-3 ✈ a	14 40	14 55	15 10		15 25	15 40	15 55		16 10	16 25	16 40		16 55	17 10	17 25		17 40	17 55	18 10		18 25	18 40	18 55	19 10
Heathrow Terminal 4 ✈ a	14 48	15 05	15 18		15 35	15 48	16 05		16 18	16 35	16 48		17 05	17 18	17 35		17 48	18 05	18 18		18 35	18 48	19 05	19 18
Heathrow Terminal 5 ✈ a	14 46	15 01	15 16		15 31	15 46	16 01		16 16	16 31	16 46		17 01	17 16	17 31		17 46	18 01	18 16		18 31	18 46	19 01	19 16

	HX 1		HX 1	HX 1	HX 1		HX 1	HX 1	HX 1		HX 1	HX 1	HX 1		HX 1	HX 1	HX 1	HX 1	HX 1	HX 1	HX 1	HX 1		
London Paddington 15 ⊖ d	19 10		19 25	19 40	19 55		20 10	20 25	20 40		20 55	21 10	21 25		21 40	21 55	22 10	22 25	22 40	22 55	23 10	23 25		
Heathrow Terminals 1-2-3 ✈ a	19 25		19 40	19 55	20 10		20 25	20 40	20 55		21 10	21 25	21 40		21 55	22 10	22 25	22 40	22 55	23 10	23 25	23 40		
Heathrow Terminal 4 ✈ a	19 35		19 48	20 05	20 18		20 35	20 48	21 05		21 18	21 35	21 48		22 05	22 18	22 35	22 48	23 05	23 18	23 35	23 48		
Heathrow Terminal 5 ✈ a	19 31		19 46	20 01	20 16		20 31	20 46	21 01		21 16	21 31	21 46		22 01	22 16	22 31	22 46	23 01	23 16	23 31	23 46		

Sundays

until 27 January

	HX 1	HX 1	HX 1		HX 1	HX 1	HX 1		HX 1	HX 1	HX 1		HX 1	HX 1	HX 1		HX 1	HX 1	HX 1		HX 1	HX 1	HX 1	HX 1
London Paddington 15 ⊖ d	05 10	05 25	05 40		05 55	06 10	06 25		06 40	06 55	07 10		07 25	07 40	07 55		08 10	08 25	08 40		08 55	09 10	09 25	09 40
Heathrow Terminals 1-2-3 ✈ a	05 26	05 41	05 56		06 11	06 26	06 41		06 56	07 11	07 26		07 41	07 56	08 11		08 27	08 41	08 56		09 11	09 25	09 40	09 55
Heathrow Terminal 4 ✈ a	05 32	05 47	06 02		06 17	06 32	06 47		07 02	07 17	07 32		07 47	08 02	08 17		08 33	08 47	09 03		09 18	09 33	09 48	10 03

	HX 1		HX 1	HX 1	HX 1		HX 1	HX 1	HX 1		HX 1	HX 1	HX 1		HX 1	HX 1	HX 1		HX 1	HX 1	HX 1		HX 1	HX 1
London Paddington 15 ⊖ d	09 55		10 10	10 25	10 40		10 55	11 10	11 25		11 40	11 55	12 10		12 25	12 40	12 55		13 10	13 25	13 40		13 55	14 10
Heathrow Terminals 1-2-3 ✈ a	10 10		10 25	10 40	10 55		11 10	11 25	11 40		11 55	12 10	12 25		12 40	12 55	13 10		13 25	13 40	13 55		14 10	14 25
Heathrow Terminal 4 ✈ a	10 18		10 33	10 48	11 03		11 18	11 33	11 48		12 03	12 18	12 33		12 48	13 03	13 18		13 33	13 48	14 03		14 18	14 33

	HX 1	HX 1	HX 1		HX 1	HX 1	HX 1		HX 1	HX 1	HX 1		HX 1	HX 1	HX 1		HX 1	HX 1	HX 1		HX 1	HX 1	HX 1	HX 1
London Paddington 15 ⊖ d	14 25	14 40	14 55		15 10	15 25	15 40		15 55	16 10	16 25		16 40	16 55	17 10		17 25	17 40	17 55		18 10	18 25	18 40	18 55
Heathrow Terminals 1-2-3 ✈ a	14 40	14 55	15 10		15 25	15 40	15 55		16 10	16 25	16 40		16 55	17 10	17 25		17 40	17 55	18 10		18 25	18 40	18 55	19 10
Heathrow Terminal 4 ✈ a	14 48	15 03	15 18		15 33	15 48	16 03		16 18	16 33	16 48		17 03	17 18	17 33		17 48	18 03	18 18		18 33	18 48	19 03	19 18

	HX 1	HX 1	HX 1	HX 1	HX 1		HX 1	HX 1	HX 1		HX 1	HX 1	HX 1		HX 1	HX 1	HX 1		HX 1	HX 1	HX 1	HX 1		
London Paddington 15 ⊖ d	19 25	19 10	19 40	19 55	20 10		20 25	20 40	20 55		21 10	21 25	21 40		21 55	22 10	22 25		22 40	22 55	23 10	23 25		
Heathrow Terminals 1-2-3 ✈ a	19 40	19 25	19 55	20 10	20 25		20 40	20 55	21 10		21 25	21 40	21 56		22 11	22 26	22 41		22 56	23 11	23 26	23 41		
Heathrow Terminal 4 ✈ a	19 48	19 33	20 03	20 18	20 33		20 48	21 03	21 18		21 33	21 46	22 02		22 17	22 32	22 47		23 02	23 17	23 32	23 50		

Sundays

3 February to 23 March

	HX 1	HX 1	HX 1		HX 1	HX 1	HX 1		HX 1	HX 1	HX 1		HX 1	HX 1	HX 1		HX 1	HX 1	HX 1		HX 1	HX 1	HX 1	HX 1
London Paddington 15 ⊖ d	05 10	05 25	05 40		05 55	06 10	06 25		06 40	06 55	07 10		07 25	07 40	07 55		08 10	08 25	08 40		08 55	09 10	09 25	09 40
Heathrow Terminals 1-2-3 ✈ a	05 26	05 41	05 56		06 11	06 26	06 41		06 56	07 11	07 26		07 41	07 56	08 11		08 27	08 41	08 56		09 11	09 26	09 41	09 55
Heathrow Terminal 4 ✈ a	05 32	05 47	06 02		06 17	06 32	06 47		07 02	07 17	07 32		07 47	08 02	08 17		08 33	08 47	09 02		09 17	09 32	09 47	10 02

For general notes see front of timetable
For details of catering facilities see
Directory of Train Operators

Table 118

Sundays

3 February to 23 March

London → Heathrow Airport

Network Diagram - see first page of Table 116

	HX 1		HX 1	HX 1	HX 1		HX 1	HX 1	HX 1		HX 1	HX 1	HX 1		HX 1	HX 1	HX 1		HX 1	HX 1	HX 1		HX 1	HX 1
London Paddington 15 ⊖ d	09 55		10 10	10 25	10 40		10 55	11 10	11 25		11 40	11 55	12 10		12 25	12 40	12 55		13 10	13 25	13 40		13 55	14 10
Heathrow Terminals 1-2-3 ✈ a	10 11		10 26	10 41	10 56		11 11	11 26	11 41		11 56	12 11	12 26		12 41	12 56	13 11		13 26	13 41	13 56		14 11	14 26
Heathrow Terminal 4 ✈ a	10 17		10 32	10 47	11 02		11 17	11 32	11 47		12 02	12 17	12 32		12 47	13 02	13 17		13 32	13 47	14 02		14 17	14 32

	HX 1	HX 1	HX 1		HX 1	HX 1	HX 1		HX 1	HX 1	HX 1		HX 1	HX 1	HX 1		HX 1	HX 1	HX 1		HX 1	HX 1	HX 1	HX 1
London Paddington 15 ⊖ d	14 25	14 40	14 55		15 10	15 25	15 40		15 55	16 10	16 25		16 40	16 55	17 10		17 25	17 40	17 55		18 10	18 25	18 40	18 55
Heathrow Terminals 1-2-3 ✈ a	14 41	14 56	15 11		15 26	15 41	15 56		16 11	16 26	16 41		16 56	17 11	17 26		17 41	17 56	18 11		18 26	18 41	18 56	19 11
Heathrow Terminal 4 ✈ a	14 47	15 02	15 17		15 32	15 47	16 02		16 17	16 32	16 47		17 02	17 17	17 32		17 47	18 02	18 17		18 32	18 47	19 02	19 17

	HX 1		HX 1	HX 1	HX 1		HX 1	HX 1	HX 1		HX 1	HX 1	HX 1		HX 1	HX 1	HX 1	HX 1	HX 1	HX 1	HX 1	HX 1		
London Paddington 15 ⊖ d	19 10		19 25	19 40	19 55		20 10	20 25	20 40		20 55	21 10	21 25		21 40	21 55	22 10	22 25	22 40	22 55	23 10	23 25		
Heathrow Terminals 1-2-3 ✈ a	19 26		19 41	19 56	20 11		20 26	20 41	20 56		21 11	21 26	21 41		21 56	22 11	22 26	22 41	22 56	23 11	23 26	23 41		
Heathrow Terminal 4 ✈ a	19 32		19 47	20 02	20 17		20 32	20 47	21 02		21 17	21 32	21 47		22 02	22 17	22 32	22 47	23 02	23 17	23 32	23 50		

Sundays

from 30 March

	HX 1	HX 1	HX 1		HX 1	HX 1	HX 1		HX 1	HX 1	HX 1		HX 1	HX 1	HX 1		HX 1	HX 1	HX 1		HX 1	HX 1	HX 1	HX 1
London Paddington 15 ⊖ d	05 10	05 25	05 40		05 55	06 10	06 25		06 40	06 55	07 10		07 25	07 40	07 55		08 10	08 25	08 40		08 55	09 10	09 25	09 40
Heathrow Terminals 1-2-3 ✈ a	05 26	05 41	05 56		06 11	06 26	06 41		06 56	07 11	07 26		07 41	07 56	08 11		08 27	08 41	08 56		09 11	09 26	09 41	09 55
Heathrow Terminal 4 ✈ a	*05 40*	*05 51*	*06 06*			*06 35*	*06 53*		*07 06*		*07 35*		*07 53*	*08 06*			*08 35*	*08 53*	*09 06*			*09 35*	*09 53*	*10 06*
Heathrow Terminal 5 ✈ a	05 32	05 47	06 03		06 17	06 32	06 50		07 03	07 17	07 32		07 50	08 03	08 17		08 33	08 50	09 03		09 17	09 32	09 50	10 03

	HX 1		HX 1	HX 1	HX 1		HX 1	HX 1	HX 1		HX 1	HX 1	HX 1		HX 1	HX 1	HX 1		HX 1	HX 1	HX 1		HX 1	HX 1
London Paddington 15 ⊖ d	09 55		10 10	10 25	10 40		10 55	11 10	11 25		11 40	11 55	12 10		12 25	12 40	12 55		13 10	13 25	13 40		13 55	14 10
Heathrow Terminals 1-2-3 ✈ a	10 11		10 26	10 41	10 56		11 11	11 26	11 41		11 56	12 11	12 26		12 41	12 56	13 11		13 26	13 41	13 56		14 11	14 26
Heathrow Terminal 4 ✈ a			*10 35*	*10 53*	*11 06*			*11 35*	*11 53*		*12 06*		*12 35*		*12 53*	*13 06*			*13 35*	*13 53*	*14 06*			*14 35*
Heathrow Terminal 5 ✈ a	10 17		10 32	10 50	11 03		11 17	11 32	11 50		12 03	12 17	12 32		12 50	13 03	13 17		13 32	13 50	14 03		14 17	14 32

	HX 1	HX 1	HX 1		HX 1	HX 1	HX 1		HX 1	HX 1	HX 1		HX 1	HX 1	HX 1		HX 1	HX 1	HX 1		HX 1	HX 1	HX 1	HX 1
London Paddington 15 ⊖ d	14 25	14 40	14 55		15 10	15 25	15 40		15 55	16 10	16 25		16 40	16 55	17 10		17 25	17 40	17 55		18 10	18 25	18 40	18 55
Heathrow Terminals 1-2-3 ✈ a	14 41	14 56	15 11		15 26	15 41	15 56		16 11	16 26	16 41		16 56	17 11	17 26		17 41	17 56	18 11		18 26	18 41	18 56	19 11
Heathrow Terminal 4 ✈ a	*14 53*	*15 06*			*15 35*	*15 53*	*16 06*			*16 35*	*16 53*		*17 06*		*17 35*		*17 53*	*18 06*			*18 35*	*18 53*	*19 06*	
Heathrow Terminal 5 ✈ a	14 50	15 03	15 17		15 32	15 50	16 03		16 17	16 32	16 50		17 03	17 17	17 32		17 50	18 03	18 17		18 32	18 50	19 03	19 17

	HX 1		HX 1	HX 1	HX 1		HX 1	HX 1	HX 1		HX 1	HX 1	HX 1		HX 1	HX 1	HX 1	HX 1	HX 1	HX 1	HX 1	HX 1		
London Paddington 15 ⊖ d	19 10		19 25	19 40	19 55		20 10	20 25	20 40		20 55	21 10	21 25		21 40	21 55	22 10	22 25	22 40	22 55	23 10	23 25		
Heathrow Terminals 1-2-3 ✈ a	19 26		19 41	19 56	20 11		20 26	20 41	20 56		21 11	21 26	21 41		21 56	22 11	22 26	22 41	22 56	23 11	23 26	23 41		
Heathrow Terminal 4 ✈ a	*19 35*		*19 53*	*20 06*			*20 35*	*20 53*	*21 06*			*21 35*	*21 53*		*22 06*		*22 35*	*22 53*	*23 06*		*23 35*	*23 53*		
Heathrow Terminal 5 ✈ a	19 32		19 50	20 03	20 17		20 32	20 50	21 03		21 17	21 32	21 50		22 03	22 17	22 32	22 50	23 03	23 17	23 32	23 50		

For general notes see front of timetable
For details of catering facilities see
Directory of Train Operators

Table 118

Mondays to Fridays

until 26 March

Heathrow Airport → London

Network Diagram - see first page of Table 116

Miles			HX 1	HX 1	HX 1	HX 1		HX 1	HX 1	HX 1	HX 1		HX 1	HX 1	HX 1	HX 1		HX 1	HX 1	HX 1	HX 1		HX 1	HX 1	HX 1
0	Heathrow Terminal 4	d	05 07	05 25	05 40	05 55	.....	06 10	06 25	06 40	06 55	.....	07 10	07 25	07 40	07 55	.....	08 10	08 25	08 40	08 55	.....	09 10	09 25	09 40
1¾	Heathrow Terminals 1-2-3	d	05 12	05 33	05 48	06 03	.	06 18	06 33	06 48	07 03	.	07 18	07 33	07 48	08 03	.	08 18	08 33	08 48	09 03	.	09 18	09 33	09 48
16½	London Paddington 15	a	05 28	05 49	06 04	06 19	.....	06 34	06 49	07 04	07 19	.....	07 34	07 49	08 04	08 19	.....	08 34	08 49	09 04	09 19	.....	09 34	09 49	10 04

		HX 1	HX 1	HX 1		HX 1	HX 1	HX 1	HX 1		HX 1	HX 1	HX 1	HX 1		HX 1	HX 1	HX 1	HX 1		HX 1	HX 1	HX 1	HX 1	HX 1
Heathrow Terminal 4	d	09 55	10 10	10 25	.....	10 40	10 55	11 10	11 25	.....	11 40	11 55	12 10	12 25	.....	12 40	12 55	13 10	13 25	.....	13 40	13 55	14 10	14 25	14 40
Heathrow Terminals 1-2-3	d	10 03	10 18	10 33	.	10 48	11 03	11 18	11 33	.	11 48	12 03	12 18	12 33	.	12 48	13 03	13 18	13 33	.	13 48	14 03	14 18	14 33	14 48
London Paddington 15	a	10 19	10 34	10 49	.....	11 04	11 19	11 34	11 49	.....	12 04	12 19	12 34	12 49	.....	13 04	13 19	13 34	13 49	.....	14 04	14 19	14 34	14 49	15 04

		HX 1		HX 1	HX 1	HX 1	HX 1		HX 1	HX 1	HX 1	HX 1		HX 1	HX 1	HX 1	HX 1		HX 1	HX 1	HX 1	HX 1		HX 1	HX 1
Heathrow Terminal 4	d	14 55	.....	15 10	15 25	15 40	15 55	.....	16 10	16 25	16 40	16 55	.....	17 10	17 25	17 40	17 55	.....	18 10	18 25	18 40	18 55	.....	19 10	19 25
Heathrow Terminals 1-2-3	d	15 03	.	15 18	15 33	15 48	16 03	.	16 18	16 33	16 48	17 03	.	17 18	17 33	17 48	18 03	.	18 18	18 33	18 48	19 03	.	19 18	19 33
London Paddington 15	a	15 19	.....	15 34	15 49	16 04	16 19	.....	16 34	16 49	17 04	17 19	.....	17 34	17 49	18 04	18 20	.....	18 34	18 49	19 04	19 19	.....	19 34	19 49

		HX 1	HX 1	HX 1	HX 1		HX 1	HX 1	HX 1	HX 1		HX 1	HX 1	HX 1	HX 1		HX 1	HX 1	HX 1	HX 1		HX 1			
Heathrow Terminal 4	d	19 40	19 55	20 10	20 25	.....	20 40	20 55	21 10	21 25	.....	21 40	21 55	22 10	22 25	.....	22 40	22 55	23 10	23 25	.....	23 40	.....	.....	.....
Heathrow Terminals 1-2-3	d	19 48	20 03	20 18	20 33	.	20 48	21 03	21 18	21 33	.	21 48	22 03	22 18	22 33	.	22 48	23 03	23 18	23 33	.	23 48	.	.	.
London Paddington 15	a	20 04	20 19	20 34	20 49	.....	21 04	21 19	21 34	21 49	.....	22 04	22 19	22 34	22 49	.....	23 04	23 19	23 34	23 49	.....	00 04	.....	.....	.....

Mondays to Fridays

from 27 March

		HX 1	HX 1	HX 1	HX 1		HX 1	HX 1	HX 1	HX 1		HX 1	HX 1	HX 1	HX 1		HX 1	HX 1	HX 1	HX 1		HX 1	HX 1	HX 1	HX 1
Heathrow Terminal 5	d	05 07	05 27	05 42	05 57	.....	06 12	06 27	06 42	06 57	.....	07 12	07 27	07 42	07 57	.....	08 12	08 27	08 42	08 57	.....	09 12	09 27	09 42	09 57
Heathrow Terminal 4	d	.	*05 23*	*05 31*	*05 51*	.	*06 05*	*06 21*	*06 35*	*06 51*	.	*07 05*	*07 21*	*07 35*	*07 51*	.	*08 05*	*08 21*	*08 35*	*08 51*	.	*09 05*	*09 21*	*09 35*	*09 51*
Heathrow Terminals 1-2-3	d	05 12	05 33	05 48	06 03	.....	06 18	06 33	06 48	07 03	.....	07 18	07 33	07 48	08 03	.....	08 18	08 33	08 48	09 03	.....	09 18	09 33	09 48	10 03
London Paddington 15	a	05 28	05 49	06 04	06 19	.	06 34	06 49	07 04	07 19	.	07 34	07 49	08 04	08 19	.	08 34	08 49	09 04	09 19	.	09 34	09 49	10 04	10 19

		HX 1	HX 1		HX 1	HX 1	HX 1	HX 1		HX 1	HX 1	HX 1	HX 1		HX 1	HX 1	HX 1	HX 1		HX 1	HX 1	HX 1	HX 1		HX 1
Heathrow Terminal 5	d	10 12	10 27	.....	10 42	10 57	11 12	11 27	.....	11 42	11 57	12 12	12 27	.....	12 42	12 57	13 12	13 27	.....	13 42	13 57	14 12	14 27	.....	14 42
Heathrow Terminal 4	d	*10 05*	*10 21*	.	*10 35*	*10 51*	*11 05*	*11 21*	.	*11 35*	*11 51*	*12 05*	*12 21*	.	*12 35*	*12 51*	*13 05*	*13 21*	.	*13 35*	*13 51*	*14 05*	*14 21*	.	*14 35*
Heathrow Terminals 1-2-3	d	10 18	10 33	.....	10 48	11 03	11 18	11 33	.....	11 48	12 03	12 18	12 33	.....	12 48	13 03	13 18	13 33	.....	13 48	14 03	14 18	14 33	.....	14 48
London Paddington 15	a	10 34	10 49	.	11 04	11 19	11 34	11 49	.	12 04	12 19	12 34	12 49	.	13 04	13 19	13 34	13 49	.	14 04	14 19	14 34	14 49	.	15 04

		HX 1	HX 1	HX 1	HX 1		HX 1	HX 1	HX 1	HX 1		HX 1	HX 1	HX 1	HX 1		HX 1	HX 1	HX 1	HX 1		HX 1	HX 1	HX 1	HX 1
Heathrow Terminal 5	d	14 57	15 12	15 27	15 42	.....	15 57	16 12	16 27	16 42	.....	16 57	17 12	17 27	17 42	.....	17 57	18 12	18 27	18 42	.....	18 57	19 12	19 27	19 42
Heathrow Terminal 4	d	*14 51*	*15 05*	*15 21*	*15 35*	.	*15 51*	*16 05*	*16 21*	*16 35*	.	*16 51*	*17 05*	*17 21*	*17 35*	.	*17 51*	*18 05*	*18 21*	*18 35*	.	*18 51*	*19 05*	*19 21*	*19 35*
Heathrow Terminals 1-2-3	d	15 03	15 18	15 33	15 48	.....	16 03	16 18	16 33	16 48	.....	17 03	17 18	17 33	17 48	.....	18 03	18 18	18 33	18 48	.....	19 03	19 18	19 33	19 48
London Paddington 15	a	15 19	15 34	15 49	16 04	.	16 19	16 34	16 49	17 04	.	17 19	17 34	17 49	18 04	.	18 20	18 34	18 49	19 04	.	19 19	19 34	19 49	20 04

		HX 1	HX 1		HX 1	HX 1	HX 1	HX 1		HX 1	HX 1	HX 1	HX 1		HX 1	HX 1	HX 1	HX 1		HX 1	HX 1				
Heathrow Terminal 5	d	19 57	20 12	.....	20 27	20 42	20 57	21 12	.....	21 27	21 42	21 57	22 12	.....	22 27	22 42	22 57	23 12	.....	23 27	23 42	.....	.....	.....	.....
Heathrow Terminal 4	d	*19 51*	*20 05*	.	*20 21*	*20 35*	*20 51*	*21 05*	.	*21 21*	*21 35*	*21 51*	*22 05*	.	*22 21*	*22 35*	*22 51*	*23 05*	.	*23 21*	*23 35*	.	.	.	.
Heathrow Terminals 1-2-3	d	20 03	20 18	.....	20 33	20 48	21 03	21 18	.....	21 33	21 48	22 03	22 18	.....	22 33	22 48	23 03	23 18	.....	23 33	23 48	.....	.....	.....	.....
London Paddington 15	a	20 19	20 34	.	20 50	21 04	21 19	21 34	.	21 49	22 04	22 19	22 34	.	22 49	23 04	23 19	23 34	.	23 49	00 04	.	.	.	.

Saturdays

until 22 March

		HX 1	HX 1	HX 1	HX 1		HX 1	HX 1	HX 1	HX 1		HX 1	HX 1	HX 1	HX 1		HX 1	HX 1	HX 1	HX 1		HX 1	HX 1	HX 1	HX 1
Heathrow Terminal 4	d	05 07	05 25	05 40	05 55	.....	06 10	06 25	06 40	06 55	.....	07 10	07 25	07 40	07 55	.....	08 10	08 25	08 40	08 55	.....	09 10	09 25	09 40	09 55
Heathrow Terminals 1-2-3	d	05 12	05 33	05 48	06 03	.	06 18	06 33	06 48	07 03	.	07 18	07 33	07 48	08 03	.	08 18	08 33	08 48	09 03	.	09 18	09 33	09 48	10 03
London Paddington 15	a	05 28	05 49	06 04	06 19	.....	06 34	06 49	07 04	07 19	.....	07 34	07 49	08 04	08 19	.....	08 34	08 49	09 04	09 19	.....	09 34	09 49	10 04	10 19

		HX 1	HX 1		HX 1	HX 1	HX 1	HX 1		HX 1	HX 1	HX 1	HX 1		HX 1	HX 1	HX 1	HX 1		HX 1	HX 1	HX 1	HX 1		HX 1
Heathrow Terminal 4	d	10 10	10 25	.....	10 40	10 55	11 10	11 25	.....	11 40	11 55	12 10	12 25	.....	12 40	12 55	13 10	13 25	.....	13 40	13 55	14 10	14 25	.....	14 40
Heathrow Terminals 1-2-3	d	10 18	10 33	.	10 48	11 03	11 18	11 33	.	11 48	12 03	12 18	12 33	.	12 48	13 03	13 18	13 33	.	13 48	14 03	14 18	14 33	.	14 48
London Paddington 15	a	10 34	10 49	.....	11 04	11 19	11 34	11 49	.....	12 04	12 19	12 34	12 49	.....	13 04	13 19	13 34	13 49	.....	14 04	14 19	14 34	14 49	.....	15 04

		HX 1	HX 1	HX 1	HX 1		HX 1	HX 1	HX 1	HX 1		HX 1	HX 1	HX 1	HX 1		HX 1	HX 1	HX 1	HX 1		HX 1	HX 1	HX 1	HX 1
Heathrow Terminal 4	d	14 55	15 10	15 25	15 40	.....	15 55	16 10	16 25	16 40	.....	16 55	17 10	17 25	17 40	.....	17 55	18 10	18 25	18 40	.....	18 55	19 10	19 25	19 40
Heathrow Terminals 1-2-3	d	15 03	15 18	15 33	15 48	.	16 03	16 18	16 33	16 48	.	17 03	17 18	17 33	17 48	.	18 03	18 18	18 33	18 48	.	19 03	19 18	19 33	19 48
London Paddington 15	a	15 19	15 34	15 49	16 04	.....	16 19	16 34	16 49	17 04	.....	17 19	17 34	17 49	18 04	.....	18 19	18 34	18 49	19 04	.....	19 19	19 34	19 49	20 04

For general notes see front of timetable
For details of catering facilities see
Directory of Train Operators

Table 118

Saturdays
until 22 March

Heathrow Airport → London

Network Diagram - see first page of Table 116

	HX 1	HX 1		HX 1	HX 1	HX 1	HX 1		HX 1	HX 1	HX 1	HX 1		HX 1	HX 1	HX 1	HX 1		HX 1	HX 1				
Heathrow Terminal 4 d	19 55	20 10	.....	20 25	20 40	20 55	21 10	.....	21 25	21 40	21 55	22 10	.....	22 25	22 40	22 55	23 10	.....	23 25	23 40	.....	.....	.....	.....
Heathrow Terminals 1-2-3 d	20 03	20 18	.	20 33	20 48	21 03	21 18	.	21 33	21 48	22 03	22 18	.	22 33	22 48	23 03	23 18	.	23 33	23 48	.	.	.	.
London Paddington 15 ⊖ a	20 19	20 34	.....	20 49	21 04	21 19	21 34	.....	21 49	22 04	22 19	22 34	.....	22 49	23 04	23 19	23 34	.....	23 49	00 04	.....	.....	.....	.....

Saturdays
from 29 March

	HX 1	HX 1	HX 1	HX 1		HX 1	HX 1	HX 1	HX 1		HX 1	HX 1	HX 1	HX 1		HX 1	HX 1	HX 1	HX 1		HX 1	HX 1	HX 1	HX 1
Heathrow Terminal 5 d	05 07	05 27	05 42	05 57	.....	06 12	06 27	06 42	06 57	.....	07 12	07 27	07 42	07 57	.....	08 12	08 27	08 42	08 57	.....	09 12	09 27	09 42	09 57
Heathrow Terminal 4 d	.	05 23	05 32	05 51	.	06 05	06 21	06 35	06 51	.	07 05	07 21	07 35	07 51	.	08 05	08 21	08 35	08 51	.	09 05	09 21	09 35	09 51
Heathrow Terminals 1-2-3 d	05 12	05 33	05 48	06 03	.....	06 18	06 33	06 48	07 03	.....	07 18	07 33	07 48	08 03	.....	08 18	08 33	08 48	09 03	.....	09 18	09 33	09 48	10 03
London Paddington 15 ⊖ a	05 28	05 49	06 04	06 19	.	06 34	06 49	07 04	07 19	.	07 34	07 49	08 04	08 19	.	08 34	08 49	09 04	09 19	.	09 34	09 49	10 04	10 19

	HX 1	HX 1		HX 1	HX 1	HX 1	HX 1		HX 1	HX 1	HX 1	HX 1		HX 1	HX 1	HX 1	HX 1		HX 1	HX 1	HX 1	HX 1		HX 1
Heathrow Terminal 5 d	10 12	10 27	.....	10 42	10 57	11 12	11 27	.....	11 42	11 57	12 12	12 27	.....	12 42	12 57	13 12	13 27	.....	13 42	13 57	14 12	14 27	.....	14 42
Heathrow Terminal 4 d	10 05	10 21	.	10 35	10 51	11 05	11 21	.	11 35	11 51	12 05	12 21	.	12 35	12 51	13 05	13 21	.	13 35	13 51	14 05	14 21	.	14 35
Heathrow Terminals 1-2-3 d	10 18	10 33	.....	10 48	11 03	11 18	11 33	.....	11 48	12 03	12 18	12 33	.....	12 48	13 03	13 18	13 33	.....	13 48	14 03	14 18	14 33	.....	14 48
London Paddington 15 ⊖ a	10 34	10 49	.	11 04	11 19	11 34	11 49	.	12 04	12 19	12 34	12 49	.	13 04	13 19	13 34	13 49	.	14 04	14 19	14 34	14 49	.	15 04

	HX 1	HX 1	HX 1	HX 1		HX 1	HX 1	HX 1	HX 1		HX 1	HX 1	HX 1	HX 1		HX 1	HX 1	HX 1	HX 1		HX 1	HX 1	HX 1	HX 1
Heathrow Terminal 5 d	14 57	15 12	15 27	15 42	.....	15 57	16 12	16 27	16 42	.....	16 57	17 12	17 27	17 42	.....	17 57	18 12	18 27	18 42	.....	18 57	19 12	19 27	19 42
Heathrow Terminal 4 d	14 51	15 05	15 21	15 35	.	15 51	16 05	16 21	16 35	.	16 51	17 05	17 21	17 35	.	17 51	18 05	18 21	18 35	.	18 51	19 05	19 21	19 35
Heathrow Terminals 1-2-3 d	15 03	15 18	15 33	15 48	.....	16 03	16 18	16 33	16 48	.....	17 03	17 18	17 33	17 48	.....	18 03	18 18	18 33	18 48	.....	19 03	19 18	19 33	19 48
London Paddington 15 ⊖ a	15 19	15 34	15 49	16 04	.	16 19	16 34	16 49	17 04	.	17 19	17 34	17 49	18 04	.	18 19	18 34	18 49	19 04	.	19 19	19 34	19 49	20 04

	HX 1	HX 1		HX 1	HX 1	HX 1	HX 1		HX 1	HX 1	HX 1	HX 1		HX 1	HX 1	HX 1	HX 1		HX 1	HX 1				
Heathrow Terminal 5 d	19 57	20 12	.....	20 27	20 42	20 57	21 12	.....	21 27	21 42	21 57	22 12	.....	22 27	22 42	22 57	23 12	.....	23 27	23 42	.....	.....	.....	.....
Heathrow Terminal 4 d	19 51	20 05	.	20 21	20 35	20 51	21 05	.	21 18	21 35	21 51	22 05	.	22 18	22 35	22 51	23 05	.	23 21	23 35	.....	.....	.....	.....
Heathrow Terminals 1-2-3 d	20 03	20 18	.....	20 33	20 48	21 03	21 18	.....	21 33	21 48	22 03	22 18	.....	22 33	22 48	23 03	23 18	.....	23 33	23 48	.	.	.	.
London Paddington 15 ⊖ a	20 19	20 34	.	20 49	21 04	21 19	21 34	.	21 49	22 04	22 19	22 34	.	22 49	23 04	23 19	23 34	.	23 49	00 04	.	.	.	.

Sundays
until 27 January

	HX 1	HX 1	HX 1	HX 1		HX 1	HX 1	HX 1	HX 1		HX 1	HX 1	HX 1	HX 1		HX 1	HX 1	HX 1	HX 1		HX 1	HX 1	HX 1	HX 1
Heathrow Terminal 4 d	05 03	05 18	05 33	05 48	.....	06 03	06 18	06 33	06 48	.....	07 03	07 18	07 33	07 48	.....	08 03	08 18	08 33	08 48	.....	08 55	09 10	09 25	09 40
Heathrow Terminals 1-2-3 d	05 08	05 23	05 38	05 53	.	06 08	06 23	06 38	06 53	.	07 08	07 23	07 38	07 53	.	08 08	08 23	08 38	08 53	.	09 03	09 18	09 33	09 48
London Paddington 15 ⊖ a	05 24	05 39	05 54	06 09	.....	06 24	06 39	06 54	07 09	.....	07 24	07 39	07 54	08 09	.....	08 24	08 39	08 54	09 09	.....	09 19	09 34	09 49	10 04

	HX 1	HX 1		HX 1	HX 1	HX 1	HX 1		HX 1	HX 1	HX 1	HX 1		HX 1	HX 1	HX 1	HX 1		HX 1	HX 1	HX 1	HX 1		HX 1
Heathrow Terminal 4 d	09 55	10 10	.....	10 25	10 40	10 55	11 10	.....	11 25	11 40	11 55	12 10	.....	12 25	12 40	12 55	13 10	.....	13 25	13 40	13 55	14 10	.....	14 25
Heathrow Terminals 1-2-3 d	10 03	10 18	.	10 33	10 48	11 03	11 18	.	11 33	11 48	12 03	12 18	.	12 33	12 48	13 03	13 18	.	13 33	13 48	14 03	14 18	.	14 33
London Paddington 15 ⊖ a	10 19	10 34	.....	10 49	11 04	11 19	11 34	.....	11 49	12 04	12 19	12 34	.....	12 49	13 04	13 19	13 34	.....	13 49	14 04	14 19	14 34	.....	14 49

	HX 1	HX 1	HX 1	HX 1		HX 1	HX 1	HX 1	HX 1		HX 1	HX 1	HX 1	HX 1		HX 1	HX 1	HX 1	HX 1		HX 1	HX 1	HX 1	HX 1
Heathrow Terminal 4 d	14 40	14 55	15 10	15 25	.....	15 40	15 55	16 10	16 25	.....	16 40	16 55	17 10	17 25	.....	17 40	17 55	18 10	18 25	.....	18 40	18 55	19 10	19 25
Heathrow Terminals 1-2-3 d	14 48	15 03	15 18	15 33	.	15 48	16 03	16 18	16 33	.	16 48	17 03	17 18	17 33	.	17 48	18 03	18 18	18 33	.	18 48	19 03	19 18	19 33
London Paddington 15 ⊖ a	15 04	15 19	15 34	15 49	.....	16 04	16 19	16 34	16 49	.....	17 04	17 19	17 34	17 49	.....	18 04	18 19	18 34	18 49	.....	19 04	19 19	19 34	19 48

	HX 1	HX 1		HX 1	HX 1	HX 1	HX 1		HX 1	HX 1	HX 1	HX 1		HX 1	HX 1	HX 1	HX 1		HX 1	HX 1	HX 1			
Heathrow Terminal 4 d	19 40	19 55	.....	20 10	20 25	20 40	20 55	.....	21 10	21 25	21 48	22 03	.....	22 18	22 33	22 48	23 03	.....	23 18	23 33	23 42	.....	.....	.....
Heathrow Terminals 1-2-3 d	19 48	20 03	.	20 18	20 33	20 48	21 03	.	21 18	21 33	21 53	22 08	.	22 23	22 38	22 53	23 08	.	23 23	23 38	23 47	.	.	.
London Paddington 15 ⊖ a	20 04	20 19	.....	20 34	20 49	21 04	21 19	.....	21 34	21 49	22 09	22 24	.....	22 44	22 54	23 09	23 28	.....	23 39	23 54	00 03	.....	.....	.....

Sundays
3 February to 23 March

	HX 1	HX 1	HX 1	HX 1		HX 1	HX 1	HX 1	HX 1		HX 1	HX 1	HX 1	HX 1		HX 1	HX 1	HX 1	HX 1		HX 1	HX 1	HX 1	HX 1
Heathrow Terminal 4 d	05 03	05 18	05 33	05 48	.....	06 03	06 18	06 33	06 48	.....	07 03	07 18	07 33	07 48	.....	08 03	08 18	08 33	08 48	.....	09 03	09 18	09 33	09 48
Heathrow Terminals 1-2-3 d	05 08	05 23	05 38	05 53	.	06 08	06 23	06 38	06 53	.	07 08	07 23	07 38	07 53	.	08 08	08 23	08 38	08 53	.	09 08	09 23	09 38	09 53
London Paddington 15 ⊖ a	05 24	05 39	05 54	06 09	.....	06 24	06 39	06 54	07 09	.....	07 24	07 39	07 54	08 09	.....	08 24	08 39	08 54	09 09	.....	09 24	09 39	09 54	10 09

For general notes see front of timetable
For details of catering facilities see
Directory of Train Operators

Table 118

Sundays

3 February to 23 March

Heathrow Airport → London

Network Diagram - see first page of Table 116

		HX 1	HX 1		HX 1	HX 1	HX 1	HX 1		HX 1	HX 1	HX 1	HX 1		HX 1	HX 1	HX 1	HX 1		HX 1	HX 1	HX 1	HX 1		HX 1
Heathrow Terminal 4	✈ d	10 03	10 18		10 33	10 48	11 03	11 18		11 33	11 48	12 03	12 18		12 33	12 48	13 03	13 18		13 33	13 48	14 03	14 18		14 33
Heathrow Terminals 1-2-3	✈ d	10 08	10 23		10 38	10 53	11 08	11 23		11 38	11 53	12 08	12 23		12 38	12 53	13 08	13 23		13 38	13 53	14 08	14 23		14 38
London Paddington 15	⊖ a	10 24	10 39		10 54	11 10	11 24	11 39		11 54	12 09	12 24	12 39		12 54	13 09	13 24	13 39		13 54	14 09	14 24	14 39		14 54

		HX 1	HX 1	HX 1	HX 1		HX 1	HX 1	HX 1	HX 1		HX 1	HX 1	HX 1	HX 1		HX 1	HX 1	HX 1	HX 1		HX 1	HX 1	HX 1	HX 1
Heathrow Terminal 4	✈ d	14 48	15 03	15 18	15 33		15 48	16 03	16 18	16 33		16 48	17 03	17 18	17 33		17 48	18 03	18 18	18 33		18 48	19 03	19 18	19 33
Heathrow Terminals 1-2-3	✈ d	14 53	15 08	15 23	15 38		15 53	16 08	16 23	16 38		16 53	17 08	17 23	17 38		17 53	18 08	18 23	18 38		18 53	19 08	19 23	19 38
London Paddington 15	⊖ a	15 09	15 24	15 39	15 54		16 09	16 24	16 39	16 54		17 09	17 24	17 39	17 54		18 09	18 24	18 39	18 54		19 09	19 24	19 39	19 54

		HX 1	HX 1		HX 1	HX 1	HX 1	HX 1		HX 1	HX 1	HX 1	HX 1		HX 1	HX 1	HX 1	HX 1		HX 1	HX 1	HX 1			
Heathrow Terminal 4	✈ d	19 48	20 03		20 18	20 33	20 48	21 03		21 18	21 33	21 48	22 03		22 18	22 33	22 48	23 03		23 18	23 33	23 42			
Heathrow Terminals 1-2-3	✈ d	19 53	20 08		20 23	20 38	20 53	21 08		21 23	21 38	21 53	22 08		22 23	22 38	22 53	23 08		23 23	23 38	23 47			
London Paddington 15	⊖ a	20 09	20 25		20 39	20 54	21 09	21 24		21 39	21 54	22 09	22 24		22 41	22 54	23 09	23 27		23 39	23 54	00 03			

Sundays

from 30 March

		HX 1	HX 1	HX 1	HX 1		HX 1	HX 1	HX 1	HX 1		HX 1	HX 1	HX 1	HX 1		HX 1	HX 1	HX 1	HX 1		HX 1	HX 1	HX 1	HX 1
Heathrow Terminal 5	✈ d	05 03	05 18	05 33	05 48		06 03	06 18	06 33	06 48		07 03	07 18	07 33	07 48		08 03	08 18	08 33	08 48		09 03	09 18	09 33	09 48
Heathrow Terminal 4	✈ d	.	.	.	.		*05 53*	*06 07*	*06 22*	*06 40*		*06 53*	*07 07*	*07 22*	*07 40*		*07 53*	*08 07*	*08 22*	*08 40*		*08 53*	*09 07*	*09 22*	*09 40*
Heathrow Terminals 1-2-3	✈ d	05 08	05 23	05 38	05 53		06 08	06 23	06 38	06 53		07 08	07 23	07 38	07 53		08 08	08 23	08 38	08 53		09 08	09 23	09 38	09 53
London Paddington 15	⊖ a	05 24	05 39	05 54	06 09		06 24	06 39	06 54	07 09		07 24	07 39	07 54	08 09		08 24	08 39	08 54	09 09		09 24	09 41	09 54	10 09

		HX 1	HX 1		HX 1	HX 1	HX 1	HX 1		HX 1	HX 1	HX 1	HX 1		HX 1	HX 1	HX 1	HX 1		HX 1	HX 1	HX 1	HX 1		HX 1
Heathrow Terminal 5	✈ d	10 03	10 18		10 33	10 48	11 03	11 18		11 33	11 48	12 03	12 18		12 33	12 48	13 03	13 18		13 33	13 48	14 03	14 18		14 33
Heathrow Terminal 4	✈ d	*09 53*	*10 07*		*10 22*	*10 40*	*10 53*	*11 07*		*11 22*	*11 40*	*11 53*	*12 07*		*12 22*	*12 40*	*12 53*	*13 07*		*13 22*	*13 40*	*13 53*	*14 07*		*14 22*
Heathrow Terminals 1-2-3	✈ d	10 08	10 23		10 38	10 53	11 08	11 23		11 38	11 53	12 08	12 23		12 38	12 53	13 08	13 23		13 38	13 53	14 08	14 23		14 38
London Paddington 15	⊖ a	10 24	10 39		10 54	11 09	11 24	11 39		11 54	12 09	12 24	12 40		12 54	13 09	13 24	13 39		13 54	14 09	14 24	14 39		14 54

		HX 1	HX 1	HX 1	HX 1		HX 1	HX 1	HX 1	HX 1		HX 1	HX 1	HX 1	HX 1		HX 1	HX 1	HX 1	HX 1		HX 1	HX 1	HX 1	HX 1
Heathrow Terminal 5	✈ d	14 48	15 03	15 18	15 33		15 48	16 03	16 18	16 33		16 48	17 03	17 18	17 33		17 48	18 03	18 18	18 33		18 48	19 03	19 18	19 33
Heathrow Terminal 4	✈ d	*14 40*	*14 53*	*15 07*	*15 22*		*15 40*	*15 53*	*16 07*	*16 22*		*16 40*	*16 53*	*17 07*	*17 22*		*17 40*	*17 53*	*18 07*	*18 22*		*18 40*	*18 53*	*19 07*	*19 22*
Heathrow Terminals 1-2-3	✈ d	14 53	15 08	15 23	15 38		15 53	16 08	16 23	16 38		16 53	17 08	17 23	17 38		17 53	18 08	18 23	18 38		18 53	19 08	19 23	19 38
London Paddington 15	⊖ a	15 09	15 24	15 39	15 54		16 09	16 24	16 39	16 54		17 09	17 24	17 39	17 54		18 09	18 24	18 41	18 54		19 09	19 24	19 42	19 54

		HX 1	HX 1		HX 1	HX 1	HX 1	HX 1		HX 1	HX 1	HX 1	HX 1		HX 1	HX 1	HX 1	HX 1		HX 1	HX 1	HX 1			
Heathrow Terminal 5	✈ d	19 48	20 03		20 18	20 33	20 48	21 03		21 18	21 33	21 48	22 03		22 18	22 33	22 48	23 03		23 18	23 33	23 48			
Heathrow Terminal 4	✈ d	*19 40*	*19 53*		*20 07*	*20 22*	*20 40*	*20 53*		*21 07*	*21 22*	*21 40*	*21 53*		*22 07*	*22 22*	*22 40*	*22 53*		*23 07*	*23 22*	*23 40*			
Heathrow Terminals 1-2-3	✈ d	19 53	20 08		20 23	20 38	20 53	21 08		21 23	21 38	21 53	22 08		22 23	22 38	22 53	23 08		23 23	23 38	23 53			
London Paddington 15	⊖ a	20 09	20 24		20 42	20 54	21 09	21 24		21 41	21 54	22 10	22 24		22 39	22 54	23 09	23 24		23 39	23 54	00 09			

For general notes see front of timetable
For details of catering facilities see
Directory of Train Operators

Slough → Windsor & Eton

Network Diagram - see first page of Table 116

Mondays to Fridays

Miles		GW 1	GW 1	GW 1	GW 1	GW 1	GW 1	GW 1	GW 1	GW 1	GW 1	GW 1	GW 1		GW 1	GW 1	GW 1	GW 1	GW 1	GW 1	GW 1	GW 1	GW 1	GW 1	GW 1
—	London Paddington 15 ⊖ d	03 34	.....	05 48	06 07	06 15	06 48	.....	07 21	07 51	.....	08 21	08 51	.....	09 21	09 51	10 21	10 51	11 21	11 51	12 21	12 51	13 21	13 51	14 15
—	Reading 7 d	04 40	05 16	05 57	06 05	06 32	06 45	07 02	07 07	07 41	07 57	08 12	08 31	.	09 19	10 04	10 25	10 56	11 19	11 56	12 27	12 55	13 27	13 56	14 27
0	**Slough 3 d**	**05 38**	**05 58**	**06 18**	**06 37**	**06 55**	**07 13**	**07 31**	**07 55**	**08 13**	**08 31**	**08 55**	**09 13**	.....	**09 53**	**10 20**	**10 50**	**11 20**	**11 50**	**12 20**	**12 50**	**13 20**	**13 50**	**14 20**	**14 50**
2¾	**Windsor & Eton Central a**	**05 44**	**06 04**	**06 24**	**06 43**	**07 01**	**07 19**	**07 37**	**08 01**	**08 19**	**08 37**	**09 01**	**09 19**	.	**09 59**	**10 26**	**10 56**	**11 26**	**11 56**	**12 26**	**12 56**	**13 26**	**13 56**	**14 26**	**14 56**

	GW 1	GW 1	GW 1		GW 1	GW 1	GW 1	GW 1	GW 1	GW 1	GW 1	GW 1	GW 1	GW 1	GW 1	GW 1	GW 1	GW 1	GW 1	GW 1	GW 1	GW 1	GW 1		
London Paddington 15 ⊖ d	14 51	15 21	15 51	.....	16 21	16 30	16 45	17 14	17 17	17 44	18 14	18 17	18 51	19 21	19 51	20 00	20 19	20 51	21 00	21 30	21 48	22 21	22b48	.....	.....
Reading 7 d	14 57	15 27	15 56	.	16 04	16 34	16 56	17 18	17 34	.	18 04	18 34	18 56	19 04	19 34	20 04	20 19	20 34	20 56	21 26	21 34	22c11	22e50	.	.
Slough 3 d	**15 20**	**15 50**	**16 21**	.....	**16 42**	**17 00**	**17 21**	**17 40**	**17 58**	**18 16**	**18 40**	**18 58**	**19 16**	**19 42**	**20 10**	**20 33**	**20 51**	**21 10**	**21 33**	**21 57**	**22 20**	**22 50**	**23 21**	.....	.....
Windsor & Eton Central a	**15 26**	**15 56**	**16 27**	.	**16 48**	**17 06**	**17 27**	**17 46**	**18 04**	**18 22**	**18 46**	**19 04**	**19 22**	**19 48**	**20 16**	**20 39**	**20 57**	**21 16**	**21 39**	**22 03**	**22 26**	**22 56**	**23 27**	.	.

Saturdays

	GW 1	GW 1	GW 1		GW 1	GW 1	GW 1		GW 1	GW 1	GW 1		GW 1	GW 1	GW 1		GW 1	GW 1	GW 1		GW 1	GW 1	GW 1		GW 1
London Paddington 15 ⊖ d	05 45	06 15	06 51	.....	07 15	07 51	08 15	.....	08 51	09 15	09 51	.....	10 15	10 51	11 15	.....	11 51	12f18	12 45	.....	13 15	13 51	14 15	.....	14 51
Reading 7 d	05 49	06 19	06 57	.	07 26	07 49	08 19	.	08 49	09 28	09 49	.	10 23	10 49	11 26	.	11 49	12 27	12 49	.	13 28	13 49	14 27	.	14 49
Slough 3 d	**06 20**	**06 50**	**07 20**	.....	**07 50**	**08 20**	**08 50**	.....	**09 20**	**09 50**	**10 20**	.....	**10 50**	**11 20**	**11 50**	.....	**12 20**	**12 50**	**13 20**	.....	**13 50**	**14 20**	**14 50**	.....	**15 20**
Windsor & Eton Central a	**06 26**	**06 56**	**07 26**	.	**07 56**	**08 26**	**08 56**	.	**09 26**	**09 56**	**10 26**	.	**10 56**	**11 26**	**11 56**	.	**12 26**	**12 56**	**13 26**	.	**13 56**	**14 26**	**14 56**	.	**15 26**

	GW 1	GW 1	GW 1		GW 1	GW 1	GW 1		GW 1	GW 1	GW 1		GW 1	GW 1	GW 1		GW 1	GW 1	GW 1		GW 1	GW 1			
London Paddington 15 ⊖ d	15 15	15 51	16 15	.....	16 51	17 15	17 45	.....	18 21	18 45	19 15	.....	19 51	20 21	20 51	.....	21 15	21 51	22 32	.....	23 00	23 33	.....	.....	.....
Reading 7 d	15 27	15 49	16 27	.	16 49	17g27	17h49	.	18 27	18 49	19 27	.	19 49	20 34	20j55	.	21 25	21 54	22 33	.	22 45	23 25	.	.	.
Slough 3 d	**15 50**	**16 20**	**16 50**	.....	**17 20**	**17 50**	**18 20**	.....	**18 50**	**19 20**	**19 50**	.....	**20 20**	**20 50**	**21 20**	.....	**21 50**	**22 20**	**22 55**	.....	**23 21**	**23 55**	.....	.....	.....
Windsor & Eton Central a	**15 56**	**16 26**	**16 56**	.	**17 26**	**17 56**	**18 26**	.	**18 56**	**19 26**	**19 56**	.	**20 26**	**20 56**	**21 26**	.	**21 56**	**22 26**	**23 01**	.	**23 27**	**00 01**	.	.	.

Sundays

	GW 1	GW 1		GW 1	GW 1		GW 1	GW 1		GW 1	GW 1		GW 1	GW 1		GW 1	GW 1		GW 1	GW 1		GW 1	GW 1		GW 1
London Paddington 15 ⊖ d	07 43	08 16	.....	08 44	09 15	.....	09 44	10 15	.....	10 44	11 16	.....	11 44	12 16	.....	12 44	13 15	.....	13 44	14 15	.....	14 44	15 15	.....	15 44
Reading 7 d	07 22	08 22	.	08 52	09 18	.	09 52	10 18	.	10 52	11 18	.	11 52	12 25	.	12 52	13 24	.	13 52	14 25	.	14 52	15 18	.	15 52
Slough 3 d	**08 22**	**08 52**	.....	**09 22**	**09 52**	.....	**10 22**	**10 52**	.....	**11 22**	**11 52**	.....	**12 22**	**12 52**	.....	**13 22**	**13 52**	.....	**14 22**	**14 52**	.....	**15 22**	**15 52**	.....	**16 22**
Windsor & Eton Central a	**08 28**	**08 58**	.	**09 28**	**09 58**	.	**10 28**	**10 58**	.	**11 28**	**11 58**	.	**12 28**	**12 58**	.	**13 28**	**13 58**	.	**14 28**	**14 58**	.	**15 28**	**15 58**	.	**16 28**

	GW 1	GW 1		GW 1	GW 1		GW 1	GW 1		GW 1	GW 1		GW 1	GW 1		GW 1	GW 1		GW 1	GW 1					
London Paddington 15 ⊖ d	16 15	16 44	.....	17 15	17 44	.....	18 15	18 44	.....	19 15	19 44	.....	20 15	20 44	.....	21 15	21 45	.....	22 15	22 44	.....	.....	.....	.....	.....
Reading 7 d	16 25	16 52	.	17 24	17 52	.	18 25	18 46	.	19 18	19 52	.	20 25	20 48	.	21 24	21 46	.	22 24	22 52	.	.	.	.	.
Slough 3 d	**16 52**	**17 22**	.....	**17 52**	**18 22**	.....	**18 52**	**19 22**	.....	**19 52**	**20 22**	.....	**20 52**	**21 22**	.....	**21 52**	**22 22**	.....	**22 52**	**23 22**	.....	.....	.....	.....	.....
Windsor & Eton Central a	**16 58**	**17 28**	.	**17 58**	**18 28**	.	**18 58**	**19 28**	.	**19 58**	**20 28**	.	**20 58**	**21 28**	.	**21 58**	**22 28**	.	**22 58**	**23 28**	.	.	.	.	.

For general notes see front of timetable
For details of catering facilities see Directory of Train Operators

b Fridays dep. 2251
c Fridays dep. 2216
e Fridays dep. 2304
f From 29 March dep. 1215
g From 29 March dep. 1725. Until 26 January dep. 1732
h From 29 March dep. 1752

Connection times on Sundays may vary. Please cross-check with Table 117

Windsor & Eton → Slough

Network Diagram - see first page of Table 116

Mondays to Fridays

Miles			GW 1	GW 1	GW 1	GW 1	GW 1	GW 1	GW 1	GW 1	GW 1	GW 1	GW 1	GW 1		GW 1	GW 1	GW 1	GW 1	GW 1	GW 1	GW 1	GW 1	GW 1	GW 1	GW 1
0	Windsor & Eton Central	d	05 48	06 08	06 28	06 46	07 04	07 22	07 40	08 04	08 22	08 40	09 04	09 22	.....	10 02	10 30	11 00	11 30	12 00	12 30	13 00	13 30	14 00	14 30	15 00
2¾	Slough 3	a	05 54	06 14	06 34	06 52	07 10	07 28	07 46	08 10	08 28	08 46	09 10	09 28	.	10 08	10 36	11 06	11 36	12 06	12 36	13 06	13 36	14 06	14 36	15 06
—	Reading 7	a	*06 13*	*06 39*	*07 12*	*07 18*	*07 42*	*07 51*	*08 21*	*08 42*	*08 51*	*09 21*	.....	*09 51*	.....	*10 42*	*11 12*	*11 42*	*12 12*	*12 42*	*13 12*	*13 42*	*14 12*	*14 42*	*15 12*	*15 42*
—	London Paddington 15	a	*06 30*	.	*07 00*	*07 16*	*07 44*	*08 09*	*08 13*	*08 42*	*09 11*	*09 15*	*10 00*	*10 09*	.	*10 37*	*10 59*	*11 29*	*12 12*	*12 29*	*12 59*	*13 26*	*13 58*	*14 29*	*14 59*	*15 28*

		GW 1	GW 1	GW 1		GW 1	GW 1	GW 1	GW 1	GW 1	GW 1	GW 1	GW 1	GW 1	GW 1	GW 1	GW 1	GW 1	GW 1	GW 1	GW 1	GW 1	GW 1	GW 1		
Windsor & Eton Central	d	15 30	16 00	16 30	.....	16 51	17 10	17 30	17 49	18 07	18 28	18 49	19 07	19 26	19 53	20 20	20 42	21 00	21 20	21 44	22 08	22 30	23 00	23 32	.....	.....
Slough 3	a	15 36	16 06	16 36	.	16 57	17 16	17 36	17 55	18 13	18 34	18 55	19 13	19 32	19 59	20 26	20 48	21 06	21 26	21 50	22 14	22 36	23 06	23 38	.	.
Reading 7	a	*16 14*	*16 45*	*17 03*	.....	*17 43*	*17 59*	*18 18*	*18 26*	*18 46*	*19 16*	*19 21*	*19 46*	*19 51*	*20 21*	*20 52*	*21 21*	*21 42*	*21 51*	*22 17*	22b56	23c02	23e40	00f01	.....	.....
London Paddington 15	a	*15 59*	*16 27*	*16 59*	.	*17 27*	*17 53*	*17 58*	*18 42*	.	*18 58*	*19 29*	.	*19 59*	*20 28*	*21 12*	.	*21 27*	*21 58*	*22 30*	22g52	23h25	23j41	*00 16*	.	.

Saturdays

		GW 1	GW 1		GW 1	GW 1		GW 1	GW 1		GW 1	GW 1		GW 1	GW 1		GW 1	GW 1		GW 1	GW 1		GW 1	GW 1		GW 1
Windsor & Eton Central	d	06 30	07 00	.....	07 30	08 00	.....	08 30	09 00	.....	09 30	10 00	.....	10 30	11 00	.....	11 30	12 00	.....	12 30	13 00	.....	13 30	14 00	.....	14 30
Slough 3	a	06 36	07 06	.	07 36	08 06	.	08 36	09 06	.	09 36	10 06	.	10 36	11 06	.	11 36	12 06	.	12 36	13 06	.	13 36	14 06	.	14 36
Reading 7	a	*07 13*	*07 41*	.....	*08 11*	*08 41*	.....	*09 11*	*09 41*	.....	*10 11*	*10 41*	.....	*11 11*	*11 41*	.....	*12 11*	*12 41*	.....	*13 11*	*13 41*	.....	*14 11*	*14 41*	.....	*15 11*
London Paddington 15	a	*07 10*	*07 31*	.	*07 57*	*08 40*	.	*09 10*	*09 40*	.	*09 58*	*10 40*	.	*11 10*	*11 40*	.	*11 58*	*12 40*	.	*12 58*	*13 40*	.	*13 59*	*14 40*	.	*14 58*

		GW 1	GW 1		GW 1	GW 1		GW 1	GW 1		GW 1	GW 1		GW 1	GW 1		GW 1	GW 1	GW 1	GW 1	GW 1	GW 1	GW 1	GW 1		
Windsor & Eton Central	d	15 00	15 30	.....	16 00	16 30	.....	17 00	17 30	.....	18 00	18 30	.....	19 00	19 30	.....	20 00	20 30	21 00	21 30	22 00	22 30	23 04	23 32	.....	.....
Slough 3	a	15 06	15 36	.	16 06	16 36	.	17 06	17 36	.	18 06	18 36	.	19 06	19 36	.	20 06	20 36	21 06	21 36	22 06	22 36	23 10	23 38	.	.
Reading 7	a	*15 41*	*16 11*	.....	*16 41*	*17 11*	.....	*17 41*	*18 11*	.....	*18 41*	*19 11*	.....	*19 41*	*20 11*	.....	*20 41*	*21 11*	*21 41*	*22 11*	*22 43*	*23 06*	*23 33*	*00 07*	.....	.....
London Paddington 15	a	*15 40*	*15 58*	.	*16 40*	*16 58*	.	*17 40*	*17 59*	.	*18 40*	*18 58*	.	*19 40*	*19 58*	.	*20 40*	*21 06*	21k29	*21 58*	*22 28*	*23 07*	.	*00 06*	.	.

Sundays

		GW 1	GW 1		GW 1	GW 1		GW 1	GW 1		GW 1	GW 1		GW 1	GW 1		GW 1	GW 1		GW 1	GW 1		GW 1	GW 1		GW 1
Windsor & Eton Central	d	00 05	08 35	.....	09 05	09 35	.....	10 05	10 35	.....	11 05	11 35	.....	12 05	12 35	.....	13 05	13 35	.....	14 05	14 35	.....	15 05	15 35	.....	16 05
Slough 3	a	00 11	08 41	.	09 11	09 41	.	10 11	10 41	.	11 11	11 41	.	12 11	12 41	.	13 11	13 41	.	14 11	14 41	.	15 11	15 41	.	16 11
Reading 7	a	*00 42*	*09 09*	.....	*09 39*	*10 09*	.....	*10 39*	*11 09*	.....	*11 39*	*12 09*	.....	*12 39*	*13 09*	.....	*13 39*	*14 09*	.....	*14 39*	*15 09*	.....	*15 39*	*16 10*	.....	*16 39*
London Paddington 15	a	*01 02*	*09 20*	.	*09 43*	*10 23*	.	*10 49*	*11 16*	.	*11 49*	*12 20*	.	*12 49*	*13 04*	.	*13 49*	*14 08*	.	*14 49*	*15 04*	.	*15 49*	*16 20*	.	*16 49*

		GW 1	GW 1		GW 1	GW 1		GW 1	GW 1		GW 1	GW 1 A		GW 1 B	GW 1		GW 1	GW 1		GW 1	GW 1	GW 1	GW 1 A	GW 1 B		
Windsor & Eton Central	d	16 35	17 05	.....	17 35	18 05	.....	18 35	19 05	.....	19 35	20 05	.....	20 06	20 35	.....	21 05	21 35	.....	22 05	22 35	23 05	23 35	23 36	.....	.....
Slough 3	a	16 41	17 11	.	17 41	18 11	.	18 41	19 11	.	19 41	20 11	.	20 12	20 41	.	21 11	21 41	.	22 11	22 41	23 11	23 41	23 42	.	.
Reading 7	a	*17 10*	*17 39*	.....	*18 10*	*18 39*	.....	*19 10*	*19 39*	.....	*20 10*	*20 38*	.....	*20 39*	*21 10*	.....	*21 39*	*22 13*	.....	*22 40*	*23 10*	*23 43*	*00 10*	*00 10*	.....	.....
London Paddington 15	a	*17 04*	*17 49*	.	*18 08*	*18 49*	.	*19 04*	*19 52*	.	*20 16*	*21 08*	.	*20 49*	*21 20*	.	*21 44*	*22 18*	.	*23 05*	*23 22*	*23 49*	*00 40*	*00 20*	.	.

For general notes see front of timetable
For details of catering facilities see Directory of Train Operators

- A Until 27 January
- B From 3 February
- b Fridays arr. 2243
- c Fridays arr. 2255
- e Fridays arr. 2325
- f Fridays arr. 0018
- g Fridays arr. 2242
- h Fridays arr. 2315
- j Fridays arr. 2336

Connection times on Sundays may vary. Please cross-check with Table 117

Table 120

Mondays to Fridays

Maidenhead → Marlow

Network Diagram - see first page of Table 116

Miles			GW MX 1	GW 1	GW 1	GW 1	GW 1	GW 1	GW 1	GW 1	GW 1	GW 1	GW 1	GW 1	GW 1	GW 1	GW 1	GW 1	GW 1
—	London Paddington 15 ⊖	d		03 34	05 24		05b48		06 30		06b48		07 30		08b21	08b51	09b51	10b51	11b51
—	Reading 7	d		05 16	05 45		06 15		06 50		07 07		07 57		08 48	09 19	10 19	11 19	12 19
0	**Maidenhead 3**	d	23p48	05 49	06 08		06 40		07 12		07 42		08 15		09 05	09 37	10 37	11 37	12 37
1¼	Furze Platt	d	23p52	05 53	06 12		06 44		07 16		07 46		08 19		09 09	09 41	10 41	11 41	12 41
3	Cookham	d	23p55	05 56							07 49		08 22		09 12	09 44	10 44	11 44	12 44
4½	Bourne End 3	a	23p59	06 01	06 20		06 52		07 24		07 54		08 26		09 16	09 48	10 48	11 48	12 48
—		d	00 03	06 05		06 25		06 57		07 28		07 58		08 29		09 52	10 52	11 52	12 52
7¼	**Marlow**	a	00 11	06 13		06 32		07 04		07 35		08 04		08 36		10 00	11 00	12 00	13 00

		GW 1	GW 1	GW 1	GW 1	GW 1	GW 1	GW 1	GW 1	GW 1	GW 1	GW 1	GW 1	GW 1	GW 1	GW 1	GW 1	GW 1
London Paddington 15 ⊖	d	12b51	13b51	14b51	16 00	17 18	17 44		18 18		18 44		19 06		20 00	21 00	21c57	22 59
Reading 7	d	13 19	14 19	15 19	16 19	17 34	17 49		18 19		18 49		19 19		20 19	21 20	22e00	23 16
Maidenhead 3	d	13 37	14 37	15 37	16 42	17 52	18 15		18 47		19 15		19 44		20 42	21 42	22 45	23 48
Furze Platt	d	13 41	14 41	15 41	16 46	17 56	18 19		18 51		19 19		19 48		20 46	21 46	22 49	23 52
Cookham	d	13 44	14 44	15 44	16 49	17 59	18 23		18 54		19 23		19 51		20 49	21 49	22 52	23 55
Bourne End 3	a	13 48	14 48	15 48	16 53	18 03	18 28		18 58		19 28		19 55		20 53	21 53	22 56	23 59
	d	13 52	14 52	15 52	16 57	18 07		18 33		19 02		19 33		20 01	20 57	21 57	23 00	00 03
Marlow	a	14 00	15 00	16 00	17 05	18 15		18 40		19 09		19 40		20 08	21 05	22 05	23 08	00 11

Saturdays

		GW 1	GW 1	GW 1	GW 1	GW 1	GW 1	GW 1	GW 1	GW 1	GW 1	GW 1	GW 1	GW 1	GW 1	GW 1	GW 1	GW 1	GW 1	GW 1
London Paddington 15 ⊖	d		05 45	06b51	07b51	08b51	09b51	10b51	11b51	12 45	13b51	14b51	15b51	16b51	17 45	18 45	19b51	20b51	21b51	23b00
Reading 7	d		06 04	07 04	08 04	09 04	10 04	11 04	12 04	13 04	14 04	15 04	16 04	17 04	18 04	19 04	20 04	21 09	22 16	23 16
Maidenhead 3	d	23p48	06 33	07 33	08 33	09 33	10 33	11 33	12 33	13 33	14 33	15 33	16 33	17 33	18 33	19 33	20 33	21 33	22 33	23 33
Furze Platt	d	23p52	06 37	07 37	08 37	09 37	10 37	11 37	12 37	13 37	14 37	15 37	16 37	17 37	18 37	19 37	20 37	21 37	22 37	23 37
Cookham	d	23p55	06 40	07 40	08 40	09 40	10 40	11 40	12 40	13 40	14 40	15 40	16 40	17 40	18 40	19 40	20 40	21 40	22 40	23 40
Bourne End 3	a	23p59	06 44	07 44	08 44	09 44	10 44	11 44	12 44	13 44	14 44	15 44	16 44	17 44	18 44	19 44	20 44	21 44	22 44	23 44
	d	00 03	06 48	07 48	08 48	09 48	10 48	11 48	12 48	13 48	14 48	15 48	16 48	17 48	18 48	19 48	20 48	21 48	22 48	23 48
Marlow	a	00 11	06 55	07 55	08 55	09 55	10 55	11 55	12 55	13 55	14 55	15 55	16 55	17 55	18 55	19 55	20 55	21 55	22 55	23 55

Sundays

until 27 January

		GW 1	GW 1	GW 1	GW 1	GW 1	GW 1	GW 1	GW 1	GW 1	GW 1	GW 1	GW 1	GW 1
London Paddington 15 ⊖	d	08 44	09 44	10 44	11 44	12 44	13 44	14 44	15 44	16 44	17 44	18 44	19 44	20 44
Reading 7	d	09 18	10 18	11 18	12 18	13 18	14 18	15 18	16 18	17 18	18 18	19 18	20 18	21 24
Maidenhead 3	d	09 34	10 34	11 34	12 34	13 34	14 34	15 34	16 34	17 34	18 34	19 34	20 34	21 40
Furze Platt	d	09 38	10 38	11 38	12 38	13 38	14 38	15 38	16 38	17 38	18 38	19 38	20 38	21 44
Cookham	d	09 41	10 41	11 41	12 41	13 41	14 41	15 41	16 41	17 41	18 41	19 41	20 42	21 48
Bourne End 3	a	09 45	10 45	11 45	12 45	13 45	14 45	15 45	16 45	17 45	18 45	19 45	20 45	21 51
	d	09 49	10 49	11 49	12 49	13 49	14 49	15 49	16 49	17 49	18 49	19 49	20 49	21 55
Marlow	a	09 55	10 55	11 55	12 55	13 55	14 55	15 55	16 55	17 55	18 55	19 55	20 55	22 01

Sundays

from 3 February

		GW 1	GW 1	GW 1	GW 1	GW 1	GW 1	GW 1	GW 1	GW 1	GW 1	GW 1	GW 1	GW 1	GW 1
London Paddington 15 ⊖	d	08 44	09 44	10 44	11 44	12 44	13 44	14 44	15 44	16 44	17 44		18 44	19 44	20 44
Reading 7	d	08 52	09 52	10 52	11 52	12 52	13 52	14 52	15 52	16 52	18 18		19 18	20 18	21f22
Maidenhead 3	d	09 32	10 32	11 32	12 32	13 32	14 32	15 32	16 32	17 32	18 34	18 34	19 34	20 34	21 40
Furze Platt	d	09 36	10 36	11 36	12 36	13 36	14 36	15 36	16 36	17 36	18 38	18 38	19 38	20 38	21 44
Cookham	d	09 39	10 39	11 39	12 39	13 39	14 39	15 39	16 39	17 39	18 41	18 41	19 41	20 42	21 48
Bourne End 3	a	09 43	10 43	11 43	12 43	13 43	14 43	15 43	16 43	17 43	18 45	18 45	19 45	20 45	21 51
	d	09 48	10 48	11 48	12 48	13 48	14 48	15 48	16 48	17 48	18 49	18 49	19 49	20 49	21 55
Marlow	a	09 55	10 55	11 55	12 55	13 55	14 55	15 55	16 55	17 55	18 55	18 55	19 55	20 55	22 01

For general notes see front of timetable
For details of catering facilities see
Directory of Train Operators

b Change at Slough and Maidenhead
c Fridays dep. 2159
e Fridays dep. 2216
f From 30 March dep. 2108

Marlow → Maidenhead

Network Diagram - see first page of Table 116

Miles			GW 1	GW 1		GW 1	GW 1		GW 1	GW 1		GW 1	GW 1		GW 1	GW 1		GW 1	GW 1		GW 1	GW 1		GW 1	GW 1	GW 1
0	**Marlow**	d	00 13	06 14			06 46			07 18			07 46			08 18			08 38			10 06		11 06	12 06	13 06
2¾	Bourne End 3	a	00 20	06 21			06 53			07 25			07 53			08 25			08 45			10 13		11 13	12 13	13 13
—		d	00 24			06 24			06 56			07 28			07 56			08 28	08 49		09 19	10 16		11 17	12 17	13 17
4¼	Cookham	d	00 28			06 28			07 00			07 32			08 00			08 32	08 53		09 23	10 20		11 21	12 21	13 21
6	Furze Platt	d	00 31			06 31			07 03			07 35			08 03			08 35	08 56		09 26	10 23		11 24	12 24	13 24
7¼	**Maidenhead 3**	a	00 34			06 36			07 08			07 40			08 08			08 40	09 00		09 30	10 28		11 28	12 28	13 28
—	Reading 7	a	00b53			06 54			07 42			08 12			08 42			09 12	09 24		09 52	10 52		11 52	12 52	13 52
—	London Paddington 15 ⊖	a	01c24			07 08			07 44			08 13			08 42			09 15	09 27		10e09	11 12		12 12	13 12	14 12

		GW 1		GW 1	GW 1		GW 1	GW 1		GW 1	GW 1		GW 1	GW 1		GW 1	GW 1		GW 1	GW 1		GW 1	GW 1	GW 1		
Marlow	d	14 06		15 06	16 06		17 07	18 21			18 51			19 20			19 51			20 15		21 07	22 07	23 15		
Bourne End 3	a	14 13		15 13	16 13		17 14	18 28			18 58			19 27			19 58			20 22		21 14	22 14	23 22		
	d	14 17		15 17	16 17		17 18			18 31			19 01			19 30			20 11	20 26		21 18	22 18	23 26		
Cookham	d	14 21		15 21	16 21		17 22			18 35			19 05			19 34			20 15	20 30		21 22	22 22	23 30		
Furze Platt	d	14 24		15 24	16 24		17 25			18 38			19 08			19 37			20 18	20 33		21 25	22 25	23 33		
Maidenhead 3	a	14 28		15 28	16 28		17 29			18 42			19 12			19 41			20 25	20 37		21 29	22 29	23 37		
Reading 7	a	14 52		15 52	16 52		17 54			19 10			19 46			20 05			20 43	21 12		21 52	22f56	23 57		
London Paddington 15 ⊖	a	15 12		16 12	17 12		18 12			19e29			19e59			20e28			21 12	21e27		22 14	23g59	01h24		

Saturdays

		GW 1	GW 1	GW 1		GW 1	GW 1	GW 1		GW 1	GW 1	GW 1		GW 1	GW 1	GW 1		GW 1	GW 1	GW 1		GW 1	GW 1	GW 1		
Marlow	d	00 13	07 07	08 07		09 07	10 07	11 07		12 07	13 07	14 07		15 07	16 07	17 07		18 07	19 07	20 07		21 07	22 07	23 07		
Bourne End 3	a	00 20	07 14	08 14		09 14	10 14	11 14		12 14	13 14	14 14		15 14	16 14	17 14		18 14	19 14	20 14		21 14	22 14	23 14		
	d	00 23	07 18	08 18		09 18	10 18	11 18		12 18	13 18	14 18		15 18	16 18	17 18		18 18	19 18	20 18		21 18	22 18	23 18		
Cookham	d	00 27	07 22	08 22		09 22	10 22	11 22		12 22	13 22	14 22		15 22	16 22	17 22		18 22	19 22	20 22		21 22	22 22	23 22		
Furze Platt	d	00 31	07 25	08 25		09 25	10 25	11 25		12 25	13 25	14 25		15 25	16 25	17 25		18 25	19 25	20 25		21 25	22 25	23 25		
Maidenhead 3	a	00 35	07 29	08 29		09 29	10 29	11 29		12 29	13 29	14 29		15 29	16 29	17 29		18 29	19 29	20 29		21 29	22 29	23 29		
Reading 7	a	00 53	07 52	08 52		09 52	10 52	11 52		12 52	13 52	14 52		15 52	16 52	17 52		18 52	19 52	20 52		21 52	23j19	00 19		
London Paddington 15 ⊖	a	01 22	08 10	09 10		10 10	11 10	12 10		13 10	14 10	15 10		16 10	17 10	18 10		19 10	20 10	21e06		22 28	23 28	00 16		

Sundays

until 27 January

		GW 1		GW 1		GW 1		GW 1		GW 1		GW 1		GW 1		GW 1		GW 1		GW 1	GW 1	GW 1	GW 1	GW 1		
Marlow	d	00 07		09 58		10 58		11 58		12 58		13 58		14 58		15 58		16 58		17 58	18 58	19 58	20 58	22 03		
Bourne End 3	a	00 14		10 05		11 05		12 05		13 05		14 05		15 05		16 05		17 05		18 05	19 05	20 05	21 05	22 10		
	d	00 18		10 09		11 09		12 09		13 09		14 09		15 09		16 09		17 09		18 09	19 09	20 09	21 09	22 14		
Cookham	d	00 22		10 13		11 13		12 13		13 13		14 13		15 13		16 13		17 13		18 13	19 13	20 13	21 13	22 18		
Furze Platt	d	00 25		10 16		11 16		12 16		13 16		14 16		15 16		16 16		17 16		18 16	19 16	20 16	21 16	22 21		
Maidenhead 3	a	00 29		10 19		11 19		12 19		13 19		14 19		15 19		16 19		17 19		18 19	19 19	20 19	21 19	22 24		
Reading 7	a	01 06		10 38		11 37		12 38		13 38		14 38		15 38		16 38		17 38		18 38	19 38	20 38	21 38	23 10		
London Paddington 15 ⊖	a			11 12		12 12		13 11		14e08		15 11		16 11		17e07		18e08		19e08	20 11	21e08	22 18	23 18		

Sundays

from 3 February

		GW 1		GW 1		GW 1		GW 1		GW 1		GW 1		GW 1		GW 1		GW 1		GW 1	GW 1	GW 1	GW 1	GW 1		
Marlow	d	00 07		09 58		10 58		11 58		12 58		13 58		14 58		15 58		16 58		17 58	18 58	19 58	20 58	22 03		
Bourne End 3	a	00 14		10 05		11 05		12 05		13 05		14 05		15 05		16 05		17 05		18 05	19 05	20 05	21 05	22 10		
	d	00 18		10 09		11 09		12 09		13 09		14 09		15 09		16 09		17 09		18 09	19 09	20 09	21 09	22 14		
Cookham	d	00 22		10 13		11 13		12 13		13 13		14 13		15 13		16 13		17 13		18 13	19 13	20 13	21 13	22 18		
Furze Platt	d	00 25		10 16		11 16		12 16		13 16		14 16		15 16		16 16		17 16		18 16	19 16	20 17	21 16	22 21		
Maidenhead 3	a	00 28		10 19		11 19		12 19		13 19		14 19		15 19		16 19		17 19		18 19	19 19	20 20	21 19	22 24		
Reading 7	a	01 08		10 39		11 39		12 39		13 39		14 39		15 39		16 39		17 39		18 39	19 39	20 39	21 39	23 10		
London Paddington 15 ⊖	a			11k04		12m04		13 04		14 04		15 04		16n04		17 04		18q04		19 04	20r08	21 05	22t16	23 22		

For general notes see front of timetable
For details of catering facilities see Directory of Train Operators

- **b** Mondays arr. 0132
- **c** Mondays arr. 0118
- **e** Change at Maidenhead and Slough
- **f** Fridays arr. 2246
- **g** Mondays to Thursdays arr. 2341, change at Maidenhead and Slough
- **h** Fridays arr. 0122
- **j** 2 February to 22 March arr. 2252
- **k** From 30 March arr. 1103
- **m** From 30 March arr. 1203
- **n** From 30 March arr. 1603
- **q** From 30 March arr. 1803
- **r** From 30 March arr. 2003
- **t** From 30 March arr. 2207

Twyford → Henley-on-Thames

Network Diagram - see first page of Table 116

Mondays to Fridays

Miles			GW 1	GW 1	GW 1	GW 1	GW 1	GW 1	GW 1	GW 1	GW 1	GW 1	GW 1	GW 1	GW 1
—	London Paddington 15	⊖ d	03b34	05b24	06c07	06 30	07c21	07c51	08 30	09 00	10 00	11 00	12 00	13 00	14 00
—	Reading 7	d	05 33	06 14	06 36	07 07	08 06	08 31	09 04	09 34	10 34	11 34	12 34	13 34	14 34
0	**Twyford 3**	d	05 42	06 23	06 52	07 27	08 14	08 44	09 22	09 52	10 50	11 50	12 50	13 50	14 50
1¾	Wargrave	d	05 46	06 27	06 56	07 31	08 19	08 48	09 26	09 56	10 54	11 54	12 54	13 54	14 54
2¾	Shiplake	d	05 49	06 30	06 59	07 34	08 22	08 51	09 29	09 59	10 57	11 57	12 57	13 57	14 57
4½	**Henley-on-Thames**	a	05 54	06 35	07 04	07 39	08 26	08 56	09 34	10 04	11 02	12 02	13 02	14 02	15 02

		GW 1	GW 1	GW 1	GW 1	GW 1	GW 1	GW 1	GW 1	GW 1	GW 1	GW 1	GW 1
London Paddington 15	⊖ d	15 00	16 00	17 06	17e14	18 06	18f14	19 06	19c21	20 00	21 00	21g57	22h48
Reading 7	d	15 34	16 34	17 19	17 49	18 19	18 49	19 19	19 49	20 34	21 34	22j00	23 16
Twyford 3	d	15 50	16 50	17 30	17 58	18 30	18 58	19 36	20 08	20 50	21 50	22 52	23 37
Wargrave	d	15 54	16 54	17 34	18 03	18 34	19 03	19 41	20 12	20 54	21 54	22 56	23 41
Shiplake	d	15 57	16 57	17 37	18 07	18 37	19 07	19 44	20 15	20 57	21 57	22 59	23 44
Henley-on-Thames	a	16 02	17 02	17 42	18 12	18 42	19 12	19 49	20 20	21 02	22 02	23 04	23 49

Saturdays

		GW 1	GW 1	GW 1	GW 1	GW 1	GW 1	GW 1	GW 1	GW 1	GW 1	GW 1	GW 1	GW 1	GW 1	GW 1	GW 1	GW 1	GW 1
London Paddington 15	⊖ d	05 45	07 00	08 00	09 00	10 00	11 00	12 00	13 00	14 00	15 00	16 00	17 00	18 00	19 00	20 00	21 00	21k51	23c00
Reading 7	d	06 34	07 34	08 34	09 35	10 34	11 34	12 34	13 34	14 34	15 35	16 35	17 34	18 34	19 34	20 34	21 34	22 35	23 16
Twyford 3	d	06 50	07 50	08 50	09 50	10 50	11 50	12 50	13 50	14 50	15 50	16 50	17 50	18 50	19 50	20 50	21 50	22 50	23 50
Wargrave	d	06 54	07 54	08 54	09 54	10 54	11 54	12 54	13 54	14 54	15 54	16 54	17 54	18 54	19 54	20 54	21 54	22 54	23 54
Shiplake	d	06 57	07 57	08 57	09 57	10 57	11 57	12 57	13 57	14 57	15 57	16 57	17 57	18 57	19 57	20 57	21 57	22 57	23 57
Henley-on-Thames	a	07 02	08 02	09 02	10 02	11 02	12 02	13 02	14 02	15 02	16 02	17 02	18 02	19 02	20 02	21 02	22 02	23 02	00 02

Sundays

		GW 1	GW 1 A	GW 1	GW 1	GW 1	GW 1	GW 1	GW 1	GW 1	GW 1	GW 1	GW 1	GW 1	GW 1
London Paddington 15	⊖ d	08b44		09 44	10 44	11 44	12 44	13 44	14 44	15 44	16 44	17 44	18 44	19 44	20 44
Reading 7	d	09 30	09 30	10 18	11m18	12 18	13 18	14 18	15 18	16 18	17 18	18 18	19 18	20 18	21n24
Twyford 3	d	09 38	09 39	10 38	11 38	12 38	13 38	14 38	15 38	16 38	17 38	18 38	19 38	20 38	21 38
Wargrave	d	09 42	09 43	10 42	11 42	12 42	13 42	14 42	15 42	16 42	17 42	18 42	19 42	20 42	21 42
Shiplake	d	09 45	09 46	10 45	11 45	12 45	13 45	14 45	15 45	16 45	17 45	18 45	19 45	20 45	21 45
Henley-on-Thames	a	09 51	09 51	10 50	11 50	12 50	13 50	14 50	15 50	16 50	17 50	18 50	19 50	20 50	21 50

For general notes see front of timetable
For details of catering facilities see Directory of Train Operators

A From 3 February
b Change at Twyford
c Change at Slough and Twyford
e By changing at Twyford, passengers may depart at 1718
f By changing at Twyford, passengers may depart at 1818
g Fridays dep. 2159
h Change at Slough and Twyford. Fridays dep. 2251
j Fridays dep. 2216
k 2 February to 22 March dep. 2200
m 3 February to 23 March dep. 1122
n 3 February to 23 March dep. 2122. From 30 March dep. 2108

Henley-on-Thames → Twyford

Network Diagram - see first page of Table 116

Miles			GW	GW	GW	GW	GW	GW	GW	GW	GW	GW	GW	GW	GW
			MX												
			1	1	1	1	1	1	1	1	1	1	1	1	1
0	**Henley-on-Thames**	d	23p52	06 06	06 38	07 09	07 43	08 29	09 02	09 37	10 08	11 08	12 08	13 08	14 08
1¾	Shiplake	d	23p56	06 10	06 42	07 14	07 48	08 33	09 06	09 41	10 12	11 12	12 12	13 12	14 12
2¾	Wargrave	d	23p59	06 13	06 45	07 17	07 51	08 36	09 09	09 44	10 15	11 15	12 15	13 15	14 15
4½	**Twyford** 3	a	00 04	06 18	06 50	07 22	07 56	08 41	09 14	09 49	10 20	11 20	12 20	13 20	14 20
—	Reading 7	a	00 17	06 40	07 12	07 42	08 12	08 54	09 24	10 12	10 42	11 42	12 42	13 42	14 42
—	London Paddington 15 ⊖	a	01b24	07 00	07 27	07 54	08 27	09 27	10c09	10c37	11 12	12 12	13 12	14 12	15 12

		GW	GW	GW	GW	GW	GW	GW	GW	GW	GW	GW	GW	GW
		1	1	1	1	1	1	1	1	1	1	1	1	1
Henley-on-Thames	d	15 08	16 20	17 09	17 45	18 14	18 45	19 16	19 52	20 25	21 07	22 07	23 07	23 52
Shiplake	d	15 12	16 24	17 13	17 49	18 18	18 49	19 20	19 56	20 29	21 11	22 11	23 11	23 56
Wargrave	d	15 15	16 27	17 16	17 52	18 21	18 52	19 23	19 59	20 32	21 14	22 14	23 14	23 59
Twyford 3	a	15 20	16 32	17 21	17 57	18 26	18 57	19 30	20 04	20 37	21 19	22 19	23 19	00 04
Reading 7	a	15 42	16 45	17 35	18 15	18 46	19 10	19 46	20 25	20 52	21 42	22e39	23 40	00 17
London Paddington 15 ⊖	a	16 12	17c27	18 12	18c58	19c29	19c59	20c28	21 00	21c27	22 14	23f15	00 16	01g24

Saturdays

		GW	GW	GW	GW	GW	GW	GW	GW	GW	GW	GW	GW	GW	GW	GW	GW	GW	GW
		1	1	1	1	1	1	1	1	1	1	1	1	1	1	1	1	1	1
Henley-on-Thames	d	23p52	07 08	08 08	09 08	10 08	11 08	12 08	13 08	14 08	15 08	16 08	17 08	18 08	19 08	20 08	21 08	22 08	23 08
Shiplake	d	23p56	07 12	08 12	09 12	10 12	11 12	12 12	13 12	14 12	15 12	16 12	17 12	18 12	19 12	20 12	21 12	22 12	23 12
Wargrave	d	23p59	07 15	08 15	09 15	10 15	11 15	12 15	13 15	14 15	15 15	16 15	17 15	18 15	19 15	20 15	21 15	22 15	23 15
Twyford 3	a	00 04	07 20	08 20	09 20	10 20	11 20	12 20	13 20	14 20	15 20	16 20	17 20	18 20	19 20	20 20	21 20	22 20	23 20
Reading 7	a	00 17	07 41	08 41	09 41	10 41	11 41	12 41	13 41	14 41	15 41	16 41	17 41	18 41	19 41	20 41	21 41	22 43	23 43
London Paddington 15 ⊖	a	01b22	08 10	09 10	10 10	11 10	12 10	13 10	14 10	15 10	16 10	17 10	18 10	19 10	20 10	21c06	22 28	23 28	00 16

Sundays

		GW	GW	GW	GW	GW	GW	GW	GW	GW	GW	GW	GW	GW	GW
		1	1	1	1	1	1	1	1	1	1	1	1	1	1
Henley-on-Thames	d	00 08	10 03	11 03	12 03	13 03	14 03	15 03	16 03	17 03	18 03	19 03	20 03	21 03	22 03
Shiplake	d	00 12	10 07	11 07	12 07	13 07	14 07	15 07	16 07	17 07	18 07	19 07	20 07	21 07	22 07
Wargrave	d	00 15	10 10	11 10	12 10	13 10	14 10	15 10	16 10	17 10	18 10	19 10	20 10	21 10	22 10
Twyford 3	a	00 20	10 15	11 15	12 15	13 15	14 15	15 15	16 15	17 15	18 15	19 15	20 15	21 15	22 15
Reading 7	a	00 42	10h39	11j39	12k39	13m39	14n39	15q39	16r39	17t39	18v39	19w39	20y39	21z39	22A40
London Paddington 15 ⊖	a	.	11B12	12C20	13D18	14E18	15G20	16H20	17J20	18K20	19L20	20N20	21Q20	22U18	23V22

For general notes see front of timetable
For details of catering facilities see Directory of Train Operators

- **A** From 30 March arr. 2239
- **B** 3 February to 23 March arr. 1120. From 30 March arr. 1121
- **C** Until 27 January arr. 1212
- **D** Until 27 January arr. 1311
- **E** Until 27 January arr. 1408, change at Twyford and Slough
- **G** Until 27 January arr. 1511
- **H** Until 27 January arr. 1611
- **J** From 30 March arr. 1718. Until 27 January arr. 1707, change at Twyford and Slough
- **K** Until 27 January arr. 1808, change at Twyford and Slough
- **L** Until 27 January arr. 1908, change at Twyford and Slough
- **N** Until 27 January arr. 2011
- **Q** Until 27 January arr. 2108, change at Twyford and Slough
- **U** 3 February to 23 March arr. 2216. From 30 March arr. 2248
- **V** Until 27 January arr. 2318
- **b** Change at Twyford
- **c** Change at Twyford and Slough
- **e** Fridays arr. 2243
- **f** Mondays to Thursdays arr. 2341, change at Twyford and Slough
- **g** Change at Twyford. Fridays arr. 0122
- **h** Until 27 January arr. 1038
- **j** Until 27 January arr. 1137
- **k** Until 27 January arr. 1238
- **m** Until 27 January arr. 1338
- **n** Until 27 January arr. 1438
- **q** Until 27 January arr. 1538
- **r** Until 27 January arr. 1638
- **t** Until 27 January arr. 1738
- **v** Until 27 January arr. 1838
- **w** Until 27 January arr. 1938
- **y** Until 27 January arr. 2038
- **z** Until 27 January arr. 2138

Reading → Basingstoke

Network Diagram - see first page of Table 116

Mondays to Fridays

Miles			GW	GW	GW	GW	GW	XC	GW	GW	XC	GW	GW	XC	GW	GW	XC	GW	GW
			1	1	1	1	1	1 ◇	1	1	1 ◇	1	1	1 ◇	1	1	R 1	1	1
—	London Paddington 15 ⊖	d	03 34	05 27	05 48	06 30	07 00		07 21	08 00		08 30	09 05		09 30	10 05		10 30	11 05
0	**Reading 7**	d	05 37	06 07	06 39	07 07	07 39	07 45	08 07	08 39	08 45	09 07	09 39	09 45	10 07	10 39	10 45	11 07	11 39
1	Reading West	d	05 40	06 10	06 42	07 10	07 42		08 10	08 42		09 10	09 42		10 10	10 42		11 10	11 42
7¼	Mortimer	d	05 48	06 18	06 50	07 18	07 50		08 18	08 50		09 18	09 50		10 18	10 50		11 18	11 50
10½	Bramley (Hants)	d	05 53	06 23	06 55	07 23	07 55		08 23	08 55		09 23	09 55		10 23	10 55		11 23	11 55
15½	**Basingstoke**	a	06 01	06 31	07 03	07 31	08 03	08 08	08 31	09 03	09 08	09 31	10 03	10 08	10 32	11 03	11 08	11 31	12 03

		XC	GW	GW	XC	GW	GW	XC	GW	GW	XC	GW	GW	XC	GW	GW	XC	GW
		R 1	1	1	R 1	1	1	R 1	1	1	R 1	1	1	R 1	1	1	1 ◇	1
London Paddington 15 ⊖	d		11 30	12 05		12 30	13 05		13 30	14 05		14 30	15 05		15 30	16 05		16 30
Reading 7	d	11 45	12 07	12 39	12 45	13 07	13 39	13 45	14 07	14 39	14 45	15 07	15 39	15 45	16 07	16 39	16 45	17 07
Reading West	d		12 10	12 42		13 10	13 42		14 10	14 42		15 10	15 42		16 10	16 42		17 10
Mortimer	d		12 18	12 50		13 18	13 50		14 18	14 50		15 18	15 50		16 18	16 50		17 19
Bramley (Hants)	d		12 23	12 55		13 23	13 55		14 23	14 55		15 23	15 55		16 23	16 55		17 24
Basingstoke	a	12 08	12 31	13 03	13 08	13 31	14 03	14 08	14 31	15 03	15 08	15 31	16 03	16 08	16 32	17 03	17 08	17 32

		GW	XC	GW	GW	XC	GW	GW	XC	GW	GW	XC	GW	GW	XC	GW	XC	GW	GW
		1	R 1	1	1	R 1	1	1	R 1	1	1	R 1	1	1	R 1	1	1 ◇	1	1
London Paddington 15 ⊖	d	17 03	17 06	17 33	18 03	18 06	18 30	19 03		19 30	20 00		20 19	20 51		21 21	21 48	21b48	22c45
Reading 7	d	17 39	17 45	18 07	18 39	18 45	19 07	19 39	19 45	20 07	20 39	20 45	21 07	21 41	21 45	22 10	22 45	22 51	23 34
Reading West	d	17 42		18 10	18 42		19 10	19 42		20 10	20 42		21 10	21 44		22 13		22 54	23 37
Mortimer	d	17 50		18 18	18 50		19 18	19 50		20 18	20 50		21 18	21 52		22 21		23 02	23 45
Bramley (Hants)	d	17 55		18 23	18 55		19 23	19 55		20 23	20 55		21 23	21 57		22 26		23 07	23 50
Basingstoke	a	18 03	18 08	18 32	19 04	19 08	19 31	20 03	20 08	20 31	21 03	21 08	21 31	22 05	22 08	22 34	23 08	23 15	23 58

Saturdays

		GW	GW	GW	GW	GW	GW	GW	XC	GW	GW	XC	GW	GW	XC	GW	GW	XC
		1	1	1	1	1	1 A	1 B	1 ◇	1	1	1 ◇	1	1	1 ◇	1	1	1 ◇
London Paddington 15 ⊖	d	05 12	05 25	06e30	07f00	07 30	07 51	08 00	08g00	08h30	09 05		09 21	10j00		10k30	11 05	
Reading 7	d	06 07	06 39	07 07	07 39	08 07	08 36	08 39	08 45	09 07	09 39	09 45	10 07	10 39	10 45	11 07	11 39	11 45
Reading West	d	06 10	06 42	07 10	07 42	08 10	08 39	08 42		09 10	09 42		10 10	10 42		11 10	11 42	
Mortimer	d	06 18	06 50	07 18	07 50	08 18	08 47	08 50		09 18	09 50		10 18	10 50		11 18	11 50	
Bramley (Hants)	d	06 23	06 55	07 23	07 55	08 23	08 55	08 55		09 23	09 55		10 23	10 55		11 23	11 55	
Basingstoke	a	06 32	07 03	07 32	08 03	08 31	09 03	09 03	09 08	09 31	10 03	10 08	10 31	11 03	11 06	11 31	12 03	12 08

		GW	GW	XC	GW	GW	XC	GW	GW	XC	GW	GW	XC	GW	GW	XC	GW	GW
		1	1	1 ◇	1	1	1 ◇	1	1	1 ◇	1	1	1 ◇	1	1	1 ◇	1	1
London Paddington 15 ⊖	d	11m30	12 05		12n30	13 05		13q30			14r30	15t00		15v30	16 05		16w30	17y00
Reading 7	d	12 07	12 39	12 45	13 07	13 39	13 45	14 07	14 39	14 45	15 07	15 39	15 45	16 07	16 39	16 45	17 07	17 39
Reading West	d	12 10	12 42		13 10	13 42		14 10	14 42		15 10	15 42		16 10	16 42		17 10	17 42
Mortimer	d	12 18	12 50		13 18	13 50		14 18	14 50		15 18	15 50		16 18	16 50		17 18	17 50
Bramley (Hants)	d	12 23	12 55		13 23	13 55		14 23	14 55		15 23	15 55		16 23	16 55		17 23	17 55
Basingstoke	a	12 31	13 03	13 08	13 31	14 03	14 08	14 31	15 03	15 08	15 31	16 03	16 08	16 31	17 03	17 08	17 31	18 03

		XC	GW	GW	XC	GW	GW	XC	GW	GW	XC	GW	GW	XC	GW	GW	XC	GW
		1 ◇	1	1	1 ◇	1	1	1 ◇	1	1	1 ◇	1	1	1 ◇	1	1	1 ◇	1
London Paddington 15 ⊖	d		17 30	18 05		18 30	19 05		19z30	20 05		20C30	20 51		21 30	22D00		22 30
Reading 7	d	17 45	18 07	18 39	18 45	19 07	19 39	19 45	20 07	20 39	20 45	21 07	21 39	21 45	22 07	22 39	22 45	23 07
Reading West	d		18 10	18 42		19 10	19 42		20 10	20 42		21 10	21 42		22 10	22 42		23 10
Mortimer	d		18 18	18 50		19 18	19 50		20 18	20 50		21 18	21 50		22 18	22 50		23 18
Bramley (Hants)	d		18 23	18 55		19 23	19 55		20 23	20 55		21 23	21 55		22 23	22 55		23 23
Basingstoke	a	18 08	18 31	19 03	19 08	19 31	20 03	20 08	20 31	21 03	21 08	21 31	22 03	22 08	22 31	23 03	23 08	23 31

For general notes see front of timetable
For details of catering facilities see Directory of Train Operators

- A 2 February to 22 March
- B Until 26 January and from 29 March
- C Until 26 January dep. 2021
- D 2 February to 22 March dep. 2151
- b Fridays dep. 2215
- c Fridays dep. 2251
- e 2 February to 22 March dep. 0621
- f 2 February to 22 March dep. 0651
- g 2 February to 22 March dep. 0751
- h 2 February to 22 March dep. 0821
- j 2 February to 22 March dep. 0951
- k 2 February to 22 March dep. 1021
- m 2 February to 22 March dep. 1121
- n 2 February to 22 March dep. 1221
- q 2 February to 22 March dep. 1321
- r 2 February to 22 March dep. 1421
- t 2 February to 22 March dep. 1451
- v 2 February to 22 March dep. 1521
- w 2 February to 22 March dep. 1621
- y 2 February to 22 March dep. 1651
- z 2 February to 22 March dep. 1921

Table 122

Sundays

Reading → Basingstoke

Network Diagram - see first page of Table 116

		GW	GW		GW	GW		XC	GW		XC	GW		XC	GW		XC	GW		XC	GW		XC	GW		XC
		1	1		1	1		1 ◇ ☕	1		1 ◇ ☕	1		1 ◇ ☕	1		1 ◇ ☕	1		1 ◇ ☕	1		R 1 ☕	1		R 1 ☕
London Paddington 15 ... ⊖	d	.....	*06 43*	.....	*08b37*	*09c33*	.....	*10e03*	*10 42*	.....	*11f07*	*11 42*	.....	*12 03*	*12 42*	.....	*13 03*	*13 42*	.....	*14 03*	*14 42*	.....	*15 03*	*15 42*	.....	*16 03*
Reading 7	d	07 27	08 27	.	09 27	10 27	.	10 50	11 27	.	11 50	12 27	.	12 50	13 27	.	13 50	14 27	.	14 50	15 27	.	15 50	16 27	.	16 50
Reading West	d	07 30	08 30	.....	09 30	10 30	.....	.....	11 30	.....	.....	12 30	.....	.....	13 30	.....	.....	14 30	.....	.....	15 30	.....	.....	16 30	.....	.....
Mortimer	d	07 38	08 38	.	09 38	10 38	.	.	11 38	.	.	12 38	.	.	13 38	.	.	14 38	.	.	15 38	.	.	16 38	.	.
Bramley (Hants)	d	07 43	08 43	.....	09 43	10 43	.....	.....	11 43	.....	.....	12 43	.....	.....	13 43	.....	.....	14 43	.....	.....	15 43	.....	.....	16 43	.....	.....
Basingstoke	a	07 51	08 51	.	09 51	10 51	.	11 08	11 51	.	12 08	12 51	.	13 08	13 51	.	14 08	14 51	.	15 08	15 51	.	16 08	16 51	.	17 08

		GW	XC		GW	XC		GW	XC		GW	XC		GW	XC		GW	XC		GW						
		1	R 1 ☕		1	R 1 ☕		1	R 1		1	R 1		1	R 1		1	1 ◇		1						
London Paddington 15 ... ⊖	d	*16 42*	*17 03*	.....	*17 42*	*18 03*	.....	*18g42*	*19 03*	.....	*19 42*	*20 03*	.....	*20h42*	*21 03*	.....	*21j42*	*22k03*	.....	*22m42*	.....	.....	.....	.....	.....	.....
Reading 7	d	17 27	17 50	.	18 27	18 50	.	19 27	19 50	.	20 27	20 50	.	21 27	21 50	.	22 27	22 50	.	23 27	.	.	.	.	.	.
Reading West	d	17 30	.....	.....	18 30	.....	.....	19 30	.....	.....	20 30	.....	.....	21 30	.....	.....	22 30	.....	.....	23 30	.....	.....	.....	.....	.....	.....
Mortimer	d	17 38	.	.	18 38	.	.	19 38	.	.	20 38	.	.	21 38	.	.	22 38	.	.	23 38	.	.	.	.	.	.
Bramley (Hants)	d	17 43	.....	.....	18 43	.....	.....	19 43	.....	.....	20 43	.....	.....	21 43	.....	.....	22 43	.....	.....	23 43	.....	.....	.....	.....	.....	.....
Basingstoke	a	17 51	18 08	.	18 51	19 08	.	19 51	20 08	.	20 51	21 08	.	21 51	22 08	.	22 51	23 08	.	23 51	.	.	.	.	.	.

For general notes see front of timetable
For details of catering facilities see Directory of Train Operators

- **b** From 30 March dep. 0816
- **c** From 30 March dep. 0942
- **e** Until 27 January dep. 0957
- **f** From 3 February dep. 1100
- **g** From 30 March dep. 1837
- **h** From 30 March dep. 2030
- **j** From 30 March dep. 2130
- **k** 3 February to 23 March dep. 2145
- **m** From 30 March dep. 2237

Basingstoke → Reading

Network Diagram - see first page of Table 116

Mondays to Fridays

Miles			GW MO	GW MX	XC	GW	GW	XC	GW	GW	XC	GW	GW	XC	GW	GW	XC	GW	GW	XC	GW
			1	1	1 ◇ ☕	1	1	1 ◇ ☕	1	1	1 ◇ ☕	1	1	1 ◇ ☕	1	1	R 1 ☕	1	1	R 1 ☕	1
0	**Basingstoke**	d	23p57	00 02	05 47	06 07	06 37	06 47	07 07	07 37	07 47	08 07	08 37	08 47	09 07	09 37	09 47	10 07	10 37	10 47	11 07
5	Bramley (Hants)	d	00 04	00 09		06 14	06 44		07 14	07 44		08 14	08 44		09 14	09 44		10 14	10 44		11 14
8¼	Mortimer	d	00 09	00 14		06 19	06 49		07 19	07 49		08 19	08 49		09 19	09 49		10 19	10 49		11 19
14½	Reading West	d	00 17	00 22		06 27	06 57		07 27	07 57		08 27	08 57		09 27	09 57		10 27	10 57		11 27
15½	**Reading 7**	a	00 20	00 26	06 04	06 30	07 00	07 04	07 30	08 00	08 04	08 30	09 00	09 04	09 30	10 00	10 04	10 30	11 00	11 04	11 30
—	London Paddington 15	⊖ a		01 48	07 00	07 16		07 42	08 06	08 38	08 41	09 09	09 38	09 44	10 09	10 39	10 44	11 15	11 41	11 41	12 15

		GW	XC	GW	GW	XC	GW	GW	XC	GW	GW	XC	GW	GW	XC	GW	GW	XC	GW	GW
		1	R 1 ☕	1	1	R 1 ☕	1	1	R 1 ☕	1	1	R 1 ☕	1	1	R 1 ☕	1	1	R 1 ☕	1	1
Basingstoke	d	11 37	11 47	12 07	12 37	12 47	13 07	13 37	13 47	14 07	14 37	14 47	15 07	15 37	15 47	16 07	16 37	16 47	17 07	17 37
Bramley (Hants)	d	11 44		12 14	12 44		13 14	13 44		14 14	14 44		15 14	15 44		16 14	16 44		17 14	17 44
Mortimer	d	11 49		12 19	12 49		13 19	13 49		14 19	14 49		15 19	15 49		16 19	16 49		17 19	17 49
Reading West	d	11 57		12 27	12 57		13 27	13 57		14 27	14 57		15 27	15 57		16 27	16 57		17 27	17 57
Reading 7	a	12 00	12 04	12 31	13 00	13 04	13 30	14 00	14 04	14 30	15 00	15 04	15 31	16 00	16 04	16 30	17 00	17 04	17 30	18 00
London Paddington 15	⊖ a	12 39	12 42	13 15	13 42	13 42	14 15	14 39	14 42	15 15	15 42	15 42	16 15	16 39	16 44	17 15	17 42	17 42	18 15	18 39

		XC	GW	GW	XC	GW	GW	XC	GW	GW	XC	GW	GW	GW	GW	GW
		R 1 ☕	1	1	1 ◇ ☕	1	1	1 ◇ ☕	1	1	1 ◇	1	1	1	1	1
Basingstoke	d	17 47	18 07	18 37	18 47	19 07	19 37	19 47	20 07	20 37	20 47	21 10	21 40	22 20	22 55	23 30
Bramley (Hants)	d		18 14	18 44		19 14	19 44		20 14	20 44		21 17	21 47	22 27	23 02	23 37
Mortimer	d		18 19	18 49		19 19	19 49		20 19	20 49		21 22	21 52	22 32	23 07	23 42
Reading West	d		18 27	18 57		19 27	19 57		20 27	20 57		21 30	22 01	22 40	23 15	23 50
Reading 7	a	18 04	18 31	19 00	19 04	19 31	20 00	20 04	20 30	21 00	21 04	21 33	22 04	22 44	23 18	23 53
London Paddington 15	⊖ a	18 45	19 15		19 42	20 15	20 39	20 44	21 15		21 58	22 15	22b52	23c36	00 22	01e02

Saturdays

		GW	GW	XC	GW	GW	XC	GW	GW	XC	GW	GW	XC	GW	GW	XC	GW	GW
		1	1	1 ◇ ☕	1	1	1 ◇ ☕	1	1	1 ◇ ☕	1	1	1 ◇ ☕	1	1	1 ◇ ☕	1	1
Basingstoke	d	00 02	06 37	06 47	07 07	07 37	07 47	08 07	08 37	08 47	09 07	09 37	09 47	10 07	10 37	10 47	11 07	11 37
Bramley (Hants)	d	00 09	06 44		07 14	07 44		08 14	08 44		09 14	09 44		10 14	10 44		11 14	11 44
Mortimer	d	00 14	06 49		07 19	07 49		08 19	08 49		09 19	09 49		10 19	10 49		11 19	11 49
Reading West	d	00 22	06 57		07 27	07 57		08 27	08 57		09 27	09 57		10 27	10 57		11 27	11 57
Reading 7	a	00 26	07 00	07 04	07 31	08 00	08 04	08 31	09 00	09 04	09 31	10 00	10 04	10 31	11 00	11 04	11 31	12 00
London Paddington 15	⊖ a	01 48		07f53	08g14	08 40	08h45	09j15		09k44	10m06		10 52	11 15		11n42		

		XC	GW	GW	XC	GW	GW	XC	GW	GW	XC	GW	GW	XC	GW	GW	XC	GW
		1 ◇ ☕	1	1	1 ◇ ☕	1	1	1 ◇ ☕	1	1	1 ◇ ☕	1	1	1 ◇ ☕	1	1	1 ◇ ☕	1
Basingstoke	d	11 47	12 07	12 37	12 47	13 07	13 37	13 47	14 07	14 37	14 47	15 07	15 37	15 47	16 07	16 37	16 47	17 07
Bramley (Hants)	d		12 14	12 44		13 14	13 44		14 14	14 44		15 14	15 44		16 14	16 44		17 14
Mortimer	d		12 19	12 49		13 19	13 49		14 19	14 49		15 19	15 49		16 19	16 49		17 19
Reading West	d		12 27	12 57		13 27	13 57		14 27	14 57		15 27	15 57		16 27	16 57		17 27
Reading 7	a	12 04	12 31	13 00	13 04	13 31	14 00	14 04	14 31	15 00	15 04	15 31	16 00	16 04	16 31	17 00	17 04	17 31
London Paddington 15	⊖ a	12 52	13q15		13r42	14t25		14 53	15v15		15w42	16y15		16 52	17z15		17A42	18 19

		GW	XC	GW	GW	XC	GW	GW	XC	GW	GW	XC	GW	GW	GW	GW	GW	GW
		1	1 ◇ ☕	1	1	1 ◇ ☕	1	1	1 ◇ ☕	1	1	1 ◇	1	1	1	1	1	1
Basingstoke	d	17 37	17 47	18 07	18 37	18 47	19 07	19 37	19 47	20 07	20 37	20 47	21 07	21 37	22 07	22 37	23 07	23 37
Bramley (Hants)	d	17 44		18 14	18 44		19 14	19 44		20 14	20 44		21 14	21 44	22 14	22 44	23 14	23 44
Mortimer	d	17 49		18 19	18 49		19 19	19 49		20 19	20 49		21 19	21 49	22 19	22 49	23 19	23 49
Reading West	d	17 57		18 27	18 57		19 27	19 57		20 27	20 57		21 27	21 57	22 27	22 57	23 27	23 57
Reading 7	a	18 00	18 04	18 31	19 00	19 04	19 31	20 00	20 04	20 31	21 00	21 04	21 31	22 00	22 31	23 00	23 31	00 01
London Paddington 15	⊖ a	18B52	18 52	19C15		19D42	20E15		21G06	21 19		21 58	22H16	23 07	23J20	00 06	00 32	

For general notes see front of timetable
For details of catering facilities see Directory of Train Operators

- **A** 2 February to 22 March arr. 1753
- **B** From 29 March arr. 1838
- **C** 2 February to 22 March arr. 1940
- **D** 2 February to 22 March arr. 1952
- **E** 2 February to 22 March arr. 2021
- **G** From 29 March arr. 2058
- **H** 2 February to 22 March arr. 2222
- **J** Until 26 January arr. 2329
- **b** Fridays arr. 2242
- **c** Fridays arr. 2329
- **e** Fridays arr. 0054
- **f** Until 26 January arr. 0745
- **g** 2 February to 22 March arr. 0840
- **h** 2 February to 22 March arr. 0850
- **j** 2 February to 22 March arr. 0928
- **k** 2 February to 22 March arr. 0951
- **m** Until 26 January arr. 1010
- **n** 2 February to 22 March arr. 1152
- **q** 2 February to 22 March arr. 1323
- **r** 2 February to 22 March arr. 1351
- **t** 2 February to 22 March arr. 1419
- **v** 2 February to 22 March arr. 1523
- **w** 2 February to 22 March arr. 1552
- **y** 2 February to 22 March arr. 1622
- **z** 2 February to 22 March arr. 1723

Table 122

Sundays

Basingstoke → Reading

Network Diagram - see first page of Table 116

		GW	GW	XC	GW	XC	GW	XC	GW	XC	GW	GW	XC	GW	XC	GW	XC	GW
		1	1	1 ◇	1	1 ◇	1	R 1	1	R 1	1	1	R 1	1	R 1	1	R 1	1
											A	B						
				☕		☕		☕		☕			☕		☕		☕	
Basingstoke	d	07 57	08 57	09 47	09 57	10 47	10 57	11 47	11 57	12 47	12 57	12 57	13 47	13 57	14 47	14 57	15 47	15 57
Bramley (Hants)	d	08 04	09 04	.	10 04	.	11 04	.	12 04	.	13 04	13 04	.	14 04	.	15 04	.	16 04
Mortimer	d	08 09	09 09	.	10 09	.	11 09	.	12 09	.	13 09	13 09	.	14 09	.	15 09	.	16 09
Reading West	d	08 17	09 17	.	10 17	.	11 17	.	12 17	.	13 17	13 18	.	14 17	.	15 17	.	16 17
Reading 7	a	08 20	09 20	10 05	10 20	11 05	11 20	12 05	12 20	13 05	13 20	13 21	14 05	14 20	15 05	15 20	16 05	16 20
London Paddington 15 ⊖	a	*09 39*	.	*10b54*	*11c07*	*11e56*	.	*13 00*	*13f07*	*13 57*	*14 10*	*14 22*	*14g57*	*15h08*	*15j57*	*16k08*	*16m54*	.

		XC	GW	XC	GW	XC	GW	XC	GW	XC	GW	GW	XC	GW	GW	GW	GW
		R 1	1	R 1	1	1 ◇	1	1 ◇	1	1 ◇	1	1	1 ◇	1	1	1	1
											C	D					
		☕		☕		☕		☕									
Basingstoke	d	16 47	16 57	17 47	17 57	18 47	18 57	19 47	19 57	20 47	20 57	20 57	21 47	21 57	22 57	23 37	23 57
Bramley (Hants)	d	.	17 04	.	18 04	.	19 04	.	20 04	.	21 04	21 04	.	22 04	23 04	23 44	00 04
Mortimer	d	.	17 09	.	18 09	.	19 09	.	20 09	.	21 09	21 09	.	22 09	23 09	23 49	00 09
Reading West	d	.	17 17	.	18 17	.	19 17	.	20 17	.	21 17	21 19	.	22 17	23 17	23 58	00 17
Reading 7	a	17 05	17 20	18 05	18 20	19 05	19 20	20 05	20 20	21 05	21 20	21 22	22 05	22 20	23 20	00 01	00 20
London Paddington 15 ⊖	a	*17 58*	*18n21*	*18 59*	*19q10*	*19r58*	*20t16*	*20v56*	*21w16*	*21y59*	*22z23*	*22 30*	*23E01*	*23 23*	*00 17*	*01 18*	.

For general notes see front of timetable
For details of catering facilities see Directory of Train Operators

- **A** Until 27 January
- **B** From 3 February
- **C** Until 23 March
- **D** From 30 March
- **E** From 30 March arr.2307

- **b** From 3 February arr. 1104
- **c** From 3 February arr. 1113
- **e** 3 February to 23 March arr. 1204
- **f** From 3 February arr. 1326
- **g** From 30 March arr.1503
- **h** From 3 February arr. 1523
- **j** 3 February to 23 March arr. 1604
- **k** 3 February to 23 March arr. 1623
- **m** 3 February to 23 March arr. 1701

- **n** Until 27 January arr. 1810
- **q** From 3 February arr. 1925
- **r** From 3 February arr. 2003
- **t** From 3 February arr. 2026
- **v** 3 February to 23 March arr. 2100
- **w** From 3 February arr. 2125
- **y** Until 27 January arr. 2153
- **z** 3 February to 23 March arr. 2239

Network Diagram for Table 123

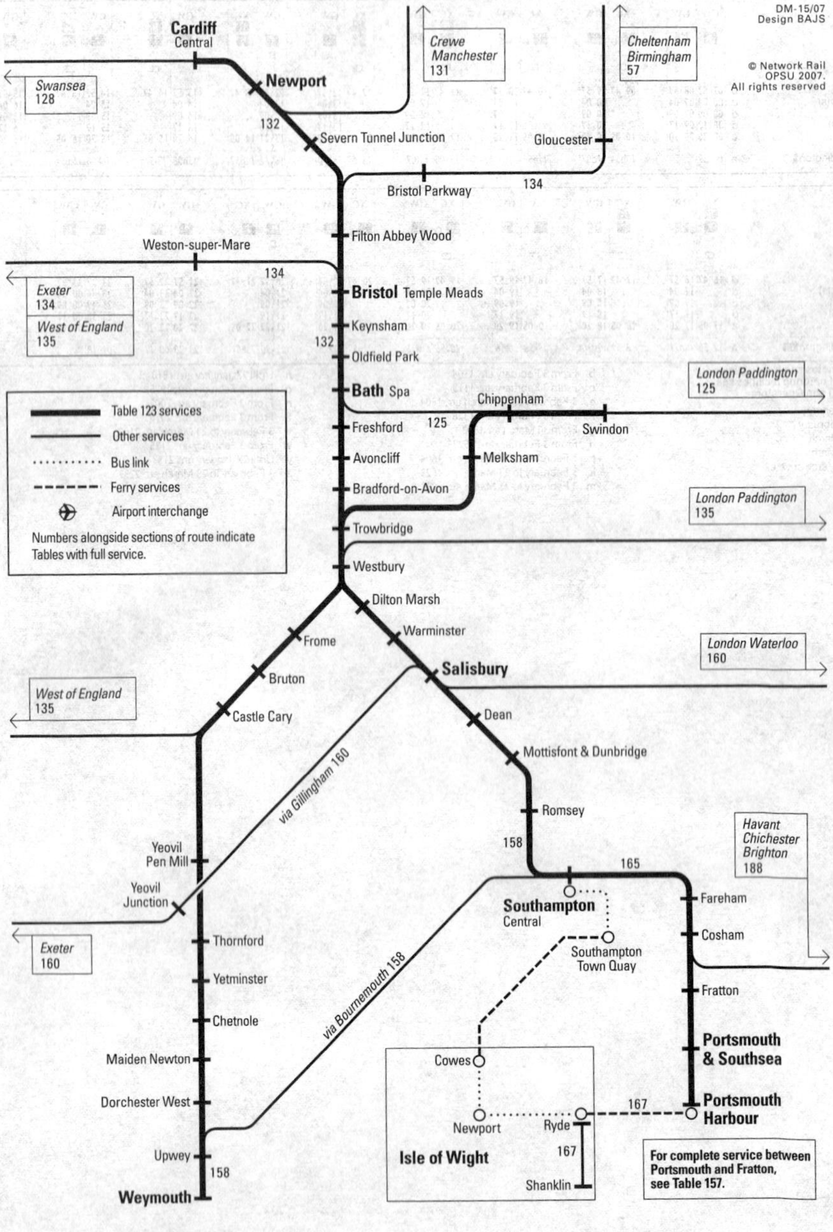

DM-15/07
Design BAJS
© Network Rail OPSU 2007. All rights reserved
Cardiff Central
Newport
Swansea 128
132
Severn Tunnel Junction
Crewe Manchester 131
Cheltenham Birmingham 57
Gloucester
Bristol Parkway
134
Filton Abbey Wood
Weston-super-Mare
134
Exeter 134
West of England 135
Bristol Temple Meads
Keynsham
132
Oldfield Park
Bath Spa
London Paddington 125
Chippenham
125
Swindon
Freshford
Avoncliff
Melksham
Bradford-on-Avon
London Paddington 135
Trowbridge
Westbury
Table 123 services
Other services
Bus link
Ferry services
Airport interchange
Numbers alongside sections of route indicate Tables with full service.
Dilton Marsh
Frome
Warminster
London Waterloo 160
Salisbury
Bruton
West of England 135
Castle Cary
Dean
Mottisfont & Dunbridge
via Gillingham 160
Romsey
Havant Chichester Brighton 188
158
165
Yeovil Pen Mill
Yeovil Junction
Southampton Central
Fareham
Cosham
Exeter 160
Southampton Town Quay
Thornford
Yetminster
Fratton
via Bournemouth 158
Chetnole
Portsmouth & Southsea
Maiden Newton
Cowes
Dorchester West
167
Portsmouth Harbour
Newport
Ryde
Upwey
158
Isle of Wight
167
Shanklin
Weymouth
For complete service between Portsmouth and Fratton, see Table 157.

South Wales and Bristol → Weymouth and Portsmouth

Network Diagram - see first page of Table 123

Miles	Miles	Miles			GW	GW	GW	GW	GW	GW	GW	GW	GW	GW	GW	GW	SW	GW	GW	GW	GW	GW	GW	GW
					MX				◇ ⊥	◇	A	B	◇ ⊥	C	◇ ⊥	◇ D	[1] ◇ E		[1] ◇ ⊥	◇ ⊥		◇ G	◇ ⊥	
—	—	—	Swansea [7]	d									05 24		06 29			06b59		07 29			08 29	
0	0	—	**Cardiff Central [7]**	d									06 30		07 30			08 00		08 30			09 30	
11¾	11¾	—	Newport (South Wales)	d									06 44		07 44			08 15		08 44			09 44	
21¾	21¾	—	Severn Tunnel Jn	d									06 55		07 55			08 25					09c25	
33¾	33¾	—	Filton Abbey Wood	d									07 09	07 28	08 09	08 27		08 50		09 09		09 22	10 09	
38¼	38¼	—	**Bristol Temple Meads [10]**	d	23p16				05 45			06 43	07 22	07 49	08 22	08 40	08 50	09 09		09 22		09 49	10 22	
42¾	42¾	—	Keynsham	d	23p23				05 52			06 50		07 56		08 47	08 57	09 16				09 56		
48¾	48¾	—	Oldfield Park	d	23p29				05 59			06 56		08 03		08 54		09 23				10 03		
—	—	—	London Paddington [15] ⊖	d									05 27	06 30		07 00			08 18	08 00		08 30	09 00	
—	—	0	Swindon	d							06 18		06 26	07 30		08 00				09 01		09 31	09 56	
—	—	16¾	Chippenham	d							06 34		06 40	07 44		08 15				09 15		09 45	10 10	
—	—	23	Melksham	d							06 43													
49¾	49¾	—	**Bath Spa [7]**	d	23p35				06 02			07 00	07 36	08 07	08 36	08 57	09 05	09 27		09 35		10 07	10 36	
56¾	56¾	—	Freshford	d	23p45				06 12			07 09		08 17		09 06						10 17		
57¾	57¾	—	Avoncliff	d	23e47				06x14			07x11		08x18		09x08						10x18		
59	59	—	Bradford-on-Avon	d	23p51				06 18			07 15	07 47	08 23	08 47	09 12	09 20	09 38				10 23	10 47	
62¼	62¼	28½	Trowbridge	d	23p57				06 25		06 53	07 21	07 53	08 29	08 53	09 18	09 27	09 44		09 50		10 29	10 53	
—	—	—	Plymouth	d									05 35			07f47				07 47				08 55
—	—	—	Exeter St Davids [6]	d						05f47	05g10		06 39			08f49				08 49				09 57
66¼	66¼	32½	**Westbury**	a	00 04				06 32		07 00	07 30	08 01	08 36	09 01	09 25	09 33	09 51	09 54	09 57		10 36	11 00	
—	—	—		d	00 04	05 26	05 49	06 25	06 35	06 39	07 03		08 01		09 01	09 28	09 39		09 54	09 58	10 08	10 36	11 01	11 07
—	72	—	Frome	d	00a15			06a35		06 48						09 38						10 46		
—	82½	—	Bruton	d						06 59						09 49						10 57		
—	86	—	Castle Cary	a						07 04						09 53			10 11			11 02		
—	—	—		d						07 04						09 54						11 03		
—	97¾	—	Yeovil Pen Mill	d						07 21						10 08						11 16		
—	101	—	Thornford	d						07x25						10x13								
—	102	—	Yetminster	d						07x28						10x16						11x22		
—	104	—	Chetnole	d						07x32						10x19								
—	110½	—	Maiden Newton	d						07 43						10 31						11 35		
—	118¼	—	Dorchester West	d						07 53						10 40						11h49		
—	122¾	—	Upwey	a						08 00						10 48						12 01		
—	125¼	—	**Weymouth**	a						08 05						10 55						12 06		
67¾	—	—	Dilton Marsh	d							07x07										10 11			11x09
71	—	—	Warminster	d		05 34	05 56		06 43		07 13		08 08		09 08		09 46			10 07	10a18		11 08	11 16
90¾	—	—	**Salisbury**	a		05 58	06 19		07 10		07 36		08 32		09 32		10 09			10 31			11 32	11 38
—	—	—		d			06 20		07 11		07 36		08 32		09 32					10 32			11 32	11 39
99¾	—	—	Dean	d																				
103½	—	—	Mottisfont & Dunbridge	d																				
107¼	—	—	Romsey	d			06 38		07 30		07 56		08 50		09 50					10 51			11 50	12j02
115½	—	—	**Southampton Central**	a			06 49		07 41		08 09		09 02		10 02					11 02			12 02	12 18
—	—	—	Bournemouth	a			07 45		08 42		09 11		10 00		11 00					12 00				13 00
130	—	—	Fareham	a			07 14		08 05		08 59		09 26		10 26					11 26			12 26	12 59
—	—	—		d			07 15		08 06				09 27		10 27					11 27			12 27	
135¾	—	—	Cosham	a			07 23		08 14		09 08		09 35		10 35					11 35			12 35	13 08
139½	—	—	Fratton	a			07 34		08 21		09 35		09 43		10 43					11 43			12 43	13 36
140½	—	—	Portsmouth & Southsea	a			07 38		08 24		09 40		09 47		10 47					11 47			12 47	13 40
141¼	—	—	**Portsmouth Harbour**	a			07 45		08 30				09 52		10 52					11 52			12 52	
—	—	—	Havant	a			07k46		08m40				09k51		10k51					11k51			12k50	
—	—	—	Chichester [4]	a			08k08		08m55				10k09		11k08					12k08			13k08	
—	—	—	Barnham	a			08k16		09m03				10k18		11k18					12k18			13k18	
—	—	—	Worthing [4]	a			08k56		09m25				10k54		11k54					12k54			13k54	
—	—	—	Shoreham-by-Sea	a			09k05		09m34				11k04		12k04					13k04			14k04	
—	—	—	Hove [2]	a			09k14		09m43				11k13		12k13					13k13			14k13	
—	—	—	Brighton [10]	a			09k19		09m48				11k18		12k18					13k18			14k18	

For general notes see front of timetable
For details of catering facilities see Directory of Train Operators

- **A** From Gloucester (Table 125)
- **B** From Taunton (Table 134)
- **C** From Bristol Parkway (Table 132)
- **D** From Worcester Shrub Hill (Table 57)
- **E** To London Waterloo (Table 160)
- **G** From Gloucester (Table 134)
- **b** Change at Cardiff Central and Bristol Temple Meads
- **c** Change at Bristol Temple Meads
- **e** Previous night.
- Stops on request, passengers wishing to alight must inform the guard and those wishing to join must give a hand signal to the driver
- **f** Change at Castle Cary
- **g** Change at Salisbury
- **h** Arr. 1144
- **j** Arr. 1158
- **k** Change at Fareham
- **m** Change at Fratton

South Wales and Bristol → Weymouth and Portsmouth

Network Diagram - see first page of Table 123

		GW	GW	GW		GW	GW	GW	GW	GW	GW	GW		GW	GW	GW	GW	GW	SW	GW		GW	GW	GW	GW	GW
			◇	■1 ◇		◇	◇	◇	■1 ◇	◇		◇			◇	◇	■1 ◇		■1 ◇	◇			◇		◇	■1 ◇
		A		B		C		A			C				A			C					A	D		
			☕	⊠			☕		☕	☕		☕				☕	🍴			☕					☕	☕
Swansea ■7	d		09 29				10 29			11 29		12 29				13 29				14 29				14b55		
Cardiff Central ■7	d		10 30				11 30			12 30		13 30				14 30				15 30				16c00	16 30	
Newport (South Wales)	d		10 44				11 44			12 44		13 44				14 44				15 44				16c15	16 44	
Severn Tunnel Jn	d		10c25				11c25			12c25		13c25				14c25				15c25			16 22	16c25	16 55	
Filton Abbey Wood	d	10 22	11 09			11 22	12 09	12 22		13 09	13 22	14 09			14 22	15 09		15 22		16 09			16 49	16 50	17 09	
Bristol Temple Meads ■10	d	10 49	11 22			11 49	12 22	12 39		13 22	13 49	14 22			14 49	15 22		15 43	15 52	16 22			16 56	17 07	17 22	
Keynsham	d	10 56				11 56		12 46			13 56				14 56			15 50					17 03	17 14		
Oldfield Park	d	11 03				12 03		12 53			14 03				15 03			15 57						17 21	17 32	
London Paddington ■15 ⊖	d	09 30	10 00	11 05		10 30	11 00		12 18	12 00	12 30	13 00			13 30	14 00	15 05			15 00				15 30		16 33
Swindon	d	10 31	10 56			11 31	11 56			12 56	13 31	13 56			14 31	14 56				15 56				16 31		
Chippenham	d	10 45	11 10			11 45	12 10			13 10	13 45	14 10			14 45	15 10				16 10				16 45		
Melksham	d																									
Bath Spa ■7	d	11 07	11 36			12 07	12 36	12 57		13 36	14 07	14 36			15 07	15 36		16 01	16 06	16 36			17 07	17 25	17 36	
Freshford	d	11 17				12 17		13 06			14 17				15 17			16 09					17 17	17 35		
Avoncliff	d	11x18				12x18		13x07			14x18				15x18			16x11					17x18	17x36		
Bradford-on-Avon	d	11 23	11 47			12 23	12 47	13 12		13 47	14 23	14 47			15 23	15 47		16 15	16 22	16 47			17 23	17 41		
Trowbridge	d	11 29	11 53			12 29	12 53	13 18		13 53	14 29	14 53			15 29	15 53		16 21	16 28	16 53			17 29	17 47	17 53	
Plymouth	d					10 45		10e45				12f25		12 55												
Exeter St Davids ■6	d		10g10			11 54		11 54		12g10		13g35		13 57		14g10										
Westbury	a	11 36	12 01	12 22		12 36	13 01	13 25	13 57	14 01	14 36	15 01			15 36	16 01	16 22	16 28	16 36	17 01			17 36	17 56	18 00	18 03
	d		12 01	12 22		12 37	13 01	13 27	13 58	14 01		15 01		15 08	15 36	16 01	16 22		16 39	17 01		17 08	17 38		18 01	18 03
Frome	d					12 46									15 46								17 47			
Bruton	d					12 58									15 57								17 59			
Castle Cary	a			12 40		13 03			14 15						16 01		16 40						18 03			18 21
	d					13 03									16 10								18 11			
Yeovil Pen Mill	d					13 17									16 23								18 24			
Thornford	d					13x22									16x27								18x28			
Yetminster	d					13x25									16x30								18x31			
Chetnole	d					13x29									16x34								18x35			
Maiden Newton	d					13 41									16 45								18 46			
Dorchester West	d					13 54									16 55								18 58			
Upwey	a					14 00									17 02								19 06			
Weymouth	a					14 09									17 07								19 13			
Dilton Marsh	d							13x29						15 11								17 11				
Warminster	d		12 08				13 08	13 36		14 08		15 08		15a18		16 08			16 47	17 08		17a18			18 08	
Salisbury	a		12 32				13 32	13 58		14 32		15 32				16 32			17 09	17 32					18 31	
	d		12 32				13 32	13 59		14 32		15 32				16 32				17 32					18 32	
Dean	d																									
Mottisfont & Dunbridge	d																									
Romsey	d		12 50				13 50	14 19		14 50		15 50				16 50				17 50					18 50	
Southampton Central	a		13 02				14 02	14 32		15 02		16 02				17 02				18 04					19 01	
Bournemouth	a		14 00				15 00	15 15		16 00		17 04				18 04				18 49						
Fareham	a		13 26				14 26	14 55		15 26		16 26				17 26				18 26					19 26	
	d		13 27				14 27	14 56		15 27		16 27				17 27				18 27					19 27	
Cosham	a		13 35				14 35	15 04		15 35		16 35				17 35				18 35					19 35	
Fratton	a		13 43				14 43	15 36		15 43		16 47				17 43				18 47					19 43	
Portsmouth & Southsea	a		13 47				14 47	15 40		15 47		16 51				17 47				18 51					19 48	
Portsmouth Harbour	a		13 52				14 52			15 52		16 57				17 52				18 57					19 52	
Havant	a		13h51				14h51	15 10		15h50		16h51				17h50				18h50						
Chichester ■4	a		14h08				15h08	15 21		16h08		17h09				18h08				19h05						
Barnham	a		14h18				15h18	15 29		16h18		17h18				18h18				19h14						
Worthing ■4	a		14h54					15 45		16h54		17h54				18h52				19h50						
Shoreham-by-Sea	a		15h04					15 56		17h04		18h04				19h02				20h02						
Hove ■2	a		15h13					16 07		17h13		18h13				19h14				20h13						
Brighton ■10	a		15h18					16 14		17h18		18h18				19h18				20h18						

For general notes see front of timetable
For details of catering facilities see Directory of Train Operators

A From Great Malvern (Table 71)
B **The Mayflower**
C From Gloucester (Table 134)
D From Bristol Parkway (Table 132)
b Change at Cardiff Central and Bristol Temple Meads
c Change at Bristol Temple Meads
e Change at Exeter St Davids and Westbury
f Change at Exeter St Davids and Salisbury
g Change at Salisbury
h Change at Fareham

South Wales and Bristol → Weymouth and Portsmouth

Network Diagram - see first page of Table 123

		GW	GW	GW	GW	GW	GW	GW	GW	GW	GW	GW	GW	GW	GW	GW	GW	GW	GW	SW	GW
		◇	1 ◇		1 ◇	◇			1 ◇	◇	1 ◇		◇	◇	1 ◇	◇	1 ◇	◇		1	
		A		B			C	D				A		E							
			🛒		🍴	🛒			🛒	🛒	🍴		🛒		🍴		🛒	🛒			
Swansea 7	d			15b55		16 29				17 29			18 29					19 29	19 55		20b55
Cardiff Central 7	d			17c00		17 30				18 30			19 30					20 30	21 00		22 00
Newport (South Wales)	d			17c15		17 44				18 44			19 44					20 44	21 14		22 17
Severn Tunnel Jn	d			17c25		17 55				18 54			19c25	20 22				20c21	21 24		22 33
Filton Abbey Wood	d	17 22		17 50		18 09		18 22		19 09		19 22	20 09	20 49		20 22		21 09	21 41		22 52
Bristol Temple Meads 10	d	17 49		18 07		18 22		18 49		19 22		19 49	20 22	20 56		20 49		21 22	22 00	22 25	23 16
Keynsham	d	17 56		18 14				18 56				19 56		21 03		20 56			22 08		23 23
Oldfield Park	d	18 03		18 21				19 03				20 03				21 03			22 15		23 29
London Paddington 15 ⊖	d		17 06	16 30	17 33		17 45	17 30	18 06		18 36	18 30			19 45		20 35	19 30	20 00	20 45	21 45
Swindon	d			17 31			18 45	18 31				19 31						20 26	21 01	21 46	22 52
Chippenham	d			17 45			19 01	18 45				19 45						20 40	21 15	22 00	23 13
Melksham	d						19 11														
Bath Spa 7	d	18 07		18 25		18 36		19 07		19 36		20 07	20 36	21 07		21 07		21 36	22 19	22 38	23 35
Freshford	d	18 17		18 35				19 17				20 17		21 17		21 17			22 27		23 45
Avoncliff	d	18x18		18x36				19x18				20x18		21x18		21x18			22x30		23x47
Bradford-on-Avon	d	18 23		18 41		18 47		19 23		19 47		20 23	20 47	21 23		21 23		21 47	22 33	22 51	23 51
Trowbridge	d	18 29		18 47		18 53	19 20	19 29		19 53		20 29	20 53	21 29		21 29		21 53	22 39	22 57	23 57
Plymouth	d					15e00			17 00				18e02								
Exeter St Davids 6	d					16f10			18 02	18f10			19f10					20f15			
Westbury	a	18 36	18 53	18 56	18 57	19 01	19 27	19 36	19 52	20 01	20 02	20 36	21 01	21 36	21 05	21 36	21 57	22 01	22 47	23 04	00 04
	d	18 36			18 58	19 01		19 37	19 54	20 01	20 03	20 36	21 01	21 36	21 06	21 36	21 58	22 01		23 04	00 04
Frome	d	18 46							20a03			20a47		21 46		21 46					00a15
Bruton	d	18 57												21 57		21 57					
Castle Cary	a	19 02			19 15						20 20			22 02	21 23	22 02	22 15				
	d	19 03												22 02		22 02					
Yeovil Pen Mill	d	19 16												22 15		22 15					
Thornford	d	19x21												22x20		22x20					
Yetminster	d	19x24												22x23		22x23					
Chetnole	d	19x28												22x26		22x26					
Maiden Newton	d	19 40												22 38		22 38					
Dorchester West	d	19 52												22 48		22 48					
Upwey	a	19 58												22 55		22 54					
Weymouth	a	20 06												23 02		23 02					
Dilton Marsh	d							19 40										22x04			
Warminster	d					19 08		19 46		20 08			21 08					22 08		23 11	
Salisbury	a					19 32		20 08		20 32			21 32					22 32		23 34	
	d					19 33		20 11		20 32			21 32					22 32			
Dean	d																				
Mottisfont & Dunbridge	d																				
Romsey	d					19 51		20 32		20 50			21 50					22 50			
Southampton Central	a					20 04		20 45		21 03			22 04					23 04			
Bournemouth	a					21 00				22 09			23 16					00 16			
Fareham	a					20 26				21 26			22 39					23 27			
	d					20 27				21 27			22 40					23 27			
Cosham	a					20 44				21 48			22g45					23 59			
Fratton	a					20 47				21 43			22 55					23 43			
Portsmouth & Southsea	a					20 51				21 47			23 00					23 47			
Portsmouth Harbour	a					20 57				21 52			23 04					23 52			
Havant	a					20h50				21h54			23h14								
Chichester 4	a					21h05				22h05			23h25								
Barnham	a					21h14				22h13			23h33								
Worthing 4	a					21h55				22j52											
Shoreham-by-Sea	a					22h05				23j02											
Hove 2	a					22h17				23j13											
Brighton 10	a					22h22				23j18											

For general notes see front of timetable
For details of catering facilities see Directory of Train Operators

A From Gloucester (Table 134)
B From Bristol Parkway (Table 132)
C From Cheltenham Spa (Table 125)
D From Worcester Foregate Street (Table 71)
E From Great Malvern (Table 71)
b Change at Cardiff Central and Bristol Temple Meads
c Change at Bristol Temple Meads
e Change at Exeter St Davids and Salisbury
f Change at Salisbury
g Change at Southampton Central
h Change at Fareham
j Change at Fratton

Saturdays

until 26 January

South Wales and Bristol → Weymouth and Portsmouth

Network Diagram - see first page of Table 123

		GW	GW ◇	GW ◇	GW	GW A	GW ◇	GW	GW ◇	GW B	SW 1 ◇ C	GW 1 ◇	GW ◇	GW	GW D	GW ◇	GW	GW E
Swansea 7	d					04 00	04 59		06 29				07 29			08 29		
Cardiff Central 7	d					04 55	06 30		07 30				08 30			09 30		
Newport (South Wales)	d					05 09	06 44		07 44				08 44			09 44		
Severn Tunnel Jn	d						06 55		07 55				08b25			09b25		
Filton Abbey Wood	d						07 10		08 10	08 23			09 09		09 23	10 09		10 22
Bristol Temple Meads 10	d	23p16		05 45		06 43	07 24	07 49	08 24	08 40	08 50		09 24		09 49	10 24		10 49
Keynsham	d	23p23		05 52		06 50		07 56		08 47	08 57				09 56			10 56
Oldfield Park	d	23p29		05 59		06 56		08 02		08 54					10 03			11 03
London Paddington 15 ⊖	d								07 00			08 18	08 00		08 30	09 00		
Swindon	d								07 56				08 56		09 31	09 56		
Chippenham	d								08 10				09 10		09 45	10 10		
Melksham	d																	
Bath Spa 7	d	23p35		06 02		07 00	07 37	08 06	08 37	08 57	09 05		09 37		10 07	10 37		11 07
Freshford	d	23p45		06 12		07 09		08 15		09 06					10 16			11 15
Avoncliff	d	23c47		06x14		07x11		08x17		09x08					10x19			11x18
Bradford-on-Avon	d	23p51		06 18		07 15	07 48	08 21	08 48	09 12	09 20		09 48		10 22	10 48		11 21
Trowbridge	d	23p57		06 24		07 21	07 54	08 27	08 54	09 18	09 27		09 54		10 28	10 54		11 27
Plymouth	d									07e54			06f55					
Exeter St Davids 6	d			05g10					06g41	08e56			08g25					
Westbury	a	00 04		06 31		07 28	08 01	08 34	09 01	09 25	09 33	09 54	10 01		10 34	11 01		11 34
	d	00 04	06 36	06 39	07 03		08 02		09 02	09 28	09 39	09 56	10 02	10 08	10 35	11 02	11 07	
Frome	d	00a15	06 45							09 38					10 45			
Bruton	d		06 57							09 49					10 57			
Castle Cary	a		07 02							09 53		10 12			11 02			
	d		07 02							09 54					11 02			
Yeovil Pen Mill	d		07 16							10 08					11 16			
Thornford	d		07x21							10x13					11x20			
Yetminster	d		07x24							10x16					11x23			
Chetnole	d		07x28							10x19					11x27			
Maiden Newton	d		07 39							10 31					11 41			
Dorchester West	d		07 49							10 38					11h56			
Upwey	a		07 55							10 48					12 02			
Weymouth	a		08 01							10 54					12 08			
Dilton Marsh	d				07x06									10x10			11x10	
Warminster	d			06 46	07 13		08 09		09 09		09 46		10 09	10a16		11 09	11 16	
Salisbury	a			07 15	07 35		08 32		09 32		10 09		10 31			11 32	11 38	
	d			07 24	07 37		08 33		09 33				10 32			11 33	11 39	
Dean	d																	
Mottisfont & Dunbridge	d																	
Romsey	d			07 44	07 56		08 51		09 51				10 50			11 51	12 02	
Southampton Central	a			08 02	08 07		09 02		10 02				11 02			12 02	12 18	
Bournemouth	a				09 10		10 00		11 00				12 00				13 00	
Fareham	a			08 26	08 59		09 26		10 26				11 26			12 26	12 59	
	d			08 26			09 26		10 26				11 26			12 26		
Cosham	a			08 34	09 08		09 34		10 34				11 34			12 34	13 08	
Fratton	a			08 41	09 36		09 41		10 41				11 41			12 41	13 36	
Portsmouth & Southsea	a			08 45	09 40		09 45		10 45				11 45			12 45	13 40	
Portsmouth Harbour	a			08 49			09 49		10 49				11 49			12 49		
Havant	a			08j50			09j50		10j50				11j50			12j50		
Chichester 4	a			09j08			10j08		11j08				12j08			13j08		
Barnham	a			09j18			10j18		11j18				12j18			13j18		
Worthing 4	a			09j54			10j54		11j54				12j54			13j54		
Shoreham-by-Sea	a			10j04			11j04		12j04				13j04			14j04		
Hove 2	a			10j13			11j13		12j13				13j13			14j13		
Brighton 10	a			10j18			11j18		12j18				13j18			14j18		

For general notes see front of timetable
For details of catering facilities see Directory of Train Operators

A From Taunton (Table 134)
B From Worcester Shrub Hill (Table 57)
C To London Waterloo (Table 160)
D From Gloucester (Table 134)
E From Great Malvern (Table 71)
b Change at Bristol Temple Meads
c Previous night.
Stops on request, passengers wishing to alight must inform the guard and those wishing to join must give a hand signal to the driver
e Change at Castle Cary
f Change at Exeter St Davids and Salisbury
g Change at Salisbury
h Arr. 1151
j Change at Fareham

Table 123

Saturdays

until 26 January

South Wales and Bristol → Weymouth and Portsmouth

Network Diagram - see first page of Table 123

		GW	GW	GW	GW	GW	SW	GW	GW	GW	GW	GW	GW	GW	GW	SW	GW	GW
		◇	1 ◇	◇	◇		1 ◇	1 ◇	◇		◇		◇	◇		1 ◇	◇	
				A		B	C			A			B		A			
		🍴	☕		🍴			☕	🍴		🍴		🍴	🍴			🍴	
Swansea 7	d	09 29			10 29				11 29		12 29			13 29			13 55	
Cardiff Central 7	d	10 30			11 30				12 30		13 30			14 30			15 30	
Newport (South Wales)	d	10 44			11 44				12 44		13 44			14 44			15 44	
Severn Tunnel Jn	d	10b25			11b25				12b25		13b26						15b25	
Filton Abbey Wood	d	11 09		11 23	12 09	12 22			13 09	13 23	14 09		14 23	15 09	15 23		16 09	
Bristol Temple Meads 10	d	11 24		11 49	12 24	12 39	13 10		13 24	13 49	14 24		14 49	15 24	15 43	15 52	16 24	
Keynsham	d			11 56		12 46				13 56			14 56		15 50			
Oldfield Park	d			12 03		12 53				14 03			15 03		15 57			
London Paddington 15 ⊖	d	10 00	11 05	10 30	11 00			12 18	12 00		13 00		13 30	14 00			15 00	
Swindon	d	10 56		11 31	11 56				12 56		13 56		14 31	14 56			15 56	
Chippenham	d	11 10		11 45	12 10				13 10		14 10		14 45	15 10			16 10	
Melksham	d																	
Bath Spa 7	d	11 37		12 07	12 37	12 56	13 22		13 37	14 07	14 37		15 07	15 37	16 01	16 04	16 37	
Freshford	d			12 16						14 16			15 15		16 10			
Avoncliff	d			12x19						14x19			15x18		16x13			
Bradford-on-Avon	d	11 48		12 22	12 48	13 08			13 48	14 22	14 48		15 21	15 48	16 16	16 20	16 48	
Trowbridge	d	11 54		12 28	12 54	13 15	13 35		13 54	14 28	14 54		15 27	15 54	16 22	16 26	16 54	
Plymouth	d	08c25			09c25	10e46					12c25	12 55	12f55					
Exeter St Davids 6	d	10g10			11g08	12 07			12g10		13g35	13 57	13f57	14g10				
Westbury	a	12 01	12 22	12 35	13 01	13 22	13 48	13 54	14 01	14 35	15 01		15 34	16 01	16 29	16 36	17 01	
	d	12 02	12 22	12 36	13 02	13 27	13 53	13 55	14 02		15 02	15 08	15 35	16 02		16 39	17 02	17 08
Frome	d			12 48									15 44					
Bruton	d			12 59									15 55					
Castle Cary	a		12 40	13 04				14 12					16 00					
	d			13 05									16 13					
Yeovil Pen Mill	d			13 18									16 26					
Thornford	d			13x23														
Yetminster	d			13x26									16x31					
Chetnole	d			13x30														
Maiden Newton	d			13 42									16 44					
Dorchester West	d			13 55									16 54					
Upwey	a			14 02														
Weymouth	a			14 08									17 07					
Dilton Marsh	d					13x30						15 11						17 11
Warminster	d	12 09			13 09	13 36	14 00		14 09		15 09	15a17		16 09		16 47	17 09	17a17
Salisbury	a	12 32			13 32	13 58	14 24		14 32		15 32			16 32		17 09	17 32	
	d	12 33			13 33	13 59			14 33		15 33			16 33			17 33	
Dean	d																	
Mottisfont & Dunbridge	d																	
Romsey	d	12 51			13 51	14 19			14 51		15 51			16 51			17 51	
Southampton Central	a	13 02			14 02	14 32			15 02		16 02			17 02			18 02	
Bournemouth	a	14 00			15 00	15 15			16 00		17 00			18 00			19 00	
Fareham	a	13 26			14 26	14 55			15 26		16 26			17 26			18 26	
	d	13 26			14 26	14 56			15 26		16 26			17 26			18 26	
Cosham	a	13 34			14 34	15 04			15 34		16 34			17 34			18 34	
Fratton	a	13 41			14 41	15 36			15 41		16 41			17 41			18 42	
Portsmouth & Southsea	a	13 45			14 45	15 40			15 45		16 45			17 45			18 46	
Portsmouth Harbour	a	13 49			14 49				15 49		16 49			17 49			18 49	
Havant	a	13h50			14h50	15 11			15h50		16h50			17h50			18h50	
Chichester 4	a	14h08			15h08	15 22			16h08		17h08			18h08			19h05	
Barnham	a	14h18			15h18	15 30			16h18		17h18			18h18			19h14	
Worthing 4	a	14h54				15 45			16h54		17h54			18h54			19h54	
Shoreham-by-Sea	a	15h04				15 56			17h04		18h04			19h04			20h04	
Hove 2	a	15h13				16 07			17h13		18h13			19h13			20h15	
Brighton 10	a	15h18				16 14			17h18		18h18			19h18			20h20	

For general notes see front of timetable
For details of catering facilities see Directory of Train Operators

- A From Gloucester (Table 134)
- B From Great Malvern (Table 71)
- C To London Waterloo (Table 160)
- b Change at Bristol Temple Meads
- c Change at Exeter St Davids and Salisbury
- e Change at Exeter St Davids and Westbury
- f Change at Castle Cary
- g Change at Salisbury
- h Change at Fareham

Table 123

until 26 January

South Wales and Bristol → Weymouth and Portsmouth

Network Diagram - see first page of Table 123

		GW	GW	GW	GW	GW	GW	GW	GW	GW	GW	GW	GW	GW	GW	GW	GW	SW	GW
		◇ A	◇	1 ◇	◇ B	◇		C	◇	1 ◇	B	◇	1 ◇	◇ D	E	◇		1	
Swansea 7	d		15 29			16 29			17 29			18 29				19 29		19b55	20b55
Cardiff Central 7	d		16 30			17 30			18 30			19 30				20 30		21 00	22 00
Newport (South Wales)	d		16 44			17 44			18 44			19 44				20 44		21 15	22 16
Severn Tunnel Jn	d		16 55			17 55			18c25			19c25				20c15		21 25	22 33
Filton Abbey Wood	d	16 23	17 10		17 23	18 10		18 22	19 09		19 22	20 09		20 23		21 09		21 42	22 52
Bristol Temple Meads 10	d	16 49	17 24		17 49	18 24		18 49	19 24		19 49	20 24		20 49		21 24	21 51	22 23	23 10
Keynsham	d	16 56			17 56			18 56			19 56			20 56			21 58		23 17
Oldfield Park	d	17 02			18 03			19 03			20 03			21 02			22 04		23 23
London Paddington 15 ⊖	d	15 30		17 05	16 30	17 00		17 30	18 00	19 05	18 30	19 00	20 05	19 30	20 00	20 00		20 00	21 30
Swindon	d	16 31			17 31	17 56		18 31	18 56		19 31	19 56		20 31	21 08	21 01		21 01	22 31
Chippenham	d	16 45			17 45	18 10		18 45	19 10		19 45	20 10		20 45	21 24	21 15		21 15	22 45
Melksham	d														21 34				
Bath Spa 7	d	17 07	17 37		18 07	18 37		19 07	19 37		20 07	20 37		21 07		21 37	22 07	22 36	23 27
Freshford	d	17 15			18 16			19 15			20 16			21 15			22 17		23 36
Avoncliff	d	17x18			18x19			19x17			20x18			21x18			22x18		23x38
Bradford-on-Avon	d	17 21	17 48		18 22	18 48		19 21	19 48		20 22	20 48		21 21		21 48	22 23	22 47	23 42
Trowbridge	d	17 27	17 54		18 28	18 54		19 27	19 54		20 28	20 54		21 27	21 43	21 54	22 29	22 53	23 48
Plymouth	d		15e04		16f54	16 54					17 54					18e25			
Exeter St Davids 6	d		16g10		17f53	17 53			18g10		18 56	19g10				20g15			
Westbury	a	17 34	18 01	18 22	18 35	19 01		19 34	20 01	20 27	20 35	21 01	21 25	21 34	21 51	22 01	22 36	23 02	23 55
	d	17 35	18 02	18 22	18 36	19 02	19 06		20 02	20 29	20 37	21 02	21 25	21 35		22 02		23 04	23 55
Frome	d	17 44			18 46						20a46			21 44					00a05
Bruton	d	17 55			19 00									21 55					
Castle Cary	a	18 00		18 40	19 05					20 45			21 44	22 00					
	d	18 14			19 05									22 00					
Yeovil Pen Mill	d	18 29			19 19									22 13					
Thornford	d	18x34			19x23									22x18					
Yetminster	d	18x38			19x26									22x21					
Chetnole	d	18x41			19x30									22x24					
Maiden Newton	d	18 55			19 43									22 37					
Dorchester West	d	19h12			19 54									22 47					
Upwey	a	19 20			20 02									22 53					
Weymouth	a	19 26			20 08									22 59					
Dilton Marsh	d						19x09									22x04			
Warminster	d		18 09			19 09	19 15		20 09			21 09				22 09		23 11	
Salisbury	a		18 32			19 32	19 38		20 32			21 32				22 31		23 34	
	d		18 33			19 33	19 39		20 33			21 33				22 32			
Dean	d																		
Mottisfont & Dunbridge	d																		
Romsey	d		18 51			19 51	20 02		20 51			21 51				22 51			
Southampton Central	a		19 03			20 02	20 18		21 02			22 02				23 02			
Bournemouth	a		20 00				21 00		22 09			23 16				00 16			
Fareham	a		19 26			20 26	20 59		21 26			22 25				23 25			
	d		19 26			20 26			21 26			22 25				23 26			
Cosham	a		19 34			20 44	21 08		21 48			22 48				23 58			
Fratton	a		19 42			20 40	21 36		21 42			22 41				23 40			
Portsmouth & Southsea	a		19 45			20 44	21 40		21 45			22 45				23 44			
Portsmouth Harbour	a		19 49			20 49			21 49			22 49				23 48			
Havant	a		19j51			20j50			21j54			22j54							
Chichester 4	a		20j06			21j05			22j05			23j09							
Barnham	a		20j14			21j14			22j13			23k24							
Worthing 4	a		20j52			21j55			22k52			23k58							
Shoreham-by-Sea	a		21j02			22j05			23k02			00k08							
Hove 2	a		21j14			22j17			23k13			00k20							
Brighton 10	a		21j18			22j22			23k18			00k25							

For general notes see front of timetable
For details of catering facilities see Directory of Train Operators

A From Worcester Foregate Street (Table 71)
B From Gloucester (Table 134)
C From Great Malvern (Table 71)
D From Worcester Shrub Hill (Table 57)
E From Cheltenham Spa (Table 125)
b Change at Cardiff Central and Bristol Temple Meads
c Change at Bristol Temple Meads
e Change at Exeter St Davids and Salisbury
f Change at Castle Cary
g Change at Salisbury
h Arr. 1903
j Change at Fareham
k Change at Fratton

2 February to 22 March

South Wales and Bristol → Weymouth and Portsmouth

Network Diagram - see first page of Table 123

		GW	GW ◇	GW ◇	GW	GW A	GW ◇	GW	GW ◇	GW B	SW 1 ◇ C	GW 1 ◇	GW ◇	GW	GW D	GW ◇	GW	GW E
Swansea 7	d					*04 00*			*06 29*				*07 09*			*07 45*		
Cardiff Central 7	d					*04 55*	06 30		07 30				08 30			09 30		
Newport (South Wales)	d					*05 09*	06 44		07 44				08 44			09 44		
Severn Tunnel Jn	d						06 55		07 55				*08b25*			*09b25*		
Filton Abbey Wood	d						07 10		08 10	08 23			09 09		09 23	10 09		10 22
Bristol Temple Meads 10	d	23p16		05 45		06 43	07 24	07 49	08 24	08 40	08 50		09 24		09 49	10 24		10 49
Keynsham	d	23p23		05 52		06 50		07 56		08 47	08 57				09 56			10 56
Oldfield Park	d	23p29		05 59		06 56		08 02		08 54					10 03			11 03
London Paddington 15 ⊖	d									*07 15*		08 18	*07 30*			*08 42*		
Swindon	d								*08 00*				*09 00*			*10 00*		
Chippenham	d								*08 14*				*09 14*			*10 14*		
Melksham	d																	
Bath Spa 7	d	23p35		06 02		07 00	07 37	08 06	08 37	08 57	09 05		09 37		10 07	10 37		11 07
Freshford	d	23p45		06 12		07 09		08 15		09 06					10 16			11 15
Avoncliff	d	23c47		06x14		07x11		08x17		09x08					10x19			11x18
Bradford-on-Avon	d	23p51		06 18		07 15	07 48	08 21	08 48	09 12	09 20		09 48		10 22	10 48		11 21
Trowbridge	d	23p57		06 24		07 21	07 54	08 27	08 54	09 18	09 27		09 54		10 28	10 54		11 27
Plymouth	d									*07e54*			*06f55*					
Exeter St Davids 6	d			*05g10*					*06g41*	*08e56*			*08g25*					
Westbury	a	00 04		06 31		07 28	08 01	08 34	09 01	09 25	09 33	09 55	10 01		10 34	11 01		11 34
	d	00 04	06 36	06 39	07 03		08 02		09 02	09 28	09 39	09 57	10 02	10 08	10 35	11 02	11 07	
Frome	d	00a15	06 45							09 38					10 45			
Bruton	d		06 57							09 49					10 57			
Castle Cary	a		07 01							09 53		10 13			11 02			
	d		07 02							09 54					11 02			
Yeovil Pen Mill	d		07 16							10 08					11 16			
Thornford	d		07x21							10x13					11x20			
Yetminster	d		07x24							10x16					11x23			
Chetnole	d		07x28							10x19					11x27			
Maiden Newton	d		07 39							10 31					11 41			
Dorchester West	d		07 49							10 38					11h56			
Upwey	a		07 55							10 48					12 02			
Weymouth	a		08 01							10 54					12 08			
Dilton Marsh	d				07 06									10x10			11x10	
Warminster	d			06 46	07 13		08 09		09 09		09 46		10 09	10a16		11 09	11 16	
Salisbury	a			07 15	07 35		08 32		09 32		10 09		10 31			11 32	11 38	
	d			07 24	07 37		08 33		09 33				10 32			11 33	11 39	
Dean	d																	
Mottisfont & Dunbridge	d																	
Romsey	d			07 44	07 56		08 51		09 51				10 50			11 51	12 02	
Southampton Central	a			08 02	08 07		09 02		10 02				11 02			12 02	12 18	
Bournemouth	a				*09 10*		*10 00*		*11 00*				*12 00*				*13 00*	
Fareham	a			08 26	*08 59*		09 26		10 26				11 26			12 26	*12 59*	
	d			08 26			09 26		10 26				11 26			12 26		
Cosham	a			08 34	*09 08*		09 34		10 34				11 34			12 34	*13 08*	
Fratton	a			08 41	*09 36*		09 41		10 41				11 41			12 41	*13 36*	
Portsmouth & Southsea	a			08 45	*09 40*		09 45		10 45				11 45			12 45	*13 40*	
Portsmouth Harbour	a			08 49			09 49		10 49				11 49			12 49		
Havant	a			*08j50*			*09j50*		*10j50*				*11j50*			*12j50*		
Chichester 4	a			*09j08*			*10j08*		*11j08*				*12j08*			*13j08*		
Barnham	a			*09j18*			*10j18*		*11j18*				*12j18*			*13j18*		
Worthing 4	a			*09j54*			*10j54*		*11j54*				*12j54*			*13j54*		
Shoreham-by-Sea	a			*10j04*			*11j04*		*12j04*				*13j04*			*14j04*		
Hove 2	a			*10j13*			*11j13*		*12j13*				*13j13*			*14j13*		
Brighton 10	a			*10j18*			*11j18*		*12j18*				*13j18*			*14j18*		

For general notes see front of timetable
For details of catering facilities see Directory of Train Operators

A From Taunton (Table 134)
B From Worcester Shrub Hill (Table 57)
C To London Waterloo (Table 160)
D From Gloucester (Table 134)
E From Great Malvern (Table 71)
b Change at Bristol Temple Meads
c Previous night.
Stops on request, passengers wishing to alight must inform the guard and those wishing to join must give a hand signal to the driver
e Change at Castle Cary
f Change at Exeter St Davids and Salisbury
g Change at Salisbury
h Arr. 1151
j Change at Fareham

Saturdays

2 February to 22 March

South Wales and Bristol → Weymouth and Portsmouth

Network Diagram - see first page of Table 123

		GW	GW	GW	GW	GW	SW	GW	GW	GW	GW	GW	GW	GW	GW	GW	SW	GW
		◇	**1** ◇	◇	◇		**1** ◇	**1** ◇	◇		◇		◇	◇			**1** ◇	◇
				A		B	C			A			B			A		
Swansea 7	d	*09 10*			*10 29*				*11 10*		*11 55*			*13 10*				*14 29*
Cardiff Central 7	d	10 30			11 30				12 30		13 30			14 30				15 30
Newport (South Wales)	d	10 44			11 44				12 44		13 44			14 44				15 44
Severn Tunnel Jn	d	*10b25*			*11b25*				*12b25*		*13b26*							*15b25*
Filton Abbey Wood	d	11 09		11 23	12 09	12 22			13 09	13 23	14 09		14 23	15 09		15 23		16 09
Bristol Temple Meads 10	d	11 24		11 49	12 24	12 39	13 10		13 24	13 49	14 24		14 49	15 24		15 43	15 52	16 24
Keynsham	d			11 56		12 46				13 56			14 56			15 50		
Oldfield Park	d			12 03		12 53				14 03			15 03			15 57		
London Paddington 15 ⊖	d		11 05	*10 15*	*10 42*	*11 15*		12 18	*11 42*	*12 15*	*12 42*		*13 15*	*13 42*		*14 15*		
Swindon	d	*11 00*			*12 00*				*13 00*		*14 00*			*15 00*	15 29		*15 00*	*16 00*
Chippenham	d	*11 14*			*12 14*				*13 14*		*14 14*			*15 14*	15 45		*15 14*	*16 14*
Melksham	d														15 55			
Bath Spa 7	d	11 37		12 07	12 37	12 56	13 22		13 37	14 07	14 37		15 07	15 37		16 01	16 04	16 37
Freshford	d			12 16						14 16			15 15			16 10		
Avoncliff	d			12x19						14x19			15x18			16x13		
Bradford-on-Avon	d	11 48		12 22	12 48	13 08	13 35		13 48	14 22	14 48		15 21	15 48		16 16	16 20	16 48
Trowbridge	d	11 54		12 28	12 54	13 15	13 42		13 54	14 28	14 54		15 27	15 54	16 04	16 22	16 26	16 54
Plymouth	d	*08c25*			*09c25*	*10e46*					*12c25*	*12 55*	*14f00*				*14e00*	
Exeter St Davids 6	d	*10g10*			*11g08*	*12 07*			*12g10*		*13g35*	*13 57*	*15h09*	*14g10*			*15 09*	
Westbury	a	12 01	12 22	12 35	13 01	13 22	13 48	13 56	14 01	14 35	15 01		15 34	16 01	16 11	16 29	16 36	17 01
	d	12 02	12 22	12 36	13 02	13 27	13 53	13 56	14 02		15 02	15 08	15 35	16 02			16 39	17 02
Frome	d			12 48									15 44					
Bruton	d			12 57									15 55					
Castle Cary	a		12 40	13 02				14 14					16 00					
	d			13 02									16 13					
Yeovil Pen Mill	d			13 16									16 23					
Thornford	d			13x20														
Yetminster	d			13x23									16x31					
Chetnole	d			13x27														
Maiden Newton	d			13 41									16 44					
Dorchester West	d			13 55									16 54					
Upwey	a			14 02														
Weymouth	a			14 08									17 07					
Dilton Marsh	d					13x30						15 11						
Warminster	d	12 09			13 09	13 36	14 00		14 09		15 09	15a17		16 09			16 47	17 09
Salisbury	a	12 32			13 32	13 58	14 24		14 32		15 32			16 32			17 09	17 32
	d	12 33			13 33	13 59			14 33		15 33			16 33				17 33
Dean	d																	
Mottisfont & Dunbridge	d																	
Romsey	d	12 51			13 51	14 19			14 51		15 51			16 51				17 51
Southampton Central	a	13 02			14 02	14 32			15 02		16 02			17 02				18 02
Bournemouth	a	*14 00*			*15 00*	*15 15*			*16 00*		*17 00*			*18 00*				*19 00*
Fareham	a	13 26			14 26	14 55			15 26		16 26			17 26				18 26
	d	13 26			14 26	14 56			15 26		16 26			17 26				18 26
Cosham	a	13 34			14 34	15 04			15 34		16 34			17 34				18 34
Fratton	a	13 41			14 41	*15 36*			15 41		16 41			17 41				18 42
Portsmouth & Southsea	a	13 45			14 45	*15 40*			15 45		16 45			17 45				18 46
Portsmouth Harbour	a	13 49			14 49				15 49		16 49			17 49				18 49
Havant	a	*13j50*			*14j50*	15 11			*15j50*		*16j50*			*17j50*				*18j50*
Chichester 4	a	*14j08*			*15j08*	15 22			*16j08*		*17j08*			*18j08*				*19j05*
Barnham	a	*14j18*			*15j18*	15 30			*16j18*		*17j18*			*18j18*				*19j14*
Worthing 4	a	*14j54*				15 45			*16j54*		*17j54*			*18j54*				*19j54*
Shoreham-by-Sea	a	*15j04*				15 56			*17j04*		*18j04*			*19j04*				*20j04*
Hove 2	a	*15j13*				16 07			*17j13*		*18j13*			*19j13*				*20j15*
Brighton 10	a	*15j18*				16 14			*17j18*		*18j18*			*19j18*				*20j20*

For general notes see front of timetable
For details of catering facilities see Directory of Train Operators

A From Gloucester (Table 134)
B From Great Malvern (Table 71)
C To London Waterloo (Table 160)
b Change at Bristol Temple Meads
c Change at Exeter St Davids and Salisbury
e Change at Exeter St Davids and Westbury
f Change at Exeter St Davids and Castle Cary
g Change at Salisbury
h Change at Castle Cary
j Change at Fareham

Table 123

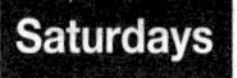

2 February to 22 March

South Wales and Bristol → Weymouth and Portsmouth

Network Diagram - see first page of Table 123

		GW	GW		GW	GW		GW	GW		GW	GW		GW	GW	GW	GW	GW	GW	GW	GW	GW	SW	GW		
			◇		◇	1 ◇		◇	◇					◇	1 ◇		◇	1 ◇	◇		◇		1			
			A					B				C				B			D	E						
					⚲	☕			⚲					⚲	☕		⚲	☕			⚲					
Swansea 7	d				15 10				15 55					17 29			18 29				19 29		19b55	20b55		
Cardiff Central 7	d				16 30				17 30					18 30			19 30				20 30		21 00	22 00		
Newport (South Wales)	d				16 44				17 44					18 44			19 44				20 44		21 15	22 16		
Severn Tunnel Jn	d				16 55				17 55					18c25			19c25				20c15		21 25	22 33		
Filton Abbey Wood	d		16 23		17 10			17 23	18 10			18 22		19 09		19 22	20 09		20 23		21 09		21 42	22 52		
Bristol Temple Meads 10	d		16 49		17 24			17 49	18 24			18 49		19 24		19 49	20 24		20 49		21 24	21 51	22 23	23 10		
Keynsham	d		16 56					17 56				18 56				19 56			20 56			21 58		23 17		
Oldfield Park	d		17 02					18 03				19 03				20 03			21 02			22 04		23 23		
London Paddington 15 ⊖	d		15 15		15 42	17 05		16 15						17 30	19 05	18 15	18 30	20 05	19 15			20 15	20 30	21 30		
Swindon	d				17 00				18 00											21 08	21 00		21 00			
Chippenham	d				17 14				18 14											21 24	21 14		21 14			
Melksham	d																			21 34						
Bath Spa 7	d		17 07		17 37			18 07	18 37			19 07		19 37		20 07	20 37		21 07		21 37	22 07	22 36	23 27		
Freshford	d		17 15					18 16				19 15				20 16			21 15			22 17		23 36		
Avoncliff	d		17x18					18x19				19x17				20x18			21x18			22x18		23x38		
Bradford-on-Avon	d		17 21		17 48			18 22	18 48			19 21		19 48		20 22	20 48		21 21		21 48	22 23	22 47	23 42		
Trowbridge	d		17 27		17 54			18 28	18 54			19 27		19 54		20 28	20 54		21 27	21 43	21 54	22 29	22 53	23 48		
Plymouth	d				14e50			16f54	16 54							17 54					18g25					
Exeter St Davids 6	d				16e10			17f53	17 53					18e10		17 56	19e10				20e15					
Westbury	a		17 34		18 01	18 22			19 01			19 34		20 01	20 27	20 35	21 01	21 25	21 34	21 51	22 01	22 36	23 02	23 55		
	d	17 08	17 35		18 02	18 22			19 02		19 06			20 02	20 29	20 37	21 02	21 25	21 35		22 02		23 04	23 55		
Frome	d		17 44					18 46								20a46			21 44					00a05		
Bruton	d		17 55					19 00											21 55							
Castle Cary	a		18 00			18 40		19 05							20 45			21 44	22 00							
	d		18 14					19 05											22 00							
Yeovil Pen Mill	d		18 29					19 19											22 13							
Thornford	d		18x34					19x23											22x18							
Yetminster	d		18x38					19x26											22x21							
Chetnole	d		18x41					19x30											22x24							
Maiden Newton	d		18 55					19 43											22 37							
Dorchester West	d		19h12					19 54											22 47							
Upwey	a		19 20					20 02											22 53							
Weymouth	a		19 26					20 08											22 59							
Dilton Marsh	d	17 11									19x09										22x04					
Warminster	d	17a17			18 09				19 09		19 15			20 09			21 09				22 09		23 11			
Salisbury	a				18 32				19 32		19 39			20 32			21 32				22 31		23 34			
	d				18 33				19 33		19 40			20 33			21 33				22 32					
Dean	d																									
Mottisfont & Dunbridge	d																									
Romsey	d				18 51				19 51		20 02			20 51			21 51				22 51					
Southampton Central	a				19 02				20 02		20 18			21 02			22 02				23 02					
Bournemouth	a				20 00						21 00			22 09			23 16				00 16					
Fareham	a				19 26				20 26		20 59			21 26			22 25				23 25					
	d				19 26				20 26					21 26			22 25				23 26					
Cosham	a				19 34				20 44		21 08			21 48			22 48				23 58					
Fratton	a				19 42				20 40		21 36			21 42			22 41				23 40					
Portsmouth & Southsea	a				19 45				20 44		21 40			21 45			22 45				23 44					
Portsmouth Harbour	a				19 49				20 49					21 49			22 49				23 48					
Havant	a				19j51				20j50					21j54			22j54									
Chichester 4	a				20j06				21j05					22j05			23j09									
Barnham	a				20j14				21j14					22j13			23k24									
Worthing 4	a				20j52				21j55					22k52			23k58									
Shoreham-by-Sea	a				21j02				22j05					23k02			00k08									
Hove 2	a				21j14				22j17					23k13			00k20									
Brighton 10	a				21j18				22j22					23k18			00k25									

For general notes see front of timetable
For details of catering facilities see Directory of Train Operators

A From Worcester Foregate Street (Table 71)
B From Gloucester (Table 134)
C From Great Malvern (Table 71)
D From Worcester Shrub Hill (Table 57)
E From Cheltenham Spa (Table 125)
b Change at Cardiff Central and Bristol Temple Meads
c Change at Bristol Temple Meads
e Change at Salisbury
f Change at Castle Cary
g Change at Exeter St Davids and Salisbury
h Arr. 1903
j Change at Fareham
k Change at Fratton

Table 123

Saturdays
from 29 March

South Wales and Bristol → Weymouth and Portsmouth

Network Diagram - see first page of Table 123

Station		GW	GW ◇	GW ◇	GW	GW A	GW ◇ B	GW	GW ◇ B 🚲	GW C	SW [1] ◇ D	GW [1] ◇ 🛒	GW ◇ B 🚲		GW	GW E	GW ◇ B 🚲	GW	GW G	GW ◇ B 🚲	GW [1] ◇ 🛒	GW ◇ E	GW ◇ B 🚲	GW G	SW [1] ◇ D	GW ◇ B 🚲
Swansea [7]	d																									
Cardiff Central [7]	d																									
Newport (South Wales)	d																									
Severn Tunnel Jn	d																									
Filton Abbey Wood	d						07 09		07 59	08 23			09 09			09 23	10 09		10 22	11 09		11 23	12 09	12 22		13 09
Bristol Temple Meads [10]	d	23p16		05 45		06 43	07 24	07 49	08 24	08 40	08 50		09 24			09 49	10 24		10 49	11 24		11 49	12 24	12 39	13 10	13 24
Keynsham	d	23p23		05 52		06 50		07 56		08 47	08 57					09 56			10 56			11 56		12 46		
Oldfield Park	d	23p29		05 59		06 56		08 02		08 54						10 03			11 03			12 03		12 53		
London Paddington [15] ⊖	d								*07 00*		*07 00*	08 18	*08 00*			*08 30*	*09 00*			*10 00*	11 05	*10 30*	*11 00*			*12 00*
Swindon	d								*07 56*		*07 56*		*08 56*			*09 31*	*09 56*			*10 56*		*11 31*	*11 56*			*12 56*
Chippenham	d								*08 10*		*08 10*		*09 10*			*09 45*	*10 10*			*11 10*		*11 45*	*12 10*			*13 10*
Melksham	d																									
Bath Spa [7]	d	23p35		06 02		07 00	07 37	08 06	08 37	08 57	09 05		09 37			10 07	10 37		11 07	11 37		12 07	12 37	12 56	13 22	13 37
Freshford	d	23p45		06 12		07 09		08 15		09 06						10 16			11 15			12 16				
Avoncliff	d	23b47		06x14		07x11		08x17		09x08						10x19			11x18			12x19				
Bradford-on-Avon	d	23p51		06 18		07 15	07 48	08 21	08 48	09 12	09 20		09 48			10 22	10 48		11 21	11 48		12 22	12 48	13 08	13 35	13 48
Trowbridge	d	23p57		06 24		07 21	07 54	08 27	08 54	09 18	09 27		09 54			10 28	10 54		11 27	11 54		12 28	12 54	13 15	13 42	13 54
Plymouth	d									*07c54*			*06e55*							*08e25*			*09e25*	*10f46*		
Exeter St Davids [6]	d			*05g10*					*06g41*	*08c56*			*08g25*							*10g10*			*11g08*	*12 07*		*12g10*
Westbury	a	00 04		06 31		07 28	08 01	08 34	09 01	09 25	09 33	09 54	10 01			10 34	11 01		11 34	12 01	12 22	12 35	13 01	13 22	13 48	14 01
	d	00 04	06 36	06 39	07 03		08 02		09 02	09 28	09 39	09 56	10 02		10 08	10 35	11 02	11 07		12 02	12 22	12 36	13 02	13 27	13 53	14 02
Frome	d	00a15	06 45							09 38						10 45						12 48				
Bruton	d		06 57							09 49						10 57						12 59				
Castle Cary	a		07 02							09 53		10 12				11 02					12 40	13 04				
	d		07 02							09 54						11 02						13 05				
Yeovil Pen Mill	d		07 16							10 08						11 16						13 18				
Thornford	d		07x21							10x13						11x20						13x23				
Yetminster	d		07x24							10x16						11x23						13x26				
Chetnole	d		07x28							10x19						11x27						13x30				
Maiden Newton	d		07 39							10 31						11 41						13 42				
Dorchester West	d		07 49							10 38						11h56						13 55				
Upwey	a		07 55							10 48						12 02						14 02				
Weymouth	a		08 01							10 54						12 08						14 08				
Dilton Marsh	d				07 06										10x10			11x10						13x30		
Warminster	d			06 46	07 13		08 09		09 09		09 46		10 09		10a16		11 09	11 16		12 09			13 09	13 36	14 00	14 09
Salisbury	a			07 15	07 35		08 32		09 32		10 09		10 31				11 32	11 38		12 32			13 32	13 58	14 24	14 32
	d			07 24	07 37		08 33		09 33				10 32				11 33	11 39		12 33			13 33	13 59		14 33
Dean	d																									
Mottisfont & Dunbridge	d																									
Romsey	d			07 44	07 56		08 51		09 51				10 50				11 51	12 02		12 51			13 51	14 19		14 51
Southampton Central	a			08 02	08 07		09 02		10 02				11 02				12 02	12 18		13 02			14 02	14 32		15 02
Bournemouth	a				*09 10*		*10 00*		*11 00*				*12 00*					*13 00*		*14 00*			*15 00*	*15 15*		*16 00*
Fareham	a			08 26	*08 59*		09 26		10 26				11 26				12 26	*12 59*		13 26			14 26	14 55		15 26
	d			08 26			09 26		10 26				11 26				12 26			13 26			14 26	14 56		15 26
Cosham	a			08 34	*09 08*		09 34		10 34				11 34				12 34	*13 08*		13 34			14 34	15 04		15 34
Fratton	a			08 41	*09 36*		09 41		10 41				11 41				12 41	*13 36*		13 41			14 41	*15 36*		15 41
Portsmouth & Southsea	a			08 45	*09 40*		09 45		10 45				11 45				12 45	*13 40*		13 45			14 45	*15 40*		15 45
Portsmouth Harbour	a			08 49			09 49		10 49				11 49				12 49			13 49			14 49			15 49
Havant	a			*08j50*			*09j50*		*10j50*				*11j50*				*12j50*			*13j50*			*14j50*	15 11		*15j50*
Chichester [4]	a			*09j08*			*10j08*		*11j08*				*12j08*				*13j08*			*14j08*			*15j08*	15 22		*16j08*
Barnham	a			*09j18*			*10j18*		*11j18*				*12j18*				*13j18*			*14j18*			*15j18*	15 30		*16j18*
Worthing [4]	a			*09j54*			*10j54*		*11j54*				*12j54*				*13j54*			*14j54*				15 45		*16j54*
Shoreham-by-Sea	a			*10j04*			*11j04*		*12j04*				*13j04*				*14j04*			*15j04*				15 56		*17j04*
Hove [2]	a			*10j13*			*11j13*		*12j13*				*13j13*				*14j13*			*15j13*				16 07		*17j13*
Brighton [10]	a			*10j18*			*11j18*		*12j18*				*13j18*				*14j18*			*15j18*				16 14		*17j18*

For general notes see front of timetable
For details of catering facilities see Directory of Train Operators

- **A** From Taunton (Table 134)
- **B** From Bristol Parkway (Table 132)
- **C** From Worcester Shrub Hill (Table 57)
- **D** To London Waterloo (Table 160)
- **E** From Gloucester (Table 134)
- **G** From Great Malvern (Table 71)
- **b** Previous night.
  Stops on request, passengers wishing to alight must inform the guard and those wishing to join must give a hand signal to the driver
- **c** Change at Castle Cary
- **e** Change at Exeter St Davids and Salisbury
- **f** Change at Exeter St Davids and Westbury
- **g** Change at Salisbury
- **h** Arr. 1151
- **j** Change at Fareham

Saturdays

from 29 March

South Wales and Bristol → Weymouth and Portsmouth

Network Diagram - see first page of Table 123

		GW	GW		GW	GW	GW	GW	SW	GW	GW	GW	GW	GW	GW	GW	GW	GW	GW	GW	GW	GW	SW	GW		
			◇			◇	◇		1 ◇	◇		◇	◇	◇			◇		◇	◇			1			
		A	B			C	B	A		B		D	B	A		C	B	A	B	B						
			⚲			⚲	⚲			⚲			⚲				⚲		⚲	⚲						
Swansea 7	d																									
Cardiff Central 7	d																									
Newport (South Wales)	d																									
Severn Tunnel Jn	d																									
Filton Abbey Wood	d	13 23	14 09			14 23	15 09	15 23		16 09		16 23	17 09	17 23		18 22	19 09	19 23	20 09	21 09			21 42			
Bristol Temple Meads 10	d	13 49	14 24			14 49	15 24	15 43	15 52	16 24		16 49	17 24	17 49		18 49	19 24	19 49	20 24	21 24		21 51	22 23	23 10		
Keynsham	d	13 56				14 56		15 50				16 56		17 56		18 56		19 56				21 58		23 17		
Oldfield Park	d	14 03				15 03		15 57				17 02	17 35	18 03		19 03		20 03				22 04		23 23		
London Paddington 15 ⊖	d		13 00			13 30	14 00			15 00		15 30		16 30		17 30	18 00	18 30	19 00	20 00		20 30		21 30		
Swindon	d		13 56			14 31	14 56			15 56		16 31		17 31		18 31	18 56	19 31	19 56	21 01	21 20	21 31		22 31		
Chippenham	d		14 10			14 45	15 10			16 10		16 45		17 45		18 45	19 10	19 45	20 10	21 15	21 36	21 45		22 45		
Melksham	d																				21 46					
Bath Spa 7	d	14 07	14 37			15 07	15 37	16 01	16 04	16 37		17 07	17 37	18 07		19 07	19 37	20 07	20 37	21 37		22 07	22 36	23 27		
Freshford	d	14 16				15 15		16 10				17 15		18 16		19 15		20 16				22 17		23 36		
Avoncliff	d	14x19				15x18		16x13				17x18		18x19		19x17		20x18				22x18		23x38		
Bradford-on-Avon	d	14 22	14 48			15 21	15 48	16 16	16 20	16 48		17 21	17 48	18 22		19 21	19 48	20 22	20 48	21 48		22 23	22 47	23 42		
Trowbridge	d	14 28	14 54			15 27	15 54	16 22	16 26	16 54		17 27	17 54	18 28		19 27	19 54	20 28	20 54	21 54	21 59	22 29	22 53	23 48		
Plymouth	d		12b25				12b55						15b04				16b54		17c42	18b25						
Exeter St Davids 6	d		13c35				14c10						16c10				18c10		19c10	20c15						
Westbury	a	14 35	15 01			15 34	16 01	16 29	16 36	17 01		17 34	18 01	18 35		19 34	20 01	20 35	21 01	22 01	22 07	22 36	23 02	23 55		
	d		15 02		15 08		16 02		16 39	17 02	17 08		18 02		19 06		20 02		21 02	22 02			23 04			
Frome	d																									
Bruton	d																									
Castle Cary	a																									
	d																									
Yeovil Pen Mill	d																									
Thornford	d																									
Yetminster	d																									
Chetnole	d																									
Maiden Newton	d																									
Dorchester West	d																									
Upwey	a																									
Weymouth	a																									
Dilton Marsh	d				15 11						17 11				19x09					22x04						
Warminster	d		15 09		15a17		16 09		16 47	17 09	17a17		18 09		19 15		20 09		21 09	22 09			23 11			
Salisbury	a		15 32				16 32		17 09	17 32			18 32		19 39		20 32		21 32	22 31			23 34			
	d		15 33				16 33			17 33			18 33		19 40		20 33		21 33	22 32						
Dean	d																									
Mottisfont & Dunbridge	d																									
Romsey	d		15 51				16 51			17 51			18 51		20 02		20 51		21 51	22 51						
Southampton Central	a		16 02				17 02			18 02			19 03		20 18		21 02		22 02	23 02						
Bournemouth	a		17 00				18 00			19 00			20 00		21 00		22 09		23 16	00 16						
Fareham	a		16 26				17 26			18 26			19 26		20 59		21 26		22 25	23 25						
	d		16 26				17 26			18 26			19 26				21 26		22 25	23 26						
Cosham	a		16 34				17 34			18 34			19 34		21 08		21 48		22 48	23 58						
Fratton	a		16 41				17 41			18 42			19 42		21 36		21 42		22 41	23 40						
Portsmouth & Southsea	a		16 45				17 45			18 46			19 45		21 40		21 45		22 45	23 44						
Portsmouth Harbour	a		16 49				17 49			18 49			19 49		21 49		21 49		22 49	23 48						
Havant	a		16e50				17e50			18e50			19e51				21e54		22e54							
Chichester 4	a		17e08				18e08			19e05			20e06				22e05		23e09							
Barnham	a		17e18				18e18			19e14			20e14				22e13		23f24							
Worthing 4	a		17e54				18e54			19e54			20e52				22f52		23f58							
Shoreham-by-Sea	a		18e04				19e04			20e04			21e02				23f02		00f08							
Hove 2	a		18e13				19e13			20e15			21e14				23f13		00f20							
Brighton 10	a		18e18				19e18			20e20			21e18				23f18		00f25							

For general notes see front of timetable
For details of catering facilities see Directory of Train Operators

- **A** From Gloucester (Table 134)
- **B** From Bristol Parkway (Table 132)
- **C** From Great Malvern (Table 71)
- **D** From Worcester Foregate Street (Table 71)
- **b** Change at Exeter St Davids and Salisbury
- **c** Change at Salisbury
- **e** Change at Fareham
- **f** Change at Fratton

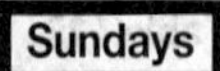

until 27 January

South Wales and Bristol → Weymouth and Portsmouth

Network Diagram - see first page of Table 123

		GW ◇	GW 1 ◇	GW 1 ◇	GW ◇	GW ◇	GW 1 ◇	GW ◇	GW ◇	GW ◇	GW 1 ◇	GW ◇	GW 1 ◇	GW ◇	SW 1 ◇ A	GW ◇	GW 1 ◇	GW ◇
Swansea 7	d				07 59	08 59		09 59	10 59			11 59		12 59		13 59		14 59
Cardiff Central 7	d	08 05			09 15	10 15		11 15	12 15			13 15		14 15		15 15		16 15
Newport (South Wales)	d	08 23			09 29	10 29		11 29	12 29			13 29		14 29		15 29		16 29
Severn Tunnel Jn	d	08 39			09 39	10 39		11 39	12 39			13 39		14 39		15 39		16 39
Filton Abbey Wood	d	08 54			09 56	10 54		11 54	12 57			13 54		14 54		15 56		16 57
Bristol Temple Meads 10	d	09 10			10 10	11 10		12 10	13 10	13 20		14 10		15 10	16 04	16 10		17 10
Keynsham	d	09 17				11 17			13 17	13 27				15 17	16 11			17 17
Oldfield Park	d	09 24				11 24			13 24	13 34				15 24				17 24
London Paddington 15 ⊖	d		08 57	09 57	08 00	09 07	11 18		11 07		12 57	12 07	13 57	13 07	14 07		15 57	15 07
Swindon	d				09 19	10 16			12 16			13 17		14 17	15 17			16 17
Chippenham	d				09 34	10 32			12 31			13 31		14 31	15 31			16 31
Melksham	d																	
Bath Spa 7	d	09 27			10 22	11 27		12 22	13 27	13 37		14 23		15 27	16 20	16 24		17 27
Freshford	d				10 32			12 32		13 48		14 33				16 34		
Avoncliff	d				10x34			12x34		13x51		14x36				16x36		
Bradford-on-Avon	d	09 39			10 38	11 39		12 38	13 39	13 54		14 39		15 39	16 31	16 40		17 39
Trowbridge	d	09 45			10 44	11 46		12 44	13 46	14 00		14 45		15 45	16 37	16 46		17 45
Plymouth	d				08 45			10 35				11b45		13 44		14c06		15 45
Exeter St Davids 6	d	08 30			09 51			11 36				13c18		14 47		15c18		16 46
Westbury	a	09 52	10 25		10 51	11 53	12 43	12 51	13 53	14 07	14 16	14 52		15 54	16 44	16 53	17 22	17 52
	d	09 53			11 00	12 03	12 43	12 55	14 03	14 30		15 00		15 58	16 46	16 58	17 29	18 00
Frome	d									14 49								
Bruton	d									15 00								
Castle Cary	a			11 36			13 01			15 05			15 36				17 46	
	d									15 06								
Yeovil Pen Mill	d									15 19								
Thornford	d									15x24								
Yetminster	d									15x27								
Chetnole	d									15x31								
Maiden Newton	d									15 43								
Dorchester West	d									15 53								
Upwey	a									15 59								
Weymouth	a									16 05								
Dilton Marsh	d	09x56				12x06			14x06					16x01		17x01		
Warminster	d	10 02			11 07	12 12		13 02	14 12			15 07		16 07	16 53	17 07		18 07
Salisbury	a	10 26			11 29	12 34		13 25	14 39			15 30		16 30	17 16	17 30		18 30
	d	10 31			11 31	12 36		13 29	14 48			15 31		16 31		17 31		18 31
Dean	d																	
Mottisfont & Dunbridge	d																	
Romsey	d	10 50			11 49	12 56		13 47	15 10			15 51		16 49		17 49		18 49
Southampton Central	a	11 00			12 04	13 06		13 58	15 20			16 06		17 04		18 04		19 04
Bournemouth	a	12 23			13 23	14 23		14 35	16 23			17 23		18 23		19 23		20 23
Fareham	a	11 25			12 28	13 33		14 22	15 50			16 28		17 28		18 28		19 28
	d	11 26			12 29	13 34		14 23	15 51			16 29		17 29		18 29		19 29
Cosham	a	11 33			12 37	13 41		14 31	16 00			16 37		17 37		18 37		19 37
Fratton	a	11 40			12 44	14 04		14 38	16 30			16 44		17 44		18 44		19 44
Portsmouth & Southsea	a	11 44			12 47	14 08		14 41	16 33			16 47		17 47		18 47		19 47
Portsmouth Harbour	a	11 51			12 51	14 13		14 46	16 51			16 51		17 51		18 51		19 51
Havant	a	11e59			12e59	14 03		14e59	16 11			16e59		17e59		18e59		19e59
Chichester 4	a	12e14			13e14	14 19		15e14	16 22			17e14		18e14		19e14		20e14
Barnham	a	12e22			13e22	14 27		15e22	16 30			17e22		18e22		19e22		20e22
Worthing 4	a	12e37			13e37	14 44		15e37	16 45			17e37		18e37		19e37		20e37
Shoreham-by-Sea	a	12e47			13e47	14 51		15e47	16 51			17e47		18e47		19e47		20e47
Hove 2	a	12e53			13e53	14 59		15e53	16 58			17e53		18e53		19e53		20e53
Brighton 10	a	13f00			14f00	15 06		16f00	17 05			18f00		19f00		20f00		21f00

For general notes see front of timetable
For details of catering facilities see Directory of Train Operators

A To London Waterloo (Table 160)
b Change at Exeter St Davids and Salisbury
c Change at Salisbury
e Change at Fratton
f Change at Fratton and Hove

Table 123

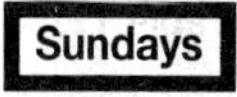

until 27 January

South Wales and Bristol → Weymouth and Portsmouth

Network Diagram - see first page of Table 123

		GW	GW	GW	GW	GW	GW	GW	GW	GW	GW	GW	GW	SW	GW	GW
		◇	◇		◇	1 ◇	◇	1 ◇	◇	◇	1 ◇	◇	◇	1		◇
		A														
			🛒		🛒	☕	🛒	☕	🛒	🛒	☕		🛒			🛒
Swansea 7	d		15 59		16 29				17 35				18 29			20 35
Cardiff Central 7	d		17 15		17 45		18 15		18 45	19 15		19b25	20 15		20b55	22 05
Newport (South Wales)	d		17 29		17 59		18 29		18 59	19 29		19b39	20 29		21b09	22 23
Severn Tunnel Jn	d		17 40				18 39		19 09				20 39			22 39
Filton Abbey Wood	d		17 55		18 24		18 56		19 25	19 52			20 54		21 54	22 56
Bristol Temple Meads 10	d	17 50	18 10		18 50		19 10		19 50	20 10		20 50	21 10	21 35	22 15	23 10
Keynsham	d	17 57	18 17				19 17					20 57			22 22	
Oldfield Park	d	18 04	18 24				19 24					21 04			22 29	
London Paddington 15 ⊖	d	16 07		17 12	17 07	17 57		18 57	18 07		19 57	19 07			20 07	21 07
Swindon	d	17 17		18 31	18 17				19 17			20 17			21 17	22 20
Chippenham	d	17 31		18 47	18 31				19 31			20 31			21 31	22 33
Melksham	d			18 57												
Bath Spa 7	d	18 07	18 27		19 02		19 27		20 02	20 22		21 07	21 22	21 49	22 32	23 22
Freshford	d	18 17	18 37							20 32		21 18			22 43	
Avoncliff	d	18x20	18x39							20x34		21x21			22x46	
Bradford-on-Avon	d	18 23	18 43		19 14		19 39			20 38		21 24	21 36	22 00	22 49	23 34
Trowbridge	d	18 29	18 50	19 06	19 20		19 45		20 18	20 44		21 30	21 42	22 06	22 55	23 40
Plymouth	d	15c45	16e02						18 10			19c15	19 15			
Exeter St Davids 6	d	16c46	17e18						19 15	19e20		20c19	20 19			
Westbury	a	18 36	18 57	19 13	19 27	19 32	19 52		20 25	20 51	21 29	21 37	21 49	22 13	23 02	23 47
	d	18 38	19 01		19 29		19 53		20 27	20 55	21 31	21 38	21 55	22 15		23 50
Frome	d	18 47										21 48				
Bruton	d	18 59										21 59				
Castle Cary	a	19 04						20 29			21 48	22 04				
	d	19 06										22 05				
Yeovil Pen Mill	d	19 20										22 18				
Thornford	d	19x24										22x23				
Yetminster	d	19x27										22x26				
Chetnole	d	19x31										22x30				
Maiden Newton	d	19 43										22 42				
Dorchester West	d	19 53										22 52				
Upwey	a	20 00										22 58				
Weymouth	a	20 05										23 03				
Dilton Marsh	d		19x04				19x56									23x53
Warminster	d		19 10		19 37		20 02		20 34	21 02			22 02	22 22		23a58
Salisbury	a		19 33		19 59		20 25		20 57	21 25			22 25	22 46		
	d		19 36		20 00		20 30		20 58	21 29			22 29			
Dean	d															
Mottisfont & Dunbridge	d															
Romsey	d		19 55		20 19		20 48		21 16	21 47			22 48			
Southampton Central	a		20 06		20 31		20 59		21 27	21 58			22 59			
Bournemouth	a		21 23		21 32				22 23	22 35			00 21			
Fareham	a		20 28		20 54		21 22		21 49	22 22			23 21			
	d		20 29		20 55		21 23		21 50	22 23			23 22			
Cosham	a		20 44		21 19		21 54		22 19	22 54			23 54			
Fratton	a		21 04		21 09		21 36		22 07	22 36			23 37			
Portsmouth & Southsea	a		21 08		21 15		21 39		22 12	22 39			23 40			
Portsmouth Harbour	a		21 13		21 23		21 46		22 20	22 46			23 44			
Havant	a		20 52		21f32		21f49		22f32	22f49						
Chichester 4	a		21 03		21f53		22f14		22f53	23f14						
Barnham	a		21 11		22f01		22f22		23f01	23f22						
Worthing 4	a		21 34		22f29		23f00									
Shoreham-by-Sea	a		21 44		22f39		23f09									
Hove 2	a		21 55		22f51		23f21									
Brighton 10	a		22 01		22f56		23f25									

For general notes see front of timetable
For details of catering facilities see Directory of Train Operators

A From Weston-super-Mare (Table 134)
b Change at Bristol Parkway and Bristol Temple Meads
c Change at Castle Cary
e Change at Salisbury
f Change at Fratton

Sundays

3 February to 23 March

South Wales and Bristol → Weymouth and Portsmouth

Network Diagram - see first page of Table 123

		GW	GW	GW	GW	GW	GW	GW	GW	GW	GW	GW	GW	GW	GW	GW	SW	GW
		1 ◇	◇	1 ◇	1 ◇	◇	◇	◇	1 ◇	◇	◇	◇	1 ◇	◇	1 ◇	◇	1 ◇	◇
																	A	
Swansea 7	d					07 59	08 45	09 45			10 45			11 45		12 45	13 45	13 45
Cardiff Central 7	d		08 05			09 15	10 15	11 15			12 15			13 15		14 15	14 41	15 15
Newport (South Wales)	d		08 23			09 29	10 29	11 29			12 29			13 29		14 29	14 55	15 29
Severn Tunnel Jn	d		08 39			09 39	10 39	11 39			12 39			13 39		14 39		15 39
Filton Abbey Wood	d		08 54			09 56	10 54	11 54			12 57			13 54		14 54		15 56
Bristol Temple Meads 10	d		09 10			10 10	11 10				13 10	13 20		14 10		15 10	16 04	16 10
Keynsham	d		09 17				11 17				13 17	13 27				15 17	16 11	
Oldfield Park	d		09 24				11 24				13 24	13 34				15 24		
London Paddington 15 ⊖	d	08 30		09 00	10 00	08 00	09 03	10 03	11 30		11 03		13 00	12 03	14 00	13 03	14 03	
Swindon	d					09 10	10 10	11 10			12 10			13 10		14 10	15 15	
Chippenham	d					09 24	10 24	11 24			12 24			13 24		14 22	15 27	
Melksham	d																	
Bath Spa 7	d		09 27			10 23	11 27	12 23			13 27	13 37		14 23		15 27	16 20	16 24
Freshford	d					10 33		12 33				13 48		14 33				16 34
Avoncliff	d					10x36		12x35				13x51		14x36				16x36
Bradford-on-Avon	d		09 39			10 39	11 39	12 39			13 39	13 54		14 39		15 39	16 31	16 40
Trowbridge	d		09 45			10 45	11 46	12 45			13 46	14 00		14 45		15 45	16 37	16 46
Plymouth	d					08 45			10 35					11b45		13 44		14c06
Exeter St Davids 6	d		08 30			09 51			11 36					13c18		14 45		15c18
Westbury	a	09 50	09 52	10 28		10 52	11 53	12 52	12 54	←	13 53	14 07	14 25	14 52		15 54	16 44	16 53
	d		09 53			11 00	12 03	12 55	12 54	12 55	14 03	14 30		15 00		15 58	16 46	16 58
Frome	d							→				14e49						
Bruton	d											15 00						
Castle Cary	a				11 39				13 12			15 05			15 39			
	d											15 06						
Yeovil Pen Mill	d											15 19						
Thornford	d											15x24						
Yetminster	d											15x27						
Chetnole	d											15x31						
Maiden Newton	d											15 43						
Dorchester West	d											15 53						
Upwey	a											15 59						
Weymouth	a											16 05						
Dilton Marsh	d		09x56				12x06				14x06					16x01		17x01
Warminster	d		10 02			11 07	12 12			13 02	14 12			15 07		16 07	16 53	17 07
Salisbury	a		10 26			11 29	12 34			13 25	14 39			15 30		16 30	17 16	17 30
	d		10 31			11 31	12 36			13 29	14 48			15 31		16 31		17 31
Dean	d																	
Mottisfont & Dunbridge	d																	
Romsey	d		10 50			11 49	12 56			13 47	15 10			15 51		16 49		17 49
Southampton Central	a		11 00			12 04	13 06			13 58	15 20			16 06		17 04		18 04
Bournemouth	a		12 23			13 23	14 23			14 35	16 23			17 23		18 23		19 23
Fareham	a		11 25			12 28	13 33			14 22	15 50			16 28		17 28		18 28
	d		11 26			12 29	13 34			14 23	15 51			16 29		17 29		18 29
Cosham	a		11 33			12 37	13 41			14 31	16 00			16 37		17 37		18 37
Fratton	a		11 40			12 44	14 04			14 38	16 30			16 44		17 44		18 44
Portsmouth & Southsea	a		11 44			12 47	14 08			14 41	16 33			16 47		17 47		18 47
Portsmouth Harbour	a		11 51			12 51	14 13			14 46	16 51			16 51		17 51		18 51
Havant	a		11f59			12f59	14 03			14f59	16 11			16f59		17f59		18f59
Chichester 4	a		12f14			13f14	14 19			15f14	16 22			17f14		18f14		19f14
Barnham	a		12f22			13f22	14 27			15f22	16 30			17f22		18f22		19f22
Worthing 4	a		12f37			13f37	14 44			15f37	16 45			17f37		18f37		19f37
Shoreham-by-Sea	a		12f47			13f47	14 51			15f47	16 51			17f47		18f47		19f47
Hove 2	a		12f53			13f53	14 59			15f53	16 58			17f53		18f53		19f53
Brighton 10	a		13g00			14g00	15 06			16g00	17 05			18g00		19g00		20g00

For general notes see front of timetable
For details of catering facilities see Directory of Train Operators

A To London Waterloo (Table 160)
b Change at Exeter St Davids and Salisbury
c Change at Salisbury
e Arr. 1440
f Change at Fratton
g Change at Fratton and Hove

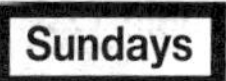

3 February to 23 March

South Wales and Bristol → Weymouth and Portsmouth

Network Diagram - see first page of Table 123

		GW	GW	GW	GW	GW	GW	GW	GW	GW	GW	GW	GW	GW	GW	SW	GW	GW
		1 ◇	◇	◇	◇		◇	1 ◇	◇	1 ◇	◇	◇	1 ◇	◇	◇	1		◇
				A														
		☕	🛒		🛒		🛒	☕	🛒	☕	🛒	🛒	☕		🛒			🛒
Swansea 7	d		14 45	15 45			16 45				17 45			18 45			20 05	20 35
Cardiff Central 7	d		16 15	16 41	17 15		17 45		18 15		18 45	19 15		19 41	20 15		21 01	22 05
Newport (South Wales)	d		16 29	16 55	17 29		18 01		18 29		19 01	19 29		19 55	20 29		21 15	22 23
Severn Tunnel Jn	d		16 39		17 40				18 39		19 11				20 39			22 39
Filton Abbey Wood	d		16 57		17 55		18 25		18 56		19 26	19 52			20 58		21 54	22 56
Bristol Temple Meads 10	d		17 10	17 50	18 10		18 50		19 10		19 50	20 10		20 50	21 11	21 35	22 15	23 10
Keynsham	d		17 17	17 57	18 17				19 17					20 57			22 22	
Oldfield Park	d		17 24	18 04	18 24				19 24					21 04			22 29	
London Paddington 15 ⊖	d	16 00	15 03	16 03			17 03	18 00	17 30	19 00		18 03	20 00	19 03			20 03	21 33
Swindon	d		16 15	17 15		18 31	18 15				19 18			20 17			21 18	22 39
Chippenham	d		16 27	17 27		18 47	18 29				19 32			20 30			21 32	22 52
Melksham	d					18 57												
Bath Spa 7	d		17 27	18 07	18 27		19 02		19 27		20 02	20 22		21 07	21 23	21 49	22 32	23 22
Freshford	d			18 17	18 37							20 32		21 18			22 43	
Avoncliff	d			18x20	18x39							20x34		21x21			22x46	
Bradford-on-Avon	d		17 39	18 23	18 43		19 14		19 39			20 38		21 24	21 36	22 00	22 49	23 34
Trowbridge	d		17 45	18 29	18 50	19 06	19 20		19 45		20 18	20 44		21 30	21 42	22 06	22 55	23 40
Plymouth	d		15b25	15c45	16e02						18 10			19c15	19 15	19 55		
Exeter St Davids 6	d		16e33	16c46	17e18						19 15	19e20		20c19	20 19	20 55		
Westbury	a	17 28	17 52	18 36	18 57	19 13	19 27	19 32	19 52		20 25	20 51	21 32	21 37	21 49	22 13	23 02	23 47
	d	17 29	17 55	18 38	19 01		19 29		19 53		20 27	20 55	21 34	21 38	21 55	22 15		23 50
Frome	d			18 47										21 48				
Bruton	d			18 59										21 59				
Castle Cary	a	17 46		19 04						20 37			21 51	22 04				
	d			19 06										22 05				
Yeovil Pen Mill	d			19 20										22 18				
Thornford	d			19x24										22x23				
Yetminster	d			19x27										22x26				
Chetnole	d			19x31										22x30				
Maiden Newton	d			19 43										22 42				
Dorchester West	d			19 53										22 52				
Upwey	a			20 00										22 58				
Weymouth	a			20 05										23 03				
Dilton Marsh	d				19x04				19x56									23x53
Warminster	d		18 02		19 10		19 37		20 02		20 34	21 02			22 02	22 22		23a58
Salisbury	a		18 30		19 33		19 59		20 25		20 57	21 25			22 25	22 46		
	d		18 31		19 36		20 00		20 30		20 58	21 29			22 29			
Dean	d																	
Mottisfont & Dunbridge	d																	
Romsey	d		18 49		19 55		20 19		20 48		21 16	21 47			22 48			
Southampton Central	a		19 04		20 06		20 31		20 59		21 27	21 58			22 59			
Bournemouth	a		20 23		21 23		21 32				22 23	22 35			00 21			
Fareham	a		19 28		20 28		20 54		21 22		21 49	22 22			23 21			
	d		19 29		20 29		20 55		21 23		21 50	22 23			23 22			
Cosham	a		19 37		20 44		21 19		21 54		22 19	22 54			23 54			
Fratton	a		19 44		21 04		21 09		21 36		22 07	22 36			23 37			
Portsmouth & Southsea	a		19 47		21 08		21 15		21 39		22 12	22 39			23 40			
Portsmouth Harbour	a		19 51		21 13		21 23		21 46		22 20	22 46			23 44			
Havant	a		19f59		20 52		21f32		21f49		22f32	22f49						
Chichester 4	a		20f14		21 03		21f53		22f14		22f53	23f14						
Barnham	a		20f22		21 11		22f01		22f22		23f01	23f22						
Worthing 4	a		20f37		21 34		22f29		23f00									
Shoreham-by-Sea	a		20f47		21 44		22f39		23f09									
Hove 2	a		20f53		21 55		22f51		23f21									
Brighton 10	a		21g00		22 01		22f56		23f25									

For general notes see front of timetable
For details of catering facilities see Directory of Train Operators

A From Weston-super-Mare (Table 134)
b Change at Exeter St Davids and Salisbury
c Change at Castle Cary
e Change at Salisbury
f Change at Fratton
g Change at Fratton and Hove

Table 123

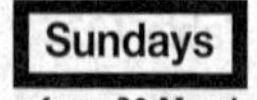

from 30 March

South Wales and Bristol → Weymouth and Portsmouth

Network Diagram - see first page of Table 123

		GW ◇ A	GW ◇ A	GW ◇ A	GW ◇ B	GW ◇ A	GW ◇	GW ◇ A	GW ◇	GW 1 ◇	GW ◇ A	SW 1 ◇ C	GW ◇ A	GW 1 ◇
Swansea 7	d													
Cardiff Central 7	d													
Newport (South Wales)	d													
Severn Tunnel Jn	d													
Filton Abbey Wood	d	08 54	09 55	10 54	11 54	12 54		13 54			14 54		15 56	
Bristol Temple Meads 10	d	09 10	10 10	11 10		13 10	13 20	14 10			15 10	16 04	16 10	
Keynsham	d	09 17		11 17		13 17	13 27				15 17	16 11		
Oldfield Park	d	09 24		11 24		13 24	13 34				15 24			
London Paddington 15 ⊖	d		*08 00*	*09 03*	*10 03*	*11 37*		*12 03*		13 37	*13 03*	*14 03*		15 37
Swindon	d		*09 12*	*10 17*	*11 17*	*12 17*		*13 17*			*14 17*	*15 17*		
Chippenham	d		*09 26*	*10 31*	*11 31*	*12 31*		*13 31*			*14 31*	*15 31*		
Melksham	d													
Bath Spa 7	d	09 27	10 22	11 27	12 22	13 27	13 37	14 23			15 27	16 20	16 24	
Freshford	d		10 32		12 32		13 48	14 33					16 34	
Avoncliff	d		10x34		12x34		13x51	14x36					16x36	
Bradford-on-Avon	d	09 39	10 38	11 39	12 38	13 39	13 54	14 39			15 39	16 31	16 40	
Trowbridge	d	09 45	10 44	11 46	12 44	13 46	14 00	14 45			15 45	16 37	16 46	
Plymouth	d				*09b50*			*11b45*				*13 44*	*14c06*	
Exeter St Davids 6	d		*09c20*		*11c20*			*13c18*				*14 45*	*15c18*	
Westbury	a	09 52	10 51	11 53	12 51	13 53	14 07	14 52		15 07	15 54	16 44	16 53	17 04
	d	09 53	11 00	12 03	12 55	14 03		15 00			15 58	16 46	16 58	
Frome	d													
Bruton	d													
Castle Cary	a													
	d								15 05					
Yeovil Pen Mill	d								15 18					
Thornford	d								15x23					
Yetminster	d								15x26					
Chetnole	d								15x30					
Maiden Newton	d								15 42					
Dorchester West	d								15 52					
Upwey	a								15 58					
Weymouth	a								16 03					
Dilton Marsh	d	09x56		12x06		14x06					16x01		17x01	
Warminster	d	10 02	11 07	12 12	13 02	14 12		15 07			16 07	16 53	17 07	
Salisbury	a	10 26	11 29	12 34	13 25	14 39		15 30			16 30	17 16	17 30	
	d	10 31	11 31	12 36	13 29	14 48		15 31			16 31		17 31	
Dean	d													
Mottisfont & Dunbridge	d													
Romsey	d	10 50	11 49	12 56	13 47	15 10		15 51			16 49		17 49	
Southampton Central	a	11 00	12 04	13 06	13 58	15 20		16 06			17 04		18 04	
Bournemouth	a	*12 23*	*13 23*	*14 23*	*14 35*	*16 23*		*17 23*			*18 23*		*19 23*	
Fareham	a	11 25	12 28	13 33	14 22	15 50		16 28			17 28		18 28	
	d	11 26	12 29	13 34	14 23	15 51		16 29			17 29		18 29	
Cosham	a	11 33	12 37	13 41	14 31	16 00		16 37			17 37		18 37	
Fratton	a	11 40	12 44	*14 04*	14 38	*16 30*		16 44			17 44		18 44	
Portsmouth & Southsea	a	11 44	12 47	*14 08*	14 41	*16 33*		16 47			17 47		18 47	
Portsmouth Harbour	a	11 51	12 51	*14 13*	14 46	*16 51*		16 51			17 51		18 51	
Havant	a	*11e59*	*12e59*	14 03	*14e59*	16 11		*16e59*			*17e59*		*18e59*	
Chichester 4	a	*12e14*	*13e14*	14 19	*15e14*	16 22		*17e14*			*18e14*		*19e14*	
Barnham	a	*12e22*	*13e22*	14 27	*15e22*	16 30		*17e22*			*18e22*		*19e22*	
Worthing 4	a	*12e37*	*13e37*	14 44	*15e37*	16 45		*17e37*			*18e37*		*19e37*	
Shoreham-by-Sea	a	*12e47*	*13e47*	14 51	*15e47*	16 51		*17e47*			*18e47*		*19e47*	
Hove 2	a	*12e53*	*13e53*	14 59	*15e53*	16 58		*17e53*			*18e53*		*19e53*	
Brighton 10	a	*13f00*	*14f00*	15 06	*16f00*	17 05		*18f00*			*19f00*		*20f00*	

For general notes see front of timetable
For details of catering facilities see Directory of Train Operators

A From Bristol Parkway (Table 132)
B From Bristol Parkway (Table 134)
C To London Waterloo (Table 160)
b Change at Exeter St Davids and Salisbury
c Change at Salisbury
e Change at Fratton
f Change at Fratton and Hove

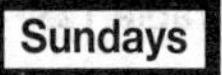

Sundays

from 30 March

South Wales and Bristol → Weymouth and Portsmouth

Network Diagram - see first page of Table 123

		GW	GW	GW	GW	GW	GW	GW	GW	GW	GW	GW	GW	GW	SW	GW	GW
		◇	◇	◇		◇	◇	◇	◇	[1] ◇	◇	◇	[1] ◇	◇	[1]		◇
		A	B	A		A		A	A		A			A			A
Swansea [7]	d																
Cardiff Central [7]	d																
Newport (South Wales)	d																
Severn Tunnel Jn	d																
Filton Abbey Wood	d	16 57		17 55		18 24		18 56	19 25		19 52			20 54		21 54	22 56
Bristol Temple Meads [10]	d	17 10	17 55	18 10		18 50		19 10	19 50		20 10	20 50		21 11	21 35	22 15	23 10
Keynsham	d	17 17	18 02	18 17				19 17				20 57				22 22	
Oldfield Park	d	17 24	18 09	18 24				19 24				21 04				22 29	
London Paddington [15] ⊖	d	15 03	16 03		17 03	17 03		17 33	18 03	19 00		19 03	20 00			20 03	21 03
Swindon	d	16 17	17 17		18 31	18 17		18 48	19 17			20 17				21 20	22 20
Chippenham	d	16 33	17 31		18 47	18 31		19 00	19 31			20 31				21 33	22 33
Melksham	d				18 57												
Bath Spa [7]	d	17 27	18 12	18 27		19 02		19 27	20 02		20 22	21 07		21 23	21 49	22 32	23 22
Freshford	d		18 22	18 37							20 32	21 18				22 43	
Avoncliff	d		18x25	18x39							20x34	21x21				22x46	
Bradford-on-Avon	d	17 39	18 28	18 43		19 14		19 39			20 38	21 24		21 36	22 00	22 49	23 34
Trowbridge	d	17 45	18 34	18 50	19 06	19 20		19 45	20 18		20 44	21 30		21 42	22 06	22 55	23 40
Plymouth	d	15b25		16b10					17 35			19c22		19 22			
Exeter St Davids [6]	d	16e33		17e18					18 37		19e20	20c26		20 26			
Westbury	a	17 52	18 41	18 57	19 13	19 27		19 52	20 25	20 32	20 51	21 37	21 38	21 50	22 13	23 02	23 47
	d	17 55		19 01		19 29		19 53	20 27		20 55	21 38	21 40	21 55	22 15		23 50
Frome	d											21 48					
Bruton	d											21 59					
Castle Cary	a											22 04	21 56				
	d						19 28					22 05					
Yeovil Pen Mill	d						19 41					22 18					
Thornford	d						19x46					22x23					
Yetminster	d						19x49					22x26					
Chetnole	d						19x53					22x30					
Maiden Newton	d						20 05					22 42					
Dorchester West	d						20 15					22 52					
Upwey	a						20 21					22 58					
Weymouth	a						20 26					23 03					
Dilton Marsh	d			19x04				19x56									23x53
Warminster	d	18 02		19 10		19 37		20 02	20 34		21 02			22 02	22 22		23a58
Salisbury	a	18 30		19 33		19 59		20 25	20 57		21 25			22 25	22 46		
	d	18 31		19 36		20 00		20 30	20 58		21 29			22 29			
Dean	d																
Mottisfont & Dunbridge	d																
Romsey	d	18 49		19 55		20 19		20 48	21 16		21 47			22 48			
Southampton Central	a	19 04		20 06		20 31		20 59	21 27		21 58			22 59			
Bournemouth	a	20 23		21 23		21 32			22 23		22 35			00 21			
Fareham	a	19 28		20 28		20 54		21 22	21 49		22 22			23 21			
	d	19 29		20 29		20 55		21 23	21 50		22 23			23 22			
Cosham	a	19 37		20 44		21 19		21 54	22 19		22 54			23 54			
Fratton	a	19 44		21 04		21 09		21 36	22 07		22 36			23 37			
Portsmouth & Southsea	a	19 47		21 08		21 15		21 39	22 12		22 39			23 40			
Portsmouth Harbour	a	19 51		21 13		21 23		21 46	22 20		22 46			23 44			
Havant	a	19f59		20 52		21f32		21f49	22f32		22f49						
Chichester [4]	a	20f14		21 03		21f53		22f14	22f53		23f14						
Barnham	a	20f22		21 11		22f01		22f22	23f01		23f22						
Worthing [4]	a	20f37		21 34		22f29		23f00									
Shoreham-by-Sea	a	20f47		21 44		22f39		23f09									
Hove [2]	a	20f53		21 55		22f51		23f21									
Brighton [10]	a	21g00		22 01		22f56		23f25									

For general notes see front of timetable
For details of catering facilities see Directory of Train Operators

A From Bristol Parkway (Table 132)
B From Weston-super-Mare (Table 134)
b Change at Exeter St Davids and Salisbury
c Change at Castle Cary
e Change at Salisbury
f Change at Fratton
g Change at Fratton and Hove

Portsmouth and Weymouth → Bristol and South Wales

Network Diagram - see first page of Table 123

Miles	Miles	Miles			GW	GW 1◇ ⌶	GW 1◇ ⌶	GW A	GW	GW B	GW 1◇ ⊠	SW 1	GW ◇ C	GW D	GW 1◇ ⌷	GW ◇ ⌶	GW 1◇ ⌷	GW ◇ C	GW A	GW ◇ ⌶	GW	GW ◇ D	GW 1◇ ⊠
—	—	—	Brighton 10	d																			
—	—	—	Hove 2	d																			
—	—	—	Shoreham-by-Sea	d																			
—	—	—	Worthing 4	d																			
—	—	—	Barnham	d												05b20							
—	—	—	Chichester 4	d												05b28							
—	—	—	Havant	d												05b39							
0	—	—	**Portsmouth Harbour**	d												06 00				06 51	06c04		
¾	—	—	Portsmouth & Southsea	d												06 04				06 55	06 23		
1¼	—	—	Fratton	d												06 08				06 59	06e47		
5½	—	—	Cosham	d												06 15				07 08	07 38		
11¼	—	—	Fareham	a												06 23				07 17			
—	—	—		d												06 24				07 20	07 47		
—	—	—	Bournemouth	d												05 57					07 30		
25¾	—	—	**Southampton Central**	d												06 46				07 54	08 24		
34	—	—	Romsey	d												07 00				08 09	08 35		
37¾	—	—	Mottisfont & Dunbridge	d																			
41½	—	—	Dean	d																			
50½	—	—	**Salisbury**	a												07 18				08 27	09 00		
—	—	—		d				06 12				06 40				07 20				08 28	09 03		
70½	—	—	Warminster	d				06 32				07 00		07 23		07 42				08 48	09 23		
73½	—	—	Dilton Marsh	d				06x36						07x27		07x46					09x27		
—	0	—	**Weymouth**	d									05 40					06 32				08 11	
—	2½	—	Upwey	d									05 45					06 37				08 16	
—	7	—	Dorchester West	d									05 54					06 45				08 24	
—	14¾	—	Maiden Newton	d									06 05					06 57				08 35	
—	21¼	—	Chetnole	d									06x13					07x04				08x42	
—	23¾	—	Yetminster	d									06x16					07x07				08x46	
—	24½	—	Thornford	d									06x18					07x10				08x48	
—	27½	—	Yeovil Pen Mill	d									06 26					07f30				08 56	
—	39¼	—	Castle Cary	a									06 38					07 42				09 08	
—	—	—		d							06 43		06 46		07 29			07 43				09 08	09 39
—	42¾	—	Bruton	d									06 52					07 49				09 14	
—	53¼	—	Frome	d			06 12		06 43				07 04					08 02				09 26	
75	59	0	**Westbury**	a			06 22	06 40	06 56		07 01	07 06	07 13	07 31	07 46	07 50	⟵	08 12		08 54	09 33	09 36	09 57
—	—	—		d	05 58	06 10	06 23	06 42	06 57	07 02	07 03	07 07	07 18	07 38	07 54	07 52	07 54	08 17	08 45	08 56		09 38	09 58
—	—	—	Exeter St Davids 6	a											⟶	10g33						11 06	
—	—	—	Plymouth	a												11h48						12j23	
79	63	4	Trowbridge	d	06 04			06 48	07 03	07 08		07 13	07 24	07 44		07 58		08 23	08 51	09 02		09 44	
82¼	66¼	—	Bradford-on-Avon	d	06 10			06 54	07 09			07 20	07 30	07 50		08 04		08 29	08 57	09 10		09 50	
83½	67½	—	Avoncliff	d	06x12			06x56	07x11				07x32	07x52		08x06		08x31	08x59	09 13		09x52	
84½	68½	—	Freshford	d	06 15			06 59	07 15				07 36	07 55		08 09		08 34	09 02	09 15		09 55	
91½	75½	—	Bath Spa 7	a	06 26			07 10	07 26			07 32	07 47	08 06		08 20		08 45	09 13	09 24		10 06	
—	—	9½	Melksham	d						07 17										09 34			
—	—	15¾	Chippenham	a	06 54					07 30		07 54		08 24		08 43		09 24	09 54			10 24	
—	—	32½	Swindon	a	07 09					07 48		08 09		08 39		09 02		09 39	10 09			10 40	
—	—	—	London Paddington 15 ⊖	a	08 14	07 51	08 09			09 06	08 38	09 15		09 44		10 15	09 22	10 44	11 15			11 41	11 23
92½	76½	—	Oldfield Park	a	06 30			07 14	07 30			07 36	07 51	08 10		08 24		08 49	09 17			10 10	
98½	82½	—	Keynsham	a	06 38			07 21	07 37			07 43	07 58	08 17		08 31		08 56	09 24			10 17	
103	87	—	**Bristol Temple Meads 10**	a	06 46			07 29	07 45			07 52	08 06	08 25		08 39		09 04	09 32	09 41		10 25	
107½	91½	—	Filton Abbey Wood	a	07 01			07 47	08 02				08 23	08 47		09 00		09 20	09 47	10 01		10 47	
119½	119½	—	Severn Tunnel Jn	a	07 14								08k46					09k45	10k48				
129½	113½	—	Newport (South Wales)	a	07 26				08 24				08k59			09 23		09k58	10m29	10 23			
141¼	125¼	—	**Cardiff Central 7**	a	07 45				08 42				09m23			09 40		10k17	10m48	10 40			
—	—	—	Swansea 7	a	08 49				09n44							10 43		11q43					

For general notes see front of timetable
For details of catering facilities see Directory of Train Operators

A To Gloucester (Table 134)
B To Cheltenham Spa (Table 125)
C To Bristol Parkway (Table 132)
D To Great Malvern (Table 71)
b Change at Fratton
c Change at Fratton and Southampton Central
e Change at Cosham and Southampton Central
f Arr. 0717
g Change at Salisbury
h Change at Salisbury and Exeter St Davids
j Change at Westbury and Exeter St Davids
k Change at Bristol Temple Meads
m Change at Bristol Parkway
n Change at Newport (South Wales)
q Change at Bristol Temple Meads and Cardiff Central

Portsmouth and Weymouth → Bristol and South Wales

Network Diagram - see first page of Table 123

		GW	GW	GW	GW	GW	GW	GW	GW	GW	GW	GW	GW	GW	SW	GW	GW	GW	GW	GW	GW	GW
		◇ ⌶	A	1 ◇ ⊠	◇ ⌶	◇ B	◇ ⌶	◇ A	1 ◇ ⌶	◇ ⌶	◇ A	C	D	◇ ⌶	1 ◇ E	1 ◇ ⊠	◇ ⌶	B	1 ◇ ⌶	◇ ⌶	◇ A	◇ ⌶
Brighton [10]	d	07b06			08c07	09 00	09e03			10e03				11e03			12e03			13e03		14e03
Hove [2]	d	07b10			08c11	09 04	09e07			10e07				11e07			12e07			13e07		14e07
Shoreham-by-Sea	d	07b16			08c20	09 13	09e17			10e16				11e16			12e16			13e16		14e16
Worthing [4]	d	07b23			08c28	09 22	09e26			10e25				11e25			12e25			13e25		14e25
Barnham	d	07b45			09b00	09 38	09b58			10b57				11b57			12b57			13b57		14b57
Chichester [4]	d	07b53			09b08	09 47	10b06			11b05				12b05			13b05			14b05		15b05
Havant	d	08b04			09b26	09 59	10b22			11b23				12b23			13b23			14b23		15b23
Portsmouth Harbour	d	08 22			09 22	09 32	10 22			11 22				12 22			13 22			14 22		15 22
Portsmouth & Southsea	d	08 27			09 27	09 36	10 27			11 27				12 27			13 27			14 27		15 27
Fratton	d	08 31			09 31	09 40	10 31			11 31				12 31			13 31			14 31		15 31
Cosham	d	08 39			09 39	10 05	10 39			11 39				12 39			13 39			14 39		15 39
Fareham	a	08 46			09 46	10 13	10 46			11 46				12 46			13 46			14 46		15 46
	d	08 47			09 47	10 14	10 47			11 47				12 47			13 47			14 47		15 47
Bournemouth	d	08 10			09 18	09 55	10 21			11 21				12 21			13 21			14 21		15 21
Southampton Central	d	09 10			10 10	10 40	11 10			12 10			12 26	13 10			14 10			15 10		16 10
Romsey	d	09 21			10 21	10 51	11 21			12 21			12 39	13 21			14 21			15 21		16 21
Mottisfont & Dunbridge	d																					
Dean	d																					
Salisbury	a	09 40			10 40	11 10	11 40			12 40			13 02	13 40			14 40			15 40		16 40
	d	09 41			10 41	11 11	11 41			12 41			13 08	13 41	13 52		14 41			15 41		16 41
Warminster	d	10 01	10 28		11 01	11 31	12 01			13 01			13 31	14 01	14 12		15 01	15 28		16 01		17 01
Dilton Marsh	d		10x32										13x35					15x32				
Weymouth	d							11 11			13 11										15 11	
Upwey	d							11 16			13 16										15 16	
Dorchester West	d							11 24			13 25										15 25	
Maiden Newton	d							11 36			13 43										15 36	
Chetnole	d							11x43			13x50										15x45	
Yetminster	d							11x46			13x53										15x48	
Thornford	d							11x49			13x56										15x50	
Yeovil Pen Mill	d							11 57			14 04										15 57	
Castle Cary	a							12 08			14 16										16 09	
	d							12 09	12 44		14 16					14 43			15 44		16 10	
Bruton	d							12 27			14 22										16 16	
Frome	d							12 39			14 35										16 29	
Westbury	a	10 07	10 36		11 07	11 38	12 07	12 48	13 02	13 07	14 44		13 39	14 07	14 18	15 01	15 07	15 36	16 01	16 07	16 38	17 07
	d	10 08	10 38	11 02	11 08	11 38	12 08	12 49	13 03	13 08	14 45	13 38	13 45	14 08	14 19	15 02	15 08	15 38	16 01	16 08	16 38	17 08
Exeter St Davids [6]	a	11f42			12f33		13 32	13g32						15f42						17 32	17g32	
Plymouth	a	13h09			13h48		14 36	14g36						16f57						18 39	18g39	
Trowbridge	d	10 14	10 44		11 14	11 44	12 14	12 55		13 14	14 51	13 44	13 51	14 14	14 25		15 14	15 44		16 14	16 44	17 14
Bradford-on-Avon	d	10 20	10 50		11 20	11 50	12 20	13 01		13 20	14 57	13 50	13 57	14 20	14 31		15 20	15 50		16 20	16 50	17 20
Avoncliff	d		10x52			11x52		13x03			15 00	13x52	13x59					15x52			16x52	
Freshford	d		10 55			11 55		13 05			15 02	13 55	14 02					15 55			16 55	
Bath Spa [7]	a	10 33	11 07		11 33	12 07	12 33	13 17		13 33	15 13	14 07	14 13	14 33	14 45		15 33	16 07		16 33	17 08	17 33
Melksham	d																					
Chippenham	a	10 54			11 54		12 54	13 24		13 54				14 54	15 24		15 54			16 54		17 54
Swindon	a	11 09			12 09		13 09	13 39		14 09				15 09	15 39		16 09			17 09		18 09
London Paddington [15] ⊖	a	12 15		12 23	13 15		14 15	14 42	14 49	15 15				16 15	16 44	16 22	17 15		17 53	18 15		19 15
Oldfield Park	a		11 10			12 10		13 20			15 17	14 10						16 10			17 10	
Keynsham	a		11 17			12 17		13 27			15 25	14 17						16 17			17 19	
Bristol Temple Meads [10]	a	10 47	11 26		11 47	12 26	12 47	13 47		13 47	15 32	14 26		14 47	15 00		15 47	16 26		16 47	17 27	17 47
Filton Abbey Wood	a	11 01	11 47		12 01	12 47	13 01	13 51		14 01	15 47	14 47	14 40	15 00	15 29		16 01	16 47		17 00	17 47	18 01
Severn Tunnel Jn	a	11j45			12j45		13j47			14j45					15 45		16j47			17 13		18 14
Newport (South Wales)	a	11 24			12 24		13 24			14 24				15 24	15 58		16 24			17 25		18 26
Cardiff Central [7]	a	11 41			12 41		13 41			14 41				15 41	16 16		16 42			17 45		18 43
Swansea [7]	a	12 43			13 43		14 43			15 43				16 43			17k43			18k46		19 48

For general notes see front of timetable
For details of catering facilities see Directory of Train Operators

A To Gloucester (Table 134)
B To Great Malvern (Table 71)
C To Worcester Foregate Street (Table 71)
D To Bristol Parkway (Table 134)
E From London Waterloo (Table 160)
b Change at Fareham
c Change at Barnham and Fareham
e Change at Fratton
f Change at Salisbury
g Change at Castle Cary
h Change at Salisbury and Exeter St Davids
j Change at Bristol Temple Meads
k Change at Newport (South Wales)

Portsmouth and Weymouth → Bristol and South Wales

Network Diagram - see first page of Table 123

		GW	GW	GW	GW	GW	GW	GW	GW	GW	GW	GW	GW	GW	SW	GW	GW	GW	GW	GW
			◇	◇	◇	1 ◇	1 ◇		◇	◇	1		1 ◇	◇	1 ◇	1	◇	◇	◇	
		A	B					C	D											
Brighton 10	d			15b03	16b03				17 00	17b03				18c14				19c14		20b03
Hove 2	d			15b07	16b07				17 04	17b07				18e25				19e20		20b07
Shoreham-by-Sea	d			15b16	16b16				17 13	17b16				18e33				19e28		20b19
Worthing 4	d			15b25	16b25				17 22	17b25				18e44				19e40		20b29
Barnham	d			15e57	16e57				17 38	18e01				18e59				19e56		20e57
Chichester 4	d			16e05	17e05				17 47	18e09				19e07				20e04		21e05
Havant	d			16e23	17e19				17 58	18e23				19e22				20e25		21e26
Portsmouth Harbour	d			16 22	17 22				17f28	18 22				19 22				20 22		21 22
Portsmouth & Southsea	d			16 27	17 27				17 36	18 27				19 27				20 27		21 27
Fratton	d			16 31	17 31				17 40	18 31				19 31				20 31		21 31
Cosham	d			16 39	17 39				18 05	18 39				19 39				20 32		21g44
Fareham	a			16 46	17 46				18 12	18 46				19 46				20 46		21 48
	d			16 47	17 47				18 13	18 47				19 47				20 47		21h48
Bournemouth	d			16 21	17 21				17 59	18 21				19 21				20 21		21 12
Southampton Central	d			17 10	18 10				18 40	19 10				20 10				21 10	21 20	22 22
Romsey	d			17 21	18 21				18 51	19 21				20 21				21 21	21 31	22 33
Mottisfont & Dunbridge	d																			22 38
Dean	d																			22 44
Salisbury	a			17 40	18 40				19 10	19 40				20 41				21 40	21 56	22 58
	d			17 41	18 41				19 11	19 41				20 41	20 57			21 41	21 58	23 00
Warminster	d	17 28		18 01	19 01				19 30	20 01				21 01	21 17			22 01	22 18	23 20
Dilton Marsh	d	17x32							19x35										22x22	23x24
Weymouth	d		17 11														20 02			
Upwey	d		17 16														20 07			
Dorchester West	d		17 25														20 17			
Maiden Newton	d		17 36														20 28			
Chetnole	d		17x44														20x35			
Yetminster	d		17x47														20x39			
Thornford	d		17x50														20x41			
Yeovil Pen Mill	d		17 57														20 49			
Castle Cary	a		18 08														21 01			
	d		18 10			18 52							20 43				21 02			
Bruton	d		18 15														21 08			
Frome	d		18 27								20 17					21 15	21 20			
Westbury	a	17 36	18 36	18 07	19 07	19 10			19 38	20 07	20 27		21 01	21 07	21 23	21 24	21 29	22 07	22 26	23 30
	d	17 38	18 38	18 08	19 08	19 11	19 18	19 32	19 38	20 08		20 38	21 03	21 08	21 24		21 38	22 08	22 41	
Exeter St Davids 6	a	19 18		19j57	20j36				21 15	21j55							23k15			
Plymouth	a	20m48		21m17	21n48				22m24								23k22			
Trowbridge	d	17 44	18 44	18 14	19 14			19 38	19 44	20 14		20 44		21 14	21 30		21 44	22 14	22 47	
Bradford-on-Avon	d	17 50	18 50	18 22	19 20				19 50	20 20		20 50		21 21	21 36		21 50	22 20	22 53	
Avoncliff	d	17x52	18 52						19x52			20x52					21x52		22x55	
Freshford	d	17 55	18 55						19 55			20 55					21 55		22 59	
Bath Spa 7	a	18 08	19 06	18 35	19 35				20 08	20 35		21 06		21 35	21 50		22 06	22 34	23 11	
Melksham	d							19 47												
Chippenham	a			18 54	19 54			20 01		20 54				22 07				22 57		
Swindon	a			19 09	20 09			20 19		21 09				22 23				23 13		
London Paddington 15 ⊖	a			20 15	21 15	20 39	21 02	21 30		22 15			22 30	23q36				00 32		
Oldfield Park	a	18 10	19 10						20 10			21 10					22 10		23 14	
Keynsham	a	18 17	19 17						20 17			21 17			21 58		22 17		23 22	
Bristol Temple Meads 10	a	18 27	19 25	18 50	19 49				20 27	20 50		21 27		21 50	22 06		22 27	22 48	23 30	
Filton Abbey Wood	a	18 47	19 47	19 01	20 00				20 47	21 01				22 00				23 00		
Severn Tunnel Jn	a			19r47	20r46					21r48				22 16				23 16		
Newport (South Wales)	a			19 25	20 23					21 28				22 35				23 35		
Cardiff Central 7	a			19 41	20 41					21 45				22 54				23 55		
Swansea 7	a			20 46	21 42					23 00				00 25				02 10		

For general notes see front of timetable
For details of catering facilities see Directory of Train Operators

A To Great Malvern (Table 71)
B To Cheltenham Spa (Table 134)
C To Cheltenham Spa (Table 125)
D To Worcester Shrub Hill (Table 57)
b Change at Fratton
c Change at Hove and Fareham
e Change at Fareham
f Change at Fratton and Cosham
g Change at Southampton Central
h By changing at Southampton Central, passengers may depart at 2153
j Change at Salisbury
k Change at Castle Cary
m Change at Westbury and Exeter St Davids
n Change at Salisbury and Exeter St Davids
q Fridays arr. 2329
r Change at Bristol Temple Meads

Table 123

Saturdays

until 26 January

Portsmouth and Weymouth → Bristol and South Wales

Network Diagram - see first page of Table 123

		GW	GW	SW	GW	GW	GW	GW	GW	GW	GW	GW	GW	GW	SW	GW	GW	GW	GW	GW	GW	GW	SW
				[1]		◇	◇		◇		◇	[1] ◇	◇	◇	[1] ◇	◇	◇	◇	[1] ◇	◇		◇	[1] ◇
		A			B		A				B	☕				A	C		A ☕		B		D
Brighton [10]	d								05b27				07c03	08c03			09 00	09c03		10c03		11c03	
Hove [2]	d								05b31				07c07	08c07			09 04	09c07		10c07		11c07	
Shoreham-by-Sea	d								05b43				07c16	08c16			09 13	09c17		10c16		11c16	
Worthing [4]	d								05b53				07c25	08c25			09 22	09c25		10c25		11c25	
Barnham	d					05c30			06c27				07b57	08b57			09 41	09b57		10b57		11b57	
Chichester [4]	d					05c38			06c35				08b05	09b05			09 49	10b05		11b05		12b05	
Havant	d					05c49			06c46				08b23	09b23			10 00	10b23		11b23		12b23	
Portsmouth Harbour	d					06 00			07 04				08 22	09 22			09e28	10 22		11 22		12 22	
Portsmouth & Southsea	d					06 04			07 08				08 27	09 27			09 36	10 27		11 27		12 27	
Fratton	d					06 08			07 13				08 31	09 31			09 40	10 31		11 31		12 31	
Cosham	d					06 15			07 20	07 44			08 39	09 39			10 06	10 39		11 39	11 44	12 39	
Fareham	a					06 24			07 28				08 46	09 46			10 14	10 46		11 46		12 46	
	d					06 25			07 29	07 53			08 47	09 47			10 15	10 47		11 47	11 53	12 47	
Bournemouth	d					05 42			06 42	07 45			08 21	09 21			09 59	10 21		11 21	11 45	12 21	
Southampton Central	d					06 47			07 52	08 27			09 10	10 10			10 40	11 10		12 10	12 27	13 10	
Romsey	d					06 59			08 09	08 38			09 21	10 21			10 51	11 21		12 21	12 38	13 21	
Mottisfont & Dunbridge	d																						
Dean	d																						
Salisbury	a					07 22			08 29	09 03			09 40	10 40			11 10	11 40		12 40	13 03	13 40	
	d	06 03		06 40		07 23			08 32	09 04			09 41	10 41	10 52		11 11	11 41		12 41	13 04	13 41	13 52
Warminster	d	06 23		07 00	07 23	07 43			08 53	09 25			10 01	11 01	11 12		11 32	12 01		13 01	13 25	14 01	14 12
Dilton Marsh	d	06x27			07x28					09x29											13x29		
Weymouth	d						06 27				08 11					11 10							
Upwey	d						06 32				08 16					11 15							
Dorchester West	d						06 40				08 23					11 23							
Maiden Newton	d						06 52				08 35					11 42							
Chetnole	d						06x59				08x42					11x50							
Yetminster	d						07x02				08x45					11x54							
Thornford	d						07x05				08x48					11x56							
Yeovil Pen Mill	d						07f25				08 56					12 03							
Castle Cary	a						07 37				09 07					12 14							
	d						07 37				09 08	09 46				12 26			12 44				
Bruton	d						07 43				09 13					12 31							
Frome	d		06 37				07 56				09 25					12 43							
Westbury	a	06 31	06 46	07 06	07 31	07 49	08 05		08 59	09 33	09 35		10 07	11 07	11 18	12 51	11 38	12 07	13 02	13 07	13 33	14 07	14 18
	d	06 38	06 51	07 07	07 38	07 52	08 38	09 03	09 08		09 38		10 08	11 08	11 19	12 52	11 48	12 08	13 03	13 08	13 38	14 08	14 19
Exeter St Davids [6]	a								10g32		11 06		11g56	12g30				13 32		14g19		15g42	
Plymouth	a								11h48		12j23			13h48				14 36		15h48		16g58	
Trowbridge	d	06 44	06 57	07 13	07 44	07 58	08 44	09 09	09 14		09 44		10 14	11 14	11 25	12 58	11 54	12 14		13 14	13 44	14 14	14 25
Bradford-on-Avon	d	06 49	07 03	07 19	07 50	08 04	08 50		09 20		09 50		10 20	11 20	11 31	13 04	12 00	12 20		13 20	13 50	14 20	14 31
Avoncliff	d	06x51	07x05		07x53		08x53				09x52						12x03				13x52		
Freshford	d	06 55	07 09		07 55		08 55				09 55						12 05				13 55		
Bath Spa [7]	a	07 06	07 20	07 32	08 07	08 17	09 08		09 33		10 06		10 34	11 33	11 45	13 17	12 16	12 33		13 33	14 08	14 33	14 44
Melksham	d							09 18															
Chippenham	a	07 24		07 54		08 54		09 30	09 54		10 24		10 54	11 54						13 54		14 54	15 54
Swindon	a	07 40		08 09		09 09		09 48	10 09		10 39		11 09	12 09						14 09		15 09	16 09
London Paddington [15] ⊖	a	08 45		09 15		10 14		10 59	11 15		11 42	11 22	12 15	13 15					14 46	15 15		16 15	17 15
Oldfield Park	a	07 10	07 24	07 36	08 11		09 12				10 10					13 21	12 20				14 12		
Keynsham	a	07 17	07 31	07 43	08 18		09 19				10 17					13 27	12 27				14 18		
Bristol Temple Meads [10]	a	07 25	07 39	07 52	08 26	08 31	09 27		09 47		10 25		10 48	11 47	12 00	13 36	12 35	12 47		13 47	14 26	14 47	15 00
Filton Abbey Wood	a	07 47	08 00	08 29	08 47	09k00	09 47		10 00		10 47		11 00	12 00		13 47	12 47	13 00		14 00	14 47	15 00	15 29
Severn Tunnel Jn	a			08 45		09m45			10m45				11m45	12m45				13m45		14m45			15 47
Newport (South Wales)	a		08 23	09 00		09 23			10 23				11 22	12 22				13 22		14 22		15 22	15 59
Cardiff Central [7]	a		08 42	09 21		09 40			10 40				11 40	12 39				13 40		14 39		15 39	16 15
Swansea [7]	a		09 56			10 43			11 43				12 43	13 43				14 43		15 43		16 43	

For general notes see front of timetable
For details of catering facilities see Directory of Train Operators

A To Gloucester (Table 134)
B To Great Malvern (Table 71)
C To Worcester Foregate Street (Table 71)
D From London Waterloo (Table 160)
b Change at Fareham
c Change at Fratton
e Change at Fratton and Cosham
f Arr. 0711
g Change at Salisbury
h Change at Salisbury and Exeter St Davids
j Change at Westbury and Exeter St Davids
k By changing at Bristol Temple Meads, passengers may arrive at 0847
m Change at Bristol Temple Meads

Table 123

Saturdays

until 26 January

Portsmouth and Weymouth → Bristol and South Wales

Network Diagram - see first page of Table 123

		GW	GW	GW	GW		GW	GW	GW	GW	GW	GW		GW	GW	GW	GW	GW	GW	GW	SW	GW	GW	GW		
		◇	**1** ◇	◇	◇		◇	◇	**1** ◇	◇	◇	◇		**1** ◇	◇		**1** ◇	◇	**1**	◇	**1** ◇	◇	◇			
		A						A				B				B					C					
			☕						☕					☕			☕									
Brighton **10**	d				12b03		13b03			14b03	15b03				16b03	17 00		17b03		18b03			19b03			
Hove **2**	d				12b07		13b07			14b07	15b07				16b07	17 04		17b07		18b07			19b07			
Shoreham-by-Sea	d				12b16		13b16			14b16	15b16				16b16	17 13		17b17		18b16			19b19			
Worthing **4**	d				12b25		13b25			14b25	15b25				16b25	17 22		17b25		18b25			19b29			
Barnham	d				12c57		13c57			14c57	15c57				16c57	17 41		17c57		18c57			19c57			
Chichester **4**	d				13c05		14c05			15c05	16c05				17c05	17 49		18c05		19c05			20c05			
Havant	d				13c23		14c23			15c23	16c23				17c23	18 00		18c23		19c23			20c26			
Portsmouth Harbour	d				13 22		14 22			15 22	16 22				17 22	17 32		18 22		19 22			20 22			
Portsmouth & Southsea	d				13 27		14 27			15 27	16 27				17 27	17 36		18 27		19 27			20 27			
Fratton	d				13 31		14 31			15 31	16 31				17 31	17 40		18 31		19 31			20 31			
Cosham	d				13 39		14 39			15 39	16 39				17 39	18 06		18 39		19 39			20 32	20 44		
Fareham	a				13 46		14 46			15 46	16 46				17 46	18 14		18 46		19 46			20 44			
	d				13 47		14 47			15 47	16 47				17 47	18 15		18 47		19 47			20 47	20 53		
Bournemouth	d				13 21		14 21			15 21	16 21				17 21	17 59		18 21		19 21			20 21			
Southampton Central	d				14 10		15 10			16 10	17 10				18 10	18 40		19 10		20 10			21 10	21 27		
Romsey	d				14 21		15 21			16 21	17 21				18 21	18 51		19 21		20 21			21 21	21 38		
Mottisfont & Dunbridge	d																									
Dean	d																									
Salisbury	a				14 40		15 40			16 40	17 40				18 40	19 10		19 40		20 40			21 40	22 03		
	d				14 41		15 41			16 41	17 41				18 41	19 11		19 41		20 41	20 57		21 41	22 04		
Warminster	d				15 01		16 01			17 01	18 01				19 01	19 31		20 01		21 01	21 17		22 01	22 25		
Dilton Marsh	d															19x36								22x29		
Weymouth	d	13 10						15 10				17 10										19 58				
Upwey	d	13 15						15 15				17 15										20 03				
Dorchester West	d	13 24						15 23				17 24										20 11				
Maiden Newton	d	13e44						15f37				17 36										20 23				
Chetnole	d	13x51						15x45				17x43										20x30				
Yetminster	d	13x54						15x48				17x46										20x33				
Thornford	d	13x57						15x51				17x49										20x36				
Yeovil Pen Mill	d	14 05						15 58				17 57										20 44				
Castle Cary	a	14 16						16 09				18 08										20 56				
	d	14 17	14 43					16 10	16 00			18 10		18 38			19 46					20 56				
Bruton	d	14 22						16 15				18 15										21 02				
Frome	d	14 34						16 27				18 27							20 53			21 15				
Westbury	a	14 44	15 01		15 07		16 07	16 36	16 17	17 07	18 07	18 36		18 56	19 07	19 39	20 03	20 07	21 02	21 07	21 23	21 25	22 08	22 33		
	d	14 45	15 02	15 03	15 08		16 08	16 38	16 19	17 08	18 08	18 38		18 57	19 08	19 48	20 05	20 08		21 08	21 24	21 38	22 08	22 38		
Exeter St Davids **6**	a						17g36				19g57							21 38		22 36		22h36				
Plymouth	a						18j48				21j17							22 43		23 47		23h47				
Trowbridge	d	14 51		15 09	15 14		16 14	16 44		17 14	18 14	18 44			19 14	19 54		20 14		21 14	21 30	21 44	22 14	22 44		
Bradford-on-Avon	d	14 57			15 20		16 20	16 50		17 20	18 20	18 50			19 20	20 00		20 20		21 20	21 36	21 50	22 20	22 50		
Avoncliff	d	14x59						16 52				18x52				20x02						21x52		22x52		
Freshford	d	15 03						16 56				18 55				20 05						21 55		22 55		
Bath Spa **7**	a	15 14			15 33		16 33	17 07		17 33	18 33	19 06			19 33	20 16		20 33		21 37	21 50	22 06	22 34	23 06		
Melksham	d			15 18																						
Chippenham	a			15 28	15 54		16 54			17 54	18 54				19 54			20 57					22 57			
Swindon	a			15 47	16 09		17 09			18 09	19 09				20 09			21 13					23 13			
London Paddington **15** ⊖	a		16 22		17 15		18 15		18 07	19 15	20 15			20 21	21 15		21 28	22 16					00 32			
Oldfield Park	a	15 18						17 11				19 10				20 21						22 10		23 10		
Keynsham	a	15 24						17 17				19 17				20 28					21 58	22 17		23 17		
Bristol Temple Meads 10	a	15 32			15 47		16 47	17 25		17 47	18 47	19 26			19 47	20 35		20 47		21 51	22 06	22 27	22 48	23 25		
Filton Abbey Wood	a	15 47			16 00		17 00	17 47		18 00	19 00	19 47			20 00	20 47		21 00		22 02			23 00			
Severn Tunnel Jn	a				16k45		17 13			18 13	19k47							21k45		22 18			23 16			
Newport (South Wales)	a				16 24		17 25			18 25	19 24				20 22			21 26		22 35			23 33			
Cardiff Central 7	a				16 41		17 44			18 41	19 40				20 39			21 42		22 56			23 54			
Swansea **7**	a				17 43		18m46			19 43	20 48				21 47			22m46		00 01						

For general notes see front of timetable
For details of catering facilities see Directory of Train Operators

- **A** To Gloucester (Table 134)
- **B** To Cheltenham Spa (Table 57)
- **C** From London Waterloo (Table 160)
- **b** Change at Fratton
- **c** Change at Fareham
- **e** Arr. 1333
- **f** Arr. 1532
- **g** Change at Salisbury
- **h** Change at Castle Cary
- **j** Change at Salisbury and Exeter St Davids
- **k** Change at Bristol Temple Meads
- **m** Change at Newport (South Wales)

Table 123

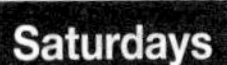

2 February to 22 March

Portsmouth and Weymouth → Bristol and South Wales

Network Diagram - see first page of Table 123

	GW	GW	SW	GW	GW	GW	GW	GW	GW	GW	GW	GW	SW	GW	GW	GW	GW	GW	GW	GW	GW	SW
			1		◇	◇		◇		◇	1 ◇	◇	1 ◇	◇	◇	◇	◇	1 ◇	◇		◇	1 ◇
	A			B		A				B					A	C				B		D
Brighton 10 d								05b27				07c03		08c03		09 00	09c03		10c03		11c03	
Hove 2 d								05b31				07c07		08c07		09 04	09c07		10c07		11c07	
Shoreham-by-Sea d								05b43				07c16		08c16		09 13	09c17		10c16		11c16	
Worthing 4 d								05b53				07c25		08c25		09 22	09c25		10c25		11c25	
Barnham d					05c30			06c27				07b57		08b57		09 41	09b57		10b57		11b57	
Chichester 4 d					05c38			06c35				08b05		09b05		09 49	10b05		11b05		12b05	
Havant d					05c49			06c46				08b23		09b23		10 00	10b23		11b23		12b23	
Portsmouth Harbour d					06 00			07 04				08 22		09 22		09e28	10 22		11 22		12 22	
Portsmouth & Southsea d					06 04			07 08				08 27		09 27		09 36	10 27		11 27		12 27	
Fratton d					06 08			07 13				08 31		09 31		09 40	10 31		11 31		12 31	
Cosham d					06 15			07 20	07 44			08 39		09 39		10 06	10 39		11 39	11 44	12 39	
Fareham a					06 24			07 28				08 46		09 46		10 14	10 46		11 46		12 46	
Fareham d					06 25			07 29	07 53			08 47		09 47		10 15	10 47		11 47	11 53	12 47	
Bournemouth d					05 42			06 42	07 45			08 21		09 21		09 59	10 21		11 21	11 45	12 21	
Southampton Central d					06 47			07 52	08 27			09 10		10 10		10 40	11 10		12 10	12 27	13 10	
Romsey d					06 59			08 09	08 38			09 21		10 21		10 51	11 21		12 21	12 38	13 21	
Mottisfont & Dunbridge d																						
Dean d																						
Salisbury a					07 22			08 29	09 03			09 40		10 40		11 10	11 40		12 40	13 03	13 40	
Salisbury d	06 03		06 40		07 23			08 32	09 04			09 41	10 52	10 41		11 11	11 41		12 41	13 04	13 41	13 52
Warminster d	06 23		07 00	07 23	07 43			08 53	09 25			10 01	11 12	11 01		11 32	12 01		13 01	13 25	14 01	14 12
Dilton Marsh d	06x27			07x28					09x29											13x30		
Weymouth d						06 27				08 11					11 10							
Upwey d						06 32				08 16					11 15							
Dorchester West d						06 40				08 23					11 23							
Maiden Newton d						06 52				08 35					11f42							
Chetnole d						06x59				08x42					11x50							
Yetminster d						07x02				08x45					11x54							
Thornford d						07x05				08x48					11x56							
Yeovil Pen Mill d						07g25				08 56					12 03							
Castle Cary a						07 37				09 07					12 14							
Castle Cary d						07 37				09 08	09 46				12 26			12 44				
Bruton d						07 43				09 13					12 31							
Frome d		06 37				07 56				09 25					12 42							
Westbury a	06 31	06 46	07 06	07 31	07 49	08 05		08 59	09 33	09 35		10 07	11 18	11 07	12 51	11 38	12 07	13 02	13 07	13 33	14 07	14 18
Westbury d	06 38	06 51	07 07	07 38	07 52	08 38	09 03	09 08		09 38		10 08	11 19	11 08	12 52	11 48	12 08	13 10	13 08	13 38	14 08	14 19
Exeter St Davids 6 a								10h32		11 08		11h56		12h30			13 32		14h19	15 06	15h42	
Plymouth a								11j48		12k23				13j48			14 36		15j48	16k25	16h58	
Trowbridge d	06 44	06 57	07 13	07 44	07 58	08 44	09 09	09 14		09 44		10 14	11 25	11 14	12 58	11 54	12 14		13 14	13 44	14 14	14 25
Bradford-on-Avon d	06 49	07 03	07 19	07 50	08 04	08 50		09 20		09 50		10 20	11 31	11 20	13 04	12 00	12 20		13 20	13 50	14 20	14 31
Avoncliff d	06x51	07x05		07x53		08x53				09x52						12x03				13x52		
Freshford d	06 55	07 09		07 55		08 55				09 55						12 05				13 55		
Bath Spa 7 a	07 06	07 20	07 32	08 07	08 17	09 08		09 33		10 06		10 34	11 45	11 33	13 17	12 16	12 33		13 33	14 08	14 33	14 45
Melksham d							09 18															
Chippenham a			07 54		08 54		09 30	09 54				10 54		12 00					13 54		14 54	15 54
Swindon a			08 10		09 10		09 48	10 09				11 10		12 15					14 10		15 10	16 10
London Paddington 15 ⊖ a			09 55		10 20			11 14			11 22	12 57		13 56			14 19	14 52	15 56			16 53
Oldfield Park a	07 10	07 24	07 36	08 11		09 12				10 10					13 21	12 20				14 12		
Keynsham a	07 17	07 31	07 43	08 18		09 19				10 17					13 27	12 27				14 18		
Bristol Temple Meads 10 a	07 25	07 39	07 52	08 26	08 31	09 27		09 47		10 25		10 48	12 00	11 47	13 36	12 35	12 47		13 47	14 26	14 47	15 00
Filton Abbey Wood a	07 47	08 00	08 29	08 47	09m00	09 47		10 00		10 47		11 00		12 00	13 47	12 47	13 00		14 00	14 47	15 00	15 29
Severn Tunnel Jn a			08 45		09n45			10n45				11n45		12n45			13n45		14n45			15 47
Newport (South Wales) a		08 23	09 00		09 23			10 23				11 22		12 22			13 22		14 22		15 22	15 43
Cardiff Central 7 a		08 42	09 21		09 40			10 40				11 40		12 39			13 40		14 39		15 39	16 02
Swansea 7 a		09 56			11 01			11 56				12 56		13 56			14 56		15 56		16 56	17 01

For general notes see front of timetable
For details of catering facilities see Directory of Train Operators

A To Gloucester (Table 134)
B To Great Malvern (Table 71)
C To Worcester Foregate Street (Table 71)
D From London Waterloo (Table 160)
b Change at Fareham
c Change at Fratton
e Change at Fratton and Cosham
f Arr. 1126
g Arr. 0711
h Change at Salisbury
j Change at Salisbury and Exeter St Davids
k Change at Westbury and Exeter St Davids
m By changing at Bristol Temple Meads, passengers may arrive at 0847
n Change at Bristol Temple Meads

Table 123

2 February to 22 March

Portsmouth and Weymouth → Bristol and South Wales

Network Diagram - see first page of Table 123

		GW ◇ A	GW **1** ◇ ☕	GW **1**	GW ◇	GW ◇	GW **1** ◇ ☕	GW ◇ A	GW ◇	GW ◇	GW ◇ B	GW **1** ◇ ☕	GW ◇	GW B	GW **1** ◇ ☕	GW ◇	GW **1**	GW ◇	SW **1** ◇ C	GW ◇	GW ◇	GW
Brighton **10**	d				12b03	13b03			14b03	15b03			16b03	17 00		17b03		18 03			19b03	
Hove **2**	d				12b07	13b07			14b07	15b07			16b07	17 04		17b07		18 07			19b07	
Shoreham-by-Sea	d				12b16	13b16			14b16	15b16			16b16	17 13		17b17		18 16			19b19	
Worthing **4**	d				12b25	13b25			14b25	15b25			16b25	17 22		17b25		18 25			19b29	
Barnham	d				12c57	13c57			14c57	15c57			16c57	17 41		17c57		18 57			19c57	
Chichester **4**	d				13c05	14c05			15c05	16c05			17c05	17 49		18c05		19 05			20c05	
Havant	d				13c23	14c23			15c23	16c23			17c23	18 00		18c23		19 23			20c26	
Portsmouth Harbour	d				13 22	14 22			15 22	16 22			17 22	17 32		18 22		19 22			20 22	
Portsmouth & Southsea	d				13 27	14 27			15 27	16 27			17 27	17 36		18 27		19 27			20 27	
Fratton	d				13 31	14 31			15 31	16 31			17 31	17 40		18 31		19 31			20 31	
Cosham	d				13 39	14 39			15 39	16 39			17 39	18 06		18 39		19 39			20 32	20 44
Fareham	a				13 46	14 46			15 46	16 46			17 46	18 14		18 46		19 46			20 44	
	d				13 47	14 47			15 47	16 47			17 47	18 15		18 47		19 47			20 47	20 53
Bournemouth	d				13 21	14 21			15 21	16 21			17 21	17 59		18 21		19 21			20 21	
Southampton Central	d				14 10	15 10			16 10	17 10			18 10	18 40		19 10		20 10			21 10	21 27
Romsey	d				14 21	15 21			16 21	17 21			18 21	18 51		19 21		20 21			21 21	21 38
Mottisfont & Dunbridge	d																					
Dean	d																					
Salisbury	a				14 40	15 40			16 40	17 40			18 40	19 10		19 40		20 40			21 40	22 03
	d				14 41	15 41			16 41	17 41			18 41	19 11		19 41		20 41	20 57		21 41	22 04
Warminster	d				15 01	16 01			17 01	18 01			19 01	19 31		20 01		21 01	21 17		22 01	22 25
Dilton Marsh	d													19x36								22x29
Weymouth	d	13 10						15 10			17 10									19 58		
Upwey	d	13 15						15 15			17 15									20 03		
Dorchester West	d	13 24						15 23			17 24									20 11		
Maiden Newton	d	13e44						15f37			17 36									20 23		
Chetnole	d	13x51						15x45			17x43									20x30		
Yetminster	d	13x54						15x48			17x46									20x33		
Thornford	d	13x57						15x51			17x49									20 36		
Yeovil Pen Mill	d	14 05						15 58			17 57									20 44		
Castle Cary	a	14 16						16 09			18 08									20 56		
	d	14 17	14 43				16 00	16 10			18 10	18 38			19 46					20 56		
Bruton	d	14 22						16 15			18 15									21 02		
Frome	d	14 34						16 27			18 27						20 53			21 15		
Westbury	a	14 44	15 01		15 07	16 07	16 17	16 36	17 07	18 07	18 36	18 56	19 07	19 39	20 03	20 07	21 02	21 07	21 23	21 25	22 08	22 33
	d	14 45	15 02	15 03	15 08	16 08	16 19	16 38	17 08	18 08	18 38	18 57	19 08	19 48	20 05	20 08		21 08	21 24	21 32	22 08	22 38
Exeter St Davids **6**	a					17g36				19g57						21 38		22 36		22h36		
Plymouth	a					18j48				21j17						22 43		23 47		23h47		
Trowbridge	d	14 51		15 09	15 14	16 14		16 44	17 14	18 14	18 44		19 14	19 54		20 14		21 14	21 30	21 44	22 14	22 44
Bradford-on-Avon	d	14 57			15 20	16 20		16 50	17 20	18 20	18 50		19 20	20 00		20 20		21 20	21 36	21 50	22 20	22 50
Avoncliff	d	14x59						16 52			18x52			20x02						21x52		22x52
Freshford	d	15 03						16 56			18 55			20 05						21 55		22 55
Bath Spa **7**	a	15 14			15 33	16 33		17 07	17 33	18 33	19 06		19 33	20 16		20 33		21 35	21 50	22 06	22 34	23 06
Melksham	d			15 18																		
Chippenham	a			15 28	15 54																	
Swindon	a			15 47	16 10																	
London Paddington **15**	⊖ a		16 22		17 53	18 19	18 03		19 58			20 21	21 19		21 36	22 22					00 37	
Oldfield Park	a	15 18						17 11			19 10			20 21						22 10		23 10
Keynsham	a	15 24						17 17			19 17			20 28					21 58	22 17		23 17
Bristol Temple Meads 10	a	15 32			15 47	16 47		17 25	17 47	18 47	19 26		19 47	20 35		20 47		21 49	22 06	22 27	22 48	23 25
Filton Abbey Wood	a	15 47			16 00	17 00		17 47	18 00	19 00	19 47		20 00	20 47		21 00		22 00			23 00	
Severn Tunnel Jn	a				16k45	17 13			18 13	19k45						21k45		22 16			23 16	
Newport (South Wales)	a				16 24	17 25			18 25	19 24			20 22			21 26		22 32			23 31	00 37
Cardiff Central 7	a				16 41	17 44			18 41	19 40			20 39			21 42		22 52			23 51	01 00
Swansea **7**	a				17 58	18 56			19 56				22 03			23 00		00 10			01 02	

For general notes see front of timetable
For details of catering facilities see Directory of Train Operators

- **A** To Gloucester (Table 134)
- **B** To Cheltenham Spa (Table 57)
- **C** From London Waterloo (Table 160)
- **b** Change at Fratton
- **c** Change at Fareham
- **e** Arr. 1333
- **f** Arr. 1532
- **g** Change at Salisbury
- **h** Change at Castle Cary
- **j** Change at Salisbury and Exeter St Davids
- **k** Change at Bristol Temple Meads

Table 123

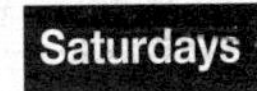

Saturdays

from 29 March

Portsmouth and Weymouth → Bristol and South Wales

Network Diagram - see first page of Table 123

	GW	GW	GW	SW	GW		GW	GW	GW	GW	GW		GW	GW		GW	GW		SW	GW	GW	GW			GW
				1			◇	◇		◇			◇	1 ◇		◇	◇		1 ◇	◇	◇	◇			◇
		A			B		C	A		C			B			C	C			A	D	C			C
Brighton 10 d										05b27						07c03	08c03				09 00	09c03			10c03
Hove 2 d										05b31						07c07	08c07				09 04	09c07			10c07
Shoreham-by-Sea d										05b43						07c16	08c16				09 13	09c17			10c16
Worthing 4 d										05b53						07c25	08c25				09 22	09c25			10c25
Barnham d							05c30			06c27						07b57	08b57				09 41	09b57			10b57
Chichester 4 d							05c38			06c35						08b05	09b05				09 49	10b05			11b05
Havant d							05c49			06c46						08b23	09b23				10 00	10b23			11b23
Portsmouth Harbour d							06 00			07 04						08 22	09 22				09e28	10 22			11 22
Portsmouth & Southsea d							06 04			07 08						08 27	09 27				09 36	10 27			11 27
Fratton d							06 08			07 13						08 31	09 31				09 40	10 31			11 31
Cosham d							06 15			07 20	07 44					08 39	09 39				10 06	10 39			11 39
Fareham a							06 24			07 28						08 46	09 46				10 14	10 46			11 46
Fareham d							06 25			07 29	07 53					08 47	09 47				10 15	10 47			11 47
Bournemouth d							05 42			06 42	07 45					08 21	09 21				09 59	10 21			11 21
Southampton Central d							06 47			07 52	08 27					09 10	10 10				10 40	11 10			12 10
Romsey d							06 59			08 09	08 38					09 21	10 21				10 51	11 21			12 21
Mottisfont & Dunbridge d																									
Dean d																									
Salisbury a							07 22			08 29	09 03					09 40	10 40				11 10	11 40			12 40
Salisbury d		06 03		06 40			07 23			08 32	09 04					09 41	10 41		10 52		11 11	11 41			12 41
Warminster d		06 23		07 00	07 23		07 43			08 53	09 25					10 01	11 01		11 12		11 32	12 01			13 01
Dilton Marsh d		06x27			07x28						09x29														
Weymouth d								06 27					08 11							11 10					
Upwey d								06 32					08 16							11 15					
Dorchester West d								06 40					08 23							11 23					
Maiden Newton d								06 52					08 35							11f42					
Chetnole d								06x59					08x42							11x50					
Yetminster d								07x02					08x45							11x54					
Thornford d								07x05					08x48							11x56					
Yeovil Pen Mill d								07g25					08 56							12 03					
Castle Cary a								07 37					09 07							12 14					
Castle Cary d								07 37					09 08	09 46						12 26					
Bruton d								07 43					09 13							12 31					
Frome d			06 37					07 56					09 25							12 43					
Westbury a		06 31	06 46	07 06	07 31		07 49	08 05		08 59	09 33		09 35			10 07	11 07		11 18	12 51	11 38	12 07			13 07
Westbury d	05 58	06 38	06 51	07 07	07 38		07 52	08 38	09 03	09 08			09 38			10 08	11 08		11 19	12 52	11 48	12 08			13 08
Exeter St Davids 6 a										10h32			11 06			11h56	12h30					13 32			14h19
Plymouth a										11j48			12k23				13j48					14 36			15j48
Trowbridge d	06 04	06 44	06 57	07 13	07 44		07 58	08 44	09 09	09 14			09 44			10 14	11 14		11 25	12 58	11 54	12 14			13 14
Bradford-on-Avon d	06 10	06 49	07 03	07 19	07 50		08 04	08 50		09 20			09 50			10 20	11 20		11 31	13 04	12 00	12 20			13 20
Avoncliff d	06x12	06x51	07x05		07x53			08x53					09x52								12x03				
Freshford d	06 15	06 55	07 09		07 55			08 55					09 55								12 05				
Bath Spa 7 a	06 26	07 06	07 20	07 32	08 07		08 17	09 08		09 33			10 06			10 34	11 33		11 45	13 17	12 16	12 33			13 33
Melksham d									09 18																
Chippenham a	06 54	07 24		07 54			08 54		09 30	09 54			10 24			10 54	11 54								13 54
Swindon a	07 09	07 40		08 09			09 09		09 52	10 09			10 39			11 09	12 09								14 09
London Paddington 15 ⊖ a	08 14	08 45		09 15			10 14			11 15			11 42	11 22		12m12	13 15								15 15
Oldfield Park a	06 30	07 10	07 24	07 36	08 11			09 12					10 10							13 21	12 20				
Keynsham a	06 38	07 17	07 31	07 43	08 18			09 19					10 17							13 27	12 27				
Bristol Temple Meads 10 a	06 46	07 25	07 39	07 52	08 26		08 31	09 27		09 47			10 25			10 48	11 47		12 00	13 36	12 35	12 47			13 47
Filton Abbey Wood a		07 47			08 47		09n00	09 47		10 00			10 47			11 00	12 00			13 47	12 47	13 00			14 00
Severn Tunnel Jn a																									
Newport (South Wales) a																									
Cardiff Central 7 a																									
Swansea 7 a																									

For general notes see front of timetable
For details of catering facilities see Directory of Train Operators

A To Gloucester (Table 134)
B To Great Malvern (Table 71)
C To Bristol Parkway (Table 132)
D To Worcester Foregate Street (Table 71)
b Change at Fareham
c Change at Fratton
e Change at Fratton and Cosham
f Arr. 1136
g Arr. 0711
h Change at Salisbury
j Change at Salisbury and Exeter St Davids
k Change at Westbury and Exeter St Davids
m Change at Bath Spa and Swindon
n By changing at Bristol Temple Meads, passengers may arrive at 0847

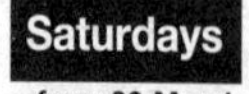

from 29 March

Portsmouth and Weymouth → Bristol and South Wales

Network Diagram - see first page of Table 123

		GW 1◇	GW A	GW ◇ B	SW 1◇ C	GW ◇ D		GW	GW ◇ B	GW ◇ B	GW ◇ D	GW ◇ B		GW ◇ B	GW ◇ E	GW ◇ B	GW E	GW ◇ B		GW ◇ B	SW 1◇ C	GW ◇	GW ◇ B	GW		
Brighton 10	d			11b03					12b03	13b03		14b03		15b03		16b03	17 00	17b03		18b03			19b03			
Hove 2	d			11b07					12b07	13b07		14b07		15b07		16b07	17 04	17b07		18b07			19b07			
Shoreham-by-Sea	d			11b16					12b16	13b16		14b16		15b16		16b16	17 13	17b17		18b16			19b19			
Worthing 4	d			11b25					12b25	13b25		14b25		15b25		16b25	17 22	17b25		18b25			19b29			
Barnham	d			11c57					12c57	13c57		14c57		15c57		16c57	17 41	17c57		18c57			19c57			
Chichester 4	d			12c05					13c05	14c05		15c05		16c05		17c05	17 49	18c05		19c05			20c05			
Havant	d			12c23					13c23	14c23		15c23		16c23		17c23	18 00	18c23		19c23			20c26			
Portsmouth Harbour	d			12 22					13 22	14 22		15 22		16 22		17 22	17 32	18 22		19 22			20 22			
Portsmouth & Southsea	d			12 27					13 27	14 27		15 27		16 27		17 27	17 36	18 27		19 27			20 27			
Fratton	d			12 31					13 31	14 31		15 31		16 31		17 31	17 40	18 31		19 31			20 31			
Cosham	d		11 44	12 39					13 39	14 39		15 39		16 39		17 39	18 06	18 39		19 39			20 32	20 44		
Fareham	a			12 46					13 46	14 46		15 46		16 46		17 46	18 14	18 46		19 46			20 44			
	d		11 53	12 47					13 47	14 47		15 47		16 47		17 47	18 15	18 47		19 47			20 47	20 53		
Bournemouth	d		11 45	12 21					13 21	14 21		15 21		16 21		17 21	17 59	18 21		19 21			20 21			
Southampton Central	d		12 27	13 10					14 10	15 10		16 10		17 10		18 10	18 40	19 10		20 10			21 10	21 27		
Romsey	d		12 38	13 21					14 21	15 21		16 21		17 21		18 21	18 51	19 21		20 21			21 21	21 38		
Mottisfont & Dunbridge	d																									
Dean	d																									
Salisbury	a		13 04	13 40					14 40	15 40		16 40		17 40		18 40	19 10	19 40		20 40			21 40	22 02		
	d		13 05	13 41	13 52				14 41	15 41		16 41		17 41		18 41	19 11	19 41		20 41	20 57		21 41	22 04		
Warminster	d		13 25	14 01	14 12				15 01	16 01		17 01		18 01		19 01	19 31	20 01		21 01	21 17		22 01	22 25		
Dilton Marsh	d		13x29														19x36							22x30		
Weymouth	d																									
Upwey	d																									
Dorchester West	d																									
Maiden Newton	d																									
Chetnole	d																									
Yetminster	d																									
Thornford	d																									
Yeovil Pen Mill	d																									
Castle Cary	a																									
	d	12 44																								
Bruton	d																									
Frome	d																									
Westbury	a	13 02	13 33	14 07	14 18				15 07	16 07		17 07		18 07		19 07	19 39	20 07		21 07	21 23		22 08	22 33		
	d	13 03	13 38	14 08	14 19	14 43		15 03	15 08	16 08	16 38	17 08		18 08	18 38	19 08	19 48	20 08		21 08	21 24	21 38	22 08	22 38		
Exeter St Davids 6	a			15e42						17e36				19e57				21e53		22e41						
Plymouth	a			16e58						18f48				21f36				23f09		00f12						
Trowbridge	d		13 44	14 14	14 25	14 49		15 09	15 14	16 14	16 44	17 14		18 14	18 44	19 14	19 54	20 14		21 14	21 30	21 44	22 14	22 44		
Bradford-on-Avon	d		13 50	14 20	14 31	14 55			15 20	16 20	16 50	17 20		18 20	18 50	19 20	20 00	20 20		21 20	21 36	21 50	22 20	22 50		
Avoncliff	d		13x52			14x57					16x52				18x52		20x02					21x52		22x53		
Freshford	d		13 55			15 01					16 56				18 56		20 05					21 55		22 55		
Bath Spa 7	a		14 08	14 33	14 45	15 12			15 33	16 33	17 07	17 33		18 33	19 07	19 33	20 16	20 33		21 37	21 50	22 06	22 34	23 06		
Melksham	d							15 18																		
Chippenham	a			14 54	15 54			15 28	15 54	16 54		17 54		18 54		19 54		20 57					22 57			
Swindon	a			15 09	16 09			15 31	16 09	17 09		18 09		19 09		20 09		21 13					23 13			
London Paddington 15 ⊖	a	14 46		16 15	17 15				17 15	18 15		19 15		20 15		21 15		22 16					00 32			
Oldfield Park	a		14 12			15 16					17 11				19 11		20 21					22 10		23 10		
Keynsham	a		14 18			15 22					17 17				19 18		20 28				21 58	22 17		23 17		
Bristol Temple Meads 10	a		14 26	14 47	15 00	15 30			15 47	16 47	17 25	17 47		18 47	19 27	19 47	20 35	20 47		21 51	22 06	22 27	22 48	23 25		
Filton Abbey Wood	a		14 47	15 00	15 29	15 47			16 00	17 00	17 47	18 00		19 00	19 47	20 00	20 47	21 00		22 02			23 00			
Severn Tunnel Jn	a																									
Newport (South Wales)	a																							00 37		
Cardiff Central 7	a																							01 00		
Swansea 7	a																									

For general notes see front of timetable
For details of catering facilities see Directory of Train Operators

- **A** To Great Malvern (Table 71)
- **B** To Bristol Parkway (Table 132)
- **C** From London Waterloo (Table 160)
- **D** To Gloucester (Table 134)
- **E** To Cheltenham Spa (Table 57)

- **b** Change at Fratton
- **c** Change at Fareham
- **e** Change at Salisbury
- **f** Change at Salisbury and Exeter St Davids

Table 123

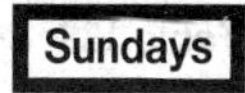

until 27 January

Portsmouth and Weymouth → Bristol and South Wales

Network Diagram - see first page of Table 123

		GW	GW	GW	GW	GW	GW	GW	SW	GW	GW	GW	GW	GW
		1 ◇		1 ◇	◇	1 ◇	◇	◇	1 ◇	◇	◇	1 ◇	◇	◇
									A					
		🍽		🍽	🛒	🍽	🛒			🛒		🍽	🛒	🛒
Brighton 10	d				07b23		09b17	11 10		11b17			12b17	13b17
Hove 2	d				07b26		09b26	11 14		11b26			12b26	13b26
Shoreham-by-Sea	d				07b38		09b38	11 20		11b38			12b38	13b38
Worthing 4	d				07b47		09b48	11 29		11b48			12b48	13b48
Barnham	d				08b20		10b12	11 46		12b12			13b12	14b12
Chichester 4	d				08b28		10b20	11 58		12b20			13b20	14b20
Havant	d				08b49		10b53	12 10		12b51			13b51	14b51
Portsmouth Harbour	d				09 08		11 08	11c32		13 08			14 08	15 08
Portsmouth & Southsea	d				09 12		11 12	11 42		13 12			14 12	15 12
Fratton	d				09 16		11 16	11 46		13 16			14 16	15 16
Cosham	d				09 23		11 23	12 23		13 23			14 23	15 23
Fareham	a				09 31		11 31	12 31		13 31			14 31	15 31
	d				09 32		11 32	12 32		13 32			14 32	15 32
Bournemouth	d				08 50		10 50	11 50		12 50			13 50	14 50
Southampton Central	d				09 54		11 54	12 54		13 54			14 54	15 54
Romsey	d				10 05		12 06	13 06		14 06			15 06	16 06
Mottisfont & Dunbridge	d													
Dean	d													
Salisbury	a				10 24		12 24	13 24		14 24			15 24	16 24
	d				10 30		12 28	13 28	13 58	14 28			15 28	16 28
Warminster	d				10 50		12 48	13 47	14 18	14 48			15 48	16 48
Dilton Marsh	d				10x55					14x53			15x53	16x53
Weymouth	d										14 00			
Upwey	d										14 05			
Dorchester West	d										14 13			
Maiden Newton	d										14 25			
Chetnole	d										14x32			
Yetminster	d										14x35			
Thornford	d										14x38			
Yeovil Pen Mill	d										14 46			
Castle Cary	a										14 57			
	d	09 20				12 27					14 59	15 33		
Bruton	d										15 05			
Frome	d		09 35								15 18			
Westbury	a	09 36	09 44		10 57	12 45	12 53	13 54	14 24	14 55	15 27	15 50	15 55	16 55
	d	09 39	09 56	10 54	10 58	12 45	12 55	13 55	14 25	15 01	15 31	15 51	15 58	16 59
Exeter St Davids 6	a				12e49		14e46	15 24		16e46	16f25			18 38
Plymouth	a				14g11		16g05	16 28		18g21	17f37			19 40
Trowbridge	d		10 02		11 04		13 01	14 01	14 32	15 07	15 37		16 04	17 05
Bradford-on-Avon	d		10 07		11 10		13 07	14 07	14 38	15 13	15 43		16 10	17 11
Avoncliff	d		10x10				13x10	14x10			15x46		16x13	
Freshford	d		10 12				13 13	14 12			15 49		16 16	
Bath Spa 7	a		10 23		11 25		13 25	14 23	14 52	15 27	16 00		16 28	17 25
Melksham	d													
Chippenham	a		10 54		12 24		14 24		15 24		16 24		16 54	17 54
Swindon	a		11 08		12 39		14 40		15 40		16 40		17 10	18 10
London Paddington 15 ⊖	a	11 21	12 22	12 28	13 55	14 22	15 57		16 54		17 54	17 36	18 27	19 24
Oldfield Park	a		10 27		11 28		13 28	14 27			16 03			17 28
Keynsham	a		10 34		11 35		13 35	14 34			16 11			17 35
Bristol Temple Meads 10	a		10 43		11 43		13 43	14 42	15 06	15 40	16 19		16 41	17 43
Filton Abbey Wood	a				11 54		13 54	14 54		15 54	16 50		16 54	17 54
Severn Tunnel Jn	a				12 10		14 07	15 07		16 07			17 10	18 07
Newport (South Wales)	a				12 24		14 20	15 20		16 21			17 23	18 21
Cardiff Central 7	a				12 39		14 35	15 38		16 36			17 38	18 36
Swansea 7	a				13 43		15 43	16 43		17 43			18 48	19 47

For general notes see front of timetable
For details of catering facilities see Directory of Train Operators

A From London Waterloo (Table 160)
b Change at Fratton
c Change at Fratton and Cosham
e Change at Salisbury
f Change at Castle Cary
g Change at Salisbury and Exeter St Davids

until 27 January

Portsmouth and Weymouth → Bristol and South Wales

Network Diagram - see first page of Table 123

		GW	GW 1 ◇	GW ◇	GW ◇	GW ◇	GW ◇	GW A	GW ◇	GW 1 ◇	SW 1 ◇ B	GW ◇	GW ◇	GW 1 ◇	GW ◇	GW ◇	GW ◇
Brighton 10	d			14b17	15 47				16b17			17 47				18b17	20b17
Hove 2	d			14b26	15 51				16b26			17 51				18b26	20b26
Shoreham-by-Sea	d			14b38	15 57				16b38			17 57				18b38	20b38
Worthing 4	d			14b48	16 08				16b48			18 08				18b48	20b48
Barnham	d			15b12	16 25				17b12			18 25				19b12	21b12
Chichester 4	d			15b20	16 34				17b20			18 34				19b20	21b20
Havant	d			15b51	16 48	16b51			17b51			18 48	18b51			19b51	21b51
Portsmouth Harbour	d			16 08	16 17	17 08			18 08			18 17	19 08			20 08	22 07
Portsmouth & Southsea	d			16 12	16 22	17 12			18 12			18 22	19 12			20 12	22 12
Fratton	d			16 16	16 26	17 16			18 16			18 26	19 16			20 16	22 16
Cosham	d			16 23	16 55	17 23			18 23			18 35	19 23			20 23	22 23
Fareham	a			16 31	17 02	17 31			18 31			19 00	19 31			20 31	22 31
	d			16 32	17 03	17 32			18 32			19 01	19 32			20 32	22 32
Bournemouth	d			15 50	16 40	16 50			17 50			18 50				19 50	21 06
Southampton Central	d			16 54	17 26	17 54			18 54			19 30	19 54			20 54	22 54
Romsey	d			17 06	17 39	18 06			19 06			19 42	20 06			21 06	23 05
Mottisfont & Dunbridge	d																23 10
Dean	d																23 16
Salisbury	a			17 24	18 01	18 24			19 24			20 00	20 24			21 24	23 29
	d			17 28	18 02	18 28			19 28		19 58	20 03	20 28			21 28	23 30
Warminster	d			17 48	18 22	18 48			19 48		20 18	20 28	20 48			21 48	23 50
Dilton Marsh	d				18x27							20x33				21x53	23x55
Weymouth	d						18 00								20 09		
Upwey	d						18 05								20 14		
Dorchester West	d						18 13								20 22		
Maiden Newton	d						18 25								20 34		
Chetnole	d						18x32								20x41		
Yetminster	d						18x35								20x44		
Thornford	d						18x38								20x47		
Yeovil Pen Mill	d						18 46								20 55		
Castle Cary	a						18 57								21 06		
	d		17 37				18 59			20 05				21 10	21 15		
Bruton	d						19 05								21 21		
Frome	d						19 18								21 34		
Westbury	a		17 54	17 57	18 30	18 53	19 27		19 53	20 22	20 24	20 36	20 53	21 28	21 43	21 55	23 57
	d	17 05	17 57	18 01	18 34	19 01	19 30	19 35	20 01	20 24	20 32	20 39	21 01	21 28	21 46	22 01	
Exeter St Davids 6	a						20 39						22c46			00c30	
Plymouth	a						21 43										
Trowbridge	d	17 11		18 07	18 40	19 07	19 36	19 42	20 07		20 38	20 45	21 07		21 52	22 07	
Bradford-on-Avon	d				18 46	19 13	19 42		20 13		20 44	20 51	21 13		21 58	22 13	
Avoncliff	d				18x49		19x45					20x54			22 01		
Freshford	d				18 52		19 48					20 56			22 04		
Bath Spa 7	a			18 25	19 03	19 27	20 01		20 27		20 59	21 09	21 27		22 15	22 28	
Melksham	d	17 21						19 52									
Chippenham	a	17 31		18 54	19 24	19 54	20 24	20 02			21 25		22 29				
Swindon	a	17 48		19 10	19 40	20 10	20 40	20 20			21 41		22 45				
London Paddington 15 ⊖	a	19 10	19 34	20 24	20 55	21 26	21 59	21 40		21 53	23 01		00 17	23 23			
Oldfield Park	a				19 06		20 04					21 13			22 18		
Keynsham	a				19 14		20 12				21 08	21 20			22 26		
Bristol Temple Meads 10	a			18 38	19 22	19 40	20 20		20 40		21 16	21 28	21 40		22 34	22 41	
Filton Abbey Wood	a			18 55		19 54	20 50		20 54				21 56			22 54	
Severn Tunnel Jn	a			19 08		20 10			21 07				22 13			23 09	
Newport (South Wales)	a			19 21		20 23			21 20				22 32			23 31	
Cardiff Central 7	a			19 38		20 38			21 38				22 51			23 50	
Swansea 7	a			20 52		21 47			22 44				23 54			00 57	

For general notes see front of timetable
For details of catering facilities see Directory of Train Operators

A To Cheltenham Spa (Table 125)
B From London Waterloo (Table 160)
b Change at Fratton
c Change at Salisbury

Table 123

Sundays

3 February to 23 March

Portsmouth and Weymouth → Bristol and South Wales

Network Diagram - see first page of Table 123

		GW	GW	GW	GW	GW	GW	GW	SW	GW	GW	GW	GW	GW	GW
		1 ◇		**1** ◇	◇	**1** ◇	◇	◇	**1** ◇	◇	◇	**1** ◇	◇	◇	
									A						
		🍴		🍴	🛒	🍴	🛒			🛒		🍴	🛒	🛒	
Brighton 10	d				07b23		09b17	11 10		11b17			12b17	13b17	
Hove 2	d				07b26		09b26	11 14		11b26			12b26	13b26	
Shoreham-by-Sea	d				07b38		09b38	11 20		11b38			12b38	13b38	
Worthing 4	d				07b47		09b48	11 29		11b48			12b48	13b48	
Barnham	d				08b20		10b12	11 46		12b12			13b12	14b12	
Chichester 4	d				08b28		10b20	11 58		12b20			13b20	14b20	
Havant	d				08b49		10b53	12 10		12b51			13b51	14b51	
Portsmouth Harbour	d				09 08		11 08	11c32		13 08			14 08	15 08	
Portsmouth & Southsea	d				09 12		11 12	11 42		13 12			14 12	15 12	
Fratton	d				09 16		11 16	11 46		13 16			14 16	15 16	
Cosham	d				09 23		11 23	12 23		13 23			14 23	15 23	
Fareham	a				09 31		11 31	12 31		13 31			14 31	15 31	
	d				09 32		11 32	12 32		13 32			14 32	15 32	
Bournemouth	d				08 50		10 50	11 50		12 50			13 50	14 50	
Southampton Central	d				09 54		11 54	12 54		13 54			14 54	15 54	
Romsey	d				10 05		12 06	13 06		14 06			15 06	16 06	
Mottisfont & Dunbridge	d														
Dean	d														
Salisbury	a				10 24		12 24	13 24		14 24			15 24	16 24	
	d				10 30		12 28	13 28	13 58	14 28			15 28	16 28	
Warminster	d				10 50		12 48	13 47	14 18	14 48			15 48	16 48	
Dilton Marsh	d				10 55					14x53			15x53	16x53	
Weymouth	d										14 00				
Upwey	d										14 05				
Dorchester West	d										14 13				
Maiden Newton	d										14 25				
Chetnole	d										14x32				
Yetminster	d										14x35				
Thornford	d										14x38				
Yeovil Pen Mill	d										14 46				
Castle Cary	a										14 57				
	d	09 20				12 27					14 59	15 32			
Bruton	d										15 05				
Frome	d		09 35								15 18				
Westbury	a	09 36	09 44		10 57	12 45	12 53	13 54	14 24	14 55	15 27	15 48	15 55	16 55	
	d	09 42	09 56	10 54	10 58	12 45	12 55	13 55	14 25	15 01	15 35	15 50	15 58	16 59	17 05
Exeter St Davids 6	a		11 35		12e49		14e46	15 32		16e46	16f28			18 38	
Plymouth	a		12 38		14g19			16 36		18g13	17f40			19 40	
Trowbridge	d		10 02		11 04		13 01	14 01	14 32	15 07	15 43		16 04	17 05	17 11
Bradford-on-Avon	d		10 07		11 10		13 07	14 07	14 38	15 13	15 49		16 10	17 11	
Avoncliff	d		10x10				13x10	14x10			15x52		16x13		
Freshford	d		10 12				13 13	14 12			15 55		16 16		
Bath Spa 7	a		10 23		11 25		13 25	14 23	14 52	15 27	16 06		16 28	17 25	
Melksham	d														17 21
Chippenham	a		11 29		12 29		14 29		15 29				16 50	17 49	17 31
Swindon	a		11 45		12 45		14 45		15 45				17 06	18 05	17 48
London Paddington 15	⊖ a	11 21	12 57	12 33	13 52	14 22	15 53	16 52		17 57	18 31	17 37	18 52	20 01	
Oldfield Park	a		10 27		11 28		13 28	14 27			16 09			17 28	
Keynsham	a		10 34		11 35		13 35	14 34			16 17			17 35	
Bristol Temple Meads 10	a		10 43		11 43		13 43	14 42	15 06	15 40	16 25		16 41	17 43	
Filton Abbey Wood	a				11 54		13 54	14 54		15 54	16 50		16 54	17 54	
Severn Tunnel Jn	a				12 10		14 07	15 07		16 07			17 10	18 07	
Newport (South Wales)	a		11 55		12 23		14 20	15 20	15 55	16 20			17 23	18 20	
Cardiff Central 7	a		12 12		12 38		14 35	15 38	16 12	16 35			17 38	18 35	
Swansea 7	a		13 07		14 07		16 07		17 07	18 07			19 10	20 10	

For general notes see front of timetable
For details of catering facilities see Directory of Train Operators

A From London Waterloo (Table 160)
b Change at Fratton
c Change at Fratton and Cosham
e Change at Salisbury
f Change at Castle Cary
g Change at Salisbury and Exeter St Davids

Table 123

Sundays

3 February to 23 March

Portsmouth and Weymouth → Bristol and South Wales

Network Diagram - see first page of Table 123

		GW	GW	GW	GW	GW	GW	GW	GW	SW	GW	GW	GW	GW	GW	GW	GW
		1 ◇	◇	◇	◇		◇	◇	1 ◇	1 ◇	◇	◇	1 ◇	◇	1 ◇	◇	◇
						A				B							
		⊡	⌆		⌆			⌆	⊡			⌆	⊡		⊡	⌆	⌆
Brighton 10	d		14b17	15 47				16b17			17 47					18b17	20b17
Hove 2	d		14b26	15 51				16b26			17 51					18b26	20b26
Shoreham-by-Sea	d		14b38	15 57				16b38			17 57					18b38	20b38
Worthing 4	d		14b48	16 08				16b48			18 08					18b48	20b48
Barnham	d		15b12	16 25				17b12			18 25					19b12	21b12
Chichester 4	d		15b20	16 34				17b20			18 34					19b20	21b20
Havant	d		15b51	16 48	16b51			17b51			18 48	18b51				19b51	21b51
Portsmouth Harbour	d		16 08	16 17	17 08			18 08			18 17	19 08				20 08	22 07
Portsmouth & Southsea	d		16 12	16 22	17 12			18 12			18 22	19 12				20 12	22 12
Fratton	d		16 16	16 26	17 16			18 16			18 26	19 16				20 16	22 16
Cosham	d		16 23	16 55	17 23			18 23			18 35	19 23				20 23	22 23
Fareham	a		16 31	17 02	17 31			18 31			19 00	19 31				20 31	22 31
	d		16 32	17 03	17 32			18 32			19 01	19 32				20 32	22 32
Bournemouth	d		15 50	16 40	16 50			17 50			18 50					19 50	21 06
Southampton Central	d		16 54	17 26	17 54			18 54			19 30	19 54				20 54	22 54
Romsey	d		17 06	17 39	18 06			19 06			19 42	20 06				21 06	23 05
Mottisfont & Dunbridge	d																23 10
Dean	d																23 16
Salisbury	a		17 24	18 01	18 24			19 24			20 00	20 24				21 24	23 29
	d		17 28	18 02	18 28			19 28		19 58	20 03	20 28				21 28	23 30
Warminster	d		17 48	18 22	18 48			19 48		20 18	20 28	20 48				21 48	23 50
Dilton Marsh	d			18x27							20x33					21x53	23x55
Weymouth	d						18 00							20 09			
Upwey	d						18 05							20 14			
Dorchester West	d						18 13							20 22			
Maiden Newton	d						18 25							20 34			
Chetnole	d						18x32							20x41			
Yetminster	d						18x35							20x44			
Thornford	d						18x38							20x47			
Yeovil Pen Mill	d						18 46							20 55			
Castle Cary	a						18 57							21 06			
	d	17 37					18 59		20 05				21 10	21 15			
Bruton	d						19 05							21 21			
Frome	d						19 18							21 34			
Westbury	a	17 54	17 57	18 30	18 53		19 27	19 53	20 22	20 24	20 36	20 53	21 27	21 43		21 55	23 57
	d	17 57	18 01	18 34	19 01	19 28	19 40	20 01	20 24	20 25	20 39	21 01	21 28	21 46	22 00	22 01	
Exeter St Davids 6	a						20 39					22 42				00e30	
Plymouth	a						21 43					23 50					
Trowbridge	d		18 07	18 40	19 07	19 34	19 48	20 07		20 31	20 45	21 07		21 52		22 07	
Bradford-on-Avon	d			18 46	19 13		19 54	20 13		20 37	20 51	21 13		21 58		22 13	
Avoncliff	d			18x49			19x57				20x54			22 01			
Freshford	d			18 52			20 00				20 56			22 04			
Bath Spa 7	a		18 25	19 03	19 27		20 11	20 27		20 51	21 09	21 27		22 15		22 28	
Melksham	d					19 45											
Chippenham	a		18 54		19 55	19 59		20 54		21 54		21 54				23 07	
Swindon	a		19 10		20 11	20 19		21 10		22 10		22 10				23 23	
London Paddington 15	⊖ a	19 35	20 51		21 32			22 49	21 59	00 27		00 27	23 24		23 32		
Oldfield Park	a			19 06			20 14				21 13			22 18			
Keynsham	a			19 14			20 22			21 00	21 20			22 26			
Bristol Temple Meads 10	a		18 38	19 22	19 40		20 30	20 40		21 08	21 28	21 40		22 34		22 41	
Filton Abbey Wood	a		18 54		19 54		20 50	20 54				21 56				22 54	
Severn Tunnel Jn	a		19 07		20 10			21 07				22 13				23 07	
Newport (South Wales)	a		19 20		20 23			21 20		21 56		22 27				23 28	
Cardiff Central 7	a		19 38		20 38			21 38		22 16		22 46				23 47	
Swansea 7	a		21 10		22 07					23 11		00 19				01 26	

For general notes see front of timetable
For details of catering facilities see Directory of Train Operators

A To Cheltenham Spa (Table 125)
B From London Waterloo (Table 160)
b Change at Fratton
c Change at Fareham
e Change at Salisbury

Table 123

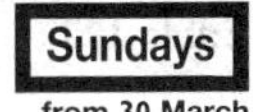

from 30 March

Portsmouth and Weymouth → Bristol and South Wales

Network Diagram - see first page of Table 123

		GW	GW ◇ A	GW ◇ A	GW ◇	GW ◇ A	SW 1 ◇ B	GW ◇ A	GW ◇	GW ◇ A	GW 1 ◇	GW ◇ A	GW	GW ◇ A	GW 1 ◇	GW ◇	GW ◇	GW ◇ A
Brighton 10	d		07b23	09b17		11 10		11b17		12b17		13b17		14b17			15 47	15 47
Hove 2	d		07b26	09b26		11 14		11b26		12b26		13b26		14b26			15 51	15 51
Shoreham-by-Sea	d		07b38	09b38		11 20		11b38		12b38		13b38		14b38			15 57	15 57
Worthing 4	d		07b47	09b48		11 29		11b48		12b48		13b48		14b48			16 08	16 08
Barnham	d		08b20	10b12		11 46		12b12		13b12		14b12		15b12			16 25	16 25
Chichester 4	d		08b28	10b20		11 58		12b20		13b20		14b20		15b20			16 34	16 34
Havant	d		08b49	10b53		12 10		12b51		13b51		14b51		15b51			16 48	16b51
Portsmouth Harbour	d		09 08	11 08		11c32		13 08		14 08		15 08		16 08			16 17	17 08
Portsmouth & Southsea	d		09 12	11 12		11 42		13 12		14 12		15 12		16 12			16 22	17 12
Fratton	d		09 16	11 16		11 46		13 16		14 16		15 16		16 16			16 26	17 16
Cosham	d		09 23	11 23		12 23		13 23		14 23		15 23		16 23			16 55	17 23
Fareham	a		09 31	11 31		12 31		13 31		14 31		15 31		16 31			17 02	17 31
	d		09 32	11 32		12 32		13 32		14 32		15 32		16 32			17 03	17 32
Bournemouth	d		08 50	10 50		11 50		12 50		13 50		14 50		15 50			16 40	16 50
Southampton Central	d		09 54	11 54		12 54		13 54		14 54		15 54		16 54			17 26	17 54
Romsey	d		10 05	12 06		13 06		14 06		15 06		16 06		17 06			17 39	18 06
Mottisfont & Dunbridge	d																	
Dean	d																	
Salisbury	a		10 24	12 24		13 24		14 24		15 24		16 24		17 24			18 01	18 24
	d		10 30	12 28		13 28	13 58	14 28		15 28		16 28		17 28			18 02	18 28
Warminster	d		10 50	12 48		13 47	14 18	14 48		15 48		16 48		17 48			18 22	18 48
Dilton Marsh	d		10x55					14x53		15x53		16x53					18x27	
Weymouth	d				13 32											17 32		
Upwey	d				13 37											17 37		
Dorchester West	d				13 46											17 46		
Maiden Newton	d				14e00											18f00		
Chetnole	d				14x07											18x07		
Yetminster	d				14x10											18x10		
Thornford	d				14x13											18x13		
Yeovil Pen Mill	d				14 21											18 21		
Castle Cary	a				14 32											18 32		
	d																	
Bruton	d																	
Frome	d	09 35																
Westbury	a	09 44	10 57	12 53		13 54	14 24	14 55		15 55		16 55		17 57			18 30	18 53
	d	09 50	10 58	12 55		13 55	14 25	15 01	15 31	15 58	16 24	16 59	17 05	18 01	18 27		18 34	19 01
Exeter St Davids 6	a		12g49	14g46			16 49	16g46				18g46						20g49
Plymouth	a		14h48	16h07			17 58	17 58				19 55						22h48
Trowbridge	d	09 56	11 04	13 01		14 01	14 32	15 07	15 37	16 04		17 05	17 11	18 07			18 40	19 07
Bradford-on-Avon	d	10 01	11 10	13 07		14 07	14 38	15 13	15 43	16 10		17 11					18 46	19 13
Avoncliff	d	10x04		13x10		14x10			15x46	16x13							18x49	
Freshford	d	10 06		13 13		14 12			15 49	16 16							18 52	
Bath Spa 7	a	10 17	11 25	13 25		14 23	14 52	15 27	16 00	16 28		17 25		18 25			19 03	19 31
Melksham	d												17 21					
Chippenham	a	10 54	12 24	14 24			15 24		16 24	16 54		17 54	17 31	18 54			19 24	19 54
Swindon	a	11 08	12 39	14 40			15 40		16 40	17 10		18 10	17 48	19 10			19 40	20 10
London Paddington 15 ⊖	a	12 22	13 55	15 56			16 53		17 52	18 21	18 09	19 23	19 23	20 23	20 09		20 56	21 25
Oldfield Park	a	10 21	11 28	13 28		14 27			16 03			17 28					19 06	
Keynsham	a	10 28	11 35	13 35		14 34			16 11			17 35					19 14	
Bristol Temple Meads 10	a	10 37	11 43	13 43		14 42	15 06	15 40	16 19	16 41		17 43		18 38			19 22	19 45
Filton Abbey Wood	a		11 54	13 54		14 54		15 54	16 50	16 54		17 54		18 54				19 56
Severn Tunnel Jn	a																	
Newport (South Wales)	a																	
Cardiff Central 7	a																	
Swansea 7	a																	

For general notes see front of timetable
For details of catering facilities see Directory of Train Operators

- **A** To Bristol Parkway (Table 132)
- **B** From London Waterloo (Table 160)
- **b** Change at Fratton
- **c** Change at Fratton and Cosham
- **e** Arr. 1355
- **f** Arr. 1755
- **g** Change at Salisbury
- **h** Change at Salisbury and Exeter St Davids

Table 123

Sundays

from 30 March

Portsmouth and Weymouth → Bristol and South Wales

Network Diagram - see first page of Table 123

		GW	GW	GW	GW	SW	GW	GW	GW	GW	GW	GW
		◇		◇	1 ◇	1 ◇	◇	◇	1 ◇	◇	◇	◇
				A		B		A		A		
				⊥	⊏			⊥	⊏	⊥		⊥
Brighton 10	d			16b17			17 47			18b17		20b17
Hove 2	d			16b26			17 51			18b26		20b26
Shoreham-by-Sea	d			16b38			17 57			18b38		20b38
Worthing 4	d			16b48			18 08			18b48		20b48
Barnham	d			17b12			18 25			19b12		21b12
Chichester 4	d			17b20			18 34			19b20		21b20
Havant	d			17b51			18 48	18b51		19b51		21b51
Portsmouth Harbour	d			18 08			18 17	19 08		20 08		22 07
Portsmouth & Southsea	d			18 12			18 22	19 12		20 12		22 12
Fratton	d			18 16			18 26	19 16		20 16		22 16
Cosham	d			18 23			18 35	19 23		20 23		22 23
Fareham	a			18 31			19 00	19 31		20 31		22 31
	d			18 32			19 01	19 32		20 32		22 32
Bournemouth	d			17 50			18 50			19 50		21 06
Southampton Central	d			18 54			19 30	19 54		20 54		22 54
Romsey	d			19 06			19 42	20 06		21 06		23 05
Mottisfont & Dunbridge	d											23 10
Dean	d											23 16
Salisbury	a			19 24			20 00	20 24		21 24		23 29
	d			19 28		19 58	20 03	20 28		21 28		23 30
Warminster	d			19 48		20 18	20 28	20 48		21 48		23 50
Dilton Marsh	d						20x33			21x53		23x55
Weymouth	d										20 40	
Upwey	d										20 45	
Dorchester West	d										20 53	
Maiden Newton	d										21 05	
Chetnole	d										21x12	
Yetminster	d										21x15	
Thornford	d										21x18	
Yeovil Pen Mill	d										21 26	
Castle Cary	a										21 37	
	d								21 26		21 38	
Bruton	d										21 44	
Frome	d										21 57	
Westbury	a			19 53		20 24	20 36	20 53	21 46	21 55	22 06	23 57
	d	19 30	19 35	20 01	20 15	20 32	20 43	21 01	21 46	22 01	22 09	
Exeter St Davids 6	a					22 23		22c46		00c30	22e50	
Plymouth	a					23 32		23 57			23e57	
Trowbridge	d	19 36	19 42	20 07		20 38	20 49	21 07		22 07	22 15	
Bradford-on-Avon	d	19 42		20 13		20 44	20 55	21 13		22 13	22 21	
Avoncliff	d	19x45					20x58				22x24	
Freshford	d	19 48					21 00				22 27	
Bath Spa 7	a	19 59		20 27		20 59	21 11	21 27		22 28	22 38	
Melksham	d		19 52									
Chippenham	a	20 24	20 02			21 24		22 29				
Swindon	a	20 40	20 20			21 40		22 49				
London Paddington 15 ⊖	a	22 05	22 05		21 59	23 07		00 11	23 30			
Oldfield Park	a	20 02					21 15				22 41	
Keynsham	a	20 10				21 08	21 22				22 49	
Bristol Temple Meads 10	a	20 18		20 40		21 16	21 30	21 40		22 41	22 57	
Filton Abbey Wood	a	20 50		20 54				21 56		22 54		
Severn Tunnel Jn	a											
Newport (South Wales)	a											
Cardiff Central 7	a											
Swansea 7	a											

For general notes see front of timetable
For details of catering facilities see Directory of Train Operators

A To Bristol Parkway (Table 132)
B From London Waterloo (Table 160)
b Change at Fratton
c Change at Salisbury
e Change at Castle Cary

Route Diagram for Table 125

DM-12/06
Design BAJS

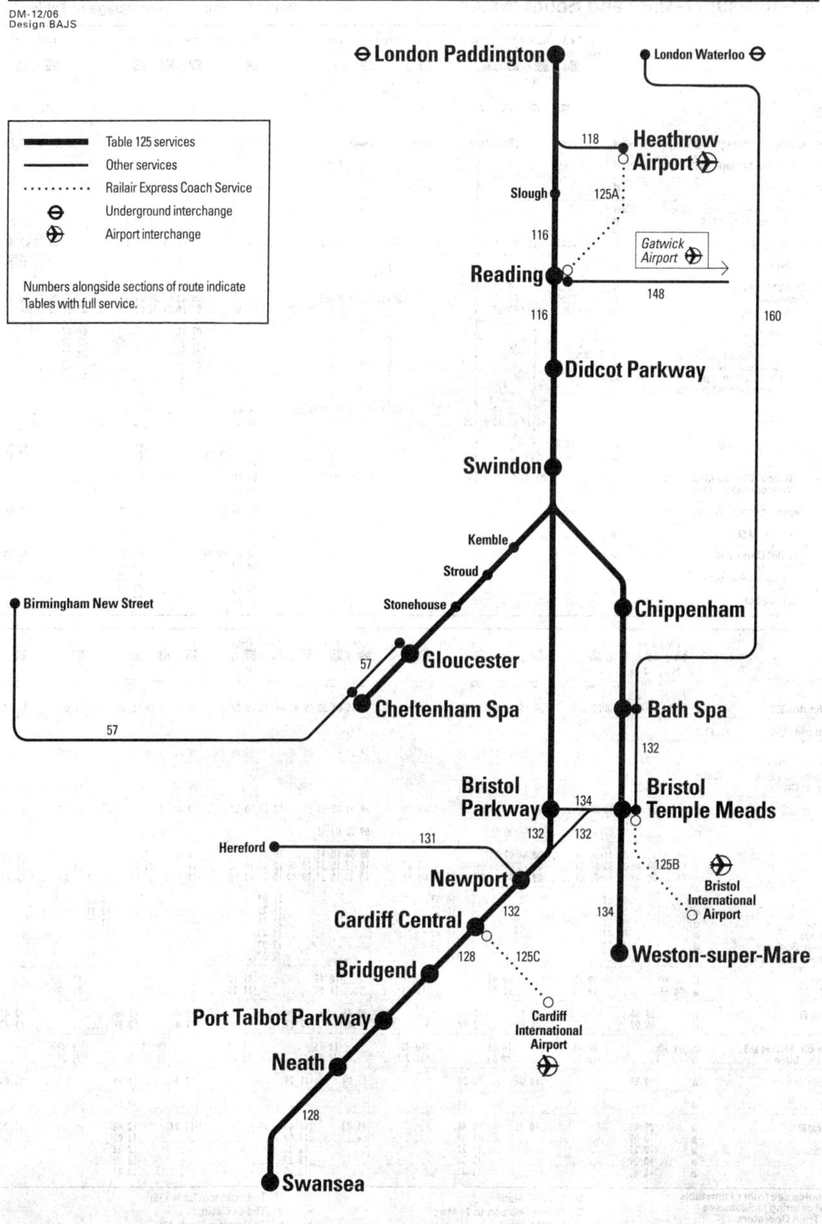
London Paddington
London Waterloo
Table 125 services
Other services
Railair Express Coach Service
Underground interchange
Airport interchange
Numbers alongside sections of route indicate Tables with full service.
118
Heathrow Airport
Slough
125A
116
Gatwick Airport
Reading
148
116
160
Didcot Parkway
Swindon
Kemble
Stroud
Stonehouse
Birmingham New Street
Chippenham
Gloucester
57
Cheltenham Spa
57
Bath Spa
132
Bristol Parkway
134
Bristol Temple Meads
132
132
Hereford
131
125B
Newport
Bristol International Airport
132
134
Cardiff Central
Weston-super-Mare
128
125C
Bridgend
Port Talbot Parkway
Cardiff International Airport
Neath
128
Swansea

London and Oxford → Swindon, Cheltenham Spa, Bristol, Weston-super-Mare and South Wales

Route Diagram - see first page of Table 125

Miles	Miles	Miles			GW MX	GW MX 1◇	GW MO 1◇ A	GW MX 1◇	GW MO 1◇ A		GW MO 1◇ B	GW MO C (Bus)	GW MO 1◇ D	GW MO 1◇ B	GW E		GW 1◇	GW	GW 1◇	GW 1◇	GW 1◇		GW G	GW 1◇	GW 1◇
0	0	0	**London Paddington** 15 ⊖	d		22p45		23p30	23p37		23p37		23p45				05 27		05 30	06 30	06 45			07 00	07 15
—	—	—	**London Waterloo** 15 ⊖	d										←											
18½	18½	18½	Slough 3	d							23p57			23p57			04 05		05 49	06 23	06 33			07 04	
—	—	—	Heathrow Terminal 1 Bus (Bus)	d							→														
—	—	—	Gatwick Airport 10	d																05 15	05 31				05 57
36	36	36	**Reading** 7	d		23p18		00 06	00 13			00 20	00 21	00 22			05 57		06 07	06 57	07 11			07 27	07 41
—	—	—	Oxford	d															06 15	06 38				07 02	07 30
53¼	53¼	53¼	Didcot Parkway	d		23p37		00 24											06 23	07 12				07 42	07 56
77¼	77¼	77¼	**Swindon**	a		23p56		00 43				01s25	00s58	00s58			06 25		06 42	07 30	07 40			08 00	08 15
—	—	—		d	23p33	23p56	23p58	00 43							06 18		06 26		06 50	07 30	07 40		07 54	08 00	08 15
—	—	91	Kemble	d	23p47														07 10				08 07		
—	—	102¼	Stroud	d	00 02														07 25				08 22		
—	—	105	Stonehouse	d	00 07														07 30				08 27		
—	—	113¾	Gloucester 7	a	00 23														07 48				08 47		
—	—	120¼	**Cheltenham Spa**	a															08 03				09 03		
—	—	—	**Birmingham New Street** 12	a															08 57				09 57		
—	94	—	Chippenham	d			00 11	00 58				02 00	01s13	01s13	06a34		06 40			07 44				08 15	
—	107	—	Bath Spa 7	a			00 27	01 13	01 20				01s27	01s27			06 54			07 59				08 30	
111¾	—	—	Bristol Parkway 7	a		00 22															08 06				08 41
—	—	—		d		00 22												07 36			08 07				08 42
117¾	118½	—	**Bristol Temple Meads** 10	a			00 43	01s29	01 35				01 45	01 45			07 10			08 17				08 45	
—	137½	—	Weston-super-Mare	a													08 25							09 23	
133½	—	—	Newport (South Wales)	a		00 52		02s12									07 44	08 05			08 29				09 04
—	—	—	Hereford 7	a													08 54				09 54				
145¼	—	—	**Cardiff Central** 7	a		01 12		02 33									08 01	08 28			08 48				09 23
165¼	—	—	Bridgend	a		01 36											08 22				09 09				
177¾	—	—	Port Talbot Parkway	a		01 49											08 35				09 22				
183¼	—	—	Neath	a		01 56											08 43				09 29				
192¾	—	—	**Swansea** 7	a		02 10											08 56				09 44				

		GW 1◇ H	GW 1◇ J	GW 1◇	GW 1◇		GW 1◇	GW 1◇	GW 1◇	GW	GW 1◇		GW 1◇	GW 1◇	GW 1◇	GW 1◇	GW 1◇ K L		GW 1◇	GW 1◇	GW 1◇	GW	GW 1◇		GW 1◇
London Paddington 15 ⊖	d	07 30	07 45	07 48	08 00		08 15	08 30	08 45		09 00		09 15	09 30	09 45	09 48	10 00		10 15	10 30	10 45		11 00		11 15
London Waterloo 15 ⊖	d																								
Slough 3	d		07 37		07 44		08 07	08 14	08 37		08 44		09 07		09 37		09 44		10 07	10 14	10 37		10 44		11 07
Heathrow Terminal 1 Bus (Bus)	d																								
Gatwick Airport 10	d		06b02				06 59		07b03		07 58				08b14				09 17				10 03		
Reading 7	d	07 57	08 11	08 16	08 27		08 41	08 57	09 11		09 27		09 41	09 57	10 11	10 16	10 27		10 41	10 57	11 11		11 27		11 41
Oxford	d			08 07	08 21			08 55					09 20	09 55					10 21	10 55					11 21
Didcot Parkway	d			08 31	08 42		08 56	09 12					09 56	10 12		10 31			10 56	11 12					11 56
Swindon	a	08 26	08 40	08 53	09 01		09 15	09 31	09 40		09 56		10 15	10 31	10 40	10 53	10 56		11 15	11 31	11 40		11 56		12 15
	d	08 26	08 40	08 54	09 01		09 15	09 31	09 40	09 54	09 56		10 15	10 31	10 40	10 54	10 56		11 15	11 31	11 40	11 54	11 56		12 15
Kemble	d			09 07						10 07						11 07						12 07			
Stroud	d			09 22						10 22						11 22						12 22			
Stonehouse	d			09 27						10 27						11 27						12 27			
Gloucester 7	a			09 43						10 47						11 43						12 47			
Cheltenham Spa	a			10 03						11 03						12 03						13 03			
Birmingham New Street 12	a			10 57						11 57						12 57						13 57			
Chippenham	d	08 40			09 15			09 45			10 10			10 45			11 10			11 45			12 10		
Bath Spa 7	a	08 55			09 30			10 00			10 25			11 00			11 25			12 00			12 25		
Bristol Parkway 7	a		09 06				09 41		10 06				10 41		11 06				11 41		12 06				12 41
	d		09 07				09 42		10 07				10 42		11 07				11 42		12 07				12 42
Bristol Temple Meads 10	a	09 10			09 45			10 15			10 42			11 15			11 42			12 15			12 42		
Weston-super-Mare	a				10 23			10 59			11 21			11 59			12 08			12 59			13 21		
Newport (South Wales)	a		09 29				10 04		10 29				11 04		11 29				12 04		12 29				13 04
Hereford 7	a		10 22						11 54						12 25						13 54				
Cardiff Central 7	a		09 48				10 23		10 48				11 23		11 48				12 23		12 48				13 23
Bridgend	a		10 09						11 09						12 08						13 09				
Port Talbot Parkway	a		10 22						11 22						12 21						13 22				
Neath	a		10 29						11 30						12 29						13 29				
Swansea 7	a		10 45						11 43						12 45						13 45				

For general notes see front of timetable
For details of catering facilities see Directory of Train Operators

A 4 February to 24 March
B From 31 March
C From 4 February to 24 March
D Until 28 January
E From Gloucester to Southampton Central (Table 123)
G From Westbury (Table 123)
H To Penzance (Table 135)
J **The St David**
K To Paignton (Table 135)
L **The Torbay Express**
b Change at Redhill

London and Oxford → Swindon, Cheltenham Spa, Bristol, Weston-super-Mare and South Wales

Route Diagram - see first page of Table 125

		GW	GW	GW	GW	GW		GW	GW	GW	GW	SW		GW	GW	GW	GW	GW		GW	GW	GW	GW	GW	GW
		1◇	1◇	1◇	1◇	1◇		1◇	1◇		1◇	1◇		1◇	1◇	1◇	1◇	1◇		1◇	1◇	1◇		1◇	1◇
				A																					
		⊼	☒	⊼	☕	☕		☕	☒		⊼			⊼	⊼	☕	⊼	⊼		⊼	☕	☕		⊼	⊼
London Paddington 15 ⊖	d	11 30	11 45	11 48	12 00	12 15		12 30	12 45		13 00			13 15	13 30	13 45	13 48	14 00		14 15	14 30	14 45		15 00	15 15
London Waterloo 15 ⊖	d											12 20													
Slough 3	d	11 14	11 37		11 44	12 07		12 14	12 37		12 44			13 07	13 14	13 37		13 44		14 07	14 14	14 31		14 44	15 07
Heathrow Terminal 1 Bus 🚌	d																								
Gatwick Airport 10	d		10b08		11 03				11b08		12 03					12b08		13 03				13b08		14 03	
Reading 7	d	11 56	12 11	12 16	12 27	12 41		12 57	13 11		13 27			13 41	13 57	14 11	14 16	14 27		14 41	14 57	15 11		15 27	15 41
Oxford	d	11 55				12 21		12 55						13 21	13 55					14 21	14 55				15 21
Didcot Parkway	d	12 12		12 31		12 56		13 12						13 56	14 12		14 31			14 56	15 12				15 56
Swindon	a	12 31	12 40	12 53	12 56	13 15		13 31	13 40		13 56			14 15	14 31	14 40	14 53	14 56		15 15	15 31	15 40		15 56	16 15
	d	12 31	12 40	12 54	12 56	13 15		13 31	13 40	13 54	13 56			14 15	14 31	14 40	14 54	14 56		15 15	15 31	15 40	15 54	15 56	16 15
Kemble	d			13 07						14 07							15 07						16 07		
Stroud	d			13 22						14 22							15 22						16 22		
Stonehouse	d			13 27						14 27							15 27						16 27		
Gloucester 7	a			13 43						14 47							15 43						16 47		
Cheltenham Spa	a			14 03						15 03							16 03						17 03		
Birmingham New Street 12	a			14 57						15 57							16 57						17 57		
Chippenham	d	12 45			13 10			13 45			14 10				14 45			15 10			15 45			16 10	
Bath Spa 7	a	13 00			13 25			14 00			14 25	14 45			15 00			15 25			16 00			16 25	
Bristol Parkway 7	a		13 06			13 41			14 06					14 41		15 06				15 41		16 06			16 41
	d		13 07			13 42			14 07					14 42		15 07				15 42		16 07			16 42
Bristol Temple Meads 10	a	13 15			13 42			14 15			14 42	15 00			15 15			15 42			16 15			16 42	
Weston-super-Mare	a	13 58			14 21			14 59			15 21				15 59			16 25			16 48			17 25	
Newport (South Wales)	a		13 29			14 05			14 29					15 04		15 29				16 04		16 29			17 04
Hereford 7	a		14 25						15 53							16 25						17 54			
Cardiff Central 7	a		13 48			14 23			14 48					15 23		15 48				16 23		16 48			17 23
Bridgend	a		14 09						15 09							16 09						17 09			
Port Talbot Parkway	a		14 22						15 22							16 22						17 22			
Neath	a		14 29						15 29							16 29						17 29			
Swansea 7	a		14 45						15 43							16 45						17 43			

		GW		GW	GW	GW	GW	GW		GW	GW	GW	GW	GW		GW	GW	GW	GW	GW		GW	GW	GW	GW
		1◇		1◇	1◇	1◇	1◇	1◇		1◇		1◇	1◇	1◇		1◇		1◇	1◇	1◇		1◇	1◇	1◇	1◇
								B						B		C	D		E	G					
		⊼		⊼	⊼	⊼	☕	☕		⊼		☕	☕	⊼		⊼		⊼	⊼	☕		⊼	⊼	⊼	⊼
London Paddington 15 ⊖	d	15 30		15 45	15 48	16 00	16 15	16 30		16 45		17 00	17 15	17 30		17 45		17 48	18 00	18 15		18 30	18 45	18 48	19 00
London Waterloo 15 ⊖	d																								
Slough 3	d	15 14		15 37		15 55	16 07	16 19		16 48		16 57		17 17		17 33			17 52	18 03		18 20	18 33		18 50
Heathrow Terminal 1 Bus 🚌	d																								
Gatwick Airport 10	d			14b08			15 03			15b08		16 03				16b08				17 03					17b23
Reading 7	d	15 57		16 11	16 16	16 27	16 41	16 57		17 11		17 27	17 41	17 57		18 11		18 16	18 27	18 41		18 57	19 11	19 16	19 27
Oxford	d	15 55					16 21	16 53				17 21		17 51					18 21			18 55			19 21
Didcot Parkway	d	16 12			16 32		16 56	17 12		17 26		17 42	17 56	18 12				18 31	18 42	18 56		19 12		19 31	19 42
Swindon	a	16 31		16 40	16 54	16 56	17 15	17 31		17 45		18 01	18 15	18 31		18 40		18 53	19 00	19 15		19 31	19 40	19 53	20 01
	d	16 31		16 40	16 54	16 56	17 15	17 31		17 45	17 54	18 01	18 15	18 31		18 40	18 45	18 54	19 00	19 15		19 31	19 40	19 54	20 01
Kemble	d				17 08						18 07							19 08						20 07	
Stroud	d				17 24						18 22							19 24						20 22	
Stonehouse	d				17 29						18 27							19 29						20 27	
Gloucester 7	a				17 47						18 47							19 47						20 43	
Cheltenham Spa	a				18 03						19 03							20 03						21 03	
Birmingham New Street 12	a				18 57						19 57							20 57						21 52	
Chippenham	d	16 45				17 10		17 45				18 15		18 45			19a01		19 15			19 45			20 15
Bath Spa 7	a	17 00				17 25		18 00				18 30		19 00					19 30			20 00			20 30
Bristol Parkway 7	a			17 06			17 42			18 12			18 41			19 11				19 41			20 06		
	d			17 07			17 42			18 13			18 42			19 11				19 42			20 07		
Bristol Temple Meads 10	a	17 15				17 42		18 15				18 45		19 15					19 45			20 15			20 45
Weston-super-Mare	a	17 51				18 26		18 53				19 29		19 47					20 29			20 53			21 28
Newport (South Wales)	a			17 29			18 04			18 36			19 04			19 34				20 04			20 29		
Hereford 7	a			18 24						19 54						20 39				21 14					
Cardiff Central 7	a			17 48			18 23			18 53			19 23			19 50				20 21			20 48		
Bridgend	a			18 09			18 53			19 13			19 49			20 11				20 42			21 09		
Port Talbot Parkway	a			18 22			19 06			19 26			20 02			20 24				20 57			21 22		
Neath	a			18 29			19 13			19 34			20 09			20 32				21 04			21 29		
Swansea 7	a			18 46			19 34			19 48			20 23			20 46				21 20			21 42		

For general notes see front of timetable
For details of catering facilities see Directory of Train Operators

A **The Cheltenham Spa Express**
B To Taunton (Table 134)
C To Carmarthen (Table 128)
D From Cheltenham Spa to Westbury (Table 123)
E **The Bristolian**
G **The Red Dragon**
b Change at Redhill

Table 125

Mondays to Fridays

London and Oxford → Swindon, Cheltenham Spa, Bristol, Weston-super-Mare and South Wales

Route Diagram - see first page of Table 125

		GW	GW	GW	GW	GW	GW	GW	GW	GW	GW	GW	GW	GW	GW	GW	GW	GW
												FO	FX		FO	FX	FO	FX
		1 ◇		1 ◇	1 ◇	1 ◇	1 ◇	1 ◇		1 ◇	1 ◇	1 ◇	1 ◇		1 ◇	1 ◇	1 ◇	1 ◇
			A								B				C			
		🛒		🛒	🛒	☕	🛒	🛒		☕	☕	☕	☕		🛒	🛒	🛒	🛒
London Paddington 15	⊖ d	19 15		19 30	19 48	20 00	20 15	20 45		21 15	21 45	22 15	22 15		22 45	22 45	23 30	23 30
London Waterloo 15	⊖ d																	
Slough 3	d	*19 07*		*19 28*	*19 41*	*19 44*	*20 07*	*20 36*		*21 07*	*21 37*	*22 05*			*22 39*	*22 43*	*23 39*	
Heathrow Terminal 1 Bus	🚌 d																	
Gatwick Airport 10	d	*18 03*				*18b23*		*19 16*		*20 03*	*20c11*	*21 03*			*21c11*		*21c11*	
Reading 7	d	19 41		19 57	20 16	20 27	20 41	21 12		21 41	22 12	22 41	22 49		23 11	23 18	00 02	00 06
Oxford	d				*19 55*	*20 20*		*20 53*		*21 20*	*21 53*	*22 34*			*23 05*	*23 05*	*23 55*	
Didcot Parkway	d	19 56			20 31	20 42	20 56	21 27		22 00	22 32	23 00	23 07		23 30	23 37	00 20	00 24
Swindon	a	20 15		20 26	20 53	21 01	21 15	21 46		22 20	22 50	23 19	23 26		23 50	23 56	00 39	00 43
	d	20 15	20 23	20 26	20 54	21 01	21 15	21 46	21 54	22 20	22 52	23 19	23 28	23 33	23 50	23 56	00 39	00 43
Kemble	d		20 37		21 11				22 07					23 47				
Stroud	d		20 52		21 26				22 22					00 02				
Stonehouse	d		20 57		21 31				22 27					00 07				
Gloucester 7	a		21 13		21 47				22 43					00 23				
Cheltenham Spa	a		21 26		22 05				23 03					*00 52*				
Birmingham New Street 12	a		*22 48*		*23 43*													
Chippenham	d			20 40		21 15		22 00			23 13	23 33	23 40				00 54	00 58
Bath Spa 7	a			20 55		21 30		22 15			23 26	23 48	23 55				01 09	01 13
Bristol Parkway 7	a	20 41					21 41			22 46					00 16	00 22		
	d	20 42					21 42			22 46					00 17	00 22		
Bristol Temple Meads 10	a			21 10		21 45		22 30			23 41	00 05	00 11				01s25	01s29
Weston-super-Mare	a			21 44		*22 28*		*23 39*			00s13							
Newport (South Wales)	a	21 04					22 04			23 15					00 48	00 52	02s06	02s12
Hereford 7	a	*22 00*					*23 05*			*01 46*					*01 46*	*01 53*	*05e13*	
Cardiff Central 7	a	21 22					22 28			23 37					01 04	01 12	02 23	02 33
Bridgend	a	21 42					22 55			23 57					01 28	01 36		
Port Talbot Parkway	a	21 55					23 08			00 10					01 41	01 49		
Neath	a	22 03					23 15			00 18					01 48	01 56		
Swansea 7	a	22 18					23 31			00 32					02 10	02 10		

Saturdays

until 26 January

		GW	GW	GW	GW	GW	GW	GW	GW	GW	GW	GW	GW	GW	GW	GW	GW	GW	GW	GW	GW	GW	GW	GW	GW
			1 ◇	1 ◇		1 ◇	1 ◇	1 ◇	1 ◇	1 ◇	1 ◇	1 ◇	1 ◇	1 ◇		1 ◇	1 ◇	1 ◇	1 ◇	1 ◇	1 ◇	1 ◇		1 ◇	1 ◇
								D																	
				🛒		☕	☕	☕	☕	☕	☕	☕	☕	☕		☕	☕	☕	☕	☕	☕	☕		☕	☕
London Paddington 15	⊖ d		22p45	23p30		06 30	07 00	07 30	07 45	08 00	08 15	08 30	08 45	09 00		09 30	09 45	10 00	10 15	10 30	10 45	11 00		11 30	11 45
London Waterloo 15	⊖ d																								
Slough 3	d					*06 18*	*06 48*	*07 14*	*07 31*	*07 45*	*08 07*	*08 14*	*08 31*	*08 45*			*09 31*	*09 45*	*10 07*	*10 14*	*10 30*	*10 45*		*11 14*	*11 31*
Heathrow Terminal 1 Bus	🚌 d																								
Gatwick Airport 10	d					*05 15*	*06 03*			*07 03*			*07b08*	*08 03*			*08b08*	*09 03*			*09b08*	*10 03*			*10b08*
Reading 7	d		23p11	00 02		06 55	07 27	07 57	08 11	08 27	08 41	08 57	09 11	09 27		09 57	10 11	10 27	10 41	10 57	11 11	11 27		11 57	12 11
Oxford	d					*06 55*		*07 55*			*08 21*								*10 21*	*10 52*				*11 55*	
Didcot Parkway	d		23p30	00 20		07 12		08 12			08 56	09 12				10 12			10 56	11 12				12 12	
Swindon	a		23p50	00 39		07 30	07 56	08 30	08 40	08 56	09 15	09 31	09 40	09 56		10 31	10 40	10 56	11 15	11 31	11 40	11 56		12 31	12 40
	d	23p33	23p50	00 39	07 15	07 30	07 56	08 30	08 40	08 56	09 15	09 31	09 40	09 56	10 14	10 31	10 40	10 56	11 15	11 31	11 40	11 56	12 14	12 31	12 40
Kemble	d	23p47			07 30						09 30				10 28				11 30				12 28		
Stroud	d	00 02			07 45						09 45				10 43				11 45				12 43		
Stonehouse	d	00 07			07 50						09 50				10 48				11 50				12 48		
Gloucester 7	a	00 23			08 06						10 06				11 04				12 06				13 04		
Cheltenham Spa	a	*00 52*			08 23						10 23				11 20				12 23				13 20		
Birmingham New Street 12	a				*09 26*						*11 26*				*12 26*				*13 26*				*14 26*		
Chippenham	d			00 54		07 45	08 10	08 45		09 10		09 45		10 10		10 45		11 10		11 45		12 10		12 45	
Bath Spa 7	a			01 09		08 00	08 24	09 00		09 24		10 00		10 25		11 00		11 25		12 00		12 25		13 00	
Bristol Parkway 7	a		00 16						09 06				10 06				11 06				12 06				13 06
	d		00 17						09 07				10 07				11 07				12 07				13 07
Bristol Temple Meads 10	a			01s25		08 15	08 40	09 15		09 40		10 15		10 42		11 15		11 42		12 15		12 42		13 15	
Weston-super-Mare	a					*08 59*	*09 21*	*09 59*				*10 59*		*11 21*				*12 21*		*12 59*		*13 21*		*13 59*	
Newport (South Wales)	a		00 48	02s06					09 30				10 31				11 29				12 31				13 29
Hereford 7	a		*01 53*						*10 54*				*11 54*				*12 25*				*13 54*				*14 25*
Cardiff Central 7	a		01 04	02 23					09 48				10 48				11 48				12 48				13 48
Bridgend	a		01 28						10 09				11 09				12 09				13 09				14 09
Port Talbot Parkway	a		01 41						10 22				11 22				12 22				13 22				14 22
Neath	a		01 48						10 30				11 30				12 30				13 30				14 30
Swansea 7	a		02 10						10 43				11 43				12 43				13 43				14 43

For general notes see front of timetable
For details of catering facilities see Directory of Train Operators

A From Westbury (Table 123)
B To Exeter St Davids (Table 135)
C 🛒 to Reading
D To Penzance (Table 135)

b Change at Redhill
c Change at Redhill and Reading
e By bus

Table 125

Saturdays

until 26 January

London and Oxford → Swindon, Cheltenham Spa, Bristol, Weston-super-Mare and South Wales

Route Diagram - see first page of Table 125

		GW		GW	GW	GW	GW	SW	GW	GW	GW	GW	GW	GW	GW	GW	GW	GW	GW	GW	GW	GW	GW	GW	GW
		1◇		1◇	1◇	1◇	1◇	1◇		1◇	1◇	1◇	1◇	1◇	1◇	1◇		1◇	1◇	1◇	1◇	1◇	1◇	1◇	
																						A			
		☕		☕	☕	☕	☕			☕	☕	☕	☕	☕	☕	☕		☕	☕	☕	☕	☕	☕	☕	
London Paddington 15 ⊖	d	12 00		12 15	12 30	12 45	13 00			13 30	13 45	14 00	14 15	14 30	14 45	15 00		15 30	15 45	16 00	16 15	16 30	16 45	17 00	
London Waterloo 15 ⊖	d							12 20																	
Slough 3	d	*11 45*		*12 07*	*12 34*		*12 45*			*13 14*	*13 31*	*13 45*	*14 07*	*14 14*	*14 31*	*14 45*		*15 14*	*15 31*		*16 07*	*16 14*	*16 31*	*16 45*	
Heathrow Terminal 1 Bus 🚌	d																								
Gatwick Airport 10	d	*11 03*				*11b08*	*12 03*				*12b08*	*13 03*			*13b08*	*14 03*			*14b08*		*15 03*		*15b08*	*16 03*	
Reading 7	d	12 27		12 41	12 58	13 11	13 27			13 57	14 11	14 27	14 41	14 57	15 11	15 27		15 57	16 11	16 27	16 41	16 57	17 11	17 27	
Oxford	d			*12 21*	*12 52*					*13 55*			*14 21*	*14 55*				*15 55*			*16 21*	*16 51*			
Didcot Parkway	d			12 56	13 15					14 12			14 56	15 12				16 12			16 56	17 12			
Swindon	a	12 56		13 15	13 33	13 40	13 56			14 31	14 40	14 56	15 15	15 31	15 40	15 56		16 31	16 40	16 56	17 15	17 31	17 40	17 56	
	d	12 56		13 15	13 35	13 40	13 56		14 14	14 31	14 40	14 56	15 15	15 31	15 40	15 56	16 14	16 31	16 40	16 56	17 15	17 31	17 40	17 56	18 14
Kemble	d			13 30					14 28				15 30				16 28				17 30				18 28
Stroud	d			13 45					14 43				15 45				16 43				17 45				18 43
Stonehouse	d			13 50					14 48				15 50				16 48				17 50				18 48
Gloucester 7	a			14 06					15 04				16 06				17 04				18 06				19 04
Cheltenham Spa	a			14 23					15 20				16 23				17 20				18 23				19 20
Birmingham New Street 12	a			*15 27*					*16 26*				*17 26*				*18 26*				*19 27*				*20 31*
Chippenham	d	13 10			13 49		14 10			14 45		15 10		15 45		16 10		16 45		17 10		17 45		18 10	
Bath Spa 7	a	13 25			14 02		14 25	14 44		15 00		15 25		16 00		16 25		17 00		17 25		18 00		18 25	
Bristol Parkway 7	a					14 06					15 06				16 06				17 06				18 06		
	d					14 07					15 07				16 07				17 07				18 07		
Bristol Temple Meads 10	a	13 42			14 17		14 42	14 59		15 15		15 42		16 15		16 42		17 15		17 42		18 15		18 42	
Weston-super-Mare	a	*14 21*								*15 59*		*16 21*		*16 59*		*17 21*		*17 59*				18 50		*19 23*	
Newport (South Wales)	a					14 31					15 29				16 32				17 29				18 31		
Hereford 7	a					*15 52*					*16 25*				*17 54*				*18 25*				*19 55*		
Cardiff Central 7	a					14 48					15 48				16 48				17 47				18 48		
Bridgend	a					15 09					16 09				17 10				18 09				19 09		
Port Talbot Parkway	a					15 22					16 22				17 23				18 24				19 22		
Neath	a					15 30					16 30				17 30				18 32				19 30		
Swansea 7	a					15 43					16 43				17 43				18 46				19 43		

		GW	GW	GW	GW	GW	GW	GW	GW	GW	GW	GW	SW	GW	GW	GW	GW	GW	GW	GW	GW	GW	GW		
		1◇	1◇	1◇	1◇	1◇	1◇	1◇	1◇	1◇	1◇	1◇	1◇		1◇	1◇	1◇	1◇		1◇	1◇	1◇	1◇		
			B			C		C						D		E				E					
		☕	☕	☕	☕	☕	☕	☕	☕	☕	☕	☕			☕	☕	☕	☕		☕		☕	☕		
London Paddington 15 ⊖	d	17 30	17 45	18 00	18 15	18 30	18 45	19 00	19 15	19 30	19 45	20 00			20 15	20 30	20 45	21 30		21 45	22 00	22 30	23 30		
London Waterloo 15 ⊖	d												19 20												
Slough 3	d	*17 14*	*17 31*	*17 45*	*18 01*	*18 14*	*18 37*	*18 45*	*19 01*	*19 14*	*19 31*	*19 45*			*20 07*		*20 38*	*21 14*			*21 44*	*22 17*	*23 20*		
Heathrow Terminal 1 Bus 🚌	d																								
Gatwick Airport 10	d		*16b08*	*17 03*			*17b08*	*18 03*			*18b08*	*19 03*					*19b08*	*20 03*			*21 03*		*21b11*		
Reading 7	d	17 56	18 11	18 27	18 41	18 57	19 11	19 27	19 41	19 57	20 11	20 27			20 41	20 57	21 11	21 57		22 12	22 27	22 57	23 59		
Oxford	d	*17 55*			*18 21*	*18 55*			*19 21*	*19 55*		*20 20*						*21 53*					*23 09*		
Didcot Parkway	d	18 12			18 56	19 12			19 56	20 12		20 42			20 56	21 12		22 12		22 32	22 42	23 16	00 16		
Swindon	a	18 31	18 40	18 56	19 15	19 31	19 40	19 56	20 15	20 31	20 40	21 01			21 15	21 31	21 45	22 31		22 50	23 01	23 36	00 36		
	d	18 31	18 40	18 56	19 15	19 31	19 40	19 56	20 15	20 31	20 40	21 01		21 08	21 15	21 31	21 46	22 31	22 35	22 52	23 01	23 37	00 36		
Kemble	d				19 30										21 30				22 49						
Stroud	d				19 45										21 45				23 04						
Stonehouse	d				19 50										21 50				23 09						
Gloucester 7	a				20 07										22 05				23 25						
Cheltenham Spa	a				20 23										22 23										
Birmingham New Street 12	a				*21 52*																				
Chippenham	d	18 45		19 10		19 45		20 10		20 45		21 15		21a24		21 45		22 45		23 13		23 50	00 50		
Bath Spa 7	a	19 00		19 25		20 00		20 25		21 00		21 30	21 49			21 59		23 00		23 26		00 05	01 05		
Bristol Parkway 7	a		19 12				20 07		20 41		21 06						22 11				23 27				
	d		19 12				20 07		20 42		21 06						22 12				23 29				
Bristol Temple Meads 10	a	19 15		19 42		20 15		20 42		21 15		21 47	22 05			22 16		23 15		23 41		00 20	01 21		
Weston-super-Mare	a	19 52		*20 23*		20 37		21 13		*22 23*						22 41				00 13					
Newport (South Wales)	a		19 35				20 31		21 04		21 31						22 45				00 01				
Hereford 7	a		*20 39*						*21 57*		*22 59*														
Cardiff Central 7	a		19 52				20 48		21 22		21 47						23 06				00 23				
Bridgend	a		20 13				21 09		21 42		22 09						23 27								
Port Talbot Parkway	a		20 26				21 22		21 55		22 22						23 40								
Neath	a		20 34				21 30		22 03		22 29						23 48								
Swansea 7	a		20 48				21 47		22 18		22 46						00 01								

For general notes see front of timetable
For details of catering facilities see Directory of Train Operators

- **A** To Paignton (Table 135)
- **B** To Carmarthen (Table 128)
- **C** To Taunton (Table 134)
- **D** From Cheltenham Spa to Westbury (Table 123)
- **E** To Exeter St.Davids (Table 135)
- **b** Change at Redhill

Table 125

Saturdays

London and Oxford → Swindon, Cheltenham Spa, Bristol, Weston-super-Mare and South Wales

2 February to 22 March

Route Diagram - see first page of Table 125

		GW	GW 1◇	GW 1◇	GW 1◇	GW	GW 1◇	GW 1◇	GW 1◇	GW 1◇	GW 1◇	GW 1◇	GW 1◇	GW 1◇	GW	GW 1◇	GW 1◇	GW 1◇	GW 1◇	GW 1◇	GW 1◇	GW 1◇		GW	GW 1◇
				🛏	A ☕		☕	☕	☕	☕	☕	☕	☕	☕		☕	☕	☕	☕	☕	☕	☕			☕
London Paddington 15 ⊖	d		22p45	23p30				07 15	07 37		08 15	08 37					09 37	10 15	10 37			11 15			
London Waterloo 15 ⊖	d																								
Slough 3	d							*07 07*	*07 14*			*08 31*						*10 07*	*10 30*			*11 07*			
Heathrow Terminal 1 Bus	d																								
Gatwick Airport 10	d							*06 03*				*07b08*						*09 03*	*09b08*			*10 03*			
Reading 7	d		23p11	00 02				07 41	08 02		08 41	09 02					10 02	10 41	11 02			11 41			
Oxford	d																								
Didcot Parkway	d		23p30	00 20																					
Swindon	a		23p50	00 39																					
	d	23p33	23p50	00 39		07 15	07 25			08 25			09 12	09 25	10 14	10 25				11 12	11 25			12 14	12 25
Kemble	d	23p47				07 30							09 25		10 28					11 25				12 28	
Stroud	d	00 02				07 45							09 40		10 43					11 40				12 43	
Stonehouse	d	00 07				07 50							09 45		10 48					11 45				12 48	
Gloucester 7	a	00 23				08 06							10 01		11 04					12 00				13 04	
Cheltenham Spa	a	*00 52*				08 23							10 18		11 20					12 18				13 20	
Birmingham New Street 12	a					*09 26*							*11 26*		*12 26*					*13 26*				*14 26*	
Chippenham	d			00 54			07 39			08 39				09 39		10 39					11 39				12 39
Bath Spa 7	a			01 09			07 52	08 46	09 17	08 53	09 49	10 12		09 54		10 52	11 17	11 47	12 17		11 53	12 46			12 52
Bristol Parkway 7	a		00 16					09 15										12 16				13 15			
	d		00 17		07 13			09 20										12 20				13 20			
Bristol Temple Meads 10	a			01s25			08 06	09 00	09 32	09 07	10 03	10 30		10 08		11 06	11 32	12 01	12 35		12 07	13 00			13 06
Weston-super-Mare	a							*09 59*		*10 59*		*11 21*		*11 31*				*12 59*	*13 21*			*13 59*			
Newport (South Wales)	a		00 48	02s06	07 34			09 42			10 45							12 43				13 41			
Hereford 7	a		*01 53*		*08 54*			*10 54*										*13 54*				*14 54*			
Cardiff Central 7	a		01 04	02 23	07 51			10 00			11 02							13 00				14 00			
Bridgend	a		01 28		08 12			10 21			11 23							13 21				14 21			
Port Talbot Parkway	a		01 41		08 25			10 34			11 36							13 34				14 34			
Neath	a		01 48		08 33			10 42			11 43							13 41				14 42			
Swansea 7	a		02 10		08 48			10 57			11 58							13 56				14 59			

		GW 1◇		GW 1◇		GW 1◇	GW 1◇	GW 1◇	SW 1◇	GW 1◇	GW 1◇	GW 1◇	GW		GW 1◇	GW 1◇	GW 1◇	GW	GW 1◇	GW 1◇	GW	GW 1◇	GW 1◇	GW 1◇	GW 1◇
		☕		☕		☕	☕	☕		☕	☕	☕			☕	☕	☕		☕	☕		☕	☕	☕	☕
London Paddington 15 ⊖	d	11 37		12 15				12 37		13 15		13 37			14 15				15 15	15 37			16 15		
London Waterloo 15 ⊖	d								12 20																
Slough 3	d			*12 07*						*13 01*		*13 31*			*14 07*				*15 07*	*15 31*			*16 07*		
Heathrow Terminal 1 Bus	d																								
Gatwick Airport 10	d			*11 03*						*12 03*		*12b08*			*13 03*				*14 03*	*14b08*			*15 03*		
Reading 7	d	12 02		12 41				13 02		13 41		14 04			14 41				15 41	16 02			16 41		
Oxford	d																								
Didcot Parkway	d																								
Swindon	a																								
	d					13 12	13 25				14 25		14 14			15 12	15 25	15 29			16 14	16 25		17 12	17 25
Kemble	d					13 25							14 28			15 25					16 28			17 25	
Stroud	d					13 40							14 43			15 40					16 43			17 40	
Stonehouse	d					13 45							14 48			15 45					16 48			17 45	
Gloucester 7	a					14 01							15 04			16 01					17 04			18 01	
Cheltenham Spa	a					14 18							15 20			16 18					17 20			18 18	
Birmingham New Street 12	a					*15 27*							*16 26*			*17 26*					*18 26*			*19 27*	
Chippenham	d						13 39				14 39						15 39	15a45				16 39			17 39
Bath Spa 7	a	13 23		13 46			13 52	14 14	14 44	14 46	14 53	15 20			15 46		15 52		16 47	17 17		16 53	17 46		17 52
Bristol Parkway 7	a			14 15						15 17					16 15				17 15				18 15		
	d			14 20						15 22					16 20				17 20				18 20		
Bristol Temple Meads 10	a	13 41		14 00			14 06	14 31	14 59	15 00	15 07	15 36			16 00		16 06		17 01	17 36		17 07	18 00		18 06
Weston-super-Mare	a			*14 59*						*15 59*		*16 21*			*16 59*				*17 59*	*18 21*			*19 00*		
Newport (South Wales)	a			14 43						15 41					16 43				17 42				18 43		
Hereford 7	a			*15 52*						*16 54*					*17 54*				*18 54*				*19 55*		
Cardiff Central 7	a			15 00						16 00					17 00				18 00				19 00		
Bridgend	a			15 21						16 21					17 21				18 22				19 21		
Port Talbot Parkway	a			15 34						16 34					17 34				18 35				19 34		
Neath	a			15 42						16 42					17 42				18 43				19 42		
Swansea 7	a			15 57						16 59					17 57				18 56				19 59		

For general notes see front of timetable
For details of catering facilities see
Directory of Train Operators

A From Bristol Temple Meads (Table 132)
b Change at Redhill

Table 125

Saturdays

2 February to 22 March

London and Oxford → Swindon, Cheltenham Spa, Bristol, Weston-super-Mare and South Wales

Route Diagram - see first page of Table 125

		GW 1◇ ☕	GW 1◇ A ☕	GW 1◇ ☕	GW	GW 1◇ ☕	GW 1◇ ☕	GW 1◇ ☕	GW 1◇ ☕	GW 1◇ ☕		SW 1◇	GW B	GW 1◇ ☕	GW 1◇ ☕	GW 1◇ ☕	GW 1◇ ☕	GW 1◇ ☕	GW 1◇ ☕	GW	GW 1◇	GW 1◇ ☕	GW 1◇ ☕		
London Paddington 15 ⊖	d	17 03	17 15	17 37		18 15	18 30			19 15				20 15	20 37		21 15	21 37			22 15	22 37			
London Waterloo 15 ⊖	d											19 20													
Slough 3	d					*18 01*	*18 14*			*19 01*				*20 07*	*20 14*		*21 08*	*21 14*			*22 08*	*22 17*			
Heathrow Terminal 1 Bus	d																								
Gatwick Airport 10	d					*17 03*				*18 03*				*19 03*			*20 03*				*21 03*				
Reading 7	d	17 30	17 41	18 02		18 41	18 57			19 41				20 41	21 03		21 41	22 02			22 41	23 07			
Oxford	d																								
Didcot Parkway	d																								
Swindon	a																								
	d				18 14			19 15	20 25				21 08			21 15			22 25	22 35			23 25		
Kemble	d				18 28			19 30								21 30				22 49					
Stroud	d				18 43			19 45								21 45				23 04					
Stonehouse	d				18 48			19 50								21 50				23 09					
Gloucester 7	a				19 04			20 06								22 05				23 25					
Cheltenham Spa	a				19 20			20 23								22 23									
Birmingham New Street 12	a				*20 31*			*21 52*																	
Chippenham	d								20 39				21a24						22 39				23 39		
Bath Spa 7	a	18 36	18 46	19 17		19 46	20 04		20 52	20 53		21 49		21 51	22 17		22 46	23 09	22 52		23 47	00 14	23 52		
Bristol Parkway 7	a		19 15			20 15				21 16				22 20			23 15								
	d		19 20			20 21				21 21				22 24			23 20								
Bristol Temple Meads 10	a	18 51	19 00	19 32		20 00	20 18		21 06	21 07		22 05		22 05	22 32		23 00	23 25	23 06		00 01	00 29	00 06		
Weston-super-Mare	a	19 23		19 53			20 40			*22 23*					22s57										
Newport (South Wales)	a		19 43			20 49				21 50				22 50			23 47				00 37				
Hereford 7	a					*21 57*				*22 59*															
Cardiff Central 7	a		20 03			21 05				22 11				23 10			00 07				01 00				
Bridgend	a		20 25			21 27				22 33				23 32			00 29								
Port Talbot Parkway	a		20 38			21 40				22 46				23 45			00 42								
Neath	a		20 45			21 47				22 53				23 52			00 49								
Swansea 7	a		20 58			22 04				23 09				00 10			01 02								

Saturdays

from 29 March

		GW	GW 1◇	GW 1◇ trolley	GW 1◇ ☕	GW 1◇ ☕	GW 1◇ ☕		GW 1◇ C ☕	GW 1◇ ☕	GW 1◇ ☕	GW 1◇ ☕	GW 1◇ ☕	GW 1◇ ☕		GW 1◇ ☕	GW 1◇ ☕	GW 1◇ ☕	GW 1◇ ☕	GW 1◇ ☕	GW 1◇ ☕		GW 1◇ ☕	GW 1◇ ☕	GW 1◇ ☕
London Paddington 15 ⊖	d		22p45	23p30	06 30	06 45	07 00		07 30	07 45	08 00	08 30	08 45	09 00		09 30	09 45	10 00	10 30	10 45	11 00		11 30	11 45	12 00
London Waterloo 15 ⊖	d																								
Slough 3	d				*06 18*		*06 48*		*07 14*	*07 31*	*07 45*	*08 14*	*08 31*	*08 45*			*09 31*	*09 45*	*10 14*	*10 30*	*10 45*		*11 14*	*11 31*	*11 45*
Heathrow Terminal 1 Bus	d																								
Gatwick Airport 10	d				*05 15*	*05 31*	*06 03*				*07 03*		*07c08*	*08 03*			*08c08*	*09 03*		*09c08*	*10 03*			*10c08*	*11 03*
Reading 7	d		23p11	00 02	06 55	07 11	07 27		07 57	08 11	08 27	08 57	09 11	09 27		09 57	10 11	10 27	10 57	11 11	11 27		11 57	12 11	12 27
Oxford	d				*06 55*				*07 55*			*08 21*	*08 55*				*09 52*		*10 52*				*11 55*		
Didcot Parkway	d		23p30	00 20	07 12	07 26			08 12	08 27		09 12	09 26			10 12	10 27		11 12	11 27			12 12	12 27	
Swindon	a		23p50	00 39	07 30	07 45	07 56		08 30	08 45	08 56	09 31	09 45	09 56		10 31	10 45	10 56	11 31	11 45	11 56		12 31	12 45	12 56
	d	23p33	23p50	00 39	07 30	07 45	07 56		08 30	08 47	08 56	09 31	09 45	09 56		10 31	10 47	10 56	11 31	11 47	11 56		12 31	12 47	12 56
Kemble	d	23p47				08 00				09 00			10 00				11 00			12 00				13 00	
Stroud	d	00 02				08 15				09 15			10 15				11 15			12 15				13 15	
Stonehouse	d	00 07				08 21				09 21			10 21				11 21			12 21				13 21	
Gloucester 7	a	00 23				08 36				09 36			10 36				11 36			12 36				13 36	
Cheltenham Spa	a	*00 52*				*08 55*				*09 56*			*10 56*				*11 56*			*12 56*				*13 55*	
Birmingham New Street 12	a					*09 45*				*10 45*			*11 45*				*12 46*			*13 45*				*14 45*	
Chippenham	d			00 54	07 45		08 10		08 45		09 10	09 45		10 10		10 45		11 10	11 45		12 10		12 45		13 10
Bath Spa 7	a			01 09	08 00		08 24		09 00		09 24	10 00		10 25		11 00		11 25	12 00		12 25		13 00		13 25
Bristol Parkway 7	a		00 16																						
	d		00 17																						
Bristol Temple Meads 10	a			01s25	08 15		08 40		09 15		09 40	10 15		10 42		11 15		11 42	12 15		12 42		13 15		13 42
Weston-super-Mare	a				*08 59*		*09 23*		*09 59*		*10 24*	*10 59*		*11 21*				*12 21*	*12 59*		*13 21*		*13 59*		*14 59*
Newport (South Wales)	a		00 48	02s06		09 19				10 18			11 19				12 17			13 19				14 17	
Hereford 7	a		*01 53*	*05e13*		*11e45*				*12e15*			*13e45*				*14e15*			*15e45*				*16e15*	
Cardiff Central 7	a		01 04	02 23		09 38				10 38			11 38				12 38			13 38				14 38	
Bridgend	a		01 28			10 00				11 00			12 00				13 00			14 00				15 00	
Port Talbot Parkway	a		01 41			10 13				11 13			12 14				13 13			14 16				15 13	
Neath	a		01 48			10 20				11 20			12 21				13 20			14 23				15 20	
Swansea 7	a		02 10			10 39				11 38			12 37				13 37			14 40				15 38	

For general notes see front of timetable
For details of catering facilities see Directory of Train Operators

A To Carmarthen (Table 128)
B From Cheltenham Spa to Westbury (Table 123)
C To Penzance (Table 135)

c Change at Redhill
e By bus

Table 125

Saturdays

from 29 March

London and Oxford → Swindon, Cheltenham Spa, Bristol, Weston-super-Mare and South Wales

Route Diagram - see first page of Table 125

		GW	GW	GW	GW	SW	GW	GW	GW	GW	GW	GW	GW	GW	GW	GW	GW	GW	GW	GW	GW	GW
		1 ◇	1 ◇	1 ◇	1 ◇	1 ◇	1 ◇	1 ◇	1 ◇	1 ◇	1 ◇	1 ◇	1 ◇	1 ◇	1 ◇	1 ◇	1 ◇	1 ◇	1 ◇	1 ◇	1 ◇	1 ◇
																		A				B
		☕	☕	☕	☕		☕	☕	☕	☕	☕	☕	☕	☕	☕	☕	☕	☕	☕	☕	☕	☕
London Paddington 15 ⊖	d	12 30	12 45	13 00	13 05		13 30	13 45	14 00	14 05	14 30	14 45	15 00	15 30	15 45	16 00	16 05	16 30	16 45	17 00	17 30	17 45
London Waterloo 15 ⊖	d					12 20																
Slough 3	d	12 14	12 31	12 45	13 01		13 14	13 31	13 45	14 07	14 14	14 31	14 45	15 14	15 31		16 07	16 14	16 31	16 45	17 14	17 31
Heathrow Terminal 1 Bus	d																					
Gatwick Airport 10	d		11b08	12 03				12b08	13 03			13b08	14 03		14b08		15 03		15b08	16 03		16b08
Reading 7	d	12 58	13 11	13 27	13 32		13 57	14 11	14 27	14 32	14 57	15 11	15 27	15 57	16 11	16 27	16 32	16 57	17 11	17 27	17 56	18 11
Oxford	d	12 52					13 55				14 55			15 55				16 51			17 55	
Didcot Parkway	d	13 15	13 27				14 12	14 27			15 12	15 27		16 12	16 27			17 12			18 12	
Swindon	a	13 33	13 45	13 56			14 31	14 47	14 56		15 31	15 45	15 56	16 31	16 46	16 56		17 31	17 41	17 56	18 31	18 41
	d	13 35	13 47	13 56			14 31	14 48	14 56		15 31	15 47	15 56	16 31	16 47	16 56		17 31	17 42	17 56	18 31	18 42
Kemble	d		14 00					15 02				16 00			17 01				17 56			18 56
Stroud	d		14 15					15 17				16 15			17 16				18 11			19 11
Stonehouse	d		14 21					15 22				16 21			17 21				18 16			19 16
Gloucester 7	a		14 36					15 37				16 37			17 36				18 37			19 33
Cheltenham Spa	a		14 55					15 56				16 55			17 55				18 55			19 55
Birmingham New Street 12	a		15 45					16 45				17 45			18 46				19 45			20 41
Chippenham	d	13 49		14 10			14 45		15 10		15 45		16 10	16 45		17 10		17 45		18 10	18 45	
Bath Spa 7	a	14 02		14 25		14 44	15 00		15 25		16 00		16 25	17 00		17 25		18 00		18 25	19 00	
Bristol Parkway 7	a																					
	d																					
Bristol Temple Meads 10	a	14 17		14 42	14 39	14 59	15 15		15 42	15 36	16 15		16 42	17 15		17 42	17 34	18 15		18 42	19 15	
Weston-super-Mare	a			15 21	15 21		15 59		16 21	16 21	16 59		17 21	17 59			18 21	18 50		19 23	19 52	
Newport (South Wales)	a		15 19					16 19				17 20			18 24				19 20			20 16
Hereford 7	a		17c45					18c15				19c45			20c30							21c55
Cardiff Central 7	a		15 38					16 38				17 37			18 41				19 38			20 36
Bridgend	a		16 00					17 00				17 59			19 04				20 00			20 58
Port Talbot Parkway	a		16 13					17 13				18 12			19 17				20 13			21 11
Neath	a		16 20					17 20				18 19			19 24				20 20			21 18
Swansea 7	a		16 36					17 39				18 37			19 37				20 37			21 31

		GW	GW	GW	GW	GW	GW	GW	GW	GW	GW	GW	SW	GW	GW	GW	GW	GW	GW	GW
		1 ◇	1 ◇	1 ◇	1 ◇	1 ◇	1 ◇	1 ◇	1 ◇	1 ◇	1 ◇	1 ◇	1 ◇		1 ◇	1 ◇	1 ◇	1 ◇	1 ◇	1 ◇
				C		C									D					
		☕	☕	☕	☕	☕	☕	☕	☕	☕	☕	☕			☕	☕	☕		☕	☕
London Paddington 15 ⊖	d	18 00	18 05	18 30	18 45	19 00	19 05	19 15	19 30	19 45	20 00	20 05			20 30	20 45	21 30	22 00	22 30	23 30
London Waterloo 15 ⊖	d												19 20							
Slough 3	d	17 45	18 01	18 14	18 37	18 45	19 01		19 14	19 31	19 45	20 07			20 14	20 38	21 14	21 44	22 17	23 20
Heathrow Terminal 1 Bus	d																			
Gatwick Airport 10	d	17 03			17b08	18 03				18b08	19 03					19b08	20 03	21 03		21b11
Reading 7	d	18 27	18 32	18 57	19 11	19 27	19 32	19 41	19 57	20 11	20 27	20 33			20 57	21 11	21 57	22 27	22 57	23 59
Oxford	d			18 55				19 21	19 55		20 20				20 53		21 53			23 09
Didcot Parkway	d			19 12				19 55	20 12		20 42				21 12	21 30	22 12	22 42	23 16	00 16
Swindon	a	18 56		19 31	19 41	19 56		20 15	20 31	20 40	21 01				21 31	21 50	22 31	23 01	23 36	00 36
	d	18 56		19 31	19 42	19 56		20 17	20 31	20 42	21 01			21 20	21 31	21 51	22 31	23 01	23 37	00 36
Kemble	d				19 56			20 30		20 55						22 05		23 16		
Stroud	d				20 11			20 45		21 10						22 20		23 31		
Stonehouse	d				20 16			20 51		21 16						22 25		23 37		
Gloucester 7	a				20 31			21 06		21 33						22 40		23 52		
Cheltenham Spa	a				21 05			21 25		21 55										
Birmingham New Street 12	a				21 52					23 02										
Chippenham	d	19 10		19 45		20 10			20 45		21 15			21a36	21 45		22 45		23 50	00 50
Bath Spa 7	a	19 25		20 00		20 25			21 00		21 30		21 49		22 00		23 00		00 05	01 05
Bristol Parkway 7	a																			
	d																			
Bristol Temple Meads 10	a	19 42	19 32	20 15		20 42	20 58		21 15		21 47	21 57	22 05		22 15		23 15		00 20	01 21
Weston-super-Mare	a	20 23	20 23	20 37		21 13			22 23						22s39					
Newport (South Wales)	a				21 15			21 49		22 24						23 32		00 42		
Hereford 7	a							22e59												
Cardiff Central 7	a				21 37			22 13		22 45						23 57		01 05		
Bridgend	a				22 00			22 34		23 06										
Port Talbot Parkway	a				22 13			22 47		23 19										
Neath	a				22 20			22 55		23 27										
Swansea 7	a				22 37			23 11		23 44										

For general notes see front of timetable
For details of catering facilities see Directory of Train Operators

A To Paignton (Table 135)
B To Carmarthen (Table 128)
C To Taunton (Table 134)
D To Exeter St Davids (Table 135)

b Change at Redhill
c By bus
e From 5 April arr. 2350, by bus

Table 125

until 27 January

London and Oxford → Swindon, Cheltenham Spa, Bristol, Weston-super-Mare and South Wales

Route Diagram - see first page of Table 125

		GW	GW	GW	GW	GW	GW	GW	GW	GW	GW	GW	GW	GW	GW	GW	GW	SW
		1 ◇	1 ◇	1 ◇	1 ◇	1 ◇	1 ◇		1 ◇	1 ◇	1 ◇	1 ◇	1 ◇	1 ◇	1 ◇	1 ◇	1 ◇	1 ◇
			A								B			C		B		
		☕	☕	☕	☕	☕	☕		☕	☕	☕	☕	☕	☕	☕	☕	☕	
London Paddington 15	⊖ d	23p30	08 00	08 33	08 37	09 07	09 30		10 07	10 27	10 37	11 07	11 37	12 07	12 27	12 37	13 07	
London Waterloo 15	⊖ d																	12 15
Slough 3	d		07 14	08 25	08 47	09 01	09 39			10 15	10 39	10 58	11 39	12 00	12 15	12 39	12 58	
Heathrow Terminal 1 Bus	🚌 d																	
Gatwick Airport 10	d		07 07			08 07				09 07			10 11	11 07			12 07	
Reading 7	d	23p59	08 43	09 11	09 17	09 41	10 07		10 44	11 04	11 12	11 42	12 11	12 42	13 05	13 12	13 42	
Oxford	d		07c45	09 05		09 38				10 38		11 38		12 05	12 50		13 38	
Didcot Parkway	d	00 16	08 58	09 29	09 34	09 59			11 00	11 20		11 58		12 58	13 19		13 58	
Swindon	a	00 36	09 18	09 48	09 53	10 16	10 39		11 18	11 37	11 41	12 16	12 40	13 17	13 37	13 41	14 16	
	d	00 36	09 19	09 50	09 55	10 16	10 42	10 45	11 18	11 38	11 44	12 16	12 40	13 17	13 38	13 44	14 17	
Kemble	d				10 08			10 59		11 53					13 53			
Stroud	d				10 23			11 14		12 09					14 09			
Stonehouse	d				10 28			11 19		12 14					14 14			
Gloucester 7	a				10 44			11 35		12 29					14 29			
Cheltenham Spa	a				11 00			11 48		12 46					14 46			
Birmingham New Street 12	a				11 51			12 51		13 40					15 44			
Chippenham	d	00 50	09 34			10 32			11 33			12 31		13 31			14 31	
Bath Spa 7	a	01 05	09 47			10 47			11 48			12 46		13 45			14 45	14 52
Bristol Parkway 7	a			10 14			11 06				12 08		13 08			14 08		
	d			10 16			11 10				12 10		13 10			14 10		
Bristol Temple Meads 10	a	01 21	10 01			11 02			12 04			13 02		14 01			15 00	15 06
Weston-super-Mare	a					12 01			12 32			13 31						15 49
Newport (South Wales)	a			10 37			11 31				12 31		13 31			14 31		
Hereford 7	a						12 40				13 40					15 41		
Cardiff Central 7	a			10 54			11 48				12 48		13 48			14 48		
Bridgend	a			11 15			12 09				13 09		14 10			15 09		
Port Talbot Parkway	a			11 28			12 22				13 22		14 23			15 22		
Neath	a			11 36			12 30				13 30		14 30			15 30		
Swansea 7	a			11 50			12 43				13 43		14 45			15 43		

		GW	GW	GW	GW	GW	GW	GW	GW	GW	GW	GW	GW	GW	GW	GW	GW
			1 ◇	1 ◇	1 ◇	1 ◇	1 ◇	1 ◇	1 ◇	1 ◇	1 ◇	1 ◇	1 ◇			1 ◇	1 ◇
						B	D										
			☕	☕	☕	☕	☕	☕	☕	☕	☕	☕	☕			☕	☕
London Paddington 15	⊖ d		13 37	14 07	14 27	14 37	15 07	15 37	16 07	16 27	16 37	17 07	17 12			17 37	18 07
London Waterloo 15	⊖ d																
Slough 3	d		13 39	13 58	14 15	14 39	14 58	15 39	15 58	16 15	16 39	16 58	17 15			17 39	17 58
Heathrow Terminal 1 Bus	🚌 d																
Gatwick Airport 10	d			13 07			14 07		15 07			16 07					17 07
Reading 7	d		14 11	14 42	15 05	15 12	15 42	16 13	16 42	17 05	17 13	17 42	17 48			18 13	18 42
Oxford	d			14 38			15 05		16 05	16 50		17 05					18 41
Didcot Parkway	d			14 58	15 19		15 58		16 58	17 19		17 58					18 58
Swindon	a		14 40	15 17	15 37	15 41	16 17	16 41	17 17	17 38	17 42	18 15	18 18			18 42	19 17
	d	14 21	14 42	15 17	15 38	15 44	16 17	16 43	17 17	17 39	17 48	18 17	18 20	18 21	18 31	18 50	19 17
Kemble	d	14e38			15 53					17 53				18 35			
Stroud	d	14 53			16 09					18 09				18 49			
Stonehouse	d	14 58			16 14					18 14				18 54			
Gloucester 7	a	15 19			16 29					18 29				19 18			
Cheltenham Spa	a	15 33			16 46					18 47				19 46			
Birmingham New Street 12	a	16 26			17 45					19 45				20 45			
Chippenham	d			15 31			16 31		17 31			18 31			18a47		19 31
Bath Spa 7	a			15 45			16 45		17 45			18 45					19 45
Bristol Parkway 7	a		15 08			16 08		17 08			18 12		18 45			19 14	
	d		15 10			16 10		17 10			18 14		18 46			19 16	
Bristol Temple Meads 10	a			16 00			17 00		18 00			19 01					20 00
Weston-super-Mare	a			16 47			17 29		18 36			19 32					20 53
Newport (South Wales)	a		15 32			16 31		17 33			18 35		19 11			19 37	
Hereford 7	a		16 40			17 44					19 38						
Cardiff Central 7	a		15 48			16 48		17 50			18 52		19 27			19 54	
Bridgend	a		16 10			17 09		18 12			19 13		19 48			20 15	
Port Talbot Parkway	a		16 23			17 22		18 25			19 26		20 01			20 28	
Neath	a		16 30			17 30		18 32			19 34		20 09			20 36	
Swansea 7	a		16 43			17 43		18 48			19 47		20 23			20 52	

For general notes see front of timetable
For details of catering facilities see Directory of Train Operators

- **A** To Penzance (Table 135)
- **B** To Carmarthen (Table 128)
- **C** To Plymouth (Table 135)
- **D** To Taunton (Table 134)
- **c** By bus
- **e** Arr. 1435

Table 125

Sundays

until 27 January

London and Oxford → Swindon, Cheltenham Spa, Bristol, Weston-super-Mare and South Wales

Route Diagram - see first page of Table 125

		GW 1◇ ☕	GW 1◇ ☕	GW 1◇ A ☕	SW 1◇	GW B	GW 1◇ ☕	GW 1◇ ☕	GW 1◇ ☕	GW 1◇	GW 1◇	GW 1◇	GW	GW 1◇ ☕	GW 1◇ ☕	GW 1◇ ☕	GW 1◇ ☕
London Paddington 15 ⊖	d	18 27	18 37	19 07			19 37	20 07	20 27	20 37	21 07	21 37		22 07	22 37	23 07	23 45
London Waterloo 15 ⊖	d				18 15												
Slough 3	d	*18 15*	*18 39*	*18 58*			*19 39*	*19 57*	*20 15*		*20 58*	*21 15*		*21 59*	*22 16*	*23 00*	*23 47*
Heathrow Terminal 1 Bus 🚌	d																
Gatwick Airport 10	d			*18 07*				*19 07*			*20 07*			*21 07*		*22 07*	*22 07*
Reading 7	d	19 05	19 11	19 42			20 12	20 42	21 06	21 14	21 42	22 13		22 43	23 14	23 46	00 21
Oxford	d			*19 05*				*20 05*	*20 50*		*21 05*			*22 05*	*22 58*		
Didcot Parkway	d	19 19		19 58				20 58	21 20		22 00			22 59	23 30	00s02	00s38
Swindon	a	19 38	19 42	20 17			20 41	21 16	21 39	21 44	22 20	22 47		23 19	23 50	00s22	00s58
	d	19 39	19 48	20 17		20 27	20 42	21 17	21 40	21 45	22 20	22 48	22 57	23 20	23 51		
Kemble	d	19 53				20 41			21 54				23 11				
Stroud	d	20 09				20 56			22 09				23 26				
Stonehouse	d	20 14				21 01			22 14				23 31				
Gloucester 7	a	20 29				21 17			22 30				23 50				
Cheltenham Spa	a	20 45				21 30			22 45				00 04				
Birmingham New Street 12	a	*21 44*				*22 45*			*23 44*								
Chippenham	d			20 31				21 31			22 33			23 34		00s39	01s14
Bath Spa 7	a			20 45	20 59			21 45			22 47			23 48		00s52	01s27
Bristol Parkway 7	a		20 12				21 07			22 09		23 13			00s16		
	d		20 14				21 08			22 11		23 14					
Bristol Temple Meads 10	a			21 00	21 16			22 02			23 03			00 03	00 29	01 06	01 45
Weston-super-Mare	a			21 31				*23 03*			23 32						
Newport (South Wales)	a		20 35				21 30			22 38		23 42					
Hereford 7	a		*21 43*							*00 04*							
Cardiff Central 7	a		20 52				21 47			22 59		00 02					
Bridgend	a		21 13				22 09			23 20		00 24					
Port Talbot Parkway	a		21 26				22 24			23 33		00 37					
Neath	a		21 34				22 31			23 41		00 44					
Swansea 7	a		21 47				22 44			23 54		00 57					

Sundays

3 February to 23 March

		GW 🚌	GW 1◇ ☕	GW 1◇ ☕	GW 🚌	GW 1◇ ☕	GW 🚌	GW 1◇ ☕	GW 🚌	GW 1◇ ☕	GW 🚌	GW 🚌	GW 1◇ ☕	GW 1◇ ☕	GW 🚌	GW 🚌	GW 1	GW 🚌	GW 🚌	GW 1◇ ☕	GW 1◇ ☕	GW 🚌
London Paddington 15 ⊖	d			08 00						09 03				10 03							11 03	
London Waterloo 15 ⊖	d																					
Slough 3	d			*07 16*						*09 01*				*09 56*							*11 01*	
Heathrow Terminal 1 Bus 🚌	d																					
Gatwick Airport 10	d			*06 07*						*08 07*				*09 07*							*10 11*	
Reading 7	d			08 37	08 45					09 42	09 50			10 42	10 20			10 50			11 45	11 20
Oxford	d																					
Didcot Parkway	d	08 15					09 15					10 15							11 15			
Swindon	a	09 05			09 50		10 05				10 55	11 05			11 25			11 55	12 05			12 25
	d		09 10			09 55		10 10	10 30				11 10			11 30	11 30			12 10		
Kemble	d					10 08											11 45					
Stroud	d					10 23											12 00					
Stonehouse	d					10 28											12 05					
Gloucester 7	a					10 44											12 22					
Cheltenham Spa	a					11 00											12 35					
Birmingham New Street 12	a					*11 51*											*13 40*					
Chippenham	d		09 24					10 24					11 24							12 24		
Bath Spa 7	a		09 37	09 43				10 37		10 53			11 37	11 52						12 37	12 51	
Bristol Parkway 7	a			10 12					11 25	11 27				12 27		12 25					13 27	
	d			10 19						11 34				12 34							13 34	
Bristol Temple Meads 10	a		09 53	09 57				10 53		11 07			11 51	12 06						12 51	13 05	
Weston-super-Mare	a												*12 50*								*14 07*	
Newport (South Wales)	a			10 40						11 55				12 55							13 55	
Hereford 7	a			*12 40*						*13 40*											*15 41*	
Cardiff Central 7	a			10 57						12 12				13 12							14 12	
Bridgend	a			11 18						12 33				13 33							14 33	
Port Talbot Parkway	a			11 31						12 46				13 46							14 46	
Neath	a			11 39						12 54				13 54							14 55	
Swansea 7	a			11 53						13 07				14 07							15 08	

For general notes see front of timetable
For details of catering facilities see Directory of Train Operators

A To Exeter St Davids (Table 135)
B From Westbury (Table 123)

Table 125

Sundays

London and Oxford → Swindon, Cheltenham Spa, Bristol, Weston-super-Mare and South Wales

3 February to 23 March

Route Diagram - see first page of Table 125

	GW 🚌		GW 🚌	GW 1 ◇ ☕	GW 🚌	GW 1 ◇ ☕	GW 🚌		GW 1 ◇ ☕	GW 🚌	GW 🚌	GW 🚌	GW 1 ◇ ☕		SW 1 ◇	GW 1 ◇ ☕	GW 🚌	GW 🚌	GW		GW 🚌	GW 🚌	GW 1 ◇ ☕	GW 1 ◇ ☕
London Paddington 15 ⊖ d									12 03							13 03								14 03
London Waterloo 15 ⊖ d															12 15									
Slough 3 d									*12 00*							*13 01*								*14 01*
Heathrow Terminal 1 Bus 🚌 d																								
Gatwick Airport 10 d									*11 07*							*12 07*								*13 07*
Reading 7 d			11 50						12 42	12 20	12 50					13 42	13 20				13 50			14 42
Oxford d																								
Didcot Parkway d					12 15							13 15										14 20		
Swindon a			12 55		13 05					13 25	13 55	14 05					14 25				14 55	15 10		
d	12 30			13 00		13 10	13 30						14 10					14 30	14 30				15 15	
Kemble d				13 13															14 44					
Stroud d				13 28															14 59					
Stonehouse d				13 33															15 04					
Gloucester 7 a				13 48															15 19					
Cheltenham Spa a				14 16															15 33					
Birmingham New Street 12 a				*15 44*															*16 39*					
Chippenham d						13 24							14 22										15 27	
Bath Spa 7 a						13 37			13 55				14 37		14 52	14 58							15 42	15 53
Bristol Parkway 7 a	13 25						14 25		14 27							15 27		15 25						16 27
d									14 34							15 34								16 34
Bristol Temple Meads 10 a						13 51			14 09				14 51		15 06	15 12							15 57	16 07
Weston-super-Mare a															*15 49*	*16 08*							*16 47*	
Newport (South Wales) a									14 55							15 55								16 55
Hereford 7 a									*16 40*							*17 44*								*18 13*
Cardiff Central 7 a									15 12							16 12								17 12
Bridgend a									15 33							16 33								17 33
Port Talbot Parkway a									15 46							16 46								17 46
Neath a									15 54							16 54								17 54
Swansea 7 a									16 07							17 07								18 07

	GW 🚌	GW 🚌	GW 🚌		GW 1 ◇ ☕	GW 🚌	GW 1 ◇ A ☕	GW 🚌	GW 🚌		GW 1 ◇ ☕	GW 🚌	GW 🚌	GW 1 ◇ ☕	GW 1 ◇ ☕		GW 🚌	GW 🚌	GW	GW 🚌	GW 🚌		GW 1 ◇ ☕	GW 🚌
London Paddington 15 ⊖ d											15 03				16 03									
London Waterloo 15 ⊖ d																								
Slough 3 d											*15 01*				*16 01*									
Heathrow Terminal 1 Bus 🚌 d																								
Gatwick Airport 10 d											*14 07*				*15 07*									
Reading 7 d	14 20		14 50					15 20			15 42	15 50			16 42		16 20			16 50				17 20
Oxford d																								
Didcot Parkway d						15 20							16 20								17 20			
Swindon a	15 25		15 55			16 10		16 25				16 55	17 10				17 25			17 55	18 10			18 25
d		15 30			16 00		16 15		16 30					17 15				17 30	17 40				18 15	
Kemble d					16 13														17 54					
Stroud d					16 28														18 08					
Stonehouse d					16 33														18 13					
Gloucester 7 a					16 49														18 29					
Cheltenham Spa a					17 05														*18 58*					
Birmingham New Street 12 a					*17 51*														*19 45*					
Chippenham d							16 27							17 27									18 29	
Bath Spa 7 a							16 42				16 51			17 42	17 53								18 42	
Bristol Parkway 7 a		16 25							17 25		17 27				18 27			18 25						
d											17 34				18 34									
Bristol Temple Meads 10 a							16 57				17 05			17 57	18 07								18 56	
Weston-super-Mare a							17 26				*17 48*			*18 36*	*19 37*									
Newport (South Wales) a											17 55				18 55									
Hereford 7 a											*19 38*													
Cardiff Central 7 a											18 12				19 13									
Bridgend a											18 33				19 34									
Port Talbot Parkway a											18 46				19 47									
Neath a											18 54				19 54									
Swansea 7 a											19 10				20 10									

For general notes see front of timetable
For details of catering facilities see
Directory of Train Operators

A To Taunton (Table 134)

Table 125

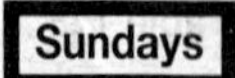

Sundays

London and Oxford → Swindon, Cheltenham Spa, Bristol, Weston-super-Mare and South Wales

3 February to 23 March

Route Diagram - see first page of Table 125

		GW 1◇	GW	GW 1◇	GW	GW		GW 1◇	GW	GW 1◇	GW	GW 1◇		GW	GW	GW 1◇ A	SW 1◇	GW		GW	GW 1◇	GW	GW B	GW	GW 1◇
London Paddington 15 ⊖	d	17 03		17 30								18 03									19 03				
London Waterloo 15 ⊖	d																18 15								
Slough 3	d	*17 01*		*17 15*								*18 00*									*19 00*				
Heathrow Terminal 1 Bus	d																								
Gatwick Airport 10	d	*16 07*										*17 07*									*18 07*				
Reading 7	d	17 42	17 50	18 05							18 20	18 42		18 50				19 20			19 42	19 50			
Oxford	d																								
Didcot Parkway	d								18 20						19 20									20 20	
Swindon	a		18 55						19 10		19 25			19 55	20 10			20 25				20 55		21 10	
	d				18 30	18 31		19 00		19 18						20 17				19 30			20 27		21 18
Kemble	d							19 13															20 41		
Stroud	d							19 28															20 56		
Stonehouse	d							19 33															21 01		
Gloucester 7	a							19 49															21 17		
Cheltenham Spa	a							20 06															21 30		
Birmingham New Street 12	a							*20 57*															*22 45*		
Chippenham	d					18a47				19 32						20 30									21 32
Bath Spa 7	a	18 51		19 10						19 45		19 57				20 45	20 51				20 58				21 45
Bristol Parkway 7	a	19 27			19 25							20 27								20 25	21 27				
	d	19 34										20 34									21 34				
Bristol Temple Meads 10	a	19 05		19 28						19 59		20 11				20 59	21 08				21 12				21 59
Weston-super-Mare	a			19 56								*20 53*				21 29					*22 19*				
Newport (South Wales)	a	19 55										20 55									21 56				
Hereford 7	a	*21 43*																							
Cardiff Central 7	a	20 12										21 12									22 16				
Bridgend	a	20 33										21 33									22 38				
Port Talbot Parkway	a	20 46										21 46									22 51				
Neath	a	20 54										21 54									22 58				
Swansea 7	a	21 10										22 07									23 11				

		GW		GW 1◇	GW	GW	GW 1◇	GW 1◇		GW	GW 1◇	GW	GW 1◇	GW		GW	GW 1◇	GW	GW 1◇	GW		GW 1◇			
London Paddington 15 ⊖	d			20 03			21 03						21 33				22 37					23 37			
London Waterloo 15 ⊖	d																								
Slough 3	d			*19 59*			*21 01*						*21 15*				*22 16*					*23 15*			
Heathrow Terminal 1 Bus	d																								
Gatwick Airport 10	d			*19 07*			*20 07*										*21 07*					*22 07*			
Reading 7	d	20 20		20 41	20 50	21 20	21 42					21 50	22 07			22 20	23 13			23 20		00 13			
Oxford	d																								
Didcot Parkway	d									21 40								23 00							
Swindon	a	21 25			21 55	22 25				22 30		22 55				23 25		23 50		00 25					
	d							22 00			22 39			23 00					23 58	00 25					
Kemble	d							22 13						23 14											
Stroud	d							22 28						23 29											
Stonehouse	d							22 33						23 34											
Gloucester 7	a							22 54						23 50											
Cheltenham Spa	a							23 10						00 04											
Birmingham New Street 12	a																								
Chippenham	d										22 52								00 11	01 00					
Bath Spa 7	a			22 00			22 48				23 07		23 13				00 21		00 27			01 20			
Bristol Parkway 7	a			22 29									23 42												
	d			22 35									23 49												
Bristol Temple Meads 10	a			22 14			23 04				23 23		23 27				00 37		00 43			01 35			
Weston-super-Mare	a																								
Newport (South Wales)	a			23 03									00 11												
Hereford 7	a			*00 04*																					
Cardiff Central 7	a			23 24									00 32												
Bridgend	a			23 45									00 53												
Port Talbot Parkway	a			23 58									01 06												
Neath	a			00 06									01 13												
Swansea 7	a			00 19									01 26												

For general notes see front of timetable
For details of catering facilities see Directory of Train Operators

A To Exeter St Davids (Table 135)
B From Westbury (Table 123)

Table 125

Sundays
from 30 March

London and Oxford → Swindon, Cheltenham Spa, Bristol, Weston-super-Mare and South Wales

Route Diagram - see first page of Table 125

		GW	GW	GW	GW	GW	GW	GW	GW	GW	GW	GW	GW	GW	GW	GW		GW	SW	GW	GW	GW	GW	GW	GW
		1 ◇	1 ◇	1 ◇	1 ◇	1 ◇	1 ◇	1 ◇	1 ◇	1 ◇	1 ◇	1 ◇	1 ◇	1 ◇	1 ◇	1 ◇		1 ◇	1 ◇	1 ◇	1 ◇	1 ◇	1 ◇	1 ◇	1 ◇
			A				B				C	B		D						B					E
London Paddington 15 ⊖	d	23p30	08 00	08 03	09 00	09 03	09 30	10 00	10 03	10 30	11 03	11 30	11 37	12 03	12 30	13 00		13 03		13 30	13 37	14 03	14 30	14 37	15 03
London Waterloo 15 ⊖	d																		12 15						
Slough 3	d		07 16		08 47		09 15	10 00		10 15	11 00	11 15		12 00	12 15	13 00				13 15		14 00	14 15		15 00
Heathrow Terminal 1 Bus	d																								
Gatwick Airport 10	d		06 07	07 07		08 07	08 31		09 07			10 07		11 07				12 07				13 07			14 07
Reading 7	d	23p59	08 37	08 42	09 36	09 42	10 07	10 35	10 42	11 07	11 42	12 07	12 13	12 42	13 07	13 37		13 42		14 07	14 10	14 42	15 07	15 14	15 42
Oxford	d		07c45				09c30			10c30		11c30			12c30					13c30			14c30		
Didcot Parkway	d	00 16	08 52	08 58		09 58	10 23		10 58	11 23	11 58	12 23		12 58	13 23			13 58		14 23		14 58	15 23		15 58
Swindon	a	00 36	09 11	09 16		10 17	10 41	11 07	11 17	11 41	12 17	12 41		13 17	13 41			14 16		14 41		15 17	15 41		16 17
	d	00 36	09 12	09 18		10 17	10 43	11 08	11 17	11 43	12 17	12 43		13 17	13 43			14 17		14 43		15 17	15 43		16 17
Kemble	d			09 31			10 56			11 56		12 56			13 56					14 56			15 56		
Stroud	d			09 46			11 11			12 11		13 11			14 11					15 11			16 11		
Stonehouse	d			09 52			11 17			12 17		13 17			14 17					15 17			16 17		
Gloucester 7	a			10 07			11 32			12 32		13 32			14 32					15 32			16 32		
Cheltenham Spa	a			10 46			11 57			12 56		13 48			14 55					15 55			16 55		
Birmingham New Street 12	a			11e51			12e51			13 40		14e57			15 44					16 39			17 45		
Chippenham	d	00 50	09 26			10 31			11 31		12 31			13 31				14 31				15 31			16 33
Bath Spa 7	a	01 05	09 40		10 28	10 46		11 31	11 46		12 46		13 10	13 48		14 29		14 46	14 52			15 46			16 47
Bristol Parkway 7	a																								
	d																								
Bristol Temple Meads 10	a	01 21	09 54		10 41	11 00			12 00		13 00			14 02				15 00	15 06		15 45	16 00		16 23	17 02
Weston-super-Mare	a		10 36			12 01			12 31		13 28			14 40					15 49			16 41			17 29
Newport (South Wales)	a			10 50			12 16			13 15		14 15			15 16					16 15			17 15		
Hereford 7	a			12c30						15c15		16c20			17c30					18c20			19c15		
Cardiff Central 7	a			11 07			12 33			13 32		14 32			15 33					16 32			17 32		
Bridgend	a			11 28			12 54			13 53		14 53			15 54					16 58			17 58		
Port Talbot Parkway	a			11 41			13 11			14 06		15 06			16 07					17 11			18 11		
Neath	a			11 49			13 19			14 14		15 14			16 15					17 19			18 19		
Swansea 7	a			12 03			13 34			14 34		15 39			16 34					17 34			18 34		

		GW	GW	GW	GW	GW	GW	GW	GW	GW	GW	GW	GW	SW	GW	GW	GW	GW	GW	GW	GW	GW	GW
		1 ◇	1 ◇	1 ◇	1 ◇		1 ◇	1 ◇	1 ◇	1 ◇	1 ◇	1 ◇	1 ◇	1 ◇	1 ◇	1 ◇	1 ◇	1 ◇	1 ◇	1 ◇	1 ◇	1 ◇	1 ◇
													G										
London Paddington 15 ⊖	d	15 30	16 03	16 30	17 03		17 30	17 33	18 00	18 03	18 30	18 42	19 03		19 30	20 03	20 30	21 03	21 30	22 03	22 37	23 03	23 37
London Waterloo 15 ⊖	d													18 15									
Slough 3	d	15 15	16 00	16 15	17 00		17 15			18 00	18 15	19 02	18 55		19 15	20 00	20 15	20 47	21 15	21 47	22 16	23 15	23 57
Heathrow Terminal 1 Bus	d																						
Gatwick Airport 10	d		15 07		16 07					17 07			18 07			19 07		20 07		21 07		22 07	22 07
Reading 7	d	16 07	16 42	17 07	17 42		18 07	18 12	18 36	18 43	19 07	19 21	19 42		20 07	20 42	21 06	21 42	22 07	22 43	23 15	23 50	00 22
Oxford	d	15c30		16c30			17c30				18c30				19c30		20c30		21c30		22c30		
Didcot Parkway	d	16 23	16 58	17 23	17 58		18 23	18 28		18 58	19 23	19 36	19 58		20 23	21 00	21 23	22 00	22 24	22 59	23 34	00s06	
Swindon	a	16 41	17 17	17 41	18 15		18 41	18 46		19 17	19 41	19 54	20 17		20 41	21 20	21 41	22 20	22 43	23 19	23 54	00s26	00s58
	d	16 43	17 17	17 43	18 17	18 31	18 43	18 48		19 17	19 43	20 00	20 17		20 43	21 20	21 43	22 20	22 44	23 20	23 55		
Kemble	d	16 56		17 56			18 56					20 20			20 56		21 56		22 58				
Stroud	d	17 11		18 11			19 11					20 35			21 11		22 11		23 13				
Stonehouse	d	17 17		18 17			19 17					20 40			21 17		22 17		23 18				
Gloucester 7	a	17 38		18 35			19 32				20 21	20 54			21 32		22 32		23 33				
Cheltenham Spa	a	17 55		18 56			19 47				20 58	21 17			21 47		22 56		23 59				
Birmingham New Street 12	a	18 45		19 45			20 45				21 44				22 45								
Chippenham	d		17 31		18 31	18a47		19 00		19 31			20 31			21 33		22 33		23 34		00s43	01s13
Bath Spa 7	a		17 46		18 46			19 15		19 46			20 46	20 59		21 48		22 48		23 48		00s56	01s27
Bristol Parkway 7	a																				00s21		
	d																						
Bristol Temple Meads 10	a		18 00		19 00			19 31	19 37	20 00			21 00	21 16		22 04		23 04		00 03	00 34	01 10	01 45
Weston-super-Mare	a		18 36		19 30					20 53			21 30			23 04		23 31					
Newport (South Wales)	a	18 21		19 18			20 15				21 04				22 21		23 21		00 23				
Hereford 7	a			21c35							22c45	22 40											
Cardiff Central 7	a	18 38		19 39			20 32				21 21				22 44		23 42		00 44				
Bridgend	a	18 59		20 00			20 53				21 42				23 06		00 03		01 05				
Port Talbot Parkway	a	19 12		20 13			21 06				21 55				23 19		00 16		01 18				
Neath	a	19 20		20 20			21 14				22 03				23 26		00 24		01 25				
Swansea 7	a	19 37		20 33			21 27				22 16				23 39		00 37		01 38				

For general notes see front of timetable
For details of catering facilities see Directory of Train Operators

- **A** To Penzance (Table 135)
- **B** To Carmarthen (Table 128)
- **C** To Paignton (Table 135)
- **D** To Plymouth (Table 135)
- **E** To Taunton (Table 134)
- **G** To Exeter St Davids (Table 135)
- **c** By bus
- **e** Change at Gloucester and Cheltenham Spa

South Wales, Weston-super-Mare, Bristol, Cheltenham Spa and Swindon → Oxford and London

Route Diagram - see first page of Table 125

Miles	Miles	Miles			GW 1◇	GW 1◇	GW	GW 1◇	GW 1◇	GW 1◇	GW 1◇	GW 1◇	GW 1◇	GW 1◇	GW 1◇	GW 1◇	GW	GW 1◇	GW 1◇	GW 1◇	GW 1◇	GW 1◇	GW 1◇	GW	GW 1◇
							A										C		D	E		G			H
					🛒	☕		🛒	🛒	☕	🛒	🛒	🛒	☕	🛒	🛒		🛒	⊠	✕	🛒	⊠	🛒		☕
0	—	—	**Swansea 7**	d				04 00		04 58				05 24				05 59		06 29			06 59		
9½	—	—	Neath	d				04 12		05 09				05 36				06 10		06 40			07 10		
15	—	—	Port Talbot Parkway	d				04 19		05 17				05 43				06 18		06 48			07 18		
27¼	—	—	Bridgend	d				04 31		05 28				05 55				06 29		06 59			07 29		
47½	—	—	**Cardiff Central 7**	d				05 15		05 54				06 20				06 55		07 25			07 55		
—	—	—	Hereford 7	d										*05 23*						*06 42*			*07 16*		
59¼	—	—	Newport (South Wales)	d				05 33		06 08				06 34				07 09		07 39			08 09		
—	0	—	Weston-super-Mare	d												06 24			06 48			07 27			07 50
—	19	—	**Bristol Temple Meads 10**	d	04 47	05 30			06 00			06 30	06 40			07 00			07 30			08 00		08 13	08 30
81	—	—	Bristol Parkway 7	a				06 00		06 29				06 55				07 30		08 00			08 30		
—	—	—		d	04u57			06 01		06 31				06 57				07 32		08 02			08 32		
—	30½	—	Bath Spa 7	d		05 43			06 13			06 43	06 52			07 13			07 43			08 13		08 31	08 43
—	43½	—	Chippenham	d		05 55			06 25			06 55	07 05			07 25	07 30		07 55			08 25		08 45	08 55
—	—	—	Birmingham New Street 12	d																	*05 30*				
—	—	0	**Cheltenham Spa**	d							05 56				06 31						07 27				
—	—	6½	Gloucester 7	d			05 29				06 12				06 47						07 43				
—	—	15½	Stonehouse	d			05 42				06 25				07 00		08a26				07 55				
—	—	18	Stroud	d			05 47				06 31				07 06						08 01				
—	—	29¼	Kemble	d			06 01				06 46				07 21						08 15				
115½	60¼	43	**Swindon**	a	05 23	06 09	06 16	06 27	06 39	06 56	07 00	07 09	07 19	07 24	07 35	07 39	07 48	07 57	08 09	08 27	08 31	08 39	08 57	09 02	09 09
—	—	—		d	05 23	06 11		06 28	06 41	06 58	07 02	07 11	07 21	07 25	07 36	07 41		07 59	08 11	08 29	08 33	08 41	08 59		09 11
139½	84¼	67	Didcot Parkway	a	05 41	06 28		06 45	06 58		07 19	07 28		07 42	07 54	08 00		08 16	08 28	08 46	08 52	08 58			09 28
—	—	—	Oxford	a	*06 21*			*07 17*		*07 42*		*07 48*		*08 00*				*08 41*		*09 14*		*09 39*			*10 13*
156¾	101½	84½	**Reading 7**	a	05 57	06 43		07 02	07 14	07 29	07 35	07 44		07 58	08 12	08 15		08 32	08 44	09 01	09 06	09 14	09 27		09 44
—	—	—	Gatwick Airport 10	a	*07 54*				*09 02*							*09 59*							*10 51*		
—	—	—	Heathrow Terminal 1 Bus	a	*07 17*	*07 57*		*08 17*	*08 37*			*08 57*		*09 17*		*09 37*			*09 45*		*10 05*		*10 25*		*10 45*
174¼	119	101¾	Slough 3	a	06 11	06 58			*07 55*	*08 07*		*08 19*		*08 38*		*08 57*			*09 25*		*09 45*		*09 51*		
—	—	—	**London Waterloo 15**	⊖ a																					
192¾	137½	120¼	**London Paddington 15**	⊖ a	06 30	07 16		07 32	07 42	08 01	08 06	08 14	08 18	08 30	08 41	08 44		09 06	09 15	09 29	09 38	09 44	09 59		10 15

		GW 1◇	GW 1◇	SW 1◇	GW 1◇		GW 1◇	GW 1◇	GW 1◇	GW	GW 1◇	GW 1◇	GW 1◇	GW 1◇	GW 1◇	GW 1◇	GW 1◇	GW 1◇	GW 1◇	GW	GW 1◇	GW 1◇	GW 1◇	GW 1◇	GW 1◇
									J		K										L			N	
		🛒	🛒		🛒		⊠	🛒	⊠		🛒	☕	🛒	☕	🛒	🛒	🛒	🛒	☕		☕	☕	🛒	⊠	🛒
Swansea 7	d	07 29					07 59		08 29					09 29					10 29					11 29	
Neath	d	07 40					08 10		08 40					09 40					10 40					11 40	
Port Talbot Parkway	d	07 48					08 18		08 48					09 48					10 48					11 48	
Bridgend	d	07 59					08 29		08 59					09 59					10 59					11 59	
Cardiff Central 7	d	08 25					08 55		09 25			09 55		10 25			10 55		11 25			11 55		12 25	
Hereford 7	d	*07 48*					*08 09*		*08 48*					*09 47*			*10 08*		*10 48*					*11 48*	
Newport (South Wales)	d	08 39					09 10		09 39			10 09		10 39			11 09		11 39			12 09		12 39	
Weston-super-Mare	d				*08 30*			*08 40*			09 27		*09 40*			*10 10*		*10 40*					*11 40*		
Bristol Temple Meads 10	d			08 50	09 00			09 30			10 00		10 30			11 00		11 30			12 00		12 30		
Bristol Parkway 7	a	09 00					09 30		10 00			10 30		11 00			11 30		12 00			12 30		13 00	
	d	09 02					09 32		10 02			10 32		11 02			11 32		12 02			12 32		13 02	
Bath Spa 7	d			09 05	09 13			09 43			10 13		10 43			11 13		11 43			12 13		12 43		
Chippenham	d				09 25			09 55			10 25		10 55			11 25		11 55			12 25		12 55		
Birmingham New Street 12	d		*07 40*							*08 40*					*09 40*					*10 40*					*11 40*
Cheltenham Spa	d		08 31							09 38					10 31					11 38					12 31
Gloucester 7	d		08 46							09 51					10 46					11 51					12 46
Stonehouse	d		08 59							10 03					10 59					12 03					12 59
Stroud	d		09 04							10 08					11 04					12 08					13 04
Kemble	d		09 19							10 22					11 19					12 22					13 19
Swindon	a	09 27	09 34		09 39		09 57	10 09	10 27	10 38	10 40	10 57	11 09	11 27	11 34	11 39	11 57	12 09	12 27	12 38	12 39	12 57	13 09	13 27	13 34
	d	09 29	09 35		09 41		09 59	10 11	10 29		10 41	10 59	11 11	11 29	11 35	11 41	11 59	12 11	12 29		12 41	12 59	13 11	13 29	13 35
Didcot Parkway	a		09 52				10 16	10 28	10 46			11 16	11 28	11 46	11 52		12 16	12 28	12 46			13 16	13 28	13 46	13 52
Oxford	a		*10 30*						*11 13*					*12 13*	*12 30*				*13 13*					*14 13*	*14 30*
Reading 7	a	09 57	10 09		10 09		10 32	10 44	11 01		11 09	11 32	11 44	12 01	12 07	12 09	12 32	12 44	13 01		13 09	13 32	13 44	14 01	14 07
Gatwick Airport 10	a								*12 33*		*12 50*					*13 50*					*14 50*				
Heathrow Terminal 1 Bus	a				*11 05*			*11 45*			*12 05*		*12 45*			*13 05*		*13 45*			*14 05*		*14 45*		
Slough 3	a	*10 17*			*10 38*			*11 09*			*11 45*		*12 09*			*12 40*		*13 08*			*13 40*		*14 09*		
London Waterloo 15	⊖ a			11 49																					
London Paddington 15	⊖ a	10 27	10 39		10 44		11 02	11 15	11 32		11 41	12 02	12 15	12 32	12 39	12 42	13 02	13 15	13 29		13 42	14 02	14 15	14 32	14 39

For general notes see front of timetable
For details of catering facilities see Directory of Train Operators

A To Southampton Central (Table 123)
C From Westbury (Table 123) to Cheltenham Spa
D **The Bristolian**
E **The Red Dragon**
G From Plymouth (Table 135)
H From Exeter St Davids (Table 135)
J From Carmarthen (Table 128)
K From Paignton (Table 135)
L From Penzance (Table 135)
N **The St David**

South Wales, Weston-super-Mare, Bristol, Cheltenham Spa and Swindon → Oxford and London

Route Diagram - see first page of Table 125

		GW	GW	GW	GW	GW	GW		GW	GW	GW	GW	GW	GW	GW	GW	GW	SW	GW	GW	GW	GW	GW	GW	GW
		[1] ◇	[1] ◇	[1] ◇	[1] ◇		[1] ◇		[1] ◇	[1] ◇	[1] ◇	[1] ◇	[1] ◇	[1] ◇	[1] ◇	[1] ◇		[1] ◇	[1] ◇	[1] ◇	[1] ◇	[1] ◇	[1] ◇	[1] ◇	[1] ◇
												A													
		🛒	🛒	🛒	🍽		🛒		🛒	🍽	🍽	🛒	🍽	🍽	🛒	🍽			🛒	🛒	🛒	🍽	🛒	🛒	🛒
Swansea [7]	d				12 29						13 29					14 29						15 29			
Neath	d				12 40						13 40					14 40						15 40			
Port Talbot Parkway	d				12 48						13 48					14 48						15 48			
Bridgend	d				12 59						13 59					14 59						15 59			
Cardiff Central [7]	d		12 55		13 25				13 55		14 25			14 55		15 25				15 55		16 25			16 55
Hereford [7]	d		*12 09*		*12 48*						*13 48*			*14 09*		*14 48*						*15 48*			*16 09*
Newport (South Wales)	d		13 09		13 39				14 09		14 39			15 09		15 39				16 09		16 39			17 09
Weston-super-Mare	d	*12 10*		*12 42*						*13 40*			*14 10*		*14 40*				*15 10*		*15 51*			*16 10*	
Bristol Temple Meads [10]	d	13 00		13 30			14 00			14 30			15 00		15 30			15 52	16 00		16 30			17 00	
Bristol Parkway [7]	a		13 30		14 00				14 30		15 00			15 30		16 00				16 30		17 00			17 30
	d		13 32		14 02				14 32		15 02			15 32		16 02				16 32		17 02			17 32
Bath Spa [7]	d	13 13		13 43			14 13			14 43			15 13		15 43			16 06	16 13		16 43			17 13	
Chippenham	d	13 25		13 55			14 25			14 55			15 25		15 55				16 25		16 55			17 25	
Birmingham New Street [12]	d					*12 40*						*13 40*					*14 40*						*15 40*		
Cheltenham Spa	d					13 38						14 31					15 38						16 31		
Gloucester [7]	d					13 51						14 46					15 51						16 46		
Stonehouse	d					14 03						14 59					16 03						16 59		
Stroud	d					14 08						15 04					16 08						17 04		
Kemble	d					14 22						15 19					16 22						17 19		
Swindon	a	13 39	13 57	14 09	14 27	14 38	14 39		14 57	15 09	15 27	15 34	15 39	15 57	16 09	16 27	16 38		16 39	16 57	17 09	17 27	17 34	17 39	17 57
	d	13 41	13 59	14 11	14 29		14 41		14 59	15 11	15 29	15 35	15 41	15 59	16 11	16 29			16 41	16 59	17 11	17 29	17 35	17 41	17 59
Didcot Parkway	a		14 16	14 28	14 46				15 16	15 28	15 46	15 52		16 16	16 28	16 46				17 16	17 28		17 52		18 16
Oxford	a				*15 13*						*16 13*	*16 30*			*17 02*	*17 23*				*17 41*	*17 47*				*18 39*
Reading [7]	a	14 09	14 32	14 44	15 01		15 09		15 32	15 44	16 01	16 07	16 12	16 32	16 44	17 01			17 09	17 32	17 44	17 57	18 07	18 13	18 32
Gatwick Airport [10]	a	*15 50*					*17 00*						*17 50*									*19 52*		*19 50*	
Heathrow Terminal 1 Bus	🚌 a	*15 05*		*15 45*			*16 05*			*16 45*		*17 05*	*17 25*		*17 45*				*18 05*		*18 45*			*19 15*	
Slough [3]	a	*14 40*		*15 10*			*15 40*			*16 09*			*16 40*		*17 09*				*17 31*	*18 15*		*18 25*		*18 40*	
London Waterloo [15]	⊖ a																	18 45							
London Paddington [15]	⊖ a	14 42	15 02	15 15	15 30		15 42		16 02	16 15	16 30	16 39	16 44	17 02	17 15	17 30			17 42	18 02	18 15	18 27	18 39	18 45	19 02

		GW	GW	GW	GW	GW	GW	GW	GW	GW	GW	GW	GW	GW	GW	GW	GW	GW	GW	GW	GW	GW	GW
															FO	FX		FO	FX	FO	FX		
		[1] ◇	[1] ◇		[1] ◇	[1] ◇	[1] ◇	[1] ◇	[1] ◇	[1] ◇		[1] ◇		[1] ◇	[1] ◇	[1] ◇	[1] ◇	[1] ◇	[1] ◇	[1] ◇	[1] ◇		[1] ◇
				B							C					D		E	E		D		G
		🍽	🍽		🛒	🛒	🛒	🍽	🛒	🍽		🍽		🛒	🛒	🛒	🛒	🍽	🍽	🛒	🛒		🛒
Swansea [7]	d		16 29					17 29				18 29			19 29	19 29				20 29	20 29		
Neath	d		16 40					17 40				18 40			19 40	19 40				20 40	20 40		
Port Talbot Parkway	d		16 48					17 48				18 48			19 48	19 48				20 48	20 48		
Bridgend	d		16 59					17 59				18 59			19 59	19 59				20 59	20 59		
Cardiff Central [7]	d		17 25			17 55		18 25				19 25			20 25	20 25				21 25	21 25		
Hereford [7]	d		*16 48*									*18 48*								*20 48*	*20 48*		
Newport (South Wales)	d		17 39			18 09		18 39				19 39			20 39	20 39				21 39	21 39		
Weston-super-Mare	d	17 08			*17 14*		18 09			*18 40*				*19 47*									22 00
Bristol Temple Meads [10]	d	17 30			18 00		18 31			19 30				20 30				21 40	21 40				22 33
Bristol Parkway [7]	a		18 00			18 30		19 00				20 00			21 00	21 00				22 00	22 00		
	d		18 02			18 32		19 02				20 02			21 02	21 02				22 02	22 02		
Bath Spa [7]	d	17 43			18 13		18 43			19 43				20 43				21 56	21 56				22 46
Chippenham	d	17 55			18 25		18 55			19 55	20 02			20 55				22 08	22 08				22 58
Birmingham New Street [12]	d			*16 40*					*17 40*				*19 10*				*19 40*					*21 10*	
Cheltenham Spa	d			17 38					18 31				20 00				20 48					22 00	
Gloucester [7]	d			17 51					18 46				20 13				21 05					22 13	
Stonehouse	d			18 03					18 59		20a57		20 25				21 18					22 25	
Stroud	d			18 08					19 04				20 30				21 23					22 30	
Kemble	d			18 22					19 19				20 44				21 37					22 45	
Swindon	a	18 09	18 27	18 38	18 39	18 57	19 10	19 27	19 34	20 09	20 19	20 27	21 00	21 09	21 27	21 27	21 53	22 23	22 23	22 27	22 27	23 00	23 13
	d	18 11	18 29		18 41	18 59	19 11	19 29	19 35	20 11		20 29		21 11	21 29	21 29		22 24	22 24	22 29	22 29		23 14
Didcot Parkway	a	18 28	18 46			19 16	19 29	19 46	19 52	20 28		20 46		21 28	21 50	21 50				22 46	22 46		23 31
Oxford	a	*19 00*	*19 12*			*19 45*		*20 12*	*20 24*	*21 02*		*21 30*		*22 13*	*22 36*	*22 36*				*23 13*	*23 13*		*00 22*
Reading [7]	a	18 44	19 01		19 09	19 32	19 45	20 01	20 12	20 44		21 01		21 44	22 15	22 15		22 55	22 55	23 06	23 06		23 52
Gatwick Airport [10]	a							*21 47*		*22b28*		*23 04*			*00 11*	*00 11*				*01 01*	*01 01*		
Heathrow Terminal 1 Bus	🚌 a	*19 45*			*20 15*		*20 45*		*21 15*	*21 45*				*22 45*	*23 45*	*23 45*							
Slough [3]	a	*19 09*			*19 40*		*20 09*		*20 45*	*21 09*		*21 38*		*22c26*	*23 00*	*23 04*		*23 17*	*23 21*	*23 42*	*23 42*		*00e41*
London Waterloo [15]	⊖ a																						
London Paddington [15]	⊖ a	19 15	19 32		19 42	20 02	20 15	20 30	20 44	21 15		21 30		22 15	22 45	22 56		23 29	23 36	23 42	23 50		00 32

For general notes see front of timetable
For details of catering facilities see Directory of Train Operators

A The Cheltenham Spa Express
B To Westbury (Table 123)
C From Westbury (Table 123) to Cheltenham Spa
D 🛒 to Reading, 🍽 from Reading
E From Penzance (Table 135)
G From Taunton (Table 134). 🛒 to Reading
b Change at Reading and Redhill
c Fridays arr. 2224
e Fridays arr. 0036

Table 125

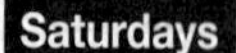

South Wales, Weston-super-Mare, Bristol, Cheltenham Spa and Swindon → Oxford and London

until 26 January

Route Diagram - see first page of Table 125

		GW	GW	GW	GW	GW		GW	GW	GW	GW	GW		GW	GW	GW	GW	SW		GW	GW	GW	GW	GW	GW
		1◇		1◇	1◇	1◇		1◇	1◇	1◇	1◇	1◇		1◇	1◇	1◇	1◇	1◇		1◇		1◇	1◇	1◇	1◇
														A										B	
		⊡		⊡	⊡	⊡		⊡	⊡	⊡	⊡	⊡		⊡	⊡	⊡	⊡			⊡		⊡	⊡	⊡	⊡
Swansea 7	d			04 00	04 59				05 59		06 29				06 59		07 29					07 59			08 29
Neath	d			04 11	05 10				06 10		06 40				07 10		07 40					08 10			08 40
Port Talbot Parkway	d			04 19	05 18				06 18		06 48				07 18		07 48					08 18			08 48
Bridgend	d			04 30	05 29				06 29		06 59				07 29		07 59					08 29			08 59
Cardiff Central 7	d			04 55	05 55				06 55		07 25				07 55		08 25					08 55			09 25
Hereford 7	d								*05 42*						*07 16*		*07 48*					*08 10*			*08 48*
Newport (South Wales)	d			05 09	06 09				07 09		07 39				08 09		08 39					09 09			09 39
Weston-super-Mare	d							06 24						07 28		*07 34*				08 28				09 00	
Bristol Temple Meads 10	d	05 30		06 00		06 30		07 00		07 30				08 00		08 30		08 50		09 00				09 30	
Bristol Parkway 7	a			05 37	06 30				07 30		08 00				08 30		09 00					09 30			10 00
	d			05 42	06 32				07 32		08 02				08 32		09 02					09 32			10 02
Bath Spa 7	d	05 43		06 13		06 43		07 13		07 43				08 13		08 43		09 05		09 13				09 43	
Chippenham	d	05 55		06 25		06 55		07 25		07 55				08 25		08 55				09 25	09 30			09 55	
Birmingham New Street 12	d											*05 30*													
Cheltenham Spa	d		05 30									07 27											09 00		
Gloucester 7	d		05 44									07 43											09 16		
Stonehouse	d		05 56									07 55											09 29		
Stroud	d		06 01									08 01											09 34		
Kemble	d		06 16									08 15											09 48		
Swindon	a	06 09	06 32	06 39	06 57	07 09		07 40	07 57	08 09	08 27	08 31		08 39	08 57	09 09	09 27			09 39	09 48	09 57	10 02	10 09	10 27
	d	06 11		06 41	06 59	07 11		07 42	07 59	08 11	08 29	08 33		08 41	08 59	09 11	09 29			09 41		09 59	10 04	10 11	10 29
Didcot Parkway	a	06 28		06 58	07 16	07 28		07 59	08 16	08 28	08 46	08 51		08 58	09 16	09 28	09 46					10 16	10 21	10 28	
Oxford	a	*07 03*		*07 28*		*08 00*			*08 39*			*09 15*		*09 31*			*10 13*							*11 13*	
Reading 7	a	06 43		07 14	07 32	07 44		08 14	08 32	08 44	09 02	09 07		09 14	09 33	09 44	10 01			10 09		10 32	10 37	10 45	10 59
Gatwick Airport 10	a			*08 50*				*09 50*						*10 50*											*12 53*
Heathrow Terminal 1 Bus	a	*07 55*		*08 25*		*08 55*		*09 25*		*09 55*				*10 25*		*10 55*	*11 25*								*11 55*
Slough 3	a	*07 12*		*07 39*	*08 15*	*08 25*		*08 55*	*09 15*	*09 25*				*09 41*	*10 15*	*10 25*	*10 36*					*11 15*		*11 25*	
London Waterloo 15 ⊖	a																	11 49							
London Paddington 15 ⊖	a	07 14		07 45	08 01	08 14		08 45	09 06	09 15	09 30	09 36		09 44	10 06	10 14	10 31			10 42		10 59	11 07	11 15	11 31

		GW		GW	GW	GW	GW	GW		GW	GW	GW	GW	GW		GW	GW	GW	GW	GW		GW	GW	SW	GW
		1◇		1◇	1◇	1◇	1◇	1◇		1◇	1◇	1◇	1◇	1◇		1◇	1◇	1◇	1◇			1◇	1◇	1◇	1◇
										C															
		⊡		⊡	⊡	⊡	⊡	⊡		⊡	⊡	⊡	⊡	⊡		⊡	⊡	⊡	⊡			⊡	⊡		⊡
Swansea 7	d				09 29					10 29		11 29				12 29			13 29						
Neath	d				09 40					10 40		11 40				12 40			13 40						
Port Talbot Parkway	d				09 48					10 48		11 48				12 48			13 48						
Bridgend	d				09 59					10 59		11 59				12 59			13 59						
Cardiff Central 7	d				10 25					11 25		12 25				13 25			14 25						
Hereford 7	d				*09 47*					*10 48*		*11 48*				*12 48*			*13 48*						
Newport (South Wales)	d				10 39					11 39		12 39				13 39			14 39						
Weston-super-Mare	d			*09 40*				*10 43*			*11 08*			*12 41*			*13 08*	*13 39*					*14 39*	*15 08*	
Bristol Temple Meads 10	d	10 00		10 30		11 00		11 30			12 00			13 30			14 00	14 30					15 30	15 52	16 00
Bristol Parkway 7	a				11 00					12 00		13 00				14 00			15 00						
	d				11 02					12 02		13 02				14 02			15 02						
Bath Spa 7	d	10 13		10 43		11 13		11 43			12 13			13 43			14 13	14 43					15 43	16 04	16 13
Chippenham	d	10 25		10 55		11 25		11 55			12 25			13 55			14 25	14 55		15 28			15 55		16 25
Birmingham New Street 12	d																								
Cheltenham Spa	d						11 00						13 00									15 00			
Gloucester 7	d						11 16						13 16									15 16			
Stonehouse	d						11 29						13 29									15 29			
Stroud	d						11 34						13 34									15 34			
Kemble	d						11 48						13 48									15 48			
Swindon	a	10 39		11 09	11 27	11 39	12 02	12 09		12 27	12 39	13 27	14 02	14 09		14 27	14 39	15 09	15 27	15 47		16 02	16 09		16 39
	d	10 41		11 11	11 29	11 41	12 04	12 11		12 29	12 41	13 29	14 04	14 11		14 29	14 41	15 11	15 29			16 04	16 11		16 41
Didcot Parkway	a			11 28	11 46		12 21	12 28		12 46		13 46	14 21	14 28		14 46		15 28	15 46			16 21	16 28		
Oxford	a				*12 13*					*13 13*		*14 13*				*15 13*			*16 13*				*17 13*		
Reading 7	a	11 09		11 44	12 02	12 09	12 36	12 44		13 01	13 09	14 01	14 36	14 44		15 01	15 09	15 44	16 01			16 36	16 44		17 09
Gatwick Airport 10	a	*12 50*			*13 50*						*14 50*	*15 50*					*16 50*		*17 50*						
Heathrow Terminal 1 Bus	a	*12 25*		*12 55*	*13 25*			*13 55*			*14 25*	*15 25*		*15 55*			*16 25*	*16 55*	*17 25*				*17 55*		*18 25*
Slough 3	a	*11 40*		*12 25*	*12 40*			*13 25*			*13 41*	*14 30*		*15 25*			*15 40*	*16 25*	*16 40*				*17 25*		*17 40*
London Waterloo 15 ⊖	a																							18 49	
London Paddington 15 ⊖	a	11 42		12 15	12 32	12 42	13 06	13 15		13 36	13 42	14 30	15 06	15 15		15 31	15 42	16 15	16 30			17 06	17 15		17 42

For general notes see front of timetable
For details of catering facilities see Directory of Train Operators

A From Taunton (Table 134)
B From Paignton (Table 135)
C From Carmarthen (Table 128)

Table 125

Saturdays

until 26 January

South Wales, Weston-super-Mare, Bristol, Cheltenham Spa and Swindon → Oxford and London

Route Diagram - see first page of Table 125

Station		GW	GW	GW		GW	GW	GW	GW	GW		GW	GW	GW	GW	GW		GW	GW	GW	GW	GW			
			1 ◇	1 ◇		1 ◇	1 ◇	1 ◇	1 ◇			1 ◇	1 ◇	1 ◇	1 ◇	1 ◇			1 ◇	1 ◇		1 ◇			
																		A				B			
			☕	☕		☕	☕	☕	☕			☕	☕	☕	☕	☕			☕	☕					
Swansea 7	d			15 29				16 29					17 29			18 29				19 29					
Neath	d			15 40				16 40					17 40			18 40				19 40					
Port Talbot Parkway	d			15 48				16 48					17 48			18 48				19 48					
Bridgend	d			15 59				16 59					17 59			18 59				19 59					
Cardiff Central 7	d			16 25				17 25					18 25			19 25				20 25					
Hereford 7	d			15 48				16 48								18 11				18 48					
Newport (South Wales)	d			16 39				17 39					18 39			19 39				20 39					
Weston-super-Mare	d		15 39				16 39		17 08			17 39			18 08				20 10			21 59			
Bristol Temple Meads 10	d		16 30				17 30		18 00			18 30			19 30				20 33			22 33			
Bristol Parkway 7	a			17 00				18 00					19 00			20 00				21 00					
	d			17 02				18 02					19 02			20 02				21 02					
Bath Spa 7	d		16 43				17 43		18 13			18 43			19 43				20 46			22 46			
Chippenham	d		16 55				17 55		18 25			18 55			19 55				20 58			22 58			
Birmingham New Street 12	d	15 10								17 10								19 10			20 10				
Cheltenham Spa	d	16 01				17 00				18 01				19 00				20 01			21 28				
Gloucester 7	d	16 15				17 16				18 15				19 15				20 15			21 42				
Stonehouse	d	16 27				17 29				18 27				19 29				20 27			21 54				
Stroud	d	16 32				17 34				18 32				19 33				20 32			21 59				
Kemble	d	16 47				17 48				18 47				19 47				20 47			22 14				
Swindon	a	17 02	17 09	17 27		18 02	18 09	18 27	18 39	19 02		19 09	19 27	20 02	20 09	20 27		21 03	21 13	21 27	22 29	23 13			
	d		17 11	17 29		18 04	18 11	18 29	18 41			19 11	19 29	20 04	20 11	20 29			21 14	21 29		23 14			
Didcot Parkway	a		17 28	17 46		18 21	18 28	18 46				19 28	19 46	20 21	20 28	20 46			21 31			23 31			
Oxford	a			18 13				19 13					20 16			21 13			21 55			00b23			
Reading 7	a		17 44	18 01		18 36	18 44	19 01	19 09			19 44	20 01	20 38	20 44	21 03			21 48	21 58		23 52			
Gatwick Airport 10	a			19 52									21 47			23 03			00 10	01 00					
Heathrow Terminal 1 Bus	🚌 a		18 55	19 25			19 55		20 25				21 05						22 45	23 45					
Slough 3	a		18 25	18 40			19 25		19 40			20 25	20 45		21 35	21 38				22 42		00 30			
London Waterloo 15	⊖ a																								
London Paddington 15	⊖ a		18 15	18 31		19 06	19 15	19 31	19 42			20 15	20 31	21 09	21 15	21 36			22 16	22 31		00 32			

Saturdays

2 February to 22 March

Station		GW	GW	GW	GW	GW	GW	GW	GW		SW	GW	GW	GW	GW	GW	GW	GW	GW	GW	GW	GW	GW	GW	GW
			1 ◇	1 ◇	1 ◇	1 ◇	1 ◇	1 ◇	1 ◇		1 ◇		1 ◇	1 ◇	1 ◇	1 ◇	1 ◇	1 ◇	1 ◇	1 ◇	1 ◇	1 ◇	1 ◇	1 ◇	
							B																		
			☕	☕	☕	☕	☕	☕	☕				☕	☕	☕	☕	☕	☕	☕	☕	☕	☕	☕	☕	
Swansea 7	d		04 00						06 29										10 29						
Neath	d		04 11						06 40										10 40						
Port Talbot Parkway	d		04 19						06 48										10 48						
Bridgend	d		04 30						06 59										10 59						
Cardiff Central 7	d		04 55						07 25										11 25						
Hereford 7	d								05 42										10 48						
Newport (South Wales)	d		05 09						07 39										11 39						
Weston-super-Mare	d			06 24			07 28		07 34					09 40	10 08	10 43	11 08		11 40	12 08	12 41	13 08	13 39	14 08	
Bristol Temple Meads 10	d		06 00	07 00	07 17		08 00	08 17	08 30		08 50		09 17	10 17	11 00	11 17	12 00	12 17	12 30	13 00	13 17	14 00	14 17	15 00	
Bristol Parkway 7	a		05 37						08 00										12 00						
	d		05 42						08 10										12 10						
Bath Spa 7	d		06 13	07 13	07 30		08 13	08 30	08 43		09 05		09 30	10 30	11 13	11 30	12 13	12 30	12 43	13 13	13 30	14 13	14 30	15 13	
Chippenham	d				07 42			08 42				09 30	09 42	10 42		11 42		12 42			13 42		14 42		15 28
Birmingham New Street 12	d					05 30																			
Cheltenham Spa	d	05 30				07 27																			
Gloucester 7	d	05 44				07 43																			
Stonehouse	d	05 56				07 55																			
Stroud	d	06 01				08 01																			
Kemble	d	06 16				08 15																			
Swindon	a	06 32			07 57	08 29		08 57				09 48	09 57	10 57		11 57		12 57			13 57		14 57		15 47
	d																								
Didcot Parkway	a																								
Oxford	a																								
Reading 7	a		07 27	08 29			09 27		09 57						12 27		13 27		13 57	14 31		15 25		16 27	
Gatwick Airport 10	a		08 50	09 50			10 50								13 50		14 50			15 50		16 50		17 50	
Heathrow Terminal 1 Bus	🚌 a		08 25	09 25			10 25		10 55						13 25		14 25		14 55	15 25		16 25		17 25	
Slough 3	a		07 55	08 55			09 41		10 25						12 56		13 55		14 25	14 55		15 56		16 56	
London Waterloo 15	⊖ a										11 49														
London Paddington 15	⊖ a		07 58	08 58			10 01		10 27						12 59		13 58		14 26	15 03		15 56		16 59	

For general notes see front of timetable
For details of catering facilities see Directory of Train Operators

A To Westbury (Table 123)
B From Taunton (Table 134)
b By bus

Table 125

Saturdays

2 February to 22 March

South Wales, Weston-super-Mare, Bristol, Cheltenham Spa and Swindon → Oxford and London

Route Diagram - see first page of Table 125

		GW	GW	SW	GW	GW	GW	GW	GW	GW	GW	GW	GW	GW	GW	GW	GW	GW	GW	GW	GW	GW	GW
		1 ◇		1 ◇	1 ◇	1 ◇	1 ◇	1 ◇	1 ◇	1 ◇		1 ◇	1 ◇	1 ◇	1 ◇	1 ◇	1 ◇		1 ◇	1 ◇		1 ◇	1 ◇
																		A				B	
		☕			☕	☕	☕	☕	☕	☕		☕	☕	☕	☕	☕	☕		☕	☕			☕
Swansea 7	d							14 29							17 29	18 29				19 29			
Neath	d							14 40							17 40	18 40				19 40			
Port Talbot Parkway	d							14 48							17 48	18 48				19 48			
Bridgend	d							14 59							17 59	18 59				19 59			
Cardiff Central 7	d							15 25							18 25	19 25				20 25			
Hereford 7	d							*14 48*							*16 48*	*18 11*				*18 48*			
Newport (South Wales)	d							15 39							18 39	19 39				20 39			
Weston-super-Mare	d	*14 39*		*15 08*				*15 39*	*16 08*			*17 08*			*18 08*							22 00	
Bristol Temple Meads 10	d	15 17		15 52	16 00	16 17		16 30	17 00	17 17		18 00	18 17	19 17	19 30		20 17		21 17			22 33	22 40
Bristol Parkway 7	a							16 00							19 00	20 00				21 00			
	d							16 10							19 10	20 10				21 10			
Bath Spa 7	d	15 30		16 04	16 13	16 30		16 43	17 13	17 30		18 13	18 30	19 30	19 43	20 43	20 30		21 30	21 43		22 46	22 53
Chippenham	d	15 42				16 42				17 42			18 42	19 42			20 42		21 42				23 05
Birmingham New Street 12	d		*15 10*				*15 40*				*17 10*							*19 10*			*20 10*		
Cheltenham Spa	d		16 01				16 31				18 01							20 01			21 28		
Gloucester 7	d		16 15				16 46				18 15							20 15			21 42		
Stonehouse	d		16 27				16 59				18 27							20 27			21 54		
Stroud	d		16 32				17 04				18 32							20 32			21 59		
Kemble	d		16 47				17 19				18 47							20 47			22 14		
Swindon	a	15 57	17 02			16 57	17 34			17 57	19 02		18 57	19 57			20 57	21 03	21 57		22 29		23 20
	d																						
Didcot Parkway	a																						
Oxford	a																						
Reading 7	a				17 27			17 57	18 27			19 28			20 57	21 57				22 57		23 56	
Gatwick Airport 10	a							*19 52*	*19 50*			*21 47*			*23 03*	*00 10*				*01 00*			
Heathrow Terminal 1 Bus	a				*18 25*			*18 55*	*19 25*			*20 25*			*22 45*								
Slough 3	a				*17 55*			*18 25*	*18 56*			*20 15*			*21 35*					*23 43*		*00 30*	
London Waterloo 15 ⊖	a			18 49																			
London Paddington 15 ⊖	a				17 59			18 26	18 59			19 57			21 26	22 27				23 26		00 37	

Saturdays

from 29 March

		GW	GW	GW		GW	GW	GW		GW	GW	GW		GW	GW	SW		GW	GW	GW		GW	GW	GW	GW
		1 ◇	1 ◇	1 ◇		1 ◇	1 ◇	1 ◇		1 ◇	1 ◇	1 ◇		1 ◇	1 ◇	1 ◇		1 ◇		1 ◇		1 ◇	1 ◇	1 ◇	1 ◇
											B							C		D					
		☕	☕	☕		☕	☕	☕		☕	☕	☕		☕	☕			☕		☕		☕	☕	☕	☕
Swansea 7	d		04 00					05 29		05 59				06 29	06 59							07 29			08 29
Neath	d		04 11					05 40		06 10				06 40	07 10							07 40			08 40
Port Talbot Parkway	d		04 19					05 48		06 18				06 48	07 18							07 48			08 48
Bridgend	d		04 30					05 59		06 29				06 59	07 29							07 59			08 59
Cardiff Central 7	d		04 55					06 25		06 55				07 25	07 55							08 25			09 25
Hereford 7	d							*04b58*						*06b00*											*08b00*
Newport (South Wales)	d		05 09					06 39		07 09				07 39	08 09							08 39			09 39
Weston-super-Mare	d					06 24					07 28	*07 34*						08 28		09 00			*09 09*	*09 40*	
Bristol Temple Meads 10	d	05 30		06 30		07 00	07 30				08 00	08 30				08 50		09 00		09 30			10 00	10 30	
Bristol Parkway 7	a																								
	d																								
Bath Spa 7	d	05 43		06 43		07 13	07 43				08 13	08 43				09 05		09 13		09 43			10 13	10 43	
Chippenham	d	05 55		06 55		07 25	07 55				08 25	08 55						09 25	09 30	09 55			10 25	10 55	
Birmingham New Street 12	d							*05 30*							*07 30*										*08c40*
Cheltenham Spa	d		*05 37*					*07 06*						*07 45*	*08 11*										*09 31*
Gloucester 7	d		06 03					07 25		07 53				08 26	08 53							09 23			10 26
Stonehouse	d		06 17					07 38		08 06				08 39	09 06							09 36			10 39
Stroud	d		06 23					07 44		08 12				08 45	09 12							09 42			10 45
Kemble	d		06 37					08e00		08 26				09 00	09 26							10 00			11 00
Swindon	a	06 09	06 51	07 09		07 40	08 09	08 14		08 39	08 39	09 09		09 14	09 39			09 39	09 52	10 09		10 14	10 39	11 09	11 14
	d	06 11	06 51	07 11		07 42	08 11	08 14		08 41	08 41	09 11		09 14	09 45			09 41		10 11		10 14	10 41	11 11	11 14
Didcot Parkway	a	06 28		07 28		07 59	08 28	08 32		08 58	08 58	09 28		09 32	10 02					10 28				11 28	
Oxford	a	*07 03*		*08 00*		*08 39*		*09 15*			*09 31*			*10 13*	*10 30*					*11 13*					
Reading 7	a	06 43	07 21	07 44		08 14	08 44	08 48		09 14	09 14	09 44		09 48	10 19			10 09		10 45		10 46	11 09	11 44	11 43
Gatwick Airport 10	a		*08 50*			*09 50*					*10 50*									*12 53*			*12 50*		
Heathrow Terminal 1 Bus	a	*07 55*	*08 25*	*08 55*		*09 25*		*09 55*			*10 25*			*10 55*	*11 25*					*11 55*			*12 25*		
Slough 3	a	*07 12*	*07 55*	*08 25*		*08 55*		*09 25*			*09 41*			*10 25*	*10 55*					*11 25*			*11 40*		
London Waterloo 15 ⊖	a															11 49									
London Paddington 15 ⊖	a	07 14	07 56	08 14		08 45	09 15	09 17		09 44	09 44	10 14		10 16	10 55			10 42		11 15		11 17	11 42	12 15	12 12

For general notes see front of timetable
For details of catering facilities see Directory of Train Operators

- **A** To Westbury (Table 123)
- **B** From Taunton (Table 134)
- **C** From Exeter St Davids (Table 135)
- **D** From Paignton (Table 135)
- **b** By bus
- **c** Change at Cheltenham Spa and Gloucester
- **e** Arr. 0757

Table 125

Saturdays

from 29 March

South Wales, Weston-super-Mare, Bristol, Cheltenham Spa and Swindon → Oxford and London

Route Diagram - see first page of Table 125

		GW		GW	GW	GW		GW	GW	GW		GW	GW	GW		GW	GW	SW		GW	GW	GW		GW	GW
		1 ◇		1 ◇	1 ◇	1 ◇		1 ◇	1 ◇	1 ◇		1 ◇	1 ◇	1 ◇			1 ◇	1 ◇		1 ◇	1 ◇	1 ◇		1 ◇	1 ◇
		☕		☕	☕	☕		☕	☕	☕		☕	☕	☕			☕			☕	☕	☕		☕	☕
Swansea 7	d				09 29				11 29				12 29												
Neath	d				09 40				11 40				12 40												
Port Talbot Parkway	d				09 48				11 48				12 48												
Bridgend	d				09 59				11 59				12 59												
Cardiff Central 7	d				10 25				12 25				13 25												
Hereford 7	d				09b00				11b00				12b00												
Newport (South Wales)	d				10 39				12 39				13 39												
Weston-super-Mare	d			10 44		11 08		12 41		13 08		13 39		14 08			14 39	15 08							15 39
Bristol Temple Meads 10	d	11 00		11 30		12 00		13 30		14 00		14 30		14 57			15 30	15 52		16 00	16 02	16 09			16 30
Bristol Parkway 7	a																					→			
	d																								
Bath Spa 7	d	11 13		11 43		12 13		13 43		14 13		14 43					15 43	16 04		16 13				←	16 43
Chippenham	d	11 25		11 55		12 25		13 55		14 25		14 55				15 28	15 55			16 25				16 25	16 55
Birmingham New Street 12	d				09c40				11 30				12c40							→					
Cheltenham Spa	d				10 45				12 11				13 45												
Gloucester 7	d				11 26				13 26				14 26												
Stonehouse	d				11 39				13 39				14 39												
Stroud	d				11 45				13 45				14 45												
Kemble	d				12 00				14 00				15 00												
Swindon	a	11 39		12 09	12 14	12 39		14 09	14 14	14 39		15 09	15 14			15 51	16 09							16 39	17 09
	d	11 41		12 11	12 14	12 41		14 11	14 14	14 41		15 11	15 14				16 11							16 41	17 11
Didcot Parkway	a			12 28	12 32			14 28	14 32			15 28	15 32				16 28								17 28
Oxford	a				13 13				15 13				16 13				17 13								
Reading 7	a	12 09		12 44	12 48	13 09		14 44	14 48	15 09		15 44	15 48	15 54			16 44				17 00			17 09	17 44
Gatwick Airport 10	a					14 50				16 50				17 50											
Heathrow Terminal 1 Bus	a				13 55	14 25			15 55	16 25				16 55							17 55			18 25	
Slough 3	a				13 25	13 41			15 25	15 40				16 25			17 25							17 40	
London Waterloo 15 ⊖	a																	18 49							
London Paddington 15 ⊖	a	12 42		13 15	13 16	13 42		15 15	15 17	15 42		16 15	16 17	16 25			17 15				17 29			17 42	18 15

		GW	GW	GW		GW	GW	GW		GW	GW	GW		GW	GW	GW		GW	GW	GW		GW			
		1 ◇	1 ◇	1 ◇		1 ◇	1 ◇	1 ◇		1 ◇	1 ◇	1 ◇		1 ◇	1 ◇	1 ◇		1 ◇	1 ◇	1 ◇		1 ◇			
																						A			
		☕	☕	☕		☕	☕	☕		☕	☕	☕		☕	☕	☕		☕	☕	☕					
Swansea 7	d	14 29					15 29				16 29				17 29			18 29		19 29					
Neath	d	14 40					15 40				16 40				17 40			18 40		19 40					
Port Talbot Parkway	d	14 48					15 48				16 48				17 48			18 48		19 48					
Bridgend	d	14 59					15 59				16 59				17 59			18 59		19 59					
Cardiff Central 7	d	15 25					16 25				17 25				18 25			19 25		20 25					
Hereford 7	d	14b00					15b00				16b00				17b00			18b00		19b00					
Newport (South Wales)	d	15 39					16 39				17 39				18 39			19 39		20 39					
Weston-super-Mare	d		←	16 08		16 39		17 08		17 39		18 08							20 10			22 00			
Bristol Temple Meads 10	d		16 09	17 09		17 30		18 00		18 30		18 58		19 30		20 05			20 33			22 33			
Bristol Parkway 7	a																								
	d																								
Bath Spa 7	d					17 43		18 13		18 43				19 43					20 46			22 46			
Chippenham	d					17 55		18 25		18 55				19 55					20 58			22 58			
Birmingham New Street 12	d	14c40					15c40				16c40				17c40			18c40		20c10					
Cheltenham Spa	d	15 31					16 45				17 45				18 45			19 45		21 02					
Gloucester 7	d	16 26					17 26				18 26				19 26			20 23		21 28					
Stonehouse	d	16 39					17 39				18 39				19 39			20 36		21 41					
Stroud	d	16 45					17 45				18 45				19 45			20 42		21 46					
Kemble	d	17 00					18 00				19 00				20 00			20 56		22e04					
Swindon	a	17 14				18 09	18 14	18 39		19 09	19 14			20 09	20 14			21 10	21 13	22 18		23 13			
	d	17 14				18 11	18 14	18 41		19 11	19 14			20 11	20 14			21 10	21 14	22 18		23 14			
Didcot Parkway	a	17 32				18 28	18 32			19 28	19 32			20 28	20 32			21 28	21 31			23 31			
Oxford	a	18 13					19 13				20 16				21 13				21 55			00b23			
Reading 7	a	17 48	17 50	18 07		18 44	18 48	19 09		19 44	19 48	20 27		20 44	20 48	21 30		21 44	21 48	22 47		23 52			
Gatwick Airport 10	a		19 52	19 50							21 47	21 59			23 03				00 10	01 00					
Heathrow Terminal 1 Bus	a		18 55	19 25			19 55	20 25			21 05	21 35							22 45	23 45					
Slough 3	a	18 25	18 05	18 40			19 25	19 40			20 25	20 47			21 10			22 09	22 42	23 43		00 30			
London Waterloo 15 ⊖	a																								
London Paddington 15 ⊖	a	18 16	18 23	18 38		19 15	19 17	19 42		20 15	20 16	20 58		21 15	21 16	21 59		22 16	22 16	23 16		00 32			

For general notes see front of timetable
For details of catering facilities see Directory of Train Operators

A From Taunton (Table 134)
b By bus
c Change at Cheltenham Spa and Gloucester
e Arr. 2159

Table 125

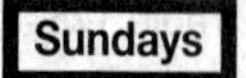

Sundays

until 27 January

South Wales, Weston-super-Mare, Bristol, Cheltenham Spa and Swindon → Oxford and London

Route Diagram - see first page of Table 125

		GW	GW		GW	GW		GW	GW		GW	GW		GW	GW		GW	GW		GW	GW		GW	GW	GW
		1 ◇	1 ◇		1 ◇	1 ◇		1 ◇			1 ◇	1 ◇		1 ◇	1 ◇		1 ◇	1 ◇		1 ◇	1 ◇			1 ◇	1 ◇
																		A						A	
Swansea 7	d							07 59				08 59					09 59				10 59				11 59
Neath	d							08 11				09 11					10 11				11 11				12 11
Port Talbot Parkway	d							08 18				09 18					10 18				11 18				12 18
Bridgend	d							08 30				09 30					10 30				11 30				12 30
Cardiff Central 7	d				07 45			08 55				09 55					10 55				11 55				12 55
Hereford 7	d																10 11								
Newport (South Wales)	d				08 03			09 13				10 09					11 09				12 09				13 09
Weston-super-Mare	d					08 28					09 14				10 28			10 51							
Bristol Temple Meads 10	d	07 40	08 10			09 00					10 00			10 30	11 00			12 00						13 00	
Bristol Parkway 7	a				08 34			09 34				10 30					11 30				12 30				13 30
	d				08 34			09 36				10 31					11 32				12 32				13 32
Bath Spa 7	d	07 53	08 23			09 13					10 13			10 43	11 13			12 13						13 13	
Chippenham	d	08 05	08 35			09 25					10 25			10 55	11 25			12 25						13 25	
Birmingham New Street 12	d																			10 30			11 40		
Cheltenham Spa	d								09 35											11 46			12 35		
Gloucester 7	d								09 49											12 04			12 49		
Stonehouse	d								10 01											12 17			13 01		
Stroud	d								10 06											12 22			13 06		
Kemble	d								10 20											12 36			13 20		
Swindon	a	08 20	08 49		09 00	09 38		10 01	10 35		10 40	10 56		11 08	11 40		11 57	12 39		12 50	12 57		13 36	13 40	13 57
	d	08 20	08 50		09 00	09 41		10 02			10 41	10 59		11 11	11 41		11 59	12 41		12 51	12 59			13 41	13 59
Didcot Parkway	a	08 39	09 08			09 59					10 58				11 58			12 58						13 58	
Oxford	a	09 14	09 31			10 29					11 25				12 27			13 27						14 25	
Reading 7	a	08 55	09 25		09 32	10 13		10 31			11 13	11 27		11 38	12 13		12 27	13 13		13 19	13 27			14 14	14 27
Gatwick Airport 10	a				11 30			12 30						13 30			14 30				15 30				16 30
Heathrow Terminal 1 Bus	a	09 55	10 25		10 55	11 25		11 55				12 25		12 55			13 25				14 25				15 25
Slough 3	a	09 24			10 01	10 55		11 09				11 56		12 14			12 57	13 47			13 55				14 56
London Waterloo 15	⊖ a																								
London Paddington 15	⊖ a	09 35	10 03		10 16	10 54		11 07			11 55	12 08		12 22	12 55		13 07	13 55		13 59	14 10			14 54	15 08

		GW		GW	GW		GW	GW		GW	GW		SW	GW		GW	GW		GW	GW		GW	GW		GW
		1 ◇		1 ◇	1 ◇		1 ◇	1 ◇		1 ◇	1 ◇		1 ◇	1 ◇		1 ◇			1 ◇			1 ◇	1 ◇		1 ◇
																							A		B
Swansea 7	d				12 59			13 59						14 59								15 59			16 29
Neath	d				13 11			14 11						15 11								16 11			16 41
Port Talbot Parkway	d				13 18			14 18						15 18								16 18			16 48
Bridgend	d				13 30			14 30						15 30								16 30			17 00
Cardiff Central 7	d				13 55			14 55						15 55								16 55			17 25
Hereford 7	d				12 46									15 11											
Newport (South Wales)	d				14 09			15 09						16 09								17 09			17 39
Weston-super-Mare	d	13 30					14 28			15 29									16 15				16 58		
Bristol Temple Meads 10	d	14 00					15 00			16 00			16 04			16 30			17 00				17 30		
Bristol Parkway 7	a				14 30			15 30						16 30								17 30			18 00
	d				14 32			15 32						16 32								17 32			18 02
Bath Spa 7	d	14 13					15 13			16 13			16 20			16 43			17 13				17 43		
Chippenham	d	14 25					15 25			16 25						16 55			17 25	17 31			17 55		
Birmingham New Street 12	d			12 40							14 40						15 40								
Cheltenham Spa	d			13 46							15 46						16 35								
Gloucester 7	d			14 03							16 04						16 49								
Stonehouse	d			14 17							16 16						17 01								
Stroud	d			14 22							16 22						17 06								
Kemble	d			14 36							16 36						17 21								
Swindon	a	14 40		14 50	14 57		15 40	15 57		16 40	16 50			16 57		17 10	17 36		17 40	17 48		17 57	18 10		18 27
	d	14 41		14 52	14 59		15 41	15 59		16 41	16 51			16 59		17 11			17 41			17 59	18 11		18 29
Didcot Parkway	a	14 58					15 58			16 58									17 58						
Oxford	a	15 27					16 25			17 25									18 27						
Reading 7	a	15 14		15 20	15 27		16 14	16 27		17 14	17 19			17 27		17 42			18 15			18 27	18 44		18 59
Gatwick Airport 10	a				17 30			18 30						19 30											20 43
Heathrow Terminal 1 Bus	a				16 25			17 25						18 25		18 55						19 25			19 55
Slough 3	a				15 56		16 45	16 56		17 48				17 56		18 41						18 56			19 31
London Waterloo 15	⊖ a												18 58												
London Paddington 15	⊖ a	15 57		15 59	16 08		16 54	17 11		17 54	17 59			18 10		18 27			18 54			19 10	19 24		19 41

For general notes see front of timetable
For details of catering facilities see Directory of Train Operators

A From Plymouth (Table 135)
B From Carmarthen (Table 128)

Table 125

until 27 January

South Wales, Weston-super-Mare, Bristol, Cheltenham Spa and Swindon → Oxford and London

Route Diagram - see first page of Table 125

		GW 1◇ A ☕	GW 1◇ ☕	GW 1◇ B ☕	GW 1◇ ☕	GW 1◇ ☕	GW 1◇ C ☕	GW D	GW	GW 1◇ E ☕	GW 1◇ ☕	GW 1◇ ☕	GW 1◇	GW 1◇ E ☕	GW 1◇ B ☕	GW
Swansea 7	d				17 29					18 29				19 59		
Neath	d				17 41					18 41				20 11		
Port Talbot Parkway	d				17 48					18 48				20 18		
Bridgend	d				18 00					19 00				20 30		
Cardiff Central 7	d				18 25					19 25				20 55		
Hereford 7	d				*17 09*					*18 02*				*20 12*		
Newport (South Wales)	d				18 39					19 39				21 09		
Weston-super-Mare	d	17 30				*18 16*	18 54						20 38		*21 19*	
Bristol Temple Meads 10	d	18 00		18 30		19 00	19 30				20 00		21 00		22 05	
Bristol Parkway 7	a				19 00					20 00				21 30		
	d				19 02					20 02				21 32		
Bath Spa 7	d	18 13		18 43		19 13	19 43				20 13		21 13		22 18	
Chippenham	d	18 25		18 55		19 25	19 55	20 04			20 25		21 27		22 30	
Birmingham New Street 12	d		*16 40*						*17 40*			*18 40*				*20 30*
Cheltenham Spa	d		17 46						*18 22*			19 46				21 42
Gloucester 7	d		18 04						19 30			20 03				22 00
Stonehouse	d		18 17					21a01	19 47			20 15				22 12
Stroud	d		18 22						19 52			20 21				22 17
Kemble	d		18 36						20 07			20b43				22 32
Swindon	a	18 40	18 50	19 10	19 27	19 40	20 10	20 20	20 22	20 27	20 40	20 57	21 41	21 57	22 45	22 47
	d	18 41	18 52	19 11	19 29	19 41	20 11			20 29	20 41	21 02	21 42	21 59	22 52	
Didcot Parkway	a	18 59				19 58					20 58		22 00			
Oxford	a	*19 25*				*20 25*					*21 25*		*22 27*			
Reading 7	a	19 14	19 20	19 44	19 58	20 14	20 45			20 57	21 16	21 31	22 16	22 35	23 26	
Gatwick Airport 10	a					*21 46*	*22 39*					*23 30*	*00 10*	*00 43*		
Heathrow Terminal 1 Bus	🚌 a		*20 25*		*21 05*	*21 35*				*21 55*		*22 45*		*23 45*		
Slough 3	a		*19 56*		*20 41*	*20 45*				*21 41*	*21 48*	*22 10*	*22 47*	*23 15*	*00 05*	
London Waterloo 15	⊖ a															
London Paddington 15	⊖ a	19 58	20 00	20 24	20 40	20 55	21 26			21 40	21 59	22 23	23 01	23 26	00 17	

Sundays

3 February to 23 March

			GW 1◇ ☕	GW 🚌	GW 1	GW 🚌	GW 🚌	GW 1◇ ☕	GW 1◇ ☕		GW 🚌	GW 🚌	GW 🚌	GW	GW 1◇ ☕	GW 1◇ ☕	GW 🚌	GW 🚌	GW 1◇ ☕	GW 🚌	GW 🚌	GW 1◇ ☕
Swansea 7	d														07 59				08 45			
Neath	d														08 11				08 57			
Port Talbot Parkway	d														08 18				09 04			
Bridgend	d														08 30				09 16			
Cardiff Central 7	d							07 45							08 55				09 41			
Hereford 7	d																					
Newport (South Wales)	d							08 03							09 13				09 55			
Weston-super-Mare	d																					
Bristol Temple Meads 10	d		07 40		08 05			09 00	09 05						10 00	10 05			10 45			11 05
Bristol Parkway 7	a							08 33							09 34				10 16			
	d							08 39					10 25		09 41				10 22		11 25	
Bath Spa 7	d		07 53		08 17			09 12	09 18						10 12	10 18			10 57			11 18
Chippenham	d				08 30				09 31							10 31						11 30
Birmingham New Street 12	d																					
Cheltenham Spa	d													09 35								
Gloucester 7	d													09 49								
Stonehouse	d													10 01								
Stroud	d													10 06								
Kemble	d													10 20								
Swindon	a				08 45				09 45				11 20	10 35		10 45					12 20	11 45
	d	07 50		08 10		08 50	08 55			09 50	09 55	10 10					10 50	10 55		11 20		
Didcot Parkway	a			09 00			09 45				10 45							11 45				
Oxford	a																					
Reading 7	a	08 50	09 01			09 55		10 30		10 55		11 15			11 23		11 55		12 08	12 25		
Gatwick Airport 10	a		*11 30*					*12 30*							*13 30*				*14 30*			
Heathrow Terminal 1 Bus	🚌 a		*09 55*					*11 25*							*12 25*				*13 25*			
Slough 3	a		*09 44*					*11 18*							*12 18*				*12 35*			
London Waterloo 15	⊖ a																					
London Paddington 15	⊖ a		09 46					11 13							12 06				12 57			

For general notes see front of timetable
For details of catering facilities see Directory of Train Operators

A From Paignton (Table 135)
B From Plymouth (Table 135)
C From Taunton (Table 134)
D From Westbury (Table 123) to Cheltenham Spa
E From Carmarthen (Table 128)
b Arr. 2035

Table 125

Sundays

South Wales, Weston-super-Mare, Bristol, Cheltenham Spa and Swindon → Oxford and London

3 February to 23 March

Route Diagram - see first page of Table 125

		GW		GW	GW	GW	GW	GW		GW	GW	GW	GW	GW		GW	GW	GW	GW	GW		GW	GW	GW	GW
					1 ◇			1 ◇			1 ◇		1 ◇				1 ◇							1 ◇	1 ◇
		🚌		🚌		🚌	🚌			🚌		🚌		🚌		🚌		🚌	🚌			🚌	🚌		
					☕			☕			☕		☕				☕							☕	☕
Swansea 7	d				09 45								10 45											11 45	
Neath	d				09 57								10 57											11 57	
Port Talbot Parkway	d				10 04								11 04											12 04	
Bridgend	d				10 16								11 16											12 16	
Cardiff Central 7	d				10 41								11 41											12 41	
Hereford 7	d												10 11												
Newport (South Wales)	d				10 55								11 55											12 55	
Weston-super-Mare	d												11 56											12 54	
Bristol Temple Meads 10	d				11 45			12 05					12 45				13 05							13 45	14 05
Bristol Parkway 7	a				11 16								12 16											13 16	
	d				11 23		12 25						12 23	13 25								14 25		13 23	
Bath Spa 7	d				11 57			12 18					12 57				13 18							13 57	14 18
Chippenham	d							12 30									13 30								14 30
Birmingham New Street 12	d										10 30									12 10					
Cheltenham Spa	d										11 46									13 05					
Gloucester 7	d										12 04									13 19					
Stonehouse	d										12 17									13 31					
Stroud	d										12 22									13 36					
Kemble	d										12 36									13 50					
Swindon	a						13 20	12 45			12 50			14 20			13 45			14 06		15 20			14 45
	d	11 50		11 55		12 20				12 55		12 58				13 25		13 55	13 55				14 25		
Didcot Parkway	a			12 45						13 45								14 45							
Oxford	a																								
Reading 7	a	12 55			13 08	13 25						14 03	14 08			14 30			15 00				15 30	15 08	
Gatwick Airport 10	a				15 30								16 30											17 30	
Heathrow Terminal 1 Bus	🚌 a				14 25								15 25											16 25	
Slough 3	a				13 37								14 35											15 40	
London Waterloo 15	⊖ a																								
London Paddington 15	⊖ a				13 52								14 53											15 53	

		GW	GW	GW		GW	GW	GW	GW	GW		GW	GW	SW	GW	GW		GW	GW	GW	GW	GW		GW	GW
				1 ◇				1 ◇		1 ◇			1 ◇	1 ◇		1 ◇			1 ◇					1 ◇	
		🚌	🚌			🚌	🚌		🚌			🚌			🚌			🚌		🚌	🚌				🚌
				☕				☕		☕			☕			☕			☕					☕	
Swansea 7	d			12 45									13 45											14 45	
Neath	d			12 57									13 57											14 57	
Port Talbot Parkway	d			13 04									14 04											15 04	
Bridgend	d			13 16									14 16											15 16	
Cardiff Central 7	d			13 41									14 41											15 41	
Hereford 7	d			12 46																				14 17	
Newport (South Wales)	d			13 55									14 55											15 55	
Weston-super-Mare	d												14 54											16 00	
Bristol Temple Meads 10	d			14 45				15 05					15 45	16 04		16 20			16 25					16 45	
Bristol Parkway 7	a			14 16									15 16											16 16	
	d			14 23		15 25							15 23											16 23	16 25
Bath Spa 7	d			14 57				15 18					15 57	16 20		16 33			16 39					16 57	
Chippenham	d							15 30											16 51						
Birmingham New Street 12	d									13 30												15 30			
Cheltenham Spa	d									14 46												16 30			
Gloucester 7	d									15 03												16 44			
Stonehouse	d									15 16												16 56			
Stroud	d									15 22												17 01			
Kemble	d									15 35												17 15			
Swindon	a					16 20		15 45		15 50									17 06			17 30			17 20
	d	14 55	14 55				15 25		15 55			15 55			16 25			16 55		17 11	17 13				
Didcot Parkway	a	15 45							16 45											18 01					
Oxford	a																								
Reading 7	a		16 00	16 08			16 30					17 00	17 08		17 30	17 45		18 00			18 18			18 07	
Gatwick Airport 10	a			18 30												19 30									
Heathrow Terminal 1 Bus	🚌 a			17 25									18 25			18 55									
Slough 3	a			16 34									17 32			18 18								18 35	
London Waterloo 15	⊖ a													18 58											
London Paddington 15	⊖ a			16 52									17 57			18 31								18 52	

For general notes see front of timetable
For details of catering facilities see Directory of Train Operators

Table 125

Sundays

3 February to 23 March

South Wales, Weston-super-Mare, Bristol, Cheltenham Spa and Swindon → Oxford and London

Route Diagram - see first page of Table 125

		GW 1◇ ☕	GW 🚌	GW	GW 1◇ ☕	GW 🚌		GW 🚌	GW 1◇ ☕	GW 1◇ ☕	GW 🚌	GW 🚌		GW 1◇ ☕	GW 1◇ ☕	GW 🚌	GW 1◇ ☕	GW 🚌		GW 🚌	GW 1◇ A ☕	GW 1◇ ☕	GW	GW 1◇ ☕	GW 🚌
Swansea 7	d									15 45							16 45							17 45	
Neath	d									15 57							16 57							17 57	
Port Talbot Parkway	d									16 04							17 04							18 04	
Bridgend	d									16 16							17 16							18 16	
Cardiff Central 7	d									16 41							17 41							18 41	
Hereford 7	d									15 11														17 09	
Newport (South Wales)	d									16 55							17 55							18 55	
Weston-super-Mare	d	16 15												17 26	17 49						18 54	18 16			
Bristol Temple Meads 10	d	17 05			17 25					17 45				18 05	18 30		18 45				19 25	19 31		19 45	
Bristol Parkway 7	a									17 16							18 16							19 16	
	d									17 23	17 25						18 23	18 25						19 23	19 25
Bath Spa 7	d	17 18			17 38					17 57				18 18	18 43		18 57				19 37	19 44		19 57	
Chippenham	d			17 31	17 50										18 55							19 56			
Birmingham New Street 12	d								16 30														17 30		
Cheltenham Spa	d								17 35														18 16		
Gloucester 7	d								17 53														19 30		
Stonehouse	d								18 05														19 44		
Stroud	d								18 11														19 49		
Kemble	d								18 25														20 04		
Swindon	a			17 48	18 05				18 40		18 20				19 10			19 20				20 11	20 19		20 20
	d		17 40			18 10		18 15				18 55				19 25		19 20		19 55					20 30
Didcot Parkway	a					19 00												20 10							21 20
Oxford	a																								
Reading 7	a	18 27	18 45					19 20		19 08		20 00		19 31		20 30	20 08			21 00	20 48			21 09	
Gatwick Airport 10	a	20 30															21 46				22 31			23 30	
Heathrow Terminal 1 Bus	🚌 a	19 25								20 25							21 05				21 55			22 45	
Slough 3	a	19 18								19 36				20 18			20 34							21 36	
London Waterloo 15	⊖ a																								
London Paddington 15	⊖ a	19 25								20 01				20 26			20 51				21 32			21 51	

		GW B		GW 🚌	GW 🚌	GW 1◇ ☕	GW 🚌	GW 1◇ ☕		GW 🚌	GW 🚌	GW 1◇ ☕	GW 🚌	GW 1◇ ☕		GW 🚌	GW 🚌	GW	GW 1◇ ☕	GW 1◇ ☕		GW 🚌	GW 🚌		
Swansea 7	d											18 45							20 05						
Neath	d											18 57							20 17						
Port Talbot Parkway	d											19 04							20 24						
Bridgend	d											19 16							20 36						
Cardiff Central 7	d											19 41							21 01						
Hereford 7	d											18 50							20 12						
Newport (South Wales)	d											19 55							21 15						
Weston-super-Mare	d					19 42								21 00						22 05					
Bristol Temple Meads 10	d					20 30						20 45		21 30					22 05	22 43					
Bristol Parkway 7	a											20 16							21 40						
	d									21 45		20 23	20 22						21 47						
Bath Spa 7	d					20 43						20 57		21 43					22 17	22 56					
Chippenham	d	20 01				20 55								21 55						23 08					
Birmingham New Street 12	d							19 30										20 30							
Cheltenham Spa	d							20 35										21 42							
Gloucester 7	d							20 50										22 00							
Stonehouse	d	21a01						21 03										22 12							
Stroud	d							21 08										22 17							
Kemble	d							21 23										22 31							
Swindon	a	20 19				21 10		21 37		22 40			21 17	22 10				22 46		23 23					
	d			20 25	20 55		21 20				21 50		21 17			22 17	22 20					23 30	23 30		
Didcot Parkway	a												22 07			23 07						00 20			
Oxford	a																								
Reading 7	a			21 30	22 00		22 25				22 55	22 08					23 25		23 26				00 35		
Gatwick Airport 10	a											00 10							01 17						
Heathrow Terminal 1 Bus	🚌 a											23 45													
Slough 3	a											22 36							00 05						
London Waterloo 15	⊖ a																								
London Paddington 15	⊖ a											22 49							00 27						

For general notes see front of timetable
For details of catering facilities see Directory of Train Operators

A From Taunton (Table 134)
B From Westbury (Table 123) to Cheltenham Spa

Table 125

Sundays

from 30 March

South Wales, Weston-super-Mare, Bristol, Cheltenham Spa and Swindon → Oxford and London

Route Diagram - see first page of Table 125

		GW	GW	GW		GW	GW	GW		GW	GW	GW		GW	GW	GW		GW	GW	GW		GW	GW	GW	GW
		1 ◊	1 ◊	1 ◊		1 ◊	1 ◊	1 ◊		1 ◊	1 ◊	1 ◊		1 ◊	1 ◊	1 ◊		1 ◊	1 ◊	1 ◊		1 ◊	1 ◊	1 ◊	1 ◊
																A				A					
Swansea 7	d										08 29				09 29				10 29			11 29			12 29
Neath	d										08 41				09 41				10 41			11 41			12 41
Port Talbot Parkway	d										08 48				09 48				10 48			11 48			12 48
Bridgend	d										09 00				10 00				11 00			12 00			13 00
Cardiff Central 7	d					07 55					09 25				10 25				11 25			12 25			13 25
Hereford 7	d																					10b11			
Newport (South Wales)	d					08 13					09 39				10 39				11 39			12 39			13 39
Weston-super-Mare	d			08 28										10 20		10 51								13 15	
Bristol Temple Meads 10	d	07 40	08 25	09 00			09 33	10 00		10 30				11 00		12 00		12 39		13 00			13 47	14 00	
Bristol Parkway 7	a		08 34																						
	d		08 35																						
Bath Spa 7	d	07 53		09 13			09 46	10 13		10 43		11 03		11 13		12 13				13 13				14 13	
Chippenham	d	08 05		09 25				10 25		10 55				11 25		12 25				13 25				14 25	
Birmingham New Street 12	d																		11c10			11 46			12 30
Cheltenham Spa	d										09 58								11 57			12 45			13 12
Gloucester 7	d					09 05					10 22				11 22				12 22			13 22			14 22
Stonehouse	d					09 19					10 36				11 36				12 36			13 36			14 36
Stroud	d					09 24					10 42				11 42				12 42			13 42			14 42
Kemble	d					09 38					10 57				11 57				12 57			13 57			14 57
Swindon	a	08 19	09 01	09 39		09 52	10 10	10 39		11 08	11 10	11 25		11 39	12 09	12 39			13 10	13 40		14 10		14 40	15 10
	d	08 20	09 01	09 41		09 54	10 12	10 41		11 11	11 14	11 26		11 41	12 11	12 41			13 13	13 41		14 11		14 41	15 11
Didcot Parkway	a	08 38	09 19	09 58		10 11		10 58		11 28	11 33			11 58	12 28	12 58			13 34	13 58		14 28		14 58	15 28
Oxford	a			10b45		11b15					12b15				13b15				14b15			15b15			16b15
Reading 7	a	08 54	09 35	10 14		10 29	10 40	11 13		11 43	11 50	11 56		12 14	12 44	13 14		13 40	13 49	14 14		14 44	14 50	15 13	15 44
Gatwick Airport 10	a	10 31	11 30				12 30					13 30			14 30				15 30			16 30			17 30
Heathrow Terminal 1 Bus	a	09 55	10 55			11 25	11 55	12 25				12 55		13 25	13 55	14 25			14 55	15 25		15 55		16 25	16 55
Slough 3	a	09 43	10 18	10 43			11 18	11 43		12 18				12 44	13 18	13 43				14 44		15 18		15 43	16 18
London Waterloo 15	⊖ a																								
London Paddington 15	⊖ a	09 39	10 22	11 04		11 12	11 27	11 56		12 22	12 33	12 42		12 59	13 26	13 55		14 22	14 30	15 03		15 23	15 32	15 56	16 23

		GW		GW	GW	GW		GW	GW	SW		GW	GW	GW		GW	GW	GW		GW	GW	GW		GW	GW
		1 ◊		1 ◊	1 ◊	1 ◊		1 ◊	1 ◊	1 ◊		1 ◊	1 ◊	1 ◊		1 ◊		1 ◊		1 ◊	1 ◊	1 ◊		1 ◊	1 ◊
																		A						B	A
Swansea 7	d				13 29								14 29							15 29					
Neath	d				13 41								14 41							15 41					
Port Talbot Parkway	d				13 48								14 48							15 48					
Bridgend	d				14 00								15 00							16 00					
Cardiff Central 7	d				14 25								15 25							16 25					
Hereford 7	d				12b55															14b25	16 30				
Newport (South Wales)	d				14 39								15 39							16 39					
Weston-super-Mare	d			14 20				15 30	←							16 15		16 58						17 34	17 49
Bristol Temple Meads 10	d	14 52		15 00		15 45		16 00	15 45	16 04		16 30		16 52		17 00		17 30				17 47		18 05	18 30
Bristol Parkway 7	a					→																			
	d																								
Bath Spa 7	d			15 13				16 13		16 20		16 43				17 13		17 43						18 18	18 43
Chippenham	d			15 25				16 25				16 55				17 25	17 31	17 55						18 31	18 55
Birmingham New Street 12	d				14c10								14 30							16c10					
Cheltenham Spa	d				14 58								15 15							17 04	17 44				
Gloucester 7	d				15 22								16 22							17 22					
Stonehouse	d				15 36								16 36							17 36					
Stroud	d				15 42								16 42							17 42					
Kemble	d				15 57								16 57							17 57					
Swindon	a			15 40	16 10			16 40				17 10	17 10			17 40	17 48	18 10		18 10	18 25			18 46	19 10
	d			15 41	16 11			16 41				17 11	17 15			17 41		18 11		18 15	18 27			18 47	19 11
Didcot Parkway	a			15 58	16 28			16 58				17 28	17 34			17 58		18 29		18 34	18 44			19 04	19 28
Oxford	a				17b15								18b15							19b15					
Reading 7	a	15 49		16 13	16 44			17 13	17 23			17 43	17 50	17 55		18 14		18 44		18 50	18 59	19 25		19 20	19 44
Gatwick Airport 10	a				18 30								19 30							20 30					
Heathrow Terminal 1 Bus	a			17 25	17 55				18 25				18 55			19 25				19 55				20 25	
Slough 3	a			16 44	17 18			17 40				18 18				18 44				19 16	19 16				20 18
London Waterloo 15	⊖ a									18 58															
London Paddington 15	⊖ a	16 31		16 53	17 22			17 52	18 09			18 21	18 35	18 39		18 56		19 23		19 30	19 39	20 09		20 03	20 23

For general notes see front of timetable
For details of catering facilities see Directory of Train Operators

- **A** From Plymouth (Table 135)
- **B** From Paignton (Table 135)
- **b** By bus
- **c** Change at Cheltenham Spa and Gloucester

Sundays

from 30 March

South Wales, Weston-super-Mare, Bristol, Cheltenham Spa and Swindon → Oxford and London

Route Diagram - see first page of Table 125

		GW	GW	GW		GW	GW	GW		GW	GW			GW	GW	GW		GW	GW	GW
		1 ◇	1 ◇	1 ◇		1 ◇	1 ◇	1 ◇			1 ◇			1 ◇	1 ◇	1 ◇		1 ◇	1 ◇	1 ◇
		A					B									A			A	C
		☕	☕	☕		☕	☕	☕			☕			☕	☕	☕		☕	☕	☕
Swansea 7	d	16 29				17 29										18 29			19 59	
Neath	d	16 41				17 41										18 41			20 11	
Port Talbot Parkway	d	16 48				17 48										18 48			20 18	
Bridgend	d	17 00				18 00										19 00			20 30	
Cardiff Central 7	d	17 25				18 25										19 25			20 55	
Hereford 7	d	15b25									18 30					17b15			19b30	
Newport (South Wales)	d	17 39				18 39										19 39			21 09	
Weston-super-Mare	d			18 16			18 54											20 38		21 19
Bristol Temple Meads 10	d		18 54	19 00			19 30							20 00	20 24			21 00		22 05
Bristol Parkway 7	a																			
	d																			
Bath Spa 7	d			19 13			19 43							20 13				21 14		22 18
Chippenham	d			19 25			19 55			20 04				20 25				21 27		22 30
Birmingham New Street 12	d	16 30				17 40										18 30			20 30	
Cheltenham Spa	d	17 15				18 26					19 43					19 15			21 14	
Gloucester 7	d	18 22				19 22										20 22			21 52	
Stonehouse	d	18 36				19 36										20 36			22 06	
Stroud	d	18 42				19 42										20 42			22 12	
Kemble	d	18 57				19 57										20 57			22 26	
Swindon	a	19 10		19 40		20 09	20 10	←		20 20	20 32			20 40		21 10		21 41	22 40	22 49
	d	19 15		19 41		20 13	20 11	20 13			20 34			20 41		21 11		21 42	22 45	22 52
Didcot Parkway	a	19 33		19 58		→		20 33						20 58		21 29		22 00	23 04	
Oxford	a	20b15						21b15								22b15		23b15	00b27	
Reading 7	a	19 49	19 54	20 13			20 41	20 49			21 02			21 17	21 20	21 52		22 16	23 20	23 28
Gatwick Airport 10	a	21 30						22 31								23 30				01 17
Heathrow Terminal 1 Bus	🚌 a	21 05		21 35				21 55							22 45			23 45		
Slough 3	a			20 43				21 17			21 18				22 11			22 50		00 05
London Waterloo 15	⊖ a																			
London Paddington 15	⊖ a	20 29	20 39	20 56			21 25	21 29			21 44			22 05	22 17	22 30		23 09	00 10	00 11

For general notes see front of timetable
For details of catering facilities see Directory of Train Operators

A From Carmarthen (Table 128)
B From Taunton (Table 134)
C From Plymouth (Table 135)

b By bus

Reading → Heathrow Railair Link

Express Coach Service

Sunday service operates on Bank Holiday Mondays.

		GW	GW	GW	GW	GW	GW	GW	GW	GW	GW	GW	GW	GW	GW	GW	GW	GW	GW	GW	GW	GW	GW	GW	GW	GW
Reading	d	04 00	05 00	05 30	06 00	06 20	06 40	07 00	07 20	07 40	08 00	08 20	08 40	09 05	09 25	09 45	10 05	10 25	10 45	11 05	11 25	11 45	12 05	12 25	12 45	13 05
Heathrow Terminal 1 Bus	a	04 40	05 40	06 10	06 40	07 17	07 37	07 57	08 17	08 37	08 57	09 17	09 37	09 45	10 05	10 25	10 45	11 05	11 25	11 45	12 05	12 25	12 45	13 05	13 25	13 45
Heathrow Terminal 2 Bus	a	04 42	05 42	06 12	06 42	07 19	07 39	07 59	08 19	08 39	08 59	09 19	09 39	09 47	10 07	10 27	10 47	11 07	11 27	11 47	12 07	12 27	12 47	13 07	13 27	13 47
Heathrow Terminal 3 Bus	a	04 45	05 45	06 15	06 45	07 22	07 42	08 02	08 22	08 42	09 02	09 22	09 42	09 50	10 10	10 30	10 50	11 10	11 30	11 50	12 10	12 30	12 50	13 10	13 30	13 50

		GW	GW	GW	GW	GW	GW	GW	GW	GW	GW	GW	GW	GW	GW	GW	GW	GW	GW	GW	GW	GW	GW	GW		
Reading	d	13 25	13 45	14 05	14 25	14 45	15 05	15 25	15 45	16 05	16 25	16 45	17 05	17 25	17 45	18 05	18 35	19 05	19 35	20 05	20 35	21 05	22 05	23 05	.....	.....
Heathrow Terminal 1 Bus	a	14 05	14 25	14 45	15 05	15 25	15 45	16 05	16 25	16 45	17 05	17 25	17 45	18 05	18 25	18 45	19 15	19 45	20 15	20 45	21 15	21 45	22 45	23 45	.	.
Heathrow Terminal 2 Bus	a	14 07	14 27	14 47	15 07	15 27	15 47	16 07	16 27	16 47	17 07	17 27	17 47	18 07	18 27	18 47	19 17	19 47	20 17	20 47	21 17	21 47	22 47	23 47	.....	.....
Heathrow Terminal 3 Bus	a	14 10	14 30	14 50	15 10	15 30	15 50	16 10	16 30	16 50	17 10	17 30	17 50	18 10	18 30	18 50	19 20	19 50	20 20	20 50	21 20	21 50	22 50	23 50	.	.

Saturdays

		GW	GW		GW	GW		GW	GW		GW	GW		GW	GW		GW	GW		GW	GW		GW	GW		GW
Reading	d	04 00	05 15	.....	05 45	06 15	.....	06 45	07 15	.....	07 45	08 15	.....	08 45	09 15	.....	09 45	10 15	.....	10 45	11 15	.....	11 45	12 15	.....	12 45
Heathrow Terminal 1 Bus	a	04 40	05 55	.	06 25	06 55	.	07 25	07 55	.	08 25	08 55	.	09 25	09 55	.	10 25	10 55	.	11 25	11 55	.	12 25	12 55	.	13 25
Heathrow Terminal 2 Bus	a	04 42	05 57	.....	06 27	06 57	.....	07 27	07 57	.....	08 27	08 57	.	09 27	09 57	.....	10 27	10 57	.....	11 27	11 57	.	12 27	12 57	.....	13 27
Heathrow Terminal 3 Bus	a	04 45	06 00	.....	06 30	07 00	.....	07 30	08 00	.	08 30	09 00	.	09 30	10 00	.	10 30	11 00	.	11 30	12 00	.	12 30	13 00	.	13 30

		GW	GW		GW	GW		GW	GW		GW	GW		GW	GW		GW	GW	GW	GW	GW	GW	GW	GW		
Reading	d	13 15	13 45	.....	14 15	14 45	.....	15 15	15 45	.....	16 15	16 45	.....	17 15	17 45	.....	18 15	18 45	19 15	19 45	20 25	20 55	22 05	23 05	.....	.....
Heathrow Terminal 1 Bus	a	13 55	14 25	.	14 55	15 25	.	15 55	16 25	.	16 55	17 25	.	17 55	18 25	.	18 55	19 25	19 55	20 25	21 05	21 35	22 45	23 45	.	.
Heathrow Terminal 2 Bus	a	13 57	14 27	.....	14 57	15 27	.....	15 57	16 27	.....	16 57	17 27	.....	17 57	18 27	.....	18 57	19 27	19 57	20 27	21 07	21 37	22 47	23 47	.....	.....
Heathrow Terminal 3 Bus	a	14 00	14 30	.	15 00	15 30	.	16 00	16 30	.....	17 00	17 30	.....	18 00	18 30	.....	19 00	19 30	20 00	20 30	21 10	21 40	22 50	23 50	.	.

Sundays

Also Bank Holiday Mondays.

		GW	GW	GW		GW	GW	GW		GW	GW	GW		GW	GW	GW		GW	GW	GW		GW	GW	GW		GW
Reading	d	04 00	05 15	05 45	.....	06 15	06 45	07 15	.....	07 45	08 15	08 45	.....	09 15	09 45	10 15	.....	10 45	11 15	11 45	.....	12 15	12 45	13 15	.....	13 45
Heathrow Terminal 1 Bus	a	04 40	05 55	06 25	.	06 55	07 25	07 55	.	08 25	08 55	09 25	.	09 55	10 25	10 55	.	11 25	11 55	12 25	.	12 55	13 25	13 55	.	14 25
Heathrow Terminal 2 Bus	a	04 42	05 57	06 27	.....	06 57	07 27	07 57	.....	08 27	08 57	09 27	.....	09 57	10 27	10 57	.....	11 27	11 57	12 27	.....	12 57	13 27	13 57	.....	14 27
Heathrow Terminal 3 Bus	a	04 45	06 00	06 30	.	07 00	07 30	08 00	.	08 30	09 00	09 30	.	10 00	10 30	11 00	.	11 30	12 00	12 30	.	13 00	13 30	14 00	.	14 30

		GW	GW	GW		GW	GW	GW		GW	GW	GW		GW	GW	GW		GW	GW	GW		GW	GW			
Reading	d	14 15	14 45	15 15	.....	15 45	16 15	16 45	.....	17 15	17 45	18 15	.....	18 45	19 15	19 45	.....	20 25	20 55	21 15	.....	22 05	23 05	.....	.....	.....
Heathrow Terminal 1 Bus	a	14 55	15 25	15 55	.	16 25	16 55	17 25	.	17 55	18 25	18 55	.	19 25	19 55	20 25	.	21 05	21 35	21 55	.	22 45	23 45	.	.	.
Heathrow Terminal 2 Bus	a	14 57	15 27	15 57	.....	16 27	16 57	17 27	.....	17 57	18 27	18 57	.....	19 27	19 57	20 27	.....	21 07	21 37	21 57	.....	22 47	23 47	.....	.....	.....
Heathrow Terminal 3 Bus	a	15 00	15 30	16 00	.	16 30	17 00	17 30	.	18 00	18 30	19 00	.	19 30	20 00	20 30	.	21 10	21 40	22 00	.	22 50	23 50	.	.	.

For general notes see front of timetable
For details of catering facilities see Directory of Train Operators

Heathrow → Reading Railair Link

Express Coach Service

Sunday service operates on Bank Holiday Mondays.

		GW	GW	GW	GW	GW	GW	GW	GW	GW	GW	GW	GW	GW	GW	GW	GW	GW	GW	GW	GW	GW	GW	GW	GW	GW
Heathrow Central Bus Stn	d	05 05	06 05	06 35	07 05	07 32	07 52	08 12	08 32	08 52	09 12	09 32	09 52	10 05	10 25	10 45	11 05	11 25	11 45	12 05	12 25	12 45	13 05	13 25	13 45	14 05
Reading	a	05 48	06 48	07 18	07 48	08 28	08 48	09 08	09 21	09 41	09 55	10 15	10 35	10 48	11 08	11 28	11 48	12 08	12 28	12 48	13 08	13 28	13 48	14 08	14 28	14 48

		GW	GW	GW	GW	GW	GW	GW	GW	GW	GW	GW	GW	GW	GW	GW	GW	GW	GW	GW	GW	GW	GW	GW		
Heathrow Central Bus Stn	d	14 25	14 45	15 05	15 25	15 45	16 05	16 25	16 45	17 05	17 25	17 45	18 05	18 25	18 45	19 05	19 35	20 05	20 35	21 05	21 35	22 05	23 05	23 59	.....	.....
Reading	a	15 08	15 28	15 48	16 08	16 28	16 48	17 08	17 28	17 48	18 08	18 28	18 48	19 08	19 28	19 48	20 18	20 48	21 18	21 48	22 18	22 48	23 48	00 43	.	.

Saturdays

		GW	GW		GW	GW		GW	GW		GW	GW		GW	GW		GW	GW		GW	GW		GW	GW		GW
Heathrow Central Bus Stn	d	05 05	06 10	.....	06 40	07 10	.....	07 40	08 10	.....	08 40	09 10	.....	09 40	10 10	.....	10 40	11 10	.....	11 40	12 10	.....	12 40	13 10	.....	13 40
Reading	a	05 48	06 53	.	07 23	07 53	.	08 23	08 53	.	09 23	09 53	.	10 23	10 53	.	11 23	11 53	.	12 23	12 53	.	13 23	13 53	.	14 23

		GW	GW		GW	GW		GW	GW		GW	GW		GW	GW		GW	GW	GW	GW	GW	GW	GW	GW		
Heathrow Central Bus Stn	d	14 10	14 40	.....	15 10	15 40	.....	16 10	16 40	.....	17 10	17 40	.....	18 10	18 40	.....	19 10	19 40	20 10	20 40	21 20	22 00	23 05	23 59	.....	.....
Reading	a	14 53	15 23	.	15 53	16 23	.	16 53	17 23	.	17 53	18 23	.	18 53	19 23	.	19 53	20 23	20 53	21 23	22 03	22 43	23 48	00 43	.	.

Sundays

Also Bank Holiday Mondays.

		GW	GW	GW		GW	GW	GW		GW	GW	GW		GW	GW	GW		GW	GW	GW		GW	GW	GW		GW
Heathrow Central Bus Stn	d	05 05	06 10	06 40	.....	07 10	07 40	08 10	.....	08 40	09 10	09 40	.....	10 10	10 40	11 10	.....	11 40	12 10	12 40	.....	13 10	13 40	14 10	.....	14 40
Reading	a	05 48	06 53	07 23	.	07 53	08 23	08 53	.	09 23	09 53	10 23	.	10 53	11 23	11 53	.	12 23	12 53	13 23	.	13 53	14 23	14 53	.	15 23

		GW	GW	GW		GW	GW	GW		GW	GW	GW		GW	GW	GW		GW	GW	GW		GW	GW			
Heathrow Central Bus Stn	d	15 10	15 40	16 10	.....	16 40	17 10	17 40	.....	18 10	18 40	19 10	.....	19 40	20 10	20 40	.....	21 20	22 00	23 05	.....	23 59	23 59	.....	.....	.....
Reading	a	15 53	16 23	16 53	.	17 23	17 53	18 23	.	18 53	19 23	19 53	.	20 23	20 53	21 23	.	22 03	22 43	23 48	.	00 43	00 43	.	.	.

For general notes see front of timetable
For details of catering facilities see
Directory of Train Operators

Bristol — Bristol International Airport

Bus service

		GW	GW	GW	GW		GW	GW	GW	GW		GW	GW	GW	GW		GW	GW	GW	GW		GW	GW	GW	GW		GW
Bristol Temple Meads	d	05 25	06 10	06 25	06 40	....	06 55	07 10	07 25	07 40	....	07 55	08 10	08 25	08 40	....	08 55	09 10	09 25	09 40	....	09 55	10 10	10 25	10 40	....	10 55
Bristol Internatl Airport	a	05 50	06 35	06 50	07 05	.	07 20	07 35	07 50	08 05	.	08 20	08 35	08 50	09 05	.	09 20	09 35	09 50	10 05	.	10 20	10 35	10 50	11 05	.	11 20

		GW	GW	GW	GW		GW	GW	GW	GW		GW	GW	GW	GW		GW	GW	GW	GW		GW	GW	GW	GW		GW SX
Bristol Temple Meads	d	11 10	11 25	11 40	11 55	....	12 10	12 25	12 40	12 55	....	13 10	13 25	13 40	13 55	....	14 10	14 25	14 40	14 55	....	15 10	15 25	15 40	15 55	....	16 10
Bristol Internatl Airport	a	11 35	11 50	12 05	12 20	.	12 35	12 50	13 05	13 20	.	13 35	13 50	14 05	14 20	.	14 35	14 50	15 05	15 20	.	15 35	15 50	16 05	16 20	.	16 35

		GW	GW SX	GW	GW SX		GW	GW SX	GW	GW SX		GW	GW SX	GW	GW SX		GW	GW	GW	GW		GW	GW	GW	GW	
Bristol Temple Meads	d	16 25	16 40	16 55	17 10	....	17 25	17 40	17 55	18 10	....	18 25	18 40	18 55	19 10	....	19 25	19 55	20 25	20 55	....	21 25	21 55	22 25	22 55	....
Bristol Internatl Airport	a	16 50	17 05	17 20	17 35	.	17 50	18 05	18 20	18 35	.	18 50	19 05	19 20	19 35	.	19 50	20 20	20 50	21 20	.	21 50	22 20	22 50	23 20	.

Sundays

		GW	GW		GW	GW		GW	GW		GW	GW		GW	GW		GW	GW		GW	GW		GW	GW		GW	GW
Bristol Temple Meads	d	05 25	05 55	....	06 25	06 55	....	07 25	07 55	....	08 25	08 55	....	09 25	09 55	....	10 25	10 55	....	11 25	11 55	....	12 25	12 55	....	13 25	13 55
Bristol Internatl Airport	a	05 45	06 20	.	06 50	07 20	.	07 50	08 20	.	08 50	09 20	.	09 50	10 20	.	10 50	11 20	.	11 50	12 20	.	12 50	13 20	.	13 50	14 20

		GW	GW		GW	GW		GW	GW		GW	GW		GW	GW		GW	GW		GW	GW		GW	GW		GW	GW
Bristol Temple Meads	d	14 25	14 40	....	14 55	15 10	....	15 25	15 40	....	15 55	16 10	....	16 25	16 40	....	16 55	17 10	....	17 25	17 40	....	17 55	18 10	....	18 25	18 40
Bristol Internatl Airport	a	14 50	15 05	.	15 20	15 35	.	15 50	16 05	.	16 20	16 35	.	16 50	17 05	.	17 20	17 35	.	17 50	18 05	.	18 20	18 35	.	18 50	19 05

		GW	GW		GW	GW		GW	GW		GW	GW		GW	GW		GW	GW		GW	GW		GW	GW	GW	
Bristol Temple Meads	d	18 55	19 10	....	19 25	19 40	....	19 55	20 10	....	20 25	20 40	....	20 55	21 10	....	21 25	21 40	....	21 55	22 10	....	22 25	22 40	22 55	....
Bristol Internatl Airport	a	19 20	19 35	.	19 50	20 05	.	20 20	20 35	.	20 50	21 05	.	21 20	21 35	.	21 50	22 05	.	22 20	22 35	.	22 50	23 05	23 20	.

Mondays to Saturdays

		GW	GW	GW	GW		GW	GW	GW	GW		GW	GW	GW	GW		GW	GW	GW	GW		GW	GW	GW	GW		GW
Bristol Internatl Airport	d	06 15	06 45	07 00	07 15	....	07 30	07 45	08 00	08 15	....	08 30	08 45	09 00	09 15	....	09 30	09 45	10 00	10 15	....	10 30	10 45	11 00	11 15	....	11 30
Bristol Temple Meads	a	06 40	07 10	07 25	07 40	.	07 55	08 10	08 25	08 40	.	08 55	09 10	09 25	09 40	.	09 55	10 10	10 25	10 40	.	10 55	11 10	11 25	11 40	.	11 55

		GW	GW	GW	GW		GW	GW	GW	GW		GW	GW	GW	GW		GW	GW	GW	GW		GW	GW	GW SX	GW		GW SX
Bristol Internatl Airport	d	11 45	12 00	12 15	12 30	....	12 45	13 00	13 15	13 30	....	13 45	14 00	14 15	14 30	....	14 45	15 00	15 15	15 30	....	15 45	16 00	16 15	16 30	....	16 45
Bristol Temple Meads	a	12 10	12 25	12 40	12 55	.	13 10	13 25	13 40	13 55	.	14 10	14 25	14 40	14 55	.	15 10	15 25	15 40	15 55	.	16 10	16 25	16 40	16 55	.	17 10

		GW	GW SX	GW	GW SX		GW	GW SX	GW	GW SX		GW	GW SX	GW	GW		GW	GW	GW	GW		GW	GW	GW	GW	
Bristol Internatl Airport	d	17 00	17 15	17 30	17 45	....	18 00	18 15	18 30	18 45	....	19 00	19 15	19 30	20 00	....	20 30	21 00	21 30	22 00	....	22 15	22 45	23 15	23 45	....
Bristol Temple Meads	a	17 25	17 40	17 55	18 10	.	18 25	18 40	18 55	19 10	.	19 25	19 40	19 55	20 25	.	20 55	21 25	21 55	22 25	.	22 40	23 10	23 40	00 10	.

Sundays

		GW	GW		GW	GW		GW	GW		GW	GW		GW	GW		GW	GW		GW	GW		GW	GW		GW	GW
Bristol Internatl Airport	d	06 00	07 00	....	07 30	08 00	....	08 30	09 00	....	09 30	10 00	....	10 30	11 00	....	11 30	12 00	....	12 30	13 00	....	13 30	14 00	....	14 30	14 45
Bristol Temple Meads	a	06 25	07 25	.	07 55	08 25	.	08 55	09 25	.	09 55	10 25	.	10 55	11 25	.	11 55	12 25	.	12 55	13 25	.	13 55	14 25	.	14 55	15 10

		GW	GW		GW	GW		GW	GW		GW	GW		GW	GW		GW	GW		GW	GW		GW	GW		GW	GW
Bristol Internatl Airport	d	15 00	15 15	....	15 30	15 45	....	16 00	16 15	....	16 30	16 45	....	17 00	17 15	....	17 30	17 45	....	18 00	18 15	....	18 30	18 45	....	19 00	19 15
Bristol Temple Meads	a	15 25	15 40	.	15 55	16 10	.	16 25	16 40	.	16 55	17 10	.	17 25	17 40	.	17 55	18 10	.	18 25	18 40	.	18 55	19 10	.	19 25	19 40

		GW	GW		GW	GW		GW	GW		GW	GW		GW	GW		GW	GW		GW	GW	GW	GW	GW	GW	
Bristol Internatl Airport	d	19 30	19 45	....	20 00	20 15	....	20 30	20 45	....	21 00	21 15	....	21 30	21 45	....	22 00	22 15	....	22 30	22 45	23 00	23 15	23 30	23 45	....
Bristol Temple Meads	a	19 55	20 10	.	20 25	20 40	.	20 55	21 10	.	21 25	21 40	.	21 55	22 10	.	22 25	22 40	.	22 55	23 10	23 25	23 40	23 55	00 10	.

For general notes see front of timetable
For details of catering facilities see Directory of Train Operators

Table 125C

Mondays to Fridays

Cardiff — Cardiff International Airport
Bus Service

		GW	GW	GW	GW	GW	GW	GW	GW	GW	GW	GW	GW	GW
Cardiff Central Bus Stn	d	05 10	08 00	08 57	10 02	11 02	12 02	13 02	14 02	15 02	16 02	17 12	17 40	18 20
Cardiff International Apt	a	05 39	08 35	09 26	10 31	11 31	12 31	13 31	14 31	15 31	16 33	17 50	18 12	18 50

Saturdays

		GW	GW	GW	GW	GW	GW	GW	GW	GW	GW	GW	GW	GW
Cardiff Central Bus Stn	d	05 10	08 02	09 02	10 02	11 02	12 02	13 02	14 02	15 02	16 02	17 12	17 40	18 20
Cardiff International Apt	a	05 39	08 31	09 31	10 31	11 31	12 31	13 31	14 31	15 31	16 31	17 41	18 12	18 49

Sundays

		GW	GW	GW	GW	GW	GW	GW
Cardiff Central Bus Stn	d	08 30	10 02	12 02	14 02	16 02	18 02	19 15
Cardiff International Apt	a	08 59	10 31	12 31	14 31	16 31	18 31	19 44

Mondays to Fridays

		GW	GW	GW	GW	GW	GW	GW	GW	GW	GW	GW	GW	GW	GW	GW
Cardiff International Apt	d	07 16	07 51	09 35	10 35	11 05	11 35	12 35	13 35	14 35	15 05	15 35	16 40	17 41	18 51	20 25
Cardiff Central Bus Stn	a	07 50	08 32	10 06	11 06	11 36	12 06	13 06	14 06	15 06	15 36	16 06	17 16	18 12	19 21	20 55

Saturdays

		GW	GW	GW	GW	GW	GW	GW	GW	GW	GW	GW	GW	GW
Cardiff International Apt	d	07 25	08 00	09 35	10 35	11 35	12 35	13 35	14 35	15 35	16 40	17 40	18 51	20 25
Cardiff Central Bus Stn	a	07 56	08 31	10 06	11 06	12 06	13 06	14 06	15 06	16 06	17 11	18 11	19 23	20 55

Sundays

		GW	GW	GW	GW	GW	GW	GW
Cardiff International Apt	d	09 05	10 40	12 40	14 40	16 40	18 40	20 25
Cardiff Central Bus Stn	a	09 35	11 10	13 10	15 10	17 10	19 10	21 01

For general notes see front of timetable
For details of catering facilities see Directory of Train Operators

London and Oxford → Worcester and Hereford

Network Diagram - see first page of Table 116

Mondays to Fridays

Miles	Station		GW 1	GW 1 ◇	GW 1	GW 1 ◇	GW 1 ◇	GW 1 ◇	GW 1 ◇	GW 1 ◇	GW 1 ◇	GW 1	GW 1 ◇	GW 1 ◇	GW 1 ◇	GW 1 ◇	GW 1 ◇	GW 1 ◇
															A			
				🛒		🛒	🛒	🛒	🛒	🛒	🛒		☕	🛒	☕	🛒		
0	**London Paddington** 15 ⊖	d		05 42	06 30	07 51	08 51	09 51	11 51	13 51	15 51		17 21	17 51	18 21	19 21	20 19	21 48
18½	Slough 3	d		06 03	07 01	08 07	09 07	10 07	12 07	14 07	16 07					19 37	20 36	22 05
36	Reading 7	d		06 20	07 23	08 23	09 23	10 23	12 23	14 23	16 23		17 50	18 21	18 50	19 53	20 53	22 21
53¼	Didcot Parkway	d		06 37	07 48													
63½	**Oxford**	d		06 55	08 02	08 49	09 56	10 49	12 56	14 49	16 49	17 31	18 16	18 55	19 19	20 21	21 19	22 52
70¼	Hanborough	d		07 05	08 13	08 59	10 06	10 59	13 06	14 59	16 59	17 40	18 27	19 05		20 31	21 28	23 01
71½	Combe	d										17x42						
75	Finstock	d										17x48						
76¾	Charlbury	d		07 13	08 21	09 07	10 14	11 07	13 14	15 07	17 07	17 52	18 35	19 14	19 33	20 39	21 36	23 09
80¼	Ascott-under-Wychwood	d										17x57						
81¾	Shipton	d										18x00		19x20				23x14
84¾	Kingham	d		07 22	08 30	09 16	10 23	11 16	13 23	15 16	17 16	18 05	18 45	19 26	19 46	20 48	21 45	23 19
91¾	Moreton-in-Marsh	a		07 30	08 37	09 24	10 31	11 24	13 31	15 24	17 24	18 14	18 53	19 37	19 54	20 56	21 52	23 28
—		d		07 31	08 38	09 25	10 32	11 25	13 32	15 25	17 25	18 15	18 54	19 37	19 58	20 57	21 53	23 28
101¾	Honeybourne	d		07 42	08 49	09 36	10 43	11 36	13 43	15 36	17 36	18 26	19 05		20 09	21 08	22 04	23 39
106¾	Evesham	a		07 50	08 56	09 44	10 51	11 44	13 51	15 44	17 44	18 33	19 13	19 54	20 17	21 16	22 11	23 47
—		d	06 11	07 56	09 02	09 56	10 52	11 56	13 52	15 45	17 46	18 42	19 21	19 56	20 19	21 23	22 12	23 47
112¾	Pershore	d	06 18	08 03	09 09	10 03	10 59	12 04	13 59	15 52	17 53	18 49	19 28	20 03	20 26	21 30	22 19	23 55
120½	**Worcester Shrub Hill** 7	a	06 29	08 15	09 21	10 22	11 11	12 20	14 11	16 14	18 09	19 10	19 44	20 22	20 39	21 41	22 31	00 07
121¼	**Worcester Foregate Street** 7	a	06 39	08 20	09 26	10 26	11 16	12 26	14 15	16 18		19 15	19 48		20 42	21 57	22 33	
128	Malvern Link	a				10 35	11 25		14 24	16 27			19 57		20 52	22 09	22 43	
128¾	Great Malvern	a				10 42	11 29		14 28	16 34			20 01		20 56	22 13	22 48	
131¾	Colwall	a					11 34		14 33				20 07		21 02			
136	Ledbury	a					11 42		14 41				20 15		21 10			
149¾	**Hereford** 7	a					12 05		15 04				20 36		21 31			

Saturdays

Station		GW 1 ◇	GW 1 ◇	GW 1 ◇	GW 1 ◇	GW 1 ◇	GW 1 ◇	GW 1 ◇	GW 1 ◇	GW 1 ◇	GW 1 ◇	GW 1 ◇	GW 1 ◇	GW 1 ◇	GW 1 ◇	GW 1 ◇	GW 1 ◇	GW 1 ◇	GW 1 ◇
						B	C	B	C	B	C	B	C						
		☕	☕	☕	☕	☕	☕	☕	☕	☕	☕	☕	☕	☕	☕	☕	☕		
London Paddington 15 ⊖	d	05 42	06 51	07 51	08 51	09 51	09 51	10 51	10 51	11 51	11 51	13 51	13 51	14 51	15 51	16 51	18 21	19 51	21 51
Slough 3	d	05 57	07 07	08 07	09 07	10 07	10 07	11 07	11 07	12 07	12 07	14 07	14 07	15 07	16 07	17 07	18 37	20 07	22 08
Reading 7	d	06 14	07 23	08 23	09 23	10 23	10 23	11 23	11 23	12 23	12 23	14 23	14 23	15 23	16 23	17 23	18 53	20 23	22 23
Didcot Parkway	d	06 29					10 39		11 38		12 39		14 39						
Oxford	d	06 48	07 48	08 48	09 48	10 48	10 52	11 48	11 52	12 48	12 52	14 48	14 52	15 48	16 48	17 48	19 19	20 49	22 48
Hanborough	d	06 58	07 59	08 59	09 59	10 59	11 03	11 59	12 02	12 59	13 03	14 59	15 03	15 59	16 59	17 58	19 30	20 58	22 57
Combe	d																		
Finstock	d																		
Charlbury	d	07 06	08 07	09 07	10 07	11 07	11 11	12 07	12 11	13 07	13 11	15 07	15 11	16 07	17 07	18 07	19 38	21 06	23 05
Ascott-under-Wychwood	d																		
Shipton	d											15x14	15x18			18x14		21x11	23x10
Kingham	d	07 16	08 17	09 17	10 17	11 17	11 21	12 17	12 21	13 17	13 21	15 20	15 24	16 17	17 17	18 20	19 48	21 16	23 15
Moreton-in-Marsh	a	07 24	08 25	09 25	10 25	11 25	11 29	12 25	12 29	13 25	13 29	15 28	15 32	16 25	17 25	18 28	19 56	21 24	23 23
	d	07 24	08 27	09 27	10 27	11 27	11 31	12 27	12 30	13 27	13 31	15 29	15 33	16 27	17 27	18 29	19 58	21 24	23 23
Honeybourne	d	07 35	08 38	09 38	10 38	11 38	11 42	12 38	12 41	13 38	13 42	15 40	15 44	16 38	17 38	18 40	20 09	21 35	23 34
Evesham	a	07 46	08 45	09 45	10 45	11 45	11 49	12 45	12 49	13 45	13 49	15 48	15 52	16 45	17 45	18 47	20 16	21 43	23 41
	d	07 58	08 48	09 57	10 47	11 48	11 52	12 48	12 51	13 48	13 52	15 57	16 01	16 48	17 48	18 50	20 19	21 45	23 43
Pershore	d	08 06	08 55	10 04	10 54	11 55	11 59	12 55	12 59	13 55	13 59	16 04	16 08	16 55	17 55	18 57	20 26	21 53	23 51
Worcester Shrub Hill 7	a	08 20	09 07	10 22	11 06	12 06	12 10	13 07	13 10	14 06	14 10	16 22	16 22	17 07	18 07	19 14	20 38	22 04	00 02
Worcester Foregate Street 7	a	08 26	09 11	10 26	11 11	12 10	12 14	13 11	13 14	14 10	14 14	16 26	16 26	17 11	18 11	19 18	20 46	22 08	
Malvern Link	a		09 20	10 36	11 20							16 35	16 35	17 20	18 20	19 28	20 55	22 17	
Great Malvern	a	08 37	09 25	10 39	11 24	12 21	12 25			14 21	14 25	16 39	16 39	17 25	18 25	19 32	20 59	22 21	
Colwall	a					12 27	12 31			14 27	14 31					19 38	21 05		
Ledbury	a					12 34	12 38			14 34	14 38					19 45	21 13		
Hereford 7	a					12 53	12 57			14 53	14 57					20 02	21 32		

For general notes see front of timetable
For details of catering facilities see Directory of Train Operators

A **The Cathedrals Express**
B Until 26 January and from 29 March
C 2 February to 22 March

Table 126

Sundays

until 27 January

London and Oxford → Worcester and Hereford

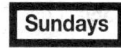

Network Diagram - see first page of Table 116

		GW 1◇ ☕	GW 1◇ ☕	GW 1◇ ☕	GW 1◇ ☕	GW 1◇ ☕	GW 1◇ ☕	GW 1◇ ☕	GW 1◇ ☕	GW 1◇ ☕	GW 1◇ ☕	GW 1◇ ☕	GW 1◇ ☕
London Paddington 15 ⊖	d	08 03	09 35	10 42	12 42	13 42	14 42	15 42	16 42	17 42	18 42	19 42	21 42
Slough 3	d	08 25	09 53	10 58	12 58	13 58	14 58	15 58	16 58	17 58	18 58	19 57	21 59
Reading 7	d	08 46	10 13	11 20	13 20	14 20	15 20	16 20	17 20	18 20	19 20	20 20	22 20
Didcot Parkway	d	09 00	10 30	11 36	13 37	14 36	15 36	16 36	17 36	18 36	19 36	20 35	22 38
Oxford	d	09 15	10 45	11 50	13 50	14 50	15 50	16 50	17 50	18 50	19 50	20 50	22 50
Hanborough	d	09 26	10 55	12 00	14 01		16 00		18 00	19 00	20 01	20 59	23 02
Combe	d												
Finstock	d												
Charlbury	d	09 33	11 03	12 09	14 09	15 04	16 08	17 04	18 09	19 09	20 10	21 07	23 10
Ascott-under-Wychwood	d												
Shipton	d												
Kingham	d	09 42	11 13	12 19	14 19	15 15	16 18	17 14	18 19	19 19	20 20	21 16	23 19
Moreton-in-Marsh	a	09 50	11 21	12 27	14 27	15 23	16 26	17 22	18 27	19 27	20 28	21 23	23 26
	d	09 56	11 23	12 28	14 29	15 24	16 28	17 24	18 28	19 28	20 29	21 24	23 27
Honeybourne	d	10 07	11 34	12 39		15 35	16 39	17 35	18 39	19 39	20 40	21 35	23 38
Evesham	a	10 13	11 41	12 47	14 45	15 44	16 46	17 44	18 47	19 47	20 48	21 41	23 44
	d	10 15	11 44	12 48	14 47	15 48	16 49	17 49	18 49	19 49	20 50	21 49	23 46
Pershore	d	10 22	11 51	12 56	14 55	15 55	16 56	17 56	18 57	19 57	20 58	21 56	23 53
Worcester Shrub Hill 7	a	10 33	12 03	13 07	15 06	16 07	17 08	18 08	19 08	20 06	21 09	22 07	00 04
Worcester Foregate Street 7	a	10 37	12 07	13 11	15 10		17 12		19 12	20 12	21 13	22 11	
Malvern Link	a	10 47	12 17	13 21			17 21		19 22	20 22	21 23	22 20	
Great Malvern	a	10 50	12 20	13 25	15 21		17 25		19 26	20 26	21 27	22 28	
Colwall	a		12 27	13 31			17 32				21 33		
Ledbury	a		12 34	13 39	15 32		17 39				21 40		
Hereford 7	a		12 54	14 04	15 51		17 58				21 59		

Sundays

3 February to 23 March

		GW 1◇ ☕	GW 1◇ ☕	GW 1◇ ☕	GW 1◇ ☕	GW 1◇ ☕	GW 1◇ ☕	GW 1◇ ☕	GW 1◇ ☕	GW 1◇ ☕	GW 1◇ ☕	GW 1◇ ☕	GW 1◇ ☕
London Paddington 15 ⊖	d	08 03	09 30	10 42	12 42	13 42	14 42	15 42	16 42	17 42	18 42	19 42	21 42
Slough 3	d	08 25	09 52	11 01	13 01	14 01	15 01	16 01	17 01	18 00	19 00	19 59	21 59
Reading 7	d	08 44	10 09	11 20	13 21	14 20	15 20	16 20	17 20	18 20	19 20	20 20	22 19
Didcot Parkway	d	09 05	10 28	11 36	13 37	14 36	15 35	16 36	17 36	18 36	19 36	20 35	22 39
Oxford	d	09 15	10 45	11 50	13 50	14 50	15 50	16 50	17 50	18 50	19 50	20 50	22 50
Hanborough	d	09 26	10 55	12 00	14 01		16 00		18 00	19 00	20 00	20 59	23 02
Combe	d												
Finstock	d												
Charlbury	d	09 33	11 03	12 09	14 09	15 04	16 08	17 04	18 09	19 09	20 09	21 07	23 10
Ascott-under-Wychwood	d												
Shipton	d												
Kingham	d	09 42	11 13	12 19	14 19	15 15	16 18	17 14	18 19	19 19	20 19	21 16	23 19
Moreton-in-Marsh	a	09 50	11 21	12 27	14 27	15 23	16 26	17 22	18 27	19 27	20 27	21 23	23 26
	d	09 56	11 23	12 28	14 29	15 24	16 28	17 24	18 28	19 28	20 28	21 24	23 27
Honeybourne	d	10 07	11 34	12 39		15 35	16 39	17 35	18 39	19 39	20 39	21 34	23 38
Evesham	a	10 13	11 41	12 47	14 45	15 44	16 46	17 44	18 47	19 47	20 47	21 41	23 44
	d	10 15	11 44	12 48	14 47	15 48	16 49	17 49	18 49	19 49	20 49	21 51	23 46
Pershore	d	10 22	11 51	12 56	14 55	15 55	16 56	17 56	18 57	19 57	20 57	21 58	23 53
Worcester Shrub Hill 7	a	10 33	12 03	13 07	15 06	16 07	17 08	18 08	19 08	20 08	21 07	22 09	00 04
Worcester Foregate Street 7	a	10 37	12 07	13 11	15 10		17 12		19 12	20 12	21 12	22 13	
Malvern Link	a	10 47	12 17	13 21			17 21		19 22	20 22	21 22	22 22	
Great Malvern	a	10 50	12 20	13 25	15 21		17 25		19 26	20 25	21 26	22 25	
Colwall	a		12 27	13 31			17 32				21 32		
Ledbury	a		12 34	13 39	15 32		17 39				21 39		
Hereford 7	a		12 54	14 04	15 50		17 58				21 58		

For general notes see front of timetable
For details of catering facilities see
Directory of Train Operators

Table 126

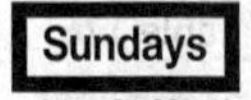

from 30 March

London and Oxford → Worcester and Hereford

Network Diagram - see first page of Table 116

		GW	GW	GW	GW	GW	GW	GW	GW	GW	GW	GW	GW	GW
		1 ◇ ☕	1 ◇ ☕	1 ◇ ☕	1 ◇ ☕	1 ◇ ☕	1 ◇ ☕	1 ◇ ☕	1 ◇ ☕	1 ◇ ☕	1 ◇ ☕	1 ◇ ☕	1 ◇ ☕	1 ◇ ☕
London Paddington 15 ⊖	d											18 42		
Slough 3	d											19 02		
Reading 7	d											19 21		
Didcot Parkway	d											19 36		
Oxford	d	09 15	10 45	11 50	13 50	14 50	15 50	16 50	17 50	18 50	19 50		20 50	22 50
Hanborough	d	09 26	10 55	12 00	14 01		16 00		18 00	18 59	20 01		20 59	23 02
Combe	d													
Finstock	d													
Charlbury	d	09 33	11 03	12 09	14 09	15 04	16 08	17 04	18 08	19 08	20 08		21 08	23 10
Ascott-under-Wychwood	d													
Shipton	d													
Kingham	d	09 42	11 13	12 19	14 19	15 15	16 17	17 14	18 17	19 17	20 17		21 16	23 19
Moreton-in-Marsh	a	09 50	11 21	12 27	14 27	15 23	16 24	17 21	18 24	19 24	20 25		21 23	23 26
	d	09 57	11 22	12 28	14 29	15 24	16 25	17 22	18 25	19 24	20 25		21 24	23 27
Honeybourne	d	10 08	11 33	12 39		15 35	16 36	17 33	18 36	19 36	20 36		21 34	23 38
Evesham	a	10 14	11 41	12 47	14 45	15 44	16 43	17 40	18 43	19 43	20 44		21 42	23 44
	d	10 16	11 44	12 48	14 47	15 48	16 46	17 45	18 46	19 48	20 49		21 45	23 46
Pershore	d	10 23	11 51	12 56	14 55	15 55	16 53	17 52	18 54	19 56	20 57		21 53	23 53
Worcester Shrub Hill 7	a	10 34	12 03	13 07	15 06	16 07	17 04	18 04	19 05	20 06	21 07	21 38	22 05	00 04
Worcester Foregate Street 7	a	10 37	12 07	13 11	15 10		17 09		19 09	20 11	21 11	21 50	22 09	
Malvern Link	a	10 47	12 17	13 21			17 19		19 18	20 21		22 01	22 18	
Great Malvern	a	10 50	12 20	13 25	15 21		17 22		19 22	20 25		22 05	22 21	
Colwall	a		12 27	13 31								22 13		
Ledbury	a		12 34	13 39								22 20		
Hereford 7	a		12 54	14 04								22 40		

For general notes see front of timetable
For details of catering facilities see Directory of Train Operators

Hereford and Worcester → Oxford and London

Network Diagram - see first page of Table 116

Mondays to Fridays

Miles	Station		GW	GW	GW	GW	GW	GW	GW	GW	GW	GW	GW	GW	GW	GW	GW	GW	GW	GW
																FO	FX	FO	FX
			1 ◇	1 ◇	1 ◇	1	1 ◇	1 ◇	1 ◇	1 ◇	1 ◇	1 ◇	1 ◇	1 ◇	1 ◇	1	1 ◇	1 ◇	1 ◇	1 ◇
					A		B C											D		
			⌶		⊠		⊠	⌶		⌶	⌶	⌶	⌶	⌶	⌶		⌶	⊡ ⌶	⌶	
0	**Hereford 7**	d			05 42		06 43					13 23	15 19							
13¾	Ledbury	d			06 00		07 00					13 41	15 36							
18	Colwall	d			06 07		07 08					13 48	15 43							
20¾	Great Malvern	d		05 31	06 13		07 15			11 06		13 53	15 51	17 06					22 33	22 33
21¾	Malvern Link	d		05 34	06 17		07 19			11 10		13 57	15 55	17 10						
28½	**Worcester Foregate Street 7**	d		05 42	06 28	06 52	07 29	08 37	09 37	11 26	12 40	14 08	16 06	17 21	18 50	19 27	20 58	20 58	22 45	22 45
29¼	**Worcester Shrub Hill 7**	d		05 46	06 32	06 55	07 34	08 41	09 40	11 31	12 44	14 14	16 10	17 25	18 54	19 30	21 02	21 02	22 49	22 49
37	Pershore	d		05 55	06 41	07 05	07 43	08 50	09 49	11 40	12 53	14 22	16 25	17 34	19 09	19 45	21 11	21 11	22 58	22 58
43	Evesham	a		06 02	06 49	07 12	07 52	08 58	09 56	11 48	13 01	14 30	16 33	17 42	19 17	19 52	21 19	21 19	23 06	23 06
—		d		06 03	06 49	07 12	07 54	09 00	09 58	11 49	13 02	14 44	16 35	17 48	19 19	20 21	21 21	21 21	23 07	23 07
48	Honeybourne	d		06 09	06 56		08 01	09 06	10 04	11 56	13 08	14 51	16 41	17 54		20 28	21 27	21 27	23 13	23 14
58	Moreton-in-Marsh	a		06 22	07 09	07 28	08 13	09 19	10 17	12 08	13 21	15 03	16 54	18 07	19 35	20 40	21 40	21 40	23 26	23 26
—		d	05 50	06 22	07 09	07 29	08 14	09 19	10 18	12 13	13 21	15 16	16 56	18 20	19 35	20 41	21 40	21 40	23 26	23 26
65	Kingham	d	05 58	06 30	07 18	07 36	08 23	09 29	10 25	12 21	13 30	15 25	17 05	18 28	19 44	20 19	21 49	21 49	23 35	23 36
68	Shipton	d	06x02			07x41								18x33						
69¼	Ascott-under-Wychwood	d				07x44														
73	Charlbury	d	06 10	06 39	07 29	07 50	08 33	09 38	10 34	12 31	13 40	15 35	17 18	18 46	19 54	20 58	21 59	21 59	23 45	23 46
74¾	Finstock	d				07x52														
78¼	Combe	d				07x56														
79¼	Hanborough	d	06 17	06 46	07 37	08 00		09 45	10 41	12 39	13 47	15 43	17 25		20 01	21 05	22 08	22 06		
86½	**Oxford**	a	06 28	06 55	07 48	08 12	08 48	09 58	10 58	12 58	13 58	15 58	17 36	18 58	20 23	21 19	22 19	22 19	23 59	23 59
96½	Didcot Parkway	a	06 42	07 09															00 18	00 18
113¾	Reading 7	a	06 57	07 25	08 22		09 14	10 24	11 25	13 25	14 25	16 25	18 03	19 26	20 55		22 45	22 45	00 28	00 36
131½	Slough 3	a						10 38		13 40	14 40			19 40	21 09		23 00	23 04	00 42	00 55
149¾	**London Paddington 15**	⊖ a	07 29	07 58	08 51		09 47	10 59	11 58	13 58	14 59	16 59	18 31	19 59	21 27		23 22	23 25	01 00	01 16

Saturdays

Station		GW	GW	GW	GW	GW	GW	GW	GW	GW	GW	GW	GW	GW
		1 ◇	1 ◇	1 ◇	1 ◇	1 ◇	1 ◇	1 ◇	1 ◇	1 ◇	1 ◇	1 ◇	1 ◇	1 ◇
		E	G	G	E	G	E	G	E	G	E	G	E	G
				⊡	⊡	⊡	⊡	⊡	⊡	⊡		⊡	⊡	⊡
Hereford 7	d					07 22	07 22							
Ledbury	d					07 40	07 40							
Colwall	d					07 47	07 47							
Great Malvern	d	06 03	06 03	07 08	07 08	07 52	07 52	09 08	09 08	09 48	09 48	11 05	11 05	11 45
Malvern Link	d	06 06	06 06	07 12	07 12	07 56	07 56	09 12	09 12	09 52	09 52	11 09	11 09	11 49
Worcester Foregate Street 7	d	06 19	06 19	07 23	07 23	08 07	08 01	09 21	09 21	10 03	10 03	11 22	11 22	12 00
Worcester Shrub Hill 7	d	06 23	06 23	07 27	07 27	08 17	08 17	09 27	09 27	10 27	10 27	11 26	11 26	12 24
Pershore	d	06 32	06 32	07 36	07 36	08 31	08 31	09 36	09 36	10 36	10 36	11 35	11 35	12 33
Evesham	a	06 39	06 39	07 44	07 44	08 39	08 39	09 44	09 44	10 44	10 44	11 43	11 43	12 41
	d	06 41	06 41	07 54	07 54	08 50	08 50	09 53	09 53	10 56	10 56	11 56	11 56	12 56
Honeybourne	d	06 48	06 48	08 00	08 00	08 56	08 56	10 00	10 00	11 03	11 03	12 03	12 03	13 03
Moreton-in-Marsh	a	07 00	07 00	08 12	08 12	09 08	09 08	10 11	10 11	11 14	11 14	12 14	12 14	13 14
	d	07 00	07 00	08 13	08 13	09 09	09 09	10 16	10 16	11 16	11 16	12 16	12 16	13 16
Kingham	d	07 08	07 08	08 22	08 22	09 18	09 18	10 25	10 25	11 25	11 25	12 25	12 25	13 24
Shipton	d	07 12	07x12	08x27	08 27									
Ascott-under-Wychwood	d													
Charlbury	d	07 19	07 19	08 35	08 35	09 29	09 39	10 35	10 35	11 35	11 35	12 35	12 35	13 35
Finstock	d													
Combe	d													
Hanborough	d	07 26	07 26	08 43	08 43	09 37	09 37	10 43	10 43	11 43	11 43	12 43	12 43	13 43
Oxford	a	07 36	07 36	08 58	08 58	09 55	09 54	10 58	10 58	11 58	11 58	12 58	12 58	13 58
Didcot Parkway	a	07 48			09 12		10 08		11 12		12 12		13 12	
Reading 7	a	08 06	08 08	09 26	09 28	10 21	10 23	11 25	11 28	12 25	12 28	13 27	13 27	14 25
Slough 3	a			09 41	09 42	10 36	10 38	11 40	11 42	12 40	12 42	13 41	13 42	14 40
London Paddington 15	⊖ a	08 38	08 40	09 58	10 00	10 54	10 56	11 58	12 00	12 58	13 00	13 59	14 00	14 58

Station		GW	GW	GW	GW	GW	GW	GW	GW	GW	GW	GW	GW	GW	GW
		◇ 1	1 ◇	1 ◇	1 ◇	1 ◇	1 ◇	1 ◇	1 ◇	◇ 1	1 ◇	1 ◇	1 ◇	◇ 1	1
		E	G	E	G	E	G	E	G	E	G	E	G	E	
		⊡	⊡	⊡	⊡	⊡	⊡	⊡	⊡	⊡	⊡	⊡	⊡	⊡	
Hereford 7	d				13 20	13 20	15 23	15 23							
Ledbury	d				13 39	13 39	15 40	15 40							
Colwall	d				13 46	13 46	15 47	15 47							
Great Malvern	d	11 45			14 05	14 05	15 53	15 53	17 08	17 08	18 08	18 08	18 45	18 45	22 40
Malvern Link	d	11 49			14 09	14 09	15 57	15 57	17 12	17 12	18 12	18 12	18 49	18 49	22 43
Worcester Foregate Street 7	d	12 00	13 22	13 22	14 21	14 21	16 06	16 06	17 23	17 23	18 23	18 23	19 01	19 01	22 51
Worcester Shrub Hill 7	d	12 24	13 26	13 26	14 28	14 28	16 27	16 27	17 27	17 27	18 27	18 27	19 15	19 15	22 55
Pershore	d	12 33	13 35	13 35	14 36	14 36	16 35	16 35	17 36	17 36	18 36	18 36	19 24	19 24	23 04
Evesham	a	12 41	13 43	13 43	14 44	14 44	16 43	16 43	17 44	17 44	18 44	18 44	19 32	19 32	23 12
	d	12 56	13 56	13 56	14 54	14 54	16 56	16 56	17 56	17 56	18 56	18 56	19 34	19 34	
Honeybourne	d	13 03	14 03	14 03	15 01	15 01	17 03	17 03	18 03	18 03	19 03	19 03	19 41	19 41	
Moreton-in-Marsh	a	13 14	14 14	14 14	15 12	15 12	17 14	17 14	18 14	18 14	19 14	19 14	19 52	19 52	
	d	13 16	14 16	14 16	15 14	15 14	17 16	17 16	18 16	18 16	19 26	19 26	20 16	20 16	
Kingham	d	13 24	14 25	14 25	15 23	15 23	17 25	17 25	18 25	18 25	19 35	19 35	20 25	20 25	
Shipton	d				15x28	15 28									
Ascott-under-Wychwood	d														
Charlbury	d	13 35	14 35	14 35	15 36	15 36	17 35	17 35	18 35	18 35	19 50	19 50	20 35	20 35	
Finstock	d														
Combe	d														
Hanborough	d	13 43	14 43	14 43	15 44	15 44	17 43	17 43	18 43	18 43			20 43	20 43	
Oxford	a	13 57	14 58	14 59	15 59	15 59	17 58	17 58	18 58	18 58	20 07	20 07	20 58	20 58	
Didcot Parkway	a	14 11		15 12		16 12		18 12		19 12		20 21		21 12	
Reading 7	a	14 28	15 25	15 28	16 26	16 28	18 25	18 28	19 25	19 28	20 33	20 36	21 24	21 27	
Slough 3	a	14 42	15 40	15 43	16 40	16 43	18 40	18 42	19 40	19 42	20 47	20 51	21 38	21 42	
London Paddington 15	⊖ a	15 00	15 58	16 00	16 58	17 00	18 58	19 00	19 58	20 00	21 06	21 10	21 58	22 02	

For general notes see front of timetable
For details of catering facilities see Directory of Train Operators

A All Tuesdays to Fridays, also Mondays until 24 March from Abergavenny (Table 131).
⊠ all Tuesdays to Fridays, also Mondays until 24 March.
⊠ Mondays from 31 March

B From Abergavenny (Table 131)

C **The Cathedrals Express**

D ⌶ to Reading, ⊡ from Reading

E 2 February to 22 March

G Until 26 January and from 29 March

Table 126

until 27 January

Hereford and Worcester → Oxford and London

Network Diagram - see first page of Table 116

		GW	GW	GW	GW	GW	GW	GW	GW	GW	GW	GW
		1 ◇	1 ◇	1 ◇	1 ◇	1 ◇	1 ◇	1 ◇	1 ◇	1 ◇	1 ◇	1 ◇
Hereford 7	d				13 30	14 30		16 30		18 30		
Ledbury	d				13 48	14 57		16 47		18 48		
Colwall	d				13 55	15 04		16 55		18 55		
Great Malvern	d	09 01	11 08	13 06	14 01	15 09		17 00		19 08	20 08	21 05
Malvern Link	d	09 04	11 11	13 09	14 05	15 13		17 04		19 12	20 12	21 09
Worcester Foregate Street 7	d	09 13	11 19	13 20	14 16	15 24		17 21		19 23	20 23	21 23
Worcester Shrub Hill 7	d	09 17	11 23	13 24	14 20	15 29	16 25	17 26	18 25	19 27	20 27	21 27
Pershore	d	09 26	11 32	13 34	14 29	15 37	16 34	17 34	18 34	19 36	20 36	21 36
Evesham	a	09 33	11 39	13 41	14 39	15 45	16 42	17 42	18 44	19 44	20 44	21 44
	d	09 35	11 46	13 42	14 51	15 50	16 51	17 47	18 51	19 51	20 51	21 47
Honeybourne	d	09 40	11 52	13 48	14 58	15 55	16 57	17 53	18 58	19 58	20 58	21 53
Moreton-in-Marsh	a	09 53	12 04	14 01	15 09	16 08	17 09	18 05	19 09	20 09	21 09	22 05
	d	09 53	12 05	14 01	15 11	16 09	17 09	18 06	19 11	20 11	21 11	22 06
Kingham	d	10 00	12 12	14 09	15 19	16 18	17 19	18 15	19 20	20 20	21 20	22 15
Shipton	d											
Ascott-under-Wychwood	d											
Charlbury	d	10 10	12 21	14 20	15 30	16 28	17 30	18 26	19 30	20 30	21 30	22 25
Finstock	d											
Combe	d											
Hanborough	d	10 17	12 28	14 27	15 38	16 36	17 37		19 38	20 38	21 38	
Oxford	a	10 27	12 41	14 37	15 48	16 46	17 47	18 40	19 49	20 48	21 48	22 38
Didcot Parkway	a	10 49	13 01	14 49	16 01	17 01	18 01	18 52	20 01	21 02	22 01	22 52
Reading 7	a	11 06	13 20	15 04	16 18	17 18	18 18	19 06	20 18	21 19	22 19	23 06
Slough 3	a	11 26	13 47	15 23	16 45	17 48	18 45	19 31	20 45	21 41	22 42	23 29
London Paddington 15	⊖ a	11 46	14 08	15 43	17 07	18 08	19 08	19 52	21 08	22 03	23 05	23 51

Sundays

3 February to 23 March

		GW	GW	GW	GW	GW	GW	GW	GW	GW	GW	GW
		1 ◇	1 ◇	1 ◇	1 ◇	1 ◇	1 ◇	1 ◇	1 ◇	1 ◇	1 ◇	1 ◇
Hereford 7	d				13 30	14 30		16 30		18 30		
Ledbury	d				13 48	14 57		16 47		18 48		
Colwall	d				13 55	15 04		16 55		18 55		
Great Malvern	d	09 01	11 08	13 06	14 01	15 09		17 00		19 08	20 08	21 05
Malvern Link	d	09 04	11 11	13 09	14 05	15 13		17 04		19 12	20 12	21 09
Worcester Foregate Street 7	d	09 13	11 19	13 20	14 14	15 24		17 20		19 21	20 23	21 23
Worcester Shrub Hill 7	d	09 17	11 21	13 24	14 18	15 28	16 25	17 25	18 25	19 25	20 27	21 27
Pershore	d	09 26	11 32	13 34	14 29	15 37	16 34	17 33	18 34	19 36	20 36	21 36
Evesham	a	09 33	11 39	13 41	14 37	15 45	16 42	17 41	18 42	19 44	20 44	21 44
	d	09 35	11 46	13 42	14 51	15 50	16 51	17 47	18 51	19 50	20 50	21 47
Honeybourne	d	09 40	11 52	13 48	14 58	15 55	16 56	17 53	18 58	19 57	20 58	21 53
Moreton-in-Marsh	a	09 53	12 05	14 01	15 09	16 08	17 09	18 05	19 10	20 09	21 09	22 05
	d	09 53	12 05	14 01	15 11	16 09	17 09	18 06	19 11	20 11	21 11	22 06
Kingham	d	10 00	12 12	14 09	15 19	16 18	17 18	18 15	19 20	20 20	21 20	22 15
Shipton	d											
Ascott-under-Wychwood	d											
Charlbury	d	10 10	12 21	14 20	15 30	16 28	17 29	18 26	19 29	20 30	21 30	22 25
Finstock	d											
Combe	d											
Hanborough	d	10 17	12 28	14 27	15 38	16 36	17 37		19 38	20 38	21 38	
Oxford	a	10 27	12 39	14 36	15 49	16 46	17 47	18 47	19 49	20 48	21 48	22 40
Didcot Parkway	a	10 49	13 02	14 49	16 02	17 00	18 02	19 02	20 03	21 02	22 02	22 52
Reading 7	a	11 04	13 20	15 04	16 17	17 15	18 17	19 19	20 18	21 18	22 18	23 07
Slough 3	a	11 23	13 37	15 34	16 34	17 32	18 35	19 36	20 34	21 36	22 36	23 26
London Paddington 15	⊖ a	11 51	13 57	15 56	17 01	17 58	18 59	20 02	21 00	22 00	23 00	23 51

For general notes see front of timetable
For details of catering facilities see
Directory of Train Operators

Table 126

Sundays
from 30 March

Hereford and Worcester → Oxford and London

Network Diagram - see first page of Table 116

		GW 1 ◇ trolley	GW 1 ◇ buffet	GW 1 ◇ trolley	GW 1 ◇ buffet	GW 1 ◇ buffet	GW 1 ◇ buffet	GW 1 ◇ buffet	GW 1 ◇ buffet	GW 1 ◇ buffet	GW 1 ◇ buffet	GW 1 ◇ buffet	GW 1 ◇ trolley
Hereford 7	d				13 30	14 30		16 30			18 30		
Ledbury	d				13 48	14 57		16 47			18 47		
Colwall	d				13 55	15 04		16 55			18 54		
Great Malvern	d	09 01	11 08	13 06	14 01	15 09		17 00		18 45	18 59	20 08	21 05
Malvern Link	d	09 04	11 11	13 09	14 05	15 13		17 04		18 48	19 03	20 12	21 09
Worcester Foregate Street 7	d	09 13	11 19	13 20	14 14	15 24		17 20		18 59	19 19	20 22	21 20
Worcester Shrub Hill 7	d	09 17	11 21	13 24	14 18	15 28	16 25	17 25	18 25	19 16	19 24	20 25	21 24
Pershore	d	09 26	11 32	13 34	14 30	15 38	16 34		18 34	19 27		20 34	21 33
Evesham	a	09 33	11 39	13 41	14 37	15 45	16 41		18 41	19 34		20 42	21 40
	d	09 35	11 46	13 42	14 45	15 48	16 51		18 48	19 46		20 47	21 46
Honeybourne	d	09 40	11 52	13 48	14 51	15 53	16 56		18 54	19 52		20 54	21 53
Moreton-in-Marsh	a	09 53	12 05	14 01	15 03	16 06	17 09		19 07	20 05		21 06	22 04
	d	09 53	12 05	14 01	15 04	16 07	17 09		19 07	20 06		21 07	22 05
Kingham	d	10 00	12 12	14 09	15 11	16 14	17 16		19 14	20 13		21 14	22 12
Shipton	d												
Ascott-under-Wychwood	d												
Charlbury	d	10 10	12 20	14 21	15 20	16 22	17 25		19 22	20 22		21 23	22 22
Finstock	d												
Combe	d												
Hanborough	d	10 17	12 28	14 28	15 27	16 30	17 33		19 30	20 29		21 30	
Oxford	a	10 27	12 42	14 42	15 38	16 41	17 44		19 41	20 41		21 41	22 43
Didcot Parkway	a							18 44			20 51		
Reading 7	a							18 59			21 08		
Slough 3	a							19 16			21 24		
London Paddington 15	⊖ a							19 39			21 53		

For general notes see front of timetable
For details of catering facilities see Directory of Train Operators

Table 126A

Mondays to Fridays

Kingham — Chipping Norton

Bus Service

		GW	GW	GW	GW	GW	GW	GW	GW	GW	GW	GW	GW	GW
Kingham	d	07 07	07 43	08 35	09 32	11 30	13 15	14 05	16 20	17 15	18 08	18 50	19 20	19 50
Chipping Norton West St	a	07 18	07 56	08 48	09 50	11 48	13 28	14 18	16 33	17 28	18 21	19 03	19 33	20 03

Saturdays

		GW	GW	GW	GW	GW	GW	GW	GW	GW	GW	GW
Kingham	d	08 10	09 15	10 10	11 15	12 10	13 10	15 15	16 15	17 15	18 18	19 45
Chipping Norton West St	a	08 23	09 28	10 29	11 34	12 29	13 23	15 28	16 28	17 28	18 31	19 58

Mondays to Fridays

		GW	GW	GW	GW	GW	GW	GW	GW	GW	GW	GW	GW	GW
Chipping Norton West St	d	06 52	07 20	08 00	09 00	10 48	12 35	13 35	15 55	16 40	17 35	18 25	19 05	19 35
Kingham	a	07 05	07 33	08 13	09 13	11 03	12 50	13 48	16 08	16 55	17 48	18 38	19 16	19 47

Saturdays

		GW	GW	GW	GW	GW	GW	GW	GW	GW	GW	GW
Chipping Norton West St	d	07 40	08 35	09 30	10 40	11 40	12 40	13 35	15 40	16 45	17 40	19 25
Kingham	a	07 53	08 48	09 43	10 58	11 58	12 53	13 48	15 53	16 58	17 53	19 38

For general notes see front of timetable
For details of catering facilities see
Directory of Train Operators

No Sunday Service

Route Diagram for Tables 127, 128

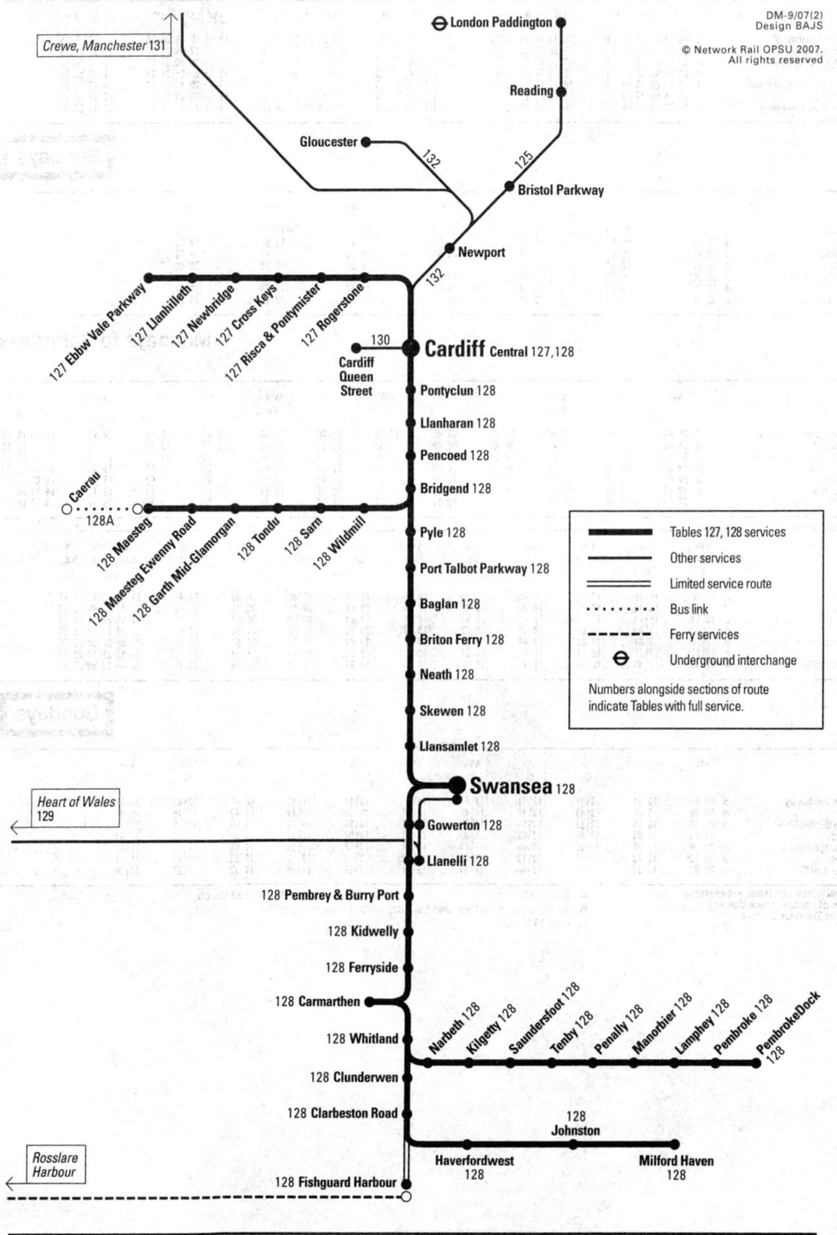

Crewe, Manchester 131
London Paddington
DM-9/07(2)
Design BAJS
© Network Rail OPSU 2007. All rights reserved
Reading
Gloucester
132
125
Bristol Parkway
Newport
132
127 Ebbw Vale Parkway
127 Llanhilleth
127 Newbridge
127 Cross Keys
127 Risca & Pontymister
127 Rogerstone
130
Cardiff Queen Street
Cardiff Central 127,128
Pontyclun 128
Llanharan 128
Pencoed 128
Bridgend 128
Caerau
128A
128 Maesteg
128 Maesteg Ewenny Road
128 Garth Mid-Glamorgan
128 Tondu
128 Sarn
128 Wildmill
Pyle 128
Port Talbot Parkway 128
Baglan 128
Briton Ferry 128
Neath 128
Skewen 128
Llansamlet 128
Swansea 128
Heart of Wales 129
Gowerton 128
Llanelli 128
128 Pembrey & Burry Port
128 Kidwelly
128 Ferryside
128 Carmarthen
128 Whitland
128 Clunderwen
128 Clarbeston Road
Narberth 128
Kilgetty 128
Saundersfoot 128
Tenby 128
Penally 128
Manorbier 128
Lamphey 128
Pembroke 128
PembrokeDock 128
128 Johnston
Haverfordwest 128
Milford Haven 128
Rosslare Harbour
128 Fishguard Harbour
Tables 127, 128 services
Other services
Limited service route
Bus link
Ferry services
Underground interchange
Numbers alongside sections of route indicate Tables with full service.

Cardiff Central — Ebbw Vale Parkway

Route Diagram - see first page of Table 127

Mondays to Saturdays

Miles	Station		AW	AW	AW	AW	AW	AW	AW	AW	AW	AW	AW	AW	AW	AW	AW	AW	AW
0	**Cardiff Central 7**	d	06 35	07 35	08 35	09 35	10 35	11 35	12 35	13 35	14 35	15 35	16 35	17 35	18 35	19 35	20 35	21 35	22 35
14	Rogerstone	d	06 56	07 56	08 56	09 56	10 56	11 56	12 56	13 56	14 56	15 56	16 56	17 56	18 56	19 56	20 56	21 56	22 56
15¼	Risca & Pontymister	d	07 00	08 00	09 00	10 00	11 00	12 00	13 00	14 00	15 00	16 00	17 00	18 00	19 00	20 00	21 00	22 00	23 00
17¼	Cross Keys	d	07 05	08 05	09 05	10 05	11 05	12 05	13 05	14 05	15 05	16 05	17 05	18 05	19 05	20 05	21 05	22 05	23 05
20¾	Newbridge (Ebbw Vale)	d	07 13	08 13	09 13	10 13	11 13	12 13	13 13	14 13	15 13	16 13	17 13	18 13	19 13	20 13	21 13	22 13	23 13
23½	Llanhilleth	d	07 19	08 19	09 19	10 19	11 19	12 19	13 19	14 19	15 19	16 19	17 19	18 19	19 19	20 19	21 19	22 19	23 19
28¾	**Ebbw Vale Parkway**	a	07 31	08 31	09 31	10 31	11 31	12 31	13 31	14 31	15 31	16 31	17 31	18 31	19 31	20 31	21 31	22 31	23 31

Sundays

Station		AW	AW	AW	AW	AW	AW	AW
Cardiff Central 7	d	07 40	09 30	11 30	13 30	15 30	17 30	19 30
Rogerstone	d	08 03	09 51	11 51	13 51	15 51	17 51	19 51
Risca & Pontymister	d	08 07	09 55	11 55	13 55	15 55	17 55	19 55
Cross Keys	d	08 12	10 00	12 00	14 00	16 00	18 00	20 00
Newbridge (Ebbw Vale)	d	08 20	10 08	12 08	14 08	16 08	18 08	20 08
Llanhilleth	d	08 26	10 14	12 14	14 14	16 14	18 14	20 14
Ebbw Vale Parkway	a	08 38	10 26	12 26	14 26	16 26	18 26	20 26

Mondays to Saturdays

Miles	Station		AW	AW SX	AW SO	AW	AW	AW	AW	AW SX	AW SO	AW	AW	AW SO	AW SX
0	**Ebbw Vale Parkway**	d	06 40	07 40	07 40	08 40	09 40	10 40	11 40	12 40	12 40	13 40	14 40	15 40	15 40
5¼	Llanhilleth	d	06 48	07 48	07 48	08 48	09 48	10 48	11 48	12 48	12 48	13 48	14 48	15 48	15 48
8	Newbridge (Ebbw Vale)	d	06 54	07 54	07 54	08 54	09 54	10 54	11 54	12 54	12 54	13 54	14 54	15 54	15 54
11½	Cross Keys	d	07 02	08 02	08 02	09 02	10 02	11 02	12 02	13 02	13 02	14 02	15 02	16 02	16 02
13½	Risca & Pontymister	d	07 07	08 07	08 07	09 07	10 07	11 07	12 07	13 07	13 07	14 07	15 07	16 07	16 07
14¾	Rogerstone	d	07 11	08 11	08 11	09 11	10 11	11 11	12 11	13 11	13 11	14 11	15 11	16 11	16 11
28¾	**Cardiff Central 7**	a	07 37	08 36	08 38	09 37	10 37	11 37	12 37	13 36	13 37	14 37	15 37	16 37	16 41

Station		AW SO A	AW B	AW	AW SO	AW SX	AW SO	AW SX	AW SO	AW SX	AW SO	AW SX	AW SO	AW SX
Ebbw Vale Parkway	d	16 40	16 40	17 40	18 40	18 40	19 40	19 40	20 40	20 40	21 41	21 41	22 41	22 41
Llanhilleth	d	16 48	16 48	17 48	18 48	18 48	19 48	19 48	20 48	20 48	21 49	21 49	22 49	22 49
Newbridge (Ebbw Vale)	d	16 54	16 54	17 54	18 54	18 54	19 54	19 54	20 54	20 54	21 55	21 55	22 55	22 55
Cross Keys	d	17 02	17 02	18 02	19 02	19 02	20 02	20 02	21 02	21 02	22 03	22 03	23 03	23 03
Risca & Pontymister	d	17 07	17 07	18 07	19 07	19 07	20 07	20 07	21 07	21 07	22 08	22 08	23 08	23 08
Rogerstone	d	17 11	17 11	18 11	19 11	19 11	20 11	20 11	21 11	21 11	22 12	22 12	23 12	23 12
Cardiff Central 7	a	17 40	17 43	18 37	19 38	19 40	20 38	20 39	21 36	21 38	22 39	22 40	23 39	23 45

Sundays

Station		AW	AW	AW C	AW D	AW C	AW D	AW C	AW D	AW	AW C	AW D
Ebbw Vale Parkway	d	08 41	10 41	12 41	12 41	14 41	14 41	16 41	16 41	18 41	20 41	20 41
Llanhilleth	d	08 49	10 49	12 49	12 49	14 49	14 49	16 49	16 49	18 49	20 49	20 49
Newbridge (Ebbw Vale)	d	08 55	10 55	12 55	12 55	14 55	14 55	16 55	16 55	18 55	20 55	20 55
Cross Keys	d	09 03	11 03	13 03	13 03	15 03	15 03	17 03	17 03	19 03	21 03	21 03
Risca & Pontymister	d	09 08	11 08	13 08	13 08	15 08	15 08	17 08	17 08	19 08	21 08	21 08
Rogerstone	d	09 12	11 12	13 12	13 12	15 12	15 12	17 12	17 12	19 12	21 12	21 12
Cardiff Central 7	a	09 37	11 37	13 37	13 40	15 37	15 41	17 37	17 40	19 37	21 37	21 38

For general notes see front of timetable
For details of catering facilities see Directory of Train Operators

A From 29 March
B All Mondays to Fridays, also Saturdays until 22 March
C Until 23 March
D From 30 March

Table 128

Cardiff → Maesteg, Swansea and West Wales

Route Diagram - see first page of Table 127

Miles	Miles			AW	AW	AW	AW	GW	AW	GW	GW	GW	GW	GW	GW	AW	AW	AW	AW	AW	AW	AW
				MX	MO	MO	MX	MO	MX	MX	MO	MO	MO	MO	MX							
					◇	◇	◇	1 ◇	◇	1 ◇	1 ◇	1 ◇	1 ◇	1 ◇	1 ◇		◇	1		1		◇
					A	B		C			B	D	C	B		E						
				(trolley)				(buffet)		(buffet)	(buffet)		(buffet)	(buffet)	(trolley)					(trolley)		(trolley)
—	—	London Paddington 15 ⊖	d					20p03		21p15	20p30	21p37	21p33	21p30	22p45							
—	—	Reading 7	d					20p41		21p41	21p06	22p13	22p07	22p07	23p18							
—	—	Manchester Piccadilly 10 (connection)	d	17p34																		
—	—	Gloucester 7	d								22p33			23p35								
—	—	Bristol Parkway 7	d					22p35		22p46		23p14	23p49		00 22							
—	—	Newport (South Wales)	d	20p46				23p05		23p15	23p23	23p43	00 12	00 24	00 52							
—	—	Cardiff Queen Street 3	d																			
0	—	**Cardiff Central 7**	d	21p07	22p35	22p35		23p25	23p15	23p37	23p43	00 05	00 34	00 46	01 12							05 40
11	—	Pontyclun	d						23p27													05 52
14	—	Llanharan	d						23p32													05 57
16¼	—	Pencoed	d						23p36													06 02
20¼	0	Bridgend	d	21p28	22p54	22p54		23p45	23p42	23p57	00 03	00 25	00 54	01 06	01 36							06 08
—	1	Wildmill	d																			
—	2¼	Sarn	d																			
—	3	Tondu	d																			
—	7	Garth (Mid Glamorgan)	d																			
—	7¾	Maesteg (Ewenny Road)	d																			
—	8¼	Maesteg	a																			
26¼	—	Pyle	d	21p35					23p50													06 16
32½	—	Port Talbot Parkway	d	21p43	23p07	23p07		23p59	23p59	00 10	00 17	00 38	01 07	01 19	01 49							06 24
34½	—	Baglan	d						00 02													06 28
36¼	—	Briton Ferry	d						00 06													06 31
38	—	Neath	d	21p50	23p14	23p14		00 07	00 10	00 18	00 25	00 45	01 14	01 26	01 56							06 35
41¾	—	Skewen	d						00 13													06 39
43½	—	Llansamlet	d						00 17													06 43
47½	—	**Swansea 7**	a	22p03	23p26	23p26		00 19	00 25	00 32	00 37	00 57	01 26	01 38	02 10							06 52
—	—		d	22p25	23p30	23p40	23p45		00 45								04 36				05 50	06 54
53	—	Gowerton	d	22p35	23b40	23b50			00c56												06x01	
58¾	—	Llanelli	a	22p42	23p47	23p57	00 01		01s02								04 52				06 08	07 10
—	—		d	22p42	23p47	23p57	00 01														06 08	07 11
62¾	—	Pembrey & Burry Port	d	22p48	23p53	00 03			01s08												06 14	07 17
68	—	Kidwelly	d	22 54	23b59	00x09			01c14												06x21	07x23
72¼	—	Ferryside	d	22 59	00x05	00x15			01c20												06x27	07x29
79¼	—	**Carmarthen**	a	23p11	00 17	00 27	00 25		01 37												06 40	07 42
—	—		d	23p17	00 19	00 29	00 27											04 55	05 45	06 05	06 43	07 44
93¼	0	Whitland	a	23p31	00 34	00 44	00 42											05 11	06 01	06 19	07 00	07 59
—	—		d	23p32	00 34	00 44	00 43											05 11	06 01	06 20	07 00	08 00
—	5¼	Narberth	d																06x10		07x09	
—	10¾	Kilgetty	d																06x19		07x19	
—	11½	Saundersfoot	d																06x20		07x21	
—	15¾	**Tenby**	a																06 27		07 28	
—	—		d																06 30		07 42	
—	17	Penally	d																06x33		07x45	
—	20½	Manorbier	d																06 39		07 52	
—	23¾	Lamphey	d																06x46		07x59	
—	25¼	Pembroke	d																06 49		08 02	
—	27¼	**Pembroke Dock**	a																07 04		08 17	
98¾	—	Clunderwen	d	23 38														05x18		06x26		08x06
105¼	0	Clarbeston Road	d	23 45	00x46	00x56	00x56											05x26		06x33		08x13
—	5¼	Haverfordwest	d	23p54														05e40		06 41		08 22
—	10	Johnston	d	00x01														05x47		06x49		08x29
—	14	**Milford Haven**	a	00 11														05 57		07 04		08 44
121	—	**Fishguard Harbour**	a		01 15	01 25	01 23															
—	—	(ship)	d													02 45						
—	—	Rosslare Harbour (ship)	a													06 15						

For general notes see front of timetable
For details of catering facilities see Directory of Train Operators

A Until 24 March
B From 31 March
C 4 February to 24 March
D Until 28 January
E Ship service

b Previous night.
Stops on request, passengers wishing to alight must inform the guard and those wishing to join must give a hand signal to the driver
c Stops, on request, to set down only
e Arr. 0534

Cardiff → Maesteg, Swansea and West Wales

Route Diagram - see first page of Table 127

	AW	AW	AW ◇	AW A	AW ◇ B	GW 1 ◇	AW ◇ C	AW	GW 1 ◇	AW	AW ◇ B	AW	AW A	GW 1 ◇ D ☒	AW ◇	AW A	GW 1 ◇	AW ◇	AW	AW ◇
London Paddington 15 ⊖ d						05 27			06 45					07 45			08 45			
Reading 7 d						05 56			07 11					08 11			09 11			
Manchester Piccadilly 10 d															06 38					07 28
Gloucester 7 d				05 50									07 58			08 58				
Bristol Parkway 7 d									08 07					09 07			10 07			
Newport (South Wales) d				06 44	07 35	07 45			08 31		08 37		08 51	09 31	09 37	09 52	10 31			10 38
Cardiff Queen Street 3 d																				
Cardiff Central 7 d	05 51		06 52	07 04	07 58	08 01	08 09	08 21	08 48		09 04	09 14	09 21	09 48	10 04	10 21	10 48	10 55		11 04
Pontyclun d	06 03			07 16				08 33					09 33			10 33				
Llanharan d	06 08			07 21				08 38					09 38			10 38				
Pencoed d	06 12			07 25				08 42					09 42			10 42				
Bridgend d	06 20		07 12	07 32	08 17	08 22	08 29	08 49	09 09		09 23	09 34	09 49	10 09	10 23	10 49	11 09			11 23
Wildmill d	06 22			07 35				08 52					09 52			10 52				
Sarn d	06 25			07 38				08 55					09 55			10 55				
Tondu d	06 29			07 41				08 58					09 58			10 58				
Garth (Mid Glamorgan) d	06 38			07 51				09 08					10 08			11 08				
Maesteg (Ewenny Road) d	06 41			07 53				09 10					10 10			11 10				
Maesteg a	06 46			07 59				09 15					10 15			11 15				
Pyle d			07 19				08 37					09 42								
Port Talbot Parkway d			07 28		08 30	08 35	08 45		09 22		09 36	09 50		10 22	10 36		11 22			11 36
Baglan d			07 31				08 49					09 54								
Briton Ferry d			07 35				08 52					09 57								
Neath d			07 39		08 37	08 43	08 56		09 29		09 43	10 01		10 29	10 43		11 29			11 43
Skewen d			07 42				09 00					10 05								
Llansamlet d			07 46				09 04					10 09								
Swansea 7 a			07 54		08 49	08 56	09 13		09 44		09 56	10 20		10 45	10 58		11 43			11 56
d		07 50	08 05		09 00		09 15			09 50	10 05				11 05				11 50	12 05
Gowerton d		08x01			09x15					10x01									12x01	
Llanelli a		08 08	08 23		09 19		09 31			10 08	10 23				11 20			11 57	12 08	12 20
d		08 08	08 23		09 19					10 08	10 24				11 21			11 58	12 08	12 21
Pembrey & Burry Port d		08 14	08 29		09 24					10 14	10 29				11 26				12 14	12 26
Kidwelly d		08x21								10x21									12x21	
Ferryside d		08x27								10x27									12x27	
Carmarthen a		08 40	08 51		09 47					10 40	10 51				11 46				12 40	12 51
d		08 56			09 52					10 56					11 52				12 56	
Whitland a		09 12			10 13					11 12					12 13			12 33	13 12	
d		09 12			10 14					11 12					12 14			12 33	13 12	
Narberth d		09x21								11x21									13x21	
Kilgetty d		09x30								11x30									13x30	
Saundersfoot d		09x31								11x31									13x31	
Tenby a		09 38								11 38									13 38	
d		09 43								11 43									13 43	
Penally d		09x46								11x46									13x46	
Manorbier d		09 52								11 52									13 52	
Lamphey d		09x59								11x59									13x59	
Pembroke d		10 02								12 02									14 02	
Pembroke Dock a		10 17								12 17									14 17	
Clunderwen d					10x20										12x20					
Clarbeston Road d					10x27										12x27					
Haverfordwest d					10 35										12 35					
Johnston d					10x43										12x43					
Milford Haven a					10 58										12 58					
Fishguard Harbour a																		13 14		
⛴ d																				
Rosslare Harbour ⛴ a																				

For general notes see front of timetable
For details of catering facilities see Directory of Train Operators

A From Cheltenham Spa (Table 57)
B From Crewe (Table 131)
C To Shrewsbury (Table 129)
D **The St David**

Cardiff → Maesteg, Swansea and West Wales

Route Diagram - see first page of Table 127

	AW	AW	GW	AW	AW		AW	GW	AW	AW	AW		AW	AW	GW	AW	AW		GW	AW	AW	AW	AW	GW
			1 ◇	◇			◇	1 ◇	◇						1 ◇	◇			1 ◇		◇			1 ◇
					A								A	B									A	
			⊠	⚲				⊠	⚲						⊠	⚲			⊠		⚲			⊡
London Paddington 15 ⊖ d			09 45					10 45							11 45				12 45					13 45
Reading 7 d			10 11					11 11							12 11				13 11					14 11
Manchester Piccadilly 10 ⛴ d				08 34					09 34							10 34					11 34			
Gloucester 7 d					10 58								11 58										13 58	
Bristol Parkway 7 d			11 07					12 07							13 07				14 07					15 07
Newport (South Wales) d			11 31	11 38	11 52			12 31	12 38				12 52		13 31	13 38			14 31		14 38		14 53	15 31
Cardiff Queen Street 3 d																								
Cardiff Central 7 d	11 14	11 21	11 48	12 04	12 21			12 48	13 04		13 14		13 21		13 48	14 04	14 21		14 48		15 04	15 14	15 21	15 48
Pontyclun d		11 33			12 33								13 33				14 33						15 33	
Llanharan d		11 38			12 38								13 38				14 38						15 38	
Pencoed d		11 42			12 42								13 42				14 42						15 42	
Bridgend d	11 34	11 49	12 09	12 23	12 49			13 09	13 23		13 34		13 49		14 09	14 23	14 49		15 09		15 23	15 34	15 49	16 09
Wildmill d		11 52			12 52								13 52				14 52						15 52	
Sarn d		11 55			12 55								13 55				14 55						15 55	
Tondu d		11 58			12 58								13 58				14 58						15 58	
Garth (Mid Glamorgan) d		12 08			13 08								14 08				15 08						16 08	
Maesteg (Ewenny Road) d		12 10			13 10								14 10				15 10						16 10	
Maesteg a		12 15			13 15								14 15				15 15						16 15	
Pyle d	11 42										13 42											15 42		
Port Talbot Parkway d	11 50		12 22	12 36				13 22	13 36		13 50				14 22	14 36			15 22		15 36	15 50		16 22
Baglan d	11 54										13 54											15 54		
Briton Ferry d	11 57										13 57											15 57		
Neath d	12 01		12 29	12 43				13 29	13 43		14 01				14 29	14 43			15 29		15 43	16 01		16 29
Skewen d	12 05										14 05											16 05		
Llansamlet d	12 09										14 09											16 09		
Swansea 7 a	12 20		12 45	12 56				13 45	13 56		14 20				14 45	14 56			15 43		15 56	16 20		16 43
d				13 05			13 16		14 00	14 05						15 05				15 50	16 05			
Gowerton d										14x17										16x01				
Llanelli a				13 20			13 32		14 15	14 24						15 23				16 08	16 20			
d				13 21					14 16	14 24						15 24				16 08	16 21			
Pembrey & Burry Port d				13 26					14 21	14 30						15 29				16 14	16 26			
Kidwelly d										14x37										16x21				
Ferryside d										14x43										16x27				
Carmarthen a				13 46					14 47	14 56						15 49				16 40	16 51			
d				13 52						14 59						15 52				16 56				
Whitland a				14 06						15 15						16 15				17 12				
d				14 07						15 15						16 16				17 12				
Narberth d										15x24										17x21				
Kilgetty d										15x33										17x30				
Saundersfoot d										15x34										17x31				
Tenby a										15 41										17 38				
d										15 43										17 43				
Penally d										15x46										17x46				
Manorbier d										15 52										17 52				
Lamphey d										15x59										17x59				
Pembroke d										16 02										18 02				
Pembroke Dock a										16 17										18 17				
Clunderwen d				14x13												16x22								
Clarbeston Road d				14x20												16x29								
Haverfordwest d				14 28												16 37								
Johnston d				14x36												16x45								
Milford Haven a				14 51												17 00								
Fishguard Harbour a																								
⛴ d														14 30										
Rosslare Harbour ⛴ a														18 00										

For general notes see front of timetable
For details of catering facilities see Directory of Train Operators

A From Cheltenham Spa (Table 57)
B Ship service

Cardiff → Maesteg, Swansea and West Wales

Route Diagram - see first page of Table 127

		AW		AW	GW	AW	AW	AW		AW	AW	AW	GW	AW		AW	GW	GW	AW	AW		AW	GW	AW	GW
		R			1 ◇		R				◇		1 ◇	R			1 ◇	1 ◇	R				1 ◇		1 ◇
				A												A						A			
		⊼			🍽	⊼	⊼	⊼					⊼	⊼			🍽	⊼	⊼				🍽		⊼
London Paddington 15 ⊖	d				14 45								15 45				16 15	16 45					17 15		17 45
Reading 7	d				15 11								16 11				16 41	17 11					17 41		18 11
Manchester Piccadilly 10 ⛴	d	12 34					13 34							14 34					15 34						
Gloucester 7	d			14 58												16 58						17 58			
Bristol Parkway 7	d				16 07								17 07				17 42	18 13					18 42		19 11
Newport (South Wales)	d	15 38		15 52	16 31		16 38						17 31	17 38		17 52	18 05	18 38	18 47			18 52	19 05		19 34
Cardiff Queen Street 3	d																								
Cardiff Central 7	d	16 04		16 21	16 48		17 04			17 21		17 38	17 48	18 04		18 21	18 28	18 53	19 04			19 12	19 24	19 37	19 50
Pontyclun	d			16 33						17 32						18 33						19 26			
Llanharan	d			16 38						17 38						18 38						19 31			
Pencoed	d			16 42						17 41						18 42						19 35			
Bridgend	d	16 23		16 49	17 09		17 25			17 48		17 58	18 09	18 26		18 49	18 53	19 13	19 23			19b45	19 49	19 56	20 11
Wildmill	d			16 52						17 51						18 52						19 48			
Sarn	d			16 55						17 54						18 55						19 51			
Tondu	d			16 58						17 57						18 58						19 54			
Garth (Mid Glamorgan)	d			17 08						18 07						19 08						20 04			
Maesteg (Ewenny Road)	d			17 10						18 09						19 10						20 06			
Maesteg	a			17 15						18 14						19 15						20 11			
Pyle	d						17 31					18 06												20 04	
Port Talbot Parkway	d	16 36			17 22		17 39					18 14	18 22	18 42			19 06	19 26	19 35				20 02	20 12	20 24
Baglan	d						17 41					18 18												20 16	
Briton Ferry	d						17 46					18 21												20 19	
Neath	d	16 43			17 29		17 50					18 25	18 30	18 49			19 13	19 34	19 42				20 09	20 23	20 32
Skewen	d						17 53					18 29												20 27	→
Llansamlet	d						17 57					18 33												20 31	
Swansea 7	a	16 56			17 43		18 05					18 44	18 46	19 01			19 34	19 48	19 56				20 23	20 42	
	d	17 05				17 50	18 09				18 21			19 05					20 00	20 05					
Gowerton	d	17x16				18x01	18x19													20x17					
Llanelli	a	17 23				18 08	18 26				18 37			19 20					20 15	20 24					
	d	17 23				18 08	18 26							19 21					20 16	20 24					
Pembrey & Burry Port	d	17 29				18 14	18 32							19 26					20 21	20 30					
Kidwelly	d	17x35				18x21	18x38													20x37					
Ferryside	d	17x40				18x27	18x43													20x43					
Carmarthen	a	17 52				18 40	19 00	←						19 46					20 46	20 56					
	d	17 55				19 05		19 05						19 52						20 59					
Whitland	a	18 13				→		19 21						20 06						21 15					
	d	18 14						19 21						20 07						21 15					
Narberth	d							19x30												21x24					
Kilgetty	d							19x39												21x34					
Saundersfoot	d							19x40												21x36					
Tenby	a							19 47												21 43					
	d							19 52												21 44					
Penally	d							19x55												21x47					
Manorbier	d							20 02												21 54					
Lamphey	d							20x09												22x01					
Pembroke	d							20 12												22 04					
Pembroke Dock	a							20 22												22 17					
Clunderwen	d	18x20												20x13											
Clarbeston Road	d	18x27												20x20											
Haverfordwest	d	18 35												20 28											
Johnston	d	18x43												20x36											
Milford Haven	a	18 58												20 51											
Fishguard Harbour	a																								
	⛴ d																								
Rosslare Harbour	⛴ a																								

For general notes see front of timetable
For details of catering facilities see Directory of Train Operators

A From Cheltenham Spa (Table 57)
b Arr. 1942

Cardiff → Maesteg, Swansea and West Wales

Route Diagram - see first page of Table 127

		AW	AW	GW		GW	AW	GW	AW	AW		GW	AW	AW	AW	GW		AW	AW	AW	GW	GW	GW		
																						FO	FX		
		R		1 ◇		1 ◇		1 ◇	R			1 ◇		◇		1 ◇			◇	◇	1 ◇	1 ◇	1 ◇		
			A			B	A			A			A												
		🛒		🛒		🍴		🛒	🛒			🛒		🛒		🛒					🍴	🛒	🛒		
London Paddington 15 ⊖	d					18 15		18 45				19 15				20 15					21 15	22 45	22 45		
Reading 7	d					18 41		19 11				19 41				20 41					21 41	23 11	23 18		
Manchester Piccadilly 10 🚌	d	16 34							17 34					18 34											
Gloucester 7	d		18 58							19 58															
Bristol Parkway 7	d					19 42		20 07				20 42				21 42					22 46	00 17	00 22		
Newport (South Wales)	d	19 40	19 51			20 05		20 31	20 46	20 52		21 05		21 38		22 05					23 15	00 48	00 52		
Cardiff Queen Street 3	d																								
Cardiff Central 7	d	20 00	20 15			20 22	←	20 48	21 07	21 21		21 22	←	22 09	22 25	22 35		←		23 15	23 37	01 04	01 12		
Pontyclun	d		20 39							21 40					22 37					23 27					
Llanharan	d		20 44				20 44			21 45			21 45		22 42			22 42		23 32					
Pencoed	d		→				20 48			→			21 49		→			22 46		23 36					
Bridgend	d	20 19				20 42	20 55	21 09	21 28			21 42	21 56	22 28		22 55		23 02		23 42	23 57	01 28	01 36		
Wildmill	d						20 58						21 59					23 05							
Sarn	d						21 01						22 02					23 08							
Tondu	d						21 04						22 05					23 11							
Garth (Mid Glamorgan)	d						21 14						22 15					23 21							
Maesteg (Ewenny Road)	d						21 16						22 17					23 23							
Maesteg	a						21 20						22 21					23 29							
Pyle	d								21 35											23 50					
Port Talbot Parkway	d	20 35				20 57		21 22	21 43			21 55		22 41		23 08				23 59	00 10	01 41	01 49		
Baglan	d																			00 02					
Briton Ferry	d			←																00 06					
Neath	d			20 32		21 04		21 29	21 50			22 03		22 48		23 15				00 10	00 18	01 48	01 56		
Skewen	d																			00 13					
Llansamlet	d																			00 17					
Swansea 7	a			20 46		21 20		21 42	22 03			22 18		23 00		23 31				00 25	00 32	02 10	02 10		
	d			21 00					22 25					23 06					23 45	00 45					
Gowerton	d								22x35					23x21						00b56					
Llanelli	a	21 05		21 16					22 42					23 27					00 01	01s02					
	d	21 05		21 16					22 42					23 28					00 01						
Pembrey & Burry Port	d	21 11		21 23					22 48					23 33						01s08					
Kidwelly	d								22x54					23x39						01b14					
Ferryside	d								22x59					23x45						01b20					
Carmarthen	a	21 30		21 49					23 11					00 03					00 25	01 37					
	d	22 04							23 17										00 27						
Whitland	a	22 20							23 31										00 42						
	d	22 21							23 32										00 43						
Narberth	d																								
Kilgetty	d																								
Saundersfoot	d																								
Tenby	a																								
	d																								
Penally	d																								
Manorbier	d																								
Lamphey	d																								
Pembroke	d																								
Pembroke Dock	a																								
Clunderwen	d	22x27							23x38																
Clarbeston Road	d	22x34							23x45										00x56						
Haverfordwest	d	22 42							23 54																
Johnston	d	22x50							00x01																
Milford Haven	a	23 05							00 11																
Fishguard Harbour	a																		01 23						
⛴	d																								
Rosslare Harbour ⛴	a																								

For general notes see front of timetable
For details of catering facilities see
Directory of Train Operators

A From Cheltenham Spa (Table 57)
B **The Red Dragon**
b Stops, on request, to set down only

Table 128

until 26 January

Cardiff → Maesteg, Swansea and West Wales

Route Diagram - see first page of Table 127

		AW	AW	AW	AW	GW	GW	AW	AW	AW	AW	AW	AW	AW	AW	AW	AW	AW	GW	GW	AW	AW	AW
		R	◇		◇	1 ◇	1 ◇	A	◇	1		1		◇			◇		1	1 ◇ B	◇ C	◇ D	
London Paddington 15	⊖ d					21p15	22p45																
Reading 7	d					21p41	23p11																
Manchester Piccadilly 10	d	17p34																					
Gloucester 7	d																	05 50					
Bristol Parkway 7	d					22p46	00 17													07 13			
Newport (South Wales)	d	20p46				23p15	00 48											06 44		07 36	07 41		
Cardiff Queen Street 3	d																						
Cardiff Central 7	d	21p07			23p15	23p37	01 04							05 40	05 51		06 52	07 04		07 53	08 04	08 09	08 21
Pontyclun	d				23p27									05 52	06 03			07 16					08 33
Llanharan	d				23p32									05 57	06 08			07 21					08 38
Pencoed	d				23p36									06 02	06 12			07 25					08 42
Bridgend	d	21p28			23p42	23p57	01 28							06 08	06 20		07 12	07 32		08 13	08 23	08 29	08 49
Wildmill	d														06 22			07 35					08 52
Sarn	d														06 25			07 38					08 55
Tondu	d														06 29			07 41					08 58
Garth (Mid Glamorgan)	d														06 38			07 51					09 08
Maesteg (Ewenny Road)	d														06 41			07 53					09 10
Maesteg	a														06 46			07 59					09 15
Pyle	d	21p35			23p50									06 16			07 20					08 37	
Port Talbot Parkway	d	21p43			23p59	00 10	01 41							06 24			07 28			08 26	08 36	08 45	
Baglan	d				00 02									06 28			07 32					08 49	
Briton Ferry	d				00 06									06 31			07 35					08 52	
Neath	d	21p50			00 10	00 18	01 48							06 35			07 39			08 34	08 43	08 56	
Skewen	d				00 13									06 39			07 43					09 00	
Llansamlet	d				00 17									06 43			07 47					09 04	
Swansea 7	a	22p03			00 25	00 32	02 10							06 51			07 55			08 48	08 55	09 13	
	d	22p25	23p45	00 05	00 45				04 36				05 50	06 54		07 50	08 05		08 13		09 00	09 15	
Gowerton	d	22b35		00x16	00c56								06x01			08x01					09x15		
Llanelli	a	22p42	00 01	00 23	01s02				04 52				06 08	07 10		08 08	08 23		08 29		09 19	09 31	
	d	22p42	00 01	00 23									06 08	07 11		08 08	08 23		08 34		09 19		
Pembrey & Burry Port	d	22p48		00 29	01s08								06 14	07 17		08 14	08 29		08 41		09 24		
Kidwelly	d	22b54		00x36	01c14								06x21	07x23		08x21							
Ferryside	d	22b59		00x41	01c20								06x27	07x29		08x27							
Carmarthen	a	23p11	00 25	00 59	01 37								06 40	07 42		08 40	08 51		09 08		09 47		
	d	23p17	00 27							04 55	05 45	06 05	06 43	07 42		08 56					09 52		
Whitland	a	23p31	00 42							05 11	06 01	06 19	07 00	07 59		09 12					10 13		
	d	23p32	00 43							05 11	06 01	06 20	07 00	08 00		09 12					10 14		
Narberth	d										06x10		07x09			09x21							
Kilgetty	d										06x19		07x19			09x30							
Saundersfoot	d										06x20		07x21			09x31							
Tenby	a										06 27		07 28			09 38							
	d										06 30		07 42			09 43							
Penally	d										06x33		07x45			09x46							
Manorbier	d										06 39		07 52			09 52							
Lamphey	d										06x46		07x59			09x59							
Pembroke	d										06 49		08 02			10 02							
Pembroke Dock	a										07 04		08 17			10 17							
Clunderwen	d	23b38								05x18		06x26		08x06							10x20		
Clarbeston Road	d	23b45	00x56							05x26		06x33		08x13							10x27		
Haverfordwest	d	23p54								05e40		06 41		08 22							10 35		
Johnston	d	00x01								05x47		06x49		08x29							10x43		
Milford Haven	a	00 11								05 57		07 04		08 44							10 58		
Fishguard Harbour	a		01 23																				
	⛴ d							02 45															
Rosslare Harbour	⛴ a							06 15															

For general notes see front of timetable
For details of catering facilities see Directory of Train Operators

A Ship service

B From Bristol Temple Meads (Table 132)

C From Crewe (Table 131)

D To Shrewsbury (Table 129)

b Previous night.
Stops on request, passengers wishing to alight must inform the guard and those wishing to join must give a hand signal to the driver

c Stops, on request, to set down only

e Arr. 0534

Table 128

until 26 January

Cardiff → Maesteg, Swansea and West Wales

Route Diagram - see first page of Table 127

	AW	AW	AW	AW		GW	AW	AW	GW	AW	AW	AW	AW		AW	GW	AW	AW	AW	GW	AW	AW		AW
		◇				1 ◇	◇		1 ◇	◇		◇				1 ◇	◇		◇	1 ◇	◇			
		A		B				B										B						
	⚲	⚲				☕	⚲		☕	⚲	⚲	⚲				☕	⚲			☕	⚲			
London Paddington 15 ⊖ d						07 45			08 45							09 45				10 45				
Reading 7 d						08 11			09 11							10 11				11 11				
Manchester Piccadilly 10 ⛴ d							06 38					07 28					08 34				09 34			
Gloucester 7 d				07 58				08 58										10 58						
Bristol Parkway 7 d						09 07			10 07							11 07				12 07				
Newport (South Wales) d		08 37		08 52		09 32	09 36	09 52	10 32			10 38				11 32	11 38	11 52		12 32	12 38			
Cardiff Queen Street 3 d																								
Cardiff Central 7 d		09 04	09 14	09 21		09 49	10 04	10 21	10 49	10 57		11 04	11 14		11 21	11 48	12 04	12 21		12 48	13 04			13 14
Pontyclun d				09 33				10 33							11 33			12 33						
Llanharan d				09 38				10 38							11 38			12 38						
Pencoed d				09 42				10 42							11 42			12 42						
Bridgend d		09 23	09 34	09 49		10 09	10 23	10 49	11 09			11 23	11 34		11 49	12 09	12 23	12 49		13 09	13 23			13 34
Wildmill d				09 52				10 52							11 52			12 52						
Sarn d				09 55				10 55							11 55			12 55						
Tondu d				09 58				10 58							11 58			12 58						
Garth (Mid Glamorgan) d				10 08				11 08							12 08			13 08						
Maesteg (Ewenny Road) d				10 10				11 10							12 10			13 10						
Maesteg a				10 15				11 15							12 15			13 15						
Pyle d			09 42										11 42											13 42
Port Talbot Parkway d		09 36	09 50			10 22	10 36		11 22			11 36	11 50			12 22	12 36			13 22	13 36			13 50
Baglan d			09 54										11 54											13 54
Briton Ferry d			09 57										11 57											13 57
Neath d		09 43	10 01			10 30	10 43		11 30			11 43	12 01			12 30	12 43			13 30	13 43			14 01
Skewen d			10 05										12 05											14 05
Llansamlet d			10 09										12 09											14 09
Swansea 7 a		09 56	10 20			10 43	11 01		11 43			11 56	12 20			12 43	12 56			13 43	13 56			14 20
d	09 50	10 05					11 05				11 50	12 05					13 05		13 16		14 00	14 05		
Gowerton d	10x01										12x01											14x17		
Llanelli a	10 08	10 23					11 21			11 58	12 08	12 20					13 20		13 32		14 15	14 24		
d	10 08	10 24					11 21			11 58	12 08	12 21					13 21				14 16	14 24		
Pembrey & Burry Port d	10 14	10 29					11 27				12 14	12 26					13 26				14 21	14 30		
Kidwelly d	10x21										12x21											14x37		
Ferryside d	10x27										12x27											14x43		
Carmarthen a	10 40	10 51					11 47				12 40	12 51					13 46				14 47	14 56		
d	10 56						11 52				12 56						13 52					14 59		
Whitland a	11 12						12 13			12 33	13 12						14 06					15 15		
d	11 12						12 14			12 34	13 12						14 07					15 15		
Narberth d	11x21										13x21											15x24		
Kilgetty d	11x30										13x30											15x33		
Saundersfoot d	11x31										13x31											15x34		
Tenby a	11 38										13 38											15 41		
d	11 43										13 43											15 43		
Penally d	11x46										13x46											15x46		
Manorbier d	11 52										13 52											15 52		
Lamphey d	11x59										13x59											15x59		
Pembroke d	12 02										14 02											16 02		
Pembroke Dock a	12 17										14 17											16 17		
Clunderwen d							12x20										14x13							
Clarbeston Road d							12x27										14x20							
Haverfordwest d							12 36										14 28							
Johnston d							12x43										14x36							
Milford Haven a							12 58										14 51							
Fishguard Harbour a										13 14														
⛴ d																								
Rosslare Harbour ⛴ a																								

For general notes see front of timetable
For details of catering facilities see Directory of Train Operators

A From Crewe (Table 131)
B From Cheltenham Spa (Table 57)

until 26 January

Cardiff → Maesteg, Swansea and West Wales

Route Diagram - see first page of Table 127

		AW	AW	GW	AW	AW	GW	AW	AW	AW	AW	GW	AW	AW	GW	AW	AW	AW	AW	AW	AW	GW	AW
													R				R						R
				1 ◇	◇		1 ◇		◇			1 ◇			1 ◇					◇		1 ◇	
		A	B								A			A									
				☕	🛒		☕		🛒			☕	🛒		☕	🛒	🛒	🛒				☕	🛒
London Paddington 15 ⊖	d			11 45			12 45					13 45			14 45							15 45	
Reading 7	d			12 11			13 11					14 11			15 11							16 11	
Manchester Piccadilly 10 🚌	d				10 34				11 34				12 34				13 34						14 34
Gloucester 7	d	11 58									13 58			14 58									
Bristol Parkway 7	d			13 07			14 07					15 07			16 07							17 07	
Newport (South Wales)	d	12 52		13 32	13 38		14 32		14 38		14 54	15 32	15 38	15 52	16 32		16 38					17 32	17 38
Cardiff Queen Street 3	d																						
Cardiff Central 7	d	13 21		13 48	14 04	14 21	14 48		15 04	15 14	15 21	15 48	16 04	16 21	16 49		17 04		17 21		17 38	17 47	18 02
Pontyclun	d	13 33				14 33					15 33			16 33					17 33				
Llanharan	d	13 38				14 38					15 38			16 38					17 38				
Pencoed	d	13 42				14 42					15 42			16 42					17 42				
Bridgend	d	13 49		14 09	14 23	14 49	15 09		15 23	15 34	15 49	16 09	16 23	16 49	17 10		17 25		17 49		17 58	18 09	18 21
Wildmill	d	13 52				14 52					15 52			16 52					17 52				
Sarn	d	13 55				14 55					15 55			16 55					17 55				
Tondu	d	13 58				14 58					15 58			16 58					17 58				
Garth (Mid Glamorgan)	d	14 08				15 08					16 08			17 08					18 08				
Maesteg (Ewenny Road)	d	14 10				15 10					16 10			17 10					18 10				
Maesteg	a	14 15				15 15					16 15			17 15					18 15				
Pyle	d									15 42							17 32				18 06		
Port Talbot Parkway	d			14 22	14 36		15 22		15 36	15 50		16 22	16 36		17 23		17 40				18 14	18 24	18 34
Baglan	d									15 54							17 43				18 18		
Briton Ferry	d									15 57							17 47				18 21		
Neath	d			14 30	14 43		15 30		15 43	16 01		16 30	16 43		17 30		17 51				18 25	18 32	18 41
Skewen	d									16 05							17 55				18 29		
Llansamlet	d									16 09							17 59				18 33		
Swansea 7	a			14 43	14 56		15 43		15 56	16 20		16 43	16 56		17 43		18 06				18 44	18 46	18 56
	d				15 05			15 50	16 05				17 05			17 50	18 09			18 21			19 05
Gowerton	d							16x01					17x20			18x01	18x19						
Llanelli	a				15 23			16 08	16 20				17 27			18 08	18 26			18 37			19 20
	d				15 24			16 08	16 21				17 27			18 08	18 26						19 21
Pembrey & Burry Port	d				15 29			16 14	16 26				17 33			18 14	18 32						19 26
Kidwelly	d							16x21					17x39			18x21	18x38						
Ferryside	d							16x27					17x44			18x27	18x43						
Carmarthen	a				15 49			16 40	16 51				17 56			18 40	19 00	←					19 46
	d				15 52			16 56					17 59			19 05 →		19 05					19 52
Whitland	a				16 15			17 12					18 13					19 21					20 06
	d				16 16			17 12					18 14					19 21					20 07
Narberth	d							17x21										19x30					
Kilgetty	d							17x30										19x39					
Saundersfoot	d							17x31										19x40					
Tenby	a							17 38										19 47					
	d							17 43										19 52					
Penally	d							17x46										19x55					
Manorbier	d							17 52										20 02					
Lamphey	d							17x59										20x09					
Pembroke	d							18 02										20 12					
Pembroke Dock	a							18 17										20 22					
Clunderwen	d				16x22								18x20										20x13
Clarbeston Road	d				16x29								18x27										20x20
Haverfordwest	d				16 37								18 35										20 28
Johnston	d				16x45								18x43										20x36
Milford Haven	a				17 00								18 58										20 51
Fishguard Harbour	a																						
🚢	d		14 30																				
Rosslare Harbour 🚢	a		18 00																				

For general notes see front of timetable
For details of catering facilities see Directory of Train Operators

A From Cheltenham Spa (Table 57)
B Ship service

until 26 January

Cardiff → Maesteg, Swansea and West Wales

Route Diagram - see first page of Table 127

		AW	GW	AW	AW		AW	AW	GW	AW	GW	AW	GW	AW		AW	GW	AW	GW	AW	AW	AW	GW		
			[1] ◇	[R]					[1] ◇	[R]	[1] ◇		[1] ◇	[R]			[1] ◇		[1] ◇	◇	◇	◇	[1] ◇		
		A					A					A				A		A							
			☕	⌶					☕	⌶	☕		☕	⌶			☕		☕	⌶			☕		
London Paddington [15] ⊖	d		16 45						17 45				18 45				19 15		19 45				20 45		
Reading [7]	d		17 11						18 11				19 11				19 41		20 11				21 11		
Manchester Piccadilly [10] 🚊	d			15 34						16 34				17 34						18 34					
Gloucester [7]	d	16 58					17 58					18 58				19 58									
Bristol Parkway [7]	d		18 07						19 12				20 07				20 42		21 06				22 12		
Newport (South Wales)	d	17 52	18 32	18 41			18 52		19 35	19 43		19 52	20 32	20 46		20 52	21 05		21 31	21 39			22 46		
Cardiff Queen Street [3]	d																								
Cardiff Central [7]	d	18 21	18 48	19 04			19 21	19 38	19 53	20 00		20 21	20 48	21 07		21 21	21 22		21 48	22 09		22 41	23 06		
Pontyclun	d	18 33					19 33					20 33				21 40		⟵				22 53			
Llanharan	d	18 38					19 38					20 38				21 45		21 45				22 58			
Pencoed	d	18 42					19 42					20 42				⟶		21 49				23 02			
Bridgend	d	18 49	19 09	19 23			19 49	19 58	20 13	20 19		20 49	21 09	21 28			21 42	21 56	22 09	22 28		23 08	23 27		
Wildmill	d	18 52					19 52					20 52						21 59							
Sarn	d	18 55					19 55					20 55						22 02							
Tondu	d	18 58					19 58					20 58						22 05							
Garth (Mid Glamorgan)	d	19 08					20 08					21 08						22 15							
Maesteg (Ewenny Road)	d	19 10					20 10					21 10						22 17							
Maesteg	a	19 15					20 15					21 15						22 22							
Pyle	d							20 06						21 35								23 16			
Port Talbot Parkway	d		19 22	19 36				20 14	20 26	20 32			21 22	21 43			21 55		22 22	22 41		23 24	23 40		
Baglan	d							20 18														23 27			
Briton Ferry	d							20 21			⟵											23 31			
Neath	d		19 30	19 43				20 25	20 34		20 34		21 30	21 50			22 03		22 29	22 48		23 35	23 48		
Skewen	d							20 29	⟶													23 38			
Llansamlet	d							20 33														23 42			
Swansea [7]	a		19 43	19 56				20 44			20 48		21 47	22 03			22 18		22 46	23 00		23 51	00 01		
	d			20 00	20 05						21 00			22 25						23 06	23 45	00 05			
Gowerton	d				20x17									22x35						23x21		00b16			
Llanelli	a			20 15	20 24					21 04	21 25			22 42						23 27	00 01	00s22			
	d			20 16	20 24					21 04	21 25			22 42						23 28	00 01				
Pembrey & Burry Port	d			20 21	20 30					21 10	21 32			22 48						23 33		00s28			
Kidwelly	d				20x37									22x54						23x39		00b35			
Ferryside	d				20x43									22x59						23x45		00b41			
Carmarthen	a			20 46	20 56					21 29	21 55			23 11						00 03	00 25	00 58			
	d				20 59					22 04				23 17							00 27				
Whitland	a				21 15					22 21				23 31							00 42				
	d				21 15					22 21				23 32							00 43				
Narberth	d				21x24																				
Kilgetty	d				21x34																				
Saundersfoot	d				21x36																				
Tenby	a				21 43																				
	d				21 44																				
Penally	d				21x47																				
Manorbier	d				21 54																				
Lamphey	d				22x01																				
Pembroke	d				22 04																				
Pembroke Dock	a				22 19																				
Clunderwen	d									22x27				23x38											
Clarbeston Road	d									22x34				23x45							00x56				
Haverfordwest	d									22 43				23a53											
Johnston	d									22x50															
Milford Haven	a									23 05															
Fishguard Harbour	a																				01 23				
⛴	d																								
Rosslare Harbour ⛴	a																								

For general notes see front of timetable
For details of catering facilities see Directory of Train Operators

A From Cheltenham Spa (Table 57)
b Stops, on request, to set down only

2 February to 22 March

Cardiff → Maesteg, Swansea and West Wales

Route Diagram - see first page of Table 127

		AW	AW	AW	AW	GW	GW	AW		AW	AW	AW	AW	AW	AW	AW		AW	AW	AW	GW	GW	AW	AW	AW
		R	◇		◇	1 ◇	1 ◇	A		◇	1		1		◇				◇		1	1 ◇ B	◇ C	◇ D	
		⊼				⊓									⊼						⊓	⊓	⊼		
London Paddington 15 ⊖	d					21p15	22p45																		
Reading 7	d					21p41	23p11																		
Manchester Piccadilly 10 ⇌	d	17p34																							
Gloucester 7	d																			05 50					
Bristol Parkway 7	d					22p46	00 17															07 13			
Newport (South Wales)	d	20p46				23p15	00 48													06 44		07 36	07 41		
Cardiff Queen Street 3	d																								
Cardiff Central 7	d	21p07			23p15	23p37	01 04								05 40	05 51			06 52	07 04		07 53	08 04	08 09	08 21
Pontyclun	d				23p27										05 52	06 03				07 16					08 33
Llanharan	d				23p32										05 57	06 08				07 21					08 38
Pencoed	d				23p36										06 02	06 12				07 25					08 42
Bridgend	d	21p28			23p42	23p57	01 28								06 08	06 20			07 12	07 32		08 13	08 23	08 29	08 49
Wildmill	d															06 22				07 35					08 52
Sarn	d															06 25				07 38					08 55
Tondu	d															06 29				07 41					08 58
Garth (Mid Glamorgan)	d															06 38				07 51					09 08
Maesteg (Ewenny Road)	d															06 41				07 53					09 10
Maesteg	a															06 46				07 59					09 15
Pyle	d	21p35			23p50										06 16				07 20					08 37	
Port Talbot Parkway	d	21p43			23p59	00 10	01 41								06 24				07 28			08 26	08 36	08 45	
Baglan	d				00 02										06 28				07 32					08 49	
Briton Ferry	d				00 06										06 31				07 35					08 52	
Neath	d	21p50			00 10	00 18	01 48								06 35				07 39			08 34	08 43	08 56	
Skewen	d				00 13										06 39				07 43					09 00	
Llansamlet	d				00 17										06 43				07 47					09 04	
Swansea 7	a	22p03			00 25	00 32	02 10								06 51				07 55			08 48	08 55	09 13	
	d	22p25	23p45	00 05	00 45					04 36				05 50	06 54			07 50	08 05		08 13		09 00	09 15	
Gowerton	d	22b35		00x16	00c56									06x01				08x01					09x15		
Llanelli	a	22p42	00 01	00 23	01s02					04 52				06 08	07 10			08 08	08 23		08 29		09 19	09 31	
	d	22p42	00 01	00 23										06 08	07 11			08 08	08 23		08 34		09 19		
Pembrey & Burry Port	d	22p48		00 29	01s08									06 14	07 17			08 14	08 29		08 41		09 24		
Kidwelly	d	22b54		00x36	01c14									06x21	07x23			08x21							
Ferryside	d	22b59		00x41	01c20									06x27	07x29			08x27							
Carmarthen	a	23p11	00 25	00 59	01 37									06 40	07 42			08 40	08 51		09 08		09 47		
	d	23p17	00 27								04 55	05 45	06 05	06 43	07 42			08 56					09 52		
Whitland	a	23p31	00 42								05 11	06 01	06 19	07 00	07 59			09 12					10 13		
	d	23p32	00 43								05 11	06 01	06 20	07 00	08 00			09 12					10 14		
Narberth	d											06x10		07x09				09x21							
Kilgetty	d											06x19		07x19				09x30							
Saundersfoot	d											06x20		07x21				09x31							
Tenby	a											06 27		07 28				09 38							
	d											06 30		07 42				09 43							
Penally	d											06x33		07x45				09x46							
Manorbier	d											06 39		07 52				09 52							
Lamphey	d											06x46		07x59				09x59							
Pembroke	d											06 49		08 02				10 02							
Pembroke Dock	a											07 04		08 17				10 17							
Clunderwen	d	23b38									05x18		06x26		08x06								10x20		
Clarbeston Road	d	23b45	00x56								05x26		06x33		08x13								10x27		
Haverfordwest	d	23p54									05e40		06 41		08 22								10 35		
Johnston	d	00x01									05x47		06x49		08x29								10x43		
Milford Haven	a	00 11									05 57		07 04		08 44								10 58		
Fishguard Harbour	a		01 23																						
⛴	d							02 45																	
Rosslare Harbour ⛴	a							06 15																	

For general notes see front of timetable
For details of catering facilities see Directory of Train Operators

A Ship service

B From Bristol Temple Meads (Table 132)
C From Crewe (Table 131)
D To Shrewsbury (Table 129)

b Previous night.
Stops on request, passengers wishing to alight must inform the guard and those wishing to join must give a hand signal to the driver
c Stops, on request, to set down only
e Arr. 0534

Saturdays

2 February to 22 March

Cardiff → Maesteg, Swansea and West Wales

Route Diagram - see first page of Table 127

		AW		AW ◇ A	AW	AW B	AW ◇	GW 1 ◇	AW B	AW ◇		AW	GW 1 ◇	AW ◇	AW	AW	AW ◇	AW B		AW ◇	GW 1 ◇	AW ◇	AW	AW	AW B
		⌶		⌶			⌶	⑂		⌶		⌶	⑂	⌶			⌶				⑂	⌶			
London Paddington 15 ⊖	d							07 15					08 15								10 15				
Reading 7	d							07 41					08 41								10 41				
Manchester Piccadilly 10 ⇌	d						06 38							07 28			08 34					09 34			
Gloucester 7	d					07 58			08 58									10 58							11 58
Bristol Parkway 7	d							09 20					10 20								12 20				
Newport (South Wales)	d			08 37		08 52	09 36	09 44	09 52				10 44	10 38			11 38	11 52			12 45	12 38			12 52
Cardiff Queen Street 3	d																								
Cardiff Central 7	d			09 04	09 14	09 21	09 55	10 01	10 21	10 55			11 01	11 04	11 14	11 21	12 04	12 21			13 01	13 04		13 14	13 21
Pontyclun	d					09 33			10 33							11 33		12 33							13 33
Llanharan	d					09 38			10 38							11 38		12 38							13 38
Pencoed	d					09 42			10 42							11 42		12 42							13 42
Bridgend	d			09 23	09 34	09 49	10 11	10 21	10 49				11 21	11 23	11 34	11 49	12 23	12 49			13 22	13 23		13 34	13 49
Wildmill	d					09 52			10 52							11 52		12 52							13 52
Sarn	d					09 55			10 55							11 55		12 55							13 55
Tondu	d					09 58			10 58							11 58		12 58							13 58
Garth (Mid Glamorgan)	d					10 08			11 08							12 08		13 08							14 08
Maesteg (Ewenny Road)	d					10 10			11 10							12 10		13 10							14 10
Maesteg	a					10 15			11 15							12 15		13 15							14 15
Pyle	d				09 42										11 42									13 42	
Port Talbot Parkway	d			09 36	09 50		10 24	10 34					11 34	11 36	11 50		12 36				13 35	13 36		13 50	
Baglan	d				09 54										11 54						↳			13 54	
Briton Ferry	d				09 57										11 57									13 57	
Neath	d			09 43	10 01		10 31	10 42					11 41	11 43	12 01		12 43					13 43		14 01	
Skewen	d				10 05										12 05									14 05	
Llansamlet	d				10 09										12 09									14 09	
Swansea 7	a			09 56	10 20		10 49	10 57					11 56	11 56	12 20		12 56					13 56		14 20	
	d	09 50		10 05			11 05					11 50		12 05			13 05			13 16		14 00	14 05		
Gowerton	d	10x01										12x01											14x17		
Llanelli	a	10 08		10 23			11 21			11 58		12 08		12 20			13 20			13 32		14 15	14 24		
	d	10 08		10 24			11 21			11 58		12 08		12 21			13 21					14 16	14 24		
Pembrey & Burry Port	d	10 14		10 29			11 27					12 14		12 26			13 26					14 21	14 30		
Kidwelly	d	10x21										12x21											14x37		
Ferryside	d	10x27										12x27											14x43		
Carmarthen	a	10 40		10 51			11 47					12 40		12 51			13 46					14 47	14 56		
	d	10 56					11 52					12 56					13 52						14 59		
Whitland	a	11 12					12 13			12 33		13 12					14 06						15 15		
	d	11 12					12 14			12 34		13 12					14 07						15 15		
Narberth	d	11x21										13x21											15x24		
Kilgetty	d	11x30										13x30											15x33		
Saundersfoot	d	11x31										13x31											15x34		
Tenby	a	11 38										13 38											15 41		
	d	11 43										13 43											15 43		
Penally	d	11x46										13x46											15x46		
Manorbier	d	11 52										13 52											15 52		
Lamphey	d	11x59										13x59											15x59		
Pembroke	d	12 02										14 02											16 02		
Pembroke Dock	a	12 17										14 17											16 17		
Clunderwen	d						12x20										14x13								
Clarbeston Road	d						12x27										14x20								
Haverfordwest	d						12 36										14 28								
Johnston	d						12x43										14x36								
Milford Haven	a						12 58										14 51								
Fishguard Harbour	a									13 14															
⛴	d																								
Rosslare Harbour ⛴	a																								

For general notes see front of timetable
For details of catering facilities see Directory of Train Operators

A From Crewe (Table 131)
B From Cheltenham Spa (Table 57)

2 February to 22 March

Cardiff → Maesteg, Swansea and West Wales

Route Diagram - see first page of Table 127

	AW	AW	GW		AW	AW	AW	GW	AW	AW	AW		GW	AW	AW	GW	AW	AW	AW		AW	AW	AW	GW
											R							R					R	
		◇	1 ◇				◇	1 ◇					1 ◇			1 ◇					◇			1 ◇
	A									B				B										
		🛒	🍽				🛒	🍽			🛒		🍽		🛒	🍽	🛒	🛒					🛒	🍽
London Paddington 15 ⊖ d			11 15					12 15					13 15			14 15								15 15
Reading 7 d			11 41					12 41					13 41			14 41								15 41
Manchester Piccadilly 10 d		10 34					11 34				12 34							13 34					14 34	
Gloucester 7 d										13 58				14 58										
Bristol Parkway 7 d			13 20					14 20					15 22			16 20								17 20
Newport (South Wales) d		13 38	13 45				14 38	14 45		14 54	15 38		15 46	15 52		16 45		16 38					17 38	17 46
Cardiff Queen Street 3 d																								
Cardiff Central 7 d		14 04	14 02		14 21		15 04	15 02	15 14	15 21	16 04		16 03	16 21		17 02		17 04	17 21			17 38	18 02	18 01
Pontyclun d					14 33					15 33				16 33					17 33					
Llanharan d					14 38					15 38				16 38					17 38					
Pencoed d					14 42					15 42				16 42					17 42					
Bridgend d		14 23	14 23		14 49		15 23	15 23	15 34	15 49	16 23		16 24	16 49		17 23		17 25	17 49			17 58	18 21	18 23
Wildmill d					14 52					15 52				16 52					17 52					
Sarn d					14 55					15 55				16 55					17 55					
Tondu d					14 58					15 58				16 58					17 58					
Garth (Mid Glamorgan) d					15 08					16 08				17 08					18 08					
Maesteg (Ewenny Road) d					15 10					16 10				17 10					18 10					
Maesteg a					15 15					16 15				17 15					18 15					
Pyle d									15 42									17 32				18 06		
Port Talbot Parkway d		14 36	14 36				15 36	15 36	15 50		16 36		16 37			17 36		17 40				18 14	18 34	18 36
Baglan d									15 54									17 43				18 18		
Briton Ferry d									15 57									17 47				18 21		
Neath d		14 43	14 43				15 43	15 43	16 01		16 43		16 44			17 43		17 51				18 25	18 41	18 44
Skewen d									16 05									17 55				18 29		
Llansamlet d									16 09									17 59				18 33		
Swansea 7 a		14 56	15 00				15 56	15 58	16 20		16 56		17 01			17 58		18 06				18 44	18 56	18 57
d		15 05				15 50	16 05				17 05				17 50			18 09			18 21		19 05	
Gowerton d						16x01					17x20				18x01			18x19						
Llanelli a		15 23				16 08	16 20				17 27				18 08			18 26			18 37		19 20	
d		15 24				16 08	16 21				17 27				18 08			18 26					19 21	
Pembrey & Burry Port d		15 29				16 14	16 26				17 33				18 14			18 32					19 26	
Kidwelly d						16x21					17x39				18x21			18x38						
Ferryside d						16x27					17x44				18x27			18x43						
Carmarthen a		15 49				16 40	16 51				17 56				18 40		←	19 00					19 46	
d		15 52				16 56					17 59				19 05		19 05						19 52	
Whitland a		16 15				17 12					18 13				→		19 21						20 06	
d		16 16				17 12					18 14						19 21						20 07	
Narberth d						17x21											19x30							
Kilgetty d						17x30											19x39							
Saundersfoot d						17x31											19x40							
Tenby a						17 38											19 47							
d						17 43											19 52							
Penally d						17x46											19x55							
Manorbier d						17 52											20 02							
Lamphey d						17x59											20x09							
Pembroke d						18 02											20 12							
Pembroke Dock a						18 17											20 22							
Clunderwen d		16x22									18x20												20x13	
Clarbeston Road d		16x29									18x27												20x20	
Haverfordwest d		16 37									18 35												20 28	
Johnston d		16x45									18x43												20x36	
Milford Haven a		17 00									18 58												20 51	
Fishguard Harbour a																								
⛴ d	14 30																							
Rosslare Harbour ⛴ a	18 00																							

For general notes see front of timetable
For details of catering facilities see Directory of Train Operators

A Ship service
B From Cheltenham Spa (Table 57)

Table 128

Saturdays

2 February to 22 March

Cardiff → Maesteg, Swansea and West Wales

Route Diagram - see first page of Table 127

		AW	AW	GW	AW	AW	AW	AW	GW	AW	GW	AW	AW	GW	AW	AW	AW	GW	GW	GW	GW
		A	R	1 ◇		A		R	1 ◇	A	1 ◇	R	A	1 ◇	◇	◇	◇	Bus	1 ◇	Bus	1 ◇
			trolley	buffet				trolley	buffet		buffet	trolley		buffet	trolley				buffet		buffet
London Paddington 15 ⊖	d			16 15					17 15		18 15			19 15					20 15		21 15
Reading 7	d			16 41					17 41		18 41			19 41					20 41		21 41
Manchester Piccadilly 10	d		15 34					16 34				17 34			18 34						
Gloucester 7	d	16 58				17 58				18 58			19 58								
Bristol Parkway 7	d			18 20					19 20		20 21			21 21					22 24		23 20
Newport (South Wales)	d	17 52	18 41	18 46		18 52		19 37	19 44	19 52	20 49	20 46	20 52	21 46	21 39			22 48	22 50	22 48	23 47
Cardiff Queen Street 3	d																				
Cardiff Central 7	d	18 21	19 04	19 02		19 21	19 38	20 00	20 03	20 21	21 06	21 09	21 21	22 07	22 09		22 41		23 11		00 08
Pontyclun	d	18 33				19 33				20 33			21 40				22 53				
Llanharan	d	18 38				19 38				20 38			21 45				22 58				
Pencoed	d	18 42				19 42				20 42			21 49				23 02				
Bridgend	d	18 49	19 23	19 23		19 49	19 58	20 19	20 25	20 49	21 27	21 28	21 56	22 28	22 28		23 08		23 32	23s33	00 29
Wildmill	d	18 52				19 52				20 52			21 59								
Sarn	d	18 55				19 55				20 55			22 02								
Tondu	d	18 58				19 58				20 58			22 05								
Garth (Mid Glamorgan)	d	19 08				20 08				21 08			22 15								
Maesteg (Ewenny Road)	d	19 10				20 10				21 10			22 17								
Maesteg	a	19 15				20 15				21 15			22 22								
Pyle	d						20 06					21 35					23 16				
Port Talbot Parkway	d		19 36	19 36			20 14	20 32	20 38		21 40	21 43		22 41	22 41		23 24		23 45	23s58	00 42
Baglan	d						20 18										23 27				
Briton Ferry	d						20 21										23 31				
Neath	d		19 43	19 44			20 25		20 45		21 47	21 50		22 48	22 48		23 35		23 52	00a10	00 49
Skewen	d						20 29										23 38				
Llansamlet	d						20 33										23 42				
Swansea 7	a		19 56	20 01			20 44		20 58		22 04	22 03		23 04	23 00		23 51	23 58	00 10		01 02
	d		20 00		20 05				21 03			22 25			23 06	23 45	00 05				
Gowerton	d				20x17							22x35			23x21		00b16				
Llanelli	a		20 15		20 24			21 04	21 25			22 42			23 27	00 01	00s22				
	d		20 16		20 24			21 04	21 25			22 42			23 28	00 01					
Pembrey & Burry Port	d		20 21		20 30			21 10	21 32			22 48			23 33		00s28				
Kidwelly	d				20x37							22x54			23x39		00b35				
Ferryside	d				20x43							22x59			23x45		00b41				
Carmarthen	a		20 46		20 56			21 29	21 55			23 11			00 03	00 25	00 58				
	d				20 59			22 06				23 17				00 27					
Whitland	a				21 15			22 21				23 31				00 42					
	d				21 15			22 21				23 32				00 43					
Narberth	d				21x24																
Kilgetty	d				21x34																
Saundersfoot	d				21x36																
Tenby	a				21 43																
	d				21 44																
Penally	d				21x47																
Manorbier	d				21 54																
Lamphey	d				22x01																
Pembroke	d				22 04																
Pembroke Dock	a				22 19																
Clunderwen	d							22x27				23x38									
Clarbeston Road	d							22x34				23x45				00x56					
Haverfordwest	d							22 43				23a53									
Johnston	d							22x50													
Milford Haven	a							23 05													
Fishguard Harbour	a															01 23					
	d																				
Rosslare Harbour	a																				

For general notes see front of timetable
For details of catering facilities see Directory of Train Operators

A From Cheltenham Spa (Table 57)
b Stops, on request, to set down only

from 29 March

Cardiff → Maesteg, Swansea and West Wales

Route Diagram - see first page of Table 127

		AW	AW	AW	AW	GW	GW	AW	AW	AW	AW	AW		AW	AW	AW	AW	AW	AW	GW	AW	AW	AW	AW	AW
		R	◇		◇	1 ◇	1 ◇	A	◇	1		1			◇			◇		1		◇ B			
London Paddington 15 ⊖	d					21p15	22p45																		
Reading 7	d					21p41	23p11																		
Manchester Piccadilly 10	d	17p34																							
Gloucester 7	d																		05 50						
Bristol Parkway 7	d					22p46	00 17																		
Newport (South Wales)	d	20p46				23p15	00 48												06 44		07 40				08 40
Cardiff Queen Street 3	d																								
Cardiff Central 7	d	21p07			23p15	23p37	01 04								05 40	05 51		06 52	07 04		08 04	08 09	08 21		09 04
Pontyclun	d				23p27										05 52	06 03			07 16				08 33		
Llanharan	d				23p32										05 57	06 08			07 21				08 38		
Pencoed	d				23p36										06 02	06 12			07 25				08 42		
Bridgend	d	21p28			23p42	23p57	01 28								06 08	06 20		07 12	07 32		08 23	08 29	08 49		09 23
Wildmill	d															06 22			07 35				08 52		
Sarn	d															06 25			07 38				08 55		
Tondu	d															06 29			07 41				08 58		
Garth (Mid Glamorgan)	d															06 38			07 51				09 08		
Maesteg (Ewenny Road)	d															06 41			07 53				09 10		
Maesteg	a															06 46			07 59				09 15		
Pyle	d	21p35			23p50										06 16			07 20				08 37			
Port Talbot Parkway	d	21p43			23p59	00 10	01 41								06 24			07 28			08 36	08 45			09 36
Baglan	d				00 02										06 28			07 32				08 49			
Briton Ferry	d				00 06										06 31			07 35				08 52			
Neath	d	21p50			00 10	00 18	01 48								06 35			07 39			08 43	08 56			09 43
Skewen	d				00 13										06 39			07 43				09 00			
Llansamlet	d				00 17										06 43			07 47				09 04			
Swansea 7	a	22p03			00 25	00 32	02 10								06 51			07 55			08 55	09 13			09 56
	d	22p25	23p45	00 05	00 45				04 36					05 50	06 54		07 50	08 05		08 13	09 00	09 15		09 50	10 05
Gowerton	d	22b35		00x16	00c56									06x01			08x01				09x15			10x01	
Llanelli	a	22p42	00 01	00 23	01s02				04 52					06 08	07 10		08 08	08 23		08 29	09 19	09 31		10 08	10 23
	d	22p42	00 01	00 23										06 08	07 11		08 08	08 23		08 34	09 19			10 08	10 24
Pembrey & Burry Port	d	22p48		00 29	01s08									06 14	07 17		08 14	08 29		08 41	09 24			10 14	10 29
Kidwelly	d	22b54		00x36	01c14									06x21	07x23		08x21							10x21	
Ferryside	d	22b59		00x41	01c20									06x27	07x29		08x27							10x27	
Carmarthen	a	23p11	00 25	00 59	01 37									06 40	07 42		08 40	08 51		09 08	09 47			10 40	10 51
	d	23p17	00 27							04 55	05 45	06 05		06 43	07 42		08 56				09 52			10 56	
Whitland	a	23p31	00 42							05 11	06 01	06 19		07 00	07 59		09 12				10 13			11 12	
	d	23p32	00 43							05 11	06 01	06 20		07 00	08 00		09 12				10 14			11 12	
Narberth	d										06x10			07x09			09x21							11x21	
Kilgetty	d										06x19			07x19			09x30							11x30	
Saundersfoot	d										06x20			07x21			09x31							11x31	
Tenby	a										06 27			07 28			09 38							11 38	
	d										06 30			07 42			09 43							11 43	
Penally	d										06x33			07x45			09x46							11x46	
Manorbier	d										06 39			07 52			09 52							11 52	
Lamphey	d										06x46			07x59			09x59							11x59	
Pembroke	d										06 49			08 02			10 02							12 02	
Pembroke Dock	a										07 04			08 17			10 17							12 17	
Clunderwen	d	23b38								05x18		06x26			08x06						10x20				
Clarbeston Road	d	23b45	00x56							05x26		06x33			08x13						10x27				
Haverfordwest	d	23p54								05e40		06 41			08 22						10 35				
Johnston	d	00x01								05x47		06x49			08x29						10x43				
Milford Haven	a	00 11								05 57		07 04			08 44						10 58				
Fishguard Harbour	a		01 23																						
	d							02 45																	
Rosslare Harbour	a							06 15																	

For general notes see front of timetable
For details of catering facilities see Directory of Train Operators

A Ship service
B To Shrewsbury (Table 129)

b Previous night. Stops on request, passengers wishing to alight must inform the guard and those wishing to join must give a hand signal to the driver
c Stops, on request, to set down only
e Arr. 0534

Table 128

from 29 March

Cardiff → Maesteg, Swansea and West Wales

Route Diagram - see first page of Table 127

		AW		AW	GW	AW	AW	GW	AW	AW	AW	AW	AW	GW		AW	AW	AW	GW	AW	AW	AW	AW	AW	GW
					1 ◇			1 ◇	◇					1 ◇				◇	1 ◇						1 ◇
				A			A										A						A	B	
					☕			☕	🛒	🛒				☕					☕						☕
London Paddington 15 ⊖	d				06 45			07 45						08 45					09 45						10 45
Reading 7	d				07 11			08 11						09 11					10 11						11 11
Manchester Piccadilly 10 🚌	d																								
Gloucester 7	d			07 58	08 37		08 58	09 37						10 37			10 58		11 37				11 58		12 37
Bristol Parkway 7	d																								
Newport (South Wales)	d			08 52	09 19	09 40	09 52	10 20			10 40			11 19		11 40	11 52		12 20	12 40			12 52		13 20
Cardiff Queen Street 3	d																								
Cardiff Central 7	d	09 14		09 21	09 40	10 04	10 21	10 40	10 55		11 04	11 14	11 21	11 40		12 04	12 21		12 39	13 04		13 14	13 21		13 39
Pontyclun	d			09 33			10 33						11 33				12 33						13 33		
Llanharan	d			09 38			10 38						11 38				12 38						13 38		
Pencoed	d			09 42			10 42						11 42				12 42						13 42		
Bridgend	d	09 34		09 49	10 00	10 23	10 49	11 00			11 23	11 34	11 49	12 00		12 23	12 49		13 00	13 23		13 34	13 49		14 00
Wildmill	d			09 52			10 52						11 52				12 52						13 52		
Sarn	d			09 55			10 55						11 55				12 55						13 55		
Tondu	d			09 58			10 58						11 58				12 58						13 58		
Garth (Mid Glamorgan)	d			10 08			11 08						12 08				13 08						14 08		
Maesteg (Ewenny Road)	d			10 10			11 10						12 10				13 10						14 10		
Maesteg	a			10 15			11 15						12 15				13 15						14 15		
Pyle	d	09 42										11 42										13 42			
Port Talbot Parkway	d	09 50			10 13	10 36		11 13			11 36	11 50		12 14		12 36			13 13	13 36		13 50			14 16
Baglan	d	09 54										11 54										13 54			
Briton Ferry	d	09 57										11 57										13 57			
Neath	d	10 01			10 20	10 43		11 20			11 43	12 01		12 21		12 43			13 20	13 43		14 01			14 23
Skewen	d	10 05										12 05										14 05			
Llansamlet	d	10 09										12 09										14 09			
Swansea 7	a	10 20			10 39	11 01		11 38			11 56	12 20		12 37		13 01			13 37	13 56		14 20			14 40
	d					11 05				11 50	12 05					13 05		13 16		14 00	14 05				
Gowerton	d									12x01											14x17				
Llanelli	a					11 21			11 58	12 08	12 20					13 20		13 32		14 15	14 24				
	d					11 21			11 58	12 08	12 21					13 21				14 16	14 24				
Pembrey & Burry Port	d					11 27				12 14	12 26					13 26				14 21	14 30				
Kidwelly	d									12x21											14x37				
Ferryside	d									12x27											14x43				
Carmarthen	a					11 47				12 40	12 51					13 46				14 47	14 56				
	d					11 52				12 56						13 52					14 59				
Whitland	a					12 13			12 33	13 12						14 06					15 15				
	d					12 14			12 34	13 12						14 07					15 15				
Narberth	d									13x21											15x24				
Kilgetty	d									13x30											15x33				
Saundersfoot	d									13x31											15x34				
Tenby	a									13 38											15 41				
	d									13 43											15 43				
Penally	d									13x46											15x46				
Manorbier	d									13 52											15 52				
Lamphey	d									13x59											15x59				
Pembroke	d									14 02											16 02				
Pembroke Dock	a									14 17											16 17				
Clunderwen	d					12x20										14x13									
Clarbeston Road	d					12x27										14x20									
Haverfordwest	d					12 36										14 28									
Johnston	d					12x43										14x36									
Milford Haven	a					12 58										14 51									
Fishguard Harbour	a								13 14																
	⛴ d																							14 30	
Rosslare Harbour	⛴ a																							18 00	

For general notes see front of timetable
For details of catering facilities see Directory of Train Operators

A From Cheltenham Spa (Table 57)
B Ship service

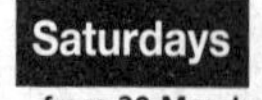

from 29 March

Cardiff → Maesteg, Swansea and West Wales

Route Diagram - see first page of Table 127

	AW	AW	GW		AW	AW	AW	AW	GW	AW	AW	GW	AW	AW	AW		AW	AW	GW	AW	AW	AW	GW	AW
			1 ◇						1 ◇			1 ◇						◇	1 ◇				1 ◇	
								A			A											A		
			🍴						🍴			🍴	🚌		🚌				🍴				🍴	
London Paddington 15 ⊖ d			11 45						12 45			13 45							14 45				15 45	
Reading 7 d			12 11						13 11			14 11							15 11				16 11	
Manchester Piccadilly 10 🚢 d																								
Gloucester 7 d			13 37					13 58	14 37		14 58	15 39							16 38			16 58	17 38	
Bristol Parkway 7 d																								
Newport (South Wales) d	13 40		14 20			14 40		14 54	15 20	15 40	15 52	16 21		16 40					17 21		17 40	17 52	18 26	18 40
Cardiff Queen Street 3 d																								
Cardiff Central 7 d	14 04	14 21	14 39			15 04	15 14	15 21	15 39	16 04	16 21	16 39		17 04			17 21		17 38	17 38	18 02	18 21	18 42	19 04
Pontyclun d		14 33						15 33			16 33						17 33					18 33		
Llanharan d		14 38						15 38			16 38						17 38					18 38		
Pencoed d		14 42						15 42			16 42						17 42					18 42		
Bridgend d	14 23	14 49	15 00			15 23	15 34	15 49	16 00	16 23	16 49	17 00		17 23			17 49		17 59	17 58	18 21	18 49	19 04	19 23
Wildmill d		14 52						15 52			16 52						17 52					18 52		
Sarn d		14 55						15 55			16 55						17 55					18 55		
Tondu d		14 58						15 58			16 58						17 58					18 58		
Garth (Mid Glamorgan) d		15 08						16 08			17 08						18 08					19 08		
Maesteg (Ewenny Road) d		15 10						16 10			17 10						18 10					19 10		
Maesteg a		15 15						16 15			17 15						18 15					19 15		
Pyle d							15 42							17 30						18 06				
Port Talbot Parkway d	14 36		15 13			15 36	15 50		16 13	16 36		17 13		17 38					18 12	18 14	18 34		19 17	19 36
Baglan d							15 54							17 42						18 18				
Briton Ferry d							15 57							17 45						18 21				
Neath d	14 43		15 20			15 43	16 01		16 20	16 43		17 20		17 49					18 19	18 25	18 41		19 24	19 43
Skewen d							16 05							17 54						18 29				
Llansamlet d							16 09							17 58						18 33				
Swansea 7 a	14 56		15 38			15 56	16 20		16 36	16 56		17 39		18 05					18 37	18 44	18 56		19 37	19 56
d	15 05				15 50	16 05				17 05			17 50	18 09				18 21			19 05			20 00
Gowerton d					16x01					17x20			18x01	18x19										
Llanelli a	15 23				16 08	16 20				17 27			18 08	18 26				18 37			19 20			20 15
d	15 24				16 08	16 21				17 27			18 08	18 26							19 21			20 16
Pembrey & Burry Port d	15 29				16 14	16 26				17 33			18 14	18 32							19 26			20 21
Kidwelly d					16x21					17x39			18x21	18x38										
Ferryside d					16x27					17x44			18x27	18x43										
Carmarthen a	15 49				16 40	16 51				17 56			18 40	19 00	←						19 46			20 46
d	15 52				16 56					17 59			19 05 →		19 05						19 52			
Whitland a	16 06				17 12					18 13					19 21						20 06			
d	16 07				17 12					18 14					19 21						20 07			
Narberth d					17x21										19x30									
Kilgetty d					17x30										19x39									
Saundersfoot d					17x31										19x40									
Tenby a					17 38										19 47									
d					17 43										19 52									
Penally d					17x46										19x55									
Manorbier d					17 52										20 02									
Lamphey d					17x59										20x09									
Pembroke d					18 02										20 12									
Pembroke Dock a					18 17										20 22									
Clunderwen d	16x13									18x20											20x13			
Clarbeston Road d	16x20									18x27											20x20			
Haverfordwest d	16 28									18 35											20 28			
Johnston d	16x36									18x43											20x36			
Milford Haven a	16 51									18 58											20 51			
Fishguard Harbour a																								
🚢 d																								
Rosslare Harbour 🚢 a																								

For general notes see front of timetable
For details of catering facilities see Directory of Train Operators

A From Cheltenham Spa (Table 57)

Table 128

from 29 March

Cardiff → Maesteg, Swansea and West Wales

Route Diagram - see first page of Table 127

		AW	AW	GW	AW	AW	AW	GW	AW	AW	GW	AW	GW	AW	GW	AW	GW	AW	AW	GW	AW	AW
				1 ◇				1 ◇			1 ◇		1 ◇		1 ◇	◇		◇				
			A				A			A												
														bus			bus		bus	bus	bus	bus
				catering				catering			catering		catering		catering							
London Paddington 15 ⊖	d			16 45				17 45			18 45		19 15		19 45							
Reading 7	d			17 11				18 11			19 11		19 41		20 11							
Manchester Piccadilly 10 ⛴	d																					
Gloucester 7	d		17 58	18 38			18 58	19 35		19 58	20 33		21 07		21 34							
Bristol Parkway 7	d																					
Newport (South Wales)	d		18 52	19 21		19 40	19 52	20 16	20 44	20 52	21 15	21 50	21 53		22 25		22 48			22 48		
Cardiff Queen Street 3	d																					
Cardiff Central 7	d		19 21	19 39	19 38	20 00	20 21	20 38	21 07	21 21	21 38	22 11	22 13	22 28	22 45			22 52			23 13	
Pontyclun	d		19 33				20 33			21 40				22 53				23 04	←			
Llanharan	d		19 38				20 38			21 45				23 01				23 09	23 01			
Pencoed	d		19 42				20 42			21 49				→				23 13	23 09			
Bridgend	d		19 49	20 00	19 58	20 19	20 49	20 58	21 28	21 56	22 00	22 31	22 34		23 06			23 19	23 24	23s33	23 50	
Wildmill	d		19 52				20 52			21 59												
Sarn	d		19 55				20 55			22 02												
Tondu	d		19 58				20 58			22 05												
Garth (Mid Glamorgan)	d		20 08				21 08			22 15												
Maesteg (Ewenny Road)	d		20 10				21 10			22 17												
Maesteg	a		20 15				21 15			22 22												
Pyle	d				20 06				21 36									23 27	23 39			
Port Talbot Parkway	d			20 13	20 14	20 35		21 11	21 44		22 13	22 43	22 47		23 19			23 36	23 59	23s58	00 15	
Baglan	d				20 18													23 39	00 04			
Briton Ferry	d				20 21													23 43	00 12			
Neath	d			20 20	20 25			21 18	21 51		22 20	22 50	22 55		23 27			23 47	00 20	00a10	00 30	←
Skewen	d				20 29													23 50	00 28			00 28
Llansamlet	d				20 33													23 54	→			00 36
Swansea 7	a			20 37	20 44			21 31	22 03		22 37	23 03	23 11		23 44		23 58	00 02			00 48	00 51
	d	20 05						21 38	22 25			23 06				23 45		00 05				
Gowerton	d	20x17							22x35			23x21						00b16				
Llanelli	a	20 24				21 04		21 56	22 42			23 27				00 01		00s22				
	d	20 24				21 04		21 56	22 42			23 28				00 01						
Pembrey & Burry Port	d	20 30				21 10		22 03	22 48			23 33						00s28				
Kidwelly	d	20x37							22x54			23x39						00b35				
Ferryside	d	20x43							22x59			23x45						00b41				
Carmarthen	a	20 56				21 29		22 26	23 11			00 03				00 25		00 58				
	d	20 59				22 06			23 17							00 27						
Whitland	a	21 15				22 21			23 31							00 42						
	d	21 15				22 21			23 32							00 43						
Narberth	d	21x24																				
Kilgetty	d	21x34																				
Saundersfoot	d	21x36																				
Tenby	a	21 43																				
	d	21 44																				
Penally	d	21x47																				
Manorbier	d	21 54																				
Lamphey	d	22x01																				
Pembroke	d	22 04																				
Pembroke Dock	a	22 19																				
Clunderwen	d					22x27			23x38													
Clarbeston Road	d					22x34			23x45							00x56						
Haverfordwest	d					22 43			23a53													
Johnston	d					22x50																
Milford Haven	a					23 05																
Fishguard Harbour	a															01 23						
	⛴ d																					
Rosslare Harbour	⛴ a																					

For general notes see front of timetable
For details of catering facilities see Directory of Train Operators

A From Cheltenham Spa (Table 57)
b Stops, on request, to set down only

until 27 January

Cardiff → Maesteg, Swansea and West Wales

Route Diagram - see first page of Table 127

		AW ◇	AW ◇	AW A	AW ◇	AW ◇	GW 1 ◇	AW	AW ◇ B	GW 1 ◇	AW A	AW	AW	GW 1 ◇	GW 1 ◇	AW ◇ C	AW ◇ D	AW	GW 1 ◇	GW 1 ◇
London Paddington 15 ⊖	d						08 33			09 30				10 37	11 37				12 37	13 37
Reading 7	d						09 11			10 07				11 12	12 11				13 12	14 11
Manchester Piccadilly 10	d																			
Gloucester 7	d																			
Bristol Parkway 7	d						10 16			11 10				12 10	13 10				14 10	15 10
Newport (South Wales)	d				09 10		10 39		11 02	11 33				12 32	13 32	13 38			14 32	15 33
Cardiff Queen Street 3	d																			
Cardiff Central 7	d		22p41		09 30		10 56		11 20	11 49				12 50	13 51	14 03			14 50	15 50
Pontyclun	d		22p53		09 42															
Llanharan	d		22p58		09 48															
Pencoed	d		23p02		09 52															
Bridgend	d		23p08		09 58		11 16		11 40	12 10				13 09	14 11	14 24			15 09	16 11
Wildmill	d																			
Sarn	d																			
Tondu	d																			
Garth (Mid Glamorgan)	d																			
Maesteg (Ewenny Road)	d																			
Maesteg	a																			
Pyle	d		23p16		10 06															
Port Talbot Parkway	d		23p24		10 14		11 29		11 54	12 23				13 23	14 24	14 38			15 23	16 23
Baglan	d		23p27		10 17															
Briton Ferry	d		23p31		10 21															
Neath	d		23p35		10 25		11 37		12 02	12 31				13 30	14 31	14 46			15 30	16 31
Skewen	d		23p38		10 29															
Llansamlet	d		23p42		10 33															
Swansea 7	a		23p51		10 40		11 50		12 14	12 43				13 43	14 45	14 58			15 43	16 43
	d	23p45	00 05		10 43	11 09			12 17					13 48		15 06	15 16		15 53	
Gowerton	d		00b16		10x54	11x20			12x28								15x27			
Llanelli	a	00 01	00s22		11 00	11 27			12 34					14 05		15 22	15 34		16 10	
	d	00 01			11 06				12 35					14 06		15 22			16 11	
Pembrey & Burry Port	d		00s28		11 12				12 40					14 12		15 28			16 18	
Kidwelly	d		00b35		11x18				12x47											
Ferryside	d		00b41		11x24				12x53											
Carmarthen	a	00 25	00 58		11 37				13 05					14 38		15 53			16 43	
	d	00 27			12 05				13 08			14 05	14 20					16 05		
Whitland	a	00 42			12 20				13 23			14 21	14 36					16 21		
	d	00 43			12 24			12 30	13 24			14 21	14 36					16 21		
Narberth	d							12x39					14x45							
Kilgetty	d							12x48					14x55							
Saundersfoot	d							12x50					14x57							
Tenby	a							13 00					15 04							
	d												15 21							
Penally	d												15x24							
Manorbier	d												15 31							
Lamphey	d												15x38							
Pembroke	d												15 42							
Pembroke Dock	a												15 53							
Clunderwen	d				12x31							14x28						16x28		
Clarbeston Road	d	00x56			12x38							14x36						16x36		
Haverfordwest	d				12 47							14 44						16 44		
Johnston	d				12x55							14x52						16x52		
Milford Haven	a				13 06							15 05						17 05		
Fishguard Harbour	a	01 23							14 00											
	(ship) d			02 45							14 30									
Rosslare Harbour	(ship) a			06 15							18 00									

For general notes see front of timetable
For details of catering facilities see Directory of Train Operators

- **A** Ship service
- **B** From Hereford (Table 131)
- **C** From Crewe (Table 131)
- **D** To Crewe (Table 131)
- **b** Stops, on request, to set down only

Cardiff → Maesteg, Swansea and West Wales

Route Diagram - see first page of Table 127

		AW	AW	GW	GW	AW		GW	GW	GW	AW	GW	AW	GW	AW	GW	GW
			R			R					R						
				1 ◇	1 ◇			1 ◇	1 ◇	1 ◇		1 ◇	◇	1 ◇	◇	1 ◇	1 ◇
						A											
			⌶	ꝒD	ꝒD	⌶		ꝒD	ꝒD	ꝒD	⌶	ꝒD		ꝒD			
London Paddington 15 ⊖	d			14 37	15 37			16 37	17 12	17 37		18 37		19 37		20 37	21 37
Reading 7	d			15 12	16 13			17 13	17 48	18 13		19 11		20 12		21 14	22 13
Manchester Piccadilly 10 ⇌	d		12 33			14 34					16 37						
Gloucester 7	d																
Bristol Parkway 7	d			16 10	17 10			18 14	18 46	19 16		20 14		21 08		22 11	23 14
Newport (South Wales)	d		16 02	16 32	17 33	18 01		18 35	19 12	19 38	20 02	20 37		21 32		22 39	23 43
Cardiff Queen Street 3	d																
Cardiff Central 7	d		16 18	16 50	17 52	18 18		18 52	19 29	19 55	20 22	20 52	21 30	21 49	22 35	23 00	00 05
Pontyclun	d		16 32										21 42				
Llanharan	d		16 37										21 46				
Pencoed	d		16 41										21 50				
Bridgend	d		16 45	17 10	18 13	18 38		19 13	19 49	20 16	20 42	21 14	21 57	22 10	22 54	23 20	00 25
Wildmill	d																
Sarn	d																
Tondu	d																
Garth (Mid Glamorgan)	d																
Maesteg (Ewenny Road)	d																
Maesteg	a																
Pyle	d												22 04				
Port Talbot Parkway	d		16 59	17 23	18 26	18 52		19 26	20 02	20 29	20 56	21 26	22 12	22 24	23 07	23 34	00 38
Baglan	d												22 16				
Briton Ferry	d												22 19				
Neath	d		17 07	17 31	18 33	19 00		19 35	20 10	20 37	21 04	21 35	22 23	22 32	23 14	23 42	00 45
Skewen	d												22 28				
Llansamlet	d												22 32				
Swansea 7	a		17 20	17 43	18 48	19 12		19 47	20 23	20 52	21 16	21 47	22 39	22 44	23 26	23 54	00 57
	d		17 25	17 48		19 17					21 19		22 50		23 30		
Gowerton	d		17x36			19x27					21x30				23x40		
Llanelli	a		17 42	18 05		19 35					21 36		23 05		23 47		
	d		17 43	18 07		19 35					21 37		23 06		23 47		
Pembrey & Burry Port	d		17 49	18 13		19 42					21 43		23 12		23 53		
Kidwelly	d		17x55								21x49				23x59		
Ferryside	d		18x01								21x55				00x05		
Carmarthen	a		18 14	18 38		20 02					22 08		23 34		00 17		
	d	17 05	18 16			20 09					22 10				00 19		
Whitland	a	17 21	18 31			20 24					22 25				00 34		
	d	17 21	18 33			20 26	20 34				22 27				00 34		
Narberth	d	17x30					20x43										
Kilgetty	d	17x40					20x52										
Saundersfoot	d	17x42					20x54										
Tenby	a	17 49					21 01										
	d	17 50					21 05										
Penally	d	17x53					21x08										
Manorbier	d	18 00					21 14										
Lamphey	d	18x07					21x22										
Pembroke	d	18 11					21 25										
Pembroke Dock	a	18 25					21 40										
Clunderwen	d		18x39			20x33					22x33						
Clarbeston Road	d		18x46			20x40					22x40				00x46		
Haverfordwest	d		18 55			20x50					22 49						
Johnston	d		19x02			20x58					22x56						
Milford Haven	a		19 17			21 15					23 11						
Fishguard Harbour	a														01 15		
⛴	d																
Rosslare Harbour ⛴	a																

For general notes see front of timetable
For details of catering facilities see Directory of Train Operators

A ⌶ To Pembroke Dock

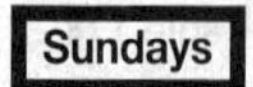
Sundays

3 February to 23 March

Cardiff → Maesteg, Swansea and West Wales

Route Diagram - see first page of Table 127

Station		AW ◇	AW ◇	GW 1◇	AW A	AW ◇	AW ◇	GW 1◇	AW	AW ◇ B	GW 1◇	AW A	AW	AW	GW 1◇	AW ◇ C	GW 1◇	AW ◇ D	AW	GW 1◇
London Paddington 15 ⊖	d			21p15				08 00			09 03				10 03		11 03			12 03
Reading 7	d			21p41				08 37			09 42				10 42		11 45			12 42
Manchester Piccadilly 10	d																			
Gloucester 7	d																			
Bristol Parkway 7	d			23p20				10 19			11 34				12 34		13 34			14 34
Newport (South Wales)	d			23p47		09 10		10 42		11 02	11 57				12 56	13 38	13 57			14 56
Cardiff Queen Street 3	d																			
Cardiff Central 7	d		22p41	00 08		09 30		10 59		11 20	12 13				13 14	14 03	14 14			15 14
Pontyclun	d		22p53			09 42														
Llanharan	d		22p58			09 48														
Pencoed	d		23p02			09 52														
Bridgend	d		23p08	00 29		09 58		11 19		11 40	12 34				13 34	14 24	14 34			15 34
Wildmill	d																			
Sarn	d																			
Tondu	d																			
Garth (Mid Glamorgan)	d																			
Maesteg (Ewenny Road)	d																			
Maesteg	a																			
Pyle	d		23p16			10 06														
Port Talbot Parkway	d		23p24	00 42		10 14		11 32		11 54	12 46				13 47	14 38	14 47			15 47
Baglan	d		23p27			10 17														
Briton Ferry	d		23p31			10 21														
Neath	d		23p35	00 49		10 25		11 40		12 02	12 55				13 55	14 46	14 56			15 55
Skewen	d		23p38			10 29														
Llansamlet	d		23p42			10 33														
Swansea 7	a		23p51	01 02		10 40		11 53		12 14	13 07				14 07	14 58	15 08			16 07
	d	23p45	00 05			10 50	11 00			12 17					14 12	15 06		15 16		16 17
Gowerton	d		00b16			11x01	11x11			12x28								15x27		
Llanelli	a	00 01	00s22			11 07	11 18			12 34					14 29	15 25		15 34		16 34
	d	00 01				11 08				12 35					14 31	15 25				16 35
Pembrey & Burry Port	d		00s28			11 14				12 40					14 37	15 31				16 42
Kidwelly	d		00b35			11x20				12x47										
Ferryside	d		00b41			11x26				12x53										
Carmarthen	a	00 25	00 58			11 39				13 05					15 04	15 56				17 03
	d	00 27				12 05				13 08			14 05	14 20					16 05	
Whitland	a	00 42				12 20				13 23			14 21	14 36					16 21	
	d	00 43				12 24			12 30	13 24			14 21	14 36					16 21	
Narberth	d								12x39					14x45						
Kilgetty	d								12x48					14x55						
Saundersfoot	d								12x50					14x57						
Tenby	a								13 00					15 04						
	d													15 21						
Penally	d													15x24						
Manorbier	d													15 31						
Lamphey	d													15x38						
Pembroke	d													15 42						
Pembroke Dock	a													15 53						
Clunderwen	d					12x31							14x28						16x28	
Clarbeston Road	d	00x56				12x38							14x36						16x36	
Haverfordwest	d					12 47							14 44						16 44	
Johnston	d					12x55							14x52						16x52	
Milford Haven	a					13 06							15 05						17 05	
Fishguard Harbour	a	01 23								14 00										
⛴	d				02 45							14 30								
Rosslare Harbour ⛴	a				06 15							18 00								

For general notes see front of timetable
For details of catering facilities see Directory of Train Operators

A Ship service
B From Hereford (Table 131)
C From Crewe (Table 131)
D To Crewe (Table 131)
b Stops, on request, to set down only

3 February to 23 March

Cardiff → Maesteg, Swansea and West Wales

Route Diagram - see first page of Table 127

		GW	AW	AW	GW	GW	AW		GW	GW	AW	GW	AW	GW	AW	GW	GW
				R			R				R						
		1 ◇			1 ◇	1 ◇			1 ◇	1 ◇		1 ◇	◇	1 ◇	◇	1 ◇	1 ◇
							A										
		☕		🍴	☕	☕	🍴		☕	☕	🍴	☕		☕		☕	☕
London Paddington 15 ⊖	d	13 03			14 03	15 03			16 03	17 03		18 03		19 03		20 03	21 33
Reading 7	d	13 42			14 42	15 42			16 42	17 42		18 42		19 42		20 41	22 07
Manchester Piccadilly 10 🚌	d			12 33			14 34				16 37						
Gloucester 7	d																
Bristol Parkway 7	d	15 34			16 34	17 34			18 34	19 34		20 34		21 34		22 35	23 49
Newport (South Wales)	d	15 57		16 02	16 56	17 56	18 03		18 55	19 56	20 02	20 57		21 57		23 05	00 12
Cardiff Queen Street 3	d																
Cardiff Central 7	d	16 13		16 18	17 14	18 13	18 20		19 13	20 13	20 22	21 12	21 30	22 18	22 35	23 25	00 34
Pontyclun	d			16 32									21 42				
Llanharan	d			16 37									21 46				
Pencoed	d			16 41									21 50				
Bridgend	d	16 34		16 45	17 34	18 34	18 40		19 34	20 34	20 42	21 34	21 57	22 39	22 54	23 45	00 54
Wildmill	d																
Sarn	d																
Tondu	d																
Garth (Mid Glamorgan)	d																
Maesteg (Ewenny Road)	d																
Maesteg	a																
Pyle	d												22 04				
Port Talbot Parkway	d	16 46		16 59	17 47	18 47	18 54		19 47	20 47	20 56	21 46	22 12	22 51	23 07	23 59	01 07
Baglan	d												22 16				
Briton Ferry	d												22 19				
Neath	d	16 55		17 07	17 55	18 55	19 02		19 55	20 55	21 04	21 55	22 23	22 59	23 14	00 07	01 14
Skewen	d												22 28				
Llansamlet	d												22 32				
Swansea 7	a	17 07		17 20	18 07	19 10	19 14		20 10	21 10	21 16	22 07	22 39	23 11	23 26	00 19	01 26
	d			17 25	18 17		19 19				21 19		22 50		23 30		
Gowerton	d			17x36			19x29				21x30				23x40		
Llanelli	a			17 42	18 39		19 37				21 36		23 05		23 47		
	d			17 43	18 40		19 37				21 37		23 06		23 47		
Pembrey & Burry Port	d			17 49	18 47		19 44				21 43		23 12		23 53		
Kidwelly	d			17x55							21x49				23x59		
Ferryside	d			18x01							21x55				00x05		
Carmarthen	a			18 14	19 11		20 04				22 08		23 34		00 17		
	d		17 10	18 16			20 09				22 10				00 19		
Whitland	a		17 26	18 31			20 24				22 25				00 34		
	d		17 26	18 33			20 26	20 34			22 27				00 34		
Narberth	d		17x35					20x43									
Kilgetty	d		17x45					20x52									
Saundersfoot	d		17x47					20x54									
Tenby	a		17 54					21 01									
	d		17 55					21 05									
Penally	d		17x58					21x08									
Manorbier	d		18 05					21 14									
Lamphey	d		18x12					21x22									
Pembroke	d		18 16					21 25									
Pembroke Dock	a		18 30					21 40									
Clunderwen	d			18x39			20x33				22x33						
Clarbeston Road	d			18x46			20x40				22x40				00x46		
Haverfordwest	d			18 55			20 50				22 49						
Johnston	d			19x02			20x58				22x56						
Milford Haven	a			19 17			21 15				23 11						
Fishguard Harbour	a														01 15		
⛴	d																
Rosslare Harbour ⛴	a																

For general notes see front of timetable
For details of catering facilities see Directory of Train Operators

A 🍴 To Pembroke Dock

Table 128

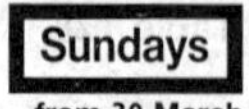
Sundays

from 30 March

Cardiff → Maesteg, Swansea and West Wales

Route Diagram - see first page of Table 127

		AW	AW	AW	AW		AW	AW	AW	AW		AW	GW	AW	AW		AW	AW	GW	AW		GW	AW	AW	AW
		◇		◇					A	◇		◇	1 ◇						1 ◇	A		1 ◇		◇ B	
			(bus)		(bus)		(bus)	(bus)					(restaurant)				(trolley)		(restaurant)			(restaurant)			(trolley)
London Paddington 15 ⊖	d												08 03						09 30			10 30			
Reading 7	d												08 42						10 07			11 07			
Manchester Piccadilly 10 (train)	d																								
Gloucester 7	d												10 08						11 33			12 33			
Bristol Parkway 7	d																								
Newport (South Wales)	d									09 10			10 52		11 02				12 18			13 16			
Cardiff Queen Street 3	d																								
Cardiff Central 7	d		22p28	22p52			23p13			09 30			11 09		11 20				12 34			13 34	14 03		
Pontyclun	d		22p53	23p04						09 42															
Llanharan	d		23p01	23p09	⟵					09 48															
Pencoed	d		23p09	23p13	23p09					09 52															
Bridgend	d		⟶	23p19	23p24		23p50			09 58			11 29		11 40				12 55			13 54	14 24		
Wildmill	d																								
Sarn	d																								
Tondu	d																								
Garth (Mid Glamorgan)	d																								
Maesteg (Ewenny Road)	d																								
Maesteg	a																								
Pyle	d			23p27	23p39					10 06															
Port Talbot Parkway	d			23p36	23p59		00 15			10 14			11 42		11 54				13 11			14 07	14 38		
Baglan	d			23p39	00 04					10 17															
Briton Ferry	d			23p43	00 12					10 21															
Neath	d			23p47	00 20		00 30	⟵		10 25			11 50		12 02				13 20			14 15	14 46		
Skewen	d			23p50	00 28			00 28		10 29															
Llansamlet	d			23p54	⟶			00 36		10 33															
Swansea 7	a			00 02			00 48	00 51		10 40			12 03		12 14				13 34			14 34	14 59		
	d	23p45		00 05						10 45		11 00			12 17				13 41				15 06	15 16	
Gowerton	d			00b16						10x59		11x11			12x28									15x27	
Llanelli	a	00 01		00s22						11 05		11 18			12 34				13 57				15 22	15 34	
	d	00 01								11 06					12 35				13 58				15 22		
Pembrey & Burry Port	d			00s28						11 12					12 40				14 05				15 28		
Kidwelly	d			00b35						11x18					12x47										
Ferryside	d			00b41						11x24					12x53										
Carmarthen	a	00 25		00 58						11 37					13 05				14 26				15 53		
	d	00 27								12 05					13 08		14 05	14 20							16 05
Whitland	a	00 42								12 20					13 23		14 21	14 36							16 21
	d	00 43								12 24				12 30	13 24		14 21	14 36							16 21
Narberth	d													12x39				14x45							
Kilgetty	d													12x48				14x55							
Saundersfoot	d													12x50				14x57							
Tenby	a													13 00				15 04							
	d																	15 21							
Penally	d																	15x24							
Manorbier	d																	15 31							
Lamphey	d																	15x38							
Pembroke	d																	15 42							
Pembroke Dock	a																	15 53							
Clunderwen	d									12x31							14x28								16x28
Clarbeston Road	d	00x56								12x38							14x36								16x36
Haverfordwest	d									12 47							14 44								16 44
Johnston	d									12x55							14x52								16x52
Milford Haven	a									13 06							15 05								17 05
Fishguard Harbour	a	01 23													14 00										
(ship)	d								02 45											14 30					
Rosslare Harbour (ship)	a								06 15											18 00					

For general notes see front of timetable
For details of catering facilities see Directory of Train Operators

A Ship service
B To Crewe (Table 131)
b Stops, on request, to set down only

Table 128

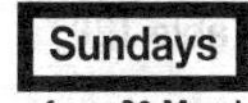

Sundays

from 30 March

Cardiff → Maesteg, Swansea and West Wales

Route Diagram - see first page of Table 127

		GW	GW		AW	AW	GW	GW		AW	AW	GW	GW		AW	GW	GW	AW		AW	GW	GW	GW		
		1 ◇	1 ◇				1 ◇	1 ◇		R		1 ◇	1 ◇			1 ◇	1 ◇			◇	1 ◇	1 ◇	1 ◇		
		☕	☕				☕	☕				☕	☕			☕	☕				☕	☕	☕		
London Paddington 15 ⊖	d	11 30	12 30				13 30	14 30				15 30	16 30			17 30	18 30				19 30	20 30	21 30		
Reading 7	d	12 07	13 07				14 07	15 07				16 07	17 07			18 07	19 07				20 07	21 06	22 07		
Manchester Piccadilly 10 ⇌	d																								
Gloucester 7	d	13 33	14 33				15 33	16 33				17 39	18 37			19 33	20 22				21 33	22 33	23 35		
Bristol Parkway 7	d																								
Newport (South Wales)	d	14 17	15 17			16 00	16 17	17 16				18 22	19 18			20 16	21 06	21 16			22 23	23 23	00 24		
Cardiff Queen Street 3	d																								
Cardiff Central 7	d	14 34	15 35			16 18	16 38	17 39			18 18	18 39	19 39		20 21	20 33	21 21	21 33		22 35	22 46	23 43	00 46		
Pontyclun	d					16 32												21 45							
Llanharan	d					16 36												21 49							
Pencoed	d					16 40												21 53							
Bridgend	d	14 54	15 55			16 45	16 59	17 59			18 38	19 00	20 00		20 41	20 54	21 43	22 00		22 54	23 07	00 03	01 06		
Wildmill	d																								
Sarn	d																								
Tondu	d																								
Garth (Mid Glamorgan)	d																								
Maesteg (Ewenny Road)	d																								
Maesteg	a																								
Pyle	d																	22 07							
Port Talbot Parkway	d	15 07	16 08			16 58	17 11	18 12			18 52	19 13	20 13		20 55	21 07	21 55	22 15		23 07	23 19	00 17	01 19		
Baglan	d																	22 19							
Briton Ferry	d																	22 22							
Neath	d	15 15	16 16			17 05	17 20	18 20			19 00	19 21	20 21		21 03	21 15	22 04	22 26		23 14	23 27	00 25	01 26		
Skewen	d																	22 31							
Llansamlet	d																	22 35							
Swansea 7	a	15 39	16 34			17 17	17 34	18 34			19 12	19 37	20 33		21 15	21 27	22 16	22 42		23 26	23 39	00 37	01 38		
	d	15 47				17 24	17 40				19 17				21 40			22 50		23 40					
Gowerton	d					17x34					19x27				21x51					23x50					
Llanelli	a	16 07				17 41	17 57				19 35				21 57			23 05		23 57					
	d	16 08				17 41	17 58				19 35				21 58			23 06		23 57					
Pembrey & Burry Port	d	16 15				17 47	18 05				19 42				22 04			23 12		00 03					
Kidwelly	d					17x53									22x10					00x09					
Ferryside	d					17x59									22x16					00x15					
Carmarthen	a	16 37				18 11	18 29				20 02				22 29			23 34		00 27					
	d				17 05	18 14					20 09				22 35					00 29					
Whitland	a				17 21	18 29					20 24				22 50					00 44					
	d				17 21	18 30				20 26	20 34				22 50					00 44					
Narberth	d				17x30						20x43														
Kilgetty	d				17x40						20x52														
Saundersfoot	d				17x42						20x54														
Tenby	a				17 49						21 01														
	d				17 50						21 05														
Penally	d				17x53						21x08														
Manorbier	d				18 00						21 14														
Lamphey	d				18x07						21x22														
Pembroke	d				18 11						21 25														
Pembroke Dock	a				18 25						21 40														
Clunderwen	d					18x36				20x33					22x57										
Clarbeston Road	d					18x43				20x40					23x04					00x56					
Haverfordwest	d					18 52				20 50					23 12										
Johnston	d					18x59				20x58					23x20										
Milford Haven	a					19 14				21 15					23 35										
Fishguard Harbour	a																			01 25					
⛴	d																								
Rosslare Harbour ⛴	a																								

For general notes see front of timetable
For details of catering facilities see
Directory of Train Operators

West Wales, Swansea and Maesteg → Cardiff

Route Diagram - see first page of Table 127

Miles	Miles	Station		AW	AW	AW	AW	AW	GW	GW	GW	GW	AW	GW	GW	AW	AW	GW	AW	GW
				MO	MO	MO	MX		MO											
								◇	1 ◇	1 ◇	1 ◇	1 ◇	◇	1 ◇	1 ◇		◇	1 ◇		1 ◇
				A	B	B			C	D					E					
									⊤	⊤	⊡	⊡	⊤	⊤	✕		⊤	⊤		⊤
—	—	Rosslare Harbour ⛴	d																	
—	—	**Fishguard Harbour** ⛴	a																	
0	—		d					01 50												
—	0	**Milford Haven**	d	21p35	21p35	23p50	00 15													
—	4	Johnston	d	21b42	21b42	23b57	00x22													
—	8¾	Haverfordwest	d	21p50	21p50	00 07	00 30													
15¾	14	Clarbeston Road	d	21b58	21b58	00x14	00x37	02x10												
22¼	—	Clunderwen	d	22b06	22b06	00x23	00x44													
—	0	**Pembroke Dock**	d																	
—	2	Pembroke	d																	
—	3½	Lamphey	d																	
—	7	Manorbier	d																	
—	10¼	Penally	d																	
—	11½	**Tenby**	a																	
—	—		d																	
—	15¾	Saundersfoot	d																	
—	16½	Kilgetty	d																	
—	22	Narberth	d																	
27¾	27¼	Whitland	a	22p12	22p12	00 29	00 50	02 22												
—	—		d	22p13	22p13	00 30	00 50	02 22												
41¾	—	**Carmarthen**	a	22p30	22p32	00 46	01 12	02 39												
—	—		d	22p35	22p37			02 44					05 04				05 50		06 18	
48¾	—	Ferryside	d	22b45	22b47												06x00		06x28	
53	—	Kidwelly	d	22b51	22b53												06x05		06x33	
58¼	—	Pembrey & Burry Port	d	22p59	23p01								05 22				06 12		06 40	
62¼	—	Llanelli	a	23p05	23p07			03 06					05 27				06 17		06 45	
—	—		d	23p05	23p07			03 07					05 28				06 18		06 46	
68	—	Gowerton	d	23b12	23b14														06x52	
73½	—	**Swansea** 7	a	23p26	23p28			03 25									06 35		07 06	
—	—		d	23p35	23p35				04 00	04 00	04 58	05 24		05 59	06 29		06 40	06 59	07 09	07 29
77¼	—	Llansamlet	d																07 16	
79¼	—	Skewen	d																07 20	
83	—	Neath	d	23p46	23p46				04 12	04 12	05 09	05 36		06 10	06 40		06 51	07 10	07 24	07 40
84¾	—	Briton Ferry	d																07 27	
86¼	—	Baglan	d																07 31	
88¼	—	Port Talbot Parkway	d	23p54	23p54				04 19	04 19	05 17	05 43	06 01	06 18	06 48		06 58	07 18	07 35	07 48
94¾	—	Pyle	d														07 04		07 42	
—	0	Maesteg	d													06 49				
—	½	Maesteg (Ewenny Road)	d													06 51				
—	1¼	Garth (Mid Glamorgan)	d													06 54				
—	5¼	Tondu	d													07 03				
—	6	Sarn	d													07 06				
—	7¼	Wildmill	d													07 08				
100¾	8¼	Bridgend	d	00 07	00 07				04 31	04 31	05 28	05 55	06 13	06 29	06 59	07 12	07 17	07 29	07 50	07 59
104¾	—	Pencoed	d										06 19			07 18			07 56	
107	—	Llanharan	d													07 22			08 00	
110	—	Pontyclun	d										06 26			07 26			08 04	
121	—	**Cardiff Central** 7	a	00 50	00 50				04 53	04 56	05 51	06 17	06 40	06 52	07 22	07 43	07 45	07 52	08 18	08 22
—	—	Cardiff Queen Street 3	a																	
—	—	Newport (South Wales)	a						05 32	05 32	06 07	06 33	07 02	07 08	07 38		08 03	08 08		08 38
—	—	Bristol Parkway 7	a						06 00	06 00	06 29	06 55		07 30	08 00			08 30		09 00
—	—	Gloucester 7	a																	
—	—	Manchester Piccadilly 10	a										10 13				11 13			
—	—	Reading 7	a						07 02	07 02	07 29	07 58		08 32	09 01			09 27		09 57
—	—	London Paddington 15 ⊖	a						07 32	07 32	08 01	08 30		09 06	09 29			09 59		10 27

For general notes see front of timetable
For details of catering facilities see Directory of Train Operators

A Until 24 March

B From 31 March

C 4 February to 24 March

D All Tuesdays to Fridays, also Mondays until 28 January and from 31 March

E **The Red Dragon**

b Previous night.

Stops on request, passengers wishing to alight must inform the guard and those wishing to join must give a hand signal to the driver

West Wales, Swansea and Maesteg → Cardiff

Route Diagram - see first page of Table 127

		AW	AW	GW	GW	AW	AW	AW	AW	GW	AW	AW	GW	AW	AW	AW	AW	GW	AW	AW
		◇		[1] ◇	[1] ◇	◇		◇		[1] ◇	◇		[1] ◇	◇				[1] ◇	◇	
							A	B							A			C		A
		[trolley]		⊠	⊠	[trolley]			[trolley]	[restaurant]	[trolley]		[restaurant]	[trolley]			[trolley]	⊠	[trolley]	
Rosslare Harbour (ship)	d																			
Fishguard Harbour (ship)	a																			
	d																			
Milford Haven	d	06 05				07 05								09 10						
Johnston	d	06x12				07x12								09x17						
Haverfordwest	d	06 20				07 20								09 25						
Clarbeston Road	d	06x27				07x27								09x32						
Clunderwen	d	06x33				07x33								09x38						
Pembroke Dock	d								07 05								09 05			
Pembroke	d								07 13								09 13			
Lamphey	d								07x16								09x16			
Manorbier	d								07 25								09 24			
Penally	d								07x30								09x29			
Tenby	a								07 33								09 32			
	d								07 40								09 42			
Saundersfoot	d								07x48								09x49			
Kilgetty	d								07x50								09x51			
Narberth	d								08x00								10x00			
Whitland	a	06 39				07 39			08 08					09 44			10 08			
	d	06 40				07 40			08 08					09 45			10 09			
Carmarthen	a	06 56				07 56			08 27					10 01			10 26			
	d	07 00			07 30	07 59			08 30		09 00			10 05			10 30		11 05	
Ferryside	d				07 42	08x09			08x40								10x40			
Kidwelly	d				07 49	08x14			08x46								10x46			
Pembrey & Burry Port	d	07 18			07 56	08 21			08 53		09 18			10 22			10 53		11 23	
Llanelli	a	07 23			08 02	08 26			08 59		09 23			10 28			10 59		11 28	
	d	07 24			08 04	08 27		08 45	09 00		09 26			10 28			11 00		11 29	
Gowerton	d	07x30				08x33		08x53	09x07								11x07			
Swansea [7]	a	07 43			08 22	08 46		09 07	09 22		09 46			10 45			11 22		11 46	
	d	07 45		07 59	08 29	08 55		09 10		09 29	09 55		10 29	10 55		11 10		11 29	11 55	
Llansamlet	d							09 17								11 17				
Skewen	d							09 21								11 21				
Neath	d	07 56		08 10	08 40	09 06		09 25		09 40	10 06		10 40	11 06		11 25		11 40	12 06	
Briton Ferry	d							09 29								11 28				
Baglan	d							09 32								11 32				
Port Talbot Parkway	d	08 03		08 18	08 48	09 13		09 36		09 48	10 13		10 48	11 13		11 36		11 48	12 13	
Pyle	d	08 10						09 43								11 43				
Maesteg	d		08 00				09 17					10 17			11 17					12 17
Maesteg (Ewenny Road)	d		08 02				09 19					10 19			11 19					12 19
Garth (Mid Glamorgan)	d		08 05				09 22					10 22			11 22					12 22
Tondu	d		08 14				09 31					10 31			11 31					12 31
Sarn	d		08 17				09 34					10 34			11 34					12 34
Wildmill	d		08 19				09 36					10 36			11 36					12 36
Bridgend	d	08 18	08 23	08 29	08 59	09 25	09 40	09 52		09 59	10 25	10 40	10 59	11 25	11 40	11 54		11 59	12 25	12 40
Pencoed	d	08 24					09 46					10 46			11 46					12 46
Llanharan	d		08 31				09 50					10 50			11 50					12 50
Pontyclun	d	08 31					09 54					10 54			11 54					12 54
Cardiff Central [7]	a	08 44	08 48	08 52	09 22	09 47	10 09	10 17		10 22	10 47	11 15	11 22	11 47	12 09	12 17		12 22	12 47	13 09
Cardiff Queen Street [3]	a																			
Newport (South Wales)	a	09 02		09 08	09 38	10 04	10 25			10 38	11 03		11 38	12 03	12 25			12 38	13 03	13 25
Bristol Parkway [7]	a			09 30	10 00					11 00			12 00					13 00		
Gloucester [7]	a						11 20								13 20					14 20
Manchester Piccadilly [10] (ship)	a	12 13				13 13					14 13			15 13					16 13	
Reading [7]	a			10 32	11 01					12 01			13 01					14 01		
London Paddington [15]	⊖ a			11 02	11 32					12 32			13 29					14 32		

For general notes see front of timetable
For details of catering facilities see Directory of Train Operators

A To Cheltenham Spa (Table 57)
B From Shrewsbury (Table 129)
C **The St David**

West Wales, Swansea and Maesteg → Cardiff

Route Diagram - see first page of Table 127

Station		GW	AW	AW		AW	AW	AW	AW		GW	AW	AW	GW		AW	AW	AW	AW		AW	GW	AW	AW
		1 ◇	◇			◇					1 ◇	R		1 ◇		R	◇					1 ◇	R	
				A									B					B						B
		[restaurant]	[trolley]								[restaurant]	[trolley]		[restaurant]		[trolley]	[trolley]				[trolley]	[restaurant]	[trolley]	
Rosslare Harbour	⛴ d			09 00																				
Fishguard Harbour	⛴ a			12 30																				
	d																13 34							
Milford Haven	d		11 10													13 10								
Johnston	d		11x17													13x17								
Haverfordwest	d		11 25													13 25								
Clarbeston Road	d		11x32													13x32								
Clunderwen	d		11x38													13x38								
Pembroke Dock	d								11 05												13 05			
Pembroke	d								11 13												13 13			
Lamphey	d								11x16												13x16			
Manorbier	d								11 24												13 24			
Penally	d								11x29												13x29			
Tenby	a								11 32												13 32			
	d								11 42												13 42			
Saundersfoot	d								11x49												13x49			
Kilgetty	d								11x51												13x51			
Narberth	d								12x00												14x00			
Whitland	a		11 44						12 08							13 44	14 06				14 13			
	d		11 45						12 09							13 45	14 06				14 13			
Carmarthen	a		12 01						12 26							14 01					14 31			
	d		12 05						12 30			13 05				14 05					14 34		15 05	
Ferryside	d								12x40												14x44			
Kidwelly	d								12x46												14x50			
Pembrey & Burry Port	d		12 23						12 53			13 23				14 23					14 57		15 23	
Llanelli	a		12 28						12 59			13 28				14 28	14 43				15 03		15 28	
	d		12 29			12 33			13 00			13 29				14 29	14 43				15 04		15 29	
Gowerton	d								13x07							14x35								
Swansea 7	a		12 46			13 01			13 22			13 48				14 48					15 22		15 46	
	d	12 29	12 50					13 10			13 29	13 55		14 29		14 55			15 10			15 29	15 55	
Llansamlet	d							13 17											15 17					
Skewen	d							13 21											15 21					
Neath	d	12 40	13 06					13 25			13 40	14 06		14 40		15 06			15 25			15 40	16 06	
Briton Ferry	d							13 28											15 28					
Baglan	d							13 32											15 32					
Port Talbot Parkway	d	12 48	13 13					13 36			13 48	14 13		14 48		15 13			15 36			15 48	16 13	
Pyle	d							13 43											15 43					
Maesteg	d						13 17						14 17					15 17						16 17
Maesteg (Ewenny Road)	d						13 19						14 19					15 19						16 19
Garth (Mid Glamorgan)	d						13 22						14 22					15 22						16 22
Tondu	d						13 31						14 31					15 31						16 31
Sarn	d						13 34						14 34					15 34						16 34
Wildmill	d						13 36						14 36					15 36						16 36
Bridgend	d	12 59	13 25				13 40	13 54			13 59	14 25	14 40	14 59		15 25		15 40	15 54			15 59	16 25	16 40
Pencoed	d						13 46						14 46					15 46						16 46
Llanharan	d						13 50						14 50					15 50						16 50
Pontyclun	d						13 54						14 54					15 54						16 54
Cardiff Central 7	a	13 22	13 47				14 12	14 16			14 22	14 47	15 09	15 22		15 47	16 04	16 10	16 18			16 22	16 47	17 09
Cardiff Queen Street 3	a																							
Newport (South Wales)	a	13 38	14 03								14 38	15 03	15 25	15 38		16 03		16 25				16 38	17 03	17 27
Bristol Parkway 7	a	14 00									15 00			16 00								17 00		
Gloucester 7	a												16 21					17 21						18 20
Manchester Piccadilly 10	⛴ a		17 11									18 12				19 13							20 18	
Reading 7	a	15 01									16 01			17 01								17 57		
London Paddington 15	⊖ a	15 30									16 30			17 30								18 27		

For general notes see front of timetable
For details of catering facilities see
Directory of Train Operators

A Ship service
B To Cheltenham Spa (Table 57)

West Wales, Swansea and Maesteg → Cardiff

Route Diagram - see first page of Table 127

		GW	AW	AW	AW	AW	GW	AW	AW	AW	GW	AW	AW	AW	AW	AW	AW	GW	GW	AW
												FX	FO		FX	FO		FO	FX	
		1 ◇	R	A			1 ◇	◇	◇		1 ◇	◇	◇	A				1 ◇	1 ◇	◇ B
Rosslare Harbour	d																			
Fishguard Harbour	a																			
	d																			
Milford Haven	d		15 10										17 10		17 10					
Johnston	d		15x17										17x17		17x17					
Haverfordwest	d		15 25										17 25		17 25					
Clarbeston Road	d		15x32										17x32		17x32					
Clunderwen	d		15x38										17x38		17x39					
Pembroke Dock	d					15 05											17 05			
Pembroke	d					15 13											17 13			
Lamphey	d					15x16											17x16			
Manorbier	d					15 24											17 24			
Penally	d					15x29											17x29			
Tenby	a					15 32											17 32			
	d					15 44											17 42			
Saundersfoot	d					15x51											17x49			
Kilgetty	d					15x53											17x51			
Narberth	d					16x02											18x00			
Whitland	a		15 44			16 10							17 44		17 45		18 08			
	d		15 45			16 11							17 45		17 45		18 09			
Carmarthen	a		16 01			16 28							18 01		18 02		18 26			
	d		16 05			16 31		17 01					18 05		18 06		18 30			19 10
Ferryside	d					16x41		17x11					18x15		18x16		18x40			
Kidwelly	d					16x47		17x16					18x20		18x21		18x46			
Pembrey & Burry Port	d		16 23			16 54		17 23					18 27		18 28		18 53			19 28
Llanelli	a		16 28			17 00		17 28					18 32		18 34		18 59			19 33
	d		16 29			17 01		17 29	17 36				18 33		18 34		19 00			19 34
Gowerton	d		16x35			17x08			17x44								19x07			
Swansea 7	a		16 48			17 22		17 46	18 06				18 51		18 51		19 22			19 51
	d	16 29	16 55		17 10		17 29	17 55			18 29	18 58	18 58		19 10	19 10		19 29	19 29	19 55
Llansamlet	d				17 17										19 17	19 17				
Skewen	d				17 21										19 21	19 21				
Neath	d	16 40	17 06		17 25		17 40	18 06			18 40	19 09	19 09		19 25	19 25		19 40	19 40	20 06
Briton Ferry	d				17 28										19 28	19 28				
Baglan	d				17 32										19 32	19 32				
Port Talbot Parkway	d	16 48	17 13		17 36		17 48	18 13			18 48	19 16	19 16		19 36	19 36		19 48	19 48	20 13
Pyle	d				17 43										19 43	19 43				
Maesteg	d			17 17						18 20				19 20						
Maesteg (Ewenny Road)	d			17 19						18 22				19 22						
Garth (Mid Glamorgan)	d			17 22						18 25				19 25						
Tondu	d			17 31						18 34				19 34						
Sarn	d			17 34						18 37				19 37						
Wildmill	d			17 36						18 39				19 39						
Bridgend	d	16 59	17 25	17 40	17 54		17 59	18 25		18 43	18 59	19 28	19 28	19 43	19 54	19 54		19 59	19 59	20 25
Pencoed	d			17 46						18 49				19 49						
Llanharan	d			17 50						18 53				19 53						
Pontyclun	d			17 54	18 04					18 57				19 57						
Cardiff Central 7	a	17 22	17 47	18 09	18 17		18 22	18 48		19 13	19 22	19 50	19 50	20 12	20 18	20 18		20 22	20 22	20 47
Cardiff Queen Street 3	a																			
Newport (South Wales)	a	17 38	18 03	18 25			18 38	19 05			19 38	20 22	20 22	20 28				20 38	20 38	21 08
Bristol Parkway 7	a	18 00					19 00				20 00							21 00	21 00	
Gloucester 7	a			19 20										21 22						
Manchester Piccadilly 10	a		21 13					22 12				23 49	23 49							
Reading 7	a	19 01					20 01				21 01							22 15	22 15	
London Paddington 15 ⊖	a	19 32					20 30				21 30							22 45	22 56	

For general notes see front of timetable
For details of catering facilities see Directory of Train Operators

A To Cheltenham Spa (Table 57)
B To Chester (Table 131)

Table 128 West Wales, Swansea and Maesteg → Cardiff

Mondays to Fridays

Route Diagram - see first page of Table 127

		AW		GW	GW	AW	AW		AW	AW	AW	AW		AW	AW	AW	AW	AW	AW	AW	AW	AW		
				FO	FX	FX	FO				FX	FO		FX										
				1 ◇	1 ◇	◇	◇					◇			◇									
		A				B	B										A					C		
				🍴	🍴																			
Rosslare Harbour ⛴	d																					21 15		
Fishguard Harbour ⛴	a																					00 45		
	d																							
Milford Haven	d					19 10	19 10									21 20					23 15			
Johnston	d					19x17	19x17									21x27					23x22			
Haverfordwest	d					19 25	19 25									21 35					23 30			
Clarbeston Road	d					19x32	19x32									21x42					23x39			
Clunderwen	d					19x38	19x38									21 48					23x47			
Pembroke Dock	d									19 16									21 11	22 24				
Pembroke	d									19 24									21 19	22 32				
Lamphey	d									19x27									21x22	22x35				
Manorbier	d									19 36									21 31	22 43				
Penally	d									19x41									21x36	22x48				
Tenby	a									19 44									21 39	22 51				
	d									19 49									21 45	22 53				
Saundersfoot	d									19x56									21x53	23x00				
Kilgetty	d									19x58									21x55	23x02				
Narberth	d									20x07									22x05	23x11				
Whitland	a					19 44	19 44			20 15						21 54			22 13	23 19	23 56			
	d					19 45	19 45			20 16						21 55			22 14	23 20	23 57			
Carmarthen	a					20 01	20 01			20 33						22 16			22 32	23 40	00 18			
	d					20 05	20 05			20 36	21 05	21 05							22 35					
Ferryside	d									20x46	21x15	21x15							22x45					
Kidwelly	d									20x52	21x20	21x20							22x51					
Pembrey & Burry Port	d					20 23	20 23			20 59	21 27	21 27							22 58					
Llanelli	a					20 28	20 28			21 05	21 32	21 32							23 04					
	d					20 29	20 29			21 10	21 33	21 33			21 44				23 05					
Gowerton	d														21x52				23x12					
Swansea 7	a					20 50	20 50			21 33	21 52	21 52			22 13				23 27					
	d			20 29	20 29	20 55	20 55			21 35		21 55		21 55				22 30						
Llansamlet	d									21 42								22 37						
Skewen	d									21 46								22 41						
Neath	d			20 40	20 40	21 06	21 06			21 50		22 06		22 06				22 45						
Briton Ferry	d									21 53								22 48						
Baglan	d									21 57								22 52						
Port Talbot Parkway	d			20 48	20 48	21 13	21 13			22 01		22 13		22 13				22 56						
Pyle	d									22 08								23 03						
Maesteg	d	20 20							21 22								22 23							
Maesteg (Ewenny Road)	d	20 22							21 24								22 25							
Garth (Mid Glamorgan)	d	20 25							21 27								22 28							
Tondu	d	20 34							21 36								22 37							
Sarn	d	20 37							21 39								22 40							
Wildmill	d	20 39							21 41								22 42							
Bridgend	d	20 43		20 59	20 59	21 25	21 25		21 45	22 16		22 25		22 27			22 47	23 11						
Pencoed	d	20 49							21 51								22 53							
Llanharan	d	20 53							21 55			22 33		22 35			22 57							
Pontyclun	d	20 57							21 59								23 01							
Cardiff Central 7	a	21 11		21 22	21 22	21 47	21 47		22 17	22 39		22 50		22 53			23 16	23 36						
Cardiff Queen Street 3	a																							
Newport (South Wales)	a	21 27		21 38	21 38	22 12	22 13										23 36							
Bristol Parkway 7	a			22 00	22 00																			
Gloucester 7	a	22 22															00 38							
Manchester Piccadilly 10 ⛴	a																							
Reading 7	a			23 06	23 06																			
London Paddington 15 ⊖	a			23 42	23 50																			

For general notes see front of timetable
For details of catering facilities see Directory of Train Operators

A To Cheltenham Spa (Table 57)
B To Crewe (Table 131)
C Ship service

Table 128

Saturdays

until 26 January

West Wales, Swansea and Maesteg → Cardiff

Route Diagram - see first page of Table 127

Station		AW	AW	GW	GW	AW	GW		GW	AW	AW	GW	AW	GW		AW	AW	GW	GW	AW	AW		AW	AW
			◇	[1] ◇	[1] ◇	◇	[1] ◇		[1] ◇		◇	[1] ◇		[1] ◇		◇		[1] ◇	[1] ◇	◇	A		◇ B	
				☕	☕	🛒	☕		☕		🛒	☕		☕		🛒		☕	☕	🛒				🛒
Rosslare Harbour ⛴	d																							
Fishguard Harbour ⛴	a																							
	d		01 50																					
Milford Haven	d	00 15														06 05				07 05				
Johnston	d	00x22														06x12				07x12				
Haverfordwest	d	00 30														06 20				07 20				
Clarbeston Road	d	00x37	02x10													06x27				07x27				
Clunderwen	d	00x44														06x33				07x33				
Pembroke Dock	d																							07 05
Pembroke	d																							07 13
Lamphey	d																							07x16
Manorbier	d																							07 25
Penally	d																							07x30
Tenby	a																							07 33
	d																							07 40
Saundersfoot	d																							07x48
Kilgetty	d																							07x50
Narberth	d																							08x00
Whitland	a	00 50	02 22													06 39				07 39				08 08
	d	00 50	02 22													06 40				07 40				08 08
Carmarthen	a	01 12	02 39													06 56				07 56				08 27
	d		02 44			05 04					05 50		06 18			07 00				07 59				08 30
Ferryside	d										06x00		06x28							08x09				08x40
Kidwelly	d										06x05		06x33							08x14				08x46
Pembrey & Burry Port	d					05 22					06 12		06 40			07 18				08 21				08 53
Llanelli	a		03 06			05 27					06 17		06 45			07 23				08 26				08 59
	d		03 06			05 28					06 18		06 46			07 24				08 27			08 45	09 00
Gowerton	d												06x52			07x30				08x33			08x53	09x07
Swansea [7]	a		03 24								06 35		07 06			07 43				08 48			09 07	09 22
	d			04 00	04 59		05 59		06 29		06 40	06 59	07 09	07 29		07 45		07 59	08 29	08 55			09 10	
Llansamlet	d												07 16										09 17	
Skewen	d												07 20										09 21	
Neath	d			04 11	05 10		06 10		06 40		06 51	07 10	07 24	07 40		07 56		08 10	08 40	09 06			09 25	
Briton Ferry	d												07 27										09 29	
Baglan	d												07 31										09 32	
Port Talbot Parkway	d			04 19	05 18	06 01	06 18		06 48		06 58	07 18	07 35	07 48		08 03		08 18	08 48	09 13			09 36	
Pyle	d										07 04		07 42			08 10							09 43	
Maesteg	d									06 49							08 00				09 17			
Maesteg (Ewenny Road)	d									06 51							08 02				09 19			
Garth (Mid Glamorgan)	d									06 54							08 05				09 22			
Tondu	d									07 03							08 14				09 31			
Sarn	d									07 06							08 17				09 34			
Wildmill	d									07 08							08 19				09 36			
Bridgend	d			04 30	05 29	06 13	06 29		06 59	07 12	07 17	07 29	07 50	07 59		08 18	08 23	08 29	08 59	09 25	09 40		09 52	
Pencoed	d					06 19				07 18			07 56			08 24					09 46			
Llanharan	d									07 22			08 00				08 31				09 50			
Pontyclun	d					06 26				07 26			08 04			08 31					09 54			
Cardiff Central [7]	a			04 53	05 52	06 40	06 52		07 22	07 43	07 45	07 52	08 18	08 22		08 44	08 48	08 52	09 22	09 47	10 09		10 17	
Cardiff Queen Street [3]	a																							
Newport (South Wales)	a			05 09	06 08	07 02	07 08		07 38		08 02	08 08		08 38		09 02		09 08	09 38	10 03	10 25			
Bristol Parkway [7]	a			05 37	06 30		07 30		08 00			08 30		09 00				09 30	10 00					
Gloucester [7]	a																				11 21			
Manchester Piccadilly [10] ⛴	a					10 13					11 13					12 13				13 13				
Reading [7]	a			07 14	07 32		08 32		09 02			09 33		10 01				10 32	10 59					
London Paddington [15] ⊖	a			07 45	08 01		09 06		09 30			10 06		10 31				10 59	11 31					

For general notes see front of timetable
For details of catering facilities see Directory of Train Operators

A To Cheltenham Spa (Table 57)
B From Shrewsbury (Table 129)

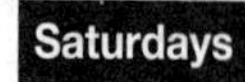

until 26 January

West Wales, Swansea and Maesteg → Cardiff

Route Diagram - see first page of Table 127

		GW	AW	AW	GW	AW	AW	AW	AW	GW	AW	AW	GW	AW	AW	AW	AW	AW	AW	GW	AW
		1 ◇	◇		1 ◇	◇				1 ◇	◇		1 ◇	◇		◇				1 ◇	R
							A					A			B						
Rosslare Harbour	d														09 00						
Fishguard Harbour	a														12 30						
	d																				
Milford Haven	d					09 10								11 10							
Johnston	d					09x17								11x17							
Haverfordwest	d					09 25								11 25							
Clarbeston Road	d					09x32								11x32							
Clunderwen	d					09x38								11x38							
Pembroke Dock	d								09 05										11 05		
Pembroke	d								09 13										11 13		
Lamphey	d								09x16										11x16		
Manorbier	d								09 24										11 24		
Penally	d								09x29										11x29		
Tenby	a								09 32										11 32		
	d								09 42										11 42		
Saundersfoot	d								09x49										11x49		
Kilgetty	d								09x51										11x51		
Narberth	d								10x00										12x00		
Whitland	a					09 44			10 08					11 44					12 08		
	d					09 45			10 09					11 45					12 09		
Carmarthen	a					10 01			10 26					12 01					12 26		
	d		09 00		09 35	10 05			10 30		11 05			12 05					12 30		13 05
Ferryside	d								10x40										12x40		
Kidwelly	d								10x46										12x46		
Pembrey & Burry Port	d		09 18		09 56	10 22			10 53		11 23			12 23					12 53		13 23
Llanelli	a		09 23		10 01	10 28			10 59		11 28			12 28					12 59		13 28
	d		09 26		10 03	10 28			11 00		11 29			12 29		12 33			13 00		13 29
Gowerton	d								11x07										13x07		
Swansea 7	a		09 46		10 21	10 45			11 22		11 46			12 46		13 01			13 22		13 48
	d	09 29	09 55		10 29	10 55		11 10		11 29	11 55		12 29	12 50				13 10		13 29	13 55
Llansamlet	d							11 17										13 17			
Skewen	d							11 21										13 21			
Neath	d	09 40	10 06		10 40	11 06		11 25		11 40	12 06		12 40	13 06				13 25		13 40	14 06
Briton Ferry	d							11 28										13 28			
Baglan	d							11 32										13 32			
Port Talbot Parkway	d	09 48	10 13		10 48	11 13		11 36		11 48	12 13		12 48	13 13				13 36		13 48	14 13
Pyle	d							11 43										13 43			
Maesteg	d			10 17			11 17					12 17					13 17				
Maesteg (Ewenny Road)	d			10 19			11 19					12 19					13 19				
Garth (Mid Glamorgan)	d			10 22			11 22					12 22					13 22				
Tondu	d			10 31			11 31					12 31					13 31				
Sarn	d			10 34			11 34					12 34					13 34				
Wildmill	d			10 36			11 36					12 36					13 36				
Bridgend	d	09 59	10 25	10 40	10 59	11 25	11 40	11 54		11 59	12 25	12 40	12 59	13 25			13 40	13 54		13 59	14 25
Pencoed	d			10 46			11 46					12 46					13 46				
Llanharan	d			10 50			11 50					12 50					13 50				
Pontyclun	d			10 54			11 54					12 54					13 54				
Cardiff Central 7	a	10 22	10 47	11 15	11 22	11 47	12 09	12 17		12 22	12 47	13 09	13 22	13 47			14 12	14 16		14 22	14 47
Cardiff Queen Street 3	a																				
Newport (South Wales)	a	10 38	11 03		11 38	12 03	12 25			12 38	13 03	13 25	13 38	14 03						14 38	15 03
Bristol Parkway 7	a	11 00			12 00					13 00			14 00							15 00	
Gloucester 7	a						13 20					14 20									
Manchester Piccadilly 10	a		14 13			15 13					16 13			17 13							18 10
Reading 7	a	12 02			13 01					14 01			15 01							16 01	
London Paddington 15 ⊖	a	12 32			13 36					14 30			15 31							16 30	

For general notes see front of timetable
For details of catering facilities see Directory of Train Operators

A To Cheltenham Spa (Table 57)
B Ship service

Saturdays

until 26 January

West Wales, Swansea and Maesteg → Cardiff

Route Diagram - see first page of Table 127

		AW	AW	AW	AW	AW	AW		GW	AW	AW	GW	AW	AW		AW	AW	GW	AW	AW	AW		GW	AW
			R	◇					1 ◇	R		1 ◇	R					1 ◇	◇	◇			1 ◇	◇
		A			A						A			A										
			[trolley]	[trolley]			[trolley]		[buffet]	[trolley]		[buffet]	[trolley]					[buffet]	[trolley]				[buffet]	[trolley]
Rosslare Harbour [ship]	d																							
Fishguard Harbour [ship]	a																							
	d			13 34																				
Milford Haven	d		13 10										15 10											17 10
Johnston	d		13x17										15x17											17x17
Haverfordwest	d		13 25										15 25											17 25
Clarbeston Road	d		13x32										15x32											17x32
Clunderwen	d		13x38										15x38											17x38
Pembroke Dock	d						13 05										15 05							
Pembroke	d						13 13										15 13							
Lamphey	d						13x16										15x16							
Manorbier	d						13 24										15 24							
Penally	d						13x29										15x29							
Tenby	a						13 32										15 32							
	d						13 42										15 44							
Saundersfoot	d						13x49										15x51							
Kilgetty	d						13x51										15x53							
Narberth	d						14x00										16x02							
Whitland	a		13 44	14 06			14 13						15 44				16 10							17 44
	d		13 45	14 06			14 13						15 45				16 11							17 45
Carmarthen	a		14 01				14 31						16 01				16 28							18 05
	d		14 05				14 34			15 05			16 05				16 31		17 01					18 07
Ferryside	d						14x44										16x41		17x11					18x17
Kidwelly	d						14x50										16x47		17x16					18x23
Pembrey & Burry Port	d		14 23				14 57			15 23			16 23				16 54		17 23					18 29
Llanelli	a		14 28	14 43			15 03			15 28			16 28				17 00		17 28					18 35
	d		14 29	14 43			15 04			15 29			16 29				17 01		17 29	17 36				18 35
Gowerton	d		14x35										16x35				17x08			17x44				
Swansea 7	a		14 48				15 22			15 46			16 48				17 22		17 46	18 06				18 52
	d		14 55			15 10			15 29	15 55		16 29	16 55			17 10		17 29	17 55				18 29	18 55
Llansamlet	d					15 17										17 17								
Skewen	d					15 21										17 21								
Neath	d		15 06			15 25			15 40	16 06		16 40	17 06			17 25		17 40	18 06				18 40	19 06
Briton Ferry	d					15 28										17 28								
Baglan	d					15 32										17 32								
Port Talbot Parkway	d		15 13			15 36			15 48	16 13		16 48	17 13			17 36		17 48	18 13				18 48	19 13
Pyle	d					15 43										17 43								
Maesteg	d	14 17			15 17						16 17			17 17							18 20			
Maesteg (Ewenny Road)	d	14 19			15 19						16 19			17 19							18 22			
Garth (Mid Glamorgan)	d	14 22			15 22						16 22			17 22							18 25			
Tondu	d	14 31			15 31						16 31			17 31							18 34			
Sarn	d	14 34			15 34						16 34			17 34							18 37			
Wildmill	d	14 36			15 36						16 36			17 36							18 39			
Bridgend	d	14 40	15 25		15 40	15 54			15 59	16 26	16 40	16 59	17 25	17 40		17 55		17 59	18 25		18 43		18 59	19 25
Pencoed	d	14 46			15 46						16 46			17 46							18 49			
Llanharan	d	14 50			15 50						16 50			17 50							18 53			
Pontyclun	d	14 54			15 54						16 54			17 54		18 05					18 57			
Cardiff Central 7	a	15 09	15 46	16 02	16 09	16 17			16 22	16 47	17 09	17 22	17 47	18 09		18 18		18 22	18 47		19 16		19 22	19 50
Cardiff Queen Street 3	a																							
Newport (South Wales)	a	15 25	16 03		16 23				16 38	17 03	17 27	17 38	18 03	18 25				18 38	19 05				19 38	20 23
Bristol Parkway 7	a								17 00			18 00						19 00					20 00	
Gloucester 7	a	16 20			17 20						18 20			19 20										
Manchester Piccadilly 10 [ferry]	a		19 16							20 13			21 13						22 13					23 50
Reading 7	a								18 01			19 01						20 01					21 03	
London Paddington 15 ⊖	a								18 31			19 31						20 31					21 36	

For general notes see front of timetable
For details of catering facilities see
Directory of Train Operators

A To Cheltenham Spa (Table 57)

Table 128

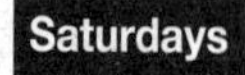

until 26 January

West Wales, Swansea and Maesteg → Cardiff

Route Diagram - see first page of Table 127

		AW	AW	AW	GW	AW	AW		AW	AW	AW		AW	AW		AW	AW	AW	AW	AW	AW	AW		
		A			1 ◇	◇ B			◇ C				◇	◇		1					1	D		
Rosslare Harbour ⛴	d																					21 15		
Fishguard Harbour ⛴	a																					00 45		
	d																							
Milford Haven	d								19 10							21 20					23 15			
Johnston	d								19x17							21x27					23x22			
Haverfordwest	d								19 25							21 35					23 30			
Clarbeston Road	d								19x32							21x42					23x39			
Clunderwen	d								19x38							21 48					23x47			
Pembroke Dock	d			17 05							19 16								21 11	22 22				
Pembroke	d			17 13							19 24								21 19	22 30				
Lamphey	d			17x16							19x27								21x22	22x33				
Manorbier	d			17 24							19 36								21 31	22 41				
Penally	d			17x29							19x41								21x36	22x46				
Tenby	a			17 32							19 44								21 39	22 49				
	d			17 42							19 47								21 45	22 51				
Saundersfoot	d			17x49							19x54								21x53	22x58				
Kilgetty	d			17x51							19x56								21x55	23x00				
Narberth	d			18x00							20x05								22x05	23x09				
Whitland	a			18 08					19 44		20 13					21 54			22 13	23 17	23 56			
	d			18 09					19 45		20 14					21 55			22 14	23 18	23 57			
Carmarthen	a			18 26					20 01		20 33					22 16			22 32	23 40	00 18			
	d			18 30		19 10			20 05		20 35		21 05						22 35					
Ferryside	d			18x40							20x46		21x15						22x45					
Kidwelly	d			18x46							20x52		21x20						22x51					
Pembrey & Burry Port	d			18 53		19 28			20 23		20 59		21 27						22 58					
Llanelli	a			18 59		19 33			20 28		21 05		21 32						23 04					
	d			19 00		19 34			20 29		21 06		21 33	21 44					23 05					
Gowerton	d			19x07										21x52					23x12					
Swansea 7	a			19 22		19 51			20 50		21 24		21 50	22 13					23 29					
	d		19 10		19 29	19 55			20 55			21 35	21 55					22 20						
Llansamlet	d		19 17									21 42						22 27						
Skewen	d		19 21									21 46						22 31						
Neath	d		19 25		19 40	20 06			21 06			21 50	22 06					22 35						
Briton Ferry	d		19 28									21 53						22 38						
Baglan	d		19 32									21 57						22 42						
Port Talbot Parkway	d		19 36		19 48	20 13			21 13			22 01	22 13					22 46						
Pyle	d		19 43									22 08						22 53						
Maesteg	d	19 20					20 20			21 22							22 23							
Maesteg (Ewenny Road)	d	19 22					20 22			21 24							22 25							
Garth (Mid Glamorgan)	d	19 25					20 25			21 27							22 28							
Tondu	d	19 34					20 34			21 36							22 37							
Sarn	d	19 37					20 37			21 39							22 40							
Wildmill	d	19 39					20 39			21 41							22 42							
Bridgend	d	19 43	19 53		19 59	20 25	20 43		21 25	21 45		22 16	22 25				22 47	23 01						
Pencoed	d	19 49					20 49			21 51							22 53							
Llanharan	d	19 53					20 53			21 55			22 33				22 57							
Pontyclun	d	19 57					20 57			21 59							23 01							
Cardiff Central 7	a	20 12	20 17		20 22	20 47	21 12		21 47	22 17		22 39	22 50				23 16	23 26						
Cardiff Queen Street 3	a																							
Newport (South Wales)	a	20 28			20 38	21 07	21 28		22 06								23 37							
Bristol Parkway 7	a				21 00																			
Gloucester 7	a	21 22					22 22										00 42							
Manchester Piccadilly 10 ⛴	a																							
Reading 7	a				21 58																			
London Paddington 15 ⊖	a				22 31																			

For general notes see front of timetable
For details of catering facilities see Directory of Train Operators

A To Cheltenham Spa (Table 57)
B To Chester (Table 131)
C To Crewe (Table 131)
D Ship service

Table 128

2 February to 22 March

West Wales, Swansea and Maesteg → Cardiff

Route Diagram - see first page of Table 127

		AW	AW	GW	AW	GW	AW	AW	AW	AW	AW	AW	AW	AW	AW	AW	AW	GW	AW	AW	AW	AW	AW	AW
			◇	1 ◇	◇	1 ◇		◇		◇		◇		◇		◇		1 ◇	◇				◇	
													A	B						A				A
				🍽	🛒	🍽		🛒		🛒		🛒			🛒	🛒		🍽	🛒			🛒	🛒	
Rosslare Harbour ⛴	d																							
Fishguard Harbour ⛴	a																							
	d		01 50																					
Milford Haven	d	00 15								06 05		07 05							09 10					
Johnston	d	00x22								06x12		07x12							09x17					
Haverfordwest	d	00 30								06 20		07 20							09 25					
Clarbeston Road	d	00x37	02x10							06x27		07x27							09x32					
Clunderwen	d	00x44								06x33		07x33							09x38					
Pembroke Dock	d														07 05							09 05		
Pembroke	d														07 13							09 13		
Lamphey	d														07x16							09x16		
Manorbier	d														07 25							09 24		
Penally	d														07x30							09x29		
Tenby	a														07 33							09 32		
	d														07 40							09 42		
Saundersfoot	d														07x48							09x49		
Kilgetty	d														07x50							09x51		
Narberth	d														08x00							10x00		
Whitland	a	00 50	02 22							06 39		07 39			08 08				09 44			10 08		
	d	00 50	02 22							06 40		07 40			08 08				09 45			10 09		
Carmarthen	a	01 12	02 39							06 56		07 56			08 27				10 01			10 26		
	d		02 44		05 04			05 50	06 18	07 00		07 59			08 30	09 00		09 35	10 05			10 30	11 05	
Ferryside	d							06x00	06x28			08x09			08x40							10x40		
Kidwelly	d							06x05	06x33			08x14			08x46							10x46		
Pembrey & Burry Port	d				05 22			06 12	06 40	07 18		08 21			08 53	09 18		09 56	10 22			10 53	11 23	
Llanelli	a		03 06		05 27			06 17	06 45	07 23		08 26			08 59	09 23		10 01	10 28			10 59	11 28	
	d		03 06		05 28			06 18	06 46	07 24		08 27		08 45	09 00	09 26		10 03	10 28			11 00	11 29	
Gowerton	d								06x52	07x30		08x33		08x53	09x07							11x07		
Swansea 7	a		03 24					06 35	07 06	07 43		08 48		09 07	09 22	09 46		10 21	10 45			11 22	11 46	
	d			04 00		06 29		06 40	07 09	07 45		08 55		09 10		09 55		10 29	10 55		11 10		11 55	
Llansamlet	d								07 16					09 17							11 17			
Skewen	d								07 20					09 21							11 21			
Neath	d			04 11		06 40		06 51	07 24	07 56		09 06		09 25		10 06		10 40	11 06		11 25		12 06	
Briton Ferry	d								07 27					09 29							11 28			
Baglan	d								07 31					09 32							11 32			
Port Talbot Parkway	d			04 19	06 01	06 48		06 58	07 35	08 03		09 13		09 36		10 13		10 48	11 13		11 36		12 13	
Pyle	d							07 04	07 42	08 10				09 43							11 43			
Maesteg	d						06 49				08 00		09 17				10 17			11 17				12 17
Maesteg (Ewenny Road)	d						06 51				08 02		09 19				10 19			11 19				12 19
Garth (Mid Glamorgan)	d						06 54				08 05		09 22				10 22			11 22				12 22
Tondu	d						07 03				08 14		09 31				10 31			11 31				12 31
Sarn	d						07 06				08 17		09 34				10 34			11 34				12 34
Wildmill	d						07 08				08 19		09 36				10 36			11 36				12 36
Bridgend	d			04 30	06 13	06 59	07 12	07 17	07 50	08 18	08 23	09 25	09 40	09 52		10 25	10 40	10 59	11 25	11 40	11 54		12 25	12 40
Pencoed	d				06 19		07 18		07 56	08 24			09 46				10 46			11 46				12 46
Llanharan	d						07 22		08 00		08 31		09 50				10 50			11 50				12 50
Pontyclun	d				06 26		07 26		08 04	08 31			09 54				10 54			11 54				12 54
Cardiff Central 7	a			04 53	06 40	07 22	07 43	07 45	08 18	08 44	08 48	09 47	10 09	10 17		10 47	11 15	11 22	11 47	12 09	12 17		12 47	13 09
Cardiff Queen Street 3	a																							
Newport (South Wales)	a			05 09	07 02	07 38		08 02		09 02		10 03	10 25			11 03		11 38	12 03	12 25			13 03	13 25
Bristol Parkway 7	a			05 37		08 00												12 00						
Gloucester 7	a												11 21							13 20				14 20
Manchester Piccadilly 10 🚌	a				10 13			11 13		12 13		13 13				14 13			15 13				16 13	
Reading 7	a			07 21		09 57												13 57						
London Paddington 15 ⊖	a			07 58		10 27												14 26						

For general notes see front of timetable
For details of catering facilities see Directory of Train Operators

A To Cheltenham Spa (Table 57)
B From Shrewsbury (Table 129)

Table 128

2 February to 22 March

West Wales, Swansea and Maesteg → Cardiff

Route Diagram - see first page of Table 127

		AW	AW	AW	AW	AW	AW	AW	AW	GW	AW	AW	AW	AW	AW	AW	AW	AW	AW	AW	AW	GW	AW	AW
								R			R					R		R						
		◇		◇						1 ◇		◇										1 ◇	◇	◇
			A						B				B				B		B					
		⌶						⌶		⌶	⌶	⌶			⌶	⌶		⌶				⌶	⌶	
Rosslare Harbour ⛴	d		09 00																					
Fishguard Harbour ⛴	a		12 30																					
	d											13 34												
Milford Haven	d	11 10									13 10							15 10						
Johnston	d	11x17									13x17							15x17						
Haverfordwest	d	11 25									13 25							15 25						
Clarbeston Road	d	11x32									13x32							15x32						
Clunderwen	d	11x38									13x38							15x38						
Pembroke Dock	d						11 05								13 05						15 05			
Pembroke	d						11 13								13 13						15 13			
Lamphey	d						11x16								13x16						15x16			
Manorbier	d						11 24								13 24						15 24			
Penally	d						11x29								13x29						15x29			
Tenby	a						11 32								13 32						15 32			
	d						11 42								13 42						15 44			
Saundersfoot	d						11x49								13x49						15x51			
Kilgetty	d						11x51								13x51						15x53			
Narberth	d						12x00								14x00						16x02			
Whitland	a	11 44					12 08				13 44	14 06			14 13			15 44			16 10			
	d	11 45					12 09				13 45	14 06			14 13			15 45			16 11			
Carmarthen	a	12 01					12 26				14 01				14 31			16 01			16 28			
	d	12 05					12 30	13 05			14 05				14 34	15 05		16 05			16 31		17 01	
Ferryside	d						12x40								14x44						16x41		17x11	
Kidwelly	d						12x46								14x50						16x47		17x16	
Pembrey & Burry Port	d	12 23					12 53	13 23			14 23				14 57	15 23		16 23			16 54		17 23	
Llanelli	a	12 28					12 59	13 28			14 28	14 43			15 03	15 28		16 28			17 00		17 28	
	d	12 29		12 33			13 00	13 29			14 29	14 43			15 04	15 29		16 29			17 01		17 29	17 36
Gowerton	d						13x07				14x35							16x35			17x08			17x44
Swansea 7	a	12 46		13 01			13 22	13 48			14 48				15 22	15 46		16 48			17 22		17 46	18 06
	d	12 50				13 10		13 55		14 29	14 55			15 10		15 55		16 55		17 10		17 29	17 55	
Llansamlet	d					13 17								15 17						17 17				
Skewen	d					13 21								15 21						17 21				
Neath	d	13 06				13 25		14 06		14 40	15 06			15 25		16 06		17 06		17 25		17 40	18 06	
Briton Ferry	d					13 28								15 28						17 28				
Baglan	d					13 32								15 32						17 32				
Port Talbot Parkway	d	13 13				13 36		14 13		14 48	15 13			15 36		16 13		17 13		17 36		17 48	18 13	
Pyle	d					13 43								15 43						17 43				
Maesteg	d				13 17				14 17				15 17				16 17		17 17					
Maesteg (Ewenny Road)	d				13 19				14 19				15 19				16 19		17 19					
Garth (Mid Glamorgan)	d				13 22				14 22				15 22				16 22		17 22					
Tondu	d				13 31				14 31				15 31				16 31		17 31					
Sarn	d				13 34				14 34				15 34				16 34		17 34					
Wildmill	d				13 36				14 36				15 36				16 36		17 36					
Bridgend	d	13 25			13 40	13 54		14 25	14 40	14 59	15 25		15 40	15 54		16 26	16 40	17 25	17 40	17 55		17 59	18 25	
Pencoed	d				13 46				14 46				15 46				16 46		17 46					
Llanharan	d				13 50				14 50				15 50				16 50		17 50					
Pontyclun	d				13 54				14 54				15 54				16 54		17 54	18 05				
Cardiff Central 7	a	13 47			14 12	14 16		14 47	15 09	15 22	15 46	16 02	16 09	16 17		16 47	17 09	17 47	18 09	18 18		18 22	18 47	
Cardiff Queen Street 3	a																							
Newport (South Wales)	a	14 03						15 03	15 25	15 38	16 03		16 23			17 03	17 27	18 03	18 25			18 38	19 05	
Bristol Parkway 7	a									16 00												19 00		
Gloucester 7	a								16 20				17 20				18 20		19 20					
Manchester Piccadilly 10 ⛴	a	17 13						18 10			19 16					20 13		21 13					22 13	
Reading 7	a									17 57												20 57		
London Paddington 15 ⊖	a									18 26												21 26		

For general notes see front of timetable
For details of catering facilities see Directory of Train Operators

A Ship service
B To Cheltenham Spa (Table 57)

Table 128

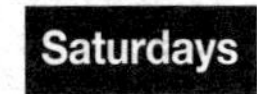

2 February to 22 March

West Wales, Swansea and Maesteg → Cardiff

Route Diagram - see first page of Table 127

		AW	GW	AW	AW	AW	AW	GW	AW	AW	AW	AW	AW	AW	AW	AW	AW	AW	AW	AW	AW	AW	AW
			1 ◇	◇				1 ◇	◇		◇				◇	◇							
					A				B		C												D
			☕	🍴				☕															
Rosslare Harbour ⛴	d																						21 15
Fishguard Harbour ⛴	a																						00 45
	d																						
Milford Haven	d			17 10							19 10						21 20					23 15	
Johnston	d			17x17							19x17						21x27					23x22	
Haverfordwest	d			17 25							19 25						21 35					23 30	
Clarbeston Road	d			17x32							19x32						21x42					23x39	
Clunderwen	d			17x38							19x38						21 48					23x47	
Pembroke Dock	d						17 05						19 16							21 11	22 22		
Pembroke	d						17 13						19 24							21 19	22 30		
Lamphey	d						17x16						19x27							21x22	22x33		
Manorbier	d						17 24						19 36							21 31	22 41		
Penally	d						17x29						19x41							21x36	22x46		
Tenby	a						17 32						19 44							21 39	22 49		
	d						17 42						19 47							21 45	22 51		
Saundersfoot	d						17x49						19 54							21x53	22x58		
Kilgetty	d						17x51						19 56							21x55	23x00		
Narberth	d						18x00						20 05							22x05	23x09		
Whitland	a			17 44			18 08				19 44		20 13				21 54			22 13	23 17	23 56	
	d			17 45			18 09				19 45		20 14				21 55			22 14	23 18	23 57	
Carmarthen	a			18 05			18 26				20 01		20 33				22 16			22 32	23 40	00 18	
	d			18 07			18 30		19 10		20 05		20 35		21 05					22 35			
Ferryside	d			18x17			18x40						20x46		21x15					22x45			
Kidwelly	d			18x23			18x46						20x52		21x20					22x51			
Pembrey & Burry Port	d			18 29			18 53		19 28		20 23		20 59		21 27					22 58			
Llanelli	a			18 35			18 59		19 33		20 28		21 05		21 32					23 04			
	d			18 35			19 00		19 34		20 29		21 06		21 33	21 44				23 05			
Gowerton	d						19x07									21x52				23x12			
Swansea 7	a			18 52			19 22		19 51		20 50		21 24		21 50	22 13				23 29			
	d		18 29	18 55		19 10		19 29	19 55		20 55			21 35	21 55				22 20				
Llansamlet	d					19 17								21 42					22 27				
Skewen	d					19 21								21 46					22 31				
Neath	d		18 40	19 06		19 25		19 40	20 06		21 06			21 50	22 06				22 35				
Briton Ferry	d					19 28								21 53					22 38				
Baglan	d					19 32								21 57					22 42				
Port Talbot Parkway	d		18 48	19 13		19 36		19 48	20 13		21 13			22 01	22 13				22 46				
Pyle	d					19 43								22 08					22 53				
Maesteg	d	18 20			19 20					20 20		21 22						22 23					
Maesteg (Ewenny Road)	d	18 22			19 22					20 22		21 24						22 25					
Garth (Mid Glamorgan)	d	18 25			19 25					20 25		21 27						22 28					
Tondu	d	18 34			19 34					20 34		21 36						22 37					
Sarn	d	18 37			19 37					20 37		21 39						22 40					
Wildmill	d	18 39			19 39					20 39		21 41						22 42					
Bridgend	d	18 43	18 59	19 25	19 43	19 53		19 59	20 25	20 43	21 25	21 45		22 16	22 25			22 47	23 01				
Pencoed	d	18 49			19 49					20 49		21 51						22 53					
Llanharan	d	18 53			19 53					20 53		21 55			22 33			22 57					
Pontyclun	d	18 57			19 57					20 57		21 59						23 01					
Cardiff Central 7	a	19 16	19 22	19 50	20 12	20 17		20 22	20 47	21 12	21 47	22 17		22 39	22 50			23 16	23 26				
Cardiff Queen Street 3	a																						
Newport (South Wales)	a		19 38	20 23	20 28			20 38	21 07	21 28	22 06							23 37					
Bristol Parkway 7	a		20 00					21 00															
Gloucester 7	a				21 22					22 22								00 42					
Manchester Piccadilly 10 ⛴	a			23 50																			
Reading 7	a		21 57					22 57															
London Paddington 15 ⊖	a		22 27					23 26															

For general notes see front of timetable
For details of catering facilities see Directory of Train Operators

A To Cheltenham Spa (Table 57)
B To Chester (Table 131)
C To Crewe (Table 131)
D Ship service

Table 128

Saturdays

from 29 March

West Wales, Swansea and Maesteg → Cardiff

Route Diagram - see first page of Table 127

		AW	AW	GW	GW	AW	GW	GW	AW	AW	GW	AW	AW	AW	GW	AW	AW	AW	AW	GW	AW
		1	◇	1 ◇	1 ◇		1 ◇	1 ◇			1 ◇				1 ◇			◇		1 ◇	
																	A	B			
				☕	☕		☕	☕			☕				☕				🛒	☕	
Rosslare Harbour ⛴	d																				
Fishguard Harbour ⛴	a																				
	d		01 50																		
Milford Haven	d	00 15											06 05			07 05					
Johnston	d	00x22											06x12			07x12					
Haverfordwest	d	00 30											06 20			07 20					
Clarbeston Road	d	00x37	02x10										06x27			07x27					
Clunderwen	d	00x44											06x33			07x33					
Pembroke Dock	d																		07 05		
Pembroke	d																		07 13		
Lamphey	d																		07x16		
Manorbier	d																		07 25		
Penally	d																		07x30		
Tenby	a																		07 33		
	d																		07 40		
Saundersfoot	d																		07x48		
Kilgetty	d																		07x50		
Narberth	d																		08x00		
Whitland	a	00 50	02 22										06 39			07 39			08 08		
	d	00 50	02 22										06 40			07 40			08 08		
Carmarthen	a	01 12	02 39										06 56			07 56			08 27		
	d		02 44			05 04				05 50		06 18	07 00			07 59			08 30		09 00
Ferryside	d									06x00		06x28				08x09			08x40		
Kidwelly	d									06x05		06x33				08x14			08x46		
Pembrey & Burry Port	d					05 22				06 12		06 40	07 18			08 21			08 53		09 18
Llanelli	a		03 06			05 27				06 17		06 45	07 23			08 26			08 59		09 23
	d		03 06			05 28				06 18		06 46	07 24			08 27		08 45	09 00		09 26
Gowerton	d											06x52	07x30			08x33		08x53	09x07		
Swansea 7	a		03 24							06 35		07 06	07 43			08 48		09 07	09 22		09 46
	d			04 00	05 29		05 59	06 29		06 40	06 59	07 09	07 45		08 29	08 55		09 10		09 29	09 55
Llansamlet	d											07 16						09 17			
Skewen	d											07 20						09 21			
Neath	d			04 11	05 40		06 10	06 40		06 51	07 10	07 24	07 56		08 40	09 06		09 25		09 40	10 06
Briton Ferry	d											07 27						09 29			
Baglan	d											07 31						09 32			
Port Talbot Parkway	d			04 19	05 48	06 01	06 18	06 48		06 58	07 18	07 35	08 03		08 48	09 13		09 36		09 48	10 13
Pyle	d									07 04		07 42	08 10					09 43			
Maesteg	d								06 49					08 00			09 17				
Maesteg (Ewenny Road)	d								06 51					08 02			09 19				
Garth (Mid Glamorgan)	d								06 54					08 05			09 22				
Tondu	d								07 03					08 14			09 31				
Sarn	d								07 06					08 17			09 34				
Wildmill	d								07 08					08 19			09 36				
Bridgend	d			04 30	05 59	06 13	06 29	06 59	07 12	07 17	07 29	07 50	08 18	08 23	08 59	09 25	09 40	09 52		09 59	10 25
Pencoed	d					06 19			07 18			07 56	08 24				09 46				
Llanharan	d								07 22			08 00		08 31			09 50				
Pontyclun	d					06 26			07 26			08 04	08 31				09 54				
Cardiff Central 7	a			04 53	06 22	06 40	06 52	07 22	07 43	07 45	07 52	08 18	08 44	08 48	09 22	09 47	10 09	10 17		10 22	10 46
Cardiff Queen Street 3	a																				
Newport (South Wales)	a			05 09	06 38	07 05	07 08	07 38		08 05	08 08		09 05		09 38	10 05	10 25			10 38	11 05
Bristol Parkway 7	a																				
Gloucester 7	a			05 59	07 24		07 52	08 25			08 52				10 25		11 21			11 25	
Manchester Piccadilly 10 ⛴	a																				
Reading 7	a			07 21	08 50		09 14	09 48			10 19				11 43					12 48	
London Paddington 15 ⊖	a			07 56	09 19		09 44	10 16			10 57				12 12					13 16	

For general notes see front of timetable
For details of catering facilities see Directory of Train Operators

A To Cheltenham Spa (Table 57)
B From Shrewsbury (Table 129)

Table 128

from 29 March

West Wales, Swansea and Maesteg → Cardiff

Route Diagram - see first page of Table 127

		AW	AW	AW	AW	AW	GW	AW	AW	GW	AW	AW	AW	AW	AW	AW	AW	AW	GW	AW
							1 ◇			1 ◇			◇						1 ◇	
				A					A			B						A		
						🚌	☕			☕									☕	
Rosslare Harbour ⛴	d											09 00								
Fishguard Harbour ⛴	a											12 30								
	d																			
Milford Haven	d		09 10								11 10									13 10
Johnston	d		09x17								11x17									13x17
Haverfordwest	d		09 25								11 25									13 25
Clarbeston Road	d		09x32								11x32									13x32
Clunderwen	d		09x38								11x38									13x38
Pembroke Dock	d					09 05										11 05				
Pembroke	d					09 13										11 13				
Lamphey	d					09x16										11x16				
Manorbier	d					09 24										11 24				
Penally	d					09x29										11x29				
Tenby	a					09 32										11 32				
	d					09 42										11 42				
Saundersfoot	d					09x49										11x49				
Kilgetty	d					09x51										11x51				
Narberth	d					10x00										12x00				
Whitland	a		09 44			10 08					11 44					12 08				13 44
	d		09 45			10 09					11 45					12 09				13 45
Carmarthen	a		10 01			10 26					12 01					12 26				14 01
	d		10 05			10 30		11 05			12 05					12 30	13 05			14 05
Ferryside	d					10x40										12x40				
Kidwelly	d					10x46										12x46				
Pembrey & Burry Port	d		10 23			10 53		11 23			12 23					12 53	13 23			14 23
Llanelli	a		10 28			10 59		11 28			12 28					12 59	13 28			14 28
	d		10 29			11 00		11 29			12 29		12 33			13 00	13 29			14 29
Gowerton	d					11x07										13x07				14x35
Swansea 7	a		10 46			11 22		11 46			12 46		13 01			13 22	13 48			14 48
	d		10 55		11 10		11 29	11 55		12 29	12 50				13 10		13 55		14 29	14 55
Llansamlet	d				11 17										13 17					
Skewen	d				11 21										13 21					
Neath	d		11 06		11 25		11 40	12 06		12 40	13 06				13 25		14 06		14 40	15 06
Briton Ferry	d				11 28										13 28					
Baglan	d				11 32										13 32					
Port Talbot Parkway	d		11 13		11 36		11 48	12 13		12 48	13 13				13 36		14 13		14 48	15 13
Pyle	d				11 43										13 43					
Maesteg	d	10 17		11 17					12 17					13 17				14 17		
Maesteg (Ewenny Road)	d	10 19		11 19					12 19					13 19				14 19		
Garth (Mid Glamorgan)	d	10 22		11 22					12 22					13 22				14 22		
Tondu	d	10 31		11 31					12 31					13 31				14 31		
Sarn	d	10 34		11 34					12 34					13 34				14 34		
Wildmill	d	10 36		11 36					12 36					13 36				14 36		
Bridgend	d	10 40	11 25	11 40	11 54		11 59	12 25	12 40	12 59	13 25			13 40	13 54		14 25	14 40	14 59	15 25
Pencoed	d	10 46		11 46					12 46					13 46				14 46		
Llanharan	d	10 50		11 50					12 50					13 50				14 50		
Pontyclun	d	10 54		11 54					12 54					13 54				14 54		
Cardiff Central 7	a	11 15	11 46	12 09	12 17		12 22	12 46	13 09	13 22	13 47			14 12	14 16		14 46	15 09	15 22	15 46
Cardiff Queen Street 3	a																			
Newport (South Wales)	a		12 05	12 25			12 38	13 05	13 25	13 38	14 05						15 05	15 25	15 38	16 05
Bristol Parkway 7	a																			
Gloucester 7	a			13 20			13 25		14 20	14 25								16 20	16 25	
Manchester Piccadilly 10 ⛴	a																			
Reading 7	a						14 48			15 48									17 48	
London Paddington 15 ⊖	a						15 17			16 17									18 16	

For general notes see front of timetable
For details of catering facilities see
Directory of Train Operators

A To Cheltenham Spa (Table 57)
B Ship service

Table 128

Saturdays

from 29 March

West Wales, Swansea and Maesteg → Cardiff

Route Diagram - see first page of Table 127

		AW	AW	AW	AW	GW		AW	AW	GW	AW	AW		AW	AW	GW	AW	AW		AW	GW	AW	AW	AW
		◇				1 ◇				1 ◇						1 ◇		◇			1 ◇			
			A						A			A											A	
Rosslare Harbour	d																							
Fishguard Harbour	a																							
	d	13 34																						
Milford Haven	d										15 10											17 10		
Johnston	d										15x17											17x17		
Haverfordwest	d										15 25											17 25		
Clarbeston Road	d										15x32											17x32		
Clunderwen	d										15x38											17x38		
Pembroke Dock	d				13 05										15 05									
Pembroke	d				13 13										15 13									
Lamphey	d				13x16										15x16									
Manorbier	d				13 24										15 24									
Penally	d				13x29										15x29									
Tenby	a				13 32										15 32									
	d				13 42										15 44									
Saundersfoot	d				13x49										15x51									
Kilgetty	d				13x51										15x53									
Narberth	d				14x00										16x02									
Whitland	a	14 06			14 13						15 44				16 10							17 44		
	d	14 06			14 13						15 45				16 11							17 45		
Carmarthen	a				14 31						16 01				16 28							18 05		
	d				14 34			15 05			16 04				16 31		17 01					18 07		
Ferryside	d				14x44										16x41		17x11					18x17		
Kidwelly	d				14x50										16x47		17x16					18x23		
Pembrey & Burry Port	d				14 57			15 23			16 22				16 54		17 23					18 29		
Llanelli	a	14 43			15 03			15 28			16 27				17 00		17 28					18 35		
	d	14 43			15 04			15 29			16 28				17 01		17 29	17 36				18 35		
Gowerton	d										16x34				17x08			17x44						
Swansea 7	a				15 22			15 46			16 47				17 22		17 46	18 06				18 52		
	d			15 10		15 29		15 55		16 29	16 55			17 10		17 29	17 55				18 29	18 55		19 10
Llansamlet	d			15 17										17 17										19 17
Skewen	d			15 21										17 21										19 21
Neath	d			15 25		15 40		16 06		16 40	17 06			17 25		17 40	18 06				18 40	19 06		19 25
Briton Ferry	d			15 28										17 28										19 28
Baglan	d			15 32										17 32										19 32
Port Talbot Parkway	d			15 36		15 48		16 13		16 48	17 13			17 36		17 48	18 13				18 48	19 13		19 36
Pyle	d			15 43										17 43										19 43
Maesteg	d		15 17						16 17			17 17								18 20			19 20	
Maesteg (Ewenny Road)	d		15 19						16 19			17 19								18 22			19 22	
Garth (Mid Glamorgan)	d		15 22						16 22			17 22								18 25			19 25	
Tondu	d		15 31						16 31			17 31								18 34			19 34	
Sarn	d		15 34						16 34			17 34								18 37			19 37	
Wildmill	d		15 36						16 36			17 36								18 39			19 39	
Bridgend	d		15 40	15 54		15 59		16 26	16 40	16 59	17 25	17 40		17 55		17 59	18 25			18 43	18 59	19 25	19 43	19 53
Pencoed	d		15 46						16 46			17 46								18 49			19 49	
Llanharan	d		15 50						16 50			17 50								18 53			19 53	
Pontyclun	d		15 54						16 54			17 54		18 05						18 57			19 57	
Cardiff Central 7	a	16 02	16 09	16 17		16 22		16 47	17 09	17 22	17 47	18 09		18 18		18 22	18 46			19 16	19 22	19 47	20 12	20 17
Cardiff Queen Street 3	a																							
Newport (South Wales)	a		16 23			16 38		17 05	17 27	17 38	18 05	18 25				18 38	19 05				19 38	20 05	20 28	
Bristol Parkway 7	a																							
Gloucester 7	a		17 20			17 25			18 20	18 25		19 20				19 25					20 22		21 22	
Manchester Piccadilly 10	a																							
Reading 7	a					18 48				19 48						20 48					21 44			
London Paddington 15	⊖ a					19 17				20 16						21 16					22 16			

For general notes see front of timetable
For details of catering facilities see Directory of Train Operators

A To Cheltenham Spa (Table 57)

from 29 March

West Wales, Swansea and Maesteg → Cardiff

Route Diagram - see first page of Table 127

		AW	GW 1 ◇	AW	AW	AW	AW	AW	AW	AW ◇	AW ◇	AW	AW	AW	AW	AW	AW	AW A
Rosslare Harbour	d																	21 15
Fishguard Harbour	a																	00 45
	d																	
Milford Haven	d					19 10						21 20					23 15	
Johnston	d					19x17						21x27					23x22	
Haverfordwest	d					19 25						21 35					23 30	
Clarbeston Road	d					19x32						21x42					23x39	
Clunderwen	d					19x38						21 48					23x47	
Pembroke Dock	d	17 05						19 16							21 11	22 22		
Pembroke	d	17 13						19 24							21 19	22 30		
Lamphey	d	17x16						19x27							21x22	22x33		
Manorbier	d	17 24						19 36							21 31	22 41		
Penally	d	17x29						19x41							21x36	22x46		
Tenby	a	17 32						19 44							21 39	22 49		
	d	17 42						19 47							21 45	22 51		
Saundersfoot	d	17x49						19x54							21x53	22x58		
Kilgetty	d	17x51						19x56							21x55	23x00		
Narberth	d	18x00						20x05							22x05	23x09		
Whitland	a	18 08				19 44		20x13				21 54			22 13	23 17	23 56	
	d	18 09				19 45		20 14				21 55			22 14	23 18	23 57	
Carmarthen	a	18 26				20 01		20 33				22 16			22 32	23 40	00 18	
	d	18 30		19 10		20 05		20 35		21 05					22 35			
Ferryside	d	18x40						20x46		21x15					22x45			
Kidwelly	d	18x46						20x52		21x20					22x51			
Pembrey & Burry Port	d	18 53		19 28		20 23		20 59		21 27					22 58			
Llanelli	a	18 59		19 33		20 28		21 05		21 32					23 04			
	d	19 00		19 34		20 29		21 06		21 33	21 44				23 05			
Gowerton	d	19x07									21x52				23x12			
Swansea 7	a	19 22		19 51		20 50		21 24		21 50	22 13				23 29			
	d		19 29	19 55		20 55			21 35	21 55				22 20				
Llansamlet	d								21 42					22 27				
Skewen	d								21 46					22 31				
Neath	d		19 40	20 06		21 06			21 50	22 06				22 35				
Briton Ferry	d								21 53					22 38				
Baglan	d								21 57					22 42				
Port Talbot Parkway	d		19 48	20 13		21 13			22 01	22 13				22 46				
Pyle	d								22 08					22 53				
Maesteg	d				20 20		21 22						22 23					
Maesteg (Ewenny Road)	d				20 22		21 24						22 25					
Garth (Mid Glamorgan)	d				20 25		21 27						22 28					
Tondu	d				20 34		21 36						22 37					
Sarn	d				20 37		21 39						22 40					
Wildmill	d				20 39		21 41						22 42					
Bridgend	d		19 59	20 25	20 43	21 25	21 45		22 16	22 25			22 47	23 01				
Pencoed	d				20 49		21 51						22 53					
Llanharan	d				20 53		21 55			22 33			22 57					
Pontyclun	d				20 57		21 59						23 01					
Cardiff Central 7	a		20 22	20 47	21 12	21 47	22 17		22 39	22 50			23 16	23 26				
Cardiff Queen Street 3	a																	
Newport (South Wales)	a		20 38	21 07	21 28	22 06							23 37					
Bristol Parkway 7	a																	
Gloucester 7	a		21 26		22 22								00 42					
Manchester Piccadilly 10	a																	
Reading 7	a		22 47															
London Paddington 15	⊖ a		23 16															

For general notes see front of timetable
For details of catering facilities see
Directory of Train Operators

A Ship service

Table 128

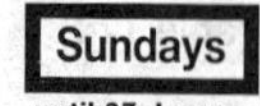

until 27 January

West Wales, Swansea and Maesteg → Cardiff

Route Diagram - see first page of Table 127

		AW	GW	GW	GW	GW	AW	GW	AW	GW	AW	GW	AW	GW	AW	AW	GW
		◇	1 ◇	1 ◇	1 ◇	1 ◇	◇	1 ◇	A	1 ◇	◇	1 ◇		1 ◇	R	1	1 ◇
			☕	☕	☕	☕	🛒	☕		☕	🛒	☕		☕	🛒		☕
Rosslare Harbour ⛴	d								09 00								
Fishguard Harbour ⛴	a								12 30								
	d	01 50														14 30	
Milford Haven	d														13 35		
Johnston	d														13x42		
Haverfordwest	d														13 50		
Clarbeston Road	d	02x10													13x57		
Clunderwen	d														14x04		
Pembroke Dock	d																
Pembroke	d																
Lamphey	d																
Manorbier	d																
Penally	d																
Tenby	a																
	d												13 05				
Saundersfoot	d												13x13				
Kilgetty	d												13x15				
Narberth	d												13x25				
Whitland	a	02 21											13 33		14 10	15 01	
	d	02 22											13 34		14 11	15 02	
Carmarthen	a	02 38											13 52		14 28	15 20	
	d	02 41					10 30				12 35		14 00		14 42		
Ferryside	d						10x40				12x45		14x10				
Kidwelly	d						10x45				12x51		14x16				
Pembrey & Burry Port	d						10 52				12 58		14 23		15 00		
Llanelli	a	03 03					10 58				13 04		14 29		15 06		
	d	03 04					10 58				13 04		14 30		15 06		
Gowerton	d						11x05						14x37				
Swansea 7	a	03 21					11 18				13 21		14 52		15 25		
	d	03 25	07 59	08 59	09 59	10 59	11 22	11 59		12 59	13 35	13 59		14 59	15 30		15 59
Llansamlet	d						11 29										
Skewen	d						11 33										
Neath	d	03 36	08 11	09 11	10 11	11 11	11 37	12 11		13 11	13 47	14 11		15 11	15 41		16 11
Briton Ferry	d						11 40										
Baglan	d						11 44										
Port Talbot Parkway	d	03 43	08 18	09 18	10 18	11 18	11 48	12 18		13 18	13 55	14 18		15 18	15 49		16 18
Pyle	d						11 55										
Maesteg	d																
Maesteg (Ewenny Road)	d																
Garth (Mid Glamorgan)	d																
Tondu	d																
Sarn	d																
Wildmill	d																
Bridgend	d	03 55	08 30	09 30	10 30	11 30	12 03	12 30		13 30	14 08	14 30		15 30	16 02		16 30
Pencoed	d						12 09								16 08		
Llanharan	d						12 13								16 12		
Pontyclun	d						12 17								16 16		
Cardiff Central 7	a	04 44	08 52	09 52	10 52	11 52	12 31	12 52		13 52	14 30	14 52		15 52	16 28		16 52
Cardiff Queen Street 3	a																
Newport (South Wales)	a		09 12	10 08	11 08	12 08	12 47	13 08		14 08	14 48	15 08		16 08	16 49		17 08
Bristol Parkway 7	a		09 34	10 30	11 30	12 30		13 30		14 30		15 30		16 30			17 30
Gloucester 7	a																
Manchester Piccadilly 10 ⛴	a						16 12				18 26				20 14		
Reading 7	a		10 31	11 27	12 27	13 27		14 27		15 27		16 27		17 27			18 27
London Paddington 15 ⊖	a		11 07	12 08	13 07	14 10		15 08		16 08		17 11		18 10			19 10

For general notes see front of timetable
For details of catering facilities see
Directory of Train Operators

A Ship service

Table 128

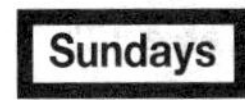

Sundays
until 27 January

West Wales, Swansea and Maesteg → Cardiff

Route Diagram - see first page of Table 127

		AW	GW		AW	GW		AW	AW		GW	AW		GW	AW		AW	AW	AW	AW	AW	AW		
					R			R				R												
		◇	1 ◇			1 ◇					1 ◇			1 ◇	◇									
					A			A				B			C		D					E		
			⊡		✕	⊡		✕			⊡	✕		⊡										
Rosslare Harbour ⛴	d																					21 15		
Fishguard Harbour ⛴	a																					00 45		
	d																							
Milford Haven	d				15 35							17 35						19 35	21 35		23 15			
Johnston	d				15x42							17x42						19x42	21x42		23x22			
Haverfordwest	d				15 50							17 50						19 50	21 50		23 30			
Clarbeston Road	d				15x57							17x57						19x58	21x58		23x37			
Clunderwen	d				16x04							18x05						20x05	22x06		23x44			
Pembroke Dock	d								16 05								19 05			22 05				
Pembroke	d								16 13								19 13			22 13				
Lamphey	d								16x16								19x16			22x16				
Manorbier	d								16 25								19 24			22 25				
Penally	d								16x30								19x29			22x30				
Tenby	a								16 33								19 32			22 33				
	d								16 35								19 35			22 35				
Saundersfoot	d								16x43								19x42			22x43				
Kilgetty	d								16x45								19x44			22x45				
Narberth	d								16x55								19x53			22x55				
Whitland	a				16 10				17 03			18 11					20 01	20 11	22 12	23 03	23 50			
	d				16 10				17 04			18 11					20 04	20 12	22 13	23 04	23 51			
Carmarthen	a				16 27				17 25			18 28					20 21	20 30	22 30	23 25	00 07			
	d		15 39		16 31						17 39	18 35		19 09			20 35		22 35					
Ferryside	d				16x41							18x45					20x45		22x45					
Kidwelly	d				16x46							18x50					20x51		22x51					
Pembrey & Burry Port	d		15 59		16 53						17 59	18 57		19 29			20 59		22 59					
Llanelli	a		16 04		16 59						18 04	19 03		19 34			21 05		23 05					
	d	15 45	16 06		16 59						18 06	19 03		19 36	19 52		21 05		23 05					
Gowerton	d	15x52			17x06							19x10			19x59		21x12		23x12					
Swansea 7	a	16 07	16 22		17 19			←			18 22	19 27		19 52	20 13		21 26		23 26					
	d		16 29		17 35 →	17 29		17 35			18 29	19 35		19 59	20 35		21 35		23 35					
Llansamlet	d																21 42							
Skewen	d																21 46							
Neath	d		16 41			17 41		17 46			18 41	19 46		20 11	20 46		21 50		23 46					
Briton Ferry	d																21 53							
Baglan	d																21 57							
Port Talbot Parkway	d		16 48			17 48		17 54			18 48	19 54		20 18	20 54		22 01		23 54					
Pyle	d																22 08							
Maesteg	d																							
Maesteg (Ewenny Road)	d																							
Garth (Mid Glamorgan)	d																							
Tondu	d																							
Sarn	d																							
Wildmill	d																							
Bridgend	d		17 00			18 00		18 07			19 00	20 07		20 30	21 07		22 16		00 07					
Pencoed	d																22 22							
Llanharan	d																22 26							
Pontyclun	d																22 30							
Cardiff Central 7	a		17 22			18 22		18 26			19 22	20 29		20 52	21 30		22 44		00 50					
Cardiff Queen Street 3	a																							
Newport (South Wales)	a		17 38			18 38		18 48			19 38	20 48		21 08			23 07							
Bristol Parkway 7	a		18 00			19 00					20 00			21 30										
Gloucester 7	a																							
Manchester Piccadilly 10 ⛴	a							22 07																
Reading 7	a		18 59			19 58					20 57			22 35										
London Paddington 15 ⊖	a		19 41			20 40					21 40			23 26										

For general notes see front of timetable
For details of catering facilities see Directory of Train Operators

A Conveys portion to Holyhead,detached at Shrewsbury
B To Crewe (Table 131)
C From Shrewsbury (Table 129)
D To Hereford (Table 131)
E Ship service

Table 128

Sundays

3 February to 23 March

West Wales, Swansea and Maesteg → Cardiff

Route Diagram - see first page of Table 127

		AW	AW	GW	GW	GW	GW	AW	GW	AW	GW	AW	GW	GW	AW	AW	AW
		◇		1 ◇	1 ◇	1 ◇	1 ◇	◇	1 ◇	A	1 ◇	◇	1 ◇	1 ◇		R	
Rosslare Harbour	d									09 00							
Fishguard Harbour	a									12 30							
	d	01 50															14 30
Milford Haven	d															13 35	
Johnston	d															13x42	
Haverfordwest	d															13 50	
Clarbeston Road	d	02x10														13x57	
Clunderwen	d															14x04	
Pembroke Dock	d																
Pembroke	d																
Lamphey	d																
Manorbier	d																
Penally	d																
Tenby	a																
	d														13 05		
Saundersfoot	d														13x13		
Kilgetty	d														13x15		
Narberth	d														13x25		
Whitland	a	02 21													13 33	14 10	15 01
	d	02 22													13 34	14 11	15 02
Carmarthen	a	02 38													13 52	14 28	15 20
	d	02 41						10 15				12 35			14 00	14 42	
Ferryside	d							10x25				12x45			14x10		
Kidwelly	d							10x30				12x51			14x16		
Pembrey & Burry Port	d							10 37				12 58			14 23	15 00	
Llanelli	a	03 03						10 43				13 04			14 29	15 06	
	d	03 04						10 43				13 04			14 30	15 06	
Gowerton	d							10x50							14x37		
Swansea 7	a	03 21						11 06				13 21			14 52	15 25	
	d		03 35	07 59	08 45	09 45	10 45	11 10	11 45		12 45	13 35	13 45	14 45		15 30	
Llansamlet	d							11 17									
Skewen	d							11 21									
Neath	d		03 53	08 11	08 57	09 57	10 57	11 25	11 57		12 57	13 47	13 57	14 57		15 41	
Briton Ferry	d							11 28									
Baglan	d							11 32									
Port Talbot Parkway	d		04 05	08 18	09 04	10 04	11 04	11 36	12 04		13 04	13 55	14 04	15 04		15 49	
Pyle	d							11 43									
Maesteg	d																
Maesteg (Ewenny Road)	d																
Garth (Mid Glamorgan)	d																
Tondu	d																
Sarn	d																
Wildmill	d																
Bridgend	d		04 30	08 30	09 16	10 16	11 16	11 51	12 16		13 16	14 08	14 16	15 16		16 02	
Pencoed	d							11 57								16 08	
Llanharan	d							12 01								16 12	
Pontyclun	d							12 05								16 16	
Cardiff Central 7	a		05 05	08 52	09 38	10 38	11 38	12 19	12 38		13 38	14 30	14 38	15 38		16 28	
Cardiff Queen Street 3	a																
Newport (South Wales)	a			09 12	09 54	10 54	11 54	12 47	12 54		13 54	14 48	14 54	15 54		16 47	
Bristol Parkway 7	a			09 34	10 16	11 16	12 16		13 16		14 16		15 16	16 16			
Gloucester 7	a																
Manchester Piccadilly 10	a							16 12				18 26				20 14	
Reading 7	a			11 23	12 08	13 08	14 08		15 08		16 08		17 08	18 07			
London Paddington 15 ⊖	a			12 06	12 57	13 52	14 53		15 53		16 52		17 57	18 52			

For general notes see front of timetable
For details of catering facilities see
Directory of Train Operators

A Ship service

Table 128

Sundays

3 February to 23 March

West Wales, Swansea and Maesteg → Cardiff

Route Diagram - see first page of Table 127

		GW	AW	GW	AW	AW	GW	GW	AW	GW	AW	AW	AW	AW	AW	AW	AW
					R				R								
		1 ◊	◊	1 ◊			1 ◊	1 ◊		1 ◊	◊						
					A				B		C	D					E
		☕		☕	🍴		☕	☕	🍴	☕							
Rosslare Harbour (ship)	d																21 15
Fishguard Harbour (ship)	a																00 45
	d																
Milford Haven	d				15 35				17 35				19 35	21 35		23 15	
Johnston	d				15x42				17x42				19x42	21x42		23x22	
Haverfordwest	d				15 50				17 50				19 50	21 50		23 30	
Clarbeston Road	d				15x57				17x57				19x58	21x58		23x37	
Clunderwen	d				16x04				18x05				20x05	22x06		23x44	
Pembroke Dock	d					16 05						19 05			22 05		
Pembroke	d					16 13						19 13			22 13		
Lamphey	d					16x16						19x16			22x16		
Manorbier	d					16 25						19 24			22 25		
Penally	d					16x30						19x29			22x30		
Tenby	a					16 33						19 32			22 33		
	d					16 35						19 35			22 35		
Saundersfoot	d					16x43						19x42			22x43		
Kilgetty	d					16x45						19x44			22x45		
Narberth	d					16x55						19x53			22x55		
Whitland	a				16 10	17 03			18 11			20 01	20 11	22 12	23 03	23 50	
	d				16 10	17 04			18 11			20 04	20 12	22 13	23 04	23 51	
Carmarthen	a				16 27	17 25			18 28			20 21	20 30	22 30	23 25	00 07	
	d			15 39	16 31			17 55	18 35	19 15		20 35		22 35			
Ferryside	d				16x41				18x45			20x45		22x45			
Kidwelly	d				16x46				18x50			20x51		22x51			
Pembrey & Burry Port	d			15 59	16 53			18 15	18 57	19 35		20 59		22 59			
Llanelli	a			16 04	16 59			18 20	19 03	19 40		21 05		23 05			
	d		15 45	16 06	16 59			18 22	19 03	19 42	19 52	21 05		23 05			
Gowerton	d		15x52		17x06				19x10		19x59	21x12		23x12			
Swansea 7	a		16 07	16 24	17 19			18 38	19 27	19 58	20 13	21 26		23 26			
	d	15 45		16 45	17 35		17 45	18 45	19 35	20 05	20 35	21 35		23 35			
Llansamlet	d											21 42					
Skewen	d											21 46					
Neath	d	15 57		16 57	17 46		17 57	18 57	19 46	20 17	20 46	21 50		23 46			
Briton Ferry	d											21 53					
Baglan	d											21 57					
Port Talbot Parkway	d	16 04		17 04	17 54		18 04	19 04	19 54	20 24	20 54	22 01		23 54			
Pyle	d											22 08					
Maesteg	d																
Maesteg (Ewenny Road)	d																
Garth (Mid Glamorgan)	d																
Tondu	d																
Sarn	d																
Wildmill	d																
Bridgend	d	16 16		17 16	18 07		18 16	19 16	20 07	20 36	21 07	22 16		00 07			
Pencoed	d											22 22					
Llanharan	d											22 26					
Pontyclun	d											22 30					
Cardiff Central 7	a	16 38		17 38	18 26		18 38	19 38	20 29	20 58	21 30	22 44		00 50			
Cardiff Queen Street 3	a																
Newport (South Wales)	a	16 54		17 54	18 48		18 54	19 54	20 48	21 14		23 07					
Bristol Parkway 7	a	17 16		18 16			19 16	20 16		21 40							
Gloucester 7	a																
Manchester Piccadilly 10 (ship)	a				22 07												
Reading 7	a	19 08		20 08			21 09	22 08		23 26							
London Paddington 15 (Underground)	a	20 01		20 51			21 51	22 49		00 27							

For general notes see front of timetable
For details of catering facilities see Directory of Train Operators

A Conveys portion to Holyhead, detached at Shrewsbury
B To Crewe (Table 131)
C From Shrewsbury (Table 129)
D To Hereford (Table 131)
E Ship service

Table 128

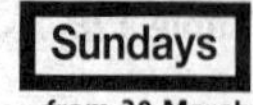
Sundays

from 30 March

West Wales, Swansea and Maesteg → Cardiff

Route Diagram - see first page of Table 127

		AW ◇	AW 🚌	GW 1 ◇		GW 1 ◇	GW 1 ◇	AW		GW 1 ◇	GW 1 ◇	AW A		AW	GW 1 ◇	AW		GW 1 ◇	AW	AW		GW 1 ◇	AW	AW
Rosslare Harbour ⛴	d											09 00												
Fishguard Harbour ⛴	a											12 30												
	d	01 50																						14 30
Milford Haven	d																			13 35				
Johnston	d																			13x42				
Haverfordwest	d																			13 50				
Clarbeston Road	d	02x10																		13x57				
Clunderwen	d																			14x04				
Pembroke Dock	d																							
Pembroke	d																							
Lamphey	d																							
Manorbier	d																							
Penally	d																							
Tenby	a																							
	d																		13 05					
Saundersfoot	d																		13x13					
Kilgetty	d																		13x15					
Narberth	d																		13x25					
Whitland	a	02 21																	13 33	14 10				15 01
	d	02 22																	13 34	14 11				15 02
Carmarthen	a	02 38																	13 52	14 30				15 20
	d	02 41						10 15											14 00	14 41				
Ferryside	d							10x25						12x45					14x10					
Kidwelly	d							10x30						12x51					14x16					
Pembrey & Burry Port	d							10 37						12 58					14 23	14 59				
Llanelli	a	03 03						10 42						13 03					14 29	15 05				
	d	03 04						10 43						13 04					14 30	15 05				
Gowerton	d							10x49											14x37					
Swansea 7	a	03 21						11 07						13 21		←			14 52	15 22			←	
	d		03 35	08 29		09 29	10 29	11 10		11 29	12 29			13 35 →	13 29	13 35		14 29		15 35 →		15 29	15 35	
Llansamlet	d							11 17																
Skewen	d							11 21																
Neath	d		03 53	08 41		09 41	10 41	11 25		11 41	12 41				13 41	13 47		14 41				15 41	15 47	
Briton Ferry	d							11 28																
Baglan	d							11 32																
Port Talbot Parkway	d		04 05	08 48		09 48	10 48	11 36		11 48	12 48				13 48	13 54		14 48				15 48	15 55	
Pyle	d							11 42																
Maesteg	d																							
Maesteg (Ewenny Road)	d																							
Garth (Mid Glamorgan)	d																							
Tondu	d																							
Sarn	d																							
Wildmill	d																							
Bridgend	d		04 30	09 00		10 00	11 00	11 50		12 00	13 00				14 00	14 06		15 00				16 00	16 08	
Pencoed	d							11 56															16 14	
Llanharan	d							12 00															16 18	
Pontyclun	d							12 04															16 22	
Cardiff Central 7	a		05 05	09 22		10 22	11 22	12 18		12 22	13 22				14 22	14 28		15 22				16 22	16 36	
Cardiff Queen Street 3	a																							
Newport (South Wales)	a			09 38		10 38	11 38			12 38	13 38				14 38			15 38				16 38		
Bristol Parkway 7	a																							
Gloucester 7	a			10 21		11 21	12 21			13 21	14 21				15 21			16 21				17 21		
Manchester Piccadilly 10 ⛴	a																							
Reading 7	a			11 50		12 44	13 49			14 44	15 44				16 44			17 50				18 50		
London Paddington 15 ⊖	a			12 33		13 26	14 30			15 23	16 23				17 22			18 35				19 30		

For general notes see front of timetable
For details of catering facilities see Directory of Train Operators

A Ship service

Sundays

from 30 March

West Wales, Swansea and Maesteg → Cardiff

Route Diagram - see first page of Table 127

		AW	GW	AW	GW	AW	AW	GW	AW	GW	AW	AW	AW	AW	AW	AW	AW
		◇	1 ◇		1 ◇			1 ◇		1 ◇	◇						
											A						B
			☕		☕			☕		☕							
Rosslare Harbour ⛴	d																21 15
Fishguard Harbour ⛴	a																00 45
	d																
Milford Haven	d			15 35					17 35				19 35	21 35		23 50	
Johnston	d			15x42					17x42				19x42	21x42		23x57	
Haverfordwest	d			15 50					17 50				19 50	21 50		00 07	
Clarbeston Road	d			15x57					17x57				19x58	21x58		00x14	
Clunderwen	d			16x03					18x04				20x05	22x06		00x23	
Pembroke Dock	d						16 05					19 05			22 05		
Pembroke	d						16 13					19 13			22 13		
Lamphey	d						16x16					19x16			22x16		
Manorbier	d						16 25					19 24			22 25		
Penally	d						16x30					19x29			22x30		
Tenby	a						16 33					19 32			22 33		
	d						16 35					19 35			22 35		
Saundersfoot	d						16x43					19x42			22x43		
Kilgetty	d						16x45					19x44			22x45		
Narberth	d						16x55					19x53			22x55		
Whitland	a			16 09			17 03		18 10			20 01	20 11	22 12	23 03	00 29	
	d			16 10			17 04		18 11			20 04	20 12	22 13	23 04	00 30	
Carmarthen	a			16 26			17 25		18 31			20 21	20 30	22 32	23 25	00 46	
	d		15 39	16 30				17 39	18 35	19 09		20 35		22 37			
Ferryside	d			16x40					18x45			20x45		22x47			
Kidwelly	d			16x45					18x50			20x51		22x53			
Pembrey & Burry Port	d		15 59	16 52				17 59	18 57	19 29		20 59		23 01			
Llanelli	a		16 04	16 57				18 04	19 02	19 34		21 05		23 07			
	d	15 45	16 06	16 58				18 06	19 03	19 36	19 52	21 05		23 07			
Gowerton	d	15x52		17x04					19x09		19x59	21x12		23x14			
Swansea 7	a	16 07	16 22	17 17		←		18 22	19 25	19 52	20 13	21 26		23 28			
	d		16 29	17 35 →	17 29	17 35		18 29	19 35	19 59	20 35	21 35		23 35			
Llansamlet	d											21 42					
Skewen	d											21 46					
Neath	d		16 41		17 41	17 47		18 41	19 46	20 11	20 46	21 50		23 46			
Briton Ferry	d											21 53					
Baglan	d											21 57					
Port Talbot Parkway	d		16 48		17 48	17 54		18 48	19 53	20 18	20 54	22 01		23 54			
Pyle	d											22 08					
Maesteg	d																
Maesteg (Ewenny Road)	d																
Garth (Mid Glamorgan)	d																
Tondu	d																
Sarn	d																
Wildmill	d																
Bridgend	d		17 00		18 00	18 06		19 00	20 05	20 30	21 07	22 16		00 07			
Pencoed	d											22 22					
Llanharan	d											22 26					
Pontyclun	d											22 30					
Cardiff Central 7	a		17 22		18 22	18 28		19 22	20 27	20 52	21 30	22 46		00 50			
Cardiff Queen Street 3	a																
Newport (South Wales)	a		17 38		18 38			19 38		21 08							
Bristol Parkway 7	a																
Gloucester 7	a		18 21		19 21			20 21		21 51							
Manchester Piccadilly 10 ⛴	a																
Reading 7	a		19 49		20 49			21 52		23 20							
London Paddington 15 ⊖	a		20 29		21 29			22 30		00 10							

For general notes see front of timetable
For details of catering facilities see Directory of Train Operators

A From Shrewsbury (Table 129)
B Ship service

Table 128A

Mondays to Fridays

Maesteg — Caerau

Bus Service

		AW	AW	AW	AW	AW	AW	AW	AW	AW	AW	AW	AW	AW	AW	AW	AW	AW
Cardiff Central	128 d	05 51	07 04	08 21	09 21	10 21	11 21	12 21	13 21	14 21	15 21	16 21	17 21	18 21	19 12	20b22	21b22	22b35
Bridgend	128 d	06 20	07 32	08 49	09 49	10 49	11 49	12 49	13 49	14 49	15 49	16 49	17 48	18 49	19 45	20 55	21 56	23 02
Maesteg	d	**06 51**	**08 05**	**09 20**	**10 20**	**11 20**	**12 20**	**13 20**	**14 20**	**15 20**	**16 20**	**17 20**	**18 22**	**19 21**	**20 26**	**21 25**	**22 26**	**23 34**
Caerau (Square)	a	**07 00**	**08 14**	**09 29**	**10 29**	**11 29**	**12 29**	**13 29**	**14 29**	**15 29**	**16 29**	**17 29**	**18 31**	**19 30**	**20 35**	**21 34**	**22 35**	**23 43**
Caerau Park	a	**07 10**	**08 24**	**09 39**	**10 39**	**11 39**	**12 39**	**13 39**	**14 39**	**15 39**	**16 39**	**17 39**	**18 41**	**19 40**	**20 45**	**21 44**	**22 45**	**23 53**

Saturdays

		AW	AW	AW	AW	AW	AW	AW	AW	AW	AW	AW	AW	AW	AW	AW	AW
Cardiff Central	128 d	05 51	07 04	08 21	09 21	10 21	11 21	12 21	13 21	14 21	15 21	16 21	17 21	18 21	19 21	20 21	21c21
Bridgend	128 d	06 20	07 32	08 49	09 49	10 49	11 49	12 49	13 49	14 49	15 49	16 49	17 49	18 49	19 49	20 49	21 56
Maesteg	d	**06 51**	**08 05**	**09 20**	**10 20**	**11 20**	**12 20**	**13 20**	**14 20**	**15 20**	**16 20**	**17 20**	**18 22**	**19 21**	**20 26**	**21 25**	**22 26**
Caerau (Square)	a	**07 00**	**08 14**	**09 29**	**10 29**	**11 29**	**12 29**	**13 29**	**14 29**	**15 29**	**16 29**	**17 29**	**18 31**	**19 30**	**20 35**	**21 34**	**22 35**
Caerau Park	a	**07 10**	**08 24**	**09 39**	**10 39**	**11 39**	**12 39**	**13 39**	**14 39**	**15 39**	**16 39**	**17 39**	**18 41**	**19 40**	**20 45**	**21 44**	**22 45**

Mondays to Fridays

		AW	AW	AW	AW	AW	AW	AW	AW	AW	AW	AW	AW	AW	AW	AW	AW
Caerau Park	d	**06 24**	**07 35**	**08 50**	**09 50**	**10 50**	**11 50**	**12 50**	**13 50**	**14 50**	**15 50**	**16 50**	**17 50**	**18 50**	**19 50**	**20 50**	**21 50**
Caerau (Square)	d	**06 34**	**07 45**	**09 00**	**10 00**	**11 00**	**12 00**	**13 00**	**14 00**	**15 00**	**16 00**	**17 00**	**18 00**	**19 00**	**20 00**	**21 00**	**22 00**
Maesteg	a	**06 44**	**07 55**	**09 10**	**10 10**	**11 10**	**12 10**	**13 10**	**14 10**	**15 10**	**16 10**	**17 10**	**18 10**	**19 10**	**20 10**	**21 10**	**22 12**
Bridgend	128 a	07 11	08 22	09 39	10 39	11 39	12 39	13 39	14 39	15 39	16 39	17 39	18 42	19 42	20 42	21 44	22 45
Cardiff Central	128 a	07 43	08 48	10 09	11 15	12 09	13 09	14 12	15 09	16 10	17 09	18 09	19 13	20 12	21 11	22 17	23 16

Saturdays

		AW	AW	AW	AW	AW	AW	AW	AW	AW	AW	AW	AW	AW	AW	AW	AW
Caerau Park	d	**06 24**	**07 35**	**08 50**	**09 50**	**10 50**	**11 50**	**12 50**	**13 50**	**14 50**	**15 50**	**16 50**	**17 50**	**18 50**	**19 50**	**20 50**	**21 50**
Caerau (Square)	d	**06 34**	**07 45**	**09 00**	**10 00**	**11 00**	**12 00**	**13 00**	**14 00**	**15 00**	**16 00**	**17 00**	**18 00**	**19 00**	**20 00**	**21 00**	**22 00**
Maesteg	a	**06 44**	**07 55**	**09 10**	**10 10**	**11 10**	**12 10**	**13 10**	**14 10**	**15 10**	**16 10**	**17 10**	**18 10**	**19 10**	**20 10**	**21 10**	**22 10**
Bridgend	128 a	07 11	08 22	09 39	10 39	11 39	12 39	13 39	14 39	15 39	16 39	17 39	18 42	19 42	20 42	21 44	22 45
Cardiff Central	128 a	07 43	08 48	10 09	11 15	12 09	13 09	14 12	15 09	16 09	17 09	18 09	19 16	20 12	21 12	22 17	23 16

For general notes see front of timetable
For details of catering facilities see Directory of Train Operators

b Change at Bridgend and Maesteg
c Until 26 January dep. 2122

No Sunday Service

Network Diagram for Tables 129, 131

DM-14/06
Design BAJS

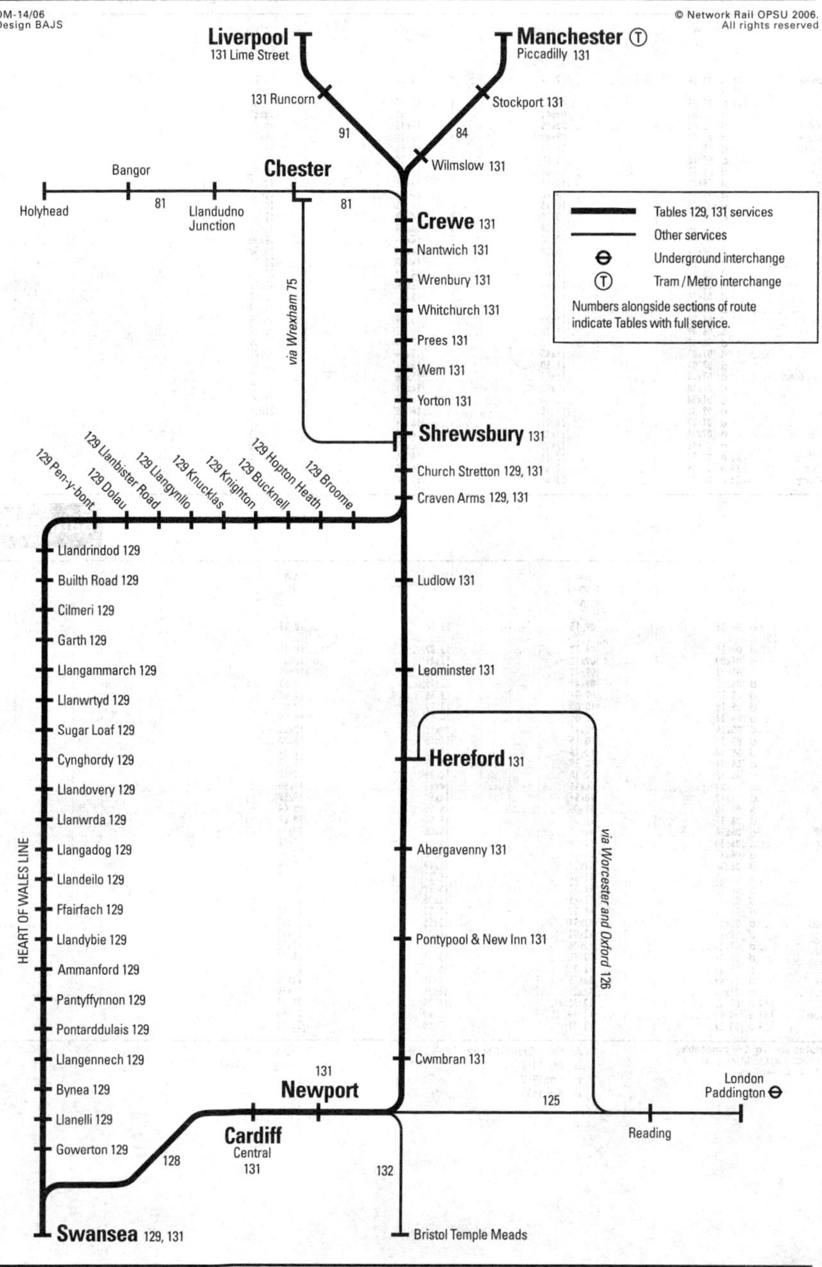

Liverpool
131 Lime Street
Manchester
Piccadilly 131
131 Runcorn
Stockport 131
91
84
Wilmslow 131
Bangor
Chester
Holyhead
81
Llandudno Junction
81
via Wrexham 75
Crewe 131
Nantwich 131
Wrenbury 131
Whitchurch 131
Prees 131
Wem 131
Yorton 131
Shrewsbury 131
Church Stretton 129, 131
Craven Arms 129, 131
129 Pen-y-bont
129 Llanbister Road
129 Dolau
129 Llangynllo
129 Knucklas
129 Knighton
129 Bucknell
129 Hopton Heath
129 Broome
Llandrindod 129
Builth Road 129
Cilmeri 129
Garth 129
Llangammarch 129
Llanwrtyd 129
Sugar Loaf 129
Cynghordy 129
Llandovery 129
Llanwrda 129
Llangadog 129
Llandeilo 129
Ffairfach 129
Llandybie 129
Ammanford 129
Pantyffynnon 129
Pontarddulais 129
Llangennech 129
Bynea 129
Llanelli 129
Gowerton 129
HEART OF WALES LINE
Swansea 129, 131
128
Cardiff
Central
131
Newport
131
132
Bristol Temple Meads
Ludlow 131
Leominster 131
Hereford 131
Abergavenny 131
Pontypool & New Inn 131
Cwmbran 131
via Worcester and Oxford 126
125
Reading
London
Paddington
Tables 129, 131 services
Other services
Underground interchange
Tram / Metro interchange
Numbers alongside sections of route indicate Tables with full service.

Swansea → Shrewsbury

HEART OF WALES LINE

Route Diagram - see first page of Table 129

Miles	Station		AW ◇	AW ◇ A	AW ◇	AW ◇
0	**Swansea 7**	128 d	04 36	09 15	13 16	18 21
5½	Gowerton	128 d				
11¼	Llanelli	128 d	04 55	09 37	13 37	18 41
14	Bynea	d	05x00	09x42	13x41	18x45
16	Llangennech	d	05x03	09x45	13x45	18x49
18¼	Pontarddulais	d	05x07	09x49	13x49	18x53
23	Pantyffynnon	d	05 15	09 57	13 56	19 00
24¼	Ammanford	d	05 18	10 00	13 59	19 03
26	Llandybie	d	05 22	10 04	14 04	19 08
30	Ffairfach	d	05x29	10x11	14x11	19x15
30¾	Llandeilo	d	05 34	10 16	14b16	19c20
36½	Llangadog	d	05 44	10 26	14 25	19 29
38¼	Llanwrda	d	05 47	10 29	14 29	19 33
42	Llandovery	d	05 56	10 38	14e38	19f42
46¾	Cynghordy	d	06x04	10x46	14x46	19x50
49½	Sugar Loaf	d	06x12	10x54	14x54	19x58
53½	Llanwrtyd	a	06 18	11 00	15 00	20 04
—		d	06 21	11 07	15 02	20 08
56¾	Llangammarch	d	06x26	11x13	15x08	20x14
58½	Garth (Powys)	d	06x30	11x16	15x11	20x17
62	Cilmeri	d	06x35	11x21	15x16	20x22
64	Builth Road	d	06x38	11x24	15x19	20x25
69¾	Llandrindod	a	06 49	11 36	15 31	20 37
—		d	06 55	11 38	15 39	20 39
73¼	Pen-y-bont	d	07x02	11x45	15x46	20x46
76¼	Dolau	d	07 07	11 50	15 51	20 51
79¾	Llanbister Road	d	07x13	11x57	15x56	20x57
82¾	Llangynllo	d	07x18	12x02	16x01	21x02
86¾	Knucklas	d	07x24	12x08	16x07	21x08
89¼	Knighton	d	07 31	12 15	16 15	21g16
93½	Bucknell	d	07 37	12 21	16 21	21 22
96½	Hopton Heath	d	07x41	12x25	16x25	21x26
99	Broome	d	07x45	12x29	16x29	21x30
101½	Craven Arms	131 a	07 52	12 36	16 36	21 37
108¾	Church Stretton	131 a	08 05	12 49	16 49	21 50
121½	**Shrewsbury**	131 a	08 21	13 07	17 10	22 12

Saturdays

Station		AW ◇	AW ◇ A	AW ◇	AW ◇
Swansea 7	128 d	04 36	09 15	13 16	18 21
Gowerton	128 d				
Llanelli	128 d	04 55	09 37	13 37	18 41
Bynea	d	05x00	09x42	13x41	18x45
Llangennech	d	05x03	09x45	13x45	18x49
Pontarddulais	d	05x07	09x49	13x49	18x53
Pantyffynnon	d	05 15	09 57	13 56	19 00
Ammanford	d	05 18	10 00	13 59	19 03
Llandybie	d	05 22	10 04	14 04	19 08
Ffairfach	d	05x29	10x11	14x11	19x15
Llandeilo	d	05 34	10 16	14b16	19c20
Llangadog	d	05 44	10 26	14 25	19 29
Llanwrda	d	05 47	10 29	14 29	19 33
Llandovery	d	05 56	10 38	14e38	19f42
Cynghordy	d	06x04	10x46	14x46	19x50
Sugar Loaf	d	06x12	10x54	14x54	19x58
Llanwrtyd	a	06 18	11 00	15 00	20 04
	d	06 21	11 07	15 02	20 08
Llangammarch	d	06x26	11x13	15x08	20x14
Garth (Powys)	d	06x30	11x16	15x11	20x17
Cilmeri	d	06x35	11x21	15x16	20x22
Builth Road	d	06x38	11x24	15x19	20x25
Llandrindod	a	06 49	11 36	15 31	20 37
	d	06 55	11 38	15 39	20 39
Pen-y-bont	d	07x02	11x45	15x46	20x46
Dolau	d	07 07	11 50	15 51	20 51
Llanbister Road	d	07x13	11x57	15x56	20x57
Llangynllo	d	07x18	12x02	16x01	21x02
Knucklas	d	07x24	12x08	16x07	21x08
Knighton	d	07 31	12 15	16 15	21g16
Bucknell	d	07 37	12 21	16 21	21 22
Hopton Heath	d	07x41	12x25	16x25	21x26
Broome	d	07x45	12x29	16x29	21x30
Craven Arms	131 a	07 52	12 36	16 36	21 37
Church Stretton	131 a	08 05	12 49	16 49	21 50
Shrewsbury	131 a	08 21	13 07	17 10	22 12

For general notes see front of timetable
For details of catering facilities see Directory of Train Operators

A From Cardiff Central (Table 128)
b Arr. 1413
c Arr. 1917
e Arr. 1435
f Arr. 1939
g Arr. 2113

Table 129

Sundays

Swansea → Shrewsbury
HEART OF WALES LINE

Route Diagram - see first page of Table 129

		AW ◇ A	AW ◇ B	AW ◇ C
Swansea 7	128 d	11§00	11§09	15 16
Gowerton	128 d	11x11	11x20	15x27
Llanelli	128 d	11§29	11§29	15 38
Bynea	d	11x34	11x34	15x43
Llangennech	d	11x38	11x38	15x46
Pontarddulais	d	11x42	11x42	15x50
Pantyffynnon	d	11§49	11§49	15 58
Ammanford	d	11§52	11§52	16 01
Llandybie	d	11§57	11§57	16 05
Ffairfach	d	12x04	12x04	16x12
Llandeilo	d	12b09	12b09	16 17
Llangadog	d	12§18	12§18	16 27
Llanwrda	d	12§22	12§22	16 30
Llandovery	d	12c31	12c31	16 39
Cynghordy	d	12x39	12x39	16x47
Sugar Loaf	d	12x47	12x47	16x55
Llanwrtyd	a	12§53	12§53	17 01
	d	12§55	12§55	17 04
Llangammarch	d	13x01	13x01	17x09
Garth (Powys)	d	13x04	13x04	17x13
Cilmeri	d	13x09	13x09	17x18
Builth Road	d	13x12	13x12	17x21
Llandrindod	a	13§24	13§24	17 32
	d	14§05	14§05	17 58
Pen-y-bont	d	14x12	14x12	18x05
Dolau	d	14§17	14§17	18 10
Llanbister Road	d	14x22	14x22	18x15
Llangynllo	d	14x27	14x27	18x20
Knucklas	d	14x33	14x33	18x26
Knighton	d	14§41	14§41	18 34
Bucknell	d	14§47	14§47	18 40
Hopton Heath	d	14x51	14x51	18x44
Broome	d	14x55	14x55	18x48
Craven Arms	131 a	15§02	15§02	18 55
Church Stretton	131 a	15§15	15§15	19 08
Shrewsbury	131 a	15§33	15§33	19 23

For general notes see front of timetable
For details of catering facilities see Directory of Train Operators

A From 3 February
B Until 27 January
C To Crewe (Table 131)

b Arr. 1206
c Arr. 1228

Shrewsbury → Swansea

HEART OF WALES LINE

Route Diagram - see first page of Table 129

Mondays to Fridays

Miles	Station			AW ◇ A	AW ◇	AW ◇	AW ◇
0	**Shrewsbury**	131	d	05 19	09 05	14 05	18 05
12¾	Church Stretton	131	d	05 36	09 22	14 23	18 23
20	Craven Arms	131	d	05 50	09 35	14 36	18 35
22½	Broome		d	05x55	09x40	14x41	18x40
25	Hopton Heath		d	05x59	09x44	14x45	18x44
28	Bucknell		d	06x03	09x48	14x49	18x48
32¼	Knighton		d	06 12	09 57	14 58	18 57
34¾	Knucklas		d	06x17	10x02	15x03	19x02
38¾	Llangynllo		d	06x25	10x10	15x11	19x10
41¾	Llanbister Road		d	06x29	10x14	15x15	19x14
45¼	Dolau		d	06x35	10x20	15x21	19x20
48½	Pen-y-bont		d	06x39	10x24	15x25	19x24
51¾	Llandrindod		a	06 48	10 33	15 34	19 33
—			d	06 55	10 35	15 38	19 35
57½	Builth Road		d	07x04	10x44	15x47	19x44
59½	Cilmeri		d	07x07	10x47	15x50	19x47
63	Garth (Powys)		d	07x12	10x52	15x55	19x52
64¾	Llangammarch		d	07x15	10x56	15x59	19x56
68	Llanwrtyd		a	07 21	11 02	16 05	20 02
—			d	07 24	11 09	16 07	20 13
70¾	Sugar Loaf		d	07x30	11x15	16x13	20x19
74¾	Cynghordy		d	07x36	11x21	16x20	20x25
79½	Llandovery		d	07 48	11 33	16b32	20 37
83¼	Llanwrda		d	07x54	11x39	16x37	20x43
85	Llangadog		d	07x57	11x42	16x41	20x46
90¾	Llandeilo		d	08c09	11e54	16 52	20f58
91½	Ffairfach		d	08 11	11 56	16 55	21 00
95½	Llandybie		d	08x18	12x03	17x02	21x07
97¼	Ammanford		d	08x22	12x07	17x06	21x11
98½	Pantyffynnon		d	08 25	12 10	17 09	21 14
103¼	Pontarddulais		d	08x32	12x17	17x15	21x21
105½	Llangennech		d	08x36	12x21	17x19	21x25
107½	Bynea		d	08x39	12x24	17x22	21x28
110¼	Llanelli	128	a	08 43	12 30	17 28	21 42
116	Gowerton	128	a	08x53	....	17x44	21x52
121½	**Swansea** 7	128	a	09 07	13 01	18 06	22 13

Saturdays

Station			AW ◇ A	AW ◇	AW ◇	AW ◇
Shrewsbury	131	d	05 19	09 05	14 05	18 05
Church Stretton	131	d	05 36	09 22	14 23	18 23
Craven Arms	131	d	05 50	09 35	14 36	18 35
Broome		d	05x55	09x40	14x41	18x40
Hopton Heath		d	05x59	09x44	14x45	18x44
Bucknell		d	06x03	09x48	14x49	18x48
Knighton		d	06 12	09 57	14 58	18 57
Knucklas		d	06x17	10x02	15x03	19x02
Llangynllo		d	06x25	10x10	15x11	19x10
Llanbister Road		d	06x29	10x14	15x15	19x14
Dolau		d	06x35	10x20	15x21	19x20
Pen-y-bont		d	06x39	10x24	15x25	19x24
Llandrindod		a	06 48	10 33	15 34	19 33
		d	06 55	10 35	15 38	19 35
Builth Road		d	07x04	10x44	15x47	19x44
Cilmeri		d	07x07	10x47	15x50	19x47
Garth (Powys)		d	07x12	10x52	15x55	19x52
Llangammarch		d	07x15	10x56	15x59	19x56
Llanwrtyd		a	07 21	11 02	16 05	20 02
		d	07 24	11 09	16 07	20 13
Sugar Loaf		d	07x30	11x15	16x13	20x19
Cynghordy		d	07x36	11x21	16x20	20x25
Llandovery		d	07 48	11 33	16b32	20 37
Llanwrda		d	07x54	11x39	16x37	20x43
Llangadog		d	07x57	11x42	16x41	20x46
Llandeilo		d	08c09	11e54	16 52	20f58
Ffairfach		d	08 11	11 56	16 55	21 00
Llandybie		d	08x18	12x03	17x02	21x07
Ammanford		d	08x22	12x07	17x06	21x11
Pantyffynnon		d	08 25	12 10	17 09	21 14
Pontarddulais		d	08x32	12x17	17x15	21x21
Llangennech		d	08x36	12x21	17x19	21x25
Bynea		d	08x39	12x24	17x22	21x28
Llanelli	128	a	08 43	12 30	17 34	21 42
Gowerton	128	a	08x53	....	17x44	21x52
Swansea 7	128	a	09 07	13 01	18 06	22 13

For general notes see front of timetable
For details of catering facilities see Directory of Train Operators

A To Cardiff Central (Table 128)
b Arr. 1629
c Arr. 0806
e Arr. 1151
f Arr. 2055

Sundays

Shrewsbury → Swansea

HEART OF WALES LINE

Route Diagram - see first page of Table 129

Station			AW ◇	AW ◇ A
Shrewsbury	131	d	12 07	16 24
Church Stretton	131	d	12 24	16 42
Craven Arms	131	d	12 36	16 53
Broome		d	12x42	16x59
Hopton Heath		d	12x46	17x03
Bucknell		d	12x50	17x07
Knighton		d	12 59	17 16
Knucklas		d	13x04	17x21
Llangynllo		d	13x12	17x29
Llanbister Road		d	13x16	17x33
Dolau		d	13x22	17x39
Pen-y-bont		d	13x26	17x43
Llandrindod		a	13 34	17 52
		d	13 38	17 57
Builth Road		d	13x47	18x06
Cilmeri		d	13x50	18x09
Garth (Powys)		d	13x55	18x14
Llangammarch		d	13x59	18x18
Llanwrtyd		a	14 05	18 24
		d	14 10	18 26
Sugar Loaf		d	14x16	18x32
Cynghordy		d	14x22	18x39
Llandovery		d	14 34	18b51
Llanwrda		d	14x40	18x56
Llangadog		d	14x43	19x00
Llandeilo		d	15c07	19 11
Ffairfach		d	15 09	19 14
Llandybie		d	15x16	19x21
Ammanford		d	15x20	19x25
Pantyffynnon		d	15 23	19 28
Pontarddulais		d	15x30	19x34
Llangennech		d	15x34	19x38
Bynea		d	15x37	19x41
Llanelli	128	a	15 42	19 49
Gowerton	128	a	15x52	19x59
Swansea 7	128	a	16 07	20 13

For general notes see front of timetable
For details of catering facilities see Directory of Train Operators

A To Cardiff Central (Table 128)
b Arr. 1848
c Arr. 1452

Network Diagram for Table 130

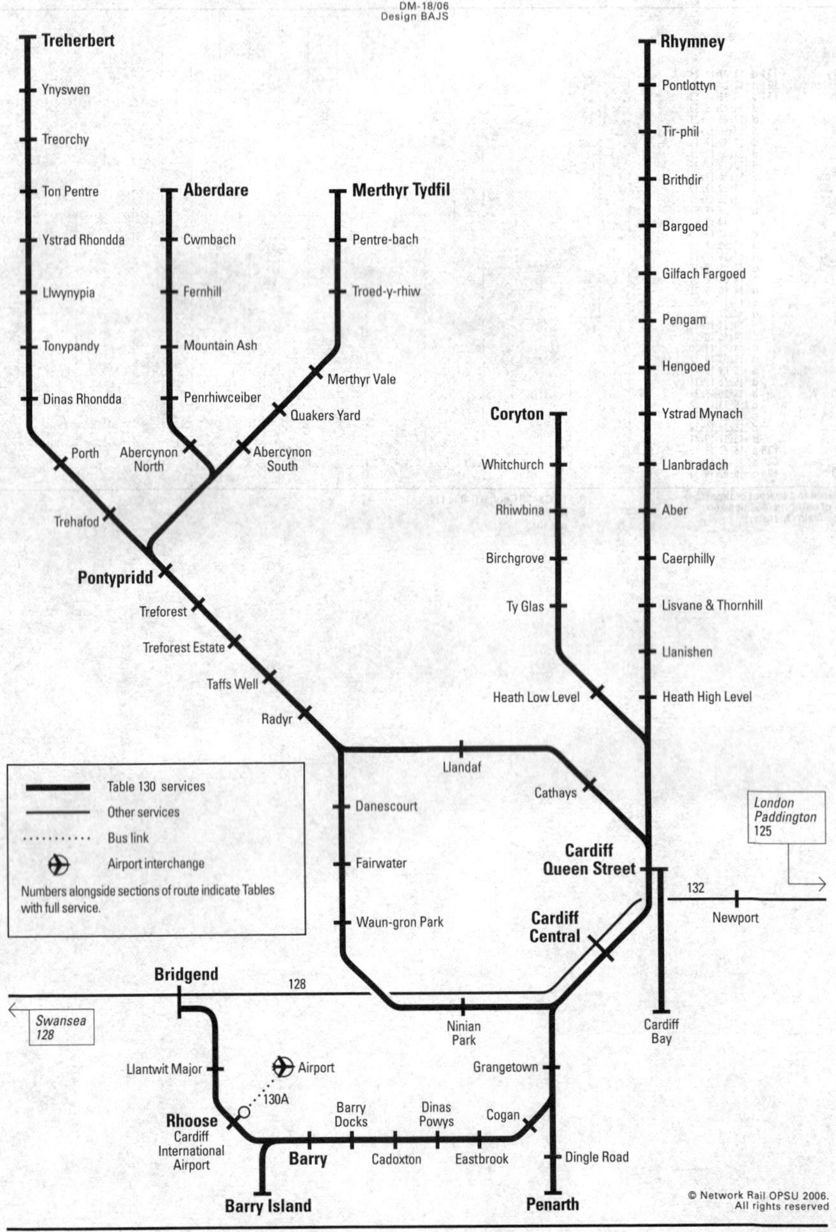

DM-18/06
Design BAJS
Treherbert
Ynyswen
Treorchy
Ton Pentre
Ystrad Rhondda
Llwynypia
Tonypandy
Dinas Rhondda
Porth
Trehafod
Aberdare
Cwmbach
Fernhill
Mountain Ash
Penrhiwceiber
Abercynon North
Merthyr Tydfil
Pentre-bach
Troed-y-rhiw
Merthyr Vale
Quakers Yard
Abercynon South
Pontypridd
Treforest
Treforest Estate
Taffs Well
Radyr
Rhymney
Pontlottyn
Tir-phil
Brithdir
Bargoed
Gilfach Fargoed
Pengam
Hengoed
Ystrad Mynach
Llanbradach
Aber
Caerphilly
Lisvane & Thornhill
Llanishen
Heath High Level
Coryton
Whitchurch
Rhiwbina
Birchgrove
Ty Glas
Heath Low Level
Llandaf
Cathays
Danescourt
Fairwater
Waun-gron Park
Cardiff Queen Street
Cardiff Central
London Paddington 125
132
Newport
Cardiff Bay
Table 130 services
Other services
Bus link
Airport interchange
Numbers alongside sections of route indicate Tables with full service.
Bridgend
128
Swansea 128
Ninian Park
Grangetown
Llantwit Major
Airport
130A
Rhoose Cardiff International Airport
Barry Docks
Dinas Powys
Cogan
Barry
Cadoxton
Eastbrook
Dingle Road
Barry Island
Penarth

Treherbert, Aberdare, Merthyr, Pontypridd, Rhymney and Coryton → Cardiff, Penarth, Barry, Barry Island and Bridgend

Network Diagram - see first page of Table 130

Miles	Miles	Miles	Miles	Miles			AW	AW	AW	AW	AW	AW	AW	AW	AW	AW	AW	AW	AW	AW		AW	AW	AW	AW	AW
																			A						B	
0	—	—	—	—	**Treherbert**	d									05 47									06 17		
½	—	—	—	—	Ynyswen	d									05 49									06 19		
1¼	—	—	—	—	Treorchy	d									05 51									06 21		
2¾	—	—	—	—	Ton Pentre	d									05 53									06 23		
3¼	—	—	—	—	Ystrad Rhondda	a									05 56									06 26		
—	—	—	—	—		d									05 58									06 28		
4½	—	—	—	—	Llwynypia	d									06 00									06 30		
5½	—	—	—	—	Tonypandy	d									06 03									06 33		
6	—	—	—	—	Dinas Rhondda	d									06 05									06 35		
7½	—	—	—	—	Porth	d									06 09									06 39		
8¾	—	—	—	—	Trehafod	d									06 12									06 42		
—	—	0	—	—	**Merthyr Tydfil**	d																				
—	—	1½	—	—	Pentre-bach	d																				
—	—	2¾	—	—	Troed Y Rhiw	d																				
—	—	4½	—	—	Merthyr Vale	d																				
—	—	6¾	—	—	Quakers Yard	d																				
—	—	8¼	—	—	Abercynon South	d																				
—	—	—	—	0	**Aberdare** 3	d																				
—	—	—	—	1½	Cwmbach	d																				
—	—	—	—	2¾	Fernhill	d																				
—	—	—	—	3¾	Mountain Ash	a																				
—	—	—	—	—		d																				
—	—	—	—	5	Penrhiwceiber	d																				
—	—	—	—	7½	Abercynon North	d																				
10¾	—	11½	—	11	**Pontypridd** 3	a									06 18									06 47		
—	—	—	—	—		d			05 24						06 18									06 48		
11½	—	—	—	—	Trefforest	d			05 27						06 21									06 51		
14	—	—	—	—	Trefforest Estate	d			05 31						06 24											
16¼	—	—	—	—	Taffs Well 3	d			05 34						06 28									06 58		
18¼	—	—	0	—	Radyr 3	a			05 37						06 31									07 01	←	
—	—	—	—	—		d			05 37						06 31									07 01	07 04	
—	—	—	1½	—	Danescourt	d																			07 08	
—	—	—	2	—	Fairwater	d																			07 10	
—	—	—	2¼	—	Waun-gron Park	d																			07 12	
—	—	—	3¾	—	Ninian Park	d																			07 15	
19¼	—	—	—	—	Llandaf	d			05 40						06 34									07 04		
21¾	—	—	—	—	Cathays	d			05 45						06 39									07 09		
—	0	—	—	—	**Rhymney** 3	d																06 14				
—	1	—	—	—	Pontlottyn	d																06 17				
—	3½	—	—	—	Tir-phil	d																06 21				
—	4½	—	—	—	Brithdir	d																06 24				
—	6	—	—	—	Bargoed	d																06b32				
—	6½	—	—	—	Gilfach Fargoed	d																06 34				
—	7½	—	—	—	Pengam	d																06 37				
—	9¼	—	—	—	Hengoed	d																06 40				
—	10½	—	—	—	Ystrad Mynach 3	d																06 43				
—	13	—	—	—	Llanbradach	d																06 48				
—	15	—	—	—	Aber	d																06 52				
—	15¾	—	—	—	Caerphilly 3	d							06 10									06 55				
—	18¼	—	—	—	Lisvane & Thornhill	d							06 14									06 59				
—	19¼	—	—	—	Llanishen	d							06 16									07 01				
—	20¼	—	—	—	Heath High Level	d							06 19									07 04				
—	—	0	—	—	**Coryton**	d													06 45							
—	—	½	—	—	Whitchurch (Cardiff)	d													06 46							
—	—	¾	—	—	Rhiwbina	d													06 48							
—	—	1¼	—	—	Birchgrove	d													06 50							
—	—	1½	—	—	Ty Glas	d													06 51							
—	—	2¼	—	—	Heath Low Level	d													06 54							
22½	22¾	4¾	—	—	**Cardiff Queen Street** 3	a			05 49				06 25		06 44				06 59			07 09		07 14		
—	—	—	—	—		d			05 51				06 26	06 42	06 45			06 57	07 00			07 11	07 12	07 16		07 27
—	—	5¾	—	—	**Cardiff Bay**	a								06 46				07 01					07 16			07 31
23	23¼	—	4¾	—	**Cardiff Central** 7	a			05 53				06 29		06 48				07 04			07 14		07 18	07 20	
—	—	—	—	—		d	05 25	05 41	05 55	06 16	06 25	06 36	06 41			06 56	07 01			07 10		07 16				
24	24¼	—	—	—	Grangetown	d	05 29	05 45	05 59	06 20	06 29	06 40	06 45			07 00	07 05			07 14		07 20				
—	26¾	—	—	—	Dingle Road	d				06 26		06 44					07 11					07 26				
—	27	—	—	—	**Penarth**	a				06 31		06 49					07 16					07 31				
25¾	—	—	—	—	Cogan	d	05 33	05 48	06 03		06 33		06 48			07 03				07 18						
26½	—	—	—	—	Eastbrook	d	05 35	05 51	06 05		06 35		06 51			07 06				07 20						
27½	—	—	—	—	Dinas Powys	d	05 37	05 53	06 07		06 37		06 53			07 08				07 22						
29½	—	—	—	—	Cadoxton	d	05 42	05 57	06 12		06 42		06 57			07 12				07 27						
30¼	—	—	—	—	Barry Docks	d	05 45	06 00	06 15		06 45		07 00			07 15				07 30						
31½	—	0	—	—	**Barry** 3	d	05 49	06 05	06 19		06 49		07 05			07 19				07 34						
32¼	—	—	—	—	**Barry Island**	a	05 55		06 25		06 55					07 25				07 40						
—	—	3¼	—	—	Rhoose Cardiff Int Airport ✈	d		06 12					07 12													
—	—	9¾	—	—	Llantwit Major	d		06 22					07 22													
—	—	19	—	—	**Bridgend**	a		06 39					07 39													

For general notes see front of timetable
For details of catering facilities see
Directory of Train Operators

A To Radyr
B To Coryton
b Arr. 0627

Treherbert, Aberdare, Merthyr, Pontypridd, Rhymney and Coryton → Cardiff, Penarth, Barry, Barry Island and Bridgend

Network Diagram - see first page of Table 130

		AW	AW	AW	AW	AW	AW	AW	AW	AW	AW	AW		AW	AW	AW	AW	AW	AW	AW	AW	AW	AW	AW	AW	AW
			A					B						A				B					A			
Treherbert	d						06 47									07 17										
Ynyswen	d						06 49									07 19										
Treorchy	d						06 51									07 21										
Ton Pentre	d						06 53									07 23										
Ystrad Rhondda	a						06 56									07 26										
	d						06 58									07 28										
Llwynypia	d						07 00									07 30										
Tonypandy	d						07 03									07 33										
Dinas Rhondda	d						07 05									07 35										
Porth	d						07 09									07 39										
Trehafod	d						07 12									07 42										
Merthyr Tydfil	d			06 39																				07 39		
Pentre-bach	d			06 43																				07 43		
Troed Y Rhiw	d			06 46																				07 46		
Merthyr Vale	d			06 50																				07 50		
Quakers Yard	d			06 55																				07 55		
Abercynon South	d			06 59																				07 59		
Aberdare 3	d									06 52										07 22						
Cwmbach	d									06 55										07 25						
Fernhill	d									06 58										07 28						
Mountain Ash	a									07 01										07 31						
	d									07 04										07 34						
Penrhiwceiber	d									07 07										07 37						
Abercynon North	d									07 15										07 45						
Pontypridd 3	a			07 07			07 17			07 23						07 47				07 53				08 07		
	d			07 09			07 18			07 24						07 48				07 54				08 09		
Trefforest	d			07 12			07 21			07 27						07 51				07 57				08 12		
Trefforest Estate	d			07 16																				08 16		
Taffs Well 3	d			07 20			07 28			07 34						07 58				08 04				08 20		
Radyr 3	a			07 23			07 31			07 37						08 01				08 07				08 23		
	d			07 23			07 31	07 34		07 37						08 01		08 04		08 07				08 23		
Danescourt	d							07 38										08 08								
Fairwater	d							07 40										08 10								
Waun-gron Park	d							07 42										08 12								
Ninian Park	d							07 45										08 15								
Llandaf	d			07 26			07 34		←	07 40						08 04			←	08 10				08 26		
Cathays	d			07 31			07 39		07 39	07 45						08 09			08 09	08 15				08 31		
Rhymney 3	d	06 37					↪				07 02					↪					07 24				07 44	
Pontlottyn	d	06 40									07 05										07 27				07 47	
Tir-phil	d	06 44									07 09										07 31				07 51	
Brithdir	d	06 47									07 12										07 34				07 54	
Bargoed	d	06 51			07 02						07 17				07 32						07b45				08 02	
Gilfach Fargoed	d				07 04						07 19										07 47					
Pengam	d	06 55			07 07						07 22				07 37						07 50				08 07	
Hengoed	d	06 59			07 10						07 25				07 40						07 54				08 10	
Ystrad Mynach 3	d	07 01			07 13						07 28				07 43						07 57				08 13	
Llanbradach	d	07 06			07 18						07 33				07 48						08 02				08 18	
Aber	d	07 10			07 22						07 37				07 52						08 07				08 22	
Caerphilly 3	d	07 13			07 25						07 40				07 55						08 10				08 25	
Lisvane & Thornhill	d	07 17			07 29						07 44				07 59						08 14				08 29	
Llanishen	d	07 19			07 31						07 46				08 01						08 16				08 31	
Heath High Level	d	07 22			07 34						07 49				08 04						08 19				08 34	
Coryton	d		07 15											07 45									08 15			
Whitchurch (Cardiff)	d		07 16											07 46									08 16			
Rhiwbina	d		07 18											07 48									08 18			
Birchgrove	d		07 20											07 50									08 20			
Ty Glas	d		07 21											07 51									08 21			
Heath Low Level	d		07 24											07 54									08 24			
Cardiff Queen Street 3	a	07 27	07 29	07 34	07 38				07 44	07 49	07 54			07 59	08 09				08 14	08 19	08 24		08 29	08 34	08 39	
	d	07 28	07 31	07 36	07 41	07 42			07 46	07 51	07 56	07 57		08 01	08 11		08 12		08 16	08 21	08 26	08 27	08 31	08 36	08 41	08 42
Cardiff Bay	a					07 46						08 01					08 16					08 31				08 46
Cardiff Central 7	a	07 31	07 34	07 39	07 44			07 50	07 52	07 54	07 59			08 04	08 14			08 20	08 22	08 24	08 29		08 34	08 39	08 47	
	d	07 32		07 41	07 46					07 55	08 01				08 16					08 25	08 31			08 41		
Grangetown	d	07 36		07 45	07 50					07 59	08 05				08 20					08 29	08 35			08 45		
Dingle Road	d	07 41			07 56						08 11				08 26						08 41					
Penarth	a	07 46			08 01						08 16				08 31						08 46					
Cogan	d			07 48						08 03										08 33				08 48		
Eastbrook	d			07 51						08 05										08 35				08 51		
Dinas Powys	d			07 53						08 07										08 37				08 53		
Cadoxton	d			07 57						08 12										08 42				08 57		
Barry Docks	d			08 00						08 15										08 45				09 00		
Barry 3	d			08 05						08 19										08 49				09 05		
Barry Island	a									08 25										08 55						
Rhoose Cardiff Int Airport ✈	d			08 12																				09 12		
Llantwit Major	d			08 22																				09 22		
Bridgend	a			08 39																				09 39		

For general notes see front of timetable
For details of catering facilities see Directory of Train Operators

A To Radyr
B To Coryton
b Arr. 0737

Treherbert, Aberdare, Merthyr, Pontypridd, Rhymney and Coryton → Cardiff, Penarth, Barry, Barry Island and Bridgend

Network Diagram - see first page of Table 130

		AW	AW A	AW		AW	AW	AW	AW B	AW	AW	AW	AW A	AW	AW	AW	AW	AW B	AW		AW	AW	AW	AW A	AW	AW
Treherbert	d	07 47									08 17												08 47			
Ynyswen	d	07 49									08 19												08 49			
Treorchy	d	07 51									08 21												08 51			
Ton Pentre	d	07 53									08 23												08 53			
Ystrad Rhondda	a	07 56									08 26												08 56			
	d	07 58									08 28												08 58			
Llwynypia	d	08 00									08 30												09 00			
Tonypandy	d	08 03									08 33												09 03			
Dinas Rhondda	d	08 05									08 35												09 05			
Porth	d	08 09									08 39												09 09			
Trehafod	d	08 12									08 42												09 12			
Merthyr Tydfil	d																		08 39							
Pentre-bach	d																		08 43							
Troed Y Rhiw	d																		08 46							
Merthyr Vale	d																		08 50							
Quakers Yard	d																		08 55							
Abercynon South	d																		08 59							
Aberdare 3	d					07 52									08 22											08 52
Cwmbach	d					07 55									08 25											08 55
Fernhill	d					07 58									08 28											08 58
Mountain Ash	a					08 01									08 31											09 01
	d					08 04									08 34											09 04
Penrhiwceiber	d					08 07									08 37											09 07
Abercynon North	d					08 15									08 45											09 15
Pontypridd 3	a	08 17				08 23					08 47				08 53				09 07				09 17			09 23
	d	08 18				08 24					08 48				08 54				09 09				09 18			09 24
Trefforest	d	08 21				08 27					08 51				08 57				09 12				09 21			09 27
Trefforest Estate	d																		09 16							
Taffs Well 3	d	08 28				08 34					08 58				09 04				09 20				09 28			09 34
Radyr 3	a	08 31				08 37					09 01				09 07				09 23				09 31			09 37
	d	08 31	08 34			08 37					09 01		09 04		09 07				09 23				09 31	09 34		09 37
Danescourt	d		08 38										09 08											09 38		
Fairwater	d		08 40										09 10											09 40		
Waun-gron Park	d		08 42										09 12											09 42		
Ninian Park	d		08 45										09 15											09 45		
Llandaf	d	08 34		←		08 40					09 04			←	09 10				09 26				09 34		←	09 40
Cathays	d	08 39		08 39		08 45					09 09			09 09	09 15				09 31				09 39		09 39	09 45
Rhymney 3	d	→									→					08 30							→			
Pontlottyn	d															08 33										
Tir-phil	d															08 37										
Brithdir	d															08 40										
Bargoed	d						08 17			08 32						08b47					09 02					
Gilfach Fargoed	d						08 19																			
Pengam	d						08 22			08 37						08 52					09 07					
Hengoed	d						08 25			08 40						08 55					09 10					
Ystrad Mynach 3	d						08 28			08 43						08 58					09 13					
Llanbradach	d						08 33			08 48						09 03					09 18					
Aber	d						08 37			08 52						09 07					09 22					
Caerphilly 3	d						08 40			08 55						09 10					09 25					
Lisvane & Thornhill	d						08 44			08 59						09 14					09 29					
Llanishen	d						08 46			09 01						09 16					09 31					
Heath High Level	d						08 49			09 04						09 19					09 34					
Coryton	d								08 45									09 15								
Whitchurch (Cardiff)	d								08 46									09 16								
Rhiwbina	d								08 48									09 18								
Birchgrove	d								08 50									09 20								
Ty Glas	d								08 51									09 21								
Heath Low Level	d								08 54									09 24								
Cardiff Queen Street 3	a			08 44		08 49	08 54		08 59	09 09				09 14	09 19	09 24		09 29	09 34		09 39				09 44	09 49
	d			08 46		08 51	08 56	08 57	09 01	09 11		09 12		09 16	09 21	09 26	09 27	09 31	09 36		09 41	09 42			09 46	09 51
Cardiff Bay	a							09 01				09 16					09 31					09 46				
Cardiff Central 7	a		08 50	08 52		08 54	08 59		09 04	09 14			09 20	09 22	09 24	09 29		09 34	09 39		09 46			09 50	09 52	09 54
	d					08 55	09 01			09 16					09 25	09 31			09 41		09 46					09 55
Grangetown	d					08 59	09 05			09 20					09 29	09 35			09 45		09 50					09 59
Dingle Road	d						09 11			09 26						09 41					09 56					
Penarth	a						09 16			09 31						09 46					10 01					
Cogan	d					09 03									09 33				09 48							10 03
Eastbrook	d					09 05									09 35				09 51							10 05
Dinas Powys	d					09 07									09 37				09 53							10 07
Cadoxton	d					09 12									09 42				09 57							10 12
Barry Docks	d					09 15									09 45				10 00							10 15
Barry 3	d					09 19									09 49				10 05							10 19
Barry Island	a					09 25									09 55											10 25
Rhoose Cardiff Int Airport ✈	d																		10 12							
Llantwit Major	d																		10 22							
Bridgend	a																		10 40							

For general notes see front of timetable
For details of catering facilities see Directory of Train Operators

A To Coryton
B To Radyr
b Arr. 0844

Treherbert, Aberdare, Merthyr, Pontypridd, Rhymney and Coryton → Cardiff, Penarth, Barry, Barry Island and Bridgend

Network Diagram - see first page of Table 130

		AW	AW	AW	AW	AW	AW	AW	AW	AW	AW	AW	AW	AW	AW	AW	AW	AW	AW	AW	AW	AW	AW	AW	AW
				A					B					A					B			MTX			A
Treherbert	d						09 17											09 47							
Ynyswen	d						09 19											09 49							
Treorchy	d						09 21											09 51							
Ton Pentre	d						09 23											09 53							
Ystrad Rhondda	a						09 26											09 56							
	d						09 28											09 58							
Llwynypia	d						09 30											10 00							
Tonypandy	d						09 33											10 03							
Dinas Rhondda	d						09 35											10 05							
Porth	d						09 39											10 09							
Trehafod	d						09 42											10 12							
Merthyr Tydfil	d														09 39										
Pentre-bach	d														09 43										
Troed Y Rhiw	d														09 46										
Merthyr Vale	d														09 50										
Quakers Yard	d														09 55										
Abercynon South	d														09 59							09 51			
Aberdare 3	d										09 22										09 52				
Cwmbach	d										09 25										09 55	10a09			
Fernhill	d										09 28										09 58				
Mountain Ash	a										09 31										10 01				
	d										09 34										10 04				
Penrhiwceiber	d										09 37										10 07	09a57			
Abercynon North	d										09 45										10 15				
Pontypridd 3	a						09 47				09 53				10 07			10 17			10 23				
	d				09 39		09 48				09 54				10 09			10 18			10 24				
Trefforest	d				09 42		09 51				09 57				10 12			10 21			10 27				
Trefforest Estate	d				09 46										10 16										
Taffs Well 3	d				09 50		09 58				10 04				10 20			10 28			10 34				
Radyr 3	a				09 53		10 01				10 07				10 23			10 31			10 37				
	d				09 53		10 01		10 04		10 07				10 23			10 31	10 34		10 37				
Danescourt	d								10 08										10 38						
Fairwater	d								10 10										10 40						
Waun-gron Park	d								10 12										10 42						
Ninian Park	d								10 15										10 45						
Llandaf	d				09 56		10 04			←	10 10				10 26			10 34		←	10 40				
Cathays	d				10 01		10 09			10 09	10 15				10 31			10 39		10 39	10 45				
Rhymney 3	d						→					09 29						→							
Pontlottyn	d											09 32													
Tir-phil	d											09 36													
Brithdir	d											09 39													
Bargoed	d	09 17				09 32						09b47				10 02							10 17		
Gilfach Fargoed	d	09 19																					10 19		
Pengam	d	09 22				09 37						09 52				10 07							10 22		
Hengoed	d	09 25				09 40						09 55				10 10							10 25		
Ystrad Mynach 3	d	09 28				09 43						09 58				10 13							10 28		
Llanbradach	d	09 33				09 48						10 03				10 18							10 33		
Aber	d	09 37				09 52						10 07				10 22							10 37		
Caerphilly 3	d	09 40				09 55						10 10				10 25							10 40		
Lisvane & Thornhill	d	09 44				09 59						10 14				10 29							10 44		
Llanishen	d	09 46				10 01						10 16				10 31							10 46		
Heath High Level	d	09 49				10 04						10 19				10 34							10 49		
Coryton	d			09 45										10 15											10 45
Whitchurch (Cardiff)	d			09 46										10 16											10 46
Rhiwbina	d			09 48										10 18											10 48
Birchgrove	d			09 50										10 20											10 50
Ty Glas	d			09 51										10 21											10 51
Heath Low Level	d			09 54										10 24											10 54
Cardiff Queen Street 3	a	09 54		09 59	10 04	10 09				10 14	10 19	10 24		10 29	10 34	10 39				10 44	10 49		10 54		10 59
	d	09 56	09 57	10 01	10 06	10 11		10 12		10 16	10 21	10 26	10 27	10 31	10 36	10 41	10 42			10 46	10 51		10 56	10 57	11 01
Cardiff Bay	a		10 01					10 16					10 31				10 46							11 01	
Cardiff Central 7	a	09 59		10 04	10 09	10 14			10 20	10 22	10 24	10 29		10 34	10 39	10 44			10 50	10 52	10 54		10 59		11 04
	d	10 01			10 10	10 16					10 25	10 31			10 41	10 46					10 55		11 01		
Grangetown	d	10 05			10 14	10 20					10 29	10 35			10 45	10 50					10 59		11 05		
Dingle Road	d	10 11				10 26						10 41				10 56							11 11		
Penarth	a	10 16				10 31						10 46				11 01							11 16		
Cogan	d				10 18						10 33				10 48						11 03				
Eastbrook	d				10 20						10 35				10 51						11 05				
Dinas Powys	d				10 22						10 37				10 53						11 07				
Cadoxton	d				10 27						10 42				10 57						11 12				
Barry Docks	d				10 30						10 45				11 00						11 15				
Barry 3	d				10 34						10 49				11 05						11 19				
Barry Island	a				10 40						10 55										11 25				
Rhoose Cardiff Int Airport ✈	d														11 12										
Llantwit Major	d														11 22										
Bridgend	a														11 39										

For general notes see front of timetable
For details of catering facilities see Directory of Train Operators

A To Radyr
B To Coryton
b Arr. 0942

Table 130

Mondays to Fridays

Treherbert, Aberdare, Merthyr, Pontypridd, Rhymney and Coryton → Cardiff, Penarth, Barry, Barry Island and Bridgend

Network Diagram - see first page of Table 130

		AW	AW		AW A	AW	AW	AW	AW	AW B	AW	AW	AW	AW	AW A	AW	AW	AW		AW	AW B	AW	AW	AW	AW A	AW
Treherbert	d							10 17						10 47									11 17			
Ynyswen	d							10 19						10 49									11 19			
Treorchy	d							10 21						10 51									11 21			
Ton Pentre	d							10 23						10 53									11 23			
Ystrad Rhondda	a							10 26						10 56									11 26			
	d							10 28						10 58									11 28			
Llwynypia	d							10 30						11 00									11 30			
Tonypandy	d							10 33						11 03									11 33			
Dinas Rhondda	d							10 35						11 05									11 35			
Porth	d							10b52						11 09									11 39			
Trehafod	d							10 55						11 12									11 42			
Merthyr Tydfil	d										10 39															
Pentre-bach	d										10 43															
Troed Y Rhiw	d										10 46															
Merthyr Vale	d										10 50															
Quakers Yard	d										10 55															
Abercynon South	d										10 59															
Aberdare 3	d					10 22											10 52									
Cwmbach	d					10 25											10 55									
Fernhill	d					10 28											10 58									
Mountain Ash	a					10 31											11 01									
	d					10 34											11 04									
Penrhiwceiber	d					10 37											11 07									
Abercynon North	d					10 45											11 15									
Pontypridd 3	a					10 53		11 01			11 07			11 17			11 23						11 47			
	d					10 54		11 04			11 09			11 18			11 24						11 48			
Trefforest	d					10 57		11 07			11 12			11 21			11 27						11 51			
Trefforest Estate	d										11 16															
Taffs Well 3	d					11 04		11 13			11 20			11 28			11 34						11 58			
Radyr 3	a					11 07		11 17			11 23			11 31			11 37						12 01			
	d				11 04	11 07		11 17			11 23			11 31	11 34		11 37						12 01		12 04	
Danescourt	d				11 08										11 38										12 08	
Fairwater	d				11 10										11 40										12 10	
Waun-gron Park	d				11 12										11 42										12 12	
Ninian Park	d				11 15										11 45										12 15	
Llandaf	d					11 10					11 26			11 34		←	11 40						12 04			←
Cathays	d					11 15					11 31			11 39		11 39	11 45						12 09			12 09
Rhymney 3	d						10 29							→									→			
Pontlottyn	d						10 32																			
Tir-phil	d						10 36																			
Brithdir	d						10 39																			
Bargoed	d	10 32					10c47					11 02						11 17				11 32				
Gilfach Fargoed	d																	11 19								
Pengam	d	10 37					10 52					11 07						11 22				11 37				
Hengoed	d	10 40					10 55					11 10						11 25				11 40				
Ystrad Mynach 3	d	10 43					10 58					11 13						11 28				11 43				
Llanbradach	d	10 48					11 03					11 18						11 33				11 48				
Aber	d	10 52					11 07					11 22						11 37				11 52				
Caerphilly 3	d	10 55					11 10					11 25						11 40				11 55				
Lisvane & Thornhill	d	10 59					11 14					11 29						11 44				11 59				
Llanishen	d	11 01					11 16					11 31						11 46				12 01				
Heath High Level	d	11 04					11 19					11 34						11 49				12 04				
Coryton	d									11 15											11 45					
Whitchurch (Cardiff)	d									11 16											11 46					
Rhiwbina	d									11 18											11 48					
Birchgrove	d									11 20											11 50					
Ty Glas	d									11 21											11 51					
Heath Low Level	d									11 24											11 54					
Cardiff Queen Street 3	a	11 09				11 19	11 24			11 29	11 34	11 39				11 44	11 49	11 54			11 59	12 09				12 14
	d	11 11	11 12			11 21	11 26		11 27	11 31	11 36	11 41	11 42			11 46	11 51	11 56		11 57	12 01	12 11		12 12		12 16
Cardiff Bay	a		11 16						11 31				11 46							12 01				12 16		
Cardiff Central 7	a	11 14			11 20	11 24	11 29	11 34		11 34	11 39	11 44			11 50	11 52	11 54	11 59			12 04	12 14			12 20	12 22
	d	11 16				11 25	11 31				11 41	11 46					11 55	12 01				12 16				
Grangetown	d	11 20				11 29	11 35				11 45	11 50					11 59	12 05				12 20				
Dingle Road	d	11 26					11 41					11 56						12 11				12 26				
Penarth	a	11 31					11 46					12 01						12 16				12 31				
Cogan	d					11 33					11 48						12 03									
Eastbrook	d					11 35					11 51						12 05									
Dinas Powys	d					11 37					11 53						12 07									
Cadoxton	d					11 42					11 57						12 12									
Barry Docks	d					11 45					12 00						12 15									
Barry 3	d					11 49					12 05						12 19									
Barry Island	a					11 55											12 25									
Rhoose Cardiff Int Airport ✈	d										12 12															
Llantwit Major	d										12 22															
Bridgend	a										12 39															

For general notes see front of timetable
For details of catering facilities see Directory of Train Operators

A To Coryton
B To Radyr
b Arr. 1038
c Arr. 1042

Treherbert, Aberdare, Merthyr, Pontypridd, Rhymney and Coryton → Cardiff, Penarth, Barry, Barry Island and Bridgend

Network Diagram - see first page of Table 130

		AW	AW	AW	AW	AW	AW	AW	AW	AW		AW	AW	AW	AW	AW	AW	AW	AW	AW	AW	AW	AW	AW	AW	AW
					A					B					A					B					A	
Treherbert	d								11 47										12 17							
Ynyswen	d								11 49										12 19							
Treorchy	d								11 51										12 21							
Ton Pentre	d								11 53										12 23							
Ystrad Rhondda	a								11 56										12 26							
	d								11 58										12 28							
Llwynypia	d								12 00										12 30							
Tonypandy	d								12 03										12 33							
Dinas Rhondda	d								12 05										12 35							
Porth	d								12 09										12 39							
Trehafod	d								12 12										12 42							
Merthyr Tydfil	d					11 39																				12 39
Pentre-bach	d					11 43																				12 43
Troed Y Rhiw	d					11 46																				12 46
Merthyr Vale	d					11 50																				12 50
Quakers Yard	d					11 55																				12 55
Abercynon South	d					11 59																				12 59
Aberdare [3]	d	11 22																				12 22				
Cwmbach	d	11 25																				12 25				
Fernhill	d	11 28																				12 28				
Mountain Ash	a	11 31																				12 31				
	d	11 34																				12 34				
Penrhiwceiber	d	11 37																				12 37				
Abercynon North	d	11 45																				12 45				
Pontypridd [3]	a	11 53				12 07			12 17										12 48			12 53				13 07
	d	11 54				12 09			12 18							12 39			12 48			12 54				13 09
Trefforest	d	11 57				12 12			12 21							12 42			12 51			12 57				13 12
Trefforest Estate	d					12 16										12 46										13 16
Taffs Well [3]	d	12 04				12 20			12 28							12 50			12 58			13 04				13 20
Radyr [3]	a	12 07				12 23			12 31							12 53			13 01			13 07				13 23
	d	12 07				12 23			12 31	12 34						12 53			13 01	13 04		13 07				13 23
Danescourt	d									12 38										13 08						
Fairwater	d									12 40										13 10						
Waun-gron Park	d									12 42										13 12						
Ninian Park	d									12 45										13 15						
Llandaf	d	12 10				12 26			12 34			←				12 56			13 04		←	13 10				13 26
Cathays	d	12 15				12 31			12 39			12 39				13 01			13 09		13 09	13 15				13 31
Rhymney [3]	d		11 29						→										→				12 29			
Pontlottyn	d		11 32																				12 32			
Tir-phil	d		11 36																				12 36			
Brithdir	d		11 39																				12 39			
Bargoed	d		11b47				12 02						12 17				12 32						12c47			
Gilfach Fargoed	d												12 19													
Pengam	d		11 52				12 07						12 22				12 37						12 52			
Hengoed	d		11 55				12 10						12 25				12 40						12 55			
Ystrad Mynach [3]	d		11 58				12 13						12 28				12 43						12 58			
Llanbradach	d		12 03				12 18						12 33				12 48						13 03			
Aber	d		12 07				12 22						12 37				12 52						13 07			
Caerphilly [3]	d		12 10				12 25						12 40				12 55						13 10			
Lisvane & Thornhill	d		12 14				12 29						12 44				12 59						13 14			
Llanishen	d		12 16				12 31						12 46				13 01						13 16			
Heath High Level	d		12 19				12 34						12 49				13 04						13 19			
Coryton	d				12 15										12 45										13 15	
Whitchurch (Cardiff)	d				12 16										12 46										13 16	
Rhiwbina	d				12 18										12 48										13 18	
Birchgrove	d				12 20										12 50										13 20	
Ty Glas	d				12 21										12 51										13 21	
Heath Low Level	d				12 24										12 54										13 24	
Cardiff Queen Street [3]	a	12 19	12 24		12 29	12 34	12 39					12 44	12 54		12 59	13 04	13 09				13 14	13 19	13 24		13 29	13 34
	d	12 21	12 26	12 27	12 31	12 36	12 41	12 42				12 46	12 56	12 57	13 01	13 06	13 11	13 12			13 16	13 21	13 26	13 27	13 31	13 36
Cardiff Bay	a			12 31				12 46						13 01				13 16						13 31		
Cardiff Central [7]	a	12 24	12 29		12 34	12 39	12 44			12 50		12 52	12 59		13 04	13 09	13 14			13 20	13 22	13 24	13 29		13 34	13 40
	d	12 25	12 31			12 41	12 46					12 55	13 01			13 10	13 16					13 25	13 31			13 41
Grangetown	d	12 29	12 35			12 45	12 50					12 59	13 05			13 14	13 20					13 29	13 35			13 45
Dingle Road	d		12 41				12 56						13 11				13 26						13 41			
Penarth	a		12 46				13 01						13 16				13 31						13 46			
Cogan	d	12 33				12 48						13 03				13 18						13 33				13 48
Eastbrook	d	12 35				12 51						13 05				13 20						13 35				13 51
Dinas Powys	d	12 37				12 53						13 07				13 22						13 37				13 53
Cadoxton	d	12 42				12 57						13 12				13 27						13 42				13 57
Barry Docks	d	12 45				13 00						13 15				13 30						13 45				14 00
Barry [3]	d	12 49				13 05						13 19				13 34						13 49				14 05
Barry Island	a	12 55										13 25				13 40						13 55				
Rhoose Cardiff Int Airport ✈	d					13 12																				14 12
Llantwit Major	d					13 22																				14 22
Bridgend	a					13 39																				14 39

For general notes see front of timetable
For details of catering facilities see Directory of Train Operators

A To Radyr
B To Coryton
b Arr. 1142
c Arr. 1242

Treherbert, Aberdare, Merthyr, Pontypridd, Rhymney and Coryton → Cardiff, Penarth, Barry, Barry Island and Bridgend

Network Diagram - see first page of Table 130

		AW	AW	AW	AW	AW	AW	AW	AW	AW	AW	AW	AW	AW	AW	AW	AW		AW	AW	AW	AW	AW	AW	AW	AW
						A					B				A						B					A
Treherbert	d				12 47								13 17												13 47	
Ynyswen	d				12 49								13 19												13 49	
Treorchy	d				12 51								13 21												13 51	
Ton Pentre	d				12 53								13 23												13 53	
Ystrad Rhondda	a				12 56								13 26												13 56	
	d				12 58								13 28												13 58	
Llwynypia	d				13 00								13 30												14 00	
Tonypandy	d				13 03								13 33												14 03	
Dinas Rhondda	d				13 05								13 35												14 05	
Porth	d				13 09								13 39												14 09	
Trehafod	d				13 12								13 42												14 12	
Merthyr Tydfil	d																					13 39				
Pentre-bach	d																					13 43				
Troed Y Rhiw	d																					13 46				
Merthyr Vale	d																					13 50				
Quakers Yard	d																					13 55				
Abercynon South	d																					13 59				
Aberdare 3	d							12 52																		
Cwmbach	d							12 55																		
Fernhill	d							12 58																		
Mountain Ash	a							13 01																		
	d							13 04																		
Penrhiwceiber	d							13 07																		
Abercynon North	d							13 15									13 45									
Pontypridd 3	a				13 17			13 23					13 47				13 53					14 07			14 17	
	d		13 39		13 18			13 24					13 48				13 54					14 09			14 18	
Trefforest	d		13 42		13 21			13 27					13 51				13 57					14 12			14 21	
Trefforest Estate	d		13 46																			14 16				
Taffs Well 3	d		13 50		13 28			13 34					13 58				14 04					14 20			14 28	
Radyr 3	a		13 53		13 31			13 37					14 01				14 07					14 23			14 31	
	d		13 53		13 31	13 34		13 37					14 01		14 04		14 07					14 23			14 31	14 34
Danescourt	d					13 38									14 08											14 38
Fairwater	d					13 40									14 10											14 40
Waun-gron Park	d					13 42									14 12											14 42
Ninian Park	d					13 45									14 15											14 45
Llandaf	d		13 56		13 34		←	13 40					14 04			←	14 10					14 26			14 34	
Cathays	d		14 01		13 39		13 39	13 45					14 09			14 09	14 15					14 31			14 39	
Rhymney 3	d				↪								↪						13 29						↪	
Pontlottyn	d																		13 32							
Tir-phil	d																		13 36							
Brithdir	d																		13 39							
Bargoed	d	13 02							13 17			13 32							13b47				14 02			
Gilfach Fargoed	d								13 19																	
Pengam	d	13 07							13 22			13 37							13 52				14 07			
Hengoed	d	13 10							13 25			13 40							13 55				14 10			
Ystrad Mynach 3	d	13 13							13 28			13 43							13 58				14 13			
Llanbradach	d	13 18							13 33			13 48							14 03				14 18			
Aber	d	13 22							13 37			13 52							14 07				14 22			
Caerphilly 3	d	13 25							13 40			13 55							14 10				14 25			
Lisvane & Thornhill	d	13 29							13 44			13 59							14 14				14 29			
Llanishen	d	13 31							13 46			14 01							14 16				14 31			
Heath High Level	d	13 34							13 49			14 04							14 19				14 34			
Coryton	d										13 45										14 15					
Whitchurch (Cardiff)	d										13 46										14 16					
Rhiwbina	d										13 48										14 18					
Birchgrove	d										13 50										14 20					
Ty Glas	d										13 51										14 21					
Heath Low Level	d										13 54										14 24					
Cardiff Queen Street 3	a	13 39	14 04				13 44	13 49	13 54		13 59	14 09				14 14	14 19		14 24		14 29	14 34	14 39			
	d	13 41	14 06	13 42			13 46	13 51	13 56	13 57	14 01	14 11		14 12		14 16	14 21		14 26	14 27	14 31	14 36	14 41	14 42		
Cardiff Bay	a			13 46						14 01				14 16						14 31				14 46		
Cardiff Central 7	a	13 44	14 09			13 50	13 52	13 54	13 59		14 04	14 14			14 20	14 22	14 24		14 29		14 34	14 39	14 44			14 50
	d	13 46	14 10					13 55	14 01			14 16					14 25		14 31			14 41	14 46			
Grangetown	d	13 50	14 14					13 59	14 05			14 20					14 29		14 35			14 45	14 50			
Dingle Road	d	13 56							14 11			14 26							14 41				14 56			
Penarth	a	14 01							14 16			14 31							14 46				15 01			
Cogan	d		14 18					14 03									14 33					14 48				
Eastbrook	d		14 20					14 05									14 35					14 51				
Dinas Powys	d		14 22					14 07									14 37					14 53				
Cadoxton	d		14 25					14 12									14 41					14 57				
Barry Docks	d		14 30					14 15									14 44					15 00				
Barry 3	d		14 34					14 19									14 48					15 05				
Barry Island	a		14 40					14 25									14 55									
Rhoose Cardiff Int Airport ✈	d																					15 12				
Llantwit Major	d																					15 22				
Bridgend	a																					15 39				

For general notes see front of timetable
For details of catering facilities see Directory of Train Operators

A To Coryton
B To Radyr
b Arr. 1342

Treherbert, Aberdare, Merthyr, Pontypridd, Rhymney and Coryton → Cardiff, Penarth, Barry, Barry Island and Bridgend

Network Diagram - see first page of Table 130

		AW	AW	AW	AW	AW A	AW	AW	AW		AW B	AW	AW	AW	AW	AW A	AW	AW	AW	AW	AW B	AW	AW	AW		AW
Treherbert	d													14 17						14 47						
Ynyswen	d													14 19						14 49						
Treorchy	d													14 21						14 51						
Ton Pentre	d													14 23						14 53						
Ystrad Rhondda	a													14 26						14 56						
	d													14 28						14 58						
Llwynypia	d													14 30						15 00						
Tonypandy	d													14 33						15 03						
Dinas Rhondda	d													14 35						15 05						
Porth	d													14b52						15 09						
Trehafod	d													14 55						15 12						
Merthyr Tydfil	d																14 39									
Pentre-bach	d																14 43									
Troed Y Rhiw	d																14 46									
Merthyr Vale	d																14 50									
Quakers Yard	d																14 55									
Abercynon South	d																14 59									
Aberdare 3	d		13 52									14 22											14 52			
Cwmbach	d		13 55									14 25											14 55			
Fernhill	d		13 58									14 28											14 58			
Mountain Ash	a		14 01									14 31											15 01			
	d		14 04									14 34											15 04			
Penrhiwceiber	d		14 07									14 37											15 07			
Abercynon North	d		14 15									14 45											15 15			
Pontypridd 3	a		14 23									14 53		15 01			15 07			15 17			15 23			
	d		14 24				14 39					14 54		15 04			15 09			15 18			15 24			
Trefforest	d		14 27				14 42					14 57		15 07			15 12			15 21			15 27			
Trefforest Estate	d						14 46										15 16									
Taffs Well 3	d		14 34				14 50					15 04		15 13			15 20			15 28			15 34			
Radyr 3	a		14 37				14 53					15 07		15 17			15 23			15 31			15 37			
	d		14 37				14 53				15 04	15 07		15 17			15 23			15 31	15 34		15 37			
Danescourt	d										15 08										15 38					
Fairwater	d										15 10										15 40					
Waun-gron Park	d										15 12										15 42					
Ninian Park	d										15 15										15 45					
Llandaf	d	←	14 40				14 56					15 10					15 26			15 34		←	15 40			
Cathays	d	14 39	14 45				15 01					15 15					15 31			15 39		15 39	15 45			
Rhymney 3	d												14 29							→						
Pontlottyn	d												14 32													
Tir-phil	d												14 36													
Brithdir	d												14 39													
Bargoed	d			14 17				14 32					14c47					15 02						15 17		
Gilfach Fargoed	d			14 19																				15 19		
Pengam	d			14 22				14 37					14 52					15 07						15 22		
Hengoed	d			14 25				14 40					14 55					15 10						15 25		
Ystrad Mynach 3	d			14 28				14 43					14 58					15 13						15 28		
Llanbradach	d			14 33				14 48					15 03					15 18						15 33		
Aber	d			14 37				14 52					15 07					15 22						15 37		
Caerphilly 3	d			14 40				14 55					15 10					15 25						15 40		
Lisvane & Thornhill	d			14 44				14 59					15 14					15 29						15 44		
Llanishen	d			14 46				15 01					15 16					15 31						15 46		
Heath High Level	d			14 49				15 04					15 19					15 34						15 49		
Coryton	d					14 45										15 15										
Whitchurch (Cardiff)	d					14 46										15 16										
Rhiwbina	d					14 48										15 18										
Birchgrove	d					14 50										15 20										
Ty Glas	d					14 51										15 21										
Heath Low Level	d					14 54										15 24										
Cardiff Queen Street 3	a	14 44	14 49	14 54		14 59	15 04	15 09				15 19	15 24			15 29	15 34	15 39				15 44	15 49	15 54		
	d	14 46	14 51	14 56	14 57	15 01	15 06	15 11	15 12			15 21	15 26		15 27	15 31	15 36	15 41	15 42			15 46	15 51	15 56		15 57
Cardiff Bay	a				15 01				15 16						15 31				15 46							16 01
Cardiff Central 7	a	14 52	14 54	14 59		15 04	15 09	15 14			15 20	15 24	15 29	15 33		15 34	15 39	15 44			15 50	15 52	15 54	15 59		
	d		14 55	15 01			15 10	15 16				15 25	15 31				15 41	15 46					15 55	16 01		
Grangetown	d		14 59	15 05			15 14	15 20				15 29	15 35				15 45	15 50					15 59	16 05		
Dingle Road	d			15 11				15 26					15 41					15 56						16 11		
Penarth	a			15 16				15 31					15 46					16 01						16 16		
Cogan	d		15 03				15 18					15 33					15 48						16 03			
Eastbrook	d		15 05				15 20					15 35					15 51						16 05			
Dinas Powys	d		15 07				15 22					15 37					15 53						16 07			
Cadoxton	d		15 12				15 27					15 42					15 57						16 12			
Barry Docks	d		15 15				15 30					15 45					16 00						16 15			
Barry 3	d		15 19				15 34					15 49					16 05						16 19			
Barry Island	a		15 25				15 40					15 55											16 25			
Rhoose Cardiff Int Airport ✈	d																16 12									
Llantwit Major	d																16 22									
Bridgend	a																16 39									

For general notes see front of timetable
For details of catering facilities see Directory of Train Operators

A To Radyr
B To Coryton
b Arr. 1438
c Arr. 1442

Treherbert, Aberdare, Merthyr, Pontypridd, Rhymney and Coryton → Cardiff, Penarth, Barry, Barry Island and Bridgend

Network Diagram - see first page of Table 130

		AW A	AW	AW	AW	AW B	AW	AW	AW	AW	AW A	AW	AW	AW	AW	AW B	AW	AW	AW	AW	AW A	AW	AW	AW	AW
Treherbert	d			15 17											15 47									16 17	
Ynyswen	d			15 19											15 49									16 19	
Treorchy	d			15 21											15 51									16 21	
Ton Pentre	d			15 23											15 53									16 23	
Ystrad Rhondda	a			15 26											15 56									16 26	
	d			15 28											15 58									16 28	
Llwynypia	d			15 30											16 00									16 30	
Tonypandy	d			15 33											16 03									16 33	
Dinas Rhondda	d			15 35											16 05									16 35	
Porth	d			15 39											16 09									16 39	
Trehafod	d			15 42											16 12									16 42	
Merthyr Tydfil	d											15 39													
Pentre-bach	d											15 43													
Troed Y Rhiw	d											15 46													
Merthyr Vale	d											15 50													
Quakers Yard	d											15 55													
Abercynon South	d											15 59													
Aberdare 3	d							15 22										15 52							
Cwmbach	d							15 25										15 55							
Fernhill	d							15 28										15 58							
Mountain Ash	a							15 31										16 01							
	d							15 34										16 04							
Penrhiwceiber	d							15 37										16 07							
Abercynon North	d							15 45										16 15							
Pontypridd 3	a			15 47				15 53				16 07			16 17			16 23						16 47	
	d			15 48				15 54				16 09			16 18			16 24				16 39		16 48	
Trefforest	d			15 51				15 57				16 12			16 21			16 27				16 42		16 51	
Trefforest Estate	d											16 16										16 46			
Taffs Well 3	d			15 58				16 04				16 20			16 28			16 34				16 50		16 58	
Radyr 3	a			16 01				16 07				16 23			16 31			16 37				16 53		17 01	
	d			16 01		16 04		16 07				16 23			16 31	16 34		16 37				16 53		17 01	
Danescourt	d					16 08										16 38									
Fairwater	d					16 10										16 40									
Waun-gron Park	d					16 12										16 42									
Ninian Park	d					16 15										16 45									
Llandaf	d			16 04			←	16 10				16 26			16 34		←	16 40				16 56		17 04	
Cathays	d			16 09			16 09	16 15				16 31			16 39		16 39	16 45				17 01		17 09	
Rhymney 3	d			→					15 29						→									→	
Pontlottyn	d								15 32																
Tir-phil	d								15 36																
Brithdir	d								15 39																
Bargoed	d		15 32						15b47				16 02						16 17				16 32		
Gilfach Fargoed	d																		16 19						
Pengam	d		15 37						15 52				16 07						16 22				16 37		
Hengoed	d		15 40						15 55				16 10						16 25				16 40		
Ystrad Mynach 3	d		15 43						15 58				16 13						16 28				16 43		
Llanbradach	d		15 48						16 03				16 18						16 33				16 48		
Aber	d		15 52						16 07				16 22						16 37				16 52		
Caerphilly 3	d		15 55						16 10				16 25						16 40				16 55		
Lisvane & Thornhill	d		15 59						16 14				16 29						16 44				16 59		
Llanishen	d		16 01						16 16				16 31						16 46				17 01		
Heath High Level	d		16 04						16 19				16 34						16 49				17 04		
Coryton	d	15 45									16 15										16 45				
Whitchurch (Cardiff)	d	15 46									16 16										16 46				
Rhiwbina	d	15 48									16 18										16 48				
Birchgrove	d	15 50									16 20										16 50				
Ty Glas	d	15 51									16 21										16 51				
Heath Low Level	d	15 54									16 24										16 54				
Cardiff Queen Street 3	a	15 59	16 09				16 14	16 19	16 24		16 29	16 34	16 39				16 44	16 49	16 54		16 59	17 04	17 09		
	d	16 01	16 11		16 12		16 16	16 21	16 26	16 27	16 31	16 36	16 41	16 42			16 46	16 51	16 56	16 57	17 01	17 06	17 11		17 12
Cardiff Bay	a				16 16					16 31				16 46						17 01					17 16
Cardiff Central 7	a	16 04	16 14			16 20	16 22	16 24	16 32		16 34	16 39	16 44			16 50	16 52	16 54	16 59		17 04	17 09	17 14		
	d		16 16					16 25				16 41	16 46					16 55	17 01			17 10	17 16		
Grangetown	d		16 20					16 29				16 45	16 50					16 59	17 05			17 14	17 20		
Dingle Road	d		16 26										16 56						17 11				17 26		
Penarth	a		16 31										17 01						17 16				17 31		
Cogan	d							16 33				16 48						17 03				17 18			
Eastbrook	d							16 35				16 51						17 05				17 20			
Dinas Powys	d							16 37				16 53						17 07				17 22			
Cadoxton	d							16 42				16 57						17 12				17 27			
Barry Docks	d							16 45				17 00						17 15				17 30			
Barry 3	d							16 49				17 05						17 19				17 34			
Barry Island	a							16 55										17 25				17 40			
Rhoose Cardiff Int Airport ✈	d											17 12													
Llantwit Major	d											17 22													
Bridgend	a											17 39													

For general notes see front of timetable
For details of catering facilities see Directory of Train Operators

A To Radyr
B To Coryton
b Arr. 1542

Treherbert, Aberdare, Merthyr, Pontypridd, Rhymney and Coryton → Cardiff, Penarth, Barry, Barry Island and Bridgend

Network Diagram - see first page of Table 130

		AW A	AW	AW	AW	AW	AW B	AW	AW	AW	AW	AW A	AW	AW	AW	AW	AW B	AW	AW	AW	AW	AW A	AW	AW
Treherbert	d										16 47									17 17				
Ynyswen	d										16 49									17 19				
Treorchy	d										16 51									17 21				
Ton Pentre	d										16 53									17 23				
Ystrad Rhondda	a										16 56									17 26				
	d										16 58									17 28				
Llwynypia	d										17 00									17 30				
Tonypandy	d										17 03									17 33				
Dinas Rhondda	d										17 05									17 35				
Porth	d										17 09									17 39				
Trehafod	d										17 12									17 42				
Merthyr Tydfil	d							16 39																
Pentre-bach	d							16 43																
Troed Y Rhiw	d							16 46																
Merthyr Vale	d							16 50																
Quakers Yard	d							16 55																
Abercynon South	d							16 59																
Aberdare 3	d			16 22										16 52										17 22
Cwmbach	d			16 25										16 55										17 25
Fernhill	d			16 28										16 58										17 28
Mountain Ash	a			16 31										17 01										17 31
	d			16 34										17 04										17 34
Penrhiwceiber	d			16 37										17 07										17 37
Abercynon North	d			16 45										17 15										17 45
Pontypridd 3	a			16 53				17 07			17 17			17 23						17 47				17 53
	d			16 54				17 09			17 18			17 24				17 39		17 48				17 54
Trefforest	d			16 57				17 12			17 21			17 27				17 42		17 51				17 57
Trefforest Estate	d							17 16										17 46						
Taffs Well 3	d			17 04				17 20			17 28			17 34				17 50		17 58				18 04
Radyr 3	a			17 07				17 23			17 31			17 37				17 53		18 01				18 07
	d	17 04		17 07				17 23			17 31	17 34		17 37				17 53		18 01		18 04		18 07
Danescourt	d	17 08										17 38										18 08		
Fairwater	d	17 10										17 40										18 10		
Waun-gron Park	d	17 12										17 42										18 12		
Ninian Park	d	17 15										17 45										18 15		
Llandaf	d		←	17 10				17 26			17 34		←	17 40				17 56		18 04			←	18 10
Cathays	d		17 09	17 15				17 31			17 39		17 39	17 45				18 01		18 09			18 09	18 15
Rhymney 3	d				16 29						→									→				
Pontlottyn	d				16 32																			
Tir-phil	d				16 36																			
Brithdir	d				16 39																			
Bargoed	d				16b47				17 02						17 17				17 32					
Gilfach Fargoed	d														17 19									
Pengam	d				16 52				17 07						17 22				17 37					
Hengoed	d				16 55				17 10						17 25				17 40					
Ystrad Mynach 3	d				16 58				17 13						17 28				17 43					
Llanbradach	d				17 03				17 18						17 33				17 48					
Aber	d				17 07				17 22						17 37				17 52					
Caerphilly 3	d				17 10				17 25						17 40				17 55					
Lisvane & Thornhill	d				17 14				17 29						17 44				17 59					
Llanishen	d				17 16				17 31						17 46				18 01					
Heath High Level	d				17 19				17 34						17 49				18 04					
Coryton	d						17 15										17 45							
Whitchurch (Cardiff)	d						17 16										17 46							
Rhiwbina	d						17 18										17 48							
Birchgrove	d						17 20										17 50							
Ty Glas	d						17 21										17 51							
Heath Low Level	d						17 24										17 54							
Cardiff Queen Street 3	a		17 14	17 19	17 24		17 29	17 34	17 39				17 44	17 49	17 54		17 59	18 04	18 09				18 14	18 19
	d		17 16	17 21	17 26	17 27	17 31	17 36	17 41	17 42			17 46	17 51	17 56	17 57	18 01	18 06	18 11		18 12		18 16	18 21
Cardiff Bay	a					17 31				17 46						18 01					18 16			
Cardiff Central 7	a	17 20	17 22	17 24	17 29		17 34	17 39	17 44			17 50	17 52	17 54	17 59		18 04	18 09	18 14			18 20	18 22	18 24
	d			17 25	17 31			17 41	17 46					17 55	18 01			18 10	18 16					18 25
Grangetown	d			17 29	17 35			17 45	17 50					17 59	18 05			18 14	18 20					18 29
Dingle Road	d				17 41				17 56						18 11				18 26					
Penarth	a				17 46				18 01						18 16				18 31					
Cogan	d			17 33				17 48						18 03				18 18						18 33
Eastbrook	d			17 35				17 51						18 05				18 20						18 35
Dinas Powys	d			17 37				17 53						18 07				18 22						18 37
Cadoxton	d			17 42				17 57						18 12				18 27						18 42
Barry Docks	d			17 45				18 00						18 15				18 30						18 45
Barry 3	d			17 49				18 05						18 19				18 34						18 49
Barry Island	a			17 55										18 25				18 40						18 55
Rhoose Cardiff Int Airport ✈	d							18 12																
Llantwit Major	d							18 22																
Bridgend	a							18 39																

For general notes see front of timetable
For details of catering facilities see Directory of Train Operators

A To Coryton
B To Radyr
b Arr. 1642

Treherbert, Aberdare, Merthyr, Pontypridd, Rhymney and Coryton → Cardiff, Penarth, Barry, Barry Island and Bridgend

Network Diagram - see first page of Table 130

		AW	AW	AW A	AW	AW	AW	AW B	AW	AW	AW	AW	AW	AW
Treherbert	d					17 47								
Ynyswen	d					17 49								
Treorchy	d					17 51								
Ton Pentre	d					17 53								
Ystrad Rhondda	a					17 56								
	d					17 58								
Llwynypia	d					18 00								
Tonypandy	d					18 03								
Dinas Rhondda	d					18 05								
Porth	d					18 09								
Trehafod	d					18 12								
Merthyr Tydfil	d				17 39									
Pentre-bach	d				17 43									
Troed Y Rhiw	d				17 46									
Merthyr Vale	d				17 50									
Quakers Yard	d				17 55									
Abercynon South	d				17 59									
Aberdare [3]	d									17 52				
Cwmbach	d									17 55				
Fernhill	d									17 58				
Mountain Ash	a									18 01				
	d									18 04				
Penrhiwceiber	d									18 07				
Abercynon North	d									18 15				
Pontypridd [3]	a				18 07	18 17				18 23				
	d				18 09	18 18				18 24				18 39
Trefforest	d				18 12	18 21				18 27				18 42
Trefforest Estate	d				18 16									18 46
Taffs Well [3]	d				18 20	18 28				18 34				18 50
Radyr [3]	a				18 23	18 31				18 37				18 53
	d				18 23	18 31		18 34		18 37				18 53
Danescourt	d							18 38						
Fairwater	d							18 40						
Waun-gron Park	d							18 42						
Ninian Park	d							18 45						
Llandaf	d				18 26	18 34			←	18 40				18 56
Cathays	d				18 31	18 39			18 39	18 45				19 01
Rhymney [3]	d	17 29				→								
Pontlottyn	d	17 32												
Tir-phil	d	17 36												
Brithdir	d	17 39												
Bargoed	d	17b47									18 17			
Gilfach Fargoed	d										18 19			
Pengam	d	17 52									18 22			
Hengoed	d	17 55									18 25			
Ystrad Mynach [3]	d	17 58									18 28			
Llanbradach	d	18 03									18 33			
Aber	d	18 07									18 37			
Caerphilly [3]	d	18 10									18 40			
Lisvane & Thornhill	d	18 14									18 44			
Llanishen	d	18 16									18 46			
Heath High Level	d	18 19									18 49			
Coryton	d			18 15									18 45	
Whitchurch (Cardiff)	d			18 16									18 46	
Rhiwbina	d			18 18									18 48	
Birchgrove	d			18 20									18 50	
Ty Glas	d			18 21									18 51	
Heath Low Level	d			18 24									18 54	
Cardiff Queen Street [3]	a	18 24		18 29	18 34				18 44	18 49	18 54		18 59	19 04
	d	18 26	18 27	18 31	18 36		18 42		18 46	18 51	18 56	18 57	19 01	19 06
Cardiff Bay	a		18 31				18 46					19 01		
Cardiff Central [7]	a	18 29		18 34	18 39			18 50	18 52	18 54	18 59		19 06	19 10
	d	18 31			18 41					18 55	19 01			
Grangetown	d	18 35			18 45					18 59	19 05			
Dingle Road	d	18 41									19 11			
Penarth	a	18 46									19 16			
Cogan	d				18 48					19 03				
Eastbrook	d				18 51					19 05				
Dinas Powys	d				18 53					19 07				
Cadoxton	d				18 57					19 12				
Barry Docks	d				19 00					19 15				
Barry [3]	d				19 05					19 19				
Barry Island	a									19 25				
Rhoose Cardiff Int Airport ✈	d				19 12									
Llantwit Major	d				19 22									
Bridgend	a				19 39									

		AW	AW	AW	AW	AW	AW	AW A	AW	AW	AW	AW
Treherbert	d		18 17								18 47	
Ynyswen	d		18 19								18 49	
Treorchy	d		18 21								18 51	
Ton Pentre	d		18 23								18 53	
Ystrad Rhondda	a		18 26								18 56	
	d		18 28								18 58	
Llwynypia	d		18 30								19 00	
Tonypandy	d		18 33								19 03	
Dinas Rhondda	d		18 35								19 05	
Porth	d		18 39								19 09	
Trehafod	d		18 42								19 12	
Merthyr Tydfil	d								18 39			
Pentre-bach	d								18 43			
Troed Y Rhiw	d								18 46			
Merthyr Vale	d								18 50			
Quakers Yard	d								18 55			
Abercynon South	d								18 59			
Aberdare [3]	d				18 22							18 52
Cwmbach	d				18 25							18 55
Fernhill	d				18 28							18 58
Mountain Ash	a				18 31							19 01
	d				18 34							19 04
Penrhiwceiber	d				18 37							19 07
Abercynon North	d				18 45							19 15
Pontypridd [3]	a		18 47		18 53				19 07		19 17	19 23
	d		18 48		18 54				19 09		19 18	19 24
Trefforest	d		18 51		18 57				19 12		19 21	19 27
Trefforest Estate	d								19 16			
Taffs Well [3]	d		18 58		19 04				19 20		19 28	19 34
Radyr [3]	a		19 01		19 07				19 23		19 31	19 37
	d		19 01	19 04	19 07				19 23		19 31	19 37
Danescourt	d			19 08								
Fairwater	d			19 10								
Waun-gron Park	d			19 12								
Ninian Park	d			19 15								
Llandaf	d		19 04		19 10				19 26		19 34	19 40
Cathays	d		19 09		19 15				19 31		19 39	19 45
Rhymney [3]	d											
Pontlottyn	d											
Tir-phil	d											
Brithdir	d											
Bargoed	d					18 48						
Gilfach Fargoed	d					18 50						
Pengam	d					18 53						
Hengoed	d					18 56						
Ystrad Mynach [3]	d					18 59						
Llanbradach	d					19 04						
Aber	d					19 08						
Caerphilly [3]	d					19 11						
Lisvane & Thornhill	d					19 15						
Llanishen	d					19 17						
Heath High Level	d					19 20						
Coryton	d							19 15				
Whitchurch (Cardiff)	d							19 16				
Rhiwbina	d							19 18				
Birchgrove	d							19 20				
Ty Glas	d							19 21				
Heath Low Level	d							19 24				
Cardiff Queen Street [3]	a		19 14		19 19	19 24		19 30	19 34		19 44	19 49
	d	19 12	19 16		19 21	19 26	19 27	19 32	19 36	19 42	19 46	19 51
Cardiff Bay	a	19 16					19 31			19 46		
Cardiff Central [7]	a		19 22	19 22	19 24	19 29		19 35	19 39		19 52	19 57
	d				19 25	19 31			19 41			
Grangetown	d				19 29	19 35			19 45			
Dingle Road	d					19 41						
Penarth	a					19 46						
Cogan	d				19 33				19 48			
Eastbrook	d				19 35				19 51			
Dinas Powys	d				19 37				19 53			
Cadoxton	d				19 42				19 57			
Barry Docks	d				19 45				20 00			
Barry [3]	d				19 49				20 05			
Barry Island	a				19 55							
Rhoose Cardiff Int Airport ✈	d								20 12			
Llantwit Major	d								20 22			
Bridgend	a								20 39			

For general notes see front of timetable
For details of catering facilities see Directory of Train Operators

A To Radyr
B To Coryton
b Arr. 1742

Treherbert, Aberdare, Merthyr, Pontypridd, Rhymney and Coryton → Cardiff, Penarth, Barry, Barry Island and Bridgend

Network Diagram - see first page of Table 130

		AW	AW	AW	AW	AW		AW	AW	AW A	AW	AW	AW	AW	AW	AW	AW	AW	AW	AW	AW		AW	AW	AW A	AW
Treherbert	d				19 17									19 47												
Ynyswen	d				19 19									19 49												
Treorchy	d				19 21									19 51												
Ton Pentre	d				19 23									19 53												
Ystrad Rhondda	a				19 26									19 56												
	d				19 28									19 58												
Llwynypia	d				19 30									20 00												
Tonypandy	d				19 33									20 03												
Dinas Rhondda	d				19 35									20 05												
Porth	d				19 39									20 09												
Trehafod	d				19 42									20 12												
Merthyr Tydfil	d										19 39															20 39
Pentre-bach	d										19 43															20 43
Troed Y Rhiw	d										19 46															20 46
Merthyr Vale	d										19 50															20 50
Quakers Yard	d										19 55															20 55
Abercynon South	d										19 59															20 59
Aberdare 3	d														19 52					20 22						
Cwmbach	d														19 55					20 25						
Fernhill	d														19 58					20 28						
Mountain Ash	a														20 01					20 31						
	d														20 04					20 34						
Penrhiwceiber	d														20 07					20 37						
Abercynon North	d							19 43							20 15					20 45						
Pontypridd 3	a				19 47			19 53			20 07			20 17	20 23					20 53						21 07
	d				19 48			19 54			20 09			20 18	20 24					20 54						21 09
Trefforest	d				19 51			19 57			20 12			20 21	20 27					20 57						21 12
Trefforest Estate	d										20 16															21 16
Taffs Well 3	d				19 58			20 04			20 20			20 28	20 34					21 04						21 20
Radyr 3	a				20 01			20 07			20 23			20 31	20 37					21 07						21 23
	d				20 01	20 04		20 07			20 23			20 31	20 37			21 04		21 07						21 23
Danescourt	d					20 08												21 08			←					
Fairwater	d					20 10												21 10 →			21 10					
Waun-gron Park	d					20 12															21 12					
Ninian Park	d					20 15															21 15					
Llandaf	d				20 04			20 10			20 26			20 34	20 40					21 10						21 26
Cathays	d				20 09			20 15			20 31			20 39	20 45					21 15						21 31
Rhymney 3	d											19 45														
Pontlottyn	d											19 48														
Tir-phil	d											19 52														
Brithdir	d											19 55														
Bargoed	d											19 59														
Gilfach Fargoed	d											20 01														
Pengam	d											20 04														
Hengoed	d											20 07														
Ystrad Mynach 3	d											20 10														
Llanbradach	d											20 15														
Aber	d											20 19														
Caerphilly 3	d	19 40										20 22				20 40										
Lisvane & Thornhill	d	19 44										20 26				20 44										
Llanishen	d	19 46										20 28				20 46										
Heath High Level	d	19 49										20 31				20 49										
Coryton	d									20 15															21 15	
Whitchurch (Cardiff)	d									20 16															21 16	
Rhiwbina	d									20 18															21 18	
Birchgrove	d									20 20															21 20	
Ty Glas	d									20 21															21 21	
Heath Low Level	d									20 24															21 24	
Cardiff Queen Street 3	a	19 54			20 14			20 19		20 29	20 34	20 39		20 44	20 50	20 54				21 19					21 29	21 34
	d	19 56	19 57	20 12	20 16			20 21	20 27	20 31	20 36	20 41	20 42	20 46	20 51	20 57	20 57		21 12	21 21				21 27	21 31	21 36
Cardiff Bay	a		20 01	20 16					20 31				20 46				21 01		21 16					21 31		
Cardiff Central 7	a	19 59			20 19	20 22		20 24		20 34	20 39	20 47		20 52	20 58	21 02				21 24	21 26				21 34	21 39
	d	20 01			20 20			20 31			20 41					21 02				21 25			21 31			21 41
Grangetown	d	20 05			20 24			20 35			20 45					21 06				21 29			21 35			21 45
Dingle Road	d	20 11						20 41								21 12							21 41			
Penarth	a	20 16						20 46								21 16							21 46			
Cogan	d				20 28						20 48									21 33						21 48
Eastbrook	d				20 30						20 51									21 35						21 51
Dinas Powys	d				20 32						20 53									21 37						21 53
Cadoxton	d				20 37						20 57									21 42						21 57
Barry Docks	d				20 40						21 00									21 45						22 00
Barry 3	d				20 44						21 05									21 49						22 05
Barry Island	a				20 50															21 55						
Rhoose Cardiff Int Airport ✈	d										21 12															22 12
Llantwit Major	d										21 22															22 22
Bridgend	a										21 39															22 39

For general notes see front of timetable
For details of catering facilities see
Directory of Train Operators

A To Radyr

Treherbert, Aberdare, Merthyr, Pontypridd, Rhymney and Coryton → Cardiff, Penarth, Barry, Barry Island and Bridgend

Network Diagram - see first page of Table 130

		AW	AW	AW	AW	AW	AW	AW	AW	AW	AW	AW	AW	AW	AW	AW	AW	AW	AW	AW	AW	AW
Treherbert	d			20 47										21 47								
Ynyswen	d			20 49										21 49								
Treorchy	d			20 51										21 51								
Ton Pentre	d			20 53										21 53								
Ystrad Rhondda	a			20 56										21 56								
	d			20 58										21 58								
Llwynypia	d			21 00										22 00								
Tonypandy	d			21 03										22 03								
Dinas Rhondda	d			21 05										22 05								
Porth	d			21 09										22 09								
Trehafod	d			21 12										22 12								
Merthyr Tydfil	d											21 39								22 39		
Pentre-bach	d											21 43								22 43		
Troed Y Rhiw	d											21 46								22 46		
Merthyr Vale	d											21 50								22 50		
Quakers Yard	d											21 55								22 55		
Abercynon South	d											21 59								22 59		
Aberdare 3	d								21 22						21 52							22 52
Cwmbach	d								21 25						21 55							22 55
Fernhill	d								21 28						21 58							22 58
Mountain Ash	a								21 31						22 01							23 01
	d								21 34						22 04							23 04
Penrhiwceiber	d								21 37						22 07							23 07
Abercynon North	d								21 45						22 15							23 15
Pontypridd 3	a			21 17					21 53			22 07		22 17	22 23					23 09		23 23
	d			21 18					21 54			22 09		22 18	22 24					23 09		23 24
Trefforest	d			21 21					21 57			22 12		22 21	22 27					23 12		23 27
Trefforest Estate	d											22 16										
Taffs Well 3	d			21 28					22 04			22 20		22 28	22 34					23 20		23 34
Radyr 3	a			21 31					22 07			22 23		22 31	22 37					23 23		23 37
	d			21 31				22 04	22 07			22 23		22 31	22 37					23 23		23 37
Danescourt	d							22 08														
Fairwater	d							22 10														
Waun-gron Park	d							22 12														
Ninian Park	d							22 15														
Llandaf	d			21 34					22 10			22 26		22 34	22 40					23 26		23 40
Cathays	d			21 39					22 15			22 31		22 39	22 45					23 31		23 45
Rhymney 3	d		20 48							21 33												
Pontlottyn	d		20 51							21 36												
Tir-phil	d		20 55							21 40												
Brithdir	d		20 58							21 43												
Bargoed	d		21 02							21 47												
Gilfach Fargoed	d		21 04							21 49												
Pengam	d		21 07							21 52												
Hengoed	d		21 10							21 55												
Ystrad Mynach 3	d		21 13							21 58												
Llanbradach	d		21 18							22 03												
Aber	d		21 22							22 07												
Caerphilly 3	d		21 25		21 40					22 10												
Lisvane & Thornhill	d		21 29		21 45					22 14												
Llanishen	d		21 31		21 47					22 16												
Heath High Level	d		21 34		21 49					22 19												
Coryton	d																					
Whitchurch (Cardiff)	d																					
Rhiwbina	d																					
Birchgrove	d																					
Ty Glas	d																					
Heath Low Level	d																					
Cardiff Queen Street 3	a		21 42	21 47	21 54				22 19	22 24		22 34		22 44	22 49					23 34		23 49
	d	21 42	21 44	21 49	21 56	21 57	22 12		22 21	22 26	22 27	22 36	22 42	22 46	22 51	22 57	23 12		23 27	23 36	23 42	23 56
Cardiff Bay	a	21 46				22 01	22 16				22 31		22 46			23 01	23 16		23 31		23 46	
Cardiff Central 7	a		21 47	21 52	22 00			22 22	22 24	22 29		22 39		22 52	22 57					23 42		00 02
	d				22 01				22 25	22 31		22 41		23 12				23 30				
Grangetown	d				22 05				22 29	22 35		22 45		23 16				23 34				
Dingle Road	d				22 11					22 41				23 20								
Penarth	a				22 16					22 46				23 25								
Cogan	d								22 33			22 48						23 37				
Eastbrook	d								22 35			22 51						23 40				
Dinas Powys	d								22 37			22 53						23 42				
Cadoxton	d								22 42			22 57						23 46				
Barry Docks	d								22 45			23 00						23 49				
Barry 3	d								22 49			23 05						23 54				
Barry Island	a								22 55									23 59				
Rhoose Cardiff Int Airport ✈	d											23 12										
Llantwit Major	d											23 22										
Bridgend	a											23 39										

For general notes see front of timetable
For details of catering facilities see Directory of Train Operators

Treherbert, Aberdare, Merthyr, Pontypridd, Rhymney and Coryton → Cardiff, Penarth, Barry, Barry Island and Bridgend

Network Diagram - see first page of Table 130

		AW	AW	AW	AW	AW	AW	AW	AW	AW	AW	AW	AW	AW	AW	AW	AW	AW	AW		AW	AW	AW	AW	AW	AW	AW
											A			B	C						C					B	
Treherbert	d									05 47									06 17								
Ynyswen	d									05 49									06 19								
Treorchy	d									05 51									06 21								
Ton Pentre	d									05 53									06 23								
Ystrad Rhondda	a									05 56									06 26								
	d									05 58									06 28								
Llwynypia	d									06 00									06 30								
Tonypandy	d									06 03									06 33								
Dinas Rhondda	d									06 05									06 35								
Porth	d									06 09									06 39								
Trehafod	d									06 12									06 42								
Merthyr Tydfil	d																										06 39
Pentre-bach	d																										06 43
Troed Y Rhiw	d																										06 46
Merthyr Vale	d																										06 50
Quakers Yard	d																										06 55
Abercynon South	d																										06 59
Aberdare 3	d																					06 22					
Cwmbach	d																					06 25					
Fernhill	d																					06 28					
Mountain Ash	a																					06 31					
	d																					06 34					
Penrhiwceiber	d																					06 37					
Abercynon North	d																					06 45					
Pontypridd 3	a									06 18									06 47			06 53					07 07
	d			05 24						06 18									06 48			06 54					07 09
Trefforest	d			05 27						06 21									06 51			06 57					07 12
Trefforest Estate	d			05 31						06 24												07 01					07 16
Taffs Well 3	d			05 34						06 28					06 53				06 58			07 04					07 20
Radyr 3	a			05 37						06 31					06 56				07 01		⟵	07 07					07 23
	d			05 37						06 31					07 04				07 01		07 04	07 07					07 23
Danescourt	d														⟶						07 08						
Fairwater	d																				07 10						
Waun-gron Park	d																				07 12						
Ninian Park	d																				07 15						
Llandaf	d			05 40						06 34									07 04			07 10					07 26
Cathays	d			05 45						06 39									07 09			07 15					07 31
Rhymney 3	d																06 14							06 37			
Pontlottyn	d																06 17							06 40			
Tir-phil	d																06 21							06 44			
Brithdir	d																06 24							06 47			
Bargoed	d																06b32							06 51			
Gilfach Fargoed	d																06 34										
Pengam	d																06 37							06 55			
Hengoed	d																06 40							06 59			
Ystrad Mynach 3	d																06 43							07 01			
Llanbradach	d																06 48							07 06			
Aber	d																06 52							07 10			
Caerphilly 3	d							06 10									06 55							07 13			
Lisvane & Thornhill	d							06 14									06 59							07 17			
Llanishen	d							06 16									07 01							07 19			
Heath High Level	d							06 19									07 04							07 22			
Coryton	d													06 45											07 15		
Whitchurch (Cardiff)	d													06 46											07 16		
Rhiwbina	d													06 48											07 18		
Birchgrove	d													06 50											07 20		
Ty Glas	d													06 51											07 21		
Heath Low Level	d													06 54											07 24		
Cardiff Queen Street 3	a			05 49				06 25		06 44				06 59			07 09		07 14			07 19		07 27	07 29	07 34
	d			05 51				06 26	06 42	06 45			06 57	07 00			07 11	07 12	07 16			07 21	07 27	07 28	07 31	07 36
Cardiff Bay	a								06 46				07 01					07 16					07 31				
Cardiff Central 7	a			05 53				06 29		06 48				07 04			07 14		07 18		07 20	07 24		07 31	07 34	07 39
	d	05 25	05 41	05 55	06 16	06 25	06 36	06 41			06 55	07 01				07 10	07 16					07 25		07 32		07 41
Grangetown	d	05 29	05 45	05 59	06 20	06 29	06 40	06 45			06 59	07 05				07 14	07 20					07 29		07 36		07 45
Dingle Road	d				06 26		06 44					07 11					07 26							07 41			
Penarth	a				06 31		06 49					07 16					07 31							07 46			
Cogan	d	05 33	05 48	06 03		06 33		06 48			07 03					07 18						07 33				07 48
Eastbrook	d	05 35	05 51	06 05		06 35		06 51			07 05					07 20						07 35				07 51
Dinas Powys	d	05 37	05 53	06 07		06 37		06 53			07 07					07 22						07 37				07 53
Cadoxton	d	05 42	05 57	06 12		06 42		06 57			07 12					07 27						07 42				07 57
Barry Docks	d	05 45	06 00	06 15		06 45		07 00			07 15					07 30						07 45				08 00
Barry 3	d	05 49	06 05	06 19		06 49		07 05			07 19					07 34						07 49				08 05
Barry Island	a	05 55		06 25		06 55					07 25					07 40						07 55				
Rhoose Cardiff Int Airport ✈	d		06 12					07 12																		08 12
Llantwit Major	d		06 22					07 22																		08 22
Bridgend	a		06 39					07 39																		08 39

For general notes see front of timetable
For details of catering facilities see Directory of Train Operators

A From 29 March from Newport (South Wales) (Table 132). Until 22 March from Hereford (Table 131)
B To Radyr
C To Coryton
b Arr. 0627

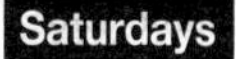

Treherbert, Aberdare, Merthyr, Pontypridd, Rhymney and Coryton → Cardiff, Penarth, Barry, Barry Island and Bridgend

Network Diagram - see first page of Table 130

		AW	AW	AW	AW	AW	AW	AW	AW	AW	AW	AW	AW	AW	AW		AW	AW	AW	AW	AW	AW	AW	AW	AW	AW
					A					B					A								B			
Treherbert	d			06 47									07 17													
Ynyswen	d			06 49									07 19													
Treorchy	d			06 51									07 21													
Ton Pentre	d			06 53									07 23													
Ystrad Rhondda	a			06 56									07 26													
	d			06 58									07 28													
Llwynypia	d			07 00									07 30													
Tonypandy	d			07 03									07 33													
Dinas Rhondda	d			07 05									07 35													
Porth	d			07 09									07 39													
Trehafod	d			07 12									07 42													
Merthyr Tydfil	d																							07 39		
Pentre-bach	d																							07 43		
Troed Y Rhiw	d																							07 46		
Merthyr Vale	d																							07 50		
Quakers Yard	d																							07 55		
Abercynon South	d																				07 21			07 59		
Aberdare 3	d						06 52											07 22	07 22							
Cwmbach	d						06 55											07 25	07 25		07a39					
Fernhill	d						06 58											07 28	07 28							
Mountain Ash	a						07 01											07 31	07 31							
	d						07 04											07 34	07 34							
Penrhiwceiber	d						07 07											07 37	07 37		07a27					
Abercynon North	d						07 15											07 45								
Pontypridd 3	a			07 17			07 23						07 47					07 53	07 54					08 07		
	d			07 18			07 24				07 39		07 48					07 54	07 54					08 09		
Trefforest	d			07 21			07 27				07 42		07 51					07 57	07 57					08 12		
Trefforest Estate	d										07 46													08 16		
Taffs Well 3	d			07 28			07 34				07 50		07 58					08 04	08 04					08 20		
Radyr 3	a			07 31			07 37				07 53		08 01					08 07	08 07					08 23		
	d			07 31	07 34		07 37				07 53		08 01		08 04			08 07	08 07					08 23		
Danescourt	d				07 38										08 08											
Fairwater	d				07 40										08 10											
Waun-gron Park	d				07 42										08 12											
Ninian Park	d				07 45										08 15											
Llandaf	d			07 34		←	07 40				07 56		08 04				←	08 10	08 10					08 26		
Cathays	d			07 39		07 39	07 45				08 01		08 09				08 09	08 15	08 15					08 31		
Rhymney 3	d			→				07 02					→							07 24					07 44	
Pontlottyn	d							07 05												07 27					07 47	
Tir-phil	d							07 09												07 31					07 51	
Brithdir	d							07 12												07 34					07 54	
Bargoed	d	07 02						07 17				07 32								07b45					08 02	
Gilfach Fargoed	d	07 04						07 19												07 47						
Pengam	d	07 07						07 22				07 37								07 50					08 07	
Hengoed	d	07 10						07 25				07 40								07 54					08 10	
Ystrad Mynach 3	d	07 13						07 28				07 43								07 57					08 13	
Llanbradach	d	07 18						07 33				07 48								08 02					08 18	
Aber	d	07 22						07 37				07 52								08 07					08 22	
Caerphilly 3	d	07 25						07 40				07 55								08 10					08 25	
Lisvane & Thornhill	d	07 29						07 44				07 59								08 14					08 29	
Llanishen	d	07 31						07 46				08 01								08 16					08 31	
Heath High Level	d	07 34						07 49				08 04								08 19					08 34	
Coryton	d									07 45													08 15			
Whitchurch (Cardiff)	d									07 46													08 16			
Rhiwbina	d									07 48													08 18			
Birchgrove	d									07 50													08 20			
Ty Glas	d									07 51													08 21			
Heath Low Level	d									07 54													08 24			
Cardiff Queen Street 3	a	07 39				07 44	07 49	07 54		07 59	08 04	08 09					08 14	08 19	08 19	08 24			08 29	08 34	08 39	
	d	07 41	07 42			07 46	07 51	07 56	07 57	08 01	08 06	08 11		08 12			08 16	08 21	08 21	08 26		08 27	08 31	08 36	08 41	08 42
Cardiff Bay	a		07 46						08 01					08 16								08 31				08 46
Cardiff Central 7	a	07 44			07 50	07 52	07 54	07 59		08 04	08 09	08 14			08 20		08 22	08 24	08 24	08 29			08 34	08 39	08 47	
	d	07 46					07 55	08 01			08 10	08 16						08 25	08 25	08 31				08 41		
Grangetown	d	07 50					07 59	08 05			08 14	08 20						08 29	08 29	08 35				08 45		
Dingle Road	d	07 56						08 11				08 26								08 41						
Penarth	a	08 01						08 16				08 31								08 46						
Cogan	d						08 03				08 18							08 33	08 33					08 48		
Eastbrook	d						08 05				08 20							08 35	08 35					08 51		
Dinas Powys	d						08 07				08 22							08 37	08 37					08 53		
Cadoxton	d						08 12				08 27							08 42	08 42					08 57		
Barry Docks	d						08 15				08 30							08 45	08 45					09 00		
Barry 3	d						08 19				08 34							08 49	08 49					09 05		
Barry Island	a						08 25				08 40							08 55	08 55							
Rhoose Cardiff Int Airport ✈	d																							09 12		
Llantwit Major	d																							09 22		
Bridgend	a																							09 39		

For general notes see front of timetable
For details of catering facilities see Directory of Train Operators

A To Coryton
B To Radyr
b Arr. 0737

Treherbert, Aberdare, Merthyr, Pontypridd, Rhymney and Coryton → Cardiff, Penarth, Barry, Barry Island and Bridgend

Network Diagram - see first page of Table 130

		AW	AW A	AW	AW	AW	AW	AW	AW B	AW	AW	AW	AW	AW A	AW	AW	AW	AW	AW B	AW	AW	AW	AW	AW A	AW
Treherbert	d	07 47										08 17											08 47		
Ynyswen	d	07 49										08 19											08 49		
Treorchy	d	07 51										08 21											08 51		
Ton Pentre	d	07 53										08 23											08 53		
Ystrad Rhondda	a	07 56										08 26											08 56		
	d	07 58										08 28											08 58		
Llwynypia	d	08 00										08 30											09 00		
Tonypandy	d	08 03										08 33											09 03		
Dinas Rhondda	d	08 05										08 35											09 05		
Porth	d	08 09										08 39											09 09		
Trehafod	d	08 12										08 42											09 12		
Merthyr Tydfil	d																			08 39					
Pentre-bach	d																			08 43					
Troed Y Rhiw	d																			08 46					
Merthyr Vale	d																			08 50					
Quakers Yard	d																			08 55					
Abercynon South	d																			08 59					
Aberdare 3	d				07 52	07 52										08 22									
Cwmbach	d				07 55	07 55										08 25									
Fernhill	d				07 58	07 58										08 28									
Mountain Ash	a				08 01	08 01										08 31									
	d				08 04	08 04										08 34									
Penrhiwceiber	d				08 07	08 07										08 37									
Abercynon North	d				08 15											08 45									
Pontypridd 3	a	08 17			08 23	08 24						08 47				08 53				09 07			09 17		
	d	08 18			08 24	08 24				08 39		08 48				08 54				09 09			09 18		
Trefforest	d	08 21			08 27	08 27				08 42		08 51				08 57				09 12			09 21		
Trefforest Estate	d									08 46										09 16					
Taffs Well 3	d	08 28			08 34	08 34				08 50		08 58				09 04				09 20			09 28		
Radyr 3	a	08 31			08 37	08 37				08 53		09 01				09 07				09 23			09 31		
	d	08 31	08 34		08 37	08 37				08 53		09 01		09 04		09 07				09 23			09 31	09 34	
Danescourt	d		08 38											09 08										09 38	
Fairwater	d		08 40											09 10										09 40	
Waun-gron Park	d		08 42											09 12										09 42	
Ninian Park	d		08 45											09 15										09 45	
Llandaf	d	08 34		←	08 40	08 40				08 56		09 04			←	09 10				09 26			09 34		←
Cathays	d	08 39		08 39	08 45	08 45				09 01		09 09			09 09	09 15				09 31			09 39		09 39
Rhymney 3	d	↪										↪					08 30						↪		
Pontlottyn	d																08 33								
Tir-phil	d																08 37								
Brithdir	d																08 40								
Bargoed	d						08 17				08 32						08b47				09 02				
Gilfach Fargoed	d						08 19																		
Pengam	d						08 22				08 37						08 52				09 07				
Hengoed	d						08 25				08 40						08 55				09 10				
Ystrad Mynach 3	d						08 28				08 43						08 58				09 13				
Llanbradach	d						08 33				08 48						09 03				09 18				
Aber	d						08 37				08 52						09 07				09 22				
Caerphilly 3	d						08 40				08 55						09 10				09 25				
Lisvane & Thornhill	d						08 44				08 59						09 14				09 29				
Llanishen	d						08 46				09 01						09 16				09 31				
Heath High Level	d						08 49				09 04						09 19				09 34				
Coryton	d								08 45										09 15						
Whitchurch (Cardiff)	d								08 46										09 16						
Rhiwbina	d								08 48										09 18						
Birchgrove	d								08 50										09 20						
Ty Glas	d								08 51										09 21						
Heath Low Level	d								08 54										09 24						
Cardiff Queen Street 3	a			08 44	08 49	08 49	08 54		08 59	09 04	09 09				09 14	09 19	09 24		09 29	09 34	09 39				09 44
	d			08 46	08 51	08 51	08 56	08 57	09 01	09 06	09 11		09 12		09 16	09 21	09 26	09 27	09 31	09 36	09 41	09 42			09 46
Cardiff Bay	a							09 01					09 16					09 31				09 46			
Cardiff Central 7	a		08 50	08 52	08 54	08 54	08 59		09 04	09 09	09 14			09 20	09 22	09 24	09 29		09 34	09 39	09 44			09 50	09 52
	d				08 55	08 55	09 01			09 10	09 16					09 25	09 31			09 41	09 46				
Grangetown	d				08 59	08 59	09 05			09 14	09 20					09 29	09 35			09 45	09 50				
Dingle Road	d						09 11				09 26						09 41				09 56				
Penarth	a						09 16				09 31						09 46				10 01				
Cogan	d				09 03	09 03				09 18						09 33				09 48					
Eastbrook	d				09 05	09 05				09 20						09 35				09 51					
Dinas Powys	d				09 07	09 07				09 22						09 37				09 53					
Cadoxton	d				09 12	09 12				09 27						09 42				09 57					
Barry Docks	d				09 15	09 15				09 30						09 45				10 00					
Barry 3	d				09 19	09 19				09 34						09 49				10 05					
Barry Island	a				09 25	09 25				09 40						09 55									
Rhoose Cardiff Int Airport ✈	d																			10 12					
Llantwit Major	d																			10 22					
Bridgend	a																			10 39					

For general notes see front of timetable
For details of catering facilities see Directory of Train Operators

A To Coryton
B To Radyr
b Arr. 0844

Treherbert, Aberdare, Merthyr, Pontypridd, Rhymney and Coryton → Cardiff, Penarth, Barry, Barry Island and Bridgend

Network Diagram - see first page of Table 130

		AW	AW	AW	AW A	AW	AW		AW	AW	AW B	AW	AW	AW	AW	AW A	AW	AW	AW	AW	AW B	AW	AW	AW	AW	AW A
Treherbert	d								09 17											09 47						
Ynyswen	d								09 19											09 49						
Treorchy	d								09 21											09 51						
Ton Pentre	d								09 23											09 53						
Ystrad Rhondda	a								09 26											09 56						
	d								09 28											09 58						
Llwynypia	d								09 30											10 00						
Tonypandy	d								09 33											10 03						
Dinas Rhondda	d								09 35											10 05						
Porth	d								09 39											10 09						
Trehafod	d								09 42											10 12						
Merthyr Tydfil	d																09 39									
Pentre-bach	d																09 43									
Troed Y Rhiw	d																09 46									
Merthyr Vale	d																09 50									
Quakers Yard	d																09 55									
Abercynon South	d																09 59									
Aberdare 3	d	08 52											09 22										09 52			
Cwmbach	d	08 55											09 25										09 55			
Fernhill	d	08 58											09 28										09 58			
Mountain Ash	a	09 01											09 31										10 01			
	d	09 04											09 34										10 04			
Penrhiwceiber	d	09 07											09 37										10 07			
Abercynon North	d	09 15											09 45										10 15			
Pontypridd 3	a	09 23							09 47				09 53				10 07			10 17			10 23			
	d	09 24				09 39			09 48				09 54				10 09			10 18			10 24			
Trefforest	d	09 27				09 42			09 51				09 57				10 12			10 21			10 27			
Trefforest Estate	d					09 46											10 16									
Taffs Well 3	d	09 34				09 50			09 58				10 04				10 20			10 28			10 34			
Radyr 3	a	09 37				09 53			10 01				10 07				10 23			10 31			10 37			
	d	09 37				09 53			10 01		10 04		10 07				10 23			10 31	10 34		10 37			
Danescourt	d										10 08										10 38					
Fairwater	d										10 10										10 40					
Waun-gron Park	d										10 12										10 42					
Ninian Park	d										10 15										10 45					
Llandaf	d	09 40				09 56			10 04			←	10 10				10 26			10 34		←	10 40			
Cathays	d	09 45				10 01			10 09			10 09	10 15				10 31			10 39		10 39	10 45			
Rhymney 3	d								↪					09 29						↪						
Pontlottyn	d													09 32												
Tir-phil	d													09 36												
Brithdir	d													09 39												
Bargoed	d		09 17				09 32							09b47				10 02						10 17		
Gilfach Fargoed	d		09 19																					10 19		
Pengam	d		09 22				09 37							09 52				10 07						10 22		
Hengoed	d		09 25				09 40							09 55				10 10						10 25		
Ystrad Mynach 3	d		09 28				09 43							09 58				10 13						10 28		
Llanbradach	d		09 33				09 48							10 03				10 18						10 33		
Aber	d		09 37				09 52							10 07				10 22						10 37		
Caerphilly 3	d		09 40				09 55							10 10				10 25						10 40		
Lisvane & Thornhill	d		09 44				09 59							10 14				10 29						10 44		
Llanishen	d		09 46				10 01							10 16				10 31						10 46		
Heath High Level	d		09 49				10 04							10 19				10 34						10 49		
Coryton	d				09 45											10 15										10 45
Whitchurch (Cardiff)	d				09 46											10 16										10 46
Rhiwbina	d				09 48											10 18										10 48
Birchgrove	d				09 50											10 20										10 50
Ty Glas	d				09 51											10 21										10 51
Heath Low Level	d				09 54											10 24										10 54
Cardiff Queen Street 3	a	09 49	09 54		09 59	10 04	10 09					10 14	10 19	10 24		10 29	10 34	10 39				10 44	10 49	10 54		10 59
	d	09 51	09 56	09 57	10 01	10 06	10 11			10 12		10 16	10 21	10 26	10 27	10 31	10 36	10 41	10 42			10 46	10 51	10 56	10 57	11 01
Cardiff Bay	a			10 01						10 16					10 31				10 46						11 01	
Cardiff Central 7	a	09 54	09 59		10 04	10 09	10 14				10 20	10 22	10 24	10 29		10 34	10 39	10 44			10 50	10 52	10 54	10 59		11 04
	d	09 55	10 01			10 10	10 16						10 25	10 31			10 41	10 46					10 55	11 01		
Grangetown	d	09 59	10 05			10 14	10 20						10 29	10 35			10 45	10 50					10 59	11 05		
Dingle Road	d		10 11				10 26							10 41				10 56						11 11		
Penarth	a		10 16				10 31							10 46				11 01						11 16		
Cogan	d	10 03				10 18							10 33				10 48						11 03			
Eastbrook	d	10 05				10 20							10 35				10 51						11 05			
Dinas Powys	d	10 07				10 22							10 37				10 53						11 07			
Cadoxton	d	10 12				10 27							10 42				10 57						11 12			
Barry Docks	d	10 15				10 30							10 45				11 00						11 15			
Barry 3	d	10 19				10 34							10 49				11 05						11 19			
Barry Island	a	10 25				10 40							10 55										11 25			
Rhoose Cardiff Int Airport ✈	d																11 12									
Llantwit Major	d																11 22									
Bridgend	a																11 39									

For general notes see front of timetable
For details of catering facilities see Directory of Train Operators

A To Radyr
B To Coryton
b Arr. 0942

Table 130

Saturdays

Treherbert, Aberdare, Merthyr, Pontypridd, Rhymney and Coryton → Cardiff, Penarth, Barry, Barry Island and Bridgend

Network Diagram - see first page of Table 130

		AW	AW		AW	AW	AW	AW	AW	AW	AW	AW	AW	AW	AW	AW	AW	AW	AW	AW	AW	AW		AW	AW	AW
						A					B					A					B					
Treherbert	d								10 17						10 47										11 17	
Ynyswen	d								10 19						10 49										11 19	
Treorchy	d								10 21						10 51										11 21	
Ton Pentre	d								10 23						10 53										11 23	
Ystrad Rhondda	a								10 26						10 56										11 26	
	d								10 28						10 58										11 28	
Llwynypia	d								10 30						11 00										11 30	
Tonypandy	d								10 33						11 03										11 33	
Dinas Rhondda	d								10 35						11 05										11 35	
Porth	d								10b52						11 09										11 39	
Trehafod	d								10 55						11 12										11 42	
Merthyr Tydfil	d											10 39														
Pentre-bach	d											10 43														
Troed Y Rhiw	d											10 46														
Merthyr Vale	d											10 50														
Quakers Yard	d											10 55														
Abercynon South	d											10 59														
Aberdare 3	d						10 22										10 52									
Cwmbach	d						10 25										10 55									
Fernhill	d						10 28										10 58									
Mountain Ash	a						10 31										11 01									
	d						10 34										11 04									
Penrhiwceiber	d						10 37										11 07									
Abercynon North	d						10 45										11 15									
Pontypridd 3	a						10 53		11 01			11 07			11 17			11 23							11 47	
	d	10 39					10 54		11 04			11 09			11 18			11 24				11 39			11 48	
Trefforest	d	10 42					10 57		11 07			11 12			11 21			11 27				11 42			11 51	
Trefforest Estate	d	10 46										11 16										11 46				
Taffs Well 3	d	10 50					11 04		11 13			11 20			11 28			11 34				11 50			11 58	
Radyr 3	a	10 53					11 07		11 17			11 23			11 31			11 37				11 53			12 01	
	d	10 53				11 04	11 07		11 17			11 23			11 31	11 34		11 37				11 53			12 01	
Danescourt	d					11 08										11 38										
Fairwater	d					11 10										11 40										
Waun-gron Park	d					11 12										11 42										
Ninian Park	d					11 15										11 45										
Llandaf	d	10 56					11 10					11 26			11 34		←	11 40				11 56			12 04	
Cathays	d	11 01					11 15					11 31			11 39		11 39	11 45				12 01			12 09	
															→										→	
Rhymney 3	d							10 29																		
Pontlottyn	d							10 32																		
Tir-phil	d							10 36																		
Brithdir	d							10 39																		
Bargoed	d		10 32					10c47					11 02						11 17					11 32		
Gilfach Fargoed	d																		11 19							
Pengam	d		10 37					10 52					11 07						11 22					11 37		
Hengoed	d		10 40					10 55					11 10						11 25					11 40		
Ystrad Mynach 3	d		10 43					10 58					11 13						11 28					11 43		
Llanbradach	d		10 48					11 03					11 18						11 33					11 48		
Aber	d		10 52					11 07					11 22						11 37					11 52		
Caerphilly 3	d		10 55					11 10					11 25						11 40					11 55		
Lisvane & Thornhill	d		10 59					11 14					11 29						11 44					11 59		
Llanishen	d		11 01					11 16					11 31						11 46					12 01		
Heath High Level	d		11 04					11 19					11 34						11 49					12 04		
Coryton	d										11 15										11 45					
Whitchurch (Cardiff)	d										11 16										11 46					
Rhiwbina	d										11 18										11 48					
Birchgrove	d										11 20										11 50					
Ty Glas	d										11 21										11 51					
Heath Low Level	d										11 24										11 54					
Cardiff Queen Street 3	a	11 04	11 09				11 20	11 24			11 29	11 34	11 39				11 44	11 49	11 54		11 59	12 04		12 09		
	d	11 06	11 11		11 12		11 21	11 26		11 27	11 31	11 36	11 41	11 42			11 46	11 51	11 56	11 57	12 01	12 06		12 11		12 12
Cardiff Bay	a				11 16					11 31				11 46						12 01						12 16
Cardiff Central 7	a	11 09	11 14			11 20	11 24	11 29	11 33		11 34	11 39	11 44			11 50	11 52	11 54	11 59		12 04	12 09		12 14		
	d	11 10	11 16				11 25	11 31				11 41	11 46					11 55	12 01			12 10		12 16		
Grangetown	d	11 14	11 20				11 29	11 35				11 45	11 50					11 59	12 05			12 14		12 20		
Dingle Road	d		11 26					11 41					11 56						12 11					12 26		
Penarth	a		11 31					11 46					12 01						12 16					12 31		
Cogan	d	11 18					11 33					11 48						12 03				12 18				
Eastbrook	d	11 20					11 35					11 51						12 05				12 20				
Dinas Powys	d	11 22					11 37					11 53						12 07				12 22				
Cadoxton	d	11 27					11 42					11 57						12 12				12 27				
Barry Docks	d	11 30					11 45					12 00						12 15				12 30				
Barry 3	d	11 34					11 49					12 05						12 19				12 34				
Barry Island	a	11 40					11 55											12 25				12 40				
Rhoose Cardiff Int Airport ✈	d											12 12														
Llantwit Major	d											12 22														
Bridgend	a											12 39														

For general notes see front of timetable
For details of catering facilities see Directory of Train Operators

A To Coryton
B To Radyr
b Arr. 1038
c Arr. 1042

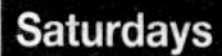

Treherbert, Aberdare, Merthyr, Pontypridd, Rhymney and Coryton → Cardiff, Penarth, Barry, Barry Island and Bridgend

Network Diagram - see first page of Table 130

		AW A	AW	AW	AW	AW	AW B	AW	AW	AW	AW	AW A	AW	AW	AW	AW B	AW	AW		AW	AW	AW A	AW	AW	AW	AW
Treherbert	d										11 47										12 17					
Ynyswen	d										11 49										12 19					
Treorchy	d										11 51										12 21					
Ton Pentre	d										11 53										12 23					
Ystrad Rhondda	a										11 56										12 26					
	d										11 58										12 28					
Llwynypia	d										12 00										12 30					
Tonypandy	d										12 03										12 33					
Dinas Rhondda	d										12 05										12 35					
Porth	d										12 09										12 39					
Trehafod	d										12 12										12 42					
Merthyr Tydfil	d							11 39																		
Pentre-bach	d							11 43																		
Troed Y Rhiw	d							11 46																		
Merthyr Vale	d							11 50																		
Quakers Yard	d							11 55																		
Abercynon South	d							11 59																		
Aberdare 3	d			11 22																				12 22		
Cwmbach	d			11 25																				12 25		
Fernhill	d			11 28																				12 28		
Mountain Ash	a			11 31																				12 31		
	d			11 34																				12 34		
Penrhiwceiber	d			11 37																				12 37		
Abercynon North	d			11 45																				12 45		
Pontypridd 3	a			11 53				12 07			12 17										12 48			12 53		
	d			11 54				12 09			12 18						12 39				12 48			12 54		
Trefforest	d			11 57				12 12			12 21						12 42				12 51			12 57		
Trefforest Estate	d							12 16									12 46									
Taffs Well 3	d			12 04				12 20			12 28						12 50				12 58			13 04		
Radyr 3	a			12 07				12 23			12 31						12 53				13 01			13 07		
	d	12 04		12 07				12 23			12 31	12 34					12 53				13 01	13 04		13 07		
Danescourt	d	12 08										12 38										13 08				
Fairwater	d	12 10										12 40										13 10				
Waun-gron Park	d	12 12										12 42										13 12				
Ninian Park	d	12 15										12 45										13 15				
Llandaf	d		←	12 10				12 26			12 34		←				12 56				13 04		←	13 10		
Cathays	d		12 09	12 15				12 31			12 39		12 39				13 01				13 09		13 09	13 15		
Rhymney 3	d				11 29						↳										↳				12 29	
Pontlottyn	d				11 32																				12 32	
Tir-phil	d				11 36																				12 36	
Brithdir	d				11 39																				12 39	
Bargoed	d				11b47				12 02					12 17				12 32							12c47	
Gilfach Fargoed	d													12 19												
Pengam	d				11 52				12 07					12 22				12 37							12 52	
Hengoed	d				11 55				12 10					12 25				12 40							12 55	
Ystrad Mynach 3	d				11 58				12 13					12 28				12 43							12 58	
Llanbradach	d				12 03				12 18					12 33				12 48							13 03	
Aber	d				12 07				12 22					12 37				12 52							13 07	
Caerphilly 3	d				12 10				12 25					12 40				12 55							13 10	
Lisvane & Thornhill	d				12 14				12 29					12 44				12 59							13 14	
Llanishen	d				12 16				12 31					12 46				13 01							13 16	
Heath High Level	d				12 19				12 34					12 49				13 04							13 19	
Coryton	d						12 15									12 45										
Whitchurch (Cardiff)	d						12 16									12 46										
Rhiwbina	d						12 18									12 48										
Birchgrove	d						12 20									12 50										
Ty Glas	d						12 21									12 51										
Heath Low Level	d						12 24									12 54										
Cardiff Queen Street 3	a		12 14	12 19	12 24		12 29	12 34	12 39				12 44	12 54		12 59	13 04	13 09					13 14	13 19	13 24	
	d		12 16	12 21	12 26	12 27	12 31	12 36	12 41	12 42			12 46	12 56	12 57	13 01	13 06	13 11		13 12			13 16	13 21	13 26	13 27
Cardiff Bay	a					12 31				12 46					13 01					13 16						13 31
Cardiff Central 7	a	12 20	12 22	12 24	12 29		12 34	12 39	12 44			12 50	12 52	12 59		13 04	13 09	13 14				13 20	13 22	13 24	13 29	
	d			12 25	12 31			12 41	12 46				12 55	13 01			13 10	13 16						13 25	13 31	
Grangetown	d			12 29	12 35			12 45	12 50				12 59	13 05			13 14	13 20						13 29	13 35	
Dingle Road	d				12 41				12 56					13 11				13 26							13 41	
Penarth	a				12 46				13 01					13 16				13 31							13 46	
Cogan	d			12 33				12 48					13 03				13 18							13 33		
Eastbrook	d			12 35				12 51					13 05				13 20							13 35		
Dinas Powys	d			12 37				12 53					13 07				13 22							13 37		
Cadoxton	d			12 42				12 57					13 12				13 27							13 42		
Barry Docks	d			12 45				13 00					13 15				13 30							13 45		
Barry 3	d			12 49				13 05					13 19				13 34							13 49		
Barry Island	a			12 55									13 25				13 40							13 55		
Rhoose Cardiff Int Airport ✈	d							13 12																		
Llantwit Major	d							13 22																		
Bridgend	a							13 39																		

For general notes see front of timetable
For details of catering facilities see Directory of Train Operators

A To Coryton
B To Radyr
b Arr. 1142
c Arr. 1242

Table 130

Saturdays

Treherbert, Aberdare, Merthyr, Pontypridd, Rhymney and Coryton → Cardiff, Penarth, Barry, Barry Island and Bridgend

Network Diagram - see first page of Table 130

		AW A	AW	AW	AW	AW	AW B	AW	AW	AW	AW	AW A	AW	AW		AW	AW	AW B	AW	AW	AW	AW	AW A	AW	AW	AW
Treherbert	d					12 47										13 17										
Ynyswen	d					12 49										13 19										
Treorchy	d					12 51										13 21										
Ton Pentre	d					12 53										13 23										
Ystrad Rhondda	a					12 56										13 26										
	d					12 58										13 28										
Llwynypia	d					13 00										13 30										
Tonypandy	d					13 03										13 33										
Dinas Rhondda	d					13 05										13 35										
Porth	d					13 09										13 39										
Trehafod	d					13 12										13 42										
Merthyr Tydfil	d		12 39																					13 39		
Pentre-bach	d		12 43																					13 43		
Troed Y Rhiw	d		12 46																					13 46		
Merthyr Vale	d		12 50																					13 50		
Quakers Yard	d		12 55																					13 55		
Abercynon South	d		12 59																					13 59		
Aberdare 3	d								12 52																	
Cwmbach	d								12 55																	
Fernhill	d								12 58																	
Mountain Ash	a								13 01																	
	d								13 04																	
Penrhiwceiber	d								13 07																	
Abercynon North	d								13 15											13 45						
Pontypridd 3	a		13 07			13 17			12 23							13 47				13 53				14 07		
	d		13 09			13 18			13 24				13 39			13 48				13 54				14 09		
Trefforest	d		13 12			13 21			13 27				13 42			13 51				13 57				14 12		
Trefforest Estate	d		13 16										13 46											14 16		
Taffs Well 3	d		13 20			13 28			13 34				13 50			13 58				14 04				14 20		
Radyr 3	a		13 23			13 31			13 37				13 53			14 01				14 07				14 23		
	d		13 23			13 31	13 34		13 37				13 53			14 01		14 04		14 07				14 23		
Danescourt	d						13 38											14 08								
Fairwater	d						13 40											14 10								
Waun-gron Park	d						13 42											14 12								
Ninian Park	d						13 45											14 15								
Llandaf	d		13 26			13 34		←	13 40				13 56			14 04			←	14 10				14 26		
Cathays	d		13 31			13 39		13 39	13 45				14 01			14 09			14 09	14 15				14 31		
Rhymney 3	d					→										→					13 29					
Pontlottyn	d																				13 32					
Tir-phil	d																				13 36					
Brithdir	d																				13 39					
Bargoed	d			13 02						13 17				13 32							13b47				14 02	
Gilfach Fargoed	d									13 19																
Pengam	d			13 07						13 22				13 37							13 52				14 07	
Hengoed	d			13 10						13 25				13 40							13 55				14 10	
Ystrad Mynach 3	d			13 13						13 28				13 43							13 58				14 13	
Llanbradach	d			13 18						13 33				13 48							14 03				14 18	
Aber	d			13 22						13 37				13 52							14 07				14 22	
Caerphilly 3	d			13 25						13 40				13 55							14 10				14 25	
Lisvane & Thornhill	d			13 29						13 44				13 59							14 14				14 29	
Llanishen	d			13 31						13 46				14 01							14 16				14 31	
Heath High Level	d			13 34						13 49				14 04							14 19				14 34	
Coryton	d	13 15										13 45											14 15			
Whitchurch (Cardiff)	d	13 16										13 46											14 16			
Rhiwbina	d	13 18										13 48											14 18			
Birchgrove	d	13 20										13 50											14 20			
Ty Glas	d	13 21										13 51											14 21			
Heath Low Level	d	13 24										13 54											14 24			
Cardiff Queen Street 3	a	13 29	13 34	13 39				13 44	13 49	13 54		13 59	14 04	14 09					14 14	14 19	14 24		14 29	14 34	14 39	
	d	13 31	13 36	13 41	13 42			13 46	13 51	13 56	13 57	14 01	14 06	14 11			14 12		14 16	14 21	14 26	14 27	14 31	14 36	14 41	14 42
Cardiff Bay	a				13 46						14 01						14 16					14 31				14 46
Cardiff Central 7	a	13 34	13 40	13 44			13 50	13 52	13 54	13 59		14 04	14 09	14 14				14 20	14 22	14 24	14 29		14 34	14 39	14 44	
	d		13 41	13 46					13 55	14 01			14 10	14 16						14 25	14 31			14 41	14 46	
Grangetown	d		13 45	13 50					13 59	14 05			14 14	14 20						14 29	14 35			14 45	14 50	
Dingle Road	d			13 56						14 11				14 26							14 41				14 56	
Penarth	a			14 01						14 16				14 31							14 46				15 01	
Cogan	d		13 48						14 03				14 18							14 33				14 48		
Eastbrook	d		13 51						14 05				14 20							14 35				14 51		
Dinas Powys	d		13 53						14 07				14 22							14 37				14 53		
Cadoxton	d		13 57						14 12				14 27							14 42				14 57		
Barry Docks	d		14 00						14 15				14 30							14 45				15 00		
Barry 3	d		14 05						14 19				14 34							14 49				15 05		
Barry Island	a								14 25				14 40							14 55						
Rhoose Cardiff Int Airport ✈	d		14 12																					15 12		
Llantwit Major	d		14 22																					15 22		
Bridgend	a		14 39																					15 39		

For general notes see front of timetable
For details of catering facilities see Directory of Train Operators

A To Radyr
B To Coryton
b Arr. 1342

Treherbert, Aberdare, Merthyr, Pontypridd, Rhymney and Coryton → Cardiff, Penarth, Barry, Barry Island and Bridgend

Network Diagram - see first page of Table 130

		AW	AW A	AW	AW	AW	AW	AW B	AW	AW	AW	AW A	AW	AW	AW	AW	AW B	AW	AW	AW	AW	AW A	AW	AW	AW
Treherbert	d	13 47													14 17						14 47				
Ynyswen	d	13 49													14 19						14 49				
Treorchy	d	13 51													14 21						14 51				
Ton Pentre	d	13 53													14 23						14 53				
Ystrad Rhondda	a	13 56													14 26						14 56				
	d	13 58													14 28						14 58				
Llwynypia	d	14 00													14 30						15 00				
Tonypandy	d	14 03													14 33						15 03				
Dinas Rhondda	d	14 05													14 35						15 05				
Porth	d	14 09													14b52						15 09				
Trehafod	d	14 12													14 55						15 12				
Merthyr Tydfil	d																	14 39							
Pentre-bach	d																	14 43							
Troed Y Rhiw	d																	14 46							
Merthyr Vale	d																	14 50							
Quakers Yard	d																	14 55							
Abercynon South	d																	14 59							
Aberdare 3	d				13 52								14 22											14 52	
Cwmbach	d				13 55								14 25											14 55	
Fernhill	d				13 58								14 28											14 58	
Mountain Ash	a				14 01								14 31											15 01	
	d				14 04								14 34											15 04	
Penrhiwceiber	d				14 07								14 37											15 07	
Abercynon North	d				14 15								14 45											15 15	
Pontypridd 3	a	14 17			14 23								14 53		15 01			15 07			15 17			15 23	
	d	14 18			14 24				14 39				14 54		15 04			15 09			15 18			15 24	
Trefforest	d	14 21			14 27				14 42				14 57		15 07			15 12			15 21			15 27	
Trefforest Estate	d								14 46									15 16							
Taffs Well 3	d	14 28			14 34				14 50				15 04		15 13			15 20			15 28			15 34	
Radyr 3	a	14 31			14 37				14 53				15 07		15 17			15 23			15 31			15 37	
	d	14 31	14 34		14 37				14 53			15 04	15 07		15 17			15 23			15 31	15 34		15 37	
Danescourt	d		14 38									15 08										15 38			
Fairwater	d		14 40									15 10										15 40			
Waun-gron Park	d		14 42									15 12										15 42			
Ninian Park	d		14 45									15 15										15 45			
Llandaf	d	14 34		←	14 40				14 56				15 10					15 26			15 34		←	15 40	
Cathays	d	14 39		14 39	14 45				15 01				15 15					15 31			15 39		15 39	15 45	
Rhymney 3	d	↪												14 29							↪				
Pontlottyn	d													14 32											
Tir-phil	d													14 36											
Brithdir	d													14 39											
Bargoed	d					14 17				14 32				14c47					15 02						15 17
Gilfach Fargoed	d					14 19																			15 19
Pengam	d					14 22				14 37				14 52					15 07						15 22
Hengoed	d					14 25				14 40				14 55					15 10						15 25
Ystrad Mynach 3	d					14 28				14 43				14 58					15 13						15 28
Llanbradach	d					14 33				14 48				15 03					15 18						15 33
Aber	d					14 37				14 52				15 07					15 22						15 37
Caerphilly 3	d					14 40				14 55				15 10					15 25						15 40
Lisvane & Thornhill	d					14 44				14 59				15 14					15 29						15 44
Llanishen	d					14 46				15 01				15 16					15 31						15 46
Heath High Level	d					14 49				15 04				15 19					15 34						15 49
Coryton	d							14 45									15 15								
Whitchurch (Cardiff)	d							14 46									15 16								
Rhiwbina	d							14 48									15 18								
Birchgrove	d							14 50									15 20								
Ty Glas	d							14 51									15 21								
Heath Low Level	d							14 54									15 24								
Cardiff Queen Street 3	a			14 44	14 49	14 54		14 59	15 04	15 09			15 19	15 24			15 29	15 34	15 39				15 44	15 49	15 54
	d			14 46	14 51	14 56	14 57	15 01	15 06	15 11	15 12		15 21	15 26		15 27	15 31	15 36	15 41	15 42			15 46	15 51	15 56
Cardiff Bay	a						15 01				15 16					15 31				15 46					
Cardiff Central 7	a		14 50	14 52	14 54	14 59		15 04	15 09	15 14		15 20	15 24	15 29	15 33		15 34	15 39	15 44			15 50	15 52	15 54	15 59
	d				14 55	15 01			15 10	15 16			15 25	15 31				15 41	15 46					15 55	16 01
Grangetown	d				14 59	15 05			15 14	15 20			15 29	15 35				15 45	15 50					15 59	16 05
Dingle Road	d					15 11				15 26				15 41					15 56						16 11
Penarth	a					15 16				15 31				15 46					16 01						16 16
Cogan	d				15 03				15 18				15 33					15 48						16 03	
Eastbrook	d				15 05				15 20				15 35					15 51						16 05	
Dinas Powys	d				15 07				15 22				15 37					15 53						16 07	
Cadoxton	d				15 12				15 27				15 42					15 57						16 12	
Barry Docks	d				15 15				15 30				15 45					16 00						16 15	
Barry 3	d				15 19				15 34				15 49					16 05						16 19	
Barry Island	a				15 25				15 40				15 55											16 25	
Rhoose Cardiff Int Airport ✈	d																	16 12							
Llantwit Major	d																	16 22							
Bridgend	a																	16 39							

For general notes see front of timetable
For details of catering facilities see Directory of Train Operators

A To Coryton
B To Radyr
b Arr. 1438
c Arr. 1442

Table 130

Saturdays

Treherbert, Aberdare, Merthyr, Pontypridd, Rhymney and Coryton → Cardiff, Penarth, Barry, Barry Island and Bridgend

Network Diagram - see first page of Table 130

		AW	AW A	AW	AW	AW		AW	AW B	AW	AW	AW	AW	AW A	AW	AW	AW	AW	AW B	AW	AW	AW	AW	AW A	AW	AW
Treherbert	d					15 17												15 47								
Ynyswen	d					15 19												15 49								
Treorchy	d					15 21												15 51								
Ton Pentre	d					15 23												15 53								
Ystrad Rhondda	a					15 26												15 56								
	d					15 28												15 58								
Llwynypia	d					15 30												16 00								
Tonypandy	d					15 33												16 03								
Dinas Rhondda	d					15 35												16 05								
Porth	d					15 39												16 09								
Trehafod	d					15 42												16 12								
Merthyr Tydfil	d														15 39											
Pentre-bach	d														15 43											
Troed Y Rhiw	d														15 46											
Merthyr Vale	d														15 50											
Quakers Yard	d														15 55											
Abercynon South	d														15 59											
Aberdare 3	d										15 22										15 52					
Cwmbach	d										15 25										15 55					
Fernhill	d										15 28										15 58					
Mountain Ash	a										15 31										16 01					
	d										15 34										16 04					
Penrhiwceiber	d										15 37										16 07					
Abercynon North	d										15 45										16 15					
Pontypridd 3	a					15 47					15 53				16 07			16 17			16 23					
	d			15 39		15 48					15 54				16 09			16 18			16 24				16 39	
Trefforest	d			15 42		15 51					15 57				16 12			16 21			16 27				16 42	
Trefforest Estate	d			15 46											16 16										16 46	
Taffs Well 3	d			15 50		15 58					16 04				16 20			16 28			16 34				16 50	
Radyr 3	a			15 53		16 01					16 07				16 23			16 31			16 37				16 53	
	d			15 53		16 01			16 04		16 07				16 23			16 31	16 34		16 37				16 53	
Danescourt	d								16 08										16 38							
Fairwater	d								16 10										16 40							
Waun-gron Park	d								16 12										16 42							
Ninian Park	d								16 15										16 45							
Llandaf	d			15 56		16 04				←	16 10				16 26			16 34		←	16 40				16 56	
Cathays	d			16 01		16 09				16 09	16 15				16 31			16 39		16 39	16 45				17 01	
Rhymney 3	d					→						15 29						→								
Pontlottyn	d											15 32														
Tir-phil	d											15 36														
Brithdir	d											15 39														
Bargoed	d				15 32							15b47				16 02						16 17				16 32
Gilfach Fargoed	d																					16 19				
Pengam	d				15 37							15 52				16 07						16 22				16 37
Hengoed	d				15 40							15 55				16 10						16 25				16 40
Ystrad Mynach 3	d				15 43							15 58				16 13						16 28				16 43
Llanbradach	d				15 48							16 03				16 18						16 33				16 48
Aber	d				15 52							16 07				16 22						16 37				16 52
Caerphilly 3	d				15 55							16 10				16 25						16 40				16 55
Lisvane & Thornhill	d				15 59							16 14				16 29						16 44				16 59
Llanishen	d				16 01							16 16				16 31						16 46				17 01
Heath High Level	d				16 04							16 19				16 34						16 49				17 04
Coryton	d		15 45											16 15										16 45		
Whitchurch (Cardiff)	d		15 46											16 16										16 46		
Rhiwbina	d		15 48											16 18										16 48		
Birchgrove	d		15 50											16 20										16 50		
Ty Glas	d		15 51											16 21										16 51		
Heath Low Level	d		15 54											16 24										16 54		
Cardiff Queen Street 3	a		15 59	16 04	16 09					16 14	16 19	16 24		16 29	16 34	16 39				16 44	16 49	16 54		16 59	17 04	17 09
	d	15 57	16 01	16 06	16 11			16 12		16 16	16 21	16 26	16 27	16 31	16 36	16 41	16 42			16 46	16 51	16 56	16 57	17 01	17 06	17 11
Cardiff Bay	a	16 01						16 16					16 31				16 46						17 01			
Cardiff Central 7	a		16 04	16 09	16 14				16 20	16 22	16 24	16 32		16 34	16 39	16 44			16 50	16 52	16 54	16 59		17 04	17 09	17 14
	d			16 10	16 16						16 25				16 41	16 46					16 55	17 01			17 10	17 16
Grangetown	d			16 14	16 20						16 29				16 45	16 50					16 59	17 05			17 14	17 20
Dingle Road	d				16 26											16 56						17 11				17 26
Penarth	a				16 31											17 01						17 16				17 31
Cogan	d			16 18							16 33				16 48						17 03				17 18	
Eastbrook	d			16 20							16 35				16 51						17 05				17 20	
Dinas Powys	d			16 22							16 37				16 53						17 07				17 22	
Cadoxton	d			16 27							16 42				16 57						17 12				17 27	
Barry Docks	d			16 30							16 45				17 00						17 15				17 30	
Barry 3	d			16 34							16 49				17 05						17 19				17 34	
Barry Island	a			16 40							16 55										17 25				17 40	
Rhoose Cardiff Int Airport ✈	d														17 12											
Llantwit Major	d														17 22											
Bridgend	a														17 39											

For general notes see front of timetable
For details of catering facilities see Directory of Train Operators

A To Radyr
B To Coryton
b Arr. 1542

Table 130

Treherbert, Aberdare, Merthyr, Pontypridd, Rhymney and Coryton → Cardiff, Penarth, Barry, Barry Island and Bridgend

Network Diagram - see first page of Table 130

		AW		AW	AW A	AW	AW	AW	AW	AW B	AW	AW	AW	AW	AW A	AW	AW	AW	AW	AW B	AW		AW	AW	AW	AW A
Treherbert	d	16 17												16 47										17 17		
Ynyswen	d	16 19												16 49										17 19		
Treorchy	d	16 21												16 51										17 21		
Ton Pentre	d	16 23												16 53										17 23		
Ystrad Rhondda	a	16 26												16 56										17 26		
	d	16 28												16 58										17 28		
Llwynypia	d	16 30												17 00										17 30		
Tonypandy	d	16 33												17 03										17 33		
Dinas Rhondda	d	16 35												17 05										17 35		
Porth	d	16 39												17 09										17 39		
Trehafod	d	16 42												17 12										17 42		
Merthyr Tydfil	d										16 39															
Pentre-bach	d										16 43															
Troed Y Rhiw	d										16 46															
Merthyr Vale	d										16 50															
Quakers Yard	d										16 55															
Abercynon South	d										16 59															
Aberdare 3	d						16 22										16 52									
Cwmbach	d						16 25										16 55									
Fernhill	d						16 28										16 58									
Mountain Ash	a						16 31										17 01									
	d						16 34										17 04									
Penrhiwceiber	d						16 37										17 07									
Abercynon North	d						16 45										17 15									
Pontypridd 3	a	16 47					16 53				17 07			17 17			17 23							17 47		
	d	16 48					16 54				17 09			17 18			17 24				17 39			17 48		
Trefforest	d	16 51					16 57				17 12			17 21			17 27				17 42			17 51		
Trefforest Estate	d										17 16										17 46					
Taffs Well 3	d	16 58					17 04				17 20			17 28			17 34				17 50			17 58		
Radyr 3	a	17 01					17 07				17 23			17 31			17 37				17 53			18 01		
	d	17 01			17 04		17 07				17 23			17 31	17 34		17 37				17 53			18 01		18 04
Danescourt	d				17 08										17 38											18 08
Fairwater	d				17 10										17 40											18 10
Waun-gron Park	d				17 12										17 42											18 12
Ninian Park	d				17 15										17 45											18 15
Llandaf	d	17 04				←	17 10				17 26			17 34		←	17 40				17 56			18 04		
Cathays	d	17 09				17 09	17 15				17 31			17 39		17 39	17 45				18 01			18 09		
Rhymney 3	d	→						16 29						→										→		
Pontlottyn	d							16 32																		
Tir-phil	d							16 36																		
Brithdir	d							16 39																		
Bargoed	d							16b47				17 02						17 17					17 32			
Gilfach Fargoed	d																	17 19								
Pengam	d							16 52				17 07						17 22					17 37			
Hengoed	d							16 55				17 10						17 25					17 40			
Ystrad Mynach 3	d							16 58				17 13						17 28					17 43			
Llanbradach	d							17 03				17 18						17 33					17 48			
Aber	d							17 07				17 22						17 37					17 52			
Caerphilly 3	d							17 10				17 25						17 40					17 55			
Lisvane & Thornhill	d							17 14				17 29						17 44					17 59			
Llanishen	d							17 16				17 31						17 46					18 01			
Heath High Level	d							17 19				17 34						17 49					18 04			
Coryton	d									17 15										17 45						
Whitchurch (Cardiff)	d									17 16										17 46						
Rhiwbina	d									17 18										17 48						
Birchgrove	d									17 20										17 50						
Ty Glas	d									17 21										17 51						
Heath Low Level	d									17 24										17 54						
Cardiff Queen Street 3	a					17 14	17 19	17 24		17 29	17 34	17 39				17 44	17 49	17 54		17 59	18 04		18 09			
	d			17 12		17 16	17 21	17 26	17 27	17 31	17 36	17 41	17 42			17 46	17 51	17 56	17 57	18 01	18 06		18 11		18 12	
Cardiff Bay	a			17 16					17 31				17 46						18 01						18 16	
Cardiff Central 7	a				17 20	17 22	17 24	17 29		17 34	17 39	17 44			17 50	17 52	17 54	17 59		18 04	18 09		18 14			18 20
	d						17 25	17 31			17 41	17 46					17 55	18 01			18 10		18 16			
Grangetown	d						17 29	17 35			17 45	17 50					17 59	18 05			18 14		18 20			
Dingle Road	d							17 41				17 56						18 11					18 26			
Penarth	a							17 46				18 01						18 16					18 31			
Cogan	d						17 33				17 48						18 03				18 18					
Eastbrook	d						17 35				17 51						18 05				18 20					
Dinas Powys	d						17 37				17 53						18 07				18 22					
Cadoxton	d						17 42				17 57						18 12				18 27					
Barry Docks	d						17 45				18 00						18 15				18 30					
Barry 3	d						17 49				18 05						18 19				18 34					
Barry Island	a						17 55										18 25				18 40					
Rhoose Cardiff Int Airport ✈	d										18 12															
Llantwit Major	d										18 22															
Bridgend	a										18 39															

For general notes see front of timetable
For details of catering facilities see Directory of Train Operators

A To Coryton
B To Radyr
b Arr. 1642

Table 130

Saturdays

Treherbert, Aberdare, Merthyr, Pontypridd, Rhymney and Coryton → Cardiff, Penarth, Barry, Barry Island and Bridgend

Network Diagram - see first page of Table 130

		AW	AW	AW	AW	AW	AW	AW	AW	AW	AW	AW	AW	AW	AW	AW	AW	AW	AW	AW	AW	AW	AW	AW	AW
						A				B													A		
Treherbert	d							17 47										18 17							
Ynyswen	d							17 49										18 19							
Treorchy	d							17 51										18 21							
Ton Pentre	d							17 53										18 23							
Ystrad Rhondda	a							17 56										18 26							
	d							17 58										18 28							
Llwynypia	d							18 00										18 30							
Tonypandy	d							18 03										18 33							
Dinas Rhondda	d							18 05										18 35							
Porth	d							18 09										18 39							
Trehafod	d							18 12										18 42							
Merthyr Tydfil	d						17 39																	18 39	
Pentre-bach	d						17 43																	18 43	
Troed Y Rhiw	d						17 46																	18 46	
Merthyr Vale	d						17 50																	18 50	
Quakers Yard	d						17 55																	18 55	
Abercynon South	d						17 59																	18 59	
Aberdare 3	d		17 22									17 52								18 22					
Cwmbach	d		17 25									17 55								18 25					
Fernhill	d		17 28									17 58								18 28					
Mountain Ash	a		17 31									18 01								18 31					
	d		17 34									18 04								18 34					
Penrhiwceiber	d		17 37									18 07								18 37					
Abercynon North	d		17 45									18 15								18 45					
Pontypridd 3	a		17 53				18 07	18 17				18 23						18 47		18 53				19 07	
	d		17 54				18 09	18 18				18 24				18 39		18 48		18 54				19 09	
Trefforest	d		17 57				18 12	18 21				18 27				18 42		18 51		18 57				19 12	
Trefforest Estate	d						18 16									18 46								19 16	
Taffs Well 3	d		18 04				18 20	18 28				18 34				18 50		18 58		19 04				19 20	
Radyr 3	a		18 07				18 23	18 31				18 37				18 53		19 01		19 07				19 23	
	d		18 07				18 23	18 31		18 34		18 37				18 53		19 01	19 04	19 07				19 23	
Danescourt	d									18 38									19 08						
Fairwater	d									18 40									19 10						
Waun-gron Park	d									18 42									19 12						
Ninian Park	d									18 45									19 15						
Llandaf	d	←	18 10				18 26	18 34			←	18 40				18 56		19 04		19 10				19 26	
Cathays	d	18 09	18 15				18 31	18 39			18 39	18 45				19 01		19 09		19 15				19 31	
Rhymney 3	d			17 29				→																	
Pontlottyn	d			17 32																					
Tir-phil	d			17 36																					
Brithdir	d			17 39																					
Bargoed	d			17b47									18 17								18 48				
Gilfach Fargoed	d												18 19								18 50				
Pengam	d			17 52									18 22								18 53				
Hengoed	d			17 55									18 25								18 56				
Ystrad Mynach 3	d			17 58									18 28								18 59				
Llanbradach	d			18 03									18 33								19 04				
Aber	d			18 07									18 37								19 08				
Caerphilly 3	d			18 10									18 40								19 11				
Lisvane & Thornhill	d			18 14									18 44								19 15				
Llanishen	d			18 16									18 46								19 17				
Heath High Level	d			18 19									18 49								19 20				
Coryton	d					18 15									18 45								19 15		
Whitchurch (Cardiff)	d					18 16				19a08					18 46								19 16		
Rhiwbina	d					18 18									18 48								19 18		
Birchgrove	d					18 20									18 50								19 20		
Ty Glas	d					18 21									18 51								19 21		
Heath Low Level	d					18 24									18 54								19 24		
Cardiff Queen Street 3	a	18 14	18 19	18 24		18 29	18 34				18 44	18 49	18 54		18 59	19 04		19 14		19 19	19 24		19 30	19 34	
	d	18 16	18 21	18 26	18 27	18 31	18 36		18 42		18 46	18 51	18 56	18 57	19 01	19 06	19 12	19 16		19 21	19 26	19 27	19 32	19 36	19 42
Cardiff Bay	a				18 31				18 46					19 01			19 16					19 31			19 46
Cardiff Central 7	a	18 22	18 24	18 29		18 34	18 39			18 50	18 52	18 54	18 59		19 06	19 10		19 22	19 22	19 24	19 29		19 35	19 39	
	d		18 25	18 31			18 41					18 55	19 01							19 25	19 31			19 41	
Grangetown	d		18 29	18 35			18 45					18 59	19 05							19 29	19 35			19 45	
Dingle Road	d			18 41									19 11								19 41				
Penarth	a			18 46									19 16								19 46				
Cogan	d		18 33				18 48					19 03								19 33				19 48	
Eastbrook	d		18 35				18 51					19 05								19 35				19 51	
Dinas Powys	d		18 37				18 53					19 07								19 37				19 53	
Cadoxton	d		18 42				18 57					19 12								19 42				19 57	
Barry Docks	d		18 45				19 00					19 15								19 45				20 00	
Barry 3	d		18 49				19 05					19 19								19 49				20 05	
Barry Island	a		18 55									19 25								19 55					
Rhoose Cardiff Int Airport ✈	d						19 12																	20 12	
Llantwit Major	d						19 22																	20 22	
Bridgend	a						19 39																	20 39	

For general notes see front of timetable
For details of catering facilities see Directory of Train Operators

A To Radyr
B To Coryton
b Arr. 1742

Table 130

Treherbert, Aberdare, Merthyr, Pontypridd, Rhymney and Coryton → Cardiff, Penarth, Barry, Barry Island and Bridgend

Network Diagram - see first page of Table 130

		AW	AW A	AW	AW	AW	AW	AW	AW	AW	AW	AW B	AW	AW	AW	AW	AW	AW	AW	AW	AW	AW	AW	AW	AW
Treherbert	d	18 47					19 17									19 47									
Ynyswen	d	18 49					19 19									19 49									
Treorchy	d	18 51					19 21									19 51									
Ton Pentre	d	18 53					19 23									19 53									
Ystrad Rhondda	a	18 56					19 26									19 56									
	d	18 58					19 28									19 58									
Llwynypia	d	19 00					19 30									20 00									
Tonypandy	d	19 03					19 33									20 03									
Dinas Rhondda	d	19 05					19 35									20 05									
Porth	d	19 09					19 39									20 09									
Trehafod	d	19 12					19 42									20 12									
Merthyr Tydfil	d												19 39												
Pentre-bach	d												19 43												
Troed Y Rhiw	d												19 46												
Merthyr Vale	d												19 50												
Quakers Yard	d												19 55												
Abercynon South	d												19 59												
Aberdare 3	d		18 52														19 52					20 22			
Cwmbach	d		18 55														19 55					20 25			
Fernhill	d		18 58														19 58					20 28			
Mountain Ash	a		19 01														20 01					20 31			
	d		19 04														20 04					20 34			
Penrhiwceiber	d		19 07														20 07					20 37			
Abercynon North	d		19 15						19 43								20 15					20 45			
Pontypridd 3	a	19 17	19 23				19 47		19 53				20 07			20 17	20 23					20 53			
	d	19 18	19 24				19 48		19 54				20 09			20 18	20 24					20 54			
Trefforest	d	19 21	19 27				19 51		19 57				20 12			20 21	20 27					20 57			
Trefforest Estate	d												20 16												
Taffs Well 3	d	19 28	19 34				19 58		20 04				20 20			20 28	20 34					21 04			
Radyr 3	a	19 31	19 37				20 01		20 07				20 23			20 31	20 37					21 07			
	d	19 31	19 37				20 01	20 04	20 07				20 23			20 31	20 37			21 04		21 07			
Danescourt	d							20 08		←										21 08			←		
Fairwater	d							20 10 →		20 10										21 10 →			21 10		
Waun-gron Park	d									20 12													21 12		
Ninian Park	d									20 15													21 15		
Llandaf	d	19 34	19 40				20 04		20 10				20 26			20 34	20 40					21 10			
Cathays	d	19 39	19 45				20 09		20 15				20 31			20 39	20 45					21 15			
Rhymney 3	d													19 45											
Pontlottyn	d													19 48											
Tir-phil	d													19 52											
Brithdir	d													19 55											
Bargoed	d													19 59											
Gilfach Fargoed	d													20 01											
Pengam	d													20 04											
Hengoed	d													20 07											
Ystrad Mynach 3	d													20 10											
Llanbradach	d													20 15											
Aber	d													20 19											
Caerphilly 3	d			19 40										20 22				20 40							
Lisvane & Thornhill	d			19 44										20 26				20 44							
Llanishen	d			19 46										20 28				20 46							
Heath High Level	d			19 49										20 31				20 49							
Coryton	d											20 15													
Whitchurch (Cardiff)	d											20 16													
Rhiwbina	d											20 18													
Birchgrove	d											20 20													
Ty Glas	d											20 21													
Heath Low Level	d											20 24													
Cardiff Queen Street 3	a	19 44	19 49	19 54			20 14		20 19			20 29	20 34	20 39		20 44	20 50	20 54				21 19			
	d	19 46	19 51	19 56	19 57	20 12	20 16		20 21		20 27	20 31	20 36	20 41	20 42	20 46	20 51	20 56	20 57		21 12	21 21		21 26	21 27
Cardiff Bay	a				20 01	20 16					20 31				20 46				21 01		21 16				21 31
Cardiff Central 7	a	19 52	19 57	19 59			20 19		20 24	20 26		20 34	20 39	20 47		20 52	20 57	20 59				21 24	21 26		
	d			20 01			20 20		20 31				20 41					21 01				21 25		21 31	
Grangetown	d			20 05			20 24		20 35				20 45					21 05				21 29		21 35	
Dingle Road	d			20 11					20 41									21 11						21 41	
Penarth	a			20 16					20 46									21 16						21 46	
Cogan	d						20 28						20 48									21 33			
Eastbrook	d						20 30						20 51									21 35			
Dinas Powys	d						20 32						20 53									21 37			
Cadoxton	d						20 37						20 57									21 42			
Barry Docks	d						20 40						21 00									21 45			
Barry 3	d						20 44						21 05									21 49			
Barry Island	a						20 50															21 55			
Rhoose Cardiff Int Airport ✈	d												21 12												
Llantwit Major	d												21 22												
Bridgend	a												21 39												

For general notes see front of timetable
For details of catering facilities see Directory of Train Operators

A Until 9 February
B To Radyr

Treherbert, Aberdare, Merthyr, Pontypridd, Rhymney and Coryton → Cardiff, Penarth, Barry, Barry Island and Bridgend

Network Diagram - see first page of Table 130

Station		AW A	AW		AW	AW	AW	AW	AW		AW	AW	AW	AW	AW	AW	AW	AW	AW	AW	AW	AW	AW	AW		
Treherbert	d					20 47										21 47										
Ynyswen	d					20 49										21 49										
Treorchy	d					20 51										21 51										
Ton Pentre	d					20 53										21 53										
Ystrad Rhondda	a					20 56										21 56										
	d					20 58										21 58										
Llwynypia	d					21 00										22 00										
Tonypandy	d					21 03										22 03										
Dinas Rhondda	d					21 05										22 05										
Porth	d					21 09										22 09										
Trehafod	d					21 12										22 12										
Merthyr Tydfil	d		20 39												21 39								22 39			
Pentre-bach	d		20 43												21 43								22 43			
Troed Y Rhiw	d		20 46												21 46								22 46			
Merthyr Vale	d		20 50												21 50								22 50			
Quakers Yard	d		20 55												21 55								22 55			
Abercynon South	d		20 59												21 59								22 59			
Aberdare 3	d											21 22						21 52								
Cwmbach	d											21 25						21 55								
Fernhill	d											21 28						21 58								
Mountain Ash	a											21 31						22 01								
	d											21 34						22 04								
Penrhiwceiber	d											21 37						22 07								
Abercynon North	d											21 45						22 15								
Pontypridd 3	a		21 07			21 17						21 53			22 07		22 17	22 23					23 07			
	d		21 09			21 18						21 54			22 09		22 18	22 24					23 09			
Trefforest	d		21 12			21 21						21 57			22 12		22 21	22 27					23 12			
Trefforest Estate	d		21 16												22 16											
Taffs Well 3	d		21 20			21 28						22 04			22 20		22 28	22 34					23 20			
Radyr 3	a		21 23			21 31						22 07			22 23		22 31	22 37					23 23			
	d		21 23			21 31					22 04	22 07			22 23		22 31	22 37					23 23			
Danescourt	d										22 08															
Fairwater	d										22 10															
Waun-gron Park	d										22 12															
Ninian Park	d										22 15															
Llandaf	d		21 26			21 34						22 10			22 26		22 34	22 40					23 26			
Cathays	d		21 31			21 39						22 15			22 31		22 39	22 45					23 31			
Rhymney 3	d			20 48									21 33													
Pontlottyn	d			20 51									21 36													
Tir-phil	d			20 55									21 40													
Brithdir	d			20 58									21 43													
Bargoed	d			21 02									21 47													
Gilfach Fargoed	d			21 04									21 49													
Pengam	d			21 07									21 52													
Hengoed	d			21 10									21 55													
Ystrad Mynach 3	d			21 13									21 58													
Llanbradach	d			21 18									22 03													
Aber	d			21 22									22 07													
Caerphilly 3	d			21 25			21 40						22 10													
Lisvane & Thornhill	d			21 29			21 45						22 14													
Llanishen	d			21 31			21 47						22 16													
Heath High Level	d			21 34			21 49						22 19													
Coryton	d	21 15																								
Whitchurch (Cardiff)	d	21 16																								
Rhiwbina	d	21 18																								
Birchgrove	d	21 20																								
Ty Glas	d	21 21																								
Heath Low Level	d	21 24																								
Cardiff Queen Street 3	a	21 29	21 34	21 42		21 47	21 54					22 19	22 24		22 34		22 44	22 49					23 34			
	d	21 31	21 36	21 44	21 42	21 49	21 56	21 57	22 12			22 21	22 26	22 27	22 36	22 42	22 46	22 51	22 57	23 12		23 27	23 36	23 42		
Cardiff Bay	a				21 46			22 01	22 16					22 31		22 46			23 01	23 16		23 31		23 46		
Cardiff Central 7	a	21 34	21 39	21 47		21 52	22 00				22 22	22 24	22 29		22 42		22 52	22 57					23 42			
	d		21 41				22 01					22 25	22 31				23 12				23 30					
Grangetown	d		21 45				22 05					22 29	22 35				23 16				23 34					
Dingle Road	d						22 11						22 41				23 20									
Penarth	a						22 16						22 46				23 25									
Cogan	d		21 48									22 33									23 37					
Eastbrook	d		21 51									22 35									23 40					
Dinas Powys	d		21 53									22 37									23 42					
Cadoxton	d		21 57									22 42									23 46					
Barry Docks	d		22 00									22 45									23 49					
Barry 3	d		22 05									22 49									23 54					
Barry Island	a											22 55									23 59					
Rhoose Cardiff Int Airport ✈	d		22 12																							
Llantwit Major	d		22 22																							
Bridgend	a		22 39																							

For general notes see front of timetable
For details of catering facilities see Directory of Train Operators

A To Radyr

Table 130

Sundays

Treherbert, Aberdare, Merthyr, Pontypridd, Rhymney and Coryton → Cardiff, Penarth, Barry, Barry Island and Bridgend

Network Diagram - see first page of Table 130

		AW	AW	AW	AW	AW	AW	AW		AW	AW	AW	AW	AW	AW	AW		AW	AW	AW	AW	AW	AW	AW		AW
Treherbert	d			08 17								10 17														
Ynyswen	d			08 19								10 19														
Treorchy	d			08 21								10 21														
Ton Pentre	d			08 23								10 23														
Ystrad Rhondda	a			08 26								10 26														
	d			08 28								10 28														
Llwynypia	d			08 30								10 30														
Tonypandy	d			08 33								10 33														
Dinas Rhondda	d			08 35								10 35														
Porth	d			08 39								10 39														
Trehafod	d			08 42								10 42														
Merthyr Tydfil	d						09 39															11 39				
Pentre-bach	d						09 43															11 43				
Troed Y Rhiw	d						09 46															11 46				
Merthyr Vale	d						09 50															11 50				
Quakers Yard	d						09 55															11 55				
Abercynon South	d						09 59															11 59				
Aberdare 3	d							09 52							10 52											
Cwmbach	d							09 55							10 55											
Fernhill	d							09 58							10 58											
Mountain Ash	a							10 01							11 01											
	d							10 04							11 04											
Penrhiwceiber	d							10 07							11 07											
Abercynon North	d							10 15							11 15											
Pontypridd 3	a			08 47			10 07	10 23				10 47			11 23							12 07				
	d			08 48			10 09	10 24				10 48			11 24							12 09				
Trefforest	d			08 51			10 12	10 27				10 51			11 27							12 12				
Trefforest Estate	d																									
Taffs Well 3	d			08 58			10 20	10 34				10 58			11 34							12 20				
Radyr 3	a			09 01			10 23	10 37				11 01			11 37							12 23				
	d			09 01			10 23	10 37				11 01			11 37							12 23				
Danescourt	d																									
Fairwater	d																									
Waun-gron Park	d																									
Ninian Park	d																									
Llandaf	d			09 04			10 26	10 40				11 04			11 40							12 26				
Cathays	d			09 09			10 31	10 45				11 09			11 45							12 31				
Rhymney 3	d					09 29														11 29						
Pontlottyn	d					09 32														11 32						
Tir-phil	d					09 36														11 36						
Brithdir	d					09 39														11 39						
Bargoed	d					09b47														11c47						
Gilfach Fargoed	d					09 49														11 49						
Pengam	d					09 52														11 52						
Hengoed	d					09 55														11 55						
Ystrad Mynach 3	d					09 58														11 58						
Llanbradach	d					10 03														12 03						
Aber	d					10 07														12 07						
Caerphilly 3	d					10 10														12 10						
Lisvane & Thornhill	d					10 14														12 14						
Llanishen	d					10 16														12 16						
Heath High Level	d					10 19														12 19						
Coryton	d																									
Whitchurch (Cardiff)	d																									
Rhiwbina	d																									
Birchgrove	d																									
Ty Glas	d																									
Heath Low Level	d																									
Cardiff Queen Street 3	a			09 14		10 24	10 34	10 49				11 14			11 49					12 24		12 34				
	d			09 16		10 26	10 36	10 51		10 57	11 12	11 16	11 27	11 42	11 51	11 57		12 12		12 26	12 27	12 36	12 42			12 57
Cardiff Bay	a									11 01	11 16		11 31	11 46		12 01		12 16			12 31		12 46			13 01
Cardiff Central 7	a			09 19		10 29	10 39	10 54				11 19			11 57					12 29		12 39				
	d	08 25	08 41	09 25	10 25	10 31	10 41	10 55				11 25							12 25	12 31		12 41		12 55		
Grangetown	d	08 29	08 45	09 29	10 29	10 35	10 45	10 59				11 29							12 29	12 35		12 45		12 59		
Dingle Road	d					10 41														12 41						
Penarth	a					10 46														12 46						
Cogan	d	08 33	08 49	09 33	10 33		10 48	11 03				11 33							12 33			12 48		13 03		
Eastbrook	d	08 35	08 51	09 35	10 35		10 51	11 05				11 35							12 35			12 51		13 05		
Dinas Powys	d	08 37	08 53	09 37	10 37		10 53	11 07				11 37							12 37			12 53		13 07		
Cadoxton	d	08 42	08 58	09 42	10 42		10 57	11 12				11 42							12 42			12 57		13 12		
Barry Docks	d	08 45	09 01	09 45	10 45		11 00	11 15				11 45							12 45			13 00		13 15		
Barry 3	d	08 49	09 05	09 49	10 49		11 05	11 19				11 49							12 49			13 05		13 19		
Barry Island	a	08 55		09 55	10 55			11 25				11 55							12 55					13 25		
Rhoose Cardiff Int Airport ✈	d		09 12				11 12															13 12				
Llantwit Major	d		09 22				11 22															13 22				
Bridgend	a		09 39				11 39															13 39				

For general notes see front of timetable
For details of catering facilities see Directory of Train Operators

b Arr. 0942
c Arr. 1142

Table 130

Sundays

Treherbert, Aberdare, Merthyr, Pontypridd, Rhymney and Coryton → Cardiff, Penarth, Barry, Barry Island and Bridgend

Network Diagram - see first page of Table 130

		AW	AW	AW	AW	AW	AW	AW		AW	AW	AW	AW	AW	AW	AW		AW	AW	AW	AW	AW	AW	AW		AW
Treherbert	d		12 17																14 17							
Ynyswen	d		12 19																14 19							
Treorchy	d		12 21																14 21							
Ton Pentre	d		12 23																14 23							
Ystrad Rhondda	a		12 26																14 26							
	d		12 28																14 28							
Llwynypia	d		12 30																14 30							
Tonypandy	d		12 33																14 33							
Dinas Rhondda	d		12 35																14 35							
Porth	d		12 39																14 39							
Trehafod	d		12 42																14 42							
Merthyr Tydfil	d												13 39													
Pentre-bach	d												13 43													
Troed Y Rhiw	d												13 46													
Merthyr Vale	d												13 50													
Quakers Yard	d												13 55													
Abercynon South	d												13 59													
Aberdare 3	d					12 52																14 52				
Cwmbach	d					12 55																14 55				
Fernhill	d					12 58																14 58				
Mountain Ash	a					13 01																15 01				
	d					13 04																15 04				
Penrhiwceiber	d					13 07																15 07				
Abercynon North	d					13 15																15 15				
Pontypridd 3	a		12 47			13 23							14 07						14 47			15 23				
	d		12 48			13 24							14 09						14 48			15 24				
Trefforest	d		12 51			13 27							14 12						14 51			15 27				
Trefforest Estate	d																									
Taffs Well 3	d		12 58			13 34							14 20						14 58			15 34				
Radyr 3	a		13 01			13 37							14 23						15 01			15 37				
	d		13 01			13 37							14 23						15 01			15 37				
Danescourt	d																									
Fairwater	d																									
Waun-gron Park	d																									
Ninian Park	d																									
Llandaf	d		13 04			13 40							14 26						15 04			15 40				
Cathays	d		13 09			13 45							14 31						15 09			15 45				
Rhymney 3	d										13 29															
Pontlottyn	d										13 32															
Tir-phil	d										13 36															
Brithdir	d										13 39															
Bargoed	d										13b47															
Gilfach Fargoed	d										13 49															
Pengam	d										13 52															
Hengoed	d										13 55															
Ystrad Mynach 3	d										13 58															
Llanbradach	d										14 03															
Aber	d										14 07															
Caerphilly 3	d										14 10															
Lisvane & Thornhill	d										14 14															
Llanishen	d										14 16															
Heath High Level	d										14 19															
Coryton	d																									
Whitchurch (Cardiff)	d																									
Rhiwbina	d																									
Birchgrove	d																									
Ty Glas	d																									
Heath Low Level	d																									
Cardiff Queen Street 3	a		13 14			13 49					14 24		14 34						15 14			15 49				
	d	13 12	13 16	13 27	13 42	13 51	13 57	14 12			14 26	14 27	14 36	14 42		14 57		15 12	15 16	15 27	15 42	15 51	15 57	16 12		
Cardiff Bay	a	13 16		13 31	13 46		14 01	14 16				14 31		14 46		15 01		15 16		15 31	15 46		16 01	16 16		
Cardiff Central 7	a		13 19			13 57					14 29		14 39						15 19			15 57				
	d		13 25							14 25	14 31		14 41		14 55				15 25							16 25
Grangetown	d		13 29							14 29	14 35		14 45		14 59				15 29							16 29
Dingle Road	d										14 41															
Penarth	a										14 46															
Cogan	d		13 33							14 33			14 48		15 03				15 33							16 33
Eastbrook	d		13 35							14 35			14 51		15 05				15 35							16 35
Dinas Powys	d		13 37							14 37			14 53		15 07				15 37							16 37
Cadoxton	d		13 42							14 42			14 57		15 12				15 42							16 42
Barry Docks	d		13 45							14 45			15 00		15 15				15 45							16 45
Barry 3	d		13 49							14 49			15 05		15 19				15 49							16 49
Barry Island	a		13 55							14 55					15 25				15 55							16 55
Rhoose Cardiff Int Airport ✈	d												15 12													
Llantwit Major	d												15 22													
Bridgend	a												15 39													

For general notes see front of timetable
For details of catering facilities see
Directory of Train Operators

b Arr. 1342

Table 130

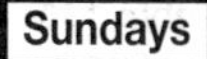

Treherbert, Aberdare, Merthyr, Pontypridd, Rhymney and Coryton → Cardiff, Penarth, Barry, Barry Island and Bridgend

Network Diagram - see first page of Table 130

		AW	AW	AW	AW	AW	AW	AW	AW	AW	AW	AW	AW	AW	AW	AW	AW	AW	AW	AW	AW	AW
					A																	
Treherbert	d						16 17						18 17						20 17			
Ynyswen	d						16 19						18 19						20 19			
Treorchy	d						16 21						18 21						20 21			
Ton Pentre	d						16 23						18 23						20 23			
Ystrad Rhondda	a						16 26						18 26						20 26			
	d						16 28						18 28						20 28			
Llwynypia	d						16 30						18 30						20 30			
Tonypandy	d						16 33						18 33						20 33			
Dinas Rhondda	d						16 35						18 35						20 35			
Porth	d						16 39						18 39						20 39			
Trehafod	d						16 42						18 42						20 42			
Merthyr Tydfil	d			15 39							17 39						19 39					21 39
Pentre-bach	d			15 42							17 43						19 43					21 43
Troed Y Rhiw	d			15 46							17 46						19 46					21 46
Merthyr Vale	d			15 50							17 50						19 50					21 50
Quakers Yard	d			15 55							17 55						19 55					21 55
Abercynon South	d			15 59							17 59						19 59					21 59
Aberdare 3	d							16 52						18 52						20 52		
Cwmbach	d							16 55						18 55						20 55		
Fernhill	d							16 58						18 58						20 58		
Mountain Ash	a							17 01						19 01						21 01		
	d							17 04						19 03						21 04		
Penrhiwceiber	d							17 07						19 07						21 07		
Abercynon North	d							17 15						19 15						21 15		
Pontypridd 3	a			16 07			16 47	17 23			18 08		18 47	19 23			20 07		20 47	21 23		22 07
	d			16 09			16 48	17 24			18 09		18 48	19 24			20 09		20 48	21 24		22 09
Trefforest	d			16 12			16 51	17 27			18 12		18 51	19 27			20 12		20 51	21 27		22 12
Trefforest Estate	d																					
Taffs Well 3	d			16 20			16 58	17 34			18 20		18 58	19 34			20 20		20 58	21 34		22 20
Radyr 3	a			16 23			17 01	17 37			18 23		19 01	19 37			20 23		21 01	21 37		22 23
	d			16 23			17 01	17 37			18 23		19 01	19 37			20 23		21 01	21 37		22 23
Danescourt	d																					
Fairwater	d																					
Waun-gron Park	d																					
Ninian Park	d																					
Llandaf	d			16 26			17 04	17 40			18 26		19 04	19 40			20 26		21 04	21 40		22 26
Cathays	d			16 31			17 09	17 45			18 31		19 09	19 45			20 31		21 09	21 45		22 31
Rhymney 3	d	15 29								17 29						19 29						
Pontlottyn	d	15 32								17 32						19 32						
Tir-phil	d	15 36								17 36						19 36						
Brithdir	d	15 39								17 39						19 39						
Bargoed	d	15b47								17c47						19e47						
Gilfach Fargoed	d	15 49								17 49						19 49						
Pengam	d	15 52								17 52						19 52						
Hengoed	d	15 55								17 55						19 55						
Ystrad Mynach 3	d	15 58								17 58						19 58						
Llanbradach	d	16 03								18 03						20 03						
Aber	d	16 07								18 07						20 07						
Caerphilly 3	d	16 10								18 10						20 10						
Lisvane & Thornhill	d	16 14								18 14						20 14						
Llanishen	d	16 16								18 16						20 16						
Heath High Level	d	16 19								18 19						20 19						
Coryton	d																					
Whitchurch (Cardiff)	d																					
Rhiwbina	d																					
Birchgrove	d																					
Ty Glas	d																					
Heath Low Level	d																					
Cardiff Queen Street 3	a	16 24		16 34			17 14	17 49		18 24	18 34		19 14	19 49		20 24	20 34		21 14	21 49		22 34
	d	16 26	16 27	16 36	16 40		17 16	17 51		18 26	18 36		19 16	19 51		20 26	20 36		21 16	21 51		22 36
Cardiff Bay	a		16 31																			
Cardiff Central 7	a	16 29		16 39	16 44		17 19	17 57		18 29	18 39		19 19	19 54		20 30	20 39		21 19	21 57		22 42
	d	16 31		16 41		16 55	17 25		18 25	18 31	18 41	18 55	19 25	19 55	20 25	20 31	20 41	20 55	21 25		22 25	
Grangetown	d	16 35		16 45		16 59	17 29		18 29	18 35	18 45	18 59	19 29	19 59	20 29	20 35	20 45	20 59	21 29		22 29	
Dingle Road	d	16 41								18 41						20 41						
Penarth	a	16 46								18 46						20 46						
Cogan	d			16 48		17 03	17 33		18 33		18 48	19 03	19 33	20 03	20 33		20 48	21 03	21 33		22 33	
Eastbrook	d			16 51		17 05	17 35		18 35		18 51	19 05	19 35	20 05	20 35		20 51	21 05	21 35		22 35	
Dinas Powys	d			16 53		17 07	17 37		18 37		18 53	19 07	19 37	20 07	20 37		20 53	21 07	21 37		22 37	
Cadoxton	d			16 57		17 12	17 42		18 42		18 57	19 12	19 42	20 12	20 42		20 57	21 12	21 42		22 42	
Barry Docks	d			17 00		17 15	17 45		18 45		19 00	19 15	19 45	20 15	20 45		21 00	21 15	21 45		22 45	
Barry 3	d			17 05		17 19	17 49		18 49		19 05	19 19	19 49	20 19	20 49		21 05	21 19	21 49		22 49	
Barry Island	a					17 25	17 55		18 55			19 25	19 55	20 25	20 55			21 25	21 55		22 55	
Rhoose Cardiff Int Airport ✈	d			17 12							19 12						21 12					
Llantwit Major	d			17 22							19 22						21 22					
Bridgend	a			17 39							19 39						21 39					

For general notes see front of timetable
For details of catering facilities see Directory of Train Operators

A From Cardiff Bay
b Arr. 1542
c Arr. 1742
e Arr. 1942

Bridgend, Barry Island, Barry, Penarth and Cardiff → Coryton. Rhymney, Pontypridd, Merthyr, Aberdare and Treherbert

Network Diagram - see first page of Table 130

Miles	Miles	Miles	Miles	Miles			AW	AW	AW	AW	AW	AW	AW	AW	AW	AW	AW	AW	AW	AW	AW	AW A	AW	AW	AW	AW B
—	—	0	—	—	**Bridgend**	d									05 42											
—	—	9¼	—	—	Llantwit Major	d									05 56											
—	—	15¾	—	—	Rhoose Cardiff Int Airport ✈	d									06 06											
0	—	—	—	—	**Barry Island**	d							05 56						06 26							
¾	—	19	—	—	**Barry** 3	d							06 00		06 15				06 30							
2	—	—	—	—	Barry Docks	d							06 04		06 19				06 34							
2¾	—	—	—	—	Cadoxton	d							06 07		06 22				06 37							
4¾	—	—	—	—	Dinas Powys	d							06 11		06 26				06 41							
5¾	—	—	—	—	Eastbrook	d							06 13		06 28				06 43							
6½	—	—	—	—	Cogan	d							06 15		06 30				06 45							
—	0	—	—	—	**Penarth**	d										06 32								07 02		
—	¼	—	—	—	Dingle Road	d										06 34								07 04		
8¼	2¾	—	—	—	Grangetown	d							06 19		06 34	06 38			06 49					07 08		
9¼	3¾	—	—	—	**Cardiff Central** 7	a							06 24		06 39	06 44			06 54					07 14		
—	—	—	0	—		d	05 26	05 46		06 11	06 16	06 21	06 26	06 36	06 41	06 46		06 51	06 56		07 06	07 06	07 11	07 16		07 21
—	—	0	—	—	**Cardiff Bay**	d											06 49			07 04					07 19	
9¾	4¼	1	—	—	**Cardiff Queen Street** 3	a	05 29	05 49		06 14	06 19	06 24	06 29	06 39	06 44	06 49	06 53	06 54	06 59	07 08	07 09		07 14	07 19	07 23	07 24
—	—	—	—	—		d	05 30	05 50		06 15	06 20	06 25	06 30	06 40	06 45	06 50		06 55	07 00		07 10		07 15	07 20		07 25
—	—	3½	—	—	Heath Low Level	d						06 30						07 00								07 30
—	—	4¼	—	—	Ty Glas	d						06 33						07 03								07 33
—	—	4¾	—	—	Birchgrove	d						06 34						07 04								07 34
—	—	5¼	—	—	Rhiwbina	d						06 36						07 06								07 36
—	—	5½	—	—	Whitchurch (Cardiff)	d						06 38						07 08								07 38
—	—	6	—	—	**Coryton**	a						06 43						07 13								07 43
—	6¾	—	—	—	Heath High Level	d		05 54			06 25					06 55								07 25		
—	7¾	—	—	—	Llanishen	d		05 57			06 28					06 58								07 28		
—	8¾	—	—	—	Lisvane & Thornhill	d		06 00			06 30					07 00								07 30		
—	11¼	—	—	—	Caerphilly 3	d		06a09			06 36					07 06								07 36		
—	12	—	—	—	Aber	d					06 38					07 08								07 38		
—	14	—	—	—	Llanbradach	d					06 42					07 12								07 42		
—	16¾	—	—	—	Ystrad Mynach 3	d					06 47					07 17								07 47		
—	17¾	—	—	—	Hengoed	d					06 50					07 20								07 50		
—	19½	—	—	—	Pengam	d					06 53					07 23								07 53		
—	20½	—	—	—	Gilfach Fargoed	d																				
—	21	—	—	—	Bargoed	d					07a01					07a31								08a01		
—	22½	—	—	—	Brithdir	d																				
—	23½	—	—	—	Tir-phil	d																				
—	26	—	—	—	Pontlottyn	d																				
—	27	—	—	—	**Rhymney** 3	a																				
10½	—	—	—	—	Cathays	d	05 33			06 18			06 33	06 43	06 48				07 03		07 13		07 18			
13	—	—	—	—	Llandaf	d	05 37			06 22			06 37	06 47	06 52				07 07		07 17		07 22			
—	—	—	1	—	Ninian Park	d																07 10				
—	—	—	2½	—	Waun-gron Park	d																07 13				
—	—	—	3	—	Fairwater	d																07 15				
—	—	—	3½	—	Danescourt	d																07 17				
14	—	—	4¾	—	Radyr 3	a	05 40			06 24			06 40	06 50	06 54				07 10		07 20	07 24	07 25			
—	—	—	—	—		d	05 40			06 24			06 40	06 50	06 55				07 10		07 20		07 25			
16	—	—	—	—	Taffs Well 3	d	05 44			06 28			06 44	06 54	06 59				07 14		07 24		07 29			
18¼	—	—	—	—	Trefforest Estate	d	05 48						06 48						07 18							
20¾	—	—	—	—	Trefforest	d	05 52			06 35			06 52	07 01	07 06				07 22		07 31		07 36			
21¾	—	0	—	0	**Pontypridd** 3	a	05 56			06 38			06 56	07 04	07 09				07 32		07 34		07 39			
—	—	—	—	—		d	05 58		06 15	06 41			06 58	07 06	07 11						07 36		07 41			
—	—	—	—	3½	Abercynon North	d			06 22	06 51					07 21								07 51			
—	—	—	—	6	Penrhiwceiber	d			06 27	06 57					07 27								07 57			
—	—	—	—	7¼	Mountain Ash	a			06 31	07 00					07 30								08 00			
—	—	—	—	—		d			06 33	07 03					07 33								08 03			
—	—	—	—	8¼	Fernhill	d			06 36	07 05					07 35								08 05			
—	—	—	—	9½	Cwmbach	d			06 39	07 09					07 39								08 09			
—	—	—	—	11	**Aberdare** 3	a			06 47	07 16					07 46								08 16			
—	—	3½	—	—	Abercynon South	d	06 04						07 04													
—	—	4¾	—	—	Quakers Yard	d	06 08						07 08													
—	—	7	—	—	Merthyr Vale	d	06b18						07 14													
—	—	8¾	—	—	Troed Y Rhiw	d	06 21						07 17													
—	—	10	—	—	Pentre-bach	d	06 24						07 20													
—	—	11½	—	—	**Merthyr Tydfil**	a	06 32						07 28													
23½	—	—	—	—	Trehafod	d								07 11							07 41					
24¾	—	—	—	—	Porth	d								07 15							07 45					
26¼	—	—	—	—	Dinas Rhondda	d								07 19							07 49					
26¾	—	—	—	—	Tonypandy	d								07 21							07 51					
27¾	—	—	—	—	Llwynypia	d								07 23							07 53					
29	—	—	—	—	Ystrad Rhondda	a								07 26							07 56					
—	—	—	—	—		d								07 29							07 59					
29½	—	—	—	—	Ton Pentre	d								07 31							08 01					
30¾	—	—	—	—	Treorchy	d								07 34							08 04					
31¾	—	—	—	—	Ynyswen	d								07 37							08 07					
32¼	—	—	—	—	**Treherbert**	a								07 43							08 13					

For general notes see front of timetable
For details of catering facilities see Directory of Train Operators

A From Coryton
B From Taffs Well
b Arr. 0613

Bridgend, Barry Island, Barry, Penarth and Cardiff → Coryton. Rhymney, Pontypridd, Merthyr, Aberdare and Treherbert

Network Diagram - see first page of Table 130

		AW	AW	AW	AW	AW A	AW	AW	AW	AW B	AW	AW		AW	AW	AW A	AW	AW	AW	AW B	AW	AW	AW	AW	AW A	AW
Bridgend	d						06 42																			07 42
Llantwit Major	d						06 56																			07 56
Rhoose Cardiff Int Airport ✈	d						07 06																			08 06
Barry Island	d	06 56									07 26						07 41				07 56					
Barry 3	d	07 00					07 15				07 30						07 45				08 00					08 15
Barry Docks	d	07 04					07 19				07 34						07 49				08 04					08 19
Cadoxton	d	07 07					07 22				07 37						07 52				08 07					08 22
Dinas Powys	d	07 11					07 26				07 41						07 56				08 11					08 26
Eastbrook	d	07 13					07 28				07 43						07 58				08 13					08 28
Cogan	d	07 15					07 30				07 45						08 00				08 15					08 30
Penarth	d		07 17					07 32				07 47						08 02				08 17				
Dingle Road	d		07 19					07 34				07 49						08 04				08 19				
Grangetown	d	07 19	07 23				07 34	07 38			07 49	07 53					08 04	08 08			08 19	08 23				08 34
Cardiff Central 7	a	07 24	07 29				07 39	07 44			07 55	07 59					08 09	08 14			08 24	08 29				08 39
	d	07 26	07 31		07 36	07 36	07 41	07 46		07 51	07 56	08 01			08 06	08 06	08 11	08 16		08 21	08 26	08 31		08 36	08 36	08 41
Cardiff Bay	d			07 34					07 49					08 04					08 19				08 34			
Cardiff Queen Street 3	a	07 29	07 34	07 38	07 39		07 44	07 49	07 53	07 54	08 00	08 04		08 08	08 09		08 14	08 19	08 23	08 24	08 29	08 34	08 38	08 39		08 44
	d	07 30	07 35		07 40		07 45	07 50		07 55	08 00	08 05			08 10		08 15	08 20		08 25	08 30	08 35		08 40		08 45
Heath Low Level	d									08 00										08 30						
Ty Glas	d									08 03										08 33						
Birchgrove	d									08 04										08 34						
Rhiwbina	d									08 06										08 36						
Whitchurch (Cardiff)	d									08 08										08 38						
Coryton	a									08 13										08 43						
Heath High Level	d		07 40					07 55				08 10						08 25				08 40				
Llanishen	d		07 43					07 58				08 13						08 28				08 43				
Lisvane & Thornhill	d		07 45					08 00				08 15						08 30				08 45				
Caerphilly 3	d		07 51					08 06				08 21						08 36				08 51				
Aber	d		07 53					08 08				08 23						08 38				08 53				
Llanbradach	d		07 57					08 12				08 27						08 42				08 57				
Ystrad Mynach 3	d		08 02					08 17				08 32						08 47				09 02				
Hengoed	d		08 05					08 20				08 35						08 50				09 05				
Pengam	d		08 08					08 23				08 38						08 53				09 08				
Gilfach Fargoed	d											08 41														
Bargoed	d		08 14					08a31				08a48						08 59				09a16				
Brithdir	d		08 18															09 03								
Tir-phil	d		08 21															09 06								
Pontlottyn	d		08 25															09 10								
Rhymney 3	a		08 31															09 16								
Cathays	d	07 33			07 43		07 48				08 03				08 13		08 18				08 33			08 43		08 48
Llandaf	d	07 37			07 47		07 52				08 07				08 17		08 22				08 37			08 47		08 52
Ninian Park	d					07 40										08 10									08 40	
Waun-gron Park	d					07 43										08 13									08 43	
Fairwater	d					07 45										08 15									08 45	
Danescourt	d					07 47										08 17									08 47	
Radyr 3	a	07 40			07 50	07 54	07 55				08 10				08 20	08 24	08 25				08 40			08 50	08 54	08 55
	d	07 40			07 50		07 55				08 10				08 20		08 25				08 40			08 50		08 55
Taffs Well 3	d	07 44			07 54		07 59				08 14				08 24		08 29				08 44			08 54		08 59
Trefforest Estate	d	07 48									08 18										08 48					
Trefforest	d	07 52			08 01		08 06				08 22				08 31		08 36				08 52			09 01		09 06
Pontypridd 3	a	07 56			08 04		08 09				08 32				08 34		08 39				08 56			09 04		09 09
	d	07 58			08 06		08 11								08 36		08 41				08 58			09 06		09 11
Abercynon North	d						08 21										08 51									09 21
Penrhiwceiber	d						08 27										08 57									09 27
Mountain Ash	a						08 30										09 00									09 30
	d						08 33										09 03									09 33
Fernhill	d						08 35										09 05									09 35
Cwmbach	d						08 39										09 09									09 39
Aberdare 3	a						08 46										09 16									09 46
Abercynon South	d	08 04																			09 04					
Quakers Yard	d	08 08																			09 08					
Merthyr Vale	d	08 14																			09 14					
Troed Y Rhiw	d	08 17																			09 17					
Pentre-bach	d	08 20																			09 20					
Merthyr Tydfil	a	08 28																			09 28					
Trehafod	d				08 11										08 41									09 11		
Porth	d				08 15										08 45									09 15		
Dinas Rhondda	d				08 19										08 49									09 19		
Tonypandy	d				08 21										08 51									09 21		
Llwynypia	d				08 23										08 53									09 23		
Ystrad Rhondda	a				08 26										08 56									09 26		
	d				08 29										08 59									09 29		
Ton Pentre	d				08 31										09 01									09 31		
Treorchy	d				08 34										09 04									09 34		
Ynyswen	d				08 37										09 07									09 37		
Treherbert	a				08 43										09 13									09 43		

For general notes see front of timetable
For details of catering facilities see Directory of Train Operators

A From Coryton
B From Radyr

Bridgend, Barry Island, Barry, Penarth and Cardiff → Coryton. Rhymney, Pontypridd, Merthyr, Aberdare and Treherbert

Network Diagram - see first page of Table 130

		AW	AW	AW A	AW	AW	AW	AW	AW B	AW	AW	AW	AW A	AW	AW	AW	AW	AW B			AW	AW	AW	AW A	AW	AW
Bridgend	d																				08 42					
Llantwit Major	d																				08 56					
Rhoose Cardiff Int Airport ✈	d																				09 06					
Barry Island	d				08 26					08 41				08 56											09 26	
Barry 3	d				08 30					08 45				09 00							09 15				09 30	
Barry Docks	d				08 34					08 49				09 04							09 19				09 34	
Cadoxton	d				08 37					08 52				09 07							09 22				09 37	
Dinas Powys	d				08 41					08 56				09 11							09 26				09 41	
Eastbrook	d				08 43					08 58				09 13							09 28				09 43	
Cogan	d				08 45					09 00				09 15							09 30				09 45	
Penarth	d	08 32				08 47									09 17							09 32				09 47
Dingle Road	d	08 34				08 49									09 19							09 34				09 49
Grangetown	d	08 38			08 49	08 53				09 04				09 19	09 23						09 34	09 38			09 49	09 53
Cardiff Central 7	a	08 44			08 54	08 59				09 09				09 24	09 29						09 39	09 44			09 54	09 59
	d	08 46		08 51	08 56	09 01		09 06	09 06	09 11	09 16		09 21	09 26	09 31		09 36	09 36			09 41	09 46		09 51	09 56	10 01
Cardiff Bay	d		08 49				09 04					09 19				09 34							09 49			
Cardiff Queen Street 3	a	08 49	08 53	08 54	08 59	09 04	09 08	09 09		09 14	09 19	09 23	09 24	09 29	09 34	09 38	09 39				09 44	09 49	09 53	09 54	09 59	10 04
	d	08 50		08 55	09 00	09 05		09 10		09 15	09 20		09 25	09 30	09 35		09 40				09 45	09 50		09 55	10 00	10 05
Heath Low Level	d			09 00									09 30											10 00		
Ty Glas	d			09 03									09 33											10 03		
Birchgrove	d			09 04									09 34											10 04		
Rhiwbina	d			09 06									09 36											10 06		
Whitchurch (Cardiff)	d			09 08									09 38											10 08		
Coryton	a			09 13									09 43											10 13		
Heath High Level	d	08 55				09 10					09 25				09 40							09 55				10 10
Llanishen	d	08 58				09 13					09 28				09 43							09 58				10 13
Lisvane & Thornhill	d	09 00				09 15					09 30				09 45							10 00				10 15
Caerphilly 3	d	09 06				09 21					09 36				09 51							10 06				10 21
Aber	d	09 08				09 23					09 38				09 53							10 08				10 23
Llanbradach	d	09 12				09 27					09 42				09 57							10 12				10 27
Ystrad Mynach 3	d	09 17				09 32					09 47				10 02							10 17				10 32
Hengoed	d	09 20				09 35					09 50				10 05							10 20				10 35
Pengam	d	09 23				09 38					09 53				10 08							10 23				10 38
Gilfach Fargoed	d					09 41																				10 41
Bargoed	d	09a31				09a48					09 59				10a16							10a31				10a48
Brithdir	d										10 03															
Tir-phil	d										10 06															
Pontlottyn	d										10 10															
Rhymney 3	a										10 16															
Cathays	d				09 03			09 13		09 18				09 33			09 43				09 48				10 03	
Llandaf	d				09 07			09 17		09 22				09 37			09 47				09 52				10 07	
Ninian Park	d								09 10									09 40								
Waun-gron Park	d								09 13									09 43								
Fairwater	d								09 15									09 45								
Danescourt	d								09 17									09 47								
Radyr 3	a				09 10			09 20	09 24	09 25				09 40			09 50	09 54			09 55				10 10	
	d				09 10			09 20		09 25				09 40			09 50				09 55				10 10	
Taffs Well 3	d				09 14			09 24		09 29				09 44			09 54				09 59				10 14	
Trefforest Estate	d				09 18									09 48											10 18	
Trefforest	d				09 22			09 31		09 36				09 52			10 01				10 06				10 22	
Pontypridd 3	a				09 32			09 34		09 39				09 56			10 04				10 09				10 32	
	d							09 36		09 41				09 58			10 06				10 11					
Abercynon North	d									09 51											10 21					
Penrhiwceiber	d									09 57											10 27					
Mountain Ash	a									10 00											10 30					
	d									10 03											10 33					
Fernhill	d									10 05											10 35					
Cwmbach	d									10 09											10 39					
Aberdare 3	a									10 16											10 46					
Abercynon South	d													10 04												
Quakers Yard	d													10 08												
Merthyr Vale	d													10 14												
Troed Y Rhiw	d													10 17												
Pentre-bach	d													10 20												
Merthyr Tydfil	a													10 28												
Trehafod	d							09 41									10 11									
Porth	d							09 45									10 15									
Dinas Rhondda	d							09 49									10 19									
Tonypandy	d							09 51									10 21									
Llwynypia	d							09 53									10 23									
Ystrad Rhondda	a							09 56									10 26									
	d							09 59									10 29									
Ton Pentre	d							10 01									10 31									
Treorchy	d							10 04									10 34									
Ynyswen	d							10 07									10 37									
Treherbert	a							10 13									10 43									

For general notes see front of timetable
For details of catering facilities see Directory of Train Operators

A From Radyr
B From Coryton

Bridgend, Barry Island, Barry, Penarth and Cardiff → Coryton. Rhymney, Pontypridd, Merthyr, Aberdare and Treherbert

Network Diagram - see first page of Table 130

Station		AW	AW	AW	AW	AW	AW	AW	AW	AW	AW	AW	AW	AW	AW	AW	AW	AW	AW	AW	AW	AW	AW	AW	AW	AW
				A				B					A				B					A				B
Bridgend	d													09 42												
Llantwit Major	d													09 56												
Rhoose Cardiff Int Airport ✈	d													10 06												
Barry Island	d				09 41				09 56										10 26				10 41			
Barry 3	d				09 45				10 00					10 15					10 30				10 45			
Barry Docks	d				09 49				10 04					10 19					10 34				10 49			
Cadoxton	d				09 52				10 07					10 22					10 37				10 52			
Dinas Powys	d				09 56				10 11					10 26					10 41				10 56			
Eastbrook	d				09 58				10 13					10 28					10 43				10 58			
Cogan	d				10 00				10 15					10 30					10 45				11 00			
Penarth	d					10 02				10 17					10 32					10 47				11 02		
Dingle Road	d					10 04				10 19					10 34					10 49				11 04		
Grangetown	d				10 04	10 08			10 19	10 23				10 34	10 38				10 49	10 53			11 04	11 08		
Cardiff Central 7	a				10 09	10 14			10 24	10 29				10 43	10 44				10 54	10 59			11 10	11 14		
	d		10 06	10 06	10 11	10 16		10 21	10 26	10 31		10 36	10 36		10 46		10 51	10 51	10 56	11 01		11 06	11 11	11 16		11 21
Cardiff Bay	d	10 04					10 19				10 34					10 49					11 04				11 19	
Cardiff Queen Street 3	a	10 08	10 09		10 14	10 19	10 23	10 24	10 29	10 34	10 38	10 39			10 49	10 53	10 54		10 59	11 04	11 08		11 14	11 19	11 23	11 24
	d		10 10		10 15	10 20		10 25	10 30	10 35		10 40			10 50		10 55		11 00	11 05			11 15	11 20		11 25
Heath Low Level	d							10 30									11 00									11 30
Ty Glas	d							10 33									11 03									11 33
Birchgrove	d							10 34									11 04									11 34
Rhiwbina	d							10 36									11 06									11 36
Whitchurch (Cardiff)	d							10 38									11 08									11 38
Coryton	a							10 43									11 13									11 43
Heath High Level	d					10 25				10 40					10 55					11 10				11 25		
Llanishen	d					10 28				10 43					10 58					11 13				11 28		
Lisvane & Thornhill	d					10 30				10 45					11 00					11 15				11 30		
Caerphilly 3	d					10 36				10 51					11 06					11 21				11 36		
Aber	d					10 38				10 53					11 08					11 23				11 38		
Llanbradach	d					10 42				10 57					11 12					11 27				11 42		
Ystrad Mynach 3	d					10 47				11 02					11 17					11 32				11 47		
Hengoed	d					10 50				11 05					11 20					11 35				11 50		
Pengam	d					10 53				11 08					11 23					11 38				11 53		
Gilfach Fargoed	d																			11 41						
Bargoed	d					10 59				11a16					11a31					11a48				11 59		
Brithdir	d					11 03																		12 03		
Tir-phil	d					11 06																		12 06		
Pontlottyn	d					11 10																		12 10		
Rhymney 3	a					11 16																		12 16		
Cathays	d		10 13		10 18				10 33			10 43							11 03				11 18			
Llandaf	d		10 17		10 22				10 37			10 47							11 07				11 22			
Ninian Park	d			10 10									10 40									11 10				
Waun-gron Park	d			10 13									10 43									11 13				
Fairwater	d			10 15									10 45									11 15				
Danescourt	d			10 17									10 47									11 17				
Radyr 3	a		10 20	10 24	10 25				10 40			10 50	10 54					11 02	11 10			11 24	11 25			
	d		10 20		10 25				10 40			10 50						11 05	11 10				11 25			
Taffs Well 3	d		10 24		10 29				10 44			10 54						11 09	11 14				11 29			
Trefforest Estate	d								10 48										11 18							
Trefforest	d		10 31		10 36				10 52			11 01						11 16	11 22				11 36			
Pontypridd 3	a		10 34		10 39				10 56			11 04						11 19	11 32				11 39			
	d		10 36		10 41				10 58			11 06						11 23					11 41			
Abercynon North	d				10 51																		11 51			
Penrhiwceiber	d				10 57																		11 57			
Mountain Ash	a				11 00																		12 00			
	d				11 03																		12 03			
Fernhill	d				11 05																		12 05			
Cwmbach	d				11 09																		12 09			
Aberdare 3	a				11 16																		12 16			
Abercynon South	d								11 04																	
Quakers Yard	d								11 08																	
Merthyr Vale	d								11 14																	
Troed Y Rhiw	d								11 17																	
Pentre-bach	d								11 20																	
Merthyr Tydfil	a								11 28																	
Trehafod	d		10 41									11 11						11 28								
Porth	d		10 45									11 15						11b45								
Dinas Rhondda	d		10 49									11 19						11 49								
Tonypandy	d		10 51									11 21						11 51								
Llwynypia	d		10 53									11 23						11 53								
Ystrad Rhondda	a		10 56									11 26						11 56								
	d		10 59									11 29						11 59								
Ton Pentre	d		11 01									11 31						12 01								
Treorchy	d		11 04									11 34						12 04								
Ynyswen	d		11 07									11 37						12 07								
Treherbert	a		11 13									11 43						12 14								

For general notes see front of timetable
For details of catering facilities see Directory of Train Operators

A From Coryton
B From Radyr
b Arr. 1131

Bridgend, Barry Island, Barry, Penarth and Cardiff → Coryton. Rhymney, Pontypridd, Merthyr, Aberdare and Treherbert

Network Diagram - see first page of Table 130

		AW	AW		AW	AW	AW	AW	AW	AW	AW	AW	AW	AW	AW	AW	AW	AW	AW	AW	AW	AW	AW	AW	AW	AW
							A					B					A				B					A
Bridgend	d								10 42																	
Llantwit Major	d								10 56																	
Rhoose Cardiff Int Airport ✈	d								11 06																	
Barry Island	d	10 56											11 26					11 41				11 56				
Barry 3	d	11 00							11 15				11 30					11 45				12 00				
Barry Docks	d	11 04							11 19				11 34					11 49				12 04				
Cadoxton	d	11 07							11 22				11 37					11 52				12 07				
Dinas Powys	d	11 11							11 26				11 41					11 56				12 11				
Eastbrook	d	11 13							11 28				11 43					11 58				12 13				
Cogan	d	11 15							11 30				11 45					12 00				12 15				
Penarth	d		11 17							11 32				11 47					12 02				12 17			
Dingle Road	d		11 19							11 34				11 49					12 04				12 19			
Grangetown	d	11 19	11 23						11 34	11 38			11 49	11 53				12 04	12 08			12 19	12 23			
Cardiff Central 7	a	11 24	11 29						11 42	11 44			11 54	11 59				12 09	12 14			12 24	12 29			
	d	11 26	11 31			11 36	11 36	11 41		11 46		11 51	11 56	12 01		12 06	12 06	12 11	12 16		12 21	12 26	12 31		12 36	12 36
Cardiff Bay	d				11 34						11 49				12 04					12 19				12 34		
Cardiff Queen Street 3	a	11 29	11 34		11 38	11 39		11 44		11 49	11 53	11 54	11 59	12 04	12 08	12 09		12 14	12 19	12 23	12 24	12 29	12 34	12 38	12 39	
	d	11 30	11 35			11 40		11 45		11 50		11 55	12 00	12 05		12 10		12 15	12 20		12 25	12 30	12 35		12 40	
Heath Low Level	d											12 00									12 30					
Ty Glas	d											12 03									12 33					
Birchgrove	d											12 04									12 34					
Rhiwbina	d											12 06									12 36					
Whitchurch (Cardiff)	d											12 08									12 38					
Coryton	a											12 13									12 43					
Heath High Level	d		11 40							11 55				12 10					12 25				12 40			
Llanishen	d		11 43							11 58				12 13					12 28				12 43			
Lisvane & Thornhill	d		11 45							12 00				12 15					12 30				12 45			
Caerphilly 3	d		11 51							12 06				12 21					12 36				12 51			
Aber	d		11 53							12 08				12 23					12 38				12 53			
Llanbradach	d		11 57							12 12				12 27					12 42				12 57			
Ystrad Mynach 3	d		12 02							12 17				12 32					12 47				13 02			
Hengoed	d		12 05							12 20				12 35					12 50				13 05			
Pengam	d		12 08							12 23				12 38					12 53				13 08			
Gilfach Fargoed	d													12 41												
Bargoed	d		12a16							12a31				12a48					12 59				13a16			
Brithdir	d																		13 03							
Tir-phil	d																		13 06							
Pontlottyn	d																		13 10							
Rhymney 3	a																		13 16							
Cathays	d	11 33				11 43		11 48					12 03			12 13		12 18				12 33			12 43	
Llandaf	d	11 37				11 47		11 52					12 07			12 17		12 22				12 37			12 47	
Ninian Park	d						11 40										12 10									12 40
Waun-gron Park	d						11 43										12 13									12 43
Fairwater	d						11 45										12 15									12 45
Danescourt	d						11 47										12 17									12 47
Radyr 3	a	11 40				11 50	11 54	11 55					12 10			12 20	12 24	12 25				12 40			12 50	12 54
	d	11 40				11 50		11 55					12 10			12 20		12 25				12 40			12 50	
Taffs Well 3	d	11 44				11 54		11 59					12 14			12 24		12 29				12 44			12 54	
Trefforest Estate	d	11 48											12 18									12 48				
Trefforest	d	11 52				12 01		12 06					12 22			12 31		12 36				12 52			13 01	
Pontypridd 3	a	11 56				12 04		12 09					12 32			12 34		12 40				12 56			13 04	
	d	11 58				12 06		12 11								12 36						12 58			13 06	
Abercynon North	d							12 22																		
Penrhiwceiber	d							12 28																		
Mountain Ash	a							12 31																		
	d							12 33																		
Fernhill	d							12 35																		
Cwmbach	d							12 39																		
Aberdare 3	a							12 46																		
Abercynon South	d	12 04																				13 04				
Quakers Yard	d	12 08																				13 08				
Merthyr Vale	d	12 14																				13 14				
Troed Y Rhiw	d	12 17																				13 17				
Pentre-bach	d	12 20																				13 20				
Merthyr Tydfil	a	12 28																				13 28				
Trehafod	d					12 11										12 41									13 11	
Porth	d					12 15										12 45									13 15	
Dinas Rhondda	d					12 19										12 49									13 19	
Tonypandy	d					12 21										12 51									13 21	
Llwynypia	d					12 23										12 53									13 23	
Ystrad Rhondda	a					12 26										12 56									13 26	
	d					12 29										12 59									13 29	
Ton Pentre	d					12 31										13 01									13 31	
Treorchy	d					12 34										13 04									13 34	
Ynyswen	d					12 37										13 07									13 37	
Treherbert	a					12 43										13 13									13 43	

For general notes see front of timetable
For details of catering facilities see Directory of Train Operators

A From Coryton
B From Radyr

Bridgend, Barry Island, Barry, Penarth and Cardiff → Coryton. Rhymney, Pontypridd, Merthyr, Aberdare and Treherbert

Network Diagram - see first page of Table 130

		AW	AW	AW	AW A	AW	AW	AW	AW	AW B	AW	AW	AW	AW A	AW	AW	AW	AW	AW B	AW	AW	AW	AW A	AW	AW
Bridgend	d	11 42																		12 42					
Llantwit Major	d	11 56																		12 56					
Rhoose Cardiff Int Airport ✈	d	12 06																		13 06					
Barry Island	d					12 26					12 41				12 56									13 26	
Barry 3	d	12 15				12 30					12 45				13 00					13 15				13 30	
Barry Docks	d	12 19				12 34					12 49				13 04					13 19				13 34	
Cadoxton	d	12 22				12 37					12 52				13 07					13 22				13 37	
Dinas Powys	d	12 26				12 41					12 56				13 11					13 26				13 41	
Eastbrook	d	12 28				12 43					12 58				13 13					13 28				13 43	
Cogan	d	12 30				12 45					13 00				13 15					13 30				13 45	
Penarth	d		12 32				12 47					13 02				13 17					13 32				13 47
Dingle Road	d		12 34				12 49					13 04				13 19					13 34				13 49
Grangetown	d	12 34	12 38			12 49	12 53				13 04	13 08			13 19	13 23				13 34	13 38			13 49	13 53
Cardiff Central 7	a	12 39	12 44			12 54	12 59				13 09	13 14			13 24	13 29				13 39	13 44			13 54	13 59
	d	12 41	12 46		12 51	12 56	13 01		13 06	13 06	13 11	13 16		13 21	13 26	13 31		13 36	13 36	13 41	13 46		13 51	13 56	14 01
Cardiff Bay	d			12 49				13 04					13 19				13 34					13 49			
Cardiff Queen Street 3	a	12 44	12 49	12 53	12 54	12 59	13 04	13 08	13 09		13 14	13 19	13 23	13 24	13 29	13 34	13 38	13 39		13 44	13 49	13 53	13 54	13 59	14 04
	d	12 45	12 50		12 55	13 00	13 05		13 10		13 15	13 20		13 25	13 30	13 35		13 40		13 45	13 50		13 55	14 00	14 05
Heath Low Level	d				13 00									13 30									14 00		
Ty Glas	d				13 03									13 33									14 03		
Birchgrove	d				13 04									13 34									14 04		
Rhiwbina	d				13 06									13 36									14 06		
Whitchurch (Cardiff)	d				13 08									13 38									14 08		
Coryton	a				13 13									13 43									14 13		
Heath High Level	d		12 55				13 10					13 25				13 40					13 55				14 10
Llanishen	d		12 58				13 13					13 28				13 43					13 58				14 13
Lisvane & Thornhill	d		13 00				13 15					13 30				13 45					14 00				14 15
Caerphilly 3	d		13 06				13 21					13 36				13 51					14 06				14 21
Aber	d		13 08				13 23					13 38				13 53					14 08				14 23
Llanbradach	d		13 12				13 27					13 42				13 57					14 12				14 27
Ystrad Mynach 3	d		13 17				13 32					13 47				14 02					14 17				14 32
Hengoed	d		13 20				13 35					13 50				14 05					14 20				14 35
Pengam	d		13 23				13 38					13 53				14 08					14 23				14 38
Gilfach Fargoed	d						13 41																		14 41
Bargoed	d		13a31				13a48					13 59				14a16					14a31				14a48
Brithdir	d											14 03													
Tir-phil	d											14 06													
Pontlottyn	d											14 10													
Rhymney 3	a											14 16													
Cathays	d	12 48				13 03			13 13		13 18				13 33			13 43		13 48				14 03	
Llandaf	d	12 52				13 07			13 17		13 22				13 37			13 47		13 52				14 07	
Ninian Park	d									13 10									13 40						
Waun-gron Park	d									13 13									13 43						
Fairwater	d									13 15									13 45						
Danescourt	d									13 17									13 47						
Radyr 3	a	12 55				13 10			13 20	13 24	13 25				13 40			13 50	13 54	13 55				14 10	
	d	12 55				13 10			13 20		13 25				13 40			13 50		13 55				14 10	
Taffs Well 3	d	12 59				13 14			13 24		13 29				13 44			13 54		13 59				14 14	
Trefforest Estate	d					13 18									13 48									14 18	
Trefforest	d	13 06				13 22			13 31		13 36				13 52			14 01		14 06				14 22	
Pontypridd 3	a	13 09				13 32			13 34		13 39				13 56			14 04		14 09				14 32	
	d	13 11							13 36		13 41				13 58			14 06		14 11					
Abercynon North	d	13 21									13 51									14 21					
Penrhiwceiber	d	13 27									13 57									14 27					
Mountain Ash	a	13 30									14 00									14 30					
	d	13 33									14 03									14 33					
Fernhill	d	13 35									14 05									14 35					
Cwmbach	d	13 39									14 09									14 39					
Aberdare 3	a	13 46									14 16									14 46					
Abercynon South	d														14 04										
Quakers Yard	d														14 08										
Merthyr Vale	d														14 14										
Troed Y Rhiw	d														14 17										
Pentre-bach	d														14 20										
Merthyr Tydfil	a														14 28										
Trehafod	d								13 41									14 11							
Porth	d								13 45									14 15							
Dinas Rhondda	d								13 49									14 19							
Tonypandy	d								13 51									14 21							
Llwynypia	d								13 53									14 23							
Ystrad Rhondda	a								13 56									14 26							
	d								13 59									14 29							
Ton Pentre	d								14 01									14 31							
Treorchy	d								14 04									14 34							
Ynyswen	d								14 07									14 37							
Treherbert	a								14 13									14 43							

For general notes see front of timetable
For details of catering facilities see Directory of Train Operators

A From Radyr
B From Coryton

Bridgend, Barry Island, Barry, Penarth and Cardiff → Coryton. Rhymney, Pontypridd, Merthyr, Aberdare and Treherbert

Network Diagram - see first page of Table 130

Station		AW	AW	AW A	AW	AW	AW	AW B	AW	AW	AW	AW	AW A	AW	AW	AW	AW B		AW	AW	AW	AW	AW A	AW	AW	AW
Bridgend	d													13 42												
Llantwit Major	d													13 56												
Rhoose Cardiff Int Airport ✈	d													14 06												
Barry Island	d				13 41				13 56											14 26				14 41		
Barry 3	d				13 45				14 00					14 15						14 30				14 45		
Barry Docks	d				13 49				14 04					14 19						14 34				14 49		
Cadoxton	d				13 52				14 07					14 22						14 37				14 52		
Dinas Powys	d				13 56				14 11					14 26						14 41				14 56		
Eastbrook	d				13 58				14 13					14 28						14 43				14 58		
Cogan	d				14 00				14 15					14 30						14 45				15 00		
Penarth	d					14 02				14 17					14 32						14 47				15 02	
Dingle Road	d					14 04				14 19					14 34						14 49				15 04	
Grangetown	d				14 04	14 08			14 19	14 23				14 34	14 38					14 49	14 53			15 04	15 08	
Cardiff Central 7	a				14 09	14 14			14 24	14 29				14 39	14 44					14 54	14 59			15 09	15 14	
	d		14 06	14 06	14 11	14 16		14 21	14 26	14 31		14 36	14 36	14 41	14 46		14 51		14 51	14 56	15 01		15 06	15 11	15 16	
Cardiff Bay	d	14 04					14 19				14 34					14 49						15 04				15 19
Cardiff Queen Street 3	a	14 08	14 09		14 14	14 19	14 23	14 24	14 29	14 34	14 38	14 39		14 44	14 49	14 53	14 54			14 59	15 04	15 08		15 14	15 19	15 23
	d		14 10		14 15	14 20		14 25	14 30	14 35		14 40		14 45	14 50		14 55			15 00	15 05			15 15	15 20	
Heath Low Level	d							14 30									15 00									
Ty Glas	d							14 33									15 03									
Birchgrove	d							14 34									15 04									
Rhiwbina	d							14 36									15 06									
Whitchurch (Cardiff)	d							14 38									15 08									
Coryton	a							14 43									15 13									
Heath High Level	d					14 25				14 40					14 55						15 10				15 25	
Llanishen	d					14 28				14 43					14 58						15 13				15 28	
Lisvane & Thornhill	d					14 30				14 45					15 00						15 15				15 30	
Caerphilly 3	d					14 36				14 51					15 06						15 21				15 36	
Aber	d					14 38				14 53					15 08						15 23				15 38	
Llanbradach	d					14 42				14 57					15 12						15 27				15 42	
Ystrad Mynach 3	d					14 47				15 02					15 17						15 32				15 47	
Hengoed	d					14 50				15 05					15 20						15 35				15 50	
Pengam	d					14 53				15 08					15 23						15 38				15 53	
Gilfach Fargoed	d																				15 41					
Bargoed	d					14 59				15a16					15a31						15a48				15 59	
Brithdir	d					15 03																			16 03	
Tir-phil	d					15 06																			16 06	
Pontlottyn	d					15 10																			16 10	
Rhymney 3	a					15 16																			16 16	
Cathays	d		14 13		14 18				14 33			14 43		14 48						15 03				15 18		
Llandaf	d		14 17		14 22				14 37			14 47		14 52						15 07				15 22		
Ninian Park	d			14 10									14 40										15 10			
Waun-gron Park	d			14 13									14 43										15 13			
Fairwater	d			14 15									14 45										15 15			
Danescourt	d			14 17									14 47										15 17			
Radyr 3	a		14 20	14 24	14 25				14 40			14 50	14 54	14 55					15 02	15 10			15 24	15 25		
	d		14 20		14 25				14 40			14 50		14 55					15 02	15 10				15 25		
Taffs Well 3	d		14 24		14 29				14 44			14 54		14 59					15 06	15 14				15 29		
Trefforest Estate	d								14 48											15 18						
Trefforest	d		14 31		14 36				14 52			15 01		15 06					15 13	15 22				15 36		
Pontypridd 3	a		14 34		14 39				14 56			15 04		15 09					15 16	15 32				15 39		
	d		14 36		14 41				14 58			15 06		15 11					15 23					15 41		
Abercynon North	d				14 51									15 21										15 51		
Penrhiwceiber	d				14 57									15 27										15 57		
Mountain Ash	a				15 00									15 30										16 00		
	d				15 03									15 33										16 03		
Fernhill	d				15 05									15 35										16 05		
Cwmbach	d				15 09									15 39										16 09		
Aberdare 3	a				15 16									15 46										16 16		
Abercynon South	d								15 04																	
Quakers Yard	d								15 08																	
Merthyr Vale	d								15 14																	
Troed Y Rhiw	d								15 17																	
Pentre-bach	d								15 20																	
Merthyr Tydfil	a								15 28																	
Trehafod	d		14 41									15 11							15 28							
Porth	d		14 45									15 15							15b45							
Dinas Rhondda	d		14 49									15 19							15 49							
Tonypandy	d		14 51									15 21							15 51							
Llwynypia	d		14 53									15 23							15 53							
Ystrad Rhondda	a		14 56									15 26							15 56							
	d		14 59									15 29							15 59							
Ton Pentre	d		15 01									15 31							16 01							
Treorchy	d		15 04									15 34							16 04							
Ynyswen	d		15 07									15 37							16 07							
Treherbert	a		15 13									15 43							16 14							

For general notes see front of timetable
For details of catering facilities see
Directory of Train Operators

A From Coryton
B From Radyr
b Arr. 1531

Bridgend, Barry Island, Barry, Penarth and Cardiff → Coryton. Rhymney, Pontypridd, Merthyr, Aberdare and Treherbert

Network Diagram - see first page of Table 130

Station		AW A	AW	AW	AW	AW	AW B	AW	AW	AW	AW A	AW	AW	AW	AW	AW B	AW	AW	AW	AW A	AW	AW	AW	AW		AW B
Bridgend	d							14 42																		
Llantwit Major	d							14 56																		
Rhoose Cardiff Int Airport ✈	d							15 06																		
Barry Island	d		14 56									15 26					15 41				15 56					
Barry [3]	d		15 00					15 15				15 30					15 45				16 00					
Barry Docks	d		15 04					15 19				15 34					15 49				16 04					
Cadoxton	d		15 07					15 22				15 37					15 52				16 07					
Dinas Powys	d		15 11					15 26				15 41					15 56				16 11					
Eastbrook	d		15 13					15 28				15 43					15 58				16 13					
Cogan	d		15 15					15 30				15 45					16 00				16 15					
Penarth	d			15 17					15 32				15 47					16 02				16 17				
Dingle Road	d			15 19					15 34				15 49					16 04				16 19				
Grangetown	d		15 19	15 23				15 34	15 38			15 49	15 53				16 04	16 08			16 19	16 23				
Cardiff Central [7]	a		15 24	15 29				15 39	15 44			15 54	15 59				16 10	16 14			16 24	16 29				
	d	15 21	15 26	15 31		15 36	15 36	15 41	15 46		15 51	15 56	16 01		16 06	16 06	16 11	16 16		16 21	16 26	16 31		16 36		16 36
Cardiff Bay	d				15 34					15 49				16 04					16 19				16 34			
Cardiff Queen Street [3]	a	15 24	15 29	15 34	15 38	15 39		15 44	15 49	15 53	15 54	15 59	16 04	16 08	16 09		16 14	16 19	16 23	16 24	16 29	16 34	16 38	16 39		
	d	15 25	15 30	15 35		15 40		15 45	15 50		15 55	16 00	16 05		16 10		16 15	16 20		16 25	16 30	16 35		16 40		
Heath Low Level	d	15 30									16 00									16 30						
Ty Glas	d	15 33									16 03									16 33						
Birchgrove	d	15 34									16 04									16 34						
Rhiwbina	d	15 36									16 06									16 36						
Whitchurch (Cardiff)	d	15 38									16 08									16 38						
Coryton	a	15 43									16 13									16 43						
Heath High Level	d			15 40					15 55				16 10					16 25				16 40				
Llanishen	d			15 43					15 58				16 13					16 28				16 43				
Lisvane & Thornhill	d			15 45					16 00				16 15					16 30				16 45				
Caerphilly [3]	d			15 51					16 06				16 21					16 36				16 51				
Aber	d			15 53					16 08				16 23					16 38				16 53				
Llanbradach	d			15 57					16 12				16 27					16 42				16 57				
Ystrad Mynach [3]	d			16 02					16 17				16 32					16 47				17 02				
Hengoed	d			16 05					16 20				16 35					16 50				17 05				
Pengam	d			16 08					16 23				16 38					16 53				17 08				
Gilfach Fargoed	d												16 41													
Bargoed	d			16a16					16a31				16a48					16 59				17a16				
Brithdir	d																	17 03								
Tir-phil	d																	17 06								
Pontlottyn	d																	17 10								
Rhymney [3]	a																	17 16								
Cathays	d		15 33			15 43		15 48				16 03			16 13		16 18				16 33			16 43		
Llandaf	d		15 37			15 47		15 52				16 07			16 17		16 22				16 37			16 47		
Ninian Park	d						15 40									16 10										16 40
Waun-gron Park	d						15 43									16 13										16 43
Fairwater	d						15 45									16 15										16 45
Danescourt	d						15 47									16 17										16 47
Radyr [3]	a		15 40			15 50	15 54	15 55				16 10			16 20	16 24	16 25				16 40			16 50		16 54
	d		15 40			15 50		15 55				16 10			16 20		16 25				16 40			16 50		
Taffs Well [3]	d		15 44			15 54		15 59				16 14			16 24		16 29				16 44			16 54		
Trefforest Estate	d		15 48									16 18									16 48					
Trefforest	d		15 52			16 01		16 06				16 22			16 31		16 36				16 52			17 01		
Pontypridd [3]	a		15 56			16 04		16 09				16 32			16 34		16 39				16 56			17 04		
	d		15 58			16 06		16 11							16 36		16 41				16 58			17 06		
Abercynon North	d							16 21									16 51									
Penrhiwceiber	d							16 27									16 57									
Mountain Ash	a							16 30									17 00									
	d							16 33									17 03									
Fernhill	d							16 35									17 05									
Cwmbach	d							16 39									17 09									
Aberdare [3]	a							16 46									17 16									
Abercynon South	d		16 04																		17 04					
Quakers Yard	d		16 08																		17 08					
Merthyr Vale	d		16 14																		17 14					
Troed Y Rhiw	d		16 17																		17 17					
Pentre-bach	d		16 20																		17 20					
Merthyr Tydfil	a		16 28																		17 28					
Trehafod	d					16 11									16 41									17 11		
Porth	d					16 15									16 45									17 15		
Dinas Rhondda	d					16 19									16 49									17 19		
Tonypandy	d					16 21									16 51									17 21		
Llwynypia	d					16 23									16 53									17 23		
Ystrad Rhondda	a					16 26									16 56									17 26		
	d					16 29									16 59									17 29		
Ton Pentre	d					16 31									17 01									17 31		
Treorchy	d					16 34									17 04									17 34		
Ynyswen	d					16 37									17 07									17 37		
Treherbert	a					16 43									17 13									17 43		

For general notes see front of timetable
For details of catering facilities see Directory of Train Operators

A From Radyr
B From Coryton

Bridgend, Barry Island, Barry, Penarth and Cardiff → Coryton. Rhymney, Pontypridd, Merthyr, Aberdare and Treherbert

Network Diagram - see first page of Table 130

Station		AW	AW	AW	AW	AW	AW	AW	AW	AW	AW	AW	AW	AW	AW	AW	AW	AW	AW	AW	AW	AW	AW	AW	AW	AW
					A					B				A					B				A			
Bridgend	d	15 42																		16 42						
Llantwit Major	d	15 56																		16 56						
Rhoose Cardiff Int Airport ✈	d	16 06																		17 06						
Barry Island	d					16 26					16 41				16 56									17 26		
Barry 3	d	16 15				16 30					16 45				17 00					17 15				17 30		
Barry Docks	d	16 19				16 34					16 49				17 04					17 19				17 34		
Cadoxton	d	16 22				16 37					16 52				17 07					17 22				17 37		
Dinas Powys	d	16 26				16 41					16 56				17 11					17 26				17 41		
Eastbrook	d	16 28				16 43					16 58				17 13					17 28				17 43		
Cogan	d	16 30				16 45					17 00				17 15					17 30				17 45		
Penarth	d		16 32									17 02				17 17					17 32				17 47	
Dingle Road	d		16 34									17 04				17 19					17 34				17 49	
Grangetown	d	16 34	16 38			16 49					17 04	17 08			17 19	17 23				17 34	17 38			17 49	17 53	
Cardiff Central 7	a	16 39	16 44			16 54					17 09	17 14			17 24	17 29				17 39	17 44			17 54	17 59	
	d	16 41	16 46		16 51	16 56	17 01		17 06	17 06	17 11	17 16		17 21	17 26	17 31		17 36	17 36	17 41	17 46		17 51	17 56	18 01	
Cardiff Bay	d			16 49				17 04					17 19				17 34					17 49				18 04
Cardiff Queen Street 3	a	16 44	16 49	16 53	16 54	16 59	17 04	17 08	17 09		17 14	17 19	17 23	17 24	17 29	17 34	17 38	17 39		17 44	17 49	17 53	17 54	17 59	18 04	18 08
	d	16 45	16 50		16 55	17 00	17 05		17 10		17 15	17 20		17 25	17 30	17 35		17 40		17 45	17 50		17 55	18 00	18 05	
Heath Low Level	d				17 00									17 30									18 00			
Ty Glas	d				17 03									17 33									18 03			
Birchgrove	d				17 04									17 34									18 04			
Rhiwbina	d				17 06									17 36									18 06			
Whitchurch (Cardiff)	d				17 08									17 38									18 08			
Coryton	a				17 13									17 43									18 13			
Heath High Level	d		16 55				17 10					17 25				17 40					17 55				18 10	
Llanishen	d		16 58				17 13					17 28				17 43					17 59				18 13	
Lisvane & Thornhill	d		17 00				17 15					17 30				17 45					18 02				18 15	
Caerphilly 3	d		17 06				17 21					17 36				17 51					18 07				18 21	
Aber	d		17 08				17 23					17 38				17 53					18 10				18 23	
Llanbradach	d		17 12				17 27					17 42				17 57					18 14				18 27	
Ystrad Mynach 3	d		17 17				17 33					17 47				18 02					18 20				18 32	
Hengoed	d		17 20				17 35					17 50				18 05					18 23				18 35	
Pengam	d		17 23				17 39					17 53				18 08					18 27				18 38	
Gilfach Fargoed	d						17 42									18 11					18 30				18 41	
Bargoed	d		17a31				17 47					18a01				18 16					18b44				18a48	
Brithdir	d						17 50									18 20					18 48					
Tir-phil	d						17 53									18 23					18 51					
Pontlottyn	d						17 58									18 27					18 55					
Rhymney 3	a						18 04									18 33					19 01					
Cathays	d	16 48				17 03			17 13		17 18				17 33			17 43		17 48				18 03		
Llandaf	d	16 52				17 07			17 17		17 22				17 37			17 47		17 52				18 07		
Ninian Park	d									17 10									17 40							
Waun-gron Park	d									17 13									17 43							
Fairwater	d									17 15									17 45							
Danescourt	d									17 17									17 47							
Radyr 3	a	16 55				17 10			17 20	17 24	17 25				17 40			17 50	17 54	17 55				18 10		
	d	16 55				17 10			17 20		17 25				17 40			17 50		17 55				18 10		
Taffs Well 3	d	16 59				17 14			17 24		17 29				17 44			17 54		17 59				18 14		
Trefforest Estate	d					17 18									17 48									18 18		
Trefforest	d	17 06				17 22			17 31		17 36				17 52			18 01		18 06				18 22		
Pontypridd 3	a	17 09				17 32			17 34		17 39				17 56			18 04		18 09				18 29		
	d	17 11							17 36		17 41				17 58			18 06		18 11						
Abercynon North	d	17 21									17 51									18 21						
Penrhiwceiber	d	17 27									17 57									18 27						
Mountain Ash	a	17 30									18 00									18 30						
	d	17 33									18 03									18 33						
Fernhill	d	17 35									18 05									18 35						
Cwmbach	d	17 39									18 09									18 39						
Aberdare 3	a	17 46									18 16									18 46						
Abercynon South	d														18 04											
Quakers Yard	d														18 08											
Merthyr Vale	d														18 14											
Troed Y Rhiw	d														18 17											
Pentre-bach	d														18 20											
Merthyr Tydfil	a														18 28											
Trehafod	d								17 41									18 11								
Porth	d								17 45									18 15								
Dinas Rhondda	d								17 49									18 19								
Tonypandy	d								17 51									18 21								
Llwynypia	d								17 53									18 23								
Ystrad Rhondda	a								17 56									18 26								
	d								17 59									18 29								
Ton Pentre	d								18 01									18 31								
Treorchy	d								18 04									18 34								
Ynyswen	d								18 07									18 37								
Treherbert	a								18 13									18 43								

For general notes see front of timetable
For details of catering facilities see Directory of Train Operators

A From Radyr
B From Coryton
b Arr. 1834

Bridgend, Barry Island, Barry, Penarth and Cardiff → Coryton. Rhymney, Pontypridd, Merthyr, Aberdare and Treherbert

Network Diagram - see first page of Table 130

		AW	AW A	AW	AW	AW	AW B	AW	AW	AW	AW	AW A	AW	AW	AW	AW B	AW	AW	AW	AW	AW	AW	AW	AW	AW
Bridgend	d												17 42												
Llantwit Major	d												17 56												
Rhoose Cardiff Int Airport ✈	d												18 06												
Barry Island	d			17 41				17 56									18 26				18 41		18 56		
Barry 3	d			17 45				18 00					18 15				18 30				18 45		19 00		
Barry Docks	d			17 49				18 04					18 19				18 34				18 49		19 04		
Cadoxton	d			17 52				18 07					18 22				18 37				18 52		19 07		
Dinas Powys	d			17 56				18 11					18 26				18 41				18 56		19 11		
Eastbrook	d			17 58				18 13					18 28				18 43				18 58		19 13		
Cogan	d			18 00				18 15					18 30				18 45				19 00		19 15		
Penarth	d				18 02				18 17					18 32				18 47						19 17	
Dingle Road	d				18 04				18 19					18 34				18 49						19 19	
Grangetown	d			18 04	18 08			18 19	18 23				18 34	18 38			18 49	18 53			19 04		19 19	19 23	
Cardiff Central 7	a			18 09	18 14			18 24	18 29				18 39	18 44			18 57	18 59			19 09		19 25	19 29	
	d	18 06	18 06	18 11	18 16		18 21	18 26	18 31		18 36	18 36	18 41			18 51		19 01		19 06	19 11		19 26	19 31	
Cardiff Bay	d					18 19				18 34					18 49				19 04			19 19			19 34
Cardiff Queen Street 3	a	18 09		18 14	18 19	18 23	18 24	18 29	18 34	18 38	18 38		18 44		18 53	18 54		19 04	19 08	19 09	19 14	19 23	19 29	19 34	19 38
	d	18 10		18 15	18 20		18 25	18 30	18 35		18 40		18 50			18 55		19 05		19 10	19 15		19 30	19 35	
Heath Low Level	d						18 30									19 00									
Ty Glas	d						18 33									19 03									
Birchgrove	d						18 34									19 04									
Rhiwbina	d						18 36									19 06									
Whitchurch (Cardiff)	d						18 38									19 08									
Coryton	a						18 43									19 13									
Heath High Level	d				18 25				18 40									19 10						19 40	
Llanishen	d				18 28				18 43									19 13						19 43	
Lisvane & Thornhill	d				18 30				18 45									19 15						19 45	
Caerphilly 3	d				18 36				18 51									19a24						19 51	
Aber	d				18 38				18 53															19 53	
Llanbradach	d				18 42				18 57															19 57	
Ystrad Mynach 3	d				18a51				19 02															20 02	
Hengoed	d								19 05															20 05	
Pengam	d								19 08															20 08	
Gilfach Fargoed	d								19 11															20 11	
Bargoed	d								19 16															20 16	
Brithdir	d								19 20															20 20	
Tir-phil	d								19 23															20 23	
Pontlottyn	d								19 27															20 27	
Rhymney 3	a								19 33															20 33	
Cathays	d	18 13		18 18				18 33			18 43		18 52							19 13	19 18		19 33		
Llandaf	d	18 17		18 22				18 37			18 47		18 56							19 17	19 22		19 37		
Ninian Park	d		18 10									18 40													
Waun-gron Park	d		18 13									18 43													
Fairwater	d		18 15									18 45													
Danescourt	d		18 17									18 47													
Radyr 3	a	18 20	18 24	18 25				18 40			18 50	18 54	18 58							19 20	19 25		19 40		
	d	18 20		18 25				18 40			18 50		18 58							19 20	19 25		19 40		
Taffs Well 3	d	18 24		18 29				18 44			18 54		19 03							19 24	19 29		19 44		
Trefforest Estate	d							18 48															19 48		
Trefforest	d	18 31		18 36				18 52			19 01		19 10							19 31	19 36		19 52		
Pontypridd 3	a	18 34		18 42				18 56			19 04		19 13							19 34	19 39		19 56		
	d	18 36						18 58			19 06		19 14							19 36	19 41		19 58		
Abercynon North	d												19 21								19 51				
Penrhiwceiber	d												19 26								19 57				
Mountain Ash	a												19 30								20 00				
	d												19 33								20 03				
Fernhill	d												19 35								20 05				
Cwmbach	d												19 39								20 09				
Aberdare 3	a												19 46								20 16				
Abercynon South	d							19 04															20 04		
Quakers Yard	d							19 08															20 08		
Merthyr Vale	d							19 14															20 14		
Troed Y Rhiw	d							19 17															20 17		
Pentre-bach	d							19 20															20 20		
Merthyr Tydfil	a							19 28															20 28		
Trehafod	d	18 41									19 11									19 41					
Porth	d	18 45									19 15									19 45					
Dinas Rhondda	d	18 49									19 19									19 49					
Tonypandy	d	18 51									19 21									19 51					
Llwynypia	d	18 53									19 23									19 53					
Ystrad Rhondda	a	18 56									19 26									19 56					
	d	18 59									19 29									19 59					
Ton Pentre	d	19 01									19 31									20 01					
Treorchy	d	19 04									19 34									20 04					
Ynyswen	d	19 07									19 37									20 07					
Treherbert	a	19 13									19 43									20 13					

For general notes see front of timetable
For details of catering facilities see Directory of Train Operators

A From Coryton
B From Radyr

Bridgend, Barry Island, Barry, Penarth and Cardiff → Coryton. Rhymney, Pontypridd, Merthyr, Aberdare and Treherbert

Network Diagram - see first page of Table 130

		AW	AW	AW	AW	AW	AW	AW	AW	AW	AW	AW	AW	AW		AW	AW	AW	AW	AW	AW	AW	AW	AW	AW	AW
			A														A									
Bridgend	d			18 42														19 42								
Llantwit Major	d			18 56														19 56								
Rhoose Cardiff Int Airport ✈	d			19 06														20 06								
Barry Island	d						19 26					19 56												20 56		
Barry 3	d			19 15			19 30					20 00						20 16						21 00		
Barry Docks	d			19 19			19 34					20 04						20 19						21 04		
Cadoxton	d			19 22			19 37					20 07						20 22						21 07		
Dinas Powys	d			19 26			19 41					20 11						20 26						21 11		
Eastbrook	d			19 28			19 43					20 13						20 28						21 13		
Cogan	d			19 30			19 45					20 15						20 30						21 15		
Penarth	d							19 47					20 17								20 47					21 17
Dingle Road	d							19 49					20 19								20 49					21 19
Grangetown	d			19 34			19 49	19 53				20 19	20 23					20 34			20 53			21 19		21 23
Cardiff Central 7	a			19 43			19 56	19 59				20 24	20 29					20 40			21 00			21 25		21 33
	d	19 36	19 36			19 51		20 01		20 11		20 26	20 31			20 36	20 36	20 41		20 51	21 01			21 26	21 31	
Cardiff Bay	d				19 49				20 04		20 19			20 34					20 49			21 04	21 19			
Cardiff Queen Street 3	a	19 39			19 53	19 54		20 04	20 08	20 14	20 23	20 29	20 34	20 38		20 39		20 44	20 53	20 54	21 04	21 08	21 23	21 29	21 34	
	d	19 40				19 55		20 05		20 15		20 30	20 35			20 40		20 45		20 55	21 05			21 30	21 35	
Heath Low Level	d					20 00														21 00						
Ty Glas	d					20 03														21 03						
Birchgrove	d					20 04														21 04						
Rhiwbina	d					20 06														21 06						
Whitchurch (Cardiff)	d					20 08														21 08						
Coryton	a					20 13														21 13						
Heath High Level	d							20 10					20 40								21 10				21 40	
Llanishen	d							20 13					20 43								21 13				21 43	
Lisvane & Thornhill	d							20 15					20 45								21 15				21 45	
Caerphilly 3	d							20a28					20 51								21a28				21 51	
Aber	d												20 53												21 53	
Llanbradach	d												20 57												21 57	
Ystrad Mynach 3	d												21 02												22 02	
Hengoed	d												21 05												22 05	
Pengam	d												21 08												22 08	
Gilfach Fargoed	d												21 11												22 11	
Bargoed	d												21 16												22 16	
Brithdir	d												21 20												22 20	
Tir-phil	d												21 23												22 23	
Pontlottyn	d												21 27												22 27	
Rhymney 3	a												21 33												22 33	
Cathays	d	19 43								20 18		20 33				20 43		20 48						21 33		
Llandaf	d	19 47								20 22		20 37				20 47		20 52						21 37		
Ninian Park	d		19 40														20 40									
Waun-gron Park	d		19 43														20 43									
Fairwater	d		19 45														20 45									
Danescourt	d		19 47														20 47									
Radyr 3	a	19 50	19 54							20 25		20 40				20 50	20 54	20 55						21 40		
	d	19 50								20 25		20 40				20 50		20 55						21 40		
Taffs Well 3	d	19 54								20 29		20 44				20 54		20 59						21 44		
Trefforest Estate	d											20 48												21 48		
Trefforest	d	20 01								20 36		20 52				21 01		21 06						21 52		
Pontypridd 3	a	20 04								20 39		20 56				21 04		21 09						21 56		
	d	20 06								20 41		20 58				21 06		21 11						21 58		
Abercynon North	d									20 51								21 21								
Penrhiwceiber	d									20 57								21 27								
Mountain Ash	a									21 00								21 30								
	d									21 03								21 33								
Fernhill	d									21 05								21 35								
Cwmbach	d									21 09								21 39								
Aberdare 3	a									21 16								21 46								
Abercynon South	d											21 04												22 04		
Quakers Yard	d											21 08												22 08		
Merthyr Vale	d											21 14												22 14		
Troed Y Rhiw	d											21 17												22 17		
Pentre-bach	d											21 20												22 20		
Merthyr Tydfil	a											21 28												22 28		
Trehafod	d	20 11														21 11										
Porth	d	20 15														21 15										
Dinas Rhondda	d	20 19														21 19										
Tonypandy	d	20 21														21 21										
Llwynypia	d	20 23														21 23										
Ystrad Rhondda	a	20 26														21 26										
	d	20 29														21 29										
Ton Pentre	d	20 31														21 31										
Treorchy	d	20 34														21 34										
Ynyswen	d	20 37														21 37										
Treherbert	a	20 43														21 43										

For general notes see front of timetable
For details of catering facilities see
Directory of Train Operators

A From Coryton

Bridgend, Barry Island, Barry, Penarth and Cardiff → Coryton. Rhymney, Pontypridd, Merthyr, Aberdare and Treherbert

Network Diagram - see first page of Table 130

Station		AW	AW	AW A	AW	AW	AW	AW	AW	AW	AW	AW	AW	AW	AW	AW	AW	AW	AW	AW	AW	AW	AW	AW
Bridgend	d				20 42									21 42									22 42	
Llantwit Major	d				20 56									21 56									22 56	
Rhoose Cardiff Int Airport ✈	d				21 06									22 06									23 06	
Barry Island	d										21 56									22 56				
Barry 3	d				21 15						22 00			22 15						23 00			23 15	
Barry Docks	d				21 19						22 04			22 19						23 04			23 19	
Cadoxton	d				21 22						22 07			22 22						23 07			23 22	
Dinas Powys	d				21 26						22 11			22 26						23 11			23 26	
Eastbrook	d				21 28						22 13			22 28						23 13			23 28	
Cogan	d				21 30						22 15			22 30						23 15			23 30	
Penarth	d						21 47					22 17						22 47				23 26		
Dingle Road	d						21 49					22 19						22 49				23 28		
Grangetown	d				21 34		21 53				22 19	22 23		22 34				22 53		23 19		23 32	23 34	
Cardiff Central 7	a				21 39		21 59				22 26	22 33		22 39				23 00		23 24		23 38	23 42	
	d		21 36	21 36	21 41		22 01		22 11			22 35		22 41	22 46			23 15		23 26				
Cardiff Bay	d	21 34				21 49		22 04		22 19			22 34			22 49	23 04		23 19		23 34			23 49
Cardiff Queen Street 3	a	21 38	21 39		21 44	21 53	22 04	22 08	22 14	22 23		22 38	22 38	22 44	22 49	22 53	23 08	23 18	23 23	23 29	23 38			23 53
	d		21 40		21 45		22 05		22 15			22 39		22 45	22 50			23 19		23 30				
Heath Low Level	d																							
Ty Glas	d																							
Birchgrove	d																							
Rhiwbina	d																							
Whitchurch (Cardiff)	d																							
Coryton	a																							
Heath High Level	d						22 10					22 44						23 24						
Llanishen	d						22 13					22 47						23 27						
Lisvane & Thornhill	d						22 15					22 49						23 29						
Caerphilly 3	d						22a24					22 55						23 35						
Aber	d											22 57						23 37						
Llanbradach	d											23 01						23 41						
Ystrad Mynach 3	d											23 06						23a50						
Hengoed	d											23 09												
Pengam	d											23 12												
Gilfach Fargoed	d											23 15												
Bargoed	d											23 20												
Brithdir	d											23 24												
Tir-phil	d											23 27												
Pontlottyn	d											23 31												
Rhymney 3	a											23 37												
Cathays	d		21 43		21 48				22 18					22 48	22 53					23 33				
Llandaf	d		21 47		21 52				22 22					22 52	22 57					23 37				
Ninian Park	d			21 40																				
Waun-gron Park	d			21 43																				
Fairwater	d			21 45																				
Danescourt	d			21 47																				
Radyr 3	a		21 50	21 54	21 55				22 25					22 55	22 59					23 40				
	d		21 50		21 55				22 25					22 55	22 59					23 40				
Taffs Well 3	d		21 54		21 59				22 29					22 59	23 03					23 44				
Trefforest Estate	d																			23 48				
Trefforest	d		22 01		22 06				22 36					23 06	23 10					23 52				
Pontypridd 3	a		22 04		22 09				22 43					23 09	23 14					00 01				
	d		22 06		22 11									23 11	23 15									
Abercynon North	d				22 21									23 21										
Penrhiwceiber	d				22 27									23 27										
Mountain Ash	a				22 30									23 30										
	d				22 33									23 33										
Fernhill	d				22 35									23 35										
Cwmbach	d				22 39									23 39										
Aberdare 3	a				22 46									23 46										
Abercynon South	d																							
Quakers Yard	d																							
Merthyr Vale	d																							
Troed Y Rhiw	d																							
Pentre-bach	d																							
Merthyr Tydfil	a																							
Trehafod	d		22 11												23 20									
Porth	d		22 15												23 24									
Dinas Rhondda	d		22 19												23 28									
Tonypandy	d		22 21												23 30									
Llwynypia	d		22 23												23 32									
Ystrad Rhondda	a		22 26												23 35									
	d		22 29												23 38									
Ton Pentre	d		22 31												23 40									
Treorchy	d		22 34												23 43									
Ynyswen	d		22 37												23 46									
Treherbert	a		22 43												23 52									

For general notes see front of timetable
For details of catering facilities see Directory of Train Operators

A From Coryton

Table 130

Saturdays

Bridgend, Barry Island, Barry, Penarth and Cardiff → Coryton, Rhymney, Pontypridd, Merthyr, Aberdare and Treherbert

Network Diagram - see first page of Table 130

		AW	AW	AW	AW	AW	AW	AW	AW	AW	AW	AW	AW	AW	AW	AW	AW A	AW	AW	AW		AW B	AW	AW	AW	AW
Bridgend	d									05 42																
Llantwit Major	d									05 56																
Rhoose Cardiff Int Airport ✈	d									06 06																
Barry Island	d							05 56						06 26									06 56			
Barry 3	d							06 00		06 15				06 30									07 00			
Barry Docks	d							06 04		06 19				06 34									07 04			
Cadoxton	d							06 07		06 22				06 37									07 07			
Dinas Powys	d							06 11		06 26				06 41									07 11			
Eastbrook	d							06 13		06 28				06 43									07 13			
Cogan	d							06 15		06 30				06 45									07 15			
Penarth	d										06 32								07 02					07 17		
Dingle Road	d										06 34								07 04					07 19		
Grangetown	d							06 19		06 34	06 38			06 49					07 08				07 19	07 23		
Cardiff Central 7	a							06 24		06 39	06 44			06 54					07 14				07 24	07 29		
	d	05 26	05 46		06 11	06 16	06 21	06 26	06 36	06 41	06 46		06 51	06 56		07 06	07 06	07 11	07 16			07 21	07 26	07 31		07 36
Cardiff Bay	d											06 49			07 04					07 19					07 34	
Cardiff Queen Street 3	a	05 29	05 49		06 14	06 19	06 24	06 29	06 39	06 44	06 49	06 53	06 54	06 59	07 08	07 09		07 14	07 19	07 23		07 24	07 29	07 34	07 38	07 39
	d	05 30	05 50		06 15	06 20	06 25	06 30	06 40	06 45	06 50		06 55	07 00		07 10		07 15	07 20			07 25	07 30	07 35		07 40
Heath Low Level	d						06 30						07 00									07 30				
Ty Glas	d						06 33						07 03									07 33				
Birchgrove	d						06 34						07 04									07 34				
Rhiwbina	d						06 36						07 06									07 36				
Whitchurch (Cardiff)	d						06 38						07 08									07 38				
Coryton	a						06 43						07 13									07 43				
Heath High Level	d		05 54			06 25					06 55								07 25					07 40		
Llanishen	d		05 57			06 28					06 58								07 28					07 43		
Lisvane & Thornhill	d		06 00			06 30					07 00								07 30					07 45		
Caerphilly 3	d		06a09			06 36					07 06								07 36					07 51		
Aber	d					06 38					07 08								07 38					07 53		
Llanbradach	d					06 42					07 12								07 42					07 57		
Ystrad Mynach 3	d					06 47					07 17								07 47					08 02		
Hengoed	d					06 50					07 20								07 50					08 05		
Pengam	d					06 53					07 23								07 53					08 08		
Gilfach Fargoed	d																									
Bargoed	d					07a01					07a31								08a01					08 14		
Brithdir	d																							08 18		
Tir-phil	d																							08 21		
Pontlottyn	d																							08 25		
Rhymney 3	a																							08 31		
Cathays	d	05 33			06 18			06 33	06 43	06 48				07 03		07 13		07 18					07 33			07 43
Llandaf	d	05 37			06 22			06 37	06 47	06 52				07 07		07 17		07 22					07 37			07 47
Ninian Park	d																07 10									
Waun-gron Park	d																07 13									
Fairwater	d																07 15									
Danescourt	d																07 17									
Radyr 3	a	05 39			06 24			06 40	06 50	06 54				07 10		07 20	07 24	07 25					07 40			07 50
	d	05 40			06 24			06 40	06 50	06 55				07 10		07 20		07 25					07 40			07 50
Taffs Well 3	d	05 44			06 28			06 44	06 54	06 59				07 14		07 24		07 29					07 44			07 54
Trefforest Estate	d	05 48						06 48						07 18									07 48			
Trefforest	d	05 52			06 35			06 52	07 01	07 06				07 22		07 31		07 36					07 52			08 01
Pontypridd 3	a	05 56			06 38			06 56	07 04	07 09				07 32		07 34		07 39					07 56			08 04
	d	05 58		06 15	06 41			06 58	07 06	07 11						07 36		07 41					07 58			08 06
Abercynon North	d			06 22	06 51					07 21								07 51								
Penrhiwceiber	d			06 27	06 57					07 27								07 57								
Mountain Ash	a			06 31	07 00					07 30								08 00								
	d			06 33	07 03					07 33								08 03								
Fernhill	d			06 36	07 05					07 35								08 05								
Cwmbach	d			06 39	07 09					07 39								08 09								
Aberdare 3	a			06 47	07 16					07 46								08 16								
Abercynon South	d	06 04						07 04															08 04			
Quakers Yard	d	06 08						07 08															08 08			
Merthyr Vale	d	06b18						07 14															08 14			
Troed Y Rhiw	d	06 21						07 17															08 17			
Pentre-bach	d	06 24						07 20															08 20			
Merthyr Tydfil	a	06 32						07 28															08 28			
Trehafod	d								07 11							07 41										08 11
Porth	d								07 15							07 45										08 15
Dinas Rhondda	d								07 19							07 49										08 19
Tonypandy	d								07 21							07 51										08 21
Llwynypia	d								07 23							07 53										08 23
Ystrad Rhondda	a								07 26							07 56										08 26
	d								07 29							07 59										08 29
Ton Pentre	d								07 31							08 01										08 31
Treorchy	d								07 34							08 04										08 34
Ynyswen	d								07 37							08 07										08 37
Treherbert	a								07 43							08 13										08 43

For general notes see front of timetable
For details of catering facilities see
Directory of Train Operators

A From Coryton
B From Taffs Well
b Arr. 0613

Table 130

Saturdays

Bridgend, Barry Island, Barry, Penarth and Cardiff → Coryton, Rhymney, Pontypridd, Merthyr, Aberdare and Treherbert

Network Diagram - see first page of Table 130

		AW A	AW	AW	AW	AW B	AW	AW	AW	AW	AW A	AW	AW	AW	AW B	AW	AW		AW	AW	AW A	AW	AW	AW	AW	AW
Bridgend	d		06 42																				07 42	07 42		
Llantwit Major	d		06 56																				07 56	07 56		
Rhoose Cardiff Int Airport	d		07 06																				08 06	08 06		
Barry Island	d						07 26					07 41				07 56										
Barry 3	d		07 15				07 30					07 45				08 00							08 15	08 15		
Barry Docks	d		07 19				07 34					07 49				08 04							08 19	08 19		
Cadoxton	d		07 22				07 37					07 52				08 07							08 22	08 22		
Dinas Powys	d		07 26				07 41					07 56				08 11							08 26	08 26		
Eastbrook	d		07 28				07 43					07 58				08 13							08 28	08 28		
Cogan	d		07 30				07 45					08 00				08 15							08 30	08 30		
Penarth	d			07 32				07 47					08 02				08 17								08 32	
Dingle Road	d			07 34				07 49					08 04				08 19								08 34	
Grangetown	d		07 34	07 38			07 49	07 53				08 04	08 08			08 19	08 23						08 34	08 34	08 38	
Cardiff Central 7	a		07 39	07 44			07 55	07 59				08 09	08 14			08 24	08 29						08 39	08 39	08 44	
	d	07 36	07 41	07 46		07 51	07 56	08 01		08 06	08 06	08 11	08 16		08 21	08 26	08 31			08 36	08 36		08 41	08 41	08 46	
Cardiff Bay	d				07 49				08 04					08 19					08 34							08 49
Cardiff Queen Street 3	a		07 44	07 49	07 53	07 54	07 59	08 04	08 08	08 09		08 14	08 19	08 23	08 24	08 29	08 34		08 38	08 39			08 44	08 44	08 49	08 53
	d		07 45	07 50		07 55	08 00	08 05		08 10		08 15	08 20		08 25	08 30	08 35			08 40			08 45	08 45	08 50	
Heath Low Level	d					08 00									08 30											
Ty Glas	d					08 03									08 33											
Birchgrove	d					08 04									08 34											
Rhiwbina	d					08 06									08 36											
Whitchurch (Cardiff)	d					08 08					07 46				08 38											
Coryton	a					08 13									08 43											
Heath High Level	d			07 55				08 10					08 25				08 40								08 55	
Llanishen	d			07 58				08 13					08 28				08 43								08 58	
Lisvane & Thornhill	d			08 00				08 15					08 30				08 45								09 00	
Caerphilly 3	d			08 06				08 21					08 36				08 51								09 06	
Aber	d			08 08				08 23					08 38				08 53								09 08	
Llanbradach	d			08 12				08 27					08 42				08 57								09 12	
Ystrad Mynach 3	d			08 17				08 32					08 47				09 02								09 17	
Hengoed	d			08 20				08 35					08 50				09 05								09 20	
Pengam	d			08 23				08 38					08 53				09 08								09 23	
Gilfach Fargoed	d							08 41																		
Bargoed	d			08a31				08a48					08 59				09a16								09a31	
Brithdir	d												09 03													
Tir-phil	d												09 06													
Pontlottyn	d												09 10													
Rhymney 3	a												09 16													
Cathays	d		07 48				08 03			08 13		08 18				08 33				08 43			08 48	08 48		
Llandaf	d		07 52				08 07			08 17		08 22				08 37				08 47			08 52	08 52		
Ninian Park	d	07 40									08 10										08 40					
Waun-gron Park	d	07 43									08 13										08 43					
Fairwater	d	07 45									08 15										08 45					
Danescourt	d	07 47									08 17										08 47					
Radyr 3	a	07 54	07 55				08 10			08 20	08 24	08 25				08 40				08 50	08 54		08 55	08 55		
	d		07 55				08 10			08 20		08 25				08 40				08 50			08 55	08 55		
Taffs Well 3	d		07 59				08 14			08 24		08 29				08 44				08 54			08 59	08 59		
Trefforest Estate	d						08 18									08 48										
Trefforest	d		08 06				08 22			08 31		08 36				08 52				09 01			09 06	09 06		
Pontypridd 3	a		08 09				08 32			08 34		08 39				08 56				09 04			09 09	09 09		
	d		08 11							08 36		08 41				08 58				09 06			09 11	09 11		
Abercynon North	d		08 21									08 51											09 21			
Penrhiwceiber	d		08 27									08 57										09 07	09 27	09 27		
Mountain Ash	a		08 30									09 00											09 30	09 30		
	d		08 33									09 03											09 33	09 33		
Fernhill	d		08 35									09 05											09 35	09 35		
Cwmbach	d		08 39									09 09										08 55	09 39	09 39		
Aberdare 3	a		08 46									09 16											09 46	09 46		
Abercynon South	d															09 04						09a15				
Quakers Yard	d															09 08										
Merthyr Vale	d															09 14										
Troed Y Rhiw	d															09 17										
Pentre-bach	d															09 20										
Merthyr Tydfil	a															09 28										
Trehafod	d									08 41										09 11						
Porth	d									08 45										09 15						
Dinas Rhondda	d									08 49										09 19						
Tonypandy	d									08 51										09 21						
Llwynypia	d									08 53										09 23						
Ystrad Rhondda	a									08 56										09 26						
	d									08 59										09 29						
Ton Pentre	d									09 01										09 31						
Treorchy	d									09 04										09 34						
Ynyswen	d									09 07										09 37						
Treherbert	a									09 13										09 43						

For general notes see front of timetable
For details of catering facilities see
Directory of Train Operators

A From Coryton
B From Radyr

Table 130

Saturdays

Bridgend, Barry Island, Barry, Penarth and Cardiff → Coryton, Rhymney, Pontypridd, Merthyr, Aberdare and Treherbert

Network Diagram - see first page of Table 130

		AW A	AW	AW	AW	AW	AW B	AW	AW	AW	AW A	AW	AW	AW		AW	AW B	AW	AW	AW	AW A	AW	AW	AW	AW	AW B
Bridgend	d																	08 42								
Llantwit Major	d																	08 56								
Rhoose Cardiff Int Airport ✈	d																	09 06								
Barry Island	d		08 26					08 41				08 56										09 26				
Barry 3	d		08 30					08 45				09 00						09 15				09 30				
Barry Docks	d		08 34					08 49				09 04						09 19				09 34				
Cadoxton	d		08 37					08 52				09 07						09 22				09 37				
Dinas Powys	d		08 41					08 56				09 11						09 26				09 41				
Eastbrook	d		08 43					08 58				09 13						09 28				09 43				
Cogan	d		08 45					09 00				09 15						09 30				09 45				
Penarth	d			08 47									09 17						09 32				09 47			
Dingle Road	d			08 49									09 19						09 34				09 49			
Grangetown	d		08 49	08 53				09 04				09 19	09 23					09 34	09 38			09 49	09 53			
Cardiff Central 7	a		08 54	08 59				09 09				09 24	09 29					09 39	09 44			09 54	09 59			
	d	08 51	08 56	09 01		09 06	09 06	09 11	09 16		09 21	09 26	09 31			09 36	09 36	09 41	09 46		09 51	09 56	10 01		10 06	10 06
Cardiff Bay	d				09 04					09 19				09 34						09 49				10 04		
Cardiff Queen Street 3	a	08 54	08 59	09 04	09 08	09 09		09 14	09 19	09 23	09 24	09 29	09 34	09 38		09 39		09 44	09 49	09 53	09 54	09 59	10 04	10 08	10 09	
	d	08 55	09 00	09 05		09 10		09 15	09 20		09 25	09 30	09 35			09 40		09 45	09 50		09 55	10 00	10 05		10 10	
Heath Low Level	d	09 00									09 30										10 00					
Ty Glas	d	09 03									09 33										10 03					
Birchgrove	d	09 04									09 34										10 04					
Rhiwbina	d	09 06									09 36										10 06					
Whitchurch (Cardiff)	d	09 08									09 38										10 08					
Coryton	a	09 13									09 43										10 13					
Heath High Level	d			09 10					09 25				09 40						09 55				10 10			
Llanishen	d			09 13					09 28				09 43						09 58				10 13			
Lisvane & Thornhill	d			09 15					09 30				09 45						10 00				10 15			
Caerphilly 3	d			09 21					09 36				09 51						10 06				10 21			
Aber	d			09 23					09 38				09 53						10 08				10 23			
Llanbradach	d			09 27					09 42				09 57						10 12				10 27			
Ystrad Mynach 3	d			09 32					09 47				10 02						10 17				10 32			
Hengoed	d			09 35					09 50				10 05						10 20				10 35			
Pengam	d			09 38					09 53				10 08						10 23				10 38			
Gilfach Fargoed	d			09 41																			10 41			
Bargoed	d			09a48					09 59				10a16						10a31				10a48			
Brithdir	d								10 03																	
Tir-phil	d								10 06																	
Pontlottyn	d								10 10																	
Rhymney 3	a								10 16																	
Cathays	d		09 03			09 13		09 18				09 33				09 43		09 48				10 03			10 13	
Llandaf	d		09 07			09 17		09 22				09 37				09 47		09 52				10 07			10 17	
Ninian Park	d						09 10										09 40									10 10
Waun-gron Park	d						09 13										09 43									10 13
Fairwater	d						09 15										09 45									10 15
Danescourt	d						09 17										09 47									10 17
Radyr 3	a		09 10			09 20	09 24	09 25				09 40				09 50	09 54	09 55				10 10			10 20	10 24
	d		09 10			09 20		09 25				09 40				09 50		09 55				10 10			10 20	
Taffs Well 3	d		09 14			09 24		09 29				09 44				09 54		09 59				10 14			10 24	
Trefforest Estate	d		09 18									09 48										10 18				
Trefforest	d		09 22			09 31		09 36				09 52				10 01		10 06				10 22			10 31	
Pontypridd 3	a		09 32			09 34		09 39				09 56				10 04		10 09				10 32			10 34	
	d					09 36		09 41				09 58				10 06		10 11							10 36	
Abercynon North	d							09 51										10 21								
Penrhiwceiber	d							09 57										10 27								
Mountain Ash	a							10 00										10 30								
	d							10 03										10 33								
Fernhill	d							10 05										10 35								
Cwmbach	d							10 09										10 39								
Aberdare 3	a							10 16										10 46								
Abercynon South	d											10 04														
Quakers Yard	d											10 08														
Merthyr Vale	d											10 14														
Troed Y Rhiw	d											10 17														
Pentre-bach	d											10 20														
Merthyr Tydfil	a											10 28														
Trehafod	d					09 41										10 11									10 41	
Porth	d					09 45										10 15									10 45	
Dinas Rhondda	d					09 49										10 19									10 49	
Tonypandy	d					09 51										10 21									10 51	
Llwynypia	d					09 53										10 23									10 53	
Ystrad Rhondda	a					09 56										10 26									10 56	
	d					09 59										10 29									10 59	
Ton Pentre	d					10 01										10 31									11 01	
Treorchy	d					10 04										10 34									11 04	
Ynyswen	d					10 07										10 37									11 07	
Treherbert	a					10 13										10 43									11 13	

For general notes see front of timetable
For details of catering facilities see Directory of Train Operators

A From Radyr
B From Coryton

Table 130

Bridgend, Barry Island, Barry, Penarth and Cardiff → Coryton, Rhymney, Pontypridd, Merthyr, Aberdare and Treherbert

Network Diagram - see first page of Table 130

		AW	AW	AW	AW A	AW	AW	AW	AW	AW B	AW		AW	AW	AW A	AW	AW	AW	AW	AW B	AW	AW	AW	AW A	AW	AW
Bridgend	d										09 42															
Llantwit Major	d										09 56															
Rhoose Cardiff Int Airport ✈	d										10 06															
Barry Island	d	09 41				09 56											10 26				10 41				10 56	
Barry 3	d	09 45				10 00					10 15						10 30				10 45				11 00	
Barry Docks	d	09 49				10 04					10 19						10 34				10 49				11 04	
Cadoxton	d	09 52				10 07					10 22						10 37				10 52				11 07	
Dinas Powys	d	09 56				10 11					10 26						10 41				10 56				11 11	
Eastbrook	d	09 58				10 13					10 28						10 43				10 58				11 13	
Cogan	d	10 00				10 15					10 30						10 45				11 00				11 15	
Penarth	d		10 02				10 17						10 32					10 47				11 02				11 17
Dingle Road	d		10 04				10 19						10 34					10 49				11 04				11 19
Grangetown	d	10 04	10 08			10 19	10 23				10 34		10 38				10 49	10 53			11 04	11 08			11 19	11 23
Cardiff Central 7	a	10 09	10 14			10 24	10 29				10 42		10 44				10 54	10 59			11 09	11 14			11 24	11 29
	d	10 11	10 16		10 21	10 26	10 31		10 36	10 36			10 46		10 51	10 51	10 56	11 01		11 06	11 11	11 16		11 21	11 26	11 31
Cardiff Bay	d			10 19				10 34						10 49					11 04				11 19			
Cardiff Queen Street 3	a	10 14	10 19	10 23	10 24	10 29	10 34	10 38	10 39				10 49	10 53	10 54		10 59	11 04	11 08		11 14	11 19	11 23	11 24	11 29	11 34
	d	10 15	10 20		10 25	10 30	10 35		10 40				10 50		10 55		11 00	11 05			11 15	11 20		11 25	11 30	11 35
Heath Low Level	d				10 30										11 00									11 30		
Ty Glas	d				10 33										11 03									11 33		
Birchgrove	d				10 34										11 04									11 34		
Rhiwbina	d				10 36										11 06									11 36		
Whitchurch (Cardiff)	d				10 38										11 08									11 38		
Coryton	a				10 43										11 13									11 43		
Heath High Level	d		10 25				10 40						10 55					11 10				11 25				11 40
Llanishen	d		10 28				10 43						10 58					11 13				11 28				11 43
Lisvane & Thornhill	d		10 30				10 45						11 00					11 15				11 30				11 45
Caerphilly 3	d		10 36				10 51						11 06					11 21				11 36				11 51
Aber	d		10 38				10 53						11 08					11 23				11 38				11 53
Llanbradach	d		10 42				10 57						11 12					11 27				11 42				11 57
Ystrad Mynach 3	d		10 47				11 02						11 17					11 32				11 47				12 02
Hengoed	d		10 50				11 05						11 20					11 35				11 50				12 05
Pengam	d		10 53				11 08						11 23					11 38				11 53				12 08
Gilfach Fargoed	d																	11 41								
Bargoed	d		10 59				11a16						11a31					11a48				11 59				12a16
Brithdir	d		11 03																			12 03				
Tir-phil	d		11 06																			12 06				
Pontlottyn	d		11 10																			12 10				
Rhymney 3	a		11 16																			12 16				
Cathays	d	10 18				10 33			10 43								11 03				11 18				11 33	
Llandaf	d	10 22				10 37			10 47								11 07				11 22				11 37	
Ninian Park	d									10 40										11 10						
Waun-gron Park	d									10 43										11 13						
Fairwater	d									10 45										11 15						
Danescourt	d									10 47										11 17						
Radyr 3	a	10 25				10 40			10 50	10 54						11 02	11 10			11 24	11 25				11 40	
	d	10 25				10 40			10 50							11 05	11 10				11 25				11 40	
Taffs Well 3	d	10 29				10 44			10 54							11 09	11 14				11 29				11 44	
Trefforest Estate	d					10 48											11 18								11 48	
Trefforest	d	10 36				10 52			11 01							11 16	11 22				11 36				11 52	
Pontypridd 3	a	10 39				10 56			11 04							11 19	11 32				11 39				11 56	
	d	10 41				10 58			11 06							11 23					11 41				11 58	
Abercynon North	d	10 51																			11 51					
Penrhiwceiber	d	10 57																			11 57					
Mountain Ash	a	11 00																			12 00					
	d	11 03																			12 03					
Fernhill	d	11 05																			12 05					
Cwmbach	d	11 09																			12 09					
Aberdare 3	a	11 16																			12 16					
Abercynon South	d					11 04																			12 04	
Quakers Yard	d					11 08																			12 08	
Merthyr Vale	d					11 14																			12 14	
Troed Y Rhiw	d					11 17																			12 17	
Pentre-bach	d					11 20																			12 20	
Merthyr Tydfil	a					11 28																			12 28	
Trehafod	d								11 11							11 28										
Porth	d								11 15							11b45										
Dinas Rhondda	d								11 19							11 49										
Tonypandy	d								11 21							11 51										
Llwynypia	d								11 23							11 53										
Ystrad Rhondda	a								11 26							11 56										
	d								11 29							11 59										
Ton Pentre	d								11 31							12 01										
Treorchy	d								11 34							12 04										
Ynyswen	d								11 37							12 07										
Treherbert	a								11 43							12 14										

For general notes see front of timetable
For details of catering facilities see Directory of Train Operators

A From Radyr
B From Coryton
b Arr. 1131

Table 130

Saturdays

Bridgend, Barry Island, Barry, Penarth and Cardiff → Coryton, Rhymney, Pontypridd, Merthyr, Aberdare and Treherbert

Network Diagram - see first page of Table 130

Station		AW	AW	AW	AW	AW	AW	AW		AW	AW	AW	AW	AW	AW	AW	AW	AW	AW	AW	AW	AW	AW	AW	AW	AW
				A						B					A				B					A		
Bridgend	d					10 42																			11 42	
Llantwit Major	d					10 56																			11 56	
Rhoose Cardiff Int Airport ✈	d					11 06																			12 06	
Barry Island	d										11 26					11 41				11 56						
Barry 3	d					11 15					11 30					11 45				12 00					12 15	
Barry Docks	d					11 19					11 34					11 49				12 04					12 19	
Cadoxton	d					11 22					11 37					11 52				12 07					12 22	
Dinas Powys	d					11 26					11 41					11 56				12 11					12 26	
Eastbrook	d					11 28					11 43					11 58				12 13					12 28	
Cogan	d					11 30					11 45					12 00				12 15					12 30	
Penarth	d						11 32					11 47					12 02				12 17					12 32
Dingle Road	d						11 34					11 49					12 04				12 19					12 34
Grangetown	d					11 34	11 38				11 49	11 53				12 04	12 08			12 19	12 23				12 34	12 38
Cardiff Central 7	a					11 44	11 44				11 54	11 59				12 09	12 14			12 24	12 29				12 39	12 44
	d		11 36	11 36	11 41		11 46			11 51	11 56	12 01		12 06	12 06	12 11	12 16		12 21	12 26	12 31		12 36	12 36	12 41	12 46
Cardiff Bay	d	11 34						11 49					12 04					12 19				12 34				
Cardiff Queen Street 3	a	11 38	11 39		11 44		11 49	11 53		11 54	11 59	12 04	12 08	12 09		12 14	12 19	12 23	12 24	12 29	12 34	12 38	12 39		12 44	12 49
	d		11 40		11 45		11 50			11 55	12 00	12 05		12 10		12 15	12 20		12 25	12 30	12 35		12 40		12 45	12 50
Heath Low Level	d									12 00									12 30							
Ty Glas	d									12 03									12 33							
Birchgrove	d									12 04									12 34							
Rhiwbina	d									12 06									12 36							
Whitchurch (Cardiff)	d									12 08									12 38							
Coryton	a									12 13									12 43							
Heath High Level	d						11 55					12 10					12 25				12 40					12 55
Llanishen	d						11 58					12 13					12 28				12 43					12 58
Lisvane & Thornhill	d						12 00					12 15					12 30				12 45					13 00
Caerphilly 3	d						12 06					12 21					12 36				12 51					13 06
Aber	d						12 08					12 23					12 38				12 53					13 08
Llanbradach	d						12 12					12 27					12 42				12 57					13 12
Ystrad Mynach 3	d						12 17					12 32					12 47				13 02					13 17
Hengoed	d						12 20					12 35					12 50				13 05					13 20
Pengam	d						12 23					12 38					12 53				13 08					13 23
Gilfach Fargoed	d											12 41														
Bargoed	d						12a31					12a48					12 59				13a16					13a31
Brithdir	d																13 03									
Tir-phil	d																13 06									
Pontlottyn	d																13 10									
Rhymney 3	a																13 16									
Cathays	d		11 43		11 48						12 03			12 13		12 18				12 33			12 43		12 48	
Llandaf	d		11 47		11 52						12 07			12 17		12 22				12 37			12 47		12 52	
Ninian Park	d			11 40											12 10									12 40		
Waun-gron Park	d			11 43											12 13									12 43		
Fairwater	d			11 45											12 15									12 45		
Danescourt	d			11 47											12 17									12 47		
Radyr 3	a		11 50	11 54	11 54						12 10			12 20	12 24	12 25				12 40			12 50	12 54	12 55	
	d		11 50		11 55						12 10			12 20		12 25				12 40			12 50		12 55	
Taffs Well 3	d		11 54		11 59						12 14			12 24		12 29				12 44			12 54		12 59	
Trefforest Estate	d										12 18									12 48						
Trefforest	d		12 01		12 06						12 22			12 31		12 36				12 52			13 01		13 06	
Pontypridd 3	a		12 04		12 09						12 32			12 34		12 40				12 56			13 04		13 09	
	d		12 06		12 11									12 36						12 58			13 06		13 11	
Abercynon North	d				12 22																				13 21	
Penrhiwceiber	d				12 28																				13 27	
Mountain Ash	a				12 31																				13 30	
	d				12 33																				13 33	
Fernhill	d				12 35																				13 35	
Cwmbach	d				12 39																				13 39	
Aberdare 3	a				12 46																				13 46	
Abercynon South	d																			13 04						
Quakers Yard	d																			13 08						
Merthyr Vale	d																			13 14						
Troed Y Rhiw	d																			13 17						
Pentre-bach	d																			13 20						
Merthyr Tydfil	a																			13 28						
Trehafod	d		12 11											12 41									13 11			
Porth	d		12 15											12 45									13 15			
Dinas Rhondda	d		12 19											12 49									13 19			
Tonypandy	d		12 21											12 51									13 21			
Llwynypia	d		12 23											12 53									13 23			
Ystrad Rhondda	a		12 26											12 56									13 26			
	d		12 29											12 59									13 29			
Ton Pentre	d		12 31											13 01									13 31			
Treorchy	d		12 34											13 04									13 34			
Ynyswen	d		12 37											13 07									13 37			
Treherbert	a		12 43											13 13									13 43			

For general notes see front of timetable
For details of catering facilities see Directory of Train Operators

A From Coryton
B From Radyr

Bridgend, Barry Island, Barry, Penarth and Cardiff → Coryton, Rhymney, Pontypridd, Merthyr, Aberdare and Treherbert

Network Diagram - see first page of Table 130

		AW	AW	AW	AW		AW	AW	AW	AW	AW	AW	AW	AW	AW	AW	AW	AW	AW	AW	AW	AW	AW	AW	AW	AW
			A						B				A					B				A				
Bridgend	d																		12 42							
Llantwit Major	d																		12 56							
Rhoose Cardiff Int Airport ✈	d																		13 06							
Barry Island	d			12 26						12 41				12 56									13 26			
Barry 3	d			12 30						12 45				13 00					13 15				13 30			
Barry Docks	d			12 34						12 49				13 04					13 19				13 34			
Cadoxton	d			12 37						12 52				13 07					13 22				13 37			
Dinas Powys	d			12 41						12 56				13 11					13 26				13 41			
Eastbrook	d			12 43						12 58				13 13					13 28				13 43			
Cogan	d			12 45						13 00				13 15					13 30				13 45			
Penarth	d				12 47						13 02				13 17					13 32				13 47		
Dingle Road	d				12 49						13 04				13 19					13 34				13 49		
Grangetown	d			12 49	12 53					13 04	13 08			13 19	13 23				13 34	13 38			13 49	13 53		
Cardiff Central 7	a			12 54	12 59					13 09	13 14			13 24	13 29				13 39	13 44			13 54	13 59		
	d		12 51	12 56	13 01			13 06	13 06	13 11	13 16		13 21	13 26	13 31		13 36	13 36	13 41	13 46		13 51	13 56	14 01		14 06
Cardiff Bay	d	12 49					13 04					13 19				13 34					13 49				14 04	
Cardiff Queen Street 3	a	12 53	12 54	12 59	13 04		13 08	13 09		13 14	13 19	13 23	13 24	13 29	13 34	13 38	13 39		13 44	13 49	13 53	13 54	13 59	14 04	14 08	14 09
	d		12 55	13 00	13 05			13 10		13 15	13 20		13 25	13 30	13 35		13 40		13 45	13 50		13 55	14 00	14 05		14 10
Heath Low Level	d		13 00										13 30									14 00				
Ty Glas	d		13 03										13 33									14 03				
Birchgrove	d		13 04										13 34									14 04				
Rhiwbina	d		13 06										13 36									14 06				
Whitchurch (Cardiff)	d		13 08										13 38									14 08				
Coryton	a		13 13										13 43									14 13				
Heath High Level	d				13 10						13 25				13 40					13 55				14 10		
Llanishen	d				13 13						13 28				13 43					13 58				14 13		
Lisvane & Thornhill	d				13 15						13 30				13 45					14 00				14 15		
Caerphilly 3	d				13 21						13 36				13 51					14 06				14 21		
Aber	d				13 23						13 38				13 53					14 08				14 23		
Llanbradach	d				13 27						13 42				13 57					14 12				14 27		
Ystrad Mynach 3	d				13 32						13 47				14 02					14 17				14 32		
Hengoed	d				13 35						13 50				14 05					14 20				14 35		
Pengam	d				13 38						13 53				14 08					14 23				14 38		
Gilfach Fargoed	d				13 41																			14 41		
Bargoed	d				13a48						13 59				14a16					14a31				14a48		
Brithdir	d										14 03															
Tir-phil	d										14 06															
Pontlottyn	d										14 10															
Rhymney 3	a										14 16															
Cathays	d			13 03				13 13		13 18				13 33			13 43		13 48				14 03			14 13
Llandaf	d			13 07				13 17		13 22				13 37			13 47		13 52				14 07			14 17
Ninian Park	d								13 10									13 40								
Waun-gron Park	d								13 13									13 43								
Fairwater	d								13 15									13 45								
Danescourt	d								13 17									13 47								
Radyr 3	a			13 10				13 20	13 24	13 25				13 40			13 50	13 54	13 55				14 10			14 20
	d			13 10				13 20		13 25				13 40			13 50		13 55				14 10			14 20
Taffs Well 3	d			13 14				13 24		13 29				13 44			13 54		13 59				14 14			14 24
Trefforest Estate	d			13 18										13 48									14 18			
Trefforest	d			13 22				13 31		13 36				13 52			14 01		14 06				14 22			14 31
Pontypridd 3	a			13 32				13 34		13 39				13 56			14 04		14 09				14 32			14 34
	d							13 36		13 41				13 58			14 06		14 11							14 36
Abercynon North	d									13 51									14 21							
Penrhiwceiber	d									13 57									14 27							
Mountain Ash	a									14 00									14 30							
	d									14 03									14 33							
Fernhill	d									14 05									14 35							
Cwmbach	d									14 09									14 39							
Aberdare 3	a									14 16									14 46							
Abercynon South	d													14 04												
Quakers Yard	d													14 08												
Merthyr Vale	d													14 14												
Troed Y Rhiw	d													14 17												
Pentre-bach	d													14 20												
Merthyr Tydfil	a													14 28												
Trehafod	d							13 41									14 11									14 41
Porth	d							13 45									14 15									14 45
Dinas Rhondda	d							13 49									14 19									14 49
Tonypandy	d							13 51									14 21									14 51
Llwynypia	d							13 53									14 23									14 53
Ystrad Rhondda	a							13 56									14 26									14 56
	d							13 59									14 29									14 59
Ton Pentre	d							14 01									14 31									15 01
Treorchy	d							14 04									14 34									15 04
Ynyswen	d							14 07									14 37									15 07
Treherbert	a							14 13									14 43									15 13

For general notes see front of timetable
For details of catering facilities see Directory of Train Operators

A From Radyr
B From Coryton

Saturdays

Bridgend, Barry Island, Barry, Penarth and Cardiff → Coryton, Rhymney, Pontypridd, Merthyr, Aberdare and Treherbert

Network Diagram - see first page of Table 130

		AW A		AW	AW	AW	AW B	AW	AW	AW	AW	AW A	AW	AW	AW	AW B	AW	AW	AW	AW	AW A	AW		AW	AW	AW B
Bridgend	d												13 42													
Llantwit Major	d												13 56													
Rhoose Cardiff Int Airport ✈	d												14 06													
Barry Island	d			13 41				13 56										14 26				14 41				
Barry 3	d			13 45				14 00					14 15					14 30				14 45				
Barry Docks	d			13 49				14 04					14 19					14 34				14 49				
Cadoxton	d			13 52				14 07					14 22					14 37				14 52				
Dinas Powys	d			13 56				14 11					14 26					14 41				14 56				
Eastbrook	d			13 58				14 13					14 28					14 43				14 58				
Cogan	d			14 00				14 15					14 30					14 45				15 00				
Penarth	d				14 02				14 17					14 32					14 47					15 02		
Dingle Road	d				14 04				14 19					14 34					14 49					15 04		
Grangetown	d			14 04	14 08			14 19	14 23				14 34	14 38				14 49	14 53			15 04		15 08		
Cardiff Central 7	a			14 09	14 14			14 24	14 29				14 39	14 44				14 54	14 59			15 09		15 14		
	d	14 06		14 11	14 16		14 21	14 26	14 31		14 36	14 36	14 41	14 46		14 51	14 51	14 56	15 01		15 06	15 11		15 16		15 21
Cardiff Bay	d					14 19				14 34					14 49					15 04					15 19	
Cardiff Queen Street 3	a			14 14	14 19	14 23	14 24	14 29	14 34	14 38	14 39		14 44	14 49	14 53	14 54		14 59	15 04	15 08		15 14		15 19	15 23	15 24
	d			14 15	14 20		14 25	14 30	14 35		14 40		14 45	14 50		14 55		15 00	15 05			15 15		15 20		15 25
Heath Low Level	d						14 30									15 00										15 30
Ty Glas	d						14 33									15 03										15 33
Birchgrove	d						14 34									15 04										15 34
Rhiwbina	d						14 36									15 06										15 36
Whitchurch (Cardiff)	d						14 38									15 08										15 38
Coryton	a						14 43									15 13										15 43
Heath High Level	d				14 25				14 40					14 55					15 10					15 25		
Llanishen	d				14 28				14 43					14 58					15 13					15 28		
Lisvane & Thornhill	d				14 30				14 45					15 00					15 15					15 30		
Caerphilly 3	d				14 36				14 51					15 06					15 21					15 36		
Aber	d				14 38				14 53					15 08					15 23					15 38		
Llanbradach	d				14 42				14 57					15 12					15 27					15 42		
Ystrad Mynach 3	d				14 47				15 02					15 17					15 32					15 47		
Hengoed	d				14 50				15 05					15 20					15 35					15 50		
Pengam	d				14 53				15 08					15 23					15 38					15 53		
Gilfach Fargoed	d																		15 41							
Bargoed	d				14 59				15a16					15a31					15a48					15 59		
Brithdir	d				15 03																			16 03		
Tir-phil	d				15 06																			16 06		
Pontlottyn	d				15 10																			16 10		
Rhymney 3	a				15 16																			16 16		
Cathays	d			14 18				14 33			14 43		14 48					15 03				15 18				
Llandaf	d			14 22				14 37			14 47		14 52					15 07				15 22				
Ninian Park	d	14 10										14 40									15 10					
Waun-gron Park	d	14 13										14 43									15 13					
Fairwater	d	14 15										14 45									15 15					
Danescourt	d	14 17										14 47									15 17					
Radyr 3	a	14 24		14 25				14 40			14 50	14 54	14 55				15 02	15 10			15 24	15 25				
	d			14 25				14 40			14 50		14 55				15 02	15 10				15 25				
Taffs Well 3	d			14 29				14 44			14 54		14 59				15 06	15 14				15 29				
Trefforest Estate	d							14 48										15 18								
Trefforest	d			14 36				14 52			15 01		15 06				15 13	15 22				15 36				
Pontypridd 3	a			14 39				14 56			15 04		15 09				15 16	15 32				15 39				
	d			14 41				14 58			15 06		15 11				15 23					15 41				
Abercynon North	d			14 51									15 21									15 51				
Penrhiwceiber	d			14 57									15 27									15 57				
Mountain Ash	a			15 00									15 30									16 00				
	d			15 03									15 33									16 03				
Fernhill	d			15 05									15 35									16 05				
Cwmbach	d			15 09									15 39									16 09				
Aberdare 3	a			15 16									15 46									16 16				
Abercynon South	d							15 04																		
Quakers Yard	d							15 08																		
Merthyr Vale	d							15 14																		
Troed Y Rhiw	d							15 17																		
Pentre-bach	d							15 20																		
Merthyr Tydfil	a							15 28																		
Trehafod	d										15 11						15 28									
Porth	d										15 15						15b45									
Dinas Rhondda	d										15 19						15 49									
Tonypandy	d										15 21						15 51									
Llwynypia	d										15 23						15 53									
Ystrad Rhondda	a										15 26						15 56									
	d										15 29						15 59									
Ton Pentre	d										15 31						16 01									
Treorchy	d										15 34						16 04									
Ynyswen	d										15 37						16 07									
Treherbert	a										15 43						16 14									

For general notes see front of timetable
For details of catering facilities see Directory of Train Operators

A From Coryton
B From Radyr
b Arr. 1531

Table 130

Saturdays

Bridgend, Barry Island, Barry, Penarth and Cardiff → Coryton, Rhymney, Pontypridd, Merthyr, Aberdare and Treherbert

Network Diagram - see first page of Table 130

		AW	AW	AW	AW	AW A	AW	AW	AW	AW B	AW	AW	AW	AW	AW A	AW	AW	AW	AW B		AW	AW	AW	AW	AW A	AW
Bridgend	d						14 42																			15 42
Llantwit Major	d						14 56																			15 56
Rhoose Cardiff Int Airport ✈	d						15 06																			16 06
Barry Island	d	14 56									15 26					15 41					15 56					
Barry 3	d	15 00					15 15				15 30					15 45					16 00					16 15
Barry Docks	d	15 04					15 19				15 34					15 49					16 04					16 19
Cadoxton	d	15 07					15 22				15 37					15 52					16 07					16 22
Dinas Powys	d	15 11					15 26				15 41					15 56					16 11					16 26
Eastbrook	d	15 13					15 28				15 43					15 58					16 13					16 28
Cogan	d	15 15					15 30				15 45					16 00					16 15					16 30
Penarth	d		15 17					15 32				15 47					16 02					16 17				
Dingle Road	d		15 19					15 34				15 49					16 04					16 19				
Grangetown	d	15 19	15 23				15 34	15 38			15 49	15 53				16 04	16 08				16 19	16 23				16 34
Cardiff Central 7	a	15 24	15 29				15 39	15 44			15 54	15 59				16 09	16 14				16 24	16 29				16 39
	d	15 26	15 31		15 36	15 36	15 41	15 46		15 51	15 56	16 01		16 06	16 06	16 11	16 16		16 21		16 26	16 31		16 36	16 36	16 41
Cardiff Bay	d			15 34					15 49				16 04					16 19					16 34			
Cardiff Queen Street 3	a	15 29	15 34	15 38	15 39		15 44	15 49	15 53	15 54	15 59	16 04	16 08	16 09		16 14	16 19	16 23	16 24		16 29	16 34	16 38	16 39		16 44
	d	15 30	15 35		15 40		15 45	15 50		15 55	16 00	16 05		16 10		16 15	16 20		16 25		16 30	16 35		16 40		16 45
Heath Low Level	d									16 00									16 30							
Ty Glas	d									16 03									16 33							
Birchgrove	d									16 04									16 34							
Rhiwbina	d									16 06									16 36							
Whitchurch (Cardiff)	d									16 08									16 38							
Coryton	a									16 13									16 43							
Heath High Level	d		15 40					15 55				16 10					16 25					16 40				
Llanishen	d		15 43					15 58				16 13					16 28					16 43				
Lisvane & Thornhill	d		15 45					16 00				16 15					16 30					16 45				
Caerphilly 3	d		15 51					16 06				16 21					16 36					16 51				
Aber	d		15 53					16 08				16 23					16 38					16 53				
Llanbradach	d		15 57					16 12				16 27					16 42					16 57				
Ystrad Mynach 3	d		16 02					16 17				16 32					16 47					17 02				
Hengoed	d		16 05					16 20				16 35					16 50					17 05				
Pengam	d		16 08					16 23				16 38					16 53					17 08				
Gilfach Fargoed	d											16 41														
Bargoed	d		16a16					16a31				16a48					16 59					17a16				
Brithdir	d																17 03									
Tir-phil	d																17 06									
Pontlottyn	d																17 10									
Rhymney 3	a																17 16									
Cathays	d	15 33			15 43		15 48				16 03			16 13		16 18					16 33			16 43		16 48
Llandaf	d	15 37			15 47		15 52				16 07			16 17		16 22					16 37			16 47		16 52
Ninian Park	d					15 40									16 10										16 40	
Waun-gron Park	d					15 43									16 13										16 43	
Fairwater	d					15 45									16 15										16 45	
Danescourt	d					15 47									16 17										16 47	
Radyr 3	a	15 40			15 50	15 54	15 55				16 10			16 20	16 24	16 25					16 40			16 50	16 54	16 55
	d	15 40			15 50		15 55				16 10			16 20		16 25					16 40			16 50		16 55
Taffs Well 3	d	15 44			15 54		15 59				16 14			16 24		16 29					16 44			16 54		16 59
Trefforest Estate	d	15 48									16 18										16 48					
Trefforest	d	15 52			16 01		16 06				16 22			16 31		16 36					16 52			17 01		17 06
Pontypridd 3	a	15 56			16 04		16 09				16 32			16 34		16 39					16 56			17 04		17 09
	d	15 58			16 06		16 11							16 36		16 41					16 58			17 06		17 11
Abercynon North	d						16 21									16 51										17 21
Penrhiwceiber	d						16 27									16 57										17 27
Mountain Ash	a						16 30									17 00										17 30
	d						16 33									17 03										17 33
Fernhill	d						16 35									17 05										17 35
Cwmbach	d						16 39									17 09										17 39
Aberdare 3	a						16 46									17 16										17 46
Abercynon South	d	16 04																			17 04					
Quakers Yard	d	16 08																			17 08					
Merthyr Vale	d	16 14																			17 14					
Troed Y Rhiw	d	16 17																			17 17					
Pentre-bach	d	16 20																			17 20					
Merthyr Tydfil	a	16 28																			17 28					
Trehafod	d				16 11									16 41										17 11		
Porth	d				16 15									16 45										17 15		
Dinas Rhondda	d				16 19									16 49										17 19		
Tonypandy	d				16 21									16 51										17 21		
Llwynypia	d				16 23									16 53										17 23		
Ystrad Rhondda	a				16 26									16 56										17 26		
	d				16 29									16 59										17 29		
Ton Pentre	d				16 31									17 01										17 31		
Treorchy	d				16 34									17 04										17 34		
Ynyswen	d				16 37									17 07										17 37		
Treherbert	a				16 44									17 13										17 43		

For general notes see front of timetable
For details of catering facilities see Directory of Train Operators

A From Coryton
B From Radyr

Table 130

Saturdays

Bridgend, Barry Island, Barry, Penarth and Cardiff → Coryton, Rhymney, Pontypridd, Merthyr, Aberdare and Treherbert

Network Diagram - see first page of Table 130

		AW	AW	AW A	AW	AW	AW	AW	AW B	AW	AW	AW	AW A	AW	AW	AW	AW	AW B	AW	AW	AW	AW A	AW	AW	AW
Bridgend	d																		16 42						
Llantwit Major	d																		16 56						
Rhoose Cardiff Int Airport ✈	d																		17 06						
Barry Island	d				16 26					16 41				16 56									17 26		
Barry [3]	d				16 30					16 45				17 00					17 15				17 30		
Barry Docks	d				16 34					16 49				17 04					17 19				17 34		
Cadoxton	d				16 37					16 52				17 07					17 22				17 37		
Dinas Powys	d				16 41					16 56				17 11					17 26				17 41		
Eastbrook	d				16 43					16 58				17 13					17 28				17 43		
Cogan	d				16 45					17 00				17 15					17 30				17 45		
Penarth	d	16 32									17 02				17 17					17 32				17 47	
Dingle Road	d	16 34									17 04				17 19					17 34				17 49	
Grangetown	d	16 38			16 49					17 04	17 08			17 19	17 23				17 34	17 38			17 49	17 53	
Cardiff Central [7]	a	16 44			16 54					17 09	17 14			17 24	17 29				17 39	17 44			17 54	17 59	
	d	16 46		16 51	16 56	17 01		17 06	17 06	17 11	17 16		17 21	17 26	17 31		17 36	17 36	17 41	17 46		17 51	17 56	18 01	
Cardiff Bay	d		16 49				17 04					17 19				17 34					17 49				18 04
Cardiff Queen Street [3]	a	16 49	16 53	16 54	16 59	17 04	17 08	17 09		17 14	17 19	17 23	17 24	17 29	17 34	17 38	17 39		17 44	17 49	17 53	17 54	17 59	18 04	18 08
	d	16 50		16 55	17 00	17 05		17 10		17 15	17 20		17 25	17 30	17 35		17 40		17 45	17 50		17 55	18 00	18 05	
Heath Low Level	d			17 00									17 30									18 00			
Ty Glas	d			17 03									17 33									18 03			
Birchgrove	d			17 04									17 34									18 04			
Rhiwbina	d			17 06									17 36									18 06			
Whitchurch (Cardiff)	d			17 08									17 38									18 08			
Coryton	a			17 13									17 43									18 13			
Heath High Level	d	16 55				17 10					17 25				17 40					17 55				18 10	
Llanishen	d	16 58				17 13					17 28				17 43					17 59				18 13	
Lisvane & Thornhill	d	17 00				17 15					17 30				17 45					18 02				18 15	
Caerphilly [3]	d	17 06				17 21					17 36				17 51					18 07				18 21	
Aber	d	17 08				17 23					17 38				17 53					18 10				18 23	
Llanbradach	d	17 12				17 27					17 42				17 57					18 14				18 27	
Ystrad Mynach [3]	d	17 17				17 33					17 47				18 02					18 20				18 32	
Hengoed	d	17 20				17 35					17 50				18 05					18 23				18 35	
Pengam	d	17 23				17 39					17 53				18 08					18 27				18 38	
Gilfach Fargoed	d					17 42									18 11					18 30				18 41	
Bargoed	d	17a31				17 47					18a01				18 16					18b44				18a48	
Brithdir	d					17 50									18 20					18 48					
Tir-phil	d					17 53									18 23					18 51					
Pontlottyn	d					17 58									18 27					18 55					
Rhymney [3]	a					18 04									18 33					19 01					
Cathays	d				17 03			17 13		17 18				17 33			17 43		17 48				18 03		
Llandaf	d				17 07			17 17		17 22				17 37			17 47		17 52				18 07		
Ninian Park	d								17 10									17 40							
Waun-gron Park	d								17 13									17 43							
Fairwater	d								17 15									17 45							
Danescourt	d								17 17									17 47							
Radyr [3]	a				17 10			17 20	17 24	17 25				17 40			17 50	17 54	17 55				18 10		
	d				17 10			17 20		17 25				17 40			17 50		17 55				18 10		
Taffs Well [3]	d				17 14			17 24		17 29				17 44			17 54		17 59				18 14		
Trefforest Estate	d				17 18									17 48									18 18		
Trefforest	d				17 22			17 31		17 36				17 52			18 01		18 06				18 22		
Pontypridd [3]	a				17 32			17 34		17 39				17 56			18 04		18 09				18 29		
	d							17 36		17 41				17 58			18 06		18 11						
Abercynon North	d									17 51									18 21						
Penrhiwceiber	d									17 57									18 27						
Mountain Ash	a									18 00									18 30						
	d									18 03									18 33						
Fernhill	d									18 05									18 35						
Cwmbach	d									18 09									18 39						
Aberdare [3]	a									18 16									18 46						
Abercynon South	d													18 04											
Quakers Yard	d													18 08											
Merthyr Vale	d													18 14											
Troed Y Rhiw	d													18 17											
Pentre-bach	d													18 20											
Merthyr Tydfil	a													18 28											
Trehafod	d							17 41									18 11								
Porth	d							17 45									18 15								
Dinas Rhondda	d							17 49									18 19								
Tonypandy	d							17 51									18 21								
Llwynypia	d							17 53									18 23								
Ystrad Rhondda	a							17 56									18 26								
	d							17 59									18 29								
Ton Pentre	d							18 01									18 31								
Treorchy	d							18 04									18 34								
Ynyswen	d							18 07									18 37								
Treherbert	a							18 13									18 43								

For general notes see front of timetable
For details of catering facilities see Directory of Train Operators

A From Radyr
B From Coryton
b Arr. 1834

Table 130

Bridgend, Barry Island, Barry, Penarth and Cardiff → Coryton, Rhymney, Pontypridd, Merthyr, Aberdare and Treherbert

Network Diagram - see first page of Table 130

		AW	AW A	AW	AW	AW	AW B	AW	AW	AW	AW	AW A	AW C		AW	AW	AW B	AW	AW	AW	AW	AW	AW	AW	AW	AW
Bridgend	d												17 42													
Llantwit Major	d												17 56													
Rhoose Cardiff Int Airport ✈	d												18 06													
Barry Island	d			17 41				17 56										18 26				18 41		18 56		
Barry 3	d			17 45				18 00					18 15					18 30				18 45		19 00		
Barry Docks	d			17 49				18 04					18 19					18 34				18 49		19 04		
Cadoxton	d			17 52				18 07					18 22					18 37				18 52		19 07		
Dinas Powys	d			17 56				18 11					18 26					18 41				18 56		19 11		
Eastbrook	d			17 58				18 13					18 28					18 43				18 58		19 13		
Cogan	d			18 00				18 15					18 30					18 45				19 00		19 15		
Penarth	d				18 02				18 17						18 32				18 47						19 17	
Dingle Road	d				18 04				18 19						18 34				18 49						19 19	
Grangetown	d			18 04	18 08			18 19	18 23				18 34		18 38			18 49	18 53			19 04		19 19	19 23	
Cardiff Central 7	a			18 09	18 14			18 25	18 29				18 39		18 45			18 57	18 59			19 09		19 25	19 29	
	d	18 06	18 06	18 11	18 16		18 21	18 26	18 31		18 36	18 36	18 41				18 50		19 01		19 06	19 11		19 26	19 31	
Cardiff Bay	d					18 19				18 34						18 49				19 04			19 19			19 34
Cardiff Queen Street 3	a	18 09		18 14	18 19	18 23	18 24	18 29	18 34	18 38	18 38		18 44			18 53	18 54		19 04	19 08	19 09	19 14	19 23	19 29	19 34	19 38
	d	18 10		18 15	18 20		18 25	18 30	18 35		18 40		18 50				18 55		19 05		19 10	19 15		19 30	19 35	
Heath Low Level	d						18 30										18 59									
Ty Glas	d						18 33										19 02									
Birchgrove	d						18 34										19 03									
Rhiwbina	d						18 36										19 05									
Whitchurch (Cardiff)	d						18 38										19 08									
Coryton	a						18 43										19 13									
Heath High Level	d				18 25				18 40										19 10						19 40	
Llanishen	d				18 28				18 43										19 13						19 43	
Lisvane & Thornhill	d				18 30				18 45										19 15						19 45	
Caerphilly 3	d				18 36				18 51										19a24						19 51	
Aber	d				18 38				18 53																19 53	
Llanbradach	d				18 42				18 57																19 57	
Ystrad Mynach 3	d				18a51				19 02																20 02	
Hengoed	d								19 05																20 05	
Pengam	d								19 08																20 08	
Gilfach Fargoed	d								19x11																20 11	
Bargoed	d								19 16																20 16	
Brithdir	d								19 20																20 20	
Tir-phil	d								19 23																20 23	
Pontlottyn	d								19 27																20 27	
Rhymney 3	a								19 33																20 33	
Cathays	d	18 13		18 18				18 33			18 43		18 52								19 13	19 18		19 33		
Llandaf	d	18 17		18 22				18 37			18 47		18 56								19 17	19 22		19 37		
Ninian Park	d		18 10									18 40														
Waun-gron Park	d		18 13									18 43														
Fairwater	d		18 15									18 45														
Danescourt	d		18 17									18 47														
Radyr 3	a	18 20	18 24	18 25				18 40			18 50	18 54	18 58								19 20	19 25		19 40		
	d	18 20		18 25				18 40			18 50		18 58								19 20	19 25		19 40		
Taffs Well 3	d	18 24		18 29				18 44			18 54		19 03								19 24	19 29		19 44		
Trefforest Estate	d							18 48																19 48		
Trefforest	d	18 31		18 36				18 52			19 01		19 10								19 31	19 36		19 52		
Pontypridd 3	a	18 34		18 42				18 56			19 04		19 13								19 34	19 39		19 56		
	d	18 36						18 58			19 06		19 14								19 36	19 41		19 58		
Abercynon North	d												19 21									19 53				
Penrhiwceiber	d												19 26									19 57				
Mountain Ash	a												19 30									20 00				
	d												19 33									20 03				
Fernhill	d												19 35									20 05				
Cwmbach	d												19 39									20 09				
Aberdare 3	a												19 46									20 16				
Abercynon South	d							19 04																20 04		
Quakers Yard	d							19 08																20 08		
Merthyr Vale	d							19 14																20 14		
Troed Y Rhiw	d							19 17																20 17		
Pentre-bach	d							19 20																20 20		
Merthyr Tydfil	a							19 28																20 28		
Trehafod	d	18 41									19 11										19 41					
Porth	d	18 45									19 15										19 45					
Dinas Rhondda	d	18 49									19 19										19 49					
Tonypandy	d	18 51									19 21										19 51					
Llwynypia	d	18 53									19 23										19 53					
Ystrad Rhondda	a	18 56									19 26										19 56					
	d	18 59									19 29										19 59					
Ton Pentre	d	19 01									19 31										20 01					
Treorchy	d	19 04									19 34										20 04					
Ynyswen	d	19 07									19 37										20 07					
Treherbert	a	19 13									19 43										20 13					

For general notes see front of timetable
For details of catering facilities see Directory of Train Operators

A From Coryton
B From Radyr
C Until 9 February

Table 130

Saturdays

Bridgend, Barry Island, Barry, Penarth and Cardiff → Coryton, Rhymney, Pontypridd, Merthyr, Aberdare and Treherbert

Network Diagram - see first page of Table 130

Station		AW	AW A	AW	AW	AW	AW	AW	AW	AW		AW	AW	AW	AW	AW	AW A	AW	AW	AW	AW	AW	AW	AW	AW	AW
Bridgend	d			18 42														19 42								
Llantwit Major	d			18 56														19 56								
Rhoose Cardiff Int Airport ✈	d			19 06														20 06								
Barry Island	d						19 26						19 56											20 56		
Barry 3	d			19 15			19 30						20 00					20 15						21 00		
Barry Docks	d			19 19			19 34						20 04					20 19						21 04		
Cadoxton	d			19 22			19 37						20 07					20 22						21 07		
Dinas Powys	d			19 26			19 41						20 11					20 26						21 11		
Eastbrook	d			19 28			19 43						20 13					20 28						21 13		
Cogan	d			19 30			19 45						20 15					20 30						21 15		
Penarth	d							19 47						20 17							20 47					21 17
Dingle Road	d							19 49						20 19							20 49					21 19
Grangetown	d			19 34			19 49	19 53					20 19	20 23				20 34			20 53			21 19		21 23
Cardiff Central 7	a			19 42			19 56	19 59					20 25	20 29				20 39			20 59			21 25		21 33
	d	19 36	19 36			19 51		20 01		20 11			20 26	20 31		20 36	20 36	20 41		20 51	21 01			21 26	21 31	
Cardiff Bay	d				19 49				20 04			20 19			20 34				20 49			21 04	21 19			
Cardiff Queen Street 3	a	19 39			19 53	19 54		20 04	20 08	20 14		20 23	20 29	20 34	20 38	20 39		20 44	20 53	20 54	21 04	21 08	21 23	21 29	21 34	
	d	19 40				19 55		20 05		20 15			20 30	20 35		20 40		20 45		20 55	21 05			21 30	21 35	
Heath Low Level	d					20 00														21 00						
Ty Glas	d					20 03														21 03						
Birchgrove	d					20 04														21 04						
Rhiwbina	d					20 06														21 06						
Whitchurch (Cardiff)	d					20 08														21 08						
Coryton	a					20 13														21 13						
Heath High Level	d							20 10						20 40							21 10				21 40	
Llanishen	d							20 13						20 43							21 13				21 43	
Lisvane & Thornhill	d							20 15						20 45							21 15				21 45	
Caerphilly 3	d							20a28						20 51							21a28				21 51	
Aber	d													20 53											21 53	
Llanbradach	d													20 57											21 57	
Ystrad Mynach 3	d													21 02											22 02	
Hengoed	d													21 05											22 05	
Pengam	d													21 08											22 08	
Gilfach Fargoed	d													21 11											22 11	
Bargoed	d													21 16											22 16	
Brithdir	d													21 20											22 20	
Tir-phil	d													21 23											22 23	
Pontlottyn	d													21 27											22 27	
Rhymney 3	a													21 33											22 33	
Cathays	d	19 43								20 18			20 33			20 43		20 48						21 33		
Llandaf	d	19 47								20 22			20 37			20 47		20 52						21 37		
Ninian Park	d		19 40														20 40									
Waun-gron Park	d		19 43														20 43									
Fairwater	d		19 45														20 45									
Danescourt	d		19 47														20 47									
Radyr 3	a	19 50	19 54							20 25			20 40			20 50	20 54	20 55						21 40		
	d	19 50								20 25			20 40			20 50		20 55						21 40		
Taffs Well 3	d	19 54								20 29			20 44			20 54		20 59						21 44		
Trefforest Estate	d												20 48											21 48		
Trefforest	d	20 01								20 36			20 52			21 01		21 06						21 52		
Pontypridd 3	a	20 04								20 39			20 56			21 04		21 09						21 56		
	d	20 06								20 41			20 58			21 06		21 11						21 58		
Abercynon North	d									20 51								21 21								
Penrhiwceiber	d									20 57								21 27								
Mountain Ash	a									21 00								21 30								
	d									21 03								21 33								
Fernhill	d									21 05								21 35								
Cwmbach	d									21 09								21 39								
Aberdare 3	a									21 16								21 46								
Abercynon South	d												21 04											22 04		
Quakers Yard	d												21 08											22 08		
Merthyr Vale	d												21 14											22 14		
Troed Y Rhiw	d												21 17											22 17		
Pentre-bach	d												21 20											22 20		
Merthyr Tydfil	a												21 28											22 28		
Trehafod	d	20 11														21 11										
Porth	d	20 15														21 15										
Dinas Rhondda	d	20 19														21 19										
Tonypandy	d	20 21														21 21										
Llwynypia	d	20 23														21 23										
Ystrad Rhondda	a	20 26														21 26										
	d	20 29														21 29										
Ton Pentre	d	20 31														21 31										
Treorchy	d	20 34														21 34										
Ynyswen	d	20 37														21 37										
Treherbert	a	20 43														21 43										

For general notes see front of timetable
For details of catering facilities see
Directory of Train Operators

A From Coryton

Table 130

Saturdays

Bridgend, Barry Island, Barry, Penarth and Cardiff → Coryton, Rhymney, Pontypridd, Merthyr, Aberdare and Treherbert

Network Diagram - see first page of Table 130

		AW	AW	AW A	AW	AW	AW	AW	AW	AW	AW	AW	AW	AW	AW	AW	AW	AW	AW	AW	AW	AW	AW
Bridgend	d												21 42									22 42	
Llantwit Major	d												21 56									22 56	
Rhoose Cardiff Int Airport ✈	d												22 06									23 06	
Barry Island	d									21 56									22 56				
Barry 3	d									22 00			22 15						23 00			23 15	
Barry Docks	d									22 04			22 19						23 04			23 19	
Cadoxton	d									22 07			22 22						23 07			23 22	
Dinas Powys	d									22 11			22 26						23 11			23 26	
Eastbrook	d									22 13			22 28						23 13			23 28	
Cogan	d									22 15			22 30						23 15			23 30	
Penarth	d					21 47					22 17						22 47				23 26		
Dingle Road	d					21 49					22 19						22 49				23 28		
Grangetown	d					21 53				22 19	22 23		22 34				22 53		23 19		23 32	23 35	
Cardiff Central 7	a					21 59				22 26	22 31		22 39				23 00		23 24		23 39	23 42	
	d		21 36	21 36		22 01		22 11			22 35		22 41	22 46			23 15		23 26				
Cardiff Bay	d	21 34			21 49		22 04		22 19			22 34			22 49	23 04		23 19		23 34			23 49
Cardiff Queen Street 3	a	21 38	21 39		21 53	22 04	22 08	22 14	22 23		22 38	22 38	22 44	22 49	22 53	23 08	23 18	23 23	23 29	23 38			23 53
	d		21 40			22 05		22 15			22 39		22 45	22 50			23 19		23 30				
Heath Low Level	d																						
Ty Glas	d																						
Birchgrove	d																						
Rhiwbina	d																						
Whitchurch (Cardiff)	d																						
Coryton	a																						
Heath High Level	d					22 10					22 44						23 24						
Llanishen	d					22 13					22 47						23 27						
Lisvane & Thornhill	d					22 15					22 49						23 29						
Caerphilly 3	d					22a24					22 55						23 35						
Aber	d										22 57						23 37						
Llanbradach	d										23 01						23 41						
Ystrad Mynach 3	d										23 06						23a50						
Hengoed	d										23 09												
Pengam	d										23 12												
Gilfach Fargoed	d										23 15												
Bargoed	d										23 20												
Brithdir	d										23 24												
Tir-phil	d										23 27												
Pontlottyn	d										23 31												
Rhymney 3	a										23 37												
Cathays	d		21 43					22 18					22 48	22 53					23 33				
Llandaf	d		21 47					22 22					22 52	22 57					23 37				
Ninian Park	d			21 40																			
Waun-gron Park	d			21 43																			
Fairwater	d			21 45																			
Danescourt	d			21 47																			
Radyr 3	a		21 50	21 54				22 25					22 55	22 59					23 40				
	d		21 50					22 25					22 55	22 59					23 40				
Taffs Well 3	d		21 54					22 29					22 59	23 03					23 44				
Trefforest Estate	d																		23 48				
Trefforest	d		22 01					22 36					23 06	23 10					23 52				
Pontypridd 3	a		22 04					22 43					23 09	23 14					00 01				
	d		22 06										23 11	23 15									
Abercynon North	d												23 21										
Penrhiwceiber	d												23 27										
Mountain Ash	a												23 30										
	d												23 33										
Fernhill	d												23 35										
Cwmbach	d												23 39										
Aberdare 3	a												23 46										
Abercynon South	d																						
Quakers Yard	d																						
Merthyr Vale	d																						
Troed Y Rhiw	d																						
Pentre-bach	d																						
Merthyr Tydfil	a																						
Trehafod	d		22 11											23 20									
Porth	d		22 15											23 24									
Dinas Rhondda	d		22 19											23 28									
Tonypandy	d		22 21											23 30									
Llwynypia	d		22 23											23 32									
Ystrad Rhondda	a		22 26											23 35									
	d		22 29											23 38									
Ton Pentre	d		22 31											23 40									
Treorchy	d		22 34											23 43									
Ynyswen	d		22 37											23 46									
Treherbert	a		22 43											23 52									

For general notes see front of timetable
For details of catering facilities see Directory of Train Operators

A From Coryton

Table 130

Sundays

Bridgend, Barry Island, Barry, Penarth and Cardiff → Coryton, Rhymney, Pontypridd, Merthyr, Aberdare and Treherbert

Network Diagram - see first page of Table 130

		AW	AW	AW	AW	AW	AW	AW	AW	AW A	AW	AW	AW	AW	AW	AW	AW	AW	AW	AW	AW	AW	AW	AW
Bridgend	d								09 42													11 42		
Llantwit Major	d								09 56													11 56		
Rhoose Cardiff Int Airport ✈	d								10 06													12 06		
Barry Island	d				08 56		09 56								10 56			11 26		11 56				
Barry 3	d				09 00		10 00		10 15						11 00			11 30		12 00		12 15		
Barry Docks	d				09 04		10 04		10 19						11 04			11 34		12 04		12 19		
Cadoxton	d				09 07		10 07		10 22						11 07			11 37		12 07		12 22		
Dinas Powys	d				09 11		10 11		10 26						11 11			11 41		12 11		12 26		
Eastbrook	d				09 13		10 13		10 28						11 13			11 43		12 13		12 28		
Cogan	d				09 15		10 15		10 30						11 15			11 45		12 15		12 30		
Penarth	d											10 47												
Dingle Road	d											10 49												
Grangetown	d				09 19		10 19		10 34			10 53			11 19			11 49		12 19		12 34		
Cardiff Central 7	a				09 24		10 24		10 42			10 58			11 24			11 57		12 24		12 42		
	d	08 26	08 41	08 41	09 41	10 16	10 26	09 06		10 49		11 06			11 41			12 16		12 26				
Cardiff Bay	d										11 04		11 19	11 34		11 49	12 04		12 19		12 34		12 49	13 04
Cardiff Queen Street 3	a	08 29	08 44	08 44	09 44	10 19	10 29			10 52	11 08	11 09	11 23	11 38	11 44	11 53	12 08	12 19	12 23	12 29	12 38		12 53	13 08
	d	08 30	08 45	08 45	09 45	10 20	10 30					11 10			11 45			12 20		12 30				
Heath Low Level	d																							
Ty Glas	d																							
Birchgrove	d																							
Rhiwbina	d																							
Whitchurch (Cardiff)	d																							
Coryton	a																							
Heath High Level	d					10 25												12 25						
Llanishen	d					10 28												12 28						
Lisvane & Thornhill	d					10 30												12 30						
Caerphilly 3	d					10 36												12 36						
Aber	d					10 38												12 38						
Llanbradach	d					10 42												12 42						
Ystrad Mynach 3	d					10 47												12 47						
Hengoed	d					10 50												12 50						
Pengam	d					10 53												12 53						
Gilfach Fargoed	d					10 56												12 56						
Bargoed	d					10 59												12 59						
Brithdir	d					11 03												13 03						
Tir-phil	d					11 06												13 06						
Pontlottyn	d					11 10												13 10						
Rhymney 3	a					11 17												13 17						
Cathays	d	08 33	08 48	08 48	09 48		10 33	09 13				11 13			11 48					12 33				
Llandaf	d	08 37	08 52	08 52	09 52		10 37	09 17				11 17			11 52					12 37				
Ninian Park	d																							
Waun-gron Park	d																							
Fairwater	d																							
Danescourt	d																							
Radyr 3	a	08 40	08 55	08 55	09 55		10 40	09 20				11 20			11 55					12 40				
	d	08 40	08 55	08 55	09 55		10 40	09 20				11 20			11 55					12 40				
Taffs Well 3	d	08 44	08 59	08 59	09 59		10 44	09 24				11 24			11 59					12 44				
Trefforest Estate	d							09 31																
Trefforest	d	08 52	09 06	09 06	10 06		10 52	09 34				11 31			12 06					12 52				
Pontypridd 3	a	08 56	09 09	09 09	10 09		10 56	09 36				11 34			12 09					12 56				
	d	08 58	09 11	09 11	10 11		10 58	09 36				11 36			12 11					12 58				
Abercynon North	d		09 21		10 21										12 22									
Penrhiwceiber	d		09 27	09 27	10 27										12 28									
Mountain Ash	a		09 30	09 30	10 30										12 31									
	d		09 33	09 33	10 33										12 33									
Fernhill	d		09 35	09 35	10 35										12 35									
Cwmbach	d		09 39	09 39	10 39										12 39									
Aberdare 3	a		09 46	09 46	10 46										12 46									
Abercynon South	d	09 04					11 04													13 04				
Quakers Yard	d	09 08					11 14													13 08				
Merthyr Vale	d	09 14					11b17													13c14				
Troed Y Rhiw	d	09 17					11 20													13 17				
Pentre-bach	d	09 20					11 28													13 20				
Merthyr Tydfil	a	09 28					11 32													13 28				
Trehafod	d							09 41				11 41												
Porth	d							09 45				11 45												
Dinas Rhondda	d							09 49				11 49												
Tonypandy	d							09 51				11 51												
Llwynypia	d							09 53				11 53												
Ystrad Rhondda	a							09 56				11 56												
	d							09 59				11 59												
Ton Pentre	d							10 01				12 01												
Treorchy	d							10 04				12 04												
Ynyswen	d							10 07				12 07												
Treherbert	a							10 13				12 13												

For general notes see front of timetable
For details of catering facilities see Directory of Train Operators

A To Cardiff Bay
b Arr. 1113
c Arr. 1313

Table 130

Bridgend, Barry Island, Barry, Penarth and Cardiff → Coryton, Rhymney, Pontypridd, Merthyr, Aberdare and Treherbert

Network Diagram - see first page of Table 130

		AW	AW	AW	AW	AW	AW	AW	AW	AW	AW	AW	AW	AW	AW	AW	AW	AW	AW	AW	AW	AW	AW
Bridgend	d											13 42											
Llantwit Major	d											13 56											
Rhoose Cardiff Int Airport ✈	d											14 06											
Barry Island	d				12 56			13 26		13 56								14 56			15 26		15 56
Barry 3	d				13 00			13 30		14 00		14 15						15 00			15 30		16 00
Barry Docks	d				13 04			13 34		14 04		14 19						15 04			15 34		16 04
Cadoxton	d				13 07			13 37		14 07		14 22						15 07			15 37		16 07
Dinas Powys	d				13 11			13 41		14 11		14 26						15 11			15 41		16 11
Eastbrook	d				13 13			13 43		14 13		14 28						15 13			15 43		16 13
Cogan	d				13 15			13 45		14 15		14 30						15 15			15 45		16 15
Penarth	d	12 47													14 47								
Dingle Road	d	12 49													14 49								
Grangetown	d	12 53			13 19			13 49		14 19		14 34			14 53			15 19			15 49		16 19
Cardiff Central 7	a	12 58			13 24			13 57		14 24		14 42			14 58			15 24			15 57		16 24
	d	13 06			13 41			14 16		14 26					15 06			15 41			16 16		16 26
Cardiff Bay	d		13 19	13 34		13 49	14 04		14 19		14 34		14 49	15 04		15 19	15 34		15 49	16 04		16 19	
Cardiff Queen Street 3	a	13 09	13 23	13 38	13 44	13 53	14 08	14 19	14 23	14 29	14 38		14 53	15 08	15 09	15 23	15 38	15 44	15 53	16 08	16 19	16 23	16 29
	d	13 10			13 45			14 20		14 30					15 10			15 45			16 20		16 30
Heath Low Level	d																						
Ty Glas	d																						
Birchgrove	d																						
Rhiwbina	d																						
Whitchurch (Cardiff)	d																						
Coryton	a																						
Heath High Level	d							14 25													16 25		
Llanishen	d							14 28													16 28		
Lisvane & Thornhill	d							14 30													16 30		
Caerphilly 3	d							14 36													16 36		
Aber	d							14 38													16 38		
Llanbradach	d							14 42													16 42		
Ystrad Mynach 3	d							14 47													16 47		
Hengoed	d							14 50													16 50		
Pengam	d							14 53													16 53		
Gilfach Fargoed	d							14 56													16 56		
Bargoed	d							14 59													16 59		
Brithdir	d							15 03													17 03		
Tir-phil	d							15 06													17 06		
Pontlottyn	d							15 10													17 10		
Rhymney 3	a							15 17													17 17		
Cathays	d	13 13			13 48					14 33					15 13			15 48					16 33
Llandaf	d	13 17			13 52					14 37					15 17			15 52					16 37
Ninian Park	d																						
Waun-gron Park	d																						
Fairwater	d																						
Danescourt	d																						
Radyr 3	a	13 20			13 55					14 40					15 20			15 55					16 40
	d	13 20			13 55					14 40					15 20			15 55					16 40
Taffs Well 3	d	13 24			13 59					14 44					15 24			15 59					16 44
Trefforest Estate	d																						
Trefforest	d	13 31			14 06					14 52					15 31			16 06					16 52
Pontypridd 3	a	13 34			14 09					14 56					15 34			16 09					16 56
	d	13 36			14 11					14 58					15 36			16 11					16 58
Abercynon North	d				14 21													16 21					
Penrhiwceiber	d				14 27													16 27					
Mountain Ash	a				14 30													16 30					
	d				14 33													16 33					
Fernhill	d				14 35													16 35					
Cwmbach	d				14 39													16 39					
Aberdare 3	a				14 46													16 46					
Abercynon South	d									15 04													17 04
Quakers Yard	d									15 08													17 08
Merthyr Vale	d									15b14													17c14
Troed Y Rhiw	d									15 17													17 17
Pentre-bach	d									15 20													17 20
Merthyr Tydfil	a									15 28													17 28
Trehafod	d	13 41													15 41								
Porth	d	13 45													15 45								
Dinas Rhondda	d	13 49													15 49								
Tonypandy	d	13 51													15 51								
Llwynypia	d	13 53													15 53								
Ystrad Rhondda	a	13 56													15 56								
	d	13 59													15 59								
Ton Pentre	d	14 01													16 01								
Treorchy	d	14 04													16 04								
Ynyswen	d	14 07													16 07								
Treherbert	a	14 13													16 13								

For general notes see front of timetable
For details of catering facilities see Directory of Train Operators

b Arr. 1513
c Arr. 1713

Table 130

Sundays

Bridgend, Barry Island, Barry, Penarth and Cardiff → Coryton, Rhymney, Pontypridd, Merthyr, Aberdare and Treherbert

Network Diagram - see first page of Table 130

		AW A	AW	AW	AW	AW	AW	AW	AW	AW	AW	AW	AW	AW	AW	AW	AW	AW	AW	AW	AW
Bridgend	d		15 42					17 42					19 42							21 42		20 42
Llantwit Major	d		15 56					17 56					19 56							21 56		20 56
Rhoose Cardiff Int Airport ✈	d		16 06					18 06					20 06							22 06		21 06
Barry Island	d				16 56	17 26	17 56			18 56	19 26	19 56		20 26		20 56	21 26	21 56		22 56	
Barry 3	d		16 15		17 00	17 30	18 00	18 15		19 00	19 30	20 00	20 15	20 30		21 00	21 30	22 00	22 15	23 00	21 15
Barry Docks	d		16 19		17 04	17 34	18 04	18 19		19 04	19 34	20 04	20 19	20 34		21 04	21 34	22 04	22 19	23 04	21 19
Cadoxton	d		16 22		17 07	17 37	18 07	18 22		19 07	19 37	20 07	20 22	20 37		21 07	21 37	22 07	22 22	23 07	21 22
Dinas Powys	d		16 26		17 11	17 41	18 11	18 26		19 11	19 41	20 11	20 26	20 41		21 11	21 41	22 11	22 26	23 11	21 26
Eastbrook	d		16 28		17 13	17 43	18 13	18 28		19 13	19 43	20 13	20 28	20 43		21 13	21 43	22 13	22 28	23 13	21 28
Cogan	d		16 30		17 15	17 45	18 15	18 30		19 15	19 45	20 15	20 30	20 45		21 15	21 45	22 15	22 30	23 15	21 30
Penarth	d			16 47					18 47						20 47						
Dingle Road	d			16 49					18 49						20 49						
Grangetown	d		16 34	16 53	17 19	17 49	18 19	18 34	18 53	19 19	19 49	20 19	20 34	20 49	20 53	21 19	21 49	22 19	22 34	23 19	21 34
Cardiff Central 7	a		16 42	16 58	17 24	17 57	18 24	18 42	18 58	19 24	19 57	20 24	20 42	20 57	20 59	21 27	21 54	22 27	22 42	23 27	21 39
	d			17 06	17 41	18 16	18 26		19 06	19 41	20 16	20 26		21 06	21 16		22 06				21 41
Cardiff Bay	d	16 34																			
Cardiff Queen Street 3	a	16 37		17 09	17 44	18 19	18 29		19 09	19 44	20 19	20 29		21 09	21 19		22 09				21 44
	d			17 10	17 45	18 20	18 30		19 10	19 45	20 20	20 30		21 10	21 20		22 10				21 45
Heath Low Level	d																				
Ty Glas	d																				
Birchgrove	d																				
Rhiwbina	d																				
Whitchurch (Cardiff)	d																				
Coryton	a																				
Heath High Level	d					18 25					20 25				21 25						
Llanishen	d					18 28					20 28				21 28						
Lisvane & Thornhill	d					18 30					20 30				21 30						
Caerphilly 3	d					18 36					20 36				21 36						
Aber	d					18 38					20 38				21 38						
Llanbradach	d					18 42					20 42				21 42						
Ystrad Mynach 3	d					18 47					20 47				21 47						
Hengoed	d					18 50					20 50				21 50						
Pengam	d					18 53					20 53				21 53						
Gilfach Fargoed	d					18 56					20 56				21 56						
Bargoed	d					18 59					20 59				21 59						
Brithdir	d					19 03					21 03				22 03						
Tir-phil	d					19 06					21 06				22 06						
Pontlottyn	d					19 10					21 10				22 10						
Rhymney 3	a					19 17					21 17				22 17						
Cathays	d			17 13	17 48		18 33		19 13	19 48		20 33		21 13			22 13				21 48
Llandaf	d			17 17	17 52		18 37		19 17	19 52		20 37		21 17			22 17				21 52
Ninian Park	d																				
Waun-gron Park	d																				
Fairwater	d																				
Danescourt	d																				
Radyr 3	a			17 20	17 55		18 40		19 20	19 55		20 40		21 20			22 20				21 55
	d			17 20	17 55		18 40		19 20	19 55		20 40		21 20			22 20				21 55
Taffs Well 3	d			17 24	17 59		18 44		19 24	19 59		20 44		21 24			22 24				21 59
Trefforest Estate	d																				
Trefforest	d			17 31	18 06		18 52		19 31	20 06		20 52		21 31			22 31				22 06
Pontypridd 3	a			17 34	18 09		18 56		19 34	20 09		20 56		21 34			22 34				22 09
	d			17 36	18 11		18 58		19 36	20 11		20 58		21 36			22 36				22 11
Abercynon North	d				18 21					20 21											22 21
Penrhiwceiber	d				18 27					20 27											22 27
Mountain Ash	a				18 30					20 30											22 30
	d				18 33					20 33											22 33
Fernhill	d				18 35					20 35											22 35
Cwmbach	d				18 39					20 39											22 39
Aberdare 3	a				18 46					20 46											22 46
Abercynon South	d						19 04					21 04									
Quakers Yard	d						19 08					21 08									
Merthyr Vale	d						19 14					21b14									
Troed Y Rhiw	d						19 17					21 17									
Pentre-bach	d						19 20					21 20									
Merthyr Tydfil	a						19 28					21 28									
Trehafod	d			17 41					19 41					21 41			22 41				
Porth	d			17 45					19 45					21 45			22 45				
Dinas Rhondda	d			17 49					19 49					21 49			22 49				
Tonypandy	d			17 51					19 51					21 51			22 51				
Llwynypia	d			17 53					19 53					21 53			22 53				
Ystrad Rhondda	a			17 56					19 56					21 56			22 56				
	d			17 59					19 59					21 59			22 59				
Ton Pentre	d			18 01					20 01					22 01			23 01				
Treorchy	d			18 04					20 04					22 04			23 04				
Ynyswen	d			18 07					20 07					22 07			23 07				
Treherbert	a			18 13					20 13					22 13			23 13				

For general notes see front of timetable
For details of catering facilities see Directory of Train Operators

A To Cardiff Central
b Arr. 2113

Table 130A

Mondays to Saturdays

Rhoose (Cardiff Intl Airport) — Cardiff International Airport

Bus Service

		AW	AW	AW		AW	AW	AW		AW	AW	AW		AW	AW	AW		AW	AW	AW		AW	AW	AW		
Rhoose Cardiff Int Airport	d	06 16	07 16	08 16	.....	09 16	10 16	11 16	.....	12 16	13 16	14 16	.....	15 16	16 16	17 16	.....	18 16	19 16	20 16	.....	21 16	22 16	23 16	.....	.....
Cardiff International Apt	a	06 23	07 23	08 23	.	09 23	10 23	11 23	.	12 23	13 23	14 23	.	15 23	16 23	17 23	.	18 23	19 23	20 23	.	21 23	22 23	23 23	.	.

Sundays

		AW		AW		AW		AW		AW		AW		AW		AW		AW		AW	AW	AW	AW	AW		
Rhoose Cardiff Int Airport	d	09 16	.....	10 16	.....	11 16	.....	12 16	.....	13 16	.....	14 16	.....	15 16	.....	16 16	.....	17 16	.....	18 16	19 16	20 16	21 16	22 16	.....	.....
Cardiff International Apt	a	09 23	.	10 23	.	11 23	.	12 23	.	13 23	.	14 23	.	15 23	.	16 23	.	17 23	.	18 23	19 23	20 23	21 23	22 23	.	.

Mondays to Saturdays

		AW	AW	AW		AW	AW	AW		AW	AW	AW		AW	AW	AW		AW	AW	AW		AW	AW	AW		
Cardiff International Apt	d	05 51	06 51	07 51	.....	08 51	09 51	10 51	.....	11 51	12 51	13 51	.....	14 51	15 51	16 51	.....	17 51	18 51	19 51	.....	20 51	21 51	22 51	.....	.....
Rhoose Cardiff Int Airport	a	05 58	06 58	07 58	.	08 58	09 58	10 58	.	11 58	12 58	13 58	.	14 58	15 58	16 58	.	17 58	18 58	19 58	.	20 58	21 58	22 58	.	.

Sundays

		AW	AW		AW	AW		AW	AW		AW	AW		AW	AW		AW	AW		AW	AW		AW			
Cardiff International Apt	d	08 51	09 51	.....	10 51	11 51	.....	12 51	13 51	.....	14 51	15 51	.....	16 51	17 51	.....	18 51	19 51	.....	20 51	21 51	.....	22 51	.....	.....	.....
Rhoose Cardiff Int Airport	a	08 58	09 58	.	10 58	11 58	.	12 58	13 58	.	14 58	15 58	.	16 58	17 58	.	18 58	19 58	.	20 58	21 58	.	22 58	.	.	.

For general notes see front of timetable
For details of catering facilities see
Directory of Train Operators

Cardiff → Crewe, Liverpool and Manchester

Route Diagram - see first page of Table 129

Miles	Miles			AW	AW	AW	AW	AW	GW	AW	GW	AW	AW	AW	AW	AW	AW	AW	AW
				MX ◇ A	MX		MX ◇	MO ◇	[1] ◇ B ⊠	◇ 🛒	[1] ◇ C D ⊠	◇ 🛒	◇		◇ E 🛒	◇ 🛒	◇ E 🛒		◇ A 🛒
—	—	Swansea [7]	d	20p55						*04 00*			04 36		*05 24*	*05 59*	06 40		07 45
0	0	**Cardiff Central [7]**	d	21p56	00 30		04 00	04 00		05 10		05 35			06 50	07 20	07 50		08 50
—	—	London Paddington [15] ⊖	d														*05 27*		*06 45*
—	—	Reading [7]	d														*05 56*		*07 11*
—	—	Bristol Temple Meads [10]	d												*05 54*	*06 50*	*07 15*		*08 19*
11¾	11¾	**Newport (South Wales)**	d	22p15	00 57		04 18	04 18		05 28		05 53			07 04	07 34	08 04		09 04
18¾	18¾	Cwmbran	d	22p25	01 08		04 28	04 29		05 38		06 03			07 15	07 44	08 16		09 15
21¾	21¾	Pontypool and New Inn	d	22p31	01 14		04 34	04 35		05 44		06 09				07 49			09 20
31¼	31¼	Abergavenny	d	22p40	01 25		04 45	04 46	05⟆11	05 54	06 09	06 22			07 28	08 00	08 29		09 28
55¼	55¼	**Hereford [7]**	a	23p05	01 53		05 12	05 13	05⟆34	06 18	06 32	06 47			07 54	08 25	08 54		09 54
—	—		d	23p06			05 23	05 23		06 25		06 48			07 56	08 28	08 56		09 56
67¾	67¾	Leominster	d	23p20			05 36	05 36		06 38		07 02			08 09		09 09		10 09
78¾	78¾	Ludlow	d	23p31			05 47	05 47		06 49		07 13			08 20	08 49	09 20		10 20
86	86	Craven Arms	d	23p39			05 56	05 56		06 58		07 21	07 53		08 29		09 29		10 29
93¼	93¼	Church Stretton	d	23p48			06 08	06 08		07 07		07 30	08 06		08 38		09 38		10 38
106	106	**Shrewsbury**	a	00 02			06 22	06 22		07 22		07 44	08 21		08 52	09 15	09 52		10 52
—	—		d	00 12		06 03	06 26	06 26		07 30		07 46		08 26	08 54	09 30	09 54	10 26	10 54
113¼	113¼	Yorton	d	00x20		06x13								08x36				10x36	
116¾	116¾	Wem	d	00 25		06 19	06 38	06 38				07 58		08 42				10 42	
120	120	Prees	d	00x30		06x23								08x46				10x46	
125	125	Whitchurch (Shrops)	d	00 37		06 31	06 47	06 47				08 07		08 54				10 54	
129¾	129¾	Wrenbury	d	00x42		06x37								09x00				11x00	
134¼	134¼	Nantwich	d	00 48		06 44	06 56	06 56				08 16		09 07				11 07	
138¾	138¾	**Crewe [10]**	a	00 58		06 54	07 05	07 05				08 25		09 17	09 25		10 25	11 17	11 25
—	—	Chester	a				*07 59*	*07 59*		08 28		*09 26*		*09 57*	*10 27*	10 28	*11 17*	*11 59*	*12 27*
—	—	Llandudno Junction	a				*09*b*19*	*09*b*19*		09 26		*10 24*		*11*b*17*		11 24	*12 07*	*13*b*17*	
—	—	Bangor (Gwynedd)	a							09 43		*10 46*				11 41	*12 26*		
—	—	Holyhead	a							10 20		*11 30*				12 20	*13 03*		
—	161½	Runcorn	a				*07 47*	*07 47*				*09 08*			*10 03*		*11 03*		*12 25*
—	174½	**Liverpool Lime Street [10]**	a				*08 11*	*08 11*				*09 31*			*10 26*		*11 26*		*12 47*
157¾	—	Wilmslow	a				07 29	07 29				08 44			09 44		10 44		11 44
163¾	—	Stockport	a				07 46	07 46				08 53			09 54		10 53		11 53
169¾	—	**Manchester Piccadilly [10]** ⛴	a			*08 02*	08 10	08 10				09 13			10 13		11 13		12 13

		AW	AW	AW	AW	GW	AW	AW	AW	AW	AW	AW	AW	GW	AW	AW	AW	AW	AW	AW
		◇ 🛒	◇ A 🛒		◇ E 🛒	[1] ◇ 🛒	◇	◇ 🛒	◇ A 🛒		◇ E 🛒	◇ 🛒	◇ A 🛒	[1] ◇ 🛒		[R] E 🛒	◇	◇ 🛒	[R] A 🛒	
Swansea [7]	d	*07 59*	08 55		09 55		09 15		10 55		11 55		12 50			13 55	13 16		14 55	
Cardiff Central [7]	d	09 20	09 50		10 50		08 09	11 20	11 50		12 50	13 20	13 50			14 50		15 20	15 50	16 06
London Paddington [15] ⊖	d	*07 45*			*08 45*	08 51		*09 45*			*10 45*	*11 45*		11 51		*12 45*		*13 45*		*14 15*
Reading [7]	d	*08 11*			*09 11*	09 23		*10 11*			*11 11*	*12 11*		12 23		*13 11*		*14 11*		*14 41*
Bristol Temple Meads [10]	d	*08 54*	*09 19*					*10 54*	*11 19*		*11 54*	*12 54*	*13 19*			*14 19*		*14 54*	*15 19*	
Newport (South Wales)	d	09 34	10 04		11 04			11 34	12 04		13 04	13 34	14 04			15 04		15 34	16 04	16 22
Cwmbran	d	09 44	10 15		11 15			11 44	12 15		13 15	13 43	14 15			15 15		15 44	16 15	16 34
Pontypool and New Inn	d							11 49				13 48						15 49		16 40
Abergavenny	d	09 57	10 28		11 28			12 00	12 28		13 28	14 00	14 28			15 28		16 00	16 28	16a55
Hereford [7]	a	10 22	10 54		11 54	12 05		12 25	12 54		13 54	14 25	14 54	15 04		15 53		16 25	16 54	
	d	10 23	10 56		11 56			12 28	12 56		13 56	14 28	14 56			15 55		16 28	16 56	
Leominster	d		11 09		12 09				13 09		14 09		15 09			16 08			17 09	
Ludlow	d	10 45	11 20		12 20			12 49	13 20		14 20	14 49	15 20			16 19		16 49	17 20	
Craven Arms	d		11 29		12 29		12 36		13 29		14 29		15 29			16 28	16 37		17 29	
Church Stretton	d		11 37		12 38		12 50		13 38		14 38		15 38				16 50		17 38	
Shrewsbury	a	11 11	11 51		12 52		13 07	13 15	13 52		14 52	15 17	15 52			16 48	17 10	17 15	17 52	
	d	11 30	11 54	12 26	12 54			13 30	13 54	14 26	14 54	15 30	15 54		16 26	16 50		17 30	17 54	
Yorton	d			12x36						14x36					16x36					
Wem	d			12 42						14 42					16 42	17 01				
Prees	d			12x46						14x46					16x46					
Whitchurch (Shrops)	d			12 54						14 54					16 54	17 10				
Wrenbury	d			13x00						15x00					17x00					
Nantwich	d			13 07						15 07					17 07					
Crewe [10]	a		12 25	13 17	13 24				14 24	15 18	15 24		16 25		17 17	17 26			18 24	
Chester	a	12 28	*13 32*	*13 57*	*14 27*			14 28	*15 26*	*15 57*	*16 27*	16 28	*17 26*		*17 53*	*18 29*		18 25	*19 25*	
Llandudno Junction	a	13 24	*14 22*	*15*b*18*				15 25	*16 24*	*17*b*17*		17 24	*18 25*		*18 49*	*19*b*26*		19 26	*20 44*	
Bangor (Gwynedd)	a	13 48	*14 55*					15 47	*16 46*			17 47	*18 47*		*19 05*	*19*b*49*		19 49	*21 03*	
Holyhead	a	14 30	*15 30*					16 30	*17 20*			18 30	*19 20*		*19 41*	*20*b*30*		20 30	*21 40*	
Runcorn	a		*13 03*		*14 25*				*15 03*		*16 25*		*17 03*			*18 25*			*19 05*	
Liverpool Lime Street [10]	a		*13 26*		*14 47*				*15 26*		*16 48*		*17 26*			*18 47*			*19 29*	
Wilmslow	a		12 44		13 44				14 44		15 44		16 44			17 44			18 44	
Stockport	a		12 53		13 53				14 53		15 53		16 53			17 54			18 53	
Manchester Piccadilly [10] ⛴	a		13 13		14 13				15 13		16 13		17 11			18 12			19 13	

For general notes see front of timetable
For details of catering facilities see Directory of Train Operators

- **A** From Milford Haven (Table 128)
- **B** All Tuesdays to Fridays, also Mondays until 24 March. To London Paddington (Table 126)
- **C** To London Paddington (Table 126)
- **D** **The Cathedrals Express**
- **E** From Carmarthen (Table 128)
- **b** Change at Crewe and Chester

Cardiff → Crewe, Liverpool and Manchester

Route Diagram - see first page of Table 129

		AW	AW [R] A	AW [R]	AW [R] B	AW	AW ◇ A	GW [1] ◇	AW ◇	AW ◇	AW ◇ C	GW [1] ◇ D	AW ◇ A	AW ◇ E	AW ◇ B
Swansea [7]	d		15 55		16 55		17 55		18 29	18 21	18 58		19 55		20 55
Cardiff Central [7]	d		16 50	17 20	17 50		18 50		19 34		20 10		20 53		21 56
London Paddington [15] ⊖	d		14 45	15 45			16 45	17 21	17 45		18 15	18 21	19 15		20 15
Reading [7]	d		15 11	16 11			17 11	17 50	18 11		18 41	18 50	19 41		20 41
Bristol Temple Meads [10]	d		15 54	16 54	17 19		18 19		18 54		19 25		20 19		21 19
Newport (South Wales)	d		17 04	17 34	18 04		19 06		19 49		20 25		21 10		22 15
Cwmbran	d		17 15	17 44	18 15		19 15		19 58		20 35		21 21		22 25
Pontypool and New Inn	d			17 49	18 20				20 03		20 41				22 31
Abergavenny	d		17 28	18 00	18 28		19 28		20 13		20 48		21 34		22 40
Hereford [7]	a		17 54	18 24	18 54		19 54	20 30	20 39		21 14	21 30	22 00		23 05
	d		17 56	18 26	18 56		19 56		20 40		21 16		22 01		23 06
Leominster	d		18 09	18 39	19 09		20 09		20 54		21 29		22 15		23 20
Ludlow	d		18 20	18 49	19 20		20 20		21 01		21 40		22 26		23 31
Craven Arms	d		18 29		19 29		20 29		21 13	21 37	21 49		22 34		23 39
Church Stretton	d		18 38		19 38		20 38		21 22	21 50	22 02		22 43		23 48
Shrewsbury	a		18 52	19 16	19 52		20 52		21 36	22 12	22 16		22 57		00 02
	d	18 26	18 54	19 30	19 54	20 26	20 54		21 38		22 17		22 59	23 29	00 12
Yorton	d	18x36				20x36					22x26		23x08		00x20
Wem	d	18 42				20 42					22 31		23 13		00 25
Prees	d	18x46				20x46					22x35		23x17		00x30
Whitchurch (Shrops)	d	18 54				20 54					22 42		23 24		00 37
Wrenbury	d	19x00				21x00					22x48		23x30		00x42
Nantwich	d	19 07				21 07					22 54		23 36		00 48
Crewe [10]	a	19 17	19 25		20 26	21 17	21 24				23 03		23 46	00 01	00 58
Chester	a		20 02	20 31	21 27	21 49	22 11		22 32				00 16	00 28	
Llandudno Junction	a			21 28		22 39			23 38					01 16	
Bangor (Gwynedd)	a			21 51		22 55			00 01					01 33	
Holyhead	a			22 35		23 30			00 47					02 06	
Runcorn	a	19 53	20 25		21 21		22 25								
Liverpool Lime Street [10]	a	20 18	20 47		21 45		22 47								
Wilmslow	a		19 44		20 45		21 44				23 23				
Stockport	a		19 53		20 53		21 53				23 33				
Manchester Piccadilly [10]	a		20 18		21 13		22 12				23 49			01b35	

Saturdays

until 22 March

		AW ◇ B	AW	AW	AW ◇	AW ◇	AW ◇	AW ◇	AW	AW ◇ A	AW ◇	AW ◇ A	AW	AW ◇ B	AW ◇	AW ◇ B	AW	AW ◇ A	AW ◇	AW ◇	GW [1] ◇	AW ◇ B	AW	AW ◇ A	AW ◇
Swansea [7]	d	20p55				04 00		04 36		04c59	05c59	06 40		07 45	07e45	08 55		09 55	09 15			10 55		11 55	
Cardiff Central [7]	d	21p56	00 30		04 00	05 10	05 35			06 50	07 20	07 50		08 50	09 20	09 50		10 50	08 09	11 20		11 50		12 50	13 20
London Paddington [15] ⊖	d															07f15		08g45		09c45	09 51			10h15	11g45
Reading [7]	d															07j41		09g11		10c11	10 23			10k41	12g11
Bristol Temple Meads [10]	d										06 50	06 58		07 54	08 54	09 19		10 19		10 54		11 19		12 19	12 53
Newport (South Wales)	d	22p15	00 53		04 18	05 25	05 53			07 04	07 34	08 04		09 04	09 34	10 04		11 04		11 34		12 04		13 04	13 34
Cwmbran	d	22p25	01 04		04 28	05 39	06 03			07 15	07 44	08 15		09 15	09 44	10 15		11 15		11 44		12 15		13 15	13 44
Pontypool and New Inn	d	22p31	01 10		04 34	05 45	06 09				07 49			09 20						11 49					13 49
Abergavenny	d	22p40	01 20		04 45	05 55	06 22			07 28	08 00	08 28		09 28	09 57	10 28		11 28		12 00		12 28		13 28	14 00
Hereford [7]	a	23p05	01 46		05 12	06 19	06 47			07 54	08 25	08 54		09 54	10 22	10 54		11 54		12 25	12 53	12 54		13 54	14 25
	d	23p06	01 48		05 23	06 25	06 48			07 56	08 28	08 56		09 56	10 24	10 56		11 56		12 28		12 56		13 56	14 28
Leominster	d	23p20	02 01		05 36	06 38	07 02			08 09		09 09		10 09		11 09		12 09				13 09		14 09	
Ludlow	d	23p31	02 12		05 47	06 49	07 13			08 20	08 49	09 20		10 20	10 46	11 20		12 20		12 49		13 20		14 20	14 49
Craven Arms	d	23p39	02 22		05 56	06 58	07 21	07 53		08 29		09 29		10 29		11 29		12 29	12 36			13 29		14 29	
Church Stretton	d	23p48	02 31		06 08	07 07	07 30	08 06		08 38		09 38		10 38		11 38		12 38	12 50			13 38		14 38	
Shrewsbury	a	00 02	02 49		06 22	07 22	07 44	08 21		08 52	09 15	09 52		10 52	11 12	11 52		12 52	13 07	13 15		13 52		14 52	15 17
	d	00 12		06 03	06 26	07 30	07 46		08 26	08 54	09 30	09 54	10 26	10 54	11 30	11 54	12 26	12 54		13 30		13 54	14 26	14 54	15 30
Yorton	d	00x20		06x13					08x36				10x36				12x36						14x36		
Wem	d	00 25		06 19	06 38		07 58		08 42				10 42				12 42						14 42		
Prees	d	00x30		06x23					08x46				10x46				12x46						14x46		
Whitchurch (Shrops)	d	00 37		06 31	06 47		08 07		08 54				10 54				12 54						14 54		
Wrenbury	d	00x42		06x37					09x00				11x00				13x00						15x00		
Nantwich	d	00 48		06 44	06 56		08 16		09 07				11 07				13 07						15 07		
Crewe [10]	a	00 58		06 57	07 05		08 28		09 17	09 28		10 28	11 20	11 28		12 28	13 20	13 28				14 28	15 20	15 28	
Chester	a				07 57	08 28	09 26		09 57	10 27	10 28	11 09	11 59		12 25	13 31	13 57	14 27		14 28		15 26	15 57	16 27	16 28
Llandudno Junction	a				09m19	09 26	10 24		11m17		11 26	12 02	13m17		13 24	14 21	15m18			15 25		16 24	17m17		17 24
Bangor (Gwynedd)	a					09 43	10 46				11 43	12 18			13 48	14 54				15 47		16 46			17 47
Holyhead	a					10 20	11 30				12 20	12 53			14 30	15 30				16 30		17 20			18 30
Runcorn	a				07 46		09 04			10 09		11 08		12 09		13 08		14 08				15 09		16 09	
Liverpool Lime Street [10]	a				08 10		09 31			10 31		11 31		12 31		13 30		14 32				15 31		16 33	
Wilmslow	a				07 33		08 48			09 48		10 48		11 48		12 48		13 48				14 48		15 48	
Stockport	a			07 42	07 42		08 56			09 58		10 58		11 58		12 58		13 58				14 58		15 58	
Manchester Piccadilly [10]	a			08 00	08 00		09 12			10 13		11 13		12 13		13 13		14 13				15 13		16 13	

For general notes see front of timetable
For details of catering facilities see Directory of Train Operators

- A From Carmarthen (Table 128)
- B From Milford Haven (Table 128)
- C Fridays from Milford Haven (Table 128).
- D **The Cathedrals Express**
- E From Birmingham New Street (Table 74)
- b Change at Crewe
- c Until 26 January only
- e Until 26 January dep. 0759
- f Until 26 January dep. 0745
- g Until 26 January
- h Until 26 January dep. 1045
- j Until 26 January dep. 0811
- k Until 26 January dep. 1111
- m Change at Crewe and Chester

Table 131

until 22 March

Cardiff → Crewe, Liverpool and Manchester

Route Diagram - see first page of Table 129

		GW	AW	AW	AW	AW	AW	AW	AW	AW	AW	AW	AW	AW	AW	GW	AW	AW	AW	GW	AW	AW	AW
		1 ◇ 🍴	◇ A 🛒		R B 🛒	◇	◇ 🛒	R A 🛒			R B 🛒	◇ 🛒	R A 🛒		◇ B 🛒	1 ◇ 🍴	◇ 🛒	◇	◇ A 🛒	1 ◇ 🍴	◇ B	◇ C	◇ A
Swansea 7	d		12 50		13 55	13 16		14 55			15 55		16 55		17 55		18 29	18 21	18 55		19 55		20 55
Cardiff Central 7	d		13 50		14 50		15 20	15 50	16 06		16 50	17 20	17 50		18 50		19 34		20 10		20 53		21 50
London Paddington 15 ⊖	d	11 51	11b15		12c15		13e45	13f15			14g15	15h45	15f15		16j15	16 51	17k45			18 21	18m15		19n15
Reading 7	d	12 23	11q41		12r41		14e11	13f41			14t41	16v11	15v41		16w41	17 23	18k11			18 53	18y41		19z41
Bristol Temple Meads 10	d		13 19		14 19		14 53	15 19			16D07	16 53	17 19		18 19		18 53		19 24		20E07		21 19
Newport (South Wales)	d		14 04		15 04		15 34	16 04	16 22		17 04	17 34	18 04		19 05		19 49		20 25		21 09		22 08
Cwmbran	d		14 15		15 15		15 44	16 15	16 32		17 15	17 44	18 15		19 16		20 00		20 35		21 20		22 19
Pontypool and New Inn	d						15 49		16 38			17 49	18 21				20 04		20 41				22 25
Abergavenny	d		14 28		15 28		16 00	16 28	16a53		17 28	18 00	18 28		19 29		20 15		20 48		21 33		22 34
Hereford 7	a	14 53	14 54		15 52		16 25	16 54			17 54	18 25	18 54		19 55	20 02	20 39		21 14	21 32	21 57		22 59
	d		14 56		15 54		16 28	16 56			17 56	18 26	18 56		19 56		20 41		21 16		21 59		23 00
Leominster	d		15 09		16 07			17 09			18 09	18 39	19 09		20 09		20 54		21 29		22 12		23 13
Ludlow	d		15 20		16 18		16 49	17 20			18 20	18 49	19 20		20 20		21 01		21 40		22 23		23 24
Craven Arms	d		15 29		16 27	16 37		17 29			18 29		19 29		20 29		21 13	21 37	21 49		22 32		23 33
Church Stretton	d		15 38			16 50		17 38			18 38		19 38		20 38		21 22	21 50	22 02		22 41		23 42
Shrewsbury	a		15 52		16 47	17 10	17 15	17 52			18 52	19 16	19 52		20 52		21 36	22 12	22 16		22 55		23 56
	d		15 54	16 26	16 49		17 30	17 54		18 26	18 54	19 30	19 54	20 26	20 54		21 38		22 17		22 56	23 29	23 57
Yorton	d			16x36						18x36				20x36					22x26		23x05		00x06
Wem	d			16 42	17 01					18 42				20 42					22 31		23 10		00 10
Prees	d			16x46						18x46				20x46					22x35		23x15		00x15
Whitchurch (Shrops)	d			16 54	17 10					18 54				20 54					22 42		23 22		00 21
Wrenbury	d			17x00						19x00				21x00					22x48		23x28		00x27
Nantwich	d			17 07						19 07				21 07					22 54		23 34		00 32
Crewe 10	a		16 28	17 20	17 28			18 28		19 23	19 28		20 26	21 20	21 27				23 03		23 44	00 01	00 44
Chester	a		17 26	17 54	18 29		18 25	19 25			20 02	20 26	21 27		22 09		22 32				00 10	00 24	
Llandudno Junction	a		18 25	18 49	19G26		19 26	20 37				21 28	22 25				23 33						
Bangor (Gwynedd)	a		18 47	19 05	19G49		19 49	20 55				21 51	22 42				00H25						
Holyhead	a		19 20	19 36	20G30		20 30	21 33				22 35	23 30				01H45						
Runcorn	a		17 09		18 09			19 08			20 08		21 08		22 08								
Liverpool Lime Street 10	a		17 30		18 28			19 32			20 30		21 27		22 27								
Wilmslow	a		16 48		17 48			18 48			19 48		20 45		21 46				23 22				
Stockport	a		16 58		17 58			18 58			19 59		20 56		21 57				23 33				
Manchester Piccadilly 10 ✈	a		17 13		18 10			19 16			20 13		21 13		22 13				23 50				

Saturdays

from 29 March

		AW	AW	AW	AW	AW	AW	AW	AW	AW	AW	AW	AW	AW	AW	AW	AW	AW	AW	AW	AW	AW	AW	AW	AW
		◇ A			◇	🚌	◇	🚌	◇	◇	🚌		◇ 🛒	🚌		🚌	◇ 🛒	🚌		◇ 🛒	🚌		🚌	◇ 🛒	🚌
Swansea 7	d	20p55								04 36	04 00														
Cardiff Central 7	d	21p56	00 30			04 15		04 40			05 40			06 15											
London Paddington 15 ⊖	d																								06 45
Reading 7	d																								07 11
Bristol Temple Meads 10	d																								
Newport (South Wales)	d	22p15	00 53			04 45		05 10			06 10			06 45		07 15		08 15			08 45		09 15		10 15
Cwmbran	d	22p25	01 04			05 00		05 25			06 25			07 00		07 30		08 30			09 00		09 30		10 30
Pontypool and New Inn	d	22p31	01 10			05 15		05 40			06 40			07 15									09 45		
Abergavenny	d	22p40	01 20			05 30		05 55			06 55			07 30		08 00		09 00			09 30		10 00		11 00
Hereford 7	a	23p05	01 46			06 15		06 40			07 40			08 15		08 45		09 45			10 15		10 45		11 45
	d	23p06	01 48		05 23		06 25		06 51				07 56		08 28		08 56			10 00		10 28		11 00	
Leominster	d	23p20	02 01		05 36		06 38		07 04				08 09				09 09			10 13				11 13	
Ludlow	d	23p31	02 12		05 47		06 49		07 15				08 20		08 49		09 20			10 24		10 49		11 24	
Craven Arms	d	23p39	02 22		05 56		06 58		07 24	07 53			08 29				09 29			10 33				11 33	
Church Stretton	d	23p48	02 31		06 08		07 07		07 33	08 06			08 38				09 38			10 42				11 42	
Shrewsbury	a	00 02	02 49		06 22		07 22		07 47	08 21			08 52		09 15		09 52			10 56		11 15		11 56	
	d	00 12		06 03	06 26		07 30		07 48			08 26	08 54		09 30		09 54		10 26	10 57		11 30		11 57	
Yorton	d	00x20		06x13								08x36							10x36						
Wem	d	00 25		06 19	06 38				08 00			08 42							10 42						
Prees	d	00x30		06x23								08x46							10x46						
Whitchurch (Shrops)	d	00 37		06 31	06 47				08 09			08 54							10 54						
Wrenbury	d	00x42		06x37								09x00							11x00						
Nantwich	d	00 48		06 44	06 56				08 19			09 07							11 07						
Crewe 10	a	00 58		06 57	07 05				08 28			09 17	09 28				10 27		11 20	11 28				12 28	
Chester	a				07 57		08 28		09 26			09 57	10 27		10 28		11 09		11 59			12 25		13 31	
Llandudno Junction	a				09G19		09 26		10 24			11G17			11 26		12 02		13G17			13 24		14 21	
Bangor (Gwynedd)	a						09 43		10 46						11 43		12 18					13 48		14 54	
Holyhead	a						10 20		11 30						12 20		12 53					14 30		15 30	
Runcorn	a				07 46				09 04				10 09				11 08			12 09				13 08	
Liverpool Lime Street 10	a				08 10				09 31				10 31				11 31			12 31				13 30	
Wilmslow	a				07 33				08 48				09 48				10 48			11 48				12 48	
Stockport	a				07 42				08 56				09 58				10 58			11 58				12 58	
Manchester Piccadilly 10 ✈	a				08 00				09 12				10 13				11 13			12 13				13 13	

For general notes see front of timetable
For details of catering facilities see Directory of Train Operators

- **A** From Milford Haven (Table 128)
- **B** From Carmarthen (Table 128)
- **C** From Birmingham New Street (Table 74)
- **D** Until 26 January dep. 1553
- **E** Until 26 January dep. 1953
- **G** Change at Crewe and Chester
- **H** By bus
- **b** 2 February to 23 March only
- **c** Until 26 January dep. 1245
- **e** Until 26 January
- **f** 2 February to 22 March only
- **g** Until 26 January dep. 1445
- **h** Until 26 January dep. 1545
- **j** Until 26 January dep. 1645
- **k** Until 26 January only
- **m** Until 26 January dep. 1915
- **n** Until 26 January dep. 1945
- **q** 2 February to 22 March only
- **r** Until 26 January dep. 1311
- **t** Until 26 January dep. 1511
- **v** Until 26 January dep. 1611
- **w** Until 26 January dep. 1711
- **y** Until 26 January dep. 1941
- **z** Until 26 January dep. 2011

Table 131

Saturdays

from 29 March

Cardiff → Crewe, Liverpool and Manchester

Route Diagram - see first page of Table 129

		AW	AW	AW	AW	AW	AW	GW	AW	AW	AW	AW	AW	AW	AW	GW	AW	AW	AW	AW	AW	AW	AW	AW	AW
			◇ 🛒	◇	🚌		🚌	1 ◇ ☕	◇ 🛒	🚌		◇ 🛒	🚌		🚌	1 ◇ ☕	◇ 🛒	🚌		R 🛒	◇	🚌		🚌	R 🛒
Swansea 7	d			09 15																	13 16				
Cardiff Central 7	d			08 09																					
London Paddington 15	⊖ d				07 45			09 51		08 45			09 45			11 51		10 45				11 45			
Reading 7	d				08 11			10 23		09 11			10 11			12 23		11 11				12 11			
Bristol Temple Meads 10	d																								
Newport (South Wales)	d				10 45		11 15			12 15			12 45		13 15			14 15				14 45		15 15	
Cwmbran	d				11 00		11 30			12 30			13 00		13 30			14 30				15 00		15 30	
Pontypool and New Inn	d				11 15								13 15									15 15			
Abergavenny	d				11 30		12 00			13 00			13 30		14 00			15 00				15 30		16 00	
Hereford 7	a				12 15		12 45	12 53		13 45			14 15		14 45	14 53		15 45				16 15		16 45	
	d		11 56			12 28			13 00			13 56		14 28			15 00			15 54			16 28		17 00
Leominster	d		12 09						13 13			14 09					15 13			16 07					17 13
Ludlow	d		12 20			12 49			13 24			14 20		14 49			15 24			16 18			16 49		17 24
Craven Arms	d		12 29	12 36					13 33			14 29					15 33			16 27	16 37				17 33
Church Stretton	d		12 38	12 50					13 42			14 38					15 42				16 50				17 42
Shrewsbury	a		12 52	13 07		13 15			13 56			14 52		15 17			15 56			16 47	17 10		17 15		17 56
	d	12 26	12 54			13 30			13 57		14 26	14 54		15 30			15 57		16 26	16 49			17 30		17 57
Yorton	d	12x36									14x36								16x36						
Wem	d	12 42									14 42								16 42	17 01					
Prees	d	12x46									14x46								16x46						
Whitchurch (Shrops)	d	12 54									14 54								16 54	17 10					
Wrenbury	d	13x00									15x00								17x00						
Nantwich	d	13 07									15 07								17 07						
Crewe 10	a	13 20	13 28						14 28		15 20	15 28					16 28		17 20	17 28					18 28
Chester	a	13 57	14 27			14 28			15 26		15 57	16 27		16 28			17 26		17 54	18 29			18 25		19 25
Llandudno Junction	a	15b18				15 25			16 24		17b17			17 24			18 25		18 49	19b26			19 26		20 37
Bangor (Gwynedd)	a					15 47			16 46					17 47			18 47		19 05	19b49			19 49		20 55
Holyhead	a					16 30			17 20					18 30			19 20		19 36	20b30			20 30		21 33
Runcorn	a		14 08						15 09			16 09					17 09			18 09					19 08
Liverpool Lime Street 10	a		14 32						15 31			16 33					17 30			18 28					19 32
Wilmslow	a		13 48						14 48			15 48					16 48			17 48					18 48
Stockport	a		13 58						14 58			15 58					16 58			17 58					18 58
Manchester Piccadilly 10	✈ a		14 13						15 13			16 13					17 13			18 10					19 16

		AW	AW	AW	AW	AW	AW	AW	AW	AW	AW	GW	AW	AW	AW	AW	AW	GW	AW	AW	AW	AW	AW	AW
		🚌		R 🛒	🚌		🚌	R 🛒	🚌		◇ 🛒	1 ◇ ☕	🚌		◇	🚌	◇	1 ◇ ☕	🚌	◇	🚌	◇ A		🚌
Swansea 7	d														18 21				18 55					
Cardiff Central 7	d																		19 55					
London Paddington 15	⊖ d	12 45			13 45				14 45			16 51	15 45					18 21	17 45					19 15
Reading 7	d	13 11			14 11				15 11			17 23	16 11					18 53	18 11					19 41
Bristol Temple Meads 10	d																							
Newport (South Wales)	d	16 15			16 45		17 15		18 15				19 00			19 15			20 25		21 15			22 20
Cwmbran	d	16 30			17 00		17 30		18 30				19 15			19 30			20 40		21 30			22s35
Pontypool and New Inn	d				17 15				18 45				19 30						20 55					22s50
Abergavenny	d	17 00			17 30		18 00		19 00				19 45			20 00			21 10		22 00			23s05
Hereford 7	a	17 45			18 15		18 45		19 45			20 02	20 30			20 45		21 32	21 55		22 45			23 50
	d			17 56		18 26		19 00			19 56			20 40			21 16			22 05			23 00	
Leominster	d			18 09		18 39		19 12			20 09			20 54			21 29			22 18			23 13	
Ludlow	d			18 20		18 49		19 23			20 20			21 01			21 40			22 29			23 24	
Craven Arms	d			18 29				19 33			20 29			21 13	21 37		21 49			22 38			23 33	
Church Stretton	d			18 38				19 42			20 38			21 22	21 50		22 02			22 47			23 42	
Shrewsbury	a			18 52		19 16		19 56			20 52			21 36	22 12		22 16			23 01			23 56	
	d		18 26	18 54		19 30		19 57		20 26	20 54			21 38			22 17			23 02		23 29	23 57	
Yorton	d		18x36							20x36							22x26			23x11			00x06	
Wem	d		18 42							20 42							22 31			23 16			00 10	
Prees	d		18x46							20x46							22x35			23x21			00x15	
Whitchurch (Shrops)	d		18 54							20 54							22 42			23 28			00 21	
Wrenbury	d		19x00							21x00							22x48			23x34			00x27	
Nantwich	d		19 07							21 07							22 54			23 40			00 32	
Crewe 10	a		19 23	19 28				20 28		21 20	21 27						23 03			23 50		00 01	00 44	
Chester	a			20 02		20 26		21 27			22 09			22 32						00 16		00 24		
Llandudno Junction	a					21 28		22 25						23 33										
Bangor (Gwynedd)	a					21 51		22 42						00c25										
Holyhead	a					22 35		23 30						01c45										
Runcorn	a			20 08				21 08			22 08													
Liverpool Lime Street 10	a			20 30				21 27			22 27													
Wilmslow	a			19 48				20 48			21 46						23 22							
Stockport	a			19 59				20 59			21 56						23 33							
Manchester Piccadilly 10	✈ a			20 13				21 13			22 13						23 50							

For general notes see front of timetable
For details of catering facilities see
Directory of Train Operators

A From Birmingham New Street (Table 74)
b Change at Crewe and Chester
c By bus

Table 131

Sundays

until 27 January

Cardiff → Crewe, Liverpool and Manchester

Route Diagram - see first page of Table 129

		AW	AW	AW	AW	AW	AW		GW	AW	GW	AW	AW	GW	AW	AW	GW	AW	AW	AW		AW	GW	AW	AW
		◇					◇		[1] ◇	◇	[1] ◇	◇	◇	[1] ◇	◇	[R]	[1] ◇	◇		[R]		[R]	[1] ◇	◇	
		A								B			B			A				A		A		C	D
Swansea [7]	d	20p55					09 59			11 22		11 09	13 35		13 59	15 30		15 16	15 59	17 35		19 35			21 35
Cardiff Central [7]	d	21p50	08 34				11 35			12 35			14 35		15 35	16 35			17 05	18 35		20 35			22 50
London Paddington [15] ⊖	d						09 30		09 35	10 37	10 42		12 37	12 42	13 37	14 37	14 42			16 37		18 37	18 42		20 37
Reading [7]	d						10 07		10 13	11 12	11 20		13 12	13 20	14 11	15 12	15 20			17 13		19 11	19 20		21 14
Bristol Temple Meads [10]	d						09 50			11 48			13 48		14 48	15 48				17 48		19 48			21 48
Newport (South Wales)	d	22p08	08 54				11 49			12 49			14 49		15 50	16 51			17 20	18 50		20 50			23 09
Cwmbran	d	22p19	09 04				12 00			13 00			15 01		16 00	17 02			17 30	19 00		21 00			23 19
Pontypool and New Inn	d	22p25	09 10							13 06			15 07			17 08			17 36			21 07			23 25
Abergavenny	d	22p34	09 20				12 14			13 16			15 17		16 14	17 18			17 46	19 14		21 17			23 35
Hereford [7]	a	22p59	09 50				12 40		12 54	13 40	14 04		15 41	15 51	16 40	17 44	17 58		18 13	19 38		21 43	21 59		00 04
	d	23p00			10 00		12 44			13 42			15 42		16 42	17 46				19 40		21 45			
Leominster	d	23p13			10 25		12 57			13 55			15 56		16 55	17 59				19 53		21 58			
Ludlow	d	23p24			10 50		13 09			14 07			16 07		17 07	18 11				20 05		22 10			
Craven Arms	d	23p33			11 10		13 18			14 16		15 02	16 17			18 20		18 55		20 14		22 19			
Church Stretton	d	23p42			11 30		13 28			14 26		15 15	16 24			18 30		19 08		20 24		22 29			
Shrewsbury	a	23p56			12 00		13 43			14 41		15 33	16 39		17 35	18 45		19 23		20 39		22 44			
	d	23p57		10 58		12 40	13 44	13 52		14 46			16 41		17 37	18 46		19 25		20 42	20 46	22 45		23 50	
Yorton	d	00x06				12x49							16x52					19x34				22x54			
Wem	d	00 10				12 54							16 57					19 39				23 00			
Prees	d	00x15				12x59							17x02					19x44				23x04			
Whitchurch (Shrops)	d	00 21				13 06							17 09					19 51				23 11			
Wrenbury	d	00x27				13x12							17x15					19x57				23x17			
Nantwich	d	00 32				13 18							17 26					20 03				23 24			
Crewe [10]	a	00 44		11 30		13 34	14 21			15 23			17 37		18 12	19 27		20 15		21 24		23 36		00 20	
Chester	a			12 20		14 15		14 59		16 17			18 20		18 55	20 20		20 56		22 20	21 34			00 48	
Llandudno Junction	a			13b25		15 10		15 59		17 09			19b29		20 40			21 51		23 33	22 49			01 39	
Bangor (Gwynedd)	a			13b51		15 34		16 22		17 26			19b52		20 57			22 14		23 50	23 12			01 56	
Holyhead	a					16c58		16 58		18 02			20b25		21 26			22 50		00 26	23 51			02 27	
Runcorn	a			12 45			14 52			16 00					18 50	20 00		20 49		21 59					
Liverpool Lime Street [10]	a			13 11			15 18			16 24					19 13	20 24		21 15		22 24					
Wilmslow	a			11 50		13 54	14 44			15 44			17 58		18 50	19 48		20 50		21 45					
Stockport	a			12 01		14 05	14 55			15 55			18 11		19e28	19 59		21e28		21 56					
Manchester Piccadilly [10]	a			12 16		14 20	15 11			16 12			18 26		19 21	20 14		21 20		22 07					

Sundays

3 February to 23 March

		AW	AW	AW	AW	AW	AW		GW	AW	GW	AW	AW	GW	AW	AW	GW	AW	AW	AW		AW	GW	AW	AW
		◇					◇		[1] ◇	◇	[1] ◇	◇	◇	[1] ◇	◇	[R]	[1] ◇	◇		[R]		[R]	[1] ◇		
		A								B			B			A				A		A			D
Swansea [7]	d	20p55					09 45			11 10		11 00	13 35		13 45	15 30		15 16	15 45	17 35		19 35			21 35
Cardiff Central [7]	d	21p50	08 34				11 35			12 35			14 35		15 35	16 35			17 05	18 35		20 35			22 50
London Paddington [15] ⊖	d						08 00		09 30	09 03	10 42		11 03	12 42	12 03	13 03	14 42		14 03	15 03		17 03	18 42		20 03
Reading [7]	d						08 37		10 09	09 42	11 20		11 45	13 21	12 42	13 42	15 20		14 42	15 42		17 42	19 20		20 41
Bristol Temple Meads [10]	d						10 04			11 48			13 48		14 48	15 48			16 15	17 48		19 48			22 20
Newport (South Wales)	d	22p08	08 54				11 49			12 49			14 49		15 50	16 49			17 20	18 50		20 50			23 09
Cwmbran	d	22p19	09 04				12 00			13 00			15 01		16 00	17 02			17 30	19 00		21 00			23 19
Pontypool and New Inn	d	22p25	09 10							13 06			15 07			17 08			17 36			21 07			23 25
Abergavenny	d	22p34	09 20				12 14			13 16			15 17		16 14	17 18			17 46	19 14		21 17			23 35
Hereford [7]	a	22p59	09 50				12 40		12 54	13 40	14 04		15 41	15 50	16 40	17 44	17 58		18 13	19 38		21 43	21 58		00 04
	d	23p00			10 00		12 44			13 42			15 42		16 42	17 46				19 40		21 45			
Leominster	d	23p13			10 25		12 57			13 55			15 56		16 55	17 59				19 53		21 58			
Ludlow	d	23p24			10 50		13 09			14 07			16 07		17 07	18 11				20 05		22 10			
Craven Arms	d	23p33			11 10		13 18			14 16		15 02	16 17			18 20		18 55		20 14		22 19			
Church Stretton	d	23p42			11 30		13 28			14 26		15 15	16 24			18 30		19 08		20 24		22 29			
Shrewsbury	a	23p56			12 00		13 43			14 41		15 33	16 39		17 35	18 45		19 23		20 39		22 44			
	d	23p57		10 58		12 40	13 44	13 52		14 46			16 41		17 37	18 46		19 25		20 42	20 46	22 45		23 50	
Yorton	d	00x06				12x49							16x52					19x34				22x54			
Wem	d	00 10				12 54							16 57					19 39				23 00			
Prees	d	00x15				12x59							17x02					19x44				23x04			
Whitchurch (Shrops)	d	00 21				13 06							17 09					19 51				23 11			
Wrenbury	d	00x27				13x12							17x15					19x57				23x17			
Nantwich	d	00 32				13 18							17 26					20 03				23 24			
Crewe [10]	a	00 44		11 30		13 34	14 21			15 23			17 37		18 12	19 27		20 15		21 24		23 36		00 20	
Chester	a			12 20		14 15		14 59		16 17			18 20		18 55	20 20		20 56		22 20	21 34	00 48		00 48	
Llandudno Junction	a			13b25		15 10		15 59		17 09			19b29		20 40			21 51		23 33	22 49	01 39		01 39	
Bangor (Gwynedd)	a			13b51		15 34		16 22		17 26			19b52		20 57			22 14		23 50	23 12	01 56		01 56	
Holyhead	a					16c58		16 58		18 02			20b25		21 26			22 50		00 26	23 51	02 27		02 27	
Runcorn	a			12 45			14 52			16 00					18 50	20 00		20 49		21 59					
Liverpool Lime Street [10]	a			13 11			15 18			16 24					19 13	20 24		21 15		22 24					
Wilmslow	a			11 50		13 54	14 44			15 44			17 58		18 50	19 48		20 50		21 45					
Stockport	a			12 01		14 05	14 55			15 55			18 11		19e28	19 59		21e28		21 56					
Manchester Piccadilly [10]	a			12 16		14 20	15 11			16 12			18 26		19 21	20 14		21 20		22 07					

For general notes see front of timetable
For details of catering facilities see Directory of Train Operators

A From Milford Haven (Table 128)
B From Carmarthen (Table 128)
C From Birmingham New Street (Table 74)
D From Pembroke Dock (Table 128)

b Change at Crewe and Chester
c Change at Crewe and Bangor (Gwynedd)
e Change at Crewe and Wilmslow

Table 131

Sundays

from 30 March

Cardiff → Crewe, Liverpool and Manchester

Route Diagram - see first page of Table 129

		AW	AW	AW	AW	AW	AW	AW	AW	AW	AW	AW	AW	AW
				Bus	Bus	Bus	Bus			Bus		◇	Bus	◇ Trolley
Swansea 7	d						08 29			09 29		11 00	11 29	
Cardiff Central 7	d				08 00		10 25			11 25			13 10	
London Paddington 15	⊖ d						08 03						10 30	
Reading 7	d						08 42						11 07	
Bristol Temple Meads 10	d													
Newport (South Wales)	d				08 35	09 00	11 00			12 00			13 45	
Cwmbran	d				08 50	09 15	11 15			12 15			14 00	
Pontypool and New Inn	d				09 05	09 30				12 30			14 15	
Abergavenny	d				09 20	09 45	11 45			12 45			14 30	
Hereford 7	a				10 05	10 30	12 30			13 30			15 15	
	d	23p00		10 00					12 44		13 42			15 42
Leominster	d	23p13		10 25					12 57		13 55			15 56
Ludlow	d	23p24		10 50					13 09		14 07			16 07
Craven Arms	d	23p33		11 10					13 18		14 16	15 02		16 17
Church Stretton	d	23p42		11 30					13 28		14 26	15 15		16 24
Shrewsbury	a	23p56		12 00					13 43		14 41	15 33		16 39
	d	23p57	10 58					12 40	13 44		14 42			16 41
Yorton	d	00x06						12x49						16x52
Wem	d	00 10						12 54						16 57
Prees	d	00x15						12x59						17x02
Whitchurch (Shrops)	d	00 21						13 06						17 09
Wrenbury	d	00x27						13x12						17x15
Nantwich	d	00 32						13 18						17 21
Crewe 10	a	00 44	11 30					13 34	14 21		15 22			17 32
Chester	a		12 20					14 15	15 20		16 17			18 20
Llandudno Junction	a		13b25					15 10			17 09			19b29
Bangor (Gwynedd)	a		13b51					15 34			17 26			19b52
Holyhead	a							16c58			18 02			20b25
Runcorn	a		12 45						14 52		16 00			
Liverpool Lime Street 10	a		13 11						15 18		16 24			
Wilmslow	a		11 50					13 54	14 44		15 44			17 55
Stockport	a		12 01					14 05	14 55		15 55			18 06
Manchester Piccadilly 10	⛴ a		12 16					14 20	15 11		16 12			18 20

		AW	AW	AW	AW	AW	AW	AW	AW	AW	AW	GW	AW	AW	AW
		Bus		Bus		◇	Bus	Bus		Bus		1 ◇ Trolley	Bus	◇ A	Bus
Swansea 7	d	12 29		13 35		15 16	14 29	15 35		18 29			19 35		
Cardiff Central 7	d	14 15		15 25			16 15	17 10		19 30			20 40		20 45
London Paddington 15	⊖ d	11 30		12 30			13 30	14 30		16 30		18 42	18 30		
Reading 7	d	12 07		13 07			14 07	15 07		17 07		19 21	19 07		
Bristol Temple Meads 10	d														
Newport (South Wales)	d	14 50		16 00			16 50	17 45		20 05			21 15		21 20
Cwmbran	d	15 05		16 15			17 05	18 00		20 20			21 30		21s35
Pontypool and New Inn	d			16 30			17 20			20 35			21 45		21s50
Abergavenny	d	15 35		16 45			17 35	18 30		20 50			22 00		22s05
Hereford 7	a	16 20		17 30			18 20	19 15		21 35		22 40	22 45		22s50
	d		16 42		17 46				19 40		21 45				
Leominster	d		16 55		17 59				19 53		21 58				23s15
Ludlow	d		17 07		18 11				20 05		22 10				23s35
Craven Arms	d				18 20	18 55			20 14		22 19				23s55
Church Stretton	d				18 30	19 08			20 24		22 29				00s10
Shrewsbury	a		17 35		18 45	19 23			20 39		22 44				00s40
	d		17 37		18 46	19 25			20 42		22 45			23 50	
Yorton	d					19x34					22x54				01s00
Wem	d					19 39					23 00				01s15
Prees	d					19x44					23x04				01s30
Whitchurch (Shrops)	d					19 51					23 11				01s45
Wrenbury	d					19x57					23x17				02s05
Nantwich	d					20 03					23 24				02s20
Crewe 10	a		18 12		19 27	20 15			21 19		23 36			00 20	02 40
Chester	a		18 55		20 20	20 56			22 20					00 48	
Llandudno Junction	a		20 40			21 51			23 33					01 39	
Bangor (Gwynedd)	a		20 57			22 14			23 50					01 56	
Holyhead	a		21 26			22 50			00 26					02 27	
Runcorn	a		18 50		20 00	20 49			21 59						
Liverpool Lime Street 10	a		19 13		20 24	21 15			22 24						
Wilmslow	a		18 50		19 48	20 50			21 43						
Stockport	a		19e13		19 59	21e13			21 54						
Manchester Piccadilly 10	⛴ a		19 21		20 14	21 20			22 07						

For general notes see front of timetable
For details of catering facilities see Directory of Train Operators

A From Birmingham New Street (Table 74)
b Change at Crewe and Chester
c Change at Crewe and Bangor (Gwynedd)
e Change at Crewe and Wilmslow

Manchester, Liverpool and Crewe → Cardiff

Route Diagram - see first page of Table 129

Miles	Miles			AW MO A 🚌	AW MX ◇	AW MO	AW MO B	AW C	GW MO 1 ◇ ⊠	AW ◇	AW ◇ D [trolley]	GW 1 ◇ E ⊠	AW ◇	AW ◇ G [trolley]	AW ◇ [trolley]	AW ◇ D [trolley]	AW	AW ◇ G [trolley]
0	—	**Manchester Piccadilly 10** 🚢	d		21p34	22p46										06 38		07 28
6	—	Stockport	d		21p46	22p54										06 48		07 37
12	—	Wilmslow	d		21p54	23p02										06 56		07 46
—	0	**Liverpool Lime Street 10**	d													06 27		07 18
—	13	Runcorn	d													06 43		07 35
—	—	Holyhead	d								02 15		02 15		04 27			05 32
—	—	Bangor (Gwynedd)	d								02 42		02 42		05 00			06 01
—	—	Llandudno Junction	d								03 00		03 00		05 18			06 21
—	—	Chester	d								03 40		05 07	04 55	06 12	06 30		07 30
31	35½	**Crewe 10**	d		22p18	23p25					04 54			05 55		07 18	07 27	08 08
35½	40	Nantwich	d		22p25	23p33					05 01			06 02			07 34	08 15
40	44½	Wrenbury	d		22b31	23b38								06x08			07x41	
44¾	49¼	Whitchurch (Shrops)	d		22p38	23p46					05 12			06 14			07 49	08 26
49¾	54¼	Prees	d		22b44	23b52								06x20			07x55	
53	57½	Wem	d		22p48	23p57					05 20			06 24			08 01	08 35
56½	61	Yorton	d		22b54	00x02								06x29			08x06	
63¾	68¼	**Shrewsbury**	a		23p04	00 14					05 32		06 07	06 40	07 07	07 47	08 17	08 44
—	—		d		23p06					05 19	05 40		06 20	06 45	07 16	07 49		08 49
76½	81	Church Stretton	d		23p22					05 36	05 55			07 00		08 04		09 04
83¾	88¼	Craven Arms	d		23p30					05 50	06 03			07 08		08 12		09 12
91	95½	Ludlow	d		23p38						06 11		06 47	07 16	07 43	08 20		09 20
102	106½	Leominster	d		23p48						06 22		06 58	07 27	07 53	08 31		09 31
114½	119	**Hereford 7**	a		00 03						06 36		07 12	07 45	08 08	08 45		09 45
—	—		d	23p25	00 04		05 23	05 23	05 42		06 42	06 43	07 16	07 48	08 09	08 48		09 47
138½	143	Abergavenny	d	00 05	00 27		05 48	05 48			07 05		07 39	08 11	08 32	09 11		10 10
148	152½	Pontypool and New Inn	d	00 25	00 37		05 59	05 59			07 15		07 49		08 42			10 20
151	155½	Cwmbran	d	00 35	00 42		06 04	06 04			07 20		07 54	08 23	08 47	09 23		10 24
158	162½	**Newport (South Wales)**	a	00 55	00 56		06 16	06 16			07 33		08 04	08 34	08 58	09 34		10 34
—	—	Bristol Temple Meads 10	a				07 18	07 18			08 18		08 53	09 18	09 52	10 18		11 18
—	—	Reading 7	a				07 58	07 58	08 22		09 01	09 14	09 27	09 57	10 32	11 01		12 01
—	—	London Paddington 15 ⊖	a				08 30	08 30	08 51		09 29	09 47	09 59	10 27	11 02	11 32		12 32
169¾	174¼	**Cardiff Central 7**	a	01 30	01 22		06 51	06 59		10 17	07 50		08 29	08 53	09 18	09 53		10 54
—	—	Swansea 7	a							09 07	08 49		09 44	09 56	10 43	10 58		11 56

		AW ◇	AW ◇ [trolley]	AW ◇ D [trolley]	AW	AW ◇ G [trolley]	AW ◇ [trolley]	AW ◇ D [trolley]	AW	GW 1 ◇ [trolley]	AW ◇ G [trolley]	AW ◇ [trolley]	AW R D [trolley]	AW ◇	AW	GW 1 ◇ [trolley]	AW R G [trolley]	AW ◇ [trolley]
Manchester Piccadilly 10 🚢	d			08 34		09 34		10 34			11 34		12 34				13 34	
Stockport	d			08 44		09 42		10 42			11 42		12 42				13 42	
Wilmslow	d			08 52		09 54		10 54			11 54		12 54				13 54	
Liverpool Lime Street 10	d			08 19		09 19		10 19			11 19		12 15				13 19	
Runcorn	d			08 35		09 35		10 35			11 35		12 31				13 35	
Holyhead	d		06 15	06 45		07 15	08 10				09 50	10 30					11 40	12 35
Bangor (Gwynedd)	d		06 59	07 12		08 01	09 04				10 18	11 03					12 19	13 04
Llandudno Junction	d		07 17	07 31		08 27	09 27				10 36	11 26					12 42	13 27
Chester	d		08 20	08 30		09 19	10 20	10 29			11 28	12 20	12 29				13 33	14 20
Crewe 10	d			09 17	09 27	10 17		11 18	11 26		12 18		13 18		13 26		14 18	
Nantwich	d				09 34				11 34						13 34			
Wrenbury	d				09x41				11x41						13x41			
Whitchurch (Shrops)	d				09 49				11 49						13 49			
Prees	d				09x55				11x55						13x55			
Wem	d				10 01				12 01						14 01			
Yorton	d				10x06				12x06						14x06			
Shrewsbury	a		09 16	09 46	10 17	10 46	11 15	11 46	12 17		12 46	13 15	13 46		14 17		14 46	15 15
	d	09 05	09 18	09 49		10 49	11 18	11 48			12 49	13 18	13 49	14 05			14 49	15 18
Church Stretton	d	09 22		10 04		11 04		12 03			13 04		14 04	14 23			15 04	
Craven Arms	d	09 35		10 12		11 12		12 11			13 12		14 12	14 36			15 12	
Ludlow	d		09 44	10 20		11 20	11 45	12 19			13 20	13 45	14 20				15 20	15 45
Leominster	d			10 31		11 31		12 30			13 31		14 31				15 31	
Hereford 7	a		10 07	10 45		11 45	12 08	12 44			13 45	14 08	14 45				15 44	16 08
	d		10 08	10 48		11 48	12 09	12 48		13 23	13 48	14 09	14 48			15 19	15 48	16 09
Abergavenny	d		10 32	11 11		12 11	12 32	13 11			14 11	14 32	15 11				16 11	16 32
Pontypool and New Inn	d						12 42					14 42						16 42
Cwmbran	d		10 46	11 23		12 23	12 47	13 23			14 23	14 47	15 23				16 23	16 47
Newport (South Wales)	a		10 58	11 34		12 34	12 58	13 34			14 34	14 58	15 34				16 34	16 57
Bristol Temple Meads 10	a		11 52	12 18		13 17	13 52	14 19			15 18	15 51	16 18					17 52
Reading 7	a		12 32	13 01		14 01	14 32	15 01		16 25	16 01	16 32	17 01			18 03	17 57	18 32
London Paddington 15 ⊖	a		13 02	13 29		14 32	15 02	15 30		16 59	16 30	17 02	17 30			18 31	18 27	19 02
Cardiff Central 7	a		11 20	11 53		12 53	13 21	13 53			14 53	15 20	15 53				16 53	17 15
Swansea 7	a	13 01	12 43	12 56		13 56	14 43	14 56			15 56	16 43	16 56	18 06			18 05	18 44

For general notes see front of timetable
For details of catering facilities see Directory of Train Operators

A From 31 March
B From 24 March
C All Tuesdays to Fridays, also Mondays until 17 March
D To Milford Haven (Table 128)
E **The Cathedrals Express**
G To Carmarthen (Table 128)
b Previous night.
Stops on request, passengers wishing to alight must inform the guard and those wishing to join must give a hand signal to the driver

Manchester, Liverpool and Crewe → Cardiff

Route Diagram - see first page of Table 129

		AW	AW	AW	AW	AW	AW	AW	AW	AW	AW	AW	AW	AW	AW FO	AW FX	AW
		[R] A 🚲		[R] B 🚲	◇ 🚲	[R] A 🚲	◇		[R] A 🚲	◇ 🚲	◇ B 🚲		◇ 🚲	◇	◇	◇	
Manchester Piccadilly [10]	d	14 34		15 34		16 34		16 34	17 34		18 34		19 34	20 34	21 34	21 34	22 34
Stockport	d	14 42		15 42		16 42		16 42	17 42		18 42		19 43	20 46	21 46	21 46	22 42
Wilmslow	d	14 54		15 54		16 54			17 51		18 54		19 54	20 54	21 54	21 54	22 50
Liverpool Lime Street [10]	d	14 15		15 19		16 15			17 18		18 15		19 19	19 49	20 40	20 40	21 40
Runcorn	d	14 31		15 35		16 31			17 36		18 31		19 35	20 05	20 58	20 58	21 59
Holyhead	d			13 35	14 35				15 39	16 35			17 27	18b35	19 35	19 35	
Bangor (Gwynedd)	d			14 14	15 04				16 17	17 04			18 06	19b14	20 14	20 14	
Llandudno Junction	d			14 37	15 27				16 40	17 27			18 29	19b32	20 37	20 37	20b56
Chester	d	14 30		15 30	16 20	16 31			17 31	18 20	18 30		19 22	20 30	21 33	21 33	22 14
Crewe [10]	d	15 18	15 26	16 18		17 18		17 27	18 18		19 18	19 26	20 18	21 18	22 18	22 18	23 16
Nantwich	d		15 34	16 25				17 34	18 25			19 34		21 25	22 25	22 25	23 23
Wrenbury	d		15x41					17x41				19x41		21x32	22x31	22x31	23x30
Whitchurch (Shrops)	d		15 49	16 36				17 49	18 36			19 49		21 39	22 38	22 38	23 38
Prees	d		15x55					17x55				19x55		21x45	22x44	22x44	23x44
Wem	d		16 01	16 45				18 01	18 45			20 01		21 50	22 48	22 48	23 50
Yorton	d		16x06					18x06				20x06		21x56	22x54	22x54	23x55
Shrewsbury	a	15 46	16 17	16 57	17 15	17 46		18 17	18 57	19 15	19 46	20 17	20 46	22 04	23 04	23 04	00 07
	d	15 48		16 59	17 18	17 49	18 05		18 59	19 17	19 49		20 49	22 07	23 06	23 06	
Church Stretton	d	16 03		17 14		18 04	18 23		19 14		20 04		21 04	22 22	23 22	23 22	
Craven Arms	d	16 11		17 22		18 12	18 35		19 22		20 12		21 12	22 30	23 30	23 30	
Ludlow	d	16 19		17 30	17 45	18 20			19 30	19 45	20 20		21 20	22 38	23 38	23 38	
Leominster	d	16 30		17 41		18 31			19 41		20 31		21 31	22 49	23 48	23 48	
Hereford [7]	a	16 44		17 52	18 08	18 45			19 55	20 08	20 45		21 45	23 03	00 03	00 03	
	d	16 48		17 56	18 09	18 48			19 57	20 09	20 48		21 49	23 05	00 04	00 04	
Abergavenny	d	17 11		18 19	18 33	19 11			20 20	20 33	21 11		22 12	23 28	00 27	00 27	
Pontypool and New Inn	d				18 42					20 42			22 22		00 37	00 37	
Cwmbran	d	17 23		18 31	18 47	19 23			20 32	20 47	21 23		22 24	23 40	00 42	00 42	
Newport (South Wales)	a	17 34		18 45	18 58	19 34			20 45	20 58	21 34		22 38	23 51	00 53	00 56	
Bristol Temple Meads [10]	a	18 18			19 52	20 18				21 53	23 00		00 04				
Reading [7]	a	19 01				21 01					23 06						
London Paddington [15] ⊖	a	19 32				21 30					23c50						
Cardiff Central [7]	a	17 54		19 01	19 24	19 54			21 01	21 19	21 57		23 04	00 17	01 14	01 22	
Swansea [7]	a	19 01		19 56	20 42	21 20	22 13		22 03		23 00		00 25	02 10			

Saturdays

until 22 March

		AW	AW	AW	AW	AW	GW	AW	AW	AW	AW	AW	AW	AW	AW	AW	AW	AW	AW	AW	AW	GW	AW	AW	AW
		◇	C	◇	◇ A 🚲	◇	[1] ◇ 🍴	◇ B 🚲	◇ 🚲	◇ E 🚲	◇ D		◇ B 🚲	◇	◇ 🚲	◇ A 🚲		◇ B 🚲	◇ 🚲	◇ A 🚲		[1] ◇ 🍴	◇ B 🚲	◇ 🚲	[R] A 🚲
Manchester Piccadilly [10]	d	21p34						05 05		06 28	06 38	06 38	07 28			08 34	08 34	09 34		10 34			11 34		12 34
Stockport	d	21p46						05 15		06 48	06 48	06 48	07 37			08 44	08 44	09 42		10 43			11 42		12 42
Wilmslow	d	21p54						05 23		06 55	06 55		07 46			08 52		09 51		10 51			11 51		12 51
Liverpool Lime Street [10]	d									06 07	06 07		07 12			08 12		09 15		10 15			11 15		12 15
Runcorn	d									06 24	06 24		07 28			08 28		09 31		10 31			11 31		12 31
Holyhead	d				02 15				04 27				05 35		06 15	06 45		07 15	08 25				09 50	10 30	
Bangor (Gwynedd)	d				02 42				05 00				06 04		06 59	07 12		08 01	09 04				10 18	11 03	
Llandudno Junction	d				03 00				05 18				06 24		07 17	07 31		08 27	09 27				10 36	11 26	
Chester	d				03 40			04 55	06 12	06 30	06 30		07 30		08 20	08 30		09 19	10 20	10 29			11 28	12 20	12 29
Crewe [10]	d	22p18			04 54			05 55		07 18	07 18	07 27	08 08			09 17	09 27	10 17		11 18	11 26		12 18		13 18
Nantwich	d	22p25			05 01			06 02				07 34	08 15				09 34				11 34				
Wrenbury	d	22e31						06x08				07x41					09x41				11x41				
Whitchurch (Shrops)	d	22p38			05 12			06 14				07 49	08 26				09 49				11 49				
Prees	d	22e44						06x20				07x55					09x55				11x55				
Wem	d	22p48			05 20			06 24				08 01	08 35				10 01				12 01				
Yorton	d	22e54						06x29				08x06					10x06				12x06				
Shrewsbury	a	23p04			05 32			06 40	07 07	07 46	07 46	08 18	08 44		09 16	09 46	10 19	10 46	11 15	11 46	12 19		12 46	13 15	13 46
	d	23p06		05 19	05 40	06 23		06 45	07 16	07 49	07 49		08 49	09 05	09 18	09 49		10 49	11 18	11 49			12 49	13 18	13 49
Church Stretton	d	23p22		05 36	05 55			07 00		08 04	08 04		09 04	09 22		10 04		11 04		12 04			13 04		14 04
Craven Arms	d	23p30		05 50	06 03			07 08		08 12	08 12		09 12	09 35		10 12		11 12		12 12			13 12		14 12
Ludlow	d	23p38			06 11	06 49		07 16	07 43	08 20	08 20		09 20		09 45	10 20		11 20	11 45	12 20			13 20	13 45	14 20
Leominster	d	23p48			06 22	07 00		07 27	07 53	08 31	08 31		09 31			10 31		11 31		12 31			13 31		14 31
Hereford [7]	a	00 03			06 36	07 14		07 45	08 08	08 45	08 45		09 45		10 08	10 45		11 45	12 08	12 45			13 45	14 08	14 45
	d	00 04	05 42		06 49	07 16	07 22	07 48	08 10	08 48	08 48		09 47		10 09	10 48		11 48	12 09	12 48		13 20	13 48	14 09	14 48
Abergavenny	d	00 27	06 07		07 12	07 39		08 11	08 33	09 11	09 11		10 10		10 33	11 11		12 11	12 33	13 11			14 11	14 32	15 11
Pontypool and New Inn	d	00 37	06 18		07 22	07 49			08 43	09 23			10 20						12 42					14 42	
Cwmbran	d	00 42	06 23		07 27	07 54		08 24	08 48	09 23	09 23		10 24		10 46	11 23		12 23	12 48	13 23			14 23	14 47	15 23
Newport (South Wales)	a	00 53	06 34		07 39	08 04		08 34	08 58	09 34	09 34		10 34		10 58	11 34		12 34	12 58	13 34			14 34	14 58	15 34
Bristol Temple Meads [10]	a		07 18		08 18	08 52		09 18	09 51	10 18	10 18		11 18		11 52	12 18		13 18	13 52	14 18			15 18	15 52	16 18
Reading [7]	a		09f51			09g33	10 21	10g01	10g32	10g59			13h51			13j01		14g01		15g01		16 26	16j01		17k51
London Paddington [15] ⊖	a		10m20			10g06	10 54	10g31	10g59	11g31			14n19			13j36		14g30		15g31		16 58	16j30		18q19
Cardiff Central [7]	a	01 14	06 54	10 17	07 55	08 25		08 51	09 18	09 52	09 52		10 52		11 20	11 53		12 53	13 19	13 53			14 53	15 20	15 53
Swansea [7]	a		08 48	09 07	08 55			09 56		11 01	10 49		11 56	13 01		12 56		13 56		14 56			15 56		16 56

For general notes see front of timetable
For details of catering facilities see Directory of Train Operators

- **A** To Milford Haven (Table 128)
- **B** To Carmarthen (Table 128)
- **C** To Barry Island (Table 130)
- **D** From 2 February To Milford Haven (Table 128)
- **E** Until 26 January To Milford Haven (Table 128)
- **b** Change at Chester and Crewe
- **c** Fridays arr. 2342
- **e** Previous night. Stops on request, passengers wishing to alight must inform the guard and those wishing to join must give a hand signal to the driver
- **f** Until 26 January arr. 0832
- **g** Until 26 January only
- **h** Until 26 January arr. 1202
- **j** Until 26 January
- **k** From 2 February only.
- **m** Until 26 January arr. 0906
- **n** Until 26 January arr. 1232
- **q** Until 26 January arr. 1831

until 22 March

Manchester, Liverpool and Crewe → Cardiff

Route Diagram - see first page of Table 129

		AW	AW	GW	AW	AW	AW	AW	AW	AW	AW	AW	AW	AW	AW	AW	AW	AW	AW	AW	AW	AW	AW
					R		R		R		R	R			R	R							
		◇		1 ◇		◇				◇			◇				◇	◇		◇	◇	◇	
					A		B		A		C	D			E	G		A					
Manchester Piccadilly 10	d				13 34		14 34		15 34		16 34	16 34			17 34	17 34		18 34		19 34	20 34	21 34	22 34
Stockport	d				13 42		14 42		15 42		16 43	16 43			17 42	17 42		18 43		19 42	20 46	21 45	22 42
Wilmslow	d				13 54		14 51		15 51		16 51	16 51			17 51	17 51		18 51		19 54	20 54	21 54	22 51
Liverpool Lime Street 10	d				13 15		14 15		15 10		16 15	16 15			17 15	17 15		18 10		18 40	20 10	21 16	
Runcorn	d				13 31		14 31		15 26		16 31	16 31			17 31	17 31		18 26		18 58	20 26	21 34	
Holyhead	d				11 40	12 35			13 35	14 35					15 39	15 39	16 35			17 35	18b35	19 35	20b35
Bangor (Gwynedd)	d				12 19	13 04			14 14	15 04					16 17	16 17	17 04			18 14	19b14	20 14	21b05
Llandudno Junction	d				12 42	13 27			14 37	15 27					16 40	16 40	17 27			18 37	19b32	20 37	21b32
Chester	d				13 33	14 20	14 30		15 30	16 20	16 31	16 31			17 31	17 31	18 20	18 30		19 34	20 30	21 33	22 33
Crewe 10	d		13 26		14 18		15 18	15 26	16 15		17 18	17 18		17 26	18 18	18 18		19 18	19 28	20 18	21 18	22 18	23 16
Nantwich	d		13 34					15 34	16 23					17 34	18 25	18 25			19 34		21 25	22 25	23 23
Wrenbury	d		13x41					15x41						17x41					19x41		21x32	22x31	23x30
Whitchurch (Shrops)	d		13 49					15 49	16 33		17 33	17 33		17 49	18 36	18 36			19 49		21 39	22 38	23 38
Prees	d		13x55					15x55						17x55					19x55		21x45	22x44	23x44
Wem	d		14 01					16 01	16 41					18 01	18 45	18 45			20 01		21 50	22 48	23 50
Yorton	d		14x06					16x06						18x06					20x06		21x56	22x54	23x55
Shrewsbury	a		14 19		14 46	15 15	15 46	16 19	16 54	17 15	17 46	17 46		18 19	18 57	18 57	19 15	19 46	20 19	20 46	22 04	23 04	00 07
	d	14 05			14 49	15 18	15 49		16 55	17 18	17 49	17 49	18 05		18 59	18 59	19 18	19 49		20 49	22 07	23 06	
Church Stretton	d	14 23			15 04		16 04		17 10		18 04	18 04	18 23		19 14	19 14		20 04		21 04	22 22	23 22	
Craven Arms	d	14 36			15 12		16 12		17 18		18 12	18 12	18 35		19 22	19 22		20 12		21 12	22 30	23 30	
Ludlow	d				15 20	15 45	16 20		17 26	17 47	18 20	18 20			19 30	19 30	19 45	20 20		21 20	22 38	23 38	
Leominster	d				15 31		16 31		17 36		18 31	18 31			19 41	19 41		20 31		21 31	22 49	23 48	
Hereford 7	a				15 45	16 08	16 45		17 51	18 10	18 45	18 45			19 55	19 55	20 08	20 45		21 45	23 03	00 03	
	d			15 23	15 48	16 09	16 48		17 53	18 11	18 48	18 48			19 57	19 57	20 09	20 48		21 48	23 05	00 04	
Abergavenny	d				16 11	16 32	17 11		18 16	18 34	19 13	19 13			20 20	20 20	20 33	21 11		22 11	23 28	00 27	
Pontypool and New Inn	d					16 42				18 44							20 42			22 21		00 37	
Cwmbran	d				16 23	16 47	17 23		18 29	18 48	19 25	19 25			20 32	20 32	20 47	21 23		22 23	23 40	00 42	
Newport (South Wales)	a				16 34	16 58	17 34		18 39	19 00	19 37	19 41			20 45	20 46	20 59	21 35		22 40	23 52	00 53	
Bristol Temple Meads 10	a				17 18	17 52	18 18		19 18	19 52	20 18	20 43					21 52	23 00					
Reading 7	a			18 25	18c01		20e51			21f52	22 52	21 58											
London Paddington 15 ⊖	a			18 58	18c31		21g19			22h22	23 20	22 31											
Cardiff Central 7	a				16 53	17 20	17 54		18 55	19 22	19 54	19 54			21 01	21 06	21 20	22 00		23 01	00 17	01 19	
Swansea 7	a	18 06			18 06	18 44	18 56		19 56	20 44		21 47	22 13		22 03	22 03		23 00		00 10			

Saturdays

from 29 March

		AW	AW	AW	AW	AW	AW	GW	AW	AW	AW	AW	AW	AW	AW	AW	AW	AW		AW	AW	AW	AW	AW	AW
			◇					1 ◇		◇				◇			◇	◇					◇		
		Bus		Bus		Bus			Bus		Bus		Bus			Bus				Bus		Bus			Bus
Manchester Piccadilly 10	d									05 05				06 38			07 28						08 34		
Stockport	d									05 15				06 48			07 37						08 44		
Wilmslow	d									05 23				06 55			07 46						08 52		
Liverpool Lime Street 10	d													06 07			07 12						08 12		
Runcorn	d													06 24			07 28						08 28		
Holyhead	d				02 15							04 27					05 35				06 15		06 45		
Bangor (Gwynedd)	d				02 42							05 00					06 04				06 59		07 12		
Llandudno Junction	d				03 00							05 18					06 24				07 17		07 31		
Chester	d				03 40					04 55		06 12		06 30			07 30				08 20		08 30		
Crewe 10	d				04 54					05 55				07 18	07 27		08 08						09 17	09 27	
Nantwich	d				05 01					06 02					07 34		08 15							09 34	
Wrenbury	d									06x08					07x41									09x41	
Whitchurch (Shrops)	d				05 12					06 14					07 49		08 26							09 49	
Prees	d									06x20					07x55									09x55	
Wem	d				05 20					06 24					08 01		08 35							10 01	
Yorton	d									06x29					08x06									10x06	
Shrewsbury	a				05 32					06 40		07 07		07 46	08 18		08 44				09 16		09 46	10 19	
	d		05 19		05 40		06 23			06 45		07 16		07 49			08 49	09 05			09 18		09 49		
Church Stretton	d		05 36		05 55					07 00				08 04			09 04	09 22					10 04		
Craven Arms	d		05 50		06 03					07 08				08 12			09 12	09 35					10 12		
Ludlow	d				06 11		06 49			07 16		07 43		08 20			09 20				09 45		10 20		
Leominster	d				06 22		07 00			07 27		07 53		08 31			09 31						10 31		
Hereford 7	a				06 40		07 15			07 50		08 15		08 50			09 50				10 15		10 50		
	d	04 58		06 00		07 00		07 22	07 30		08 00		08 30			09 00				10 00		10 30			11 00
Abergavenny	d	05 38		06 40		07 40			08 10		08 40		09 10			09 40				10 40		11 10			11 40
Pontypool and New Inn	d	05 58		07 00		08 00			08 30				09 30							11 00					
Cwmbran	d	06 08		07 10		08 10			08 40		09 10		09 40			10 10				11 10		11 40			12 10
Newport (South Wales)	a	06 28		07 30		08 30			09 00		09 30		10 00			10 30				11 30		12 00			12 30
Bristol Temple Meads 10	a																								
Reading 7	a	08 50		09 48				10 21			11 43					12 48									14 48
London Paddington 15 ⊖	a	09 19		10 16				10 54			12 12					13 16									15 17
Cardiff Central 7	a		10 17																						
Swansea 7	a		09 07															13 01							

For general notes see front of timetable
For details of catering facilities see Directory of Train Operators

A To Carmarthen (Table 128)
B To Milford Haven (Table 128)
C From 2 February. To Milford Haven (Table 128)
D Until 26 January. To Milford Haven (Table 128)
E Until 26 January. To Haverfordwest (Table 128)
G From 2 February. To Haverfordwest (Table 128)
b Change at Chester and Crewe
c Until 26 January only
e Until 26 January arr. 1901
f Until 26 January arr. 2103
g Until 26 January arr. 1931
h Until 26 January arr. 2136

Saturdays

from 29 March

Manchester, Liverpool and Crewe → Cardiff

Route Diagram - see first page of Table 129

		AW	AW	AW	AW	AW	AW	AW	GW	AW	AW	AW	AW	AW		AW	AW	AW	GW	AW	AW	AW	AW	AW	AW
		◇ trolley	bus		bus	◇ trolley		bus	1 ◇ buffet	◇ trolley	bus		bus	R trolley		◇		bus	1 ◇ buffet	R trolley	bus		bus	R trolley	
Manchester Piccadilly 10	d	09 34				10 34				11 34				12 34						13 34				14 34	
Stockport	d	09 42				10 43				11 42				12 42						13 42				14 42	
Wilmslow	d	09 51				10 51				11 51				12 51						13 54				14 51	
Liverpool Lime Street 10	d	09 15				10 15				11 15				12 15						13 15				14 15	
Runcorn	d	09 31				10 31				11 31				12 31						13 31				14 31	
Holyhead	d	07 15		08 25						09 50		10 30								11 40		12 35			
Bangor (Gwynedd)	d	08 01		09 04						10 18		11 03								12 19		13 04			
Llandudno Junction	d	08 27		09 27						10 36		11 26								12 42		13 27			
Chester	d	09 19		10 20		10 29				11 28		12 20		12 29						13 33		14 20		14 30	
Crewe 10	d	10 17				11 18	11 26			12 18				13 18			13 26			14 18				15 18	15 26
Nantwich	d						11 34										13 34								15 34
Wrenbury	d						11x41										13x41								15x41
Whitchurch (Shrops)	d						11 49										13 49								15 49
Prees	d						11x55										13x55								15x55
Wem	d						12 01										14 01								16 01
Yorton	d						12x06										14x06								16x06
Shrewsbury	a	10 46		11 15		11 46	12 19			12 46		13 15		13 46			14 19			14 46		15 15		15 46	16 19
	d	10 49		11 18		11 49				12 49		13 18		13 49		14 05				14 49		15 18		15 49	
Church Stretton	d	11 04				12 04				13 04				14 04		14 23				15 04				16 04	
Craven Arms	d	11 12				12 12				13 12				14 12		14 36				15 12				16 12	
Ludlow	d	11 20		11 45		12 20				13 20		13 45		14 20						15 20		15 45		16 20	
Leominster	d	11 31				12 31				13 31				14 31						15 31				16 31	
Hereford 7	a	11 50		12 15		12 50				13 50		14 15		14 50						15 50		16 15		16 50	
	d		12 00		12 30			13 00	13 20		14 00		14 30					15 00	15 23		16 00		16 30		
Abergavenny	d		12 40		13 10			13 40			14 40		15 10					15 40			16 40		17 10		
Pontypool and New Inn	d				13 30								15 30										17 30		
Cwmbran	d		13 10		13 40			14 10			15 10		15 40					16 10			17 10		17 40		
Newport (South Wales)	a		13 30		14 00			14 30			15 30		16 00					16 30			17 30		18 00		
Bristol Temple Meads 10	a																								
Reading 7	a		15 48						16 26		17 48							18 48	18 25		19 48				
London Paddington 15	⊖ a		16 17						16 58		18 16							19 17	18 58		20 16				
Cardiff Central 7	a																								
Swansea 7	a															18 06									

		AW	AW	AW	AW	AW	AW	AW	AW	AW	AW	AW	AW	AW	AW	AW	AW	AW	AW	AW	AW	AW	AW		
		bus	R trolley	bus		bus	R trolley	◇		bus	R trolley	bus		bus	◇ trolley		bus	◇ trolley	bus	◇	bus	◇			
Manchester Piccadilly 10	d		15 34				16 34				17 34				18 34			19 34		20 34		21 34	22 34		
Stockport	d		15 42				16 43				17 42				18 43			19 42		20 46		21 45	22 42		
Wilmslow	d		15 51				16 51				17 51				18 51			19 54		20 54		21 54	22 51		
Liverpool Lime Street 10	d		15 10				16 15				17 15				18 10			18 40		20 10		21 16			
Runcorn	d		15 26				16 31				17 31				18 26			18 58		20 26		21 34			
Holyhead	d		13 35		14 35						15 39		16 35					17 35		18b35		19 35	20b35		
Bangor (Gwynedd)	d		14 14		15 04						16 17		17 04					18 14		19b14		20 14	21b05		
Llandudno Junction	d		14 37		15 27						16 40		17 27					18 37		19b32		20 37	21b32		
Chester	d		15 30		16 20		16 31				17 31		18 20		18 30			19 34		20 30		21 33	22 33		
Crewe 10	d		16 15				17 18		17 26		18 18				19 18	19 28		20 18		21 18		22 18	23 16		
Nantwich	d		16 23						17 34		18 25					19 34				21 25		22 25	23 23		
Wrenbury	d								17x41							19x41				21x32		22x31	23x30		
Whitchurch (Shrops)	d		16 33				17 33		17 49		18 36					19 49				21 39		22 38	23 38		
Prees	d								17x55							19x55				21x45		22x44	23x44		
Wem	d		16 41						18 01		18 45					20 01				21 50		22 48	23 50		
Yorton	d								18x06							20x06				21x56		22x54	23x55		
Shrewsbury	a		16 54		17 15		17 46		18 19		18 57		19 15		19 46	20 19		20 46		22 04		23 04	00 07		
	d		16 55		17 18		17 49	18 05			18 59		19 18		19 49			20 49		22 07		23 06			
Church Stretton	d		17 10				18 04	18 23			19 14				20 04			21 04		22 22		23 22			
Craven Arms	d		17 18				18 12	18 35			19 22				20 12			21 12		22 30		23 30			
Ludlow	d		17 26		17 47		18 20				19 30		19 45		20 20			21 20		22 38		23 38			
Leominster	d		17 36				18 31				19 41				20 31			21 31		22 49		23 48			
Hereford 7	a		17 52		18 15		18 50				20 00		20 15		20 50			21 50		23 10		00 05			
	d	17 00		18 00		18 30				19 00		20 10		20 30			21 00		22 00		23 20				
Abergavenny	d	17 40		18 40		19 10				19 40		20 50		21 10			21 40		22 40		00 01				
Pontypool and New Inn	d					19 30								21 30					22 55		00 16				
Cwmbran	d	18 10		19 10		19 40				20 10		21 20		21 40			22 10		23 10		00 30				
Newport (South Wales)	a	18 30		19 30		20 00				20 30		21 40		22 00			22 30		23 30		00 50				
Bristol Temple Meads 10	a																								
Reading 7	a	20 48		21 44						22 47															
London Paddington 15	⊖ a	21 16		22 16						23 16															
Cardiff Central 7	a													22 35			23 05		00 05		01 25				
Swansea 7	a							22 13						23 44			00c48								

For general notes see front of timetable
For details of catering facilities see Directory of Train Operators

b Change at Chester and Crewe
c By bus

Table 131

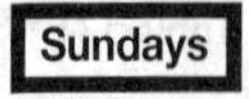
Sundays

until 27 January

Manchester, Liverpool and Crewe → Cardiff

Route Diagram - see first page of Table 129

		AW	AW	AW	AW	AW	GW	AW	GW	AW	GW	AW	AW	AW	GW	AW	AW	AW	AW	AW	AW	AW
										R		R		R			R	R	R	R		
		◇		◇	◇	◇	1 ◇	◇	1 ◇		1 ◇		◇		1 ◇						◇	
				A	B					C		D					C					
			🚌																			
					⊼		☕	⊼	☕	⊼	☕	⊼		⊼	☕		⊼	⊼	⊼	⊼		
Manchester Piccadilly 10	d	21p34			09 14					12 33		14 34		15 49			16 37	17 06		18 37	20 46	22 46
Stockport	d	21p45			09 10					12 42		14 42		15 58			16 45	16 45		18 45	20 54	22 54
Wilmslow	d	21p54			09 41					12 54		14 55		16 06			16 54	17 31		18 55	21 02	23 02
Liverpool Lime Street 10	d				09 53					11 56		13 56		15 31			15 56	17 27		17 56		
Runcorn	d				10 09					12 14		14 14		15 49			16 14	17 43			20 14	22 05
Holyhead	d							10 35				13 14		13b31				15 57	17 25			
Bangor (Gwynedd)	d							11 04				13 41		13b58				16b32	17 53			19b55
Llandudno Junction	d							11 22				13 59		14b16				16b54	18 11			20b18
Chester	d				10 11			12 20		12 25		14 46		15 25			16 25	17 52	19 07			22 25
Crewe 10	d	22p18	06 40		10 50					13 23		15 24		16 32			17 22	18 40		19 20	21 35	23 25
Nantwich	d	22p25	06 50		10 57					13 30							17 29			19 27		23 33
Wrenbury	d	22c31			11x03					13x36							17x35			19 33		23x38
Whitchurch (Shrops)	d	22p38	07 20		11 10					13 44							17 43			19 41		23 46
Prees	d	22c44			11x15					13x49							17x48			19 46		23x52
Wem	d	22p48			11 20					13 55							17 54			19 52		23 57
Yorton	d	22c54			11x25					13x59							17x58			19 56		00x02
Shrewsbury	a	23p04	07 50		11 36			13 15		14 09		15 52		17 05			18 08	19 13	19 59	20 06	22 09	00 14
	d	23p06	07 50		11 45	12 07		13 16		14 10		16 08	16 24	17 08			18 09	19 18		20 13	22 13	
Church Stretton	d	23p22	08 15		12 01	12 24		13 32		14 26		16 24	16 42				18 25			20 29	22 28	
Craven Arms	d	23p30	08 35		12 09	12 36		13 41		14 35		16 32	16 53				18 34			20 37	22 36	
Ludlow	d	23p38	08 55		12 18			13 49		14 43		16 41		17 37			18 42	19 47		20 46	22 44	
Leominster	d	23p48	09 20		12 29			14 01		14 55		16 52					18 54			20 57	22 55	
Hereford 7	a	00 03	09 50		12 44			14 15		15 09		17 07		18 00			19 08	20 10		21 12	23 09	
	d	00 04		10 11	12 46		13 30	14 17	14 30	15 11	16 30	17 09		18 02	18 30	18 50	19 10	20 12		21 13	23 14	
Abergavenny	d	00 27		10 34	13 10			14 40		15 34		17 32		18 25		19 13	19 33	20 35		21 37	23 37	
Pontypool and New Inn	d	00 37		10 45	13 20			14 51		15 45		17 43				19 24	19 44			21 47	23 47	
Cwmbran	d	00 42		10 50	13 25			14 56		15 50		17 48		18 38		19 29	19 49	20 48		21 52	23 52	
Newport (South Wales)	a	00 53		11 00	13 37			15 09		16 00		17 58		18 51		19 46	20 00	21 00		22 03	00 01	
Bristol Temple Meads 10	a			12 03	15 04			16 06		17 06		19 06		19 34			21 04			23 06		
Reading 7	a			12 27	15 27		16 18		17 18	17 27	19 06	19 58		20 57	21 19			22 35				
London Paddington 15 ⊖	a			13 07	16 08		17 07		18 08	18 10	19 52	20 40		21 40	22 03			23 26				
Cardiff Central 7	a	01 19		11 17	13 54			15 31		16 17		18 16	21 30	19 13		20 05	20 17	21 21		22 28	00 29	
Swansea 7	a			12 14	14 58	16 07		16 43		17 20		19 12	20 13	20 23			21 16	22 39		23 26		

Sundays

3 February to 23 March

		AW	AW	AW	AW	AW	GW	AW	GW	AW	GW	AW	AW	AW	GW	AW	AW	AW	AW	AW	AW	AW
										R		R		R			R	R	R	R		
		◇		◇	◇	◇	1 ◇	◇	1 ◇		1 ◇		◇		1 ◇						◇	
				A	B					C		D					C					
			🚌																			
					⊼		☕	⊼	☕	⊼	☕	⊼		⊼	☕		⊼	⊼	⊼	⊼		
Manchester Piccadilly 10	d	21p34			09 14					12 33		14 34		15 49			16 37	17 06		18 37	20 46	22 46
Stockport	d	21p45			09 10					12 42		14 42		15 58			16 45	16 45		18 45	20 54	22 54
Wilmslow	d	21p54			09 41					12 54		14 55		16 06			16 54	17 31		18 55	21 02	23 02
Liverpool Lime Street 10	d				09 53					11 56		13 56		15 31			15 56	17 27		17 56		
Runcorn	d				10 09					12 14		14 14		15 49			16 14	17 43			20 14	22 05
Holyhead	d							10 35				13 14		13b31				15 57	17 25			
Bangor (Gwynedd)	d							11 04				13 41		13b58				16b32	17 53			19b55
Llandudno Junction	d							11 22				13 59		14b16				16b54	18 11			20b18
Chester	d				10 11			12 20		12 25		14 46		15 25			16 25	17 52	19 07			22 25
Crewe 10	d	22p18	06 40		10 50					13 23		15 24		16 32			17 22	18 40		19 20	21 35	23 25
Nantwich	d	22p25	06 50		10 57					13 30							17 29			19 27		23 33
Wrenbury	d	22c31			11x03					13x36							17x35			19 33		23x38
Whitchurch (Shrops)	d	22p38	07 20		11 10					13 44							17 43			19 41		23 46
Prees	d	22c44			11x15					13x49							17x48			19 46		23x52
Wem	d	22p48			11 20					13 55							17 54			19 52		23 57
Yorton	d	22c54			11x25					13x59							17x58			19 56		00x02
Shrewsbury	a	23p04	07 50		11 36			13 15		14 09		15 52		17 05			18 08	19 13	19 59	20 06	22 09	00 14
	d	23p06	07 50		11 45	12 07		13 16		14 10		16 08	16 24	17 08			18 09	19 18		20 13	22 13	
Church Stretton	d	23p22	08 15		12 01	12 24		13 32		14 26		16 24	16 42				18 25			20 29	22 28	
Craven Arms	d	23p30	08 35		12 09	12 36		13 41		14 35		16 32	16 53				18 34			20 37	22 36	
Ludlow	d	23p38	08 55		12 18			13 49		14 43		16 41		17 37			18 42	19 47		20 46	22 44	
Leominster	d	23p48	09 20		12 29			14 01		14 55		16 52					18 54			20 57	22 55	
Hereford 7	a	00 03	09 50		12 44			14 15		15 09		17 07		18 00			19 08	20 10		21 12	23 09	
	d	00 04		10 11	12 46		13 30	14 17	14 30	15 11	16 30	17 09		18 02	18 30	18 50	19 10	20 12		21 13	23 14	
Abergavenny	d	00 27		10 34	13 10			14 40		15 34		17 32		18 25		19 13	19 33	20 35		21 37	23 37	
Pontypool and New Inn	d	00 37		10 45	13 20			14 51		15 45		17 43				19 24	19 44			21 47	23 47	
Cwmbran	d	00 42		10 50	13 25			14 56		15 50		17 48		18 38		19 29	19 49	20 48		21 52	23 52	
Newport (South Wales)	a	00 53		11 00	13 37			15 09		16 00		18 01		18 51		19 46	20 00	21 00		22 03	00 01	
Bristol Temple Meads 10	a			12 34	14 34			16 06		17 06		19 06		19 36		20 34	21 08	21 58		23 06		
Reading 7	a			14 08	16 08		16 17	18 07	17 15	19 08	19 19	21 09			21 18	22 08		23 26				
London Paddington 15 ⊖	a			14 53	16 52		17 01	18 52	17 58	20 01	20 02	21 51			22 00	22 49		00 27				
Cardiff Central 7	a	01 19		11 17	13 54			15 31		16 17		18 18	21 30	19 13		20 05	20 17	21 21		22 28	00 29	
Swansea 7	a			12 14	14 58	16 07		17 07		17 20		19 14	20 13			21 10	21 16	22 39		23 26		

For general notes see front of timetable
For details of catering facilities see Directory of Train Operators

- **A** To Fishguard Harbour (Table 128)
- **B** To Carmarthen (Table 128)
- **C** To Milford Haven (Table 128)
- **D** To Pembroke Dock (Table 128)
- **b** Change at Chester and Crewe
- **c** Previous night. Stops on request, passengers wishing to alight must inform the guard and those wishing to join must give a hand signal to the driver

Table 131

Sundays
from 30 March

Manchester, Liverpool and Crewe → Cardiff

Route Diagram - see first page of Table 129

		AW	AW	AW	AW	AW	AW	AW	AW	AW	AW	AW	GW	AW
											R			R
							◇						1 ◇	
		Bus	Bus	Bus	Bus			Bus		Bus		Bus		
													Buffet	
Manchester Piccadilly 10	✈ d					09 24					12 33			14 34
Stockport	d					09 33					12 44			14 42
Wilmslow	d					09 41					12 54			14 55
Liverpool Lime Street 10	d					09 53					11 56			13 56
Runcorn	d					10 09					12 14			14 14
Holyhead	d								10 35					13 14
Bangor (Gwynedd)	d								11 04					13 41
Llandudno Junction	d								11 22					13 59
Chester	d					10 11			12 20		12 25			14 46
Crewe 10	d			06 40		10 50					13 23			15 24
Nantwich	d			06 50		10 57					13 30			
Wrenbury	d					11x03					13x36			
Whitchurch (Shrops)	d			07 20		11 10					13 44			
Prees	d					11x15					13x49			
Wem	d					11 20					13 55			
Yorton	d					11x25					13x59			
Shrewsbury	a			07 50		11 36			13 15		14 09			15 52
	d			07 50		11 45	12 07		13 16		14 10			16 08
Church Stretton	d			08 15		12 01	12 24		13 32		14 26			16 24
Craven Arms	d			08 35		12 09	12 36		13 41		14 35			16 32
Ludlow	d			08 55		12 18			13 49		14 43			16 41
Leominster	d			09 20		12 29			14 01		14 55			16 52
Hereford 7	a			09 50		12 45			14 15		15 10			17 07
	d	23p20	00 15		10 11			12 55		14 25		15 25	16 30	
Abergavenny	d	00 01	00 55		10 51			13 35		15 05		16 05		
Pontypool and New Inn	d	00 16	01 10		11 11			13 55		15 25		16 25		
Cwmbran	d	00 30	01 25		11 21			14 05		15 35		16 35		
Newport (South Wales)	a	00 50	01 45		11 40			14 25		15 54		16 55		
Bristol Temple Meads 10	a													
Reading 7	a				14 44			16 44		18 50		19 49	18 59	
London Paddington 15	⊖ a				15 23			17 22		19 30		20 29	19 39	
Cardiff Central 7	a	01 25	02 20		12 10			15 00		16 24		17 30		
Swansea 7	a				13 34		16 07	16 34		17 34		18 34		

		AW	AW	AW	AW	GW	AW	AW	AW	AW	AW	AW	AW	AW	AW	AW
				R			R					R				
			◇			1 ◇								◇		
												A				
		Bus			Bus			Bus		Bus			Bus		Bus	
						Buffet						Trolley				
Manchester Piccadilly 10	✈ d			15 40			16 37		17 24			18 37		20 46		22 46
Stockport	d			15 49			16 45		17 33			18 45		20 54		22 54
Wilmslow	d			15 56			16 54		17 41			18 55		21 02		23 02
Liverpool Lime Street 10	d			15 31			15 56		17 27			17 56		19 56		21 47
Runcorn	d			15 49			16 14		17 43			18 14		20 14		22 05
Holyhead	d			13b31					15 57		17 25	16 48		18b40		
Bangor (Gwynedd)	d			13b58					16b32		17 53	17 27		19b09		19b55
Llandudno Junction	d			14b16					16b54		18 11	17 46		19b27		20b18
Chester	d			15 25			16 25		17 52		19 07	18 42		20 55		22 25
Crewe 10	d			16 32			17 22		18 40			19 20		21 35		23 25
Nantwich	d						17 29					19 27				23 33
Wrenbury	d						17x35					19 33				23x38
Whitchurch (Shrops)	d						17 43					19 41				23 46
Prees	d						17x48					19 46				23x52
Wem	d						17 54					19 52				23 57
Yorton	d						17x58					19 56				00x02
Shrewsbury	a			17 05			18 08		19 13		19 59	20 06		22 09		00 14
	d		16 24	17 08			18 09		19 18		20 13			22 13		
Church Stretton	d		16 42				18 25				20 29			22 28		
Craven Arms	d		16 53				18 34				20 37			22 36		
Ludlow	d			17 37			18 42		19 47		20 46			22 44		
Leominster	d						18 54				20 57			22 55		
Hereford 7	a			18 00			19 15		20 10		21 15			23 15		
	d	17 15			18 10	18 30		19 30		20 30			21 45		23 25	
Abergavenny	d	17 55			18 50			20 10		21 10			22 25		00 05	
Pontypool and New Inn	d	18 15						20 30					22 45		00 25	
Cwmbran	d	18 25			19 15			20 40		21 40			22 55		00 35	
Newport (South Wales)	a	18 45			19 35			21 00		22 00			23 15		00 55	
Bristol Temple Meads 10	a															
Reading 7	a	21 52				21 01		23 20								
London Paddington 15	⊖ a	22 30				21 44		00 10								
Cardiff Central 7	a	19 20	21 30		20 10			21 35		22 35			23 50		01 30	
Swansea 7	a	20 33	20 13		21 15			23 26		23 39			01 38			

For general notes see front of timetable
For details of catering facilities see Directory of Train Operators

A Trolley from Crewe
b Change at Chester and Crewe

Network Diagram for Tables 132, 133 ,134

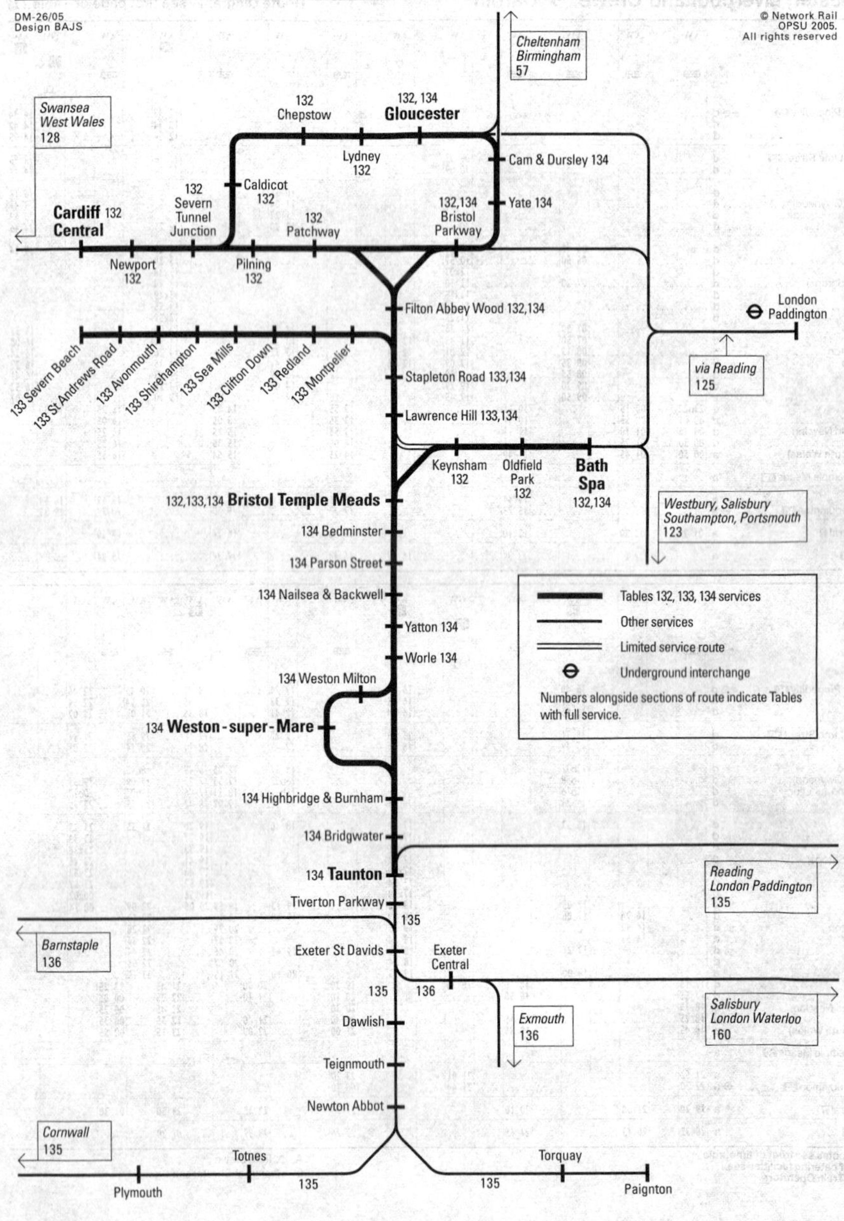

DM-26/05
Design BAJS
© Network Rail
OPSU 2005.
All rights reserved
Cheltenham
Birmingham
57
Swansea
West Wales
128
132
Chepstow
132, 134
Gloucester
Lydney
132
Cam & Dursley 134
Caldicot
132
132
Severn
Tunnel
Junction
Cardiff 132
Central
132
Patchway
132,134
Bristol
Parkway
Yate 134
Newport
132
Pilning
132
Filton Abbey Wood 132,134
London
Paddington
133 Severn Beach
133 St Andrews Road
133 Avonmouth
133 Shirehampton
133 Sea Mills
133 Clifton Down
133 Redland
133 Montpelier
Stapleton Road 133,134
via Reading
125
Lawrence Hill 133,134
Keynsham
132
Oldfield
Park
132
Bath
Spa
132,134
132,133,134 Bristol Temple Meads
Westbury, Salisbury
Southampton, Portsmouth
123
134 Bedminster
134 Parson Street
134 Nailsea & Backwell
Yatton 134
Worle 134
134 Weston Milton
134 Weston-super-Mare
Tables 132, 133, 134 services
Other services
Limited service route
Underground interchange
Numbers alongside sections of route indicate Tables with full service.
134 Highbridge & Burnham
134 Bridgwater
134 Taunton
Reading
London Paddington
135
Tiverton Parkway
135
Barnstaple
136
Exeter St Davids
Exeter
Central
135
136
Salisbury
London Waterloo
160
Exmouth
136
Dawlish
Teignmouth
Newton Abbot
Cornwall
135
Totnes
Torquay
135
135
Plymouth
Paignton

Cardiff → Gloucester, Bristol and Bath Spa

Network Diagram - see first page of Table 132

Miles	Miles	Miles			AW	AW	AW	AW	GW	GW	GW	AW	GW	GW		GW	GW	GW	AW	GW	GW	GW	AW	GW	GW	GW
					MX	MX																				
							◇	◇	1 ◇	◇	1 ◇	◇	1 ◇	1 ◇		1 ◇	1 ◇			1 ◇	1 ◇	◇	◇	1 ◇		1 ◇
					A													B	C					D	E	
								⊥	🍽	⊥	⊥	⊥	⊥	⊥		🍽	⊥			🍽	⊥	⊥	⊥	⊠		⊥
0	0	0	**Cardiff Central 7**	d	23p20	00 30	04 00	05 10			05 15	05 35				05 54			06 12	06 20		06 30	06 50			06 55
11¾	11¾	11¾	Newport (South Wales)	a	23p36	00 48	04 16	05 26			05 32	05 51				06 07			06 25	06 33		06 43	07 02			07 08
—	—	—		d	23p39						05 33					06 08			06 27	06 34		06 44				07 09
21¾	21¾	21¾	Severn Tunnel Jn	d	23p57														06 38			06 55				
—	—	22½	Caldicot	d	23p59														06 40							
—	—	29¼	Chepstow	d	00 08														06 49							
—	—	37	Lydney	d	00 17														06 58							
—	—	56½	**Gloucester 7**	a	00 38														07 20							
28¾	28¾	—	Pilning	d																						
32¼	32¼	—	Patchway	d																						
—	33½	—	**Bristol Parkway 7**	a							06 00					06 29				06 55						07 30
—	—	—		d																					07 25	
33¾	—	—	Filton Abbey Wood	d																		07 09			07 28	
38¼	—	—	**Bristol Temple Meads 10**	a																		07 18			07 40	
—	—	—		d					05 30	05 45			06 00	06 30			06 40	06 43			07 00	07 22		07 30	07 49	
42¾	—	—	Keynsham	d						05 52								06 50							07 56	
48¾	—	—	Oldfield Park	d						05 59								06 56							08 03	
49¾	—	—	**Bath Spa 7**	a					05 41	06 00			06 11	06 41			06 51	06 59			07 11	07 35		07 41	08 05	

		XC		AW	AW	AW	GW	GW	GW	GW	GW	XC	AW		GW	GW	SW	GW	GW	GW	GW	GW	GW	XC		AW
				MO																						
		1 ◇				◇	1 ◇	1 ◇		◇	1 ◇	◇	◇		◇	1 ◇	1 ◇		1 ◇	1 ◇		◇	1 ◇	◇		◇
		G		H	J		K		L			N			Q		U	V						N		
		🍽				⊥	✕	⊠		⊥	🍽	⊥	⊥			⊥			⊥	⊥		⊥	⊥	⊥		⊥
Cardiff Central 7	d	07 00		07 05	07 12	07 20	07 25			07 30		07 45	07 50			07 55		08 00		08 25		08 30		08 45		08 50
Newport (South Wales)	a	07 13		07 19	07 25	07 32	07 38			07 43		07 57	08 03			08 08		08 13		08 38		08 43		08 58		09 02
	d	07 15		07 27	07 27		07 39			07 44		07 59				08 09		08 15		08 39		08 44		08 59		
Severn Tunnel Jn	d	07 25		07 38	07 38					07 55								08 25								
Caldicot	d			07 40	07 40																					
Chepstow	d			07 49	07 49																					
Lydney	d			07 58	07 58																					
Gloucester 7	a			08 20	08 20							08 43												09 43		
Pilning	d																									
Patchway	d	07 39																08 39								
Bristol Parkway 7	a						08 00									08 30				09 00						
	d														08 24											
Filton Abbey Wood	d	07 47								08 09					08 27			08 42				09 09				
Bristol Temple Meads 10	a	07 53								08 18					08 36			08 53				09 18				
	d							08 00	08 13	08 22	08 30				08 40		08 50		09 00		09 09	09 22	09 30			
Keynsham	d								08 20						08 47		08 57				09 16					
Oldfield Park	d								08 27						08 54						09 23					
Bath Spa 7	a							08 11	08 29	08 35	08 41				08 56		09 04		09 11		09 25	09 34	09 41			

		GW	GW	GW	GW	AW	AW	GW	GW	GW	XC		AW	GW	GW	GW	GW	AW	GW	GW	GW	XC		AW	GW	GW
		◇	1 ◇		1 ◇		◇	1 ◇	◇	1 ◇	◇		◇		1 ◇		1 ◇		1 ◇	◇	1 ◇	◇		◇	◇	1 ◇
		X		V		C					N			Y		V		A				N			X	
			⊠		🍽		⊥	⊠	⊥	⊥	⊥		⊥		🍽		⊥		🍽	⊥	⊥	⊥		⊥		⊥
Cardiff Central 7	d		08 55	09 00		09 12	09 20	09 25	09 30		09 45		09 50		09 55	10 00		10 12	10 25	10 30		10 45		10 50		10 55
Newport (South Wales)	a		09 08	09 13		09 25	09 32	09 38	09 43		09 58		10 04		10 08	10 13		10 25	10 38	10 43		10 58		11 03		11 08
	d		09 10	09 15		09 27		09 39	09 44		09 59				10 09	10 15		10 27	10 39	10 44		10 59				11 09
Severn Tunnel Jn	d			09 25		09 38										10 25		10 38								
Caldicot	d					09 40												10 40								
Chepstow	d					09 49												10 49								
Lydney	d					09 58												10 58								
Gloucester 7	a					10 20					10 43							11 20				11 43				
Pilning	d																									
Patchway	d			09 39												10 39										
Bristol Parkway 7	a		09 30					10 00							10 30				11 00							11 30
	d	09 19												10 19											11 19	
Filton Abbey Wood	d	09 22		09 42					10 09					10 22		10 42				11 09					11 22	
Bristol Temple Meads 10	a	09 35		09 52					10 18					10 34		10 52				11 18					11 35	
	d	09 49			10 00				10 22	10 30				10 49			11 00			11 22	11 30				11 49	
Keynsham	d	09 56												10 56											11 56	
Oldfield Park	d	10 03												11 03											12 03	
Bath Spa 7	a	10 05			10 11				10 35	10 41				11 05			11 11			11 35	11 41				12 05	

For general notes see front of timetable
For details of catering facilities see Directory of Train Operators

- **A** From Maesteg (Table 128) to Cheltenham Spa (Table 57)
- **B** From Taunton (Table 134)
- **C** To Cheltenham Spa (Table 57)
- **D** **The Bristolian**
- **E** To Westbury (Table 123)
- **G** To Newcastle (Table 51)
- **H** From 24 March. To Cheltenham Spa (Table 57)
- **J** All Tuesdays to Fridays, also Mondays until 17 March. To Cheltenham Spa (Table 57)
- **K** **The Red Dragon**
- **L** To Swindon (Table 125)
- **N** ⊥ from Newport (South Wales)
- **Q** From Worcester Shrub Hill (Table 57) to Weymouth (Table 123)
- **U** To London Waterloo (Table 160)
- **V** To Taunton (Table 134)
- **X** From Gloucester (Table 134) to Weymouth (Table 123)
- **Y** From Great Malvern (Table 71) to Westbury (Table 123)

Cardiff → Gloucester, Bristol and Bath Spa

Network Diagram - see first page of Table 132

		GW	AW	GW	GW	GW	GW	XC	AW	GW		GW	GW	GW	AW	GW	GW	GW	XC	AW	GW		GW	GW	GW	AW
			◇	[1] ◇	[1] ◇	◇	[1] ◇	◇	◇	◇		[1] ◇		[1] ◇		[1] ◇	◇	[1] ◇	◇	◇			[1] ◇		[1] ◇	
		A						B		C			A		D	E					G			A		D
			trolley	buffet	buffet	trolley	trolley	trolley	trolley			buffet		trolley		⊠	trolley	trolley		trolley			trolley		trolley	
Cardiff Central [7]	d	11 00	11 20		11 25	11 30		11 45	11 50			11 55	12 00		12 12	12 25	12 30		12 45	12 50			12 55	13 00		13 12
Newport (South Wales)	a	11 13	11 32		11 38	11 43		11 58	12 03			12 08	12 13		12 25	12 38	12 43		12 58	13 03			13 08	13 13		13 25
	d	11 15			11 39	11 44		11 59				12 09	12 15		12 27	12 39	12 44		12 59				13 09	13 15		13 27
Severn Tunnel Jn	d	11 25											12 25		12 38									13 25		13 39
Caldicot	d														12 40											13 41
Chepstow	d														12 49											13 50
Lydney	d														12 58											13 59
Gloucester [7]	a							12 44							13 20				13 45							14 20
Pilning	d																									
Patchway	d	11 39											12 39											13 39		
Bristol Parkway [7]	a				12 00							12 30				13 00							13 30			
	d									12 19											13 19					
Filton Abbey Wood	d	11 42				12 09				12 22			12 42				13 09				13 22			13 42		
Bristol Temple Meads [10]	a	11 52				12 18				12 35			12 52				13 17				13 34			13 52		
	d			12 00		12 22	12 30			12 39				13 00			13 22	13 30			13 49				14 00	
Keynsham	d									12 46											13 56					
Oldfield Park	d									12 53											14 03					
Bath Spa [7]	a			12 11		12 35	12 41			12 55				13 11			13 35	13 41			14 05				14 11	

		AW	GW	GW	GW	XC	AW	GW	GW		GW	GW	GW	GW	GW	XC	AW	GW	GW	GW		SW	AW	AW	GW	GW
		◇	[1] ◇	◇	[1] ◇	◇	◇	◇	[1] ◇			[1] ◇	[1] ◇	◇		◇	R	[1] ◇	[1] ◇			[1] ◇		◇	[1] ◇	[1] ◇
								H			A				G					A			D			
		trolley	buffet	trolley	buffet		trolley		trolley			buffet	buffet	trolley			trolley	trolley	buffet					trolley	trolley	buffet
Cardiff Central [7]	d	13 20	13 25	13 30		13 45	13 50		13 55		14 00		14 25	14 30		14 45	14 50		14 55	15 00			15 12	15 20		15 25
Newport (South Wales)	a	13 32	13 38	13 43		13 58	14 03		14 08		14 13		14 38	14 43		14 58	15 03		15 08	15 13			15 25	15 32		15 38
	d		13 39	13 44		13 59			14 09		14 15		14 39	14 44		14 59			15 09	15 15			15 27			15 39
Severn Tunnel Jn	d										14 25									15 25			15 38			
Caldicot	d																						15 40			
Chepstow	d																						15 49			
Lydney	d																						15 58			
Gloucester [7]	a					14 45										15 45							16 21			
Pilning	d																									
Patchway	d										14 39									15 39						
Bristol Parkway [7]	a		14 00						14 30				15 00						15 30							16 00
	d							14 19							15 19											
Filton Abbey Wood	d			14 09				14 22			14 42			15 09	15 22					15 42						
Bristol Temple Meads [10]	a			14 19				14 34			14 52			15 18	15 36					15 51						
	d			14 22	14 30			14 49				15 00		15 22	15 43			15 30				15 52			16 00	
Keynsham	d							14 56							15 50											
Oldfield Park	d							15 03							15 57											
Bath Spa [7]	a			14 35	14 41			15 05				15 11		15 35	15 59			15 41				16 05			16 11	

		GW	GW	XC	GW	AW	GW	GW		GW	AW	GW	GW	AW	GW	GW	XC	AW	GW		GW	GW	GW	GW	GW	AW
		◇	[1] ◇	◇		R	[1] ◇	[1] ◇				[1] ◇			[1] ◇	◇	◇	R	[1] ◇		◇	[1] ◇		[1] ◇		
					H					A			J	D							K		A		J	D
		trolley	trolley			trolley	trolley	trolley				trolley			buffet	trolley		trolley	buffet		trolley	trolley		trolley		
Cardiff Central [7]	d	15 30		15 45		15 50	15 55			16 00	16 06			16 12	16 25	16 30	16 45	16 50				16 55	17 00			17 12
Newport (South Wales)	a	15 43		15 58		16 03	16 08			16 13	16 21			16 25	16 38	16 43	16 58	17 03				17 08	17 13			17 27
	d	15 44		15 59			16 09			16 15				16 27	16 39	16 44	16 59					17 09	17 15			17 27
Severn Tunnel Jn	d									16 25				16 39		16 55							17 25			17 38
Caldicot	d													16 41												17 40
Chepstow	d													16 50												17 49
Lydney	d													16 59												17 58
Gloucester [7]	a			16 44										17 21			17 45									18 20
Pilning	d																									
Patchway	d									16 39													17 39			
Bristol Parkway [7]	a						16 30								17 00							17 30				
	d				16 19								16 47								17 19				17 47	
Filton Abbey Wood	d	16 09			16 22					16 42			16 50			17 09					17 22		17 42		17 50	
Bristol Temple Meads [10]	a	16 18			16 34					16 51			17 02			17 18					17 36		17 52		18 02	
	d	16 22	16 30		16 49			16 30				17 00	17 07			17 22			17 31		17 49			18 00	18 07	
Keynsham	d				16 56								17 14								17 56				18 14	
Oldfield Park	d				17 03								17 21			17 32					18 03				18 21	
Bath Spa [7]	a	16 35	16 41		17 05			16 41				17 11	17 24			17 35			17 41		18 05			18 11	18 24	

For general notes see front of timetable
For details of catering facilities see Directory of Train Operators

A To Taunton (Table 134)
B trolley from Newport (South Wales)
C From Great Malvern (Table 71) to Brighton (Table 123)
D From Maesteg (Table 128) to Cheltenham Spa (Table 57)
E **The St David**
G From Gloucester (Table 134) to Westbury (Table 123)
H From Great Malvern (Table 71) to Weymouth (Table 123)
J To Westbury (Table 123)
K From Gloucester (Table 134) to Weymouth (Table 123)

Table 132

Cardiff → Gloucester, Bristol and Bath Spa

Network Diagram - see first page of Table 132

Mondays to Fridays

		AW	GW	GW	GW	XC	AW		GW	GW	GW	AW	GW	GW	GW	XC	AW	GW		GW	GW	GW	AW	GW	GW	GW
		R	1◇	◇	1◇	◇	R			1◇			1◇	◇	1◇	◇	◇				1◇	◇	◇	1◇	◇	
									A		B	C						D		B					E	B
		🛒	☕	🛒	🛒		🛒			🛒			☕	🛒	☕	🛒	🛒				☕	🛒	🛒	🛒		
Cardiff Central 7	d	17 20	17 25	17 30		17 45	17 50			17 55	18 00	18 12	18 25	18 30		18 45	18 50			19 00	19 25	19 30	19 34			19 55
Newport (South Wales)	a	17 32	17 38	17 43		17 58	18 03			18 08	18 13	18 25	18 38	18 42		18 59	19 05			19 13	19 38	19 43	19 47			20 08
	d		17 39	17 44		17 59				18 09	18 15	18 27	18 39	18 44		18 59				19 15	19 39	19 44				20 10
Severn Tunnel Jn	d			17 55							18 25	18 38		18 54						19 25						20 21
Caldicot	d											18 40														
Chepstow	d											18 49														
Lydney	d											18 58														
Gloucester 7	a					18 44						19 20				19 46										
Pilning	d																									
Patchway	d										18 39									19 39						20 35
Bristol Parkway 7	a		18 00							18 30			19 00								20 00					
	d								18 19									19 19							20 19	
Filton Abbey Wood	d			18 09					18 22		18 42			19 09				19 22		19 42		20 09			20 22	20 38
Bristol Temple Meads 10	a			18 18					18 34		18 52			19 18				19 36		19 52		20 18			20 34	20 48
	d			18 22	18 31				18 49					19 22	19 30			19 49				20 22		20 30	20 49	
Keynsham	d								18 56									19 56							20 56	
Oldfield Park	d								19 03									20 03							21 03	
Bath Spa 7	a			18 34	18 42				19 05					19 35	19 41			20 05				20 35		20 41	21 05	

		XC	AW	AW	GW	GW		XC	AW	GW	GW	AW	GW	AW	AW	SW	GW		GW	GW	GW	GW	AW			
		◇	◇		1◇	◇		◇	◇	1◇			1◇	FX ◇	FO ◇	1	1◇				FO	FX				
				C							G	C							B				C			
			🛒		🛒	🛒				☕			🛒				🛒									
Cardiff Central 7	d	20 00	20 10	20 15	20 25	20 30		20 50	20 53		21 00	21 14	21 25	21 56	21 56				22 00		23 00	23 00	23 20			
Newport (South Wales)	a	20 13	20 22	20 28	20 38	20 43		21 02	21 08		21 12	21 27	21 38	22 12	22 13				22 14		23 14	23 15	23 36			
	d	20 15		20 30	20 39	20 44		21 04			21 14	21 29	21 39						22 17		23 16	23 17	23 39			
Severn Tunnel Jn	d			20 41							21 24	21 40							22 33		23 32	23 32	23 57			
Caldicot	d			20 43								21 42											23 59			
Chepstow	d			20 52								21 51											00 08			
Lydney	d			21 01								22 01											00 17			
Gloucester 7	a	20 56		21 22				21 46				22 22											00 38			
Pilning	d																									
Patchway	d										21 37								22 47		23 46	23 46				
Bristol Parkway 7	a				21 00								22 00													
	d																									
Filton Abbey Wood	d					21 09					21 41								22 51		23 50	23 50				
Bristol Temple Meads 10	a					21 18					21 53								23 00		00 04	00 04				
	d					21 22				21 40	22 00					22 25	22 33			23 16						
Keynsham	d										22 08									23 23						
Oldfield Park	d										22 15									23 29						
Bath Spa 7	a					21 35				21 54	22 17					22 36	22 44			23 32						

Saturdays

until 26 January

		AW	AW	AW	GW	GW	GW		AW	AW	GW	GW	GW	GW		AW	GW	AW	GW	GW	GW		GW	GW	AW	AW
				◇	1◇	◇	1◇		◇	◇	1◇	1◇		1◇			◇	◇	1◇	1◇				1◇		◇
		C					H						J			K							L		K	
					☕		☕		🛒	🛒	☕	☕		☕				🛒	☕	☕				☕		🛒
Cardiff Central 7	d	23p20	00 30	04 00			04 55		05 10	05 35		05 55				06 12	06 30	06 50		06 55			07 00		07 12	07 20
Newport (South Wales)	a	23p36	00 48	04 16			05 09		05 23	05 51		06 08				06 25	06 43	07 02		07 08			07 13		07 25	07 32
	d	23p39					05 09					06 09				06 27	06 44			07 09			07 15		07 27	
Severn Tunnel Jn	d	23p57														06 38	06 55						07 25		07 38	
Caldicot	d	23p59														06 40									07 40	
Chepstow	d	00 08														06 49									07 49	
Lydney	d	00 17														06 58									07 58	
Gloucester 7	a	00 38														07 20									08 21	
Pilning	d																									
Patchway	d																						07 39			
Bristol Parkway 7	a						05 37					06 30								07 30						
	d						05 42																			
Filton Abbey Wood	d																07 10						07 42			
Bristol Temple Meads 10	a						05 53										07 18						07 52			
	d				05 30	05 45	06 00				06 30		06 43	07 00			07 24		07 30		07 49			08 00		
Keynsham	d					05 52							06 50								07 56					
Oldfield Park	d					05 59							06 56								08 02					
Bath Spa 7	a				05 41	06 01	06 11				06 41		06 59	07 11			07 35		07 41		08 05			08 11		

For general notes see front of timetable
For details of catering facilities see Directory of Train Operators

- **A** From Worcester Foregate Street (Table 71) to Westbury (Table 123)
- **B** To Taunton (Table 134)
- **C** From Maesteg (Table 128) to Cheltenham Spa (Table 57)
- **D** From Gloucester (Table 134) to Frome (Table 123)
- **E** From Great Malvern (Table 71) to Weymouth (Table 123)
- **G** To Westbury (Table 123)
- **H** From Swansea (Table 125)
- **J** From Taunton (Table 134)
- **K** To Cheltenham Spa (Table 57)
- **L** To Weston-super-Mare (Table 134)

until 26 January

Cardiff → Gloucester, Bristol and Bath Spa

Network Diagram - see first page of Table 132

		GW 1◇ 🍴	GW ◇ 🛒	GW 1◇ 🍴	XC ◇ A 🛒		AW ◇ 🛒	GW B	GW 1◇ 🍴	SW 1◇ C	GW 1◇ 🍴	GW D		GW 1◇ 🍴	GW ◇ 🛒	GW 1◇ 🍴	GW E	XC ◇ A 🛒	AW ◇ 🛒		GW 1◇ 🍴	XC 1◇ G 🍴	AW H	AW ◇ 🛒	GW 1◇ 🍴	GW 1◇ 🍴
Cardiff Central 7	d	07 25	07 30		07 45		07 50		07 55			08 00		08 25	08 30			08 45	08 50		08 55	09 00	09 12	09 20	09 25	
Newport (South Wales)	a	07 38	07 43		07 57		08 02		08 08			08 13		08 38	08 43			08 57	09 02		09 08	09 13	09 25	09 32	09 38	
	d	07 39	07 44		07 59				08 09			08 15		08 39	08 44			08 59			09 09	09 15	09 27		09 39	
Severn Tunnel Jn	d		07 55									08 25										09 25	09 38			
Caldicot	d																						09 40			
Chepstow	d																						09 49			
Lydney	d																						09 58			
Gloucester 7	a				08 43													09 44					10 20			
Pilning	d											08 32														
Patchway	d											08 40										09 35				
Bristol Parkway 7	a	08 00							08 30					09 00							09 30				10 00	
	d							08 20									09 19									
Filton Abbey Wood	d		08 10					08 23				08 43			09 09		09 23					09 40				
Bristol Temple Meads 10	a		08 18					08 34				08 52			09 18		09 35					09 51				
	d		08 24	08 30				08 40		08 50	09 00				09 24	09 30	09 49									10 00
Keynsham	d							08 47		08 57							09 56									
Oldfield Park	d							08 54									10 03									
Bath Spa 7	a		08 35	08 41				08 56		09 04	09 11				09 35	09 41	10 05									10 11

		GW ◇ 🛒	GW 1◇ 🍴		XC ◇ A 🛒	AW ◇ 🛒	GW J	GW D	GW 1◇ 🍴	AW K		GW 1◇ 🍴	GW ◇ 🛒	GW 1◇ 🍴	XC ◇ A 🛒	AW ◇ 🛒	GW ◇ E		GW D	AW ◇ 🛒	GW 1◇ 🍴	GW 1◇ 🍴	GW ◇ 🛒	XC ◇ A 🛒		AW ◇ 🛒
Cardiff Central 7	d	09 30			09 45	09 50		10 00		10 12		10 25	10 30		10 45	10 50			11 00	11 20		11 25	11 30	11 45		11 50
Newport (South Wales)	a	09 43			09 58	10 03		10 13		10 25		10 38	10 43		10 58	11 03			11 13	11 32		11 38	11 43	11 58		12 03
	d	09 44			09 59			10 15		10 27		10 39	10 44		10 59				11 15			11 39	11 44	11 59		
Severn Tunnel Jn	d							10 25		10 38									11 25							
Caldicot	d									10 40																
Chepstow	d									10 49																
Lydney	d									10 58																
Gloucester 7	a				10 45					11 21					11 45									12 46		
Pilning	d																									
Patchway	d							10 39											11 39							
Bristol Parkway 7	a											11 00										12 00				
	d						10 19										11 19									
Filton Abbey Wood	d	10 09					10 22	10 42					11 09				11 23		11 42				12 09			
Bristol Temple Meads 10	a	10 18					10 35	10 52					11 18				11 35		11 52				12 18			
	d	10 24	10 30				10 49		11 00				11 24	11 30			11 49				12 00		12 24			
Keynsham	d						10 56										11 56									
Oldfield Park	d						11 03										12 03									
Bath Spa 7	a	10 35	10 41				11 05		11 11				11 35	11 41			12 05				12 11		12 35			

		GW L	GW D	SW 1◇ C	AW K	GW 1◇ 🍴	GW ◇ 🛒		GW 1◇ 🍴	XC ◇	AW ◇ 🛒	GW N	GW D	GW 1◇ 🍴		AW K	AW ◇ 🛒	GW 1◇ 🍴	GW ◇ 🛒	GW 1◇ 🍴	XC ◇		AW ◇ 🛒	GW ◇ Q 🛒	GW 1◇ 🍴	GW ◇ 🛒
Cardiff Central 7	d		12 00		12 12	12 25	12 30			12 45	12 50		13 00			13 12	13 20	13 25	13 30		13 45		13 50		14 25	14 30
Newport (South Wales)	a		12 13		12 25	12 38	12 43			12 58	13 03		13 13			13 25	13 32	13 38	13 43		13 58		14 03		14 38	14 43
	d		12 15		12 27	12 39	12 44			12 59			13 15			13 27		13 39	13 44		13 59				14 39	14 44
Severn Tunnel Jn	d		12 25		12 38								13 26			13 38										
Caldicot	d				12 40											13 40										
Chepstow	d				12 49											13 49										
Lydney	d				12 58											13 58										
Gloucester 7	a				13 20					13 45						14 20					14 44					
Pilning	d																									
Patchway	d		12 39										13 39													
Bristol Parkway 7	a					13 00												14 00							15 00	
	d	12 19										13 19												14 19		
Filton Abbey Wood	d	12 22	12 42				13 09					13 23	13 43						14 09					14 23		15 09
Bristol Temple Meads 10	a	12 35	12 52				13 18					13 35	13 52						14 18					14 34		15 18
	d	12 39		13 10			13 24		13 30			13 49		14 00					14 24	14 30				14 49		15 24
Keynsham	d	12 46										13 56												14 56		
Oldfield Park	d	12 53										14 03												15 03		
Bath Spa 7	a	12 55		13 21			13 35		13 41			14 05		14 11					14 35	14 41				15 05		15 35

For general notes see front of timetable
For details of catering facilities see Directory of Train Operators

A 🛒 from Newport (South Wales)

B From Worcester Shrub Hill (Table 57) to Weymouth (Table 123)
C To London Waterloo (Table 160)
D To Taunton (Table 134)
E From Gloucester (Table 134) to Weymouth (Table 123)
G To Newcastle (Table 51)

H To Cheltenham Spa (Table 57)
J From Great Malvern (Table 71) to Westbury (Table 123)
K From Maesteg (Table 128) to Cheltenham Spa (Table 57)
L From Great Malvern (Table 71) to Brighton (Table 123)
N From Gloucester (Table 134) to Westbury (Table 123)
Q From Great Malvern (Table 71) to Weymouth (Table 123)

Table 132

Saturdays

until 26 January

Cardiff → Gloucester, Bristol and Bath Spa

Network Diagram - see first page of Table 132

		GW	XC	AW	GW		SW	GW	GW	AW	AW	GW		XC	AW	GW	GW	GW	AW		AW	GW	GW	GW	XC	AW
		1 ◇	◇	**R**			**1** ◇		**1** ◇		◇	◇		◇	**R**	**1** ◇	◇					**1** ◇	◇	**1** ◇	◇	**R**
					A			B		C							D	B			C					
		☕		🛒					☕		🛒	🛒			🛒	☕						☕	🛒	☕		🛒
Cardiff Central 7	d		14 45	14 50				15 00		15 12	15 20	15 30		15 45	15 50			16 00	16 06		16 12	16 25	16 30		16 45	16 50
Newport (South Wales)	a		14 58	15 03				15 13		15 25	15 32	15 43		15 58	16 03			16 13	16 21		16 23	16 38	16 43		16 58	17 03
	d		14 59					15 15		15 27		15 44		15 59				16 15			16 26	16 39	16 44		16 59	
Severn Tunnel Jn	d							15 25		15 38								16 25			16 37		16 55			
Caldicot	d									15 40											16 38					
Chepstow	d									15 49											16 47					
Lydney	d									15 58											16 56					
Gloucester 7	a		15 45							16 20				16 44							17 20				17 45	
Pilning	d																									
Patchway	d							15 39										16 39								
Bristol Parkway 7	a																					17 00				
	d				15 19												16 19									
Filton Abbey Wood	d				15 23			15 42				16 09					16 23	16 42					17 10			
Bristol Temple Meads 10	a				15 35			15 52				16 18					16 34	16 52					17 18			
	d	15 30			15 43		15 52		16 00			16 24				16 30	16 49						17 24	17 30		
Keynsham	d				15 50												16 56									
Oldfield Park	d				15 57												17 02						17 35			
Bath Spa 7	a	15 41			15 59		16 05		16 11			16 35				16 41	17 05						17 37	17 41		

		GW	GW		GW	AW	AW	GW	GW	GW		XC	AW	GW	GW	AW	GW		GW	GW	XC	AW	GW	GW		GW
		◇			**1** ◇		◇	**1** ◇	◇	**1** ◇		◇	**R**				**1** ◇		◇	**1** ◇	◇	◇				**1** ◇
		E	B			C								G	B	C							H	B		
					☕		🛒	☕	🛒	☕			🛒				☕		🛒	☕		🛒				☕
Cardiff Central 7	d		17 00			17 12	17 20	17 25	17 30			17 45	17 50		18 00	18 12	18 25		18 30		18 45	18 50		19 00		19 25
Newport (South Wales)	a		17 13			17 27	17 32	17 38	17 43			17 58	18 03		18 13	18 25	18 38		18 43		18 59	19 05		19 13		19 38
	d		17 15			17 27		17 39	17 44			17 59			18 15	18 27	18 39		18 44		18 59			19 15		19 39
Severn Tunnel Jn	d		17 25			17 38			17 55						18 25	18 38								19 25		
Caldicot	d					17 40										18 40										
Chepstow	d					17 49										18 49										
Lydney	d					17 58										18 58										
Gloucester 7	a					18 20						18 43				19 20					19 44					
Pilning	d																									
Patchway	d		17 39												18 39									19 39		
Bristol Parkway 7	a							18 00									19 00									20 00
	d	17 19												18 19									19 19			
Filton Abbey Wood	d	17 23	17 42						18 10					18 22	18 42				19 09				19 22	19 42		
Bristol Temple Meads 10	a	17 35	17 52						18 18					18 35	18 52				19 18				19 36	19 52		
	d	17 49			18 00				18 24	18 30				18 49					19 24	19 30			19 49			
Keynsham	d	17 56												18 56									19 56			
Oldfield Park	d	18 03												19 03									20 03			
Bath Spa 7	a	18 05			18 11				18 35	18 41				19 05					19 35	19 41			20 05			

		GW	AW	GW	GW	GW	XC		AW	AW	GW	GW	XC	AW		GW	GW	AW	AW	SW	GW	GW	GW	AW		
		◇	◇	**1** ◇	◇		◇		◇		**1** ◇	◇	◇	◇					◇	**1**	**1** ◇					
					J	K				C							K	L						L		
		🛒	🛒	☕					🛒		☕	🛒														
Cardiff Central 7	d	19 30	19 34			19 50	20 00		20 10	20 15	20 25	20 30	20 50	20 53			21 00	21 15	21 50			22 00		23 20		
Newport (South Wales)	a	19 43	19 48			20 03	20 13		20 23	20 28	20 38	20 43	21 02	21 07			21 13	21 28	22 06			22 13		23 37		
	d	19 44				20 05	20 15			20 30	20 39	20 44	21 04				21 15	21 30				22 16		23 40		
Severn Tunnel Jn	d					20 15				20 41							21 25	21 41				22 33		23 57		
Caldicot	d									20 43								21 43						23 59		
Chepstow	d									20 52								21 52						00 08		
Lydney	d									21 01								22 01						00 17		
Gloucester 7	a						20 56			21 22			21 46					22 22						00 42		
Pilning	d																									
Patchway	d					20 29											21 39					22 48				
Bristol Parkway 7	a										21 00															
	d				20 19																					
Filton Abbey Wood	d	20 09			20 23	20 34						21 09					21 42					22 52				
Bristol Temple Meads 10	a	20 18			20 36	20 43						21 18					21 52					23 00				
	d	20 24		20 33	20 49							21 24				21 51				22 23	22 33		23 10			
Keynsham	d				20 56											21 58							23 17			
Oldfield Park	d				21 02											22 04							23 23			
Bath Spa 7	a	20 35		20 44	21 05							21 35				22 07				22 34	22 44		23 26			

For general notes see front of timetable
For details of catering facilities see Directory of Train Operators

A From Gloucester (Table 134) to Westbury (Table 123)
B To Taunton (Table 134)
C From Maesteg (Table 128) to Cheltenham Spa (Table 57)
D From Worcester Foregate Street (Table 71) to Weymouth (Table 123)
E From Gloucester (Table 134) to Weymouth (Table 123)
G From Great Malvern (Table 71) to Westbury (Table 123)
H From Gloucester (Table 134) to Frome (Table 123)
J From Worcester Shrub Hill (Table 57) to Weymouth (Table 123)
K To Exeter St Davids (Table 135)
L From Maesteg (Table 128))

Saturdays

2 February to 22 March

Cardiff → Gloucester, Bristol and Bath Spa

Network Diagram - see first page of Table 132

		AW	AW	AW	GW	GW	AW	AW	GW		GW	GW	AW	GW	AW	GW	GW	GW		GW	GW	AW	AW	GW	GW	GW
				◇	◇	1◇	◇	◇			1◇	1◇		◇	◇	1◇				1◇	1◇		◇	1◇	◇	1◇
		A				B			C				D					E				D		B		
						🍴	🛒	🛒			🍴	🍴			🛒	🍴				🍴	🍴		🛒	🍴	🛒	🍴
Cardiff Central 7	d	23p20	00 30	04 00		04 55	05 10	05 35					06 12	06 30	06 50			07 00				07 12	07 20	07 25	07 30	
Newport (South Wales)	a	23p36	00 48	04 16		05 09	05 23	05 51					06 25	06 43	07 02			07 13				07 25	07 32	07 38	07 43	
	d	23p39				05 09							06 27	06 44				07 15				07 27		07 39	07 44	
Severn Tunnel Jn	d	23p57											06 38	06 55				07 25				07 38			07 55	
Caldicot	d	23p59											06 40									07 40				
Chepstow	d	00 08											06 49									07 49				
Lydney	d	00 17											06 58									07 58				
Gloucester 7	a	00 38											07 20									08 21				
Pilning	d																									
Patchway	d																	07 39								
Bristol Parkway 7	a					05 37																		08 00		
	d					05 42																		08 10		
Filton Abbey Wood	d													07 10				07 42						→	08 10	
Bristol Temple Meads 10	a					05 53								07 18				07 52							08 18	
	d				05 45	06 00			06 43		07 00	07 17		07 24		07 30	07 49			08 00	08 17				08 24	08 17
Keynsham	d				05 52				06 50								07 56									
Oldfield Park	d				05 59				06 56								08 02									
Bath Spa 7	a				06 01	06 11			06 59		07 11	07 28		07 35		07 41	08 05			08 11	08 28				08 35	08 28

		GW	XC	AW		GW	SW	GW	GW	GW	GW	XC	AW		GW	XC	AW	AW	XC	GW	GW	XC		AW	GW	GW
		1◇	◇	◇			1◇		1◇	◇	1◇	◇	◇			1◇		◇	◇	◇	1◇	◇		◇		
		B	G			H	J	K				G			L	N	D					G			Q	K
		🍴	🛒	🛒					🍴	🛒	🍴	🛒	🛒			🍴		🛒	🍴	🛒	🍴	🛒		🛒		
Cardiff Central 7	d		07 45	07 50				08 00		08 30		08 45	08 50			09 00	09 12	09 20		09 30		09 45		09 50		10 00
Newport (South Wales)	a		07 57	08 02				08 13		08 43		08 57	09 02			09 13	09 25	09 32		09 43		09 58		10 03		10 13
	d		07 59					08 15		08 44		08 59				09 15	09 27			09 44		09 59				10 15
Severn Tunnel Jn	d							08 25								09 25	09 38									10 25
Caldicot	d																09 40									
Chepstow	d																09 49									
Lydney	d																09 58									
Gloucester 7	a		08 43									09 44					10 20					10 45				
Pilning	d							08 32																		
Patchway	d							08 40								09 35										10 39
Bristol Parkway 7	a	←																								
	d	08 10				08 20									09 19										10 19	
Filton Abbey Wood	d					08 23		08 43		09 09					09 23	09 40				10 09					10 22	10 42
Bristol Temple Meads 10	a	08 22				08 34		08 52		09 18					09 35	09 51				10 18					10 35	10 52
	d	08 30				08 40	08 50		09 17	09 24	09 17				09 49				10 17	10 24	10 30				10 49	
Keynsham	d					08 47	08 57								09 56										10 56	
Oldfield Park	d					08 54									10 03										11 03	
Bath Spa 7	a	08 41				08 56	09 04		09 28	09 35	09 28				10 05				10 28	10 35	10 41				11 05	

		GW	GW	AW	GW	XC	AW	GW		GW	AW	GW	GW	GW	GW	GW	XC		AW	GW	GW	GW	SW	AW	GW	GW
		1◇	1◇		◇	◇	◇	◇			◇	1◇	1◇	1◇	◇	1◇	◇		◇			1◇	1◇		1◇	◇
				A		G		L		K				U		U	G			V	K		J	A		
		🍴	🍴		🛒	🛒	🛒				🛒	🍴	🍴	🍴	🛒	🍴	🛒		🛒			🍴			🍴	🛒
Cardiff Central 7	d			10 12	10 30	10 45	10 50			11 00	11 20			11 25	11 30		11 45		11 50		12 00			12 12		12 30
Newport (South Wales)	a			10 25	10 43	10 58	11 03			11 13	11 32			11 38	11 43		11 58		12 03		12 13			12 25		12 43
	d			10 27	10 44	10 59				11 15				11 39	11 44		11 59				12 15			12 27		12 44
Severn Tunnel Jn	d			10 38						11 25											12 25			12 38		
Caldicot	d			10 40																				12 40		
Chepstow	d			10 49																				12 49		
Lydney	d			10 58																				12 58		
Gloucester 7	a			11 21		11 45											12 46							13 20		
Pilning	d																									
Patchway	d									11 39											12 39					
Bristol Parkway 7	a													12 00		←										
	d							11 19						12 10		12 10				12 19						
Filton Abbey Wood	d				11 09			11 23		11 42				→	12 09					12 22	12 42					13 09
Bristol Temple Meads 10	a				11 18			11 35		11 52					12 18	12 22				12 35	12 52					13 18
	d	11 00	11 17		11 24			11 49				12 00	12 17		12 24	12 30				12 39		13 00	13 10		13 17	13 24
Keynsham	d							11 56												12 46						
Oldfield Park	d							12 03												12 53						
Bath Spa 7	a	11 11	11 28		11 35			12 05				12 11	12 28		12 35	12 41				12 55		13 11	13 21		13 28	13 35

For general notes see front of timetable
For details of catering facilities see Directory of Train Operators

- **A** From Maesteg (Table 128) to Cheltenham Spa (Table 57)
- **B** From Swansea (Table 125)
- **C** From Taunton (Table 134)
- **D** To Cheltenham Spa (Table 57)
- **E** To Weston-super-Mare (Table 134)
- **G** 🛒 from Newport (South Wales)
- **H** From Worcester Shrub Hill (Table 57) to Weymouth (Table 123)
- **J** To London Waterloo (Table 160)
- **K** To Taunton (Table 134)
- **L** From Gloucester (Table 134) to Weymouth (Table 123)
- **N** To Newcastle (Table 51)
- **Q** From Great Malvern (Table 71) to Westbury (Table 123)
- **U** From Carmarthen (Table 128)
- **V** From Great Malvern (Table 71) to Brighton (Table 123)

Table 132

Saturdays

2 February to 22 March

Cardiff → Gloucester, Bristol and Bath Spa

Network Diagram - see first page of Table 132

		GW	XC		AW	GW	GW	GW	GW	AW	AW	GW		GW	XC	AW	GW	GW	GW	GW	GW		XC	AW	GW	SW
		1◇	◇		◇			1◇	1◇		◇	◇		1◇	◇	◇	◇	1◇	1◇	◇	1◇		◇	R		1◇
						A	B			C							D								A	
		⊡			⊤			⊡	⊡		⊤	⊤		⊡		⊤	⊤	⊡	⊡	⊤	⊡			⊤		
Cardiff Central 7	d		12 45		12 50		13 00			13 12	13 20	13 30			13 45	13 50				14 30			14 45	14 50		
Newport (South Wales)	a		12 58		13 03		13 13			13 25	13 32	13 43			13 58	14 03				14 43			14 58	15 03		
	d		12 59				13 15			13 27		13 44			13 59					14 44			14 59			
Severn Tunnel Jn	d						13 26			13 38																
Caldicot	d									13 40																
Chepstow	d									13 49																
Lydney	d									13 58																
Gloucester 7	a		13 45							14 20					14 44								15 45			
Pilning	d																									
Patchway	d						13 39																			
Bristol Parkway 7	a																									
	d					13 19											14 19								15 19	
Filton Abbey Wood	d					13 23	13 43					14 09					14 23			15 09					15 23	
Bristol Temple Meads 10	a					13 35	13 52					14 18					14 34			15 18					15 35	
	d	13 30				13 49		14 00	14 17			14 24		14 30			14 49	15 00	15 17	15 24	15 30				15 43	15 52
Keynsham	d					13 56											14 56								15 50	
Oldfield Park	d					14 03											15 03								15 57	
Bath Spa 7	a	13 41				14 05		14 11	14 28			14 35		14 41			15 05	15 11	15 28	15 35	15 41				15 59	16 05

		GW	GW	GW	AW	AW	GW		GW	XC	AW	GW	GW	GW	AW	GW		GW	AW	GW	XC	AW	GW	GW	GW	GW
			1◇	1◇		◇	1◇		◇	◇	R	1◇	◇			1◇		1◇		◇	◇	R	◇		1◇	1◇
		B			C		E					E	G	B					C				H	B		
			⊡	⊡		⊤	⊡		⊤		⊤	⊡				⊡		⊡		⊤		⊤			⊡	⊡
Cardiff Central 7	d	15 00			15 12	15 20	15 25		15 30	15 45	15 50			16 00	16 06				16 12	16 30	16 45	16 50		17 00		
Newport (South Wales)	a	15 13			15 25	15 32	15 38		15 43	15 58	16 03			16 13	16 21				16 23	16 43	16 58	17 03		17 13		
	d	15 15			15 27		15 39		15 44	15 59				16 15					16 26	16 44	16 59			17 15		
Severn Tunnel Jn	d	15 25			15 38									16 25					16 37	16 55				17 25		
Caldicot	d				15 40														16 38							
Chepstow	d				15 49														16 47							
Lydney	d				15 58														16 56							
Gloucester 7	a				16 20					16 44									17 20		17 45					
Pilning	d																									
Patchway	d	15 39												16 39										17 39		
Bristol Parkway 7	a						16 00					←														
	d						16 10					16 10	16 19										17 19			
Filton Abbey Wood	d	15 42					→		16 09				16 23	16 42						17 10			17 23	17 42		
Bristol Temple Meads 10	a	15 52							16 18			16 22	16 34	16 52						17 18			17 35	17 52		
	d		16 00	16 17					16 24			16 30	16 49			17 00		17 17		17 24			17 49		18 00	18 17
Keynsham	d												16 56										17 56			
Oldfield Park	d												17 02										18 03			
Bath Spa 7	a		16 11	16 28					16 35			16 41	17 05			17 11		17 28		17 35			18 05		18 11	18 28

		AW		AW	GW	XC	AW	GW	GW	AW	GW		GW	GW	GW	XC	AW	GW	GW	GW		GW	GW	AW	GW	GW
				◇	◇	◇	R				1◇		1◇	◇	1◇	◇	◇			1◇		1◇	◇	◇	1◇	◇
		C						J	B	C	E				E			K	B			E			E	L
				⊤	⊤		⊤				⊡		⊡	⊤	⊡		⊤			⊡		⊡	⊤	⊤	⊡	
Cardiff Central 7	d	17 12		17 20	17 30	17 45	17 50		18 00	18 12	18 25			18 30		18 45	18 50		19 00			19 25	19 30	19 34		
Newport (South Wales)	a	17 27		17 32	17 43	17 58	18 03		18 13	18 25	18 38			18 43		18 59	19 05		19 13			19 38	19 43	19 48		
	d	17 27			17 44	17 59			18 15	18 27	18 39			18 44		18 59			19 15			19 39	19 44			
Severn Tunnel Jn	d	17 38			17 55				18 25	18 38									19 25							
Caldicot	d	17 40								18 40																
Chepstow	d	17 49								18 49																
Lydney	d	17 58								18 58																
Gloucester 7	a	18 20				18 43				19 20						19 44										
Pilning	d																									
Patchway	d								18 39										19 39							
Bristol Parkway 7	a										19 00				←							20 00			←	
	d							18 19			19 10				19 10			19 19				20 10			20 10	20 19
Filton Abbey Wood	d				18 10			18 22	18 42		→			19 09				19 22	19 42			→	20 09			20 23
Bristol Temple Meads 10	a				18 18			18 35	18 52					19 18	19 22			19 36	19 52				20 18		20 22	20 36
	d				18 24			18 49					19 17	19 24	19 30			19 49		20 17			20 24		20 30	20 49
Keynsham	d							18 56										19 56								20 56
Oldfield Park	d							19 03										20 03								21 02
Bath Spa 7	a				18 35			19 05					19 28	19 35	19 41			20 05		20 28			20 35		20 41	21 05

For general notes see front of timetable
For details of catering facilities see Directory of Train Operators

- **A** From Gloucester (Table 134) to Westbury (Table 123)
- **B** To Taunton (Table 134)
- **C** From Maesteg (Table 128) to Cheltenham Spa (Table 57)
- **D** From Great Malvern (Table 71) to Weymouth (Table 123)
- **E** From Swansea (Table 125)
- **G** From Worcester Foregate Street (Table 71) to Weymouth (Table 123)
- **H** From Gloucester (Table 134) to Weymouth (Table 123)
- **J** From Great Malvern (Table 71) to Westbury (Table 123)
- **K** From Gloucester (Table 134) to Frome (Table 123)
- **L** From Worcester Shrub Hill (Table 57) to Weymouth (Table 123)

Table 132

Cardiff → Gloucester, Bristol and Bath Spa

Network Diagram - see first page of Table 132

		GW	XC	AW	GW	AW		GW	GW	GW	XC	AW	GW	GW	AW		AW	SW	GW	GW	GW	GW	AW			
			◇	◇	1 ◇			1 ◇	◇	1 ◇	◇	◇					◇	1	1 ◇	1 ◇						
		A				B		C		C				A	B								D			
				[trolley]	[restaurant]			[restaurant]	[trolley]	[restaurant]										[restaurant]						
Cardiff Central 7	d	19 50	20 00	20 10		20 15		20 25	20 30		20 50	20 53		21 00	21 15		21 50				22 00		23 20			
Newport (South Wales)	a	20 03	20 13	20 23		20 28		20 38	20 43		21 02	21 07		21 13	21 28		22 06				22 13		23 37			
	d	20 05	20 15			20 30		20 39	20 44		21 04			21 15	21 30						22 16		23 40			
Severn Tunnel Jn	d	20 15				20 41								21 25	21 41						22 33		23 57			
Caldicot	d					20 43									21 43								23 59			
Chepstow	d					20 52									21 52								00 08			
Lydney	d					21 01									22 01								00 17			
Gloucester 7	a		20 56			21 22					21 46				22 22								00 42			
Pilning	d																									
Patchway	d	20 29												21 39							22 48					
Bristol Parkway 7	a							21 00		←																
	d							21 10		21 10																
Filton Abbey Wood	d	20 34						→	21 09					21 42							22 52					
Bristol Temple Meads 10	a	20 43							21 18	21 22				21 52							23 00					
	d				21 17				21 24	21 30			21 51					22 23	22 33	22 40		23 10				
Keynsham	d												21 58									23 17				
Oldfield Park	d												22 04									23 23				
Bath Spa 7	a				21 28				21 35	21 41			22 07					22 34	22 44	22 51		23 26				

		AW	AW	AW	AW	GW	GW		GW	AW	GW	GW	GW	AW		AW	GW	AW	GW	GW	GW		GW	GW	GW	AW
						1 ◇	◇		1 ◇		1 ◇		1 ◇				1 ◇		◇	1 ◇			1 ◇	1 ◇	◇	
		B										E		G					H						H	G
				[bus]	[bus]	[restaurant]			[restaurant]	[bus]	[restaurant]		[restaurant]			[bus]	[restaurant]			[restaurant]			[restaurant]	[restaurant]	[trolley]	
Cardiff Central 7	d	23p20	00 30	04 15	04 40				04 55	05 40				06 12		06 15	06 25	06 50					06 55			07 12
Newport (South Wales)	a	23p36	00 48	04 45	05 10				05 09	06 10				06 25		06 45	06 38	07 05					07 08			07 25
	d	23p39							05 09					06 27			06 39						07 09			07 27
Severn Tunnel Jn	d	23p57												06 38												07 38
Caldicot	d	23p59												06 40												07 40
Chepstow	d	00 08												06 49												07 49
Lydney	d	00 17												06 58												07 58
Gloucester 7	a	00 38							05 59					07 20			07 24						07 52			08 21
Pilning	d																									
Patchway	d																									
Bristol Parkway 7	a																									
	d																		07 06						07 55	
Filton Abbey Wood	d																		07 09						07 59	
Bristol Temple Meads 10	a																		07 18						08 08	
	d					05 30	05 45				06 30	06 43	07 00						07 24	07 30	07 49			08 00	08 24	
Keynsham	d						05 52					06 50									07 56					
Oldfield Park	d						05 59					06 56									08 02					
Bath Spa 7	a					05 41	06 01				06 41	06 59	07 11						07 35	07 41	08 05			08 11	08 35	

		GW	GW	XC	AW		GW	SW	GW	GW	GW	GW		GW	XC	AW	GW	GW	GW		AW	GW	GW	XC	AW	GW
		1 ◇	1 ◇	◇				1 ◇	1 ◇	1 ◇	◇	1 ◇		1 ◇	◇			1 ◇	◇			1 ◇	1 ◇	◇		
				J			K	L			H				J		N		H		G			J		Q
		[restaurant]	[restaurant]	[trolley]					[restaurant]	[restaurant]	[trolley]	[restaurant]		[restaurant]	[trolley]			[restaurant]	[trolley]			[restaurant]	[restaurant]	[trolley]		
Cardiff Central 7	d	07 25		07 45	07 50				07 55					08 25	08 45	08 50					09 12	09 25		09 45	09 50	
Newport (South Wales)	a	07 38		07 57	08 05				08 08					08 38	08 57	09 05					09 25	09 38		09 58	10 05	
	d	07 39		07 59					08 09					08 39	08 59						09 27	09 39		09 59		
Severn Tunnel Jn	d																				09 38					
Caldicot	d																				09 40					
Chepstow	d																				09 49					
Lydney	d																				09 58					
Gloucester 7	a	08 25		08 43					08 52					09 22	09 44						10 20	10 25		10 45		
Pilning	d																									
Patchway	d																									
Bristol Parkway 7	a																									
	d						08 20				09 06						09 19		10 06							10 19
Filton Abbey Wood	d						08 23				09 09						09 23		10 09							10 22
Bristol Temple Meads 10	a						08 34				09 17						09 35		10 17							10 35
	d		08 30				08 40	08 50		09 00	09 24	09 30					09 49	10 00	10 24				10 30			10 49
Keynsham	d						08 47	08 57									09 56									10 56
Oldfield Park	d						08 54										10 03									11 03
Bath Spa 7	a		08 41				08 56	09 04		09 11	09 35	09 41					10 05	10 11	10 35				10 41			11 05

For general notes see front of timetable
For details of catering facilities see Directory of Train Operators

A To Exeter St Davids (Table 135)
B From Maesteg (Table 128) to Cheltenham Spa (Table 57)
C From Swansea (Table 125)
D From Maesteg (Table 128))
E From Taunton (Table 134)
G To Cheltenham Spa (Table 57)
H To Portsmouth Harbour (Table 123)
J [trolley] from Newport (South Wales)
K From Worcester Shrub Hill (Table 57) to Weymouth (Table 123)
L To London Waterloo (Table 160)
N From Gloucester (Table 134) to Weymouth (Table 123)
Q From Great Malvern (Table 71) to Westbury (Table 123)

Table 132

Saturdays

from 29 March

Cardiff → Gloucester, Bristol and Bath Spa

Network Diagram - see first page of Table 132

		GW	GW		AW	GW	GW	XC	AW	GW		GW	GW	GW	XC	AW	GW		SW	GW	AW	GW	GW	XC		AW
		1 ◇	◇			1 ◇	1 ◇	◇		◇		1 ◇	◇	1 ◇	◇				1 ◇	◇		1 ◇	1 ◇	◇		
			A		B			C		D			A		C		E		G	A	B					
		☕	🛒			☕	☕	🛒				☕	🛒	☕	🛒					🛒		☕	☕			
Cardiff Central 7	d				10 12	10 25		10 45	10 50					11 25	11 45	11 50					12 12	12 25		12 45		12 50
Newport (South Wales)	a				10 25	10 38		10 58	11 05					11 38	11 58	12 05					12 25	12 38		12 58		13 05
	d				10 27	10 39		10 59						11 39	11 59						12 27	12 39		12 59		
Severn Tunnel Jn	d				10 38																12 38					
Caldicot	d				10 40																12 40					
Chepstow	d				10 49																12 49					
Lydney	d				10 58																12 58					
Gloucester 7	a				11 21	11 25		11 45						12 22	12 46						13 20	13 25		13 45		
Pilning	d																									
Patchway	d																									
Bristol Parkway 7	a																									
	d		11 06							11 19			12 06				12 19			13 06						
Filton Abbey Wood	d		11 09							11 23			12 09				12 22			13 09						
Bristol Temple Meads 10	a		11 17							11 35			12 17				12 35			13 17						
	d	11 00	11 24				11 30			11 49		12 00	12 24				12 39		13 10	13 24			13 30			
Keynsham	d									11 56							12 46									
Oldfield Park	d									12 03							12 53									
Bath Spa 7	a	11 11	11 35				11 41			12 05		12 11	12 35				12 55		13 21	13 35			13 41			

		GW	GW	GW	AW	GW	GW		XC	AW	GW	GW	GW	XC		AW	GW	SW	GW	GW	AW		GW	GW	XC	AW
			1 ◇	◇		1 ◇	1 ◇		◇		◇	◇	1 ◇	◇				1 ◇	1 ◇	◇			1 ◇	1 ◇	◇	
		H		A	B						J	A					H			A	B					
			☕	🛒		☕	☕				🛒	🛒	☕						☕	🛒			☕	☕		
Cardiff Central 7	d				13 12	13 25			13 45	13 50				14 45		14 50					15 12		15 25		15 45	15 50
Newport (South Wales)	a				13 25	13 38			13 58	14 05				14 58		15 05					15 25		15 38		15 58	16 05
	d				13 27	13 39			13 59					14 59							15 27		15 39		15 59	
Severn Tunnel Jn	d				13 38																15 38					
Caldicot	d				13 40																15 40					
Chepstow	d				13 49																15 49					
Lydney	d				13 58																15 58					
Gloucester 7	a				14 20	14 25			14 44					15 45							16 20		16 25		16 44	
Pilning	d																									
Patchway	d																									
Bristol Parkway 7	a																									
	d	13 19		14 06							14 19	15 06					15 19			16 06						
Filton Abbey Wood	d	13 23		14 09							14 23	15 09					15 23			16 09						
Bristol Temple Meads 10	a	13 35		14 17							14 34	15 17					15 35			16 17						
	d	13 49	14 00	14 24			14 30				14 49	15 24	15 30				15 43	15 52	16 00	16 24				16 30		
Keynsham	d	13 56									14 56						15 50									
Oldfield Park	d	14 03									15 03						15 57									
Bath Spa 7	a	14 05	14 11	14 35			14 41				15 05	15 35	15 41				15 59	16 05	16 11	16 35				16 41		

		GW	GW	AW	GW		GW	XC	AW	GW	GW	AW		GW	GW	XC	AW	GW	GW		AW	GW	GW	XC	AW	GW
		◇	◇		1 ◇		1 ◇	◇		◇	1 ◇			1 ◇	1 ◇	◇			◇			1 ◇	1 ◇	◇		
		K	A	B						H		B						J	A		B					H
			🛒		☕		☕				☕			☕	☕				🛒			☕	☕			
Cardiff Central 7	d			16 12	16 25			16 45	16 50			17 12		17 25		17 45	17 50				18 12	18 25		18 45	18 50	
Newport (South Wales)	a			16 23	16 38			16 58	17 05			17 27		17 38		17 58	18 05				18 25	18 38		18 59	19 05	
	d			16 26	16 39			16 59				17 27		17 39		17 59					18 27	18 39		18 59		
Severn Tunnel Jn	d			16 37								17 38									18 38					
Caldicot	d			16 38								17 40									18 40					
Chepstow	d			16 47								17 49									18 49					
Lydney	d			16 56								17 58									18 58					
Gloucester 7	a			17 20	17 25			17 45				18 20		18 25		18 43					19 20	19 25		19 44		
Pilning	d																									
Patchway	d																									
Bristol Parkway 7	a																									
	d	16 19	17 06							17 19								18 19	19 06							19 20
Filton Abbey Wood	d	16 23	17 09							17 23								18 22	19 09							19 23
Bristol Temple Meads 10	a	16 34	17 17							17 32								18 35	19 17							19 37
	d	16 49	17 24				17 30			17 49	18 00				18 30			18 49	19 24				19 30			19 49
Keynsham	d	16 56								17 56								18 56								19 56
Oldfield Park	d	17 02								18 03								19 03								20 03
Bath Spa 7	a	17 05	17 35				17 41			18 05	18 11				18 41			19 05	19 35				19 41			20 05

		GW	AW		GW	AW	GW	XC	GW	AW		GW	XC	AW	GW	AW	AW		SW	GW	GW	AW				
		1 ◇			◇		1 ◇	◇	◇			1 ◇	◇						1	1 ◇						
					A				A	B						L						L				
						🚌																				
		☕			🛒		☕		🛒			☕														
Cardiff Central 7	d	19 25	19 50			19 50		20 00		20 15		20 25	20 50	20 53		21 15	21 50					23 20				
Newport (South Wales)	a	19 38	20 05			20 20		20 13		20 28		20 38	21 02	21 07		21 28	22 06					23 37				
	d	19 39						20 15		20 30		20 39	21 04			21 30						23 40				
Severn Tunnel Jn	d									20 41						21 41						23 57				
Caldicot	d									20 43						21 43						23 59				
Chepstow	d									20 52						21 52						00 08				
Lydney	d									21 01						22 01						00 17				
Gloucester 7	a	20 22						20 56		21 22		21 26	21 46			22 22						00 42				
Pilning	d																									
Patchway	d																									
Bristol Parkway 7	a																									
	d				20 06				21 06																	
Filton Abbey Wood	d				20 09				21 09																	
Bristol Temple Meads 10	a				20 17				21 17																	
	d				20 24		20 33		21 24						21 51				22 23	22 33	23 10					
Keynsham	d														21 58						23 17					
Oldfield Park	d														22 04						23 23					
Bath Spa 7	a				20 35		20 44		21 35						22 07				22 34	22 44	23 26					

For general notes see front of timetable
For details of catering facilities see Directory of Train Operators

- **A** To Portsmouth Harbour (Table 123)
- **B** From Maesteg (Table 128) to Cheltenham Spa (Table 57)
- **C** 🛒 from Newport (South Wales)
- **D** From Gloucester (Table 134) to Weymouth (Table 123)
- **E** From Great Malvern (Table 71) to Brighton (Table 123)
- **G** To London Waterloo (Table 160)
- **H** From Gloucester (Table 134) to Westbury (Table 123)
- **J** From Great Malvern (Table 71) to Westbury (Table 123)
- **K** From Worcester Foregate Street (Table 71) to Westbury (Table 123)
- **L** From Maesteg (Table 128))

Table 132

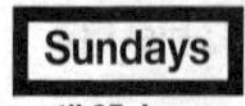

until 27 January

Cardiff → Gloucester, Bristol and Bath Spa

Network Diagram - see first page of Table 132

		AW	GW	GW	GW	GW	GW		AW	GW	GW	GW	GW	GW		GW	GW	AW	GW	GW	GW		AW	XC	GW	XC
			1◇	1◇	1◇	1◇	◇			1◇	1◇	◇	1◇	1◇		1◇	◇		1◇	1◇	◇		◇	◇	1◇	1◇
		A										B						C								
			⊥P	⊥P	⊥P	⊥P	⊤o			⊥P	⊥P	⊤o	⊥P	⊥P		⊥P	⊤o		⊥P	⊥P	⊤o		⊤o		⊥P	⊥P
Cardiff Central 7	d	23p20			07 45		08 05		08 34	08 55		09 15		09 55			10 15	10 30	10 55		11 15		11 35	11 50	11 55	12 00
Newport (South Wales)	a	23p37			08 01		08 21		08 52	09 12		09 27		10 08			10 27	10 43	11 08		11 27		11 47	12 02	12 08	12 13
	d	23p40			08 03		08 23			09 13		09 29		10 09			10 29	10 45	11 09		11 29			12 04	12 09	12 15
Severn Tunnel Jn	d	23p57					08 39					09 39					10 39	10 56			11 39					
Caldicot	d	23p59																10 58								
Chepstow	d	00 08																11 07								
Lydney	d	00 17																11 16								
Gloucester 7	a	00 42																11 43						12 45		
Pilning	d																									
Patchway	d											09 52														
Bristol Parkway 7	a				08 34					09 34				10 30					11 30						12 30	13 08
	d																									
Filton Abbey Wood	d						08 54					09 56					10 54				11 54					
Bristol Temple Meads 10	a						09 04					10 06					11 03				12 03					12 48
	d		07 40	08 10		09 00	09 10				10 00	10 10	10 30			11 00	11 10			12 00	12 10					
Keynsham	d						09 17										11 17									
Oldfield Park	d						09 24										11 24									
Bath Spa 7	a		07 52	08 21		09 12	09 26				10 11	10 21	10 42			11 12	11 26			12 12	12 21					

		GW	GW	AW	AW		GW	GW	GW	GW	XC	GW		GW	GW	AW	AW	XC	GW		GW	SW	GW	AW	GW	XC
		1◇	◇		◇		◇	1◇	1◇	◇	◇	1◇		1◇	◇		◇	◇	1◇		1◇	1◇	◇	◇	1◇	◇
			D	C												C						E	B			
		⊥P	⊤o		⊤o			⊥P	⊥P	⊤o		⊥P		⊥P	⊤o		⊤o		⊥P		⊥P		⊤o	⊤o	⊥P	
Cardiff Central 7	d		12 15	12 30	12 35			12 55		13 15	13 50	13 55			14 15	14 30	14 35	14 50	14 55				15 15	15 35		15 50
Newport (South Wales)	a		12 27	12 43	12 47			13 08		13 27	14 02	14 08			14 27	14 43	14 48	15 02	15 08				15 27	15 48		16 02
	d		12 29	12 45				13 09		13 29	14 04	14 09			14 29	14 45		15 04	15 09				15 29			16 04
Severn Tunnel Jn	d		12 39	12 56						13 39					14 39	14 56							15 39			
Caldicot	d			12 58												14 58										
Chepstow	d			13 07												15 07										
Lydney	d			13 16												15 16										
Gloucester 7	a			13 42							14 45					15 37		15 45								16 44
Pilning	d																									
Patchway	d		12 51																				15 52			
Bristol Parkway 7	a							13 30				14 30							15 30							
	d																									
Filton Abbey Wood	d		12 57							13 54					14 54								15 56			
Bristol Temple Meads 10	a		13 05							14 04					15 04								16 06			
	d	13 00	13 10				13 20		14 00	14 10				15 00	15 10						16 00	16 04	16 10		16 30	
Keynsham	d		13 17				13 27								15 17							16 11				
Oldfield Park	d		13 24				13 34								15 24											
Bath Spa 7	a	13 12	13 26				13 37		14 11	14 23				15 12	15 26						16 12	16 18	16 23		16 41	

		GW	GW		GW	AW	AW	XC	GW	AW		GW	GW	GW	GW	GW	GW		GW	XC	GW	GW	GW	AW		AW
		1◇	1◇		◇		R	◇	1◇			1◇	◇	1◇	◇	1◇	1◇		◇	◇	1◇	◇	1◇			R
						C							G									B		C		
		⊥P	⊥P		⊤o		⊤o		⊥P			⊥P		⊥P	⊤o	⊥P	⊥P		⊤o		⊥P	⊤o	⊥P			⊤o
Cardiff Central 7	d	15 55			16 15	16 30	16 35	16 50	16 55	17 05					17 15	17 25			17 45	17 50		18 15	18 25	18 30		18 35
Newport (South Wales)	a	16 08			16 27	16 43	16 49	17 02	17 08	17 18					17 28	17 38			17 57	18 02		18 27	18 38	18 43		18 48
	d	16 09			16 29	16 45		17 04	17 09						17 29	17 39			17 59	18 04		18 29	18 39	18 45		
Severn Tunnel Jn	d				16 39	16 56									17 40							18 39		18 56		
Caldicot	d					16 58																		18 58		
Chepstow	d					17 07																		19 07		
Lydney	d					17 16																		19 16		
Gloucester 7	a					17 37		17 45												18 45				19 38		
Pilning	d																									
Patchway	d																					18 52				
Bristol Parkway 7	a	16 30							17 30							18 00							19 00			
	d																									
Filton Abbey Wood	d				16 57										17 55				18 24			18 56				
Bristol Temple Meads 10	a				17 06										18 03				18 34			19 06				
	d		17 00		17 10							17 30	17 50	18 00	18 10		18 30		18 50		19 00	19 10				
Keynsham	d				17 17								17 57		18 17							19 17				
Oldfield Park	d				17 24								18 04		18 24							19 24				
Bath Spa 7	a		17 12		17 26							17 42	18 06	18 12	18 26		18 42		19 01		19 12	19 26				

For general notes see front of timetable
For details of catering facilities see Directory of Train Operators

A From Maesteg (Table 128))
B To Portsmouth Harbour (Table 123)
C To Cheltenham Spa (Table 57)
D To Brighton (Table 123)
E To London Waterloo (Table 160)
G From Weston-super-Mare (Table 134)

Table 132

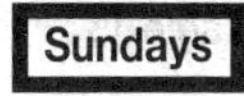

until 27 January

Cardiff → Gloucester, Bristol and Bath Spa

Network Diagram - see first page of Table 132

		GW	GW	XC	GW	GW	GW	XC	GW	GW	GW	AW	AW	GW	SW	GW	GW	XC	GW	AW	AW
		1 ◇	◇	◇	1 ◇	◇	1 ◇	◇	◇	1 ◇	◇		R	1 ◇	1	1 ◇			◇		
																			A		
Cardiff Central	d		18 45	18 50		19 15	19 25	19 50			20 15	20 30	20 35	20 55				21 40	22 05	22 30	22 50
Newport (South Wales)	a		18 57	19 02		19 28	19 38	20 02			20 27	20 43	20 48	21 08				21 53	22 21	22 47	23 07
	d		18 59	19 04		19 29	19 39	20 04			20 29	20 45		21 09				21 55	22 23	22 49	
Severn Tunnel Jn	d		19 09								20 39	20 56							22 39	23 06	
Caldicot	d											20 58								23 08	
Chepstow	d											21 07								23 17	
Lydney	d											21 16								23 26	
Gloucester	a			19 45				20 45				21 37						22 42		23 47	
Pilning	d																				
Patchway	d																		22 52		
Bristol Parkway	a						20 00							21 30							
	d																				
Filton Abbey Wood	d		19 25			19 52					20 54								22 56		
Bristol Temple Meads	a		19 34			20 02					21 04								23 06		
	d	19 30	19 50		20 00	20 10			20 50	21 00	21 10				21 35	22 05	22 15		23 10		
Keynsham	d								20 57								22 22				
Oldfield Park	d								21 04								22 29				
Bath Spa	a	19 42	20 01		20 11	20 21			21 07	21 13	21 22				21 47	22 17	22 32		23 21		

Sundays

3 February to 23 March

		AW	GW	GW	GW	GW	GW	AW	GW	GW	GW	GW	GW	GW	AW	GW	GW	GW	AW	GW	XC	GW
			1 ◇	1	1 ◇	1 ◇	◇		1 ◇	1 ◇	◇	1 ◇	1 ◇	◇		1 ◇	1 ◇	◇	◇	1 ◇	◇	1 ◇
		B							C		D	C			E	C				C		
Cardiff Central	d	23p20			07 45		08 05	08 34	08 55		09 15	09 41		10 15	10 30	10 41		11 15	11 35	11 41	11 50	
Newport (South Wales)	a	23p37			08 01		08 21	08 52	09 12		09 27	09 54		10 27	10 43	10 54		11 27	11 47	11 54	12 02	
	d	23p40			08 03		08 23		09 13		09 29	09 55		10 29	10 45	10 55		11 29		11 55	12 04	
Severn Tunnel Jn	d	23p57					08 39				09 39			10 39	10 56			11 39				
Caldicot	d	23p59													10 58							
Chepstow	d	00 08													11 07							
Lydney	d	00 17													11 16							
Gloucester	a	00 42													11 43						12 45	
Pilning	d																					
Patchway	d										09 52											
Bristol Parkway	a				08 33				09 34			10 16				11 16				12 16		
	d				08 39				09 41			10 22				11 23				12 23		
Filton Abbey Wood	d						08 54				09 56			10 54				11 54				
Bristol Temple Meads	a				08 52		09 04		09 52		10 06	10 34		11 03		11 34				12 34		
	d		07 40	08 05	09 00	09 05	09 10		10 00	10 05	10 10	10 45	11 05	11 10		11 45	12 05			12 45		13 05
Keynsham	d						09 17							11 17								
Oldfield Park	d						09 24							11 24								
Bath Spa	a		07 51	08 16	09 11	09 17	09 26		10 11	10 17	10 23	10 56	11 16	11 26		11 56	12 16	12 22		12 56		13 16

		GW	AW	AW	GW	GW	GW	GW	GW	XC	GW	GW	AW	AW	GW	XC	SW	GW	AW	GW	GW	GW
		◇		◇	◇	1 ◇	1 ◇	◇	1 ◇	◇	1 ◇	◇		◇	1 ◇	◇	1 ◇	◇	◇	1 ◇	1 ◇	1 ◇
		G	E			C			C				E		C		H	D				C
Cardiff Central	d	12 15	12 30	12 35		12 41		13 15	13 41	13 50		14 15	14 30	14 35	14 41	14 50		15 15	15 35			15 41
Newport (South Wales)	a	12 27	12 43	12 47		12 54		13 27	13 54	14 02		14 27	14 43	14 48	14 54	15 02		15 27	15 48			15 54
	d	12 29	12 45			12 55		13 29	13 55	14 04		14 29	14 45		14 55	15 04		15 29				15 55
Severn Tunnel Jn	d	12 39	12 56					13 39				14 39	14 56					15 39				
Caldicot	d		12 58										14 58									
Chepstow	d		13 07										15 07									
Lydney	d		13 16										15 16									
Gloucester	a		13 42							14 45			15 37			15 45						
Pilning	d																					
Patchway	d	12 51																15 52				
Bristol Parkway	a					13 16			14 16						15 16							16 16
	d					13 23			14 23						15 23							16 23
Filton Abbey Wood	d	12 57						13 54				14 54						15 56				
Bristol Temple Meads	a	13 05				13 34		14 04	14 34			15 04			15 34			16 06				16 34
	d	13 10			13 20	13 45	14 05	14 10	14 45		15 05	15 10			15 45		16 04	16 10		16 20	16 25	16 45
Keynsham	d	13 17			13 27							15 17					16 11					
Oldfield Park	d	13 24			13 34							15 24										
Bath Spa	a	13 26			13 37	13 56	14 16	14 23	14 56		15 16	15 26			15 56		16 18	16 23		16 32	16 37	16 56

For general notes see front of timetable
For details of catering facilities see Directory of Train Operators

- **A** To Warminster (Table 123)
- **B** From Maesteg (Table 128))
- **C** From Swansea (Table 125)
- **D** To Portsmouth Harbour (Table 123)
- **E** To Cheltenham Spa (Table 57)
- **G** To Brighton (Table 123)
- **H** To London Waterloo (Table 160)

Table 132

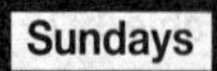

3 February to 23 March

Cardiff → Gloucester, Bristol and Bath Spa

Network Diagram - see first page of Table 132

		XC	GW	GW	AW	AW	GW	GW	XC	AW	GW	GW	GW	GW	GW	GW	XC	GW	GW	AW	AW	GW
						R															R	
		◇	1◇	◇			1◇	1◇	◇		◇	1◇	◇	1◇	1◇	◇	◇	◇	1◇			1◇
					A			B			C				D			E		A		
			🍴	🛒		🛒	🍴	🍴				🍴	🛒	🍴	🍴	🛒		🛒	🍴		🛒	🍴
Cardiff Central 7	d	15 50		16 15	16 30	16 35		16 41	16 50	17 05			17 15		17 41	17 45	17 50	18 15		18 30	18 35	
Newport (South Wales)	a	16 02		16 27	16 43	16 47		16 54	17 02	17 18			17 28		17 54	17 59	18 02	18 27		18 43	18 48	
	d	16 04		16 29	16 45			16 55	17 04				17 29		17 55	18 01	18 04	18 29		18 45		
Severn Tunnel Jn	d			16 39	16 56								17 40					18 39		18 56		
Caldicot	d				16 58															18 58		
Chepstow	d				17 07															19 07		
Lydney	d				17 16															19 16		
Gloucester 7	a	16 44			17 37				17 45								18 46			19 38		
Pilning	d																					
Patchway	d																	18 52				
Bristol Parkway 7	a							17 16							18 16							
	d							17 23							18 23							
Filton Abbey Wood	d			16 57									17 55			18 25		18 56				
Bristol Temple Meads 10	a			17 06				17 34					18 03		18 34	18 35		19 06				
	d		17 05	17 10			17 25	17 45			17 50	18 05	18 10	18 30	18 45	18 50		19 10	19 25			19 31
Keynsham	d			17 17							17 57		18 17					19 17				
Oldfield Park	d			17 24							18 04		18 24					19 24				
Bath Spa 7	a		17 17	17 26			17 36	17 56			18 06	18 17	18 26	18 41	18 56	19 01		19 26	19 36			19 42

		GW	GW	XC	GW	GW	GW	XC	GW	GW	GW	AW	AW	SW	GW	GW	XC	GW	GW	AW	AW
													R								
		1◇	◇	◇	◇	1◇	1◇	◇	◇	◇	1◇			1	1◇			1◇	◇		
		B					D								D				G		
		🍴	🛒		🛒	🍴	🍴			🛒	🍴		🛒		🍴			🍴	🛒		
Cardiff Central 7	d	18 41	18 45	18 50	19 15		19 41	19 50		20 15		20 30	20 35		21 01		21 40		22 05	22 30	22 50
Newport (South Wales)	a	18 54	18 59	19 04	19 27		19 54	20 02		20 27		20 43	20 48		21 14		21 53		22 21	22 47	23 07
	d	18 55	19 01	19 04	19 29		19 55	20 04		20 29		20 45			21 15		21 55		22 23	22 49	
Severn Tunnel Jn	d		19 11							20 39		20 56							22 39	23 06	
Caldicot	d											20 58								23 08	
Chepstow	d											21 07								23 17	
Lydney	d											21 16								23 26	
Gloucester 7	a			19 46				20 45				21 37					22 42			23 47	
Pilning	d																				
Patchway	d																		22 52		
Bristol Parkway 7	a	19 16					20 16								21 40						
	d	19 23					20 23								21 47						
Filton Abbey Wood	d		19 26		19 52					20 58									22 56		
Bristol Temple Meads 10	a	19 34	19 36		20 01		20 34			21 08					21 58				23 06		
	d	19 45	19 50		20 10	20 30	20 45		20 50	21 11	21 30			21 35	22 05	22 15		22 43	23 10		
Keynsham	d								20 57							22 22					
Oldfield Park	d								21 04							22 29					
Bath Spa 7	a	19 56	20 01		20 21	20 41	20 56		21 07	21 23	21 41			21 47	22 16	22 32		22 54	23 21		

Sundays

from 30 March

		AW	GW	GW	GW	AW	GW	GW	GW	GW	GW	GW	GW	GW	GW	AW	AW	GW	GW	GW	AW	XC	GW
			1◇	1◇	1◇		◇	1◇	1◇	◇	1◇	1◇	1◇	◇	1◇			1◇	◇	1◇		◇	1◇
		H					E			E				J			A		E				
						🚌										🚌					🚌		
			🍴	🍴	🍴		🛒	🍴	🍴	🛒	🍴	🍴	🍴	🛒	🍴			🍴	🛒	🍴			🍴
Cardiff Central 7	d	23p20			07 55	08 00					09 25				10 25	10 25	10 30			11 25	11 25	11 50	
Newport (South Wales)	a	23p37			08 11	08 35					09 38				10 38	11 00	10 43			11 38	12 00	12 02	
	d	23p40			08 13						09 39				10 39		10 45			11 39		12 04	
Severn Tunnel Jn	d	23p57															10 56						
Caldicot	d	23p59															10 58						
Chepstow	d	00 08															11 07						
Lydney	d	00 17															11 16						
Gloucester 7	a	00 42			09 03						10 21				11 21		11 43			12 21		12 45	
Pilning	d																						
Patchway	d																						
Bristol Parkway 7	a																						
	d						08 50			09 50				10 51					11 50				
Filton Abbey Wood	d						08 54			09 55				10 54					11 54				
Bristol Temple Meads 10	a						09 04			10 05				11 03					12 04				
	d		07 40	09 00			09 10	09 33	10 00	10 10		10 30	11 00	11 10				12 00	12 10				13 00
Keynsham	d						09 17							11 17									
Oldfield Park	d						09 24							11 24									
Bath Spa 7	a		07 52	09 12			09 26	09 45	10 12	10 21		10 42	11 12	11 26				12 12	12 21				13 12

For general notes see front of timetable
For details of catering facilities see Directory of Train Operators

- **A** To Cheltenham Spa (Table 57)
- **B** From Swansea (Table 125)
- **C** From Weston-super-Mare (Table 134)
- **D** From Carmarthen (Table 128)
- **E** To Portsmouth Harbour (Table 123)
- **G** To Warminster (Table 123)
- **H** From Maesteg (Table 128))
- **J** To Brighton (Table 123)

Sundays

from 30 March

Cardiff → Gloucester, Bristol and Bath Spa

Network Diagram - see first page of Table 132

		GW	GW	GW	AW		AW	GW	GW	GW	XC	AW		GW	GW	GW	AW	XC	GW		GW	AW	AW	SW	GW	GW
		◇	◇	1◇				1◇	◇	1◇	◇			1◇	◇	1◇		◇	1◇		1◇			1◇	◇	1◇
		A			B				C						C		B							D	C	
		🛒		☕			🚌	☕	🛒	☕		🚌		☕	🛒	☕			☕		☕	🚌			🛒	☕
Cardiff Central [7]	d			12 25	12 30		13 10			13 25	13 50	14 15				14 25	14 30	14 50			15 25	15 25	15 35			
Newport (South Wales)	a			12 38	12 43		13 45			13 38	14 02	14 50				14 38	14 43	15 02			15 38	16 00	15 48			
	d			12 39	12 45					13 39	14 04					14 39	14 45	15 04			15 39					
Severn Tunnel Jn	d				12 56												14 56									
Caldicot	d				12 58												14 58									
Chepstow	d				13 07												15 07									
Lydney	d				13 16												15 16									
Gloucester [7]	a			13 21	13 42					14 21	14 45					15 21	15 37	15 45			16 21					
Pilning	d																									
Patchway	d																									
Bristol Parkway [7]	a																									
	d	12 50							13 50						14 50										15 50	
Filton Abbey Wood	d	12 54							13 54						14 54										15 56	
Bristol Temple Meads [10]	a	13 03							14 04						15 04										16 06	
	d	13 10	13 20					14 00	14 10					15 00	15 10				16 00					16 04	16 10	16 30
Keynsham	d	13 17	13 27												15 17									16 11		
Oldfield Park	d	13 24	13 34												15 24											
Bath Spa [7]	a	13 26	13 37					14 12	14 23					15 12	15 26				16 11					16 18	16 23	16 42

		XC	AW		GW	GW	GW	GW	AW	XC		AW	GW	GW	GW	GW	GW		GW	XC	GW	GW	GW	GW		GW
		◇			1◇	◇	1◇	1◇		◇			◇	1◇	◇	1◇	1◇		◇	◇	1◇	◇	1◇	1◇		◇
						C			B				E		A				C			C				C
			🚌		☕	🛒	☕	☕				🚌		☕	🛒	☕	☕		🛒		☕	🛒	☕	☕		🛒
Cardiff Central [7]	d	15 50	16 15				16 25		16 30	16 50		17 10				17 25				17 50			18 25			
Newport (South Wales)	a	16 02	16 50				16 38		16 43	17 02		17 45				17 38				18 02			18 38			
	d	16 04					16 39		16 45	17 04						17 39				18 04			18 39			
Severn Tunnel Jn	d								16 56																	
Caldicot	d								16 58																	
Chepstow	d								17 07																	
Lydney	d								17 16																	
Gloucester [7]	a	16 45					17 21		17 37	17 45						18 21				18 45			19 21			
Pilning	d																									
Patchway	d																									
Bristol Parkway [7]	a																									
	d					16 50									17 50				18 20			18 50				19 20
Filton Abbey Wood	d					16 57									17 55				18 24			18 56				19 25
Bristol Temple Meads [10]	a					17 06									18 03				18 34			19 05				19 34
	d				17 00	17 10		17 30					17 55	18 05	18 10		18 30		18 50		19 00	19 10		19 30		19 50
Keynsham	d					17 17							18 02		18 17							19 17				
Oldfield Park	d					17 24							18 09		18 24							19 24				
Bath Spa [7]	a				17 12	17 26		17 42					18 11	18 17	18 26		18 42		19 01		19 12	19 26		19 42		20 01

		AW	XC	GW	GW	GW	AW		XC	GW	GW	GW	AW	AW		AW	SW	GW	GW	GW	XC		GW	AW		
			◇	1◇	◇	1◇			◇	◇	1◇	◇					1	1◇	1◇				◇			
		B			C							C											G			
				☕	🛒	☕	🚌				☕	🛒		🚌		🚌		☕	☕				🛒			
Cardiff Central [7]	d	18 30	18 50			19 25	19 30		19 50				20 30	20 40		20 45		20 55			21 40			22 30		
Newport (South Wales)	a	18 43	19 02			19 38	20 05		20 02				20 43	21 15		21 20		21 08			21 53			22 47		
	d	18 45	19 04			19 39			20 04				20 45					21 09			21 55			22 49		
Severn Tunnel Jn	d	18 56											20 56											23 06		
Caldicot	d	18 58											20 58											23 08		
Chepstow	d	19 07											21 07											23 17		
Lydney	d	19 16											21 16											23 26		
Gloucester [7]	a	19 38	19 46			20 21			20 45				21 37					21 51			22 42			23 47		
Pilning	d																									
Patchway	d																									
Bristol Parkway [7]	a																									
	d				19 49							20 50											22 50			
Filton Abbey Wood	d				19 52							20 54											22 56			
Bristol Temple Meads [10]	a				20 02							21 04											23 06			
	d			20 00	20 10					20 50	21 00	21 11					21 35		22 05	22 15			23 10			
Keynsham	d									20 57										22 22						
Oldfield Park	d									21 04										22 29						
Bath Spa [7]	a			20 12	20 21					21 07	21 14	21 23					21 47		22 17	22 32			23 21			

For general notes see front of timetable
For details of catering facilities see Directory of Train Operators

A To Brighton (Table 123)
B To Cheltenham Spa (Table 57)
C To Portsmouth Harbour (Table 123)
D To London Waterloo (Table 160)
E From Weston-super-Mare (Table 134)
G To Warminster (Table 123)

Bath Spa, Bristol and Gloucester → Cardiff

Network Diagram - see first page of Table 132

Miles	Miles	Miles			AW	AW	GW	GW	GW	GW	GW	AW	AW	GW	GW	GW	GW	GW	AW	AW	AW	GW	XC		GW	AW
					MX	MO	MO	MO	MX	MO	MO	MX	MO	MO	MO	MX	MO		MO							
						◇	1◇	1◇	1◇	1◇	1◇	◇		1◇	1◇	1◇	1◇									◇
					A	B	C	D		E	E		D 🚌	G	H		E		J	K	L		N			
							⊓	⊓	⊤	⊓	⊓			⊓	⊓	⊤	⊓									⊤
0	—	—	**Bath Spa 7**	d			23p15			00 23	00 27			00 53	00 57	01 13	01 23								06 28	
1	—	—	Oldfield Park	d																					06 31	
7	—	—	Keynsham	d																					06 38	
11½	—	—	**Bristol Temple Meads 10**	a			23p27			00 37	00 43			01 06	01 10	01s29	01 37								06 46	
—	—	—		d			23p34											05 54				06 22			06 50	
16	—	—	Filton Abbey Wood	d														06 01				06 33			07 02	
—	0	—	**Bristol Parkway 7**	a			23p42																			
—	—	—		d			23p49		00 22																	
17½	—	—	Patchway	d														06 05				06 37				
21	4¾	—	Pilning	d																						
—	—	0	**Gloucester 7**	d	22p58			23p35													05 50		06 16			
—	—	19½	Lydney	d	23p17																06 09		06 35			
—	—	27¼	Chepstow	d	23p27																06 19		06 44			
—	—	34	Caldicot	d	23p35																06 26		06 53			
28	11¾	34¾	Severn Tunnel Jn	d	23p38													06 16			06 29	06 49			07 15	
38	21¾	44¾	Newport (South Wales)	a	23p59		00 11	00 23	00 52							02s12		06 27			06 41	07 01	07 06		07 26	
—	—	—		d	00 01	00 03	00 12	00 24	00 52			00 58	00 55					06 29	06 33	06 41	06 44	07 02	07 07		07 28	07 35
49¾	33½	56½	**Cardiff Central 7**	a	00 22	00 29	00 32	00 44	01 12			01 22	01 30			02 33		06 45	06 51	06 59	07 00	07 20	07 27		07 45	07 50

		GW	XC	GW	GW	AW	GW	SW	GW	GW	GW	AW	AW	AW	GW	GW	XC	GW	GW	GW		GW	AW	AW	GW	GW
		1◇				◇		1	1◇	◇	1◇	◇		◇	1◇		◇		◇	1◇		1◇	◇		◇	1◇
		Q	U	V	X					Y	Z		L			AA		BB				CC		L	Y	
		⊓							⊓		⊤	⊤		⊤	⊓				⊤	⊤		⊠	⊤			⊠
Bath Spa 7	d	06 56			07 12		07 28	07 34		07 48	08 00							08 08	08 22	08 30					08 47	08 55
Oldfield Park	d				07 14		07 31	07 37		07 51								08 11	08 24						08 49	
Keynsham	d				07 22		07 38	07 44		07 58	08 09							08 18	08 32						08 57	09 10
Bristol Temple Meads 10	a	07 10			07 29		07 45	07 52		08 06	08 17							08 25	08 39	08 45					09 04	
	d	07 15		07 19	07 41		07 54			08 13						08 19		08 41	08 54						09 10	
Filton Abbey Wood	d	07 22		07 30	07 48		08 02			08 24						08 30		08 48	09 01						09 20	
Bristol Parkway 7	a			07 33	07 52					08 30								08 51							09 25	
	d			07 36					08 07						08 42							09 07				
Patchway	d			07 39												08 34										
Pilning	d																									
Gloucester 7	d		07 00										07 58				08 25							08 58		
Lydney	d		07 19										08 17											09 17		
Chepstow	d		07 28										08 27											09 27		
Caldicot	d		07 37										08 34											09 35		
Severn Tunnel Jn	d		07 40	07 52									08 37			08 46								09 38		
Newport (South Wales)	a	07 44	07 50	08 05			08 24		08 29				08 49		09 04	08 59	09 07		09 23			09 29		09 50		
	d	07 45	07 52	08 11		08 08	08 26		08 31			08 37	08 51	08 59	09 05	09 03	09 07		09 24			09 31	09 37	09 52		
Cardiff Central 7	a	08 01	08 12	08 28		08 29	08 42		08 48			08 53	09 10	09 18	09 23	09 24	09 29		09 40			09 48	09 53	10 10		

		GW	GW	XC	GW	GW	GW	GW	GW	AW	AW	GW	GW	XC	GW	GW	GW		GW	GW	AW	AW	GW	GW	XC	GW
			1◇	◇		◇	1◇	1◇	1◇	◇	◇	1◇		◇	◇	1◇	◇		1◇	1◇	◇			1◇	◇	
		AA			DD								AA		EE							L	V			FF
			⊤	⊤		⊤	⊤	⊓	⊤	⊤	⊤	⊓		⊤		⊤	⊤		⊠	⊓	⊤			⊤	⊤	
Bath Spa 7	d				09 15	09 26	09 30		10 00						10 09	10 25	10 35			11 00						11 08
Oldfield Park	d				09 17										10 11											11 10
Keynsham	d				09 25	09 34									10 18											11 17
Bristol Temple Meads 10	a				09 32	09 41	09 45		10 15						10 26	10 42	10 47			11 15						11 26
	d	09 19			09 41	09 54							10 19		10 41		10 54						11 19			11 41
Filton Abbey Wood	d	09 30			09 48	10 01							10 30		10 48		11 02						11 30			11 48
Bristol Parkway 7	a				09 51										10 52											11 51
	d		09 42					10 07				10 42							11 07					11 42		
Patchway	d	09 34											10 34										11 34			
Pilning	d																									
Gloucester 7	d			09 22										10 22								10 58			11 22	
Lydney	d																					11 17				
Chepstow	d																					11 27				
Caldicot	d																					11 35				
Severn Tunnel Jn	d	09 46											10 48									11 38	11 46			
Newport (South Wales)	a	09 58	10 04	10 09		10 23		10 29				11 04	11 05	11 10			11 24		11 29			11 50	11 58	12 04	12 09	
	d	09 59	10 05	10 09		10 24		10 31		10 38	10 58	11 05	11 07	11 10			11 25		11 31		11 38	11 52	11 59	12 05	12 09	
Cardiff Central 7	a	10 17	10 23	10 30		10 40		10 48		10 54	11 20	11 23	11 25	11 32			11 41		11 47		11 53	12 10	12 17	12 23	12 32	

For general notes see front of timetable
For details of catering facilities see Directory of Train Operators

- **A** From Cheltenham Spa (Table 57)
- **B** Until 24 March
- **C** 4 February to 24 March. To Swansea (Table 125)
- **D** From 31 March
- **E** 4 February to 24 March
- **G** Until 28 January
- **H** From 31 March
- **J** From 24 March
- **K** All Tuesdays to Fridays, also Mondays until 17 March
- **L** From Cheltenham Spa (Table 57) to Maesteg (Table 128)
- **N** From Worcester Shrub Hill (Table 57)
- **Q** From London Paddington to Swansea (Table 125)
- **U** From Birmingham New Street (Table 57)
- **V** From Taunton (Table 134)
- **X** From Salisbury (Table 123) to Gloucester (Table 134)
- **Y** From Weymouth (Table 123)
- **Z** From London Paddington (Table 125)
- **AA** From Weston-super-Mare (Table 134)
- **BB** From Warminster (Table 123) to Great Malvern (Table 71)
- **CC** **The St David**
- **DD** From Westbury (Table 123) to Gloucester (Table 134)
- **EE** From Weymouth (Table 123) to Great Malvern (Table 71)
- **FF** From Warminster (Table 123) to Gloucester (Table 134)

Bath Spa, Bristol and Gloucester → Cardiff

Network Diagram - see first page of Table 132

		GW	GW	SW	GW	GW	AW	AW	AW	GW	GW	XC	GW	GW		GW	GW	GW	AW	GW	GW	XC	GW	GW	GW	GW
		[1] ◇	◇	[1] ◇	[1] ◇	[1] ◇	◇		◇	[1] ◇		◇	◇	[1] ◇		◇	[1] ◇	[1] ◇	◇		[1] ◇	◇	◇	[1] ◇	◇	[1] ◇
		A						B			C		D							C			E			
		⚲	⚲		☒	⚲	⚲		⚲	⚲		⚲		⚲		⚲	☒	⚲	⚲		⊡	⚲		⊡	⚲	☒
Bath Spa [7]	d	11 25	11 35	11 46		12 00							12 08	12 25		12 35		13 00					13 08	13 25	13 35	
Oldfield Park	d												12 10										13 10			
Keynsham	d												12 17										13 17			
Bristol Temple Meads [10]	a	11 42	11 47	12 05		12 15							12 26	12 42		12 47		13 15					13 26	13 42	13 47	
	d		11 54								12 19		12 41			12 54				13 19			13 41		13 54	
Filton Abbey Wood	d		12 02								12 30		12 48			13 02				13 30			13 48		14 02	
Bristol Parkway [7]	a												12 51										13 51			
	d				12 07					12 42							13 07				13 42					14 07
Patchway	d										12 34									13 34						
Pilning	d																									
Gloucester [7]	d							11 58				12 22										13 22				
Lydney	d							12 17																		
Chepstow	d							12 27																		
Caldicot	d							12 35																		
Severn Tunnel Jn	d							12 38			12 46									13 46						
Newport (South Wales)	a		12 24		12 29			12 50		13 04	13 04	13 09				13 24	13 29			13 58	14 04	14 10			14 24	14 29
	d		12 25		12 31		12 38	12 52	12 58	13 05	13 05	13 09				13 25	13 31		13 38	13 59	14 05	14 10			14 25	14 31
Cardiff Central [7]	a		12 41		12 48		12 54	13 10	13 21	13 23	13 27	13 34				13 41	13 48		13 54	14 15	14 23	14 32			14 41	14 49

		GW	AW	AW	AW	GW	GW	XC	GW	GW	GW		GW	SW	GW	GW	AW	AW	GW	GW	XC	GW	GW	GW	GW	GW
		[1] ◇	◇		◇	[1] ◇		◇			[1] ◇		◇	[1] ◇	[1] ◇	[1] ◇	[R]			[1] ◇	◇	◇	[1] ◇	◇	[1] ◇	[1] ◇
				B			C		G									B	C			E				
		⊡	⚲		⚲	⚲					⚲		⚲		⊡	⚲	⚲			⚲	⚲		⚲	⚲	⊡	⊡
Bath Spa [7]	d	14 00							14 08	14 15	14 25		14 35	14 46		15 00						15 15	15 25	15 35		16 00
Oldfield Park	d								14 11													15 17				
Keynsham	d								14 18													15 25				
Bristol Temple Meads [10]	a	14 15							14 26		14 42		14 47	15 00		15 15						15 32	15 42	15 47		16 15
	d						14 19		14 41				14 54						15 19			15 41		15 54		
Filton Abbey Wood	d						14 30		14 48	14 40			15 01						15 30			15 48		16 02		
Bristol Parkway [7]	a								14 51	14 45												15 51				
	d					14 42									15 07					15 42					16 07	
Patchway	d						14 34												15 34							
Pilning	d																									
Gloucester [7]	d			13 58				14 22										14 58			15 22					
Lydney	d			14 17														15 17								
Chepstow	d			14 27														15 27								
Caldicot	d			14 36														15 35								
Severn Tunnel Jn	d			14 39			14 46											15 39	15 46							
Newport (South Wales)	a			14 51		15 04	14 58	15 09					15 24		15 29			15 51	15 58	16 04	16 09			16 24	16 29	
	d		14 38	14 53	14 58	15 05	15 02	15 09					15 25		15 31		15 38	15 52	15 59	16 05	16 09			16 25	16 31	
Cardiff Central [7]	a		14 54	15 10	15 20	15 23	15 24	15 32					15 41		15 48		15 53	16 09	16 16	16 23	16 32			16 42	16 49	

		AW	AW	GW	GW	XC	GW	GW		GW	GW	GW	AW	AW	GW	GW	XC	GW	GW	GW	GW	GW	AW	AW	GW	GW
		[R]	◇	[1] ◇		◇		[1] ◇		◇	[1] ◇	[1] ◇	[R]			[1] ◇	◇	◇	[1] ◇	◇	[1] ◇	[1] ◇	[R]			[1] ◇
					C		J							B	C			E						B	C	
		⚲	⚲	⚲		⚲		⚲		⚲	⚲	⚲	⚲			⊡	⚲		⚲	⚲	⚲	⊡	⚲			⊡
Bath Spa [7]	d						16 08	16 25		16 35		17 00						17 08	17 25	17 35		18 00				
Oldfield Park	d						16 10											17 10								
Keynsham	d						16 17											17 19								
Bristol Temple Meads [10]	a						16 26	16 42		16 47		17 15						17 27	17 42	17 47		18 15				
	d				16 19		16 41			16 54					17 19			17 41		17 54					18 19	
Filton Abbey Wood	d				16 30		16 48			17 01					17 30			17 48		18 02					18 30	
Bristol Parkway [7]	a						16 51											17 51								
	d			16 42							17 07					17 42					18 13					18 42
Patchway	d				16 36										17 34										18 34	
Pilning	d																									
Gloucester [7]	d					16 26								16 58			17 25							17 58		
Lydney	d													17 17										18 17		
Chepstow	d													17 27										18 27		
Caldicot	d													17 36										18 35		
Severn Tunnel Jn	d				16 48					17 14				17 39	17 46					18 15				18 38	18 46	
Newport (South Wales)	a			17 04	17 00	17 09				17 25	17 29			17 51	17 58	18 04	18 09			18 26	18 36			18 50	18 58	19 04
	d	16 38	16 57	17 05	17 02	17 09				17 27	17 31		17 38	17 52	18 01	18 05	18 10			18 28	18 38		18 47	18 52	18 59	19 05
Cardiff Central [7]	a	16 54	17 15	17 23	17 24	17 32				17 45	17 48		17 54	18 10	18 16	18 23	18 32			18 43	18 53		19 01	19 10	19 15	19 23

For general notes see front of timetable
For details of catering facilities see Directory of Train Operators

- **A** **The Torbay Express**
- **B** From Cheltenham Spa (Table 57) to Maesteg (Table 128)
- **C** From Taunton (Table 134)
- **D** From Brighton (Table 123) to Great Malvern (Table 71)
- **E** From Weymouth (Table 123) to Gloucester (Table 134)
- **G** From Westbury (Table 123) to Worcester Foregate Street (Table 71)
- **J** From Warminster (Table 123) to Great Malvern (Table 71)

Bath Spa, Bristol and Gloucester → Cardiff

Network Diagram - see first page of Table 132

		GW	AW	XC	GW		GW	GW	GW	AW	AW	XC	GW	XC	GW	GW	GW	GW	GW	AW	AW	AW	GW	GW	XC	GW
			◇	◇	[1] ◇		◇	[1] ◇	[1] ◇	[R]		[R] [1]	[1] ◇	◇	◇	[1] ◇	◇	[1] ◇	[1] ◇	[R]		◇	[1] ◇		◇	◇
		A		B							C	D	E		G	H					C			J		K
			⌶	⌶	🍴		⌶	⌶	⌶	⌶		🍴	🍴			⌶	⌶	⌶	⌶	⌶		⌶	⌶			
Bath Spa [7]	d	18 08			18 30		18 35	19 00							19 08	19 30	19 37		20 00							20 08
Oldfield Park	d	18 10													19 11											20 10
Keynsham	d	18 17													19 18											20 17
Bristol Temple Meads [10]	a	18 27			18 45		18 50	19 15							19 25	19 45	19 49		20 15							20 27
	d	18 41					18 54					19 25			19 41		19 54							20 19		20 41
Filton Abbey Wood	d	18 48					19 01					19 31			19 48		20 01							20 30		20 48
Bristol Parkway [7]	a	18 51													19 51											20 51
	d								19 11				19 42					20 07					20 42			
Patchway	d											19 37												20 34		
Pilning	d																									
Gloucester [7]	d			18 29							18 58			19 25							19 58				20 26	
Lydney	d										19 17										20 17					
Chepstow	d										19 27										20 27					
Caldicot	d										19 34										20 35					
Severn Tunnel Jn	d										19 37	19 49									20 38			20 46		
Newport (South Wales)	a			19 14			19 25		19 34		19 50	19 59	20 04	20 10			20 23	20 29			20 50		21 04	21 01	21 10	
	d		19 00	19 16			19 26		19 34	19 40	19 51	20 01	20 05	20 11			20 24	20 31		20 46	20 52	20 58	21 05	21 02	21 12	
Cardiff Central [7]	a		19 24	19 36			19 41		19 50	19 57	20 11	20 19	20 21	20 29			20 41	20 48		21 01	21 10	21 19	21 22	21 24	21 31	

		GW		GW	GW	AW	GW	GW	GW	GW	GW	SW	GW	GW	AW	AW	GW	GW	GW	GW	AW	AW	GW	GW		
																							FO	FSX		
		[1] ◇		◇	[1] ◇	◇			[1] ◇	[1] ◇	◇	[1] ◇	◇	[1] ◇	◇		[1] ◇	◇	◇	[1] ◇	◇		[1] ◇	[1] ◇		
											L					N		L				N				
		⌶		⌶	⌶	⌶			⌶	🍴	⌶			⌶	⌶		🍴	⌶		🍴			🍴			
Bath Spa [7]	d	20 30		20 35	20 55			21 08		21 30	21 35	21 51	22 08	22 15				22 35	23 11	23 28			23 48	22 35		
Oldfield Park	d							21 10					22 10						23 14							
Keynsham	d							21 18				21 59	22 17						23 22							
Bristol Temple Meads [10]	a	20 45		20 50	21 10			21 27		21 45	21 50	22 06	22 27	22 30				22 48	23 30	23 41			00 05	00 11		
	d			20 54			21 19				21 54							22 54								
Filton Abbey Wood	d			21 01			21 30				22 01							23 01								
Bristol Parkway [7]	a																									
	d								21 42								22 46									
Patchway	d						21 34				22 05							23 05								
Pilning	d																									
Gloucester [7]	d															21 58						22 58				
Lydney	d															22 17						23 17				
Chepstow	d															22 27						23 27				
Caldicot	d															22 35						23 35				
Severn Tunnel Jn	d						21 49				22 16					22 38		23 16				23 38				
Newport (South Wales)	a			21 28			22 00		22 04		22 35					22 57	23 15	23 35				23 59				
	d			21 30		21 38	22 02		22 05		22 36				22 41	22 58	23 15	23 35			23 52	00 01				
Cardiff Central [7]	a			21 45		21 57	22 22		22 28		22 54				23 04	23 18	23 37	23 55			00 17	00 22				

Saturdays

until 26 January

		AW	GW	AW	GW	AW	AW		XC	GW	GW	AW	XC	GW		AW	GW	SW	GW	AW	AW		AW	GW	XC	GW
			[1] ◇	◇	[1] ◇						[1] ◇	◇				◇		[1]	[1] ◇	◇			◇		◇	
		N				Q	U		V		X		Y	Z							C			AA		A
					⌶						🍴	⌶							🍴	⌶			⌶			
Bath Spa [7]	d				01 09									07 07			07 22	07 34	08 00							08 09
Oldfield Park	d													07 10			07 25	07 37								08 11
Keynsham	d													07 17			07 32	07 44								08 18
Bristol Temple Meads [10]	a				01s25									07 25			07 39	07 52	08 15							08 26
	d									06 50	06 58			07 41			07 54							08 19		08 41
Filton Abbey Wood	d									07 01				07 48			08 01							08 30		08 48
Bristol Parkway [7]	a										07 06			07 51												08 51
	d		00 17								07 13															
Patchway	d																							08 34		
Pilning	d																									
Gloucester [7]	d	22p58					05 50		06 16				07 00								07 58				08 25	
Lydney	d	23p17					06 09		06 35				07 19								08 17					
Chepstow	d	23p27					06 19		06 44				07 28								08 27					
Caldicot	d	23p35					06 27		06 53				07 37								08 35					
Severn Tunnel Jn	d	23p38					06 30			07 14			07 40								08 38			08 46		
Newport (South Wales)	a	23p59	00 48		02s06		06 42		07 05	07 26	07 34		07 50				08 23				08 50			09 00	09 06	
	d	00 01	00 48	00 55		06 38	06 44		07 06	07 28	07 36	07 40	07 52			08 06	08 24			08 37	08 52		09 01	09 03	09 07	
Cardiff Central [7]	a	00 22	01 04	01 14	02 23	06 54	07 00		07 26	07 43	07 51	07 54	08 12			08 25	08 42			08 51	09 10		09 18	09 21	09 29	

For general notes see front of timetable
For details of catering facilities see Directory of Train Operators

- **A** From Warminster (Table 123) to Great Malvern (Table 71)
- **B** ⌶ to Newport (South Wales)
- **C** From Cheltenham Spa (Table 57) to Maesteg (Table 128)
- **D** From Newcastle (Table 51)
- **E** **The Red Dragon**
- **G** From Weymouth (Table 123) to Cheltenham Spa (Table 57)
- **H** **The Bristolian**
- **J** From Taunton (Table 134)
- **K** From Brighton (Table 123) to Worcester Shrub Hill (Table 57)
- **L** From Portsmouth Harbour (Table 123)
- **N** From Cheltenham Spa (Table 57)
- **Q** To Barry Island (Table 130)
- **U** To Maesteg (Table 128)
- **V** From Worcester Shrub Hill (Table 57)
- **X** To Swansea (Table 125)
- **Y** From Birmingham New Street (Table 57)
- **Z** From Salisbury (Table 123) to Gloucester (Table 134)
- **AA** From Weston-super-Mare (Table 134)

Bath Spa, Bristol and Gloucester → Cardiff

Network Diagram - see first page of Table 132

		GW	GW	GW	GW		AW	AW	GW	XC	GW	GW		GW	GW	GW	AW	GW	GW		GW	AW	XC	GW	GW	AW
		◇	1 ◇	1 ◇	1 ◇		◇			◇	◇	1 ◇		◇	1 ◇	1 ◇	◇		◇		1 ◇	◇	◇	◇	1 ◇	◇
								A	B		C							B	D							
			☕	☕	☕		🛒			🛒		☕			☕	☕	🛒				☕	🛒			☕	🛒
Bath Spa [7]	d	08 19	08 25		09 00						09 09	09 25		09 35		10 00			10 08		10 25			10 35		
Oldfield Park	d										09 12								10 10							
Keynsham	d										09 19								10 17							
Bristol Temple Meads [10]	a	08 31	08 40		09 15						09 27	09 40		09 47		10 15			10 25		10 42			10 48		
	d	08 54							09 19		09 41			09 54				10 19	10 41					10 54		
Filton Abbey Wood	d	09 01							09 30		09 48			10 01				10 30	10 48					11 00		
Bristol Parkway [7]	a										09 51								10 51							
	d			09 07											10 07										11 07	
Patchway	d								09 34									10 34								
Pilning	d																									
Gloucester [7]	d							08 58		09 22													10 22			
Lydney	d							09 17																		
Chepstow	d							09 27																		
Caldicot	d							09 35																		
Severn Tunnel Jn	d							09 38	09 46									10 46								
Newport (South Wales)	a	09 23		09 30				09 50	09 58	10 04				10 23	10 31			10 58					11 04	11 22	11 29	
	d	09 23		09 32			09 36	09 52	09 59	10 06				10 23	10 32		10 38	10 59				10 58	11 05	11 22	11 32	11 38
Cardiff Central [7]	a	09 40		09 48			09 52	10 10	10 16	10 25				10 40	10 48		10 52	11 18				11 20	11 25	11 40	11 48	11 53

		AW	GW		XC	GW	GW	GW	SW	GW		GW	AW	AW	GW	GW	GW		AW	XC	GW	GW	GW	AW		GW
					◇	1 ◇	1 ◇	◇	1 ◇	1 ◇		1 ◇	◇			◇	1 ◇		◇	◇	◇	1 ◇	1 ◇	◇		
		A	E											A	E	G										E
						☕	☕			☕		☕	🛒				☕		🛒			☕	☕	🛒		
Bath Spa [7]	d					11 00	11 25	11 35	11 46			12 00				12 18	12 25				12 35		13 00			
Oldfield Park	d															12 20										
Keynsham	d															12 28										
Bristol Temple Meads [10]	a					11 15	11 42	11 47	12 00			12 15				12 35	12 42				12 47		13 15			
	d		11 19					11 53							12 19	12 41					12 53					13 19
Filton Abbey Wood	d		11 30					12 00							12 30	12 48					13 00					13 30
Bristol Parkway [7]	a															12 51										
	d									12 07												13 07				
Patchway	d		11 34												12 34											13 34
Pilning	d																									
Gloucester [7]	d	10 58			11 22									11 58						12 22						
Lydney	d	11 17												12 17												
Chepstow	d	11 27												12 27												
Caldicot	d	11 35												12 35												
Severn Tunnel Jn	d	11 38	11 46											12 38	12 46											13 45
Newport (South Wales)	a	11 50	11 58		12 04			12 22		12 31				12 50	12 58					13 04	13 22	13 29				13 57
	d	11 52	11 59		12 05			12 22		12 32			12 38	12 52	12 59				12 58	13 05	13 22	13 32		13 38		13 58
Cardiff Central [7]	a	12 10	12 15		12 25			12 39		12 48			12 53	13 10	13 18				13 19	13 25	13 40	13 48		13 53		14 13

		XC	GW	GW	GW	GW	GW		AW	AW	AW	GW	XC	GW		GW	GW	SW	GW	GW	AW		AW	GW	XC	GW
																					R					
		◇	◇	1 ◇	◇	1 ◇	1 ◇		◇		◇		◇			1 ◇	◇	1 ◇	1 ◇	1 ◇					◇	◇
			C							A		E		H									A	E		C
				☕		☕	☕		🛒		🛒					☕			☕	☕	🛒					
Bath Spa [7]	d		13 18	13 25	13 35		14 03							14 09		14 25	14 35	14 46		15 00						15 15
Oldfield Park	d		13 21											14 12												15 18
Keynsham	d		13 28											14 19												15 25
Bristol Temple Meads [10]	a		13 36	13 42	13 47		14 17							14 26		14 42	14 47	15 00		15 15						15 32
	d		13 41		13 53							14 19		14 41			14 53							15 19		15 41
Filton Abbey Wood	d		13 48		14 00							14 30		14 48			15 00							15 30		15 48
Bristol Parkway [7]	a		13 51											14 51												15 51
	d					14 07													15 07							
Patchway	d											14 34												15 34		
Pilning	d																							15 40		
Gloucester [7]	d	13 22								13 58			14 22										14 58		15 22	
Lydney	d									14 17													15 17			
Chepstow	d									14 27													15 27			
Caldicot	d									14 37													15 35			
Severn Tunnel Jn	d									14 40		14 45											15 38	15 48		
Newport (South Wales)	a	14 04			14 22	14 31				14 52		14 57	15 04				15 22		15 29				15 50	15 59	16 04	
	d	14 06			14 22	14 32			14 38	14 54	14 58	15 02	15 06				15 22		15 32		15 38		15 52	16 01	16 06	
Cardiff Central [7]	a	14 25			14 39	14 48			14 53	15 11	15 20	15 24	15 25				15 39		15 48		15 53		16 07	16 15	16 25	

For general notes see front of timetable
For details of catering facilities see Directory of Train Operators

- **A** From Cheltenham Spa (Table 57) to Maesteg (Table 128)
- **B** From Weston-super-Mare (Table 134)
- **C** From Weymouth (Table 123) to Gloucester (Table 134)
- **D** From Weymouth (Table 123) to Great Malvern (Table 71)
- **E** From Taunton (Table 134)
- **G** From Brighton (Table 123) to Worcester Foregate Street (Table 71)
- **H** From Southampton Central (Table 123) to Great Malvern (Table 71)

Bath Spa, Bristol and Gloucester → Cardiff

Network Diagram - see first page of Table 132

		GW	GW	GW	GW		AW	AW	GW	XC	GW	GW		GW	GW	AW	AW	GW	GW		XC	GW	GW	GW	GW	AW
		1 ◇	◇	1 ◇	1 ◇		R	◇		◇	1 ◇	◇		1 ◇	1 ◇	R			◇		◇	1 ◇	◇	1 ◇	1 ◇	R
									A								B	A	C							
		☕		☕	☕		🛒	🛒			☕			☕	☕	🛒						☕		☕	☕	🛒
Bath Spa 7	d	15 25	15 35		16 00						16 25	16 35			17 00				17 08			17 25	17 35		18 00	
Oldfield Park	d																		17 11							
Keynsham	d																		17 18							
Bristol Temple Meads 10	a	15 42	15 47		16 15						16 42	16 47			17 15				17 25			17 42	17 47		18 15	
	d		15 53						16 19			16 53						17 19	17 41				17 53			
Filton Abbey Wood	d		16 00						16 30			17 00						17 30	17 48				18 00			
Bristol Parkway 7	a																		17 51							
	d			16 07										17 07										18 07		
Patchway	d								16 34									17 34								
Pilning	d																									
Gloucester 7	d									16 26							16 58				17 25					
Lydney	d																17 17									
Chepstow	d																17 27									
Caldicot	d																17 35									
Severn Tunnel Jn	d								16 45			17 14					17 38	17 45					18 14			
Newport (South Wales)	a		16 24	16 32					17 00	17 07		17 25		17 29			17 50	17 57			18 06		18 25	18 31		
	d		16 24	16 32			16 38	16 58	17 02	17 08		17 25		17 32		17 38	17 52	17 58			18 08		18 25	18 32		18 40
Cardiff Central 7	a		16 41	16 48			16 53	17 20	17 21	17 25		17 44		17 47		17 54	18 10	18 13			18 25		18 41	18 48		18 54

		AW	GW		AW	XC	GW	GW	GW	GW		AW	AW	XC	XC	GW	GW		GW	GW	GW	AW	AW	AW		GW
					◇	◇	1 ◇	◇	1 ◇	1 ◇		R		1 ◇	◇	◇	1 ◇		◇	1 ◇	1 ◇	R		◇		1 ◇
		B	A										B	D		E							B			
					🛒		☕		☕	☕		🛒		☕			☕			☕	☕	🛒		🛒		☕
Bath Spa 7	d						18 25	18 35	19 00							19 08	19 25		19 35		20 01					
Oldfield Park	d															19 10										
Keynsham	d															19 17										
Bristol Temple Meads 10	a						18 42	18 47	19 15							19 26	19 42		19 47		20 15					
	d		18 19					18 53						19 24		19 40			19 53							
Filton Abbey Wood	d		18 30					19 00						19 33		19 48			20 00							
Bristol Parkway 7	a															19 51										
	d									19 12										20 07						20 42
Patchway	d		18 34											19 37												
Pilning	d																									
Gloucester 7	d	17 58				18 30							18 58		19 25								19 58			
Lydney	d	18 17											19 17										20 17			
Chepstow	d	18 27											19 27										20 27			
Caldicot	d	18 35											19 34										20 35			
Severn Tunnel Jn	d	18 38	18 45										19 37	19 48									20 38			
Newport (South Wales)	a	18 50	18 57			19 12		19 24		19 35			19 50	19 59	20 06				20 22	20 31			20 50			21 04
	d	18 52	18 58		19 00	19 14		19 24		19 35		19 43	19 52	20 00	20 08				20 22	20 32		20 46	20 52	20 59		21 05
Cardiff Central 7	a	19 10	19 13		19 22	19 33		19 40		19 52		19 54	20 10	20 19	20 25				20 39	20 48		21 01	21 10	21 20		21 22

		GW	GW	GW	GW	GW	AW	SW	GW	GW	GW	SW	GW	AW		GW	AW	GW	GW	GW	GW	AW	AW	GW		
			1 ◇	◇	1 ◇	1 ◇	◇	1 ◇		1 ◇	◇	1 ◇	1 ◇	◇		1 ◇		◇	◇	1 ◇		◇		1 ◇		
		G							A		H	J					K		H							
			☕		☕	☕	🛒			☕			☕	🛒		☕				☕						
Bath Spa 7	d	20 18	20 25	20 35		21 00		21 51		21 30	21 39	21 51	21 59					22 08	22 35	23 00	23 08					
Oldfield Park	d	20 21																22 10			23 10					
Keynsham	d	20 28						21 59				21 59						22 18			23 17					
Bristol Temple Meads 10	a	20 35	20 42	20 47		21 15		22 00		21 47	21 51	22 06	22 16					22 29	22 48	23 15	23 25					
	d	20 41		20 53					21 19		21 54								22 54							
Filton Abbey Wood	d	20 48		21 00					21 30		22 02								23 01							
Bristol Parkway 7	a	20 51																								
	d				21 06											22 12								23 29		
Patchway	d								21 34		22 07								23 05							
Pilning	d																									
Gloucester 7	d																21 58						22 58			
Lydney	d																22 17						23 17			
Chepstow	d																22 27						23 27			
Caldicot	d																22 35						23 35			
Severn Tunnel Jn	d								21 45		22 18						22 38		23 16				23 38			
Newport (South Wales)	a			21 26	21 31				22 02		22 35					22 45	22 55		23 33				23 57	00 01		
	d			21 26	21 31		21 39		22 04		22 36			22 42		22 46	22 57		23 35			23 53	23 58	00 01		
Cardiff Central 7	a			21 42	21 47		22 00		22 23		22 56			23 01		23 06	23 18		23 54			00 17	00 18	00 23		

For general notes see front of timetable
For details of catering facilities see Directory of Train Operators

A From Taunton (Table 134)

B From Cheltenham Spa (Table 57) to Maesteg (Table 128)

C From Weymouth (Table 123) to Gloucester (Table 134)

D From Newcastle (Table 51)

E From Weymouth (Table 123) to Cheltenham Spa (Table 57)

G From Brighton (Table 123) to Cheltenham Spa (Table57)

H From Portsmouth Harbour (Table 123)

J From London Waterloo (Table 160)

K From Cheltenham Spa (Table 57)

Saturdays

2 February to 22 March

Bath Spa, Bristol and Gloucester → Cardiff

Network Diagram - see first page of Table 132

		AW	GW	AW	GW	AW	AW	XC	GW	GW	AW		XC	GW	AW	GW	SW	GW	AW	AW	AW	GW		XC	GW	GW
			1 ◇	◇	1 ◇					1 ◇	◇				◇		1	1 ◇	◇		◇			◇		◇
		A				B	C	D		E			G	H						J		K			L	
					🛒					☕	🛒							☕	🛒		🛒					
Bath Spa 7	d				01 09									07 07		07 22	07 34	07 54							08 09	08 29
Oldfield Park	d													07 10		07 25	07 37								08 11	
Keynsham	d													07 17		07 32	07 44								08 18	
Bristol Temple Meads 10	a				01s25									07 25		07 39	07 52	08 06							08 26	08 41
	d								06 50	06 58				07 41		07 54						08 19			08 41	08 54
Filton Abbey Wood	d								07 01					07 48		08 01						08 30			08 48	09 01
Bristol Parkway 7	a									07 06				07 51											08 51	
	d		00 17							07 13																
Patchway	d																					08 34				
Pilning	d																									
Gloucester 7	d	22p58					05 50	06 16					07 00							07 58				08 25		
Lydney	d	23p17					06 09	06 35					07 19							08 17						
Chepstow	d	23p27					06 19	06 44					07 28							08 27						
Caldicot	d	23p35					06 27	06 53					07 37							08 35						
Severn Tunnel Jn	d	23p38					06 30		07 14				07 40							08 38		08 46				
Newport (South Wales)	a	23p59	00 48		02s06		06 42	07 05	07 26	07 34			07 50			08 23				08 50		09 00		09 06		09 23
	d	00 01	00 48	00 55		06 38	06 44	07 06	07 28	07 36	07 40		07 52		08 06	08 24			08 37	08 52	09 01	09 03		09 07		09 23
Cardiff Central 7	a	00 22	01 04	01 14	02 23	06 54	07 00	07 26	07 43	07 51	07 54		08 12		08 25	08 42			08 51	09 10	09 18	09 21		09 29		09 40

		AW	GW	AW	GW	GW	XC	GW	GW	GW		AW	GW	GW	GW	GW	GW	GW	AW	XC	GW		GW	AW	AW	GW
		◇	1 ◇		1 ◇		◇	◇	1 ◇	◇		◇	1 ◇	1 ◇		◇	1 ◇	1 ◇	◇	◇	◇		1 ◇	◇		
			E	J		K		N					E		K	Q									J	U
		🛒	☕		☕		🛒		☕			🛒	☕	☕			☕	☕	🛒				☕	🛒		
Bath Spa 7	d		08 48		08 55			09 09	09 17	09 35			09 50	09 56		10 08	10 13	10 30			10 35		10 54			
Oldfield Park	d							09 12								10 10										
Keynsham	d							09 19								10 17										
Bristol Temple Meads 10	a		09 00		09 07			09 27	09 32	09 47			10 03	10 08		10 25	10 30	10 45			10 48		11 06			
	d		09 07			09 19		09 41		09 54			10 09		10 19	10 41					10 54					11 19
Filton Abbey Wood	d					09 30		09 48		10 01					10 30	10 48					11 00					11 30
Bristol Parkway 7	a		09 15					09 51					10 18			10 51										
	d		09 20										10 22													
Patchway	d					09 34									10 34											11 34
Pilning	d																									
Gloucester 7	d			08 58			09 22													10 22					10 58	
Lydney	d			09 17																					11 17	
Chepstow	d			09 27																					11 27	
Caldicot	d			09 35																					11 35	
Severn Tunnel Jn	d			09 38		09 46									10 46										11 38	11 46
Newport (South Wales)	a		09 42	09 50		09 58	10 04			10 23			10 45		10 58					11 04	11 22				11 50	11 58
	d	09 36	09 44	09 52		09 59	10 06			10 23		10 38	10 46		10 59				10 58	11 05	11 22			11 38	11 52	11 59
Cardiff Central 7	a	09 52	10 00	10 10		10 16	10 25			10 40		10 52	11 02		11 18				11 20	11 25	11 40			11 53	12 10	12 15

		XC	GW	GW	GW	AW	GW	AW	GW		SW	GW	GW	GW	GW	AW	XC	GW	AW	GW		GW	GW	XC	GW	GW
		◇	1 ◇	1 ◇	◇	◇	1 ◇		1 ◇		1 ◇		◇	1 ◇	1 ◇	◇	◇	◇	◇	1 ◇		1 ◇		◇	◇	1 ◇
							E	J				U	V							E			U		N	
			☕	☕		🛒	☕		☕					☕	☕	🛒			🛒	☕		☕				☕
Bath Spa 7	d		11 30	11 17	11 35		11 48		11 55		12 01		12 13	12 18	12 30			12 35		12 48		12 54			13 18	13 24
Oldfield Park	d												12 15												13 21	
Keynsham	d												12 23												13 28	
Bristol Temple Meads 10	a		11 45	11 32	11 47		12 00		12 07		12 15		12 30	12 35	12 45			12 47		13 00		13 06			13 36	13 41
	d				11 53		12 07					12 19	12 41					12 53		13 07			13 19		13 41	
Filton Abbey Wood	d				12 00							12 30	12 48					13 00					13 30		13 48	
Bristol Parkway 7	a						12 15						12 51							13 15					13 51	
	d						12 20													13 20						
Patchway	d											12 34											13 34			
Pilning	d																									
Gloucester 7	d	11 22						11 58									12 22							13 22		
Lydney	d							12 17																		
Chepstow	d							12 27																		
Caldicot	d							12 35																		
Severn Tunnel Jn	d							12 38				12 46											13 45			
Newport (South Wales)	a	12 04			12 22		12 44	12 50				12 58					13 04	13 22		13 41			13 57	14 04		
	d	12 05			12 22	12 38	12 45	12 52				12 59				12 58	13 05	13 22	13 38	13 44			13 58	14 06		
Cardiff Central 7	a	12 25			12 39	12 53	13 01	13 10				13 18				13 19	13 25	13 40	13 53	14 00			14 13	14 25		

For general notes see front of timetable
For details of catering facilities see Directory of Train Operators

- **A** From Cheltenham Spa (Table 57)
- **B** To Barry Island (Table 130)
- **C** To Maesteg (Table 128)
- **D** From Worcester Shrub Hill (Table 57)
- **E** To Swansea (Table 125)
- **G** From Birmingham New Street (Table 57)
- **H** From Salisbury (Table 123) to Gloucester (Table 134)
- **J** From Cheltenham Spa (Table 57) to Maesteg (Table 128)
- **K** From Weston-super-Mare (Table 134)
- **L** From Warminster (Table 123) to Great Malvern (Table 71)
- **N** From Weymouth (Table 123) to Gloucester (Table 134)
- **Q** From Weymouth (Table 123) to Great Malvern (Table 71)
- **U** From Taunton (Table 134)
- **V** From Brighton (Table 123) to Worcester Foregate Street (Table 71)

2 February to 22 March

Bath Spa, Bristol and Gloucester → Cardiff

Network Diagram - see first page of Table 132

		GW	GW	AW	GW	AW	GW	AW		GW	XC	GW	GW	GW	GW	SW	AW	GW	GW		AW	GW	XC	SW	GW	GW
																	R									
		[1] ◇	◇	◇	[1] ◇		[1] ◇	◇			◇		[1] ◇	[1] ◇	◇	[1] ◇		[1] ◇	[1] ◇				◇	[1] ◇	◇	[1] ◇
					A	B				C		D						A			B	C			E	
		☕		🛒	☕		☕	🛒					☕	☕			🛒	☕	☕							☕
Bath Spa [7]	d	13 30	13 35		13 48		13 54					14 09	14 15	14 30	14 35	14 45		14 47	14 55					15 01	15 15	15 21
Oldfield Park	d											14 12													15 18	
Keynsham	d											14 19													15 25	
Bristol Temple Meads [10]	a	13 45	13 47		14 00		14 06					14 26	14 31	14 45	14 47	14 59		15 00	15 07					15 15	15 32	15 37
	d		13 53		14 07					14 19		14 41			14 53			15 07				15 19			15 41	
Filton Abbey Wood	d		14 00							14 30		14 48			15 00							15 30			15 48	
Bristol Parkway [7]	a				14 15							14 51						15 15							15 51	
	d				14 20													15 20								
Patchway	d									14 34												15 34				
Pilning	d																					15 40				
Gloucester [7]	d					13 58					14 22										14 58		15 22			
Lydney	d					14 17															15 17					
Chepstow	d					14 27															15 27					
Caldicot	d					14 37															15 35					
Severn Tunnel Jn	d					14 40				14 45											15 38	15 48				
Newport (South Wales)	a		14 22		14 43	14 52				14 57	15 04				15 22			15 41			15 50	15 59	16 04			
	d		14 22	14 38	14 44	14 54		14 58		15 02	15 06				15 22		15 38	15 44			15 52	16 01	16 06			
Cardiff Central [7]	a		14 39	14 53	15 00	15 11		15 20		15 24	15 25				15 39		15 53	16 00			16 07	16 15	16 25			

		GW	GW	AW	GW	GW	AW		GW	XC	GW	GW	AW	GW	AW	GW	GW	XC		GW	GW	GW	GW	AW	GW	AW
				R									R											R		
		[1] ◇	◇		[1] ◇	[1] ◇	◇			◇	[1] ◇	◇		[1] ◇		[1] ◇		◇		◇	[1] ◇	[1] ◇	◇		[1] ◇	
					A				C					A	B		C			E					A	B
		☕		🛒	☕	☕	🛒				☕		🛒	☕		☕					☕	☕		🛒	☕	
Bath Spa [7]	d	15 30	15 35		15 48	15 54					16 30	16 35		16 49		16 55				17 08	17 18	17 30	17 35		17 48	
Oldfield Park	d																			17 11						
Keynsham	d																			17 18						
Bristol Temple Meads [10]	a	15 45	15 47		16 00	16 06					16 45	16 47		17 01		17 07				17 25	17 36	17 45	17 47		18 00	
	d		15 53		16 07				16 19			16 53		17 08			17 19			17 42			17 53		18 07	
Filton Abbey Wood	d		16 00						16 30			17 00					17 30			17 48			18 00			
Bristol Parkway [7]	a				16 15									17 16						17 51					18 15	
	d				16 20									17 21											18 20	
Patchway	d								16 34								17 34									
Pilning	d																									
Gloucester [7]	d									16 26					16 58			17 25								17 58
Lydney	d														17 17											18 17
Chepstow	d														17 27											18 27
Caldicot	d														17 35											18 35
Severn Tunnel Jn	d								16 45			17 14			17 38		17 45						18 14			18 38
Newport (South Wales)	a		16 24		16 43				17 00	17 07		17 25		17 42	17 50		17 57	18 06					18 25		18 43	18 50
	d		16 24	16 38	16 44		16 58		17 02	17 08		17 25	17 38	17 45	17 52		17 58	18 08					18 25	18 40	18 44	18 52
Cardiff Central [7]	a		16 41	16 53	17 00		17 20		17 21	17 25		17 44	17 54	18 00	18 10		18 13	18 25					18 41	18 54	19 00	19 10

		GW	GW	GW	AW	XC		GW	GW	AW	GW	AW	XC	XC	GW	GW	GW		GW	GW	AW	AW	GW	AW	GW	AW
										R											R					
		[1] ◇		[1] ◇	◇	◇		◇	[1] ◇		[1] ◇		[1] ◇	◇	◇	[1] ◇	◇		[1] ◇	[1] ◇				◇	◇	◇
			C								G	B	H		J				A			B	K			
		☕		☕	🛒				☕	🛒	☕		☕			☕			☕	☕	🛒			🛒		🛒
Bath Spa [7]	d	17 54		18 30				18 35	18 37		18 48				19 08	19 18	19 35		19 48	20 04			20 18		20 35	
Oldfield Park	d														19 10								20 21			
Keynsham	d														19 17								20 28			
Bristol Temple Meads [10]	a	18 06		18 45				18 47	18 51		19 00				19 26	19 32	19 47		20 00	20 18			20 35		20 47	
	d		18 19					18 53			19 07		19 24		19 40		19 53		20 07				20 41		20 53	
Filton Abbey Wood	d		18 30					19 00					19 33		19 48		20 00						20 48		21 00	
Bristol Parkway [7]	a										19 15				19 51				20 15				20 51			
	d										19 20								20 21							
Patchway	d		18 34										19 37													
Pilning	d																									
Gloucester [7]	d					18 30						18 58		19 25								19 58				
Lydney	d											19 17										20 17				
Chepstow	d											19 27										20 27				
Caldicot	d											19 34										20 35				
Severn Tunnel Jn	d		18 45									19 37	19 48									20 38				
Newport (South Wales)	a		18 57			19 12		19 24			19 43	19 50	19 59	20 06			20 22		20 49			20 52			21 26	
	d		18 58		19 00	19 14		19 24		19 37	19 44	19 52	20 00	20 08			20 22		20 49		20 46	20 52		20 59	21 26	21 39
Cardiff Central [7]	a		19 13		19 22	19 33		19 40		19 54	20 03	20 10	20 19	20 25			20 39		21 05		21 06	21 11		21 20	21 42	22 00

For general notes see front of timetable
For details of catering facilities see Directory of Train Operators

A To Swansea (Table 125)

B From Cheltenham Spa (Table 57) to Maesteg (Table 128)

C From Taunton (Table 134)

D From Southampton Central (Table 123) to Great Malvern (Table 71)

E From Weymouth (Table 123) to Gloucester (Table 134)

G To Carmarthen (Table 128)

H From Newcastle (Table 51)

J From Weymouth (Table 123) to Cheltenham Spa (Table 57)

K From Brighton (Table 123) to Cheltenham Spa (Table 57)

Table 132

2 February to 22 March

Bath Spa, Bristol and Gloucester → Cardiff

Network Diagram - see first page of Table 132

		GW	GW	GW	GW	GW	SW	AW	GW	AW	GW	GW	GW	GW	GW	GW	GW	GW	AW	AW	GW	GW
		1◇	1◇		1◇	◇	1◇	◇	1◇		1◇	◇	1◇	◇	1◇	1◇		1◇	◇		1◇	1◇
			A	B		C	D		A	E				C	A							
		☕	☕		☕			🍴	☕		☕		☕		☕	☕		☕				☕
Bath Spa 7	d	20 54	20 54		21 30	21 37	21 51		21 52		22 02	22 08	22 17	22 35	22 48	22 54	23 08	23 13			23 49	23 54
Oldfield Park	d											22 10					23 10					
Keynsham	d						21 59					22 18					23 17					
Bristol Temple Meads 10	a	21 06	21 07		21 45	21 49	22 06		22 05		22 17	22 29	22 32	22 48	23 00	23 06	23 25	23 31			00 02	00 06
	d		21 13	21 19		21 53			22 11					22 54	23 07						00 08	
Filton Abbey Wood	d			21 30		22 00								23 01								
Bristol Parkway 7	a		21 22						22 20						23 15							
	d		21 26						22 24						23 20							
Patchway	d			21 34		22 05								23 05								
Pilning	d																					
Gloucester 7	d									21 58										22 58		
Lydney	d									22 17										23 17		
Chepstow	d									22 27										23 27		
Caldicot	d									22 35										23 35		
Severn Tunnel Jn	d			21 45		22 16				22 38				23 16						23 38		
Newport (South Wales)	a		21 50	22 02		22 32			22 50	22 55				23 31	23 47					23 57	00 37	
	d		21 51	22 04		22 32		22 42	22 50	22 57				23 32	23 47				23 53	23 58	00 37	
Cardiff Central 7	a		22 11	22 23		22 52		23 01	23 10	23 15				23 51	00 07				00 17	00 18	01 00	

Saturdays

from 29 March

		AW	GW	AW	GW	AW	AW	XC	GW	AW	XC	GW	GW	SW	GW	AW	AW	XC	GW	GW	GW	GW	GW
			1◇	◇	1◇									1	1◇			◇	1◇		◇	1◇	1◇
		E				G	H	J			K	L					N			Q	C		
					🍴										☕				☕			☕	☕
Bath Spa 7	d				01 09				06 28			07 07	07 22	07 34	08 00					08 09	08 19	08 25	09 00
Oldfield Park	d								06 31			07 10	07 25	07 37						08 11			
Keynsham	d								06 38			07 17	07 32	07 44						08 18			
Bristol Temple Meads 10	a				01s25				06 46			07 25	07 39	07 52	08 15					08 26	08 31	08 40	09 15
	d											07 41								08 41	08 54		
Filton Abbey Wood	d											07 48								08 48	09 01		
Bristol Parkway 7	a											07 51								08 51	09 04		
	d		00 17																				
Patchway	d																						
Pilning	d																						
Gloucester 7	d	22p58					05 50	06 16			07 00						07 58	08 25	08 37				
Lydney	d	23p17					06 09	06 35			07 19						08 17						
Chepstow	d	23p27					06 19	06 44			07 28						08 27						
Caldicot	d	23p35					06 27	06 53			07 37						08 35						
Severn Tunnel Jn	d	23p38					06 30				07 40						08 38						
Newport (South Wales)	a	23p59	00 48		02s06		06 42	07 05			07 50						08 50	09 06	09 19				
	d	00 01	00 48	00 55		06 38	06 44	07 06		07 40	07 52					08 40	08 52	09 07	09 19				
Cardiff Central 7	a	00 22	01 04	01 14	02 23	06 54	07 00	07 26		07 54	08 12					08 54	09 10	09 29	09 38				

		AW	AW	XC	GW	GW	GW	GW	GW	AW	XC	GW	GW	GW	GW	AW	AW	GW	XC	GW	GW	GW	SW
				◇	1◇	◇	1◇	◇	1◇		◇	1◇	◇	1◇	◇			1◇	◇	1◇	1◇	◇	1◇
			N			U		C					V		C		N					C	
				🍴	☕		☕		☕			☕		☕				☕		☕	☕		
Bath Spa 7	d					09 09	09 25	09 35	10 00				10 08	10 25	10 35			11 00			11 25	11 35	11 46
Oldfield Park	d					09 12							10 10										
Keynsham	d					09 19							10 17										
Bristol Temple Meads 10	a					09 27	09 40	09 47	10 15				10 25	10 42	10 48			11 15			11 42	11 47	12 00
	d					09 41		09 54					10 41		10 54							11 53	
Filton Abbey Wood	d					09 48		10 01					10 48		11 00							12 00	
Bristol Parkway 7	a					09 51		10 04					10 51		11 04							12 04	
	d																						
Patchway	d																						
Pilning	d																						
Gloucester 7	d		08 58	09 22	09 37						10 22	10 37					10 58		11 22	11 37			
Lydney	d		09 17														11 17						
Chepstow	d		09 27														11 27						
Caldicot	d		09 35														11 35						
Severn Tunnel Jn	d		09 38														11 38						
Newport (South Wales)	a		09 50	10 04	10 18						11 04	11 19					11 50		12 04	12 17			
	d	09 40	09 52	10 06	10 20					10 40	11 05	11 19				11 40	11 52		12 05	12 20			
Cardiff Central 7	a	09 54	10 10	10 25	10 38					10 54	11 25	11 38				11 54	12 10		12 25	12 38			

For general notes see front of timetable
For details of catering facilities see Directory of Train Operators

- **A** To Swansea (Table 125)
- **B** From Taunton (Table 134)
- **C** From Portsmouth Harbour (Table 123)
- **D** From London Waterloo (Table 160)
- **E** From Cheltenham Spa (Table 57)
- **G** To Barry Island (Table 130)
- **H** To Maesteg (Table 128)
- **J** From Worcester Shrub Hill (Table 57)
- **K** From Birmingham New Street (Table 57)
- **L** From Salisbury (Table 123) to Gloucester (Table 134)
- **N** From Cheltenham Spa (Table 57) to Maesteg (Table 128)
- **Q** From Warminster (Table 123) to Great Malvern (Table 71)
- **U** From Weymouth (Table 123) to Gloucester (Table 134)
- **V** From Weymouth (Table 123) to Great Malvern (Table 71)

Saturdays
from 29 March

Bath Spa, Bristol and Gloucester → Cardiff

Network Diagram - see first page of Table 132

		GW	AW	AW	XC	GW	GW	GW	GW	GW	AW	XC	GW	GW	GW	GW	GW	AW	AW	XC	GW	GW	GW
		1◇			◇	1◇	◇	1◇	◇	1◇		◇	1◇	◇	1◇	◇	1◇			◇	1◇		1◇
				A			B		C					D		C			A			E	
		🍴				🍴		🍴		🍴			🍴		🍴		🍴				🍴		🍴
Bath Spa 7	d	12 00					12 18	12 25	12 35	13 00				13 18	13 25	13 35	14 03					14 09	14 25
Oldfield Park	d						12 20							13 21								14 12	
Keynsham	d						12 28							13 28								14 19	
Bristol Temple Meads 10	a	12 15					12 35	12 42	12 47	13 15				13 36	13 42	13 47	14 17					14 26	14 42
	d						12 41		12 53					13 41		13 53						14 41	
Filton Abbey Wood	d						12 48		13 00					13 48		14 00						14 48	
Bristol Parkway 7	a						12 51		13 04					13 51		14 04						14 51	
	d																						
Patchway	d																						
Pilning	d																						
Gloucester 7	d			11 58	12 22	12 37						13 22	13 37						13 58	14 22	14 37		
Lydney	d			12 17															14 17				
Chepstow	d			12 27															14 27				
Caldicot	d			12 35															14 37				
Severn Tunnel Jn	d			12 38															14 40				
Newport (South Wales)	a			12 50	13 04	13 19						14 04	14 17						14 52	15 04	15 19		
	d		12 40	12 52	13 05	13 20					13 40	14 06	14 20					14 40	14 54	15 06	15 20		
Cardiff Central 7	a		12 54	13 10	13 25	13 38					13 54	14 25	14 38					14 54	15 11	15 25	15 38		

		GW	SW	GW	AW	AW	XC	GW	GW	GW	GW	GW	AW	XC	GW	GW	GW	GW	AW	AW	XC	GW	GW
		◇	1◇	1◇			◇	1◇	◇	1◇	◇	1◇		◇	1◇	1◇	◇	1◇			◇	1◇	◇
		C				A			G		C						C			A			G
				🍴				🍴		🍴		🍴			🍴	🍴		🍴				🍴	
Bath Spa 7	d	14 35	14 46	15 00					15 13	15 25	15 35	16 00				16 25	16 35	17 00					17 08
Oldfield Park	d								15 16														17 11
Keynsham	d								15 23														17 18
Bristol Temple Meads 10	a	14 47	15 00	15 15					15 30	15 42	15 47	16 15				16 42	16 47	17 15					17 25
	d	14 53							15 41		15 53						16 53						17 41
Filton Abbey Wood	d	15 00							15 48		16 00						17 00						17 48
Bristol Parkway 7	a	15 04							15 51		16 04						17 04						17 51
	d																						
Patchway	d																						
Pilning	d																						
Gloucester 7	d					14 58	15 22	15 39						16 26	16 38					16 58	17 25	17 38	
Lydney	d					15 17														17 17			
Chepstow	d					15 27														17 27			
Caldicot	d					15 35														17 35			
Severn Tunnel Jn	d					15 38														17 38			
Newport (South Wales)	a					15 50	16 04	16 19						17 07	17 20					17 50	18 06	18 24	
	d				15 40	15 52	16 06	16 21					16 40	17 08	17 21				17 40	17 52	18 08	18 26	
Cardiff Central 7	a				15 54	16 07	16 25	16 38					16 54	17 25	17 37				17 54	18 10	18 25	18 41	

		GW	GW	GW	AW	AW	XC	GW	GW	GW	GW	AW	AW	XC	GW	GW	GW	GW	GW	AW	AW	GW	GW
		1◇	◇	1◇			◇	1◇	1◇	◇	1◇			◇	1◇	◇	1◇	◇	1◇			1◇	
			C			A				C			A			H		C			A		J
		🍴		🍴				🍴	🍴		🍴				🍴		🍴		🍴			🍴	
Bath Spa 7	d	17 25	17 35	18 00					18 25	18 35	19 00					19 08	19 25	19 35	20 01				20 18
Oldfield Park	d															19 11							20 21
Keynsham	d															19 18							20 28
Bristol Temple Meads 10	a	17 42	17 47	18 15					18 42	18 47	19 15					19 27	19 42	19 47	20 15				20 35
	d		17 53							18 53						19 40		19 53					20 41
Filton Abbey Wood	d		18 00							19 00						19 48		20 00					20 48
Bristol Parkway 7	a		18 04							19 04						19 51		20 04					20 51
	d																						
Patchway	d																						
Pilning	d																						
Gloucester 7	d					17 58	18 30	18 38					18 58	19 25	19 35						19 58	20 33	
Lydney	d					18 17							19 17								20 17		
Chepstow	d					18 27							19 27								20 27		
Caldicot	d					18 35							19 34								20 35		
Severn Tunnel Jn	d					18 38							19 37								20 38		
Newport (South Wales)	a					18 50	19 12	19 20					19 50	20 06	20 16						20 50	21 15	
	d				18 40	18 52	19 14	19 21				19 40	19 52	20 08	20 16					20 44	20 52	21 15	
Cardiff Central 7	a				18 54	19 10	19 33	19 38				19 57	20 10	20 25	20 36					20 59	21 10	21 37	

For general notes see front of timetable
For details of catering facilities see Directory of Train Operators

- **A** From Cheltenham Spa (Table 57) to Maesteg (Table 128)
- **B** From Brighton (Table 123) to Worcester Foregate Street (Table 71)
- **C** From Portsmouth Harbour (Table 123)
- **D** From Weymouth (Table 123) to Gloucester (Table 134)
- **E** From Southampton Central (Table 123) to Great Malvern (Table 71)
- **G** From Westbury (Table 123) to Gloucester (Table 134)
- **H** From Westbury (Table 123) to Cheltenham Spa (Table 57)
- **J** From Brighton (Table 123) to Cheltenham Spa (Table 57)

Table 132

Saturdays

from 29 March

Bath Spa, Bristol and Gloucester → Cardiff

Network Diagram - see first page of Table 132

		GW	GW	GW	AW	GW	GW	AW		GW	GW	SW	GW	GW	AW	AW		GW	GW	GW	GW	AW	AW	GW		
		1◇	◇	1◇		1◇	1◇			1◇	◇	1◇	1◇	◇				1◇	◇	1◇				1◇		
			A								A	B				C			A							
		☕		☕		☕	☕	🚌		☕			☕		🚌			☕		☕		🚌				
Bath Spa 7	d	20 25	20 35	21 00			21 30				21 39	21 51	22 00	22 08					22 35	23 00	23 08					
Oldfield Park	d													22 10							23 10					
Keynsham	d											21 59		22 18							23 17					
Bristol Temple Meads 10	a	20 42	20 47	21 15			21 47				21 51	22 06	22 15	22 27					22 48	23 15	23 25					
	d		20 53								21 54								22 54							
Filton Abbey Wood	d		21 00								22 02								23 01							
Bristol Parkway 7	a		21 04								22 06								23 04							
	d																									
Patchway	d																									
Pilning	d																									
Gloucester 7	d					21 07				21 34						21 58		22 42					22 58	23 53		
Lydney	d															22 17							23 17			
Chepstow	d															22 27							23 27			
Caldicot	d															22 35							23 35			
Severn Tunnel Jn	d															22 38							23 38			
Newport (South Wales)	a					21 49				22 24						22 55		23 32					23 57	00 42		
	d				21 50	21 53		22 00		22 25					22 30	22 57		23 32				23 30	23 58	00 42		
Cardiff Central 7	a				22 11	22 13		22 35		22 45					23 05	23 18		23 57				00 05	00 18	01 05		

Sundays

until 27 January

		GW	GW	AW	GW		AW	GW	GW	GW		XC	GW	AW	AW		GW	GW	XC	GW		GW	GW	AW	GW	GW
		1◇	1◇	◇	1◇		◇	◇	1◇	1◇				◇			1◇	1◇	◇	◇		1◇	1◇		1◇	1◇
								D												A				C		
			☕		☕				☕	☕							☕	☕		🛒		☕	☕		☕	☕
Bath Spa 7	d		00 05		01 06				09 49				10 25				10 49			11 25		11 48			12 46	
Oldfield Park	d												10 27							11 28						
Keynsham	d												10 35							11 35						
Bristol Temple Meads 10	a		00 20		01 21				10 01				10 43				11 02			11 43		12 04			13 02	
	d							09 50												11 48						
Filton Abbey Wood	d							09 57												11 55						
Bristol Parkway 7	a																									
	d	23p29								10 16								11 10					12 10			13 10
Patchway	d																			11 59						
Pilning	d																									
Gloucester 7	d											10 11			10 33				11 22					12 33		
Lydney	d														10 52									12 52		
Chepstow	d														11 02									13 02		
Caldicot	d														11 10									13 10		
Severn Tunnel Jn	d							10 10							11 13					12 10				13 13		
Newport (South Wales)	a	00 01						10 21		10 37		10 54			11 25			11 31	12 04	12 24			12 31	13 25		13 31
	d	00 01		00 55			09 10	10 23		10 39		10 54		11 02	11 27			11 33	12 05	12 25			12 32	13 27		13 32
Cardiff Central 7	a	00 23		01 19			09 25	10 37		10 54		11 13		11 17	11 45			11 48	12 25	12 39			12 48	13 45		13 48

		AW		XC	GW	GW	GW		XC	AW	GW	AW		GW	SW	GW	AW		XC	GW	GW	GW		GW	XC	GW
																	R									
		◇		◇	◇	1◇	1◇		◇	◇	◇			1◇	1◇	1◇			◇	◇	1◇	1◇		◇	◇	◇
												C														A
		🛒			🛒	☕	☕			🛒				☕		☕	🛒			🛒	☕	☕				🛒
Bath Spa 7	d				13 26	13 46					14 25			14 47	14 54					15 28	15 47			16 01		16 28
Oldfield Park	d				13 29						14 27													16 03		
Keynsham	d				13 36						14 35													16 12		
Bristol Temple Meads 10	a				13 43	14 01					14 42			15 00	15 06					15 40	16 00			16 19		16 41
	d				13 48						14 48									15 48						16 48
Filton Abbey Wood	d				13 55						14 55									15 55						16 55
Bristol Parkway 7	a																									
	d						14 10									15 10						16 10				
Patchway	d																									16 59
Pilning	d																									
Gloucester 7	d			13 26					14 22			14 32							15 26						16 26	
Lydney	d											14 51														
Chepstow	d											15 01														
Caldicot	d											15 09														
Severn Tunnel Jn	d				14 08						15 08	15 12								16 08						17 10
Newport (South Wales)	a			14 08	14 20		14 31		15 04		15 20	15 24				15 32			16 08	16 21		16 31			17 08	17 23
	d	13 38		14 09	14 21		14 32		15 05	15 11	15 21	15 26				15 33	16 02		16 08	16 21		16 32			17 08	17 23
Cardiff Central 7	a	13 54		14 29	14 35		14 48		15 25	15 31	15 38	15 45				15 48	16 17		16 29	16 36		16 48			17 29	17 38

For general notes see front of timetable
For details of catering facilities see Directory of Train Operators

A From Portsmouth Harbour (Table 123)
B From London Waterloo (Table 160)
C From Cheltenham Spa (Table 57)
D From Exeter St Davids (Table 135)

Table 132

until 27 January

Bath Spa, Bristol and Gloucester → Cardiff

Network Diagram - see first page of Table 132

		AW	GW	GW	GW	AW	XC	GW	GW	GW	GW	AW	XC	GW		GW	AW	GW	GW		GW	AW	XC	AW		XC
			1◇	1◇	1◇	R	◇	◇	1◇	1◇	1◇	R	◇	1◇		◇		1◇	1◇		◇		R 1	R		◇
		A															A									
			☕	☕		🛒		🛒	☕	☕	☕	🛒		☕		🛒		☕	☕				☕	🛒		
Bath Spa 7	d		16 47		17 08			17 26	17 47	17 25						18 25		18 46			19 04					
Oldfield Park	d				17 11			17 29													19 06					
Keynsham	d				17 18			17 36													19 14					
Bristol Temple Meads 10	a		17 00		17 25			17 43	18 00	17 42						18 38		19 01			19 22					
	d				17 41			17 48								18 48							19 24			
Filton Abbey Wood	d				17 48			17 55								18 56										
Bristol Parkway 7	a				17 51																					
	d			17 10							18 14			18 46					19 16							
Patchway	d																									
Pilning	d																									
Gloucester 7	d	16 33					17 26						18 23				18 33									19 26
Lydney	d	16 52															18 52									
Chepstow	d	17 02															19 02									
Caldicot	d	17 11															19 11									
Severn Tunnel Jn	d	17 14						18 08								19 09	19 14									
Newport (South Wales)	a	17 27		17 33			18 08	18 21			18 35		19 05	19 11		19 21	19 26		19 37				19 51			20 12
	d	17 27		17 33		18 01	18 09	18 21			18 35	18 52	19 06	19 12		19 22	19 27		19 38			19 46	19 52	20 02		20 13
Cardiff Central 7	a	17 45		17 50		18 16	18 26	18 36			18 52	19 13	19 26	19 27		19 38	19 45		19 54			20 05	20 11	20 17		20 33

		GW	GW	GW	GW		AW	GW	AW	GW		GW	SW	GW	AW		GW	GW	GW	GW	AW	GW	GW	GW		
		◇	1◇	1◇	◇		R	◇		1◇		1◇	1◇	◇	R		◇	1◇	1◇	◇		1◇	1◇	1◇		
		B							A				C				B									
		🛒	☕	☕			🛒	🛒		☕		☕			🛒		🛒	☕		🛒				☕		
Bath Spa 7	d	19 28	19 47		20 02			20 28		20 47			21 01	21 11			21 28	21 46		22 28		22 47		23 49		
Oldfield Park	d				20 04									21 13												
Keynsham	d				20 13								21 08	21 21												
Bristol Temple Meads 10	a	19 40	20 00		20 20			20 40		21 00			21 16	21 28			21 40	22 02		22 41		23 03		00 03		
	d	19 48						20 48									21 48			22 48						
Filton Abbey Wood	d	19 55						20 55									21 57			22 55						
Bristol Parkway 7	a																									
	d			20 14								21 08							22 11				23 14			
Patchway	d	19 59															22 01									
Pilning	d																									
Gloucester 7	d								20 33												22 33					
Lydney	d								20 52												22 52					
Chepstow	d								21 02												23 02					
Caldicot	d								21 10												23 10					
Severn Tunnel Jn	d	20 10						21 08	21 13								22 14			23 10	23 15					
Newport (South Wales)	a	20 23		20 35				21 20	21 25			21 30					22 32		22 38	23 31	23 35		23 42			
	d	20 23		20 37			21 02	21 21	21 27			21 32			22 04		22 32		22 39	23 31	23 36		23 43			
Cardiff Central 7	a	20 38		20 52			21 21	21 38	21 46			21 47			22 28		22 51		22 59	23 50	23 56		00 02			

Sundays

3 February to 23 March

		GW	GW	AW	GW		AW	GW	GW	GW		XC	GW	GW	AW		AW	GW	XC	GW		GW	GW	AW	GW	AW
		1◇	1◇	◇			◇	◇	1◇	1◇				1◇	◇			1◇	◇	◇		1◇	1◇		1◇	◇
										D								D		B			E	A		
					🚌																					
			☕					🛒	☕	☕				☕				☕		🛒		☕	☕		☕	🛒
Bath Spa 7	d	23p49	00 15		01 44				09 39	09 45			10 25	10 39				10 54		11 25		11 39	11 54		12 39	
Oldfield Park	d												10 27							11 28						
Keynsham	d												10 35							11 35						
Bristol Temple Meads 10	a	00 02	00 29		02 18				09 53	09 57			10 43	10 53				11 07		11 43		11 51	12 06		12 51	
	d	00 08						09 50		10 04								11 15		11 48			12 15			
Filton Abbey Wood	d							09 57												11 55						
Bristol Parkway 7	a									10 12								11 27					12 27			
	d									10 19								11 34					12 34			
Patchway	d																			11 59						
Pilning	d																									
Gloucester 7	d											10 11					10 33		11 22					12 33		
Lydney	d																10 52							12 52		
Chepstow	d																11 02							13 02		
Caldicot	d																11 10							13 10		
Severn Tunnel Jn	d							10 10									11 13			12 10				13 13		
Newport (South Wales)	a	00 37						10 21		10 40		10 54					11 25	11 55	12 04	12 23			12 55	13 25		
	d	00 37		00 55			09 10	10 23		10 42		10 54			11 02		11 27	11 57	12 05	12 23			12 56	13 27		13 38
Cardiff Central 7	a	01 00		01 19			09 25	10 37		10 57		11 13			11 17		11 45	12 12	12 25	12 38			13 12	13 45		13 54

For general notes see front of timetable
For details of catering facilities see Directory of Train Operators

A From Cheltenham Spa (Table 57)
B From Portsmouth Harbour (Table 123)
C From London Waterloo (Table 160)
D To Swansea (Table 125)
E To Carmarthen (Table 128)

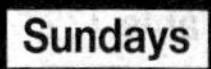

Sundays

3 February to 23 March

Bath Spa, Bristol and Gloucester → Cardiff

Network Diagram - see first page of Table 132

		GW	XC	GW	GW	GW	XC	AW	GW	AW	GW	SW	GW	AW	XC	GW	GW	GW	GW	XC	GW
		1◇	◇	◇	1◇	1◇	◇	◇	◇		1◇	1◇	1◇	R	◇	◇	1◇	1◇	◇	◇	◇
		A				B				C			A					B			D
		🍴		🛒	🍴	🍴		🛒			🍴		🍴	🛒		🛒	🍴	🍴			🛒
Bath Spa 7	d	12 52		13 26	13 39	13 56			14 25		14 38	14 54	15 00			15 28	15 43	15 54	16 07		16 28
Oldfield Park	d			13 29					14 27										16 09		
Keynsham	d			13 36					14 35										16 18		
Bristol Temple Meads 10	a	13 05		13 43	13 51	14 09			14 42		14 51	15 06	15 12			15 40	15 57	16 07	16 25		16 41
	d	13 15		13 48		14 15			14 48				15 19			15 48		16 15			16 48
Filton Abbey Wood	d			13 55					14 55							15 55					16 55
Bristol Parkway 7	a	13 27				14 27							15 27					16 27			
	d	13 34				14 34							15 34					16 34			
Patchway	d																				16 59
Pilning	d																				
Gloucester 7	d		13 26				14 22			14 32					15 26					16 26	
Lydney	d									14 51											
Chepstow	d									15 01											
Caldicot	d									15 09											
Severn Tunnel Jn	d			14 08					15 08	15 12						16 08					17 10
Newport (South Wales)	a	13 55	14 08	14 20		14 55	15 04		15 20	15 24			15 55		16 08	16 20		16 55		17 08	17 23
	d	13 57	14 09	14 21		14 56	15 05	15 11	15 21	15 26			15 57	16 02	16 08	16 21		16 56		17 08	17 23
Cardiff Central 7	a	14 12	14 29	14 35		15 12	15 25	15 31	15 38	15 45			16 12	16 17	16 29	16 35		17 12		17 29	17 38

		AW	GW	GW	AW	XC	GW	GW	AW	GW	XC	GW	AW	GW	AW	GW	GW	GW	AW	XC	GW
			1◇	1◇	R	◇	◇	1◇	R	1◇	◇	◇		1◇		1◇	◇	1◇	R	◇	◇
		C		A						A			C			A					D
			🍴	🍴	🛒		🛒	🍴	🛒	🍴		🛒		🍴		🍴		🍴	🛒		🛒
Bath Spa 7	d		16 43	16 52			17 26	17 43		17 54		18 25		18 44		18 52	19 04	19 12			19 28
Oldfield Park	d						17 29										19 06				
Keynsham	d						17 36										19 14				
Bristol Temple Meads 10	a		16 57	17 05			17 43	17 57		18 07		18 38		18 56		19 05	19 22	19 28			19 40
	d			17 15			17 48			18 15		18 48				19 15					19 48
Filton Abbey Wood	d						17 55					18 55									19 55
Bristol Parkway 7	a			17 27						18 27						19 27					
	d			17 34						18 34						19 34					
Patchway	d																				19 59
Pilning	d																				
Gloucester 7	d	16 33				17 26					18 23		18 33							19 26	
Lydney	d	16 52											18 52								
Chepstow	d	17 02											19 02								
Caldicot	d	17 11											19 11								
Severn Tunnel Jn	d	17 14					18 08					19 08	19 14								20 10
Newport (South Wales)	a	17 27		17 55		18 08	18 20			18 55	19 05	19 20	19 26			19 55				20 12	20 23
	d	17 27		17 56	18 03	18 09	18 21		18 52	18 55	19 06	19 21	19 27		19 46	19 56			20 02	20 13	20 23
Cardiff Central 7	a	17 45		18 12	18 18	18 26	18 35		19 13	19 13	19 26	19 38	19 45		20 05	20 12			20 17	20 33	20 38

		GW	GW	GW	AW	GW	AW	GW	SW	GW	GW	AW	GW	GW	GW	GW	AW	GW	GW	GW
		1◇	1◇	◇	R	◇		1◇	1◇	1◇	◇	R	◇	1◇	1◇	◇		1◇	1◇	1◇
			A				C		E	A			D		A					A
		🍴	🍴		🛒	🛒		🍴		🍴		🛒	🛒	🍴	🍴	🛒		🍴	🍴	🍴
Bath Spa 7	d	19 47	19 59	20 12		20 28		20 46	20 53	20 59	21 11		21 28	21 47	22 01	22 28		22 50	23 07	23 15
Oldfield Park	d			20 14							21 13									
Keynsham	d			20 23					21 00		21 21									
Bristol Temple Meads 10	a	19 59	20 11	20 30		20 40		20 59	21 08	21 12	21 28		21 40	21 59	22 14	22 41		23 04	23 23	23 27
	d		20 18			20 48				21 19			21 48		22 20	22 48				23 34
Filton Abbey Wood	d					20 55							21 57			22 55				
Bristol Parkway 7	a		20 27							21 27					22 29					23 42
	d		20 34							21 34					22 35					23 49
Patchway	d												22 01							
Pilning	d																			
Gloucester 7	d						20 33										22 33			
Lydney	d						20 52										22 52			
Chepstow	d						21 02										23 02			
Caldicot	d						21 10										23 10			
Severn Tunnel Jn	d					21 08	21 13						22 14			23 08	23 15			
Newport (South Wales)	a		20 55			21 20	21 25			21 56			22 27		23 03	23 28	23 35			00 11
	d		20 57		21 02	21 21	21 27			21 57		22 04	22 27		23 05	23 28	23 36			00 12
Cardiff Central 7	a		21 12		21 21	21 38	21 46			22 16		22 28	22 46		23 24	23 47	23 56			00 32

For general notes see front of timetable
For details of catering facilities see Directory of Train Operators

A To Swansea (Table 125)
B To Carmarthen (Table 128)
C From Cheltenham Spa (Table 57)
D From Portsmouth Harbour (Table 123)
E From London Waterloo (Table 160)

Sundays
from 30 March

Bath Spa, Bristol and Gloucester → Cardiff

Network Diagram - see first page of Table 132

		GW	GW	AW	GW	AW	GW	GW	XC	GW	GW	GW	AW	AW	AW	XC	GW	GW	GW	GW	AW	GW
		1 ◇	1 ◇		1 ◇	◇	1 ◇	1 ◇			1 ◇	1 ◇				◇	1 ◇	◇ A	1 ◇	1 ◇	B	1 ◇
			☕	🚌	☕		☕	☕			☕	☕			🚌		☕	🚲	☕	☕		☕
Bath Spa 7	d		00 05		01 06		09 40			10 19	10 29	10 46						11 25	11 46			12 46
Oldfield Park	d									10 21								11 28				
Keynsham	d									10 29								11 35				
Bristol Temple Meads 10	a		00 20		01 21		09 54			10 37	10 41	11 00						11 43	12 00			13 00
	d																	11 48				
Filton Abbey Wood	d																	11 55				
Bristol Parkway 7	a																	11 58				
	d																					
Patchway	d																					
Pilning	d																					
Gloucester 7	d	23p53						10 08	10 11					10 33		11 22	11 33			12 33	12 37	
Lydney	d													10 52							12 56	
Chepstow	d													11 02							13 06	
Caldicot	d													11 10							13 14	
Severn Tunnel Jn	d													11 13							13 17	
Newport (South Wales)	a	00 42						10 50	10 54					11 25		12 04	12 16			13 15	13 29	
	d	00 42		00 50		09 10		10 52	10 55				11 02	11 27	11 40	12 05	12 18			13 16	13 31	
Cardiff Central 7	a	01 05		01 25		09 25		11 07	11 13				11 17	11 45	12 10	12 25	12 33			13 32	13 49	

		XC	GW	GW	GW	AW	XC	GW	AW	GW	GW	SW	AW	AW	XC	GW	GW	GW	GW	XC	AW	GW
		◇	1 ◇	◇ A	1 ◇		◇	1 ◇	B	◇ C	1 ◇	1 ◇	1		◇	1 ◇	◇ A	1 ◇	◇	◇		1 ◇
			☕	🚲	☕	🚌		☕			☕			🚌		☕	🚲	☕			🚌	☕
Bath Spa 7	d			13 26	13 48					14 25	14 46	14 54					15 28	15 46	16 01			
Oldfield Park	d			13 29						14 27									16 03			
Keynsham	d			13 36						14 35									16 12			
Bristol Temple Meads 10	a			13 43	14 02					14 42	15 00	15 06					15 40	16 00	16 19			
	d			13 48						14 48							15 48					
Filton Abbey Wood	d			13 55						14 55							15 55					
Bristol Parkway 7	a			13 58						14 58							15 58					
	d																					
Patchway	d																					
Pilning	d																					
Gloucester 7	d	13 26	13 33				14 22	14 33	14 37						15 26	15 33				16 26		16 33
Lydney	d								14 56													
Chepstow	d								15 06													
Caldicot	d								15 14													
Severn Tunnel Jn	d								15 17													
Newport (South Wales)	a	14 08	14 15				15 04	15 16	15 29						16 08	16 15				17 08		17 15
	d	14 09	14 17			14 25	15 05	15 17	15 31				16 00	15 54	16 08	16 17				17 08	16 55	17 16
Cardiff Central 7	a	14 29	14 32			15 00	15 25	15 33	15 49				16 14	16 24	16 29	16 32				17 29	17 30	17 32

		AW	GW	GW	XC	GW	GW	GW	AW	XC	GW	AW	GW	GW	GW	GW	AW	XC	GW	GW	GW	GW
		B	◇ A	1 ◇	◇	1 ◇	◇ A	1 ◇		◇	1 ◇	B	◇ A	1 ◇	◇	1 ◇		◇	1 ◇	◇ A	1 ◇	◇
			🚲	☕		☕	🚲	☕	🚌		☕		🚲	☕		☕	🚌		☕	🚲	☕	
Bath Spa 7	d		16 28	16 48			17 26	17 46					18 25	18 46	19 04	19 16				19 32	19 46	20 00
Oldfield Park	d						17 29								19 06							20 02
Keynsham	d						17 36								19 14							20 11
Bristol Temple Meads 10	a		16 41	17 02			17 43	18 00					18 38	19 00	19 22	19 31				19 45	20 00	20 18
	d		16 48				17 48						18 48							19 49		
Filton Abbey Wood	d		16 55				17 55						18 55							19 56		
Bristol Parkway 7	a		16 58				17 58						18 58							20 00		
	d																					
Patchway	d																					
Pilning	d																					
Gloucester 7	d	16 37			17 26	17 39				18 23	18 37	18 42						19 26	19 33			
Lydney	d	16 56										19 01										
Chepstow	d	17 06										19 11										
Caldicot	d	17 14										19 19										
Severn Tunnel Jn	d	17 17										19 22										
Newport (South Wales)	a	17 30			18 08	18 21				19 05	19 18	19 34						20 08	20 15			
	d	17 30			18 09	18 22			18 45	19 06	19 18	19 36					19 35	20 09	20 16			
Cardiff Central 7	a	17 48			18 26	18 38			19 20	19 26	19 39	19 53					20 10	20 29	20 32			

		GW	GW	AW	AW	AW	GW	SW	GW	AW	GW	GW	GW	GW	GW	GW	GW	AW	AW	GW	GW
		1 ◇	◇ A			B	1 ◇	1 ◇ D	◇		1 ◇	◇ A	1 ◇	1 ◇	◇ A	◇	1 ◇			1 ◇	1 ◇
		☕	🚲		🚌		☕			🚌	☕	🚲	☕	☕	🚲		☕	🚌		☕	☕
Bath Spa 7	d		20 28				20 46	21 01	21 13			21 28	21 48		22 28	22 39	22 48				23 49
Oldfield Park	d								21 15							22 41					
Keynsham	d							21 08	21 23							22 50					
Bristol Temple Meads 10	a		20 40				21 00	21 16	21 30			21 40	22 04		22 41	22 57	23 04				00 03
	d		20 48									21 48			22 48						
Filton Abbey Wood	d		20 55									21 57			22 55						
Bristol Parkway 7	a		20 58									22 00			22 58						
	d																				
Patchway	d																				
Pilning	d																				
Gloucester 7	d	20 22				20 33					21 33			22 33					22 37	23 35	
Lydney	d					20 52													22 56		
Chepstow	d					21 02													23 06		
Caldicot	d					21 10													23 14		
Severn Tunnel Jn	d					21 13													23 19		
Newport (South Wales)	a	21 04				21 25					22 21			23 21					23 36	00 23	
	d	21 06		21 16	21 00	21 27				22 00	22 23			23 23				23 15	23 37	00 24	
Cardiff Central 7	a	21 21		21 30	21 35	21 46				22 35	22 44			23 42				23 50	23 57	00 44	

For general notes see front of timetable
For details of catering facilities see Directory of Train Operators

A From Portsmouth Harbour (Table 123)
B From Cheltenham Spa (Table 57)
C From Brighton (Table 123)
D From London Waterloo (Table 160)

Table 133

Bristol → Avonmouth and Severn Beach

Network Diagram - see first page of Table 132

Mondays to Fridays

Miles			GW	GW	GW	GW	GW	GW	GW	GW (bus)	GW	GW ◇	GW	GW	GW	GW ◇	GW	GW		GW	GW	GW (bus)	GW	GW	GW (bus)	GW
0	Bristol Temple Meads 10	d	05 31	06 09	06 22	06 45	06 50	07 19	07 45		08 09	08 13	08 19	08 46	08 49	09 10	09 19	09 49		10 19	10 49		11 19	11 49		12 19
1	Lawrence Hill	d	05 34	06 12	06 25	06 48	06 54	07 22	07 48		08 12	08 16	08 22	08 49	08 52	09 13	09 22	09 52		10 22	10 51		11 22	11 51		12 22
1½	Stapleton Road	d	05 36	06 14	06a27	06 50	06a56	07a24	07a50		08 14	08a18	08a24	08a51	08 55	09a15	09a24	09 54		10a24	10 53		11a24	11 53		12a24
2¾	Montpelier	d	05 40	06 18		06 54					08 18				08 59			09 58			10 58			11 58		
3¼	Redland	d	05 42	06 20		06 56					08 20				09 01			10 00			11 00			12 00		
4	Clifton Down	d	05 45	06b32		06 59					08c30				09 04			10 03			11 03			12 03		
6	Sea Mills	d	05 49	06 36		07 03					08 34				09 08			10 07			11 07			12 07		
7¼	Shirehampton	d	05 52	06 39		07 06					08 38				09 11			10 10			11 10			12 10		
9	Avonmouth 2	d	05 56	06a44		07 10				08 18	08 42				09e19			10a15			11a15	11 18		12a15	12 18	
10	St Andrews Road	d	05x59			07x13				08x21	08x45				09x22							11x21			12x21	
13½	Severn Beach	a	06 08			07 22				08 33	08 53				09 31							11 33			12 33	

		GW	GW (bus)	GW	GW	GW (bus)	GW	GW	GW (bus)	GW	GW	GW	GW (bus)	GW	GW	GW	GW (bus)	GW	GW	GW	GW	GW	GW	GW
Bristol Temple Meads 10	d	12 49		13 19	13 49		14 19	14 49		15 19	15 49	16 04		16 19	16 49	17 10		17 19	17 49	18 19	19 18	20 19	21 19	21 45
Lawrence Hill	d	12 51		13 22	13 51		14 22	14 51		15 22	15 51	16 07		16 22	16 51	17 13		17 22	17 51	18 22	19 21	20 22	21 22	21 48
Stapleton Road	d	12 53		13a24	13 53		14a24	14 53		15a24	15 53	16a09		16a24	16 53	17a15		17a24	17 53	18a24	19 23	20a24	21a24	21 50
Montpelier	d	12 58			13 58			14 58			15 58				16 58				17 58		19 27			21 53
Redland	d	13 00			14 00			15 00			16 00				17 00				18 00		19 29			21 55
Clifton Down	d	13 03			14 03			15 03			16 03				17 03				18 03		19 32			21 58
Sea Mills	d	13 07			14 07			15 07			16 07				17 07				18 07		19 36			22 02
Shirehampton	d	13 10			14 10			15 10			16 10				17 10				18 10		19 39			22 06
Avonmouth 2	d	13a15	13 18		14a15	14 18		15a15	15 18		16a15		16 18		17a15		17 18		18 14		19 43			22 10
St Andrews Road	d		13x21			14x21			15x21				16x21				17x21		18x17		19x46			22x13
Severn Beach	a		13 33			14 33			15 33				16 33				17 33		18 26		19 55			22 22

Saturdays until 22 March

		GW	GW	GW	GW	GW	GW	GW	GW	GW	GW	GW	GW	GW	GW	GW	GW	GW
Bristol Temple Meads 10	d	06 06	06 50	07 13	07 46	08 13	08 19	09 13	09 19	10 13	10 19	11 13	11 19	12 13	12 19	13 13	13 19	14 13
Lawrence Hill	d	06 09	06 53	07 16	07 49	08 16	08 22	09 16	09 22	10 16	10 22	11 16	11 22	12 16	12 22	13 16	13 22	14 16
Stapleton Road	d	06 11	06a55	07 18	07a51	08 18	08a24	09 18	09a24	10 18	10a24	11 18	11a24	12 18	12a24	13 18	13a24	14 18
Montpelier	d	06 14		07 21		08 21		09 21		10 21		11 21		12 21		13 21		14 21
Redland	d	06 16		07 23		08 23		09 23		10 23		11 23		12 23		13 23		14 23
Clifton Down	d	06 19		07 26		08 26		09 26		10 26		11 26		12 26		13 26		14 26
Sea Mills	d	06 23		07 30		08 30		09 30		10 30		11 30		12 30		13 30		14 30
Shirehampton	d	06 27		07 34		08 34		09 34		10 34		11 34		12 34		13 34		14 34
Avonmouth 2	d	06 31		07 38		08 38		09 38		10 38		11 38		12 38		13 38		14 38
St Andrews Road	d	06x34		07x41		08x41		09x41		10x41		11x41		12x41		13x41		14x41
Severn Beach	a	06 41		07 48		08 48		09 48		10 48		11 48		12 48		13 48		14 48

		GW	GW	GW	GW	GW	GW	GW	GW	GW	GW	GW	GW	GW
Bristol Temple Meads 10	d	14 19	15 13	15 19	16 13	16 19	17 13	17 19	18 13	18 19	19 13	20 13	21 19	22 25
Lawrence Hill	d	14 22	15 16	15 22	16 16	16 22	17 16	17 22	18 16	18 22	19 16	20 16	21 22	22 28
Stapleton Road	d	14a24	15 18	15a24	16 18	16a24	17 18	17a24	18 18	18a24	19 18	20 18	21a24	22 30
Montpelier	d		15 21		16 21		17 21		18 21		19 21	20 21		22 33
Redland	d		15 23		16 23		17 23		18 23		19 23	20 23		22 35
Clifton Down	d		15 26		16 26		17 26		18 26		19 26	20 26		22 38
Sea Mills	d		15 30		16 30		17 30		18 30		19 30	20 30		22 42
Shirehampton	d		15 34		16 34		17 34		18 34		19 34	20 34		22 46
Avonmouth 2	d		15 38		16 38		17 38		18 38		19 38	20 38		22 50
St Andrews Road	d		15x41		16x41		17x41		18x41		19x41	20x41		22x53
Severn Beach	a		15 48		16 48		17 48		18 48		19 48	20 48		23 00

Saturdays from 29 March

		GW	GW	GW	GW	GW	GW	GW	GW	GW	GW	GW	GW	GW
Bristol Temple Meads 10	d	06 06	07 13	07 46	08 13	09 13	10 13	11 13	11 19	12 13	12 19	13 13	13 19	14 13
Lawrence Hill	d	06 09	07 16	07 49	08 16	09 16	10 16	11 16	11 22	12 16	12 22	13 16	13 22	14 16
Stapleton Road	d	06 11	07 18	07a51	08 18	09 18	10 18	11 18	11a24	12 18	12a24	13 18	13a24	14 18
Montpelier	d	06 14	07 21		08 21	09 21	10 21	11 21		12 21		13 21		14 21
Redland	d	06 16	07 23		08 23	09 23	10 23	11 23		12 23		13 23		14 23
Clifton Down	d	06 19	07 26		08 26	09 26	10 26	11 26		12 26		13 26		14 26
Sea Mills	d	06 23	07 30		08 30	09 30	10 30	11 30		12 30		13 30		14 30
Shirehampton	d	06 27	07 34		08 34	09 34	10 34	11 34		12 34		13 34		14 34
Avonmouth 2	d	06 31	07 38		08 38	09 38	10 38	11 38		12 38		13 38		14 38
St Andrews Road	d	06x34	07x41		08x41	09x41	10x41	11x41		12x41		13x41		14x41
Severn Beach	a	06 41	07 48		08 48	09 48	10 48	11 48		12 48		13 48		14 48

For general notes see front of timetable
For details of catering facilities see Directory of Train Operators

b Arr. 0622
c Arr. 0822
e Arr. 0916

The bus service between Avonmouth and Severn Beach is operated by South Gloucestershire County Council. Valid Rail Tickets are accepted.

from 29 March

Bristol → Avonmouth and Severn Beach

Network Diagram - see first page of Table 132

		GW		GW		GW		GW		GW		GW		GW		GW		GW		GW		GW	GW	GW		
Bristol Temple Meads 10	d	14 19		15 13		15 19		16 13		16 19		17 13		17 19		18 13		18 19		19 13		20 13	20 19	22 25		
Lawrence Hill	d	14 22		15 16		15 22		16 16		16 22		17 16		17 22		18 16		18 22		19 16		20 16	20 22	22 28		
Stapleton Road	d	14a24		15 18		15a24		16 18		16a24		17 18		17a24		18 18		18a24		19 18		20 18	20a24	22 30		
Montpelier	d			15 21				16 21				17 21				18 21				19 21		20 21		22 33		
Redland	d			15 23				16 23				17 23				18 23				19 23		20 23		22 35		
Clifton Down	d			15 26				16 26				17 26				18 26				19 26		20 26		22 38		
Sea Mills	d			15 30				16 30				17 30				18 30				19 30		20 30		22 42		
Shirehampton	d			15 34				16 34				17 34				18 34				19 34		20 34		22 46		
Avonmouth 2	d			15 38				16 38				17 38				18 38				19 38		20 38		22 50		
St Andrews Road	d			15x41				16x41				17x41				18x41				19x41		20x41		22x53		
Severn Beach	a			15 48				16 48				17 48				18 48				19 48		20 48		23 00		

For general notes see front of timetable
For details of catering facilities see
Directory of Train Operators

No Sunday Service

The bus service between Avonmouth and Severn Beach is operated by South Gloucestershire County Council. Valid Rail Tickets are accepted.

Severn Beach and Avonmouth → Bristol

Network Diagram - see first page of Table 132

Miles			GW	GW	GW	GW	GW		GW	GW	GW	GW	GW		GW	GW	GW	GW	GW		GW	GW	GW	GW	GW	GW
									🚌		◇							🚌	◇			🚌		🚌		
0	**Severn Beach**	d	06 09				07 23		07 59			09 05			09 36			10 59				11 59		12 59		
3½	St Andrews Road	d	06x15				07x29		08x11			09x11			09x42			11x11				12x11		13x11		
4½	Avonmouth 2	d	06 19		06 46		07 33		08a14	08 18		09 17			09 46		10 18	11a14			11 18	12a14	12 18	13a14		13 18
6	Shirehampton	d	06 23		06 49		07 37			08 21		09 21			09 50		10 21				11 21		12 21			13 21
7½	Sea Mills	d	06 27		06 53		07 41			08 25		09 25			09 54		10 25				11 25		12 25			13 25
9½	Clifton Down	d	06 32		07b04		07 46			08c33		09 30			10e03		10 30				11 30		12 30			13 30
10¼	Redland	d	06 35		07 06		07 48			08 35		09 32			10 05		10 33				11 33		12 33			13 33
10¾	Montpelier	d	06 37		07 08		07 50			08 37		09 34			10 07		10 35				11 35		12 35			13 35
12	Stapleton Road	d	06 41	07 09	07 13	07 34	07 55				09 29	09 39	09 44			10 29	10 39		11 29		11 39		12 39		13 29	13 39
12½	Lawrence Hill	d	06 44	07 11	07 15	07 36	07 57				09 31	09 41				10 31	10 41		11 31		11 42		12 42		13 31	13 42
13½	**Bristol Temple Meads 10**	a	06 47	07 15	07 20	07 40	08 01			08 44	09 35	09 46	09 48		10 15	10 34	10 46		11 35		11 46		12 46		13 34	13 46

		GW		GW	GW	GW	GW	GW		GW	GW	GW	GW	GW		GW	GW	GW	GW	GW	GW	GW	GW	GW		
		🚌		◇			🚌			🚌			🚌													
Severn Beach	d	13 59					14 59			15 59			16 59							18 36			21 35			
St Andrews Road	d	14x11					15x11			16x11			17x11							18x42			21x41			
Avonmouth 2	d	14a14			14 18		15a14	15 18		16a14	16 18		17a14			17 18				18 46			21 45			
Shirehampton	d				14 21			15 21			16 21					17 21				18 50			21 49			
Sea Mills	d				14 25			15 25			16 25					17 25				18 54			21 53			
Clifton Down	d				14 30			15 30			16 30					17 30				18 59			22f00			
Redland	d				14 33			15 33			16 33					17 33				19 01			22 02			
Montpelier	d				14 35			15 35			16 35					17 35				19 03			22 04			
Stapleton Road	d			14 29	14 39	14 56		15 39			16 39	16 57				17 39	17 57	18 19	18 29	19 08	19 29	21 47	22 09	23 57		
Lawrence Hill	d			14 31	14 42	14 58		15 42			16 42	16 59		17 21		17 42	17 59	18 21	18 31	19 10	19 31	21 50	22 11	23 59		
Bristol Temple Meads 10	a			14 34	14 46	15 03		15 46			16 46	17 03		17 24		17 46	18 03	18 25	18 34	19 15	19 36	21 53	22 15	00 04		

Saturdays

until 22 March

		GW		GW		GW		GW		GW		GW		GW		GW		GW		GW		GW		GW
																◇								
Severn Beach	d	07 03				08 03				09 03				10 03				11 03				12 03				13 03
St Andrews Road	d	07x09				08x09				09x09				10x09				11x09				12x09				13x09
Avonmouth 2	d	07 13				08 13				09 13				10 13				11 13				12 13				13 13
Shirehampton	d	07 17				08 17				09 17				10 17				11 17				12 17				13 17
Sea Mills	d	07 21				08 21				09 21				10 21				11 21				12 21				13 21
Clifton Down	d	07 27				08 27				09 27				10 27				11 27				12 27				13 27
Redland	d	07 29				08 29				09 29				10 29				11 29				12 29				13 29
Montpelier	d	07 31				08 31				09 31				10 31				11 31				12 31				13 31
Stapleton Road	d	07 36		08 29		08 36		09 29		09 36		10 27		10 36		11 29		11 36		12 29		12 36		13 27		13 36
Lawrence Hill	d	07 38		08 31		08 38		09 31		09 38		10 29		10 38		11 31		11 38		12 31		12 38		13 29		13 38
Bristol Temple Meads 10	a	07 41		08 34		08 41		09 35		09 41		10 35		10 41		11 35		11 41		12 35		12 41		13 35		13 41

		GW		GW		GW		GW		GW		GW		GW		GW	GW	GW	GW	GW	GW	GW	GW	GW		
		◇								◇				◇							◇					
Severn Beach	d			14 03				15 03				16 03				17 03		18 03		19 03		20 03	21 03	23 03		
St Andrews Road	d			14x09				15x09				16x09				17x09		18x09		19x09		20x09	21x09	23x09		
Avonmouth 2	d			14 13				15 13				16 13				17 13		18 13		19 13		20 13	21 13	23 13		
Shirehampton	d			14 17				15 17				16 17				17 17		18 17		19 17		20 17	21 17	23 17		
Sea Mills	d			14 21				15 21				16 21				17 21		18 21		19 21		20 21	21 21	23 21		
Clifton Down	d			14 27				15 27				16 27				17 27		18 27		19 27		20 27	21 27	23 27		
Redland	d			14 29				15 29				16 29				17 29		18 29		19 29		20 29	21 29	23 29		
Montpelier	d			14 31				15 31				16 31				17 31		18 31		19 31		20 31	21 31	23 31		
Stapleton Road	d	14 28		14 36		15 27		15 36		16 27		16 36		17 28		17 36	18 29	18 36	19 28	19 36	20 27	20 36	21 36	23 36		
Lawrence Hill	d	14 30		14 38		15 29		15 38		16 29		16 38		17 30		17 38	18 31	18 38	19 30	19 38	20 29	20 38	21 38	23 38		
Bristol Temple Meads 10	a	14 34		14 41		15 35		15 41		16 34		16 41		17 35		17 41	18 35	18 41	19 36	19 41	20 36	20 41	21 41	23 41		

For general notes see front of timetable
For details of catering facilities see Directory of Train Operators

b Arr. 0658
c Arr. 0830
e Arr. 0958
f Arr. 2157

The bus service between Avonmouth and Severn Beach is operated by South Gloucestershire County Council. Valid Rail Tickets are accepted.

Saturdays

from 29 March

Severn Beach and Avonmouth → Bristol

Network Diagram - see first page of Table 132

		GW	GW	GW	GW	GW	GW	GW	GW ◇	GW	GW	GW	GW	GW
Severn Beach	d	07 03		08 03		09 03		10 03		11 03		12 03		13 03
St Andrews Road	d	07x09		08x09		09x09		10x09		11x09		12x09		13x09
Avonmouth 2	d	07 13		08 13		09 13		10 13		11 13		12 13		13 13
Shirehampton	d	07 17		08 17		09 17		10 17		11 17		12 17		13 17
Sea Mills	d	07 21		08 21		09 21		10 21		11 21		12 21		13 21
Clifton Down	d	07 27		08 27		09 27		10 27		11 27		12 27		13 27
Redland	d	07 29		08 29		09 29		10 29		11 29		12 29		13 29
Montpelier	d	07 31		08 31		09 31		10 31		11 31		12 31		13 31
Stapleton Road	d	07 36	08 29	08 36	09 29	09 36	10 27	10 36	11 29	11 36	12 29	12 36	13 27	13 36
Lawrence Hill	d	07 38	08 31	08 38	09 31	09 38	10 29	10 38	11 31	11 38	12 31	12 38	13 29	13 38
Bristol Temple Meads 10	a	07 41	08 34	08 41	09 35	09 41	10 35	10 41	11 35	11 41	12 35	12 41	13 35	13 41

		GW ◇ H	GW	GW	GW	GW ◇	GW	GW	GW	GW	GW	GW	GW	GW	GW
Severn Beach	d		14 03		15 03		16 03	17 03		18 03		19 03	20 03	21 03	23 03
St Andrews Road	d		14x09		15x09		16x09	17x09		18x09		19x09	20x09	21x09	23x09
Avonmouth 2	d		14 13		15 13		16 13	17 13		18 13		19 13	20 13	21 13	23 13
Shirehampton	d		14 17		15 17		16 17	17 17		18 17		19 17	20 17	21 17	23 17
Sea Mills	d		14 21		15 21		16 21	17 21		18 21		19 21	20 21	21 21	23 21
Clifton Down	d		14 27		15 27		16 27	17 27		18 27		19 27	20 27	21 27	23 27
Redland	d		14 29		15 29		16 29	17 29		18 29		19 29	20 29	21 29	23 29
Montpelier	d		14 31		15 31		16 31	17 31		18 31		19 31	20 31	21 31	23 31
Stapleton Road	d	14 28	14 36	15 27	15 36	16 27	16 36	17 36	18 29	18 36	19 30	19 36	20 36	21 36	23 36
Lawrence Hill	d	14 30	14 38	15 29	15 38	16 29	16 38	17 38	18 31	18 38	19 32	19 38	20 38	21 38	23 38
Bristol Temple Meads 10	a	14 34	14 41	15 35	15 41	16 34	16 41	17 41	18 35	18 41	19 37	19 41	20 41	21 41	23 41

For general notes see front of timetable
For details of catering facilities see
Directory of Train Operators

No Sunday Service

The bus service between Avonmouth and Severn Beach is operated by South Gloucestershire County Council. Valid Rail Tickets are accepted.

Gloucester → Taunton

Network Diagram - see first page of Table 132

Miles	Station		GW MX ◇ A	GW ◇ B	GW	GW ◇	GW C	GW	GW ◇ trolley	GW D	GW	XC [1] ◇ buffet	GW E	GW	XC [1] ◇ buffet	GW ◇ trolley	GW	GW ◇ G	XC [1] ◇ H buffet	GW A	GW	XC [1] ◇ buffet	GW ◇ trolley	GW	GW ◇ J	XC [1] ◇ H buffet
0	**Gloucester** [7]	d						06 21					07 16					07 48							08 42	
13	Cam & Dursley	d						06 35					07 29					08 02							08 57	
28	Yate	d						06 48					07 42					08 15							09 10	
—	London Paddington [15] ⊖	d																								
—	Bath Spa [7]	d																								
34	**Bristol Parkway** [7]	a						06 58					07 51					08 24							09 19	
—		d						06 58		07 25			07 51	08 12	07 55		08 12	08 24	08 26		08 46	08 55		09 12	09 19	09 25
35¼	Filton Abbey Wood	d	22p51					07 02	07 09	07 28		07 47	07 54	08 15 →		08 09	08 15	08 27		08 42	08 50		09 09	09 15	09 22	
38¼	Stapleton Road	d					06 41	07 09		07 34															09 29	
38¾	Lawrence Hill	d					06 44	07 11		07 36															09 31	
39¾	**Bristol Temple Meads** [10]	a	23p00				06 47	07 15	07 18	07 40		07 52	08 03		08 11	08 18	08 23	08 36	08 41	08 53	08 59	09 11	09 18	09 23	09 35	09 41
—		d	23p06	05 31	06 19	06 48	06 51	07 19			07 51						08 25		08 44	08 55				09 25		09 44
40¾	Bedminster	d	23p09				06 54				07 54						08 28							09 28		
41½	Parson Street	d	23p12				06 57				07 56						08 30							09 30		
47¾	Nailsea & Backwell	d	23p20		06 29		07 05	07 29			08 04						08 38			09 05				09 38		
51¾	Yatton	d	23p25		06 35		07 10	07 35			08 10						08 44			09 11				09 44		
55¾	Worle	d	23p31		06 41		07 16	07 41			08 16						08 50			09 17				09 50		
58½	Weston Milton	d	23p36				07 20				08 21						08 55							09 55		
59¾	**Weston-super-Mare**	a	23p40	05 50	06 46	07 07	07 25	07 46			08 25						08 59			09 23				09 59		
—		d	23p41	05 52	06 50	07 10		07 48												09 28						
67¼	Highbridge & Burnham	d	23p52	06 02	07 00			07 59												09 39						
73½	Bridgwater	d	00 02	06 10	07 08			08 07												09 47						
85¼	**Taunton**	a	00 14	06 23	07 23	07 36		08 21											09 15	10 03						10 15

Station		GW	GW A		XC [1] ◇ buffet	GW ◇ trolley	GW	GW K	XC [R] [1] buffet	GW A	XC [R] [1] buffet	GW ◇ trolley	GW	GW ◇ J	XC [1] ◇ buffet	GW [1] ◇ L trolley	GW A	XC [1] ◇ buffet	GW ◇ trolley	GW	GW ◇ N	XC [1] ◇ buffet	GW A	XC [1] ◇ buffet	GW ◇ trolley	GW A
Gloucester [7]	d							09 42						10 42							11 42					
Cam & Dursley	d							09 57						10 57							11 57					
Yate	d							10 10						11 10							12 10					
London Paddington [15] ⊖	d															10 00										
Bath Spa [7]	d															11 25										
Bristol Parkway [7]	a							10 19						11 19							12 19					
	d	09 34			09 55		10 12	10 19	10 25		10 55		11 12	11 19	11 25			11 55		12 12	12 19	12 25		12 55		
Filton Abbey Wood	d	09 37	09 42			10 09	10 15	10 22		10 42		11 09	11 15	11 22			11 42		12 09	12 15	12 22		12 42		13 09	
Stapleton Road	d	09 44						10 29						11 29												
Lawrence Hill	d							10 31						11 31												
Bristol Temple Meads [10]	a	09 48	09 52		10 11	10 18	10 23	10 34	10 41	10 52	11 11	11 18	11 23	11 35	11 41	11 42	11 52	12 11	12 18	12 23	12 35	12 41	12 52	13 11	13 17	
	d		09 55				10 25		10 44	10 53	11 14		11 25		11 44	11 46	11 53			12 25		12 44	12 53	13 11		
Bedminster	d						10 28						11 28							12 28						
Parson Street	d						10 30						11 30							12 30						
Nailsea & Backwell	d		10 05				10 38			11 04			11 38				12 04			12 38			13 04			
Yatton	d		10 11				10 44			11 10			11 44				12 10			12 44			13 10			←
Worle	d		10 17				10 50			11 16			11 50				12 16			12 50			13 16 →			13 16
Weston Milton	d						10 55						11 55							12 55						
Weston-super-Mare	a		10 23				10 59			11 21	11 32		11 59			12 08	12 21			12 59						13 21
	d		10 24							11 23	11 42					12 10	12 23									13 23
Highbridge & Burnham	d		10 35							11 34							12 34									13 36
Bridgwater	d		10 43							11 42							12 42									13 44
Taunton	a		10 59						11 15	11 59	12 03				12 15	12 31	12 59					13 15		13 42		13 59

Station		GW	GW D	XC [1] ◇ buffet	GW A		XC [1] ◇ buffet	GW ◇ trolley	GW	GW ◇ Q	XC [1] ◇ buffet	GW A	GW	XC [R] [1] buffet	GW ◇ trolley	GW A	GW	GW D	XC [R] [1] buffet	GW A	XC [1] ◇ buffet	GW [1] ◇ buffet	GW ◇ trolley	GW	GW ◇ Q	XC [R] [1] buffet
Gloucester [7]	d		12 42							13 42								14 42							15 42	
Cam & Dursley	d		12 57							13 57								14 57							15 57	
Yate	d		13 10							14 10								15 10							16 10	
London Paddington [15] ⊖	d																					14 30				
Bath Spa [7]	d																					16 00				
Bristol Parkway [7]	a		13 19							14 19								15 19							16 19	
	d	13 12	13 19	13 25			13 55		14 12	14 19	14 25		14 47	14 55			15 12	15 19	15 25		15 55			16 12	16 19	16 25
Filton Abbey Wood	d	13 15	13 22		13 42			14 09	14 15	14 22		14 42	14 50		15 09		15 15	15 22		15 42			16 09	16 15	16 22	
Stapleton Road	d		13 29							14 29			14 56					15 29							16 29	
Lawrence Hill	d		13 31							14 31			14 58					15 31							16 31	
Bristol Temple Meads [10]	a	13 23	13 34	13 41	13 52		14 11	14 19	14 23	14 34	14 41	14 52	15 03	15 11	15 18		15 23	15 36	15 41	15 51	16 11	16 15	16 18	16 23	16 34	16 41
	d	13 25		13 44	13 53				14 25		14 44	14 53		15 11			15 25		15 44	15 53		16 18		16 25		16 44
Bedminster	d	13 28							14 28								15 28			15 56				16 28		
Parson Street	d	13 30							14 30								15 30			15 58				16 30		
Nailsea & Backwell	d	13 38			14 04				14 38			15 04					15 38			16 06		16 26		16 38		
Yatton	d	13 44			14 10				14 44			15 10				←	15 44			16 12		16 31		16 44		
Worle	d	13 50			14 16				14 50			15 16 →				15 16	15 50			16 18		16 38		16 50		
Weston Milton	d	13 55							14 55								15 55			16 22				16 55		
Weston-super-Mare	a	13 59			14 21				14 59							15 21	15 59			16 25		16 48		16 59		
	d				14 23											15 26				16 25						
Highbridge & Burnham	d				14 34											15 37				16 37						
Bridgwater	d				14 42											15 45				16 45						
Taunton	a			14 15	14 59						15 15			15 42		16 01			16 15	17 00						17 15

For general notes see front of timetable
For details of catering facilities see Directory of Train Operators

- **A** From Cardiff Central (Table 132)
- **B** To Penzance (Table 135)
- **C** From Severn Beach (Table 133)
- **D** To Westbury (Table 123)
- **E** From Cheltenham Spa (Table 57)
- **G** From Worcester Shrub Hill (Table 57) to Weymouth (Table 123)
- **H** From Derby (Table 57)
- **J** To Weymouth (Table 123)
- **K** From Great Malvern (Table 71) to Westbury (Table 123)
- **L** **The Torbay Express**
- **N** From Great Malvern (Table 71) to Brighton (Table 123)
- **Q** From Great Malvern (Table 71) to Weymouth (Table 123)

Gloucester → Taunton

Network Diagram - see first page of Table 132

Mondays to Fridays

		GW	GW	XC	GW	GW	GW		GW	GW	XC	GW	GW	XC	GW	GW	GW	GW	XC	GW	GW	GW	GW	XC	GW	XC
				[1] ◇		[1] ◇	◇			◇	[R] [1]			[1] ◇	[1] ◇	◇			[R] [1]	[1] ◇		[1] ◇	◇	[R] [1]		[1] ◇
		A	B		A					C		A	B					D			A				E	
				☕		trolley	trolley				☕			☕	☕	trolley			☕	☕		trolley	trolley	☕		☕
Gloucester [7]	d									16 42								17 42						18 38	18 42	
Cam & Dursley	d									16 57								17 57							18 57	
Yate	d									17 10								18 10							19 10	
London Paddington [15] ⊖	d					15 30									16 30							17 30				
Bath Spa [7]	d					17 00									18 00							19 00				
Bristol Parkway [7]	a									17 19								18 19						19 05	19 19	
	d		16 47	16 55					17 12	17 19	17 25		17 47	17 55			18 11	18 19	18 25					19 06	19 19	19 25
Filton Abbey Wood	d	16 42	16 50				17 09		17 15	17 22		17 42	17 50			18 09	18 14	18 22			18 42		19 09		19 22	
Stapleton Road	d		16 56							17 29			17 56				18 19	18 29							19 29	
Lawrence Hill	d		16 58						17 21	17 31			17 58				18 21	18 31							19 31	
Bristol Temple Meads [10]	a	16 51	17 02	17 11		17 15	17 18		17 24	17 36	17 41	17 52	18 02	18 11	18 15	18 18	18 25	18 34	18 41		18 52	19 15	19 18	19 22	19 36	19 41
	d	16 53		17 11		17 18			17 25		17 44	17 53			18 22		18 25		18 44		18 55	19 16				19 44
Bedminster	d	16 56							17 29			17 56					18 29				18 59					
Parson Street	d	16 58							17 31			17 59					18 31				19 02					
Nailsea & Backwell	d	17 06				17 28			17 39			18 07			18 32		18 39				19 10	19 25				
Yatton	d	17 12			←	17 34			17 45			18 13			18 38		18 45				19 15	19 31				
Worle	d	17 18			17 18	17 40			17 51			18 19			18 43		18 51				19 21	19 36				
Weston Milton	d	→			17 22				17 56			18 23			18 48		18 56				19 25	19 42				
Weston-super-Mare	a				17 25	17 51			18 00			18 26			→		18 59				19 29	→				
	d				17 27							18 28									19 30					
Highbridge & Burnham	d				17 37							18 39								←	19 41					
Bridgwater	d				17 45							18 47								19 13	19 49					
Taunton	a			17 42	18 00						18 15	19 01							19 15	19 30	20 04					20 15

		GW	GW	GW	XC	GW	GW	GW	GW	XC	GW	GW	XC	GW	XC	GW	GW	GW	XC	GW	GW	XC	GW	GW
			[1] ◇		[R] [1]	[1] ◇	◇		◇	[1] ◇		[1] ◇	[R] [1]	◇	[1] ◇				[1] ◇		[1] ◇	[1] ◇	[1] ◇	
				A					G		A					H		J		A				A
			trolley			trolley	trolley					trolley		trolley							trolley		☕	
Gloucester [7]	d								19 44									21 15			22 49			
Cam & Dursley	d								19 57									21 28						
Yate	d								20 10									21 41						
London Paddington [15] ⊖	d					18 30						19 30											21 45	
Bath Spa [7]	d					20 00						20 55											23 28	
Bristol Parkway [7]	a								20 19									21 50			23 16			
	d	19 31			19 55			20 11	20 19	20 25			20 55		21 25			21 50	22 25		23 18	23 25		
Filton Abbey Wood	d	19 34		19 42			20 09	20 14	20 22		20 38			21 09		21 41				22 52				23 50
Stapleton Road	d								20 29							21 47								23 57
Lawrence Hill	d								20 31							21 50								23 59
Bristol Temple Meads [10]	a	19 43		19 52	20 11	20 15	20 18	20 25	20 34	20 41	20 48	21 10	21 11	21 18	21 41	21 53		22 02	22 41	23 00	23 30	23 41	23 41	00 04
	d			19 55	20 14	20 16				20 44	20 55	21 13			21 44		21 55			23 06			23 45	
Bedminster	d			19 59							20 59						21 59			23 09				
Parson Street	d			20 02							21 01						22 01			23 11				
Nailsea & Backwell	d			20 10		20 27					21 09	21 21					22 09			23 19			23s55	
Yatton	d			20 15		20 32					21 15	21 27					22 15			23 25			23s59	
Worle	d		←	20 21		20 39					21 21	21 33					22 21			23 31			00s06	
Weston Milton	d		19 42	20 25		20 44					21 25						22 25			23 36				
Weston-super-Mare	a		19 45	20 29	20 39	20 52					21 28	21 44					22 28			23 39			00s13	
	d		19 58	20 30							21 30						22 30			23 41				
Highbridge & Burnham	d		20 06	20 41							21 41						22 41			23 51			00s24	
Bridgwater	d		20 13	20 49							21 49						22 49			23 59			00s31	
Taunton	a		20 30	21 04						21 15	22 03				22 15		23 03			00 14			00s42	

Saturdays

until 26 January

		GW	GW	GW	GW	GW	GW	GW	GW	GW	GW	XC	GW	GW	GW	GW	GW	GW	XC	XC	XC	GW	GW	GW	XC	GW
		[1] ◇		◇			◇		◇			[1] ◇		[1] ◇	◇				[1] ◇	[1] ◇	[1] ◇	◇			[1] ◇	
								A			K	L	A			A		C						N		A
		☕		trolley					trolley			☕		☕	trolley				☕	☕	☕	trolley			☕	
Gloucester [7]	d					06 21					07 40							08 42						09 42		
Cam & Dursley	d					06 36					07 53							08 56						09 56		
Yate	d					06 50					08 07							09 10						10 10		
London Paddington [15] ⊖	d													07 30												
Bath Spa [7]	d													09 00												
Bristol Parkway [7]	a					07 00					08 15							09 19						10 19		
	d	05 42				07 00				08 12	08 20	08 25					09 12	09 19	09 25		09 58		10 12	10 19	10 25	
Filton Abbey Wood	d					07 03	07 10	07 42	08 10	08 15	08 23		08 43		09 09		09 15	09 23		09 40		10 09	10 15	10 22		10 42
Stapleton Road	d										08 29							09 31						10 27		
Lawrence Hill	d										08 31							09 35						10 29		
Bristol Temple Meads [10]	a	05 53				07 13	07 18	07 52	08 18	08 23	08 34	08 41	08 52	09 15	09 18		09 23		09 41	09 51	10 13	10 18	10 23	10 35	10 41	10 52
	d		06 20	06 48	06 53	07 17		07 53		08 25		08 44	08 53	09 17			09 25		09 44				10 25		10 44	10 53
Bedminster	d				06 56					08 28							09 28						10 28			
Parson Street	d				06 58					08 30							09 30						10 30			
Nailsea & Backwell	d		06 30		07 06	07 28		08 04		08 38			09 04				09 38						10 38			11 04
Yatton	d		06 36		07 12	07 33		08 10		08 44			09 10			←	09 44						10 44			11 10
Worle	d		06 42		07 18	07 39		08 16		08 50			09 16			09 16	09 50						10 50			11 16
Weston Milton	d				07 23					08 55			→				09 55						10 55			
Weston-super-Mare	a		06 47	07 11	07 28	07 45		08 21		08 59						09 21	09 59						10 59			11 21
	d		06 49	07 12		07 47										09 30										11 23
Highbridge & Burnham	d		07 00			07 58										09 46										11 34
Bridgwater	d		07 08			08 05										09 54										11 42
Taunton	a		07 22	07 38		08 21						09 15		09 50		10 08			10 15						11 15	11 56

For general notes see front of timetable
For details of catering facilities see Directory of Train Operators

A From Cardiff Central (Table 132)
B To Westbury (Table 123)
C To Weymouth (Table 123)
D From Worcester Foregate Street (Table 71) to Southampton (Table 123)
E To Frome (Table 123)
G From Great Malvern (Table 71) to Weymouth (Table 123)
H From Cardiff Central (Table 132) to Westbury (Table 123)
J From Cheltenham Spa (Table 57)
K From Worcester Shrub Hill (Table 57) to Weymouth (Table 123)
L From Derby (Table 57)
N From Great Malvern (Table 71) to Westbury (Table 123)

Table 134

Saturdays

until 26 January

Gloucester → Taunton

Network Diagram - see first page of Table 132

		XC	GW	GW	GW	XC	GW	XC	GW	GW		GW	XC	GW	XC	GW	GW	GW	XC	GW	XC	GW	GW	GW	XC	XC
		1◇	◇		◇	1◇		1◇	◇				1◇		1◇	◇			1◇		1◇	◇		◇	1◇	1◇
					A		B					C		B				D		B				E		
		☕	🛒			☕		☕	🛒				☕		☕	🛒			☕		☕	🛒		🛒	☕	☕
Gloucester 7	d				10 42							11 42						12 42						13 42		
Cam & Dursley	d				10 56							11 56						12 56						13 56		
Yate	d				11 10							12 10						13 10						14 10		
London Paddington 15 ⊖	d																									
Bath Spa 7	d																									
Bristol Parkway 7	a				11 19							12 19						13 19						14 19		
	d	10 58		11 12	11 19	11 25		11 58		12 12		12 19	12 25		12 58		13 12	13 19	13 25		13 58		14 12	14 19	14 25	14 58
Filton Abbey Wood	d		11 09	11 15	11 23		11 42		12 09	12 15		12 22		12 42		13 09	13 15	13 23		13 43		14 09	14 15	14 23		
Stapleton Road	d				11 29							12 29						13 27						14 28		
Lawrence Hill	d				11 31							12 31						13 29						14 30		
Bristol Temple Meads 10	a	11 13	11 18	11 23	11 35	11 41	11 52	12 13	12 18	12 23		12 35	12 41	12 52	13 13	13 18	13 23	13 35	13 41	13 52	14 13	14 18	14 23	14 34	14 41	15 11
	d	11 14		11 25		11 44	11 53			12 25			12 44	12 53			13 25		13 44	13 53			14 25		14 44	15 11
Bedminster	d			11 28						12 28							13 28						14 28			
Parson Street	d			11 30						12 30							13 30						14 30			
Nailsea & Backwell	d			11 38			12 04			12 38				13 04			13 38			14 04			14 38			
Yatton	d			11 44			12 10			12 44				13 10			13 44			14 10			14 44			
Worle	d			11 50			12 16			12 50				13 16			13 50			14 16			14 50			
Weston Milton	d			11 55						12 55							13 55						14 55			
Weston-super-Mare	a	11 31		11 59			12 21			12 59				13 21			13 59			14 21			14 59			
	d	11 42					12 23							13 23						14 23						
Highbridge & Burnham	d						12 34							13 34						14 34						
Bridgwater	d						12 42							13 42						14 42						
Taunton	a	12 03				12 15	12 56						13 15	13 56					14 15	14 56					15 15	15 42

		GW	GW	GW	XC	GW	XC	GW	GW	GW	XC	GW	XC	GW	GW	GW	XC	GW	XC	GW	GW	GW	GW	XC	GW	GW
		◇			1◇		1◇	◇		◇	1◇		1◇	◇		◇	1◇		1◇	1◇	◇			1◇	1◇	
				D		B				G		B				A		B		H			J		H	B
		🛒			☕		☕	🛒			☕		☕	🛒			☕		☕	☕	🛒			☕	☕	
Gloucester 7	d			14 42						15 42						16 42							17 42			
Cam & Dursley	d			14 56						15 56						16 56							17 56			
Yate	d			15 10						16 10						17 10							18 10			
London Paddington 15 ⊖	d																			16 30						
Bath Spa 7	d																			18 00						
Bristol Parkway 7	a			15 19						16 19						17 19							18 19			
	d		15 12	15 19	15 25		15 58		16 12	16 19	16 25		16 58		17 12	17 19	17 25		17 58			18 12	18 19	18 25		
Filton Abbey Wood	d	15 09	15 15	15 23		15 42		16 09	16 15	16 23		16 42		17 10	17 15	17 23		17 42			18 10	18 14	18 22			18 42
Stapleton Road	d			15 27						16 27						17 28							18 29			
Lawrence Hill	d			15 29						16 29						17 30							18 31			
Bristol Temple Meads 10	a	15 18	15 23	15 35	15 41	15 52	16 13	16 18	16 23	16 34	16 41	16 52	17 13	17 18	17 23	17 35	17 41	17 52	18 13	18 15	18 18	18 23	18 35	18 41		18 52
	d		15 25		15 44	15 53			16 25		16 44	16 53			17 25		17 44	17 53		18 19		18 26		18 44		18 53
Bedminster	d		15 28						16 28						17 28							18 29				
Parson Street	d		15 30						16 30						17 30							18 31				
Nailsea & Backwell	d		15 38			16 04			16 38			17 04			17 38			18 04		18 31		18 39				19 04
Yatton	d		15 44			16 10			16 44			17 10			17 44			18 10		18 37		18 45				19 10
Worle	d		15 50			16 16			16 50			17 16			17 50			18 16		18 42		18 51				19 16
Weston Milton	d		15 55						16 55						17 55					18 47		18 56				19 20
Weston-super-Mare	a		15 59			16 21			16 59			17 21			17 59			18 21		18 50		19 00			←	19 23
	d					16 23						17 23						18 23		18 54 →					18 54	19 25
Highbridge & Burnham	d					16 34						17 34						18 34								19 36
Bridgwater	d					16 42						17 42						18 42								19 44
Taunton	a				16 15	16 56					17 15	17 56					18 15	18 56						19 15	19 19	19 58

		GW	GW	XC	GW	GW	XC	GW	XC	GW	GW	GW	GW	XC	GW	GW	XC	GW	XC	GW	GW	GW	XC	GW		
		1◇	◇	1◇			1◇		1◇	1◇	◇		◇	1◇	1◇		1◇	◇	1◇			1◇	1◇			
						K		B					L			N				N	Q	U				
		☕	🛒	☕			☕		☕	☕	🛒				☕			🛒				☕				
Gloucester 7	d			18 39		18 42							19 44								21 15					
Cam & Dursley	d					18 56							19 56								21 28					
Yate	d					19 10							20 10								21 41					
London Paddington 15 ⊖	d	17 30								18 30					19 00							20 30				
Bath Spa 7	d	19 00								20 01					20 25							21 59				
Bristol Parkway 7	a			19 06		19 19							20 19								21 51					
	d			19 08	19 16	19 19	19 25		19 58			20 17	20 19	20 25			20 58		21 25		21 51		22 25			
Filton Abbey Wood	d		19 09		19 19	19 22		19 42			20 09	20 20	20 23			20 34		21 09		21 42				22 52		
Stapleton Road	d					19 28							20 27													
Lawrence Hill	d					19 30							20 29													
Bristol Temple Meads 10	a	19 15	19 18	19 24	19 28	19 36	19 41	19 52	20 13	20 15	20 18	20 29	20 36	20 41	20 42	20 42	21 13	21 18	21 41	21 52	22 04	22 16	22 41	23 00		
	d	19 16					19 44	19 53		20 15				20 44	20 49	20 56			21 44	21 53		22 16				
Bedminster	d															20 59										
Parson Street	d															21 01										
Nailsea & Backwell	d	19 29						20 04							20 58	21 09				22 04		22 27				
Yatton	d	19 35						20 09							21 04	21 15				22 10		22 33				
Worle	d							20 15								21 21				22 16						
Weston Milton	d							20 19								21 25										
Weston-super-Mare	a	19 52						20 23		20 37					21 13	21 28				22 25		22 41				
	d							20 24		20 37					21 13	21 30				22 27		22 42				
Highbridge & Burnham	d							20 35							21 24	21 41				22 38		22 52				
Bridgwater	d							20 43							21 31	21 49				22 46		22 59				
Taunton	a						20 15	20 58		21 06				21 15	21 47	22 03			22 15	23 00		23 09				

For general notes see front of timetable
For details of catering facilities see Directory of Train Operators

- **A** To Weymouth (Table 123)
- **B** From Cardiff Central (Table 132)
- **C** From Great Malvern (Table 71) to Brighton (Table 123)
- **D** To Westbury (Table 123)
- **E** From Great Malvern (Table 71) to Weymouth (Table 123)
- **G** From Worcester Foregate Street (Table 71) to Weymouth (Table 123)
- **H** To Paignton (Table 135)
- **J** From Great Malvern (Table 71) to Westbury (Table 123)
- **K** To Frome (Table 123)
- **L** From Worcester Shrub Hill (Table 57) to Weymouth (Table 123)
- **N** From Cardiff Central (Table 132) to Exeter St Davids (Table 135)
- **Q** From Cheltenham Spa (Table 57)
- **U** To Exeter St Davids (Table 135)

Table 134

2 February to 22 March

Gloucester → Taunton

Network Diagram - see first page of Table 132

		GW 1◇ ☕	GW	GW ◇ 🛒	GW	GW	GW ◇	GW A	GW	GW ◇ 🛒	GW 1◇ ☕	GW B	XC 1◇ ☕	GW A	GW	GW 1◇ ☕	GW ◇ 🛒	GW A	GW	GW C	XC 1◇ ☕	XC 1◇ ☕
Gloucester 7	d					06 21						07 40								08 42		
Cam & Dursley	d					06 36						07 53								08 56		
Yate	d					06 50						08 07								09 10		
London Paddington 15	⊖ d															07 30						
Bath Spa 7	d															09 04						
Bristol Parkway 7	a					07 00						08 15								09 19		
	d	05 42				07 00			07 55		08 10	08 20	08 25		09 02					09 19	09 25	
Filton Abbey Wood	d					07 03	07 10	07 42	07 59	08 10		08 23		08 43	09 05		09 09			09 23		09 40
Stapleton Road	d											08 29								09 29		
Lawrence Hill	d											08 31								09 31		
Bristol Temple Meads 10	a	05 53				07 13	07 18	07 52	08 07	08 18	08 22	08 34	08 41	08 52	09 13	09 18	09 18		←	09 35	09 41	09 51
	d		06 20	06 48	06 53	07 17		07 53	08 25				08 44	08 53	09 25	09 20			09 25		09 44	
Bedminster	d				06 56				08 28						→				09 28			
Parson Street	d				06 58				08 30										09 30			
Nailsea & Backwell	d		06 30		07 06	07 28		08 04	08 38					09 04					09 38			
Yatton	d		06 36		07 12	07 33		08 10	08 44					09 10				←	09 44			
Worle	d		06 42		07 18	07 39		08 16	08 50					09 16				09 16	09 50			
Weston Milton	d				07 23				08 55					→					09 55			
Weston-super-Mare	a		06 47	07 11	07 28	07 45		08 21	08 59									09 21	09 59			
	d		06 49	07 12		07 47												09 30				
Highbridge & Burnham	d		07 00			07 58												09 44				
Bridgwater	d		07 08			08 05												09 52				
Taunton	a		07 22	07 38		08 21							09 15			09 53		10 06			10 15	

		XC 1◇ ☕	GW	GW ◇ 🛒	GW D	XC 1◇ ☕	GW A	XC 1◇ ☕	GW	GW ◇ 🛒	GW ◇ C	XC 1◇ ☕	GW A	XC 1◇ ☕	GW	GW ◇ 🛒	GW 1◇ ☕	GW E	XC 1◇ ☕	GW A	XC 1◇ ☕
Gloucester 7	d				09 42						10 42							11 42			
Cam & Dursley	d				09 56						10 56							11 56			
Yate	d				10 10						11 10							12 10			
London Paddington 15	⊖ d																				
Bath Spa 7	d																				
Bristol Parkway 7	a				10 19						11 19							12 19			
	d	09 58	10 02		10 19	10 25		10 58	11 02		11 19	11 25		11 58	12 02		12 10	12 19	12 25		12 58
Filton Abbey Wood	d		10 05	10 09	10 22		10 42		11 05	11 09	11 23		11 42		12 05	12 09		12 22		12 42	
Stapleton Road	d				10 27						11 29							12 29			
Lawrence Hill	d				10 29						11 31							12 31			
Bristol Temple Meads 10	a	10 13	10 13	10 18	10 35	10 41	10 52	11 13	11 13	11 18	11 35	11 41	11 52	12 13	12 13	12 18	12 22	12 35	12 41	12 52	13 13
	d		10 25			10 44	10 53	11 14	11 25			11 44	11 53		12 25				12 44	12 53	
Bedminster	d		10 28						11 28						12 28						
Parson Street	d		10 30						11 30						12 30						
Nailsea & Backwell	d		10 38				11 04		11 38				12 04		12 38					13 04	
Yatton	d		10 44				11 10		11 44				12 10		12 44					13 10	
Worle	d		10 50				11 16		11 50				12 16		12 50					13 16	
Weston Milton	d		10 55						11 55						12 55						
Weston-super-Mare	a		10 59				11 21	11 31	11 59				12 21		12 59					13 21	
	d						11 23	11 42					12 23							13 23	
Highbridge & Burnham	d						11 34						12 34							13 34	
Bridgwater	d						11 42						12 42							13 42	
Taunton	a					11 15	11 56	12 03				12 15	12 56						13 15	13 56	

		GW	GW ◇ 🛒	GW G	XC 1◇ ☕	GW A	XC 1◇ ☕	GW	GW ◇ 🛒	GW ◇ H 🛒	XC 1◇ ☕	GW 1◇ J ☕	XC 1◇ ☕	GW	GW ◇ 🛒	GW G	XC 1◇ ☕	GW A	XC 1◇ ☕	GW	GW ◇ 🛒
Gloucester 7	d			12 42						13 42						14 42					
Cam & Dursley	d			12 56						13 56						14 56					
Yate	d			13 10						14 10						15 10					
London Paddington 15	⊖ d											13 15									
Bath Spa 7	d											14 50									
Bristol Parkway 7	a			13 19						14 19		15 17				15 19					
	d	13 02		13 19	13 25		13 58	14 02		14 19	14 25		14 58	15 02		15 19	15 25		15 58	16 02	
Filton Abbey Wood	d	13 05	13 09	13 23		13 43		14 05	14 09	14 23				15 05	15 09	15 23		15 42		16 05	16 09
Stapleton Road	d			13 27						14 28						15 27					
Lawrence Hill	d			13 29						14 30						15 29					
Bristol Temple Meads 10	a	13 13	13 18	13 35	13 41	13 52	14 13	14 13	14 18	14 34	14 41	15 02	15 11	15 13	15 18	15 35	15 41	15 52	16 13	16 13	16 18
	d	13 25			13 44	13 53		14 25			14 44		15 11	15 25			15 44	15 53		16 25	
Bedminster	d	13 28						14 28						15 28						16 28	
Parson Street	d	13 30						14 30						15 30						16 30	
Nailsea & Backwell	d	13 38				14 04		14 38						15 38				16 04		16 38	
Yatton	d	13 44				14 10		14 44						15 44				16 10		16 44	
Worle	d	13 50				14 16		14 50						15 50				16 16		16 50	
Weston Milton	d	13 55						14 55						15 55						16 55	
Weston-super-Mare	a	13 59				14 21		14 59						15 59				16 21		16 59	
	d					14 23												16 23			
Highbridge & Burnham	d					14 34												16 34			
Bridgwater	d					14 42												16 42			
Taunton	a				14 15	14 56					15 15		15 42				16 15	16 56			

For general notes see front of timetable
For details of catering facilities see Directory of Train Operators

- **A** From Cardiff Central (Table 132)
- **B** From Worcester Shrub Hill (Table 57) to Weymouth (Table 123)
- **C** To Weymouth (Table 123)
- **D** From Great Malvern (Table 71) to Westbury (Table 123)
- **E** From Great Malvern (Table 71) to Brighton (Table 123)
- **G** To Westbury (Table 123)
- **H** From Great Malvern (Table 71) to Weymouth (Table 123)
- **J** To Swansea (Table 125)

Saturdays

2 February to 22 March

Gloucester → Taunton

Network Diagram - see first page of Table 132

		GW 1◇ ☕	GW ◇ A	XC 1◇ ☕	GW B		XC 1◇ ☕	GW	GW ◇ 🛒	GW ◇ C		XC 1◇ ☕	GW B	XC 1◇ ☕	GW		GW ◇ 🛒	GW D	XC 1◇ ☕	GW B		GW	GW ◇ 🛒	GW 1◇ ☕	XC 1◇ ☕	GW 1◇ ☕
Gloucester 7	d		15 42							16 42								17 42							18 39	
Cam & Dursley	d		15 56							16 56								17 56								
Yate	d		16 10							17 10								18 10								
London Paddington 15 ⊖	d																							17 30		
Bath Spa 7	d																							19 06		
Bristol Parkway 7	a		16 19							17 19								18 19							19 06	
	d	16 10	16 19	16 25			16 58	17 02		17 19		17 25		17 58	18 02			18 19	18 25			19 02			19 08	19 10
Filton Abbey Wood	d		16 23		16 42			17 05	17 10	17 23			17 42		18 04		18 10	18 22		18 42		19 05	19 09			
Stapleton Road	d		16 27							17 28								18 29								
Lawrence Hill	d		16 29							17 30								18 31								
Bristol Temple Meads 10	a	16 22	16 34	16 41	16 52		17 13	17 13	17 18	17 35		17 41	17 52	18 13	18 13		18 18	18 35	18 41	18 52		19 14	19 18	19 20	19 24	19 22
	d			16 44	16 53			17 25				17 44	17 53		18 26				18 44	18 53				19 20		
Bedminster	d							17 28							18 29											
Parson Street	d							17 30							18 31											
Nailsea & Backwell	d				17 04			17 38					18 04		18 39					19 04				19 34		
Yatton	d				17 10			17 44					18 10		18 45					19 10				19 40		
Worle	d				17 16			17 50					18 16		18 51					19 16						
Weston Milton	d							17 55							18 56					19 20						
Weston-super-Mare	a				17 21			17 59					18 21		19 00					19 23				19 52		
	d				17 23								18 23							19 25						
Highbridge & Burnham	d				17 34								18 34							19 36						
Bridgwater	d				17 42								18 42							19 44						
Taunton	a			17 15	17 56							18 15	18 56						19 15	19 58						

		GW E		XC 1◇ ☕	GW B	XC 1◇ ☕	GW 1◇ ☕		GW ◇ 🛒	GW 1◇ ☕	GW	GW ◇ G		XC 1◇	GW H	XC 1◇	GW ◇ 🛒	GW 1◇ ☕	XC 1◇	GW H	GW J	GW 1◇ K ☕	XC 1◇	GW		
Gloucester 7	d	18 42										19 44									21 15					
Cam & Dursley	d	18 56										19 56									21 28					
Yate	d	19 10										20 10									21 41					
London Paddington 15 ⊖	d						18 30															20 30				
Bath Spa 7	d						20 04															22 02				
Bristol Parkway 7	a	19 19										20 19									21 51					
	d	19 19		19 25		19 58				20 10	20 17	20 19		20 25		20 58		21 10	21 25		21 51		22 25			
Filton Abbey Wood	d	19 22			19 42				20 09		20 20	20 23			20 34		21 09			21 42				22 52		
Stapleton Road	d	19 28										20 27														
Lawrence Hill	d	19 30										20 29														
Bristol Temple Meads 10	a	19 36		19 41	19 52	20 13	20 18		20 18	20 22	20 29	20 36		20 41	20 43	21 13	21 18	21 22	21 41	21 52	22 04	22 17	22 41	23 00		
	d			19 44	19 53		20 18							20 44	20 56				21 44	21 53		22 17				
Bedminster	d														20 59											
Parson Street	d														21 01											
Nailsea & Backwell	d				20 04										21 09					22 04		22s27				
Yatton	d				20 09										21 15					22 10		22s33				
Worle	d				20 15										21 21					22 16						
Weston Milton	d				20 19										21 25											
Weston-super-Mare	a				20 23		20 39								21 28					22 23		22s41				
	d				20 24										21 30					22 25						
Highbridge & Burnham	d				20 35										21 41					22 36		22 53				
Bridgwater	d				20 43										21 49					22 44		23 00				
Taunton	a			20 15	20 58									21 15	22 03				22 15	22 58		23 11				

Saturdays

from 29 March

		GW	GW ◇ 🛒	GW	GW		GW ◇	GW	GW ◇ 🛒	GW		GW G	XC 1◇ L ☕	GW	GW 1◇ ☕		GW ◇ 🛒	GW	GW	GW C		XC 1◇ ☕	GW	XC 1◇ ☕	GW ◇ 🛒	GW
Gloucester 7	d				06 21							07 40								08 42						
Cam & Dursley	d				06 36							07 53								08 56						
Yate	d				06 50							08 07								09 10						
London Paddington 15 ⊖	d														07 30											
Bath Spa 7	d														09 00											
Bristol Parkway 7	a				07 00							08 15								09 19						
	d				07 00		07 06	07 40	07 55	08 12		08 20	08 25	08 42			09 06		09 12	09 19		09 25		09 58	10 06	10 12
Filton Abbey Wood	d				07 03		07 09	07 42	07 59	08 15		08 23		08 44			09 09		09 15	09 23					10 09	10 15
Stapleton Road	d											08 29								09 29						
Lawrence Hill	d											08 31								09 31						
Bristol Temple Meads 10	a				07 13		07 18	07 52	08 08	08 23		08 34	08 41	08 54	09 15		09 17		09 23	09 35		09 41		10 13	10 17	10 23
	d	06 20	06 48	06 53	07 17			07 53		08 25			08 44	08 55	09 17				09 25			09 44	09 56			10 25
Bedminster	d			06 56						08 28									09 28							10 28
Parson Street	d			06 58						08 30									09 30							10 30
Nailsea & Backwell	d	06 30		07 06	07 28			08 04		08 38				09 06					09 38				10 07			10 38
Yatton	d	06 36		07 12	07 33			08 10		08 44				09 12				←	09 44				10 13			10 44
Worle	d	06 42		07 18	07 39			08 16		08 50				09 18				09 18	09 50				10 19			10 50
Weston Milton	d			07 23						08 55				→					09 55							10 55
Weston-super-Mare	a	06 47	07 11	07 28	07 45			08 21		08 59								09 23	09 59				10 24			10 59
	d	06 49	07 12		07 47													09 30					10 26			
Highbridge & Burnham	d	07 00			07 58													09 44					10 37			
Bridgwater	d	07 08			08 05													09 52					10 45			
Taunton	a	07 22	07 38		08 21								09 15		09 50			10 06				10 15	10 59			

For general notes see front of timetable
For details of catering facilities see Directory of Train Operators

A From Worcester Foregate Street (Table 71) to Weymouth (Table 123)
B From Cardiff Central (Table 132)
C To Weymouth (Table 123)
D From Great Malvern (Table 71) to Westbury (Table 123)
E To Frome (Table 123)
G From Worcester Shrub Hill (Table 57) to Weymouth (Table 123)
H From Cardiff Central (Table 132) to Exeter St Davids (Table 135)
J From Cheltenham Spa (Table 57)
K To Exeter St Davids (Table 135)
L From Derby (Table 57)

Table 134

Saturdays

from 29 March

Gloucester → Taunton

Network Diagram - see first page of Table 132

		GW	XC	GW	XC	GW	GW	GW	XC	GW	XC	GW	GW	GW	XC	GW	XC	GW	GW	GW	XC
			1 ◇		1 ◇	◇		◇	1 ◇		1 ◇	◇			1 ◇		1 ◇	◇			1 ◇
		A						B						C						D	
Gloucester 7	d	09 42						10 42						11 42						12 42	
Cam & Dursley	d	09 56						10 56						11 56						12 56	
Yate	d	10 10						11 10						12 10						13 10	
London Paddington 15	⊖ d																				
Bath Spa 7	d																				
Bristol Parkway 7	a	10 19						11 19						12 19						13 19	
	d	10 19	10 25	10 40	10 58	11 06	11 12	11 19	11 25	11 40	11 58	12 06	12 12	12 19	12 25	12 40	12 58	13 06	13 12	13 19	13 25
Filton Abbey Wood	d	10 22		10 42		11 09	11 15	11 23		11 42		12 09	12 15	12 22		12 42		13 09	13 15	13 23	
Stapleton Road	d	10 27						11 29						12 29						13 27	
Lawrence Hill	d	10 29						11 31						12 31						13 29	
Bristol Temple Meads 10	a	10 35	10 41	10 52	11 13	11 17	11 23	11 35	11 41	11 52	12 13	12 17	12 23	12 35	12 41	12 52	13 13	13 17	13 23	13 35	13 41
	d		10 44	10 53	11 14		11 25		11 44	11 53			12 25		12 44	12 53			13 25		13 44
Bedminster	d						11 28						12 28						13 28		
Parson Street	d						11 30						12 30						13 30		
Nailsea & Backwell	d			11 04			11 38			12 04			12 38			13 04			13 38		
Yatton	d			11 10			11 44			12 10			12 44			13 10			13 44		
Worle	d			11 16			11 50			12 16			12 50			13 16			13 50		
Weston Milton	d						11 55						12 55						13 55		
Weston-super-Mare	a			11 21	11 31		11 59			12 21			12 59			13 21			13 59		
	d			11 23	11 42					12 23						13 23					
Highbridge & Burnham	d			11 34						12 34						13 36					
Bridgwater	d			11 42						12 42						13 44					
Taunton	a		11 15	11 56	12 03				12 15	12 56					13 15	13 58					14 15

		XC	GW	GW	GW	GW	XC	GW	XC	GW	GW	GW	GW	GW	XC	GW	XC	GW	GW	GW	XC
		1 ◇	◇		◇	1 ◇	1 ◇		1 ◇	◇				1 ◇	1 ◇		1 ◇	◇		◇	1 ◇
					A								D							E	
Gloucester 7	d				13 42								14 42							15 42	
Cam & Dursley	d				13 56								14 56							15 56	
Yate	d				14 10								15 10							16 10	
London Paddington 15	⊖ d					13 05								14 05							
Bath Spa 7	d																				
Bristol Parkway 7	a				14 19								15 19							16 19	
	d	13 58	14 06	14 12	14 19		14 25	14 40	14 58	15 06		15 12	15 19		15 25	15 40	15 58	16 06	16 12	16 19	16 25
Filton Abbey Wood	d		14 09	14 15	14 23			14 42		15 09		15 15	15 23			15 42		16 09	16 15	16 23	
Stapleton Road	d				14 28								15 27							16 27	
Lawrence Hill	d				14 30								15 29							16 29	
Bristol Temple Meads 10	a	14 13	14 17	14 23	14 34	14 39	14 41	14 52	15 11	15 17		15 23	15 35	15 36	15 41	15 52	16 13	16 17	16 23	16 34	16 41
	d			14 25		14 41	14 44	14 53	15 11			15 25		15 38	15 44	15 53			16 25		16 44
Bedminster	d			14 28								15 28							16 28		
Parson Street	d			14 30								15 30							16 30		
Nailsea & Backwell	d			14 38				15 04				15 38				16 04			16 38		
Yatton	d			14 44				15 10			←	15 44				16 10			16 44		
Worle	d			14 50				15 16 ↳			15 16	15 50				16 16			16 50		
Weston Milton	d			14 55								15 55							16 55		
Weston-super-Mare	a			14 59							15 21	15 59				16 21			16 59		
	d										15 26					16 23					
Highbridge & Burnham	d										15 37					16 34					
Bridgwater	d										15 45					16 42					
Taunton	a					15 13	15 15		15 42		15 59			16 10	16 15	16 56					17 15

		GW	XC	GW	GW	GW	GW	XC	GW	XC	GW	GW	GW	XC	GW	GW	XC	GW	GW	GW	GW	XC
			1 ◇	◇		◇	1 ◇	1 ◇		1 ◇	1 ◇			1 ◇	1 ◇		1 ◇	1 ◇	◇		1 ◇	1 ◇
						D					G		A		G							
Gloucester 7	d					16 42							17 42									
Cam & Dursley	d					16 56							17 56									
Yate	d					17 10							18 10									
London Paddington 15	⊖ d						16 05				16 30							17 30			18 05	
Bath Spa 7	d										18 00							19 00				
Bristol Parkway 7	a					17 19							18 19									
	d	16 40	16 58	17 06	17 12	17 19		17 25	17 40	17 58		18 12	18 19	18 25		18 40	18 58		19 06	19 16		19 25
Filton Abbey Wood	d	16 42		17 09	17 15	17 23			17 42			18 14	18 22			18 42			19 09	19 19		
Stapleton Road	d												18 29									
Lawrence Hill	d												18 31									
Bristol Temple Meads 10	a	16 52	17 13	17 17	17 23	17 32	17 34	17 41	17 52	18 13	18 15	18 23	18 35	18 41		18 52	19 13	19 15	19 17	19 28	19 32	19 41
	d	16 53			17 25		17 36	17 44	17 53		18 19	18 26		18 44		18 53		19 16			19 34	19 44
Bedminster	d				17 28							18 29										
Parson Street	d				17 30							18 31										
Nailsea & Backwell	d	17 04			17 38				18 04		18 31	18 39				19 04		19 29				
Yatton	d	17 10			17 44				18 10		18 37	18 45				19 10		19 35				
Worle	d	17 16			17 50				18 16		18 42	18 51				19 16						
Weston Milton	d				17 55						18 47	18 56				19 20						
Weston-super-Mare	a	17 21			17 59				18 21		18 50	19 00			←	19 23		19 52				
	d	17 23							18 23		18 54 ↳				18 54	19 25						
Highbridge & Burnham	d	17 34							18 34							19 36						
Bridgwater	d	17 42							18 42							19 44						
Taunton	a	17 56					18 08	18 15	18 56					19 15	19 19	19 58					20 06	20 15

For general notes see front of timetable
For details of catering facilities see Directory of Train Operators

A From Great Malvern (Table 71) to Westbury (Table 123)
B To Weymouth (Table 123)
C From Great Malvern (Table 71) to Brighton (Table 123)
D To Westbury (Table 123)
E From Worcester Foregate Street (Table 71) to Westbury (Table 123)
G To Paignton (Table 135)

Saturdays
from 29 March

Gloucester → Taunton

Network Diagram - see first page of Table 132

		GW	XC	GW	GW	GW	XC	GW	GW	GW	XC	GW	GW	GW	XC	GW	GW	GW	GW	XC
			[1]◊	[1]◊	◊		[1]◊	[1]◊		[1]◊	[1]◊	◊	[1]◊		[1]◊				[1]◊	[1]◊
									A					A		A	B	A	A	
			☕	☕	⊼			☕		☕		⊼	☕						☕	
Gloucester [7]	d																21 15			
Cam & Dursley	d																21 28			
Yate	d																21 41			
London Paddington [15] ⊖	d			18 30				19 00		19 05									20 30	
Bath Spa [7]	d			20 01				20 25											22 00	
Bristol Parkway [7]	a																21 51			
	d	19 40	19 58		20 06	20 17	20 25		20 40		20 58	21 06			21 25	21 40	21 51			22 25
Filton Abbey Wood	d	19 42			20 09	20 20			20 42			21 09				21 42				
Stapleton Road	d																			
Lawrence Hill	d																			
Bristol Temple Meads [10]	a	19 52	20 13	20 15	20 17	20 29	20 41	20 42	20 52	20 58	21 13	21 17			21 41	21 52	22 04		22 15	22 41
	d	19 53		20 15			20 44	20 49	20 56	20 59					21 44	21 53			22 15	
Bedminster	d								20 59											
Parson Street	d								21 01											
Nailsea & Backwell	d	20 04						20 58	21 09							22 04			22s25	
Yatton	d	20 10						21 04	21 15					←		22 10		←	22s31	
Worle	d	20 16							21 21 →					21 21		22 16 →		22 16		
Weston Milton	d	20 20												21 25						
Weston-super-Mare	a	20 23		20 37				21 13					←	21 28				22 23	22s39	
	d	20 25		20 37				21 13 →					21 13	21 30				22 25		
Highbridge & Burnham	d	20 36											21 24	21 41				22 36	22 51	
Bridgwater	d	20 44											21 31	21 49				22 44	22 58	
Taunton	a	20 58		21 06			21 15			21 33			21 47	22 03	22 15			22 58	23 09	

Sundays
until 27 January

		GW	GW	GW	GW	GW	GW	GW	GW	XC	GW	XC	GW	GW	GW	XC	XC	GW	GW	XC	XC	GW
		◊	◊	◊	◊	[1]◊	◊		◊	[1]◊	◊	[1]◊		[1]◊	◊	[1]◊	[1]◊	[1]◊	◊	[1]◊	[1]◊	◊
			C		C								B									
				⊼		☕	⊼		⊼	☕	⊼	☕		☕	⊼	☕	☕	☕	⊼	☕	☕	⊼
Gloucester [7]	d												12 13									
Cam & Dursley	d												12 25									
Yate	d												12 39									
London Paddington [15] ⊖	d					08 00								11 07				12 07				
Bath Spa [7]	d					09 49								12 46				13 46				
Bristol Parkway [7]	a												12 48									
	d									11 25		12 25	12 49			12 55	13 25			13 55	14 25	
Filton Abbey Wood	d			08 54			09 56		10 54		11 54		12 52		12 57				13 54			14 54
Stapleton Road	d																					
Lawrence Hill	d																					
Bristol Temple Meads [10]	a			09 04		10 01	10 06		11 03	11 38	12 03	12 38	13 00	13 02	13 05	13 14	13 38	14 01	14 04	14 14	14 38	15 04
	d	07 30	08 15		09 05	10 03		10 10		11 44		12 44		13 02			13 44	14 01			14 44	
Bedminster	d																					
Parson Street	d																					
Nailsea & Backwell	d		08 25		09 14			10 19						13 12								
Yatton	d		08 30		09 19			10 25						13 17								
Worle	d		08 36		09 25			10 31						13 22								
Weston Milton	d																					
Weston-super-Mare	a	07 49	08 42		09 31			10 40		12 01				13 31								
	d	07 50	08 43		09 32			10 41		12 02												
Highbridge & Burnham	d		08 54		09 43			10 52														
Bridgwater	d		09 02		09 50			10 59														
Taunton	a	08 16	09 15		10 03	10 36		11 16		12 23		13 15					14 15	14 35			15 15	

		XC	GW	XC	GW	GW	GW	XC	XC	GW	GW	XC	GW	XC	GW	GW	GW	XC	GW	XC	GW	GW
				R					R					R						R		
		[1]◊		[1]		◊		[1]◊	[1]	[1]◊	◊	[1]◊		[1]	◊			[1]◊	◊	[1]	[1]◊	◊
							D									D	A					
		☕		☕		⊼		☕	☕	☕	⊼	☕		☕	⊼			☕	⊼	☕	☕	⊼
Gloucester [7]	d						15 14									17 16						
Cam & Dursley	d						15 27									17 29						
Yate	d						15 40									17 42						
London Paddington [15] ⊖	d									15 07											17 07	
Bath Spa [7]	d									16 47											18 46	
Bristol Parkway [7]	a						15 49									17 51						
	d	14 55		15 25			15 50	15 55	16 25			16 55		17 25		17 51		17 55		18 25		
Filton Abbey Wood	d					15 56	16 01				16 57				17 55	17 58			18 24			18 56
Stapleton Road	d																					
Lawrence Hill	d																					
Bristol Temple Meads [10]	a	15 11		15 38		16 06	16 10	16 14	16 38	17 00	17 06	17 14		17 38	18 03	18 07		18 14	18 34	18 38	19 01	19 06
	d	15 11	15 16	15 44	15 50		16 16		16 44	17 02			17 16	17 44			18 10			18 44	19 02	
Bedminster	d		15 19		15 53								17 19									
Parson Street	d		15 21		15 56																	
Nailsea & Backwell	d		15 29		16 04		16 25			17 12			17 28				18 19				19 13	
Yatton	d		15 35		16 10		16 31			17 17			17 34				18 25				19 19	
Worle	d		15 41		16 19		16 37			17 22			17 40				18 31				19 24	
Weston Milton	d		15 46				16 42						17 45									
Weston-super-Mare	a		15 49		16 26		16 47			17 29			17 48				18 36				19 32	
	d				16 27					17 31							18 40					
Highbridge & Burnham	d				16 38												18 50					
Bridgwater	d				16 46												18 58					
Taunton	a	15 43		16 15	17 02				17 15	17 53				18 15			19 11			19 15		

For general notes see front of timetable
For details of catering facilities see Directory of Train Operators

A To Exeter St Davids (Table 135)
B From Cheltenham Spa (Table 57)
C To Penzance (Table 135)
D From Worcester Shrub Hill (Table 57)

Sundays
until 27 January

Gloucester → Taunton

Network Diagram - see first page of Table 132

Station		XC	GW	GW	XC	GW	GW	XC	GW	XC	GW	GW	GW	XC	XC	GW	GW	XC	GW	GW	XC
		R 1		◇	R 1		◇	1 ◇		R 1		1 ◇	◇	1 ◇	R 1			1 ◇	1 ◇	◇	1 ◇
												A				B					
		🍴		🛒	🍴		🛒	🍴				🍴	🛒	🍴						🛒	🍴
Gloucester [7]	d	18 39														21 15					
Cam & Dursley	d															21 28					
Yate	d															21 41					
London Paddington [15] ⊖	d											19 07							21 07		
Bath Spa [7]	d											20 47							22 47		
Bristol Parkway [7]	a	19 07														21 50					
	d	19 08			19 25			20 01		20 25				20 58	21 25	21 51		22 25			23 25
Filton Abbey Wood	d			19 25			19 52						20 54			21 54				22 56	
Stapleton Road	d																				
Lawrence Hill	d																				
Bristol Temple Meads [10]	a	19 24		19 34	19 38		20 02	20 16		20 38		21 00	21 04	21 14	21 38	22 03		22 41	23 03	23 06	23 41
	d		19 25		19 44				20 25	20 44		21 02			21 44		22 30		23 03		
Bedminster	d		19 28						20 28								22 33				
Parson Street	d		19 30														22 35				
Nailsea & Backwell	d		19 38						20 36			21 11					22 43		23 14		
Yatton	d		19 44			←			20 41		←	21 16					22 49		23 20		
Worle	d		19 50			19 50			20 47		20 47	21 21					22 55		23 25		
Weston Milton	d		→			19 54			→								23 00				
Weston-super-Mare	a					19 57					20 53	21 31					23 03		23 32		
	d					19 59					20 57	21 32									
Highbridge & Burnham	d					20 09					21 10										
Bridgwater	d					20 17					21 17										
Taunton	a				20 15	20 32				21 15	21 32	21 53			22 15						

Sundays
3 February to 23 March

Station		GW	GW	GW	GW	GW	GW	GW	GW	GW	GW	GW	GW	GW	XC	GW	GW	GW	XC	GW	GW	GW	GW	XC
				1 ◇		◇		1 ◇		◇		1 ◇	◇	1 ◇	1 ◇	◇		1 ◇	1 ◇		◇		1 ◇	1 ◇
																				C				
		🚌	🚌		🚌		🚌		🚌		🚌													
				🍴		🛒		🍴		🛒		🍴	🛒	🍴	🍴	🛒		🍴	🍴		🛒		🍴	🍴
Gloucester [7]	d																			12 13				
Cam & Dursley	d																			12 25				
Yate	d																			12 39				
London Paddington [15] ⊖	d																							
Bath Spa [7]	d																							
Bristol Parkway [7]	a																			12 48				
	d			08 39				09 41				10 22		11 23	11 25			12 23	12 25	12 49			13 23	13 25
Filton Abbey Wood	d					08 54				09 56			10 54			11 54				12 52	12 57			
Stapleton Road	d																							
Lawrence Hill	d																							
Bristol Temple Meads [10]	a			08 52		09 04		09 52		10 06		10 34	11 03	11 34	11 38	12 04		12 34	12 38	13 00	13 05		13 34	13 38
	d	07 30	08 15		08 55		09 50		09 56		10 10				11 50		12 08		12 50			13 25		13 50
Bedminster	d																							
Parson Street	d																							
Nailsea & Backwell	d		08 35		09 15		10 10				10 30						12 17					13 34		
Yatton	d		08 50		09 30		10 25				10 45						12 22					13 39		
Worle	d		09 05		09 45		10 40				11 00						12 45					14 02		
Weston Milton	d																							
Weston-super-Mare	a	08 10	09 20		10 00		10 55				11 15						12 50					14 07		
	d	08 10	09 20		10 00		10 55				11 15											14 08		
Highbridge & Burnham	d	08 30	09 40		10 20		11 15															14 18		
Bridgwater	d	08 45	09 55		10 35		11 30															14 26		
Taunton	a	09 10	10 20		11 00		11 55		11 01		11 55				12 59				14 15			14 40		15 15

Station		GW	GW	XC	GW	GW	GW	XC	GW	GW	GW	GW	XC	GW	GW	GW	GW	XC	GW	GW	GW	GW	GW
		◇	1 ◇	1 ◇	◇		1 ◇	R 1		◇		1 ◇	R 1	1 ◇	◇		1 ◇	R 1	◇			1 ◇	◇
											B			D						B	A		
		🛒	🍴	🍴	🛒		🍴	🍴		🛒		🍴	🍴	🍴	🛒		🍴	🍴	🛒			🍴	🛒
Gloucester [7]	d										15 14									17 16			
Cam & Dursley	d										15 27									17 29			
Yate	d										15 40									17 42			
London Paddington [15] ⊖	d																						
Bath Spa [7]	d													16 43									
Bristol Parkway [7]	a										15 49									17 51			
	d		14 23	14 25			15 23	15 25			15 50	16 23	16 25				17 23	17 25		17 51		18 23	
Filton Abbey Wood	d	13 54			14 54					15 56	16 01				16 57				17 55	17 58			18 33
Stapleton Road	d																						
Lawrence Hill	d																						
Bristol Temple Meads [10]	a	14 04	14 34	14 38	15 04		15 34	15 38		16 06	16 10	16 34	16 38	16 57	17 06		17 34	17 38	18 03	18 07		18 34	18 43
	d			14 50		15 16		15 50	15 50		16 16		16 44	17 03		17 16		17 44			18 10		
Bedminster	d					15 19			15 53							17 19							
Parson Street	d					15 21			15 56														
Nailsea & Backwell	d					15 29			16 04		16 25			17 12		17 28					18 19		
Yatton	d					15 35			16 10		16 31			17 17		17 34					18 25		
Worle	d					15 41			16 19		16 37					17 40					18 31		
Weston Milton	d					15 46					16 42					17 45							
Weston-super-Mare	a					15 49		16 08	16 26		16 47			17 26		17 48					18 36		
	d							16 13	16 27					17 28							18 40		
Highbridge & Burnham	d								16 38												18 50		
Bridgwater	d								16 46												18 58		
Taunton	a			16 15				16 33	17 02				17 15	17 50				18 15			19 11		

For general notes see front of timetable
For details of catering facilities see Directory of Train Operators

A To Exeter St Davids (Table 135)
B From Worcester Shrub Hill (Table 57)
C From Cheltenham Spa (Table 57)
D From Swindon (Table 125)

3 February to 23 March

Gloucester → Taunton

Network Diagram - see first page of Table 132

		XC R 1 ☕	GW	GW ◇ 🛒	GW 1 ◇ ☕	GW 1 ◇ ☕	GW ◇ 🛒	XC R 1 ☕		GW ◇ 🛒	GW	GW 1 ◇ ☕	XC R 1	GW	GW 1 ◇ A ☕	GW ◇ 🛒	XC R 1	GW	GW 1 ◇ ☕	GW B	XC R 1	GW ◇ 🛒	GW 🚌	XC 1 ◇ ☕		
Gloucester [7]	d	18 07																		21 15						
Cam & Dursley	d																			21 28						
Yate	d																			21 41						
London Paddington [15] ⊖	d				17 30																					
Bath Spa [7]	d				19 12										20 46											
Bristol Parkway [7]	a	18 35																		21 50						
	d	18 36				19 23		19 25				20 23	20 25				21 25		21 47	21 51	22 25			23 25		
Filton Abbey Wood	d			18 56			19 33			19 52						20 58				21 54		22 56				
Stapleton Road	d																									
Lawrence Hill	d																									
Bristol Temple Meads [10]	a	18 47		19 06	19 28	19 34	19 43	19 38		20 01		20 34	20 38		20 59	21 08	21 38		21 58	22 03	22 41	23 06		23 41		
	d	18 50	19 05		19 29			19 44			20 25		20 44		21 02		21 44	21 46					23 33			
Bedminster	d		19 08								20 28							21 49								
Parson Street	d		19 10															21 51								
Nailsea & Backwell	d		19 18		19 39						20 36				21 11			21 59					23 53			
Yatton	d		19 24		19 44						20 41			←	21 16			22 05					00 08			
Worle	d		19 30		19 49						20 47			20 47	21 21			22 11					00 23			
Weston Milton	d		19 34								→							22 16								
Weston-super-Mare	a		19 37		19 56									20 53	21 29			22 19					00 38			
	d													20 57	21 30											
Highbridge & Burnham	d													21 10												
Bridgwater	d													21 17												
Taunton	a	19 21						20 15					21 15	21 32	21 51		22 15									

Sundays

from 30 March

		GW 🛒	GW ◇ C	GW ◇ 🛒	GW	GW 1 ◇ ☕	GW ◇ 🛒	GW		GW 1 ◇ ☕	GW ◇ 🛒	XC 1 ◇ ☕	GW 1 ◇ ☕	GW ◇ D 🛒	XC 1 ◇ ☕	GW E		GW 1 ◇ G ☕	GW ◇ 🛒	XC 1 ◇ ☕	XC 1 ◇ ☕	GW 1 ◇ ☕	GW ◇ 🛒	XC 1 ◇ ☕		XC 1 ◇ ☕
Gloucester [7]	d															12 11										
Cam & Dursley	d															12 23										
Yate	d															12 36										
London Paddington [15] ⊖	d					08 00				09 00			10 03					11 03				12 03				
Bath Spa [7]	d					09 40				10 29			11 46					12 46				13 48				
Bristol Parkway [7]	a															12 46										
	d			08 50			09 50				10 51	11 25		11 50	12 25	12 46			12 50	12 58	13 25		13 50	13 58		14 25
Filton Abbey Wood	d			08 54			09 55				10 54			11 54		12 49			12 54				13 54			
Stapleton Road	d																									
Lawrence Hill	d																									
Bristol Temple Meads [10]	a			09 04		09 54	10 05			10 41	11 03	11 38	12 00	12 04	12 38	12 58		13 00	13 03	13 13	13 38	14 02	14 04	14 13		14 38
	d	07 30	08 15		09 05	09 57		10 10		10 41		11 44	12 02		12 44			13 02			13 44	14 03				14 44
Bedminster	d																									
Parson Street	d																									
Nailsea & Backwell	d		08 25		09 14			10 19					12 12					13 11								
Yatton	d		08 30		09 19			10 25					12 18					13 17								
Worle	d		08 36		09 25			10 31					12 24					13 22								
Weston Milton	d																									
Weston-super-Mare	a	07 49	08 42		09 31			10 36				12 01	12 31					13 28								
	d	07 50	08 43		09 32			10 41				12 02						13 29								
Highbridge & Burnham	d		08 54		09 43			10 52																		
Bridgwater	d		09 02		09 50			10 59																		
Taunton	a	08 16	09 15		10 03	10 30		11 16		11 17		12 26			13 15			13 53			14 15	14 37				15 15

		GW ◇ 🛒	XC 1 ◇ ☕	GW	XC R 1 ☕	GW 1 ◇ ☕	GW	GW B		GW ◇ 🛒	XC 1 ◇ ☕	XC R 1 ☕	GW 1 ◇ ☕	GW ◇ 🛒	XC 1 ◇ ☕	GW		XC R 1 ☕	GW ◇ 🛒	GW B	GW H	XC 1 ◇ ☕	GW ◇ 🛒	XC R 1 ☕		GW 1 ◇ ☕
Gloucester [7]	d							15 11												17 16						
Cam & Dursley	d							15 24												17 29						
Yate	d							15 37												17 42						
London Paddington [15] ⊖	d					13 37							15 03													17 03
Bath Spa [7]	d												16 48													18 46
Bristol Parkway [7]	a							15 46												17 53						
	d	14 50	14 58		15 25			15 46		15 50	15 58	16 25		16 50	16 58			17 25	17 50	17 55		18 02	18 20	18 25		
Filton Abbey Wood	d	14 54						15 50		15 56				16 57					17 55	17 59			18 24			
Stapleton Road	d																									
Lawrence Hill	d																									
Bristol Temple Meads [10]	a	15 04	15 11		15 38	15 45		15 59		16 06	16 13	16 38	17 02	17 06	17 13			17 38	18 03	18 08		18 17	18 34	18 38		19 00
	d		15 11	15 16	15 44	15 47	15 50	16 10				16 44	17 02			17 16		17 44			18 10			18 44		19 02
Bedminster	d			15 19			15 53									17 19										
Parson Street	d			15 21			15 56																			
Nailsea & Backwell	d			15 29			16 04	16 19					17 12			17 28					18 19					19 13
Yatton	d			15 35			16 10	16 25					17 17			17 34					18 25					19 19
Worle	d			15 41			16 19	16 31					17 22			17 40					18 31					19 24
Weston Milton	d			15 46				16 36								17 45										
Weston-super-Mare	a			15 49			16 26	16 41					17 29			17 48					18 36					19 31
	d						16 27						17 31								18 40					
Highbridge & Burnham	d						16 38														18 50					
Bridgwater	d						16 46														18 58					
Taunton	a		15 43		16 15	16 20	17 02					17 15	17 56					18 15			19 11			19 15		

For general notes see front of timetable
For details of catering facilities see Directory of Train Operators

- **A** From Swindon (Table 125) to Exeter St Davids (Table 135)
- **B** From Worcester Shrub Hill (Table 57)
- **C** To Penzance (Table 135)
- **D** To Portsmouth Harbour (Table 123)
- **E** From Cheltenham Spa (Table 57)
- **G** To Paignton (Table 135)
- **H** To Exeter St Davids (Table 135)

Table 134

Sundays

from 30 March

Gloucester → Taunton

Network Diagram - see first page of Table 132

		GW	GW	XC	GW	XC	GW	GW		XC	GW	XC	GW	GW	GW	XC		XC	GW	GW	XC	GW	GW	XC		
				R		R						R						R								
		◇		1	◇	1		◇		1 ◇		1		1 ◇	◇	1 ◇		1			1 ◇	1 ◇	◇	1 ◇		
														A					B							
		⊥o		⊥P	⊥o	⊥P		⊥o		⊥P				⊥P	⊥o							⊥P	⊥o			
Gloucester 7	d	.	.	18 39	.	.	.	.	.	.	.	.	.	.	.	.	.	.	21 15	.	.	.	.	.	.	.
Cam & Dursley	d	.	.	.	.	.	.	.	.	.	.	.	.	.	.	.	.	.	21 28	.	.	.	.	.	.	.
Yate	d	.	.	.	.	.	.	.	.	.	.	.	.	.	.	.	.	.	21 41	.	.	.	.	.	.	.
London Paddington 15	⊖ d	.	.	.	.	.	.	.	.	.	.	.	.	19 03	.	.	.	.	.	.	.	21 03	.	.	.	.
Bath Spa 7	d	.	.	.	.	.	.	.	.	.	.	.	.	20 46	.	.	.	.	.	.	.	22 48	.	.	.	.
Bristol Parkway 7	a	.	.	19 07	.	.	.	.	.	.	.	.	.	.	.	.	.	.	21 50	.	.	.	.	.	.	.
	d	18 50	.	19 08	19 20	19 25	.	19 49	.	20 01	.	20 25	.	.	20 50	20 58	.	21 25	21 51	.	22 25	.	22 50	23 25	.	.
Filton Abbey Wood	d	18 56	.	.	19 25	.	.	19 52	.	.	.	.	.	.	20 54	.	.	.	21 54	.	.	.	22 56	.	.	.
Stapleton Road	d	.	.	.	.	.	.	.	.	.	.	.	.	.	.	.	.	.	.	.	.	.	.	.	.	.
Lawrence Hill	d	.	.	.	.	.	.	.	.	.	.	.	.	.	.	.	.	.	.	.	.	.	.	.	.	.
Bristol Temple Meads 10	a	19 05	.	19 24	19 34	19 38	.	20 02	.	20 16	.	20 38	.	21 00	21 04	21 14	.	21 38	22 03	.	22 41	23 04	23 06	23 41	.	.
	d	.	19 18	.	.	19 44	.	.	.	.	20 25	20 44	.	21 02	.	.	.	21 44	.	22 30	.	23 05	.	.	.	.
Bedminster	d	.	.	.	.	.	.	.	.	.	20 28	.	.	.	.	.	.	.	.	22 33	.	.	.	.	.	.
Parson Street	d	.	.	.	.	.	.	.	.	.	.	.	.	.	.	.	.	.	.	22 36	.	.	.	.	.	.
Nailsea & Backwell	d	.	19 28	.	.	.	.	.	.	.	20 36	.	.	21 11	.	.	.	.	.	22 44	.	23 13	.	.	.	.
Yatton	d	.	19 34	.	.	.	.	.	.	.	20 41	.	←	21 17	.	.	.	.	.	22 49	.	23 19	.	.	.	.
Worle	d	.	19 40	.	.	.	←	.	.	.	20 47	.	20 47	21 22	.	.	.	.	.	22 55	.	23 24	.	.	.	.
Weston Milton	d	.	19 45	.	.	.	19 45	.	.	.	→	.	.	.	.	.	.	.	.	23 01	.	.	.	.	.	.
Weston-super-Mare	a	.	→	.	.	.	19 48	.	.	.	.	.	20 53	21 30	.	.	.	.	.	23 04	.	23 31	.	.	.	.
	d	.	.	.	.	.	19 59	.	.	.	.	.	20 57	21 30	.	.	.	.	.	.	.	.	.	.	.	.
Highbridge & Burnham	d	.	.	.	.	.	20 09	.	.	.	.	.	21 10	.	.	.	.	.	.	.	.	.	.	.	.	.
Bridgwater	d	.	.	.	.	.	20 17	.	.	.	.	.	21 17	.	.	.	.	.	.	.	.	.	.	.	.	.
Taunton	a	.	.	.	.	20 15	20 32	.	.	.	.	21 15	21 32	21 57	.	.	.	22 15	.	.	.	.	.	.	.	.

For general notes see front of timetable
For details of catering facilities see
Directory of Train Operators

A To Exeter St Davids (Table 135)
B From Worcester Shrub Hill (Table 57)

Table 134

Taunton → Gloucester

Mondays to Fridays

Network Diagram - see first page of Table 132

Miles			GW	GW	XC	GW	GW	GW	GW	XC	GW	GW	GW	GW	XC	GW	GW	GW	GW	XC	GW	GW	GW	GW	XC	GW
			MO		R ■1				■1 ◇	■1 ◇	■1 ◇		■1 ◇		■1 ◇				■1 ◇	■1 ◇	◇		■1 ◇		■1 ◇	
			A			B	C	D				B	E	G		H	G		J		K	B	G			L
			🚌		☕				🛒	☕	☕		⊠		☕				⊠	☕			☕		☕	
0	**Taunton**	d					05 30					06 02		06 34	06 51				06 56				07 14	07 32	07 51	
11¾	Bridgwater	d					05 41					06 14		06 47					07 07				07 24	07 44		
18	Highbridge & Burnham	d					05 48					06 22		06 55					07 14				07 32	07 52		
25¾	**Weston-super-Mare**	a					06 00					06 33		07 06					07 26				07 43	08 03		
—		d					06 02		06 24			06 34	06 48	07 08			←		07 27			07 33	07 50	08 08		
27	Weston Milton	d							06 28			06 38	06 52	07 12								07 36	07 53	08 11		
29½	Worle	d					06 07		06 33			06 43	06 57	07 17			07 17		07 34			07 41	07 59	08 16		
33½	Yatton	d					06 13		06 39			06 48	07 03	→			07 23		07 40			07 46	08 05	→		
37½	Nailsea & Backwell	d					06 19		06 46			06 54	07 10				07 29		07 45			07 52	08 11			
43¾	Parson Street	d										07 04					07 38					08 02				
44½	Bedminster	d										07 06					07 41					08 04				
45½	**Bristol Temple Meads** [10]	a					06 31		06 57			07 09	07 21		07 25		07 44		07 57			08 07	08 22		08 25	
—		d	00 45	05 54	06 15	06 22	06 43	06 50	07 00	07 00	07 15	07 19	07 30		07 30	07 41	07 45	07 54	08 00	08 00	08 13	08 19	08 30		08 30	08 41
46½	Lawrence Hill	d				06 25		06 54				07 22					07 48				08 16	08 22				
47	Stapleton Road	d				06 27		06 56				07 24					07 51				08 18	08 24				
50	Filton Abbey Wood	d		06a00		06a32		07a01			07a21	07 30				07 48	07 56	08a02			08 24	08a30				08 48
51¼	**Bristol Parkway** [7]	a	01 05		06 23					07 08		07 33			07 38	07 51	08 03			08 08	08 30				08 38	08 51
—		d			06 25											07 52										08 52
—	Bath Spa [7]	a					06 59		07 11				07 41						08 11				08 41			
—	London Paddington [15]	⊖ a							08 44				09 15						09 44				10 15			
57½	Yate	d														08 01										09 01
72¼	Cam & Dursley	d														08 13										09 13
85¼	**Gloucester** [7]	a			06 55											08 31										09 29

		GW	GW	XC	GW	GW	GW	XC	GW	GW	GW	GW	XC	GW	XC	GW	GW	GW	XC	GW	XC	GW	GW	GW	GW	XC
			◇	■1 ◇	◇			R ■1			◇	■1 ◇	■1 ◇		■1 ◇	◇		◇	■1 ◇		R ■1			◇		■1 ◇
					K	B			N			Q		B		U				B		V			B	
			🛒	☕				☕			🛒	☕	☕		☕			🛒	☕		☕			🛒		☕
Taunton	d			08 06			08 37	08 51				09 04			09 51					10 07	10 51				11 04	11 16
Bridgwater	d						08 49													10 19					11 16	
Highbridge & Burnham	d						08 57													10 27					11 24	
Weston-super-Mare	a			08 29			09 09					09 25								10 39					11 35	
	d	←		08 30		08 40	09 10			←		09 27		09 40			10 10			10 40			11 10		11 40	
Weston Milton	d					08 43	09 14							09 43			10 13						11 13		→	
Worle	d	08 16				08 48	09 19			09 19		09 35		09 48			10 18			10 46			11 18			
Yatton	d	08 22				08 53	→			09 24		09 40		09 53			10 23			10 52			11 23			
Nailsea & Backwell	d	08 28				08 59				09 30		09 46		09 59			10 29			10 58			11 29			
Parson Street	d	08 38				09 09				09 40				10 09			10 39						11 39			
Bedminster	d	08 41				09 11				09 43				10 11			10 41						11 41			
Bristol Temple Meads [10]	a	08 44		08 50		09 14		09 27		09 46		09 55		10 14	10 25		10 44			11 11	11 25		11 44			11 53
	d	08 46	08 54	09 00	09 10	09 19		09 30	09 41	09 47	09 54	10 00	10 00	10 19	10 30	10 41	10 46	10 54	11 00	11 19	11 30	11 41	11 46	11 54		12 00
Lawrence Hill	d	08 49			09 13	09 22								10 22						11 22						
Stapleton Road	d	08 51			09 15	09 24								10 24						11 24						
Filton Abbey Wood	d	08 57	09a00		09 20	09a29			09 48	09 54	10a01			10a29		10 48	10 53	11a01		11a29		11 48	11 53	12a01		
Bristol Parkway [7]	a	09 03		09 08	09 25			09 38	09 51	10 03			10 08		10 38	10 51	10 58		11 08		11 38	11 51	11 58			12 08
	d								09 52							10 52						11 52				
Bath Spa [7]	a											10 11														
London Paddington [15]	⊖ a											11 42														
Yate	d								10 01							11 01						12 01				
Cam & Dursley	d								10 13							11 13						12 13				
Gloucester [7]	a								10 31							11 30						12 29				

		GW	GW	XC	GW	GW	GW	XC	GW	XC	GW	GW	GW	GW	XC	GW	XC	GW	GW	GW	GW	XC	GW	XC	GW	GW
		■1 ◇		R ■1	◇		◇	■1 ◇		R ■1	◇		◇		■1 ◇		R ■1				◇	R ■1		R ■1	◇	
			B		X				B		K			B		B		Y	Z				B		K	
		☕		☕			🛒	☕		☕			🛒		☕		☕				🛒	☕		☕		
Taunton	d	11 22		11 51					12 07	12 51				13 07	13 16		13 51						14 07	14 51		
Bridgwater	d								12 19					13 19									14 19			
Highbridge & Burnham	d								12 27					13 27									14 27			
Weston-super-Mare	a		←						12 38					13 38		←							14 38			
	d		11 40			12 10			12 42			13 10		13 40		13 40				14 10			14 40			15 10
Weston Milton	d					12 13						13 13		→						14 13						15 13
Worle	d		11 46			12 18			12 48			13 18				13 46				14 18			14 46			15 18
Yatton	d		11 52			12 23			12 54			13 23				13 52				14 23			14 52			15 23
Nailsea & Backwell	d		11 58			12 29			13 00			13 29				13 58				14 29			14 58			15 29
Parson Street	d					12 39						13 39								14 39						15 39
Bedminster	d					12 41						13 41								14 41						15 41
Bristol Temple Meads [10]	a	11 55	12 11	12 25		12 44			13 13	13 25		13 44			13 54	14 11	14 25			14 44			15 11	15 25		15 44
	d	12 00	12 19	12 30	12 41	12 46	12 54	13 00	13 19	13 30	13 41	13 46	13 54		14 00	14 19	14 30		14 41	14 46	14 54	15 00	15 19	15 30	15 41	15 46
Lawrence Hill	d		12 22						13 22							14 22							15 22			
Stapleton Road	d		12 24						13 24							14 24							15 24			
Filton Abbey Wood	d		12a29		12 48	12 53	13a01		13a29		13 48	13 53	14a01			14a29		14 40	14 48	14 53	15a00		15a29		15 48	15 53
Bristol Parkway [7]	a			12 38	12 51	12 58		13 08		13 38	13 51	13 58			14 08		14 38	14 45	14 51	14 58		15 08		15 38	15 51	15 58
	d				12 52						13 52								14 52						15 52	
Bath Spa [7]	a	12 11																								
London Paddington [15]	⊖ a	13 42																								
Yate	d				13 01						14 01								15 01						16 01	
Cam & Dursley	d				13 13						14 13								15 13						16 13	
Gloucester [7]	a				13 29						14 29								15 29						16 31	

For general notes see front of timetable
For details of catering facilities see Directory of Train Operators

- **A** From 4 February to 24 March
- **B** To Cardiff Central (Table 132)
- **C** To Westbury (Table 123)
- **D** From Westbury to Cardiff Central (Table 123)
- **E** **The Bristolian**
- **G** From Exeter St Davids (Table 135)
- **H** From Salisbury (Table 123)
- **J** From Plymouth (Table 135)
- **K** From Weymouth (Table 123)
- **L** From Warminster (Table 123) to Great Malvern (Table 71)
- **N** From Westbury (Table 123)
- **Q** From Paignton (Table 135)
- **U** From Weymouth (Table 123) to Great Malvern (Table 71)
- **V** From Warminster (Table 123)
- **X** From Brighton (Table 123) to Great Malvern (Table 71)
- **Y** From Southampton Central (Table 123)
- **Z** From Westbury (Table 123) to Worcester Foregate Street (Table 71)

Taunton → Gloucester

Network Diagram - see first page of Table 132

		GW	XC	GW	GW	XC	GW	GW	GW	XC	GW	GW	GW	XC	GW	GW	GW	GW	XC	GW	XC	GW	GW	GW	GW	XC
		◇	R 1			R 1			◇	R 1			1 ◇	R 1	◇			◇	1 ◇		1 ◇	1 ◇			◇	1 ◇
				A			B					A			C		A			A			B			
		🛒	☕			☕			🛒	☕			☕	☕				🛒	☕		☕	🛒			🛒	☕
Taunton	d		15 14	15 18		15 51						16 07		16 51			17 07		17 21		17 51					
Bridgwater	d			15 30								16 19					17 19									
Highbridge & Burnham	d			15 38								16 27					17 27									
Weston-super-Mare	a		15 34	15 49								16 38					17 38									
	d		15 36	15 51				16 10				16 40	17 02			17 10	17 40					18 08		18 15		
Weston Milton	d							16 13								17 13				←						
Worle	d							16 18				16 46				17 18	17 46 →			17 46				18 21		
Yatton	d							16 23				16 52				17 23				17 52				18 26		
Nailsea & Backwell	d							16 29				16 58				17 29				17 58				18 32		
Parson Street	d							16 39								17 39				18 07						
Bedminster	d							16 41								17 41				18 10						
Bristol Temple Meads 10	a		15 55	16 11		16 25		16 44				17 11	17 22	17 25		17 44			17 55	18 13	18 25	18 29		18 45		
	d	15 54	16 00	16 19	16 26	16 30	16 41	16 46	16 54	17 00	17 10	17 19	17 30	17 30	17 41	17 46		17 54	18 00	18 19	18 30	18 31	18 41	18 47	18 54	19 00
Lawrence Hill	d			16 22							17 13	17 22								18 22						
Stapleton Road	d			16 24							17 15	17 24								18 24						
Filton Abbey Wood	d	16a01		16a29			16 48	16 53	17a00		17 21	17a29			17 48	17 53		18a01		18a29			18 48	18 54	19a01	
Bristol Parkway 7	a		16 08		16 37	16 38	16 51	16 58		17 08	17 25			17 38	17 51	17 58			18 08		18 38		18 51	18 58		19 08
	d						16 52								17 52								18 52			
Bath Spa 7	a												17 41									18 42				
London Paddington 15 ⊖	a												19 15									20 15				
Yate	d						17 01								18 01								19 01			
Cam & Dursley	d						17 13								18 13								19 13			
Gloucester 7	a						17 29								18 31								19 29			

		GW	XC	XC	GW	GW	GW	GW	XC	GW	GW	GW	GW	GW	GW	GW	GW	GW	XC	GW	GW	GW	GW	GW		
														FO	FX											
			R 1	1 ◇	◇		◇		1 ◇	◇	◇			1 ◇	1 ◇		◇	1	1 ◇		1 ◇	◇				
					D			A	E	G		A	H			H										
			☕	☕			🛒		☕		🛒			☕	☕		🛒				🛒	🛒				
Taunton	d	18 07		18 52				19 11	19 51				20 28	21 06	21 06						21 30		22 20	22 45		
Bridgwater	d	18 19						19 23					20 41								21 40			22 57		
Highbridge & Burnham	d	18 27						19 31					20 48								21 47			23 05		
Weston-super-Mare	a	18 38						19 42					20 59								21 57		22 44	23 16		
	d	18 40				19 10		19 47					21 01					21 30			21 59		22 46	23 18		
Weston Milton	d	18 43				19 13							21 04					21 33						23 21		
Worle	d	18 48				19 18		19 53					21 09					21 37			22 05			23 26		
Yatton	d	18 54				19 23		19 59					21 15					21 42			22 10			23 32		
Nailsea & Backwell	d	19 00				19 29		20 05					21 21					21 48			22 16			23 38		
Parson Street	d	19 09				19 39							21 30											23 48		
Bedminster	d	19 12				19 41							21 33											23 51		
Bristol Temple Meads 10	a	19 15		19 25		19 44		20 17	20 25				21 36	21 39	21 39	←		21 59			22 28		23 06	23 54		
	d		19 25	19 30	19 41	19 46	19 54	20 19	20 30	20 41	20 54	21 19	21 45 →	21 40	21 40	21 45	21 54		22 00	22 10	22 33	22 54				
Lawrence Hill	d					19 49		20 22				21 22				21 48										
Stapleton Road	d					19 51		20 24				21 24				21a50										
Filton Abbey Wood	d		19a31		19 48	19 57	20a00	20a29		20 48	21a01	21a29					22a00			22 17		23a00				
Bristol Parkway 7	a			19 38	19 51	20 03			20 38	20 51									22 08	22 20						
	d				19 52					20 52										22 21						
Bath Spa 7	a													21 54	21 54						22 44					
London Paddington 15 ⊖	a													23 29	23 36						00 32					
Yate	d				20 01					21 01										22 30						
Cam & Dursley	d				20 13					21 13										22 42						
Gloucester 7	a				20 29					21 29										23 01						

Saturdays

until 26 January

		XC	GW	GW	GW	GW	GW	XC	GW	GW	GW	GW	XC	GW		GW	XC	GW	GW	GW	XC	GW	GW	GW	XC	GW
		1 ◇			1 ◇	1 ◇		1 ◇				1 ◇	1 ◇				1 ◇			◇	1 ◇		1 ◇		1 ◇	◇
			J	A			K		L	K				A				B				A				C
		☕			☕	☕		☕				☕	☕				☕				☕		☕		☕	
Taunton	d		05 26				06 13	06 38				07 00				07 32	07 51						08 34	08 38	08 51	
Bridgwater	d		05 37				06 26					07 10				07 44								08 50		
Highbridge & Burnham	d		05 44				06 34					07 17				07 52								08 58		
Weston-super-Mare	a		05 54				06 45	06 58				07 26				08 02							08 54	09 08		
	d		06 02			06 24	06 49	07 00				07 28		07 34		08 09						08 40	09 00	09 09		
Weston Milton	d						06 52							07 37		08 12			←					09 12		
Worle	d		06 07			06 31	06 57					07 34		07 42		08 16 →			08 16			08 48		09 17 →		
Yatton	d		06 13			06 36	07 03					07 40		07 47					08 22			08 53				
Nailsea & Backwell	d		06 19			06 42	07 09					07 45		07 53					08 28			08 59				
Parson Street	d						07 19							08 03					08 38							
Bedminster	d						07 21							08 05					08 41							
Bristol Temple Meads 10	a		06 31			06 53	07 24	07 27		←		07 57		08 08			08 25		08 44			09 12	09 20		09 25	
	d	06 15	06 43	06 50	06 58	07 00	07 46 →	07 30	07 41	07 46	07 54	08 00	08 00	08 19			08 30	08 41	08 46	08 54	09 00	09 19	09 30		09 30	09 41
Lawrence Hill	d			06 53						07 49				08 22								09 22				
Stapleton Road	d			06 56						07 51				08 24								09 24				
Filton Abbey Wood	d			07a01					07 48	07 57	08a00			08a29				08 48	08 53	09a00		09a29				09 48
Bristol Parkway 7	a	06 23			07 06			07 38	07 51	08 03			08 08				18 38	08 51	08 56		09 08				09 38	09 51
	d	06 25							07 52									08 52								09 52
Bath Spa 7	a		06 59			07 11						08 11											09 41			
London Paddington 15 ⊖	a					08 45						09 44											11 15			
Yate	d								08 01									09 01								10 01
Cam & Dursley	d								08 15									09 13								10 15
Gloucester 7	a	06 54							08 31									09 29								10 31

For general notes see front of timetable
For details of catering facilities see Directory of Train Operators

A To Cardiff Central (Table 132)

B From Warminster (Table 123) to Great Malvern (Table 71)

C From Weymouth (Table 123)

D From Weymouth (Table 123) to Cheltenham Spa (Table 57)

E ☕ to Bristol Temple Meads

G From Brighton (Table 123) to Worcester Shrub Hill (Table 57)

H To Severn Beach (Table 133)

J To Westbury (Table 123)

K From Exeter St Davids (Table 135)

L From Salisbury (Table 123)

Taunton → Gloucester

Network Diagram - see first page of Table 132

		GW	GW ◇	XC 1 ◇ ☕	GW A		XC 1 ◇ ☕	GW ◇ B	GW	GW ◇	XC 1 ◇ ☕	GW A	XC 1 ◇ ☕	GW	GW A	GW ◇	XC 1 ◇ ☕	GW A	XC 1 ◇ ☕		GW ◇ C	GW	GW ◇	XC 1 ◇ ☕	GW A	XC 1 ◇ ☕
Taunton	d						09 51					10 11	10 51		11 07		11 16		11 51						12 11	12 51
Bridgwater	d											10 23			11 19										12 22	
Highbridge & Burnham	d											10 31			11 27										12 29	
Weston-super-Mare	a											10 42			11 38			←							12 39	
	d				09 40				10 08			10 43		11 08	11 40			11 40				12 08			12 41	
Weston Milton	d	←							10 11					11 11	→							12 11				
Worle	d	09 17			09 46				10 16			10 50		11 16				11 46				12 16			12 47	
Yatton	d	09 23			09 51				10 21			10 56		11 21				11 51				12 21			12 53	
Nailsea & Backwell	d	09 29			09 57				10 27			11 02		11 27				11 57				12 27			12 59	
Parson Street	d	09 38							10 37					11 37								12 37				
Bedminster	d	09 41							10 39					11 39								12 39				
Bristol Temple Meads [10]	a	09 44			10 10		10 25		10 42			11 14	11 25	11 42			11 55	12 10	12 25			12 42			13 11	13 25
	d	09 46	09 54	10 00	10 19		10 30	10 41	10 46	10 54	11 00	11 19	11 30	11 46		11 53	12 00	12 19	12 30		12 41	12 46	12 53	13 00	13 19	13 30
Lawrence Hill	d				10 22							11 22						12 22							13 22	
Stapleton Road	d				10 24							11 24						12 24							13 24	
Filton Abbey Wood	d	09 53	10a00		10a29			10 48	10 53	11a00		11a29		11 53		12a00		12a29			12 48	12 53	13a00		13a29	
Bristol Parkway [7]	a	09 57		10 08			10 38	10 51	10 56		11 08		11 38	11 56			12 08		12 38		12 51	12 56		13 08		13 38
	d							10 52													12 52					
Bath Spa [7]	a																									
London Paddington [15]	⊖ a																									
Yate	d							11 01													13 01					
Cam & Dursley	d							11 13													13 15					
Gloucester [7]	a							11 29													13 33					

		GW ◇ D	GW	GW ◇	XC 1 ◇ ☕	GW A	XC 1 ◇ ☕	GW E	GW	GW ◇		XC 1 ◇ ☕	GW A	XC 1 ◇ ☕	GW ◇ D	GW	GW A	GW ◇	XC 1 ◇ ☕	GW A	XC 1 ◇ ☕	GW	GW ◇	XC 1 ◇ ☕		GW A
Taunton	d					13 07	13 51						14 07	14 51			15 07		15 16		15 51					16 07
Bridgwater	d					13 18							14 18				15 18									16 18
Highbridge & Burnham	d					13 25							14 25				15 25									16 25
Weston-super-Mare	a					13 35							14 35				15 35			←						16 35
	d		13 08			13 39			14 08				14 39			15 08	15 39			15 39		16 08				16 39
Weston Milton	d		13 11						14 11							15 11	→					16 11				
Worle	d		13 16			13 45			14 16				14 45			15 16				15 45		16 16				16 45
Yatton	d		13 21			13 51			14 21				14 51			15 21				15 51		16 21				16 51
Nailsea & Backwell	d		13 27			13 57			14 27				14 57			15 27				15 57		16 27				16 57
Parson Street	d		13 37						14 37							15 37						16 37				
Bedminster	d		13 39						14 39							15 39						16 39				
Bristol Temple Meads [10]	a		13 42			14 09	14 25		14 42				15 09	15 25		15 42			15 55	16 09	16 25	16 42				17 09
	d	13 41	13 46	13 53	14 00	14 19	14 30	14 41	14 46	14 53		15 00	15 19	15 30	15 41	15 46		15 53	16 00	16 19	16 30	16 44	16 53	17 00		17 19
Lawrence Hill	d					14 22							15 22							16 22						17 22
Stapleton Road	d					14 24							15 24							16 24						17 24
Filton Abbey Wood	d	13 48	13 53	14a00		14a29		14 48	14 53	15a00			15a29		15 48	15 53		16a00		16a29		16 53	17a00			17a29
Bristol Parkway [7]	a	13 51	13 56		14 08		14 38	14 51	14 56			15 08		15 38	15 51	15 56			16 08		16 38	16 56		17 08		
	d	13 52						14 52							15 52											
Bath Spa [7]	a																									
London Paddington [15]	⊖ a																									
Yate	d	14 01						15 01							16 01											
Cam & Dursley	d	14 13						15 13							16 13											
Gloucester [7]	a	14 29						15 31							16 29											

		XC 1 ◇ ☕	GW ◇ D	GW	GW ◇	XC 1 ◇ ☕	GW A	XC 1 ◇ ☕	GW	GW ◇	XC 1 ◇	XC 1 ◇ ☕	XC 1 ◇ ☕	GW ◇ G	GW	GW ◇	XC 1 ◇ ☕	GW 1 ◇ ☕	GW H	GW ◇	GW A	GW ◇	GW 1 ◇	GW ◇		
Taunton	d	16 51					17 07	17 51					18 51				19 51				20 07		21 30			
Bridgwater	d						17 18														20 18		21 40			
Highbridge & Burnham	d						17 25														20 25		21 47			
Weston-super-Mare	a						17 35														20 36		21 57			
	d			17 08			17 39		18 08						19 08			20 10			20 40		21 59			
Weston Milton	d			17 11					18 11						19 11						20 43					
Worle	d			17 16			17 45		18 16						19 16						20 47		22 06			
Yatton	d			17 21			17 51		18 21						19 21						20 53		22 11			
Nailsea & Backwell	d			17 27			17 57		18 27						19 27						20 59		22 16			
Parson Street	d			17 37					18 37						19 37						21 09					
Bedminster	d			17 39					18 39						19 39						21 11					
Bristol Temple Meads [10]	a	17 25		17 42			18 09	18 25	18 42				19 25		19 42		20 25	20 30			21 14		22 28			
	d	17 30	17 41	17 46	17 53	18 00	18 19	18 30	18 46	18 53	19 00	19 24	19 30	19 40	19 46	19 53	20 30	20 33	20 41	20 53	21 19	21 54	22 33	22 54		
Lawrence Hill	d						18 22														21 22					
Stapleton Road	d						18 24														21 24					
Filton Abbey Wood	d		17 48	17 53	18a00		18a29		18 53	19a00		19a32		19 48	19 53	20a00			20 48	21a00	21a29	22a02		23a00		
Bristol Parkway [7]	a	17 38	17 51	17 56		18 08		18 38	18 56		19 08		19 38	19 51	19 56		20 38		20 51							
	d		17 52											19 52					20 52							
Bath Spa [7]	a																	20 44					22 44			
London Paddington [15]	⊖ a																	22 16					00 32			
Yate	d		18 01											20 01					21 01							
Cam & Dursley	d		18 13											20 13					21 13							
Gloucester [7]	a		18 32											20 31					21 31							

For general notes see front of timetable
For details of catering facilities see Directory of Train Operators

A To Cardiff Central (Table 132)

B From Weymouth (Table 123) to Great Malvern (Table 71)

C From Brighton (Table 123) to Worcester Foregate Street (Table 71)

D From Weymouth (Table 123)

E From Southampton Central (Table 123) to Great Malvern (Table 71)

G From Weymouth (Table 123) to Cheltenham Spa (Table 57)

H From Brighton (Table 123) to Cheltenham Spa (Table 57)

Table 134

Saturdays

2 February to 22 March

Taunton → Gloucester

Network Diagram - see first page of Table 132

		XC	GW	GW	GW	GW	GW	XC	GW	GW	GW	XC	GW	GW	XC	GW	GW	GW	XC	GW	GW	GW
		1◇			1◇	1◇		1◇			1◇	1◇			1◇			◇	1◇	1◇		
			A	B			C		D				B			E					B	
		🍴			🍴	🍴		🍴			🍴	🍴			🍴				🍴	🍴		
Taunton	d		05 26				05 57	06 38			07 00			07 32	07 51							08 38
Bridgwater	d		05 37				06 07				07 10			07 44								08 50
Highbridge & Burnham	d		05 44				06 15				07 17			07 52								08 58
Weston-super-Mare	a		05 54				06 26	06 58			07 26			08 02								09 08
	d		06 02			06 24	06 30	07 00			07 28		07 34	08 09							08 40	09 09
Weston Milton	d						06 33						07 37	08 12			←					09 12
Worle	d		06 07			06 31	06 38				07 35		07 42	08 16 →			08 16				08 48	09 17 →
Yatton	d		06 13			06 36	06 44				07 40		07 47				08 22				08 53	
Nailsea & Backwell	d		06 19			06 42	06 50				07 45		07 53				08 28				08 59	
Parson Street	d						07 00						08 03				08 38					
Bedminster	d						07 02						08 05				08 41					
Bristol Temple Meads 10	a		06 31			06 53	07 05	07 27			07 56		08 08		08 25		08 44				09 12	
	d	06 15	06 43	06 50	06 58	07 00	07 08	07 30	07 41	07 54	08 00	08 00	08 19		08 30	08 41	08 46	08 54	09 00	09 08	09 19	
Lawrence Hill	d			06 53			07 11						08 22								09 22	
Stapleton Road	d			06 56			07 13						08 24								09 24	
Filton Abbey Wood	d			07a01			07 19		07 48	08a00			08a29			08 48	08 53	09a00			09a29	
Bristol Parkway 7	a	06 23			07 06		07 22	07 38	07 51			08 08			08 38	08 51	08 56		09 08	09 16		
	d	06 25							07 52							08 52						
Bath Spa 7	a		06 59			07 11					08 11											
London Paddington 15	⊖ a					08 58					10 01											
Yate	d								08 01							09 01						
Cam & Dursley	d								08 15							09 13						
Gloucester 7	a	06 54							08 31							09 29						

		XC	GW	GW	GW	XC	GW	XC	GW	GW	GW	XC	GW	XC	GW	GW	GW	XC	GW	GW	XC	GW
		1◇	◇		◇	1◇		1◇	◇		◇	1◇		1◇			◇	1◇	1◇		1◇	◇
			G				B		H				B			B				B		J
		🍴				🍴		🍴				🍴		🍴				🍴	🍴		🍴	
Taunton	d	08 51						09 51					10 11	10 51		11 07		11 16			11 51	
Bridgwater	d												10 23			11 19						
Highbridge & Burnham	d												10 31			11 27						
Weston-super-Mare	a												10 42			11 38				←		
	d						09 40			10 08			10 43		11 08	11 40 →				11 40		
Weston Milton	d			←						10 11					11 11							
Worle	d			09 17			09 46			10 16			10 50		11 16					11 46		
Yatton	d			09 23			09 51			10 21			10 56		11 21					11 51		
Nailsea & Backwell	d			09 29			09 57			10 27			11 02		11 27					11 57		
Parson Street	d			09 38						10 37					11 37							
Bedminster	d			09 41						10 39					11 39							
Bristol Temple Meads 10	a	09 25		09 44			10 10	10 25		10 42			11 14	11 25	11 42			11 55		12 10	12 25	
	d	09 30	09 41	09 46	09 54	10 00	10 19	10 30	10 41	10 46	10 54	11 00	11 19	11 30	11 46		11 53	12 00	12 07	12 19	12 30	12 41
Lawrence Hill	d						10 22						11 22							12 22		
Stapleton Road	d						10 24						11 24							12 24		
Filton Abbey Wood	d		09 48	09 53	10a00		10a29		10 48	10 53	11a00		11a29		11 53		12a00			12a29		12 48
Bristol Parkway 7	a	09 38	09 51	09 57		10 08		10 38	10 51	10 56		11 08		11 38	11 56			12 08	12 16		12 38	12 51
	d		09 52						10 52													12 52
Bath Spa 7	a																					
London Paddington 15	⊖ a																					
Yate	d		10 01						11 01													13 01
Cam & Dursley	d		10 15						11 13													13 15
Gloucester 7	a		10 31						11 29													13 33

		GW	GW	XC	GW	GW	XC	GW	GW	GW	XC	GW	GW	XC	GW	GW	GW	XC	GW	GW	XC	GW
			◇	1◇	1◇		1◇	◇		◇	1◇	1◇		1◇			◇	1◇	1◇		1◇	◇
						B		G					B		K					B		G
				🍴	🍴		🍴				🍴	🍴		🍴				🍴	🍴		🍴	
Taunton	d					12 11	12 51						13 07	13 51						14 07	14 51	
Bridgwater	d					12 22							13 18							14 18		
Highbridge & Burnham	d					12 29							13 25							14 25		
Weston-super-Mare	a					12 39							13 35							14 35		
	d	12 08				12 41			13 08				13 39			14 08				14 39		
Weston Milton	d	12 11							13 11							14 11						
Worle	d	12 16				12 47			13 16				13 45			14 16				14 45		
Yatton	d	12 21				12 53			13 21				13 51			14 21				14 51		
Nailsea & Backwell	d	12 27				12 59			13 27				13 57			14 27				14 57		
Parson Street	d	12 37							13 37							14 37						
Bedminster	d	12 39							13 39							14 39						
Bristol Temple Meads 10	a	12 42				13 11	13 25		13 42				14 09	14 25		14 42				15 09	15 25	
	d	12 46	12 53	13 00	13 07	13 19	13 30	13 41	13 46	13 53	14 00	14 07	14 19	14 30	14 41	14 46	14 53	15 00	15 09	15 19	15 30	15 41
Lawrence Hill	d					13 22							14 22							15 22		
Stapleton Road	d					13 24							14 24							15 24		
Filton Abbey Wood	d	12 53	13a00			13a29		13 48	13 53	14a00			14a29		14 48	14 53	15a00			15a29		15 48
Bristol Parkway 7	a	12 56		13 08	13 15		13 38	13 51	13 56		14 08	14 15		14 38	14 51	14 56		15 08	15 17		15 38	15 51
	d							13 52							14 52							15 52
Bath Spa 7	a																					
London Paddington 15	⊖ a																					
Yate	d							14 01							15 01							16 01
Cam & Dursley	d							14 13							15 13							16 13
Gloucester 7	a							14 29							15 31							16 29

For general notes see front of timetable
For details of catering facilities see Directory of Train Operators

A To Westbury (Table 123)

B To Cardiff Central (Table 132)

C From Exeter St Davids (Table 135)

D From Salisbury (Table 123)

E From Warminster (Table 123) to Great Malvern (Table 71)

G From Weymouth (Table 123)

H From Weymouth (Table 123) to Great Malvern (Table 71)

J From Brighton (Table 123) to Worcester Foregate Street (Table 71)

K From Southampton Central (Table 123) to Great Malvern (Table 71)

Table 134

Taunton → Gloucester

Saturdays

2 February to 22 March

Network Diagram - see first page of Table 132

		GW	GW A	GW ◇	XC 1 ◇ ☕	GW 1 ◇ ☕		GW A	XC 1 ◇ ☕	GW	GW ◇	XC 1 ◇ ☕		GW 1 ◇ ☕	GW A	XC 1 ◇ ☕	GW ◇ B	GW		GW ◇	XC 1 ◇ ☕	GW 1 ◇ ☕	GW A	XC 1 ◇ ☕		GW
Taunton	d		15 07		15 16				15 51						16 07	16 51							17 07	17 51		
Bridgwater	d		15 18												16 18								17 18			
Highbridge & Burnham	d		15 25												16 25								17 25			
Weston-super-Mare	a		15 35					←							16 35								17 35			
	d	15 08	15 39					15 39		16 08					16 39			17 08					17 39			18 08
Weston Milton	d	15 11	→							16 11								17 11								18 11
Worle	d	15 16						15 45		16 16					16 45			17 16					17 45			18 16
Yatton	d	15 21						15 51		16 21					16 51			17 21					17 51			18 21
Nailsea & Backwell	d	15 27						15 57		16 27					16 57			17 27					17 57			18 27
Parson Street	d	15 37								16 37								17 37								18 37
Bedminster	d	15 39								16 39								17 39								18 39
Bristol Temple Meads 10	a	15 42			15 55			16 09	16 25	16 42					17 09	17 25		17 42					18 09	18 25		18 42
	d	15 46		15 53	16 00	16 07		16 19	16 30	16 44	16 53	17 00		17 07	17 19	17 30	17 41	17 46		17 53	18 00	18 07	18 19	18 30		18 46
Lawrence Hill	d							16 22							17 22								18 22			
Stapleton Road	d							16 24							17 24								18 24			
Filton Abbey Wood	d	15 53		16a00				16a29		16 53	17a00				17a29		17 48	17 53		18a00			18a29			18 53
Bristol Parkway 7	a	15 56			16 08	16 15			16 38	16 56		17 08		17 15		17 38	17 51	17 56			18 08	18 15		18 38		18 56
	d																17 52									
Bath Spa 7	a																									
London Paddington 15 ⊖	a																									
Yate	d																18 01									
Cam & Dursley	d																18 13									
Gloucester 7	a																18 32									

		GW ◇	XC 1 ◇	GW 1 ◇ ☕	XC 1 ◇ ☕	XC 1 ◇ ☕		GW ◇ C	GW	GW ◇	GW 1 ◇ ☕	XC 1 ◇ ☕		GW D	GW ◇	GW 1 ◇ ☕	GW A	GW ◇		GW 1 ◇ ☕	GW 1 ◇	GW ◇	GW 1 ◇ ☕			
Taunton	d					18 51						19 51					20 07				21 30					
Bridgwater	d																20 18				21 40					
Highbridge & Burnham	d																20 25				21 47					
Weston-super-Mare	a																20 36				21 57					
	d								19 08								20 40				21 59					
Weston Milton	d								19 11								20 43									
Worle	d								19 16								20 47				22 06					
Yatton	d								19 21								20 53				22 11					
Nailsea & Backwell	d								19 27								20 59				22 17					
Parson Street	d								19 37								21 09									
Bedminster	d								19 39								21 11									
Bristol Temple Meads 10	a					19 25			19 42			20 25					21 14				22 28					
	d	18 53	19 00	19 07	19 24	19 30		19 40	19 46	19 53	20 07	20 30		20 41	20 53	21 08	21 19	21 53		22 11	22 33	22 54	23 07			
Lawrence Hill	d																21 22									
Stapleton Road	d																21 24									
Filton Abbey Wood	d	19a00			19a32			19 48	19 53	20a00				20 48	21a00		21a29	22a00				23a00				
Bristol Parkway 7	a		19 08	19 15		19 38		19 51	19 56		20 15	20 38		20 51		21 16				22 22			23 15			
	d							19 52						20 52												
Bath Spa 7	a																				22 44					
London Paddington 15 ⊖	a																				00 37					
Yate	d							20 01						21 01												
Cam & Dursley	d							20 13						21 13												
Gloucester 7	a							20 31						21 31												

Saturdays

from 29 March

		XC 1 ◇ ☕	GW E	GW 1 ◇ ☕	GW G	XC 1 ◇ ☕	GW H	GW G	XC 1 ◇ ☕	GW 1 ◇ ☕	GW	GW	XC 1 ◇ ☕	GW J	GW	GW ◇	XC 1 ◇ ☕	GW	GW 1 ◇ ☕	GW	XC 1 ◇ ☕	GW ◇ B	GW	GW ◇	XC 1 ◇ ☕	GW
Taunton	d		05 26		06 13	06 38				07 00		07 32	07 51						08 34	08 38	08 51					
Bridgwater	d		05 37		06 26					07 10		07 44								08 50						
Highbridge & Burnham	d		05 44		06 34					07 17		07 52								08 58						
Weston-super-Mare	a		05 54		06 45	06 58				07 26		08 02							08 54	09 08						
	d		06 02	06 24	06 49	07 00				07 28	07 34	08 09						08 40	09 00	09 09						09 40
Weston Milton	d				06 52						07 37	08 12			←					09 12			←			
Worle	d		06 07	06 31	06 57					07 34	07 42	08 16			08 16			08 48		09 17			09 17			09 46
Yatton	d		06 13	06 36	07 03					07 40	07 47	→			08 22			08 53		→			09 23			09 51
Nailsea & Backwell	d		06 19	06 42	07 09					07 45	07 53				08 28			08 59					09 29			09 57
Parson Street	d				07 19						08 03				08 38								09 38			
Bedminster	d				07 21						08 05				08 41								09 41			
Bristol Temple Meads 10	a		06 31	06 53	07 24	07 27		←		07 57	08 08		08 25		08 44			09 12	09 20		09 25		09 44			10 10
	d	06 15	06 43	07 00	07 46	07 30	07 41	07 46	08 00	08 00			08 30	08 41	08 46	08 54	09 00		09 30		09 30	09 41	09 46	09 54	10 00	
Lawrence Hill	d				→			07 49																		
Stapleton Road	d							07 51																		
Filton Abbey Wood	d						07 48	07 57						08 48	08 53	09 01						09 48	09 53	10 01		
Bristol Parkway 7	a	06 23				07 38	07 51	08 03	08 08				08 38	08 51	08 56	09 04	09 08				09 38	09 51	09 57	10 04	10 08	
	d	06 25					07 52							08 52								09 52				
Bath Spa 7	a		06 59	07 11						08 11									09 41							
London Paddington 15 ⊖	a			08 45						09 44									11 15							
Yate	d						08 01							09 01								10 01				
Cam & Dursley	d						08 15							09 13								10 15				
Gloucester 7	a	06 54					08 31							09 29								10 31				

For general notes see front of timetable
For details of catering facilities see Directory of Train Operators

- **A** To Cardiff Central (Table 132)
- **B** From Weymouth (Table 123)
- **C** From Weymouth (Table 123) to Cheltenham Spa (Table 57)
- **D** From Brighton (Table 123) to Cheltenham Spa (Table 57)
- **E** To Westbury (Table 123)
- **G** From Exeter St Davids (Table 135)
- **H** From Salisbury (Table 123)
- **J** From Warminster (Table 123) to Great Malvern (Table 71)

Table 134

Taunton → Gloucester

Network Diagram - see first page of Table 132

		XC		GW	GW	GW	XC	GW	XC	GW	GW	GW	XC	GW	XC	GW	GW	GW	XC	GW	XC	GW	GW	GW	XC	GW
		[1] ◇		◇		◇	[1] ◇		[1] ◇			◇	[1] ◇		[1] ◇	◇		◇	[1] ◇		[1] ◇	◇		◇	[1] ◇	
				A												B						C				
		☕					☕		☕				☕		☕				☕		☕				☕	
Taunton	d	09 51						10 11	10 51		11 07		11 16		11 51					12 11	12 51					13 07
Bridgwater	d							10 23			11 19									12 22						13 18
Highbridge & Burnham	d							10 31			11 27									12 29						13 25
Weston-super-Mare	a							10 42			11 38			⟵						12 39						13 35
	d				10 08			10 44		11 08	11 40			11 40			12 08			12 41			13 08			13 39
Weston Milton	d				10 11					11 11	⟶						12 11						13 11			
Worle	d				10 16			10 50		11 16				11 46			12 16			12 47			13 16			13 45
Yatton	d				10 21			10 56		11 21				11 51			12 21			12 53			13 21			13 51
Nailsea & Backwell	d				10 27			11 02		11 27				11 57			12 27			12 59			13 27			13 57
Parson Street	d				10 37					11 37							12 37						13 37			
Bedminster	d				10 39					11 39							12 39						13 39			
Bristol Temple Meads [10]	a	10 25			10 42			11 15	11 25	11 42			11 55	12 10	12 25		12 42			13 11	13 25		13 42			14 09
	d	10 30		10 41	10 46	10 54	11 00	11 19	11 30	11 46		11 53	12 00	12 19	12 30	12 41	12 46	12 53	13 00	13 19	13 30	13 41	13 46	13 53	14 00	14 19
Lawrence Hill	d							11 22						12 22						13 22						14 22
Stapleton Road	d							11 24						12 24						13 24						14 24
Filton Abbey Wood	d			10 48	10 53	11 00		11 30		11 53		12 00		12 30		12 48	12 53	13 00		13 30		13 48	13 53	14 00		14 30
Bristol Parkway [7]	a	10 38		10 51	10 56	11 04	11 08	11 33	11 38	11 56		12 04	12 08	12 33	12 38	12 51	12 56	13 04	13 08	13 33	13 38	13 51	13 56	14 04	14 08	14 33
	d			10 52												12 52						13 52				
Bath Spa [7]	a																									
London Paddington [15]	⊖ a																									
Yate	d			11 01												13 01						14 01				
Cam & Dursley	d			11 13												13 15						14 13				
Gloucester [7]	a			11 29												13 33						14 29				

		XC	GW	GW		GW	GW	GW	XC	GW	XC	GW	GW	GW	GW	XC	GW	GW	GW	XC	GW	GW	GW	XC	GW	GW
		[1] ◇					◇	[1] ◇	[1] ◇		[1] ◇	◇			◇	[1] ◇	[1] ◇	[1] ◇		[1] ◇			◇	[1] ◇	[1] ◇	
			D									E														
		☕						☕	☕		☕					☕	☕	☕		☕				☕	☕	
Taunton	d	13 51				14 07		14 22			14 51			15 07		15 16	15 28	15 34		15 51		16 07			16 35	
Bridgwater	d					14 18								15 18								16 18				
Highbridge & Burnham	d					14 25								15 25								16 25				
Weston-super-Mare	a					14 35				⟵				15 35					⟵			16 35				⟵
	d			14 08		14 39				14 39			15 08	15 39					15 39		16 08	16 39				16 39
Weston Milton	d			14 11		⟶							15 11	⟶							16 11	⟶				
Worle	d			14 16						14 45			15 16						15 45		16 16					16 45
Yatton	d			14 21						14 51			15 21						15 51		16 21					16 51
Nailsea & Backwell	d			14 27						14 57			15 27						15 57		16 27					16 57
Parson Street	d			14 37									15 37								16 37					
Bedminster	d			14 39									15 39								16 39					
Bristol Temple Meads [10]	a	14 25		14 42				14 55		15 09	15 25		15 42			15 55	16 01	16 07	16 09	16 25	16 42				17 08	17 09
	d	14 30	14 41	14 46			14 53	14 57	15 00	15 19	15 30	15 41	15 46		15 53	16 00	16 02	16 09	16 19	16 30	16 44		16 53	17 00	17 09	17 19
Lawrence Hill	d									15 22									16 22							17 22
Stapleton Road	d									15 24									16 24							17 24
Filton Abbey Wood	d		14 48	14 53			15 00			15 30		15 48	15 53		16 00				16 30		16 53		17 00			17 30
Bristol Parkway [7]	a	14 38	14 51	14 56			15 04		15 08	15 33	15 38	15 51	15 56		16 04	16 08			16 33	16 38	16 56		17 04	17 08		17 33
	d		14 52									15 52														
Bath Spa [7]	a																									
London Paddington [15]	⊖ a							16 25									17 29	18 23							18 38	
Yate	d		15 01									16 01														
Cam & Dursley	d		15 13									16 13														
Gloucester [7]	a		15 31									16 29														

		XC	GW	GW	GW	XC	GW	XC	GW	GW	GW	XC	XC	GW	GW	GW	GW	XC	GW	GW	GW	GW	GW	GW		
		[1] ◇	◇		◇	[1] ◇		[1] ◇		◇	[1] ◇	[1] ◇	[1] ◇	◇		◇		[1] ◇	[1] ◇		◇	◇	[1] ◇	◇		
			E											G						H						
		☕				☕		☕			☕		☕					☕	☕							
Taunton	d	16 51					17 07	17 51			18 17		18 51				19 07	19 51					21 30			
Bridgwater	d						17 18										19 18						21 40			
Highbridge & Burnham	d						17 25										19 25						21 47			
Weston-super-Mare	a						17 35										19 35						21 57			
	d			17 08			17 39		18 08						19 08		19 39		20 10				21 59			
Weston Milton	d			17 11					18 11						19 11											
Worle	d			17 16			17 45		18 16						19 16		19 45						22 06			
Yatton	d			17 21			17 51		18 21						19 21		19 51						22 11			
Nailsea & Backwell	d			17 27			17 57		18 27						19 27		19 57						22 16			
Parson Street	d			17 37					18 37						19 37											
Bedminster	d			17 39					18 39						19 39											
Bristol Temple Meads [10]	a	17 25		17 42			18 09	18 25	18 42		18 50		19 25		19 42		20 09	20 25	20 30				22 28			
	d	17 30	17 41	17 46	17 53	18 00	18 19	18 30	18 46	18 53	18 58	19 00	19 30	19 40	19 46	19 53	20 19	20 30	20 33	20 41	20 53	21 54	22 33	22 54		
Lawrence Hill	d						18 22										20 22									
Stapleton Road	d						18 24										20 24									
Filton Abbey Wood	d		17 48	17 53	18 00		18 30		18 53	19 00				19 48	19 53	20 00	20 30			20 48	21 00	22 02		23 01		
Bristol Parkway [7]	a	17 38	17 51	17 56	18 04	18 08	18 33	18 38	18 56	19 04		19 08	19 38	19 51	19 56	20 04	20 33	20 38		20 51	21 04	22 06		23 04		
	d		17 52											19 52						20 52						
Bath Spa [7]	a																		20 44				22 44			
London Paddington [15]	⊖ a										20 58								22 16				00 32			
Yate	d		18 01											20 01						21 01						
Cam & Dursley	d		18 13											20 15						21 13						
Gloucester [7]	a		18 32											20 33						21 31						

For general notes see front of timetable
For details of catering facilities see Directory of Train Operators

A From Weymouth (Table 123) to Great Malvern (Table 71)
B From Brighton (Table 123) to Worcester Foregate Street (Table 71)
C From Weymouth (Table 123)
D From Southampton Central (Table 123) to Great Malvern (Table 71)
E From Westbury (Table 123)
G From Westbury (Table 123) to Cheltenham Spa (Table 57)
H From Brighton (Table 123) to Cheltenham Spa (Table 57)

Table 134

Sundays

until 27 January

Taunton → Gloucester

Network Diagram - see first page of Table 132

		GW	XC	GW	GW	XC	GW		XC	GW	XC	GW	XC	GW		XC	GW	GW	GW	XC	GW		XC	GW	GW	XC
		1◇	1◇		◇	1◇	1◇		1◇		1◇	◇	1◇	1◇		R 1			1◇	1◇			R 1	◇	1◇	1◇
				A	B													C								
		☕	☕			☕	☕		☕		☕	🛒	☕	☕		☕			☕	☕			☕	🛒	☕	☕
Taunton	d				08 45					10 22	10 51		11 16	11 20		11 51	12 10		12 21				12 51			
Bridgwater	d				08 56					10 33							12 21									
Highbridge & Burnham	d				09 03					10 40							12 28									
Weston-super-Mare	a				09 12					10 49							12 37									
	d	08 28			09 14		10 28			10 51							12 39				←				13 30	
Weston Milton	d				09 17												12 42				12 42					
Worle	d	08 34			09 21		10 34			10 57							→									
Yatton	d	08 39			09 27		10 39			11 02											12 49				13 40	
Nailsea & Backwell	d	08 44			09 33		10 44			11 08											12 55				13 46	
Parson Street	d																									
Bedminster	d																				13 06					
Bristol Temple Meads 10	a	08 55			09 45		10 55			11 20	11 25		11 55	11 56		12 25			12 55		13 09		13 25		13 57	
	d	09 00	09 15	09 44	09 50	10 30	11 00		11 00		11 30	11 48	12 00	12 00		12 30		12 44	13 00	13 00			13 30	13 48	14 00	14 00
Lawrence Hill	d																									
Stapleton Road	d																									
Filton Abbey Wood	d			09 51	09a56							11a54						12 51						13a54		
Bristol Parkway 7	a		09 23	09 54		10 38			11 08		11 38		12 08			12 38		12 54		13 08			13 38			14 08
	d		09 25	09 55														12 55								
Bath Spa 7	a	09 12					11 12							12 12					13 12						14 11	
London Paddington 15 ⊖	a	10 54					12 55							13 55					14 54						15 57	
Yate	d			10 04														13 04								
Cam & Dursley	d			10 16														13 16								
Gloucester 7	a		09 55	10 32														13 32								

		GW	XC	GW	GW		GW	XC	XC	GW	XC	GW		XC	GW	GW	GW	XC	GW		XC	GW	GW	GW	XC	GW
			R 1		◇		1◇	1◇	R 1	◇	R 1			R 1		◇		1◇	1◇		R 1	◇	◇	1◇	1◇	1◇
				C											C								D	E		
			☕				☕	☕	☕	🛒	☕			☕		🛒		☕	☕		☕	🛒		☕	☕	☕
Taunton	d	13 20	13 51						14 51		15 06	15 21		15 51					16 36		16 51			17 04		17 45
Bridgwater	d	13 31										15 32														
Highbridge & Burnham	d	13 38										15 39														
Weston-super-Mare	a	13 47									15 28	15 48							16 57					17 25		
	d	13 49					14 28				15 29	15 51					16 15		16 58				17 07	17 30		
Weston Milton	d	13 52										15 54					16 18						17 11			
Worle	d	13 56					14 34					15 58					16 23						17 16	17 36		
Yatton	d	14 01					14 39					16 03					16 28						17 22	17 41		
Nailsea & Backwell	d	14 07					14 44					16 09					16 34						17 28	17 47		
Parson Street	d																16 44									
Bedminster	d																16 46						17 37			
Bristol Temple Meads 10	a	14 19	14 25				14 55		15 25		15 50	16 21		16 25			16 49		17 19		17 25		17 40	17 58		18 24
	d		14 30	14 44	14 48		15 00	15 00	15 30	15 48	16 00			16 30	16 44	16 48		17 00	17 30		17 30	17 48	17 50	18 00	18 00	18 30
Lawrence Hill	d																									
Stapleton Road	d																									
Filton Abbey Wood	d			14 51	14a54					15a54					16 51	16a54						17a54				
Bristol Parkway 7	a		14 38	14 54				15 08	15 38		16 08			16 38	16 54			17 08			17 38				18 08	
	d			14 55											16 55											
Bath Spa 7	a						15 12												17 42				18 06	18 12		18 42
London Paddington 15 ⊖	a						16 54												19 24					19 58		20 24
Yate	d			15 04											17 04											
Cam & Dursley	d			15 16											17 16											
Gloucester 7	a			15 35											17 35											

		XC	GW		GW	GW	XC	GW	XC	GW		GW	XC	GW	GW	GW	GW		GW	GW	XC	GW	GW	GW		
		R 1			◇		1◇	1◇	1◇	◇		◇	1◇		◇	1◇	◇			1◇	1◇		◇			
			C									G		A												
		☕			🛒			☕	☕	🛒		🛒	☕		🛒		🛒			☕			🛒			
Taunton	d	17 51						18 26	18 51			19 10	19 51						20 45	21 22		21 35				
Bridgwater	d							18 36				19 22							20 57			21 46				
Highbridge & Burnham	d							18 43				19 30							21 05			21 53				
Weston-super-Mare	a							18 53				19 41							21 16			22 03				
	d					18 16		18 54				19 42				20 38			21 19			22 05		23 15		
Weston Milton	d					18 19													21 22			22 08		23 18		
Worle	d					18 24		19 00				19 47							21 27					23 23		
Yatton	d					18 29		19 05				19 53							21 32			22 15		23 28		
Nailsea & Backwell	d					18 35		19 10				19 59							21 38			22 21		23 34		
Parson Street	d					18 45																				
Bedminster	d					18 47													21 49					23 45		
Bristol Temple Meads 10	a	18 25				18 50		19 25	19 25			20 11	20 25			20 58			21 52	21 57		22 33		23 48		
	d	18 30	18 44		18 48		19 00	19 30	19 30	19 48			20 30	20 44	20 48	21 00	21 48			22 05	22 10		22 48			
Lawrence Hill	d																									
Stapleton Road	d																									
Filton Abbey Wood	d		18 51		18a55					19a54				20 51	20a54		21a56						22a54			
Bristol Parkway 7	a	18 38	18 54				19 08		19 38				20 38	20 54							22 18					
	d		18 55											20 55												
Bath Spa 7	a							19 42								21 13				22 17						
London Paddington 15 ⊖	a							21 26								23 01				00 17						
Yate	d		19 04											21 04												
Cam & Dursley	d		19 16											21 16												
Gloucester 7	a		19 34											21 32												

For general notes see front of timetable
For details of catering facilities see Directory of Train Operators

- **A** To Cheltenham Spa (Table 57)
- **B** From Exeter St Davids (Table 135) to Cardiff Central (Table 132)
- **C** To Worcester Shrub Hill (Table 57)
- **D** To Weymouth (Table 123)
- **E** From Paignton (Table 135)
- **G** From Penzance (Table 135)

Table 134

Sundays

3 February to 23 March

Taunton → Gloucester

Network Diagram - see first page of Table 132

		XC	GW	GW	GW	GW	XC	GW	GW	XC	GW	GW	GW	GW	XC	GW	GW	GW	XC	GW	GW	GW
		1◇			1◇		1◇		1◇	1◇		◇		1◇	R 1	◇		1◇	R 1		◇	1◇
				A												B	C					
		☕	🚌		☕	🚌	☕	🚌	☕	☕	🚌	🛒	🚌	☕	☕			☕	☕		🛒	☕
Taunton	d					08 50		08 50		10 01			10 21		11 06	11 27			11 56			
Bridgwater	d							09 15					10 46			11 38						
Highbridge & Burnham	d							09 30					11 01			11 45						
Weston-super-Mare	a					09 30		09 50					11 21			11 55						
	d		08 24			09 30		09 50			10 25		11 21			11 56				12 54		
Weston Milton	d							10 00														
Worle	d		08 39					10 10			10 40					12 02				12 59		
Yatton	d		08 54					10 25			10 55					12 07				13 04		
Nailsea & Backwell	d		09 09					10 40			11 10					12 13				13 10		
Parson Street	d																					
Bedminster	d																					
Bristol Temple Meads 10	a		09 34			10 10		11 05		11 11	11 35		12 01		12 10	12 30			13 10	13 27		
	d	09 15		09 44	10 04		10 30	11 05	11 15	11 30		11 48		12 15	12 30		12 44	13 15	13 30		13 48	14 15
Lawrence Hill	d																					
Stapleton Road	d																					
Filton Abbey Wood	d			09 51				11 25				11a54					12 51				13a54	
Bristol Parkway 7	a	09 23		09 54	10 12		10 38		11 27	11 38				12 27	12 38		12 54	13 27	13 38			14 27
	d	09 25		09 55													12 55					
Bath Spa 7	a																					
London Paddington 15 ⊖	a																					
Yate	d			10 04													13 04					
Cam & Dursley	d			10 16													13 16					
Gloucester 7	a	09 55		10 32													13 32					

		XC	GW	GW	GW	XC	GW	GW	GW	GW	XC	GW	GW	GW	GW	XC	GW	GW	GW	GW	XC	GW
		R 1		◇	1◇	R 1		◇	1◇		R 1		◇		1◇	R 1	◇	◇	1◇	1◇	R 1	
			C									C						D	E			C
		☕			☕	☕		🛒	☕		☕		🛒		☕	☕	🛒		☕	☕	☕	
Taunton	d	12 56				13 56				15 21	15 28					16 51			17 04		17 51	
Bridgwater	d									15 32												
Highbridge & Burnham	d									15 39												
Weston-super-Mare	a									15 48	15 57								17 25			
	d						14 54			15 51	16 00			16 15				17 07	17 26			
Weston Milton	d						14 57			15 54				16 18				17 10				
Worle	d						15 00			15 58				16 23				17 14	17 32			
Yatton	d						15 06			16 03				16 28				17 20	17 37			
Nailsea & Backwell	d						15 12			16 09				16 34				17 26	17 43			
Parson Street	d													16 44								
Bedminster	d						15 27							16 46				17 35				
Bristol Temple Meads 10	a	14 10				15 16	15 30			16 21	16 25			16 49		17 25		17 38	17 55		18 25	
	d	14 30	14 44	14 48	15 19	15 30		15 48	16 15		16 30	16 44	16 48		17 15	17 30	17 48	17 50	18 05	18 15	18 30	18 44
Lawrence Hill	d																					
Stapleton Road	d																					
Filton Abbey Wood	d		14 51	14a54				15a54				16 51	16a54				17a54					18 51
Bristol Parkway 7	a	14 38	14 54		15 27	15 38			16 27		16 38	16 54			17 27	17 38				18 27	18 38	18 54
	d		14 55									16 55										18 55
Bath Spa 7	a																	18 06	18 17			
London Paddington 15 ⊖	a																		20 26			
Yate	d		15 04									17 04										19 04
Cam & Dursley	d		15 16									17 16										19 16
Gloucester 7	a		15 35									17 35										19 34

		GW	GW	GW	GW	XC	GW	GW	GW	XC	GW	GW	GW	GW	GW	GW	XC	GW	GW	GW	GW	GW
		◇		1◇	1◇	1◇	◇	◇	1◇	1◇		◇		1◇	1◇	◇	1◇	1◇		◇		1◇
								G		H	A				J							
		🛒		☕	☕	☕	🛒	🛒	☕	☕		🛒		☕	☕	🛒		☕		🛒		☕
Taunton	d				18 26	18 51		19 10		19 51									21 35			
Bridgwater	d				18 36			19 22											21 46			
Highbridge & Burnham	d				18 43			19 30											21 53			
Weston-super-Mare	a				18 52			19 41											22 03			
	d		18 16		18 54			19 42					20 15		21 00				22 05		22 22	
Weston Milton	d		18 19										20 18						22 08		22 25	
Worle	d		18 24		19 00			19 47					20 23		21 06						22 30	
Yatton	d		18 29		19 05			19 53					20 28		21 11				22 15		22 35	
Nailsea & Backwell	d		18 35		19 10			19 59					20 34		21 16				22 21		22 41	
Parson Street	d		18 45																			
Bedminster	d		18 47										20 45								22 52	
Bristol Temple Meads 10	a		18 50		19 25	19 25		20 11		20 25			20 48		21 27				22 33		22 55	
	d	18 48		19 15	19 25	19 30	19 48		20 18	20 30	20 44	20 48		21 19	21 30	21 48	22 10	22 20		22 48		23 34
Lawrence Hill	d																					
Stapleton Road	d																					
Filton Abbey Wood	d	18a54					19a54				20 51	20a54				21a56				22a54		
Bristol Parkway 7	a			19 27		19 38			20 27	20 38	20 54			21 27			22 18	22 29				23 42
	d										20 55											
Bath Spa 7	a				19 36										21 41							
London Paddington 15 ⊖	a				21 32																	
Yate	d										21 04											
Cam & Dursley	d										21 16											
Gloucester 7	a										21 32											

For general notes see front of timetable
For details of catering facilities see Directory of Train Operators

A To Cheltenham Spa (Table 57)
B From Exeter St Davids (Table 135)
C To Worcester Shrub Hill (Table 57)
D To Weymouth (Table 123)
E From Paignton (Table 135)
G From Penzance (Table 135)
H ☕ to Bristol Temple Meads
J To Swindon (Table 125)

Table 134

Sundays

from 30 March

Taunton → Gloucester

Network Diagram - see first page of Table 132

		GW	GW	XC	GW	GW	GW	GW	XC	GW	XC	GW	XC	GW	XC		GW	XC	GW	GW	XC	GW	GW	XC	GW	GW
		1◇	1◇	1◇	◇	1◇		◇	1◇	1◇	1◇		1◇	◇	1◇		1◇	R 1			1◇	1◇		R 1	◇	1◇
					A		B	A												C						
		☕	☕	☕	🛒	☕		🛒	☕	☕	☕		☕	🛒	☕		☕	☕			☕	☕		☕	🛒	☕
Taunton	d				08 45	08 58						10 22	10 51		11 16		11 20	11 51	12 10			12 21		12 51		
Bridgwater	d				08 56							10 33							12 21							
Highbridge & Burnham	d				09 03							10 40							12 28							
Weston-super-Mare	a				09 12							10 49							12 37							
	d		08 28		09 14					10 20		10 51							12 39				←			13 15
Weston Milton	d				09 17														12 42 →				12 42			
Worle	d		08 34		09 21					10 26		10 57														
Yatton	d		08 39		09 27			←		10 31		11 02											12 49			13 24
Nailsea & Backwell	d		08 44		09 33 →			09 33		10 36		11 08											12 55			13 30
Parson Street	d																									
Bedminster	d																						13 06			
Bristol Temple Meads 10	a		08 55			09 32		09 45		10 47		11 20	11 25		11 55		11 56	12 25				12 55	13 09	13 25		13 41
	d	08 25	09 00	09 15		09 33	09 44	09 50	10 30	11 00	11 00		11 30	11 48	12 00		12 00	12 30		12 44	13 00	13 00		13 30	13 48	14 00
Lawrence Hill	d																									
Stapleton Road	d																									
Filton Abbey Wood	d						09 51	09 57						11 55						12 51					13 55	
Bristol Parkway 7	a	08 34		09 23			09 54	10 00	10 38		11 08		11 38	11 58	12 08			12 38		12 54	13 08			13 38	13 58	
	d	08 35		09 25			09 55													12 55						
Bath Spa 7	a		09 12			09 45				11 12							12 12					13 12				14 12
London Paddington 15 ⊖	a	10 22	11 04			11 27				12 59							13 55					15 03				15 56
Yate	d						10 04													13 04						
Cam & Dursley	d						10 16													13 16						
Gloucester 7	a			09 55			10 32													13 35						

		XC	GW	XC	GW	GW	GW		XC	XC	XC	GW	GW	XC	GW	XC	GW	GW	GW	XC	GW	XC		GW	GW	XC
		1◇		R 1		◇	1◇		1◇	R 1	R 1	1◇	◇	R 1		R 1		◇		1◇	1◇	R 1		◇	◇	1◇
					C												C								D	
		☕		☕			☕		☕	☕	☕	☕	🛒	☕		☕		🛒		☕	☕	☕		🛒		☕
Taunton	d		13 20	13 51						14 51	15 06	15 10			15 21	15 51					16 36	16 51				
Bridgwater	d		13 31												15 32											
Highbridge & Burnham	d		13 38												15 39											
Weston-super-Mare	a		13 47								15 28			←	15 48						16 57					
	d		13 49				14 20				15 29 →			15 29	15 51				16 15		16 58				17 07	
Weston Milton	d		13 52												15 54				16 18						17 10	
Worle	d		13 56				14 27								15 58				16 23						17 14	
Yatton	d		14 01				14 32								16 03				16 28						17 20	
Nailsea & Backwell	d		14 07				14 37								16 09				16 34						17 26	
Parson Street	d																		16 44							
Bedminster	d																		16 46						17 35	
Bristol Temple Meads 10	a		14 19	14 25			14 48			15 25		15 44		15 50	16 21	16 25			16 49		17 19	17 25			17 38	
	d	14 00		14 30	14 44	14 48	15 00		15 00	15 30		15 45	15 48	16 00		16 30	16 44	16 48		17 00	17 30	17 30		17 48	17 55	18 00
Lawrence Hill	d																									
Stapleton Road	d																									
Filton Abbey Wood	d				14 51	14 55							15 55				16 51	16 55						17 55		
Bristol Parkway 7	a	14 08		14 38	14 54	14 58			15 08	15 38			15 58	16 08		16 38	16 54	16 58		17 08		17 38		17 58		18 08
	d				14 55												16 55									
Bath Spa 7	a						15 12														17 42				18 11	
London Paddington 15 ⊖	a						16 53					18 09									19 23					
Yate	d				15 04												17 04									
Cam & Dursley	d				15 16												17 16									
Gloucester 7	a				15 35												17 35									

		GW	GW	XC	GW	GW	GW	XC	GW	XC	GW	GW	GW	XC	GW	GW	GW	GW	GW	GW	XC	GW	GW	GW		
		1◇	1◇	R 1		◇		1◇	1◇	1◇	◇	◇	1◇	1◇		◇	1◇	◇		1◇	1◇		◇			
		E			C							G			B											
		☕	☕	☕		🛒			☕	☕	🛒	🛒	☕	☕		🛒	☕	🛒		☕			🛒			
Taunton	d	17 04	17 45	17 51					18 26	18 51		19 15	19 45	19 51					20 45	21 22		21 35				
Bridgwater	d								18 36			19 27							20 56			21 46				
Highbridge & Burnham	d								18 43			19 35							21 03			21 53				
Weston-super-Mare	a	17 25							18 52			19 46							21 16			22 03				
	d	17 34					18 16		18 54			19 49					20 38		21 19			22 05		23 15		
Weston Milton	d						18 19												21 22			22 08		23 18		
Worle	d	17 40					18 24		19 00			19 54							21 26					23 23		
Yatton	d	17 45					18 29		19 05			20 00							21 31			22 15		23 28		
Nailsea & Backwell	d	17 51					18 35		19 10			20 06							21 37			22 21		23 34		
Parson Street	d						18 45																			
Bedminster	d						18 47												21 48					23 45		
Bristol Temple Meads 10	a	18 03	18 24	18 25			18 50		19 25	19 25		20 18	20 22	20 25			20 58		21 51	21 57		22 33		23 48		
	d	18 05	18 30	18 30	18 44	18 48		19 00	19 30	19 30	19 49		20 24	20 30	20 44	20 48	21 00	21 48		22 05	22 10		22 48			
Lawrence Hill	d																									
Stapleton Road	d																									
Filton Abbey Wood	d				18 51	18 55					19 56				20 51	20 55		21 57					22 55			
Bristol Parkway 7	a			18 38	18 54	18 58		19 08		19 38	20 00			20 38	20 54	20 58		22 00			22 18		22 58			
	d				18 55										20 55											
Bath Spa 7	a	18 17	18 42						19 42								21 12			22 17						
London Paddington 15 ⊖	a	20 03	20 23						21 25				22 17				23 07			00 11						
Yate	d				19 04										21 04											
Cam & Dursley	d				19 16										21 16											
Gloucester 7	a				19 35										21 35											

For general notes see front of timetable
For details of catering facilities see Directory of Train Operators

A From Exeter St Davids (Table 135)
B To Cheltenham Spa (Table 57)
C To Worcester Shrub Hill (Table 57)
D To Westbury (Table 123)
E From Paignton (Table 135)
G From Penzance (Table 135)

Route Diagram for Tables 135, 136, 139, 140, 142, 143, 144

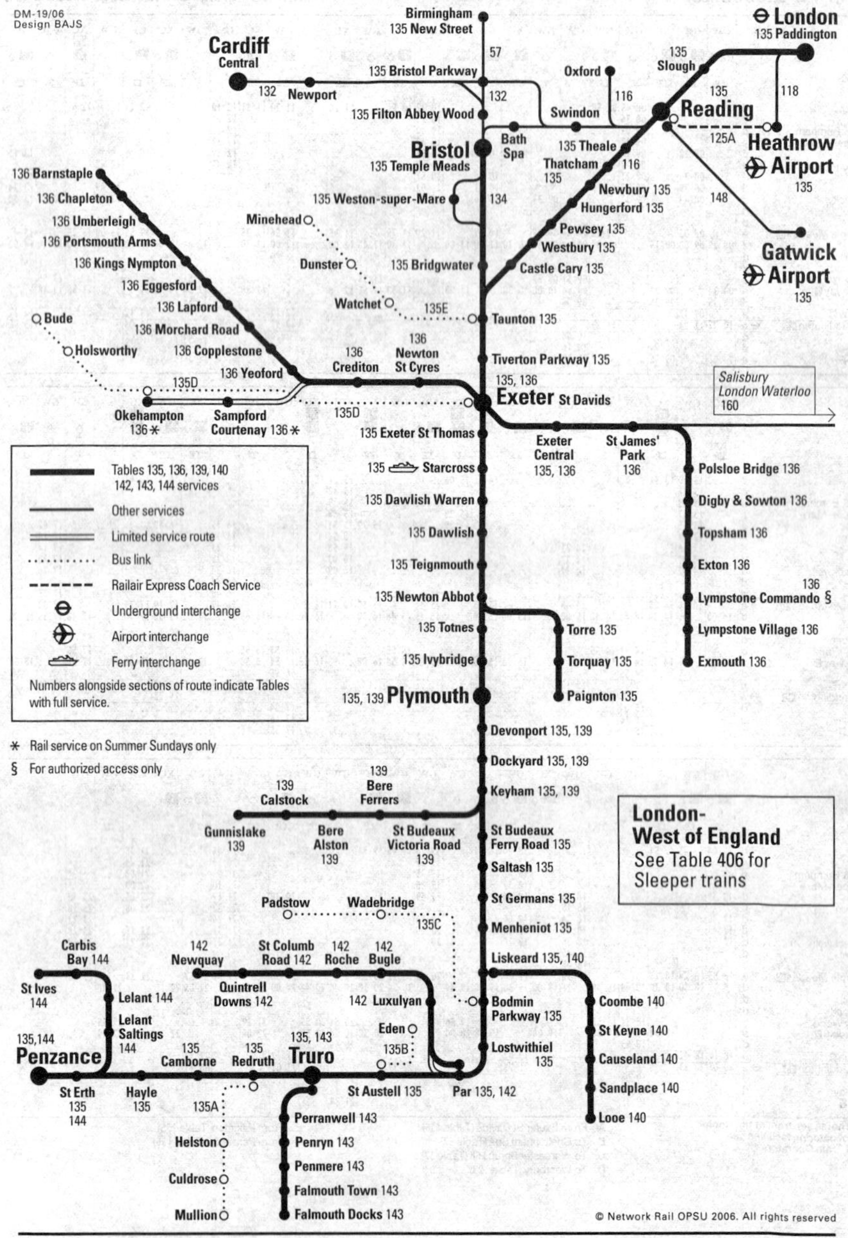
DM-19/06
Design BAJS
Birmingham
135 New Street
57
London
135 Paddington
Cardiff
Central
132 Newport
135 Bristol Parkway
Oxford
135 Slough
132
116
135
118
135 Filton Abbey Wood
Swindon
Reading
Bath Spa
135 Theale
125A
Heathrow Airport
135
Bristol
135 Temple Meads
Thatcham 135
116
136 Barnstaple
Newbury 135
148
136 Chapleton
135 Weston-super-Mare
134
Hungerford 135
136 Umberleigh
Minehead
Pewsey 135
136 Portsmouth Arms
Westbury 135
Gatwick Airport
135
136 Kings Nympton
Dunster
135 Bridgwater
Castle Cary 135
136 Eggesford
Watchet
135E
136 Lapford
Bude
136 Morchard Road
Taunton 135
Holsworthy
136 Copplestone
136 Crediton
136 Newton St Cyres
Tiverton Parkway 135
136 Yeoford
135D
135, 136
Exeter St Davids
Salisbury
London Waterloo
160
Okehampton 136 *
Sampford Courtenay 136 *
135D
135 Exeter St Thomas
Exeter Central 135, 136
St James' Park 136
135 Starcross
Polsloe Bridge 136
135 Dawlish Warren
Digby & Sowton 136
135 Dawlish
Topsham 136
135 Teignmouth
Exton 136
136
135 Newton Abbot
Lympstone Commando §
135 Totnes
Torre 135
Lympstone Village 136
135 Ivybridge
Torquay 135
Exmouth 136
135, 139 Plymouth
Paignton 135
Tables 135, 136, 139, 140 142, 143, 144 services
Other services
Limited service route
Bus link
Railair Express Coach Service
Underground interchange
Airport interchange
Ferry interchange
Numbers alongside sections of route indicate Tables with full service.
Devonport 135, 139
* Rail service on Summer Sundays only
§ For authorized access only
Dockyard 135, 139
139 Calstock
139 Bere Ferrers
Keyham 135, 139
London-
West of England
See Table 406 for Sleeper trains
Gunnislake 139
Bere Alston 139
St Budeaux Victoria Road 139
St Budeaux Ferry Road 135
Saltash 135
St Germans 135
Padstow
Wadebridge
135C
Menheniot 135
Carbis Bay 144
142 Newquay
St Columb Road 142
142 Roche
142 Bugle
Liskeard 135, 140
St Ives 144
Lelant 144
Quintrell Downs 142
142 Luxulyan
Bodmin Parkway 135
Coombe 140
Lelant Saltings 144
Eden
St Keyne 140
135,144
Penzance
135 Camborne
135 Redruth
135, 143
Truro
135B
Lostwithiel 135
Causeland 140
St Erth 135 144
Hayle 135
135A
St Austell 135
Par 135, 142
Sandplace 140
Perranwell 143
Looe 140
Helston
Penryn 143
Penmere 143
Culdrose
Falmouth Town 143
Mullion
Falmouth Docks 143

Sleeper services are published in Table 406

London and Birmingham → Devon and Cornwall

Network Diagram - see first page of Table 135

Miles	Miles			GW MX ■1 ✕	GW MX ■1◇ 🛏	GW MO ■1◇ ☕	XC MO ■1◇ ☕	GW MX ■1◇ ☕	GW	GW		XC MX ■1◇ ☕	GW MO ■1◇ ☕	GW ■1	GW	GW	GW ◇	GW A		GW	GW ◇	GW	GW	GW	XC ■1◇ ☕
0	—	**London Paddington** [15] ⊖	d	19p03	20p35	23p50		23p45																	
—	—	**London Waterloo** [15] ⊖	d																						
18½	—	Slough [3]	d																						
—	—	Heathrow Terminal 1 Bus	d																						
—	—	Gatwick Airport [10]	d																						
—	—	Oxford	d																						
36	—	**Reading** [7]	d	19p32	21p02	00u37		00u37																	
41¾	—	Theale	d																						
49½	—	Thatcham	d																						
53	—	Newbury	d	19p49	21p18																				
61½	—	Hungerford	d																						
75½	—	Pewsey	d		21p39																				
95¼	—	Westbury	d		21p58																				
115¼	—	Castle Cary	d		22p16																				
—	0	**Birmingham New Street** [12]	d																						06 10
—	—	Cardiff Central [7]	d																						
—	—	Newport (South Wales)	d																						
—	—	Swindon	d																						
—	87	Bristol Parkway [7]	d																						07 55
—	88¼	Filton Abbey Wood	d																						
—	—	Bath Spa [7]	d																						
—	92¾	**Bristol Temple Meads** [10]	d													05 31				06 48				08 11
—	112¾	Weston-super-Mare	d													05 52				07 10				
—	126½	Bridgwater	d													06 10								
143	138¾	Taunton	d	20p55	22p59			03b55									06 25				07 38				08 43
157½	—	Tiverton Parkway	d		23p20												06 40				07 53				
173¾	—	**Exeter St Davids** [6]	a	21p20	23p43	04 05		04 44									06 58				08 11				09 07
—	—	Exeter Central	a			*05 13*											*07 13*				*08 29*				
—	—	Exmouth	a			*06 03*											*07 40*				*09 15*				
—	—	Barnstaple	a																		*10 21*				
—	—	Exmouth	d														*06 05*			07 15		07 50		08 20	
—	—	Exeter Central	d														*06 32*			07 39		08 19		08 44	
—	—	**Exeter St Davids** [6]	d	21p22	23p45	04 37		04 47		05 40					06 15		07 00			07 48	08 13	08 29		08 56	09 07
174¾	—	Exeter St Thomas	d							05 43					06 18		07 02			07 51				08 59	
182¼	—	Starcross	d												06 26		07 11			07 59				09 07	
184¼	—	Dawlish Warren	d												06 31		07 15			08 04				09c19 →	
185¾	—	Dawlish	d							05 55					06 35		07 19			08 08	08 26	08 42			
188¾	—	Teignmouth	d							06 00					06 40		07 24			08 13	08 31	08 47			
193¾	—	Newton Abbot	a	21p42	00 04	04 57		05 07		06 07					06 46		07 31			08 19	08 37	08 53			
—	0		d	21p43	00 06	04 57		05 09	05 42	06 08					06 48	07 06	07 31			08 21	08 38	08 54	09 02		
—	5¼	Torre	d						05 50	06 17					06 56	07 15				08 29		09 02			
—	6	Torquay	d						05 53	06 20					06 59	07 20				08 32		09 05			09 36
—	8¼	Paignton	a						06 00	06 25					07 05	07 26				08 38		09 13			09 47
202½	—	Totnes	d	21p57	00 18												07 45				08 51		09 14		
214	—	Ivybridge	d														08 01				09 08		09 31		
225¾	—	**Plymouth**	a	22p24	00 47	05 37		05 47					←				08 15				09 22		09 47		
—	—		d	22p26		06 30 →	05 50	05 50				06 30	06 30	07 05			08 19	08 28			09 23				
227	—	Devonport	d											07 10				08 31							
227½	—	Dockyard	d																						
228	—	Keyham	d																						
228¾	—	St Budeaux Ferry Road	d																						
230	—	Saltash	d	22p36										07 18			08 27	08 38							
235	—	St Germans	d	22p43										07 25			08 34	08 45							
240½	—	Menheniot	d															08 53							
243½	—	Liskeard [3]	d	22p55			06 16	06 16				06 53	07 00	07 37			08 46	08 59			09 47				
—	—	Looe	a									*07 44*	*07 44*								*10 24*				
252½	—	Bodmin Parkway	d	23p07			06 30	06 30				07 06	07 14	07 49			08 58				09 59				
256	—	Lostwithiel	d	23p12			06 36	06 36				07 11	07 20	07 55			09 03				10 04				
260½	—	Par [3]	d	23p19			06 43	06 43				07 18	07 27	08 02			09 10	09 25			10 11				
—	—	Newquay	a											*10 13*				10 15							
265	—	St Austell	d	23p27			06 51	06 51				07 25	07 36	08 10			09 18				10 19				
279½	—	Truro	d	23p44			07 11	07 11				07 42	07 55	08 28			09 36				10 40				
—	—	Falmouth Docks	a				*07 54*							*08 54*			*10 08*				*11 10*				
288½	—	Redruth	d	23p57			07 24	07 24				07 53	08 10	08 40			09 49				10 53				
292	—	Camborne	d	00 04			07 32	07 32				08 00	08 18	08 47			09 55				10 59				
298	—	Hayle	d	00 12			07 40	07 40				08 08	08 26	08 56			10 03				11 06				
299½	—	St Erth [2]	d	00 17			07 45	07 45				08 12	08 31	09 00			10 06				11 09				
—	—	St Ives	a				*08 28*					*08 28*		*09 24*			*10 23*				*11 23*				
305¼	—	**Penzance**	a	00 35			08 01	08 01				08 27	08 47	09 14			10 19				11 24				

For general notes see front of timetable
For details of catering facilities see Directory of Train Operators

A From Gunnislake (Table 139)
b Arr. 0336
c Arr. 0911

Sleeper services are published in Table 406

London and Birmingham → Devon and Cornwall

Network Diagram - see first page of Table 135

		GW	GW	XC		GW	GW	GW	SW	XC	SW	GW		GW	GW	GW	XC	GW	GW	GW		GW	XC	SW	XC
				1 ◇			1 ◇		1 ◇	1 ◇	1 ◇			1 ◇	1 ◇		R 1		1 ◇	1 ◇			R 1	1 ◇	1 ◇
																			A	B		C			
				☕			⊠		☕	☕	☕			⊤	☕		☕		⊤	⊠			☕	☕	☕
London Paddington 15	⊖ d						07 30							08 18	09 05				10 00	10 05					
London Waterloo 15	⊖ d								07 10															09 20	
Slough 3	d																								
Heathrow Terminal 1 Bus	d																								
Gatwick Airport 10	d													*06 59*	*07 58*				*08b14*						
Oxford	d													*08 15*	*08 50*				*09 43*	*10 00*					
Reading 7	d						07 57							08 47	09 32				10 27	10 32					
Theale	d													08 55											
Thatcham	d													09 04											
Newbury	d													09 10											
Hungerford	d													09 20											
Pewsey	d													09 35											
Westbury	d													09 54											
Castle Cary	d													10 11											
Birmingham New Street 12	d			07 10						08 10							09 10						09 40		10 10
Cardiff Central 7	d																								
Newport (South Wales)	d																								
Swindon	d						08 26												10 56						
Bristol Parkway 7	d			08 26						09 25							10 25						10 55		11 25
Filton Abbey Wood	d																								
Bath Spa 7	d						08 55												11 25						
Bristol Temple Meads 10	d			08 44			09 13			09 44							10 44		11 46 →				11 14		11 44
Weston-super-Mare	d																						11 42		
Bridgwater	d																								
Taunton	d			09 17			09 46			10 17				10 33	10 48		11 17						12 05		12 17
Tiverton Parkway	d			09 29						10 29				10 46	11 01		11 29						12 17		12 29
Exeter St Davids 6	a			09 43			10 12			10 43				11 06	11 17		11 43			12 10			12 31		12 43
Exeter Central	a			*10 13*										*11 21*	*11 36*		*12 13*			*12 21*					
Exmouth	a			*10 45*										*11 45*	*12 15*					*12 45*					
Barnstaple	a														*12 28*										
Exmouth	d		08 50			09 20			*09 50*			10 20					*10 50*	11 20					*11 50*		
Exeter Central	d		09 14	*09 24*		09 44			10 30			10 43					*11 18*	11 43				12 08	*12 16*	12 30	
Exeter St Davids 6	d		09 20	09 45		09 57	10 13		10 39	10 45		10 50			11 18		11 45	11 51		12 10		12 15	12 33	12 39	12 45
Exeter St Thomas	d					10 00						10 53						11 54							
Starcross	d	←				10 08					←	11 01						12 02							
Dawlish Warren	d	09 19				10 13			10c57 →		10 57	11 06						12 07						12e57 →	
Dawlish	d	09 23	09 33			10 17					11 01	11 10						12 11				12 28	12 45		
Teignmouth	d	09 28	09 38			10 22					11 06	11 15						12 16				12 33	12 50		
Newton Abbot	a	09 34	09 44	10 02		10 28	10 33	←		11 02	11 12	11 21			11 38		12 02	12 22		12 31		12 39	12 56		13 02
	d	09 38	09 46	10 04		10 42	10 34	10 42		11 04	11 14	11 23			11 39		12 04	12 24		12 31		12 40	12 57		13 04
Torre	d	09 46				→		10 50				11 31						12 32							
Torquay	d	09 49						10 53			11 25	11 34						12 35					13 08		
Paignton	a	09 55						10 59			11 31	11 40						12 41					13 20		
Totnes	d		09 59	10 17			10 47			11 17					11 52		12 17					12 52			13 17
Ivybridge	d		10 16																			13 09			
Plymouth	a		10 30	10 48			11 15			11 48					12 23		12 48			13 09		13 25			13 48
	d		10 32				11 17									12 44				13 10		13 33			
Devonport	d																					13 36			
Dockyard	d																					13x38			
Keyham	d																					13x40			
St Budeaux Ferry Road	d																								
Saltash	d		10 40													12 52									
St Germans	d															12 59									
Menheniot	d																								
Liskeard 3	d		10 57				11 41									13 11				13 34					
Looe	a		*12 19*																	*14 15*					
Bodmin Parkway	d		11 09				11 53									13 23				13 47					
Lostwithiel	d															13 28									
Par 3	d		11 19				12 05									13 35				13 57					
Newquay	a		*12 14*																	*14 50*					
St Austell	d		11 27				12 12									13 43				14 05					
Truro	d		11 44				12 29									14 00				14 22					
Falmouth Docks	a		*13 02*																	*14 52*					
Redruth	d		11 57				12 42									14 13				14 35					
Camborne	d		12 03				12 49									14 19				14 42					
Hayle	d						12 58													14 51					
St Erth 2	d		12 13				13 02									14 29				14 55					
St Ives	a		*12 53*													*14 53*				*15 23*					
Penzance	a		12 24				13 21									14 41				15 12					

For general notes see front of timetable
For details of catering facilities see Directory of Train Operators

A **The Torbay Express**
B **The Cornish Riviera**
C To Gunnislake (Table 139)
b Change at Redhill
c Arr. 1050
e Arr. 1250

Sleeper services are published in Table 406

London and Birmingham → Devon and Cornwall

Network Diagram - see first page of Table 135

	SW	GW	GW	GW	GW		XC	GW	GW	XC	XC	GW	GW		GW	GW	GW	XC	GW	SW	GW		XC	GW
	1◇	1◇		1◇			1◇		1◇	1◇	1◇		1◇			1◇		1◇		1◇			R 1	1◇
		A		B					C															
	⊡	⚲		⊠			⊡		✕	⊡	⊡		⚲			⊡		⊡		⊡			⊡	⊠
London Paddington 15 ⊖ d				11 05					12 05				12 18			13 05								14 05
London Waterloo 15 ⊖ d																				12 20				
Slough 3 d																								
Heathrow Terminal 1 Bus d																								
Gatwick Airport 10 d				10 03					11 03							12 03								13 03
Oxford d				11 00					12 00				12 15			13 00								14 00
Reading 7 d				11 32					12 32				12 47			13 32								14 32
Theale d													12 55											
Thatcham d													13 04											
Newbury d													13 10											
Hungerford d													13 20											
Pewsey d				12 03									13 39											
Westbury d				12 22									13 58											
Castle Cary d				12 40									14 16											
Birmingham New Street 12 d							11 10			11 40	12 10							13 10					13 40	
Cardiff Central 7 d																								
Newport (South Wales) d																								
Swindon d																								
Bristol Parkway 7 d							12 25			12 55	13 25							14 25					14 55	
Filton Abbey Wood d																								
Bath Spa 7 d		←																						
Bristol Temple Meads 10 d		11 46					12 44			13 11	13 44							14 44					15 11	
Weston-super-Mare d		12 10																						
Bridgwater d																								
Taunton d		12 32		13 02			13 17			13b50	14 17		14a40			14 48		15 17					15 43	15 48
Tiverton Parkway d				13 15			13 29			14 02	14 29					15 01		15 29					15 55	16 01
Exeter St Davids 6 a		12 58		13 32			13 43		14 10	14 16	14 43					15 18		15 43					16 10	16 18
Exeter Central a		13 21		13 48			14 13		14 21	14 48	15 21					15 33		16 13		15 39			16 21	16 39
Exmouth a		13 45		14 12					14 45	15 15	15 45					16 15							16 45	17 15
Barnstaple a		14 20								15 30						16 35								17 45
Exmouth d			12 20	12 50				13 20			13 50	14 20				14 20		14 50					15 20	
Exeter Central d			12 43	13 14				13 45			14 14	14 43				14 43		15 14					15 46	
Exeter St Davids 6 d		13 00	13 05	13 33			13 45	13 51	14 11	14 18	14 45	14 50				15 19		15 45		15 50			16 12	16 19
Exeter St Thomas d			13 08					13 54				14 53												
Starcross d	←		13 16					14 02				15 01												
Dawlish Warren d	12 57		13 21					14 07				15 06												
Dawlish d	13 01	13 13	13 25					14 11		14 30		15 10								16 02				
Teignmouth d	13 06	13 19	13 30					14 16		14 35		15 15								16 07				
Newton Abbot a	13 13	13 26	13 36	13 53			14 02	14 22	14 31	14 41	15 02	15 21				15 40		16 02		16 14			16 30	16 39
Newton Abbot d	13 13	13 27	13 38	13 54			14 04	14 24	14 32	14 42	15 04	15 23				15 40	15 56	16 04	16 08	16 14			16 31	16 40
Torre d			13 46					14 32				15 31							16 16					
Torquay d		13 39	13 49					14 35		14 53		15 34							16 19					
Paignton a		13 50	13 55					14 42		15 05		15 40							16 24					
Totnes d	13 26			14 07			14 17				15 17					15 54	16 08	16 17		16 26			16 44	16 53
Ivybridge d	13 41																16 24			16 42				
Plymouth a	13 56			14 36			14 48		15 09		15 48					16 25	16 40	16 48		16 57			17 15	17 21
Plymouth d					14 41				15 11						15 57						17 06			17 25
Devonport d															16 00						17 09			
Dockyard d															16x02						17x11			
Keyham d															16x04						17x13			
St Budeaux Ferry Road d															16 06						17 15			
Saltash d															16 11						17 20			17 35
St Germans d															16 18						17 27			17 43
Menheniot d															16 26						17 35			
Liskeard 3 d					15 05				15 35						16 32						17a41			17 57
Looe a					15 44				17 05						17 05									18 32
Bodmin Parkway d					15 17				15 47						16 44									18 10
Lostwithiel d															16 49									18 15
Par 3 d					15 27				15 57						16 56									18 21
Newquay a																								
St Austell d					15 35				16 05						17 03									18 29
Truro d					15 53				16 23						17 22									18 47
Falmouth Docks a									16 50						17 48									19 14
Redruth d					16 06				16 35						17 35									18 59
Camborne d					16 12				16 43						17 43									19 07
Hayle d					16 20										17 50									19 16
St Erth 2 d					16 23				16 53						17 54									19 20
St Ives a					16 54				17 24						18 12									
Penzance a					16 36				17 11						18 06									19 37

For general notes see front of timetable
For details of catering facilities see Directory of Train Operators

A The Torbay Express
B The Mayflower
C The Royal Duchy

b Arr. 1342

Sleeper services are published in Table 406

London and Birmingham → Devon and Cornwall

Network Diagram - see first page of Table 135

		GW	XC	GW	GW	GW	GW	GW		XC	SW	XC	GW	GW	XC	GW		GW	GW	GW	GW	XC	GW	GW	GW
			R							R					R							R			
			1					1 ◇		1	1 ◇	1 ◇	1 ◇		1	1 ◇		1 ◇		1 ◇		1	1 ◇	1 ◇	1 ◇
					A	B				C					D										
			☕					☕		☕	☕	☕	☕		☕	☕		🍴		☕		☕	🍴	☕	🍴
London Paddington 15	⊖ d							15 05					16 05			16 30		16 33		17 03			17 06		17 30
London Waterloo 15	⊖ d										14 20														
Slough 3	d																	16u48							
Heathrow Terminal 1 Bus	🚌 d																								
Gatwick Airport 10	d							*14 03*					*15 03*							*16 03*					
Oxford	d							*15 00*					*16 00*			*16 15*		*16 30*		*17 00*					*17 15*
Reading 7	d							15 32					16 32			16 57		17 04		17 32			17 37		17 57
Theale	d																						17 45		
Thatcham	d																						17 54		
Newbury	d																	17 20		17 48			18 01		
Hungerford	d																	17 29					18 14		
Pewsey	d							16 03										17 44					18 32		
Westbury	d							16 22										18 03					18a53		
Castle Cary	d							16 40										18 21							
Birmingham New Street 12	d		14 10							15 10		15 40			16 10							17 10			
Cardiff Central 7	d																								
Newport (South Wales)	d																								
Swindon	d															17 31									18 31
Bristol Parkway 7	d		15 25							16 25		16 58			17 25							18 25			
Filton Abbey Wood	d																								
Bath Spa 7	d															18 00								←	19 00
Bristol Temple Meads 10	d		15 44							16 44		17 11			17 44	18 22 →						18 44		18 22	19 16
Weston-super-Mare	d																							18 56	19 58
Bridgwater	d																							19 13	→
Taunton	d		16 17					17 03		17 17		17 44	17 48		18 17			18 43		18 53		19 17		19a30	
Tiverton Parkway	d		16 29					17 16		17 29		17 56	18 01		18 29			18 56		19 06		19 29			
Exeter St Davids 6	a		16 43					17 32		17 43		18 10	18 18		18 43			19 18		19 22		19 43			
Exeter Central	a		*17 21*					*17 43*		*17 53*		*18 21*			*18 52*							*19 52*			
Exmouth	a		*17 48*							*18 19*		*18 48*			*19 19*							*20 18*			
Barnstaple	a									*19 04*					*20 19*										
Exmouth	d	15 50		16 20			16 50					*17 20*		17 50						*18 20*	18 54				
Exeter Central	d	16 17	*16 32*	16 42			17 14			*17 35*	17 35	*17 56*		18 18						*19 01*	19 18				
Exeter St Davids 6	d	16 23	16 45	16 51			17 21	17 33		17 45	17 49	18 12	18 21	18 25	18 45					19 23	19 28	19 45			
Exeter St Thomas	d	16 26		16 54			17 24				17 52			18 28							19 31				
Starcross	d	16 34		17 02			17 32				18 00			18 36							19 39				
Dawlish Warren	d	16 39		17 07			17 37				18 04			18 41							19 44				
Dawlish	d	16 43		17 11			17 41				18 08	18 24		18 45							19 48				
Teignmouth	d	16 48		17 16			17 46				18 13	18 29		18 50							19 53				
Newton Abbot	a	16 54	17 02	17 22			17 52	17 57		18 08	18 20	18 35	18 42	18 56	19 02				←	19 43	19 59	20 02			
	d	16 56	17 04	17 24		17 29	17 54	17 58		18 09	18 21	18 36	18 42	19 09	19 04				19 09	19 44	20 08	20 04			
Torre	d	17 04		17 32			18 02				18 30			→					19 17		→				
Torquay	d	17 07		17 35			18 05				18 34								19 20						
Paignton	a	17 13		17 41			18 11				18 40								19 26						
Totnes	d		17 17			17 41		18 11		18 22		18 49	18 56		19 17					19 58		20 17			
Ivybridge	d					17 58																			
Plymouth	a		17 48			18 13		18 39		18 52		19 20	19 24		19 48					20 25		20 48			
	d		17 55		18 12	18 16		18 40		19 00			19 26		19 50					20 27					
Devonport	d				18 15	18 19																			
Dockyard	d				18x17	18x21																			
Keyham	d				18x19	18x23																			
St Budeaux Ferry Road	d				18 21																				
Saltash	d				18 26								19 36												
St Germans	d				18 33								19 43												
Menheniot	d				18 41																				
Liskeard 3	d		18 18		18 47			19 04		19 23			19 55		20 13					20 51					
Looe	a							*19 40*																	
Bodmin Parkway	d		18 31		18 59			19 16		19 35			20 07		20 26					21 04					
Lostwithiel	d				19 04					19 41										21 09					
Par 3	d		18 41		19b33			19 26		19 47			20 17		20 36					21 15					
Newquay	a				20 23			*20 23*																	
St Austell	d		18 48					19 34		19 54			20 25		20 42					21 23					
Truro	d		19 05					19 53		20 11			20 43		21 00					21 42					
Falmouth Docks	a							*20 23*							*21 27*										
Redruth	d		19 17					20 05		20 22			20 55		21 14					21 54					
Camborne	d		19 24					20 13		20 29			21 03		21 21					22 02					
Hayle	d									20 36			21 12							22 10					
St Erth 2	d		19 34					20 23		20 41			21 16		21 31					22 15					
St Ives	a		*19 53*					*20 43*							*21 48*										
Penzance	a		19 49					20 41		20 56			21 29		21 47					22 30					

For general notes see front of timetable
For details of catering facilities see Directory of Train Operators

A From Gunnislake (Table 139)
B To Gunnislake (Table 139)
C From Glasgow Central (Table 51)
D ☕ to Plymouth
b Arr. 1913

Sleeper services are published in Table 406

London and Birmingham → Devon and Cornwall

Network Diagram - see first page of Table 135

		GW		GW	GW	GW	XC	GW	GW	GW		GW	GW	XC	GW	GW	GW	XC		GW	GW	GW	GW		
																						FO	FX		
		1 ◇			1 ◇	1 ◇	1 ◇	1 ◇	1 ◇	1 ◇		1		1 ◇		1 ◇		1 ◇		1 ◇	1 ◇	1 ◇	◇		
					A			B						C								D			
		⊡			✕	⊡	⊡	⊼	⊼	⊡		✕		⊡		⊡				⊼	⊡	⊡	⊡		
London Paddington 15 ⊖	d	17 33			18 03			18 06		18 36		19 03				19 45				20 35	21 45	23 45	23 45		
London Waterloo 15 ⊖	d																								
Slough 3	d																								
Heathrow Terminal 1 Bus	d																								
Gatwick Airport 10	d	16b08						17 03				18 03				18 03					20c11	22 23			
Oxford	d				18 00					18 30		18 43				19 30					21 20	23 55			
Reading 7	d	18 02			18 32			18 36		19 03		19 32				20 11				21 02	22 12	00u37	00u37		
Theale	d							18 45																	
Thatcham	d							18 54																	
Newbury	d	18 18						19 01		19 19		19 49				20 26				21 18					
Hungerford	d							19 15		19 29															
Pewsey	d	18 39						19 34		19 44						20 47				21 39					
Westbury	d	18 58						19a52		20 03						21 06				21 58					
Castle Cary	d	19 16								20 20						21 23				22 16					
Birmingham New Street 12	d						18 10							19 10				20 10							
Cardiff Central 7	d																								
Newport (South Wales)	d																								
Swindon	d																				22 52				
Bristol Parkway 7	d						19 25							20 25				21 25							
Filton Abbey Wood	d																								
Bath Spa 7	d																				23 28				
Bristol Temple Meads 10	d						19 44		←					20 44				21 44			23 45				
Weston-super-Mare	d								19 58																
Bridgwater	d								20 13																
Taunton	d	19 38			19 47		20 17		20a30	20 42		20 55		21 17		21 45		22s15		22 59	00s42	03 40	03e55		
Tiverton Parkway	d	19 51					20 29			20 55				21 29		21 58		22s45		23 20	01s18				
Exeter St Davids 6	a	20 07			20 13		20 43			21 15		21 20		21 43		22 15		23 10		23 43	01 45	04 36	04 44		
Exeter Central	a	20 18					20 52							21 52		22f33						05 13	05 13		
Exmouth	a						21 18							22 18								06 03	06 03		
Barnstaple	a						22 05															06 56	06 58		
Exmouth	d				19 20							20 20		20 20		21 20		22 20							
Exeter Central	d				19 52	←	20 31					20 44		20 44		21 50		22 44							
Exeter St Davids 6	d	20 19 →			20 15	20 19	20 45					21 22	21 28	21 45		22 16	22 30	23 13		23 45		04 47	04 47		
Exeter St Thomas	d					20 23							21 31				22 33								
Starcross	d					20 32							21 39				22 41								
Dawlish Warren	d					20 36							21 44				22 46								
Dawlish	d					20 41							21 48				22 50								
Teignmouth	d					20 47							21 53				22 55								
Newton Abbot	a			←	20 35	20 54	21 02					21 42	21 59	22 02	←	22 37	23 01	23 33		00 04		05 07	05 07		
	d			20 08	20 36	20 54	21 04					21 43	22 08	22 04	22 08	22 37	23 10	23 34		00 06		05 09	05 09		
Torre	d			20 16		21 03							→		22 16		23 18								
Torquay	d			20 19		21 07									22 19		23 21								
Paignton	a			20 25		21 20									22 26		23 28								
Totnes	d				20 49		21 17					21 57		22 17		22 51		23 47		00 18					
Ivybridge	d																								
Plymouth	a				21 17		21 48					22 24		22 48		23 22		00 18		00 47		05 47	05 47		
	d				21 19							22 26										05 50	05 50		
Devonport	d																								
Dockyard	d																								
Keyham	d																								
St Budeaux Ferry Road	d																								
Saltash	d											22 36													
St Germans	d											22 43													
Menheniot	d																								
Liskeard 3	d				21 43							22 55										06 16	06 16		
Looe	a																					07 43	07 44		
Bodmin Parkway	d				21 55							23 07										06 30	06 30		
Lostwithiel	d											23 12										06 36	06 36		
Par 3	d				22 05							23 19										06 43	06 43		
Newquay	a																								
St Austell	d				22 13							23 27										06 51	06 51		
Truro	d				22 31							23 44										07 10	07 11		
Falmouth Docks	a																					07 53	07 54		
Redruth	d				22 43							23 57										07 24	07 24		
Camborne	d											00 04										07 31	07 32		
Hayle	d											00 12										07 40	07 40		
St Erth 2	d											00 17										07 45	07 45		
St Ives	a																					09 19	08 28		
Penzance	a				23 10							00 35										08 00	08 01		

For general notes see front of timetable
For details of catering facilities see Directory of Train Operators

- **A** **The Golden Hind**
- **B** To Frome (Table 123)
- **C** ⊡ to Bristol Temple Meads
- **D** **The Night Riviera**

- **b** Change at Redhill
- **c** Change at Redhill and Reading
- **e** Arr. 0336
- **f** Fridays arr. 2300

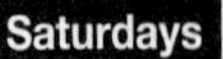

until 26 January

Sleeper services are published in Table 406

London and Birmingham → Devon and Cornwall

Network Diagram - see first page of Table 135

		GW	GW	GW	GW	GW	XC	GW	GW	GW	GW	GW	SW	GW	GW	GW	XC	GW	GW	GW	SW	XC	SW
		1	1 ◇		1 ◇		1 ◇					◇	1				1 ◇		1 ◇		1 ◇	1 ◇	1 ◇
					A																		
		✕	🛒		☕		☕					🛒			🛒	🛒	☕		☕		☕	☕	☕
London Paddington 15 ⊖	d	19p03	20 35		23p45														07 30				
London Waterloo 15 ⊖	d																				07 10		
Slough 3	d																						
Heathrow Terminal 1 Bus 🚌	d																						
Gatwick Airport 10	d																		*06 03*				
Oxford	d																		*07 15*				
Reading 7	d	19p32	21 02		00u37														07 57				
Theale	d																						
Thatcham	d																						
Newbury	d	19p49	21 18																				
Hungerford	d																						
Pewsey	d		21 39																				
Westbury	d		21 58																				
Castle Cary	d		22 16																				
Birmingham New Street 12	d																07 10					08 10	
Cardiff Central 7	d																						
Newport (South Wales)	d																						
Swindon	d																		08 30				
Bristol Parkway 7	d																08 25					09 25	
Filton Abbey Wood	d																						
Bath Spa 7	d																		09 00				
Bristol Temple Meads 10	d											06 48					08 44		09 17			09 44	
Weston-super-Mare	d											07 12											
Bridgwater	d																						
Taunton	d	20p55	22 59		03b40							07 38					09 17		09 51			10 17	
Tiverton Parkway	d		23 20									07 59					09 29					10 29	
Exeter St Davids 6	a	21p20	23 43		04 36							08 17					09 43		10 17			10 43	
Exeter Central	a				*05 13*							*08 29*					*10 13*					*11 11*	
Exmouth	a				*06 03*							*09 15*					*10 45*						
Barnstaple	a				*06 56*							*10 20*											
Exmouth	d										07 18		*07 50*	08 20		08 50		09 20	*09 20*	*09 50*			
Exeter Central	d										07 42		08 27	08 44		09 14	*09 24*	09 44	*09 44*	*10 14*	10 29		
Exeter St Davids 6	d	21p22	23 45		04 47	05 29		06 00	06 14		07 48	08 19	08 37	08 50		09 20	09 45	09 52	10 18	10 25	10 38	10 45	
Exeter St Thomas	d					05 32		06 03	06 17		07 51			08 53				09 55					
Starcross	d					05 40		06 11	06 25		07 59			09 01				10 03					←
Dawlish Warren	d					05 45		06 16	06 30		08 04			09 06				10 08			11c00		11 00
Dawlish	d					05 49		06 20	06 34		08 08	08 32	08 50	09 10		09 33		10 12			→		11 04
Teignmouth	d					05 54		06 25	06 39		08 13	08 37	08 55	09 15		09 38		10 17					11 09
Newton Abbot	a	21p42	00 04		05 07	06 00		06 31	06 45		08 19	08 43	09 01	09 21		09 44	10 03	10 23	10 38	10 46		11 03	11 15
	d	21p43	00 06		05 09	06 02		06 33	06 47	07 37	08 21	08 44	09 06	09 23		09 46	10 04	10 25	10 39	10 48		11 04	11 17
Torre	d					06 10		06 41	06 55	07 45	08 29			09 31				10 33		10 56			
Torquay	d					06 13		06 44	06 58	07 48	08 32		09 17	09 34				10 36		10 59			11 28
Paignton	a					06 19		06 50	07 04	07 55	08 38		09 23	09 40				10 42		11 05			11 34
Totnes	d	21p57	00 18									08 57				09 59	10 17		10 52			11 17	
Ivybridge	d											09 14				10 16							
Plymouth	a	22p24	00 47		05 47							09 28				10 30	10 48		11 20			11 48	
	d	22p26			05 50		06 30					09 29			10 00	10 34			11 23				
Devonport	d														10 03								
Dockyard	d																						
Keyham	d																						
St Budeaux Ferry Road	d																						
Saltash	d	22p36													10 10	10 43							
St Germans	d	22p43													10 17								
Menheniot	d														10 25								
Liskeard 3	d	22p55			06 16		06 53					09 53			10 31	11 02			11 46				
Looe	a						*07 43*					*10 23*							*12 38*				
Bodmin Parkway	d	23p07			06 30		07 06					10 05			10 43	11 14			11 58				
Lostwithiel	d	23p12			06 36		07 11					10 10			10 48								
Par 3	d	23p19		06 10	06 43		07 18					10 17			10 55	11 24			12 09				
Newquay	a															*12 20*							
St Austell	d	23p27		06 17	06 51		07 25					10 25			11 03	11 32			12 16				
Truro	d	23p44		06 35	07 10		07 42					10 42			11 20	11 49			12 34				
Falmouth Docks	a				*07 53*		*08 53*								*11 48*				*13 10*				
Redruth	d	23p57		06 48	07 24		07 53					10 55			11 33	12 02			12 46				
Camborne	d	00 04		06 54	07 31		08 00					11 01			11 39	12 08			12 54				
Hayle	d	00 12		07 01	07 40		08 08					11 08			11 47				13 03				
St Erth 2	d	00 17		07 04	07 45		08 12					11 10			11 50	12 18			13 07				
St Ives	a			*07 43*			*09 19*					*11 21*			*12 21*	*12 53*			*13 21*				
Penzance	a	00 35		07 17	08 00		08 27					11 26			12 02	12 31			13 23				

For general notes see front of timetable
For details of catering facilities see Directory of Train Operators

A The Night Riviera
b Arr. 0336
c Arr. 1049

Saturdays

until 26 January

Sleeper services are published in Table 406

London and Birmingham → Devon and Cornwall

Network Diagram - see first page of Table 135

		GW		GW 1 ◇	GW 1 ◇	GW	XC 1 ◇	GW	GW 1 ◇	GW		XC 1 ◇	SW 1 ◇	XC 1 ◇	SW 1 ◇	GW	GW 1 ◇	GW		XC 1 ◇	GW	GW 1 ◇	SW 1 ◇	XC 1 ◇	GW
London Paddington 15 ⊖	d			08 18	09 05				10 05								11 05					12 05			
London Waterloo 15 ⊖	d												09 20										11 20		
Slough 3	d																								
Heathrow Terminal 1 Bus	d																								
Gatwick Airport 10	d			*07 03*	*08 03*												*10 03*					*11 03*			
Oxford	d			*08 15*	*08 43*												*11 00*					*12 00*			
Reading 7	d			08 49	09 32				10 32								11 32					12 32			
Theale	d			08 58																					
Thatcham	d			09 06																					
Newbury	d			09 12																					
Hungerford	d			09 21																					
Pewsey	d			09 36													12 03								
Westbury	d			09 56													12 22								
Castle Cary	d			10 13													12 40								
Birmingham New Street 12	d						09 10					09 40		10 10						11 10				12 10	
Cardiff Central 7	d																								
Newport (South Wales)	d																								
Swindon	d																								
Bristol Parkway 7	d						10 25					10 58		11 25						12 25				13 25	
Filton Abbey Wood	d																								
Bath Spa 7	d																								
Bristol Temple Meads 10	d						10 44					11 14		11 44						12 44				13 44	
Weston-super-Mare	d											11 42													
Bridgwater	d																								
Taunton	d			10 35	10 48		11 17					12 05		12 17			13 02			13 17				14 17	
Tiverton Parkway	d			10 48	11 01		11 29					12 17		12 29			13 15			13 29				14 29	
Exeter St Davids 6	a			11 06	11 17		11 43		12 10			12 31		12 43			13 32			13 43		14 10		14 43	
Exeter Central	a			*11 21*	*11 48*		*12 13*					*12 48*		*13 21*						*14 13*		*14 21*		*15 21*	
Exmouth	a			*11 45*	*12 14*		*12 45*					*13 14*		*13 42*								*14 45*		*15 45*	
Barnstaple	a			*12 20*										*14 23*											
Exmouth	d	10 20					*10 50*	11 20				*11 50*				12 20	*12 50*				13 20		*13 50*		14 20
Exeter Central	d	10 43					*11 14*	11 43				*12 14*	12 27			12 43	*13 14*				13 46		*14 19*		14 43
Exeter St Davids 6	d	10 50			11 18		11 45	11 50	12 10			12 33	12 39	12 45		12 50	13 33			13 45	13 51	14 11	14 28	14 45	14 50
Exeter St Thomas	d	10 53						11 53								12 53					13 54				14 53
Starcross	d	11 01						12 01							←	13 01					14 02				15 01
Dawlish Warren	d	11 06						12 06					13b00		13 00	13 06					14 07		14 39		15 06
Dawlish	d	11 10						12 10				12 45	→		13 04	13 10					14 11		14 43		15 10
Teignmouth	d	11 15						12 15				12 50			13 09	13 15					14 16		14 48		15 15
Newton Abbot	a	11 21			11 38		12 03	12 21	12 31			12 56		13 03	13 15	13 21	13 53			14 03	14 22	14 31	14 55	15 03	15 21
	d	11 23			11 39		12 04	12 23	12 31	12 40		12 57		13 04	13 16	13 23	13 54			14 04	14 24	14 32	14 56	15 04	15 23
Torre	d	11 31						12 35								13 31					14 32		15 05		15 31
Torquay	d	11 34						12 38				13 08				13 34					14 35		15 09		15 34
Paignton	a	11 40						12 44				13 20				13 41					14 42		15 15		15 40
Totnes	d				11 52		12 17			12 52				13 17	13 28		14 07			14 17				15 17	
Ivybridge	d									13 09					13 44										
Plymouth	a				12 23		12 48		13 09	13 25				13 48	13 59		14 36			14 48		15 09		15 48	
	d					12 44			13 10									14 41				15 11			
Devonport	d																								
Dockyard	d																								
Keyham	d																								
St Budeaux Ferry Road	d																								
Saltash	d					12 52																			
St Germans	d					12 59																			
Menheniot	d					13 07																			
Liskeard 3	d					13 15			13 34									15 05				15 35			
Looe	a					*14 16*												*15 42*				*16 59*			
Bodmin Parkway	d					13 27			13 47									15 17				15 47			
Lostwithiel	d					13 33												15 22							
Par 3	d					13 40			13 57									15 29				15 57			
Newquay	a					*14 55*																			
St Austell	d					13 47			14 05									15 37				16 05			
Truro	d					14 05			14 22									15 54				16 23			
Falmouth Docks	a					*14 58*												*16 21*				*17 14*			
Redruth	d					14 18			14 35									16 06				16 35			
Camborne	d					14 24			14 42									16 12				16 43			
Hayle	d					14 31			14 51									16 20							
St Erth 2	d					14 34			14 55									16 23				16 53			
St Ives	a					*14 53*												*16 54*				*17 24*			
Penzance	a					14 46			15 12									16 36				17 11			

For general notes see front of timetable
For details of catering facilities see
Directory of Train Operators

b Arr. 1250

until 26 January

Sleeper services are published in Table 406

London and Birmingham → Devon and Cornwall

Network Diagram - see first page of Table 135

		GW	GW	GW	SW	XC	SW	GW	XC	GW	XC	GW		GW	GW	GW	SW	XC	SW	SW		GW	GW	XC	GW
		1 ◇	1 ◇		1 ◇	1 ◇	1 ◇		1 ◇	1 ◇	1 ◇						1 ◇	1 ◇	1 ◇	1		1 ◇		1 ◇	1 ◇
				A											A									B	
		⊡	⊡		⊡	⊡	⊡		⊡	⊡	⊡			🚲			⊡	⊡	⊡			⊡		⊡	⊡
London Paddington 15 ⊖	d	12 18	13 05							14 05												16 05			16 30
London Waterloo 15 ⊖	d				12 20												14 20								
Slough 3	d	12 34																							
Heathrow Terminal 1 Bus 🚌	d																								
Gatwick Airport 10	d		*12 03*																			*15 03*			
Oxford	d	*12 15*	*12 43*																			*15 43*			*16 15*
Reading 7	d	12 49	13 32							14 32												16 32			16 57
Theale	d	12 58																							
Thatcham	d	13 06																							
Newbury	d	13 12																							
Hungerford	d	13 21																							
Pewsey	d	13 35																							
Westbury	d	13 55																							
Castle Cary	d	14 12																							
Birmingham New Street 12	d					13 10			13 40		14 10							15 10						16 10	
Cardiff Central 7	d																								
Newport (South Wales)	d																								
Swindon	d																								17 31
Bristol Parkway 7	d					14 25			14 58		15 25							16 25						17 25	
Filton Abbey Wood	d																								
Bath Spa 7	d																								18 00
Bristol Temple Meads 10	d					14 44			15 11		15 44							16 44						17 44	18 19
Weston-super-Mare	d																								18 54
Bridgwater	d																								→
Taunton	d	14a34	14 48			15 17			15 43	15 50	16 17							17 17				17 48		18 17	
Tiverton Parkway	d		15 01			15 29			15 55	16 03	16 29							17 29				18 01		18 29	
Exeter St Davids 6	a		15 18			15 43			16 10	16 20	16 43							17 43				18 18		18 43	
Exeter Central	a		*15 33*			*16 13*			*16 21*		*17 21*							*17 54*						*18 52*	
Exmouth	a		*16 14*						*16 45*		*17 45*							*18 19*						*19 18*	
Barnstaple	a		*16 36*						*17 45*									*19 01*						*20 19*	
Exmouth	d				15 20	*14 50*		15 20			*15 50*	16 20				16 50				*17 20*			17 50		
Exeter Central	d				15 46	*15 31*	15 39	15 46			*16 24*	16 42				17 14				17 53			18 19		
Exeter St Davids 6	d		15 19		15 54	15 45	15 51	15 54	16 12	16 21	16 45	16 51				17 21	17 42	17 45		18 02		18 19	18 26	18 45	
Exeter St Thomas	d				15 57			15 57				16 54				17 24							18 29		
Starcross	d				16 05			16 05				17 02				17 32							18 38		
Dawlish Warren	d				16 10			16 10				17 07				17 37			←	18 15			18 42		
Dawlish	d				16 14		16 03	16 14				17 11				17 41	18 05		18 05	18 19			18 46		
Teignmouth	d				16 19		16 08	16 19				17 16				17 46	→		18 10	18 24			18 51		
Newton Abbot	a		15 40		16 25	16 03	16 15	16 25	16 30	16 41	17 03	17 22				17 52		18 03	18 16	18 30		18 39	18 58	19 03	
	d		15 40	15 56	16 27	16 04	16 15	16 27	16 31	16 42	17 04	17 24			17 29	17 54		18 04	18 20	18 32		18 39	18 59	19 04	
Torre	d				16 35			16 35				17 32				18 02							19 07		
Torquay	d				16 38			16 38				17 35				18 05				18 43			19 10		
Paignton	a				16 44			16 44				17 41				18 11				18 50			19 17		
Totnes	d		15 54	16 08		16 17	16 27		16 44	16 55	17 17				17 41			18 17	18 32			18 53		19 17	
Ivybridge	d			16 24			16 43								17 58				18 48						
Plymouth	a		16 25	16 40		16 48	16 58		17 15	17 23	17 48				18 13			18 48	19 02			19 21		19 48	
	d			16 44						17 25	17 55			17 59	18 16			19 00	19 11			19 25		19 50	
Devonport	d			16 47										18 02	18 19										
Dockyard	d			16x48										18 04	18x21										
Keyham	d			16x50										18 06	18x23										
St Budeaux Ferry Road	d													18 08											
Saltash	d													18 13					19 19						
St Germans	d													18 19					19 26						
Menheniot	d													18 27											
Liskeard 3	d									17 49	18 18			18 33				19 23	19 38			19 50		20 13	
Looe	a													*19 39*											
Bodmin Parkway	d									18 03	18 31			18 45				19 35	19 50			20 05		20 26	
Lostwithiel	d													18 51					19 56						
Par 3	d									18 13	18 41			18 58				19 45	20 03			20 15		20 36	
Newquay	a																								
St Austell	d									18 21	18 48			19 05				19 52	20 11			20 23		20 42	
Truro	d									18 39	19 06			19 23				20b11	20 29			20 40		21 00	
Falmouth Docks	a										*20 19*			*20 19*										*21 27*	
Redruth	d									18 51	19 17			19 36				20 22	20 41			20 53		21 11	
Camborne	d									18 59	19 23			19 42				20 28	20 47			21 00		21 17	
Hayle	d													19 49								21 09			
St Erth 2	d									19 09	19 33			19 53				20 38				21 13		21 27	
St Ives	a										*20 38*			*20 38*										*21 45*	
Penzance	a									19 23	19 49			20 04				20 59	21 05			21 27		21 43	

For general notes see front of timetable
For details of catering facilities see Directory of Train Operators

A To Gunnislake (Table 139)
B ⊡ to Plymouth
b Arr. 2008

Table 135

Saturdays

until 26 January

Sleeper services are published in Table 406

London and Birmingham → Devon and Cornwall

Network Diagram - see first page of Table 135

		GW	GW	XC	GW	GW	GW	XC	GW	GW	GW	GW	GW	XC	GW	GW	GW	XC	GW	GW	GW
			1 ◇	1 ◇	1 ◇		1 ◇	1 ◇	1 ◇			1 ◇	1 ◇	1 ◇	1 ◇		1 ◇	1 ◇			1 ◇
		A												B							
			☕	☕	☕		☕	☕	☕			☕	☕	☕	☕		☕				☕
London Paddington 15	⊖ d		17 05				18 05		18 30			19 00	19 05				20 05				20 30
London Waterloo 15	⊖ d																				
Slough 3	d																				
Heathrow Terminal 1 Bus	🚌 d																				
Gatwick Airport 10	d						*17 03*					*18 03*					*19 03*				
Oxford	d						*18 00*		*18 15*			*18 43*	*19 00*				*19 43*				
Reading 7	d		17 32				18 32		18 57			19 27	19 32				20 32				20 57
Theale	d																				
Thatcham	d																				
Newbury	d												19 49				20 46				
Hungerford	d																				
Pewsey	d		18 03										20 10				21 06				
Westbury	d		18 22										20 29				21 25				
Castle Cary	d		18 40										20 45				21 44				
Birmingham New Street 12	d			17 10				18 10						19 10				20 10			
Cardiff Central 7	d															19 50				21 00	
Newport (South Wales)	d															20 05				21 15	
Swindon	d								19 31			19 56									21 31
Bristol Parkway 7	d			18 24				19 25						20 25				21 25			
Filton Abbey Wood	d															20 34				21 42	
Bath Spa 7	d								20 01			20 25			←						21 59
Bristol Temple Meads 10	d			18 44	←			19 44	20 15			20 49 →		20 44	20 49	20 56		21 44		21 53	22 16
Weston-super-Mare	d				18 54				20 37						21 13	21 30				22 27	22 42
Bridgwater	d														21 31	21 49			←	22 46	22 59
Taunton	d		19 02	19 17	19 20		19 47	20 17	21a06				21 07	21 17	21a47	22b21	22 06	22 17	22 21	23 01	23 10
Tiverton Parkway	d		19 15	19 29	19 33			20 29					21 20	21 29		→	22 19	22 29	22 36	23 16	23 24
Exeter St Davids 6	a		19 32	19 43	19 50		20 13	20 43					21 38	21 43			22 36	22 43	22 55	23 35	23 44
Exeter Central	a			*19 52*	*20 18*		*20 25*	*20 52*					*21 48*					*23 00*	*23 13*		
Exmouth	a			*20 18*				*21 17*					*22 14*						*23 39*		
Barnstaple	a							*22 05*													
Exmouth	d	*18 20*		*18 54*		19 20	*19 20*						*20 26*				*21 20*				
Exeter Central	d	*18 52*		*19 18*		19 44	*19 52*						*20 50*				*21 48*				
Exeter St Davids 6	d	19 09	19 33	19 45	19 50	19 54	20 15	20 45		20 53			21 39	21 45			22 37	22 45			
Exeter St Thomas	d	19 12				19 57				20 56											
Starcross	d	19 20				20 05				21 04											
Dawlish Warren	d	19 25				20 11				21 09											
Dawlish	d	19 29			20 03	20 15				21 13							22 49				
Teignmouth	d	19 34			20 09	20 20				21 18							22 55				
Newton Abbot	a	19 40	19 53	20 03	20 16	20 26	20 35	21 03		21 24			21 59	22 05			23 02	23 11			
	d	19 42	19 53	20 04	20 17	20 28	20 36	21 04		21 26			22 00	22 07			23 03	23 12			
Torre	d	19 50			20 27	20 36				21 34											
Torquay	d	19 53			20 30	20 39				21 37											
Paignton	a	19 59			20 41	20 45				21 43											
Totnes	d		20 07	20 17			20 49	21 17					22 13	22 22			23 16	23 27			
Ivybridge	d																				
Plymouth	a		20 36	20 48			21 17	21 48					22 43	22 55			23 47	23 59			
	d		20 38				21 19														
Devonport	d																				
Dockyard	d																				
Keyham	d																				
St Budeaux Ferry Road	d																				
Saltash	d		20 49																		
St Germans	d		20 56																		
Menheniot	d																				
Liskeard 3	d		21 07				21 43														
Looe	a																				
Bodmin Parkway	d		21 20				21 55														
Lostwithiel	d		21 26																		
Par 3	d		21 33				22 05														
Newquay	a																				
St Austell	d		21 41				22 13														
Truro	d						22 31				22 48										
Falmouth Docks	a		21 59																		
Redruth	d		22 11				22 43				23 01										
Camborne	d		22 19				22 51				23 07										
Hayle	d		22 28																		
St Erth 2	d						23 03				23 16										
St Ives	a																				
Penzance	a						23 17				23 29										

For general notes see front of timetable
For details of catering facilities see Directory of Train Operators

A From Barnstaple (Table 136)
B ☕ to Bristol Temple Meads
b Arr. 2203

Table 135

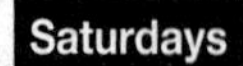

2 February to 22 March

Sleeper services are published in Table 406

London and Birmingham → Devon and Cornwall

Network Diagram - see first page of Table 135

		GW	GW	GW	GW		GW	XC	GW	GW		GW	GW	GW	SW		GW	GW	GW	XC		GW	GW	GW	SW
		1	1 ◇		◇ 1			1 ◇						◇	1					1 ◇			1 ◇		1 ◇
					A																				
		✕	⊤		⊐			⊐						⊤				⊤	⊤	⊐			⊐		⊐
London Paddington 15 ⊖	d	19p03	20 35		23p45																		07 30		
London Waterloo 15 ⊖	d																								07 10
Slough 3	d																								
Heathrow Terminal 1 Bus	d																								
Gatwick Airport 10	d																						*06 03*		
Oxford	d																						*07 15*		
Reading 7	d	19p32	21 02		00u37																		07 57		
Theale	d																								
Thatcham	d																								
Newbury	d	19p49	21 18																						
Hungerford	d																								
Pewsey	d		21 18																						
Westbury	d		21 58																						
Castle Cary	d		22 16																						
Birmingham New Street 12	d																			07 10					
Cardiff Central 7	d																								
Newport (South Wales)	d																								
Swindon	d																								
Bristol Parkway 7	d																			08 25					
Filton Abbey Wood	d																								
Bath Spa 7	d																						09 04		
Bristol Temple Meads 10	d												06 48							08 44			09 20		
Weston-super-Mare	d												07 10												
Bridgwater	d																								
Taunton	d	20p55	22 59		03b40								07 36							09 17			09 54		
Tiverton Parkway	d		23 20										07 53							09 29					
Exeter St Davids 6	a	21p20	23 43		04 36								08 11							09 43			10 20		
Exeter Central	a				*05 13*								*08 29*							*10 14*					
Exmouth	a				*06 03*								*09 15*							*10 45*					
Barnstaple	a				*06 56*								*10 20*												
Exmouth	d											07 18		*07 50*		08 20		08 50				09 20		*09 50*	
Exeter Central	d											07 42		08 27		08 44		09 14	*09 24*			09 44		*10 14*	10 29
Exeter St Davids 6	d	21p22	23 45		04 47		05 29		06 00	06 14			07 48	08 13	08 37		08 50		09 20	09 45		09 52	10 21	10 25	10 38
Exeter St Thomas	d						05 32		06 03	06 17			07 51				08 53					09 55			
Starcross	d						05 40		06 11	06 25			07 59				09 01					10 03			
Dawlish Warren	d						05 45		06 16	06 30			08 04				09 06					10 08			11c00 →
Dawlish	d						05 49		06 20	06 34			08 08	08 26	08 50		09 10		09 33			10 12			
Teignmouth	d						05 54		06 25	06 39			08 13	08 31	08 55		09 15		09 38			10 17			
Newton Abbot	a	21p42	00 04		05 07		06 00		06 31	06 45			08 19	08 37	09 01		09 21		09 44	10 03		10 23	10 41	10 46	
	d	21p43	00 06		05 09		06 02		06 33	06 47		07 37	08 21	08 38	09 06		09 23		09 46	10 04		10 25	10 42	10 48	
Torre	d						06 10		06 41	06 55		07 45	08 29				09 31					10 33		10 56	
Torquay	d						06 13		06 44	06 58		07 48	08 32		09 17		09 34					10 36		10 59	
Paignton	a						06 19		06 50	07 04		07 55	08 38		09 23		09 40					10 42		11 05	
Totnes	d	21p57	00 18											08 51					09 59	10 17			10 55		
Ivybridge	d													09 08					10 16						
Plymouth	a	22p24	00 47		05 47									09 22					10 30	10 48			11 23		
	d	22p26			05 50			06 30						09 23				10 00	10 34				11 26		
Devonport	d																	10 03							
Dockyard	d																								
Keyham	d																								
St Budeaux Ferry Road	d																								
Saltash	d	22p36																10 10	10 43						
St Germans	d	22p43																10 17							
Menheniot	d																	10 25							
Liskeard 3	d	22p55			06 16			06 53						09 47				10 31	11 02				11 49		
Looe	a							*07 43*						*10 23*									*12 38*		
Bodmin Parkway	d	23p07			06 30			07 06						09 59				10 43	11 14				12 01		
Lostwithiel	d	23p12			06 36			07 11						10 04				10 48							
Par 3	d	23p19		06 10	06 43			07 18						10 11				10 55	11 24				12 12		
Newquay	a																		*12 20*						
St Austell	d	23p27		06 17	06 51			07 25						10 19				11 03	11 32				12 19		
Truro	d	23p44		06 35	07 10			07 42						10 40				11 20	11 49				12 37		
Falmouth Docks	a				*07 53*			*08 53*										*11 48*					*13 10*		
Redruth	d	23p57		06 48	07 24			07 53						10 53				11 33	12 02				12 49		
Camborne	d	00 04		06 54	07 31			08 00						10 59				11 39	12 08				12 57		
Hayle	d	00 12		07 01	07 40			08 08						11 06				11 47					13 06		
St Erth 2	d	00 17		07 04	07 45			08 12						11 09				11 50	12 18				13 10		
St Ives	a			*07 43*				*09 19*						*11 21*				*12 21*	*12 53*				*13 21*		
Penzance	a	00 35		07 17	08 00			08 27						11 24				12 02	12 31				13 26		

For general notes see front of timetable
For details of catering facilities see Directory of Train Operators

A **The Night Riviera**
b Arr. 0336
c Arr. 1049

2 February to 22 March

Sleeper services are published in Table 406

London and Birmingham → Devon and Cornwall

Network Diagram - see first page of Table 135

	XC	SW		GW	GW	GW	GW		XC	GW	GW			GW	XC	SW	XC		SW	GW	GW	GW		XC
	1◇	1◇			1◇	1◇			1◇		1◇				1◇	1◇	1◇		1◇		1◇			1◇
	☕	☕			☕	☕	🚌		☕		☕				☕	☕	☕		☕		☕	🚌		☕
London Paddington 15 ⊖ d					08 18	09 05					10 05										11 05			
London Waterloo 15 ⊖ d																09 20								
Slough 3 d																								
Heathrow Terminal 1 Bus 🚌 d																								
Gatwick Airport 10 d					*07 03*	*08 03*															*10 03*			
Oxford d					*08 15*	*08 43*															*11 00*			
Reading 7 d					08 49	09 32					10 32										11 32			
Theale d					08 58																			
Thatcham d					09 07																			
Newbury d					09 13																			
Hungerford d					09 23																			
Pewsey d					09 37																12 03			
Westbury d					09 57																12 22			
Castle Cary d					10 14																12 40			
Birmingham New Street 12 d	08 10								09 10						09 40		10 10							11 10
Cardiff Central 7 d																								
Newport (South Wales) d																								
Swindon d																								
Bristol Parkway 7 d	09 25								10 25						10 58		11 25							12 25
Filton Abbey Wood d																								
Bath Spa 7 d																								
Bristol Temple Meads 10 d	09 44								10 44						11 14		11 44							12 44
Weston-super-Mare d															11 42									
Bridgwater d																								
Taunton d	10 17				10 36	10 48			11 17						12 05		12 17				13 02			13 17
Tiverton Parkway d	10 29				10 49	11 01			11 29						12 17		12 29				13 15			13 29
Exeter St Davids 6 a	10 43				11 08	11 17			11 43		12 10				12 31		12 43				13 32			13 43
Exeter Central a	*11 11*				*11 21*	*11 48*			*12 13*						*12 48*		*13 21*							*14 13*
Exmouth a					*11 45*	*12 14*			*12 45*						*13 14*		*13 42*							
Barnstaple a					*12 20*												*14 23*							
Exmouth d				10 20					*10 50*	11 20					*11 50*					12 20	*12 50*			
Exeter Central d				10 43					*11 14*	11 43					*12 14*	12 27				12 43	*13 14*			
Exeter St Davids 6 d	10 45			10 50		11 18			11 45	11 50	12 10				12 33	12 39	12 45			12 50	13 33			13 45
Exeter St Thomas d				10 53						11 53										12 53				
Starcross d		←		11 01						12 01									←	13 01				
Dawlish Warren d		11 00		11 06						12 06						13b00			13b00	13 06				
Dawlish d		11 04		11 10						12 10					12 45	→			13 04	13 10				
Teignmouth d		11 09		11 15						12 15					12 50				13 09	13 15				
Newton Abbot a	11 03	11 15		11 21		11 38			12 03	12 21	12 31				12 56		13 03		13 15	13 21	13 53			14 03
Newton Abbot d	11 04	11 17		11 23		11 39			12 04	12 23	12 31			12 40	12 57		13 04		13 16	13 23	13 54			14 04
Torre d				11 31						12 35										13 31				
Torquay d		11 28		11 34						12 38					13 08					13 34				
Paignton a		11 34		11 40						12 44					13 20					13 41				
Totnes d	11 17					11 52			12 17					12 52			13 17		13 28		14 07			14 17
Ivybridge d														13 09					13 44					
Plymouth a	11 48					12 23			12 48		13 09			13 25			13 48		13 59		14 36			14 48
Plymouth d							12 44				13 19											14 41		
Devonport d																								
Dockyard d																								
Keyham d																								
St Budeaux Ferry Road d																								
Saltash d							12 52																	
St Germans d							12 59																	
Menheniot d							13 07																	
Liskeard 3 d							13 15				13 34											15 05		
Looe a							*14 16*															*15 42*		
Bodmin Parkway d							13 27				13 47											15 17		
Lostwithiel d							13 33															15 22		
Par 3 d							13 40				13 57											15 29		
Newquay a							*14 55*																	
St Austell d							13 47				14 05											15 37		
Truro d							14 05				14 22											15 54		
Falmouth Docks a							*14 58*															*16 21*		
Redruth d							14 18				14 35											16 06		
Camborne d							14 24				14 42											16 12		
Hayle d							14 31				14 51											16 20		
St Erth 2 d							14 34				14 55											16 23		
St Ives a							*14 53*															*16 54*		
Penzance a							14 46				15 12											16 36		

For general notes see front of timetable
For details of catering facilities see
Directory of Train Operators

b Arr. 1250

Table 135

2 February to 22 March

Sleeper services are published in Table 406

London and Birmingham → Devon and Cornwall

Network Diagram - see first page of Table 135

		GW	GW 1◇	SW 1◇	XC 1◇	GW	GW 1◇	GW 1◇	GW	XC 1◇	SW 1◇	GW	XC 1◇	XC 1◇	GW	GW	GW	GW	SW 1◇	XC 1◇	SW 1◇
																	A				
London Paddington 15 ⊖	d		12 05				12 18	13 05													
London Waterloo 15 ⊖	d			11 20															14 20		
Slough 3	d						12 34														
Heathrow Terminal 1 Bus	d																				
Gatwick Airport 10	d		*11 03*					*12 03*													
Oxford	d		*12 00*				*12 15*	*12 43*													
Reading 7	d		12 32				12 50	13 32													
Theale	d						12 59														
Thatcham	d						13 07														
Newbury	d						13 14														
Hungerford	d						13 22														
Pewsey	d						13 37														
Westbury	d						13 56														
Castle Cary	d						14 14														
Birmingham New Street 12	d				12 10					13 10			13 40	14 10						15 10	
Cardiff Central 7	d																				
Newport (South Wales)	d																				
Swindon	d																				
Bristol Parkway 7	d				13 25					14 25			14 58	15 25						16 25	
Filton Abbey Wood	d																				
Bath Spa 7	d																				
Bristol Temple Meads 10	d				13 44					14 44			15 11	15 44						16 44	
Weston-super-Mare	d																				
Bridgwater	d																				
Taunton	d				14 17		14 37	14 48		15 17			15 43	16 17						17 17	
Tiverton Parkway	d				14 29		14 50	15 01		15 29			15 55	16 29						17 29	
Exeter St Davids 6	a		14 10		14 43		15 06	15 18		15 43			16 10	16 43						17 43	
Exeter Central	a		*14 21*				*15 21*	*15 33*		*16 13*			*16 21*	*17 21*						*17 54*	
Exmouth	a		*14 45*				*15 45*	*16 14*					*16 45*	*17 45*						*18 19*	
Barnstaple	a							*16 36*					*17 45*							*19 01*	
Exmouth	d	13 20		*13 50*		14 20				*14 50*		15 20		*15 50*	16 20			16 50			
Exeter Central	d	13 46		14 19		14 43				*15 31*	15 39	15 46		*16 24*	16 42			17 14	17 33		
Exeter St Davids 6	d	13 51	14 11	14 28	14 45	14 50		15 19		15 45	15 51	15 54	16 12	16 45	16 51			17 21	17 42	17 45	
Exeter St Thomas	d	13 54				14 53						15 57			16 54			17 24			
Starcross	d	14 02				15 01						16 05			17 02			17 32			
Dawlish Warren	d	14 07		14 39		15 06						16 10			17 07			17 37			←
Dawlish	d	14 11		14 43		15 10					16 03	16 14			17 11			17 41	18 05 →		18 05
Teignmouth	d	14 16		14 48		15 15					16 08	16 19			17 16			17 46			18 10
Newton Abbot	a	14 22	14 31	14 55	15 03	15 21		15 40		16 03	16 15	16 25	16 30	17 03	17 22			17 52		18 03	18 16
	d	14 24	14 32	14 56	15 04	15 23		15 40	15 56	16 04	16 15	16 27	16 31	17 04	17 24		17 29	17 54		18 04	18 20
Torre	d	14 32		15 05		15 31						16 35			17 32			18 02			
Torquay	d	14 35		15 09		15 34						16 38			17 35			18 05			
Paignton	a	14 42		15 15		15 40						16 44			17 41			18 11			
Totnes	d				15 17			15 54	16 08	16 17	16 27		16 44	17 17			17 41			18 17	18 32
Ivybridge	d								16 24		16 43						17 58				18 48
Plymouth	a		15 09		15 48			16 25	16 40	16 48	16 58		17 15	17 48			18 13			18 48	19 02
	d		15 11						16 44					17 55		17 59	18 16			19 00	19 11
Devonport	d								16 47							18 02	18 19				
Dockyard	d								16x48							18 04	18x21				
Keyham	d								16x50							18 06	18x23				
St Budeaux Ferry Road	d															18 08					
Saltash	d															18 13					19 19
St Germans	d															18 19					19 26
Menheniot	d															18 27					
Liskeard 3	d		15 35											18 18		18 33				19 23	19 38
Looe	a		*16 59*													*19 39*					
Bodmin Parkway	d		15 47											18 31		18 45				19 35	19 50
Lostwithiel	d															18 51					19 56
Par 3	d		15 57											18 41		18 58				19 45	20 03
Newquay	a																				
St Austell	d		16 05											18 48		19 05				19 52	20 11
Truro	d		16 23											19 06		19 23				20 11	20 29
Falmouth Docks	a		*17 14*													*20 19*					
Redruth	d		16 35											19 17		19 36				20 22	20 41
Camborne	d		16 43											19 23		19 42				20 28	20 47
Hayle	d															19 49					
St Erth 2	d		16 53											19 33		19 53				20 38	
St Ives	a		*17 24*													*20 38*					
Penzance	a		17 11											19 49		20 04				20 59	21 05

For general notes see front of timetable
For details of catering facilities see Directory of Train Operators

A To Gunnislake (Table 139)

Table 135

2 February to 22 March

Sleeper services are published in Table 406

London and Birmingham → Devon and Cornwall

Network Diagram - see first page of Table 135

		SW	GW	GW	XC	GW	GW	XC	GW	GW	XC	GW	GW	XC	GW	GW	XC	GW	GW	GW
		1	1 ◇		1 ◇		1 ◇	1 ◇		1 ◇	1 ◇		1 ◇	1 ◇		1 ◇	1 ◇			1 ◇
					A	B														
			⊡		⊡		⊡	⊡		⊡	⊡		⊡	⊡		⊡				⊡
London Paddington 15 ⊖	d		16 05				17 05			18 05			19 05			20 05				20 30
London Waterloo 15 ⊖	d																			
Slough 3	d																			
Heathrow Terminal 1 Bus 🚌	d																			
Gatwick Airport 10	d		*15 03*							*17 03*			*18 03*			*19 03*				
Oxford	d		*15 43*							*18 00*			*19 00*			*19 43*				*20 15*
Reading 7	d		16 32				17 32			18 32			19 32			20 32				20 56
Theale	d																			
Thatcham	d																			
Newbury	d												19 49			20 46				
Hungerford	d																			
Pewsey	d						18 03						20 10			21 06				
Westbury	d						18 22						20 29			21 25				
Castle Cary	d						18 40						20 45			21 44				
Birmingham New Street 12	d				16 10			17 10			18 10			19 10			20 10			
Cardiff Central 7	d														19 50				21 00	
Newport (South Wales)	d														20 05				21 15	
Swindon	d																			
Bristol Parkway 7	d				17 25			18 25			19 25			20 25			21 25			
Filton Abbey Wood	d														20 34				21 42	
Bath Spa 7	d																			22 02
Bristol Temple Meads 10	d				17 44			18 44			19 44			20 44	20 56		21 44		21 53	22 17
Weston-super-Mare	d														21 30				22 25	
Bridgwater	d														21 49			⟵	22 44	23 00
Taunton	d		17 48		18 17		19 02	19 17		19 47	20 17		21 07	21 17	22b21	22 06	22 17	22 21	22 59	23 12
Tiverton Parkway	d		18 01		18 29		19 15	19 29			20 29		21 20	21 29	⟶	22 19	22 29	22 36	23 14	23 25
Exeter St Davids 6	a		18 18		18 43		19 32	19 43		20 13	20 43		21 38	21 43		22 36	22 43	22 55	23 33	23 45
Exeter Central	a				*18 52*			*19 52*		*20 25*	*20 52*		*21 48*				*23 00*	*23 13*		
Exmouth	a				*19 18*			*20 18*			*21 18*		*22 14*					*23 39*		
Barnstaple	a				*20 19*						*22 05*									
Exmouth	d	*17 20*		17 50		*18 20*		*18 54*	19 20				*20 26*			*21 20*				
Exeter Central	d	17 53		18 19		*18 52*		*19 18*	19 44	*19 52*			*20 50*			*21 48*				
Exeter St Davids 6	d	18 02	18 19	18 26	18 45	19 09	19 33	19 45	19 54	20 15	20 45	20 53	21 39	21 45		22 37	22 45			
Exeter St Thomas	d			18 29		19 12			19 57			20 56								
Starcross	d			18 38		19 20			20 05			21 04								
Dawlish Warren	d	18 15		18 42		19 25			20 11			21 09								
Dawlish	d	18 19		18 46		19 29			20 15			21 13				22 49				
Teignmouth	d	18 24		18 51		19 34			20 20			21 18				22 55				
Newton Abbot	a	18 30	18 39	18 58	19 03	19 40	19 53	20 03	20 26	20 35	21 03	21 24	21 59	22 05		23 02	23 11			
	d	18 32	18 39	18 59	19 04	19 42	19 53	20 04	20 28	20 36	21 04	21 26	22 00	22 07		23 03	23 12			
Torre	d			19 07		19 50			20 36			21 34								
Torquay	d	18 43		19 10		19 53			20 39			21 37								
Paignton	a	18 50		19 17		19 59			20 45			21 43								
Totnes	d		18 53		19 17		20 07	20 17		20 49	21 17		22 13	22 22		23 16	23 27			
Ivybridge	d																			
Plymouth	a		19 21		19 48		20 36	20 48		21 17	21 48		22 43	22 55		23 47	23 59			
	d		19 25		19 50		20 38			21 19										
Devonport	d																			
Dockyard	d																			
Keyham	d																			
St Budeaux Ferry Road	d																			
Saltash	d						20 49													
St Germans	d						20 56													
Menheniot	d																			
Liskeard 3	d		19 50		20 13					21 43										
Looe	a																			
Bodmin Parkway	d		20 05		20 26		21 20			21 55										
Lostwithiel	d						21 26													
Par 3	d		20 15		20 36		21 33			22 05										
Newquay	a																			
St Austell	d		20 23		20 42		21 41			22 13										
Truro	d		20 40		21 00		21 59			22 31										
Falmouth Docks	a				*21 27*															
Redruth	d		20 53		21 11		22 11			22 43										
Camborne	d		21 00		21 17		22 19			22 51										
Hayle	d		21 09				22 28													
St Erth 2	d		21 13		21 27		22 32			23 03										
St Ives	a				*21 45*															
Penzance	a		21 27		21 43		22 45			23 17										

For general notes see front of timetable
For details of catering facilities see Directory of Train Operators

A ⊡ to Plymouth
B From Barnstaple (Table 136)
b Arr. 2203

from 29 March

Sleeper services are published in Table 406

London and Birmingham → Devon and Cornwall

Network Diagram - see first page of Table 135

		GW	GW	GW	GW	XC	GW	GW	GW	GW	GW	SW	GW	GW	GW	XC	GW	GW	GW	SW	XC
		1 ✕	1 ◇ 🛒			1 ◇ ☕					◇ 🛒	1		🛒	🛒	1 ◇ ☕		1 ◇ ☕		1 ◇ ☕	1 ◇ ☕
London Paddington 15 ⊖	d	19p03	20p35															07 30			
London Waterloo 15 ⊖	d																			07 10	
Slough 3	d																				
Heathrow Terminal 1 Bus	d																				
Gatwick Airport 10	d																	*06 03*			
Oxford	d																	*07 15*			
Reading 7	d	19p32	21p02															07 57			
Theale	d																				
Thatcham	d																				
Newbury	d	19p49	21p18																		
Hungerford	d																				
Pewsey	d		21p39																		
Westbury	d		21p58																		
Castle Cary	d		22p16																		
Birmingham New Street 12	d															07 10					08 10
Cardiff Central 7	d																				
Newport (South Wales)	d																				
Swindon	d																	08 30			
Bristol Parkway 7	d															08 25					09 25
Filton Abbey Wood	d																				
Bath Spa 7	d																	09 00			
Bristol Temple Meads 10	d										06 48					08 44		09 17			09 44
Weston-super-Mare	d										07 10										
Bridgwater	d																				
Taunton	d	20p55	22 59								07 36					09 17		09 51			10 17
Tiverton Parkway	d		23 20								07 53					09 29					10 29
Exeter St Davids 6	a	21p20	23 43								08 11					09 43		10 17			10 43
Exeter Central	a										*08 29*					*10 13*					*11 11*
Exmouth	a										*09 15*					*10 45*					
Barnstaple	a										*10 20*										
Exmouth	d									07 18	*07 18*	*07 50*	08 20		08 50		09 20		*09 50*		
Exeter Central	d									07 42		08 27	08 44		09 14	*09 24*	09 44		*10 14*	10 29	
Exeter St Davids 6	d	21p22	23 47		05 29		06 00	06 14		07 48	08 13	08 37	08 50		09 20	09 45	09 52	10 18	10 25	10 38	10 45
Exeter St Thomas	d				05 32		06 03	06 17		07 51			08 53				09 55				
Starcross	d				05 40		06 11	06 25		07 59			09 01				10 03				
Dawlish Warren	d				05 45		06 16	06 30		08 04			09 06				10 08			11b00 →	
Dawlish	d				05 49		06 20	06 34		08 08	08 26	08 50	09 10		09 33		10 12				
Teignmouth	d				05 54		06 25	06 39		08 13	08 31	08 55	09 15		09 38		10 17				
Newton Abbot	a	21p42	00 18		06 00		06 31	06 45		08 19	08 37	09 01	09 21		09 44	10 03	10 23	10 38	10 46		11 03
	d	21p43			06 02		06 33	06 47	07 37	08 21	08 38	09 06	09 23		09 46	10 04	10 25	10 39	10 48		11 04
Torre	d				06 10		06 41	06 55	07 45	08 29			09 31				10 33		10 56		
Torquay	d				06 13		06 44	06 58	07 48	08 32		09 17	09 34				10 36		10 59		
Paignton	a				06 19		06 50	07 04	07 55	08 38		09 23	09 40				10 42		11 05		
Totnes	d	21p57									08 51				09 59	10 17		10 52			11 17
Ivybridge	d										09 08				10 16						
Plymouth	a	22p24	00 47								09 22				10 30	10 48		11 20			11 48
	d	22p26				06 30					09 23			10 00	10 34			11 23			
Devonport	d													10 03							
Dockyard	d																				
Keyham	d																				
St Budeaux Ferry Road	d																				
Saltash	d	22p36												10 10	10 43						
St Germans	d	22p43												10 17							
Menheniot	d													10 25							
Liskeard 3	d	22p55				06 53					09 47			10 31	11 02			11 46			
Looe	a					*07 43*					*10 23*							*12 38*			
Bodmin Parkway	d	23p07				07 06					09 59			10 43	11 14			11 58			
Lostwithiel	d	23p12				07 11					10 04			10 48							
Par 3	d	23p19		06 10		07 18					10 11			10 55	11 24			12 09			
Newquay	a														*12 20*						
St Austell	d	23p27		06 17		07 25					10 19			11 03	11 32			12 16			
Truro	d	23p44		06 35		07 42					10 40			11 20	11 49			12 34			
Falmouth Docks	a					*08 53*								*11 48*				*13 10*			
Redruth	d	23p57		06 48		07 53					10 53			11 33	12 02			12 46			
Camborne	d	00 04		06 54		08 00					10 59			11 39	12 08			12 54			
Hayle	d	00 12		07 01		08 08					11 06			11 47				13 03			
St Erth 2	d	00 17		07 04		08 12					11 09			11 50	12 18			13 07			
St Ives	a			*07 43*		*09 19*					*11 21*			*12 21*	*12 53*			*13 21*			
Penzance	a	00 35		07 17		08 27					11 24			12 02	12 31			13 23			

For general notes see front of timetable
For details of catering facilities see Directory of Train Operators

b Arr. 1049

Saturdays
from 29 March

Sleeper services are published in Table 406

London and Birmingham → Devon and Cornwall

Network Diagram - see first page of Table 135

		SW 1◇	GW	GW 1◇	GW 1◇	GW	XC 1◇	GW	GW ◇1	GW	XC 1◇	SW 1◇	XC 1◇	SW 1◇	GW	GW 1◇	GW	XC 1◇	GW	GW 1◇
London Paddington 15 ⊖	d			08 18	09 05				10 05							11 05				12 05
London Waterloo 15 ⊖	d											09 20								
Slough 3	d																			
Heathrow Terminal 1 Bus	d																			
Gatwick Airport 10	d			*07 03*	*08 03*											*10 03*				*11 03*
Oxford	d			*08 15*	*08 43*											*11 00*				*12 00*
Reading 7	d			08 49	09 32				10 32							11 32				12 32
Theale	d			08 58																
Thatcham	d			09 06																
Newbury	d			09 12																
Hungerford	d			09 21																
Pewsey	d			09 36												12 03				
Westbury	d			09 56												12 22				
Castle Cary	d			10 13												12 40				
Birmingham New Street 12	d						09 10				09 40		10 10					11 10		
Cardiff Central 7	d																			
Newport (South Wales)	d																			
Swindon	d																			
Bristol Parkway 7	d						10 25				10 58		11 25					12 25		
Filton Abbey Wood	d																			
Bath Spa 7	d																			
Bristol Temple Meads 10	d						10 44				11 14		11 44					12 44		
Weston-super-Mare	d										11 42									
Bridgwater	d																			
Taunton	d			10 35	10 48		11 17				12 05		12 17			13 02		13 17		
Tiverton Parkway	d			10 48	11 01		11 29				12 17		12 29			13 15		13 29		
Exeter St Davids 6	a			11 06	11 17		11 43		12 10		12 31		12 43			13 32		13 43		14 10
Exeter Central	a			*11 21*	*11 48*		*12 13*				*12 48*		*13 21*					*14 13*		*14 21*
Exmouth	a			*11 45*	*12 14*		*12 45*				*13 14*		*13 42*							*14 45*
Barnstaple	a			*12 20*									*14 23*							
Exmouth	d		10 20		*10 20*		*10 50*	11 20			*11 50*				12 20	*12 50*			13 20	
Exeter Central	d		10 43		*10 43*		*11 14*	11 43			*12 14*	12 27			12 43	*13 14*			13 46	
Exeter St Davids 6	d		10 50		11 18		11 45	11 50	12 10		12 33	12 39	12 45		12 50	13 33		13 45	13 51	14 11
Exeter St Thomas	d		10 53					11 53							12 53				13 54	
Starcross	d	←	11 01					12 01						←	13 01				14 02	
Dawlish Warren	d	11 00	11 06					12 06				13b00		13 00	13 06				14 07	
Dawlish	d	11 04	11 10					12 10			12 45	→		13 04	13 10				14 11	
Teignmouth	d	11 09	11 15					12 15			12 50			13 09	13 15				14 16	
Newton Abbot	a	11 15	11 21		11 38		12 03	12 21	12 31		12 56		13 03	13 15	13 21	13 53		14 03	14 22	14 31
	d	11 17	11 23		11 39		12 04	12 23	12 31	12 40	12 57		13 04	13 16	13 23	13 54		14 04	14 24	14 32
Torre	d		11 31					12 35							13 31				14 32	
Torquay	d	11 28	11 34					12 38			13 08				13 34				14 35	
Paignton	a	11 34	11 40					12 44			13 20				13 41				14 42	
Totnes	d				11 52		12 17			12 52			13 17	13 28		14 07		14 17		
Ivybridge	d									13 09				13 44						
Plymouth	a				12 23		12 48		13 09	13 25			13 48	13 59		14 36		14 48		15 09
	d					12 44			13 10								14 41			15 11
Devonport	d																			
Dockyard	d																			
Keyham	d																			
St Budeaux Ferry Road	d																			
Saltash	d					12 52														
St Germans	d					12 59														
Menheniot	d					13 07														
Liskeard 3	d					13 15			13 34								15 05			15 35
Looe	a					*14 16*											*15 42*			*16 59*
Bodmin Parkway	d					13 27			13 47								15 17			15 47
Lostwithiel	d					13 33											15 22			
Par 3	d					13 40			13 57								15 29			15 57
Newquay	a					*14 55*														
St Austell	d					13 47			14 05								15 37			16 05
Truro	d					14 05											15 54			16 23
Falmouth Docks	a					*14 58*											*16 21*			*17 14*
Redruth	d					14 18			14 35								16 06			16 35
Camborne	d					14 24			14 42								16 12			16 43
Hayle	d					14 31			14 51								16 20			
St Erth 2	d					14 34			14 55								16 23			16 53
St Ives	a					*14 53*											*16 54*			*17 24*
Penzance	a					14 46			15 12								16 36			17 11

For general notes see front of timetable
For details of catering facilities see Directory of Train Operators

b Arr. 1250

Table 135

Saturdays

from 29 March

Sleeper services are published in Table 406

London and Birmingham → Devon and Cornwall

Network Diagram - see first page of Table 135

		SW	XC	GW	GW	GW	XC	SW	GW	XC	GW	XC	GW	GW	GW	GW	SW	XC	SW	SW	GW
		1 ◇	1 ◇			1 ◇	1 ◇	1 ◇		1 ◇	1 ◇	1 ◇					1 ◇	1 ◇	1 ◇	1	
					A										A						
		☕	☕			☕	☕	☕		☕	☕	☕		🍴			☕	☕	☕		
London Paddington 15	⊖ d					13 05					14 05										
London Waterloo 15	⊖ d	11 20															14 20				
Slough 3	d																				
Heathrow Terminal 1 Bus	🚌 d																				
Gatwick Airport 10	d					*12 03*					*13 03*										
Oxford	d					*12 43*					*14 00*										
Reading 7	d					13 32					14 32										
Theale	d																				
Thatcham	d																				
Newbury	d																				
Hungerford	d																				
Pewsey	d																				
Westbury	d																				
Castle Cary	d																				
Birmingham New Street 12	d		12 10				13 10			13 40		14 10						15 10			
Cardiff Central 7	d																				
Newport (South Wales)	d																				
Swindon	d						14 25														
Bristol Parkway 7	d		13 25							14 58		15 25						16 25			
Filton Abbey Wood	d																				
Bath Spa 7	d																				
Bristol Temple Meads 10	d		13 44			14 41	14 44			15 11	15 38	15 44						16 44			
Weston-super-Mare	d																				
Bridgwater	d																				
Taunton	d		14 17			15 14	15 17			15 43	16 11	16 17						17 17			
Tiverton Parkway	d		14 29				15 29			15 55	16 24	16 29						17 29			
Exeter St Davids 6	a		14 43				15 43			16 10	16 41	16 45						17 43			
Exeter Central	a		*15 21*			*16 13*				*16 21*		*17 21*						*17 54*			
Exmouth	a		*15 45*							*16 45*		*17 45*						*18 19*			
Barnstaple	a		*16 36*							*17 45*								*19 01*			
Exmouth	d	*13 50*		14 20		*14 50*			15 20		*15 50*		16 20			16 50				*17 20*	17 50
Exeter Central	d	14 19		14 43		*15 31*		15 39	15 46		*16 24*		16 42			17 14	17 33			17 53	18 19
Exeter St Davids 6	d	14 28	14 45	14 50		15 44	15 45	15 51	15 54	16 12	16 41	16 43	16 51			17 21	17 42	17 45		18 02	18 26
Exeter St Thomas	d			14 53					15 57				16 54			17 24					18 29
Starcross	d			15 01					16 05				17 02			17 32					18 38
Dawlish Warren	d	14 39		15 06					16 10				17 07			17 37			⟵	18 15	18 42
Dawlish	d	14 43		15 10				16 03	16 14				17 11			17 41	18 05		18 05	18 19	18 46
Teignmouth	d	14 48		15 15				16 08	16 19				17 16			17 46	⟶		18 10	18 24	18 51
Newton Abbot	a	14 55	15 03	15 21		16 05	16 03	16 15	16 25	16 30	17 02	17 03	17 22			17 52		18 03	18 16	18 30	18 58
	d	14 56	15 04	15 23	15 56	16 05	16 04	16 15	16 27	16 31	17 02	17 04	17 24		17 29	17 54		18 04	18 20	18 32	18 59
Torre	d	15 05		15 31					16 35				17 32			18 02					19 07
Torquay	d	15 09		15 34					16 38				17 35			18 05				18 43	19 10
Paignton	a	15 15		15 40					16 44				17 41			18 11				18 50	19 17
Totnes	d		15 17		16 08	16 19	16 17	16 27		16 44	17 16	17 17			17 41			18 17	18 32		
Ivybridge	d				16 24			16 43							17 58				18 48		
Plymouth	a		15 48		16 40	16 48	16 48	16 58		17 15	17 44	17 48			18 13			18 48	19 02		
	d				16 44						17 45	17 55		17 59	18 16			19 00	19 11		
Devonport	d				16 47									18 02	18 19						
Dockyard	d				16x48									18 04	18x21						
Keyham	d				16x50									18 06	18x23						
St Budeaux Ferry Road	d													18 08							
Saltash	d													18 13					19 19		
St Germans	d													18 19					19 26		
Menheniot	d													18 27							
Liskeard 3	d										18 11	18 18		18 33				19 23	19 38		
Looe	a													*19 39*							
Bodmin Parkway	d										18 26	18 31		18 45				19 35	19 50		
Lostwithiel	d													18 51					19 56		
Par 3	d										18 36	18 41		18 58				19 45	20 03		
Newquay	a																				
St Austell	d										18 44	18 48		19 05				19 52	20 11		
Truro	d										19 01	19 06		19 23				20 11	20 29		
Falmouth Docks	a													*20 19*							
Redruth	d										19 14	19 17		19 36				20 22	20 41		
Camborne	d										19 21	19 23		19 42				20 28	20 47		
Hayle	d													19 49							
St Erth 2	d										19 32	19 33		19 53				20 38			
St Ives	a													*20 38*							
Penzance	a										19 45	19 49		20 04				20 59	21 05		

For general notes see front of timetable
For details of catering facilities see
Directory of Train Operators

A To Gunnislake (Table 139)

Table 135

Saturdays

from 29 March

Sleeper services are published in Table 406

London and Birmingham → Devon and Cornwall

Network Diagram - see first page of Table 135

		GW	XC		GW	XC	GW	GW		GW	XC	GW	GW		XC	GW	GW	GW		GW	XC	GW	GW		
		1 ◇	1 ◇			1 ◇	1 ◇			1 ◇	1 ◇		1 ◇		1 ◇	1 ◇	1 ◇	1 ◇			1 ◇		1 ◇		
			A		B										C										
		☕	☕			☕	☕			☕	☕		☕		☕	☕	☕	☕					☕		
London Paddington 15	⊖ d	16 05					16 30			18 05			18 30			19 00	19 05						20 30		
London Waterloo 15	⊖ d																								
Slough 3	d																								
Heathrow Terminal 1 Bus	🚌 d																								
Gatwick Airport 10	d	*15 03*								*17 03*						*18 03*									
Oxford	d	*15 43*					*16 15*			*18 00*			*18 15*			*18 43*	*19 00*						*20 15*		
Reading 7	d	16 32					16 57			18 32			18 57			19 27	19 32						20 57		
Theale	d																								
Thatcham	d																								
Newbury	d																19 49								
Hungerford	d																								
Pewsey	d																20 10								
Westbury	d																								
Castle Cary	d																								
Birmingham New Street 12	d		16 10			17 10					18 10				19 10						20 10				
Cardiff Central 7	d																								
Newport (South Wales)	d																								
Swindon	d						17 31						19 31			19 56							21 31		
Bristol Parkway 7	d		17 25			18 25					19 25				20 25					20 40	21 25	21 40			
Filton Abbey Wood	d																			20 42		21 42			
Bath Spa 7	d						18 00						20 01			20 25							22 00		
Bristol Temple Meads 10	d	17 36	17 44			18 44	18 19			19 34	19 44		20 15		20 44	20 49	20 59	←		20 56	21 44	21 53	22 15		
Weston-super-Mare	d						18 54						20 37			21 13		21 13		21 30		22 25			
Bridgwater	d															→		21 31		21 49		22 44	22 58		
Taunton	d	18 09	18 17			19 17	19 20			20 07	20 17		21a06		21 17		21 33	21a47		22 04	22 17	22 59	23 10		
Tiverton Parkway	d	18 22	18 29			19 29	19 33				20 29				21 29		21 46			22 19	22 29	23 14	23 23		
Exeter St Davids 6	a	18 39	18 43			19 43	19 50			20 33	20 43				21 43		22 04			22 38	22 43	23 33	23 43		
Exeter Central	a		*18 52*			*19 52*	*20 18*				*20 52*										*23 00*				
Exmouth	a		*19 18*			*20 18*					*21 18*										*23 39*				
Barnstaple	a		*20 19*								*22 05*														
Exmouth	d				*18 20*	*18 54*		*19 20*							*20 26*		*21 20*								
Exeter Central	d				*18 52*	*19 18*		*19 44*		*19 52*					*20 50*		*21 48*								
Exeter St Davids 6	d	18 39	18 45		19 09	19 45	19 50	19 54		20 34	20 45	20 53			21 45		22 05				22 45				
Exeter St Thomas	d				19 12			19 57				20 56													
Starcross	d				19 20			20 05				21 04													
Dawlish Warren	d				19 25			20 11				21 09													
Dawlish	d				19 29		20 03	20 15				21 13													
Teignmouth	d				19 34		20 09	20 20				21 18													
Newton Abbot	a	19 00	19 03		19 40	20 03	20 16	20 26		20 54	21 03	21 24			22 05		22 25				23 11				
	d	19 00	19 04		19 42	20 04	20 17	20 28		20 55	21 04	21 26			22 07		22 26				23 12				
Torre	d				19 50		20 27	20 36				21 34													
Torquay	d				19 53		20 30	20 39				21 37													
Paignton	a				19 59		20 41	20 45				21 43													
Totnes	d	19 14	19 17			20 17				21 08	21 17				22 22		22 39				23 27				
Ivybridge	d																								
Plymouth	a	19 42	19 48			20 48				21 36	21 48				22 55		23 09				23 59				
	d	19 44	19 50							21 38															
Devonport	d																								
Dockyard	d																								
Keyham	d																								
St Budeaux Ferry Road	d																								
Saltash	d																								
St Germans	d																								
Menheniot	d																								
Liskeard 3	d	20 09	20 13							22 02															
Looe	a																								
Bodmin Parkway	d	20 21	20 26							22 14															
Lostwithiel	d																								
Par 3	d	20 31	20 36							22 25															
Newquay	a																								
St Austell	d	20 39	20 42							22 32															
Truro	d	20 57	21 00							22 50															
Falmouth Docks	a		*21 27*																						
Redruth	d	21 09	21 11							23 02															
Camborne	d	21 17	21 17							23 12															
Hayle	d	21 26																							
St Erth 2	d	21 30	21 27							23 22															
St Ives	a		*21 45*																						
Penzance	a	21 43	21 43							23 36															

For general notes see front of timetable
For details of catering facilities see Directory of Train Operators

A ☕ to Plymouth
B From Barnstaple (Table 136)
C ☕ to Bristol Temple Meads

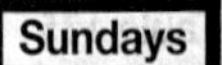

Sundays

until 27 January

Sleeper services are published in Table 406

London and Birmingham → Devon and Cornwall

Network Diagram - see first page of Table 135

	XC	GW	GW	GW	GW	GW	SW	GW	GW	GW	GW	SW	GW	GW	GW	XC	GW	SW	GW	XC	GW
	1 ◇		◇		◇		1 ◇	1 ◇			1 ◇	1 ◇		1 ◇		1 ◇		1 ◇	1 ◇	1 ◇	
																		A			
	🍴	🛒						🍴	🛒		🍴	🍴		🍴		🍴		🍴	🍴	🍴	🛒
London Paddington 15 ⊖ d								08 00			08 57			09 57					10 57		
London Waterloo 15 ⊖ d												08 15						09 15			
Slough 3 d																					
Heathrow Terminal 1 Bus 🚌 d																					
Gatwick Airport 10 d								07 07						08 07					09 07		
Oxford d											07b45			09 38					10 38		
Reading 7 d								08 43			09 32			10 34					11 32		
Theale d																					
Thatcham d																					
Newbury d											09 48										
Hungerford d																					
Pewsey d									09 20					11 07							12 05
Westbury d											10 28										
Castle Cary d														11 37							
Birmingham New Street 12 d																10 10				11 10	
Cardiff Central 7 d																					
Newport (South Wales) d																					
Swindon d								09 19	10a05												12a50
Bristol Parkway 7 d																11 25				12 25	
Filton Abbey Wood d																					
Bath Spa 7 d								09 49													
Bristol Temple Meads 10 d			07 30		08 15			10 03								11 44				12 44	
Weston-super-Mare d			07 50		08 43											12 02					
Bridgwater d					09 02																
Taunton d			08 18		09 17			10 36			11 04			11 57		12 24			12 47	13 17	
Tiverton Parkway d			08 33		09 32			10 50			11 17									13 29	
Exeter St Davids 6 a			08 51		09 50			11 07			11 34			12 26		12 48			13 14	13 43	
Exeter Central a			09 23		10 35			11 23			12 28								13 28		
Exmouth a					11 00			11 53			12 54								13 53		
Barnstaple a			10 55								13 02									15 09	
Exmouth d														11 10	12 05					13 05	
Exeter Central d				08 56			10 46					11 29		11 37	12 30			12 46		13 29	
Exeter St Davids 6 d			08 53	09 25	09 52	10 10	10 56	11 08			11 35	11 40		12 27	12 35	12 49	←	12 55	13 15	13 45	
Exeter St Thomas d				09 28		10 13									12 39 →		12 39				
Starcross d				09 36		10 21											12 47				
Dawlish Warren d				09 41		10 26											13c02				
Dawlish d			09 06	09 45	10 05	10 30	11 11	11 21								13 02	13 07	13 12			
Teignmouth d			09 11	09 50	10 10	10 35	11 16	11 27								13 07	13 12	13 20			
Newton Abbot a			09 17	09 56	10 16	10 41	11 23	11 33			11 55	12 01		12 47		13 13	13 19	13 26		14 03	
d			09 18	09 58	10 17	10 43	11 24	11 34		11 42	11 57	12 02	12 30	12 49		13 15	13 21	13 31		14 04	
Torre d				10 06		10 51				11 50			12 38				13 30				
Torquay d				10 09		10 54	11 35			11 53			12 41			13 26	13 34	13 43			
Paignton a				10 15		11 00	11 42			11 59			12 47			13 37	13 40	13 49			
Totnes d			09 31		10 30			11 47			12 09	12 17		13 01						14 17	
Ivybridge d			09 48									12 33									
Plymouth a			10 02		10 59			12 15			12 37	12 47		13 34					14 11	14 48	
d	09 10	09 30	10 03		11 00			12 17			12 40								14 13		
Devonport d			10 07																		
Dockyard d																					
Keyham d																					
St Budeaux Ferry Road d																					
Saltash d			10 14		11 09																
St Germans d			10 21		11 16																
Menheniot d			10 29		11 24																
Liskeard 3 d	09 33	09 54	10 35		11 30			12 41			13 02								14 37		
Looe a																					
Bodmin Parkway d	09 45	10 06	10 47		11 42			12 53			13 15								14 50		
Lostwithiel d		10 11	10 52		11 47																
Par 3 d	09 55	10 18	10 59		11 54			13 04			13 25										
Newquay a																					
St Austell d	10 02	10 26	11 06		12 02			13 11			13 32								15 05		
Truro d	10 19	10 44	11 24		12 20			13 29			13 52								15 27		
Falmouth Docks a		11 34			12 49			13 58			14 57								15 59		
Redruth d	10 30	10 57	11 37		12 34			13 41			14 03								15 39		
Camborne d	10 37	11 03	11 43		12 40			13 49			14 12								15 47		
Hayle d		11 11	11 50		12 47																
St Erth 2 d	10 50	11 14	11 54		12 50			14 01			14 23								15 59		
St Ives a			12 13		13 15						15 19								16 25		
Penzance a	11 06	11 32	12 05		13 03			14 16			14 40								16 14		

For general notes see front of timetable
For details of catering facilities see Directory of Train Operators

A Also stops at Chard Jn. S.B arr. 1158 dep. 1203

b Change at Didcot Parkway and Reading. By bus to Didcot Parkway

c Arr. 1251

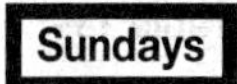

until 27 January

Sleeper services are published in Table 406

London and Birmingham → Devon and Cornwall

Network Diagram - see first page of Table 135

		GW	GW	GW	GW	XC		SW	GW	GW	GW	XC	GW		XC	GW	GW	GW	XC	SW		GW	GW	XC	GW
		1 ◇ ☕		1 ◇ ☕	🛒	1 ◇ ☕		1 ◇ ☕	1 ◇ ☕		1 ◇ ☕	1 ◇ ☕			1 ◇ ☕		1 ◇ ☕		R 1 ☕	1 ◇ ☕			1 ◇ ☕	R 1 ☕	
London Paddington 15	⊖ d	11 18		11 57					12 07		12 57						13 57						14 57		
London Waterloo 15	⊖ d							11 15												13 15					
Slough 3	d																								
Heathrow Terminal 1 Bus	🚌 d																								
Gatwick Airport 10	d	*10 11*							*11 07*								*12 07*						*13 07*		
Oxford	d	*11 15*		*11 45*							*12 50*						*13 47*						*14 47*		
Reading 7	d	11 53		12 32					12 42		13 32						14 34						15 32		
Theale	d																								
Thatcham	d																								
Newbury	d			12 48													14 51								
Hungerford	d																								
Pewsey	d	12 24																				15 27			
Westbury	d	12 43									14 19														
Castle Cary	d	13 01															15 36								
Birmingham New Street 12	d					12 10						13 10			13 40				14 10					15 10	
Cardiff Central 7	d																								
Newport (South Wales)	d																								
Swindon	d								13 17													16 12			
Bristol Parkway 7	d					13 25						14 25			14 55				15 25					16 25	
Filton Abbey Wood	d																								
Bath Spa 7	d								13 46																
Bristol Temple Meads 10	d					13 44			14 01			14 44			15 11				15 44					16 44	
Weston-super-Mare	d																								
Bridgwater	d																								
Taunton	d	13 23		13b59		14 17			14 35		14 54	15 17			15 44		15 58		16 17				16 49	17 17	
Tiverton Parkway	d	13 36				14 29					15 07	15 29			15 56				16 29				17 02	17 29	
Exeter St Davids 6	a	13 53		14 25					15 02		15 24	15 43			16 11		16 25		16 43				17 18	17 43	
Exeter Central	a	*14 28*							*15 21*						*16 28*		*16 36*						*17 28*	*18 38*	
Exmouth	a	*14 54*							*15 53*						*16 54*								*17 53*	*19 03*	
Barnstaple	a											*17 08*											*19 06*	*19 06*	
Exmouth	d					*14 10*						*15 10*							*16 10*					*17 10*	
Exeter Central	d					*14 34*		14 43				*15 34*							*16 34*	16 43				*17 34*	
Exeter St Davids 6	d	13 54	14 05	14 25		14 45		14 52	15 02	15 10	15 25	15 45	16 03		16 12		16 25		16 45	16 57			17 20	17 45	17 50
Exeter St Thomas	d		14 08							15 13															17 53
Starcross	d		14 16							15 21															18 01
Dawlish Warren	d		14 21							15 26															18 06
Dawlish	d	14 07	14 25							15 30			16 16							17 10					18 10
Teignmouth	d	14 13	14 30							15 35			16 21							17 15					18 15
Newton Abbot	a	14 20	14 36	14 46		15 03		15 19	15 23	15 41	15 45	16 03	16 27		16 32	←	16 45		17 03	17 22			17 39	18 03	18 21
	d	14 21	14 38	14 47		15 04		15 21	15 24	15 43	15 45	16 04	16 38		16 33	16 38	16 45	16 55	17 04	17 26			17 40	18 04	18 23
Torre	d		14 46							15 51			→					17 03							18 31
Torquay	d	14 33	14 49					15 32		15 54								17 06		17 37					18 34
Paignton	a	14 40	14 55					15 38		16 01								17 12		17 43					18 40
Totnes	d			15 00		15 17					16 00	16 17			16 45	16 53	17 01		17 17				17 54	18 17	
Ivybridge	d															17 10									
Plymouth	a			15 30		15 48			16 05		16 28	16 48			17 18	17 24	17 37		17 48				18 21	18 48	
	d				15 36						16 30					17 25			17 55				18 23	18 55	
Devonport	d																								
Dockyard	d																								
Keyham	d																								
St Budeaux Ferry Road	d																								
Saltash	d															17 34									
St Germans	d															17 41									
Menheniot	d															17 49									
Liskeard 3	d				16 00						16 57					17 55			18 24				18 47	19 18	
Looe	a																								
Bodmin Parkway	d				16 12						17 09					18 07			18 37				18 59	19 31	
Lostwithiel	d				16 17											18 12									
Par 3	d				16 24						17 21					18 19			18 47				19 10	19 41	
Newquay	a																								
St Austell	d				16 32						17 27					18 27			18 54				19 17	19 48	
Truro	d				16 50						17 49					18 45			19 11				19 35	20 05	
Falmouth Docks	a				*17 18*						*18 53*												*20 04*		
Redruth	d				17 03						18 00					18 59			19 22				19 47	20 16	
Camborne	d				17 09						18 08					19 05			19 29				19 55	20 23	
Hayle	d				17 17											19 12									
St Erth 2	d				17 20						18 20					19 15			19 39				20 09	20 33	
St Ives	a				*17 45*						*18 39*					*19 33*									
Penzance	a				17 39						18 37					19 29			19 54				20 21	20 48	

For general notes see front of timetable
For details of catering facilities see
Directory of Train Operators

b Arr. 1352

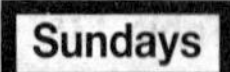

Sundays
until 27 January

Sleeper services are published in Table 406

London and Birmingham → Devon and Cornwall

Network Diagram - see first page of Table 135

		GW	GW	GW	XC		GW	GW	GW	XC	GW	GW		XC	SW	GW	XC	GW	GW	GW	XC	GW	GW
		1 ◇		1 ◇	R 1			1 ◇		R 1		1 ◇		R 1	1 ◇	1 ◇	R 1		1 ◇	1 ◇	R 1	1 ◇	1 ◇
					A																		
		☕		☕	☕			☕		☕		☕		☕	☕	☕	☕		☕	☕		☕	☕
London Paddington 15	⊖ d	15 07		15 57				16 57				17 57				18 57			19 07	19 57		20 57	23 50
London Waterloo 15	⊖ d														17 15								
Slough 3	d																						
Heathrow Terminal 1 Bus	🚌 d																						
Gatwick Airport 10	d	*14 07*						*15 07*				*16 07*				*17 07*			*18 07*			*19 07*	*22 07*
Oxford	d			*15 48*				*16 50*				*17 50*				*18 47*						*20 50*	*22 58*
Reading 7	d	15 42		16 32				17 32				18 33				19 32			19 42	20 34		21 33	00u37
Theale	d																						
Thatcham	d																						
Newbury	d			16 48								18 51								20 51			
Hungerford	d																						
Pewsey	d											19 12								21 12			
Westbury	d			17b29								19 34								21 31			
Castle Cary	d			17 47												20 29				21 49			
Birmingham New Street 12	d				16 10					17 10				18 10			19 10				20 10		
Cardiff Central 7	d																						
Newport (South Wales)	d																						
Swindon	d	16 17																	20 17				
Bristol Parkway 7	d				17 25					18 25				19 25			20 25				21 25		
Filton Abbey Wood	d																						
Bath Spa 7	d	16 47																	20 47				
Bristol Temple Meads 10	d	17 02			17 44				18 10	18 44				19 44			20 44		21 02		21 44		
Weston-super-Mare	d	17 31							18 40										21 32				
Bridgwater	d								18 58														
Taunton	d	17a53		18 08	18 17			18 49	19 11	19 17		20 08		20 17		20 51	21 17		21 54	22 09	22 17	22s51	
Tiverton Parkway	d			18 22	18 29			19 01	19 26	19 29		20 22		20 29		21 04	21 29		22 07	22 22	22 29	23s04	
Exeter St Davids 6	a			18 38	18 43			19 18	19 42	19 45		20 39		20 45		21 21	21 43		22 24	22 39	22 45	23 23	04 05
Exeter Central	a			*19 23*	*19 23*			*19 38*	*20 38*							*21 38*			*22 33*		*23 13*		*05 13*
Exmouth	a							*20 03*	*21 06*							*22 03*			*22 58*		*23 44*		*06 03*
Barnstaple	a								*21 06*														
Exmouth	d			*17 10*	*18 10*		18 10	*18 10*		*19 10*				*20 10*	*20 10*		*21 10*	21 10			*22 10*		
Exeter Central	d			*17 34*	*18 35*		18 35	*18 43*		*19 34*				*20 34*	20 46		*21 35*	21 35			*22 34*		
Exeter St Davids 6	d			18 38	18 45		18 52	19 19		19 48	20 05	20 39		20 45	20 55	21 21	21 45	21 53		22 39	22 49		04 37
Exeter St Thomas	d						18 55				20 08							21 57					
Starcross	d						19 03				20 16							22 06					
Dawlish Warren	d						19 08				20 21							22 10					
Dawlish	d						19 12				20 25				21 08	21 35		22 14					
Teignmouth	d						19 17				20 30				21 13	21 41		22 19					
Newton Abbot	a			18 59	19 03		19 23	19 39		20 06	20 36	21 00		21 06	21 19	21 47	22 03	22 26		23 00	23 10		04 57
	d			19 00	19 04		19 25	19 39		20 07	20 38	21 01		21 08	21 21	21 48	22 04	22 27		23 00	23 11		04 57
Torre	d						19 33				20 46							22 35					
Torquay	d						19 36				20 49				21 32			22 38					
Paignton	a						19 42				20 55				21 38			22 45					
Totnes	d				19 17			19 53		20 20		21 16		21 24		22 02	22 17			23 14	23 27		
Ivybridge	d																						
Plymouth	a			19 40	19 48			20 21		20 51		21 43		21 56		22 30	22 48			23 47	23 59		05 37
	d		19 25		19 55			20 23				21 45											06 30
Devonport	d																						
Dockyard	d																						
Keyham	d																						
St Budeaux Ferry Road	d																						
Saltash	d																						
St Germans	d																						
Menheniot	d																						
Liskeard 3	d		19 49		20 18			20 47				22 08											07 00
Looe	a																						*07 44*
Bodmin Parkway	d		20 01		20 31			20 59				22 20											07 14
Lostwithiel	d		20 06																				07 20
Par 3	d		20 13		20 41			21 10				22 32											07 27
Newquay	a																						
St Austell	d		20 21		20 48			21 17				22 40											07 36
Truro	d		20 39		21 05			21 35				22 56											07 55
Falmouth Docks	a		*21 13*					*22 23*															*08 54*
Redruth	d		20 52		21 16			21 47				23 10											08 10
Camborne	d		20 58		21 27			21 55				23 16											08 18
Hayle	d		21 06																				08 26
St Erth 2	d		21 09		21 37			22 07				23 28											08 31
St Ives	a																						*09 24*
Penzance	a		21 29		21 52			22 20				23 43											08 47

For general notes see front of timetable
For details of catering facilities see Directory of Train Operators

A ☕ to Plymouth
b Arr. 1722

Sundays

3 February to 23 March

Sleeper services are published in Table 406

London and Birmingham → Devon and Cornwall

Network Diagram - see first page of Table 135

	XC	GW	GW		GW	GW	GW		GW	GW	SW		GW	GW	SW		GW	GW	GW		SW	GW	XC	GW
	1 ◇ ☕	🛒	🛒			◇			1 ◇	1 ◇ ☕	1 ◇			1 ◇ ☕	1 ◇ ☕			1 ◇ ☕			1 ◇ ☕	1 ◇ ☕	1 ◇ ☕	
London Paddington 15 ⊖ d										08 30				09 00				10 00				11 00		
London Waterloo 15 ⊖ d															08 15						09 15			
Slough 3 d																								
Heathrow Terminal 1 Bus 🚌 d																								
Gatwick Airport 10 d														07 07				08 07				09 07		
Oxford d														07b45				09 38				10 38		
Reading 7 d										09 04				09 37				10 37				11 40		
Theale d																								
Thatcham d																								
Newbury d														09 54										
Hungerford d																								
Pewsey d																		11 10						
Westbury d										09 52				10 28										
Castle Cary d																		11 40						
Birmingham New Street 12 d																							10 10	
Cardiff Central 7 d																								
Newport (South Wales) d																								
Swindon d																								
Bristol Parkway 7 d																							11 25	
Filton Abbey Wood d																								
Bath Spa 7 d																								
Bristol Temple Meads 10 d																							11 50	
Weston-super-Mare d																								
Bridgwater d																								
Taunton d						09 17				10 26				11 05				12 00				12 55	13 01	
Tiverton Parkway d						09 32				10 41				11 18									13 14	
Exeter St Davids 6 a						09 50				10 57				11 35				12 27				13 23	13 28	
Exeter Central a						10 35								12 28										
Exmouth a						11 00								12 54										
Barnstaple a														13 02									15 09	
Exmouth d																		11 10	12 05					13 05
Exeter Central d					08 56				10 46						11 29			11 37	12 30		12 46			13 29
Exeter St Davids 6 d					09 25	09 52	10 10		10 56	10 58				11 35	11 40			12 28	12 35		12 55	13 23	13 31	13 50
Exeter St Thomas d			08 53		09 28		10 13												12 39					13 53
Starcross d					09 36		10 21												12 47					14 01
Dawlish Warren d					09 41		10 26				←								13c02					14 06
Dawlish d			09 06		09 45	10 05	10 30		11 20	11 14	11 20								13 07		13 12		13 43	14 10
Teignmouth d			09 11		09 50	10 10	10 35		→	11 19	11 26								13 12		13 20		13 49	14 15
Newton Abbot a			09 17		09 56	10 16	10 41			11 25	11 33			11 56	12 01			12 48	13 19		13 26		13 55	14 21
Newton Abbot d			09 18		09 58	10 17	10 43			11 25	11 34		11 42	11 57	12 02		12 30	12 50	13 21		13 31		13 56	14 23
Torre d					10 06		10 51						11 50				12 38		13 30					14 31
Torquay d					10 09		10 54				11 44		11 53				12 41		13 34		13 43			14 34
Paignton a					10 15		11 00				11 52		11 59				12 47		13 40		13 49			14 40
Totnes d			09 31			10 30				11 40				12 10	12 17			13 02					14 09	
Ivybridge d			09 48												12 33									
Plymouth a			10 02			10 59				12 08				12 38	12 47			13 35				14 19	14 40	
Plymouth d	09 10	09 30	10 03			11 00				12 10				12 40								14 21		
Devonport d			10 07																					
Dockyard d																								
Keyham d																								
St Budeaux Ferry Road d																								
Saltash d			10 14			11 09																		
St Germans d			10 21			11 16																		
Menheniot d			10 35			11 24																		
Liskeard 3 d	09 33	09 54				11 30				12 33				13 02								14 45		
Looe a																								
Bodmin Parkway d	09 45	10 06	10 47			11 42				12 46				13 16								14 57		
Lostwithiel d		10 11	10 52			11 47																		
Par 3 d	09 55	10 18	10 59			11 54				12 57				13 26										
Newquay a																								
St Austell d	10 02	10 26	11 06			12 02				13 04				13 33								15 13		
Truro d	10 19	10 44	11 24			12 20				13 21				13 52								15 30		
Falmouth Docks a		11 34				12 49								14 57								15 59		
Redruth d	10 30	10 57	11 37			12 34				13 34				14 04								15 43		
Camborne d	10 37	11 03	11 43			12 40				13 41				14 12								15 50		
Hayle d		11 11	11 50			12 47																		
St Erth 2 d	10 50	11 14	11 54			12 50				13 54				14 24								16 03		
St Ives a		12 13				13 15								15 19								16 25		
Penzance a	11 06	11 32	12 11			13 03				14 08				14 40								16 14		

For general notes see front of timetable
For details of catering facilities see Directory of Train Operators

b Change at Didcot Parkway and Reading. By bus to Didcot Parkway

c Arr. 1251

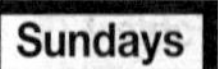
Sundays

3 February to 23 March

Sleeper services are published in Table 406

London and Birmingham → Devon and Cornwall

Network Diagram - see first page of Table 135

		GW	GW	GW	XC	SW	GW	GW	XC	GW	GW	GW	XC	SW	XC	GW	XC	GW	GW
		1 ◇	1 ◇		1 ◇	1 ◇		1 ◇	1 ◇		1 ◇		1 ◇	1 ◇	R 1	1 ◇	R 1		
		☕	☕	🛒	☕	☕		☕	☕		☕		☕	☕	☕	☕	☕		🛒
London Paddington 15	⊖ d	11 30	12 00					13 00			14 00					15 00			
London Waterloo 15	⊖ d					11 15								13 15					
Slough 3	d																		
Heathrow Terminal 1 Bus	🚌 d																		
Gatwick Airport 10	d	*10 11*						*11 07*			*12 07*					*13 07*			
Oxford	d	*11 15*	*11 50*					*12 50*			*13 50*					*14 38*			
Reading 7	d	12 04	12 37					13 37			14 37					15 37			
Theale	d																		
Thatcham	d																		
Newbury	d		12 54								14 54								
Hungerford	d																		
Pewsey	d	12 35																	
Westbury	d	12 54						14 27											
Castle Cary	d	13 12									15 39								
Birmingham New Street 12	d				11 10				12 10				13 10		14 10		15 10		
Cardiff Central 7	d																		
Newport (South Wales)	d																		
Swindon	d																		
Bristol Parkway 7	d				12 25				13 25				14 25		15 25		16 25		
Filton Abbey Wood	d																		
Bath Spa 7	d																		
Bristol Temple Meads 10	d				12 50				13 50				14 50		15 50		16 44		
Weston-super-Mare	d														16 13				
Bridgwater	d																		
Taunton	d	13 34	13 59		14 17			15 02	15 17		16 01		16 17		16 35	16 57	17 17		
Tiverton Parkway	d	13 47			14 29			15 15	15 29				16 29		16 47	17 10	17 29		
Exeter St Davids 6	a	14 04	14 25		14 43			15 32	15 43		16 28		16 43		17 01	17 26	17 43		
Exeter Central	a	*14 28*							*16 28*						*17 21*		*18 38*		
Exmouth	a	*14 54*							*16 54*						*17 53*		*19 03*		
Barnstaple	a								*17 08*								*19 06*		
Exmouth	d				*14 10*				*15 10*				*16 10*				*17 10*		
Exeter Central	d				*14 34*	14 43			*15 34*				*16 34*	16 43			*17 34*		
Exeter St Davids 6	d	14 05	14 25		14 45	14 52	15 10	15 33	15 45	16 03	16 28		16 45	16 57	17 05	17 28	17 45	17 50	
Exeter St Thomas	d						15 13											17 53	
Starcross	d						15 21											18 01	
Dawlish Warren	d						15 26											18 06	
Dawlish	d	14 18					15 30			16 16				17 10	17 17			18 10	
Teignmouth	d	14 24					15 35			16 21				17 15	17 22			18 15	
Newton Abbot	a	14 31	14 46		15 03	15 19	15 41	15 53	16 03	16 27	16 48		17 03	17 22	17 28	17 48	18 03	18 21	
	d	14 32	14 47		15 04	15 21	15 43	15 53	16 04	16 38	16 48	16 55	17 04	17 26	17 29	17 48	18 04	18 23	
Torre	d						15 51					17 03						18 31	
Torquay	d	14 44				15 32	15 54					17 06		17 37				18 34	
Paignton	a	14 52				15 38	16 01					17 12		17 43				18 40	
Totnes	d		15 00		15 17			16 08	16 17	16 53	17 04		17 17		17 42	18 03	18 17		
Ivybridge	d									17 10									
Plymouth	a		15 30		15 48			16 36	16 48	17 24	17 40		17 48		18 13	18 30	18 48		
	d			15 36				16 38		17 25					18 13	18 31	18 55		19 25
Devonport	d																		
Dockyard	d																		
Keyham	d																		
St Budeaux Ferry Road	d																		
Saltash	d									17 34									
St Germans	d									17 41									
Menheniot	d									17 49									
Liskeard 3	d			16 00				17 00		17 55					18 36	18 55	19 18		19 49
Looe	a																		
Bodmin Parkway	d			16 12				17 13		18 07					18 48	19 08	19 31		20 01
Lostwithiel	d			16 17						18 12									20 06
Par 3	d			16 24				17 25		18 19						19 19	19 41		20 13
Newquay	a																		
St Austell	d			16 32				17 31		18 27					19 02	19 26	19 48		20 21
Truro	d			16 50				17 50		18 45					19 20	19 43	20 05		20 39
Falmouth Docks	a			*17 18*				*18 53*								*20 12*			*21 13*
Redruth	d			17 03				18 02		18 59					19 31	19 56	20 16		20 52
Camborne	d			17 09				18 09		19 05					19 37	20 03	20 29		20 58
Hayle	d			17 17						19 12									21 06
St Erth 2	d			17 20				18 22		19 15						20 16	20 39		21 09
St Ives	a			*17 45*				*18 39*		*19 33*									
Penzance	a			17 39				18 38		19 29					20 00	20 28	20 54		21 29

For general notes see front of timetable
For details of catering facilities see
Directory of Train Operators

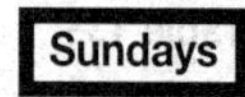

3 February to 23 March

Sleeper services are published in Table 406

London and Birmingham → Devon and Cornwall

Network Diagram - see first page of Table 135

		GW	XC	GW	GW	GW	XC	GW	GW	XC	SW	GW	XC	GW	GW	GW	XC	GW	GW
		1◇	R 1		1◇		R 1		1◇	R 1	1◇	1◇	R 1		1◇	1◇	R 1	1◇	1◇
			A																
		☕	☕		☕		☕		☕	☕	☕	☕	☕		☕	☕		☕	☕
London Paddington 15	⊖ d	16 00			17 00				18 00			19 00				20 00		21 00	23 50
London Waterloo 15	⊖ d										17 15								
Slough 3	d																		
Heathrow Terminal 1 Bus	🚌 d																		
Gatwick Airport 10	d	*14 07*			*15 07*				*16 07*			*17 07*				*18 07*		*19 07*	*22 07*
Oxford	d	*15 50*			*16 48*				*17 50*			*18 50*				*19 51*		*20 50*	*22 58*
Reading 7	d	16 37			17 37				18 37			19 37				20 37		21 37	00u37
Theale	d																		
Thatcham	d																		
Newbury	d	16 54							18 54							20 54			
Hungerford	d																		
Pewsey	d								19 15							21 15			
Westbury	d	17 29							19 34							21 34			
Castle Cary	d	17 47										20 37				21 52			
Birmingham New Street 12	d		16 10				17 10			18 10			19 10				20 10		
Cardiff Central 7	d																		
Newport (South Wales)	d																		
Swindon	d														20 17				
Bristol Parkway 7	d		17 25				18 36			19 25			20 25				21 25		
Filton Abbey Wood	d																		
Bath Spa 7	d														20 46				
Bristol Temple Meads 10	d		17 44			18 10	18 50			19 44			20 44		21 02		21 44		
Weston-super-Mare	d					18 40									21 30				
Bridgwater	d					18 58													
Taunton	d	18 08	18 17		18 57	19 11	19 23		20 08	20 17		20 59	21 17		21 52	22 12	22 17	22s56	
Tiverton Parkway	d	18 22	18 29		19 09	19 26	19 35		20 22	20 29		21 12	21 29		22 05	22 25	22 29	23s10	
Exeter St Davids 6	a	18 38	18 43		19 26	19 42	19 48		20 39	20 45		21 29	21 43		22 22	22 42	22 45	23 28	04 05
Exeter Central	a		*19 23*		*19 38*		*20 38*					*21 38*			*22 33*		*23 13*		*05 13*
Exmouth	a				*20 03*		*21 06*					*22 03*			*22 58*		*23 44*		*06 03*
Barnstaple	a					*21 06*													
Exmouth	d		*18 10*	18 10			*19 10*			*20 10*			*21 10*	21 10			*22 10*		
Exeter Central	d		*18 35*	18 35	*18 43*		*19 34*			*20 34*	20 46		*21 35*	21 35			*22 34*		
Exeter St Davids 6	d	18 38	18 45	18 52	19 28		19 51	20 05	20 39	20 45	20 55	21 30	21 45	21 53		22 42	22 49		04 37
Exeter St Thomas	d			18 55				20 08						21 57					
Starcross	d			19 03				20 16						22 06					
Dawlish Warren	d			19 08				20 21						22 10					
Dawlish	d			19 12				20 25			21 08	21 44		22 14					
Teignmouth	d			19 17				20 30			21 13	21 49		22 19					
Newton Abbot	a	18 59	19 03	19 23	19 47		20 09	20 36	21 00	21 06	21 19	21 56	22 03	22 26		23 03	23 10		04 57
	d	19 00	19 04	19 25	19 48		20 10	20 38	21 01	21 08	21 21	21 56	22 04	22 27		23 03	23 11		04 57
Torre	d			19 33				20 46						22 35					
Torquay	d			19 36				20 49			21 32			22 38					
Paignton	a			19 42				20 55			21 38			22 45					
Totnes	d		19 17		20 01		20 23		21 16	21 24		22 11	22 17			23 17	23 27		
Ivybridge	d																		
Plymouth	a	19 40	19 48		20 29		20 54		21 43	21 56		22 39	22 48			23 50	23 59		05 37
	d		19 55		20 31				21 45										06 30
Devonport	d																		
Dockyard	d																		
Keyham	d																		
St Budeaux Ferry Road	d																		
Saltash	d																		
St Germans	d																		
Menheniot	d																		
Liskeard 3	d		20 18		20 55				22 08										07 00
Looe	a																		*07 44*
Bodmin Parkway	d		20 31		21 08				22 20										07 14
Lostwithiel	d																		07 20
Par 3	d		20 41		21 19				22 32										07 27
Newquay	a																		
St Austell	d		20 48		21 26				22 40										07 36
Truro	d		21 05		21 47				22 56										07 55
Falmouth Docks	a				*22 23*														*08 54*
Redruth	d		21 16		22 00				23 10										08 10
Camborne	d		21 27		22 07				23 16										08 18
Hayle	d																		08 26
St Erth 2	d		21 37		22 20				23 28										08 31
St Ives	a																		*09 24*
Penzance	a		21 52		22 32				23 43										08 47

For general notes see front of timetable
For details of catering facilities see
Directory of Train Operators

A ☕ to Plymouth

Table 135

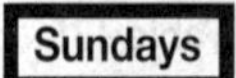

from 30 March

Sleeper services are published in Table 406

London and Birmingham → Devon and Cornwall

Network Diagram - see first page of Table 135

		XC	GW	GW	GW	GW		GW	SW	GW	GW	GW	XC	SW	GW	GW	GW	GW		SW	XC	GW	GW	GW	GW
		1 ◇				◇			1 ◇	1 ◇			1 ◇	1 ◇	1 ◇			1 ◇		1 ◇	1 ◇			1 ◇	1 ◇
																				A					
												bus					bus						bus		
		⊡	⊼	⊼						⊡			⊡	⊡	⊡			⊡		⊡	⊡			⊡	⊡
London Paddington 15 ⊖	d									08 00					09 00			10 00						11 03	11 37
London Waterloo 15 ⊖	d													08 15						09 15					
Slough 3	d																								
Heathrow Terminal 1 Bus (bus)	d																								
Gatwick Airport 10	d									*06 07*					*07 07*			*08 31*						*09 07*	*10 07*
Oxford	d														*07b45*									*09b30*	*10b30*
Reading 7	d									08 37					09 36			10 35						11 42	12 13
Theale	d																								
Thatcham	d																								
Newbury	d																								
Hungerford	d																								
Pewsey	d											09 20					10 15						11 21		
Westbury	d																								
Castle Cary	d																								
Birmingham New Street 12	d												10 10								11 10				
Cardiff Central 7	d																								
Newport (South Wales)	d																								
Swindon	d									09 12		10a05					11a00	11 08					12a06	12 17	
Bristol Parkway 7	d												11 25								12 25				
Filton Abbey Wood	d																								
Bath Spa 7	d									09 40					10 29			11 32						12 46	13 11
Bristol Temple Meads 10	d			07 30		08 15				09 57			11 44								12 44			13 02	
Weston-super-Mare	d			07 50		08 43																		13 29	
Bridgwater	d					09 02							12 02												
Taunton	d			08 18		09 17				10 30			12 27		11 19			12 21			13 17			13 53	13 58
Tiverton Parkway	d			08 33		09 32				10 45					11 32						13 29			14 07	14 13
Exeter St Davids 6	a			08 51		09 50				11 00			12 55		11 48			12 49			13 43			14 25	14 32
Exeter Central	a			*09 23*		*10 35*				*11 23*					*12 28*						*14 28*				
Exmouth	a			*09 56*		*11 00*				*11 53*					*12 54*						*14 54*				
Barnstaple	a			*10 55*											*13 02*						*15 09*				
Exmouth	d					*09 10*			*10 00*						*11 10*			*12 05*			*13 05*				
Exeter Central	d				*08 56*	*09 34*			10 46					11 29	*11 37*			*12 30*		12 46	*13 29*				
Exeter St Davids 6	d			08 53	09 25	09 52		10 10	10 56	11 00			12 56	11 40	11 49			12 50		13 01	13 45	13 50		14 26	14 32
Exeter St Thomas	d				09 28			10 13														13 53			
Starcross	d				09 36			10 21														14 01			
Dawlish Warren	d				09 41			10 26					13 09									14 06			
Dawlish	d			09 06	09 45	10 05		10 30	11 11	11 15										13 14		14 10		14 40	
Teignmouth	d			09 11	09 50	10 10		10 35	11 16	11 21			13 14							13 20		14 15		14 45	
Newton Abbot	a			09 17	09 56	10 16		10 41	11 23	11 27			13 20	12 01	12 09			13 10		13 26	14 03	14 21		14 52	14 56
	d			09 18	09 58	10 17		10 43	11 24	11 27	11 42			12 02	12 10	12 30		13 11		13 31	14 04	14 23		14 52	14 56
Torre	d				10 06			10 51			11 50					12 38						14 31			
Torquay	d				10 09			10 54	11 35		11 53		13 13			12 41				13 43		14 34		15 05	
Paignton	a				10 15			11 00	11 42		11 59		13 44			12 47				13 49		14 40		15 11	
Totnes	d			09 31		10 30				11 41				12 17	12 24			13 25			14 17				15 09
Ivybridge	d			09 48										12 33											
Plymouth	a			10 02		10 59				12 09				12 47	12 54			13 55			14 48				15 37
	d	09 10	09 30	10 03		11 00				12 12					12 57										
Devonport	d			10 07																					
Dockyard	d																								
Keyham	d																								
St Budeaux Ferry Road	d																								
Saltash	d			10 14		11 09																			
St Germans	d			10 21		11 16																			
Menheniot	d			10 29		11 24																			
Liskeard 3	d	09 33	09 54	10 35		11 30				12 35					13 19										
Looe	a																								
Bodmin Parkway	d	09 45	10 06	10 47		11 42				12 47					13 32										
Lostwithiel	d		10 11	10 52		11 47																			
Par 3	d	09 55	10 18	10 59		11 54				12 58					13 42										
Newquay	a																								
St Austell	d	10 02	10 26	11 06		12 02				13 05					13 49										
Truro	d	10 19	10 44	11 24		12 20				13 23					14 09										
Falmouth Docks	a	*11 34*	*11 34*			*12 49*				*13 58*					*14 57*										
Redruth	d	10 30	10 57	11 37		12 34				13 35					14 20										
Camborne	d	10 37	11 03	11 43		12 40				13 43					14 29										
Hayle	d		11 11	11 50		12 47																			
St Erth 2	d	10 50	11 14	11 54		12 50				13 55					14 45										
St Ives	a	*12 13*		*12 13*		*13 15*				*14 14*					*15 19*										
Penzance	a	11 06	11 32	12 05		13 03				14 10					15 02										

For general notes see front of timetable
For details of catering facilities see Directory of Train Operators

A Also stops at Chard Jn. S.B arr. 1158 dep. 1203

b Change at Didcot Parkway and Reading. By bus to Didcot Parkway

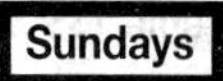

from 30 March

Sleeper services are published in Table 406

London and Birmingham → Devon and Cornwall

Network Diagram - see first page of Table 135

		XC	SW	GW	GW	GW	XC	GW	GW	GW	XC	GW	GW	XC	GW	GW	SW	GW	XC	GW	GW
		1 ◇	1 ◇	1 ◇			1 ◇	1 ◇			1 ◇			R 1	1 ◇		1 ◇	1 ◇	R 1		1 ◇
		☕	☕	☕		🚲	☕	☕	🚌		☕			☕	☕	🚌	☕	☕	☕		☕
London Paddington 15 ⊖	d			12 03				13 00							13 37			14 37			15 03
London Waterloo 15 ⊖	d		11 15														13 15				
Slough 3	d																				
Heathrow Terminal 1 Bus 🚌	d																				
Gatwick Airport 10	d			*11 07*											*12 07*			*13 07*			*14 07*
Oxford	d							*11b30*							*12b30*			*13b30*			
Reading 7	d			12 42				13 37							14 10			15 14			15 42
Theale	d																				
Thatcham	d																				
Newbury	d														14 28						
Hungerford	d																				
Pewsey	d								13 45						14 49	14 50					
Westbury	d														15c13						
Castle Cary	d																				
Birmingham New Street 12	d	12 10					13 10				13 40			14 10					15 10		
Cardiff Central 7	d																				
Newport (South Wales)	d																				
Swindon	d			13 17					14a30							15a35					16 17
Bristol Parkway 7	d	13 25					14 25				14 58			15 25					16 25		
Filton Abbey Wood	d																				
Bath Spa 7	d			13 48				14 31													16 48
Bristol Temple Meads 10	d	13 44		14 03			14 44				15 11			15 44	15 47				16 44		17 02
Weston-super-Mare	d																				17 31
Bridgwater	d																				
Taunton	d	14 17		14 37			15 17	15 22			15 44			16 17	16 21			17 04	17 17		17a56
Tiverton Parkway	d	14 29					15 29				15 56			16 29				17 18	17 29		
Exeter St Davids 6	a	14 43	14 46	15 04			15 43	15 49			16 11			16 43	16 49			17 35	17 43		
Exeter Central	a		14 42	*15 21*							*16 28*				*17 21*				*18 38*		
Exmouth	a			*15 53*							*16 54*				*17 53*				*19 03*		
Barnstaple	a						*17 08*												*19 06*		
Exmouth	d	*14 10*					*15 10*							*16 10*	*16 10*				*17 10*		
Exeter Central	d	*14 34*	14 43				*15 34*							*16 34*	*16 34*		16 43		*17 34*		
Exeter St Davids 6	d	14 45	14 52	15 04	15 10		15 45	15 51		16 03	16 12			16 45	16 51		16 57	17 35	17 45	17 50	
Exeter St Thomas	d				15 13															17 53	
Starcross	d				15 21															18 01	
Dawlish Warren	d				15 26															18 06	
Dawlish	d				15 30					16 16							17 10			18 10	
Teignmouth	d				15 35					16 21							17 15			18 15	
Newton Abbot	a	15 03	15 19	15 25	15 41		16 03	16 10		16 27	16 32	⟵		17 03	17 10		17 22	17 55	18 03	18 21	
	d	15 04	15 21	15 26	15 43		16 04	16 10		16 38	16 33	16 38	16 55	17 04	17 10		17 26	17 55	18 04	18 23	
Torre	d				15 51					⟶			17 03							18 31	
Torquay	d		15 32		15 54								17 06				17 37			18 34	
Paignton	a		15 38		16 01								17 12				17 43			18 40	
Totnes	d	15 17					16 17	16 24			16 45	16 53		17 17	17 25			18 10	18 17		
Ivybridge	d											17 10									
Plymouth	a	15 48		16 07			16 48	16 52			17 18	17 24		17 48	17 58			18 37	18 48		
	d					16 10		17 00				17 25		17 55				18 38	18 55		
Devonport	d																				
Dockyard	d																				
Keyham	d																				
St Budeaux Ferry Road	d																				
Saltash	d											17 34									
St Germans	d											17 41									
Menheniot	d											17 49									
Liskeard 3	d					16 34		17 24				17 55		18 24				19 02	19 18		
Looe	a																				
Bodmin Parkway	d					16 46		17 37				18 07		18 37				19 15	19 31		
Lostwithiel	d					16 51						18 12									
Par 3	d					16 58		17 49				18 19		18 47				19 26	19 41		
Newquay	a																				
St Austell	d					17 06		17 55				18 27		18 54				19 33	19 48		
Truro	d					17 24		18 14				18 45		19 11				19 50	20e11		
Falmouth Docks	a							*18 53*						*20 04*							
Redruth	d					17 37		18 26				18 59		19 22				20 03	20f27		
Camborne	d					17 43		18 33				19 05		19 29				20 10	20 36		
Hayle	d					17 51						19 12									
St Erth 2	d					17 54		18 46				19 15		19 39				20 23	20 46		
St Ives	a					*18 39*						*19 33*									
Penzance	a					18 12		19 02				19 29		19 54				20 35	21 01		

For general notes see front of timetable
For details of catering facilities see Directory of Train Operators

b Change at Didcot Parkway and Reading. By bus to Didcot Parkway

c Arr. 1507

e Arr. 2004

f Arr.2021

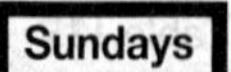

Sundays

from 30 March

Sleeper services are published in Table 406

London and Birmingham → Devon and Cornwall

Network Diagram - see first page of Table 135

Station		GW	XC	GW		GW	GW	GW	XC	GW		GW	XC	SW	XC	GW		GW	GW	XC	GW	GW	GW		
			R						R				R		R					R					
			1	1 ◇			1 ◇		1			1 ◇	1	1 ◇	1			1 ◇	1 ◇	1	1 ◇	1 ◇	1 ◇		
			A																						
		⊼	⊡	⊡			⊡		⊡			⊡	⊡	⊡	⊡			⊡	⊡		⊡	⊡	⊡		
London Paddington 15	⊖ d			15 37			16 37					18 00						19 00	19 03		20 00	21 00	23 50		
London Waterloo 15	⊖ d													17 15											
Slough 3	d																								
Heathrow Terminal 1 Bus	d																								
Gatwick Airport 10	d						*15 07*					*16 07*						*17 07*	*18 07*			*19 07*			
Oxford	d			*14b30*			*15b30*					*16b30*						*17b30*			*18b30*	*19b30*			
Reading 7	d			16 12			17 14					18 36						19 38	19 42		20 37	21 37	00 37		
Theale	d																								
Thatcham	d																								
Newbury	d			16 31														19 55			21 00				
Hungerford	d																								
Pewsey	d																	20 15			21 20				
Westbury	d			17c11														20e39			21 40				
Castle Cary	d																				21 57				
Birmingham New Street 12	d		16 10						17 10				18 10		19 10					20 10					
Cardiff Central 7	d																								
Newport (South Wales)	d																								
Swindon	d																		20 17						
Bristol Parkway 7	d		17 25						18 25				19 25		20 25					21 25					
Filton Abbey Wood	d																								
Bath Spa 7	d																		20 46						
Bristol Temple Meads 10	d		17 44					18 10	18 44				19 44		20 44				21 02	21 44					
Weston-super-Mare	d							18 40											21 30						
Bridgwater	d							18 58																	
Taunton	d		18 17	18 22			18 56	19 11	19 17			20 08	20 17		21 17			21 52	21 58	22 17	22 19	22s56			
Tiverton Parkway	d		18 29	18 35			19 09	19 26	19 29			20 22	20 29		21 29			22 06	22 12	22 29	22 32	23s10			
Exeter St Davids 6	a		18 43	18 51			19 28	19 42	19 45			20 39	20 45		21 43			22 23	22 31	22 43	22 50	23 28	04 05		
Exeter Central	a			*19 23*			*19 38*		*20 38*				*21 23*					*22 33*			*23 13*				
Exmouth	a						*20 03*		*21 06*				*22 03*					*22 58*			*23 44*				
Barnstaple	a							*21 06*																	
Exmouth	d		*18 10*			18 10			*19 10*				*20 10*		*21 10*	21 10				*22 10*					
Exeter Central	d		*18 35*	*18 43*		18 35			*19 34*				*20 34*	20 46	*21 35*	21 35				*22 34*					
Exeter St Davids 6	d		18 45	18 53		18 55	19 29		19 48	20 05		20 41	20 45	20 55	21 45	21 53		22 24		22 45	22 50		04 37		
Exeter St Thomas	d					18 59				20 08						21 57									
Starcross	d					19 07				20 16						22 06									
Dawlish Warren	d					19 12				20 21						22 10									
Dawlish	d					19 16				20 25				21 08		22 14		22 37							
Teignmouth	d					19 21				20 30				21 13		22 19		22 43							
Newton Abbot	a		19 03	19 12		19 27	19 48		20 06	20 36		21 00	21 06	21 19	22 03	22 26		22 49		23 03	23 11		04 57		
	d		19 04	19 14		19 29	19 49		20 07	20 38		21 01	21 08	21 21	22 04	22 27		22 50		23 04	23 11		04 57		
Torre	d					19 37				20 46						22 35									
Torquay	d					19 40				20 49				21 32		22 38									
Paignton	a					19 46				20 55				21 38		22 45									
Totnes	d		19 17				20 02		20 20			21 16	21 24		22 17			23 04		23 17	23 24				
Ivybridge	d																								
Plymouth	a		19 48	19 55			20 30		20 51			21 43	21 56		22 48			23 32		23 48	23 57		05 37		
	d	19 25	19 55				20 32					21 45											06 30		
Devonport	d																								
Dockyard	d																								
Keyham	d																								
St Budeaux Ferry Road	d																								
Saltash	d																								
St Germans	d																								
Menheniot	d																								
Liskeard 3	d	19 49	20 18				20 56					22 08											07 00		
Looe	a																								
Bodmin Parkway	d	20 01	20 31				21 08					22 20											07 14		
Lostwithiel	d	20 06																					07 29		
Par 3	d	20 13	20 41				21 19					22 32											07 27		
Newquay	a																								
St Austell	d	20 21	20 48				21 26					22 40											07 36		
Truro	d	20 39	21 05				21 48					22 56											07 55		
Falmouth Docks	a	*21 13*					22 23																		
Redruth	d	20 52	21 16				22 00					23 10											08 10		
Camborne	d	20 58	21 23				22 08					23 16											08 18		
Hayle	d	21 06																					08 26		
St Erth 2	d	21 09	21 33				22 20					23 28											08 31		
St Ives	a																								
Penzance	a	21 29	21 48				22 33					23 43											08 47		

For general notes see front of timetable
For details of catering facilities see Directory of Train Operators

A ⊡ to Plymouth
b Change at Didcot Parkway and Reading. By bus to Didcot Parkway
c Arr. 1704
e Arr. 2032

Sleeper services are published in Table 406

Cornwall and Devon → Birmingham and London

Network Diagram - see first page of Table 135

Miles	Miles			GW	GW	GW	GW	GW	GW	GW	GW	XC	GW	GW	GW	GW	GW	GW	GW	GW	GW	XC	GW	XC	GW
				MX	MO	MO	MX																		
					1◇	1◇	1◇	1◇	1◇	1◇		1◇	1◇	1◇	1◇		1◇			1◇	1◇	1◇		1◇	
					A	B _9D_	C		D																E
					🛒	🛒	🛒	🍴	🍴	⊠		🛒	⊠	🛒	🛒		🍴			🛒	⊠	🛒		🛒	
0	—	**Penzance**	d		21p15	21p15	22p00																		
—	—	St Ives	d																						
5¾	—	St Erth 2	d		21p25	21p25	22p10																		
7¼	—	Hayle	d				22p14																		
13¼	—	Camborne	d		21p37	21p37	22p24																		
16¾	—	Redruth	d		21p44	21p44	22p32																		
—	—	Falmouth Docks	d																						
25¾	—	Truro	d		21p57	21p57	22p44																		
40¼	—	St Austell	d		22p15	22p15	23p02																		
—	—	Newquay	d																						
44¾	—	Par 3	d				23p11																		
49¼	—	Lostwithiel	d				23p19																		
52¾	—	Bodmin Parkway	d		22p32	22p32	23p26																		
—	—	Looe	d																						
61¾	—	Liskeard 3	d		22p47	22p47	23p41																		
65	—	Menheniot	d																						
70½	—	St Germans	d																						
75¼	—	Saltash	d																						
76¾	—	St Budeaux Ferry Road	d																						
77¼	—	Keyham	d																						
77¾	—	Dockyard	d																						
78¼	—	Devonport	d																						
79½	—	**Plymouth**	a		23p13	23p13	00 07																		
—	—		d		23p20	23p20	00 20						05 24	05 35			06 00					06 25		06 40	
90¼	—	Ivybridge	d																						
102¾	—	Totnes	d		23p48	23p48	00 48						05 51	06 03								06 50		07 05	
—	0	Paignton	d	23p32												06 07			06 42						07 09
—	2¼	Torquay	d	23p37												06 12			06 47						07 14
—	3	Torre	d	23p40												06 15			06 50						07 17
111½	8¼	Newton Abbot	a	23p48	23p59	23p59	01 00						06 03	06 15		06 23	06 34		06 58			07 01	←	07 16	07 25
—	—		d	23p50	00 01	00 01	01 01						06 04	06 16		06 25	06 35		07 08 →			07 03	07 08	07 18	07 32 →
116½	—	Teignmouth	d	23p57									06 11			06 32							07 15		
119¾	—	Dawlish	d	00 02									06 17			06 37		←					07 20		
121	—	Dawlish Warren	d	00 06												06b46 →		06 46					07c30 →		
123	—	Starcross	d	00 09														06 49							
130½	—	Exeter St Thomas	d	00 18														06 58							
131½	—	**Exeter St Davids 6**	a	00 22	00 26	00 26	01 23						06 29	06 37			06 54	07 02				07 21		07 36	
—	—	Exeter Central	a										*06 44*	*06 48*				07 13							
—	—	Exmouth	a											*07 13*				07 40							
—	—	Barnstaple	d																						
—	—	Exmouth	d											*06 05*								*06 48*			
—	—	Exeter Central	d											*06 29*	*06 32*							*07 13*			
—	—	**Exeter St Davids 6**	d		01 27	01 27	01 27			05 47	06 00	06 23	06 31	06 39	06 45		06 55					07 23		07 38	
148	—	Tiverton Parkway	d							06 07	06 17	06 37		06 54	06 59							07 37		07 52	
162¼	—	Taunton	d				02 32			06 21	06 34	06 51	06 56	07 07	07 14		07 19					07 51		08 06	
—	11¾	Bridgwater	a								06 46		07 06		07 23						←				
—	25¾	Weston-super-Mare	a								07 06		07 26 →		07 43 →						07 26			08 29	
—	45½	**Bristol Temple Meads 10**	a								07 44	07 25									07 57	08 25		08 50	
—	—	Bath Spa 7	a																		08 11				
—	—	Filton Abbey Wood	a								07 56														
—	51¼	Bristol Parkway 7	a								08 03	07 38										08 38		09 08	
—	—	Swindon	a																		08 39				
—	—	Newport (South Wales)	a																						
—	—	Cardiff Central 7	a																						
—	138¼	**Birmingham New Street 12**	a									08 57										09 57		10 26	
190	—	Castle Cary	d							06 43				07 29						←					
209¾	—	Westbury	d					06 10	06 23	07 03				07e54 →						07 54					
230	—	Pewsey	d					06 29	06 41	07 22										08 13					
243¾	—	Hungerford	a					06 41	06 57																
252¼	—	Newbury	a					06 51	07 11	07 41										08 33					
255¾	—	Thatcham	a					06 58	07 18																
264½	—	Theale	a					07 07	07 27																
269¼	—	**Reading 7**	a		03s39	04s18	04s28	07 18	07 41	08 07							08 33			08 52	09 14				
—	—	Oxford	a					*08f00*	*08 20*	*08 47*							*09 06*			*09 34*	*09 47*				
—	—	Gatwick Airport 10	a			*05 54*		*09 02*	*09g47*	*09 59*										*10g39*	*10 51*				
—	—	Heathrow Terminal 1 Bus	a					*08 37*	*08 57*	*09 37*							*09 45*			*10 05*	*10 25*				
286¾	—	Slough 3	a																						
—	—	**London Waterloo 15**	⊖ a																						
305¼	—	**London Paddington 15**	⊖ a		05 10	05 10	05 20	07 51	08 09	08 38							09 00			09 22	09 44				

For general notes see front of timetable
For details of catering facilities see Directory of Train Operators

A 4 February to 24 March
B Until 28 January and from 31 March. First Class seating accommodation also available
C First Class seating accommodation also available
D From Frome (Table 123)
E To St James' Park (Table 136)

b Arr. 0640
c Arr. 0723
e Arr. 0746
f Change at Reading and Didcot Parkway
g Change at Reading and Redhill

Sleeper services are published in Table 406

Cornwall and Devon → Birmingham and London

Network Diagram - see first page of Table 135

		GW	GW	GW	GW	GW	GW	XC	GW	GW		GW	GW	XC	GW	GW	GW	GW	GW	XC		XC	GW	GW	XC
			1◇			1◇	1◇	R 1	1◇	1◇				1◇			1◇	1◇		R 1		1◇	1◇		R 1
			A		B																				
			✕			☕	☕	☕	☕	⊠				☕			☕	⊠		☕		☕	☕		☕
Penzance	d		05 05	05 23						05 42		06 04						06 43		07 30			07 43		08 30
St Ives	d																			*07 08*			*07 38*		
St Erth 2	d											06 12						06 54		07 38			07 53		08 38
Hayle	d			05 32								06 15						06 57					07 57		
Camborne	d			05 42						06 02		06 25						07 07		07 48			08 08		08 48
Redruth	d		05 26	05 48						06 09		06 31						07 14		07 54			08 15		08 54
Falmouth Docks	d																	*06 57*					*07 57*		
Truro	d		05 39	05a58						06 21		06 43						07 27		08 06			08 27		09 06
St Austell	d		05 56							06 39		07 00						07 44		08 22			08 45		09 22
Newquay	d																								
Par 3	d									06 46		07 07						07 51		08 29					09 29
Lostwithiel	d									06 52		07 14						07 58							
Bodmin Parkway	d		06 12							06 59		07 20						08 04		08 40			09 01		09 40
Looe	d									*06 41*								*07 46*							
Liskeard 3	d		06 27							07 12		07 34						08 17		08 52			09 14		09 52
Menheniot	d									07 18		07 39						08 23							
St Germans	d									07 27		07 46						08 31					09 25		
Saltash	d									07 34		07 53						08 38					09 32		
St Budeaux Ferry Road	d											07 57													
Keyham	d											07x59													
Dockyard	d											08x01													
Devonport	d											08 03													
Plymouth	a		06 52							07 45		08 09						08 49		09 14			09 43		10 18
	d		06 55					07 25		07 47		08 10		08 25				08 55		09 25			09 45		10 25
Ivybridge	d											08 25													
Totnes	d							07 50		08 14		08 39		08 50				09 22		09 50			10 12		10 50
Paignton	d					07 38							08 42			09 14						10 02		10 25	
Torquay	d					07 44							08 47			09 19						10 08		10 30	
Torre	d					07 48							08 50			09 22								10 33	
Newton Abbot	a		07 30		←	07 58		08 01	←	08 25		08 53	08 58	09 01	←	09 30		09 33	←	10 01		10 18	10 24	10 41	11 01
	d		07 30		07 32	08 06		08 03	08 06	08 27			09 07	09 03	09 07	09 38		09 35	09 38	10 03		10 19	10 25	10 43	11 03
Teignmouth	d				07 40	→			08 13				→		09 14	→			09 45			10 26	10 32	10 50	
Dawlish	d	←			07 45				08 19						09 19				09 50			10 31	10 38	10 55	
Dawlish Warren	d	07 30			07 49										09 23				09 54					10 59	
Starcross	d	07 33			07 52				08 26						09 26				09 57					11 02	
Exeter St Thomas	d	07 42			08 01				08 35						09 35				10 06					11 11	
Exeter St Davids 6	a	07 46	07 50		08 05			08 21	08 38	08 47				09 21	09 39			09 55	10 10	10 21		10 43	10 51	11 15	11 21
Exeter Central	a	07 52	*08 03*		08 11				*08 49*	*08 58*					*09 48*			*10 13*	10 21	*10 48*				11 21	*11 36*
Exmouth	a	08 17			*08 45*				*09 15*	*09 45*					*10 15*				10 45	*11 15*				11 45	
Barnstaple	d							*07 04*										*08 41*							
Exmouth	d		*07 15*						*07 50*					*08 50*				*09 20*		*09 50*			*10 20*		
Exeter Central	d		*07 39*					*08 12*	*08 19*					*09 14*				*09 44*		*10 14*			*10 43*		
Exeter St Davids 6	d		07 52					08 23	08 40	08 49				09 23				09 57		10 23		10 48	10 53		11 23
Tiverton Parkway	d							08 37		09 03				09 37				10 11		10 37		11 01	11 07		11 37
Taunton	d		08 16					08 51	09 04	09 18				09 51				10 26		10 51		11 16	11 22		11 51
Bridgwater	a						←										←								
Weston-super-Mare	a						07 43		09 25																
Bristol Temple Meads 10	a						08 22	09 27	09 55					10 25			09 55			11 25		11 53	11 55		12 25
Bath Spa 7	a						08 41		→								10 11						12 11		
Filton Abbey Wood	a																								
Bristol Parkway 7	a							09 38						10 38						11 38		12 08			12 38
Swindon	a						09 09										10 40						12 39		
Newport (South Wales)	a																								
Cardiff Central 7	a																								
Birmingham New Street 12	a							10 57						11 57						12 57		13 26			13 57
Castle Cary	d									09 39															
Westbury	d									09 58								11 02							
Pewsey	d									10 17															
Hungerford	a																								
Newbury	a																								
Thatcham	a																								
Theale	a																								
Reading 7	a		09 34				09 44			10 51							11 09	11 51					13 09		
Oxford	a						*10 18*			*11 34*							*11 47*	*12 34*					*13 47*		
Gatwick Airport 10	a						*11b39*			*12b39*							*12 50*	*13c39*							
Heathrow Terminal 1 Bus	🚌 a						*10 45*										*12 05*	*13 05*					*14 05*		
Slough 3	a																								
London Waterloo 15	⊖ a																								
London Paddington 15	⊖ a		10 01				10 15			11 23							11 41	12 23					13 42		

For general notes see front of timetable
For details of catering facilities see Directory of Train Operators

A **The Golden Hind**
B To St James' Park (Table 136)
b Change at Reading and Redhill
c Change at Reading and Redhill

Sleeper services are published in Table 406

Cornwall and Devon → Birmingham and London

Network Diagram - see first page of Table 135

Station		GW	GW	GW	GW	XC	GW	XC	GW	GW	GW	SW	XC	GW	SW	GW	GW	GW	XC	GW	XC	GW	GW	GW	XC
		1	1 ◇			R 1		1 ◇		1		1 ◇	R 1		1 ◇		1 ◇		R 1	◇	R 1	1 ◇	1 ◇		R 1
		A			B		B																C		
		☕	🛒			☕		☕		✕		☕	☕		☕		⊠		☕		☕	🛒	☕		☕
Penzance	d	08 45				09 30				10 00				10 36						11 40					
St Ives	d	08 35								09 27				10 25						11 25					
St Erth 2	d	08 56				09 38				10 11				10 44						11 48					
Hayle	d													10 47						11 52					
Camborne	d	09 08				09 48				10 22				10 57						12 01					
Redruth	d	09 15				09 54				10 29				11 03						12 07					
Falmouth Docks	d	08 57								10 11										11 47					
Truro	d	09 27				10 06				10 41				11 15						12 19					
St Austell	d	09 45				10 22				10 59				11 32						12 36					
Newquay	d									10 18															
Par 3	d					10 29				11 06				11 39						12 44					
Lostwithiel	d													11 46											
Bodmin Parkway	d	10 01				10 40				11 17				11 52						12 55					
Looe	d					10 25														12 33					
Liskeard 3	d	10 14				10 52				11 30				12 05						13 08					
Menheniot	d													12 10											
St Germans	d													12 17											
Saltash	d													12 24											
St Budeaux Ferry Road	d																								
Keyham	d				11x00																				
Dockyard	d				11x02																				
Devonport	d				11 04																				
Plymouth	a	10 39			11 08	11 17				11 57				12 37						13 32					
	d	10 45			11 10	11 25		11 50		12 00			12 25				12 55		13 25	13 33					14 25
Ivybridge	d				11 25															13 48					
Totnes	d				11 39	11 50		12 15		12 27			12 50				13 22		13 50	14 02					14 50
Paignton	d			11 23					12 19			12 35				13 14					14 03		14 15	14 25	
Torquay	d			11 28					12 24			12 41				13 19					14 09		14 21	14 30	
Torre	d			11 31					12 27							13 22								14 33	
Newton Abbot	a			11 39	11 53	12 01		12 26	12 35	12 38	←	12 51	13 01			13 30	13 34	←	14 01	14 14	14 19		14 32	14 41	15 01
	d			11 41	11 53	12 03		12 28	12 44 →	12 40	12 44	12 53	13 03			13 43 →	13 35	13 43	14 03	14 15	14 21		14 33	14 43	15 03
Teignmouth	d			11 48	12 00						12 51	13 00			←			13 50			14 28		14 40	14 50	
Dawlish	d			11 53	12 05		←				12 56	13 05 →			13 05			13 55			14 33		14 46	14 55	
Dawlish Warren	d			11 57	12b16 →		12 16				13 00				13c16			13 59						14 59	
Starcross	d			12 00			12 19				13 03							14 02						15 02	
Exeter St Thomas	d			12 09			12 28				13 12							14 11						15 11	
Exeter St Davids 6	a	11 38		12 14		12 21	12 34	12 46		13 00	13 16		13 21		13 27		13 55	14 15	14 21	14 38	14 44		14 59	15 15	15 21
Exeter Central	a	11 48		12 21			12 48				13 21				13 38		14 13	14 21		14 48				15 21	15 33
Exmouth	a	12 15		12 45			13 15				13 45				14 12			14 45		15 15				15 45	16 15
Barnstaple	d	10 30															12 41								
Exmouth	d	10 50	11 20					11 50		12 20			12 50				13 20		13 50				14 20		14 50
Exeter Central	d	11 18	11 43			12 08		12 30		12 43			13 14				13 45		14 14				14 43		15 14
Exeter St Davids 6	d	11 40	11 54			12 23		12 48		13 02			13 23				13 57		14 23		14 46		15 01		15 23
Tiverton Parkway	d		12 08			12 37		13 02		13 16			13 37						14 37		15 00		15 15		15 37
Taunton	d		12 23			12 51		13 16		13 31			13 51				14 22		14 51		15 14	15 23	15 30		15 51
Bridgwater	a																								
Weston-super-Mare	a																				15 34				
Bristol Temple Meads 10	a					13 25		13 54					14 25						15 25		15 55				16 25
Bath Spa 7	a																								
Filton Abbey Wood	a																								
Bristol Parkway 7	a					13 38		14 08					14 38						15 38		16 08				16 38
Swindon	a																								
Newport (South Wales)	a																								
Cardiff Central 7	a																								
Birmingham New Street 12	a					14 57		15 26					15 57						16 57		17 26				17 57
Castle Cary	d		12 44														14 43					15 44			
Westbury	d		13 03														15 02					16 01			
Pewsey	d		13 22																			16 26 →			
Hungerford	a		13 38																						
Newbury	a		13 48																						
Thatcham	a		13 54																						
Theale	a		14 03																						
Reading 7	a	13 17	14 15							14 51							15 51						16 51		
Oxford	a	14 06	14 47							15 34							16 34						17 34		
Gatwick Airport 10	a	14 50	15 50							16e56							17 50						18e58		
Heathrow Terminal 1 Bus 🚌	a	14 25	15 25							16 05							17 05						18 05		
Slough 3	a																								
London Waterloo 15 ⊖	a														16 49										
London Paddington 15 ⊖	a	13 45	14 49							15 23							16 22						17 22		

For general notes see front of timetable
For details of catering facilities see Directory of Train Operators

- A **The Cornish Riviera**
- B From Gunnislake (Table 139)
- C **The Torbay Express**
- b Arr. 1208
- c Arr. 1308
- e Change at Reading and Redhill

Sleeper services are published in Table 406

Cornwall and Devon → Birmingham and London

Network Diagram - see first page of Table 135

		GW	SW	GW	GW	GW	GW	GW	GW	XC	XC	GW	GW	XC	GW	GW	GW	GW	GW	GW	XC	GW	SW	GW	GW
			1 ◇		1 ◇	1 ◇				R 1	1 ◇	1 ◇		1 ◇					1 ◇		1 ◇		1 ◇		1 ◇
						A		B				C			D										
			☕		🍷	✕				☕	☕	☕		☕					☕		☕				🍷
Penzance	d	12 42										14 00					14 50								
St Ives	d	*12 25*										*13 55*					*14 25*								
St Erth 2	d	12 50										14 11					14 58								
Hayle	d																15 01								
Camborne	d	13 01										14 22					15 11								
Redruth	d	13 07										14 29					15 17								
Falmouth Docks	d											*13 27*					*14 57*								
Truro	d	13 19										14 41					15 28								
St Austell	d	13 36										14 59					15 45								
Newquay	d	*12 42*													14 52										
Par 3	d	13 44										15 06			15 40		15 55								
Lostwithiel	d	13 50															16 01								
Bodmin Parkway	d	13 56										15 17					16 07								
Looe	d											*14 30*					*15 49*								
Liskeard 3	d	14 09										15 30					16 20								
Menheniot	d																16 25								
St Germans	d	14 20															16 33								
Saltash	d	14 27															16 40								
St Budeaux Ferry Road	d																16 46								
Keyham	d							15x01									16x47								
Dockyard	d							15x03									16x49								
Devonport	d							15 05									16 52								
Plymouth	a	14 38						15 09				15 55			16 25		16 55								
	d		14 47			15 00		15 11		15 25		16 00		16 25		16 44			17 00		17 25		17 48		
Ivybridge	d		15 02					15 26								16 59							18 03		
Totnes	d		15 16			15 27		15 39		15 50		16 27		16 50		17 13			17 27		17 50		18 17		
Paignton	d			15 19					15 43		16 15		16 27					17 19				17 50		18 21	
Torquay	d			15 24					15 46		16 21		16 32					17 24				17 55		18 26	
Torre	d			15 27					15 49				16 34					17 27				17 58		18 29	
Newton Abbot	a		15 27	15 35		15 39	←	15 53	15 58	16 01	16 31	16 39	16 43	17 01		17 27		17 35	17 39	←	18 01	18 06	18 28	18 37	
	d		15 29	15 44		15 40	15 44			16 03	16 33	16 40	16 44	17 03				17 43	17 40	17 43	18 03	18 08	18 30	18 45	
Teignmouth	d		15 36	→			15 51						16 51					→		17 50		18 15	18 37	→	
Dawlish	d		15 41				15 56						16 56							17 55		18 20	18 42		
Dawlish Warren	d		15 45				16 00						17 00							17 59		18 24	18 46		
Starcross	d						16 03						17 04							18 03		18 27			
Exeter St Thomas	d						16 12						17 13							18 12		18 36			
Exeter St Davids 6	a		15 56			16 00	16 16			16 21	16 51	17 00	17 16	17 21					18 00	18 15	18 21	18 40	18 57		
Exeter Central	a		16 13			*16 13*	16 21			*16 39*			17 21	*17 43*					*18 13*	18 21		18 52	19 13		
Exmouth	a					*16 45*	16 45			*17 15*			17 48	*18 19*						18 48		19 19			
Barnstaple	d					*14 35*					*15 42*								*16 50*						
Exmouth	d					*15 20*					*16 20*			*16 50*					*17 20*						
Exeter Central	d					*15 46*					*16 42*			*17 14*					*17 46*		*17 56*				
Exeter St Davids 6	d					16 02				16 23	16 53	17 01		17 23					18 02		18 23				
Tiverton Parkway	d					16 17				16 37	17 07	17 16		17 37					18 17		18 38				
Taunton	d					16 31				16 51	17 21	17 30		17 51					18 31		18 52				
Bridgwater	a																								
Weston-super-Mare	a																								
Bristol Temple Meads 10	a									17 25	17 55			18 25							19 25				
Bath Spa 7	a																								
Filton Abbey Wood	a																								
Bristol Parkway 7	a									17 38	18 08			18 38							19 38				
Swindon	a																								
Newport (South Wales)	a																								
Cardiff Central 7	a																								
Birmingham New Street 12	a									18 57	19 26			19 57							20 57				
Castle Cary	d																		18 52						
Westbury	d				←														19 11						19 18
Pewsey	d				16 26																				19 36
Hungerford	a				16 38																				19 52
Newbury	a				16 48														19 45						20 05
Thatcham	a				16 54																				20 11
Theale	a				17 03																				20 20
Reading 7	a				17 17	17 51						18 51							20 07						20 33
Oxford	a				*18 06*	*18 34*						*19 34*							*20 47*						*21 16*
Gatwick Airport 10	a				*19 07*	*19 50*						*21 47*													
Heathrow Terminal 1 Bus	a				*18 25*	*19 15*						*20 15*							*21 15*						*21 45*
Slough 3	a				17 31																				
London Waterloo 15 ⊖	a		19 49																				22 57		
London Paddington 15 ⊖	a				17 53	18 22						19 24							20 39						21 02

For general notes see front of timetable
For details of catering facilities see Directory of Train Operators

A **The Mayflower**
B From Gunnislake (Table 139)
C **The Royal Duchy**
D To Gunnislake (Table 139)

Sleeper services are published in Table 406

Cornwall and Devon → Birmingham and London

Network Diagram - see first page of Table 135

		GW	GW	GW	XC	GW	GW	SW	GW	GW	GW	GW	GW	GW	GW	GW	GW	GW	GW	XC	GW	GW	GW
										FO	FX											FX	FO
		1 ◇			1 ◇		1 ◇	1		1 ◇	1 ◇		1 ◇			1		1		1 ◇		1 ◇	1 ◇
					A								B	C	D								
		⊠			⊐P		⌶			⊐P	⊐P		⌶									⊐P	⊐P
Penzance	d	16 00				16 44				17 35	17 35						19 05	20 11		20 55		22 00	22 00
St Ives	d	15 56				16 25				17 27	17 27						18 55	20 00		20 46		21 51	21 51
St Erth 2	d	16 11				16 52				17 46	17 46						19 13	20 21		21 03		22 10	22 10
Hayle	d					16 55				17 49	17 49						19 16	20 25		21 06		22 14	22 14
Camborne	d	16 22				17 05				17 59	17 59						19 26	20 35		21 16		22 24	22 24
Redruth	d	16 29				17 11				18 06	18 06						19 32	20 42		21 22		22 32	22 32
Falmouth Docks	d	14 57				16 53											19 16	20 26				21 30	21 30
Truro	d	16 41				17 23				18 19	18 19						19 44	20 55		21 34		22 44	22 44
St Austell	d	16 59				17 40				18 36	18 36						20 01	21 12		21 50		23 02	23 02
Newquay	d	14 52																20 25					
Par 3	d	17 06				17 47				18 43	18 43						20 08	21 20		21 57		23 11	23 11
Lostwithiel	d	17 15				17 54											20 15	21 27				23 19	23 19
Bodmin Parkway	d	17 22				18 00				18 55	18 55						20 21	21 33		22 08		23 26	23 26
Looe	d	17 06								18 35	18 35						19 43	19 43					
Liskeard 3	d	17 35	17 49			18 13				19 08	19 08						20 34	21 46		22 20		23 41	23 41
Menheniot	d		17 54														20 39						
St Germans	d		18 01			18 24											20 46	21 57					
Saltash	d		18 08			18 31											20 53	22 03					
St Budeaux Ferry Road	d																20 59						
Keyham	d																21x01						
Dockyard	d																21x03						
Devonport	d																21 05						
Plymouth	a	17 59	18 18			18 41				19 33	19 33						21 09	22 15		22 51		00 07	00 07
	d	18 02			18 25	18 43				19 35	19 35						21 13					00 20	00 20
Ivybridge	d					18 58											21 29						
Totnes	d	18 29			18 50	19 12				20 02	20 02						21 43					00 48	00 48
Paignton	d							19 10	19 30			20 30				21 28			22 30		23 32		
Torquay	d							19 16	19 35			20 35				21 34			22 35		23 37		
Torre	d								19 38			20 38				21 38			22 38		23 40		
Newton Abbot	a	18 40		←	19 01	19 24		19 26	19 46	20 14	20 14	20 46				21 48	21 55		22 46		23 48	01 00	01 00
	d	18 42		18 45	19 03	19 25		19 28	19 48	20 15	20 15	20 48					21 55		22 48		23 50	01 01	01 01
Teignmouth	d			18 52				19 35	19 55			20 55					22 02		22 55		23 57		
Dawlish	d			18 57				19 40	20 00			21 00					22 07		23 00		00 02		
Dawlish Warren	d			19 01				19 44	20 04			21 04					22 11		23 04		00 06		
Starcross	d			19 05					20 07			21 07					22 15		23 07		00 09		
Exeter St Thomas	d			19 14					20 16			21 16					22 24		23 16		00 18		
Exeter St Davids 6	a	19 02		19 17	19 21	19 46		19 59	20 20	20 35	20 35	21 20					22 28		23 20		00 22	01 23	01 23
Exeter Central	a	19 13			19 52			20 18		20 52	20 52	21 52					23b00						
Exmouth	a				20 18					21 18	21 18	22 18											
Barnstaple	d				18 06					19 24	19 24				20 22								
Exmouth	d	18 20					19 20							20 20	20 20							23 45	23 45
Exeter Central	d	18 50					19 44			19 52	19 52			20 44	20 44							00 09	00 09
Exeter St Davids 6	d	19 04			19 23		19 53			20 37	20 37			21 26	21 45							01 27	01 27
Tiverton Parkway	d	19 18			19 37		20 08			20 52	20 52			21 42	22 01								
Taunton	d	19 33			19 51		20 22			21 06	21 06		21 30	22c20	22 20							02 32	02 47
Bridgwater	a												21 40										
Weston-super-Mare	a												21 57	22 44	22 44								
Bristol Temple Meads 10	a				20 25					21 39	21 39		22 28	23 06	23 06								
Bath Spa 7	a									21 54	21 54		22 44										
Filton Abbey Wood	a																						
Bristol Parkway 7	a				20 38																		
Swindon	a									22 23	22 23		23 13										
Newport (South Wales)	a																						
Cardiff Central 7	a																						
Birmingham New Street 12	a				21 57																		
Castle Cary	d						20 43																
Westbury	d						21 03																
Pewsey	d						21 21																
Hungerford	a																						
Newbury	a						21 41																
Thatcham	a																						
Theale	a																						
Reading 7	a	20 51					22 00			22 55	22 55		23 52									04s28	04s27
Oxford	a	21 34					22 50			23 51	23 33		00e34									06 21	06 17
Gatwick Airport 10	a	22f28					00f11															06 56	05 53
Heathrow Terminal 1 Bus	a	22 45					23 45															05 40	05 55
Slough 3	a																						
London Waterloo 15	⊖ a																						
London Paddington 15	⊖ a	21 22					22 30			23 29	23 36		00 32									05 20	

For general notes see front of timetable
For details of catering facilities see Directory of Train Operators

- **A** ⊐P to Bristol Temple Meads
- **B** ⌶ to Reading
- **C** Until 15 February
- **D** From 18 February
- **b** Fridays only
- **c** Arr.2157
- **e** Fridays arr. 0107
- **f** Change at Reading and Redhill

until 26 January

Sleeper services are published in Table 406

Cornwall and Devon → Birmingham and London

Network Diagram - see first page of Table 135

		GW	GW	GW	GW	XC	GW	GW	XC	GW	GW	GW	GW	XC	GW	GW	GW	GW	GW	XC	GW
			1 ◇			1 ◇	1 ◇		1 ◇			1 ◇	1 ◇	1 ◇		1 ◇		1 ◇		1 ◇	
																		A			
			🍴			🍴	🍴		🍴			🍴	🍴	🍴		🍴		🍽		🍴	
Penzance	d		22p00		05 30													06 04			
St Ives	d																				
St Erth [2]	d		22p10															06 12			
Hayle	d		22p14															06 15			
Camborne	d		22p24		05 47													06 25			
Redruth	d		22p32		05 53													06 31			
Falmouth Docks	d																				
Truro	d		22p44		06a04													06 43			
St Austell	d		23p02															07 00			
Newquay	d																				
Par [3]	d		23p11															07 07	07 25		
Lostwithiel	d		23p19															07 14	07 32		
Bodmin Parkway	d		23p26															07 20	07 38		
Looe	d																	*06 45*			
Liskeard [3]	d		23p41															07 34	07 51		
Menheniot	d																	07 39			
St Germans	d																	07 46			
Saltash	d																	07 53			
St Budeaux Ferry Road	d																	07 57			
Keyham	d																	07 59			
Dockyard	d																	08 01			
Devonport	d																	08 03			
Plymouth	a		00 07															08 09	08 16		
	d		00 20						06 25			06 55		07 25		07 54		08 10		08 25	
Ivybridge	d																	08 25			
Totnes	d		00 48						06 50					07 50		08 21		08 39		08 50	
Paignton	d	23p32						06 23		06 54	07 08		07 17		08 13						09 11
Torquay	d	23p37						06 28		06 59	07 13		07 23		08 18						09 16
Torre	d	23p40						06 31		07 02	07 16		07 26		08 21						09 19
Newton Abbot	a	23p48	01 00					06 39	07 01	07 10	07 25	07 30	07 36	08 01	08 29	08 33	←	08 52		09 01	09 27
	d	23p50	01 01					06 41	07 03	07 11		07 31	07 37	08 03	08 39 →	08 34	08 39	08 52		09 03	09 38
Teignmouth	d	23p57						06 48		07 18			07 44				08 46				09 45
Dawlish	d	00 02						06 53		07 23			07 50				08 51				09 50
Dawlish Warren	d	00 06						06 57		07 27							08 55				09 54
Starcross	d	00 09						07 00		07 30							08 58				09 57
Exeter St Thomas	d	00 18						07 09		07 39							09 07				10 06
Exeter St Davids [6]	a	00 22	01 23					07 11	07 21	07 43		07 51	08 03	08 21		08 54	09 11	09 16		09 21	10 10
Exeter Central	a							07 17		07 49		*08 03*	*08 18*	*08 49*			09 21			*09 48*	10 21
Exmouth	a							07 43		08 15			*08 44*	*09 15*			09 45			*10 14*	10 45
Barnstaple	d													*07 03*							
Exmouth	d		*23 45*						*06 15*			*07 18*		*07 50*		*08 20*				*08 50*	
Exeter Central	d		*00 09*						*06 39*			*07 42*		*08 14*		*08 44*				*09 14*	
Exeter St Davids [6]	d		01 27	05 20		06 10			07 23			07 53	08 05	08 23		08 56				09 23	
Tiverton Parkway	d			05 37		06 24			07 37				08 19	08 37		09 11				09 37	
Taunton	d		02 47	05 54		06 38	07 00		07 51			08 18	08 34	08 51		09 25				09 51	
Bridgwater	a			06 06			07 09														
Weston-super-Mare	a			06 26		06 58	07 26						08 54								
Bristol Temple Meads [10]	a			07 05		07 27	07 57		08 25				09 20	09 25						10 25	
Bath Spa [7]	a						08 11						09 41								
Filton Abbey Wood	a			07 18																	
Bristol Parkway [7]	a			07 22		07 38			08 38					09 38						10 38	
Swindon	a						08 39						10 09								
Newport (South Wales)	a																				
Cardiff Central [7]	a																				
Birmingham New Street [12]	a					08 57			09 57					10 58						11 57	
Castle Cary	d															09 46					
Westbury	d																				
Pewsey	d															10 18					
Hungerford	a																				
Newbury	a																				
Thatcham	a																				
Theale	a																				
Reading [7]	a		04s27				09 14					09 35	10 45			10 51					
Oxford	a		*06 21*				*09 47*					*10 18*	*11 19*			*11 34*					
Gatwick Airport [10]	a		*05 54*				*10 50*					*11b39*				*12b39*					
Heathrow Terminal 1 Bus 🚌	a		*05 40*				*10 25*					*10 55*				*11 55*					
Slough [3]	a																				
London Waterloo [15]	⊖ a																				
London Paddington [15]	⊖ a		05 25				09 44					10 10	11 15			11 22					

For general notes see front of timetable
For details of catering facilities see
Directory of Train Operators

A To Barnstaple (Table 136)
b Change at Reading and Redhill

Saturdays

until 26 January

Sleeper services are published in Table 406

Cornwall and Devon → Birmingham and London

Network Diagram - see first page of Table 135

		XC	XC		SW	GW	GW	XC		GW	GW	GW	GW		GW	XC	GW	GW		GW	SW	XC	GW		GW
		1◇	1◇		1◇	1◇		1◇			1◇	1◇				1◇		1			1◇	1◇			
															A										
		☕	☕		☕	☕		☕			☕	☕				☕		☕			☕	☕	🛒		
Penzance	d	07 30				08 03		08 30			08 48					09 30		10 00					10 36		
St Ives	d					*07 46*										*09 22*							*10 25*		
St Erth [2]	d	07 38				08 14		08 38			08 59					09 38		10 11					10 44		
Hayle	d					08 17																	10 47		
Camborne	d	07 48				08 27		08 48			09 10					09 48		10 22					10 57		
Redruth	d	07 54				08 34		08 54			09 17					09 54		10 29					11 03		
Falmouth Docks	d	*06 53*				*07 56*					*08 56*							*10 09*							
Truro	d	08 06				08 47		09 06			09 29					10 06		10 41					11 15		
St Austell	d	08 22				09 04		09 22			09 47					10 22		10 59					11 32		
Newquay	d																	*10 13*							
Par [3]	d	08 29				09 11		09 29			09 54					10 29		11 06					11 39		
Lostwithiel	d																						11 46		
Bodmin Parkway	d	08 40				09 23		09 40			10 05					10 40		11 17					11 52		
Looe	d	*07 46*																*10 25*							
Liskeard [3]	d	08 52				09 36		09 52			10 18					10 52		11 30					12 05		
Menheniot	d																						12 10		
St Germans	d																						12 17		
Saltash	d																						12 24		
St Budeaux Ferry Road	d																								
Keyham	d														11x00										
Dockyard	d														11x02										
Devonport	d														11 04										
Plymouth	a	09 14				10 01		10 19			10 43				11 08	11 16		11 57					12 37		
	d	09 25				10 05		10 25			10 46				11 10	11 25		12 00				12 25			
Ivybridge	d														11 25										
Totnes	d	09 50				10 32		10 50							11 39	11 50		12 27				12 50			
Paignton	d		10 05		10 12		10 30			10 46			11 17				12 12				12 34				13 15
Torquay	d		10 11		10 18		10 35			10 51			11 22				12 17				12 40				13 20
Torre	d				10 21		10 38			10 54			11 25				12 20								13 23
Newton Abbot	a	10 01	10 21		10 29	10 43	10 46	11 01		11 02	11 21		11 33		11 53	12 01	12 28	12 38			12 50	13 01			13 31
	d	10 03	10 22		10 31	10 45	10 48	11 03		11 07	11 22		11 35			12 03	12 30	12 40			12 53	13 03			13 43
Teignmouth	d		10 29		10 38		10 55			11 14			11 42				12 37				13 00				→
Dawlish	d		10 34		10 43		11 00			11 19			11 47				12 42			⟵	13 05				
Dawlish Warren	d				10 47		11 03						11 51				12b52			12 52	13c15				
Starcross	d									11 24			11 54				→			12 55	→				
Exeter St Thomas	d									11 33			12 03							13 04					
Exeter St Davids [6]	a	10 21	10 46		10 58	11 05	11 14	11 21		11 36	11 42		12 07			12 21		13 00		13 09		13 21			
Exeter Central	a	*10 48*					11 21	*11 48*		*11 48*	*12 13*		12 21			*12 48*				13 21					
Exmouth	a	*11 14*					11 45	*12 15*		*12 14*			12 45			*13 14*				13 42		*14 14*			
Barnstaple	d	*08 41*										*10 40*													
Exmouth	d	*09 20*	*09 50*			*10 20*		*10 50*				*11 20*						*12 20*				*12 50*			
Exeter Central	d	*09 44*	*10 29*			*10 43*		*11 14*				*11 43*				*11 53*		*12 43*				*13 14*			
Exeter St Davids [6]	d	10 23	10 48			11 06		11 23			11 44	11 54				12 23		13 02				13 23			
Tiverton Parkway	d	10 37	11 01			11 21		11 37				12 09				12 37		13 16				13 37			
Taunton	d	10 51	11 16			11 35		11 51				12 23				12 51		13 31				13 51			
Bridgwater	a																								
Weston-super-Mare	a																								
Bristol Temple Meads [10]	a	11 25	11 55					12 25								13 25						14 25			
Bath Spa [7]	a																								
Filton Abbey Wood	a																								
Bristol Parkway [7]	a	11 38	12 08					12 38								13 38						14 38			
Swindon	a																								
Newport (South Wales)	a																								
Cardiff Central [7]	a																								
Birmingham New Street [12]	a	12 57	13 26					13 57								14 57						15 57			
Castle Cary	d											12 44													
Westbury	d											13 03													
Pewsey	d											13 22													
Hungerford	a											13 39													
Newbury	a											13 49													
Thatcham	a											13 55													
Theale	a											14 04													
Reading [7]	a					12 53					13 22	14 19						14 51							
Oxford	a					*13 34*					*14 06*	*15 06*						*15 34*							
Gatwick Airport [10]	a					*14e39*					*14 50*	*15 50*						*16e39*							
Heathrow Terminal 1 Bus	a					*13 55*					*14 25*	*15 25*						*15 55*							
Slough [3]	a																								
London Waterloo [15] ⊖	a				14 49																				
London Paddington [15] ⊖	a					13 23					13 51	14 46						15 23							

For general notes see front of timetable
For details of catering facilities see
Directory of Train Operators

A From Gunnislake (Table 139)
b Arr. 1245
c Arr. 1308
e Change at Reading and Redhill

Table 135

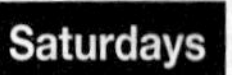

until 26 January

Sleeper services are published in Table 406

Cornwall and Devon → Birmingham and London

Network Diagram - see first page of Table 135

		SW	GW	GW	XC		GW	XC	GW	GW		GW	XC	GW	SW		GW	GW	XC	SW		GW	XC	GW	GW
		1◇	1◇		1◇			1◇	1◇	1◇			1◇		1◇		1◇		1◇	1			1◇		1◇
																		A							
		☕	☕		☕		🍴	☕	☕	☕			☕		☕		☕		☕				☕		☕
Penzance	d		10 58				11 45																		
St Ives	d		10 25				11 25																		
St Erth 2	d		11 09				11 53																		
Hayle	d						11 57																		
Camborne	d		11 20				12 06																		
Redruth	d		11 27				12 12																		
Falmouth Docks	d						11 51																		
Truro	d		11 39				12 24																		
St Austell	d		11 57				12 41																		
Newquay	d																								
Par 3	d						12 49																		
Lostwithiel	d																								
Bodmin Parkway	d		12 13				13 00																		
Looe	d						12 40																		
Liskeard 3	d		12 26				13 13																		
Menheniot	d																								
St Germans	d																								
Saltash	d																								
St Budeaux Ferry Road	d																								
Keyham	d																	15x01							
Dockyard	d																	15x03							
Devonport	d																	15 05							
Plymouth	a		12 51				13 38											15 09							
	d		12 55		13 25				14 00				14 25		14 50		15 04	15 11	15 25				16 25	16 34	16 54
Ivybridge	d														15 05			15 26						16 49	
Totnes	d		13 22		13 50								14 50		15 19		15 31	15 39	15 50				16 50	17 03	
Paignton	d							14 05				14 25		14 53						15 52		16 19			
Torquay	d							14 11				14 30		14 58						15 58		16 24			
Torre	d											14 33		15 01								16 27			
Newton Abbot	a		13 34	←	14 01			14 21	14 35			14 41	15 01	15 09	15 30		15 42	15 53	16 01	16 08		16 35	17 01	17 17	17 29
	d		13 35	13 43	14 03			14 22	14 37			14 42	15 03	15 11	15 32		15 44		16 03	16 10		16 43	17 03		17 31
Teignmouth	d			13 50				14 29				14 49		15 18	15 39					16 17		16 50			
Dawlish	d	←		13 55				14 34				14 54		15 23	15 44					16 22		16 55			
Dawlish Warren	d	13 15		13 59								14 58		15 27	15 48							16 59			
Starcross	d			14 02								15 02		15 30								17 02			
Exeter St Thomas	d			14 11								15 11		15 39								17 11			
Exeter St Davids 6	a	13 24	13 55	14 15	14 21			14 46	14 57			15 14	15 21	15 42	15 59		16 04		16 21	16 35		17 15	17 21		17 51
Exeter Central	a	13 38	14 13	14 21	14 48							15 21	15 33		16 13		16 13			16 43		17 21	17 43		18 13
Exmouth	a			14 45	15 14							15 45	16 14				16 45		17 45	17 14		17 45	18 19		
Barnstaple	d																14 35	14 35					15 42		
Exmouth	d		13 20						14 20								15 20		15 50				16 50		
Exeter Central	d		13 46					14 16	14 43								15 46		16 14				17 14		17 33
Exeter St Davids 6	d		13 57		14 23			14 48	14 59				15 23				16 06		16 23				17 23		17 53
Tiverton Parkway	d				14 37			15 01	15 13				15 37				16 20		16 37				17 37		
Taunton	d		14 22		14 51			15 16	15 28	15 34			15 51				16 35		16 51				17 51		18 17
Bridgwater	a																								
Weston-super-Mare	a																								
Bristol Temple Meads 10	a				15 25			15 55					16 25						17 25				18 25		
Bath Spa 7	a																								
Filton Abbey Wood	a																								
Bristol Parkway 7	a				15 38			16 08					16 38						17 38				18 38		
Swindon	a																								
Newport (South Wales)	a																								
Cardiff Central 7	a																								
Birmingham New Street 12	a				16 57			17 26					17 57						18 57				19 57		
Castle Cary	d		14 43							16 00															18 38
Westbury	d		15 02							16 19															18 57
Pewsey	d									16 38															
Hungerford	a									16 54															
Newbury	a									17 04															19 31
Thatcham	a									17 11															
Theale	a									17 20															
Reading 7	a		15 51						16 50	17 30							17 53								19 50
Oxford	a		16 34						17b30	18 06							18 34								20b30
Gatwick Airport 10	a		17c39						18c39								19c39								21 47
Heathrow Terminal 1 Bus	🚌 a		16 55						17 55	18 25							18 55								21 05
Slough 3	a									17 45															
London Waterloo 15	⊖ a	16 49													19 49										
London Paddington 15	⊖ a		16 22						17 23	18 07							18 23								20 21

For general notes see front of timetable
For details of catering facilities see Directory of Train Operators

A From Gunnislake (Table 139)
b Change at Reading and Didcot Parkway
c Change at Reading and Redhill

until 26 January

Sleeper services are published in Table 406

Cornwall and Devon → Birmingham and London

Network Diagram - see first page of Table 135

Station		XC	GW		SW	GW	SW	XC		GW	SW	GW	GW		GW	GW	GW	GW		GW	XC
		1 ◇ ☕			1 ◇	1 ◇ ☕	1 ◇	1 ◇ ☕			1				1	1 ◇		◇ 🍴			1 ◇
Penzance	d					15 54												19 08			20 45
St Ives	d					15 25												18 55			20 00
St Erth 2	d					16 05												19 16			20 53
Hayle	d																	19 20			20 57
Camborne	d					16 16												19 29			21 06
Redruth	d					16 23												19 35			21 13
Falmouth Docks	d					15 01												18 28			20 26
Truro	d					16 35												19 47			21 24
St Austell	d					16 53												20 04			21 40
Newquay	d					15 10															
Par 3	d					17 00												20 12			21 48
Lostwithiel	d					17 07												20 19			
Bodmin Parkway	d					17 14												20 25			21 59
Looe	d					15 49												19 43			
Liskeard 3	d					17 27												20 38			22 11
Menheniot	d																	20 43			
St Germans	d																	20 50			
Saltash	d																	20 59			
St Budeaux Ferry Road	d																	21 03			
Keyham	d																	21x05			
Dockyard	d																	21x07			
Devonport	d																	21 09			
Plymouth	a					17 52												21 12			22 40
	d	17 25			17 42	17 54		18 25										21 18			
Ivybridge	d				17 57													21 33			
Totnes	d	17 50			18 11	18 21		18 50										21 47			
Paignton	d		17 52							18 52	19 14	19 22	20 06		20 35		21 07			21 50	
Torquay	d		17 57							18 57	19 20	19 27	20 11		20 41		21 12			21 55	
Torre	d		18 00							19 00		19 30	20 14				21 15			21 58	
Newton Abbot	a	18 01	18 08		18 22	18 33		19 01		19 08	19 30	19 38	20 22		20 51		21 23	21 59		22 06	
	d	18 03	18 10		18 24	18 34		19 03		19 10	19 32	19 40	20 24		20 53		21 25	21 59		22 08	
Teignmouth	d		18 17		18 31		←			19 17	19 39	19 47	20 31				21 32	22 06		22 15	
Dawlish	d		18 22		18 36		18 36			19 22	19 44	19 52	20 36				21 37	22 11		22 20	
Dawlish Warren	d		18 26		→		18b48			19 26	19 49	19 56	20 40				21 41	22 15		22 24	
Starcross	d		18 29							19 29		19 59	20 43				21 44	22 19		22 27	
Exeter St Thomas	d		18 38							19 38		20 08	20 52				21 53	22 27		22 36	
Exeter St Davids 6	a	18 21	18 42			18 54	19 00	19 21		19 42	20 00	20 12	20 56		21 13		21 57	22 30		22 40	
Exeter Central	a		18 52				19 13			19 52	20 18	20 25			21 48					23 00	
Exmouth	a		19 18							20 18		21 18			22 14					23 39	
Barnstaple	d	16 48						18 00													
Exmouth	d	17 20				17 50		18 20													
Exeter Central	d	17 53				18 19															
Exeter St Davids 6	d	18 23				18 56		19 23													
Tiverton Parkway	d	18 37				19 10		19 37													
Taunton	d	18 51				19 25		19 51								21 30					
Bridgwater	a															21 40					
Weston-super-Mare	a															21 57					
Bristol Temple Meads 10	a	19 25						20 25								22 28					
Bath Spa 7	a															22 44					
Filton Abbey Wood	a																				
Bristol Parkway 7	a	19 38						20 38													
Swindon	a															23 13					
Newport (South Wales)	a																				
Cardiff Central 7	a																				
Birmingham New Street 12	a	20 57						21 57													
Castle Cary	d					19 46															
Westbury	d					20 05															
Pewsey	d					20 23															
Hungerford	a																				
Newbury	a																				
Thatcham	a																				
Theale	a																				
Reading 7	a					20 58										23 52					
Oxford	a					21 34										00c55					
Gatwick Airport 10	a					23 03															
Heathrow Terminal 1 Bus	🚌 a					22 45															
Slough 3	a																				
London Waterloo 15	⊖ a						22 57														
London Paddington 15	⊖ a					21 28										00 32					

For general notes see front of timetable
For details of catering facilities see Directory of Train Operators

b Arr. 1840

c Change at Reading and Didcot Parkway. By bus from Didcot Parkway

Table 135

Saturdays

2 February to 22 March

Sleeper services are published in Table 406

Cornwall and Devon → Birmingham and London

Network Diagram - see first page of Table 135

		GW	GW	GW	GW	XC	GW	GW	XC	GW	GW	GW	GW	XC	GW	GW	GW	GW	GW	XC
			1 ◇			1 ◇	1 ◇		1 ◇			1 ◇	1 ◇	1 ◇		1 ◇		1 ◇		1 ◇
																		A		
			☕			☕	☕		☕			☕	☕	☕		☕		trolley		☕
Penzance	d		22p00		05 30													06 04		
St Ives	d																			
St Erth 2	d		22p10															06 12		
Hayle	d		22p14															06 15		
Camborne	d		22p24		05 47													06 25		
Redruth	d		22p32		05 53													06 31		
Falmouth Docks	d																			
Truro	d		22p44		06a04													06 43		
St Austell	d		23p02															07 00		
Newquay	d																			
Par 3	d		23p11															07 07	07 25	
Lostwithiel	d		23p19															07 14	07 32	
Bodmin Parkway	d		23p26															07 20	07 38	
Looe	d																	*06 45*		
Liskeard 3	d		23p41															07 34	07 51	
Menheniot	d																	07 39		
St Germans	d																	07 46		
Saltash	d																	07 53		
St Budeaux Ferry Road	d																	07 57		
Keyham	d																	07 59		
Dockyard	d																	08 01		
Devonport	d																	08 03		
Plymouth	a		00 07															08 09	08 16	
	d		00 20						06 25			06 55		07 25		07 54		08 10		08 25
Ivybridge	d																	08 25		
Totnes	d		00 48						06 50					07 50		08 21		08 39		08 50
Paignton	d	23p32						06 23		06 54	07 08		07 17		08 13					
Torquay	d	23p37						06 28		06 59	07 13		07 23		08 18					
Torre	d	23p40						06 31		07 02	07 16		07 26		08 21					
Newton Abbot	a	23p48	01 00					06 39	07 01	07 10	07 25	07 30	07 36	08 01	08 29	08 33	←	08 52		09 01
	d	23p50	01 01					06 41	07 03	07 11		07 31	07 37	08 03	08 39 →	08 34	08 39	08 52		09 03
Teignmouth	d	23p57						06 48		07 18			07 44				08 46			
Dawlish	d	00 02						06 53		07 23			07 50				08 51			
Dawlish Warren	d	00 06						06 57		07 27							08 55			
Starcross	d	00 09						07 00		07 30							08 58			
Exeter St Thomas	d	00 18						07 09		07 39							09 07			
Exeter St Davids 6	a	00 22	01 23					07 11	07 21	07 43		07 51	08 03	08 21		08 54	09 11	09 16		09 21
Exeter Central	a							07 17		07 49		*08 03*	*08 18*	*08 49*			09 21			*09 48*
Exmouth	a							07 43		08 15			*08 44*	*09 15*			09 45			*10 14*
Barnstaple	d													*07 03*						
Exmouth	d		*23 45*						*06 15*			*07 18*		*07 50*		*08 20*				*08 50*
Exeter Central	d		*00 09*						*06 39*			*07 42*		*08 14*		*08 44*				*09 14*
Exeter St Davids 6	d		01 27	05 20		06 10			07 23			07 53	08 05	08 23		08 56				09 23
Tiverton Parkway	d			05 37		06 24			07 37				08 19	08 37		09 11				09 37
Taunton	d		02 47	05 54		06 38	07 00		07 51			08 18	08 34	08 51		09 25				09 51
Bridgwater	a			06 06			07 09													
Weston-super-Mare	a			06 26		06 58	07 26						08 54							
Bristol Temple Meads 10	a			07 05		07 27	07 56		08 25				09 19	09 25						10 25
Bath Spa 7	a						08 11						09 41							
Filton Abbey Wood	a			07 18																
Bristol Parkway 7	a			07 22		07 38			08 38					09 38						10 38
Swindon	a												10 09							
Newport (South Wales)	a																			
Cardiff Central 7	a																			
Birmingham New Street 12	a					08 57			09 57					10 58						11 57
Castle Cary	d															09 46				
Westbury	d																			
Pewsey	d															10 18				
Hungerford	a																			
Newbury	a																			
Thatcham	a																			
Theale	a																			
Reading 7	a		04s27				09 21					09 35	10 43			10 51				
Oxford	a		*06 21*				*10 06*					*10 18*	*11 19*			*11 34*				
Gatwick Airport 10	a		*05 54*				*10 50*					*11b39*				*12b39*				
Heathrow Terminal 1 Bus	a		*05 40*				*10 25*					*10 55*				*11 55*				
Slough 3	a																			
London Waterloo 15 ⊖	a																			
London Paddington 15 ⊖	a		05 25				09 55					10 06	11 14			11 22				

For general notes see front of timetable
For details of catering facilities see
Directory of Train Operators

A To Barnstaple (Table 136)
b Change at Reading and Redhill

Table 135

2 February to 22 March

Sleeper services are published in Table 406

Cornwall and Devon → Birmingham and London

Network Diagram - see first page of Table 135

		GW	XC	XC	SW	GW	GW	XC	GW	GW	GW	GW	GW	XC	GW	GW	GW	SW	XC
			1◇	1◇	1◇	1◇		1◇		1◇	1◇		A	1◇		1		1◇	1◇
			☕	☕	☕	☕		☕		☕	☕			☕		☕		☕	☕
Penzance	d		07 30			08 03		08 30		08 48				09 30		10 00			
St Ives	d					*07 46*								*09 22*					
St Erth 2	d		07 38			08 14		08 38		08 59				09 38		10 11			
Hayle	d					08 17													
Camborne	d		07 48			08 27		08 48		09 10				09 48		10 22			
Redruth	d		07 54			08 34		08 54		09 17				09 54		10 29			
Falmouth Docks	d		*06 53*			*07 56*				*08 56*						*10 09*			
Truro	d		08 06			08 47		09 06		09 29				10 06		10 41			
St Austell	d		08 22			09 04		09 22		09 47				10 22		10 59			
Newquay	d															*10 13*			
Par 3	d		08 29			09 11		09 29		09 54				10 29		11 06			
Lostwithiel	d																		
Bodmin Parkway	d		08 40			09 23		09 40		10 05				10 40		11 17			
Looe	d		*07 46*													*10 25*			
Liskeard 3	d		08 52			09 36		09 52		10 18				10 52		11 30			
Menheniot	d																		
St Germans	d																		
Saltash	d																		
St Budeaux Ferry Road	d																		
Keyham	d												11x00						
Dockyard	d												11x02						
Devonport	d												11 04						
Plymouth	a		09 14			10 01		10 16		10 43			11 08	11 16		11 57			
	d		09 25			10 05		10 25		10 46			11 10	11 25		12 00			12 25
Ivybridge	d												11 25						
Totnes	d		09 50			10 32		10 50					11 39	11 50		12 27			12 50
Paignton	d	09 11		10 05	10 12		10 30		10 46			11 17			12 12			12 25	
Torquay	d	09 16		10 11	10 18		10 35		10 51			11 22			12 17			12 31	
Torre	d	09 19			10 21		10 38		10 54			11 25			12 20				
Newton Abbot	a	09 27	10 01	10 21	10 29	10 43	10 46	11 01	11 02	11 21		11 33	11 53	12 01	12 28	12 38		12 41	13 01
	d	09 38	10 03	10 22	10 31	10 45	10 48	11 03	11 07	11 22		11 35		12 03	12 30	12 40		12 44	13 03
Teignmouth	d	09 45		10 29	10 38		10 55		11 14			11 42			12 37			12 51	
Dawlish	d	09 50		10 34	10 43		11 00		11 19			11 47			12 42		←	12 56	
Dawlish Warren	d	09 54			10 47		11 03					11 51			12b52		12 52	13c01	
Starcross	d	09 57							11 24			11 54			→		12 55		
Exeter St Thomas	d	10 06							11 33			12 03					13 04		
Exeter St Davids 6	a	10 10	10 21	10 46	10 58	11 05	11 14	11 21	11 36	11 42		12 07		12 21		13 00	13 09	13 10	13 21
Exeter Central	a	10 21	*10 48*				11 21		*11 48*	*12 13*		12 21		*12 48*		*13 21*	13 21	*13e21*	
Exmouth	a	10 45	*11 14*				11 45		*12 14*			12 45		*13 15*			13 42	*13 42*	
Barnstaple	d		*08 41*								*10 40*							→	
Exmouth	d		*09 20*	*09 50*		*10 20*		*10 50*			*11 20*					*12 20*			*12 50*
Exeter Central	d		*09 44*	*10 29*		*10 43*		*11 14*			*11 43*					*12 43*			*13 14*
Exeter St Davids 6	d		10 23	10 48		11 06		11 23		11 44	11 54			12 23		13 02			13 23
Tiverton Parkway	d		10 37	11 01		11 21		11 37			12 09			12 37		13 16			13 37
Taunton	d		10 51	11 16		11 35		11 51			12 23			12 51		13 31			13 51
Bridgwater	a																		
Weston-super-Mare	a																		
Bristol Temple Meads 10	a		11 25	11 55				12 25						13 25					14 25
Bath Spa 7	a																		
Filton Abbey Wood	a																		
Bristol Parkway 7	a		11 38	12 08				12 38						13 38					14 38
Swindon	a																		
Newport (South Wales)	a																		
Cardiff Central 7	a																		
Birmingham New Street 12	a		12 57	13 26				13 57						14 57					15 57
Castle Cary	d										12 44								
Westbury	d										13f10								
Pewsey	d										13 27								
Hungerford	a										13 45								
Newbury	a										13 55								
Thatcham	a										14 01								
Theale	a										14 10								
Reading 7	a					12 53				13 22	14 22					14 51			
Oxford	a					*13 34*				*14 06*	*15 06*					*15 34*			
Gatwick Airport 10	a					*14g39*				*14 50*	*15 50*					*16g39*			
Heathrow Terminal 1 Bus	a					*13 55*				*14 25*	*15 25*					*15 55*			
Slough 3	a																		
London Waterloo 15 ⊖	a				14 49														
London Paddington 15 ⊖	a					13 23				13 51	14 52					15 23			

For general notes see front of timetable
For details of catering facilities see Directory of Train Operators

A From Gunnislake (Table 139)
b Arr. 1245
c Arr. 1308
e Change at Exeter St Davids
f Arr. 1302
g Change at Reading and Redhill

Saturdays

2 February to 22 March

Sleeper services are published in Table 406

Cornwall and Devon → Birmingham and London

Network Diagram - see first page of Table 135

		GW	GW	SW		GW	GW	XC		GW	XC	GW		GW	GW	XC		GW	SW	GW		XC	SW	GW	XC
				1 ◇		1 ◇		1 ◇			1 ◇	1 ◇		1 ◇		1 ◇			1 ◇			1 ◇	1		1 ◇
																				A					
		🛒		☕		☕		☕		🛒	☕	☕		☕		☕			☕			☕			☕
Penzance	d	10 36				10 58				11 45															
St Ives	d	*10 25*				*10 25*				*11 25*															
St Erth 2	d	10 44				11 09				11 53															
Hayle	d	10 47								11 57															
Camborne	d	10 57				11 20				12 06															
Redruth	d	11 03				11 27				12 12															
Falmouth Docks	d									*11 51*															
Truro	d	11 15				11 39				12 24															
St Austell	d	11 32				11 57				12 41															
Newquay	d																								
Par 3	d	11 39								12 49															
Lostwithiel	d	11 46																							
Bodmin Parkway	d	11 52				12 13				13 00															
Looe	d									*12 40*															
Liskeard 3	d	12 05				12 26				13 13															
Menheniot	d	12 10																							
St Germans	d	12 17																							
Saltash	d	12 24																							
St Budeaux Ferry Road	d																								
Keyham	d																			15x01					
Dockyard	d																			15x03					
Devonport	d																			15 05					
Plymouth	a	12 37				12 51				13 38										15 09					
	d					12 55		13 25				14 00				14 25			14 50	15 11		15 25			16 25
Ivybridge	d																		15 05	15 26					
Totnes	d					13 22		13 50								14 50			15 19	15 39		15 50			16 50
Paignton	d		13 15								14 05				14 25			14 53					15 52	16 19	
Torquay	d		13 20								14 11				14 30			14 58					15 58	16 24	
Torre	d		13 23												14 33			15 01						16 27	
Newton Abbot	a		13 31			13 34	←	14 01			14 21	14 35			14 41	15 01		15 09	15 30	15 53		16 01	16 08	16 35	17 01
	d		13 43			13 35	13 43	14 03			14 22	14 37			14 42	15 03		15 11	15 32			16 03	16 10	16 43	17 03
Teignmouth	d		→				13 50				14 29				14 49			15 18	15 39				16 17	16 50	
Dawlish	d			←			13 55				14 34				14 54			15 23	15 44				16 22	16 55	
Dawlish Warren	d			13 15			13 59								14 58			15 27	15 48					16 59	
Starcross	d						14 02								15 02			15 30						17 02	
Exeter St Thomas	d						14 11								15 11			15 39						17 11	
Exeter St Davids 6	a			13 24		13 55	14 15	14 21			14 46	14 57			15 14	15 21		15 42	15 59			16 21	16 35	17 15	17 21
Exeter Central	a			13 38		*14 13*	14 21	*14 48*							15 21	*15 33*			16 13				16 43	17 21	*17 43*
Exmouth	a						14 45	*15 14*							15 45	*16 14*			*16 45*				*17 14*	17 45	*18 19*
Barnstaple	d																					*14 35*			*15 42*
Exmouth	d			*12 50*		*13 20*						*14 20*										*15 50*			*16 50*
Exeter Central	d			13 39		*13 46*					*14 16*	*14 43*										*16 14*			*17 14*
Exeter St Davids 6	d			13 35		13 57		14 23			14 48	14 59		15 09		15 23						16 23			17 23
Tiverton Parkway	d							14 37			15 01	15 13				15 37						16 37			17 37
Taunton	d					14 22		14 51			15 16	15 28		15 34		15 51						16 51			17 51
Bridgwater	a																								
Weston-super-Mare	a																								
Bristol Temple Meads 10	a							15 25			15 55					16 25						17 25			18 25
Bath Spa 7	a																								
Filton Abbey Wood	a																								
Bristol Parkway 7	a							15 38			16 08					16 38						17 38			18 38
Swindon	a																								
Newport (South Wales)	a																								
Cardiff Central 7	a																								
Birmingham New Street 12	a							16 57			17 26					17 57						18 57			19 57
Castle Cary	d					14 43								16 00											
Westbury	d					15 02								16 19											
Pewsey	d													16 38											
Hungerford	a													16 50											
Newbury	a													17 00											
Thatcham	a													17 06											
Theale	a													17 15											
Reading 7	a					15 51						16 50		17 26											
Oxford	a					*16 34*						*17 34*		*18 06*											
Gatwick Airport 10	a					*17b39*						*18b39*		*18 50*											
Heathrow Terminal 1 Bus	🚌 a					*16 55*						*17 55*		*18 25*											
Slough 3	a													17 40											
London Waterloo 15	⊖ a			16 49															19 49						
London Paddington 15	⊖ a					16 22						17 23		18 03											

For general notes see front of timetable
For details of catering facilities see
Directory of Train Operators

A From Gunnislake (Table 139)
b Change at Reading and Redhill

Table 135

Saturdays

2 February to 22 March

Sleeper services are published in Table 406

Cornwall and Devon → Birmingham and London

Network Diagram - see first page of Table 135

		GW		GW 1◇ ☕	XC 1◇ ☕	GW		SW 1◇	GW 1◇ ☕	SW 1◇		XC 1◇ ☕	GW	SW 1		GW	GW	GW 1	GW 1◇	GW	GW ◇ 🚲	GW	XC 1◇		
Penzance	d								15 54												19 08		20 45		
St Ives	d								*15 25*												*18 55*		*20 00*		
St Erth 2	d								16 05												19 16		20 53		
Hayle	d																				19 20		20 57		
Camborne	d								16 16												19 29		21 06		
Redruth	d								16 23												19 35		21 13		
Falmouth Docks	d								*15 01*												*18 28*		*20 26*		
Truro	d								16 35												19 47		21 24		
St Austell	d								16 53												20 04		21 40		
Newquay	d								*15 10*																
Par 3	d								17 00												20 12		21 48		
Lostwithiel	d								17 07												20 19				
Bodmin Parkway	d								17 14												20 25		21 59		
Looe	d								*15 49*												*19 43*				
Liskeard 3	d								17 27												20 38		22 11		
Menheniot	d																				20 43				
St Germans	d																				20 50				
Saltash	d																				20 59				
St Budeaux Ferry Road	d																				21 03				
Keyham	d																				21x05				
Dockyard	d																				21x07				
Devonport	d																				21 09				
Plymouth	a								17 52												21 12		22 40		
	d	16 34		16 54	17 25			17 42	17 54			18 25									21 18				
Ivybridge	d	16 49						17 57													21 33				
Totnes	d	17 03			17 50			18 11	18 21			18 50									21 47				
Paignton	d					17 52							18 52	19 14		19 22	20 06	20 35		21 07		21 50			
Torquay	d					17 57							18 57	19 20		19 27	20 11	20 41		21 12		21 55			
Torre	d					18 00							19 00			19 30	20 14			21 15		21 58			
Newton Abbot	a	17 17		17 29	18 01	18 08		18 22	18 33			19 01	19 08	19 30		19 38	20 22	20 51		21 23	21 59	22 06			
	d			17 31	18 03	18 10		18 24	18 34			19 03	19 10	19 32		19 40	20 24	20 53		21 25	21 59	22 08			
Teignmouth	d					18 17		18 31		←			19 17	19 39		19 47	20 31			21 32	22 06	22 15			
Dawlish	d					18 22		18 36		18 36			19 22	19 44		19 52	20 36			21 37	22 11	22 20			
Dawlish Warren	d					18 26		→		18b48			19 26	19 49		19 56	20 40			21 41	22 15	22 24			
Starcross	d					18 29							19 29			19 59	20 43			21 44	22 19	22 27			
Exeter St Thomas	d					18 38							19 38			20 08	20 52			21 53	22 27	22 36			
Exeter St Davids 6	a			17 51	18 21	18 42			18 54	19 00		19 21	19 42	20 00		20 12	20 56	21 13		21 57	22 30	22 40			
Exeter Central	a			*18 13*		18 52				19 13			19 52	20 18		20 25		*21 48*				*23 00*			
Exmouth	a					19 18				*20 18*			20 18			*21 18*		*22 14*				*23 39*			
Barnstaple	d				*16 48*							*18 00*													
Exmouth	d				*17 20*				*17 50*	*18 20*		*18 20*													
Exeter Central	d			*17 33*	*17 53*				*18 19*	19 14															
Exeter St Davids 6	d			17 53	18 23				18 56	19 10		19 23													
Tiverton Parkway	d				18 37				19 10			19 37													
Taunton	d			18 17	18 51				19 25			19 51							21 30						
Bridgwater	a																		21 40						
Weston-super-Mare	a																		21 57						
Bristol Temple Meads 10	a				19 25							20 25							22 28						
Bath Spa 7	a																		22 44						
Filton Abbey Wood	a																								
Bristol Parkway 7	a				19 38							20 38													
Swindon	a																								
Newport (South Wales)	a																								
Cardiff Central 7	a																								
Birmingham New Street 12	a				20 57							21 57													
Castle Cary	d			18 38					19 46																
Westbury	d			18 57					20 05																
Pewsey	d								20 28																
Hungerford	a																								
Newbury	a			19 31																					
Thatcham	a																								
Theale	a																								
Reading 7	a			19 50					21 06										23 55						
Oxford	a			*20 34*					*21 34*										*00c55*						
Gatwick Airport 10	a			*21 47*					*23 03*																
Heathrow Terminal 1 Bus 🚌	a			*21 05*					*22 45*																
Slough 3	a																								
London Waterloo 15 ⊖	a									22 57															
London Paddington 15 ⊖	a			20 21					21 24										00 37						

For general notes see front of timetable
For details of catering facilities see
Directory of Train Operators

b Arr. 1840

c Change at Reading and Didcot Parkway. By bus from Didcot Parkway

Saturdays

from 29 March

Sleeper services are published in Table 406

Cornwall and Devon → Birmingham and London

Network Diagram - see first page of Table 135

		GW	GW	GW	GW	XC	GW	XC	GW	GW	GW	GW	XC	GW	GW	GW	GW	GW	XC	GW
			1 ◇			1 ◇	1 ◇	1 ◇			1 ◇	1 ◇	1 ◇		1 ◇		1 ◇		1 ◇	
																	A			
			☕			☕	☕	☕			☕	☕	☕		☕		🛒		☕	
Penzance	d		22p00		05 30												06 04			
St Ives	d																			
St Erth 2	d		22p10														06 12			
Hayle	d		22p14														06 15			
Camborne	d		22p24		05 47												06 25			
Redruth	d		22p32		05 53												06 31			
Falmouth Docks	d																			
Truro	d		22p44		06a04												06 43			
St Austell	d		23p02														07 00			
Newquay	d																			
Par 3	d		23p11														07 07	07 25		
Lostwithiel	d		23p19														07 14	07 32		
Bodmin Parkway	d		23p26														07 20	07 38		
Looe	d																*06 45*			
Liskeard 3	d		23p41														07 34	07 51		
Menheniot	d																07 39			
St Germans	d																07 46			
Saltash	d																07 53			
St Budeaux Ferry Road	d																07 57			
Keyham	d																07 59			
Dockyard	d																08 01			
Devonport	d																08 03			
Plymouth	a		00 07														08 09	08 16		
	d		00 20					06 25			06 55		07 25		07 54		08 10		08 25	
Ivybridge	d																08 25			
Totnes	d		00 48					06 50					07 50		08 21		08 39		08 50	
Paignton	d	23p32							06 54	07 08		07 17		08 13						09 11
Torquay	d	23p37							06 59	07 13		07 23		08 18						09 16
Torre	d	23p40							07 02	07 16		07 26		08 21						09 19
Newton Abbot	a	23p48	01 00					07 01	07 10	07 25	07 30	07 36	08 01	08 29	08 33	←	08 52		09 01	09 27
	d	23p50	01 01					07 03	07 11		07 31	07 37	08 03	08 39	08 34	08 39	08 52		09 03	09 38
Teignmouth	d	23p57							07 18			07 44		→		08 46				09 45
Dawlish	d	00 02							07 23			07 50				08 51				09 50
Dawlish Warren	d	00 06							07 27							08 55				09 54
Starcross	d	00 09							07 30							08 58				09 57
Exeter St Thomas	d	00 18							07 39							09 07				10 06
Exeter St Davids 6	a	00 22	01 23					07 21	07 43		07 51	08 03	08 21		08 54	09 11	09 16		09 21	10 10
Exeter Central	a								07 49		*08 03*	*08 18*	*08 49*			09 21			*09 48*	10 21
Exmouth	a								08 15			*08 44*	*09 15*			09 45			*10 14*	10 45
Barnstaple	d												*07 03*							
Exmouth	d		*23 45*					*06 15*			*07 18*		*07 50*		*08 20*				*08 50*	
Exeter Central	d		*00 09*					*06 39*			*07 42*		*08 14*		*08 44*				*09 14*	
Exeter St Davids 6	d		01 27	05 39		06 10		07 23			07 53	08 05	08 23		08 56				09 23	
Tiverton Parkway	d			05 56		06 24		07 37				08 19	08 37		09 11				09 37	
Taunton	d		02 47	06 13		06 38	07 00	07 51			08 18	08 34	08 51		09 25				09 51	
Bridgwater	a			06 25			07 09													
Weston-super-Mare	a			06 45		06 58	07 26					08 54								
Bristol Temple Meads 10	a			07 24		07 27	07 57	08 25				09 20	09 25						10 25	
Bath Spa 7	a						08 11					09 41								
Filton Abbey Wood	a			07 56																
Bristol Parkway 7	a			08 03		07 38		08 38					09 38						10 38	
Swindon	a						08 39					10 09								
Newport (South Wales)	a																			
Cardiff Central 7	a																			
Birmingham New Street 12	a					08 57		09 57					10 58						11 57	
Castle Cary	d														09 46					
Westbury	d																			
Pewsey	d														10 18					
Hungerford	a																			
Newbury	a																			
Thatcham	a																			
Theale	a																			
Reading 7	a		04s27				09 14				09 35	10 45			10 51					
Oxford	a		*06 21*				*09 47*				*10 18*	*11 19*			*11 34*					
Gatwick Airport 10	a		*05 54*				*10 50*				*11b39*				*12b39*					
Heathrow Terminal 1 Bus	🚌 a		*05 40*				*10 25*				*10 55*				*11 55*					
Slough 3	a																			
London Waterloo 15	⊖ a																			
London Paddington 15	⊖ a		05 25				09 44				10 06	11 15			11 22					

For general notes see front of timetable
For details of catering facilities see Directory of Train Operators

A To Barnstaple (Table 136)
b Change at Reading and Redhill

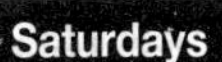

from 29 March

Sleeper services are published in Table 406

Cornwall and Devon → Birmingham and London

Network Diagram - see first page of Table 135

		XC	XC	SW	GW	GW	XC	GW	GW	GW	GW	GW	XC	GW	GW	GW	SW	XC	GW
		1 ◇	1 ◇	1 ◇	1 ◇		1 ◇		1 ◇	1 ◇			1 ◇		1		1 ◇	1 ◇	
												A							
Penzance	d	07 30			08 03		08 30		08 48				09 30		10 00				10 36
St Ives	d				*07 46*								*09 22*						*10 25*
St Erth 2	d	07 38			08 14		08 38		08 59				09 38		10 11				10 44
Hayle	d				08 17														10 47
Camborne	d	07 48			08 27		08 48		09 10				09 48		10 22				10 57
Redruth	d	07 54			08 34		08 54		09 17				09 54		10 29				11 03
Falmouth Docks	d	*06 53*			*07 56*				*08 56*						*10 09*				
Truro	d	08 06			08 47		09 06		09 29				10 06		10 41				11 15
St Austell	d	08 22			09 04		09 22		09 47				10 22		10 59				11 32
Newquay	d														*10 13*				
Par 3	d	08 29			09 11		09 29		09 54				10 29		11 06				11 39
Lostwithiel	d																		11 46
Bodmin Parkway	d	08 40			09 23		09 40		10 05				10 40		11 17				11 52
Looe	d	*07 46*													*10 25*				
Liskeard 3	d	08 52			09 36		09 52		10 18				10 52		11 30				12 05
Menheniot	d																		12 10
St Germans	d																		12 17
Saltash	d																		12 24
St Budeaux Ferry Road	d																		
Keyham	d											11x00							
Dockyard	d											11x02							
Devonport	d											11 04							
Plymouth	a	09 14			10 01		10 19		10 43			11 08	11 16		11 57				12 37
	d	09 25			10 05		10 25		10 46			11 10	11 25		12 00			12 25	
Ivybridge	d											11 25							
Totnes	d	09 50			10 32		10 50					11 39	11 50		12 27			12 50	
Paignton	d		10 05	10 12		10 30		10 46			11 17			12 12			12 34		
Torquay	d		10 11	10 18		10 35		10 51			11 22			12 17			12 40		
Torre	d			10 21		10 38		10 54			11 25			12 20					
Newton Abbot	a	10 01	10 21	10 29	10 43	10 46	11 01	11 02	11 21		11 33	11 53	12 01	12 28	12 38		12 50	13 01	
	d	10 03	10 22	10 31	10 45	10 48	11 03	11 07	11 22		11 35		12 03	12 30	12 40		12 53	13 03	
Teignmouth	d		10 29	10 38		10 55		11 14			11 42			12 37			13 00		
Dawlish	d		10 34	10 43		11 00		11 19			11 47			12 42		←	13 05		
Dawlish Warren	d			10 47		11 03					11 51			12b53 →		12 53	13c15 →		
Starcross	d							11 24			11 54					12 56			
Exeter St Thomas	d							11 33			12 03					13 05			
Exeter St Davids 6	a	10 21	10 46	10 58	11 05	11 14	11 21	11 36	11 42		12 07		12 21		13 00	13 09		13 21	
Exeter Central	a	*10 48*				11 21		*11 48*	*12 13*		12 21		*12 48*		*13 21*	13 21		*13 38*	
Exmouth	a	*11 14*				11 45		*12 14*	*12 45*		12 45		*13 14*			13 45			
Barnstaple	d	*08 41*								*10 40*									
Exmouth	d	*09 20*	*09 50*		*10 20*		*10 50*			*11 20*					*12 20*			*12 50*	
Exeter Central	d	*09 44*	*10 29*		*10 43*		*11 14*			*11 43*			*11 53*		*12 43*			*13 14*	
Exeter St Davids 6	d	10 23	10 48		11 06		11 23		11 44	11 54			12 23		13 02			13 23	
Tiverton Parkway	d	10 37	11 01		11 21		11 37			12 09			12 37		13 16			13 37	
Taunton	d	10 51	11 16		11 35		11 51			12 23			12 51		13 31			13 51	
Bridgwater	a																		
Weston-super-Mare	a																		
Bristol Temple Meads 10	a	11 25	11 55				12 25						13 25					14 25	
Bath Spa 7	a																		
Filton Abbey Wood	a																		
Bristol Parkway 7	a	11 38	12 08				12 38						13 38					14 38	
Swindon	a																		
Newport (South Wales)	a																		
Cardiff Central 7	a																		
Birmingham New Street 12	a	12 57	13 26				13 57						14 57					15 57	
Castle Cary	d									12 44									
Westbury	d									13 03									
Pewsey	d									13 22									
Hungerford	a									13 39									
Newbury	a									13 49									
Thatcham	a									13 55									
Theale	a									14 04									
Reading 7	a				12 53				13 22	14 19					14 51				
Oxford	a				*13 34*				*14 06*	*15 06*					*15 34*				
Gatwick Airport 10	a				*14e39*				*14 50*	*15 50*					*16e39*				
Heathrow Terminal 1 Bus	a				*13 55*				*14 25*	*15 25*					*15 55*				
Slough 3	a																		
London Waterloo 15 ⊖	a			14 49															
London Paddington 15 ⊖	a				13 23				13 51	14 46					15 23				

For general notes see front of timetable
For details of catering facilities see Directory of Train Operators

A From Gunnislake (Table 139)
b Arr. 1245
c Arr. 1308
e Change at Reading and Redhill

Saturdays

from 29 March

Sleeper services are published in Table 406

Cornwall and Devon → Birmingham and London

Network Diagram - see first page of Table 135

		GW	SW	GW		GW	XC	GW		XC	GW	GW		GW	XC	GW		SW	GW	GW		XC	SW	GW	XC
			1 ◇	1 ◇			1 ◇			1 ◇	1 ◇	1 ◇			1 ◇			1 ◇	1 ◇	A		1 ◇	1		1 ◇
Penzance	d			10 58				11 45																	
St Ives	d							*11 25*																	
St Erth 2	d			11 09				11 53																	
Hayle	d							11 57																	
Camborne	d			11 20				12 06																	
Redruth	d			11 27				12 12																	
Falmouth Docks	d							*11 51*																	
Truro	d			11 39				12 24																	
St Austell	d			11 57				12 41																	
Newquay	d																								
Par 3	d							12 49																	
Lostwithiel	d																								
Bodmin Parkway	d			12 13				13 00																	
Looe	d							*12 40*																	
Liskeard 3	d			12 26				13 13																	
Menheniot	d																								
St Germans	d																								
Saltash	d																								
St Budeaux Ferry Road	d																								
Keyham	d																			15x01					
Dockyard	d																			15x03					
Devonport	d																			15 05					
Plymouth	a			12 51				13 38												15 09					
	d			12 55			13 25				14 00				14 25			14 50	15 04	15 11		15 25			16 25
Ivybridge	d																	15 05		15 26					
Totnes	d			13 22			13 50								14 50			15 19	15 31	15 39		15 50			16 50
Paignton	d	13 15								14 05				14 25		14 53							15 52	16 19	
Torquay	d	13 20								14 11				14 30		14 58							15 58	16 24	
Torre	d	13 23												14 33		15 01								16 27	
Newton Abbot	a	13 31		13 34		←	14 01			14 21	14 35			14 41	15 01	15 09		15 30	15 42	15 53		16 01	16 08	16 35	17 01
	d	13 43		13 35		13 43	14 03			14 22	14 37			14 42	15 03	15 11		15 32	15 44			16 03	16 10	16 43	17 03
Teignmouth	d	→				13 50				14 29				14 49		15 18		15 39					16 17	16 50	
Dawlish	d		←			13 55				14 34				14 54		15 23		15 44					16 22	16 55	
Dawlish Warren	d		13 15			13 59								14 58		15 27		15 48						16 59	
Starcross	d					14 02								15 02		15 30								17 02	
Exeter St Thomas	d					14 11								15 11		15 39								17 11	
Exeter St Davids 6	a		13 24	13 55		14 15	14 21			14 46	14 57			15 14	15 21	15 42		15 59	16 04			16 21	16 35	17 15	17 21
Exeter Central	a		13 38	*14 13*		14 21	*14 48*				*15 21*			15 21	*15 33*				*16 13*				16 43	17 21	*17 43*
Exmouth	a					14 45	*15 14*				*15 45*			15 45	*16 14*				*16 45*				*17 14*	17 45	*18 19*
Barnstaple	d																		*14 35*						*15 42*
Exmouth	d			*13 20*							*14 20*								*15 20*			*15 50*			*16 50*
Exeter Central	d			*13 46*						*14 16*	*14 43*								*15 46*			*16 14*			*17 14*
Exeter St Davids 6	d			13 57			14 23			14 48	14 59	15 09			15 23				16 06			16 23			17 23
Tiverton Parkway	d						14 37			15 01	15 13				15 37				16 20			16 37			17 37
Taunton	d			14 22			14 51			15 16	15 28	15 34			15 51				16 35			16 51			17 51
Bridgwater	a																								
Weston-super-Mare	a																								
Bristol Temple Meads 10	a			14 55			15 25			15 55	16 01	16 07			16 25				17 08			17 25			18 25
Bath Spa 7	a																								
Filton Abbey Wood	a																								
Bristol Parkway 7	a						15 38			16 08					16 38							17 38			18 38
Swindon	a																								
Newport (South Wales)	a																								
Cardiff Central 7	a																								
Birmingham New Street 12	a						16 57			17 26					17 57							18 57			19 57
Castle Cary	d																								
Westbury	d																								
Pewsey	d											16 58													
Hungerford	a											17 14													
Newbury	a											17 24													
Thatcham	a											17 31													
Theale	a											17 40													
Reading 7	a			15 54							17 00	17 50							18 07						
Oxford	a			*16 34*							*17 34*	*18 34*							*18 47*						
Gatwick Airport 10	a			*17b39*							*18 50*	*19b39*							*19 50*						
Heathrow Terminal 1 Bus	a			*16 55*							*17 55*	*18 55*							*19 25*						
Slough 3	a											18 05													
London Waterloo 15	⊖ a		16 49															19 49							
London Paddington 15	⊖ a			16 25							17 29	18 23							18 38						

For general notes see front of timetable
For details of catering facilities see
Directory of Train Operators

A From Gunnislake (Table 139)
b Change at Reading and Redhill

Table 135

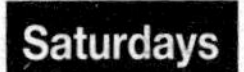

from 29 March

Sleeper services are published in Table 406

Cornwall and Devon → Birmingham and London

Network Diagram - see first page of Table 135

		GW		GW **1** ◇ ☕	XC **1** ◇ ☕	GW		SW **1** ◇	GW **1** ◇ ☕	SW **1** ◇		XC **1** ◇ ☕	GW	SW **1**		GW	GW	GW **1**	GW **1** ◇	GW	GW ◇	GW	XC **1** ◇		
Penzance	d								15 54												19 08		20 45		
St Ives	d																				*18 55*		*20 00*		
St Erth **2**	d								16 05												19 16		20 53		
Hayle	d																				19 20		20 57		
Camborne	d								16 16												19 29		21 06		
Redruth	d								16 23												19 35		21 13		
Falmouth Docks	d																				*18 28*		*20 26*		
Truro	d								16 35												19 47		21 24		
St Austell	d								16 53												20 04		21 40		
Newquay	d																								
Par **3**	d								17 00												20 12		21 48		
Lostwithiel	d								17 07												20 19				
Bodmin Parkway	d								17 14												20 25		21 59		
Looe	d																				*19 43*				
Liskeard **3**	d								17 27												20 38		22 11		
Menheniot	d																				20 43				
St Germans	d																				20 50				
Saltash	d																				20 59				
St Budeaux Ferry Road	d																				21 03				
Keyham	d																				21x05				
Dockyard	d																				21x07				
Devonport	d																				21 09				
Plymouth	a								17 52												21 12		22 40		
	d	16 34		16 54	17 25			17 42	17 54			18 25									21 18				
Ivybridge	d	16 49						17 57													21 33				
Totnes	d	17 03			17 50			18 11	18 21			18 50									21 47				
Paignton	d					17 52							18 52	19 14		19 22	20 06	20 35		21 07		21 50			
Torquay	d					17 57							18 57	19 20		19 27	20 11	20 41		21 12		21 55			
Torre	d					18 00							19 00			19 30	20 14			21 15		21 58			
Newton Abbot	a	17 17		17 29	18 01	18 08		18 22	18 33			19 01	19 08	19 30		19 38	20 22	20 51		21 23	21 59	22 06			
	d			17 31	18 03	18 10		18 24	18 34			19 03	19 10	19 32		19 40	20 24	20 53		21 25	21 59	22 08			
Teignmouth	d					18 17		18 31					19 17	19 39		19 47	20 31			21 32	22 06	22 15			
Dawlish	d					18 22		18 36		←			19 22	19 44		19 52	20 36			21 37	22 11	22 20			
Dawlish Warren	d					18 26		18b48 →		18 48			19 26	19 49		19 56	20 40			21 41	22 15	22 24			
Starcross	d					18 29							19 29			19 59	20 43			21 44	22 19	22 27			
Exeter St Thomas	d					18 38							19 38			20 08	20 52			21 53	22 27	22 36			
Exeter St Davids 6	a			17 51	18 21	18 42			18 54	19 00		19 21	19 42	20 00		20 12	20 56	21 13		21 57	22 30	22 40			
Exeter Central	a			*18 13*		18 52				19 13			19 52	20 18		20 25		*21 48*				*23 00*			
Exmouth	a					19 18							20 18	*21 17*		*21 18*		*22 14*				*23 39*			
Barnstaple	d				*16 48*							*18 00*													
Exmouth	d				*17 20*							*18 20*													
Exeter Central	d			*17 33*	*17 53*																				
Exeter St Davids 6	d			17 53	18 23				18 56			19 23													
Tiverton Parkway	d				18 37				19 10			19 37													
Taunton	d			18 17	18 51				19 25			19 51							21 30						
Bridgwater	a																		21 40						
Weston-super-Mare	a																		21 57						
Bristol Temple Meads 10	a			18 50	19 25				19 58			20 25							22 28						
Bath Spa **7**	a																		22 44						
Filton Abbey Wood	a																								
Bristol Parkway **7**	a				19 38							20 38													
Swindon	a																		23 13						
Newport (South Wales)	a																								
Cardiff Central **7**	a																								
Birmingham New Street 12	a				20 57							21 57													
Castle Cary	d																								
Westbury	d																								
Pewsey	d								20 56																
Hungerford	a																								
Newbury	a			20 09																					
Thatcham	a																								
Theale	a																								
Reading 7	a			20 27					21 30										23 52						
Oxford	a			*21 22*															*00c55*						
Gatwick Airport **10**	a			*21 59*																					
Heathrow Terminal 1 Bus 🚌	a			*21 35*																					
Slough **3**	a																								
London Waterloo 15 ⊖	a							22 57		22 57															
London Paddington 15 ⊖	a			20 58					21 59										00 32						

For general notes see front of timetable
For details of catering facilities see Directory of Train Operators

b Arr. 1840

c Change at Reading and Didcot Parkway. By bus from Didcot Parkway

Table 135

Sundays

until 27 January

Sleeper services are published in Table 406

Cornwall and Devon → Birmingham and London

Network Diagram - see first page of Table 135

		GW	GW	GW	GW	XC	XC	GW	GW	XC	GW	GW	GW	GW	XC	GW	GW	SW	XC	GW	GW	XC	XC	GW	GW
										R					R				R			R	R		
		◇	1 ◇	1 ◇	bus	1 ◇	1 ◇	1 ◇		1	1 ◇		bus	1 ◇	1		1 ◇	1 ◇	1		1 ◇	1	1	1 ◇	
			trolley	trolley		trolley	trolley	trolley		trolley	trolley			trolley	trolley		trolley	trolley	trolley		trolley	trolley	trolley	trolley	
Penzance	d										08 30				09 30		09 50		10 30		10 50	11 30			
St Ives	d																								
St Erth 2	d										08 40				09 38		10 00		10 38		11 00	11 38			
Hayle	d										08 44														
Camborne	d										08 54				09 48		10 12		10 48		11 13	11 48			
Redruth	d										09 00				09 54		10 18		10 54		11 19	11 54			
Falmouth Docks	d																					*11 37*			
Truro	d										09 15				10 06		10 30		11 06		11 32	12 06			
St Austell	d										09 31				10 22		10 48		11 22		11 49	12 22			
Newquay	d																								
Par 3	d										09 39				10 29		10 55		11 29		11 56	12 29			
Lostwithiel	d																								
Bodmin Parkway	d										09 51				10 40		11 07		11 40		12 09	12 40			
Looe	d																								
Liskeard 3	d										10 04				10 52		11 20		11 52		12 22	12 52			
Menheniot	d																								
St Germans	d										10 15														
Saltash	d										10 23														
St Budeaux Ferry Road	d																								
Keyham	d																								
Dockyard	d																								
Devonport	d																								
Plymouth	a										10 32				11 19		11 45		12 16		12 47	13 21			
	d			08 45		09 25		09 50		10 25	10 35			10 50	11 25		11 45		12 25		12 50	13 25		13 44	
Ivybridge	d																								
Totnes	d			09 11		09 50		10 17		10 50	11 02			11 18	11 50		12 15		12 50		13 17	13 50		14 10	
Paignton	d								10 25			11 04				12 08		12 25		12 55			13 59		14 20
Torquay	d								10 30			11 09				12 13		12 31		13 00			14 05		14 25
Torre	d								10 33			11 12				12 16				13 03					14 28
Newton Abbot	a			09 24		10 01		10 29	10 41	11 01	11 14	11 20		11 29	12 01	12 24	12 28	12 41	13 01	13 11	13 28	14 01	14 15	14 23	14 36
	d			09 26		10 03		10 30	10 43	11 03	11 15			11 31	12 03		12 28	12 44	13 03	13 13	13 30	14 03	14 16	14 24	14 38
Teignmouth	d			09 33					10 50									12 51		13 20			14 24		14 45
Dawlish	d			09 38					10 55									12 58		13 25			14 29		14 50
Dawlish Warren	d								10 59											13 29					14 54
Starcross	d								11 02											13 32					14 57
Exeter St Thomas	d								11 11											13 41					15 06
Exeter St Davids 6	a			09 51		10 21		10 50	11 15	11 21	11 35			11 51	12 21		12 49	13 13	13 21	13 46	13 50	14 21	14 41	14 46	15 10
Exeter Central	a					*10 35*		*11 23*	11 28					*12 28*				13 21			*14 28*				15 28
Exmouth	a					*11 00*			11 53					*12 54*				*13 53*			*14 54*				15 53
Barnstaple	d																*11 10*						*13 19*		
Exmouth	d													*11 10*			*12 05*				*13 05*		*14 10*		
Exeter Central	d			*08 56*						*10 46*				*11 37*			*12 30*	13 22			*13 29*		*14 34*		
Exeter St Davids 6	d	08 15	08 30	09 51		10 23	10 48	10 52		11 23	11 36			11 53	12 23		12 50	13 18	13 23		13 52	14 23	14 43	14 47	
Tiverton Parkway	d	08 30	08 44			10 37	11 01	11 06		11 37	11 52			12 07	12 37				13 37		14 05	14 37			
Taunton	d	08 45	08 58	10 16		10 51	11 16	11 20		11 51	12 05			12 21	12 51		13 15		13 51		14 20	14 51	15 06	15 11	
Bridgwater	a	08 55																							
Weston-super-Mare	a	09 12																					15 28		
Bristol Temple Meads 10	a	09 45				11 25	11 55	11 56		12 25				12 55	13 25				14 25			15 25	15 50		
Bath Spa 7	a							12 12						13 12											
Filton Abbey Wood	a	09 56																							
Bristol Parkway 7	a					11 38	12 08			12 38					13 38				14 38			15 38	16 08		
Swindon	a				11d10			12 39					13d10	13 40											
Newport (South Wales)	a	10 21																							
Cardiff Central 7	a	10 37																							
Birmingham New Street 12	a					12 51	13 26			13 51					14 57				15 51			16 57	17 26		
Castle Cary	d		09 20								12 27													15 33	
Westbury	d		09 39	10 54							12 45													15 51	
Pewsey	d		09 57		11a55						13 05		13a55											16 10	
Hungerford	a																								
Newbury	a		10 16	11 28							13 24													16 30	
Thatcham	a																								
Theale	a																								
Reading 7	a		10 37	11 48				13 13			13 42			14 14			14 38				15 38			16 48	
Oxford	a		*11 35*	*12 35*				*13 49*			*14 35*			*15 04*			*15 35*				*16 35*			*17 36*	
Gatwick Airport 10	a		*12 30*	*13 30*							*15 30*						*16 30*				*17 30*			*18 30*	
Heathrow Terminal 1 Bus (bus)	a		*11 55*	*12 55*				*14 25*			*14 55*			*15 25*			*15 55*				*16 55*			*17 55*	
Slough 3	a																								
London Waterloo 15	⊖ a																	16 58							
London Paddington 15	⊖ a		11 21	12 28				13 55			14 22			14 54			15 22				16 21			17 36	

For general notes see front of timetable
For details of catering facilities see
Directory of Train Operators

Table 135

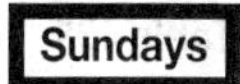

until 27 January

Sleeper services are published in Table 406

Cornwall and Devon → Birmingham and London

Network Diagram - see first page of Table 135

		SW		GW	GW	XC	GW	GW	SW	XC	SW	GW	GW	SW	SW	GW	GW	GW	W		XC	GW	GW	GW	GW
		1 ◇ ☕		🚌		R 1 ☕		1 ◇ ☕	1 ◇ ☕	R 1 ☕	1 ◇ ☕	1 ◇ ☕	1 ◇ ☕	1 ◇	1 ◇ ☕		1 ◇ ☕	1 ◇ ☕			R 1 ☕	1 ◇ ☕		◇ 🛒	1 ◇ ☕
Penzance	d				12 25										13 50							14 46		15 08	
St Ives	d														13 30							14 30			
St Erth 2	d				12 32										14 00							14 57		15 17	
Hayle	d														14 03									15 20	
Camborne	d				12 44										14 13							15 08		15 30	
Redruth	d				12 50										14 19							15 15		15 36	
Falmouth Docks	d				11 37										14 01									15 00	
Truro	d				13 02										14 31							15 29		15 48	
St Austell	d				13 20										14 48							15 46		16 05	
Newquay	d																								
Par 3	d				13 28										14 56							15 53		16 13	
Lostwithiel	d				13 35										15 03									16 19	
Bodmin Parkway	d				13 42										15 08							16 05		16 25	
Looe	d																								
Liskeard 3	d				13 56										15 22							16 18		16 38	
Menheniot	d														15 29									16 43	
St Germans	d														15 37									16 50	
Saltash	d														15 44									16 59	
St Budeaux Ferry Road	d																								
Keyham	d																								
Dockyard	d																								
Devonport	d																								
Plymouth	a				14 20										15 53							16 43		17 07	
	d	14 06				14 25		15 05		15 25			15 45		16 02		16 10				16 25	16 50		17 08	
Ivybridge	d	14 21													16 17									17 24	
Totnes	d	14 35				14 50		15 32		15 50			16 12		16 31		16 42				16 50	17 17		17 39	
Paignton	d						15 02		15 27			15 51		16 10		16 31							17 20		
Torquay	d						15 07		15 33			15 56		16 16		16 36							17 25		
Torre	d						15 10									16 39							17 28		
Newton Abbot	a	14 46				15 01	15 18	15 44	15 48	16 01		16 07	16 24	16 30	16 42	16 47	16 53				17 01	17 28	17 36	17 51	
	d	14 47				15 03	15 20	15 45	15 49	16 03		16 08	16 25	16 32	16 43		16 55				17 03	17 30	17 38	17 52	
Teignmouth	d	14 54					15 27		15 56		←	16 16											17 45	18 00	
Dawlish	d	14 59					15 32		16 01		16 01	16 20											17 50	18 05	
Dawlish Warren	d						15 43		→		16b17												17 54		
Starcross	d						15 46																17 57		
Exeter St Thomas	d						15 55																18 06		
Exeter St Davids 6	a	15 14				15 21	15 59	16 05		16 21	16 28	16 34	16 45	16 53	17 05		17 15				17 21	17 50	18 10	18 19	
Exeter Central	a	15 21						16 28			16 36			17 21			17 28								
Exmouth	a	15 53						16 54									17 53		17 53						
Barnstaple	d										15 11	15 11													
Exmouth	d							15 10			15 10		16 10						16 10			17 10			
Exeter Central	d							15 34			16 37		16 34				16 43		17 23			17 34			
Exeter St Davids 6	d					15 23		16 07		16 23	16 33	16 36	16 46				17 17		17 18		17 23	17 52		18 35 →	
Tiverton Parkway	d					15 37		16 22		16 37		16 51	17 02				17 32				17 37	18 05			
Taunton	d					15 51		16 36		16 51		17 04	17 15				17 45				17 51	18 20			
Bridgwater	a																								
Weston-super-Mare	a							16 57				17 25						←							
Bristol Temple Meads 10	a					16 25		17 19		17 25		17 58					18 24	17 58			18 25				←
Bath Spa 7	a							17 42				→						18 12							18 42
Filton Abbey Wood	a																→								
Bristol Parkway 7	a					16 38				17 38											18 38				
Swindon	a			16d35				18 10										18 40							19 10
Newport (South Wales)	a																								
Cardiff Central 7	a																								
Birmingham New Street 12	a					17 51				18 57											19 51				
Castle Cary	d												17 37												
Westbury	d												17 57												
Pewsey	d			17a20									18 15												
Hungerford	a																								
Newbury	a												18 34												
Thatcham	a																								
Theale	a																								
Reading 7	a							18 44					18 53					19 14				19 38			19 44
Oxford	a												19 35					20 25							20 35
Gatwick Airport 10	a												20 43												21 46
Heathrow Terminal I Bus 🚌	a												19 55					20 25							21 05
Slough 3	a																								
London Waterloo 15 ⊖	a	18 58									20 04			20 58					20 58						
London Paddington 15 ⊖	a							19 24					19 34					19 58				20 21			20 24

For general notes see front of timetable
For details of catering facilities see Directory of Train Operators

b Arr. 1605

Table 135

Sundays

until 27 January

Sleeper services are published in Table 406

Cornwall and Devon → Birmingham and London

Network Diagram - see first page of Table 135

		GW	GW	XC	GW	GW	SW	GW	GW	XC	GW	GW	GW	GW	GW	GW	GW	GW	GW	SW	XC	GW	GW
			1 ◇	1 ◇	◇	1 ◇	1 ◇	1 ◇	1 ◇	1 ◇		1 ◇			1 ◇					1	1 ◇		1 ◇
		🚌	☕	☕	🍴	☕	☕	☕	☕	☕		☕	🚌		☕	🚌		☕	🍴				☕
Penzance	d								16 15			17 20						19 00	20 00		20 55		21 15
St Ives	d								*15 39*			*17 02*						*18 45*	*19 40*				*19 40*
St Erth 2	d								16 26			17 30						19 09	20 09				21 25
Hayle	d																		20 12				
Camborne	d								16 37			17 42						19 21	20 21		21 11		21 37
Redruth	d								16 44			17 49						19 27	20 27		21 17		21 44
Falmouth Docks	d								*16 04*			*17 21*						*19 00*	*20 07*				*21 20*
Truro	d								16 56			18 00						19 39	20 40		21 29		21 57
St Austell	d								17 14			18 19						19 57	20 57		21 45		22 15
Newquay	d																						
Par 3	d								17 20			18 25						20 04	21 04		21 53		
Lostwithiel	d																	20 11					
Bodmin Parkway	d								17 32			18 37						20 18	21 15		22 04		22 32
Looe	d																						
Liskeard 3	d								17 45			18 50						20 34	21 28		22 16		22 47
Menheniot	d																	20 39					
St Germans	d																	20 46					
Saltash	d																	20 55					
St Budeaux Ferry Road	d																						
Keyham	d																						
Dockyard	d																						
Devonport	d																	21 01					
Plymouth	a								18 10			19 15						21 04	21 53		22 45		23 13
	d			17 25		17 50			18 10	18 25		19 15			19 55			21 15					23 20
Ivybridge	d																						
Totnes	d			17 50		18 16			18 40	18 50		19 45						21 42					23 48
Paignton	d						18 23				18 55			19 50			21 00			22 10		23 00	
Torquay	d						18 29				19 00			19 55			21 05			22 16		23 05	
Torre	d										19 03			19 58			21 08					23 08	
Newton Abbot	a			18 01		18 28	18 39		18 51	19 01	19 11	19 57		20 06	20 31		21 16	21 54		22 26		23 16	23 59
	d			18 03		18 29	18 41		18 52	19 03	19 13	19 58		20 08	20 32		21 18	21 54		22 28		23 18	00 01
Teignmouth	d						18 48				19 20			20 15			21 25	22 01		22 35		23 25	
Dawlish	d						18 53				19 25			20 20			21 30	22 06		22 40		23 30	
Dawlish Warren	d						18 57				19 29			20 24			21 34			22 44		23 34	
Starcross	d										19 32			20 27			21 37					23 37	
Exeter St Thomas	d										19 41			20 36			21 46					23 46	
Exeter St Davids 6	a			18 22		18 50	19 08		19 13	19 21	19 45	20 18		20 40	20 53		21 50	22 21		22 55		23 50	00 26
Exeter Central	a			*18 38*			19 23		*19 23*	*19 38*		*20 38*			*21 23*			*22 33*		23 13			
Exmouth	a			*19 03*						*20 03*		*21 06*			*22 03*			*22 58*		*23 44*			
Barnstaple	d					*17 17*									*19 10*								
Exmouth	d					*18 10*						*19 10*			*20 10*								*23 47*
Exeter Central	d				←	*18 35*			*18 43*			*19 34*			*20 46*								*00 11*
Exeter St Davids 6	d			18 23	18 35	18 50			19 15	19 23		20 19			20 55								01 27
Tiverton Parkway	d			18 37	18 53				19 28	19 37		20 35			21 09								
Taunton	d		18 26	18 51	19 10	19 15			19 42	19 51		20 47			21 22								
Bridgwater	a		18 36		19 21																		
Weston-super-Mare	a		18 53		19 41																		
Bristol Temple Meads 10	a		19 25	19 25	20 11			←		20 25					21 57								
Bath Spa 7	a		19 42					19 42							22 17								
Filton Abbey Wood	a		→																				
Bristol Parkway 7	a			19 38						20 38													
Swindon	a	19d15						20 10					21d08		22 45	22d55							
Newport (South Wales)	a																						
Cardiff Central 7	a																						
Birmingham New Street 12	a			20 57						21 51													
Castle Cary	d								20 05			21 10											
Westbury	d								20 24			21 28											
Pewsey	d	20a00										21 48	21a53			23a40							
Hungerford	a																						
Newbury	a					20 22						22 07											
Thatcham	a																						
Theale	a																						
Reading 7	a					20 40		20 45	21 12			22 29			23 26								04s18
Oxford	a							*21 35*	*21 50*			*23 29*			*00 35*								*06 21*
Gatwick Airport 10	a							*22 39*	*23 30*			*00b58*											*05 54*
Heathrow Terminal 1 Bus 🚌	a					*21 35*		*21 55*	*22 45*			*23 45*											*05 40*
Slough 3	a																						
London Waterloo 15	⊖ a						22 58																
London Paddington 15	⊖ a					21 24		21 26	21 53			23 23			00 17								05 10

For general notes see front of timetable
For details of catering facilities see Directory of Train Operators

b Change at Reading and Redhill

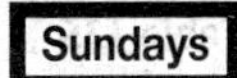

3 February to 23 March

Sleeper services are published in Table 406

Cornwall and Devon → Birmingham and London

Network Diagram - see first page of Table 135

		GW	GW	XC	GW	XC	GW		GW	GW	XC	GW	GW	XC		GW	GW	SW	XC	GW	GW		GW	XC	GW
			1◇ ☕	1◇ ☕	1◇ ☕	R 1 ☕	1◇ ☕		◇		R 1 ☕	1◇ ☕		R 1 ☕			1◇ ☕	1◇ ☕	R 1 ☕		1◇ ☕		1◇ ☕	R 1 ☕	
Penzance	d											08 30		09 30			09 50		10 30		10 50			12 00	
St Ives	d																								
St Erth 2	d											08 40		09 38			10 00		10 38		11 00			12 08	
Hayle	d											08 44													
Camborne	d											08 54		09 48			10 12		10 48		11 12			12 18	
Redruth	d											09 00		09 54			10 18		10 54		11 18			12 24	
Falmouth Docks	d																							*11 37*	
Truro	d											09 15		10 06			10 30		11 06		11 30			12 36	
St Austell	d											09 31		10 22			10 48		11 22		11 48			12 52	
Newquay	d																								
Par 3	d											09 39		10 29			10 55		11 29		11 55			12 59	
Lostwithiel	d																								
Bodmin Parkway	d											09 51		10 40			11 07		11 40		12 07			13 10	
Looe	d																								
Liskeard 3	d											10 04		10 52			11 20		11 52		12 20			13 22	
Menheniot	d																								
St Germans	d											10 15													
Saltash	d											10 23													
St Budeaux Ferry Road	d																								
Keyham	d																								
Dockyard	d																								
Devonport	d																								
Plymouth	a											10 32		11 16			11 45		12 16		12 45			13 46	
	d			08 35	08 45	09 40	09 50				10 25	10 35		11 30			11 45		12 30		12 50		13 44	13 55	
Ivybridge	d																								
Totnes	d			09 00	09 11	10 05	10 16				10 50	11 02		11 55			12 15		12 55		13 17		14 10	14 20	
Paignton	d									10 25			11 04			12 08		12 25		12 55					14 20
Torquay	d									10 30			11 09			12 13		12 31		13 00					14 25
Torre	d									10 33			11 12			12 16				13 03					14 28
Newton Abbot	a			09 11	09 24	10 16	10 29			10 41	11 01	11 14	11 20	12 06		12 24	12 27	12 41	13 06	13 11	13 28		14 23	14 31	14 36
	d			09 13	09 26	10 18	10 31			10 43	11 03	11 15		12 08			12 28	12 44	13 08	13 13	13 30		14 24	14 33	14 38
Teignmouth	d				09 33					10 50	11 10							12 51		13 20				14 40	14 45
Dawlish	d				09 38					10 55	11 15							12 58		13 25				14 45	14 50
Dawlish Warren	d									10 59										13 29					14 54
Starcross	d									11 02										13 32					14 57
Exeter St Thomas	d									11 11										13 41					15 06
Exeter St Davids 6	a			09 31	09 51	10 36	10 51			11 15	11 26	11 35		12 26			12 49	13 13	13 26	13 46	13 50		14 44	14 56	15 10
Exeter Central	a				*10 35*		*11 23*			11 28		*12 28*						13 21			*14 28*				15 28
Exmouth	a				*11 00*					11 53		*12 54*						*13 53*			*14 54*				15 53
Barnstaple	d																*11 10*						*13 19*		
Exmouth	d													*11 10*			*12 05*				*13 05*		*14 10*		
Exeter Central	d			*08 56*					*10 46*					*11 37*			*12 30*				*13 29*		*14 34*	*14 43*	
Exeter St Davids 6	d	08 15	08 30	09 33	09 51	10 38	10 51		10 57		11 28	11 36		12 28			12 50		13 28		13 52		14 45	15 00	
Tiverton Parkway	d	08 30	08 44	09 47		10 52	11 07		11 12		11 42	11 52		12 42					13 42		14 05			15 14	
Taunton	d	08a44	08 58	10 01	10 16	11 06	11 20		11 27		11 56	12 05		12 56			13 15		13 56		14 20		15 10	15 28	
Bridgwater	a								11 37																
Weston-super-Mare	a								11 55															15 57	
Bristol Temple Meads 10	a			11 11		12 10			12 30		13 10			14 10					15 16					16 25	
Bath Spa 7	a																								
Filton Abbey Wood	a																								
Bristol Parkway 7	a			11 38		12 38					13 38			14 38					15 38					16 38	
Swindon	a																								
Newport (South Wales)	a																								
Cardiff Central 7	a																								
Birmingham New Street 12	a			12 51		13 51					14 57			15 51					16 57					17 51	
Castle Cary	d		09 20									12 27											15 32		
Westbury	d		09b42		10 54							12 45											15 50		
Pewsey	d		10 00									13 05											16 08		
Hungerford	a																								
Newbury	a		10 19		11 28							13 24											16 28		
Thatcham	a																								
Theale	a																								
Reading 7	a		10 38		11 49		12 41					13 42					14 33				15 38		16 47		
Oxford	a		*11 35*		*12 35*		*13 34*					*14 35*					*15 27*				*16 35*		*17 35*		
Gatwick Airport 10	a		*12 30*		*13 30*		*14 30*					*15 30*					*16 30*				*17 30*		*18 30*		
Heathrow Terminal 1 Bus	🚌 a		*11 55*		*12 55*		*13 55*					*14 55*					*15 55*				*16 55*		*17 55*		
Slough 3	a																								
London Waterloo 15	⊖ a																	16 58							
London Paddington 15	⊖ a		11 21		12 33		13 25					14 22					15 22				16 21		17 37		

For general notes see front of timetable
For details of catering facilities see Directory of Train Operators

b Arr. 0936

Table 135

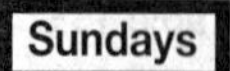

Sundays

3 February to 23 March

Sleeper services are published in Table 406

Cornwall and Devon → Birmingham and London

Network Diagram - see first page of Table 135

		SW	GW	GW	GW	GW		SW	XC	SW	GW	GW	SW		SW	GW	GW	GW		SW		XC	GW	GW	GW
		1 ◇ ☕			1 ◇ ☕			1 ◇ ☕	R 1 ☕	1 ◇ ☕	1 ◇ ☕	1 ◇ ☕	1 ◇		1 ◇ ☕		1 ◇ ☕	1 ◇ ☕		1 ◇		R 1 ☕	1 ◇ ☕		◇ 🛒
Penzance	d		12 25		12 50										13 50								14 46		15 08
St Ives	d				*12 30*										*13 30*								*14 30*		
St Erth 2	d		12 32		13 00										14 00								14 57		15 17
Hayle	d														14 03										15 20
Camborne	d		12 44		13 12										14 13								15 08		15 30
Redruth	d		12 50		13 18										14 19								15 15		15 36
Falmouth Docks	d		*11 37*		*12 52*										*14 01*										*15 00*
Truro	d		13 02		13 30										14 31								15b29		15 48
St Austell	d		13 20		13 49										14 48								15 46		16 05
Newquay	d																								
Par 3	d		13 28		13 55										14 56								15 53		16 13
Lostwithiel	d		13 35												15 03										16 19
Bodmin Parkway	d		13 42		14 07										15 08								16 05		16 25
Looe	d																								
Liskeard 3	d		13 56		14 20										15 22								16 18		16 38
Menheniot	d														15 29										16 43
St Germans	d														15 37										16 50
Saltash	d														15 44										16 59
St Budeaux Ferry Road	d																								
Keyham	d																								
Dockyard	d																								
Devonport	d																								
Plymouth	a		14 20		14 46										15 53								16 43		17 07
	d	14 06			14 50				15 25			15 45			16 02		16 10					16 25	16 50		17 08
Ivybridge	d	14 21													16 17										17 24
Totnes	d	14 35			15 17				15 50			16 12			16 31		16 40					16 50	17 17		17 39
Paignton	d			15 02				15 27			15 51		16 10			16 31								17 20	
Torquay	d			15 07				15 33			15 56		16 16			16 36								17 25	
Torre	d			15 10												16 39								17 28	
Newton Abbot	a	14 46		15 18	15 28			15 48	16 01		16 08	16 24	16 30		16 42	16 47	16 51					17 01	17 28	17 36	17 51
	d	14 47		15 20	15 30			15 49	16 03		16 08	16 25	16 32		16 43		16 53					17 03	17 30	17 38	17 52
Teignmouth	d	14 54		15 27				15 56		←	16 16													17 45	18 00
Dawlish	d	14 59		15 32		←		16 01		16 01	16 21													17 50	18 05
Dawlish Warren	d			15c43		15 43		→		16e17														17 54	
Starcross	d			→		15 46																		17 57	
Exeter St Thomas	d					15 55																		18 06	
Exeter St Davids 6	a	15 14			15 50	15 59			16 21	16 28	16 35	16 45	16 53		17 05		17 13					17 21	17 50	18 10	18 19
Exeter Central	a	15 21				*16 28*				16 36			17 21				*17 28*								
Exmouth	a	*15 53*				*16 54*											*17 53*			*17 53*					
Barnstaple	d										*15 11*														
Exmouth	d				*15 10*							*16 10*								*16 10*			*17 10*		
Exeter Central	d				*15 34*							*16 34*					*16 43*			*17 23*			*17 34*		
Exeter St Davids 6	d				15 50				16 23		16 36	16 46					17 17			17 18		17 23	17 52		18 35 →
Tiverton Parkway	d				16 05				16 37		16 51	17 02					17 32					17 37	18 05		
Taunton	d				16 20				16 51		17 04	17 15					17 45					17 51	18 20		
Bridgwater	a																	←							
Weston-super-Mare	a										17 25 →							17 25							
Bristol Temple Meads 10	a								17 25									17 55				18 25			
Bath Spa 7	a																	18 17							
Filton Abbey Wood	a																								
Bristol Parkway 7	a								17 38													18 38			
Swindon	a																								
Newport (South Wales)	a																								
Cardiff Central 7	a																								
Birmingham New Street 12	a								18 57													19 51			
Castle Cary	d											17 37													
Westbury	d											17 57													
Pewsey	d											18 15													
Hungerford	a																								
Newbury	a											18 34													
Thatcham	a																								
Theale	a																								
Reading 7	a				17 38							18 53					19 02	19 31					19 38		
Oxford	a				*18 35*												*19 35*	*20 25*					*20 35*		
Gatwick Airport 10	a				*19 30*																		*21 46*		
Heathrow Terminal 1 Bus 🚌	a				*18 55*							*19 55*					*20 25*						*21 05*		
Slough 3	a																								
London Waterloo 15	⊖ a	18 58								20 04			20 58							20 58					
London Paddington 15	⊖ a				18 21							19 35					19 54	20 26					20 28		

For general notes see front of timetable
For details of catering facilities see Directory of Train Operators

b Arr. 1526
c Arr. 1535
e Arr. 1605

Sundays

3 February to 23 March

Sleeper services are published in Table 406

Cornwall and Devon → Birmingham and London

Network Diagram - see first page of Table 135

		GW	XC	GW	GW	SW	GW	GW	XC	GW	GW	GW	GW	GW	GW	GW	SW	XC	GW	GW
		1 ◇	1 ◇	◇	1 ◇	1 ◇	1 ◇	1 ◇	1 ◇		1 ◇		1 ◇				1	1 ◇		1 ◇
									A											
		🍴	🍴	🛒	🍴	🍴	🍴	🍴	🍴		🍴		🍴		🍴	🛒				🍴
Penzance	d							16 15			17 20				19 00	20 00		20 55		21 15
St Ives	d							15 39			17 02				18 45	19 40				
St Erth 2	d							16 26			17 30				19 09	20 09				21 25
Hayle	d															20 12				
Camborne	d							16 37			17 42				19 21	20 21		21 11		21 37
Redruth	d							16 44			17 49				19 27	20 27		21 17		21 44
Falmouth Docks	d							16 04			17 21				19 00			20 15		
Truro	d							16 56			18 00				19 39	20 40		21 29		21 57
St Austell	d							17 14			18 19				19 57	20 57		21 45		
Newquay	d																			
Par 3	d							17 20			18 25				20 04	21 04		21 53		
Lostwithiel	d														20 11					
Bodmin Parkway	d							17 32			18 37				20 18	21 15		22 04		22 32
Looe	d																			
Liskeard 3	d							17 45			18 50				20 34	21 28		22 16		22 47
Menheniot	d														20 39					
St Germans	d														20 46					
Saltash	d														20 55					
St Budeaux Ferry Road	d																			
Keyham	d																			
Dockyard	d																			
Devonport	d														21 01					
Plymouth	a							18 10			19 15				21 04	21 53		22 45		23 13
	d		17 25		17 50			18 10	18 25		19 15		19 55		21 15					23 20
Ivybridge	d																			
Totnes	d		17 50		18 16			18 40	18 50		19 45				21 42					23 48
Paignton	d					18 23				18 55		19 50		21 00			22 10		23 00	
Torquay	d					18 29				19 00		19 55		21 05			22 16		23 05	
Torre	d									19 03		19 58		21 08					23 08	
Newton Abbot	a		18 01		18 28	18 39		18 51	19 01	19 11	19 56	20 06	20 31	21 16	21 54		22 26		23 16	23 59
	d		18 03		18 29	18 41		18 52	19 03	19 13	19 58	20 08	20 32	21 18	21 54		22 28		23 18	00 01
Teignmouth	d					18 48				19 20		20 15		21 25	22 01		22 35		23 25	
Dawlish	d					18 53				19 25		20 20		21 30	22 06		22 40		23 30	
Dawlish Warren	d					18 57				19 29		20 24		21 34			22 44		23 34	
Starcross	d									19 32		20 27		21 37					23 37	
Exeter St Thomas	d									19 41		20 36		21 46					23 46	
Exeter St Davids 6	a		18 22		18 50	19 08		19 13	19 21	19 45	20 18	20 40	20 53	21 50	22 21		22 55		23 50	00 26
Exeter Central	a		18 38			19 23		19 23	19 38		20 38		21 23		22 33		23 13			
Exmouth	a		19 03						20 03		21 06		22 03		22 58		23 44			
Barnstaple	d				17 17								19 10							
Exmouth	d				18 10						19 10		20 10							
Exeter Central	d			←	18 35			18 43			19 34		20 46							
Exeter St Davids 6	d		18 23	18 35	18 50			19 15	19 23		20 19		20 55							01 27
Tiverton Parkway	d		18 37	18 53				19 28	19 37		20 34		21 08							
Taunton	d	18 26	18 51	19 10	19 15			19 42	19 51		20 47		21 22							
Bridgwater	a	18 35		19 21																
Weston-super-Mare	a	18 52		19 41																
Bristol Temple Meads 10	a	19 25	19 25	20 11			←		20 25											
Bath Spa 7	a	19 36					19 36													
Filton Abbey Wood	a	→																		
Bristol Parkway 7	a		19 38						20 38											
Swindon	a																			
Newport (South Wales)	a																			
Cardiff Central 7	a																			
Birmingham New Street 12	a		20 57						21 55											
Castle Cary	d							20 05			21 10									
Westbury	d							20 24			21 28		22 00							
Pewsey	d										21 47									
Hungerford	a																			
Newbury	a				20 19						22 06									
Thatcham	a																			
Theale	a																			
Reading 7	a				20 42		20 48	21 14			22 31		22 48							03s39
Oxford	a						21 35	21 50			23 29		23 48							
Gatwick Airport 10	a						22 31	23 30					00b58							
Heathrow Terminal 1 Bus 🚌	a						21 55	22 45					23 45							
Slough 3	a																			
London Waterloo 15 ⊖	a					22 58														
London Paddington 15 ⊖	a				21 24		21 32	21 59			23 24		23 32							05 10

For general notes see front of timetable
For details of catering facilities see Directory of Train Operators

A 🍴 to Bristol Temple Meads
b Change at Reading and Redhill

Sundays
from 30 March

Sleeper services are published in Table 406

Cornwall and Devon → Birmingham and London

Network Diagram - see first page of Table 135

		GW	GW	GW	XC	XC		GW	GW	XC	GW	GW		GW	XC	GW	GW	SW		XC	GW	GW	XC	XC	GW
		◇	1 ◇	1 ◇	1 ◇	1 ◇		1 ◇		R 1	1 ◇			1 ◇	R 1		1 ◇	1 ◇		R 1		1 ◇	R 1	R 1	1 ◇
Penzance	d										08 30				09 30		09 50			10 30		10 50	11 30		
St Ives	d																								
St Erth 2	d										08 40				09 38		10 00			10 38		11 00	11 38		
Hayle	d										08 44														
Camborne	d										08 54				09 48		10 12			10 48		11 12	11 48		
Redruth	d										09 00				09 54		10 18			10 54		11 18	11 54		
Falmouth Docks	d																						*11 37*		
Truro	d										09 15				10 06		10 30			11 06		11 30	12 06		
St Austell	d										09 31				10 22		10 48			11 22		11 48	12 22		
Newquay	d																								
Par 3	d										09 39				10 29		10 55			11 29		11 55	12 29		
Lostwithiel	d																								
Bodmin Parkway	d										09 51				10 40		11 07			11 40		12 07	12 40		
Looe	d																								
Liskeard 3	d										10 04				10 52		11 20			11 52		12 20	12 52		
Menheniot	d																								
St Germans	d										10 15														
Saltash	d										10 24														
St Budeaux Ferry Road	d																								
Keyham	d																								
Dockyard	d																								
Devonport	d																								
Plymouth	a										10 33				11 18		11 45			12 16		12 45	13 21		
	d			08 45	09 25			09 50		10 25	10 35			10 50	11 25		11 45			12 25		12 50	13 25		13 44
Ivybridge	d																								
Totnes	d			09 13	09 50			10 17		10 50	11 03			11 18	11 50		12 15			12 50		13 17	13 50		14 10
Paignton	d								10 25			11 04				12 08		12 25			12 55			13 59	
Torquay	d								10 30			11 09				12 13		12 31			13 00			14 05	
Torre	d								10 33			11 12				12 16					13 03				
Newton Abbot	a			09 24	10 01			10 29	10 41	11 01	11 14	11 20		11 29	12 01	12 24	12 27	12 41		13 01	13 11	13 28	14 01	14 15	14 23
	d			09 26	10 03			10 30	10 43	11 03	11 16			11 31	12 03		12 29	12 44		13 03	13 13	13 30	14 03	14 16	14 24
Teignmouth	d			09 33					10 50									12 51			13 20			14 24	
Dawlish	d			09 38					10 55									12 58			13 25			14 29	
Dawlish Warren	d								10 59												13 29				
Starcross	d								11 02												13 32				
Exeter St Thomas	d								11 11												13 41				
Exeter St Davids 6	a			09 51	10 21			10 50	11 15	11 21	11 36			11 51	12 21		12 49	13 13		13 21	13 46	13 50	14 21	14 41	14 44
Exeter Central	a				*10 35*			*11 23*	11 28					*12 28*				*13 21*				*14 28*			
Exmouth	a				*11 00*				11 53					*12 54*				*13 53*				*14 54*			
Barnstaple	d																*11 10*							*13 19*	
Exmouth	d			*09 10*		*10 00*								*11 10*								*13 05*		*14 10*	
Exeter Central	d			*09 34*		*10 24*				*10 46*				*11 37*								*13 29*		*14 34*	
Exeter St Davids 6	d	08 15	08 30	09 52	10 23	10 48		10 52		11 23	11 37			11 53	12 23		12 50			13 23		13 52	14 23	14 43	14 45
Tiverton Parkway	d	08 30	08 44		10 37	11 01		11 06		11 37	11 52			12 07	12 37					13 37		14 05	14 37		
Taunton	d	08 45	08 58	10 17	10 51	11 16		11 20		11 51	12 06			12 21	12 51		13 15			13 51		14 20	14 51	15 06	15 10
Bridgwater	a	08 55																							
Weston-super-Mare	a	09 12																						15 28	
Bristol Temple Meads 10	a	09 45	09 32		11 25	11 55		11 56		12 25				12 55	13 25					14 25			15 25	15 50	15 44
Bath Spa 7	a		09 45	11 02				12 12						13 12											
Filton Abbey Wood	a	09 56																							
Bristol Parkway 7	a	10 00			11 38	12 08				12 38					13 38					14 38			15 38	16 08	
Swindon	a		10 10	11 25				12 39						13 40											
Newport (South Wales)	a																								
Cardiff Central 7	a																								
Birmingham New Street 12	a				12 51	13 26				13 51					14 57					15 51			16 57	17 26	
Castle Cary	d																								
Westbury	d																								16b24
Pewsey	d																								16 42
Hungerford	a																								
Newbury	a																								17 01
Thatcham	a																								
Theale	a																								
Reading 7	a		10 40	11 56				13 14			13 40			14 14			14 50					15 49			17 23
Oxford	a		*12c15*	*13c15*							*15c15*						*16c15*					*17c15*			
Gatwick Airport 10	a		*12 30*	*13 30*							*15 30*						*16 30*					*17 30*			
Heathrow Terminal 1 Bus	a		*11 55*	*12 55*				*14 25*			*14 55*			*15 25*			*15 55*					*16 55*			*18 25*
Slough 3	a																								
London Waterloo 15	⊖ a																	16 58							
London Paddington 15	⊖ a		11 27	12 42				13 55			14 22			15 03			15 32					16 31			18 09

For general notes see front of timetable
For details of catering facilities see Directory of Train Operators

b Arr. 1617
c Change at Reading and Didcot Parkway. By bus from Didcot Parkway

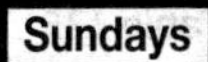

Sundays

from 30 March

Sleeper services are published in Table 406

Cornwall and Devon → Birmingham and London

Network Diagram - see first page of Table 135

		GW	SW	GW	XC	GW	GW	GW	GW	SW	XC	SW	GW	GW	SW	SW	GW	GW	XC	GW	GW
			1 ◇ ☕		R 1 ☕		1 ◇ ☕		1 ◇ ☕	1 ◇ ☕	R 1 ☕	1 ◇ ☕	1 ◇ ☕	1 ◇ ☕	1 ◇	1 ◇ ☕		1 ◇ ☕	R 1 ☕	1 ◇ ☕	
Penzance	d			12 25			12 47									13 50				14 46	
St Ives	d						*12 30*									*13 30*				*14 30*	
St Erth 2	d			12 32			12 57									14 00				14 57	
Hayle	d															14 03					
Camborne	d			12 44			13 09									14 13				15 08	
Redruth	d			12 50			13 15									14 19				15 15	
Falmouth Docks	d			*11 37*			*12 52*									*14 01*					
Truro	d			13 02			13 27									14 31				15 29	
St Austell	d			13 20			13 46									14 48				15 46	
Newquay	d																				
Par 3	d			13 28			13 52									14 56				15 53	
Lostwithiel	d			13 35												15 03					
Bodmin Parkway	d			13 42			14 04									15 08				16 05	
Looe	d																				
Liskeard 3	d			13 56			14 17									15 22				16 18	
Menheniot	d															15 29					
St Germans	d															15 37					
Saltash	d															15 44					
St Budeaux Ferry Road	d																				
Keyham	d																				
Dockyard	d																				
Devonport	d																				
Plymouth	a			14 20			14 43									15 53				16 43	
	d		14 06		14 25		14 50		15 05		15 25			15 45		16 02		16 10	16 25	16 50	
Ivybridge	d		14 21													16 17					
Totnes	d		14 35		14 50		15 17		15 32		15 50			16 12		16 31		16 39	16 50	17 17	
Paignton	d	14 20				15 02				15 27			15 51		16 10		16 31				17 20
Torquay	d	14 25				15 07				15 33			15 56		16 16		16 36				17 25
Torre	d	14 28				15 10											16 39				17 28
Newton Abbot	a	14 36	14 46		15 01	15 18	15 28		15 44	15 48	16 01		16 08	16 24	16 30	16 42	16 47	16 51	17 01	17 28	17 36
	d	14 38	14 47		15 03	15 20	15 30		15 45	15 49	16 03		16 08	16 25	16 32	16 43		16 52	17 03	17 30	17 38
Teignmouth	d	14 45	14 54			15 27				15 56		←	16 16								17 45
Dawlish	d	14 50	14 59			15 32		←		16 01		16 01	16 21								17 50
Dawlish Warren	d	14 54				15b43 →		15 43		→		16c17									17 54
Starcross	d	14 57						15 46													17 57
Exeter St Thomas	d	15 06						15 55													18 06
Exeter St Davids 6	a	15 10	15 14		15 21		15 50	15 59	16 05		16 21	16 28	16 35	16 45	16 53	17 05		17 12	17 21	17 50	18 10
Exeter Central	a	15 28	15 21						*16 28*			16 36						*17 21*			
Exmouth	a	15 53	*15 53*						*16 54*									*17 53*			
Barnstaple	d												*15 11*								
Exmouth	d		*14 10*				*15 10*							*16 10*						*17 10*	
Exeter Central	d		15 23				*15 34*							*16 34*				*16 43*		*17 34*	
Exeter St Davids 6	d		15 18		15 23		15 50		16 07		16 23		16 36	16 46				17 17	17 23	17 52	
Tiverton Parkway	d				15 37		16 05		16 22		16 37		16 51	17 00				17 32	17 37	18 05	
Taunton	d				15 51		16 20		16 36		16 51		17 04	17 15				17 45	17 51	18 20	
Bridgwater	a																				
Weston-super-Mare	a								16 57				17 25								
Bristol Temple Meads 10	a				16 25				17 19		17 25		18 03					18 24	18 25		
Bath Spa 7	a								17 42				18 17					18 42			
Filton Abbey Wood	a																				
Bristol Parkway 7	a				16 38						17 38								18 38		
Swindon	a								18 10				18 46					19 10			
Newport (South Wales)	a																				
Cardiff Central 7	a																				
Birmingham New Street 12	a				17 51						18 57								19 51		
Castle Cary	d																				
Westbury	d													18e27							
Pewsey	d													18 45							
Hungerford	a																				
Newbury	a													19 04							
Thatcham	a																				
Theale	a																				
Reading 7	a						17 55		18 44				19 20	19 25				19 44		19 54	
Oxford	a						*19f15*		*20f15*											*21f15*	
Gatwick Airport 10	a						*19 30*		*20 30*											*21 30*	
Heathrow Terminal 1 Bus	🚌 a						*18 55*		*19 55*					*20 25*						*21 05*	
Slough 3	a																				
London Waterloo 15	⊖ a		18 58									20 04			20 58						
London Paddington 15	⊖ a						18 39		19 23				20 03	20 09				20 23		20 39	

For general notes see front of timetable
For details of catering facilities see Directory of Train Operators

b Arr. 1535
c Arr. 1605
e Arr. 1819
f Change at Reading and Didcot Parkway. By bus from Didcot Parkway

Table 135

Sundays

from 30 March

Sleeper services are published in Table 406

Cornwall and Devon → Birmingham and London

Network Diagram - see first page of Table 135

		GW ◇	GW 1 ◇	XC 1 ◇		GW 1 ◇	GW ◇	SW 1 ◇	GW 1 ◇	XC 1 ◇		GW	GW 1 ◇	GW	GW 1 ◇	GW		GW	GW	SW 1	XC 1 ◇	GW	GW 1 ◇		
Penzance	d	15 08							16 15				17 20					19 00	20 00		20 55		21 15		
St Ives	d								*15 39*				*17 02*					*18 45*	*19 40*				*19 40*		
St Erth 2	d	15 17							16 26				17 30					19 09	20 09				21 25		
Hayle	d	15 20																	20 12						
Camborne	d	15 30							16 37				17 42					19 21	20 21		21 11		21 37		
Redruth	d	15 36							16 44				17 49					19 27	20 27		21 17		21 44		
Falmouth Docks	d	*15 00*							*16 24*				*17 21*					*19 00*	*20 07*				*21 20*		
Truro	d	15 48							16 56				18 00					19 39	20 40		21 29		21 57		
St Austell	d	16 05							17 14				18 19					19 57	20 57		21 45		22 15		
Newquay	d																								
Par 3	d	16 13							17 20				18 25					20 04	21 04		21 53				
Lostwithiel	d	16 19																20 11							
Bodmin Parkway	d	16 25							17 32				18 37					20 18	21 15		22 04		22 32		
Looe	d																								
Liskeard 3	d	16 38							17 45				18 50					20 34	21 28		22 16		22 47		
Menheniot	d	16 43																20 39							
St Germans	d	16 50																20 46							
Saltash	d	16 59																20 55							
St Budeaux Ferry Road	d																								
Keyham	d																								
Dockyard	d																								
Devonport	d																	21 01							
Plymouth	a	17 07							18 09				19 15					21 04	21 53		22 45		23 13		
	d	17 08		17 25		17 35			18 10	18 25			19 22		19 55			21 15					23 20		
Ivybridge	d	17 24																							
Totnes	d	17 39		17 50		18 02			18 40	18 50			19 52					21 42					23 48		
Paignton	d							18 23				18 55		19 50		21 00				22 10		23 00			
Torquay	d							18 29				19 00		19 55		21 05				22 16		23 05			
Torre	d											19 03		19 58		21 08						23 08			
Newton Abbot	a	17 51		18 01		18 13		18 39	18 54	19 01		19 11	20 03	20 06	20 31	21 16		21 54		22 26		23 16	23 59		
	d	17 52		18 03		18 14		18 41	18 55	19 03		19 13	20 05	20 08	20 32	21 18		21 54		22 28		23 18	00 01		
Teignmouth	d	18 00						18 48				19 20		20 15		21 25		22 01		22 35		23 25			
Dawlish	d	18 05						18 53				19 25		20 20		21 30		22 06		22 40		23 30			
Dawlish Warren	d							18 57				19 29		20 24		21 34				22 44		23 34			
Starcross	d											19 32		20 27		21 37						23 37			
Exeter St Thomas	d											19 41		20 36		21 46						23 46			
Exeter St Davids 6	a	18 19		18 22		18 35		19 08	19 15	19 21		19 45	20 25	20 40	20 53	21 50		22 21		22 55		23 50	00 26		
Exeter Central	a			*18 38*			←			*19 38*			*20 38*		*21 23*			*22 33*		23 13					
Exmouth	a			*19 03*						*20 03*			*21 06*		*22 03*			*22 58*		23 44					
Barnstaple	d						*17 17*						*19 10*												
Exmouth	d								*18 10*				*19 10*		*20 10*								*23 47*		
Exeter Central	d								*18 43*				*19 34*		*20 46*								*00 11*		
Exeter St Davids 6	d	18 41 ↪		18 23		18 37	18 41		19 17	19 23			20 26		20 55								01 27		
Tiverton Parkway	d			18 37			18 58		19 31	19 37			20 41		21 08										
Taunton	d		18 26	18 51		19 00	19 15		19 45	19 51			21b00		21 22										
Bridgwater	a		18 35				19 26																		
Weston-super-Mare	a		18 52				19 46																		
Bristol Temple Meads 10	a		19 25	19 25			20 18		20 22	20 25					21 57										
Bath Spa 7	a		19 42												22 17										
Filton Abbey Wood	a																								
Bristol Parkway 7	a			19 38						20 38															
Swindon	a		20 10												22 49										
Newport (South Wales)	a																								
Cardiff Central 7	a																								
Birmingham New Street 12	a			20 57						21 51															
Castle Cary	d												21 26												
Westbury	d					20c15							21 46												
Pewsey	d												22 06												
Hungerford	a																								
Newbury	a					20 53							22 25												
Thatcham	a																								
Theale	a																								
Reading 7	a		20 41			21 14			21 20				22 43		23 28								04s18		
Oxford	a		*22e15*						*23e15*				*00e27*		*00e55*								*06 21*		
Gatwick Airport 10	a		*22 31*						*23 30*				*00f58*										*05 54*		
Heathrow Terminal 1 Bus	a		*21 55*						*22 45*				*23 45*										*05 40*		
Slough 3	a																								
London Waterloo 15	⊖ a							22 58																	
London Paddington 15	⊖ a		21 25			21 59			22 17				23 30		00 11								05 10		

For general notes see front of timetable
For details of catering facilities see Directory of Train Operators

b Arr. 2054
c Arr. 2008
e Change at Reading and Didcot Parkway. By bus from Didcot Parkway
f Change at Reading and Redhill

Mondays to Fridays

Redruth — Helston and Culdrose

Bus Service

		GW A	GW A	GW	GW A	GW	GW A	GW A	GW A	GW	GW	GW	GW A	GW A	GW
Redruth	d	08 00	09 15	10 15	11 15	12 15	13 15	14 15	15 15	16 15	17 00	18 15	19 15	21 15	23 15
Helston (Woolworths)	a	08 47	09 47	10 47	11 47	12 47	13 47	14 47	15 47	16 47	17 32	18 47	19 47	21 47	23 41
Culdrose (R.N.A.S.)	a			11 00		13 00				17 00	17 50	18 55			
Mullion Holiday Park	a														

Saturdays

		GW A	GW A	GW	GW	GW	GW	GW	GW	GW	GW	GW	GW	GW	GW
Redruth	d	08 15	09 15	10 15	11 15	12 15	13 15	14 15	15 15	16 15	17 15	18 15	19 15	21 15	23 15
Helston (Woolworths)	a	08 47	09 47	10 47	11 47	12 47	13 47	14 47	15 47	16 47	17 47	18 47	19 47	21 47	23 41
Culdrose (R.N.A.S.)	a			11 00	12 00	13 00	14 00	15 00	16 00	17 00	18 00	18 55	19 55	21 55	
Mullion Holiday Park	a														

Sundays

		GW	GW	GW A	GW	GW	GW
Redruth	d	09 50	11 50	13 50	15 50	17 50	23 00
Helston (Woolworths)	a	10 19	12 19	14 19	16 19	18s19	23s29
Culdrose (R.N.A.S.)	a	10 35	12 35		16 35	18 35	23 45
Mullion Holiday Park	a						

Mondays to Fridays

		GW	GW	GW	GW	GW	GW	GW	GW	GW	GW	GW	GW	GW	GW	GW
Mullion Holiday Park	d															
Culdrose (R.N.A.S.)	d	06 55	08 01	09 21	10 14	11 14	12 14	13 00	14 14	15 09	16 14	17 14	17 14	18 14	18 14	19 39
Helston (Woolworths)	d	07 05	08 06	09 27	10 27	11 27	12 27	13 10	14 27	15 15	16 27	17 27	17 27	18 27	18 27	19 47
Redruth	a	07 39	08 55	10 01	11 01	12 01	13 01	13 40	15 01	16 01	17 01	18 01	18 01	18 59	18 59	20 19

Saturdays

		GW	GW	GW	GW	GW	GW	GW	GW	GW	GW	GW	GW
Mullion Holiday Park	d												
Culdrose (R.N.A.S.)	d	07 19	08 19	09 19	10 14	11 14	12 14	13 14	14 14	15 14	16 14	18 14	19 39
Helston (Woolworths)	d	07 27	08 27	09 27	10 27	11 27	12 27	13 27	14 27	15 27	16 27	18 27	19 47
Redruth	a	08 01	09 01	10 01	11 01	12 01	13 01	14 01	15 01	16 01	17 01	18 59	20 19

Sundays

		GW	GW	GW	GW	GW
Mullion Holiday Park	d					
Culdrose (R.N.A.S.)	d		10 35	12 35	14 35	16 35
Helston (Woolworths)	d	08 50	10 50	12 50	14 50	16 50
Redruth	a	09 21	11 21	13 21	15 21	17 21

For general notes see front of timetable
For details of catering facilities see Directory of Train Operators

A From Redruth

Mondays to Fridays

St. Austell — Eden Project

Bus Service

		GW	GW	GW	GW	GW	GW	GW	GW	GW	GW	GW	GW	GW	GW
St Austell	d	08 50	08 50	09 30	10 30	10 55	11 40	12 40	13 10	13 50	15 15	15 50	16 50	17 30	17 30
Eden Project	a	09 10	09 10	09 50	10 50	11 15	12 00	13 00	13 30	14 10	15 35	16 10	17 10	17 50	17 50

Saturdays

		GW	GW	GW	GW	GW	GW	GW	GW	GW	GW	GW	GW	GW	GW
St Austell	d	08 50	09 30	10 30	11 40	12 40	12 50	13 50	15 35	15 50	15 55	16 35	16 50	17 20	17 30
Eden Project	a	09 10	09 50	10 50	12 00	13 00	13 10	14 10	15 55	16 10	16 15	16 55	17 10	17 40	17 50

Sundays

		GW	GW	GW	GW	GW	GW	GW	GW	GW	GW	GW	GW	GW
St Austell	d	08 50	10 00	10 40	11 35	12 30	13 35	15 00	15 20	15 40	16 30	16 35	17 20	17 35
Eden Project	a	09 10	10 20	11 00	11 55	12 50	13 55	15 20	15 40	16 00	16 50	16 55	17 40	17 55

Mondays to Fridays

		GW	GW	GW	GW	GW	GW	GW	GW	GW	GW	GW	GW	GW
Eden Project	d	09 10	09 50	11 00	12 10	13 10	15 05	16 00	16 30	16 30	17 00	17 10	18 00	18 00
St Austell	a	09 30	10 10	11 20	12 30	13 30	15 25	16 20	16 50	16 50	17 20	17 30	18 20	18 20

Saturdays

		GW	GW	GW	GW	GW	GW	GW	GW	GW	GW	GW	GW
Eden Project	d	09 10	09 50	11 00	12 10	13 10	14 20	15 05	16 30	17 00	17 10	18 00	18 00
St Austell	a	09 30	10 10	11 20	12 30	13 30	14 40	15 25	16 50	17 20	17 30	18 20	18 20

Sundays

		GW	GW	GW	GW	GW	GW	GW	GW	GW	GW	GW	GW	GW
Eden Project	d	10 10	10 20	11 00	11 55	12 50	14 40	15 20	16 15	16 35	17 00	17 10	17 50	18 00
St Austell	a	10 30	10 40	11 20	12 15	13 10	15 00	15 40	16 35	16 55	17 20	17 30	18 10	18 20

For general notes see front of timetable
For details of catering facilities see
Directory of Train Operators

Table 135C

Mondays to Saturdays

Bodmin — Wadebridge and Padstow
Bus Service

		GW 🚌	GW 🚌	GW 🚌	GW 🚌	GW 🚌	GW 🚌	GW 🚌	GW 🚌	GW 🚌	GW 🚌	GW 🚌	GW 🚌	GW 🚌	GW 🚌
Bodmin Parkway	d	07 25	08 30	09 30	10 30	11 30	12 30	13 30	14 30	15 30	16 30	17 30	18 30	19 30	22 00
Bodmin Tsb Bus Stop	a														
Bodmin Mount Folly	a	07 35	08 40	09 40	10 40	11 40	12 40	13 40	14 40	15 40	16 40	17 40	18 40	19 40	22 10
Wadebridge Bus Station	a	07 55	09 00	10 00	11 00	12 00	13 00	14 00	15 00	16 00	17 00	18 00	19 00	20 00	22 30
Padstow Old Rly Station	a	08 27	09 27	10 27	11 27	12 27	13 27	14 27	15 27	16 27	17 27	18 27	19 27	20 27	22 57

Sundays

		GW 🚌	GW 🚌	GW 🚌	GW 🚌	GW 🚌	GW 🚌
Bodmin Parkway	d	09 30	11 30	13 30	15 30	17 30	19 30
Bodmin Tsb Bus Stop	a						
Bodmin Mount Folly	a	09 40	11 40	13 40	15 40	17 40	19 40
Wadebridge Bus Station	a	10 00	12 00	14 00	16 00	18 00	20 00
Padstow Old Rly Station	a	10 27	12 27	14 27	16 27	18 27	20 27

Mondays to Saturdays

		GW 🚌	GW 🚌	GW 🚌	GW 🚌	GW 🚌	GW 🚌	GW 🚌	GW 🚌	GW 🚌	GW 🚌	GW 🚌	GW 🚌	GW 🚌	GW 🚌
Padstow Old Rly Station	d	06 30	07 30	08 30	09 30	10 30	11 30	12 30	13 30	14 30	15 30	16 30	17 30	18 30	20 30
Wadebridge Bus Station	d	06 55	07 55	08 55	09 55	10 55	11 55	12 55	13 55	14 55	15 55	16 55	17 55	18 55	20 55
Bodmin Mount Folly	d														
Bodmin Tsb Bus Stop	d	07 17	08 17	09 17	10 17	11 17	12 17	13 17	14 17	15 17	16 17	17 17	18 17	19 17	21 17
Bodmin Parkway	a	07 25	08 25	09 25	10 25	11 25	12 25	13 25	14 25	15 25	16 25	17 25	18 25	19 25	21 25

Sundays

		GW 🚌	GW 🚌	GW 🚌	GW 🚌	GW 🚌	GW 🚌
Padstow Old Rly Station	d	08 30	10 30	12 30	14 30	16 30	18 30
Wadebridge Bus Station	d	08 55	10 55	12 55	14 55	16 55	18 55
Bodmin Mount Folly	d						
Bodmin Tsb Bus Stop	d	09 17	11 17	13 17	15 17	17 17	19 17
Bodmin Parkway	a	09 25	11 25	13 25	15 25	17 25	19 25

For general notes see front of timetable
For details of catering facilities see
Directory of Train Operators

Mondays to Fridays

Exeter — Okehampton, Holsworthy and Bude

Bus Service

		GW	GW	GW	GW	GW	GW FO
Exeter St Davids	d	09 50	11 50	13 50	15 40	17 55	20 40
Okehampton West Street	a	10 25	12 25	14 25	16 25	18 30	21 30
Okehampton Fore Street	a						
Holsworthy Library	a						
Holsworthy Church	a	10 58	12 58	14 58	16 58	19 03	22 03
Bude Strand	a	11 20	13 20	15 20	17 20	19 25	22 25

Saturdays

		GW	GW	GW	GW	GW	GW	GW	GW	GW	GW	GW	GW	GW	GW	GW	GW
Exeter St Davids	d	09 25	10 25	11 25	12 25	13 25	13 55	14 25	15 25	15 55	16 25	16 55	17 25	17 55	18 25	19 40	20 40
Okehampton West Street	a	10 00	11 10	12 00	13 10	14 00	14 40	15 00	16 10	16 30	17 00	17 45	18 15	18 45	19 15	20 30	21 30
Okehampton Fore Street	a																
Holsworthy Library	a																
Holsworthy Church	a	10 33		12 33		14 33					17 33		18 48		19 48	21 03	22 03
Bude Strand	a	10 55		12 55		14 55					17 55		19 10	20 00	20 10	21 25	22 25

Sundays

		GW	GW
Exeter St Davids	d	12 25	17 25
Okehampton West Street	a	13 15	18 15
Okehampton Fore Street	a		
Holsworthy Library	a		
Holsworthy Church	a	13 48	18 48
Bude Strand	a	14 10	19 10

Mondays to Fridays

		GW	GW	GW	GW	GW	GW	GW FO
Bude Strand	d	06 40	09 00	11 30	13 30	15 25	15 30	17 30
Holsworthy Library	d							
Holsworthy Church	d	07 02	09 22	11 52	13 52	15 57	15 57	17 52
Okehampton West Street	d	07 40	10 00	12 30	14 30	16 35	16 35	18 25
Okehampton Fore Street	d							
Exeter St Davids	a	08 15	10 35	13 05	15 05	17 15	17 15	19 07

Saturdays

		GW	GW	GW	GW	GW	GW	GW	GW	GW	GW	GW	GW	GW	GW	GW
Bude Strand	d	05 45	06 40	08 15	09 15			11 15		13 15				15 30	17 15	17 30
Holsworthy Library	d															
Holsworthy Church	d		07 02	08 37	09 37			11 37		13 37				15 57	17 37	17 52
Okehampton West Street	d	07 00	07 40	09 15	10 15	10 45	11 15	12 15	13 15	14 15	14 45	15 15	16 15	16 35	18 10	18 25
Okehampton Fore Street	d															
Exeter St Davids	a	07 40	08 20	10 00	10 50	11 20	12 00	12 50	14 00	14 50	15 30	15 50	17 00	17 10	18 50	19 07

Sundays

		GW	GW
Bude Strand	d	10 10	15 10
Holsworthy Library	d		
Holsworthy Church	d	10 32	15 32
Okehampton West Street	d	11 10	16 10
Okehampton Fore Street	d		
Exeter St Davids	a	12 00	17 00

For general notes see front of timetable
For details of catering facilities see Directory of Train Operators

Table 135E

Mondays to Saturdays

Taunton — Watchet, Dunster and Minehead

Bus Service

		GW	GW		GW	GW		GW	GW		GW	GW		GW	GW		GW	GW		GW	GW		GW	GW	GW
Taunton	d	05 41	07 14		07 44	08 14		08 44	09 14		09 44	10 14		10 44	11 14		11 44	12 14		12 44	13 14		13 44	14 14	14 44
Watchet (West Somerset Ry)	a	06 25	07 58		08 28	08 58		09 32	09 58		10 32	11 02		11 32	12 02		12 32	13 02		13 32	14 02		14 32	15 02	15 32
Dunster Steep	a	06 39	08 15		08 45	09 15		09 49	10 15		10 49	11 19		11 49	12 19		12 49	13 19		13 49	14 19		14 49	15 19	15 49
Minehead Parade	a	06 47	08 23		08 53	09 23		09 57	10 27		10 57	11 27		11 57	12 27		12 57	13 27		13 57	14 27		14 57	15 27	15 57
Minehead Bancks Street	a																								

		GW		GW	GW		GW	GW		GW	GW		GW	GW		GW	GW		GW	GW		GW			
								SX		SO															
Taunton	d	15 14		15 44	16 14		16 44	17 09		17 09	17 29		17 59	18 29		19 16	20 16		21 16	22 16		23 16			
Watchet (West Somerset Ry)	a	16 02		16 32	16 58		16 28	17 51		17 53	18 13		18 43	19 13		20 00	21 00		22 00	23 00		23 59			
Dunster Steep	a	16 19		16 49	17 15		17 45	18 08		18 10	18 30		19 00	19 30		20 14	21 14		22 14	23 14		00 14			
Minehead Parade	a	16 27		16 57	17 23		17 53	18 16		18 18	18 38		19 08	19 38		20 22	21 22		22 22	23 22		00 22			
Minehead Bancks Street	a																								

Sundays

		GW	GW	GW	GW	GW	GW	GW	GW	GW	GW
Taunton	d	09 35	11 35	12 35	13 35	14 35	15 35	16 35	17 35	19 35	23 15
Watchet (West Somerset Ry)	a	10 18	12 18	13 18	14 18	15 18	16 18	17 18	18 18	20 18	23 58
Dunster Steep	a	10 32	12 32	13 32	14 32	15 32	16 32	17 32	18 32	20 32	00 12
Minehead Parade	a	10 40	12 40	13 40	14 40	15 40	16 40	17 40	18 40	20 40	00 20
Minehead Bancks Street	a										

Mondays to Saturdays

		GW	GW		GW	GW		GW	GW		GW	GW		GW	GW		GW	GW		GW	GW		GW	GW	GW
			SX		SO			SO																	
Minehead Bancks Street	d	05 50	07 00		07 10	07 20		07 42	08 17		08 47	09 17		09 47	10 17		10 47	11 17		11 47	12 17		12 47	13 17	13 47
Minehead Parade	d																								
Dunster Steep	d	05 58	07 08		07 18	07 28		07 50	08 25		08 55	09 25		09 55	10 25		10 55	11 25		11 55	12 25		12 55	13 25	13 55
Watchet (West Somerset Ry)	d	06 13	07 26		07 36	07 46		08 08	08 43		09 13	09 43		10 13	10 43		11 13	11 43		12 13	12 43		13 13	13 43	14 13
Taunton	a	06 55	08 14		08 18	08 33		08 50	09 25		09 55	10 25		10 55	11 29		11 59	12 29		12 59	13 29		14 00	14 29	14 59

		GW		GW	GW		GW	GW		GW	GW		GW	GW		GW	GW		GW	GW		GW	GW		
														SX		SO									
Minehead Bancks Street	d	14 17		14 47	15 17		15 47	16 17		16 47	17 17		17 47	18 17		18 17	18 45		19 45	20 35		21 35	22 35		
Minehead Parade	d																								
Dunster Steep	d	14 25		14 55	15 25		15 55	16 25		16 55	17 25		17 55	18 25		18 25	18 53		19 53	20 43		21 43	22 43		
Watchet (West Somerset Ry)	d	14 43		15 13	15 43		16 13	16 43		17 13	17 43		18 13	19 43		19 43	19 08		20 08	20 58		21 58	22 58		
Taunton	a	15 29		15 59	16 29		16 59	17 29		17 59	18 29		19 00	19 25		19 29	19 50		20 50	21 40		22 40	23 40		

Sundays

		GW	GW	GW	GW	GW	GW	GW	GW	GW
Minehead Bancks Street	d	08 55	10 55	12 55	13 55	14 55	15 55	16 55	17 55	18 55
Minehead Parade	d									
Dunster Steep	d	09 03	11 03	13 03	14 03	15 03	16 03	17 03	18 03	19 03
Watchet (West Somerset Ry)	d	09 18	11 18	13 18	14 18	15 18	16 18	17 18	18 18	19 18
Taunton	a	10 00	12 00	14 00	15 00	16 00	17 00	18 00	19 00	20 00

For general notes see front of timetable
For details of catering facilities see Directory of Train Operators

Exmouth → Exeter → Barnstaple

Network Diagram - see first page of Table 135

Miles			GW MX	GW MO	GW	GW	SW 1	GW	GW	SW 1	GW A	SW 1	GW A	GW A	GW	GW B	SW 1	GW A	GW	SW 1 ◊ ☕	GW A
0	**Exmouth**	d	23p45	23p47		06 05			06 48		07 15		07 50	08 20		08 50		09 20	09 50		10 20
2	Lympstone Village	d	23p49	23p51		06 09			06 52		07 19		07 54	08 24		08 54		09 24	09 54		10 24
3	Lympstone Commando	d	23b51	23b53		06x11			06x54		07x21		07x56	08x26		08x56		09x26	09x56		
3½	Exton	d	23b53	23b54		06x13			06x56		07x23		07x58	08x28		08x58		09x28	09x58		
5	Topsham	d	23p57	23p59		06 17			07 01		07 27		08c06	08 32		09 02		09 32	10 02		10 33
7	Digby & Sowton	d	00 01	00 03		06 21			07 05		07 31		08 10	08 36		09 06		09 36	10 06		10 37
9	Polsloe Bridge	d	00 04	00 06		06 24			07 08		07 34		08 14	08 39		09 09		09 39	10 09		
10	St James' Park	d	00 07	00 09		06 27			07 11		07 37		08 16	08 42		09 12		09 42	10 12		
10½	**Exeter Central**	a	00 09	00 11		06 29			07 13		07 39		08 18	08 44		09 14		09 44	10 14		10 42
—		d	00 09	00 11		06 29	06 32		07 13	07 32	07 39	08 12	08 19	08 44	09 04	09 14	09 24	09 44	10 14	10 30	10 43
11¼	**Exeter St Davids** 5	a	00 13	00 14		06 33	06 35		07 17	07 35	07 42	08 15	08 22	08 47	09 07	09 17	09 27	09 47	10 17	10 33	10 46
—		d			05 56			06 51							09 12						
15½	Newton St Cyres	d																			
18¼	Crediton	d			06 06			07 01							09e30						
—	Sampford Courtenay	d																			
—	Okehampton	a																			
21¾	Yeoford	d			06x13			07x08							09x37						
24½	Copplestone	d			06x19			07x14							09x42						
26¼	Morchard Road	d						07x16							09x45						
28¾	Lapford	d						07x20													
32½	Eggesford	d			06 31			07f50							09 57						
36¼	Kings Nympton	d						07x56													
39¼	Portsmouth Arms	d						08x00													
43½	Umberleigh	d			06x46			08x06							10x12						
45¾	Chapelton	d						08x10													
50¼	**Barnstaple**	a			06 58			08 16							10 21						

		GW	SW 1 ◊ ☕	GW A	GW C	GW	SW 1 ◊ ☕	GW A	GW	SW 1 ◊ ☕	GW A	GW	GW A	GW	SW 1 ◊ ☕	GW	GW A	SW 1	GW	GW A
Exmouth	d	10 50		11 20		11 50		12 20	12 50		13 20	13 50	14 20	14 50		15 20	15 50			16 20
Lympstone Village	d	10 54		11 24		11 54		12 24	12 54		13 24	13 54	14 24	14 54		15 24	15 54			16 24
Lympstone Commando	d	10x56				11x56			12x56			13x56		14x56		15x26	15x56			
Exton	d	10x58				11x58			12x58			13x58		14x58		15x28	15x58			
Topsham	d	11 02		11 33		12 02		12 33	13 02		13 33	14 02	14 33	15 02		15 33	16 02			16 32
Digby & Sowton	d	11 06		11 37		12 06		12 37	13 06		13 37	14 06	14 37	15 06		15 36	16 06			16 36
Polsloe Bridge	d	11 09				12 09			13 09			14 09		15 09		15 39	16 09			
St James' Park	d	11 12				12 12			13 12			14 12		15 12		15 43	16 12			
Exeter Central	a	11 14		11 43		12 14		12 42	13 14		13 44	14 14	14 42	15 14		15 45	16 14			16 41
	d	11 18	11 38	11 43	12 08	12 16	12 30	12 43	13 14	13 38	13 45	14 14	14 43	15 14	15 39	15 46	16 17	16 23	16 32	16 42
Exeter St Davids 6	a	11 21	11 42	11 48	12 11	12 19	12 33	12 46	13 17	13 41	13 48	14 17	14 46	15 17	15 42	15 49	16 20	16 26	16 35	16 45
	d	11 27							13 19			14 26		15 33					16 36	
Newton St Cyres	d																			
Crediton	d	11 38							13 29			14 36		15 44					16 47	
Sampford Courtenay	d																			
Okehampton	a																			
Yeoford	d	11x45							13x36			14x43		15x51					16x54	
Copplestone	d	11x50							13x42			14x49		15x57					16x59	
Morchard Road	d											14x51							17x02	
Lapford	d																		17x06	
Eggesford	d	12 02							13 54			15 04		16 09					17g18	
Kings Nympton	d																		17x24	
Portsmouth Arms	d																			
Umberleigh	d	12x17							14x09			15x19		16x24					17x34	
Chapelton	d																			
Barnstaple	a	12 28							14 20			15 30		16 35					17 45	

		GW A	SW 1 ◊ ☕	GW	SW 1	GW A	GW	SW 1	GW A	GW	SW 1 ◊ ☕	SW 1 ▼ ☕	GW	GW	SW 1 ◊ ☕	SW FO 1 ◊ ☕	GW	SW FO 1 ◊ ☕	SW FX 1 ◊ ☕	GW
Exmouth	d	16 50		17 20		17 50	18 20		18 54	19 20			20 20	21 20			22 20			23 45
Lympstone Village	d	16 54		17 24		17 54	18 24		18 58	19 24			20 24	21 24			22 24			23 49
Lympstone Commando	d	16x56		17x26		17x56	18x26		19x00	19x26			20 26	21x26			22x26			23x51
Exton	d	16x58		17x28		17x58	18x28		19x02	19x28			20 28	21x28			22x28			23x53
Topsham	d	17 02		17 34		18h06	18 35		19 06	19 32			20 32	21 32			22 32			23 57
Digby & Sowton	d	17 06		17 38		18 10	18 39		19 10	19 36			20 36	21 36			22 36			00 01
Polsloe Bridge	d	17 09		17 41		18 13	18 42		19 13	19 39			20 39	21 39			22 39			00 04
St James' Park	d	17 12		17 45		18 16	18 45		19 16	19 42			20 42	21 42			22 42			00 07
Exeter Central	a	17 14		17 46		18 18	18 47		19 18	19 44			20 44	21 44			22 44			00 09
	d	17 14	17 35	17 46	17 56	18 18	18 50	19 01	19 18	19 44	19 52	20 31	20 44	21 44	21 50	22 38	22 44	23 51	23 58	00 09
Exeter St Davids 6	a	17 17	17 38	17 53	17 59	18 21	18 53	19 04	19 21	19 47	19 57	20 36	20 47	21 48	21 55	22 41	22 48	23 54	00 01	00 13
	d			17 55			19 08						20 55							
Newton St Cyres	d			18x02			19x16						21x02							
Crediton	d			18 08			19 22						21 09							
Sampford Courtenay	d																			
Okehampton	a																			
Yeoford	d			18x15			19x29						21x16							
Copplestone	d			18x21			19x35						21x21							
Morchard Road	d			18x23			19x38						21x24							
Lapford	d			18x27			19x42						21x27							
Eggesford	d			18 36			19 51						21 37							
Kings Nympton	d			18x42			19x57						21x43							
Portsmouth Arms	d			18x46			20x01						21x47							
Umberleigh	d			18x53			20x08						21x53							
Chapelton	d			18x56			20x11						21x57							
Barnstaple	a			19 04			20 19						22 05							

For general notes see front of timetable
For details of catering facilities see Directory of Train Operators

A To Paignton (Table 135)
B To Penzance (Table 135)
C To Gunnislake (Table 139)
b Previous night.
Stops on request, passengers wishing to alight must inform the guard and those wishing to join must give a hand signal to the driver
c Arr. 0801
e Arr. 0922
f Arr. 0728
g Arr. 1713
h Arr. 1801

Exmouth → Exeter → Barnstaple

Network Diagram - see first page of Table 135

		GW	GW	SW	GW	GW	SW	GW	GW	SW	GW	GW	GW	SW	GW	GW	SW	GW
				1			1			1			1 ◇	1			1 ◇	
								A			A	B	C		A			A
												🍴	🍴				☕	
Exmouth	d	23p45			06 15			07 18	07 50		08 20	08 50			09 20	09 50		10 20
Lympstone Village	d	23p49			06 19			07 22	07 54		08 24	08 54			09 24	09 54		10 24
Lympstone Commando	d	23b51			06x21			07x24	07x56		08x26	08x56			09x26	09x56		10x26
Exton	d	23b53			06x23			07x26	07x58		08x28	08x58			09x28	09x58		
Topsham	d	23p57			06 27			07 30	08 01		08 32	09 02			09 32	10 02		10 33
Digby & Sowton	d	00 01			06 31			07 34	08 05		08 36	09 06			09 36	10 06		10 37
Polsloe Bridge	d	00 04			06 34			07 37	08 08		08 39	09 09			09 39	10 09		
St James' Park	d	00 07			06 37			07 40	08 11		08 42	09 12			09 42	10 12		
Exeter Central	a	00 09			06 39			07 42	08 14		08 44	09 14			09 44	10 14		10 42
	d	00 09		06 32	06 39		07 36	07 42	08 14	08 27	08 44	09 14		09 24	09 44	10 14	10 29	10 43
Exeter St Davids 6	a	00 13		06 35	06 43		07 39	07 45	08 17	08 30	08 47	09 17		09 27	09 47	10 18	10 32	10 46
	d		05 56			06 51							09 18					
Newton St Cyres	d																	
Crediton	d		06 05			07 01							09 29					
Sampford Courtenay	d																	
Okehampton	a																	
Yeoford	d		06x12			07x08							09x36					
Copplestone	d		06x18			07x14							09x42					
Morchard Road	d					07x16							09x44					
Lapford	d					07x20												
Eggesford	d		06 30			07c50							09 56					
Kings Nympton	d					07x56												
Portsmouth Arms	d					08x00												
Umberleigh	d		06x45			08x06							10x11					
Chapelton	d					08x10												
Barnstaple	a		06 56			08 16							10 20					

		GW	GW	SW	GW	SW	GW	GW	SW	GW	GW	SW	GW	GW	GW	SW	GW	GW
				1 ◇		1 ◇			1 ◇			1 ◇				1 ◇		
			A				A			A			A				A	
				☕		☕			☕			☕				☕		
Exmouth	d	10 50	11 20		11 50		12 20	12 50		13 20	13 50		14 20	14 50			15 20	15 50
Lympstone Village	d	10 54	11 24		11 54		12 24	12 54		13 24	13 54		14 24	14 54			15 24	15 54
Lympstone Commando	d	10x56	11x26		11x56		12x26	12x56		13x26	13x56			14x56			15x26	15x56
Exton	d	10x58			11x58			12x58			13x58			14x58			15x28	15x58
Topsham	d	11 02	11 33		12 02		12 33	13 02		13 33	14 02		14 33	15 02			15 33	16 02
Digby & Sowton	d	11 06	11 37		12 06		12 37	13 06		13 37	14 06		14 37	15 06			15 37	16 06
Polsloe Bridge	d	11 09			12 09			13 09			14 09			15 09			15 40	16 09
St James' Park	d	11 12			12 12			13 12			14 12			15 12			15 43	16 12
Exeter Central	a	11 14	11 42		12 14		12 42	13 14		13 43	14 14		14 42	15 14			15 45	16 14
	d	11 14	11 43	11 53	12 14	12 27	12 43	13 14	13 39	13 46	14 16	14 19	14 43	15 14	15 31	15 39	15 46	16 14
Exeter St Davids 6	a	11 17	11 46	11 56	12 18	12 30	12 46	13 17	13 42	13 49	14 19	14 22	14 46	15 18	15 34	15 42	15 49	16 17
	d	11 19						13 19			14 26				15 35			16 36
Newton St Cyres	d																	
Crediton	d	11 30						13 29			14 36				15 46			16 47
Sampford Courtenay	d																	
Okehampton	a																	
Yeoford	d	11x37						13x36			14x43				15x52			16x54
Copplestone	d	11x43						13x42			14x49				15x59			17x00
Morchard Road	d							13x45			14x51							17x02
Lapford	d																	17x06
Eggesford	d	11 54						13 57			15 04				16 08			17e18
Kings Nympton	d							14 03										17x24
Portsmouth Arms	d																	
Umberleigh	d	12x10						14x13			15x19				16x24			17x34
Chapelton	d																	
Barnstaple	a	12 20						14 23			15 30				16 33			17 45

		SW	GW	GW	SW	GW	SW	GW	GW	SW	GW	GW	SW	GW	GW	SW	SW	GW	GW
		1			1 ◇		1			1			1 ◇			1 ◇	1 ◇		
			A	A				A				A							
					☕								☕			☕	☕		
Exmouth	d		16 20	16 50		17 20		17 50	18 20		18 54	19 20		20 26	21 20			22 20	23 41
Lympstone Village	d		16 24	16 54		17 24		17 54	18 24		18 58	19 24		20 30	21 24			22 24	23 45
Lympstone Commando	d			16x56		17x26		17x56	18x26		19x00	19x26		20x32	21x26			22x26	23x47
Exton	d			16x58		17x28		17x58	18x28		19x02	19x28		20x34	21x28			22x28	23x49
Topsham	d		16 32	17 02		17 33		18f06	18 35		19 06	19 32		20 38	21 32			22 32	23 53
Digby & Sowton	d		16 36	17 06		17 37		18 10	18 39		19 10	19 36		20 42	21 36			22 36	23 57
Polsloe Bridge	d			17 09		17 40		18 13	18 42		19 13	19 39		20 45	21 39			22 39	00 01
St James' Park	d			17 12		17 43		18 17	18 45		19 16	19 42		20 48	21 42			22 42	00 03
Exeter Central	a		16 41	17 14		17 45		18 19	18 47		19 18	19 44		20 50	21 44			22 44	00 05
	d	16 24	16 42	17 14	17 33	17 45	17 53	18 19	18 52	19 01	19 18	19 44	19 52	20 50	21 44	21 48	22 38	22 44	00 05
Exeter St Davids 6	a	16 27	16 45	17 17	17 36	17 48	17 56	18 22	18 55	19 04	19 22	19 47	19 57	20 53	21 48	21 53	22 41	22 48	00 09
	d					17 50			19 08					20 55					
Newton St Cyres	d					17 57			19 16					21x02					
Crediton	d					18 03			19 22					21 09					
Sampford Courtenay	d																		
Okehampton	a																		
Yeoford	d					18x10			19x29					21x16					
Copplestone	d					18x16			19x35					21x21					
Morchard Road	d					18x19			19x38					21x24					
Lapford	d					18x23			19x42					21x27					
Eggesford	d					18 32			19 51					21 37					
Kings Nympton	d					18x38			19x57					21x43					
Portsmouth Arms	d					18x43			20x01					21x47					
Umberleigh	d					18x49			20x08					21x53					
Chapelton	d					18x53			20x11					21x57					
Barnstaple	a					19 01			20 19					22 05					

For general notes see front of timetable
For details of catering facilities see Directory of Train Operators

A To Paignton (Table 135)

B To Penzance (Table 135)

C From Penzance (Table 135)

b Previous night.

Stops on request, passengers wishing to alight must inform the guard and those wishing to join must give a hand signal to the driver

c Arr. 0728

e Arr. 1713

f Arr. 1801

Table 136

Sundays

Exmouth → Exeter → Barnstaple

Network Diagram - see first page of Table 135

		GW	SW [1]	GW	GW	GW	SW [1] ◇	SW [1] ◇	GW	GW	SW [1] ◇	GW	GW	SW [1] ◇
				A	B	B				C				
								☕			☕			☕
Exmouth	d	23p41			09⌇10	10⌇00			11 10	12 05		13 05	14 10	
Lympstone Village	d	23p45			09⌇14	10⌇04			11 14	12 09		13 09	14 14	
Lympstone Commando	d	23b47			09x16	10x06			11x16	12x11		13x11	14x16	
Exton	d	23b49			09x18	10x07			11x17	12x12		13x12	14x17	
Topsham	d	23p53			09⌇22	10⌇12			11 22	12 17		13 17	14 22	
Digby & Sowton	d	23p57			09⌇26	10⌇16			11 26	12 21		13 21	14 26	
Polsloe Bridge	d	00 01			09⌇29	10⌇19			11 29	12 24		13 24	14 29	
St James' Park	d	00 03			09⌇32	10⌇22			11 32	12 27		13 27	14 32	
Exeter Central	a	00 05			09⌇34	10⌇24			11 34	12 29		13 29	14 34	
	d	00 05	08 56		09⌇34	10⌇24	10 46	11 29	11 37	12 30	12 46	13 29	14 34	14 43
Exeter St Davids [6]	a	00 09	08 59		09⌇37	10⌇27	10 49	11 32	11 40	12 33	12 49	13 32	14 37	14 46
	d			09⌇41	09⌇42				11 55			13 55		
Newton St Cyres	d			09x49	09x49							14x03		
Crediton	d			09⌇57	09⌇57				12 10			14 10		
Sampford Courtenay	d													
Okehampton	a													
Yeoford	d			10x04	10x04				12x17			14x18		
Copplestone	d			10x09	10x09				12x23			14x23		
Morchard Road	d			10x12	10x12				12x26			14x26		
Lapford	d			10x16	10x16							14x30		
Eggesford	d			10⌇26	10⌇26				12 37			14 40		
Kings Nympton	d			10x33	10x33							14x47		
Portsmouth Arms	d			10x37	10x37							14x51		
Umberleigh	d			10x44	10x44				12x52			14x58		
Chapelton	d			10x48	10x48							15x02		
Barnstaple	a			10⌇55	10⌇55				13 02			15 09		

		GW	GW	SW [1] ◇	GW	GW	GW	SW [1] ◇	GW	GW	SW [1] ◇	GW	GW	SW [1] ◇	GW	GW
						D	E					C				
				☕				☕			☕			☕		
Exmouth	d	15 10	16 10		17 10	18⌇10	18⌇10		19 10	20 10		21 10	22 10		23 01	23 47
Lympstone Village	d	15 14	16 14		17 14	18⌇14	18⌇14		19 14	20 14		21 14	22 14		23 05	23 51
Lympstone Commando	d	15x16	16x16		17x16	18x16	18x16		19x16	20x16		21x16	22x16		23x07	23x53
Exton	d	15x17	16x17		17x17	18x17	18x17		19x17	20x17		21x17	22x17		23x08	23x54
Topsham	d	15 22	16 22		17 22	18⌇22	18⌇22		19 22	20 22		21 22	22 22		23 13	23 59
Digby & Sowton	d	15 26	16 26		17 26	18⌇26	18⌇26		19 26	20 26		21 26	22 26		23 17	00 03
Polsloe Bridge	d	15 29	16 29		17 29	18⌇29	18⌇29		19 29	20 29		21 29	22 29		23 20	00 06
St James' Park	d	15 32	16 32		17 32	18⌇32	18⌇32		19 32	20 32		21 32	22 32		23 23	00 09
Exeter Central	a	15 34	16 34		17 34	18⌇34	18⌇34		19 34	20 34		21 34	22 34		23 25	00 11
	d	15 34	16 34	16 43	17 34	18⌇35	18⌇35	18 43	19 34	20 34	20 46	21 35	22 34	22 43	23 25	00 11
Exeter St Davids [6]	a	15 37	16 37	16 46	17 37	18⌇38	18⌇39	18 46	19 37	20 39	20 49	21 38	22 38	22 46	23 28	00 14
	d	15 54			18 00				19 49							
Newton St Cyres	d	16x02							19x57							
Crediton	d	16 09			18 14				20 07							
Sampford Courtenay	d															
Okehampton	a															
Yeoford	d	16x16			18x21				20x14							
Copplestone	d	16x22			18x27				20x20							
Morchard Road	d	16x25			18x30				20x23							
Lapford	d	16x29							20x27							
Eggesford	d	16c39			18 41				20 37							
Kings Nympton	d	16x45							20x43							
Portsmouth Arms	d	16x50							20x48							
Umberleigh	d	16x56			18x56				20x54							
Chapelton	d	17x00							20x58							
Barnstaple	a	17 08			19 06				21 06							

For general notes see front of timetable
For details of catering facilities see Directory of Train Operators

A Until 23 March

B From 30 March

C To Paignton (Table 135)

D From 30 March. To Paignton (Table 135)

E Until 23 March. To Paignton (Table 135)

b Previous night.

Stops on request, passengers wishing to alight must inform the guard and those wishing to join must give a hand signal to the driver

c Arr. 1635

Barnstaple → Exeter → Exmouth

Network Diagram - see first page of Table 135

Miles	Station		SW	GW	GW	SW	GW	GW	GW	SW	GW	GW	SW	GW	GW	GW	GW	SW	GW
			1 ◇			1 ◇				1			1 ◇					1 ◇	
								A	A		A								A
			☕			☕							☕					☕	
0	**Barnstaple**	d										07 04					08 41		
4¼	Chapelton	d										07x10							
6¾	Umberleigh	d										07x14					08x49		
10¾	Portsmouth Arms	d										07x21							
13¾	Kings Nympton	d										07x26							
17½	Eggesford	d										07 35					09 07		
21½	Lapford	d										07x41							
23¾	Morchard Road	d										07x45							
25½	Copplestone	d										07x49					09x18		
28½	Yeoford	d										07x53					09x22		
—	Okehampton	d																	
—	Sampford Courtenay	d																	
32	Crediton	d										08 00					09 30		
34¾	Newton St Cyres	d										08x04							
39	**Exeter St Davids** 6	a										08 15					09 40		
—		d	05 10	05 35	06 00	06 41	06 45	07 10	07 49	08 00	08 06	08 15	08 25	08 46	08 55	09 18	09 45	10 10	10 18
39¾	**Exeter Central**	a	05 13	05 38	06 03	06 44	06 48	07 13	07 52	08 03	08 11	08 18	08 29	08 49	08 58	09 21	09 48	10 13	10 21
—		d		05 38	06 03		06 48	07 14	07 52		08 12	08 18		08 49		09 21	09 48		10 21
40¼	St James' Park	d		05 40	06 05		06 50	07 16	07 54		08a16	08 20		08 51			09 50		
41¼	Polsloe Bridge	d		05 43	06 08		06 53	07 19	07 57			08 23		08 54			09 53		
43¼	Digby & Sowton	d		05 47	06 12		06 57	07 22	08 01			08 27		08 58		09 27	09 57		10 27
45¼	Topsham	d		05 51	06 18		07 01	07 27	08 05			08 32		09 02		09 32	10 02		10 32
46¾	Exton	d		05x53	06x20		07x03	07x30	08x07			08x35		09x05			10x05		
47¼	Lympstone Commando	d		05x55	06x22		07x05	07x31	08x09			08x37		09x07			10x07		
48¼	Lympstone Village	d		05 57	06 24		07 07	07 34	08 11			08 39		09 09		09 37	10 09		10 37
50¼	**Exmouth**	a		06 03	06 30		07 13	07 40	08 17			08 45		09 15		09 45	10 15		10 45

Station		GW	GW	GW	GW	SW	GW	GW	GW	SW	GW	SW	GW	GW	GW	SW	GW	SW
						1 ◇				1 ◇		1 ◇		◇		1		1 ◇
			A				A		A				A	B	A			
						☕				☕		☕						☕
Barnstaple	d			10 30							12 41						14 35	
Chapelton	d																	
Umberleigh	d			10x38							12x49						14x43	
Portsmouth Arms	d																	
Kings Nympton	d																	
Eggesford	d			10 56							13 07						15 03	
Lapford	d																	
Morchard Road	d			11x05													15x12	
Copplestone	d			11x08							13x18						15x15	
Yeoford	d			11x13							13x22						15x20	
Okehampton	d																	
Sampford Courtenay	d																	
Crediton	d			11 19							13 29						15 26	
Newton St Cyres	d																	
Exeter St Davids 6	a			11 32							13 40						15 38	
	d	10 45	11 18	11 33	11 45	12 10	12 18	12 45	13 18	13 35	13 45	14 10	14 18	14 45	15 18	15 30	15 45	16 10
Exeter Central	a	10 48	11 21	11 36	11 48	12 13	12 21	12 48	13 21	13 38	13 48	14 13	14 21	14 48	15 21	15 33	15 48	16 13
	d	10 48	11 21		11 48		12 21	12 48	13 21		13 48		14 21	14 48	15 21		15 48	
St James' Park	d	10 50			11 50			12 50			13 50			14 50			15 50	
Polsloe Bridge	d	10 53			11 53			12 53			13 53			14 53			15 53	
Digby & Sowton	d	10 57	11 27		11 57		12 27	12 57	13 27		13 57		14 27	14 57	15 27		15 57	
Topsham	d	11 02	11 32		12 02		12 32	13 02	13 32		14 02		14 32	15 02	15 32		16 03	
Exton	d	11x05			12x04			13x05			14x04			15x05			16x05	
Lympstone Commando	d	11x07			12x06			13x07			14x06			15x07			16x07	
Lympstone Village	d	11 09	11 37		12 08		12 37	13 09	13 37		14 08		14 37	15 09	15 37		16 09	
Exmouth	a	11 15	11 45		12 15		12 45	13 15	13 45		14 12		14 45	15 15	15 45		16 15	

Station		GW	SW	GW	GW	SW	GW	SW	GW	GW	SW	GW	GW	SW	GW	SW	GW	SW	SW
																		FX	FO
			1			1		1 ◇			1 ◇			1		1		1	1
		A			A				A	A									
								☕											
Barnstaple	d			15 42			16 50					18 06			19 24		20 22		
Chapelton	d											18x12							
Umberleigh	d			15x50			16x58					18x16			19x32		20x30		
Portsmouth Arms	d											18x22							
Kings Nympton	d						17x09					18x27							
Eggesford	d			16 08			17 17					18 37			19 52		20 48		
Lapford	d											18x43							
Morchard Road	d											18x47							
Copplestone	d			16x19			17x27					18x50			20x02		20x58		
Yeoford	d			16 23			17x32					18x55			20x07		21x03		
Okehampton	d																		
Sampford Courtenay	d																		
Crediton	d			16 30			17 38					19 01			20 14		21 09		
Newton St Cyres	d											19x05			20x18		21x13		
Exeter St Davids 6	a			16 40			17 48					19 13			20 26		21 25		
	d	16 18	16 36	16 45	17 18	17 40	17 50	18 10	18 18	18 49	19 10	19 22	19 49	20 15	20 49	21 00	21 49	22 30	22 57
Exeter Central	a	16 21	16 39	16 48	17 21	17 43	17 53	18 13	18 21	18 52	19 13	19 26	19 52	20 18	20 52	21 03	21 52	22 33	23 00
	d	16 21		16 48	17 21		17 53		18 21	18 52			19 52		20 52		21 52		
St James' Park	d			16 50	17 23		17 55		18 23	18 54			19 54		20 54		21 54		
Polsloe Bridge	d			16 53	17 26		17 58		18 26	18 57			19 57		20 57		21 57		
Digby & Sowton	d	16 27		16 57	17 30		18 02		18 30	19 01			20 01		21 01		22 01		
Topsham	d	16 32		17 02	17 34		18 06		18 34	19 06			20 05		21 05		22 05		
Exton	d			17x05	17x37		18x09		18x37	19x09			20x07		21x07		22x07		
Lympstone Commando	d			17x07	17x39		18x11		18x39	19x11			20x09		21x09		22x09		
Lympstone Village	d	16 37		17 09	17 41		18 13		18 41	19 13			20 11		21 11		22 11		
Exmouth	a	16 45		17 15	17 48		18 19		18 48	19 19			20 18		21 18		22 18		

For general notes see front of timetable
For details of catering facilities see Directory of Train Operators

A From Paignton (Table 135)
B From Penzance (Table 135)

Table 136

Saturdays

Barnstaple → Exeter → Exmouth

Network Diagram - see first page of Table 135

		SW	GW	SW	GW	GW	GW	SW	GW	SW	GW	GW	GW	SW	GW	GW	SW	GW	GW	SW	GW	GW	GW	SW	SW	GW
		1◇		1◇				1		1◇				1◇			1◇			1◇				1◇	1◇	
						A	A					A			A			A			A		A			A
		☕		☕						☕				☕			☕			☕				☕	☕	
Barnstaple	d								07 03				08 41						10 40							
Chapelton	d								07x09																	
Umberleigh	d								07x13				08x49						10x48							
Portsmouth Arms	d								07x20																	
Kings Nympton	d								07x25																	
Eggesford	d								07 34				09 08						11 06							
Lapford	d								07x39																	
Morchard Road	d								07x43										11x14							
Copplestone	d								07x47				09x18						11x18							
Yeoford	d								07x51				09x23						11x22							
Okehampton	d																									
Sampford Courtenay	d																									
Crediton	d								08 00				09 31						11 30							
Newton St Cyres	d								08x03																	
Exeter St Davids 6	a								08 13				09 43						11 42							
	d	05 10	05 35	06 41	06 45	07 14	07 46	08 00	08 15	08 25	08 46	09 18	09 45	10 10	10 18	10 45	11 08	11 18	11 45	12 10	12 18	12 45	13 18	13 35	14 10	14 18
Exeter Central	a	05 13	05 38	06 44	06 48	07 17	07 49	08 03	08 18	08 29	08 49	09 21	09 48	10 13	10 21	10 48	11 11	11 21	11 48	12 13	12 21	12 48	13 21	13 38	14 13	14 21
	d		05 38		06 48	07 17	07 49		08 18		08 49	09 21	09 48		10 21	10 48		11 21	11 48		12 21	12 48	13 21			14 21
St James' Park	d		05 40		06 50	07 19	07 51		08 20		08 51		09 50			10 50			11 50			12 50				
Polsloe Bridge	d		05 43		06 53	07 22	07 54		08 23		08 54		09 53			10 53			11 53			12 53				
Digby & Sowton	d		05 47		06 57	07 26	07 58		08 27		08 58	09 27	09 57		10 27	10 57		11 27	11 57		12 27	12 57	13 27			14 27
Topsham	d		05 51		07 01	07 31	08 03		08 32		09 02	09 32	10 02		10 32	11 02		11 32	12 02		12 32	13 02	13 32			14 32
Exton	d		05x53		07x03	07x34	08x06		08x35		09x05		10x05			11x05			12x05			13x05				
Lympstone Commando	d		05x55		07x05	07x36	08x08		08x37		09x07		10x07			11x07			12x07			13x07				
Lympstone Village	d		05 57		07 07	07 38	08 10		08 39		09 09	09 37	10 09		10 37	11 09		11 37	12 09		12 37	13 09	13 37			14 37
Exmouth	a		06 03		07 14	07 43	08 15		08 44		09 15	09 45	10 14		10 45	11 14		11 45	12 14		12 45	13 14	13 42			14 45

		GW	GW	GW	SW	GW	SW	GW	SW	GW	GW	SW	GW	SW	GW	GW	SW	GW	SW	GW	GW	SW	GW	SW	GW
					1		1◇		1			1		1◇			1◇		1			1		1	
			A								A				A	B		A							
							☕							☕											
Barnstaple	d					14 35				15 42			16 48			18 00					19 24		20 22		22 06
Chapelton	d															18x06									22x12
Umberleigh	d					14x43				15x50			16x56			18x10					19x32		20x30		22x16
Portsmouth Arms	d															18x17									22x22
Kings Nympton	d												17x07			18x22									22x27
Eggesford	d					15 03				16 10			17 16			18 32					19 51		20 48		22 35
Lapford	d															18x38									22x40
Morchard Road	d					15x12										18x42									22x44
Copplestone	d					15x15				16x20			17x27			18x46					20x01		20x58		22x47
Yeoford	d					15x20				16x24			17x31			18x50					20x06		21x03		22x52
Okehampton	d																								
Sampford Courtenay	d																								
Crediton	d					15 26				16 30			17 38			18 56					20 13		21 09		22 58
Newton St Cyres	d															19x00					20x17		21x13		23x02
Exeter St Davids 6	a					15 41				16 43			17 48			19 07					20 26		21 22		23 09
	d	14 45	15 18	15 23	15 30	15 45	16 10	16 18	16 40	16 45	17 18	17 40	17 50	18 10	18 49		19 10	19 49	20 15	20 22	20 49	21 00	21 45	22 57	23 10
Exeter Central	a	14 48	15 21	15 26	15 33	15 48	16 13	16 21	16 43	16 48	17 21	17 43	17 54	18 13	18 52		19 13	19 52	20 18	20 25	20 52	21 03	21 48	23 00	23 13
	d	14 48	15 21			15 48		16 21		16 49	17 21		17 54		18 52			19 52			20 52		21 48		23 14
St James' Park	d	14 50				15 50				16 51	17 23		17 56		18 54			19 54			20 54		21 50		23 16
Polsloe Bridge	d	14 53				15 53				16 54	17 26		17 58		18 57			19 57			20 57		21 53		23 19
Digby & Sowton	d	14 57	15 27			15 57		16 27		16 57	17 30		18 02		19 01			20 01			21 01		21 57		23 22
Topsham	d	15 02	15 32			16 02		16 32		17 02	17 34		18 06		19 07			20 06			21 05		22 01		23 26
Exton	d	15x05				16x05				17x05	17x37		18x09		19x09			20x09			21x07		22x04		23x29
Lympstone Commando	d	15x07				16x07				17x07	17x39		18x11		19x11			20x11			21x09		22x06		23x31
Lympstone Village	d	15 09	15 37			16 09		16 37		17 10	17 41		18 13		19 13			20 13			21 11		22 08		23 34
Exmouth	a	15 14	15 45			16 14		16 45		17 14	17 45		18 19		19 18			20 18			21 18		22 14		23 39

Sundays

		GW	SW	GW	GW	SW	GW	GW	SW	GW	GW	SW	GW	GW	SW	SW	GW	GW	SW	GW	GW	SW	GW	GW	SW	GW
			1◇			1◇			1◇			1◇			1◇	1◇			1◇			1			1	
		C		C			A						A													
			☕			☕			☕			☕			☕	☕			☕							
Barnstaple	d							11 10			13 19			15 11				17 17			19 10			21 30		
Chapelton	d							11x16						15x17				17x23			19x16					
Umberleigh	d							11x20			13x27			15x21				17x27			19x20			21x38		
Portsmouth Arms	d							11x27						15x28				17x34			19x27					
Kings Nympton	d							11x32						15x33				17x39			19x32					
Eggesford	d							11 42			13 46			15 42				17 49			19 41			21 58		
Lapford	d							11x48						15x48				17x55			19x47					
Morchard Road	d							11x53			13x54			15x53				18x00			19x52					
Copplestone	d							11x56			13x57			15x56				18x03			19x55					
Yeoford	d							12x01			14x01			16x01				18x08			20x00					
Okehampton	d																									
Sampford Courtenay	d																									
Crediton	d							12 09			14 09			16 08				18 18			20 06			22 16		
Newton St Cyres	d							12x13						16x12				18x22			20x10					
Exeter St Davids 6	a							12 23			14 22			16 22				18 33			20 20			22 29		
	d	08 25	09 20	09 25	10 32	11 20	11 25	12 25	13 18	13 25	14 25	15 18	15 25	16 25	16 33	17 18	17 25	18 35	19 20	19 35	20 35	21 20	21 35	22 30	23 10	23 16
Exeter Central	a	08 28	09 23	09 28	10 35	11 23	11 28	12 28	13 21	13 28	14 28	15 21	15 28	16 28	16 36	17 21	17 28	18 38	19 23	19 38	20 38	21 23	21 38	22 33	23 13	23 19
	d	08 28		09 28	10 36		11 29	12 29		13 29	14 29		15 29	16 29			17 29	18 39		19 39	20 39		21 39	22 34		23 20
St James' Park	d	08 30		09 33	10 38		11 31	12 31		13 31	14 31		15 31	16 31			17 31	18 41		19 41	20 41		21 41	22 36		23 22
Polsloe Bridge	d	08 33		09 36	10 41		11 34	12 34		13 34	14 34		15 34	16 34			17 34	18 44		19 44	20 46		21 44	22 39		23 25
Digby & Sowton	d	08 37		09 39	10 44		11 37	12 38		13 37	14 38		15 37	16 38			17 37	18 47		19 47	20 50		21 47	22 42		23 28
Topsham	d	08 42		09 44	10 49		11 42	12 42		13 42	14 42		15 42	16 42			17 42	18 52		19 52	20 54		21 52	22 47		23 33
Exton	d	08x44		09x47	10x52		11x45	12x45		13x45	14x45		15x45	16x45			17x45	18x55		19x55	20x57		21x55	22x50		23x36
Lympstone Commando	d	08x46		09x48	10x54		11x47	12x47		13x47	14x47		15x47	16x47			17x47	18x57		19x57	20x59		21x57	22x52		23x38
Lympstone Village	d	08 48		09 51	10 56		11 49	12 50		13 49	14 50		15 49	16 50			17 49	18 59		19 59	21 02		21 59	22 54		23 40
Exmouth	a	08 53		09 56	11 00		11 53	12 54		13 53	14 54		15 53	16 54			17 53	19 03		20 03	21 06		22 03	22 58		23 44

For general notes see front of timetable
For details of catering facilities see
Directory of Train Operators

A From Paignton (Table 135)
B To Paignton (Table 135)
C From 30 March

Plymouth → Gunnislake

Network Diagram - see first page of Table 135

Miles			GW	GW	GW [1]	GW	GW	GW	GW A	GW	GW B	GW	GW	GW C	GW
0	**Plymouth**	d	05 37	06 42	07 05	08 28	09 34	11 30	13 33	15 57	16 35	17 06	18 12	18 16	21 24
1¼	Devonport	d	.	06 45	07a09	08a31	09 37	11 33	13 36	16 00	16 39	17 09	18 15	18 19	21 27
1¾	Dockyard	d	.	06x47	.	.	09x39	11x35	13x38	16x02	16x40	17x11	18x17	18x21	21x29
2¼	Keyham	d	.	06x49	.	.	09x41	11x37	13x40	16x04	16x42	17x13	18x19	18x23	21x31
—	St Budeaux Ferry Road	a	.	.	.	.	.	.	.	16 06	.	17 15	18 21	.	.
3¼	St Budeaux Victoria Road	d	05 43	06 52	.	.	09 44	11 40	13 43	.	16 45	.	.	18 26	21 34
7½	Bere Ferrers	d	.	07x00	.	.	09x52	11x47	13x51	.	16x52	.	.	18x34	21x42
10¼	Bere Alston	a	05 55	07 06	.	.	09 58	11 53	13 57	.	16 58	.	.	18 40	21 48
—		d	05 58	07 08	.	.	10 00	11 55	13 59	.	17 01	.	.	18 42	21 50
12	Calstock	d	06a05	07x15	.	.	10x07	12x03	14x06	.	17x07	.	.	18x49	21x57
15	**Gunnislake**	a	.	07 27	.	.	10 20	12 15	14 18	.	17 20	.	.	19 02	22 09

Saturdays

		GW	GW	GW ⊥	GW	GW	GW C	GW ⊥	GW C	GW
Plymouth	d	06 45	09 34	10 00	11 30	13 35	16 44	17 59	18 16	21 24
Devonport	d	06 48	09 37	10a03	11 33	13 38	16 47	18 02	18 19	21 27
Dockyard	d	06x49	09x39	.	11x35	13x39	16x48	18 04	18x21	21x29
Keyham	d	06x51	09x41	.	11x37	13x41	16x50	18 06	18x23	21x31
St Budeaux Ferry Road	a	.	.	.	.	.	.	18 07	.	.
St Budeaux Victoria Road	d	06 55	09 44	.	11 40	13 45	16 54	.	18 26	21 34
Bere Ferrers	d	07x02	09x52	.	11x47	13x52	17x01	.	18x34	21x42
Bere Alston	a	07 09	09 58	.	11 53	13 59	17 08	.	18 40	21 48
	d	07 10	10 00	.	11 55	14 00	17 09	.	18 42	21 50
Calstock	d	07x18	10x07	.	12x03	14x08	17x17	.	18x49	21x57
Gunnislake	a	07 30	10 20	.	12 15	14 20	17 29	.	19 02	22 09

Sundays

		GW	GW ◊ ⊥	GW	GW	GW	GW
Plymouth	d	09 35	10 03	11 40	13 45	15 45	17 45
Devonport	d	09 38	10a07	11 43	13 48	15 48	17 48
Dockyard	d	09x40	.	11x45	13x50	15x50	17x50
Keyham	d	09x42	.	11x47	13x52	15x52	17x52
St Budeaux Ferry Road	a	.	.	.	.	.	.
St Budeaux Victoria Road	d	09 45	.	11 50	13 55	15 55	17 55
Bere Ferrers	d	09x53	.	11x58	14x03	16x03	18x03
Bere Alston	a	09 59	.	12 04	14 09	16 09	18 09
	d	10 02	.	12 07	14 12	16 12	18 12
Calstock	d	10x09	.	12x14	14x19	16x19	18x19
Gunnislake	a	10 21	.	12 26	14 31	16 31	18 31

For general notes see front of timetable
For details of catering facilities see Directory of Train Operators

A From Exeter Central (Table 135)
B From Newquay (Table 142)
C From Newton Abbot (Table 135)

Gunnislake → Plymouth

Network Diagram - see first page of Table 135

Miles			GW	GW	GW A	GW B	GW	GW C	GW	GW A	GW	GW	GW
0	**Gunnislake**	d			07 34	10 23	12 19	14 24		17 24	19 07		22 15
3	Calstock	d	06 08		07x46	10x35	12x31	14x36		17x36	19x19		22x27
4¾	Bere Alston	a	06 14		07 52	10 41	12 37	14 42		17 43	19 25		22 33
—		d	06 17		07 55	10 44	12 40	14 45		17 45	19 28		22 36
7½	Bere Ferrers	d	06x22		08x00	10x49	12x45	14x50		17x50	19x33		22x41
11¾	St Budeaux Victoria Road	d	06 30		08 09	10 58	12 54	14 59		17 59	19 42		22 50
—	St Budeaux Ferry Road	d		07 57					16 46			20 59	
12¾	Keyham	d	06x32	07x59	08x11	11x00	12x56	15x01	16x47	18x01	19x44	21x01	22x52
13¼	Dockyard	d	06x34	08x01	08x13	11x02	12x58	15x03	16x49	18x03	19x46	21x03	22x54
13¾	Devonport	d	06 36	08 03	08 15	11 04	13 00	15 05	16 52	18 05	19 48	21 05	22 56
15	**Plymouth**	a	06 39	08 09	08 19	11 08	13 04	15 09	16 55	18 09	19 52	21 09	23 00

Saturdays

		GW 1 ◇ 🚲	GW	GW C	GW	GW C	GW	GW	GW ◇ 🚲
Gunnislake	d		07 42	10 23	12 19	14 24	17 33	19 07	
Calstock	d		07x54	10x35	12x31	14x36	17x45	19x19	
Bere Alston	a		08 00	10 41	12 37	14 42	17 51	19 25	
	d		08 02	10 44	12 39	14 44	17 53	19 28	
Bere Ferrers	d		08x07	10x49	12x44	14x49	17x58	19x33	
St Budeaux Victoria Road	d		08 16	10 58	12 53	14 58	18 07	19 42	
St Budeaux Ferry Road	d	07 57							21 03
Keyham	d	07 59	08x19	11x00	12x56	15x01	18x10	19x44	21x05
Dockyard	d	08 01	08x21	11x02	12x58	15x03	18x12	19x46	21x07
Devonport	d	08 03	08 23	11 04	13 00	15 05	18 14	19 48	21 09
Plymouth	a	08 09	08 27	11 08	13 04	15 09	18 18	19 52	21 12

Sundays

		GW	GW	GW	GW	GW	GW 🚌
Gunnislake	d	10 25	12 45	14 45	16 55	18 37	
Calstock	d	10x37	12x57	14x57	17x07	18x49	
Bere Alston	a	10 43	13 03	15 03	17 13	18 55	
	d	10 45	13 05	15 05	17 15	18 57	
Bere Ferrers	d	10x51	13x11	15x11	17x21	19x03	
St Budeaux Victoria Road	d	10 59	13 19	15 19	17 29	19 11	
St Budeaux Ferry Road	d						
Keyham	d	11x02	13x22	15x22	17x32	19x14	
Dockyard	d	11x04	13x24	15x24	17x34	19x16	
Devonport	d	11 06	13 26	15 26	17 36	19 18	21 01
Plymouth	a	11 10	13 30	15 30	17 40	19 22	21 04

For general notes see front of timetable
For details of catering facilities see Directory of Train Operators

A To Newquay (Table 142)
B To Exeter St Davids (Table 135)
C To Newton Abbot (Table 135)

Liskeard — Looe

Network Diagram - see first page of Table 135

Mondays to Fridays

Miles			GW	GW	GW	GW	GW	GW	GW	GW	GW
0	**Liskeard 3**	d	06 10	07 15	09 56	11 50	13 45	15 15	16 36	18 02	19 11
2	Coombe	a					13 51			18 08	
—		d					13 54			18 11	
3¾	St Keyne	d	06x23	07x28		12x03	14x01	15x28	16x49	18x18	19x24
5	Causeland	d	06x26	07x31		12x06	14x05	15x31	16x52	18x22	19x27
6½	Sandplace	d	06x30	07x35		12x10	14x08	15x35	16x56	18x25	19x31
8¾	**Looe**	a	06 39	07 44	10 24	12 19	14 15	15 44	17 05	18 32	19 40

Saturdays

		GW	GW	GW	GW	GW	GW	GW	GW	GW
Liskeard 3	d	06 12	07 15	09 56	12 10	13 45	15 15	16 31	17 57	19 11
Coombe	a					13 51			18 03	
	d					13 54			18 06	
St Keyne	d	06x25	07x28		12x23	14x01	15x28	16x44	18x13	19x24
Causeland	d	06x28	07x31		12x26	14x05	15x31	16x47	18x17	19x27
Sandplace	d	06x32	07x35		12x30	14x08	15x35	16x51	18x20	19x31
Looe	a	06 41	07 44	10 24	12 39	14 15	15 44	17 00	18 27	19 40

Mondays to Fridays

Miles			GW	GW	GW	GW	GW	GW	GW	GW	GW
0	**Looe**	d	06 41	07 46	10 25	12 33	14 30	15 49	17 06	18 35	19 43
2¼	Sandplace	d	06x46	07x51		12x38	14x35	15x54	17x11	18x40	19x48
3¾	Causeland	d	06x50	07x55		12x42	14x39	15x58	17x15	18x44	19x52
5	St Keyne	d	06x54	07x59		12x46	14x43	16x02	17x19	18x48	19x56
6¾	Coombe	a				12 54	14 51				
—		d				12 57	14 54				
8¾	**Liskeard 3**	a	07 07	08 12	10 49	13 03	15 00	16 15	17 32	19 01	20 09

Saturdays

		GW	GW	GW	GW	GW	GW	GW	GW	GW
Looe	d	06 45	07 46	10 25	12 40	14 30	15 49	17 10	18 30	19 43
Sandplace	d		07x51		12x45	14x35	15x54	17x15	18x35	19x48
Causeland	d		07x55		12x49	14x39	15x58	17x19	18x39	19x52
St Keyne	d		07x59		12x53	14x43	16x02	17x23	18x43	19x56
Coombe	a		08 07			14 51				
	d		08 10			14 54				
Liskeard 3	a	07 10	08 16	10 50	13 07	15 00	16 16	17 37	18 57	20 10

For general notes see front of timetable
For details of catering facilities see Directory of Train Operators

No Sunday Service

Table 142

Mondays to Fridays

Par — Newquay

Network Diagram - see first page of Table 135

Miles			GW A	GW	GW	GW A
0	**Par** [3]	d	09 23	11 24	14 00	19 33
4¼	Luxulyan	d	09x34	11x35	14x11	19x44
6¼	Bugle	d	09x40	11x41	14x17	19x50
8¾	Roche	d	09x45	11x46	14x22	19x55
14½	St Columb Road	d	09x56	11x57	14x33	20x06
18¼	Quintrell Downs	d	10x04	12x05	14x41	20x14
20¾	**Newquay**	a	10 13	12 14	14 50	20 23

Saturdays

		GW	GW
Par [3]	d	11 28	14 03
Luxulyan	d	11x39	14x14
Bugle	d	11x45	14x20
Roche	d	11x50	14x25
St Columb Road	d	12x01	14x36
Quintrell Downs	d	12x09	14x44
Newquay	a	12 20	14 55

Mondays to Fridays

Miles			GW	GW	GW B	GW
0	**Newquay**	d	10 18	12 42	14 52	20 25
2½	Quintrell Downs	d	10 24	12 48	14 58	20 31
6½	St Columb Road	d		12x56	15x06	20x39
12	Roche	d		13x07	15x17	20x50
14½	Bugle	d		13x12	15x22	20x55
16½	Luxulyan	d		13x17	15x27	21x00
20¾	**Par** [3]	a	11 03	13 30	15 39	21 13

Saturdays

		GW	GW	GW
Newquay	d	10 13	12 42	15 10
Quintrell Downs	d	10 19	12x48	15x16
St Columb Road	d	10x27	12x56	15x24
Roche	d	10x38	13x07	15x35
Bugle	d	10x43	13x12	15x40
Luxulyan	d	10x48	13x17	15x45
Par [3]	a	11 01	13 30	15 58

For general notes see front of timetable
For details of catering facilities see Directory of Train Operators

A From Gunnislake (Table 139)
B To Gunnislake (Table 139)

No Sunday Service

Table 143

Mondays to Fridays

Truro — Falmouth

Network Diagram - see first page of Table 135

Miles			GW	GW	GW	GW	GW	GW	GW	GW	GW	GW	GW	GW
0	**Truro**	d	06 31	07 31	08 32	09 45	10 47	12 39	14 29	16 28	17 26	18 52	20 00	21 04
$4\frac{1}{2}$	Perranwell	d	06 38	07 38	08 39	09 52	10 54	12 46	14 36	16 35	17 33	18 59	20 07	21 11
$8\frac{1}{4}$	Penryn	d	06 45	07 45	08 45	09 59	11 01	12 53	14 43	16 41	17 39	19 05	20 14	21 18
$10\frac{1}{2}$	Penmere	d	06 49	07 49	08 49	10 03	11 05	12 57	14 47	16 45	17 43	19 09	20 18	21 22
$11\frac{3}{4}$	Falmouth Town	d	06 51	07 51	08 51	10 05	11 07	12 59	14 49	16 47	17 45	19 11	20 20	21 24
$12\frac{1}{4}$	**Falmouth Docks**	a	06 54	07 54	08 54	10 08	11 10	13 02	14 52	16 50	17 48	19 14	20 23	21 27

Saturdays

		GW	GW	GW	GW	GW	GW	GW	GW	GW	GW	GW	GW
Truro	d	06 25	07 30	08 30	09 43	11 25	12 47	14 35	15 58	16 51	18 02	19 56	21 04
Perranwell	d	06 32	07 37	08 37	09 50	11 32	12 54	14 42	16 05	16 58	18 09	20 03	21 11
Penryn	d	06 39	07 44	08 44	09 57	11 39	13 01	14 49	16 12	17 05	18 16	20 10	21 18
Penmere	d	06 43	07 48	08 48	10 01	11 43	13 05	14 53	16 16	17 09	18 20	20 14	21 22
Falmouth Town	d	06 45	07 50	08 50	10 03	11 45	13 07	14 55	16 18	17 11	18 22	20 16	21 24
Falmouth Docks	a	06 48	07 53	08 53	10 06	11 48	13 10	14 58	16 21	17 14	18 25	20 19	21 27

Sundays

		GW	GW	GW	GW	GW A	GW B	GW	GW	GW C	GW D	GW	GW
Truro	d	11 11	12 26	13 35	14 34	15 36	15 55	16 55	18 30	19 41	19 49	20 50	22 00
Perranwell	d	11 18	12 33	13 42	14 41	15 43	16 02	17 02	18 37	19 48	19 56	20 57	22 07
Penryn	d	11 25	12 40	13 49	14 48	15 50	16 09	17 09	18 44	19 55	20 03	21 04	22 14
Penmere	d	11 29	12 44	13 53	14 52	15 53	16 12	17 13	18 48	19 59	20 07	21 08	22 18
Falmouth Town	d	11 31	12 46	13 55	14 54	15 56	16 15	17 15	18 50	20 01	20 09	21 10	22 20
Falmouth Docks	a	11 34	12 49	13 58	14 57	15 59	16 18	17 18	18 53	20 04	20 12	21 13	22 23

Mondays to Fridays

Miles			GW	GW	GW	GW	GW	GW	GW	GW	GW	GW	GW	GW
0	**Falmouth Docks**	d	06 57	07 57	08 57	10 11	11 47	13 27	14 57	16 53	18 22	19 16	20 26	21 30
$\frac{1}{2}$	Falmouth Town	d	06 59	07 59	08 59	10 13	11 49	13 29	14 59	16 55	18 24	19 18	20 28	21 32
2	Penmere	d	07 02	08 02	09 02	10 16	11 52	13 32	15 02	16 58	18 27	19 21	20 31	21 35
4	Penryn	d	07 07	08 07	09 06	10 21	11 57	13 37	15 07	17 03	18 31	19 25	20 36	21 40
8	Perranwell	d	07 14	08 14	09 13	10 28	12 04	13 44	15 14	17 10	18 38	19 32	20 43	21 47
$12\frac{1}{4}$	**Truro**	a	07 21	08 21	09 20	10 35	12 11	13 51	15 21	17 17	18 45	19 39	20 50	21 54

Saturdays

		GW	GW	GW	GW	GW	GW	GW	GW	GW	GW	GW	GW
Falmouth Docks	d	06 53	07 56	08 56	10 09	11 51	13 13	15 01	16 24	17 25	18 28	20 26	21 31
Falmouth Town	d	06 55	07 58	08 58	10 11	11 53	13 15	15 03	16 26	17 27	18 30	20 28	21 33
Penmere	d	06 58	08 01	09 01	10 14	11 56	13 18	15 06	16 29	17 30	18 33	20 31	21 36
Penryn	d	07 03	08 06	09 06	10 19	12 01	13 23	15 11	16 34	17 35	18 38	20 36	21 41
Perranwell	d	07 10	08 13	09 13	10 26	12 08	13 30	15 18	16 41	17 42	18 45	20 43	21 48
Truro	a	07 17	08 20	09 20	10 33	12 15	13 37	15 25	16 48	17 49	18 52	20 50	21 55

Sundays

		GW	GW	GW	GW	GW A	GW B	GW	GW C	GW D	GW C	GW D	GW	GW
Falmouth Docks	d	11 37	12 52	14 01	15 00	16 04	16 24	17 21	19 00	19 00	20 07	20 15	21 20	22 26
Falmouth Town	d	11 39	12 54	14 03	15 02	16 06	16 26	17 23	19 02	19 02	20 09	20 17	21 22	22 28
Penmere	d	11 42	12 57	14 06	15 05	16 09	16 29	17 26	19 05	19 05	20 12	20 20	21 25	22 31
Penryn	d	11 47	13 02	14 11	15 10	16 13	16 33	17 31	19 10	19 10	20 17	20 25	21 30	22 36
Perranwell	d	11 54	13 09	14 18	15 17	16 20	16 40	17 38	19 17	19 17	20 24	20 32	21 37	22 43
Truro	a	12 01	13 17	14 25	15 25	16 27	16 47	17 45	19 24	19 26	20 31	20 39	21 44	22 50

For general notes see front of timetable
For details of catering facilities see Directory of Train Operators

A Until 23 March
B From 30 March
C Until 27 January and from 30 March
D 3 February to 23 March

St. Erth — St. Ives

Mondays to Fridays

Network Diagram - see first page of Table 135

Miles			GW	GW	GW	GW	GW	GW	GW	GW	GW	GW	GW	GW	GW	GW	GW	GW	GW	GW	GW	GW	GW	GW	GW	GW
—	Penzance	d	06 37	06 43	07 43	09 02	09 30	10 00	10 36		11 40		12 42		14 00		14 50		16 00		16 44	17 35		19 05	20 11	20 55
0	St Erth 2	d	06 45	07 24	08 17	09 10	10 11	10 41	11 11	11 41	12 11	12 41	13 11	13 41	14 11	14 41	15 11	15 41	16 11	16 41	17 12	17 59	18 36	19 40	20 30	21 35
¾	Lelant Saltings	d				09 13	10 14	10 44	11 14	11 44	12 14	12 44	13 14	13 44	14 14	14 44	15 14	15 44	16 14	16 44	17 15	18 02	18 39	19 43	20 33	21 38
1	Lelant	d	06x48	07x27	08x20	09x15														16x46	17x35	18x04	18x41	19x45	20x35	21x40
3	Carbis Bay	d	06 53	07 32	08 25	09 20	10 20	10 50	11a28	11 50	12a28	12 50	13a28	13 50	14a28	14 50	15a28	15 50	16a28	16 51	17 21	18 09	18 46	19 50	20 40	21 45
4¼	St Ives	a	06 57	07 36	08 28	09 24	10 23	10 53	11 23	11 53	12 23	12 53	13 23	13 53	14 23	14 53	15 23	15 53	16 23	16 54	17 24	18 12	18 49	19 53	20 43	21 48

Saturdays

		GW	GW	GW	GW	GW	GW	GW	GW	GW	GW	GW	GW	GW	GW	GW	GW	GW	GW	GW	GW	GW	GW	GW
Penzance	d	06 55	06 04	08 58	10 00		10 58		11 45							15b54					19 08		20 45
St Erth 2	d	07 03	07 32	09 06	10 11	10 41	11 11	11 41	12 11	12 41	13 11	13 41	14 11	14 41	15 11	15 41	16 11	16 41	17 12	17 59	18 36	19 23	20 25	21 32
Lelant Saltings	d			09 09		10 44		11 44		12 44		13 44		14 44		15 44	16a34	16 44	17 15	18 02	18 39	19 26	20 28	21 35
Lelant	d	07x06	07x35	09x11														16x46		18x04	18x41	19x28	20x30	21x37
Carbis Bay	d	07 11	07 40	09 16	10 18	10 50	11 18	11 50	12 18	12 50	13 18	13 50	14 18	14 50	15 18	15 50	16 18	16 51	17 21	18 09	18 46	19 33	20 35	21 42
St Ives	a	07 14	07 43	09 20	10 21	10 53	11 21	11 53	12 21	12 53	13 21	13 53	14 21	14 53	15 21	15 53	16 21	16 54	17 24	18 12	18 49	19 36	20 38	21 45

Sundays

		GW	GW	GW	GW	GW	GW	GW	GW	GW
Penzance	d	11 50		13 50	14 46	15 08	16 15	17 20		19 00
St Erth 2	d	12 00	13 02	14 01	15 06	16 12	16 46	17 32	18 26	19 20
Lelant Saltings	d	12 03	13 05	14 04	15 09	16 15	16 49	17 35	18 29	19 23
Lelant	d	12x05	13x07	14x06	15x11	16x17	16x51	17x37	18x31	19x25
Carbis Bay	d	12 10	13 12	14 11	15 16	16 22	16 56	17 42	18 36	19 30
St Ives	a	12 13	13 15	14 14	15 19	16 25	16 59	17 45	18 39	19 33

Mondays to Fridays

Miles			GW	GW	GW	GW	GW	GW	GW	GW	GW	GW	GW	GW	GW	GW	GW	GW	GW	GW	GW	GW	GW	GW	GW	GW
0	St Ives	d	07 08	07 38	08 35	09 27	10 25	10 55	11 25	11 55	12 25	12 55	13 25	13 55	14 25	14 55	15 25	15 56	16 25	16 57	17 27	18 17	18 55	20 00	20 46	21 51
1¼	Carbis Bay	d	07 11	07 41	08 38	09 30	10 28	10 59	11 28	11 50	12 28	12 50	13 28	13 50	14 28	14 50	15 28	15 50	16 28	17 00	17 30	18 20	18 58	20 03	20 49	21 54
3¼	Lelant	d	07x16	07x46	08x43	09x35															17x35	18x25	19x03	20x08	20x54	21x59
3½	Lelant Saltings	d				09 38		11 05	11 35	12 05	12 35	13 05	13 35	14 05	14 35	15 05	15 35	16 05	16 35	17 07	17 38	18 28	19 06	20 11	20 57	22 02
4¼	St Erth 2	a	07 19	07 49	08 46	09 40	10 38	11 08	11 38	12 08	12 38	13 08	13 37	14 08	14 38	15 08	15 38	16 08	16 38	17 10	17 40	18 31	19 09	20 13	21 00	22 04
—	Penzance	a	08 01		08 57	10 19	11 24			12 24				14 41	15 12			16 36	17 11		18 06		19 37	20 41	21 29	22 15

Saturdays

		GW	GW	GW	GW	GW	GW	GW	GW	GW	GW	GW	GW	GW	GW	GW	GW	GW	GW	GW	GW	GW	GW	GW
St Ives	d	07 17	07 46	09 23	10 25	10 56	11 25	11 56	12 25	12 56	13 25	13 56	14 25	14 56	15 25	15 56	16 25	16 57	17 27	18 17	18 55	20 00	20 45	21 50
Carbis Bay	d	07 20	07 49	09 26	10 28	10 59	11 28	11 59	12 28	12 59	13 28	13 59	14 28	14 59	15 28	15 59	16 28	17 00	17 30	18 20	18 58	20 03	20 48	21 53
Lelant	d	07x25	07x54	09x31															17x35	18x25	19x03	20x08	20 53	21x58
Lelant Saltings	d			09 34	10 35		11 35		12 35		13 35		14 35		15 35		16 35		17 38	18 28	19 06	20 11	20 56	22 01
St Erth 2	a	07 28	07 57	09 36	10 38	11 08	11 38	12 08	12 38	13 08	13 38	14 08	14 38	15 08	15 38	16 08	16 38	17 09	17 40	18 30	19 08	20 13	20 58	22 04
Penzance	a		08 27		11 24		12 02	12 31	13c23	13e26		14 46				16 36	17 11				19f49	20 59	21g27	22 13

Sundays

		GW	GW	GW	GW	GW	GW	GW	GW	GW
St Ives	d	12 30	13 30	14 30	15 39	16 30	17 02	17 48	18 45	19 40
Carbis Bay	d	12 33	13 33	14 33	15 42	16 33	17 05	17 51	18 48	19 43
Lelant	d	12x38	13x38	14x38	15x47	16x38	17x10	17x56	18x53	19x48
Lelant Saltings	d	12 41	13 41	14 41	15 50	16 41	17 13	17 59	18 56	19 51
St Erth 2	a	12 43	13 43	14 43	15 52	16 43	17 15	18 01	18 58	19 53
Penzance	a	13 03		15h02	16j14		17k39		19 29	20 08

For general notes see front of timetable
For details of catering facilities see Directory of Train Operators

b Until 22 March only
c Until 26 January and from 29 March only
e 2 February to 22 March only
f From 29 March arr. 1945
g From 29 March arr. 2143
h From 30 March only
j Until 23 March only
k From 30 March arr. 1812

Network Diagram for Tables 148, 149

DM-36/04
Design BAJS

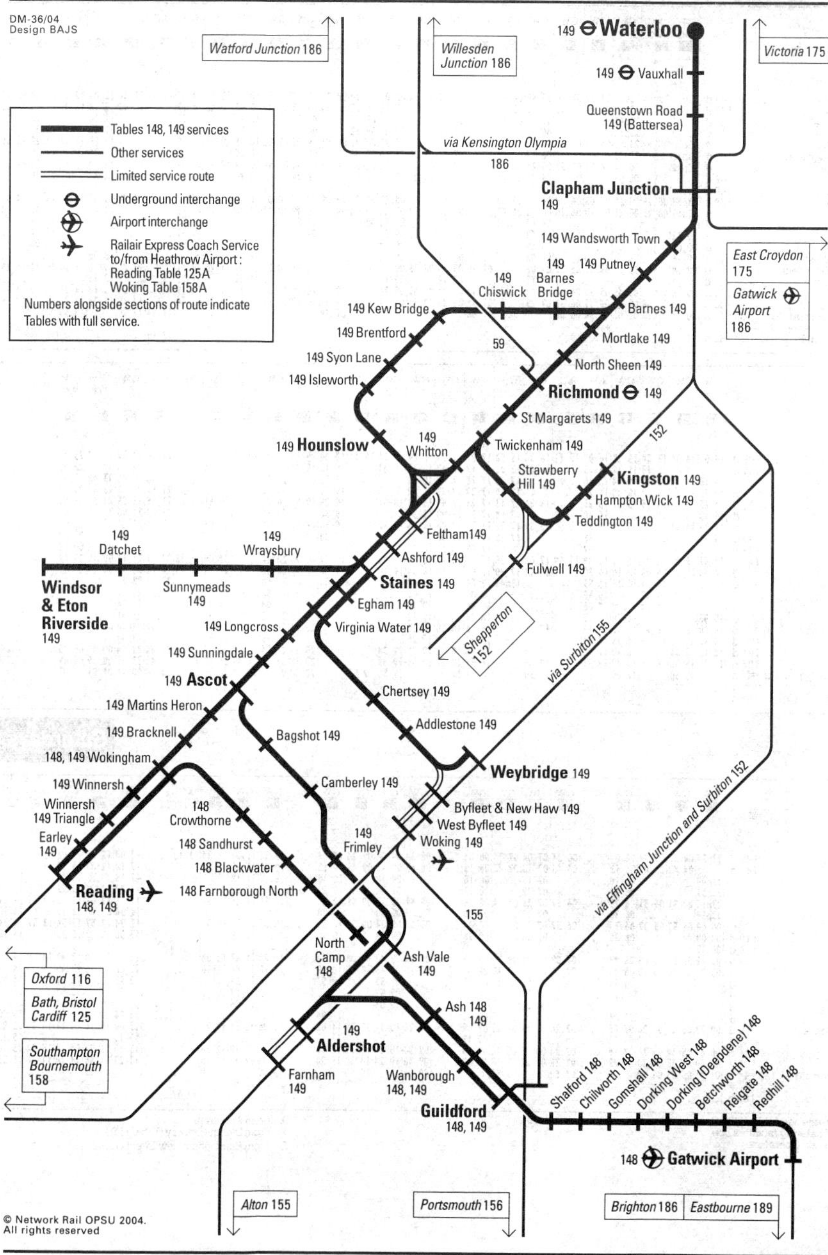

Tables 148, 149 services
Other services
Limited service route
Underground interchange
Airport interchange
Railair Express Coach Service to/from Heathrow Airport: Reading Table 125A Woking Table 158A
Numbers alongside sections of route indicate Tables with full service.
Watford Junction 186
Willesden Junction 186
149 Waterloo
Victoria 175
149 Vauxhall
Queenstown Road 149 (Battersea)
via Kensington Olympia
186
Clapham Junction 149
149 Wandsworth Town
149 Putney
East Croydon 175
Gatwick Airport 186
149 Chiswick
149 Barnes Bridge
149 Kew Bridge
Barnes 149
149 Brentford
Mortlake 149
59
149 Syon Lane
North Sheen 149
149 Isleworth
Richmond 149
St Margarets 149
149 Hounslow
149 Whitton
Twickenham 149
152
Strawberry Hill 149
Kingston 149
Hampton Wick 149
Teddington 149
Feltham 149
149 Datchet
149 Wraysbury
Ashford 149
Fulwell 149
Windsor & Eton Riverside 149
Sunnymeads 149
Staines 149
Egham 149
149 Longcross
Virginia Water 149
Shepperton 152
149 Sunningdale
via Surbiton 155
149 Ascot
Chertsey 149
149 Martins Heron
Addlestone 149
149 Bracknell
Bagshot 149
148, 149 Wokingham
Weybridge 149
149 Winnersh
Camberley 149
Winnersh 149 Triangle
148 Crowthorne
Byfleet & New Haw 149
West Byfleet 149
Earley 149
148 Sandhurst
149 Frimley
Woking 149
via Effingham Junction and Surbiton 152
148 Blackwater
Reading 148, 149
148 Farnborough North
155
North Camp 148
Ash Vale 149
Oxford 116
Bath, Bristol Cardiff 125
Ash 148 149
149 Aldershot
Southampton Bournemouth 158
Farnham 149
Wanborough 148, 149
Shalford 148
Chilworth 148
Gomshall 148
Dorking West 148
Dorking (Deepdene) 148
Betchworth 148
Reigate 148
Redhill 148
Guildford 148, 149
148 Gatwick Airport
Alton 155
Portsmouth 156
Brighton 186
Eastbourne 189

Reading → Guildford, Redhill, and Gatwick Airport

Network Diagram - see first page of Table 148

Miles	Station		GW MO 1	XC MO 1◇ A	GW MX 1	GW 1	GW 1	GW 1	GW 1	GW 1	GW 1	GW 1	GW 1	GW 1	GW 1	GW 1	GW 1	GW 1	GW 1	GW 1	XC 1◇ ☕	GW 1	GW 1	GW 1	GW 1	GW 1
0	**Reading** 7	149 d	23p15	23p45	23p34	04 34	05 34	05 50	06 07	06 34	07 04	07 34	08 04	08 20	08 34	09 04	09 34	10 04	10 34	11 04	11 08	11 34	12 04	12 34	13 04	13 34
6¾	Wokingham	149 d	23p24		23p43	04 43	05 43	06 00	06 16	06 43	07 13	07 43	08 13	08 29	08 43	09 13	09 44	10 13	10 43	11 13		11 43	12 13	12 43	13 13	13 43
10	Crowthorne	d			23p48			06 05	06 21		07 18	07 48	08 18	08 34		09 18		10 18		11 18			12 18		13 18	
11½	Sandhurst	d	23p30		23p52			06 09	06 25		07 22	07 52	08 22	08 38		09 22		10 22		11 22			12 22		13 22	
13¼	Blackwater	d	23p34		23p55	04 51	05 51	06 12	06 28	06 51	07 25	07 55	08 25	08 41	08 51	09 25	09 52	10 25	10 51	11 25		11 51	12 25	12 51	13 25	13 51
15¼	Farnborough North	d	23p38		23p59			06 17	06 33		07 30	08 00	08 30	08 46		09 30		10 30		11 30			12 30		13 30	
17¼	North Camp	d	23p42		00 04	04 57	05 57	06 21	06 37	06 57	07 34	08 04	08 34	08 50	08 57	09 34	09 58	10 34	10 57	11 34		11 57	12 34	12 57	13 34	13 57
19¼	Ash 3	149 d			00 08			06 25	06 41		07 38	08 08	08 38	08 54		09 38		10 38		11 38			12 38		13 38	
21¼	Wanborough	149 d			00 12			06 29																		
25¾	**Guildford**	149 a	23p53	00 25	00 19	05 08	06 08	06 36	06 50	07 08	07 47	08 17	08 47	09 03	09 09	09 47	10 09	10 47	11 08	11 47		12 08	12 47	13 08	13 47	14 08
—		d	23p55	00 26	00 21	05 10	06 10	06 43	06 57	07 10	07 48	08 18	08 48	09 04	09 10	09 48	10 11	10 48	11 10	11 48		12 10	12 48	13 10	13 48	14 10
27¾	Shalford	d						06 48	07a02		07 53		08 53	09a10		09 53				11 53			12 53		13 53	
29¾	Chilworth	d	00 02					06 52			07 57		08 57			09 57				11 57					13 57	
33¼	Gomshall	d	00 09					06 58			08 04		09 04			10 04				12 04					14 04	
38¼	Dorking West	d	00 16					07 06			08 11		09 12					11 04					13 06			
39	Dorking Deepdene	d	00 19		00 37	05 26	06 26	07 08		07 26	08 14	08 35	09 14		09 30	10 11	10 27	11 07	11 26	12 11		12 26	13 08	13 26	14 11	14 26
41¾	Betchworth	d						07 13			08 19		09 19					11 12					13 13			
44¼	Reigate	186 d	00 26		00 45	05 34	06 34	07 18		07 34	08 24	08 42	09 24		09 37	10 19	10 35	11 17	11 34	12 19		12 34	13 18	13 34	14 19	14 34
46¼	**Redhill**	186 a	00 30	00 58	00 49	05 39	06 38	07 23		07 38	08 29	08 51	09 29		09 41	10 24	10 39	11 22	11 38	12 24		12 38	13 23	13 38	14 24	14 38
52¼	**Gatwick Airport** 10	186 ✈ a	00 43	01 17	01 01	05 54	06 56			07 54		09 02			09 59		10 51		11 50		12 33	12 50		13 50		14 50
—	Brighton 10	186 a																			13 15					

Station		GW 1	GW 1	GW 1	GW 1	GW 1	XC 1◇ ☕	GW 1	GW 1	GW 1	GW 1	GW 1	GW 1	XC R 1 ☕	GW 1	GW 1	GW 1	XC R 1	GW 1	XC 1◇	GW 1	GW 1	GW FO 1	GW FX 1		
Reading 7	149 d	14 04	14 34	15 04	15 28	16 04	16 11	16 34	16 50	17 04	17 34	18 04	18 34	18 11	19 04	19 34	20 04	20 09	20 34	21 06	21 34	22 34	23 34	23 34		
Wokingham	149 d	14 13	14 43	15 13	15 39	16 13		16 43	17 00	17 13	17 43	18 13	18 43		19 13	19 43	20 13		20 43		21 43	22 43		23 43		
Crowthorne	d	14 18		15 18	15 44	16 18			17 06	17 18	17 48	18 18			19 18		20 18				21 48	22 48	23 48	23 48		
Sandhurst	d	14 22		15 22	15 48	16 22			17 10	17 22	17 52	18 22			19 22		20 22				21 52	22 52	23 52	23 52		
Blackwater	d	14 25	14 51	15 25	15 51	16 25		16 51	17 13	17 25	17 55	18 25	18 51		19 25	19 51	20 25		20 51		21 55	22 55	23 55	23 55		
Farnborough North	d	14 30		15 30		16 30			17 18	17 30	18 00	18 30			19 30		20 30				22 00	23 00	23 59	23 59		
North Camp	d	14 34	14 57	15 34	15 57	16 34		16 57	17 22	17 34	18 04	18 34	18 57		19 34	19 57	20 34		20 57		22 04	23 04	00 04	00 04		
Ash 3	149 d	14 38		15 38		16 38			17 26	17 38	18 08	18 38			19 38		20 38				22 08	23 08	00 08	00 08		
Wanborough	149 d					16 42				17 42		18 42											00 12	00 12		
Guildford	149 a	14 47	15 08	15 47	16 09	16 49	16 59	17 08	17 35	17 49	18 17	18 49	19 08		19 47	20 08	20 47		21 08	21 33	22 17	23 17	00 19	00 19		
	d	14 48	15 10	15 48	16 10	16 50		17 10	17 40	17 51	18 18	18 54	19 10		19 48	20 10	20 48		21 10	21 43	22 18	23 18	00 21	00 21		
Shalford	d	14 53		15 53	16 15	16 55			17a45	17 56		18 59			19a54		20 54				22 23	23 23				
Chilworth	d			15 57		16 59				18 00		19 03					20 58		21 17			23 27				
Gomshall	d			16 04		17 06				18 06		19 10					21 04		21 24			23 34				
Dorking West	d	15 06			16 28	17 13				18 14		19 17					21 12		21 31			23 41				
Dorking Deepdene	d	15 08	15 26	16 11	16 30	17 16		17 26		18 16	18 35	19 20	19 26			20 26	21 14		21 34		22 37	23 44	00 37	00 37		
Betchworth	d	15 13		16 16	16 35	17 21				18 21		19 25					21 19		21 39			23 49				
Reigate	186 d	15 18	15 34	16 21	16 40	17 26		17 34		18 26	18 42	19 30	19 34			20 34	21 24		21 44		22 44	23 54	00 45	00 45		
Redhill	186 a	15 25	15 38	16 26	16 47	17 31		17 38		18 31	18 52	19 35	19 38			20 38	21 28	21 34	21 48	22 10	22 48	23 58	00 49	00 49		
Gatwick Airport 10	186 ✈ a		15 50		17 00			17 50			19 07		19 50	19 52		20 50		21 47	22 04	22 32	23 04	00 11	01 01	01 01		
Brighton 10	186 a													20 30												

Saturdays

Station		GW 1	GW 1	GW 1	GW 1		GW 1	GW 1	GW 1	GW 1		GW 1	GW 1	GW 1	GW 1		GW 1	GW 1	GW 1	XC 1◇ B ☕		GW 1	GW 1	GW 1	GW 1	GW 1
Reading 7	149 d	23p34	04 34	05 34	06 04		06 34	07 04	07 34	08 04		08 34	09 04	09 34	10 04		10 34	11 04	11 34	11 13		12 04	12 34	13 04	13 34	14 04
Wokingham	149 d		04 43	05 43	06 13		06 43	07 13	07 43	08 13		08 43	09 13	09 43	10 13		10 43	11 13	11 43			12 13	12 43	13 13	13 43	14 13
Crowthorne	d	23p48			06 18			07 18		08 18			09 18		10 18			11 18				12 18		13 18		14 18
Sandhurst	d	23p52			06 22			07 22		08 22			09 22		10 22			11 22				12 22		13 22		14 22
Blackwater	d	23p55	04 51	05 51	06 25		06 51	07 25	07 51	08 25		08 51	09 25	09 51	10 25		10 51	11 25	11 51			12 25	12 51	13 25	13 51	14 25
Farnborough North	d	23p59			06 30			07 30		08 30			09 30		10 30			11 30				12 30		13 30		14 30
North Camp	d	00 04	04 57	05 57	06 34		06 57	07 34	07 57	08 34		08 57	09 34	09 57	10 34		10 57	11 34	11 57			12 34	12 57	13 34	13 57	14 34
Ash 3	149 d	00 08			06 38			07 38		08 38			09 38		10 38			11 38				12 38		13 38		14 38
Wanborough	149 d	00 12																								
Guildford	149 a	00 19	05 08	06 08	06 47		07 08	07 47	08 08	08 47		09 08	09 47	10 08	10 47		11 08	11 47	12 08			12 47	13 08	13 47	14 08	14 47
	d	00 21	05 10	06 10	06 48		07 10	07 48	08 10	08 48		09 10	09 48	10 10	10 48		11 10	11 48	12 10			12 48	13 10	13 48	14 10	14 48
Shalford	d				06 53			07 53		08 53			09 53		10 53			11 53				12 53		13 53		14 53
Chilworth	d							07 57					09 57					11 57						13 57		
Gomshall	d							08 04					10 04					12 04						14 04		
Dorking West	d				07 06					09 06					11 06							13 06				15 06
Dorking Deepdene	d	00 37	05 26	06 26	07 08		07 26	08 11	08 26	09 08		09 26	10 11	10 26	11 08		11 26	12 11	12 26			13 08	13 26	14 11	14 26	15 08
Betchworth	d				07 13					09 13					11 13							13 13				15 13
Reigate	186 d	00 45	05 34	06 34	07 18		07 34	08 19	08 34	09 18		09 34	10 19	10 34	11 18		11 34	12 19	12 34			13 18	13 34	14 19	14 34	15 18
Redhill	186 a	00 49	05 38	06 38	07 23		07 38	08 24	08 38	09 23		09 38	10 24	10 38	11 24		11 38	12 24	12 38			13 23	13 38	14 24	14 38	15 23
Gatwick Airport 10	186 ✈ a	01 01	05 53	06 50			07 50		08 50			09 50		10 50			11 50		12 50	12 53			13 50		14 50	
Brighton 10	186 a																			13 37						

For general notes see front of timetable
For details of catering facilities see
Directory of Train Operators

A From 31 March.
From Didcot Parkway (Table 116)

B From Birmingham New Street (Table 116)

Table 148

Saturdays

Reading → Guildford, Redhill, and Gatwick Airport

Network Diagram - see first page of Table 148

		GW 1	GW 1	GW 1	GW 1	XC 1 ◇ A ☕	GW 1	GW 1	GW 1	GW 1	GW 1	XC 1 ◇ A ☕	GW 1	GW 1	GW 1	XC 1 ◇ A ☕	GW 1	GW 1	GW 1	GW 1
Reading 7	149 d	14 34	15 04	15 34	16 04	16 13	16 34	17 04	17 34	18 04	18 34	18 13	19 04	19 34	20 04	20 13	20 34	21 34	22 34	23 34
Wokingham	149 d	14 43	15 13	15 43	16 13		16 43	17 13	17 43	18 13	18 43		19 13	19 43	20 13		20 43	21 43	22 43	
Crowthorne	d		15 18		16 18			17 18		18 18			19 18		20 18			21 48	22 48	23 48
Sandhurst	d		15 22		16 22			17 22		18 22			19 22		20 22			21 52	22 52	23 52
Blackwater	d	14 51	15 25	15 51	16 25		16 51	17 25	17 51	18 25	18 51		19 25	19 51	20 25		20 51	21 55	22 55	23 55
Farnborough North	d		15 30		16 30			17 30		18 30			19 30		20 30			22 00	23 00	23 59
North Camp	d	14 57	15 34	15 57	16 34		16 57	17 34	17 57	18 34	18 57		19 34	19 57	20 34		20 57	22 04	23 04	00 04
Ash 3	149 d		15 38		16 38			17 38		18 38			19 38		20 38			22 08	23 08	00 08
Wanborough	149 d																			00 12
Guildford	149 a	15 08	15 47	16 08	16 47	16 58	17 08	17 47	18 08	18 47	19 08		19 47	20 08	20 47	20 58	21 08	22 17	23 17	00 19
	d	15 10	15 48	16 10	16 48		17 10	17 48	18 10	18 48	19 10		19 48	20 10	20 48	21 00	21 10	22 18	23 18	00 21
Shalford	d		15 53		16 53			17 53		18 53			19 53		20 53		21 15	22 23	23 23	
Chilworth	d		15 57					17 57					19 57				21 19		23 27	
Gomshall	d		16 04					18 04					20 04				21 25		23 34	
Dorking West	d				17 06					19 06					21 06			22 36	23 41	
Dorking Deepdene	d	15 26	16 11	16 26	17 08		17 26	18 11	18 26	19 08	19 26		20 11	20 26	21 08		21 33	22 38	23 44	00 37
Betchworth	d				17 13					19 13					21 13			22 43	23 49	
Reigate	186 d	15 34	16 19	16 34	17 18		17 34	18 19	18 34	19 18	19 34		20 19	20 34	21 18		21 40	22 48	23 54	00 45
Redhill	186 a	15 38	16 24	16 38	17 23		17 38	18 24	18 38	19 23	19 38		20 24	20 38	21 23	21 28	21 44	22 52	23 58	00 49
Gatwick Airport 10	186 ✈ a	15 50		16 50			17 50		18 50		19 50	19 52		20 50		21 47	21 59	23 03	00 10	01 00
Brighton 10	186 a											20 28								

Sundays

		GW 1	GW 1	GW 1	GW 1	GW 1	GW 1	GW 1	GW 1	GW 1	GW 1	GW 1	GW 1	GW 1	GW 1	GW 1	XC 1 ◇ B ☕	GW 1	XC 1 ◇ C ☕	XC 1 ◇ B ☕	GW 1 D	GW 1 E	GW 1	GW 1	GW 1	XC 1 ◇ G
Reading 7	149 d	23p34	06 04	07 02	08 03	09 01	10 03	11 01	12 03	13 01	14 03	15 00	16 03	17 00	18 03	19 00	19 12	20 03	20 15	20 21	21 00	21 00	22 03	22 34	23 15	23 45
Wokingham	149 d		06 13	07 11	08 11	09 12	10 11	11 12	12 11	13 12	14 11	15 12	16 11	17 12	18 11	19 12		20 11			21 12	21 12	22 11	22 43	23 24	
Crowthorne	d	23p48	06 18		08 17		10 17		12 17		14 17		16 17		18 17			20 17					22 17	22 48		
Sandhurst	d	23p52		07 17		09 19		11 19		13 19		15 19		17 19		19 19					21 19	21 19		22 52	23 30	
Blackwater	d	23p55	06 23	07 21	08 21	09 22	10 21	11 22	12 21	13 22	14 21	15 22	16 21	17 22	18 21	19 22		20 21			21 22	21 22	22 21	22 55	23 34	
Farnborough North	d	23p59		07 25		09 27		11 27		13 27		15 27		17 27		19 27					21 27	21 27		23 00	23 38	
North Camp	d	00 04	06 30	07 29	08 29	09 31	10 29	11 31	12 29	13 31	14 29	15 31	16 29	17 31	18 29	19 31		20 29			21 31	21 31	22 29	23 04	23 42	
Ash 3	149 d	00 08	06 34		08 33		10 33		12 33		14 33		16 33		18 33			20 33					22 33	23 08		
Wanborough	149 d	00 12																								
Guildford	149 a	00 19	06 43	07 40	08 42	09 42	10 42	11 42	12 42	13 42	14 42	15 42	16 42	17 42	18 42	19 42	19 51	20 42	20 50	20 50	21 42	21 42	22 42	23 17	23 53	00 25
	d	00 21	06 44	07 42	08 43	09 43	10 43	11 43	12 43	13 43	14 43	15 43	16 43	17 43	18 43	19 43	19 55	20 43	20 55	20 55	21 43	21 43	22 43	23 18	23 55	00 26
Shalford	d		06 49		08 48		10 48		12 48		14 48		16 48		18 48			20 48					22 48	23 23		
Chilworth	d			07 49		09 51		11 51		13 51		15 51		17 51		19 51					21 51	21 51		23 27	00 02	
Gomshall	d			07 56		09 57		11 57		13 57		15 57		17 57		19 57					21 57	21 57		23 34	00 09	
Dorking West	d			08 03		10 05		12 05		14 05		16 05		18 05		20 05					22 05	22 05		23 41	00 16	
Dorking Deepdene	d	00 37	07 03	08 06	09 02	10 07	11 02	12 07	13 02	14 07	15 02	16 07	17 02	18 07	19 02	20 07		21 02			22 07	22 07	23 02	23 44	00 19	
Betchworth	d		07 08		09 07		11 07		13 07		15 07		17 07		19 07			21 07					23 07	23 49		
Reigate	186 d	00 45	07 13	08 13	09 12	10 15	11 12	12 15	13 12	14 15	15 12	16 15	17 12	18 15	19 12	20 15		21 12			22 15	22 15	23 12	23 54	00 26	
Redhill	186 a	00 49	07 17	08 17	09 17	10 20	11 17	12 19	13 17	14 19	15 17	16 19	17 17	18 19	19 17	20 19	20 26	21 17	21 31	21 31	22 19	22 21	23 17	23 58	00 30	00 58
Gatwick Airport 10	186 ✈ a	01 00	07 30	08 30	09 30	10 31	11 30	12 30	13 30	14 30	15 30	16 30	17 30	18 30	19 30	20 30	20 43	21 30	21 46	21 46	22 31	22 39	23 30	00 10	00 43	01 17
Brighton 10	186 a																21 13									

For general notes see front of timetable
For details of catering facilities see Directory of Train Operators

A From Birmingham New Street (Table 116)
B Until 27 January. From Birmingham New Street (Table 116)
C 3 February to 23 March. From Birmingham New Street (Table 116)
D From 3 February
E Until 27 January
G From 30 March. From Didcot Parkway (Table 116)

Gatwick Airport, Redhill and Guildford → Reading

Network Diagram - see first page of Table 148

Miles	Station		GW MO 1	XC 1 ◇	GW 1	XC 1 ◇ A	GW 1	XC 1 ◇ A	GW 1	GW 1	GW 1	GW 1	GW 1	GW 1	GW 1	GW 1	GW 1	XC 1 ◇ A	GW 1	GW 1	GW 1	GW 1	GW 1	GW 1
—	Brighton 10	186 d																09 21						
0	**Gatwick Airport 10**	186 ✈ d	23p07	05 15	05 31	05 45	05 57				06 59		07 58			09 17		09 46	10 03		11 03		12 03	
5¾	**Redhill**	186 d	23p19	05 33	05 44	06 04	06 14		06 24		07 11	07 28	08 09	08 33		09 29	09 34		10 14	10 34	11 14	11 34	12 14	12 34
7¼	Reigate	186 d	23p23		05 49		06 18		06 28		07 15	07 32	08 13	08 37		09 33	09 38		10 18	10 38	11 18	11 38	12 18	12 38
10¼	Betchworth	d							06 33			07 37		08 42			09 43			10 43				12 43
13¼	Dorking Deepdene	d	23p30		05 56		06 25		06 37		07 22	07 41	08 20	08 46		09 40	09 47		10 25	10 47	11 25	11 45	12 25	12 47
14	Dorking West	d	23p33						06 40			07 44		08 49			09 50			10 50				12 50
18¾	Gomshall	d	23p41						06 48		07 30	07 52		08 57			09 58					11 53		
22¼	Chilworth	d	23p47						06 54			07 58		09 03			10 04					11 59		
24¼	Shalford	d							06 58	07 21		08 02		09 07	09 31		10 08			11 03		12 03		13 03
26½	**Guildford**	a	23p54	05 59	06 11	06 35	06 41	⟵	07 02	07 25	07 40	08 06	08 36	09 11	09 35	09 56	10 12		10 42	11 07	11 42	12 07	12 42	13 07
—		d	23p56	06 00	06 12	06 51 ⟶	06 42	06 51	07 04	07 26	07 42	08 12	08 37	09 12	09 36	09 57	10 13		10 43	11 09	11 43	12 09	12 43	13 09
30¾	Wanborough	149 d			06 20				07 11			08 20		09 20										
32¾	Ash 3	149 d			06 24		06 52		07 16	07 36	07 52	08 24		09 24	09 46		10 23			11 18		12 18		13 18
34¾	North Camp	d	00 08		06 28		06 56		07 20	07 41	07 56	08 28	08 49	09 28	09 50		10 27		10 55	11 22	11 55	12 22	12 55	13 22
36¾	Farnborough North	d	00 12		06 32		07 00		07 24	07 45	08 00	08 32		09 32			10 31			11 26		12 26		13 26
38¾	Blackwater	d	00 16		06 37		07 04		07 28	07 49	08 04	08 37	08 56	09 37	09 56		10 35		11 02	11 31	12 02	12 31	13 02	13 31
40¾	Sandhurst	d	00 20		06 40		07 08		07 32	07 53	08 08	08 40		09 40			10 39			11 34		12 34		13 34
42¼	Crowthorne	d			06 44		07 12		07 36	07 57	08 12	08 44		09 44			10 43			11 38		12 38		13 38
45¼	Wokingham	149 d	00 27		06 49		07 17		07 41	08 02	08 17	08 49	09 04	09 51	10 04		10 48		11 10	11 43	12 10	12 43	13 10	13 43
52¼	**Reading 7**	149 a	00 36	06 30	06 58		07 28	07 35	07 50	08 16	08 28	08 59	09 16	10 00	10 16	10 27	10 57	11 35	11 19	11 53	12 19	12 53	13 19	13 53

Station		GW 1	GW 1	GW 1	GW 1	XC R 1	GW 1	GW 1	GW 1	GW 1	GW 1	XC 1 ◇	GW 1	GW 1	GW 1	GW 1	GW 1	GW 1	GW 1	GW 1	GW 1	GW 1	GW 1
Brighton 10	186 d					14 22																	
Gatwick Airport 10	186 ✈ d	13 03		14 03		14 51	15 03		16 03		17 03				18 03		19 16		20 03		21 03		22 23
Redhill	186 d	13 14	13 34	14 14	14 34		15 14	15 29	16 14	16 32	17 14			17 44	18 14	18 43	19 27		20 14	20 34	21 14	21 35	22 33
Reigate	186 d	13 18	13 38	14 18	14 38		15 18	15 34	16 18	16 36	17 18			17 49	18 18	18 47	19 31		20 18	20 40	21 18	21 39	22 38
Betchworth	d				14 43			15 38		16 41				17 53		18 52				20 45		21 44	22 43
Dorking Deepdene	d	13 25	13 45	14 25	14 47		15 25	15 43	16 25	16 45	17 25			17 58	18 25	18 56	19 38		20 25	20 49	21 25	21 48	22 47
Dorking West	d				14 50			15 45						18 00		18 59				20 52		21 51	22 50
Gomshall	d		13 53					15 53		16 53				18 08		19 07				21 00		21 59	22 58
Chilworth	d		13 59					15 59		16 59				18 14		19 13				21 06		22 05	23 04
Shalford	d		14 03		15 03			16 03		17 03			18 08	18 18		19 17		20 08		21 10		22 09	23 08
Guildford	a	13 42	14 07	14 42	15 07		15 42	16 07	16 42	17 07	17 41		18 12	18 22	18 41	19 21	19 54	20 12	20 43	21 14	21 42	22 13	23 12
	d	13 43	14 09	14 43	15 09		15 43	16 14	16 43	17 09	17 46	17 57	18 13	18 24	18 49	19 36	19 55	20 13	20 43	21 15	21 42	22 14	23 14
Wanborough	149 d																						23 21
Ash 3	149 d		14 18		15 18			16 23		17 18	17 55		18 23	18 33		19 45		20 23		21 25		22 23	23 26
North Camp	d	13 55	14 22	14 55	15 22		15 55	16 27	16 55	17 22	18 00		18 27	18 37	19 01	19 49	20 07	20 27	20 55	21 29	21 54	22 27	23 30
Farnborough North	d		14 26		15 26			16 31		17 26	18 04		18 31	18 41		19 53		20 31		21 33		22 31	23 34
Blackwater	d	14 02	14 31	15 02	15 31		16 02	16 36	17 02	17 31	18b11		18 35	18 46	19 07	19 58	20 14	20 35	21 02	21 37	22 02	22 36	23 38
Sandhurst	d		14 34		15 34			16 39		17 34			18 39	18 49		20 01		20 39		21 41		22 39	23 42
Crowthorne	d		14 38		15 38			16 43		17 38			18 43	18 56		20 05		20 43		21 45		22 43	23 46
Wokingham	149 d	14 10	14 43	15 10	15 43		16 10	16 48	17 10	17 43	18 19		18 51	19 01	19 15	20 10	20 22	20 48	21 10	21 50	22 10	22 48	23 51
Reading 7	149 a	14 19	14 54	15 19	15 53	16 36	16 23	16 59	17 19	17 53	18 28	18 38	19 00	19 16	19 25	20 20	20 37	20 58	21 20	22 00	22 19	23 00	00 02

Saturdays

Station		XC 1 ◇	GW 1	XC 1 ◇ A	GW 1	GW 1	GW 1	GW 1	GW 1	GW 1	GW 1	GW 1	XC 1 ◇ A	GW 1	GW 1	GW 1	GW 1	GW 1	GW 1	GW 1	GW 1	GW 1
Brighton 10	186 d												09 15									
Gatwick Airport 10	186 ✈ d	05 15	05 31	05 45	06 03		07 03		08 03		09 03		09 47	10 03		11 03		12 03		13 03		14 03
Redhill	186 d	05 33	05 43	05 52	06 14	06 34	07 14	07 34	08 14	08 34	09 14	09 34		10 14	10 34	11 14	11 34	12 14	12 34	13 14	13 34	14 14
Reigate	186 d		05 47		06 18	06 38	07 18	07 38	08 18	08 38	09 18	09 38		10 18	10 38	11 18	11 38	12 18	12 38	13 18	13 38	14 18
Betchworth	d					06 43				08 43					10 43				12 43			
Dorking Deepdene	d		05 54		06 25	06 47	07 25	07 45	08 25	08 47	09 25	09 45		10 25	10 47	11 25	11 45	12 25	12 47	13 25	13 45	14 25
Dorking West	d					06 50				08 50					10 50				12 50			
Gomshall	d							07 53				09 53					11 53				13 53	
Chilworth	d							07 59				09 59					11 59				13 59	
Shalford	d					07 03		08 03		09 03		10 03			11 03		12 03		13 03		14 03	
Guildford	a	05 59	06 10		06 41	07 07	07 41	08 07	08 42	09 07	09 42	10 07		10 42	11 07	11 42	12 07	12 42	13 07	13 42	14 07	14 42
	d	06 00	06 12		06 43	07 09	07 43	08 09	08 43	09 09	09 43	10 09		10 43	11 09	11 43	12 09	12 43	13 09	13 43	14 09	14 43
Wanborough	149 d		06 20																			
Ash 3	149 d		06 24			07 18		08 18		09 18		10 18			11 18		12 18		13 18		14 18	
North Camp	d		06 28		06 55	07 22	07 55	08 22	08 55	09 22	09 55	10 22		10 55	11 22	11 55	12 22	12 55	13 22	13 55	14 22	14 55
Farnborough North	d		06 32			07 26		08 26		09 26		10 26			11 26		12 26		13 26		14 26	
Blackwater	d		06 37		07 02	07 31	08 02	08 31	09 02	09 31	10 02	10 31		11 02	11 31	12 02	12 31	13 02	13 31	14 02	14 31	15 02
Sandhurst	d		06 40			07 34		08 34		09 34		10 34			11 34		12 34		13 34		14 34	
Crowthorne	d		06 44			07 38		08 38		09 38		10 38			11 38		12 38		13 38		14 38	
Wokingham	149 d		06 49		07 10	07 43	08 10	08 43	09 10	09 43	10 10	10 43		11 10	11 43	12 10	12 43	13 10	13 43	14 10	14 43	15 10
Reading 7	149 a	06 35	07 02	07 36	07 19	07 53	08 19	08 53	09 19	09 53	10 19	10 53	11 35	11 19	11 53	12 19	12 53	13 19	13 53	14 19	14 53	15 19

For general notes see front of timetable
For details of catering facilities see Directory of Train Operators

A To Birmingham New Street (Table 116)
b Arr. 3 minutes earlier

Table 148

Gatwick Airport, Redhill and Guildford → Reading

Network Diagram - see first page of Table 148

	GW 1	XC 1 ◇ A ☕	GW 1	GW 1	GW 1	GW 1	GW 1	XC 1 ◇ A ☕	GW 1	GW 1	GW 1	GW 1	GW 1	GW 1	GW 1	GW 1	GW 1	GW 1	GW 1
Brighton 10 186 d		14 22																	
Gatwick Airport 10 186 ✈ d		14 54	15 03		16 03		17 03			18 03		19 03		20 03		21 03		22 22	23 18
Redhill 186 d	14 34		15 14	15 34	16 14	16 34	17 14		17 34	18 14	18 34	19 14	19 34	20 14	20 34	21 14	21 36	22 34	23 29
Reigate 186 d	14 38		15 18	15 38	16 18	16 38	17 18		17 38	18 18	18 38	19 18	19 38	20 18	20 38	21 18	21 40	22 38	23 33
Betchworth d	14 43					16 43					18 43				20 43			22 43	
Dorking Deepdene d	14 47		15 25	15 45	16 25	16 47	17 25		17 45	18 25	18 47	19 25	19 45	20 25	20 47	21 25	21 47	22 47	23 40
Dorking West d	14 50					16 50					18 50				20 50			22 50	
Gomshall d				15 53					17 53				19 53				21 55	22 58	
Chilworth d				15 59					17 59				19 59				22 01	23 04	
Shalford d	15 03			16 03		17 03			18 03		19 03		20 03		21 03		22 05	23 08	
Guildford a	15 07		15 42	16 07	16 42	17 07	17 42		18 07	18 42	19 07	19 42	20 07	20 42	21 07	21 42	22 12	23 12	23 59
d	15 09		15 43	16 09	16 43	17 09	17 43	17 58	18 09	18 43	19 09	19 43	20 09	20 43	21 09	21 43	22 14	23 14	00 01
Wanborough 149 d																		23 21	
Ash 3 149 d	15 18			16 18		17 18			18 18		19 18		20 18		21 18		22 23	23 26	
North Camp d	15 22		15 55	16 22	16 55	17 22	17 55		18 22	18 55	19 22	19 55	20 22	20 55	21 22	21 55	22 27	23 30	00 13
Farnborough North d	15 26			16 26		17 26			18 26		19 26		20 26		21 26		22 31	23 34	
Blackwater d	15 31		16 02	16 31	17 02	17 31	18 02		18 31	19 02	19 31	20 02	20 31	21 02	21 31	22 02	22 36	23 38	00 20
Sandhurst d	15 34			16 34		17 34			18 34		19 34		20 34		21 34		22 39	23 42	
Crowthorne d	15 38			16 38		17 38			18 38		19 38		20 38		21 38		22 43	23 46	
Wokingham 149 d	15 43		16 10	16 43	17 10	17 43	18 10		18 43	19 10	19 43	20 10	20 43	21 10	21 43	22 10	22 48	23 51	00 28
Reading 7 149 a	15 53	16 35	16 19	16 53	17 19	17 53	18 19	18 35	18 53	19 19	19 53	20 19	20 53	21 19	21 53	22 19	22 57	23 59	00 37

Sundays

	GW 1	GW 1	GW 1	GW 1	XC 1 ◇ B ☕	GW 1	GW 1 C	GW 1 D	XC 1 ◇ E ☕	GW 1 D	GW 1 C	GW 1	GW 1	GW 1	GW 1	GW 1	GW 1	GW 1	GW 1	GW 1	GW 1	GW 1	GW 1	GW 1
Brighton 10 186 d					07 50				09 40															
Gatwick Airport 10 186 ✈ d	23p18	06 07	07 07	08 07	08 31	09 07	10 07	10 07	10 11			11 07	12 07	13 07	14 07	15 07	16 07	17 07	18 07	19 07	20 07	21 07	22 07	23 07
Redhill 186 d	23p29	06 19	07 19	08 19	08 48	09 19	10 21	10 21	10 33			11 19	12 19	13 19	14 20	15 19	16 20	17 19	18 20	19 19	20 20	21 19	22 19	23 19
Reigate 186 d	23p33	06 23	07 23	08 23		09 23	10 25	10 25				11 23	12 23	13 23	14 24	15 23	16 24	17 23	18 24	19 23	20 24	21 23	22 23	23 23
Betchworth d		06 28		08 28			10 30	10 30					12 28		14 29		16 29		18 29		20 29		22 28	
Dorking Deepdene d	23p40	06 32	07 30	08 32		09 30	10 34	10 34				11 30	12 32	13 30	14 33	15 30	16 33	17 30	18 33	19 30	20 33	21 30	22 32	23 30
Dorking West d			07 33			09 33						11 33		13 33		15 33		17 33		19 33		21 33		23 33
Gomshall d			07 41			09 41						11 41		13 41		15 41		17 41		19 41		21 41		23 41
Chilworth d			07 47			09 47						11 47		13 47		15 47		17 47		19 47		21 47		23 47
Shalford d		06 46		08 46			10 48	10 48					12 46		14 47		16 47		18 47		20 47		22 46	
Guildford a	23p59	06 50	07 54	08 54	09 09	09 54	10 54	10 54	10 57	←	←	11 54	12 54	13 54	14 54	15 54	16 54	17 54	18 54	19 54	20 54	21 54	22 54	23 54
d	00 01	06 51	07 56	08 56	09 11	09 56	11 02	11 02	10 58	11 02	11 02	11 56	12 56	13 56	14 56	15 56	16 56	17 56	18 56	19 56	20 55	21 56	22 55	23 56
Wanborough 149 d							→	→																
Ash 3 149 d		07 01		09 05						11 11	11 11		13 05		15 05		17 05		19 05		21 05		23 05	
North Camp d	00 13	07 05	08 08	09 09		10 08				11 15	11 21	12 08	13 09	14 08	15 09	16 08	17 09	18 08	19 09	20 08	21 09	22 08	23 09	00 08
Farnborough North d			08 12			10 12						12 12		14 12		16 12		18 12		20 12		22 12		00 12
Blackwater d	00 20	07 11	08 16	09 16		10 16				11 22	11 28	12 16	13 16	14 16	15 16	16 16	17 16	18 16	19 16	20 16	21 16	22 16	23 16	00 16
Sandhurst d			08 20			10 20						12 20		14 20		16 20		18 20		20 20		22 20		00 20
Crowthorne d		07 16		09 21						11 27	11 33		13 21		15 21		17 21		19 21		21 21		23 21	
Wokingham 149 d	00 28	07 21	08 27	09 26		10 27				11 32	11 38	12 27	13 26	14 27	15 26	16 27	17 26	18 27	19 26	20 27	21 26	22 27	23 26	00 27
Reading 7 149 a	00 37	07 30	08 35	09 35	09 46	10 35			11 36	11 40	11 46	12 35	13 35	14 35	15 35	16 35	17 35	18 35	19 35	20 35	21 35	22 36	23 37	00 36

For general notes see front of timetable
For details of catering facilities see Directory of Train Operators

A To Birmingham New Street (Table 116)
B From 30 March. To Didcot Parkway (Table 116)
C Until 27 January
D From 3 February
E Until 23 March. To Birmingham New Street (Table 116)

South West Trains
A Stagecoach Company

These notes apply to Tables 149 to 156, 158, 160, 165 and 167

Christmas and New Year Holiday 2007/8

Saturday 23 December	—	A normal Sunday service will operate
Monday 24 December	—	A normal Saturday service will operate until 1900 hours when trains will be revised to enable a complete shutdown by 2200 hours
Tuesday 25 December	—	No service
Wednesday 26 Decenber	—	No service
Thursday 27 December	—	A normal Saturday service will operate with additional peak hour sevices. On Table 167 servies commence approximately one hour later than normal
Friday 28 December	—	A normal Saturday service will operate with additional peak hour sevices
Saturday 29 December	—	A normal Saturday service will operate
Sunday 30 December	—	A normal Sunday service will operate
Monday 31 December	—	A normal Saturday service will operate. On Table 167 services will finish approximately two hours earlier than normal
Tuesday 1 January	—	A normal Sunday service will operate. On Table 167 a special service will operate commencing after 0800
Wednesday 2 January	—	A normal weekday service will operate

Easter Holiday

Friday 21 March	—	A normal Saturday service will operate
Monday 24 March	—	A normal Saturday service will operate

Engineering Works
Major engineering works will be taking place in the Clapham Junction area and many services will be directed via alternative routes, or will start/terminate at different stations.

May Day Holiday

Monday 5 May	—	A normal Saturday service will operate

For details of Bank Holiday service alterations, please see first page of this Table

London → Hounslow, Richmond, Kingston, Windsor, Weybridge, Ascot, Guildford and Reading

Network Diagram - see first page of Table 148

Miles	Miles	Miles			SW	SW	SW	SW	SW	SW	SW	SW	SW	SW	SW	SW	SW	SW	SW	SW	SW		SW	SW	SW
					MO	MO	MO	MO	MX	MX	MX	MX	MX	MX	MX	MX	MX	MX							
					1	1			1	1											1			1	1
							A													B					
0	—	0	**London Waterloo** 15 ⊖	d	23p09	23p39		23p44	22p50	23p20	23p22	23p28		23p35	23p33	23p52	23p58		00 18						05 05
1¼	—	1¼	Vauxhall ⊖	d	23p13	23p43		23p48			23p26	23p32			23p37	23p56	00 02		00 22						05 09
2¾	—	2¾	Queenstown Rd.(Battersea)	d				23p51			23p29				23p40	23p59			00 25						05 12
4	—	4	**Clapham Junction** 10	d	23p19	23p49		23p54	22p58	23p28	23p32	23p38		23p43	23p43	00 02	00 08		00 28						05 15
4¾	—	4¾	Wandsworth Town	d				23p57			23p35				23p46	00 05			00 31						05 18
5¾	—	5¾	Putney	d	23p23	23p53		23p59			23p38	23p42			23p49	00 08	00 12		00 34						05 21
7	0	7	Barnes	d				00 03			23p43				23p52	00 13			00 37						05 24
—	½	—	Barnes Bridge	d							23p45					00 15									
—	1½	—	Chiswick	d							23p47		←			00 17		←							
—	2½	—	Kew Bridge	d							23p50		23p50			00 20		00 20							
—	3½	—	Brentford	d							→		23p53			→		00 23							
—	4¼	—	Syon Lane	d									23p55					00 25							
—	5	—	Isleworth	d									23p57					00 27							
—	6½	—	**Hounslow**	d									00 01					00 31							
8¼	—	8¼	Mortlake	d				00 05							23p54				00 39						05 26
9	—	9	North Sheen	d				00 07							23p56				00 41						05 28
9¾	—	9¾	**Richmond** ⊖	d	23p29	23p59		00 10	23p06	23p37		23p48		23p51	23p59		00 18		00 44						05 31
10¾	—	10¾	St Margarets	d				00 12							00 01				00 46						05 33
11¼	—	11¼	Twickenham	a	23p32	00 02		00 14	23p10	23p41		23p51		23p55	00 03		00 21		00 48						05 35
—	—	—		d	23p33	00 03		00 15	23p10	23p41		23p52		23p55	00 04		00 22		00 49	04 52					05 36
12¼	—	—	Strawberry Hill	d											00 07				00s52	04 55					
12½	—	—	Fulwell	a																					
13½	—	—	Teddington	a											00 10				00s55	04 58					
14¾	—	—	Hampton Wick	a											00 14				00s58	05 01					
15¼	—	—	**Kingston**	a											00 16				01 00	05 03					
—	—	12½	Whitton	d				00 18				23p55					00 25								05 39
—	—	14¾	Feltham	d	23p39	00 09		00 22	23p16	23p48		23p59	00 06	00 01			00 29	00 36							05 43
—	—	17½	Ashford (Surrey)	d				00 26				00 03	00 10				00 33	00 40							05 47
0	—	19	**Staines**	d	23p45	00 15	00 21	00a30	23p23	23p56		00 07	00 15	00 08			00a37	00a46			05 23		05 45		05 53
2½	—	—	Wraysbury	d								00 11													
3¾	—	—	Sunnymeads	d								00 14													
4¾	—	—	Datchet	d								00 17													
6¾	—	—	**Windsor & Eton Riverside**	a								00 21													
—	—	21	Egham	d	23p50	00 20	00s25		23p27	00 01			00 20	00 12							05 27		05 50		05 57
0	—	23¼	Virginia Water	a	23p54	00 24	00s29		23p31	00 05			00 24	00 16							05 31		05 54		06 01
—	—	—		d	23p54	00 24			23p31	00 05			00 24	00 16							05 31		05 54		06 01
2½	—	—	Chertsey §	d			00s34						00 29										05 59		
4	—	—	Addlestone §	d			00s38						00 32										06 02		
5¾	—	—	**Weybridge**	a									00 37										06 07		
—	—	25¼	Longcross	d																					
—	—	27	Sunningdale	d	23p59	00 29			23p37	00 10				00 22							05 37				06 07
—	0	29	**Ascot** 3	d	00 04	00 34			23p43	00 15				00 26							05 43				06 13
—	3¼	—	Bagshot	d																					
—	6½	—	Camberley	a																					
—	—	—		d																					
—	8¾	—	Frimley	d																					
—	12	—	Ash Vale	d																					
—	14½	—	**Aldershot**	a																					
—	—	—		d																				06 08	
—	17¼	—	Ash 3	d																				06 15	
—	19¼	—	Wanborough	d																				06 18	
—	23½	—	**Guildford**	a																				06 25	
—	—	31¼	Martins Heron	d	00 08	00 38			23p47	00 19				00 30							05 47				06 17
—	—	32¼	Bracknell	d	00 11	00 41			23p50	00 23				00 34							05 50				06 20
—	—	36¾	**Wokingham**	d	00 18	00 48			23p57	00 31				00 40							05 57				06 27
—	—	38¾	Winnersh	d	00 21	00 51			00 01	00 35											06 00				06 30
—	—	39¼	Winnersh Triangle	d	00 23	00 53			00 02	00 37											06 02				06 32
—	—	40½	Earley	d	00 26	00 56			00 05	00 39											06 05				06 35
—	—	43½	**Reading** 7	a	00 31	01 01			00 10	00 44				00 49							06 10				06 40

For general notes see front of timetable
For details of catering facilities see Directory of Train Operators

§ Passengers to/from London may travel via Weybridge. See Table 155.

A To Woking
B To London Waterloo (Table 152)

For details of Bank Holiday service alterations, please see first page of this Table

London → Hounslow, Richmond, Kingston, Windsor, Weybridge, Ascot, Guildford and Reading

Network Diagram - see first page of Table 148

		SW	SW	SW	SW	SW	SW	SW	SW	SW	SW	SW	SW	SW	SW	SW	SW	SW	SW	SW	SW	SW	SW	SW
					1	1	1						1	1								1	1	
			A					B		A	B					B		A	B	B				
London Waterloo 15	⊖ d		05 33				05 50		05 58	06 03	06 15			06 20	06 22		06 28	06 33	06 45				06 50	06 52
Vauxhall	⊖ d		05 37						06 02	06 07	06 19				06 26		06 32	06 37	06 49					06 56
Queenstown Rd.(Battersea)	d		05 40							06 10	06 22				06 29			06 40	06 52					06 59
Clapham Junction 10	d		05 43				05 58		06 08	06 13	06 25			06 28	06 32		06 38	06 43	06 55				06 58	07 02
Wandsworth Town	d		05 46							06 16	06 28				06 35			06 46	06 58					07 05
Putney	d		05 49						06 12	06 19	06 31				06 38	←	06 42	06 49	07 01					07 08
Barnes	d		05 52							06 22	06 35				06 43	06 35		06 52	07 05					07 13
Barnes Bridge	d										→				06 45				→					07 15
Chiswick	d														06 47						←			07 17
Kew Bridge	d														06 50						06 50			07 20
Brentford	d														→						06 53			→
Syon Lane	d																				06 55			
Isleworth	d																				06 57			
Hounslow	d																			06 48	07 01			
Mortlake	d		05 54							06 24						06 37		06 54						
North Sheen	d		05 56							06 26						06 39		06 56						
Richmond	⊖ d		05 59				06 06		06 18	06 29				06 36		06 42	06 48	06 59					07 06	
St Margarets	d		06 01							06 31						06 44		07 01						
Twickenham	a		06 03				06 10		06 21	06 33				06 40		06 46	06 51	07 03					07 10	
	d	05 52	06 04				06 10	06 17	06 22	06 34				06 40		06 47	06 52	07 04					07 10	
Strawberry Hill	d		06 07							06 37								07 07						
Fulwell	a																							
Teddington	a		06 10							06 40								07 10						
Hampton Wick	a		06 14							06 44								07 14						
Kingston	a		06 16							06 46								07 16						
Whitton	d	05 55						06a20	06 25							06a50	06 55			06a53				
Feltham	d	05 59					06 16		06 29					06 46			06 59				07 06		07 16	
Ashford (Surrey)	d	06 03							06 33								07 03				07 10			
Staines	d	06 07		06 15			06 23		06 37			06 45		06 53			07 07				07 15		07 23	
Wraysbury	d	06 11							06 41								07 11							
Sunnymeads	d	06 14							06 44								07 14							
Datchet	d	06 17							06 47								07 17							
Windsor & Eton Riverside	a	06 21							06 51								07 21							
Egham	d			06 20			06 27					06 50		06 57							07 20		07 27	
Virginia Water	a			06 24			06 31					06 54		07 01							07 24		07 31	
	d			06 24			06 31					06 54		07 01							07 24		07 31	
Chertsey §	d			06 29								06 59									07 29			
Addlestone §	d			06 32								07 02									07 32			
Weybridge	a			06 37								07 07									07 37			
Longcross	d						06 35							07 05									07 35	
Sunningdale	d						06 37							07 07									07 37	
Ascot 3	d					06 23	06 43						06 53	07 13								07 23	07 43	
Bagshot	d					06 29							06 59									07 29		
Camberley	a					06 35							07 05									07 35		
	d					06 39							07 09									07 39		
Frimley	d					06 43							07 13									07 43		
Ash Vale	d					06 49							07 19									07 49		
Aldershot	a					06 54							07 24									07 54		
	d				06 38	07 08							07 38									08 08		
Ash 3	d				06 45	07 15							07 45									08 15		
Wanborough	d				06 48	07 18							07 48									08 18		
Guildford	a				06 55	07 25							07 55									08 25		
Martins Heron	d						06 47							07 17									07 47	
Bracknell	d						06 50							07 20									07 50	
Wokingham	d						06 57							07 27									07 57	
Winnersh	d						07 00							07 30									08 00	
Winnersh Triangle	d						07 02							07 32									08 02	
Earley	d						07 05							07 35									08 05	
Reading 7	a						07 10							07 40									08 10	

For general notes see front of timetable
For details of catering facilities see Directory of Train Operators

§ Passengers to/from London may travel via Weybridge. See Table 155.

A To London Waterloo (Table 152)
B To London Waterloo

For details of Bank Holiday service alterations, please see first page of this Table

London → Hounslow, Richmond, Kingston, Windsor, Weybridge, Ascot, Guildford and Reading

Network Diagram - see first page of Table 148

		GW	SW	SW	SW	SW	SW	SW	SW	SW	SW	SW	SW	SW	SW	SW	SW	SW	SW	SW	SW	SW	SW	SW
		[1]	[1]							[1]		[1]								[1]		[1]		
		A		B		C		B	C				B		C			B	C				B	
London Waterloo [15]	⊖ d				06 58	07 03		07 15		07 20	07 22			07 28	07 33		07 37	07 45		07 50	07 52			07 58
Vauxhall	⊖ d				07 02	07 07		07 19			07 26			07 32	07 37		07 41	07 49			07 56			08 02
Queenstown Rd.(Battersea)	d					07 10		07 22			07 29				07 40		07 44	07 52			07 59			
Clapham Junction [10]	d				07 08	07 13		07 25		07 28	07 32			07 38	07 43		07 47	07 55		07 58	08 02			08 08
Wandsworth Town	d					07 16		07 28			07 35				07 46		07 50	07 58			08 05			
Putney	d			←	07 12	07 19		07 31			07 38		←	07 42	07 49		07 53	08 01			08 08		←	08 12
Barnes	d			07 05		07 22		07 35			07 43		07 35		07 52		07 57	08 05			08 13		08 05	
Barnes Bridge	d							→			07 45						08 00	→			08 15			
Chiswick	d						←				07 47					←	08 02				08 17			
Kew Bridge	d						07 20				07 50					07 50	08 05				08 20			
Brentford	d						07 23				→					07 53	08 08				→			
Syon Lane	d						07 25									07 55	08 10							
Isleworth	d						07 27									07 57	08 12							
Hounslow	d						07 31									08 01	08a18							
Mortlake	d			07 07		07 24							07 37		07 54								08 07	
North Sheen	d			07 09		07 26							07 39		07 56								08 09	
Richmond	⊖ d			07 12	07 18	07 29				07 36			07 42	07 48	07 59					08 06			08 12	08 18
St Margarets	d			07 14		07 31							07 44		08 01								08 14	
Twickenham	a			07 16	07 21	07 33				07 40			07 46	07 51	08 03					08 10			08 16	08 21
	d			07 17	07 22	07 34			07 37	07 40			07 47	07 52	08 04				08 07	08 10			08 17	08 22
Strawberry Hill	d					07 37			07b47						08 07				08c17					
Fulwell	a																							
Teddington	a					07 40			07 50						08 10				08 20					
Hampton Wick	a					07 44			07 52						08 14				08 22					
Kingston	a					07 46			07 54						08 16				08 24					
Whitton	d			07a20	07 25								07a50	07 55									08a20	08 25
Feltham	d				07 29		07 36			07 46				07 59		08 06				08 16				08 29
Ashford (Surrey)	d				07 33		07 40							08 03		08 10								08 33
Staines	d				07 37		07 45			07 53				08 07		08 15				08 23				08 37
Wraysbury	d				07 41									08 11										08 41
Sunnymeads	d				07 44									08 14										08 44
Datchet	d				07 47									08 17										08 47
Windsor & Eton Riverside	a				07 51									08 21										08 51
Egham	d						07 50			07 57						08 20				08 27				
Virginia Water	a						07 54			08 01						08 24				08 31				
	d						07 54			08 01						08 24				08 31				
Chertsey §	d						07 59									08 29								
Addlestone §	d						08 02									08 32								
Weybridge	a						08 07									08 37								
Longcross	d									08 05										08 35				
Sunningdale	d									08 07										08 37				
Ascot [3]	d		07 53							08 13		08 23								08 43		08 53		
Bagshot	d		07 59									08 29										08 59		
Camberley	a		08 05									08 37										09 05		
	d		08 09									08 39										09 09		
Frimley	d		08 13									08 43										09 13		
Ash Vale	d		08 19									08 49										09 19		
Aldershot	a		08 24									08 54										09 25		
	d		08 38									09 08										09 38		
Ash [3]	d		08 45									09 15										09 45		
Wanborough	d		08 48									09 18										09 48		
Guildford	a		08 55									09 25										09 55		
Martins Heron	d									08 17										08 47				
Bracknell	d									08 20										08 50				
Wokingham	d	08 17								08 27										08 57				
Winnersh	d	08 21								08 30										09 00				
Winnersh Triangle	d									08 32										09 02				
Earley	d									08 35										09 05				
Reading [7]	a	08 28								08 40										09 10				

For general notes see front of timetable
For details of catering facilities see Directory of Train Operators

§ Passengers to/from London may travel via Weybridge. See Table 155.

A From Gatwick Airport (Table 148)
B To London Waterloo
C To London Waterloo (Table 152)

b Arr. 0740
c Arr. 0810

For details of Bank Holiday service alterations, please see first page of this Table

London → Hounslow, Richmond, Kingston, Windsor, Weybridge, Ascot, Guildford and Reading

Network Diagram - see first page of Table 148

		SW	SW 1	SW	SW	SW	SW	SW 1	SW		SW 1	SW	SW	SW	SW 1	SW	SW	SW	SW	SW 1	SW	SW 1	SW	SW	SW
		A		A		B	B					B		A		A		B	B				B		A
London Waterloo [15]	⊖ d	08 03	08 07			08 10	08 15	08 20	08 22				08 28	08 33	08 37			08 40	08 43	08 50	08 52			08 58	09 03
Vauxhall	⊖ d	08 07				08 14	08 19		08 26				08 32	08 37				08 44	08 47		08 56			09 02	09 07
Queenstown Rd.(Battersea)	d	08 10				08 17	08 22		08 29					08 40				08 47	08 50		08 59				09 10
Clapham Junction [10]	d	08 13	08 15			08 20	08 25	08 28	08 32				08 38	08 43	08 45			08 50	08 55	08 58	09 02			09 08	09 13
Wandsworth Town	d	08 16				08 23	08 28		08 35					08 46				08 53	08 58		09 05				09 16
Putney	d	08 19		←		08 26	08 31		08 38			←	08 42	08 49		←		08 56	09 01		09 08		←	09 12	09 19
Barnes	d	08 22		08 22		08 28	08 35		08 43			08 35		08 52		08 52		08 58	09 05		09 13		09 05		09 22
Barnes Bridge	d	→				08 30	→		08 45					→				09 00	→		09 15				
Chiswick	d				←	08 33			08 47								←	09 02			09 17				
Kew Bridge	d				08 20	08 35			08 50 →								08 50	09 05			09 20 →				
Brentford	d				08 23	08 38											08 53	09 08							
Syon Lane	d				08 25	08 40											08 55	09 10							
Isleworth	d				08 27	08 42											08 57	09 12							
Hounslow	d				08 31	08 48											09 01	09 18							
Mortlake	d			08 24								08 37				08 54							09 07		09 24
North Sheen	d			08 26								08 39				08 56							09 09		09 26
Richmond	⊖ d		08 23	08 29				08 36				08 42	08 48		08 53	08 59				09 06			09 12	09 18	09 29
St Margarets	d			08 31								08 44				09 01							09 14		09 31
Twickenham	a		08 27	08 33				08 40				08 46	08 51		08 57	09 03				09 10			09 16	09 21	09 33
	d		08 27	08 34				08 40				08 47	08 52		08 57	09 04				09 10			09 17	09 22	09 34
Strawberry Hill	d			08 37												09 07									09 37
Fulwell	a																								
Teddington	a			08 40												09 10									09 40
Hampton Wick	a			08 44												09 14									09 44
Kingston	a			08 46												09 16									09 46
Whitton	d					08a53						08a50	08 55					09a23					09a20	09 25	
Feltham	d		08 33		08 36			08 46					08 59		09 03		09 07			09 16				09 29	
Ashford (Surrey)	d		08 37		08 40								09 03		09 07		09 10							09 33	
Staines	d		08 41		08 45			08 53					09 07		09 11		09 15			09 23				09 37	
Wraysbury	d												09 11											09 41	
Sunnymeads	d												09 14											09 44	
Datchet	d												09 17											09 47	
Windsor & Eton Riverside	a												09 21											09 51	
Egham	d		08 46		08 50			08 57							09 16		09 20			09 27					
Virginia Water	a		08 50		08 54			09 01							09 20		09 24			09 31					
	d		08 50		08 54			09 01							09 20		09 24			09 31					
Chertsey §	d				08 59												09 29								
Addlestone §	d				09 02												09 32								
Weybridge	a				09 07												09 37								
Longcross	d		08 53																						
Sunningdale	d		08 57					09 07							09 25					09 37					
Ascot [3]	d		09 01					09 13			09 23				09 30					09 43		09 53			
Bagshot	d										09 29											09 59			
Camberley	a										09 35											10 05			
	d										09 39											10 09			
Frimley	d										09 43											10 13			
Ash Vale	d										09 49											10 19			
Aldershot	a										09 54											10 24			
	d										10 08											10 38			
Ash [3]	d										10 15											10 45			
Wanborough	d										10 18											10 48			
Guildford	a										10 25											10 55			
Martins Heron	d		09 05					09 17							09 34					09 47					
Bracknell	d		09 09					09 20							09 37					09 50					
Wokingham	d		09 17					09 27							09 46					09 57					
Winnersh	d		09 20					09 30												10 00					
Winnersh Triangle	d		09 22					09 32												10 02					
Earley	d		09 25					09 35												10 05					
Reading [7]	a		09 30					09 40							09 55					10 10					

For general notes see front of timetable
For details of catering facilities see Directory of Train Operators

A To London Waterloo (Table 152)
B To London Waterloo

§ Passengers to/from London may travel via Weybridge. See Table 155.

For details of Bank Holiday service alterations, please see first page of this Table

London → Hounslow, Richmond, Kingston, Windsor, Weybridge, Ascot, Guildford and Reading

Network Diagram - see first page of Table 148

		SW	SW	SW	SW [1]		SW	SW [1]	SW	SW	SW	SW	SW	SW	SW [1]	SW	SW [1]	SW	SW	SW	SW		SW	SW	SW [1]
			A	A					A		B		A	A				A		B			A	A	
London Waterloo [15] ⊖	d		09 07	09 15	09 20		09 22			09 28	09 33		09 37	09 45	09 50	09 52			09 58	10 03			10 07	10 15	10 20
Vauxhall ⊖	d		09 11	09 19			09 26			09 32	09 37		09 41	09 49		09 56			10 02	10 07			10 11	10 19	
Queenstown Rd.(Battersea)	d		09 14	09 22			09 29				09 40		09 44	09 52		09 59				10 10			10 14	10 22	
Clapham Junction [10]	d		09 17	09 25	09 28		09 32			09 38	09 43		09 47	09 55	09 58	10 02			10 08	10 13			10 17	10 25	10 28
Wandsworth Town	d		09 20	09 28			09 35				09 46		09 50	09 58		10 05				10 16			10 20	10 28	
Putney	d		09 23	09 31			09 38		←	09 42	09 49		09 53	10 01		10 08		←	10 12	10 19			10 23	10 31	
Barnes	d		09 28	09 35			09 43		09 35		09 52		09 58	10 05		10 13		10 05		10 22			10 28	10 35	
Barnes Bridge	d		09 30	→			09 45						10 00	→		10 15							10 30	→	
Chiswick	d	←	09 32				09 47					←	10 02			10 17					←		10 32		
Kew Bridge	d	09 20	09 35				09 50					09 50	10 05			10 20					10 20		10 35		
Brentford	d	09 23	09 38				→					09 53	10 08			→					10 23		10 38		
Syon Lane	d	09 25	09 40									09 55	10 10								10 25		10 40		
Isleworth	d	09 27	09 42									09 57	10 12								10 27		10 42		
Hounslow	d	09 31	09b48									10 01	10c18								10 31		10e48		
Mortlake	d								09 37		09 54							10 07		10 24					
North Sheen	d								09 39		09 56							10 09		10 26					
Richmond ⊖	d				09 36				09 42	09 48	09 59				10 06			10 12	10 18	10 29					10 36
St Margarets	d								09 44		10 01							10 14		10 31					
Twickenham	a				09 40				09 46	09 51	10 03				10 10			10 16	10 21	10 33					10 40
	d				09 40				09 47	09 52	10 04				10 10			10 17	10 22	10 34					10 40
Strawberry Hill	d										10 07									10 37					
Fulwell	a																								
Teddington	a										10 10									10 40					
Hampton Wick	a										10 14									10 44					
Kingston	a										10 16									10 46					
Whitton	d		09a53						09a50	09 55			10a23					10a20	10 25				10a53		
Feltham	d	09 36			09 46					09 59		10 06			10 16				10 29		10 36				10 46
Ashford (Surrey)	d	09 40								10 03		10 10							10 33		10 40				
Staines	d	09 45			09 53					10 07		10 15			10 23				10 37		10 45				10 53
Wraysbury	d									10 11									10 41						
Sunnymeads	d									10 14									10 44						
Datchet	d									10 17									10 47						
Windsor & Eton Riverside	a									10 21									10 52						
Egham	d	09 50			09 57							10 20			10 27						10 50				10 57
Virginia Water	a	09 54			10 01							10 24			10 31						10 54				11 01
	d	09 54			10 01							10 24			10 31						10 54				11 01
Chertsey §	d	09 59										10 29									10 59				
Addlestone §	d	10 02										10 32									11 02				
Weybridge	a	10 07										10 37									11 07				
Longcross	d																								
Sunningdale	d				10 07										10 37										11 07
Ascot [3]	d				10 13			10 23							10 43		10 53								11 13
Bagshot	d							10 29									10 59								
Camberley	a							10 35									11 05								
	d							10 39									11 09								
Frimley	d							10 43									11 13								
Ash Vale	d							10 49									11 19								
Aldershot	a							10 54									11 24								
	d							11 08									11 38								
Ash [3]	d							11 15									11 45								
Wanborough	d							11 18									11 48								
Guildford	a							11 25									11 55								
Martins Heron	d				10 17										10 47										11 17
Bracknell	d				10 20										10 50										11 20
Wokingham	d				10 27										10 57										11 27
Winnersh	d				10 30										11 00										11 30
Winnersh Triangle	d				10 32										11 02										11 32
Earley	d				10 35										11 05										11 35
Reading [7]	a				10 40										11 10										11 40

For general notes see front of timetable
For details of catering facilities see Directory of Train Operators

§ Passengers to/from London may travel via Weybridge. See Table 155.

A To London Waterloo
B To London Waterloo (Table 152)
b Arr. 0945
c Arr. 1015
e Arr. 1045

For details of Bank Holiday service alterations, please see first page of this Table

London → Hounslow, Richmond, Kingston, Windsor, Weybridge, Ascot, Guildford and Reading

Network Diagram - see first page of Table 148

Station		SW	SW 1	SW	SW	SW	SW	SW	SW	SW 1	SW	SW 1	SW	SW	SW	SW		SW	SW	SW 1	SW	SW 1	SW
				A		B		A	A				A		B			A	A				A
London Waterloo 15 ⊖	d	10 22			10 28	10 33		10 37	10 45	10 50	10 52			10 58	11 03			15 07	15 15	15 20	15 22		
Vauxhall ⊖	d	10 26			10 32	10 37		10 41	10 49		10 56			11 02	11 07			15 12	15 19		15 26		
Queenstown Rd.(Battersea)	d	10 29				10 40		10 44	10 52		10 59				11 10			15 15	15 22		15 29		
Clapham Junction 10	d	10 32			10 38	10 43		10 47	10 55	10 58	11 02			11 08	11 13			15 18	15 25	15 28	15 32		
Wandsworth Town	d	10 35				10 46		10 50	10 58		11 05				11 16			15 20	15 28		15 35		
Putney	d	10 38		←	10 42	10 49		10 53	11 01		11 08		←	11 12	11 19			15 23	15 31		15 38		←
Barnes	d	10 43		10 35		10 52		10 58	11 05		11 13		11 05		11 22			15 27	15 35		15 43		15 35
Barnes Bridge	d	10 45						11 00	→		11 15							15 30	→		15 45		
Chiswick	d	10 47					←	11 02			11 17					←		15 32			15 47		
Kew Bridge	d	10 50					10 50	11 05			11 20					11 20		15 35			15 50		
Brentford	d	→					10 53	11 08			→					11 23		15 38			→		
Syon Lane	d						10 55	11 10								11 25		15 40					
Isleworth	d						10 57	11 12								11 27		15 42					
Hounslow	d						11 01	11b18								11 31		15c48					
Mortlake	d			10 37		10 54							11 07		11 24								15 37
North Sheen	d			10 39		10 56							11 09		11 26								15 39
Richmond ⊖	d			10 42	10 48	10 59				11 06			11 12	11 18	11 29					15 36			15 42
St Margarets	d			10 44		11 01							11 14		11 31								15 44
Twickenham	a			10 46	10 51	11 03				11 10			11 17	11 21	11 33					15 40			15 46
	d			10 47	10 52	11 04				11 10			11 17	11 22	11 34					15 40			15 47
Strawberry Hill	d					11 07									11 37								
Fulwell	a																						
Teddington	a					11 10									11 40								
Hampton Wick	a					11 14									11 44		and at						
Kingston	a					11 16									11 46		the same						
Whitton	d			10a50	10 55			11a23					11a20	11 25				15a53					15a50
Feltham	d				10 59		11 06			11 16				11 29		11 36	minutes			15 46			
Ashford (Surrey)	d				11 03		11 10							11 33		11 40							
Staines	d				11 07		11 15			11 23				11 37		11 45	past			15 53			
Wraysbury	d				11 11									11 41			each						
Sunnymeads	d				11 14									11 44									
Datchet	d				11 17									11 47			hour until						
Windsor & Eton Riverside	a				11 21									11 51									
Egham	d						11 20			11 27						11 50				15 57			
Virginia Water	a						11 24			11 31						11 54				16 01			
	d						11 24			11 31						11 54				16 01			
Chertsey §	d						11 29									11 59							
Addlestone §	d						11 32									12 02							
Weybridge	a						11 37									12 07							
Longcross	d																						
Sunningdale	d									11 37										16 07			
Ascot 3	d		11 23							11 43		11 53								16 13		16 23	
Bagshot	d		11 29									11 59										16 29	
Camberley	a		11 35									12 05										16 35	
	d		11 39									12 09										16 39	
Frimley	d		11 43									12 13										16 43	
Ash Vale	d		11 49									12 19										16 49	
Aldershot	a		11 54									12 24										16 54	
	d		12 08									12 38										17 08	
Ash 3	d		12 15									12 45										17 15	
Wanborough	d		12 18									12 48										17 18	
Guildford	a		12 25									12 55										17 25	
Martins Heron	d									11 47										16 17			
Bracknell	d									11 50										16 20			
Wokingham	d									11 57										16 27			
Winnersh	d									12 00										16 30			
Winnersh Triangle	d									12 02										16 32			
Earley	d									12 05										16 35			
Reading 7	a									12 10										16 40			

For general notes see front of timetable
For details of catering facilities see Directory of Train Operators

§ Passengers to/from London may travel via Weybridge. See Table 155.

A To London Waterloo
B To London Waterloo (Table 152)
b Arr. 1115
c Arr. 1545

For details of Bank Holiday service alterations, please see first page of this Table

London → Hounslow, Richmond, Kingston, Windsor, Weybridge, Ascot, Guildford and Reading

Network Diagram - see first page of Table 148

		SW	SW	SW	SW	SW	SW	SW	SW	SW	SW	SW	SW	SW		SW	SW	SW	SW	SW	SW	SW	SW	SW	SW
							1		1				1						1		1				1
			A		B	B				B		A		A			B	B				B		A	
London Waterloo 15	⊖ d	15 28	15 33		15 37	15 45	15 50	15 52			15 58	16 01	16 05				16 07	16 15	16 20	16 22			16 28	16 31	16 35
Vauxhall	⊖ d	15 32	15 37		15 41	15 49		15 56			16 02	16 05	16 09				16 11	16 19		16 26			16 32	16 35	16 39
Queenstown Rd.(Battersea)	d		15 40		15 44	15 52		15 59				16 08					16 14	16 22		16 29				16 38	
Clapham Junction 10	d	15 38	15 43		15 47	15 55	15 58	16 02			16 08	16 11	16 15				16 17	16 25	16 28	16 32			16 38	16 41	16 45
Wandsworth Town	d		15 46		15 50	15 58		16 05				16 14					16 20	16 28		16 35				16 44	
Putney	d	15 42	15 49		15 53	16 01		16 08		←	16 12	16 17		←			16 23	16 31		16 38		←	16 42	16 47	
Barnes	d		15 52		15 57	16 05		16 13		16 05		16 22		16 22			16 27	16 35		16 43		16 35		16 52	
Barnes Bridge	d				16 00	→		16 15				→					16 30	→		16 45				→	
Chiswick	d			←	16 02			16 17								←	16 32			16 47					
Kew Bridge	d			15 50	16 05			16 20								16 20	16 35			16 50					
Brentford	d			15 53	16 08			→								16 23	16 38			→					
Syon Lane	d			15 55	16 10											16 25	16 40								
Isleworth	d			15 57	16 12											16 27	16 42								
Hounslow	d			16 01	16b18											16 31	16c48								
Mortlake	d		15 54							16 07				16 24								16 37			
North Sheen	d		15 56							16 09				16 26								16 39			
Richmond	⊖ d	15 48	15 59				16 06			16 12	16 18		16 23	16 29					16 36			16 42	16 48		16 53
St Margarets	d		16 01							16 14				16 31								16 44			
Twickenham	a	15 51	16 03				16 10			16 16	16 21		16 27	16 33					16 40			16 46	16 51		16 57
	d	15 52	16 04				16 10			16 17	16 22		16 27	16 34					16 40			16 47	16 52		16 57
Strawberry Hill	d		16 07											16 37											
Fulwell	a																								
Teddington	a		16 10											16 42											
Hampton Wick	a		16 14											16 46											
Kingston	a		16 16											16 48											
Whitton	d	15 55			16a23					16a20	16 25						16a53					16a50	16 55		
Feltham	d	15 59		16 06			16 16				16 29		16 33			16 36			16 46				16 59		17 03
Ashford (Surrey)	d	16 03		16 10							16 33		16 37			16 40							17 03		17 07
Staines	d	16 07		16 15			16 23				16 37		16 41			16 45			16 53				17 07		17 11
Wraysbury	d	16 11									16 41												17 11		
Sunnymeads	d	16 14									16 44												17 14		
Datchet	d	16 17									16 47												17 17		
Windsor & Eton Riverside	a	16 21									16 51												17 23		
Egham	d			16 20			16 27						16 46			16 50			16 57						17 16
Virginia Water	a			16 24			16 31						16 50			16 54			17 01						17 20
	d			16 24			16 31						16 50			16 54			17 01						17 20
Chertsey §	d			16 29												16 59									
Addlestone §	d			16 32												17 02									
Weybridge	a			16 37												17 07									
Longcross	d																								17 23
Sunningdale	d						16 37						16 55						17 07						17 27
Ascot 3	d						16 43		16 53				17 00						17 13		17 23				17 31
Bagshot	d								16 59												17 29				
Camberley	a								17 05												17 35				
	d								17 09												17 39				
Frimley	d								17 13												17 43				
Ash Vale	d								17 19												17 49				
Aldershot	a								17 24												17 54				
	d								17 38												18 08				
Ash 3	d								17 45												18 15				
Wanborough	d								17 48												18 18				
Guildford	a								17 55												18 25				
Martins Heron	d						16 47						17 04						17 17						17 35
Bracknell	d						16 50						17 07						17 20						17 39
Wokingham	d						16 57						17 17						17 27						17 47
Winnersh	d						17 00												17 30						
Winnersh Triangle	d						17 02												17 32						
Earley	d						17 05												17 35						
Reading 7	a						17 10						17 27						17 42						17 58

For general notes see front of timetable
For details of catering facilities see Directory of Train Operators

§ Passengers to/from London may travel via Weybridge. See Table 155.

A To London Waterloo (Table 152)
B To London Waterloo
b Arr. 1615
c Arr. 1645

For details of Bank Holiday service alterations, please see first page of this Table

London → Hounslow, Richmond, Kingston, Windsor, Weybridge, Ascot, Guildford and Reading

Network Diagram - see first page of Table 148

		SW A	SW	SW B	SW B	SW [1]	SW	SW B	SW	SW A	SW [1]	SW A	SW	SW [1]	SW B	SW	SW B	SW [1]	SW	SW [1]	SW B	SW	SW A	SW [1]
London Waterloo [15]	⊖ d			16 37	16 45	16 50	16 52		16 58	17 01	17 05				17 07	17 13	17 15	17 20	17 22			17 28	17 31	17 35
Vauxhall	⊖ d			16 41	16 49		16 56		17 02	17 05	17 09				17 11	17 17	17 19		17 26			17 32	17 35	17 39
Queenstown Rd.(Battersea)	d			16 44	16 52		16 59			17 08					17 14		17 22		17 29				17 38	
Clapham Junction [10]	d			16 47	16 55	16 58	17 02		17 08	17 11	17 15				17 17	17 23	17 25	17 28	17 32			17 38	17 41	17 45
Wandsworth Town	d			16 50	16 58		17 05			17 14					17 20		17 28		17 35				17 44	
Putney	d	←		16 53	17 01		17 08	←	17 12	17 17		←			17 23	17 27	17 31		17 38		←	17 42	17 47	
Barnes	d	16 52		16 57	17 05		17 13	17 05		17 22		17 22			17 27		17 35		17 43		17 35		17 52	
Barnes Bridge	d			17 00	→		17 15			→					17 30		→		17 45				→	
Chiswick	d		←	17 02			17 17						←		17 32				17 47					
Kew Bridge	d		16 50	17 05			17 20						17 20		17 35				17 50					
Brentford	d		16 53	17 08			→						17 23		17 38				→					
Syon Lane	d		16 55	17 10									17 25		17 40									
Isleworth	d		16 57	17 12									17 27		17 42									
Hounslow	d		17 01	17b18									17 31		17c48									
Mortlake	d	16 54						17 07				17 24									17 37			
North Sheen	d	16 56						17 09				17 26									17 39			
Richmond	⊖ d	16 59				17 06		17 12	17 18		17 23	17 29				17 33		17 36			17 42	17 48		17 53
St Margarets	d	17 01						17 14				17 31									17 44			
Twickenham	a	17 03				17 10		17 16	17 21		17 27	17 33				17 37		17 40			17 46	17 51		17 57
	d	17 04				17 10		17 17	17 22		17 27	17 34				17 37		17 40			17 47	17 52		17 57
Strawberry Hill	d	17 07										17 37				17 41								
Fulwell	a																							
Teddington	a	17 12										17 42				17 46								
Hampton Wick	a	17 16										17 46												
Kingston	a	17 18										17 48												
Whitton	d			17a23				17a20	17 25						17a53						17a50	17 55		
Feltham	d		17 06			17 16			17 29		17 33		17 36					17 46				17 59		18 03
Ashford (Surrey)	d		17 10						17 33		17 37		17 40									18 03		18 07
Staines	d		17 15			17 23			17 37		17 41		17 45					17 53				18 07		18 11
Wraysbury	d								17 41													18 11		
Sunnymeads	d								17 44													18 14		
Datchet	d								17 47													18 17		
Windsor & Eton Riverside	a								17 53													18 23		
Egham	d		17 20			17 27					17 46		17 50					17 57						18 16
Virginia Water	a		17 24			17 31					17 50		17 54					18 01						18 20
	d		17 24			17 31					17 50		17 54					18 01						18 20
Chertsey §	d		17 29										17 59											
Addlestone §	d		17 32										18 02											
Weybridge	a		17 40										18 10											
Longcross	d																							
Sunningdale	d					17 37					17 55							18 07						18 25
Ascot [3]	d					17 43					18 00							18 13		18 23				18 30
Bagshot	d										18 06									18 29				
Camberley	a										18 12									18 35				
	d										18 13									18 39				
Frimley	d										18 17									18 43				
Ash Vale	d										18 24									18 49				
Aldershot	a										18 31									18 54				
	d													18 38						19 08				
Ash [3]	d													18 45						19 15				
Wanborough	d													18 48						19 18				
Guildford	a													18 55						19 25				
Martins Heron	d					17 47												18 17						18 34
Bracknell	d					17 50												18 20						18 37
Wokingham	d					17 57												18 27						18 47
Winnersh	d					18 00												18 30						
Winnersh Triangle	d					18 02												18 32						
Earley	d					18 05												18 35						
Reading [7]	a					18 12												18 43						18 57

For general notes see front of timetable
For details of catering facilities see Directory of Train Operators

§ Passengers to/from London may travel via Weybridge. See Table 155.

A To London Waterloo (Table 152)
B To London Waterloo
b Arr. 1715
c Arr. 1745

For details of Bank Holiday service alterations, please see first page of this Table

London → Hounslow, Richmond, Kingston, Windsor, Weybridge, Ascot, Guildford and Reading

Network Diagram - see first page of Table 148

		SW	SW	SW	SW	SW		SW 1	SW	SW	SW	SW	SW 1	SW	SW	SW 1	SW	SW	SW	SW 1	SW	SW 1	SW	SW	SW
		A		B	C	B				B		A		A			B	C	B				B		A
London Waterloo 15	⊖ d			17 37	17 43	17 45		17 50	17 52		17 58	18 01	18 05				18 07	18 13	18 15	18 20	18 22			18 28	18 31
Vauxhall	⊖ d			17 41	17 47	17 49			17 56		18 02	18 05	18 09				18 11	18 17	18 19		18 26			18 32	18 35
Queenstown Rd.(Battersea)	d			17 44		17 52			17 59			18 08					18 14		18 22		18 29				18 38
Clapham Junction 10	d			17 47	17 53	17 55		17 58	18 02		18 08	18 11	18 15				18 17	18 23	18 25	18 28	18 32			18 38	18 41
Wandsworth Town	d			17 50		17 58			18 05			18 14					18 20		18 28		18 35				18 44
Putney	d	←		17 53	17 57	18 01			18 08	←	18 12	18 17		←			18 23	18 27	18 31		18 38		←	18 42	18 47
Barnes	d	17 52		17 57		18 05			18 13	18 05		18 22		18 22			18 27		18 35		18 43		18 35		18 52
Barnes Bridge	d			18 00		→			18 15			→					18 30		→		18 45				→
Chiswick	d		←	18 02					18 17						←		18 32				18 47				
Kew Bridge	d		17 50	18 05					18 20						18 20		18 35				18 50				
Brentford	d		17 53	18 08					→						18 23		18 38				→				
Syon Lane	d		17 55	18 10											18 25		18 40								
Isleworth	d		17 57	18 12											18 27		18 42								
Hounslow	d		18 01	18b18											18 31		18c48								
Mortlake	d	17 54								18 07				18 24									18 37		
North Sheen	d	17 56								18 09				18 26									18 39		
Richmond	⊖ d	17 59			18 03			18 06		18 12	18 18		18 23	18 29				18 33		18 36			18 42	18 48	
St Margarets	d	18 01								18 14				18 31									18 44		
Twickenham	a	18 03			18 07			18 10		18 16	18 21		18 27	18 33				18 37		18 40			18 46	18 51	
	d	18 04			18 07			18 10		18 17	18 22		18 27	18 34				18 37		18 40			18 47	18 52	
Strawberry Hill	d	18 07			18 11									18 37				18 41							
Fulwell	a				18 13													18 43							
Teddington	a	18 12												18 42											
Hampton Wick	a	18 16												18 46											
Kingston	a	18 18												18 48											
Whitton	d			18a23						18a20	18 25						18a53						18a50	18 55	
Feltham	d		18 06					18 16			18 29		18 33		18 36					18 46				18 59	
Ashford (Surrey)	d		18 10								18 33		18 37		18 40									19 03	
Staines	d		18 15					18 23			18 37		18 41		18 45					18 53				19 07	
Wraysbury	d										18 41													19 11	
Sunnymeads	d										18 44													19 14	
Datchet	d										18 47													19 17	
Windsor & Eton Riverside	a										18 53													19 23	
Egham	d		18 20					18 27					18 46		18 50					18 57					
Virginia Water	a		18 24					18 31					18 50		18 54					19 01					
	d		18 24					18 31					18 50		18 54					19 01					
Chertsey §	d		18 29												18 59										
Addlestone §	d		18 32												19 02										
Weybridge	a		18 40												19 10										
Longcross	d							18 35																	
Sunningdale	d							18 37					18 55							19 07					
Ascot 3	d							18 43					19 00							19 13		19 23			
Bagshot	d												19 06									19 29			
Camberley	a												19 12									19 35			
	d												19 13									19 39			
Frimley	d												19 17									19 43			
Ash Vale	d												19 24									19 49			
Aldershot	a												19 31									19 54			
	d															19 38						20 08			
Ash 3	d															19 45						20 15			
Wanborough	d															19 48						20 18			
Guildford	a															19 55						20 25			
Martins Heron	d							18 47												19 17					
Bracknell	d							18 50												19 20					
Wokingham	d							18 57												19 27					
Winnersh	d							19 00												19 30					
Winnersh Triangle	d							19 02												19 32					
Earley	d							19 05												19 35					
Reading 7	a							19 12												19 42					

For general notes see front of timetable
For details of catering facilities see Directory of Train Operators

§ Passengers to/from London may travel via Weybridge. See Table 155.

A To London Waterloo (Table 152)
B To London Waterloo
C To Shepperton (Table 152)

b Arr. 1815
c Arr. 1845

For details of Bank Holiday service alterations, please see first page of this Table

London → Hounslow, Richmond, Kingston, Windsor, Weybridge, Ascot, Guildford and Reading

Network Diagram - see first page of Table 148

		SW 1		SW	SW	SW	SW	SW	SW 1	SW	SW 1	SW	SW	SW	SW 1	SW	SW	SW	SW	SW 1		SW	SW 1	SW	SW
				A		B	C	B				B		A		A		B	B					B	
London Waterloo 15	⊖ d	18 35				18 37	18 43	18 45	18 50	18 52			18 58	19 01	19 05			19 07	19 15	19 20		19 22			19 28
Vauxhall	⊖ d	18 39				18 41	18 47	18 49		18 56			19 02	19 05	19 09			19 11	19 19			19 26			19 32
Queenstown Rd.(Battersea)	d					18 44		18 52		18 59				19 08				19 14	19 22			19 29			
Clapham Junction 10	d	18 45				18 47	18 53	18 55	18 58	19 02			19 08	19 11	19 15			19 17	19 25	19 28		19 32			19 38
Wandsworth Town	d					18 50		18 58		19 05				19 14				19 20	19 28			19 35			
Putney	d			←		18 53	18 57	19 01		19 08		←	19 12	19 17		←		19 23	19 31			19 38		←	19 42
Barnes	d			18 52		18 57		19 05		19 13		19 05		19 22		19 22		19 27	19 35			19 43		19 35	
Barnes Bridge	d					19 00		→		19 15				→				19 30	→			19 45			
Chiswick	d				←	19 02				19 17							←	19 32				19 47			
Kew Bridge	d				18 50	19 05				19 20 →							19 20	19 35				19 50 →			
Brentford	d				18 53	19 08											19 23	19 38							
Syon Lane	d				18 55	19 10											19 25	19 40							
Isleworth	d				18 57	19 12											19 27	19 42							
Hounslow	d				19 01	19b18											19 31	19c48							
Mortlake	d			18 54								19 07				19 24								19 37	
North Sheen	d			18 56								19 09				19 26								19 39	
Richmond	⊖ d	18 53		18 59			19 03		19 06			19 12	19 18		19 23	19 29				19 36				19 42	19 48
St Margarets	d			19 01								19 14				19 31								19 44	
Twickenham	a	18 57		19 03			19 07		19 10			19 16	19 21		19 27	19 33				19 40				19 46	19 51
	d	18 57		19 04			19 07		19 10			19 17	19 22		19 27	19 34				19 40				19 47	19 52
Strawberry Hill	d			19 07			19 11									19 37									
Fulwell	a						19 13																		
Teddington	a			19 12												19 42									
Hampton Wick	a			19 16												19 46									
Kingston	a			19 18												19 48									
Whitton	d					19a23						19a20	19 25					19a53						19a50	19 55
Feltham	d	19 03			19 06				19 16				19 29		19 33		19 36			19 46					19 59
Ashford (Surrey)	d	19 07			19 10								19 33		19 37		19 40								20 03
Staines	d	19 11			19 15				19 23				19 37		19 41		19 45			19 53					20 07
Wraysbury	d												19 41												20 11
Sunnymeads	d												19 44												20 14
Datchet	d												19 47												20 17
Windsor & Eton Riverside	a												19 53												20 21
Egham	d	19 16			19 20				19 27						19 46		19 50			19 57					
Virginia Water	a	19 20			19 24				19 31						19 50		19 54			20 01					
	d	19 20			19 24				19 31						19 50		19 54			20 01					
Chertsey §	d				19 29												19 59								
Addlestone §	d				19 31												20 02								
Weybridge	a				19 40												20 10								
Longcross	d																								
Sunningdale	d	19 25							19 37						19 55					20 07					
Ascot 3	d	19 30							19 43		19 53				20 00					20 13			20 23		
Bagshot	d										19 59												20 29		
Camberley	a										20 05												20 35		
	d										20 09												20 39		
Frimley	d										20 13												20 43		
Ash Vale	d										20 19												20 49		
Aldershot	a										20 24												20 54		
	d										20 38												21 08		
Ash 3	d										20 45												21 15		
Wanborough	d										20 48												21 18		
Guildford	a										20 55												21 25		
Martins Heron	d	19 34							19 47						20 04					20 17					
Bracknell	d	19 37							19 50						20 07					20 20					
Wokingham	d	19 47							19 57						20 17					20 27					
Winnersh	d								20 00											20 30					
Winnersh Triangle	d								20 02											20 32					
Earley	d								20 05											20 35					
Reading 7	a	19 57							20 12						20 25					20 40					

For general notes see front of timetable
For details of catering facilities see Directory of Train Operators

§ Passengers to/from London may travel via Weybridge. See Table 155.

A To London Waterloo (Table 152)
B To London Waterloo
C To Shepperton (Table 152)

b Arr. 1915
c Arr. 1945

For details of Bank Holiday service alterations, please see first page of this Table

London → Hounslow, Richmond, Kingston, Windsor, Weybridge, Ascot, Guildford and Reading

Network Diagram - see first page of Table 148

		SW	SW	SW	SW	SW 1	SW	SW 1	SW	SW	SW	SW	SW	SW	SW 1	SW		SW 1	SW 1	SW	SW	SW	SW	SW	SW
		A		B	B				B		A		B	B						B		A		B	B
London Waterloo 15 ⊖	d	19 33		19 37	19 45	19 50	19 52			19 58	20 03		20 07	20 15	20 20	20 22					20 28	20 33		20 37	20 45
Vauxhall ⊖	d	19 37		19 41	19 49		19 56			20 02	20 07		20 11	20 19		20 26					20 32	20 37		20 41	20 49
Queenstown Rd.(Battersea)	d	19 40		19 44	19 52		19 59				20 10		20 14	20 22		20 29						20 40		20 44	20 52
Clapham Junction 10	d	19 43		19 47	19 55	19 58	20 02			20 08	20 13		20 17	20 25	20 28	20 32					20 38	20 43		20 47	20 55
Wandsworth Town	d	19 46		19 50	19 58		20 05				20 16		20 20	20 28		20 35						20 46		20 50	20 58
Putney	d	19 49		19 53	20 01		20 08		←	20 12	20 19		20 23	20 31		20 38				←	20 42	20 49		20 53	21 01
Barnes	d	19 52		19 57	20 05		20 13		20 05		20 22		20 27	20 35		20 43				20 35		20 52		20 57	21 05
Barnes Bridge	d			20 00	→		20 15						20 30	→		20 45								21 00	→
Chiswick	d		←	20 02			20 17					←	20 32			20 47							←	21 02	
Kew Bridge	d		19 50	20 05			20 20					20 20	20 35			20 50							20 50	21 05	
Brentford	d		19 53	20 08			→					20 23	20 38			→							20 53	21 08	
Syon Lane	d		19 55	20 10								20 25	20 40										20 55	21 10	
Isleworth	d		19 57	20 12								20 27	20 42										20 57	21 12	
Hounslow	d		20 01	20b18								20 31	20c48										21 01	21e18	
Mortlake	d	19 54							20 07		20 24									20 37		20 54			
North Sheen	d	19 56							20 09		20 26									20 39		20 56			
Richmond ⊖	d	19 59				20 06			20 12	20 18	20 29				20 36					20 42	20 48	20 59			
St Margarets	d	20 01							20 14		20 31									20 44		21 01			
Twickenham	a	20 03				20 10			20 16	20 21	20 33				20 40					20 46	20 51	21 03			
	d	20 04				20 10			20 17	20 22	20 34				20 40					20 47	20 52	21 04			
Strawberry Hill	d	20 07									20 37											21 07			
Fulwell	a																								
Teddington	a	20 10									20 40											21 10			
Hampton Wick	a	20 14									20 44											21 14			
Kingston	a	20 16									20 46											21 16			
Whitton	d			20a23					20a20	20 25			20a53							20a50	20 55			21a23	
Feltham	d		20 06			20 16				20 29		20 36			20 46						20 59		21 06		
Ashford (Surrey)	d		20 10							20 33		20 40									21 03		21 10		
Staines	d		20 15			20 23				20 37		20 45			20 53						21 07		21 15		
Wraysbury	d									20 41											21 11				
Sunnymeads	d									20 44											21 14				
Datchet	d									20 47											21 17				
Windsor & Eton Riverside	a									20 51											21 21				
Egham	d		20 20			20 27						20 50			20 57								21 20		
Virginia Water	a		20 24			20 31						20 54			21 01								21 24		
	d		20 24			20 31						20 54			21 01								21 24		
Chertsey §	d		20 29									20 59											21 29		
Addlestone §	d		20 32									21 02											21 32		
Weybridge	a		20 37									21 07											21 37		
Longcross	d																								
Sunningdale	d					20 37									21 07										
Ascot 3	d					20 43		20 53							21 13			21 23							
Bagshot	d							20 59										21 29							
Camberley	a							21 05										21 35							
	d							21 09										21 39							
Frimley	d							21 13										21 43							
Ash Vale	d							21 19										21 49							
Aldershot	a							21 24										21 54							
	d							21 38										22 08	22 38						
Ash 3	d							21 45										22 15	22 45						
Wanborough	d							21 48										22 18	22 48						
Guildford	a							21 55										22 25	22 55						
Martins Heron	d					20 47									21 17										
Bracknell	d					20 50									21 20										
Wokingham	d					20 57									21 27										
Winnersh	d					21 00									21 30										
Winnersh Triangle	d					21 02									21 32										
Earley	d					21 05									21 35										
Reading 7	a					21 10									21 40										

For general notes see front of timetable
For details of catering facilities see Directory of Train Operators

§ Passengers to/from London may travel via Weybridge. See Table 155.

A To London Waterloo (Table 152)
B To London Waterloo
b Arr. 2015
c Arr. 2045
e Arr. 2115

For details of Bank Holiday service alterations, please see first page of this Table

London → Hounslow, Richmond, Kingston, Windsor, Weybridge, Ascot, Guildford and Reading

Network Diagram - see first page of Table 148

		SW 1	SW	SW	SW	SW	SW	SW	SW	SW 1	SW	SW 1	SW	SW	SW	SW	SW	SW	SW 1	SW	SW	SW	SW	SW
				A		B		A	A				A		B		A						B	
London Waterloo 15 ⊖	d	20 50	20 52		20 58	21 03		21 07	21 15	21 20	21 22			21 28	21 33		21 37	21 45	21 50		21 52	21 58	22 03	
Vauxhall ⊖	d		20 56		21 02	21 07		21 11	21 19		21 26			21 32	21 37		21 41	21 49			21 56	22 02	22 07	
Queenstown Rd.(Battersea)	d		20 59			21 10		21 14	21 22		21 29				21 40		21 44	21 52			21 59		22 10	
Clapham Junction 10	d	20 58	21 02		21 08	21 13		21 17	21 25	21 28	21 32			21 38	21 43		21 47	21 55	21 58		22 02	22 08	22 13	
Wandsworth Town	d		21 05			21 16		21 20	21 28		21 35				21 46		21 50	21 58			22 05		22 16	
Putney	d		21 08	←	21 12	21 19		21 23	21 31		21 38		←	21 42	21 49		21 53	22 01		←	22 08	22 12	22 19	
Barnes	d		21 13	21 05		21 22		21 27	21 35		21 43		21 35		21 52		21 57	22 05		22 05	22 13		22 22	
Barnes Bridge	d		21 15					21 30	→		21 45						22 00	→			22 15			
Chiswick	d		21 17				←	21 32			21 47					←	22 02				22 17			←
Kew Bridge	d		21 20				21 20	21 35			21 50					21 50	22 05				22 20			22 20
Brentford	d		→				21 23	21 38			→					21 53	22 08				→			22 23
Syon Lane	d						21 25	21 40								21 55	22 10							22 25
Isleworth	d						21 27	21 42								21 57	22 12							22 27
Hounslow	d						21 31	21b48								22 01	22c18							22 31
Mortlake	d			21 07		21 24							21 37		21 54					22 07			22 24	
North Sheen	d			21 09		21 26							21 39		21 56					22 09			22 26	
Richmond ⊖	d	21 06		21 12	21 18	21 29				21 36			21 42	21 48	21 59				22 06	22 12		22 18	22 29	
St Margarets	d			21 14		21 31							21 44		22 01					22 14			22 31	
Twickenham	a	21 10		21 16	21 21	21 33				21 40			21 46	21 51	22 03				22 10	22 17		22 21	22 33	
	d	21 10		21 17	21 22	21 34				21 40			21 47	21 52	22 04				22 10			22 22	22 34	
Strawberry Hill	d					21 37									22 07								22 37	
Fulwell	a																							
Teddington	a					21 40									22 10								22 40	
Hampton Wick	a					21 44									22 14								22 44	
Kingston	a					21 46									22 16								22 46	
Whitton	d			21a20	21 25			21a53					21a50	21 55			22a23					22 25		
Feltham	d	21 16			21 29		21 36			21 46				21 59		22 06			22 16			22 29		22 36
Ashford (Surrey)	d				21 33		21 40							22 03		22 10						22 33		22 40
Staines	d	21 23			21 37		21 45			21 53				22 07		22 15			22 23			22 37		22 45
Wraysbury	d				21 41									22 11								22 41		
Sunnymeads	d				21 44									22 14								22 44		
Datchet	d				21 47									22 17								22 47		
Windsor & Eton Riverside	a				21 51									22 21								22 51		
Egham	d	21 27					21 50			21 57						22 20			22 27					22 50
Virginia Water	a	21 31					21 54			22 01						22 24			22 31					22 54
	d	21 31					21 54			22 01						22 24			22 31					22 54
Chertsey §	d						21 59									22 29								22 59
Addlestone §	d						22 02									22 32								23 02
Weybridge	a						22 07									22 37								23 07
Longcross	d																							
Sunningdale	d	21 37								22 07									22 37					
Ascot 3	d	21 43								22 13		22 23							22 43					
Bagshot	d											22 29												
Camberley	a											22 35												
	d											22 39												
Frimley	d											22 43												
Ash Vale	d											22 49												
Aldershot	a											22 54												
	d											23 08												
Ash 3	d											23 15												
Wanborough	d											23 18												
Guildford	a											23 25												
Martins Heron	d	21 47								22 17									22 47					
Bracknell	d	21 50								22 20									22 50					
Wokingham	d	21 57								22 27									22 57					
Winnersh	d	22 00								22 30									23 00					
Winnersh Triangle	d	22 02								22 32									23 02					
Earley	d	22 05								22 35									23 05					
Reading 7	a	22 10								22 40									23 10					

For general notes see front of timetable
For details of catering facilities see Directory of Train Operators

A To London Waterloo
B To London Waterloo (Table 152)
b Arr. 2145
c Arr. 2215

§ Passengers to/from London may travel via Weybridge. See Table 155.

For details of Bank Holiday service alterations, please see first page of this Table

London → Hounslow, Richmond, Kingston, Windsor, Weybridge, Ascot, Guildford and Reading

Network Diagram - see first page of Table 148

		SW 1	SW	SW	SW	SW 1	SW	SW 1	SW	SW	SW	SW	SW 1	SW	SW	SW	SW	SW	SW	SW	SW
					A	B			C		A	C									
London Waterloo 15 ⊖	d	22 20	22 22	22 28	22 33			22 50	22 52	22 58	23 03		23 20	23 22	23 28	23 35	23 33		23 52	23 58	
Vauxhall ⊖	d		22 26	22 32	22 37				22 56	23 02	23 07			23 26	23 32		23 37		23 56	00 02	
Queenstown Rd.(Battersea)	d		22 29		22 40				22 59		23 10			23 29			23 40		23 59		
Clapham Junction 10	d	22 28	22 32	22 38	22 43			22 58	23 02	23 08	23 13		23 28	23 32	23 38	23 43	23 43		00 02	00 08	
Wandsworth Town	d		22 35		22 46				23 05		23 16			23 35			23 46		00 05		
Putney	d		22 38	22 42	22 49				23 08	23 12	23 19			23 38	23 42		23 49		00 08	00 12	
Barnes	d		22 43		22 52				23 13		23 22			23 43			23 52		00 13		
Barnes Bridge	d		22 45						23 15					23 45					00 15		
Chiswick	d		22 47				←		23 17			←		23 47				←	00 17		←
Kew Bridge	d		22 50				22 50		23 20			23 20		23 50				23 50	00 20		00 20
Brentford	d		→				22 53		→			23 23		→				23 53	→		00 23
Syon Lane	d						22 55					23 25						23 55			00 25
Isleworth	d						22 57					23 27						23 57			00 27
Hounslow	d						23 01					23 31						00 01			00 31
Mortlake	d				22 54						23 24						23 54				
North Sheen	d				22 56						23 26						23 56				
Richmond ⊖	d	22 36		22 48	22 59			23 06		23 18	23 29		23 37		23 48	23 51	23 59			00 18	
St Margarets	d				23 01						23 31						00 01				
Twickenham	a	22 40		22 51	23 03			23 10		23 21	23 33		23 41		23 51	23 55	00 03			00 21	
	d	22 40		22 52	23 04			23 10		23 22	23 34		23 41		23 52	23 55	00 04			00 22	
Strawberry Hill	d				23 07						23 37						00 07				
Fulwell	a																				
Teddington	a				23 10						23 40						00 10				
Hampton Wick	a				23 14						23 44						00 14				
Kingston	a				23 16						23 46						00 16				
Whitton	d			22 55						23 25					23 55					00 25	
Feltham	d	22 46		22 59			23 06	23 16		23 29		23 36	23 48		23 59	00 01		00 06		00 29	00 36
Ashford (Surrey)	d			23 03			23 10			23 33		23 40			00 03			00 10		00 33	00 40
Staines	d	22 53		23 07			23 15	23 23		23 37		23 44	23 56		00 07	00 08		00 15		00a37	00a46
Wraysbury	d			23 11						23 41					00 11						
Sunnymeads	d			23 14						23 44					00 14						
Datchet	d			23 17						23 47					00 17						
Windsor & Eton Riverside	a			23 21						23 51					00 21						
Egham	d	22 57					23 20	23 27				23 49	00 01			00 12		00 20			
Virginia Water	a	23 01					23 24	23 31				23 53	00 05			00 16		00 24			
	d	23 01					23 24	23 31				23 53	00 05			00 16		00 24			
Chertsey §	d						23 29					23 58						00 29			
Addlestone §	d						23 32					00a01						00 32			
Weybridge	a						23 37											00 37			
Longcross	d																				
Sunningdale	d	23 07						23 37					00 10			00 22					
Ascot 3	d	23 13				23 23		23 43					00 15			00 26					
Bagshot	d					23 29															
Camberley	a					23 35															
	d					23 39															
Frimley	d					23 43															
Ash Vale	d					23 49															
Aldershot	a					23 54															
	d																				
Ash 3	d																				
Wanborough	d																				
Guildford	a																				
Martins Heron	d	23 17						23 47					00 19			00 30					
Bracknell	d	23 20						23 50					00 23			00 34					
Wokingham	d	23 27						23 57					00 31			00 40					
Winnersh	d	23 30						00 01					00 35								
Winnersh Triangle	d	23 32						00 02					00 37								
Earley	d	23 35						00 05					00 39								
Reading 7	a	23 40						00 10					00 44			00 49					

For general notes see front of timetable
For details of catering facilities see Directory of Train Operators

§ Passengers to/from London may travel via Weybridge. See Table 155.

A To London Waterloo (Table 152)
B To Farnham (Table 155)
C To Woking (Table 155)

Table 149

Saturdays

London → Hounslow, Richmond, Kingston, Windsor, Weybridge, Ascot, Guildford and Reading

Network Diagram - see first page of Table 148

		SW 1	SW 1	SW	SW	SW	SW	SW	SW	SW		SW 1	SW	SW	SW	SW 1	SW	SW 1	SW	SW 1		SW	SW	SW	SW 1
												A			B				C					B	
London Waterloo 15 ⊖	d	22p50	23p20	23p22	23p28		23p35	23p33	23p52	23p58				00 18				05 05						05 33	
Vauxhall ⊖	d			23p26	23p32			23p37	23p56	00 02				00 22				05 09						05 37	
Queenstown Rd.(Battersea)	d			23p29				23p40	23p59					00 25				05 12						05 40	
Clapham Junction 10	d	22p58	23p28	23p32	23p38		23p43	23p43	00 02	00 08				00 28				05 15						05 43	
Wandsworth Town	d			23p35				23p46	00 05					00 31				05 18						05 46	
Putney	d			23p38	23p42			23p49	00 08	00 12				00 34				05 21						05 49	
Barnes	d			23p43				23p52	00 13					00 37				05 24						05 52	
Barnes Bridge	d			23p45					00 15																
Chiswick	d			23p47		←			00 17				←												
Kew Bridge	d			23p50 →		23p50			00 20 →				00 20												
Brentford	d					23p53							00 23												
Syon Lane	d					23p55							00 25												
Isleworth	d					23p57							00 27												
Hounslow	d					00 01							00 31												
Mortlake	d							23p54						00 39				05 26						05 54	
North Sheen	d							23p56						00 41				05 28						05 56	
Richmond ⊖	d	23p06	23p37		23p48		23p51	23p59		00 18				00 44				05 31						05 59	
St Margarets	d							00 01						00 46				05 33						06 01	
Twickenham	a	23p10	23p41		23p51		23p55	00 03		00 21				00 48				05 35						06 03	
	d	23p10	23p41		23p52		23p55	00 04		00 22				00 49	04 52			05 36	05 38			05 52		06 04	
Strawberry Hill	d							00 07						00s52	04 55									06 07	
Fulwell	a																								
Teddington	a							00 10						00s55	04 58									06 10	
Hampton Wick	a							00 14						00s58	05 01									06 14	
Kingston	a							00 16						01 00	05 03									06 16	
Whitton	d				23p55					00 25								05 39	05a41			05 55			
Feltham	d	23p16	23p48		23p59	00 06	00 01			00 29			00 36					05 43				05 59			
Ashford (Surrey)	d				00 03	00 10				00 33			00 40					05 47				06 03			
Staines	d	23p23	23p56		00 07	00 15	00 08			00a37			00a46			05 23	05 45	05 53				06 07	06 15		
Wraysbury	d				00 11																	06 11			
Sunnymeads	d				00 14																	06 14			
Datchet	d				00 17																	06 17			
Windsor & Eton Riverside	a				00 21																	06 21			
Egham	d	23p27	00 01			00 20	00 12									05 27	05 50	05 57					06 20		
Virginia Water	a	23p31	00 05			00 24	00 16									05 31	05 54	06 01					06 24		
	d	23p31	00 05			00 24	00 16									05 31	05 54	06 01					06 24		
Chertsey §	d					00 29											05 59						06 29		
Addlestone §	d					00 32											06 02						06 32		
Weybridge	a					00 37											06 07						06 37		
Longcross	d																								
Sunningdale	d	23p37	00 10				00 22									05 38		06 07							
Ascot 3	d	23p43	00 15				00 26					00 29				05 43		06 13							
Bagshot	d											00 35													
Camberley	a											00 40													
	d											00 41													
Frimley	d											00 45													
Ash Vale	d											00 52													
Aldershot	a											00 57													
	d																			06 08					06 38
Ash 3	d																			06 15					06 45
Wanborough	d																			06 18					06 48
Guildford	a																			06 25					06 55
Martins Heron	d	23p47	00 19				00 30									05 47		06 17							
Bracknell	d	23p50	00 23				00 34									05 50		06 20							
Wokingham	d	23p57	00 31				00 40									05 57		06 27							
Winnersh	d	00 01	00 35													06 00		06 30							
Winnersh Triangle	d	00 02	00 37													06 03		06 32							
Earley	d	00 05	00 39													06 05		06 35							
Reading 7	a	00 10	00 44				00 49									06 10		06 40							

For general notes see front of timetable
For details of catering facilities see Directory of Train Operators

§ Passengers to/from London may travel via Weybridge. See Table 155.

A To Farnham (Table 155)
B To London Waterloo (Table 152)
C To London Waterloo

Table 149

London → Hounslow, Richmond, Kingston, Windsor, Weybridge, Ascot, Guildford and Reading

Network Diagram - see first page of Table 148

		SW 1	SW	SW	SW	SW 1	SW 1	SW 1		SW	SW	SW	SW	SW 1	SW	SW	SW	SW		SW	SW 1	SW 1	SW 1	SW	SW 1
				A								A					A	B							
London Waterloo 15	⊖ d	05 50	05 58	06 03				06 20		06 22	06 28	06 33		06 50	06 52	06 58	07 03	07 15					07 20	07 22	
Vauxhall	⊖ d		06 02	06 07						06 26	06 32	06 37			06 56	07 02	07 07	07 19						07 26	
Queenstown Rd.(Battersea)	d			06 10						06 29		06 40			06 59		07 10	07 22						07 29	
Clapham Junction 10	d	05 58	06 08	06 13				06 28		06 32	06 38	06 43		06 58	07 02	07 08	07 13	07 25					07 28	07 32	
Wandsworth Town	d			06 16						06 35		06 46			07 05		07 16	07 28						07 35	
Putney	d		06 12	06 19						06 38	06 42	06 49			07 08	07 12	07 19	07 31						07 38	
Barnes	d			06 22						06 43		06 52			07 13		07 22	07 35						07 43	
Barnes Bridge	d									06 45					07 15			→						07 45	
Chiswick	d									06 47			←		07 17					←				07 47	
Kew Bridge	d									06 50			06 50		07 20					07 20				07 50	
Brentford	d									→			06 53		→					07 23				→	
Syon Lane	d												06 55							07 25					
Isleworth	d												06 57							07 27					
Hounslow	d												07 01							07 31					
Mortlake	d			06 24								06 54					07 24								
North Sheen	d			06 26								06 56					07 26								
Richmond	⊖ d	06 06	06 18	06 29				06 36			06 48	06 59		07 06		07 18	07 29						07 36		
St Margarets	d			06 31								07 01					07 31								
Twickenham	a	06 10	06 21	06 33				06 40			06 51	07 03		07 10		07 21	07 33						07 40		
	d	06 10	06 22	06 34				06 40			06 52	07 04		07 10		07 22	07 34						07 40		
Strawberry Hill	d			06 37								07 07					07 37								
Fulwell	a																								
Teddington	a			06 40								07 10					07 40								
Hampton Wick	a			06 44								07 14					07 44								
Kingston	a			06 46								07 16					07 46								
Whitton	d		06 25								06 55					07 25									
Feltham	d	06 16	06 29					06 46			06 59		07 06	07 16		07 29				07 36			07 46		
Ashford (Surrey)	d		06 33								07 03		07 10			07 33				07 40					
Staines	d	06 23	06 37		06 45			06 53			07 07		07 15	07 23		07 37				07 45			07 53		
Wraysbury	d		06 41								07 11					07 41									
Sunnymeads	d		06 44								07 14					07 44									
Datchet	d		06 47								07 17					07 47									
Windsor & Eton Riverside	a		06 51								07 21					07 51									
Egham	d	06 27			06 50			06 57					07 20	07 27						07 50			07 57		
Virginia Water	a	06 31			06 54			07 01					07 24	07 31						07 54			08 01		
	d	06 31			06 54			07 01					07 24	07 31						07 54			08 01		
Chertsey §	d				06 59								07 29							07 59					
Addlestone §	d				07 02								07 32							08 02					
Weybridge	a				07 07								07 37							08 07					
Longcross	d																								
Sunningdale	d	06 37						07 07						07 37									08 07		
Ascot 3	d	06 43					06 53	07 13						07 43								07 53	08 13		08 23
Bagshot	d						06 59															07 59			08 29
Camberley	a						07 05															08 05			08 35
	d						07 09															08 09			08 39
Frimley	d						07 13															08 13			08 43
Ash Vale	d						07 19															08 19			08 49
Aldershot	a						07 24															08 24			08 54
	d					07 08	07 38														08 08	08 38			09 08
Ash 3	d					07 15	07 45														08 15	08 45			09 15
Wanborough	d					07 18	07 48														08 18	08 48			09 18
Guildford	a					07 25	07 55														08 25	08 55			09 25
Martins Heron	d	06 47						07 17						07 47									08 17		
Bracknell	d	06 50						07 20						07 50									08 20		
Wokingham	d	06 57						07 27						07 57									08 27		
Winnersh	d	07 00						07 30						08 00									08 30		
Winnersh Triangle	d	07 02						07 32						08 02									08 32		
Earley	d	07 05						07 35						08 05									08 35		
Reading 7	a	07 10						07 40						08 10									08 40		

For general notes see front of timetable
For details of catering facilities see Directory of Train Operators

A To London Waterloo (Table 152)
B To London Waterloo

§ Passengers to/from London may travel via Weybridge. See Table 155.

Table 149

London → Hounslow, Richmond, Kingston, Windsor, Weybridge, Ascot, Guildford and Reading

Network Diagram - see first page of Table 148

		SW	SW	SW	SW	SW	SW	SW 1	SW	SW 1	SW	SW	SW	SW	SW	SW	SW 1	SW	SW 1	SW	SW	SW	SW
		A		B		A	A				A		B		A	A				A		B	
London Waterloo 15	⊖ d		07 28	07 33		07 37	07 45	07 50	07 52			07 58	08 03		08 07	08 15	08 20	08 22			08 28	08 33	
Vauxhall	⊖ d		07 32	07 37		07 41	07 49		07 56			08 02	08 07		08 11	08 19		08 26			08 32	08 37	
Queenstown Rd.(Battersea)	d			07 40		07 44	07 52		07 59				08 10		08 14	08 22		08 29				08 40	
Clapham Junction 10	d		07 38	07 43		07 47	07 55	07 58	08 02			08 08	08 13		08 17	08 25	08 28	08 32			08 38	08 43	
Wandsworth Town	d			07 46		07 50	07 58		08 05				08 16		08 20	08 28		08 35				08 46	
Putney	d	←	07 42	07 49		07 53	08 01		08 08		←	08 12	08 19		08 23	08 31		08 38		←	08 42	08 49	
Barnes	d	07 35		07 52		07 58	08 05		08 13		08 05		08 22		08 28	08 35		08 43		08 35		08 52	
Barnes Bridge	d					08 00	→		08 15						08 30	→		08 45					
Chiswick	d				←	08 02			08 17					←	08 32			08 47					←
Kew Bridge	d				07 50	08 05			08 20					08 20	08 35			08 50					08 50
Brentford	d				07 53	08 08			→					08 23	08 38			→					08 53
Syon Lane	d				07 55	08 10								08 25	08 40								08 55
Isleworth	d				07 57	08 12								08 27	08 42								08 57
Hounslow	d				08 01	08b18								08 31	08c48								09 01
Mortlake	d	07 37		07 54							08 07		08 24							08 37		08 54	
North Sheen	d	07 39		07 56							08 09		08 26							08 39		08 56	
Richmond	⊖ d	07 42	07 48	07 59				08 06			08 12	08 18	08 29				08 36			08 42	08 48	08 59	
St Margarets	d	07 44		08 01							08 14		08 31							08 44		09 01	
Twickenham	a	07 46	07 51	08 03				08 10			08 16	08 21	08 33				08 40			08 46	08 51	09 03	
	d	07 47	07 52	08 04				08 10			08 17	08 22	08 34				08 40			08 47	08 52	09 04	
Strawberry Hill	d			08 07									08 37									09 07	
Fulwell	a																						
Teddington	a			08 10									08 40									09 10	
Hampton Wick	a			08 14									08 44									09 14	
Kingston	a			08 16									08 46									09 16	
Whitton	d	07a50	07 55			08a23					08a20	08 25			08a53					08a50	08 55		
Feltham	d		07 59		08 06			08 16				08 29		08 36			08 46				08 59		09 06
Ashford (Surrey)	d		08 03		08 10							08 33		08 40							09 03		09 10
Staines	d		08 07		08 15			08 23				08 37		08 45			08 53				09 07		09 15
Wraysbury	d		08 11									08 41									09 11		
Sunnymeads	d		08 14									08 44									09 14		
Datchet	d		08 17									08 47									09 17		
Windsor & Eton Riverside	a		08 21									08 51									09 21		
Egham	d				08 20			08 27						08 50			08 57						09 20
Virginia Water	a				08 24			08 31						08 54			09 01						09 24
	d				08 24			08 31						08 54			09 01						09 24
Chertsey §	d				08 29									08 59									09 29
Addlestone §	d				08 32									09 02									09 32
Weybridge	a				08 37									09 07									09 37
Longcross	d																						
Sunningdale	d							08 37									09 07						
Ascot 3	d							08 43		08 53							09 13		09 23				
Bagshot	d									08 59									09 29				
Camberley	a									09 05									09 35				
	d									09 09									09 39				
Frimley	d									09 13									09 43				
Ash Vale	d									09 19									09 49				
Aldershot	a									09 24									09 54				
	d									09 38									10 08				
Ash 3	d									09 45									10 15				
Wanborough	d									09 48									10 18				
Guildford	a									09 55									10 25				
Martins Heron	d							08 47									09 17						
Bracknell	d							08 50									09 20						
Wokingham	d							08 57									09 27						
Winnersh	d							09 00									09 30						
Winnersh Triangle	d							09 02									09 32						
Earley	d							09 05									09 35						
Reading 7	a							09 10									09 40						

For general notes see front of timetable
For details of catering facilities see Directory of Train Operators

§ Passengers to/from London may travel via Weybridge. See Table 155.

A To London Waterloo
B To London Waterloo (Table 152)
b Arr. 0815
c Arr. 0845

Table 149

London → Hounslow, Richmond, Kingston, Windsor, Weybridge, Ascot, Guildford and Reading

Network Diagram - see first page of Table 148

		SW	SW	SW 1	SW	SW 1	SW	SW	SW	SW	SW	SW	SW 1	SW	SW 1	SW	SW	SW	SW	SW	SW	SW 1	SW
		A	A				A		B		A	A				A		B		A	A		
London Waterloo 15	⊖ d	08 37	08 45	08 50	08 52			08 58	09 03		09 07	09 15	09 20	09 22			09 28	09 33		09 37	09 45	09 50	09 52
Vauxhall	⊖ d	08 41	08 49		08 56			09 02	09 07		09 11	09 19		09 26			09 32	09 37		09 41	09 49		09 56
Queenstown Rd.(Battersea)	d	08 44	08 52		08 59				09 10		09 14	09 22		09 29				09 40		09 44	09 52		09 59
Clapham Junction 10	d	08 47	08 55	08 58	09 02			09 08	09 13		09 17	09 25	09 28	09 32			09 38	09 43		09 47	09 55	09 58	10 02
Wandsworth Town	d	08 50	08 58		09 05				09 16		09 20	09 28		09 35				09 46		09 50	09 58		10 05
Putney	d	08 53	09 01		09 08		←	09 12	09 19		09 23	09 31		09 38		←	09 42	09 49		09 53	10 01		10 08
Barnes	d	08 58	09 05		09 13		09 05		09 22		09 28	09 35		09 43		09 35		09 52		09 58	10 05		10 13
Barnes Bridge	d	09 00	→		09 15						09 30	→		09 45						10 00	→		10 15
Chiswick	d	09 02			09 17					←	09 32			09 47					←	10 02			10 17
Kew Bridge	d	09 05			09 20					09 20	09 35			09 50					09 50	10 05			10 20
Brentford	d	09 08			→					09 23	09 38			→					09 53	10 08			→
Syon Lane	d	09 10								09 25	09 40								09 55	10 10			
Isleworth	d	09 12								09 27	09 42								09 57	10 12			
Hounslow	d	09b18								09 31	09c48								10 01	10e18			
Mortlake	d						09 07		09 24							09 37		09 54					
North Sheen	d						09 09		09 26							09 39		09 56					
Richmond	⊖ d			09 06			09 12	09 18	09 29				09 36			09 42	09 48	09 59				10 06	
St Margarets	d						09 14		09 31							09 44		10 01					
Twickenham	a			09 10			09 16	09 21	09 33				09 40			09 46	09 51	10 03				10 10	
	d			09 10			09 17	09 22	09 34				09 40			09 47	09 52	10 04				10 10	
Strawberry Hill	d								09 37									10 07					
Fulwell	a																						
Teddington	a								09 40									10 10					
Hampton Wick	a								09 44									10 14					
Kingston	a								09 46									10 16					
Whitton	d	09a23					09a20	09 25			09a53					09a50	09 55			10a23			
Feltham	d			09 16				09 29		09 36			09 46				09 59		10 06			10 16	
Ashford (Surrey)	d							09 33		09 40							10 03		10 10				
Staines	d			09 23				09 37		09 45			09 53				10 07		10 15			10 23	
Wraysbury	d							09 41									10 11						
Sunnymeads	d							09 44									10 14						
Datchet	d							09 47									10 17						
Windsor & Eton Riverside	a							09 51									10 21						
Egham	d			09 27						09 50			09 57						10 20			10 27	
Virginia Water	a			09 31						09 54			10 01						10 24			10 31	
	d			09 31						09 54			10 01						10 24			10 31	
Chertsey §	d									09 59									10 29				
Addlestone §	d									10 02									10 32				
Weybridge	a									10 07									10 37				
Longcross	d																						
Sunningdale	d			09 37									10 07									10 37	
Ascot 3	d			09 43		09 53							10 13		10 23							10 43	
Bagshot	d					09 59									10 29								
Camberley	a					10 05									10 35								
	d					10 09									10 39								
Frimley	d					10 13									10 43								
Ash Vale	d					10 19									10 49								
Aldershot	a					10 24									10 54								
	d					10 38									11 08								
Ash 3	d					10 45									11 15								
Wanborough	d					10 48									11 18								
Guildford	a					10 55									11 25								
Martins Heron	d			09 47									10 17									10 47	
Bracknell	d			09 50									10 20									10 50	
Wokingham	d			09 57									10 27									10 57	
Winnersh	d			10 00									10 30									11 00	
Winnersh Triangle	d			10 02									10 32									11 02	
Earley	d			10 05									10 35									11 05	
Reading 7	a			10 10									10 40									11 10	

For general notes see front of timetable
For details of catering facilities see Directory of Train Operators

§ Passengers to/from London may travel via Weybridge. See Table 155.

A To London Waterloo
B To London Waterloo (Table 152)
b Arr. 0915
c Arr. 0945
e Arr. 1015

Table 149

London → Hounslow, Richmond, Kingston, Windsor, Weybridge, Ascot, Guildford and Reading

Network Diagram - see first page of Table 148

		SW 1	SW A	SW		SW B	SW	SW A	SW A	SW 1	SW	SW 1	SW 1	SW A	SW	SW B	SW	SW A	SW A	SW 1	SW	SW A
London Waterloo 15 ⊖	d			09 58		20 03		20 07	20 15	20 20	20 22				20 28	20 33		20 37	20 45	20 50	20 52	
Vauxhall ⊖	d			10 02		20 07		20 11	20 19		20 26				20 32	20 37		20 41	20 49		20 56	
Queenstown Rd.(Battersea)	d					20 10		20 14	20 22		20 29					20 40		20 44	20 52		20 59	
Clapham Junction 10	d			10 08		20 13		20 17	20 25	20 28	20 32				20 38	20 43		20 47	20 55	20 58	21 02	
Wandsworth Town	d					20 16		20 20	20 28		20 35					20 46		20 50	20 58		21 05	
Putney	d		←	10 12		20 19		20 23	20 31		20 38			←	20 42	20 49		20 53	21 01		21 08	←
Barnes	d		10 05			20 22		20 28	20 35		20 43			20 35		20 52		20 58	21 05		21 13	21 05
Barnes Bridge	d							20 30	→		20 45							21 00	→		21 15	
Chiswick	d						←	20 32			20 47						←	21 02			21 17	
Kew Bridge	d						20 20	20 35			20 50 →						20 50	21 05			21 20 →	
Brentford	d						20 23	20 38									20 53	21 08				
Syon Lane	d						20 25	20 40									20 55	21 10				
Isleworth	d						20 27	20 42									20 57	21 12				
Hounslow	d						20 31	20b48									21 01	21c18				
Mortlake	d		10 07			20 24								20 37		20 54		21a38				21 07
North Sheen	d		10 09			20 26								20 39		20 56						21 09
Richmond ⊖	d		10 12	10 18		20 29				20 36				20 42	20 48	20 59				21 06		21 12
St Margarets	d		10 14			20 31								20 44		21 01						21 14
Twickenham	a		10 16	10 21		20 33				20 40				20 46	20 51	21 03				21 10		21 16
	d		10 17	10 22		20 34				20 40				20 47	20 52	21 04				21 10		21 17
Strawberry Hill	d					20 37										21 07						
Fulwell	a																					
Teddington	a					20 40										21 10						
Hampton Wick	a				and at	20 44										21 14						
Kingston	a				the same	20 46										21 16						
Whitton	d		10a20	10 25				20a53						20a50	20 55			21a23				21a20
Feltham	d			10 29	minutes		20 36			20 46					20 59		21 06			21 16		
Ashford (Surrey)	d			10 33			20 40								21 03		21 10					
Staines	d			10 37	past		20 45			20 53					21 07		21 15			21 23		
Wraysbury	d			10 41	each										21 11							
Sunnymeads	d			10 44											21 14							
Datchet	d			10 47	hour until										21 17							
Windsor & Eton Riverside	a			10 51											21 21							
Egham	d						20 50			20 57							21 20			21 27		
Virginia Water	a						20 54			21 01							21 24			21 31		
	d						20 54			21 01							21 24			21 31		
Chertsey §	d						20 59										21 29					
Addlestone §	d						21 02										21 32					
Weybridge	a						21 07										21 37					
Longcross	d																					
Sunningdale	d									21 07										21 37		
Ascot 3	d	10 53								21 13		21 23								21 43		
Bagshot	d	10 59										21 29										
Camberley	a	11 05										21 35										
	d	11 09										21 39										
Frimley	d	11 13										21 43										
Ash Vale	d	11 19										21 49										
Aldershot	a	11 24										21 54										
	d	11 38										22 08	22 38									
Ash 3	d	11 45										22 15	22 45									
Wanborough	d	11 48										22 18	22 48									
Guildford	a	11 55										22 25	22 55									
Martins Heron	d									21 17										21 47		
Bracknell	d									21 20										21 50		
Wokingham	d									21 27										21 57		
Winnersh	d									21 30										22 00		
Winnersh Triangle	d									21 32										22 02		
Earley	d									21 35										22 05		
Reading 7	a									21 40										22 10		

For general notes see front of timetable
For details of catering facilities see Directory of Train Operators

§ Passengers to/from London may travel via Weybridge. See Table 155.

A To London Waterloo
B To London Waterloo (Table 152)
b Arr. 2045
c Arr. 2115

Table 149

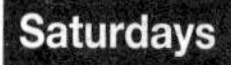

London → Hounslow, Richmond, Kingston, Windsor, Weybridge, Ascot, Guildford and Reading

Network Diagram - see first page of Table 148

	SW	SW	SW	SW	SW	SW 1	SW	SW 1	SW	SW	SW	SW	SW	SW	SW 1	SW	SW	SW	SW	SW	SW 1	SW
		A		B	B				B		A		B						A			
London Waterloo 15 ⊖ d	20 58	21 03		21 07	21 15	21 20	21 22			21 28	21 33		21 37	21 45	21 50		21 52	21 58	22 03		22 20	22 22
Vauxhall ⊖ d	21 02	21 07		21 11	21 19		21 26			21 32	21 37		21 41	21 49			21 56	22 02	22 07			22 26
Queenstown Rd.(Battersea) d		21 10		21 14	21 22		21 29				21 40		21 44	21 52			21 59		22 10			22 29
Clapham Junction 10 d	21 08	21 13		21 17	21 25	21 28	21 32			21 38	21 43		21 47	21 55	21 58		22 02	22 08	22 13		22 28	22 32
Wandsworth Town d		21 16		21 20	21 28		21 35				21 46		21 50	21 58			22 05		22 16			22 35
Putney d	21 12	21 19		21 23	21 31		21 38		←	21 42	21 49		21 53	22 01		←	22 08	22 12	22 19			22 38
Barnes d		21 22		21 28	21 35		21 43		21 35		21 52		21 58	22 05		22 05	22 13		22 22			22 43
Barnes Bridge d				21 30	→		21 45						22 00	→			22 15					22 45
Chiswick d			←	21 32			21 47					←	22 02				22 17			←		22 47
Kew Bridge d			21 20	21 35			21 50					21 50	22 05				22 20			22 20		22 50
Brentford d			21 23	21 38			→					21 53	22 08				→			22 23		→
Syon Lane d			21 25	21 40								21 55	22 10							22 25		
Isleworth d			21 27	21 42								21 57	22 12							22 27		
Hounslow d			21 31	21b48								22 01	22c18							22 31		
Mortlake d		21 24							21 37		21 54					22 07			22 24			
North Sheen d		21 26							21 39		21 56					22 09			22 26			
Richmond ⊖ d	21 18	21 29				21 36			21 42	21 48	21 59				22 06	22 12		22 18	22 29		22 36	
St Margarets d		21 31							21 44		22 01					22 14			22 31			
Twickenham a	21 21	21 33				21 40			21 46	21 51	22 03				22 10	22 16		22 21	22 33		22 40	
d	21 22	21 34				21 40			21 47	21 52	22 04				22 10			22 22	22 34		22 40	
Strawberry Hill d		21 37									22 07								22 37			
Fulwell a																						
Teddington a		21 40									22 10								22 40			
Hampton Wick a		21 44									22 14								22 44			
Kingston a		21 46									22 16								22 46			
Whitton d	21 25			21a53					21a50	21 55			22a23					22 25				
Feltham d	21 29		21 36			21 46				21 59		22 06			22 16			22 29		22 36	22 46	
Ashford (Surrey) d	21 33		21 40							22 03		22 10						22 33		22 40		
Staines d	21 37		21 45			21 53				22 07		22 15			22 23			22 37		22 45	22 53	
Wraysbury d	21 41									22 11								22 41				
Sunnymeads d	21 44									22 14								22 44				
Datchet d	21 47									22 17								22 47				
Windsor & Eton Riverside a	21 51									22 21								22 51				
Egham d			21 50			21 57						22 20			22 27					22 50	22 57	
Virginia Water a			21 54			22 01						22 24			22 31					22 54	23 01	
d			21 54			22 01						22 24			22 31					22 54	23 01	
Chertsey § d			21 59									22 29								22 59		
Addlestone § d			22 02									22 32								23 02		
Weybridge a			22 07									22 37								23 07		
Longcross d																						
Sunningdale d						22 07									22 37						23 07	
Ascot 3 d						22 13		22 23							22 43						23 13	
Bagshot d								22 29														
Camberley a								22 35														
d								22 39														
Frimley d								22 43														
Ash Vale d								22 49														
Aldershot a								22 54														
d								23 08														
Ash 3 d								23 15														
Wanborough d								23 18														
Guildford a								23 25														
Martins Heron d						22 17									22 47						23 17	
Bracknell d						22 20									22 50						23 20	
Wokingham d						22 27									22 57						23 27	
Winnersh d						22 30									23 00						23 30	
Winnersh Triangle d						22 32									23 02						23 32	
Earley d						22 35									23 05						23 35	
Reading 7 a						22 40									23 10						23 40	

For general notes see front of timetable
For details of catering facilities see Directory of Train Operators

§ Passengers to/from London may travel via Weybridge. See Table 155.

A To London Waterloo (Table 152)
B To London Waterloo
b Arr. 2145
c Arr. 2215

London → Hounslow, Richmond, Kingston, Windsor, Weybridge, Ascot, Guildford and Reading

Network Diagram - see first page of Table 148

		SW		SW	SW	SW	SW	SW	SW	SW	SW	SW		SW	SW	SW	SW	SW	SW	SW	SW				
					1		1					1													
				A				B		A	B														
London Waterloo 15	⊖ d	22 28		22 33			22 50	22 52	22 58	23 03		23 20		23 22	23 28	23 35	23 33		23 52	23 58					
Vauxhall	⊖ d	22 32		22 37				22 56	23 02	23 07				23 26	23 32		23 37		23 56	00 02					
Queenstown Rd.(Battersea)	d			22 40				22 59		23 10				23 29			23 40		23 59						
Clapham Junction 10	d	22 38		22 43			22 58	23 02	23 08	23 13		23 28		23 32	23 38	23 43	23 43		00 02	00 08					
Wandsworth Town	d			22 46				23 05		23 16				23 35			23 46		00 05						
Putney	d	22 42		22 49				23 08	23 12	23 19				23 38	23 42		23 49		00 08	00 12					
Barnes	d			22 52				23 13		23 22				23 43			23 52		00 13						
Barnes Bridge	d							23 15						23 45					00 15						
Chiswick	d					←		23 17			←			23 47				←	00 17		←				
Kew Bridge	d					22 50		23 20			23 20			23 50				23 50	00 20		00 20				
Brentford	d					22 53		→			23 23			→				23 53	→		00 23				
Syon Lane	d					22 55					23 25							23 55			00 25				
Isleworth	d					22 57					23 27							23 57			00 27				
Hounslow	d					23 01					23 31							00 01			00 31				
Mortlake	d			22 54						23 24							23 54								
North Sheen	d			22 56						23 26							23 56								
Richmond	⊖ d	22 48		22 59			23 06		23 18	23 29		23 37			23 48	23 51	23 59			00 18					
St Margarets	d			23 01						23 31							00 01								
Twickenham	a	22 51		23 03			23 10		23 21	23 33		23 41			23 51	23 55	00 03			00 21					
	d	22 52		23 04			23 10		23 22	23 34		23 41			23 52	23 55	00 04			00 22					
Strawberry Hill	d			23 07						23 37							00 07								
Fulwell	a																								
Teddington	a			23 10						23 40							00 10								
Hampton Wick	a			23 14						23 44							00 14								
Kingston	a			23 16						23 46							00 16								
Whitton	d	22 55							23 25						23 55					00 25					
Feltham	d	22 59				23 06	23 16		23 29		23 36	23 48			23 59	00 01		00 06		00 29	00 36				
Ashford (Surrey)	d	23 03				23 10			23 33		23 40				00 03			00 10		00 33	00 40				
Staines	d	23 07				23 15	23 23		23 37		23 44	23 56			00 07	00 08		00 15		00a37	00a46				
Wraysbury	d	23 11							23 41						00 11										
Sunnymeads	d	23 14							23 44						00 14										
Datchet	d	23 17							23 47						00 17										
Windsor & Eton Riverside	a	23 21							23 51						00 21										
Egham	d					23 20	23 27				23 49	00 01				00 12		00 20							
Virginia Water	a					23 24	23 31				23 53	00 05				00 16		00 24							
	d					23 24	23 31				23 53	00 05				00 16		00 24							
Chertsey §	d					23 29					23 58							00 29							
Addlestone §	d					23 32					00a01							00 32							
Weybridge	a					23 37												00 37							
Longcross	d																								
Sunningdale	d						23 37					00 10				00 22									
Ascot 3	d				23 23		23 43					00 15				00 26									
Bagshot	d				23 29																				
Camberley	a				23 35																				
	d				23 39																				
Frimley	d				23 43																				
Ash Vale	d				23 49																				
Aldershot	a				23 54																				
	d																								
Ash 3	d																								
Wanborough	d																								
Guildford	a																								
Martins Heron	d						23 47					00 19				00 30									
Bracknell	d						23 50					00 23				00 34									
Wokingham	d						23 57					00 31				00 40									
Winnersh	d						00 01					00 35													
Winnersh Triangle	d						00 02					00 37													
Earley	d						00 05					00 39													
Reading 7	a						00 10					00 44				00 49									

For general notes see front of timetable
For details of catering facilities see Directory of Train Operators

§ Passengers to/from London may travel via Weybridge. See Table 155.

A To London Waterloo (Table 152)
B To Woking (Table 155)

London → Hounslow, Richmond, Kingston, Windsor, Weybridge, Ascot, Guildford and Reading

Network Diagram - see first page of Table 148

		SW 1	SW 1	SW	SW	SW	SW		SW	SW	SW	SW	SW	SW 1		SW	SW	SW 1	SW	SW 1	SW		SW 1	SW 1	SW
																A			B		A				
London Waterloo 15	⊖ d	22p50	23p20	23p22	23p28		23p35		23p33	23p52	23p58		00 18			06 14	06 44			07 09	07 14				07 44
Vauxhall	⊖ d			23p26	23p32				23p37	23p56	00 02		00 22			06 18	06 48			07 13	07 18				07 48
Queenstown Rd.(Battersea)	d			23p29					23p40	23p59			00 25			06 21	06 51				07 21				07 51
Clapham Junction 10	d	22p58	23p28	23p32	23p38		23p43		23p43	00 02	00 08		00 28			06 24	06 54			07 19	07 24				07 54
Wandsworth Town	d			23p35					23p46	00 05			00 31			06 27	06 57				07 27				07 57
Putney	d			23p38	23p42				23p49	00 08	00 12		00 34			06 30	07 00			07 23	07 30				08 00
Barnes	d			23p43					23p52	00 13			00 37			06 33	07 03				07 33				08 03
Barnes Bridge	d			23p45						00 15															
Chiswick	d			23p47		←				00 17		←													
Kew Bridge	d			23p50		23p50				00 20		00 20													
Brentford	d			→		23p53				→		00 23													
Syon Lane	d					23p55						00 25													
Isleworth	d					23p57						00 27													
Hounslow	d					00 01						00 31													
Mortlake	d								23p54				00 39			06 35	07 05				07 35				08 05
North Sheen	d								23p56				00 41			06 37	07 07				07 37				08 07
Richmond	⊖ d	23p06	23p37		23p48		23p51		23p59		00 18		00 44			06 40	07 10			07 29	07 40				08 10
St Margarets	d								00 01				00 46			06 42	07 12				07 42				08 12
Twickenham	a	23p10	23p41		23p51		23p55		00 03		00 21		00 48			06 44	07 14			07 32	07 44				08 14
	d	23p10	23p41		23p52		23p55		00 04		00 22		00 49			06 45	07 15			07 33	07 45				08 15
Strawberry Hill	d								00 07				00s52			06 49					07 49				
Fulwell	a																								
Teddington	a								00 10				00s55			06 52					07 52				
Hampton Wick	a								00 14				00s58			06 57					07 57				
Kingston	a								00 16				01 00			06 59					07 59				
Whitton	d				23p55						00 25						07 18								08 18
Feltham	d	23p16	23p48		23p59	00 06	00 01				00 29	00 36					07 22			07 39					08 22
Ashford (Surrey)	d				00 03	00 10					00 33	00 40					07 26								08 26
Staines	d	23p23	23p56		00 07	00 15	00 08				00a37	00a46		06 32			07 30		07 42	07 45				08 15	08 30
Wraysbury	d				00 11												07 34								08 34
Sunnymeads	d				00 14												07 37								08 37
Datchet	d				00 17												07 40								08 40
Windsor & Eton Riverside	a				00 21												07 44								08 44
Egham	d	23p27	00 01			00 20	00 12							06 37					07 47	07 50				08 20	
Virginia Water	a	23p31	00 05			00 24	00 16							06 41					07 51	07 54				08 24	
	d	23p31	00 05			00 24	00 16							06 41					07 51	07 54				08 24	
Chertsey §	d					00 29								06 46					07 56						
Addlestone §	d					00 32								06 49					07a59						
Weybridge	a					00 37								06 53											
Longcross	d																								
Sunningdale	d	23p37	00 10				00 22													07 59				08 29	
Ascot 3	d	23p43	00 15				00 26													08 04			08 13	08 34	
Bagshot	d																						08 19		
Camberley	a																						08 25		
	d																						08 25		
Frimley	d																						08 29		
Ash Vale	d																						08 36		
Aldershot	a																						08 41		
	d																	07 50					08 50		
Ash 3	d																	07 57					08 57		
Wanborough	d																	08 00					09 00		
Guildford	a																	08 07					09 07		
Martins Heron	d	23p47	00 19				00 30													08 08				08 38	
Bracknell	d	23p50	00 23				00 34													08 11				08 41	
Wokingham	d	23p57	00 31				00 40													08 18				08 48	
Winnersh	d	00 01	00 35																	08 21				08 51	
Winnersh Triangle	d	00 02	00 37																	08 23				08 53	
Earley	d	00 05	00 39																	08 26				08 56	
Reading 7	a	00 10	00 44				00 49													08 31				09 04	

For general notes see front of timetable
For details of catering facilities see Directory of Train Operators

§ Passengers to/from London may travel via Weybridge. See Table 155.

A To London Waterloo (Table 152)
B To Woking (Table 155)

Table 149

Sundays

London → Hounslow, Richmond, Kingston, Windsor, Weybridge, Ascot, Guildford and Reading

Network Diagram - see first page of Table 148

		SW	SW	SW	SW	SW	SW	SW	SW	SW	SW	SW	SW	SW	SW		SW	SW	SW	SW	SW
			1		1	1			1		1		1				1		1		1
		A		B				A		B					A			B			
London Waterloo 15	⊖ d	07 50	08 09	08 14		08 39	08 44	08 50	09 09	09 14		09 25	09 39	09 44	09 50		13 09	13 14		13 25	13 39
Vauxhall	⊖ d	07 54	08 13	08 18		08 43	08 48	08 54	09 13	09 18		09 29	09 43	09 48	09 54		13 13	13 18		13 29	13 43
Queenstown Rd.(Battersea)	d	07 57		08 21			08 51	08 57		09 21				09 51	09 57			13 21			
Clapham Junction 10	d	08 00	08 19	08 24		08 49	08 54	09 00	09 19	09 24		09 35	09 49	09 54	10 00		13 19	13 24		13 35	13 49
Wandsworth Town	d	08 03		08 27			08 57	09 03		09 27				09 57	10 03			13 27			
Putney	d	08 06	08 23	08 30		08 53	09 00	09 06	09 23	09 30		09 39	09 53	10 00	10 06		13 23	13 30		13 39	13 53
Barnes	d	08 09		08 33			09 03	09 09		09 33				10 03	10 09			13 33			
Barnes Bridge	d	08 11						09 11							10 11						
Chiswick	d	08 13						09 13							10 13						
Kew Bridge	d	08 16						09 16							10 16						
Brentford	d	08 19						09 19							10 19						
Syon Lane	d	08 21						09 21							10 21						
Isleworth	d	08 23						09 23							10 23						
Hounslow	d	08 27						09 27							10 27						
Mortlake	d			08 35			09 05			09 35				10 05				13 35			
North Sheen	d			08 37			09 07			09 37				10 07				13 37			
Richmond	⊖ d		08 29	08 40		08 59	09 10		09 29	09 40		09 45	09 59	10 10			13 29	13 40		13 45	13 59
St Margarets	d			08 42			09 12			09 42				10 12				13 42			
Twickenham	a		08 32	08 44		09 02	09 14		09 32	09 44		09 48	10 02	10 14			13 32	13 44		13 48	14 02
	d		08 33	08 45		09 03	09 15		09 33	09 45		09 49	10 03	10 15			13 33	13 45		13 49	14 03
Strawberry Hill	d			08 49						09 49								13 49			
Fulwell	a																				
Teddington	a			08 52						09 52								13 52			
Hampton Wick	a			08 57						09 57						and at		13 57			
Kingston	a			08 59						09 59						the same		13 59			
Whitton	d						09 18					09 52		10 18						13 52	
Feltham	d	08 33	08 39			09 09	09 22	09 33	09 39			09 56	10 09	10 22	10 33	minutes	13 39			13 56	14 09
Ashford (Surrey)	d	08 37					09 26	09 37				10 00		10 26	10 37					14 00	
Staines	d	08 41	08 45			09 15	09 30	09 41	09 45			10 04	10 15	10 30	10 41	past	13 45			14 04	14 15
Wraysbury	d						09 34							10 34		each					
Sunnymeads	d						09 37							10 37							
Datchet	d						09 40					10 12		10 40		hour until				14 12	
Windsor & Eton Riverside	a						09 44					10 16		10 44						14 16	
Egham	d	08 45	08 50			09 20		09 45	09 50				10 20		10 45		13 50				14 20
Virginia Water	a	08 49	08 54			09 24		09 49	09 54				10 24		10 49		13 54				14 24
	d	08 49	08 54			09 24		09 49	09 54				10 24		10 49		13 54				14 24
Chertsey §	d	08 55						09 55							10 55						
Addlestone §	d	08a58						09a58							10a58						
Weybridge	a																				
Longcross	d																				
Sunningdale	d		08 59			09 29			09 59				10 29				13 59				14 29
Ascot 3	d		09 04		09 13	09 34			10 04		10 13		10 34				14 04		14 13		14 34
Bagshot	d				09 19						10 19								14 19		
Camberley	a				09 25						10 25								14 25		
	d				09 25						10 25								14 25		
Frimley	d				09 29						10 29								14 29		
Ash Vale	d				09 36						10 36								14 36		
Aldershot	a				09 41						10 41								14 41		
	d				09 50						10 50								14 50		
Ash 3	d				09 57						10 57								14 57		
Wanborough	d				10 00						11 00								15 00		
Guildford	a				10 07						11 07								15 07		
Martins Heron	d		09 08			09 38			10 08				10 38				14 08				14 38
Bracknell	d		09 11			09 41			10 11				10 41				14 11				14 41
Wokingham	d		09 18			09 48			10 18				10 48				14 18				14 48
Winnersh	d		09 21			09 51			10 21				10 51				14 21				14 51
Winnersh Triangle	d		09 23			09 53			10 23				10 53				14 23				14 53
Earley	d		09 26			09 56			10 26				10 56				14 26				14 56
Reading 7	a		09 31			10 01			10 31				11 04				14 31				15 03

For general notes see front of timetable
For details of catering facilities see Directory of Train Operators

§ Passengers to/from London may travel via Weybridge. See Table 155.

A To Woking (Table 155)
B To London Waterloo (Table 152)

Table 149

Sundays

London → Hounslow, Richmond, Kingston, Windsor, Weybridge, Ascot, Guildford and Reading

Network Diagram - see first page of Table 148

		SW	SW A	SW	SW 1	SW B	SW 1	SW	SW 1	SW	SW A	SW		SW 1	SW B	SW 1	SW 1	SW	SW A	SW
London Waterloo 15 ⊖	d	13 44	13 50	13 55	14 09	14 14		14 25	14 39	14 44	14 50	14 55		20 09	20 14		20 39	20 44	20 50	20 55
Vauxhall ⊖	d	13 48	13 54	13 59	14 13	14 18		14 29	14 43	14 48	14 54	14 59		20 13	20 18		20 43	20 48	20 54	20 59
Queenstown Rd.(Battersea)	d	13 51	13 57	14 02		14 21				14 51	14 57	15 02			20 21			20 51	20 57	21 02
Clapham Junction 10	d	13 54	14 00	14 05	14 19	14 24		14 35	14 49	14 54	15 00	15 05		20 19	20 24		20 49	20 54	21 00	21 05
Wandsworth Town	d	13 57	14 03	14 08		14 27				14 57	15 03	15 08			20 27			20 57	21 03	21 08
Putney	d	14 00	14 06	14 11	14 23	14 30		14 39	14 53	15 00	15 06	15 11		20 23	20 30		20 53	21 00	21 06	21 11
Barnes	d	14 03	14 09	14 14		14 33				15 03	15 09	15 14			20 33			21 03	21 09	21 14
Barnes Bridge	d		14 11								15 11								21 11	
Chiswick	d		14 13								15 13								21 13	
Kew Bridge	d		14 16								15 16								21 16	
Brentford	d		14 19								15 19								21 19	
Syon Lane	d		14 21								15 21								21 21	
Isleworth	d		14 23								15 23								21 23	
Hounslow	d		14 27								15 27								21 27	
Mortlake	d	14 05		14 16		14 35				15 05		15 16			20 35			21 05		21 16
North Sheen	d	14 07		14 18		14 37				15 07		15 18			20 37			21 07		21 18
Richmond ⊖	d	14 10		14 21	14 29	14 40		14 45	14 59	15 10		15 21		20 29	20 40		20 59	21 10		21 21
St Margarets	d	14 12		14 23		14 42				15 12		15 23			20 42			21 12		21 23
Twickenham	a	14 14		14 25	14 32	14 44		14 48	15 02	15 14		15 25		20 32	20 44		21 02	21 14		21 25
	d	14 15		14 26	14 33	14 45		14 49	15 03	15 15		15 26		20 33	20 45		21 03	21 15		21 26
Strawberry Hill	d			14 29		14 49						15 29			20 49					21 29
Fulwell	a																			
Teddington	a			14 32		14 52						15 32			20 52					21 32
Hampton Wick	a			14 35		14 57						15 35	and at		20 57					21 35
Kingston	a			14 37		14 59						15 37	the same		20 59					21 37
Whitton	d	14 18						14 52		15 18								21 18		
Feltham	d	14 22	14 33		14 39			14 56	15 09	15 22	15 33		minutes	20 39			21 09	21 22	21 33	
Ashford (Surrey)	d	14 26	14 37					15 00		15 26	15 37							21 26	21 37	
Staines	d	14 30	14 41		14 45			15 04	15 15	15 30	15 41		past	20 45			21 15	21 30	21 41	
Wraysbury	d	14 34								15 34			each					21 34		
Sunnymeads	d	14 37								15 37								21 37		
Datchet	d	14 40						15 12		15 40			hour until					21 40		
Windsor & Eton Riverside	a	14 44						15 16		15 44								21 44		
Egham	d		14 45		14 50				15 20		15 45			20 50			21 20		21 45	
Virginia Water	a		14 49		14 54				15 24		15 49			20 54			21 24		21 49	
	d		14 49		14 54				15 24		15 49			20 54			21 24		21 49	
Chertsey §	d		14 55								15 55								21 55	
Addlestone §	d		14a58								15a58								21a58	
Weybridge	a																			
Longcross	d																			
Sunningdale	d				14 59				15 29					20 59			21 29			
Ascot 3	d				15 04		15 13		15 34					21 04		21 13	21 34			
Bagshot	d						15 19									21 19				
Camberley	a						15 25									21 25				
	d						15 25									21 25				
Frimley	d						15 29									21 29				
Ash Vale	d						15 36									21 36				
Aldershot	a						15 41									21 41				
	d						15 50									21 50				
Ash 3	d						15 57									21 57				
Wanborough	d						16 00									22 00				
Guildford	a						16 07									22 07				
Martins Heron	d				15 08				15 38					21 08			21 38			
Bracknell	d				15 11				15 41					21 11			21 41			
Wokingham	d				15 18				15 48					21 18			21 48			
Winnersh	d				15 21				15 51					21 21			21 51			
Winnersh Triangle	d				15 23				15 53					21 23			21 53			
Earley	d				15 26				15 56					21 26			21 56			
Reading 7	a				15 31				16 01					21 31			22 01			

For general notes see front of timetable
For details of catering facilities see Directory of Train Operators

§ Passengers to/from London may travel via Weybridge. See Table 155.

A To Woking (Table 155)
B To London Waterloo (Table 152)

London → Hounslow, Richmond, Kingston, Windsor, Weybridge, Ascot, Guildford and Reading

Network Diagram - see first page of Table 148

		SW 1	SW	SW 1	SW 1	SW	SW	SW	SW 1	SW	SW 1	SW 1	SW	SW	SW	SW 1	SW	SW 1	SW
			A				B			A	C			B					
London Waterloo 15 ⊖	d	21 09	21 14		21 39	21 44	21 50	21 55	22 09	22 14		22 39	22 44	22 50	22 55	23 09	23 14	23 39	23 44
Vauxhall ⊖	d	21 13	21 18		21 43	21 48	21 54	21 59	22 13	22 18		22 43	22 48	22 54	22 59	23 13	23 18	23 43	23 48
Queenstown Rd.(Battersea)	d		21 21			21 51	21 57	22 02		22 21			22 51	22 57	23 02		23 21		23 51
Clapham Junction 10	d	21 19	21 24		21 49	21 54	22 00	22 05	22 19	22 24		22 49	22 54	23 00	23 05	23 19	23 24	23 49	23 54
Wandsworth Town	d		21 27			21 57	22 03	22 08		22 27			22 57	23 03	23 08		23 27		23 57
Putney	d	21 23	21 30		21 53	22 00	22 06	22 11	22 23	22 30		22 53	23 00	23 06	23 11	23 23	23 30	23 53	23 59
Barnes	d		21 33			22 03	22 09	22 14		22 33			23 03	23 09	23 14		23 33		00 03
Barnes Bridge	d						22 11							23 11					
Chiswick	d						22 13							23 13					
Kew Bridge	d						22 16							23 16					
Brentford	d						22 19							23 19					
Syon Lane	d						22 21							23 21					
Isleworth	d						22 23							23 23					
Hounslow	d						22 27							23 27					
Mortlake	d		21 35			22 05		22 16		22 35			23 05		23 16		23 35		00 05
North Sheen	d		21 37			22 07		22 18		22 37			23 07		23 18		23 37		00 07
Richmond ⊖	d	21 29	21 40		21 59	22 10		22 21	22 29	22 40		22 59	23 10		23 21	23 29	23 40	23 59	00 10
St Margarets	d		21 42			22 12		22 23		22 42			23 12		23 23		23 42		00 12
Twickenham	a	21 32	21 44		22 02	22 14		22 25	22 32	22 44		23 02	23 14		23 25	23 32	23 44	00 02	00 14
	d	21 33	21 45		22 03	22 15		22 26	22 33	22 45		23 03	23 15		23 26	23 33	23 45	00 03	00 15
Strawberry Hill	d		21 49					22 29		22 49					23 29		23a48		
Fulwell	a																		
Teddington	a		21 52					22 32		22 52					23 32				
Hampton Wick	a		21 57					22 35		22 57					23 35				
Kingston	a		21 59					22 37		22 59					23 37				
Whitton	d					22 18							23 18						00 18
Feltham	d	21 39			22 09	22 22	22 33		22 39			23 09	23 22	23 33		23 39		00 09	00 22
Ashford (Surrey)	d					22 26	22 37						23 26	23 37					00 26
Staines	d	21 45			22 15	22 30	22 41		22 45			23 15	23 30	23 41		23 45		00 15	00a30
Wraysbury	d					22 34							23 34						
Sunnymeads	d					22 37							23 37						
Datchet	d					22 40							23 40						
Windsor & Eton Riverside	a					22 44							23 44						
Egham	d	21 50			22 20		22 45		22 50			23 20		23 45		23 50		00 20	
Virginia Water	a	21 54			22 24		22 49		22 54			23 24		23 49		23 54		00 24	
	d	21 54			22 24		22 49		22 54			23 24		23 49		23 54		00 24	
Chertsey §	d						22 55							23 55					
Addlestone §	d						22a58							23a58					
Weybridge	a																		
Longcross	d																		
Sunningdale	d	21 59			22 29				22 59			23 29				23 59		00 29	
Ascot 3	d	22 04		22 13	22 34				23 04		23 13	23 34				00 04		00 34	
Bagshot	d			22 19							23 19								
Camberley	a			22 25							23 25								
	d			22 25							23 25								
Frimley	d			22 29							23 29								
Ash Vale	d			22 36							23 36								
Aldershot	a			22 41							23 41								
	d			22 50															
Ash 3	d			22 57															
Wanborough	d			23 00															
Guildford	a			23 07															
Martins Heron	d	22 08			22 38				23 08			23 38				00 08		00 38	
Bracknell	d	22 11			22 41				23 11			23 41				00 11		00 41	
Wokingham	d	22 18			22 48				23 20			23 48				00 18		00 48	
Winnersh	d	22 21			22 51				23 24			23 51				00 21		00 51	
Winnersh Triangle	d	22 23			22 53				23 26			23 53				00 23		00 53	
Earley	d	22 26			22 56				23 28			23 56				00 26		00 56	
Reading 7	a	22 31			23 01				23 33			00 01				00 31		01 01	

For general notes see front of timetable
For details of catering facilities see Directory of Train Operators

§ Passengers to/from London may travel via Weybridge. See Table 155.

A To London Waterloo (Table 152)
B To Woking (Table 155)
C To Farnham (Table 155)

Reading, Guildford, Ascot, Weybridge, Windsor, Kingston, Richmond and Hounslow → London

For details of Bank Holiday service alterations, please see first page of this Table

Network Diagram - see first page of Table 148

Miles	Miles	Miles	Miles			SW MO	SW MO A	SW MO 1	SW MX B	SW MX B	SW MX 1	SW	SW	SW C	SW	SW	SW	SW A	SW	SW A	SW 1	SW		SW	SW
—	—	0	—	**Reading 7**	d			22p54			23p12										05 42				
—	—	3	—	Earley	d			22p59			23p17										05 47				
—	—	4¼	—	Winnersh Triangle	d			23p01			23p19										05 49				
—	—	4¾	—	Winnersh	d			23p03			23p21										05 51				
—	—	6¾	—	**Wokingham**	d			23p08			23p26										05 56				
—	—	11¼	—	Bracknell	d			23p14			23p32										06 02				
—	—	12¼	—	Martins Heron	d			23p17			23p35										06 05				
—	0	—	—	**Guildford**	d																				
—	4¼	—	—	Wanborough	d																				
—	6¼	—	—	Ash 3	d																				
—	9	—	—	**Aldershot**	a																				
—	—	—	—		d																				
—	11½	—	—	Ash Vale	d																				
—	14¾	—	—	Frimley	d																				
—	17	—	—	Camberley	a																				
—	—	—	—		d																				
—	20¼	—	—	Bagshot	d																				
—	23½	14½	—	**Ascot 3**	d			23p22			23p40										06 10				
—	—	16½	—	Sunningdale	d			23p25			23p43										06 13				
—	—	18¼	—	Longcross	d																				
0	—	—	—	**Weybridge**	d																				
1¾	—	—	—	Addlestone §	d		23p04											05 37							
3¼	—	—	—	Chertsey §	d		23p07											05 40							
5¾	—	20¼	—	Virginia Water	a		23p12	23p30			23p49							05 45			06 19				
—	—	—	—		d		23p12	23p30			23p49							05 54			06 19				
—	—	22½	—	Egham	d		23p16	23p34			23p53							05 57			06 23				
—	—	—	0	**Windsor & Eton Riverside**	d	23p01													05 53						
—	—	—	2	Datchet	d	23p04													05 56						
—	—	—	3	Sunnymeads	d	23p07													05 59						
—	—	—	4¼	Wraysbury	d	23p10													06 02						
—	—	24½	6¾	**Staines**	d	23p16	23p21	23p39			23p59	04 58			05 38			06 03	06 08		06 29				06 33
—	—	26	—	Ashford (Surrey)	d	23p19	23p24					05 01			05 41			06 06	06 11						06 36
—	—	28¾	—	Feltham	d	23p24	23p29	23p46			00 05	05 06			05 46			06 11	06 16		06 35				06 41
—	—	31	—	Whitton	d	23p28						05 10			05 50				06 20			06 20			
0	—	—	—	**Kingston**	d				23p29	23p55							05 59							06 29	
½	—	—	—	Hampton Wick	d				23p31	23p57							06 01							06 31	
1¾	—	—	—	Teddington	d				23p35	23p59							06 05							06 35	
2¾	—	—	—	Fulwell	d									05 36											
3	—	—	—	Strawberry Hill	d				23p38	00 03				05 38			06 08							06 38	
4	—	32¼	—	Twickenham	a	23p31		23p51	23p42	00 06	00 10	05 13		05 42	05 53		06 12		06 23		06 40			06 42	
—	—	—	—		d	23p32		23p51	23p43		00 11	05 13		05 43	05 53		06 13		06 23		06 41			06 43	
4½	—	32¾	—	St Margarets	d	23p34			23p45			05 15		05 45			06 15							06 45	
5½	—	33¾	—	**Richmond**	⊖ d	23p37		23p56	23p49		00 15	05 19		05 49	05 58		06 19		06 28		06 45			06 49	
6¼	—	34½	—	North Sheen	d	23p39			23p51			05 21		05 51			06 21							06 51	
7	—	35¼	—	Mortlake	d	23p42			23p53			05 23		05 53			06 23							06 53	
—	0	—	—	**Hounslow**	d		23p35						05 31			06 01		06 16				06 31			06 46
—	—	—	—	Isleworth	d		23p38						05 34			06 04		06 19				06 34			06 49
—	2¼	—	—	Syon Lane	d		23p40						05 36			06 06		06 21		←		06 36			06 51
—	3	—	—	Brentford	d		23p42						05 39			06 09		06 24		06 24		06 39			06 54
—	4	—	—	Kew Bridge	d		23p45						05 41			06 11		→		06 26		06 41			→
—	5	—	—	Chiswick	d		23p47						05 44			06 14				06 29		06 44			
—	6	—	—	Barnes Bridge	d		23p50						05 46			06 16				06 31		06 46			
8¼	6½	36½	—	Barnes	d	23p45	23p53		23p56			05 26	05 48	05 56		06 19	06 26			06 34		06 49		06 56	
9¾	—	37¾	—	Putney	d	23p48	23p56	00 02	23p59			05 29	05 51	05 59	06 04	06 22	06 29		06 34	06 37	06 52	06 52		06 59	
10½	—	38¾	—	Wandsworth Town	d	23p51	23p59		00 02			05 32	05 54	06 02		06 25	06 32			06 40		06 55		07 02	
11¼	—	39½	—	**Clapham Junction 10**	d	23p54	00 02	00 07	00 05		00 24	05 35	05 57	06 05	06 09	06 28	06 35		06 39	06 43	06 56	06 58		07 05	
12½	—	41¾	—	Queenstown Rd.(Battersea)	d	23p57	00 05		00 08			05 38	06 00	06 08		06 31	06 38			06 46		07 01		07 08	
14	—	42¼	—	Vauxhall	⊖ d	00 01	00 08	00 12	00 12			05 42	06 04	06 12	06 15	06 35	06 42		06 45	06 50		07 05		07 12	
15¼	—	43½	—	**London Waterloo 15**	⊖ a	00 05	00 13	00 17	00 16		00 32	05 46	06 08	06 16	06 19	06 39	06 46		06 49	06 56	07 07	07 11		07 18	

For general notes see front of timetable
For details of catering facilities see Directory of Train Operators

§ Passengers to/from London may travel via Weybridge. See Table 155.

A From Woking (Table 155)
B From London Waterloo (Table 152)
C From Shepperton (Table 152)

For details of Bank Holiday service alterations, please see first page of this Table

Reading, Guildford, Ascot, Weybridge, Windsor, Kingston, Richmond and Hounslow → London

Network Diagram - see first page of Table 148

		SW	SW	SW	SW	SW	SW	SW	SW	SW	SW	SW	SW	SW	SW	SW	SW	SW		SW	SW	SW	SW	SW	SW
			1			1			A			B	1	1	B	1				A			B	1	1
Reading 7	d					06 12										06 42									
Earley	d					06 17										06 47									
Winnersh Triangle	d					06 19										06 49									
Winnersh	d					06 21										06 51									
Wokingham	d					06 26										06 56									
Bracknell	d					06 32										07 02									
Martins Heron	d					06 35										07 05									
Guildford	d													06 30											07 00
Wanborough	d													06 36											07 06
Ash 3	d													06 40											07 10
Aldershot	a													06 47											07 17
	d		06 00										06 30											07 00	
Ash Vale	d		06 04										06 34											07 04	
Frimley	d		06 10										06 40											07 10	
Camberley	a		06 14										06 44											07 14	
	d		06 18										06 47											07 17	
Bagshot	d		06 23										06 52											07 22	
Ascot 3	d		06a30			06 40							06 59			07 10								07 29	
Sunningdale	d					06 43							07 02			07 13								07 32	
Longcross	d																								
Weybridge	d							06 33										07 03							
Addlestone §	d							06 37										07 07							
Chertsey §	d							06 40										07 10							
Virginia Water	a					06 49		06 45					07 09			07 19		07 15						07 38	
	d					06 49		06 54					07 09			07 19		07 24						07 38	
Egham	d					06 53		06 57					07 13			07 23		07 27						07 42	
Windsor & Eton Riverside	d	06 23								06 53											07 23				
Datchet	d	06 26								06 56											07 26				
Sunnymeads	d	06 29								06 59											07 29				
Wraysbury	d	06 32								07 02											07 32				
Staines	d	06 38				06 59		07 03		07 08			07 18			07 29		07 33			07 38			07 48	
Ashford (Surrey)	d	06 41						07 06		07 11			07 21					07 36			07 41			07 51	
Feltham	d	06 46				07 05		07 11		07 16			07 26			07 35		07 41			07 46			07 56	
Whitton	d	06 50			06 53		06 50			07 20			07 30				07 20				07 50			08 00	
Kingston	d								06 59											07 29					
Hampton Wick	d								07 01											07 31					
Teddington	d								07 05											07 35					
Fulwell	d											07 12											07 42		
Strawberry Hill	d								07 08			07 14								07 38			07 44		
Twickenham	a	06 53			06 56	07 10			07 12	07 23		07 18	07 33			07 40				07 42	07 53		07 48	08 03	
	d	06 53			06 58	07 11			07 13	07 23		07 27	07 33			07 41				07 43	07 53		07 57	08 03	
St Margarets	d				07 00				07 15			07 29								07 45			07 59		
Richmond	⊖ d	06 58			07 04	07 15			07 19	07 28		07 32	07 38			07 45				07 49	07 58		08 02	08 08	
North Sheen	d				07 06				07 21			07 34								07 51			08 04		
Mortlake	d				07 08				07 23			07 37								07 53			08 07		
Hounslow	d				06 48		07 01	07 16									07 31	07 46							
Isleworth	d						07 04	07 19									07 34	07 49							
Syon Lane	d			←			07 06	07 21			←						07 36	07 51				←			
Brentford	d			06 54			07 09	07 24			07 24						07 39	07 54				07 54			
Kew Bridge	d			06 56			07 11	→			07 26						07 41	→				07 56			
Chiswick	d			06 59			07 14				07 29						07 44					07 59			
Barnes Bridge	d			07 01			07 16				07 31				←		07 46					08 01			
Barnes	d			07 04	07 11		07 19		07 26		07 34	07 40			07 40		07 49			07 56		08 04	08 10		
Putney	d	07 04		07 07	07 14	07 22	07 22		07 29	07 34	07 37	→			07 43		07 52			07 59	08 04	08 07	→		
Wandsworth Town	d			07 10	07 17		07 25		07 32		07 40				07 46		07 55			08 02		08 10			
Clapham Junction 10	d	07 09		07 13	07 20	07 26	07 28		07 35	07 39	07 43		07 46		07 49	07 54	07 58			08 05	08 09	08 13		08 17	
Queenstown Rd.(Battersea)	d			07 16	07 23		07 31		07 38		07 46				07 52		08 01			08 08		08 16			
Vauxhall	⊖ d	07 15		07 20	07 27		07 35		07 42	07 45	07 50		07 53		07 56		08 05			08 12	08 15	08 20		08 23	
London Waterloo 15	⊖ a	07 21		07 28	07 34	07 37	07 43		07 48	07 49	07 58		07 59		08 04	08 06	08 11			08 18	08 21	08 28		08 29	

For general notes see front of timetable
For details of catering facilities see Directory of Train Operators

§ Passengers to/from London may travel via Weybridge. See Table 155.

A From London Waterloo (Table 152)
B From Shepperton (Table 152)

For details of Bank Holiday service alterations, please see first page of this Table

Reading, Guildford, Ascot, Weybridge, Windsor, Kingston, Richmond and Hounslow → London

Network Diagram - see first page of Table 148

		SW	SW	SW	SW	SW	SW	SW	SW	SW	SW	SW	SW	SW		SW	SW	SW	SW	SW	SW	SW	SW	SW	SW
			1				1					1		1								1	1		
		A				B		B			A		A				B								B
Reading 7	d		07 12				07 24							07 42									08 12		
Earley	d		07 17											07 47									08 17		
Winnersh Triangle	d		07 19											07 49									08 19		
Winnersh	d		07 21											07 51									08 21		
Wokingham	d		07 26				07 33							07 56									08 26		
Bracknell	d		07 32				07 39							08 02									08 32		
Martins Heron	d		07 35				07 42							08 05									08 35		
Guildford	d																					07 30			
Wanborough	d																					07 36			
Ash 3	d																					07 40			
Aldershot	a																					07 47			
	d											07 30										08 00			
Ash Vale	d											07 34										08 04			
Frimley	d											07 40										08 10			
Camberley	a											07 44										08 14			
	d											07 47										08 18			
Bagshot	d											07 52										08 23			
Ascot 3	d		07 40				07 47					07 59		08 10								08a30	08 40		
Sunningdale	d		07 43				07 50					08 02		08 13									08 43		
Longcross	d													08 16									08 46		
Weybridge	d				07 33													08 03							
Addlestone §	d				07 37													08 07							
Chertsey §	d				07 40													08 10							
Virginia Water	a				07 45		07 55					08 08		08 19				08 15					08 50		
	d				07 51		07 55					08 08		08 19				08 24					08 50		
Egham	d		07 50		07 54		07 58					08 12		08 23				08 27					08 53		
Windsor & Eton Riverside	d								07 53										08 23						
Datchet	d								07 56										08 26						
Sunnymeads	d								07 59										08 29						
Wraysbury	d								08 02										08 32						
Staines	d		07 56		08 00		08 04		08 08			08 18		08 29				08 33	08 38				08 59		
Ashford (Surrey)	d				08 03				08 11			08 21						08 36	08 41						
Feltham	d		08 03		08 08		08 12		08 16			08 26		08 35				08 41	08 46				09 05		
Whitton	d			07 50					08 20			08 30				08 20			08 50		08 53			08 50	
Kingston	d					07 59											08 29								08 59
Hampton Wick	d					08 01											08 31								09 01
Teddington	d					08 05											08 35								09 05
Fulwell	d										08 12														
Strawberry Hill	d					08 08					08 14						08 38								09 08
Twickenham	a		08 09			08 12	08 17		08 23		08 18	08 33		08 40			08 42		08 53		08 56		09 10		09 12
	d		08 09			08 13	08 18		08 23		08 27	08 33		08 41			08 43		08 53		08 58		09 11		09 13
St Margarets	d					08 15					08 29						08 45				09 00				09 15
Richmond	⊖ d		08 14			08 19	08 24		08 28		08 32	08 38		08 45			08 49		08 58		09 04		09 15		09 19
North Sheen	d					08 21					08 34						08 51				09 06				09 21
Mortlake	d					08 23					08 37						08 53				09 08			08 37	09 23
Hounslow	d			08 01	08 16											08 31		08 46						09 01	
Isleworth	d			08 04	08 19											08 34		08 49						09 04	
Syon Lane	d			08 06	08 21											08 36		08 51		←				09 06	
Brentford	d			08 09	08 24					←						08 39		08 54		08 54				09 09	
Kew Bridge	d			08 11	08 26					08 26						08 41		→		08 56				09 11	
Chiswick	d			08 14	→					08 29						08 44				08 59				09 14	
Barnes Bridge	d	←		08 16				←		08 31			←			08 46				09 01				09 16	
Barnes	d	08 10		08 19		08 26		08 26		08 34	08 40		08 40			08 49	08 56			09 04	09 11			09 19	09 26
Putney	d	08 13		08 22		→		08 29	08 34	08 37	→		08 43			08 52	08 59		09 04	09 07	09 14			09 22	09 29
Wandsworth Town	d	08 16		08 25				08 32		08 40			08 46			08 55	09 02			09 10	09 17			09 25	09 32
Clapham Junction 10	d	08 19	08 22	08 28			08 33	08 35	08 39	08 43		08 47	08 49	08 54		08 58	09 05		09 09	09 13	09 20		09 24	09 28	09 35
Queenstown Rd.(Battersea)	d	08 22		08 31				08 38		08 46			08 52			09 01	09 08			09 16	09 23			09 31	09 38
Vauxhall	⊖ d	08 26		08 35			08 38	08 42	08 45	08 50		08 53	08 56			09 05	09 12		09 15	09 20	09 27			09 35	09 42
London Waterloo 15	⊖ a	08 34	08 36	08 43			08 46	08 49	08 49	08 58		09 00	09 04	09 06		09 13	09 18		09 21	09 28	09 34		09 34	09 43	09 48

For general notes see front of timetable
For details of catering facilities see
Directory of Train Operators

§ Passengers to/from London may travel via Weybridge. See Table 155.

A From Shepperton (Table 152)
B From London Waterloo (Table 152)

For details of Bank Holiday service alterations, please see first page of this Table

Reading, Guildford, Ascot, Weybridge, Windsor, Kingston, Richmond and Hounslow → London

Network Diagram - see first page of Table 148

		SW	SW	SW	SW	SW 1	SW 1	SW	SW	SW		SW	SW	SW	SW 1	SW 1	SW	SW	SW	SW	SW 1	SW	SW	SW 1	SW 1
									A									A							
Reading 7	d						08 42									09 12					09 25				09 42
Earley	d						08 47									09 17					09 30				09 47
Winnersh Triangle	d						08 49									09 19					09 32				09 49
Winnersh	d						08 51									09 21					09 34				09 51
Wokingham	d						08 56									09 26					09 39				09 56
Bracknell	d						09 02									09 32					09 46				10 02
Martins Heron	d						09 05									09 35					09 49				10 05
Guildford	d					08 00									08 30									09 00	
Wanborough	d					08 06									08 36									09 06	
Ash 3	d					08 10									08 40									09 10	
Aldershot	a					08 17									08 47									09 17	
	d					08 30									09 00									09 30	
Ash Vale	d					08 34									09 04									09 34	
Frimley	d					08 40									09 10									09 40	
Camberley	a					08 44									09 14									09 44	
	d					08 48									09 18									09 48	
Bagshot	d					08 53									09 23									09 53	
Ascot 3	d					09a00	09 10								09a30	09 40					09 55			10a00	10 10
Sunningdale	d						09 13									09 43					09 58				10 13
Longcross	d						09 16																		
Weybridge	d	08 33								09 03									09 33						
Addlestone §	d	08 37								09 07									09 37						
Chertsey §	d	08 40								09 10									09 40						
Virginia Water	a	08 45					09 19			09 15						09 49			09 45		10 03				10 19
	d	08 54					09 19			09 24						09 49			09 54		10 03				10 19
Egham	d	08 57					09 23			09 27						09 53			09 57		10 06				10 23
Windsor & Eton Riverside	d		08 53									09 23								09 53					
Datchet	d		08 56									09 26								09 56					
Sunnymeads	d		08 59									09 29								09 59					
Wraysbury	d		09 02									09 32								10 02					
Staines	d	09 03	09 08				09 29			09 33		09 38				09 59			10 03	10 08	10 14				10 29
Ashford (Surrey)	d	09 06	09 11							09 36		09 41							10 06	10 11					
Feltham	d	09 11	09 16				09 35			09 41		09 46				10 05			10 11	10 16	10 20				10 35
Whitton	d		09 20		09 23			09 20				09 50		09 53			09 50			10 20			10 23		
Kingston	d								09 29									09 59							
Hampton Wick	d								09 31									10 01							
Teddington	d								09 35									10 05							
Fulwell	d																								
Strawberry Hill	d								09 38									10 08							
Twickenham	a		09 23		09 26		09 40		09 42			09 53		09 56		10 10		10 12		10 23	10 27		10 28		10 40
	d		09 23		09 28		09 41		09 43			09 53		09 58		10 11		10 13		10 23	10 27		10 28		10 41
St Margarets	d				09 30				09 45					10 00				10 15					10 30		
Richmond	⊖ d		09 28		09 34		09 45		09 49			09 58		10 04		10 15		10 19		10 28	10 32		10 34		10 45
North Sheen	d				09 36				09 51					10 06				10 21					10 36		
Mortlake	d				09 38			09 07	09 53					10 08				10 23					10 38		
Hounslow	d	09 16						09 31		09 46							10 01		10 16						
Isleworth	d	09 19						09 34		09 49							10 04		10 19						
Syon Lane	d	09 21		←				09 36		09 51			←				10 06		10 21						
Brentford	d	09 24		09 24				09 39		09 54			09 54				10 09		10 24			←			
Kew Bridge	d	→		09 26				09 41		→			09 56				10 11		10 26			10 26			
Chiswick	d			09 29				09 44					09 59				10 14		→			10 29			
Barnes Bridge	d			09 31				09 46					10 01				10 16					10 31			
Barnes	d			09 34	09 41			09 49	09 56				10 04	10 11			10 19	10 26				10 34	10 41		
Putney	d		09 34	09 37	09 44			09 52	09 59			10 04	10 07	10 14			10 22	10 29		10 34		10 37	10 44		
Wandsworth Town	d			09 40	09 47			09 55	10 02				10 10	10 17			10 25	10 32				10 40	10 47		
Clapham Junction 10	d		09 39	09 43	09 50		09 54	09 58	10 05			10 09	10 13	10 20		10 24	10 28	10 35		10 39	10 42	10 43	10 50		10 54
Queenstown Rd.(Battersea)	d			09 46	09 53			10 01	10 08				10 16	10 23			10 31	10 38				10 46	10 53		
Vauxhall	⊖ d		09 45	09 50	09 57			10 05	10 12			10 15	10 20	10 27			10 35	10 42		10 45		10 50	10 57		
London Waterloo 15	⊖ a		09 49	09 58	10 02		10 04	10 11	10 16			10 19	10 26	10 32		10 34	10 41	10 46		10 49	10 53	10 56	11 02		11 04

For general notes see front of timetable
For details of catering facilities see Directory of Train Operators

§ Passengers to/from London may travel via Weybridge. See Table 155.

A From London Waterloo (Table 152)

For details of Bank Holiday service alterations, please see first page of this Table

Reading, Guildford, Ascot, Weybridge, Windsor, Kingston, Richmond and Hounslow → London

Network Diagram - see first page of Table 148

Station		SW	SW	SW	SW	SW		SW	SW	SW		SW	SW	SW	SW	SW	SW	SW	SW	SW	SW	SW	SW	SW	SW
						1				1		1							1	1					
			A											A								A			
Reading 7	d					09 56						10 12								10 42					
Earley	d					10 01						10 17								10 47					
Winnersh Triangle	d					10 03						10 19								10 49					
Winnersh	d					10 05						10 21								10 51					
Wokingham	d					10 10						10 26								10 56					
Bracknell	d					10 16						10 32								11 02					
Martins Heron	d					10 19						10 35								11 05					
Guildford	d									09 30									10 00						
Wanborough	d									09 36									10 06						
Ash 3	d									09 40									10 10						
Aldershot	a									09 47									10 17						
	d									10 00									10 30						
Ash Vale	d									10 04									10 34						
Frimley	d									10 10									10 40						
Camberley	a									10 14									10 44						
	d									10 18									10 48						
Bagshot	d									10 23									10 53						
Ascot 3	d					10 25				10a30		10 40							11a00	11 10					
Sunningdale	d					10 28						10 43								11 13					
Longcross	d																								
Weybridge	d			10 03											10 33								11 03		
Addlestone §	d			10 07											10 37								11 07		
Chertsey §	d			10 10											10 40								11 10		
Virginia Water	a			10 15		10 33						10 49			10 45					11 19			11 15		
	d			10 24		10 33						10 49			10 54					11 19			11 24		
Egham	d			10 27		10 36						10 53			10 57					11 23			11 27		
Windsor & Eton Riverside	d				10 23											10 53								11 23	
Datchet	d				10 26											10 56								11 26	
Sunnymeads	d				10 29											10 59								11 29	
Wraysbury	d				10 32											11 02								11 32	
Staines	d			10 33	10 38	10 44						10 59			11 03	11 08				11 29			11 33	11 38	
Ashford (Surrey)	d			10 36	10 41										11 06	11 11							11 36	11 41	
Feltham	d			10 41	10 46	10 50						11 05			11 11	11 16				11 35			11 41	11 46	
Whitton	d	10 20			10 50				10 53				10 50			11 20		11 23			11 20			11 50	
Kingston	d		10 29											10 59								11 29			
Hampton Wick	d		10 31											11 01								11 31			
Teddington	d		10 35											11 05								11 35			
Fulwell	d																								
Strawberry Hill	d		10 38											11 08								11 38			
Twickenham	a		10 42		10 53	10 57			10 58			11 10		11 12		11 23		11 26		11 40		11 42		11 53	
	d		10 43		10 53	10 57			10 58			11 11		11 13		11 23		11 28		11 41		11 43		11 53	
St Margarets	d		10 45						11 00					11 15				11 30				11 45			
Richmond	⊖ d		10 49		10 58	11 02			11 04			11 15		11 19		11 28		11 34		11 45		11 49		11 58	
North Sheen	d		10 51						11 06					11 21				11 36				11 51			
Mortlake	d		10 53						11 08					11 23				11 38				11 53			
Hounslow	d	10 31		10 46									11 01		11 16						11 31		11 46		
Isleworth	d	10 34		10 49									11 04		11 19						11 34		11 49		
Syon Lane	d	10 36		10 51									11 06		11 21		←				11 36		11 51		←
Brentford	d	10 39		10 54				←					11 09		11 24		11 24				11 39		11 54		11 54
Kew Bridge	d	10 41		10 56				10 56					11 11		→		11 26				11 41		→		11 56
Chiswick	d	10 44		→				10 59					11 14				11 29				11 44				11 59
Barnes Bridge	d	10 46						11 01					11 16				11 31				11 46				12 01
Barnes	d	10 49	10 56					11 04	11 11				11 19	11 26			11 34	11 41			11 49	11 56			12 04
Putney	d	10 52	10 59		11 04			11 07	11 14				11 22	11 29		11 34	11 37	11 44			11 52	11 59		12 04	12 07
Wandsworth Town	d	10 55	11 02					11 10	11 17				11 25	11 32			11 40	11 47			11 55	12 02			12 10
Clapham Junction 10	d	10 58	11 05		11 09	11 12		11 13	11 20			11 24	11 29	11 35		11 39	11 43	11 50		11 54	11 58	12 05		12 09	12 13
Queenstown Rd.(Battersea)	d	11 01	11 08					11 16	11 23				11 32	11 38			11 46	11 53			12 01	12 08			12 16
Vauxhall	⊖ d	11 05	11 12		11 15			11 20	11 27				11 35	11 42		11 45	11 50	11 57			12 05	12 12		12 15	12 20
London Waterloo 15	⊖ a	11 11	11 16		11 19	11 26		11 27	11 32			11 34	11 41	11 46		11 49	11 56	12 02		12 04	12 11	12 16		12 19	12 26

For general notes see front of timetable
For details of catering facilities see Directory of Train Operators

A From London Waterloo (Table 152)

§ Passengers to/from London may travel via Weybridge. See Table 155.

For details of Bank Holiday service alterations, please see first page of this Table

Reading, Guildford, Ascot, Weybridge, Windsor, Kingston, Richmond and Hounslow → London

Network Diagram - see first page of Table 148

		SW	SW 1		SW 1	SW	SW	SW A	SW	SW 1	GW 1 B	SW	SW	SW 1	SW	SW A	SW	SW	SW	SW	SW 1	SW 1
Reading 7	d				15 12						15 28			15 42								16 12
Earley	d				15 17									15 47								16 17
Winnersh Triangle	d				15 19									15 49								16 19
Winnersh	d				15 21						15 35			15 51								16 21
Wokingham	d				15 26						15a38			15 56								16 26
Bracknell	d				15 32									16 02								16 32
Martins Heron	d				15 35									16 05								16 35
Guildford	d		10 30							15 00											15 30	
Wanborough	d		10 36							15 06											15 36	
Ash 3	d		10 40							15 10											15 40	
Aldershot	a		10 47							15 17											15 47	
	d		11 00							15 30											16 00	
Ash Vale	d		11 04							15 34											16 04	
Frimley	d		11 10							15 40											16 10	
Camberley	a		11 14							15 44											16 14	
	d		11 18							15 48											16 18	
Bagshot	d		11 23							15 53											16 23	
Ascot 3	d		11a30		15 40					16a00				16 10							16a30	16 40
Sunningdale	d				15 43									16 13								16 43
Longcross	d																					
Weybridge	d						15 33										16 03					
Addlestone §	d						15 37										16 07					
Chertsey §	d						15 40										16 10					
Virginia Water	a			**and at**	15 49		15 45							16 19			16 15					16 49
	d				15 49		15 54							16 19			16 24					16 49
Egham	d			**the same**	15 53		15 57							16 23			16 27					16 53
Windsor & Eton Riverside	d			**minutes**					15 53									16 23				
Datchet	d								15 56									16 26				
Sunnymeads	d			**past**					15 59									16 29				
Wraysbury	d								16 02									16 32				
Staines	d			**each**	15 59		16 03		16 08					16 29			16 33	16 38				16 59
Ashford (Surrey)	d			**hour until**			16 06		16 11								16 36	16 41				
Feltham	d				16 05		16 11		16 16					16 35			16 41	16 46				17 05
Whitton	d	11 53				15 50			16 20				16 23		16 20			16 50		16 53		
Kingston	d							15 59								16 29						
Hampton Wick	d							16 01								16 31						
Teddington	d							16 05								16 35						
Fulwell	d																					
Strawberry Hill	d							16 08								16 38						
Twickenham	a	11 56			16 10			16 12	16 23				16 26	16 40		16 42		16 53		16 56		17 10
	d	11 58			16 11			16 13	16 23				16 28	16 41		16 43		16 53		16 58		17 11
St Margarets	d	12 00						16 15					16 30			16 45				17 00		
Richmond	⊖ d	12 04			16 15			16 19	16 28				16 34	16 45		16 49		16 58		17 04		17 15
North Sheen	d	12 06						16 21					16 36			16 51				17 06		
Mortlake	d	12 08						16 23					16 38			16 53				17 08		
Hounslow	d					16 01	16 16								16 31		16 46					
Isleworth	d					16 04	16 19								16 34		16 49					
Syon Lane	d					16 06	16 21					←			16 36		16 51		←			
Brentford	d					16 09	16 24					16 24			16 39		16 54		16 54			
Kew Bridge	d					16 11	→					16 26			16 41		→		16 56			
Chiswick	d					16 14						16 29			16 44				16 59			
Barnes Bridge	d					16 16						16 31			16 46				17 01			
Barnes	d	12 11				16 19		16 26				16 34	16 41		16 49	16 56			17 04	17 11		
Putney	d	12 14				16 22		16 29	16 34			16 37	16 44		16 52	16 59		17 04	17 07	17 14		
Wandsworth Town	d	12 17				16 25		16 32				16 40	16 47		16 55	17 02			17 10	17 17		
Clapham Junction 10	d	12 20			16 24	16 28		16 35	16 39			16 43	16 50	16 54	16 58	17 05		17 09	17 13	17 20		17 24
Queenstown Rd.(Battersea)	d	12 23				16 31		16 38				16 46	16 53		17 01	17 08			17 16	17 23		
Vauxhall	⊖ d	12 27				16 35		16 42	16 45			16 50	16 57		17 05	17 12		17 15	17 20	17 27		
London Waterloo 15	⊖ a	12 32			16 34	16 41		16 49	16 49			16 54	17 02	17 04	17 11	17 19		17 19	17 24	17 32		17 34

For general notes see front of timetable
For details of catering facilities see Directory of Train Operators

§ Passengers to/from London may travel via Weybridge. See Table 155.

A From London Waterloo (Table 152)
B To Gatwick Airport (Table 148)

Reading, Guildford, Ascot, Weybridge, Windsor, Kingston, Richmond and Hounslow → London

For details of Bank Holiday service alterations, please see first page of this Table

Network Diagram - see first page of Table 148

Station		SW	SW	SW	SW	SW	SW	SW	SW	SW	SW	SW	SW	SW	SW	SW	SW	SW		SW	SW	SW	SW	SW	SW
								1	1					1			1				1			1	
			A								A											A			
Reading 7	d								16 42								17 12				17 22				
Earley	d								16 47								17 17				17 27				
Winnersh Triangle	d								16 49								17 19				17 29				
Winnersh	d								16 51								17 21				17 31				
Wokingham	d								16 56								17 26				17 36				
Bracknell	d								17 02								17 32				17 42				
Martins Heron	d								17 05								17 35				17 45				
Guildford	d							16 00						16 30										17 00	
Wanborough	d							16 06						16 36										17 06	
Ash 3	d							16 10						16 40										17 10	
Aldershot	a							16 17						16 47										17 17	
	d							16 30						17 00										17 30	
Ash Vale	d							16 34						17 04										17 34	
Frimley	d							16 40						17 10										17 40	
Camberley	a							16 44						17 14										17 44	
	d							16 48						17 18										17 48	
Bagshot	d							16 53						17 23										17 53	
Ascot 3	d							17a00	17 10					17a30			17 40				17a49			18a00	
Sunningdale	d								17 13								17 43								
Longcross	d								17 16																
Weybridge	d			16 33								17 03								17 37					
Addlestone §	d			16 37								17 07								17 41					
Chertsey §	d			16 40								17 10								17 44					
Virginia Water	a			16 45					17 19			17 15					17 49			17 49					
	d			16 54					17 19			17 24					17 49			17 54					
Egham	d			16 57					17 23			17 27					17 53			17 57					
Windsor & Eton Riverside	d				16 53								17 23										17 53		
Datchet	d				16 56								17 26										17 56		
Sunnymeads	d				16 59								17 29										17 59		
Wraysbury	d				17 02								17 32										18 02		
Staines	d			17 03	17 08				17 29			17 33	17 38				17 59			18 03			18 08		
Ashford (Surrey)	d			17 06	17 11							17 36	17 41							18 06			18 11		
Feltham	d			17 11	17 16				17 35			17 41	17 46				18 05			18 11			18 16		
Whitton	d	16 50			17 20		17 23			17 20			17 50			17 53		17 50					18 20		
Kingston	d		16 59								17 29											17 59			
Hampton Wick	d		17 01								17 31											18 01			
Teddington	d		17 05								17 35											18 05			
Fulwell	d																								
Strawberry Hill	d		17 08								17 38											18 08			
Twickenham	a		17 12		17 23		17 26		17 40		17 42		17 53			17 56	18 10					18 12	18 23		
	d		17 13		17 23		17 28		17 41		17 43		17 53			17 58	18 11					18 13	18 23		
St Margarets	d		17 15				17 30				17 45					18 00						18 15			
Richmond	⊖ d		17 19		17 28		17 34		17 45		17 49		17 58			18 04	18 15					18 19	18 28		
North Sheen	d		17 21				17 36				17 51					18 06						18 21			
Mortlake	d		17 23				17 38				17 53					18 08						18 23			
Hounslow	d	17 01		17 16						17 31		17 46						18 01		18 16					
Isleworth	d	17 04		17 19						17 34		17 49						18 04		18 19					
Syon Lane	d	17 06		17 21		←				17 36		17 51			←			18 06		18 21					←
Brentford	d	17 09		17 24 →		17 24				17 39		17 54 →			17 54			18 09		18 24 →					18 24
Kew Bridge	d	17 11				17 26				17 41					17 56			18 11							18 26
Chiswick	d	17 14				17 29				17 44					17 59			18 14							18 29
Barnes Bridge	d	17 16				17 31				17 46					18 01			18 16							18 31
Barnes	d	17 19	17 26			17 34	17 41			17 49	17 56				18 04	18 11		18 19				18 26			18 34
Putney	d	17 22	17 29		17 34	17 37	17 44			17 52	17 59		18 04		18 07	18 14		18 22				18 29	18 34		18 37
Wandsworth Town	d	17 25	17 32			17 40	17 47			17 55	18 02				18 10	18 17		18 25				18 32			18 40
Clapham Junction 10	d	17 28	17 35		17 39	17 43	17 50		17 54	17 58	18 05		18 09		18 13	18 20	18 24	18 28				18 35	18 39		18 43
Queenstown Rd.(Battersea)	d	17 31	17 38			17 46	17 53			18 01	18 08				18 16	18 23		18 31				18 38			18 46
Vauxhall	⊖ d	17 35	17 42		17 45	17 50	17 57			18 05	18 12		18 15		18 20	18 27		18 35				18 42	18 45		18 50
London Waterloo 15	⊖ a	17 41	17 49		17 49	17 54	18 02		18 04	18 11	18 19		18 19		18 24	18 32	18 34	18 41				18 49	18 49		18 54

For general notes see front of timetable
For details of catering facilities see Directory of Train Operators

§ Passengers to/from London may travel via Weybridge. See Table 155.

A From London Waterloo (Table 152)

For details of Bank Holiday service alterations, please see first page of this Table

Reading, Guildford, Ascot, Weybridge, Windsor, Kingston, Richmond and Hounslow → London

Network Diagram - see first page of Table 148

		SW	SW 1	SW	SW	SW 1	SW	SW	SW	SW	SW 1	SW 1	SW	SW		SW	SW	SW 1	SW	SW	SW 1	SW	SW	SW 1	SW
							A							A											A
Reading 7	d		17 42			17 52						18 12									18 42			18 52	
Earley	d		17 47			17 57						18 17									18 47			18 57	
Winnersh Triangle	d		17 49			17 59						18 19									18 49			18 59	
Winnersh	d		17 51			18 01						18 21									18 51			19 01	
Wokingham	d		17 56			18 06						18 26									18 56			19 06	
Bracknell	d		18 02			18 12						18 32									19 02			19 12	
Martins Heron	d		18 05			18 15						18 35									19 05			19 15	
Guildford	d										17 30							18 00							
Wanborough	d										17 36							18 06							
Ash 3	d										17 40							18 10							
Aldershot	a										17 47							18 17							
	d										18 00							18 30							
Ash Vale	d										18 04							18 34							
Frimley	d										18 10							18 40							
Camberley	a										18 14							18 44							
	d										18 18							18 48							
Bagshot	d										18 23							18 53							
Ascot 3	d		18 10			18a20					18a30	18 40						19a00			19 10			19a19	
Sunningdale	d		18 13									18 43									19 13				
Longcross	d		18 16									18 46									19 16				
Weybridge	d				18 07											18 37							19 07		
Addlestone §	d				18 11											18 41							19 11		
Chertsey §	d				18 14											18 44							19 14		
Virginia Water	a		18 19		18 19							18 49				18 49					19 19		19 19		
	d		18 19		18 24							18 49				18 54					19 19		19 24		
Egham	d		18 23		18 27							18 53				18 57					19 23		19 27		
Windsor & Eton Riverside	d							18 23									18 53								
Datchet	d							18 26									18 56								
Sunnymeads	d							18 29									18 59								
Wraysbury	d							18 32									19 02								
Staines	d		18 29		18 33			18 38				18 59				19 03	19 08				19 29		19 33		
Ashford (Surrey)	d				18 36			18 41								19 06	19 11						19 36		
Feltham	d		18 35		18 41			18 46				19 05				19 11	19 16				19 35		19 41		
Whitton	d	18 23		18 20				18 50		18 53			18 50				19 20			19 23		19 20			
Kingston	d						18 29							18 59											19 29
Hampton Wick	d						18 31							19 01											19 31
Teddington	d						18 35							19 05											19 35
Fulwell	d																								
Strawberry Hill	d						18 38							19 08											19 38
Twickenham	a	18 26	18 40				18 42	18 53		18 56		19 10		19 12			19 23			19 26	19 40				19 42
	d	18 28	18 41				18 43	18 53		18 58		19 11		19 13			19 23			19 28	19 41				19 43
St Margarets	d	18 30					18 45			19 00				19 15						19 30					19 45
Richmond	⊖ d	18 34	18 45				18 49	18 58		19 04		19 15		19 19			19 28			19 34	19 45				19 49
North Sheen	d	18 36					18 51			19 06				19 21						19 36					19 51
Mortlake	d	18 38					18 53			19 08				19 23						19 38					19 53
Hounslow	d			18 31	18 46								19 01			19 16						19 31	19 46		
Isleworth	d			18 34	18 49								19 04			19 19						19 34	19 49		
Syon Lane	d			18 36	18 51				←				19 06			19 21			←			19 36	19 51		
Brentford	d			18 39	18 54				18 54				19 09			19 24			19 24			19 39	19 54		
Kew Bridge	d			18 41	→				18 56				19 11			→			19 26			19 41	→		
Chiswick	d			18 44					18 59				19 14						19 29			19 44			
Barnes Bridge	d			18 46					19 01				19 16						19 31			19 46			
Barnes	d	18 41		18 49			18 56		19 04	19 11			19 19	19 26					19 34	19 41		19 49			19 56
Putney	d	18 44		18 52			18 59	19 04	19 07	19 14			19 22	19 29			19 34		19 37	19 44		19 52			19 59
Wandsworth Town	d	18 47		18 55			19 02		19 10	19 17			19 25	19 32					19 40	19 47		19 55			20 02
Clapham Junction 10	d	18 51	18 54	18 58			19 05	19 09	19 13	19 20		19 24	19 28	19 35			19 39		19 43	19 50	19 54	19 58			20 05
Queenstown Rd.(Battersea)	d	18 53		19 01			19 08		19 16	19 23			19 31	19 38					19 46	19 53		20 01			20 08
Vauxhall	⊖ d	18 57		19 05			19 12	19 15	19 20	19 27			19 35	19 42			19 45		19 50	19 57		20 05			20 12
London Waterloo 15	⊖ a	19 02	19 04	19 09			19 16	19 19	19 26	19 32		19 34	19 41	19 46			19 49		19 56	20 02	20 04	20 10			20 16

For general notes see front of timetable
For details of catering facilities see
Directory of Train Operators

§ Passengers to/from London may travel via Weybridge. See Table 155.

A From London Waterloo (Table 152)

For details of Bank Holiday service alterations, please see first page of this Table

Reading, Guildford, Ascot, Weybridge, Windsor, Kingston, Richmond and Hounslow → London

Network Diagram - see first page of Table 148

	SW	SW	SW	SW	SW	SW	SW	SW	SW		SW	SW	SW	SW	SW	SW	SW	SW	SW	SW	SW	SW	SW	SW
				1	1								1	1					1			1		
							A									A								
Reading 7 d					19 12									19 42								20 12		
Earley d					19 17									19 47								20 17		
Winnersh Triangle d					19 19									19 49								20 19		
Winnersh d					19 21									19 51								20 21		
Wokingham d					19 26									19 56								20 26		
Bracknell d					19 32									20 02								20 32		
Martins Heron d					19 35									20 05								20 35		
Guildford d				18 30									19 00						19 30					
Wanborough d				18 36									19 06						19 36					
Ash 3 d				18 40									19 10						19 40					
Aldershot a				18 47									19 17						19 47					
d				19 00									19 30						20 00					
Ash Vale d				19 04									19 34						20 04					
Frimley d				19 10									19 40						20 10					
Camberley a				19 14									19 44						20 14					
d				19 18									19 48						20 18					
Bagshot d				19 23									19 53						20 23					
Ascot 3 d				19a30	19 40								20a00	20 10					20a30			20 40		
Sunningdale d					19 43									20 13								20 43		
Longcross d					19 46																			
Weybridge d								19 37									20 03							20 33
Addlestone § d								19 41									20 07							20 37
Chertsey § d								19 44									20 10							20 40
Virginia Water a					19 49			19 49						20 19			20 15					20 49		20 45
d					19 49			19 54						20 19			20 24					20 49		20 54
Egham d					19 53			19 57						20 23			20 27					20 53		20 57
Windsor & Eton Riverside d	19 23								19 53									20 23						
Datchet d	19 26								19 56									20 26						
Sunnymeads d	19 29								19 59									20 29						
Wraysbury d	19 32								20 02									20 32						
Staines d	19 38				19 59			20 03	20 08					20 29			20 33	20 38				20 59		21 03
Ashford (Surrey) d	19 41							20 06	20 11								20 36	20 41						21 06
Feltham d	19 46				20 05			20 11	20 16					20 35			20 41	20 46				21 05		21 11
Whitton d	19 50		19 53			19 50			20 20			20 23			20 20			20 50			20 53		20 50	
Kingston d							19 59									20 29								
Hampton Wick d							20 01									20 31								
Teddington d							20 05									20 35								
Fulwell d																								
Strawberry Hill d							20 08									20 38								
Twickenham a	19 53		19 56		20 10		20 12		20 23			20 26		20 40		20 42		20 53			20 56	21 10		
d	19 53		19 58		20 11		20 13		20 23			20 28		20 41		20 43		20 53			20 58	21 11		
St Margarets d			20 00				20 15					20 30				20 45					21 00			
Richmond ⊖ d	19 58		20 04		20 15		20 19		20 28			20 34		20 45		20 49		20 58			21 04	21 15		
North Sheen d			20 06				20 21					20 36				20 51					21 06			
Mortlake d			20 08				20 23					20 38				20 53					21 08			
Hounslow d						20 01		20 16							20 31		20 46						21 01	21 16
Isleworth d						20 04		20 19							20 34		20 49						21 04	21 19
Syon Lane d		←				20 06		20 21			←				20 36		20 51			←			21 06	21 21
Brentford d		19 54				20 09		20 24			20 24				20 39		20 54			20 54			21 09	21 24
Kew Bridge d		19 56				20 11		→			20 26				20 41		→			20 56			21 11	→
Chiswick d		19 59				20 14					20 29				20 44					20 59			21 14	
Barnes Bridge d		20 01				20 16					20 31				20 46					21 01			21 16	
Barnes d		20 04	20 11			20 19	20 26				20 34	20 41			20 49	20 56				21 04	21 11		21 19	
Putney d	20 05	20 07	20 14			20 22	20 29		20 34		20 37	20 44			20 52	20 59		21 04		21 07	21 14		21 22	
Wandsworth Town d		20 10	20 17			20 25	20 32				20 40	20 47			20 55	21 02				21 10	21 17		21 25	
Clapham Junction 10 d	20 09	20 13	20 20		20 24	20 28	20 35		20 39		20 43	20 50		20 54	20 58	21 05		21 09		21 13	21 20	21 24	21 28	
Queenstown Rd.(Battersea) d		20 16	20 23			20 31	20 38				20 46	20 53			21 01	21 08				21 16	21 23		21 31	
Vauxhall ⊖ d	20 15	20 20	20 27			20 35	20 42		20 45		20 50	20 57			21 05	21 12		21 15		21 20	21 27		21 35	
London Waterloo 15 ⊖ a	20 19	20 26	20 32		20 34	20 41	20 46		20 49		20 56	21 02		21 04	21 11	21 16		21 19		21 26	21 32	21 34	21 41	

For general notes see front of timetable
For details of catering facilities see Directory of Train Operators

§ Passengers to/from London may travel via Weybridge. See Table 155.

A From London Waterloo (Table 152)

For details of Bank Holiday service alterations, please see first page of this Table

Reading, Guildford, Ascot, Weybridge, Windsor, Kingston, Richmond and Hounslow → London

Network Diagram - see first page of Table 148

		SW A	SW	SW 1	SW 1	SW		SW	SW 1	SW	SW A	SW	SW	SW	SW	SW 1	SW	SW	SW A	SW	SW 1	SW 1	SW	SW	SW 1
Reading 7	d								20 42							21 12									21 42
Earley	d								20 47							21 17									21 47
Winnersh Triangle	d								20 49							21 19									21 49
Winnersh	d								20 51							21 21									21 51
Wokingham	d								20 56							21 26									21 56
Bracknell	d								21 02							21 32									22 02
Martins Heron	d								21 05							21 35									22 05
Guildford	d			20 00	20 30																21 00	21 30			
Wanborough	d			20 06	20 36																21 06	21 36			
Ash 3	d			20 10	20 40																21 10	21 40			
Aldershot	a			20 17	20 47																21 17	21 47			
	d			20 30																	21 30				
Ash Vale	d			20 34																	21 34				
Frimley	d			20 40																	21 40				
Camberley	a			20 44																	21 44				
	d			20 48																	21 48				
Bagshot	d			20 53																	21 53				
Ascot 3	d			21a00					21 10							21 40					22a00				22 10
Sunningdale	d								21 13							21 43									22 13
Longcross	d																								
Weybridge	d											21 03						21 33							
Addlestone §	d											21 07						21 37							
Chertsey §	d											21 10						21 40							
Virginia Water	a								21 19			21 15				21 49		21 45							22 19
	d								21 19			21 24				21 49		21 54							22 19
Egham	d								21 23			21 27				21 53		21 57							22 23
Windsor & Eton Riverside	d		20 53										21 23							21 53					
Datchet	d		20 56										21 26							21 56					
Sunnymeads	d		20 59										21 29							21 59					
Wraysbury	d		21 02										21 32							22 02					
Staines	d		21 08						21 29			21 33	21 38			21 59		22 03		22 08					22 29
Ashford (Surrey)	d		21 11									21 36	21 41					22 06		22 11					
Feltham	d		21 16						21 35			21 41	21 46			22 05		22 11		22 16					22 35
Whitton	d		21 20					21 23		21 20			21 50		21 53		21 50			22 20				22 23	
Kingston	d	20 59									21 29								21 59						
Hampton Wick	d	21 01									21 31								22 01						
Teddington	d	21 05									21 35								22 05						
Fulwell	d																								
Strawberry Hill	d	21 08									21 38								22 08						
Twickenham	a	21 12	21 23					21 26	21 40		21 42		21 53		21 56	22 10			22 12	22 23				22 26	22 40
	d	21 13	21 23					21 28	21 41		21 43		21 53		21 58	22 11			22 13	22 23				22 28	22 41
St Margarets	d	21 15						21 30			21 45				22 00				22 15					22 30	
Richmond	⊖ d	21 19	21 28					21 34	21 45		21 49		21 58		22 04	22 15			22 19	22 28				22 34	22 45
North Sheen	d	21 21						21 36			21 51				22 06				22 21					22 36	
Mortlake	d	21 23						21 38			21 53				22 08				22 23					22 38	
Hounslow	d									21 31		21 46					22 01	22 16							
Isleworth	d									21 34		21 49					22 04	22 19							
Syon Lane	d					←				21 36		21 51		←			22 06	22 21					←		
Brentford	d					21 24				21 39		21 54		21 54			22 09	22 24					22 24		
Kew Bridge	d					21 26				21 41		→		21 56			22 11	→					22 26		
Chiswick	d					21 29				21 44				21 59			22 14						22 29		
Barnes Bridge	d					21 31				21 46				22 01			22 16						22 31		
Barnes	d	21 26				21 34		21 41		21 49	21 56			22 04	22 11		22 19		22 26				22 34	22 41	
Putney	d	21 29	21 34			21 37		21 44		21 52	21 59		22 04	22 07	22 14		22 22		22 29	22 34			22 37	22 44	
Wandsworth Town	d	21 32				21 40		21 47		21 55	22 02			22 10	22 17		22 25		22 32				22 40	22 47	
Clapham Junction 10	d	21 35	21 39			21 43		21 50	21 54	21 58	22 05		22 09	22 13	22 20	22 24	22 28		22 35	22 39			22 43	22 50	22 54
Queenstown Rd.(Battersea)	d	21 38				21 46		21 53		22 01	22 08			22 16	22 23		22 31		22 38				22 46	22 53	
Vauxhall	⊖ d	21 42	21 45			21 50		21 57		22 05	22 12		22 15	22 20	22 27		22 35		22 42	22 45			22 50	22 57	
London Waterloo 15	⊖ a	21 46	21 49			21 56		22 02	22 04	22 11	22 16		22 19	22 26	22 32	22 34	22 41		22 46	22 49			22 56	23 01	23 04

For general notes see front of timetable
For details of catering facilities see Directory of Train Operators

§ Passengers to/from London may travel via Weybridge. See Table 155.

A From London Waterloo (Table 152)

For details of Bank Holiday service alterations, please see first page of this Table

Reading, Guildford, Ascot, Weybridge, Windsor, Kingston, Richmond and Hounslow → London

Network Diagram - see first page of Table 148

		SW		SW	SW	SW	SW	SW	SW	SW	SW	SW	SW	SW	SW	SW	SW	SW	SW	SW		SW	SW		
							1			1	1			1					1			1	1		
		A							A						A			A							
Reading 7	d						22 12							22 42					23 12						
Earley	d						22 17							22 47					23 17						
Winnersh Triangle	d						22 19							22 49					23 19						
Winnersh	d						22 21							22 51					23 21						
Wokingham	d						22 26							22 56					23 26						
Bracknell	d						22 32							23 02					23 32						
Martins Heron	d						22 35							23 05					23 35						
Guildford	d									22 00	22 30											23 00	23 30		
Wanborough	d									22 06	22 36											23 06	23 36		
Ash 3	d									22 10	22 40											23 10	23 40		
Aldershot	a									22 17	22 47											23 17	23 47		
	d									22 30												23 30			
Ash Vale	d									22 34												23 34			
Frimley	d									22 40												23 40			
Camberley	a									22 44												23 44			
	d									22 48												23 48			
Bagshot	d									22 53												23 53			
Ascot 3	d						22 40			23a00				23 10					23 40			00a01			
Sunningdale	d						22 43							23 13					23 43						
Longcross	d																								
Weybridge	d			22 03				22 33								23 03				23 33					
Addlestone §	d			22 07				22 37								23 07				23 37					
Chertsey §	d			22 10				22 40								23 10				23 40					
Virginia Water	a			22 15			22 49	22 45						23 19		23 15			23 49	23 45					
	d			22 24			22 49	22 54						23 19		23 24			23 49	23 54					
Egham	d			22 27			22 53	22 57						23 23		23 27			23 53	23 57					
Windsor & Eton Riverside	d				22 23							22 53					23 23								
Datchet	d				22 26							22 56					23 26								
Sunnymeads	d				22 29							22 59					23 29								
Wraysbury	d				22 32							23 02					23 32								
Staines	d			22 33	22 38		22 59	23 03				23 08		23 29		23a32	23a37		23 59	00a02					
Ashford (Surrey)	d			22 36	22 41			23 06				23 11													
Feltham	d			22 41	22 46		23 05	23 11				23 16		23 35					00 05						
Whitton	d				22 50							23 20													
Kingston	d	22 29							22 59						23 29			23 55							
Hampton Wick	d	22 31							23 01						23 31			23 57							
Teddington	d	22 35							23 05						23 35			23 59							
Fulwell	d																								
Strawberry Hill	d	22 38							23 08						23 38			00 03							
Twickenham	a	22 42			22 53		23 10		23 12			23 23		23 40	23 42			00 06	00 10						
	d	22 43			22 53		23 11		23 13			23 23		23 41	23 43				00 11						
St Margarets	d	22 45							23 15						23 45										
Richmond	⊖ d	22 49			22 58		23 15		23 19			23 28		23 45	23 49				00 15						
North Sheen	d	22 51							23 21						23 51										
Mortlake	d	22 53							23 23						23 53										
Hounslow	d			22 46				23 16																	
Isleworth	d			22 49				23 19																	
Syon Lane	d			22 51		←		23 21					←												
Brentford	d			22 54 →		22 54		23 24 →					23 24												
Kew Bridge	d					22 56							23 26												
Chiswick	d					22 59							23 29												
Barnes Bridge	d					23 01							23 31												
Barnes	d	22 56				23 04			23 26				23 34		23 56										
Putney	d	22 59			23 04	23 07			23 29			23 34	23 37		23 59										
Wandsworth Town	d	23 02				23 10			23 32				23 40		00 02										
Clapham Junction 10	d	23 05			23 09	23 13	23 24		23 35			23 39	23 43	23 54	00 05				00 24						
Queenstown Rd.(Battersea)	d	23 08				23 16			23 38				23 46		00 08										
Vauxhall	⊖ d	23 12			23 15	23 20			23 42			23 45	23 50		00 12										
London Waterloo 15	⊖ a	23 16			23 19	23 26	23 34		23 46			23 49	23 56	00 03	00 16				00 32						

For general notes see front of timetable
For details of catering facilities see Directory of Train Operators

§ Passengers to/from London may travel via Weybridge. See Table 155.

A From London Waterloo (Table 152)

Table 149

Saturdays

Reading, Guildford, Ascot, Weybridge, Windsor, Kingston, Richmond and Hounslow → London

Network Diagram - see first page of Table 148

		SW	SW	SW [1]	SW	SW	SW	SW	SW	SW	SW	SW	SW [1]		SW	SW [1]	SW	SW	SW	SW [1]	SW	SW	SW	SW	SW [1]
		A	A							B		B									A				
Reading [7]	d			23p12									05 42							06 12					06 42
Earley	d			23p17									05 47							06 17					06 47
Winnersh Triangle	d			23p19									05 49							06 19					06 49
Winnersh	d			23p21									05 51							06 21					06 51
Wokingham	d			23p26									05 56							06 26					06 56
Bracknell	d			23p32									06 02							06 32					07 02
Martins Heron	d			23p35									06 05							06 35					07 05
Guildford	d																								
Wanborough	d																								
Ash [3]	d																								
Aldershot	a																								
	d															06 00									
Ash Vale	d															06 04									
Frimley	d															06 10									
Camberley	a															06 14									
	d															06 18									
Bagshot	d															06 23									
Ascot [3]	d			23p40									06 10			06a30				06 40					07 10
Sunningdale	d			23p43									06 13							06 43					07 13
Longcross	d																								
Weybridge	d																					06 33			
Addlestone §	d									05 37												06 37			
Chertsey §	d									05 40												06 40			
Virginia Water	a			23p49						05 45			06 19							06 49		06 45			07 19
	d			23p49						05 54			06 19							06 49		06 54			07 19
Egham	d			23p53						05 57			06 23							06 53		06 57			07 23
Windsor & Eton Riverside	d										05 53							06 23					06 53		
Datchet	d										05 56							06 26					06 56		
Sunnymeads	d										05 59							06 29					06 59		
Wraysbury	d										06 02							06 32					07 02		
Staines	d			23p59	04 58		05 38			06 03	06 08		06 29				06 33	06 38		06 59		07 03	07 08		07 29
Ashford (Surrey)	d				05 01		05 41			06 06	06 11						06 36	06 41				07 06	07 11		
Feltham	d			00 05	05 06		05 46			06 11	06 16		06 35				06 41	06 46		07 05		07 11	07 16		07 35
Whitton	d				05 10		05 50	05 41			06 20							06 50					07 20		
Kingston	d	23p29	23p55						05 59						06 29						06 59				
Hampton Wick	d	23p31	23p57						06 01						06 31						07 01				
Teddington	d	23p35	23p59						06 05						06 35						07 05				
Fulwell	d																								
Strawberry Hill	d	23p38	00 03			05 38			06 08						06 38						07 08				
Twickenham	a	23p42	00 06	00 10	05 13	05 41	05 53		06 12		06 23		06 40		06 42			06 53		07 10	07 12		07 23		07 40
	d	23p43		00 11	05 13	05 43	05 53		06 13		06 23		06 41		06 43			06 53		07 11	07 13		07 23		07 41
St Margarets	d	23p45			05 15	05 45			06 15						06 45						07 15				
Richmond	⊖ d	23p49		00 15	05 19	05 49	05 58		06 19		06 28		06 45		06 49			06 58		07 15	07 19		07 28		07 45
North Sheen	d	23p51			05 21	05 51			06 21						06 51						07 21				
Mortlake	d	23p53			05 23	05 53			06 23						06 53						07 23				
Hounslow	d							05 46		06 16							06 46					07 16			
Isleworth	d							05 49		06 19							06 49					07 19			
Syon Lane	d							05 51		06 21		←					06 51		←			07 21		←	
Brentford	d							05 54		06 24		06 24					06 54		06 54			07 24		07 24	
Kew Bridge	d							05 56		→		06 26					→		06 56			→		07 26	
Chiswick	d							05 59				06 29							06 59					07 29	
Barnes Bridge	d							06 01				06 31							07 01					07 31	
Barnes	d	23p56			05 26	05 56		06 04	06 26			06 34			06 56				07 04		07 26			07 34	
Putney	d	23p59			05 29	05 59	06 04	06 07	06 29		06 34	06 37			06 59			07 04	07 07		07 29		07 34	07 37	
Wandsworth Town	d	00 02			05 32	06 02		06 10	06 32			06 40			07 02				07 10		07 32			07 40	
Clapham Junction [10]	d	00 05		00 24	05 35	06 05	06 09	06 13	06 35		06 39	06 43	06 54		07 05			07 09	07 13	07 24	07 35		07 39	07 43	07 54
Queenstown Rd.(Battersea)	d	00 08			05 38	06 08		06 16	06 38			06 46			07 08				07 16		07 38			07 46	
Vauxhall	⊖ d	00 12			05 42	06 12	06 15	06 20	06 42		06 45	06 50			07 12			07 15	07 20		07 42		07 45	07 50	
London Waterloo [15]	⊖ a	00 16		00 32	05 46	06 16	06 19	06 26	06 46		06 51	06 56	07 04		07 16			07 19	07 26	07 34	07 47		07 49	07 56	08 04

For general notes see front of timetable
For details of catering facilities see Directory of Train Operators

§ Passengers to/from London may travel via Weybridge. See Table 155.

A From London Waterloo (Table 152)
B From Woking (Table 155)

Table 149

Saturdays

Reading, Guildford, Ascot, Weybridge, Windsor, Kingston, Richmond and Hounslow → London

Network Diagram - see first page of Table 148

		SW	SW	SW	SW	SW 1	SW	SW	SW 1	SW	SW	SW	SW	SW	SW	SW 1	SW 1	SW	SW	SW	SW	SW	SW
			A								A								A				
Reading 7	d								07 12								07 42						
Earley	d								07 17								07 47						
Winnersh Triangle	d								07 19								07 49						
Winnersh	d								07 21								07 51						
Wokingham	d								07 26								07 56						
Bracknell	d								07 32								08 02						
Martins Heron	d								07 35								08 05						
Guildford	d					06 30										07 00							
Wanborough	d					06 36										07 06							
Ash 3	d					06 40										07 10							
Aldershot	a					06 47										07 17							
	d					07 00										07 30							
Ash Vale	d					07 04										07 34							
Frimley	d					07 10										07 40							
Camberley	a					07 14										07 44							
	d					07 18										07 48							
Bagshot	d					07 23										07 53							
Ascot 3	d					07a30			07 40							08a00	08 10						
Sunningdale	d								07 43								08 13						
Longcross	d																						
Weybridge	d			07 03								07 33								08 03			
Addlestone §	d			07 07								07 37								08 07			
Chertsey §	d			07 10								07 40								08 10			
Virginia Water	a			07 15					07 49			07 45					08 19			08 15			
	d			07 24					07 49			07 54					08 19			08 24			
Egham	d			07 27					07 53			07 57					08 23			08 27			
Windsor & Eton Riverside	d				07 23								07 53								08 23		
Datchet	d				07 26								07 56								08 26		
Sunnymeads	d				07 29								07 59								08 29		
Wraysbury	d				07 32								08 02								08 32		
Staines	d			07 33	07 38				07 59			08 03	08 08				08 29			08 33	08 38		
Ashford (Surrey)	d			07 36	07 41							08 06	08 11							08 36	08 41		
Feltham	d			07 41	07 46				08 05			08 11	08 16				08 35			08 41	08 46		
Whitton	d				07 50					07 50			08 20		08 23			08 20			08 50		08 53
Kingston	d		07 29								07 59								08 29				
Hampton Wick	d		07 31								08 01								08 31				
Teddington	d		07 35								08 05								08 35				
Fulwell	d																						
Strawberry Hill	d		07 38								08 08								08 38				
Twickenham	a		07 42		07 53				08 10		08 12		08 23		08 26		08 40		08 42		08 53		08 56
	d		07 43		07 53			07 58	08 11		08 13		08 23		08 28		08 41		08 43		08 53		08 58
St Margarets	d		07 45					08 00			08 15				08 30				08 45				09 00
Richmond	⊖ d		07 49		07 58			08 04	08 15		08 19		08 28		08 34		08 45		08 49		08 58		09 04
North Sheen	d		07 51					08 06			08 21				08 36				08 51				09 06
Mortlake	d		07 53					08 08			08 23				08 38				08 53				09 08
Hounslow	d	07 31		07 46						08 01		08 16						08 31		08 46			
Isleworth	d	07 34		07 49						08 04		08 19						08 34		08 49			
Syon Lane	d	07 36		07 51			←			08 06		08 21		←				08 36		08 51		←	
Brentford	d	07 39		07 54			07 54			08 09		08 24		08 24				08 39		08 54		08 54	
Kew Bridge	d	07 41		→			07 56			08 11		→		08 26				08 41		→		08 56	
Chiswick	d	07 44					07 59			08 14				08 29				08 44				08 59	
Barnes Bridge	d	07 46					08 01			08 16				08 31				08 46				09 01	
Barnes	d	07 49	07 56				08 04	08 11		08 19	08 26			08 34	08 41			08 49	08 56			09 04	09 11
Putney	d	07 52	07 59		08 04		08 07	08 14		08 22	08 29		08 34	08 37	08 44			08 52	08 59		09 04	09 07	09 14
Wandsworth Town	d	07 55	08 02				08 10	08 17		08 25	08 32			08 40	08 47			08 55	09 02			09 10	09 17
Clapham Junction 10	d	07 58	08 05		08 09		08 13	08 20	08 24	08 28	08 35		08 39	08 43	08 50		08 54	08 58	09 05		09 09	09 13	09 21
Queenstown Rd.(Battersea)	d	08 01	08 08				08 16	08 23		08 31	08 38			08 46	08 53			09 01	09 08			09 16	09 23
Vauxhall	⊖ d	08 05	08 12		08 15		08 20	08 27		08 35	08 42		08 45	08 50	08 57			09 05	09 12		09 15	09 20	09 27
London Waterloo 15	⊖ a	08 11	08 16		08 19		08 26	08 32	08 34	08 41	08 46		08 49	08 56	09 02		09 04	09 11	09 16		09 19	09 26	09 32

For general notes see front of timetable
For details of catering facilities see Directory of Train Operators

§ Passengers to/from London may travel via Weybridge. See Table 155.

A From London Waterloo (Table 152)

Reading, Guildford, Ascot, Weybridge, Windsor, Kingston, Richmond and Hounslow → London

Network Diagram - see first page of Table 148

Station		SW 1	SW 1	SW	SW A	SW	SW	SW	SW		SW 1	SW 1	SW	SW A	SW	SW	SW 1	SW	SW	SW 1	SW	SW	SW A
Reading 7	d		08 12									19 42								20 12			
Earley	d		08 17									19 47								20 17			
Winnersh Triangle	d		08 19									19 49								20 19			
Winnersh	d		08 21									19 51								20 21			
Wokingham	d		08 26									19 56								20 26			
Bracknell	d		08 32									20 02								20 32			
Martins Heron	d		08 35									20 05								20 35			
Guildford	d	07 30									19 00						19 30						
Wanborough	d	07 36									19 06						19 36						
Ash 3	d	07 40									19 10						19 40						
Aldershot	a	07 47									19 17						19 47						
	d	08 00									19 30						20 00						
Ash Vale	d	08 04									19 34						20 04						
Frimley	d	08 10									19 40						20 10						
Camberley	a	08 14									19 44						20 14						
	d	08 18									19 48						20 18						
Bagshot	d	08 23									19 53						20 23						
Ascot 3	d	08a30	08 40								20a00	20 10					20a30			20 40			
Sunningdale	d		08 43									20 13								20 43			
Longcross	d																						
Weybridge	d					08 33									20 03							20 33	
Addlestone §	d					08 37									20 07							20 37	
Chertsey §	d					08 40									20 10							20 40	
Virginia Water	a		08 49			08 45				and at the same minutes past each hour until		20 19			20 15					20 49		20 45	
	d		08 49			08 54						20 19			20 24					20 49		20 54	
Egham	d		08 53			08 57						20 23			20 27					20 53		20 57	
Windsor & Eton Riverside	d						08 53									20 23							
Datchet	d						08 56									20 26							
Sunnymeads	d						08 59									20 29							
Wraysbury	d						09 02									20 32							
Staines	d		08 59			09 03	09 08					20 29			20 33	20 38				20 59		21 03	
Ashford (Surrey)	d					09 06	09 11								20 36	20 41						21 06	
Feltham	d		09 05			09 11	09 16					20 35			20 41	20 46				21 05		21 11	
Whitton	d			08 50			09 20		09 23				20 20			20 50			20 53		20 50		
Kingston	d				08 59									20 29									20 59
Hampton Wick	d				09 01									20 31									21 01
Teddington	d				09 05									20 35									21 05
Fulwell	d																						
Strawberry Hill	d				09 08									20 38									21 08
Twickenham	a		09 10		09 12		09 23		09 26			20 40		20 42		20 53			20 56	21 10			21 12
	d		09 11		09 13		09 23		09 28			20 41		20 43		20 53			20 58	21 11			21 13
St Margarets	d				09 15				09 30					20 45					21 00				21 15
Richmond ⊖	d		09 15		09 19		09 28		09 34			20 45		20 49		20 58			21 04	21 15			21 19
North Sheen	d				09 21				09 36					20 51					21 06				21 21
Mortlake	d				09 23				09 38					20 53					21 08				21 23
Hounslow	d			09 01		09 16							20 31		20 46						21 01	21 16	
Isleworth	d			09 04		09 19							20 34		20 49						21 04	21 19	
Syon Lane	d			09 06		09 21		←					20 36		20 51			←			21 06	21 21	
Brentford	d			09 09		09 24		09 24					20 39		20 54			20 54			21 09	21 24	
Kew Bridge	d			09 11		→		09 26					20 41		→			20 56			21 11	→	
Chiswick	d			09 14				09 29					20 44					20 59			21 14		
Barnes Bridge	d			09 16				09 31					20 46					21 01			21 16		
Barnes	d			09 19	09 26			09 34	09 41				20 49	20 56				21 04	21 11		21 19		21 26
Putney	d			09 22	09 29		09 34	09 37	09 44				20 52	20 59		21 04		21 07	21 14		21 22		21 29
Wandsworth Town	d			09 25	09 32			09 40	09 47				20 55	21 02				21 10	21 17		21 25		21 32
Clapham Junction 10	d		09 24	09 28	09 35		09 39	09 43	09 50			20 54	20 58	21 05		21 09		21 13	21 21	21 24	21 28		21 35
Queenstown Rd.(Battersea)	d			09 31	09 38			09 46	09 53				21 01	21 08				21 16	21 23		21 31		21 38
Vauxhall ⊖	d			09 35	09 42		09 45	09 50	09 57				21 05	21 12		21 15		21 20	21 27		21 35		21 42
London Waterloo 15 ⊖	a		09 34	09 41	09 46		09 49	09 56	10 02			21 04	21 11	21 16		21 19		21 26	21 32	21 34	21 41		21 46

For general notes see front of timetable
For details of catering facilities see Directory of Train Operators

§ Passengers to/from London may travel via Weybridge. See Table 155.

A From London Waterloo (Table 152)

Table 149

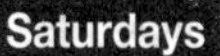

Reading, Guildford, Ascot, Weybridge, Windsor, Kingston, Richmond and Hounslow → London

Network Diagram - see first page of Table 148

		SW		SW 1	SW 1	SW	SW	SW 1	SW	SW A	SW	SW	SW	SW	SW 1		SW	SW	SW A	SW	SW 1	SW 1	SW	SW	SW 1
Reading 7	d							20 42							21 12										21 42
Earley	d							20 47							21 17										21 47
Winnersh Triangle	d							20 49							21 19										21 49
Winnersh	d							20 51							21 21										21 51
Wokingham	d							20 56							21 26										21 56
Bracknell	d							21 02							21 32										22 02
Martins Heron	d							21 05							21 35										22 05
Guildford	d			20 00	20 30																21 00	21 30			
Wanborough	d			20 06	20 36																21 06	21 36			
Ash 3	d			20 10	20 40																21 10	21 40			
Aldershot	a			20 17	20 47																21 17	21 47			
	d			20 30																	21 30				
Ash Vale	d			20 34																	21 34				
Frimley	d			20 40																	21 40				
Camberley	a			20 44																	21 44				
	d			20 48																	21 48				
Bagshot	d			20 53																	21 53				
Ascot 3	d			21a00				21 10							21 40						22a00				22 10
Sunningdale	d							21 13							21 43										22 13
Longcross	d																								
Weybridge	d										21 03							21 33							
Addlestone §	d										21 07							21 37							
Chertsey §	d										21 10							21 40							
Virginia Water	a							21 19			21 15				21 49			21 45							22 19
	d							21 19			21 24				21 49			21 54							22 19
Egham	d							21 23			21 27				21 53			21 57							22 23
Windsor & Eton Riverside	d	20 53										21 23								21 53					
Datchet	d	20 56										21 26								21 56					
Sunnymeads	d	20 59										21 29								21 59					
Wraysbury	d	21 02										21 32								22 02					
Staines	d	21 08						21 29			21 33	21 38			21 59			22 03		22 08					22 29
Ashford (Surrey)	d	21 11									21 36	21 41						22 06		22 11					
Feltham	d	21 16						21 35			21 41	21 46			22 05			22 11		22 16					22 35
Whitton	d	21 20					21 23		21 20			21 50		21 53			21 50			22 20				22 23	
Kingston	d									21 29									21 59						
Hampton Wick	d									21 31									22 01						
Teddington	d									21 35									22 05						
Fulwell	d																								
Strawberry Hill	d									21 38									22 08						
Twickenham	a	21 23					21 26	21 40		21 42		21 53		21 56	22 10				22 12	22 23				22 26	22 40
	d	21 23					21 28	21 41		21 43		21 53		21 58	22 11				22 13	22 23				22 28	22 41
St Margarets	d						21 30			21 45				22 00					22 15					22 30	
Richmond	⊖ d	21 28					21 34	21 45		21 49		21 58		22 04	22 15				22 19	22 28				22 34	22 45
North Sheen	d						21 36			21 51				22 06					22 21					22 36	
Mortlake	d						21 38			21 53				22 08					22 23					22 38	
Hounslow	d								21 31		21 46						22 01	22 16							
Isleworth	d								21 34		21 49						22 04	22 19							
Syon Lane	d					←			21 36		21 51		←				22 06	22 21					←		
Brentford	d					21 24			21 39		21 54		21 54				22 09	22 24					22 24		
Kew Bridge	d					21 26			21 41		→		21 56				22 11	→					22 26		
Chiswick	d					21 29			21 44				21 59				22 14						22 29		
Barnes Bridge	d					21 31			21 46				22 01				22 16						22 31		
Barnes	d					21 34	21 41		21 49	21 56			22 04	22 11			22 19		22 26				22 34	22 41	
Putney	d	21 34				21 37	21 44		21 52	21 59		22 04	22 07	22 14			22 22		22 29	22 34			22 37	22 44	
Wandsworth Town	d					21 40	21 47		21 55	22 02			22 10	22 18			22 25		22 32				22 40	22 47	
Clapham Junction 10	d	21 39				21 43	21 50	21 54	21 58	22 05		22 09	22 13	22 21	22 24		22 28		22 35	22 39			22 43	22 50	22 54
Queenstown Rd.(Battersea)	d					21 46	21 53		22 01	22 08			22 16	22 23			22 31		22 38				22 46	22 53	
Vauxhall	⊖ d	21 45				21 50	21 57		22 05	22 12		22 15	22 20	22 27			22 35		22 42	22 45			22 50	22 57	
London Waterloo 15	⊖ a	21 49				21 56	22 02	22 04	22 11	22 16		22 19	22 26	22 32	22 34		22 41		22 46	22 49			22 56	23 02	23 04

For general notes see front of timetable
For details of catering facilities see Directory of Train Operators

A From London Waterloo (Table 152)

§ Passengers to/from London may travel via Weybridge. See Table 155.

Table 149

Saturdays

Reading, Guildford, Ascot, Weybridge, Windsor, Kingston, Richmond and Hounslow → London

Network Diagram - see first page of Table 148

		SW	SW	SW	SW	SW 1		SW	SW	SW 1	SW 1	SW	SW	SW 1	SW	SW	SW	SW	SW 1		SW	SW 1	SW 1		
		A							A						A			A					B		
Reading 7	d					22 12								22 42					23 12						
Earley	d					22 17								22 47					23 17						
Winnersh Triangle	d					22 19								22 49					23 19						
Winnersh	d					22 21								22 51					23 21						
Wokingham	d					22 26								22 56					23 26						
Bracknell	d					22 32								23 02					23 32						
Martins Heron	d					22 35								23 05					23 35						
Guildford	d									22 00	22 30											23 00	23 30		
Wanborough	d									22 06	22 36											23 06	23 36		
Ash 3	d									22 10	22 40											23 10	23 40		
Aldershot	a									22 17	22 47											23 17	23 47		
	d									22 30												23 30			
Ash Vale	d									22 34												23 34			
Frimley	d									22 40												23 40			
Camberley	a									22 44												23 44			
	d									22 48												23 48			
Bagshot	d									22 53												23 53			
Ascot 3	d					22 40				23a00				23 10					23 40			00a01			
Sunningdale	d					22 43								23 13					23 43						
Longcross	d																								
Weybridge	d		22 03					22 33								23 03					23 33				
Addlestone §	d		22 07					22 37								23 07					23 37				
Chertsey §	d		22 10					22 40								23 10					23 40				
Virginia Water	a		22 15			22 49		22 45						23 19		23 15			23 49		23 45				
	d		22 24			22 49		22 54						23 19		23 24			23 49		23 54				
Egham	d		22 27			22 53		22 57						23 23		23 27			23 53		23 57				
Windsor & Eton Riverside	d			22 23								22 53					23 23								
Datchet	d			22 26								22 56					23 26								
Sunnymeads	d			22 29								22 59					23 29								
Wraysbury	d			22 32								23 02					23 32								
Staines	d		22 33	22 38		22 59		23 03				23 08		23 29		23a32	23a37		23 59		00a02				
Ashford (Surrey)	d		22 36	22 41				23 06				23 11													
Feltham	d		22 41	22 46		23 05		23 11				23 16		23 35					00 05						
Whitton	d			22 50								23 20													
Kingston	d	22 29							22 59						23 29			23 55							
Hampton Wick	d	22 31							23 01						23 31			23 57							
Teddington	d	22 35							23 05						23 35			23 59							
Fulwell	d																								
Strawberry Hill	d	22 38							23 08						23 38			00 04							
Twickenham	a	22 42		22 53		23 10			23 12			23 23		23 40	23 42			00 07	00 10						
	d	22 43		22 53		23 11			23 13			23 23		23 41	23 43				00 12						
St Margarets	d	22 45							23 15						23 45										
Richmond	⊖ d	22 49		22 58		23 15			23 19			23 28		23 45	23 49				00 16						
North Sheen	d	22 51							23 21						23 51										
Mortlake	d	22 53							23 23						23 53										
Hounslow	d		22 46					23 16																	
Isleworth	d		22 49					23 19																	
Syon Lane	d		22 51		←			23 21					←												
Brentford	d		22 54		22 54			23 24					23 24												
Kew Bridge	d		→		22 56			→					23 26												
Chiswick	d				22 59								23 29												
Barnes Bridge	d				23 01								23 31												
Barnes	d	22 56			23 04				23 26				23 34		23 56										
Putney	d	22 59		23 04	23 07				23 29			23 34	23 37		23 59										
Wandsworth Town	d	23 02			23 10				23 32				23 40		00 02										
Clapham Junction 10	d	23 05		23 09	23 13	23 24			23 35			23 39	23 43	23 54	00 05				00 25						
Queenstown Rd.(Battersea)	d	23 08			23 16				23 38				23 46		00 08										
Vauxhall	⊖ d	23 12		23 15	23 20				23 42			23 45	23 50		00 12										
London Waterloo 15	⊖ a	23 16		23 19	23 26	23 34			23 47			23 49	23 56	00 02	00 16				00 33						

For general notes see front of timetable
For details of catering facilities see Directory of Train Operators

§ Passengers to/from London may travel via Weybridge. See Table 155.

A From London Waterloo (Table 152)
B To Farnham (Table 155)

Table 149

Sundays

Reading, Guildford, Ascot, Weybridge, Windsor, Kingston, Richmond and Hounslow → London

Network Diagram - see first page of Table 148

		SW	SW	SW	SW	SW		SW	SW	SW	SW	SW		SW	SW	SW	SW	SW		SW	SW	SW	SW	SW	SW
				1											1	1		1				1	1		1
		A	A			A		A			A			B			A				B			A	
Reading 7	d			23p12												07 54		08 24					08 54		09 24
Earley	d			23p17												07 59		08 29					08 59		09 29
Winnersh Triangle	d			23p19												08 01		08 31					09 01		09 31
Winnersh	d			23p21												08 03		08 33					09 03		09 33
Wokingham	d			23p26												08 08		08 38					09 08		09 38
Bracknell	d			23p32												08 14		08 44					09 14		09 44
Martins Heron	d			23p35												08 17		08 47					09 17		09 47
Guildford	d														07 17							08 17			
Wanborough	d														07 23							08 23			
Ash 3	d														07 27							08 27			
Aldershot	a														07 34							08 34			
	d														07 40							08 40			
Ash Vale	d														07 45							08 45			
Frimley	d														07 51							08 51			
Camberley	a														07 55							08 55			
	d														07 55							08 55			
Bagshot	d														08 01							09 01			
Ascot 3	d			23p40											08a07	08 22		08 52				09a07	09 22		09 52
Sunningdale	d			23p43												08 25		08 55					09 25		09 55
Longcross	d																								
Weybridge	d									07 00															
Addlestone §	d									07 04				08 04							09 04				
Chertsey §	d									07 07				08 07							09 07				
Virginia Water	a			23p49						07 12				08 12		08 30		09 00			09 12		09 30		10 00
	d			23p49						07 12				08 12		08 30		09 00			09 12		09 30		10 00
Egham	d			23p53						07 16				08 16		08 34		09 04			09 16		09 34		10 04
Windsor & Eton Riverside	d								07 01			08 01								09 01					
Datchet	d								07 04			08 04								09 04					
Sunnymeads	d								07 07			08 07								09 07					
Wraysbury	d								07 10			08 10								09 10					
Staines	d			23p59					07 16	07 21		08 16		08 21		08 39		09 09		09 16	09 21		09 39		10 09
Ashford (Surrey)	d								07 19	07 24		08 19		08 24						09 19	09 24				
Feltham	d			00 05					07 24	07 29		08 24		08 29		08 46		09 16		09 24	09 29		09 46		10 16
Whitton	d								07 28			08 28								09 28					
Kingston	d	23p29	23p55		01 17	02 16		06 49			07 49						08 49							09 49	
Hampton Wick	d	23p31	23p57		01s19			06 51			07 51						08 51							09 51	
Teddington	d	23p35	23p59		01s22			06 56			07 56						08 56							09 56	
Fulwell	d																								
Strawberry Hill	d	23p38	00 04		01 25	02s26		06 59			07 59						08 59							09 59	
Twickenham	a	23p42	00 07	00 10		02 30		07 02	07 31		08 02	08 31				08 51	09 02	09 21		09 31			09 51	10 02	10 21
	d	23p43		00 12				07 03	07 32		08 03	08 32				08 51	09 03	09 21		09 32			09 51	10 03	10 21
St Margarets	d	23p45						07 05	07 34		08 05	08 34					09 05			09 34				10 05	
Richmond	⊖ d	23p49		00 16				07 09	07 37		08 09	08 37				08 56	09 09	09 26		09 37			09 56	10 09	10 26
North Sheen	d	23p51						07 11	07 39		08 11	08 39					09 11			09 39				10 11	
Mortlake	d	23p53						07 13	07 42		08 13	08 42					09 13			09 42				10 13	
Hounslow	d									07 35				08 35							09 35				
Isleworth	d									07 38				08 38							09 38				
Syon Lane	d									07 40				08 40							09 40				
Brentford	d									07 42				08 42							09 42				
Kew Bridge	d									07 45				08 45							09 45				
Chiswick	d									07 47				08 47							09 47				
Barnes Bridge	d									07 50				08 50							09 50				
Barnes	d	23p56						07 16	07 45	07 53	08 16	08 45		08 53			09 16			09 45	09 53			10 16	
Putney	d	23p59						07 19	07 48	07 56	08 19	08 48		08 56		09 02	09 19	09 32		09 48	09 56		10 02	10 19	10 32
Wandsworth Town	d	00 02						07 22	07 51	07 59	08 22	08 51		08 59			09 22			09 51	09 59			10 22	
Clapham Junction 10	d	00 05		00 25				07 25	07 54	08 02	08 25	08 54		09 02		09 07	09 25	09 37		09 54	10 02		10 07	10 25	10 37
Queenstown Rd.(Battersea)	d	00 08						07 28	07 57	08 05	08 28	08 57		09 05			09 28			09 57	10 05			10 28	
Vauxhall	⊖ d	00 12						07 32	08 00	08 08	08 32	09 00		09 08		09 12	09 32	09 42		10 00	10 08		10 12	10 32	10 42
London Waterloo 15	⊖ a	00 16		00 33				07 41	08 10	08 13	08 41	09 10		09 13		09 23	09 41	09 53		10 10	10 13		10 23	10 41	10 53

For general notes see front of timetable
For details of catering facilities see Directory of Train Operators

§ Passengers to/from London may travel via Weybridge. See Table 155.

A From London Waterloo (Table 152)
B From Woking (Table 155)

Table 149

Sundays

Reading, Guildford, Ascot, Weybridge, Windsor, Kingston, Richmond and Hounslow → London

Network Diagram - see first page of Table 148

		SW		SW	SW	SW	SW	SW		SW	SW	SW	SW	SW		SW	SW	SW	SW	SW		SW	SW	SW	SW
					1	1				1			1	1				1				1	1		
				A				B				A					B			A					B
Reading [7]	d					09 54				10 24				10 54				11 24					11 54		
Earley	d					09 59				10 29				10 59				11 29					11 59		
Winnersh Triangle	d					10 01				10 31				11 01				11 31					12 01		
Winnersh	d					10 03				10 33				11 03				11 33					12 03		
Wokingham	d					10 08				10 38				11 08				11 38					12 08		
Bracknell	d					10 14				10 44				11 14				11 44					12 14		
Martins Heron	d					10 17				10 47				11 17				11 47					12 17		
Guildford	d				09 17								10 17									11 17			
Wanborough	d				09 23								10 23									11 23			
Ash [3]	d				09 27								10 27									11 27			
Aldershot	a				09 34								10 34									11 34			
	d				09 40								10 40									11 40			
Ash Vale	d				09 45								10 45									11 45			
Frimley	d				09 51								10 51									11 51			
Camberley	a				09 55								10 55									11 55			
	d				09 55								10 55									11 55			
Bagshot	d				10 01								11 01									12 01			
Ascot [8]	d				10a07	10 22				10 52			11a07	11 22				11 52				12a07	12 22		
Sunningdale	d					10 25				10 55				11 25				11 55					12 25		
Longcross	d																								
Weybridge	d																								
Addlestone §	d			10 04								11 04								12 04					
Chertsey §	d			10 07								11 07								12 07					
Virginia Water	a			10 12		10 30				11 00		11 12		11 30				12 00		12 12			12 30		
	d			10 12		10 30				11 00		11 12		11 30				12 00		12 12			12 30		
Egham	d			10 16		10 34				11 04		11 16		11 34				12 04		12 16			12 34		
Windsor & Eton Riverside	d	10 01					10 34				11 01					11 34			12 01					12 34	
Datchet	d	10 04					10 37				11 04					11 37			12 04					12 37	
Sunnymeads	d	10 07									11 07								12 07						
Wraysbury	d	10 10									11 10								12 10						
Staines	d	10 16		10 21		10 39	10 45			11 09	11 16	11 21		11 39		11 45		12 09	12 16	12 21			12 39	12 45	
Ashford (Surrey)	d	10 19		10 24			10 48				11 19	11 24				11 48			12 19	12 24				12 48	
Feltham	d	10 24		10 29		10 46	10 53			11 16	11 24	11 29		11 46		11 53		12 16	12 24	12 29			12 46	12 53	
Whitton	d	10 28					10 57				11 28					11 57			12 28					12 57	
Kingston	d							10 49									11 49								12 49
Hampton Wick	d							10 51									11 51								12 51
Teddington	d							10 56									11 56								12 56
Fulwell	d																								
Strawberry Hill	d							10 59									11 59								12 59
Twickenham	a	10 31				10 51	11 00	11 02		11 21	11 31			11 51		12 00	12 02	12 21	12 31				12 51	13 00	13 02
	d	10 32				10 51	11 01	11 03		11 21	11 32			11 51		12 01	12 03	12 21	12 32				12 51	13 01	13 03
St Margarets	d	10 34						11 05			11 34						12 05		12 34						13 05
Richmond	⊖ d	10 37				10 56	11 05	11 09		11 26	11 37			11 56		12 05	12 09	12 26	12 37				12 56	13 05	13 09
North Sheen	d	10 39						11 11			11 39						12 11		12 39						13 11
Mortlake	d	10 42						11 13			11 42						12 13		12 42						13 13
Hounslow	d			10 35								11 35								12 35					
Isleworth	d			10 38								11 38								12 38					
Syon Lane	d			10 40								11 40								12 40					
Brentford	d			10 42								11 42								12 42					
Kew Bridge	d			10 45								11 45								12 45					
Chiswick	d			10 47								11 47								12 47					
Barnes Bridge	d			10 50								11 50								12 50					
Barnes	d	10 45		10 53				11 16			11 45	11 53					12 16		12 45	12 53					13 16
Putney	d	10 48		10 56		11 02	11 14	11 19		11 32	11 48	11 56		12 02		12 14	12 19	12 32	12 48	12 56			13 02	13 14	13 19
Wandsworth Town	d	10 51		10 59				11 22			11 51	11 59					12 22		12 51	12 59					13 22
Clapham Junction [10]	d	10 54		11 04		11 07	11 18	11 25		11 37	11 54	12 04		12 07		12 18	12 25	12 37	12 54	13 02			13 07	13 18	13 25
Queenstown Rd.(Battersea)	d	10 58		11 09				11 33			11 58	12 09					12 33		12 58	13 05					13 28
Vauxhall	⊖ d	11 02		11 13		11 16	11 26	11 37		11 45	12 02	12 13		12 16		12 26	12 37	12 45	13 02	13 08			13 12	13 24	13 32
London Waterloo [15]	⊖ a	11 10		11 19		11 23	11 34	11 41		11 53	12 10	12 19		12 23		12 34	12 41	12 53	13 10	13 13			13 23	13 34	13 41

For general notes see front of timetable
For details of catering facilities see Directory of Train Operators

§ Passengers to/from London may travel via Weybridge. See Table 155.

A From Woking (Table 155)
B From London Waterloo (Table 152)

Table 149

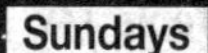
Sundays

Reading, Guildford, Ascot, Weybridge, Windsor, Kingston, Richmond and Hounslow → London

Network Diagram - see first page of Table 148

		SW 1	SW	SW	SW	SW 1	SW 1	SW	SW	SW 1	SW	SW	SW	SW 1	SW 1	SW	SW	SW 1		SW
					A				B				A				B			
Reading 7	d	12 24					12 54			13 24					13 54			14 24		
Earley	d	12 29					12 59			13 29					13 59			14 29		
Winnersh Triangle	d	12 31					13 01			13 31					14 01			14 31		
Winnersh	d	12 33					13 03			13 33					14 03			14 33		
Wokingham	d	12 38					13 08			13 38					14 08			14 38		
Bracknell	d	12 44					13 14			13 44					14 14			14 44		
Martins Heron	d	12 47					13 17			13 47					14 17			14 47		
Guildford	d					12 17								13 17						
Wanborough	d					12 23								13 23						
Ash 3	d					12 27								13 27						
Aldershot	a					12 34								13 34						
	d					12 40								13 40						
Ash Vale	d					12 45								13 45						
Frimley	d					12 51								13 51						
Camberley	a					12 55								13 55						
	d					12 55								13 55						
Bagshot	d					13 01								14 01						
Ascot 3	d	12 52				13a07	13 22			13 52				14a07	14 22			14 52		
Sunningdale	d	12 55					13 25			13 55					14 25			14 55		
Longcross	d																			
Weybridge	d																			
Addlestone §	d				13 04								14 04							
Chertsey §	d				13 07								14 07							
Virginia Water	a	13 00			13 12		13 30			14 00			14 12		14 30			15 00	and at the same minutes past each hour until	
	d	13 00			13 12		13 30			14 00			14 12		14 30			15 00		
Egham	d	13 04			13 16		13 34			14 04			14 16		14 34			15 04		
Windsor & Eton Riverside	d			13 01				13 34				14 01				14 34				
Datchet	d			13 04				13 37				14 04				14 37				
Sunnymeads	d			13 07								14 07								
Wraysbury	d			13 10								14 10								
Staines	d	13 09		13 16	13 21		13 39	13 45		14 09		14 16	14 21		14 39	14 45		15 09		
Ashford (Surrey)	d			13 19	13 24			13 48				14 19	14 24			14 48				
Feltham	d	13 16		13 24	13 29		13 46	13 53		14 16		14 24	14 29		14 46	14 53		15 16		
Whitton	d			13 28				13 57				14 28				14 57				
Kingston	d		13 11						13 49		14 11						14 49			21 11
Hampton Wick	d		13 13						13 51		14 13						14 51			21 13
Teddington	d		13 16						13 56		14 16						14 56			21 16
Fulwell	d																			
Strawberry Hill	d		13 19						13 59		14 19						14 59			21 19
Twickenham	a	13 21	13 22	13 31			13 51	14 00	14 02	14 21	14 22	14 31			14 51	15 00	15 02	15 21		21 22
	d	13 21	13 23	13 32			13 51	14 01	14 03	14 21	14 23	14 32			14 51	15 01	15 03	15 21		21 23
St Margarets	d		13 25	13 34					14 05		14 25	14 34					15 05			21 25
Richmond	⊖ d	13 26	13 29	13 37			13 56	14 05	14 09	14 26	14 29	14 37			14 56	15 05	15 09	15 26		21 29
North Sheen	d		13 31	13 39					14 11		14 31	14 39					15 11			21 31
Mortlake	d		13 33	13 42					14 13		14 33	14 42					15 13			21 33
Hounslow	d				13 35								14 35							
Isleworth	d				13 38								14 38							
Syon Lane	d				13 40								14 40							
Brentford	d				13 42								14 42							
Kew Bridge	d				13 45								14 45							
Chiswick	d				13 47								14 47							
Barnes Bridge	d				13 50								14 50							
Barnes	d		13 36	13 45	13 53				14 16		14 36	14 45	14 53				15 16			21 36
Putney	d	13 32	13 39	13 48	13 56		14 02	14 14	14 19	14 32	14 39	14 48	14 56		15 02	15 14	15 19	15 32		21 39
Wandsworth Town	d		13 42	13 51	13 59				14 22		14 42	14 51	14 59				15 22			21 42
Clapham Junction 10	d	13 37	13 45	13 54	14 02		14 07	14 18	14 25	14 37	14 45	14 54	15 02		15 07	15 18	15 25	15 37		21 45
Queenstown Rd.(Battersea)	d		13 48	13 57	14 05				14 28		14 48	14 57	15 05				15 28			21 48
Vauxhall	⊖ d	13 42	13 52	14 00	14 08		14 12	14 24	14 32	14 42	14 52	15 00	15 08		15 12	15 24	15 32	15 42		21 52
London Waterloo 15	⊖ a	13 53	13 59	14 10	14 13		14 23	14 29	14 36	14 48	14 59	15 05	15 13		15 18	15 29	15 36	15 48		21 59

For general notes see front of timetable
For details of catering facilities see Directory of Train Operators

A From Woking (Table 155)
B From London Waterloo (Table 152)

§ Passengers to/from London may travel via Weybridge. See Table 155.

Table 149

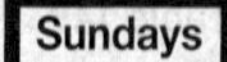

Reading, Guildford, Ascot, Weybridge, Windsor, Kingston, Richmond and Hounslow → London

Network Diagram - see first page of Table 148

		SW	SW	SW	SW	SW		SW	SW	SW	SW	SW		SW	SW	SW	SW	SW		SW	SW	SW	SW		
				1	1			1				1		1		1					1	1	1		
			A			B					A				B					A					
Reading 7	d				20 54			21 24						21 54		22 24							22 54		
Earley	d				20 59			21 29						21 59		22 29							22 59		
Winnersh Triangle	d				21 01			21 31						22 01		22 31							23 01		
Winnersh	d				21 03			21 33						22 03		22 33							23 03		
Wokingham	d				21 08			21 38						22 08		22 38							23 08		
Bracknell	d				21 14			21 44						22 14		22 44							23 14		
Martins Heron	d				21 17			21 47						22 17		22 47							23 17		
Guildford	d			20 17								21 17									22 17	23 17			
Wanborough	d			20 23								21 23									22 23	23 23			
Ash 3	d			20 27								21 27									22 27	23 27			
Aldershot	a			20 34								21 34									22 34	23 34			
	d			20 40								21 40									22 40				
Ash Vale	d			20 45								21 45									22 45				
Frimley	d			20 51								21 51									22 51				
Camberley	a			20 55								21 55									22 55				
	d			20 55								21 55									22 55				
Bagshot	d			21 01								22 01									23 01				
Ascot 3	d			21a07	21 22			21 52				22a07		22 22		22 52					23a07		23 22		
Sunningdale	d				21 25			21 55						22 25		22 55							23 25		
Longcross	d																								
Weybridge	d																								
Addlestone §	d		21 04								22 04									23 04					
Chertsey §	d		21 07								22 07									23 07					
Virginia Water	a		21 12		21 30			22 00			22 12			22 30		23 00				23 12			23 30		
	d		21 12		21 30			22 00			22 12			22 30		23 00				23 12			23 30		
Egham	d		21 16		21 34			22 04			22 16			22 34		23 04				23 16			23 34		
Windsor & Eton Riverside	d	21 01								22 01								23 01							
Datchet	d	21 04								22 04								23 04							
Sunnymeads	d	21 07								22 07								23 07							
Wraysbury	d	21 10								22 10								23 10							
Staines	d	21 16	21 21		21 39			22 09		22 16	22 21			22 39		23 09		23 16		23 21			23 39		
Ashford (Surrey)	d	21 19	21 24							22 19	22 24							23 19		23 24					
Feltham	d	21 24	21 29		21 46			22 16		22 24	22 29			22 46		23 16		23 24		23 29			23 46		
Whitton	d	21 28								22 28								23 28							
Kingston	d					21 49			22 11						22 49		23 11								
Hampton Wick	d					21 51			22 13						22 51		23 13								
Teddington	d					21 56			22 16						22 56		23 16								
Fulwell	d																								
Strawberry Hill	d					21 59			22 19						22 59		23 19								
Twickenham	a	21 31			21 51	22 02		22 21	22 22	22 31				22 51	23 02	23 21	23 22	23 31					23 51		
	d	21 32			21 51	22 03		22 21	22 23	22 32				22 51	23 03	23 21	23 23	23 32					23 51		
St Margarets	d	21 34				22 05			22 25	22 34					23 05		23 25	23 34							
Richmond	⊖ d	21 37			21 56	22 09		22 26	22 29	22 37				22 56	23 09	23 26	23 29	23 37					23 56		
North Sheen	d	21 39				22 11			22 31	22 39					23 11		23 31	23 39							
Mortlake	d	21 42				22 13			22 33	22 42					23 13		23 33	23 42							
Hounslow	d		21 35								22 35									23 35					
Isleworth	d		21 38								22 38									23 38					
Syon Lane	d		21 40								22 40									23 40					
Brentford	d		21 42								22 42									23 42					
Kew Bridge	d		21 45								22 45									23 45					
Chiswick	d		21 47								22 47									23 47					
Barnes Bridge	d		21 50								22 50									23 50					
Barnes	d	21 45	21 53			22 16			22 36	22 45	22 53				23 16		23 36	23 45		23 53					
Putney	d	21 48	21 56		22 02	22 19		22 32	22 39	22 48	22 56			23 02	23 19	23 32	23 39	23 48		23 56			00 02		
Wandsworth Town	d	21 51	21 59			22 22			22 42	22 51	22 59				23 22		23 42	23 51		23 59					
Clapham Junction 10	d	21 54	22 02		22 07	22 25		22 37	22 45	22 54	23 02			23 07	23 25	23 37	23 45	23 54		00 02			00 07		
Queenstown Rd.(Battersea)	d	21 57	22 05			22 28			22 48	22 57	23 05				23 28		23 48	23 57		00 05					
Vauxhall	⊖ d	22 00	22 08		22 12	22 32		22 42	22 52	23 00	23 08			23 12	23 32	23 42	23 52	00 01		00 08			00 12		
London Waterloo 15	⊖ a	22 05	22 13		22 18	22 36		22 48	22 59	23 05	23 13			23 18	23 36	23 48	23 59	00 05		00 13			00 17		

For general notes see front of timetable
For details of catering facilities see Directory of Train Operators

§ Passengers to/from London may travel via Weybridge. See Table 155.

A From Woking (Table 155)
B From London Waterloo (Table 152)

Network Diagram for Table 152

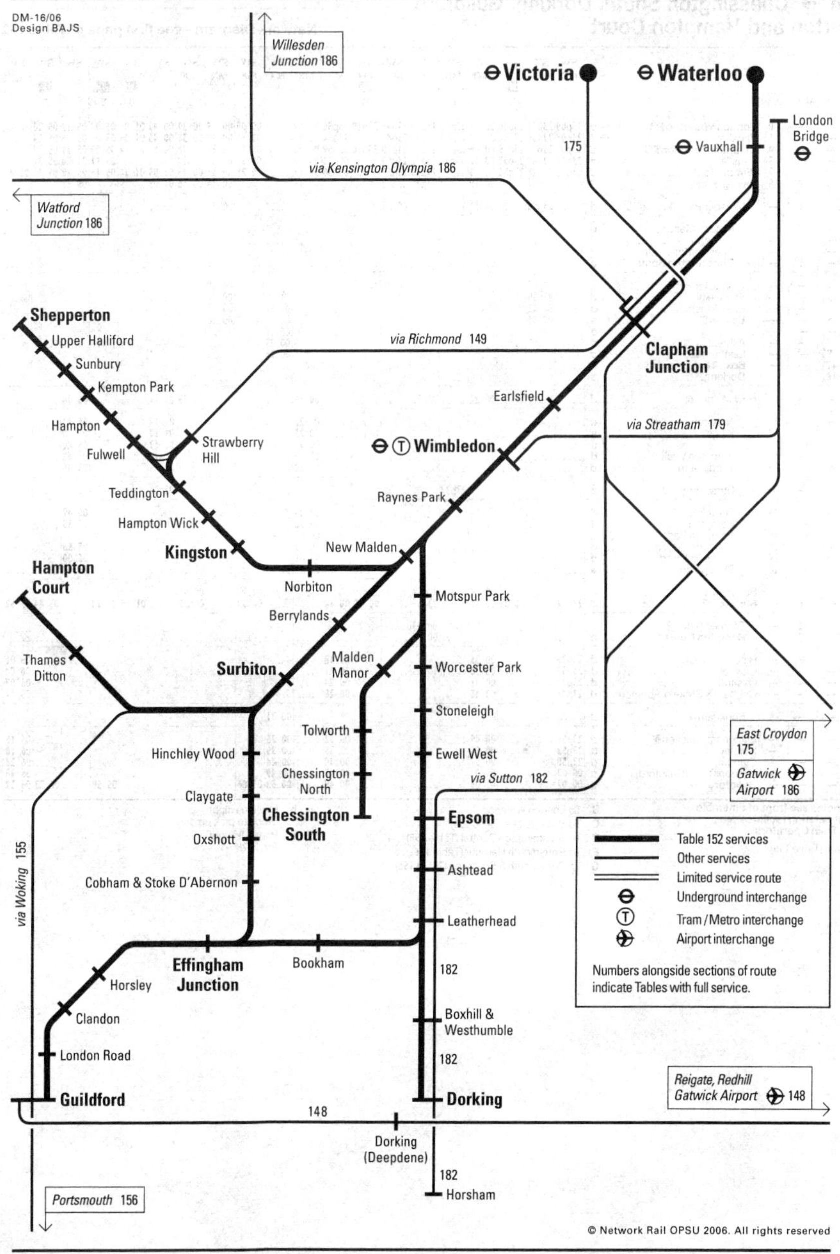
DM-16/06
Design BAJS
Willesden Junction 186
Victoria
Waterloo
London Bridge
175
Vauxhall
via Kensington Olympia 186
Watford Junction 186
Shepperton
Upper Halliford
Sunbury
Kempton Park
Hampton
Fulwell
Strawberry Hill
Teddington
Hampton Wick
Kingston
via Richmond 149
Clapham Junction
Earlsfield
via Streatham 179
Wimbledon
Raynes Park
New Malden
Norbiton
Hampton Court
Berrylands
Thames Ditton
Surbiton
Malden Manor
Motspur Park
Worcester Park
Stoneleigh
Tolworth
Hinchley Wood
Chessington North
Ewell West
via Sutton 182
Claygate
Chessington South
Epsom
Oxshott
Ashtead
Cobham & Stoke D'Abernon
via Woking 155
Leatherhead
Effingham Junction
Bookham
Horsley
182
Clandon
London Road
Boxhill & Westhumble
182
Guildford
Dorking
148
Dorking (Deepdene)
182
Horsham
Portsmouth 156
East Croydon 175
Gatwick Airport 186
Reigate, Redhill Gatwick Airport 148
Table 152 services
Other services
Limited service route
Underground interchange
Tram/Metro interchange
Airport interchange
Numbers alongside sections of route indicate Tables with full service.

For details of Bank Holiday service alterations, please see first page of Table 149

London → Chessington South, Dorking, Guildford Shepperton and Hampton Court

Network Diagram - see first page of Table 152

Miles	Miles	Miles	Miles	Miles			SW MO	SW MO	SW MO 1 A	SW MO	SW MX B	SW MX	SW MX	SW MX 1 C	SW MX	SW MX	SW MX	SW MX	SW MX	SW MX	SW	SW 1 D	SW 1 E	SW	SW 1 G	SW
0	—	—	—	0	**London Waterloo 15** ⊖	d	23p00	23p32	23p40	00 01	23p03	23p30	23p41	23p48	23p50	23p57		00 09	00 15	00 27	00 42	01 05	05 00	05 12	05 20	
1¼	—	—	—	1¼	Vauxhall ⊖	d	23p04	23p36	23p44	00 04	23p07	23p34	23p45		23p54	00 01		00 13	00 19	00 31	00 46	01 09	05 04	05 16	05 24	
4	—	—	—	4	**Clapham Junction 10**	d	23p09	23p41	23p49	00 09	23p13	23p39	23p50	23b56	23p59	00 06		00 18	00 24	00 36	00 51	01 14	05 09	05 21	05 29	
5½	—	—	—	5½	Earlsfield	d	23p12	23p44	23p52	00 12	00a08	23p42	23p53		00 02	00 09		00 21	00 27	00s39			05 12	05 24	05 32	
7¼	—	—	—	7¼	**Wimbledon 6** ⊖	d	23p16	23p48	23p56	00 16		23p46	23p57		00 06	00 13		00 25	00 31	00 43	01 05	01 20	05 16	05 28	05 36	05 49
8¾	—	0	0	8¾	Raynes Park 6	d		23p52		00 19		23p49	23p59			00 16			00 34	00 46	01 08			05 31		
—	—	1	1	—	Motspur Park	d		23p55					00 03						00 37							
—	—	—	2½	—	Malden Manor	d																				
—	—	—	3½	—	Tolworth	d																				
—	—	—	4½	—	Chessington North	d																				
—	—	—	5¼	—	**Chessington South**	a																				
—	—	2	—	—	Worcester Park	d		23p57					00 05						00 39							
—	—	3½	—	—	Stoneleigh	d		23p59					00 08				←		00 42							
—	—	4¼	—	—	Ewell West	d		00 03					00 11				00 11		00 45							
—	—	5½	—	—	**Epsom 3**	a		00 06					→				00 15		00 48							
—	—	—	—	—		d											00 19									
—	—	7½	—	—	Ashtead	d											00 23									
—	0	9¼	—	—	Leatherhead	d											00 26									
—	—	12½	—	—	Boxhill & Westhumble	d																				
—	—	13¼	—	—	**Dorking 4**	a																				
9¾	—	—	—	9¾	New Malden 6	d				00 22		23p52				00 19				00 49	01 11			05 34		
—	—	—	—	11¼	Norbiton	d										00 22					01 14			05 37		
—	—	—	—	12	Kingston	a										00 25					01 17			05 40		
—	—	—	—	—		d										00 25					01 17			05 40		
—	—	—	—	12½	Hampton Wick	d										00 27					01s22			05 42		
—	—	—	—	13¾	Teddington	d										00 30					01s25			05 45		
—	—	—	—	—	Strawberry Hill	a					23p37										01 28					
—	—	—	—	14¾	Fulwell	d										00 34								05 49		
—	—	—	—	16¼	Hampton	d										00 38								05 53		
—	—	—	—	18¼	Kempton Park	d										00 41										
—	—	—	—	18¾	Sunbury	d										00 43								05 58		
—	—	—	—	19¼	Upper Halliford	d										00 45								06 00		
—	—	—	—	20¾	**Shepperton**	a										00 48								06 03		
11	—	—	—	—	Berrylands	d				00 24		23p54								00s51						
12	—	—	0	—	**Surbiton 6**	d	23c32		00 05	00 31		23p59		00 10	00 14			00 33		00a55		01 28	05 24		05 44	05 57
—	—	—	2	—	Thames Ditton	d						00 03														
—	—	—	3	—	**Hampton Court**	a						00 06														
14	—	—	—	—	Hinchley Wood	d	23p36			00 35					00 18											06 01
15¼	—	—	—	—	Claygate	d	23p39			00 38					00 21											06 04
17	—	—	—	—	Oxshott	d	23p42			00 41					00 24											06 07
19	—	—	—	—	Cobham & Stoke d'Abernon	d	23p46			00 45					00 28											06 11
—	2½	—	—	—	Bookham	d											00 31									
21½	4¼	—	—	—	Effingham Junction 6	d	23p50			00 49					00 32		00 36									06 15
22¼	—	—	—	—	Horsley	d	23p53			00 52					00 35		00 39									06 18
25½	—	—	—	—	Clandon	d	23p58			00 57					00 40		00 44									06 23
28¾	—	—	—	—	London Road (Guildford)	d	00 03			01 02					00 45		00 49									06 28
30	—	—	—	—	**Guildford**	a	00 07			01 06					00 49		00 53	01 06					05 59		06 23	06 32

For general notes see front of timetable
For details of catering facilities see Directory of Train Operators

A To Farnham (Table 155)
B To London Waterloo
C To Basingstoke (Table 155)
D To Southampton Central (Table 158)
E To Portsmouth Harbour (Table 156)
G To Portsmouth & Southsea (Table 156)

b Previous night. Stops to pick up only
c Previous night. Arr. 2328

For details of Bank Holiday service alterations, please see first page of Table 149

London → Chessington South, Dorking, Guildford Shepperton and Hampton Court

Network Diagram - see first page of Table 152

	SW	SW	SW	SW	SW	SW	SW	SW	SW	SW	SW		SN	SW	SW	SW	SW	SW	SW	SW	SW	SW	SW	SW	SW
							1											1					1		
	A	B		C			D		B				E			B		G					H		
London Waterloo 15 ⊖ d	05 33		05 47	05 50		06 03	06 12	06 06		06 12	06 16			06 20	06 24	06 27	06 33	06 42	06 36	06 39	06 42	06 46	06 53	06 50	06 54
Vauxhall ⊖ d	05 37		05 51	05 54		06 07		06 10		06 16	06 20			06 24	06 28	06 31	06 37		06 40	06 43	06 46	06 50		06 54	06 58
Clapham Junction 10 d	05 43		05 56	05 59		06 12	06u19	06 15		06 21	06 25			06 29	06 33	06 36	06 42	06u49	06 45	06 48	06 51	06 55	07u00	06 59	07 03
Earlsfield d	06a35		05 59	06 02		06 15		06 18		06 24	06 28			06 32	06 36	06 39	06 45		06 48	06 51	06 54	06 58		07 02	07 06
Wimbledon 6 ⊖ d			06 03	06 06	06 15	06 19		06 22		06 28	06 32			06 36	06 40	06 43	06 49		06 52	06 55	06 58	07 02		07 06	07 10
Raynes Park 6 d			06 06		06 18			06 25		06 31	06 35				06 43	06 46			06 55		07 01	07 05			07 13
Motspur Park d			06 09		06 20						06 38				06 46							07 08			07 16
Malden Manor d					06 24						06 41											07 11			
Tolworth d					06 26						06 44											07 14			
Chessington North d					06 29						06 47											07 17			
Chessington South a					06 31						06 49											07 19			
Worcester Park d			06 11												06 48					07 01					07 18
Stoneleigh d			06 14												06 51										07 21
Ewell West d			06 17												06 54										07 24
Epsom 3 a			06 20												06 57					07 08					07 27
d			06 21										06 49		06 58					07 08					07 28
Ashtead d			06 25												07 02					07 12					07 32
Leatherhead d			06 28										06 56		07 05					07 15					07 35
Boxhill & Westhumble d																									
Dorking 4 a															07 11										07 41
New Malden 6 d								06 28		06 34						06 49			06 58		07 04				
Norbiton d										06 37						06 52					07 07				
Kingston a										06 40						06 55					07 10				
d		05 59							06 29	06 40						06 59					07 10				
Hampton Wick d		06 01							06 31	06 42						07 01					07 12				
Teddington d		06 05							06 35	06 45						07 05					07 15				
Strawberry Hill a	06 07	06 08							06 38							07 08									
Fulwell d										06 49											07 19				
Hampton d										06 53											07 23				
Kempton Park d																									
Sunbury d										06 58											07 28				
Upper Halliford d										07 00											07 30				
Shepperton a										07 03											07 33				
Berrylands d								06 30											07 00						
Surbiton 6 d				06 14		06 27	06 30	06 35						06 44			06 57	07 00	07 05				07 11	07 14	
Thames Ditton d								06 39											07 09						
Hampton Court a								06 42											07 12						
Hinchley Wood d						06 31											07 01								
Claygate d						06 34											07 04								
Oxshott d						06 37											07 07								
Cobham & Stoke d'Abernon d						06 41											07 11								
Bookham d			06 33										07 01							07 21					
Effingham Junction 6 d			06 37			06 45							07 05				07 15			07a24					
Horsley d						06 48											07 18								
Clandon d						06 53											07 23								
London Road (Guildford) d			06 46			06 58											07 28								
Guildford a			06 50			07 02							07 17	07 20			07 32							07 47	

For general notes see front of timetable
For details of catering facilities see Directory of Train Operators

- **A** To London Waterloo
- **B** To London Waterloo (Table 149)
- **C** To Woking (Table 155)
- **D** To Weymouth (Table 158)
- **E** From Sutton (Surrey) (Table 182)
- **G** To Portsmouth Harbour (Table 158)
- **H** To Alton (Table 155)

For details of Bank Holiday service alterations, please see first page of Table 149

London → Chessington South, Dorking, Guildford Shepperton and Hampton Court

Network Diagram - see first page of Table 152

		SW	SW	SW	SW	SN	SW	SW	SW	SW	SW	SW	SW	SW	SW	SW	SW	SW	SW		SW	SW	SW	SW	SW	SW
				1						1					1						1					1
		A		B		C				D	E		A		B						D			A		B
London Waterloo 15	⊖ d	06 57	07 03	07 12	07 06		07 09	07 12	07 16	07 23	07 20	07 24	07 27	07 33	07 42	07 36	07 39	07 42	07 46		07 53	07 50	07 54	07 57	08 03	08 12
Vauxhall	⊖ d	07 01	07 07		07 10		07 13	07 16	07 20		07 24	07 28	07 31	07 37		07 40	07 43	07 46	07 50			07 54	07 58	08 01	08 07	
Clapham Junction 10	d	07 06	07 12	07u20	07 15		07 18	07 21	07 25	07u30	07 29	07 33	07 36	07 42		07 45	07 48	07 51	07 55		08u00	07 59	08 03	08 06	08 12	08u19
Earlsfield	d	07 09	07 15		07 18		07 21	07 24	07 28		07 32	07 36	07 39	07 45		07 48	07 51	07 54	07 58			08 02	08 06	08 09	08 15	
Wimbledon 6	⊖ d	07 13	07 19		07 22		07 25	07 28	07 32		07 36	07 40	07 43	07 49		07 52	07 55	07 58	08 02			08 06	08 10	08 13	08 19	
Raynes Park 6	d	07 16			07 25		07 28	07 31	07 35			07 43	07 46			07 55	07 58	08 01	08 05				08 13	08 16		
Motspur Park	d						07 31		07 38			07 46					08 01		08 08				08 16			
Malden Manor	d								07 41										08 11							
Tolworth	d								07 44										08 14							
Chessington North	d								07 47										08 17							
Chessington South	a								07 49										08 19							
Worcester Park	d						07 33					07 48					08 03						08 18			
Stoneleigh	d						07 36					07 51					08 06						08 21			
Ewell West	d						07 39					07 54					08 09						08 24			
Epsom 3	a						07 42					07 58					08 15						08 27			
	d					07 38						07 58					08 15						08 28			
Ashtead	d					07 42						08 02					08 19						08 32			
Leatherhead	d					07 45						08 05					08 22						08 35			
Boxhill & Westhumble	d																									
Dorking 4	a											08 12											08 41			
New Malden 6	d	07 19			07 28			07 34					07 49			07 58		08 04						08 19		
Norbiton	d	07 22						07 37					07 52					08 07						08 22		
Kingston	a	07 25						07 40					07 55					08 10						08 25		
	d	07 29						07 40					07 59					08 10						08 29		
Hampton Wick	d	07 31						07 42					08 01					08 12						08 31		
Teddington	d	07 35						07 45					08 05					08 15						08 35		
Strawberry Hill	a	07 38											08 08											08 38		
Fulwell	d							07 49										08 19								
Hampton	d							07 53										08 23								
Kempton Park	d							07 56										08 26								
Sunbury	d							07 58										08 28								
Upper Halliford	d							08 00										08 30								
Shepperton	a							08 03										08 33								
Berrylands	d				07 30											08 00										
Surbiton 6	d		07 27	07 30	07 35					07 41	07 44			07 57	08 00	08 05					08 11	08 14			08 27	08 30
Thames Ditton	d				07 39											08 09										
Hampton Court	a				07 42											08 12										
Hinchley Wood	d		07 31											08 01											08 31	
Claygate	d		07 34											08 04											08 34	
Oxshott	d		07 37											08 07											08 37	
Cobham & Stoke d'Abernon	d		07 41											08 11											08 41	
Bookham	d					07 50											08 28									
Effingham Junction 6	d		07 45			07 54								08 15			08 32								08 45	
Horsley	d		07 48											08 18			08 34								08 48	
Clandon	d		07 53											08 23			08 39								08 53	
London Road (Guildford)	d		07 58			08 03								08 28			08 44								08 58	
Guildford	a		08 02			08 07								08 32			08 48					08 50			09 04	

For general notes see front of timetable
For details of catering facilities see Directory of Train Operators

A To London Waterloo (Table 149)
B To Basingstoke (Table 155)
C From London Bridge (Table 182)
D To Alton (Table 155)
E To Woking (Table 155)

For details of Bank Holiday service alterations, please see first page of Table 149

London → Chessington South, Dorking, Guildford Shepperton and Hampton Court

Network Diagram - see first page of Table 152

		SW	SW	SW	SW	SW 1 A	SW B	SW	SW C	SW	SW 1 D	SW	SW	SW	SW	SW 1 A	SW B	SW	SW C	SW	SW 1 D	SW	SW	SW	SW	SW 1 A
London Waterloo 15 ⊖	d	08 06	08 09	08 12	08 16	08 23	08 20	08 24	08 27	08 33	08 42	08 36	08 39	08 42	08 46	08 53	08 50	08 54	08 57	09 03	09 12	09 06	09 09	09 12	09 16	09 23
Vauxhall ⊖	d	08 10	08 13	08 16	08 20		08 24	08 28	08 31	08 37		08 40	08 43	08 46	08 50		08 54	08 58	09 01	09 07		09 10	09 13	09 16	09 20	
Clapham Junction 10	d	08 15	08 18	08 21	08 25		08 29	08 33	08 36	08 42		08 45	08 48	08 51	08 55	09u00	08 59	09 03	09 06	09 12	09u19	09 15	09 18	09 21	09 25	
Earlsfield	d	08 18	08 21	08 24	08 28		08 32	08 36	08 39	08 45		08 48	08 51	08 54	08 58		09 02	09 06	09 09	09 15		09 18	09 21	09 24	09 28	
Wimbledon 6 ⊖	d	08 22	08 25	08 28	08 32		08 36	08 40	08 43	08 49		08 52	08 55	08 58	09 02		09 06	09 10	09 13	09 19		09 22	09 25	09 28	09 32	
Raynes Park 6	d	08 25	08 28	08 31	08 35			08 43	08 46			08 55	08 58	09 01	09 05			09 13	09 16			09 25	09 28	09 31	09 35	
Motspur Park	d		08 31		08 38			08 46					09 01		09 08			09 16					09 31		09 38	
Malden Manor	d				08 41										09 11										09 41	
Tolworth	d				08 44										09 14										09 44	
Chessington North	d				08 47										09 17										09 47	
Chessington South	a				08 49										09 19										09 49	
Worcester Park	d		08 33					08 48					09 03					09 18					09 33			
Stoneleigh	d		08 36					08 51					09 06					09 21					09 36			
Ewell West	d		08 39					08 54					09 09					09 24					09 39			
Epsom 3	a		08 42					08 57					09 16					09 27					09 42			
	d		08 47					08 58					09 17					09 28					09 47			
Ashtead	d		08 51					09 02					09 21					09 32					09 51			
Leatherhead	d		08 54					09 05					09 24					09 35					09 54			
Boxhill & Westhumble	d																									
Dorking 4	a							09 11										09 41								
New Malden 6	d	08 28		08 34					08 49			08 58		09 04					09 19			09 28		09 34		
Norbiton	d			08 37					08 52					09 07					09 22					09 37		
Kingston	a			08 40					08 55					09 10					09 25					09 40		
	d			08 40					08 59					09 10					09 29					09 40		
Hampton Wick	d			08 42					09 01					09 12					09 31					09 42		
Teddington	d			08 45					09 05					09 15					09 35					09 45		
Strawberry Hill	a								09 08										09 38							
Fulwell	d			08 49										09 19										09 49		
Hampton	d			08 53										09 23										09 53		
Kempton Park	d			08 56										09 26										09 56		
Sunbury	d			08 58										09 28										09 58		
Upper Halliford	d			09 00										09 30										10 00		
Shepperton	a			09 03										09 33										10 03		
Berrylands	d	08 30										09 00										09 30				
Surbiton 6	d	08 35				08 41	08 44			08 57	09 00	09 05				09 11	09 14			09 27	09 30	09 35				09 41
Thames Ditton	d	08 39										09 09										09 39				
Hampton Court	a	08 42										09 12										09 42				
Hinchley Wood	d									09 01										09 31						
Claygate	d									09 04										09 34						
Oxshott	d									09 07										09 37						
Cobham & Stoke d'Abernon	d									09 11										09 41						
Bookham	d		08 59										09 29										09 59			
Effingham Junction 6	d		09 03							09 15			09 33							09 45			10 03			
Horsley	d		09 06							09 18			09 36							09 48			10 06			
Clandon	d		09 11							09 23			09 41							09 53			10 11			
London Road (Guildford)	d		09 16							09 28			09 46							09 58			10 16			
Guildford	a		09 20							09 32			09 50							10 02			10 20			

For general notes see front of timetable
For details of catering facilities see Directory of Train Operators

A To Alton (Table 155)
B To Woking (Table 155)
C To London Waterloo (Table 149)
D To Basingstoke (Table 155)

For details of Bank Holiday service alterations, please see first page of Table 149

London → Chessington South, Dorking, Guildford Shepperton and Hampton Court

Network Diagram - see first page of Table 152

Station		SW	SW		SW	SW	SW		SW	SW	SW	SW	SW	SW	SW	SW	SW	SW	SW	SW	SW	SW	SW	SW	SW	SW
							1						1					1					1			
		A			B		C						D	A		B		C					E	A		B
London Waterloo 15 ⊖	d	09 20	09 24		09 27	09 33	09 42		09 36	09 39	09 42	09 46	09 53	09 50	09 54	09 57	10 03	10 12	10 06	10 09	10 12	10 16	10 23	10 20	10 24	10 27
Vauxhall ⊖	d	09 24	09 28		09 31	09 37			09 40	09 43	09 46	09 50		09 54	09 58	10 01	10 07		10 10	10 13	10 16	10 20		10 24	10 28	10 31
Clapham Junction 10	d	09 29	09 33		09 36	09 42			09 45	09 48	09 51	09 55	10u00	09 59	10 03	10 06	10 12	10u19	10 15	10 18	10 21	10 25		10 29	10 33	10 36
Earlsfield	d	09 32	09 36		09 39	09 45			09 48	09 51	09 54	09 58		10 02	10 06	10 09	10 15		10 18	10 21	10 24	10 28		10 32	10 36	10 39
Wimbledon 6 ⊖	d	09 36	09 40		09 43	09 49			09 52	09 55	09 58	10 02		10 06	10 10	10 13	10 19		10 22	10 25	10 28	10 32		10 36	10 40	10 43
Raynes Park 6	d		09 43		09 46				09 55	09 58	10 01	10 05			10 13	10 16			10 25	10 28	10 31	10 35			10 43	10 46
Motspur Park	d		09 46							10 01		10 08			10 16					10 31		10 38			10 46	
Malden Manor	d											10 11										10 41				
Tolworth	d											10 14										10 44				
Chessington North	d											10 17										10 47				
Chessington South	a											10 19										10 49				
Worcester Park	d		09 48							10 03					10 18					10 33					10 48	
Stoneleigh	d		09 51							10 06					10 21					10 36					10 51	
Ewell West	d		09 54							10 09					10 24					10 39					10 54	
Epsom 3	a		09 57							10 16					10 27					10 46					10 57	
	d		09 58							10 17					10 28					10 47					10 58	
Ashtead	d		10 02							10 21					10 32					10 51					11 02	
Leatherhead	d		10 05							10 24					10 35					10 54					11 05	
Boxhill & Westhumble	d																									
Dorking 4	a		10 11												10 41										11 11	
New Malden 6	d				09 49				09 58		10 04					10 19			10 28		10 34					10 49
Norbiton	d				09 52						10 07					10 22					10 37					10 52
Kingston	a				09 55						10 10					10 25					10 40					10 55
	d				09 59						10 10					10 29					10 40					10 59
Hampton Wick	d				10 01						10 12					10 31					10 42					11 01
Teddington	d				10 05						10 15					10 35					10 45					11 05
Strawberry Hill	a				10 08											10 38										11 08
Fulwell	d										10 19										10 49					
Hampton	d										10 23										10 53					
Kempton Park	d										10 26										10 56					
Sunbury	d										10 28										10 58					
Upper Halliford	d										10 30										11 00					
Shepperton	a										10 33										11 03					
Berrylands	d								10 00										10 30							
Surbiton 6	d	09 44				09 57	10 00		10 05				10 11	10 14			10 27	10 30	10 35				10 41	10 44		
Thames Ditton	d								10 09										10 39							
Hampton Court	a								10 12										10 42							
Hinchley Wood	d					10 01											10 31									
Claygate	d					10 04											10 34									
Oxshott	d					10 07											10 37									
Cobham & Stoke d'Abernon	d					10 11											10 41									
Bookham	d									10 29										10 59						
Effingham Junction 6	d					10 15				10 33							10 45			11 03						
Horsley	d					10 18				10 36							10 48			11 06						
Clandon	d					10 23				10 41							10 53			11 11						
London Road (Guildford)	d					10 28				10 46							10 58			11 16						
Guildford	a					10 32				10 50							11 02			11 20						

For general notes see front of timetable
For details of catering facilities see Directory of Train Operators

A To Woking (Table 155)
B To London Waterloo (Table 149)
C To Basingstoke (Table 155)
D To Alton (Table 155)
E To Farnham (Table 155)

For details of Bank Holiday service alterations, please see first page of Table 149

London → Chessington South, Dorking, Guildford Shepperton and Hampton Court

Network Diagram - see first page of Table 152

		SW	SW 1 A		SW	SW	SW	SW	SW 1 B	SW C	SW	SW D	SW	SW 1 A	SW	SW	SW	SW	SW 1 B	SW C	SW	SW D	SW	SW 1 A
London Waterloo 15 ⊖	d	10 33	10 42	and at the same minutes past each hour until	15 36	15 39	15 42	15 46	15 53	15 50	15 54	15 57	16 03	16 12	16 06	16 09	16 12	16 16	16 25	16 20	16 24	16 27	16 33	16 42
Vauxhall ⊖	d	10 37			15 40	15 43	15 46	15 50		15 54	15 58	16 01	16 07		16 10	16 13	16 16	16 20		16 24	16 28	16 31	16 37	
Clapham Junction 10	d	10 42			15 45	15 48	15 51	15 55	16u00	15 59	16 03	16 06	16 12	16u19	16 15	16 18	16 21	16 25		16 29	16 33	16 36	16 42	
Earlsfield	d	10 45			15 48	15 51	15 54	15 58		16 02	16 06	16 09	16 15		16 18	16 21	16 24	16 28		16 32	16 36	16 39	16 45	
Wimbledon 6 ⊖	d	10 49			15 52	15 55	15 58	16 02		16 06	16 10	16 13	16 19		16 22	16 25	16 28	16 32		16 36	16 40	16 43	16 49	
Raynes Park 6	d				15 55	15 58	16 01	16 05			16 13	16 16			16 25	16 28	16 31	16 35			16 43	16 46		
Motspur Park	d					16 01		16 08			16 16					16 31		16 38			16 46			
Malden Manor	d							16 11										16 41						
Tolworth	d							16 14										16 44						
Chessington North	d							16 17										16 47						
Chessington South	a							16 19										16 51						
Worcester Park	d					16 03					16 18					16 33					16 48			
Stoneleigh	d					16 06					16 21					16 36					16 51			
Ewell West	d					16 09					16 24					16 39					16 54			
Epsom 3	a					16 16					16 27					16 46					16 57			
	d					16 17					16 28					16 47					17 01			
Ashtead	d					16 21					16 32					16 51					17 05			
Leatherhead	d					16 24					16 35					16 54					17 08			
Boxhill & Westhumble	d																				17 13			
Dorking 4	a										16 41										17 18			
New Malden 6	d				15 58		16 04					16 19			16 28		16 34					16 49		
Norbiton	d						16 07					16 22					16 37					16 52		
Kingston	a						16 10					16 25					16 40					16 55		
	d						16 10					16 29					16 40					16 59		
Hampton Wick	d						16 12					16 31					16 42					17 01		
Teddington	d						16 15					16 35					16 45					17 05		
Strawberry Hill	a											16 38										17 08		
Fulwell	d						16 19										16 49							
Hampton	d						16 23										16 53							
Kempton Park	d						16 26										16 56							
Sunbury	d						16 28										16 58							
Upper Halliford	d						16 30										17 00							
Shepperton	a						16 33										17 05							
Berrylands	d				16 00										16 30									
Surbiton 6	d	10 57	11 00		16 05				16 11	16 14			16 27	16 30	16 35				16 41	16 44			16 57	17 00
Thames Ditton	d				16 09										16 39									
Hampton Court	a				16 12										16 44									
Hinchley Wood	d	11 01											16 31										17 01	
Claygate	d	11 04											16 34										17 04	
Oxshott	d	11 07											16 37										17 07	
Cobham & Stoke d'Abernon	d	11 11											16 41										17 11	
Bookham	d					16 29										16 59								
Effingham Junction 6	d	11 15				16 33							16 45			17 03							17 15	
Horsley	d	11 18				16 36							16 48			17 06							17 18	
Clandon	d	11 23				16 41							16 53			17 11							17 23	
London Road (Guildford)	d	11 28				16 46							16 58			17 16							17 28	
Guildford	a	11 32				16 50							17 04			17 22							17 34	

For general notes see front of timetable
For details of catering facilities see Directory of Train Operators

A To Basingstoke (Table 155)
B To Alton (Table 155)
C To Woking (Table 155)
D To London Waterloo (Table 149)

For details of Bank Holiday service alterations, please see first page of Table 149

London → Chessington South, Dorking, Guildford Shepperton and Hampton Court

Network Diagram - see first page of Table 152

		SW	SN	SW	SW	SW	SW	SW	SW	SW 1	SW	SW	SN	SW	SW	SW	SW 1	SW	SW	SW		SW	SW 1	SW	SW	SN
			A				B		C				A				D	B		C						A
London Waterloo 15 ⊖	d	16 36		16 39	16 42	16 46	16 50	16 54	16 57	17 02	17 02	17 06		17 09	17 12	17 16	17 23	17 20	17 24	17 27		17 30	17 32	17 32	17 36	
Vauxhall ⊖	d	16 40		16 43	16 46	16 50	16 54	16 58	17 01		17 07	17 10		17 13	17 16	17 20		17 24	17 28	17 31		17 34		17 37	17 40	
Clapham Junction 10	d	16 45		16 48	16 51	16 55	16 59	17 03	17 06		17 12	17 15		17 18	17 22	17 25		17 29	17 33	17 36		17 39		17 42	17 45	
Earlsfield	d	16 48		16 51	16 54	16 58	17 02	17 06	17 09		17 15	17 18		17 21	17 25	17 28		17 32	17 36	17 39		17 42		17 45	17 48	
Wimbledon 6 ⊖	d	16 52		16 55	16 58	17 02	17 06	17 10	17 13		17 19	17 22		17 25	17 29	17 32		17 36	17 40	17 43		17 46		17 49	17 52	
Raynes Park 6	d	16 55		16 58	17 01	17 05		17 13	17 16			17 25		17 28	17 32	17 35			17 43	17 46		17 49			17 55	
Motspur Park	d			17 01		17 08		17 16						17 31		17 38						17 52				
Malden Manor	d					17 11										17 41										
Tolworth	d					17 14										17 44										
Chessington North	d					17 17										17 47										
Chessington South	a					17 21										17 51										
Worcester Park	d			17 03				17 18						17 33					17 47			17 54				
Stoneleigh	d			17 06				17 21						17 36								17 57				
Ewell West	d			17 09				17 24						17 39								18 00				
Epsom 3	a			17 12				17 27						17 42					17 54			18 06				
	d		17 07	17 17				17 31					17 38	17 47					17 54							18 13
Ashtead	d		17 11	17 21				17 35					17 42	17 51					17 58							18 17
Leatherhead	d		17 14	17 24				17 38					17 45	17 54					18 01							18 20
Boxhill & Westhumble	d							17 43											18 06							
Dorking 4	a							17 48											18 11							
New Malden 6	d	16 58			17 04				17 19			17 28			17 35					17 49					17 58	
Norbiton	d				17 07				17 22						17 38					17 52						
Kingston	a				17 10				17 25						17 41					17 55						
	d				17 10				17 29						17 41					17 59						
Hampton Wick	d				17 12				17 31						17 43					18 01						
Teddington	d				17 15				17 35						17 46					18 05						
Strawberry Hill	a								17 38											18 08						
Fulwell	d				17 19										17 50											
Hampton	d				17 23										17 54											
Kempton Park	d				17 26										17 57											
Sunbury	d				17 28										17 59											
Upper Halliford	d				17 30										18 01											
Shepperton	a				17 35										18 06											
Berrylands	d	17 00										17 30													18 00	
Surbiton 6	d	17 05					17 14			17 18	17 27	17 35					17 39	17 44					17 48	17 57	18 05	
Thames Ditton	d	17 09										17 39													18 09	
Hampton Court	a	17 14										17 44													18 14	
Hinchley Wood	d										17 31													18 05		
Claygate	d										17 34													18 07		
Oxshott	d										17 37													18 11		
Cobham & Stoke d'Abernon	d										17 41													18 14		
Bookham	d		17 19	17 29									17 50	17 59												18 25
Effingham Junction 6	d		17 23	17 33							17 45		17 54	18a05										18 19		18 29
Horsley	d			17 36							17 48		17 56											18 21		18 31
Clandon	d			17 41							17 53		18 01											18 26		18 36
London Road (Guildford)	d			17 46							17 58		18 06											18 31		18 41
Guildford	a		17 38	17 52						17 56	18 04		18 13										18 29	18 38		18 47

For general notes see front of timetable
For details of catering facilities see Directory of Train Operators

A From London Bridge (Table 182)
B To Woking (Table 155)
C To London Waterloo (Table 149)
D To Basingstoke (Table 155)

For details of Bank Holiday service alterations, please see first page of Table 149

London → Chessington South, Dorking, Guildford Shepperton and Hampton Court

Network Diagram - see first page of Table 152

	SW	SW	SW	SW	SW	SW	SW	SW	SW	SW	SW	SW	SW	SW	SW	SW	SW	SW	SW	SW	SW	SW	SW	SW	SW
					1					1							1					1			
		A			B	C		D		C				A			B	C		D		B			A
London Waterloo 15 ⊖ d	17 39	17 43	17 42	17 46	17 53	17 50	17 54	17 57	18 00	18 02	18 02	18 06	18 09	18 13	18 12	18 16	18 23	18 20	18 24	18 27	18 30	18 32	18 32	18 36	18 43
Vauxhall ⊖ d	17 43	17 47	17 46	17 50		17 54	17 58	18 01	18 04		18 07	18 10	18 13	18 17	18 16	18 20		18 24	18 28	18 31	18 34		18 37	18 40	18 47
Clapham Junction 10 d	17 48	17 53	17 52	17 55		17 59	18 03	18 06	18 09		18 12	18 15	18 18	18 23	18 22	18 25		18 29	18 33	18 36	18 39		18 42	18 45	18 53
Earlsfield d	17 51		17 55	17 58		18 02	18 06	18 09	18 12		18 15	18 18	18 21		18 25	18 28		18 32	18 36	18 39	18 42		18 45	18 48	
Wimbledon 6 ⊖ ⛴ d	17 55		17 59	18 02		18 06	18 10	18 13	18 16		18 19	18 22	18 25		18 29	18 32		18 36	18 40	18 43	18 46		18 49	18 52	
Raynes Park 6 d	17 58		18 02	18 05			18 13	18 16	18 19			18 25	18 28		18 32	18 35			18 43	18 46	18 49			18 55	
Motspur Park d	18 01			18 08					18 22				18 31			18 38					18 52				
Malden Manor d				18 11												18 41									
Tolworth d				18 14												18 44									
Chessington North d				18 17												18 47									
Chessington South a				18 21												18 51									
Worcester Park d	18 03						18 17		18 24				18 33						18 47		18 54				
Stoneleigh d	18 06								18 27				18 36								18 57				
Ewell West d	18 09								18 30				18 39								19 00				
Epsom 3 a	18 20						18 24		18 35				18 43						18 54		19 05				
d	18 20						18 24						18 47						18 54						
Ashtead d	18 24						18 28						18 51						18 58						
Leatherhead d	18 28						18 31						18 54						19 01						
Boxhill & Westhumble d							18 36												19 06						
Dorking 4 a							18 41												19 11						
New Malden 6 d			18 05					18 19				18 28			18 35					18 49				18 58	
Norbiton d			18 08					18 22							18 38					18 52					
Kingston a			18 11					18 25							18 41					18 55					
d			18 11					18 29							18 41					18 59					
Hampton Wick d			18 13					18 31							18 43					19 01					
Teddington d			18 16					18 35							18 46					19 05					
Strawberry Hill a		18 11						18 38						18 41						19 08					19 11
Fulwell d		18 13	18 20											18 43	18 50										19 13
Hampton d		18 17	18 24											18 47	18 54										19 17
Kempton Park d			18 27												18 57										
Sunbury d		18 21	18 29											18 51	18 59										19 21
Upper Halliford d		18 23	18 31											18 53	19 01										19 23
Shepperton a		18 28	18 40											18 58	19 10										19 28
Berrylands d												18 30												19 00	
Surbiton 6 d					18 09	18 14				18 18	18 27	18 35					18 40	18 44				18 48	18 57	19 05	
Thames Ditton d												18 39												19 09	
Hampton Court a												18 44												19 14	
Hinchley Wood d											18 35												19 01		
Claygate d											18 37												19 04		
Oxshott d											18 41												19 07		
Cobham & Stoke d'Abernon d											18 44												19 11		
Bookham d	18 33												18 59												
Effingham Junction 6 d	18a44										18 49		19 03										19 15		
Horsley d											18 51		19 06										19 18		
Clandon d											18 56		19 11										19 23		
London Road (Guildford) d											19 01		19 16										19 28		
Guildford a											19 07		19 22										19 34		

For general notes see front of timetable
For details of catering facilities see Directory of Train Operators

A Via Richmond (Table 149)
B To Basingstoke (Table 155)
C To Woking (Table 155)
D To London Waterloo (Table 149)

London → Chessington South, Dorking, Guildford Shepperton and Hampton Court

For details of Bank Holiday service alterations, please see first page of Table 149

Network Diagram - see first page of Table 152

		SW	SW	SW		SW	SW	SW	SW	SW	SW	SW	SW	SW	SW	SW	SW	SW	SW	SW	SW	SW	SW	SW	SW	SW
							A		B		1 A							A		B		1 C				
London Waterloo 15 ⊖	d	18 48	18 39	18 42		18 46	18 50	18 54	18 57	19 00	19 02	19 02	19 06	19 09	19 12	19 16	19 23	19 20	19 24	19 27	19 33	19 42	19 36	19 39	19 42	19 46
Vauxhall ⊖	d		18 43	18 46		18 50	18 54	18 58	19 01	19 04		19 07	19 10	19 13	19 16	19 20		19 24	19 28	19 31	19 37		19 40	19 43	19 46	19 50
Clapham Junction 10	d		18 48	18 52		18 55	18 59	19 03	19 06	19 09		19 12	19 15	19 18	19 22	19 25		19 29	19 33	19 36	19 42		19 45	19 48	19 51	19 55
Earlsfield	d		18 51	18 55		18 58	19 02	19 06	19 09	19 12		19 15	19 18	19 21	19 25	19 28		19 32	19 36	19 39	19 45		19 48	19 51	19 54	19 58
Wimbledon 6 ⊖ 🚋	d		18 55	18 59		19 02	19 06	19 10	19 13	19 16		19 19	19 22	19 25	19 29	19 32		19 36	19 40	19 43	19 49		19 52	19 55	19 58	20 02
Raynes Park 6	d		18 58	19 02		19 05		19 13	19 16	19 19			19 25	19 28	19 32	19 35				19 46			19 55	19 58	20 01	20 05
Motspur Park	d		19 01			19 08				19 22				19 31		19 38								20 01		20 08
Malden Manor	d					19 11										19 41										20 11
Tolworth	d					19 14										19 44										20 14
Chessington North	d					19 17										19 47										20 17
Chessington South	a					19 21										19 49										20 19
Worcester Park	d		19 03					19 17		19 24				19 33					19 46					20 03		
Stoneleigh	d		19 06							19 27				19 36										20 06		
Ewell West	d		19 09							19 30				19 39										20 09		
Epsom 3	a		19 13					19 29		19 33				19 43					19 53					20 12		
	d		19 17					19 30						19 47					19 54					20 17		
Ashtead	d		19 21					19 34						19 51					19 58					20 21		
Leatherhead	d		19 24					19 37						19 54					20 01					20 24		
Boxhill & Westhumble	d							19 42											20 06							
Dorking 4	a							19 46											20 08							
New Malden 6	d			19 05					19 19				19 28		19 35					19 49			19 58		20 04	
Norbiton	d			19 08					19 22						19 38					19 52					20 07	
Kingston	a			19 11					19 25						19 41					19 55					20 10	
	d			19 11					19 29						19 41					19 59					20 10	
Hampton Wick	d			19 13					19 31						19 43					20 01					20 12	
Teddington	d			19 16					19 35						19 46					20 05					20 15	
Strawberry Hill	a								19 38											20 08						
Fulwell	d			19 20											19 50										20 19	
Hampton	d			19 24											19 54										20 23	
Kempton Park	d			19 27											19 57										20 26	
Sunbury	d			19 29											19 59										20 28	
Upper Halliford	d			19 31											20 01										20 30	
Shepperton	a			19 37											20 04										20 33	
Berrylands	d												19 30										20 00			
Surbiton 6	d	19 06					19 14				19 18	19 27	19 35				19a39	19 44			19 57	20 00	20 05			
Thames Ditton	d												19 39										20 09			
Hampton Court	a												19 42										20 12			
Hinchley Wood	d	19 10										19 31									20 01					
Claygate	d	19 13										19 34									20 04					
Oxshott	d	19 16										19 37									20 07					
Cobham & Stoke d'Abernon	d	19 20										19 41									20 11					
Bookham	d		19 29											19 59										20 29		
Effingham Junction 6	d	19 24	19 33									19 45		20 03							20 15			20 33		
Horsley	d	19 27	19 36									19 48		20 06							20 18			20 36		
Clandon	d	19 32	19 41									19 53		20 11							20 23			20 41		
London Road (Guildford)	d	19 37	19 46									19 58		20 16							20 28			20 46		
Guildford	a	19 43	19 52									20 02		20 20							20 32			20 50		

For general notes see front of timetable
For details of catering facilities see
Directory of Train Operators

A To Woking (Table 155)
B To London Waterloo (Table 149)
C To Basingstoke (Table 155)

London → Chessington South, Dorking, Guildford Shepperton and Hampton Court

For details of Bank Holiday service alterations, please see first page of Table 149

Network Diagram - see first page of Table 152

		SW	SW	SW	SW	SW	SW	SW	SW	SW	SW	SW	SW	SW	SW	SW	SW	SW	SW	SW	SW	SW	SW	SW	SW
		1					1					1					1					1			
		A	B		C		D					A	B		C		D					A	B		C
London Waterloo 15 ⊖	d	19 53	19 50	19 54	19 57	20 03	20 12	20 06	20 09	20 12	20 16	20 23	20 20	20 24	20 27	20 33	20 42	20 36	20 39	20 42	20 46	20 53	20 50	20 54	20 57
Vauxhall ⊖	d		19 54	19 58	20 01	20 07		20 10	20 13	20 16	20 20		20 24	20 28	20 31	20 37		20 40	20 43	20 46	20 50		20 54	20 58	21 01
Clapham Junction 10	d	20u00	19 59	20 03	20 06	20 12	20u19	20 15	20 18	20 21	20 25		20 29	20 33	20 36	20 42		20 45	20 48	20 51	20 55	21u00	20 59	21 03	21 06
Earlsfield	d		20 02	20 06	20 09	20 15		20 18	20 21	20 24	20 28		20 32	20 36	20 39	20 45		20 48	20 51	20 54	20 58		21 02	21 06	21 09
Wimbledon 6 ⊖ 🚋	d		20 06	20 10	20 13	20 19		20 22	20 25	20 28	20 32		20 36	20 40	20 43	20 49		20 52	20 55	20 58	21 02		21 06	21 10	21 13
Raynes Park 6	d			20 13	20 16			20 25	20 28	20 31	20 35			20 43	20 46			20 55	20 58	21 01	21 05			21 13	21 16
Motspur Park	d			20 16					20 31		20 38			20 46					21 01		21 08			21 16	
Malden Manor	d										20 41										21 11				
Tolworth	d										20 44										21 14				
Chessington North	d										20 47										21 17				
Chessington South	a										20 49										21 19				
Worcester Park	d			20 18					20 33					20 48					21 03					21 18	
Stoneleigh	d			20 21					20 36					20 51					21 06					21 21	
Ewell West	d			20 24					20 39					20 54					21 09					21 24	
Epsom 3	a			20 27					20 42					20 57					21 12					21 27	
	d								20 47										21 17						
Ashtead	d								20 51										21 21						
Leatherhead	d								20 54										21 24						
Boxhill & Westhumble	d								20 59																
Dorking 4	a								21 01																
New Malden 6	d				20 19			20 28		20 34					20 49			20 58		21 04					21 19
Norbiton	d				20 22					20 37					20 52					21 07					21 22
Kingston	a				20 25					20 40					20 55					21 10					21 25
	d				20 29					20 40					20 59					21 10					21 29
Hampton Wick	d				20 31					20 42					21 01					21 12					21 31
Teddington	d				20 35					20 45					21 05					21 15					21 35
Strawberry Hill	a				20 38										21 08										21 38
Fulwell	d									20 49										21 19					
Hampton	d									20 53										21 23					
Kempton Park	d									20 56										21 26					
Sunbury	d									20 58										21 28					
Upper Halliford	d									21 00										21 30					
Shepperton	a									21 03										21 33					
Berrylands	d							20 30										21 00							
Surbiton 6	d	20 11	20 14			20 27	20 30	20 35				20 41	20 44			20 57	21 00	21 05				21 11	21 14		
Thames Ditton	d							20 39										21 09							
Hampton Court	a							20 42										21 12							
Hinchley Wood	d					20 31										21 01									
Claygate	d					20 34										21 04									
Oxshott	d					20 37										21 07									
Cobham & Stoke d'Abernon	d					20 41										21 11									
Bookham	d																		21 29						
Effingham Junction 6	d					20 45										21 15			21 33						
Horsley	d					20 48										21 18			21 36						
Clandon	d					20 53										21 23			21 41						
London Road (Guildford)	d					20 58										21 28			21 46						
Guildford	a					21 02										21 32			21 50						

For general notes see front of timetable
For details of catering facilities see Directory of Train Operators

A To Alton (Table 155)
B To Woking (Table 155)
C To London Waterloo (Table 149)
D To Basingstoke (Table 155)

For details of Bank Holiday service alterations, please see first page of Table 149

London → Chessington South, Dorking, Guildford Shepperton and Hampton Court

Network Diagram - see first page of Table 152

		SW	SW	SW 1 A	SW	SW 1 B	SW C	SW	SW D	SW	SW 1 E	SW	SW	SW	SW	SW 1 B	SW	SW	SW D	SW	SW	SW 1 A	SW	SW 1 B	SW C
London Waterloo 15 ⊖	d	21 03	21 09	21 12	21 12	21 23	21 20	21 24	21 27	21 33	21 42	21 36	21 39	21 42	21 46	21 53	21 50	21 54	21 57	22 03	22 09	22 12	22 12	22 23	22 20
Vauxhall ⊖	d	21 07	21 13		21 16		21 24	21 28	21 31	21 37		21 40	21 43	21 46	21 50		21 54	21 58	22 01	22 07	22 13		22 16		22 24
Clapham Junction 10	d	21 12	21 18	21u19	21 21		21 29	21 33	21 36	21 42		21 45	21 48	21 51	21 55	22u00	21 59	22 03	22 06	22 12	22 18	22u19	22 21	22u30	22 29
Earlsfield	d	21 15	21 21		21 24		21 32	21 36	21 39	21 45		21 48	21 51	21 54	21 58		22 02	22 06	22 09	22 15	22 21		22 24		22 32
Wimbledon 6 ⊖	d	21 19	21 25		21 28		21 36	21 40	21 43	21 49		21 52	21 55	21 58	22 02		22 06	22 10	22 13	22 19	22 25		22 28		22 36
Raynes Park 6	d		21 28		21 31			21 43	21 46			21 55	21 58	22 01	22 05			22 13	22 16		22 28		22 31		
Motspur Park	d		21 31					21 46					22 01		22 08			22 16			22 31				
Malden Manor	d														22 11										
Tolworth	d														22 14										
Chessington North	d														22 17										
Chessington South	a														22 19										
Worcester Park	d		21 33					21 48					22 03					22 18			22 33				
Stoneleigh	d		21 36					21 51					22 06					22 21			22 36				
Ewell West	d		21 39					21 54					22 09					22 24			22 39				
Epsom 3	a		21 42					21 57					22 12					22 27			22 42				
	d		21 47										22 17								22 47				
Ashtead	d		21 51										22 21								22 51				
Leatherhead	d		21 54										22 24								22 54				
Boxhill & Westhumble	d		21 59																		22 59				
Dorking 4	a		22 01																		23 01				
New Malden 6	d				21 34				21 49			21 58		22 04					22 19				22 34		
Norbiton	d				21 37				21 52					22 07					22 22				22 37		
Kingston	a				21 40				21 55					22 10					22 25				22 40		
	d				21 40				21 59					22 10					22 29				22 40		
Hampton Wick	d				21 42				22 01					22 12					22 31				22 42		
Teddington	d				21 45				22 05					22 15					22 35				22 45		
Strawberry Hill	a								22 08										22 38						
Fulwell	d				21 49									22 19									22 49		
Hampton	d				21 53									22 23									22 53		
Kempton Park	d				21 56									22 26									22 56		
Sunbury	d				21 58									22 28									22 58		
Upper Halliford	d				22 00									22 30									23 00		
Shepperton	a				22 03									22 33									23 03		
Berrylands	d											22 00													
Surbiton 6	d	21 27		21 30		21 41	21 44			21 57	22 00	22 05				22 11	22 14			22 27		22 30		22 41	22 44
Thames Ditton	d											22 09													
Hampton Court	a											22 12													
Hinchley Wood	d	21 31								22 01										22 31					
Claygate	d	21 34								22 04										22 34					
Oxshott	d	21 37								22 07										22 37					
Cobham & Stoke d'Abernon	d	21 41								22 11										22 41					
Bookham	d												22 29												
Effingham Junction 6	d	21 45								22 15			22 33							22 45					
Horsley	d	21 48								22 18			22 36							22 48					
Clandon	d	21 53								22 23			22 41							22 53					
London Road (Guildford)	d	21 58								22 28			22 46							22 58					
Guildford	a	22 02								22 32			22 50				22 47			23 06					

For general notes see front of timetable
For details of catering facilities see Directory of Train Operators

A To Basingstoke (Table 155)
B To Alton (Table 155)
C To Woking (Table 155)
D To London Waterloo (Table 149)
E To Portsmouth Harbour (Table 158)

London → Chessington South, Dorking, Guildford Shepperton and Hampton Court

For details of Bank Holiday service alterations, please see first page of Table 149

Network Diagram - see first page of Table 152

		SW A	SW	SW 1 B	SW	SW	SW	SW 1 C	SW D	SW A	SW	SW	SW	SW 1 B	SW	SW 1 C	SW D	SW E	SW	SW	SW 1 B	SW	SW	SW
London Waterloo 15 ⊖	d	22 27	22 33	22 42	22 36	22 39	22 42	22 53	22 50	22 57	23 00	23 03	23 09	23 12	23 12	23 23	23 20	23 27	23 30	23 41	23 48	23 50	23 57	
Vauxhall ⊖	d	22 31	22 37		22 40	22 43	22 46		22 54	23 01	23 04	23 07	23 13		23 16		23 24	23 31	23 34	23 45		23 54	00 01	
Clapham Junction 10	d	22 36	22 42	22u49	22 45	22 48	22 51	23u00	22 59	23 06	23 09	23 12	23 18	23u19	23 21	23u30	23 29	23 36	23 39	23 50	23u56	23 59	00 06	
Earlsfield	d	22 39	22 45		22 48	22 51	22 54		23 02	23 09	23 12	23 15	23 21		23 24		23 32	23 39	23 42	23 53		00 02	00 09	
Wimbledon 6 ⊖	d	22 43	22 49		22 52	22 55	22 58		23 06	23 13	23 16	23 19	23 25		23 28		23 36	23 43	23 46	23 57		00 06	00 13	
Raynes Park 6	d	22 46			22 55	22 58	23 01			23 16	23 19		23 28		23 31			23 46	23 49	23 59			00 16	
Motspur Park	d					23 01					23 22		23 31							00 03				
Malden Manor	d										23 25													
Tolworth	d										23 28													
Chessington North	d										23 31													
Chessington South	a										23 33													
Worcester Park	d					23 03							23 33							00 05				
Stoneleigh	d					23 06							23 36							00 08				←
Ewell West	d					23 09							23 39							00 11				00 11
Epsom 3	a					23 12							23 42							→				00 15
	d					23 17							23 47											00 19
Ashtead	d					23 21							23 51											00 23
Leatherhead	d					23 24							23 54											00 26
Boxhill & Westhumble	d												23 59											
Dorking 4	a												00 01											
New Malden 6	d	22 49			22 58		23 04			23 19					23 34			23 49	23 52				00 19	
Norbiton	d	22 52					23 07			23 22					23 37			23 52					00 22	
Kingston	a	22 55					23 10			23 25					23 40			23 55					00 25	
	d	22 59					23 10			23 29					23 40			23 55					00 25	
Hampton Wick	d	23 01					23 12			23 31					23 42			23 57					00 27	
Teddington	d	23 05					23 15			23 35					23 45			23 59					00 30	
Strawberry Hill	a	23 08								23 38								00 03						
Fulwell	d						23 19								23 49								00 34	
Hampton	d						23 23								23 53								00 38	
Kempton Park	d						23 26								23 56								00 41	
Sunbury	d						23 28								23 58								00 43	
Upper Halliford	d						23 30								23 59								00 45	
Shepperton	a						23 33								00 05								00 48	
Berrylands	d				23 00														23 54					
Surbiton 6	d		22 57	23 00	23 05			23 11	23 14			23 27		23 30		23 41	23 44		23 59		00 10	00 14		
Thames Ditton	d				23 09														00 03					
Hampton Court	a				23 12														00 06					
Hinchley Wood	d		23 01									23 31										00 18		
Claygate	d		23 04									23 34										00 21		
Oxshott	d		23 07									23 37										00 24		
Cobham & Stoke d'Abernon	d		23 11									23 41										00 28		
Bookham	d					23 29																		00 31
Effingham Junction 6	d		23 15			23 33						23 45										00 32		00 36
Horsley	d		23 18			23 36						23 48										00 35		00 39
Clandon	d		23 23			23 41						23 53										00 40		00 44
London Road (Guildford)	d		23 28			23 46						23 58										00 45		00 49
Guildford	a		23 32			23 54						00 02										00 49		00 53

For general notes see front of timetable
For details of catering facilities see Directory of Train Operators

A To London Waterloo (Table 149)
B To Basingstoke (Table 155)
C To Alton (Table 155)
D To Woking (Table 155)
E To Twickenham (Table 149)

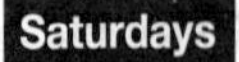

For details of Bank Holiday service alterations, please see first page of Table 149

London → Chessington South, Dorking, Guildford Shepperton and Hampton Court

Network Diagram - see first page of Table 152

		SW	SW	SW	SW	SW	SW	SW	SW	SW	SW	SW	SW		SW	SW	SW	SW	SW	SW	SW	SW	SW	SW	SW	SW
				1								1	1			1			1							
				A								B	C			D	E	G	A		E			G	E	
London Waterloo 15 ⊖	d	23p30	23p41	23p48	23p50	23p57		00 09	00 15	00 27	00 42	01 05	05 00		05 12	05 20		05 50	06 12	06 06		06 12	06 16	06 20	06 27	06 33
Vauxhall ⊖	d	23p34	23p45		23p54	00 01		00 13	00 19	00 31	00 46	01 09	05 04		05 16	05 24		05 54		06 10		06 16	06 20	06 24	06 31	06 37
Clapham Junction 10	d	23p39	23p50	23b56	23p59	00 06		00 18	00 24	00 36	00 51	01 14	05 09		05 21	05 29		05 59	06u19	06 15		06 21	06 25	06 29	06 36	06 42
Earlsfield	d	23p42	23p53		00 02	00 09		00 21	00 27	00s39			05 12		05 24	05 32		06 02		06 18		06 24	06 28	06 32	06 39	06 45
Wimbledon 6 ⊖	d	23p46	23p57		00 06	00 13		00 25	00 31	00 43	01 05	01 20	05 16		05 28	05 36		06 06		06 22		06 28	06 32	06 36	06 43	06 49
Raynes Park 6	d	23p49	23p59			00 16			00 34	00 46	01 08				05 31					06 25		06 31	06 35		06 46	
Motspur Park	d		00 03						00 37														06 38			
Malden Manor	d																						06 41			
Tolworth	d																						06 44			
Chessington North	d																						06 47			
Chessington South	a																						06 49			
Worcester Park	d		00 05						00 39																	
Stoneleigh	d		00 08				←		00 42																	
Ewell West	d		00 11				00 11		00 45																	
Epsom 3	a		→				00 15		00 48																	
	d						00 19																			
Ashtead	d						00 23																			
Leatherhead	d						00 26																			
Boxhill & Westhumble	d																									
Dorking 4	a																									
New Malden 6	d	23p52				00 19				00 49	01 11				05 34					06 28		06 34			06 49	
Norbiton	d					00 22					01 14				05 37							06 37			06 52	
Kingston	a					00 25					01 17				05 40							06 40			06 55	
	d					00 25					01 17				05 40		05 59				06 29	06 40			06 59	
Hampton Wick	d					00 27					01s22				05 42		06 01				06 31	06 42			07 01	
Teddington	d					00 30					01s25				05 45		06 05				06 35	06 45			07 05	
Strawberry Hill	a										01 28						06 08				06 38				07 08	
Fulwell	d					00 34									05 49							06 49				
Hampton	d					00 38									05 53							06 53				
Kempton Park	d					00 41									05 56							06 56				
Sunbury	d					00 43									05 58							06 58				
Upper Halliford	d					00 45									06 00							07 00				
Shepperton	a					00 48									06 03							07 03				
Berrylands	d	23p54								00s51										06 30						
Surbiton 6	d	23p59		00 10	00 14			00 33		00a55		01 28	05 24			05 44		06 14	06 30	06 35				06 44		06 57
Thames Ditton	d	00 03																		06 39						
Hampton Court	a	00 06																		06 42						
Hinchley Wood	d				00 18																					07 01
Claygate	d				00 21																					07 04
Oxshott	d				00 24																					07 07
Cobham & Stoke d'Abernon	d				00 28																					07 11
Bookham	d						00 31																			
Effingham Junction 6	d				00 32		00 36																			07 15
Horsley	d				00 35		00 39																			07 18
Clandon	d				00 40		00 44																			07 23
London Road (Guildford)	d				00 45		00 49																			07 28
Guildford	a				00 49		00 53	01 06					05 59			06 23										07 32

For general notes see front of timetable
For details of catering facilities see Directory of Train Operators

A To Basingstoke (Table 155)
B To Southampton Central (Table 158)
C To Haslemere (Table 156)
D To Portsmouth Harbour (Table 156)
E To London Waterloo (Table 149)
G To Woking (Table 155)
b Previous night.
Stops to pick up only

Table 152

Saturdays

For details of Bank Holiday service alterations, please see first page of Table 149

London → Chessington South, Dorking, Guildford Shepperton and Hampton Court

Network Diagram - see first page of Table 152

		SW [1] A	SW	SW	SW	SW	SW [1] B	SW C	SW D	SW	SW [1] E	SW	SW	SW	SW	SW [1] B	SW C	SW	SW D	SW	SW [1] E	SW	SW	SW
London Waterloo [15] ⊖	d	06 42	06 36	06 39	06 42	06 46	06 53	06 50	06 57	07 03	07 12	07 06	07 09	07 12	07 16	07 23	07 20	07 24	07 27	07 33	07 42	07 36	07 39	07 42
Vauxhall ⊖	d		06 40	06 43	06 46	06 50		06 54	07 01	07 07		07 10	07 13	07 16	07 20		07 24	07 28	07 31	07 37		07 40	07 43	07 46
Clapham Junction [10]	d	06u49	06 45	06 48	06 51	06 55	07u00	06 59	07 06	07 12	07u19	07 15	07 18	07 21	07 25	07u30	07 29	07 33	07 36	07 42		07 45	07 48	07 51
Earlsfield	d		06 48	06 51	06 54	06 58		07 02	07 09	07 15		07 18	07 21	07 24	07 28		07 32	07 36	07 39	07 45		07 48	07 51	07 54
Wimbledon [6] ⊖	d		06 52	06 55	06 58	07 02		07 06	07 13	07 19		07 22	07 25	07 28	07 32		07 36	07 40	07 43	07 49		07 52	07 55	07 58
Raynes Park [6]	d		06 55	06 58	07 01	07 05			07 16			07 25	07 28	07 31	07 35			07 43	07 46			07 55	07 58	08 01
Motspur Park	d			07 01		07 08							07 31		07 38			07 46					08 01	
Malden Manor	d					07 11									07 41									
Tolworth	d					07 14									07 44									
Chessington North	d					07 17									07 47									
Chessington South	a					07 19									07 49									
Worcester Park	d			07 03									07 33					07 48					08 03	
Stoneleigh	d			07 06									07 36					07 51					08 06	
Ewell West	d			07 09									07 39					07 54					08 09	
Epsom [3]	a			07 16									07 46					07 57					08 16	
	d			07 17									07 47					07 58					08 17	
Ashtead	d			07 21									07 51					08 02					08 21	
Leatherhead	d			07 24									07 54					08 05					08 24	
Boxhill & Westhumble	d																							
Dorking [4]	a																	08 11						
New Malden [6]	d		06 58		07 04				07 19			07 28		07 34					07 49			07 58		08 04
Norbiton	d				07 07				07 22					07 37					07 52					08 07
Kingston	a				07 10				07 25					07 40					07 55					08 10
	d				07 10				07 29					07 40					07 59					08 10
Hampton Wick	d				07 12				07 31					07 42					08 01					08 12
Teddington	d				07 15				07 35					07 45					08 05					08 15
Strawberry Hill	a								07 38										08 08					
Fulwell	d				07 19									07 49										08 19
Hampton	d				07 23									07 53										08 23
Kempton Park	d				07 26									07 56										08 26
Sunbury	d				07 28									07 58										08 28
Upper Halliford	d				07 30									08 00										08 30
Shepperton	a				07 33									08 03										08 33
Berrylands	d		07 00									07 30										08 00		
Surbiton [6]	d	07 00	07 05				07 11	07 14		07 27	07 30	07 35				07 41	07 44			07 57	08 00	08 05		
Thames Ditton	d		07 09									07 39										08 09		
Hampton Court	a		07 12									07 42										08 12		
Hinchley Wood	d									07 31										08 01				
Claygate	d									07 34										08 04				
Oxshott	d									07 37										08 07				
Cobham & Stoke d'Abernon	d									07 41										08 11				
Bookham	d			07 29									07 59										08 29	
Effingham Junction [6]	d			07 33						07 45			08 03							08 15			08 33	
Horsley	d			07 36						07 48			08 06							08 18			08 36	
Clandon	d			07 41						07 53			08 11							08 23			08 41	
London Road (Guildford)	d			07 46						07 58			08 16							08 28			08 46	
Guildford	a			07 50						08 02			08 20							08 32			08 50	

For general notes see front of timetable
For details of catering facilities see Directory of Train Operators

- **A** To Portsmouth Harbour (Table 158)
- **B** To Alton (Table 155)
- **C** To Woking (Table 155)
- **D** To London Waterloo (Table 149)
- **E** To Basingstoke (Table 155)

For details of Bank Holiday service alterations, please see first page of Table 149

London → Chessington South, Dorking, Guildford Shepperton and Hampton Court

Network Diagram - see first page of Table 152

		SW	SW 1	SW	SW	SW			SW	SW 1	SW	SW	SW	SW	SW 1	SW	SW	SW	SW	SW 1	SW	SW	SW	SW	SW 1	SW
			A	B		C				D					A	B		C		D					A	B
London Waterloo 15 ⊖	d	07 46	07 53	07 50	07 54	07 57			08 03	08 12	08 06	08 09	08 12	08 16	08 23	08 20	08 24	08 27	08 33	08 42	08 36	08 39	08 42	08 46	08 53	08 50
Vauxhall ⊖	d	07 50		07 54	07 58	08 01			08 07		08 10	08 13	08 16	08 20		08 24	08 28	08 31	08 37		08 40	08 43	08 46	08 50		08 54
Clapham Junction 10	d	07 55	08u00	07 59	08 03	08 06			08 12	08u19	08 15	08 18	08 21	08 25		08 29	08 33	08 36	08 42		08 45	08 48	08 51	08 55	09u00	08 59
Earlsfield	d	07 58		08 02	08 06	08 09			08 15		08 18	08 21	08 24	08 28		08 32	08 36	08 39	08 45		08 48	08 51	08 54	08 58		09 02
Wimbledon 6 ⊖	d	08 02		08 06	08 10	08 13			08 19		08 22	08 25	08 28	08 32		08 36	08 40	08 43	08 49		08 52	08 55	08 58	09 02		09 06
Raynes Park 6	d	08 05			08 13	08 16					08 25	08 28	08 31	08 35			08 43	08 46			08 55	08 58	09 01	09 05		
Motspur Park	d	08 08			08 16							08 31		08 38			08 46					09 01		09 08		
Malden Manor	d	08 11												08 41										09 11		
Tolworth	d	08 14												08 44										09 14		
Chessington North	d	08 17												08 47										09 17		
Chessington South	a	08 19												08 49										09 19		
Worcester Park	d				08 18							08 33					08 48					09 03				
Stoneleigh	d				08 21							08 36					08 51					09 06				
Ewell West	d				08 24							08 39					08 54					09 09				
Epsom 3	a				08 27							08 46					08 57					09 16				
	d				08 28							08 47					08 58					09 17				
Ashtead	d				08 32							08 51					09 02					09 21				
Leatherhead	d				08 35							08 54					09 05					09 24				
Boxhill & Westhumble	d																									
Dorking 4	a				08 41												09 11									
New Malden 6	d					08 19					08 28		08 34					08 49			08 58		09 04			
Norbiton	d					08 22							08 37					08 52					09 07			
Kingston	a					08 25							08 40					08 55					09 10			
	d					08 29							08 40					08 59					09 10			
Hampton Wick	d					08 31							08 42					09 01					09 12			
Teddington	d					08 35							08 45					09 05					09 15			
Strawberry Hill	a					08 38												09 08								
Fulwell	d												08 49										09 19			
Hampton	d												08 53										09 23			
Kempton Park	d												08 56										09 26			
Sunbury	d												08 58										09 28			
Upper Halliford	d												09 00										09 30			
Shepperton	a												09 03										09 33			
Berrylands	d										08 30										09 00					
Surbiton 6	d		08 11	08 14					08 27	08 30	08 35				08 41	08 44			08 57	09 00	09 05				09 11	09 14
Thames Ditton	d										08 39										09 09					
Hampton Court	a										08 42										09 12					
Hinchley Wood	d								08 31										09 01							
Claygate	d								08 34										09 04							
Oxshott	d								08 37										09 07							
Cobham & Stoke d'Abernon	d								08 41										09 11							
Bookham	d											08 59										09 29				
Effingham Junction 6	d								08 45			09 03							09 15			09 33				
Horsley	d								08 48			09 06							09 18			09 36				
Clandon	d								08 53			09 11							09 23			09 41				
London Road (Guildford)	d								08 58			09 16							09 28			09 46				
Guildford	a								09 02			09 20							09 32			09 50				

For general notes see front of timetable
For details of catering facilities see Directory of Train Operators

A To Alton (Table 155)
B To Woking (Table 155)
C To London Waterloo (Table 149)
D To Basingstoke (Table 155)

Table 152

Saturdays

For details of Bank Holiday service alterations, please see first page of Table 149

London → Chessington South, Dorking, Guildford Shepperton and Hampton Court

Network Diagram - see first page of Table 152

		SW	SW		SW	SW ■1	SW	SW	SW	SW	SW ■1	SW	SW	SW	SW	SW ■1	SW	SW	SW	SW	SW ■1	SW	SW
			A	and at the same minutes past each hour until		B					C	D		A		B					C	D	
London Waterloo ■15 ⊖	d	08 54	08 57		19 03	19 12	19 06	19 09	19 12	19 16	19 23	19 20	19 24	19 27	19 33	19 42	19 36	19 39	19 42	19 46	19 53	19 50	19 54
Vauxhall ⊖	d	08 58	09 01		19 07		19 10	19 13	19 16	19 20		19 24	19 28	19 31	19 37		19 40	19 43	19 46	19 50		19 54	19 58
Clapham Junction ■10	d	09 03	09 06		19 12	19u19	19 15	19 18	19 21	19 25		19 29	19 33	19 36	19 42		19 45	19 48	19 51	19 55	20u00	19 59	20 03
Earlsfield	d	09 06	09 09		19 15		19 18	19 21	19 24	19 28		19 32	19 36	19 39	19 45		19 48	19 51	19 54	19 58		20 02	20 06
Wimbledon ■6 ⊖ 🚋	d	09 10	09 13		19 19		19 22	19 25	19 28	19 32		19 36	19 40	19 43	19 49		19 52	19 55	19 58	20 02		20 06	20 10
Raynes Park ■6	d	09 13	09 16				19 25	19 28	19 31	19 35			19 43	19 46			19 55	19 58	20 01	20 05			20 13
Motspur Park	d	09 16						19 31		19 38			19 46					20 01		20 08			20 16
Malden Manor	d									19 41										20 11			
Tolworth	d									19 44										20 14			
Chessington North	d									19 47										20 17			
Chessington South	a									19 49										20 19			
Worcester Park	d	09 18						19 33					19 48					20 03					20 18
Stoneleigh	d	09 21						19 36					19 51					20 06					20 21
Ewell West	d	09 24						19 39					19 54					20 09					20 24
Epsom ■3	a	09 27						19 42					19 57					20 12					20 27
	d	09 28						19 47					19 58					20 17					
Ashtead	d	09 32						19 51					20 02					20 21					
Leatherhead	d	09 35						19 54					20 05					20 24					
Boxhill & Westhumble	d																						
Dorking ■4	a	09 41											20 11										
New Malden ■6	d		09 19				19 28		19 34					19 49			19 58		20 04				
Norbiton	d		09 22						19 37					19 52					20 07				
Kingston	a		09 25						19 40					19 55					20 10				
	d		09 29						19 40					19 59					20 10				
Hampton Wick	d		09 31						19 42					20 01					20 12				
Teddington	d		09 35						19 45					20 05					20 15				
Strawberry Hill	a		09 38											20 08									
Fulwell	d								19 49										20 19				
Hampton	d								19 53										20 23				
Kempton Park	d								19 56										20 26				
Sunbury	d								19 58										20 28				
Upper Halliford	d								20 00										20 30				
Shepperton	a								20 03										20 33				
Berrylands	d						19 30										20 00						
Surbiton ■6	d				19 27	19 30	19 35				19 41	19 44			19 57	20 00	20 05				20 11	20 14	
Thames Ditton	d						19 39										20 09						
Hampton Court	a						19 42										20 12						
Hinchley Wood	d				19 31										20 01								
Claygate	d				19 34										20 04								
Oxshott	d				19 37										20 07								
Cobham & Stoke d'Abernon	d				19 41										20 11								
Bookham	d							19 59										20 29					
Effingham Junction ■6	d				19 45			20 03							20 15			20 33					
Horsley	d				19 48			20 06							20 18			20 36					
Clandon	d				19 53			20 11							20 23			20 41					
London Road (Guildford)	d				19 58			20 16							20 28			20 46					
Guildford	a				20 02			20 20							20 32			20 50					

For general notes see front of timetable
For details of catering facilities see Directory of Train Operators

A To London Waterloo (Table 149)
B To Basingstoke (Table 155)
C To Alton (Table 155)
D To Woking (Table 155)

Saturdays

For details of Bank Holiday service alterations, please see first page of Table 149

London → Chessington South, Dorking, Guildford Shepperton and Hampton Court

Network Diagram - see first page of Table 152

		SW	SW	SW	SW	SW	SW	SW		SW	SW	SW	SW	SW	SW	SW	SW	SW	SW	SW	SW		SW	SW	SW	SW
				1						1					1					1						
		A		B						C	D		A		E					C	D			A		
London Waterloo 15 ⊖	d	19 57	20 03	20 12	20 06	20 09	20 12	20 16		20 23	20 20	20 24	20 27	20 33	20 42	20 36	20 39	20 42	20 46	20 53	20 50		20 54	20 57	21 03	21 09
Vauxhall ⊖	d	20 01	20 07		20 10	20 13	20 16	20 20			20 24	20 28	20 31	20 37		20 40	20 43	20 46	20 50		20 54		20 58	21 01	21 07	21 13
Clapham Junction 10	d	20 06	20 12	20u19	20 15	20 18	20 21	20 25			20 29	20 33	20 36	20 42		20 45	20 48	20 51	20 55	21u00	20 59		21 03	21 06	21 12	21 18
Earlsfield	d	20 09	20 15		20 18	20 21	20 24	20 28			20 32	20 36	20 39	20 45		20 48	20 51	20 54	20 58		21 02		21 06	21 09	21 15	21 21
Wimbledon 6 ⊖	d	20 13	20 19		20 22	20 25	20 28	20 32			20 36	20 40	20 43	20 49		20 52	20 55	20 58	21 02		21 06		21 10	21 13	21 19	21 25
Raynes Park 6	d	20 16			20 25	20 28	20 31	20 35				20 43	20 46			20 55	20 58	21 01	21 05				21 13	21 16		21 28
Motspur Park	d					20 31		20 38				20 46					21 01		21 08				21 16			21 31
Malden Manor	d							20 41											21 11							
Tolworth	d							20 44											21 14							
Chessington North	d							20 47											21 17							
Chessington South	a							20 49											21 19							
Worcester Park	d					20 33						20 48					21 03						21 18			21 33
Stoneleigh	d					20 36						20 51					21 06						21 21			21 36
Ewell West	d					20 39						20 54					21 09						21 24			21 39
Epsom 3	a					20 42						20 57					21 12						21 27			21 42
	d					20 47											21 17									21 47
Ashtead	d					20 51											21 21									21 51
Leatherhead	d					20 54											21 24									21 54
Boxhill & Westhumble	d																									
Dorking 4	a					21 00																				22 00
New Malden 6	d	20 19			20 28		20 34						20 49			20 58		21 04						21 19		
Norbiton	d	20 22					20 37						20 52					21 07						21 22		
Kingston	a	20 25					20 40						20 55					21 10						21 25		
	d	20 29					20 40						20 59					21 10						21 29		
Hampton Wick	d	20 31					20 42						21 01					21 12						21 31		
Teddington	d	20 35					20 45						21 05					21 15						21 35		
Strawberry Hill	a	20 38											21 08											21 38		
Fulwell	d						20 49											21 19								
Hampton	d						20 53											21 23								
Kempton Park	d						20 56											21 26								
Sunbury	d						20 58											21 28								
Upper Halliford	d						21 00											21 30								
Shepperton	a						21 03											21 33								
Berrylands	d				20 30											21 00										
Surbiton 6	d		20 27	20 30	20 35					20 41	20 44			20 57	21 00	21 05				21 11	21 14				21 27	
Thames Ditton	d				20 39											21 09										
Hampton Court	a				20 42											21 12										
Hinchley Wood	d		20 31											21 01											21 31	
Claygate	d		20 34											21 04											21 34	
Oxshott	d		20 37											21 07											21 37	
Cobham & Stoke d'Abernon	d		20 41											21 11											21 41	
Bookham	d																21 29									
Effingham Junction 6	d		20 45											21 15			21 33								21 45	
Horsley	d		20 48											21 18			21 36								21 48	
Clandon	d		20 53											21 23			21 41								21 53	
London Road (Guildford)	d		20 58											21 28			21 46								21 58	
Guildford	a		21 02											21 32			21 50								22 02	

For general notes see front of timetable
For details of catering facilities see Directory of Train Operators

A To London Waterloo (Table 149)
B To Basingstoke (Table 155)
C To Alton (Table 155)
D To Woking (Table 155)
E To Portsmouth Harbour (Table 158)

Table 152

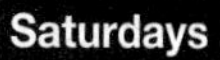

For details of Bank Holiday service alterations, please see first page of Table 149

London → Chessington South, Dorking, Guildford Shepperton and Hampton Court

Network Diagram - see first page of Table 152

		SW	SW	SW	SW	SW	SW	SW	SW	SW	SW	SW	SW	SW	SW	SW	SW	SW	SW	SW	SW	SW	SW	SW
		1		1					1					1						1		1		
		A		B	C		D		E					B			D			A		B	C	D
London Waterloo 15	⊖ d	21 12	21 12	21 23	21 20	21 24	21 27	21 33	21 42	21 36	21 39	21 42	21 46	21 53	21 50	21 54	21 57	22 03	22 09	22 12	22 12	22 23	22 20	22 27
Vauxhall	⊖ d		21 16		21 24	21 28	21 31	21 37		21 40	21 43	21 46	21 50		21 54	21 58	22 01	22 07	22 13		22 16		22 24	22 31
Clapham Junction 10	d	21u19	21 21		21 29	21 33	21 36	21 42		21 45	21 48	21 51	21 55	22u00	21 59	22 03	22 06	22 12	22 18	22u19	22 21	22u30	22 29	22 36
Earlsfield	d		21 24		21 32	21 36	21 39	21 45		21 48	21 51	21 54	21 58		22 02	22 06	22 09	22 15	22 21		22 24		22 32	22 39
Wimbledon 6	⊖ d		21 28		21 36	21 40	21 43	21 49		21 52	21 55	21 58	22 02		22 06	22 10	22 13	22 19	22 25		22 28		22 36	22 43
Raynes Park 6	d		21 31			21 43	21 46			21 55	21 58	22 01	22 05			22 13	22 16		22 28		22 31			22 46
Motspur Park	d					21 46					22 01		22 08			22 16			22 31					
Malden Manor	d												22 11											
Tolworth	d												22 14											
Chessington North	d												22 17											
Chessington South	a												22 19											
Worcester Park	d					21 48					22 03					22 18			22 33					
Stoneleigh	d					21 51					22 06					22 21			22 36					
Ewell West	d					21 54					22 09					22 24			22 39					
Epsom 3	a					21 57					22 12					22 27			22 42					
	d										22 17								22 47					
Ashtead	d										22 21								22 51					
Leatherhead	d										22 24								22 54					
Boxhill & Westhumble	d																							
Dorking 4	a																		23 00					
New Malden 6	d		21 34				21 49			21 58		22 04					22 19				22 34			22 49
Norbiton	d		21 37				21 52					22 07					22 22				22 37			22 52
Kingston	a		21 40				21 55					22 10					22 25				22 40			22 55
	d		21 40				21 59					22 10					22 29				22 40			22 59
Hampton Wick	d		21 42				22 01					22 12					22 31				22 42			23 01
Teddington	d		21 45				22 05					22 15					22 35				22 45			23 05
Strawberry Hill	a						22 08										22 38							23 08
Fulwell	d		21 49									22 19									22 49			
Hampton	d		21 53									22 23									22 53			
Kempton Park	d		21 56									22 26									22 56			
Sunbury	d		21 58									22 28									22 58			
Upper Halliford	d		22 00									22 30									23 00			
Shepperton	a		22 03									22 33									23 03			
Berrylands	d									22 00														
Surbiton 6	d	21 30		21 41	21 44			21 57	22 00	22 05				22 11	22 14			22 27		22 30		22 41	22 44	
Thames Ditton	d									22 09														
Hampton Court	a									22 12														
Hinchley Wood	d							22 01										22 31						
Claygate	d							22 04										22 34						
Oxshott	d							22 07										22 37						
Cobham & Stoke d'Abernon	d							22 11										22 41						
Bookham	d										22 29													
Effingham Junction 6	d							22 15			22 33							22 45						
Horsley	d							22 18			22 36							22 48						
Clandon	d							22 23			22 41							22 53						
London Road (Guildford)	d							22 28			22 46							22 58						
Guildford	a							22 32			22 50				22 47			23 02						

For general notes see front of timetable
For details of catering facilities see Directory of Train Operators

A To Basingstoke (Table 155)
B To Alton (Table 155)
C To Woking (Table 155)
D To London Waterloo (Table 149)
E To Portsmouth Harbour (Table 158)

Table 152

Saturdays

For details of Bank Holiday service alterations, please see first page of Table 149

London → Chessington South, Dorking, Guildford Shepperton and Hampton Court

Network Diagram - see first page of Table 152

		SW	SW 1 A	SW	SW	SW	SW 1 B	SW C	SW D	SW	SW	SW	SW 1 A		SW	SW 1 B	SW C	SW E	SW	SW	SW 1 A	SW	SW	SW		
London Waterloo 15 ⊖	d	22 33	22 42	22 36	22 39	22 42	22 53	22 50	22 57	23 00	23 03	23 09	23 12		23 12	23 23	23 20	23 27	23 30	23 41	23 48	23 50	23 57			
Vauxhall ⊖	d	22 37		22 40	22 43	22 46		22 54	23 01	23 04	23 07	23 13			23 16		23 24	23 31	23 34	23 45		23 54	00 01			
Clapham Junction 10	d	22 42	22u49	22 45	22 48	22 51	23u00	22 59	23 06	23 09	23 12	23 18	23u19		23 21	23u30	23 29	23 36	23 39	23 50	23u56	23 59	00 06			
Earlsfield	d	22 45		22 48	22 51	22 54		23 02	23 09	23 12	23 15	23 21			23 24		23 32	23 39	23 42	23 53		00 02	00 09			
Wimbledon 6 ⊖	d	22 49		22 52	22 55	22 58		23 06	23 13	23 16	23 19	23 25			23 28		23 36	23 43	23 46	23 57		00 06	00 13			
Raynes Park 6	d			22 55	22 58	23 01			23 16	23 19		23 28			23 31			23 46	23 49	00 01			00 16			
Motspur Park	d				23 01					23 22		23 31								00 02						
Malden Manor	d									23 25																
Tolworth	d									23 28																
Chessington North	d									23 31																
Chessington South	a									23 33																
Worcester Park	d				23 03							23 33								00 05						
Stoneleigh	d				23 06							23 36								00 08				←		
Ewell West	d				23 09							23 39								00 10 →				00 10		
Epsom 3	a				23 12							23 42												00 15		
	d				23 17							23 47												00 19		
Ashtead	d				23 21							23 51												00 23		
Leatherhead	d				23 24							23 54												00 26		
Boxhill & Westhumble	d																									
Dorking 4	a											00 01														
New Malden 6	d			22 58		23 04			23 19						23 34			23 49	23 52				00 19			
Norbiton	d					23 07			23 22						23 37			23 52					00 22			
Kingston	a					23 10			23 25						23 40			23 55					00 25			
	d					23 10			23 29						23 40			23 55					00 25			
Hampton Wick	d					23 12			23 31						23 42			23 57					00 27			
Teddington	d					23 15			23 35						23 45			23 59					00 30			
Strawberry Hill	a								23 38									00 04								
Fulwell	d					23 19									23 49								00 34			
Hampton	d					23 23									23 53								00 38			
Kempton Park	d					23 26									23 56								00 41			
Sunbury	d					23 28									23 58								00 43			
Upper Halliford	d					23 30									23 59								00 45			
Shepperton	a					23 33									00 03								00 48			
Berrylands	d			23 00															23 54							
Surbiton 6	d	22 57	23 00	23 05			23 11	23 14			23 27		23 30			23 41	23 44		23 59		00 10	00 14				
Thames Ditton	d			23 09															00 03							
Hampton Court	a			23 12															00 06							
Hinchley Wood	d	23 01									23 31											00 18				
Claygate	d	23 04									23 34											00 21				
Oxshott	d	23 07									23 37											00 24				
Cobham & Stoke d'Abernon	d	23 11									23 41											00 28				
Bookham	d				23 29																			00 31		
Effingham Junction 6	d	23 15			23 33						23 45											00 32		00 36		
Horsley	d	23 18			23 36						23 48											00 35		00 39		
Clandon	d	23 23			23 41						23 53											00 40		00 44		
London Road (Guildford)	d	23 28			23 46						23 58											00 45		00 49		
Guildford	a	23 32			23 54						00 02											00 49		00 53		

For general notes see front of timetable
For details of catering facilities see Directory of Train Operators

A To Basingstoke (Table 155)
B To Alton (Table 155)
C To Woking (Table 155)
D To London Waterloo (Table 149)
E To Twickenham (Table 149)

Sundays

London → Chessington South, Dorking, Guildford Shepperton and Hampton Court

For details of Bank Holiday service alterations, please see first page of Table 149

Network Diagram - see first page of Table 152

Station		SW	SW	SW	SW	SW	SW	SW	SW	SW	SW	SW	SW	SW	SW	SW	SW	SW		SW	SW	SW	SW	SW	SW	SW
				1								1														
				A								B	C	D							D					
London Waterloo 15	⊖ d	23p30	23p41	23p48	23p50	23p57		00 09	00 15	00 27	00 42	01 05	01 42	06 18		06 57				07 10	07 18		07 27		07 40	07 48
Vauxhall	⊖ d	23p34	23p45		23p54	00 01		00 13	00 19	00 31	00 46	01 09	01 46	06 22		07 01				07 14	07 22		07 31		07 44	07 52
Clapham Junction 10	d	23p39	23p50	23b56	23p59	00 06		00 18	00 24	00 36	00 51	01 14	01 51	06 27		07 06				07 19	07 27		07 36		07 49	07 57
Earlsfield	d	23p42	23p53		00 02	00 09		00 21	00 27	00s39						07 09				07 22	07 30		07 39		07 52	08 00
Wimbledon 6	⊖ d	23p46	23p57		00 06	00 13		00 25	00 31	00 43	01 05	01 20	02c04	06 34	06 48	07 13	07 16	07 18		07 26	07 34	07 37	07 43	07 48	07 56	08 04
Raynes Park 6	d	23p49	00 01			00 16			00 34	00 46	01 08		02 07	06 37	06 52	07 16		07 22			07 37	07 40	07 46	07 52		08 07
Motspur Park	d		00 02						00 37						06 55			07 25				07 43		07 55		
Malden Manor	d																					07 46				
Tolworth	d																					07 49				
Chessington North	d																					07 52				
Chessington South	a																					07 54				
Worcester Park	d		00 05						00 39						06 57			07 27						07 57		
Stoneleigh	d		00 08				←		00 42						07 00			07 30						08 00		
Ewell West	d		00 10				00 10		00 45						07 03			07 33						08 03		
Epsom 3	a		→				00 15		00 48						07 06			07 36						08 06		
	d						00 19																	08 08		
Ashtead	d						00 23																	08 12		
Leatherhead	d						00 26																	08 15		
Boxhill & Westhumble	d																									
Dorking 4	a																									
New Malden 6	d	23p52				00 19				00 49	01 11		02 09	06 40		07 19					07 40		07 49			08 10
Norbiton	d					00 22					01 14		02 13	06 43							07 43					08 13
Kingston	a					00 25					01 17		02 15	06 46							07 46					08 16
	d					00 25					01 17		02 16	06 49							07 49					08 16
Hampton Wick	d					00 27					01s22		02s21	06 51							07 51					08 18
Teddington	d					00 30					01s25		02s23	06 56							07 56					08 21
Strawberry Hill	a										01 28		02s26	06 59							07 59					
Fulwell	d					00 34																				08 25
Hampton	d					00 38																				08 29
Kempton Park	d					00 41																				08 32
Sunbury	d					00 43																				08 34
Upper Halliford	d					00 45																				08 36
Shepperton	a					00 48																				08 39
Berrylands	d	23p54								00s51						07 21							07 51			
Surbiton 6	d	23p59		00 10	00 14			00 33		00a55		01 28				07 25	07e32			07 35			07 55		08 05	
Thames Ditton	d	00 03														07 30							08 00			
Hampton Court	a	00 06														07 33							08 03			
Hinchley Wood	d				00 18												07 36									
Claygate	d				00 21												07 39									
Oxshott	d				00 24												07 42									
Cobham & Stoke d'Abernon	d				00 28												07 46									
Bookham	d						00 31																	08 20		
Effingham Junction 6	d				00 32		00 36										07 50							08 24		
Horsley	d				00 35		00 39										07 53							08 27		
Clandon	d				00 40		00 44										07 58							08 32		
London Road (Guildford)	d				00 45		00 49										08 03							08 37		
Guildford	a				00 49		00 53	01 06									08 07			08 13				08 41	08 40	

For general notes see front of timetable
For details of catering facilities see Directory of Train Operators

A To Basingstoke (Table 155)
B To Southampton Central (Table 158)
C To Twickenham (Table 149)
D To London Waterloo (Table 149)

b Previous night. Stops to pick up only
c Arr. 0156
e Arr. 0728

Table 152

Sundays

For details of Bank Holiday service alterations, please see first page of Table 149

London → Chessington South, Dorking, Guildford Shepperton and Hampton Court

Network Diagram - see first page of Table 152

		SW	SW		SW	SW	SW 1 A	SW	SW	SW B	SW	SW	SW	SW	SW	SW	SW			SW	SW	SW 1 A	SW	SW	SW B
London Waterloo 15 ⊖	d		07 57			08 02	08 07		08 10	08 18	08 21	08 27	08 32	08 40	08 48	08 51	08 57				12 02	12 07		12 10	12 18
Vauxhall ⊖	d		08 01			08 06			08 14	08 22	08 25	08 31	08 36	08 44	08 52	08 55	09 01				12 06			12 14	12 22
Clapham Junction 10	d		08 06			08 11	08 15		08 19	08 27	08 30	08 36	08 41	08 49	08 57	09 00	09 06				12 11	12 15		12 19	12 27
Earlsfield	d		08 09			08 14			08 22	08 30	08 33	08 39	08 44	08 52	09 00	09 03	09 09				12 14			12 22	12 30
Wimbledon 6 ⊖	d	08 07	08 13		08 16	08 18	08 22		08 26	08 34	08 37	08 43	08 48	08 56	09 04	09 07	09 13			12 16	12 18	12 22		12 26	12 34
Raynes Park 6	d	08 10	08 16			08 22				08 37	08 40	08 46	08 52		09 07	09 10	09 16				12 22				12 37
Motspur Park	d	08 13				08 25					08 43		08 55			09 13					12 25				
Malden Manor	d	08 16									08 46					09 16									
Tolworth	d	08 19									08 49					09 19									
Chessington North	d	08 22									08 52					09 22									
Chessington South	a	08 24									08 54					09 24									
Worcester Park	d					08 27							08 57								12 27				
Stoneleigh	d					08 30							09 00								12 30				
Ewell West	d					08 33							09 03								12 33				
Epsom 3	a					08 36							09 06								12 36				
	d					08 38							09 08								12 38				
Ashtead	d					08 42							09 12								12 42				
Leatherhead	d					08 45							09 15								12 45				
Boxhill & Westhumble	d																	and at							
Dorking 4	a					08 51															12 51				
New Malden 6	d		08 19							08 40		08 49			09 10		09 19	the same							12 40
Norbiton	d									08 43					09 13			minutes							12 43
Kingston	a									08 46					09 16			past							12 46
	d									08 49					09 16										12 49
Hampton Wick	d									08 51					09 18			each							12 51
Teddington	d									08 56					09 21										12 56
Strawberry Hill	a									08 59								hour until							12 59
Fulwell	d														09 25										
Hampton	d														09 29										
Kempton Park	d														09 32										
Sunbury	d														09 34										
Upper Halliford	d														09 36										
Shepperton	a														09 39										
Berrylands	d		08 21					←				08 51					09 21						←		
Surbiton 6	d		08 25		08b32		08 30	08 32	08 35			08 55		09 05			09 25			12c32		12 30	12 32	12 35	
Thames Ditton	d		08 30		→							09 00					09 30			→					
Hampton Court	a		08 33									09 03					09 33								
Hinchley Wood	d							08 36															12 36		
Claygate	d							08 39															12 39		
Oxshott	d							08 42															12 42		
Cobham & Stoke d'Abernon	d							08 46															12 46		
Bookham	d												09 20												
Effingham Junction 6	d							08 50					09 24										12 50		
Horsley	d							08 53					09 27										12 53		
Clandon	d							08 58					09 32										12 58		
London Road (Guildford)	d							09 03					09 37										13 03		
Guildford	a							09 07	09 10				09 41	09 40									13 07	13 13	

For general notes see front of timetable
For details of catering facilities see Directory of Train Operators

A To Alton (Table 155) and to Basingstoke (Table 155)
B To London Waterloo (Table 149)
b Arr. 0828
c Arr. 1228

For details of Bank Holiday service alterations, please see first page of Table 149

London → Chessington South, Dorking, Guildford Shepperton and Hampton Court

Network Diagram - see first page of Table 152

Station		SW	SW	SW	SW	SW	SW	SW	SW	SW	SW	SW	SW	SW		SW	SW	SW	SW	SW	SW	SW	SW	SW	SW	SW
												1														
						A						B				A					A					
London Waterloo 15	⊖ d	12 21	12 27	12 32	12 40		12 48	12 51	12 57	13 00	13 02	13 07		13 10		13 18	13 21	13 27	13 32	13 40		13 48	13 51	13 57	14 00	14 02
Vauxhall	⊖ d	12 25	12 31	12 36	12 44		12 52	12 55	13 01	13 04	13 06			13 14		13 22	13 25	13 31	13 36	13 44		13 52	13 55	14 01	14 04	14 06
Clapham Junction 10	d	12 30	12 36	12 41	12 49		12 57	13 00	13 06	13 09	13 11	13 15		13 19		13 27	13 30	13 36	13 41	13 49		13 57	14 00	14 06	14 09	14 11
Earlsfield	d	12 33	12 39	12 44	12 52		13 00	13 03	13 09	13 12	13 14			13 22		13 30	13 33	13 39	13 44	13 52		14 00	14 03	14 09	14 12	14 14
Wimbledon 6	⊖ d	12 37	12 43	12 48	12 56		13 04	13 07	13 13	13 16	13 18	13 22		13 26		13 34	13 37	13 43	13 48	13 56		14 04	14 07	14 13	14 16	14 18
Raynes Park 6	d	12 40	12 46	12 52			13 07	13 10	13 16		13 22					13 37	13 40	13 46	13 52			14 07	14 10	14 16		14 22
Motspur Park	d	12 43		12 55				13 13			13 25						13 43		13 55				14 13			14 25
Malden Manor	d	12 46						13 16									13 46						14 16			
Tolworth	d	12 49						13 19									13 49						14 19			
Chessington North	d	12 52						13 22									13 52						14 22			
Chessington South	a	12 54						13 24									13 54						14 24			
Worcester Park	d			12 57							13 27								13 57							14 27
Stoneleigh	d			13 00							13 30								14 00							14 30
Ewell West	d			13 03							13 33								14 03							14 33
Epsom 3	a			13 06							13 36								14 06							14 36
	d			13 08							13 38								14 08							14 38
Ashtead	d			13 12							13 42								14 12							14 42
Leatherhead	d			13 15							13 45								14 15							14 45
Boxhill & Westhumble	d																									
Dorking 4	a										13 51															14 51
New Malden 6	d		12 49				13 10		13 19							13 40		13 49				14 10		14 19		
Norbiton	d						13 13									13 43						14 13				
Kingston	a						13 16									13 46						14 16				
	d					13 11	13 16									13 49					14 11	14 16				
Hampton Wick	d					13 13	13 18									13 51					14 13	14 18				
Teddington	d					13 16	13 21									13 56					14 16	14 21				
Strawberry Hill	a					13 19										13 59					14 19					
Fulwell	d						13 25															14 25				
Hampton	d						13 29															14 29				
Kempton Park	d						13 32															14 32				
Sunbury	d						13 34															14 34				
Upper Halliford	d						13 36															14 36				
Shepperton	a						13 39															14 39				
Berrylands	d		12 51						13 21				←					13 51						14 21		
Surbiton 6	d		12 55		13 05				13 25	13b32		13 30	13 32	13 35				13 55		14 05				14 25	14c32	
Thames Ditton	d		13 00						13 30	→								14 00						14 30	→	
Hampton Court	a		13 03						13 33									14 03						14 33		
Hinchley Wood	d												13 36													
Claygate	d												13 39													
Oxshott	d												13 42													
Cobham & Stoke d'Abernon	d												13 46													
Bookham	d			13 20															14 20							
Effingham Junction 6	d			13 24									13 50						14 24							
Horsley	d			13 27									13 53						14 27							
Clandon	d			13 32									13 58						14 32							
London Road (Guildford)	d			13 37									14 03						14 37							
Guildford	a			13 41	13 43								14 07	14 13					14 41	14 43						

For general notes see front of timetable
For details of catering facilities see Directory of Train Operators

A To London Waterloo (Table 149)
B To Alton (Table 155) and to Basingstoke (Table 155)
b Arr. 1328
c Arr. 1428

Table 152

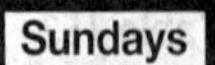

For details of Bank Holiday service alterations, please see first page of Table 149

London → Chessington South, Dorking, Guildford Shepperton and Hampton Court

Network Diagram - see first page of Table 152

Station		SW	SW	SW	SW	SW	SW	SW	SW	SW	SW	SW	SW
		1 A			B					B			
London Waterloo 15 ⊖	d	14 07		14 10	14 18	14 21	14 27	14 32	14 40		14 48	14 51	14 57
Vauxhall ⊖	d			14 14	14 22	14 25	14 31	14 36	14 44		14 52	14 55	15 01
Clapham Junction 10	d	14 15		14 19	14 27	14 30	14 36	14 41	14 49		14 57	15 00	15 06
Earlsfield	d			14 22	14 30	14 33	14 39	14 44	14 52		15 00	15 03	15 09
Wimbledon 6 ⊖	d	14 22		14 26	14 34	14 37	14 43	14 48	14 56		15 04	15 07	15 13
Raynes Park 6	d				14 37	14 40	14 46	14 52			15 07	15 10	15 16
Motspur Park	d					14 43		14 55				15 13	
Malden Manor	d					14 46						15 16	
Tolworth	d					14 49						15 19	
Chessington North	d					14 52						15 22	
Chessington South	a					14 54						15 24	
Worcester Park	d							14 57					
Stoneleigh	d							15 00					
Ewell West	d							15 03					
Epsom 3	a							15 06					
	d							15 08					
Ashtead	d							15 12					
Leatherhead	d							15 15					
Boxhill & Westhumble	d												
Dorking 4	a												
New Malden 6	d				14 40		14 49				15 10		15 19
Norbiton	d				14 43						15 13		
Kingston	a				14 46						15 16		
	d				14 49					15 11	15 16		
Hampton Wick	d				14 51					15 13	15 18		
Teddington	d				14 56					15 16	15 21		
Strawberry Hill	a				14 59					15 19			
Fulwell	d										15 25		
Hampton	d										15 29		
Kempton Park	d										15 32		
Sunbury	d										15 34		
Upper Halliford	d										15 36		
Shepperton	a										15 39		
Berrylands	d		←				14 51						15 21
Surbiton 6	d	14 30	14 32	14 35			14 55		15 05				15 25
Thames Ditton	d						15 00						15 30
Hampton Court	a						15 03						15 33
Hinchley Wood	d		14 36										
Claygate	d		14 39										
Oxshott	d		14 42										
Cobham & Stoke d'Abernon	d		14 46										
Bookham	d							15 20					
Effingham Junction 6	d		14 50					15 24					
Horsley	d		14 53					15 27					
Clandon	d		14 58					15 32					
London Road (Guildford)	d		15 03					15 37					
Guildford	a		15 07	15 13				15 41	15 43				

Station		SW	SW	SW	SW	SW	SW	SW	SW	SW	SW	SW
				1 A			B				1 A	
London Waterloo 15 ⊖	d	15 00	15 02	15 07		15 10	15 18	15 21	15 27	15 32	15 37	15 40
Vauxhall ⊖	d	15 04	15 06			15 14	15 22	15 25	15 31	15 36		15 44
Clapham Junction 10	d	15 09	15 11	15 15		15 19	15 27	15 30	15 36	15 41	15 46	15 49
Earlsfield	d	15 12	15 14			15 22	15 30	15 33	15 39	15 44		15 52
Wimbledon 6 ⊖	d	15 16	15 18	15 22		15 26	15 34	15 37	15 43	15 48	15 53	15 56
Raynes Park 6	d		15 22				15 37	15 40	15 46	15 52		
Motspur Park	d		15 25					15 43		15 55		
Malden Manor	d							15 46				
Tolworth	d							15 49				
Chessington North	d							15 52				
Chessington South	a							15 54				
Worcester Park	d		15 27							15 57		
Stoneleigh	d		15 30							16 00		
Ewell West	d		15 33							16 03		
Epsom 3	a		15 36							16 06		
	d		15 38							16 08		
Ashtead	d		15 42							16 12		
Leatherhead	d		15 45							16 15		
Boxhill & Westhumble	d											
Dorking 4	a		15 51									
New Malden 6	d						15 40		15 49			
Norbiton	d						15 43					
Kingston	a						15 46					
	d						15 49					
Hampton Wick	d						15 51					
Teddington	d						15 56					
Strawberry Hill	a						15 59					
Fulwell	d											
Hampton	d											
Kempton Park	d											
Sunbury	d											
Upper Halliford	d											
Shepperton	a											
Berrylands	d				←				15 51			
Surbiton 6	d	15b32		15 30	15 32	15 35			15 55		16 02	16 05
Thames Ditton	d	→							16 00			
Hampton Court	a								16 03			
Hinchley Wood	d				15 36							
Claygate	d				15 39							
Oxshott	d				15 42							
Cobham & Stoke d'Abernon	d				15 46							
Bookham	d									16 20		
Effingham Junction 6	d				15 50					16 24		
Horsley	d				15 53					16 27		
Clandon	d				15 58					16 32		
London Road (Guildford)	d				16 03					16 37		
Guildford	a				16 07	16 13				16 41		16 43

For general notes see front of timetable
For details of catering facilities see Directory of Train Operators

A To Alton (Table 155) and to Basingstoke (Table 155)
B To London Waterloo (Table 149)
b Arr. 1528

Table 152

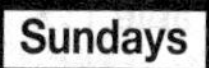

Sundays

For details of Bank Holiday service alterations, please see first page of Table 149

London → Chessington South, Dorking, Guildford Shepperton and Hampton Court

Network Diagram - see first page of Table 152

		SW	SW	SW	SW		SW	SW	SW 1	SW	SW	SW	SW	SW	SW	SW 1	SW	SW	SW	SW	SW	SW	SW 1	SW
		A				and at the same minutes past each hour until			B			A				B		A					B	
London Waterloo 15 ⊖	d		15 48	15 51	15 57		19 00	19 02	19 07		19 10	19 18	19 21	19 27	19 32	19 37	19 40		19 48	19 57	20 00	20 02	20 07	
Vauxhall ⊖	d		15 52	15 55	16 01		19 04	19 06			19 14	19 22	19 25	19 31	19 36		19 44		19 52	20 01	20 04	20 06		
Clapham Junction 10	d		15 57	16 00	16 06		19 09	19 11	19 15		19 19	19 27	19 30	19 36	19 41	19 46	19 49		19 57	20 06	20 09	20 11	20 15	
Earlsfield	d		16 00	16 03	16 09		19 12	19 14			19 22	19 30	19 33	19 39	19 44		19 52		20 00	20 09	20 12	20 14		
Wimbledon 6 ⊖	d		16 04	16 07	16 13		19 16	19 18	19 22		19 26	19 34	19 37	19 43	19 48	19 53	19 56		20 04	20 13	20 16	20 18	20 22	
Raynes Park 6	d		16 07	16 10	16 16			19 22				19 37	19 40	19 46	19 52				20 07	20 16		20 22		
Motspur Park	d			16 13				19 25					19 43		19 55							20 25		
Malden Manor	d			16 16									19 46											
Tolworth	d			16 19									19 49											
Chessington North	d			16 22									19 52											
Chessington South	a			16 24									19 54											
Worcester Park	d							19 27							19 57							20 27		
Stoneleigh	d							19 30							20 00							20 30		
Ewell West	d							19 33							20 03							20 33		
Epsom 3	a							19 36							20 06							20 36		
	d							19 38							20 08							20 38		
Ashtead	d							19 42							20 12							20 42		
Leatherhead	d							19 45							20 15							20 45		
Boxhill & Westhumble	d																							
Dorking 4	a							19 51														20 51		
New Malden 6	d		16 10		16 19							19 40		19 49					20 10	20 19				
Norbiton	d		16 13									19 43							20 13					
Kingston	a		16 16									19 46							20 16					
	d	16 11	16 16									19 49						20 11	20 16					
Hampton Wick	d	16 13	16 18									19 51						20 13	20 18					
Teddington	d	16 16	16 21									19 56						20 16	20 21					
Strawberry Hill	a	16 19										19 59						20 19						
Fulwell	d		16 25																20 25					
Hampton	d		16 29																20 29					
Kempton Park	d		16 32																20 32					
Sunbury	d		16 34																20 34					
Upper Halliford	d		16 36																20 36					
Shepperton	a		16 39																20 39					
Berrylands	d				16 21					←				19 51						20 21				←
Surbiton 6	d				16 25		19b32		19 30	19 32	19 35			19 55		20 02	20 05			20 25	20c32		20 30	20 32
Thames Ditton	d				16 30		→							20 00						20 30	→			
Hampton Court	a				16 33									20 03						20 33				
Hinchley Wood	d									19 36														20 36
Claygate	d									19 39														20 39
Oxshott	d									19 42														20 42
Cobham & Stoke d'Abernon	d									19 46														20 46
Bookham	d														20 20									
Effingham Junction 6	d									19 50					20 24									20 50
Horsley	d									19 53					20 27									20 53
Clandon	d									19 58					20 32									20 58
London Road (Guildford)	d									20 03					20 37									21 03
Guildford	a									20 07	20 13				20 41		20 43							21 07

For general notes see front of timetable
For details of catering facilities see Directory of Train Operators

A To London Waterloo (Table 149)
B To Alton (Table 155) and to Basingstoke (Table 155)
b Arr. 1928
c Arr. 2028

Table 152

Sundays

For details of Bank Holiday service alterations, please see first page of Table 149

London → Chessington South, Dorking, Guildford Shepperton and Hampton Court

Network Diagram - see first page of Table 152

		SW		SW	SW	SW	SW	SW	SW	SW	SW	SW	SW	SW	SW	SW	SW	SW	SW	SW		SW	SW	SW	SW	SW
								1							1							1				
				A				B		A					B			A				B		A		
London Waterloo 15 ⊖	d	20 10		20 18	20 21	20 27	20 32	20 37	20 40		20 48	20 57	21 00	21 02	21 07		21 10	21 18	21 21	21 32		21 37	21 40		21 48	21 57
Vauxhall ⊖	d	20 14		20 22	20 25	20 31	20 36		20 44		20 52	21 01	21 04	21 06			21 14	21 22	21 25	21 36			21 44		21 52	22 01
Clapham Junction 10	d	20 19		20 27	20 30	20 36	20 41	20 46	20 49		20 57	21 06	21 09	21 11	21 15		21 19	21 27	21 30	21 41		21 46	21 49		21 57	22 06
Earlsfield	d	20 22		20 30	20 33	20 39	20 44		20 52		21 00	21 09	21 12	21 14			21 22	21 30	21 33	21 44			21 52		22 00	22 09
Wimbledon 6 ⊖	d	20 26		20 34	20 37	20 43	20 48	20 53	20 56		21 04	21 13	21 16	21 18	21 22		21 26	21 34	21 37	21 48		21 53	21 56		22 04	22 13
Raynes Park 6	d			20 37	20 40	20 46	20 52				21 07	21 16		21 22				21 37	21 40	21 52					22 07	22 16
Motspur Park	d				20 43		20 55							21 25					21 43	21 55						
Malden Manor	d				20 46														21 46							
Tolworth	d				20 49														21 49							
Chessington North	d				20 52														21 52							
Chessington South	a				20 54														21 54							
Worcester Park	d						20 57							21 27						21 57						
Stoneleigh	d						21 00							21 30						22 00						
Ewell West	d						21 03							21 33						22 03						
Epsom 3	a						21 06							21 36						22 06						
	d						21 08							21 38						22 08						
Ashtead	d						21 12							21 42						22 12						
Leatherhead	d						21 15							21 45						22 15						
Boxhill & Westhumble	d																									
Dorking 4	a													21 51												
New Malden 6	d			20 40		20 49					21 10	21 19						21 40							22 10	22 19
Norbiton	d			20 43							21 13							21 43							22 13	
Kingston	a			20 46							21 16							21 46							22 16	
	d			20 49						21 11	21 16							21 49						22 11	22 16	
Hampton Wick	d			20 51						21 13	21 18							21 51						22 13	22 18	
Teddington	d			20 56						21 16	21 21							21 56						22 16	22 21	
Strawberry Hill	a			20 59						21 19								21 59						22 19		
Fulwell	d										21 25														22 25	
Hampton	d										21 29														22 29	
Kempton Park	d										21 32														22 32	
Sunbury	d										21 34														22 34	
Upper Halliford	d										21 36														22 36	
Shepperton	a										21 39														22 39	
Berrylands	d					20 51						21 21				←										22 21
Surbiton 6	d	20 35				20 55		21 02	21 05			21 25	21b32		21 30	21 32	21 35					22 02	22 05			22 25
Thames Ditton	d					21 00						21 30	→													22 30
Hampton Court	a					21 03						21 33														22 33
Hinchley Wood	d															21 36										
Claygate	d															21 39										
Oxshott	d															21 42										
Cobham & Stoke d'Abernon	d															21 46										
Bookham	d						21 20													22 20						
Effingham Junction 6	d						21 24									21 50				22 24						
Horsley	d						21 27									21 53				22 27						
Clandon	d						21 32									21 58				22 32						
London Road (Guildford)	d						21 37									22 03				22 37						
Guildford	a	21 13					21 41		21 43							22 07	22 13			22 41			22 43			

For general notes see front of timetable
For details of catering facilities see Directory of Train Operators

A To London Waterloo (Table 149)
B To Alton (Table 155) and to Basingstoke (Table 155)
b Arr. 2128

Table 152

Sundays

For details of Bank Holiday service alterations, please see first page of Table 149

London → Chessington South, Dorking, Guildford Shepperton and Hampton Court

Network Diagram - see first page of Table 152

		SW	SW	SW	SW	SW	SW	SW	SW	SW	SW	SW	SW	SW	SW		SW	SW	SW	SW	SW	SW	SW	SW		
				1 A			B			1 A		B							1 A					1 C		
London Waterloo 15	⊖ d	22 00	22 02	22 07		22 10	22 18	22 21	22 32	22 37	22 40		22 48	22 51	22 57		23 00	23 02	23 07		23 10	23 18	23 32	23 40		
Vauxhall	⊖ d	22 04	22 06			22 14	22 22	22 25	22 36		22 44		22 52	22 55	23 01		23 04	23 06			23 14	23 22	23 36	23 44		
Clapham Junction 10	d	22 09	22 11	22 15		22 19	22 27	22 30	22 41	22 46	22 49		22 57	23 00	23 06		23 09	23 11	23 15		23 19	23 27	23 41	23 49		
Earlsfield	d	22 12	22 14			22 22	22 30	22 33	22 44		22 52		23 00	23 03	23 09		23 12	23 14			23 22	23 30	23 44	23 52		
Wimbledon 6	⊖ d	22 16	22 18	22 22		22 26	22 34	22 37	22 48	22 53	22 56		23 04	23 07	23 13		23 16	23 18	23 22		23 26	23 34	23 48	23 56		
Raynes Park 6	d		22 22				22 37	22 40	22 52				23 07	23 10	23 16			23 22				23 37	23 52			
Motspur Park	d		22 25					22 43	22 55					23 13				23 25					23 55			
Malden Manor	d							22 46						23 16												
Tolworth	d							22 49						23 19												
Chessington North	d							22 52						23 22												
Chessington South	a							22 54						23 24												
Worcester Park	d		22 27						22 57									23 27					23 57			
Stoneleigh	d		22 30						23 00									23 30					23 59			
Ewell West	d		22 33						23 03									23 33					00 03			
Epsom 3	a		22 36						23 06									23 36					00 06			
	d		22 38						23 08																	
Ashtead	d		22 42						23 12																	
Leatherhead	d		22 45						23 15																	
Boxhill & Westhumble	d																									
Dorking 4	a		22 51																							
New Malden 6	d						22 40						23 10		23 19							23 40				
Norbiton	d						22 43						23 13									23 43				
Kingston	a						22 46						23 16									23 46				
	d						22 49					23 11	23 16									23 47				
Hampton Wick	d						22 51					23 13	23 18									23 49				
Teddington	d						22 56					23 16	23 21									23 51				
Strawberry Hill	a						22 59					23 19										23 54				
Fulwell	d												23 25													
Hampton	d												23 29													
Kempton Park	d												23 32													
Sunbury	d												23 34													
Upper Halliford	d												23 36													
Shepperton	a												23 39													
Berrylands	d				←										23 21					←						
Surbiton 6	d	22b32		22 30	22 32	22 35				23 02	23 05				23 25		23c32		23 30	23 32	23 35			00 05		
Thames Ditton	d	→													23 30		→									
Hampton Court	a														23 33											
Hinchley Wood	d				22 36															23 36						
Claygate	d				22 39															23 39						
Oxshott	d				22 42															23 42						
Cobham & Stoke d'Abernon	d				22 46															23 46						
Bookham	d								23 20																	
Effingham Junction 6	d				22 50				23 24											23 50						
Horsley	d				22 53				23 27											23 53						
Clandon	d				22 58				23 32											23 58						
London Road (Guildford)	d				23 03				23 37											00 03						
Guildford	a				23 07	23 13			23 41		23 43									00 07	00 13					

For general notes see front of timetable
For details of catering facilities see Directory of Train Operators

A To Alton (Table 155) and to Basingstoke (Table 155)
B To London Waterloo (Table 149)
C To Farnham (Table 155)

b Arr. 2228
c Arr. 2328

For details of Bank Holiday service alterations, please see first page of Table 149

Hampton Court, Shepperton, Guildford, Dorking and Chessington South → London

Network Diagram - see first page of Table 152

Miles	Miles	Miles	Miles	Miles	Station		SW MO	SW MX	SW MX	SW MX A	SW MX [1] B	SW MX A	SW MX [1] C	SW	SW D	SW [1] B	SW	SW	SW	SW	SW E	SW	SW	SW	SW A	SW E
0	—	—	—	—	**Guildford**	d			23p08					04 00			04 58			05 12			05 38			
1¼	—	—	—	—	London Road (Guildford)	d			23p11								05 01						05 41			
4½	—	—	—	—	Clandon	d			23p16								05 06						05 46			
7¼	—	—	—	—	Horsley	d			23p21								05 11						05 51			
8¾	0	—	—	—	Effingham Junction [6]	d			23p24								05 16						05 54			
—	1¾	—	—	—	Bookham	d											05 19									
11	—	—	—	—	Cobham & Stoke d'Abernon	d			23p28														05 58			
13	—	—	—	—	Oxshott	d			23p31														06 01			
14¾	—	—	—	—	Claygate	d			23p34														06 04			
16	—	—	—	—	Hinchley Wood	d			23p37														06 07			
—	—	—	0	—	**Hampton Court**	d	23p45															05 54				
—	—	—	1	—	Thames Ditton	d	23p47															05 56				
18	—	—	3	—	**Surbiton** [6]	d	23p53		23p42		23p57		00 40	04 24		05 40				05 57	06 01	06 02	06 12			06 28
19	—	—	—	—	Berrylands	d	23p55															06 04				
—	—	—	—	0	**Shepperton**	d		23p11										05 23								
—	—	—	—	1½	Upper Halliford	d		23p14										05 26								
—	—	—	—	2	Sunbury	d		23p16										05 28								
—	—	—	—	2½	Kempton Park	d		23p18																		
—	—	—	—	4¼	Hampton	d		23p21										05 33								
—	—	—	—	6	Fulwell	d		23p24										05 36								
—	—	—	0	—	Strawberry Hill	d				23p37		00 07			04 55			05 38							06 07	
—	—	—	1¼	7	Teddington	d		23p29		23p41		00 11			04 59				05 44						06 11	
—	—	—	—	8¼	Hampton Wick	d		23p31		23p44		00 14			05 01				05 46						06 14	
—	—	—	—	8¾	Kingston	a		23p33		23p46		00 16			05 03				05 48						06 16	
—	—	—	—	—		d		23p34		23p49					05 04				05 49						06 19	
—	—	—	—	9½	Norbiton	d		23p36		23p51					05 06				05 51						06 21	
20	—	—	—	11	New Malden [6]	d	23p58	23p40		23p55					05 10				05 55			06 07			06 25	
—	—	0	—	—	**Dorking** [4]	d																		05 48		
—	—	¾	—	—	Boxhill & Westhumble	d																		05 50		
—	4¼	4	—	—	Leatherhead	d											05 24							05 56		
—	—	5¾	—	—	Ashtead	d											05 28							05 59		
—	—	7¾	—	—	**Epsom** [3]	a											05 32							06 04		
—	—	—	—	—		d											05 34							06 04		
—	—	9	—	—	Ewell West	d											05 37							06 07		
—	—	10	—	—	Stoneleigh	d											05 40							06 10		
—	—	11¼	—	—	Worcester Park	d											05 42							06 12		
—	0	—	—	—	**Chessington South**	d																				
—	¾	—	—	—	Chessington North	d																				
—	1¾	—	—	—	Tolworth	d																				
—	2¾	—	—	—	Malden Manor	d																				
—	3¾	12¼	—	—	Motspur Park	d											05 46							06 16		
21¼	5¼	13¼	—	12	Raynes Park [6]	d	00 01	23p43		23p58					05 13		05 49		05 58			06 10		06 19	06 28	
22¾	6¾	14¾	—	13¼	**Wimbledon** [6] ⊖	d	00a04	23p49	23p55	00 05	00 08		00 48	04 32	05 17	05 49	05 53		06 02	06 05		06 14	06 20	06 23	06 32	06 35
24½	8½	16½	—	15¼	Earlsfield	d		23p55	23p58	00 08	00 10				05 21		05 57		06 05	06 08		06 17	06 24	06 27	06 35	06 39
26	10	18	—	16¾	**Clapham Junction** [10]	d		23p59	00 02	00 12	00 14		00 55	04 44	05 25	06 01	06 01	06 05	06 09	06 12		06 21	06 28	06 31	05 43	06 43
28¾	12¾	20¾	—	19¼	Vauxhall ⊖	d		00 04	00 07	00 17	00 19				05 30	06 08	06 06	06 12	06 14	06 17		06 26	06 33	06 36	06 44	06 48
30	14	22	—	20¾	**London Waterloo** [15] ⊖	a		00 09	00 13	00 22	00 29		01 02	04 53	05 35	06 12	06 11	06 16	06 19	06 22	06 20	06 31	06 37	06 40	06 49	06 52

For general notes see front of timetable
For details of catering facilities see Directory of Train Operators

A From London Waterloo (Table 149)
B From Basingstoke (Table 155)
C From Weymouth (Table 158)
D From Twickenham (Table 149)
E From Woking (Table 155)

For details of Bank Holiday service alterations, please see first page of Table 149

Hampton Court, Shepperton, Guildford, Dorking and Chessington South → London

Network Diagram - see first page of Table 152

		SW	SW	SW	SW	SW	SW	SW	SW	SW	SW	SW	SW	SW	SW	SW	SW	SW	SW	SW	SW	SW	SW	SW	SW	SW
					1		1									1				1						
					A		B				C	D				D				D		C				
Guildford	d		05 58					06 07						06 28				06 37								06 58
London Road (Guildford)	d		06 01					06 10						06 31				06 40								07 01
Clandon	d		06 06					06 15						06 36				06 45								07 06
Horsley	d		06 11					06 20						06 41				06 50								07 11
Effingham Junction 6	d		06 16					06 24						06b48				06 54								07 16
Bookham	d		06 19											06 51												07 19
Cobham & Stoke d'Abernon	d							06 27										06 57								
Oxshott	d							06 31										07 01								
Claygate	d							06 34										07 04								
Hinchley Wood	d							06 37										07 07								
Hampton Court	d			06 24											06 54											
Thames Ditton	d			06 26											06 56											
Surbiton 6	d			06 32	06 35		06 41	06 42				06 57			07 02	07 08		07 12		07 27						
Berrylands	d			06 34											07 04											
Shepperton	d					06 11											06 41									
Upper Halliford	d					06 14											06 44									
Sunbury	d					06 16											06 46									
Kempton Park	d																									
Hampton	d					06 21											06 51									
Fulwell	d					06 24											06 54									
Strawberry Hill	d										06 37											07 07				
Teddington	d					06 29					06 41						06 59					07 11		07 20		
Hampton Wick	d					06 31					06 44						07 01					07 14		07 22		
Kingston	a					06 33					06 46						07 03					07 16		07 24		
	d					06 34					06 49						07 04					07 19		07 26		
Norbiton	d					06 36					06 51						07 06					07 21		07 28		
New Malden 6	d			06 37		06 40					06 55				07 07		07 10					07 25		07 32		
Dorking 4	d												06 32										07 02			
Boxhill & Westhumble	d												06 34										07 04			
Leatherhead	d		06 24										06 39	06 56									07 09			07 24
Ashtead	d		06 28										06 43	06 59									07 13			07 27
Epsom 3	a		06 32										06 47	07 04									07 17			07 32
	d	06 18	06 33						←				06 48	07 04					←				07 18		07 22	07 34
Ewell West	d	06 21	06 36						06 36				06 51	07 07					07 07						07 25	07 37
Stoneleigh	d	06 24	→						06 38				06 53	→					07 10						07 27	→
Worcester Park	d	06 27							06 41				06 56						07 12				07 26		07 30	
Chessington South	d									06 40											07 10					
Chessington North	d									06 42											07 12					
Tolworth	d									06 44											07 14					
Malden Manor	d									06 47											07 17					
Motspur Park	d	06 30							06 46	06 50			07 00						07 16		07 20				07 34	
Raynes Park 6	d	06 34		06 40		06 43			06 49	06 54	06 58		07 04		07 10		07 13		07 19		07 24	07 28	07 31	07 34	07 37	
Wimbledon 6 ⊖	d	06 38		06 44		06 47	06 47	06 50	06 53	06 58	07 02	07 05	07 08		07 14		07 17	07 20	07 23		07 28	07 32	07 35	07 38	07 41	
Earlsfield	d	06 42		06 47		06 50		06 54	06 57	07 01	07 05	07 08	07 11		07 17		07 20	07 24	07 27		07 31	07 35	07 38	07 42	07 45	
Clapham Junction 10	d	06 46		06 51	06 46	06 54	06 54	06 58	07 01	07 05	06 13	07 12	07 15		07 21		07 24	07 28	07 31		07 35	06 43	07 42	07 46	07 49	
Vauxhall ⊖	d	06 51		06 56		06 59		07 03	07 06	07 10	07 14	07 17	07 20		07 26		07 29	07 33	07 36		07 40	07 44	07 47	07 51	07 54	
London Waterloo 15 ⊖	a	06 55		07 03	06 56	07 06	07 04	07 09	07 12	07 17	07 21	07 24	07 27		07 33	07 28	07 36	07 39	07 42	07 49	07 47	07 51	07 54	07 57	08 00	

For general notes see front of timetable
For details of catering facilities see Directory of Train Operators

A From Alton (Table 155)
B From Basingstoke (Table 155)
C From London Waterloo (Table 149)
D From Woking (Table 155)
b Arr. 0644

For details of Bank Holiday service alterations, please see first page of Table 149

Hampton Court, Shepperton, Guildford, Dorking and Chessington South → London

Network Diagram - see first page of Table 152

		SW	SW	SW	SW	SW	SW	SW	SW	SW	SW	SW	SW	SW	SN	SW	SW	SW	SW	SW	SW	SW	SW	SW	SW	SW
				1						1									1			1	1			
		A		B						B	C		D		E		A		G			B	B			C
Guildford	d					07 07	07 17								07 26						07 37					
London Road (Guildford)	d					07 10	07 20								07 29						07 40					
Clandon	d					07 15	07 25														07 45					
Horsley	d					07 20	07 30														07 50					
Effingham Junction 6	d					07 24	07 34								07 38	07 46					07 54					
Bookham	d														07 41	07 49										
Cobham & Stoke d'Abernon	d					07 27	07 37														07 57					
Oxshott	d					07 31	07 41														08 01					
Claygate	d					07 34	07 44														08 04					
Hinchley Wood	d					07 37	07 47														08 07					
Hampton Court	d		07 24															07 54								
Thames Ditton	d		07 26															07 56								
Surbiton 6	d		07 32	07 38		07 42	07 53			07 57								08 02	08 08		08 12	08 19	08 25			
Berrylands	d		07 34															08 04								
Shepperton	d	07 00			07 11												07 30			07 41						
Upper Halliford	d	07 03			07 14												07 33			07 44						
Sunbury	d	07 05			07 16												07 35			07 46						
Kempton Park	d																									
Hampton	d	07 09			07 21												07 39			07 51						
Fulwell	d	07 12			07 24												07 42			07 54						
Strawberry Hill	d	07 14									07 37		07 47				07 44									08 07
Teddington	d				07 29						07 41		07 50							07 59						08 11
Hampton Wick	d				07 31						07 44		07 52							08 01						08 14
Kingston	a				07 33						07 46		07 54							08 03						08 16
	d				07 34						07 49		07 56							08 04						08 19
Norbiton	d				07 36						07 51		07 58							08 06						08 21
New Malden 6	d		07 37		07 40	07 46					07 55		08 02					08 07		08 10	08 16					08 25
Dorking 4	d											07 32														
Boxhill & Westhumble	d											07 34														
Leatherhead	d											07 39			07 46	07 54										
Ashtead	d											07 43			07 50	07 57										
Epsom 3	a											07 47			07 54	08 02										
	d							←				07 48		07 52		08 04								←		
Ewell West	d							07 37						07 55		08 07 →								08 07		
Stoneleigh	d							07 40						07 57										08 10		
Worcester Park	d							07 43				07 56		08 00										08 13		
Chessington South	d								07 40																08 10	
Chessington North	d								07 42																08 12	
Tolworth	d								07 44																08 14	
Malden Manor	d								07 47																08 17	
Motspur Park	d							07 46	07 50					08 04										08 16	08 20	
Raynes Park 6	d		07 40		07 43			07 50	07 54		07 58	08 01	08 04	08 07				08 10		08 13				08 20	08 24	08 28
Wimbledon 6 ⊖ 🚋	d		07 44		07 47	07 51		07 54	07 58		08 02	08 05	08 08	08 11				08 14		08 17	08 21			08 24	08 28	08 32
Earlsfield	d		07 48		07 51	07 54		07 58	08 01		08 05	08 08	08 12	08 15				08 18		08 21	08 24			08 28	08 31	08 35
Clapham Junction 10	d	07 49	07 52		07 55	07 58		08 02	08 05		07 13	08 12	08 16	08 19			08 19	08 22		08 25	08 28			08 32	08 35	07 43
Vauxhall ⊖	d	07 56	07 57		08 00	08 03		08 07	08 10		08 14	08 17	08 21	08 24			08 26	08 27		08 30	08 33			08 37	08 40	08 44
London Waterloo 15 ⊖	a	08 04	08 04	07 56	08 06	08 11	08 13	08 13	08 17	08 19	08 21	08 24	08 27	08 30			08 34	08 33	08 26	08 36	08 40	08 36	08 46	08 43	08 47	08 51

For general notes see front of timetable
For details of catering facilities see Directory of Train Operators

A Via Richmond (Table 149)
B From Woking (Table 155)
C From London Waterloo (Table 149)
D From Twickenham (Table 149)
E To London Bridge (Table 182)
G From West Byfleet (Table 155)

For details of Bank Holiday service alterations, please see first page of Table 149

Hampton Court, Shepperton, Guildford, Dorking and Chessington South → London

Network Diagram - see first page of Table 152

		SW	SW	SW	SW	SW	SW	SW	SW	SW	SW	SW	SW	SW	SW	SN	SW	SW	SW	SW	SW	SW	SW	SW	SW	SW
						1					1								1			1				
			A			B	C				D		E			G			H			D			E	
Guildford	d								07 58	08 07				08 20		08 16					08 37					08 46
London Road (Guildford)	d								08 01	08 10						08 19					08 40					
Clandon	d								08 06	08 15						08 24					08 45					
Horsley	d								08 11	08 20						08 29					08 48					
Effingham Junction 6	d								08 15	08 24						08 32	08 48				08 52					
Bookham	d								08 18							08 35	08 51									
Cobham & Stoke d'Abernon	d									08 27											08 55					
Oxshott	d									08 31											08 59					
Claygate	d									08 34											09 02					
Hinchley Wood	d									08 37											09 05					
Hampton Court	d				08 24													08 54								
Thames Ditton	d				08 26													08 56								
Surbiton 6	d				08 32	08 38				08 42	08 48			08 57				09 02	09 11		09 12	09 19				09 27
Berrylands	d				08 34													09 04								
Shepperton	d						08 00	08 11												08 41						
Upper Halliford	d						08 03	08 14												08 44						
Sunbury	d						08 05	08 16												08 46						
Kempton Park	d																									
Hampton	d						08 09	08 21												08 51						
Fulwell	d						08 12	08 24												08 54						
Strawberry Hill	d		08 17				08 14						08 37												09 07	
Teddington	d		08 20					08 29					08 41							08 59					09 11	
Hampton Wick	d		08 22					08 31					08 44							09 01					09 14	
Kingston	a		08 24					08 33					08 46							09 03					09 16	
	d		08 26					08 34					08 49							09 04					09 19	
Norbiton	d		08 28					08 36					08 51							09 06					09 21	
New Malden 6	d		08 32		08 37			08 40					08 55					09 07		09 10					09 25	
Dorking 4	d	08 02													08 31											
Boxhill & Westhumble	d	08 04													08 33											
Leatherhead	d	08 09							08 23						08 38	08 41	08 56									
Ashtead	d	08 13							08 27						08 42	08 45	08 59									
Epsom 3	a	08 17							08 31						08 46	08 49	09 04									
	d	08 18		08 22					08 34						08 48		09 04						←			
Ewell West	d			08 25					08 37						08 51		09 07						09 07			
Stoneleigh	d			08 27					08 40						08 54		→						09 10			
Worcester Park	d	08 26		08 30					08 42						08 57								09 12			
Chessington South	d											08 40												09 10		
Chessington North	d											08 42												09 12		
Tolworth	d											08 44												09 14		
Malden Manor	d											08 47												09 17		
Motspur Park	d			08 34					08 46			08 50			09 00								09 16	09 20		
Raynes Park 6	d	08 31	08 34	08 37	08 40			08 43	08 49			08 54	08 58		09 04			09 10		09 13			09 19	09 24	09 28	
Wimbledon 6 ⊖	d	08 35	08 38	08 41	08 44			08 47	08 53			08 58	09 02	09 05	09 08			09 14		09 17	09 20		09 23	09 28	09 32	09 35
Earlsfield	d	08 38	08 42	08 45	08 48			08 51	08 57			09 01	09 05	09 08	09 12			09 17		09 20	09 24		09 27	09 31	09 35	09 38
Clapham Junction 10	d	08 42	08 46	08 49	08 52		08 49	08 55	09 01			09 05	08 13	09 12	09 16			09 21		09 24	09 28		09 31	09 35	08 43	09 42
Vauxhall ⊖	d	08 47	08 51	08 54	08 57		08 56	09 00	09 06			09 10	09 14	09 17	09 21			09 26		09 29	09 33		09 36	09 40	09 44	09 47
London Waterloo 15 ⊖	a	08 54	08 57	09 00	09 03	08 59	09 04	09 06	09 12	09 01	09 06	09 17	09 21	09 24	09 27			09 33	09 29	09 36	09 39	09 40	09 42	09 47	09 51	09 54

For general notes see front of timetable
For details of catering facilities see Directory of Train Operators

A From Twickenham (Table 149)
B From Farnham (Table 155)
C Via Richmond (Table 149)
D From Woking (Table 155)
E From London Waterloo (Table 149)
G To London Bridge (Table 178)
H From Southampton Central (Table 158)

For details of Bank Holiday service alterations, please see first page of Table 149

Hampton Court, Shepperton, Guildford, Dorking and Chessington South → London

Network Diagram - see first page of Table 152

		SW	SW	SW	SW	SW	SW	SW	SW	SW	SW	SW	SW	SW	SW	SW	SW	SW	SW	SW	SW	SW	SW	SW	SW	SW
					1			1								1			1							
					A			B			C	D				A			B			C	D			
Guildford	d		08 58				09 08							09 28				09 38							09 58	
London Road (Guildford)	d		09 01				09 11							09 31				09 41							10 01	
Clandon	d		09 06				09 16							09 36				09 46							10 06	
Horsley	d		09 11				09 21							09 41				09 51							10 11	
Effingham Junction 6	d		09 16				09 24							09 46				09 54							10 16	
Bookham	d		09 19											09 49											10 19	
Cobham & Stoke d'Abernon	d						09 28											09 58								
Oxshott	d						09 31											10 01								
Claygate	d						09 34											10 04								
Hinchley Wood	d						09 37											10 07								
Hampton Court	d			09 24											09 54											10 24
Thames Ditton	d			09 26											09 56											10 26
Surbiton 6	d			09 32	09 38		09 42	09 47				09 57			10 02	10 08		10 12	10 17				10 27			10 32
Berrylands	d			09 34											10 04											10 34
Shepperton	d					09 11											09 41									
Upper Halliford	d					09 14											09 44									
Sunbury	d					09 16											09 46									
Kempton Park	d					09 18											09 48									
Hampton	d					09 21											09 51									
Fulwell	d					09 24											09 54									
Strawberry Hill	d										09 37											10 07				
Teddington	d					09 29					09 41						09 59					10 11				
Hampton Wick	d					09 31					09 44						10 01					10 14				
Kingston	a					09 33					09 46						10 03					10 16				
	d					09 34					09 49						10 04					10 19				
Norbiton	d					09 36					09 51						10 06					10 21				
New Malden 6	d			09 37		09 40					09 55				10 07		10 10					10 25				10 37
Dorking 4	d	09 02											09 35											10 05		
Boxhill & Westhumble	d	09 04																								
Leatherhead	d	09 09	09 24										09 41	09 54										10 11	10 24	
Ashtead	d	09 13	09 28										09 44	09 58										10 14	10 28	
Epsom 3	a	09 17	09 32										09 49	10 02										10 19	10 32	
	d	09 18	09 35						←				09 50	10 05						←				10 20	10 35	
Ewell West	d	09 21	09 38						09 38				09 53	10 08						10 08				10 23	10 38	
Stoneleigh	d	09 24	→						09 40				09 55	→						10 10				10 25	→	
Worcester Park	d	09 27							09 43				09 58							10 13				10 28		
Chessington South	d									09 40											10 10					
Chessington North	d									09 42											10 12					
Tolworth	d									09 44											10 14					
Malden Manor	d									09 47											10 17					
Motspur Park	d	09 30							09 46	09 50			10 01							10 16	10 20			10 31		
Raynes Park 6	d	09 34		09 40		09 43			09 49	09 53	09 58		10 04		10 10		10 13			10 19	10 23	10 28		10 34		10 40
Wimbledon 6	⊖ ⛴ d	09 38		09 44		09 47	09 50		09 53	09 57	10 02	10 05	10 08		10 14		10 17	10 20		10 23	10 27	10 32	10 35	10 38		10 44
Earlsfield	d	09 42		09 47		09 50	09 54		09 57	10 01	10 05	10 08	10 12		10 17		10 20	10 24		10 27	10 31	10 35	10 38	10 42		10 47
Clapham Junction 10	d	09 46		09 51	09 51	09 54	09 58	09 59	10 01	10 05	09 13	10 12	10 16		10 21		10 24	10 28		10 31	10 35	09 43	10 42	10 46		10 51
Vauxhall	⊖ d	09 51		09 56		09 59	10 03		10 06	10 10	10 14	10 17	10 21		10 26		10 29	10 33		10 36	10 40	10 44	10 47	10 51		10 56
London Waterloo 15	⊖ a	09 57		10 01	09 59	10 04	10 07	10 08	10 10	10 15	10 19	10 22	10 25		10 31	10 25	10 34	10 37	10 35	10 40	10 45	10 49	10 52	10 55		11 01

For general notes see front of timetable
For details of catering facilities see Directory of Train Operators

A From Alton (Table 155)
B From Basingstoke (Table 155)
C From London Waterloo (Table 149)
D From Woking (Table 155)

Table 152 — Mondays to Fridays

For details of Bank Holiday service alterations, please see first page of Table 149

Hampton Court, Shepperton, Guildford, Dorking and Chessington South → London

Network Diagram - see first page of Table 152

Station		SW 1 A	SW	SW	SW 1 B	SW	SW	SW C	SW D	SW	SW	SW	SW 1 A	SW	SW	SW 1 B	SW	SW	SW C	SW D	SW	SW	SW	SW 1 A	SW
Guildford	d			10 08							10 28				10 38							10 58			
London Road (Guildford)	d			10 11							10 31				10 41							11 01			
Clandon	d			10 16							10 36				10 46							11 06			
Horsley	d			10 21							10 41				10 51							11 11			
Effingham Junction 6	d			10 24							10 46				10 54							11 16			
Bookham	d										10 49											11 19			
Cobham & Stoke d'Abernon	d			10 28											10 58										
Oxshott	d			10 31											11 01										
Claygate	d			10 34											11 04										
Hinchley Wood	d			10 37											11 07										
Hampton Court	d											10 54											11 24		
Thames Ditton	d											10 56											11 26		
Surbiton 6	d	10 38		10 42	10 47				10 57			11 02	11 08		11 12	11 17				11 27			11 32	11 38	
Berrylands	d											11 04											11 34		
Shepperton	d		10 11											10 41											11 11
Upper Halliford	d		10 14											10 44											11 14
Sunbury	d		10 16											10 46											11 16
Kempton Park	d		10 18											10 48											11 18
Hampton	d		10 21											10 51											11 21
Fulwell	d		10 24											10 54											11 24
Strawberry Hill	d							10 37											11 07						
Teddington	d		10 29					10 41						10 59					11 11						11 29
Hampton Wick	d		10 31					10 44						11 01					11 14						11 31
Kingston	a		10 33					10 46						11 03					11 16						11 33
	d		10 34					10 49						11 04					11 19						11 34
Norbiton	d		10 36					10 51						11 06					11 21						11 36
New Malden 6	d		10 40					10 55				11 07		11 10					11 25				11 37		11 40
Dorking 4	d									10 35											11 05				
Boxhill & Westhumble	d																								
Leatherhead	d									10 41	10 54										11 11	11 24			
Ashtead	d									10 44	10 58										11 14	11 28			
Epsom 3	a									10 49	11 02										11 19	11 32			
	d					←				10 50	11 05						←				11 20	11 35			
Ewell West	d					10 38				10 53	11 08						11 08				11 23	11 38			
Stoneleigh	d					10 40				10 55	→						11 10				11 25	→			
Worcester Park	d					10 43				10 58							11 13				11 28				
Chessington South	d						10 40											11 10							
Chessington North	d						10 42											11 12							
Tolworth	d						10 44											11 14							
Malden Manor	d						10 47											11 17							
Motspur Park	d					10 46	10 50			11 01							11 16	11 20			11 31				
Raynes Park 6	d		10 43			10 49	10 53	10 58		11 04		11 10		11 13			11 19	11 23	11 28		11 34		11 40		11 43
Wimbledon 6	⊖ ⛴ d		10 47	10 50		10 53	10 57	11 02	11 05	11 08		11 14		11 17	11 20		11 23	11 27	11 32	11 35	11 38		11 44		11 47
Earlsfield	d		10 50	10 54		10 57	11 01	11 05	11 08	11 12		11 17		11 20	11 24		11 27	11 31	11 35	11 38	11 42		11 47		11 50
Clapham Junction 10	d	10 49	10 54	10 58	10 59	11 01	11 05	10 13	11 12	11 16		11 21		11 24	11 28		11 31	11 35	10 43	11 42	11 46		11 51	11 49	11 54
Vauxhall	⊖ d		10 59	11 03		11 06	11 10	11 14	11 17	11 21		11 26		11 29	11 33		11 36	11 40	11 44	11 47	11 51		11 56		11 59
London Waterloo 15	⊖ a	10 57	11 04	11 07	11 06	11 10	11 15	11 19	11 22	11 25		11 31	11 27	11 34	11 37	11 36	11 40	11 45	11 49	11 52	11 55		12 01	11 57	12 04

For general notes see front of timetable
For details of catering facilities see Directory of Train Operators

A From Alton (Table 155)
B From Basingstoke (Table 155)
C From London Waterloo (Table 149)
D From Woking (Table 155)

For details of Bank Holiday service alterations, please see first page of Table 149

Hampton Court, Shepperton, Guildford, Dorking and Chessington South → London

Network Diagram - see first page of Table 152

		SW	SW	SW	SW		SW	SW	SW	SW	SW	SW	SW	SW	SW	SW	SW	SW	SW	SW	SW	SW	SW	SW	SW
			1									1			1								1		
			A				B	C				D			A			B	C				D		
Guildford	d	11 08								16 28				16 38							16 58				17 08
London Road (Guildford)	d	11 11								16 31				16 41							17 01				17 11
Clandon	d	11 16								16 36				16 46							17 06				17 16
Horsley	d	11 21								16 41				16 51							17 11				17 21
Effingham Junction [6]	d	11 24								16 46				16 54							17 16				17 24
Bookham	d									16 49											17 19				
Cobham & Stoke d'Abernon	d	11 28												16 58											17 28
Oxshott	d	11 31												17 01											17 31
Claygate	d	11 34												17 04											17 34
Hinchley Wood	d	11 37												17 07											17 37
Hampton Court	d										16 54											17 24			
Thames Ditton	d										16 56											17 26			
Surbiton [6]	d	11 42	11 47					16 57			17 02	17 08		17 12	17 17				17 27			17 32	17 38		17 42
Berrylands	d										17 04											17 34			
Shepperton	d												16 41											17 11	
Upper Halliford	d												16 44											17 14	
Sunbury	d					and at							16 46											17 16	
Kempton Park	d												16 48											17 18	
Hampton	d					the same							16 51											17 21	
Fulwell	d												16 54											17 24	
Strawberry Hill	d					minutes	16 37											17 07							
Teddington	d					past	16 43						16 59					17 13						17 29	
Hampton Wick	d						16 46						17 01					17 16						17 31	
Kingston	a					each	16 48						17 03					17 18						17 33	
	d					hour until	16 49						17 04					17 19						17 34	
Norbiton	d						16 51						17 06					17 21						17 36	
New Malden [6]	d						16 55				17 07		17 10					17 25				17 37		17 40	
Dorking [4]	d								16 35											17 05					
Boxhill & Westhumble	d																								
Leatherhead	d								16 41	16 54										17 11	17 24				
Ashtead	d								16 44	16 58										17 14	17 28				
Epsom [3]	a								16 49	17 02										17 19	17 32				
	d			←					16 50	17 05						←				17 20	17 35				
Ewell West	d			11 38					16 53	17 08 →						17 08				17 23	17 38 →				
Stoneleigh	d			11 40					16 55							17 10				17 25					
Worcester Park	d			11 43					16 58							17 13				17 28					
Chessington South	d				11 40												17 10								
Chessington North	d				11 42												17 12								
Tolworth	d				11 44												17 14								
Malden Manor	d				11 47												17 17								
Motspur Park	d			11 46	11 50				17 01							17 16	17 20			17 31					
Raynes Park [6]	d			11 49	11 53		16 58		17 04		17 10		17 13			17 19	17 23	17 28		17 34		17 40		17 43	
Wimbledon [6] ⊖ 🚋	d	11 50		11 53	11 57		17 02	17 05	17 08		17 14		17 17	17 20		17 23	17 27	17 32	17 35	17 38		17 44		17 47	17 50
Earlsfield	d	11 54		11 57	12 01		17 05	17 08	17 12		17 17		17 20	17 24		17 27	17 31	17 35	17 38	17 42		17 47		17 50	17 54
Clapham Junction [10]	d	11 58	11 59	12 01	12 05		16 11	17 12	17 16		17 21		17 24	17 28		17 31	17 35	16 41	17 42	17 46		17 51	17 49	17 54	17 58
Vauxhall ⊖	d	12 03		12 06	12 10		17 14	17 17	17 21		17 26		17 29	17 33		17 36	17 40	17 44	17 47	17 51		17 56		17 59	18 03
London Waterloo [15] ⊖	a	12 08	12 06	12 11	12 15		17 21	17 22	17 25		17 31	17 29	17 35	17 37	17 34	17 40	17 44	17 49	17 52	17 55		18 01	17 59	18 05	18 07

For general notes see front of timetable
For details of catering facilities see Directory of Train Operators

A From Basingstoke (Table 155)
B From London Waterloo (Table 149)
C From Woking (Table 155)
D From Alton (Table 155)

For details of Bank Holiday service alterations, please see first page of Table 149

Hampton Court, Shepperton, Guildford, Dorking and Chessington South → London

Network Diagram - see first page of Table 152

		SW 1	SW	SW	SW	SW	SW	SW	SW	SW 1	SW	SW	SN	SW 1	SW	SW	SW	SW	SW	SW	SW	SW 1	SW	SW	SW 1	SW
		A			B	C				D			E	A			B	C				D			A	
Guildford	d							17 28				17 34	17 42							17 58				18 08		
London Road (Guildford)	d							17 31				17 37								18 01				18 11		
Clandon	d							17 36				17 42								18 06				18 16		
Horsley	d							17 41				17 47								18 11				18 21		
Effingham Junction 6	d							17 46				17 50	17 55							18 16				18 24		
Bookham	d							17 49												18 19						
Cobham & Stoke d'Abernon	d											17 54												18 28		
Oxshott	d											17 57												18 31		
Claygate	d											18 00												18 34		
Hinchley Wood	d											18 03												18 37		
Hampton Court	d								17 54												18 24					
Thames Ditton	d								17 56												18 26					
Surbiton 6	d	17 47				17 57			18 02	18 08		18 12		18 17				18 27			18 32	18 38		18 42	18 47	
Berrylands	d								18 04												18 34					
Shepperton	d										17 41												18 11			
Upper Halliford	d										17 44												18 14			
Sunbury	d										17 46												18 16			
Kempton Park	d										17 48												18 18			
Hampton	d										17 51												18 21			
Fulwell	d										17 54												18 24			
Strawberry Hill	d				17 37												18 07									
Teddington	d				17 43						17 59						18 13						18 29			
Hampton Wick	d				17 46						18 01						18 16						18 31			
Kingston	a				17 48						18 03						18 18						18 33			
	d				17 49						18 04						18 19						18 34			
Norbiton	d				17 51						18 06						18 21						18 36			
New Malden 6	d				17 55				18 07		18 10						18 25				18 37		18 40			
Dorking 4	d						17 35												18 05							
Boxhill & Westhumble	d																									
Leatherhead	d						17 41	17 54					18 02						18 11	18 24						
Ashtead	d						17 44	17 58					18 06						18 14	18 28						
Epsom 3	a						17 49	18 02					18 10						18 19	18 32						
	d		←				17 50	18 05							←				18 20	18 35						←
Ewell West	d		17 38				17 53	18 08							18 08				18 23	18 38						18 38
Stoneleigh	d		17 40				17 55	→							18 10				18 25	→						18 40
Worcester Park	d		17 43				17 58								18 13				18 28							18 43
Chessington South	d			17 40												18 10										
Chessington North	d			17 42												18 12										
Tolworth	d			17 44												18 14										
Malden Manor	d			17 47												18 17										
Motspur Park	d		17 46	17 50			18 01								18 16	18 20			18 31							18 46
Raynes Park 6	d		17 49	17 53	17 58		18 04		18 10		18 13				18 19	18 23	18 28		18 34		18 40		18 43			18 49
Wimbledon 6 ⊖	d		17 53	17 57	18 02	18 05	18 08		18 14		18 17	18 20			18 23	18 27	18 32	18 35	18 38		18 44		18 47	18 50		18 53
Earlsfield	d		17 57	18 01	18 05	18 08	18 12		18 17		18 20	18 24			18 27	18 31	18 35	18 38	18 42		18 47		18 50	18 54		18 57
Clapham Junction 10	d	17 59	18 01	18 05	17 11	18 12	18 16		18 21		18 24	18 28			18 31	18 35	17 41	18 42	18 46		18 51	18 49	18 54	18 58	18 59	19 01
Vauxhall ⊖	d		18 06	18 10	18 14	18 17	18 21		18 26		18 29	18 33			18 36	18 40	18 44	18 47	18 51		18 56		18 59	19 03		19 06
London Waterloo 15 ⊖	a	18 09	18 10	18 15	18 19	18 23	18 25		18 31	18 29	18 35	18 37		18 39	18 40	18 47	18 49	18 52	18 55		19 01	18 57	19 05	19 07	19 06	19 10

For general notes see front of timetable
For details of catering facilities see Directory of Train Operators

A From Basingstoke (Table 155)
B From London Waterloo (Table 149)
C From Woking (Table 155)
D From Alton (Table 155)
E To London Victoria (Table 177)

For details of Bank Holiday service alterations, please see first page of Table 149

Hampton Court, Shepperton, Guildford, Dorking and Chessington South → London

Network Diagram - see first page of Table 152

		SW	SW	SW	SW	SN	SW	SW	SW	SW	SW	SW	SW	SW	SW	SW	SN	SW	SW	SW	SW	SW	SW	SW	SW	SW
								1			1								1			1				
			A	B		C		D			E			A	B		G		D			E			A	B
Guildford	d					18 22				18 38							18 52				19 08					
London Road (Guildford)	d					18 25				18 41							18 55				19 11					
Clandon	d					18 30				18 46							19 00				19 16					
Horsley	d					18 35				18 51							19 05				19 21					
Effingham Junction 6	d					18 39				18 54						18 59	19 08				19 24					
Bookham	d					18 42										19 02	19 11									
Cobham & Stoke d'Abernon	d									18 58											19 28					
Oxshott	d									19 01											19 31					
Claygate	d									19 04											19 34					
Hinchley Wood	d									19 07											19 37					
Hampton Court	d						18 54											19 24								
Thames Ditton	d						18 56											19 26								
Surbiton 6	d			18 57			19 02	19 08		19 12	19 17				19 27			19 32	19 38		19 42	19 47				19 57
Berrylands	d						19 04											19 34								
Shepperton	d								18 36											19 06						
Upper Halliford	d								18 39											19 09						
Sunbury	d								18 41											19 11						
Kempton Park	d								18 43											19 13						
Hampton	d								18b51											19c21						
Fulwell	d								18 54											19 24						
Strawberry Hill	d		18 37											19 07											19 37	
Teddington	d		18 43						18 59					19 13						19 29					19 43	
Hampton Wick	d		18 46						19 01					19 16						19 31					19 46	
Kingston	a		18 48						19 03					19 18						19 33					19 48	
	d		18 49						19 04					19 19						19 34					19 49	
Norbiton	d		18 51						19 06					19 21						19 36					19 51	
New Malden 6	d		18 55				19 07		19 10					19 25				19 37		19 40					19 55	
Dorking 4	d				18 35							18 50														
Boxhill & Westhumble	d																									
Leatherhead	d				18 41	18 47						18 56				19 07	19 16									
Ashtead	d				18 44	18 50						18 59				19 10	19 20									
Epsom 3	a				18 50	18 58						19 04				19 15	19 24									
	d				18 50							19 05				19 20							19 35			
Ewell West	d				18 53							19 08				19 23							19 38			
Stoneleigh	d				18 55							19 10				19 25							19 40			
Worcester Park	d				18 58							19 13				19 28							19 43			
Chessington South	d	18 40											19 10											19 40		
Chessington North	d	18 42											19 12											19 42		
Tolworth	d	18 44											19 14											19 44		
Malden Manor	d	18 47											19 17											19 47		
Motspur Park	d	18 50			19 01							19 16	19 20			19 31							19 46	19 50		
Raynes Park 6	d	18 53	18 58		19 04		19 10		19 13			19 19	19 23	19 28		19 34		19 40		19 43			19 49	19 53	19 58	
Wimbledon 6 ⊖ ⛴	d	18 57	19 02	19 05	19 08		19 14		19 17	19 20		19 23	19 27	19 32	19 35	19 38		19 44		19 47	19 50		19 53	19 57	20 02	20 05
Earlsfield	d	19 01	19 05	19 08	19 12		19 17		19 20	19 24		19 27	19 31	19 35	19 38	19 42		19 47		19 50	19 54		19 57	20 01	20 05	20 08
Clapham Junction 10	d	19 05	18 11	19 12	19 16		19 21		19 24	19 28		19 31	19 35	18 41	19 42	19 46		19 51	19 49	19 54	19 58	19 59	20 01	20 05	19 11	20 12
Vauxhall ⊖	d	19 10	19 14	19 17	19 21		19 26		19 29	19 33		19 36	19 40	19 44	19 47	19 51		19 56		19 59	20 03		20 06	20 10	20 14	20 17
London Waterloo 15 ⊖	a	19 14	19 19	19 23	19 27		19 31	19 25	19 34	19 37	19 39	19 41	19 45	19 49	19 52	19 55		20 01	19 57	20 04	20 07	20 06	20 10	20 15	20 19	20 22

For general notes see front of timetable
For details of catering facilities see Directory of Train Operators

- **A** From London Waterloo (Table 149)
- **B** From Woking (Table 155)
- **C** To London Bridge (Table 182)
- **D** From Alton (Table 155)
- **E** From Basingstoke (Table 155)
- **G** To London Bridge (Table 178)
- **b** Arr. 1846
- **c** Arr. 1916

Watford Junction, Bedford and London → Brighton

Network Diagram - see first page of Table 186

	LO	SN	SN	FC	GX		SN		SN	SN	FC	GW	SN	GX	SN	LO	GW	SE	SN	SN	FC	GX	SN	
																		13						
		1	1	1	1		1		1	1	1	1	1	1	1		1		1	1	1	1	1	
															A			B					C	
London Victoria 15 ⊖ d			14 36		14 45		14 47							15 00	15 02				15 06			15 15	15 17	
Watford Junction d									14 11															
Harrow & Wealdstone ⊖ d									14 17															
Wembley Central d																								
Willesden Jn. High Level d	14 38															15 08								
Shepherds Bush § ⊖ d																								
Kensington Olympia ⊖ d	14 47								14 42							15 17								
West Brompton ⊖ d	14 49								14 45							15 19								
Imperial Wharf § d																								
Clapham Junction 10 d	14a59		14 42				14 53		14 54						15 08	15a29			15 12				15 23	
Bedford 7 d				13 25							13 40										13 55			
Luton 10 d				13 49							14 04										14 19			
Luton Airport Parkway 7 ✈ d				13 51							14 06										14 21			
St Albans d				14 03							14 18										14 33			
St Pancras International 15 ⊖ d				14 24							14 39										14 54			
Farringdon 3 ⊖ d				14 29							14 44										14 59			
City Thameslink 3 d				14 31							14 46										15 01			
London Blackfriars 3 ⊖ d				14 35							14 50										15 05			
London Bridge 4 ⊖ d		14 33		14 41							14 56							15 03			15 11			
Norwood Junction 2 d		14 46																15 16						
East Croydon a		14 49	14 52	14 54			15 03		15 07		15 09				15 18			15 19	15 22		15 24		15 33	
d		14 51	14 52	14 54			15 03		15 07		15 09				15 18			15 21	15 22		15 24		15 33	
Purley 4 d		14 57																15 26						
Coulsdon South d		15 00																15 30						
Merstham d		15 06																15 35						
Redhill a		15 09								←					15 30			15 38						
d		15 10								15 10		15 14			15 30		15 34	15 39						
Tonbridge 4 a		→																16 08						
Reigate a												15 18					15 38							
Earlswood (Surrey) d										15 12														
Salfords d										15 16														
Horley 4 d										15 19					15 36									
Gatwick Airport 10 ✈ a				15 10	15 15		15 18		15 22	15 23	15 25		←	15 30	15 39						15 40	15 45	15 48	
d				15 11			15 19		15 28	15 24	15 26		15 28		15 40						15 41		15 49	
Three Bridges 4 a				15 15					→	15 29			15 33		15 44						15 45			
d				15 15						15 30			15 33		15 45						15 45			
Crawley d										15 33					15 48									
Ifield d										15 36														
Faygate d																								
Littlehaven d										15 42														
Horsham 4 a										15 47					15 56									
Balcombe d				15 21																				
Haywards Heath 3 a				15 26			15 30				15 36		15 42								15 54		16 00	
d				15 27			15 34	15 37			15 38		15 46								15 55		16 04	16 07
Wivelsfield 4 d				15 31									15 50								15 59			16 11
Lewes 4 a							15 48																	16 22
Burgess Hill 4 d				15 33									15 52								16 01		16 09	
Hassocks 4 d				15 36									15 55							←	16 04			
Preston Park d				15 43									16 02							16 02	16 11			
Hove 2 a								15 51					→										16 21	
Brighton 10 a			15 27	15 51							15 56								15 58	16 07	16 19			

For general notes see front of timetable
For details of catering facilities see Directory of Train Operators

§ It is unknown at the time of going to press, when this station will open. For further details please contact National Rail Enquiries 08457-484950 or see local publicity.

A To Portsmouth Harbour (Table 188) and to Bognor Regis (Table 188)

B To Tunbridge Wells (Table 206)

C To Littlehampton (Table 188)

Table 186

Saturdays

Watford Junction, Bedford and London → Brighton

Network Diagram - see first page of Table 186

	GW	SE	FC	GX	SN	LO	SN	SN	FC	GX	SN		SN	SN	FC	GW	SN	GX	SN	GW	SE	SN	SN
		88																			13		
	1	1	1	1	1		1	1	1	1	1		1	1	1	1	1	1	1	1		1	1
		A			B														C		D		
London Victoria 15 ⊖ d				15 30	15 32			15 36		15 45	15 47							16 00	16 02			16 06	
Watford Junction d													15 11										
Harrow & Wealdstone ⊖ d													15 17										
Wembley Central d																							
Willesden Jn. High Level d						15 38																	
Shepherds Bush § ⊖ d																							
Kensington Olympia ⊖ d						15 47							15 42										
West Brompton ⊖ d						15 49							15 45										
Imperial Wharf § d																							
Clapham Junction 10 d					15 38	15a59		15 42			15 53		15 54						16 08			16 12	
Bedford 7 d			14 10						14 25						14 40								
Luton 10 d			14 34						14 49						15 04								
Luton Airport Parkway 7 ✈ d			14 36						14 51						15 06								
St Albans d			14 48						15 03						15 18								
St Pancras International 15 ⊖ d			15 09						15 24						15 39								
Farringdon 3 ⊖ d			15 14						15 29						15 44								
City Thameslink 3 d			15 16						15 31						15 46								
London Blackfriars 3 ⊖ d			15 20						15 35						15 50								
London Bridge 4 ⊖ d			15 26				15 33		15 41						15 56						16 03		
Norwood Junction 2 d							15 46														16 16		
East Croydon a			15 39		15 48		15 49	15 52	15 54		16 03		16 07		16 09				16 18		16 19	16 22	
d			15 39		15 48		15 51	15 52	15 54		16 03		16 07		16 09				16 18		16 21	16 22	
Purley 4 d							15 57														16 26		
Coulsdon South d							16 00														16 30		
Merstham d							16 06														16 35		
Redhill a					16 00		16 09							←					16 30		16 38		
d	15 41	15 44			16 00		16 10							16 10		16 14			16 30	16 34	16 39		
Tonbridge 4 a							↪														17 08		
Reigate a																16 18				16 38			
Earlswood (Surrey) d														16 12									
Salfords d														16 16									
Horley 4 d		15 51												16 19					16 36				
Gatwick Airport 10 ✈ a	15 50	15 55	15 55	16 00	16 08				16 10	16 15	16 18		16 22	16 23	16 25		←	16 30	16 39				
d		15 55	15 56		16 09				16 11		16 19		16 28	16 24	16 26		16 28		16 40				
Three Bridges 4 a		16 00			16 14				16 15				↪	16 29			16 33		16 44				
d		16 01			16 14				16 15					16 30			16 33		16 45				
Crawley d		16 04			16 18									16 33					16 48				
Ifield d		16 07												16 36									
Faygate d																							
Littlehaven d		16 13												16 42									
Horsham 4 a		16 16			16 26									16 47					16 56				
Balcombe d									16 21														
Haywards Heath 3 a			16 06						16 26		16 30				16 36		16 42						
d			16 08						16 27		16 34	16 37			16 38		16 46						
Wivelsfield 4 d									16 31								16 50						
Lewes 4 a											16 48												
Burgess Hill 4 d									16 33								16 52						
Hassocks 4 d									16 36								16 55						←
Preston Park d									16 43								17 02						17 02
Hove 2 a												16 51					↪						
Brighton 10 a			16 26					16 27	16 51						16 56							16 58	17 07

For general notes see front of timetable
For details of catering facilities see Directory of Train Operators

§ It is unknown at the time of going to press, when this station will open. For further details please contact National Rail Enquiries 08457-484950 or see local publicity.

A From Tunbridge Wells (Table 209)

B To Southampton Central (Table 188) and to Bognor Regis (Table 188)

C To Portsmouth Harbour (Table 188) and to Bognor Regis (Table 188)

D To Tunbridge Wells (Table 206)

Table 186

Saturdays

Watford Junction, Bedford and London → Brighton

Network Diagram - see first page of Table 186

	FC	GX	SN		GW	SE	FC		GX	LO	SN	SN	SN	FC	GX	SN		SN	SN	FC	GW	SN	GX	LO
						88																		
	1	1	1		1	1	1		1		1	1	1	1	1	1		1	1	1	1	1	1	
			A			B					C													
London Victoria 15 ⊖ d		16 15	16 17						16 30		16 32		16 36		16 45	16 47							17 00	
Watford Junction d																		16 11						
Harrow & Wealdstone ⊖ d																		16 17						
Wembley Central d																								
Willesden Jn. High Level d										16 08														16 38
Shepherds Bush § ⊖ d																								
Kensington Olympia ⊖ d										16 17								16 42						16 47
West Brompton ⊖ d										16 19								16 45						16 49
Imperial Wharf § d																								
Clapham Junction 10 d			16 23							16a29	16 38		16 42			16 53		16 54						16a59
Bedford 7 d	14 55						15 10							15 25						15 40				
Luton 10 d	15 19						15 34							15 49						16 04				
Luton Airport Parkway 7 ✈ d	15 21						15 36							15 51						16 06				
St Albans d	15 33						15 48							16 03						16 18				
St Pancras International 15 ⊖ d	15 54						16 09							16 24						16 39				
Farringdon 3 ⊖ d	15 59						16 14							16 29						16 44				
City Thameslink 3 d	16 01						16 16							16 31						16 46				
London Blackfriars 3 ⊖ d	16 05						16 20							16 35						16 50				
London Bridge 4 ⊖ d	16 11						16 26					16 33		16 41						16 56				
Norwood Junction 2 d												16 46												
East Croydon a	16 24		16 33				16 39				16 48	16 49	16 52	16 54		17 03		17 07		17 09				
d	16 24		16 33				16 39				16 48	16 51	16 52	16 54		17 03		17 07		17 09				
Purley 4 d												16 57												
Coulsdon South d												17 00												
Merstham d												17 06												
Redhill a											17 00	17 09							←					
d					16 41	16 44					17 00	17 10							17 10		17 14			
Tonbridge 4 a												→												
Reigate a																					17 18			
Earlswood (Surrey) d																			17 12					
Salfords d																			17 16					
Horley 4 d						16 51													17 19					
Gatwick Airport 10 ✈ a	16 40	16 45	16 48		16 50	16 55	16 55		17 00		17 08			17 10	17 15	17 18		17 22	17 23	17 25		←	17 30	
d	16 41		16 49			16 55	16 56				17 09			17 11		17 19		17 28	17 24	17 26		17 28		
Three Bridges 4 a	16 45					17 00					17 14			17 15				→	17 29			17 33		
d	16 45					17 01					17 14			17 15					17 30			17 33		
Crawley d						17 04					17 18								17 33					
Ifield d						17 07													17 36					
Faygate d																								
Littlehaven d						17 13													17 42					
Horsham 4 a						17 16					17 26								17 47					
Balcombe d														17 21										
Haywards Heath 3 a	16 54		17 00				17 06							17 26		17 30				17 36		17 42		
d	16 55		17 04	17 07			17 08							17 27		17 34	17 37			17 38		17 46		
Wivelsfield 4 d	16 59			17 11										17 31								17 50		
Lewes 4 a				17 22												17 52								
Burgess Hill 4 d	17 01		17 09											17 33								17 52		
Hassocks 4 d	17 04													17 36								17 55		
Preston Park d	17 11													17 43								18 02		
Hove 2 a			17 21														17 51					→		
Brighton 10 a	17 19						17 26						17 27	17 51						17 56				

For general notes see front of timetable
For details of catering facilities see Directory of Train Operators

§ It is unknown at the time of going to press, when this station will open. For further details please contact National Rail Enquiries 08457-484950 or see local publicity.

A To Littlehampton (Table 188)
B From Tunbridge Wells (Table 209)
C To Southampton Central (Table 188) and to Bognor Regis (Table 188)

Watford Junction, Bedford and London → Brighton

Network Diagram - see first page of Table 186

Station		SN	GW	SE 13	SN	SN	FC	GX	SN	SN	GW	SE 88	FC	GX	LO	SN	SN	SN	FC	GX	SN	SN	SN	LO
		1	1		1	1	1	1	1		1	1	1	1		1	1	1	1	1	1		1	
		A		B					C			D				E								
London Victoria [15]	⊖ d	17 02			17 06			17 15	17 17					17 30		17 32		17 36		17 45	17 47			
Watford Junction	d																						17 11	
Harrow & Wealdstone	⊖ d																						17 17	
Wembley Central	d																							
Willesden Jn. High Level	d														17 08									17 38
Shepherds Bush §	⊖ d																							
Kensington Olympia	⊖ d														17 17								17 42	17 47
West Brompton	⊖ d														17 19								17 45	17 49
Imperial Wharf §	d																							
Clapham Junction [10]	d	17 08			17 12				17 23						17a29	17 38		17 42			17 53		17 54	17a59
Bedford [7]	d						15 55						16 10						16 25					
Luton [10]	d						16 19						16 34						16 49					
Luton Airport Parkway [7]	✈ d						16 21						16 36						16 51					
St Albans	d						16 33						16 48						17 03					
St Pancras International [15]	⊖ d						16 54						17 09						17 24					
Farringdon [3]	⊖ d						16 59						17 14						17 29					
City Thameslink [3]	d						17 01						17 16						17 31					
London Blackfriars [3]	⊖ d						17 05						17 20						17 35					
London Bridge [4]	⊖ d			17 03			17 11						17 26				17 33		17 41					
Norwood Junction [2]	d			17 16													17 46							
East Croydon	🚌 a	17 18		17 19	17 22		17 24		17 33				17 39			17 48	17 49	17 52	17 54		18 03		18 07	
	d	17 18		17 21	17 22		17 24		17 33				17 39			17 48	17 51	17 52	17 54		18 03		18 07	
Purley [4]	d			17 26													17 57							
Coulsdon South	d			17 30													18 00							
Merstham	d			17 35													18 06							
Redhill	a	17 30		17 38												18 00	18 09							
	d	17 30	17 34	17 39							17 41	17 44				18 00	18 10							
Tonbridge [4]	a			18 08													→							
Reigate	a		17 38																					
Earlswood (Surrey)	d																							
Salfords	d																							
Horley [4]	d	17 36										17 51												
Gatwick Airport [10]	✈ a	17 39					17 40	17 45	17 48		17 50	17 55	17 55	18 00		18 08			18 10	18 15	18 18		18 22	
	d	17 40					17 41		17 49			17 55	17 56			18 09			18 11		18 19		18 28 →	
Three Bridges [4]	a	17 44					17 45					18 00				18 14			18 15					
	d	17 45					17 45					18 01				18 14			18 15					
Crawley	d	17 48										18 04				18 18								
Ifield	d											18 07												
Faygate	d																							
Littlehaven	d											18 13												
Horsham [4]	a	17 56										18 16				18 26								
Balcombe	d																		18 21					
Haywards Heath [3]	a						17 54		18 00				18 06						18 26		18 30			
	d						17 55		18 04	18 07			18 08						18 27		18 34	18 37		
Wivelsfield [4]	d						17 59			18 11									18 31					
Lewes [4]	a									18 22											18 52			
Burgess Hill [4]	d						18 01		18 09										18 33					
Hassocks [4]	d					←	18 04												18 36					
Preston Park	d					18 02	18 11												18 43					
Hove [2]	a								18 21													18 51		
Brighton [10]	a				17 58	18 07	18 19						18 26					18 27	18 51					

For general notes see front of timetable
For details of catering facilities see Directory of Train Operators

§ It is unknown at the time of going to press, when this station will open. For further details please contact National Rail Enquiries 08457-484950 or see local publicity.

A To Portsmouth Harbour (Table 188) and to Bognor Regis (Table 188)
B To Tunbridge Wells (Table 206)
C To Littlehampton (Table 188)
D From Tunbridge Wells (Table 209)
E To Southampton Central (Table 188) and to Bognor Regis (Table 188)

Table 186

Saturdays

Watford Junction, Bedford and London → Brighton

Network Diagram - see first page of Table 186

		SN	FC	GW	SN	GX	SE 88	SN	GW	SE 13	SN	SN	FC	GX	SN		GW	SE 88	FC	GX	LO	SN	SN	SN
		1	1	1	1	1		1	1		1	1	1	1	1		1	1	1	1		1	1	1
								A		B					C			D				E		
London Victoria 15	⊖ d					18 00		18 02			18 06			18 15	18 17					18 30		18 32		18 36
Watford Junction	d																							
Harrow & Wealdstone	⊖ d																							
Wembley Central	d																							
Willesden Jn. High Level	d																				18 08			
Shepherds Bush §	⊖ d																							
Kensington Olympia	⊖ d																				18 17			
West Brompton	⊖ d																				18 19			
Imperial Wharf §	d																							
Clapham Junction 10	d							18 08			18 12				18 23						18a29	18 38		18 42
Bedford 7	d		16 40										16 55						17 10					
Luton 10	d		17 04										17 19						17 34					
Luton Airport Parkway 7	✈ d		17 06										17 21						17 36					
St Albans	d		17 18										17 33						17 48					
St Pancras International 15	⊖ d		17 39										17 54						18 09					
Farringdon 3	⊖ d		17 44										17 59						18 14					
City Thameslink 3	d		17 46										18 01						18 16					
London Blackfriars 3	⊖ d		17 50										18 05						18 20					
London Bridge 4	⊖ d		17 56							18 03			18 11						18 26				18 33	
Norwood Junction 2	d									18 16													18 46	
East Croydon	⇌ a		18 09					18 18		18 19	18 22		18 24		18 33				18 39			18 48	18 49	18 52
	d		18 09					18 18		18 21	18 22		18 24		18 33				18 39			18 48	18 51	18 52
Purley 4	d									18 26													18 57	
Coulsdon South	d									18 30													19 00	
Merstham	d									18 35													19 06	
Redhill	a	←						18 30		18 38												19 00	19 09	
	d	18 10		18 14			18 27	18 30	18 34	18 39							18 41	18 44				19 00	19 10	
Tonbridge 4	a									19 08													→	
Reigate	a			18 18					18 38															
Earlswood (Surrey)	d	18 12																						
Salfords	d	18 16																						
Horley 4	d	18 19						18 36										18 51						
Gatwick Airport 10	✈ a	18 23	18 25		←	18 30	18 34	18 39					18 40	18 45	18 48		18 50	18 55	18 55	19 00		19 08		
	d	18 24	18 26		18 28		18 35	18 40					18 41		18 49			18 55	18 56			19 09		
Three Bridges 4	a	18 29			18 33		18 40	18 44					18 45					19 00				19 14		
	d	18 30			18 33			18 45					18 45					19 01				19 14		
Crawley	d	18 33						18 48										19 04				19 18		
Ifield	d	18 36																19 07						
Faygate	d																							
Littlehaven	d	18 42																19 13						
Horsham 4	a	18 47						18 56										19 16				19 26		
Balcombe	d																							
Haywards Heath 3	a		18 36		18 42								18 54		19 00				19 06					
	d		18 38		18 46								18 55		19 04	19 07			19 08					
Wivelsfield 4	d				18 50								18 59			19 11								
Lewes 4	a															19 22								
Burgess Hill 4	d				18 52								19 01		19 09									
Hassocks 4	d				18 55							←	19 04											
Preston Park	d				19 02							19 02	19 11											
Hove 2	a				→										19 21									
Brighton 10	a		18 56								18 58		19 07	19 19					19 26					19 27

For general notes see front of timetable
For details of catering facilities see Directory of Train Operators

§ It is unknown at the time of going to press, when this station will open. For further details please contact National Rail Enquiries 08457-484950 or see local publicity.

A To Portsmouth Harbour (Table 188) and to Bognor Regis (Table 188)
B To Tunbridge Wells (Table 206)
C To Littlehampton (Table 188)
D From Tunbridge Wells (Table 209)
E To Southampton Central (Table 188) and to Bognor Regis (Table 188)

Table 186

Watford Junction, Bedford and London → Brighton

Network Diagram - see first page of Table 186

	FC	GX	SN		SN	LO	SN	FC	GW	SN	GX		SE 88	SN	GW	SE 13	SN	SN	FC	SN	GX	SN		LO
	1	1	1		1		1	1	1	1	1			1	1		1	1	1	1	1	1		
														A								B		
London Victoria 15 ⊖ d		18 45	18 47								19 00			19 02			19 06			19 10	19 15	19 17		
Watford Junction d					18 11																			
Harrow & Wealdstone ⊖ d					18 17																			
Wembley Central d																								
Willesden Jn. High Level d						18 38																		19 08
Shepherds Bush § ⊖ d																								
Kensington Olympia ⊖ d					18 42	18 47																		19 17
West Brompton ⊖ d					18 45	18 49																		19 19
Imperial Wharf § d																								
Clapham Junction 10 d			18 53		18 54	18a59								19 08			19 12			19 16		19 23		19a29
Bedford 7 d	17 25							17 40											17 50					
Luton 10 d	17 49							18 04											18 14					
Luton Airport Parkway 7 ✈ d	17 51							18 06											18 16					
St Albans d	18 03							18 18											18 28					
St Pancras International 15 ⊖ d	18 24							18 39											18 54					
Farringdon 3 ⊖ d	18 29							18 44											18 59					
City Thameslink 3 d	18 31							18 46											19 01					
London Blackfriars 3 ⊖ d	18 35							18 50											19 04					
London Bridge 4 ⊖ d	18 41							18 56								19 03			19 11					
Norwood Junction 2 d																19 16								
East Croydon ⇌ a	18 54		19 03		19 07			19 09						19 18		19 19	19 22		19 24	19 28		19 33		
d	18 54		19 03		19 07			19 09						19 18		19 21	19 22		19 24	19 28		19 33		
Purley 4 d																19 25				19 33				
Coulsdon South d																19 29				19 37				
Merstham d																19 34				19 42				
Redhill a							⟵							19 30		19 38				⟶				
d							19 10		19 14				19 27	19 30	19 34	19 39								
Tonbridge 4 a																20 08								
Reigate a									19 18						19 38									
Earlswood (Surrey) d							19 12																	
Salfords d							19 16																	
Horley 4 d							19 19							19 36										
Gatwick Airport 10 ✈ a	19 10	19 15	19 18		19 22		19 23	19 25		⟵	19 30		19 34	19 39					19 40		19 45	19 48		
d	19 11		19 19		19 28		19 24	19 26		19 28			19 35	19 40					19 41			19 49		
Three Bridges 4 a	19 15				⟶		19 28			19 33			19 40	19 44					19 45					
d	19 15						19 30			19 33				19 45					19 45					
Crawley d							19 33							19 48										
Ifield d							19 36																	
Faygate d																								
Littlehaven d							19 42																	
Horsham 4 a							19 47							19 56										
Balcombe d	19 21																							
Haywards Heath 3 a	19 26		19 30					19 36		19 42									19 54			20 00		
d	19 27		19 34	19 37				19 38		19 46									19 55			20 04	20 07	
Wivelsfield 4 d	19 31									19 50									19 59				20 11	
Lewes 4 a			19 52																				20 22	
Burgess Hill 4 d	19 33									19 52									20 01			20 09		
Hassocks 4 d	19 36									19 55								⟵	20 04					
Preston Park d	19 43									20 02								20 02	20 11					
Hove 2 a				19 51						⟶												20 21		
Brighton 10 a	19 51							19 56									19 58	20 07	20 19					

For general notes see front of timetable
For details of catering facilities see Directory of Train Operators

§ It is unknown at the time of going to press, when this station will open. For further details please contact National Rail Enquiries 08457-484950 or see local publicity.

A To Portsmouth Harbour (Table 188) and to Bognor Regis (Table 188)

B To Littlehampton (Table 188)

Table 186

Saturdays

Watford Junction, Bedford and London → Brighton

Network Diagram - see first page of Table 186

		GW	XC	SN	FC	GX	LO	SN	SN	SN	FC	GX	SN		SN	SN	FC	GW	SN	GX	SE 88	SN	LO	SN
		1	1 ◇	1	1	1		1	1	1	1	1	1		1	1	1	1	1	1		1		1
			A					B					C									D		
London Victoria 15	⊖ d					19 30		19 32		19 36		19 45	19 47							20 00		20 02		20 06
Watford Junction	d														19 11									
Harrow & Wealdstone	⊖ d														19 17									
Wembley Central	d																							
Willesden Jn. High Level	d						19 38																20 08	
Shepherds Bush §	⊖ d																							
Kensington Olympia	⊖ d		19 02				19 47								19 42								20 17	
West Brompton	⊖ d						19 49								19 45								20 19	
Imperial Wharf §	d																							
Clapham Junction 10	d						19a59	19 38		19 42			19 53		19 54							20 08	20a29	20 12
Bedford 7	d				18 10						18 20						18 40							
Luton 10	d				18 34						18 44						19 04							
Luton Airport Parkway 7	✈ d				18 36						18 46						19 06							
St Albans	d				18 48						18 58						19 18							
St Pancras International 15	⊖ d				19 09						19 24						19 39							
Farringdon 3	⊖ d				19 14						19 29						19 44							
City Thameslink 3	d				19 16						19 31						19 46							
London Blackfriars 3	⊖ d				19 20						19 34						19 50							
London Bridge 4	⊖ d				19 26				19 33		19 41						19 56							
Norwood Junction 2	d								19 46															
East Croydon	⇌ a		19 36		19 39			19 48	19 50	19 52	19 54		20 03		20 07		20 09					20 19		20 22
	d		19 37		19 39			19 48	19 51	19 52	19 54		20 03		20 07		20 09					20 19		20 22
Purley 4	d								19 57															
Coulsdon South	d			←					20 00															
Merstham	d			19 42					20 06															
Redhill	a			19 46				20 00	20 09							←						20 30		
	d	19 41		19 46				20 00	20 10							20 10		20 14			20 27	20 31		
Tonbridge 4	a								→															
Reigate	a																	20 18						
Earlswood (Surrey)	d															20 12								
Salfords	d															20 16								
Horley 4	d			19 52												20 19								
Gatwick Airport 10	✈ a	19 50	19 52	19 55	19 56	20 00		20 08			20 10	20 15	20 18		20 22	20 23	20 25		←	20 30	20 34	20 38		
	d		19 53	19 56	19 56			20 09			20 11		20 19		20 28	20 24	20 26		20 28		20 35	20 39		
Three Bridges 4	a			20 01				20 14			20 15				→	20 29			20 33		20 40	20 44		
	d			20 01				20 14			20 15					20 33			20 33			20 44		
Crawley	d			20 05				20 18								20 36						20 48		
Ifield	d			20 07												20 39								
Faygate	d																							
Littlehaven	d			20 14												20 45								
Horsham 4	a			20 17				20 26								20 49						20 56		
Balcombe	d										20 21													
Haywards Heath 3	a		20 04		20 10					20 15	20 26		20 30				20 36		20 42					
	d		20 09		20 10					20 15	20 27		20 34	20 37			20 38		20 46					
Wivelsfield 4	d										20 31			20 41					20 50					
Lewes 4	a													20 54										
Burgess Hill 4	d										20 33		20 39						20 52					
Hassocks 4	d										20 36		20 42						20 55					
Preston Park	d										20 43		20 49						21 02					
Hove 2	a												20 53						→					
Brighton 10	a		20 28		20 28					20 29	20 51						20 56							20 58

For general notes see front of timetable
For details of catering facilities see Directory of Train Operators

§ It is unknown at the time of going to press, when this station will open. For further details please contact National Rail Enquiries 08457-484950 or see local publicity.

A From Birmingham New Street (Table 116)
B To Southampton Central (Table 188) and to Bognor Regis (Table 188)
C To Littlehampton (Table 188)
D To Portsmouth Harbour (Table 188) and to Bognor Regis (Table 188)

Table 186

Saturdays

Watford Junction, Bedford and London → Brighton

Network Diagram - see first page of Table 186

		GW	SN	FC	SN	GX	SN		GW	SN	GX	SN	LO	SN	FC		GW	SN	GX	SN		SN	SN	GX	SE
		1	1	1	1	1	1		1	1	1	1		1	1		1	1	1	1		1	1	1	88
							A					B								A					
London Victoria 15	⊖ d				20 10	20 15	20 17				20 30	20 32		20 36				20 40	20 45	20 47				21 00	
Watford Junction	d																					20 13			
Harrow & Wealdstone	⊖ d																					20 19			
Wembley Central	d																								
Willesden Jn. High Level	d												20 38												
Shepherds Bush §	⊖ d																								
Kensington Olympia	⊖ d												20 47									20 42			
West Brompton	⊖ d												20 49									20 45			
Imperial Wharf §	d																								
Clapham Junction 10	d				20 16		20 23					20 38	21a00	20 42				20 46		20 53		20 54			
Bedford 7	d			18 50											19 20										
Luton 10	d			19 14											19 44										
Luton Airport Parkway 7	✈ d			19 16											19 46										
St Albans	d			19 28											19 58										
St Pancras International 15	⊖ d			19 54											20 24										
Farringdon 3	⊖ d			19 59											20 29										
City Thameslink 3	d			20 01											20 31										
London Blackfriars 3	⊖ d			20 04											20 34										
London Bridge 4	⊖ d			20 11											20 41										
Norwood Junction 2	d																								
East Croydon	a			20 24	20 28		20 33					20 48		20 52	20 54			20 58		21 03		21 07			
	d			20 24	20 28		20 33					20 48		20 52	20 54			20 58		21 03		21 07			
Purley 4	d				20 33													21 03							
Coulsdon South	d				20 37					←								21 06							
Merstham	d				20 42					20 42								21 12							
Redhill	a				→					20 46		21 00						21 15					←		
	d	20 34							20 41	20 46		21 00					21 14	21 16					21 16		21 27
Tonbridge 4	a																	→							
Reigate	a	20 38															21 18								
Earlswood (Surrey)	d																						21 18		
Salfords	d																						21 22		
Horley 4	d									20 52													21 25		
Gatwick Airport 10	✈ a			20 41		20 45	20 48		20 50	20 56	21 00	21 08			21 10				21 15	21 18		21 22	21 28	21 30	21 34
	d			20 41			20 49			20 57		21 09			21 11					21 19			21 29		21 35
Three Bridges 4	a			20 45						21 02		21 14			21 15								21 33		21 40
	d			20 45						21 02		21 14			21 15								21 36		
Crawley	d									21 06		21 18											21 39		
Ifield	d									21 08													21 42		
Faygate	d																								
Littlehaven	d									21 15													21 48		
Horsham 4	a									21 18		21 26											21 52		
Balcombe	d			20 51																					
Haywards Heath 3	a			20 58			21 01							21 15	21 24					21 30					
	d			20 58			21 05	21 07						21 15	21 26					21 34	21 37				
Wivelsfield 4	d			21 02				21 11							21 30						21 41				
Lewes 4	a							21 22													21 54				
Burgess Hill 4	d			21 04			21 10								21 32					21 39					
Hassocks 4	d		←	21 08											21 35					21 42					
Preston Park	d		21 02	21 15											21 42					21 49					
Hove 2	a						21 21													21 53					
Brighton 10	a		21 07	21 22										21 30	21 50										

For general notes see front of timetable
For details of catering facilities see Directory of Train Operators

§ It is unknown at the time of going to press, when this station will open. For further details please contact National Rail Enquiries 08457-484950 or see local publicity.

A To Littlehampton (Table 188)

B To Southampton Central (Table 188) and to Bognor Regis (Table 188)

Watford Junction, Bedford and London → Brighton

Network Diagram - see first page of Table 186

		XC 1 ◇	LO	SN 1	SN 1	SN 1	FC 1	SN 1	GX 1	XC 1 ◇	SN 1		GW 1	SN 1	GW 1	GX 1		SN 1	LO	SN 1	FC 1	SN 1	GX 1	SN 1	
		A								A	B							C							
		🍴								🍴															
London Victoria 15	⊖ d			21 02	21 06			21 10	21 15		21 17					21 30		21 32		21 36		21 40	21 45	21 47	
Watford Junction	d																								
Harrow & Wealdstone	⊖ d																								
Wembley Central	d																								
Willesden Jn. High Level	d		21 08																21 38						
Shepherds Bush §	⊖ d																								
Kensington Olympia	⊖ d		21 17																21 47						
West Brompton	⊖ d		21 19																21 49						
Imperial Wharf §	d																								
Clapham Junction 10	d		21a29	21 08	21 12			21 16			21 23							21 38	21a59	21 42		21 46		21 53	
Bedford 7	d						19 50														20 20				
Luton 10	d						20 14														20 44				
Luton Airport Parkway 7	✈ d						20 16														20 46				
St Albans	d						20 28														20 58				
St Pancras International 15	⊖ d						20 54														21 24				
Farringdon 3	⊖ d						20 59														21 29				
City Thameslink 3	d						21 01																		
London Blackfriars 3	⊖ d						21 04														21 34				
London Bridge 4	⊖ d						21 11														21 41				
Norwood Junction 2	d																								
East Croydon	🚋 a			21 18	21 22		21 24	21 28			21 33							21 48		21 52	21 54	21 58		22 03	
	d			21 18	21 22		21 24	21 28			21 33							21 48		21 52	21 54	21 58		22 03	
Purley 4	d							21 33														22 03			
Coulsdon South	d							21 37						←								22 06			
Merstham	d							21 42						21 42								22 12			
Redhill	a	21 28		21 30				→		←				21 46				21 59				22 15			
	d	21 34		21 31						21 34			21 36	21 46	21 49			22 00				22 16			
Tonbridge 4	a	→																				→			
Reigate	a												21 40												
Earlswood (Surrey)	d																								
Salfords	d																								
Horley 4	d													21 52											
Gatwick Airport 10	✈ a			21 38		←	21 40		21 45	21 47	21 48			21 55	21 59	22 00		22 08			22 10		22 15	22 18	
	d			21 39		21 39	21 41				21 49			21 56				22 09			22 11			22 19	
Three Bridges 4	a			→		21 44	21 45				21 53			22 00				22 14			22 15				
	d					21 44	21 45				21 53			22 01				22 14			22 15				
Crawley	d													22 05				22 18							
Ifield	d													22 07											
Faygate	d																								
Littlehaven	d													22 14											
Horsham 4	a													22 17				22 26							
Balcombe	d						21 51																		
Haywards Heath 3	a				21 45	21 52	21 58				22 02									22 15	22 24			22 30	
	d				21 45	21 53	21 58				22 06	22 08								22 15	22 26			22 34	22 37
Wivelsfield 4	d					21 57	22 02					22 12									22 30			22 38	
Lewes 4	a											22 23												22 51	
Burgess Hill 4	d					21 59	22 04				22 11										22 32				
Hassocks 4	d					22 02	22 08														22 35				
Preston Park	d					22 09	22 15														22 42				
Hove 2	a										22 22														22 51
Brighton 10	a				22 00	22 15	22 22													22 30	22 50				

For general notes see front of timetable
For details of catering facilities see Directory of Train Operators

§ It is unknown at the time of going to press, when this station will open. For further details please contact National Rail Enquiries 08457-484950 or see local publicity.

A From Birmingham New Street (Table 116)
B To Bognor Regis (Table 188) and to Eastbourne (Table 189)
C To Portsmouth & Southsea (Table 188)

Table 186

Saturdays

Watford Junction, Bedford and London → Brighton

Network Diagram - see first page of Table 186

		SN	SN	GX	SE	SN	LO	SN	SN	FC	SN	GX	SN	GW	SN	GX	GW		SN	LO	SN	FC	SN	GX	
		1	1	1	88	1		1	1	1	1	1	1 A	1	1	1	1		1 B		1	1	1	1	
London Victoria 15 ⊖	d			22 00		22 02		22 06			22 10	22 15	22 17			22 30			22 32		22 36		22 40	22 45	
Watford Junction	d	21 13																							
Harrow & Wealdstone ⊖	d	21 19																							
Wembley Central	d																								
Willesden Jn. High Level	d						22 08													22 38					
Shepherds Bush § ⊖	d																								
Kensington Olympia ⊖	d	21 42					22 17													22 47					
West Brompton ⊖	d	21 45					22 19													22 49					
Imperial Wharf §	d																								
Clapham Junction 10	d	21 54				22 08	22a29	22 12			22 16		22 23						22 38	22a59	22 42		22 46		
Bedford 7	d									20 50												21 20			
Luton 10	d									21 14												21 44			
Luton Airport Parkway 7 ✈	d									21 16												21 46			
St Albans	d									21 28												21 58			
St Pancras International 15 ⊖	d									21 54												22 24			
Farringdon 3 ⊖	d									21 59												22 29			
City Thameslink 3	d																								
London Blackfriars 3 ⊖	d									22 04												22 34			
London Bridge 4 ⊖	d									22 11												22 41			
Norwood Junction 2	d																								
East Croydon 🚋	a	22 07				22 18		22 22		22 24	22 28		22 33						22 48		22 52	22 54	22 58		
	d	22 07				22 18		22 22		22 24	22 28		22 33						22 48		22 52	22 54	22 58		
Purley 4	d										22 33												23 03		
Coulsdon South	d										22 37				←								23 07		
Merstham	d										22 42				22 42								23 12		
Redhill	a		←			22 30					→				22 46				23 00				23 16		
	d		22 16		22 27	22 31								22 34	22 46		22 56		23 01				23 16		
Tonbridge 4	a																						→		
Reigate	a													22 38											
Earlswood (Surrey)	d		22 18																						
Salfords	d		22 22																						
Horley 4	d		22 25												22 52										
Gatwick Airport 10 ✈	a	22 23	22 28	22 30	22 34	22 38			←	22 40		22 45	22 50		22 55	23 00	23 03		23 08			23 10		23 15	
	d		22 29		22 35	22 39			22 39	22 41			22 51		22 56				23 09			23 11			
Three Bridges 4	a		22 33		22 41	→			22 44	22 45			22 55		23 00				23 14			23 15			
	d		22 36						22 44	22 45			22 55		23 01				23 15			23 15			
Crawley	d		22 39												23 04				23 18						
Ifield	d		22 42												23 07										
Faygate	d																								
Littlehaven	d		22 48												23 13										
Horsham 4	a		22 52												23 16				23 26						
Balcombe	d									22 51															
Haywards Heath 3	a							22 45	22 52	22 58			23 04								23 15	23 24			
	d							22 45	22 53	22 58			23 04								23 15	23 26			
Wivelsfield 4	d								22 57	23 02												23 30			
Lewes 4	a																								
Burgess Hill 4	d								22 59	23 04			23 10									23 32			
Hassocks 4	d								23 02	23 08												23 35			
Preston Park	d								23 09	23 15												23 42			
Hove 2	a												23 21												
Brighton 10	a							23 00	23 15	23 22											23 30	23 50			

For general notes see front of timetable
For details of catering facilities see
Directory of Train Operators

§ It is unknown at the time of going to press, when this station will open. For further details please contact National Rail Enquiries 08457-484950 or see local publicity.

A To Bognor Regis (Table 188)
B To Chichester (Table 188)

Watford Junction, Bedford and London → Brighton

Network Diagram - see first page of Table 186

		SN 1		SN 1	GX 1	SN 1	GW 1	SN 1	LO	SN 1	SN 1	FC 1	SN 1	GX 1	SN 1	SN 1	GX 1	SN 1		FC	GX 1	SN 1	FC	FC 1	SN 1
															A										
London Victoria 15	⊖ d	22 47			23 00			23 02		23 06			23 10	23 15	23 17		23 30	23 32			23 45	23 47			
Watford Junction	d					22 11																			23 13
Harrow & Wealdstone	⊖ d					22 17																			23 19
Wembley Central	d																								
Willesden Jn. High Level	d								23 08																
Shepherds Bush §	⊖ d																								
Kensington Olympia	⊖ d					22 42			23 17																23 42
West Brompton	⊖ d					22 45			23 19																23 45
Imperial Wharf §	d																								
Clapham Junction 10	d	22 53				22a52		23 08	23a29	23 12			23 16		23 23			23 38				23 53			23a53
Bedford 7	d											21 50								22 10			22 40	23 10	
Luton 10	d											22 14								22 34			23 04	23 34	
Luton Airport Parkway 7	✈ d											22 16								22 36			23 06	23 36	
St Albans	d											22 28								22 48			23 18	23 48	
St Pancras International 15	⊖ d											22 54								23 24			23 54	00 24	
Farringdon 3	⊖ d											22 59								23 29			23 59	00 29	
City Thameslink 3	d																								
London Blackfriars 3	⊖ d											23 04								23 34			00 04	00 34	
London Bridge 4	⊖ d											23 11								23 41			00 16	00 41	
Norwood Junction 2	d																								
East Croydon	a	23 03						23 18		23 22		23 24	23 28		23 33			23 52		23 56		00 06	00 29	00 56	
	d	23 03						23 18		23 22		23 24	23 28		23 33			23 52		23 57		00 06	00 29	00 57	
Purley 4	d												23 33									00 12			
Coulsdon South	d												23 37									00 15			
Merstham	d												23 42									00 21			
Redhill	a			←				23 30					23 46			←		00 03				00 24			
	d			23 16			23 29	23 31					23 46			23 46		00 05				00 25			
Tonbridge 4	a												↳												
Reigate	a						23 33																		
Earlswood (Surrey)	d			23 19												23 49									
Salfords	d			23 22												23 52									
Horley 4	d			23 26												23 56						00 31			
Gatwick Airport 10	✈ a	23 18		23 28	23 30			23 38			←	23 40		23 45	23 50	23 58	00 05	00 13		00 17	00 20	00 33	00 47	01 16	
	d	23 19		23 29				23 39			23 39	23 41			23 51	23 59		00 14		00 18		00 34	00 47	01 17	
Three Bridges 4	a			23 34				↳			23 44	23 45			23 55	00 04		00 18		00 26		00 39	00 56	01 26	
	d			23 38							23 44	23 45			23 56	00 04		00 19				00 39			
Crawley	d			23 41												00 07						00 42			
Ifield	d			23 44												00 10						00 45			
Faygate	d																								
Littlehaven	d			23 50												00 16						00 51			
Horsham 4	a			23 53												00 19						00 54			
Balcombe	d											23 53						00 25							
Haywards Heath 3	a	23 30								23 45	23 52	23 58			00 04			00 30							
	d	23 34	23 37							23 45	23 53	23 58			00 05			00 30							
Wivelsfield 4	d	23 38									23 57	00 02						00 34							
Lewes 4	a	23 51																							
Burgess Hill 4	d										23 59	00 04			00 10			00 36							
Hassocks 4	d										00 02	00 08						00 40							
Preston Park	d										00 09	00 15						00 47							
Hove 2	a		23 51												00 21										
Brighton 10	a									23 59	00 15	00 22						00 51							

For general notes see front of timetable
For details of catering facilities see
Directory of Train Operators

§ It is unknown at the time of going to press, when this station will open. For further details please contact National Rail Enquiries 08457-484950 or see local publicity.

A To Chichester (Table 188)

Table 186

Sundays

Watford Junction, Bedford and London → Brighton

Network Diagram - see first page of Table 186

Station		SN 1	FC 1	SN 1	SN 1 A	SN 1	GW 1	SN 1	FC	SN 1	GX 1	SN 1 B		FC	SN 1	GW 1		FC 1	GX 1	SN 1	SN 1	SN 1	GX 1	SN 1	GX 1
London Victoria 15	⊖ d	23p02		23p10	23p17			23p32		23p47	00 01	00 05			00 14				00 30	01 00	02 02	03 00	03 30	04 00	04 30
Watford Junction	d																								
Harrow & Wealdstone	⊖ d																								
Wembley Central	d																								
Willesden Jn. High Level	d																								
Shepherds Bush §	⊖ d																								
Kensington Olympia	⊖ d																								
West Brompton	⊖ d																								
Imperial Wharf §	d																								
Clapham Junction 10	d	23p08		23p16	23p23			23p38		23p53		00 11			00 20					01 08	02 08	03 08		04 08	
Bedford 7	d		21p50						22p10					22p40				23p10							
Luton 10	d		22p14						22p34					23p04				23p34							
Luton Airport Parkway 7	✈ d		22p16						22p36					23p06				23p36							
St Albans	d		22p28						22p48					23p18				23p48							
St Pancras International 15	⊖ d		22p54						23p24					23p54				00 24							
Farringdon 3	⊖ d		22p59						23p29					23p59				00 29							
City Thameslink 3	d																								
London Blackfriars 3	⊖ d		23p04						23p34					00 04				00 34							
London Bridge 4	⊖ d		23p11						23p41					00 16				00 41							
Norwood Junction 2	d																								
East Croydon	🚋 a	23p18	23p24	23p28	23p33			23p52	23p56	00 06		00 24		00 29	00 32			00 56		01 21	02 21	03 21		04 21	
	d	23p18	23p24	23p28	23p33			23p52	23p57	00 06		00 25		00 29	00 33			00 57		01 22	02 22	03 22		04 22	
Purley 4	d			23p33						00 12					00 38					01 27	02 27	03 27		04 27	
Coulsdon South	d			23p37						00 15					00 41										
Merstham	d			23p42						00 21					00 47										
Redhill	a	23p30		23p46		←		00 03		00 24					00 50										
	d	23p31		23p46		23p46	00 03	00 05		00 25					00 51	00 53									
Tonbridge 4	a			→																					
Reigate	a																								
Earlswood (Surrey)	d					23p49																			
Salfords	d					23p52																			
Horley 4	d					23p56				00 31										01 43	02 42	03 42		04 43	
Gatwick Airport 10	✈ a	23p38	23p40		23p50	23p58	00 10	00 13	00 17	00 33	00 35	00 42		00 47	00 58	01 00		01 16	01 20	01 45	02 44	03 44	04 05	04 45	05 05
	d	23p39	23p41		23p51	23p59		00 14	00 18	00 34		00 43		00 47	01 00			01 17		01 47	02 46	03 46		04 47	
Three Bridges 4	a	23p44	23p45		23p55	00 04		00 18	00 26	00 39		00 48		00 56	01 04			01 26		01 51	03 00	04 00		04 54	
	d	23p44	23p45		23p56	00 04		00 19		00 39		00 48								01 52				04 55	
Crawley	d					00 07				00 42															
Ifield	d					00 10				00 45															
Faygate	d																								
Littlehaven	d					00 16				00 51															
Horsham 4	a					00 19				00 54															
Balcombe	d		23p53					00 25																	
Haywards Heath 3	a	23p52	23p58		00 04			00 30				00 56													
	d	23p53	23p58		00 05			00 30				01 00	01 02												
Wivelsfield 4	d	23p57	00 02					00 34																	
Lewes 4	a												01 16												
Burgess Hill 4	d	23p59	00 04		00 10			00 36																	
Hassocks 4	d	00 02	00 08					00 40																	
Preston Park	d	00 09	00 15					00 47																	
Hove 2	a				00 21							01s22													
Brighton 10	a	00 15	00 22					00 51				01s14								02 20				05 20	

For general notes see front of timetable
For details of catering facilities see
Directory of Train Operators

§ It is unknown at the time of going to press, when this station will open. For further details please contact National Rail Enquiries 08457-484950 or see local publicity.

A To Chichester (Table 188)
B To Eastbourne (Table 189)

Table 186

Sundays

Watford Junction, Bedford and London → Brighton

Network Diagram - see first page of Table 186

		GX	SN	GX	GX	GX	SN	SN	GX	GX		GW	GX	SN	GX	GW	GW	GX	SE 88	SN	FC	GX	GX	SN	SN
		1	1	1	1	1	1	1	1	1		1	1	1	1	1	1	1		1	1	1	1	1	1
																				A					
London Victoria 15 ⊖	d	05 00	05 02	05 15	05 30	05 45		05 47	06 00	06 15			06 30	06 32	06 45			07 00		07 02		07 15	07 30	07 32	07 34
Watford Junction	d																								
Harrow & Wealdstone ⊖	d																								
Wembley Central	d																								
Willesden Jn. High Level	d																								
Shepherds Bush § ⊖	d																								
Kensington Olympia ⊖	d																								
West Brompton ⊖	d																								
Imperial Wharf §	d																								
Clapham Junction 10	d		05 08					05 53						06 38						07 08				07 38	07 40
Bedford 7	d																				05 40				
Luton 10	d																				06 04				
Luton Airport Parkway 7 ✈	d																				06 06				
St Albans	d																				06 18				
St Pancras International 15 ⊖	d																				06 54				
Farringdon 3 ⊖	d																				06 59				
City Thameslink 3	d																								
London Blackfriars 3 ⊖	d																				07 04				
London Bridge 4 ⊖	d																				07 11				
Norwood Junction 2	d																								
East Croydon	a		05 22					06 05						06 51						07 23	07 26			07 50	07 53
	d		05 23					06 06						06 52						07 23	07 27			07 51	07 54
Purley 4	d		05 29											06 56						07 28					07 59
Coulsdon South	d													07 00											08 03
Merstham	d													07 05											08 08
Redhill	a							06 18						07 09						07 36				08 03	↳
	d							06 19				06 19		07 09		07 19	07 21		07 29	07 37				08 04	
Tonbridge 4	a																								
Reigate	a											06 23				07 23									
Earlswood (Surrey)	d																								
Salfords	d																								
Horley 4	d							06 22						07 15						07 44					
Gatwick Airport 10 ✈	a	05 35	05 45	05 50	06 05	06 20		06 31	06 35	06 50			07 05	07 18	07 20		07 30	07 35	07 38	07 46	07 48	07 50	08 05	08 11	
	d		05 46				06 29	06 32						07 19					07 39	07 47	07 50			08 12	
Three Bridges 4	a		05 50				06 33	06 36						07 23					07 43	07 52	07 54			08 16	
	d		05 51				06 40	06 36						07 24						07 52	07 54			08 17	
Crawley	d						06 43													07 55					
Ifield	d						06 46													07 58					
Faygate	d																								
Littlehaven	d						06 52													08 04					
Horsham 4	a						06 56													08 07					
Balcombe	d													07 30										08 23	
Haywards Heath 3	a		05 59					06 46						07 35							08 03			08 28	
	d		06 00					06 47						07 36							08 03			08 28	
Wivelsfield 4	d							06 51						07 40										08 32	
Lewes 4	a																								
Burgess Hill 4	d							06 53						07 42							08 08			08 34	
Hassocks 4	d							06 56						07 45										08 38	
Preston Park	d							07 03						07 52										08 45	
Hove 2	a																								
Brighton 10	a		06 18					07 08						07 58							08 24			08 50	

For general notes see front of timetable
For details of catering facilities see
Directory of Train Operators

A To Bognor Regis (Table 188)

§ It is unknown at the time of going to press, when this station will open. For further details please contact National Rail Enquiries 08457-484950 or see local publicity.

Table 186

Sundays

Watford Junction, Bedford and London → Brighton

Network Diagram - see first page of Table 186

Station		FC	GX	SN		SN	GW	GW	GX	SE	SN	FC	GX	SN	GX	SN	SN	SN	FC	GX		SN	SN	GW	GW
										55															
		1	1	1		1	1	1	1		1	1	1	1	1	1	1	1	1	1		1	1	1	1
										A	B			C											
London Victoria 15 ⊖	d		07 45						08 00		08 04		08 15	08 17	08 30		08 32	08 34		08 45			08 47		
Watford Junction	d																								
Harrow & Wealdstone ⊖	d																								
Wembley Central	d																								
Willesden Jn. High Level	d																								
Shepherds Bush § ⊖	d																								
Kensington Olympia ⊖	d					07 47										08 18									
West Brompton ⊖	d					07 49										08 20									
Imperial Wharf §	d																								
Clapham Junction 10	d					08a00					08 10			08 23		08a30	08 38	08 40					08 53		
Bedford 7	d	06 10										06 40							07 10						
Luton 10	d	06 34										07 04							07 34						
Luton Airport Parkway 7 ✈	d	06 36										07 06							07 36						
St Albans	d	06 48										07 18							07 48						
St Pancras International 15 ⊖	d	07 24										07 54							08 24						
Farringdon 3 ⊖	d	07 29										07 59							08 29						
City Thameslink 3	d																								
London Blackfriars 3 ⊖	d	07 34										08 04							08 34						
London Bridge 4 ⊖	d	07 41										08 11							08 41						
Norwood Junction 2	d																								
East Croydon 🚋	a	07 56									08 23	08 26		08 36			08 50	08 53	08 56				09 06		
	d	07 57									08 23	08 27		08 37			08 51	08 54	08 57				09 07		
Purley 4	d										08 29							08 59							
Coulsdon South	d			←														09 03				←			
Merstham	d			08 08														09 08				09 08			
Redhill	a			08 12							08 37						09 03	→				09 12			
	d			08 12			08 19	08 21		08 29	08 38						09 04					09 12		09 19	09 21
Tonbridge 4	a																								
Reigate	a						08 23																	09 23	
Earlswood (Surrey)	d																								
Salfords	d																								
Horley 4	d			08 22							08 44											09 22			
Gatwick Airport 10 ✈	a	08 18	08 20	08 24				08 30	08 35	08 38	08 46	08 48	08 50	08 54	09 05		09 11		09 18	09 20		09 24	09 27		09 30
	d	08 20		08 25						08 39	08 47	08 50		08 56			09 12		09 20			09 25	09 29		
Three Bridges 4	a	08 24		08 30						08 43	08 52	08 54					09 16		09 24			09 30			
	d	08 24		08 33							08 52	08 54					09 17		09 24			09 33			
Crawley	d			08 36							08 55											09 36			
Ifield	d			08 39																		09 39			
Faygate	d																								
Littlehaven	d			08 45																		09 45			
Horsham 4	a			08 49							09 04											09 49			
Balcombe	d																09 23								
Haywards Heath 3	a	08 33										09 03		09 06			09 28		09 33				09 40		
	d	08 33										09 03		09 07			09 28		09 33				09 41		
Wivelsfield 4	d																09 32						09 45		
Lewes 4	a																						09 58		
Burgess Hill 4	d	08 38										09 08		09 12			09 34		09 38						
Hassocks 4	d	08 42															09 38		09 42						
Preston Park	d																09 45								
Hove 2	a													09 24											
Brighton 10	a	08 54										09 24					09 50		09 54						

For general notes see front of timetable
For details of catering facilities see Directory of Train Operators

§ It is unknown at the time of going to press, when this station will open. For further details please contact National Rail Enquiries 08457-484950 or see local publicity.

A From Gillingham (Kent) (Table 208)

B To Bognor Regis (Table 188)

C To Portsmouth Harbour (Table 188) and to Littlehampton (Table 188)

Table 186

Sundays

Watford Junction, Bedford and London → Brighton

Network Diagram - see first page of Table 186

		GX	SE	SN	SN	FC	GX	SN	GX	SN	SN	FC	LO	GX		SN	SN	SN	GW	GW	GW	GX	SE	SN	FC
			55																				55		
		1		1	1	1	1	1	1	1	1	1		1		1	1	1	1	1	1	1		1	1
			A		B			C												D	E		A	B	
London Victoria 15	⊖ d	09 00			09 04		09 15	09 17	09 30	09 32	09 34			09 45			09 47					10 00		10 04	
Watford Junction	d																	09 22							
Harrow & Wealdstone	⊖ d																	09 28							
Wembley Central	d																								
Willesden Jn. High Level	d												09 06												
Shepherds Bush §	⊖ d																								
Kensington Olympia	⊖ d			08 48									09 15					09 47							
West Brompton	⊖ d			08a50									09 17					09 49							
Imperial Wharf §	d																								
Clapham Junction 10	d			09a00	09 10			09 23		09 38	09 40		09a26				09 53	10a00						10 10	
Bedford 7	d					07 50						08 20													08 50
Luton 10	d					08 14						08 44													09 14
Luton Airport Parkway 7	✈ d					08 16						08 46													09 16
St Albans	d					08 28						08 58													09 28
St Pancras International 15	⊖ d					08 54						09 24													09 54
Farringdon 3	⊖ d					08 59						09 29													09 59
City Thameslink 3	d																								
London Blackfriars 3	⊖ d					09 04						09 34													10 04
London Bridge 4	⊖ d					09 11						09 41													10 11
Norwood Junction 2	d																								
East Croydon	a				09 23	09 26		09 36		09 50	09 53	09 56					10 06							10 23	10 26
	d				09 23	09 27		09 37		09 51	09 54	09 57					10 07							10 23	10 27
Purley 4	d				09 29						09 59													10 29	
Coulsdon South	d										10 03					←									
Merstham	d										10 08					10 08									
Redhill	a				09 37					10 03	→					10 12								10 37	
	d		09 29		09 38					10 04						10 12			10 21	10 22	10 24		10 30	10 38	
Tonbridge 4	a																								
Reigate	a																		10 25						
Earlswood (Surrey)	d																								
Salfords	d																								
Horley 4	d				09 44											10 22								10 44	
Gatwick Airport 10	✈ a	09 35	09 38		09 46	09 48	09 50	09 54	10 05	10 11		10 18		10 20		10 24	10 27			10 31	10 31	10 35	10 38	10 46	10 48
	d		09 39		09 47	09 50		09 56		10 12		10 20				10 25	10 29						10 39	10 47	10 50
Three Bridges 4	a		09 43		09 52	09 54				10 16		10 24				10 30							10 43	10 52	10 54
	d				09 52	09 54				10 17		10 24				10 33								10 52	10 54
Crawley	d				09 55											10 36								10 55	
Ifield	d															10 39									
Faygate	d																								
Littlehaven	d															10 45									
Horsham 4	a				10 04											10 49								11 04	
Balcombe	d									10 23															
Haywards Heath 3	a					10 03		10 06		10 28		10 33					10 40								11 03
	d					10 03		10 07		10 28		10 33					10 41								11 03
Wivelsfield 4	d									10 32							10 45								
Lewes 4	a																10 58								
Burgess Hill 4	d					10 08		10 12		10 34		10 38													11 08
Hassocks 4	d									10 38		10 42													
Preston Park	d									10 45															
Hove 2	a							10 24																	
Brighton 10	a					10 24				10 50		10 54													11 24

For general notes see front of timetable
For details of catering facilities see Directory of Train Operators

§ It is unknown at the time of going to press, when this station will open. For further details please contact National Rail Enquiries 08457-484950 or see local publicity.

A From Maidstone West (Table 208)
B To Bognor Regis (Table 188)
C To Portsmouth Harbour (Table 188) and to Littlehampton (Table 188)
D From 3 February
E Until 27 January

Watford Junction, Bedford and London → Brighton

Network Diagram - see first page of Table 186

Station		GX	SN	GX	SN	SN	FC	LO		GX	SN	SN	SN	GW	GW	GX	SE	SN	FC	GX	SN	GX	SN	SN	FC
		1	1	1	1	1	1			1	1	1	1	1	1	1	55	1	1	1	1	1	1	1	1
			A														B	C			A				
London Victoria 15	⊖ d	10 15	10 17	10 30	10 32	10 34				10 45		10 47				11 00		11 04		11 15	11 17	11 30	11 32	11 34	
Watford Junction	d												10 22												
Harrow & Wealdstone	⊖ d												10 27												
Wembley Central	d																								
Willesden Jn. High Level	d							10 06																	
Shepherds Bush §	⊖ d																								
Kensington Olympia	⊖ d							10 15					10 47												
West Brompton	⊖ d							10 17					10 49												
Imperial Wharf §	d																								
Clapham Junction 10	d		10 23		10 38	10 40		10a26				10 53	11a00					11 10			11 23		11 38	11 40	
Bedford 7	d						09 20												09 50						10 20
Luton 10	d						09 44												10 14						10 44
Luton Airport Parkway 7	✈ d						09 46												10 16						10 46
St Albans	d						09 58												10 28						10 58
St Pancras International 15	⊖ d						10 24												10 54						11 24
Farringdon 3	⊖ d						10 29												10 59						11 29
City Thameslink 3	d																								
London Blackfriars 3	⊖ d						10 34												11 04						11 34
London Bridge 4	⊖ d						10 41												11 11						11 41
Norwood Junction 2	d																								
East Croydon	🚋 a		10 36		10 50	10 53	10 56					11 06						11 23	11 26		11 36		11 50	11 53	11 56
	d		10 37		10 51	10 54	10 57					11 07						11 23	11 27		11 37		11 51	11 54	11 57
Purley 4	d					10 59												11 29						11 59	
Coulsdon South	d					11 03					←													12 03	
Merstham	d					11 08					11 08													12 08	
Redhill	a				11 03	→					11 12							11 37					12 03	→	
	d				11 04						11 12			11 19	11 21		11 30	11 38					12 04		
Tonbridge 4	a																								
Reigate	a													11 23											
Earlswood (Surrey)	d																								
Salfords	d																								
Horley 4	d										11 22							11 44							
Gatwick Airport 10	✈ a	10 50	10 54	11 05	11 11		11 18			11 20	11 24	11 27			11 30	11 35	11 38	11 46	11 48	11 50	11 54	12 05	12 11		12 18
	d		10 56		11 12		11 20				11 25	11 29					11 39	11 47	11 50		11 56		12 12		12 20
Three Bridges 4	a				11 16		11 24				11 30						11 43	11 52	11 54				12 16		12 24
	d				11 17		11 24				11 33							11 52	11 54				12 17		12 24
Crawley	d										11 36							11 55							
Ifield	d										11 39														
Faygate	d																								
Littlehaven	d										11 45														
Horsham 4	a										11 49							12 04							
Balcombe	d				11 23																		12 23		
Haywards Heath 3	a		11 06		11 28		11 33					11 40							12 03		12 06		12 28		12 33
	d		11 07		11 28		11 33					11 41							12 03		12 07		12 28		12 33
Wivelsfield 4	d				11 32							11 45											12 32		
Lewes 4	a											11 58													
Burgess Hill 4	d		11 12		11 34		11 38												12 08		12 12		12 34		12 38
Hassocks 4	d				11 38		11 42																12 38		12 42
Preston Park	d				11 45																		12 45		
Hove 2	a		11 24																		12 24				
Brighton 10	a				11 50		11 54												12 24				12 49		12 54

For general notes see front of timetable
For details of catering facilities see Directory of Train Operators

§ It is unknown at the time of going to press, when this station will open. For further details please contact National Rail Enquiries 08457-484950 or see local publicity.

A To Portsmouth Harbour (Table 188) and to Littlehampton (Table 188)

B From Maidstone West (Table 208)

C To Bognor Regis (Table 188)

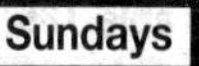

Watford Junction, Bedford and London → Brighton

Network Diagram - see first page of Table 186

Station		LO		GX	SN	SN	SN	GW	GW	GX	SE	SN	FC	GX	SN	GX	SN	SN		FC	LO	GX	SN	SN	SN
											55														
				1	1	1	1	1	1	1		1	1	1	1	1	1	1		1		1	1	1	1
											A	B			C										
London Victoria 15	⊖ d			11 45		11 47				12 00		12 04		12 15	12 17	12 30	12 32	12 34				12 45		12 47	
Watford Junction	d						11 22																		12 22
Harrow & Wealdstone	⊖ d						11 28																		12 28
Wembley Central	d																								
Willesden Jn. High Level	d	11 06																			12 06				
Shepherds Bush §	⊖ d																								
Kensington Olympia	⊖ d	11 15					11 47														12 15				12 47
West Brompton	⊖ d	11 17					11 49														12 17				12 49
Imperial Wharf §	d																								
Clapham Junction 10	d	11a26				11 53	12a00					12 10			12 23		12 38	12 40			12a26			12 53	13a00
Bedford 7	d												10 50							11 20					
Luton 10	d												11 14							11 44					
Luton Airport Parkway 7	✈ d												11 16							11 46					
St Albans	d												11 28							11 58					
St Pancras International 15	⊖ d												11 54							12 24					
Farringdon 3	⊖ d												11 59							12 29					
City Thameslink 3	d																								
London Blackfriars 3	⊖ d												12 04							12 34					
London Bridge 4	⊖ d												12 11							12 41					
Norwood Junction 2	d																								
East Croydon	🚋 a					12 06						12 23	12 26		12 36		12 50	12 53		12 56				13 06	
	d					12 07						12 23	12 27		12 37		12 51	12 54		12 57				13 07	
Purley 4	d											12 29						12 59							
Coulsdon South	d				←													13 03					←		
Merstham	d				12 08													13 08					13 08		
Redhill	a				12 12							12 37					13 03	→					13 12		
	d				12 12			12 19	12 22		12 30	12 38					13 04						13 12		
Tonbridge 4	a																								
Reigate	a							12 23																	
Earlswood (Surrey)	d																								
Salfords	d																								
Horley 4	d				12 22							12 44											13 22		
Gatwick Airport 10	✈ a			12 20	12 24	12 27			12 30	12 35	12 38	12 46	12 48	12 50	12 54	13 05	13 11			13 18		13 20	13 24	13 27	
	d				12 25	12 29					12 39	12 47	12 50		12 56		13 12			13 20			13 25	13 29	
Three Bridges 4	a				12 30						12 43	12 52	12 54				13 16			13 24			13 30		
	d				12 33							12 52	12 54				13 17			13 24			13 33		
Crawley	d				12 36							12 55											13 36		
Ifield	d				12 39																		13 39		
Faygate	d																								
Littlehaven	d				12 45																		13 45		
Horsham 4	a				12 49							13 04											13 49		
Balcombe	d																13 23								
Haywards Heath 3	a					12 40							13 03		13 06		13 28			13 33				13 40	
	d					12 41							13 03		13 07		13 28			13 33				13 41	
Wivelsfield 4	d					12 45											13 32							13 45	
Lewes 4	a					12 58																		13 58	
Burgess Hill 4	d												13 08		13 12		13 34			13 38					
Hassocks 4	d																13 38			13 42					
Preston Park	d																13 45								
Hove 2	a														13 24										
Brighton 10	a												13 24				13 50			13 54					

For general notes see front of timetable
For details of catering facilities see
Directory of Train Operators

§ It is unknown at the time of going to press, when this station will open. For further details please contact National Rail Enquiries 08457-484950 or see local publicity.

A From Maidstone West (Table 208)
B To Bognor Regis (Table 188)
C To Portsmouth Harbour (Table 188) and to Littlehampton (Table 188)

Table 186

Sundays

Watford Junction, Bedford and London → Brighton

Network Diagram - see first page of Table 186

	GW	GW	GX	SE 55	SN	FC	GX	SN	GX	SN	SN		FC	LO	GX	SN	SN	SN	GW	GW	GX	SE 55	SN	FC
	1	1	1		1	1	1	1	1	1	1		1		1	1	1	1	1	1	1		1	1
				A	B			C														A	B	
London Victoria 15 ⊖ d			13 00		13 04		13 15	13 17	13 30	13 32	13 34				13 45		13 47				14 00		14 04	
Watford Junction d																		13 22						
Harrow & Wealdstone ⊖ d																		13 28						
Wembley Central d																								
Willesden Jn. High Level d														13 06										
Shepherds Bush § ⊖ d																								
Kensington Olympia ⊖ d														13 15				13 47						
West Brompton ⊖ d														13 17				13 48						
Imperial Wharf § d																								
Clapham Junction 10 d					13 10			13 23		13 38	13 40			13a26			13 53	14a00					14 10	
Bedford 7 d						11 50							12 20											12 50
Luton 10 d						12 14							12 44											13 14
Luton Airport Parkway 7 ✈ d						12 16							12 46											13 16
St Albans d						12 28							12 58											13 28
St Pancras International 15 ⊖ d						12 54							13 24											13 54
Farringdon 3 ⊖ d						12 59							13 29											13 59
City Thameslink 3 d																								
London Blackfriars 3 ⊖ d						13 04							13 34											14 04
London Bridge 4 ⊖ d						13 11							13 41											14 11
Norwood Junction 2 d																								
East Croydon a					13 23	13 26		13 36		13 50	13 53		13 56				14 06						14 23	14 26
d					13 23	13 27		13 37		13 51	13 54		13 57				14 07						14 23	14 27
Purley 4 d					13 29						13 59												14 29	
Coulsdon South d											14 03					←								
Merstham d											14 08					14 08								
Redhill a					13 37					14 03	→					14 12							14 37	
d	13 19	13 21		13 30	13 38					14 04						14 12			14 20	14 22		14 30	14 38	
Tonbridge 4 a																								
Reigate a	13 23																		14 24					
Earlswood (Surrey) d																								
Salfords d																								
Horley 4 d					13 44											14 22							14 44	
Gatwick Airport 10 ✈ a		13 30	13 35	13 38	13 46	13 48	13 50	13 54	14 05	14 11			14 18		14 20	14 24	14 27			14 30	14 35	14 38	14 46	14 48
d				13 39	13 47	13 50		13 56		14 12			14 20			14 25	14 29					14 39	14 47	14 50
Three Bridges 4 a				13 43	13 52	13 54				14 16			14 24			14 30						14 43	14 52	14 54
d					13 52	13 54				14 17			14 24			14 33							14 52	14 54
Crawley d					13 55											14 36							14 55	
Ifield d																14 39								
Faygate d																								
Littlehaven d																14 45								
Horsham 4 a					14 04											14 49							15 04	
Balcombe d										14 23														
Haywards Heath 3 a						14 03		14 06		14 28			14 33				14 40							15 03
d						14 03		14 07		14 28			14 33				14 41							15 03
Wivelsfield 4 d										14 32							14 45							
Lewes 4 a																	14 58							
Burgess Hill 4 d						14 08		14 12		14 34			14 38											15 08
Hassocks 4 d										14 38			14 42											
Preston Park d										14 45														
Hove 2 a								14 24																
Brighton 10 a						14 24				14 50			14 54											15 24

For general notes see front of timetable
For details of catering facilities see Directory of Train Operators

§ It is unknown at the time of going to press, when this station will open. For further details please contact National Rail Enquiries 08457-484950 or see local publicity.

A From Maidstone West (Table 208)

B To Bognor Regis (Table 188)

C To Portsmouth Harbour (Table 188) and to Littlehampton (Table 188)

Table 186

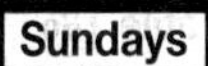

Watford Junction, Bedford and London → Brighton

Network Diagram - see first page of Table 186

		GX	SN	GX	SN	SN		FC	LO	GX	SN	SN	SN	LO	GW	GW	GX	SE	SN	FC	GX	SN		GX	SN
																		55							
		1	1	1	1	1		1		1	1	1	1		1	1	1		1	1	1	1		1	1
			A															B	C			A			
London Victoria 15	⊖ d	14 15	14 17	14 30	14 32	14 34				14 45		14 47					15 00		15 04		15 15	15 17		15 30	15 32
Watford Junction	d												14 22												
Harrow & Wealdstone	⊖ d												14 28												
Wembley Central	d																								
Willesden Jn. High Level	d								14 06					14 51											
Shepherds Bush §	⊖ d																								
Kensington Olympia	⊖ d								14 15				14 47	15 00											
West Brompton	⊖ d								14 17				14 49	15 02											
Imperial Wharf §	d																								
Clapham Junction 10	d		14 23		14 38	14 40			14a26			14 53	15a00	15a11					15 10			15 23			15 38
Bedford 7	d							13 20												13 50					
Luton 10	d							13 44												14 14					
Luton Airport Parkway 7	✈ d							13 46												14 16					
St Albans	d							13 58												14 28					
St Pancras International 15	⊖ d							14 24												14 54					
Farringdon 3	⊖ d							14 29												14 59					
City Thameslink 3	d																								
London Blackfriars 3	⊖ d							14 34												15 04					
London Bridge 4	⊖ d							14 41												15 11					
Norwood Junction 2	d																								
East Croydon	⇌ a		14 36		14 50	14 53		14 56				15 06							15 23	15 26		15 36			15 50
	d		14 37		14 51	14 54		14 57				15 07							15 23	15 27		15 37			15 51
Purley 4	d					14 59													15 29						
Coulsdon South	d					15 03					←														
Merstham	d					15 08					15 08														
Redhill	a				15 03	→					15 12								15 37						16 03
	d				15 04						15 12				15 19	15 21		15 30	15 38						16 04
Tonbridge 4	a																								
Reigate	a														15 23										
Earlswood (Surrey)	d																								
Salfords	d																								
Horley 4	d										15 22								15 44						
Gatwick Airport 10	✈ a	14 50	14 54	15 05	15 11			15 18		15 20	15 24	15 27				15 30	15 35	15 38	15 46	15 48	15 50	15 54		16 05	16 11
	d		14 56		15 12			15 20			15 25	15 29						15 39	15 47	15 50		15 56			16 12
Three Bridges 4	a				15 16			15 24			15 30							15 43	15 52	15 54					16 16
	d				15 17			15 24			15 33								15 52	15 54					16 17
Crawley	d										15 36								15 55						
Ifield	d										15 39														
Faygate	d																								
Littlehaven	d										15 45														
Horsham 4	a										15 49								16 04						
Balcombe	d				15 23																				16 23
Haywards Heath 3	a		15 06		15 28			15 33				15 40								16 03		16 06			16 28
	d		15 07		15 28			15 33				15 41								16 03		16 07			16 28
Wivelsfield 4	d				15 32							15 45													16 32
Lewes 4	a											15 58													
Burgess Hill 4	d		15 12		15 34			15 38												16 08		16 12			16 34
Hassocks 4	d				15 38			15 42																	16 38
Preston Park	d				15 45																				16 45
Hove 2	a		15 24																			16 24			
Brighton 10	a				15 50			15 54												16 24					16 50

For general notes see front of timetable
For details of catering facilities see Directory of Train Operators

§ It is unknown at the time of going to press, when this station will open. For further details please contact National Rail Enquiries 08457-484950 or see local publicity.

A To Portsmouth Harbour (Table 188) and to Littlehampton (Table 188)

B From Maidstone West (Table 208)

C To Bognor Regis (Table 188)

Table 186

Sundays

Watford Junction, Bedford and London → Brighton

Network Diagram - see first page of Table 186

		SN	FC	LO	GX	SN	SN	SN	LO	GW	GW	GX	SE	SN	FC	GX		SN	GX	SN	SN	FC	LO	GX	SN
													55												
		1	1		1	1	1	1		1	1	1		1	1	1		1	1	1	1	1		1	1
													A	B				C							
London Victoria 15	⊖ d	15 34			15 45		15 47					16 00		16 04		16 15		16 17	16 30	16 32	16 34			16 45	
Watford Junction	d							15 22																	
Harrow & Wealdstone	⊖ d							15 28																	
Wembley Central	d																								
Willesden Jn. High Level	d			15 21					15 51														16 21		
Shepherds Bush §	⊖ d																								
Kensington Olympia	⊖ d			15 30				15 48	16 00														16 30		
West Brompton	⊖ d			15 32				15 50	16 02														16 32		
Imperial Wharf §	d																								
Clapham Junction 10	d	15 40		15a41			15 53	16a00	16a11					16 10				16 23		16 38	16 40		16a41		
Bedford 7	d		14 20												14 50							15 20			
Luton 10	d		14 44												15 14							15 44			
Luton Airport Parkway 7	✈ d		14 46												15 16							15 46			
St Albans	d		14 58												15 28							15 58			
St Pancras International 15	⊖ d		15 24												15 54							16 24			
Farringdon 3	⊖ d		15 29												15 59							16 29			
City Thameslink 3	d																								
London Blackfriars 3	⊖ d		15 34												16 04							16 34			
London Bridge 4	⊖ d		15 41												16 11							16 41			
Norwood Junction 2	d																								
East Croydon	🚋 a	15 53	15 56				16 06							16 23	16 26			16 36		16 50	16 53	16 56			
	d	15 54	15 57				16 07							16 23	16 27			16 37		16 51	16 54	16 57			
Purley 4	d	15 59												16 29							16 59				
Coulsdon South	d	16 03				←															17 03				←
Merstham	d	16 08				16 08															17 08				17 08
Redhill	a	→				16 12								16 37						17 03	→				17 12
	d					16 12				16 20	16 22		16 30	16 38						17 04					17 12
Tonbridge 4	a																								
Reigate	a									16 24															
Earlswood (Surrey)	d																								
Salfords	d																								
Horley 4	d					16 22								16 44											17 22
Gatwick Airport 10	✈ a		16 18		16 20	16 24	16 27				16 30	16 35	16 38	16 46	16 48	16 50		16 54	17 05	17 11		17 18		17 20	17 24
	d		16 20			16 25	16 29						16 39	16 47	16 50			16 56		17 12		17 20			17 25
Three Bridges 4	a		16 24			16 30							16 43	16 52	16 54					17 16		17 24			17 30
	d		16 24			16 33								16 52	16 54					17 17		17 24			17 33
Crawley	d					16 36								16 55											17 36
Ifield	d					16 39																			17 39
Faygate	d																								
Littlehaven	d					16 45																			17 45
Horsham 4	a					16 49								17 04											17 49
Balcombe	d																			17 23					
Haywards Heath 3	a		16 33				16 40								17 03			17 06		17 28		17 33			
	d		16 33				16 41								17 03			17 07		17 28		17 33			
Wivelsfield 4	d						16 45													17 32					
Lewes 4	a						16 58																		
Burgess Hill 4	d		16 38												17 08			17 12		17 34		17 38			
Hassocks 4	d		16 42																	17 38		17 42			
Preston Park	d																			17 45					
Hove 2	a																	17 24							
Brighton 10	a		16 54												17 24					17 50		17 54			

For general notes see front of timetable
For details of catering facilities see Directory of Train Operators

§ It is unknown at the time of going to press, when this station will open. For further details please contact National Rail Enquiries 08457-484950 or see local publicity.

A From Maidstone West (Table 208)

B To Bognor Regis (Table 188)

C To Portsmouth Harbour (Table 188) and to Littlehampton (Table 188)

Table 186

Sundays

Watford Junction, Bedford and London → Brighton

Network Diagram - see first page of Table 186

		SN	SN	LO	GW	GW	GX	SE	SN	SN		FC	GX	SN	GX	SN	SN	FC	LO	GX	SN	SN	SN	GW	GW
		1	1		1	1	1	55	1	1		1	1	1	1	1	1	1		1	1	1	1	1	1
								A		B				C											
London Victoria 15	⊖ d	16 47					17 00		17 02	17 04			17 15	17 17	17 30	17 32	17 34			17 45		17 47			
Watford Junction	d		16 22																				17 22		
Harrow & Wealdstone	⊖ d		16 28																				17 28		
Wembley Central	d																								
Willesden Jn. High Level	d			16 51															17 21						
Shepherds Bush §	⊖ d																								
Kensington Olympia	⊖ d		16 48	17 00															17 30				17 48		
West Brompton	⊖ d		16 50	17 02															17 32				17 50		
Imperial Wharf §	d																								
Clapham Junction 10	d	16 53	17a00	17a11					17 07	17 10				17 23		17 38	17 40		17a41			17 53	18a00		
Bedford 7	d											15 50						16 20							
Luton 10	d											16 14						16 44							
Luton Airport Parkway 7	✈ d											16 16						16 46							
St Albans	d											16 28						16 58							
St Pancras International 15	⊖ d											16 54						17 24							
Farringdon 3	⊖ d											16 59						17 29							
City Thameslink 3	d																								
London Blackfriars 3	⊖ d											17 04						17 34							
London Bridge 4	⊖ d											17 11						17 41							
Norwood Junction 2	d																								
East Croydon	🚋 a	17 06							17 20	17 23		17 26		17 36		17 50	17 53	17 56				18 06			
	d	17 07							17 20	17 24		17 27		17 37		17 51	17 54	17 57				18 07			
Purley 4	d									17 29							17 59								
Coulsdon South	d																18 03				←				
Merstham	d																18 08				18 08				
Redhill	a									17 37						18 03	→				18 12				
	d				17 19	17 21		17 30		17 38						18 04					18 12			18 20	18 22
Tonbridge 4	a																								
Reigate	a				17 23																			18 24	
Earlswood (Surrey)	d																								
Salfords	d																								
Horley 4	d									17 44											18 22				
Gatwick Airport 10	✈ a	17 27				17 30	17 35	17 38	17 41	17 46		17 48	17 50	17 54	18 05	18 11		18 18		18 20	18 24	18 27			18 30
	d	17 29						17 39	17 42	17 47		17 50		17 56		18 12		18 20			18 25	18 29			
Three Bridges 4	a							17 43		17 52		17 54				18 16		18 24			18 30				
	d									17 52		17 54				18 17		18 24			18 33				
Crawley	d									17 55											18 36				
Ifield	d																				18 39				
Faygate	d																								
Littlehaven	d																				18 45				
Horsham 4	a									18 04											18 49				
Balcombe	d															18 23									
Haywards Heath 3	a	17 40										18 03		18 06		18 28		18 33				18 40			
	d	17 41										18 03		18 07		18 28		18 33				18 41			
Wivelsfield 4	d	17 45														18 32						18 45			
Lewes 4	a	17 58																				18 58			
Burgess Hill 4	d											18 08		18 12		18 34		18 38							
Hassocks 4	d															18 38		18 42							
Preston Park	d															18 45									
Hove 2	a													18 24											
Brighton 10	a								18 05			18 24				18 50		18 54							

For general notes see front of timetable
For details of catering facilities see Directory of Train Operators

§ It is unknown at the time of going to press, when this station will open. For further details please contact National Rail Enquiries 08457-484950 or see local publicity.

A From Maidstone West (Table 208)
B To Bognor Regis (Table 188)

C To Portsmouth Harbour (Table 188) and to Littlehampton (Table 188)

Table 186

Sundays

Watford Junction, Bedford and London → Brighton

Network Diagram - see first page of Table 186

		GX	SE 55	SN		SN	FC	GX	SN	LO	GX	SN	SN	FC	LO	GX	SN	SN	SN	GW		GW	GX	SE 55	SN
		1		1		1	1	1	1		1	1	1	1		1	1	1	1	1		1	1		1
			A			B			C															A	
London Victoria 15 ⊖	d	18 00		18 02		18 04		18 15	18 17		18 30	18 32	18 34			18 45		18 47					19 00		19 02
Watford Junction	d																		18 22						
Harrow & Wealdstone ⊖	d																		18 28						
Wembley Central	d																								
Willesden Jn. High Level	d									17 51					18 21										
Shepherds Bush § ⊖	d																								
Kensington Olympia ⊖	d									18 00					18 30				18 48						
West Brompton ⊖	d									18 02					18 32				18 50						
Imperial Wharf §	d																								
Clapham Junction 10	d			18 07		18 10			18 23	18a11		18 38	18 40		18a41			18 53	19a00						19 07
Bedford 7	d						16 50							17 20											
Luton 10	d						17 14							17 44											
Luton Airport Parkway 7 ✈	d						17 16							17 46											
St Albans	d						17 28							17 58											
St Pancras International 15 ⊖	d						17 54							18 24											
Farringdon 3 ⊖	d						17 59							18 29											
City Thameslink 3	d																								
London Blackfriars 3 ⊖	d						18 04							18 34											
London Bridge 4 ⊖	d						18 11							18 41											
Norwood Junction 2	d																								
East Croydon	a			18 20		18 23	18 26		18 36			18 50	18 53	18 56				19 06							19 20
	d			18 20		18 24	18 27		18 37			18 51	18 54	18 57				19 07							19 20
Purley 4	d					18 29							18 59												
Coulsdon South	d												19 03				←								
Merstham	d												19 08				19 08								
Redhill	a					18 37						19 03	→				19 12								
	d		18 30			18 38						19 04					19 12			19 19		19 21		19 30	
Tonbridge 4	a																								
Reigate	a																			19 23					
Earlswood (Surrey)	d																								
Salfords	d																								
Horley 4	d					18 44											19 22								
Gatwick Airport 10 ✈	a	18 35	18 38	18 41		18 46	18 48	18 50	18 54		19 05	19 11		19 18		19 20	19 24	19 27				19 30	19 35	19 38	19 41
	d		18 39	18 42		18 47	18 50		18 56			19 12		19 20			19 25	19 29						19 39	19 42
Three Bridges 4	a		18 43			18 52	18 54					19 16		19 24			19 30							19 43	
	d					18 52	18 54					19 17		19 24			19 33								
Crawley	d					18 55											19 36								
Ifield	d																19 39								
Faygate	d																								
Littlehaven	d																19 45								
Horsham 4	a					19 04											19 49								
Balcombe	d											19 23													
Haywards Heath 3	a						19 03		19 06			19 28		19 33				19 40							
	d						19 03		19 07			19 28		19 33				19 41							
Wivelsfield 4	d											19 32						19 45							
Lewes 4	a																	19 58							
Burgess Hill 4	d						19 08		19 12			19 34		19 38											
Hassocks 4	d											19 38		19 42											
Preston Park	d											19 45													
Hove 2	a								19 24																
Brighton 10	a			19 05			19 24					19 50		19 54											20 05

For general notes see front of timetable
For details of catering facilities see
Directory of Train Operators

§ It is unknown at the time of going to press, when this station will open. For further details please contact National Rail Enquiries 08457-484950 or see local publicity.

A From Maidstone West (Table 208)
B To Bognor Regis (Table 188)
C To Portsmouth Harbour (Table 188) and to Littlehampton (Table 188)

Table 186

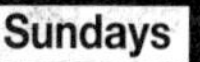

Sundays

Watford Junction, Bedford and London → Brighton

Network Diagram - see first page of Table 186

	SN	LO	FC	GX	SN	GX	SN	SN	FC	GX	SN	SN	LO	GW	GW	GX	SE 55	SN	SN	XC	SN	LO	FC
	1		1	1	1	1	1	1	1	1	1	1		1	1	1		1	1	1 ◇	1		1
	A				B												C			D 🍴	A		
London Victoria 15 ⊖ d	19 04			19 15	19 17	19 30	19 32	19 34		19 45		19 47				20 00			20 02		20 04		
Watford Junction d																		19 22					
Harrow & Wealdstone ⊖ d																		19 28					
Wembley Central d																							
Willesden Jn. High Level d		18 51											19 21									19 51	
Shepherds Bush § ⊖ d																							
Kensington Olympia ⊖ d		19 00											19 30					19 48				20 00	
West Brompton ⊖ d		19 02											19 32					19 50				20 02	
Imperial Wharf § d																							
Clapham Junction 10 d	19 10	19a11			19 23		19 38	19 40				19 53	19a41					20a00	20 07		20 10	20a11	
Bedford 7 d			17 50						18 20														18 50
Luton 10 d			18 14						18 44														19 14
Luton Airport Parkway 7 ✈ d			18 16						18 46														19 16
St Albans d			18 28						18 58														19 28
St Pancras International 15 ⊖ d			18 54						19 24														19 54
Farringdon 3 ⊖ d			18 59						19 29														19 59
City Thameslink 3 d																							
London Blackfriars 3 ⊖ d			19 04						19 34														20 04
London Bridge 4 ⊖ d			19 11						19 41														20 11
Norwood Junction 2 d																							
East Croydon 🚋 a	19 23		19 26		19 36		19 50	19 53	19 56			20 06							20 20		20 23		20 26
d	19 24		19 27		19 37		19 51	19 54	19 57			20 07							20 20		20 23		20 27
Purley 4 d	19 29							19 59													20 29		
Coulsdon South d								20 03			←												
Merstham d								20 08			20 08												
Redhill a	19 37						20 03	→			20 12									20 26	20 37		
d	19 38						20 04				20 12			20 20	20 22		20 30			20 33	20 38		
Tonbridge 4 a																							
Reigate a														20 24									
Earlswood (Surrey) d																							
Salfords d																							
Horley 4 d	19 44										20 22										20 44		
Gatwick Airport 10 ✈ a	19 46		19 48	19 50	19 54	20 05	20 11		20 18	20 20	20 24	20 27			20 30	20 35	20 38		20 41	20 43	20 46		20 48
d	19 47		19 50		19 56		20 12		20 20		20 25	20 29					20 39		20 42	20 45	20 47		20 50
Three Bridges 4 a	19 52		19 54				20 16		20 24		20 30						20 43				20 52		20 54
d	19 52		19 54				20 17		20 24		20 33										20 52		20 54
Crawley d	19 55										20 36										20 55		
Ifield d											20 39												
Faygate d																							
Littlehaven d											20 45												
Horsham 4 a	20 04										20 49										21 04		
Balcombe d							20 23																
Haywards Heath 3 a			20 03		20 06		20 28		20 33			20 40								20 54			21 03
d			20 03		20 07		20 28		20 33			20 41								20 54			21 03
Wivelsfield 4 d							20 32					20 45											
Lewes 4 a												20 58											
Burgess Hill 4 d			20 08		20 12		20 34		20 38														21 08
Hassocks 4 d							20 38		20 42														
Preston Park d							20 45																
Hove 2 a					20 24																		
Brighton 10 a			20 24				20 50		20 54										21 05	21 13			21 24

For general notes see front of timetable
For details of catering facilities see Directory of Train Operators

§ It is unknown at the time of going to press, when this station will open. For further details please contact National Rail Enquiries 08457-484950 or see local publicity.

A To Bognor Regis (Table 188)

B To Portsmouth Harbour (Table 188) and to Littlehampton (Table 188)

C From Maidstone West (Table 208)

D Until 27 January. From Birmingham New Street (Table 116)

Table 186

Sundays

Watford Junction, Bedford and London → Brighton

Network Diagram - see first page of Table 186

		GX	SN	GX	SN	SN	FC	GX		SN	LO	SN	GW	GW	GX	SE 55	XC	XC	SN	SN	LO	FC	GX	SN	GX
		1	1	1	1	1	1	1		1		1	1	1	1		1 ◇	1 ◇	1	1		1	1	1	1
			A													B	C	D		E				A	
London Victoria 15	⊖ d	20 15	20 17	20 30	20 32	20 34		20 45				20 47			21 00					21 04			21 15	21 17	21 30
Watford Junction	d																		20 22						
Harrow & Wealdstone	⊖ d																		20 28						
Wembley Central	d																								
Willesden Jn. High Level	d										20 21										20 51				
Shepherds Bush §	⊖ d																								
Kensington Olympia	⊖ d										20 30								20 48		21 00				
West Brompton	⊖ d										20 32								20 50		21 02				
Imperial Wharf §	d																								
Clapham Junction 10	d		20 23		20 38	20 40					20a43	20 53							21a00	21 10	21a11			21 23	
Bedford 7	d						19 20															19 50			
Luton 10	d						19 44															20 14			
Luton Airport Parkway 7	✈ d						19 46															20 16			
St Albans	d						19 58															20 28			
St Pancras International 15	⊖ d						20 24															20 54			
Farringdon 3	⊖ d						20 29															20 59			
City Thameslink 3	d																								
London Blackfriars 3	⊖ d						20 34															21 04			
London Bridge 4	⊖ d						20 41															21 11			
Norwood Junction 2	d																								
East Croydon	a		20 36		20 50	20 53	20 56					21 06								21 23		21 26		21 36	
	d		20 37		20 51	20 54	20 57					21 07								21 23		21 27		21 37	
Purley 4	d					20 59														21 29					
Coulsdon South	d					21 03				←															
Merstham	d					21 08				21 08															
Redhill	a				21 03	→				21 12							21 30	21 31		21 37					
	d				21 04					21 12			21 19	21 21		21 30	21 34	21 34		21 38					
Tonbridge 4	a																								
Reigate	a												21 23												
Earlswood (Surrey)	d																								
Salfords	d																								
Horley 4	d									21 22										21 44					
Gatwick Airport 10	✈ a	20 50	20 54	21 05	21 11		21 18	21 20		21 24		21 27		21 30	21 36	21 38	21 46	21 46		21 46		21 48	21 50	21 54	22 05
	d		20 56		21 12		21 20			21 25		21 29				21 39				21 47		21 50		21 56	
Three Bridges 4	a				21 16		21 24			21 30						21 43				21 52		21 54			
	d				21 17		21 24			21 33										21 52		21 54			
Crawley	d									21 36										21 55					
Ifield	d									21 39															
Faygate	d																								
Littlehaven	d									21 45															
Horsham 4	a									21 49										22 04					
Balcombe	d				21 23																				
Haywards Heath 3	a		21 06		21 28		21 33					21 40										22 03		22 06	
	d		21 07		21 28		21 33					21 41										22 03		22 07	
Wivelsfield 4	d				21 32							21 45													
Lewes 4	a											21 58													
Burgess Hill 4	d		21 12		21 34		21 38															22 08		22 12	
Hassocks 4	d				21 38		21 42																		
Preston Park	d				21 45																				
Hove 2	a		21 24																					22 24	
Brighton 10	a				21 50		21 54															22 24			

For general notes see front of timetable
For details of catering facilities see
Directory of Train Operators

§ It is unknown at the time of going to press, when this station will open. For further details please contact National Rail Enquiries 08457-484950 or see local publicity.

A To Portsmouth Harbour (Table 188) and to Littlehampton (Table 188)

B From Maidstone West (Table 208)

C Until 27 January. From Birmingham New Street (Table 116)

D 3 February to 23 March. From Birmingham New Street (Table 116)

E To Bognor Regis (Table 188)

Table 186

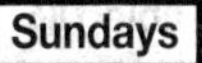

Watford Junction, Bedford and London → Brighton

Network Diagram - see first page of Table 186

		SN 1		SN 1	FC 1	GX 1	LO	SN 1	SN 1	SN 1	GW 1	GW 1 A	GX 1	GW 1 B	SN 1 C	LO	FC 1	GX 1		SN 1 D	GX 1	SN 1	SN 1	FC 1	GX 1
London Victoria 15	⊖ d	21 32		21 34		21 45			21 47				22 00		22 04			22 15		22 17	22 30	22 32	22 34		22 45
Watford Junction	d									21 22															
Harrow & Wealdstone	⊖ d									21 28															
Wembley Central	d																								
Willesden Jn. High Level	d						21 21									21 51									
Shepherds Bush §	⊖ d																								
Kensington Olympia	⊖ d						21 30			21 48						22 00									
West Brompton	⊖ d						21 32			21 50						22 02									
Imperial Wharf §	d																								
Clapham Junction 10	d	21 38		21 40			21a41		21 53	22a00					22 10	22a11				22 23		22 38	22 40		
Bedford 7	d				20 10												20 40							21 10	
Luton 10	d				20 34												21 04							21 34	
Luton Airport Parkway 7	✈ d				20 36												21 06							21 36	
St Albans	d				20 48												21 18							21 48	
St Pancras International 15	⊖ d				21 24												21 54							22 24	
Farringdon 3	⊖ d				21 29												21 59							22 29	
City Thameslink 3	d																								
London Blackfriars 3	⊖ d				21 34												22 04							22 34	
London Bridge 4	⊖ d				21 41												22 11							22 41	
Norwood Junction 2	d																								
East Croydon	🚋 a	21 50		21 53	21 56				22 06						22 23		22 26			22 36		22 50	22 53	22 56	
	d	21 51		21 54	21 57				22 07						22 23		22 27			22 37		22 51	22 54	22 57	
Purley 4	d			21 59											22 29								22 59		
Coulsdon South	d			22 03				←															23 03		
Merstham	d			22 08				22 08															23 08		
Redhill	a	22 03		→				22 12							22 37							23 03	→		
	d	22 04						22 12			22 19	22{22		22{31	22 38							23 04			
Tonbridge 4	a																								
Reigate	a										22 23														
Earlswood (Surrey)	d																								
Salfords	d																								
Horley 4	d							22 22							22 44										
Gatwick Airport 10	✈ a	22 11			22 18	22 20		22 24	22 27			22{31	22 35	22{39	22 46		22 48	22 50		22 54	23 05	23 11		23 18	23 20
	d	22 12			22 20			22 25	22 29						22 47		22 50			22 56		23 12		23 20	
Three Bridges 4	a	22 16			22 24			22 30							22 52		22 54					23 16		23 24	
	d	22 17			22 24			22 33							22 52		22 54					23 17		23 24	
Crawley	d							22 36							22 55										
Ifield	d							22 39																	
Faygate	d																								
Littlehaven	d							22 45																	
Horsham 4	a							22 49							23 04										
Balcombe	d	22 23																				23 23			
Haywards Heath 3	a	22 28			22 33				22 40								23 03			23 06		23 28		23 33	
	d	22 28			22 33				22 41								23 03			23 07		23 28		23 33	
Wivelsfield 4	d	22 32							22 45													23 32			
Lewes 4	a								22 58																
Burgess Hill 4	d	22 34			22 38												23 08			23 12		23 34		23 38	
Hassocks 4	d	22 38			22 42																	23 38		23 42	
Preston Park	d	22 45																				23 45			
Hove 2	a																			23 24					
Brighton 10	a	22 50			22 54												23 24					23 50		23 54	

For general notes see front of timetable
For details of catering facilities see
Directory of Train Operators

§ It is unknown at the time of going to press, when this station will open. For further details please contact National Rail Enquiries 08457-484950 or see local publicity.

A From 3 February
B Until 27 January
C To Bognor Regis (Table 188)
D To Worthing (Table 188)

Table 186

Sundays

Watford Junction, Bedford and London → Brighton

Network Diagram - see first page of Table 186

		LO	SN 1	SN 1	SN 1	LO	GW 1	GW 1	GX 1	SN 1	FC 1	GX 1		SN 1	SN 1	GX 1	SN 1	FC	LO	SN 1	GX 1	FC	FC 1		
London Victoria 15	⊖ d			22 47					23 00	23 04		23 15			23 17	23 30	23 32				23 45				
Watford Junction	d				22 22															23 22					
Harrow & Wealdstone	⊖ d				22 28															23 28					
Wembley Central	d																								
Willesden Jn. High Level	d	22 21				22 51													23 21						
Shepherds Bush §	⊖ d																								
Kensington Olympia	⊖ d	22 30			22 48	23 00													23 30	23 48					
West Brompton	⊖ d	22 32			22 50	23 02													23 32	23 50					
Imperial Wharf §	d																								
Clapham Junction 10	d	22a41		22 53	23a00	23a11				23 10					23 23		23 38		23a41	00 02					
Bedford 7	d										21 40							22 10				22 40	23 40		
Luton 10	d										22 04							22 34				23 04	00 04		
Luton Airport Parkway 7	✈ d										22 06							22 36				23 06	00 06		
St Albans	d										22 18							22 48				23 18	00 18		
St Pancras International 15	⊖ d										22 54							23 24				23 54	00 54		
Farringdon 3	⊖ d										22 59							23 29				23 59			
City Thameslink 3	d																								
London Blackfriars 3	⊖ d										23 04							23 34				00 04	01 04		
London Bridge 4	⊖ d										23 11							23 41				00 11			
Norwood Junction 2	d																								
East Croydon	🚋 a			23 06						23 23	23 26				23 36		23 52	23 56		00 20		00 26	01 30		
	d			23 07						23 23	23 27				23 37		23 53	23 57				00 27	01 32		
Purley 4	d									23 29															
Coulsdon South	d		←							23 33				←											
Merstham	d		23 08							23 38 →				23 38											
Redhill	a		23 12											23 42			00 05								
	d		23 12				23 19	23 21						23 42			00 05								
Tonbridge 4	a																								
Reigate	a						23 23																		
Earlswood (Surrey)	d																								
Salfords	d																								
Horley 4	d		23 22											23 50											
Gatwick Airport 10	✈ a		23 24	23 27				23 30	23 35		23 48	23 50		23 54	00 01	00 05	00 13	00 16			00 20	00 46	01 51		
	d		23 25	23 29							23 50			23 55	00 02		00 14	00 17				00 47	01 52		
Three Bridges 4	a		23 30								23 54			00 01	00 07		00 18	00 26				00 56	01 58		
	d		23 33								23 54			00 01	00 07		00 19								
Crawley	d		23 36											00 05											
Ifield	d		23 39											00 07											
Faygate	d																								
Littlehaven	d		23 45											00 14											
Horsham 4	a		23 49											00 17											
Balcombe	d																00 25								
Haywards Heath 3	a			23 40							00 03				00 16		00 30								
	d			23 41							00 03				00 16		00 30								
Wivelsfield 4	d			23 45													00 34								
Lewes 4	a			23 58																					
Burgess Hill 4	d										00 08						00 36								
Hassocks 4	d																00 40								
Preston Park	d																00 47								
Hove 2	a														00 30										
Brighton 10	a										00 24						00 51								

For general notes see front of timetable
For details of catering facilities see Directory of Train Operators

§ It is unknown at the time of going to press, when this station will open. For further details please contact National Rail Enquiries 08457-484950 or see local publicity.

Brighton → London, Bedford and Watford Junction

Network Diagram - see first page of Table 186

Miles	Miles	Miles			FC MX 1	FC MO 1	FC MX 1	FC MX 1	FC MO 1	FC MX 1	SN MX 1	SN MO 1	SN MX 1	SN MX 1	SN MO 1	SN MX 1	GX 1	FC MX 1	FC MO 1	GX 1	GW MO 1	GX 1	GW MX 1	GX 1	SN 1
0	—	—	**Brighton 10**	d	22p07	22p16		22p33	22p44					23p02	23p02			23p37	23p44						
—	0	—	Hove 2	d																					
1½	1½	—	Preston Park	d	22p11			22p37						23p06	23p06			23p41							
7¼	—	—	Hassocks 4	d	22p17			22p43	22p52					23p12	23p12			23p47	23p52						
9¼	—	—	Burgess Hill 4	d	22p21	22p26		22p47	22p56					23p16	23p16			23p51	23p56						
—	0	—	Lewes 4	d																					
10	9¼	—	Wivelsfield 4	d	22p23			22p49						23p19	23p19			23p53							
13	—	—	**Haywards Heath 3**	a	22p28	22p30	←	22p54	23p00					23p23	23p23			23p58	00 01						
—	—	—		d	22p32	22p31	22p32	22p54	23p01					23p24	23p24			23p59	00 01						
17	—	—	Balcombe	d	→		22p37	23p00							23p29			00 04							
—	0	—	**Horsham 4**	d							23p02	23p04													
—	1	—	Littlehaven	d							23p05	23p07													
—	3½	—	Faygate	d																					
—	5¾	—	Ifield	d							23p11	23p13													
—	7	—	Crawley	d							23p14	23p17													
21½	8½	—	Three Bridges 4	a		22p40	22p42	23p05	23p10	←	23p18	23p20		23p33	23p35	←		00 10	00 10						
—	—	—		d		22p40	22p42	23p12	23p10	23p12	23p18	23p22		23p47	23p42	23p47		00 10	00 10						
24¼	—	—	**Gatwick Airport 10** ✈	a		22p44	22p46	→	23p14	23p16	23p22	23p26		→	23p46	23p52		00 14	00 14						
—	—	—		d		22p45	22p46		23p15	23p16	23p23	23p27			23p47	23p53	00 05	00 15	00 15	00 20		00 35		00 50	01 05
25	—	—	Horley 4	d							23p26	23p30			23b49	23b56									01 07
27¼	—	—	Salfords	d							23p29														
29¼	—	—	Earlswood (Surrey)	d							23p33														
—	0	—	Reigate	d																	00 26		00 45		
—	—	0	Tonbridge 4	d																					
30	1¾	19¾	**Redhill**	a							23p36	23p36			23p56	00 02		00 22	00 22		00 30		00 49		
—	—	—		d							23p37	23p37			00 02	00 03		00 22	00 22						
32	—	—	Merstham	d							23p41	23p41													
35½	—	—	Coulsdon South	d							23p46	23p46	←												
37½	—	—	Purley 4	d							23p49	23p50	23p49		00 11	00 11									01 22
40½	0	—	**East Croydon**	a		23p01	23p02		23p31	23p32	→	23p55	23p55		00 16	00 16		00 35	00 35						01 27
—	—	—		d		23p02	23p02		23p32	23p32		23p56	23p58		00 17	00 17		00 36	00 36						01 28
—	1¼	—	Norwood Junction 2	a																					
—	10¼	—	**London Bridge 4** ⊖	a		23p15	23p15		23p45	23p45								00 52	00 52						
—	—	—	**London Blackfriars 3** ⊖	a		23p23	23p22		23p53	23p52								00 59	00 59						
—	—	—	City Thameslink 3	a																					
—	—	—	Farringdon 3 ⊖	a		23p27	23p28		23p57	23p58															
—	—	—	St Pancras International 15 ⊖	a		23p31	23p32		00 02	00 02								01 07	01 07						
—	—	—	St Albans	a		00 03	23p54		00 33	00 24								01 39	01 39						
—	—	—	Luton Airport Parkway 4 ✈	a		00 15	00 06		00 45	00 36								01 51	01 51						
—	—	—	Luton 7	a		00 19	00 10		00 49	00 40								01 55	01 55						
—	—	—	**Bedford 10**	a		00 45	00 35		01 15	01 07								02 20	02 20						
48¼	0	0	Clapham Junction 10	d								00 11	00 11		00 30	00 30									01 41
—	—	2	Imperial Wharf §	d																					
—	2½	2½	West Brompton ⊖	d																					
—	3½	3½	Kensington Olympia ⊖	d																					
—	—	4¾	Shepherds Bush § ⊖	d																					
—	—	6¼	Willesden Jn. High Level	a																					
—	9	—	Wembley Central	a																					
—	12½	—	Harrow & Wealdstone ⊖	a																					
—	18½	—	Watford Junction	a																					
51	—	—	**London Victoria 15** ⊖	a								00 18	00 18		00 37	00 37	00 40			00 55		01 10		01 25	01 49

For general notes see front of timetable
For details of catering facilities see
Directory of Train Operators

§ It is unknown at the time of going to press, when this station will open. For further details please contact National Rail Enquiries 08457-484950 or see local publicity.

b Previous night.
Stops to set down only

Brighton → London, Bedford and Watford Junction

Network Diagram - see first page of Table 186

Station		GX 1	SN 1	FC 1	SN 1	FC 1	SN 1	SN 1	FC	GX 1	SN 1	SN	FC 1	SN 1	LO	SN	XC 1 ◇	GX 1	GW 1	GW 1	SN	XC 1 ◇ A 🍴	FC 1	GX 1	SN
Brighton [10]	d										03 50												05 09		
Hove [2]	d																								
Preston Park	d																						05 13		
Hassocks [4]	d																						05 19		
Burgess Hill [4]	d																						05 23		
Lewes [4]	d																								
Wivelsfield [4]	d																						05 26		
Haywards Heath [3]	a										04 25												05 30		
	d										04 25												05 30		
Balcombe	d																								
Horsham [4]	d																				05 17				
Littlehaven	d																				05 20				
Faygate	d																								
Ifield	d																				05 26				
Crawley	d																				05 29				
Three Bridges [4]	a										04 45			←							05 33		05 40		
	d		01 59	02 25	02 55	03 25	03 55		04 25		04 54		04 55	04 54							05 33		05 40		
Gatwick Airport [10] ✈	a		02 03	02 29	02 59	03 29	03 59		04 29		→		04 59	05 02							05 37		05 45		
	d	01 35	02 05	02 30	03 05	03 30	04 00		04 30	04 35			05 00	05 03			05 15	05 20		05 31	05 38	05 45	05 46	05 50	
Horley [4]	d		02 07		03 07		04 03							05 05							05 40				
Salfords	d																								
Earlswood (Surrey)	d																								
Reigate	d																		05 34						
Tonbridge [4]	d																								
Redhill	a																05 22		05 39	05 41	05 47	05 54			←
	d															05 28	05 33				05 48	06 04			
Merstham	d																				05 52 →				05 52
Coulsdon South	d															05 36									05 57
Purley [4]	d		02 22		03 22		04 22					05 07		05 23		05 39									06 00
East Croydon	a		02 27	02 47	03 27	03 47	04 27		04 47			05 12	05 17	05 28		05 48							06 01		06 06
	d		02 28	02 47	03 28	03 47	04 28		04 47			05 13	05 17	05 29		05 48							06 02		06 07
Norwood Junction [2]	a											05 17													
London Bridge [4] ⊖	a											05 41	05 34										06 15		
London Blackfriars [3] ⊖	a			03 12		04 12			05 12				05 41										06 23		
City Thameslink [3]	a																						06 25		
Farringdon [3] ⊖	a								05 17				05 47										06 29		
St Pancras International [15] ⊖	a			03 21		04 21			05 21				05 51										06 33		
St Albans	a			03 53		04 53			05 53				06 23										06 54		
Luton Airport Parkway [4] ✈	a			04 05		05 05			06 05				06 35										07 06		
Luton [7]	a			04 09		05 09			06 09				06 39										07 09		
Bedford [10]	a			04 37		05 37			06 37				07 07										07 37		
Clapham Junction [10]	d		02 41		03 41		04 47	05 25						05 49	06 05	06 08									06 18
Imperial Wharf §	d																								
West Brompton ⊖	d							05 31							06 12										
Kensington Olympia ⊖	d							05 34							06 15										
Shepherds Bush § ⊖	d																								
Willesden Jn. High Level	a														06 27										
Wembley Central	a																								
Harrow & Wealdstone ⊖	a							05 51																	
Watford Junction	a							05 58																	
London Victoria [15] ⊖	a	02 20	02 49		03 49		04 54			05 10				05 58		06 18		05 55						06 20	06 25

For general notes see front of timetable
For details of catering facilities see Directory of Train Operators

§ It is unknown at the time of going to press, when this station will open. For further details please contact National Rail Enquiries 08457-484950 or see local publicity.

A To Birmingham New Street (Table 116)

Table 186

Mondays to Fridays

Brighton → London, Bedford and Watford Junction

Network Diagram - see first page of Table 186

		SN	SE 88		GW	SN	SN	SN	GX	LO	SN	FC	GX	FC	SN	GW	GX	LO	FC	SE 13	SN	SN	SN	SE 13	FC
		1			1	1	1	1	1		1	1	1	1	1	1	1		1		1	1	1		1
			A																	B			C	B	
Brighton 10	d	05 22										05 39		05 49								06 01			06 09
Hove 2	d														05 57										
Preston Park	d											05 43		05 53											06 13
Hassocks 4	d											05 49		05 59								06 09			06 19
Burgess Hill 4	d	05 31										05 53		06 03								06 12			06 23
Lewes 4	d					05 29																	06 05		
Wivelsfield 4	d											05 56		06 05								06 15			
Haywards Heath 3	a	05 36				05 46						06 00		06 09	06 12							06 19	06 22		06 29
	d	05 36				05 47						06 00		06 09	06 12							06 27			06 30
Balcombe	d	05 42										06 05													06 35
Horsham 4	d							05 41													06 15				
Littlehaven	d							05 44													06 18				
Faygate	d																								
Ifield	d							05 50													06 24				
Crawley	d							05 53													06 28				
Three Bridges 4	a	05 47						05 57				06 12		06 19	06 21						06 31	06 36			06 40
	d	05 48						05 57				06 12		06 20	06 21						06 32	06 37			06 40
Gatwick Airport 10 ✈	a	05 52				05 58		06 01				06 16		06 24	06 25						06 36	06 41			06 45
	d	05 53	05 54		05 57	05 59		06 02	06 05			06 16	06 20	06 24	06 26		06 35				06 37	06 42			06 46
Horley 4	d							06 05													06 40				
Salfords	d		05 58																		06 44				
Earlswood (Surrey)	d		06 02																		06 48				
Reigate	d															06 34									
Tonbridge 4	d																			06 14					
Redhill	a		06 05		06 08			06 12						06 32		06 38			←	06 45	06 51				
	d							06 13						06 33 →					06 33	06 46	06 51 →				
Merstham	d							06 17																	
Coulsdon South	d							06 22												06 53				←	
Purley 4	d							06 25												06 56				06 56	
East Croydon	a	06 10				06 14	←	06 30				06 32			06 41				06 43	→		06 58		07 01	07 01
	d	06 10 →				06 15	06 10	06 31				06 32			06 42				06 44			06 59		07 02	07 02
Norwood Junction 2	a																								
London Bridge 4 ⊖	a											06 46							06 58			07 14		07 18	07 16
London Blackfriars 3 ⊖	a											06 52							07 06						07 22
City Thameslink 3	a											06 55							07 09						07 25
Farringdon 3 ⊖	a											06 59							07 12						07 28
St Pancras International 15 ⊖	a											07 03							07 16						07 32
St Albans	a											07 24							07 35						07 54
Luton Airport Parkway 4 ✈	a											07 35							07 49						08 05
Luton 7	a											07 38							07 52						08 08
Bedford 10	a											08 05							08 19						08 35
Clapham Junction 10	d					06 25	06b30	06 40		06 35	06 49				06 51			07 05							
Imperial Wharf §	d																								
West Brompton ⊖	d						06 35			06 42	06 54							07 12							
Kensington Olympia ⊖	d						06 39			06 45	06 57							07 15							
Shepherds Bush § ⊖	d																								
Willesden Jn. High Level	a									06 57								07 27							
Wembley Central	a						06 57				07 17														
Harrow & Wealdstone ⊖	a						07 02				07 22														
Watford Junction	a						07 09				07 30														
London Victoria 15 ⊖	a					06 33		06 47	06 35				06 50		07 00		07 05								

For general notes see front of timetable
For details of catering facilities see Directory of Train Operators

§ It is unknown at the time of going to press, when this station will open. For further details please contact National Rail Enquiries 08457-484950 or see local publicity.

A To Tonbridge (Table 209)
B From Paddock Wood (Table 207)
C From Hastings (Table 189)

b Arr. 0625

Brighton → London, Bedford and Watford Junction

Network Diagram - see first page of Table 186

		GX [1]	LO [1]	SN [1]	SN [1]	LO	SN [1]	SN [1]	GW [1]	FC [1]	SN [1]	GX [1]	SN [1]	SN [1]	SN [1]	GW [1]	SN [1]	GX [1]	SN [1]	SN [1]	SN [1]	GW [1]	SN [1]	SN [1]	SN [1]
			A				B				B		C		B					D	E				G
Brighton [10]	d				06 20					06 24				06 41					06 47						
Hove [2]	d												06 30												
Preston Park	d									06 28			06 34						06 51						
Hassocks [4]	d				06 28					06 34			06 41						06 57						
Burgess Hill [4]	d				06 31					06 38			06 45						07 01						
Lewes [4]	d																								06 50
Wivelsfield [4]	d									06 40			06 47						07 03						07 07
Haywards Heath [3]	a				06 37					06 45			06 52	06 57					07 08						07 13
	d				06 37					06 45			07 00						07 08						07 13
Balcombe	d									06 51															07 19
Horsham [4]	d						06 35													06 55	07 04				
Littlehaven	d						06 38													06 58					
Faygate	d						06 42																		
Ifield	d						06 46													07 05					
Crawley	d						06 49													07 08	07 13				
Three Bridges [4]	a				06 46		06 52			06 56	←									07 12	07 17				07 24
	d				06 47		06 57 →			06 56	06 57						07 08			07 21					07 25
Gatwick Airport [10] ✈	a				06 51					07 01	07 02		07 11				07 12		07 21						07 29
	d	06 50			06 52				06 59	07 01	07 03	07 05	07 12				07 13	07 20	07 22						07 30
Horley [4]	d				06 55						07 05						07 15			07 27					
Salfords	d										07 09				←		07 19								
Earlswood (Surrey)	d										07 13				07 13		07 23								
Reigate	d							06 58			→					07 18						07 34			
Tonbridge [4]	d																								
Redhill	a			←	07 02			07 02	07 06	07 09					07 16	07 23	07 26					07 38		←	
	d			06 51	07 04					07 10					07 16		07 26 →							07 26	
Merstham	d			06 55											07 20									07 30	
Coulsdon South	d			07 00											07 25									07 35	
Purley [4]	d			07 05																				07 39	
East Croydon	a			07 09	07 15					07 23			07 28		07 31				07 38	07 43				07 44	07 46
	d			07 10	07 16					07 24			07 29		07 32				07 38	07 44				07 45	07 47
Norwood Junction [2]	a																								
London Bridge [4] ⊖	a												07 46		07 48										08 03
London Blackfriars [3] ⊖	a									07 50															
City Thameslink [3]	a									07 55															
Farringdon [3] ⊖	a									07 58															
St Pancras International [15] ⊖	a									08 02															
St Albans	a									08 23															
Luton Airport Parkway [4] ✈	a									08 36															
Luton [7]	a									08 39															
Bedford [10]	a									09 01															
Clapham Junction [10]	d		07 17	07 20	07 25	07 35													07 48	07 54			07 57	07 57	
Imperial Wharf §	d																								
West Brompton ⊖	d		07 24			07 42																	08 02		
Kensington Olympia ⊖	d		07 27			07 45																	08 05		
Shepherds Bush § ⊖	d																								
Willesden Jn. High Level	a		07 38			07 57																			
Wembley Central	a																						08 21		
Harrow & Wealdstone ⊖	a																						08 26		
Watford Junction	a																						08 33		
London Victoria [15] ⊖	a	07 20		07 28	07 34							07 35						07 50	07 57	08 03				08 07	

For general notes see front of timetable
For details of catering facilities see Directory of Train Operators

§ It is unknown at the time of going to press, when this station will open. For further details please contact National Rail Enquiries 08457-484950 or see local publicity.

A To Stratford Low Level (Table 59)
B From Havant (Table 188)
C From Littlehampton (Table 188)
D From Bognor Regis (Table 188)
E From Portsmouth Harbour (Table 188)
G From Eastbourne (Table 189)

Brighton → London, Bedford and Watford Junction

Network Diagram - see first page of Table 186

Station		SN 1	SN 1		GX 1	FC 1	SN 1 A	SN 1	SN 1	SN 1	SN 1 B 🛒	SN 1 🛒	LO	SN 1	SN 1 A	LO 1 C	SN 1	SN 1	SN 1	SN 1 D 🛒	LO	SN 1	GX 1	GW 1	FC 1
Brighton [10]	d					07 00						07 16													07 26
Hove [2]	d						07 11								07 20										
Preston Park	d					07 04						07 20													07 30
Hassocks [4]	d					07 10	07 21								07 30										07 36
Burgess Hill [4]	d					07 14						07 29													07 40
Lewes [4]	d																			07 23					
Wivelsfield [4]	d					07 18						07 32			07 35					07 39					
Haywards Heath [3]	a					07 23	07 29					07 36			07 40					07 43					07 46
	d					07 23	07 30					07 37			07 40					07 44					07 47
Balcombe	d																								
Horsham [4]	d		07 10					07 19			07 25														
Littlehaven	d		07 13					07 22			07 29														
Faygate	d		07 17																						
Ifield	d		07 21					07 28																	
Crawley	d		07 24					07 32			07 37														
Three Bridges [4]	a		07 27			07 32		07 35			07 40														07 56
	d		07 28			07 32		07 36			07 41											07 44			07 56
Gatwick Airport [10] ✈	a		07 32			07 37		07 40														07 48			08 00
	d		07 33		07 35	07 37		07 41														07 49	07 50	07 58	08 01
Horley [4]	d		07 36					07 43												07 59		07 52			→
Salfords	d		07 40					07 47									←					07 56			
Earlswood (Surrey)	d		07 43					07 51									07 51					07 59			
Reigate	d	07 40						→										07 51							
Tonbridge [4]	d																								
Redhill	a	07 44	07 47						←					←			07 54	07 55				08 02		08 05	
	d	07 45	07 48						07 45					07 48			07 54					08 03			
Merstham	d	→	→											07 52			07 59					08 07			
Coulsdon South	d													07 57			08 04					08 12			
Purley [4]	d													08 01								08 16			
East Croydon	a					07 53	07 57		08 00	←	08 00	08 03		08 06	08 08		08 11			08 14		08 21			
	d					07 54	07 57		08 00	07 47	08 01	08 04		08 07	08 09		08 12			08 15		08 22			
Norwood Junction [2]	a																								
London Bridge [4] ⊖	a								08 18					08 24	08 26							08 39			
London Blackfriars [3] ⊖	a					08 19																			
City Thameslink [3]	a					08 25																			
Farringdon [3] ⊖	a					08 29																			
St Pancras International [15] ⊖	a					08 33																			
St Albans	a					08 53																			
Luton Airport Parkway [4] ✈	a					09 05																			
Luton [7]	a					09 08																			
Bedford [10]	a					09 35																			
Clapham Junction [10]	d						08 07			08 10	08 11	08 14	08 05			08 17	08 21		08 24	08 24	08 35				
Imperial Wharf §	d																								
West Brompton ⊖	d									08 16			08 12			08 24			08 29		08 42				
Kensington Olympia ⊖	d									08a19			08 15			08 27			08 32		08 45				
Shepherds Bush § ⊖	d																								
Willesden Jn. High Level	a												08 27			08 37					08 57				
Wembley Central	a																		08 48						
Harrow & Wealdstone ⊖	a																		08 53						
Watford Junction	a																		09 00						
London Victoria [15] ⊖	a				08 05		08 16				08 20	08 22					08 31			08 33			08 22		

For general notes see front of timetable
For details of catering facilities see Directory of Train Operators

§ It is unknown at the time of going to press, when this station will open. For further details please contact National Rail Enquiries 08457-484950 or see local publicity.

A From Littlehampton (Table 188)
B From Bognor Regis (Table 188)
C To Stratford Low Level (Table 59)
D From Seaford (Table 189) and from Hastings (Table 189)

Brighton → London, Bedford and Watford Junction

Network Diagram - see first page of Table 186

Station		SN	SN	GX	SN	SN	FC	SN	SN	SN	SN	SN	SN	SN	GX	FC	SN	GW	GX	SN	SE 13	SN	SN	GW	FC
		1	1	1	1	1	1	1	1	1	1	1	1	1	1	1	1	1	1	1		1	1	1	1
					A			B									C			D					
			✠		✠						✠						✠			✠					
Brighton 10	d		07 33								07 47					07 50									08 02
Hove 2	d							07 41																	
Preston Park	d		07 37								07 51					07 54									08 06
Hassocks 4	d							07 51								08 00									08 12
Burgess Hill 4	d		07 46								08 00														08 16
Lewes 4	d								07 44											07 54					
Wivelsfield 4	d		07 49																	08 10					08 18
Haywards Heath 3	a		07 53					07 58	08 02		08 05					08 08				08 14					08 23
	d		07 54					07 59	08 03		08 06					08 09				08 15					08 23
Balcombe	d		07 59													08 14				08 21					
Horsham 4	d	07 40			07 46								07 51				08 09					08 14			
Littlehaven	d	07 43			07 50								07 54									08 17			
Faygate	d												07 58									08 21			
Ifield	d	07 50			07 57								08 02									08 25			
Crawley	d	07 53			08 01								08 05				08 18					08 28			
Three Bridges 4	a	07 57	08 05		08 05								08 08				08 22			08 27		08 31			08 33
	d	07 58	08 05		08 06								08 09				08 22			08 28		08 32			08 34
Gatwick Airport 10 ✈	a	08 02					←	08 12					08 13			08 22						08 36			08 38
	d	08 04		08 05			08 01	08 13					08 14		08 20	08 22			08 35			08 37			08 38
Horley 4	d	08 07											08 16				08 28					08 40			
Salfords	d	08 11										←	08 20									08 44			
Earlswood (Surrey)	d	08 14										08 14	08 24									08 47			
Reigate	d	→				08 07								08 24				08 24						08 42	
Tonbridge 4	d																				07 56				
Redhill	a					08 11	08 12					08 17	08 27	08 28				08 29				08 50		08 51	
	d						08 14					08 18	08 32									08 51 →	←		
Merstham	d											08 22	08a36 →										08 36		
Coulsdon South	d											08 28									08 36		08 41		
Purley 4	d											08 32											08 45		
East Croydon	a		08 23		08 27		08 27	08 29	08 31		08 34	08 37				08 38	08 43			08 46	08 47		08 52		08 54
	d		08 24		08 27		08 28	08 30	08 32		08 34	08 37				08 38	08 44			08 47	08 48		08 53		08 54
Norwood Junction 2	a																								
London Bridge 4 ⊖	a		08 41		08 44				08 49												09 07		09 15		09 10
London Blackfriars 3 ⊖	a						08 52									09 08									09 18
City Thameslink 3	a						08 59									09 11									09 21
Farringdon 3 ⊖	a						09 02									09 14									09 26
St Pancras International 15 ⊖	a						09 06									09 18									09 33
St Albans	a						09 28									09 41									09 53
Luton Airport Parkway 4 ✈	a						09 40									09 53									10 05
Luton 7	a						09 43									09 55									10 08
Bedford 10	a						10 09									10 21									10 37
Clapham Junction 10	d							08 41		08 43	08 44	08 49					08 53			08 57					
Imperial Wharf §	d																								
West Brompton ⊖	d									08 49															
Kensington Olympia ⊖	d									08a52															
Shepherds Bush § ⊖	d																								
Willesden Jn. High Level	a																								
Wembley Central	a																								
Harrow & Wealdstone ⊖	a																								
Watford Junction	a																								
London Victoria 15 ⊖	a			08 35				08 49			08 52	08 58			08 52		09 02		09 05	09 07					

For general notes see front of timetable
For details of catering facilities see Directory of Train Operators

§ It is unknown at the time of going to press, when this station will open. For further details please contact National Rail Enquiries 08457-484950 or see local publicity.

A From Bognor Regis (Table 188) and from Southampton Central (Table 188)

B From Littlehampton (Table 188)

C From Bognor Regis (Table 188) and from Portsmouth Harbour (Table 188)

D From Hastings (Table 189)

Brighton → London, Bedford and Watford Junction

Network Diagram - see first page of Table 186

Station		LO	SN		GX	FC	SN	LO	SN	SN	SN	FC	GX	SN	SN	SN	SN	SN	LO	FC	SE	GW	GX	SN	SN
																					13				
			[1]		[1]	[1]	[1]		[1]	[1]	[1]	[1]	[1]	[1]	[1]	[1]	[1]	[1]	[1]	[1]		[1]	[1]	[1]	[1]
			A								B										C				D
											🛒				🛒										🛒
Brighton [10]	d					08 16						08 36				08 45									
Hove [2]	d		08 11																						
Preston Park	d		08 15			08 20						08 40													
Hassocks [4]	d		08 22			08 26						08 46													
Burgess Hill [4]	d		08 26			08 30						08 50													
Lewes [4]	d										08 23														08 47
Wivelsfield [4]	d					08 33					08 39														08 59
Haywards Heath [3]	a		08 31			08 37					08 44	08 55				08 57									09 03
	d		08 31			08 38					08 44	09 00 →				08 58				← 09 00					09 06
Balcombe	d																			09 06					
Horsham [4]	d						08 35								08 49									09 00	
Littlehaven	d						08 38																	09 03	
Faygate	d																								
Ifield	d						08 44																	09 09	
Crawley	d						08 47								08 58									09 13	
Three Bridges [4]	a		08 41			08 47	08 51								09 01					09 11				09 16	09 17
	d		08 42			08 47	08 51								09 02					09 12				09 18	09 18
Gatwick Airport [10] ✈	a					08 51	08 55				08 55				09 06	09 10				09 16				09 22	09 22
	d				08 50	08 52	08 56				08 56		09 05		09 07	09 11				09 16		09 17	09 20	09 23	09 23
Horley [4]	d						08 59				08 59													09 26	
Salfords	d						09 03																	09 30	
Earlswood (Surrey)	d						09 06											← 09 06						09 33	
Reigate	d						→										09 03							→	
Tonbridge [4]	d																				08 51				
Redhill	a																09 07	09 10			09 21	09 24			
	d									← 08 51							09 14				09 22				
Merstham	d									08 55							09 18								
Coulsdon South	d									09 00							09 23				09 29				
Purley [4]	d									09 03											09 34				
East Croydon	a		09 01			09 08				09 08	09 14				09 22	09 26	09 29			09 32	→				09 39
	d		09 01			09 08				09 09	09 14				09 22	09 26	09 29			09 32					09 39
Norwood Junction [2]	a																								
London Bridge [4]	⊖ a																			09 45					
London Blackfriars [3]	⊖ a					09 37														09 52					
City Thameslink [3]	a					09 40														09 55					
Farringdon [3]	⊖ a					09 44														09 59					
St Pancras International [15]	⊖ a					09 48														10 03					
St Albans	a					10 09														10 23					
Luton Airport Parkway [4] ✈	a					10 20														10 35					
Luton [7]	a					10 24														10 38					
Bedford [10]	a					10 50														11 05					
Clapham Junction [10]	d	09 05	09 11					09 35	09 14	09 21	09 24			09 27	09 33	09 36	09 39		09 47						09 50
Imperial Wharf §	d																								
West Brompton	⊖ d	09 12						09 42	09 22					09 32					09 54						
Kensington Olympia	⊖ d	09 15						09 45	09a25					09 35					09 57						
Shepherds Bush §	⊖ d																								
Willesden Jn. High Level	a	09 27						09 57											10 12						
Wembley Central	a													09 53											
Harrow & Wealdstone	⊖ a													09 58											
Watford Junction	a													10 05											
London Victoria [15]	⊖ a		09 19		09 20					09 29	09 33		09 35		09 42	09 44	09 48						09 50		09 58

For general notes see front of timetable
For details of catering facilities see Directory of Train Operators

§ It is unknown at the time of going to press, when this station will open. For further details please contact National Rail Enquiries 08457-484950 or see local publicity.

A From Littlehampton (Table 188)
B From Hastings (Table 189)
C From Strood (Table 208)
D From Seaford (Table 189) and from Hastings (Table 189)

Brighton → London, Bedford and Watford Junction

Network Diagram - see first page of Table 186

		GW	SE 13	SN	FC	GX	SN	LO	SN	SN	GW	SN	FC	SN	XC	GX	SN	SN	SN	FC	SE 13	GW	GX	SN	LO
		1		1	1	1	1		1	1	1	1	1	1	1 ◇	1	1	1	1	1		1	1	1	
			A	B								C		C	D		E		B						
Brighton 10	d				09 00					09 17			09 04		09 21					09 34				09 49	
Hove 2	d			08 52															09 22						
Preston Park	d												09 08												
Hassocks 4	d			09 04	09 08								09 14												
Burgess Hill 4	d			09 08	09 12								09 18						09 35						
Lewes 4	d																	09 17							
Wivelsfield 4	d												09 20					09 33							
Haywards Heath 3	a			09 12	09 16								09 25		09 32			09 37	09 40	09 47					
	d			09 14	09 16								09 25		09 33			09 44		09 48					
Balcombe	d												09 31												
Horsham 4	d											09 20					09 30								
Littlehaven	d																09 33								
Faygate	d																09 37								
Ifield	d																09 41								
Crawley	d											09 29					09 44								
Three Bridges 4	a				09 26							09 32	09 36				09 47								
	d				09 27							09 33	09 37				09 48								
Gatwick Airport 10 ✈	a			09 26	09 31							09 37	09 41		09 44		09 52	09 55		10 00					
	d			09 27	09 31	09 35	09 37					09 38	09 41	←	09 46	09 50	09 52	09 56		10 01		10 03	10 05		
Horley 4	d											09 41 →		09 41			09 55								
Salfords	d								←																
Earlswood (Surrey)	d								09 33																
Reigate	d	09 24									09 37														
Tonbridge 4	d																				09 34				
Redhill	a	09 29							09 36		09 41			09 47			10 02				10 04	10 10			
	d								09 37					09 48							10 05				
Merstham	d								09 41												10 09				
Coulsdon South	d		←						09 46												10 14				
Purley 4	d		09 34						09 49												10 18				
East Croydon	a		09 40	09 42	09 47		09 52		09 54	09 55			09 57	09 59	10 03			10 11		10 16	10 23			10 24	
	d		09 40	09 43	09 47		09 52		09 55	09 56			09 57	10 00	10 08			10 12		10 17	10 24			10 24	
Norwood Junction 2	a								09 59												10 28				
London Bridge 4 ⊖	a		09 55		10 00				10 12				10 15							10 30	10 40				
London Blackfriars 3 ⊖	a				10 07								10 22							10 37					
City Thameslink 3	a				10 10								10 25							10 40					
Farringdon 3 ⊖	a				10 14								10 29							10 44					
St Pancras International 15 ⊖	a				10 18								10 33							10 48					
St Albans	a				10 39								10 53							11 09					
Luton Airport Parkway 4 ✈	a				10 50								11 05							11 20					
Luton 7	a				10 54								11 08							11 24					
Bedford 10	a				11 20								11 35							11 50					
Clapham Junction 10	d			09 53			10 03	10 05		10 05				10 09				10 22						10 34	10 35
Imperial Wharf §	d																								
West Brompton ⊖	d						10 09	10 12																	10 42
Kensington Olympia ⊖	d						10 12	10 15							10 37										10 45
Shepherds Bush § ⊖	d																								
Willesden Jn. High Level	a							10 27																	10 57
Wembley Central	a																								
Harrow & Wealdstone ⊖	a						10 29																		
Watford Junction	a						10 45																		
London Victoria 15 ⊖	a			10 00			10 05			10 13				10 16		10 20		10 28					10 35	10 40	

For general notes see front of timetable
For details of catering facilities see Directory of Train Operators

§ It is unknown at the time of going to press, when this station will open. For further details please contact National Rail Enquiries 08457-484950 or see local publicity.

- **A** From Strood (Table 208)
- **B** From Littlehampton (Table 188)
- **C** From Bognor Regis (Table 188) and from Portsmouth Harbour (Table 188)
- **D** To Birmingham New Street (Table 116)
- **E** To Tunbridge Wells (Table 209)

Brighton → London, Bedford and Watford Junction

Network Diagram - see first page of Table 186

Station		SN	FC		GW	GX	SN	SN	SN	SN	FC	GW	GX	SN	LO	SN	SN	SN	FC	GX	SN	SN	SN	FC	SE 13
		1	1		1	1	1	1	1	1	1	1	1	1		1	1	1	1	1	1	1	1	1	
		A						B										C			D				E
									🚲								🚲					🚲	🚲		
Brighton 10	d		09 37							09 55	10 04						10 19		10 07					10 34	
Hove 2	d							09 51														10 21			
Preston Park	d		09 41							09 58									10 11						
Hassocks 4	d		09 47							10 05									10 17						
Burgess Hill 4	d		09 51					10 02		10 08									10 21						
Lewes 4	d								09 49														10 20		
Wivelsfield 4	d		09 53							10 11									10 23				10 35		
Haywards Heath 3	a		09 58					10 06	10 09	10 15	10 18								10 28			10 35	10 40	10 47	
	d		09 58					10 13		10 16	10 18								10 32			10 43		10 48	
Balcombe	d																		10 37						
Horsham 4	d	09 50					10 00											10 20			10 32				
Littlehaven	d						10 03														10 35				
Faygate	d																								
Ifield	d						10 09														10 41				
Crawley	d	09 59					10 14											10 29			10 44				
Three Bridges 4	a	10 02	10 07				10 18			10 25								10 32	10 42		10 48				
	d	10 03	10 10				10 18			10 31 →				← 10 31				10 33	10 42		10 48				
Gatwick Airport 10 ✈	a	10 07	10 15				10 22	10 24			10 30			10 35				10 37	10 46		10 52	10 54		11 00	
	d	10 08	10 16			10 20	10 23	10 25			10 31		10 35	10 37				10 38	10 46	10 50	10 53	10 55		11 01	
Horley 4	d						10 26											10 41			10 55				
Salfords	d						10 30																		
Earlswood (Surrey)	d						10 33																		
Reigate	d				10 19							10 35													
Tonbridge 4	d																								10 34
Redhill	a	10 15			10 24		10 36					10 39						10 47			11 02				11 04
	d	10 16					10 37 →									← 10 37		10 48							11 05
Merstham	d															10 41									11 09
Coulsdon South	d															10 46									11 14
Purley 4	d															10 49									11 18
East Croydon 🚊	a	10 28	10 32					10 40			10 46			10 52		10 54	10 55	10 59	11 02			11 11		11 16	11 23
	d	10 28	10 32					10 40			10 47			10 52		10 55	10 55	11 00	11 02			11 11		11 17	11 24
Norwood Junction 2	a															10 59									11 28
London Bridge 4 ⊖	a		10 45								11 00					11 12			11 15					11 30	11 40
London Blackfriars 3 ⊖	a		10 52								11 07								11 22					11 37	
City Thameslink 3	a		10 55								11 10								11 25					11 40	
Farringdon 3 ⊖	a		10 59								11 14								11 29					11 44	
St Pancras International 15 ⊖	a		11 03								11 18								11 33					11 48	
St Albans	a		11 23								11 39								11 53					12 09	
Luton Airport Parkway 4 ✈	a		11 35								11 50								12 05					12 20	
Luton 7	a		11 38								11 54								12 08					12 24	
Bedford 10	a		12 05								12 20								12 35					12 50	
Clapham Junction 10	d	10 38						10 50						11 03	11 05		11 05	11 09				11 21			
Imperial Wharf §	d																								
West Brompton ⊖	d													11 09	11 12										
Kensington Olympia ⊖	d													11 12	11 15										
Shepherds Bush § ⊖	d																								
Willesden Jn. High Level	a														11 27										
Wembley Central	a																								
Harrow & Wealdstone ⊖	a													11 29											
Watford Junction	a													11 45											
London Victoria 15 ⊖	a	10 45				10 50		10 58					11 05				11 11	11 16		11 20		11 27			

For general notes see front of timetable
For details of catering facilities see Directory of Train Operators

§ It is unknown at the time of going to press, when this station will open. For further details please contact National Rail Enquiries 08457-484950 or see local publicity.

A From Bognor Regis (Table 188) and from Southampton Central (Table 188)

B From Littlehampton (Table 188)

C From Bognor Regis (Table 188) and from Portsmouth Harbour (Table 188)

D To Tunbridge Wells (Table 209)

E From Tunbridge Wells (Table 206)

Brighton → London, Bedford and Watford Junction

Network Diagram - see first page of Table 186

		GW 1	GX 1	SN 1	LO	SN 1 A	FC 1	GW 1	GX 1	SN 1	SN 1	SN 1 B	SN 1	FC 1	GW 1	GX 1	SN 1	LO	SN 1	SN 1	SN 1 C	FC 1	GX 1	SN 1 D
Brighton 10	d			10 49			10 37						10 55	11 04						11 19		11 07		
Hove 2	d											10 51												
Preston Park	d						10 41						10 58									11 11		
Hassocks 4	d						10 47						11 05									11 17		
Burgess Hill 4	d						10 51					11 02	11 08									11 21		
Lewes 4	d										10 49													
Wivelsfield 4	d						10 53						11 11									11 23		
Haywards Heath 3	a						10 58				11 05	11 08	11 15	11 18								11 28		
	d						11 02				11 13		11 16	11 18								11 32		
Balcombe	d																					11 37		
Horsham 4	d					10 50				11 00											11 20			11 32
Littlehaven	d									11 03														11 35
Faygate	d																							
Ifield	d									11 09														11 41
Crawley	d					10 59				11 14											11 29			11 44
Three Bridges 4	a					11 02	11 11			11 18			11 25								11 32	11 42		11 48
	d					11 03	11 12			11 18			11 31 →				← 11 31				11 33	11 42		11 48
Gatwick Airport 10 ✈	a					11 07	11 16			11 22	11 24			11 30			11 35				11 37	11 46		11 52
	d	11 03	11 05			11 08	11 16		11 20	11 23	11 25			11 31		11 35	11 37				11 38	11 46	11 50	11 53
Horley 4	d									11 26											11 41			11 55
Salfords	d									11 30														
Earlswood (Surrey)	d									11 33														
Reigate	d							11 17							11 34									
Tonbridge 4	d																							
Redhill	a	11 10				11 15		11 22		11 36					11 38						11 48			12 02
	d					11 16				11 37 →									← 11 37		11 49			
Merstham	d																		11 41					
Coulsdon South	d																		11 46					
Purley 4	d																		11 49					
East Croydon	a			11 23		11 27	11 32				11 40			11 46			11 52		11 54	11 55	12 00	12 02		
	d			11 24		11 28	11 32				11 40			11 47			11 52		11 55	11 55	12 00	12 02		
Norwood Junction 2	a																		11 59					
London Bridge 4 ⊖	a						11 45							12 00					12 12			12 15		
London Blackfriars 3 ⊖	a						11 52							12 07								12 22		
City Thameslink 3	a						11 55							12 10								12 25		
Farringdon 3 ⊖	a						11 59							12 14								12 29		
St Pancras International 15 ⊖	a						12 03							12 18								12 33		
St Albans	a						12 23							12 39								12 53		
Luton Airport Parkway 4 ✈	a						12 35							12 50								13 05		
Luton 7	a						12 38							12 54								13 08		
Bedford 10	a						13 05							13 20								13 35		
Clapham Junction 10	d			11 33	11 35	11 37					11 50						12 03	12 05		12 05	12 11			
Imperial Wharf §	d																							
West Brompton ⊖	d				11 42												12 09	12 12						
Kensington Olympia ⊖	d				11 45												12 12	12 15						
Shepherds Bush § ⊖	d																							
Willesden Jn. High Level	a				11 57													12 27						
Wembley Central	a																							
Harrow & Wealdstone ⊖	a																12 29							
Watford Junction	a																12 45							
London Victoria 15 ⊖	a		11 35	11 40		11 44			11 50		11 58					12 05				12 11	12 18		12 20	

For general notes see front of timetable
For details of catering facilities see Directory of Train Operators

§ It is unknown at the time of going to press, when this station will open. For further details please contact National Rail Enquiries 08457-484950 or see local publicity.

A From Bognor Regis (Table 188) and from Southampton Central (Table 188)

B From Littlehampton (Table 188)

C From Bognor Regis (Table 188) and from Portsmouth Harbour (Table 188)

D To Tunbridge Wells (Table 209)

Brighton → London, Bedford and Watford Junction

Network Diagram - see first page of Table 186

		SN	SN	FC		SE	GW	GX	SN	LO	SN	FC	GW	GX	SN	SN	SN	SN	FC	GW	GX	SN	LO	SN	SN
						13																			
		1	1	1			1	1	1		1	1	1	1	1	1	1	1	1	1	1	1		1	1
						A					B						C								
		(trolley)	(trolley)						(trolley)		(trolley)					(trolley)									(trolley)
Brighton 10	d			11 34					11 49			11 37						11 55	12 04						12 19
Hove 2	d	11 21															11 51								
Preston Park	d											11 41						11 58							
Hassocks 4	d											11 47						12 05							
Burgess Hill 4	d											11 51					12 02	12 08							
Lewes 4	d		11 20													11 50									
Wivelsfield 4	d		11 34									11 53						12 11							
Haywards Heath 3	a	11 35	11 40	11 47								11 58				12 05	12 09	12 15	12 18						
	d	11 43		11 48								12 02				12 13		12 16	12 18						
Balcombe	d																								
Horsham 4	d										11 50				12 00										
Littlehaven	d														12 03										
Faygate	d																								
Ifield	d														12 09										
Crawley	d										11 59				12 14										
Three Bridges 4	a										12 02	12 11			12 18			12 25							
	d										12 03	12 12			12 18			12 31 ↪				↩ 12 31			
Gatwick Airport 10 ✈	a	11 54		12 00							12 07	12 16			12 22	12 24			12 30			12 35			
	d	11 55		12 01			12 03	12 05			12 08	12 16		12 20	12 23	12 25			12 31		12 35	12 37			
Horley 4	d														12 26										
Salfords	d														12 30										
Earlswood (Surrey)	d														12 33										
Reigate	d												12 19							12 34					
Tonbridge 4	d					11 34																			
Redhill	a					12 04	12 10				12 15		12 24		12 36					12 38					
	d					12 05					12 16				12 37 ↪									↩ 12 37	
Merstham	d					12 09																		12 41	
Coulsdon South	d					12 14																		12 46	
Purley 4	d					12 18																		12 49	
East Croydon	a	12 10		12 16		12 23			12 23		12 27	12 32				12 40			12 46			12 52		12 54	12 55
	d	12 10		12 17		12 24			12 24		12 28	12 32				12 40			12 47			12 52		12 55	12 55
Norwood Junction 2	a					12 28																		12 59	
London Bridge 4 ⊖	a			12 30		12 40						12 45							13 00					13 12	
London Blackfriars 3 ⊖	a			12 37								12 52							13 07						
City Thameslink 3	a			12 40								12 55							13 10						
Farringdon 3 ⊖	a			12 44								12 59							13 14						
St Pancras International 15 ⊖	a			12 48								13 03							13 18						
St Albans	a			13 09								13 23							13 39						
Luton Airport Parkway 4 ✈	a			13 20								13 35							13 50						
Luton 7	a			13 24								13 38							13 54						
Bedford 10	a			13 50								14 05							14 20						
Clapham Junction 10	d	12 20							12 33	12 35	12 37					12 50						13 03	13 05		13 05
Imperial Wharf §	d																								
West Brompton ⊖	d									12 42												13 09	13 12		
Kensington Olympia ⊖	d									12 45												13 12	13 15		
Shepherds Bush § ⊖	d																								
Willesden Jn. High Level	a									12 57													13 27		
Wembley Central	a																								
Harrow & Wealdstone ⊖	a																					13 29			
Watford Junction	a																					13 45			
London Victoria 15 ⊖	a	12 28						12 35	12 40		12 44			12 50		12 57					13 05				13 11

For general notes see front of timetable
For details of catering facilities see Directory of Train Operators

§ It is unknown at the time of going to press, when this station will open. For further details please contact National Rail Enquiries 08457-484950 or see local publicity.

A From Tunbridge Wells (Table 206)

B From Bognor Regis (Table 188) and from Southampton Central (Table 188)

C From Littlehampton (Table 188)

Table 186

Brighton → London, Bedford and Watford Junction

Network Diagram - see first page of Table 186

		SN	FC	GX	SN	SN	SN	FC	SE	GW	GX	SN	LO	SN	FC	GW	GX	SN	SN	SN	SN	FC	GW	GX	SN
									13																
		1	1	1	1	1	1	1		1	1	1		1	1	1	1	1	1	1	1	1	1	1	1
		A			B				C					D						E					
						🛒	🛒					🛒		🛒					🛒						
Brighton 10	d		12 07					12 34				12 49			12 37						12 55	13 04			
Hove 2	d					12 21														12 51					
Preston Park	d		12 11												12 41						12 58				
Hassocks 4	d		12 17												12 47						13 05				
Burgess Hill 4	d		12 21												12 51					13 02	13 08				
Lewes 4	d						12 20												12 50						
Wivelsfield 4	d		12 23				12 34								12 53						13 11				
Haywards Heath 3	a		12 28			12 35	12 40	12 47							12 58				13 05	13 09	13 15	13 18			
	d		12 32			12 43		12 48							13 02				13 13		13 16	13 18			
Balcombe	d		12 37																						
Horsham 4	d	12 20			12 30									12 50				13 00							
Littlehaven	d				12 33													13 03							
Faygate	d				12 37																				
Ifield	d				12 41													13 09							
Crawley	d	12 29			12 44									12 59				13 14							
Three Bridges 4	a	12 32	12 42		12 47									13 02	13 11			13 18			13 25				←
	d	12 33	12 42		12 48									13 03	13 12			13 18			13 31 →				13 31
Gatwick Airport 10 ✈	a	12 37	12 46		12 52	12 54		13 00						13 07	13 16			13 22	13 24			13 30			13 35
	d	12 38	12 46	12 50	12 52	12 55		13 01		13 03	13 05			13 08	13 16		13 20	13 23	13 25			13 31		13 35	13 37
Horley 4	d	12 41			12 55													13 26							
Salfords	d																	13 30							
Earlswood (Surrey)	d																	13 33							
Reigate	d															13 18							13 34		
Tonbridge 4	d								12 34																
Redhill	a	12 47			13 02				13 04	13 10				13 17		13 23		13 36					13 38		
	d	12 48							13 05					13 18				13 37 →							
Merstham	d								13 09																
Coulsdon South	d								13 14																
Purley 4	d								13 18																
East Croydon	a	13 00	13 02			13 10		13 16	13 23			13 23		13 28	13 32				13 40			13 46			13 52
	d	13 00	13 02			13 10		13 17	13 24			13 24		13 29	13 32				13 40			13 47			13 52
Norwood Junction 2	a								13 28																
London Bridge 4 ⊖	a		13 15					13 30	13 40						13 45							14 00			
London Blackfriars 3 ⊖	a		13 22					13 37							13 52							14 07			
City Thameslink 3	a		13 25					13 40							13 55							14 10			
Farringdon 3 ⊖	a		13 29					13 44							13 59							14 14			
St Pancras International 15 ⊖	a		13 33					13 48							14 03							14 18			
St Albans	a		13 53					14 09							14 23							14 39			
Luton Airport Parkway 4 ✈	a		14 05					14 20							14 35							14 50			
Luton 7	a		14 08					14 24							14 38							14 54			
Bedford 10	a		14 35					14 50							15 05							15 20			
Clapham Junction 10	d	13 11				13 20						13 33	13 35	13 38					13 50						14 03
Imperial Wharf §	d																								
West Brompton ⊖	d												13 42												14 09
Kensington Olympia ⊖	d												13 45												14 12
Shepherds Bush § ⊖	d																								
Willesden Jn. High Level	a												13 57												
Wembley Central	a																								
Harrow & Wealdstone ⊖	a																								14 29
Watford Junction	a																								14 45
London Victoria 15 ⊖	a	13 18		13 20		13 27					13 35	13 40		13 46			13 50		13 58					14 05	

For general notes see front of timetable
For details of catering facilities see Directory of Train Operators

§ It is unknown at the time of going to press, when this station will open. For further details please contact National Rail Enquiries 08457-484950 or see local publicity.

A From Bognor Regis (Table 188) and from Portsmouth Harbour (Table 188)
B To Tunbridge Wells (Table 209)
C From Tunbridge Wells (Table 206)
D From Bognor Regis (Table 188) and from Southampton Central (Table 188)
E From Littlehampton (Table 188)

Brighton → London, Bedford and Watford Junction

Network Diagram - see first page of Table 186

		LO	SN	SN		SN	FC	GX	SN	SN	SN	FC	SE 13	GW	GX	SN	LO	SN	FC	GW	GX	SN	SN	SN	SN
			1	1		1	1	1	1	1	1	1		1	1	1		1	1	1	1	1	1	1	1
						A			B				C					D						E	
				⊼						⊼	⊼					⊼		⊼					⊼		
Brighton 10	d			13 19			13 07					13 34				13 49			13 37						13 55
Hove 2	d									13 21														13 51	
Preston Park	d						13 11												13 41						13 58
Hassocks 4	d						13 17												13 47						14 05
Burgess Hill 4	d						13 21												13 51					14 02	14 08
Lewes 4	d										13 20												13 50		
Wivelsfield 4	d						13 23				13 34								13 53						14 11
Haywards Heath 3	a						13 28			13 35	13 40	13 47							13 58				14 05	14 09	14 15
	d						13 32			13 43		13 48							14 02				14 13		14 16
Balcombe	d						13 37																		
Horsham 4	d					13 20			13 32									13 50				14 00			
Littlehaven	d								13 35													14 03			
Faygate	d																								
Ifield	d								13 41													14 09			
Crawley	d					13 29			13 44									13 59				14 14			
Three Bridges 4	a					13 32	13 42		13 48									14 02	14 11			14 18			14 25
	d					13 33	13 42		13 48									14 03	14 12			14 18			14 31 →
Gatwick Airport 10 ✈	a					13 37	13 46		13 52	13 54		14 00						14 07	14 16			14 22	14 24		
	d					13 38	13 46	13 50	13 53	13 55		14 01		14 03	14 05			14 08	14 16		14 20	14 23	14 25		
Horley 4	d					13 41			13 55													14 26			
Salfords	d																					14 30			
Earlswood (Surrey)	d																					14 33			
Reigate	d																			14 19					
Tonbridge 4	d												13 34												
Redhill	a		←			13 47			14 02				14 04	14 10				14 15		14 24		14 36			
	d		13 37			13 48							14 05					14 16				14 37 →			
Merstham	d		13 41										14 09												
Coulsdon South	d		13 46										14 14												
Purley 4	d		13 49										14 18												
East Croydon	a		13 54	13 55		14 00	14 02			14 10		14 16	14 23			14 23		14 27	14 32				14 40		
	d		13 55	13 55		14 00	14 02			14 10		14 17	14 24			14 24		14 28	14 32				14 40		
Norwood Junction 2	a		13 59										14 28												
London Bridge 4 ⊖	a		14 12				14 15					14 30	14 40						14 45						
London Blackfriars 3 ⊖	a						14 22					14 37							14 52						
City Thameslink 3	a						14 25					14 40							14 55						
Farringdon 3 ⊖	a						14 29					14 44							14 59						
St Pancras International 15 ⊖	a						14 33					14 48							15 03						
St Albans	a						14 53					15 09							15 23						
Luton Airport Parkway 4 ✈	a						15 05					15 20							15 35						
Luton 7	a						15 08					15 24							15 38						
Bedford 10	a						15 35					15 50							16 05						
Clapham Junction 10	d	14 05		14 05		14 11				14 20						14 33	14 35	14 37					14 50		
Imperial Wharf §	d																								
West Brompton ⊖	d	14 12															14 42								
Kensington Olympia ⊖	d	14 15															14 45								
Shepherds Bush § ⊖	d																								
Willesden Jn. High Level	a	14 27															14 57								
Wembley Central	a																								
Harrow & Wealdstone ⊖	a																								
Watford Junction	a																								
London Victoria 15 ⊖	a			14 11		14 18		14 20		14 27					14 35	14 40		14 44			14 50		14 57		

For general notes see front of timetable
For details of catering facilities see Directory of Train Operators

§ It is unknown at the time of going to press, when this station will open. For further details please contact National Rail Enquiries 08457-484950 or see local publicity.

A From Bognor Regis (Table 188) and from Portsmouth Harbour (Table 188)

B To Tunbridge Wells (Table 209)

C From Tunbridge Wells (Table 206)

D From Bognor Regis (Table 188) and from Southampton Central (Table 188)

E From Littlehampton (Table 188)

Brighton → London, Bedford and Watford Junction

Network Diagram - see first page of Table 186

Station		FC	GW	GX	SN	LO	SN	SN	SN	FC	GX	XC	SN	SN	SN	FC	SE	GW	GX	SN	LO	SN	FC	GW	GX
												R					13								
		1	1	1	1		1	1	1	1	1	1	1	1	1	1		1	1	1		1	1	1	1
									A				B				C					D			
								🛒				🍽		🛒	🛒					🛒		🛒			
Brighton 10	d	14 04						14 19		14 07		14 22				14 34				14 49			14 37		
Hove 2	d													14 21											
Preston Park	d									14 11													14 41		
Hassocks 4	d									14 17													14 47		
Burgess Hill 4	d									14 21													14 51		
Lewes 4	d														14 20										
Wivelsfield 4	d									14 23					14 34								14 53		
Haywards Heath 3	a	14 18								14 28				14 35	14 40	14 47							14 58		
	d	14 18								14 31				14 43		14 48							15 02		
Balcombe	d									14 37															
Horsham 4	d								14 20				14 32									14 50			
Littlehaven	d												14 35												
Faygate	d																								
Ifield	d												14 41												
Crawley	d								14 29				14 44									14 59			
Three Bridges 4	a								14 32	14 41			14 48									15 02	15 11		
	d				← 14 31				14 33	14 41			14 48									15 03	15 12		
Gatwick Airport 10 ✈	a	14 30			14 35				14 37	14 46		14 50	14 52	14 54		15 00						15 07	15 16		
	d	14 31		14 35	14 37				14 38	14 46	14 50	14 51	14 53	14 55		15 01		15 03	15 05			15 08	15 16		15 20
Horley 4	d								14 41				14 55												
Salfords	d																								
Earlswood (Surrey)	d																								
Reigate	d		14 34																					15 18	
Tonbridge 4	d																14 34								
Redhill	a		14 38						14 47				15 02				15 04	15 10				15 15		15 25	
	d						← 14 37		14 48								15 05					15 16			
Merstham	d						14 41										15 09								
Coulsdon South	d						14 46										15 14								
Purley 4	d						14 49										15 18								
East Croydon	a	14 46			14 52		14 54	14 55	15 00	15 01		15 08		15 09		15 16	15 23			15 23		15 27	15 32		
	d	14 47			14 52		14 55	14 55	15 00	15 01		15 09		15 10		15 17	15 24			15 24		15 28	15 32		
Norwood Junction 2	a						14 59										15 28								
London Bridge 4 ⊖	a	15 00					15 12			15 15						15 30	15 40						15 45		
London Blackfriars 3 ⊖	a	15 07								15 22						15 37							15 52		
City Thameslink 3	a	15 10								15 24						15 40							15 55		
Farringdon 3 ⊖	a	15 14								15 28						15 44							15 59		
St Pancras International 15 ⊖	a	15 18								15 33						15 48							16 03		
St Albans	a	15 39								15 53						16 09							16 23		
Luton Airport Parkway 4 ✈	a	15 50								16 05						16 20							16 36		
Luton 7	a	15 54								16 08						16 24							16 40		
Bedford 10	a	16 20								16 35						16 50							17 05		
Clapham Junction 10	d				15 03	15 05		15 05	15 11					15 20						15 33	15 35	15 37			
Imperial Wharf §	d																								
West Brompton ⊖	d				15 09	15 12															15 42				
Kensington Olympia ⊖	d				15 12	15 15						15 36									15 45				
Shepherds Bush § ⊖	d																								
Willesden Jn. High Level	a					15 27															15 57				
Wembley Central	a																								
Harrow & Wealdstone ⊖	a				15 29																				
Watford Junction	a				15 45																				
London Victoria 15 ⊖	a			15 05				15 11	15 18		15 20			15 28					15 35	15 40		15 44			15 50

For general notes see front of timetable
For details of catering facilities see Directory of Train Operators

§ It is unknown at the time of going to press, when this station will open. For further details please contact National Rail Enquiries 08457-484950 or see local publicity.

A From Bognor Regis (Table 188) and from Portsmouth Harbour (Table 188)
B To Tonbridge (Table 209)
C From Tunbridge Wells (Table 206)
D From Bognor Regis (Table 188) and from Southampton Central (Table 188)

Brighton → London, Bedford and Watford Junction

Network Diagram - see first page of Table 186

		SN	SN	SN	SN	FC	GW	GX	SN	SN	SN	LO	SN	FC	GX	SN	SN	SN	FC	SE	GW	GX	SN	LO
		1	1	1	1	1	1	1	1	1	1		1	1	1	1	1	1	1	13	1	1	1	
				A									B			C				D				
			⊥								⊥		⊥				⊥	⊥					⊥	
Brighton 10	d				14 55	15 04					15 19			15 07					15 34				15 49	
Hove 2	d			14 51													15 21							
Preston Park	d				14 58									15 11										
Hassocks 4	d				15 05									15 17										
Burgess Hill 4	d			15 02	15 08									15 21										
Lewes 4	d		14 50															15 19						
Wivelsfield 4	d				15 11									15 23				15 35						
Haywards Heath 3	a		15 05	15 09	15 15	15 18								15 28			15 35	15 39	15 48					
	d		15 13		15 16	15 18								15 32			15 44		15 48					
Balcombe	d													15 37										
Horsham 4	d	15 00											15 20			15 32								
Littlehaven	d	15 03														15 35								
Faygate	d																							
Ifield	d	15 09														15 41								
Crawley	d	15 14											15 29			15 44								
Three Bridges 4	a	15 18			15 25								15 32	15 42		15 48								
	d	15 18			15 31 →				← 15 31				15 33	15 42		15 48								
Gatwick Airport 10 ✈	a	15 22	15 24			15 30			15 35				15 37	15 46		15 52	15 55		16 00					
	d	15 23	15 25			15 31		15 35	15 37				15 38	15 46	15 50	15 53	15 56		16 01		16 03	16 05		
Horley 4	d	15 26											15 41			15 55								
Salfords	d	15 30																						
Earlswood (Surrey)	d	15 33																						
Reigate	d						15 34																	
Tonbridge 4	d																			15 34				
Redhill	a	15 36					15 38						15 47			16 02				16 04	16 10			
	d	15 37 →								← 15 37			15 48							16 05				
Merstham	d									15 41										16 09				
Coulsdon South	d									15 46										16 14				
Purley 4	d									15 49										16 18				
East Croydon	a		15 41			15 46			15 52	15 54	15 55		16 00	16 02			16 11		16 16	16 23			16 24	
	d		15 41			15 47			15 52	15 55	15 55		16 00	16 02			16 12		16 17	16 24			16 24	
Norwood Junction 2	a									15 59										16 28				
London Bridge 4 ⊖	a					16 00				16 12				16 15						16 41				
London Blackfriars 3 ⊖	a					16 07								16 24					16 48					
City Thameslink 3	a					16 10								16 28					16 52					
Farringdon 3 ⊖	a					16 14								16 31					16 56					
St Pancras International 15 ⊖	a					16 18								16 35					17 01					
St Albans	a					16 39								16 56					17 21					
Luton Airport Parkway 4 ✈	a					16 51								17 09					17 34					
Luton 7	a					16 54								17 13					17 36					
Bedford 10	a					17 20								17 38					18 00					
Clapham Junction 10	d		15 52						16 03		16 05	16 05	16 11				16 21						16 34	16 35
Imperial Wharf §	d																							
West Brompton ⊖	d								16 09			16 12												16 42
Kensington Olympia ⊖	d								16 12			16 15												16 45
Shepherds Bush § ⊖	d																							
Willesden Jn. High Level	a											16 27												16 57
Wembley Central	a								16 26															
Harrow & Wealdstone ⊖	a								16 31															
Watford Junction	a								16 45															
London Victoria 15 ⊖	a		15 58					16 05			16 11		16 20		16 20		16 29					16 35	16 41	

For general notes see front of timetable
For details of catering facilities see Directory of Train Operators

§ It is unknown at the time of going to press, when this station will open. For further details please contact National Rail Enquiries 08457-484950 or see local publicity.

A From Littlehampton (Table 188)
B From Bognor Regis (Table 188) and from Portsmouth Harbour (Table 188)
C To Tonbridge (Table 209)
D From Tunbridge Wells (Table 206)

Brighton → London, Bedford and Watford Junction

Network Diagram - see first page of Table 186

		SN	FC	SN	GX	SN	GW	SN	SN	SN	SN	FC	GX	SN	SN	SN	LO	SN	GW	SN	FC	GX	SN	SN	LO
		1	1	1	1	1	1	1	1	1	1	1	1	1	1	1		1	1	1	1	1	1	1	1
		A		A						B								C						C	D
		🍴		🍴					🍴							🍴									
Brighton [10]	d		15 37								15 55	16 04				16 19					16 07				
Hove [2]	d									15 51															
Preston Park	d		15 41								15 58										16 11				
Hassocks [4]	d		15 47								16 05										16 17				
Burgess Hill [4]	d		15 51							16 02	16 08										16 21				
Lewes [4]	d								15 50																
Wivelsfield [4]	d		15 53								16 11														
Haywards Heath [3]	a		15 58						16 05	16 09	16 15	16 18									16 25				
	d		15 58							16 13	16 16	16 19									16 26				
Balcombe	d																				16 31				
Horsham [4]	d	15 50						16 02										16 20							
Littlehaven	d							16 05																	
Faygate	d																								
Ifield	d							16 11																	
Crawley	d	15 59						16 14										16 29							
Three Bridges [4]	a	16 02	16 07					16 18			16 25							16 32			16 37				
	d	16 03	16 07			16 17		16 18			16 31 →			← 16 31				16 33			16 37				
Gatwick Airport [10] ✈	a	16 07	16 11			16 21		16 22		16 26		16 30		16 35				16 37			16 41				
	d	16 08	16 11		16 20	16 23		16 23		16 27		16 31	16 35	16 37				16 38			16 41	16 50			
Horley [4]	d							16 26																	
Salfords	d							16 30																	
Earlswood (Surrey)	d							16 33																	
Reigate	d						16 21												16 40						
Tonbridge [4]	d																								
Redhill	a	16 17					16 26	16 36										16 47	16 47						
	d	16 18 →		← 16 18				16 37 →							← 16 37			16 48 →						← 16 48	
Merstham	d														16 41										
Coulsdon South	d														16 46										
Purley [4]	d														16 49										
East Croydon	a		16 27	16 30		16 38				16 42		16 46		16 52	16 54	16 55				←	16 57			17 01	
	d		16 27	16 30		16 38				16 42		16 47		16 52	16 55 →	16 55				16 55	16 57			17 01	
Norwood Junction [2]	a																								
London Bridge [4] ⊖	a		16 42									17 02													
London Blackfriars [3] ⊖	a		16 53																		17 25				
City Thameslink [3]	a		16 56																		17 28				
Farringdon [3] ⊖	a		17 01																		17 31				
St Pancras International [15] ⊖	a		17 05																		17 35				
St Albans	a		17 26																		17 56				
Luton Airport Parkway [4] ✈	a		17 39																		18 09				
Luton [7]	a		17 42																		18 12				
Bedford [10]	a		18 10																		18 38				
Clapham Junction [10]	d			16 40		16 48				16 52				17 03		17 05	17 05			17 08			17 10	17 11	17 17
Imperial Wharf §	d																								
West Brompton ⊖	d													17 09			17 12						17 18		17 24
Kensington Olympia ⊖	d													17 12			17 15						17a21		17 27
Shepherds Bush § ⊖	d																								
Willesden Jn. High Level	a																17 27								17 38
Wembley Central	a													17 26											
Harrow & Wealdstone ⊖	a													17 31											
Watford Junction	a													17 45											
London Victoria [15] ⊖	a			16 46	16 50	16 56				16 58			17 05			17 11				17 14		17 20		17 20	

For general notes see front of timetable
For details of catering facilities see Directory of Train Operators

§ It is unknown at the time of going to press, when this station will open. For further details please contact National Rail Enquiries 08457-484950 or see local publicity.

A From Bognor Regis (Table 188) and from Southampton Central (Table 188)

B From Littlehampton (Table 188)

C From Bognor Regis (Table 188) and from Portsmouth Harbour (Table 188)

D To Stratford Low Level (Table 59)

Table 186

Mondays to Fridays

Brighton → London, Bedford and Watford Junction

Network Diagram - see first page of Table 186

	FC 1	SN 1	SN 1	SN 1	GW 1	GX 1	SN 1	SN 1	LO	FC 1	SN 1	SN 1	GX 1	SN 1	GW 1	SN	SN 1	SN 1	SN 1	FC 1	GW 1	GX 1	SN 1
												A						B					
Brighton 10 d	16 14							16 49		16 29									16 55	17 03			
Hove 2 d			16 21															16 51					
Preston Park d										16 33									16 58				
Hassocks 4 d										16 39									17 05				
Burgess Hill 4 d	16 25									16 43								17 02	17 08	17 13			
Lewes 4 d				16 19													16 51						
Wivelsfield 4 d				16 35						16 46									17 11				
Haywards Heath 3 a	16 30		16 35	16 39						16 50							17 05	17 09	17 15	17 18			←
Haywards Heath 3 d	16 38		16 44							16 50							17 13		17 21 →	17 18			17 21
Balcombe d										16 56													17 27
Horsham 4 d		16 30										16 50				17 00							
Littlehaven d		16 33														17 03							
Faygate d		16 37														17 07							
Ifield d		16 41														17 11							
Crawley d		16 44										16 59				17 14							
Three Bridges 4 a	16 47	16 47								17 02		17 02				17 17				17 27			17 32
Three Bridges 4 d	16 47	16 48								17 02		17 03				17 18				17 27			17 32
Gatwick Airport 10 a	16 52	16 52	16 55							17 06		17 07				17 22	17 24			17 31			17 36
Gatwick Airport 10 d	16 53	16 53	16 56		17 03	17 05				17 07		17 08	17 20			17 23	17 25			17 31		17 35	17 37
Horley 4 d		16 56														17 26							
Salfords d		17 00														17 30							
Earlswood (Surrey) d		17 03														17 33							
Reigate d														17 14	17 26						17 34		
Tonbridge 4 d																							
Redhill a		17 06			17 10							17 17		17 21	17 31	17 36					17 38		
Redhill d		17 07 →					← 17 07					17 18		17 22		17 37 →							
Merstham d							17 11							17 26									
Coulsdon South d							17 16							17 31									
Purley 4 d							17 19																
East Croydon a	17 08		17 11				17 24	17 25		17 27	←	17 30		17 37			17 40			17 47			17 52
East Croydon d	17 09		17 12				17 25 →	17 25		17 27	17 25	17 30		17 38			17 41			17 47			17 52
Norwood Junction 2 a																							
London Bridge 4 ⊖ a	17 29																			18 11			
London Blackfriars 3 ⊖ a	17 36									17 56										18 19			
City Thameslink 3 a	17 38									18 08										18 28			
Farringdon 3 ⊖ a	17 41									18 11										18 31			
St Pancras International 15 ⊖ a	17 45									18 15										18 35			
St Albans a	18 06									18 36										18 56			
Luton Airport Parkway 4 ✈ a	18 19									18 50										19 09			
Luton 7 a	18 22									18 53										19 12			
Bedford 10 a	18 48									19 18										19 38			
Clapham Junction 10 d			17 21					17 35	17 35		17 38	17 41		17 47			17 50						18 04
Imperial Wharf § d																							
West Brompton ⊖ d									17 42														18 09
Kensington Olympia ⊖ d									17 45														18 12
Shepherds Bush § ⊖ d																							
Willesden Jn. High Level a									17 57														
Wembley Central a																							18 28
Harrow & Wealdstone ⊖ a																							18 33
Watford Junction a																							18 45
London Victoria 15 ⊖ a			17 28			17 35		17 43			17 45	17 50	17 50	17 56			17 57					18 05	

For general notes see front of timetable
For details of catering facilities see Directory of Train Operators

§ It is unknown at the time of going to press, when this station will open. For further details please contact National Rail Enquiries 08457-484950 or see local publicity.

A From Bognor Regis (Table 188) and from Southampton Central (Table 188)

B From Littlehampton (Table 188)

Brighton → London, Bedford and Watford Junction

Network Diagram - see first page of Table 186

		SN	LO	SN	SN	LO	SN	SE	GX	SN	SN	SN	FC	GW	GX	SN	LO	SN	SN	SN	FC	GX	SN	GW	SN
								13																	
		1			1	1	1		1	1	1	1	1	1	1	1		1	1	1	1	1	1	1	1
					A	B														C					
		✕									✕	✕				✕				✕					
Brighton 10	d	17 19											17 23			17 49					17 37				
Hove 2	d										17 21														
Preston Park	d												17 27								17 41				
Hassocks 4	d												17 33								17 47				
Burgess Hill 4	d												17 37								17 51				
Lewes 4	d											17 19													
Wivelsfield 4	d											17 35	17 40												
Haywards Heath 3	a										17 35	17 39	17 45								17 56				
	d										17 43		17 46								17 56				
Balcombe	d																				18 02				
Horsham 4	d				17 20					17 30										17 50					18 00
Littlehaven	d									17 33															18 03
Faygate	d									17 37															18 07
Ifield	d									17 41															18 11
Crawley	d				17 29					17 44										17 59					18 14
Three Bridges 4	a				17 32					17 47			17 56							18 02	18 08				18 17
	d				17 33					17 48			17 56							18 03	18 12				18 18
Gatwick Airport 10 ✈	a				17 37					17 52	17 55		18 00							18 07	18 16				18 22
	d				17 38				17 50	17 53	17 56		18 01	18 03	18 05					18 08	18 16	18 20			18 23
Horley 4	d									17 56															18 26
Salfords	d									18 00															18 30
Earlswood (Surrey)	d									18 03															18 32
Reigate	d						17 44											18 06						18 26	
Tonbridge 4	d							17 20																	
Redhill	a				17 46		17 50	17 51		18 06				18 10				18 10		18 17				18 31	18 36
	d			← 17 37	17 46		17 51	17 53		18 07 →								18 21 →	← 18 07	18 18			← 18 21		18 37 →
Merstham	d			17 41															18 11				18 25		
Coulsdon South	d			17 46				18 00											18 16				18 30		
Purley 4	d			17 49															18 19						
East Croydon	a	17 54		17 55	17 58		18 08	18 11			18 11		18 16			18 24			18 25	18 29	18 31		18 38		
	d	17 55		17 56	17 59		18 08	18 11			18 12		18 17			18 24			18 26	18 30	18 32		18 39		
Norwood Junction 2	a																								
London Bridge 4 ⊖	a						18 24	18 26													18 45				
London Blackfriars 3 ⊖	a												18 49								18 55				
City Thameslink 3	a												18 54								18 58				
Farringdon 3 ⊖	a												18 57								19 01				
St Pancras International 15 ⊖	a												19 01								19 05				
St Albans	a												19 21								19 28				
Luton Airport Parkway 4 ✈	a																				19 40				
Luton 7	a												19 34								19 43				
Bedford 10	a												20 00								20 09				
Clapham Junction 10	d	18 04	18 05	18 07	18 10	18 17					18 21					18 34	18 35		18 38	18 41			18 49		
Imperial Wharf §	d																								
West Brompton ⊖	d		18 12			18 24											18 42								
Kensington Olympia ⊖	d		18 15			18 27											18 45								
Shepherds Bush § ⊖	d																								
Willesden Jn. High Level	a		18 27			18 38											18 57								
Wembley Central	a																								
Harrow & Wealdstone ⊖	a																								
Watford Junction	a																								
London Victoria 15 ⊖	a	18 11		18 14	18 20				18 20		18 28				18 35	18 40			18 45	18 50		18 50	18 56		

For general notes see front of timetable
For details of catering facilities see Directory of Train Operators

§ It is unknown at the time of going to press, when this station will open. For further details please contact National Rail Enquiries 08457-484950 or see local publicity.

A From Bognor Regis (Table 188) and from Portsmouth Harbour (Table 188)

B To Stratford Low Level (Table 59)

C From Bognor Regis (Table 188) and from Southampton Central (Table 188)

Brighton → London, Bedford and Watford Junction

Network Diagram - see first page of Table 186

		SN	SN	SN	FC		GX	SN	SN	SN	LO	SN	SN	GW	FC	GX	SN	SN	SN	SN	FC	GX	SN	LO	SN
		1	1	1	1		1	1	1	1		1	1	1	1	1	1	1	1	1	1	1	1		1
			A										B							A					
Brighton 10	d			17 55	18 03					18 19					18 07						18 34		18 49		
Hove 2	d		17 51																	18 21					
Preston Park	d			17 58											18 11										
Hassocks 4	d			18 05											18 17										
Burgess Hill 4	d		18 02	18 08	18 13										18 21					18 33					
Lewes 4	d	17 50																	18 18						
Wivelsfield 4	d			18 11											18 23				18 34						
Haywards Heath 3	a	18 05	18 09	18 15	18 18										18 28				18 38	18 41	18 47				
	d	18 13		18 22 →	18 18			← 18 22							18 32				18 45		18 48				
Balcombe	d														18 37										
Horsham 4	d												18 20					18 30							
Littlehaven	d																	18 33							
Faygate	d																	18 37							
Ifield	d																	18 41							
Crawley	d												18 29					18 44							
Three Bridges 4	a							18 31					18 32		18 42			18 47							
	d							18 31					18 33		18 42			18 48							
Gatwick Airport 10 ✈	a	18 24			18 30			18 36					18 37		18 46			18 52	18 56		19 00				
	d	18 25			18 31		18 35	18 37					18 38		18 46	18 50		18 53	18 57		19 01	19 05			
Horley 4	d																	18 56							
Salfords	d																	19 00							
Earlswood (Surrey)	d																	19 03							
Reigate	d											18 38		18 42			18 58								
Tonbridge 4	d																								
Redhill	a											18 42	18 47	18 52			19 02	19 06							
	d								← 18 37				18 47					19 07 →							← 19 07
Merstham	d								18 41																19 11
Coulsdon South	d								18 46																19 16
Purley 4	d								18 49																19 19
East Croydon	a	18 41			18 46			18 52	18 54	18 55			19 00		19 02				19 12		19 16		19 23		19 25
	d	18 42			18 47			18 52	18 55	18 55			19 00		19 02				19 12		19 17		19 24		19 26
Norwood Junction 2	a								18 59																
London Bridge 4 ⊖	a				19 00				19 12						19 15						19 30				
London Blackfriars 3 ⊖	a				19 07										19 22						19 37				
City Thameslink 3	a				19 12										19 25						19 40				
Farringdon 3 ⊖	a				19 15										19 29						19 44				
St Pancras International 15 ⊖	a				19 19										19 33						19 48				
St Albans	a				19 40										19 54						20 09				
Luton Airport Parkway 4 ✈	a				19 53										20 06						20 20				
Luton 7	a				19 56										20 09						20 24				
Bedford 10	a				20 22										20 35						20 50				
Clapham Junction 10	d	18 52						19 03		19 05	19 05		19 11						19 22				19 33	19 35	19 37
Imperial Wharf §	d																								
West Brompton ⊖	d							19 08			19 12													19 42	
Kensington Olympia ⊖	d							19 11			19 15													19 45	
Shepherds Bush § ⊖	d																								
Willesden Jn. High Level	a										19 27													19 57	
Wembley Central	a							19 26																	
Harrow & Wealdstone ⊖	a							19 31																	
Watford Junction	a							19 45																	
London Victoria 15 ⊖	a	18 59					19 05			19 11			19 17			19 20			19 29			19 35	19 40		19 44

For general notes see front of timetable
For details of catering facilities see Directory of Train Operators

§ It is unknown at the time of going to press, when this station will open. For further details please contact National Rail Enquiries 08457-484950 or see local publicity.

A From Littlehampton (Table 188)

B From Bognor Regis (Table 188) and from Portsmouth Harbour (Table 188)

Brighton → London, Bedford and Watford Junction

Network Diagram - see first page of Table 186

		SN 1 A	FC 1	GW 1	GX 1	SN 1	GW 1	SN 1	SN 1	SN 1	FC 1	GW 1	GX 1	SN 1	LO	SN 1	SN 1	SN 1	SN 1	SN 1 B	FC 1	SN 1	GX 1	SN 1	SN 1 C
Brighton 10	d		18 37														19 19		18 55		19 07				
Hove 2	d								18 52																19 22
Preston Park	d		18 41																18 59		19 11				
Hassocks 4	d		18 47																19 05		19 17				
Burgess Hill 4	d		18 51																19 09		19 21				19 33
Lewes 4	d									18 50														19 20	
Wivelsfield 4	d		18 53							19 05									19 11		19 23				
Haywards Heath 3	a		18 58						19 05	19 10									19 16		19 28			19 36	19 39
	d		19 02						19 14										19 17		19 32			19 43	
Balcombe	d																				19 37				
Horsham 4	d	18 50						19 02												19 17					
Littlehaven	d							19 05																	
Faygate	d																								
Ifield	d							19 11																	
Crawley	d	18 59						19 14												19 26					
Three Bridges 4	a	19 02	19 12					19 18											19 28	19 30	19 42				
	d	19 03	19 12					19 18			19 27								19 34		19 42				
Gatwick Airport 10 ✈	a	19 07	19 16					19 22	19 25		19 31								19 38		19 46			19 54	
	d	19 08	19 16	19 16	19 20			19 23	19 26		19 31		19 35	19 37					19 39		19 46		19 50	19 55	
Horley 4	d							19 26																	
Salfords	d							19 30																	
Earlswood (Surrey)	d							19 33																	
Reigate	d					19 21	19 30					19 34										19 47			
Tonbridge 4	d																								
Redhill	a	19 17		19 23		19 26	19 35	19 36				19 38							19 46			19 51			
	d	19 18						19 37 →								← 19 37			19 47						
Merstham	d															19 41									
Coulsdon South	d															19 46									
Purley 4	d															19 49									
East Croydon	a	19 28	19 32						19 41		19 47			19 52		19 54	19 55	←	19 59		20 02			20 10	
	d	19 29	19 32						19 41		19 47			19 52		19 55 →	19 55	19 55	20 00		20 02			20 10	
Norwood Junction 2	a																								
London Bridge 4 ⊖	a		19 45								20 00										20 15				
London Blackfriars 3 ⊖	a		19 52								20 07										20 22				
City Thameslink 3	a		19 55								20 10										20 25				
Farringdon 3 ⊖	a		19 59								20 14										20 29				
St Pancras International 15 ⊖	a		20 03								20 18										20 33				
St Albans	a		20 24								20 39										20 54				
Luton Airport Parkway 4 ✈	a		20 36								20 50										21 06				
Luton 7	a		20 39								20 54										21 09				
Bedford 10	a		21 05								21 20										21 35				
Clapham Junction 10	d	19 40							19 51					20 03	20 05		20 05	20 08	20 11					20 20	
Imperial Wharf §	d																								
West Brompton ⊖	d													20 09	20 12										
Kensington Olympia ⊖	d													20 12	20 15										
Shepherds Bush § ⊖	d																								
Willesden Jn. High Level	a														20 27										
Wembley Central	a																								
Harrow & Wealdstone ⊖	a													20 30											
Watford Junction	a													20 45											
London Victoria 15 ⊖	a	19 47			19 50				19 59				20 05				20 11	20 14	20 20				20 20	20 28	

For general notes see front of timetable
For details of catering facilities see Directory of Train Operators

§ It is unknown at the time of going to press, when this station will open. For further details please contact National Rail Enquiries 08457-484950 or see local publicity.

A From Bognor Regis (Table 188) and from Southampton Central (Table 188)

B From Portsmouth & Southsea (Table 188)

C From Bognor Regis (Table 188)

Brighton → London, Bedford and Watford Junction

Network Diagram - see first page of Table 186

	SN 1	FC 1	GW 1	GX 1		SN 1	LO	SN 1	SN 1 A	SN 1	FC 1	GX 1	SN 1	SN 1	SN 1	SN 1	FC 1	GW 1	GX 1	SN 1	LO	SN 1	SN 1	SN 1
Brighton 10 d		19 34				19 49					19 37					19 55	20 04					20 19		
Hove 2 d														19 52										
Preston Park d											19 41					19 59								
Hassocks 4 d											19 47					20 05								
Burgess Hill 4 d											19 51					20 09								
Lewes 4 d															19 53									
Wivelsfield 4 d											19 53				20 05	20 11								
Haywards Heath 3 a		19 47									19 58			20 04	20 10	20 16	20 18							
d		19 48									20 02			20 14		20 22 →	20 18							← 20 22
Balcombe d																								
Horsham 4 d	19 32								19 52				20 02											
Littlehaven d	19 35												20 05											
Faygate d																								
Ifield d	19 41												20 11											
Crawley d	19 45								20 01				20 14											
Three Bridges 4 a	19 48								20 05		20 11		20 18											20 32
d	19 51								20 05		20 12		20 18											20 32
Gatwick Airport 10 ✈ a	19 55	20 00							20 10		20 16		20 22	20 25			20 31							20 37
d	19 56	20 01	20 03	20 05					20 11		20 16	20 20	20 23	20 26			20 31		20 35	20 37				20 38
Horley 4 d	19 59												20 26											
Salfords d													20 30											
Earlswood (Surrey) d													20 33											
Reigate d										20 14								20 34						
Tonbridge 4 d																								
Redhill a	20 05		20 10						20 18	20 18			20 36					20 38						20 46
d	20 08							←	20 18				20 37 →										← 20 37	20 47
Merstham d	20 12 →							20 12															20 41	
Coulsdon South d								20 17															20 46	
Purley 4 d								20 20															20 49	
East Croydon a		20 16				20 23		20 25	20 30		20 32			20 41			20 47			20 52		20 55	20 57	20 59
d		20 17				20 24		20 26	20 30		20 32			20 42			20 47			20 52		20 55	20 57	21 00
Norwood Junction 2 a																								
London Bridge 4 ⊖ a		20 30									20 45						21 00							
London Blackfriars 3 ⊖ a		20 37									20 52						21 07							
City Thameslink 3 a		20 40									20 55						21 10							
Farringdon 3 ⊖ a		20 44									20 59						21 14							
St Pancras International 15 ⊖ a		20 48									21 03						21 18							
St Albans a		21 09									21 24						21 39							
Luton Airport Parkway 4 ✈ a		21 20									21 36						21 50							
Luton 7 a		21 24									21 39						21 54							
Bedford 10 a		21 50									22 05						22 20							
Clapham Junction 10 d						20 33	20 35	20 38	20 41					20 51						21 03	21 05	21 05	21 08	21 11
Imperial Wharf § d																								
West Brompton ⊖ d							20 42													21 09	21 12			
Kensington Olympia ⊖ d							20 45													21 12	21 15			
Shepherds Bush § ⊖ d																								
Willesden Jn. High Level a							20 57														21 27			
Wembley Central a																								
Harrow & Wealdstone ⊖ a																				21 29				
Watford Junction a																				21 45				
London Victoria 15 ⊖ a				20 35		20 40		20 46	20 50			20 50		20 59					21 05			21 11	21 14	21 20

For general notes see front of timetable
For details of catering facilities see Directory of Train Operators

§ It is unknown at the time of going to press, when this station will open. For further details please contact National Rail Enquiries 08457-484950 or see local publicity.

A From Southampton Central (Table 188)

Brighton → London, Bedford and Watford Junction

Network Diagram - see first page of Table 186

		SN	FC	GX	SN	SE	SN	FC	GW	GX	SN	LO	SN	SN	SN	FC	GX	GW	SN	SN	SN	SN	GX	SN	SN
						88																			
		1	1	1	1		1	1	1	1	1		1	1	1	1	1	1	1	1	1	1	1	1	1
					A										B										
Brighton 10	d		20 07					20 34			20 49					20 37									
Hove 2	d				20 22															20 52					
Preston Park	d		20 11													20 41									
Hassocks 4	d		20 17													20 47									
Burgess Hill 4	d		20 21		20 33											20 51									
Lewes 4	d																				20 50				
Wivelsfield 4	d		20 23													20 53					21 06				
Haywards Heath 3	a		20 28		20 37			20 47								20 58				21 06	21 10				
	d		20 32		20 38			20 48								21 02				21 14					
Balcombe	d		20 37																						
Horsham 4	d						20 32								20 52				21 02						
Littlehaven	d						20 35												21 05						
Faygate	d																								
Ifield	d						20 41												21 11						
Crawley	d						20 45								21 01				21 14						
Three Bridges 4	a		20 42		20 47		20 48								21 05	21 11			21 18						
	d		20 42		20 47	20 48	20 51								21 05	21 12			21 18						
Gatwick Airport 10 ✈	a		20 46		20 51	20 52	20 56	21 00							21 10	21 16			21 22	21 25					
	d		20 46	20 50	20 53	20 53	20 57	21 01	21 03	21 05					21 11	21 16	21 20		21 23	21 26			21 35	21 37	
Horley 4	d						20 59												21 26						
Salfords	d																		21 30						
Earlswood (Surrey)	d																		21 33						
Reigate	d	20 46												21 13				21 24				21 34			
Tonbridge 4	d																								
Redhill	a	20 50				21 01	21 06		21 10					21 17	21 18			21 28	21 36			21 38			
	d						21 08						←		21 18				21 37 →						← 21 37
Merstham	d						21 12 →						21 12												21 41
Coulsdon South	d												21 17												21 46
Purley 4	d												21 20												21 49
East Croydon	a		21 02		21 09			21 16			21 23		21 25		21 30	21 32				21 41				21 52	21 54
	d		21 02		21 10			21 17			21 24		21 26		21 30	21 32				21 41				21 52	21 57 →
Norwood Junction 2	a																								
London Bridge 4 ⊖	a		21 15					21 30								21 45									
London Blackfriars 3 ⊖	a		21 22					21 37								21 52									
City Thameslink 3	a		21 25					21 40								21 55									
Farringdon 3 ⊖	a		21 29					21 44								21 59									
St Pancras International 15 ⊖	a		21 33					21 48								22 03									
St Albans	a		21 54					22 08								22 24									
Luton Airport Parkway 4 ✈	a		22 06					22 20								22 36									
Luton 7	a		22 09					22 24								22 40									
Bedford 10	a		22 35					22 50								23 05									
Clapham Junction 10	d				21 19						21 33	21 35	21 38		21 41					21 51				22 03	
Imperial Wharf §	d																								
West Brompton ⊖	d											21 42												22 09	
Kensington Olympia ⊖	d											21 45												22 12	
Shepherds Bush § ⊖	d																								
Willesden Jn. High Level	a											21 57													
Wembley Central	a																								
Harrow & Wealdstone ⊖	a																							22 29	
Watford Junction	a																							22 45	
London Victoria 15 ⊖	a			21 20	21 29					21 35	21 40		21 47		21 48		21 50			21 58			22 05		

For general notes see front of timetable
For details of catering facilities see Directory of Train Operators

§ It is unknown at the time of going to press, when this station will open. For further details please contact National Rail Enquiries 08457-484950 or see local publicity.

A From Bognor Regis (Table 188)
B From Southampton Central (Table 188)

Brighton → London, Bedford and Watford Junction

Network Diagram - see first page of Table 186

		SN	LO	SN	SN		GW	FC	GX	SN	SE 88	SN	SN	GX	SN	LO	SN	SN	SN	FC	GX	GW	SN	SN	SN
		1		1	1		1	1	1	1		1	1	1	1		1	1	1	1	1	1	1	1	1
										A									B					C	
Brighton 10	d	21 19			21 02			21 07					21 34		21 49					21 37					
Hove 2	d									21 22														21 52	
Preston Park	d				21 06			21 11												21 41					
Hassocks 4	d				21 12			21 17												21 47					
Burgess Hill 4	d				21 16			21 21		21 32										21 51				22 02	
Lewes 4	d																						21 50		
Wivelsfield 4	d				21 18			21 23												21 53			22 02		
Haywards Heath 3	a				21 23			21 28		21 37			21 46							21 58			22 06	22 09	
	d				21 23			21 32		21 38			21 46							22 02			22 13		
Balcombe	d							21 37																	
Horsham 4	d											21 32							21 52						
Littlehaven	d											21 35													
Faygate	d																								
Ifield	d											21 41													
Crawley	d											21 45							22 01						
Three Bridges 4	a				21 32			21 42		21 47		21 48	21 55						22 05	22 11					
	d				21 33			21 42		21 47	21 48	21 51	21 56						22 05	22 12					
Gatwick Airport 10 ✈	a				21 37			21 46		21 51	21 52	21 55	22 00						22 10	22 16			22 24		
	d				21 38			21 46	21 50	21 53	21 53	21 56	22 02	22 05					22 11	22 16	22 20	22 23	22 25		
Horley 4	d											21 59													
Salfords	d																								
Earlswood (Surrey)	d																								
Reigate	d						21 44										22 09								22 32
Tonbridge 4	d																								
Redhill	a				21 46		21 48				22 01	22 05					22 13		22 18			22 30			22 36
	d				21 47							22 08						←	22 18						
Merstham	d											22 12 →						22 12							
Coulsdon South	d																	22 17							
Purley 4	d																	22 20							
East Croydon	a	21 55		←	21 59			22 02		22 09			22 17		22 23			22 25	22 30	22 32			22 40		
	d	21 55		21 57	22 00			22 02		22 10			22 17		22 24			22 26	22 30	22 32			22 41		
Norwood Junction 2	a																								
London Bridge 4 ⊖	a							22 15					22 32							22 45					
London Blackfriars 3 ⊖	a							22 22												22 52					
City Thameslink 3	a							22 25												22 55					
Farringdon 3 ⊖	a							22 29												22 59					
St Pancras International 15 ⊖	a							22 33												23 03					
St Albans	a							22 54												23 24					
Luton Airport Parkway 4 ✈	a							23 06												23 36					
Luton 7	a							23 10												23 40					
Bedford 10	a							23 35												00 07					
Clapham Junction 10	d	22 05	22 05	22 08	22 11					22 19					22 33	22 35		22 38	22 41				22 51		
Imperial Wharf §	d																								
West Brompton ⊖	d		22 12													22 42									
Kensington Olympia ⊖	d		22 15													22 45									
Shepherds Bush § ⊖	d																								
Willesden Jn. High Level	a		22 27													22 57									
Wembley Central	a																								
Harrow & Wealdstone ⊖	a																								
Watford Junction	a																								
London Victoria 15 ⊖	a	22 11		22 14	22 20				22 20	22 27				22 35	22 40			22 44	22 50		22 50		22 58		

For general notes see front of timetable
For details of catering facilities see Directory of Train Operators

§ It is unknown at the time of going to press, when this station will open. For further details please contact National Rail Enquiries 08457-484950 or see local publicity.

A From Bognor Regis (Table 188)
B From Southampton Central (Table 188)
C From Littlehampton (Table 188)

Brighton → London, Bedford and Watford Junction

Network Diagram - see first page of Table 186

		SN	GX	SN	LO	SN	SN	GW	FC	GX	SE	GX	FC	SN	FC	GX	SN	GX	GX	GW	SN	SN	FC	FC
																							FX	FO
											88													
		1	1	1		1	1	1	1	1		1	1	1	1	1	1	1	1	1	1	1	1	1
														A								B		
Brighton 10	d						22 00		22 07				22 33								23 02		23 37	
Hove 2	d																							
Preston Park	d						22 04		22 11				22 37								23 06		23 41	
Hassocks 4	d						22 10		22 17				22 43								23 12		23 47	
Burgess Hill 4	d						22 14		22 21				22 47								23 16		23 51	
Lewes 4	d													22 40										
Wivelsfield 4	d						22 16		22 23				22 49	22 54							23 19		23 53	
Haywards Heath 3	a						22 21		22 28				22 54	22 58							23 23		23 58	
	d						22 22		22 32				22 54	22 59							23 24		23 59	23 59
Balcombe	d								22 37				23 00										00 04	00 04
Horsham 4	d	22 02															23 02					23 25		
Littlehaven	d	22 05															23 05					23 28		
Faygate	d																							
Ifield	d	22 11															23 11					23 35		
Crawley	d	22 14															23 14					23 38		
Three Bridges 4	a	22 18					22 32		22 42				23 05	23 08	⟵		23 18				23 33	23 42	00 10	00 10
	d	22 21					22 32		22 42		22 48		23 12 ⟶	23 08	23 12		23 18				23 47		00 10	00 10
Gatwick Airport 10 ✈	a	22 25					22 37		22 46		22 52			23 12	23 16		23 22				23 52		00 14	00 14
	d	22 26	22 35	22 37			22 38		22 46	22 50	22 53	23 05		23 13	23 16	23 20	23 23	23 35	23 50		23 53		00 15	00 15
Horley 4	d	22 29															23 26				23s56			
Salfords	d	22 33															23 29							
Earlswood (Surrey)	d	22 36															23 33							
Reigate	d							22 44												23 54				
Tonbridge 4	d																							
Redhill	a	22 39				⟵	22 46	22 48			23 01						23 36			23 58	00 02		00 22	00 22
	d	22 40 ⟶				22 40	22 47										23 37				00 03		00 22	00 22
Merstham	d					22 44											23 41							
Coulsdon South	d					22 49											23 46							
Purley 4	d					22 52											23 49				00 11			
East Croydon	a			22 52		22 57	22 59		23 02					23 30	23 32		23 55				00 16		00 35	00 35
	d			22 52		22 58	23 00		23 02					23 30	23 32		23 58				00 17		00 36	00 36
Norwood Junction 2	a																							
London Bridge 4 ⊖	a								23 15						23 45								00 52	00 52
London Blackfriars 3 ⊖	a								23 22						23 52								00 59	00 59
City Thameslink 3	a																							
Farringdon 3 ⊖	a								23 28						23 58									
St Pancras International 15 ⊖	a								23 32						00 02								01 07	01 07
St Albans	a								23 54						00 24								01 39	01 39
Luton Airport Parkway 4 ✈	a								00 06						00 36								01 51	01 51
Luton 7	a								00 10						00 40								01 55	01 55
Bedford 10	a								00 35						01 07								02 20	02 20
Clapham Junction 10	d			23 03	23 05	23 08	23 11							23 42			00 11				00 30			
Imperial Wharf §	d																							
West Brompton ⊖	d			23 09	23 12																			
Kensington Olympia ⊖	d			23 12	23 15																			
Shepherds Bush § ⊖	d																							
Willesden Jn. High Level	a				23 27																			
Wembley Central	a																							
Harrow & Wealdstone ⊖	a			23 29																				
Watford Junction	a			23 45																				
London Victoria 15 ⊖	a		23 05			23 15	23 20			23 20		23 35		23 52		23 55	00 18	00 10	00 25		00 37			

For general notes see front of timetable
For details of catering facilities see Directory of Train Operators

§ It is unknown at the time of going to press, when this station will open. For further details please contact National Rail Enquiries 08457-484950 or see local publicity.

A From Ore (Table 189)
B From Southampton Central (Table 188)

Table 186

Saturdays

Brighton → London, Bedford and Watford Junction

Network Diagram - see first page of Table 186

Station		FC 1	FC 1	SN 1	SN 1	GX 1	FC 1	GX 1	GX 1	GW 1	GX 1	SN 1	GX 1	SN 1	FC 1	SN 1	FC 1	SN 1	FC 1	GX 1	FC 1	SN 1	XC 1 ◇	GX 1	GW 1
Brighton 10	d	22p07	22p33		23p02																	03 50			
Hove 2	d																								
Preston Park	d	22p11	22p37		23p06																				
Hassocks 4	d	22p17	22p43		23p12																				
Burgess Hill 4	d	22p21	22p47		23p16																				
Lewes 4	d																								
Wivelsfield 4	d	22p23	22p49		23p19																				
Haywards Heath 3	a	22p28	22p54		23p23																	04 24			
	d	22p32	22p54		23p24		23p59															04 25			
Balcombe	d	22p37	23p00				00 04																		
Horsham 4	d			23p02																					
Littlehaven	d			23p05																					
Faygate	d																								
Ifield	d			23p11																					
Crawley	d			23p14																					
Three Bridges 4	a	22p42	23p05	23p18	23p33		00 10															04 45			
	d	22p42	23p12	23p18	23p47		00 10							01 59	02 25	02 55	03 25	03 55	04 25		04 55	04 58			
Gatwick Airport 10 ✈	a	22p46	23p16	23p22	23p52		00 14							02 03	02 29	02 59	03 29	03 59	04 29		04 59	05 02			
	d	22p46	23p16	23p23	23p53	00 05	00 15	00 20	00 35		00 50	01 05	01 35	02 05	02 30	03 05	03 30	04 05	04 30	04 35	05 00	05 03	05 15	05 20	
Horley 4	d			23p26	23b56							01 07		02 07		03 07		04 07				05 05			
Salfords	d			23p29																					
Earlswood (Surrey)	d			23p33																					
Reigate	d									00 45															05 34
Tonbridge 4	d																								
Redhill	a			23p36	00 02		00 22			00 49													05 22		05 38
	d			23p37	00 03		00 22																05 33		
Merstham	d			23p41																					
Coulsdon South	d			23p46																					
Purley 4	d			23p49	00 11							01 22		02 22		03 22		04 22				05 24			
East Croydon	a	23p02	23p32	23p55	00 16		00 35					01 27		02 27	02 47	03 27	03 47	04 27	04 47		05 17	05 29			
	d	23p02	23p32	23p58	00 17		00 36					01 28		02 28	02 47	03 28	03 47	04 28	04 47		05 17	05 29			
Norwood Junction 2	a																								
London Bridge 4 ⊖	a	23p15	23p45				00 52																		
London Blackfriars 3 ⊖	a	23p22	23p52				00 59								03 12		04 12		05 12		05 42				
City Thameslink 3	a																								
Farringdon 3 ⊖	a	23p28	23p58																05 17		05 47				
St Pancras International 15 ⊖	a	23p32	00 02				01 07								03 21		04 21		05 21		05 51				
St Albans	a	23p54	00 24				01 39								03 53		04 53		05 53		06 23				
Luton Airport Parkway 4 ✈	a	00 06	00 36				01 51								04 05		05 05		06 05		06 35				
Luton 7	a	00 10	00 40				01 55								04 09		05 09		06 09		06 39				
Bedford 10	a	00 35	01 07				02 20								04 37		05 37		06 37		07 07				
Clapham Junction 10	d			00 11	00 30							01 41		02 41		03 41		04 41				05 49			
Imperial Wharf §	d																								
West Brompton ⊖	d																								
Kensington Olympia ⊖	d																								
Shepherds Bush § ⊖	d																								
Willesden Jn. High Level	a																								
Wembley Central	a																								
Harrow & Wealdstone ⊖	a																								
Watford Junction	a																								
London Victoria 15 ⊖	a			00 18	00 37	00 40		00 55	01 10		01 25	01 49	02 20	02 49		03 49		04 49		05 10		05 58		05 55	

For general notes see front of timetable
For details of catering facilities see Directory of Train Operators

§ It is unknown at the time of going to press, when this station will open. For further details please contact National Rail Enquiries 08457-484950 or see local publicity.

b Previous night. Stops to set down only

Table 186

Saturdays

Brighton → London, Bedford and Watford Junction

Network Diagram - see first page of Table 186

Station		FC 1	GW 1	SN 1	LO	XC 1 ◇ A	GX 1	SN 1	SN 1	SN 1	SN 1 B	FC 1	GW 1	SN 1 B	GX 1	SN 1	GX 1	SN 1	SN 1	SN 1	SN 1	LO	GW 1	FC 1	GX 1
Brighton 10	d								05 21			05 24							05 50		05 56			06 04	
Hove 2	d																			05 54					
Preston Park	d											05 28									06 00				
Hassocks 4	d											05 34									06 06				
Burgess Hill 4	d											05 38												06 14	
Lewes 4	d										05 25														
Wivelsfield 4	d											05 40									06 11				
Haywards Heath 3	a								05 34		05 40	05 45		←					06 02	06 07	06 15			06 18	
	d								05 34		05 49 →	05 45		05 49					06 11		06 22 →			06 18	
Balcombe	d											05 51													
Horsham 4	d									05 34								06 02							
Littlehaven	d									05 37								06 05							
Faygate	d																								
Ifield	d									05 43								06 11							
Crawley	d									05 47								06 14							
Three Bridges 4	a								05 43	05 50		05 56		05 59				06 18	06 20						
	d	05 20		05 33					05 44	05 51		05 56		05 59				06 18	06 20						
Gatwick Airport 10 ✈	a	05 24		05 37					05 48	05 55		06 00		06 03				06 22	06 24					06 30	
	d	05 25	05 31	05 38		05 45	05 50		05 52	05 56		06 01	06 03		06 05		06 20	06 23	06 25					06 31	06 35
Horley 4	d			05 40						05 59								06 26							
Salfords	d																	06 30							
Earlswood (Surrey)	d									06 04								06 33							
Reigate	d																						06 34		
Tonbridge 4	d																								
Redhill	a		05 39	05 47		05 51				06 07			06 12			←		06 36					06 38		
	d			05 48		05 52				06 08 →						06 08		06 37 →							
Merstham	d															06 12									
Coulsdon South	d															06 17									
Purley 4	d			05 58												06 20									
East Croydon	a	05 42		06 02		06 05		←	06 10			06 16				06 26			06 40					06 46	
	d	05 42		06 07 →		06 06		06 07	06 10			06 17				06 27			06 41					06 47	
Norwood Junction 2	a																								
London Bridge 4 ⊖	a											06 31												07 01	
London Blackfriars 3 ⊖	a	06 07										06 37												07 07	
City Thameslink 3	a																								
Farringdon 3 ⊖	a	06 13										06 41												07 13	
St Pancras International 15 ⊖	a	06 17										06 45												07 17	
St Albans	a	06 41										07 09												07 41	
Luton Airport Parkway 4 ✈	a	06 52										07 20												07 52	
Luton 7	a	06 56										07 24												07 56	
Bedford 10	a	07 23										07 52												08 23	
Clapham Junction 10	d				06 05			06 18	06 23							06 37			06 50			06 35			
Imperial Wharf §	d																								
West Brompton ⊖	d				06 12				06 29													06 42			
Kensington Olympia ⊖	d				06 15	06 50			06 32													06 45			
Shepherds Bush § ⊖	d																								
Willesden Jn. High Level	a				06 27																	06 57			
Wembley Central	a																								
Harrow & Wealdstone ⊖	a								06 56																
Watford Junction	a								07 04																
London Victoria 15 ⊖	a						06 20	06 26							06 35	06 44	06 50		06 58						07 05

For general notes see front of timetable
For details of catering facilities see Directory of Train Operators

§ It is unknown at the time of going to press, when this station will open. For further details please contact National Rail Enquiries 08457-484950 or see local publicity.

A To Birmingham New Street (Table 116)
B From Eastbourne (Table 189)

Table 186

Brighton → London, Bedford and Watford Junction

Network Diagram - see first page of Table 186

		SN	GX	SN	LO	SN	SN	SN	FC	SE 13	GW	GX	SN	SN	GW	LO	FC	GX	SN		SN	SN	SN	GW	FC
		1	1	1		1	1	1	1		1	1	1	1	1		1	1	1		1	1	1	1	1
				A										B								C			
Brighton 10	d						06 10		06 24				06 49				06 37						06 55		07 04
Hove 2	d							06 21														06 51			
Preston Park	d						06 14		06 28								06 41						06 58		
Hassocks 4	d						06 20		06 34								06 47						07 05		
Burgess Hill 4	d						06 24		06 38								06 51					07 02	07 08		
Lewes 4	d																				06 50				
Wivelsfield 4	d						06 26		06 40								06 53						07 11		
Haywards Heath 3	a	←					06 31	06 35	06 45								06 58				07 05	07 08	07 15		07 18
	d	06 22					06 39		06 45								07 02				07 13		07 16		07 18
Balcombe	d								06 51																
Horsham 4	d			06 32										06 50					07 02						
Littlehaven	d			06 35															07 05						
Faygate	d																								
Ifield	d			06 41															07 11						
Crawley	d			06 44										06 59					07 14						
Three Bridges 4	a	06 32		06 48			06 48		06 56					07 02			07 11		07 18				07 25		
	d	06 32		06 48			06 48		06 56					07 03			07 12		07 18				07 31 →		
Gatwick Airport 10 ✈	a	06 36		06 52			06 52		07 00					07 07			07 16		07 22		07 24				07 30
	d	06 37	06 50	06 53			06 54		07 01		07 03	07 05		07 08			07 16	07 20	07 23		07 25				07 31
Horley 4	d			06 55															07 26						
Salfords	d																		07 30						
Earlswood (Surrey)	d																		07 33						
Reigate	d														07 18									07 34	
Tonbridge 4	d																								
Redhill	a			07 02		←					07 10			07 15	07 23				07 36					07 38	
	d					06 37				07 05				07 16					07 37 →						
Merstham	d					06 41				07 09															
Coulsdon South	d					06 46				07 14															
Purley 4	d					06 49				07 18															
East Croydon	a	06 52				06 54	07 09		07 16	07 23			07 23	07 27			07 32				07 40				07 46
	d	06 53				06 55	07 10		07 17	07 24			07 24	07 28			07 32				07 40				07 47
Norwood Junction 2	a					06 59				07 28															
London Bridge 4 ⊖	a					07 12			07 31	07 40							07 45								08 01
London Blackfriars 3 ⊖	a								07 37								07 52								08 07
City Thameslink 3	a																								
Farringdon 3 ⊖	a								07 43								07 58								08 13
St Pancras International 15 ⊖	a								07 47								08 02								08 17
St Albans	a								08 09								08 23								08 39
Luton Airport Parkway 4 ✈	a								08 20								08 35								08 50
Luton 7	a								08 24								08 38								08 54
Bedford 10	a								08 52								09 07								09 22
Clapham Junction 10	d	07 03			07 05		07 19						07 33	07 37		07 35					07 50				
Imperial Wharf §	d																								
West Brompton ⊖	d	07 09			07 12											07 42									
Kensington Olympia ⊖	d	07 12			07 15											07 45									
Shepherds Bush § ⊖	d																								
Willesden Jn. High Level	a				07 28											07 57									
Wembley Central	a																								
Harrow & Wealdstone ⊖	a	07 29																							
Watford Junction	a	07 36																							
London Victoria 15 ⊖	a		07 20				07 27					07 35	07 40	07 44				07 50			07 57				

For general notes see front of timetable
For details of catering facilities see Directory of Train Operators

§ It is unknown at the time of going to press, when this station will open. For further details please contact National Rail Enquiries 08457-484950 or see local publicity.

A To Tonbridge (Table 209)
B From Havant (Table 188)
C From Littlehampton (Table 188)

Table 186

Saturdays

Brighton → London, Bedford and Watford Junction

Network Diagram - see first page of Table 186

		GX	SN	SN	SN	SN	LO	FC	GX	SN	SN	SN	FC	SE	GW	GX	SN	SN	GW	LO	FC	GX	SN	SN	SN
														13											
		1	1	1	1	1		1	1	1	1	1	1		1	1	1	1	1		1	1	1	1	1
						A				B								C							D
Brighton 10	d				07 19			07 07					07 34				07 49				07 37				
Hove 2	d										07 22														07 51
Preston Park	d							07 11													07 41				
Hassocks 4	d							07 17													07 47				
Burgess Hill 4	d							07 21													07 51				08 02
Lewes 4	d											07 20												07 50	
Wivelsfield 4	d							07 23				07 34									07 53				
Haywards Heath 3	a							07 28			07 35	07 40	07 47								07 58			08 05	08 09
	d							07 32			07 43		07 48								08 02			08 13	
Balcombe	d							07 37																	
Horsham 4	d					07 20				07 32								07 50					08 00		
Littlehaven	d									07 35													08 03		
Faygate	d																								
Ifield	d									07 41													08 09		
Crawley	d					07 29				07 44								07 59					08 14		
Three Bridges 4	a		←			07 32		07 42		07 48								08 02			08 11		08 18		
	d		07 31			07 33		07 42		07 48								08 03			08 12		08 18		
Gatwick Airport 10 ✈	a		07 35			07 37		07 46		07 52	07 54		08 00					08 07			08 16		08 22	08 24	
	d	07 35	07 37			07 38		07 46	07 50	07 53	07 55		08 01		08 03	08 05		08 08			08 16	08 20	08 23	08 25	
Horley 4	d					07 41				07 55													08 26		
Salfords	d																						08 30		
Earlswood (Surrey)	d																						08 33		
Reigate	d																		08 19						
Tonbridge 4	d													07 34											
Redhill	a			←		07 47				08 02				08 04	08 10			08 15	08 24				08 36		
	d			07 37		07 48								08 05				08 16					08 37 →		
Merstham	d			07 41										08 09											
Coulsdon South	d			07 46										08 14											
Purley 4	d			07 49										08 18											
East Croydon	a		07 52	07 54	07 55	07 59		08 02			08 10		08 16	08 23			08 23	08 27			08 32			08 40	
	d		07 52	07 55	07 55	08 00		08 02			08 10		08 17	08 24			08 24	08 28			08 32			08 40	
Norwood Junction 2	a			07 59										08 28											
London Bridge 4 ⊖	a			08 12				08 15					08 31	08 40							08 45				
London Blackfriars 3 ⊖	a							08 22					08 37								08 52				
City Thameslink 3	a																								
Farringdon 3 ⊖	a							08 28					08 43								08 58				
St Pancras International 15 ⊖	a							08 32					08 47								09 02				
St Albans	a							08 54					09 09								09 23				
Luton Airport Parkway 4 ✈	a							09 05					09 20								09 35				
Luton 7	a							09 08					09 24								09 38				
Bedford 10	a							09 37					09 52								10 07				
Clapham Junction 10	d		08 03		08 05	08 11	08 05				08 20						08 33	08 37		08 35				08 50	
Imperial Wharf §	d																								
West Brompton ⊖	d		08 09				08 12													08 42					
Kensington Olympia ⊖	d		08 12				08 15													08 45					
Shepherds Bush § ⊖	d																								
Willesden Jn. High Level	a						08 28													08 57					
Wembley Central	a																								
Harrow & Wealdstone ⊖	a		08 29																						
Watford Junction	a		08 37																						
London Victoria 15 ⊖	a	08 05			08 11	08 18			08 20		08 27					08 35	08 40	08 44				08 50		08 57	

For general notes see front of timetable
For details of catering facilities see Directory of Train Operators

§ It is unknown at the time of going to press, when this station will open. For further details please contact National Rail Enquiries 08457-484950 or see local publicity.

A From Bognor Regis (Table 188) and from Portsmouth Harbour (Table 188)

B To Tunbridge Wells (Table 209)

C From Bognor Regis (Table 188) and from Southampton Central (Table 188)

D From Littlehampton (Table 188)

Brighton → London, Bedford and Watford Junction

Network Diagram - see first page of Table 186

Station		SN	GW	FC	GX	SN	SN	SN	SN	LO	FC	GX	SN	SN	SN	FC	SE	GW	GX	SN	SN	GW	LO	FC	GX
		1	1	1	1	1	1	1	1		1	1	1	1	1	1	13	1	1	1	1	1		1	1
									A				B								C				
Brighton 10	d	07 55		08 04				08 19			08 07					08 34				08 49				08 37	
Hove 2	d													08 21											
Preston Park	d	07 58									08 11													08 41	
Hassocks 4	d	08 05									08 17													08 47	
Burgess Hill 4	d	08 08									08 21													08 51	
Lewes 4	d														08 20										
Wivelsfield 4	d	08 11									08 23				08 34									08 53	
Haywards Heath 3	a	08 15		08 18							08 28			08 35	08 40	08 47								08 58	
	d	08 16		08 18							08 32			08 43		08 49								09 02	
Balcombe	d										08 37														
Horsham 4	d								08 20				08 32								08 50				
Littlehaven	d												08 35												
Faygate	d																								
Ifield	d												08 41												
Crawley	d								08 29				08 44								08 59				
Three Bridges 4	a	08 25				←			08 32		08 42		08 48								09 02			09 11	
	d	08 31				08 31			08 33		08 42		08 48								09 03			09 12	
Gatwick Airport 10 ✈	a	→		08 30		08 35			08 37		08 46		08 52	08 54		09 00					09 07			09 16	
	d			08 31	08 35	08 37			08 38		08 46	08 50	08 53	08 55		09 01		09 03	09 05		09 08			09 16	09 20
Horley 4	d								08 41				08 55												
Salfords	d																								
Earlswood (Surrey)	d																								
Reigate	d		08 34																			09 18			
Tonbridge 4	d																08 34								
Redhill	a		08 38				←		08 47				09 02				09 04	09 10			09 15	09 23			
	d						08 37		08 48								09 05				09 16				
Merstham	d						08 41										09 09								
Coulsdon South	d						08 46										09 14								
Purley 4	d						08 49										09 18								
East Croydon	a			08 46		08 52	08 54	08 55	08 59		09 02			09 10		09 16	09 23			09 23	09 27			09 32	
	d			08 47		08 52	08 55	08 55	09 00		09 02			09 10		09 17	09 24			09 24	09 28			09 32	
Norwood Junction 2	a						08 59										09 28								
London Bridge 4 ⊖	a			09 01			09 12				09 15					09 30	09 40							09 45	
London Blackfriars 3 ⊖	a			09 07							09 22					09 37								09 52	
City Thameslink 3	a			09 10							09 25					09 40								09 55	
Farringdon 3 ⊖	a			09 14							09 29					09 44								09 59	
St Pancras International 15 ⊖	a			09 18							09 33					09 48								10 03	
St Albans	a			09 39							09 53					10 09								10 23	
Luton Airport Parkway 4 ✈	a			09 50							10 05					10 20								10 35	
Luton 7	a			09 54							10 08					10 24								10 38	
Bedford 10	a			10 22							10 37					10 52								11 07	
Clapham Junction 10	d					09 03		09 05	09 11	09 05				09 20						09 33	09 37		09 35		
Imperial Wharf §	d																								
West Brompton ⊖	d					09 09				09 12													09 42		
Kensington Olympia ⊖	d					09 12				09 15													09 45		
Shepherds Bush § ⊖	d																								
Willesden Jn. High Level	a									09 27													09 57		
Wembley Central	a																								
Harrow & Wealdstone ⊖	a					09 29																			
Watford Junction	a					09 36																			
London Victoria 15 ⊖	a				09 05			09 11	09 18			09 20		09 27					09 35	09 40	09 44				09 50

For general notes see front of timetable
For details of catering facilities see Directory of Train Operators

§ It is unknown at the time of going to press, when this station will open. For further details please contact National Rail Enquiries 08457-484950 or see local publicity.

A From Bognor Regis (Table 188) and from Portsmouth Harbour (Table 188)
B To Tunbridge Wells (Table 209)
C From Bognor Regis (Table 188) and from Southampton Central (Table 188)

Table 186

Brighton → London, Bedford and Watford Junction

Network Diagram - see first page of Table 186

		SN	SN	SN	SN	GW	FC	GX	SN	SN	SN	SN	LO	FC	SN	XC		GX	SN	SN	SN	FC	SE 13	GW	GX
		1	1	1	1	1	1	1	1	1	1	1		1	1	1 ◇		1	1	1	1	1		1	1
												A			A	B 🍴			C				D		
Brighton 10	d				08 55		09 04				09 19			09 07		09 15						09 34			
Hove 2	d			08 51																09 21					
Preston Park	d				08 58									09 11											
Hassocks 4	d				09 05									09 17											
Burgess Hill 4	d				09 08									09 21											
Lewes 4	d		08 50																		09 20				
Wivelsfield 4	d				09 11																09 34				
Haywards Heath 3	a		09 05	09 09	09 15		09 18							09 26		09 28				09 35	09 40	09 47			
	d		09 13		09 16		09 18							09 26		09 34				09 43		09 48			
Balcombe	d													09 32											
Horsham 4	d	09 00										09 20							09 32						
Littlehaven	d	09 03																	09 35						
Faygate	d																								
Ifield	d	09 09																	09 41						
Crawley	d	09 14										09 29							09 44						
Three Bridges 4	a	09 18			09 25				←			09 32		09 37					09 48						
	d	09 18			09 31				09 31			09 33		09 37					09 48						
Gatwick Airport 10 ✈	a	09 22	09 24		→		09 30		09 35			09 37		09 41		09 44			09 52	09 54		10 00			
	d	09 23	09 25				09 31	09 35	09 37			09 38		09 41	←	09 47		09 50	09 53	09 55		10 01		10 03	10 05
Horley 4	d	09 26										09 41			09 41				09 55						
Salfords	d	09 30										→													
Earlswood (Surrey)	d	09 33																							
Reigate	d					09 34																			
Tonbridge 4	d																						09 34		
Redhill	a	09 36				09 38				←					09 47				10 02				10 04	10 10	
	d	09 37								09 37					09 48								10 05		
Merstham	d	→								09 41													10 09		
Coulsdon South	d									09 46													10 14		
Purley 4	d									09 49													10 18		
East Croydon	a		09 40				09 46		09 52	09 54	09 55			09 57	09 59	10 02				10 10		10 16	10 23		
	d		09 40				09 47		09 52	09 55	09 55			09 57	10 00	10 03				10 10		10 17	10 24		
Norwood Junction 2	a									09 59													10 28		
London Bridge 4 ⊖	a						10 00			10 12				10 15								10 30	10 40		
London Blackfriars 3 ⊖	a						10 07							10 22								10 37			
City Thameslink 3	a						10 10							10 25								10 40			
Farringdon 3 ⊖	a						10 14							10 29								10 44			
St Pancras International 15 ⊖	a						10 18							10 33								10 48			
St Albans	a						10 39							10 53								11 09			
Luton Airport Parkway 4 ✈	a						10 50							11 05								11 20			
Luton 7	a						10 54							11 08								11 24			
Bedford 10	a						11 22							11 37								11 52			
Clapham Junction 10	d		09 50						10 03		10 05		10 05		10 11					10 20					
Imperial Wharf §	d																								
West Brompton ⊖	d								10 09				10 12												
Kensington Olympia ⊖	d								10 12				10 15			10 34									
Shepherds Bush § ⊖	d																								
Willesden Jn. High Level	a												10 27												
Wembley Central	a																								
Harrow & Wealdstone ⊖	a								10 29																
Watford Junction	a								10 35																
London Victoria 15 ⊖	a		09 57					10 05			10 11				10 18			10 20		10 27					10 35

For general notes see front of timetable
For details of catering facilities see Directory of Train Operators

§ It is unknown at the time of going to press, when this station will open. For further details please contact National Rail Enquiries 08457-484950 or see local publicity.

A From Bognor Regis (Table 188) and from Portsmouth Harbour (Table 188)
B To Birmingham New Street (Table 116)
C To Tunbridge Wells (Table 209)
D From Tunbridge Wells (Table 206)

Saturdays

Brighton → London, Bedford and Watford Junction

Network Diagram - see first page of Table 186

		SN 1	SN 1 A	GW 1	LO	FC 1	GX 1	SN 1	SN 1	SN 1 B	SN 1	GW 1	FC 1	GX 1	SN 1	SN 1	SN 1	SN 1 C	LO	FC 1	GX 1	SN 1 D	SN 1	SN 1	FC 1
Brighton 10	d	09 49				09 37					09 55		10 04				10 19			10 07					10 34
Hove 2	d									09 51													10 21		
Preston Park	d					09 41					09 58									10 11					
Hassocks 4	d					09 47					10 05									10 17					
Burgess Hill 4	d					09 51				10 02	10 08									10 21					
Lewes 4	d							09 50																10 20	
Wivelsfield 4	d					09 53					10 11									10 23				10 34	
Haywards Heath 3	a					09 58		10 05		10 08	10 15		10 18							10 28			10 35	10 40	10 47
	d					10 02		10 09		10 12	10 16		10 18							10 32			10 43		10 48
Balcombe	d																			10 37					
Horsham 4	d		09 50						10 00									10 20				10 32			
Littlehaven	d								10 03													10 35			
Faygate	d																								
Ifield	d								10 09													10 41			
Crawley	d		09 59						10 14									10 29				10 44			
Three Bridges 4	a		10 02			10 11			10 18		10 25				←			10 32		10 42		10 48			
	d		10 03			10 12			10 18		10 31 →				10 31			10 33		10 42		10 48			
Gatwick Airport 10 ✈	a		10 07			10 16		10 21	10 22	10 25			10 30		10 35			10 37		10 46		10 52	10 54		11 00
	d		10 08			10 16	10 20	10 22	10 23	10 26			10 31	10 35	10 37			10 38		10 46	10 50	10 53	10 55		11 01
Horley 4	d								10 26									10 41				10 55			
Salfords	d								10 30																
Earlswood (Surrey)	d								10 33																
Reigate	d			10 19								10 34													
Tonbridge 4	d																								
Redhill	a		10 15	10 24					10 36			10 38				←		10 47				11 02			
	d		10 16						10 37 →							10 37		10 48							
Merstham	d															10 41									
Coulsdon South	d															10 46									
Purley 4	d															10 49									
East Croydon 🚋	a	10 23	10 27			10 32		10 38		10 42			10 46		10 52	10 54	10 55	11 00		11 02			11 10		11 16
	d	10 24	10 28			10 32		10 38		10 42			10 47		10 52	10 55	10 55	11 00		11 02			11 10		11 17
Norwood Junction 2	a															10 59									
London Bridge 4	⊖ a					10 45							11 00			11 12				11 15					11 30
London Blackfriars 3	⊖ a					10 52							11 07							11 22					11 37
City Thameslink 3	a					10 55							11 10							11 25					11 40
Farringdon 3	⊖ a					10 59							11 14							11 29					11 44
St Pancras International 15	⊖ a					11 03							11 18							11 33					11 48
St Albans	a					11 23							11 39							11 53					12 09
Luton Airport Parkway 4	✈ a					11 35							11 50							12 05					12 20
Luton 7	a					11 38							11 54							12 08					12 24
Bedford 10	a					12 07							12 22							12 37					12 52
Clapham Junction 10	d	10 33	10 37		10 35			10 48		10 52					11 03		11 05	11 11	11 05				11 20		
Imperial Wharf §	d																								
West Brompton	⊖ d				10 42										11 09				11 12						
Kensington Olympia	⊖ d				10 45										11 12				11 15						
Shepherds Bush §	⊖ d																								
Willesden Jn. High Level	a				10 57														11 27						
Wembley Central	a																								
Harrow & Wealdstone	⊖ a														11 29										
Watford Junction	a														11 36										
London Victoria 15	⊖ a	10 40	10 44				10 50	10 56		10 59				11 05			11 11	11 18			11 20		11 27		

For general notes see front of timetable
For details of catering facilities see Directory of Train Operators

§ It is unknown at the time of going to press, when this station will open. For further details please contact National Rail Enquiries 08457-484950 or see local publicity.

A From Bognor Regis (Table 188) and from Southampton Central (Table 188)
B From Littlehampton (Table 188)
C From Bognor Regis (Table 188) and from Portsmouth Harbour (Table 188)
D To Tunbridge Wells (Table 209)

Brighton → London, Bedford and Watford Junction

Network Diagram - see first page of Table 186

		SE	GW	GX	SN	SN	GW	LO	FC	GX	SN	SN	SN	SN	GW	FC	GX	SN	SN	SN	SN	LO	FC	GX	SN
		13																							
			1	1	1	1	1		1	1	1	1	1	1	1	1	1	1	1	1	1		1	1	1
		A				B							C								D				E
Brighton 10	d				10 49				10 37					10 55		11 04				11 19			11 07		
Hove 2	d												10 51												
Preston Park	d								10 41					10 58									11 11		
Hassocks 4	d								10 47					11 05									11 17		
Burgess Hill 4	d								10 51				11 02	11 08									11 21		
Lewes 4	d											10 50													
Wivelsfield 4	d								10 53					11 11									11 23		
Haywards Heath 3	a								10 58			11 05	11 09	11 15		11 18							11 28		
	d								11 02			11 13		11 16		11 18							11 32		
Balcombe	d																						11 37		
Horsham 4	d					10 50					11 00										11 20				11 32
Littlehaven	d										11 03														11 35
Faygate	d																								
Ifield	d										11 09														11 41
Crawley	d					10 59					11 14										11 29				11 44
Three Bridges 4	a					11 02			11 11		11 18			11 25				←			11 32		11 42		11 48
	d					11 03			11 12		11 18			11 31 →				11 31			11 33		11 42		11 48
Gatwick Airport 10 ✈	a					11 07			11 16		11 22	11 24				11 30		11 35			11 37		11 46		11 52
	d		11 03	11 05		11 08			11 16	11 20	11 23	11 25				11 31	11 35	11 37			11 38		11 46	11 50	11 53
Horley 4	d										11 26										11 41				11 55
Salfords	d										11 30														
Earlswood (Surrey)	d										11 33														
Reigate	d						11 18								11 34										
Tonbridge 4	d	10 34																							
Redhill	a	11 04	11 10			11 15	11 24				11 36				11 38				←		11 47				12 02
	d	11 05				11 16					11 37 →								11 37		11 48				
Merstham	d	11 09																	11 41						
Coulsdon South	d	11 14																	11 46						
Purley 4	d	11 18																	11 49						
East Croydon	a	11 23			11 23	11 27			11 32			11 40				11 46		11 52	11 54	11 55	12 00		12 02		
	d	11 24			11 24	11 28			11 32			11 40				11 47		11 52	11 55	11 55	12 00		12 02		
Norwood Junction 2	a	11 28																	11 59						
London Bridge 4 ⊖	a	11 40							11 45							12 00			12 12				12 15		
London Blackfriars 3 ⊖	a								11 52							12 07							12 22		
City Thameslink 3	a								11 55							12 10							12 25		
Farringdon 3 ⊖	a								11 59							12 14							12 29		
St Pancras International 15 ⊖	a								12 03							12 18							12 33		
St Albans	a								12 23							12 39							12 53		
Luton Airport Parkway 4 ✈	a								12 35							12 50							13 05		
Luton 7	a								12 38							12 54							13 08		
Bedford 10	a								13 07							13 22							13 37		
Clapham Junction 10	d				11 33	11 37		11 35				11 50						12 03		12 05	12 11	12 05			
Imperial Wharf §	d																								
West Brompton ⊖	d							11 42										12 09				12 12			
Kensington Olympia ⊖	d							11 45										12 12				12 15			
Shepherds Bush § ⊖	d																								
Willesden Jn. High Level	a							11 57														12 27			
Wembley Central	a																								
Harrow & Wealdstone ⊖	a																	12 29							
Watford Junction	a																	12 36							
London Victoria 15 ⊖	a			11 35	11 40	11 44				11 50		11 57					12 05			12 11	12 18			12 20	

For general notes see front of timetable
For details of catering facilities see Directory of Train Operators

§ It is unknown at the time of going to press, when this station will open. For further details please contact National Rail Enquiries 08457-484950 or see local publicity.

A From Tunbridge Wells (Table 206)
B From Bognor Regis (Table 188) and from Southampton Central (Table 188)
C From Littlehampton (Table 188)
D From Bognor Regis (Table 188) and from Portsmouth Harbour (Table 188)
E To Tunbridge Wells (Table 209)

Table 186

Saturdays

Brighton → London, Bedford and Watford Junction

Network Diagram - see first page of Table 186

		SN	SN	FC	SE	GW	GX	SN	SN	GW	LO	FC	GX	SN	SN	SN	SN	GW	FC	GX	SN	SN	SN	SN
					13																			
		1	1	1		1	1	1	1	1		1	1	1	1	1	1	1	1	1	1	1	1	1
					A				B							C								D
Brighton 10	d			11 34				11 49				11 37					11 55		12 04				12 19	
Hove 2	d	11 21														11 51								
Preston Park	d											11 41					11 58							
Hassocks 4	d											11 47					12 05							
Burgess Hill 4	d											11 51				12 02	12 08							
Lewes 4	d		11 20												11 50									
Wivelsfield 4	d		11 34									11 53					12 11							
Haywards Heath 3	a	11 35	11 40	11 47								11 58			12 05	12 09	12 15		12 18					
	d	11 43		11 48								12 02			12 13		12 16		12 18					
Balcombe	d																							
Horsham 4	d								11 50					12 00										12 20
Littlehaven	d													12 03										
Faygate	d																							
Ifield	d													12 09										
Crawley	d								11 59					12 14										12 29
Three Bridges 4	a								12 02			12 11		12 18			12 25				←			12 32
	d								12 03			12 12		12 18			12 31				12 31			12 33
Gatwick Airport 10 ✈	a	11 54		12 00					12 07			12 16		12 22	12 24		→		12 30		12 35			12 37
	d	11 55		12 01		12 03	12 05		12 08			12 16	12 20	12 23	12 25				12 31	12 35	12 37			12 38
Horley 4	d													12 26										12 41
Salfords	d													12 30										
Earlswood (Surrey)	d													12 33										
Reigate	d									12 19								12 34						
Tonbridge 4	d				11 34																			
Redhill	a				12 04	12 10			12 15	12 24				12 36				12 38				←		12 47
	d				12 05				12 16					12 37 →								12 37		12 48
Merstham	d				12 09																	12 41		
Coulsdon South	d				12 14																	12 46		
Purley 4	d				12 18																	12 49		
East Croydon	a	12 10		12 16	12 23			12 23	12 27			12 32			12 40				12 46		12 52	12 54	12 55	13 00
	d	12 10		12 17	12 24			12 24	12 28			12 32			12 40				12 47		12 52	12 55	12 55	13 00
Norwood Junction 2	a				12 28																	12 59		
London Bridge 4 ⊖	a			12 30	12 40							12 45							13 00			13 12		
London Blackfriars 3 ⊖	a			12 37								12 52							13 07					
City Thameslink 3	a			12 40								12 55							13 10					
Farringdon 3 ⊖	a			12 44								12 59							13 14					
St Pancras International 15 ⊖	a			12 48								13 03							13 18					
St Albans	a			13 09								13 23							13 39					
Luton Airport Parkway 4 ✈	a			13 20								13 35							13 50					
Luton 7	a			13 24								13 38							13 54					
Bedford 10	a			13 52								14 07							14 22					
Clapham Junction 10	d	12 20						12 33	12 37		12 35				12 50						13 03		13 05	13 11
Imperial Wharf §	d																							
West Brompton ⊖	d										12 42										13 09			
Kensington Olympia ⊖	d										12 45										13 12			
Shepherds Bush § ⊖	d																							
Willesden Jn. High Level	a										12 57													
Wembley Central	a																							
Harrow & Wealdstone ⊖	a																				13 29			
Watford Junction	a																				13 37			
London Victoria 15 ⊖	a	12 27					12 35	12 40	12 44				12 50		12 57					13 05			13 11	13 18

For general notes see front of timetable
For details of catering facilities see Directory of Train Operators

§ It is unknown at the time of going to press, when this station will open. For further details please contact National Rail Enquiries 08457-484950 or see local publicity.

A From Tunbridge Wells (Table 206)
B From Bognor Regis (Table 188) and from Southampton Central (Table 188)
C From Littlehampton (Table 188)
D From Bognor Regis (Table 188) and from Portsmouth Harbour (Table 188)

Table 186

Saturdays

Brighton → London, Bedford and Watford Junction

Network Diagram - see first page of Table 186

		LO	FC	GX	SN	SN	SN	FC	SE	GW	GX	SN	SN	GW	LO	FC	GX	SN	SN	SN	SN	GW	FC	GX	SN
									13																
			1	1	1	1	1	1		1	1	1	1	1		1	1	1	1	1	1	1	1	1	1
					A				B				C							D					
Brighton 10	d		12 07					12 34				12 49				12 37					12 55		13 04		
Hove 2	d					12 21														12 51					
Preston Park	d		12 11													12 41					12 58				
Hassocks 4	d		12 17													12 47					13 05				
Burgess Hill 4	d		12 21													12 51				13 02	13 08				
Lewes 4	d						12 20												12 50						
Wivelsfield 4	d		12 23				12 34									12 53					13 11				
Haywards Heath 3	a		12 28			12 35	12 40	12 47								12 58			13 05	13 09	13 15		13 18		
	d		12 32			12 43		12 48								13 02			13 13		13 16		13 18		
Balcombe	d		12 37																						
Horsham 4	d				12 32								12 50					13 00							
Littlehaven	d				12 35													13 03							
Faygate	d																								
Ifield	d				12 41													13 09							
Crawley	d				12 44								12 59					13 14							
Three Bridges 4	a		12 42		12 48								13 02			13 11		13 18			13 25				←
	d		12 42		12 48								13 03			13 12		13 18			13 31 →				13 31
Gatwick Airport 10 ✈	a		12 46		12 52	12 54		13 00					13 07			13 16		13 22	13 24		→		13 30		13 35
	d		12 46	12 50	12 53	12 55		13 01		13 03	13 05		13 08			13 16	13 20	13 23	13 25				13 31	13 35	13 37
Horley 4	d				12 55													13 26							
Salfords	d																	13 30							
Earlswood (Surrey)	d																	13 33							
Reigate	d													13 18								13 34			
Tonbridge 4	d								12 34																
Redhill	a				13 02				13 04	13 10			13 15	13 23				13 36				13 38			
	d								13 05				13 16					13 37 →							
Merstham	d								13 09																
Coulsdon South	d								13 14																
Purley 4	d								13 18																
East Croydon	a		13 02			13 10		13 16	13 23			13 23	13 27			13 32			13 40				13 46		13 52
	d		13 02			13 10		13 17	13 24			13 24	13 28			13 32			13 40				13 47		13 52
Norwood Junction 2	a								13 28																
London Bridge 4 ⊖	a		13 15					13 30	13 40							13 45							14 00		
London Blackfriars 3 ⊖	a		13 22					13 37								13 52							14 07		
City Thameslink 3	a		13 25					13 40								13 55							14 10		
Farringdon 3 ⊖	a		13 29					13 44								13 59							14 14		
St Pancras International 15 ⊖	a		13 33					13 48								14 03							14 18		
St Albans	a		13 53					14 09								14 23							14 39		
Luton Airport Parkway 4 ✈	a		14 05					14 20								14 35							14 50		
Luton 7	a		14 08					14 24								14 38							14 54		
Bedford 10	a		14 37					14 52								15 07							15 22		
Clapham Junction 10	d	13 05				13 20						13 33	13 37		13 35				13 50						14 03
Imperial Wharf §	d																								
West Brompton ⊖	d	13 12													13 42										14 09
Kensington Olympia ⊖	d	13 15													13 45										14 12
Shepherds Bush § ⊖	d																								
Willesden Jn. High Level	a	13 27													13 57										
Wembley Central	a																								
Harrow & Wealdstone ⊖	a																								14 29
Watford Junction	a																								14 37
London Victoria 15 ⊖	a			13 20		13 27					13 35	13 40	13 44				13 50		13 57					14 05	

For general notes see front of timetable
For details of catering facilities see Directory of Train Operators

§ It is unknown at the time of going to press, when this station will open. For further details please contact National Rail Enquiries 08457-484950 or see local publicity.

A To Tunbridge Wells (Table 209)
B From Tunbridge Wells (Table 206)
C From Bognor Regis (Table 188) and from Southampton Central (Table 188)
D From Littlehampton (Table 188)

Table 186

Saturdays

Brighton → London, Bedford and Watford Junction

Network Diagram - see first page of Table 186

		SN	SN	SN	LO	FC	GX	SN	SN	SN	FC	SE	GW	GX	SN	SN	GW	LO	FC	GX	SN	SN	SN	SN	GW
												13													
		1	1	1		1	1	1	1	1	1		1	1	1	1	1		1	1	1	1	1	1	1
				A				B				C				D							E		
Brighton 10	d		13 19			13 07					13 34				13 49				13 37					13 55	
Hove 2	d								13 21														13 51		
Preston Park	d					13 11													13 41					13 58	
Hassocks 4	d					13 17													13 47					14 05	
Burgess Hill 4	d					13 21													13 51				14 02	14 08	
Lewes 4	d									13 20												13 50			
Wivelsfield 4	d					13 23				13 34									13 53					14 11	
Haywards Heath 3	a					13 28			13 35	13 40	13 47								13 58			14 05	14 09	14 15	
	d					13 32			13 43		13 48								14 02			14 13		14 16	
Balcombe	d					13 37																			
Horsham 4	d			13 20				13 32								13 50					14 00				
Littlehaven	d							13 35													14 03				
Faygate	d																								
Ifield	d							13 41													14 09				
Crawley	d			13 29				13 44								13 59					14 14				
Three Bridges 4	a			13 32		13 42		13 48								14 02			14 11		14 18			14 25	
	d			13 33		13 42		13 48								14 03			14 12		14 18			14 31 →	
Gatwick Airport 10 ✈	a			13 37		13 46		13 52	13 54		14 00					14 07			14 16		14 22	14 24			
	d			13 38		13 46	13 50	13 53	13 55		14 01		14 03	14 05		14 08			14 16	14 20	14 23	14 25			
Horley 4	d			13 41				13 55													14 26				
Salfords	d																				14 30				
Earlswood (Surrey)	d																				14 33				
Reigate	d																14 19								14 34
Tonbridge 4	d											13 34													
Redhill	a	←		13 47				14 02				14 04	14 10			14 15	14 24				14 36				14 38
	d	13 37		13 48								14 05				14 16					14 37 →				
Merstham	d	13 41										14 09													
Coulsdon South	d	13 46										14 14													
Purley 4	d	13 49										14 18													
East Croydon	a	13 54	13 55	14 00		14 02			14 10		14 16	14 23			14 23	14 27			14 32			14 40			
	d	13 55	13 55	14 00		14 02			14 10		14 17	14 24			14 24	14 28			14 32			14 40			
Norwood Junction 2	a	13 59										14 28													
London Bridge 4 ⊖	a	14 12				14 15					14 30	14 40							14 45						
London Blackfriars 3 ⊖	a					14 22					14 37								14 52						
City Thameslink 3	a					14 25					14 40								14 55						
Farringdon 3 ⊖	a					14 29					14 44								14 59						
St Pancras International 15 ⊖	a					14 33					14 48								15 03						
St Albans	a					14 53					15 09								15 23						
Luton Airport Parkway 4 ✈	a					15 05					15 20								15 35						
Luton 7	a					15 08					15 24								15 38						
Bedford 10	a					15 37					15 52								16 07						
Clapham Junction 10	d		14 05	14 11	14 05				14 20						14 33	14 37		14 35				14 50			
Imperial Wharf §	d																								
West Brompton ⊖	d				14 12													14 42							
Kensington Olympia ⊖	d				14 15													14 45							
Shepherds Bush § ⊖	d																								
Willesden Jn. High Level	a				14 27													14 57							
Wembley Central	a																								
Harrow & Wealdstone ⊖	a																								
Watford Junction	a																								
London Victoria 15 ⊖	a		14 11	14 18			14 20		14 27					14 35	14 40	14 44				14 50		14 57			

For general notes see front of timetable
For details of catering facilities see Directory of Train Operators

§ It is unknown at the time of going to press, when this station will open. For further details please contact National Rail Enquiries 08457-484950 or see local publicity.

A From Bognor Regis (Table 188) and from Portsmouth Harbour (Table 188)
B To Tunbridge Wells (Table 209)
C From Tunbridge Wells (Table 206)
D From Bognor Regis (Table 188) and from Southampton Central (Table 188)
E From Littlehampton (Table 188)

Table 186

Saturdays

Brighton → London, Bedford and Watford Junction

Network Diagram - see first page of Table 186

		FC	GX	SN	SN	SN	SN	LO	FC	GX		XC	SN	XC	SN	SN	FC	SE	GW	GX	SN	SN	GW	LO	FC
																		13							
		1	1	1	1	1	1		1	1		1 ◊	1	1 ◊	1	1	1		1	1	1	1	1		1
							A					B	C	B				D				E			
												⊡		⊡											
Brighton 10	d	14 04				14 19			14 07			14 22					14 34				14 49				14 37
Hove 2	d														14 21										
Preston Park	d								14 11																14 41
Hassocks 4	d								14 17																14 47
Burgess Hill 4	d								14 21																14 51
Lewes 4	d															14 20									
Wivelsfield 4	d								14 23							14 34									14 53
Haywards Heath 3	a	14 18							14 28						14 35	14 40	14 47								14 58
	d	14 18							14 32						14 43		14 48								15 02
Balcombe	d								14 37																
Horsham 4	d						14 20						14 32									14 50			
Littlehaven	d												14 35												
Faygate	d																								
Ifield	d												14 41												
Crawley	d						14 29						14 44									14 59			
Three Bridges 4	a			←			14 32		14 42				14 48									15 02			15 11
	d			14 31			14 33		14 42				14 48									15 03			15 12
Gatwick Airport 10 ✈	a	14 30		14 35			14 37		14 46			14 51	14 52	←	14 55		15 00					15 07			15 16
	d	14 31	14 35	14 37			14 38		14 46	14 50		14 54	14 53	14 54	14 56		15 01		15 03	15 05		15 08			15 16
Horley 4	d						14 41					→	14 55												
Salfords	d																								
Earlswood (Surrey)	d																								
Reigate	d																						15 18		
Tonbridge 4	d																	14 34							
Redhill	a				←		14 47						15 02					15 04	15 10			15 15	15 23		
	d				14 37		14 48											15 05				15 16			
Merstham	d				14 41													15 09							
Coulsdon South	d				14 46													15 14							
Purley 4	d				14 49													15 18							
East Croydon	a	14 46		14 52	14 54	14 55	15 00		15 02					15 07	15 11		15 16	15 23			15 23	15 27			15 32
	d	14 47		14 52	14 55	14 55	15 00		15 02					15 08	15 11		15 17	15 24			15 24	15 28			15 32
Norwood Junction 2	a				14 59													15 28							
London Bridge 4 ⊖	a	15 00			15 12				15 15								15 30	15 40							15 45
London Blackfriars 3 ⊖	a	15 07							15 22								15 37								15 52
City Thameslink 3	a	15 10							15 25								15 40								15 55
Farringdon 3 ⊖	a	15 14							15 29								15 44								15 59
St Pancras International 15 ⊖	a	15 18							15 33								15 48								16 03
St Albans	a	15 39							15 53								16 09								16 23
Luton Airport Parkway 4 ✈	a	15 50							16 05								16 20								16 35
Luton 7	a	15 54							16 08								16 24								16 38
Bedford 10	a	16 22							16 37								16 52								17 07
Clapham Junction 10	d			15 03		15 05	15 11	15 05							15 21						15 33	15 37		15 35	
Imperial Wharf §	d																								
West Brompton ⊖	d			15 09				15 12																15 42	
Kensington Olympia ⊖	d			15 12				15 15						15 40										15 45	
Shepherds Bush § ⊖	d																								
Willesden Jn. High Level	a							15 27																15 57	
Wembley Central	a																								
Harrow & Wealdstone ⊖	a			15 29																					
Watford Junction	a			15 37																					
London Victoria 15 ⊖	a		15 05			15 11	15 18			15 20					15 27					15 35	15 40	15 44			

For general notes see front of timetable
For details of catering facilities see Directory of Train Operators

§ It is unknown at the time of going to press, when this station will open. For further details please contact National Rail Enquiries 08457-484950 or see local publicity.

A From Bognor Regis (Table 188) and from Portsmouth Harbour (Table 188)
B To Birmingham New Street (Table 116)
C To Tunbridge Wells (Table 209)
D From Tunbridge Wells (Table 206)
E From Bognor Regis (Table 188) and from Southampton Central (Table 188)

Brighton → London, Bedford and Watford Junction

Network Diagram - see first page of Table 186

		GX	SN	SN	SN	SN	GW	FC	GX	SN	SN	SN	SN	LO	FC	GX	SN	SN	SN	FC	SE 13	GW	GX	SN	SN
		1	1	1	1	1	1	1	1	1	1	1	1		1	1	1	1	1	1		1	1	1	1
					A								B				C				D				E
Brighton 10	d					14 55		15 04				15 19			15 07					15 34				15 49	
Hove 2	d				14 51													15 21							
Preston Park	d					14 58									15 11										
Hassocks 4	d					15 05									15 17										
Burgess Hill 4	d				15 02	15 08									15 21										
Lewes 4	d			14 50															15 20						
Wivelsfield 4	d					15 11									15 23				15 34						
Haywards Heath 3	a			15 05	15 09	15 15		15 18							15 28			15 35	15 40	15 47					
	d			15 13		15 16		15 18							15 32			15 43		15 48					
Balcombe	d														15 37										
Horsham 4	d		15 00										15 20				15 32								15 50
Littlehaven	d		15 03														15 35								
Faygate	d																								
Ifield	d		15 09														15 41								
Crawley	d		15 14										15 29				15 44								15 59
Three Bridges 4	a		15 18			15 25				←			15 32		15 42		15 48								16 02
	d		15 18			15 31 →				15 31			15 33		15 42		15 48								16 03
Gatwick Airport 10 ✈	a		15 22	15 24				15 30		15 35			15 37		15 46		15 52	15 54		16 00					16 07
	d	15 20	15 23	15 25				15 31	15 35	15 37			15 38		15 46	15 50	15 53	15 55		16 01		16 03	16 05		16 08
Horley 4	d		15 26										15 41				15 55								
Salfords	d		15 30																						
Earlswood (Surrey)	d		15 33																						
Reigate	d						15 34																		
Tonbridge 4	d																				15 34				
Redhill	a		15 36				15 38				←		15 47				16 02				16 04	16 10			16 15
	d		15 37 →								15 37		15 48								16 05				16 16
Merstham	d										15 41										16 09				
Coulsdon South	d										15 46										16 14				
Purley 4	d										15 49										16 18				
East Croydon	a			15 40				15 46		15 52	15 54	15 55	16 00		16 02			16 10		16 16	16 23			16 23	16 27
	d			15 40				15 47		15 52	15 55	15 55	16 00		16 02			16 10		16 17	16 24			16 24	16 28
Norwood Junction 2	a										15 59										16 28				
London Bridge 4 ⊖	a							16 00			16 12				16 15					16 30	16 40				
London Blackfriars 3 ⊖	a							16 07							16 22					16 37					
City Thameslink 3	a							16 10							16 25					16 40					
Farringdon 3 ⊖	a							16 14							16 29					16 44					
St Pancras International 15 ⊖	a							16 18							16 33					16 48					
St Albans	a							16 39							16 53					17 09					
Luton Airport Parkway 4 ✈	a							16 50							17 05					17 20					
Luton 7	a							16 54							17 08					17 24					
Bedford 10	a							17 22							17 37					17 52					
Clapham Junction 10	d			15 50						16 03		16 05	16 11	16 05				16 20						16 33	16 37
Imperial Wharf §	d																								
West Brompton ⊖	d									16 09				16 12											
Kensington Olympia ⊖	d									16 12				16 15											
Shepherds Bush § ⊖	d																								
Willesden Jn. High Level	a													16 27											
Wembley Central	a																								
Harrow & Wealdstone ⊖	a									16 29															
Watford Junction	a									16 37															
London Victoria 15 ⊖	a	15 50		15 57					16 05			16 11	16 18			16 20		16 27					16 35	16 40	16 44

For general notes see front of timetable
For details of catering facilities see Directory of Train Operators

§ It is unknown at the time of going to press, when this station will open. For further details please contact National Rail Enquiries 08457-484950 or see local publicity.

A From Littlehampton (Table 188)
B From Bognor Regis (Table 188) and from Portsmouth Harbour (Table 188)
C To Tunbridge Wells (Table 209)
D From Tunbridge Wells (Table 206)
E From Bognor Regis (Table 188) and from Southampton Central (Table 188)

Table 186

Saturdays

Brighton → London, Bedford and Watford Junction

Network Diagram - see first page of Table 186

		GW	LO	FC	GX	SN	SN	SN	SN	GW	FC	GX	SN	SN	SN	SN	LO	FC	GX	SN	SN	SN	FC	SE 13	GW
		1		1	1	1	1	1	1	1	1	1	1	1	1	1		1	1	1	1	1	1		1
								A								B				C				D	
Brighton 10	d			15 37					15 55		16 04				16 19			16 07					16 34		
Hove 2	d							15 51													16 21				
Preston Park	d			15 41					15 58									16 11							
Hassocks 4	d			15 47					16 05									16 17							
Burgess Hill 4	d			15 51				16 02	16 08									16 21							
Lewes 4	d						15 50															16 20			
Wivelsfield 4	d			15 53					16 11									16 23				16 34			
Haywards Heath 3	a			15 58			16 05	16 09	16 15		16 18							16 28			16 35	16 40	16 47		
	d			16 02				16 13	16 16		16 18							16 32				16 43	16 48		
Balcombe	d																	16 37							
Horsham 4	d					16 00										16 20				16 32					
Littlehaven	d					16 03														16 35					
Faygate	d																								
Ifield	d					16 09														16 41					
Crawley	d					16 14										16 29				16 44					
Three Bridges 4	a			16 11		16 18			16 25				←			16 32		16 42		16 48					
	d			16 12		16 18			16 31				16 31			16 33		16 42		16 48					
Gatwick Airport 10 ✈	a			16 16		16 22		16 24	→		16 30		16 35			16 37		16 46		16 52		16 54	17 00		
	d			16 16	16 20	16 23		16 25			16 31	16 35	16 37			16 38		16 46	16 50	16 53		16 55	17 01		17 03
Horley 4	d					16 26										16 41				16 55					
Salfords	d					16 30																			
Earlswood (Surrey)	d					16 33																			
Reigate	d	16 19								16 34															
Tonbridge 4	d																							16 34	
Redhill	a	16 24				16 36				16 38				←		16 47				17 02				17 04	17 10
	d					16 37 →								16 37		16 48								17 05	
Merstham	d													16 41										17 09	
Coulsdon South	d													16 46										17 14	
Purley 4	d													16 49										17 18	
East Croydon	a			16 32				16 40			16 46		16 52	16 54	16 55	17 00		17 02				17 10	17 16	17 23	
	d			16 32				16 40			16 47		16 52	16 55	16 55	17 00		17 02				17 10	17 17	17 24	
Norwood Junction 2	a													16 59										17 28	
London Bridge 4 ⊖	a			16 45							17 00			17 12				17 15					17 30	17 40	
London Blackfriars 3 ⊖	a			16 52							17 07							17 22					17 37		
City Thameslink 3	a			16 55							17 10							17 25					17 40		
Farringdon 3 ⊖	a			16 59							17 14							17 29					17 44		
St Pancras International 15 ⊖	a			17 03							17 18							17 33					17 48		
St Albans	a			17 23							17 39							17 53					18 09		
Luton Airport Parkway 4 ✈	a			17 35							17 50							18 05					18 20		
Luton 7	a			17 38							17 54							18 08					18 24		
Bedford 10	a			18 07							18 22							18 37					18 52		
Clapham Junction 10	d		16 35					16 50					17 03		17 05	17 11	17 05					17 20			
Imperial Wharf §	d																								
West Brompton ⊖	d		16 42										17 09				17 12								
Kensington Olympia ⊖	d		16 45										17 12				17 15								
Shepherds Bush § ⊖	d																								
Willesden Jn. High Level	a		16 57														17 27								
Wembley Central	a																								
Harrow & Wealdstone ⊖	a												17 29												
Watford Junction	a												17 36												
London Victoria 15 ⊖	a				16 50			16 57				17 05			17 11	17 18			17 20			17 27			

For general notes see front of timetable
For details of catering facilities see Directory of Train Operators

§ It is unknown at the time of going to press, when this station will open. For further details please contact National Rail Enquiries 08457-484950 or see local publicity.

A From Littlehampton (Table 188)
B From Bognor Regis (Table 188) and from Portsmouth Harbour (Table 188)
C To Tunbridge Wells (Table 209)
D From Tunbridge Wells (Table 206)

Table 186

Brighton → London, Bedford and Watford Junction

Network Diagram - see first page of Table 186

		GX 1	SN 1	SN 1 A	GW 1	LO	FC 1		GX 1	SN 1	SN 1	SN 1 B	SN 1	GW 1	FC 1	GX 1	SN 1	SN 1	SN 1	SN 1 C	LO	FC 1	GX 1	SN 1 D	
Brighton 10	d		16 49				16 37						16 55		17 04				17 19			17 07			
Hove 2	d											16 51													
Preston Park	d						16 41						16 58									17 11			
Hassocks 4	d						16 47						17 05									17 17			
Burgess Hill 4	d						16 51					17 02	17 08									17 21			
Lewes 4	d										16 50														
Wivelsfield 4	d						16 53						17 11									17 23			
Haywards Heath 3	a						16 58				17 05	17 09	17 15		17 18							17 28			
	d						17 02				17 13		17 16		17 18							17 32			
Balcombe	d																					17 37			
Horsham 4	d			16 50						17 00										17 20				17 32	
Littlehaven	d									17 03														17 35	
Faygate	d																								
Ifield	d									17 09														17 41	
Crawley	d			16 59						17 14										17 29				17 44	
Three Bridges 4	a			17 02			17 11			17 18			17 25				←			17 32		17 42		17 48	
	d			17 03			17 12			17 18			17 31 →				17 31			17 33		17 42		17 48	
Gatwick Airport 10 ✈	a			17 07			17 16			17 22	17 24				17 30		17 35			17 37		17 46		17 52	
	d	17 05		17 08			17 16		17 20	17 23	17 25				17 31	17 35	17 37			17 38		17 46	17 50	17 53	
Horley 4	d									17 26										17 41				17 55	
Salfords	d									17 30															
Earlswood (Surrey)	d									17 33															
Reigate	d				17 18									17 34											
Tonbridge 4	d																								
Redhill	a			17 15	17 23					17 36				17 38				←		17 47				18 02	
	d			17 16						17 37 →								17 37		17 48					
Merstham	d																	17 41							
Coulsdon South	d																	17 46							
Purley 4	d																	17 49							
East Croydon	a		17 23	17 27			17 32				17 40				17 46		17 52	17 54	17 55	18 00		18 02			
	d		17 24	17 28			17 32				17 40				17 47		17 52	17 55	17 55	18 00		18 02			
Norwood Junction 2	a																	17 59							
London Bridge 4 ⊖	a						17 45								18 00			18 12				18 15			
London Blackfriars 3 ⊖	a						17 52								18 07							18 22			
City Thameslink 3	a						17 55								18 10							18 25			
Farringdon 3 ⊖	a						17 59								18 14							18 29			
St Pancras International 15 ⊖	a						18 03								18 18							18 33			
St Albans	a						18 23								18 39							18 53			
Luton Airport Parkway 4 ✈	a						18 35								18 50							19 05			
Luton 7	a						18 38								18 54							19 08			
Bedford 10	a						19 07								19 22							19 37			
Clapham Junction 10	d		17 33	17 37		17 35					17 50						18 03		18 05	18 11	18 05				
Imperial Wharf §	d																								
West Brompton ⊖	d					17 42											18 09				18 12				
Kensington Olympia ⊖	d					17 45											18 12				18 15				
Shepherds Bush § ⊖	d																								
Willesden Jn. High Level	a					17 57															18 27				
Wembley Central	a																								
Harrow & Wealdstone ⊖	a																18 29								
Watford Junction	a																18 37								
London Victoria 15 ⊖	a	17 35	17 40	17 44					17 50		17 57					18 05			18 11	18 18			18 20		

For general notes see front of timetable
For details of catering facilities see Directory of Train Operators

§ It is unknown at the time of going to press, when this station will open. For further details please contact National Rail Enquiries 08457-484950 or see local publicity.

A From Bognor Regis (Table 188) and from Southampton Central (Table 188)

B From Littlehampton (Table 188)

C From Bognor Regis (Table 188) and from Portsmouth Harbour (Table 188)

D To Tunbridge Wells (Table 209)

Table 186

Saturdays

Brighton → London, Bedford and Watford Junction

Network Diagram - see first page of Table 186

		SN	SN	FC	SE	GW	GX	SN	SN	GW	LO	FC	GX	SN	SN	SN	SN	GW	FC	GX	SN	SN	SN	SN	LO
					13																				
		1	1	1		1	1	1	1	1		1	1	1	1	1	1	1	1	1	1	1	1	1	
					A				B							C								D	
Brighton 10	d			17 34				17 49				17 37					17 55		18 04				18 19		
Hove 2	d	17 21														17 51									
Preston Park	d											17 41					17 58								
Hassocks 4	d											17 47					18 05								
Burgess Hill 4	d											17 51				18 02	18 08								
Lewes 4	d		17 20												17 50										
Wivelsfield 4	d		17 34									17 53					18 11								
Haywards Heath 3	a	17 35	17 40	17 47								17 58			18 05	18 09	18 15		18 18						
	d	17 43		17 48								18 02			18 13		18 16		18 18						
Balcombe	d																								
Horsham 4	d								17 50					18 00										18 20	
Littlehaven	d													18 03											
Faygate	d																								
Ifield	d													18 09											
Crawley	d								17 59					18 14										18 29	
Three Bridges 4	a								18 02			18 11		18 18			18 25				←			18 32	
	d								18 03			18 12		18 18			18 31 →				18 31			18 33	
Gatwick Airport 10 ✈	a	17 54		18 00					18 07			18 16		18 22	18 24				18 30		18 35			18 37	
	d	17 55		18 01		18 03	18 05		18 08			18 16	18 20	18 23	18 25				18 31	18 35	18 37			18 38	
Horley 4	d													18 26										18 41	
Salfords	d													18 30											
Earlswood (Surrey)	d													18 33											
Reigate	d									18 19								18 34							
Tonbridge 4	d				17 34																				
Redhill	a				18 04	18 10			18 15	18 24				18 36				18 38				←		18 47	
	d				18 05				18 16					18 37 →								18 37		18 48	
Merstham	d				18 09																	18 41			
Coulsdon South	d				18 14																	18 46			
Purley 4	d				18 18																	18 49			
East Croydon	a	18 10		18 16	18 23			18 23	18 27			18 32			18 40				18 46		18 52	18 54	18 55	19 00	
	d	18 10		18 17	18 24			18 24	18 28			18 32			18 40				18 47		18 52	18 55	18 55	19 00	
Norwood Junction 2	a				18 28																	18 59			
London Bridge 4 ⊖	a			18 30	18 40							18 45							19 00			19 12			
London Blackfriars 3 ⊖	a			18 37								18 52							19 07						
City Thameslink 3	a			18 40								18 55							19 10						
Farringdon 3 ⊖	a			18 44								18 59							19 14						
St Pancras International 15 ⊖	a			18 48								19 03							19 18						
St Albans	a			19 09								19 24							19 39						
Luton Airport Parkway 4 ✈	a			19 20								19 36							19 50						
Luton 7	a			19 24								19 39							19 54						
Bedford 10	a			19 52								20 07							20 22						
Clapham Junction 10	d	18 20						18 33	18 37		18 35				18 50						19 03		19 05	19 11	19 05
Imperial Wharf §	d																								
West Brompton ⊖	d										18 42										19 09				19 12
Kensington Olympia ⊖	d										18 45										19 12				19 15
Shepherds Bush § ⊖	d																								
Willesden Jn. High Level	a										18 57														19 27
Wembley Central	a																								
Harrow & Wealdstone ⊖	a																				19 29				
Watford Junction	a																				19 37				
London Victoria 15 ⊖	a	18 27					18 35	18 40	18 44				18 50		18 57					19 05			19 11	19 18	

For general notes see front of timetable
For details of catering facilities see Directory of Train Operators

§ It is unknown at the time of going to press, when this station will open. For further details please contact National Rail Enquiries 08457-484950 or see local publicity.

A From Tunbridge Wells (Table 206)

B From Bognor Regis (Table 188) and from Southampton Central (Table 188)

C From Littlehampton (Table 188)

D From Bognor Regis (Table 188) and from Portsmouth Harbour (Table 188)

Table 186

Saturdays

Brighton → London, Bedford and Watford Junction

Network Diagram - see first page of Table 186

		FC	GX	SE	SN	SN	SN	FC	GW	GX	SN	SN	SN	GW	LO	FC	GX	SN	SN	SN	SN	GW	FC	GX	SN
		1	1	88	1	1	1	1	1	1	1	1	1	1		1	1	1	1	1	1	1	1	1	1
													A							B					
Brighton 10	d	18 07						18 34			18 49					18 37					18 55		19 04		
Hove 2	d				18 21															18 51					
Preston Park	d	18 11														18 41					18 58				
Hassocks 4	d	18 17														18 47					19 05				
Burgess Hill 4	d	18 21														18 51				19 02	19 08				
Lewes 4	d					18 20													18 50						
Wivelsfield 4	d	18 23				18 34										18 53					19 11				
Haywards Heath 3	a	18 28			18 35	18 40		18 47								18 58			19 05	19 09	19 15		19 18		
	d	18 32			18 43			18 48								19 02			19 13		19 16		19 18		
Balcombe	d	18 37																							
Horsham 4	d						18 35						18 50					19 02							
Littlehaven	d						18 38											19 05							
Faygate	d																								
Ifield	d						18 44											19 11							
Crawley	d						18 47						18 59					19 14							
Three Bridges 4	a	18 42					18 51						19 02			19 12		19 18			19 25				←
	d	18 42		18 48			18 51						19 03			19 12		19 18			19 31				19 31
Gatwick Airport 10 ✈	a	18 46		18 52	18 54		18 55	19 00					19 07			19 16		19 22	19 24		→		19 31		19 35
	d	18 46	18 50	18 52	18 55		18 56	19 01	19 03	19 05			19 08			19 16	19 20	19 23	19 25				19 31	19 35	19 37
Horley 4	d						18 59											19 26							
Salfords	d																	19 30							
Earlswood (Surrey)	d																	19 33							
Reigate	d													19 18								19 34			
Tonbridge 4	d																								
Redhill	a			19 00			19 05		19 10				19 17	19 23				19 36				19 38			
	d						19 06					←	19 18					19 37							
Merstham	d						19 10					19 10						→							
Coulsdon South	d						→					19 15													
Purley 4	d											19 19													
East Croydon	a	19 02			19 10			19 16			19 23	19 24	19 28			19 32			19 40				19 47		19 52
	d	19 02			19 10			19 17			19 24	19 25	19 29			19 32			19 40				19 47		19 52
Norwood Junction 2	a																								
London Bridge 4 ⊖	a	19 15						19 30								19 45							20 00		
London Blackfriars 3 ⊖	a	19 22						19 37								19 52							20 07		
City Thameslink 3	a	19 25						19 40								19 55							20 10		
Farringdon 3 ⊖	a	19 29						19 44								19 59							20 14		
St Pancras International 15 ⊖	a	19 33						19 48								20 03									
St Albans	a	19 54						20 09								20 24							20 39		
Luton Airport Parkway 4 ✈	a	20 06						20 20								20 36							20 50		
Luton 7	a	20 09						20 24								20 39							20 54		
Bedford 10	a	20 37						20 52								21 07							21 22		
Clapham Junction 10	d				19 20						19 33	19 37	19 40		19 35				19 50						20 03
Imperial Wharf §	d																								
West Brompton ⊖	d														19 42										20 09
Kensington Olympia ⊖	d														19 45										20 12
Shepherds Bush § ⊖	d																								
Willesden Jn. High Level	a														19 57										
Wembley Central	a																								
Harrow & Wealdstone ⊖	a																								20 29
Watford Junction	a																								20 37
London Victoria 15 ⊖	a		19 20		19 27					19 35	19 40	19 44	19 48				19 50		19 57					20 05	

For general notes see front of timetable
For details of catering facilities see Directory of Train Operators

§ It is unknown at the time of going to press, when this station will open. For further details please contact National Rail Enquiries 08457-484950 or see local publicity.

A From Bognor Regis (Table 188) and from Southampton Central (Table 188)

B From Littlehampton (Table 188)

Table 186

Saturdays

Brighton → London, Bedford and Watford Junction

Network Diagram - see first page of Table 186

Station		SN	SN	LO		SN	SN	FC	GX	SE	SN	SN	SN	FC	GW	GX	SN	SN	SN	GW	LO	FC	GX	SN
		1	1			1	1	1	1	55	1	1	1	1	1	1	1	1	1	1		1	1	1
							A												B					
Brighton 10	d		19 19					19 07						19 34			19 49					19 37		
Hove 2	d										19 21													
Preston Park	d							19 11														19 41		
Hassocks 4	d							19 17														19 47		
Burgess Hill 4	d							19 21														19 51		
Lewes 4	d											19 20												
Wivelsfield 4	d							19 23				19 34										19 53		
Haywards Heath 3	a							19 28			19 35	19 40		19 47								19 58		
	d							19 32			19 43			19 48								20 02		
Balcombe	d							19 37																
Horsham 4	d						19 21						19 32						19 52					20 02
Littlehaven	d												19 35											20 05
Faygate	d																							
Ifield	d												19 41											20 11
Crawley	d						19 30						19 45						20 01					20 14
Three Bridges 4	a						19 33	19 42					19 48						20 05			20 12		20 18
	d						19 34	19 42		19 48			19 51						20 05			20 12		20 18
Gatwick Airport 10	✈ a						19 38	19 46		19 52	19 54		19 55	20 00					20 10			20 16		20 22
	d						19 39	19 46	19 50	19 53	19 55		19 56	20 01	20 03	20 05			20 11			20 16	20 20	20 23
Horley 4	d												19 59											20 26
Salfords	d																							20 30
Earlswood (Surrey)	d																							20 33
Reigate	d																			20 19				
Tonbridge 4	d																							
Redhill	a	←					19 46			20 01			20 05		20 10				20 18	20 24				20 36
	d	19 37					19 47						20 08					←	20 18					20 37
Merstham	d	19 41											20 12 →					20 12						→
Coulsdon South	d	19 46																20 17						
Purley 4	d	19 49																20 20						
East Croydon	a	19 54	19 55			←	19 59	20 02			20 10			20 16			20 23	20 25	20 30			20 32		
	d	19 55	19 55			19 55	20 00	20 02			20 10			20 17			20 24	20 26	20 30			20 32		
Norwood Junction 2	a	→																						
London Bridge 4	⊖ a							20 15						20 30								20 45		
London Blackfriars 3	⊖ a							20 22						20 37								20 52		
City Thameslink 3	a							20 25						20 40								20 55		
Farringdon 3	⊖ a							20 29						20 44								20 59		
St Pancras International 15	⊖ a							20 33						20 48								21 03		
St Albans	a							20 54						21 09								21 24		
Luton Airport Parkway 4	✈ a							21 06						21 20								21 36		
Luton 7	a							21 09						21 24								21 40		
Bedford 10	a							21 37						21 52								22 07		
Clapham Junction 10	d		20 05	20 05		20 08	20 11				20 20						20 33	20 38	20 41		20 35			
Imperial Wharf §	d																							
West Brompton	⊖ d			20 12																	20 42			
Kensington Olympia	⊖ d			20 15																	20 45			
Shepherds Bush §	⊖ d																							
Willesden Jn. High Level	a			20 27																	20 57			
Wembley Central	a																							
Harrow & Wealdstone	⊖ a																							
Watford Junction	a																							
London Victoria 15	⊖ a		20 11			20 14	20 17		20 20		20 27					20 35	20 40	20 44	20 50				20 50	

For general notes see front of timetable
For details of catering facilities see Directory of Train Operators

§ It is unknown at the time of going to press, when this station will open. For further details please contact National Rail Enquiries 08457-484950 or see local publicity.

A From Portsmouth & Southsea (Table 188)
B From Southampton Central (Table 188)

Table 186

Saturdays

Brighton → London, Bedford and Watford Junction

Network Diagram - see first page of Table 186

		SN	SN	SN	GW	FC	GX	SN	SN	SN	SN	SN	LO	FC	GX	SN	SE 88	SN	FC	GW	GX	SN	SN	SN	GW
		1	1	1	1	1	1	1	1	1	1	1		1	1	1		1	1	1	1	1	1	1	1
			A																					B	
Brighton 10	d			19 55		20 04				20 19				20 07					20 34			20 49			
Hove 2	d		19 52													20 22									
Preston Park	d			19 59										20 11											
Hassocks 4	d			20 05										20 17											
Burgess Hill 4	d		20 02	20 09										20 21											
Lewes 4	d	19 51																							
Wivelsfield 4	d	20 03		20 11										20 23											
Haywards Heath 3	a	20 07	20 09	20 16		20 18						←		20 28		20 36			20 47						
	d	20 13		20 22 →		20 18						20 22		20 32		20 38			20 48						
Balcombe	d													20 37											
Horsham 4	d																	20 32						20 52	
Littlehaven	d																	20 35							
Faygate	d																								
Ifield	d																	20 41							
Crawley	d																	20 45						21 01	
Three Bridges 4	a											20 32		20 42		20 47		20 48						21 05	
	d											20 32		20 42		20 48	20 48	20 51						21 05	
Gatwick Airport 10 ✈	a	20 24				20 30						20 37		20 46		20 52	20 52	20 55	21 00					21 10	
	d	20 25				20 31	20 35	20 37				20 38		20 46	20 50	20 53	20 53	20 56	21 01	21 03	21 05			21 11	
Horley 4	d																	20 59							
Salfords	d																								
Earlswood (Surrey)	d																								
Reigate	d				20 34																				21 18
Tonbridge 4	d																								
Redhill	a				20 38				←			20 46					21 02	21 05		21 10				21 18	21 23
	d								20 37			20 47						21 08					←	21 18	
Merstham	d								20 41									21 12 →					21 12		
Coulsdon South	d								20 46														21 17		
Purley 4	d								20 49														21 20		
East Croydon	a	20 40				20 46		20 52	20 54	20 55	←	20 59		21 02		21 09			21 16			21 23	21 25	21 30	
	d	20 40				20 47		20 52	20 57 →	20 55	20 57	21 00		21 02		21 10			21 17			21 24	21 26	21 30	
Norwood Junction 2	a																								
London Bridge 4 ⊖	a					21 00								21 15					21 30						
London Blackfriars 3 ⊖	a					21 07								21 22					21 37						
City Thameslink 3	a																								
Farringdon 3 ⊖	a					21 13								21 28					21 43						
St Pancras International 15 ⊖	a					21 17								21 32					21 47						
St Albans	a					21 39								21 54					22 09						
Luton Airport Parkway 4 ✈	a					21 50								22 06					22 20						
Luton 7	a					21 54								22 10					22 24						
Bedford 10	a					22 22								22 37					22 52						
Clapham Junction 10	d	20 50						21 03		21 05	21 08	21 11	21 05			21 20						21 33	21 38	21 41	
Imperial Wharf §	d																								
West Brompton ⊖	d							21 09					21 12												
Kensington Olympia ⊖	d							21 12					21 15												
Shepherds Bush § ⊖	d																								
Willesden Jn. High Level	a												21 27												
Wembley Central	a																								
Harrow & Wealdstone ⊖	a							21 29																	
Watford Junction	a							21 46																	
London Victoria 15 ⊖	a	20 57					21 05			21 11	21 14	21 20			21 20	21 27					21 35	21 40	21 44	21 48	

For general notes see front of timetable
For details of catering facilities see Directory of Train Operators

§ It is unknown at the time of going to press, when this station will open. For further details please contact National Rail Enquiries 08457-484950 or see local publicity.

A From Littlehampton (Table 188)
B From Southampton Central (Table 188)

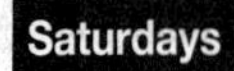

Brighton → London, Bedford and Watford Junction

Network Diagram - see first page of Table 186

		LO	FC	GX	SN	SN	SN	GX	SN	SN	GW	SN	SN	LO	FC	GX	SN	SE	LO	SN	SN	GX	SN	FC	GX
																		88							
			1	1	1	1	1	1	1	1	1	1	1		1	1	1			1	1	1	1	1	1
							A																B		
Brighton 10	d		20 37							21 19			21 00		21 07					21 49				21 37	
Hove 2	d						20 52										21 22								
Preston Park	d		20 41										21 04		21 11									21 41	
Hassocks 4	d		20 47										21 10		21 17									21 47	
Burgess Hill 4	d		20 51				21 02						21 14		21 21									21 51	
Lewes 4	d					20 50																			
Wivelsfield 4	d		20 53			21 02							21 16		21 23									21 53	
Haywards Heath 3	a		20 58			21 06	21 08						21 21		21 28		21 36							21 58	
	d		21 02			21 13							21 22		21 32		21 38							22 02	
Balcombe	d														21 37										
Horsham 4	d				21 02																21 32		21 52		
Littlehaven	d				21 05																21 35				
Faygate	d																								
Ifield	d				21 11																21 41				
Crawley	d				21 14																21 45		22 01		
Three Bridges 4	a		21 11		21 18								21 32		21 42						21 48		22 05	22 11	
	d		21 12		21 19								21 32		21 42			21 48			21 51		22 05	22 12	
Gatwick Airport 10 ✈	a		21 16		21 23	21 24							21 37		21 46		21 51	21 52			21 55		22 10	22 16	
	d		21 16	21 20	21 24	21 25		21 35	21 37				21 38		21 46	21 50	21 53	21 53			21 56	22 05	22 11	22 16	22 20
Horley 4	d				21 27																21 59				
Salfords	d				21 31																				
Earlswood (Surrey)	d				21 34																				
Reigate	d										21 40														
Tonbridge 4	d																								
Redhill	a				21 38						21 44	←	21 46					22 01			22 05		22 18		
	d				21 38 →							21 38	21 47								22 08		22 18		
Merstham	d											21 42									22 12				
Coulsdon South	d											21 47									22 17				
Purley 4	d											21 51									22 20				
East Croydon	a		21 32			21 40			21 52	21 55		21 56	21 59		22 02		22 09			22 23	22 25		22 30	22 32	
	d		21 32			21 40			21 52	21 55		21 57	22 00		22 02		22 10			22 24	22 26		22 30	22 32	
Norwood Junction 2	a																								
London Bridge 4	⊖ a		21 45												22 15									22 45	
London Blackfriars 3	⊖ a		21 52												22 22									22 52	
City Thameslink 3	a																								
Farringdon 3	⊖ a		21 58												22 28									22 58	
St Pancras International 15	⊖ a		22 02												22 32									23 02	
St Albans	a		22 24												22 54									23 24	
Luton Airport Parkway 4 ✈	a		22 36												23 06									23 36	
Luton 7	a		22 40												23 10									23 40	
Bedford 10	a		23 07												23 37									00 07	
Clapham Junction 10	d	21 35				21 50			22 03	22 05		22 08	22 11	22 05			22 20		22 35	22 33	22 38		22 41		
Imperial Wharf §	d																								
West Brompton	⊖ d	21 42							22 09					22 12					22 42						
Kensington Olympia	⊖ d	21 45							22 12					22 15					22 45						
Shepherds Bush §	⊖ d																								
Willesden Jn. High Level	a	21 57												22 27					22 57						
Wembley Central	a																								
Harrow & Wealdstone	⊖ a								22 29																
Watford Junction	a								22 46																
London Victoria 15	⊖ a			21 50		21 57		22 05		22 11		22 14	22 18			22 20	22 27			22 40	22 44	22 35	22 48		22 50

For general notes see front of timetable
For details of catering facilities see Directory of Train Operators

§ It is unknown at the time of going to press, when this station will open. For further details please contact National Rail Enquiries 08457-484950 or see local publicity.

A From Littlehampton (Table 188)
B From Southampton Central (Table 188)

Table 186

Saturdays

Brighton → London, Bedford and Watford Junction

Network Diagram - see first page of Table 186

		GW	SN	SN	LO	SN	GX	SN	FC	GW	GX	SE 88	GX	FC	SN	FC	GW	GX	SN	GX	GX	GW	SN	SN	FC
		1	1	1		1	1	1	1	1	1		1	1	1	1	1	1	1	1	1	1	1	1	1
				A											B									C	
Brighton 10	d							22 00	22 07					22 33									23 02		
Hove 2	d			21 52																					
Preston Park	d							22 04	22 11					22 37									23 06		
Hassocks 4	d							22 10	22 17					22 43									23 12		
Burgess Hill 4	d			22 02				22 14	22 21					22 47									23 16		
Lewes 4	d		21 50												22 40										
Wivelsfield 4	d		22 02					22 16	22 23					22 49	22 54								23 19		
Haywards Heath 3	a		22 06	22 08				22 21	22 28					22 54	22 58								23 23		
	d			22 12				22 22	22 32					22 54	22 59								23 24		23 59
Balcombe	d								22 37					23 00											00 04
Horsham 4	d					22 02													23 02					23 25	
Littlehaven	d					22 05													23 05					23 28	
Faygate	d																								
Ifield	d					22 11													23 11					23 35	
Crawley	d					22 14													23 14					23 38	
Three Bridges 4	a					22 18		22 32	22 42					23 05	23 08	←			23 18				23 33	23 42	00 10
	d					22 21		22 32	22 42			22 48		23 12	23 08	23 12			23 18				23 47		00 10
Gatwick Airport 10 ✈	a			22 23		22 25		22 37	22 46			22 52		→	23 12	23 16			23 22				23 52		00 14
	d	22 22		22 25		22 26	22 35	22 38	22 46		22 50	22 53	23 05		23 13	23 16	23 18	23 20	23 23	23 35	23 50		23 53		00 15
Horley 4	d					22 29													23 26				23s56		
Salfords	d					22 33													23 30						
Earlswood (Surrey)	d					22 36													23 33						
Reigate	d									22 48												23 54			
Tonbridge 4	d																								
Redhill	a	22 29				22 39		22 46		22 52		23 01					23 25		23 36			23 58	00 02		00 22
	d					22 40		22 47											23 37				00 03		00 22
Merstham	d					22 44													23 41						
Coulsdon South	d					22 49													23 46						
Purley 4	d					22 52													23 49				00 11		
East Croydon	a			22 40		22 57		22 59	23 02						23 30	23 32			23 55				00 16		00 35
	d			22 40		22 58		23 00	23 02						23 30	23 32			23 56				00 17		00 36
Norwood Junction 2	a																								
London Bridge 4 ⊖	a								23 15							23 45									00 52
London Blackfriars 3 ⊖	a								23 22							23 52									00 59
City Thameslink 3	a																								
Farringdon 3 ⊖	a								23 28							23 58									
St Pancras International 15 ⊖	a								23 32							00 02									01 07
St Albans	a								23 54							00 24									01 39
Luton Airport Parkway 4 ✈	a								00 06							00 36									01 51
Luton 7	a								00 10							00 40									01 55
Bedford 10	a								00 37							01 07									02 20
Clapham Junction 10	d			22 50	23 05	23 08		23 11							23 42				00 11				00 30		
Imperial Wharf §	d																								
West Brompton ⊖	d				23 13																				
Kensington Olympia ⊖	d				23 15																				
Shepherds Bush § ⊖	d																								
Willesden Jn. High Level	a				23 29																				
Wembley Central	a																								
Harrow & Wealdstone ⊖	a																								
Watford Junction	a																								
London Victoria 15 ⊖	a			22 57		23 14	23 05	23 17			23 20		23 35		23 52			23 55	00 18	00 10	00 25		00 37		

For general notes see front of timetable
For details of catering facilities see Directory of Train Operators

§ It is unknown at the time of going to press, when this station will open. For further details please contact National Rail Enquiries 08457-484950 or see local publicity.

A From Littlehampton (Table 188)
B From Hastings (Table 189)
C From Southampton Central (Table 188)

Table 186

Sundays

Brighton → London, Bedford and Watford Junction

Network Diagram - see first page of Table 186

		FC 1	FC 1	SN 1	SN 1	GX 1	FC 1	GX 1	GX 1	GW 1	GX 1	SN 1	GX 1	SN 1	SN 1	SN 1		GX 1	SN 1	FC 1	GX 1	SN 1	GX 1	GX 1	GW 1
Brighton 10	d	22p07	22p33		23p02														03 50						
Hove 2	d																								
Preston Park	d	22p11	22p37		23p06																				
Hassocks 4	d	22p17	22p43		23p12																				
Burgess Hill 4	d	22p21	22p47		23p16																				
Lewes 4	d																								
Wivelsfield 4	d	22p23	22p49		23p19																				
Haywards Heath 3	a	22p28	22p54		23p23																				
	d	22p32	22p54		23p24		23p59																		
Balcombe	d	22p37	23p00				00 04																		
Horsham 4	d			23p02																					
Littlehaven	d			23p05																					
Faygate	d																								
Ifield	d			23p11																					
Crawley	d			23p14																					
Three Bridges 4	a	22p42	23p05	23p18	23p33		00 10												04 45						
	d	22p42	23p12	23p18	23p47		00 10					01 10		02 10	03 10	04 10			04 58	05 10		05 30			
Gatwick Airport 10 ✈	a	22p46	23p16	23p22	23p52		00 14					01 19		02 14	03 14	04 14			05 02	05 14		05 34			
	d	22p46	23p16	23p23	23p53	00 05	00 15	00 20	00 35		00 50	01 20	01 35	02 15	03 15	04 15		04 35	05 03	05 15	05 20	05 36	05 50	06 05	06 07
Horley 4	d			23p26	23b56							01 22		02 18	03 18	04 18			05 05			05 38			
Salfords	d			23p30																					
Earlswood (Surrey)	d			23p33																					
Reigate	d									00 45															
Tonbridge 4	d																								
Redhill	a			23p36	00 02		00 22			00 49												05 46			06 15
	d			23p37	00 03		00 22															05 46			
Merstham	d			23p41																					
Coulsdon South	d			23p46																					
Purley 4	d			23p49	00 11							01 37		02 33	03 33	04 33			05 22			05 56			
East Croydon	a	23p02	23p32	23p55	00 16		00 35					01 42		02 39	03 39	04 39			05 27	05 31		06 01			
	d	23p02	23p32	23p56	00 17		00 36					01 43		02 40	03 40	04 40			05 28	05 32		06 02			
Norwood Junction 2	a																								
London Bridge 4 ⊖	a	23p15	23p45				00 52																		
London Blackfriars 3 ⊖	a	23p22	23p52				00 59													05 54					
City Thameslink 3	a																								
Farringdon 3 ⊖	a	23p28	23p58																						
St Pancras International 15 ⊖	a	23p32	00 02				01 07													06 02					
St Albans	a	23p54	00 24				01 39													06 33					
Luton Airport Parkway 4 ✈	a	00 06	00 36				01 51													06 45					
Luton 7	a	00 10	00 40				01 55													06 49					
Bedford 10	a	00 37	01 07				02 20													07 19					
Clapham Junction 10	d			00 11	00 30							01 54		02 53	03 53	04 53			05 49			06 14			
Imperial Wharf §	d																								
West Brompton ⊖	d																								
Kensington Olympia ⊖	d																								
Shepherds Bush § ⊖	d																								
Willesden Jn. High Level	a																								
Wembley Central	a																								
Harrow & Wealdstone ⊖	a																								
Watford Junction	a																								
London Victoria 15 ⊖	a			00 18	00 37	00 40		00 55	01 10		01 25	02 05	02 20	03 05	04 05	05 05		05 10	05 58		05 55	06 22	06 25	06 40	

For general notes see front of timetable
For details of catering facilities see
Directory of Train Operators

§ It is unknown at the time of going to press, when this station will open. For further details please contact National Rail Enquiries 08457-484950 or see local publicity.

b Previous night.
Stops to set down only

Sundays

Brighton → London, Bedford and Watford Junction

Network Diagram - see first page of Table 186

	FC	GX	SN	GX	FC	GX	SN	SN	SN		GX	GW	GW	FC	GX	SN	SN	GX	SN	FC	GX	SN	SE	LO
	1	1	1	1	1	1	1	1	1		1	1	1	1	1	1	1	1	1	1	1	1	55	
																							A	B
																						🚲		
Brighton 10 d	05 44				06 13		06 16							06 44					07 00	07 16				
Hove 2 d																								
Preston Park d							06 19												07 03					
Hassocks 4 d	05 52						06 26							06 52					07 10					
Burgess Hill 4 d	05 56				06 26		06 29							06 56					07 13	07 26				
Lewes 4 d																						07 20		
Wivelsfield 4 d							06 32												07 16			07 32		
Haywards Heath 3 a	06 00				06 30		06 36							07 00					07 20	07 30		07 36		
d	06 01				06 31		06 40							07 01					07 21	07 31		07 39		
Balcombe d																			07 26					
Horsham 4 d			06 04						06 34								07 04							
Littlehaven d			06 07						06 37								07 07							
Faygate d																								
Ifield d			06 13						06 43								07 13							
Crawley d			06 17						06 47								07 17							
Three Bridges 4 a	06 10		06 20		06 40		06 49		06 50					07 10			07 20		07 32	07 40				
d	06 10		06 21		06 40		06 49		06 52					07 10			07 22		07 32	07 40			07 50	
Gatwick Airport 10 ✈ a	06 14		06 25		06 44		06 53		06 57					07 14			07 26		07 37	07 44		07 51	07 54	
d	06 15	06 20		06 35	06 45	06 50	06 54		06 58		07 05	07 07		07 15	07 20		07 27	07 35	07 38	07 45	07 50	07 53	07 55	
Horley 4 d									07 00								07 30							
Salfords d																								
Earlswood (Surrey) d																								
Reigate d													07 13											
Tonbridge 4 d																								
Redhill a									07 07			07 15	07 17				07 40		07 45				08 03	
d									07 07								07 41		07 46					
Merstham d									07 11								07 45							
Coulsdon South d									07 16								07 50							
Purley 4 d									07 20								07 53							
East Croydon 🚋 a	06 31				07 01		07 09		07 26					07 31			07 58		07 58	08 01		08 09		
d	06 32				07 02		07 10		07 27					07 32			07 59		07 59	08 02		08 10		
Norwood Junction 2 a																								
London Bridge 4 ⊖ a					07 15									07 45						08 15				
London Blackfriars 3 ⊖ a	06 54				07 23									07 53						08 23				
City Thameslink 3 a																								
Farringdon 3 ⊖ a	06 58				07 27									07 57						08 27				
St Pancras International 15 ⊖ a	07 02				07 31									08 01						08 31				
St Albans a	07 33				08 03									08 33						09 03				
Luton Airport Parkway 4 ✈ a	07 45				08 15									08 45						09 15				
Luton 7 a	07 49				08 19									08 49						09 19				
Bedford 10 a	08 17				08 47									09 17						09 47				
Clapham Junction 10 d							07 24	07 35	07 40							08 05	08 09		08 12			08 24		08 30
Imperial Wharf § d																								
West Brompton ⊖ d								07 40								08 10								08 37
Kensington Olympia ⊖ d								07a43								08a13								08 40
Shepherds Bush § ⊖ d																								
Willesden Jn. High Level a																								08 50
Wembley Central a																								
Harrow & Wealdstone ⊖ a																								
Watford Junction a																								
London Victoria 15 ⊖ a		06 55		07 10		07 25	07 31		07 48		07 40				07 55		08 16	08 10	08 18		08 25	08 31		

For general notes see front of timetable
For details of catering facilities see Directory of Train Operators

§ It is unknown at the time of going to press, when this station will open. For further details please contact National Rail Enquiries 08457-484950 or see local publicity.

A To Maidstone West (Table 208)
B To Stratford Low Level (Table 59)

Table 186

Sundays

Brighton → London, Bedford and Watford Junction

Network Diagram - see first page of Table 186

		SN	SN	GX		GW	GW	FC	XC	GX	SN	SN	SN	XC	GX	SN	FC	GX	SN	SE		SN	GX	GW	GW
																				55					
		1	1	1		1	1	1	1 ◇	1	1	1	1	1 ◇	1	1	1	1	1			1	1	1	1
			A						B		C			B						D		A			
									🍴					🍴											
Brighton 10	d							07 44	07 50							08 00	08 16								
Hove 2	d										07 54														
Preston Park	d															08 03									
Hassocks 4	d							07 52								08 10									
Burgess Hill 4	d							07 56			08 04					08 13	08 26								
Lewes 4	d																		08 16						
Wivelsfield 4	d															08 16			08 31						
Haywards Heath 3	a							08 00	08 04		08 09					08 20	08 30		08 36						
	d							08 01	08 12		08 10			08 12		08 21	08 31		08 39						
Balcombe	d															08 26									
Horsham 4	d		07 42										08 04									08 42			
Littlehaven	d												08 07												
Faygate	d																								
Ifield	d												08 13												
Crawley	d		07 51										08 17									08 51			
Three Bridges 4	a		07 54					08 10					08 20			08 32	08 40					08 54			
	d		07 54					08 10					08 22			08 32	08 40			08 50		08 54			
Gatwick Airport 10 ✈	a		07 58					08 14			08 21		08 26	08 30		08 37	08 44		08 51	08 54		08 58			
	d		07 59	08 05		08 07		08 15		08 20	08 23		08 27	08 31	08 35	08 38	08 45	08 50	08 53	08 55		08 59	09 05	09 07	
Horley 4	d		08 02										08 30									09 02			
Salfords	d																								
Earlswood (Surrey)	d																								
Reigate	d						08 13																		09 12
Tonbridge 4	d																								
Redhill	a		08 08			08 15	08 17						08 40	08 43		08 45				09 03		09 08		09 15	09 17
	d		08 09										08 41			08 46						09 09			
Merstham	d												08 45												
Coulsdon South	d												08 50												
Purley 4	d		08 18										08 53									09 18			
East Croydon 🚋	a		08 24					08 31			08 39		08 58			08 58	09 01		09 09			09 24			
	d		08 25					08 32			08 40		08 59			08 59	09 02		09 10			09 25			
Norwood Junction 2	a																								
London Bridge 4 ⊖	a							08 45									09 15								
London Blackfriars 3 ⊖	a							08 53									09 23								
City Thameslink 3	a																								
Farringdon 3 ⊖	a							08 57									09 27								
St Pancras International 15 ⊖	a							09 01									09 31								
St Albans	a							09 33									10 03								
Luton Airport Parkway 4 ✈	a							09 45									10 15								
Luton 7	a							09 49									10 19								
Bedford 10	a							10 17									10 47								
Clapham Junction 10	d	08 35	08 38								08 55	09 05	09 09			09 12			09 24			09 38			
Imperial Wharf §	d																								
West Brompton ⊖	d	08 40										09 10													
Kensington Olympia ⊖	d	08 43										09 13													
Shepherds Bush § ⊖	d																								
Willesden Jn. High Level	a																								
Wembley Central	a																								
Harrow & Wealdstone ⊖	a	09 06										09 32													
Watford Junction	a	09 14										09 42													
London Victoria 15 ⊖	a		08 46	08 40						08 55	09 01		09 16		09 10	09 18		09 25	09 31			09 46	09 40		

For general notes see front of timetable
For details of catering facilities see Directory of Train Operators

§ It is unknown at the time of going to press, when this station will open. For further details please contact National Rail Enquiries 08457-484950 or see local publicity.

A From Bognor Regis (Table 188)
B From 30 March. To Didcot Parkway (Table 116)
C From Littlehampton (Table 188)
D To Maidstone West (Table 208)

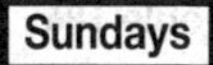

Brighton → London, Bedford and Watford Junction

Network Diagram - see first page of Table 186

		LO	FC	GX	SN	SN	SN	GX	SN	FC	GX	SN	SE	SN	GX	GW	GW	GW	XC	XC	LO	FC	GX	SN
			1	1	1	1	1	1	1	1	1	1	55	1	1	1	1	1	1 ◇	1 ◇		1	1	1
					A								B	C			D	E	G	H				A
Brighton 10	d		08 44						09 00	09 16									09 40	09 40		09 44		
Hove 2	d				08 54																			09 54
Preston Park	d								09 03															
Hassocks 4	d		08 52						09 10													09 52		
Burgess Hill 4	d		08 56		09 04				09 13	09 26												09 56		10 04
Lewes 4	d											09 16												
Wivelsfield 4	d								09 16			09 31												
Haywards Heath 3	a		09 00		09 09				09 20	09 30		09 35							09 51	09 51		10 00		10 09
	d		09 01		09 10				09 21	09 31		09 39							09 52	09 52		10 01		10 10
Balcombe	d								09 26															
Horsham 4	d						09 04							09 42										
Littlehaven	d						09 07																	
Faygate	d																							
Ifield	d						09 13																	
Crawley	d						09 17							09 51										
Three Bridges 4	a		09 10				09 20		09 32	09 40				09 54								10 10		
	d		09 10				09 22		09 32	09 40			09 50	09 54								10 10		
Gatwick Airport 10 ✈	a		09 14		09 21		09 26		09 37	09 44		09 51	09 54	09 58					10 10	10 10		10 14		10 21
	d		09 15	09 20	09 23		09 27	09 35	09 38	09 45	09 50	09 53	09 55	09 59	10 05	10 07			10 11	10 11		10 15	10 20	10 23
Horley 4	d						09 30							10 02										
Salfords	d																							
Earlswood (Surrey)	d																							
Reigate	d																10 15	10 15						
Tonbridge 4	d																							
Redhill	a						09 40		09 45				10 03	10 08		10 15	10 19	10 20	10 28	10 28				
	d						09 41		09 46					10 09					10 33	10 33				
Merstham	d						09 45																	
Coulsdon South	d						09 50																	
Purley 4	d						09 53							10 18										
East Croydon	a		09 31		09 39		09 58		09 58	10 01		10 09		10 24								10 31		10 39
	d		09 32		09 40		09 59		09 59	10 02		10 10		10 25								10 32		10 40
Norwood Junction 2	a																							
London Bridge 4 ⊖	a		09 45							10 15												10 45		
London Blackfriars 3 ⊖	a		09 53							10 23												10 53		
City Thameslink 3	a																							
Farringdon 3 ⊖	a		09 57							10 27												10 57		
St Pancras International 15 ⊖	a		10 01							10 31												11 01		
St Albans	a		10 33							11 03												11 23		
Luton Airport Parkway 4 ✈	a		10 45							11 15												11 35		
Luton 7	a		10 49							11 19												11 39		
Bedford 10	a		11 17							11 47												12 07		
Clapham Junction 10	d	09 30			09 55	10 05	10 09		10 12			10 24		10 38							10 30			10 55
Imperial Wharf §	d																							
West Brompton ⊖	d	09 37				10 10															10 37			
Kensington Olympia ⊖	d	09 40				10 13															10 40			
Shepherds Bush § ⊖	d																							
Willesden Jn. High Level	a	09 50																			10 50			
Wembley Central	a																							
Harrow & Wealdstone ⊖	a					10 35																		
Watford Junction	a					10 42																		
London Victoria 15 ⊖	a			09 55	10 01		10 16	10 10	10 18		10 25	10 31		10 46	10 40								10 55	11 01

For general notes see front of timetable
For details of catering facilities see Directory of Train Operators

§ It is unknown at the time of going to press, when this station will open. For further details please contact National Rail Enquiries 08457-484950 or see local publicity.

A From Littlehampton (Table 188) and from Portsmouth Harbour (Table 188)
B To Maidstone West (Table 208)
C From Bognor Regis (Table 188)
D From 3 February
E Until 27 January
G Until 27 January. To Birmingham New Street (Table 116)
H 3 February to 23 March. To Birmingham New Street (Table 116)

Table 186

Sundays

Brighton → London, Bedford and Watford Junction

Network Diagram - see first page of Table 186

		SN	SN	GX	SN	FC	GX	SN		SE	SN	GX	GW	GW	LO	FC	GX	SN	SN	SN	GX	SN	FC	GX	SN
										55															
		1	1	1	1	1	1	1			1	1	1	1		1	1	1	1	1	1	1	1	1	1
										A	B							C							
Brighton 10	d				10 00	10 16										10 44						11 00	11 16		
Hove 2	d																	10 54							
Preston Park	d				10 03																	11 03			
Hassocks 4	d				10 10											10 52						11 10			
Burgess Hill 4	d				10 13	10 26										10 56		11 04				11 13	11 26		
Lewes 4	d							10 16																	11 16
Wivelsfield 4	d				10 16			10 31														11 16			11 31
Haywards Heath 3	a				10 20	10 30		10 35								11 00		11 09				11 20	11 30		11 35
	d				10 21	10 31		10 39								11 01		11 10				11 21	11 31		11 39
Balcombe	d				10 26																	11 26			
Horsham 4	d		10 04								10 42									11 04					
Littlehaven	d		10 07																	11 07					
Faygate	d																								
Ifield	d		10 13																	11 13					
Crawley	d		10 17								10 51									11 17					
Three Bridges 4	a		10 20		10 32	10 40					10 54					11 10				11 20		11 32	11 40		
	d		10 22		10 32	10 40				10 50	10 54					11 10				11 22		11 32	11 40		
Gatwick Airport 10 ✈	a		10 26		10 37	10 44		10 51		10 54	10 58					11 14		11 21		11 26		11 37	11 44		11 51
	d		10 27	10 35	10 38	10 45	10 50	10 53		10 55	10 59	11 05	11 07			11 15	11 20	11 23		11 27	11 35	11 38	11 45	11 50	11 53
Horley 4	d		10 30								11 02									11 30					
Salfords	d																								
Earlswood (Surrey)	d																								
Reigate	d													11 12											
Tonbridge 4	d																								
Redhill	a		10 40		10 45					11 03	11 08		11 15	11 17						11 40		11 45			
	d		10 41		10 46						11 09									11 41		11 46			
Merstham	d		10 45																	11 45					
Coulsdon South	d		10 50																	11 50					
Purley 4	d		10 53								11 18									11 53					
East Croydon	a		10 58		10 58	11 01		11 09			11 24					11 31		11 39		11 58		11 58	12 01		12 09
	d		10 59		10 59	11 02		11 10			11 25					11 32		11 40		11 59		11 59	12 02		12 10
Norwood Junction 2	a																								
London Bridge 4 ⊖	a					11 15										11 45							12 15		
London Blackfriars 3 ⊖	a					11 23										11 53							12 23		
City Thameslink 3	a																								
Farringdon 3 ⊖	a					11 27										11 57							12 27		
St Pancras International 15 ⊖	a					11 31										12 01							12 31		
St Albans	a					11 53										12 23							12 53		
Luton Airport Parkway 4 ✈	a					12 05										12 35							13 05		
Luton 7	a					12 09										12 39							13 09		
Bedford 10	a					12 37										13 07							13 37		
Clapham Junction 10	d	11 05	11 09		11 12			11 24			11 38				11 30			11 55	12 05	12 09		12 12			12 24
Imperial Wharf §	d																								
West Brompton ⊖	d	11 10													11 37				12 10						
Kensington Olympia ⊖	d	11 13													11 40				12 13						
Shepherds Bush § ⊖	d																								
Willesden Jn. High Level	a														11 50										
Wembley Central	a																								
Harrow & Wealdstone ⊖	a	11 32																	12 32						
Watford Junction	a	11 42																	12 41						
London Victoria 15 ⊖	a		11 16	11 10	11 18		11 25	11 31			11 46	11 40					11 55	12 01		12 16	12 10	12 18		12 25	12 31

For general notes see front of timetable
For details of catering facilities see Directory of Train Operators

§ It is unknown at the time of going to press, when this station will open. For further details please contact National Rail Enquiries 08457-484950 or see local publicity.

A To Maidstone West (Table 208)
B From Bognor Regis (Table 188)
C From Littlehampton (Table 188) and from Portsmouth Harbour (Table 188)

Table 186

Sundays

Brighton → London, Bedford and Watford Junction

Network Diagram - see first page of Table 186

		SE 55 A		SN 1 B	GX 1	GW 1	GW 1	LO	FC 1	GX 1	SN 1 C	SN 1	SN 1	GX 1	SN 1	FC 1	GX 1	SN 1		SE 55 A	SN 1 B	GX 1	GW 1	GW 1	LO
Brighton 10	d								11 44						12 00	12 16									
Hove 2	d										11 54														
Preston Park	d														12 03										
Hassocks 4	d								11 52						12 10										
Burgess Hill 4	d								11 56		12 04				12 13	12 26									
Lewes 4	d																	12 16							
Wivelsfield 4	d														12 16			12 31							
Haywards Heath 3	a								12 00		12 09				12 20	12 30		12 35							
	d								12 01		12 10				12 21	12 31		12 39							
Balcombe	d														12 26										
Horsham 4	d			11 42									12 04								12 42				
Littlehaven	d												12 07												
Faygate	d																								
Ifield	d												12 13												
Crawley	d			11 51									12 17								12 51				
Three Bridges 4	a			11 54					12 10				12 20		12 32	12 40					12 54				
	d	11 50		11 54					12 10				12 22		12 32	12 40				12 50	12 54				
Gatwick Airport 10 ✈	a	11 54		11 58					12 14		12 22		12 26		12 37	12 44		12 52		12 54	12 58				
	d	11 55		11 59	12 05	12 07			12 15	12 20	12 23		12 27	12 35	12 38	12 45	12 50	12 53		12 55	12 59	13 05	13 07		
Horley 4	d			12 02									12 30								13 02				
Salfords	d																								
Earlswood (Surrey)	d																								
Reigate	d						12 15																	13 12	
Tonbridge 4	d																								
Redhill	a	12 03		12 08		12 15	12 19						12 40		12 45					13 03	13 08		13 15	13 17	
	d			12 09									12 41		12 46						13 09				
Merstham	d												12 45												
Coulsdon South	d												12 50												
Purley 4	d			12 18									12 53								13 18				
East Croydon	a			12 24					12 31		12 39		12 58		12 58	13 01		13 09			13 24				
	d			12 25					12 32		12 40		12 59		12 59	13 02		13 10			13 25				
Norwood Junction 2	a																								
London Bridge 4 ⊖	a								12 45							13 15									
London Blackfriars 3 ⊖	a								12 53							13 23									
City Thameslink 3	a																								
Farringdon 3 ⊖	a								12 57							13 27									
St Pancras International 15 ⊖	a								13 01							13 31									
St Albans	a								13 23							13 53									
Luton Airport Parkway 4 ✈	a								13 35							14 05									
Luton 7	a								13 39							14 09									
Bedford 10	a								14 07							14 37									
Clapham Junction 10	d			12 38				12 30			12 55	13 05	13 09		13 12			13 24			13 38				13 30
Imperial Wharf §	d																								
West Brompton ⊖	d							12 37				13 10													13 37
Kensington Olympia ⊖	d							12 40				13 13													13 40
Shepherds Bush § ⊖	d																								
Willesden Jn. High Level	a							12 50																	13 50
Wembley Central	a																								
Harrow & Wealdstone ⊖	a											13 32													
Watford Junction	a											13 42													
London Victoria 15 ⊖	a			12 46	12 40					12 55	13 01		13 16	13 10	13 18		13 25	13 31			13 46	13 40			

For general notes see front of timetable
For details of catering facilities see Directory of Train Operators

§ It is unknown at the time of going to press, when this station will open. For further details please contact National Rail Enquiries 08457-484950 or see local publicity.

A To Maidstone West (Table 208)
B From Bognor Regis (Table 188)
C From Littlehampton (Table 188) and from Portsmouth Harbour (Table 188)

Table 186

Sundays

Brighton → London, Bedford and Watford Junction

Network Diagram - see first page of Table 186

		FC	GX	SN	SN	SN	GX	SN	FC	GX	SN	SE 55		SN	GX	GW	GW	GW	LO	FC	GX	SN	SN	SN	GX
		1	1	1	1	1	1	1	1	1	1			1	1	1	1	1		1	1	1	1	1	1
				A								B		C		D	E					A			
Brighton 10	d	12 44						13 00	13 16											13 44					
Hove 2	d			12 54																		13 54			
Preston Park	d							13 03																	
Hassocks 4	d	12 52						13 10												13 52					
Burgess Hill 4	d	12 56		13 04				13 13	13 26											13 56		14 04			
Lewes 4	d										13 16														
Wivelsfield 4	d							13 16			13 31														
Haywards Heath 3	a	13 00		13 09				13 20	13 30		13 35									14 00		14 09			
	d	13 01		13 10				13 21	13 31		13 39									14 01		14 10			
Balcombe	d							13 26																	
Horsham 4	d					13 04								13 42										14 04	
Littlehaven	d					13 07																		14 07	
Faygate	d																								
Ifield	d					13 13																		14 13	
Crawley	d					13 17								13 51										14 17	
Three Bridges 4	a	13 10				13 20		13 32	13 40					13 54						14 10				14 20	
	d	13 10				13 22		13 32	13 40			13 50		13 54						14 10				14 22	
Gatwick Airport 10 ✈	a	13 14		13 22		13 26		13 37	13 44		13 52	13 54		13 58						14 14		14 22		14 26	
	d	13 15	13 20	13 23		13 27	13 35	13 38	13 45	13 50	13 53	13 55		13 59	14 05	14 07	14 07			14 15	14 20	14 23		14 27	14 35
Horley 4	d					13 30								14 02										14 30	
Salfords	d																								
Earlswood (Surrey)	d																								
Reigate	d																	14 15							
Tonbridge 4	d																								
Redhill	a					13 40		13 45				14 03		14 08		14 15	14 16	14 19						14 40	
	d					13 41		13 46						14 09										14 41	
Merstham	d					13 45																		14 45	
Coulsdon South	d					13 50																		14 50	
Purley 4	d					13 53								14 18										14 53	
East Croydon	a	13 31		13 39		13 58		13 58	14 01		14 09			14 24						14 31		14 39		14 58	
	d	13 32		13 40		13 59		13 59	14 02		14 10			14 25						14 32		14 40		14 59	
Norwood Junction 2	a																								
London Bridge 4 ⊖	a	13 45							14 15											14 45					
London Blackfriars 3 ⊖	a	13 53							14 23											14 53					
City Thameslink 3	a																								
Farringdon 3 ⊖	a	13 57							14 27											14 57					
St Pancras International 15 ⊖	a	14 01							14 31											15 01					
St Albans	a	14 23							14 53											15 23					
Luton Airport Parkway 4 ✈	a	14 35							15 05											15 35					
Luton 7	a	14 39							15 09											15 39					
Bedford 10	a	15 07							15 37											16 07					
Clapham Junction 10	d			13 55	14 05	14 09		14 12			14 24			14 38					14 30			14 55	15 05	15 09	
Imperial Wharf §	d																								
West Brompton ⊖	d				14 10														14 37				15 10		
Kensington Olympia ⊖	d				14 13														14 40				15 13		
Shepherds Bush § ⊖	d																								
Willesden Jn. High Level	a																		14 50						
Wembley Central	a																								
Harrow & Wealdstone ⊖	a				14 32																		15 32		
Watford Junction	a				14 42																		15 42		
London Victoria 15 ⊖	a		13 55	14 01		14 16	14 10	14 18		14 25	14 31			14 46	14 40						14 55	15 01		15 16	15 10

For general notes see front of timetable
For details of catering facilities see Directory of Train Operators

§ It is unknown at the time of going to press, when this station will open. For further details please contact National Rail Enquiries 08457-484950 or see local publicity.

A From Littlehampton (Table 188) and from Portsmouth Harbour (Table 188)

B To Maidstone West (Table 208)

C From Bognor Regis (Table 188)

D Until 27 January

E From 3 February

Table 186

Sundays

Brighton → London, Bedford and Watford Junction

Network Diagram - see first page of Table 186

		SN	FC	GX	LO	SN		SE	SN	GX	GW	GW	LO	FC	GX	SN	SN	SN	GX	SN	FC	GX		LO	SN
								55																	
		1	1	1		1			1	1	1	1		1	1	1	1	1	1	1	1	1			1
								A	B							C									
Brighton 10	d	14 00	14 16											14 44						15 00	15 16				
Hove 2	d															14 54									
Preston Park	d	14 03																		15 03					
Hassocks 4	d	14 10												14 52						15 10					
Burgess Hill 4	d	14 13	14 26											14 56		15 04				15 13	15 26				
Lewes 4	d					14 16																			15 16
Wivelsfield 4	d	14 16				14 31														15 16					15 31
Haywards Heath 3	a	14 20	14 30			14 35								15 00		15 09				15 20	15 30				15 35
	d	14 21	14 31			14 39								15 01		15 10				15 21	15 31				15 39
Balcombe	d	14 26																		15 26					
Horsham 4	d								14 42									15 04							
Littlehaven	d																	15 07							
Faygate	d																								
Ifield	d																	15 13							
Crawley	d								14 51									15 17							
Three Bridges 4	a	14 32	14 40						14 54					15 10				15 20		15 32	15 40				
	d	14 32	14 40					14 50	14 54					15 10				15 22		15 32	15 40				
Gatwick Airport 10 ✈	a	14 37	14 44			14 52		14 54	14 58					15 14		15 22		15 26		15 37	15 44				15 52
	d	14 38	14 45	14 50		14 53		14 55	14 59	15 05	15 07			15 15	15 20	15 23		15 27	15 35	15 38	15 45	15 50			15 53
Horley 4	d								15 02									15 30							
Salfords	d																								
Earlswood (Surrey)	d																								
Reigate	d											15 12													
Tonbridge 4	d																								
Redhill	a	14 45						15 03	15 08		15 15	15 17						15 40		15 45					
	d	14 46							15 09									15 41		15 46					
Merstham	d																	15 45							
Coulsdon South	d																	15 50							
Purley 4	d								15 18									15 53							
East Croydon	a	14 58	15 01			15 09			15 24					15 31		15 39		15 58		15 58	16 01				16 09
	d	14 59	15 02			15 10			15 25					15 32		15 40		15 59		15 59	16 02				16 10
Norwood Junction 2	a																								
London Bridge 4 ⊖	a		15 15											15 45							16 15				
London Blackfriars 3 ⊖	a		15 23											15 53							16 23				
City Thameslink 3	a																								
Farringdon 3 ⊖	a		15 27											15 57							16 27				
St Pancras International 15 ⊖	a		15 31											16 01							16 31				
St Albans	a		15 53											16 23							16 53				
Luton Airport Parkway 4 ✈	a		16 05											16 35							17 05				
Luton 7	a		16 09											16 39							17 09				
Bedford 10	a		16 38											17 08							17 37				
Clapham Junction 10	d	15 12			15 18	15 24			15 38				15 48			15 55	16 05	16 09		16 12				16 18	16 24
Imperial Wharf §	d																								
West Brompton ⊖	d				15 25								15 55				16 10							16 25	
Kensington Olympia ⊖	d				15 28								15 58				16 13							16 28	
Shepherds Bush § ⊖	d																								
Willesden Jn. High Level	a				15 38								16 08											16 38	
Wembley Central	a																								
Harrow & Wealdstone ⊖	a																16 32								
Watford Junction	a																16 41								
London Victoria 15 ⊖	a	15 18		15 25		15 31			15 46	15 40					15 55	16 01		16 16	16 10	16 18		16 25			16 31

For general notes see front of timetable
For details of catering facilities see Directory of Train Operators

§ It is unknown at the time of going to press, when this station will open. For further details please contact National Rail Enquiries 08457-484950 or see local publicity.

A To Maidstone West (Table 208)
B From Bognor Regis (Table 188)
C From Littlehampton (Table 188) and from Portsmouth Harbour (Table 188)

Table 186

Sundays

Brighton → London, Bedford and Watford Junction

Network Diagram - see first page of Table 186

		SE 55	SN	GX	GW	GW	LO	FC	SN	GX	SN	SN	SN	GX	SN	FC		GX	LO	SN	SE 55	SN	GX	GW	GW
			1	1	1	1		1	1	1	1	1	1	1	1	1		1		1		1	1	1	1
		A	B								C										A	B			
Brighton 10	d							15 44	15 51						16 00	16 16									
Hove 2	d										15 54														
Preston Park	d														16 03										
Hassocks 4	d							15 52							16 10										
Burgess Hill 4	d							15 56			16 04				16 13	16 26									
Lewes 4	d																			16 16					
Wivelsfield 4	d														16 16					16 31					
Haywards Heath 3	a							16 00			16 09				16 20	16 30				16 35					
	d							16 01			16 10				16 21	16 31				16 39					
Balcombe	d														16 26										
Horsham 4	d		15 42										16 04									16 42			
Littlehaven	d												16 07												
Faygate	d																								
Ifield	d												16 13												
Crawley	d		15 51										16 17									16 51			
Three Bridges 4	a		15 54					16 10					16 20		16 32	16 40						16 54			
	d	15 50	15 54					16 10					16 22		16 32	16 40					16 50	16 54			
Gatwick Airport 10 ✈	a	15 54	15 58					16 14	16 17		16 22		16 26		16 37	16 44				16 52	16 54	16 58			
	d	15 55	15 59	16 05	16 07			16 15	16 18	16 20	16 23		16 27	16 35	16 38	16 45		16 50		16 53	16 55	16 59	17 05	17 07	
Horley 4	d		16 02										16 30									17 02			
Salfords	d																								
Earlswood (Surrey)	d																								
Reigate	d					16 15																			17 12
Tonbridge 4	d																								
Redhill	a	16 03	16 08		16 15	16 19							16 40		16 45						17 03	17 08		17 15	17 17
	d		16 09										16 41		16 46							17 09			
Merstham	d												16 45												
Coulsdon South	d												16 50												
Purley 4	d		16 18										16 53									17 18			
East Croydon 🚋	a		16 24					16 31	16 34		16 39		16 58		16 58	17 01				17 09		17 24			
	d		16 25					16 32	16 35		16 40		16 59		16 59	17 02				17 10		17 25			
Norwood Junction 2	a																								
London Bridge 4 ⊖	a							16 45								17 15									
London Blackfriars 3 ⊖	a							16 53								17 23									
City Thameslink 3	a																								
Farringdon 3 ⊖	a							16 57								17 27									
St Pancras International 15 ⊖	a							17 01								17 31									
St Albans	a							17 23								17 53									
Luton Airport Parkway 4 ✈	a							17 35								18 05									
Luton 7	a							17 39								18 09									
Bedford 10	a							18 07								18 37									
Clapham Junction 10	d		16 38				16 48		16 47		16 55	17 05	17 09		17 12				17 18	17 24		17 38			
Imperial Wharf §	d																								
West Brompton ⊖	d						16 55					17 10							17 25						
Kensington Olympia ⊖	d						16 58					17 13							17 28						
Shepherds Bush § ⊖	d																								
Willesden Jn. High Level	a						17 08												17 38						
Wembley Central	a																								
Harrow & Wealdstone ⊖	a											17 32													
Watford Junction	a											17 41													
London Victoria 15 ⊖	a		16 46	16 40					16 53	16 55	17 01		17 16	17 10	17 18			17 25		17 31		17 46	17 40		

For general notes see front of timetable
For details of catering facilities see Directory of Train Operators

§ It is unknown at the time of going to press, when this station will open. For further details please contact National Rail Enquiries 08457-484950 or see local publicity.

A To Maidstone West (Table 208)

B From Bognor Regis (Table 188)

C From Littlehampton (Table 188) and from Portsmouth Harbour (Table 188)

Table 186

Sundays

Brighton → London, Bedford and Watford Junction

Network Diagram - see first page of Table 186

		LO	FC	SN	GX	SN	SN	SN	GX	SN		FC	GX	SN	SE	LO	SN	GX	GW	GW	LO	FC	SN	GX	SN
															55										
			1	1	1	1	1	1	1	1		1	1	1			1	1	1	1		1	1	1	1
						A									B		C								A
Brighton 10	d		16 44	16 51						17 00		17 16										17 44	17 51		
Hove 2	d					16 54																			17 54
Preston Park	d									17 03															
Hassocks 4	d		16 52							17 10												17 52			
Burgess Hill 4	d		16 56			17 04				17 13		17 26										17 56			18 04
Lewes 4	d													17 16											
Wivelsfield 4	d									17 16				17 31											
Haywards Heath 3	a		17 00			17 09				17 20		17 30		17 35								18 00			18 09
	d		17 01			17 10				17 21		17 31		17 39								18 01			18 10
Balcombe	d									17 26															
Horsham 4	d							17 04									17 42								
Littlehaven	d							17 07																	
Faygate	d																								
Ifield	d							17 13																	
Crawley	d							17 17									17 51								
Three Bridges 4	a		17 10					17 20		17 32		17 40					17 54					18 10			
	d		17 10					17 22		17 32		17 40			17 50		17 54					18 10			
Gatwick Airport 10 ✈	a		17 14	17 17		17 22		17 26		17 37		17 44		17 52	17 54		17 58					18 14	18 17		18 22
	d		17 15	17 18	17 20	17 23		17 27	17 35	17 38		17 45	17 50	17 53	17 55		17 59	18 05	18 07			18 15	18 18	18 20	18 23
Horley 4	d							17 30									18 02								
Salfords	d																								
Earlswood (Surrey)	d																								
Reigate	d																			18 15					
Tonbridge 4	d																								
Redhill	a							17 40		17 45					18 03		18 08		18 15	18 19					
	d							17 41		17 46							18 09								
Merstham	d							17 45																	
Coulsdon South	d							17 50																	
Purley 4	d							17 53									18 18								
East Croydon 🚋	a		17 31	17 34		17 39		17 58		17 58		18 01		18 09			18 24					18 31	18 34		18 39
	d		17 32	17 35		17 40		17 59		17 59		18 02		18 10			18 25					18 32	18 35		18 40
Norwood Junction 2	a																								
London Bridge 4 ⊖	a		17 45									18 15										18 45			
London Blackfriars 3 ⊖	a		17 53									18 23										18 53			
City Thameslink 3	a																								
Farringdon 3 ⊖	a		17 57									18 27										18 57			
St Pancras International 15 ⊖	a		18 01									18 31										19 01			
St Albans	a		18 23									18 53										19 24			
Luton Airport Parkway 4 ✈	a		18 35									19 05										19 35			
Luton 7	a		18 39									19 09										19 39			
Bedford 10	a		19 07									19 37										20 07			
Clapham Junction 10	d	17 48		17 47		17 55	18 05	18 09		18 12				18 24		18 18	18 38				18 48		18 47		18 55
Imperial Wharf §	d																								
West Brompton ⊖	d	17 55					18 10									18 25					18 55				
Kensington Olympia ⊖	d	17 58					18 13									18 28					18 58				
Shepherds Bush § ⊖	d																								
Willesden Jn. High Level	a	18 08														18 38					19 08				
Wembley Central	a																								
Harrow & Wealdstone ⊖	a						18 32																		
Watford Junction	a						18 41																		
London Victoria 15 ⊖	a			17 53	17 55	18 01		18 16	18 10	18 18			18 25	18 31			18 46	18 40					18 53	18 55	19 01

For general notes see front of timetable
For details of catering facilities see Directory of Train Operators

§ It is unknown at the time of going to press, when this station will open. For further details please contact National Rail Enquiries 08457-484950 or see local publicity.

A From Littlehampton (Table 188) and from Portsmouth Harbour (Table 188)

B To Maidstone West (Table 208)

C From Bognor Regis (Table 188)

Table 186

Sundays

Brighton → London, Bedford and Watford Junction

Network Diagram - see first page of Table 186

		SN	SN	GX		SN	FC	GX	LO	SN	SE	SN	GX	GW	GW	LO	FC	SN	GX	SN		SN	SN	GX	SN
		1	1	1		1	1	1		1	55	1	1	1	1		1	1	1	1		1	1	1	1
											A	B								C					
Brighton 10	d					18 00	18 16										18 44	18 51							19 00
Hove 2	d																			18 54					
Preston Park	d					18 03																			19 03
Hassocks 4	d					18 10											18 52								19 10
Burgess Hill 4	d					18 13	18 26										18 56			19 04					19 13
Lewes 4	d									18 16															
Wivelsfield 4	d					18 16				18 31															19 16
Haywards Heath 3	a					18 20	18 30			18 35							19 00			19 09					19 20
	d					18 21	18 31			18 39							19 01			19 10					19 21
Balcombe	d					18 26																			19 26
Horsham 4	d		18 04									18 42											19 04		
Littlehaven	d		18 07																				19 07		
Faygate	d																								
Ifield	d		18 13																				19 13		
Crawley	d		18 17									18 51											19 17		
Three Bridges 4	a		18 20			18 32	18 40					18 54					19 10						19 20		19 32
	d		18 22			18 32	18 40				18 50	18 54					19 10						19 22		19 32
Gatwick Airport 10 ✈	a		18 26			18 37	18 44			18 52	18 54	18 58					19 14	19 17		19 22			19 26		19 37
	d		18 27	18 35		18 38	18 45	18 50		18 53	18 55	18 59	19 05	19 07			19 15	19 18	19 20	19 23			19 27	19 35	19 38
Horley 4	d		18 30									19 02											19 30		
Salfords	d																								
Earlswood (Surrey)	d																								
Reigate	d														19 12										
Tonbridge 4	d																								
Redhill	a		18 40			18 45					19 03	19 08		19 15	19 17								19 40		19 45
	d		18 41			18 46						19 09											19 41		19 46
Merstham	d		18 45																				19 45		
Coulsdon South	d		18 50																				19 50		
Purley 4	d		18 53									19 18											19 53		
East Croydon	a		18 58			18 58	19 01			19 09		19 24					19 31	19 34		19 39			19 58		19 58
	d		18 59			18 59	19 02			19 10		19 25					19 32	19 35		19 40			19 59		19 59
Norwood Junction 2	a																								
London Bridge 4 ⊖	a						19 15										19 45								
London Blackfriars 3 ⊖	a						19 23										19 53								
City Thameslink 3	a																								
Farringdon 3 ⊖	a						19 27										19 57								
St Pancras International 15 ⊖	a						19 31										20 01								
St Albans	a						19 54										20 24								
Luton Airport Parkway 4 ✈	a						20 05										20 35								
Luton 7	a						20 09										20 39								
Bedford 10	a						20 37										21 07								
Clapham Junction 10	d	19 05	19 09			19 12			19 18	19 24		19 38				19 48		19 47		19 55		20 05	20 09		20 12
Imperial Wharf §	d																								
West Brompton ⊖	d	19 10							19 25							19 55						20 10			
Kensington Olympia ⊖	d	19 13							19 28							19 58						20 13			
Shepherds Bush § ⊖	d																								
Willesden Jn. High Level	a								19 38							20 08									
Wembley Central	a																								
Harrow & Wealdstone ⊖	a	19 32																				20 32			
Watford Junction	a	19 41																				20 42			
London Victoria 15 ⊖	a		19 16	19 10		19 18		19 25		19 31		19 46	19 40					19 53	19 55	20 01			20 16	20 10	20 18

For general notes see front of timetable
For details of catering facilities see Directory of Train Operators

§ It is unknown at the time of going to press, when this station will open. For further details please contact National Rail Enquiries 08457-484950 or see local publicity.

A To Maidstone West (Table 208)
B From Bognor Regis (Table 188)
C From Littlehampton (Table 188) and from Portsmouth Harbour (Table 188)

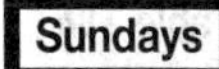
Sundays

Brighton → London, Bedford and Watford Junction

Network Diagram - see first page of Table 186

		LO	FC	GX	SN	SE	SN	GX	GW	GW	LO	FC	SN	GX		SN	SN	SN	GX	SN	FC	LO	GX	SN	SE
						55																			55
			1	1	1		1	1	1	1		1	1	1		1	1	1	1	1	1		1	1	
						A	B									C									D
Brighton [10]	d		19 16									19 44	19 51							20 00	20 16				
Hove [2]	d															19 54									
Preston Park	d																			20 03					
Hassocks [4]	d											19 52								20 10					
Burgess Hill [4]	d		19 26									19 56				20 04				20 13	20 26				
Lewes [4]	d				19 16																			20 16	
Wivelsfield [4]	d				19 31															20 16				20 31	
Haywards Heath [3]	a		19 30		19 35							20 00				20 09				20 20	20 30			20 35	
	d		19 31		19 39							20 01				20 10				20 21	20 31			20 39	
Balcombe	d																			20 26					
Horsham [4]	d						19 42											20 04							
Littlehaven	d																	20 07							
Faygate	d																								
Ifield	d																	20 13							
Crawley	d						19 51											20 17							
Three Bridges [4]	a		19 40				19 54					20 10						20 20		20 32	20 40				
	d		19 40			19 50	19 54					20 10						20 22		20 32	20 40				20 50
Gatwick Airport [10] ✈	a		19 44		19 52	19 54	19 58					20 14	20 17			20 22		20 26		20 37	20 44			20 52	20 54
	d		19 45	19 50	19 53	19 55	19 59	20 05	20 07			20 15	20 18	20 20		20 23		20 27	20 35	20 38	20 45		20 50	20 53	20 55
Horley [4]	d						20 02											20 30							
Salfords	d																								
Earlswood (Surrey)	d																								
Reigate	d									20 15															
Tonbridge [4]	d																								
Redhill	a					20 03	20 08		20 15	20 19								20 40		20 45					21 03
	d						20 09											20 41		20 46					
Merstham	d																	20 45							
Coulsdon South	d																	20 50							
Purley [4]	d						20 18											20 53							
East Croydon ⛴	a		20 01		20 09		20 24					20 31	20 34			20 39		20 58		20 58	21 01			21 09	
	d		20 02		20 10		20 25					20 32	20 35			20 40		20 59		20 59	21 02			21 10	
Norwood Junction [2]	a																								
London Bridge [4] ⊖	a		20 15									20 45									21 15				
London Blackfriars [3] ⊖	a		20 23									20 53									21 23				
City Thameslink [3]	a																								
Farringdon [3] ⊖	a		20 27									20 57									21 27				
St Pancras International [15] ⊖	a		20 31									21 01									21 31				
St Albans	a		20 54									21 24									21 54				
Luton Airport Parkway [4] ✈	a		21 05									21 35									22 05				
Luton [7]	a		21 09									21 39									22 09				
Bedford [10]	a		21 37									22 07									22 37				
Clapham Junction [10]	d	20 18			20 24		20 38				20 48		20 47			20 55	21 05	21 09		21 12		21 18		21 24	
Imperial Wharf §	d																								
West Brompton ⊖	d	20 25									20 55						21 10					21 25			
Kensington Olympia ⊖	d	20 28									20 58						21 13					21 28			
Shepherds Bush § ⊖	d																								
Willesden Jn. High Level	a	20 40									21 08											21 40			
Wembley Central	a																								
Harrow & Wealdstone ⊖	a																21 32								
Watford Junction	a																21 42								
London Victoria [15] ⊖	a			20 25	20 31		20 46	20 40					20 53	20 55		21 01		21 16	21 10	21 18			21 25	21 31	

For general notes see front of timetable
For details of catering facilities see Directory of Train Operators

§ It is unknown at the time of going to press, when this station will open. For further details please contact National Rail Enquiries 08457-484950 or see local publicity.

A To Maidstone West (Table 208)
B From Bognor Regis (Table 188)
C From Littlehampton (Table 188) and from Portsmouth Harbour (Table 188)
D To Gillingham (Kent) (Table 208)

Table 186

Sundays

Brighton → London, Bedford and Watford Junction

Network Diagram - see first page of Table 186

		SN	GX	GW	GW	LO	FC	GX		SN	SN	SN	GX	SN	LO	FC	GX	SN	SE 55	SN	LO	GX	GW	GW	GW
		1 A	1	1	1		1	1		1 B	1	1	1	1		1	1	1		1 A		1	1	1 C	1 D
Brighton 10	d						20 44							21 00		21 16									
Hove 2	d									20 54															
Preston Park	d													21 03											
Hassocks 4	d						20 52							21 10											
Burgess Hill 4	d						20 56			21 04				21 13		21 26									
Lewes 4	d																	21 16							
Wivelsfield 4	d													21 16				21 31							
Haywards Heath 3	a						21 00			21 09				21 20		21 30		21 35							
	d						21 01			21 10				21 21		21 31		21 39							
Balcombe	d													21 26											
Horsham 4	d	20 42										21 04								21 42					
Littlehaven	d											21 07													
Faygate	d																								
Ifield	d											21 13													
Crawley	d	20 51										21 17								21 51					
Three Bridges 4	a	20 54					21 10					21 20		21 32		21 40				21 54					
	d	20 54					21 10					21 22		21 32		21 40			21 50	21 54					
Gatwick Airport 10 ✈	a	20 58					21 14			21 22		21 26		21 37		21 44		21 52	21 54	21 58					
	d	20 59	21 05	21 07			21 15	21 20		21 23		21 27	21 35	21 38		21 45	21 50	21 53	21 55	21 59		22 05	22 07		
Horley 4	d	21 02										21 30								22 02					
Salfords	d																								
Earlswood (Surrey)	d																								
Reigate	d				21 12																			22 15	22 15
Tonbridge 4	d																								
Redhill	a	21 13		21 15	21 17							21 40		21 45					22 03	22 08			22 15	22 19	22 21
	d	21 13										21 41		21 46						22 09					
Merstham	d											21 45													
Coulsdon South	d											21 50													
Purley 4	d	21 23										21 53								22 18					
East Croydon	a	21 27					21 31			21 39		21 58		21 58		22 01		22 09		22 24					
	d	21 28					21 32			21 40		21 59		21 59		22 02		22 10		22 25					
Norwood Junction 2	a																								
London Bridge 4	⊖ a						21 45									22 15									
London Blackfriars 3	⊖ a						21 53									22 23									
City Thameslink 3	a																								
Farringdon 3	⊖ a						21 57									22 27									
St Pancras International 15	⊖ a						22 01									22 31									
St Albans	a						22 24									23 03									
Luton Airport Parkway 4 ✈	a						22 35									23 15									
Luton 7	a						22 39									23 19									
Bedford 10	a						23 07									23 45									
Clapham Junction 10	d	21 38				21 48				21 55	22 05	22 09		22 12	22 18			22 24		22 38	22 48				
Imperial Wharf §	d																								
West Brompton	⊖ d					21 55					22 10				22 25						22 55				
Kensington Olympia	⊖ d					21 58					22 13				22 28						22 58				
Shepherds Bush §	⊖ d																								
Willesden Jn. High Level	a					22 08									22 40						23 08				
Wembley Central	a																								
Harrow & Wealdstone	⊖ a										22 32														
Watford Junction	a										22 40														
London Victoria 15	⊖ a	21 46	21 40					21 55		22 01		22 16	22 10	22 18			22 25	22 31		22 46		22 40			

For general notes see front of timetable
For details of catering facilities see
Directory of Train Operators

§ It is unknown at the time of going to press, when this station will open. For further details please contact National Rail Enquiries 08457-484950 or see local publicity.

A From Bognor Regis (Table 188)

B From Littlehampton (Table 188) and from Portsmouth Harbour (Table 188)

C From 3 February

D Until 27 January

Table 186

Sundays

Brighton → London, Bedford and Watford Junction

Network Diagram - see first page of Table 186

		FC 1		GX 1	SN 1	GX 1	SN 1	FC 1	GX 1	SN 1 A	GX 1	GW 1	GW 1	LO	FC 1	GX 1	SN 1	GX 1		SN 1	GX 1	GW 1	FC 1		
Brighton 10	d	21 44					22 00	22 16							22 44					23 02			23 44		
Hove 2	d																								
Preston Park	d						22 03													23 06					
Hassocks 4	d	21 52					22 10								22 52					23 12			23 52		
Burgess Hill 4	d	21 56					22 13	22 26							22 56					23 16			23 56		
Lewes 4	d																								
Wivelsfield 4	d						22 16													23 19					
Haywards Heath 3	a	22 00					22 20	22 30							23 00					23 23			00 01		
	d	22 01					22 21	22 31							23 01					23 24			00 01		
Balcombe	d						22 26													23 29					
Horsham 4	d				22 04					22 42							23 04								
Littlehaven	d				22 07												23 07								
Faygate	d																								
Ifield	d				22 13												23 13								
Crawley	d				22 17					22 51							23 17								
Three Bridges 4	a	22 10			22 20		22 32	22 40		22 54					23 10		23 20			23 35			00 10		
	d	22 10			22 22		22 32	22 40		22 54					23 10		23 22			23 42			00 10		
Gatwick Airport 10 ✈	a	22 14			22 26		22 37	22 44		22 58					23 14		23 26			23 46			00 14		
	d	22 15		22 20	22 27	22 35	22 38	22 45	22 50	22 59	23 05	23 07			23 15	23 20	23 27	23 35		23 47	23 50		00 15		
Horley 4	d				22 30					23 02							23 30			23s49					
Salfords	d																								
Earlswood (Surrey)	d																								
Reigate	d												23 12									23 54			
Tonbridge 4	d																								
Redhill	a				22 40		22 45			23 08		23 15	23 17				23 36			23 56		23 58	00 22		
	d				22 41		22 46			23 09							23 37			00 02			00 22		
Merstham	d				22 45												23 41								
Coulsdon South	d				22 50												23 46								
Purley 4	d				22 53					23 17							23 50			00 11					
East Croydon	a	22 31			22 58		22 58	23 01		23 24					23 31		23 55			00 16			00 35		
	d	22 32			22 59		22 59	23 02		23 25					23 32		23 56			00 17			00 36		
Norwood Junction 2	a																								
London Bridge 4 ⊖	a	22 45						23 15							23 45								00 52		
London Blackfriars 3 ⊖	a	22 53						23 23							23 53								00 59		
City Thameslink 3	a																								
Farringdon 3 ⊖	a	22 57						23 27							23 57										
St Pancras International 15 ⊖	a	23 01						23 31							00 02								01 07		
St Albans	a	23 34						00 03							00 33								01 39		
Luton Airport Parkway 4 ✈	a	23 45						00 15							00 45								01 51		
Luton 7	a	23 49						00 19							00 49								01 55		
Bedford 10	a	00 15						00 45							01 15								02 20		
Clapham Junction 10	d				23 10		23 13			23 38				23 18			00 11			00 30					
Imperial Wharf §	d																								
West Brompton ⊖	d													23 25											
Kensington Olympia ⊖	d													23 28											
Shepherds Bush § ⊖	d																								
Willesden Jn. High Level	a													23 38											
Wembley Central	a																								
Harrow & Wealdstone ⊖	a																								
Watford Junction	a																								
London Victoria 15 ⊖	a			22 55	23 16	23 10	23 20		23 25	23 46	23 40					23 55	00 18	00 10		00 37	00 25				

For general notes see front of timetable
For details of catering facilities see
Directory of Train Operators

§ It is unknown at the time of going to press, when this station will open. For further details please contact National Rail Enquiries 08457-484950 or see local publicity.

A From Bognor Regis (Table 188)

London, Gatwick Airport & Brighton → Sussex Coast, Portsmouth and Southampton

For complete service between Three Bridges and Horsham see Table 186

Miles	Miles	Miles			SN MX 1	SN MX 1	SN MX 1	SN MX 1	SN 1	SN MX 1	SN MO 1	SN MX 1	SN 1	SN 1	SN 1	SN 1	SN 1	SN 1	SN 1	SN 1	SN 1	SN 1	SN 1		SN 1	SN 1
0	—	0	**London Victoria 15**	⊖ d	22p17	22p32		22p47	*23 06*	23p17	23p17	00 05									*04 00*					
2¾	—	—	Clapham Junction 10	d	22p23	22p38		22p53	*23 12*	23p23	23p23	00 11									*04 08*					
—	0	—	London Bridge 4	⊖ d					*23 00*	*23 11*	*23b11*	*23 53*														
10½	10¼	—	**East Croydon**	d	22p33	22p48		23p03	*23 22*	23p33	23p37	00 25									*04 22*	*04 32*				
26¾	—	—	**Gatwick Airport 10**	d	22p49	23p09		23p19	*23 19*	23p51	00 02	00 43									*04 47*	*04 52*				
29½	—	29½	**Three Bridges 4**	d	22p54	23p15			*23 15*	23p56	00 07	00 48									*04 52*	*04 58*				
—	—	31	Crawley	d		23p18																				
—	—	38	**Horsham 4**	d		23p27																				
—	—	40½	Christs Hospital	d		23p30																				
—	—	45¼	Billingshurst	d		23p36																				
—	—	50¼	Pulborough	d		23p43																				
—	—	55	Amberley	d		23p49																				
—	—	58¾	Arundel	d		23p54																				
38	—	—	Haywards Heath 3	d	23p03			23p37	*23 45*	00 05	00 16	01 00									*05 01*	*05 08*				
—	0	—	**Brighton 10**	d					00 10									05 15			05 30	05 44	05 53			
51	1½	—	Hove 2	d	23p21			23p52	00a13	00 22	00 31	01s22						05 19			05 34	05a47	05 57			
—	2	—	Aldrington	d														05 21			05 36					
—	3	—	Portslade	d	23p24			23p55		00s25	00s34	01s25						05 23			05 38					
—	3½	—	Fishersgate	d														05 25			05 40					
—	4¼	—	Southwick	d	23p27			23p58		00s28	00s37	01s28						05 27			05 42					
—	5¼	—	Shoreham-by-Sea	d	23p30			00 01		00s31	00s40	01s31						05 30			05 45		06 03			
—	8¼	—	Lancing	d	23p34			00 05		00s35	00s44	01s35						05 34			05 49					
—	9¾	—	East Worthing	d														05 37			05 52					
—	10½	—	**Worthing 4**	a	23p38			00 09		00 39	00 48	01 39						05 40			05 55		06 09			
—	—	—		d	23p39													05 40			05 55		06 09			
—	11½	—	West Worthing	d	23p41													05 42			05 57					
—	12¼	—	Durrington-on-Sea	d	23p43													05 45			06 00					
—	13	—	Goring-by-Sea	d	23p46													05 47			06 02					
0	15½	—	Angmering 3	d	23p50													05 51			06 06					
6	—	—	**Littlehampton 4**	a		*00c10*															*06c47*					
—	—	—		d													05 35		05 57	06 04						06 39
8	19¾	61	Ford 4	d	23p56	23p59											05 39	05 57	06 01	06 08	06 13					06 43
—	—	—	Bognor Regis 4	d													*05 13*	*05 49*			*06 04*		*06 11*			
—	22½	—	Barnham	a	00 01	00 04	←										05 43	06 02	06 05	06 12	06 17		06 24		←	06 47
0	—	—		d	00 06	00 05	00 06						04 58	05 05	05 20	05 36	05 44	06 02	06 06	06 27	06 18		06 24		06 27	06 48
3½	—	—	**Bognor Regis 4**	a	→		00 12									05 42			06 12	→					06 35	06 54
—	28¾	—	**Chichester 4**	d		00a12							05 06	05 13	05 28		05 52	06 10			06 26		06 32			
—	30¼	—	Fishbourne (Sussex)	d													05 55						06 35			
—	31½	—	Bosham	d													05 58						06 38			
—	33¼	—	Nutbourne	d													06 01						06 42			
—	34¼	—	Southbourne	d													06 04				06 33		06 44			
—	35¾	—	Emsworth	d													06 07				06 36		06 47			
—	37	—	Warblington	d													06 10						06 50			
0	37½	—	**Havant**	d									05 17	05 24	05 39		06 13	06 21			06 40		06 53			
—	38¼	—	Bedhampton	a													06 15						06 56			
—	41¼	—	Hilsea	a													06 20						07 01			
—	44	—	Fratton	a										05 32	05 47		06 24						07 05			
—	44¾	—	Portsmouth & Southsea	a										05 36	05 51		06 28						07 08			
—	45½	—	**Portsmouth Harbour**	a										05 40	05 55		06 32						07 12			
4	—	—	Cosham	a									05 23					06 28			06 49					
6½	—	—	Portchester	a									05 28								06 54					
9¾	—	—	Fareham	a									05 33					06 37			06 59					
13½	—	—	Swanwick	a									05 40					06 44			07 06					
24¼	—	—	**Southampton Central**	a									05 59					07 02			07 26					

For general notes see front of timetable
For details of catering facilities see
Directory of Train Operators

b Change at Gatwick Airport
c Change at Ford

London, Gatwick Airport & Brighton → Sussex Coast, Portsmouth and Southampton

For complete service between Three Bridges and Horsham see Table 186

		SN 1	SN 1	SN 1		SN 1	SN 1	SN 1	SN 1	SN 1	SN 1	SN 1	SN 1	SN 1	SN 1	SN 1	SN 1	SN 1	SN 1	SN 1		SN 1	SN 1	SN 1	SN 1	SN 1
London Victoria 15 ⊖	d			05 02		05 02							05b32	06 02					06b02	06 21		06 32		06b32		
Clapham Junction 10	d			05 08		05 08							05b38	06 08					06b08	06 27		06 38		06b38		
London Bridge 4 ⊖	d										05 31		05 50	05 55					06 21			06c43		06 43		
East Croydon	d		05 02	05 32		05 22					05 52		06 04	06 18					06 36	06 39		06 49		06 56		07e03
Gatwick Airport 10 ✈	d		05 22	05 59		05 49					06 08		06 20	06 54					06 52	07 04		07 20		07 12		07 20
Three Bridges 4	d		05 26	06 04		05 54					06 14		06 26	06 59					06 56	07 09		07 30		07 18		07 28
Crawley	d			06 07										07 03								07 34				
Horsham 4	d			06 20										07 12								07 46				
Christs Hospital	d			06 23										07 15								07 50				
Billingshurst	d			06 29										07 21								07 56				
Pulborough	d			06 36										07 28								08 03				
Amberley	d			06 42										07 34								08 09				
Arundel	d			06 47										07 39								08 14				
Haywards Heath 3	d		05 36			06 06					06 25		06 38						07 06	07 21				07 28		07 40
Brighton 10	d	05 57	06 20			06 33			06 36		06 53		07 06		07 15		07 20	07 30	07 37	07 47			07 50	08 03		08 07
Hove 2	d	06 01	06 24			06 37			06 40		06 57		07 10		07 19		07 24	07 34	07 41	07 51			07 54	08 07		08 11
Aldrington	d	06 03	06 26								06 59						07 26						07 56			
Portslade	d	06 05	06 28						06 43		07 01				07 22		07 28	07 37	07 44	07 54			07 58			08 14
Fishersgate	d	06 07	06 30								07 03						07 30						08 00			
Southwick	d	06 09	06 32						06 46		07 05				07 25		07 32	07 40	07 47	07 57			08 02			08 17
Shoreham-by-Sea	d	06 12	06 35			06 43			06 49		07 09		07 16		07 28		07 35	07 43	07 50	08 00			08 06	08 13		08 20
Lancing	d	06 16	06 39						06 53		07 13				07 32		07 39	07 47	07 54	08 04			08 10			08 24
East Worthing	d	06 19	06 42								07 16						07 42						08 13			
Worthing 4	a	06 22	06 45			06 49			06 57		07 18		07 22		07 36		07 45	07 51	07 58	08 08			08 15	08 19		08 28
	d	06 22	06 45			06 50			06 57		07 19		07 23		07 36		07 45	07 52	07 59	08 08			08 16	08 20		08 28
West Worthing	d	06 24	06a47						06 59		07a21		07 25				07 47	07 54	08 01				08 18	08 22		08 30
Durrington-on-Sea	d	06 27							07 02				07 27				07 50	07 56	08 03	08 12			08 20	08 24		08 33
Goring-by-Sea	d	06 29							07 04				07 30				07 52	07 59	08 06				08 23	08 27		08 35
Angmering 3	d	06 33							07 08				07 34				07 56	08 03	08 10	08 17			08 27	08 31		08 39
Littlehampton 4	a	06 42		07f06										07f54			08 05		08f35			08 21	08 38	08f53		
	d						07 00			07 18		07 30				07 58						08 26				
Ford 4	d			06 52			07 04		07 14	07 22		07 34	07 40	07 44		08 02		08 09	08 17			08 30		08 37		08 45
Bognor Regis 4	d			06 50			06 57			07 17					07 38			07 55						08 32		
Barnham	a			06 56		07 04	07 08		07 19	07 26		07 38	07 45	07 49	07 52	08 06		08 13	08 21	08 27		08 34		08 41		08 50
	d			07 13 →	07 00	07 05	07 09	← 07 13	07 20	07 27		07 39	07 45	07 50	07 53	08 07		08 14	08 22	08 27		08 35		08 42	08 45	08 52
Bognor Regis 4	a							07 20				07 45		07 58		08 13				08 35					08 52	08 58
Chichester 4	d				07 08	07 13	07 17		07 28	07 35			07 53		08 01			08 22	08 30			08a42		08 50		
Fishbourne (Sussex)	d						07 20			07 38					08 04											
Bosham	d					07 17				07 41					08 07											
Nutbourne	d						07 25			07 44					08 10											
Southbourne	d					07 22	07 27			07 47					08 13			08 29	08 37							
Emsworth	d					07 25	07 30			07 50					08 16			08 32	08 40							
Warblington	d					07 28				07 53					08 19											
Havant	d				07 19	07 31	07 35		07 41	07 56			08 04		08 22			08 37	08 44					09 01		
Bedhampton	a						07 37			07 58					08 24											
Hilsea	a						07 42			08 06					08 29											
Fratton	a						07 46		07 49	08 10					08 33				08 53					09 11		
Portsmouth & Southsea	a						07 50		07 53	08 15					08 37				08 56					09 16		
Portsmouth Harbour	a								07 57	08 19					08 41				09 00					09 21		
Cosham	a				07 25	07 38							08 15					08 44								
Portchester	a				07 30								08 19					08 48								
Fareham	a				07 35	07 46							08 24					08 53								
Swanwick	a				07 42	07 53							08 31					09 00								
Southampton Central	a				08 01	08 13							08 56					09 19								

For general notes see front of timetable
For details of catering facilities see Directory of Train Operators

b Change at East Croydon and Brighton
c Change at Gatwick Airport
e Change at Three Bridges and Brighton
f Change at Ford

London, Gatwick Airport & Brighton → Sussex Coast, Portsmouth and Southampton

For complete service between Three Bridges and Horsham see Table 186

		SN 1	SN 1	SN 1	SN 1	SN 1	SN 1	SN 1	SN 1	SN 1	SN 1		GW ◇ A	SN 1	SN 1	SN 1	SN 1		SN 1	SN 1	SN 1		SN 1	SN 1	SN 1	SN 1
London Victoria 15 ⊖	d	06b47	07 17			07b23		07 52			08 02					08 06			08 17		08 32				08 20	08 36
Clapham Junction 10	d	06b53	07 23			07b29		07 58			08 08					08 12			08 23		08 38				08 28	08 43
London Bridge 4 ⊖	d	07 00	07c16			07 28		07 46			07 56		07 40		07 40	07b56			08 07		08 25				08 19	08b27
East Croydon	d	07 16	07 34			07 46		08 08			08 18		07 56		07 56	08 22			08 33		08 48				08 39	08 53
Gatwick Airport 10 ✈	d	07 32	07 59			08 02		08 26			08 40		08 12		08 12	08 30			08 49		09 11				08 56	09 00
Three Bridges 4	d	07 38	08 05			08 07		08 16			08 45		08 16		08 16	08 42			08 46		09 16				09 00	09 05
Crawley	d		08 09								08 48										09 19					
Horsham 4	d		08 23								09 00	09 04 →		← 09 04							09 31	09 35 →		← 09 35		
Christs Hospital	d		08 26											09 07										09 38		
Billingshurst	d		08 32											09 13										09 44		
Pulborough	d		08 39											09 20										09 51		
Amberley	d		08 45											09 26										09 57		
Arundel	d		08 50											09 31										10 02		
Haywards Heath 3	d	07 48				08 16		08 38					08 28		08 28	08 51			09 04						09 10	09 17
Brighton 10	d	08 23				08 39	08 44		08 53				09 00		09 03	09 14				09 23					09 33	09 44
Hove 2	d	08 27				08 43	08a47	08 54	08 57				09 04		09 07	09a17			09 22	09 27					09 37	09a47
Aldrington	d	08 29							08 59											09 29						
Portslade	d	08 31							09 01						09 10				09 25	09 31					09 40	
Fishersgate	d	08 33							09 03											09 33						
Southwick	d	08 35							09 05						09 13					09 35					09 43	
Shoreham-by-Sea	d	08 39				08 49		09 00	09 08				09 13		09 17				09 30	09 39					09 46	
Lancing	d	08 43						09 04	09 12						09 21					09 43					09 50	
East Worthing	d	08 46							09 15											09 46						
Worthing 4	a	08 48				08 55		09 08	09 18				09 21		09 25				09 36	09 48					09 54	
	d	08 49				08 56		09 08	09 18				09 22		09 26				09 37	09 49					09 55	
West Worthing	d	08a51						09 10	09a20						09 28				09 39	09a51						
Durrington-on-Sea	d					08 59		09 13											09 41						09 58	
Goring-by-Sea	d					09 02		09 15											09 44						10 01	
Angmering 3	d					09 06		09 19							09 33				09 48						10 05	
Littlehampton 4	a							09 28							09e54				09 58							
	d			08 58																			09 54			
Ford 4	d		08 55	09 02										09 36	09 40								09 58	10 07		
Bognor Regis 4	d		08 49			09 00					09 09		09 26		09 26						09 39				10 00	
Barnham	a		08 59	09 06		09 15					09 26		09 36	09 40	09 44						09 57		10 02	10 11	10 14	
	d		09 00	09 07	09 08	09 16				09 22	09 27		09 38	09 41	09 45		09 52				09 58		10 03	10 12	10 15	
Bognor Regis 4	a				09 14					09 28				09 47			09 58							10 18		
Chichester 4	d		09 08	09 15		09 24					09 35		09 47		09 53						10 06		10 11		10 23	
Fishbourne (Sussex)	d			09 18																			10 14			
Bosham	d		09 12																		10 10					
Nutbourne	d		09 16																				10 19			
Southbourne	d			09 24		09 31															10 15		10 21		10 30	
Emsworth	d		09 20	09 27		09 34															10 18		10 24		10 33	
Warblington	d		09 23																				10 27			
Havant	d		09 26	09 31		09 38					09 46		09 59		10 04						10 22		10 32		10 37	
Bedhampton	a			09 34																			10 35			
Hilsea	a			09 41																			10 42			
Fratton	a			09 45							09 54				10 12								10 46			
Portsmouth & Southsea	a			09 49							09 58				10 16								10 49			
Portsmouth Harbour	a										10 02				10 20											
Cosham	a		09 32			09 45							10 05								10 29				10 44	
Portchester	a																				10 33					
Fareham	a		09 40			09 53							10 13								10 38				10 52	
Swanwick	a					10 00															10 45				10 59	
Southampton Central	a		10 03			10 19							10 38								11 02				11 18	

For general notes see front of timetable
For details of catering facilities see Directory of Train Operators

A To Great Malvern (Table 71)
b Change at East Croydon and Brighton
c Change at Gatwick Airport
e Change at Ford

London, Gatwick Airport & Brighton → Sussex Coast, Portsmouth and Southampton

For complete service between Three Bridges and Horsham see Table 186

Station		SN 1	SN 1	SN 1	SN 1 ⊥		SN 1	SN 1	SN 1 ⊥	SN 1	SN 1	SN 1		SN 1		SN 1	SN 1	SN 1	SN 1	SN 1	SN 1	SN 1 ⊥		SN 1	SN 1	SN 1 ⊥
London Victoria 15 ⊖	d		08 47		09 02		09 06		09 17			09 32					09 36			09 47		10 02		10 06		10 17
Clapham Junction 10	d		08 53		09 08		09 12		09 23			09 38					09 42			09 53		10 08		10 12		10 23
London Bridge 4 ⊖	d		08 41		08 49		09b00		09 11			09 25					09 25			09 42		09 56		09 56		10 11
East Croydon	d		09 03		09 18		09 22		09 33			09 48					09 52			10 03		10 18		10 22		10 33
Gatwick Airport 10 ✈	d		09 19		09 40		09 23		09 49			10 09					09 56			10 19		10 40		10 26	10 28	10 49
Three Bridges 4	d		09 19		09 45		09 28		09 45			10 14					10 00			10 15		10 45		10 15	10 33	10 45
Crawley	d				09 48							10 18										10 48				
Horsham 4	d				10 00	10 04						10 30	10 34 →			← 10 34						11 00	11 04			
Christs Hospital	d															10 37										
Billingshurst	d					10 13										10 43							11 13			
Pulborough	d					10 19										10 50							11 19			
Amberley	d															10 56										
Arundel	d					10 28										11 01							11 28			
Haywards Heath 3	d		09 37				09 40		10 04								10 10	10 18		10 37				10 38	10 46	11 04
Brighton 10	d			09 53			10 03	10 14		10 23							10 33	10 44			10 53			11 03	11 14	
Hove 2	d		09 52	09 57			10 07	10a17	10 22	10 27							10 37	10a47		10 52	10 57			11 07	11a17	11 22
Aldrington	d			09 59						10 29											10 59					
Portslade	d			10 01			10 10		10 25	10 31							10 40				11 01			11 10		11 25
Fishersgate	d			10 03						10 33											11 03					
Southwick	d			10 05			10 13			10 35							10 43				11 05			11 13		
Shoreham-by-Sea	d		09 58	10 09			10 16		10 30	10 39							10 46			10 58	11 09			11 16		11 30
Lancing	d		10 02	10 13			10 20			10 43							10 50			11 02	11 13			11 20		
East Worthing	d			10 16						10 46											11 16					
Worthing 4	a		10 06	10 18			10 24		10 36	10 48							10 54			11 06	11 18			11 24		11 36
	d		10 07	10 19			10 25		10 37	10 49							10 55			11 07	11 19			11 25		11 37
West Worthing	d		10 09	10a21			10 27		10 39	10a51										11 09	11a21			11 27		11 39
Durrington-on-Sea	d		10 11						10 41								10 58			11 11						11 41
Goring-by-Sea	d		10 14						10 44								11 01			11 14						11 44
Angmering 3	d		10 18				10 33		10 48								11 05			11 18				11 33		11 48
Littlehampton 4	a		10 27				10c54		10 57											11 27				11c54		11 57
	d	10 11												10 58					11 11							
Ford 4	d	10 15				10 33	10 40							11 02		11 06			11 15				11 33	11 40		
Bognor Regis 4	d				10 07		10 26					10 39					11 00					11 07		11 26		
Barnham	a	10 19			10 26	10 38	10 44					10 56		11 06		11 10	11 14		11 19			11 26	11 38	11 44		
	d	10 22			10 27	10 38	10 45				10 52	10 57		11 07		11 11	11 15		11 22			11 27	11 38	11 45		
Bognor Regis 4	a	10 28				10 45					10 58					11 17			11 28				11 45			
Chichester 4	d				10 35		10 53					11 05		11 15			11 23					11 35		11 53		
Fishbourne (Sussex)	d													11 18												
Bosham	d											11 09														
Nutbourne	d													11 23												
Southbourne	d											11 14		11 25			11 30									
Emsworth	d											11 17		11 28			11 33									
Warblington	d											11 20														
Havant	d				10 46		11 04					11 23		11 33			11 37					11 46		12 04		
Bedhampton	a													11 35												
Hilsea	a													11 42												
Fratton	a				10 54		11 12							11 46								11 54		12 12		
Portsmouth & Southsea	a				10 58		11 16							11 49								11 58		12 16		
Portsmouth Harbour	a				11 02		11 20															12 02		12 20		
Cosham	a											11 29					11 44									
Portchester	a											11 33														
Fareham	a											11 38					11 52									
Swanwick	a											11 45					11 59									
Southampton Central	a											12 02					12 18									

For general notes see front of timetable
For details of catering facilities see Directory of Train Operators

b Change at East Croydon and Brighton
c Change at Ford

London, Gatwick Airport & Brighton → Sussex Coast, Portsmouth and Southampton

For complete service between Three Bridges and Horsham see Table 186

Station																										
		SN 1	SN 1	SN 1		SN 1	SN 1	SN 1	SN 1	SN 1	SN 1		SN 1	SN 1		SN 1	SN 1	SN 1	SN 1	SN 1	SN 1		SN 1	SN 1	SN 1	SN 1
London Victoria 15 ⊖	d			10 32				10 36			10 47			11 02		11 06		11 17			11 32				11 36	
Clapham Junction 10	d			10 38				10 42			10 53			11 08		11 12		11 23			11 38				11 42	
London Bridge 4 ⊖	d	10 11		10 26				10 26			10 41			10 56		10 56		11 11	11 11		11 26				11 26	
East Croydon	d	10 24		10 48				10 52			11 03			11 18		11 22		11 33	11 24		11 48				11 52	
Gatwick Airport 10 ✈	d	10 41		11 09				10 56			11 19			11 40		11 26	11 28	11 49	11 41		12 09				11 56	
Three Bridges 4	d	10 45		11 14							11 15			11 45		11 15	11 33	11 45	11 45		12 14					
Crawley	d			11 18										11 48							12 18					
Horsham 4	d			11 30	11 34 →		← 11 34							12 00	12 04						12 30	12 34 →		← 12 34		
Christs Hospital	d						11 37																	12 37		
Billingshurst	d						11 43								12 13									12 43		
Pulborough	d						11 50								12 19									12 50		
Amberley	d						11 56																	12 56		
Arundel	d						12 01								12 28									13 01		
Haywards Heath 3	d	10 55						11 08			11 37					11 38	11 46	12 04	11 55						12 08	
Brighton 10	d	11 23						11 33	11 44				11 53			12 03	12 14		12 23						12 33	12 44
Hove 2	d	11 27						11 37	11a47		11 52		11 57			12 07	12a17	12 22	12 27						12 37	12a47
Aldrington	d	11 29											11 59						12 29							
Portslade	d	11 31						11 40					12 01			12 10		12 25	12 31						12 40	
Fishersgate	d	11 33											12 03						12 33							
Southwick	d	11 35						11 43					12 05			12 13			12 35						12 43	
Shoreham-by-Sea	d	11 39						11 46			11 58		12 09			12 16		12 30	12 39						12 46	
Lancing	d	11 43						11 50			12 02		12 13			12 20			12 43						12 50	
East Worthing	d	11 46											12 16						12 46							
Worthing 4	a	11 48						11 54			12 06		12 18			12 24		12 36	12 48						12 54	
	d	11 49						11 55			12 07		12 19			12 25		12 37	12 49						12 55	
West Worthing	d	11a51									12 09		12a21			12 27		12 39	12a51							
Durrington-on-Sea	d							11 58			12 11							12 41							12 58	
Goring-by-Sea	d							12 01			12 14							12 44							13 01	
Angmering 3	d							12 05			12 18					12 33		12 48							13 05	
Littlehampton 4	a										12 27					12b54		12 57								
	d					11 58				12 11													12 58			
Ford 4	d					12 02	12 06			12 15					12 33	12 40							13 02	13 06		
Bognor Regis 4	d			11 39				12 00						12 07		12 26					12 39				13 00	
Barnham	a			11 56		12 06	12 10	12 14		12 19				12 26	12 38	12 44					12 56		13 06	13 10	13 14	
	d		11 52	11 57		12 07	12 11	12 15		12 22				12 27	12 38	12 45				12 52	12 57		13 07	13 11	13 15	
Bognor Regis 4	a		11 58				12 17			12 28					12 45					12 58				13 17		
Chichester 4	d			12 05		12 15		12 23						12 35		12 53					13 05		13 15		13 23	
Fishbourne (Sussex)	d					12 18																	13 18			
Bosham	d			12 09																	13 09					
Nutbourne	d					12 23																	13 23			
Southbourne	d			12 14		12 25		12 30													13 14		13 25		13 30	
Emsworth	d			12 17		12 28		12 33													13 17		13 28		13 33	
Warblington	d			12 20																	13 20					
Havant	d			12 23		12 33		12 37						12 46		13 04					13 23		13 33		13 37	
Bedhampton	a					12 35																	13 35			
Hilsea	a					12 41																	13 42			
Fratton	a					12 45								12 54		13 12							13 46			
Portsmouth & Southsea	a					12 49								12 58		13 16							13 49			
Portsmouth Harbour	a													13 02		13 20										
Cosham	a			12 29				12 44													13 29				13 44	
Portchester	a			12 33																	13 33					
Fareham	a			12 38				12 52													13 38				13 52	
Swanwick	a			12 45				12 59													13 45				13 59	
Southampton Central	a			13 02				13 18													14 02				14 18	

For general notes see front of timetable
For details of catering facilities see Directory of Train Operators

b Change at Ford

London, Gatwick Airport & Brighton → Sussex Coast, Portsmouth and Southampton

For complete service between Three Bridges and Horsham see Table 186

Station		SN 1	SN 1	SN 1	SN 1		SN 1	SN 1		SN 1	SN 1	SN 1	SN 1		SN 1	SN 1	SN 1	SN 1	SN 1	SN 1	SN 1	SN 1		SN 1	SN 1	SN 1
London Victoria 15 ⊖	d		11 47		12 02		12 06			12 17			12 32				12 36			12 47		13 02		13 06		
Clapham Junction 10	d		11 53		12 08		12 12			12 23			12 38				12 42			12 53		13 08		13 12		
London Bridge 4 ⊖	d		11 41		11 56		11 56			12 11	12 11		12 26				12 26			12 41		12 56		12 56		
East Croydon	d		12 03		12 18		12 22			12 33	12 24		12 48				12 52			13 03		13 18		13 22		
Gatwick Airport 10 ✈	d		12 19		12 40		12 26	12 28		12 49	12 41		13 09				12 56			13 19		13 40		13 26	13 28	
Three Bridges 4	d		12 15		12 45		12 15	12 33		12 45	12 45		13 14							13 15		13 45		13 15	13 33	
Crawley	d				12 48								13 18									13 48				
Horsham 4	d				13 00	13 04							13 30	13 34 →		← 13 34						14 00	14 04			
Christs Hospital	d															13 37										
Billingshurst	d					13 13										13 43							14 13			
Pulborough	d					13 19										13 50							14 19			
Amberley	d															13 56										
Arundel	d					13 28										14 01							14 28			
Haywards Heath 3	d		12 37				12 38	12 46		13 04	12 55						13 08			13 37				13 38	13 46	
Brighton 10	d			12 53			13 03	13 14			13 23						13 33	13 44			13 53			14 03	14 14	
Hove 2	d		12 52	12 57			13 07	13a17		13 22	13 27						13 37	13a47		13 52	13 57			14 07	14a17	
Aldrington	d			12 59							13 29										13 59					
Portslade	d			13 01			13 10			13 25	13 31						13 40				14 01			14 10		
Fishersgate	d			13 03							13 33										14 03					
Southwick	d			13 05			13 13				13 35						13 43				14 05			14 13		
Shoreham-by-Sea	d		12 58	13 09			13 16			13 30	13 39						13 46			13 58	14 09			14 16		
Lancing	d		13 02	13 13			13 20				13 43						13 50			14 02	14 13			14 20		
East Worthing	d			13 16							13 46										14 16					
Worthing 4	a		13 06	13 18			13 24			13 36	13 48						13 54			14 06	14 18			14 24		
	d		13 07	13 19			13 25			13 37	13 49						13 55			14 07	14 19			14 25		
West Worthing	d		13 09	13a21			13 27			13 39	13a51									14 09	14a21			14 27		
Durrington-on-Sea	d		13 11							13 41							13 58			14 11						
Goring-by-Sea	d		13 14							13 44							14 01			14 14						
Angmering 3	d		13 18				13 33			13 48							14 05			14 18				14 33		
Littlehampton 4	a		13 27				13b54			13 57										14 27				14b54		
	d	13 11													13 58				14 11							
Ford 4	d	13 15				13 33	13 40								14 02	14 06			14 15				14 33	14 40		
Bognor Regis 4	d				13 07		13 26						13 39				14 00					14 07		14 26		
Barnham	a	13 19			13 26	13 38	13 44						13 56		14 06	14 10	14 14		14 19			14 26	14 38	14 44		
	d	13 22			13 27	13 38	13 45					13 52	13 57		14 07	14 11	14 15		14 22			14 27	14 38	14 45		14 52
Bognor Regis 4	a	13 28				13 45						13 58				14 17			14 28				14 45			14 58
Chichester 4	d				13 35		13 53						14 05		14 15		14 23					14 35		14 53		
Fishbourne (Sussex)	d														14 18											
Bosham	d												14 09													
Nutbourne	d														14 23											
Southbourne	d												14 14		14 25		14 30									
Emsworth	d												14 17		14 28		14 33									
Warblington	d												14 20													
Havant	d				13 46		14 04						14 23		14 33		14 37					14 46		15 04		
Bedhampton	a														14 35											
Hilsea	a														14 42											
Fratton	a				13 54		14 12								14 46							14 54		15 12		
Portsmouth & Southsea	a				13 58		14 16								14 49							14 58		15 16		
Portsmouth Harbour	a				14 02		14 20															15 02		15 20		
Cosham	a												14 29				14 44									
Portchester	a												14 33													
Fareham	a												14 38				14 52									
Swanwick	a												14 45				14 59									
Southampton Central	a												15 02				15 18									

For general notes see front of timetable
For details of catering facilities see Directory of Train Operators

b Change at Ford

London, Gatwick Airport & Brighton → Sussex Coast, Portsmouth and Southampton

For complete service between Three Bridges and Horsham see Table 186

		SN 1	SN 1	SN 1			SN 1	SN 1	SN 1	SN 1	SN 1	SN 1	SN 1	SN 1		SN 1	SN 1	SN 1	SN 1	SN 1	SN 1	SN 1		SN 1	SN 1	SN 1
London Victoria 15	d	13 17		13 32					13 36			13 47		14 02				14 06			14 17	14 32				
Clapham Junction 10	d	13 23		13 38					13 42			13 53		14 08				14 12			14 23	14 38				
London Bridge 4	d	13 11	13 11	13 26					13 26			13 41		13 56				13 56			14 11	14 26			14 11	
East Croydon	d	13 33	13 24	13 48					13 52			14 03		14 18				14 22			14 33	14 48			14 24	
Gatwick Airport 10	d	13 49	13 41	14 09					13 56			14 19		14 40				14 26	14 28		14 49	15 09			14 41	
Three Bridges 4	d	13 45	13 45	14 14								14 15		14 45				14 15	14 33		14 45	15 14			14 45	
Crawley	d			14 18										14 48								15 18				
Horsham 4	d			14 30	14 34 →			← 14 34						15 00	15 04 →		← 15 04					15 30	15 34 →			← 15 34
Christs Hospital	d							14 37									15 07									15 37
Billingshurst	d							14 43									15 13									15 43
Pulborough	d							14 50									15 20									15 50
Amberley	d							14 56																		15 56
Arundel	d							15 01									15 29									16 01
Haywards Heath 3	d	14 04	13 55						14 08			14 37						14 38	14 46		15 04				14 55	
Brighton 10	d		14 23						14 33	14 44			14 53					15 03	15 14						15 23	
Hove 2	d	14 22	14 27						14 37	14a47		14 52	14 57					15 07	15a17		15 22				15 27	
Aldrington	d		14 29										14 59												15 29	
Portslade	d	14 25	14 31						14 40				15 01					15 10			15 25				15 31	
Fishersgate	d		14 33										15 03												15 33	
Southwick	d		14 35						14 43				15 05					15 13							15 35	
Shoreham-by-Sea	d	14 30	14 39						14 46			14 58	15 09					15 16			15 30				15 39	
Lancing	d		14 43						14 50			15 02	15 13					15 20							15 43	
East Worthing	d		14 46										15 16												15 46	
Worthing 4	a	14 36	14 48						14 54			15 06	15 18					15 24			15 36				15 48	
	d	14 37	14 49						14 55			15 07	15 19					15 25			15 37				15 49	
West Worthing	d	14 39	14a51									15 09	15a21					15 27			15 39				15 51	
Durrington-on-Sea	d	14 41							14 58			15 11						15 29			15 41				15 53	
Goring-by-Sea	d	14 44							15 01			15 14						15 32			15 44				15 56	
Angmering 3	d	14 48							15 05			15 18						15 36			15 48				16 00	
Littlehampton 4	a	14 57										15 27						15b54			15 57				16 10	
	d						14 54									15 23								15 54		
Ford 4	d						14 58	15 06								15 27	15 34	15 42						15 58		16 06
Bognor Regis 4	d			14 39					15 00					15 09				15 26				15 39				
Barnham	a			14 56			15 02	15 10	15 14					15 26		15 31	15 38	15 46				15 56		16 02		16 10
	d			14 57			15 03	15 11	15 15		15 22			15 27		15 33	15 39	15 47		15 52		15 57		16 03		16 11
Bognor Regis 4	a							15 17			15 28						15 45			15 58						16 17
Chichester 4	d			15 05			15 11		15 23					15 35		15 41		15 55				16 05		16 11		
Fishbourne (Sussex)	d						15 14									15 44								16 14		
Bosham	d			15 09			15 17									15 47						16 09		16 17		
Nutbourne	d						15 20									15 50								16 20		
Southbourne	d			15 14			15 23		15 30							15 53						16 14		16 23		
Emsworth	d			15 17			15 26		15 33							15 56						16 17		16 26		
Warblington	d			15 20			15 29									15 59						16 20		16 29		
Havant	d			15 23			15 32		15 37					15 46		16 02		16 06				16 23		16 32		
Bedhampton	a						15 34									16 04								16 34		
Hilsea	a						15 41																	16 39		
Fratton	a						15 45							15 54		16 12		16 15						16 43		
Portsmouth & Southsea	a						15 49							15 58		16 15		16 19						16 49		
Portsmouth Harbour	a													16 02		16 20										
Cosham	a			15 29					15 44													16 29				
Portchester	a			15 33																		16 33				
Fareham	a			15 38					15 52													16 38				
Swanwick	a			15 45					15 59													16 45				
Southampton Central	a			16 02					16 18													17 02				

For general notes see front of timetable
For details of catering facilities see Directory of Train Operators

b Change at Ford

London, Gatwick Airport & Brighton → Sussex Coast, Portsmouth and Southampton

For complete service between Three Bridges and Horsham see Table 186

	SN 1		SN 1	SN 1	SN 1	SN 1	SN 1 ⅄		SN 1	SN 1	SN 1	SN 1	SN 1	SN 1 ⅄	SN 1	SN 1		SN 1	SN 1	SN 1	SN 1		SN 1	SN 1	SN 1
London Victoria 15 ⊖ d	14 36				14 47		15 02				15 06			15 17		15 32				15 36				15 47	
Clapham Junction 10 d	14 42				14 53		15 08				15 12			15 23		15 38				15 42				15 53	
London Bridge 4 ⊖ d	14 26				14 41		14 56				14 56			15 11	15 11	15 26				15 26				15 41	
East Croydon d	14 52				15 03		15 18				15 22			15 33	15 24	15 48				15 52				16 03	
Gatwick Airport 10 ✈ d	14 56				15 19		15 40				15 26	15 28		15 49	15 41	16 09				15 56				16 19	
Three Bridges 4 d					15 15		15 45				15 15	15 33		15 45	15 45	16 14				16 00				16 15	
Crawley d							15 48									16 18									
Horsham 4 d							16 00	16 04 →		← 16 04						16 30	16 34 →		← 16 34						
Christs Hospital d										16 07									16 37						
Billingshurst d										16 13									16 43						
Pulborough d										16 20									16 50						
Amberley d																			16 56						
Arundel d										16 29									17 01						
Haywards Heath 3 d	15 08				15 37						15 38	15 46		16 04	15 55					16 10				16 37	
Brighton 10 d	15 33		15 44			15 53					16 03	16 14			16 23					16 33	16 44				16 53
Hove 2 d	15 37		15a47		15 52	15 57					16 07	16a17		16 22	16 27					16 37	16a47			16 52	16 57
Aldrington d						15 59									16 29										16 59
Portslade d	15 40					16 01					16 10			16 25	16 31					16 40				16 55	17 01
Fishersgate d						16 03									16 33										17 03
Southwick d	15 43					16 05					16 13				16 35					16 43					17 05
Shoreham-by-Sea d	15 46				15 58	16 09					16 16			16 30	16 39					16 46					17 08
Lancing d	15 50				16 02	16 13					16 20				16 43					16 50				17 00	17 12
East Worthing d						16 16									16 46									17 04	17 15
Worthing 4 a	15 54				16 06	16 18					16 24			16 36	16 48					16 54				17 08	17 18
d	15 55				16 07	16 19					16 25			16 37	16 49					16 55				17 08	17 18
West Worthing d					16 09	16a21					16 27			16 39	16a51									17 10	17a20
Durrington-on-Sea d	15 58				16 11						16 29			16 41						16 58				17 13	
Goring-by-Sea d	16 01				16 14						16 32			16 44						17 01				17 15	
Angmering 3 d	16 05				16 18						16 36			16 48						17 05				17 19	
Littlehampton 4 a					16 27						16b54			16 57										17 28	
d									16 22									16 54							
Ford 4 d									16 26	16 34	16 42							16 58	17 06						
Bognor Regis 4 d	16 00						16 09				16 26					16 39				17 00					
Barnham a	16 14						16 26		16 30	16 38	16 46					16 56		17 02	17 10	17 14					
d	16 15			16 22			16 27		16 31	16 39	16 47		16 52			16 57		17 03	17 11	17 15			17 22		
Bognor Regis 4 a				16 28						16 45			16 58						17 17				17 28		
Chichester 4 d	16 23						16 35		16 39		16 55					17 05		17 11		17 23					
Fishbourne (Sussex) d									16 42									17 14							
Bosham d									16 45									17 17							
Nutbourne d									16 48									17 20							
Southbourne d	16 30								16 51							17 12		17 23		17 30					
Emsworth d	16 33								16 54							17 15		17 26		17 33					
Warblington d									16 57									17 29							
Havant d	16 37						16 46		17 00		17 08					17 19		17 32		17 37					
Bedhampton a									17 02									17 34							
Hilsea a									17 07									17 41							
Fratton a							16 54		17 11		17 18							17 45							
Portsmouth & Southsea a							16 58		17 15		17 22							17 49							
Portsmouth Harbour a							17 02		17 19																
Cosham a	16 44															17 26				17 44					
Portchester a																17 30									
Fareham a	16 52															17 35				17 52					
Swanwick a																17 42				17 59					
Southampton Central a	17 28															18 02				18 19					

For general notes see front of timetable
For details of catering facilities see Directory of Train Operators

b Change at Ford

London, Gatwick Airport & Brighton → Sussex Coast, Portsmouth and Southampton

For complete service between Three Bridges and Horsham see Table 186

		SN 1		SN 1	GW ◇ A	SN 1	SN 1	SN 1	SN 1	SN 1	SN 1		SN 1	SN 1	SN 1	SN 1	SN 1	SN 1	SN 1		SN 1	SN 1	SN 1	SN 1	SN 1	
		🛒								🛒	🛒												🛒			
London Victoria 15 ⊖	d	16 02			15b47		15b47	16 06		16 17	16 38				16b17	16 36			16c47				17 21	17 02		
Clapham Junction 10	d	16 08			15b53		15b53	16 12		16 23	16 45				16b23	16 42	←		16c53				17 27	17 08		
London Bridge 4 ⊖	d	15 56			15 56		15 56			16 11	16 33			16 11	16 26		16 46		16 53				17 17	16b57		
East Croydon	d	16 18			16 09		16 09	16 22		16 33	16 55			16 24	16 40	16 52	17 00		17 07				17 37	17 18		
Gatwick Airport 10 ✈	d	16 40			16 26		16 26			16 49	17 13			16 41	16 56		17 16		17 20		17 09		17 40	17 34		
Three Bridges 4	d	16 45			16 30		16 30			16 45	17 21	17 24		16 45	17 00		17 24		17 29		17 14		17 57	17 39		
Crawley	d	16 48				←					17 25	→					17 30						18 01			
Horsham 4	d	17 00	17 04 →			17 04					17 33						17 42						18 12			
Christs Hospital	d					17 07											17 46						18 15			
Billingshurst	d					17 14											17 52						18 22			
Pulborough	d					17 21											17 59						18 29			
Amberley	d					17 27											18 05									
Arundel	d					17 32											18 10						18 38			
Haywards Heath 3	d				16 40		16 40	16 46		17 04				16 55	17 10	17 16			17 38		17 24			17 48		
Brighton 10	d				17 00		17 03	17 14						17 23	17 33	17 44					17 58			18 08	18 14	
Hove 2	d				17 04		17 07	17a17		17 21				17 27	17 37	17a47			17 58		18 02			18 12	18a17	
Aldrington	d													17 29							18 04					
Portslade	d						17 10			17 24				17 31	17 40				18 01		18 06			18 15		
Fishersgate	d													17 33							18 08					
Southwick	d						17 13							17 35	17 43						18 10			18 18		
Shoreham-by-Sea	d				17 13		17 16			17 29				17 39	17 46				18 06		18 14			18 21		
Lancing	d						17 20			17 33				17 43	17 50				18 10		18 18			18 25		
East Worthing	d													17 46							18 21					
Worthing 4	a				17 21		17 24			17 37				17 48	17 54				18 14		18 23			18 29		
	d				17 22		17 25			17 38				17 49	17 55				18 14		18 24			18 30		
West Worthing	d						17 27			17 40				17 51	17 57				18 16		18 26			18 32		
Durrington-on-Sea	d						17 29			17 42				17 53	17 59				18 19		18 28			18 34		
Goring-by-Sea	d						17 32			17 45				17 56	18 02				18 21		18 31			18 37		
Angmering 3	d						17 36			17 49				18 00	18 06				18 25		18 35			18 41		
Littlehampton 4	a						17e54			17 59				18 08					18 36		18 43			18e57		
	d			17 23									17 56					18 22								
Ford 4	d			17 27		17 37	17 42						18 00		18 12		18 15	18 26						18 47		
Bognor Regis 4	d	17 09			17 26		17 26				17 39				18 00			18 19						18 41		
Barnham	a	17 26		17 31	17 36	17 41	17 46				18 00		18 04		18 16		18 19	18 30					18 46	18 51		
	d	17 27		17 32	17 38	17 42	17 47		17 52		18 01		18 05		18 17		18 20	18 31				18 32	18 47	18 52		
Bognor Regis 4	a			17 38		17 50			17 58								18 28					18 38	18 55			
Chichester 4	d	17 35			17 47		17 55				18 09		18 13		18 25			18 39						19 00		
Fishbourne (Sussex)	d	17 38											18 16					18 42								
Bosham	d	17 41											18 19					18 45								
Nutbourne	d												18 22					18 48								
Southbourne	d	17 45					18 04				18 16		18 25					18 51								
Emsworth	d	17 48					18 07				18 19		18 28					18 54								
Warblington	d						18 10						18 31					18 57								
Havant	d	17 53			17 58		18 13				18 23		18 34		18 37			19 00						19 11		
Bedhampton	a	17 55											18 36					19 02								
Hilsea	a	18 00											18 41					19 07								
Fratton	a	18 04					18 22						18 45					19 12						19 19		
Portsmouth & Southsea	a	18 08					18 25						18 49					19 16						19 23		
Portsmouth Harbour	a	18 14					18 31											19 21						19 27		
Cosham	a				18 04						18 29				18 44											
Portchester	a										18 34															
Fareham	a				18 12						18 39				18 52											
Swanwick	a										18 46				18 59											
Southampton Central	a				18 38						19 05				19 19											

For general notes see front of timetable
For details of catering facilities see Directory of Train Operators

A To Worcester Shrub Hill (Table 57)
b Change at East Croydon and Brighton
c Change at Three Bridges
e Change at Ford

London, Gatwick Airport & Brighton → Sussex Coast, Portsmouth and Southampton

For complete service between Three Bridges and Horsham see Table 186

		SN 1		SN 1	SN 1	SN 1	SN 1	SN 1	SN 1 ⚲	SN 1	SN 1	SN 1	SN 1		SN 1	SN 1		SN 1	SN 1		SN 1	SN 1	SN 1	SN 1	SN 1	SN 1
London Victoria 15 ⊖	d	17 24					17 07	17 37	17b47			17 47	18 21			17c53			18e07				18 32	18 17	18 32	18 47
Clapham Junction 10	d	17 30					17 13	17 43	17b53			17 53	18 27			17c59			18e13				18 38	18 23	18 38	18 53
London Bridge 4 ⊖	d				17 32		17 08	17c32	17 52			17f46	18 16			18 03			18 16				18 26	18c12	18 26	18 38
East Croydon	d	17 40			17 46		17 24	17 54	18 06			18 03	18 37		18g00	18 16			18 30				18 48	18 33	18 48	19 03
Gatwick Airport 10 ✈	d	17 58					17 40	17g58	18 12			18 12	18 42		18 12	18g29			18 46				19 04	18 50	19 04	19 19
Three Bridges 4	d	17 53					17 46	17g53	18 26			18 23	18 57		18 18	18 36			18 44				19 02	18 44	19 02	
Crawley	d								18 30				19 01													
Horsham 4	d								18 43				19 16	19 20 →							← 19 20					
Christs Hospital	d								18 46												19 23					
Billingshurst	d								18 53												19 30					
Pulborough	d								19 00												19 37					
Amberley	d								19 06												19 43					
Arundel	d								19 11												19 48					
Haywards Heath 3	d	18 10			18 15		17 58	18 20				18 32			18 30	18 45			18 58				19 19	19 08	19 22	19 36
Brighton 10	d						18 35	18 49							19 03	19 14								19 34	19 44	
Hove 2	d	18 25			18 36		18 39	18a53				18 58			19 07	19a17			19 20				19 35	19 38	19a47	19 52
Aldrington	d						18 41								19 09									19 40		
Portslade	d	18 28			18 39		18 43					19 01			19 11				19 23					19 42		19 55
Fishersgate	d						18 45								19 13									19 44		
Southwick	d						18 47								19 15									19 46		
Shoreham-by-Sea	d	18 33			18 44		18 51					19 06			19 19				19 28				19 41	19 50		19 59
Lancing	d	18 37			18 48		18 55					19 10			19 23				19 32					19 54		20 03
East Worthing	d						18 58								19 26									19 57		
Worthing 4	a	18 41			18 52		19 00					19 14			19 28				19 36				19 47	19 59		20 07
	d	18 44	18 47		18 52		19 01					19 14			19 29				19 40	19 42			19 48	20 00		20 08
West Worthing	d		18 49		18 54							19 16			19 31					19 44			19 50	20 02		20 10
Durrington-on-Sea	d		18 51		18 57							19 19			19 33					19 46			19 52			20 12
Goring-by-Sea	d		18 54		18 59							19 21			19 36					19 49			19 55			20 15
Angmering 3	d		18 58		19 03							19 25			19 40					19 53			19 59	20 07		20 19
Littlehampton 4	a		19 08		19 14		19h32					19 37			19h59					20 04			20 11	20h39		20 29
	d			18 56							19 29											20 06				
Ford 4	d			19 00			19 12				19 33				19 46							20 10		20 13		
Bognor Regis 4	d			18 54									19 33		19 39									20 04		
Barnham	a	18 59		19 04			19 16		19 19		19 37		19 42		19 50				19 55		19 58	20 14		20 18		
	d	18 59		19 05		19 07	19 17		19 20	19 22	19 38		19 43		19 52			19 52	19 56		19 59	20 22 →		20 18		
Bognor Regis 4	a					19 13			19 28		19 44							19 58			20 07					
Chichester 4	d	19 07		19 13			19 25			19a30			19 51		20 00				20 04					20 26		
Fishbourne (Sussex)	d			19 16															20 07							
Bosham	d			19 19															20 10							
Nutbourne	d			19 22															20 13							
Southbourne	d	19 14		19 25									19 58						20 16							
Emsworth	d	19 17		19 28									20 01						20 19							
Warblington	d			19 31															20 22							
Havant	d	19 22		19 35			19 38						20 05		20 11				20 25					20 37		
Bedhampton	a			19 37																						
Hilsea	a			19 43																						
Fratton	a			19 48									20 15		20 19											
Portsmouth & Southsea	a			19 53									20 20		20 23											
Portsmouth Harbour	a														20 27											
Cosham	a	19 28					19 44												20 32					20 44		
Portchester	a	19 33																						20 48		
Fareham	a	19 38					19 52												20 40					20 53		
Swanwick	a	19 45					19 59												20 47					21 00		
Southampton Central	a	20 04					20 18												21 06					21 18		

For general notes see front of timetable
For details of catering facilities see Directory of Train Operators

- **b** Change at Three Bridges
- **c** Change at East Croydon and Brighton
- **e** Change at East Croydon
- **f** Change at Haywards Heath
- **g** Change at Haywards Heath and Brighton
- **h** Change at Ford

London, Gatwick Airport & Brighton → Sussex Coast, Portsmouth and Southampton

For complete service between Three Bridges and Horsham see Table 186

		SN 1	SN 1	SN 1 ⚒		SN 1	SN 1	SN 1	SN 1 ⚒	SN 1	SN 1		SN 1		SN 1	SN 1	SN 1	SN 1	SN 1		SN 1	SN 1	SN 1	SN 1	SN 1	
London Victoria 15 ⊖	d	18b32		19 02				19 06	19 17		19 32					19 36	19 47		20 02			20 06	20 17		20 32	
Clapham Junction 10	d	18b38		19 08				19 12	19 23		19 38					19 42	19 53		20 08			20 12	20 23		20 38	
London Bridge 4 ⊖	d	18 34		18 56			18 38	18 56	19 12		19 27				19 12	19 27	19 41		20 01		19 41	20 01	20 11		20 28	
East Croydon	d	18 49		19 18			18 52	19 22	19 33		19 48				19 24	19 52	20 03		20 19		19 54	20 22	20 33		20 48	
Gatwick Airport 10 ✈	d	19 21		19 39			19 10	19 26	19 49		20 09				19 41	19 55	20 19		20 39		20 11	20 31	20 49		21 09	
Three Bridges 4	d	19 26		19 44				19 32	19 45		20 14				19 45	20 01	20 15		20 44		20 15		20 43		21 14	
Crawley	d	19 30		19 48							20 18								20 48						21 18	
Horsham 4	d	19 44		20 00	20 04						20 30	20 34							21 00	21 04					21 30	21 34
Christs Hospital	d	19 47			20 07							20 37								21 07						21 37
Billingshurst	d	19 53			20 13							20 43								21 13						21 43
Pulborough	d	20 00			20 20							20 50								21 20						21 50
Amberley	d				20 26							20 56								21 26						21 56
Arundel	d	20 09			20 31							21 01								21 31						22 01
Haywards Heath 3	d						19 24	19 45	20 04						19 58	20 17	20 34				20 26	20 47	21 05			
Brighton 10	d						20 03	20 14							20 30	20 44					21 03	21 14				
Hove 2	d						20 07	20a17	20 22						20 34	20a47	20 54				21 07	21a17	21 22			
Aldrington	d						20 09								20 36						21 09					
Portslade	d						20 11		20 25						20 38		20 57				21 11		21 25			
Fishersgate	d						20 13								20 40						21 13					
Southwick	d						20 15								20 42						21 15					
Shoreham-by-Sea	d						20 19		20 30						20 46		21 01				21 19		21 30			
Lancing	d						20 23		20 34						20 50		21 05				21 23		21 34			
East Worthing	d						20 26								20 53						21 26					
Worthing 4	a						20 28		20 38						20 55		21 09				21 28		21 38			
	d						20 29		20 38						20 56		21 10				21 29		21 38			
West Worthing	d						20 31		20 40						20 58		21 12				21 31		21 40			
Durrington-on-Sea	d						20 33		20 43						21 00		21 14				21 33		21 43			
Goring-by-Sea	d						20 36		20 45						21 03		21 17				21 36		21 45			
Angmering 3	d						20 40		20 49						21 07		21 21				21 40		21 49			
Littlehampton 4	a	20 20					21c01		20 58						21c35		21 29						21 58			22c16
	d					20 36							21 06													
Ford 4	d				20 36	20 40	20 46					21 06	21 10		21 13					21 36	21 46					22 06
Bognor Regis 4	d						20 36								21 04						21 39					
Barnham	a			20 26	20 40	20 44	20 50				20 56	21 10	21 14		21 17				21 26	21 40	21 50				21 56	22 10
	d		← 20 22	20 27	20 41	20 52 →	20 51			← 20 52	20 57	21 11	21 22 →		21 18			← 21 22	21 27	21 41	21 51			21 52	21 57	22 11
Bognor Regis 4	a		20 28		20 47					20 58		21 17						21 28		21 47				21 58		22 17
Chichester 4	d			20 35			20 59				21 05				21 26				21 35		21 59				22 05	
Fishbourne (Sussex)	d										21 08														22 08	
Bosham	d										21 11														22 11	
Nutbourne	d										21 14														22 14	
Southbourne	d			20 42							21 17								21 42						22 17	
Emsworth	d			20 45							21 20								21 45						22 20	
Warblington	d										21 23														22 23	
Havant	d			20 52			21 10				21 26				21 37				21 49		22 10				22 26	
Bedhampton	a																									
Hilsea	a																									
Fratton	a			21 01			21 18												21 58		22 18					
Portsmouth & Southsea	a			21 06			21 23												22 02		22 22					
Portsmouth Harbour	a						21 27												22 06		22 26					
Cosham	a										21 32				21 43										22 32	
Portchester	a										21 36															
Fareham	a										21 41				21 52										22 42	
Swanwick	a										21 48				21 59										22 49	
Southampton Central	a										22 06				22 17										23 07	

For general notes see front of timetable
For details of catering facilities see Directory of Train Operators

b Change at Gatwick Airport
c Change at Ford

London, Gatwick Airport & Brighton → Sussex Coast, Portsmouth and Southampton

For complete service between Three Bridges and Horsham see Table 186

		SN 1	SN 1	SN 1	SN 1	SN 1	SN 1	SN 1	SN 1	SN 1	SN 1	SN 1	SN 1	SN 1	SN 1	SN 1	SN 1	SN 1	SN 1	SN 1	SN 1	SN 1	SN 1	SN 1
London Victoria 15 ⊖	d			20 36	20 47			20b47	21 06		21 17	21 32		21 36		21 47	22 06		22 17	22 36	22 32		22 47	23 17
Clapham Junction 10	d		20b23	20 42	20 53			20b53	21 12		21 23	21 38		21 42		21 53	22 12		22 23	22 42	22 38		22 53	23 23
London Bridge 4 ⊖	d		20 28		20 41			20 58			21 11	21 15		21b15		21 41	21b45		22 11	22b15	22 15		22 41	23 11
East Croydon	d		20 41	20 52	21 03			21 11	21 22		21 33	21 48		21 52		22 03	22 22		22 33	22 52	22 48		23 03	23 33
Gatwick Airport 10 ✈	d		20 56		21 19			21 27			21 49	22 09		21c49		22 19	22c19		22 49	22c49	23 09		23 19	23 51
Three Bridges 4	d		21 01		21 15			21 32			21 53	22 14		21c53		22 15	22 15		22 54	22c54	23 15		23 15	23 56
Crawley	d											22 18									23 18			
Horsham 4	d											22 27									23 27			
Christs Hospital	d											22 30									23 30			
Billingshurst	d											22 36									23 36			
Pulborough	d											22 43									23 43			
Amberley	d											22 49									23 49			
Arundel	d											22 54									23 54			
Haywards Heath 3	d		21 11	21 15	21 34			21 41	21 45		22 06			22 15		22 37	22 45		23 03	23 15			23 37	00 05
Brighton 10	d		21 33	21 44				22 03	22 14					22 34	22 44		23 14			23 44				
Hove 2	d		21 37	21a47	21 54			22 07	22a17		22 23			22 38	22a47	22 52	23a17		23 21	23a47			23 52	00 22
Aldrington	d		21 39					22 09						22 40										
Portslade	d		21 41		21 57			22 11			22 26			22 42		22 55			23 24				23 55	00s25
Fishersgate	d		21 43					22 13						22 44										
Southwick	d		21 45					22 15						22 46					23 27				23 58	00s28
Shoreham-by-Sea	d		21 49		22 01			22 19			22 31			22 50		23 00			23 30				00 01	00s31
Lancing	d		21 53		22 05			22 23			22 35			22 54		23 04			23 34				00 05	00s35
East Worthing	d		21 56					22 26						22 57										
Worthing 4	a		21 58		22 09			22 28			22 39			22 59		23 08			23 38				00 09	00 39
	d		21 59		22 10			22 29			22 39			23 00		23 08			23 39					
West Worthing	d		22 01		22 12			22 31			22 41			23 02		23 10			23 41					
Durrington-on-Sea	d		22 03		22 14			22 33			22 44			23 04		23 13			23 43					
Goring-by-Sea	d		22 06		22 17			22 36			22 46			23 07		23 15			23 46					
Angmering 3	d		22 10		22 21			22 40			22 50			23 11		23 19			23 50					
Littlehampton 4	a		22e28		22 31							23e34		23 19		23 28					00e10			
	d	22 08					22 38							23 24										
Ford 4	d	22 12	22 16				22 42	22 46			22 56	23 00		23 28					23 56		23 59			
Bognor Regis 4	d		22 00					22 30																
Barnham	a	22 16	22 20				22 46	22 50			23 01	23 04		23 32					00 01		00 04			
	d	22 22 →	22 21			← 22 22	22 52 →	22 51		← 22 52	23 06 →	23 05	← 23 06	23 33				23 36	00 06 →		00 05	← 00 06		
Bognor Regis 4	a					22 28				22 58			23 12					23 42				00 12		
Chichester 4	d		22 29					22 59				23 13		23a40							00a12			
Fishbourne (Sussex)	d											23 16												
Bosham	d											23 19												
Nutbourne	d											23 22												
Southbourne	d		22 36									23 25												
Emsworth	d		22 39									23 28												
Warblington	d											23 31												
Havant	d		22 43					23 11				23 36												
Bedhampton	a																							
Hilsea	a																							
Fratton	a		22 53					23 20				23 49												
Portsmouth & Southsea	a		22 56					23 23				23 53												
Portsmouth Harbour	a		23 00					23 27																
Cosham	a																							
Portchester	a																							
Fareham	a																							
Swanwick	a																							
Southampton Central	a																							

For general notes see front of timetable
For details of catering facilities see Directory of Train Operators

b Change at East Croydon and Brighton
c Change at Haywards Heath and Brighton
e Change at Ford

London, Gatwick Airport & Brighton → Sussex Coast, Portsmouth and Southampton

For complete service between Three Bridges and Horsham see Table 186

		SN 1	SN 1	SN 1	SN 1	SN 1	SN 1	SN 1	SN 1	SN 1	SN 1	SN 1		SN 1	SN 1	SN 1	SN 1	SN 1	SN 1	SN 1	SN 1	SN 1	SN 1	SN 1		SN 1
London Victoria 15 ⊖	d	22p17	22p32		22p47	23 06	23p17	00 05									04 00									
Clapham Junction 10	d	22p23	22p38		22p53	23 12	23p23	00 11									04 08									
London Bridge 4 ⊖	d					23b00	23 11	23 53																		
East Croydon	d	22p33	22p48		23p03	23 22	23p33	00 25									04 22						05 02			
Gatwick Airport 10 ✈	d	22p49	23p09		23p19	23c19	23p51	00 43									04 47						05 22			
Three Bridges 4	d	22p54	23p15			23 15	23p56	00 48									04 52						05 28			
Crawley	d		23p18																							
Horsham 4	d		23p27																							
Christs Hospital	d		23p30																							
Billingshurst	d		23p36																							
Pulborough	d		23p43																							
Amberley	d		23p49																							
Arundel	d		23p54																							
Haywards Heath 3	d	23p03			23p37	23 45	00 05	01 00									05 01						05 42			
Brighton 10	d					00 10									05 15		05 27	05 44	05 53			06 01	06 14	06 23		
Hove 2	d	23p21			23p52	00a13	00 22	01s22							05 19		05 31	05a47	05 57			06 05	06a17	06 27		
Aldrington	d																05 33		05 59					06 29		
Portslade	d	23p24			23p55		00s25	01s25							05 22		05 35		06 01			06 08		06 31		
Fishersgate	d																05 37		06 03					06 33		
Southwick	d	23p27			23p58		00s28	01s28									05 39		06 05			06 11		06 35		
Shoreham-by-Sea	d	23p30			00 01		00s31	01s31							05 26		05 43		06 09			06 14		06 39		
Lancing	d	23p34			00 05		00s35	01s35							05 30		05 47		06 13			06 18		06 43		
East Worthing	d																05 50		06 16					06 46		
Worthing 4	a	23p38			00 09		00 39	01 39							05 34		05 52		06 18			06 22		06 48		
	d	23p39													05 35		05 53		06 19			06 23		06 49		
West Worthing	d	23p41													05 37		05 55		06a21			06 25		06a51		
Durrington-on-Sea	d	23p43													05 39		05 57					06 27				
Goring-by-Sea	d	23p46													05 42		06 00					06 30				
Angmering 3	d	23p50													05 46		06 04					06 34				
Littlehampton 4	a	00e10	00e10														06e29					06e52				
	d															05 58					06 19					
Ford 4	d	23p56	23p59												05 52	06 02	06 10					06 40				
Bognor Regis 4	d											05 13			05 43		06 04					06 26				
Barnham	a	00 01	00 04	⟵											05 57	06 06	06 14				06 26	06 44				
	d	00 06	00 05	00 06					04 55	05 15	05 20	05 30		05 38	05 57	06 07	06 15			06 22	06 27	06 45				06 52
Bognor Regis 4	a	⟶		00 12																06 28						06 58
Chichester 4	d		00a12						05 03	05 23	05 28	05 38		05 46	06 05	06 15	06 23				06 35	06 53				
Fishbourne (Sussex)	d															06 18										
Bosham	d														06 10											
Nutbourne	d															06 23										
Southbourne	d														06 14	06 25	06 30									
Emsworth	d														06 17	06 28	06 33									
Warblington	d														06 20											
Havant	d								05 14	05 34	05 39	05 49		05 57	06 23	06 33	06 37				06 46	07 04				
Bedhampton	a															06 35										
Hilsea	a															06 41										
Fratton	a									05 42		05 57		06 05		06 45					06 54	07 12				
Portsmouth & Southsea	a									05 46		06 01		06 09		06 49					06 58	07 17				
Portsmouth Harbour	a											06 05		06 16							07 02	07 21				
Cosham	a								05 22		05 49				06 30		06 44									
Portchester	a								05 27						06 34											
Fareham	a								05 32		05 57				06 39		06 52									
Swanwick	a								05 39		06 04				06 46		06 59									
Southampton Central	a								05 58		06 21				07 05		07 18									

For general notes see front of timetable
For details of catering facilities see Directory of Train Operators

b Change at East Croydon and Brighton
c Change at Haywards Heath and Brighton
e Change at Ford

London, Gatwick Airport & Brighton → Sussex Coast, Portsmouth and Southampton

For complete service between Three Bridges and Horsham see Table 186

		SN 1		SN 1	SN 1	SN 1	SN 1	SN 1	SN 1	SN 1	SN 1	SN 1		SN 1	SN 1	SN 1	SN 1	SN 1	SN 1	SN 1	SN 1	SN 1	SN 1	SN 1		SN 1
London Victoria 15 ⊖	d	05 02				05 02					05 32	05b32					06 10		06b10			06c23	06b23	06 40		07 06
Clapham Junction 10	d	05 08				05 08					05 38	05b38					06 16		06b16			06c29	06b29	06 46		07 12
London Bridge 4 ⊖	d										05e50	05 50					06e26		06 26			06 41	06 41	06f41		06 56
East Croydon	d	05 22				05 22	05 32				05 48	06 05					06 28		06 39			06 54	06 54	06 58		07 22
Gatwick Airport 10	d	05 58				05 50	05 54				06 21	06 20		06 21			06 59		06 56			07 11	07 11	07 29		07 26
Three Bridges 4	d	06 03				05 54	06 00				06 34	06 26		06 30			07 04		07 00			07 15	07 15	07 34		
Crawley	d	06 06									06 37						07 07							07 37		
Horsham 4	d	06 19									06 50						07 20							07 50		
Christs Hospital	d	06 22									06 53						07 23							07 53		
Billingshurst	d	06 28									06 59						07 29							07 59		
Pulborough	d	06 35									07 06						07 36							08 06		
Amberley	d	06 41									07 12						07 42							08 12		
Arundel	d	06 46									07 17						07 47							08 17		
Haywards Heath 3	d					06 03	06 12					06 38		06 41					07 08			07 37	07 27			07 38
Brighton 10	d					06 31	06 44		06 48	06 53		07 03		07 14	07 23				07 33	07 44			07 53			08 03
Hove 2	d					06 35	06a47		06 52	06 57		07 07		07a17	07 27				07 37	07a47		07 52	07 57			08 07
Aldrington	d									06 59					07 29								07 59			
Portslade	d					06 38			06 55	07 01		07 10			07 31				07 40				08 01			08 10
Fishersgate	d									07 03					07 33								08 03			
Southwick	d					06 41				07 05		07 13			07 35				07 43				08 05			08 13
Shoreham-by-Sea	d					06 44			06 59	07 09		07 16			07 39				07 46			07 58	08 09			08 16
Lancing	d					06 48			07 03	07 13		07 20			07 43				07 50			08 02	08 13			08 20
East Worthing	d									07 16					07 46								08 16			
Worthing 4	a					06 52			07 07	07 18		07 24			07 48				07 54			08 06	08 18			08 24
	d					06 53			07 08	07 19		07 25			07 49				07 55			08 07	08 19			08 25
West Worthing	d					06 55			07 10	07a21		07 27			07a51							08 09	08a21			08 27
Durrington-on-Sea	d					06 57			07 12										07 58			08 11				
Goring-by-Sea	d					07 00			07 15										08 01			08 14				
Angmering 3	d					07 04			07 19			07 33							08 05			08 18				08 33
Littlehampton 4	a								07 27			07g54										08 27				08g54
	d			06 54				07 11										07 58			08 11					
Ford 4	d	06 51		06 58		07 10		07 15			07 22	07 40					07 52	08 02			08 15			08 22		08 40
Bognor Regis 4	d	06 39				07 00					07 07	07 26					07 39		08 00					08 07		08 26
Barnham	a	06 55		07 02		07 14		07 19			07 27	07 44					07 57	08 06	08 14		08 19			08 27		08 44
	d	07 05 →	06 59	07 03	← 07 05	07 15		07 22			07 27	07 45				07 52	07 57	08 07	08 15		08 22			08 27		08 45
Bognor Regis 4	a				07 11			07 28								07 58					08 28					
Chichester 4	d		07 07	07 11		07 23					07 35	07 53					08 05	08 15	08 23					08 35		08 53
Fishbourne (Sussex)	d			07 14														08 18								
Bosham	d			07 17													08 10									
Nutbourne	d			07 20														08 23								
Southbourne	d		07 14	07 23		07 30											08 14	08 25	08 30							
Emsworth	d		07 17	07 26		07 33											08 17	08 28	08 33							
Warblington	d			07 29													08 20									
Havant	d		07 23	07 33		07 37					07 46	08 04					08 23	08 33	08 37					08 46		09 04
Bedhampton	a			07 35														08 35								
Hilsea	a			07 41														08 41								
Fratton	a			07 45							07 55	08 13						08 45						08 55		09 12
Portsmouth & Southsea	a			07 49							07 58	08 18						08 49						08 58		09 16
Portsmouth Harbour	a										08 02	08 22												09 02		09 20
Cosham	a		07 29			07 44											08 29		08 44							
Portchester	a		07 33														08 34									
Fareham	a		07 38			07 52											08 39		08 52							
Swanwick	a		07 45			07 59											08 46		08 59							
Southampton Central	a		08 02			08 18											09 03		09 18							

For general notes see front of timetable
For details of catering facilities see Directory of Train Operators

- **b** Change at East Croydon and Brighton
- **c** Change at East Croydon and Haywards Heath
- **e** Change at Three Bridges
- **f** Change at Gatwick Airport
- **g** Change at Ford

Table 188

Saturdays

London, Gatwick Airport & Brighton → Sussex Coast, Portsmouth and Southampton

For complete service between Three Bridges and Horsham see Table 186

		SN 1	SN 1	SN 1	SN 1		SN 1	SN 1	SN 1	SN 1	SN 1	SN 1		SN 1	SN 1		GW ◇ A	SN 1	SN 1	SN 1	SN 1	SN 1	SN 1			SN 1
London Victoria 15 ⊖	d				07 32				07 36			07 47			08 02		07b47	08 06		08 17			08 32			
Clapham Junction 10	d				07 38				07 42			07 53			08 08		07b53	08 12		08 23			08 38			
London Bridge 4 ⊖	d		07 11		07 26				07 26			07 41			07 56		07 56	07 56		08 11			08 26			
East Croydon	d		07 24		07 48				07 52			08 03			08 18		08 09	08 22		08 33			08 48			
Gatwick Airport 10 ✈	d	07 28	07 41		08 09				07 56			08 19			08 40		08 26	08 26	08 28	08 49			09 09			
Three Bridges 4	d	07 33	07 45		08 14							08 15			08 45		08 15	08 15	08 33	08 45			09 14			
Crawley	d				08 18			←							08 48								09 18			
Horsham 4	d				08 30	08 34 →		08 34							09 00	09 04							09 30	09 34 →		
Christs Hospital	d							08 37																		
Billingshurst	d							08 43								09 13										
Pulborough	d							08 50								09 19										
Amberley	d							08 56																		
Arundel	d							09 01								09 28										
Haywards Heath 3	d	07 46	07 55						08 08			08 37					08 38	08 38	08 46	09 04						
Brighton 10	d	08 14	08 23						08 33	08 44				08 53			09 00	09 03	09 14		09 23					
Hove 2	d	08a17	08 27						08 37	08a47		08 52		08 57			09 04	09 07	09a17	09 22	09 27					
Aldrington	d		08 29											08 59							09 29					
Portslade	d		08 31						08 40					09 01				09 10		09 25	09 31					
Fishersgate	d		08 33											09 03							09 33					
Southwick	d		08 35						08 43					09 05				09 13			09 35					
Shoreham-by-Sea	d		08 39						08 46			08 58		09 09			09 13	09 17		09 30	09 39					
Lancing	d		08 43						08 50			09 02		09 13				09 21			09 43					
East Worthing	d		08 46											09 16							09 46					
Worthing 4	a		08 48						08 54			09 06		09 18			09 22	09 25		09 36	09 48					
	d		08 49						08 55			09 07		09 19			09 22	09 25		09 37	09 49					
West Worthing	d		08a51									09 09		09a21				09 28		09 39	09a51					
Durrington-on-Sea	d								08 58			09 11								09 41						
Goring-by-Sea	d								09 01			09 14								09 44						
Angmering 3	d								09 05			09 18						09 34		09 48						
Littlehampton 4	a											09 27						09c54		09 57						
	d						08 58				09 11															09 58
Ford 4	d						09 02	09 06			09 15					09 33		09 40								10 02
Bognor Regis 4	d				08 39				09 00						09 07		09 26	09 26					09 39			
Barnham	a				08 56		09 06	09 10	09 14		09 19				09 26	09 38	09 40	09 44					09 56			10 06
	d			08 52	08 57		09 07	09 11	09 15		09 22				09 27	09 38	09 41	09 45				09 52	09 57			10 07
Bognor Regis 4	a			08 58				09 17			09 28					09 45						09 58				
Chichester 4	d				09 05		09 15		09 23						09 35		09 49	09 53					10 05			10 15
Fishbourne (Sussex)	d						09 18																			10 18
Bosham	d				09 09																		10 09			
Nutbourne	d						09 23																			10 23
Southbourne	d				09 14		09 25		09 30														10 14			10 25
Emsworth	d				09 17		09 28		09 33														10 17			10 28
Warblington	d				09 20																		10 20			
Havant	d				09 23		09 33		09 37						09 46		10 00	10 04					10 23			10 33
Bedhampton	a						09 35																			10 35
Hilsea	a						09 41																			10 41
Fratton	a						09 45								09 54			10 12								10 45
Portsmouth & Southsea	a						09 49								09 58			10 16								10 49
Portsmouth Harbour	a														10 02			10 20								
Cosham	a				09 29				09 44								10 06						10 29			
Portchester	a				09 33																		10 33			
Fareham	a				09 38				09 52								10 14						10 38			
Swanwick	a				09 45				09 59														10 45			
Southampton Central	a				10 02				10 18								10 38						11 02			

For general notes see front of timetable
For details of catering facilities see Directory of Train Operators

A To Worcester Foregate Street (Table 71)
b Change at East Croydon and Brighton
c Change at Ford

Table 188

London, Gatwick Airport & Brighton → Sussex Coast, Portsmouth and Southampton

For complete service between Three Bridges and Horsham see Table 186

		SN 1	SN 1	SN 1	SN 1	SN 1	SN 1	SN 1		SN 1	SN 1	SN 1		SN 1	SN 1	SN 1		SN 1	SN 1	SN 1	SN 1	SN 1	SN 1	SN 1		
London Victoria 15	⊖ d		08 36			08 47		09 02		09 06		09 17				09 32				09 36			09 47			
Clapham Junction 10	d		08 42			08 53		09 08		09 12		09 23				09 38				09 42			09 53			
London Bridge 4	⊖ d		08 26			08 41		08 56		08 56		09 11		09 11		09 26				09 26			09 41			
East Croydon	d		08 52			09 03		09 18		09 22		09 33		09 24		09 48				09 52			10 03			
Gatwick Airport 10	✈ d		08 56			09 19		09 40		09 26	09 28	09 49		09 41		10 09				09 56			10 19			
Three Bridges 4	d		08 45			09 15		09 45		09 15	09 33	09 45		09 45		10 14							10 15			
Crawley	d							09 48								10 18										
Horsham 4	d	← 09 34						10 00	10 04							10 30	10 34 →		← 10 34							
Christs Hospital	d	09 37																	10 37							
Billingshurst	d	09 43							10 13										10 43							
Pulborough	d	09 50							10 19										10 50							
Amberley	d	09 56																	10 56							
Arundel	d	10 01							10 28										11 01							
Haywards Heath 3	d		09 08			09 37				09 38	09 46	10 04		09 55						10 08			10 37			
Brighton 10	d		09 33	09 44			09 53			10 03	10 14			10 23						10 33	10 44			10 53		
Hove 2	d		09 37	09a47		09 52	09 57			10 07	10a17	10 22		10 27						10 37	10a47		10 52	10 57		
Aldrington	d						09 59							10 29										10 59		
Portslade	d		09 40				10 01			10 10		10 25		10 31						10 40				11 01		
Fishersgate	d						10 03							10 33										11 03		
Southwick	d		09 43				10 05			10 13				10 35						10 43				11 05		
Shoreham-by-Sea	d		09 46			09 58	10 09			10 16		10 30		10 39						10 46			10 58	11 09		
Lancing	d		09 50			10 02	10 13			10 20				10 43						10 50			11 02	11 13		
East Worthing	d						10 16							10 46										11 16		
Worthing 4	a		09 54			10 06	10 18			10 24		10 36		10 48						10 54			11 06	11 18		
	d		09 55			10 07	10 19			10 25		10 37		10 49						10 55			11 07	11 19		
West Worthing	d					10 09	10a21			10 27		10 39		10a51									11 09	11a21		
Durrington-on-Sea	d		09 58			10 11						10 41								10 58			11 11			
Goring-by-Sea	d		10 01			10 14						10 44								11 01			11 14			
Angmering 3	d		10 05			10 18				10 33		10 48								11 05			11 18			
Littlehampton 4	a					10 27				10b54		10 57											11 27			
	d				10 11													10 58				11 11				
Ford 4	d	10 06			10 15				10 33	10 40								11 02	11 06			11 15				
Bognor Regis 4	d		10 00					10 07		10 26						10 39				11 00						
Barnham	a	10 10	10 14		10 19			10 26	10 38	10 44						10 56		11 06	11 10	11 14		11 19				
	d	10 11	10 15		10 22			10 27	10 38	10 45					10 52	10 57		11 07	11 11	11 15		11 22				
Bognor Regis 4	a	10 17			10 28				10 45						10 58				11 17			11 28				
Chichester 4	d		10 23					10 35		10 53						11 05		11 15		11 23						
Fishbourne (Sussex)	d																	11 18								
Bosham	d															11 09										
Nutbourne	d																	11 23								
Southbourne	d		10 30													11 14		11 25		11 30						
Emsworth	d		10 33													11 17		11 28		11 33						
Warblington	d															11 20										
Havant	d		10 37					10 46		11 04						11 23		11 33		11 37						
Bedhampton	a																	11 35								
Hilsea	a																	11 41								
Fratton	a							10 54		11 12								11 45								
Portsmouth & Southsea	a							10 58		11 16								11 49								
Portsmouth Harbour	a							11 02		11 20																
Cosham	a		10 44													11 29				11 44						
Portchester	a															11 33										
Fareham	a		10 52													11 38				11 52						
Swanwick	a		10 59													11 45				11 59						
Southampton Central	a		11 18													12 02				12 18						

For general notes see front of timetable
For details of catering facilities see Directory of Train Operators

b Change at Ford

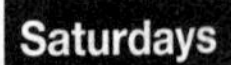

London, Gatwick Airport & Brighton → Sussex Coast, Portsmouth and Southampton

For complete service between Three Bridges and Horsham see Table 186

		SN 1		SN 1	SN 1	SN 1	SN 1	SN 1	SN 1		SN 1	SN 1		SN 1	SN 1	SN 1	SN 1	SN 1	SN 1		SN 1	SN 1	SN 1	SN 1		SN 1
London Victoria 15 ⊖	d	10 02		*10 06*		10 17			10 32					*10 36*			10 47		11 02		*11 06*		11 17			
Clapham Junction 10	d	10 08		*10 12*		10 23			10 38					*10 42*			10 53		11 08		*11 12*		11 23			
London Bridge 4 ⊖	d	*09 56*		*09 56*		*10 11*	*10 11*		*10 26*					*10 26*			*10 41*		*10 56*		*10 56*		*11 11*	*11 11*		
East Croydon	d	10 18		*10 22*		10 33	*10 24*		10 48					*10 52*			11 03		11 18		*11 22*		11 33	*11 24*		
Gatwick Airport 10 ✈	d	10 40		*10 26*	*10 28*	10 49	*10 41*		11 09					*10 56*			11 19		11 40		*11 26*	*11 28*	11 49	*11 41*		
Three Bridges 4	d	10 45		*10 15*	*10 33*	*10 45*	*10 45*		11 14								*11 15*		11 45		*11 15*	*11 33*	*11 45*	*11 45*		
Crawley	d	10 48							11 18										11 48							
Horsham 4	d	11 00	11 04						11 30	11 34 →		← 11 34							12 00	12 04						
Christs Hospital	d											11 37														
Billingshurst	d		11 13									11 43								12 13						
Pulborough	d		11 19									11 50								12 19						
Amberley	d											11 56														
Arundel	d		11 28									12 01								12 28						
Haywards Heath 3	d			*10 38*	*10 46*	11 04	*10 55*							*11 08*			11 37				*11 38*	*11 46*	12 04	*11 55*		
Brighton 10	d			11 03	11 14		11 23							11 33	11 44			11 53			12 03	12 14		12 23		
Hove 2	d			11 07	11a17	11 22	11 27							11 37	11a47		11 52	11 57			12 07	12a17	12 22	12 27		
Aldrington	d						11 29											11 59						12 29		
Portslade	d			11 10		11 25	11 31							11 40				12 01			12 10		12 25	12 31		
Fishersgate	d						11 33											12 03						12 33		
Southwick	d			11 13			11 35							11 43				12 05			12 13			12 35		
Shoreham-by-Sea	d			11 16		11 30	11 39							11 46			11 58	12 09			12 16		12 30	12 39		
Lancing	d			11 20			11 43							11 50			12 02	12 13			12 20			12 43		
East Worthing	d						11 46											12 16						12 46		
Worthing 4	a			11 24		11 36	11 48							11 54			12 06	12 18			12 24		12 36	12 48		
	d			11 25		11 37	11 49							11 55			12 07	12 19			12 25		12 37	12 49		
West Worthing	d			11 27		11 39	11a51										12 09	12a21			12 27		12 39	12a51		
Durrington-on-Sea	d					11 41								11 58			12 11						12 41			
Goring-by-Sea	d					11 44								12 01			12 14						12 44			
Angmering 3	d			11 33		11 48								12 05			12 18				12 33		12 48			
Littlehampton 4	a			*11b54*		11 57											12 27				*12b54*		12 57			
	d										11 58					12 11										
Ford 4	d		11 33	11 40							12 02	12 06				12 15				12 33	12 40					
Bognor Regis 4	d	*11 07*		*11 26*					*11 39*					*12 00*					*12 07*		*12 26*					
Barnham	a	11 26	11 38	11 44					11 56		12 06	12 10		12 14		12 19			12 26	12 38	12 44					
	d	11 27	11 38	11 45				11 52	11 57		12 07	12 11		12 15		12 22			12 27	12 38	12 45					12 52
Bognor Regis 4	a		11 45					11 58				12 17				12 28				12 45						12 58
Chichester 4	d	11 35		11 53					12 05		12 15			12 23					12 35		12 53					
Fishbourne (Sussex)	d										12 18															
Bosham	d								12 09																	
Nutbourne	d										12 23															
Southbourne	d								12 14		12 25			12 30												
Emsworth	d								12 17		12 28			12 33												
Warblington	d								12 20																	
Havant	d	11 46		12 04					12 23		12 33			12 37					12 46		13 04					
Bedhampton	a										12 35															
Hilsea	a										12 41															
Fratton	a	11 54		12 12							12 45								12 54		13 12					
Portsmouth & Southsea	a	11 58		12 16							12 49								12 58		13 16					
Portsmouth Harbour	a	12 02		12 20															13 02		13 20					
Cosham	a								12 29					12 44												
Portchester	a								12 33																	
Fareham	a								12 38					12 52												
Swanwick	a								12 45					12 59												
Southampton Central	a								13 02					13 18												

For general notes see front of timetable
For details of catering facilities see
Directory of Train Operators

b Change at Ford

Table 188

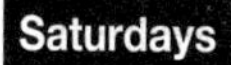

London, Gatwick Airport & Brighton → Sussex Coast, Portsmouth and Southampton

For complete service between Three Bridges and Horsham see Table 186

		SN 1		SN 1	SN 1	SN 1	SN 1	SN 1	SN 1	SN 1	SN 1			SN 1	SN 1	SN 1	SN 1	SN 1	SN 1		SN 1	SN 1	SN 1	SN 1		SN 1
London Victoria 15 ⊖	d	11 32				11 36			11 47		12 02			12 06		12 17			12 32				12 36			
Clapham Junction 10	d	11 38				11 42			11 53		12 08			12 12		12 23			12 38				12 42			
London Bridge 4 ⊖	d	11 26				11 26			11 41		11 56			11 56		12 11	12 11		12 26				12 26			
East Croydon	d	11 48				11 52			12 03		12 18			12 22		12 33	12 24		12 48				12 52			
Gatwick Airport 10 ✈	d	12 09				11 56			12 19		12 40			12 26	12 28	12 49	12 40		13 09				12 56	13 01		
Three Bridges 4	d	12 14							12 15		12 45			12 15	12 33	12 45	12 45		13 14							
Crawley	d	12 18									12 48								13 18							
Horsham 4	d	12 30	12 34 →		← 12 34						13 00	13 04							13 30	13 34 →		← 13 34				
Christs Hospital	d				12 37																	13 37				
Billingshurst	d				12 43							13 13										13 43				
Pulborough	d				12 50							13 19										13 50				
Amberley	d				12 56																	13 56				
Arundel	d				13 01							13 28										14 01				
Haywards Heath 3	d					12 08			12 37					12 38	12 46	13 04	12 55						13 08	13 18		
Brighton 10	d					12 33	12 44			12 53				13 03	13 14		13 23						13 33	13 44		
Hove 2	d					12 37	12a47		12 52	12 57				13 07	13a17	13 22	13 27						13 37	13a47		
Aldrington	d									12 59							13 29									
Portslade	d					12 40				13 01				13 10		13 25	13 31						13 40			
Fishersgate	d									13 03							13 33									
Southwick	d					12 43				13 05				13 13			13 35						13 43			
Shoreham-by-Sea	d					12 46			12 58	13 09				13 16		13 30	13 39						13 46			
Lancing	d					12 50			13 02	13 13				13 20			13 43						13 50			
East Worthing	d									13 16							13 46									
Worthing 4	a					12 54			13 06	13 18				13 24		13 36	13 48						13 54			
	d					12 55			13 07	13 19				13 25		13 37	13 49						13 55			
West Worthing	d								13 09	13a21				13 27		13 39	13a51									
Durrington-on-Sea	d					12 58			13 11							13 41							13 58			
Goring-by-Sea	d					13 01			13 14							13 44							14 01			
Angmering 3	d					13 05			13 18					13 33		13 48							14 05			
Littlehampton 4	a								13 27					13b54		13 57										
	d			12 58				13 11													13 58					14 11
Ford 4	d			13 02	13 06			13 15				13 33		13 40							14 02	14 06				14 15
Bognor Regis 4	d	12 39				13 00					13 07			13 26					13 39				14 00			
Barnham	a	12 56		13 06	13 10	13 14		13 19			13 26	13 38		13 44					13 56		14 06	14 10	14 14			14 19
	d	12 57		13 07	13 11	13 15		13 22			13 27	13 38		13 45				13 52	13 57		14 07	14 11	14 15			14 22
Bognor Regis 4	a				13 17			13 28				13 45						13 58				14 17				14 28
Chichester 4	d	13 05		13 15		13 23					13 35			13 53					14 05		14 15		14 23			
Fishbourne (Sussex)	d			13 18																	14 18					
Bosham	d	13 09																	14 09							
Nutbourne	d			13 23																	14 23					
Southbourne	d	13 14		13 25		13 30													14 14		14 25		14 30			
Emsworth	d	13 17		13 28		13 33													14 17		14 28		14 33			
Warblington	d	13 20																	14 20							
Havant	d	13 23		13 33		13 37					13 46			14 04					14 23		14 33		14 37			
Bedhampton	a			13 35																	14 35					
Hilsea	a			13 41																	14 41					
Fratton	a			13 45							13 54			14 12							14 45					
Portsmouth & Southsea	a			13 49							13 58			14 16							14 49					
Portsmouth Harbour	a										14 02			14 20												
Cosham	a	13 29				13 44													14 29				14 44			
Portchester	a	13 33																	14 33							
Fareham	a	13 38				13 52													14 38				14 52			
Swanwick	a	13 45				13 59													14 45				14 59			
Southampton Central	a	14 02				14 18													15 02				15 18			

For general notes see front of timetable
For details of catering facilities see
Directory of Train Operators

b Change at Ford

Table 188

Saturdays

London, Gatwick Airport & Brighton → Sussex Coast, Portsmouth and Southampton

For complete service between Three Bridges and Horsham see Table 186

		SN 1	SN 1	SN 1		SN 1	SN 1	SN 1	SN 1	SN 1	SN 1			SN 1	SN 1	SN 1	SN 1	SN 1	SN 1	SN 1	SN 1		SN 1	SN 1		SN 1
London Victoria 15 ⊖	d	12 47		13 02		13 06		13 17			13 32					13 36			13 47		14 02		14 06			14 17
Clapham Junction 10	d	12 53		13 08		13 12		13 23			13 38					13 42			13 53		14 08		14 12			14 23
London Bridge 4 ⊖	d	12 41		12 56		12 56		13 11	13 11		13 26					13 26			13 41		13 56		13 56			14 11
East Croydon	d	13 03		13 18		13 22		13 33	13 24		13 48					13 52			14 03		14 18		14 22			14 33
Gatwick Airport 10 ✈	d	13 19		13 40		13 26	13 28	13 49	13 41		14 09					13 56			14 19		14 40		14 26	14 28		14 49
Three Bridges 4	d	13 15		13 45		13 15	13 33	13 45	13 45		14 14								14 15		14 45		14 15	14 33		14 45
Crawley	d			13 48							14 18				←						14 48					
Horsham 4	d			14 00	14 04						14 30	14 34 →			14 34						15 00	15 04				
Christs Hospital	d														14 37											
Billingshurst	d				14 13										14 43							15 13				
Pulborough	d				14 19										14 50							15 19				
Amberley	d														14 56											
Arundel	d				14 28										15 01							15 28				
Haywards Heath 3	d	13 37				13 38	13 46	14 04	13 55							14 08			14 37				14 38	14 46		15 04
Brighton 10	d		13 53			14 03	14 14		14 23							14 33	14 44			14 53			15 03	15 14		
Hove 2	d	13 52	13 57			14 07	14a17	14 22	14 27							14 37	14a47		14 52	14 57			15 07	15a17		15 22
Aldrington	d		13 59						14 29											14 59						
Portslade	d		14 01			14 10		14 25	14 31							14 40				15 01			15 10			15 25
Fishersgate	d		14 03						14 33											15 03						
Southwick	d		14 05			14 13			14 35							14 43				15 05			15 13			
Shoreham-by-Sea	d	13 58	14 09			14 16		14 30	14 39							14 46			14 58	15 09			15 16			15 30
Lancing	d	14 02	14 13			14 20			14 43							14 50			15 02	15 13			15 20			
East Worthing	d		14 16						14 46											15 16						
Worthing 4	a	14 06	14 18			14 24		14 36	14 48							14 54			15 06	15 18			15 24			15 36
	d	14 07	14 19			14 25		14 37	14 49							14 55			15 07	15 19			15 25			15 37
West Worthing	d	14 09	14a21			14 27		14 39	14a51										15 09	15a21			15 27			15 39
Durrington-on-Sea	d	14 11						14 41								14 58			15 11							15 41
Goring-by-Sea	d	14 14						14 44								15 01			15 14							15 44
Angmering 3	d	14 18				14 33		14 48								15 05			15 18				15 33			15 48
Littlehampton 4	a	14 27				14b54		14 57											15 27				15b54			15 57
	d													14 58				15 11								
Ford 4	d				14 33	14 40								15 02	15 06			15 15				15 33	15 40			
Bognor Regis 4	d			14 07		14 26					14 39					15 00					15 07		15 26			
Barnham	a			14 26	14 38	14 44					14 56			15 06	15 10	15 14		15 19			15 26	15 38	15 44			
	d			14 27	14 38	14 45				14 52	14 57			15 07	15 11	15 15		15 22			15 27	15 38	15 45			
Bognor Regis 4	a				14 45					14 58					15 17			15 28				15 45				
Chichester 4	d			14 35		14 53					15 05			15 15		15 23					15 35		15 53			
Fishbourne (Sussex)	d													15 18												
Bosham	d										15 09															
Nutbourne	d													15 23												
Southbourne	d										15 14			15 25		15 30										
Emsworth	d										15 17			15 28		15 33										
Warblington	d										15 20															
Havant	d			14 46		15 04					15 23			15 33		15 37					15 46		16 04			
Bedhampton	a													15 35												
Hilsea	a													15 41												
Fratton	a			14 54		15 12								15 45							15 54		16 12			
Portsmouth & Southsea	a			14 58		15 16								15 49							15 58		16 16			
Portsmouth Harbour	a			15 02		15 20															16 02		16 20			
Cosham	a										15 29					15 44										
Portchester	a										15 33															
Fareham	a										15 38					15 52										
Swanwick	a										15 45					15 59										
Southampton Central	a										16 02					16 18										

For general notes see front of timetable
For details of catering facilities see Directory of Train Operators

b Change at Ford

Table 188

London, Gatwick Airport & Brighton → Sussex Coast, Portsmouth and Southampton

For complete service between Three Bridges and Horsham see Table 186

		SN 1	SN 1	SN 1		SN 1	SN 1	SN 1	SN 1	SN 1	SN 1	SN 1		SN 1		SN 1	SN 1	SN 1	SN 1	SN 1	SN 1		SN 1	SN 1		SN 1
London Victoria 15 ⊖	d			14 32				14 36			14 47			15 02		15 06		15 17			15 32					15 36
Clapham Junction 10	d			14 38				14 42			14 53			15 08		15 12		15 23			15 38					15 42
London Bridge 4 ⊖	d	14 11		14 26				14 26			14 41			14 56		14 56		15 11	15 11		15 26					15 26
East Croydon	d	14 24		14 48				14 52			15 03			15 18		15 22		15 33	15 24		15 48					15 52
Gatwick Airport 10 ✈	d	14 41		15 09				14 56			15 19			15 40		15 26	15 28	15 49	15 41		16 09					15 56
Three Bridges 4	d	14 45		15 14							15 15			15 45		15 15	15 33	15 45	15 45		16 14					
Crawley	d			15 18										15 48							16 18					
Horsham 4	d			15 30	15 34 →		← 15 34							16 00	16 04						16 30	16 34 →		← 16 34		
Christs Hospital	d						15 37																	16 37		
Billingshurst	d						15 43								16 13									16 43		
Pulborough	d						15 50								16 19									16 50		
Amberley	d						15 56																	16 56		
Arundel	d						16 01								16 28									17 01		
Haywards Heath 3	d	14 55						15 08			15 37					15 38	15 46	16 04	15 55							16 08
Brighton 10	d	15 23						15 33	15 44			15 53				16 03	16 14		16 23							16 33
Hove 2	d	15 27						15 37	15a47		15 52	15 57				16 07	16a17	16 22	16 27							16 37
Aldrington	d	15 29										15 59							16 29							
Portslade	d	15 31						15 40				16 01				16 10		16 25	16 31							16 40
Fishersgate	d	15 33										16 03							16 33							
Southwick	d	15 35						15 43				16 05				16 13			16 35							16 43
Shoreham-by-Sea	d	15 39						15 46			15 58	16 09				16 16		16 30	16 39							16 46
Lancing	d	15 43						15 50			16 02	16 13				16 20			16 43							16 50
East Worthing	d	15 46										16 16							16 46							
Worthing 4	a	15 48						15 54			16 06	16 18				16 24		16 36	16 48							16 54
	d	15 49						15 55			16 07	16 19				16 25		16 37	16 49							16 55
West Worthing	d	15a51									16 09	16a21				16 27		16 39	16a51							
Durrington-on-Sea	d							15 58			16 11							16 41								16 58
Goring-by-Sea	d							16 01			16 14							16 44								17 01
Angmering 3	d							16 05			16 18					16 33		16 48								17 05
Littlehampton 4	a										16 27					16b54		16 57								
	d					15 58				16 11													16 58			
Ford 4	d					16 02	16 06			16 15					16 33	16 40							17 02	17 06		
Bognor Regis 4	d			15 39				16 00						16 07		16 26					16 39					17 00
Barnham	a			15 56		16 06	16 10	16 14		16 19				16 26	16 38	16 44					16 56		17 06	17 10		17 14
	d		15 52	15 57		16 07	16 11	16 15		16 22				16 27	16 38	16 45				16 52	16 57		17 07	17 11		17 15
Bognor Regis 4	a		15 58				16 17			16 28					16 45					16 58				17 17		
Chichester 4	d			16 05		16 15		16 23						16 35		16 53					17 05		17 15			17 23
Fishbourne (Sussex)	d					16 18																	17 18			
Bosham	d			16 09																	17 09					
Nutbourne	d					16 23																	17 23			
Southbourne	d			16 14		16 25		16 30													17 14		17 25			17 30
Emsworth	d			16 17		16 28		16 33													17 17		17 28			17 33
Warblington	d			16 20																	17 20					
Havant	d			16 23		16 33		16 37						16 46		17 04					17 23		17 33			17 37
Bedhampton	a					16 35																	17 35			
Hilsea	a					16 41																	17 41			
Fratton	a					16 45								16 54		17 12							17 45			
Portsmouth & Southsea	a					16 49								16 58		17 16							17 49			
Portsmouth Harbour	a													17 02		17 20										
Cosham	a			16 29				16 44													17 29					17 44
Portchester	a			16 33																	17 33					
Fareham	a			16 38				16 52													17 38					17 52
Swanwick	a			16 45				16 59													17 45					17 59
Southampton Central	a			17 02				17 18													18 02					18 18

For general notes see front of timetable
For details of catering facilities see Directory of Train Operators

b Change at Ford

London, Gatwick Airport & Brighton → Sussex Coast, Portsmouth and Southampton

For complete service between Three Bridges and Horsham see Table 186

		SN	SN	SN	SN	SN		GW	SN	SN	SN	SN		SN	SN		SN	SN	SN	SN	SN	SN	SN	SN		SN
		1	1	1	1	1			1	1	1	1		1	1		1	1	1	1	1	1	1	1		1
								A																		
London Victoria 15 ⊖	d			15 47		16 02		15b47	16 06		16 17				16 32				16 36			16 47		17 02		17 06
Clapham Junction 10	d			15 53		16 08		15b53	16 12		16 23				16 38				16 42			16 53		17 08		17 12
London Bridge 4 ⊖	d			15 41		15 56		15 56	15 56		16 11	16 11			16 26				16 26			16 41		16 56		16 56
East Croydon	d			16 03		16 18		16 09	16 22		16 33	16 24			16 48				16 52			17 03		17 18		17 22
Gatwick Airport 10 ✈	d			16 19		16 40		16 26	16 26	16 28	16 49	16 41			17 09				16 56			17 19		17 40		17 26
Three Bridges 4	d			16 15		16 45		16 15	16 15	16 33	16 45	16 45			17 14							17 15		17 45		17 15
Crawley	d					16 48									17 18									17 48		
Horsham 4	d					17 00	17 04								17 30	17 34 →		← 17 34						18 00	18 04	
Christs Hospital	d																	17 37								
Billingshurst	d						17 13											17 43							18 13	
Pulborough	d						17 19											17 50							18 19	
Amberley	d																	17 56								
Arundel	d						17 28											18 01							18 28	
Haywards Heath 3	d			16 37				16 38	16 38	16 46	17 04	16 55							17 08			17 37				17 38
Brighton 10	d	16 44			16 53			17 00	17 03	17 14		17 23							17 33	17 44			17 53			18 03
Hove 2	d	16a47		16 52	16 57			17 04	17 07	17a17	17 22	17 27							17 37	17a47		17 52	17 57			18 07
Aldrington	d				16 59							17 29											17 59			
Portslade	d				17 01				17 10		17 25	17 31							17 40				18 01			18 10
Fishersgate	d				17 03							17 33											18 03			
Southwick	d				17 05				17 13			17 35							17 43				18 05			18 13
Shoreham-by-Sea	d			16 58	17 09			17 13	17 17		17 30	17 39							17 46			17 58	18 09			18 16
Lancing	d			17 02	17 13				17 21			17 43							17 50			18 02	18 13			18 20
East Worthing	d				17 16							17 46											18 16			
Worthing 4	a			17 06	17 18			17 22	17 25		17 36	17 48							17 54			18 06	18 18			18 24
	d			17 07	17 19			17 22	17 25		17 37	17 49							17 55			18 07	18 19			18 25
West Worthing	d			17 09	17a21				17 28		17 39	17a51										18 09	18a21			18 27
Durrington-on-Sea	d			17 11							17 41								17 58			18 11				
Goring-by-Sea	d			17 14							17 44								18 01			18 14				
Angmering 3	d			17 18					17 34		17 48								18 05			18 18				18 33
Littlehampton 4	a			17 27					17c54		17 57											18 27				19c03
	d		17 11														17 58				18 11					
Ford 4	d		17 15				17 33		17 40								18 02	18 06			18 15				18 33	18 40
Bognor Regis 4	d					17 07		17 26	17 26						17 39				18 00					18 07		18 33
Barnham	a		17 19			17 26	17 38	17 40	17 44						17 56		18 06	18 10	18 14		18 19			18 26	18 38	18 44
	d		17 22			17 27	17 38	17 41	17 45					17 52	17 57		18 07	18 11	18 15		18 22			18 27	18 38	18 45
Bognor Regis 4	a		17 28				17 45							17 58				18 17			18 28				18 45	
Chichester 4	d					17 35		17 49	17 53						18 05		18 15		18 23					18 35		18 53
Fishbourne (Sussex)	d																18 18									
Bosham	d														18 09											
Nutbourne	d																18 23									
Southbourne	d														18 14		18 25		18 30							
Emsworth	d														18 17		18 28		18 33							
Warblington	d														18 20											
Havant	d					17 46		18 00	18 04						18 23		18 33		18 37					18 46		19 04
Bedhampton	a																18 35									
Hilsea	a																18 41									
Fratton	a					17 54			18 12								18 45							18 54		19 12
Portsmouth & Southsea	a					17 58			18 16								18 49							18 58		19 16
Portsmouth Harbour	a					18 02			18 20															19 02		19 20
Cosham	a							18 06							18 29				18 44							
Portchester	a														18 33											
Fareham	a							18 14							18 38				18 52							
Swanwick	a														18 45				18 59							
Southampton Central	a							18 38							19 02				19 18							

For general notes see front of timetable
For details of catering facilities see Directory of Train Operators

A To Worcester Shrub Hill (Table 57)
b Change at East Croydon and Brighton
c Change at Ford

London, Gatwick Airport & Brighton → Sussex Coast, Portsmouth and Southampton

Saturdays

For complete service between Three Bridges and Horsham see Table 186

Station		SN 1		SN 1	SN 1	SN 1		SN 1	SN 1	SN 1	SN 1	SN 1	SN 1	SN 1		SN 1		SN 1	SN 1	SN 1	SN 1	SN 1		SN 1	SN 1	SN 1
London Victoria 15	⊖ d			17 17		17 32					17 36			17 47		18 02				18 17		18 32			18 36	
Clapham Junction 10	d			17 23		17 38					17 42			17 53		18 08				18 23		18 38			18 42	
London Bridge 4	⊖ d			17 11		17 26			17 11		17 26			17 41		17 56				18 11		18 26		18 11	18 26	
East Croydon	d			17 33		17 48			17 24		17 52			18 03		18 18				18 33		18 48		18 24	18 52	
Gatwick Airport 10	✈ d	17 28		17 49		18 09			17 41		17 56			18 19		18 40				18 49		19 09		18 41	18 56	
Three Bridges 4	d	17 33		17 45		18 14			17 45					18 15		18 45			18 33	18 45		19 14		18 45		
Crawley	d					18 18										18 48						19 18				
Horsham 4	d					18 30	18 34 →			← 18 34						19 00	19 04					19 30	19 34			
Christs Hospital	d									18 37													19 37			
Billingshurst	d									18 43							19 13						19 43			
Pulborough	d									18 50							19 19						19 50			
Amberley	d									18 56													19 56			
Arundel	d									19 01							19 28						20 01			
Haywards Heath 3	d	17 46		18 04					17 55		18 08			18 37				18 38	18 46	19 04				18 55	19 08	
Brighton 10	d	18 14							18 23		18 33	18 44						19 03	19 14					19 27	19 44	
Hove 2	d	18a17		18 22					18 27		18 37	18a47		18 52				19 07	19a17	19 22				19 31	19a47	
Aldrington	d								18 29									19 09						19 33		
Portslade	d			18 25					18 31		18 40			18 55				19 11		19 25				19 35		
Fishersgate	d								18 33									19 13						19 37		
Southwick	d								18 35		18 43							19 15						19 39		
Shoreham-by-Sea	d			18 30					18 39		18 46			19 00				19 19		19 30				19 43		
Lancing	d								18 43		18 50			19 04				19 23		19 34				19 47		
East Worthing	d								18 46									19 26						19 50		
Worthing 4	a			18 36					18 48		18 54			19 08				19 28		19 38				19 52		
	d			18 37					18 49		18 55			19 08				19 29		19 38				19 53		
West Worthing	d			18 39					18 51					19 10				19 31		19 40				19 55		
Durrington-on-Sea	d			18 41					18 53		18 58			19 13				19 33		19 43				19 57		
Goring-by-Sea	d			18 44					18 56		19 01			19 15				19 36		19 45				20 00		
Angmering 3	d			18 48					19 00		19 05			19 19				19 40		19 49				20 04		
Littlehampton 4	a			18 57					19 10					19 28			19b54			19 58				20b20		
	d							18 58					19 11													20 11
Ford 4	d							19 02		19 06			19 15				19 33	19 46					20 06	20 10		20 15
Bognor Regis 4	d					18 39					19 03													20 04		
Barnham	a					18 56		19 06		19 10	19 14		19 19			19 26	19 38	19 50				19 56	20 10	20 14		20 19
	d				18 52	18 57		19 07		19 11	19 15		19 22			19 27	19 38	19 51			19 52	19 57	20 11	20 15		20 22
Bognor Regis 4	a				18 58					19 17			19 28				19 45				19 58		20 17			20 28
Chichester 4	d					19 05		19 15			19 23					19 35		19 59				20 05		20 23		
Fishbourne (Sussex)	d							19 18														20 08				
Bosham	d					19 09																20 11				
Nutbourne	d							19 23														20 14				
Southbourne	d					19 14		19 25			19 30											20 17		20 30		
Emsworth	d					19 17		19 28			19 33											20 20		20 33		
Warblington	d					19 20																20 23				
Havant	d					19 23		19 33			19 37					19 46		20 10				20 26		20 37		
Bedhampton	a							19 35																		
Hilsea	a							19 41																		
Fratton	a							19 45								19 54		20 18								
Portsmouth & Southsea	a							19 49								19 58		20 22								
Portsmouth Harbour	a															20 02		20 26								
Cosham	a					19 29					19 44											20 32		20 44		
Portchester	a					19 33																20 36				
Fareham	a					19 38					19 52											20 41		20 52		
Swanwick	a					19 45					19 59											20 48		20 59		
Southampton Central	a					20 02					20 18											21 05		21 18		

For general notes see front of timetable
For details of catering facilities see Directory of Train Operators

b Change at Ford

Table 188

Saturdays

London, Gatwick Airport & Brighton → Sussex Coast, Portsmouth and Southampton

For complete service between Three Bridges and Horsham see Table 186

		SN 1	SN 1			SN 1	SN 1	SN 1	SN 1	SN 1		SN 1	SN 1	SN 1	SN 1	SN 1		SN 1		SN 1	SN 1	SN 1	SN 1	SN 1		SN 1
London Victoria 15 ⊖	d	18 47	19 02				*19 06*	19 17		19 32				*19 36*	19 47			20 02		*20 06*		20 17		20 32		
Clapham Junction 10	d	18 53	19 08				*19 12*	19 23		19 38				*19 42*	19 53			20 08		*20 12*		20 23		20 38		
London Bridge 4 ⊖	d	*18 41*	*18 56*			*18 41*	*18 56*	*19 11*		*19 26*			*19 11*	*19 26*	*19 41*			*19 56*		*19 56*		*20 11*		*20 15*		
East Croydon	d	19 03	19 18			*18 54*	*19 22*	19 33		19 48			*19 24*	*19 52*	20 03			20 19		*20 22*		20 33		20 48		
Gatwick Airport 10 ✈	d	19 19	19 40			*19 11*	*19 28*	19 49		20 09			*19 41*	*19 56*	20 19			20 39		*20 26*	*20 28*	20 49		21 09		
Three Bridges 4	d	*19 15*	19 45			*19 15*	*19 33*	*19 45*		20 14			*19 45*		*20 15*			20 44		*20 15*	*20 33*	*20 45*		21 14		
Crawley	d		19 48							20 18								20 48						21 18		
Horsham 4	d		20 00	20 04						20 30	20 34							21 00	21 04					21 30	21 34	
Christs Hospital	d										20 37								21 07						21 37	
Billingshurst	d			20 13							20 43								21 13						21 43	
Pulborough	d			20 19							20 50								21 20						21 50	
Amberley	d										20 56								21 26						21 56	
Arundel	d			20 28							21 01								21 31						22 01	
Haywards Heath 3	d	19 37				*19 27*	*19 46*	20 04					*19 55*	*20 15*	20 34					*20 38*	*20 46*	21 05				
Brighton 10	d					19 56	20 14						20 30	20 44						21 03	21 14					
Hove 2	d	19 52				20 00	20a19	20 22					20 34	20a47	20 54					21 07	21a17	21 22				
Aldrington	d					20 02							20 36							21 09						
Portslade	d	19 55				20 04		20 25					20 38		20 57					21 11		21 25				
Fishersgate	d					20 06							20 40							21 13						
Southwick	d					20 08							20 42							21 15						
Shoreham-by-Sea	d	20 00				20 12		20 30					20 46		21 01					21 19		21 30				
Lancing	d	20 04				20 16		20 34					20 50		21 05					21 23		21 34				
East Worthing	d					20 19							20 53							21 26						
Worthing 4	a	20 08				20 21		20 38					20 55		21 09					21 28		21 38				
	d	20 08				20 22		20 38					20 56		21 10					21 29		21 38				
West Worthing	d	20 10				20 24		20 40					20 58		21 12					21 31		21 40				
Durrington-on-Sea	d	20 13				20 26		20 43					21 00		21 14					21 33		21 43				
Goring-by-Sea	d	20 15				20 29		20 45					21 03		21 17					21 36		21 45				
Angmering 3	d	20 19				20 33		20 49					21 07		21 21					21 40		21 49				
Littlehampton 4	a	20 28				*21b01*		20 58					*21b35*		21 29							21 58			*22b16*	
	d											21 06														22 08
Ford 4	d			20 33		20 39					21 06	21 10	21 13						21 36	21 46					22 06	22 12
Bognor Regis 4	d					*20 33*				*20 39*			*21 04*							*21 39*						
Barnham	a		20 26	20 38		20 43				20 56	21 10	21 14	21 17					21 26	21 40	21 50				21 56	22 10	22 16
	d		20 27	20 38		20 44			20 52	20 57	21 11	21 22 →	21 18			← 21 22		21 27	21 41	21 51			21 52	21 57	22 11	22 22 →
Bognor Regis 4	a			20 45					20 58		21 17					21 28			21 47				21 58		22 17	
Chichester 4	d		20 35			20 52				21 05			21 26					21 35		21 59				22 05		
Fishbourne (Sussex)	d					20 55																		22 08		
Bosham	d									21 09														22 11		
Nutbourne	d					21 00																		22 14		
Southbourne	d					21 02				21 14								21 42						22 17		
Emsworth	d					21 05				21 17								21 45						22 20		
Warblington	d									21 20														22 23		
Havant	d		20 46			21 10				21 23			21 37					21 49		22 10				22 26		
Bedhampton	a																									
Hilsea	a																									
Fratton	a		20 54			21 18												21 59		22 18						
Portsmouth & Southsea	a		20 58			21 22												22 02		22 22						
Portsmouth Harbour	a		21 02			21 26												22 06		22 26						
Cosham	a									21 29			21 44											22 33		
Portchester	a									21 33																
Fareham	a									21 38			21 52											22 41		
Swanwick	a									21 45			21 59											22 48		
Southampton Central	a									22 02			22 18											23 05		

For general notes see front of timetable
For details of catering facilities see
Directory of Train Operators

b Change at Ford

Table 188

London, Gatwick Airport & Brighton → Sussex Coast, Portsmouth and Southampton

For complete service between Three Bridges and Horsham see Table 186

		SN 1	SN 1	SN 1	SN 1		SN 1	SN 1	SN 1	SN 1	SN 1	SN 1	SN 1	SN 1	SN 1	SN 1	SN 1		SN 1	SN 1	SN 1	SN 1	SN 1	SN 1	SN 1	
London Victoria 15 ⊖	d		20 36	20 47					21 06		21 17	21 32		21 36		21 47	22 06			22 17	22 36	22 32		22 47	23 17	
Clapham Junction 10	d		20 42	20 53					21 12		21 23	21 38		21 42		21 53	22 12			22 23	22 42	22 38		22 53	23 23	
London Bridge 4 ⊖	d		20b15	20 41				20 41	20b45		21 11	21 15		21b15		21 41	21b45			22 11	22b15	22 15		22 41	23 11	
East Croydon	d	20 24	20 52	21 03				20 54	21 22		21 33	21 48		21 52		22 03	22 22			22 33	22 52	22 48		23 03	23 33	
Gatwick Airport 10 ✈	d	20 41	20c49	21 19				21 11	21c19		21 49	22 09		21c49		22 19	22c19			22 51	22c51	23 09		23 19	23 51	
Three Bridges 4	d	20 45		21 15				21 15			21 53	22 14		21c53		22 15	22 15			22 55	22c55	23 15		23 15	23 56	
Crawley	d											22 18										23 18				
Horsham 4	d											22 27										23 27				
Christs Hospital	d											22 30										23 30				
Billingshurst	d											22 36										23 36				
Pulborough	d											22 43										23 43				
Amberley	d											22 49										23 49				
Arundel	d											22 54										23 54				
Haywards Heath 3	d	20 58	21 15	21 34				21 26	21 45		22 06			22 15		22 37	22 45			23 04	23 15			23 37	00 05	
Brighton 10	d	21 33	21 44					22 03	22 14					22 34	22 44		23 14				23 44					
Hove 2	d	21 37	21a47	21 54				22 07	22a17		22 23			22 38	22a47	22 52	23a17			23 21	23a47			23 52	00 22	
Aldrington	d	21 39						22 09						22 40												
Portslade	d	21 41		21 57				22 11			22 26			22 42		22 55				23 24				23 55	00s25	
Fishersgate	d	21 43						22 13						22 44												
Southwick	d	21 45						22 15						22 46						23 27				23 58	00s28	
Shoreham-by-Sea	d	21 49		22 01				22 19			22 31			22 50		23 00				23 30				00 01	00s31	
Lancing	d	21 53		22 05				22 23			22 35			22 54		23 04				23 34				00 05	00s35	
East Worthing	d	21 56						22 26						22 57												
Worthing 4	a	21 58		22 09				22 28			22 39			22 59		23 08				23 38				00 09	00s39	
	d	21 59		22 10				22 29			22 39			23 00		23 08				23 39						
West Worthing	d	22 01		22 12				22 31			22 41			23 02		23 10				23 41					00s41	
Durrington-on-Sea	d	22 03		22 14				22 33			22 44			23 04		23 13				23 43					00s44	
Goring-by-Sea	d	22 06		22 17				22 36			22 46			23 07		23 15				23 46					00s46	
Angmering 3	d	22 10		22 21				22 40			22 50			23 11		23 19				23 50					00s50	
Littlehampton 4	a	22e28		22 31								23e34		23 19		23 28						00e10				
	d						22 38							23 24												
Ford 4	d	22 16					22 42	22 46			22 56	23 00		23 28						23 56		23 59			00s56	
Bognor Regis 4	d	22 00						22 30																		
Barnham	a	22 20					22 46	22 50			23 01	23 04		23 32						00 01		00 04			01s01	
					←					←			←										←			
	d	22 21			22 22		22 52 →	22 51		22 52	23 06 →	23 05	23 06	23 33					23 36	00 06 →		00 05	00 06			
Bognor Regis 4	a				22 28					22 58			23 12						23 42				00 12			
Chichester 4	d	22 29						22 59				23 13		23a40								00a12			01a09	
Fishbourne (Sussex)	d											23 16														
Bosham	d											23 19														
Nutbourne	d											23 22														
Southbourne	d	22 36										23 25														
Emsworth	d	22 39										23 28														
Warblington	d											23 31														
Havant	d	22 43						23 10				23 36														
Bedhampton	a																									
Hilsea	a																									
Fratton	a	22 52						23 18				23 47														
Portsmouth & Southsea	a	22 55						23 22				23 51														
Portsmouth Harbour	a	22 59						23 26																		
Cosham	a																									
Portchester	a																									
Fareham	a																									
Swanwick	a																									
Southampton Central	a																									

For general notes see front of timetable
For details of catering facilities see
Directory of Train Operators

b Change at East Croydon and Brighton
c Change at Haywards Heath and Brighton
e Change at Ford

Table 188

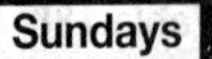

Sundays

London, Gatwick Airport & Brighton → Sussex Coast, Portsmouth and Southampton

For complete service between Three Bridges and Horsham see Table 186

		SN 1	SN 1	SN 1	SN 1	SN 1	SN 1	SN 1	SN 1	SN 1	SN 1	SN 1	SN 1		SN 1	SN 1	SN 1	SN 1	SN 1	SN 1	SN 1	SN 1	SN 1	SN 1	SN 1	
London Victoria 15 ⊖	d	22p17	22p32		22p47	*23 06*	23p17	00 05				*05 47*					07 02	*06 32*				*07 32*		08 04	08 17	
Clapham Junction 10	d	22p23	22p38		22p53	*23 12*	23p23	00 11				*05 53*					07 08	*06 38*				*07 38*		08 10	08 23	
London Bridge 4 ⊖	d					*23b00*	*23c11*	*23 53*													*07 11*	*07 41*		*07 44*	*08 11*	
East Croydon	d	22p33	22p48		23p03	*23 22*	23p33	00 25				*06 06*					07 23	*06 52*			*07 27*	*07 57*		08 23	08 37	
Gatwick Airport 10 ✈	d	22p51	23p09		23p19	*23e19*	23p51	00 43				*06 32*					07 47	*07 19*			*07 50*	*08 20*		08 47	08 56	
Three Bridges 4	d	22p55	23p15			*23 15*	23p56	00 48				*06 36*					07 52	*07 24*			*07 54*	*08 24*		08 52	*08 54*	
Crawley	d		23p18														07 55							08 55		
Horsham 4	d		23p27														08 08							09 05		
Christs Hospital	d		23p30																					09 08		
Billingshurst	d		23p36														08 16							09 14		
Pulborough	d		23p43														08 24							09 21		
Amberley	d		23p49																					09 27		
Arundel	d		23p54														08 33							09 32		
Haywards Heath 3	d	23p04			23p37	*23 45*	00 05	01 00				*06 47*						*07 36*			*08 03*	*08 33*			09 07	
Brighton 10	d					00 10						07 15			07 23			08 15		08 23	08 50	09 17				
Hove 2	d	23p21			23p52	00a13	00 22	01s22				07 18			07 26			08 18		08 26	08 53	09f26 →			09 24	
Aldrington	d														07 28					08 28	08 55					
Portslade	d	23p24			23p55		00s25	01s25							07 31					08 31	08 58					
Fishersgate	d														07 33					08 33	09 00					
Southwick	d	23p27			23p58		00s28	01s28							07 35					08 35	09 02					
Shoreham-by-Sea	d	23p30			00 01		00s31	01s31				07 24			07 38			08 24		08 38	09 05				09 30	
Lancing	d	23p34			00 05		00s35	01s35							07 42					08 42	09 09					
East Worthing	d														07 45					08 45	09 12					
Worthing 4	a	23p38			00 09		00s39	01 39				07 30			07 47			08 30		08 47	09 14				09 36	
	d	23p39										07 31			07 47			08 31		08 47	09 15				09 40	09 42
West Worthing	d	23p41					00s41								07 49					08 49	09 17					09 44
Durrington-on-Sea	d	23p43					00s44								07 52					08 52	09 19					09 46
Goring-by-Sea	d	23p46					00s46								07 54					08 54	09 22					09 49
Angmering 3	d	23p50					00s50					07 37			07 58			08 37		08 58	09 26					09 53
Littlehampton 4	a	*00g10*	*00g10*												08 07		*08g52*			09 07	09 35			*09g52*		10 02
	d									06 42	07 19		07 57		08 11				08 57	09 11						
Ford 4	d	23p56	23p59				00s56			06 46	07 23		08 01		08 15		08 38		09 01	09 15				09 39		
Bognor Regis 4	d											*07 36*			*07 57*			*08 36*		*08 57*					*09 36*	
Barnham	a	00 01	00 04	←			01s01			06 50	07 27	07 47	08 08		08 19	←	08 42	08 47	09 08	09 19			←	09 43	09 54	
	d	00 06	00 05	00 06					06 45	06 51	07 28	07 47	08 26		08 20	08 26	08 43	08 47	09 26	09 20			09 26	09 44	09 55	
Bognor Regis 4	a	→		00 12					06 51		07 34		→			08 32	08 49		→				09 32	09 50		
Chichester 4	d		00a12				01a09			06 59		07 55			08 28			08 55		09 28					10 03	
Fishbourne (Sussex)	d														08 31					09 31						
Bosham	d														08 34					09 34						
Nutbourne	d														08 37					09 37						
Southbourne	d											08 02			08 40			09 02		09 40					10 10	
Emsworth	d											08 05			08 43			09 05		09 43					10 13	
Warblington	d														08 46					09 46						
Havant	d									07 10		08 10			08 49			09 10		09 49					10 17	
Bedhampton	a														08 51					09 51						
Hilsea	a																									
Fratton	a									07 18		08 18			08 59			09 18		09 59					10 26	
Portsmouth & Southsea	a									07 22		08 22			09 03			09 22		10 03					10 29	
Portsmouth Harbour	a									07 26		08 26			09 07			09 26		10 07					10 35	
Cosham	a																									
Portchester	a																									
Fareham	a																									
Swanwick	a																									
Southampton Central	a																									

For general notes see front of timetable
For details of catering facilities see Directory of Train Operators

b Change at East Croydon and Brighton
c Change at Haywards Heath
e Change at Haywards Heath and Brighton
f Arr. 0920
g Change at Ford

Table 188

Sundays

London, Gatwick Airport & Brighton → Sussex Coast, Portsmouth and Southampton

For complete service between Three Bridges and Horsham see Table 186

		SN 1	SN 1		SN 1	SN 1	SN 1	SN 1	SN 1		SN 1	SN 1	SN 1	SN 1	SN 1	GW ◇ A		SN 1	SN 1		SN 1	SN 1	SN 1	SN 1	SN 1	SN 1
London Victoria 15 ⊖	d					07b34	08 32	09 04	09 17					08b47	10 04	09 32		09 32	10 17					09b47	10 32	11 04
Clapham Junction 10	d					07b40	08 38	09 10	09 23					08b53	10 10	09 38		09 38	10 23					09b53	10 38	11 10
London Bridge 4 ⊖	d					08 11	08 41	08 44	09 11					09 11	09 56	09 41		09 41	10 11					10 11	10 41	10 56
East Croydon	d					08 27	08 57	09 23	09 37					09 27	10 23	09 57		09 57	10 37					10 27	10 57	11 23
Gatwick Airport 10 ✈	d					08 50	09 20	09 47	09 56					09 50	10 47	10 20		10 20	10 56					10 50	11 20	11 47
Three Bridges 4	d					08 54	09 24	09 52	09 54					09 54	10 52	10 24		10 24	10 54					10 54	11 24	11 52
Crawley	d							09 55							10 55											11 55
Horsham 4	d							10 05							11 05											12 05
Christs Hospital	d							10 08							11 08											12 08
Billingshurst	d							10 14							11 14											12 14
Pulborough	d							10 21							11 21											12 21
Amberley	d							10 27							11 27											12 27
Arundel	d							10 32							11 32											12 32
Haywards Heath 3	d					09 03	09 33		10 07					10 03		10 33		10 33	11 07					11 03	11 33	
Brighton 10	d		←			09 50	10 17					←		10 50		11 10		11 17				←		11 50	12 17	
Hove 2	d		09 26			09 53	10c26		10 24			10 26		10 53		11 14		11e26	11 24			11 26		11 53	12f26	
Aldrington	d		09 28			09 55	→					10 28		10 55				→				11 28		11 55	→	
Portslade	d		09 31			09 58						10 31		10 58								11 31		11 58		
Fishersgate	d		09 33			10 00						10 33		11 00								11 33		12 00		
Southwick	d		09 35			10 02						10 35		11 02								11 35		12 02		
Shoreham-by-Sea	d		09 38			10 05			10 30			10 38		11 05		11 20			11 30			11 38		12 05		
Lancing	d		09 42			10 09						10 42		11 09								11 42		12 09		
East Worthing	d		09 45			10 12						10 45		11 12								11 45		12 12		
Worthing 4	a		09 47			10 14			10 36			10 47		11 14		11 26			11 36			11 47		12 14		
	d		09 48			10 15			10 40	10 42		10 48		11 15		11 29			11 40	11 42		11 48		12 15		
West Worthing	d		09 50			10 17				10 44		10 50		11 17						11 44		11 50		12 17		
Durrington-on-Sea	d		09 52			10 19				10 46		10 52		11 19						11 46		11 52		12 19		
Goring-by-Sea	d		09 55			10 22				10 49		10 55		11 22						11 49		11 55		12 22		
Angmering 3	d		09 59			10 26				10 53		10 59		11 26						11 53		11 59		12 26		
Littlehampton 4	a					10 35		10g52		11 02				11 35	11g52					12 02				12 35		12g52
	d	09 57									10 57										11 57					
Ford 4	d	10 01	10 05					10 38			11 01	11 05			11 38						12 01	12 05				12 38
Bognor Regis 4	d		09 57						10 36			10 57				11 36			11 36			11 57				
Barnham	a	10 08	10 11		←			10 42	10 54		11 08	11 11	←		11 42	11 45			11 54		12 08	12 11	←			12 42
	d	10 15	10 12		10 15			10 43	10 55		11 15	11 12	11 15		11 43	11 46			11 55		12 15	12 12	12 15			12 43
Bognor Regis 4	a	→			10 21			10 49			→		11 21		11 49						→		12 21			12 49
Chichester 4	d		10 20						11 03			11 20				11h58			12 03			12 20				
Fishbourne (Sussex)	d		10 23									11 23										12 23				
Bosham	d		10 26									11 26										12 26				
Nutbourne	d		10 29									11 29										12 29				
Southbourne	d		10 32									11 32										12 32				
Emsworth	d		10 35						11 10			11 35							12 10			12 35				
Warblington	d		10 38						11 13			11 38							12 13			12 38				
Havant	d		10 41						11 17			11 41				12 10			12 17			12 41				
Bedhampton	a		10 43									11 43										12 43				
Hilsea	a																									
Fratton	a		10 51						11 26			11 52							12 26			12 51				
Portsmouth & Southsea	a		10 54						11 29			11 55							12 29			12 54				
Portsmouth Harbour	a		10 58						11 35			11 59							12 35			12 58				
Cosham	a															12 16										
Portchester	a																									
Fareham	a															12 31										
Swanwick	a																									
Southampton Central	a															12 53										

For general notes see front of timetable
For details of catering facilities see Directory of Train Operators

A From 30 March to Bristol Parkway (Table 132)
b Change at East Croydon and Brighton
c Arr. 1020
e Arr. 1120
f Arr. 1220
g Change at Ford
h Arr. 1153

Table 188

London, Gatwick Airport & Brighton → Sussex Coast, Portsmouth and Southampton

For complete service between Three Bridges and Horsham see Table 186

		SN 1		SN 1	SN 1	SN 1		SN 1	SN 1	SN 1	SN 1		SN 1	SN 1	SN 1	SN 1	SN 1	SN 1	SN 1			SN 1	SN 1	SN 1	SN 1	SN 1
London Victoria 15 ⊖	d	11 17						10b47	11 32	12 04	12 17					11b47	12 32	13 04	13 17						12b47	13 32
Clapham Junction 10	d	11 23						10b53	11 38	12 10	12 23					11b53	12 38	13 10	13 23						12b53	13 38
London Bridge 4 ⊖	d	11 11						11 11	11 41	11 56	12 11					12 11	12 41	12 56	13 11						13 11	13 41
East Croydon	d	11 37						11 27	11 57	12 23	12 37					12 27	12 57	13 23	13 37						13 27	13 57
Gatwick Airport 10	d	11 56						11 50	12 20	12 47	12 56					12 50	13 20	13 47	13 56						13 50	14 20
Three Bridges 4	d	11 54						11 54	12 24	12 52	12 54					12 54	13 24	13 52	13 54						13 54	14 24
Crawley	d									12 55								13 55								
Horsham 4	d									13 05								14 05								
Christs Hospital	d									13 08								14 08								
Billingshurst	d									13 14								14 14								
Pulborough	d									13 21								14 21								
Amberley	d									13 27								14 27								
Arundel	d									13 32								14 32								
Haywards Heath 3	d	12 07						12 03	12 33		13 07					13 03	13 33		14 07						14 03	14 33
Brighton 10	d				←			12 50	13 17					←		13 50	14 17						←		14 50	15 17
Hove 2	d	12 24			12 26			12 53	13c26		13 24			13 26		13 53	14e26		14 24				14 26		14 53	15f26
Aldrington	d				12 28			12 55	→					13 28		13 55	→						14 28		14 55	→
Portslade	d				12 31			12 58						13 31		13 58							14 31		14 58	
Fishersgate	d				12 33			13 00						13 33		14 00							14 33		15 00	
Southwick	d				12 35			13 02						13 35		14 02							14 35		15 02	
Shoreham-by-Sea	d	12 30			12 38			13 05			13 30			13 38		14 05			14 30				14 38		15 05	
Lancing	d				12 42			13 09						13 42		14 09							14 42		15 09	
East Worthing	d				12 45			13 12						13 45		14 12							14 45		15 12	
Worthing 4	a	12 36			12 47			13 14			13 36			13 47		14 14			14 36				14 47		15 14	
	d	12 40	12 42		12 48			13 15			13 40	13 42		13 48		14 15			14 40	14 42			14 48		15 15	
West Worthing	d		12 44		12 50			13 17				13 44		13 50		14 17				14 44			14 50		15 17	
Durrington-on-Sea	d		12 46		12 52			13 19				13 46		13 52		14 19				14 46			14 52		15 19	
Goring-by-Sea	d		12 49		12 55			13 22				13 49		13 55		14 22				14 49			14 55		15 22	
Angmering 3	d		12 53		12 59			13 26				13 53		13 59		14 26				14 53			14 59		15 26	
Littlehampton 4	a		13 02					13 35		13g52		14 02				14 35		14g52		15 02					15 35	
	d			12 57									13 57									14 57				
Ford 4	d			13 01	13 05					13 38			14 01	14 05				14 38				15 01	15 05			
Bognor Regis 4	d	12 36			12 57						13 36			13 57					14 36				14 57			
Barnham	a	12 54		13 08	13 11	←				13 42	13 54		14 08	14 11	←			14 42	14 54			15 08	15 11	←		
	d	12 55		13 15	13 12	13 15				13 43	13 55		14 15	14 12	14 15			14 43	14 55			15 15	15 12	15 15		
Bognor Regis 4	a			→		13 21				13 49			→		14 21			14 49				→		15 21		
Chichester 4	d	13 03			13 20						14 03			14 20					15 03				15 20			
Fishbourne (Sussex)	d				13 23									14 23									15 23			
Bosham	d				13 26									14 26									15 26			
Nutbourne	d				13 29									14 29									15 29			
Southbourne	d	13 10			13 32						14 10			14 32					15 10				15 32			
Emsworth	d	13 13			13 35						14 13			14 35					15 13				15 35			
Warblington	d				13 38									14 38									15 38			
Havant	d	13 17			13 41						14 17			14 41					15 17				15 41			
Bedhampton	a				13 43									14 43									15 43			
Hilsea	a																									
Fratton	a	13 26			13 51						14 26			14 51					15 26				15 51			
Portsmouth & Southsea	a	13 29			13 54						14 29			14 54					15 29				15 54			
Portsmouth Harbour	a	13 35			13 58						14 35			14 58					15 35				15 58			
Cosham	a																									
Portchester	a																									
Fareham	a																									
Swanwick	a																									
Southampton Central	a																									

For general notes see front of timetable
For details of catering facilities see Directory of Train Operators

b Change at East Croydon and Brighton
c Arr. 1320
e Arr. 1420
f Arr. 1520
g Change at Ford

Table 188

Sundays

London, Gatwick Airport & Brighton → Sussex Coast, Portsmouth and Southampton

For complete service between Three Bridges and Horsham see Table 186

		SN 1	SN 1		SN 1	SN 1	SN 1	GW ◇	SN 1	SN 1		SN 1	SN 1		SN 1	SN 1	SN 1	SN 1	SN 1	SN 1	SN 1		SN 1		SN 1	SN 1
London Victoria 15 ⊖	d	14 04	14 17					13b47	13b47	14 32		15 04	15 17					14b47	15 32	16 04	16 17					
Clapham Junction 10	d	14 10	14 23					13b53	13b53	14 38		15 10	15 23					14b53	15 38	16 10	16 23					
London Bridge 4 ⊖	d	13 56	14 11					14 11	14 11	14 41		14 56	15 11					15 11	15 41	15 56	16 11					
East Croydon	d	14 23	14 37					14 27	14 27	14 57		15 23	15 37					15 27	15 57	16 23	16 37					
Gatwick Airport 10 ✈	d	14 47	14 56					14 50	14 50	15 20		15 47	15 56					15 50	16 20	16 47	16 56					
Three Bridges 4	d	14 52	14 54					14 54	14 54	15 24		15 52	15 54					15 54	16 24	16 52	16 54					
Crawley	d	14 55										15 55								16 55						
Horsham 4	d	15 05										16 05								17 05						
Christs Hospital	d	15 08										16 08								17 08						
Billingshurst	d	15 14										16 14								17 14						
Pulborough	d	15 21										16 21								17 21						
Amberley	d	15 27										16 27								17 27						
Arundel	d	15 32										16 32								17 32						
Haywards Heath 3	d		15 07					15 03	15 03	15 33			16 07					16 03	16 33		17 07					
Brighton 10	d					←		15 47	15 50	16 17						←		16 50	17 17						←	
Hove 2	d		15 24			15 26		15 51	15 53	16c26			16 24			16 26		16 53	17e26		17 24				17 26	
Aldrington	d					15 28			15 55	→						16 28		16 55	→						17 28	
Portslade	d					15 31			15 58							16 31		16 58							17 31	
Fishersgate	d					15 33			16 00							16 33		17 00							17 33	
Southwick	d					15 35			16 02							16 35		17 02							17 35	
Shoreham-by-Sea	d		15 30			15 38		15 57	16 05				16 30			16 38		17 05			17 30				17 38	
Lancing	d					15 42			16 09							16 42		17 09							17 42	
East Worthing	d					15 45			16 12							16 45		17 12							17 45	
Worthing 4	a		15 36			15 47		16 03	16 14				16 36			16 47		17 14			17 36				17 47	
	d		15 40	15 42		15 48		16 08	16 15				16 40	16 42		16 48		17 15			17 40	17 42			17 48	
West Worthing	d			15 44		15 50			16 17					16 44		16 50		17 17				17 44			17 50	
Durrington-on-Sea	d			15 46		15 52			16 19					16 46		16 52		17 19				17 46			17 52	
Goring-by-Sea	d			15 49		15 55			16 22					16 49		16 55		17 22				17 49			17 55	
Angmering 3	d			15 53		15 59			16 26					16 53		16 59		17 26				17 53			17 59	
Littlehampton 4	a	15f52		16 02					16 35			16f52		17 02				17 35		17f52		18 02				
	d				15 57										16 57								17 57			
Ford 4	d	15 38			16 01	16 05						16 38			17 01	17 05				17 38			18 01		18 05	
Bognor Regis 4	d		15 36			15 57							16 36			16 57					17 36				17 57	
Barnham	a	15 42	15 54		16 08	16 11	←	16 25				16 42	16 54		17 08	17 11	←			17 42	17 54		18 08		18 11	←
	d	15 43	15 55		16 15	16 12	16 15	16 25				16 43	16 55		17 15	17 12	17 15			17 43	17 55		18 15		18 12	18 15
Bognor Regis 4	a	15 49			→		16 21					16 49			→		17 21			17 49			→			18 21
Chichester 4	d		16 03			16 20		16 34					17 03			17 20					18 03				18 20	
Fishbourne (Sussex)	d					16 23										17 23									18 23	
Bosham	d					16 26										17 26									18 26	
Nutbourne	d					16 29										17 29									18 29	
Southbourne	d		16 10			16 32							17 10			17 32					18 10				18 32	
Emsworth	d		16 13			16 35							17 13			17 35					18 13				18 35	
Warblington	d					16 38										17 38									18 38	
Havant	d		16 17			16 41		16 48					17 17			17 41					18 17				18 41	
Bedhampton	a					16 43										17 43									18 43	
Hilsea	a																									
Fratton	a		16 26			16 51							17 26			17 51					18 26				18 51	
Portsmouth & Southsea	a		16 29			16 54							17 29			17 54					18 29				18 54	
Portsmouth Harbour	a		16 35			16 58							17 35			17 58					18 35				18 58	
Cosham	a							16 54																		
Portchester	a																									
Fareham	a							17 02																		
Swanwick	a																									
Southampton Central	a							17 24																		

For general notes see front of timetable
For details of catering facilities see Directory of Train Operators

b Change at East Croydon and Brighton
c Arr. 1620
e Arr. 1720
f Change at Ford

Table 188 **Sundays**

London, Gatwick Airport & Brighton → Sussex Coast, Portsmouth and Southampton

For complete service between Three Bridges and Horsham see Table 186

		GW ◇	SN 1	SN 1	SN 1	SN 1		SN 1	SN 1	SN 1	SN 1	SN 1	SN 1		SN 1		SN 1	SN 1	SN 1	SN 1	SN 1	SN 1	SN 1		SN 1	SN 1
London Victoria 15 ⊖	d	15b47	15b47	17 02	17 04	17 17						18 02	18 04		18 17						19 02	19 04	19 17			
Clapham Junction 10	d	15b53	15b53	17 07	17 10	17 23						18 07	18 10		18 23						19 07	19 10	19 23			
London Bridge 4 ⊖	d	16 11	16 11	16b44	16 56	17 11					17 11	17b44	17 44		18 11					18 11	18b44	18 44	19 11			
East Croydon	d	16 27	16 27	17 20	17 24	17 37					17 27	18 20	18 24		18 37					18 27	19 20	19 24	19 37			
Gatwick Airport 10 ✈	d	16 50	16 50	17 42	17 47	17 56					17 50	18 42	18 47		18 56					18 50	19 42	19 47	19 56			
Three Bridges 4	d	16 54	16 54	17 24	17 52	17 54					17 54	18 24	18 52		18 54					18 54	19 24	19 52	19 54			
Crawley	d				17 55								18 55									19 55				
Horsham 4	d				18 05								19 05									20 05				
Christs Hospital	d				18 08								19 08									20 08				
Billingshurst	d				18 14								19 14									20 14				
Pulborough	d				18 21								19 21									20 21				
Amberley	d				18 27								19 27									20 27				
Arundel	d				18 32								19 32									20 32				
Haywards Heath 3	d	17 03	17 03	17 33		18 07					18 03	18 33			19 07					19 03	19 33		20 07			
Brighton 10	d	17 47	17 50	18 17					←		18 50	19 17						←		19 50	20 17					←
Hove 2	d	17 51	17 53	18c26 →		18 24			18 26		18 53	19e26 →			19 24			19 26		19 53	20f26 →		20 24			20 26
Aldrington	d		17 55						18 28		18 55							19 28		19 55						20 28
Portslade	d		17 58						18 31		18 58							19 31		19 58						20 31
Fishersgate	d		18 00						18 33		19 00							19 33		20 00						20 33
Southwick	d		18 02						18 35		19 02							19 35		20 02						20 35
Shoreham-by-Sea	d	17 57	18 05			18 30			18 38		19 05				19 30			19 38		20 05			20 30			20 38
Lancing	d		18 09						18 42		19 09							19 42		20 09						20 42
East Worthing	d		18 12						18 45		19 12							19 45		20 12						20 45
Worthing 4	a	18 03	18 14			18 36			18 47		19 14				19 36			19 47		20 14			20 36			20 47
	d	18 08	18 15			18 40	18 42		18 48		19 15				19 40	19 42		19 48		20 15			20 40	20 42		20 48
West Worthing	d		18 17				18 44		18 50		19 17					19 44		19 50		20 17				20 44		20 50
Durrington-on-Sea	d		18 19				18 46		18 52		19 19					19 46		19 52		20 19				20 46		20 52
Goring-by-Sea	d		18 22				18 49		18 55		19 22					19 49		19 55		20 22				20 49		20 55
Angmering 3	d		18 26				18 53		18 59		19 26					19 53		19 59		20 26				20 53		20 59
Littlehampton 4	a		18 35		18g52		19 02				19 35		19g52			20 02				20 35		20g52		21 02		21g31
	d							18 57									19 57								20 57	
Ford 4	d				18 38			19 01	19 05				19 38				20 01	20 05				20 38			21 01	21 05
Bognor Regis 4	d					18 36			18 57						19 36			19 57					20 36			20 57
Barnham	a	18 25			18 42	18 54		19 08	19 11	←			19 42		19 54		20 08	20 11	←			20 42	20 54		21 08	21 11
	d	18 25			18 43	18 55		19 15 →	19 12	19 15			19 43		19 55		20 15 →	20 12	20 15			20 43	20 55		21 15 →	21 12
Bognor Regis 4	a				18 49					19 21			19 49						20 21			20 49				
Chichester 4	d	18 34				19 03			19 20						20 03			20 20					21 03			21 20
Fishbourne (Sussex)	d								19 23									20 23								21 23
Bosham	d								19 26									20 26								21 26
Nutbourne	d								19 29									20 29								21 29
Southbourne	d					19 10			19 32						20 10			20 32					21 10			21 32
Emsworth	d					19 13			19 35						20 13			20 35					21 13			21 35
Warblington	d								19 38									20 38								21 38
Havant	d	18 48				19 17			19 41						20 17			20 41					21 17			21 41
Bedhampton	a								19 43									20 43								21 43
Hilsea	a																									
Fratton	a					19 26			19 51						20 26			20 51					21 26			21 51
Portsmouth & Southsea	a					19 29			19 54						20 29			20 54					21 29			21 54
Portsmouth Harbour	a					19 35			19 58						20 35			20 58					21 35			21 58
Cosham	a																									
Portchester	a																									
Fareham	a	19 00																								
Swanwick	a																									
Southampton Central	a	19 22																								

For general notes see front of timetable
For details of catering facilities see Directory of Train Operators

b Change at East Croydon and Brighton
c Arr. 1820
e Arr. 1920
f Arr. 2020
g Change at Ford

Sundays

London, Gatwick Airport & Brighton → Sussex Coast, Portsmouth and Southampton

For complete service between Three Bridges and Horsham see Table 186

Station																									
		SN 1	SN 1		SN 1	SN 1	SN 1		SN 1	SN 1	SN 1	SN 1	SN 1	SN 1		SN 1		SN 1	SN 1	SN 1	SN 1	SN 1	SN 1	SN 1		
London Victoria 15 ⊖	d				20 02	20 04	20 17						21 04	21 17					20b47	21 32	22 04	22 17		23 17		
Clapham Junction 10	d				20 07	20 10	20 23						21 10	21 23					20b53	21 38	22 10	22 23		23 23		
London Bridge 4 ⊖	d		19 11		19b44	19 44	20 11					20 11	20 44	21 11					21 11	21 41	21 44	22 11		23 11		
East Croydon	d		19 27		20 20	20 23	20 37					20 27	21 23	21 37					21 27	21 57	22 23	22 37		23 37		
Gatwick Airport 10 ✈	d		19 50		20c42	20 47	20 56					20 50	21 47	21 56					21 50	22 20	22 47	22 56		00 02		
Three Bridges 4	d		19 54		20 24	20 52	20 54					20 54	21 52	21 54					21 54	22 24	22 52	22 54		00 07		
Crawley	d					20 55							21 55								22 55					
Horsham 4	d					21 05							22 05								23 05					
Christs Hospital	d					21 08							22 08								23 08					
Billingshurst	d					21 14							22 14								23 14					
Pulborough	d					21 21							22 21								23 21					
Amberley	d					21 27							22 27								23 27					
Arundel	d					21 32							22 32								23 32					
Haywards Heath 3	d		20 03		20e33		21 07					21 03		22 07					22 03	22 33		23 07		00 16		
Brighton 10	d		20 50		21 17					←		21 50							22 40	23 15						
Hove 2	d		20 53		21f26		21 24			21 26		21 53		22 24					22 43	23a18		23 24		00 31		
Aldrington	d		20 55		→					21 28		21 55							22 45							
Portslade	d		20 58							21 31		21 58							22 48			23 27		00s34		
Fishersgate	d		21 00							21 33		22 00							22 50							
Southwick	d		21 02							21 35		22 02							22 52			23 30		00s37		
Shoreham-by-Sea	d		21 05				21 30			21 38		22 05		22 30					22 55			23 33		00s40		
Lancing	d		21 09							21 42		22 09							22 59			23 37		00s44		
East Worthing	d		21 12							21 45		22 12							23 02							
Worthing 4	a		21 14				21 36			21 47		22 14		22 36					23 04			23 41		00 48		
	d		21 15				21 40	21 42		21 48		22 15		22 40	22 42				23 04							
West Worthing	d		21 17					21 44		21 50		22 17			22 44				23 06							
Durrington-on-Sea	d		21 19					21 46		21 52		22 19			22 46				23 09							
Goring-by-Sea	d		21 22					21 49		21 55		22 22			22 49				23 11							
Angmering 3	d		21 26					21 53		21 59		22 26			22 53				23 15							
Littlehampton 4	a		21 35			21g52		22 02		22g31		22 35	23g10		23 02			23g32	23 24		23g46					
	d								21 57									23 06	23 29							
Ford 4	d					21 38			22 01	22 05			22 38					23 10	23 33		23 38					
Bognor Regis 4	d						21 36			21 57				22 11												
Barnham	a	←				21 42	21 54		22 08	22 11	←		22 42	22 54				23 14	23 37		23 42		←			
	d	21 15				21 43	21 55		22 15	22 12	22 15		22 43	22 55		22 56		23 15	23 45		23 43		23 45			
Bognor Regis 4	a	21 21				21 49			→		22 21		22 49			23 02		23 21	→		23 49					
Chichester 4	d						22 03			22 20				23 03									23a52			
Fishbourne (Sussex)	d									22 23																
Bosham	d									22 26				23 07												
Nutbourne	d									22 29				23 11												
Southbourne	d						22 10			22 32				23 13												
Emsworth	d						22 13			22 35				23 16												
Warblington	d									22 38																
Havant	d						22 17			22 41				23 21												
Bedhampton	a									22 43																
Hilsea	a																									
Fratton	a						22 26			22 51				23 31												
Portsmouth & Southsea	a						22 29			22 54				23 34												
Portsmouth Harbour	a						22 35			22 58				23 38												
Cosham	a																									
Portchester	a																									
Fareham	a																									
Swanwick	a																									
Southampton Central	a																									

For general notes see front of timetable
For details of catering facilities see Directory of Train Operators

b Change at East Croydon and Brighton
c Until 27 January dep. 2045
e Until 27 January dep. 2054
f Arr. 2120
g Change at Ford

Table 188

Southampton, Portsmouth and Sussex Coast → Brighton, Gatwick Airport & London

For complete service between Horsham and Three Bridges see Table 186

Miles	Miles	Miles	Station		SN MX 1	SN MX 1	SN MX 1	SN 1	SN 1	SN 1	SN 1	SN 1	SN 1	SN 1	SN 1	SN 1	SN 1	SN 1	SN 1	SN 1	SN 1	SN 1	SN 1	SN 1	SN 1
0	—	—	**Southampton Central**	d																					
10¾	—	—	Swanwick	d																					
14½	—	—	Fareham	d																					
17¾	—	—	Portchester	d																					
20¼	—	—	Cosham	d																					
—	0	—	**Portsmouth Harbour**	d	22p44		23p15														05 34		05 47		
—	¾	—	Portsmouth & Southsea	d	22p48		23p19														05 38		05 51		
—	1½	—	Fratton	d	22p52		23p23														05 42		05 55		
—	4¼	—	Hilsea	d	22p56		23p27														05 46		05 59		
—	7¼	—	Bedhampton	d	23p01		23p33														05 51		06 04		
24¼	8	—	**Havant**	d	23p04		23p36			05 01						05 38					05 54		06 07		
—	8½	—	Warblington	d			23p38														05 56				
—	9¾	—	Emsworth	d			23p41														05 59		06 11		
—	11¼	—	Southbourne	d			23p44														06 02		06 14		
—	12¼	—	Nutbourne	d			23p47														06 04				
—	14	—	Bosham	d			23p50														06 08		06 18		
—	15¼	—	Fishbourne (Sussex)	d			23p53														06 11		06 21		
—	16¾	—	**Chichester** 4	d	23p17	23p52	23p57			05 16						05 51					06 15		06 26		
0	—	—	**Bognor Regis** 4	d					05 13				05 35	05 49					06 04	06 11					
3½	23	—	Barnham	a	23p24	23p59	00 05		05 19	05 23	←		05 41	05 55		05 58		←	06 10	06 17	06 22		06 34		
—	—	—		d	23p25	00 01	00 06	04 47	05 27 →	05 24	05 27		05 42	06 02 →		05 59		06 02	06 11	06 18	06 23		06 34		
—	—	—	Bognor Regis 4	a						*05 42*						*06 12*					*06 35*				
0	25¾	0	Ford 4	d	23p29	00 05	00 10	04 51			05 31		05 46					06 06	06 15		06 27				
—	—	2	**Littlehampton** 4	a	23p34	00 10	00 15	04 56			05 36								06 20						
2	—	—		d	23p39			05 01					*05b35*		05 50			*05b57*						06 33	
8	30	—	Angmering 3	d	23p47			05 09		05 33			05 53		06 01			06 13			06 33			06 41	
—	32½	—	Goring-by-Sea	d	23p51			05 13					05 57		06 05			06 17			06 37			06 45	
—	33¼	—	Durrington-on-Sea	d	23p53			05 15					05 59		06 08			06 19			06 40			06 47	
—	34	—	West Worthing	d	23p55			05 18					06 01		06 10			06 21			06 42			06 50	
—	35	—	**Worthing** 4	a	23p58			05 20		05 40			06 04		06 12			06 24			06 44			06 52	
—	—	—		d	23p59			05 21		05 41			06 04		06 13			06 24			06 45			06 53	
—	35¾	—	East Worthing	d	00 01			05 23					06 07					06 27			06 47				
—	37¼	—	Lancing	d	00 04			05 26		05 45			06 10		06 17			06 30			06 50			06 57	
—	40	—	Shoreham-by-Sea	d	00 08			05 31		05 49			06 14		06 21			06 34			06 54			07 01	
—	41	—	Southwick	d	00 11			05 34					06 17					06 37			06 57				
—	42	—	Fishersgate	d	00 13			05 36					06 19					06 39			06 59			07 06	
—	42½	—	Portslade	d	00 15			05 38		05 53			06 21		06 26			06 41			07 01				
—	43½	—	Aldrington	d	00 18			05 40					06 23					06 43			07 04				
0	44	—	Hove 2	d	00 20			05 43		05 57		05 59	06 26		06 30		06 36	06 46			07 06			07 11	07 17
—	45½	—	**Brighton** 10	a	00 25			05 47				06 03	06 30				06 40	06 50			07 10				07 21
13	—	—	Haywards Heath 3	a				*06 19*		06 12		*06 29*	*06 57*		06 52		*07 08*	*07 23*			*07 36*			07 29	*07 46*
—	—	2¼	Arundel	d												06 07				06 26					
—	—	6	Amberley	d																06 31					
—	—	10¾	Pulborough	d												06 16				06 37					
—	—	15¾	Billingshurst	d												06 23				06 44					
—	—	20½	Christs Hospital	d												06 29				06 50					
—	—	23	**Horsham** 4	d												06 35				06 55			07 04		
—	—	30	Crawley	d												06 49				07 08		←	07 13		
21½	—	31½	**Three Bridges** 4	a				*06 36*		06 21		*06 40*			07 24	06 52	07c24	07 32		07 12 →		07 12	07 17		*07 56*
24¾	—	—	**Gatwick Airport** 10 ✈	a				*06 41*		06 25		*06 45*	*07 11*		07 11	07 02	*07 21*	*07 37*					*07 29*		*08 00*
40½	0	—	**East Croydon**	a				*06 58*		06 41		*07 01*	*07 28*		07 28	07 31	*07 38*	*07 53*			*08 03*	07 43	07 43	07 57	*08 23*
—	10¼	—	London Bridge 4 ⊖	a				*07 14*		*07 14*		*07 16*	*07 46*		07 46	07 48	*08e03*	*08e18*			*08e26*	*08 11*			*08 41*
48¼	—	—	Clapham Junction 10	a						06 51		*07e19*			*07f47*	07g39	*07 47*	*08e10*			*08 13*	07 54		08 06	*08e40*
51	—	61	**London Victoria** 15 ⊖	a						07 00		*07h20*	*07h50*		*07j50*	07g48	*07 57*	*08c16*			*08 22*	08 03		08 16	*08h35*

For general notes see front of timetable
For details of catering facilities see Directory of Train Operators

b Change at Ford
c Change at Brighton and Haywards Heath
e Change at Brighton and East Croydon
f Change at East Croydon
g Change at Three Bridges and East Croydon
h Change at Brighton and Gatwick Airport
j Change at Gatwick Airport

Southampton, Portsmouth and Sussex Coast → Brighton, Gatwick Airport & London

For complete service between Horsham and Three Bridges see Table 186

		SN 1	SN 1	SN 1	SN 1	SN 1	SN 1	SN 1	SN 1	SN 1	SN 1	SN 1	SN 1	SN 1	SN 1	SN 1	SN 1	GW	SN 1	SN 1	SN 1	SN 1	SN 1	SN 1	SN 1
Southampton Central	d									05 48			06 10										07 06		
Swanwick	d									06 06			06 27										07 24		
Fareham	d									06 13			06 34										07 31		
Portchester	d									06 18			06 40										07 36		
Cosham	d									06 23			06 44										07 40		
Portsmouth Harbour	d			06 04											06 46			07 01			07 20				
Portsmouth & Southsea	d			06 08											06 50			07 05			07 24				
Fratton	d			06 12											06 54			07 10			07 28				
Hilsea	d														06 58										
Bedhampton	d									06 34					07 03										
Havant	d			06 20						06 37			06 53		07 06			07 20			07 36		07 47		
Warblington	d									06 39					07 08								07 49		
Emsworth	d			06 24						06 42			06 57		07 11								07 52		
Southbourne	d			06 27						06 45			07 00		07 14								07 55		
Nutbourne	d									06 48					07 16								07 58		
Bosham	d									06 51					07 20								08 01		
Fishbourne (Sussex)	d									06 54					07 23								08 04		
Chichester 4	d			06 35						06 59			07 08		07 28			07 32			07 47		08 08		
Bognor Regis 4	d	06 31			06 41			06 50	06 57					07 17						07 38		07 55			
Barnham	a	06 37		06 42	06 47			06 56	07 03	07 07			07 15	07 23	07 35			07 39		07 44	07 55	08 01	08 16		
	d	06 38		06 43	06 48			06 57	07 11				07 16	07 24	07 36			07 40		07 45	07 55	08 02	08 16		
Bognor Regis 4	a			*06 54*					*07 20*						*07 45*			*07 58*			*08 13*		*08 35*		
Ford 4	d	06 42		06 47	06 52			07 01					07 20							07 49	08 00	08 06			
Littlehampton 4	a	06 47						07 06												07 54					
	d		06 43	*06b39*							07 03		*07b00*				07 33		07 45			*07b58*		08 01	08 15
Angmering 3	d		06 51	06 56							07 11		07 26				07 41		07 53		08 06			08 10	08 23
Goring-by-Sea	d		06 55	07 00							07 15		07 30				07 45		07 57					08 14	08 27
Durrington-on-Sea	d		06 57	07 03							07 17		07 33				07 47		08 00		08 12			08 17	08 30
West Worthing	d		07 00	07 05		07 12					07 20		07 35			07 42	07 50		08 02					08 19	08 32
Worthing 4	a		07 02	07 07		07 14					07 22		07 37			07 44	07 52	07 56	08 04		08 16			08 21	08 34
	d		07 03	07 08		07 15					07 23		07 38			07 45	07 53	08 00	08 05		08 16			08 22	08 35
East Worthing	d					07 17										07 47			08 07					08 24	
Lancing	d		07 07	07 12		07 20					07 27		07 42			07 50	07 57		08 10		08 20			08 27	08 39
Shoreham-by-Sea	d		07 11	07 16		07 25					07 31		07 46			07 55	08 01	08 06	08 15		08 24			08 32	08 43
Southwick	d			07 19		07 28							07 49			07 58			08 18		08 27			08 35	
Fishersgate	d					07 30										08 00			08 20					08 37	
Portslade	d		07 16	07 22		07 32					07 36		07 52			08 02	08 06		08 22		08 31			08 39	08 48
Aldrington	d					07 34										08 04			08 24					08 41	
Hove 2	d		07 20	07 26		07 37					07 41	07 49	07 56			08 07	08 11	08 13	08 27		08 34			08 44	08 52
Brighton 10	a			07 30		07 41	←					07 53	08 00			08 11		08 19	08 31		08 38			08 48	
Haywards Heath 3	a		07 40			*08 05*	07 40				07 58	*08 23*				*08 37*	08 31		*08 55*		*08 57*			*09 16*	09 12
Arundel	d				06 57				07 18					07 32								08 11			
Amberley	d													07 37								08 16			
Pulborough	d				07 06				07 28					07 43								08 23			
Billingshurst	d				07 13				07 35					07 50								08 30			
Christs Hospital	d				07 19				07 41					07 57								08 36			
Horsham 4	d				07 25				07 46					08c09	08e09							08f49	08g49		
Crawley	d				07 37				08 01					08 18								08 58			
Three Bridges 4	a		*07 56*		07 40	*08h27*			08 05		*08 27*	*08 33*		08 22		*08 47*	08 41				*09h11*	09 01		*09 26*	*09 26*
Gatwick Airport 10 ✈	a		*08 00*		*07 48*	*08 22*					08 12	*08 38*				*08 51*	*08 51*				*09 10*	09 06		*09 31*	09 26
East Croydon	a		→		08 00	*08 34*	08 08		08 27		08 29	*08 54*		08 43		*09 08*	09 01				*09 26*	09 22		*09 47*	09 42
London Bridge 4 ⊖	a				*08 24*	*08j59*	08 26		08 44		*08k49*	*09 10*		*09 07*		*09j42*					*09j45*	*09 45*		*10 00*	*10 00*
Clapham Junction 10	a				08 10	*08 43*	*08m24*		*08m43*		08 40	*09j10*		08 53		*09j23*	09 10				*09 35*	09 32		*10j03*	09 52
London Victoria 15 ⊖	a				08 20	*08 52*	*08m33*		*08m52*		08 49	*09j19*		09 02		*09j33*	09 19				*09 44*	09 42			10 00

For general notes see front of timetable
For details of catering facilities see Directory of Train Operators

b Change at Ford
c Arr. 0801
e Arr. 0805
f Arr. 0840
g Arr. 0845
h Change at Brighton and Haywards Heath
j Change at Brighton and East Croydon
k Change at Haywards Heath
m Change at East Croydon

Southampton, Portsmouth and Sussex Coast → Brighton, Gatwick Airport & London

For complete service between Horsham and Three Bridges see Table 186

		SN 1		SN 1	SN 1	SN 1 🚌	SN 1	SN 1	SN 1	SN 1 🚌	SN 1	SN 1	SN 1	SN 1	SN 1	SN 1	SN 1		SN 1	SN 1	SN 1	SN 1	SN 1	SN 1	SN 1	SN 1
Southampton Central	d						07 36															08 10				
Swanwick	d						07 53															08 28				
Fareham	d						08 00															08 35				
Portchester	d																					08 40				
Cosham	d						08 08															08 44				
Portsmouth Harbour	d										08 10					08 26										
Portsmouth & Southsea	d								08 03		08 14					08 30										
Fratton	d								08 07		08 18					08 35										
Hilsea	d								08 11																	
Bedhampton	d								08 16																	
Havant	d						08 15		08 19		08 27					08 45						08 51				
Warblington	d								08 21													08 53				
Emsworth	d								08 24		08 31											08 56				
Southbourne	d								08 27													08 59				
Nutbourne	d								08 29																	
Bosham	d						08 22															09 03				
Fishbourne (Sussex)	d						08 25																			
Chichester 4	d						08 30		08 36		08 41					08 56			09 03			09b11				
Bognor Regis 4	d			08 13	08 19	08 26		08 32					08 49				09 00			09 09						09 26
Barnham	a			08 19	08 25	08 32	08 37	08 38	08 43		08 48		08 55			09 03	09 06		09 10	09 15		09 18				09 32
	d			08 20	08 26	08 33	08 38		08 44		08 49					09 04	09 07		09 11			09 19				09 33
Bognor Regis 4	a						08 52				08 58					09 14						09 28				
Ford 4	d			08 24	08 30	08 37			08 48							09 08	09 11		09 15							09 37
Littlehampton 4	a				08 35				08 53										09 20							
	d					08c26						08 45				08c58							09 15			
Angmering 3	d			08 30			08 47					08 53				09 14							09 23			
Goring-by-Sea	d			08 34								08 57				09 18							09 27			
Durrington-on-Sea	d			08 37			08 52					09 00				09 21							09 30			
West Worthing	d			08 39								09 02			09 09	09 23							09 32		09 39	
Worthing 4	a			08 41			08 56					09 04			09 11	09 25							09 34		09 41	
	d			08 42			08 57					09 05			09 12	09 26							09 36		09 42	
East Worthing	d			08 44											09 14										09 44	
Lancing	d			08 47			09 01					09 09			09 17	09 30									09 47	
Shoreham-by-Sea	d			08 52			09 05					09 13			09 22	09 34							09 42		09 52	
Southwick	d			08 55			09 08								09 25	09 37									09 55	
Fishersgate	d			08 57											09 27										09 57	
Portslade	d			08 59			09 11					09 18			09 29	09 40							09 47		09 59	
Aldrington	d			09 01											09 31										10 01	
Hove 2	d	08 54		09 04			09 15					09 22		09 24	09 34	09 44							09 51	09 54	10 04	
Brighton 10	a	08 58		09 08			09 19							09 28	09 38	09 48								09 58	10 08	
Haywards Heath 3	a	09 25		09 32								09 40		09 47		10 15							10 06	10 18		
Arundel	d					08 42											09 16									09 42
Amberley	d					08 47																				09 47
Pulborough	d					08 53											09 25									09 53
Billingshurst	d					09 00											09 31									09 59
Christs Hospital	d					09 06 →				← 09 06							09 38 →				← 09 38					10 06 →
Horsham 4	d									09e20	09f20										09g50	09h50				
Crawley	d									09 29											09 59					
Three Bridges 4	a	09 36								09 32				10 07		10 25					10 02			10 42		
Gatwick Airport 10 ✈	a	09 41		09 44						09 37		09 55		10 00							10 07		10 24	10 30		
East Croydon	a			09 55						09 59		10 11		10 16	10 24						10 28		10 40	10 46	10 55	
London Bridge 4 ⊖	a	10 15		10j22						10k15				10 30	10j45						10m45			11 00	11j15	
Clapham Junction 10	a			10 05						10 09		10 21			10 33						10 37		10 49	11j03	11 04	
London Victoria 15 ⊖	a			10 13						10 16		10 28		10n35	10 40						10 45		10 58	11n05	11 11	

For general notes see front of timetable
For details of catering facilities see Directory of Train Operators

b Arr. 0908
c Change at Ford
e Arr. 0910
f Arr. 0916
g Arr. 0942
h Arr. 0946
j Change at Brighton and East Croydon
k Change at Three Bridges
m Change at Gatwick Airport
n Change at Brighton and Gatwick Airport

Southampton, Portsmouth and Sussex Coast → Brighton, Gatwick Airport & London

For complete service between Horsham and Three Bridges see Table 186

		SN 1	SN 1	SN 1	SN 1	SN 1	SN 1	SN 1	SN 1		SN 1	SN 1	SN 1	SN 1	SN 1	SN 1	SN 1	SN 1	SN 1	SN 1	SN 1	SN 1	SN 1	SN 1		SN 1
							trolley					trolley		trolley					trolley				trolley			trolley
Southampton Central	d	08 36													09 11					09 36						
Swanwick	d	08 53													09 28					09 53						
Fareham	d	09 00													09 36					10 00						
Portchester	d														09 41											
Cosham	d	09 08													09 45					10 08						
Portsmouth Harbour	d		08 59			09 12					09 28													10 12		
Portsmouth & Southsea	d		09 03			09 16					09 32										10 03			10 16		
Fratton	d		09 07			09 20					09 36										10 07			10 20		
Hilsea	d		09 11																		10 11					
Bedhampton	d		09 16																		10 16					
Havant	d	09 15	09 19			09 30					09 45				09 52					10 15	10 19			10 30		
Warblington	d														09 54											
Emsworth	d	09 19	09 23												09 57					10 19	10 23					
Southbourne	d	09 22	09 26												10 00					10 22	10 26					
Nutbourne	d		09 28																		10 28					
Bosham	d														10 04											
Fishbourne (Sussex)	d		09 33																		10 33					
Chichester 4	d	09 30	09 37			09 41					09 56				10 11					10 30	10 37			10 41		
Bognor Regis 4	d			09 39								10 00	10 07						10 26			10 39				
Barnham	a	09 37	09 44	09 45		09 48					10 03	10 06	10 13		10 18				10 32	10 37	10 44	10 45		10 48		
	d	09 38	09 45			09 49					10 04	10 07	10 15		10 19				10 33	10 38	10 45			10 49		
Bognor Regis 4	a	*09 47*				*09 58*					*10 18*				*10 28*									*10 58*		
Ford 4	d		09 49								10 08	10 11	10 19						10 37		10 49					
Littlehampton 4	a		09 54										10 24								10 54					
	d						09 45				*09b54*					10 15										10 45
Angmering 3	d	09 47					09 53				10 14					10 23				10 47						10 53
Goring-by-Sea	d						09 57				10 18					10 27										10 57
Durrington-on-Sea	d						10 00				10 21					10 30										11 00
West Worthing	d						10 02		10 09		10 23					10 32		10 39								11 02
Worthing 4	a	09 54					10 04		10 11		10 25					10 34		10 41		10 54						11 04
	d	09 56					10 06		10 12		10 26					10 36		10 42		10 56						11 06
East Worthing	d								10 14									10 44								
Lancing	d	10 00					10 10		10 17		10 30							10 47		11 00						11 10
Shoreham-by-Sea	d	10 04					10 14		10 22		10 34					10 42		10 52		11 04						11 14
Southwick	d	10 07							10 25		10 37							10 55		11 07						
Fishersgate	d								10 27									10 57								
Portslade	d	10 10							10 29		10 40					10 47		10 59		11 10						
Aldrington	d								10 31									11 01								
Hove 2	d	10 14					10 21	10 24	10 34		10 44					10 51	10 54	11 04		11 14						11 21
Brighton 10	a	10 18						10 28	10 38		10 48						10 58	11 08		11 18						
Haywards Heath 3	a						10 35	*10 47*			*11 15*					11 08	*11 18*									11 35
Arundel	d											10 16							10 42							
Amberley	d																		10 47							
Pulborough	d											10 25							10 53							
Billingshurst	d				←							10 31 →		← 10 31					10 59				←			
Christs Hospital	d				10 06														11 06 →				11 06			
Horsham 4	d				10c20	10e20								10f50	10g50								11h20	11j20		
Crawley	d				10 29									10 59									11 29			
Three Bridges 4	a				10 32			*11 11*			*11 25*			11 02			*11 42*						11 32			
Gatwick Airport 10 ✈	a				10 37		10 54	*11 00*						11 07		11 24	*11 30*						11 37			11 54
East Croydon	a				10 59		11 11	*11 16*	*11 23*					11 27		11 40	*11 46*	*11 55*					12 00			12 10
London Bridge 4 ⊖	a				*11k15*			*11 30*	11m45					*11 45*			*12 00*	*12m15*					*12k15*			
Clapham Junction 10	a				11 09		11 20		*11 33*					11 37		11 49	*12m03*	*12 04*					12 11			12 19
London Victoria 15 ⊖	a				11 16		11 27	*11n35*	*11 40*					11 44		11 58	*12n05*	*12 11*					12 18			12 28

For general notes see front of timetable
For details of catering facilities see Directory of Train Operators

b Change at Ford
c Arr. 1010
e Arr. 1016
f Arr. 1040
g Arr. 1046
h Arr. 1110
j Arr. 1116
k Change at Gatwick Airport
m Change at Brighton and East Croydon
n Change at Brighton and Gatwick Airport

Table 188

Mondays to Fridays

Southampton, Portsmouth and Sussex Coast → Brighton, Gatwick Airport & London

For complete service between Horsham and Three Bridges see Table 186

		SN 1	SN 1	SN 1	SN 1	SN 1	SN 1	SN 1	SN 1	SN 1	SN 1	SN 1	SN 1	SN 1	SN 1		SN 1	SN 1	SN 1	SN 1	SN 1	SN 1	SN 1	SN 1	SN 1	SN 1
					⚲		⚲												⚲				⚲		⚲	
Southampton Central	d							10 11					10 36													11 11
Swanwick	d							10 28					10 53													11 28
Fareham	d							10 35					11 00													11 35
Portchester	d							10 40																		11 40
Cosham	d							10 45					11 08													11 45
Portsmouth Harbour	d			10 28														11 12				11 28				
Portsmouth & Southsea	d			10 32										11 03				11 16				11 32				
Fratton	d			10 36										11 07				11 20				11 36				
Hilsea	d													11 11												
Bedhampton	d													11 16												
Havant	d			10 45				10 51					11 15	11 19				11 30				11 45				11 51
Warblington	d							10 53																		11 53
Emsworth	d							10 56					11 19	11 23												11 56
Southbourne	d							10 59					11 22	11 26												11 59
Nutbourne	d													11 28												
Bosham	d							11 04																		12 04
Fishbourne (Sussex)	d													11 33												
Chichester 4	d			10 56				11b11					11 30	11 37				11 41				11 56				12c11
Bognor Regis 4	d				11 00	11 07						11 26			11 39								12 00	12 07		
Barnham	a			11 03	11 06	11 13		11 18				11 32	11 37	11 44	11 45			11 48				12 03	12 06	12 13		12 18
	d			11 04	11 07	11 15		11 19				11 33	11 38	11 45				11 49				12 04	12 07	12 15		12 19
Bognor Regis 4	a			*11 17*				*11 28*										*11 58*				*12 17*				*12 28*
Ford 4	d			11 08	11 11	11 19						11 37		11 49								12 08	12 11	12 19		
Littlehampton 4	a					11 24								11 54										12 24		
	d			*10e58*					11 15										11 45			*11e58*				
Angmering 3	d			11 14					11 23				11 47						11 53			12 14				
Goring-by-Sea	d			11 18					11 27										11 57			12 18				
Durrington-on-Sea	d			11 21					11 30										12 00			12 21				
West Worthing	d		11 09	11 23					11 32		11 39								12 02		12 09	12 23				
Worthing 4	a		11 11	11 25					11 34		11 41		11 54						12 04		12 11	12 25				
	d		11 12	11 26					11 36		11 42		11 56						12 06		12 12	12 26				
East Worthing	d		11 14								11 44										12 14					
Lancing	d		11 17	11 30							11 47		12 00						12 10		12 17	12 30				
Shoreham-by-Sea	d		11 22	11 34					11 42		11 52		12 04						12 14		12 22	12 34				
Southwick	d		11 25	11 37							11 55		12 07								12 25	12 37				
Fishersgate	d		11 27								11 57										12 27					
Portslade	d		11 29	11 40					11 47		11 59		12 10								12 29	12 40				
Aldrington	d		11 31								12 01										12 31					
Hove 2	d	11 24	11 34	11 44					11 51	11 54	12 04		12 14						12 21	12 24	12 34	12 44				
Brighton 10	a	11 28	11 38	11 48						11 58	12 08		12 18							12 28	12 38	12 48				
Haywards Heath 3	a	*11 47*		*12 15*					12 09	*12 18*									12 35	*12 47*		*13 15*				
Arundel	d				11 16							11 42											12 16			
Amberley	d											11 47														
Pulborough	d				11 25		←					11 53											12 25		←	
Billingshurst	d				11 31 →		11 31					11 59					←						12 31 →		12 31	
Christs Hospital	d											12 06 →					12 06									
Horsham 4	d						11f50	11g50									12h20	12j20							12k50	12m50
Crawley	d						11 59										12 29								12 59	
Three Bridges 4	a	*12 11*		*12 25*			12 02			*12 42*							12 32			*13 11*		*13 25*			13 02	
Gatwick Airport 10 ✈	a	*12 00*					12 07		12 24	*12 30*							12 37		12 54	*13 00*					13 07	
East Croydon	a	*12 16*	*12 23*				12 27		12 40	*12 46*	*12 55*						13 00		13 10	*13 16*	*13 23*				13 28	
London Bridge 4 ⊖	a	*12 30*	*12n45*				*12 45*			*13 00*	*13n15*						*13q15*			*13 30*	*13n45*				*13q45*	
Clapham Junction 10	a		*12 33*				12 37		12 49	*13n03*	13 04						13 11		13 19		*13 33*				13 38	
London Victoria 15 ⊖	a	*12r35*	*12 40*				12 44		12 57	*13r05*	*13 11*						13 18		13 27	*13r35*	*13 40*				13 46	

For general notes see front of timetable
For details of catering facilities see Directory of Train Operators

b Arr. 1108
c Arr. 1208
e Change at Ford
f Arr. 1140
g Arr. 1146
h Arr. 1210
j Arr. 1216
k Arr. 1240
m Arr. 1246
n Change at Brighton and East Croydon
q Change at Gatwick Airport
r Change at Brighton and Gatwick Airport

Southampton, Portsmouth and Sussex Coast → Brighton, Gatwick Airport & London

For complete service between Horsham and Three Bridges see Table 186

Station		SN 1	SN 1	SN 1	SN 1	SN 1	SN 1		SN 1	SN 1	SN 1	SN 1	SN 1	SN 1	SN 1	SN 1	SN 1	SN 1	SN 1	SN 1	SN 1	SN 1		SN 1	SN 1	SN 1
Southampton Central	d					11 36													12 11						12 36	
Swanwick	d					11 53													12 28						12 53	
Fareham	d					12 00													12 35						13 00	
Portchester	d																		12 40							
Cosham	d					12 09													12 44						13 08	
Portsmouth Harbour	d										12 12				12 28											
Portsmouth & Southsea	d						12 03				12 16				12 32											13 03
Fratton	d						12 07				12 20				12 36											13 07
Hilsea	d						12 11																			13 11
Bedhampton	d						12 16																			13 16
Havant	d					12 15	12 19				12 30				12 45				12 51						13 15	13 19
Warblington	d																		12 53							
Emsworth	d					12 19	12 23												12 56						13 19	13 23
Southbourne	d					12 22	12 26												12 59						13 22	13 26
Nutbourne	d						12 28																			13 28
Bosham	d																		13 03							
Fishbourne (Sussex)	d						12 33																			13 33
Chichester 4	d					12 30	12 37				12 41				12 56				13b11						13 30	13 37
Bognor Regis 4	d				12 26				12 39							13 00	13 07							13 26		
Barnham	a				12 32	12 37	12 44		12 45		12 48				13 03	13 06	13 13		13 18					13 32	13 37	13 44
	d				12 33	12 38	12 45				12 49				13 04	13 07	13 15		13 19					13 33	13 38	13 45
Bognor Regis 4	a										*12 58*				*13 17*				*13 28*							
Ford 4	d				12 37		12 49								13 08	13 11	13 19							13 37		13 49
Littlehampton 4	a						12 54										13 24									13 54
	d	12 15										12 45			*12c58*					13 15						
Angmering 3	d	12 23				12 47						12 53			13 14					13 23					13 47	
Goring-by-Sea	d	12 27										12 57			13 18					13 27						
Durrington-on-Sea	d	12 30										13 00			13 21					13 30						
West Worthing	d	12 32		12 39								13 02		13 09	13 23					13 32		13 39				
Worthing 4	a	12 34		12 41		12 54						13 04		13 11	13 25					13 34		13 41			13 54	
	d	12 36		12 42		12 56						13 06		13 12	13 26					13 36		13 42			13 56	
East Worthing	d			12 44										13 14								13 44				
Lancing	d			12 47		13 00						13 10		13 17	13 30							13 47			14 00	
Shoreham-by-Sea	d	12 42		12 52		13 04						13 14		13 22	13 34					13 42		13 52			14 04	
Southwick	d			12 55		13 07								13 25	13 37							13 55			14 07	
Fishersgate	d			12 57										13 27								13 57				
Portslade	d	12 47		12 59		13 10								13 29	13 40					13 47		13 59			14 10	
Aldrington	d			13 01										13 31								14 01				
Hove 2	d	12 51	12 54	13 04		13 14						13 21	13 24	13 34	13 44					13 51	13 54	14 04			14 14	
Brighton 10	a		12 58	13 08		13 18							13 28	13 38	13 48						13 58	14 08			14 18	
Haywards Heath 3	a	13 09	*13 18*									13 35	*13 47*		*14 15*					14 09	*14 18*					
Arundel	d				12 42											13 16								13 42		
Amberley	d				12 47																			13 47		
Pulborough	d				12 53											13 25		←						13 53		
Billingshurst	d				12 59					←						13 31 →		13 31						13 59		
Christs Hospital	d				13 06 →					13 06														14 06 →		
Horsham 4	d									13e20	13f20							13g50	13h50							
Crawley	d									13 29								13 59								
Three Bridges 4	a		*13 42*							13 32			*14 11*		*14 25*			14 02			*14 41*					
Gatwick Airport 10 ✈	a	13 24	*13 30*							13 37		13 54	*14 00*					14 07		14 24	*14 30*				*14 50*	
East Croydon	a	13 40	*13 46*	*13 55*						14 00		14 10	*14 16*	*14 23*				14 27		14 40	*14 46*	*14 55*			*15 08*	
London Bridge 4 ⊖	a		*14 00*	*14j15*						*14k15*			*14 30*	*14j45*				*14 45*			*15 00*	*15j15*				
Clapham Junction 10	a	13 49	*14j03*	*14 04*						14 11		14 19		*14 33*				14 37		14 49	*15j03*	*15 04*			*15j25*	
London Victoria 15 ⊖	a	13 58	*14m05*	*14 11*						14 18		14 27	*14m35*	*14 40*				14 44		14 57	*15m05*	*15 11*			*15m28*	

For general notes see front of timetable
For details of catering facilities see Directory of Train Operators

- b Arr. 1308
- c Change at Ford
- e Arr. 1310
- f Arr. 1316
- g Arr. 1340
- h Arr. 1346
- j Change at Brighton and East Croydon
- k Change at Gatwick Airport
- m Change at Brighton and Gatwick Airport

Table 188

Southampton, Portsmouth and Sussex Coast → Brighton, Gatwick Airport & London

For complete service between Horsham and Three Bridges see Table 186

Station		SN 1	SN 1	SN 1	SN 1 🛒	SN 1	SN 1	SN 1	SN 1 🛒	SN 1	SN 1 🛒	SN 1	SN 1	SN 1	SN 1	SN 1 🛒	SN 1	SN 1	SN 1	SN 1 🛒	SN 1	SN 1 🛒	SN 1	SN 1	SN 1
Southampton Central	d											13 11					13 36								
Swanwick	d											13 28					13 53								
Fareham	d											13 35					14 00								
Portchester	d											13 40													
Cosham	d											13 45					14 08								
Portsmouth Harbour	d			13 12				13 28													14 12				14 28
Portsmouth & Southsea	d			13 16				13 32										14 03			14 16				14 32
Fratton	d			13 20				13 36										14 07			14 20				14 36
Hilsea	d																	14 11							
Bedhampton	d																	14 16							
Havant	d			13 30				13 45				13 51					14 15	14 19			14 30				14 45
Warblington	d											13 53													
Emsworth	d											13 56					14 19	14 23							
Southbourne	d											13 59					14 22	14 26							
Nutbourne	d																	14 28							
Bosham	d											14 04													
Fishbourne (Sussex)	d																	14 33							
Chichester 4	d			13 41				13 56				14b11					14 30	14 37			14 41				14 56
Bognor Regis 4	d	13 39							14 00	14 07						14 26			14 39						
Barnham	a	13 45		13 48				14 03	14 06	14 13		14 18				14 32	14 37	14 44	14 45		14 48				15 03
	d			13 49				14 04	14 07	14 15		14 19				14 33	14 38	14 45			14 49				15 04
Bognor Regis 4	a			*13 58*				*14 17*				*14 28*									*14 58*				*15 17*
Ford 4	d							14 08	14 11	14 19						14 37		14 49							15 08
Littlehampton 4	a									14 24								14 54							
	d				13 45			*13c58*					14 15									14 45			*14c54*
Angmering 3	d				13 53			14 14					14 23				14 47					14 53			15 14
Goring-by-Sea	d				13 57			14 18					14 27									14 57			15 18
Durrington-on-Sea	d				14 00			14 21					14 30									15 00			15 21
West Worthing	d				14 02		14 09	14 23					14 32		14 39							15 02		15 09	15 23
Worthing 4	a				14 04		14 11	14 25					14 34		14 41		14 54					15 04		15 11	15 25
	d				14 06		14 12	14 26					14 36		14 42		14 56					15 06		15 12	15 26
East Worthing	d						14 14								14 44									15 14	
Lancing	d				14 10		14 17	14 30							14 47		15 00					15 10		15 17	15 30
Shoreham-by-Sea	d				14 14		14 22	14 34					14 42		14 52		15 04					15 14		15 22	15 34
Southwick	d						14 25	14 37							14 55		15 07							15 25	15 37
Fishersgate	d						14 27								14 57									15 27	
Portslade	d						14 29	14 40					14 47		14 59		15 10							15 29	15 40
Aldrington	d						14 31								15 01									15 31	
Hove 2	d				14 21	14 24	14 34	14 44					14 51	14 54	15 04		15 14					15 21	15 24	15 34	15 44
Brighton 10	a					14 28	14 38	14 48						14 58	15 08		15 18						15 28	15 38	15 48
Haywards Heath 3	a				14 35	*14 47*		*15 15*					15 09	*15 18*								15 35	*15 48*		*16 15*
Arundel	d								14 16							14 42									
Amberley	d															14 47									
Pulborough	d								14 25							14 53									
Billingshurst	d								14 31 →		← 14 31					14 59									
Christs Hospital	d		← 14 06													15 06 →				← 15 06					
Horsham 4	d		14e20	14f20							14g50	14h50								15j20	15k20				
Crawley	d		14 29								14 59									15 29					
Three Bridges 4	a		14 32			*15 11*		*15 25*			15 02			*15 42*						15 32			*16 07*		*16 25*
Gatwick Airport 10 ✈	a		14 37		14 54	*15 00*					15 07		15 24	*15 30*						15 37		15 55	*16 00*		
East Croydon	a		15 00		15 09	*15 16*	*15 23*				15 27		15 41	*15 46*	*15 55*					16 00		16 11	*16 16*	*16 24*	
London Bridge 4 ⊖	a		*15m15*			*15 30*	*15n45*				*15 45*			*16 00*	*16n15*					*16m15*			*16n41*	*16n56*	
Clapham Junction 10	a		15 11		15 19		*15 33*				15 37		15 51	*16n03*	*16 04*					16 11		16 21		*16 33*	
London Victoria 15 ⊖	a		15 18		15 28	*15q35*	*15 40*				15 44		15 58	*16q05*	*16 11*					16 20		16 29	*16q35*	*16 41*	

For general notes see front of timetable
For details of catering facilities see Directory of Train Operators

b Arr. 1408
c Change at Ford
e Arr. 1410
f Arr. 1416
g Arr. 1440
h Arr. 1446
j Arr. 1510
k Arr. 1516
m Change at Gatwick Airport
n Change at Brighton and East Croydon
q Change at Brighton and Gatwick Airport

Southampton, Portsmouth and Sussex Coast → Brighton, Gatwick Airport & London

For complete service between Horsham and Three Bridges see Table 186

		SN 1	SN 1	SN 1	SN 1	SN 1		SN 1	SN 1	GW ◇ A	SN 1	SN 1	SN 1	SN 1	SN 1	SN 1	SN 1	SN 1	SN 1	SN 1	SN 1		SN 1	SN 1	SN 1	SN 1
		⚲		⚲													⚲				⚲			⚲		
Southampton Central	d				14 11					14 34		14 26													15 11	
Swanwick	d				14 28																				15 28	
Fareham	d				14 35					14 56		15 02													15 35	
Portchester	d				14 40																				15 40	
Cosham	d				14 45					15 04															15 44	
Portsmouth Harbour	d															15 12				15 28						
Portsmouth & Southsea	d												15 03			15 16				15 32						
Fratton	d												15 07			15 20				15 36						
Hilsea	d												15 11													
Bedhampton	d												15 16													
Havant	d				14 51					15 11		15 15	15 19			15 30				15 45					15 51	
Warblington	d				14 53																				15 53	
Emsworth	d				14 56							15 19	15 23												15 56	
Southbourne	d				14 59							15 22	15 26												15 59	
Nutbourne	d												15 28													
Bosham	d				15 04																				16 03	
Fishbourne (Sussex)	d												15 33													
Chichester 4	d				15b11					15 22		15 30	15 37			15 41				15 56					16c11	
Bognor Regis 4	d	15 00	15 09								15 26			15 39							16 00		16 09			
Barnham	a	15 06	15 15		15 18					15 29	15 32	15 38	15 44	15 45		15 48				16 03	16 06		16 15		16 18	
	d	15 07			15 19					15 30	15 33	15 38	15 45			15 49				16 04	16 07				16 19	
Bognor Regis 4	a				*15 28*					*15 45*						*15 58*				*16 17*					*16 28*	
Ford 4	d	15 11									15 37		15 49							16 08	16 11					
Littlehampton 4	a												15 54													
	d					15 15					*15e23*						15 45		15 50	*15e54*						16 15
Angmering 3	d					15 23						15 47					15 53		16 00	16 14						16 23
Goring-by-Sea	d					15 27											15 57		16 04	16 18						16 27
Durrington-on-Sea	d					15 30											16 00		16 07	16 21						16 30
West Worthing	d					15 32			15 39								16 02		16 09	16 23						16 32
Worthing 4	a					15 34			15 41	15 45		15 54					16 04		16 11	16 25						16 34
	d					15 36			15 42	15 50		15 56					16 06		16 12	16 26						16 36
East Worthing	d								15 44										16 14							
Lancing	d								15 47			16 00					16 10		16 17	16 30						
Shoreham-by-Sea	d					15 42			15 52	15 57		16 04					16 14		16 22	16 34						16 42
Southwick	d								15 55			16 07							16 25	16 37						
Fishersgate	d								15 57										16 27							
Portslade	d					15 47			15 59			16 10							16 29	16 40						16 47
Aldrington	d								16 01										16 31							
Hove 2	d					15 51		15 54	16 04	16 08		16 14					16 21	16 24	16 34	16 44						16 51
Brighton 10	a							15 58	16 08	16 14		16 18						16 28	16 38	16 48						
Haywards Heath 3	a					16 09		*16 18*	*16 30*			*16 50*					16 35			*17 15*						17 09
Arundel	d	15 16									15 42										16 16					
Amberley	d										15 47															
Pulborough	d	15 25		←							15 53										16 25			←		
Billingshurst	d	15 31		15 31							15 59				←						16 31			16 31		
Christs Hospital	d	→									16 06				16 06						→					
Horsham 4	d			15f50	15g50						→				16h20	16j20								16k50	16m50	
Crawley	d			15 59											16 29									16 59		
Three Bridges 4	a			16 02				16 37	16 47			17 02			16 32									17 02		
Gatwick Airport 10 ✈	a			16 07		16 26		16 30	16 52			17 06			16 37		16 55							17 07		17 24
East Croydon 🚊	a			16 30		16 42		16 46	16 55	16 55					17 01		17 11		*17 25*					17 30		17 40
London Bridge 4 ⊖	a			*16n42*				*17 02*	*17q26*	*17q26*					*17 26*				*17q54*					*17 54*		
Clapham Junction 10	a			16 39		16 51		*17q03*	*17 04*	*17 04*					17 10		17 21		*17 34*					17 40		17 50
London Victoria 15 ⊖	a			16 46		16 58		*17r05*	*17 11*	*17 11*					17 20		17 28		*17 43*					17 50		17 57

For general notes see front of timetable
For details of catering facilities see Directory of Train Operators

A From Great Malvern (Table 71)
b Arr. 1508
c Arr. 1608
e Change at Ford
f Arr. 1540
g Arr. 1546
h Arr. 1610
j Arr. 1616
k Arr. 1640
m Arr. 1646
n Change at Three Bridges
q Change at Brighton and East Croydon
r Change at Brighton and Gatwick Airport

Southampton, Portsmouth and Sussex Coast → Brighton, Gatwick Airport & London

For complete service between Horsham and Three Bridges see Table 186

		SN 1	SN 1	SN 1	SN 1	SN 1	SN 1	SN 1	SN 1	SN 1	SN 1	SN 1	SN 1		SN 1	SN 1	SN 1	SN 1	SN 1	SN 1	SN 1	SN 1	SN 1	SN 1	SN 1	SN 1
										trolley					trolley		trolley									
Southampton Central	d				15 36													16 11						16 36		
Swanwick	d				15 53													16 28						16 53		
Fareham	d				16 00													16 36						17 00		
Portchester	d																	16 41								
Cosham	d				16 08													16 45						17 08		
Portsmouth Harbour	d								16 12				16 28													
Portsmouth & Southsea	d					16 03			16 16				16 32							16 46					17 03	
Fratton	d					16 07			16 20				16 36							16 50					17 07	
Hilsea	d					16 11														16 54					17 11	
Bedhampton	d					16 16																			17 16	
Havant	d				16 15	16 19			16 30				16 45					16 52		17 00				17 15	17 19	
Warblington	d																	16 54		17 02						
Emsworth	d				16 19	16 23												16 57		17 05				17 19	17 23	
Southbourne	d				16 22	16 26												17 00		17 08				17 22	17 26	
Nutbourne	d					16 28														17 10					17 28	
Bosham	d																	17 04		17 14						
Fishbourne (Sussex)	d					16 33														17 17					17 33	
Chichester 4	d				16 30	16 37			16 41				16 56					17 11		17 21				17 30	17 37	
Bognor Regis 4	d			16 26			16 39								17 00	17 09							17 26			17 39
Barnham	a			16 32	16 37	16 44	16 45		16 48				17 03		17 06	17 15		17 18		17 28			17 32	17 37	17 44	17 45
	d			16 33	16 38	16 45			16 49				17 04		17 07			17 19		17 29			17 33	17 38	17 45	
Bognor Regis 4	a								16 58				17 17					17 28		17 38				17 50		
Ford 4	d			16 37		16 49							17 08		17 11					17 33			17 37		17 49	
Littlehampton 4	a					16 54														17 38					17 54	
	d			16b22						16 45			16b54						17 15							
Angmering 3	d				16 47					16 53			17 14						17 23					17 47		
Goring-by-Sea	d									16 57			17 18						17 27							
Durrington-on-Sea	d									17 00			17 21						17 30							
West Worthing	d		16 39							17 02		17 09	17 23						17 32			17 39				
Worthing 4	a		16 41		16 54					17 04		17 11	17 25						17 34			17 41		17 54		
	d		16 42		16 56					17 06		17 12	17 26						17 36			17 42		17 56		
East Worthing	d		16 44									17 14										17 44				
Lancing	d		16 47		17 00					17 10		17 17	17 30									17 47		18 00		
Shoreham-by-Sea	d		16 52		17 04					17 14		17 22	17 34						17 42			17 52		18 04		
Southwick	d		16 55		17 07							17 25	17 37									17 55		18 07		
Fishersgate	d		16 57									17 27										17 57				
Portslade	d		16 59		17 10							17 29	17 40						17 47			17 59		18 10		
Aldrington	d		17 01									17 31										18 01				
Hove 2	d	16 54	17 04		17 14					17 21	17 24	17 34	17 44						17 51		17 54	18 04		18 14		
Brighton 10	a	16 58	17 08		17 18						17 28	17 38	17 48								17 58	18 08		18 18		
Haywards Heath 3	a	17 18			17 45					17 35	17 56		18 15						18 09		18 18					
Arundel	d			16 42											17 16								17 42			
Amberley	d			16 47																			17 47			
Pulborough	d			16 53											17 25								17 53			
Billingshurst	d			16 59											17 31		17 31						17 59			
Christs Hospital	d			17 06				17 06															18 06			
Horsham 4	d							17c20	17e20								17f50	17g50								
Crawley	d							17 29									17 59									
Three Bridges 4	a	17 27			17 56			17 32			18 08						18 02				18h31					
Gatwick Airport 10 ✈	a	17 31			18 00			17 37		17 55	18 16						18 07		18 24		18 30					
East Croydon	a	17 47	17 54		18 16			17 58		18 11		18 24					18 29		18 41		18 46	18 55				
London Bridge 4 ⊖	a	18j10	18j24					18 24				18j45					18k45				19 00	19j15				
Clapham Junction 10	a	18j02	18 04					18 10		18 21		18 33					18 41		18 51		19j02	19 04				
London Victoria 15 ⊖	a		18 11		18m35			18 20		18 28		18 40					18 50		18 59		19m05	19 11				

For general notes see front of timetable
For details of catering facilities see Directory of Train Operators

- **b** Change at Ford
- **c** Arr. 1710
- **e** Arr. 1716
- **f** Arr. 1740
- **g** Arr. 1746
- **h** Change at Brighton and Haywards Heath
- **j** Change at Brighton and East Croydon
- **k** Change at Gatwick Airport
- **m** Change at Brighton and Gatwick Airport

Southampton, Portsmouth and Sussex Coast → Brighton, Gatwick Airport & London

For complete service between Horsham and Three Bridges see Table 186

Station		SN 1	SN 1	SN 1	SN 1		SN 1	SN 1	SN 1	SN 1	SN 1	SN 1	SN 1	SN 1	SN 1	SN 1	SN 1	SN 1	SN 1	SN 1		SN 1	SN 1	SN 1	SN 1	SN 1
Southampton Central	d								17 11					17 36										18 11		
Swanwick	d								17 28					17 53										18 28		
Fareham	d								17 35					18 00										18 35		
Portchester	d								17 40															18 40		
Cosham	d								17 44					18 08										18 44		
Portsmouth Harbour	d		17 12				17 28																18 28			
Portsmouth & Southsea	d		17 16				17 32					17 46				18 03							18 32			
Fratton	d		17 20				17 36					17 50				18 07							18 36			
Hilsea	d											17 54				18 11										
Bedhampton	d															18 16										
Havant	d		17 30				17 45		17 51			18 00		18 15		18 19							18 45	18 51		
Warblington	d								17 53			18 02														
Emsworth	d								17 56			18 05				18 23								18 55		
Southbourne	d								17 59			18 08				18 26								18 58		
Nutbourne	d											18 10				18 28										
Bosham	d								18 03			18 14														
Fishbourne (Sussex)	d											18 17				18 33										
Chichester 4	d		17 41				17 56		18b11			18 21		18 26		18 37							18 56	19 07		
Bognor Regis 4	d							18 00			18 19				18 33					18 41		18 54				19 09
Barnham	a		17 48				18 03	18 06	18 18		18 25	18 28		18 33	18 39	18 44				18 47		19 00	19 03	19 14		19 15
	d		17 49				18 04	18 07	18 19			18 29		18 34	18 40	18 45				18 48			19 04	19 15		
Bognor Regis 4	a		17 58				18 28					18 38		18 55									19 13	19 28		
Ford 4	d						18 08	18 11				18 33			18 44					18 52				19 19		
Littlehampton 4	a											18 38								18 57						
	d			17 45			17c56			18 15									18 52					18c56	19 15	
Angmering 3	d			17 53			18 14			18 23				18 43	18 53				19 00				19 13		19 23	
Goring-by-Sea	d			17 57			18 18			18 27					18 57				19 04						19 27	
Durrington-on-Sea	d			18 00			18 21			18 30				18 48	19 00		←		19 07				19 18		19 30	
West Worthing	d			18 02			18 23			18 32					19 02		19 02		19 09						19 32	
Worthing 4	a			18 04			18 25			18 34				18 52	→		19 04		19 11				19 22		19 34	
	d			18 06			18 26			18 35				18 53			19 05		19 12				19 23		19 35	
East Worthing	d						18 28							18 55					19 14				19 25			
Lancing	d			18 10			18 31			18 39				18 58			19 09		19 17				19 28		19 39	
Shoreham-by-Sea	d			18 14			18 35			18 43				19 02			19 13		19 22				19 32		19 43	
Southwick	d						18 38							19 05					19 25				19 35			
Fishersgate	d						18 40							19 07					19 27				19 37			
Portslade	d						18 42			18 48				19 09			19 18		19 29				19 39		19 48	
Aldrington	d						18 45							19 12					19 31				19 42			
Hove 2	d			18 21	18 26		18 47			18 52			19 00	19 14			19 22	19 24	19 34				19 44		19 52	
Brighton 10	a				18 30		18 52						19 04	19 18				19 28	19 38				19 48			
Haywards Heath 3	a			18 41	18 47		19 28			19 05							19 39	19 47					20 16		20 04	
Arundel	d							18 16								18 52								19 24		
Amberley	d																							19 29		
Pulborough	d							18 25								19 01								19 35		
Billingshurst	d	←						18 31								19 08								19 41		
Christs Hospital	d	18 06						18 38																19 48		
Horsham 4	d	18e20	18f20					18g50	18h50							19 17								19 52		
Crawley	d	18 29						18 59								19 26								20 01		
Three Bridges 4	a	18 32			19 12		19 42	19 02		19 28						19 30	20 11	20 11						20 05	20 32	
Gatwick Airport 10	a	18 37		18 56	19 00		19 46	19 07		19 25						19 38	19 54	20 00						20 10	20 25	
East Croydon	a	19 00		19 12	19 16			19 28		19 41			19 55			19 59	20 10	20 16	20 23					20 30	20 41	
London Bridge 4	a	19j15			19 30			19j45		20 00			20k15			20j15	20 30	20 30	20k45					20j45	21 00	
Clapham Junction 10	a	19 10		19 21	19 33			19 40		19 50			20 04			20 10	20 19		20 33					20 40	20 51	
London Victoria 15	a	19 17		19 29	19m35			19 47		19 59			20 11			20 20	20 28	20m35	20 40					20 50	20 59	

For general notes see front of timetable
For details of catering facilities see Directory of Train Operators

b Arr. 1808
c Change at Ford
e Arr. 1810
f Arr. 1816
g Arr. 1842
h Arr. 1846
j Change at Gatwick Airport
k Change at Brighton and East Croydon
m Change at Brighton and Gatwick Airport

Southampton, Portsmouth and Sussex Coast → Brighton, Gatwick Airport & London

For complete service between Horsham and Three Bridges see Table 186

		SN 1	SN 1	SN 1	SN 1	SN 1	SN 1	SN 1	SN 1	SN 1	SN 1	SN 1		SN 1	SN 1	SN 1	SN 1	SN 1	SN 1	SN 1	SN 1	SN 1	SN 1	SN 1	SN 1	SN 1
Southampton Central	d			18 27								19 11					19 36							20 11		
Swanwick	d			18 47								19 28					19 53							20 28		
Fareham	d			18 56								19 35					20 00							20 35		
Portchester	d											19 40												20 40		
Cosham	d			19 04								19 44					20 08							20 44		
Portsmouth Harbour	d	18 36								19 28					19 40											20 40
Portsmouth & Southsea	d	18 41							19 03	19 32					19 44						20 03	20 32				20 44
Fratton	d	18 45							19 07	19 36					19 48						20 07	20 36				20 48
Hilsea	d	18 49							19 11												20 11					
Bedhampton	d								19 16												20 16					
Havant	d	18 55		19 11					19 19	19 45		19 52			19 57		20 15				20 20	20 45		20 51		20 57
Warblington	d	18 57							19 21						19 59						20 22					20 59
Emsworth	d	19 00							19 24			19 56			20 02						20 25			20 55		21 02
Southbourne	d	19 03							19 27			19 59			20 05						20 28			20 58		21 05
Nutbourne	d	19 05							19 29						20 07						20 30					21 07
Bosham	d	19 09							19 33						20 11						20 34					21 11
Fishbourne (Sussex)	d	19 12							19 36						20 14						20 37					21 14
Chichester [4]	d	19 15		19 22					19 40	19 56		20 07			20 18		20 26				20 41	20 56		21 07		21 18
Bognor Regis [4]	d				19 33	19 39					20 04							20 36					21 04			
Barnham	a	19 23		19 29	19 39	19 45			19 47	20 03	20 10	20 14			20 25		20 33	20 42			20 48	21 03	21 10	21 14		21 25
	d	19 23		19 30	19 40				19 49	20 04	20 11	20 15			20 27		20 34	20 43			20 50	21 04	21 11	21 15		21 26
Bognor Regis [4]	a			*19 44*					*19 58*			*20 28*					*20 47*				*20 58*	*21 17*		*21 28*		
Ford [4]	d	19 28			19 44				19 54	20 08	20 15	20 19			20 31			20 47			20 54	21 08	21 15	21 19		21 30
Littlehampton [4]	a	19 32							19 59		20 21				20 39						21 01		21 20			21 35
	d				*19b29*			19 52						20 15				*20b36*		20 52					21 15	
Angmering [3]	d			19 39	19 53			20 00		20 14				20 23			20 43	20 53		21 00		21 14			21 23	
Goring-by-Sea	d			19 43	19 57			20 04						20 27				20 57		21 04					21 27	
Durrington-on-Sea	d			19 46	20 00			20 07						20 30			20 48	21 00		21 07					21 30	
West Worthing	d			19 48	20 02			20 09						20 32				21 02		21 09					21 32	
Worthing [4]	a			19 50	20 04			20 11		20 21				20 34			20 52	21 04		21 11		21 21			21 34	
	d			19 52	20 05			20 12		20 22				20 35			20 53	21 05		21 12		21 22			21 35	
East Worthing	d			19 55				20 14		20 25							20 55			21 14		21 25				
Lancing	d			19 58	20 09			20 17		20 28				20 39			20 58	21 09		21 17		21 28			21 39	
Shoreham-by-Sea	d			20 02	20 13			20 22		20 32				20 43			21 02	21 13		21 22		21 32			21 43	
Southwick	d			20 05				20 25		20 35							21 05			21 25		21 35				
Fishersgate	d			20 07				20 27		20 37							21 07			21 27		21 37				
Portslade	d			20 09	20 18			20 29		20 39				20 48			21 09	21 18		21 29		21 39			21 48	
Aldrington	d			20 11				20 31		20 41							21 12			21 31		21 41				
Hove [2]	d		19 54	20 14	20 22		20 24	20 34		20 44				20 52		20 54	21 14	21 22	21 24	21 34		21 44			21 52	
Brighton [10]	a		19 58	20 18			20 28	20 38		20 48						20 58	21 18		21 28	21 38		21 48				
Haywards Heath [3]	a		*20 18*		20 37		*20 47*							21 06		*21 23*		21 37	*21 46*			*22 21*			22 09	
Arundel	d											20 24												21 24		
Amberley	d											20 29												21 29		
Pulborough	d											20 35												21 35		
Billingshurst	d											20 41												21 41		
Christs Hospital	d											20 48												21 48		
Horsham [4]	d											20 52												21 52		
Crawley	d											21 01												22 01		
Three Bridges [4]	a		*20c32*		20 47		*21 11*					21 05		*21 32*		*21 32*		21 47	*21 55*			*22 32*		22 05	*22 32*	
Gatwick Airport [10] ✈	a		*20 31*		20 51		*21 00*					21 10		21 25		*21 37*		21 51	*22 00*			*22 37*		22 10	22 24	
East Croydon	a		*20 47*		21 09		*21 16*	*21 23*				21 30		21 41		*21 55*		22 09	*22 17*	*22 23*		*22 59*		22 30	22 40	
London Bridge [4] ⊖	a		*21 00*		21 30		*21 30*	*21e45*				*21f45*				*22 15*		22 32	22 32	*22e45*				*22f45*		
Clapham Junction [10]	a		*21e03*		21 19			*21 33*				21 40		21 50		*22 04*		22 19		*22 33*		*23 10*		22 40	22 50	
London Victoria [15] ⊖	a		*21 11*		21 29		*21g35*	*21 40*				21 48		21 58		*22 11*		22 27	*22g35*	*22 40*		*23 20*		22 50	22 58	

For general notes see front of timetable
For details of catering facilities see Directory of Train Operators

b Change at Ford
c Change at Brighton and Haywards Heath
e Change at Brighton and East Croydon
f Change at Gatwick Airport
g Change at Brighton and Gatwick Airport

Southampton, Portsmouth and Sussex Coast → Brighton, Gatwick Airport & London

For complete service between Horsham and Three Bridges see Table 186

		SN 1	SN 1	SN 1		SN 1	SN 1	SN 1	SN 1	SN 1	SN 1	SN 1	SN 1	SN 1	SN 1	SN 1	SN 1	SN 1	SN 1		SN 1	SN 1	SN 1	SN 1		
Southampton Central	d		20 36							21 11				21 23			22 12					22 36				
Swanwick	d		20 53							21 28							22 29					22 53				
Fareham	d		21 00							21 39				21 56			22 36					23 00				
Portchester	d									21 44				22 01			22 41									
Cosham	d		21 08							21 48				22 06			22 45					23 08				
Portsmouth Harbour	d											21 40				22 15					22 44			23 15		
Portsmouth & Southsea	d							21 15				21 44				22 19					22 48			23 19		
Fratton	d							21 19				21 48				22 23					22 52			23 23		
Hilsea	d							21 23				21 52				22 27					22 56			23 27		
Bedhampton	d							21 28				21 57				22 32					23 01			23 33		
Havant	d		21 15					21 31		21 55		22 00		22 14		22 35	22 57				23 04	23 15		23 36		
Warblington	d							21 33						22 16										23 38		
Emsworth	d							21 36						22 19		22 39	23 01							23 41		
Southbourne	d							21 39						22 22		22 42	23 04							23 44		
Nutbourne	d							21 41						22 24										23 47		
Bosham	d							21 45						22 28										23 50		
Fishbourne (Sussex)	d							21 48						22 31										23 53		
Chichester 4	d		21 26					21 52		22 06		22 11		22 35		22b52	23 11				23 17	23 26	23 52	23 57		
Bognor Regis 4	d			21 39					22 00				22 30					23 15								
Barnham	a		21 33	21 45				21 59	22 06	22 13		22 18	22 36	22 42		22 59	23 19	23 21			23 24	23 33	23 59	00 05		
	d		21 34					22 00	22 07	22 14		22 19	22 37	22 48		23 00	23 19				23 25	23 34	00 01	00 06		
Bognor Regis 4	a		*21 47*					*22 17*				*22 28*		*22 58*		*23 12*					*23 42*	*00 12*				
Ford 4	d		21 38					22 04	22 11			22 23	22 41	22 52		23 04					23 29		00 05	00 10		
Littlehampton 4	a								22 16	22 22		22 28	22 46				23 31				23 34	23 42	00 10	00 15		
	d						21 52					22 33		*22c38*							23 39					
Angmering 3	d		21 44				22 00	22 11				22 41				23 11					23 47					
Goring-by-Sea	d		21 48				22 04	22 15				22 45				23 15					23 51					
Durrington-on-Sea	d		21 51				22 07	22 17				22 47				23 17					23 53					
West Worthing	d		21 53				22 09	22 19				22 49				23 19					23 55					
Worthing 4	a		21 55				22 11	22 22				22 52				23 22					23 58					
	d		21 56				22 12	22 22				22 52				23 22					23 59					
East Worthing	d		21 58				22 14	22 25				22 55				23 25					00 01					
Lancing	d		22 01				22 17	22 28				22 58				23 28					00 04					
Shoreham-by-Sea	d		22 05				22 22	22 32				23 02				23 32					00 08					
Southwick	d		22 08				22 25	22 35				23 05				23 35					00 11					
Fishersgate	d		22 10				22 27	22 37				23 07				23 37					00 13					
Portslade	d		22 12				22 29	22 39				23 09				23 39					00 15					
Aldrington	d		22 15				22 31	22 41				23 11				23 41					00 18					
Hove 2	d	21 54	22 17			22 24	22 34	22 44			22 54	23 14			23 24	23 44			23 54		00 20					
Brighton 10	a	21 58	22 22			22 28	22 38	22 48			22 58	23 18			23 28	23 48			23 58		00 25					
Haywards Heath 3	a	*22 28*				*22 54*					*23 23*				*23 58*											
Arundel	d													22 57												
Amberley	d													23 02												
Pulborough	d													23 08												
Billingshurst	d													23 14												
Christs Hospital	d													23 21												
Horsham 4	d													23 25												
Crawley	d													23 38												
Three Bridges 4	a	*22 42*				*23 05*					*23 33*			23 42	*00 10*											
Gatwick Airport 10 ✈	a	*22 46*				*23e12*					*23 52*			*23 52*	*00 14*											
East Croydon	a	*23 02*				*23 32*					*00 16*			*00 16*	*00 35*											
London Bridge 4 ⊖	a	*23 15*				*23 45*					*00 52*			*00 52*	*00 52*											
Clapham Junction 10	a	*23f25*				*00f11*					*00 29*			*00 29*	*01f02*											
London Victoria 15 ⊖	a	*23f35*				*23e52*					*00 37*			*00 37*	*00g55*											

For general notes see front of timetable
For details of catering facilities see Directory of Train Operators

b Arr. 2249
c Change at Ford
e Change at Brighton and Haywards Heath
f Change at Brighton and East Croydon
g Change at Brighton and Gatwick Airport

Southampton, Portsmouth and Sussex Coast → Brighton, Gatwick Airport & London

For complete service between Horsham and Three Bridges see Table 186

		SN 1	SN 1	SN 1	SN 1	SN 1	SN 1	SN 1	SN 1	SN 1	SN 1	SN 1	SN 1	SN 1	SN 1	SN 1		SN 1	SN 1	SN 1	SN 1	SN 1	SN 1	SN 1	SN 1	SN 1
Southampton Central	d																									
Swanwick	d																									
Fareham	d																									
Portchester	d																									
Cosham	d																									
Portsmouth Harbour	d	22p44		23p15																					06 12	
Portsmouth & Southsea	d	22p48		23p19			04 56															05 56			06 16	
Fratton	d	22p52		23p23			05 00															06 00			06 20	
Hilsea	d	22p56		23p27																		06 04				
Bedhampton	d	23p01		23p33																		06 09				
Havant	d	23p04		23p36			05 08							05 53								06 14			06 30	
Warblington	d			23p38																		06 16				
Emsworth	d			23p41										05 57								06 19				
Southbourne	d			23p44										06 00								06 22				
Nutbourne	d			23p47																		06 24				
Bosham	d			23p50																		06 28				
Fishbourne (Sussex)	d			23p53																		06 31				
Chichester 4	d	23p17	23p52	23p57			05 19							06 07							06 30	06 35			06 41	
Bognor Regis 4	d					05 13						05 43	06 04					06 26					06 39			
Barnham	a	23p24	23p59	00 05		05 19	05 27	←				05 49	06 10	06 15		←		06 32			06 37	06 42	06 45		06 48	
	d	23p25	00 01	00 06	04 47	05 31 →	05 27	05 31				05 50	06 20 →	06 15		06 20		06 33			06 38	06 43			06 49	
Bognor Regis 4	a	23 42												06 28											06 58	
Ford 4	d	23p29	00 05	00 10	04 51			05 35				05 54		06 20		06 24		06 37				06 47				
Littlehampton 4	a	23p34	00 10	00 15	04 56			05 40								06 29						06 52				
	d	23p39			05 01					05 45				05b58	06 15											06 45
Angmering 3	d	23p47			05 09					05 53		06 00			06 23						06 47					06 55
Goring-by-Sea	d	23p51			05 13					05 57		06 04			06 27											06 59
Durrington-on-Sea	d	23p53			05 15					06 00		06 07			06 30											07 02
West Worthing	d	23p55			05 18					06 02		06 09			06 32					06 39						07 04
Worthing 4	a	23p58			05 20		05 41			06 04		06 11			06 34					06 41	06 54					07 06
	d	23p59			05 21		05 42			06 05		06 12			06 35					06 42	06 56					07 07
East Worthing	d	00 01			05 23							06 14								06 44						
Lancing	d	00 04			05 26					06 09		06 17			06 39					06 47	07 00					07 11
Shoreham-by-Sea	d	00 08			05 31		05 48			06 13		06 22			06 43					06 52	07 04					07 15
Southwick	d	00 11			05 34							06 25								06 55	07 07					
Fishersgate	d	00 13			05 36							06 27								06 57						
Portslade	d	00 15			05 38					06 17		06 29			06 47					06 59	07 10					
Aldrington	d	00 18			05 40							06 31								07 01						
Hove 2	d	00 20			05 43		05 54		05 56	06 21	06 24	06 34			06 51				06 54	07 04	07 14					07 22
Brighton 10	a	00 25			05 47				06 00		06 28	06 38							06 58	07 08	07 18					
Haywards Heath 3	a				06 15		06 07		06 18	06 35	06 58	07 15			07 08				07 18							07 35
Arundel	d													06 24				06 42								
Amberley	d																	06 47								
Pulborough	d													06 33				06 53								
Billingshurst	d													06 40				06 59						←		
Christs Hospital	d																	07 06 →						07 06		
Horsham 4	d													06 50										07c20	07e20	
Crawley	d													06 59										07 29		
Three Bridges 4	a						06 20		06f32	06 48	07 11	07 25		07 02	07 25				07 42					07 32		
Gatwick Airport 10 ✈	a						06 24		06 30	06 52	07 16			07 07	07 24				07 30					07 37		07 54
East Croydon	a						06 40		06 46	07 09		07 23		07 27	07 40				07 46	07 55				07 59		08 10
London Bridge 4 ⊖	a						07 01		07 01	07 31		07g45		07 45	08 01				08 01	08g15				08h15		
Clapham Junction 10	a						06 50		07g03	07 19		07 33		07 37	07 49				08g03	08 04				08 11		08 19
London Victoria 15 ⊖	a						06 58		07j05	07 27		07 40		07 44	07 57				08j05	08 11				08 18		08 27

For general notes see front of timetable
For details of catering facilities see Directory of Train Operators

b Change at Ford
c Arr. 0710
e Arr. 0716
f Change at Brighton and Haywards Heath
g Change at Brighton and East Croydon
h Change at Gatwick Airport
j Change at Brighton and Gatwick Airport

Table 188

Saturdays

Southampton, Portsmouth and Sussex Coast → Brighton, Gatwick Airport & London

For complete service between Horsham and Three Bridges see Table 186

Station		SN 1	SN 1	SN 1	SN 1	SN 1	SN 1	SN 1	SN 1		SN 1	SN 1	GW	SN 1	SN 1	SN 1	SN 1	SN 1	SN 1	SN 1	SN 1	SN 1	SN 1	SN 1	SN 1	
Southampton Central	d							06 11							06 36											
Swanwick	d							06 28							06 53											
Fareham	d							06 35							07 00											
Portchester	d							06 40																		
Cosham	d							06 44							07 08											
Portsmouth Harbour	d			06 28									06 48						07 12				07 28			
Portsmouth & Southsea	d			06 32									06 53			07 03			07 16				07 32			
Fratton	d			06 36									06 57			07 07			07 20				07 36			
Hilsea	d															07 11										
Bedhampton	d															07 16										
Havant	d			06 45				06 51					07 10		07 15	07 19			07 30				07 45			
Warblington	d							06 53																		
Emsworth	d							06 56							07 19	07 23										
Southbourne	d							06 59							07 22	07 26										
Nutbourne	d															07 28										
Bosham	d							07 03																		
Fishbourne (Sussex)	d															07 33										
Chichester 4	d			06 56				07b11					07 21		07 30	07 37			07 41				07 56			
Bognor Regis 4	d				07 00	07 07								07 26			07 39							08 00	08 07	
Barnham	a			07 03	07 06	07 13		07 18					07 29	07 32	07 37	07 44	07 45		07 48				08 03	08 06	08 13	
	d			07 04	07 07	07 15		07 19					07 29	07 33	07 38	07 45			07 49				08 04	08 07	08 15	
Bognor Regis 4	a							07 28											07 58							
Ford 4	d			07 08	07 11	07 19								07 37		07 49							08 08	08 11	08 19	
Littlehampton 4	a					07 24										07 54									08 24	
	d			06c54					07 15											07 45			07c58			
Angmering 3	d			07 14					07 23						07 47					07 53			08 14			
Goring-by-Sea	d			07 18					07 27											07 57			08 18			
Durrington-on-Sea	d			07 21					07 30											08 00			08 21			
West Worthing	d		07 09	07 23					07 32			07 39								08 02		08 09	08 23			
Worthing 4	a		07 11	07 25					07 34			07 41	07 45		07 54					08 04		08 11	08 25			
	d		07 12	07 26					07 36			07 42	07 50		07 56					08 06		08 12	08 26			
East Worthing	d		07 14									07 44										08 14				
Lancing	d		07 17	07 30								07 47			08 00					08 10		08 17	08 30			
Shoreham-by-Sea	d		07 22	07 34					07 42			07 52	07 57		08 04					08 14		08 22	08 34			
Southwick	d		07 25	07 37								07 55			08 07							08 25	08 37			
Fishersgate	d		07 27									07 57										08 27				
Portslade	d		07 29	07 40					07 47			07 59			08 10							08 29	08 40			
Aldrington	d		07 31									08 01										08 31				
Hove 2	d	07 24	07 34	07 44					07 51		07 54	08 04	08 08		08 14					08 21	08 24	08 34	08 44			
Brighton 10	a	07 28	07 38	07 48							07 58	08 08	08 15		08 18						08 28	08 38	08 48			
Haywards Heath 3	a	07 47		08 15					08 09		08 18									08 35	08 47		09 15			
Arundel	d				07 16									07 42										08 16		
Amberley	d													07 47												
Pulborough	d				07 25		←							07 53										08 25		
Billingshurst	d				07 31		07 31							07 59				←						08 31		
Christs Hospital	d				→									08 06				08 06						→		
Horsham 4	d						07e50	07f50						→				08g20	08h20							
Crawley	d							07 59										08 29								
Three Bridges 4	a	08 11		08 25				08 02			08 42							08 32			09 11		09 25			
Gatwick Airport 10 ✈	a	08 00						08 07	08 24		08 30							08 37		08 54	09 00					
East Croydon	a	08 16	08 23					08 27	08 40		08 46	08 55	08 55					08 59		09 10	09 16	09 23				
London Bridge 4 ⊖	a	08 31	08j45					08 45			09 01	09j15	09j15					09k15			09 30	09j45				
Clapham Junction 10	a		08 33					08 37	08 49		09j03	09 04	09 04					09 11		09 19		09 33				
London Victoria 15 ⊖	a	08m35	08 40					08 44	08 57		09m05	09 11	09 11					09 18		09 27	09m35	09 40				

For general notes see front of timetable
For details of catering facilities see Directory of Train Operators

- b Arr. 0708
- c Change at Ford
- e Arr. 0740
- f Arr. 0746
- g Arr. 0810
- h Arr. 0816
- j Change at Brighton and East Croydon
- k Change at Gatwick Airport
- m Change at Brighton and Gatwick Airport

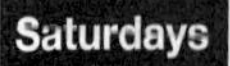

Southampton, Portsmouth and Sussex Coast → Brighton, Gatwick Airport & London

For complete service between Horsham and Three Bridges see Table 186

		SN 1	SN 1	SN 1		SN 1	SN 1	SN 1	SN 1	SN 1	SN 1	SN 1	SN 1	SN 1	SN 1	SN 1	SN 1	SN 1	SN 1	SN 1	SN 1		SN 1	SN 1	SN 1	SN 1
Southampton Central	d		07 11						07 36												08 11					
Swanwick	d		07 28						07 53												08 28					
Fareham	d		07 35						08 00												08 35					
Portchester	d		07 40																		08 40					
Cosham	d		07 44						08 09												08 44					
Portsmouth Harbour	d												08 12				08 28									
Portsmouth & Southsea	d									08 03			08 16				08 32									
Fratton	d									08 07			08 20				08 36									
Hilsea	d									08 11																
Bedhampton	d									08 16																
Havant	d		07 51						08 16	08 19			08 30				08 45				08 51					
Warblington	d		07 53																		08 53					
Emsworth	d		07 56						08 20	08 23											08 56					
Southbourne	d		07 59						08 23	08 26											08 59					
Nutbourne	d									08 29																
Bosham	d		08 03																		09 03					
Fishbourne (Sussex)	d									08 33																
Chichester 4	d		08b11						08 31	08 37			08 41				08 56				09c11					
Bognor Regis 4	d							08 26			08 39							09 00	09 07							09 26
Barnham	a		08 18					08 32	08 38	08 44	08 45		08 48				09 03	09 06	09 13		09 18					09 32
	d		08 19					08 33	08 39	08 45			08 49				09 04	09 07	09 15		09 19					09 33
Bognor Regis 4	a		*08 28*										*08 58*				*09 17*				*09 28*					
Ford 4	d							08 37		08 49							09 08	09 11	09 19							09 37
Littlehampton 4	a									08 54									09 24							
	d			08 15										08 45			*08e58*						09 15			
Angmering 3	d			08 23					08 48					08 53			09 14						09 23			
Goring-by-Sea	d			08 27										08 57			09 18						09 27			
Durrington-on-Sea	d			08 30										09 00			09 21						09 30			
West Worthing	d			08 32			08 39							09 02		09 09	09 23						09 32		09 39	
Worthing 4	a			08 34			08 41		08 55					09 04		09 11	09 25						09 34		09 41	
	d			08 36			08 42		08 56					09 05		09 12	09 26						09 36		09 42	
East Worthing	d						08 44									09 14									09 44	
Lancing	d						08 47		09 00					09 09		09 17	09 30								09 47	
Shoreham-by-Sea	d			08 42			08 52		09 04					09 13		09 22	09 34						09 42		09 52	
Southwick	d						08 55		09 07							09 25	09 37								09 55	
Fishersgate	d						08 57									09 27									09 57	
Portslade	d			08 47			08 59		09 10							09 29	09 40						09 47		09 59	
Aldrington	d						09 01									09 31									10 01	
Hove 2	d			08 51		08 54	09 04		09 14					09 21	09 24	09 34	09 44						09 51	09 54	10 04	
Brighton 10	a					08 58	09 08		09 18						09 28	09 38	09 48							09 58	10 08	
Haywards Heath 3	a			09 09		*09 18*	*09 28*							09 35	*09 47*		*10 15*						10 08	*10 18*		
Arundel	d							08 42										09 16								09 42
Amberley	d							08 47																		09 47
Pulborough	d	←						08 53										09 25		←						09 53
Billingshurst	d	08 31						08 59				←						09 31 →		09 31						09 59
Christs Hospital	d							09 06 →				09 06														10 06 →
Horsham 4	d	08f50	08g50									09h20	09j20							09k50	09m50					
Crawley	d	08 59										09 29								09 59						
Three Bridges 4	a	09 02				*09 37*						09 32			*10 11*		*10 25*			10 02				*10 42*		
Gatwick Airport 10 ✈	a	09 07		09 24		*09 30*	*09 44*					09 37		09 54	*10 00*					10 07			10 25	*10 30*		
East Croydon	a	09 27		09 40		*09 46*	*09 55*					09 59		10 10	*10 16*	*10 23*				10 27			10 42	*10 46*	*10 55*	
London Bridge 4 ⊖	a	*09 45*				*10 00*	*10n22*					*10q15*			*10 30*	*10n45*				10 45				*11 00*	*11n15*	
Clapham Junction 10	a	09 37		09 49		*10n03*	*10 04*					10 11		10 19		*10 33*				10 37			10 51	*11n03*	*11 04*	
London Victoria 15 ⊖	a	09 44		09 57		*10r05*	*10 11*					10 18		10 27	*10r35*	*10 40*				10 44			10 59	*11r05*	*11 11*	

For general notes see front of timetable
For details of catering facilities see Directory of Train Operators

b Arr. 0808
c Arr. 0908
e Change at Ford
f Arr. 0840
g Arr. 0846
h Arr. 0910
j Arr. 0916
k Arr. 0940
m Arr. 0946
n Change at Brighton and East Croydon
q Change at Three Bridges
r Change at Brighton and Gatwick Airport

Southampton, Portsmouth and Sussex Coast → Brighton, Gatwick Airport & London

For complete service between Horsham and Three Bridges see Table 186

Station		SN 1	SN 1	SN 1	SN 1	SN 1	SN 1	SN 1	SN 1	SN 1	SN 1	SN 1	SN 1	SN 1		SN 1	SN 1	SN 1	SN 1	SN 1	SN 1	SN 1	SN 1	SN 1	SN 1	SN 1
Southampton Central	d	08 36												09 11						09 36						
Swanwick	d	08 53												09 28						09 53						
Fareham	d	09 00												09 35						10 00						
Portchester	d													09 40												
Cosham	d	09 08												09 44						10 08						
Portsmouth Harbour	d					09 12				09 28														10 12		
Portsmouth & Southsea	d		09 03			09 16				09 32											10 03			10 16		
Fratton	d		09 07			09 20				09 36											10 07			10 20		
Hilsea	d		09 11																		10 11					
Bedhampton	d		09 16																		10 16					
Havant	d	09 15	09 19			09 30				09 45				09 51						10 15	10 19			10 30		
Warblington	d													09 53												
Emsworth	d	09 19	09 23											09 56						10 19	10 23					
Southbourne	d	09 22	09 26											09 59						10 22	10 26					
Nutbourne	d		09 28																		10 28					
Bosham	d													10 03												
Fishbourne (Sussex)	d		09 33																		10 33					
Chichester 4	d	09 30	09 37			09 41				09 56				10b11						10 30	10 37			10 41		
Bognor Regis 4	d			09 39							10 00	10 07							10 26			10 39				
Barnham	a	09 37	09 44	09 45		09 48				10 03	10 06	10 13		10 18					10 32	10 37	10 44	10 45		10 48		
	d	09 38	09 45			09 49				10 04	10 07	10 15		10 19					10 33	10 38	10 45			10 49		
Bognor Regis 4	a					*09 58*				*10 17*				*10 28*										*10 58*		
Ford 4	d		09 49							10 08	10 11	10 19							10 37		10 49					
Littlehampton 4	a		09 54									10 24									10 54					
	d						09 45			*09c58*						10 15									10 45	
Angmering 3	d	09 47					09 53			10 14						10 23				10 47					10 53	
Goring-by-Sea	d						09 57			10 18						10 27									10 57	
Durrington-on-Sea	d						10 00			10 21						10 30									11 00	
West Worthing	d						10 02		10 09	10 23						10 32		10 39							11 02	
Worthing 4	a	09 54					10 04		10 11	10 25						10 34		10 41		10 54					11 04	
	d	09 56					10 06		10 12	10 26						10 36		10 42		10 56					11 06	
East Worthing	d								10 14									10 44								
Lancing	d	10 00					10 10		10 17	10 30								10 47		11 00					11 10	
Shoreham-by-Sea	d	10 04					10 14		10 22	10 34						10 42		10 52		11 04					11 14	
Southwick	d	10 07							10 25	10 37								10 55		11 07						
Fishersgate	d								10 27									10 57								
Portslade	d	10 10							10 29	10 40						10 47		10 59		11 10						
Aldrington	d								10 31									11 01								
Hove 2	d	10 14					10 21	10 24	10 34	10 44						10 51	10 54	11 04		11 14					11 21	11 24
Brighton 10	a	10 18						10 28	10 38	10 48							10 58	11 08		11 18						11 28
Haywards Heath 3	a						10 35	*10 47*		*11 15*						11 09	*11 18*								11 35	*11 47*
Arundel	d										10 16								10 42							
Amberley	d																		10 47							
Pulborough	d										10 25		←						10 53							
Billingshurst	d				←						10 31		10 31						10 59				←			
Christs Hospital	d				10 06						→								11 06 →				11 06			
Horsham 4	d				10e20	10f20							10g50	10h50									11j20	11k20		
Crawley	d				10 29								10 59										11 29			
Three Bridges 4	a				10 32			*11 11*		*11 25*			11 02				*11 42*						11 32			*12 11*
Gatwick Airport 10 ✈	a				10 37		10 54	*11 00*					11 07			11 24	*11 30*						11 37		11 54	*12 00*
East Croydon	a				11 00		11 10	*11 16*	*11 23*				11 27			11 40	*11 46*	*11 55*					12 00		12 10	*12 16*
London Bridge 4 ⊖	a				*11m15*			*11 30*	*11n45*				*11 45*				*12 00*	*12n15*					*12m15*			*12 30*
Clapham Junction 10	a				11 11		11 19		*11 33*				11 37			11 49	*12n03*	*12 04*					12 11		12 19	
London Victoria 15 ⊖	a				11 18		11 27	*11q35*	*11 40*				11 44			11 57	*12q05*	*12 11*					12 18		12 27	*12q35*

For general notes see front of timetable
For details of catering facilities see Directory of Train Operators

b Arr. 1008

c Change at Ford
e Arr. 1010
f Arr. 1016
g Arr. 1040
h Arr. 1046

j Arr. 1110
k Arr. 1116
m Change at Gatwick Airport
n Change at Brighton and East Croydon
q Change at Brighton and Gatwick Airport

Table 188

Saturdays

Southampton, Portsmouth and Sussex Coast → Brighton, Gatwick Airport & London

For complete service between Horsham and Three Bridges see Table 186

	SN 1	SN 1	SN 1	SN 1	SN 1	SN 1		SN 1	SN 1	SN 1	SN 1	SN 1	SN 1	SN 1	SN 1	SN 1	SN 1	SN 1	SN 1	SN 1	SN 1	SN 1		SN 1	SN 1
Southampton Central d						10 11						10 36													11 11
Swanwick d						10 28						10 53													11 28
Fareham d						10 35						11 00													11 35
Portchester d						10 40																			11 40
Cosham d						10 44						11 08													11 44
Portsmouth Harbour d		10 28														11 12				11 28					
Portsmouth & Southsea d		10 32											11 03			11 16				11 32					
Fratton d		10 36											11 07			11 20				11 36					
Hilsea d													11 11												
Bedhampton d													11 16												
Havant d		10 45				10 51						11 15	11 19			11 30				11 45					11 51
Warblington d						10 53																			11 53
Emsworth d						10 56						11 19	11 23												11 56
Southbourne d						10 59						11 22	11 26												11 59
Nutbourne d													11 28												
Bosham d						11 03																			12 03
Fishbourne (Sussex) d													11 33												
Chichester 4 d		10 56				11b11						11 30	11 37			11 41				11 56					12c11
Bognor Regis 4 d			11 00	11 07							11 26			11 39							12 00	12 07			
Barnham a		11 03	11 06	11 13		11 18					11 32	11 37	11 44	11 45		11 48				12 03	12 06	12 13			12 18
Barnham d		11 04	11 07	11 15		11 19					11 33	11 38	11 45			11 49				12 04	12 07	12 15			12 19
Bognor Regis 4 a		11 17				11 28										11 58				12 17					12 28
Ford 4 d		11 08	11 11	11 19							11 37		11 49							12 08	12 11	12 19			
Littlehampton 4 a				11 24									11 54									12 24			
Littlehampton 4 d		10e58						11 15									11 45			11e58					
Angmering 3 d		11 14						11 23				11 47					11 53			12 14					
Goring-by-Sea d		11 18						11 27									11 57			12 18					
Durrington-on-Sea d		11 21						11 30									12 00			12 21					
West Worthing d	11 09	11 23						11 32		11 39							12 02		12 09	12 23					
Worthing 4 a	11 11	11 25						11 34		11 41		11 54					12 04		12 11	12 25					
Worthing 4 d	11 12	11 26						11 36		11 42		11 56					12 06		12 12	12 26					
East Worthing d	11 14									11 44									12 14						
Lancing d	11 17	11 30								11 47		12 00					12 10		12 17	12 30					
Shoreham-by-Sea d	11 22	11 34						11 42		11 52		12 04					12 14		12 22	12 34					
Southwick d	11 25	11 37								11 55		12 07							12 25	12 37					
Fishersgate d	11 27									11 57									12 27						
Portslade d	11 29	11 40						11 47		11 59		12 10							12 29	12 40					
Aldrington d	11 31									12 01									12 31						
Hove 2 d	11 34	11 44						11 51	11 54	12 04		12 14					12 21	12 24	12 34	12 44					
Brighton 10 a	11 38	11 48							11 58	12 08		12 18						12 28	12 38	12 48					
Haywards Heath 3 a		12 15						12 09	12 18								12 35	12 47		13 15					
Arundel d			11 16								11 42										12 16				
Amberley d											11 47														
Pulborough d			11 25		←						11 53										12 25			←	
Billingshurst d			11 31 →		11 31						11 59				←						12 31 →			12 31	
Christs Hospital d											12 06 →				12 06										
Horsham 4 d					11f50	11g50									12h20	12j20								12k50	12m50
Crawley d					11 59										12 29									12 59	
Three Bridges 4 a		12 25			12 02				12 42						12 32			13 11		13 25				13 02	
Gatwick Airport 10 ✈ a					12 07			12 24	12 30						12 37		12 54	13 00						13 07	
East Croydon a	12 23				12 27			12 40	12 46	12 55					13 00		13 10	13 16	13 23					13 27	
London Bridge 4 ⊖ a	12n45				12 45				13 00	13n15					13q15			13 30	13n45					13 45	
Clapham Junction 10 a	12 33				12 37			12 49	13n03	13 04					13 11		13 19		13 33					13 37	
London Victoria 15 ⊖ a	12 40				12 44			12 57	13r05	13 11					13 18		13 27	13r35	13 40					13 44	

For general notes see front of timetable
For details of catering facilities see Directory of Train Operators

b Arr. 1108
c Arr. 1208
e Change at Ford
f Arr. 1140
g Arr. 1146
h Arr. 1210
j Arr. 1216
k Arr. 1240
m Arr. 1246
n Change at Brighton and East Croydon
q Change at Gatwick Airport
r Change at Brighton and Gatwick Airport

Table 188

Saturdays

Southampton, Portsmouth and Sussex Coast → Brighton, Gatwick Airport & London

For complete service between Horsham and Three Bridges see Table 186

		SN 1	SN 1	SN 1	SN 1	SN 1	SN 1	SN 1	SN 1	SN 1	SN 1	SN 1	SN 1	SN 1	SN 1	SN 1		SN 1	SN 1	SN 1	SN 1	SN 1	SN 1	SN 1	SN 1	SN 1
Southampton Central	d					11 36													12 11					12 36		
Swanwick	d					11 53													12 28					12 53		
Fareham	d					12 00													12 35					13 00		
Portchester	d																		12 40							
Cosham	d					12 08													12 44					13 08		
Portsmouth Harbour	d									12 12				12 28												
Portsmouth & Southsea	d						12 03			12 16				12 32											13 03	
Fratton	d						12 07			12 20				12 36											13 07	
Hilsea	d						12 11																		13 11	
Bedhampton	d						12 16																		13 16	
Havant	d					12 15	12 19			12 30				12 45					12 51					13 15	13 19	
Warblington	d																		12 53							
Emsworth	d					12 19	12 23												12 56					13 19	13 23	
Southbourne	d					12 22	12 26												12 59					13 22	13 26	
Nutbourne	d						12 28																		13 28	
Bosham	d																		13 03							
Fishbourne (Sussex)	d						12 33																		13 33	
Chichester 4	d					12 30	12 37			12 41				12 56					13b11					13 30	13 37	
Bognor Regis 4	d				12 26			12 39							13 00	13 07							13 26			13 39
Barnham	a				12 32	12 37	12 44	12 45		12 48				13 03	13 06	13 13			13 18				13 32	13 37	13 44	13 45
	d				12 33	12 38	12 45			12 49				13 04	13 07	13 15			13 19				13 33	13 38	13 45	
Bognor Regis 4	a									*12 58*				*13 17*					*13 28*							
Ford 4	d				12 37		12 49							13 08	13 11	13 19							13 37		13 49	
Littlehampton 4	a						12 54									13 24									13 54	
	d	12 15									12 45			*12c58*						13 15						
Angmering 3	d	12 23				12 47					12 53			13 14						13 23				13 47		
Goring-by-Sea	d	12 27									12 57			13 18						13 27						
Durrington-on-Sea	d	12 30									13 00			13 21						13 30						
West Worthing	d	12 32		12 39							13 02		13 09	13 23						13 32		13 39				
Worthing 4	a	12 34		12 41		12 54					13 04		13 11	13 25						13 34		13 41		13 54		
	d	12 36		12 42		12 56					13 06		13 12	13 26						13 36		13 42		13 56		
East Worthing	d			12 44									13 14									13 44				
Lancing	d			12 47		13 00					13 10		13 17	13 30								13 47		14 00		
Shoreham-by-Sea	d	12 42		12 52		13 04					13 14		13 22	13 34						13 42		13 52		14 04		
Southwick	d			12 55		13 07							13 25	13 37								13 55		14 07		
Fishersgate	d			12 57									13 27									13 57				
Portslade	d	12 47		12 59		13 10							13 29	13 40						13 47		13 59		14 10		
Aldrington	d			13 01									13 31									14 01				
Hove 2	d	12 51	12 54	13 04		13 14					13 21	13 24	13 34	13 44						13 51	13 54	14 04		14 14		
Brighton 10	a		12 58	13 08		13 18						13 28	13 38	13 48							13 58	14 08		14 18		
Haywards Heath 3	a	13 09	*13 18*								13 35	*13 47*		*14 15*						14 09	*14 18*					
Arundel	d				12 42										13 16								13 42			
Amberley	d				12 47																		13 47			
Pulborough	d				12 53										13 25			←					13 53			
Billingshurst	d				12 59				←						13 31			13 31					13 59			
Christs Hospital	d				13 06				13 06						→								14 06			
Horsham 4	d				→				13e20	13f20								13g50	13h50				→			
Crawley	d								13 29									13 59								
Three Bridges 4	a		*13 42*						13 32			*14 11*		*14 25*				14 02			*14 42*					
Gatwick Airport 10 ✈	a	13 24	*13 30*						13 37		13 54	*14 00*						14 07		14 24	*14 30*			*14 51*		
East Croydon	a	13 40	*13 46*	*13 55*					14 00		14 10	*14 16*	*14 23*					14 27		14 40	*14 46*	*14 55*		*15 07*		
London Bridge 4 ⊖	a		*14 00*	*14j15*					*14k15*			*14 30*	*14j45*					*14 45*			*15 00*	*15j15*				
Clapham Junction 10	a	13 49	*14j03*	*14 04*					14 11		14 19		*14 33*					14 37		14 49	*15j03*	*15 04*		*15j25*		
London Victoria 15 ⊖	a	13 57	*14m05*	*14 11*					14 18		14 27	*14m35*	*14 40*					14 44		14 57	*15m05*	*15 11*		*15m27*		

For general notes see front of timetable
For details of catering facilities see Directory of Train Operators

- b Arr. 1308
- c Change at Ford
- e Arr. 1310
- f Arr. 1316
- g Arr. 1340
- h Arr. 1346
- j Change at Brighton and East Croydon
- k Change at Gatwick Airport
- m Change at Brighton and Gatwick Airport

Table 188

Southampton, Portsmouth and Sussex Coast → Brighton, Gatwick Airport & London

For complete service between Horsham and Three Bridges see Table 186

		SN 1	SN 1	SN 1	SN 1	SN 1	SN 1	SN 1	SN 1		SN 1	SN 1	SN 1	SN 1	SN 1	SN 1	SN 1	SN 1	SN 1	SN 1	SN 1	SN 1	SN 1	SN 1	SN 1	SN 1
Southampton Central	d											13 11					13 36									
Swanwick	d											13 28					13 53									
Fareham	d											13 35					14 00									
Portchester	d											13 40														
Cosham	d											13 44					14 08									
Portsmouth Harbour	d		13 12				13 28														14 12				14 28	
Portsmouth & Southsea	d		13 16				13 32											14 03			14 16				14 32	
Fratton	d		13 20				13 36											14 07			14 20				14 36	
Hilsea	d																	14 11								
Bedhampton	d																	14 16								
Havant	d		13 30				13 45					13 51					14 15	14 19			14 30				14 45	
Warblington	d											13 53														
Emsworth	d											13 56					14 19	14 23								
Southbourne	d											13 59					14 22	14 26								
Nutbourne	d																	14 28								
Bosham	d											14 03														
Fishbourne (Sussex)	d																	14 33								
Chichester 4	d		13 41				13 56					14b11					14 30	14 37			14 41				14 56	
Bognor Regis 4	d							14 00	14 07							14 26			14 39							15 00
Barnham	a		13 48				14 03	14 06	14 13			14 18				14 32	14 37	14 44	14 45		14 48				15 03	15 06
	d		13 49				14 04	14 07	14 15			14 19				14 33	14 38	14 45			14 49				15 04	15 07
Bognor Regis 4	a		*13 58*				*14 17*					*14 28*									*14 58*				*15 17*	
Ford 4	d						14 08	14 11	14 19							14 37		14 49							15 08	15 11
Littlehampton 4	a								14 24									14 54								
	d			13 45			*13c58*						14 15									14 45			*14c58*	
Angmering 3	d			13 53			14 14						14 23				14 47					14 53			15 14	
Goring-by-Sea	d			13 57			14 18						14 27									14 57			15 18	
Durrington-on-Sea	d			14 00			14 21						14 30									15 00			15 21	
West Worthing	d			14 02		14 09	14 23						14 32		14 39							15 02		15 09	15 23	
Worthing 4	a			14 04		14 11	14 25						14 34		14 41		14 54					15 04		15 11	15 25	
	d			14 06		14 12	14 26						14 36		14 42		14 56					15 06		15 12	15 26	
East Worthing	d					14 14									14 44									15 14		
Lancing	d			14 10		14 17	14 30								14 47		15 00					15 10		15 17	15 30	
Shoreham-by-Sea	d			14 14		14 22	14 34						14 42		14 52		15 04					15 14		15 22	15 34	
Southwick	d					14 25	14 37								14 55		15 07							15 25	15 37	
Fishersgate	d					14 27									14 57									15 27		
Portslade	d					14 29	14 40						14 47		14 59		15 10							15 29	15 40	
Aldrington	d					14 31									15 01									15 31		
Hove 2	d			14 21	14 24	14 34	14 44						14 51	14 54	15 04		15 14					15 21	15 24	15 34	15 44	
Brighton 10	a				14 28	14 38	14 48							14 58	15 08		15 18						15 28	15 38	15 48	
Haywards Heath 3	a			14 35	*14 47*		*15 15*						15 09	*15 18*								15 35	*15 47*		*16 15*	
Arundel	d							14 16								14 42										15 16
Amberley	d															14 47										
Pulborough	d							14 25			←					14 53										15 25
Billingshurst	d	←						14 31			14 31					14 59				←						15 31
Christs Hospital	d	14 06						→								15 06				15 06						→
Horsham 4	d	14e20	14f20								14g50	14h50				→				15j20	15k20					
Crawley	d	14 29									14 59									15 29						
Three Bridges 4	a	14 32			*15 11*		*15 25*				15 02			*15 42*						15 32			*16 11*		*16 25*	
Gatwick Airport 10 ✈	a	14 37		14 55	*15 00*						15 07		15 24	*15 30*						15 37		15 54	*16 00*			
East Croydon	a	15 00		15 11	*15 16*	*15 23*					15 27		15 40	*15 46*	*15 55*					16 00		16 10	*16 16*	*16 23*		
London Bridge 4 ⊖	a	*15m15*			*15 30*	*15n45*					*15 45*			*16 00*	*16n15*					*16m15*			*16 30*	*16n45*		
Clapham Junction 10	a	15 11		15 20		*15 33*					15 37		15 49	*16n03*	*16 04*					16 11		16 19		*16 33*		
London Victoria 15 ⊖	a	15 18		15 27	*15q35*	*15 40*					15 44		15 57	*16q05*	*16 11*					16 18		16 27	*16q35*	*16 40*		

For general notes see front of timetable
For details of catering facilities see Directory of Train Operators

b Arr. 1408

c Change at Ford
e Arr. 1410
f Arr. 1416
g Arr. 1440
h Arr. 1446

j Arr. 1510
k Arr. 1516
m Change at Gatwick Airport
n Change at Brighton and East Croydon
q Change at Brighton and Gatwick Airport

Table 188

Southampton, Portsmouth and Sussex Coast → Brighton, Gatwick Airport & London

For complete service between Horsham and Three Bridges see Table 186

		SN 1		SN 1	SN 1	SN 1	SN 1	SN 1	GW A	SN 1	SN 1	SN 1	SN 1	SN 1	SN 1	SN 1	SN 1	SN 1		SN 1	SN 1	SN 1	SN 1	SN 1	SN 1	SN 1
Southampton Central	d				14 11				14 34		14 26													15 11		
Swanwick	d				14 28																			15 28		
Fareham	d				14 35				14 56		15 02													15 35		
Portchester	d				14 40																			15 40		
Cosham	d				14 44				15 04															15 44		
Portsmouth Harbour	d														15 12					15 28						
Portsmouth & Southsea	d											15 03			15 16					15 32						
Fratton	d											15 07			15 20					15 36						
Hilsea	d											15 11														
Bedhampton	d											15 16														
Havant	d				14 51				15 11		15 15	15 19			15 30					15 45				15 51		
Warblington	d				14 53																			15 53		
Emsworth	d				14 56						15 19	15 23												15 56		
Southbourne	d				14 59						15 22	15 26												15 59		
Nutbourne	d											15 28														
Bosham	d				15 03																			16 03		
Fishbourne (Sussex)	d											15 33														
Chichester 4	d				15b11				15 22		15 30	15 37			15 41					15 56				16c11		
Bognor Regis 4	d	15 07								15 26			15 39								16 00	16 07				
Barnham	a	15 13			15 18				15 30	15 32	15 37	15 44	15 45		15 48					16 03	16 06	16 13		16 18		
	d	15 15			15 19				15 30	15 33	15 38	15 45			15 49					16 04	16 07	16 15		16 19		
Bognor Regis 4	a				*15 28*				*15 45*						*15 58*					*16 17*				*16 28*		
Ford 4	d	15 19								15 37		15 49								16 08	16 11	16 19				
Littlehampton 4	a	15 24										15 54										16 24				
	d					15 15										15 45				*15e58*					16 15	
Angmering 3	d					15 23					15 47					15 53				16 14					16 23	
Goring-by-Sea	d					15 27										15 57				16 18					16 27	
Durrington-on-Sea	d					15 30										16 00				16 21					16 30	
West Worthing	d					15 32		15 39								16 02		16 09		16 23					16 32	
Worthing 4	a					15 34		15 41	15 45		15 54					16 04		16 11		16 25					16 34	
	d					15 36		15 42	15 50		15 56					16 06		16 12		16 26					16 36	
East Worthing	d							15 44										16 14								
Lancing	d							15 47			16 00					16 10		16 17		16 30						
Shoreham-by-Sea	d					15 42		15 52	15 57		16 04					16 14		16 22		16 34					16 42	
Southwick	d							15 55			16 07							16 25		16 37						
Fishersgate	d							15 57										16 27								
Portslade	d					15 47		15 59			16 10							16 29		16 40					16 47	
Aldrington	d							16 01										16 31								
Hove 2	d					15 51	15 54	16 04	16 08		16 14					16 21	16 24	16 34		16 44					16 51	16 54
Brighton 10	a						15 58	16 08	16 14		16 18						16 28	16 38		16 48						16 58
Haywards Heath 3	a					16 09	*16 18*									16 35	*16 47*			*17 15*					17 09	*17 18*
Arundel	d									15 42											16 16					
Amberley	d									15 47																
Pulborough	d			←						15 53											16 25		←			
Billingshurst	d			15 31						15 59				←							16 31 →		16 31			
Christs Hospital	d									16 06 →				16 06												
Horsham 4	d			15f50	15g50									16h20	16j20								16k50	16m50		
Crawley	d			15 59										16 29									16 59			
Three Bridges 4	a			16 02			*16 42*							16 32			*17 11*			*17 25*			17 02			*17 42*
Gatwick Airport 10 ✈	a			16 07		16 24	*16 30*							16 37		16 54	*17 00*						17 07		17 24	*17 30*
East Croydon	a			16 27		16 40	*16 46*	*16 55*	*16 55*					17 00		17 10	*17 16*	*17 23*					17 27		17 40	*17 46*
London Bridge 4 ⊖	a			*16 45*			*17 00*	*17n15*	*17n15*					*17q15*			*17 30*	*17n45*					*17 45*			*18 00*
Clapham Junction 10	a			16 37		16 49	*17n03*	*17 04*	*17 04*					17 11		17 19		*17 33*					17 37		17 49	*18n03*
London Victoria 15 ⊖	a			16 44		16 57	*17r05*	*17 11*	*17 11*					17 18		17 27	*17r35*	*17 40*					17 44		17 57	*18r05*

For general notes see front of timetable
For details of catering facilities see Directory of Train Operators

A From Great Malvern (Table 71)
b Arr. 1508
c Arr. 1608
e Change at Ford
f Arr. 1540
g Arr. 1546
h Arr. 1610
j Arr. 1616
k Arr. 1640
m Arr. 1646
n Change at Brighton and East Croydon
q Change at Gatwick Airport
r Change at Brighton and Gatwick Airport

Table 188

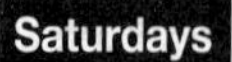

Southampton, Portsmouth and Sussex Coast → Brighton, Gatwick Airport & London

For complete service between Horsham and Three Bridges see Table 186

Station		SN 1	SN 1	SN 1	SN 1	SN 1	SN 1	SN 1	SN 1	SN 1	SN 1	SN 1	SN 1	SN 1	SN 1	SN 1	SN 1	SN 1	SN 1	SN 1	SN 1	SN 1	SN 1	SN 1	SN 1
Southampton Central	d			15 36												16 11					16 36				
Swanwick	d			15 53												16 28					16 53				
Fareham	d			16 00												16 35					17 00				
Portchester	d															16 40									
Cosham	d			16 08												16 44					17 08				
Portsmouth Harbour	d							16 12				16 28													17 12
Portsmouth & Southsea	d				16 03			16 16				16 32										17 03			17 16
Fratton	d				16 07			16 20				16 36										17 07			17 20
Hilsea	d				16 11																	17 11			
Bedhampton	d				16 16																	17 16			
Havant	d			16 15	16 19			16 30				16 45				16 51					17 15	17 19			17 30
Warblington	d															16 53									
Emsworth	d			16 19	16 23											16 56					17 19	17 23			
Southbourne	d			16 22	16 26											16 59					17 22	17 26			
Nutbourne	d				16 28																	17 28			
Bosham	d															17 03									
Fishbourne (Sussex)	d				16 33																	17 33			
Chichester 4	d			16 30	16 37			16 41				16 56				17b11					17 30	17 37			17 41
Bognor Regis 4	d		16 26			16 39							17 00	17 07						17 26			17 39		
Barnham	a		16 32	16 37	16 44	16 45		16 48				17 03	17 06	17 13		17 18				17 32	17 37	17 44	17 45		17 48
	d		16 33	16 38	16 45			16 49				17 04	17 07	17 15		17 19				17 33	17 38	17 45			17 49
Bognor Regis 4	a							*16 58*				*17 17*				*17 28*									*17 58*
Ford 4	d		16 37		16 49							17 08	17 11	17 19						17 37		17 49			
Littlehampton 4	a				16 54									17 24								17 54			
	d								16 45			*16c58*					17 15								
Angmering 3	d			16 47					16 53			17 14					17 23				17 47				
Goring-by-Sea	d								16 57			17 18					17 27								
Durrington-on-Sea	d								17 00			17 21					17 30								
West Worthing	d	16 39							17 02		17 09	17 23					17 32		17 39						
Worthing 4	a	16 41		16 54					17 04		17 11	17 25					17 34		17 41		17 54				
	d	16 42		16 56					17 06		17 12	17 26					17 36		17 42		17 56				
East Worthing	d	16 44									17 14								17 44						
Lancing	d	16 47		17 00					17 10		17 17	17 30							17 47		18 00				
Shoreham-by-Sea	d	16 52		17 04					17 14		17 22	17 34					17 42		17 52		18 04				
Southwick	d	16 55		17 07							17 25	17 37							17 55		18 07				
Fishersgate	d	16 57									17 27								17 57						
Portslade	d	16 59		17 10							17 29	17 40					17 47		17 59		18 10				
Aldrington	d	17 01									17 31								18 01						
Hove 2	d	17 04		17 14					17 21	17 24	17 34	17 44					17 51	17 54	18 04		18 14				
Brighton 10	a	17 08		17 18						17 28	17 38	17 48						17 58	18 08		18 18				
Haywards Heath 3	a								17 35	*17 47*		*18 15*					18 09	*18 18*							
Arundel	d		16 42										17 16							17 42					
Amberley	d		16 47																	17 47					
Pulborough	d		16 53										17 25							17 53					
Billingshurst	d		16 59				←						17 31		← 17 31					17 59					
Christs Hospital	d		17 06 →				17 06						→							18 06 →				← 18 06	
Horsham 4	d						17e20	17f20							17g50	17h50								18j20	18k20
Crawley	d						17 29								17 59									18 29	
Three Bridges 4	a						17 32			*18 11*		*18 25*			18 02			*18 42*						18 32	
Gatwick Airport 10 ✈	a						17 37		17 54	*18 00*					18 07		18 24	*18 30*						18 37	
East Croydon	a	*17 55*					18 00		18 10	*18 16*	*18 23*				18 27		18 40	*18 46*	*18 55*					19 00	
London Bridge 4 ⊖	a	*18m15*					*18n15*			*18 30*	*18m45*				*18 45*			*19 00*	*19m15*					*19n15*	
Clapham Junction 10	a	*18 04*					18 11		18 19		*18 33*				18 37		18 49	*19m03*	*19 04*					19 11	
London Victoria 15 ⊖	a	*18 11*					18 18		18 27	*18q35*	*18 40*				18 44		18 57	*19q05*	*19 11*					19 18	

For general notes see front of timetable
For details of catering facilities see Directory of Train Operators

b Arr. 1708
c Change at Ford
e Arr. 1710
f Arr. 1716
g Arr. 1740
h Arr. 1746
j Arr. 1810
k Arr. 1816
m Change at Brighton and East Croydon
n Change at Gatwick Airport
q Change at Brighton and Gatwick Airport

Southampton, Portsmouth and Sussex Coast → Brighton, Gatwick Airport & London

For complete service between Horsham and Three Bridges see Table 186

		SN 1	SN 1	SN 1	SN 1	SN 1	SN 1	SN 1	SN 1	SN 1	SN 1	SN 1	SN 1	SN 1	SN 1	SN 1	SN 1	SN 1	SN 1	SN 1	SN 1	SN 1	SN 1	SN 1
Southampton Central	d								17 11				17 36									18 11	
Swanwick	d								17 28				17 53									18 28	
Fareham	d								17 35				18 00									18 35	
Portchester	d								17 40													18 40	
Cosham	d								17 44				18 08									18 44	
Portsmouth Harbour	d				17 28															18 12	18 28			
Portsmouth & Southsea	d				17 32										18 03					18 16	18 32			
Fratton	d				17 36										18 07					18 20	18 36			
Hilsea	d														18 11									
Bedhampton	d														18 16									
Havant	d				17 45				17 51				18 15		18 19					18 28	18 45		18 51	
Warblington	d								17 53											18 30				
Emsworth	d								17 56				18 19		18 23					18 33			18 55	
Southbourne	d								17 59				18 22		18 26					18 36			18 58	
Nutbourne	d														18 28									
Bosham	d								18 03											18 41				
Fishbourne (Sussex)	d														18 33									
Chichester 4	d				17 56				18b11				18 30		18 37					18 46	18 56		19 07	
Bognor Regis 4	d					18 00	18 07							18 33		18 39						19 03		
Barnham	a				18 03	18 06	18 13		18 18				18 37	18 40	18 44	18 46				18 53	19 03	19 09	19 14	
	d				18 04	18 07	18 15		18 19				18 38	18 41	18 45					18 54	19 04	19 22	19 15	
Bognor Regis 4	a				*18 17*				*18 28*						*18 58*						*19 17*	→	*19 28*	
Ford 4	d				18 08	18 11	18 19							18 45	18 49					18 58	19 08		19 19	
Littlehampton 4	a						18 24													19 03				
	d	17 45			*17c58*					18 15									18 52		*18c58*		*19c11*	19 15
Angmering 3	d	17 53			18 14					18 23			18 47	18 53					19 00		19 14			19 23
Goring-by-Sea	d	17 57			18 18					18 27				18 57					19 04		19 18			19 27
Durrington-on-Sea	d	18 00			18 21					18 30				19 00			←		19 07		19 21			19 30
West Worthing	d	18 02		18 09	18 23					18 32		18 39		19 02			19 02		19 09		19 23			19 32
Worthing 4	a	18 04		18 11	18 25					18 34		18 41	18 54	→			19 04		19 11		19 25			19 34
	d	18 06		18 12	18 26					18 36		18 42	18 56				19 06		19 12		19 26			19 35
East Worthing	d			18 14								18 44							19 14					
Lancing	d	18 10		18 17	18 30							18 47	19 00				19 10		19 17		19 30			19 39
Shoreham-by-Sea	d	18 14		18 22	18 34					18 42		18 52	19 04				19 14		19 22		19 34			19 43
Southwick	d			18 25	18 37							18 55	19 07						19 25		19 37			
Fishersgate	d			18 27								18 57							19 27					
Portslade	d			18 29	18 40					18 47		18 59	19 10						19 29		19 40			19 48
Aldrington	d			18 31								19 01							19 31					
Hove 2	d	18 21	18 24	18 34	18 44					18 51	18 54	19 04	19 14				19 21	19 24	19 34		19 44			19 52
Brighton 10	a		18 28	18 38	18 48						18 58	19 08	19 18					19 28	19 38		19 48			
Haywards Heath 3	a	18 35	*18 47*		*19 15*					19 09	*19 18*						19 35	*19 47*			*20 16*			20 09
Arundel	d					18 16									18 54								19 24	
Amberley	d														18 59								19 29	
Pulborough	d					18 25									19 05								19 35	
Billingshurst	d					18 31		←							19 11								19 41	
Christs Hospital	d					18 38		18 38															19 48	
Horsham 4	d					→		18e50	18f50						19 21								19 52	
Crawley	d								18 59						19 30								20 01	
Three Bridges 4	a		*19 12*		*19 25*				19 02		*19 42*				19 33		*20 12*	*20 12*					20 05	*20 32*
Gatwick Airport 10 ✈	a	18 54	*19 00*						19 07	19 24	*19 31*				19 38		19 54	*20 00*					20 10	20 24
East Croydon	a	19 10	*19 16*	*19 23*					19 28	19 40	*19 47*	*19 55*			19 59		20 10	*20 16*	*20 23*				20 30	20 40
London Bridge 4 ⊖	a		*19 30*	19g45					19h45		*20 00*	20g15			20h15		*20 30*	*20 30*	20g45				20h45	*21 00*
Clapham Junction 10	a	19 19		*19 33*					19 40	19 49	20g03	*20 04*			20 10		20 19		*20 33*				20 40	20 49
London Victoria 15 ⊖	a	19 27	19j35	*19 40*					19 48	19 57		*20 11*			20 17		20 27	20j35	*20 40*				20 50	20 57

For general notes see front of timetable
For details of catering facilities see Directory of Train Operators

b Arr. 1808
c Change at Ford
e Arr. 1842
f Arr. 1846
g Change at Brighton and East Croydon
h Change at Gatwick Airport
j Change at Brighton and Gatwick Airport

Southampton, Portsmouth and Sussex Coast → Brighton, Gatwick Airport & London

For complete service between Horsham and Three Bridges see Table 186

		SN 1	SN 1	SN 1	SN 1	SN 1	SN 1	SN 1	SN 1	SN 1	SN 1	SN 1	SN 1		SN 1	SN 1	SN 1	SN 1	SN 1	SN 1	SN 1	SN 1	SN 1	SN 1	SN 1	SN 1
Southampton Central	d			18 36									19 11				19 36								20 11	
Swanwick	d			18 53									19 28				19 53								20 28	
Fareham	d			19 00									19 35				20 00								20 35	
Portchester	d												19 40												20 40	
Cosham	d			19 08									19 44				20 08								20 44	
Portsmouth Harbour	d									19 12	19 28												20 28			
Portsmouth & Southsea	d							19 03		19 16	19 32											20 03	20 32			
Fratton	d							19 07		19 20	19 36											20 07	20 36			
Hilsea	d							19 11														20 11				
Bedhampton	d							19 16														20 16				
Havant	d			19 15				19 19		19 28	19 45		19 52				20 15					20 19	20 45		20 51	
Warblington	d									19 30												20 21				
Emsworth	d			19 19				19 23		19 33			19 56									20 24			20 55	
Southbourne	d			19 22				19 26		19 36			19 59									20 27			20 58	
Nutbourne	d							19 28														20 29				
Bosham	d									19 41												20 33				
Fishbourne (Sussex)	d							19 33														20 36				
Chichester 4	d			19 30				19 37		19 46	19 56		20 07				20 26					20 40	20 56		21 07	
Bognor Regis 4	d				19 33				19 39			20 04						20 33	20 39					21 04		
Barnham	a	←		19 37	19 40			19 44	19 46	19 53	20 03	20 10	20 14				20 33	20 39	20 45			20 47	21 03	21 10	21 14	
	d	19 22		19 38	19 41			19 45		19 54	20 04	20 11	20 15				20 34	20 40				20 49	21 04	21 11	21 15	
Bognor Regis 4	a							*19 58*			*20 17*		*20 28*				*20 45*					*20 58*	*21 17*		*21 28*	
Ford 4	d	19 26			19 45			19 49		19 58	20 08	20 15	20 19					20 44				20 53	21 08	21 15	21 19	
Littlehampton 4	a	19 32						19 54		20 03		20 20										21 01		21 20		
	d						19 52						*20b11*		20 15						20 52					21 15
Angmering 3	d			19 47	19 53		20 00				20 14				20 23		20 43	20 53			21 00		21 14			21 23
Goring-by-Sea	d				19 57		20 04								20 27			20 57			21 04					21 27
Durrington-on-Sea	d				20 00		20 07								20 30		20 48	21 00			21 07					21 30
West Worthing	d				20 02		20 09								20 32			21 02			21 09					21 32
Worthing 4	a			19 54	20 04		20 11				20 21				20 34		20 52	21 04			21 11		21 21			21 34
	d			19 54	20 05		20 12				20 22				20 35		20 53	21 05			21 12		21 22			21 35
East Worthing	d			19 57			20 14				20 25						20 55				21 14		21 25			
Lancing	d			20 00	20 09		20 17				20 28				20 39		20 58	21 09			21 17		21 28			21 39
Shoreham-by-Sea	d			20 04	20 13		20 22				20 32				20 43		21 02	21 13			21 22		21 32			21 43
Southwick	d			20 07			20 25				20 35						21 05				21 25		21 35			
Fishersgate	d			20 09			20 27				20 37						21 07				21 27		21 37			
Portslade	d			20 11	20 17		20 29				20 39				20 48		21 09	21 18			21 29		21 39			21 48
Aldrington	d			20 13			20 31				20 41						21 12				21 31		21 41			
Hove 2	d		19 54	20 16	20 22	20 24	20 34				20 44				20 52	20 54	21 14	21 22		21 24	21 34		21 44			21 52
Brighton 10	a		19 58	20 20		20 28	20 38				20 48					20 58	21 18			21 28	21 38		21 48			
Haywards Heath 3	a		*20 18*		20 36	*20 47*					*21 21*				21 08	*21 28*		21 36		*21 58*			*22 21*			22 08
Arundel	d												20 24												21 24	
Amberley	d												20 29												21 29	
Pulborough	d												20 35												21 35	
Billingshurst	d												20 41												21 41	
Christs Hospital	d												20 48												21 48	
Horsham 4	d												20 52												21 52	
Crawley	d												21 01												22 01	
Three Bridges 4	a		*20c32*		20 47	*21 11*					*21 32*		21 05		*21 32*	*21 42*		*22 11*		*22 11*			22 32		22 05	*22 32*
Gatwick Airport 10 ✈	a		*20 30*		20 52	*21 00*					*21 37*		21 10		21 24	*21 46*		21 51		*22 16*			22 37		22 10	22 23
East Croydon	a		*20 46*		21 09	*21 16*	*21 23*						21 30		21 40	*21 55*		22 09			*22 23*		*22 59*		22 30	22 40
London Bridge 4 ⊖	a		*21 00*		*21 30*	*21 30*	*21e45*						*21f45*			*22 15*					*22e45*				*22f45*	
Clapham Junction 10	a		*21e03*		21 19		*21 33*						21 40		21 49	*22 04*		22 19			*22 33*		*23 10*		22 40	22 49
London Victoria 15 ⊖	a		*21g05*		21 27	*21g35*	*21 40*						21 48		21 57	*22 11*		22 27			*22 40*		*23 17*		22 48	22 57

For general notes see front of timetable
For details of catering facilities see Directory of Train Operators

b Change at Ford
c Change at Brighton and Haywards Heath
e Change at Brighton and East Croydon
f Change at Gatwick Airport
g Change at Brighton and Gatwick Airport

Table 188

Southampton, Portsmouth and Sussex Coast → Brighton, Gatwick Airport & London

For complete service between Horsham and Three Bridges see Table 186

		SN 1	SN 1	SN 1	SN 1	SN 1		SN 1	SN 1	SN 1	SN 1	SN 1	SN 1	SN 1	SN 1	SN 1	SN 1	SN 1	SN 1	SN 1	SN 1	SN 1		SN 1	SN 1	
Southampton Central	d			20 36							21 11				21 23			22 11				22 36				
Swanwick	d			20 53							21 28				21 45			22 28				22 53				
Fareham	d			21 00							21 39				21 55			22 39				23 00				
Portchester	d										21 44				22 00			22 44								
Cosham	d			21 08							21 48				22 04			22 48				23 08				
Portsmouth Harbour	d	20 40							21 11				21 40				22 15				22 44				23 15	
Portsmouth & Southsea	d	20 44							21 15				21 44				22 19				22 48				23 19	
Fratton	d	20 48							21 19				21 48				22 23				22 52				23 23	
Hilsea	d								21 23				21 52				22 27				22 56				23 27	
Bedhampton	d								21 28				21 57				22 32				23 01				23 33	
Havant	d	20 57		21 15					21 31		21 55		22 00		22 14		22 35	22 55			23 04	23 15			23 36	
Warblington	d	20 59							21 33						22 16										23 38	
Emsworth	d	21 02							21 36						22 19		22 39	22 59							23 41	
Southbourne	d	21 05							21 39						22 22		22 42	23 02							23 44	
Nutbourne	d	21 07							21 41						22 24										23 47	
Bosham	d	21 11							21 45						22 28										23 50	
Fishbourne (Sussex)	d	21 14							21 48						22 31										23 53	
Chichester 4	d	21 18		21 26					21 52		22 06		22 11		22 35		22b52	23 09			23 17	23 26		23 52	23 57	
Bognor Regis 4	d				21 39					22 00				22 30					23 15							
Barnham	a	21 25		21 33	21 45				21 59	22 06	22 13		22 18	22 36	22 42		22 59	23 17	23 21		23 24	23 33		23 59	00 05	
	d	21 26		21 34					22 00	22 07	22 14		22 19	22 37	22 48		23 00	23 17			23 25	23 34		00 01	00 06	
Bognor Regis 4	a			*21 47*					*22 17*				*22 28*		*22 58*		*23 12*				*23 42*	*00 12*				
Ford 4	d	21 30		21 38					22 04	22 11			22 23	22 41	22 52		23 04				23 29			00 05	00 10	
Littlehampton 4	a	21 35								22 16	22 22		22 28	22 46				23 25			23 34	23 42		00 10	00 15	
	d							21 52					22 33		*22c38*						23 39					
Angmering 3	d			21 44				22 00	22 11				22 41				23 11				23 47					
Goring-by-Sea	d			21 48				22 04	22 15				22 45				23 15				23 51					
Durrington-on-Sea	d			21 51				22 07	22 17				22 47				23 17				23 53					
West Worthing	d			21 53				22 09	22 19				22 49				23 19				23 55					
Worthing 4	a			21 55				22 11	22 22				22 52				23 22				23 58					
	d			21 56				22 12	22 22				22 52				23 22				23 59					
East Worthing	d			21 58				22 14	22 25				22 55				23 25				00 01					
Lancing	d			22 01				22 17	22 28				22 58				23 28				00 04					
Shoreham-by-Sea	d			22 05				22 22	22 32				23 02				23 32				00 08					
Southwick	d			22 08				22 25	22 35				23 05				23 35				00 11					
Fishersgate	d			22 10				22 27	22 37				23 07				23 37				00 13					
Portslade	d			22 12				22 29	22 39				23 09				23 39				00 15					
Aldrington	d			22 15				22 31	22 41				23 11				23 41				00 18					
Hove 2	d		21 54	22 17		22 24		22 34	22 44			22 54	23 14			23 24	23 44			23 54	00 20					
Brighton 10	a		21 58	22 22		22 28		22 38	22 48			22 58	23 18			23 28	23 48			23 58	00 25					
Haywards Heath 3	a		*22 28*			*22 54*						*23 23*														
Arundel	d														22 57											
Amberley	d														23 02											
Pulborough	d														23 08											
Billingshurst	d														23 14											
Christs Hospital	d														23 21											
Horsham 4	d														23 25											
Crawley	d														23 38											
Three Bridges 4	a		*22 42*			*23 05*						*23 33*			23 42											
Gatwick Airport 10 ✈	a		*22 46*			*23e12*						*23 52*			*23 52*											
East Croydon	a		*23 02*			*23 32*						*00 16*			*00 16*											
London Bridge 4 ⊖	a		*23 15*			*23 45*						*00f52*			*00 52*											
Clapham Junction 10	a		*23f25*			*00f11*						*01f02*			*01g02*											
London Victoria 15 ⊖	a		*23h52*									*00 37*			*00 37*											

For general notes see front of timetable
For details of catering facilities see Directory of Train Operators

b Arr. 2249
c Change at Ford
e Change at Brighton and Haywards Heath
f Change at Brighton and East Croydon
g Change at Three Bridges and East Croydon
h Change at Brighton and Three Bridges

Table 188

Sundays

Southampton, Portsmouth and Sussex Coast → Brighton, Gatwick Airport & London

For complete service between Horsham and Three Bridges see Table 186

		SN 1	SN 1	SN 1	SN 1	SN 1	SN 1	SN 1		SN 1	SN 1	SN 1	SN 1	SN 1	SN 1	SN 1		SN 1	SN 1	SN 1	SN 1	SN 1	SN 1	SN 1	SN 1	SN 1
Southampton Central	d																									
Swanwick	d																									
Fareham	d																									
Portchester	d																									
Cosham	d																									
Portsmouth Harbour	d	22p44		23p15								07 14				07 43					08 14				08 43	
Portsmouth & Southsea	d	22p48		23p19								07 18				07 47					08 18				08 47	
Fratton	d	22p52		23p23								07 22				07 51					08 22				08 51	
Hilsea	d	22p56		23p27																						
Bedhampton	d	23p01		23p33								07 30									08 30					
Havant	d	23p04		23p36								07 33				08 00					08 33				09 00	
Warblington	d			23p38								07 35									08 35					
Emsworth	d			23p41								07 38				08 04					08 38				09 04	
Southbourne	d			23p44								07 41				08 07					08 41				09 07	
Nutbourne	d			23p47								07 43									08 43					
Bosham	d			23p50								07 47									08 47					
Fishbourne (Sussex)	d			23p53								07 50									08 50					
Chichester 4	d	23p17	23p52	23p57								07 53				08 14					08 53				09 14	
Bognor Regis 4	d					06 57					07 36		07 57							08 36		08 57				
Barnham	a	23p24	23p59	00 05		07 03					07 42	08 01	08 03	←		08 22				08 42	09 01	09 03	←		09 22	
	d	23p25	00 01	00 06	06 06	07 05					07 43	08 08 →	08 05	08 08		08 22				08 43	09 08 →	09 05	09 08		09 22	
Bognor Regis 4	a	*23 42*														*08 32*									*09 32*	
Ford 4	d	23p29	00 05	00 10		07 09					07 47		08 09	08 12						08 47		09 09	09 12			
Littlehampton 4	a	23p34	00 10	00 15	06 13						07 52									08 52						
	d	23p39			06 21	*06*b*42*	07 14			07 41			*07*b*57*		08 14				08 41			*08*b*57*		09 14		
Angmering 3	d	23p47					07 22			07 49				08 18	08 22				08 49				09 18	09 22		
Goring-by-Sea	d	23p51					07 26			07 53				08 22	08 26				08 53				09 22	09 26		
Durrington-on-Sea	d	23p53					07 29			07 55				08 25	08 29				08 55				09 25	09 29		
West Worthing	d	23p55					07 31			07 57				08 27	08 31				08 57				09 27	09 31		
Worthing 4	a	23p58			06 34		07 33			08 00				08 29	08 33	08 37			09 00				09 29	09 33	09 37	
	d	23p59			06 34		07 35			08 00				08 30	08 41				09 00				09 30	09 41		
East Worthing	d	00 01								08 02				08 32					09 02				09 32			
Lancing	d	00 04			06 38		07 39			08 05				08 35					09 05				09 35			
Shoreham-by-Sea	d	00 08			06 42		07 43			08 09				08 39	08 47				09 09				09 39	09 47		
Southwick	d	00 11			06 45		07 46			08 12				08 42					09 12				09 42			
Fishersgate	d	00 13								08 14				08 44					09 14				09 44			
Portslade	d	00 15			06 49		07 49			08 16				08 46					09 16				09 46			
Aldrington	d	00 18								08 19				08 49				←	09 19				09 49			←
Hove 2	d	00 20			06 52		07 54	07 56		08 21				08c56 →	08 54			08 56	09 21				09e56 →	09 54		09 56
Brighton 10	a	00 25			06 56			08 00		08 26								09 00	09 25							10 00
Haywards Heath 3	a				*07 20*		08 09	*08 30*		*09 00*					09 09				*09*f*51*					10 09		
Arundel	d					07 14							08 14									09 14				
Amberley	d					07 19							08 19									09 19				
Pulborough	d					07 25							08 25									09 25				
Billingshurst	d					07 31							08 31									09 31				
Christs Hospital	d					07 38							08 38									09 38				
Horsham 4	d					07 42							08 42									09 42				
Crawley	d					07 51							08 51									09 51				
Three Bridges 4	a				*07 32*	07 54	*08 32*	*08 40*		*09 10*			08 54		*09 32*				*10 10*			09 54		*10 32*		
Gatwick Airport 10 ✈	a				*07 37*	07 58	08 21	*08 44*		*09 14*			08 58		09 21				*10*g*10*			09 58		10 21		
East Croydon	a				*07 58*	08 24	08 39	*09 01*		*09 31*			09 24		09 39				*10 31*			10 24		10 39		
London Bridge 4 ⊖	a				*08 15*	*08 45*	*09 12*	*09 15*		*09 45*			*09 45*		*10 12*				*10 45*			*10 45*		*11 12*		
Clapham Junction 10	a				*08 11*	08 37	08 54	*09*h*24*		*09*h*54*			09 37		09 54				*10*h*54*			10 37		10 54		
London Victoria 15 ⊖	a				*08 18*	08 46	09 01	*09*j*25*		*09*j*55*			09 46		10 01				*10*j*55*			10 46		11 01		

For general notes see front of timetable
For details of catering facilities see Directory of Train Operators

b Change at Ford
c Arr. 0851
e Arr. 0951
f From 30 March arr. 1000
g From 30 March arr. 1014
h Change at Brighton and East Croydon
j Change at Brighton and Gatwick Airport

Table 188

Sundays

Southampton, Portsmouth and Sussex Coast → Brighton, Gatwick Airport & London

For complete service between Horsham and Three Bridges see Table 186

		GW	SN	SN	SN	SN	SN	SN	SN	SN	SN	SN	SN	SN	SN	SN	SN	SN	SN	SN	SN	SN	SN
		◇ A	1	1	1	1	1	1	1	1	1	1	1	1	1	1	1	1	1	1	1	1	1
Southampton Central	d	08 31																					
Swanwick	d																						
Fareham	d	08 52																					
Portchester	d																						
Cosham	d	09 00																					
Portsmouth Harbour	d				09 14				09 43				10 14				10 43				11 14		
Portsmouth & Southsea	d				09 18				09 47				10 18				10 47				11 18		
Fratton	d				09 22				09 51				10 22				10 51				11 22		
Hilsea	d																						
Bedhampton	d				09 30								10 30								11 30		
Havant	d	09 11			09 33				10 00				10 33				11 00				11 33		
Warblington	d				09 35								10 35								11 35		
Emsworth	d				09 38				10 04				10 38				11 04				11 38		
Southbourne	d				09 41				10 07				10 41				11 07				11 41		
Nutbourne	d				09 43								10 43								11 43		
Bosham	d				09 47								10 47								11 47		
Fishbourne (Sussex)	d				09 50								10 50								11 50		
Chichester 4	d	09 22			09 53				10 14				10 53				11 14				11 53		
Bognor Regis 4	d			09 36		09 57						10 36		10 57						11 36		11 57	
Barnham	a	09 30		09 42	10 01	10 03	←		10 22			10 42	11 01	11 03	←		11 22			11 42	12 01	12 03	←
	d	09 30		09 43	10 08	10 05	10 08		10 22			10 43	11 08	11 05	11 08		11 22			11 43	12 08	12 05	12 08
Bognor Regis 4	a	09 50			10 21				10 49				11 21				11 49				12 21		
Ford 4	d			09 47	→	10 09	10 12					10 47	→	11 09	11 12					11 47	→	12 09	12 12
Littlehampton 4	a			09 52								10 52								11 52			
	d		09 41			09b57		10 14			10 41			10b57		11 14			11 41			11b57	
Angmering 3	d		09 49				10 18	10 22			10 49				11 18	11 22			11 49				12 18
Goring-by-Sea	d		09 53				10 22	10 26			10 53				11 22	11 26			11 53				12 22
Durrington-on-Sea	d		09 55				10 25	10 29			10 55				11 25	11 29			11 55				12 25
West Worthing	d		09 57				10 27	10 31			10 57				11 27	11 31			11 57				12 27
Worthing 4	a	09 45	10 00				10 29	10 33	10 37		11 00				11 29	11 33	11 37		12 00				12 29
	d	09 45	10 00				10 30	10 41			11 00				11 30	11 41			12 00				12 30
East Worthing	d		10 02				10 32				11 02				11 32				12 02				12 32
Lancing	d		10 05				10 35				11 05				11 35				12 05				12 35
Shoreham-by-Sea	d	09 52	10 09				10 39	10 47			11 09				11 39	11 47			12 09				12 39
Southwick	d		10 12				10 42				11 12				11 42				12 12				12 42
Fishersgate	d		10 14				10 44				11 14				11 44				12 14				12 44
Portslade	d		10 16				10 46				11 16				11 46				12 16				12 46
Aldrington	d		10 19				10 49			←	11 19				11 49			←	12 19				12 49
Hove 2	d	09 59	10 21				10c56	10 54		10 56	11 21				11e56	11 54		11 56	12 21				12f56
Brighton 10	a	10 05	10 25				→			11 00	11 25				→			12 00	12 25				→
Haywards Heath 3	a	10 30	11 00					11 09			12 00					12 09			13 00				
Arundel	d					10 14								11 14								12 14	
Amberley	d					10 19								11 19								12 19	
Pulborough	d					10 25								11 25								12 25	
Billingshurst	d					10 31								11 31								12 31	
Christs Hospital	d					10 38								11 38								12 38	
Horsham 4	d					10 42								11 42								12 42	
Crawley	d					10 51								11 51								12 51	
Three Bridges 4	a	10 40	11 10			10 54		11 32			12 10			11 54		12 32			13 10			12 54	
Gatwick Airport 10 ✈	a	10 44	11 14			10 58		11 21			12 14			11 58		12 22			13 14			12 58	
East Croydon	a	11 01	11 31			11 24		11 39			12 31			12 24		12 39			13 31			13 24	
London Bridge 4 ⊖	a	11 15	11 45			11 45		12 12			12 45			12 45		13 12			13 45			13 45	
Clapham Junction 10	a	11g24	11g54			11 37		11 54			12g54			12 37		12 54			13g54			13 37	
London Victoria 15 ⊖	a	11h25	11h55			11 46		12 01			12h55			12 46		13 01			13h55			13 46	

For general notes see front of timetable
For details of catering facilities see Directory of Train Operators

A From Romsey (Table 158)
b Change at Ford
c Arr. 1051
e Arr. 1151
f Arr. 1251
g Change at Brighton and East Croydon
h Change at Brighton and Gatwick Airport

Sundays

Southampton, Portsmouth and Sussex Coast → Brighton, Gatwick Airport & London

For complete service between Horsham and Three Bridges see Table 186

		SN 1	SN 1	SN 1		SN 1	SN 1	SN 1	SN 1	SN 1	SN 1	SN 1		SN 1	SN 1	SN 1	SN 1	SN 1	SN 1	SN 1	SN 1		SN 1	GW ◇ A	SN 1	SN 1
Southampton Central	d																							13 08		
Swanwick	d																									
Fareham	d																							13 34		
Portchester	d																									
Cosham	d																							13 42		
Portsmouth Harbour	d		11 43					12 14				12 43					13 14				13 43					
Portsmouth & Southsea	d		11 47					12 18				12 47					13 18				13 47					
Fratton	d		11 51					12 22				12 51					13 22				13 51					
Hilsea	d																									
Bedhampton	d							12 30									13 30									
Havant	d		12 00					12 33				13 00					13 33				14 00			14 04		
Warblington	d							12 35									13 35									
Emsworth	d		12 04					12 38				13 04					13 38				14 04					
Southbourne	d		12 07					12 41				13 07					13 41				14 07					
Nutbourne	d							12 43									13 43									
Bosham	d							12 47									13 47									
Fishbourne (Sussex)	d							12 50									13 50									
Chichester 4	d		12 14					12 53				13 14					13 53				14 14			14 19		
Bognor Regis 4	d						12 36		12 57							13 36		13 57								14 36
Barnham	a		12 22				12 42	13 01	13 03	←		13 22				13 42	14 01	14 03	←		14 22			14 27		14 42
	d		12 22				12 43	13 08	13 05	13 08		13 22				13 43	14 08	14 05	14 08		14 22			14 27		14 43
Bognor Regis 4	a		*12 49*					*13 21*				*13 49*					*14 21*				*14 49*			*14 49*		
Ford 4	d						12 47	→	13 09	13 12						13 47	→	14 09	14 12							14 47
Littlehampton 4	a						12 52									13 52										14 52
	d	12 14				12 41			*12*b*57*		13 14				13 41			*13*b*57*		14 14					14 41	
Angmering 3	d	12 22				12 49				13 18	13 22				13 49				14 18	14 22					14 49	
Goring-by-Sea	d	12 26				12 53				13 22	13 26				13 53				14 22	14 26					14 53	
Durrington-on-Sea	d	12 29				12 55				13 25	13 29				13 55				14 25	14 29					14 55	
West Worthing	d	12 31				12 57				13 27	13 31				13 57				14 27	14 31					14 57	
Worthing 4	a	12 33	12 37			13 00				13 29	13 33	13 37			14 00				14 29	14 33	14 37			14 44	15 00	
	d	12 41				13 00				13 30	13 41				14 00				14 30	14 41				14 45	15 00	
East Worthing	d					13 02				13 32					14 02				14 32						15 02	
Lancing	d					13 05				13 35					14 05				14 35						15 05	
Shoreham-by-Sea	d	12 47				13 09				13 39	13 47				14 09				14 39	14 47				14 51	15 09	
Southwick	d					13 12				13 42					14 12				14 42						15 12	
Fishersgate	d					13 14				13 44					14 14				14 44						15 14	
Portslade	d					13 16				13 46					14 16				14 46						15 16	
Aldrington	d			←		13 19				13 49				←	14 19				14 49				←		15 19	
Hove 2	d	12 54		12 56		13 21				13c56	13 54			13 56	14 21				14e56	14 54			14 56	15 00	15 21	
Brighton 10	a			13 00		13 25				→				14 00	14 25				→				15 00	15 06	15 25	
Haywards Heath 3	a	13 09				*14 00*					14 09				*15 00*					15 09				*15 30*	*16 00*	
Arundel	d								13 14									14 14								
Amberley	d								13 19									14 19								
Pulborough	d								13 25									14 25								
Billingshurst	d								13 31									14 31								
Christs Hospital	d								13 38									14 38								
Horsham 4	d								13 42									14 42								
Crawley	d								13 51									14 51								
Three Bridges 4	a	*13 32*				*14 10*			13 54		*14 32*				*15 10*			14 54		*15 32*				*15 40*	*16 10*	
Gatwick Airport 10 ✈	a	13 22				*14 14*			13 58		14 22				*15 14*			14 58		15 22				*15 44*	*16 14*	
East Croydon 🚌	a	13 39				*14 31*			14 24		14 39				*15 31*			15 24		15 39				*16 01*	*16 31*	
London Bridge 4 ⊖	a	*14 12*				*14 45*			*14 45*		*15 12*				*15 45*			*15 45*		*16 12*				*16 15*	*16 45*	
Clapham Junction 10	a	13 54				*14f54*			14 37		14 54				*15f54*			15 37		15 54				*16f24*	*16 47*	
London Victoria 15 ⊖	a	14 01				*14g55*			14 46		15 01				*15g55*			15 46		16 01				*16g25*	*16 53*	

For general notes see front of timetable
For details of catering facilities see Directory of Train Operators

A From 30 March from Bristol Parkway (Table 132)
b Change at Ford
c Arr. 1351
e Arr. 1451
f Change at Brighton and East Croydon
g Change at Brighton and Gatwick Airport

Table 188

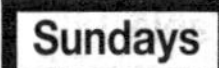

Southampton, Portsmouth and Sussex Coast → Brighton, Gatwick Airport & London

For complete service between Horsham and Three Bridges see Table 186

		SN 1	SN 1	SN 1	SN 1	SN 1	SN 1	SN 1	SN 1	SN 1	SN 1	SN 1	SN 1	SN 1	SN 1	GW ◇ A ⚓	SN 1	SN 1	SN 1	SN 1	SN 1	SN 1	SN 1
Southampton Central	d															15 22							
Swanwick	d																						
Fareham	d															15 51							
Portchester	d																						
Cosham	d															16 01							
Portsmouth Harbour	d	14 14				14 43				15 14				15 43					16 14				16 43
Portsmouth & Southsea	d	14 18				14 47				15 18				15 47					16 18				16 47
Fratton	d	14 22				14 51				15 22				15 51					16 22				16 51
Hilsea	d																						
Bedhampton	d	14 30								15 30									16 30				
Havant	d	14 33				15 00				15 33				16 00		16 11			16 33				17 00
Warblington	d	14 35								15 35									16 35				
Emsworth	d	14 38				15 04				15 38				16 04					16 38				17 04
Southbourne	d	14 41				15 07				15 41				16 07					16 41				17 07
Nutbourne	d	14 43								15 43									16 43				
Bosham	d	14 47								15 47									16 47				
Fishbourne (Sussex)	d	14 50								15 50									16 50				
Chichester 4	d	14 53				15 14				15 53				16 14		16 22			16 53				17 14
Bognor Regis 4	d		14 57						15 36		15 57							16 36		16 57			
Barnham	a	15 01	15 03	←		15 22			15 42	16 01	16 03	←		16 22		16 30		16 42	17 01	17 03	←		17 22
	d	15 08	15 05	15 08		15 22			15 43	16 08	16 05	16 08		16 22		16 30		16 43	17 08	17 05	17 08		17 22
Bognor Regis 4	a	*15 21*				*15 49*				*16 21*				*16 49*		*16 49*			*17 21*				*17 49*
Ford 4	d	→	15 09	15 12					15 47	→	16 09	16 12						16 47	→	17 09	17 12		
Littlehampton 4	a								15 52									16 52					
	d		*14b57*		15 14			15 41			*15b57*		16 14				16 41			*16b57*		17 14	
Angmering 3	d			15 18	15 22			15 49				16 18	16 22				16 49				17 18	17 22	
Goring-by-Sea	d			15 22	15 26			15 53				16 22	16 26				16 53				17 22	17 26	
Durrington-on-Sea	d			15 25	15 29			15 55				16 25	16 29				16 55				17 25	17 29	
West Worthing	d			15 27	15 31			15 57				16 27	16 31				16 57				17 27	17 31	
Worthing 4	a			15 29	15 33	15 37		16 00				16 29	16 33	16 37		16 45	17 00				17 29	17 33	17 37
	d			15 30		15 41		16 00				16 30		16 41		16 45	17 00				17 30		17 41
East Worthing	d			15 32				16 02				16 32					17 02				17 32		
Lancing	d			15 35				16 05				16 35					17 05				17 35		
Shoreham-by-Sea	d			15 39		15 47		16 09				16 39		16 47		16 52	17 09				17 39		17 47
Southwick	d			15 42				16 12				16 42					17 12				17 42		
Fishersgate	d			15 44				16 14				16 44					17 14				17 44		
Portslade	d			15 46				16 16				16 46					17 16				17 46		
Aldrington	d			15 49			←	16 19				16 49			←		17 19				17 49		
Hove 2	d			15c56		15 54	15 56	16 21				16e56		16 54	16 56	16 59	17 21				17f56		17 54
Brighton 10	a			→			16 00	16 25				→			17 00	17 05	17 25				→		
Haywards Heath 3	a					16 09		*17 00*						17 09		*17 30*	*18 00*						18 09
Arundel	d		15 14								16 14									17 14			
Amberley	d		15 19								16 19									17 19			
Pulborough	d		15 25								16 25									17 25			
Billingshurst	d		15 31								16 31									17 31			
Christs Hospital	d		15 38								16 38									17 38			
Horsham 4	d		15 42								16 42									17 42			
Crawley	d		15 51								16 51									17 51			
Three Bridges 4	a		15 54			*16 32*		*17 10*			16 54			*17 32*		*17 40*	*18 10*			17 54			*18 32*
Gatwick Airport 10 ✈	a		15 58			16 22		*17 14*			16 58			17 22		*17 44*	*18 14*			17 58			18 22
East Croydon	a		16 24			16 39		*17 31*			17 24			17 39		*18 01*	*18 31*			18 24			18 39
London Bridge 4 ⊖	a		*16 45*			*17 12*		*17 45*			*17 45*			*18 12*		*18 15*	*18 45*			*18 45*			*19 12*
Clapham Junction 10	a		16 37			16 54		*17 47*			17 37			17 54		*18g24*	*18 47*			18 37			18 54
London Victoria 15 ⊖	a		16 46			17 01		*17 53*			17 46			18 01		*18h25*	*18 53*			18 46			19 01

For general notes see front of timetable
For details of catering facilities see Directory of Train Operators

A From 30 March from Bristol Parkway (Table 132)
b Change at Ford
c Arr. 1551
e Arr. 1651
f Arr. 1751
g Change at Brighton and East Croydon
h Change at Brighton and Gatwick Airport

Table 188

Sundays

Southampton, Portsmouth and Sussex Coast → Brighton, Gatwick Airport & London

For complete service between Horsham and Three Bridges see Table 186

	SN 1	SN 1	SN 1	SN 1	SN 1	SN 1	SN 1	SN 1		SN 1	SN 1	SN 1	SN 1	SN 1	SN 1	SN 1	SN 1		SN 1	SN 1	SN 1	SN 1	SN 1	SN 1	
Southampton Central d																									
Swanwick d																									
Fareham d																									
Portchester d																									
Cosham d																									
Portsmouth Harbour d				17 14				17 43					18 14				18 43					19 14			
Portsmouth & Southsea d				17 18				17 47					18 18				18 47					19 18			
Fratton d				17 22				17 51					18 22				18 51					19 22			
Hilsea d																									
Bedhampton d				17 30									18 30									19 30			
Havant d				17 33				18 00					18 33				19 00					19 33			
Warblington d				17 35									18 35									19 35			
Emsworth d				17 38				18 04					18 38				19 04					19 38			
Southbourne d				17 41				18 07					18 41				19 07					19 41			
Nutbourne d				17 43									18 43									19 43			
Bosham d				17 47									18 47									19 47			
Fishbourne (Sussex) d				17 50									18 50									19 50			
Chichester 4 d				17 53				18 14					18 53				19 14					19 53			
Bognor Regis 4 d			17 36		17 57							18 36		18 57							19 36		19 57		
Barnham a			17 42	18 01	18 03	←		18 22				18 42	19 01	19 03	←		19 22				19 42	20 01	20 03	←	
Barnham d			17 43	18 08	18 05	18 08		18 22				18 43	19 08	19 05	19 08		19 22				19 43	20 08	20 05	20 08	
Bognor Regis 4 a				*18 21*				*18 49*					*19 21*				*19 49*					*20 21*			
Ford 4 d			17 47	→	18 09	18 12						18 47	→	19 09	19 12						19 47	→	20 09	20 12	
Littlehampton 4 a			17 52									18 52									19 52				
Littlehampton 4 d		17 41			*17b57*		18 14				18 41			*18b57*		19 14				19 41			*19b57*		
Angmering 3 d		17 49				18 18	18 22				18 49				19 18	19 22				19 49				20 18	
Goring-by-Sea d		17 53				18 22	18 26				18 53				19 22	19 26				19 53				20 22	
Durrington-on-Sea d		17 55				18 25	18 29				18 55				19 25	19 29				19 55				20 25	
West Worthing d		17 57				18 27	18 31				18 57				19 27	19 31				19 57				20 27	
Worthing 4 a		18 00				18 29	18 33	18 37			19 00				19 29	19 33	19 37			20 00				20 29	
Worthing 4 d		18 00				18 30	18 41				19 00				19 30	19 41				20 00				20 30	
East Worthing d		18 02				18 32					19 02				19 32					20 02				20 32	
Lancing d		18 05				18 35					19 05				19 35					20 05				20 35	
Shoreham-by-Sea d		18 09				18 39	18 47				19 09				19 39	19 47				20 09				20 39	
Southwick d		18 12				18 42					19 12				19 42					20 12				20 42	
Fishersgate d		18 14				18 44					19 14				19 44					20 14				20 44	
Portslade d		18 16				18 46					19 16				19 46					20 16				20 46	
Aldrington d	←	18 19				18 49				←	19 19				19 49				←	20 19				20 49	
Hove 2 d	17 56	18 21				18c56	18 54			18 56	19 21				19e56	19 54			19 56	20 21				20f56	
Brighton 10 a	18 00	18 25				→				19 00	19 25				→				20 00	20 25				→	
Haywards Heath 3 a		*19 00*					19 09				*20 00*					20 09				*21 00*					
Arundel d					18 14									19 14									20 14		
Amberley d					18 19									19 19									20 19		
Pulborough d					18 25									19 25									20 25		
Billingshurst d					18 31									19 31									20 31		
Christs Hospital d					18 38									19 38									20 38		
Horsham 4 d					18 42									19 42									20 42		
Crawley d					18 51									19 51									20 51		
Three Bridges 4 a		*19 10*			18 54		*19 32*				*20 10*			19 54		*20 32*				*21 10*			20 54		
Gatwick Airport 10 ✈ a		*19 14*			18 58		19 22				*20 14*			19 58		20 22				*21 14*			20 58		
East Croydon a		*19 31*			19 24		19 39				*20 31*			20 24		20 39				*21 31*			21 27		
London Bridge 4 ⊖ a		*19 45*			*19 45*		*20 12*				*20 45*			*20 45*		*21 12*				*21 45*			*21 45*		
Clapham Junction 10 a		*19 47*			19 37		19 54				*20 47*			20 37		20 54				*21g54*			21 37		
London Victoria 15 ⊖ a		*19 53*			19 46		20 01				*20 53*			20 46		21 01				*21h55*			21 46		

For general notes see front of timetable
For details of catering facilities see Directory of Train Operators

b Change at Ford
c Arr. 1851
e Arr. 1951
f Arr. 2051
g Change at Brighton and East Croydon
h Change at Brighton and Gatwick Airport

For details of Bank Holiday service alterations, please see first page of Table 149

Hampton Court, Shepperton, Guildford, Dorking and Chessington South → London

Network Diagram - see first page of Table 152

		SW	SW	SW	SW	SW	SW	SW	SW	SW	SW	SW	SW	SW	SW	SW	SW	SW	SW	SW	SW	SW	SW	SW	SW	SW
					1			1								1			1							1
					A			B			C	D				A			B			C	D			A
Guildford	d		19 28				19 38							19 58				20 08								
London Road (Guildford)	d		19 31				19 41							20 01				20 11								
Clandon	d		19 36				19 46							20 06				20 16								
Horsley	d		19 41				19 51							20 11				20 21								
Effingham Junction 6	d		19 46				19 54							20 16				20 24								
Bookham	d		19 49											20 19												
Cobham & Stoke d'Abernon	d						19 58											20 28								
Oxshott	d						20 01											20 31								
Claygate	d						20 04											20 34								
Hinchley Wood	d						20 07											20 37								
Hampton Court	d			19 54											20 24										20 54	
Thames Ditton	d			19 56											20 26										20 56	
Surbiton 6	d			20 02	20 08		20 12	20 17				20 27			20 32	20 38		20 42	20 47				20 57		21 02	21 08
Berrylands	d			20 04											20 34										21 04	
Shepperton	d					19 42											20 11									
Upper Halliford	d					19 45											20 14									
Sunbury	d					19 47											20 16									
Kempton Park	d					19 49											20 18									
Hampton	d					19 52											20 21									
Fulwell	d					19 54											20 24									
Strawberry Hill	d										20 07											20 37				
Teddington	d					19 59					20 11						20 29					20 41				
Hampton Wick	d					20 01					20 14						20 31					20 44				
Kingston	a					20 04					20 16						20 33					20 46				
	d					20 04					20 19						20 34					20 49				
Norbiton	d					20 06					20 21						20 36					20 51				
New Malden 6	d			20 07		20 10					20 25				20 37		20 40					20 55			21 07	
Dorking 4	d	19 33											20 05											20 35		
Boxhill & Westhumble	d																									
Leatherhead	d	19 39	19 54										20 11	20 24										20 41		
Ashtead	d	19 42	19 58										20 14	20 28										20 44		
Epsom 3	a	19 47	20 02										20 19	20 32										20 49		
	d	19 50	20 05						←				20 20	20 35						←				20 50		
Ewell West	d	19 53	20 08						20 08				20 23	20 38						20 38				20 53		
Stoneleigh	d	19 55	→						20 10				20 25	→						20 40				20 55		
Worcester Park	d	19 58							20 13				20 28							20 43				20 58		
Chessington South	d									20 10											20 40					
Chessington North	d									20 12											20 42					
Tolworth	d									20 14											20 44					
Malden Manor	d									20 17											20 47					
Motspur Park	d	20 01							20 16	20 20			20 31							20 46	20 50			21 01		
Raynes Park 6	d	20 04		20 10		20 13			20 19	20 23	20 28		20 34		20 40		20 43			20 49	20 53	20 58		21 04	21 10	
Wimbledon 6 ⊖ ⛴	d	20 08		20 14		20 17	20 20		20 23	20 27	20 32	20 35	20 38		20 44		20 47	20 50		20 53	20 57	21 02	21 05	21 08	21 14	
Earlsfield	d	20 12		20 17		20 20	20 24		20 27	20 31	20 35	20 38	20 42		20 47		20 50	20 54		20 57	21 01	21 05	21 08	21 12	21 17	
Clapham Junction 10	d	20 16		20 21		20 24	20 28		20 31	20 35	19 43	20 42	20 46		20 51	20 49	20 54	20 58	20 59	21 01	21 05	20 13	21 12	21 16	21 21	
Vauxhall ⊖	d	20 21		20 26		20 29	20 33		20 36	20 40	20 44	20 47	20 51		20 56		20 59	21 03		21 06	21 10	21 14	21 17	21 21	21 26	
London Waterloo 15 ⊖	a	20 25		20 31	20 25	20 34	20 37	20 36	20 40	20 46	20 49	20 52	20 55		21 01	20 57	21 04	21 07	21 06	21 10	21 15	21 19	21 22	21 25	21 31	21 27

For general notes see front of timetable
For details of catering facilities see Directory of Train Operators

A From Alton (Table 155)
B From Basingstoke (Table 155)
C From London Waterloo (Table 149)
D From Woking (Table 155)

For details of Bank Holiday service alterations, please see first page of Table 149

Hampton Court, Shepperton, Guildford, Dorking and Chessington South → London

Network Diagram - see first page of Table 152

		SW	SW	SW 1 A	SW	SW	SW B	SW C	SW	SW	SW 1 D	SW	SW	SW 1 A	SW	SW	SW B	SW C	SW	SW 1 D	SW	SW	SW 1 E	SW B	SW C	SW
Guildford	d		20 38						20 46				21 08									21 38				21 46
London Road (Guildford)	d		20 41						20 49				21 11									21 41				21 49
Clandon	d		20 46						20 54				21 16									21 46				21 54
Horsley	d		20 51						20 59				21 21									21 51				21 59
Effingham Junction 6	d		20 54						21 03				21 24									21 54				22 03
Bookham	d								21 06																	22 06
Cobham & Stoke d'Abernon	d		20 58										21 28									21 58				
Oxshott	d		21 01										21 31									22 01				
Claygate	d		21 04										21 34									22 04				
Hinchley Wood	d		21 07										21 37									22 07				
Hampton Court	d									21 24																
Thames Ditton	d									21 26																
Surbiton 6	d		21 12	21 17				21 27		21 32	21 38		21 42	21 47				21 57		22 08		22 12	22 17		22 27	
Berrylands	d									21 34																
Shepperton	d	20 41										21 11									21 41					
Upper Halliford	d	20 44										21 14									21 44					
Sunbury	d	20 46										21 16									21 46					
Kempton Park	d	20 48										21 18									21 48					
Hampton	d	20 51										21 21									21 51					
Fulwell	d	20 54										21 24									21 54					
Strawberry Hill	d						21 07										21 37							22 07		
Teddington	d	20 59					21 11					21 29					21 41				21 59			22 11		
Hampton Wick	d	21 01					21 14					21 31					21 44				22 01			22 14		
Kingston	a	21 03					21 16					21 33					21 46				22 03			22 16		
	d	21 04					21 19					21 34					21 49				22 04			22 19		
Norbiton	d	21 06					21 21					21 36					21 51				22 06			22 21		
New Malden 6	d	21 10					21 25			21 37		21 40					21 55				22 10			22 25		
Dorking 4	d																		21 35							
Boxhill & Westhumble	d																									
Leatherhead	d								21 11										21 41							22 11
Ashtead	d								21 14										21 44							22 14
Epsom 3	a								21 19										21 49							22 19
	d				21 05				21 20						21 35				21 50							22 20
Ewell West	d				21 08				21 23						21 38				21 53							22 23
Stoneleigh	d				21 10				21 25						21 40				21 55							22 25
Worcester Park	d				21 13				21 28						21 43				21 58							22 28
Chessington South	d					21 10										21 40										
Chessington North	d					21 12										21 42										
Tolworth	d					21 14										21 44										
Malden Manor	d					21 17										21 47										
Motspur Park	d				21 16	21 20			21 31						21 46	21 50			22 01							22 31
Raynes Park 6	d	21 13			21 19	21 23	21 28		21 34	21 40		21 43			21 49	21 53	21 58		22 04		22 13			22 28		22 34
Wimbledon 6 ⊖	d	21 17	21 20		21 23	21 27	21 32	21 35	21 38	21 44		21 47	21 50		21 53	21 57	22 02	22 05	22 08		22 17	22 20		22 32	22 35	22 38
Earlsfield	d	21 20	21 24		21 27	21 31	21 35	21 38	21 42	21 47		21 50	21 54		21 57	22 01	22 05	22 08	22 12		22 20	22 24		22 35	22 38	22 42
Clapham Junction 10	d	21 24	21 28		21 31	21 35	20 43	21 42	21 46	21 51	21 49	21 54	21 58	21 59	22 01	22 05	21 13	22 12	22 16		22 24	22 28		21 43	22 42	22 46
Vauxhall ⊖	d	21 29	21 33		21 36	21 40	21 44	21 47	21 51	21 56		21 59	22 03		22 06	22 10	22 14	22 17	22 21		22 29	22 33		22 44	22 47	22 51
London Waterloo 15 ⊖	a	21 34	21 37	21 34	21 40	21 45	21 49	21 52	21 55	22 01	21 57	22 04	22 07	22 06	22 10	22 16	22 19	22 22	22 25	22 26	22 34	22 39	22 34	22 49	22 52	22 55

For general notes see front of timetable
For details of catering facilities see Directory of Train Operators

A From Basingstoke (Table 155)
B From London Waterloo (Table 149)
C From Woking (Table 155)
D From Alton (Table 155)
E From Portsmouth Harbour (Table 158)

For details of Bank Holiday service alterations, please see first page of Table 149

Hampton Court, Shepperton, Guildford, Dorking and Chessington South → London

Network Diagram - see first page of Table 152

		SW	SW 1 A	SW	SW	SW 1 B	SW	SW C	SW	SW	SW 1 A	SW	SW	SW 1 D	SW C	SW	SW	SW	SW 1 A	SW	SW	SW	SW C	SW 1 B
Guildford	d				22 08				22 20				22 38			22 55	22 46				23 08			
London Road (Guildford)	d				22 11								22 41				22 49				23 11			
Clandon	d				22 16								22 46				22 54				23 16			
Horsley	d				22 21								22 51				22 59				23 21			
Effingham Junction 6	d				22 24								22 54				23 03				23 24			
Bookham	d																23 06							
Cobham & Stoke d'Abernon	d				22 28								22 58								23 28			
Oxshott	d				22 31								23 01								23 31			
Claygate	d				22 34								23 04								23 34			
Hinchley Wood	d				22 37								23 07								23 37			
Hampton Court	d	22 24																23 24						
Thames Ditton	d	22 26																23 26						
Surbiton 6	d	22 32	22 38		22 42	22 47			22 57		23 08		23 12	23 17		23 30		23 33	23 38		23 42			23 57
Berrylands	d	22 34																23 35						
Shepperton	d			22 11								22 41								23 11				
Upper Halliford	d			22 14								22 44								23 14				
Sunbury	d			22 16								22 46								23 16				
Kempton Park	d			22 18								22 48								23 18				
Hampton	d			22 21								22 51								23 21				
Fulwell	d			22 24								22 54								23 24				
Strawberry Hill	d							22 37							23 07								23 37	
Teddington	d			22 29				22 41				22 59			23 11					23 29			23 41	
Hampton Wick	d			22 31				22 44				23 01			23 14					23 31			23 44	
Kingston	a			22 33				22 46				23 03			23 16					23 33			23 46	
	d			22 34				22 49				23 04			23 19					23 34			23 49	
Norbiton	d			22 36				22 51				23 06			23 21					23 36			23 51	
New Malden 6	d	22 37		22 40				22 55				23 10			23 25			23 38		23 40			23 55	
Dorking 4	d									22 35														
Boxhill & Westhumble	d																							
Leatherhead	d									22 41							23 11							
Ashtead	d									22 44							23 14							
Epsom 3	a									22 49							23 19							
	d									22 50							23 20							
Ewell West	d									22 53							23 23							
Stoneleigh	d									22 55							23 25							
Worcester Park	d									22 58							23 28							
Chessington South	d						22 40															23 40		
Chessington North	d						22 42															23 42		
Tolworth	d						22 44															23 44		
Malden Manor	d						22 47															23 47		
Motspur Park	d						22 50			23 01							23 31					23 50		
Raynes Park 6	d	22 40		22 43			22 53	22 58		23 04		23 13			23 28		23b37	23 41		23 43		23 54	23 58	
Wimbledon 6 ⊖ 🚊	d	22 44		22 47	22 50		22 57	23 02	23 05	23 08		23 17	23 20		23 32	23 37	23 41	23a44		23 49	23 55	23a59	00 05	00 08
Earlsfield	d	22 47		22 50	22 54		23 01	23 05	23 08	23 12		23 20	23 24		23 35	23 41	23 44			23 55	23 58		00 08	00 10
Clapham Junction 10	d	22 51	22 53	22 54	22 58	22 59	23 05	22 13	23 12	23 16		23 24	23 28		22 43	23 45	23 48		23 53	23 59	00 02		23 13	00 14
Vauxhall ⊖	d	22 56		22 59	23 03		23 10	23 14	23 17	23 21		23 29	23 33		23 44	23 50	23 53			00 04	00 07		00 17	00 19
London Waterloo 15 ⊖	a	23 01	23 01	23 04	23 07	23 08	23 15	23 19	23 23	23 25	23 26	23 34	23 37	23 33	23 49	23 54	23 58		00 01	00 09	00 13		00 22	00 29

For general notes see front of timetable
For details of catering facilities see Directory of Train Operators

A From Alton (Table 155)
B From Basingstoke (Table 155)
C From London Waterloo (Table 149)
D From Portsmouth Harbour (Table 158)
b Arr. 2334

Table 152

Saturdays

For details of Bank Holiday service alterations, please see first page of Table 149

Hampton Court, Shepperton, Guildford, Dorking and Chessington South → London

Network Diagram - see first page of Table 152

		SW	SW	SW	SW 1	SW	SW 1	SW	SW	SW 1	SW	SW	SW	SW	SW		SW	SW	SW	SW 1	SW	SW	SW	SW	SW	SW
				A	B	A	C		D	B							A	E		G				A	E	
Guildford	d		23p08					04 00					05 12													06 28
London Road (Guildford)	d		23p11																							06 31
Clandon	d		23p16																							06 36
Horsley	d		23p21																							06 41
Effingham Junction 6	d		23p24																							06 46
Bookham	d																									06 49
Cobham & Stoke d'Abernon	d		23p28																							
Oxshott	d		23p31																							
Claygate	d		23p34																							
Hinchley Wood	d		23p37																							
Hampton Court	d													05 54					06 24							
Thames Ditton	d													05 56					06 26							
Surbiton 6	d		23p42		23p57		00 40	04 24		05 40			05 57	06 02				06 27	06 32	06 47					06 57	
Berrylands	d													06 04					06 34							
Shepperton	d	23p11																			06 11					
Upper Halliford	d	23p14																			06 14					
Sunbury	d	23p16																			06 16					
Kempton Park	d	23p18																			06 18					
Hampton	d	23p21																			06 21					
Fulwell	d	23p24																			06 24					
Strawberry Hill	d			23p37		00 07			04 55								06 07							06 37		
Teddington	d	23p29		23p41		00 11			04 59			05 44					06 11				06 29			06 41		
Hampton Wick	d	23p31		23p44		00 14			05 01			05 46					06 14				06 31			06 44		
Kingston	a	23p33		23p46		00 16			05 03			05 48					06 16				06 33			06 46		
	d	23p34		23p49					05 04			05 49					06 19				06 34			06 49		
Norbiton	d	23p36		23p51					05 06			05 51					06 21				06 36			06 51		
New Malden 6	d	23p40		23p55					05 10			05 55		06 07			06 25		06 37		06 40			06 55		
Dorking 4	d																									
Boxhill & Westhumble	d																									
Leatherhead	d																									06 54
Ashtead	d																									06 58
Epsom 3	a																									07 02
	d										05 35				06 05							06 35				07 05
Ewell West	d										05 38				06 08							06 38				07 08 →
Stoneleigh	d										05 40				06 10							06 40				
Worcester Park	d										05 43				06 13							06 43				
Chessington South	d																						06 40			
Chessington North	d																						06 42			
Tolworth	d																						06 44			
Malden Manor	d																						06 47			
Motspur Park	d										05 46				06 16							06 46	06 50			
Raynes Park 6	d	23p43		23p58					05 13		05 49	05 58		06 10	06 19		06 28		06 40		06 43	06 49	06 53	06 58		
Wimbledon 6 ⊖ ⛴	d	23p49	23p55	00 05	00 08		00 48	04 32	05 17	05 49	05 53	06 02	06 05	06 14	06 23		06 32	06 35	06 44		06 47	06 53	06 57	07 02	07 05	
Earlsfield	d	23p55	23p58	00 08	00 10				05 21		05 57	06 05	06 08	06 17	06 27		06 35	06 38	06 47		06 50	06 57	07 01	07 05	07 08	
Clapham Junction 10	d	23p59	00 02	23p13	00 14		00 55	04 44	05 25	06 01	06 01	06 09	06 12	06 21	06 31		05 43	06 42	06 51	06 59	06 54	07 01	07 05	06 13	07 12	
Vauxhall ⊖	d	00 04	00 07	00 17	00 19				05 30	06 08	06 06	06 14	06 17	06 26	06 36		06 44	06 47	06 56		06 59	07 06	07 10	07 14	07 17	
London Waterloo 15 ⊖	a	00 09	00 13	00 22	00 29		01 02	04 53	05 35	06 12	06 11	06 19	06 22	06 31	06 40		06 49	06 52	07 01	07 06	07 04	07 10	07 15	07 19	07 22	

For general notes see front of timetable
For details of catering facilities see Directory of Train Operators

A From London Waterloo (Table 149)
B From Basingstoke (Table 155)
C From Weymouth (Table 158)
D From Twickenham (Table 149)
E From Woking (Table 155)
G From Southampton Central (Table 158)

Table 152

Hampton Court, Shepperton, Guildford, Dorking and Chessington South → London

For details of Bank Holiday service alterations, please see first page of Table 149

Network Diagram - see first page of Table 152

		SW	SW 1 A	SW	SW	SW 1 B	SW	SW	SW C	SW D	SW	SW	SW 1 A	SW	SW	SW 1 E	SW	SW	SW C	SW D	SW	SW	SW 1 A	SW
Guildford	d				06 38						06 58				07 08						07 28			
London Road (Guildford)	d				06 41						07 01				07 11						07 31			
Clandon	d				06 46						07 06				07 16						07 36			
Horsley	d				06 51						07 11				07 21						07 41			
Effingham Junction 6	d				06 54						07 16				07 24						07 46			
Bookham	d										07 19										07 49			
Cobham & Stoke d'Abernon	d				06 58										07 28									
Oxshott	d				07 01										07 31									
Claygate	d				07 04										07 34									
Hinchley Wood	d				07 07										07 37									
Hampton Court	d	06 54										07 24										07 54		
Thames Ditton	d	06 56										07 26										07 56		
Surbiton 6	d	07 02	07 08		07 12	07 17				07 27		07 32	07 38		07 42	07 47				07 57		08 02	08 08	
Berrylands	d	07 04										07 34										08 04		
Shepperton	d			06 41										07 11										07 41
Upper Halliford	d			06 44										07 14										07 44
Sunbury	d			06 46										07 16										07 46
Kempton Park	d			06 48										07 18										07 48
Hampton	d			06 51										07 21										07 51
Fulwell	d			06 54										07 24										07 54
Strawberry Hill	d								07 07										07 37					
Teddington	d			06 59					07 11					07 29					07 41					07 59
Hampton Wick	d			07 01					07 14					07 31					07 44					08 01
Kingston	a			07 03					07 16					07 33					07 46					08 03
	d			07 04					07 19					07 34					07 49					08 04
Norbiton	d			07 06					07 21					07 36					07 51					08 06
New Malden 6	d	07 07		07 10					07 25			07 37		07 40					07 55			08 07		08 10
Dorking 4	d																							
Boxhill & Westhumble	d																							
Leatherhead	d										07 24										07 54			
Ashtead	d										07 28										07 58			
Epsom 3	a										07 32										08 02			
	d						←				07 35						←				08 05			
Ewell West	d						07 08				07 38						07 38				08 08			
Stoneleigh	d						07 10				→						07 40				→			
Worcester Park	d						07 13										07 43							
Chessington South	d							07 10										07 40						
Chessington North	d							07 12										07 42						
Tolworth	d							07 14										07 44						
Malden Manor	d							07 17										07 47						
Motspur Park	d						07 16	07 20									07 46	07 50						
Raynes Park 6	d	07 10		07 13			07 19	07 23	07 28			07 40		07 43			07 49	07 53	07 58			08 10		08 13
Wimbledon 6	⊖ ⛴ d	07 14		07 17	07 20		07 23	07 27	07 32	07 35		07 44		07 47	07 50		07 53	07 57	08 02	08 05		08 14		08 17
Earlsfield	d	07 17		07 20	07 24		07 27	07 31	07 35	07 38		07 47		07 50	07 54		07 57	08 01	08 05	08 08		08 17		08 20
Clapham Junction 10	d	07 21	07 19	07 24	07 28		07 31	07 35	06 43	07 42		07 51	07 51	07 54	07 58	07 59	08 01	08 05	07 13	08 12		08 21		08 24
Vauxhall	⊖ d	07 26		07 29	07 33		07 36	07 40	07 44	07 47		07 56		07 59	08 03		08 06	08 10	08 14	08 17		08 26		08 29
London Waterloo 15	⊖ a	07 31	07 27	07 34	07 37	07 33	07 40	07 45	07 49	07 52		08 01	07 58	08 04	08 07	08 06	08 10	08 15	08 19	08 22		08 31	08 25	08 34

For general notes see front of timetable
For details of catering facilities see Directory of Train Operators

A From Alton (Table 155)
B From Southampton Central (Table 158)
C From London Waterloo (Table 149)
D From Woking (Table 155)
E From Basingstoke (Table 155)

For details of Bank Holiday service alterations, please see first page of Table 149

Hampton Court, Shepperton, Guildford, Dorking and Chessington South → London

Network Diagram - see first page of Table 152

		SW	SW	SW	SW	SW	SW	SW	SW	SW	SW	SW		SW	SW	SW	SW	SW	SW	SW	SW	SW	SW	SW	SW	SW
			1								1				1								1			1
			A			B	C				D				E			B	C				D			E
Guildford	d	07 38							07 58					08 08							08 28				08 38	
London Road (Guildford)	d	07 41							08 01					08 11							08 31				08 41	
Clandon	d	07 46							08 06					08 16							08 36				08 46	
Horsley	d	07 51							08 11					08 21							08 41				08 50	
Effingham Junction 6	d	07 54							08 16					08 24							08 46				08 53	
Bookham	d								08 19												08 49					
Cobham & Stoke d'Abernon	d	07 58												08 28											08 57	
Oxshott	d	08 01												08 31											09 00	
Claygate	d	08 04												08 34											09 03	
Hinchley Wood	d	08 07												08 37											09 06	
Hampton Court	d									08 24												08 54				
Thames Ditton	d									08 26												08 56				
Surbiton 6	d	08 12	08 17				08 27			08 32	08 38			08 42	08 47				08 57			09 02	09 08		09 11	09 17
Berrylands	d									08 34												09 04				
Shepperton	d											08 11												08 41		
Upper Halliford	d											08 14												08 44		
Sunbury	d											08 16												08 46		
Kempton Park	d											08 18												08 48		
Hampton	d											08 21												08 51		
Fulwell	d											08 24												08 54		
Strawberry Hill	d					08 07												08 37								
Teddington	d					08 11						08 29						08 41						08 59		
Hampton Wick	d					08 14						08 31						08 44						09 01		
Kingston	a					08 16						08 33						08 46						09 03		
	d					08 19						08 34						08 49						09 04		
Norbiton	d					08 21						08 36						08 51						09 06		
New Malden 6	d					08 25				08 37		08 40						08 55				09 07		09 10		
Dorking 4	d							08 05												08 35						
Boxhill & Westhumble	d																									
Leatherhead	d							08 11	08 24											08 41	08 54					
Ashtead	d							08 14	08 28											08 44	08 58					
Epsom 3	a							08 19	08 32											08 49	09 02					
	d			←				08 20	08 35							←				08 50	09 05					
Ewell West	d			08 08				08 23	08 38							08 38				08 53	09 08					
Stoneleigh	d			08 10				08 25	→							08 40				08 55	→					
Worcester Park	d			08 13				08 28								08 43				08 58						
Chessington South	d				08 10												08 40									
Chessington North	d				08 12												08 42									
Tolworth	d				08 14												08 44									
Malden Manor	d				08 17												08 47									
Motspur Park	d			08 16	08 20			08 31								08 46	08 50			09 01						
Raynes Park 6	d			08 19	08 23	08 28		08 34		08 40		08 43				08 49	08 53	08 58		09 04		09 10		09 13		
Wimbledon 6 ⊖	d	08 20		08 23	08 27	08 32	08 35	08 38		08 44		08 47		08 50		08 53	08 57	09 02	09 05	09 08		09 14		09 17	09 20	
Earlsfield	d	08 24		08 27	08 31	08 35	08 38	08 42		08 47		08 50		08 54		08 57	09 01	09 05	09 08	09 12		09 17		09 20	09 24	
Clapham Junction 10	d	08 28		08 31	08 35	07 43	08 42	08 46		08 51	08 50	08 54		08 58	08 59	09 01	09 05	08 13	09 12	09 16		09 21		09 24	09 28	
Vauxhall ⊖	d	08 33		08 36	08 40	08 44	08 47	08 51		08 56		08 59		09 03		09 06	09 10	09 14	09 17	09 21		09 26		09 29	09 33	
London Waterloo 15 ⊖	a	08 37	08 34	08 40	08 45	08 49	08 52	08 55		09 01	08 58	09 04		09 07	09 06	09 10	09 15	09 19	09 22	09 25		09 31	09 25	09 34	09 37	09 35

For general notes see front of timetable
For details of catering facilities see Directory of Train Operators

A From Portsmouth Harbour (Table 158)
B From London Waterloo (Table 149)
C From Woking (Table 155)
D From Alton (Table 155)
E From Basingstoke (Table 155)

Table 152

For details of Bank Holiday service alterations, please see first page of Table 149

Hampton Court, Shepperton, Guildford, Dorking and Chessington South → London

Network Diagram - see first page of Table 152

Station		SW	SW	SW	SW	SW	SW	SW	SW	SW		SW	SW	SW	SW	SW	SW	SW	SW	SW	SW	SW	SW	SW
				A	B				1 C		and at the same minutes past each hour until		1 D			A	B			1 C			1 D	
Guildford	d						08 58					20 08										20 38		
London Road (Guildford)	d						09 01					20 11										20 41		
Clandon	d						09 06					20 16										20 46		
Horsley	d						09 11					20 21										20 51		
Effingham Junction 6	d						09 16					20 24										20 54		
Bookham	d						09 19																	
Cobham & Stoke d'Abernon	d											20 28										20 58		
Oxshott	d											20 31										21 01		
Claygate	d											20 34										21 04		
Hinchley Wood	d											20 37										21 07		
Hampton Court	d							09 24											20 54					
Thames Ditton	d							09 26											20 56					
Surbiton 6	d				09 27			09 32	09 38			20 42	20 47				20 57		21 02	21 08		21 12	21 17	
Berrylands	d							09 34											21 04					
Shepperton	d									09 11											20 41			
Upper Halliford	d									09 14											20 44			
Sunbury	d									09 16											20 46			
Kempton Park	d									09 18											20 48			
Hampton	d									09 21											20 51			
Fulwell	d									09 24											20 54			
Strawberry Hill	d			09 07												20 37								
Teddington	d			09 11						09 29						20 41					20 59			
Hampton Wick	d			09 14						09 31						20 44					21 01			
Kingston	a			09 16						09 33						20 46					21 03			
	d			09 19						09 34						20 49					21 04			
Norbiton	d			09 21						09 36						20 51					21 06			
New Malden 6	d			09 25				09 37		09 40						20 55			21 07		21 10			
Dorking 4	d					09 05												20 35						
Boxhill & Westhumble	d																							
Leatherhead	d					09 11	09 24											20 41						
Ashtead	d					09 14	09 28											20 44						
Epsom 3	a					09 19	09 32											20 49						
	d	←				09 20	09 35							←				20 50						21 05
Ewell West	d	09 08				09 23	09 38							20 38				20 53						21 08
Stoneleigh	d	09 10				09 25	→							20 40				20 55						21 10
Worcester Park	d	09 13				09 28								20 43				20 58						21 13
Chessington South	d		09 10												20 40									
Chessington North	d		09 12												20 42									
Tolworth	d		09 14												20 44									
Malden Manor	d		09 17												20 47									
Motspur Park	d	09 16	09 20			09 31								20 46	20 50			21 01						21 16
Raynes Park 6	d	09 19	09 23	09 28		09 34		09 40		09 43				20 49	20 53	20 58		21 04	21 10		21 13			21 19
Wimbledon 6 ⊖	d	09 23	09 27	09 32	09 35	09 38		09 44		09 47		20 50		20 53	20 57	21 02	21 05	21 08	21 14		21 17	21 20		21 23
Earlsfield	d	09 27	09 31	09 35	09 38	09 42		09 47		09 50		20 54		20 57	21 01	21 05	21 08	21 12	21 17		21 20	21 24		21 27
Clapham Junction 10	d	09 31	09 35	08 43	09 42	09 46		09 51	09 49	09 54		20 58	20 59	21 01	21 05	20 13	21 12	21 16	21 21		21 24	21 28		21 31
Vauxhall ⊖	d	09 36	09 40	09 44	09 47	09 51		09 56		09 59		21 03		21 06	21 10	21 14	21 17	21 21	21 26		21 29	21 33		21 36
London Waterloo 15 ⊖	a	09 40	09 45	09 49	09 52	09 55		10 01	09 57	10 04		21 07	21 06	21 10	21 15	21 19	21 23	21 25	21 31	21 26	21 34	21 37	21 34	21 40

For general notes see front of timetable
For details of catering facilities see Directory of Train Operators

A From London Waterloo (Table 149)
B From Woking (Table 155)
C From Alton (Table 155)
D From Basingstoke (Table 155)

Table 152

Saturdays

For details of Bank Holiday service alterations, please see first page of Table 149

Hampton Court, Shepperton, Guildford, Dorking and Chessington South → London

Network Diagram - see first page of Table 152

		SW	SW	SW		SW	SW	SW ■1	SW	SW	SW ■1	SW	SW	SW	SW	SW	SW ■1	SW	SW		SW ■1	SW	SW	SW	SW	SW ■1
			A	B				C			D			A	B		C				E	A	B			C
Guildford	d					20 46				21 08									21 38					21 46		
London Road (Guildford)	d					20 49				21 11									21 41					21 49		
Clandon	d					20 54				21 16									21 46					21 54		
Horsley	d					20 59				21 21									21 51					21 59		
Effingham Junction ■6	d					21 03				21 24									21 54					22 03		
Bookham	d					21 06																		22 06		
Cobham & Stoke d'Abernon	d									21 28									21 58							
Oxshott	d									21 31									22 01							
Claygate	d									21 34									22 04							
Hinchley Wood	d									21 37									22 07							
Hampton Court	d						21 24																		22 24	
Thames Ditton	d						21 26																		22 26	
Surbiton ■6	d			21 27			21 32	21 38		21 42	21 47				21 57		22 08		22 12		22 17		22 27		22 32	22 38
Berrylands	d						21 34																		22 34	
Shepperton	d								21 11									21 41								
Upper Halliford	d								21 14									21 44								
Sunbury	d								21 16									21 46								
Kempton Park	d								21 18									21 48								
Hampton	d								21 21									21 51								
Fulwell	d								21 24									21 54								
Strawberry Hill	d		21 07											21 37								22 07				
Teddington	d		21 11						21 29					21 41				21 59				22 11				
Hampton Wick	d		21 14						21 31					21 44				22 01				22 14				
Kingston	a		21 16						21 33					21 46				22 03				22 16				
	d		21 19						21 34					21 49				22 04				22 19				
Norbiton	d		21 21						21 36					21 51				22 06				22 21				
New Malden ■6	d		21 25				21 37		21 40					21 55				22 10				22 25			22 37	
Dorking ■4	d															21 35										
Boxhill & Westhumble	d																									
Leatherhead	d					21 11										21 41								22 11		
Ashtead	d					21 14										21 44								22 14		
Epsom ■3	a					21 19										21 49								22 19		
	d					21 20						21 35				21 50								22 20		
Ewell West	d					21 23						21 38				21 53								22 23		
Stoneleigh	d					21 25						21 40				21 55								22 25		
Worcester Park	d					21 28						21 43				21 58								22 28		
Chessington South	d	21 10											21 40													
Chessington North	d	21 12											21 42													
Tolworth	d	21 14											21 44													
Malden Manor	d	21 17											21 47													
Motspur Park	d	21 20				21 31						21 46	21 50			22 01								22 31		
Raynes Park ■6	d	21 23	21 28			21 34	21 40		21 43			21 49	21 53	21 58		22 04		22 13				22 28		22 34	22 40	
Wimbledon ■6 ⊖	d	21 27	21 32	21 35		21 38	21 44		21 47	21 50		21 53	21 57	22 02	22 05	22 08		22 17	22 20			22 32	22 35	22 38	22 44	
Earlsfield	d	21 31	21 35	21 38		21 42	21 47		21 50	21 54		21 57	22 01	22 05	22 08	22 12		22 20	22 24			22 35	22 38	22 42	22 47	
Clapham Junction ■10	d	21 35	20 43	21 42		21 46	21 51	21 49	21 54	21 58	21 59	22 01	22 05	21 13	22 12	22 16		22 24	22 28			21 43	22 42	22 46	22 51	22 53
Vauxhall ⊖	d	21 40	21 44	21 47		21 51	21 56		21 59	22 03		22 06	22 10	22 14	22 17	22 21		22 29	22 33			22 44	22 47	22 51	22 56	
London Waterloo ■15 ⊖	a	21 45	21 49	21 52		21 55	22 01	21 57	22 04	22 07	22 07	22 10	22 15	22 19	22 22	22 25	22 26	22 34	22 39		22 34	22 49	22 52	22 55	23 01	23 01

For general notes see front of timetable
For details of catering facilities see Directory of Train Operators

A From London Waterloo (Table 149)
B From Woking (Table 155)
C From Alton (Table 155)
D From Basingstoke (Table 155)
E From Portsmouth Harbour (Table 158)

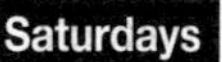

Hampton Court, Shepperton, Guildford, Dorking and Chessington South → London

For details of Bank Holiday service alterations, please see first page of Table 149

Network Diagram - see first page of Table 152

		SW	SW	SW 1 A	SW	SW B	SW	SW	SW 1 C	SW	SW		SW 1 D	SW B	SW	SW	SW	SW 1 C	SW	SW	SW	SW B	SW 1 A
Guildford	d		22 08				22 20				22 38				22 55	22 46				23 08			
London Road (Guildford)	d		22 11								22 41					22 49				23 11			
Clandon	d		22 16								22 46					22 54				23 16			
Horsley	d		22 21								22 51					22 59				23 21			
Effingham Junction 6	d		22 24								22 54					23 03				23 24			
Bookham	d															23 06							
Cobham & Stoke d'Abernon	d		22 28								22 58									23 28			
Oxshott	d		22 31								23 01									23 31			
Claygate	d		22 34								23 04									23 34			
Hinchley Wood	d		22 37								23 07									23 37			
Hampton Court	d																23 24						
Thames Ditton	d																23 26						
Surbiton 6	d		22 42	22 47			22 57		23 08		23 12		23 17		23 30		23 33	23 38		23 42			23 57
Berrylands	d																23 35						
Shepperton	d	22 11								22 41									23 11				
Upper Halliford	d	22 14								22 44									23 14				
Sunbury	d	22 16								22 46									23 16				
Kempton Park	d	22 18								22 48									23 18				
Hampton	d	22 21								22 51									23 21				
Fulwell	d	22 24								22 54									23 24				
Strawberry Hill	d					22 37								23 07								23 37	
Teddington	d	22 29				22 41				22 59				23 11					23 29			23 41	
Hampton Wick	d	22 31				22 44				23 01				23 14					23 31			23 44	
Kingston	a	22 33				22 46				23 03				23 16					23 33			23 46	
	d	22 34				22 49				23 04				23 19					23 34			23 49	
Norbiton	d	22 36				22 51				23 06				23 21					23 36			23 51	
New Malden 6	d	22 40				22 55				23 10				23 25			23 38		23 40			23 55	
Dorking 4	d							22 35															
Boxhill & Westhumble	d																						
Leatherhead	d							22 41								23 11							
Ashtead	d							22 44								23 14							
Epsom 3	a							22 49								23 19							
	d							22 50								23 20							
Ewell West	d							22 53								23 23							
Stoneleigh	d							22 55								23 25							
Worcester Park	d							22 58								23 28							
Chessington South	d				22 40																23 40		
Chessington North	d				22 42																23 42		
Tolworth	d				22 44																23 44		
Malden Manor	d				22 47																23 47		
Motspur Park	d				22 50			23 01								23 31					23 50		
Raynes Park 6	d	22 43			22 53	22 58		23 04		23 13				23 28		23b37	23 41		23 43		23 54	23 58	
Wimbledon 6	⊖ d	22 47	22 50		22 57	23 02	23 05	23 08		23 17	23 20			23 32	23 37	23 41	23 45		23 52	23 58	00a02	00 07	00 08
Earlsfield	d	22 50	22 54		23 01	23 06	23 08	23 12		23 20	23 24			23 35	23 41	23 44	23 48		23 55	00 01		00 10	00 10
Clapham Junction 10	d	22 54	22 58	22 59	23 05	22 13	23 12	23 16		23 24	23 28			22 43	23 45	23 48	23 52	23 53	23 59	00 05		23 13	00 14
Vauxhall	⊖ d	22 59	23 03		23 10	23 15	23 17	23 21		23 29	23 33			23 44	23 50	23 53	23 58		00 04	00 10		00 19	00 19
London Waterloo 15	⊖ a	23 04	23 07	23 06	23 15	23 19	23 22	23 25	23 25	23 34	23 37		23 37	23 49	23 54	23 58	00 02	00 03	00 09	00 14		00 24	00 29

For general notes see front of timetable
For details of catering facilities see Directory of Train Operators

A From Basingstoke (Table 155)
B From London Waterloo (Table 149)
C From Alton (Table 155)
D From Portsmouth Harbour (Table 158)
b Arr. 2334

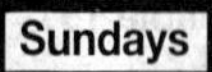

For details of Bank Holiday service alterations, please see first page of Table 149

Hampton Court, Shepperton, Guildford, Dorking and Chessington South → London

Network Diagram - see first page of Table 152

	SW	SW	SW	SW	SW	SW	SW	SW	SW	SW	SW	SW	SW	SW	SW	SW	SW	SW	SW	SW	SW	SW	SW
				1		1														1			
			A	B	A	C				D	A								A	E			
Guildford d		23p08											06 57				07 27						07 50
London Road (Guildford) d		23p11																					07 53
Clandon d		23p16																					07 58
Horsley d		23p21																					08 02
Effingham Junction 6 d		23p24																					08 06
Bookham d																							
Cobham & Stoke d'Abernon d		23p28																					08 10
Oxshott d		23p31																					08 13
Claygate d		23p34																					08 16
Hinchley Wood d		23p37																					08 19
Hampton Court d																07 35					08 05		
Thames Ditton d																07 37					08 07		
Surbiton 6 d		23p42		23p57		00 40				07 00			07 30			07 43	08 00			08 10	08 13		08 24
Berrylands d																07 45					08 15		
Shepperton d	23p11														07 11								
Upper Halliford d	23p14														07 14								
Sunbury d	23p16														07 16								
Kempton Park d	23p18														07 18								
Hampton d	23p21														07 21								
Fulwell d	23p24														07 24								
Strawberry Hill d			23p37		00 07						06 49								07 49				
Teddington d	23p29		23p41		00 11						06b55				07 29				07c55				
Hampton Wick d	23p31		23p44		00 14						06 57				07 31				07 57				
Kingston a	23p33		23p46		00 16						06 59				07 33				07 59				
d	23p34		23p49								07 04				07 34				08 04				
Norbiton d	23p36		23p51								07 06				07 36				08 06				
New Malden 6 d	23p40		23p55								07 10				07 40	07 48			08 10		08 18		
Dorking 4 d																							
Boxhill & Westhumble d																							
Leatherhead d																							
Ashtead d																							
Epsom 3 a																							
d														07 24				07 54					
Ewell West d														07 27				07 57					
Stoneleigh d														07 29				07 59					
Worcester Park d														07 32				08 02					
Chessington South d																						08 10	
Chessington North d																						08 12	
Tolworth d																						08 14	
Malden Manor d																						08 17	
Motspur Park d														07 35				08 05				08 20	
Raynes Park 6 d	23p43		23p58								07 13			07 38	07 43	07 51		08 08	08 13		08 21	08 24	
Wimbledon 6 ⊖ ⛴ d	23p52	23p58	00 07	00 08		00 48	05 31	06 12	06 42	07 08	07e19	07 31	07 38	07 42	07 47	07 55	08 08	08 12	08 17	08 17	08 25	08 28	08a33
Earlsfield d	23p55	00 01	00 10	00 10					06 46	07 11	07 22	07 34	07 41	07 46	07 50	07 58	08 11	08 16	08 20		08 28	08 31	
Clapham Junction 10 d	23p59	00 05	00 14	00 14		00 55	05 38	06 20	06 50	07 15	06 24	07 38	07 45	07 50	07 54	08 02	08 15	08 20	07 24	08 24	08 34	08 37	
Vauxhall ⊖ d	00 04	00 10	00 19	00 19			05 43	06 25	06 55	07 20	07 31	07 43	07 50	07 55	07 59	08 07	08 20	08 25	08 29		08 39	08 42	
London Waterloo 15 ⊖ a	00 09	00 14	00 24	00 29		01 02	05 54	06 34	07 04	07 30	07 41	07 53	08 00	08 04	08 07	08 17	08 30	08 34	08 39	08 39	08 47	08 50	

For general notes see front of timetable
For details of catering facilities see Directory of Train Operators

- **A** From London Waterloo (Table 149)
- **B** From Basingstoke (Table 155)
- **C** From Weymouth (Table 158)
- **D** From Woking (Table 155)
- **E** From Farnham (Table 155) and from Basingstoke (Table 155)
- **b** Arr. 0652
- **c** Arr. 0752
- **e** Arr. 0716

Table 152

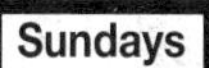

For details of Bank Holiday service alterations, please see first page of Table 149

Hampton Court, Shepperton, Guildford, Dorking and Chessington South → London

Network Diagram - see first page of Table 152

		SW	SW	SW	SW	SW	SW	SW	SW	SW	SW	SW		SW	SW	SW	SW	SW	SW	SW	SW	SW	SW	SW		SW
									A	[1] B												A	[1] B			
Guildford	d	07 57					08 27	08 20						08 50	08 57					09 27	09 20					
London Road (Guildford)	d							08 23						08 53							09 23					
Clandon	d							08 28						08 58							09 28					
Horsley	d							08 33						09 02							09 33					
Effingham Junction [6]	d							08 36						09 06							09 36					
Bookham	d							08 39													09 39					
Cobham & Stoke d'Abernon	d													09 10												
Oxshott	d													09 13												
Claygate	d													09 16												
Hinchley Wood	d													09 19												
Hampton Court	d				08 35						09 05							09 35						10 05		
Thames Ditton	d				08 37						09 07							09 37						10 07		
Surbiton [6]	d	08 30			08 43		09 00			09 10	09 13			09 24	09 30			09 43		10 00			10 10	10 13		
Berrylands	d				08 45						09 15							09 45						10 15		
Shepperton	d			08 11													09 11									
Upper Halliford	d			08 14													09 14									
Sunbury	d			08 16													09 16									
Kempton Park	d			08 18													09 18									
Hampton	d			08 21													09 21									
Fulwell	d			08 24													09 24									
Strawberry Hill	d								08 49													09 49				
Teddington	d			08 29					08b55								09 29					09c55				
Hampton Wick	d			08 31					08 57								09 31					09 57				
Kingston	a			08 33					08 59								09 33					09 59				
	d			08 34					09 04								09 34					10 04				
Norbiton	d			08 36					09 06								09 36					10 06				
New Malden [6]	d			08 40	08 48				09 10		09 18						09 40	09 48				10 10		10 18		
Dorking [4]	d															09 08										
Boxhill & Westhumble	d																									
Leatherhead	d							08 44								09 15					09 44					
Ashtead	d							08 48								09 18					09 48					
Epsom [3]	a							08 52								09 23					09 52					
	d		08 24					08 54								09 24					09 54					
Ewell West	d		08 27					08 57								09 27					09 57					
Stoneleigh	d		08 29					08 59								09 29					09 59					
Worcester Park	d		08 32					09 02								09 32					10 02					
Chessington South	d					08 40						09 10							09 40							10 10
Chessington North	d					08 42						09 12							09 42							10 12
Tolworth	d					08 44						09 14							09 44							10 14
Malden Manor	d					08 47						09 17							09 47							10 17
Motspur Park	d		08 35			08 50		09 05				09 20				09 35			09 50		10 05					10 20
Raynes Park [6]	d		08 38	08 43	08 51	08 54		09 08	09 13		09 21	09 24				09 38	09 43	09 51	09 54		10 08	10 13		10 21		10 24
Wimbledon [6] ⊖	d	08 38	08 42	08 47	08 55	08 58	09 08	09 12	09 17	09 17	09 25	09 28		09a33	09 38	09 42	09 47	09 55	09 58	10 08	10 12	10 17	10 17	10 25		10 28
Earlsfield	d	08 41	08 46	08 50	08 58	09 01	09 11	09 16	09 20		09 28	09 31			09 41	09 46	09 50	09 58	10 01	10 11	10 16	10 20		10 28		10 31
Clapham Junction [10]	d	08 45	08 50	08 54	09 02	09 09	09 15	09 20	08 24	09 24	09 32	09 36			09 45	09 50	09 54	10 02	10 05	10 15	10 20	09 24	10 24	10 32		10 36
Vauxhall ⊖	d	08 50	08 55	08 59	09 07	09 14	09 20	09 25	09 29		09 37	09 41			09 50	09 55	09 59	10 07	10 10	10 20	10 25	10 29		10 37		10 41
London Waterloo [15] ⊖	a	09 00	09 04	09 07	09 17	09 20	09 30	09 34	09 39	09 39	09 47	09 50			10 00	10 04	10 07	10 17	10 20	10 30	10 34	10 39	10 39	10 47		10 50

For general notes see front of timetable
For details of catering facilities see Directory of Train Operators

A From London Waterloo (Table 149)
B From Alton (Table 155) and from Basingstoke (Table 155)
b Arr. 0852
c Arr. 0952

Table 152

Sundays

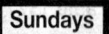

For details of Bank Holiday service alterations, please see first page of Table 149

Hampton Court, Shepperton, Guildford, Dorking and Chessington South → London

Network Diagram - see first page of Table 152

		SW	SW	SW	SW	SW	SW	SW	SW	SW	SW	SW		SW	SW	SW	SW	SW	SW	SW	SW	SW	SW	SW		SW
										A	1 B												A	1 B		
Guildford	d	09 50	09 57					10 27	10 20						10 50	10 57					11 27	11 20				
London Road (Guildford)	d	09 53							10 23						10 53							11 23				
Clandon	d	09 58							10 28						10 58							11 28				
Horsley	d	10 02							10 33						11 02							11 33				
Effingham Junction 6	d	10 06							10 36						11 06							11 36				
Bookham	d								10 39													11 39				
Cobham & Stoke d'Abernon	d	10 10													11 10											
Oxshott	d	10 13													11 13											
Claygate	d	10 16													11 16											
Hinchley Wood	d	10 19													11 19											
Hampton Court	d					10 35						11 05							11 35							12 05
Thames Ditton	d					10 37						11 07							11 37							12 07
Surbiton 6	d	10 24	10 30			10 43		11 00			11 10	11 13			11 24	11 30			11 43		12 00			12 10		12 13
Berrylands	d					10 45						11 15							11 45							12 15
Shepperton	d				10 11													11 11								
Upper Halliford	d				10 14													11 14								
Sunbury	d				10 16													11 16								
Kempton Park	d				10 18													11 18								
Hampton	d				10 21													11 21								
Fulwell	d				10 24													11 24								
Strawberry Hill	d									10 49													11 49			
Teddington	d				10 29					10b55								11 29					11c55			
Hampton Wick	d				10 31					10 57								11 31					11 57			
Kingston	a				10 33					10 59								11 33					11 59			
	d				10 34					11 04								11 34					12 04			
Norbiton	d				10 36					11 06								11 36					12 06			
New Malden 6	d				10 40	10 48				11 10		11 18						11 40	11 48				12 10			12 18
Dorking 4	d			10 08													11 08									
Boxhill & Westhumble	d																									
Leatherhead	d			10 15					10 44								11 15					11 44				
Ashtead	d			10 18					10 48								11 18					11 48				
Epsom 3	a			10 23					10 52								11 23					11 52				
	d			10 24					10 54								11 24					11 54				
Ewell West	d			10 27					10 57								11 27					11 57				
Stoneleigh	d			10 29					10 59								11 29					11 59				
Worcester Park	d			10 32					11 02								11 32					12 02				
Chessington South	d						10 40							11 10						11 40						
Chessington North	d						10 42							11 12						11 42						
Tolworth	d						10 44							11 14						11 44						
Malden Manor	d						10 47							11 17						11 47						
Motspur Park	d			10 35			10 50		11 05					11 20			11 35			11 50		12 05				
Raynes Park 6	d			10 38	10 43	10 51	10 54		11 08	11 13		11 21		11 24			11 38	11 43	11 51	11 54		12 08	12 13			12 21
Wimbledon 6 ⊖	d	10a33	10 38	10 42	10 47	10 55	10 58	11 08	11 12	11 17	11 17	11 25		11 28	11a33	11 38	11 42	11 47	11 55	11 58	12 08	12 12	12 17	12 17		12 25
Earlsfield	d		10 41	10 46	10 50	10 58	11 01	11 11	11 16	11 20		11 28		11 31		11 41	11 46	11 50	11 58	12 01	12 11	12 16	12 20			12 28
Clapham Junction 10	d		10 45	10 50	10 54	11 02	11 05	11 15	11 20	10 24	11 24	11 32		11 35		11 45	11 50	11 54	12 02	12 05	12 15	12 20	11 24	12 24		12 32
Vauxhall ⊖	d		10 50	10 55	10 59	11 07	11 10	11 20	11 25	11 29		11 37		11 40		11 50	11 55	11 59	12 07	12 10	12 20	12 25	12 29			12 37
London Waterloo 15 ⊖	a		11 00	11 04	11 07	11 17	11 20	11 30	11 34	11 39	11 39	11 47		11 50		12 00	12 04	12 07	12 17	12 20	12 30	12 34	12 39	12 39		12 47

For general notes see front of timetable
For details of catering facilities see Directory of Train Operators

A From London Waterloo (Table 149)
B From Alton (Table 155) and from Basingstoke (Table 155)
b Arr. 1052
c Arr. 1152

Table 152

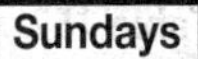

For details of Bank Holiday service alterations, please see first page of Table 149

Hampton Court, Shepperton, Guildford, Dorking and Chessington South → London

Network Diagram - see first page of Table 152

		SW	SW	SW	SW	SW	SW	SW	SW	SW	SW	SW 1	SW	SW	SW	SW	SW	SW	SW	SW	SW	SW	SW	SW 1
											A	B											A	B
Guildford	d		11 50	11 57					12 27	12 20					12 50	12 57					13 27	13 20		
London Road (Guildford)	d		11 53							12 23					12 53							13 23		
Clandon	d		11 58							12 28					12 58							13 28		
Horsley	d		12 02							12 33					13 02							13 33		
Effingham Junction 6	d		12 06							12 36					13 06							13 36		
Bookham	d									12 39												13 39		
Cobham & Stoke d'Abernon	d		12 10												13 10									
Oxshott	d		12 13												13 13									
Claygate	d		12 16												13 16									
Hinchley Wood	d		12 19												13 19									
Hampton Court	d						12 35						13 05						13 35					
Thames Ditton	d						12 37						13 07						13 37					
Surbiton 6	d		12 24	12 30			12 43		13 00			13 10	13 13		13 24	13 30			13 43		14 00			14 10
Berrylands	d						12 45						13 15						13 45					
Shepperton	d					12 11												13 11						
Upper Halliford	d					12 14												13 14						
Sunbury	d					12 16												13 16						
Kempton Park	d					12 18												13 18						
Hampton	d					12 21												13 21						
Fulwell	d					12 24												13 24						
Strawberry Hill	d										12 49												13 49	
Teddington	d					12 29					12b55							13 29					13c55	
Hampton Wick	d					12 31					12 57							13 31					13 57	
Kingston	a					12 33					12 59							13 33					13 59	
	d					12 34					13 04							13 34					14 04	
Norbiton	d					12 36					13 06							13 36					14 06	
New Malden 6	d					12 40	12 48				13 10		13 18					13 40	13 48				14 10	
Dorking 4	d				12 08												13 08							
Boxhill & Westhumble	d																							
Leatherhead	d				12 15					12 44							13 15					13 44		
Ashtead	d				12 18					12 48							13 18					13 48		
Epsom 3	a				12 23					12 52							13 23					13 52		
	d				12 24					12 54							13 24					13 54		
Ewell West	d				12 27					12 57							13 27					13 57		
Stoneleigh	d				12 29					12 59							13 29					13 59		
Worcester Park	d				12 32					13 02							13 32					14 02		
Chessington South	d	12 10						12 40						13 10						13 40				
Chessington North	d	12 12						12 42						13 12						13 42				
Tolworth	d	12 14						12 44						13 14						13 44				
Malden Manor	d	12 17						12 47						13 17						13 47				
Motspur Park	d	12 20			12 35			12 50		13 05				13 20			13 35			13 50		14 05		
Raynes Park 6	d	12 24			12 38	12 43	12 51	12 54		13 08	13 13		13 21	13 24			13 38	13 43	13 51	13 54		14 08	14 13	
Wimbledon 6 ⊖	d	12 28	12 31	12 38	12 42	12 47	12 55	12 58	13 08	13 12	13 17	13 17	13 25	13 28	13 31	13 38	13 42	13 47	13 55	13 58	14 08	14 12	14 17	14 17
Earlsfield	d	12 31	12 35	12 41	12 46	12 50	12 58	13 01	13 11	13 16	13 20		13 28	13 31	13 35	13 41	13 46	13 50	13 58	14 01	14 11	14 16	14 20	
Clapham Junction 10	d	12 35	12 39	12 45	12 50	12 54	13 02	13 05	13 15	13 20	12 24	13 24	13 32	13 35	13 39	13 45	13 50	13 54	14 02	14 05	14 15	14 20	13 24	14 24
Vauxhall ⊖	d	12 40	12 44	12 50	12 55	12 59	13 07	13 10	13 20	13 25	13 29		13 37	13 40	13 44	13 50	13 55	13 59	14 07	14 10	14 20	14 25	14 29	
London Waterloo 15 ⊖	a	12 50	12 53	13 00	13 04	13 07	13 17	13 20	13 30	13 34	13 39	13 39	13 47	13 50	13 53	14 00	14 04	14 07	14 17	14 20	14 30	14 34	14 34	14 34

For general notes see front of timetable
For details of catering facilities see Directory of Train Operators

A From London Waterloo (Table 149)
B From Alton (Table 155) and from Basingstoke (Table 155)
b Arr. 1252
c Arr. 1352

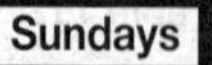

For details of Bank Holiday service alterations, please see first page of Table 149

Hampton Court, Shepperton, Guildford, Dorking and Chessington South → London

Network Diagram - see first page of Table 152

		SW	SW	SW	SW	SW	SW	SW	SW	SW	SW	SW	SW	SW	SW	SW	SW	SW		SW	SW	SW	SW
										1						1							
								A		B					A	B			and at the same minutes past each hour until				
Guildford	d			13 50	13 57								14 27	14 20						19 50	19 57		
London Road (Guildford)	d			13 53										14 23						19 53			
Clandon	d			13 58										14 28						19 58			
Horsley	d			14 02										14 33						20 02			
Effingham Junction 6	d			14 06										14 36						20 06			
Bookham	d													14 39									
Cobham & Stoke d'Abernon	d			14 10																20 10			
Oxshott	d			14 13																20 13			
Claygate	d			14 16																20 16			
Hinchley Wood	d			14 19																20 19			
Hampton Court	d	14 05							14 35								15 05						
Thames Ditton	d	14 07							14 37								15 07						
Surbiton 6	d	14 13		14 24	14 30				14 43	14 46			15 00			15 10	15 13			20 24	20 30		
Berrylands	d	14 15							14 45								15 15						
Shepperton	d						14 11																20 11
Upper Halliford	d						14 14																20 14
Sunbury	d						14 16																20 16
Kempton Park	d						14 18																20 18
Hampton	d						14 21																20 21
Fulwell	d						14 24																20 24
Strawberry Hill	d							14 29							14 49								
Teddington	d						14 29	14 32							14b55								20 29
Hampton Wick	d						14 31	14 35							14 57								20 31
Kingston	a						14 33	14 37							14 59								20 33
	d						14 34								15 04								20 34
Norbiton	d						14 36				←				15 06								20 36
New Malden 6	d	14 18					14 40		14 48		14 48				15 10		15 18						20 40
Dorking 4	d					14 08			→													20 08	
Boxhill & Westhumble	d																						
Leatherhead	d					14 15								14 44								20 15	
Ashtead	d					14 18								14 48								20 18	
Epsom 3	a					14 23								14 52								20 23	
	d					14 24								14 54								20 24	
Ewell West	d					14 27								14 57								20 27	
Stoneleigh	d					14 29								14 59								20 29	
Worcester Park	d					14 32								15 02								20 32	
Chessington South	d		14 10									14 40						15 10					
Chessington North	d		14 12									14 42						15 12					
Tolworth	d		14 14									14 44						15 14					
Malden Manor	d		14 17									14 47						15 17					
Motspur Park	d		14 20			14 35						14 50		15 05				15 20				20 35	
Raynes Park 6	d	14 21	14 24			14 38	14 43				14 51	14 54		15 08	15 13		15 21	15 24				20 38	20 43
Wimbledon 6 ⊖ ⛴	d	14 25	14 28	14 31	14 38	14 42	14 47			14 54	14 55	14 58	15 08	15 12	15 17	15 17	15 25	15 28		20 31	20 38	20 42	20 47
Earlsfield	d	14 28	14 31	14 35	14 41	14 46	14 50				14 58	15 01	15 11	15 16	15 20		15 28	15 31		20 35	20 41	20 46	20 50
Clapham Junction 10	d	14 32	14 35	14 39	14 45	14 50	14 54			15 00	15 02	15 05	15 15	15 20	14 24	15 24	15 32	15 35		20 39	20 45	20 50	20 54
Vauxhall ⊖	d	14 37	14 40	14 44	14 50	14 55	14 59				15 07	15 10	15 20	15 25	15 29		15 37	15 40		20 44	20 50	20 55	20 59
London Waterloo 15 ⊖	a	14 42	14 45	14 48	14 55	14 59	15 04			15 10	15 12	15 15	15 25	15 29	15 34	15 34	15 42	15 45		20 48	20 55	21 00	21 04

For general notes see front of timetable
For details of catering facilities see Directory of Train Operators

A From London Waterloo (Table 149)
B From Alton (Table 155) and from Basingstoke (Table 155)
b Arr. 1452

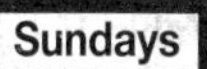

For details of Bank Holiday service alterations, please see first page of Table 149

Hampton Court, Shepperton, Guildford, Dorking and Chessington South → London

Network Diagram - see first page of Table 152

		SW	SW	SW	SW	SW	SW	SW	SW	SW		SW	SW	SW	SW	SW	SW	SW	SW	SW	SW	SW		SW	SW	SW
				1					1										1						1	
		A		B				A	B								A		B					A	B	
Guildford	d					20 27	20 20						20 50	20 57							21 27	21 20				
London Road (Guildford)	d						20 23						20 53									21 23				
Clandon	d						20 28						20 58									21 28				
Horsley	d						20 33						21 02									21 33				
Effingham Junction 6	d						20 36						21 06									21 36				
Bookham	d						20 39															21 39				
Cobham & Stoke d'Abernon	d												21 10													
Oxshott	d												21 13													
Claygate	d												21 16													
Hinchley Wood	d												21 19													
Hampton Court	d		20 35							21 05								21 35								22 05
Thames Ditton	d		20 37							21 07								21 37								22 07
Surbiton 6	d		20 43	20 46		21 00			21 10	21 13			21 24	21 30				21 43	21 46		22 00				22 10	22 13
Berrylands	d		20 45							21 15								21 45								22 15
Shepperton	d															21 11										
Upper Halliford	d															21 14										
Sunbury	d															21 16										
Kempton Park	d															21 18										
Hampton	d															21 21										
Fulwell	d															21 24										
Strawberry Hill	d	20 29						20 49									21 29							21 49		
Teddington	d	20 32						20b55								21 29	21 32							21c55		
Hampton Wick	d	20 35						20 57								21 31	21 35							21 57		
Kingston	a	20 37						20 59								21 33	21 37							21 59		
	d							21 04								21 34								22 04		
Norbiton	d				⟵			21 06								21 36				⟵				22 06		
New Malden 6	d		20 48		20 48			21 10		21 18						21 40		21 48		21 48				22 10		22 18
Dorking 4	d		⟶												21 08			⟶								
Boxhill & Westhumble	d																									
Leatherhead	d						20 44								21 15							21 44				
Ashtead	d						20 48								21 18							21 48				
Epsom 3	a						20 52								21 23							21 52				
	d						20 54								21 24							21 54				
Ewell West	d						20 57								21 27							21 57				
Stoneleigh	d						20 59								21 29							21 59				
Worcester Park	d						21 02								21 32							22 02				
Chessington South	d											21 10														
Chessington North	d											21 12														
Tolworth	d											21 14														
Malden Manor	d											21 17														
Motspur Park	d						21 05					21 20			21 35							22 05				
Raynes Park 6	d				20 51		21 08	21 13		21 21		21 24			21 38	21 43				21 51		22 08		22 13		22 21
Wimbledon 6	⊖ d			20 54	20 55	21 08	21 12	21 17	21 17	21 25		21 28	21 31	21 38	21 42	21 47			21 54	21 55	22 08	22 12		22 17	22 17	22 25
Earlsfield	d				20 58	21 11	21 16	21 20		21 28		21 31	21 35	21 41	21 46	21 50				21 58	22 11	22 16		22 20		22 28
Clapham Junction 10	d			21 00	21 02	21 15	21 20	20 24	21 24	21 32		21 35	21 39	21 45	21 50	21 54			22 00	22 02	22 15	22 20		21 24	22 24	22 32
Vauxhall	⊖ d				21 07	21 20	21 25	21 29		21 37		21 40	21 44	21 50	21 55	21 59				22 07	22 20	22 25		22 29		22 37
London Waterloo 15	⊖ a			21 10	21 12	21 25	21 29	21 35	21 34	21 42		21 45	21 48	21 55	22 00	22 04			22 10	22 12	22 25	22 29		22 35	22 34	22 42

For general notes see front of timetable
For details of catering facilities see Directory of Train Operators

A From London Waterloo (Table 149)
B From Alton (Table 155) and from Basingstoke (Table 155)
b Arr. 2052
c Arr. 2152

Table 152

Sundays

For details of Bank Holiday service alterations, please see first page of Table 149

Hampton Court, Shepperton, Guildford, Dorking and Chessington South → London

Network Diagram - see first page of Table 152

		SW	SW	SW	SW	SW	SW	SW	SW	SW	SW	SW	SW	SW	SW	SW	SW	SW	SW	SW	SW	SW	SW
								1				1								1		
							A	B			A	B							A	C		
Guildford	d		21 50	21 57					22 27	22 20					22 50	22 57						
London Road (Guildford)	d		21 53							22 23					22 53							
Clandon	d		21 58							22 28					22 58							
Horsley	d		22 02							22 33					23 02							
Effingham Junction [6]	d		22 06							22 36					23 06							
Bookham	d									22 39												
Cobham & Stoke d'Abernon	d		22 10												23 10							
Oxshott	d		22 13												23 13							
Claygate	d		22 16												23 16							
Hinchley Wood	d		22 19												23 19							
Hampton Court	d												23 05									23 45
Thames Ditton	d												23 07									23 47
Surbiton [6]	d		22 24	22 30				22 46	23 00			23 10	23 13		23 24	23 30				23 46		23 53
Berrylands	d												23 15									23 55
Shepperton	d					22 11												23 11				
Upper Halliford	d					22 14												23 14				
Sunbury	d					22 16												23 16				
Kempton Park	d					22 18												23 18				
Hampton	d					22 21												23 21				
Fulwell	d					22 24												23 24				
Strawberry Hill	d						22 29				22 49								23 29			
Teddington	d					22 29	22 32				22b55							23 29	23 32			
Hampton Wick	d					22 31	22 35				22 57							23 31	23 35			
Kingston	a					22 33	22 37				22 59							23 33	23 37			
	d					22 34					23 04							23 34				
Norbiton	d					22 36					23 06							23 36				
New Malden [6]	d					22 40					23 10		23 18					23 40				23 58
Dorking [4]	d				22 08												23 08					
Boxhill & Westhumble	d																					
Leatherhead	d				22 15					22 44							23 15					
Ashtead	d				22 18					22 48							23 18					
Epsom [3]	a				22 23					22 52							23 23					
	d				22 24					22 54							23 24					
Ewell West	d				22 27					22 57							23 27					
Stoneleigh	d				22 29					22 59							23 29					
Worcester Park	d				22 32					23 02							23 32					
Chessington South	d	22 10												23 10							23 40	
Chessington North	d	22 12												23 12							23 42	
Tolworth	d	22 14												23 14							23 44	
Malden Manor	d	22 17												23 17							23 47	
Motspur Park	d	22 20			22 35					23 05				23 20			23 35				23 50	
Raynes Park [6]	d	22 24			22 38	22 43				23 08	23 13		23 21	23 24			23 38	23 43			23 53	00 01
Wimbledon [6] ⊖	d	22 28	22 31	22 38	22 42	22 47		22 54	23 08	23 12	23 17	23 17	23 25	23 28	23 31	23 38	23 42	23 47		23 54	23a58	00a04
Earlsfield	d	22 31	22 35	22 41	22 46	22 50			23 11	23 16	23 20		23 28	23 31	23 35	23 41	23 46	23 50				
Clapham Junction [10]	d	22 35	22 39	22 45	22 50	22 54		23 00	23 15	23 20	22 24	23 24	23 32	23 35	23 39	23 45	23 50	23 54		23 59		
Vauxhall ⊖	d	22 40	22 44	22 50	22 55	22 59			23 20	23 25	23 29		23 37	23 40	23 44	23 50	23 55	23 59				
London Waterloo [15] ⊖	a	22 45	22 48	22 55	23 00	23 04		23 11	23 25	23 29	23 34	23 34	23 42	23 45	23 48	23 55	23 59	00 04		00 10		

For general notes see front of timetable
For details of catering facilities see Directory of Train Operators

A From London Waterloo (Table 149)
B From Alton (Table 155) and from Basingstoke (Table 155)
C From Alton (Table 155)

b Arr. 2252

Network Diagram for Tables 155, 156, 157

DM-29/05
Design BAJS

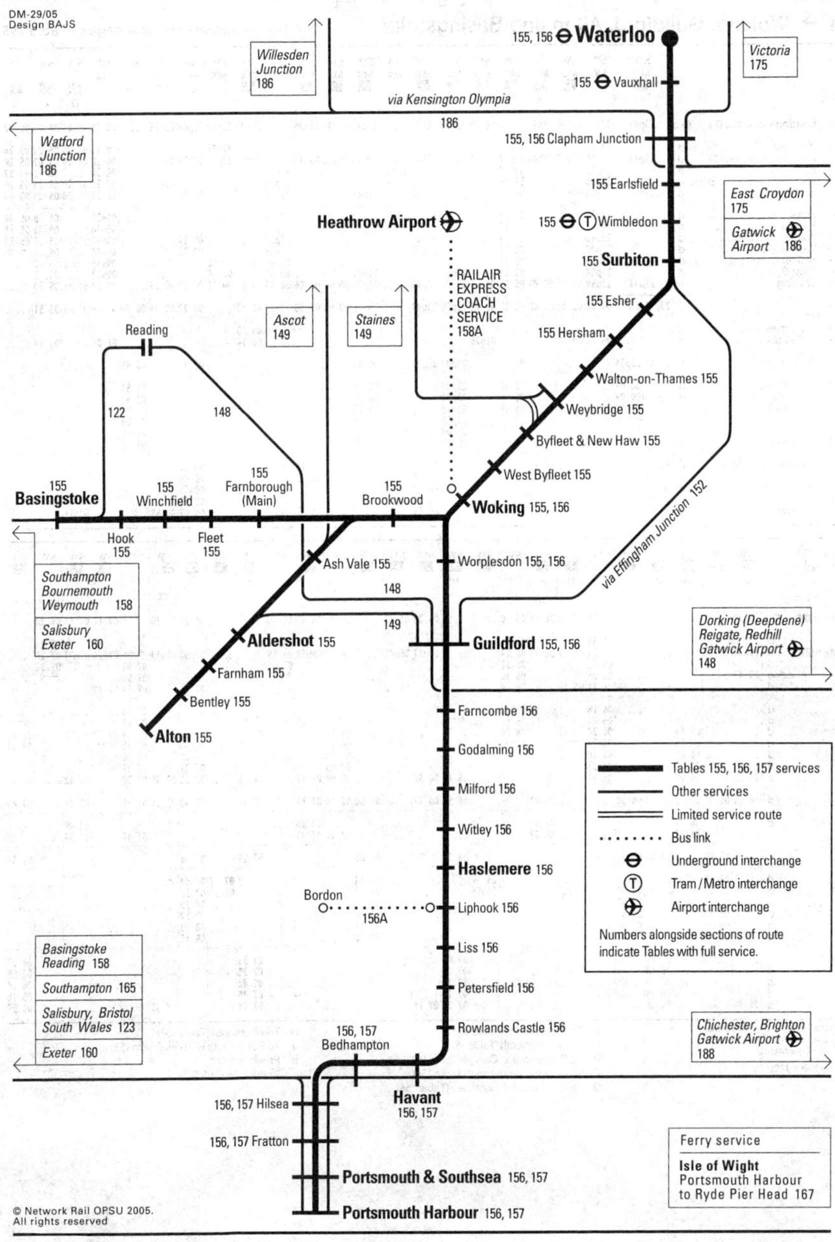

For details of Bank Holiday service alterations, please see first page of Table 149

London → Woking, Guildford, Alton and Basingstoke

Network Diagram - see first page of Table 155

Miles	Miles	Miles			SW MO 1		SW MO	SW MO 1	SW MO 1 A	SW MO 1	SW MO 1 B	SW MX 1	SW MX 1	SW MX	SW MX 1	SW MX 1	SW MX 1	SW MX	SW MX 1	SW MX	SW MX 1	SW MX 1 C	SW MX 1	SW MX	SW 1 D	SW 1 E	SW 1 G
0	—	—	**London Waterloo 15** ⊖	d	23p07		23p10	23p30	23p35	23p40	00 50	22p53	23p12	23p20	23p23	23p35	23p39		23p45	22p52	23p48	00 05		00 09	01 05	05 00	05 20
1¼	—	—	Vauxhall ⊖	d			23p14			23p44				23p24						22p56				00 13	01 09	05 04	05 24
4	—	—	Clapham Junction 10	d	23p15		23p19	23b39	23b44	23p49	00u57	23b00	23b19	23p29	23b30	23b42	23b46	←	23b52	23p02	23b56	00u12		00 18	01 14	05 09	05 29
5½	—	—	Earlsfield	d			23p22			23p52				23p32				23p32						00 21		05 12	05 32
7¼	—	—	Wimbledon 6 ⊖	d	23p22		23p26			23p56				→				23p36				00u18		00 25	01 20	05 16	05 36
12	—	—	**Surbiton 6**	d	23p30		23p35			00 05		23p11	23p30		23p41			23p44			00 10			00 33	01 28	05 24	05 44
14½	—	—	Esher	d			23p39			00 09								23p48						00s37		05 28	05 48
16	—	—	Hersham	d			23p42			00 12								23p51						00s40		05 32	05 51
17	—	—	Walton-on-Thames	d			23p45			00 15			23p37					23p54			00 17			00s43		05 35	05 54
19	—	—	Weybridge	d			23p49			00 19			23p41					23p58			00 21			00s46		05 39	→
20½	—	—	Byfleet & New Haw	d			23p51			00 21								00 01		00 06				00s49		05 42	
21½	—	—	West Byfleet	d			23p54			00 24		23p21			23p51			00 03		00 09				00s52		05 45	
24¼	0	—	**Woking**	a	23p42		23p59	00 01	00 07	00 30	01 16	23p28	23p48		23p59	00 02	00 06	00 08	00 11	00 16	00 27	00 35		00 57	01 41	05 50	
—	—	—		d	23p46	23p49	00 05	00 02	00 08	00 35	01 18	23p30	23p49		00 01	00 03	00 08		00 13		00 29	00 36	00 40	00 58	01 41	05 51	
—	2½	—	Worplesdon	d															00 18								
—	6	—	**Guildford**	a			00 13	00 10			01s26								00 24					01 06		05 59	
28	—	0	Brookwood	d	23p52	23p56				00 41		23p37	23p55		00 06						00 35		00 45				
—	—	4½	Ash Vale	d		00 04				00 48		23p44			00 14								00 53				
—	—	7	**Aldershot**	d		00 09				00 53		23p50			00 20								00 58				
—	—	10	Farnham	a		00 15				00 59		23p56			00 25								01 04				
—	—	—		d		00 15						23p57			00 26								01 04				
—	—	14	Bentley	d		00 23						00 04			00 32								01s10				
—	—	18¾	**Alton**	a		00 30						00 11			00 40								01 18				
33½	—	—	Farnborough (Main)	d	23p59				00 18				00 03				00 18				00 42				01s57		
36½	—	—	Fleet	d	00 05				00 24				00 08				00 23				00 48						
40	—	—	Winchfield	d	00 10								00 14								00s53						
42¼	—	—	Hook	d	00 15								00 18								00s58						
47¾	—	—	**Basingstoke**	a	00 22				00 39				00 25			00 22	00 35				01 07	00 55			02s11		

		SW 1 H	SW 1	SW 1 G	SW 1 J	SW 1	SW	SW 1 H	SW 1	SW	SW 1	SW 1 H	SW 1	SW 1 J	SW 1	SW	SW 1	SW	SW 1 J	SW 1	SW 1	SW 1 ◇ ☕	SW	SW 1	SW 1	SW	SW 1
London Waterloo 15 ⊖	d	05 30					05 50	06 12	06 15	06 20			06 30	06 42			06 45	06 50			06 53	07 10		07 12	07 15	07 20	
Vauxhall ⊖	d						05 54			06 24								06 54								07 24	
Clapham Junction 10	d	05u37					05 59	06u19	06u22	06 29			06u37	06u49			06u52	06 59			07u00	07u17	←	07u20	07u22	07 29	
Earlsfield	d						06 02			06 32								07 02					07 02			07 32	
Wimbledon 6 ⊖	d	05 43					06 06			06 36								→					07 06			→	
Surbiton 6	d						06 14	06 30		06 44				07 00							07 11		07 14	07 30			
Esher	d						06 18			06 48													07 18				
Hersham	d			←			06 21			06 51		←				←			←				07 21				←
Walton-on-Thames	d			05 54			06 24	06 37		06 54		06 37		07 07		06 54			07 07				07 24	07 37			07 37
Weybridge	d			05 58			06 28	→		→		06 41		→		06 58			07 11				07 28	→			07 41
Byfleet & New Haw	d			06 00			06 30									07 00							07 30				
West Byfleet	d			06 03			06 33									07 03					07 21		07 33				
Woking	a	05 59		06 08			06 38		06 41			06 48	06 56			07 08	07 11		07 18		07 26	07 35	07 38		07 42		07 48
	d	06 01	06 02	06 13	06 19	06 30			06 43			06 50	06 57		07 00	07 10	07 13		07 19		07 30	07 36	07 39		07 44		07 49
Worplesdon	d			06 18					06 48								07 18								07 49		
Guildford	a			06 23					06 53							07 20	07 23						07 47		07 54		
Brookwood	d		06 08		06 25	06 36						06 56			07 06				07 25		07 36						07 55
Ash Vale	d		06 16			06 44					06 49				07 14					07 19	07 44						
Aldershot	d		06 21			06 50					06a54				07 20					07a24	07 50						
Farnham	a		06 27			06 55									07 25						07 55						
	d		06 27			06 57									07 26						07 57						
Bentley	d		06 34			07 03									07 32						08 03						
Alton	a		06 41			07 10									07 40						08 10						
Farnborough (Main)	d				06 33							07 04							07 33								08 03
Fleet	d				06 38							07 09							07 38								08 08
Winchfield	d				06 44							07 15							07 44								08 14
Hook	d				06 48							07 19							07 48								08 18
Basingstoke	a	06 20			06 58							07 28	07 16						07 56			07 55					08 25

For general notes see front of timetable
For details of catering facilities see Directory of Train Operators

A To Salisbury (Table 160)
B To Portsmouth Harbour
C To Bournemouth (Table 158)
D To Southampton Central (Table 158)
E To Portsmouth Harbour (Table 156)
G To Portsmouth & Southsea (Table 156)
H To Weymouth (Table 158)
J To Portsmouth Harbour (Table 158)
b Previous night.
Stops to pick up only

For details of Bank Holiday service alterations, please see first page of Table 149

London → Woking, Guildford, Alton and Basingstoke

Network Diagram - see first page of Table 155

		SW 1	SW 1 ☕	SW 1	SW 1◇	SW	SW 1	SW 1	SW 1	SW 1◇ ☕	SW 1	SW	SW 1	SW 1	SW 1◇ ☕	SW 1	SW	SW 1	SW 1	SW 1◇ ☕	SW 1	SW 1	SW 1 ☕	SW 1◇ ☕	SW 1	SW	SW 1
London Waterloo 15 ⊖	d		07 30	07 23	07 35		07 38	07 45		07 50	07 42	07 50	08 00	07 53	08 05	08 09		08 12	08 15	08 20			08 30	08 35	08 23	08 20	08 39
Vauxhall ⊖	d											07 54														08 24	
Clapham Junction 10	d			07u30		←	07u45	07u52		07u57		07 59		08u00	08u12		←	08u19	08u22	08u27						08 29	08u46
Earlsfield	d					07 32						08 02 →					08 02									08 32	
Wimbledon 6 ⊖	d					07 36											08 06									08 36	
Surbiton 6	d			07 41		07 44					08 00			08 11			08 14	08 30							08 41	08 44	
Esher	d					07 48											08 18									08 48	
Hersham	d					07 51											08 21				←					08 51	
Walton-on-Thames	d					07 54					08 07						08 24	08 37			08 37					08 54	
Weybridge	d					07 58					08 11						08 28	→			08 41					08 58	
Byfleet & New Haw	d					08 00											08 30									09 00	
West Byfleet	d			07 51		08 03								08 21			08 33								08 51	09 03	
Woking	a		07 55	07 59	07 59	08 08		08 12		08 15	08 18		08 24	08 29		08 34	08 38		08 42	08 45	08 49		08 55	08 58	09 00	09 08	
	d		07 55	08 00	08 00			08 14		08 16	08 19		08 25	08 30		08 35	08 39		08 44	08 46	08 49		08 55	09 00	09 00		
Worplesdon	d							08 19											08 49								
Guildford	a		08 04					08 24					08 35				08 50		08 54				09 04				
Brookwood	d			08 06							08 25			08 36							08 55				09 06		
Ash Vale	d	07 49		08 14					08 19					08 44								08 49			09 14		
Aldershot	d	07a54		08 20					08a24					08 50								08a54			09 20		
Farnham	a			08 26										08 55											09 26		
	d			08 26										08 57											09 26		
Bentley	d			08 32										09 03													
Alton	a			08 40										09 10											09 39		
Farnborough (Main)	d						08 13				08 33					08 45					09 03						09 13
Fleet	d						08 19				08 38										09 08						09 19
Winchfield	d										08 44										09 14						
Hook	d										08 48										09 18						
Basingstoke	a				08 20		08 34			08 35	08 58				08 48	08 59				09 06	09 28						09 34

		SW 1	SW 1	SW 1◇ ☕	SW 1	SW	SW 1 ☕	SW 1	SW 1◇ ☕	SW 1	SW	SW 1	SW 1	SW 1◇ ☕	SW 1	SW 1	SW 1 ☕	SW 1◇ ☕	SW 1	SW	SW 1	SW 1	SW 1	SW 1◇ ☕	SW 1	SW	SW 1 ☕
London Waterloo 15 ⊖	d		08 45	08 50	08 42	08 50	09 00	08 53	09 05	09 09		09 12	09 15	09 20			09 30	09 35	09 23	09 20	09 39	09 45		09 50	09 42	09 50	10 00
Vauxhall ⊖	d					08 54														09 24						09 54	
Clapham Junction 10	d		08u52			08 59		09u00	09u12		←	09u19	09u22	09u27						09 29	09u46	09u52				09 59	
Earlsfield	d					09 02 →					09 02									09 32						10 02 →	
Wimbledon 6 ⊖	d										09 06									09 36							
Surbiton 6	d				09 00			09 11			09 14	09 30							09 41	09 44					10 00		
Esher	d										09 18									09 48							
Hersham	d										09 21				←					09 51							
Walton-on-Thames	d				09 07						09 24	09 37			09 37					09 54					10 07		
Weybridge	d				09 11						09 28	→			09 41					09 58					10 11		
Byfleet & New Haw	d										09 30									10 00							
West Byfleet	d							09 21			09 33								09 51	10 03							
Woking	a		09 11	09 15	09 18		09 24	09 29		09 33	09 38		09 42	09 45	09 48		09 54	09 58	09 59	10 08		10 11		10 14	10 18		10 24
	d		09 13	09 16	09 19		09 25	09 30		09 35			09 43	09 46	09 49		09 55	10 00	10 00			10 13		10 16	10 19		10 25
Worplesdon	d		09 18																			10 18					
Guildford	a		09 23				09 33						09 52				10 03					10 23					10 33
Brookwood	d				09 25			09 36							09 55				10 06						10 25		
Ash Vale	d	09 19						09 44								09 49			10 14				10 19				
Aldershot	d	09a25						09 50								09a54			10 20				10a24				
Farnham	a							09 55											10 25								
	d							09 57											10 26								
Bentley	d							10 03																			
Alton	a							10 10											10 38								
Farnborough (Main)	d				09 33					09 45					10 03						10 13				10 33		
Fleet	d				09 38										10 08						10 19				10 38		
Winchfield	d				09 44										10 14										10 44		
Hook	d				09 48										10 18										10 48		
Basingstoke	a			09 35	09 58				09 48	09 58				10 05	10 28						10 34			10 35	10 58		

For general notes see front of timetable
For details of catering facilities see
Directory of Train Operators

For details of Bank Holiday service alterations, please see first page of Table 149

London → Woking, Guildford, Alton and Basingstoke

Network Diagram - see first page of Table 155

		SW 1	SW 1 ◇ ☕	SW 1	SW	SW 1	SW 1	SW 1 ◇ ☕	SW 1	SW 1	SW 1 ☕	SW 1 ◇ ☕	SW 1	SW	SW 1	SW 1	SW 1	SW 1 ◇ ☕	SW 1	SW	SW 1 ☕	SW 1	SW 1 ◇ ☕	SW 1	SW	SW 1	SW 1
London Waterloo 15 ⊖	d	09 53	10 05	10 09		10 12	10 15	10 20			10 30	10 35	10 23	10 20	10 39	10 45		10 50	10 42	10 50	11 00	10 53	11 05	11 09		11 12	11 15
Vauxhall ⊖	d													10 24						10 54							
Clapham Junction 10	d	10u00	10u12		←	10u19	10u22	10u27						10 29	10u46	10u52				10 59		11u00	11u12		←	11u19	11u22
Earlsfield	d				10 02									10 32						11 02 →					11 02		
Wimbledon 6 ⊖ 🚊	d				10 06									10 36											11 06		
Surbiton 6	d	10 11			10 14	10 30							10 41	10 44					11 00			11 11			11 14	11 30	
Esher	d				10 18									10 48											11 18		
Hersham	d				10 21				←					10 51											11 21		
Walton-on-Thames	d				10 24	10 37 →			10 37					10 54					11 07						11 24	11 37 →	
Weybridge	d				10 28				10 41					10 58					11 11						11 28		
Byfleet & New Haw	d				10 30									11 00											11 30		
West Byfleet	d	10 21			10 33								10 51	11 03								11 21			11 33		
Woking	a	10 29		10 33	10 38		10 41	10 45	10 48		10 54	10 58	10 59	11 08		11 11		11 14	11 18		11 24	11 29		11 33	11 38		11 41
	d	10 30		10 35			10 43	10 46	10 49		10 55	11 00	11 01			11 13		11 16	11 19		11 25	11 30		11 35			11 43
Worplesdon	d															11 18											
Guildford	a						10 50				11 03					11 23					11 33						11 50
Brookwood	d	10 36							10 55				11 06						11 25			11 36					
Ash Vale	d	10 44								10 49			11 14				11 19					11 44					
Aldershot	d	10 50								10a54			11 20				11a24					11 50					
Farnham	a	10 55											11 25									11 55					
	d	10 57																				11 57					
Bentley	d	11 03																				12 03					
Alton	a	11 10																				12 10					
Farnborough (Main)	d			10 45					11 03						11 13				11 33					11 45			
Fleet	d								11 08						11 19				11 38								
Winchfield	d								11 14										11 44								
Hook	d								11 18										11 48								
Basingstoke	a		10 48	10 58				11 05	11 28						11 34			11 35	11 58				11 48	11 58			

		SW 1 ◇ ☕	SW 1	SW 1	SW 1 ☕	SW 1 ◇ ☕		SW 1	SW	SW 1	SW 1	SW 1	SW 1 ◇ ☕	SW 1	SW	SW 1 ☕	SW 1	SW 1 ◇ ☕	SW 1	SW	SW 1	SW 1	SW 1 ◇ A ☕	SW 1	SW 1	SW 1 ☕	
London Waterloo 15 ⊖	d	11 20			11 30	11 35		11 23	11 20	11 39	11 45		11 50	11 42	11 50	12 00	11 53	12 05	12 09		12 12	12 15	12 20			12 30	
Vauxhall ⊖	d								11 24						11 54												
Clapham Junction 10	d	11u27							11 29	11u46	11u52				11 59		12u00	12u12		←	12u19	12u22	12u27				
Earlsfield	d								11 32						12 02 →					12 02							
Wimbledon 6 ⊖ 🚊	d								11 36											12 06							
Surbiton 6	d							11 41	11 44					12 00			12 11			12 14	12 30						
Esher	d								11 48											12 18							
Hersham	d		←						11 51											12 21				←			
Walton-on-Thames	d		11 37						11 54					12 07						12 24	12 37 →			12 37			
Weybridge	d		11 41						11 58					12 11						12 28				12 41			
Byfleet & New Haw	d								12 00											12 30							
West Byfleet	d							11 51	12 03								12 21			12 33							
Woking	a	11 45	11 48		11 54	11 58		11 59	12 08		12 11		12 14	12 18		12 24	12 29		12 33	12 38		12 41	12 45	12 48		12 54	
	d	11 46	11 49		11 55	12 00		12 00			12 13		12 16	12 19		12 25	12 30		12 35			12 43	12 46	12 49		12 55	
Worplesdon	d										12 18																
Guildford	a				12 03						12 23					12 33						12 50				13 03	
Brookwood	d		11 55					12 06						12 25			12 36							12 55			
Ash Vale	d			11 49				12 14				12 19					12 44								12 49		
Aldershot	d			11a54				12 20				12a24					12 50								12a54		
Farnham	a							12 25									12 55										
	d							12 26									12 57										
Bentley	d																13 03										
Alton	a							12 37									13 10										
Farnborough (Main)	d		12 03							12 13				12 33					12 45					13 03			
Fleet	d		12 08							12 19				12 38										13 08			
Winchfield	d		12 14											12 44										13 14			
Hook	d		12 18											12 48										13 18			
Basingstoke	a	12 05	12 28							12 34			12 35	12 58				12 48	12 58				13 05	13 28			

For general notes see front of timetable
For details of catering facilities see Directory of Train Operators

A To Bristol Temple Meads (Table 123)

For details of Bank Holiday service alterations, please see first page of Table 149

London → Woking, Guildford, Alton and Basingstoke

Network Diagram - see first page of Table 155

	SW 1◇ ☕		SW 1	SW	SW 1 ☕	SW 1	SW 1	SW 1◇ ☕	SW 1	SW	SW 1 ☕	SW 1	SW 1◇ ☕	SW 1	SW	SW 1	SW 1	SW 1◇ ☕	SW 1	SW 1	SW 1 ☕	SW 1◇ ☕	SW 1	SW	SW 1
London Waterloo 15 ⊖ d	12 35	and at the same minutes past each hour until	14 23	14 20	14 39	14 45		14 50	14 42	14 50	15 00	14 53	15 05	15 09		15 12	15 15	15 20			15 30	15 35	15 23	15 20	15 39
Vauxhall ⊖ d				14 24						14 54														15 24	
Clapham Junction 10 d				14 29	14u46	14u52				14 59		15u00	15u12		←	15u19	15u22	15u27						15 29	15u46
Earlsfield d				14 32						15 02 →					15 02									15 32	
Wimbledon 6 ⊖ ⛴ d				14 36											15 06									15 36	
Surbiton 6 d			14 41	14 44					15 00			15 11			15 14	15 30							15 41	15 44	
Esher d				14 48											15 18									15 48	
Hersham d				14 51											15 21				←					15 51	
Walton-on-Thames d				14 54					15 07						15 24	15 37 →			15 37					15 54	
Weybridge d				14 58					15 11						15 28				15 41					15 58	
Byfleet & New Haw d				15 00											15 30									16 00	
West Byfleet d			14 51	15 03								15 21			15 33								15 51	16 03	
Woking a	12 58		14 59	15 08		15 11		15 14	15 18		15 23	15 29		15 33	15 38		15 41	15 45	15 48		15 54	15 58	15 59	16 08	
d	13 00		15 00			15 13		15 16	15 19		15 25	15 30		15 35			15 43	15 46	15 49		15 55	16 00	16 00		
Worplesdon d						15 18											15 48								
Guildford a						15 23					15 32						15 53				16 03				
Brookwood d			15 06						15 25			15 36							15 55				16 06		
Ash Vale d			15 14				15 19					15 44								15 49			16 14		
Aldershot d			15 20				15a24					15 50								15a54			16 20		
Farnham a			15 25									15 55											16 25		
d			15 26									15 57											16 26		
Bentley d												16 03													
Alton a			15 37									16 10											16 37		
Farnborough (Main) d					15 13				15 33					15 45					16 03						16 13
Fleet d					15 19				15 38										16 08						16 19
Winchfield d									15 44										16 14						
Hook d									15 48										16 18						
Basingstoke a					15 34			15 35	15 58				15 48	15 58				16 05	16 28						16 34

	SW 1	SW 1	SW 1◇ ☕	SW 1	SW	SW 1 ☕	SW 1	SW 1◇	SW 1	SW	SW 1	SW 1	SW 1◇ ☕	SW 1	SW 1	SW 1 ☕	SW 1	SW 1 ☕	SW 1	SW	SW 1	SW 1	SW 1◇ ☕	SW 1	SW	SW 1 ☕
London Waterloo 15 ⊖ d	15 45		15 50	15 42	15 50	16 00	15 53	16 05	16 09		16 12	16 15	16 20			16 30	16 25	16 35		16 20	16 39	16 45	16 50	16 42	16 50	17 00
Vauxhall ⊖ d					15 54															16 24					16 54	
Clapham Junction 10 d	15u52		15u57		15 59		16u00	16u12		←	16u19	16u22	16u27							16 29	16u46	16u52	16u57		16 59	
Earlsfield d					16 02 →					16 02										16 32					17 02	
Wimbledon 6 ⊖ ⛴ d										16 06										16 36					17 06	
Surbiton 6 d				16 00			16 11			16 14	16 30						16 41			16 44				17 00	17 14	
Esher d										16 18										16 48					17 18	
Hersham d										16 21				←						16 51					17 21 →	
Walton-on-Thames d				16 07						16 24	16 37 →			16 37						16 54				17 07		
Weybridge d				16 11						16 28				16 41						16 58				17 11		
Byfleet & New Haw d										16 30										17 00						
West Byfleet d							16 21			16 33							16 51			17 03						
Woking a	16 11		16 15	16 18		16 24	16 29		16 33	16 38		16 41	16 45	16 48		16 54	16 59	16 58		17 10		17 11		17 18		17 24
d	16 13		16 16	16 19		16 25	16 30		16 35			16 43	16 46	16 49		16 55	17 00	17 00				17 13	17u16	17 19		17 25
Worplesdon d												16 48														17 30
Guildford a	16 20					16 33						16 53				17 03						17 20				17 36
Brookwood d				16 25			16 36							16 55			17 06							17 25		
Ash Vale d		16 19					16 44								16 49		17 14		17 19							
Aldershot d		16a24					16 50								16a54		17 20		17a24							
Farnham a							16 55										17 25									
d							16 57										17 26									
Bentley d							17 03										17 32									
Alton a							17 10										17 41									
Farnborough (Main) d				16 33					16 45					17 03							17 13			17 33		
Fleet d				16 38										17 08							17 19			17 38		
Winchfield d				16 44										17 14										17 44		
Hook d				16 48										17 18										17 48		
Basingstoke a			16 35	16 58				16 48	16 58				17 05	17 30							17 34		17 35	18 00		

For general notes see front of timetable
For details of catering facilities see
Directory of Train Operators

For details of Bank Holiday service alterations, please see first page of Table 149

London → Woking, Guildford, Alton and Basingstoke

Network Diagram - see first page of Table 155

Station		SW 1	SW 1	SW 1	SW 1	SW 1	SW	SW 1	SW 1 ▼ ☕	SW 1	SW 1	SW 1 ☕	SW 1	SW	SW 1	SW 1	SW 1	SW 1	SW 1 ▼ ☕	SW 1	SW 1	SW 1	SW 1 ☕	SW 1	SW	SW 1	SW 1
London Waterloo 15 ⊖	d	16 55		17 09	17 12	17 15		17 02	17 20	17 25	17 23	17 30	17 39	17 20	17 41	17 45	17 48	17 32	17 50	17 55	17 53		18 00	18 09	17 50	18 11	18 15
Vauxhall ⊖	d													17 24											17 54		
Clapham Junction 10	d	17u02												17 29											17 59		
Earlsfield	d													17 32											18 02		
Wimbledon 6 ⊖	d													17 36											18 06		
Surbiton 6	d							17 18			17 39			17 44				17 48			18 09				18 14		
Esher	d						←	17 22						17 48				17 52							18 18		
Hersham	d						17 21	17 25						17 51				17 55							18 21		
Walton-on-Thames	d						17 24	17 29						17 54				17 59							18 24		
Weybridge	d						17 28	17 33						17 58				18 03							18 28		
Byfleet & New Haw	d						17 30	17 36						18 00				18 06							18 30		
West Byfleet	d	17 21					17 33	17 39						18 03				18 09			18 19				18 33		
Woking	a	17 29		17 32	17 36	17 38	17 43	17 44		17 50	17 51	17 54	18 02	18 10			18 11	18 14		18 20	18 23			18 32	18 40		
	d	17 30		17 34	17 37	17 40		17 46	17u46	17 51	17 52	17 56	18 04				18 13	18 16		18 21	18 26			18 34			
Worplesdon	d					17 45						18 00						18 21									
Guildford	a					17 51		17 56				18 06				18 21		18 29					18 31				18 50
Brookwood	d	17 36			17 43						18 00				18 11					18 27						18 41	
Ash Vale	d	17 44	17 49							18 03										18 35		18 49					
Aldershot	d	17 50	17a54							18 09										18 41		18a54					
Farnham	a	17 55								18 14										18 46							
	d	17 57								18 15										18 48							
Bentley	d	18 03								18 23										18 54							
Alton	a	18 12								18 32										19 03							
Farnborough (Main)	d				17 51						18 08				18 19						18 38					18 48	
Fleet	d				17 56						18 13				18 24						18 44					18 54	
Winchfield	d				18 02						18 19				18 30						18 49					18 59	
Hook	d				18 06						18 23				18 34						18 54					19 04	
Basingstoke	a			17 53	18 16				18 05		18 32		18 23		18 45		18 32		18 37		19 03			18 53		19 16	

Station		SW 1	SW 1 ◇ ☕	SW 1	SW 1	SW 1	SW	SW 1	SW 1	SW 1 ☕	SW 1	SW	SW 1 A	SW 1 ◇ ☕	SW 1	SW	SW 1	SW 1 ☕	SW 1	SW 1 ◇ ☕	SW 1	SW 1	SW	SW 1	SW 1 ◇ ☕	SW 1	SW
London Waterloo 15 ⊖	d	18 18	18 20	18 02	18 41	18 23	18 20	18 25		18 30	18 39		18 45	18 50	18 32	18 50	18 55	19 00		19 05	19 09	19 12		19 15	19 20	19 02	19 20
Vauxhall ⊖	d						18 24									18 54											19 24
Clapham Junction 10	d		18u27				18 29	18u33			18u46					18 59	19u02			19u12		19u19		19u22	19u27		19 29
Earlsfield	d						18 32									19 02											19 32
Wimbledon 6 ⊖	d						18 36		←							19 06											19 36
Surbiton 6	d			18 18		18 40	18 44		18 40						18 48	19 14										19 18	19 44
Esher	d			18 22		→	18 48								18 52	19 18										19 22	19 48
Hersham	d			18 25			18 51					←			18 55	19 21							←			19 25	19 51
Walton-on-Thames	d			18 29			18 54					18 54			18 59	19 24							19 24			19 29	→
Weybridge	d			18 33			→					18 58			19 03	→							19 28			19 33	
Byfleet & New Haw	d			18 36								19 00			19 06								19 30			19 36	
West Byfleet	d			18 39								19 03	19 08		19 09								19 33			19 39	
Woking	a	18 42	18 45	18 48				18 52	18 52	18 57	19 05	19 12	19 13	19 17	19 18		19 21	19 24			19 33	19 38	19 42	19 43	19 45	19 48	
	d	18 43	18 46					18 53	18 54	18 58	19 06		19 14	19 18	19 20		19 23	19 25			19 35	19 39		19 45	19 46		
Worplesdon	d	18 48																19 30									
Guildford	a	18 54								19 06			19 23					19 36						19 52			
Brookwood	d				19 13				19 02								19 30					19 45					
Ash Vale	d							19 05									19 37		19 49								
Aldershot	d							19 11									19 43		19a54								
Farnham	a							19 16									19 48										
	d							19 17									19 49										
Bentley	d							19 23									19 55										
Alton	a							19 32									20 04										
Farnborough (Main)	d				19 20				19 10						19 31						19 45	19 53					
Fleet	d				19 26				19 15						19 37							19 58					
Winchfield	d				19 31				19 21						19 42							20 04					
Hook	d				19 36				19 25						19 47							20 08					
Basingstoke	a		19 05		19 47				19 34		19 28			19 37	20 00					19 48	19 58	20 15			20 06		

For general notes see front of timetable
For details of catering facilities see Directory of Train Operators

A To Portsmouth Harbour (Table 156)

For details of Bank Holiday service alterations, please see first page of Table 149

London → Woking, Guildford, Alton and Basingstoke

Network Diagram - see first page of Table 155

		SW	SW	SW	SW	SW	SW	SW	SW	SW	SW	SW	SW	SW	SW	SW	SW	SW	SW	SW	SW	SW	SW	SW	SW	SW	SW
		1 ☕	1 ◇ ☕	1	1		1	1 ◇ ☕	1		1 ☕	1	1	1 ◇ ☕	1		1	1	1 ◇ ☕	1	1	1 ☕	1 ◇ ☕	1		1	1
London Waterloo 15 ⊖	d	19 30	19 35	19 25	19 39		19 45	19 50	19 42	19 50	20 00		19 53	20 05	20 09		20 12	20 15	20 20			20 30	20 35	20 23	20 20	20 39	20 45
Vauxhall ⊖	d									19 54															20 24		
Clapham Junction 10	d			19u32	19u46		19u52			19 59			20u00	20u12		←	20u19	20u22	20u27						20 29	20u46	20u52
Earlsfield	d									20 02 →						20 02									20 32		
Wimbledon 6 ⊖	d															20 06									20 36		
Surbiton 6	d								20 00				20 11			20 14	20 30							20 41	20 44		
Esher	d					←										20 18									20 48		
Hersham	d					19 51										20 21					←				20 51		
Walton-on-Thames	d					19 54			20 07							20 24	20 37 →				20 37				20 54		
Weybridge	d					19 58			20 11							20 28					20 41				20 58		
Byfleet & New Haw	d					20 00										20 30									21 00		
West Byfleet	d			19 51		20 03							20 21			20 33								20 51	21 03		
Woking	a	19 54	19 58	19 59		20 08	20 11	20 14	20 18		20 25		20 29		20 33	20 38		20 41	20 45		20 48	20 54	20 58	20 59	21 08		21 11
	d	19 55	20 00	20 00			20 13	20 16	20 19		20 25		20 30		20 35			20 43	20 49		20 49	20 55	21 00	21 00			21 13
Worplesdon	d						20 18																				21 18
Guildford	a	20 03					20 23				20 34							20 50				21 03					21 23
Brookwood	d			20 06					20 25				20 37								20 55			21 06			
Ash Vale	d			20 14								20 19	20 44							20 49				21 14			
Aldershot	d			20 20								20a24	20 50							20a54				21 20			
Farnham	a			20 25									20 56											21 25			
	d			20 26									20 57											21 26			
Bentley	d			20 32									21 03											21 32			
Alton	a			20 39									21 17											21 42			
Farnborough (Main)	d				20 13				20 33						20 45						21 03					21 13	
Fleet	d				20 19				20 38												21 08					21 19	
Winchfield	d								20 44												21 14						
Hook	d								20 48												21 18						
Basingstoke	a				20 34			20 35	20 58					20 48	20 58				21 08		21 27					21 34	

		SW	SW	SW	SW	SW	SW	SW	SW	SW	SW	SW	SW	SW	SW	SW	SW	SW	SW	SW	SW	SW	SW	SW	SW	SW	SW
		1		1	1 ☕	1	1 ◇ ☕		1	1 ◇ ☕	1	1	1 ☕	1 ◇ ☕	1		1	1	1 A		1 ☕	1	1 ☕		1	1 ☕	
London Waterloo 15 ⊖	d	20 42	20 50		21 00	20 53	21 05		21 12	21 20			21 30	21 35	21 23	21 20	21 39	21 45	21 42	21 50	22 00	21 53	22 05		22 12	22 20	22 20
Vauxhall ⊖	d		20 54													21 24				21 54							22 24
Clapham Junction 10	d		20 59			21u00	21u12	←	21u19	21u27						21 29	21u46	21u52		21 59		22u00	22u12	←	22u19	22u27	22 29
Earlsfield	d		21 02 →					21 02								21 32				22 02 →				22 02			22 32 →
Wimbledon 6 ⊖	d							21 06								21 36								22 06			
Surbiton 6	d	21 00				21 11		21 14	21 30						21 41	21 44			22 00			22 11		22 14	22 30		
Esher	d							21 18								21 48								22 18			
Hersham	d							21 21				←				21 51								22 21			
Walton-on-Thames	d	21 07						21 24	21 37 →			21 37				21 54			22 07					22 24	22 37 →		
Weybridge	d	21 11						21 28				21 41				21 58			22 11					22 28			
Byfleet & New Haw	d							21 30								22 00								22 30			
West Byfleet	d					21 21		21 33							21 51	22 03						22 21		22 33			
Woking	a	21 18			21 24	21 29	21 31	21 38		21 45		21 48	21 54	21 58	21 59	22 08		22 11	22 18		22 24	22 29	22 31	22 38		22 45	
	d	21 19			21 25	21 30	21 32			21 49		21 49	21 55	22 00	22 00			22 13	22 19		22 25	22 30	22 32	22 39		22 49	
Worplesdon	d																	22 18									
Guildford	a				21 33								22 03					22 23			22 33			22 47			
Brookwood	d	21 25				21 36						21 55			22 06				22 25			22 36					
Ash Vale	d			21 19		21 44					21 49				22 14							22 44					
Aldershot	d			21a24		21 50					21a54				22 20							22 50					
Farnham	a					21 55									22 25							22 56					
	d					21 57									22 26							22 57					
Bentley	d					22 03									22 32							23 03					
Alton	a					22 10									22 39							23 10					
Farnborough (Main)	d	21 33										22 03					22 13		22 33								
Fleet	d	21 38										22 08					22 19		22 38								
Winchfield	d	21 44										22 14							22 44								
Hook	d	21 48										22 18							22 48								
Basingstoke	a	21 58					21 51			22 08		22 28					22 34		22 58				22 51			23 10	

For general notes see front of timetable
For details of catering facilities see
Directory of Train Operators

A To Portsmouth Harbour (Table 158)

For details of Bank Holiday service alterations, please see first page of Table 149

London → Woking, Guildford, Alton and Basingstoke

Network Diagram - see first page of Table 155

		SW 1	SW 1	SW 1	SW 1	SW 1	SW	SW 1	SW 1	SW 1	SW 1	SW	SW 1	SW 1	SW 1	SW	SW 1	SW 1	SW 1	SW	SW 1	SW 1	SW 1	SW	SW 1	SW 1
														A												
London Waterloo 15	⊖ d			22 30	22 35	22 23		22 39	22 42	22 45		22 50	22 53		23 05		23 12	23 15		23 20	23 23	23 35	23 39		23 45	23 48
Vauxhall	⊖ d											22 54								23 24						
Clapham Junction 10	d					22u30	←	22u46	22u49	22u52		22 59	23u00		23u12	←	23u19	23u22		23 29	23u30	23u42	23u46	←	23u52	23u56
Earlsfield	d						22 32					23 02				23 02				23 32				23 32		
Wimbledon 6	⊖ d						22 36					→				23 06				→				23 36		
Surbiton 6	d					22 41	22 44		23 00				23 11			23 14	23 30				23 41			23 44		00 10
Esher	d						22 48									23 18								23 48		
Hersham	d		←				22 51				←					23 21			←					23 51		
Walton-on-Thames	d		22 37				22 54		23 07		23 07					23 24	23 37		23 37					23 54		00 17
Weybridge	d		22 41				22 58		→		23 11					23 28	→		23 41					23 58		00 21
Byfleet & New Haw	d						23 00									23 30								00 01		
West Byfleet	d					22 51	23 03						23 21			23 33					23 51			00 03		
Woking	a		22 48	22 54	22 58	22 59	23 08			23 11	23 18		23 28		23 31	23 38		23 41	23 48		23 59	00 02	00 06	00 08	00 11	00 27
	d		22 49	22 55	23 00	23 00				23 13	23 19		23 30		23 32			23 43	23 49		00 01	00 03	00 08		00 13	00 29
Worplesdon	d									23 18															00 18	
Guildford	a			23 03						23 24								23 51							00 24	
Brookwood	d		22 55			23 06					23 25		23 37						23 55		00 06					00 35
Ash Vale	d	22 49				23 14							23 44	23 49							00 14					
Aldershot	d	22a54				23 20							23 50	23 55							00 20					
Farnham	a					23 25							23 56	00 03							00 25					
	d					23 26							23 57								00 26					
Bentley	d					23 32							00 04								00 32					
Alton	a					23 39							00 11								00 40					
Farnborough (Main)	d		23 03					23 13			23 33								00 03				00 18			00 42
Fleet	d		23 08					23 19			23 38								00 08				00 23			00 48
Winchfield	d		23 14								23 44								00 14							00s53
Hook	d		23 18								23 48								00 18							00s58
Basingstoke	a		23 27					23 33			23 57				23 51				00 25			00 22	00 35			01 07

Saturdays

		SW 1	SW 1	SW	SW 1	SW 1	SW 1	SW	SW 1	SW 1	SW 1	SW 1		SW	SW 1	SW 1	SW 1	SW 1	SW 1	SW 1	SW 1	SW 1	SW 1	SW		SW 1	SW 1
											B				A	C	D	E	G		E	H					
London Waterloo 15	⊖ d	22p53	23p12	23p20	23p23	23p35	23p39		23p45	23p48	00 05			00 09		01 05	05 00	05 20	05 30					05 50		06 12	06 15
Vauxhall	⊖ d			23p24										00 13		01 09	05 04	05 24						05 54			
Clapham Junction 10	d	23b00	23b19	23p29	23b30	23b42	23b46	←	23b52	23b56	00u12			00 18		01 14	05 09	05 29	05u37					05 59		06u19	06u22
Earlsfield	d			23p32				23p32						00 21			05 12	05 32						06 02			
Wimbledon 6	⊖ d			→				23p36			00u18			00 25		01 20	05 16	05 36	05 43					06 06			
Surbiton 6	d	23p11	23p30		23p41			23p44		00 10				00 33		01 28	05 24	05 44						06 14		06 30	
Esher	d							23p48						00s37			05 28	05 48						06 18			
Hersham	d							23p51						00s40			05 32	05 51			←			06 21			
Walton-on-Thames	d		23p37					23p54		00 17				00s43			05 35	05 54			05 54			06 24		06 37	
Weybridge	d		23p41					23p58		00 21				00s46			05 39	→			05 58			06 28		→	
Byfleet & New Haw	d							00 01						00s49			05 42				06 00			06 30			
West Byfleet	d	23p21			23p51			00 03						00s52			05 45				06 03			06 33			
Woking	a	23p28	23p48		23p59	00 02	00 06	00 08	00 11	00 27	00 35			00 57		01 41	05 50		05 59		06 08			06 38			06 41
	d	23p30	23p49		00 01	00 03	00 08		00 13	00 29	00 36	00 40		00 58		01 41	05 51		06 01	06 02	06 13	06 19	06 30				06 43
Worplesdon	d								00 18												06 18						
Guildford	a								00 24					01 06			05 59				06 23						06 50
Brookwood	d	23p37	23p55		00 06					00 35		00 45								06 08		06 25	06 36				
Ash Vale	d	23p44			00 14							00 53			00 52					06 16			06 44				
Aldershot	d	23p50			00 20							00 58			00 57					06 21			06 50				
Farnham	a	23p56			00 25							01 04			01 02					06 27			06 55				
	d	23p57			00 26							01 04								06 27			06 57				
Bentley	d	00 04			00 32							01s10								06 34			07 03				
Alton	a	00 11			00 40							01 18								06 41			07 10				
Farnborough (Main)	d		00 03				00 18			00 42						01s57						06 33					
Fleet	d		00 08				00 23			00 48												06 38					
Winchfield	d		00 14							00s53												06 43					
Hook	d		00 18							00s58												06 48					
Basingstoke	a		00 25			00 22	00 35			01 07	00 55					02s11			06 20			06 58					

For general notes see front of timetable
For details of catering facilities see Directory of Train Operators

A From Ascot (Table 149)
B To Bournemouth (Table 158)
C To Southampton Central (Table 158)
D To Haslemere (Table 156)
E To Portsmouth Harbour (Table 156)
G To Weymouth (Table 158)
H To Portsmouth Harbour (Table 158)
b Previous night.
Stops to pick up only

Table 155

Saturdays

London → Woking, Guildford, Alton and Basingstoke

Network Diagram - see first page of Table 155

		SW	SW 1	SW 1	SW 1 A	SW 1	SW	SW 1	SW	SW 1	SW 1 A	SW 1		SW 1◇ ☕	SW	SW 1	SW 1	SW	SW 1	SW 1	SW 1◇	SW 1	SW	SW 1		SW 1	SW 1
London Waterloo 15 ⊖	d	06 20		06 30	06 42			06 45	06 50			06 53		07 10		07 12	07 15	07 20		07 30	07 35	07 23		07 39		07 45	
Vauxhall ⊖	d	06 24							06 54									07 24									
Clapham Junction 10	d	06 29		06u37	06u49			06u52	06 59			07u00		07u17	←	07u19	07u22	07 29				07u30	←	07u46		07u52	
Earlsfield	d	06 32							07 02 →						07 02			07 32 →					07 32				
Wimbledon 6 ⊖	d	06 36													07 06								07 36				
Surbiton 6	d	06 44			07 00							07 11			07 14	07 30						07 41	07 44				
Esher	d	06 48													07 18								07 48				
Hersham	d	06 51	←				←				←				07 21				←				07 51				
Walton-on-Thames	d	06 54 →	06 37		07 07 →		06 54				07 07				07 24	07 37 →			07 37				07 54				
Weybridge	d		06 41				06 58				07 11				07 28				07 41				07 58				
Byfleet & New Haw	d						07 00								07 30								08 00				
West Byfleet	d						07 03					07 21			07 33							07 51	08 03				
Woking	a		06 48	06 56			07 08	07 11			07 18	07 26		07 35	07 38		07 41		07 48	07 54	07 58	07 59	08 08			08 11	
	d		06 49	06 57		07 00		07 13			07 19	07 30		07 36			07 43		07 49	07 55	08 00	08 00				08 13	
Worplesdon	d							07 18																		08 18	
Guildford	a							07 23									07 50			08 03						08 23	
Brookwood	d		06 55			07 06					07 25	07 36							07 55			08 06					
Ash Vale	d					07 14				07 19		07 44										08 14					08 19
Aldershot	d					07 20				07a24		07 50										08 20					08a24
Farnham	a					07 25						07 55										08 25					
	d					07 26						07 57										08 26					
Bentley	d					07 32						08 03										08 32					
Alton	a					07 40						08 10										08 40					
Farnborough (Main)	d		07 03								07 33								08 03					08 13			
Fleet	d		07 08								07 38								08 08					08 19			
Winchfield	d		07 14								07 44								08 14								
Hook	d		07 18								07 48								08 18								
Basingstoke	a		07 28	07 16							07 58			07 57					08 28		08 20			08 34			

		SW 1◇ ☕	SW 1	SW	SW 1	SW 1	SW 1◇ ☕	SW 1	SW	SW 1	SW 1	SW 1◇ ☕		SW 1	SW 1	SW 1	SW 1◇ ☕	SW 1	SW	SW 1	SW 1	SW 1	SW 1◇ ☕	SW 1		SW	SW 1 ☕
London Waterloo 15 ⊖	d	07 50	07 42	07 50	08 00	07 53	08 05	08 09		08 12	08 15	08 20				08 30	08 35	08 23	08 20	08 39	08 45		08 50	08 42		08 50	09 00
Vauxhall ⊖	d			07 54															08 24							08 54	
Clapham Junction 10	d	07u57		07 59		08u00	08u12		←	08u19	08u22	08u27							08 29	08u46	08u52					08 59	
Earlsfield	d			08 02 →					08 02										08 32							09 02 →	
Wimbledon 6 ⊖	d								08 06										08 36								
Surbiton 6	d		08 00			08 11			08 14	08 30								08 41	08 44					09 00			
Esher	d								08 18										08 48								
Hersham	d								08 21					←					08 51								
Walton-on-Thames	d		08 07						08 24	08 37 →				08 37					08 54					09 07			
Weybridge	d		08 11						08 28					08 41					08 58					09 11			
Byfleet & New Haw	d								08 30										09 00								
West Byfleet	d					08 21			08 33									08 51	09 03								
Woking	a	08 15	08 18		08 24	08 29		08 33	08 38		08 41	08 45		08 48		08 54	08 58	08 59	09 08		09 11		09 14	09 18			09 24
	d	08 16	08 19		08 25	08 30		08 35			08 43	08 46		08 49		08 55	09 00	09 00			09 13		09 16	09 19			09 25
Worplesdon	d																				09 18						
Guildford	a				08 33						08 50					09 03					09 23						09 33
Brookwood	d		08 25			08 36								08 55				09 06						09 25			
Ash Vale	d					08 44									08 49			09 14				09 19					
Aldershot	d					08 50									08a54			09 20				09a24					
Farnham	a					08 55												09 25									
	d					08 57												09 26									
Bentley	d					09 03																					
Alton	a					09 10												09 38									
Farnborough (Main)	d		08 33					08 45						09 03						09 13				09 33			
Fleet	d		08 38											09 08						09 19				09 38			
Winchfield	d		08 44											09 14										09 44			
Hook	d		08 48											09 18										09 48			
Basingstoke	a	08 35	08 58				08 48	08 58				09 05		09 28						09 34			09 35	09 58			

		SW 1	SW 1◇ ☕	SW 1	SW	SW 1	SW 1	SW 1◇ ☕	SW 1	SW 1	SW 1 ☕	SW 1◇ ☕		SW 1	SW	SW 1	SW 1	SW 1	SW 1◇ ☕	SW 1	SW	SW 1 ☕	SW 1	SW 1◇ ☕		SW 1	SW
London Waterloo 15 ⊖	d	08 53	09 05	09 09		09 12	09 15	09 20			09 30	09 35		09 23	09 20	09 39	09 45		09 50	09 42	09 50	10 00	09 53	10 05		10 09	
Vauxhall ⊖	d														09 24						09 54						
Clapham Junction 10	d	09u00	09u12		←	09u19	09u22	09u27							09 29	09u46	09u52				09 59		10u00	10u12			←
Earlsfield	d				09 02										09 32						10 02 →						10 02
Wimbledon 6 ⊖	d				09 06										09 36												10 06
Surbiton 6	d	09 11			09 14	09 30								09 41	09 44					10 00			10 11				10 14
Esher	d				09 18										09 48												10 18
Hersham	d				09 21				←						09 51												10 21
Walton-on-Thames	d				09 24	09 37 →			09 37						09 54					10 07							10 24
Weybridge	d				09 28				09 41						09 58					10 11							10 28
Byfleet & New Haw	d				09 30										10 00												10 30
West Byfleet	d	09 21			09 33									09 51	10 03								10 21				10 33
Woking	a	09 29		09 33	09 38		09 41	09 45	09 48		09 54	09 58		09 59	10 08		10 11		10 14	10 18		10 24	10 29			10 33	10 38
	d	09 30		09 35			09 43	09 46	09 49		09 55	10 00		10 00			10 13		10 16	10 19		10 25	10 30			10 35	
Worplesdon	d																10 18										
Guildford	a						09 50				10 03						10 23					10 33					
Brookwood	d	09 36							09 55					10 06						10 25			10 36				
Ash Vale	d	09 44								09 49				10 14				10 19					10 44				
Aldershot	d	09 50								09a54				10 20				10a24					10 50				
Farnham	a	09 55												10 25									10 55				
	d	09 57												10 26									10 57				
Bentley	d	10 03																					11 03				
Alton	a	10 10												10 38									11 10				
Farnborough (Main)	d			09 45					10 03							10 13				10 33						10 45	
Fleet	d								10 08							10 19				10 38							
Winchfield	d								10 14											10 44							
Hook	d								10 18											10 48							
Basingstoke	a		09 48	09 58				10 05	10 28							10 34			10 35	10 58				10 48		10 58	

For general notes see front of timetable
For details of catering facilities see
Directory of Train Operators

A To Portsmouth Harbour (Table 158)

London → Woking, Guildford, Alton and Basingstoke

Network Diagram - see first page of Table 155

		SW 1	SW 1	SW 1 ◇ ☕	SW 1	SW 1		SW 1 ☕	SW 1 ◇ ☕	SW 1	SW	SW 1	SW 1	SW 1	SW 1 ◇ ☕	SW 1	SW	SW 1 ☕	SW 1	SW 1 ◇ ☕	SW 1	SW	SW 1	SW 1	SW 1 ◇ ☕	SW 1	
London Waterloo 15 ⊖	d	10 12	10 15	10 20				10 30	10 35	10 23	10 20	10 39	10 45		10 50	10 42	10 50	11 00	10 53	11 05	11 09		11 12	11 15	11 20		
Vauxhall ⊖	d										10 24						10 54										
Clapham Junction 10	d	10u19	10u22	10u27							10 29	10u46	10u52				10 59		11u00	11u12		←	11u19	11u22	11u27		
Earlsfield	d										10 32						11 02 →					11 02					
Wimbledon 6 ⊖	d										10 36											11 06					
Surbiton 6	d	10 30								10 41	10 44					11 00			11 11			11 14	11 30				
Esher	d										10 48											11 18					
Hersham	d				←						10 51											11 21				←	
Walton-on-Thames	d	10 37 →			10 37						10 54					11 07						11 24	11 37 →			11 37	
Weybridge	d				10 41						10 58					11 11						11 28				11 41	
Byfleet & New Haw	d										11 00											11 30					
West Byfleet	d									10 51	11 03								11 21			11 33					
Woking	a		10 41	10 45	10 48			10 54	10 58	10 59	11 08		11 11		11 14	11 18		11 24	11 29		11 33	11 38		11 41	11 45	11 48	
	d		10 43	10 46	10 49			10 55	11 00	11 00			11 13		11 16	11 19		11 25	11 30		11 35			11 43	11 46	11 49	
Worplesdon	d												11 18														
Guildford	a		10 50					11 03					11 23					11 33						11 50			
Brookwood	d				10 55					11 06						11 25			11 36							11 55	
Ash Vale	d					10 49				11 14				11 19					11 44								
Aldershot	d					10a54				11 20				11a24					11 50								
Farnham	a									11 25									11 55								
	d									11 26									11 56								
Bentley	d																		12 03								
Alton	a									11 38									12 10								
Farnborough (Main)	d				11 03							11 13				11 33					11 45					12 03	
Fleet	d				11 08							11 19				11 38										12 08	
Winchfield	d				11 14											11 44										12 14	
Hook	d				11 18											11 48										12 18	
Basingstoke	a			11 05	11 28							11 34			11 35	11 58				11 48	11 58				12 05	12 28	

		SW 1	and at the same minutes past each hour until		SW 1 ☕	SW 1 ◇ ☕	SW 1	SW	SW 1	SW 1	SW 1	SW 1 ◇ ☕	SW 1	SW	SW 1 ☕		SW 1	SW 1 ◇ ☕	SW 1	SW	SW 1	SW 1	SW 1 ◇ ☕	SW 1	SW 1	SW 1 ☕
London Waterloo 15 ⊖	d				16 30	16 35	16 23	16 20	16 39	16 45		16 50	16 42	16 50	17 00		16 53	17 05	17 09		17 12	17 15	17 20			17 30
Vauxhall ⊖	d							16 24						16 54												
Clapham Junction 10	d							16 29	16u46	16u52				16 59			17u00	17u12		←	17u19	17u22	17u27			
Earlsfield	d							16 32						17 02 →						17 02						
Wimbledon 6 ⊖	d							16 36												17 06						
Surbiton 6	d						16 41	16 44					17 00				17 11			17 14	17 30					
Esher	d							16 48												17 18						
Hersham	d							16 51												17 21				←		
Walton-on-Thames	d							16 54					17 07							17 24	17 37 →			17 37		
Weybridge	d							16 58					17 11							17 28				17 41		
Byfleet & New Haw	d							17 00												17 30						
West Byfleet	d						16 51	17 03									17 21			17 33						
Woking	a				16 54	16 58	16 59	17 08		17 11		17 14	17 18		17 24		17 29		17 33	17 38		17 41	17 45	17 48		17 54
	d				16 55	17 00	17 00			17 13		17 16	17 19		17 25		17 30		17 35			17 43	17 46	17 49		17 55
Worplesdon	d									17 18																
Guildford	a				17 03					17 23					17 33							17 50				18 03
Brookwood	d						17 06						17 25				17 36							17 55		
Ash Vale	d	11 49					17 14				17 19						17 44								17 49	
Aldershot	d	11a54					17 20				17a24						17 50								17a54	
Farnham	a						17 25										17 55									
	d						17 26										17 57									
Bentley	d						17 32										18 03									
Alton	a						17 42										18 10									
Farnborough (Main)	d								17 13				17 33						17 45					18 03		
Fleet	d								17 19				17 38											18 08		
Winchfield	d												17 44											18 14		
Hook	d												17 48											18 18		
Basingstoke	a								17 34			17 35	17 58					17 48	17 58				18 05	18 28		

		SW 1 ◇ ☕	SW 1	SW		SW 1	SW 1	SW 1	SW 1 ◇ ☕	SW 1	SW	SW 1 ☕	SW 1	SW 1 ☕	SW 1	SW		SW 1	SW 1	SW 1 ◇ ☕	SW 1	SW 1	SW 1 ☕	SW 1 ◇ ☕	SW 1	SW	SW 1
London Waterloo 15 ⊖	d	17 35	17 23	17 20		17 39	17 45		17 50	17 42	17 50	18 00	17 53	18 05	18 09			18 12	18 15	18 20			18 30	18 35	18 23	18 20	18 39
Vauxhall ⊖	d			17 24							17 54															18 24	
Clapham Junction 10	d			17 29		17u46	17u52				17 59		18u00	18 12		←		18u19	18u22	18u27						18 29	18u46
Earlsfield	d			17 32							18 02 →					18 02										18 32	
Wimbledon 6 ⊖	d			17 36												18 06										18 36	
Surbiton 6	d		17 41	17 44						18 00			18 11			18 14		18 30							18 41	18 44	
Esher	d			17 48												18 18										18 48	
Hersham	d			17 51												18 21					←					18 51	
Walton-on-Thames	d			17 54						18 07						18 24		18 37 →			18 37					18 54	
Weybridge	d			17 58						18 11						18 28					18 41					18 58	
Byfleet & New Haw	d			18 00												18 30										19 00	
West Byfleet	d		17 51	18 03									18 21			18 33									18 51	19 03	
Woking	a	17 58	17 59	18 08			18 11		18 14	18 18		18 24	18 29		18 33	18 38			18 41	18 45	18 48		18 54	18 58	18 59	19 08	
	d	18 00	18 00				18 13		18 16	18 19		18 25	18 30		18 35				18 43	18 46	18 49		18 55	19 00	19 00		
Worplesdon	d						18 18																				
Guildford	a						18 23					18 33							18 50				19 03				
Brookwood	d		18 06							18 25			18 36								18 55				19 06		
Ash Vale	d		18 14					18 19					18 44									18 49			19 14		
Aldershot	d		18 20					18a24					18 50									18a54			19 20		
Farnham	a		18 26										18 55												19 25		
	d		18 26										18 57												19 26		
Bentley	d		18 32										19 03												19 32		
Alton	a		18 40										19 10												19 39		
Farnborough (Main)	d					18 13				18 33					18 45						19 03						19 13
Fleet	d					18 19				18 38											19 08						19 19
Winchfield	d									18 44											19 14						
Hook	d									18 48											19 18						
Basingstoke	a					18 34			18 35	18 58				18 48	18 58					19 05	19 28						19 34

For general notes see front of timetable
For details of catering facilities see
Directory of Train Operators

London → Woking, Guildford, Alton and Basingstoke

Network Diagram - see first page of Table 155

		SW	SW	SW		SW	SW	SW	SW	SW	SW	SW	SW	SW	SW	SW		SW	SW	SW	SW	SW	SW	SW	SW	SW	SW
		1	1	1 ◇		1		1	1	1 ◇	1		1	1	1 ◇	1		1	1	1 ◇	1		1	1	1	1 ◇	1
															A												
				☕				☕		☕					☕				☕	☕						☕	
London Waterloo 15	⊖ d	18 45		18 50		18 42	18 50	19 00	18 53	19 05	19 09		19 12	19 15	19 20				19 30	19 35	19 23	19 20	19 39	19 45		19 50	19 42
Vauxhall	⊖ d						18 54															19 24					
Clapham Junction 10	d	18u52					18 59		19u00	19u12		←	19u19	19u22	19u27							19 29	19u46	19u52			
Earlsfield	d						19 02					19 02										19 32					
Wimbledon 6	⊖ ⛴ d						→					19 06										19 36					
Surbiton 6	d					19 00			19 11			19 14	19 30								19 41	19 44					20 00
Esher	d											19 18										19 48					
Hersham	d											19 21				←						19 51					
Walton-on-Thames	d					19 07						19 24	19 37			19 37						19 54					20 07
Weybridge	d					19 11						19 28	→			19 41						19 58					20 11
Byfleet & New Haw	d											19 30										20 00					
West Byfleet	d								19 21			19 33									19 51	20 03					
Woking	a	19 11		19 15		19 18		19 24	19 29		19 33	19 38		19 41	19 45	19 48			19 54	19 58	19 59	20 08		20 11		20 14	20 18
	d	19 13		19 16		19 19		19 25	19 30		19 35			19 43	19 46	19 49			19 55	20 00	20 00			20 13		20 16	20 19
Worplesdon	d	19 18																						20 18			
Guildford	a	19 23						19 33						19 50					20 03					20 23			
Brookwood	d					19 25			19 36							19 55					20 06						20 25
Ash Vale	d		19 19						19 44									19 49			20 14				20 19		
Aldershot	d		19a24						19 50									19a54			20 20				20a24		
Farnham	a								19 55												20 25						
	d								19 57												20 26						
Bentley	d								20 03												20 32						
Alton	a								20 10												20 39						
Farnborough (Main)	d					19 33					19 45					20 03							20 13				20 33
Fleet	d					19 38										20 08							20 19				20 38
Winchfield	d					19 44										20 14											20 44
Hook	d					19 48										20 18											20 48
Basingstoke	a			19 35		19 58				19 48	19 58				20 05	20 28							20 34			20 35	20 58

		SW	SW	SW		SW	SW	SW	SW	SW	SW	SW	SW	SW	SW	SW		SW	SW	SW	SW	SW	SW	SW	SW	SW	SW
			1	1		1 ◇	1		1	1	1 ◇	1	1	1	1 ◇	1			1	1	1		1	1	1	1 ◇	
																					B						
						☕					☕				☕											☕	
London Waterloo 15	⊖ d	19 50	20 00	19 53		20 05	20 09		20 12	20 15	20 20			20 30	20 35	20 23		20 20	20 39	20 45	20 42	20 50		21 00	20 53	21 05	
Vauxhall	⊖ d	19 54																20 24				20 54					
Clapham Junction 10	d	19 59		20u00		20u12		←	20u19	20u22	20u27							20 29	20u46	20u52		20 59			21u00	21u12	←
Earlsfield	d	20 02						20 02										20 32				21 02					21 02
Wimbledon 6	⊖ ⛴ d	→						20 06										20 36				→					21 06
Surbiton 6	d			20 11				20 14	20 30							20 41		20 44			21 00				21 11		21 14
Esher	d							20 18										20 48									21 18
Hersham	d							20 21				←						20 51									21 21
Walton-on-Thames	d							20 24	20 37			20 37						20 54			21 07						21 24
Weybridge	d							20 28	→			20 41						20 58			21 11						21 28
Byfleet & New Haw	d							20 30										21 00									21 30
West Byfleet	d			20 21				20 33								20 51		21 03							21 21		21 33
Woking	a		20 24	20 29			20 33	20 38		20 41	20 45	20 48		20 54	20 58	20 59		21 08		21 11	21 18			21 24	21 29	21 31	21 38
	d		20 25	20 30			20 35			20 43	20 46	20 49		20 55	21 00	21 00				21 13	21 19			21 25	21 30	21 32	
Worplesdon	d																			21 18							
Guildford	a		20 33							20 50				21 03						21 23				21 33			
Brookwood	d			20 36								20 55				21 06					21 25				21 36		
Ash Vale	d			20 44									20 49			21 14							21 19		21 44		
Aldershot	d			20 50									20a54			21 20							21a24		21 50		
Farnham	a			20 55												21 25									21 55		
	d			20 57												21 26									21 57		
Bentley	d			21 03												21 32									22 03		
Alton	a			21 10												21 39									22 10		
Farnborough (Main)	d						20 45					21 03							21 13		21 33						
Fleet	d											21 08							21 19		21 38						
Winchfield	d											21 14									21 44						
Hook	d											21 18									21 48						
Basingstoke	a					20 48	20 58				21 05	21 25							21 34		21 58					21 51	

		SW	SW	SW		SW	SW	SW	SW	SW	SW	SW	SW	SW	SW	SW		SW	SW	SW	SW	SW	SW	SW	SW	SW	SW
		1	1 ◇	1		1	1	1 ◇	1		1	1	1		1	1		1		1	1 ◇		1	1	1	1	1
													B														
			☕					☕										☕			☕					☕	
London Waterloo 15	⊖ d	21 12	21 20				21 30	21 35	21 23	21 20	21 39	21 45	21 42	21 50	22 00	21 53		22 05		22 12	22 20	22 20			22 30	22 35	22 23
Vauxhall	⊖ d									21 24				21 54								22 24					
Clapham Junction 10	d	21u19	21u27							21 29	21u46	21u52		21 59		22u00		22u12	←	22u19	22u27	22 29					22u30
Earlsfield	d									21 32				22 02					22 02			22 32					
Wimbledon 6	⊖ ⛴ d									21 36				→					22 06			→					
Surbiton 6	d	21 30							21 41	21 44			22 00			22 11			22 14	22 30							22 41
Esher	d									21 48									22 18								
Hersham	d			←						21 51									22 21				←				
Walton-on-Thames	d	21 37		21 37						21 54			22 07						22 24	22 37			22 37				
Weybridge	d	→		21 41						21 58			22 11						22 28	→			22 41				
Byfleet & New Haw	d									22 00									22 30								
West Byfleet	d								21 51	22 03						22 21			22 33								22 51
Woking	a		21 45	21 48			21 54	21 58	21 59	22 08		22 11	22 18		22 24	22 29		22 31	22 38		22 45		22 48		22 54	22 58	22 59
	d		21 49	21 49			21 55	22 00	22 00			22 13	22 19		22 25	22 30		22 32	22 39		22 49		22 49		22 55	23 00	23 00
Worplesdon	d											22 18															
Guildford	a						22 03					22 23			22 33				22 47						23 03		
Brookwood	d			21 55					22 06				22 25			22 36							22 55				23 06
Ash Vale	d					21 49			22 14							22 44								22 49			23 14
Aldershot	d					21a54			22 20							22 50								22a54			23 20
Farnham	a								22 25							22 56											23 25
	d								22 26							22 57											23 26
Bentley	d								22 32							23 03											23 32
Alton	a								22 39							23 10											23 39
Farnborough (Main)	d			22 03							22 13		22 33										23 03				
Fleet	d			22 08							22 19		22 38										23 08				
Winchfield	d			22 14									22 44										23 14				
Hook	d			22 18									22 48										23 18				
Basingstoke	a		22 08	22 25							22 34		22 58					22 51			23 09		23 25				

For general notes see front of timetable
For details of catering facilities see
Directory of Train Operators

A To Bristol Temple Meads (Table 123)
B To Portsmouth Harbour (Table 158)

Table 155

Saturdays

London → Woking, Guildford, Alton and Basingstoke

Network Diagram - see first page of Table 155

		SW	SW 1	SW 1		SW 1	SW 1	SW	SW 1	SW 1		SW 1	SW	SW 1	SW 1	SW 1		SW	SW 1	SW 1	SW 1	SW	SW 1	SW 1			
London Waterloo 15 ⊖	d		22 39	22 42		22 45		22 50	22 53			23 05		23 12	23 15			23 20	23 23	23 35	23 39		23 45	23 48			
Vauxhall ⊖	d							22 54										23 24									
Clapham Junction 10	d	←	22u46	22u49		22u52		22 59	23u00			23u12	←	23u19	23u22			23 29	23u30	23u42	23u46	←	23u52	23u56			
Earlsfield	d	22 32						23 02 →					23 02					23 32 →				23 32					
Wimbledon 6 ⊖	d	22 36											23 06									23 36					
Surbiton 6	d	22 44		23 00					23 11				23 14	23 30					23 41			23 44		00 10			
Esher	d	22 48											23 18									23 48					
Hersham	d	22 51					←						23 21			←						23 51					
Walton-on-Thames	d	22 54		23 07 →			23 07						23 24	23 37 →		23 37						23 54		00 17			
Weybridge	d	22 58					23 11						23 28			23 41						23 58		00 21			
Byfleet & New Haw	d	23 00											23 30									23 59					
West Byfleet	d	23 03							23 21				23 33						23 51			00 03					
Woking	a	23 08				23 11	23 18		23 29			23 31	23 38		23 41	23 48			23 59	00 02	00 06	00 08	00 12	00 27			
	d					23 13	23 19		23 30			23 32			23 43	23 49			00 01	00 03	00 08		00 13	00 29			
Worplesdon	d					23 18																	00 18				
Guildford	a					23 24									23 51								00 23				
Brookwood	d						23 25		23 36							23 55			00 06					00 35			
Ash Vale	d								23 44	23 49									00 14								
Aldershot	d								23 50	23a54	23 58								00 20								
Farnham	a								23 55		00a03								00 25								
	d								23 57										00 26								
Bentley	d								00 04										00 33								
Alton	a								00 11										00 40								
Farnborough (Main)	d		23 13				23 33									00 03					00 18			00 42			
Fleet	d		23 19				23 38									00 08					00 23			00 48			
Winchfield	d						23 44									00 14								00s53			
Hook	d						23 48									00 18								00s58			
Basingstoke	a		23 34				23 55					23 51				00 25				00 22	00 35			01 07			

Sundays

		SW 1	SW 1	SW	SW 1	SW 1	SW 1	SW	SW 1	SW 1	SW 1 A	SW 1	SW	SW 1 B	SW 1	SW 1		SW 1	SW	SW	SW C	SW 1 ◊	SW	SW 1	SW 1	SW 1	
London Waterloo 15 ⊖	d	22p53	23p12	23p20	23p23	23p35	23p39		23p45	23p48	00 05		00 09	01 05					07 10	07 40		07 54			08 00	08 07	
Vauxhall ⊖	d			23p24									00 13	01 09					07 14	07 44							
Clapham Junction 10	d	23b00	23b19	23p29	23b30	23b42	23b46	←	23b52	23b56	00u12		00 18	01 14					07 19	07 49		08u03			08u09	08 15	
Earlsfield	d			23p32 →				23p32					00 21						07 22	07 52							
Wimbledon 6 ⊖	d							23p36			00u18		00 25	01 20					07 26	07 56						08 22	
Surbiton 6	d	23p11	23p30		23p41			23p44		00 10			00 33	01 28					07 35	08 05						08 30	
Esher	d							23p48					00s37						07 39	08 09							
Hersham	d							23p51					00s40						07 42	08 12			←				
Walton-on-Thames	d		23p37					23p54		00 17			00s43						07 45	08 15 →			08 15				
Weybridge	d		23p41					23p58		00 21			00s46						07 49				08 19				
Byfleet & New Haw	d							23p59					00s49						07 51		08 03		08 21				
West Byfleet	d	23p21			23p51			00 03					00s52						07 54		08 06		08 24				
Woking	a	23p29	23p48		23p59	00 02	00 06	00 08	00 12	00 27	00 35		00 57	01 41					07 59		08 11	08 27	08 29		08 34	08 42	
	d	23p30	23p49		00 01	00 03	00 08		00 13	00 29	00 36	00 40	00 58	01 41	07 32	07 46		07 49	08 05			08 28	08 32		08 35	08 49	08 46
Worplesdon	d								00 18																	→	
Guildford	a								00 23				01 06		07 40				08 13				08 40		08 43		
Brookwood	d	23p36	23p55		00 06					00 35		00 45				07 52		07 56									08 52
Ash Vale	d	23p44			00 14							00 53						08 04						08 36			
Aldershot	d	23p50			00 20							00 58						08 09						08a41			
Farnham	a	23p55			00 25							01 04						08 15									
	d	23p57			00 26							01 04						08 15									
Bentley	d	00 04			00 33							01s10						08 24									
Alton	a	00 11			00 40							01 18						08 31									
Farnborough (Main)	d		00 03				00 18			00 42				01s57		07 59											08 59
Fleet	d		00 08				00 23			00 48						08 05											09 05
Winchfield	d		00 14							00s53						08 10											09 10
Hook	d		00 18							00s58						08 15											09 15
Basingstoke	a		00 25			00 22	00 35			01 07	00 55			02s11		08 22						08 47					09 22

For general notes see front of timetable
For details of catering facilities see Directory of Train Operators

A To Bournemouth (Table 158)
B To Southampton Central (Table 158)
C From Staines (Table 149)

b Previous night.
Stops to pick up only

London → Woking, Guildford, Alton and Basingstoke

Network Diagram - see first page of Table 155

	SW	SW 1◇ ☕	SW 1	SW	SW 1	SW 1	SW 1◇		SW	SW 1◇	SW	SW 1	SW 1		SW	SW 1◇ ☕	SW 1	SW	SW 1		SW 1	SW 1◇	SW	SW 1◇	SW	SW 1
London Waterloo 15 ⊖ d	08 10	08 15				08 30	08 35		08 40	08 54		09 00	09 07		09 10	09 15					09 30	09 35	09 40	09 54		10 00
Vauxhall ⊖ d	08 14								08 44						09 14								09 44			
Clapham Junction 10 d	08 19	08u22				08u39	08u42		08 49	09u03		09u09	09 15		09 19	09u22					09u39	09u42	09 49	10u03		10u09
Earlsfield d	08 22								08 52						09 22								09 52			
Wimbledon 6 ⊖ d	08 26								08 56				09 22		09 26								09 56			
Surbiton 6 d	08 35								09 05				09 30		09 35								10 05			
Esher d	08 39								09 09						09 39								10 09			
Hersham d	08 42			←					09 12		←				09 43			←					10 12		←	
Walton-on-Thames d	08 45			08 45					09 15		09 15				09 45			09 45					10 15		10 15	
Weybridge d	→			08 49					→		09 19				→			09 49					→		10 19	
Byfleet & New Haw d				08 51							09 21							09 51							10 21	
West Byfleet d				08 54							09 24							09 54							10 24	
Woking a		08 46	←	08 59		09 03	09 07			09 27	09 29	09 34	09 42			09 46	←	09 59			10 01	10 06		10 26	10 29	10 31
d		08 47	08 49	09 02		09 04	09 08			09 28	09 32	09 35	09 49	09 46		09 47	09 49	10 02			10 02	10 07		10 28	10 35	10 32
Worplesdon d													→												→	
Guildford a				09 10		09 12					09 40	09 43						10 10			10 10					10 40
Brookwood d			08 56											09 52			09 56									
Ash Vale d			09 04		09 36												10 04		10 36							
Aldershot d			09 09		09a41												10 09		10a41							
Farnham a			09 15														10 15									
d			09 15														10 15									
Bentley d			09 24														10 24									
Alton a			09 31														10 31									
Farnborough (Main) d														09 59												
Fleet d														10 05												
Winchfield d														10 10												
Hook d														10 15												
Basingstoke a		09 06					09 27			09 47				10 22		10 06						10 26		10 47		

	SW	SW 1		SW	SW 1◇ ☕	SW 1	SW	SW 1			SW 1 ☕	SW	SW 1◇ ☕	SW 1		SW	SW 1◇	SW	SW 1	SW	SW 1		SW	SW 1◇ ☕	SW 1
London Waterloo 15 ⊖ d		10 07		10 10	10 15				and at the same minutes past each hour until		15 30		15 35	15 37		15 40	15 54		16 00		16 07		16 10	16 15	
Vauxhall ⊖ d				10 14												15 44							16 14		
Clapham Junction 10 d		10 15		10 19	10u22						15u39		15u42	15 46		15 49	16u03		16u09		16 15		16 19	16u22	
Earlsfield d				10 22												15 52							16 22		
Wimbledon 6 ⊖ d		10 22		10 26										15 53		15 56					16 22		16 26		
Surbiton 6 d		10 30		10 35										16 02		16 05					16 30		16 35		
Esher d				10 39												16 09							16 39		
Hersham d				10 42			←									16 12		←					16 42		
Walton-on-Thames d				10 45			10 45							16 09		16 15		16 15					16 45		
Weybridge d				→			10 49							16 13		→		16 19					→		
Byfleet & New Haw d							10 51											16 21							
West Byfleet d							10 54											16 24							
Woking a	←	10 42			10 45	←	10 59				16 01	←	16 06	16 19			16 26	16 29	16 31	←	16 42			16 45	←
d	10 35	10 49	10 46		10 46	10 49	11 05				16 02	16 05	16 07	16 23	16 26		16 28	16 35	16 32	16 35	16 49	16 46		16 46	16 49
Worplesdon d		→																→			→				
Guildford a	10 43						11 13				16 10	16 13							16 40	16 43					
Brookwood d			10 52			10 56								16 29	16 33							16 52			16 56
Ash Vale d						11 04		11 36							16 41										17 04
Aldershot d						11 09		11a41							16 47										17 09
Farnham a						11 15									16 53										17 15
d						11 15									16 56										17 15
Bentley d						11 24																			17 24
Alton a						11 31									17 07										17 31
Farnborough (Main) d			10 59											16 36								16 59			
Fleet d			11 05											16 42								17 05			
Winchfield d			11 10																			17 10			
Hook d			11 15																			17 15			
Basingstoke a			11 22		11 05								16 26	16 54			16 47					17 22		17 05	

For general notes see front of timetable
For details of catering facilities see
Directory of Train Operators

London → Woking, Guildford, Alton and Basingstoke

Network Diagram - see first page of Table 155

		SW	SW 1		SW 1 ☕	SW	SW 1 ◇ ☕	SW 1		SW	SW 1 ◇	SW	SW 1	SW	SW 1		SW	SW 1 ◇ ☕	SW 1		SW	SW 1	SW 1 ☕	SW	SW 1 ◇ ☕	SW 1	
London Waterloo [15] ⊖	d				16 30		16 35	16 37		16 40	16 54		17 00		17 07		17 10	17 15					17 30		17 35	17 37	
Vauxhall ⊖	d									16 44							17 14										
Clapham Junction [10]	d				16u39		16u42	16 46		16 49	17u03		17u09		17 15		17 19	17u22					17u39		17u42	17 46	
Earlsfield	d									16 52							17 22										
Wimbledon [6] ⊖	d							16 53		16 56					17 22		17 26									17 53	
Surbiton [6]	d							17 02		17 05					17 30		17 35									18 02	
Esher	d									17 09							17 39										
Hersham	d	←								17 12		←					17 42				←						
Walton-on-Thames	d	16 45						17 09		17 15		17 15					17 45				17 45					18 09	
Weybridge	d	16 49						17 13		→		17 19					→				17 49					18 13	
Byfleet & New Haw	d	16 51										17 21									17 51						
West Byfleet	d	16 54										17 24									17 54						
Woking	a	16 59			17 01		17 06	17 19			17 26	17 29	17 31		17 42			17 45			17 59		18 01		18 06	18 19	
						←								←					←					←			
	d	17 05			17 02	17 05	17 07	17 23	17 26		17 28	17 35	17 32	17 35	17 49	17 46		17 46	17 49		18 05		18 02	18 05	18 07	18 23	18 26
Worplesdon	d	→										→			→						→						
Guildford	a				17 10	17 13							17 40	17 43									18 10	18 13			
Brookwood	d							17 29	17 33							17 52			17 56							18 29	18 33
Ash Vale	d		17 36						17 41										18 04			18 36					18 41
Aldershot	d		17a41						17 47										18 09			18a41					18 47
Farnham	a								17 53										18 15								18 53
	d								17 56										18 15								18 56
Bentley	d																		18 24								
Alton	a								18 07										18 31								19 07
Farnborough (Main)	d							17 36								17 59										18 36	
Fleet	d							17 42								18 05										18 42	
Winchfield	d															18 10											
Hook	d															18 15											
Basingstoke	a						17 26	17 54			17 47					18 22		18 05							18 26	18 54	

		SW	SW 1 ◇	SW	SW 1	SW	SW 1		SW	SW 1 ◇ A ☕	SW 1		SW	SW 1	SW 1 ☕	SW	SW 1 ◇ ☕	SW 1		SW	SW 1 ◇	SW	SW 1	SW	SW 1		SW
London Waterloo [15] ⊖	d	17 40	17 54		18 00		18 07		18 10	18 15					18 30		18 35	18 37		18 40	18 54		19 00		19 07		19 10
Vauxhall ⊖	d	17 44							18 14											18 44							19 14
Clapham Junction [10]	d	17 49	18u03		18u09		18 15		18 19	18u22					18u39		18u42	18 46		18 49	19u03		19u09		19 15		19 19
Earlsfield	d	17 52							18 22											18 52							19 22
Wimbledon [6] ⊖	d	17 56					18 22		18 26									18 53		18 56					19 22		19 26
Surbiton [6]	d	18 05					18 30		18 35									19 02		19 05					19 30		19 35
Esher	d	18 09							18 39											19 09							19 39
Hersham	d	18 12		←					18 42				←							19 12		←					19 42
Walton-on-Thames	d	18 15		18 15					18 45				18 45					19 09		19 15		19 15					19 45
Weybridge	d	→		18 19					→				18 49					19 13		→		19 19					→
Byfleet & New Haw	d			18 21									18 51									19 21					
West Byfleet	d			18 24									18 54									19 24					
Woking	a		18 26	18 29	18 31		18 42			18 45			18 59		19 01		19 06	19 19			19 26	19 29	19 31		19 42		
						←					←					←								←			
	d		18 28	18 35	18 32	18 35	18 49	18 46		18 46	18 49		19 05		19 02	19 05	19 07	19 23	19 26		19 28	19 35	19 32	19 35	19 49	19 46	
Worplesdon	d			→			→						→									→			→		
Guildford	a				18 40	18 43									19 10	19 13							19 40	19 43			
Brookwood	d							18 52			18 56							19 29	19 33							19 52	
Ash Vale	d										19 04			19 36					19 41								
Aldershot	d										19 09			19a41					19 47								
Farnham	a										19 15								19 53								
	d										19 15								19 56								
Bentley	d										19 24																
Alton	a										19 31								20 07								
Farnborough (Main)	d							18 59										19 36								19 59	
Fleet	d							19 05										19 42								20 05	
Winchfield	d							19 10																		20 10	
Hook	d							19 15																		20 15	
Basingstoke	a		18 47					19 22		19 05							19 26	19 54			19 47					20 22	

For general notes see front of timetable
For details of catering facilities see Directory of Train Operators

A To Bristol Temple Meads (Table 123)

Table 155

Sundays

London → Woking, Guildford, Alton and Basingstoke

Network Diagram - see first page of Table 155

		SW 1 ◇ ☕	SW 1		SW	SW 1	SW 1 ☕	SW	SW 1 ◇ ☕	SW 1		SW	SW 1 ◇	SW	SW 1	SW	SW 1		SW		SW 1 ◇ ☕	SW 1	SW	SW 1	SW 1 ☕	SW	SW 1 ◇ ☕
London Waterloo 15 ⊖	d	19 15					19 30		19 35	19 37		19 40	19 54		20 00		20 07		20 10		20 15				20 30		20 35
Vauxhall ⊖	d											19 44							20 14								
Clapham Junction 10	d	19u22					19u39		19u42	19 46		19 49	20u03		20u09		20 15		20 19		20u22				20u39		20u42
Earlsfield	d											19 52							20 22								
Wimbledon 6 ⊖	d									19 53		19 56					20 22		20 26								
Surbiton 6	d									20 02		20 05					20 30		20 35								
Esher	d											20 09							20 39								
Hersham	d				←							20 12		←					20 42				←				
Walton-on-Thames	d				19 45					20 09		20 15 →		20 15					20 45 →				20 45				
Weybridge	d				19 49					20 13				20 19									20 49				
Byfleet & New Haw	d				19 51									20 21									20 51				
West Byfleet	d				19 54									20 24									20 54				
Woking	a	19 45	←		19 59		20 01	←	20 06	20 19			20 26	20 29	20 31	←	20 42				20 45	←	20 59		21 01	←	21 06
	d	19 46	19 49		20 05		20 02	20 05	20 07	20 23	20 26		20 28	20 35	20 32	20 35	20 49	20 46			20 46	20 49	21 05		21 02	21 05	21 07
Worplesdon	d				→									→			→						→				
Guildford	a						20 10	20 13							20 40	20 43									21 10	21 13	
Brookwood	d		19 56							20 29	20 33							20 52				20 56					
Ash Vale	d		20 04			20 36					20 41											21 04		21 36			
Aldershot	d		20 09			20a41					20 47											21 09		21a41			
Farnham	a		20 15								20 53											21 15					
	d		20 15								20 56											21 15					
Bentley	d		20 24																			21 24					
Alton	a		20 31								21 07											21 31					
Farnborough (Main)	d									20 36								20 59									
Fleet	d									20 42								21 05									
Winchfield	d																	21 10									
Hook	d																	21 15									
Basingstoke	a	20 05							20 26	20 54			20 47					21 22			21 05						21 26

		SW 1		SW	SW 1 ◇	SW	SW 1	SW	SW 1		SW		SW 1 ◇ ☕	SW 1	SW	SW 1	SW 1	SW	SW 1 ◇ ☕	SW 1		SW	SW 1 ◇	SW	SW 1	SW	
London Waterloo 15 ⊖	d	20 37		20 40	20 54		21 00		21 07		21 10		21 15				21 30		21 35	21 37		21 40	21 54		22 00		
Vauxhall ⊖	d			20 44							21 14											21 44					
Clapham Junction 10	d	20 46		20 49	21u03		21u09		21 15		21 19		21u22				21u39		21u42	21 46		21 49	22u03		22u09		
Earlsfield	d			20 52							21 22											21 52					
Wimbledon 6 ⊖	d	20 53		20 56					21 22		21 26									21 53		21 56					
Surbiton 6	d	21 02		21 05					21 30		21 35									22 02		22 05					
Esher	d			21 09							21 39											22 09					
Hersham	d			21 12		←					21 42				←							22 12		←			
Walton-on-Thames	d	21 09		21 15 →		21 15					21 45 →				21 45					22 09		22 15 →		22 15			
Weybridge	d	21 13				21 19									21 49					22 13				22 19			
Byfleet & New Haw	d					21 21									21 51									22 21			
West Byfleet	d					21 24									21 54									22 24			
Woking	a	21 19			21 26	21 29	21 31	←	21 42				21 45	←	21 59		22 01	←	22 06	22 19			22 26	22 29	22 31	←	
	d	21 23	21 26		21 28	21 35	21 32	21 35	21 49	21 46			21 46	21 49	22 05		22 02	22 05	22 07	22 23	22 26		22 28	22 35	22 32	22 35	
Worplesdon	d					→			→						→									→			
Guildford	a						21 40	21 43									22 10	22 13							22 40	22 43	
Brookwood	d	21 29	21 33							21 52				21 56						22 29	22 33						
Ash Vale	d		21 41											22 04		22 36					22 41						
Aldershot	d		21 47											22 09		22a41					22 47						
Farnham	a		21 53											22 15							22 53						
	d		21 56											22 15							22 56						
Bentley	d													22 24													
Alton	a		22 07											22 31							23 07						
Farnborough (Main)	d	21 36								21 59										22 36							
Fleet	d	21 42								22 05										22 42							
Winchfield	d									22 10																	
Hook	d									22 15																	
Basingstoke	a	21 54			21 47					22 22			22 05						22 26	22 54			22 47				

For general notes see front of timetable
For details of catering facilities see
Directory of Train Operators

Table 155

Sundays

London → Woking, Guildford, Alton and Basingstoke

Network Diagram - see first page of Table 155

	SW 1		SW		SW 1	SW 1	SW	SW 1	SW 1	SW	SW 1		SW	SW 1	SW	SW 1	SW	SW 1			SW	SW 1	SW	SW 1	SW 1	
								A																B		
London Waterloo 15 ⊖ d	22 07		22 10		22 15				22 30		22 37		22 40	22 54		23 00		23 07			23 10	23 30		23 35	23 40	
Vauxhall ⊖ d			22 14										22 44								23 14				23 44	
Clapham Junction 10 d	22 15		22 19		22u22				22u39		22 46		22 49	23u03		23u09		23 15			23 19	23u39		23u44	23 49	
Earlsfield d			22 22										22 52								23 22				23 52	
Wimbledon 6 ⊖ d	22 22		22 26								22 53		22 56					23 22			23 26				23 56	
Surbiton 6 d	22 30		22 35								23 02		23 05					23 30			23 35				00 05	
Esher d			22 39										23 09								23 39				00 09	
Hersham d			22 42				←						23 12		←						23 42				00 12	
Walton-on-Thames d			22 45				22 45				23 09		23 15		23 15						23 45				00 15	
Weybridge d			→				22 49				23 13		→		23 19						23 49				00 19	
Byfleet & New Haw d							22 51								23 21						23 51				00 21	
West Byfleet d							22 54								23 24						23 54				00 24	
Woking a	22 42				22 45		22 59		23 01		23 19			23 26	23 29	23 31		23 42			23 59	00 01		00 07	00 30	
						←				←							←						←			
d	22 49	22 46			22 46	22 49	23 05		23 02	23 05	23 23	23 26		23 28	23 35	23 32	23 35	23 46	23 49		00 05	00 02	00 05	00 08	00 35	
Worplesdon d	→						→								→						→					
Guildford a									23 10	23 13						23 40	23 43					00 10	00 13			
Brookwood d		22 52				22 56					23 29	23 33						23 52	23 56						00 41	
Ash Vale d						23 04		23 36				23 41							00 04						00 48	
Aldershot d						23 09		23 42				23 47							00 09						00 53	
Farnham a						23 15		23 47				23 54							00 15						00 59	
d						23 15						23 56							00 15							
Bentley d						23 24													00 23							
Alton a						23 31						00 07							00 30							
Farnborough (Main) d		22 59									23 36							23 59						00 18		
Fleet d		23 05									23 42							00 05						00 24		
Winchfield d		23 10																00 10								
Hook d		23 15																00 15								
Basingstoke a		23 22			23 05						23 54			23 47				00 22						00 39		

For general notes see front of timetable
For details of catering facilities see
Directory of Train Operators

A From Ascot (Table 149)
B To Salisbury (Table 160)

For details of Bank Holiday service alterations, please see first page of Table 149

Basingstoke, Alton, Guildford and Woking → Waterloo

Network Diagram - see first page of Table 155

Miles	Miles	Miles			SW MO 1	SW MO 1	SW MO 1	SW MX 1	SW MX 1	SW MX 1 A	SW	SW	SW 1	SW 1	SW	SW	SW 1	SW	SW 1	SW 1	SW 1 ☕	SW	SW 1	SW 1	SW	SW 1	SW 1 ☕
0	—	—	**Basingstoke**	d		23p43		22p54		23p44				04 54					05 39	05 54	05 59						
5½	—	—	Hook	d				23p01		23p51				05 01						06 01							
7¾	—	—	Winchfield	d				23p05		23p55				05 05						06 05				←			
11¼	—	—	Fleet	d				23p10		00 01				05 10					05 50	06 10				06 10			
14½	—	—	Farnborough (Main)	d				23p16		00 06				05 16					05 56	→				06 16			
—	0	—	**Alton**	d																			05 44				
—	4¾	—	Bentley	d																			05 51				
—	8¾	—	Farnham	a																			05 56				
—	—	—		d																			05 58				
—	11¾	—	**Aldershot**	d									06 00										06 04				
—	14¾	—	Ash Vale	d									06a04										06 09				
19¾	18¾	—	Brookwood	d				23p23		00 13				05 23									06 16	06 23			
—	—	0	**Guildford**	d	23p35		00 05		23p39		04 00	05 12					05 50									06 24	06 31
—	—	3½	Worplesdon	d					23p44			05 17					05 55									06 30	
23½	—	6	**Woking**	a	23p42	00 02	00 13	23p28	23p49	00 18	04 08	05 22		05 28	←		06 00		06 05		06 18		06 21	06 28		06 35	06 39
—	—	—		d	23p45	00 03		23p33	23p56	00 20	04 10	05 33		05 29	05 33	05 43	06 01	06 04	06 06		06 19		06 22	06 29	06 32	06 37	06 41
26	—	—	West Byfleet	d				23p37		00 25		→			05 37	05 47		06 08							06 36		
27¼	—	—	Byfleet & New Haw	d				23p40							05 40			06 11							06 39		
28¾	—	—	Weybridge	d				23p43		00 29					05 43	05 51		06 14				←			06 43		
30¾	—	—	Walton-on-Thames	d				23p47		00 34					05 47	05 55		06 18				06 18			06 47		
31¾	—	—	Hersham	d				23p49							05 49			→				06 20			→		
33¼	—	—	Esher	d				23p52							05 52							06 23					
35¾	—	—	**Surbiton** 6	a				23p57		00 40	04 24			05 40	05 56	06 01						06 27	06 33	06 40			
40½	—	—	Wimbledon 6 ⊖ ⛴	a				00 08		00 48	04 31			05 48	06 04							06 35		06 47			
42¼	—	—	Earlsfield	a				00 10							06 08							06 39					
43¾	—	—	Clapham Junction 10	a	00 04	00 22		00 14	00 20	00 54	04 43			06 00	06 12		06 20		06 25		06 38	06 42	06 45	06 54		06 58	07 02
46½	—	—	Vauxhall ⊖	a				00 19						06 07	06 17							06 47					
47¾	—	—	**London Waterloo** 15 ⊖	a	00 14	00 33		00 29	00 29	01 02	04 53			06 12	06 22	06 20	06 29		06 34		06 49	06 52	06 56	07 04		07 08	07 12

		SW 1		SW 1	SW	SW 1	SW 1 ◇ ☕	SW 1	SW	SW 1 ☕	SW 1	SW 1	SW 1	SW 1	SW 1 ▼ ☕	SW 1	SW 1	SW 1 ☕	SW 1	SW 1	SW 1	SW 1	SW 1	SW 1	SW 1		SW 1
Basingstoke	d	06 24					06 31			06 36					06 52			06 54	07 06	07 17							
Hook	d	06 31																07 01	07 13								
Winchfield	d	06 35									←							07 05	07 17								
Fleet	d	06 40									06 40							07 10	07 22								
Farnborough (Main)	d	→									06 46							07 16	07 28								
Alton	d							06 14									06 44										07 14
Bentley	d							06 21									06 51										07 21
Farnham	a							06 26									06 56										07 26
	d							06 28									06 58										07 28
Aldershot	d							06 34									07 04										07 34
Ash Vale	d							06 39									07 09										07 39
Brookwood	d							06 46			06 53						07 16		07 23								07 46
Guildford	d			07 32									06 55			07 07		07 17									
Worplesdon	d			07 40									07 01														
Woking	a						06 49	06 51		06 54	06 58		07 05		07 11	07 15	07 21	07 25	07 28								07 51
	d					06 41	06 51	06 53		06 55	06 59	07 02	07 07	07 11	07 12	07 17	07 22	07 26	07 29			07 32	07 40		07 47		07 52
West Byfleet	d					06 46						07 07		07 16								07 37		07 46	07b54		
Byfleet & New Haw	d					06 49								07 19										07 49	07 57		
Weybridge	d				←	06 52						07 11		07 22								07 41		07 52	08 01		
Walton-on-Thames	d				06 47	06 57						07 16		07 27								07 46		07 57	08 06		
Hersham	d				06 49	07 00						07 19		07 30								07 49		08 00	08 09		
Esher	d				06 52	07 03						07 22		07 33								07 52		08 03	08 13		
Surbiton 6	a				06 56	07 07						07 26		07 37								07 56		08 07	08 18		
Wimbledon 6 ⊖ ⛴	a				07 04				←																		
Earlsfield	a				07 08				07 08																		
Clapham Junction 10	a				→			07 11	07 12	07 15	07 22		07 26		07 31												
Vauxhall ⊖	a								07 17																		
London Waterloo 15 ⊖	a			08 11		07 28	07 19	07 22	07 24	07 25	07 32	07 49	07 37	07 56	07 44	07 44	07 51	07 54	07 59	08 06	08 01	08 19	08 08	08 26	08 36		08 22

For general notes see front of timetable
For details of catering facilities see
Directory of Train Operators

A From Weymouth (Table 158)
b Arr. 0751

For details of Bank Holiday service alterations, please see first page of Table 149

Basingstoke, Alton, Guildford and Woking → Waterloo

Network Diagram - see first page of Table 155

		SW 1	SW 1	SW 1	SW 1	SW 1	SW 1	SW 1	SW 1	SW 1	SW 1	SW 1	SW 1	SW 1 ◇	SW 1	SW 1	SW 1	SW	SW 1	SW 1	SW 1	SW 1	SW 1		SW 1	SW 1	SW 1 ◇
				▼ ☕			A		A					☕		☕			A		A				A		☕
Basingstoke	d		07 24	07 29			07 36	07 47				07 52		07 59					08 05	08 16					08 24		08 29
Hook	d		07 31				07 43		←			07 59							08 12		←				08 31		
Winchfield	d		07 35				07 47		07 47			08 04					←		08 16		08 16				08 35		
Fleet	d		07 40				→		07 52			08 09					08 09		→		08 22				08 40		
Farnborough (Main)	d		07 46						07 58			→					08 16				08 28				→		
Alton	d														07 44												
Bentley	d														07 51												
Farnham	a														07 56												
	d					07 39									07 58												
Aldershot	d					07 46					08 00				08 04								08 30				
Ash Vale	d					07 50					08a04				08 09								08a34				
Brookwood	d		07 53			07 57									08 16		08 23										
Guildford	d	07 45								08 03						08 15		08 20				08 31					
Worplesdon	d	07 50														08 20						08 37					
Woking	a	07 54	07 58			08 03		08 05	08 08	08 11				08 18	08 21	08 26	08 28	08 30		08 34	08 38	08 41					08 48
	d	07 56	07 59		08 02	08 05		08 06	08 09	08 12			08 17	08 19	08 24	08 27	08 29	08 32		08 36	08 39	08 43				08 47	08 49
West Byfleet	d				08 06	08b16							08c26					08 36								08e54	
Byfleet & New Haw	d					08 19							08 29					08 39								08 57	
Weybridge	d				08 11	08 22							08 32					08 43								09 02	
Walton-on-Thames	d				08 15	08 27							08 36					08 47								→	
Hersham	d				08 17	08 30							08 39					→									
Esher	d				08 20	08 33							08 43														
Surbiton 6	a				08 24	08 37							08 47														
Wimbledon 6 ⊖	a																										
Earlsfield	a																										
Clapham Junction 10	a																										
Vauxhall ⊖	a																					09 03					
London Waterloo 15 ⊖	a	08 24	08 29	08 14	08 46	08 59		08 34	08 39	08 41			09 06	08 46	08 51	08 55	09 00			09 03	09 10	09 13					09 17

		SW 1	SW	SW 1	SW 1	SW 1	SW 1	SW	SW 1	SW 1	SW 1	SW 1	SW 1 ◇	SW	SW 1	SW 1 ◇	SW 1	SW 1	SW 1	SW	SW 1	SW 1		SW 1	SW 1	SW 1 ◇	SW
				☕	A	☕							☕			☕	☕									☕	
Basingstoke	d			08 35					08 42			08 54	08 59									09 17			09 24	09 31	
Hook	d											09 01													09 31		
Winchfield	d				←							09 05							←						09 35		
Fleet	d				08 40				08 54			09 10							09 10						09 40		
Farnborough (Main)	d				08 46				08 59			→							09 16			09 31			→		
Alton	d	08 14													08 44												
Bentley	d	08 21													08 51												
Farnham	a	08 26													08 56												
	d	08 28													08 58												
Aldershot	d	08 34									09 00				09 04						09 30						
Ash Vale	d	08 39									09a04				09 09						09a34						
Brookwood	d	08 46			08 53										09 16				09 23								
Guildford	d					08 54		08 46		09 03							09 17							09 32			
Worplesdon	d							08 51																09 40			
Woking	a	08 51		08 53	08 58			08 59		09 11			09 18		09 21	09 22	09 27		09 28			09 40		09 44		09 49	
	d	08 52		08 55	08 59			09 02		09 13			09 19		09 22	09 24	09 28	←	09 29	09 33		09 41		09 46		09 51	
West Byfleet	d							09 06							09 27			09 27		09 37							
Byfleet & New Haw	d						←	09 09							→					09 40							
Weybridge	d		←				09 02	09 13						←					09 36	09 43							←
Walton-on-Thames	d		08 47				09 07	09 17						09 17					09 41	09 47							09 47
Hersham	d		08 49				09 10	→						09 19						→							09 49
Esher	d		08 52				09 13							09 22													09 52
Surbiton 6	a		08 56		09 10		09 18							09 26				09 37	09 47								09 56
Wimbledon 6 ⊖	a		09 04											09 34													10 04
Earlsfield	a		09 08											09 38													10 08
Clapham Junction 10	a		09 12	09 14					09 26	09 32			09 38	09 42		09 43		09 50	09 58					10 05		10 10	10 12
Vauxhall ⊖	a		09 17											09 47													10 17
London Waterloo 15 ⊖	a	09 21	09 24	09 25	09 29	09 31	09 40		09 41	09 43			09 51	09 54		09 53	09 55	09 59	10 08			10 08		10 13		10 19	10 22

For general notes see front of timetable
For details of catering facilities see Directory of Train Operators

A From Southampton Central (Table 158)
b Arr. 0809
c Arr. 0821
e Arr. 0851

For details of Bank Holiday service alterations, please see first page of Table 149

Basingstoke, Alton, Guildford and Woking → Waterloo

Network Diagram - see first page of Table 155

		SW 1	SW 1 ◇ ☕	SW 1	SW 1 ☕	SW 1 ☕	SW	SW 1	SW 1	SW 1	SW 1 ◇ ☕	SW 1 ◇ ☕	SW	SW 1	SW 1 ☕	SW 1	SW	SW 1	SW 1	SW 1	SW 1		SW 1 ◇ ☕	SW 1 ◇ ☕	SW	SW 1	SW 1 ☕
Basingstoke	d		09 36			09 41				09 54	09 57								10 17		10 24		10 31	10 36			
Hook	d									10 01											10 31						
Winchfield	d			←						10 05						←					10 35						
Fleet	d			09 40		09 53				10 10						10 10					10 40						
Farnborough (Main)	d			09 46		09 58				→						10 16			10 31		→						
Alton	d	09 14												09 44												10 14	
Bentley	d	09 21												09 51												10 21	
Farnham	a	09 26												09 56												10 26	
	d	09 28												09 58												10 28	
Aldershot	d	09 34							10 00					10 04				10 30								10 34	
Ash Vale	d	09 39							10a04					10 09				10a34								10 39	
Brookwood	d	09 46		09 53										10 16		10 23										10 46	
Guildford	d				09 47			10 02							10 17					10 32							10 49
Worplesdon	d																			10 40							
Woking	a	09 51	09 54	09 58	09 59			10 11			10 15	10 20		10 21	10 25	10 28			10 40	10 44			10 49			10 51	10 57
	d	09 52	09 55	09 59	09 59		10 03	10 12			10 17	10 21		10 22	10 26	10 29	10 33		10 41	10 46			10 51			10 52	10 59
West Byfleet	d	09 57					10 07							10 27			10 37									10 57	
Byfleet & New Haw	d						10 10										10 40										
Weybridge	d			10 06			10 13						←			10 36	10 43								←		
Walton-on-Thames	d			10 11			10 17						10 17			10 41	10 47								10 47		
Hersham	d						→						10 19				→								10 49		
Esher	d												10 22												10 52		
Surbiton 6	a	10 07		10 17									10 26	10 37		10 47									10 56	11 07	
Wimbledon 6 ⊖	a												10 34												11 04		
Earlsfield	a												10 38												11 08		
Clapham Junction 10	a		10 14			10 24		10 31			10 36		10 42	10 48		10 58				11 05				11 12	11 12		
Vauxhall ⊖	a												10 47												11 17		
London Waterloo 15 ⊖	a	10 25	10 23	10 35	10 27	10 34		10 40			10 49	10 49	10 52	10 57	10 51	11 06			11 08	11 13			11 19	11 20	11 22	11 27	11 24

		SW 1	SW 1	SW	SW 1	SW 1	SW 1	SW 1 ◇ ☕	SW 1 ◇ ☕	SW	SW 1	SW 1 ☕	SW 1	SW	SW 1	SW 1	SW 1	SW 1	SW 1 ◇ ☕	SW 1 ◇ ☕		SW	SW 1	SW 1 ☕	SW 1	SW 1	SW
Basingstoke	d		10 41				10 54	10 57								11 17		11 24	11 31	11 36						11 41	
Hook	d						11 01											11 31									
Winchfield	d	←					11 05						←					11 35							←		
Fleet	d	10 40	10 53				11 10						11 10					11 40							11 40	11 53	
Farnborough (Main)	d	10 46	10 58				→						11 16			11 31		→							11 46	11 58	
Alton	d										10 44												11 15				
Bentley	d										10 51																
Farnham	a										10 56												11 25				
	d										10 58												11 28				
Aldershot	d					11 00					11 04				11 30								11 34				
Ash Vale	d					11a04					11 09				11a34								11 39				
Brookwood	d	10 53									11 16		11 23										11 46		11 53		
Guildford	d				11 02							11 17					11 32							11 47			
Worplesdon	d																11 40										
Woking	a	10 58			11 11			11 15	11 19		11 21	11 25	11 28			11 40	11 44		11 49				11 51	11 57	11 58		
	d	10 59		11 03	11 12			11 17	11 21		11 22	11 26	11 29	11 33		11 41	11 46		11 51				11 52	11 59	11 59		12 03
West Byfleet	d			11 07							11 27			11 37									11 57				12 07
Byfleet & New Haw	d			11 10										11 40													12 10
Weybridge	d	11 06		11 13						←			11 36	11 43								←			12 06		12 13
Walton-on-Thames	d	11 11		11 17						11 17			11 41	11 47								11 47			12 11		12 17
Hersham	d			→						11 19				→								11 49					→
Esher	d									11 22												11 52					
Surbiton 6	a	11 17								11 26	11 37		11 47									11 56	12 07		12 17		
Wimbledon 6 ⊖	a									11 34												12 04					
Earlsfield	a									11 38												12 08					
Clapham Junction 10	a		11 24		11 31			11 36		11 42	11 48		11 58				12 05			12 12		12 12				12 24	
Vauxhall ⊖	a									11 47												12 17					
London Waterloo 15 ⊖	a	11 36	11 34		11 40			11 49	11 49	11 52	11 57	11 51	12 06			12 08	12 13		12 19	12 20		12 22	12 27	12 23	12 35	12 34	

For general notes see front of timetable
For details of catering facilities see Directory of Train Operators

For details of Bank Holiday service alterations, please see first page of Table 149

Basingstoke, Alton, Guildford and Woking → Waterloo

Network Diagram - see first page of Table 155

		SW 1	SW 1	SW 1	SW 1 ◇ ☕	SW 1 ◇ ☕	SW	SW 1	SW 1 ☕	SW 1	SW	SW 1	SW 1	SW 1	SW 1	SW 1 ◇ ☕	SW 1 ◇ ☕	SW	SW 1		SW 1 ☕	SW 1		SW 1	SW	SW 1	SW 1
Basingstoke	d			11 54	11 57								12 17		12 24	12 31	12 36							12 41			
Hook	d			12 01											12 31												
Winchfield	d			12 05						←					12 35							←					
Fleet	d			12 10						12 10					12 40							12 40		12 53			
Farnborough (Main)	d			→						12 16			12 31		→							12 46		12 58			
Alton	d							11 44																			
Bentley	d							11 51																			
Farnham	a							11 56																			
	d							11 58											12 28								
Aldershot	d		12 00					12 04				12 30							12 34								13 00
Ash Vale	d		12a04					12 09				12a34							12 39								13a04
Brookwood	d							12 16		12 23									12 46			12 53					
Guildford	d	12 02							12 17					12 32							12 47					13 02	
Worplesdon	d													12 40													
Woking	a	12 11			12 15	12 19		12 21	12 25	12 28			12 40	12 44		12 49			12 51		12 57	12 58				13 11	
	d	12 12			12 17	12 21		12 22	12 26	12 29	12 33		12 41	12 46		12 51			12 52		12 59	12 59			13 03	13 12	
West Byfleet	d							12 27			12 37								12 57						13 07		
Byfleet & New Haw	d										12 40														13 10		
Weybridge	d						←			12 36	12 43							←				13 06			13 13		
Walton-on-Thames	d						12 17			12 41	12 47							12 47				13 11			13 17		
Hersham	d						12 19				→							12 49							→		
Esher	d						12 22											12 52									
Surbiton 6	a						12 26	12 37		12 47								12 56	13 07			13 17					
Wimbledon 6 ⊖ 🚊	a						12 34											13 04									
Earlsfield	a						12 38											13 08									
Clapham Junction 10	a	12 31			12 36		12 42	12 48		12 58				13 05			13 12	13 12						13 24		13 31	
Vauxhall ⊖	a						12 47											13 17									
London Waterloo 15 ⊖	a	12 40			12 49	12 49	12 52	12 57	12 51	13 06			13 08	13 13		13 19	13 20	13 22	13 25		13 23	13 35		13 34		13 40	

		SW 1	SW 1 ◇ ☕	SW 1 ◇ ☕	SW	SW 1	SW 1 ☕	SW 1	SW	SW 1	SW 1	SW 1	SW 1	SW 1 ◇ ☕	SW 1 ◇ ☕	SW	SW 1	SW 1 ☕	SW 1			SW 1	SW	SW 1	SW 1	SW 1
Basingstoke	d	12 54	12 57								13 17		13 24	13 31	13 36							15 41				15 54
Hook	d	13 01											13 31													16 01
Winchfield	d	13 05						←					13 35						←							16 05
Fleet	d	13 10						13 10					13 40						13 40			15 53				16 10
Farnborough (Main)	d	→						13 16			13 31		→						13 46			15 58				→
Alton	d					12 44											13 15									
Bentley	d					12 51																				
Farnham	a					12 56											13 25									
	d					12 58											13 28			and at						
Aldershot	d					13 04				13 30							13 34								16 00	
Ash Vale	d					13 09				13a34							13 39			the same					16a04	
Brookwood	d					13 16		13 23									13 46		13 53	minutes						
Guildford	d						13 17					13 32						13 47		past				16 00		
Worplesdon	d											13 40								each				16 06		
Woking	a		13 15	13 19		13 21	13 25	13 28			13 40	13 44		13 49			13 51	13 57	13 58	hour until				16 11		
	d		13 17	13 21		13 22	13 26	13 29	13 33		13 41	13 46		13 51			13 52	13 59	13 59				16 03	16 12		
West Byfleet	d					13 27			13 37								13 57						16 07			
Byfleet & New Haw	d								13 40														16 10			
Weybridge	d				←			13 36	13 43							←			14 06				16 13			
Walton-on-Thames	d				13 17			13 41	13 47							13 47			14 11				16 17			
Hersham	d				13 19				→							13 49							→			
Esher	d				13 22											13 52										
Surbiton 6	a				13 26	13 37		13 47								13 56	14 07		14 17							
Wimbledon 6 ⊖ 🚊	a				13 34											14 04										
Earlsfield	a				13 38											14 08										
Clapham Junction 10	a		13 36		13 42	13 48		13 58				14 05			14 12	14 12						16 24		16 31		
Vauxhall ⊖	a				13 47											14 17										
London Waterloo 15 ⊖	a		13 49	13 49	13 52	13 57	13 51	14 06			14 08	14 13		14 19	14 20	14 22	14 25	14 23	14 35			16 34		16 40		

For general notes see front of timetable
For details of catering facilities see
Directory of Train Operators

For details of Bank Holiday service alterations, please see first page of Table 149

Basingstoke, Alton, Guildford and Woking → Waterloo

Network Diagram - see first page of Table 155

		SW 1◇ ☕	SW 1◇ ☕	SW	SW 1	SW 1 ☕	SW 1	SW	SW 1	SW 1	SW 1	SW 1	SW 1◇ ☕	SW 1◇ ☕	SW	SW 1	SW 1	SW 1	SW 1	SW		SW 1 ☕	SW 1	SW 1	SW 1◇ ☕	SW 1◇ ☕	SW
Basingstoke	d	15 57								16 17		16 24	16 31	16 36					16 41					16 54	16 57		
Hook	d											16 31												17 01			
Winchfield	d						←					16 35						←						17 05			
Fleet	d						16 10					16 40						16 40	16 53					17 10			
Farnborough (Main)	d						16 16			16 31		→						16 46	16 58					→			
Alton	d				15 44											16 15											
Bentley	d				15 51																						
Farnham	a				15 56											16 25											
	d				15 58											16 28											
Aldershot	d				16 04				16 30							16 34							17 00				
Ash Vale	d				16 09				16a34							16 39							17a04				
Brookwood	d				16 16		16 23									16 46		16 53									
Guildford	d					16 17					16 32						16 47					17 00					
Worplesdon	d										16 40											17 06					
Woking	a	16 15	16 19		16 21	16 25	16 28			16 40	16 44		16 49			16 51	16 57	16 58				17 11			17 16	17 20	
	d	16 17	16 21		16 22	16 26	16 29	16 33		16 41	16 46		16 51			16 52	16 59	16 59		17 03		17 12			17 17	17 21	
West Byfleet	d				16 27			16 37								16 57				17 07							
Byfleet & New Haw	d							16 40												17 10							
Weybridge	d			←			16 36	16 43							←			17 06		17 13							←
Walton-on-Thames	d			16 17			16 41	16 47							16 47			17 11		17 17							17 17
Hersham	d			16 19				→							16 49					→							17 19
Esher	d			16 22											16 52												17 22
Surbiton 6	a			16 26	16 37		16 47								16 56	17 07		17 17									17 26
Wimbledon 6 ⊖	a			16 35											17 04												17 34
Earlsfield	a			16 38											17 08												17 38
Clapham Junction 10	a	16 36		16 42	16 48		16 58				17 05			17 12	17 12				17 24			17 31			17 36		17 42
Vauxhall ⊖	a			16 47											17 17												17 47
London Waterloo 15 ⊖	a	16 49	16 49	16 53	16 59	16 51	17 08			17 08	17 14		17 19	17 20	17 22	17 29	17 24	17 34	17 34			17 43			17 45	17 50	17 52

		SW 1	SW 1 ☕	SW 1	SW	SW 1	SW 1	SW 1	SW 1	SW 1◇ ☕	SW	SW 1◇ ☕	SW 1	SW 1	SW 1	SW 1	SW	SW 1 ☕	SW 1		SW 1	SW 1◇ ☕	SW 1◇ ☕	SW	SW 1	SW 1 ☕	SW 1
Basingstoke	d						17 17		17 24	17 31		17 36				17 41					17 54	17 57					
Hook	d								17 31												18 01						
Winchfield	d			←					17 35						←						18 05						←
Fleet	d			17 10					17 40						17 40	17 53					18 10						18 10
Farnborough (Main)	d			17 16			17 31		→						17 46	17 58					→						18 16
Alton	d	16 44											17 15												17 44		
Bentley	d	16 51																							17 51		
Farnham	a	16 56											17 25												17 56		
	d	16 58											17 28												17 58		
Aldershot	d	17 04				17 30							17 34						18 00						18 04		
Ash Vale	d	17 09				17a34							17 39						18a04						18 09		
Brookwood	d	17 16		17 23									17 46		17 53										18 16		18 23
Guildford	d		17 17					17 32						17 47				18 00								18 17	
Worplesdon	d							17 40										18 06									
Woking	a	17 21	17 25	17 28			17 40	17 44		17 49			17 51	17 58	17 58			18 11				18 15	18 19		18 21		18 28
	d	17 22	17 26	17 29	17 33		17 41	17 46		17 51			17 52	17 59	17 59		18 03	18 12				18 17	18 21		18 22		18 29
West Byfleet	d	17 27			17 37								17 57				18 07								18 27		
Byfleet & New Haw	d				17 40												18 10										
Weybridge	d			17 36	17 43						←				18 06		18 13							←			18 36
Walton-on-Thames	d			17 41	17 47						17 47				18 11		18 17							18 17			18 41
Hersham	d				→						17 49						→							18 19			
Esher	d										17 52													18 22			
Surbiton 6	a	17 37		17 47							17 56		18 07		18 17									18 26	18 37		18 47
Wimbledon 6 ⊖	a										18 04													18 34			
Earlsfield	a										18 08													18 38			
Clapham Junction 10	a	17 48		17 58				18 05			18 12	18 12				18 24		18 31				18 36		18 42	18 48		18 58
Vauxhall ⊖	a										18 17													18 47			
London Waterloo 15 ⊖	a	17 59	17 52	18 09			18 08	18 14		18 17	18 23	18 23	18 29	18 24	18 39	18 34		18 43				18 45	18 47	18 52	18 57	18 59	19 06

For general notes see front of timetable
For details of catering facilities see
Directory of Train Operators

For details of Bank Holiday service alterations, please see first page of Table 149

Basingstoke, Alton, Guildford and Woking → Waterloo

Network Diagram - see first page of Table 155

		SW	SW 1	SW 1	SW 1	SW 1	SW 1 ◇ ⊡	SW 1 ◇ ⊡	SW	SW 1	SW 1	SW	SW 1 ⊡	SW 1	SW 1	SW 1	SW 1 ◇ ⊡	SW		SW 1	SW 1 ◇ ⊡	SW 1	SW 1 ⊡	SW	SW 1	SW 1	SW 1
Basingstoke	d		18 17			18 24	18 31	18 36						18 38		18 54	19 01								19 17		
Hook	d					18 31										19 01											
Winchfield	d					18 35					←					19 05						←					
Fleet	d					18 40					18 40			18 50		19 10						19 10					
Farnborough (Main)	d		18 31			→					18 46			18 55		→						19 16			19 31		
Alton	d									18 14										18 35							
Bentley	d									18b23										18 42							
Farnham	a									18 28										18 47							
	d									18 28										18 58							
Aldershot	d				18 30					18 34					19 00					19 04							19 30
Ash Vale	d				18a34					18 39					19a04					19 09							19a34
Brookwood	d									18 46	18 53									19 16		19 23					
Guildford	d			18 32									18 55										19 21			19 32	
Worplesdon	d			18 40																						19 40	
Woking	a		18 40	18 44			18 49			18 52	18 58		19 03				19 19			19 21	19 24	19 28	19 28		19 40	19 45	
	d	18 33	18 41	18 46			18 51			18 52	18 59	19 03	19 05				19 21			19 22	19 25	19 29	19 30	19 33	19 41	19 46	
West Byfleet	d	18 37								18 57		19 07								19 27				19 37			
Byfleet & New Haw	d	18 40										19 10												19 40			
Weybridge	d	18 43							←		19 06	19 13						←				19 36		19 43			
Walton-on-Thames	d	18 47							18 47		19 11	19 17						19 17				19 41		19 47			
Hersham	d	→							18 49			→						19 19						→			
Esher	d								18 52									19 22									
Surbiton 6	a								18 56	19 08	19 17							19 26		19 37		19 47					
Wimbledon 6 ⊖ ⛴	a								19 05									19 34									
Earlsfield	a								19 08									19 38									
Clapham Junction 10	a			19 05				19 12	19 12					19 26			19 40	19 42		19 48		19 58				20 05	
Vauxhall ⊖	a								19 17									19 47									
London Waterloo 15 ⊖	a		19 08	19 14			19 19	19 20	19 23	19 25	19 39		19 29	19 38			19 49	19 52		19 57	19 51	20 06	19 59		20 08	20 14	

		SW 1	SW 1 ◇ ⊡	SW 1 ◇ ⊡	SW	SW 1	SW 1 ⊡	SW 1	SW 1	SW	SW 1	SW 1 ◇ ⊡	SW 1	SW	SW 1	SW 1	SW 1		SW 1 ◇ ⊡	SW 1	SW 1	SW	SW 1	SW 1	SW	SW 1	SW 1
Basingstoke	d	19 24	19 31	19 36					19 41								19 54		20 09				20 17				
Hook	d	19 31															20 01										
Winchfield	d	19 35						←									20 05										
Fleet	d	19 40						19 40	19 53								20 10										
Farnborough (Main)	d	→						19 46	19 58								20 16						20 31				
Alton	d					19 07									19 35											20 15	
Bentley	d														19 42												
Farnham	a					19 17									19 47											20 25	
	d					19 28									19 58											20 28	
Aldershot	d					19 34							20 00		20 04					20 30						20 34	
Ash Vale	d					19 39							20a04		20 09					20a34						20 39	
Brookwood	d					19 46		19 53							20 16		20 23									20 46	
Guildford	d						19 47				20 02					20 17								20 39			20 47
Worplesdon	d																							20 44			
Woking	a		19 49			19 51	19 57	19 58			20 11	20 19			20 21	20 25	20 28		20 29				20 40	20 49		20 51	20 57
	d		19 51			19 52	19 59	19 59		20 03	20 12	20 21			20 22	20 26	20 29		20 30			20 33	20 41	20 50		20 52	20 59
West Byfleet	d					19 57				20 07					20 27							20 37				20 57	
Byfleet & New Haw	d									20 10											←	20 40					
Weybridge	d				←			20 06		20 13				←			20 36				20 36	20 43			←		
Walton-on-Thames	d				19 47			20 11		20 17				20 17			→				20 41	20 47			20 47		
Hersham	d				19 49					→				20 19								→			20 49		
Esher	d				19 52									20 22											20 52		
Surbiton 6	a				19 56	20 07		20 17						20 26	20 37						20 47				20 56	21 07	
Wimbledon 6 ⊖ ⛴	a				20 04									20 35											21 05		
Earlsfield	a				20 08									20 38											21 08		
Clapham Junction 10	a			20 12	20 12				20 25		20 31			20 41	20 48				20 52		20 58			21 09	21 11		
Vauxhall ⊖	a				20 17									20 46											21 16		
London Waterloo 15 ⊖	a		20 19	20 20	20 22	20 25	20 23	20 36	20 34		20 40	20 49		20 52	20 57	20 50			21 00		21 06		21 08	21 19	21 22	21 27	21 27

For general notes see front of timetable
For details of catering facilities see
Directory of Train Operators

b Arr. 1820

For details of Bank Holiday service alterations, please see first page of Table 149

Basingstoke, Alton, Guildford and Woking → Waterloo

Network Diagram - see first page of Table 155

		SW 1	SW 1 ◇ ☕	SW	SW 1	SW 1 ◇ ☕	SW	SW 1	SW 1	SW 1	SW 1 ◇ ☕	SW 1	SW 1	SW	SW 1	SW		SW 1	SW 1	SW 1 A	SW 1 ◇ ☕	SW	SW 1	SW 1	SW	SW 1	SW 1
Basingstoke	d	20 24	20 36		20 41					20 54	21 09									21 24	21 36		21 41				21 54
Hook	d	20 31								21 01										21 31							22 01
Winchfield	d	20 35								21 05										21 35							22 05
Fleet	d	20 40			20 53					21 10										21 40			21 53				22 10
Farnborough (Main)	d	20 46			20 58					21 16										21 46			21 58				22 16
Alton	d							20 44										21 15								21 44	
Bentley	d							20 51																		21 51	
Farnham	a							20 56										21 28								21 56	
	d							20 58										21 28								21 58	
Aldershot	d							21 04				21 30						21 34								22 04	
Ash Vale	d							21 09				21a34						21 39								22 09	
Brookwood	d	20 53						21 16		21 23								21 46		21 53						22 16	22 23
Guildford	d								21 17						21 39				21 47								→
Worplesdon	d														21 44												
Woking	a	20 58			21 07	21 19		21 21	21 25	21 28	21 29				21 49			21 51	21 57	21 58			22 07	22 19		22 21	
	d	20 59		21 03	21 09	21 21		21 22	21 26	21 29	21 30			21 33	21 50			21 52	21 59	21 59		22 03	22 09	22 21		22 22	
West Byfleet	d			21 07				21 27						21 37				21 57				22 07				22 27	
Byfleet & New Haw	d			21 10									←	21 40								22 10				→	
Weybridge	d	21 06		21 13			←			21 36			21 36	21 43		←				22 06		22 13			←		
Walton-on-Thames	d	21 11		21 17			21 17			→			21 41	21 47		21 47				22 11		22 17			22 17		
Hersham	d			→			21 19							→		21 49						→			22 19		
Esher	d						21 22									21 52									22 22		
Surbiton 6	a	21 17					21 26	21 37					21 47			21 56		22 07		22 17					22 26		
Wimbledon 6 ⊖ ⛴	a						21 34									22 04									22 34		
Earlsfield	a						21 38									22 08									22 38		
Clapham Junction 10	a		21 14		21 33		21 42	21 48			21 52		21 58		22 09	22 12					22 14		22 33		22 42		
Vauxhall ⊖	a						21 47									22 17									22 47		
London Waterloo 15 ⊖	a	21 34	21 22		21 43	21 49	21 52	21 57	21 50		22 04		22 06		22 18	22 22		22 26	22 27	22 34	22 22		22 43	22 49	22 52		

		SW 1 ◇	SW 1	SW 1	SW	SW 1	SW 1	SW	SW 1	SW 1 A	SW 1 ◇	SW 1 A	SW	SW 1	SW		SW 1	SW 1	SW 1	SW 1	SW 1	SW 1	SW 1	SW 1	SW 1 B		
Basingstoke	d	22 09								22 24	22 36			22 41				22 54	23 12						23 44		
Hook	d									22 31								23 01							23 51		
Winchfield	d									22 35		←						23 05							23 55		
Fleet	d									22 40		22 40		22 53				23 10							00 01		
Farnborough (Main)	d									→		22 46		22 58				23 16							00 06		
Alton	d								22 15								22 44						23 15	23 44			
Bentley	d																22 51							23 51			
Farnham	a								22 25								22 56						23 25	23 56			
	d								22 28								22 58						23 28				
Aldershot	d					22 30			22 34								23 04				23 30		23 34				
Ash Vale	d			←		22a34			22 39								23 09				23a34		23 39				
Brookwood	d			22 23					22 46			22 53					23 16	23 23					23 46		00 13		
Guildford	d				22 20		22 39						22 55									23 39					
Worplesdon	d						22 44															23 44					
Woking	a	22 28		22 28	22 32		22 49		22 51		22 54	22 58	23 05	23 07			23 21	23 28	23 30	←		23 49	23 51		00 18		
	d	22 29	←	22 29	22 33		22 50		22 52		22 55	22 59	23 06	23 09			23 22	23 33	23 31	23 33		23 56			00 20		
West Byfleet	d		22 27		22 37				22 57				23 10				23 27	→		23 37					00 25		
Byfleet & New Haw	d				22 40								23 13							23 40							
Weybridge	d			22 36	22 43			←				23 06	23 16		←					23 43					00 29		
Walton-on-Thames	d			22 41	22 47			22 47				23 11	23 20		23 20					23 47					00 34		
Hersham	d				→			22 49					→		23 22					23 49							
Esher	d							22 52							23 25					23 52							
Surbiton 6	a		22 37	22 47				22 56	23 07			23 17			23 29		23 37			23 57					00 40		
Wimbledon 6 ⊖ ⛴	a							23 04							23 37					00 08					00 48		
Earlsfield	a							23 08							23 41					00 10							
Clapham Junction 10	a	22 48	22 52	22 58			23 09	23 12			23 14			23 32	23 44		23 52		23 55	00 14		00 20			00 54		
Vauxhall ⊖	a							23 17							23 49					00 19							
London Waterloo 15 ⊖	a	22 57	23 01	23 08			23 18	23 23	23 26		23 23	23 33		23 43	23 54		00 01		00 04	00 29		00 29			01 02		

For general notes see front of timetable
For details of catering facilities see
Directory of Train Operators

A From Portsmouth Harbour (Table 158)
B From Weymouth (Table 158)

Table 155

Saturdays

Basingstoke, Alton, Guildford and Woking → Waterloo

Network Diagram - see first page of Table 155

		SW 1	SW 1	SW 1	SW	SW	SW 1	SW	SW 1	SW	SW	SW 1	SW 1	SW 1	SW	SW 1	SW		SW 1	SW 1	SW 1 ◇	SW	SW 1	SW 1	SW 1	SW	SW 1
				A									B	☕		B				B	☕			B			
Basingstoke	d	22p54		23p44					04 54				05 54	05 59						06 24	06 31				06 40		
Hook	d	23p01		23p51					05 01				06 01							06 31							
Winchfield	d	23p05		23p55					05 05				06 05			←				06 35				←			
Fleet	d	23p10		00 01					05 10				06 10			06 10				06 40				06 40			
Farnborough (Main)	d	23p16		00 06					05 16				→			06 16				→				06 46			
Alton	d																						06 14				
Bentley	d																						06 21				
Farnham	a																						06 26				
	d																						06 28				
Aldershot	d						06 00																06 34				
Ash Vale	d						06a04																06 39				
Brookwood	d	23p23		00 13					05 23							06 23							06 46	06 53			
Guildford	d		23p39		04 00	05 12						06 02							06 32								07 02
Worplesdon	d		23p44			05 17													06 40								
Woking	a	23p28	23p49	00 18	04 08	05 22			05 28	←		06 11		06 18		06 28			06 44		06 49		06 51	06 58	06 58		07 11
	d	23p33	23p56	00 20	04 10	05 33		05 25	05 29	05 33	06 03	06 13		06 19		06 29	06 33		06 46		06 51		06 52	06 59	07 00	07 03	07 12
West Byfleet	d	23p37		00 25		→		05 30		05 37	06 07						06 37						06 57			07 07	
Byfleet & New Haw	d	23p40						05 33		05 40	06 10						06 40									07 10	
Weybridge	d	23p43		00 29						05 43	06 13				←	06 36	06 43					←		07 06		07 13	
Walton-on-Thames	d	23p47		00 34						05 47	06 17				06 17	06 41	06 47					06 47		07 11		07 17	
Hersham	d	23p49								05 49	→				06 19		→					06 49				→	
Esher	d	23p52								05 52					06 22							06 52					
Surbiton 6	a	23p57		00 40	04 24				05 40	05 56					06 26	06 47						06 56	07 07	07 17			
Wimbledon 6 ⊖ 🚊	a	00 08		00 48	04 31				05 48	06 04					06 34							07 04					
Earlsfield	a	00 10								06 08					06 38							07 08					
Clapham Junction 10	a	00 14	00 20	00 54	04 43			06 43	06 00	06 12		06 32		06 38	06 42	06 58			07 05			07 12	07 18		07 23		07 31
Vauxhall ⊖	a	00 19						06 49	06 07	06 17					06 47							07 17					
London Waterloo 15 ⊖	a	00 29	00 29	01 02	04 53			06 56	06 12	06 22		06 40		06 49	06 52	07 06			07 13		07 19	07 22	07 27	07 33	07 31		07 40

		SW 1	SW 1	SW 1 ◇	SW	SW 1	SW 1 ◇	SW 1	SW	SW 1		SW 1	SW 1	SW 1 ◇	SW	SW 1	SW 1	SW 1	SW	SW 1	SW 1	SW 1	SW 1	SW 1 ◇	SW	SW 1	SW 1 ◇
				☕			☕						C	☕			☕	C						☕			☕
Basingstoke	d		06 54	06 57			07 09						07 24	07 31						07 42			07 54	07 57			
Hook	d		07 01										07 31										08 01				
Winchfield	d		07 05					←					07 35					←					08 05				
Fleet	d		07 10					07 10					07 40					07 40		07 53			08 10				
Farnborough (Main)	d		→					07 16					→					07 46		07 59			→				
Alton	d					06 44										07 14										07 44	
Bentley	d					06 51										07 21										07 51	
Farnham	a					06 56										07 26										07 56	
	d					06 58										07 28										07 58	
Aldershot	d	07 00				07 04						07 30				07 34						08 00				08 04	
Ash Vale	d	07a04				07 09						07a34				07 39						08a04				08 09	
Brookwood	d					07 16		07 23								07 46		07 53								08 16	
Guildford	d									07 32							07 47				08 02						
Worplesdon	d									07 40																	
Woking	a			07 15		07 21	07 27	07 28		07 44				07 49		07 51	07 57	07 58		08 08	08 12			08 17		08 21	08 21
	d			07 17		07 22	07 29	07 29	07 33	07 46				07 51		07 52	07 59	07 59	08 03	08 09	08 14			08 18		08 22	08 23
West Byfleet	d					07 27			07 37							07 57			08 07							08 27	
Byfleet & New Haw	d								07 40										08 10								
Weybridge	d				←			07 36	07 43						←			08 06	08 13						←		
Walton-on-Thames	d				07 17			07 41	07 47						07 47			08 11	08 17						08 17		
Hersham	d				07 19				→						07 49				→						08 19		
Esher	d				07 22										07 52										08 22		
Surbiton 6	a				07 27	07 37		07 47							07 56	08 07		08 17							08 26	08 37	
Wimbledon 6 ⊖ 🚊	a				07 35										08 04										08 34		
Earlsfield	a				07 38										08 08										08 38		
Clapham Junction 10	a			07 36	07 42	07 50		07 58		08 05					08 12					08 30	08 33			08 37	08 42	08 49	
Vauxhall ⊖	a				07 47										08 17										08 47		
London Waterloo 15 ⊖	a			07 49	07 52	07 58	07 53	08 06		08 13				08 19	08 22	08 25	08 23	08 34		08 38	08 42			08 49	08 52	08 58	08 49

		SW 1	SW 1		SW	SW 1	SW 1	SW 1	SW 1	SW 1 ◇	SW 1 ◇	SW	SW 1	SW 1	SW 1	SW 1	SW	SW 1	SW 1	SW 1		SW 1 ◇	SW 1 ◇	SW	SW 1	SW 1	SW 1
		☕								☕	☕			☕								☕	☕			☕	
Basingstoke	d					08 17			08 24	08 28	08 36					08 41				08 54		08 57					
Hook	d								08 31											09 01							
Winchfield	d		←						08 35						←					09 05							←
Fleet	d		08 10						08 40						08 40	08 53				09 10							09 10
Farnborough (Main)	d		08 16			08 30			→						08 46	08 58				→							09 16
Alton	d												08 14												08 44		
Bentley	d												08 21												08 51		
Farnham	a												08 26												08 56		
	d												08 28												08 58		
Aldershot	d							08 30					08 34						09 00						09 04		
Ash Vale	d							08a34					08 39						09a04						09 09		
Brookwood	d		08 23										08 46		08 53										09 16		09 23
Guildford	d	08 17					08 32							08 47				09 02								09 17	
Worplesdon	d						08 40																				
Woking	a	08 26	08 28			08 39	08 44			08 49			08 51	08 57	08 58			09 11				09 15	09 19		09 21	09 25	09 28
	d	08 27	08 29		08 33	08 41	08 46			08 51			08 52	08 59	08 59		09 03	09 12				09 17	09 21		09 22	09 26	09 29
West Byfleet	d				08 37								08 57				09 07								09 27		
Byfleet & New Haw	d				08 40												09 10										
Weybridge	d		08 36		08 43							←			09 06		09 13							←			09 36
Walton-on-Thames	d		08 41		08 47							08 47			09 11		09 17							09 17			09 41
Hersham	d				→							08 49					→							09 19			
Esher	d											08 52												09 22			
Surbiton 6	a		08 47									08 56	09 07		09 17									09 26	09 37		09 47
Wimbledon 6 ⊖ 🚊	a											09 04												09 34			
Earlsfield	a											09 08												09 38			
Clapham Junction 10	a		08 58				09 05				09 12	09 12				09 24		09 31				09 36		09 42	09 48		09 58
Vauxhall ⊖	a											09 17												09 47			
London Waterloo 15 ⊖	a	08 51	09 06			09 08	09 13			09 19	09 20	09 22	09 25	09 23	09 35	09 34		09 40				09 49	09 49	09 52	09 57	09 52	10 06

For general notes see front of timetable
For details of catering facilities see Directory of Train Operators

A From Weymouth (Table 158)
B From Southampton Central (Table 158)
C From Portsmouth Harbour (Table 158)

Basingstoke, Alton, Guildford and Woking → Waterloo

Network Diagram - see first page of Table 155

	SW	SW 1	SW 1	SW 1	SW 1	SW 1 ◇ ☕	SW 1 ◇ ☕	SW	SW 1	SW 1 ☕	SW 1	SW 1		SW	SW 1	SW 1	SW 1	SW 1 ◇ ☕	SW 1 ◇ ☕	SW	SW 1	SW 1 ☕	SW 1	SW	SW 1	SW 1
Basingstoke d			09 17		09 24	09 31	09 36					09 41					09 54	09 57								10 17
Hook d					09 31												10 01									
Winchfield d					09 35						←						10 05						←			
Fleet d					09 40						09 40	09 53					10 10						10 10			
Farnborough (Main) d			09 31		→						09 46	09 58					→						10 16			10 31
Alton d									09 14												09 44					
Bentley d									09 21												09 51					
Farnham a									09 26												09 56					
d									09 28												09 58					
Aldershot d		09 30							09 34							10 00					10 04				10 30	
Ash Vale d		09a34							09 39							10a04					10 09				10a34	
Brookwood d									09 46		09 53										10 16		10 23			
Guildford d				09 32						09 47					10 02							10 17				
Worplesdon d				09 40																						
Woking a			09 40	09 44		09 49			09 51	09 57	09 58				10 11			10 15	10 19		10 21	10 25	10 28			10 40
d	09 33		09 41	09 46		09 51			09 52	09 59	09 59			10 03	10 12			10 17	10 21		10 22	10 26	10 29	10 33		10 41
West Byfleet d	09 37								09 57					10 07							10 27			10 37		
Byfleet & New Haw d	09 40													10 10										10 40		
Weybridge d	09 43							←			10 06			10 13						←			10 36	10 43		
Walton-on-Thames d	09 47							09 47			10 11			10 17						10 17			10 41	10 47		
Hersham d	→							09 49						→						10 19				→		
Esher d								09 52												10 22						
Surbiton [6] a								09 56	10 07		10 17									10 26	10 37		10 47			
Wimbledon [6] ⊖ a								10 04												10 34						
Earlsfield a								10 08												10 38						
Clapham Junction [10] a				10 05			10 12	10 12				10 24			10 31			10 36		10 42	10 48		10 58			
Vauxhall ⊖ a								10 17												10 47						
London Waterloo [15] ⊖ a			10 08	10 13		10 19	10 20	10 22	10 25	10 23	10 35	10 34			10 40			10 49	10 49	10 52	10 57	10 51	11 06			11 08

	SW 1	SW 1	SW 1 ◇ ☕	SW 1 ◇ ☕	SW		SW 1	SW 1 ☕	SW 1		SW 1	SW	SW 1	SW 1	SW 1	SW 1 ◇ ☕	SW 1 ◇ ☕	SW	SW 1	SW 1 ☕	SW 1	SW	SW 1	SW 1	SW 1	SW 1
Basingstoke d		10 24	10 31	10 36							10 41				10 54	10 57								11 17		11 24
Hook d		10 31													11 01											11 31
Winchfield d		10 35							←						11 05						←					11 35
Fleet d		10 40							10 40		10 53				11 10						11 10					11 40
Farnborough (Main) d		→							10 46		10 58				→						11 16			11 31		→
Alton d							10 14												10 44							
Bentley d							10 21												10 51							
Farnham a							10 26												10 56							
d							10 28												10 58							
Aldershot d							10 34							11 00					11 04				11 30			
Ash Vale d							10 39							11a04					11 09				11a34			
Brookwood d							10 46		10 53										11 16		11 23					
Guildford d	10 32							10 47					11 02							11 17					11 32	
Worplesdon d	10 40																								11 40	
Woking a	10 44		10 49				10 51	10 57	10 58				11 11			11 15	11 19		11 21	11 25	11 28			11 40	11 44	
d	10 46		10 51				10 52	10 59	10 59			11 03	11 12			11 17	11 21		11 22	11 26	11 29	11 33		11 41	11 46	
West Byfleet d							10 57					11 07							11 27			11 37				
Byfleet & New Haw d												11 10										11 40				
Weybridge d					←				11 06			11 13						←			11 36	11 43				
Walton-on-Thames d					10 47				11 11			11 17						11 17			11 41	11 47				
Hersham d					10 49							→						11 19				→				
Esher d					10 52													11 22								
Surbiton [6] a					10 56		11 07		11 17									11 26	11 37		11 47					
Wimbledon [6] ⊖ a					11 04													11 34								
Earlsfield a					11 08													11 38								
Clapham Junction [10] a	11 05			11 12	11 12						11 24		11 31			11 36		11 42	11 48		11 58				12 05	
Vauxhall ⊖ a					11 17													11 47								
London Waterloo [15] ⊖ a	11 13		11 19	11 20	11 22		11 25	11 23	11 35		11 34		11 40			11 49	11 49	11 52	11 57	11 51	12 06			12 08	12 13	

	SW 1 ◇ ☕	SW 1 ◇ ☕	SW	SW 1	SW 1 ☕	SW 1			SW 1	SW	SW 1	SW 1	SW 1	SW 1 ◇ ☕	SW 1 ◇ ☕	SW	SW 1	SW 1	SW 1	SW	SW 1	SW 1	SW 1	SW 1	SW
Basingstoke d	11 31	11 36							18 41				18 54	18 57								19 17		19 24	
Hook d													19 01											19 31	
Winchfield d						←							19 05						←					19 35	
Fleet d						11 40			18 53				19 10						19 10					19 40	
Farnborough (Main) d						11 46			18 58				→						19 16			19 31		→	
Alton d				11 15													18 44								
Bentley d							and at										18 51								
Farnham a				11 25													18 56								
d				11 28			the same										18 58								
Aldershot d				11 34								19 00					19 04				19 30				
Ash Vale d				11 39			minutes					19a04					19 09				19a34				
Brookwood d				11 46		11 53											19 16		19 23						
Guildford d					11 47		past				19 02							19 17					19 32		
Worplesdon d																							19 40		
Woking a	11 49			11 51	11 57	11 58	each				19 11			19 15	19 19		19 21	19 25	19 28			19 40	19 44		
d	11 51			11 52	11 59	11 59				19 03	19 12			19 17	19 21		19 22	19 26	19 29	19 33		19 41	19 46		
West Byfleet d				11 57			hour until			19 07							19 27			19 37					
Byfleet & New Haw d										19 10										19 40					
Weybridge d			←			12 06				19 13						←			19 36	19 43					←
Walton-on-Thames d			11 47			12 11				19 17						19 17			19 41	19 47					19 47
Hersham d			11 49							→						19 19				→					19 49
Esher d			11 52													19 22									19 52
Surbiton [6] a			11 56	12 07		12 17										19 26	19 37		19 47						19 56
Wimbledon [6] ⊖ a			12 04													19 34									20 04
Earlsfield a			12 08													19 38									20 08
Clapham Junction [10] a		12 12	12 12						19 24		19 31			19 36		19 42	19 48		19 58				20 05		20 12
Vauxhall ⊖ a			12 17													19 47									20 17
London Waterloo [15] ⊖ a	12 19	12 20	12 22	12 25	12 23	12 35			19 34		19 40			19 49	19 49	19 52	19 57	19 50	20 06			20 08	20 13		20 22

For general notes see front of timetable
For details of catering facilities see Directory of Train Operators

Basingstoke, Alton, Guildford and Woking → Waterloo

Network Diagram - see first page of Table 155

	SW 1◇ ☕		SW 1◇ ☕	SW 1	SW 1	SW 1	SW 1	SW	SW 1	SW 1◇ ☕	SW 1	SW	SW 1	SW 1	SW 1	SW 1◇ ☕	SW 1	SW 1		SW	SW 1	SW 1	SW	SW 1	SW 1	SW 1
Basingstoke d	19 31		19 36				19 41								19 54	20 09					20 17					20 24
Hook d															20 01											20 31
Winchfield d						←									20 05											20 35
Fleet d						19 40	19 53								20 10											20 40
Farnborough (Main) d						19 46	19 58								20 16						20 31					20 46
Alton d				19 15									19 44											20 15		
Bentley d													19 51													
Farnham a				19 25									19 56											20 25		
d				19 28									19 58											20 28		
Aldershot d				19 34							20 00		20 04				20 30							20 34		
Ash Vale d				19 39							20a04		20 09				20a34							20 39		
Brookwood d				19 46		19 53							20 16		20 23									20 46		20 53
Guildford d					19 47				20 02					20 17								20 39			20 49	
Worplesdon d																						20 44				
Woking a	19 49			19 51	19 57	19 58			20 11	20 19			20 21	20 25	20 28	20 29					20 40	20 49		20 51	20 57	20 58
d	19 51			19 52	19 59	19 59		20 03	20 12	20 21			20 22	20 26	20 29	20 30				20 33	20 41	20 50		20 52	20 59	20 59
West Byfleet d				19 57				20 07					20 27							20 37				20 57		
Byfleet & New Haw d								20 10										←		20 40						
Weybridge d						20 06		20 13				←			20 36			20 36		20 43			←			21 06
Walton-on-Thames d						20 11		20 17				20 17			→			20 41		20 47			20 47			21 11
Hersham d								→				20 19								→			20 49			
Esher d												20 22											20 52			
Surbiton 6 a				20 07		20 17						20 26	20 37					20 47					20 56	21 07		21 17
Wimbledon 6 ⊖ a												20 34											21 04			
Earlsfield a												20 38											21 08			
Clapham Junction 10 a			20 12				20 24		20 31			20 42	20 48			20 52		20 58				21 09	21 12			
Vauxhall ⊖ a												20 47											21 17			
London Waterloo 15 ⊖ a	20 26		20 20	20 25	20 23	20 35	20 34		20 40	20 49		20 52	20 57	20 50		21 04		21 06			21 08	21 18	21 23	21 26	21 24	21 34

	SW 1◇ ☕	SW	SW 1	SW 1◇ ☕	SW	SW 1	SW 1	SW 1	SW 1◇ ☕	SW 1	SW 1		SW	SW 1	SW	SW 1	SW 1	SW 1 A	SW 1◇ ☕	SW	SW 1	SW 1	SW	SW 1	SW 1	SW 1◇
Basingstoke d	20 36		20 41					20 54	21 09									21 24	21 36		21 41				21 54	22 09
Hook d								21 01										21 31							22 01	
Winchfield d								21 05										21 35							22 05	
Fleet d			20 53					21 10										21 40			21 53				22 10	
Farnborough (Main) d			20 58					21 16										21 46			21 58				22 16	
Alton d						20 44										21 15								21 44		
Bentley d						20 51																		21 51		
Farnham a						20 56										21 25								21 56		
d						20 58										21 28								21 58		
Aldershot d						21 04				21 30						21 34								22 04		
Ash Vale d						21 09				21a34						21 39								22 09		
Brookwood d						21 16		21 23								21 46		21 53						22 16	22 23	
Guildford d							21 17							21 39			21 49								→	
Worplesdon d														21 44												
Woking a			21 07	21 19		21 21	21 25	21 28	21 29					21 49		21 51	21 57	21 58			22 07	22 19		22 21		22 28
d		21 03	21 09	21 21		21 22	21 26	21 29	21 30				21 33	21 50		21 52	21 59	21 59		22 03	22 09	22 21		22 22		22 29
West Byfleet d		21 07				21 27							21 37			21 57				22 07				22 27		
Byfleet & New Haw d		21 10									←		21 40							22 10				→		
Weybridge d		21 13			←			21 36			21 36		21 43		←			22 06		22 13			←			
Walton-on-Thames d		21 17			21 17			→			21 41		21 47		21 47			22 11		22 17			22 17			
Hersham d		→			21 19								→		21 49					→			22 19			
Esher d					21 22										21 52								22 22			
Surbiton 6 a					21 26	21 37					21 47				21 56	22 07		22 17					22 26			
Wimbledon 6 ⊖ a					21 34										22 04								22 34			
Earlsfield a					21 38										22 08								22 38			
Clapham Junction 10 a	21 14		21 30		21 42	21 48			21 52		21 58			22 09	22 12				22 14		22 30		22 42			22 48
Vauxhall ⊖ a					21 47										22 17								22 47			
London Waterloo 15 ⊖ a	21 22		21 38	21 49	21 52	21 57	21 50		22 04		22 07			22 18	22 22	22 26	22 24	22 34	22 22		22 38	22 49	22 52			22 57

	SW 1	SW 1	SW	SW 1		SW 1	SW	SW 1	SW 1 A	SW 1◇	SW 1 A	SW	SW 1	SW	SW 1	SW 1	SW 1	SW 1	SW 1	SW 1	SW 1		SW 1	SW 1 B		
Basingstoke d									22 24	22 36			22 41			22 54	23 14							23 44		
Hook d									22 31							23 01								23 51		
Winchfield d									22 35		←					23 05								23 55		
Fleet d									22 40		22 40		22 53			23 10								00 01		
Farnborough (Main) d									→		22 46		22 58			23 16								00 06		
Alton d								22 15							22 44						23 15		23 44			
Bentley d															22 51								23 51			
Farnham a								22 25							22 56						23 25		23 56			
d								22 28							22 58						23 28					
Aldershot d				22 30				22 34							23 04			23 30			23 34					
Ash Vale d		←		22a34				22 39							23 09			23a34			23 39					
Brookwood d		22 23						22 46			22 53				23 16	23 23					23 46			00 13		
Guildford d			22 20			22 39						22 55								23 39						
Worplesdon d						22 44														23 44						
Woking a		22 28	22 32			22 49		22 51		22 54	22 58	23 05	23 07		23 21	23 28	23 32			23 49	23 51			00 18		
d	←	22 29	22 33			22 50		22 52		22 56	22 59	23 06	23 09		23 22	23 33	23 33			23 56				00 20		
West Byfleet d	22 27		22 37					22 57				23 10			23 27	23 37								00 25		
Byfleet & New Haw d			22 40									23 13				23 40										
Weybridge d		22 36	22 43				←				23 06	23 16		←		23 43			←					00 29		
Walton-on-Thames d		22 41	22 47				22 47				23 11	23 20		23 20		23 47			23 47					00 34		
Hersham d			→				22 49					→		23 22		→			23 49							
Esher d							22 52							23 25					23 52							
Surbiton 6 a	22 37	22 47					22 56	23 07			23 17			23 29	23 37				23 57					00 40		
Wimbledon 6 ⊖ a							23 04							23 37					00 08					00 48		
Earlsfield a							23 08							23 41					00 10							
Clapham Junction 10 a	22 52	22 58				23 09	23 12			23 15			23 30	23 44	23 52		23 57		00 14	00 22				00 54		
Vauxhall ⊖ a							23 17							23 49					00 19							
London Waterloo 15 ⊖ a	23 01	23 06				23 18	23 22	23 25		23 23	23 37		23 38	23 54	00 03		00 07		00 29	00 31				01 02		

For general notes see front of timetable
For details of catering facilities see
Directory of Train Operators

A From Portsmouth Harbour (Table 158)
B From Weymouth (Table 158)

Sundays

Basingstoke, Alton, Guildford and Woking → Waterloo

Network Diagram - see first page of Table 155

		SW ■1	SW ■1	SW ■1	SW	SW	SW	SW ■1	SW ■1◇	SW	SW ■1	SW ■1	SW ■1	SW ■1	SW	SW ■1	SW	SW ■1◇	SW	SW ■1	SW	SW ■1	SW ■1	SW ■1	SW ■1◇	SW	SW ■1
				A					☕									☕							☕		
Basingstoke	d	22p54		23p44				07 16	07 20					07 44				08 05				08 16			08 44		
Hook	d	23p01		23p51				07 23														08 23					
Winchfield	d	23p05		23p55				07 27			←											08 27					
Fleet	d	23p10		00 01				07 32			07 32											08 32					
Farnborough (Main)	d	23p16		00 06				→			07 38											08 38					
Alton	d																						08 15				
Bentley	d																						08b24				
Farnham	a																						08 29				
	d											07 30											08 30				
Aldershot	d											07 36	07 40										08 36	08 40			
Ash Vale	d											07 41	07a44										08 41	08a44			
Brookwood	d	23p23		00 13							07 45	07 48										08 45	08 48				
Guildford	d		23p39			06 57	07 27								07 57	08 05			08 27	08 35						08 57	09 05
Worplesdon	d		23p44																								
Woking	a	23p28	23p49	00 18		07 05	07 35		07 39		07 50	07 54		08 02	08 05	08 13		08 23	08 35	08 42		08 50	08 54		09 02	09 05	09 14
	d	23p33	23p56	00 20	06 36	07 06	07 36		07 40		07 58			08 04	08 06	08 15		08 25	08 36	08 45		08 58			09 04	09 06	09 15
West Byfleet	d	23p37		00 25	06 40	07 10	07 40								08 10				08 40							09 10	
Byfleet & New Haw	d	23p40			06 43	07 13	07 43								08 13				08 43							09 13	
Weybridge	d	23p43		00 29	06 46	07 16	07 46			←					08 16		←		08 46		←					09 16	
Walton-on-Thames	d	23p47		00 34	06 50	07 20	07 50			07 50					08 20		08 20		08 50		08 50					09 20	
Hersham	d	23p49			06 52	07 22	→			07 52					→		08 22		→		08 52					→	
Esher	d	23p52			06 55	07 25				07 55							08 25				08 55						
Surbiton 6	a	23p57		00 40	06 59	07 29				07 59	08 09						08 29				08 59	09 09					
Wimbledon 6 ⊖	a	00 08		00 48	07 07	07 37				08 07	08 16						08 37				09 07	09 16					
Earlsfield	a	00 10			07 11	07 41				08 11							08 41				09 11						
Clapham Junction 10	a	00 14	00 22	00 54	07 15	07 45			08 03	08 15	08 23			08 27		08 37	08 45	08 55		09 06	09 15	09 24			09 27		09 35
Vauxhall ⊖	a	00 19			07 20	07 50				08 20							08 50				09 20						
London Waterloo 15 ⊖	a	00 29	00 31	01 02	07 30	08 00			08 19	08 30	08 39			08 42		08 49	09 00	09 09		09 19	09 30	09 39			09 42		09 49

		SW	SW ■1◇	SW	SW ■1	SW	SW ■1	SW ■1	SW ■1	SW ■1◇	SW	SW ■1	SW ■1◇	SW ■1◇	SW	SW	SW ■1	SW	SW ■1	SW ■1	SW ■1	SW ■1◇	SW	SW ■1	SW ■1◇	SW	SW ■1◇
			☕										☕	☕			☕								☕		☕
Basingstoke	d		09 11				09 16			09 44			10 00	10 05					10 16			10 44			11 00		11 11
Hook	d						09 23												10 23								
Winchfield	d						09 27												10 27								
Fleet	d						09 32												10 32								
Farnborough (Main)	d						09 38												10 38								
Alton	d							09 15												10 15							
Bentley	d							09c24												10e24							
Farnham	a							09 29												10 29							
	d							09 30												10 30							
Aldershot	d							09 36	09 40											10 36	10 40						
Ash Vale	d							09 41	09a44											10 41	10a44						
Brookwood	d						09 45	09 48											10 45	10 48							
Guildford	d			09 27	09 35						09 57	10 05				10 27	10 35						10 57	11 05			
Worplesdon	d																										
Woking	a		09 30	09 35	09 42		09 50	09 54		10 02	10 05	10 13	10 18	10 23		10 35	10 42		10 50	10 54		11 02	11 05	11 14	11 18		11 30
	d		09 31	09 36	09 45		09 58			10 04	10 06	10 15	10 20	10 25		10 36	10 45		10 58			11 04	11 06	11 15	11 20		11 31
West Byfleet	d			09 40							10 10					10 40							11 10				
Byfleet & New Haw	d			09 43							10 13					10 43							11 13				
Weybridge	d	←		09 46		←					10 16				←	10 46		←					11 16			←	
Walton-on-Thames	d	09 20		09 50		09 50					10 20				10 20	10 50		10 50					11 20			11 20	
Hersham	d	09 22		→		09 52					→				10 22	→		10 52					→			11 22	
Esher	d	09 25				09 55									10 25			10 55								11 25	
Surbiton 6	a	09 29				09 59	10 09								10 29			10 59	11 09							11 29	
Wimbledon 6 ⊖	a	09 37				10 07	10 17								10 37			11 07	11 16							11 37	
Earlsfield	a	09 41				10 11									10 41			11 11								11 41	
Clapham Junction 10	a	09 45	09 55		10 06	10 15	10 22			10 27		10 35	10 39	10 44	10 45		11 04	11 15	11 22			11 27		11 34	11 39	11 45	11 50
Vauxhall ⊖	a	09 50				10 20									10 50			11 20								11 50	
London Waterloo 15 ⊖	a	10 00	10 08		10 21	10 30	10 39			10 42		10 49	10 54	11 03	11 00		11 19	11 30	11 39			11 40		11 49	11 52	12 00	12 03

For general notes see front of timetable
For details of catering facilities see Directory of Train Operators

A From Weymouth (Table 158)
b Arr. 0821
c Arr. 0921
e Arr. 1021

Basingstoke, Alton, Guildford and Woking → Waterloo

Network Diagram - see first page of Table 155

		SW	SW 1 ☕	SW	SW 1	SW 1	SW 1	SW 1 ◇	SW	SW 1	SW 1 ◇ ☕	SW 1 ◇ ☕	SW	SW	SW 1 ☕	SW	SW 1	SW 1	SW 1	SW 1 ◇	SW	SW 1	SW 1 ◇ ☕	SW	SW 1 ◇ ☕	SW	SW 1 ☕
Basingstoke	d				11 16			11 44			12 00	12 05					12 16			12 44			13 00		13 11		
Hook	d				11 23												12 23										
Winchfield	d				11 27												12 27										
Fleet	d				11 32												12 32										
Farnborough (Main)	d				11 38												12 38										
Alton	d					11 15												12 15									
Bentley	d					11b24												12c24									
Farnham	a					11 29												12 29									
	d					11 30												12 30									
Aldershot	d					11 36	11 40											12 36	12 40								
Ash Vale	d					11 41	11a44											12 41	12a44								
Brookwood	d				11 45	11 48											12 45	12 48									
Guildford	d	11 27	11 35						11 57	12 05				12 27	12 35						12 57	13 05				13 27	13 35
Worplesdon	d																										
Woking	a	11 35	11 42		11 50	11 54		12 02	12 05	12 13	12 18	12 23		12 35	12 42		12 50	12 54		13 02	13 05	13 13	13 18		13 30	13 35	13 42
	d	11 36	11 45		11 58			12 04	12 06	12 15	12 20	12 25		12 36	12 45		12 58			13 04	13 06	13 15	13 20		13 31	13 36	13 45
West Byfleet	d	11 40							12 10					12 40							13 10					13 40	
Byfleet & New Haw	d	11 43							12 13					12 43							13 13					13 43	
Weybridge	d	11 46		←					12 16				←	12 46		←					13 16			←		13 46	
Walton-on-Thames	d	11 50 →		11 50					12 20 →				12 20	12 50 →		12 50					13 20 →			13 20		13 50 →	
Hersham	d			11 52									12 22			12 52								13 22			
Esher	d			11 55									12 25			12 55								13 25			
Surbiton 6	a			11 59	12 09								12 29			12 59	13 09							13 29			
Wimbledon 6 ⊖ 🚋	a			12 07	12 17								12 37			13 07	13 17							13 37			
Earlsfield	a			12 11									12 41			13 11								13 41			
Clapham Junction 10	a		12 04	12 15	12 23			12 27		12 34	12 39	12 44	12 45		13 04	13 15	13 23			13 27		13 34	13 39	13 45	13 50		14 04
Vauxhall ⊖	a			12 20									12 50			13 20								13 50			
London Waterloo 15 ⊖	a		12 19	12 30	12 39			12 40		12 47	12 52	13 03	13 00		13 14	13 30	13 39			13 40		13 44	13 49	14 00	14 04		14 14

		SW	SW 1	SW 1	SW 1	SW 1 ◇	SW	SW 1	SW 1	SW 1 ◇ ☕	SW 1	SW 1 ◇ ☕	SW	SW 1	SW 1	SW	SW 1 ☕	SW	SW 1	SW 1	SW 1	SW 1 ◇	SW	SW 1	SW 1	SW 1 ◇ ☕	SW
Basingstoke	d		13 16			13 44			13 50	14 00		14 05							14 16			14 44			14 50	15 00	
Hook	d		13 23																14 23								
Winchfield	d		13 27																14 27								
Fleet	d		13 32						14 02		←								14 32						15 02		
Farnborough (Main)	d		13 38						14 08		14 08								14 38						15 08		
Alton	d			13 15					→						13 45					14 15					→		
Bentley	d			13e24																14f24							
Farnham	a			13 29											13 55					14 29							
	d			13 30											14 00					14 30							
Aldershot	d			13 36	13 40										14 06					14 36	14 40						
Ash Vale	d			13 41	13a44										14 11					14 41	14a44						
Brookwood	d		13 45	13 48							14 15				14 18				14 45	14 48							
Guildford	d						13 57	14 05								14 27	14 35						14 57	15 05			
Worplesdon	d													←													
Woking	a		13 50	13 54		14 02	14 05	14 13		14 18	14 20 →	14 23		14 20	14 24	14 35	14 42		14 50	14 54		15 02	15 05	15 13		15 18	
	d		13 58			14 04	14 06	14 15		14 20		14 25		14 28		14 36	14 45		14 58			15 04	15 06	15 15		15 20	
West Byfleet	d						14 10									14 40							15 10				
Byfleet & New Haw	d						14 13									14 43							15 13				
Weybridge	d	←					14 16						←	14 35		14 46		←					15 16				←
Walton-on-Thames	d	13 50					14 20 →						14 20	14 39		14 50 →		14 50					15 20 →				15 20
Hersham	d	13 52											14 22					14 52									15 22
Esher	d	13 55											14 25					14 55									15 25
Surbiton 6	a	13 59	14 09										14 29	14 45				14 59	15 09								15 29
Wimbledon 6 ⊖ 🚋	a	14 07	14 17										14 37	14 53				15 07	15 17								15 37
Earlsfield	a	14 11											14 41					15 11									15 41
Clapham Junction 10	a	14 15	14 23			14 27		14 34		14 39		14 44	14 45	14 59			15 04	15 15	15 23			15 27		15 34		15 39	15 45
Vauxhall ⊖	a	14 20											14 50					15 20									15 50
London Waterloo 15 ⊖	a	14 30	14 34			14 37		14 44		14 49		14 58	14 55	15 10			15 14	15 25	15 34			15 37		15 44		15 49	15 55

For general notes see front of timetable
For details of catering facilities see Directory of Train Operators

b Arr. 1121
c Arr. 1221
e Arr. 1321
f Arr. 1421

Table 155

Sundays

Basingstoke, Alton, Guildford and Woking → Waterloo

Network Diagram - see first page of Table 155

		SW 1	SW 1	SW 1 ◇ ☕	SW	SW 1	SW 1 ☕	SW	SW 1	SW 1	SW 1	SW 1 ◇	SW	SW 1
Basingstoke	d			15 11					15 16			15 44		
Hook	d								15 23					
Winchfield	d								15 27					
Fleet	d	←							15 32					
Farnborough (Main)	d	15 08							15 38					
Alton	d		14 45							15 15				
Bentley	d									15b24				
Farnham	a		14 55							15 29				
	d		15 00							15 30				
Aldershot	d		15 06							15 36	15 40			
Ash Vale	d		15 11							15 41	15a44			
Brookwood	d	15 15	15 18						15 45	15 48				
Guildford	d				15 27		15 35						15 57	16 05
Worplesdon	d													
Woking	a	15 20	15 24	15 30	15 35		15 42		15 50	15 54		16 02	16 05	16 13
	d	15 28		15 31	15 36		15 45		15 58			16 04	16 06	16 15
West Byfleet	d				15 40								16 10	
Byfleet & New Haw	d				15 43								16 13	
Weybridge	d	15 35			15 46			←					16 16	
Walton-on-Thames	d	15 39			15 50 →			15 50					16 20 →	
Hersham	d							15 52						
Esher	d					←		15 55						
Surbiton 6	a	15 45 →				15 45		15 59	16 09					
Wimbledon 6 ⊖	a					15 53		16 07	16 17					
Earlsfield	a							16 11						
Clapham Junction 10	a			15 50		15 59	16 04	16 15	16 23			16 27		16 34
Vauxhall ⊖	a							16 20						
London Waterloo 15 ⊖	a			16 04		16 10	16 14	16 25	16 34			16 37		16 44

		SW 1	SW 1 ◇ ☕	SW 1	SW 1 ◇ ☕	SW	SW 1	SW 1	SW	SW 1 ☕	SW	SW 1	SW 1	SW 1
Basingstoke	d	15 50	16 00		16 05							16 16		
Hook	d											16 23		
Winchfield	d											16 27		
Fleet	d	16 02		←								16 32		
Farnborough (Main)	d	16 08		16 08								16 38		
Alton	d	→						15 45					16 15	
Bentley	d												16c24	
Farnham	a							15 55					16 29	
	d							16 00					16 30	
Aldershot	d							16 06					16 36	16 40
Ash Vale	d							16 11					16 41	16a44
Brookwood	d			16 15				16 18				16 45	16 48	
Guildford	d								16 27	16 35				
Worplesdon	d						←							
Woking	a		16 18	16 20 →	16 23		16 20	16 24	16 35	16 42		16 50	16 54	
	d		16 20		16 25		16 28		16 36	16 45		16 58		
West Byfleet	d								16 40					
Byfleet & New Haw	d								16 43					
Weybridge	d					←	16 35		16 46		←			
Walton-on-Thames	d					16 20	16 39		16 50 →		16 50			
Hersham	d					16 22					16 52			
Esher	d					16 25					16 55			
Surbiton 6	a					16 29	16 45				16 59	17 09		
Wimbledon 6 ⊖	a					16 37	16 53				17 07	17 17		
Earlsfield	a					16 41					17 11			
Clapham Junction 10	a		16 39		16 44	16 45	16 59			17 04	17 15	17 23		
Vauxhall ⊖	a					16 50					17 20			
London Waterloo 15 ⊖	a		16 49		16 58	16 55	17 10			17 14	17 25	17 34		

		SW 1 ◇	SW	SW 1	SW 1	SW 1 ◇ ☕	SW	SW 1	SW 1	SW 1 ◇ ☕	SW	SW 1	SW 1 ☕	SW
Basingstoke	d	16 44			16 50	17 00				17 11				
Hook	d													
Winchfield	d													
Fleet	d				17 02			←						
Farnborough (Main)	d				17 08			17 08						
Alton	d				→				16 45					
Bentley	d													
Farnham	a								16 55					
	d								17 00					
Aldershot	d								17 06					
Ash Vale	d								17 11					
Brookwood	d							17 15	17 18					
Guildford	d		16 57	17 05							17 27		17 35	
Worplesdon	d													
Woking	a	17 02	17 05	17 13		17 18		17 20	17 24	17 30	17 35		17 42	
	d	17 04	17 06	17 15		17 20		17 28		17 31	17 36		17 45	
West Byfleet	d		17 10								17 40			
Byfleet & New Haw	d		17 13								17 43			
Weybridge	d		17 16				←	17 35			17 46			←
Walton-on-Thames	d		17 20 →				17 20	17 39			17 50 →			17 50
Hersham	d						17 22							17 52
Esher	d						17 25					←		17 55
Surbiton 6	a						17 29	17 45 →				17 45		17 59
Wimbledon 6 ⊖	a						17 37					17 53		18 07
Earlsfield	a						17 41							18 11
Clapham Junction 10	a	17 27		17 34		17 39	17 45			17 50		17 59	18 04	18 15
Vauxhall ⊖	a						17 50							18 20
London Waterloo 15 ⊖	a	17 37		17 44		17 49	17 55			18 04		18 10	18 14	18 25

		SW 1	SW 1	SW 1	SW 1 ◇	SW	SW 1	SW 1	SW 1 ◇ ☕	SW 1	SW 1 ◇ ☕	SW	SW 1	SW 1
Basingstoke	d	17 16			17 44			17 50	18 00		18 05			
Hook	d	17 23												
Winchfield	d	17 27												
Fleet	d	17 32						18 02		←				
Farnborough (Main)	d	17 38						18 08		18 08				
Alton	d		17 15					→						17 45
Bentley	d		17e24											
Farnham	a		17 29											17 55
	d		17 30											18 00
Aldershot	d		17 36	17 40										18 06
Ash Vale	d		17 41	17a44										18 11
Brookwood	d	17 45	17 48							18 15				18 18
Guildford	d					17 57	18 05							
Worplesdon	d												←	
Woking	a	17 50	17 54		18 02	18 05	18 13		18 18	18 20 →	18 23		18 20	18 24
	d	17 58			18 04	18 06	18 15		18 20		18 25		18 28	
West Byfleet	d					18 10								
Byfleet & New Haw	d					18 13								
Weybridge	d					18 16						←	18 35	
Walton-on-Thames	d					18 20 →						18 20	18 39	
Hersham	d											18 22		
Esher	d											18 25		
Surbiton 6	a	18 09										18 29	18 45	
Wimbledon 6 ⊖	a	18 17										18 37	18 53	
Earlsfield	a											18 41		
Clapham Junction 10	a	18 23			18 27		18 34		18 39		18 44	18 45	18 59	
Vauxhall ⊖	a											18 50		
London Waterloo 15 ⊖	a	18 34			18 37		18 44		18 49		18 58	18 55	19 10	

For general notes see front of timetable
For details of catering facilities see Directory of Train Operators

b Arr. 1521
c Arr. 1621
e Arr. 1721

Table 155

Sundays

Basingstoke, Alton, Guildford and Woking → Waterloo

Network Diagram - see first page of Table 155

		SW	SW 1 ☕	SW	SW 1	SW 1	SW 1	SW 1 ◇	SW	SW 1	SW 1	SW 1 ◇ ☕	SW	SW 1	SW 1	SW 1 ◇ ☕	SW	SW 1	SW 1 ☕	SW	SW 1	SW 1	SW 1	SW 1 ◇	SW	SW 1	SW 1
Basingstoke	d				18 16			18 44			18 50	19 00				19 11					19 16			19 44			19 50
Hook	d				18 23																19 23						
Winchfield	d				18 27																19 27						
Fleet	d				18 32						19 02			←							19 32						20 02
Farnborough (Main)	d				18 38						19 08			19 08							19 38						20 08
Alton	d					18 15					→				18 45							19 15					→
Bentley	d					18b24																19c24					
Farnham	a					18 29									18 55							19 29					
	d					18 30									19 00							19 30					
Aldershot	d					18 36	18 40								19 06							19 36	19 40				
Ash Vale	d					18 41	18a44								19 11							19 41	19a44				
Brookwood	d				18 45	18 48								19 15	19 18						19 45	19 48					
Guildford	d	18 27	18 35						18 57	19 05							19 27		19 35						19 57	20 05	
Worplesdon	d																										
Woking	a	18 35	18 42		18 50	18 54		19 02	19 05	19 13		19 18		19 20	19 24	19 30	19 35		19 42		19 50	19 54		20 02	20 05	20 13	
	d	18 36	18 45		18 58			19 04	19 06	19 15		19 20		19 28		19 31	19 36		19 45		19 58			20 04	20 06	20 15	
West Byfleet	d	18 40							19 10								19 40								20 10		
Byfleet & New Haw	d	18 43							19 13								19 43								20 13		
Weybridge	d	18 46		←					19 16				←	19 35			19 46			←					20 16		
Walton-on-Thames	d	18 50		18 50					19 20				19 20	19 39			19 50			19 50					20 20		
Hersham	d	→		18 52					→				19 22				→			19 52					→		
Esher	d			18 55									19 25					←		19 55							
Surbiton [6]	a			18 59	19 09								19 29	19 45				19 45		19 59	20 09						
Wimbledon [6] ⊖	a			19 07	19 17								19 37	→				19 53		20 07	20 17						
Earlsfield	a			19 11									19 41							20 11							
Clapham Junction [10]	a		19 04	19 15	19 23			19 27		19 34		19 39	19 45			19 50		19 59	20 04	20 15	20 23			20 27		20 34	
Vauxhall ⊖	a			19 20									19 50							20 20							
London Waterloo [15] ⊖	a		19 14	19 25	19 34			19 37		19 44		19 49	19 55			20 04		20 10	20 14	20 25	20 34			20 37		20 44	

		SW 1 ◇ ☕	SW 1	SW 1 ◇ A ☕	SW	SW 1	SW 1	SW	SW 1	SW	SW 1	SW 1	SW 1	SW 1 ◇	SW	SW 1	SW 1	SW 1 ◇ ☕	SW	SW 1	SW 1	SW 1 ◇ ☕	SW	SW 1	SW 1	SW	
Basingstoke	d	20 00		20 05							20 16			20 44			20 50	21 00				21 11					
Hook	d										20 23																
Winchfield	d										20 27																
Fleet	d		←								20 32						21 02			←							
Farnborough (Main)	d		20 08								20 38						21 08			21 08							
Alton	d						19 45					20 15					→				20 45						
Bentley	d											20e24															
Farnham	a						19 55					20 29									20 55						
	d						20 00					20 30									21 00						
Aldershot	d						20 06					20 36	20 40								21 06						
Ash Vale	d						20 11					20 41	20a44								21 11						
Brookwood	d		20 15				20 18				20 45	20 48								21 15	21 18						
Guildford	d							20 27	20 35						20 57	21 05							21 27		21 35		
Worplesdon	d					←																					
Woking	a	20 18	20 20 →	20 23		20 20	20 24	20 35	20 42		20 50	20 54		21 02	21 05	21 13		21 18		21 20	21 24	21 30	21 35		21 42		
	d	20 20		20 25		20 28		20 36	20 45		20 58			21 04	21 06	21 15		21 20		21 28		21 31	21 36		21 45		
West Byfleet	d							20 40							21 10								21 40				
Byfleet & New Haw	d							20 43							21 13								21 43				
Weybridge	d				←	20 35		20 46		←					21 16				←	21 35			21 46			←	
Walton-on-Thames	d				20 20	20 39		20 50		20 50					21 20				21 20	21 39			21 50			21 50	
Hersham	d				20 22			→		20 52					→				21 22				→			21 52	
Esher	d				20 25					20 55									21 25					←		21 55	
Surbiton [6]	a				20 29	20 45				20 59	21 09								21 29	21 45				21 45		21 59	
Wimbledon [6] ⊖	a				20 37	20 53				21 07	21 17								21 37	→				21 53		22 07	
Earlsfield	a				20 41					21 11									21 41							22 11	
Clapham Junction [10]	a	20 39		20 44	20 45	20 59			21 04	21 15	21 23			21 27		21 34		21 39	21 45			21 50		21 59	22 04	22 15	
Vauxhall ⊖	a				20 50					21 20									21 50							22 20	
London Waterloo [15] ⊖	a	20 49		20 58	20 55	21 10			21 14	21 25	21 34			21 37		21 44		21 49	21 55			22 04		22 10	22 14	22 25	

For general notes see front of timetable
For details of catering facilities see Directory of Train Operators

A From Penzance (Table 135)
b Arr. 1821
c Arr. 1921
e Arr. 2021

Table 155

Sundays

Basingstoke, Alton, Guildford and Woking → Waterloo

Network Diagram - see first page of Table 155

Station		SW 1	SW 1	SW 1	SW 1 ◇	SW	SW 1	SW 1	SW 1 ◇ ☕	SW	SW 1	SW 1	SW	SW 1	SW	SW 1	SW 1	SW 1	SW 1	SW	SW 1	SW	SW 1	SW 1	SW 1	SW 1	SW 1
Basingstoke	d	21 16			21 44			21 50	22 05							22 16			22 44						23 16		23 43
Hook	d	21 23														22 23									23 23		
Winchfield	d	21 27														22 27									23 27		
Fleet	d	21 32						22 02								22 32									23 32		
Farnborough (Main)	d	21 38						22 08								22 38									23 38		
Alton	d		21 15									21 45					22 15						22 45			23 15	
Bentley	d		21b24														22c24									23e24	
Farnham	a		21 29									21 55					22 29						22 55			23 29	
	d		21 30									22 00					22 30						23 00			23 30	
Aldershot	d		21 36	21 40								22 06					22 36	22 40					23 06			23 36	
Ash Vale	d		21 41	21a44								22 11					22 41	22a44					23 11			23 41	
Brookwood	d	21 45	21 48					22 15				22 18				22 45	22 48						23 18		23 45	23 48	
Guildford	d					21 57	22 05						22 27	22 35						22 57	23 05			23 35			
Worplesdon	d										←																
Woking	a	21 50	21 54		22 02	22 05	22 13	22 21 →	22 23		22 21	22 24	22 35	22 42		22 50	22 54		23 02	23 05	23 13		23 24	23 42	23 50	23 54	00 02
	d	21 58			22 04	22 06	22 15		22 25		22 28		22 36	22 45		22 58			23 04	23 06	23 15		23 28	23 45			00 03
West Byfleet	d					22 10							22 40							23 10							
Byfleet & New Haw	d					22 13							22 43							23 13							
Weybridge	d					22 16				←	22 35		22 46		←					23 16		←	23 35				
Walton-on-Thames	d					22 20 →				22 20	22 39		22 50 →		22 50					23 20 →		23 20	23 39				
Hersham	d									22 22					22 52							23 22					
Esher	d									22 25					22 55							23 25					
Surbiton 6	a	22 09								22 29	22 45				22 59	23 09						23 29	23 45				
Wimbledon 6 ⊖ 🚋	a	22 17								22 37	22 53				23 07	23 17						23 37	23 53				
Earlsfield	a									22 41					23 11							23 41					
Clapham Junction 10	a	22 23			22 27		22 34		22 44	22 45	22 59			23 04	23 15	23 23			23 27		23 34	23 45	23 58	00 04			00 22
Vauxhall ⊖	a									22 50					23 20							23 50					
London Waterloo 15 ⊖	a	22 34			22 37		22 44		22 58	22 55	23 11			23 14	23 25	23 34			23 37		23 44	23 55	00 10	00 14			00 33

For general notes see front of timetable
For details of catering facilities see
Directory of Train Operators

b Arr. 2121
c Arr. 2221
e Arr. 2321

London → Guildford, Haslemere and Portsmouth

Network Diagram - see first page of Table 155

Miles			SW	SW	SW	SW	SW	SW	SW	SW	SW	SW	SW	SW	SW	SW	SW	SW	SW	SW	SW	SW	SW	SW	SW	SW
			MO	MO	MO	MX	MX	MX	MX																	
			1	1	1	1	1	1	1	1	1	1	1	1	1	1	1	1	1	1	1	1	1	1	1	1
																☕						☕		☕		
0	London Waterloo 15 ⊖	d	22p30	23p00	23p30	22p30	22p45	23p15	23p45		05 00	05 20	06 15	06 45	07 15	07 30		07 45	08 00		08 15	08 30	08 45	09 00		09 15
4	Clapham Junction 10	d	22b39	23b09	23b39		22b52	23b22	23b52		05 09	05 29	06u22	06u52	07u22			07u52			08u22		08u52			09u22
24¼	Woking	a	23p01	23p31	00 01	22p54	23p11	23p41	00 11		05 50	06 08	06 41	07 11	07 42	07 55		08 12	08 24		08 42	08 55	09 11	09 24		09 42
—		d	23p02	23p32	00 02	22p55	23p13	23p43	00 13		05 51	06 13	06 43	07 13	07 44	07 55		08 14	08 25		08 44	08 55	09 13	09 25		09 43
26¾	Worplesdon	d					23p18		00 18			06 18	06 48	07 18	07 49			08 19			08 49		09 18			
30¼	Guildford	a	23p10	23p40	00 10	23p03	23p24	23p51	00 24		05 59	06 23	06 53	07 23	07 54	08 04		08 24	08 35		08 54	09 04	09 23	09 33		09 52
—		d	23p12	23p46	00 12	23p05	23p25	23p52	00 25	05 15	06 00	06 25	06 55	07 25	07 56	08 04		08 26	08 39		08 56	09 04	09 25	09 34		09 54
33½	Farncombe	d		23p53		23p11	23p31	23p58	00 31		06 06	06 31	07 01	07 31	08 02			08 32			09 02		09 31			10 00
34½	Godalming	d		23p56		23p14	23p34	00 01	00 34		06 09	06 34	07 04	07 34	08 05			08 35			09 05		09 34			10 03
36¼	Milford (Surrey)	d		00 01			23p38		00s38		06 13	06 38	07 08	07 38	08 09			08 39			09 09					10 07
38½	Witley	d		00 04			23p43		00s43		06 18	06 42	07 12	07 42	08 13			08 43			09 13					10 11
43	Haslemere 4	a	23p26	00 11	00 26	23p24	23p49	00 12	00 49	05 29	06 24	06 49	07 19	07 49	08 20	08 24	←	08 50	08 54	←	09 20	09 24	09 45	09 49	←	10 19
—		d	23p27	00 12	00 27	23p25	23p50	00 13	00 50	05 30	06 25	06 55	07 20	07 55	08 30	08 25	08 30	09 00	08 55	09 00		09 25	09 55	09 50	09 55	
46¾	Liphook	d		00 17			23p55		00s55	05 35	06 30	07 00	07 25	08 00	→		08 35	→		09 05			→		10 00	
51½	Liss	d		00 23			00 01		01s01	05 41	06 36	07 06	07 31	08 06			08 41			09 11					10 06	
55	Petersfield	d	23p38	00 28	00 38	23p36	00 06	00 24	01 06	05 46	06 41	07 11	07 36	08 11		08 36	08 46		09 06	09 16		09 36		10 01	10 11	
63¼	Rowlands Castle	d		00 38			00 16		01s16	05 56	06 51	07 21	07 46	08 21			08 56			09 26					10 21	
66½	Havant	a	23p50	00 44	00 50	23p48	00 21	00 36	01 21	06 01	06 57	07 27	07 51	08 26		08 49	09 04		09 18	09 34		09 49		10 14	10 26	
66½		d	23p51	00 45	00 51	23p49	00 22	00 37	01 22	06 02	06 58	07 28	07 52	08 27		08 50	09 05		09 19	09 35		09 50		10 15	10 27	
67¼	Bedhampton	a		00 47			00 24		01s24	06 04	07 00	07 30	07 54	08 29			09 07			09 37					10 29	
70½	Hilsea	a					00 30		01s30	06 10	07 07	07 37	08 00	08 36			09 13			09 44					10 35	
72¾	Fratton	a	23p59	00 55	01 00	23p58	00 34	00 46	01s34	06 14	07 11	07 41	08 04	08 40		08 58	09 17		09 28	09 48		09 58		10 23	10 39	
73¾	Portsmouth & Southsea	a	00 04	00 59	01 04	00 02	00 38	00 50	01 38	06 18	07 16	07 46	08 07	08 43		09 02	09 20		09 32	09 52		10 02		10 27	10 43	
74½	Portsmouth Harbour	a	00 09	01 04	01 09	00 07		00 55		06 22	07 20		08 12	08 48		09 07	09 26		09 37	09 57		10 07		10 32	10 48	

		SW	SW	SW	SW	SW	SW	SW	SW	SW	SW		SW	SW	SW	SW	SW	SW	SW	SW	SW	SW	SW	SW	SW	SW
		1	1	1	1	1	1	1	1	1	1		1	1	1	1	1	1	1	1	1	1	1	1	1	1
		☕		☕			☕		☕				☕		☕			☕		☕			☕		☕	
London Waterloo 15 ⊖	d	09 30	09 45	10 00		10 15	10 30	10 45	11 00		11 15		11 30	11 45	12 00		12 15	12 30	12 45	13 00		13 15	13 30	13 45	14 00	
Clapham Junction 10	d		09u52			10u22		10u52			11u22			11u52			12u22		12u52			13u22		13u52		
Woking	a	09 54	10 11	10 24		10 41	10 54	11 11	11 24		11 41		11 54	12 11	12 24		12 41	12 54	13 11	13 24		13 41	13 54	14 11	14 24	
	d	09 55	10 13	10 25		10 43	10 55	11 13	11 25		11 43		11 55	12 13	12 25		12 43	12 55	13 13	13 25		13 43	13 55	14 13	14 25	
Worplesdon	d		10 18					11 18						12 18					13 18					14 18		
Guildford	a	10 03	10 23	10 33		10 50	11 03	11 23	11 33		11 50		12 03	12 23	12 33		12 50	13 03	13 23	13 33		13 50	14 03	14 23	14 33	
	d	10 04	10 25	10 34		10 52	11 04	11 25	11 34		11 52		12 04	12 25	12 34		12 52	13 04	13 25	13 34		13 52	14 04	14 25	14 34	
Farncombe	d		10 31			10 58		11 31			11 58			12 31			12 58		13 31			13 58		14 31		
Godalming	d		10 34			11 01		11 34			12 01			12 34			13 01		13 34			14 01		14 34		
Milford (Surrey)	d					11 05					12 05						13 05					14 05				
Witley	d					11 09					12 09						13 09					14 09				
Haslemere 4	a	10 22	10 45	10 49	←	11 16	11 20	11 45	11 49	←	12 16		12 20	12 45	12 49	←	13 16	13 20	13 45	13 49	←	14 16	14 20	14 45	14 49	←
	d	10 23	10 55	10 50	10 55		11 21	11 55	11 50	11 55			12 21	12 55	12 50	12 55		13 21	13 55	13 50	13 55		14 21	14 55	14 50	14 55
Liphook	d		→		11 00			→		12 00				→		13 00			→		14 00			→		15 00
Liss	d				11 06					12 06						13 06					14 06					15 06
Petersfield	d	10 34		11 01	11 11		11 32		12 01	12 11			12 32		13 01	13 11		13 32		14 01	14 11		14 32		15 01	15 11
Rowlands Castle	d				11 21					12 21						13 21					14 21					15 21
Havant	a	10 48		11 14	11 26		11 49		12 14	12 26			12 49		13 14	13 26		13 49		14 14	14 26		14 49		15 15	15 26
	d	10 50		11 15	11 27		11 50		12 15	12 27			12 50		13 15	13 27		13 50		14 15	14 27		14 50		15 15	15 27
Bedhampton	a				11 29					12 29						13 29					14 29					15 29
Hilsea	a				11 35					12 35						13 35					14 35					15 35
Fratton	a	10 58		11 23	11 39		11 58		12 23	12 39			12 58		13 23	13 39		13 58		14 23	14 39		14 58		15 24	15 39
Portsmouth & Southsea	a	11 02		11 27	11 43		12 02		12 27	12 43			13 02		13 27	13 43		14 03		14 27	14 51		15 02		15 28	15 43
Portsmouth Harbour	a	11 07		11 32			12 07		12 32				13 07		13 32	13 48		14 07		14 32	14 57		15 07		15 32	15 48

		SW	SW	SW	SW	SW	SW	SW	SW	SW	SW	SW	SW	SW	SW	SW	SW	SW	SW	SW	SW	SW	SW	SW	SW	SW
		1	1	1	1	1	1	1	1	1	1	1	1	1	1	1	1	1	1	1	1	1	1	1	1	1
			☕		☕			☕			☕			☕			☕			☕			☕			
London Waterloo 15 ⊖	d	14 15	14 30	14 45	15 00		15 15	15 30		15 45	16 00		16 15	16 30		16 45	17 00		17 15	17 30		17 45	18 00		18 15	18 18
Clapham Junction 10	d	14u22		14u52			15u22			15u52			16u22			16u52										
Woking	a	14 41	14 54	15 11	15 23		15 41	15 54		16 11	16 24		16 41	16 54		17 11	17 24		17 38	17 54						18 42
	d	14 43	14 55	15 13	15 25		15 43	15 55		16 13	16 25		16 43	16 55		17 13	17 25		17 40	17 56						18 43
Worplesdon	d			15 18			15 48						16 48				17 30		17 45	18 00						18 48
Guildford	a	14 50	15 03	15 23	15 32		15 53	16 03		16 20	16 33		16 53	17 03		17 20	17 36		17 51	18 06		18 21	18 31		18 50	18 54
	d	14 52	15 04	15 25	15 34		15 55	16 04		16 22	16 34		16 55	17 04		17 22	17 37		17 54	18 08		18 23	18 33		18 51	18 57
Farncombe	d	14 58		15 31			16 01			16 28			17 01			17 28			18 00			18 29				19 03
Godalming	d	15 01		15 34			16 04			16 31			17 04			17 31			18 03	18 15		18 32	18 39			19 06
Milford (Surrey)	d	15 05					16 08			16 35			17 08			17 35			18 07			18 36				19 10
Witley	d	15 09					16 12			16 39			17 12			17 39			18 11			18 40				19 14
Haslemere 4	a	15 16	15 20	15 45	15 49	←	16 19	16 23	←	16 46	16 50	←	17 19	17 23	←	17 46	17 51	←	18 18	18 25	←	18 49	18 51	←	19 05	19 23
	d		15 21	15 55	15 50	15 55	16 29	16 24	16 29	16 55	16 51	16 55	17 29	17 24	17 29	17 56	17 52	17 56	18 31	18 26	18 31	18 56	18 52	18 56	19 06	
Liphook	d			→		16 00	→		16 34	→		17 00	→		17 34	→		18 01	→		18 36	→		19 01	19 11	
Liss	d					16 06			16 40			17 06			17 40			18 07			18 42			19 07	19 17	
Petersfield	d		15 32		16 01	16 11		16 35	16 45		17 02	17 11		17 35	17 45		18 03	18 12		18 37	18 47		19 03	19 12	19 23	
Rowlands Castle	d					16 21			16 55			17 21			17 55			18 22			18 57			19 22	19 32	
Havant	a		15 49		16 14	16 26		16 49	17 03		17 15	17 26		17 48	18 03		18 18	18 29		18 50	19 03		19 16	19 29	19 41	
	d		15 50		16 15	16 27		16 50	17 04		17 16	17 27		17 49	18 04		18 19	18 30		18 51	19 04		19 17		19 42	
Bedhampton	a					16 29			17 06			17 29			18 07			18 32			19 07				19 44	
Hilsea	a					16 35			17 11			17 35			18 12			18 38			19 12				19 50	
Fratton	a		15 58		16 23	16 37		16 58	17 15		17 24	17 39		17 58	18 16		18 28	18 42		18 59	19 16		19 25		19 56	
Portsmouth & Southsea	a		16 02		16 27	16 45		17 02	17 22		17 28	17 43		18 02	18 20		18 32	18 46		19 03			19 29			
Portsmouth Harbour	a		16 07		16 32	16 54		17 07	17 27		17 35			18 09	18 28		18 39			19 10			19 36			

For general notes see front of timetable
For details of catering facilities see
Directory of Train Operators

b Previous night.
Stops to pick up only

Table 156

Mondays to Fridays

London → Guildford, Haslemere and Portsmouth

Network Diagram - see first page of Table 155

Station		SW 1 ☕	SW 1	SW 1 ☕	SW 1	SW 1	SW 1 ☕	SW 1	SW 1	SW 1 ☕	SW 1	SW 1	SW 1 ☕	SW 1	SW 1 ☕	SW 1	SW 1 ☕	SW 1	SW 1 ☕	SW 1	SW 1	SW 1	SW 1	SW 1		
London Waterloo 15 ⊖	d	18 30	18 45	19 00		19 15	19 30		19 45	20 00		20 15	20 30	20 45	21 00		21 30	21 45	22 00		22 30	22 45	23 15	23 45		
Clapham Junction 10	d					19u22			19u52			20u22		20u52				21u52				22u52	23u22	23u52		
Woking	a	18 57	19 13	19 24		19 43	19 54		20 11	20 25		20 41	20 54	21 11	21 24		21 54	22 11	22 24		22 54	23 11	23 41	00 11		
	d	18 58	19 14	19 25		19 45	19 55		20 13	20 25		20 43	20 55	21 13	21 25		21 55	22 13	22 25		22 55	23 13	23 43	00 13		
Worplesdon	d			19 30					20 18					21 18				22 18				23 18		00 18		
Guildford	a	19 06	19 23	19 36		19 52	20 03		20 23	20 34		20 50	21 03	21 23	21 33		22 03	22 23	22 33		23 03	23 24	23 51	00 24		
	d	19 08	19 24	19 37		19 54	20 04		20 25	20 34		20 52	21 04	21 25	21 34		22 04	22 25	22 34		23 05	23 25	23 52	00 25		
Farncombe	d		19 30			20 00			20 31	20 41		20 58		21 31	21 40		22 10	22 31	22 40		23 11	23 31	23 58	00 31		
Godalming	d	19 14	19 33			20 03	20 11		20 34	20 44		21 01	21 11	21 34	21 43		22 13	22 34	22 43		23 14	23 34	00 01	00 34		
Milford (Surrey)	d		19 37			20 07			20 38			21 05		21 38				22 38				23 38		00s38		
Witley	d		19 41			20 11			20 42			21 09		21 42				22 42				23 43		00s43		
Haslemere 4	a	19 25	19 49	19 52	←	20 18	20 22	←	20 49	20 55	←	21 16	21 21	21 49	21 54	←	22 24	22 49	22 54	←	23 24	23 49	00 12	00 49		
	d	19 26	19 57 →	19 53	19 57	20 27 →	20 22	20 27	20 59 →	20 55	20 59		21 22	21 59 →	21 55	21 59	22 25	22 59 →	22 55	22 59	23 25	23 50	00 13	00 50		
Liphook	d				20 02			20 32			21 04					22 04				23 04		23 55		00s55		
Liss	d				20 08			20 38			21 10					22 10				23 10		00 01		01s01		
Petersfield	d	19 37		20 04	20 13		20 33	20 43		21 06	21 16		21 33		22 06	22 16	22 36		23 06	23 16	23 36	00 06	00 24	01 06		
Rowlands Castle	d				20 23			20 53			21 25					22 25				23 25		00 16		01s16		
Havant	a	19 50		20 18	20 28		20 48	21 00		21 19	21 30		21 46		22 18	22 30	22 48		23 18	23 30	23 48	00 21	00 36	01 21		
	d	19 51		20 19	20 29		20 49			21 20	21 31		21 46		22 19	22 31	22 49		23 19	23 31	23 49	00 22	00 37	01 22		
Bedhampton	a				20 31						21 34					22 34				23 33		00 24		01s24		
Hilsea	a				20 41						21 40					22 39				23 39		00 30		01s30		
Fratton	a	19 59		20 27	20 45		20 58			21 29	21 44		21 55		22 28	22 43	22 58		23 28	23 43	23 58	00 34	00 46	01s34		
Portsmouth & Southsea	a	20 03		20 31	20 48		21 02			21 33	21 47		21 58		22 32	22 47	23 03		23 32	23 46	00 02	00 38	00 50	01 38		
Portsmouth Harbour	a	20 10		20 36	20 56		21 07			21 38			22 02		22 38		23 08		23 37		00 07		00 55			

Saturdays

Station		SW 1	SW 1	SW 1	SW 1		SW 1	SW 1	SW 1	SW 1		SW 1		SW 1	SW 1	SW 1	SW 1	SW 1			SW 1 ☕	SW 1	SW 1 ☕	SW 1	SW 1
London Waterloo 15 ⊖	d	22p45	23p15	23p45			05 00	05 20	06 15	06 45		07 15		07 30	07 45	08 00		08 15			18 30	18 45	19 00		19 15
Clapham Junction 10	d	22b52	23b22	23b52			05 09	05 29	06u22	06u52		07u22			07u52			08u22				18u52			19u22
Woking	a	23p11	23p41	00 11			05 50	06 08	06 41	07 11		07 41		07 54	08 11	08 24		08 41			18 54	19 11	19 24		19 41
	d	23p13	23p43	00 13			05 51	06 13	06 43	07 13		07 43		07 55	08 13	08 25		08 43			18 55	19 13	19 25		19 43
Worplesdon	d	23p18		00 18				06 18		07 18					08 18							19 18			
Guildford	a	23p24	23p51	00 24			05 59	06 23	06 50	07 23		07 50		08 03	08 23	08 33		08 50	and at		19 03	19 23	19 33		19 50
	d	23p25	23p52	00 25	05 15		06 00	06 25	06 52	07 25		07 52		08 04	08 25	08 34		08 52	the same		19 04	19 25	19 34		19 52
Farncombe	d	23p31	23p58	00 31			06 06	06 31	06 58	07 31		07 58			08 31			08 58				19 31			19 58
Godalming	d	23p34	00 01	00 34			06 09	06 34	07 01	07 34		08 01			08 34			09 01	minutes			19 34			20 01
Milford (Surrey)	d	23p38		00s38			06 13		07 05			08 05						09 05							20 05
Witley	d	23p43		00s43			06 18		07 09			08 09						09 09	past						20 09
Haslemere 4	a	23p49	00 12	00 49	05 29		06 25	06 44	07 16	07 44		08 16		08 20	08 45	08 49	←	09 16			19 20	19 45	19 49	←	20 16
	d	23p50	00 13	00 50	05 29			06 45		07 45				08 21	08 55 →	08 50	08 55		each		19 21	19 55 →	19 50	19 55	
Liphook	d	23p55		00s55	05 34			06 50		07 50							09 00							20 00	
Liss	d	00 01		01s01	05 40			06 56		07 56							09 06		hour until					20 06	
Petersfield	d	00 06	00 24	01 06	05 46			07 01		08 01				08 32		09 01	09 11				19 32		20 01	20 11	
Rowlands Castle	d	00 16		01s16	05 55			07 11		08 11							09 21							20 21	
Havant	a	00 21	00 36	01 21	06 00			07 16		08 16				08 48		09 14	09 26				19 48		20 14	20 28	
	d	00 22	00 37	01 22	06 01			07 17		08 17				08 49		09 15	09 27				19 49		20 15	20 29	
Bedhampton	a	00 24		01s24	06 03			07 19		08 19							09 29							20 31	
Hilsea	a	00 30		01s30	06 09			07 25		08 25							09 35							20 39	
Fratton	a	00 34	00 46	01s34	06 13			07 29		08 29				08 58		09 23	09 39				19 58		20 23	20 43	
Portsmouth & Southsea	a	00 38	00 50	01 38	06 21			07 32		08 32				09 02		09 27	09 43				20 02		20 27	20 47	
Portsmouth Harbour	a		00 55		06 26			07 37		08 37				09 07		09 32					20 07		20 32		

Station		SW 1 ☕		SW 1	SW 1	SW 1	SW 1		SW 1	SW 1	SW 1	SW 1		SW 1	SW 1	SW 1	SW 1		SW 1	SW 1	SW 1	SW 1				
London Waterloo 15 ⊖	d	19 30		19 45	20 00		20 15		20 30	20 45	21 00			21 30	21 45	22 00			22 30	22 45	23 15	23 45				
Clapham Junction 10	d			19u52			20u22			20u52					21u52					22u52	23u22	23u52				
Woking	a	19 54		20 11	20 24		20 41		20 54	21 11	21 24			21 54	22 11	22 24			22 54	23 11	23 41	00 12				
	d	19 55		20 13	20 25		20 43		20 55	21 13	21 25			21 55	22 13	22 25			22 55	23 13	23 43	00 13				
Worplesdon	d			20 18						21 18					22 18					23 18		00 18				
Guildford	a	20 03		20 23	20 33		20 50		21 03	21 23	21 33			22 03	22 23	22 33			23 03	23 24	23 51	00 23				
	d	20 04		20 25	20 34		20 52		21 04	21 25	21 34			22 04	22 25	22 34			23 05	23 25	23 52	00 25				
Farncombe	d			20 31			20 58			21 31	21 40			22 10	22 31	22 40			23 11	23 31	23 58	00 31				
Godalming	d			20 34			21 01			21 34	21 43			22 13	22 34	22 43			23 14	23 34	00 01	00 34				
Milford (Surrey)	d						21 05			21 38					22 38					23 38		00s38				
Witley	d						21 09			21 42					22 42					23 43		00s43				
Haslemere 4	a	20 20		20 45	20 49	←	21 16		21 20	21 49	21 54	←		22 24	22 49	22 54	←		23 24	23 49	00 12	00 49				
	d	20 21		20 55 →	20 50	20 55			21 21	21 59 →	21 55	21 59		22 25	22 59 →	22 55	22 59		23 25	23 50	00 13	00 50				
Liphook	d					21 00						22 04					23 04			23 55		00s55				
Liss	d					21 06						22 10					23 10			00 01		01s01				
Petersfield	d	20 32			21 01	21 11			21 32		22 06	22 16		22 36		23 06	23 16		23 36	00 06	00 24	01 06				
Rowlands Castle	d					21 21						22 25					23 25			00 16		01s16				
Havant	a	20 48			21 14	21 26			21 45		22 18	22 30		22 48		23 18	23 30		23 48	00 21	00 36	01 21				
	d	20 49			21 15	21 27			21 46		22 19	22 31		22 49		23 19	23 31		23 49	00 22	00 37	01 22				
Bedhampton	a					21 29						22 34					23 34			00 24		01s24				
Hilsea	a					21 35						22 39					23 39			00 30		01s30				
Fratton	a	20 58			21 23	21 39			21 54		22 28	22 43		22 58		23 28	23 43		23 58	00 34	00 46	01s34				
Portsmouth & Southsea	a	21 02			21 27	21 43			21 58		22 32	22 47		23 02		23 32	23 48		00 02	00 38	00 50	01 38				
Portsmouth Harbour	a	21 07			21 32				22 03		22 36	22 52		23 07		23 37	23 54		00 07		00 55					

For general notes see front of timetable
For details of catering facilities see
Directory of Train Operators

b Previous night.
Stops to pick up only

Table 156

Sundays

London → Guildford, Haslemere and Portsmouth

Network Diagram - see first page of Table 155

		SW 1	SW 1	SW 1	SW 1	SW 1	SW 1	SW 1	SW 1	SW 1	SW 1
London Waterloo 15 ⊖	d	22p45	23p15	23p45	.	08 00	08 30	09 00	09 30	10 00	10 30
Clapham Junction 10	d	22b52	23b22	23b52	.	08u09	08u39	09u09	09u39	10u09	10u39
Woking	a	23p11	23p41	00 12	.	08 34	09 03	09 34	10 03	10 31	11 01
	d	23p13	23p43	00 13	07 32	08 35	09 04	09 35	10 04	10 32	11 02
Worplesdon	d	23p18	.	00 18	.	.	.	.	.	.	.
Guildford	a	23p24	23p51	00 23	07 40	08 43	09 12	09 43	10 12	10 40	11 10
	d	23p25	23p52	00 25	07 46	08 46	09 14	09 46	10 14	10 46	11 12
Farncombe	d	23p31	23p58	00 31	07 53	08 53	.	09 53	.	10 53	.
Godalming	d	23p34	00 01	00 34	07 56	08 56	.	09 56	.	10 56	.
Milford (Surrey)	d	23p38	.	00s38	08 00	09 00	.	10 00	.	11 00	.
Witley	d	23p43	.	00s43	08 04	09 04	.	10 04	.	11 04	.
Haslemere 4	a	23p49	00 12	00 49	08 11	09 11	09 28	10 11	10 28	11 11	11 26
	d	23p50	00 13	00 50	08 12	09 12	09 29	10 12	10 29	11 12	11 27
Liphook	d	23p55	.	00s55	08 17	09 17	.	10 17	.	11 17	.
Liss	d	00 01	.	01s01	08 23	09 23	.	10 23	.	11 23	.
Petersfield	d	00 06	00 24	01 06	08 28	09 28	09 40	10 28	10 40	11 28	11 38
Rowlands Castle	d	00 16	.	01s16	08 38	09 38	.	10 38	.	11 38	.
Havant	a	00 21	00 36	01 21	08 44	09 44	09 50	10 44	10 52	11 44	11 50
	d	00 22	00 37	01 22	08 45	09 45	09 52	10 45	10 53	11 45	11 51
Bedhampton	a	00 24	.	01s24	08 47	09 47	.	10 47	.	11 47	.
Hilsea	a	00 30	.	01s30	.	.	.	.	.	.	.
Fratton	a	00 34	00 46	01s34	08 55	09 55	10 01	10 55	11 01	11 55	12 00
Portsmouth & Southsea	a	00 38	00 50	01 38	08 59	09 59	10 05	10 59	11 05	11 59	12 04
Portsmouth Harbour	a	.	00 55	.	09 04	10 04	10 11	11 04	11 11	12 04	12 11

		SW 1	SW 1 ☕		SW 1	SW 1 ☕	SW 1	SW 1 ☕	SW 1	SW 1	SW 1	SW 1	SW 1	SW 1
London Waterloo 15 ⊖	d	11 00	11 30		19 00	19 30	20 00	20 30	21 00	21 30	22 00	22 30	23 00	23 30
Clapham Junction 10	d	11u09	11u39		19u09	19u39	20u09	20u39	21u09	21u39	22u09	22u39	23u09	23u39
Woking	a	11 31	12 01		19 31	20 01	20 31	21 01	21 31	22 01	22 31	23 01	23 31	00 01
	d	11 32	12 02		19 32	20 02	20 32	21 02	21 32	22 02	22 32	23 02	23 32	00 02
Worplesdon	d	.	.		.	.	.	.	.	.	.	.	.	.
Guildford	a	11 40	12 10	and at	19 40	20 10	20 40	21 10	21 40	22 10	22 40	23 10	23 40	00 10
	d	11 46	12 12	the same	19 46	20 12	20 46	21 12	21 46	22 12	22 46	23 12	23 46	00 12
Farncombe	d	11 53	.		19 53	.	20 53	.	21 53	.	22 53	.	23 53	.
Godalming	d	11 56	.	minutes	19 56	.	20 56	.	21 56	.	22 56	.	23 56	.
Milford (Surrey)	d	12 00	.		20 00	.	21 00	.	22 00	.	23 00	.	00 01	.
Witley	d	12 04	.	past	20 04	.	21 04	.	22 04	.	23 04	.	00 04	.
Haslemere 4	a	12 11	12 26		20 11	20 26	21 11	21 26	22 11	22 26	23 11	23 26	00 11	00 26
	d	12 12	12 27	each	20 12	20 27	21 12	21 27	22 12	22 27	23 12	23 27	00 12	00 27
Liphook	d	12 17	.		20 17	.	21 17	.	22 17	.	23 17	.	00 17	.
Liss	d	12 23	.	hour until	20 23	.	21 23	.	22 23	.	23 23	.	00 23	.
Petersfield	d	12 28	12 38		20 28	20 38	21 28	21 38	22 28	22 38	23 28	23 38	00 28	00 38
Rowlands Castle	d	12 38	.		20 38	.	21 38	.	22 38	.	23 38	.	00 38	.
Havant	a	12 44	12 50		20 44	20 50	21 44	21 50	22 44	22 50	23 44	23 50	00 44	00 50
	d	12 45	12 51		20 45	20 51	21 45	21 51	22 45	22 51	23 45	23 51	00 45	00 51
Bedhampton	a	12 47	.		20 47	.	21 47	.	22 47	.	23 47	.	00 47	.
Hilsea	a	.	.		.	.	.	.	.	.	.	.	.	.
Fratton	a	12 55	13 00		20 55	21 00	21 55	22 00	22 55	23 00	23 55	23 59	00 55	01 00
Portsmouth & Southsea	a	12 59	13 04		20 59	21 04	21 59	22 04	22 59	23 04	23 59	00 04	00 59	01 04
Portsmouth Harbour	a	13 04	13 11		21 04	21 09	22 04	22 11	23 04	23 09	00 04	00 09	01 04	01 09

For general notes see front of timetable
For details of catering facilities see
Directory of Train Operators

b Previous night.
Stops to pick up only

Table 156

Mondays to Fridays

Portsmouth, Haslemere and Guildford → London

Network diagram - see first page of Table 155

Miles			SW	SW	SW	SW	SW	SW	SW	SW	SW	SW	SW	SW	SW	SW	SW	SW	SW	SW	SW	SW	SW	SW	SW	SW
			MO	MO	MX	MX																				
			1	1	1	1	1	1	1	1	1	1	1	1	1	1	1	1	1	1	1	1	1	1	1	1
									☕			☕			☕			☕			☕		☕		☕	
0	**Portsmouth Harbour**	d	22p32	22p48	22p17	23p18	04 30		05 19		05 50	06 15			06 42		06 55	07 13		07 29	07 45		08 13		08 45	
$\frac{3}{4}$	**Portsmouth & Southsea**	d	22p37	22p53	22p24	23p24	04 35		05 24		05 55	06 20			06 47		07 00	07 18		07 33	07 50		08 18	08 24	08 50	
$1\frac{3}{4}$	Fratton	d	22p41	22p57	22p28	23p28	04 39		05 28		05 59	06 24			06 51		07 04	07 22		07 37	07 54		08 22	08 28	08 54	
4	Hilsea	d			22p32	23p32	04 43		05 32		06 03			06 42			07 08			07 41				08 32		
$7\frac{1}{4}$	Bedhampton	d		23p04	22p37	23p37	04 48		05 37		06 08			06 47			07 13			07 49				08 37		
8	**Havant**	a	22p49	23p07	22p39	23p39	04 50		05 40		06 10	06 33		06 49	06 59		07 15	07 30		07 51	08 02		08 30	08 40	09 03	
—		d	22p50	23p07	22p40	23p40	04 51		05 41		06 11	06 34		06 50	07 00	07 11	07 16	07 32		07 52	08 03		08 33	08 40	09 04	
$11\frac{1}{4}$	Rowlands Castle	d		23p13	22p46	23p46	04 57		05 46		06 16			06 56			07 22			07 58				08 46		
$19\frac{1}{2}$	Petersfield	d	23p04	23p24	22p57	23p57	05 08		05 57		06 29	06 48		07 07	07 14	07 25	07 33	07 46		08 09	08 17		08 47	08 57	09 18	
23	Liss	d		23p29	23p02	00 02	05 13		06 02		06 34			07 12	07 20		07 38			08 14				09 02		
$27\frac{3}{4}$	Liphook	d		23p36	23p09	00 09	05 20		06 09		06 41			07 19	07 27		07 45			08 21				09 09		
$31\frac{1}{2}$	**Haslemere** 4	a	23p16	23p41	23p15	00 15	05 25		06 15		06 46	07 01		07 25	07 33	07 38	07 51	07 59	←	08 27	08 31	←	09 00	09 15	09 31	
—		d	23p17	23p42	23p15	00 15	05 26	06 00	06 16	06 32	06 47	07 02	07 10	07 26	07 35	07 40	08 07	08 00	08 07	08 39	08 32	08 39	09 02	09 15	09 32	09 39
36	Witley	d		23p48	23p21	00 21	05 32	06 06		06 38			07 16			07 46	→		08 13	→		08 45				09 45
$38\frac{1}{4}$	Milford (Surrey)	d		23p52	23p25	00 25	05 36	06 11		06 42			07 21			07 50			08 17			08 49				09 49
40	Godalming	d		23p56	23p29	00 29	05 40	06 15		06 46	06 57		07 25	07 35	07 45	07 54			08 21			08 53		09 25		09 53
41	Farncombe	d		23p59	23p32	00 32	05 43	06 18		06 49	07 00		07 28	07 38		07 57			08 25			08 57		09 28		09 56
$44\frac{1}{4}$	**Guildford**	a	23p31	00 04	23p37	00 37	05 48	06 23	06 29	06 54	07 05	07 15	07 32	07 43	07 52	08 02		08 13	08 30		08 47	09 02	09 15	09 32	09 45	10 01
—		d	23p35	00 05	23p39		05 50	06 24	06 31	06 55	07 07	07 17	07 32	07 45	07 54	08 03		08 15	08 31		08 54	09 03	09 17	09 32	09 47	10 02
$47\frac{3}{4}$	Worplesdon	d			23p44		05 55	06 30		07 01			07 40	07 50				08 20	08 37					09 40		
$50\frac{1}{2}$	**Woking**	a	23p42	00 13	23p49		06 00	06 35	06 39	07 05	07 15	07 25		07 54		08 11		08 26	08 41			09 11	09 27	09 44	09 59	10 11
—		d	23p45		23p56		06 01	06 37	06 41	07 07	07 17	07 26		07 56		08 12		08 27	08 43			09 13	09 28	09 46	09 59	10 12
$70\frac{1}{2}$	Clapham Junction 10	a	00 04		00 20		06 20	06 58	07 02	07 26									09 03			09 32		10 05		10 31
$74\frac{1}{2}$	**London Waterloo** 15	⊖ a	00 14		00 29		06 29	07 08	07 12	07 37	07 44	07 54	08 11	08 24	08 32	08 41		08 55	09 13		09 31	09 43	09 55	10 13	10 27	10 40

		SW	SW	SW	SW	SW	SW	SW	SW	SW	SW	SW	SW	SW	SW	SW	SW	SW	SW	SW	SW	SW	SW	SW	SW	SW
		1	1	1	1	1	1	1	1	1	1	1	1	1	1	1	1	1	1	1	1	1	1	1	1	1
		☕		☕		☕		☕		☕		☕		☕		☕		☕		☕		☕		☕		☕
Portsmouth Harbour	d	09 15	09 17	09 45		10 15	10 17	10 45		11 15	11 17	11 45		12 15	12 17	12 45		13 15		13 45		14 15	14 17	14 45		15 15
Portsmouth & Southsea	d	09 20	09 24	09 50		10 20	10 24	10 50		11 20	11 24	11 50		12 20	12 24	12 50		13 20	13 24	13 50		14 20	14 24	14 50		15 20
Fratton	d	09 24	09 28	09 54		10 24	10 28	10 54		11 24	11 28	11 54		12 24	12 28	12 54		13 24	13 28	13 54		14 24	14 28	14 54		15 24
Hilsea	d		09 32				10 32				11 32				12 32				13 32				14 32			
Bedhampton	d		09 37				10 37				11 37				12 37				13 37				14 37			
Havant	a	09 33	09 39	10 03		10 33	10 39	11 03		11 33	11 39	12 03		12 33	12 39	13 03		13 33	13 39	14 03		14 33	14 39	15 03		15 33
	d	09 34	09 40	10 04		10 34	10 40	11 04		11 34	11 40	12 04		12 34	12 40	13 04		13 34	13 40	14 04		14 34	14 40	15 04		15 34
Rowlands Castle	d		09 46				10 46				11 46				12 46				13 46				14 46			
Petersfield	d	09 48	09 57	10 18		10 48	10 57	11 18		11 48	11 57	12 18		12 48	12 57	13 18		13 48	13 57	14 18		14 48	14 57	15 18		15 48
Liss	d		10 02				11 02				12 02				13 02				14 02				15 02			
Liphook	d		10 09				11 09				12 09				13 09				14 09				15 09			
Haslemere 4	a	10 01	10 15	10 31		11 01	11 15	11 31		12 01	12 15	12 31		13 01	13 15	13 31		14 01	14 15	14 31		15 01	15 15	15 31		16 01
	d	10 02	10 15	10 32	10 39	11 02	11 15	11 32	11 39	12 02	12 15	12 32	12 39	13 02	13 15	13 32	13 39	14 02	14 15	14 32	14 39	15 02	15 15	15 32	15 37	16 02
Witley	d				10 45				11 45				12 45				13 45				14 45				15 43	
Milford (Surrey)	d				10 49				11 49				12 49				13 49				14 49				15 47	
Godalming	d		10 25		10 53		11 25		11 53		12 25		12 53		13 25		13 53		14 25		14 53		15 25		15 51	
Farncombe	d		10 28		10 56		11 28		11 56		12 28		12 56		13 28		13 56		14 28		14 56		15 28		15 54	
Guildford	a	10 15	10 32	10 48	11 01	11 15	11 32	11 45	12 01	12 15	12 32	12 45	13 01	13 15	13 32	13 45	14 01	14 15	14 32	14 45	15 01	15 15	15 32	15 45	15 59	16 15
	d	10 17	10 32	10 49	11 02	11 17	11 32	11 47	12 02	12 17	12 32	12 47	13 02	13 17	13 32	13 47	14 02	14 17	14 32	14 47	15 02	15 17	15 32	15 47	16 00	16 17
Worplesdon	d		10 40				11 40				12 40				13 40				14 40				15 40		16 06	
Woking	a	10 25	10 44	10 57	11 11	11 25	11 44	11 57	12 11	12 25	12 44	12 57	13 11	13 25	13 44	13 57	14 11	14 25	14 44	14 57	15 11	15 25	15 44	15 57	16 11	16 25
	d	10 26	10 46	10 59	11 12	11 26	11 46	11 59	12 12	12 26	12 46	12 59	13 12	13 26	13 46	13 59	14 12	14 26	14 46	14 59	15 12	15 26	15 46	15 59	16 12	16 26
Clapham Junction 10	a		11 05		11 31		12 05		12 31		13 05		13 31		14 05		14 31		15 05		15 31		16 05		16 31	
London Waterloo 15	⊖ a	10 51	11 13	11 24	11 40	11 51	12 13	12 23	12 40	12 51	13 13	13 23	13 40	13 51	14 13	14 23	14 40	14 51	15 13	15 23	15 40	15 51	16 13	16 23	16 40	16 51

		SW	SW	SW	SW	SW	SW	SW	SW	SW	SW	SW	SW	SW	SW	SW	SW	SW	SW	SW	SW	SW	SW	SW
		1	1	1	1	1	1	1	1	1	1	1	1	1	1	1	1	1	1	1	1	1	1	1
				☕	☕			☕	☕		☕	☕		☕										
Portsmouth Harbour	d	15 17		15 45	16 15	16 17		16 45	17 15	17 17	17 45	18 15		18 45		19 15		19 45	20 15	20 17	20 45	21 15	22 17	23 18
Portsmouth & Southsea	d	15 24		15 50	16 20	16 24		16 50	17 20	17 24	17 50	18 20	18 24	18 50		19 20	19 24	19 50	20 20	20 24	20 50	21 24	22 24	23 24
Fratton	d	15 28		15 54	16 24	16 28		16 54	17 24	17 28	17 54	18 24	18 28	18 54		19 24	19 28	19 54	20 24	20 28	20 54	21 28	22 28	23 28
Hilsea	d	15 32				16 32				17 32			18 32				19 32			20 32		21 32	22 32	23 32
Bedhampton	d	15 37				16 37				17 37			18 37				19 37			20 37		21 37	22 37	23 37
Havant	a	15 40		16 03	16 33	16 39		17 03	17 33	17 39	18 03	18 33	18 39	19 03		19 33	19 39	20 03	20 33	20 39	21 03	21 39	22 39	23 39
	d	15 40	15 56	16 04	16 34	16 40	16 56	17 04	17 34	17 40	18 04	18 34	18 40	19 04		19 34	19 40	20 04	20 34	20 40	21 04	21 40	22 40	23 40
Rowlands Castle	d	15 46				16 46				17 46			18 46				19 46			20 46		21 46	22 46	23 46
Petersfield	d	15 57	16 10	16 18	16 48	16 57	17 10	17 18	17 48	17 57	18 18	18 48	18 57	19 18		19 48	19 57	20 18	20 48	20 57	21 18	21 57	22 57	23 57
Liss	d	16 02		16 23		17 02		17 23		18 02			19 02				20 02			21 02		22 02	23 02	00 02
Liphook	d	16 09		16 30		17 09		17 30		18 09			19 09				20 09			21 09		22 09	23 09	00 09
Haslemere 4	a	16 15	16 23	16 36	17 01	17 15	17 23	17 36	18 01	18 15	18 31	19 01	19 15	19 31		20 01	20 15	20 31	21 01	21 15	21 31	22 15	23 15	00 15
	d	16 15	16 24	16 37	17 02	17 15	17 32	17 37	18 02	18 15	18 32	19 02	19 15	19 32	19 39	20 02	20 15	20 32	21 02	21 15	21 32	22 15	23 15	00 15
Witley	d		16 30	16 43				17 43			18 38				19 45		20 21			21 21		22 21	23 21	00 21
Milford (Surrey)	d		16 34	16 47				17 47			18 42				19 49		20 25			21 25		22 25	23 25	00 25
Godalming	d	16 25	16 38	16 51		17 25		17 51		18 25	18 46	19 11	19 25		19 53		20 29			21 29		22 29	23 29	00 29
Farncombe	d	16 28	16 41	16 54		17 28		17 54		18 28	18 49	19 14	19 28		19 56		20 32			21 32		22 32	23 32	00 32
Guildford	a	16 32	16 46	16 59	17 15	17 32	17 45	17 59	18 15	18 32	18 54	19 19	19 32	19 47	20 01	20 15	20 37	20 45	21 16	21 37	21 46	22 37	23 37	00 37
	d	16 32	16 47	17 00	17 17	17 32	17 47	18 00	18 17	18 32	18 55	19 21	19 32	19 47	20 02	20 17	20 39	20 47	21 17	21 39	21 47	22 39	23 39	
Worplesdon	d	16 40		17 06		17 40		18 06		18 40			19 40				20 44			21 44		22 44	23 44	
Woking	a	16 44	16 57	17 11	17 25	17 44	17 58	18 11		18 44	19 03	19 28	19 45	19 57	20 11	20 25	20 49	20 57	21 25	21 49	21 57	22 49	23 49	
	d	16 46	16 59	17 12	17 26	17 46	17 59	18 12		18 46	19 05	19 30	19 46	19 59	20 12	20 26	20 50	20 59	21 26	21 50	21 59	22 50	23 56	
Clapham Junction 10	a	17 05		17 31		18 05		18 31		19 05			20 05		20 31		21 09			22 09		23 09	00 20	
London Waterloo 15	⊖ a	17 14	17 24	17 43	17 52	18 14	18 24	18 43	18 59	19 14	19 29	19 59	20 14	20 23	20 40	20 50	21 19	21 27	21 50	22 18	22 27	23 18	00 29	

For general notes see front of timetable
For details of catering facilities see
Directory of Train Operators

Table 156

Saturdays

Portsmouth, Haslemere and Guildford → London

Network diagram - see first page of Table 155

Station		SW 1	SW 1	SW 1	SW 1	SW 1	SW 1	SW 1 ☕	SW 1	SW 1 ☕	SW 1	SW 1 ☕	SW 1	SW 1 ☕	SW 1		SW 1 ☕	SW 1	SW 1	SW 1
Portsmouth Harbour	d	22p17	23p18	04 43	05 18		06 18	06 45		07 15		07 45		08 15			16 45			17 16
Portsmouth & Southsea	d	22p24	23p24	04 48	05 24		06 24	06 50		07 20	07 24	07 50		08 20	08 24		16 50		17 10	17 24
Fratton	d	22p28	23p28	04 52	05 28		06 28	06 54		07 24	07 28	07 54		08 24	08 28		16 54		17 14	17 28
Hilsea	d	22p32	23p32	04 56	05 32		06 32				07 32				08 32				17 18	17 32
Bedhampton	d	22p37	23p37	05 01	05 37		06 37				07 37				08 37				17 23	17 37
Havant	a	22p39	23p39	05 03	05 39		06 39	07 03		07 33	07 39	08 03		08 33	08 39	and at	17 03		17 25	17 39
	d	22p40	23p40	05 04	05 40		06 40	07 04		07 34	07 40	08 04		08 34	08 40		17 04		17 26	17 40
Rowlands Castle	d	22p46	23p46	05 09	05 46		06 46				07 46				08 46	the same			17 32	17 46
Petersfield	d	22p57	23p57	05 20	05 57		06 57	07 18		07 48	07 57	08 18		08 48	08 57	minutes	17 18		17 43	17 57
Liss	d	23p02	00 02	05 25	06 02		07 02				08 02				09 02				17 48	18 02
Liphook	d	23p09	00 09	05 32	06 09		07 09				08 09				09 09				17 55	18 09
Haslemere [4]	a	23p15	00 15	05 38	06 15		07 15	07 31		08 01	08 15	08 31		09 01	09 15	past	17 31		18 01	18 15
	d	23p15	00 15	05 39	06 15	06 39	07 15	07 32	07 39	08 02	08 15	08 32	08 39	09 02	09 15	each	17 32	17 39	18 02	18 15
Witley	d	23p21	00 21	05 45		06 45			07 45				08 45					17 45		
Milford (Surrey)	d	23p25	00 25	05 49		06 49			07 49				08 49			hour until		17 49		
Godalming	d	23p29	00 29	05 53	06 25	06 53	07 25		07 53		08 25		08 53		09 25			17 53		18 25
Farncombe	d	23p32	00 32	05 56	06 28	06 56	07 28		07 56		08 28		08 56		09 28			17 56		18 28
Guildford	a	23p37	00 37	06 01	06 32	07 01	07 32	07 46	08 01	08 16	08 32	08 46	09 01	09 16	09 32		17 45	18 01	18 15	18 32
	d	23p39		06 02	06 32	07 02	07 32	07 47	08 02	08 17	08 32	08 47	09 02	09 17	09 32		17 47	18 02	18 17	18 32
Worplesdon	d	23p44			06 40		07 40				08 40				09 40					18 40
Woking	a	23p49		06 11	06 44	07 11	07 44	07 57	08 12	08 26	08 44	08 57	09 11	09 25	09 44		17 57	18 11	18 25	18 44
	d	23p56		06 13	06 46	07 12	07 46	07 59	08 14	08 27	08 46	08 59	09 12	09 26	09 46		17 59	18 12	18 26	18 46
Clapham Junction [10]	a	00 20		06 32	07 05	07 31	08 05		08 33		09 05		09 31		10 05			18 31		19 05
London Waterloo [15]	⊖ a	00 29		06 40	07 13	07 40	08 13	08 23	08 42	08 51	09 13	09 23	09 40	09 52	10 13		18 23	18 40	18 51	19 13

Station		SW 1 ☕	SW 1	SW 1	SW 1	SW 1	SW 1	SW 1	SW 1	SW 1	SW 1	SW 1	SW 1	SW 1	SW 1	SW 1
Portsmouth Harbour	d	17 45		18 15		18 45		19 15		19 45	20 15		20 45	21 17	22 17	23 18
Portsmouth & Southsea	d	17 50		18 20	18 24	18 50		19 20	19 24	19 50	20 20	20 24	20 50	21 24	22 24	23 23
Fratton	d	17 54		18 24	18 28	18 54		19 24	19 28	19 54	20 24	20 28	20 54	21 28	22 28	23 28
Hilsea	d				18 32				19 32			20 32		21 32	22 32	23 32
Bedhampton	d				18 37				19 37			20 37		21 37	22 37	23 37
Havant	a	18 03		18 33	18 39	19 03		19 33	19 39	20 03	20 33	20 39	21 03	21 39	22 39	23 39
	d	18 04		18 34	18 40	19 04		19 34	19 40	20 04	20 34	20 40	21 04	21 40	22 40	23 41
Rowlands Castle	d				18 46				19 46			20 46		21 46	22 46	23 46
Petersfield	d	18 18		18 48	18 57	19 18		19 48	19 57	20 18	20 48	20 57	21 18	21 57	22 57	23 57
Liss	d				19 02				20 02			21 02		22 02	23 02	00 02
Liphook	d				19 09				20 09			21 09		22 09	23 09	00 09
Haslemere [4]	a	18 31		19 01	19 15	19 31		20 01	20 15	20 31	21 01	21 15	21 31	22 15	23 15	00 15
	d	18 32	18 39	19 02	19 15	19 32	19 39	20 02	20 15	20 32	21 02	21 15	21 32	22 15	23 15	00 15
Witley	d		18 45				19 45		20 21			21 21		22 21	23 21	00 21
Milford (Surrey)	d		18 49				19 49		20 25			21 25		22 25	23 25	00 25
Godalming	d		18 53		19 25		19 53		20 29			21 29		22 29	23 29	00 29
Farncombe	d		18 56		19 28		19 56		20 32			21 32		22 32	23 32	00 32
Guildford	a	18 45	19 01	19 15	19 32	19 46	20 01	20 15	20 37	20 47	21 15	21 37	21 47	22 37	23 37	00 37
	d	18 47	19 02	19 17	19 32	19 47	20 02	20 17	20 39	20 49	21 17	21 39	21 49	22 39	23 39	
Worplesdon	d				19 40				20 44			21 44		22 44	23 44	
Woking	a	18 57	19 11	19 25	19 44	19 57	20 11	20 25	20 49	20 57	21 25	21 49	21 57	22 49	23 49	
	d	18 59	19 12	19 26	19 46	19 59	20 12	20 26	20 50	20 59	21 26	21 50	21 59	22 50	23 56	
Clapham Junction [10]	a		19 31		20 05		20 31		21 09			22 09		23 09	00 22	
London Waterloo [15]	⊖ a	19 23	19 40	19 50	20 13	20 23	20 40	20 50	21 18	21 24	21 50	22 18	22 24	23 18	00 31	

Sundays

Station		SW 1	SW 1	SW 1	SW 1	SW 1	SW 1	SW 1	SW 1 ☕	SW 1	SW 1 ☕	SW 1	SW 1 ☕
Portsmouth Harbour	d	22p17	23p18	06 48	07 32	07 48	08 32	08 48	09 32	09 48	10 32	10 48	11 32
Portsmouth & Southsea	d	22p24	23p23	06 53	07 37	07 53	08 37	08 53	09 37	09 53	10 37	10 53	11 37
Fratton	d	22p28	23p28	06 57	07 41	07 57	08 41	08 57	09 41	09 57	10 41	10 57	11 41
Hilsea	d	22p32	23p32										
Bedhampton	d	22p37	23p37	07 04		08 04		09 04		10 04		11 04	
Havant	a	22p39	23p39	07 07	07 49	08 07	08 49	09 07	09 49	10 07	10 49	11 07	11 49
	d	22p40	23p41	07 07	07 50	08 07	08 50	09 07	09 50	10 07	10 50	11 07	11 50
Rowlands Castle	d	22p46	23p46	07 13		08 13		09 13		10 13		11 13	
Petersfield	d	22p57	23p57	07 24	08 04	08 24	09 04	09 24	10 04	10 24	11 04	11 24	12 04
Liss	d	23p02	00 02	07 29		08 29		09 29		10 29		11 29	
Liphook	d	23p09	00 09	07 36		08 36		09 36		10 36		11 36	
Haslemere [4]	a	23p15	00 15	07 41	08 16	08 41	09 16	09 41	10 16	10 41	11 16	11 41	12 16
	d	23p15	00 15	07 42	08 17	08 42	09 17	09 42	10 17	10 42	11 17	11 42	12 17
Witley	d	23p21	00 21	07 48		08 48		09 48		10 48		11 48	
Milford (Surrey)	d	23p25	00 25	07 52		08 52		09 52		10 52		11 52	
Godalming	d	23p29	00 29	07 56		08 56		09 56		10 56		11 56	
Farncombe	d	23p32	00 32	07 59		08 59		09 59		10 59		11 59	
Guildford	a	23p37	00 37	08 04	08 31	09 04	09 31	10 03	10 31	11 04	11 31	12 04	12 31
	d	23p39		08 05	08 35	09 05	09 35	10 05	10 35	11 05	11 35	12 05	12 35
Worplesdon	d	23p44											
Woking	a	23p49		08 13	08 42	09 14	09 42	10 13	10 42	11 14	11 42	12 13	12 42
	d	23p56		08 15	08 45	09 15	09 45	10 15	10 45	11 15	11 45	12 15	12 45
Clapham Junction [10]	a	00 22		08 37	09 06	09 35	10 06	10 35	11 04	11 34	12 04	12 34	13 04
London Waterloo [15]	⊖ a	00 31		08 49	09 19	09 49	10 21	10 49	11 19	11 49	12 19	12 47	13 14

For general notes see front of timetable
For details of catering facilities see Directory of Train Operators

Table 156

Sundays

Portsmouth, Haslemere and Guildford → London

Network diagram - see first page of Table 155

		SW 1		SW 1 ☕	SW 1	SW 1	SW 1	SW 1	SW 1	SW 1	SW 1	SW 1	SW 1
Portsmouth Harbour	d	11 48		18 32	18 48	19 32	19 48	20 32	20 48	21 32	21 48	22 32	22 48
Portsmouth & Southsea	d	11 53		18 37	18 53	19 37	19 53	20 37	20 53	21 37	21 53	22 37	22 53
Fratton	d	11 57		18 41	18 57	19 41	19 57	20 41	20 57	21 41	21 57	22 41	22 57
Hilsea	d												
Bedhampton	d	12 04			19 04		20 04		21 04		22 04		23 04
Havant	a	12 07	and at	18 49	19 07	19 49	20 07	20 49	21 07	21 49	22 07	22 49	23 07
	d	12 07	the same	18 50	19 07	19 50	20 07	20 50	21 07	21 50	22 07	22 50	23 07
Rowlands Castle	d	12 13			19 13		20 13		21 13		22 13		23 13
Petersfield	d	12 24	minutes	19 04	19 24	20 04	20 24	21 04	21 24	22 04	22 24	23 04	23 24
Liss	d	12 29			19 29		20 29		21 29		22 29		23 29
Liphook	d	12 36	past		19 36		20 36		21 36		22 36		23 36
Haslemere 4	a	12 41		19 16	19 41	20 16	20 41	21 16	21 41	22 17	22 41	23 16	23 41
	d	12 42	each	19 17	19 42	20 17	20 42	21 17	21 42	22 17	22 42	23 17	23 42
Witley	d	12 48			19 48		20 48		21 48		22 48		23 48
Milford (Surrey)	d	12 52	hour until		19 52		20 52		21 52		22 52		23 52
Godalming	d	12 56			19 56		20 56		21 56		22 56		23 56
Farncombe	d	12 59			19 59		20 59		21 59		22 59		23 59
Guildford	a	13 04		19 31	20 04	20 31	21 04	21 31	22 04	22 31	23 04	23 31	00 04
	d	13 05		19 35	20 05	20 35	21 05	21 35	22 05	22 35	23 05	23 35	00 05
Worplesdon	d												
Woking	a	13 13		19 42	20 13	20 42	21 13	21 42	22 13	22 42	23 13	23 42	00 13
	d	13 15		19 45	20 15	20 45	21 15	21 45	22 15	22 45	23 15	23 45	
Clapham Junction 10	a	13 34		20 04	20 34	21 04	21 34	22 04	22 34	23 04	23 34	00 04	
London Waterloo 15 ⊖	a	13 44		20 14	20 44	21 14	21 44	22 14	22 44	23 14	23 44	00 14	

For general notes see front of timetable
For details of catering facilities see Directory of Train Operators

Liphook → Liphook via Lindford, Bordon and Whitehill (circular service)

Bus Service

Mondays to Fridays

		SW	SW	SW	SW	SW	SW	SW		SW	SW	SW	SW	SW	SW	SW	SW	SW	SW	SW	SW	SW	SW		
		MX	MX																						
London Waterloo 15	⊖ 156 d	22b45	23b45		05 00	06 15	06 45	07 45		08 45	09 45	10 45	11 45	12 45	13 45	15 15	16 15	16 45	17 45	18 45	19 45	20 45	21 45		
Woking	156 d	23b13	00 13		05 51	06 43	07 13	08 14		09 13	10 13	11 13	12 13	13 13	14 13	15 43	16 43	17 13	17c56	19 14	20 13	21 13	22 13		
Guildford	156 d	23b25	00 25		06 00	06 55	07 25	08 26		09 25	10 25	11 25	12 25	13 25	14 25	15 55	16 55	17 22	18 23	19 24	20 25	21 25	22 25		
Portsmouth Harbour	156 d	23b18			05 19	06 42	06 55	07 29		09 17	10 17	11 17	12 17	13e15	14 17	15 45	16 45	17 17	18e15	19e15	20 17	21 15	22 17		
Portsmouth & Southsea	156 d	23b24			05 24	06 47	07 00	08 24		09 24	10 24	11 24	12 24	13 24	14 24	15 50	16 50	17 24	18 24	19 24	20 24	21 24	22 24		
Liphook	d	00 15	01 01		06 35	07 35	08 25	09 15		10 15	11 15	12 15	13 15	14 15	15 15	16 40	17 40	18 40	19 15	20 15	21 15	22 15	23 15		
Lindford (Liphook Road)	d	00 24	01 10	06 04	06 44	07 44	08 34	09 24		10 24	11 24	12 24	13 24	14 24	15 24	16 49	17 49	18 49	19 24	20 24	21 24	22 24	23 24		
Bordon Camp (Fire Station)	d	00 28	01 14	06 08	06 48	07 48	08 38	09 28		10 28	11 28	12 28	13 28	14 28	15 28	16 53	17 53	18 53	19 28	20 28	21 28	22 28	23 28		
Whitehill, Prince of Wales	d	00 37	01a23	06 17	06 57	07 57	08 47	09 37		10 37	11 37	12 37	13 37	14 37	15 37	17 02	18 02	19 02	19 37	20 37	21 37	22 37	23 37		
Liphook	a	00 50		06 30	07 10	08 10	09 00	09 50		10 50	11 50	12 50	13 50	14 50	15 50	17 15	18 15	19 15	19 50	20 50	21 50	22 50	23 50		
Portsmouth & Southsea	156 a			07 46	08 07	09 20	09 52	10 43		11 43	12 43	13 43	14 51	15 43	16 45	18 20	19e29		20 48	21 47	22 47	23 46	00 38		
Portsmouth Harbour	156 a				08 12	09 26	09 57	10 48		12e07	13e07	13 48	14 57	15 48	16 54	18 28	19e36		20 56	22e04	23e04	00e04	00e55		
Guildford	156 a			07 05	07 43	09 02	09 32	10 32		11 32	12 32	13 32	14 32	15 32	16 32	17 59	19 32		20 37	21 37	22 37	23 37	00 37		
Woking	156 a			07 15	07 54	09 11	09 44	10 44		11 44	12 44	13 44	14 44	15 44	16 44	18 11	19 45		20 49	21 49	22 49	23 49			
London Waterloo 15	⊖ 156 a			07 44	08 24	09 43	10 13	11 13		12 13	13 13	14 13	15 13	16 13	17 14	18 43	20 14		21 19	22 18	23 18	00 29			

Saturdays

		SW	SW	SW	SW		SW	SW	SW	SW		SW	SW	SW	SW		SW	SW	SW	SW	SW	SW	SW		
London Waterloo 15	⊖ 156 d	22b45	23b45		06 45		07 45	08 45	09 45	10 45		11 45	12 45	13 45	14 45		15 45	16 45	17 45	18 45	19 45	20 45	21 45		
Woking	156 d	23b13	00 13		07 13		08 13	09 13	10 13	11 13		12 13	13 13	14 13	15 13		16 13	17 13	18 13	19 13	20 13	21 13	22 13		
Guildford	156 d	23b25	00 25		07 25		08 25	09 25	10 25	11 25		12 25	13 25	14 25	15 25		16 25	17 25	18 25	19 25	20 25	21 25	22 25		
Portsmouth Harbour	156 d	23b18			06 18		08 15	09 15	10 15	11 15		12 15	13 15	14 15	15 15		16 15	17 16	18 15	19 15	20 15	21 17	22 17		
Portsmouth & Southsea	156 d	23b24			07 24		08 24	09 24	10 24	11 24		12 24	13 24	14 24	15 24		16 24	17 24	18 24	19 24	20 24	21 24	22 24		
Liphook	d	00 15	01 01		08 15		09 15	10 15	11 15	12 15		13 15	14 15	15 15	16 15		17 15	18 15	19 15	20 15	21 15	22 15	23 15		
Lindford (Liphook Road)	d	00 24	01 10	07 19	08 24		09 24	10 24	11 24	12 24		13 24	14 24	15 24	16 24		17 24	18 24	19 24	20 24	21 24	22 24	23 24		
Bordon Camp (Fire Station)	d	00 28	01 14	07 23	08 28		09 28	10 28	11 28	12 28		13 28	14 28	15 28	16 28		17 28	18 28	19 28	20 28	21 28	22 28	23 28		
Whitehill, Prince of Wales	d	00 37	01a23	07 32	08 37		09 37	10 37	11 37	12 37		13 37	14 37	15 37	16 37		17 37	18 37	19 37	20 37	21 37	22 37	23 37		
Liphook	a	00 50		07 45	08 50		09 50	10 50	11 50	12 50		13 50	14 50	15 50	16 50		17 50	18 50	19 50	20 50	21 50	22 50	23 50		
Portsmouth & Southsea	156 a			08 32	09 43		10 43	11 43	12 43	13 43		14 43	15 43	16 43	17 43		18 42	19 42	20 47	21 43	22 47	23 48	00 38		
Portsmouth Harbour	156 a			08 37	10 07		11 07	12 07	13 07	14 07		15 07	16 07	17 07	18 07		19 07	20 07	21 07	22 03	22 52	23 54	00 55		
Guildford	156 a			08 32	09 32		10 32	11 32	12 32	13 32		14 32	15 32	16 32	17 32		18 15	19 32	20 37	21 37	22 37	23 37	00 37		
Woking	156 a			08 44	09 44		10 44	11 44	12 44	13 44		14 44	15 44	16 44	17 44		18 25	19 44	20 49	21 49	22 49	23 49			
London Waterloo 15	⊖ 156 a			09 13	10 13		11 13	12 13	13 13	14 13		15 13	16 13	17 13	18 13		18 51	20 13	21 18	22 18	23 18	00 31			

Sundays

		SW	SW	SW	SW		SW	SW	SW	SW		SW	SW	SW	SW		SW	SW	SW	SW	SW	SW	SW		
London Waterloo 15	⊖ 156 d	22b45	23b45				08 00	09 00	10 00	11 00		12 00	13 00	14 00	15 00		16 00	17 00	18 00	19 00	20 00	21 00	22 00		
Woking	156 d	23b13	00 13		07 32		08 35	09 35	10 32	11 32		12 32	13 32	14 32	15 32		16 32	17 32	18 32	19 32	20 32	21 32	22 32		
Guildford	156 d	23b25	00 25		07 46		08 46	09 46	10 46	11 46		12 46	13 46	14 46	15 46		16 46	17 46	18 46	19 46	20 46	21 46	22 46		
Portsmouth Harbour	156 d	23f18			07 48		08 48	09 48	10 48	11 48		12 48	13 48	14 48			15 48	16 48	17 48	18 48	19 48	20 48	21 48		
Portsmouth & Southsea	156 d	23b23			07 53		08 53	09 53	10 53	11 53		12 53	13 53	14 53			15 53	16 53	17 53	18 53	19 53	20 53	21 53		
Liphook	d	00 15	01 01		08 50		09 50	10 50	11 50	12 50		13 50	14 50	15 50	16 30		17 30	18 30	19 30	20 30	21 30	22 30	23 30		
Lindford (Liphook Road)	d	00 24	01 10	07 59	08 59		09 59	10 59	11 59	12 59		13 59	14 59	15 59	16 39		17 39	18 39	19 39	20 39	21 39	22 39	23 39		
Bordon Camp (Fire Station)	d	00 28	01 14	08 03	09 03		10 03	11 03	12 03	13 03		14 03	15 03	16 03	16 43		17 43	18 43	19 43	20 43	21 43	22 43	23 43		
Whitehill, Prince of Wales	d	00 37	01a23	08 12	09 12		10 12	11 12	12 12	13 12		14 12	15 12	16 12	16 52		17 52	18 52	19 52	20 52	21 52	22 52	23a52		
Liphook	a	00 50		08 25	09 25		10 25	11 25	12 25	13 25		14 25	15 25	16 25	17 05		18 05	19 05	20 05	21 05	22 05	23 05			
Portsmouth & Southsea	156 a			09 59	10 59		11 59	12 59	13 59	14 59		15 59	16 59		17 59		18 59	19 59	20 59	21 59	22 59	23 59			
Portsmouth Harbour	156 a			10 04	11 04		12 04	13 04	14 04	15 04		16 04	17 05		18 04		19 04	20 04	21 04	22 04	23 04	00 04			
Guildford	156 a			09 04	10 03		11 04	12 04	13 04	14 04		15 04	16 04	17 04	18 04		19 04	20 04	21 04	22 04	23 04	00 04			
Woking	156 a			09 14	10 13		11 14	12 13	13 13	14 13		15 13	16 13	17 13	18 13		19 13	20 13	21 13	22 13	23 13	00 13			
London Waterloo 15	⊖ 156 a			09 49	10 49		11 49	12 47	13 44	14 44		15 44	16 44	17 44	18 44		19 44	20 44	21 44	22 44	23 44	01g02			

For general notes see front of timetable
For details of catering facilities see Directory of Train Operators

b Previous night
c Change at Guildford and Liphook
e Change at Petersfield
f Sundays
g Change at Liphook and Woking

Havant → Portsmouth Harbour
(Complete service)

Network Diagram - see first page of Table 155

		SW	SW	SW	SW	SW	SW	SW	SW	SW	SW	SW	SN	SN	SW	SN	SW	SN	SW	SW	SW	GW	SW
		MO	MO	MO	MO	MO	MX	MX	MX	MX	MX												
		1	1	1	1	1	1	1	1	1	1	1	1	1	1	1	1	1	1	1	1		1
Havant	d	23p45	23p51		00 45	00 51	23p49		00 22	00 37	01 22	04 40	05 24	05 39	06 02	06 13		06 53		06 58			
Bedhampton	d	23p47			00 47				00 25		01s24	04 43			06 05	06 15		06 56		07 01			
Hilsea	d			23p59				00 04	00 30		01s30	04 48			06 10	06 20	06 33	07 01	07 05	07 07	07 13		07 35
Fratton	d	23p56	00 01	00 04	00 56	01 01	23p59	00 08	00 34	00 47	01s34	04 52	05 33	05 48	06 15	06 25	06 38	07 05	07 09	07 12	07 17	07 35	07 39
Portsmouth & Southsea	a	23p59	00 04	00 08	00 59	01 04	00 02	00 11	00 38	00 50	01 38	04 55	05 36	05 51	06 18	06 28	06 44	07 08	07 12	07 16	07 22	07 38	07 42
	d	00 01	00 05	00 09	01 00	01 05	00 03	00 13		00 51		04 56	05 36	05 51	06 19	06 28	06 45	07 09	07 13	07 17		07 39	07 43
Portsmouth Harbour	a	00 04	00 09	00 13	01 04	01 09	00 07	00 16		00 55		04 59	05 40	05 55	06 22	06 32	06 49	07 12	07 17	07 20		07 45	07 48

		SW	SN	SN	SW	SW	SN	SW	GW	SN	SW	SW	SN	SW	SW	SN	SW	SW	SW	GW	SN	SW	SN
		1	1	1	1	1	1	1	◇	1	1	1	1	1	1	1	1	1	1	◇	1	1	1
Havant	d	07 28	07 35	07 41	07 52		07 56			08 22	08 27		08 44	08 50		09 01	09 05	09 19			09 31	09 35	09 46
Bedhampton	d	07 31	07 37		07 55		07 58			08 24	08 30						09 08				09 34	09 38	
Hilsea	d	07 37	07 42		08 00	08 03	08 06	08 10		08 29	08 36	08 43			09 04		09 13		09 31		09 41	09 44	
Fratton	d	07 42	07 47	07 50	08 04	08 07	08 11	08 15	08 21	08 34	08 40	08 48	08 53	08 59	09 08	09 13	09 17	09 29	09 37	09 44	09 46	09 49	09 55
Portsmouth & Southsea	a	07 46	07 50	07 53	08 07	08 11	08 15	08 18	08 24	08 37	08 43	08 51	08 56	09 02	09 11	09 16	09 20	09 32	09 40	09 47	09 49	09 52	09 58
	d			07 53	08 09	08 13	08 16	08 19	08 25	08 37	08 45	08 52	08 57	09 04	09 13	09 17	09 22	09 34		09 48		09 53	09 58
Portsmouth Harbour	a			07 57	08 12	08 16	08 19	08 22	08 30	08 41	08 48	08 55	09 00	09 07	09 18	09 21	09 26	09 37		09 52		09 57	10 02

		SW	SN	SW	SW	SW	SW	GW	SN	SN	SW	SN	SW	SW	SW	SW	GW	SN	SN	SW	SN	SW	SW
		1	1	1	1	1	1	◇	1	1	1	1	1	1	1	1	◇	1	1	1	1	1	1
Havant	d	09 50	10 04		10 15		10 27		10 32	10 46	10 50	11 04		11 15		11 27		11 33	11 46	11 50	12 04		12 15
Bedhampton	d						10 30		10 35							11 30		11 35					
Hilsea	d			10 03		10 32	10 35		10 42				11 03		11 32	11 35		11 42				12 03	
Fratton	d	09 59	10 13	10 08	10 24	10 37	10 40	10 43	10 46	10 55	10 59	11 13	11 08	11 24	11 37	11 40	11 42	11 46	11 55	11 59	12 13	12 08	12 24
Portsmouth & Southsea	a	10 02	10 16	10 19	10 27	10 41	10 43	10 47	10 49	10 58	11 02	11 16	11 19	11 27	11 40	11 43	11 45	11 49	11 58	12 02	12 16	12 19	12 27
	d	10 04	10 16	10 20	10 29		10 44	10 48		10 58	11 04	11 16	11 20	11 29			11 46		11 58	12 04	12 16	12 20	12 29
Portsmouth Harbour	a	10 07	10 20	10 23	10 32		10 48	10 52		11 02	11 07	11 20	11 23	11 32			11 50		12 02	12 07	12 20	12 23	12 32

		SW	SW	GW	SN	SN	SW	SN	SW	SW	SW	SW	GW	SN	SN	SW	SN	SW	SW	SW	GW	SN	SW
		1	1	◇	1	1	1	1	1	1	1	1	◇	1	1	1	1	1	1	1	◇	1	1
Havant	d		12 27		12 33	12 46	12 50	13 04		13 15		13 27		13 33	13 46	13 50	14 04		14 15			14 33	14 27
Bedhampton	d		12 30		12 35							13 30		13 35								14 35	14 30
Hilsea	d	12 31	12 35		12 41				13 03		13 32	13 35		13 42				14 03		14 32		14 42	14 35
Fratton	d	12 37	12 40	12 43	12 46	12 55	12 59	13 13	13 08	13 24	13 37	13 40	13 43	13 46	13 55	13 59	14 13	14 08	14 24	14 37	14 43	14 46	14b43
Portsmouth & Southsea	a	12 40	12 43	12 47	12 49	12 58	13 02	13 16	13 19	13 27	13 40	13 43	13 47	13 49	13 58	14 03	14 16	14 19	14 27	14 40	14 47	14 49	14 51
	d			12 48		12 58	13 04	13 16	13 20	13 29		13 44	13 47		13 58	14 04	14 16	14 20	14 29		14 47		14 53
Portsmouth Harbour	a			12 52		13 02	13 07	13 20	13 23	13 32		13 48	13 52		14 02	14 07	14 20	14 23	14 32		14 52		14 57

		SN	SW	SN	SW	SW	SW	SW	GW	SN	SN	SW	SW	SN	SN	SW	SW	SW	SN	GW	SN	SW	SN
		1	1	1	1	1	1	1	◇	1	1	1	1	1	1	1	1	1	1	◇	1	1	1
Havant	d	14 46	14 50	15 04		15 15		15 27		15 32	15 46	15 50		16 02	16 06	16 15		16 27	16 32		16 46	16 50	17 00
Bedhampton	d							15 30		15 34				16 04				16 30	16 34				17 02
Hilsea	d				15 03		15 32	15 35		15 41			16 03				16 32	16 35	16 39				17 07
Fratton	d	14 55	14 59	15 13	15 08	15 24	15 37	15 40	15 43	15 46	15 55	15 59	16 08	16 12	16 16	16 24	16 37	16 37	16 45	16 47	16 55	16 59	17 12
Portsmouth & Southsea	a	14 58	15 02	15 16	15 19	15 28	15 40	15 43	15 47	15 49	15 58	16 02	16 11	16 15	16 19	16 27	16 40	16 45	16 49	16 51	16 58	17 02	17 15
	d	14 58	15 04	15 16	15 20	15 29		15 44	15 47		15 58	16 04	16 12	16 16		16 29	16 41	16 48		16 51	16 58	17 04	17 15
Portsmouth Harbour	a	15 02	15 07	15 20	15 23	15 32		15 48	15 52		16 02	16 07	16 20	16 20		16 32	16 44	16 54		16 57	17 02	17 07	17 19

		SW	SN	SW	SW	SW	SW	SW	GW	SN	SW	SN	SW	SW	SN	SW	SW	SW	SW	SN	GW	SW	SW
		1	1	1	1	1	1	1	◇	1	1	1	1	1	1	1	1	1	1	1	◇	1	1
Havant	d		17 08	17 04	17 16			17 27		17 32	17 49	17 53		18 04	18 13	18 19			18 30	18 34		18 51	
Bedhampton	d			17 06				17 30		17 34		17 55		18 07					18 33	18 36			
Hilsea	d	17 03		17 11			17 32	17 35		17 41		18 00	18 03	18 12			18 32		18 38	18 41			19 05
Fratton	d	17 08	17 19	17 16	17 25	17 27	17 37	17 40	17 43	17 46	17 59	18 05	18 08	18 17	18 22	18 29	18 37	18 40	18 43	18 46	18 47	19 00	19 09
Portsmouth & Southsea	a	17 18	17 22	17 22	17 28	17 31	17 40	17 43	17 47	17 49	18 02	18 08	18 11	18 20	18 25	18 32	18 40	18 43	18 46	18 49	18 51	19 03	19 12
	d	17 19		17 23	17 30				17 47		18 03	18 08	18 12	18 22	18 26	18 33		18 45			18 51	19 05	19 14
Portsmouth Harbour	a	17 25		17 27	17 35				17 52		18 09	18 14	18 20	18 28	18 31	18 39		18 51			18 57	19 10	19 20

		SN	SW	SN	SW	SW	SW	GW	SN	SW	SW	SW	SN	SN	SW	SW	GW	SW	SW	SN	SW	SN	SW
		1	1	1	1	1	1	◇	1	1	1	1	1	1	1	1	◇	1	1	1	1	1	1
Havant	d	19 00	19 04	19 11	19 17				19 35	19 42	19 51		20 05	20 11	20 19			20 29	20 49	20 52		21 10	21 20
Bedhampton	d	19 02	19 07						19 37	19 45								20 32					
Hilsea	d	19 07	19 12			19 28	19 32		19 43	19 50		20 08				20 32		20 41			20 59		
Fratton	d	19 13	19a16	19 20	19 26	19 33	19 37	19 44	19 49	19a56	20 00	20 13	20 16	20 20	20 28	20 37	20 41	20 45	20 59	21 02	21 08	21 19	21 30
Portsmouth & Southsea	a	19 16		19 23	19 29	19 36	19 42	19 47	19 53		20 03	20 16	20 20	20 23	20 31	20 40	20 44	20 48	21 02	21 06	21 11	21 23	21 33
	d	19 17		19 23	19 31	19 38		19 48			20 05	20 17		20 23	20 33		20 44	20 50	21 03		21 13	21 23	21 34
Portsmouth Harbour	a	19 21		19 27	19 36	19 43		19 52			20 10	20 23		20 27	20 36		20 49	20 56	21 07		21 25	21 27	21 38

		SW	GW	SW	SW	SN	SW	SN	SW	SW	SW	SN	GW	SW	SN	SW	SW	SW	SW	GW	SN	SW	
		1	◇	1	1	1	1	1	1	1	1	1	◇	1	1	1	1	1	1	◇	1	1	
Havant	d			21 31	21 46	21 49		22 10	22 19		22 31	22 43		22 49	23 11	23 19			23 31		23 36	23 49	
Bedhampton	d			21 34							22 34								23 34				
Hilsea	d	21 32		21 40			22 06			22 31	22 39						23 24	23 32	23 39				
Fratton	d	21 37	21 41	21 44	21 55	21 59	22 10	22 19	22 29	22 36	22 44	22 53	22 56	22 59	23 20	23 29	23 33	23 37	23 43	23 43	23 50	23 59	
Portsmouth & Southsea	a	21 43	21 44	21 47	21 58	22 02	22 13	22 22	22 32	22 43	22 47	22 56	23 00	23 03	23 23	23 32	23 36	23 40	23 46	23 47	23 53	00 02	
	d		21 44		21 59	22 02	22 15	22 22	22 33			22 57	23 00	23 04	23 24	23 33	23 36			23 47		00 03	
Portsmouth Harbour	a		21 49		22 02	22 06	22 18	22 26	22 38			23 00	23 04	23 08	23 27	23 37	23 40			23 52		00 07	

For general notes see front of timetable
For details of catering facilities see Directory of Train Operators

b Arr. 1439

Table 157

Saturdays

Havant → Portsmouth Harbour

(Complete service)

Network Diagram - see first page of Table 155

		SW 1	SW 1	SW 1	SW 1	SW 1	SW 1	SN 1	SN 1	SN 1		SW 1	SW 1	SN 1	SN 1	SW 1	SN 1	SW 1	SW 1	SN 1		SN 1	SW 1	SN 1	SW 1	SW 1
Havant	d	23p49		00 22	00 37	01 22	04 40	05 34	05 49	05 57		06 01		06 33	06 46		07 04	07 17		07 33		07 46		08 04	08 17	
Bedhampton	d			00 25		01s24	04 43					06 04		06 35				07 20		07 35					08 20	
Hilsea	d		00 04	00 30		01s30	04 48					06 09	06 32	06 41		07 03		07 25	07 32	07 41			08 04		08 25	08 32
Fratton	d	23p59	00 08	00 34	00 47	01s34	04 52	05 43	05 58	06 06		06b17	06 37	06 46	06 55	07 07	07 13	07 29	07 37	07 46		07 55	08 08	08 14	08 29	08 37
Portsmouth & Southsea	a	00 02	00 11	00 38	00 50	01 38	04 55	05 46	06 01	06 09		06 21	06 40	06 49	06 58	07 10	07 17	07 32	07 40	07 49		07 58	08 11	08 18	08 32	08 40
	d	00 03	00 13		00 51		04 57		06 01	06 09		06 23			06 58	07 12	07 17	07 34				07 59	08 13	08 18	08 33	
Portsmouth Harbour	a	00 07	00 16		00 55		05 00		06 05	06 16		06 26			07 02	07 18	07 21	07 37				08 02	08 19	08 22	08 37	

		GW ◇	SN 1	SN 1	SW 1	SN 1	SW 1		SW 1	SW 1	SW 1	GW ◇	SN 1	SN 1	SW 1	SN 1	SW 1		SW 1	SW 1	SW 1	GW ◇	SN 1	SN 1	SW 1	SN 1
Havant	d		08 33	08 46	08 49	09 04			09 15		09 27		09 33	09 46	09 49	10 04			10 15		10 27		10 33	10 46	10 49	11 04
Bedhampton	d		08 35								09 30		09 35								10 30		10 35			
Hilsea	d		08 41				09 07			09 32	09 35		09 41				10 03			10 32	10 35		10 41			
Fratton	d	08 41	08 46	08 55	08 59	09 13	09 16		09 24	09 37	09 40	09 41	09 46	09 55	09 59	10 13	10c11		10 24	10 37	10 40	10 41	10 46	10 55	10 59	11 13
Portsmouth & Southsea	a	08 45	08 49	08 58	09 02	09 16	09 19		09 27	09 40	09 43	09 45	09 49	09 58	10 02	10 16	10 19		10 27	10 40	10 43	10 45	10 49	10 58	11 02	11 16
	d	08 45		08 59	09 03	09 16	09 21		09 29			09 45		09 58	10 03	10 16	10 20		10 29			10 45		10 58	11 03	11 16
Portsmouth Harbour	a	08 49		09 02	09 07	09 20	09 24		09 32			09 49		10 02	10 07	10 20	10 23		10 32			10 49		11 02	11 07	11 20

		SW 1	SW 1	SW 1		SW 1	GW ◇	SN 1	SN 1	SW 1	SN 1	SW 1	SW 1	SW 1		SW 1	GW ◇	SN 1	SN 1	SW 1	SN 1	SW 1	SW 1	SW 1		SW 1
Havant	d		11 15			11 27		11 33	11 46	11 49	12 04		12 15			12 27		12 33	12 46	12 49	13 04		13 15			13 27
Bedhampton	d					11 30		11 35								12 30		12 35								13 30
Hilsea	d	11 03		11 32		11 35		11 41				12 03		12 32		12 35		12 41				13 03		13 32		13 35
Fratton	d	11e11	11 24	11 37		11 40	11 41	11 46	11 55	11 59	12 13	12f11	12 24	12 37		12 40	12 41	12 46	12 55	12 59	13 13	13g11	13 24	13 37		13 40
Portsmouth & Southsea	a	11 19	11 27	11 40		11 43	11 45	11 49	11 58	12 02	12 16	12 19	12 27	12 40		12 43	12 45	12 49	12 58	13 02	13 16	13 19	13 27	13 40		13 43
	d	11 20	11 29				11 45		11 58	12 03	12 16	12 20	12 29				12 45		12 58	13 03	13 16	13 20	13 29			
Portsmouth Harbour	a	11 23	11 32				11 49		12 02	12 07	12 20	12 23	12 32				12 49		13 02	13 07	13 20	13 23	13 32			

		GW ◇	SN 1	SN 1	SW 1	SN 1	SW 1	SW 1	SW 1	SW 1		GW ◇	SN 1	SN 1	SW 1	SN 1	SW 1	SW 1	SW 1	SW 1		GW ◇	SN 1	SN 1	SW 1	SN 1
Havant	d		13 33	13 46	13 49	14 04		14 15		14 27			14 33	14 46	14 49	15 04		15 15		15 27			15 33	15 46	15 49	16 04
Bedhampton	d		13 35							14 30			14 35							15 30			15 35			
Hilsea	d		13 41				14 03		14 32	14 35			14 41				15 03		15 32	15 35			15 41			
Fratton	d	13 41	13 46	13 55	13 59	14 13	14h11	14 24	14 37	14 40		14 41	14 46	14 55	14 59	15 13	15j11	15 24	15 37	15 40		15 41	15 46	15 55	15 59	16 13
Portsmouth & Southsea	a	13 45	13 49	13 58	14 02	14 16	14 19	14 27	14 40	14 43		14 45	14 49	14 58	15 02	15 16	15 19	15 27	15 40	15 43		15 45	15 49	15 58	16 02	16 16
	d	13 45		13 58	14 03	14 16	14 20	14 29				14 45		14 58	15 03	15 16	15 20	15 29				15 45		15 58	16 03	16 16
Portsmouth Harbour	a	13 49		14 02	14 07	14 20	14 23	14 32				14 49		15 02	15 07	15 20	15 23	15 32				15 49		16 02	16 07	16 20

		SW 1	SW 1	SW 1	SW 1	GW ◇	SN 1		SN 1	SW 1	SN 1	SW 1	SW 1	SW 1	SW 1	GW ◇	SN 1		SN 1	SW 1	SN 1	SW 1	SW 1	SW 1	SW 1	GW ◇
Havant	d		16 15		16 27		16 33		16 46	16 49	17 04		17 15		17 27		17 33		17 46	17 49	18 04		18 15		18 27	
Bedhampton	d				16 30		16 35								17 30		17 35								18 30	
Hilsea	d	16 03		16 32	16 35		16 41					17 03		17 32	17 35		17 41					18 03		18 32	18 35	
Fratton	d	16k11	16 24	16 37	16 40	16 41	16 46		16 55	16 59	17 13	17m11	17 24	17 37	17 40	17 41	17 46		17 55	17 59	18 13	18n11	18 24	18 37	18 39	18 42
Portsmouth & Southsea	a	16 19	16 27	16 40	16 43	16 45	16 49		16 58	17 02	17 16	17 19	17 27	17 40	17 43	17 45	17 49		17 58	18 02	18 16	18 19	18 27	18 40	18 42	18 46
	d	16 20	16 29	16 41		16 45			16 58	17 03	17 16	17 20	17 29			17 45			17 58	18 03	18 16	18 20	18 29			18 46
Portsmouth Harbour	a	16 23	16 32	16 44		16 49			17 02	17 07	17 20	17 23	17 32			17 49			18 02	18 07	18 20	18 23	18 32			18 49

		SN 1	SN 1	SW 1		SN 1	SW 1	SW 1	SW 1	SW 1	GW ◇	SN 1	SN 1	SW 1		SW 1	SN 1	SW 1	SW 1	GW ◇ A	SW 1	SN 1	SW 1	SW 1		SN 1
Havant	d	18 33	18 46	18 49		19 04		19 15		19 27		19 33	19 46	19 49			20 10	20 15			20 29	20 46	20 49			21 10
Bedhampton	d	18 35								19 30		19 35									20 32					
Hilsea	d	18 41					19 03		19 32	19 35		19 41				20 03			20 32		20 39			21 06		
Fratton	d	18 46	18 55	18 59		19 13	19q11	19 24	19 37	19 39	19 42	19 46	19 55	19 59		20r11	20 19	20 24	20 37	20 41	20 44	20 55	20 59	21 10		21 19
Portsmouth & Southsea	a	18 49	18 58	19 02		19 16	19 19	19 27	19 40	19 42	19 45	19 49	19 58	20 02		20 19	20 22	20 27	20 40	20 44	20 47	20 58	21 02	21 18		21 22
	d		18 58	19 03		19 16	19 20	19 29			19 46		19 58	20 03		20 20	20 22	20 29		20 46		20 58	21 03	21 20		21 22
Portsmouth Harbour	a		19 02	19 07		19 20	19 23	19 32			19 49		20 02	20 07		20 23	20 26	20 32		20 49		21 02	21 07	21 23		21 26

		SW 1	SW 1	SW 1	GW ◇	SW 1	SN 1	SW 1	SN 1	SW 1		SW 1	GW ◇	SW 1	SN 1	SW 1	SW 1	SN 1	SW 1	SW 1	GW ◇	SW 1	SN 1	SW 1		
Havant	d	21 15		21 27		21 46	21 49		22 10	22 19				22 31	22 43	22 49		23 10	23 19			23 31	23 36	23 49		
Bedhampton	d			21 30										22 34								23 34				
Hilsea	d		21 32	21 35				22 06				22 33		22 39			23 03			23 32		23 39				
Fratton	d	21 24	21 37	21 40	21 42	21 55	21 59	22 10	22 19	22 29		22 38	22 42	22 44	22 52	22 59	23 07	23 19	23 29	23 37	23 40	23 44	23 48	23 59		
Portsmouth & Southsea	a	21 27	21 40	21 43	21 45	21 58	22 02	22 13	22 22	22 32		22 41	22 45	22 47	22 55	23 02	23 10	23 22	23 32	23 40	23 44	23 48	23 51	00 02		
	d	21 29			21 46	22 00	22 03	22 15	22 22	22 33		22 42	22 46	22 48	22 56	23 03	23 12	23 22	23 33		23 45	23 50		00 03		
Portsmouth Harbour	a	21 32			21 49	22 03	22 06	22 18	22 26	22 36		22 45	22 49	22 52	22 59	23 07	23 16	23 26	23 37		23 48	23 54		00 07		

For general notes see front of timetable
For details of catering facilities see Directory of Train Operators

A Until 22 March
b Arr. 0613
c Arr. 1007
e Arr. 1107
f Arr. 1207
g Arr. 1307
h Arr. 1407
j Arr. 1507
k Arr. 1607
m Arr. 1707
n Arr. 1807
q Arr. 1907
r Arr. 2007

Table 157

Sundays

Havant → Portsmouth Harbour
(Complete service)

Network Diagram - see first page of Table 155

		SW 1	SW 1	SW 1	SW 1	SW 1	SN 1	SW 1	SW 1	SN 1	SW 1		SW 1	SN 1	SW 1	SN 1	SW 1	SW 1	SN 1	SW 1	SW 1	SN 1		SW 1	SN 1	SW 1
Havant	d	23p49		00 22	00 37	01 22	07 10			08 10			08 45	08 49		09 10		09 45	09 49	09 52		10 17			10 41	10 45
Bedhampton	d			00 25		01s24							08 47	08 51				09 47	09 51						10 43	10 47
Hilsea	d		00 03	00 30		01s30		07 26	07 59		08 26				09 00		09 26				10 01			10 26		
Fratton	d	23p59	00 07	00 34	00 47	01s34	07 19	07 30	08 04	08 19	08 30		08 56	08 59	09 04	09 19	09 30	09 56	09 59	10 01	10 06	10 26		10 30	10 51	10 56
Portsmouth & Southsea	a	00 02	00 11	00 38	00 50	01 38	07 22	07 33	08 08	08 22	08 33		08 59	09 03	09 08	09 22	09 33	09 59	10 03	10 05	10 10	10 29		10 33	10 54	10 59
	d	00 03	00 12		00 51		07 22		08 09	08 22			09 00	09 04	09 09	09 22		10 00	10 04	10 06	10 12	10 30			10 55	11 00
Portsmouth Harbour	a	00 07	00 16		00 55		07 26		08 13	08 26			09 04	09 07	09 13	09 26		10 04	10 07	10 11	10 15	10 35			10 58	11 04

		SW 1	SW 1	SN 1	SW 1	GW ◇	SN 1	SW 1	SW 1	SW 1		SN 1	SW 1	GW ◇	SN 1	SW 1	SW 1	SW 1	SN 1	SW 1	SN 1		SW 1	SW 1	SW 1	SN 1
Havant	d	10 53		11 17			11 41	11 45	11 51			12 17			12 41	12 45	12 51		13 17		13 41		13 45	13 51		14 17
Bedhampton	d						11 43	11 47							12 43	12 47					13 43		13 47			
Hilsea	d		11 01		11 26					12 00			12 26					13 00		13 26					14 00	
Fratton	d	11 02	11 06	11 26	11 30	11 41	11 52	11 56	12 01	12 04		12 26	12 30	12 44	12 51	12 56	13 01	13 04	13 26	13 30	13 51		13 56	14 01	14 04	14 26
Portsmouth & Southsea	a	11 05	11 09	11 29	11 33	11 44	11 55	11 59	12 05	12 08		12 29	12 33	12 47	12 54	12 59	13 04	13 08	13 29	13 33	13 54		13 59	14 04	14 08	14 29
	d	11 07	11 11	11 30		11 44	11 56	12 00	12 06	12 09		12 30		12 48	12 55	13 00	13 05	13 09	13 30		13 55		14 00	14 05	14 09	14 30
Portsmouth Harbour	a	11 11	11 14	11 35		11 51	11 59	12 04	12 09	12 13		12 35		12 51	12 58	13 04	13 11	13 13	13 35		13 58		14 04	14 11	14 13	14 35

		SW 1	GW ◇	SN 1	SW 1	SW 1	SW 1	SN 1	SW 1		SN 1	SW 1	SW 1	SW 1	SN 1	SW 1	GW ◇	SN 1	SW 1	SW 1		SW 1	SN 1	SW 1	GW ◇	SN 1
Havant	d			14 41	14 45	14 51		15 17			15 41	15 45	15 51		16 17			16 41	16 44	16 51			17 17			17 41
Bedhampton	d			14 43	14 47						15 43	15 47						16 43	16 47							17 43
Hilsea	d	14 26					15 00		15 26					16 00		16 26						17 00		17 26		
Fratton	d	14 30	14 38	14 51	14 56	15 01	15 04	15 26	15 30		15 51	15 56	16 01	16 04	16 26	16 30	16 44	16 51	16 56	17 01		17 05	17 26	17 30	17 44	17 51
Portsmouth & Southsea	a	14 33	14 41	14 54	14 59	15 04	15 08	15 29	15 33		15 54	15 59	16 04	16 08	16 29	16 33	16 47	16 54	16 59	17 04		17 08	17 29	17 33	17 47	17 54
	d		14 42	14 55	15 00	15 05	15 09	15 30			15 55	16 00	16 05	16 09	16 30		16 48	16 55	17 00	17 05		17 09	17 30		17 48	17 55
Portsmouth Harbour	a		14 46	14 58	15 04	15 11	15 13	15 35			15 58	16 04	16 11	16 13	16 35		16 51	16 58	17 05	17 11		17 13	17 35		17 51	17 58

		SW 1	SW 1	SW 1	SN 1	SW 1	GW ◇	SN 1		SW 1	SW 1	SW 1	SN 1	SW 1	GW ◇	SN 1	SW 1	SW 1	SW 1		SN 1	SW 1	SN 1	SW 1	SW 1	SW 1
Havant	d	17 45	17 51		18 17			18 41		18 44	18 51		19 17			19 41	19 45	19 51			20 17		20 41	20 45	20 51	
Bedhampton	d	17 47						18 43		18 47						19 43	19 47						20 43	20 47		
Hilsea	d			18 00		18 26						19 00		19 26					20 00			20 26				21 00
Fratton	d	17 56	18 01	18 04	18 26	18 30	18 44	18 51		18 56	19 01	19 05	19 26	19 30	19 44	19 51	19 56	20 01	20 04		20 26	20 30	20 51	20 56	21 01	21 04
Portsmouth & Southsea	a	17 59	18 04	18 08	18 29	18 33	18 47	18 54		18 59	19 03	19 08	19 29	19 33	19 47	19 54	19 59	20 04	20 08		20 29	20 33	20 54	20 59	21 04	21 08
	d	18 00	18 05	18 09	18 30		18 48	18 55		19 00	19 06	19 09	19 30		19 48	19 55	20 00	20 05	20 09		20 30		20 55	21 00	21 05	21 09
Portsmouth Harbour	a	18 04	18 11	18 13	18 35		18 51	18 58		19 04	19 11	19 13	19 35		19 51	19 58	20 04	20 11	20 13		20 35		20 58	21 04	21 09	21 13

		GW ◇	SN 1	SW 1	GW ◇	SN 1	SW 1		SW 1	SW 1	GW ◇	SN 1	SW 1	GW ◇	SN 1	SW 1	SW 1	SW 1	SW 1	SN 1	GW ◇	SW 1	SW 1	SW 1		
Havant	d		21 17			21 41	21 45		21 51			22 17			22 41	22 45	22 51			23 21		23 45	23 51			
Bedhampton	d					21 43	21 47								22 43	22 47						23 47				
Hilsea	d			21 26						22 00			22 26					23 00	23 24					23 59		
Fratton	d	21 10	21 26	21 30	21 36	21 51	21 56		22 01	22 04	22 07	22 26	22 30	22 36	22 51	22 56	23 01	23 04	23 29	23 31	23 37	23 56	00 01	00 04		
Portsmouth & Southsea	a	21 15	21 29	21 33	21 39	21 54	21 59		22 04	22 08	22 12	22 29	22 33	22 39	22 54	22 59	23 04	23 08	23 32	23 34	23 40	23 59	00 04	00 08		
	d	21 15	21 30		21 40	21 55	22 00		22 05	22 09	22 12	22 30		22 40	22 55	23 00	23 05	23 09		23 35	23 41	00 01	00 05	00 09		
Portsmouth Harbour	a	21 23	21 35		21 46	21 58	22 04		22 11	22 13	22 20	22 35		22 46	22 58	23 04	23 09	23 13		23 38	23 44	00 04	00 09	00 13		

For general notes see front of timetable
For details of catering facilities see
Directory of Train Operators

Portsmouth Harbour → Havant

(Complete service)

Network Diagram - see first page of Table 155

Mondays to Fridays

		SW 1	SW 1	SW 1	SW 1	SN 1	SW 1	SN 1	SW 1	GW ◇	SN 1	SW 1	SW 1		SW 1	SW 1	SW 1	SN 1	SW 1	SN 1	SW 1	GW	SW 1	SN 1	SW 1	SW 1
Portsmouth Harbour	d	04 30	05 00		05 19	05 34	05 43	05 47	05 50	06 00	06 04	06 15			06 23		06 38		06 42	06 46	06 55	07 01	07 13	07 20	07 24	07 29
Portsmouth & Southsea	a	04 33	05 03		05 22	05 37	05 46	05 50	05 53	06 03	06 07	06 18			06 26		06 41		06 45	06 49	06 58	07 04	07 16	07 23	07 27	07 32
	d	04 35	05 05	05 16	05 24	05 38	05 48	05 51	05 55	06 04	06 08	06 20	06 23		06 28		06 43		06 47	06 50	07 00	07 05	07 18	07 24	07 29	07 33
Fratton	d	04 39	05 09	05 20	05 28	05 42	05 52	05 55	05 59	06a07	06 12	06 24	06 27		06 32		06 47		06 51	06 54	07 04	07 10	07 22	07 28	07 33	07 37
Hilsea	d	04 43	05a13	05a24	05 32	05 46	05a56	05 59	06 03				06a31		06a36	06 42	06a51			06 58	07 08				07a37	07 41
Bedhampton	d	04 48			05 37	05 51		06 04	06 08							06 47		06 34		07 03	07 13					07 49
Havant	a	04 50			05 40	05 53		06 06	06 10		06 20	06 33				06 49		06 37	06 59	07 05	07 15	07 19	07 30	07 36		07 51

		SW 1	SW 1		SW 1	SN 1	SW 1	SN 1	SW 1	SW 1	GW ◇	SN 1	SW 1	SW 1	SW 1	SN 1		SN 1	SW 1	SW 1	GW ◇	SN 1	SW 1	SW 1	SW 1	SN 1
Portsmouth Harbour	d		07 45		07 52		08 05	08 10	08 13		08 22	08 26	08 32	08 45	08 51	08 59		09 12	09 15	09 17	09 22	09 28	09 32	09 45	09 54	
Portsmouth & Southsea	a		07 48		07 55		08 08	08 13	08 16		08 26	08 29	08 35	08 48	08 54	09 02		09 15	09 18	09 22	09 26	09 31	09 35	09 48	09 57	
	d	07 36	07 50		07 57	08 03	08 10	08 14	08 18	08 24	08 27	08 30	08 36	08 50	08 56	09 03		09 16	09 20	09 24	09 27	09 32	09 36	09 50	09 59	10 03
Fratton	d	07 40	07 54		08 01	08 07	08 14	08 18	08 22	08 28	08a31	08 35	08 40	08 54	09 01	09 07		09 20	09 24	09 28	09a31	09 36	09 40	09 54	10 03	10 07
Hilsea	d	07a44			08a05	08 11	08a18			08 32			08a44		09a05	09 11				09 32			09a44		10a07	10 11
Bedhampton	d					08 16				08 37						09 16				09 37						10 16
Havant	a		08 02			08 18		08 26	08 30	08 40		08 44		09 03		09 18		09 28	09 33	09 39		09 44		10 03		10 18

		SN 1	SW 1	SW 1	GW ◇	SN 1		SW 1	SW 1	SW 1	SN 1	SN 1	SW 1	SW 1	GW ◇	SN 1	SW 1	SW 1	SW 1		SN 1	SN 1	SW 1	SW 1	GW ◇	SN 1
Portsmouth Harbour	d	10 12	10 15	10 17	10 22	10 28		10 31	10 45	10 54		11 12	11 15	11 17	11 22	11 28		11 45	11 54			12 12	12 15	12 17	12 22	12 28
Portsmouth & Southsea	a	10 15	10 18	10 22	10 26	10 31		10 34	10 48	10 57		11 15	11 18	11 22	11 26	11 31		11 48	11 57			12 15	12 18	12 22	12 26	12 31
	d	10 16	10 20	10 24	10 27	10 32		10 36	10 50	10 59	11 03	11 16	11 20	11 24	11 27	11 32	11 36	11 50	11 59		12 03	12 16	12 20	12 24	12 27	12 32
Fratton	d	10 20	10 24	10 28	10a31	10 36		10 40	10 54	11 03	11 07	11 20	11 24	11 28	11a31	11 36	11 40	11 54	12 03		12 07	12 20	12 24	12 28	12a31	12 36
Hilsea	d			10 32				10a44		11a07	11 11			11 32			11a44		12a07		12 11			12 32		
Bedhampton	d			10 37							11 16			11 37							12 16			12 37		
Havant	a	10 28	10 33	10 39		10 44			11 03		11 18	11 29	11 33	11 39		11 44		12 03			12 18	12 29	12 33	12 39		12 44

		SW 1	SW 1	SW 1	SN 1	SN 1	SW 1	SW 1	GW ◇		SN 1	SW 1	SW 1	SW 1	SN 1	SN 1	SW 1	SW 1	GW ◇	SN 1	SW 1	SW 1		SW 1	SN 1	SN 1
Portsmouth Harbour	d		12 45	12 54		13 12	13 15		13 22		13 28		13 45	13 54		14 12	14 15	14 17	14 22	14 28		14 45		14 54		15 12
Portsmouth & Southsea	a		12 48	12 57		13 15	13 18		13 26		13 31		13 48	13 57		14 15	14 18	14 22	14 26	14 31		14 48		14 57		15 15
	d	12 36	12 50	12 59	13 03	13 16	13 20	13 24	13 27		13 32	13 36	13 50	13 59	14 03	14 16	14 20	14 24	14 27	14 32	14 36	14 50		14 59	15 03	15 16
Fratton	d	12 40	12 54	13 03	13 07	13 20	13 24	13 28	13a31		13 36	13 40	13 54	14 03	14 07	14 20	14 24	14 28	14a31	14 36	14 40	14 54		15 03	15 07	15 20
Hilsea	d	12a44		13a07	13 11			13 32				13a44		14a07	14 11			14 32			14a44			15a07	15 11	
Bedhampton	d				13 16			13 37							14 16			14 37							15 16	
Havant	a		13 03		13 18	13 29	13 33	13 39			13 44		14 03		14 18	14 29	14 33	14 39		14 44		15 03			15 18	15 29

		SW 1	SW 1	GW ◇	SN 1	SW 1	SW 1	SW 1	SN 1	SN 1	SW 1	SW 1		GW ◇	SN 1	SW 1	SN 1	SW 1	SW 1	SN 1	SW 1	SN 1	SW 1	SW 1	GW ◇	SN 1
Portsmouth Harbour	d	15 15	15 17	15 22	15 28		15 45	15 54		16 12	16 15	16 17		16 22	16 28			16 45	16 54		17 03	17 12	17 15	17 17	17 22	17 28
Portsmouth & Southsea	a	15 18	15 22	15 26	15 31		15 48	15 57		16 15	16 18	16 22		16 26	16 31			16 48	16 57		17 06	17 15	17 18	17 22	17 26	17 31
	d	15 20	15 24	15 27	15 32	15 36	15 50	15 59	16 03	16 16	16 20	16 24		16 27	16 32	16 36	16 46	16 50	16 59	17 03	17 07	17 16	17 20	17 24	17 27	17 32
Fratton	d	15 24	15 28	15a31	15 36	15 40	15 54	16 03	16 07	16 20	16 24	16 28		16a31	16 36	16 40	16 50	16 54	17 03	17 07	17 11	17 20	17 24	17 28	17a31	17 36
Hilsea	d		15 32			15a44		16a07	16 11			16 32				16a44	16 54		17a07	17 11	17a15			17 32		
Bedhampton	d		15 37						16 16			16 37								17 16				17 37		
Havant	a	15 33	15 40		15 44		16 03		16 18	16 29	16 33	16 39			16 44		16 59	17 03		17 18		17 29	17 33	17 39		17 44

		SW 1		SN 1	SW 1	SW 1	SN 1	SW 1	SW 1	GW ◇	SN 1	SW 1	SN 1	SW 1	SW 1		SN 1	SW 1	SW 1	GW ◇	SN 1	SW 1	SN 1	SW 1	SW 1	SN 1
Portsmouth Harbour	d				17 45	17 54		18 15		18 22	18 28		18 36	18 45	18 54			19 15		19 22	19 28		19 40	19 45	19 54	
Portsmouth & Southsea	a				17 48	17 57		18 18		18 26	18 31		18 39	18 48	18 57			19 18		19 26	19 31		19 43	19 48	19 57	
	d	17 36		17 46	17 50	17 59	18 03	18 20	18 24	18 27	18 32	18 36	18 41	18 50	18 59		19 03	19 20	19 24	19 27	19 32	19 36	19 44	19 50	19 59	20 03
Fratton	d	17 40		17 50	17 54	18 03	18 07	18 24	18 28	18a31	18 36	18 40	18 45	18 54	19 03		19 07	19 24	19 28	19a31	19 36	19 40	19 48	19 54	20 03	20 07
Hilsea	d	17a44		17 54		18a07	18 11		18 32			18a44	18 49		19a07		19 11		19 32			19a44			20a07	20 11
Bedhampton	d						18 16		18 37								19 16		19 37							20 16
Havant	a			17 59	18 03		18 18	18 33	18 39		18 44		18 54	19 03			19 18	19 33	19 39		19 44		19 56	20 03		20 18

		SW 1	SW 1	GW ◇	SN 1		SW 1	SN 1	SW 1	SW 1	SN 1	SW 1	GW	SW 1	SN 1	SW 1	SN 1	SW 1		SW 1	SN 1	SN 1	SW 1	SW 1		
Portsmouth Harbour	d	20 15	20 17	20 22				20 40	20 45	20 54		21 15	21 22		21 40	21 54	22 15	22 17			22 44	23 15	23 18	23 24		
Portsmouth & Southsea	a	20 18	20 22	20 26				20 43	20 48	20 57		21 20	21 26		21 43	21 57	22 18	22 22			22 47	23 18	23 22	23 27		
	d	20 20	20 24	20 27	20 32		20 36	20 44	20 50	20 59	21 15	21 24	21 27	21 36	21 44	21 59	22 19	22 24		22 36	22 48	23 19	23 24	23 29		
Fratton	d	20 24	20 28	20a31	20 36		20 40	20 48	20 54	21 03	21 19	21 28	21a31	21 40	21 48	22 03	22 23	22 28		22 40	22 52	23 23	23 28	23 33		
Hilsea	d		20 32				20a44			21a07	21 23	21 32		21a44	21 52	22a07	22 27	22 32		22a44	22 56	23 27	23 32	23a37		
Bedhampton	d		20 37								21 28	21 37			21 57		22 32	22 37			23 01	23 33	23 37			
Havant	a	20 33	20 39		20 44			20 56	21 03		21 30	21 39			21 59		22 34	22 39			23 03	23 36	23 39			

Saturdays

		SW 1	SN 1	SW 1	SW 1	SN 1	SW 1	GW ◇		SN 1	SW 1	SN 1	SW 1	SW 1	GW	SW 1		SN 1	GW ◇	SN 1	SW 1	SW 1	SN 1	SW 1		SW 1
Portsmouth Harbour	d	04 43			05 18		05 54	06 00		06 12	06 18	06 28		06 45	06 48	06 54			07 04	07 12	07 15		07 28			07 45
Portsmouth & Southsea	a	04 46			05 22		05 57	06 03		06 15	06 22	06 31		06 48	06 52	06 57			07 07	07 15	07 18		07 31			07 48
	d	04 48	04 56	05 16	05 24	05 56	05 59	06 04		06 16	06 24	06 32	06 36	06 50	06 53	06 59		07 03	07 08	07 16	07 20	07 24	07 32	07 36		07 50
Fratton	d	04 52	05 00	05 20	05 28	06 00	06 03	06a07		06 20	06 28	06 36	06 40	06 54	06 57	07 03		07 07	07a12	07 20	07 24	07 28	07 36	07 40		07 54
Hilsea	d	04 56		05a24	05 32	06 04	06a07				06 32		06a44			07a07		07 11				07 32		07a44		
Bedhampton	d	05 01			05 37	06 09					06 37							07 16				07 37				
Havant	a	05 03	05 08		05 39	06 13				06 29	06 39	06 44		07 03	07 09			07 18		07 29	07 33	07 39	07 44			08 03

For general notes see front of timetable
For details of catering facilities see
Directory of Train Operators

Table 157

Saturdays

Portsmouth Harbour → Havant

(Complete service)

Network Diagram - see first page of Table 155

		SW	SN	SN	SW	SW	GW	SN	SW	SW	SW	SN	SN	SW	SW	GW	SN	SW	SW	SW	SN	SN	SW
		1	1	1	1	1	◇	1	1	1	1	1	1	1	1	◇	1	1	1	1	1	1	1
Portsmouth Harbour	d	07 54		08 12	08 15		08 22	08 28		08 45	08 54		09 12	09 15		09 22	09 28		09 45	09 54		10 12	10 15
Portsmouth & Southsea	a	07 57		08 15	08 18		08 25	08 31		08 48	08 57		09 15	09 18		09 25	09 31		09 48	09 57		10 15	10 18
	d	07 59	08 03	08 16	08 20	08 24	08 27	08 32	08 36	08 50	08 59	09 03	09 16	09 20	09 24	09 27	09 32	09 36	09 50	09 59	10 03	10 16	10 20
Fratton	d	08 03	08 07	08 20	08 24	08 28	08a30	08 36	08 40	08 54	09 03	09 07	09 20	09 24	09 28	09a30	09 36	09 40	09 54	10 03	10 07	10 20	10 24
Hilsea	d	08a07	08 11			08 32			08a44		09a07	09 11			09 32			09a44		10a07	10 11		
Bedhampton	d		08 16			08 37						09 16			09 37						10 16		
Havant	a		08 19	08 29	08 33	08 39		08 44		09 03		09 18	09 29	09 33	09 39		09 44		10 03		10 18	10 28	10 33

		SW	GW	SN	SW	SW	SW	SN	SN	SW	SW	GW	SN	SW	SW	SW	SN	SN	SW	SW	GW	SN	SW
		1	◇	1	1	1	1	1	1	1	1	◇	1	1	1	1	1	1	1	1	◇	1	1
Portsmouth Harbour	d		10 22	10 28		10 45	10 54		11 12	11 15		11 22	11 28		11 45	11 54		12 12	12 15		12 22	12 28	
Portsmouth & Southsea	a		10 25	10 31		10 48	10 57		11 15	11 18		11 25	11 31		11 48	11 57		12 15	12 18		12 25	12 31	
	d	10 24	10 27	10 32	10 36	10 50	10 59	11 03	11 16	11 20	11 24	11 27	11 32	11 36	11 50	11 59	12 03	12 16	12 20	12 24	12 27	12 32	12 36
Fratton	d	10 28	10a30	10 36	10 40	10 54	11 03	11 07	11 20	11 24	11 28	11a30	11 36	11 40	11 54	12 03	12 07	12 20	12 24	12 28	12a30	12 36	12 40
Hilsea	d	10 32			10a44		11a07	11 11			11 32			11a44		12a07	12 11			12 32			12a44
Bedhampton	d	10 37						11 16			11 37						12 16			12 37			
Havant	a	10 39		10 44		11 03		11 18	11 29	11 33	11 39		11 44		12 03		12 18	12 29	12 33	12 39		12 44	

		SW	SW	SN	SN	SW	SW	GW	SN	SW	SW	SW	SN	SN	SW	SW	GW	SN	SW	SW	SW	SN	SN
		1	1	1	1	1	1	◇	1	1	1	1	1	1	1	1	◇	1	1	1	1	1	1
Portsmouth Harbour	d	12 45	12 54		13 12	13 15		13 22	13 28		13 45	13 54		14 12	14 15		14 22	14 28		14 45	14 54		15 12
Portsmouth & Southsea	a	12 48	12 57		13 15	13 18		13 25	13 31		13 48	13 57		14 15	14 18		14 25	14 31		14 48	14 57		15 15
	d	12 50	12 59	13 03	13 16	13 20	13 24	13 27	13 32	13 36	13 50	13 59	14 03	14 16	14 20	14 24	14 27	14 32	14 36	14 50	14 59	15 03	15 16
Fratton	d	12 54	13 03	13 07	13 20	13 24	13 28	13a30	13 36	13 40	13 54	14 03	14 07	14 20	14 24	14 28	14a30	14 36	14 40	14 54	15 03	15 07	15 20
Hilsea	d		13a07	13 11			13 32			13a44		14a07	14 11			14 32			14a44		15a07	15 11	
Bedhampton	d			13 16			13 37						14 16			14 37						15 16	
Havant	a	13 03		13 18	13 29	13 33	13 39		13 44		14 03		14 18	14 29	14 33	14 39		14 44		15 03		15 18	15 29

		SW	SW	GW	SN	SW	SW	SW	SN	SN	SW	SW	GW	SN	SW	SW	SW	SN	SW	SW	SN	SW	GW
		1	1	◇	1	1	1	1	1	1	1	1	◇	1	1	1	1	1	1	1	1	1	◇
Portsmouth Harbour	d	15 15		15 22	15 28		15 45	15 54		16 12	16 15		16 22	16 28		16 45	16 54		17 01		17 12	17 16	17 22
Portsmouth & Southsea	a	15 18		15 25	15 31		15 48	15 57		16 15	16 18		16 25	16 31		16 48	16 57		17 04		17 15	17 22	17 26
	d	15 20	15 24	15 27	15 32	15 36	15 50	15 59	16 03	16 16	16 20	16 24	16 27	16 32	16 36	16 50	16 59	17 03	17 06	17 10	17 16	17 24	17 27
Fratton	d	15 24	15 28	15a30	15 36	15 40	15 54	16 03	16 07	16 20	16 24	16 28	16a31	16 36	16 40	16 54	17 03	17 07	17 10	17 14	17 20	17 28	17a31
Hilsea	d		15 32			15a44		16a07	16 11			16 32			16a44		17a07	17 11	17a14	17 18		17 32	
Bedhampton	d		15 37						16 16			16 37						17 16		17 23		17 37	
Havant	a	15 33	15 39		15 44		16 03		16 18	16 29	16 33	16 39		16 44		17 03		17 18		17 25	17 29	17 39	

		SN	SW	SW	SW	SN	SN	SW	SW	GW	SN	SW	SW	SW	SN	SN	SW	SW	GW	SN	SW	SW	SW
		1	1	1	1	1	1	1	1	◇	1	1	1	1	1	1	1	1	◇	1	1	1	1
Portsmouth Harbour	d	17 28	17 32	17 45	17 54		18 12	18 15		18 22	18 28		18 45	18 54		19 12	19 15		19 22	19 28		19 45	19 54
Portsmouth & Southsea	a	17 31	17 35	17 48	17 57		18 15	18 18		18 26	18 31		18 48	18 57		19 15	19 18		19 25	19 31		19 48	19 57
	d	17 32	17 36	17 50	17 59	18 03	18 16	18 20	18 24	18 27	18 32	18 36	18 50	18 59	19 03	19 16	19 20	19 24	19 27	19 32	19 36	19 50	19 59
Fratton	d	17 36	17 40	17 54	18 03	18 07	18 20	18 24	18 28	18a31	18 36	18 40	18 54	19 03	19 07	19 20	19 24	19 28	19a30	19 36	19 40	19 54	20 03
Hilsea	d		17a44		18a07	18 11			18 32			18a44		19a07	19 11			19 32			19a44		20a07
Bedhampton	d					18 16			18 37						19 16			19 37					
Havant	a	17 44		18 03		18 18	18 28	18 33	18 39		18 44		19 03		19 18	19 28	19 33	19 39		19 44		20 03	

		SN	SW	SW	GW	SN	SW	SN	SW	SW	SN	SW	SW	SN	SW	SN	SW	SW	SN	SN	SW	SW
		1	1	1	◇	1	1	1	1	1	1	1	1	1	1	1	1	1	1	1	1	1
Portsmouth Harbour	d		20 15		20 22	20 28		20 40	20 45	20 54	21 11	21 17		21 40	21 54	22 15	22 17		22 44	23 15	23 18	23 24
Portsmouth & Southsea	a		20 18		20 25	20 31		20 43	20 48	20 57	21 14	21 20		21 43	21 57	22 18	22 22		22 47	23 18	23 22	23 28
	d	20 03	20 20	20 24	20 27	20 32	20 36	20 44	20 50	20 59	21 15	21 24	21 36	21 44	21 59	22 19	22 24	22 36	22 48	23 19	23 23	23 29
Fratton	d	20 07	20 24	20 28	20a30	20 36	20 40	20 48	20 54	21 03	21 19	21 28	21 40	21 48	22 03	22 23	22 28	22 40	22 52	23 23	23 28	23 33
Hilsea	d	20 11		20 32			20a44			21a07	21 23	21 32	21a44	21 52	22a07	22 27	22 32	22a44	22 56	23 27	23 32	23a37
Bedhampton	d	20 16		20 37							21 28	21 37		21 57		22 32	22 37		23 01	23 33	23 37	
Havant	a	20 18	20 33	20 39		20 44		20 56	21 03		21 30	21 39		21 59		22 34	22 39		23 03	23 36	23 39	

Sundays

		SW	SW	GW	SN	SW	SW	SW	SN	SW	SN	SW	SW	SW	SN	SW	GW	SN	SW	SW	SW	SN	SW	SN
		1	1		1	1	1	1	1	1	1	1	1	1	1	1	◇	1	1	1	1	1	1	1
Portsmouth Harbour	d	06 37	06 48	07 08	07 14	07 17	07 32		07 43	07 48	08 14	08 17	08 32		08 43	08 48	09 08	09 14	09 17	09 32		09 43	09 48	10 14
Portsmouth & Southsea	a	06 40	06 51	07 11	07 17	07 20	07 35		07 46	07 51	08 17	08 20	08 35		08 46	08 51	09 11	09 17	09 20	09 35		09 46	09 51	10 17
	d	06 42	06 53	07 12	07 18	07 22	07 37	07 42	07 47	07 53	08 18	08 22	08 37	08 42	08 47	08 53	09 12	09 18	09 22	09 37	09 42	09 47	09 53	10 18
Fratton	d	06 46	06 57	07a15	07 22	07 26	07 41	07 46	07 51	07 57	08 22	08 26	08 41	08 46	08 51	08 57	09a15	09 22	09 26	09 41	09 46	09 51	09 57	10 22
Hilsea	d	06a50				07a30		07a50				08a30		08a50					09a30		09a50			
Bedhampton	d		07 04		07 30					08 04	08 30					09 04		09 30					10 04	10 30
Havant	a		07 07		07 32		07 49		07 59	08 07	08 32		08 49		08 59	09 07		09 32		09 49		09 59	10 07	10 32

		SW	SW	SW	SN	SW	GW	SN	SW	SW	SW	SN	SW	SN	SW	SW	SW	SN	SW	GW	SN	SW	SW
		1	1	1	1	1	◇	1	1	1	1	1	1	1	1	1	1	1	1	◇	1	1	1
Portsmouth Harbour	d	10 17	10 32		10 43	10 48	11 08	11 14	11 17	11 32		11 43	11 48	12 14	12 17	12 32		12 43	12 48	13 08	13 14	13 17	13 32
Portsmouth & Southsea	a	10 20	10 35		10 46	10 51	11 11	11 17	11 20	11 35		11 46	11 51	12 17	12 20	12 35		12 46	12 51	13 11	13 17	13 20	13 35
	d	10 22	10 37	10 42	10 47	10 53	11 12	11 18	11 22	11 37	11 42	11 47	11 53	12 18	12 22	12 37	12 42	12 47	12 53	13 12	13 18	13 22	13 37
Fratton	d	10 26	10 41	10 46	10 51	10 57	11a15	11 22	11 26	11 41	11 46	11 51	11 57	12 22	12 26	12 41	12 46	12 51	12 57	13a15	13 22	13 26	13 41
Hilsea	d	10a30		10a50					11a30		11a50				12a30		12a50					13a30	
Bedhampton	d					11 04		11 30					12 04	12 30					13 04		13 30		
Havant	a		10 49		10 59	11 07		11 32		11 49		11 59	12 07	12 32		12 49		12 59	13 07		13 32		13 49

For general notes see front of timetable
For details of catering facilities see
Directory of Train Operators

Table 157

Sundays

Portsmouth Harbour → Havant
(Complete service)

Network Diagram - see first page of Table 155

		SW 1	SN 1	SW 1	GW ◇	SN 1	SW 1	SW 1		SW 1	SN 1	SW 1	GW ◇	SN 1	SW 1	SW 1	SW 1		SN 1	SW 1	GW ◇	SN 1	SW 1	SW 1	SW 1	SN 1
Portsmouth Harbour	d		13 43	13 48	14 08	14 14	14 17	14 32			14 43	14 48	15 08	15 14	15 17	15 32			15 43	15 48	16 08	16 14	16 17	16 32		16 43
Portsmouth & Southsea	a		13 46	13 51	14 11	14 17	14 20	14 35			14 46	14 51	15 11	15 17	15 20	15 35			15 46	15 51	16 11	16 17	16 20	16 35		16 46
	d	13 42	13 47	13 53	14 12	14 18	14 22	14 37		14 42	14 47	14 53	15 12	15 18	15 22	15 37	15 42		15 47	15 53	16 12	16 18	16 22	16 37	16 42	16 47
Fratton	d	13 46	13 51	13 57	14a15	14 22	14 26	14 41		14 46	14 51	14 57	15a15	15 22	15 26	15 41	15 46		15 51	15 57	16a15	16 22	16 26	16 41	16 46	16 51
Hilsea	d	13a50					14a30			14a50					15a30		15a50						16a30		16a50	
Bedhampton	d			14 04		14 30						15 04		15 30						16 04		16 30				
Havant	a		13 59	14 07		14 32		14 49			14 59	15 07		15 32		15 49			15 59	16 07		16 32		16 49		16 59

		SW 1	GW ◇		SN 1	SW 1	SW 1	SW 1	SN 1	SW 1	GW ◇	SN 1		SW 1	SW 1	SW 1	SN 1	SW 1	GW ◇	SN 1	SW 1		SW 1	SW 1	SN 1	SW 1
Portsmouth Harbour	d	16 48	17 08		17 14	17 17	17 32		17 43	17 48	18 08	18 14		18 17	18 32		18 43	18 48	19 08	19 14	19 17		19 32		19 43	19 48
Portsmouth & Southsea	a	16 51	17 11		17 17	17 20	17 35		17 46	17 51	18 11	18 17		18 20	18 35		18 46	18 51	19 11	19 17	19 20		19 35		19 46	19 51
	d	16 53	17 12		17 18	17 22	17 37	17 42	17 47	17 53	18 12	18 18		18 22	18 37	18 42	18 47	18 53	19 12	19 18	19 22		19 37	19 42	19 47	19 53
Fratton	d	16 57	17a15		17 22	17 26	17 41	17 46	17 51	17 57	18a15	18 22		18 26	18 41	18 46	18 51	18 57	19a15	19 22	19 26		19 41	19 46	19 51	19 57
Hilsea	d					17a30		17a50						18a30		18a50					19a30			19a50		
Bedhampton	d	17 04			17 30					18 04		18 30						19 04		19 30						20 04
Havant	a	17 07			17 32		17 49		17 59	18 07		18 32			18 49		18 59	19 07		19 32			19 49		19 59	20 07

		GW ◇	SN 1	SW 1	SW 1	SW 1	SN 1		SW 1	SN 1	SW 1	SW 1	SW 1	SN 1	SW 1	GW ◇		SN 1	SW 1	SW 1	SW 1	SN 1	SW 1	SW 1		
Portsmouth Harbour	d	20 08	20 14	20 17	20 32		20 43		20 48	21 14	21 17	21 32		21 43	21 48	22 07		22 14	22 17	22 32		22 43	22 48	23 17		
Portsmouth & Southsea	a	20 11	20 17	20 20	20 35		20 46		20 51	21 17	21 20	21 35		21 46	21 51	22 11		22 17	22 20	22 34		22 46	22 51	23 20		
	d	20 12	20 18	20 22	20 37	20 42	20 47		20 53	21 18	21 22	21 37	21 42	21 47	21 53	22 12		22 18	22 22	22 37	22 42	22 47	22 53	23 22		
Fratton	d	20a15	20 22	20 26	20 41	20 46	20 51		20 57	21 22	21 26	21 41	21 46	21 51	21 57	22a15		22 22	22 26	22 41	22 46	22 51	22 57	23 26		
Hilsea	d			20a30		20a50					21a30		21a50						22a30		22a50			23a30		
Bedhampton	d		20 30						21 04	21 30					22 04			22 30					23 04			
Havant	a		20 32		20 49		20 59		21 07	21 32		21 49		21 59	22 07			22 32		22 49		22 59	23 07			

For general notes see front of timetable
For details of catering facilities see
Directory of Train Operators

Network Diagram for Table 158

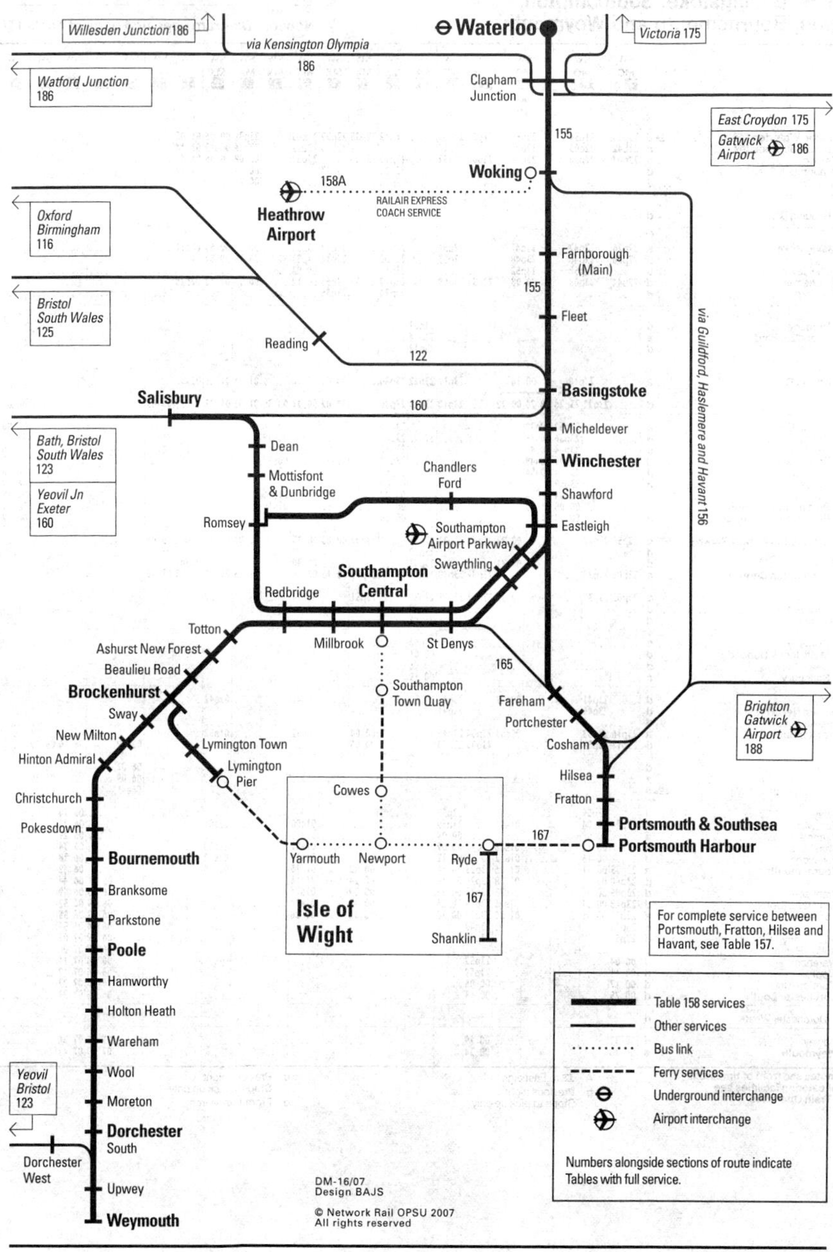

Willesden Junction 186
via Kensington Olympia
186
Waterloo
Victoria 175
Watford Junction 186
Clapham Junction
East Croydon 175
Gatwick Airport 186
155
Woking
158A
Heathrow Airport
RAILAIR EXPRESS COACH SERVICE
Oxford Birmingham 116
Farnborough (Main)
155
Bristol South Wales 125
Fleet
via Guildford, Haslemere and Havant 156
Reading
122
Basingstoke
Salisbury
160
Micheldever
Bath, Bristol South Wales 123
Dean
Winchester
Mottisfont & Dunbridge
Chandlers Ford
Yeovil Jn Exeter 160
Shawford
Romsey
Southampton Airport Parkway
Eastleigh
Swaythling
Southampton Central
Redbridge
Totton
Millbrook
St Denys
Ashurst New Forest
165
Beaulieu Road
Southampton Town Quay
Brockenhurst
Fareham
Brighton Gatwick Airport 188
Sway
Portchester
New Milton
Lymington Town
Cosham
Hinton Admiral
Lymington Pier
Hilsea
Christchurch
Cowes
Fratton
Pokesdown
Portsmouth & Southsea
167
Portsmouth Harbour
Yarmouth
Newport
Ryde
Bournemouth
167
Branksome
Isle of Wight
Shanklin
For complete service between Portsmouth, Fratton, Hilsea and Havant, see Table 157.
Parkstone
Poole
Hamworthy
Table 158 services
Holton Heath
Other services
Wareham
Bus link
Yeovil Bristol 123
Wool
Ferry services
Underground interchange
Moreton
Airport interchange
Dorchester South
Dorchester West
Numbers alongside sections of route indicate Tables with full service.
Upwey
DM-16/07
Design BAJS
© Network Rail OPSU 2007
All rights reserved
Weymouth

For details of Bank Holiday service alterations, please see first page of Table 149

London → Basingstoke, Southampton, Lymington, Bournemouth and Weymouth

Network Diagram - see first page of Table 158

Miles	Miles			SW	SW		SW		SW	SW	SW	SW	SW	SW	SW	SW	SW	SW	SW	SW	SW	SW	SW	SW	SW
				MO	MO		MO		MX	MX	MX	MX	MX	MX	MX	MX	MX	MX							
				1 ◇	1 ◇		1		1 ◇	1	1	1	1	1	1	1	1	1	1	1	1	1	1	1	1
							A ☕			☕			☕												
0	—	**London Waterloo** 15 ⊖	d	21p35	21p54		22p54		21p35	22p05		21p42	22p35	22p39	23p05		23p39	00 05	01 05						
4	—	Clapham Junction 10	d	21b42	22c03		23b03			22b12				22b46	23b12		23b46	00u12	01 14						
24¼	—	**Woking**	d	22p07	22p28		23p28		22p00	22p32		22p19	23p00		23p32		00 08	00 36	01 41						
33¼	—	Farnborough (Main)	d									22p33		23p13			00 18		01s57						
36½	—	Fleet	d									22p38		23p19			00 23								
—	—	Reading 7	d																						
47¾	—	**Basingstoke**	a	22p26	22p47		23p47			22p51		22p58		23p33	23p51		00 35	00 55	02s11						
—	—		d	22p28	22p48		23p48			22p53		23p00		23p34	23p53		00 36	00 57							
58	—	Micheldever	d		22p58		23p58					23p10			00 03										
66½	—	**Winchester**	d	22p44	23p08		00 08		22p33	23p09		23p19	23p33	23p51	00 12		00 53	01 13	02s28						
69¾	—	Shawford	d									23p24		23p55											
—	0	**Romsey**	d								23p07														
—	5¼	Chandlers Ford	a								23p14														
—	—		d								23p14														
73½	—	Eastleigh 3	a		23p18		00 18			23p17	23p22	23p30		00 01	00 20		01 01	01 21	02s37						
—	0		d		23p22	23p26	00 26	00 22		23p18	23p23	23p30		00 02	00 21	00 30	01 02	01 22		05 05					06 00
—	4½	Hedge End	d			23p32	00s32					23p36				00s36									06 06
—	5½	Botley	d			23p36	00s35					23p40				00s39									06 10
—	11	Fareham	d			23p44	00s43					23p48				00s47									06 18
—	14½	Portchester	d			23p49	00s49					23p53				00s53									06 23
—	16¾	Cosham	d			23p54	00s54					23p59				00s58									06 28
—	18¼	Hilsea	a			23p59						00 04													06 33
—	20½	Fratton	a			00 04	01s04					00 08				01s06									06 38
—	21½	**Portsmouth & Southsea**	a			00 08	01s08					00 11				01s10									06 44
—	22¼	**Portsmouth Harbour**	a			00 13	01 13					00 16				01 15									06 49
75	—	**Southampton Airport Parkway** ✈	d	22p53	23p27			00 27	22p42	23p23	23p27		23p42	00 06	00 25		01 06	01 27	02s42	05 09					
75¾	—	Swaythling	d								23p30									05 12					
77¼	—	St Denys	d					00s31			23p33				00s30				02s47	05 15					
79¼	—	**Southampton Central**	a	23p00	23p34			00 36	22p49	23p30	23p38		23p49	00 13	00 35		01 13	01 36	02 52	05 20					
—	—		d	23p03	23p35			00 37	22p51	23p31	23p39		23p51		00 36			01 37							
80¼	—	Millbrook (Hants)	d								23p42														
82	0	Redbridge	d								23p45														
—	6	**Romsey**	d								23p56														
—	9¾	Mottisfont & Dunbridge	d								00 01														
—	13½	Dean	d								00 06														
—	22½	**Salisbury**	a								00 19														
82½	—	Totton	d		23p41			00s42		23p37					00s41			01s42							
85½	—	Ashurst New Forest	d		23p45					23p41															
88	—	Beaulieu Road	d																						
92¾	—	**Brockenhurst** 3	a	23p16	23p53			00s53	23p04	23p49			00 04		00s52			01s53							
—	0		d	23p17	23p54				23p05	23p50			00 05								05 59		06 16	06 29	
—	4¾	Lymington Town	d																		06 07			06 37	
—	5¼	**Lymington Pier**	a																		06 09			06 39	
—	—	Yarmouth (I.O.W.) ⛴	a																		*06e45*			*07 15*	
95½	—	Sway	d		23p59					23p55													06 20		
98½	—	New Milton	d	23p24	00 04			01s01		23p59					01s00			02s01					06 25		
101	—	Hinton Admiral	d		00 08					00 04													06 29		
104¼	—	Christchurch	d		00 13			01s08		00 09					01s07			02s08					06 34		
106¼	—	Pokesdown	d		00 16			01s12		00 12					01s11			02s12					06 38		
108	—	**Bournemouth**	a	23p35	00 21			01 16	23p23	00 16			00 22		01 15			02 16					06 42		
—	—		d	23p40	00 22			01 18	23p28	00 18			00 24		01 16							06 11	06 44		
110¾	—	Branksome	d	23p45	00 28			01s23	23p33	00 23			00 29		01s21							06 16	06 49		
112	—	Parkstone (Dorset)	d	23p48	00 31			01s26	23p36	00 26			00 32		01s24							06 19	06 52		
113¾	—	**Poole** 4	a	23p51	00 35			01 30	23p39	00 30			00 36		01 28							06 23	06 55		
—	—		d	23p52					23p40													06 24	06 57		
116	—	Hamworthy	d	23p57					23p45													06 29	07 02		
118¾	—	Holton Heath	d																			06 33	07 06		
120¾	—	Wareham	d	00 04					23p52													06 38	07 11		
125¾	—	Wool	d	00 11					23p59													06 44	07 17		
130¼	—	Moreton (Dorset)	d	00 17					00 05													06 50	07 23		
135¾	—	**Dorchester South**	d	00 25					00 13													06 58	07 31		
—	—	Dorchester West	d																						
140½	—	Upwey	d	00 32					00 19													07 05	07 38		
142¾	—	**Weymouth**	a	00 36					00 24													07 09	07 42		

For general notes see front of timetable
For details of catering facilities see Directory of Train Operators

A ☕ to Eastleigh
b Previous night. Stops to pick up only
c Previous night. Stops to pick up only
e From 14th March

London → Basingstoke, Southampton, Lymington, Bournemouth and Weymouth

For details of Bank Holiday service alterations, please see first page of Table 149

Network Diagram - see first page of Table 158

Station		GW		SW	SW	SW	SW	SW	SW	SW	SW	SW	SW	SW	SW	SW	SW	SW		SW	SW	XC	SW	SW	SW
		◇		1	1	1	1	1	1	1	1	1	1	1	1	1	1	1		1	1	1 ◇ 🍴	1	1 ◇	1
London Waterloo 15 ⊖	d							05 30								06 30		06 12			06 42			07 35	07 38
Clapham Junction 10	d							05u37								06u37		06u19			06u49				07u45
Woking	d							06 01							06 19	06 57		06 50			07 19			08 00	
Farnborough (Main)	d														06 33			07 04			07 33				08 13
Fleet	d														06 38			07 09			07 38				08 19
Reading 7	d																					07 45			
Basingstoke	a							06 20							06 58	07 16		07 28			07 56	08 08		08 20	08 34
	d			05 40				06 21						06 55	07 00	07 18		07 30			08 00	08 10		08 21	08 36
Micheldever	d			05 50											07 10			07 41			08 10				
Winchester	d			05 59			06 18	06 38						07 11	07 19	07 34		07 50			08 19	08 25		08 38	08 52
Shawford	d						06 23							07 16				07 55			08 24				08 57
Romsey	d					05 58							07 07							08 04					
Chandlers Ford	a					06 06							07 14							08 11					
	d					06 06							07 14							08 11					
Eastleigh 3	a			06 07		06 11	06 28	06 47					07 20	07 22	07 29	07 43		08 00		08 17	08 30			08 46	09 02
	d			06 08		06 13	06 30	06 48		07 02			07 21	07 25	07 30	07 44		08 02		08 18	08 30			08 47	09 03
Hedge End	d						06 36			07 08					07 36						08 36				
Botley	d						06 40			07 12					07 40						08 40				
Fareham	d						06 50			07 20					07 48						08 48				
Portchester	d						06 55			07 25					07 53						08 53				
Cosham	d						07 00			07 29					07 58						08 58				
Hilsea	a						07 05			07 35					08 03						09 04				
Fratton	a						07 09			07 39					08 07						09 08				
Portsmouth & Southsea	a						07 12			07 42					08 11						09 11				
Portsmouth Harbour	a						07 17			07 48					08 16						09 18				
Southampton Airport Parkwy ✈	d			06 13		06 17		06 53					07 25	07 29		07 49		08 06		08 22		08 34		08 51	09 08
Swaythling	d			06 15		06 20							07 28	07 32				08 09		08 25					
St Denys	d			06 18		06 23							07 31	07 35				08 12		08 28					
Southampton Central	a			06 23		06 28		07 00					07 36	07 40		07 57		08 17		08 33		08 40		08 58	09 16
	d			06 25		06 30		07 01			07 18		07 37			07 59		08 19		08 39		08 42		09 00	09 30 ⟶
Millbrook (Hants)	d					06 32					07 20		07 40					08 21		08 41					
Redbridge	d					06 36					07 24		07 43					08 25		08 45					
Romsey	d					06 44							07 51							08 53					
Mottisfont & Dunbridge	d					06 49							07 56							08 58					
Dean	d					06 54							08 02							09 03					
Salisbury	a					07 07							08 14							09 16					
Totton	d			06 30				07 07			07 27					08 04		08 28						09 05	
Ashurst New Forest	d			06 35							07 31							08 32							
Beaulieu Road	d										07 36							08 37							
Brockenhurst 3	a			06 43				07 17			07 42					08 15		08 43				08 56		09 16	
	d			06 44	06 59			07 18	07 29		07 44	07 59				08 16	08 29	08 45				08 57	08 59	09 16	
Lymington Town	d				07 07				07 37			08 07					08 37						09 07		
Lymington Pier	a				07 09				07 39			08 09					08 39						09 09		
Yarmouth (I.O.W.) ⛴	a				*07 45*				*08b15*			*08 45*					*09 15*						*09b45*		
Sway	d			06 48				07 23			07 48					08 20		08 49						09 20	
New Milton	d			06 53				07 28			07 53					08 25		08 54						09 25	
Hinton Admiral	d			06 57				07 32			07 57					08 29		08 58						09 29	
Christchurch	d			07 02				07 37			08 02					08 34		09 03						09 34	
Pokesdown	d			07 06				07 41			08 06					08 38		09 07						09 38	
Bournemouth	a			07 10				07 45			08 10					08 42		09 11				09 15		09 43	
	d			07 11				07 49			08 11					08 43		09 12						09 43	
Branksome	d			07 16				07 54			08 16					08 48		09 17						09 48	
Parkstone (Dorset)	d			07 19				07 57			08 19					08 51		09 20						09 51	
Poole 4	a			07 23				08 01			08 23					08 55		09 24						09 56	
	d			07 24				08 02			08 24					08 56		09 25						09 56	
Hamworthy	d			07 29				08 07			08 29					09 01		09 30						10 01	
Holton Heath	d			07 33				08 11			08 33							09 34							
Wareham	d			07 38				08 16			08 38					09 08		09 39						10c11	
Wool	d			07 44				08 22			08 44					09 14		09 45							
Moreton (Dorset)	d			07 50				08 28			08 50					09 20		09 51							
Dorchester South	d			07 59				08 36			08 58					09 28		09 59						10 27	
Dorchester West	d	07 53																							
Upwey	d	08 00		08 06				08 43			09 05					09 34		10 06							
Weymouth	a	08 05		08 10				08 47			09 09					09 39		10 10						10 35	

For general notes see front of timetable
For details of catering facilities see Directory of Train Operators

b Fridays only until 21st December
Daily from 14th March

c Arr. 1008

For details of Bank Holiday service alterations, please see first page of Table 149

London → Basingstoke, Southampton, Lymington, Bournemouth and Weymouth

Network Diagram - see first page of Table 158

		SW		GW	SW	SW	SW	SW	XC	SW	SW	SW	SW	SW	SW	SW	SW	GW	SW	XC	SW	SW	SW	SW	SW
		1		◇	1 ◇	1	1	1	1 ◇	1	1 ◇	1	1	1	1 ◇	1	1	◇	1	1 ◇	1	1 ◇	1	1	1
					A						A				A							A			
					☕				☕		☕				☕					☕		☕			
London Waterloo 15 ⊖	d				08 05			08 09			08 35		08 39		09 05				09 09			09 35		09 39	
Clapham Junction 10	d				08u12								08u46		09u12									09u46	
Woking	d							08 35			09 00								09 35			10 00			
Farnborough (Main)	d							08 45					09 13						09 45					10 13	
Fleet	d												09 19											10 19	
Reading 7	d								08 45											09 45					
Basingstoke	a				08 48			08 59	09 08				09 34		09 48				09 58	10 08				10 34	
	d				08 50			09 00	09 10				09 36		09 50				10 00	10 10				10 36	
Micheldever	d							09 10											10 10						
Winchester	d				09 06			09 19	09 25		09 33		09 52		10 06				10 19	10 25		10 33		10 52	
Shawford	d												09 57											10 57	
Romsey	d						09 05										10 05								
Chandlers Ford	a						09 12										10 12								
	d						09 12										10 12								
Eastleigh 3	a						09 18	09 29					10 02				10 18		10 29					11 02	
	d						09 19	09 30					10 03				10 19		10 30					11 03	
Hedge End	d							09 36											10 36						
Botley	d							09 40											10 40						
Fareham	d							09 48											10 48						
Portchester	d							09 53											10 53						
Cosham	d							09 58											10 58						
Hilsea	a							10 03											11 03						
Fratton	a							10 07											11 07						
Portsmouth & Southsea	a							10 19											11 19						
Portsmouth Harbour	a							10 23											11 23						
Southampton Airport Parkway ✈	d				09 15		09 23		09 34		09 42		10 08		10 15		10 23			10 34		10 42		11 08	
Swaythling	d						09 26										10 26								
St Denys	d						09 29										10 29								
Southampton Central	a				09 22	←	09 34		09 40		09 49		10 15		10 22	←	10 34			10 40		10 49		11 14	
	d				09 24	09 30	09 38		09 42		09 51		10 30		10 24	10 30	10 38			10 42		10 51		11 30	
Millbrook (Hants)	d						09 40						↳				10 40							↳	
Redbridge	d						09 44										10 43								
Romsey	d						09 52										10 57								
Mottisfont & Dunbridge	d						09 57																		
Dean	d						10 02																		
Salisbury	a						10 15										11 15								
Totton	d					09 35										10 35									
Ashurst New Forest	d					09 40										10 40									
Beaulieu Road	d																								
Brockenhurst 3	a				09 37	09 51			09 56		10 04	←			10 37	10 51				10 56		11 04	←		
	d	09 29			09 38	10 16			09 57	09 59	10 05	10 16		10 29	10 38	11 16				10 57	10 59	11 05	11 16		11 29
Lymington Town	d	09 37				↳				10 07				10 37		↳					11 07				11 37
Lymington Pier	a	09 39								10 09				10 39							11 09				11 39
Yarmouth (I.O.W.) ⛴	a	*10 15*								*10 45*				*11b15*							*11 45*				*12b15*
Sway	d											10 20											11 20		
New Milton	d				09 45							10 25			10 45								11 25		
Hinton Admiral	d											10 29											11 29		
Christchurch	d				09 52							10 34			10 52								11 34		
Pokesdown	d				09 56							10 38			10 56								11 38		
Bournemouth	a				10 00				10 15		10 20	10 42			11 00					11 15		11 20	11 42		
	d				10 04						10 24	10 43			11 04							11 24	11 43		
Branksome	d										10 29	10 48										11 29	11 48		
Parkstone (Dorset)	d										10 32	10 51										11 32	11 51		
Poole 4	a				10 13						10 36	10 55			11 13							11 36	11 55		
	d				10 14						10 37				11 14							11 37			
Hamworthy	d				10 20						10 42				11 19							11 42			
Holton Heath	d				10 27										11 23										
Wareham	d				10c35						10 49				11 28							11 49			
Wool	d				10 42										11 35										
Moreton (Dorset)	d				10 48										11 41										
Dorchester South	d				10 56						11 05				11 49							12 05			
Dorchester West	d			10 42														11 50							
Upwey	d			10 49	11 02										11 55			12 01							
Weymouth	a			10 55	11 07						11 13				12 00			12 06				12 13			

For general notes see front of timetable
For details of catering facilities see Directory of Train Operators

A ☕ to Bournemouth

b Fridays only until 21st December
Daily from 14th March

c Arr. 1031

For details of Bank Holiday service alterations, please see first page of Table 149

London → Basingstoke, Southampton, Lymington, Bournemouth and Weymouth

Network Diagram - see first page of Table 158

		SW		SW	SW	SW	XC	SW	SW	SW	SW	SW	SW	SW	SW	GW	SW	XC	SW	SW	SW	SW	SW	SW	SW
		1 ◇		1	1	1	R 1	1	1 ◇	1	1	1	1 ◇	1	1	◇	1	R 1	1	1 ◇	1	1	1	1 ◇	1
		A ☕					☕		A ☕				A ☕					☕		A ☕				A ☕	
London Waterloo 15 ⊖	d	10 05				10 09			10 35		10 39		11 05				11 09			11 35		11 39		12 05	
Clapham Junction 10	d	10u12									10u46		11u12									11u46		12u12	
Woking	d					10 35			11 00								11 35			12 00					
Farnborough (Main)	d					10 45					11 13						11 45					12 13			
Fleet	d										11 19											12 19			
Reading 7	d						10 45											11 45							
Basingstoke	a	10 48				10 58	11 08				11 34		11 48				11 58	12 08				12 34		12 48	
	d	10 50				11 00	11 10				11 36		11 50				12 00	12 10				12 36		12 50	
Micheldever	d					11 10											12 10								
Winchester	d	11 06				11 19	11 25		11 33		11 52		12 06				12 19	12 25		12 33		12 52		13 06	
Shawford	d										11 57											12 57			
Romsey	d				11 05										12 05										
Chandlers Ford	a				11 12										12 12										
	d				11 12										12 12										
Eastleigh 3	a				11 18	11 29					12 02				12 18		12 29					13 02			
	d				11 19	11 30					12 03				12 19		12 30					13 03			
Hedge End	d					11 36											12 36								
Botley	d					11 40											12 40								
Fareham	d					11 48											12 48								
Portchester	d					11 53											12 53								
Cosham	d					11 58											12 58								
Hilsea	a					12 03											13 03								
Fratton	a					12 07											13 07								
Portsmouth & Southsea	a					12 19											13 19								
Portsmouth Harbour	a					12 23											13 23								
Southampton Airport Parkwy ✈	d	11 15			11 23		11 34		11 42		12 08		12 15		12 23			12 34		12 42		13 08		13 15	
Swaythling	d				11 26										12 26										
St Denys	d				11 29										12 29										
Southampton Central	a	11 22		←	11 34		11 40		11 49		12 15		12 22	←	12 34			12 40		12 49		13 15		13 22	←
	d	11 24		11 30	11 38		11 42		11 51		12 30		12 24	12 30	12 38			12 42		12 51		13 30		13 24	13 30
Millbrook (Hants)	d				11 40						→				12 40							→			
Redbridge	d				11 44										12 44										
Romsey	d				11 52										12 52										
Mottisfont & Dunbridge	d				11 57																				
Dean	d				12 02																				
Salisbury	a				12 15										13 10										
Totton	d			11 35										12 35											13 35
Ashurst New Forest	d			11 40										12 40											13 40
Beaulieu Road	d																								
Brockenhurst 3	a	11 37		11 51			11 56		12 04	←			12 37	12 51				12 56		13 04	←			13 37	13 51
	d	11 38		12 16			11 57	11 59	12 05	12 16		12 29	12 38	13 16				12 57	12 59	13 05	13 16		13 29	13 38	14 16
Lymington Town	d			→				12 07				12 37		→					13 07				13 37		→
Lymington Pier	a							12 09				12 39							13 09				13 39		
Yarmouth (I.O.W.) ⛴	a							*12 45*				*13b15*							*13 45*				*14c15*		
Sway	d									12 20											13 20				
New Milton	d	11 45								12 25			12 45								13 25			13 45	
Hinton Admiral	d									12 29											13 29				
Christchurch	d	11 52								12 34			12 52								13 34			13 52	
Pokesdown	d	11 56								12 38			12 56								13 38			13 56	
Bournemouth	a	12 00					12 15		12 20	12 42			13 00					13 15		13 20	13 42			14 00	
	d	12 04							12 24	12 43			13 04							13 24	13 43			14 04	
Branksome	d								12 29	12 48										13 29	13 48				
Parkstone (Dorset)	d								12 32	12 51										13 32	13 51				
Poole 4	a	12 13							12 36	12 55			13 13							13 36	13 55			14 13	
	d	12 14							12 37				13 14							13 37				14 14	
Hamworthy	d	12 19							12 42				13 19							13 42				14 19	
Holton Heath	d	12 23											13 23											14 23	
Wareham	d	12 28							12 49				13 28							13 49				14 28	
Wool	d	12 35											13 35											14 35	
Moreton (Dorset)	d	12 41											13 41											14 41	
Dorchester South	d	12 49							13 05				13 49							14 05				14 49	
Dorchester West	d															13 54									
Upwey	d	12 55											13 55			14 01								14 55	
Weymouth	a	13 00							13 13				14 00			14 09				14 13				15 00	

For general notes see front of timetable
For details of catering facilities see Directory of Train Operators

A ☕ to Bournemouth
b Fridays only until 21st December Daily from 14th March
c Daily 10th December to 13th March Mondays and Fridays only from 14th March

For details of Bank Holiday service alterations, please see first page of Table 149

London → Basingstoke, Southampton, Lymington, Bournemouth and Weymouth

Network Diagram - see first page of Table 158

		SW		SW	XC	SW	SW	SW	SW	SW	SW	SW	SW	SW	XC	SW	SW	SW	SW	SW	SW	SW	SW	GW	SW
					R										R										
		1		1	1	1	1 ◇	1	1	1	1 ◇	1	1	1	1	1	1 ◇	1	1	1	1 ◇	1	1	◇	1
							A				A						A				A				
					☕		☕				☕				☕		☕				☕				
London Waterloo 15 ⊖	d			12 09			12 35		12 39		13 05			13 09			13 35	13 39			14 05				14 09
Clapham Junction 10	d								12u46		13u12							13u46			14u12				
Woking	d			12 35			13 00							13 35			14 00								14 35
Farnborough (Main)	d			12 45					13 13					13 45				14 13							14 45
Fleet	d								13 19									14 19							
Reading 7	d				12 45										13 45										
Basingstoke	a			12 58	13 08				13 34		13 48			13 58	14 08			14 34			14 48				14 58
	d			13 00	13 10				13 36		13 50			14 00	14 10			14 36			14 50				15 00
Micheldever	d			13 10										14 10											15 10
Winchester	d			13 19	13 25		13 33		13 52		14 06			14 19	14 25		14 33	14 52			15 06				15 19
Shawford	d								13 57									14 57							
Romsey	d	13 05											14 05										15 05		
Chandlers Ford	a	13 12											14 12										15 12		
	d	13 12											14 12										15 12		
Eastleigh 3	a	13 18		13 29					14 02				14 18	14 29				15 02					15 18		15 29
	d	13 19		13 30					14 03				14 19	14 30				15 03					15 19		15 30
Hedge End	d			13 36										14 36											15 36
Botley	d			13 40										14 40											15 40
Fareham	d			13 48										14 48											15 48
Portchester	d			13 53										14 53											15 53
Cosham	d			13 58										14 58											15 58
Hilsea	a			14 03										15 03											16 03
Fratton	a			14 07										15 07											16 07
Portsmouth & Southsea	a			14 19										15 19											16 11
Portsmouth Harbour	a			14 23										15 23											16 20
Southampton Airport Parkwy ✈	d	13 23			13 34		13 42		14 08		14 15		14 23		14 34		14 42	15 08			15 15		15 23		
Swaythling	d	13 26											14 26										15 26		
St Denys	d	13 29											14 29										15 29		
Southampton Central	a	13 34			13 40		13 49		14 13		14 22	←	14 34		14 40		14 49	15 15			15 22	←	15 34		
	d	13 38			13 42		13 51		14 30 →		14 24	14 30	14 38		14 42		14 51	15 30 →			15 24	15 30	15 38		
Millbrook (Hants)	d	13 40											14 40										15 40		
Redbridge	d	13 44											14 44										15 44		
Romsey	d	13 52											14 52										15 52		
Mottisfont & Dunbridge	d	13 57											14 57										15 57		
Dean	d	14 02											15 02										16 02		
Salisbury	a	14 15											15 15										16 15		
Totton	d											14 35										15 35			
Ashurst New Forest	d											14 40										15 40			
Beaulieu Road	d																								
Brockenhurst 3	a				13 56		14 04	←			14 37	14 51			14 56		15 04		←		15 37	15 51			
	d				13 57	13 59	14 05	14 16		14 29	14 38	15 16			14 57	14 59	15 05		15 16	15 29	15 38	16 28			
Lymington Town	d					14 07				14 37		→				15 07				15 37		→			
Lymington Pier	a					14 09				14 39						15 09				15 39					
Yarmouth (I.O.W.) ⛴	a					*14b45*				*15 15*						*15 45*				*16b15*					
Sway	d							14 20											15 20						
New Milton	d							14 25			14 45								15 25		15 45				
Hinton Admiral	d							14 29											15 29						
Christchurch	d							14 34			14 52								15 34		15 52				
Pokesdown	d							14 38			14 56								15 38		15 56				
Bournemouth	a				14 15		14 20	14 42			15 00				15 15		15 20		15 42		16 00				
	d						14 24	14 43			15 04						15 24		15 43		16 04				
Branksome	d						14 29	14 48									15 29		15 48						
Parkstone (Dorset)	d						14 32	14 51									15 32		15 51						
Poole 4	a						14 36	14 55			15 13						15 36		15 55		16 13				
	d						14 37				15 14						15 37				16 14				
Hamworthy	d						14 42				15 19						15 42				16 19				
Holton Heath	d										15 23										16 23				
Wareham	d						14 49				15 28						15 49				16 28				
Wool	d										15 35										16 35				
Moreton (Dorset)	d										15 41										16 41				
Dorchester South	d						15 05				15 49						16 05				16 49				
Dorchester West	d																							16 55	
Upwey	d										15 55										16 55			17 02	
Weymouth	a						15 13				16 00						16 13				17 00			17 07	

For general notes see front of timetable
For details of catering facilities see Directory of Train Operators

A ☕ to Bournemouth
b Fridays only until 21st December Daily from 14th March

For details of Bank Holiday service alterations, please see first page of Table 149

London → Basingstoke, Southampton, Lymington, Bournemouth and Weymouth

Network Diagram - see first page of Table 158

		XC		SW	SW	SW	SW	SW	SW	SW	SW	SW	XC	SW	SW		SW	SW	SW	SW	SW	SW	SW	SW	XC
		R 1		1	1 ◊	1	1	1	1 ◊	1	1	1	R 1	1	1 ◊		1	1	1	1	1 ◊	1	1	1	1 ◊
					A				A						A										
		☕			☕		☕		☕	☕			☕		☕										☕
London Waterloo 15 ⊖	d				14 35		14 39		15 05			15 09			15 35				15 39		16 05			16 09	
Clapham Junction 10	d						14u46		15u12										15u46		16u12				
Woking	d				15 00							15 35			16 00									16 35	
Farnborough (Main)	d						15 13					15 45							16 13					16 45	
Fleet	d						15 19												16 19						
Reading 7	d	14 45											15 45												16 45
Basingstoke	a	15 08					15 34		15 48			15 58	16 08						16 34		16 48			16 58	17 08
	d	15 10					15 36		15 50			16 00	16 10					16 24	16 36		16 50			17 00	17 10
Micheldever	d											16 10												17 10	
Winchester	d	15 25			15 33		15 52		16 06			16 19	16 25		16 33		16 38	16 43	16 52		17 06			17 19	17 25
Shawford	d						15 57										16 42		16 57						
Romsey	d										16 05												17 05		
Chandlers Ford	a										16 12												17 12		
	d										16 12												17 12		
Eastleigh 3	a						16 02				16 18	16 29					16 48	16 51	17 02				17 18	17 29	
	d						16 03				16 19	16 30					16 49	16 52	17 03				17 19	17 30	
Hedge End	d											16 36						16 58						17 36	
Botley	d											16 40						17 02						17 40	
Fareham	d											16 48						17 10						17 48	
Portchester	d											16 53						17 15						17 53	
Cosham	d											16 58						17 20						17 58	
Hilsea	a											17 03												18 03	
Fratton	a											17 07						17 27						18 07	
Portsmouth & Southsea	a											17 18						17 31						18 11	
Portsmouth Harbour	a											17 25												18 20	
Southampton Airport Parkwy ✈	d	15 34			15 42		16 08		16 15		16 23		16 34		16 42		16 53		17 08		17 15		17 23		17 34
Swaythling	d										16 26						16 56						17 26		
St Denys	d										16 29						16 59						17 29		
Southampton Central	a	15 40			15 49		16 15		16 22	←	16 34		16 40		16 49		17 04		17 15		17 22	←	17 34		17 40
	d	15 42			15 51		16 30 →		16 24	16 30	16 38		16 42		16 53	16 56	17 06		17 30 →		17 24	17 30	17 38		17 42
Millbrook (Hants)	d										16 40												17 40		
Redbridge	d										16 44												17 44		
Romsey	d										16 52												17 52		
Mottisfont & Dunbridge	d										16 57												17 57		
Dean	d										17 02												18 02		
Salisbury	a										17 15												18 15		
Totton	d									16 35						17 01	17a11					17 35			
Ashurst New Forest	d									16 40						17 06						17 40			
Beaulieu Road	d									16 44												17 44			
Brockenhurst 3	a	15 56			16 04	←			16 37	16 51			16 56		17 07	17 14					17 37	17 51			17 56
	d	15 57		15 59	16 05	16 28		16 29	16 38				16 57	16 59	17 08	17 16				17 29	17 38				17 57
Lymington Town	d			16 07				16 37						17 07						17 37					
Lymington Pier	a			16 09				16 39						17 09						17 39					
Yarmouth (I.O.W.) ⛴	a			*16 45*				*17 15*						*17b45*						*18 15*					
Sway	d					16 32			16 43							17 20					17 43				
New Milton	d					16 37			16 48							17 25					17 48				
Hinton Admiral	d					16 41			16 52							17 29					17 52				
Christchurch	d					16 46			16 57							17 34					17 57				
Pokesdown	d					16 50			17 00							17 38					18 00				
Bournemouth	a	16 15			16 20	16 54			17 04				17 15		17 22	17 42					18 04				18 15
	d				16 24	16 55			17 06						17 24	17 43					18 09				
Branksome	d				16 29	17 00									17 29	17 48									
Parkstone (Dorset)	d				16 32	17 03									17 32	17 51									
Poole 4	a				16 36	17 07			17 15						17 36	17 55					18 18				
	d				16 37				17 16						17 37						18 19				
Hamworthy	d				16 42				17 21						17 42						18 24				
Holton Heath	d								17 25												18 28				
Wareham	d				16 49				17 30						17 49						18 33				
Wool	d								17 36												18 39				
Moreton (Dorset)	d								17 42												18 45				
Dorchester South	d				17 05				17 50						18 05						18 53				
Dorchester West	d																								
Upwey	d								17 57												19 00				
Weymouth	a				17 13				18 01						18 13						19 05				

For general notes see front of timetable
For details of catering facilities see Directory of Train Operators

A ☕ to Bournemouth

b Fridays only until 21st December
Daily from 14th March

For details of Bank Holiday service alterations, please see first page of Table 149

London → Basingstoke, Southampton, Lymington, Bournemouth and Weymouth

Network Diagram - see first page of Table 158

		SW		GW	SW		SW	SW	SW	SW		SW	SW	XC	SW	GW	SW		SW	SW	SW	SW	SW	SW	SW
		1		◇	1 ◇		1	1	1	1		1	1	R 1	1	◇	1		1	1	1	1	1	1	1
					A ☕					A ☕				☕			A ☕					A ☕			
London Waterloo 15 ⊖	d				16 35				16 39	17 05			17 09				17 35		17 39	17 48		18 05			18 09
Clapham Junction 10	d								16u46																
Woking	d				17u00								17 34						18 04	18 13					18 34
Farnborough (Main)	d								17 13																
Fleet	d								17 19																
Reading 7	d													17 45											
Basingstoke	a								17 34				17 53	18 08					18 23	18 32					18 53
	d						17 24		17 36				17 54	18 10					18 24	18 33					18 54
Micheldever	d						17 34						18 04						18 34						19 04
Winchester	d				17 33		17 43		17 52	18 01			18 14	18 25			18 31		18 44	18 50		19b01	19 05		19 14
Shawford	d						17 48						18 19						18 49				19 09		19 19
Romsey	d											18 05												19 05	
Chandlers Ford	a											18 12												19 12	
	d											18 12												19 12	
Eastleigh 3	a						17 53		18 00			18 18	18 24						18 54	18 58			19 15	19 19	19 24
	d						17 54		18 01			18 19	18 27						18 55	18 59			19 16	19 20	19 29
Hedge End	d								18 07				18 33						19 01						19 35
Botley	d								18 11				18 37						19 05						19 39
Fareham	d								18 21				18 50						19 14						19 50
Portchester	d								18 26				18 55						19 19						19 55
Cosham	d								18 31				19 00						19 24						20 00
Hilsea	a												19 05						19 28						20 08
Fratton	a								18 39				19 09						19 32						20 12
Portsmouth & Southsea	a								18 43				19 12						19 36						20 16
Portsmouth Harbour	a								18 51				19 20						19 43						20 23
Southampton Airport Parkwy ✈	d				17 42		17 59			18 10		18 23		18 34			18 40			19 03		19 10	19 20	19 25	
Swaythling	d						18 01					18 26								19 06			19 23	19 27	
St Denys	d						18 04					18 29								19 09			19 26	19 30	
Southampton Central	a				17 49		18 10			18 17		18 34		18 40			18 48			19 16		19 17	19 33	19 35	
	d				17 53	17 56				18 22	18 25	18 38		18 42			18 52	18 55				19 19		19 38	
Millbrook (Hants)	d											18 40												19 40	
Redbridge	d											18 43												19 44	
Romsey	d											18 57												19 52	
Mottisfont & Dunbridge	d											19 04												19 57	
Dean	d											19 09												20 02	
Salisbury	a											19 23												20 15	
Totton	d					18 01					18 30							19 00				19 24			
Ashurst New Forest	d					18 06					18 35							19 05							
Beaulieu Road	d																								
Brockenhurst 3	a				18 07	18 14					18 43			18 56				19 13				19 35			
	d	17 59			18 08	18 16		18 29			18 44			18 57	18 59			19 14			19 29	19 36			
Lymington Town	d	18 07						18 37							19 07						19 37				
Lymington Pier	a	18 09						18 39							19 09						19 39				
Yarmouth (I.O.W.) ⛴	a	*18 45*						*19c15*							*19 45*						*20c15*				
Sway	d					18 20					18 48							19 18				19 40			
New Milton	d					18 25					18 53							19 23				19 45			
Hinton Admiral	d					18 29					18 58							19 26				19 49			
Christchurch	d					18 34					19 02							19 32				19 54			
Pokesdown	d					18 38					19 06							19 36				19 58			
Bournemouth	a				18 22	18 44				18 49	19 10			19 15			19 20	19 40				20 02			
	d				18 24					18 50	19 11						19 21	19 41				20 06			
Branksome	d				18 29					18 55	19 16						19 26	19 46				20 11			
Parkstone (Dorset)	d				18 32					18 58	19 19						19 29	19 49				20 14			
Poole 4	a				18 36					19 02	19 26						19 33	19 56				20 18			
	d				18 37					19 03							19 34					20 19			
Hamworthy	d				18 42					19 08							19 39					20 24			
Holton Heath	d									19 12												20 28			
Wareham	d				18 49					19 17							19 46					20 33			
Wool	d									19 23												20 39			
Moreton (Dorset)	d									19 30												20 45			
Dorchester South	d				19 05					19 38							20 02					20 53			
Dorchester West	d			18 58												19 52									
Upwey	d			19 07						19 44						19 59						21 00			
Weymouth	a			19 13	19 17					19 51						20 06	20 15					21 06			

For general notes see front of timetable
For details of catering facilities see Directory of Train Operators

A ☕ to Bournemouth
b Arr. 1858

c Fridays only until 21st December
Thursday 20th March, Mondays only 24th March & from 5th May
Daily from 12th May

For details of Bank Holiday service alterations, please see first page of Table 149

London → Basingstoke, Southampton, Lymington, Bournemouth and Weymouth

Network Diagram - see first page of Table 158

	XC		SW		SW	XC	SW	SW	SW	SW	SW	SW	SW	SW	XC	SW	SW	GW	XC	SW	SW	SW		SW
	R 1		1		1	R 1	1	1	1	1	1 ◇	1	1	1	R 1	1	1 ◇	◇	R 1	1	1	1		1 ◇
			A								A						A							
	🍴		🍴			🍴					🍴				🍴		🍴		🍴					🍴
London Waterloo 15 ⊖ d			18 35						18 39		19 05			19 09			19 35				19 39			20 05
Clapham Junction 10 d									18u46		19u12										19u46			20u12
Woking d									19 06					19 35			20 00							
Farnborough (Main) d														19 45							20 13			
Fleet d																					20 19			
Reading 7 d	18 45														19 45									
Basingstoke a	19 08								19 28		19 48			19 58	20 08						20 34			20 48
d	19 10							19 24	19 30		19 50			20 00	20 10						20 36			20 50
Micheldever d									19 40					20 10										
Winchester d	19 25		19 31					19 40	19 49		20 06			20 19	20 25		20 33				20 52			21 06
Shawford d								19 45	19 54					20 24							20 57			
Romsey d													20 05											
Chandlers Ford a													20 12											
d													20 12											
Eastleigh 3 a								19 50	19 59				20 18	20 30							21 02			
d								19 51	20 00				20 19	20 30							21 03			
Hedge End d								19 57						20 36										
Botley d								20 01						20 40										
Fareham d								20a09						20 48										
Portchester d														20 53										
Cosham d														20 58										
Hilsea a														20 59										
Fratton a														21 08										
Portsmouth & Southsea a														21 11										
Portsmouth Harbour a														21 25										
Southampton Airport Parkwy ✈ d	19 34		19 40						20 05		20 15		20 23		20 34		20 42				21 08			21 15
Swaythling d													20 26											
St Denys d													20 29											
Southampton Central a	19 40		19 47						20 15		20 22		20 34		20 40		20 49				21 15			21 22
d	19 42		19 52	19 55 →			← 19 55		20 30 →		20 24	← 20 30	20 38		20 42		20 51							21 24
Millbrook (Hants) d													20 40											
Redbridge d													20 44											
Romsey d													20 52											
Mottisfont & Dunbridge d																								
Dean d																								
Salisbury a													21 10											
Totton d							20 00					20 35					20 56							21 29
Ashurst New Forest d							20 05					20 40												21 34
Beaulieu Road d																								
Brockenhurst 3 a	19 56					←	20 13				20 37	20 51			20 56		21 07		←	←				21 42
d	19 57				19 59	19 57	20 14			20 29	20 38	21 16			20 57	20 59	21 08		20 57	21 16		21 29		21 43
Lymington Town d	→				20 07					20 37		→			→	21 07						21 37		
Lymington Pier a					20 09					20 39						21 09						21 39		
Yarmouth (I.O.W.) ⛴ a					*20 45*					*21 15*						*22b00*						*22 45*		
Sway d							20 18													21 20				21 47
New Milton d							20 23				20 45									21 25				21 52
Hinton Admiral d							20 27													21 29				21 56
Christchurch d							20 32				20 52									21 34				22 01
Pokesdown d							20 36				20 56									21 38				22 05
Bournemouth a			20 20			20 24	20 40				21 00						21 22		21 26	21 42				22 09
d			20 21				20 41				21 04						21 27			21 43				22 10
Branksome d			20 26				20 46										21 32			21 48				22 15
Parkstone (Dorset) d			20 29				20 49										21 35			21 51				22 18
Poole 4 a			20 33				20 56				21 13						21 38			21 57				22 23
d			20 34								21 14						21 39							
Hamworthy d			20 39								21 19						21 44							
Holton Heath d																								
Wareham d			20 46								21 26						21 51							
Wool d											21 33						21 58							
Moreton (Dorset) d											21 39						22 04							
Dorchester South d			21 02								21 47						22 12							
Dorchester West d																		22 48						
Upwey d											21 53						22 18	22 55						
Weymouth a			21 13								21 58						22 23	23 02						

For general notes see front of timetable
For details of catering facilities see Directory of Train Operators

A 🍴 to Bournemouth
b Fridays only 14th March to 9th May
Thursday 20th March
Daily from 12th May

For details of Bank Holiday service alterations, please see first page of Table 149

London → Basingstoke, Southampton, Lymington, Bournemouth and Weymouth

Network Diagram - see first page of Table 158

		SW		SW	XC R	SW	SW	SW	XC R	SW	SW	XC R	SW	SW	SW	SW	SW	SW	XC	SW	SW	SW	SW		
		1		1	1	1	1 ◇	1	1	1 ◇	1	1	1 ◇	1	1	1	1	1	1 ◇	1	1	1	1		
							A ☕			☕			A ☕			☕				☕					
London Waterloo 15 ⊖	d			20 09			20 35	20 39		21 05			21 35		21 39	22 05		21 42		22 35	22 39	23 05	23 39		
Clapham Junction 10	d							20u46		21u12					21u46	22u12					22u46	23u12	23u46		
Woking	d			20 35			21 00			21 32			22 00			22 32		22 19		23 00		23 32	00 08		
Farnborough (Main)	d			20 45				21 13							22 13			22 33			23 13		00 18		
Fleet	d							21 19							22 19			22 38			23 19		00 23		
Reading 7	d				20 45							21 45							22 45						
Basingstoke	a			20 58	21 08			21 34		21 51		22 08			22 34	22 51		22 58	23 08		23 33	23 51	00 35		
	d			21 00	21 10			21 36		21 53		22 10		22 21	22 36	22 53		23 00	23 10		23 34	23 53	00 36		
Micheldever	d			21 10										22 31	22s46			23 10				00 03			
Winchester	d			21 19	21 25		21 33	21 52		22 09		22 25	22 33	22 40	22 55	23 09		23 19	23 25	23 33	23 51	00 12	00 53		
Shawford	d			21 24				21 57						22 45	23 00			23 24			23 55				
Romsey	d	21 05									22 07						23 07								
Chandlers Ford	a	21 12									22 14						23 14								
	d	21 12									22 14						23 14								
Eastleigh 3	a	21 18		21 30				22 02		22 17	22 22			22 50	23 05	23 17	23 22	23 30			00 01	00 20	01 01		
	d	21 19		21 30				22 03		22 18	22 23			22 51	23 06	23 18	23 23	23 30			00 02	00 21	01 02		
Hedge End	d			21 36										22 57				23 36							
Botley	d			21 40										23 01				23 40							
Fareham	d			21 48										23 10				23 48							
Portchester	d			21 53										23 15				23 53							
Cosham	d			21 58										23 20				23 59							
Hilsea	a			22 06										23 24				00 04							
Fratton	a			22 10										23 32				00 08							
Portsmouth & Southsea	a			22 13										23 36				00 11							
Portsmouth Harbour	a			22 18										23 40				00 16							
Southampton Airport Parkwy ✈	d	21 23			21 34		21 42	22 08		22 23	22 27	22 34	22 42		23 11	23 23	23 27		23 34	23 42	00 06	00 25	01 06		
Swaythling	d	21 26									22 30						23 30								
St Denys	d	21 29									22 33						23 33					00s30			
Southampton Central	a	21 34			21 40		21 49	22 15		22 30	22 38	22 46	22 49		23 18	23 30	23 38		23 47	23 49	00 13	00 35	01 13		
	d	21 38			21 42		21 51			22 31	22 39		22 51			23 31	23 39			23 51		00 36			
Millbrook (Hants)	d	21 40									22 42						23 42								
Redbridge	d	21 44									22 45						23 45								
Romsey	d	21 52									22a53						23 56								
Mottisfont & Dunbridge	d	21 57															00 01								
Dean	d	22 02															00 06								
Salisbury	a	22 15															00 19								
Totton	d									22 37						23 37						00s41			
Ashurst New Forest	d									22 41						23 41									
Beaulieu Road	d																								
Brockenhurst 3	a				21 56		22 04		←	22 49			23 04			23 49				00 04		00s52			
	d				21 57	21 59	22 05		21 57	22 50			23 05			23 50				00 05					
Lymington Town	d				→	22 07																			
Lymington Pier	a					22 09																			
Yarmouth (I.O.W.) ⛴	a					22 45																			
Sway	d									22 55						23 55									
New Milton	d									23 00						23 59						01s00			
Hinton Admiral	d									23 04						00 04									
Christchurch	d									23 09						00 09						01s07			
Pokesdown	d									23 12						00 12						01s11			
Bournemouth	a						22 20		22 26	23 16			23 23			00 16				00 22		01 15			
	d						22 24			23 18			23 28			00 18				00 24		01 16			
Branksome	d						22 29			23 23			23 33			00 23				00 29		01s21			
Parkstone (Dorset)	d						22 32			23 26			23 36			00 26				00 32		01s24			
Poole 4	a						22 36			23 30			23 39			00 30				00 36		01 28			
	d						22 37						23 40												
Hamworthy	d						22 42						23 45												
Holton Heath	d																								
Wareham	d						22 49						23 52												
Wool	d						22 55						23 59												
Moreton (Dorset)	d						23 01						00 05												
Dorchester South	d						23 09						00 13												
Dorchester West	d																								
Upwey	d						23 16						00 19												
Weymouth	a						23 20						00 24												

For general notes see front of timetable
For details of catering facilities see Directory of Train Operators

A ☕ to Bournemouth

London → Basingstoke, Southampton, Lymington, Bournemouth and Weymouth

Network Diagram - see first page of Table 158

		SW 1 ◇	SW 1 ☕	SW 1	SW 1	SW 1 ☕	SW 1	SW 1	SW 1	SW 1	SW 1	SW 1	SW 1	SW 1	SW 1	SW 1	GW ◇	SW 1	SW 1	SW 1	SW 1	SW 1	SW 1	SW 1	SW 1
London Waterloo 15 ⊖	d	21p35	22p05		21p42	22p35	22p39	23p05		23p39	00 05	01 05										05 30			
Clapham Junction 10	d		22b12				22b46	23b12		23b46	00u12	01 14										05u37			
Woking	d	22p00	22p32		22p19	23p00		23p32		00 08	00 36	01 41										06 01			
Farnborough (Main)	d				22p33		23p13			00 18		01s57													
Fleet	d				22p38		23p19			00 23															
Reading 7	d																								
Basingstoke	a		22p51		22p58		23p33	23p51		00 35	00 55	02s11										06 20			
	d		22p53		23p00		23p34	23p53		00 36	00 57											06 21			
Micheldever	d				23p10			00 03														06 31			
Winchester	d	22p33	23p09		23p19	23p33	23p51	00 12		00 53	01 13	02s28										06 41			
Shawford	d				23p24		23p55																		
Romsey	d			23p07																05 58					
Chandlers Ford	a			23p14																06 06					
	d			23p14																06 06					
Eastleigh 3	a		23p17	23p22	23p30		00 01	00 20		01 01	01 21	02s37								06 11		06 50			
	d		23p18	23p23	23p30		00 02	00 21	00 30	01 02	01 22									06 13	06 30	06 51			
Hedge End	d				23p36				00s36												06 36				
Botley	d				23p40				00s39												06 40				
Fareham	d				23p48				00s47												06 48				
Portchester	d				23p53				00s53												06 53				
Cosham	d				23p59				00s58												06 58				
Hilsea	a				00 04																07 03				
Fratton	a				00 08				01s06												07 07				
Portsmouth & Southsea	a				00 11				01s10												07 10				
Portsmouth Harbour	a				00 16				01 15												07 18				
Southampton Airport Parkwy ✈	d	22p42	23p23	23p27		23p42	00 06	00 25		01 06	01 27	02s42								06 17		06 56			
Swaythling	d			23p30																06 20					
St Denys	d			23p33				00s30				02s47								06 23					
Southampton Central	a	22p49	23p30	23p38		23p49	00 13	00 35		01 13	01 36	02 52								06 28		07 03			
	d	22p51	23p31	23p39		23p51		00 36			01 37							06 25		06 30		07 05		07 25	
Millbrook (Hants)	d			23p42																06 32					
Redbridge	d			23p45																06 36					
Romsey	d			23p56																06 44					
Mottisfont & Dunbridge	d			00 01																06 49					
Dean	d			00 06																06 54					
Salisbury	a			00 19																07 07					
Totton	d		23p37					00s41			01s42							06 30				07 10		07 30	
Ashurst New Forest	d		23p41															06 35						07 35	
Beaulieu Road	d																								
Brockenhurst 3	a	23p04	23p49			00 04		00s52			01s53							06 43				07 21		07 43	
	d	23p05	23p50			00 05							05 59		06 16	06 29		06 44	06 59			07 22	07 29	07 44	07 59
Lymington Town	d												06 07			06 37			07 07				07 37		08 07
Lymington Pier	a												06 09			06 39			07 09				07 39		08 09
Yarmouth (I.O.W.) ⛴	a												*06c45*			*07 15*			*07 45*				*08e15*		*08 45*
Sway	d		23p55												06 20			06 48				07 26		07 48	
New Milton	d		23p59					01s00			02s01				06 25			06 53				07 31		07 53	
Hinton Admiral	d		00 04												06 29			06 57				07 35		07 57	
Christchurch	d		00 09					01s07			02s08				06 34			07 02				07 40		08 02	
Pokesdown	d		00 12					01s11			02s12				06 38			07 06				07 44		08 06	
Bournemouth	a	23p23	00 16			00 22		01 15			02 16				06 42			07 10				07 48		08 10	
	d	23p28	00 18			00 24		01 16						06 11	06 44			07 11				07 49		08 11	
Branksome	d	23p33	00 23			00 29		01s21						06 16	06 49			07 16				07 54		08 16	
Parkstone (Dorset)	d	23p36	00 26			00 32		01s24						06 19	06 52			07 19				07 57		08 19	
Poole 4	a	23p39	00 30			00 36		01 28						06 23	06 55			07 23				08 01		08 23	
	d	23p40												06 24	06 57			07 24				08 02		08 24	
Hamworthy	d	23p45												06 29	07 02			07 29				08 07		08 29	
Holton Heath	d													06 33	07 06			07 33						08 33	
Wareham	d	23p52												06 38	07 11			07 38				08 14		08 38	
Wool	d	23p59												06 44	07 17			07 44				08 20		08 44	
Moreton (Dorset)	d	00 05												06 50	07 23			07 50				08 26		08 50	
Dorchester South	d	00 13												06 58	07 31			07 58				08 34		08 58	
Dorchester West	d																07 49								
Upwey	d	00 19												07 05	07 38		07 55	08 05				08 41		09 05	
Weymouth	a	00 24												07 09	07 42		08 01	08 09				08 45		09 09	

For general notes see front of timetable
For details of catering facilities see Directory of Train Operators

b Previous night.
Stops to pick up only

c From 17th May

e From 15th March

London → Basingstoke, Southampton, Lymington, Bournemouth and Weymouth

Network Diagram - see first page of Table 158

		SW 1	SW 1	SW 1	SW 1		SW 1		SW 1	SW 1	SW 1	SW 1 ◇	SW 1	SW 1	GW	SW 1 ◇	SW 1	SW 1	SW 1	XC 1 ◇	SW 1	SW 1 ◇	SW 1	SW 1	SW 1
																A						A			
																(catering)				(catering)		(catering)			
London Waterloo 15 ⊖	d			06 30							06 42	07 35	07 39			08 05			08 09			08 35		08 39	
Clapham Junction 10	d			06u37							06u49		07u46			08u12								08u46	
Woking	d		06 19	06 57							07 19	08 00							08 35			09 00			
Farnborough (Main)	d		06 33								07 33		08 13						08 45					09 13	
Fleet	d		06 38								07 38		08 19											09 19	
Reading 7	d																			08 45					
Basingstoke	a		06 58	07 16							07 58	08 20	08 34			08 48			08 58	09 08				09 34	
	d		07 00	07 18							08 00	08 21	08 36			08 50			09 00	09 10				09 36	
Micheldever	d		07 10								08 10								09 10						
Winchester	d		07 19	07 34							08 19	08 38	08 52			09 06			09 19	09 25		09 33		09 52	
Shawford	d		07 24								08 24		08 57											09 57	
Romsey	d	07 07							08 05									09 05							
Chandlers Ford	a	07 14							08 12									09 12							
	d	07 14							08 12									09 12							
Eastleigh 3	a	07 20	07 30	07 42					08 18		08 30	08 46	09 02					09 18	09 29					10 02	
	d	07 21	07 30	07 43					08 19		08 30	08 47	09 03					09 19	09 30					10 03	
Hedge End	d		07 36								08 36								09 36						
Botley	d		07 40								08 43								09 40						
Fareham	d		07 48								08 51								09 48						
Portchester	d		07 53								08 56								09 53						
Cosham	d		07 58								09 01								09 58						
Hilsea	a		08 04								09 07								10 03						
Fratton	a		08 08								09 16								10 07						
Portsmouth & Southsea	a		08 11								09 19								10 19						
Portsmouth Harbour	a		08 19								09 24								10 23						
Southampton Airport Parkway ✈	d	07 25		07 48					08 23			08 51	09 08			09 15		09 23		09 34		09 42		10 08	
Swaythling	d	07 28							08 26									09 26							
St Denys	d	07 31							08 29									09 29							
Southampton Central	a	07 36		07 55					08 34			08 58	09 15			09 22	⟵	09 34		09 40		09 49		10 15	
	d	07 37		08 00			08 22		08 38			09 00	09 30 ⟶			09 24	09 30	09 38		09 42		09 51		10 30 ⟶	
Millbrook (Hants)	d	07 40							08 40									09 40							
Redbridge	d	07 43							08 44									09 44							
Romsey	d	07 51							08 52									09 52							
Mottisfont & Dunbridge	d	07 56							08 57									09 57							
Dean	d	08 02							09 02									10 02							
Salisbury	a	08 14							09 15									10 15							
Totton	d			08 05			08 27					09 05					09 35								
Ashurst New Forest	d						08 31										09 40								
Beaulieu Road	d						08 36										09 44								
Brockenhurst 3	a			08 16			08 42					09 16				09 37	09 51			09 56		10 04	⟵		
	d			08 17	08 29		08 44			08 59		09 16		09 29		09 38	10 16			09 57	09 59	10 05	10 16		10 29
Lymington Town	d				08 37					09 07				09 37			⟶				10 07				10 37
Lymington Pier	a				08 39					09 09				09 39							10 09				10 39
Yarmouth (I.O.W.) ⛴	a				*09 15*					*09b45*				*10 15*							*10 45*				*11b15*
Sway	d			08 21			08 48					09 20											10 20		
New Milton	d			08 26			08 53					09 25				09 45							10 25		
Hinton Admiral	d			08 30			08 57					09 29											10 29		
Christchurch	d			08 35			09 02					09 34				09 52							10 34		
Pokesdown	d			08 39			09 06					09 38				09 56							10 38		
Bournemouth	a			08 43			09 10					09 43				10 00				10 15		10 20	10 42		
	d			08 44			09 11					09 43				10 04						10 24	10 43		
Branksome	d			08 49			09 16					09 48										10 29	10 48		
Parkstone (Dorset)	d			08 52			09 19					09 51										10 32	10 51		
Poole 4	a			08 56			09 23					09 56				10 13						10 36	10 55		
	d			08 57			09 24					09 56				10 14						10 37			
Hamworthy	d			09 02			09 29					10 01				10 19						10 42			
Holton Heath	d						09 33									10 23									
Wareham	d			09 09			09 38					10c11				10 28						10 49			
Wool	d			09 15			09 44									10 35									
Moreton (Dorset)	d			09 21			09 50									10 41									
Dorchester South	d			09 29			09 58					10 27				10 49						11 05			
Dorchester West	d														10 38										
Upwey	d			09 36			10 05								10 48	10 55									
Weymouth	a			09 40			10 09					10 35			10 54	11 00						11 13			

For general notes see front of timetable
For details of catering facilities see Directory of Train Operators

A (catering) to Bournemouth
b From 15th March
c Arr. 1008

London → Basingstoke, Southampton, Lymington, Bournemouth and Weymouth

Network Diagram - see first page of Table 158

		SW	SW	SW	GW	SW	XC	SW	SW	SW		SW	SW	SW	SW	SW	SW	XC	SW	SW	SW	SW	SW	SW	SW
		1 ◇	1	1		1	1 ◇	1	1 ◇	1		1	1	1 ◇	1	1	1	1 ◇	1	1 ◇	1	1	1	1 ◇	1
		A							A					A						A				A	
		☕					☕		☕					☕				☕		☕				☕	
London Waterloo 15 ⊖	d	09 05				09 09			09 35			09 39		10 05			10 09			10 35		10 39		11 05	
Clapham Junction 10	d	09u12										09u46		10u12								10u46		11u12	
Woking	d					09 35			10 00								10 35			11 00					
Farnborough (Main)	d					09 45						10 13					10 45					11 13			
Fleet	d											10 19										11 19			
Reading 7	d						09 45											10 45							
Basingstoke	a	09 48				09 58	10 08					10 34		10 48			10 58	11 06				11 34		11 48	
	d	09 50				10 00	10 10					10 36		10 50			11 00	11 07				11 36		11 50	
Micheldever	d					10 10											11 10								
Winchester	d	10 06				10 19	10 25		10 33			10 52		11 06			11 19	11 25		11 33		11 52		12 06	
Shawford	d											10 57										11 57			
Romsey	d			10 05												11 05									
Chandlers Ford	a			10 12												11 12									
	d			10 12												11 12									
Eastleigh 8	a			10 18		10 29						11 02				11 18	11 29					12 02			
	d			10 19		10 30						11 03				11 19	11 30					12 03			
Hedge End	d					10 36											11 36								
Botley	d					10 40											11 40								
Fareham	d					10 48											11 48								
Portchester	d					10 53											11 53								
Cosham	d					10 58											11 58								
Hilsea	a					11 03											12 03								
Fratton	a					11 07											12 07								
Portsmouth & Southsea	a					11 19											12 19								
Portsmouth Harbour	a					11 23											12 23								
Southampton Airport Parkwy ✈	d	10 15		10 23			10 34		10 42			11 08		11 15		11 23		11 34		11 42		12 08		12 15	
Swaythling	d			10 26												11 26									
St Denys	d			10 29												11 29									
Southampton Central	a	10 22	⟵	10 34			10 40		10 49			11 15		11 22	⟵	11 34		11 40		11 49		12 15		12 22	⟵
	d	10 24	10 30	10 38			10 42		10 51			11 30		11 24	11 30	11 38		11 42		11 51		12 30		12 24	12 30
Millbrook (Hants)	d			10 40								⟶				11 40						⟶			
Redbridge	d			10 44												11 44									
Romsey	d			10 57												11 52									
Mottisfont & Dunbridge	d															11 57									
Dean	d															12 02									
Salisbury	a			11 15												12 15									
Totton	d		10 35												11 35										12 35
Ashurst New Forest	d		10 40												11 40										12 40
Beaulieu Road	d																								
Brockenhurst 3	a	10 37	10 51				10 56		11 04	⟵				11 37	11 51			11 56		12 04	⟵			12 37	12 51
	d	10 38	11 16				10 57	10 59	11 05	11 16			11 29	11 38	12 16			11 57	11 59	12 05	12 16		12 29	12 38	13 16
Lymington Town	d		⟶					11 07					11 37		⟶				12 07				12 37		⟶
Lymington Pier	a							11 09					11 39						12 09				12 39		
Yarmouth (I.O.W.) ⛴	a							*11 45*					*12b15*						*12 45*				*13b15*		
Sway	d									11 20											12 20				
New Milton	d	10 45								11 25				11 45							12 25			12 45	
Hinton Admiral	d									11 29											12 29				
Christchurch	d	10 52								11 34				11 52							12 34			12 52	
Pokesdown	d	10 56								11 38				11 56							12 38			12 56	
Bournemouth	a	11 00					11 15		11 20	11 42				12 00				12 15		12 20	12 42			13 00	
	d	11 04							11 24	11 43				12 04						12 24	12 43			13 04	
Branksome	d								11 29	11 48										12 29	12 48				
Parkstone (Dorset)	d								11 32	11 51										12 32	12 51				
Poole 4	a	11 13							11 36	11 55				12 13						12 36	12 55			13 13	
	d	11 14							11 37					12 14						12 37				13 14	
Hamworthy	d	11 19							11 42					12 19						12 42				13 19	
Holton Heath	d	11 23												12 23										13 23	
Wareham	d	11 28							11 49					12 28						12 49				13 28	
Wool	d	11 35												12 35										13 35	
Moreton (Dorset)	d	11 41												12 41										13 41	
Dorchester South	d	11 49							12 05					12 49						13 05				13 49	
Dorchester West	d				11 56																				
Upwey	d	11 55			12 03									12 55										13 55	
Weymouth	a	12 00			12 08				12 13					13 00						13 13				14 00	

For general notes see front of timetable
For details of catering facilities see Directory of Train Operators

A ☕ to Bournemouth
b From 15th March

Table 158

Saturdays

London → Basingstoke, Southampton, Lymington, Bournemouth and Weymouth

Network Diagram - see first page of Table 158

		SW	GW	SW	XC	SW	SW	SW	SW	SW	SW	SW	SW	SW	XC		SW	SW	SW	SW	SW	SW	SW	SW	SW
		1	◇	1	1 ◇	1	1 ◇	1	1	1	1 ◇	1	1	1	1 ◇		1	1 ◇	1	1	1	1 ◇	1	1	1
							A				A							A				A			
					☕		☕				☕				☕			☕				☕			
London Waterloo 15 ⊖	d			11 09			11 35		11 39		12 05			12 09				12 35		12 39		13 05			13 09
Clapham Junction 10	d								11u46		12u12									12u46		13u12			
Woking	d			11 35			12 00							12 35				13 00							13 35
Farnborough (Main)	d			11 45					12 13					12 45						13 13					13 45
Fleet	d								12 19											13 19					
Reading 7	d				11 45										12 45										
Basingstoke	a			11 58	12 08				12 34		12 48			12 58	13 08					13 34		13 48			13 58
	d			12 00	12 10				12 36		12 50			13 00	13 10					13 36		13 50			14 00
Micheldever	d			12 10										13 10											14 10
Winchester	d			12 19	12 25		12 33		12 52		13 06			13 19	13 25			13 33		13 52		14 06			14 19
Shawford	d								12 57											13 57					
Romsey	d	12 05											13 05											14 05	
Chandlers Ford	a	12 12											13 12											14 12	
	d	12 12											13 12											14 12	
Eastleigh 3	a	12 18		12 29					13 02				13 18	13 29						14 02				14 18	14 29
	d	12 19		12 30					13 03				13 19	13 30						14 03				14 19	14 30
Hedge End	d			12 36										13 36											14 36
Botley	d			12 40										13 40											14 40
Fareham	d			12 48										13 48											14 48
Portchester	d			12 53										13 53											14 53
Cosham	d			12 58										13 58											14 58
Hilsea	a			13 03										14 03											15 03
Fratton	a			13 07										14 07											15 07
Portsmouth & Southsea	a			13 19										14 19											15 19
Portsmouth Harbour	a			13 23										14 23											15 23
Southampton Airport Parkwy ✈	d	12 23			12 34		12 42		13 08		13 15		13 23		13 34			13 42		14 08		14 15		14 23	
Swaythling	d	12 26											13 26											14 26	
St Denys	d	12 29											13 29											14 29	
Southampton Central	a	12 34			12 40		12 49		13 15		13 22	←	13 34		13 40			13 49		14 15		14 22	←	14 34	
	d	12 39			12 42		12 51		13 30 →		13 24	13 30	13 38		13 42			13 51		14 30 →		14 24	14 30	14 38	
Millbrook (Hants)	d	12b46											13 40											14 40	
Redbridge	d	12 49											13 44											14 44	
Romsey	d	12 57											13 52											14 52	
Mottisfont & Dunbridge	d												13 57											14 57	
Dean	d												14 02											15 02	
Salisbury	a	13 15											14 15											15 15	
Totton	d											13 35											14 35		
Ashurst New Forest	d											13 40											14 40		
Beaulieu Road	d											13 44													
Brockenhurst 3	a				12 56		13 04	←			13 37	13 51			13 56			14 04	←			14 37	14 51		
	d				12 57	12 59	13 05	13 16		13 29	13 38	14 16			13 57		13 59	14 05	14 16		14 29	14 38	15 16		
Lymington Town	d					13 07				13 37		→					14 07				14 37		→		
Lymington Pier	a					13 09				13 39							14 09				14 39				
Yarmouth (I.O.W.) ⛴	a					*13 45*				*14 15*							*14c45*				*15 15*				
Sway	d							13 20											14 20						
New Milton	d							13 25			13 45								14 25			14 45			
Hinton Admiral	d							13 29											14 29						
Christchurch	d							13 34			13 52								14 34			14 52			
Pokesdown	d							13 38			13 56								14 38			14 56			
Bournemouth	a				13 15		13 20	13 42			14 00				14 15			14 20	14 42			15 00			
	d						13 24	13 43			14 04							14 24	14 43			15 04			
Branksome	d						13 29	13 48										14 29	14 48						
Parkstone (Dorset)	d						13 32	13 51										14 32	14 51						
Poole 4	a						13 36	13 55			14 13							14 36	14 55			15 13			
	d						13 37				14 14							14 37				15 14			
Hamworthy	d						13 42				14 19							14 42				15 19			
Holton Heath	d										14 23											15 23			
Wareham	d						13 49				14 28							14 49				15 28			
Wool	d										14 35											15 35			
Moreton (Dorset)	d										14 41											15 41			
Dorchester South	d						14 05				14 49							15 05				15 49			
Dorchester West	d		13 55																						
Upwey	d		14 03								14 55											15 55			
Weymouth	a		14 08				14 13				15 00							15 13				16 00			

For general notes see front of timetable
For details of catering facilities see Directory of Train Operators

A ☕ to Bournemouth
b Arr. 1241
c From 15th March

Table 158

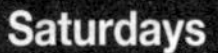

London → Basingstoke, Southampton, Lymington, Bournemouth and Weymouth

Network Diagram - see first page of Table 158

		XC	SW	SW	SW	SW	SW	SW	SW	SW	GW	SW	XC	SW	SW	SW	SW	SW	SW	SW		SW	SW	XC	SW
		1 ◇	1	1 ◇	1	1	1	1 ◇	1	1	◇	1	1 ◇	1	1 ◇	1	1	1	1 ◇	1		1	1	1 ◇	1
				A							B				A				A						
		☕		☕							🍴		☕		☕				☕					☕	
London Waterloo 15 ⊖	d			13 35	13 39			14 05				14 09			14 35		14 39		15 05				15 09		
Clapham Junction 10	d				13u46			14u12									14u46		15u12						
Woking	d			14 00								14 35			15 00								15 35		
Farnborough (Main)	d				14 13							14 45					15 13						15 45		
Fleet	d				14 19												15 19								
Reading 7	d	13 45											14 45											15 45	
Basingstoke	a	14 08			14 34			14 48				14 58	15 08				15 34		15 48				15 58	16 08	
	d	14 10			14 36			14 50				15 00	15 10				15 36		15 50				16 00	16 10	
Micheldever	d											15 10											16 10		
Winchester	d	14 25		14 33	14 52			15 06				15 19	15 25		15 33		15 52		16 06				16 19	16 25	
Shawford	d				14 57												15 57								
Romsey	d									15 05												16 05			
Chandlers Ford	a									15 12												16 12			
	d									15 12												16 12			
Eastleigh 3	a				15 02					15 18		15 29					16 02					16 18	16 29		
	d				15 03					15 19		15 30					16 03					16 19	16 30		
Hedge End	d											15 36											16 36		
Botley	d											15 40											16 40		
Fareham	d											15 48											16 48		
Portchester	d											15 53											16 53		
Cosham	d											15 58											16 58		
Hilsea	a											16 03											17 03		
Fratton	a											16 07											17 07		
Portsmouth & Southsea	a											16 19											17 19		
Portsmouth Harbour	a											16 23											17 23		
Southampton Airport Parkwy ✈	d	14 34		14 42	15 08			15 15		15 23			15 34		15 42		16 08		16 15			16 23		16 34	
Swaythling	d									15 26												16 26			
St Denys	d									15 29												16 29			
Southampton Central	a	14 40		14 49	15 15			15 22	←	15 34			15 40		15 49		16 15		16 22	←		16 34		16 40	
	d	14 42		14 51	15 30			15 24	15 30	15 38			15 42		15 51		16 30		16 24	16 30		16 38		16 42	
Millbrook (Hants)	d				→					15 40							→					16 40			
Redbridge	d									15 44												16 44			
Romsey	d									15 52												16 52			
Mottisfont & Dunbridge	d									15 57												16 57			
Dean	d									16 02												17 03			
Salisbury	a									16 15												17 15			
Totton	d								15 35											16 35					
Ashurst New Forest	d								15 40											16 40					
Beaulieu Road	d																								
Brockenhurst 3	a	14 56		15 04		←		15 37	15 51				15 56		16 04	←			16 37	16 51				16 56	
	d	14 57	14 59	15 05		15 16	15 29	15 38	16 16				15 57	15 59	16 05	16 16		16 29	16 38	17 16				16 57	16 59
Lymington Town	d		15 07				15 37		→					16 07				16 37		→					17 07
Lymington Pier	a		15 09				15 39							16 09				16 39							17 09
Yarmouth (I.O.W.) ⛴	a		*15 45*				*16b15*							*16 45*				*17c15*							*17b45*
Sway	d					15 20										16 20									
New Milton	d					15 25		15 45								16 25			16 45						
Hinton Admiral	d					15 29										16 29									
Christchurch	d					15 34		15 52								16 34			16 52						
Pokesdown	d					15 38		15 56								16 38			16 56						
Bournemouth	a	15 15		15 20		15 42		16 00					16 15		16 20	16 42			17 00					17 15	
	d			15 24		15 43		16 04							16 24	16 43			17 04						
Branksome	d			15 29		15 48									16 29	16 48									
Parkstone (Dorset)	d			15 32		15 51									16 32	16 51									
Poole 4	a			15 36		15 55		16 13							16 36	16 55			17 13						
	d			15 37				16 14							16 37				17 14						
Hamworthy	d			15 42				16 19							16 42				17 19						
Holton Heath	d							16 23											17 23						
Wareham	d			15 49				16 28							16 49				17 28						
Wool	d							16 35											17 35						
Moreton (Dorset)	d							16 41											17 41						
Dorchester South	d			16 05				16 49							17 05				17 49						
Dorchester West	d										16 54														
Upwey	d							16 55											17 55						
Weymouth	a			16 13				17 00			17 07				17 13				18 00						

For general notes see front of timetable
For details of catering facilities see Directory of Train Operators

A ☕ to Bournemouth
B Until 22 March
b From 15th March
c Until 8th March and from 17th May

London → Basingstoke, Southampton, Lymington, Bournemouth and Weymouth

Network Diagram - see first page of Table 158

		SW	SW	SW	SW	SW	SW	SW	SW	XC	SW	SW	SW	SW	SW	SW	GW	SW	SW	SW	GW	SW	XC	SW	SW
		1 ◇	1	1	1	1 ◇	1	1	1	1 ◇	1	1 ◇	1	1	1	1	◇	1 ◇	1	1	◇	1	1 ◇	1	1 ◇
		A				A						A					B	A			B				A
		☕				☕				☕		☕						☕					☕		☕
London Waterloo 15 ⊖	d	15 35		15 39		16 05			16 09			16 35		16 39				17 05				17 09			17 35
Clapham Junction 10	d			15u46		16u12								16u46				17u12							
Woking	d	16 00							16 35			17 00										17 35			18 00
Farnborough (Main)	d			16 13					16 45					17 13								17 45			
Fleet	d			16 19										17 19											
Reading 7	d									16 45													17 45		
Basingstoke	a			16 34		16 48			16 58	17 08				17 34				17 48				17 58	18 08		
	d			16 36		16 50			17 00	17 10			17 24	17 36				17 50				18 00	18 10		
Micheldever	d								17 10				17 34									18 10			
Winchester	d	16 33		16 52		17 06			17 19	17 25		17 33	17 43	17 52				18 06				18 19	18 25		18 33
Shawford	d			16 57									17 48	17 57											
Romsey	d							17 05												18 05					
Chandlers Ford	a							17 12												18 12					
	d							17 12												18 12					
Eastleigh 3	a			17 02				17 18	17 29				17 53	18 02						18 18		18 29			
	d			17 03				17 19	17 30				17 54	18 03						18 19		18 30			
Hedge End	d								17 36													18 36			
Botley	d								17 40													18 40			
Fareham	d								17 48													18 48			
Portchester	d								17 53													18 53			
Cosham	d								17 58													18 58			
Hilsea	a								18 03													19 03			
Fratton	a								18 07													19 07			
Portsmouth & Southsea	a								18 19													19 19			
Portsmouth Harbour	a								18 23													19 23			
Southampton Airport Parkwy ✈	d	16 42		17 08		17 15		17 23		17 34		17 42	17 59	18 08				18 15		18 23			18 34		18 42
Swaythling	d							17 26					18 01							18 26					
St Denys	d							17 29					18 04							18 29					
Southampton Central	a	16 49		17 15		17 22	←	17 34		17 40		17 49	18 10	18 15				18 22	←	18 34			18 40		18 49
	d	16 51		17 30		17 24	17 30	17 38		17 42		17 51		18 30				18 24	18 30	18 38			18 42		18 51
Millbrook (Hants)	d			→				17 40						→						18 40					
Redbridge	d							17 44												18 43					
Romsey	d							17 52												18 57					
Mottisfont & Dunbridge	d							17 57												19 04					
Dean	d							18 02												19 09					
Salisbury	a							18 15												19 23					
Totton	d						17 35												18 35						
Ashurst New Forest	d						17 40												18 40						
Beaulieu Road	d						17 44																		
Brockenhurst 3	a	17 04	←			17 37	17 51			17 56		18 04			←			18 37	18 51				18 56		19 04
	d	17 05	17 16		17 29	17 38	18 16			17 57	17 59	18 05			18 16	18 29		18 38	19 16				18 57	18 59	19 05
Lymington Town	d				17 37		→				18 07					18 37			→					19 07	
Lymington Pier	a				17 39						18 09					18 39								19 09	
Yarmouth (I.O.W.) ⛴	a				*18b15*						*18 45*					*19c15*								*19 45*	
Sway	d		17 20												18 20										
New Milton	d		17 25			17 45									18 25			18 45							
Hinton Admiral	d		17 29												18 29										
Christchurch	d		17 34			17 52									18 34			18 52							
Pokesdown	d		17 38			17 56									18 38			18 56							
Bournemouth	a	17 20	17 42			18 00				18 15		18 20			18 42			19 00					19 15		19 20
	d	17 24	17 43			18 04						18 24			18 43			19 04							19 24
Branksome	d	17 29	17 48									18 29			18 48										19 29
Parkstone (Dorset)	d	17 32	17 51									18 32			18 51										19 32
Poole 4	a	17 36	17 55			18 13						18 36			18 55			19 13							19 36
	d	17 37				18 14						18 37						19 14							19 37
Hamworthy	d	17 42				18 19						18 42						19 19							19 42
Holton Heath	d					18 23												19 23							
Wareham	d	17 49				18 28						18 49						19 28							19 49
Wool	d					18 35												19 35							
Moreton (Dorset)	d					18 41												19 41							
Dorchester South	d	18 05				18 49						19 05						19 49							20 05
Dorchester West	d																19 12				19 54				
Upwey	d					18 55											19 21	19 55			20 02				
Weymouth	a	18 13				19 00						19 13					19 26	20 00			20 08				20 13

For general notes see front of timetable
For details of catering facilities see Directory of Train Operators

A ☕ to Bournemouth
B Until 22 March
b Until 8th March and from 17th May
c From 17th May

Table 158

London → Basingstoke, Southampton, Lymington, Bournemouth and Weymouth

Network Diagram - see first page of Table 158

		SW 1	SW 1		SW 1	SW 1	SW 1	SW 1	SW 1	XC 1 ◇	SW 1	SW 1 ◇	SW 1	SW 1	SW 1	SW 1 ◇	SW 1	SW 1	SW 1	XC 1 ◇	SW 1	SW 1 ◇	SW 1	SW 1	SW 1
						A						A				A						A			
						☕				☕		☕				☕				☕		☕			
London Waterloo 15 ⊖	d		17 39			18 05			18 09			18 35		18 39		19 05			19 09			19 35		19 39	
Clapham Junction 10	d		17u46			18 12								18u46		19u12								19u46	
Woking	d								18 35			19 00							19 35			20 00			
Farnborough (Main)	d		18 13						18 45					19 13					19 45					20 13	
Fleet	d		18 19											19 19										20 19	
Reading 7	d									18 45										19 45					
Basingstoke	a		18 34			18 48			18 58	19 08				19 34		19 48			19 58	20 08				20 34	
	d		18 36			18 50			19 00	19 10				19 36		19 50			20 00	20 10				20 36	
Micheldever	d								19 10										20 10						
Winchester	d		18 52			19 06			19 19	19 25		19 33		19 52		20 06			20 19	20 25		20 33		20 52	
Shawford	d		18 57											19 57										20 57	
Romsey	d							19 05										20 05							
Chandlers Ford	a							19 12										20 12							
	d							19 12										20 12							
Eastleigh 3	a		19 02					19 18	19 29					20 02				20 18	20 29					21 02	
	d		19 03					19 19	19 30					20 03				20 19	20 30					21 03	
Hedge End	d								19 36										20 36						
Botley	d								19 40										20 40						
Fareham	d								19 48										20 48						
Portchester	d								19 53										20 53						
Cosham	d								19 58										20 58						
Hilsea	a								20 03										21 06						
Fratton	a								20 07										21 10						
Portsmouth & Southsea	a								20 19										21 18						
Portsmouth Harbour	a								20 23										21 23						
Southampton Airport Parkwy ✈	d		19 08			19 15		19 23		19 34		19 42		20 08		20 15		20 23		20 34		20 42		21 08	
Swaythling	d							19 26										20 26							
St Denys	d							19 29										20 29							
Southampton Central	a		19 15			19 22	←	19 34		19 40		19 49		20 15		20 22	←	20 34		20 40		20 49		21 15	
	d		19 30			19 24	19 30	19 38		19 42		19 51		20 30		20 24	20 30	20 39		20 42		20 51			
Millbrook (Hants)	d		↳					19 40						↳				20b46							
Redbridge	d							19 44										20 49							
Romsey	d							19 52										20 57							
Mottisfont & Dunbridge	d							19 57																	
Dean	d							20 02																	
Salisbury	a							20 15										21 15							
Totton	d						19 35										20 35								
Ashurst New Forest	d						19 40										20 40								
Beaulieu Road	d																								
Brockenhurst 3	a	←				19 37	19 51			19 56		20 04	←			20 37	20 51			20 56		21 04	←		
	d	19 16			19 29	19 38	20 16			19 57	19 59	20 05	20 16		20 29	20 38	21 16			20 57	20 59	21 05	21 16		21 29
Lymington Town	d				19 37		↳				20 07				20 37		↳				21 07				21 37
Lymington Pier	a				19 39						20 09				20 39						21 09				21 39
Yarmouth (I.O.W.) ⛴	a				*20c15*						*20 45*				*21e30*						*22c00*				*22 45*
Sway	d	19 20											20 20										21 20		
New Milton	d	19 25				19 45							20 25			20 45							21 25		
Hinton Admiral	d	19 29											20 29										21 29		
Christchurch	d	19 34				19 52							20 34			20 52							21 34		
Pokesdown	d	19 38				19 56							20 38			20 56							21 38		
Bournemouth	a	19 42				20 00				20 15		20 20	20 42			21 00				21 15		21 20	21 42		
	d	19 43				20 04						20 24	20 43			21 04						21 24	21 43		
Branksome	d	19 48										20 29	20 48									21 29	21 48		
Parkstone (Dorset)	d	19 51										20 32	20 51									21 32	21 51		
Poole 4	a	19 55				20 13						20 36	20 55			21 13						21 36	21 55		
	d					20 14						20 37				21 14						21 37			
Hamworthy	d					20 19						20 42				21 19						21 42			
Holton Heath	d					20 23																			
Wareham	d					20 28						20 49				21 27						21 49			
Wool	d					20 35										21 34						21 55			
Moreton (Dorset)	d					20 41										21 40						22 01			
Dorchester South	d					20 49						21 05				21 47						22 09			
Dorchester West	d																								
Upwey	d					20 55										21 54						22 16			
Weymouth	a					21 02						21 13				21 58						22 20			

For general notes see front of timetable
For details of catering facilities see Directory of Train Operators

A ☕ to Bournemouth
b Arr. 2041
c From 17th May
e Until 10th May arrives 15 minutes earlier

Table 158

Saturdays

London → Basingstoke, Southampton, Lymington, Bournemouth and Weymouth

Network Diagram - see first page of Table 158

		SW	SW	SW	XC	SW	GW	SW	SW	SW	SW	SW	XC	SW	SW	SW	SW	SW	XC	SW	SW	SW	SW
		1 ◇	1	1	1 ◇	1	◇	1 ◇	1	1 ◇	1	1	1 ◇	1 ◇	1	1	1	1	1 ◇	1	1	1	1
							A	B						B									
		🛒						🛒		🛒				🛒		🛒				🛒			
London Waterloo 15 ⊖	d	20 05		20 09				20 35	20 39	21 05		20 42		21 35	21 39	22 05		21 42		22 35	22 39	23 05	23 39
Clapham Junction 10	d	20u12							20u46	21u12					21u46	22u12					22u46	23u12	23u46
Woking	d			20 35				21 00		21 32		21 19		22 00		22 32		22 19		23 00		23 32	00 08
Farnborough (Main)	d			20 45					21 13			21 33			22 13			22 33			23 13		00 18
Fleet	d								21 19			21 38			22 19			22 38			23 19		00 23
Reading 7	d				20 45								21 45						22 45				
Basingstoke	a	20 48		20 58	21 08				21 34	21 51		21 58	22 08		22 34	22 51		22 58	23 08		23 34	23 51	00 35
	d	20 50		21 00	21 10				21 36	21 53		22 00	22 10		22 36	22 53		23 00	23 08		23 36	23 53	00 36
Micheldever	d			21 10								22 10			22s46			23 10				00 03	
Winchester	d	21 06		21 19	21 25			21 33	21 52	22 09		22 19	22 25	22 33	22 56	23 09		23 19	23 23	23 33	23 52	00 12	00 53
Shawford	d								21 57						23 00						23 57		
Romsey	d		21 05								22 07						23 08						
Chandlers Ford	a		21 12								22 14						23 16						
	d		21 12								22 14						23 16						
Eastleigh 3	a		21 18	21 29					22 02	22 17	22 23	22 29			23 06	23 17	23 22	23 29			00 02	00 20	01 01
	d		21 19	21 30					22 03	22 18	22 24	22 30			23 07	23 18	23 23	23 30			00 03	00 21	01 02
Hedge End	d			21 36								22 36						23 36					
Botley	d			21 40								22 40						23 40					
Fareham	d			21 48								22 48						23 48					
Portchester	d			21 53								22 53						23 53					
Cosham	d			21 58								22 58						23 58					
Hilsea	a			22 06								23 03						00 03					
Fratton	a			22 10								23 07						00 07					
Portsmouth & Southsea	a			22 13								23 10						00 11					
Portsmouth Harbour	a			22 18								23 16						00 16					
Southampton Airport Parkwy ✈	d	21 15	21 23		21 34			21 42	22 08	22 23	22 28		22 34	22 42	23 11	23 23	23 27		23 34	23 42	00 08	00 26	01 06
Swaythling	d		21 26								22 31						23 30						
St Denys	d		21 29								22 34						23 33					00s30	
Southampton Central	a	21 22	21 34		21 40			21 49	22 15	22 30	22 39		22 48	22 49	23 18	23 30	23 38		23 45	23 49	00 15	00 35	01 13
	d	21 24	21 38		21 42			21 51		22 31	22 40			22 51		23 31	23 40			23 51		00 36	
Millbrook (Hants)	d		21 40								22 43						23 42						
Redbridge	d		21 44								22 46						23 49						
Romsey	d		21 52								22a55						23 57						
Mottisfont & Dunbridge	d		21 57														00 02						
Dean	d		22 02														00 08						
Salisbury	a		22 15														00 20						
Totton	d	21 29								22 37						23 37						00s41	
Ashurst New Forest	d	21 34								22 41						23 41							
Beaulieu Road	d																						
Brockenhurst 3	a	21 42			21 56			22 04		22 49				23 04		23 49				00 04		00s52	
	d	21 43			21 57	21 59		22 05		22 50				23 05		23 50				00 05			
Lymington Town	d					22 07																	
Lymington Pier	a					22 09																	
Yarmouth (I.O.W.) ⛴	a					22 45																	
Sway	d	21 47								22 55						23 55							
New Milton	d	21 52								23 00						23 59						01s00	
Hinton Admiral	d	21 56								23 04						00 04							
Christchurch	d	22 01								23 09						00 09						01s07	
Pokesdown	d	22 05								23 12						00 12						01s11	
Bournemouth	a	22 09			22 15			22 20		23 16				23 23		00 16				00 22		01 15	
	d	22 10						22 24		23 18				23 28		00 18				00 24		01 16	
Branksome	d	22 15						22 29		23 23				23 33		00 23				00 29		01s21	
Parkstone (Dorset)	d	22 18						22 32		23 26				23 36		00 26				00 32		01s24	
Poole 4	a	22 23						22 36		23 30				23 39		00 30				00 36		01 29	
	d							22 37						23 40									
Hamworthy	d							22 42						23 45									
Holton Heath	d																						
Wareham	d							22 49						23 52									
Wool	d							22 55						23 59									
Moreton (Dorset)	d							23 01						00 05									
Dorchester South	d							23 09						00 13									
Dorchester West	d						22 47																
Upwey	d						22 54	23 16						00 19									
Weymouth	a						22 59	23 20						00 24									

For general notes see front of timetable
For details of catering facilities see Directory of Train Operators

A Until 22 March
B 🛒 to Bournemouth

Table 158

London → Basingstoke, Southampton, Lymington, Bournemouth and Weymouth

Network Diagram - see first page of Table 158

		SW	SW	SW	SW	SW	SW	SW	SW	SW	SW	SW	SW	SW		SW	SW	SW	SW	SW		SW
		1 ◇	1 ☕	1	1	1 ☕	1	1	1	1	1	1	1	1		1	1	1	1	1 ◇		1
London Waterloo 15 ⊖	d	21p35	22p05		21p42	22p35	22p39	23p05	23p39	00 05	01 05									07 54		
Clapham Junction 10	d		22b12				22b46	23b12	23b46	00u12	01 14									08u03		
Woking	d	22p00	22p32		22p19	23p00		23p32	00 08	00 36	01 41									08 28		
Farnborough (Main)	d				22p33		23p13		00 18		01s57											
Fleet	d				22p38		23p19		00 23													
Reading 7	d																					
Basingstoke	a		22p51		22p58		23p34	23p51	00 35	00 55	02s11									08 47		
	d		22p53		23p00		23p36	23p53	00 36	00 57				07 48						08 49		
Micheldever	d				23p10			00 03						07 58						08 59		
Winchester	d	22p33	23p09		23p19	23p33	23p52	00 12	00 53	01 13	02s28			08 08						09 08		
Shawford	d						23p57							08 12								
Romsey	d			23p08									07 38						08 35			
Chandlers Ford	a			23p16									07 45						08 42			
	d			23p16									07 45						08 42			
Eastleigh 3	a		23p17	23p22	23p29		00 02	00 20	01 01	01 21	02s37		07 51	08 18					08 48	09 18		
	d		23p18	23p23	23p30		00 03	00 21	01 02	01 22			07 54	08 22	08 26				08 54	09 22	09 26	
Hedge End	d				23p36										08 32						09 32	
Botley	d				23p40										08 36						09 36	
Fareham	d				23p48										08 44						09 44	
Portchester	d				23p53										08 49						09 49	
Cosham	d				23p58										08 54						09 54	
Hilsea	a				00 03										09 00						10 01	
Fratton	a				00 07										09 04						10 05	
Portsmouth & Southsea	a				00 11										09 08						10 10	
Portsmouth Harbour	a				00 16										09 13						10 15	
Southampton Airport Parkwy ✈	d	22p42	23p23	23p27		23p42	00 08	00 26	01 06	01 27	02s42		07 58	08 27					08 58	09 27		
Swaythling	d			23p30									08 01						09 01			
St Denys	d			23p33				00s30			02s47		08 04						09 04			
Southampton Central	a	22p49	23p30	23p38		23p49	00 15	00 35	01 13	01 36	02 52		08 09	08 34					09 09	09 34		
	d	22p51	23p31	23p40		23p51		00 36		01 37			08 10	08 35			09 03		09 10	09 35		
Millbrook (Hants)	d			23p42									08 13						09 13			
Redbridge	d			23p49									08 16						09 16			
Romsey	d			23p57									08 24						09 24			
Mottisfont & Dunbridge	d			00 02									08 29						09 29			
Dean	d			00 08									08 35						09 35			
Salisbury	a			00 20									08 47						09 47			
Totton	d		23p37					00s41		01s42				08 41						09 41		
Ashurst New Forest	d		23p41											08 45						09 45		
Beaulieu Road	d													08 50						09 50		
Brockenhurst 3	a	23p04	23p49			00 04		00s52		01s53				08 56			09 16			09 56		
	d	23p05	23p50			00 05								08 57		08 59	09 17	09 29		09 57		09 59
Lymington Town	d															09 07		09 37				10 07
Lymington Pier	a															09 09		09 39				10 09
Yarmouth (I.O.W.) ⛴	a															*10 15*		*10 15*				*10 45*
Sway	d		23p55											09 01						10 01		
New Milton	d		23p59					01s00		02s01				09 06			09 24			10 06		
Hinton Admiral	d		00 04											09 10						10 10		
Christchurch	d		00 09					01s07		02s08				09 15						10 15		
Pokesdown	d		00 12					01s11		02s12				09 19						10 19		
Bournemouth	a	23p23	00 16			00 22		01 15		02 16				09 23			09 35			10 23		
	d	23p28	00 18			00 24		01 16				08 40		09 25			09 40			10 25		
Branksome	d	23p33	00 23			00 29		01s21				08 45					09 45					
Parkstone (Dorset)	d	23p36	00 26			00 32		01s24				08 48					09 48					
Poole 4	a	23p39	00 30			00 36		01 29				08 51		09 34			09 51			10 34		
	d	23p40										08 52					09 52					
Hamworthy	d	23p45										08 57					09 57					
Holton Heath	d																					
Wareham	d	23p52										09 04					10 04					
Wool	d	23p59										09 11					10 11					
Moreton (Dorset)	d	00 05										09 17					10 17					
Dorchester South	d	00 13										09 25					10 25					
Dorchester West	d																					
Upwey	d	00 19										09 32					10 32					
Weymouth	a	00 24										09 36					10 36					

For general notes see front of timetable
For details of catering facilities see Directory of Train Operators

b Previous night.
Stops to pick up only

London → Basingstoke, Southampton, Lymington, Bournemouth and Weymouth

Network Diagram - see first page of Table 158

		SW		SW	SW	SW		SW		SW	SW	SW	SW			SW	XC	SW	SW	SW		SW		SW	XC
		1 ◇		1	1	1 ◇		1		1 ◇	1	1	1 ◇			1	1 ◇	1 ◇	1	1		1 ◇		1	1 ◇
																		A							
																	[trolley]	[trolley]							[trolley]
London Waterloo 15 ⊖	d	08 35				08 54				09 35			09 54					10 35				10 54			
Clapham Junction 10	d	08u42				09u03				09u42			10u03					10u42				11u03			
Woking	d	09 08				09 28				10 08			10 28					11 07				11 28			
Farnborough (Main)	d																								
Fleet	d																								
Reading 7	d																10 50								11 50
Basingstoke	a	09 27				09 47				10 27			10 47				11 08	11 26				11 47			12 08
	d	09 29				09 48				10 29			10 48				11 10	11 28				11 48			12 10
Micheldever	d					09 58							10 58									11 58			
Winchester	d	09 45				10 08				10 45			11 08				11 25	11 44				12 08			12 25
Shawford	d					10 12																12 12			
Romsey	d				09 35							10 35								11 35					
Chandlers Ford	a				09 42							10 42								11 42					
	d				09 42							10 42								11 42					
Eastleigh 3	a				09 48	10 18						10 48	11 18							11 48		12 18			
	d				09 55	10 22	10 26					10 55	11 22	11 26						11 54		12 22	12 26		
Hedge End	d						10 32							11 32									12 32		
Botley	d						10 36							11 36									12 36		
Fareham	d						10 44							11 44									12 44		
Portchester	d						10 49							11 49									12 49		
Cosham	d						10 54							11 54									12 54		
Hilsea	a						11 01							12 00									13 00		
Fratton	a						11 05							12 04									13 04		
Portsmouth & Southsea	a						11 09							12 08									13 08		
Portsmouth Harbour	a						11 14							12 13									13 13		
Southampton Airport Parkwy ✈	d	09 54			09 59	10 27				10 54		10 59	11 27				11 34	11 53		11 58		12 27			12 34
Swaythling	d				10 01							11 01								12 01					
St Denys	d				10 04							11 04								12 04					
Southampton Central	a	10 01			10 09	10 34				11 01		11 09	11 34				11 42	12 00		12 09		12 34			12 42
	d	10 04			10 10	10 35				11 04		11 10	11 35				11 44	12 03		12 10		12 35			12 44
Millbrook (Hants)	d				10 13							11 13								12 13					
Redbridge	d				10 16							11 16								12 16					
Romsey	d				10 24							11 24								12 24					
Mottisfont & Dunbridge	d											11 29													
Dean	d											11 35													
Salisbury	a				10 44							11 50								12 43					
Totton	d					10 41							11 41									12 41			
Ashurst New Forest	d					10 45							11 45									12 45			
Beaulieu Road	d					10 50							11 50									12 50			
Brockenhurst 3	a	10 17				10 56				11 17			11 56				12 02	12 16				12 56			13 02
	d	10 18		10 29		10 57		10 59		11 18	11 29		11 57			11 59	12 03	12 17	12 29			12 57		12 59	13 03
Lymington Town	d			10 37				11 07			11 37					12 07			12 37					13 07	
Lymington Pier	a			10 39				11 09			11 39					12 09			12 39					13 09	
Yarmouth (I.O.W.) ⛴	a			*11 45*				*11 45*			*12b15*					*12c45*			*13b15*					*13 45*	
Sway	d					11 01							12 01									13 01			
New Milton	d	10 25				11 06				11 25			12 06					12 24				13 06			
Hinton Admiral	d					11 10							12 10									13 10			
Christchurch	d					11 15							12 15									13 15			
Pokesdown	d					11 19							12 19									13 19			
Bournemouth	a	10 35				11 23				11 35			12 23				12 32	12 35				13 23			13 32
	d	10 40				11 25				11 40			12 25					12 40				13 25			
Branksome	d	10 45								11 45								12 45							
Parkstone (Dorset)	d	10 48								11 48								12 48							
Poole 4	a	10 51				11 34				11 51			12 34					12 51				13 34			
	d	10 52								11 52								12 52							
Hamworthy	d	10 57								11 57								12 57							
Holton Heath	d																								
Wareham	d	11 04								12 04								13 04							
Wool	d	11 11								12 11								13 11							
Moreton (Dorset)	d	11 17								12 17								13 17							
Dorchester South	d	11 25								12 25								13 25							
Dorchester West	d																								
Upwey	d	11 32								12 32								13 32							
Weymouth	a	11 36								12 36								13 36							

For general notes see front of timetable
For details of catering facilities see Directory of Train Operators

A [trolley] to Bournemouth
b From 16th March
c Until 9th March and from 18th May

Table 158

Sundays

London → Basingstoke, Southampton, Lymington, Bournemouth and Weymouth

Network Diagram - see first page of Table 158

Station		SW 1◇ A ☕	SW 1	SW 1	SW 1◇		SW 1	XC 1◇ ☕	SW 1◇ A ☕	SW 1	SW 1	SW 1◇		SW 1	GW ◇	XC 1◇ ☕	SW 1◇ A ☕	SW 1	SW 1	SW 1◇	
London Waterloo 15 ⊖	d	11 35			11 54				12 35			12 54					13 35			13 54	
Clapham Junction 10	d	11u42			12u03				12u42			13u03					13u42			14u03	
Woking	d	12 07			12 28				13 07			13 28					14 07			14 28	
Farnborough (Main)	d																				
Fleet	d																				
Reading 7	d							12 50								13 50					
Basingstoke	a	12 26			12 47			13 08	13 26			13 47				14 08	14 26			14 47	
	d	12 28			12 48			13 10	13 28			13 48				14 10	14 28			14 48	
Micheldever	d				12 58							13 58								14 58	
Winchester	d	12 44			13 08			13 25	13 44			14 08				14 25	14 44			15 08	
Shawford	d											14 12									
Romsey	d			12 35							13 35								14 35		
Chandlers Ford	a			12 42							13 42								14 42		
	d			12 42							13 42								14 42		
Eastleigh 3	a			12 48	13 18						13 48	14 18							14 48	15 18	
	d			12 54	13 22	13 26					13 54	14 22	14 26						14 54	15 22	15 26
Hedge End	d					13 32							14 32								15 32
Botley	d					13 36							14 36								15 36
Fareham	d					13 44							14 44								15 45
Portchester	d					13 49							14 49								15 50
Cosham	d					13 54							14 54								15 55
Hilsea	a					14 00							15 00								16 00
Fratton	a					14 04							15 04								16 04
Portsmouth & Southsea	a					14 08							15 08								16 08
Portsmouth Harbour	a					14 13							15 13								16 13
Southampton Airport Parkwy ✈	d	12 53		12 58	13 27			13 34	13 53		13 58	14 27				14 34	14 53		14 58	15 27	
Swaythling	d			13 01							14 01								15 01		
St Denys	d			13 04							14 04								15 04		
Southampton Central	a	13 00		13 09	13 34			13 42	14 00		14 09	14 34				14 42	15 00		15 09	15 34	
	d	13 03		13 10	13 35			13 44	14 03		14 10	14 35				14 44	15 03		15 10	15 35	
Millbrook (Hants)	d			13 13							14 13								15 13		
Redbridge	d			13 16							14 16								15 16		
Romsey	d			13 24							14 24								15 24		
Mottisfont & Dunbridge	d			13 29															15 29		
Dean	d			13 38															15 35		
Salisbury	a			13 50							14 43								15 50		
Totton	d				13 41							14 41								15 41	
Ashurst New Forest	d				13 45							14 45								15 45	
Beaulieu Road	d				13 50							14 50								15 50	
Brockenhurst 3	a	13 16			13 56			14 02	14 16			14 56				15 02	15 16			15 56	
	d	13 17	13 29		13 57		13 59	14 03	14 17	14 29		14 57		14 59		15 03	15 17	15 29		15 57	
Lymington Town	d		13 37				14 07			14 37				15 07				15 37			
Lymington Pier	a		13 39				14 09			14 39				15 09				15 39			
Yarmouth (I.O.W.) ⛴	a		*14 15*				*14b45*			*15 15*				*15 45*				*16b15*			
Sway	d				14 01							15 01								16 01	
New Milton	d	13 24			14 06				14 24			15 06					15 24			16 06	
Hinton Admiral	d				14 10							15 10								16 10	
Christchurch	d				14 15							15 15								16 15	
Pokesdown	d				14 19							15 19								16 19	
Bournemouth	a	13 35			14 23			14 32	14 35			15 23				15 32	15 35			16 23	
	d	13 40			14 25				14 40			15 25					15 40			16 25	
Branksome	d	13 45							14 45								15 45				
Parkstone (Dorset)	d	13 48							14 48								15 48				
Poole 4	a	13 51			14 34				14 51			15 34					15 51			16 34	
	d	13 52							14 52								15 52				
Hamworthy	d	13 57							14 57								15 57				
Holton Heath	d																				
Wareham	d	14 04							15 04								16 04				
Wool	d	14 11							15 11								16 11				
Moreton (Dorset)	d	14 17							15 17								16 17				
Dorchester South	d	14 25							15 25								16 25				
Dorchester West	d														15 53						
Upwey	d	14 32							15 32						16 00		16 32				
Weymouth	a	14 36							15 36						16 05		16 36				

For general notes see front of timetable
For details of catering facilities see Directory of Train Operators

A ☕ to Bournemouth
b From 16th March

London → Basingstoke, Southampton, Lymington, Bournemouth and Weymouth

Network Diagram - see first page of Table 158

		SW	XC	SW	SW	SW	SW		SW	XC	SW	SW	SW	SW		SW	XC	SW	SW	SW	SW	
										R							R					
		1	1 ◊	1 ◊	1	1	1 ◊		1	1	1 ◊	1	1	1 ◊		1	1	1 ◊	1	1	1 ◊	
				A							A							A				
			☕	☕						☕	☕						☕	☕				
London Waterloo 15 ⊖	d			14 35			14 54				15 35			15 54				16 35			16 54	
Clapham Junction 10	d			14u42			15u03				15u42			16u03				16u42			17u03	
Woking	d			15 07			15 28				16 07			16 28				17 07			17 28	
Farnborough (Main)	d																					
Fleet	d																					
Reading 7	d		14 50							15 50							16 50					
Basingstoke	a		15 08	15 26			15 47			16 08	16 26			16 47			17 08	17 26			17 47	
	d		15 10	15 28			15 48			16 10	16 28			16 48			17 10	17 28			17 48	
Micheldever	d						15 58							16 58							17 58	
Winchester	d		15 25	15 44			16 08			16 25	16 44			17 08			17 25	17 44			18 08	
Shawford	d						16 12														18 12	
Romsey	d					15 35							16 35							17 35		
Chandlers Ford	a					15 42							16 42							17 42		
	d					15 42							16 42							17 42		
Eastleigh 3	a					15 48	16 18						16 48	17 18						17 48	18 18	
	d					15 54	16 22	16 26					16 54	17 22	17 26					17 54	18 22	18 26
Hedge End	d							16 32							17 32							18 32
Botley	d							16 36							17 36							18 36
Fareham	d							16 44							17 44							18 44
Portchester	d							16 49							17 49							18 49
Cosham	d							16 54							17 54							18 54
Hilsea	a							17 00							18 00							19 00
Fratton	a							17 04							18 04							19 04
Portsmouth & Southsea	a							17 08							18 08							19 08
Portsmouth Harbour	a							17 13							18 13							19 13
Southampton Airport Parkwy ✈	d		15 34	15 53		15 58	16 27			16 34	16 53		16 58	17 27			17 34	17 53		17 58	18 27	
Swaythling	d					16 01							17 01							18 01		
St Denys	d					16 04							17 04							18 04		
Southampton Central	a		15 42	16 00		16 09	16 34			16 42	17 00		17 09	17 34			17 42	18 00		18 09	18 34	
	d		15 44	16 03		16 10	16 35			16 44	17 03		17 10	17 35			17 44	18 03		18 10	18 35	
Millbrook (Hants)	d					16 13							17 13							18 13		
Redbridge	d					16 16							17 16							18 16		
Romsey	d					16 24							17 24							18 24		
Mottisfont & Dunbridge	d												17 29									
Dean	d												17 35									
Salisbury	a					16 43							17 50							18 43		
Totton	d						16 41							17 41							18 41	
Ashurst New Forest	d						16 45							17 45							18 45	
Beaulieu Road	d						16 50							17 50							18 50	
Brockenhurst 3	a		16 02	16 16			16 56			17 02	17 16			17 56			18 02	18 16			18 56	
	d	15 59	16 03	16 17	16 29		16 57		16 59	17 03	17 17	17 29		17 57		17 59	18 03	18 17	18 29		18 57	
Lymington Town	d	16 07			16 37				17 07			17 37				18 07			18 37			
Lymington Pier	a	16 09			16 39				17 09			17 39				18 09			18 39			
Yarmouth (I.O.W.) ⛴	a	*16 45*			*17 15*				*17b45*			*18 15*				*18 45*			*19b15*			
Sway	d						17 01							18 01							19 01	
New Milton	d			16 24			17 06				17 24			18 06				18 24			19 06	
Hinton Admiral	d						17 10							18 10							19 10	
Christchurch	d						17 15							18 15							19 15	
Pokesdown	d						17 19							18 19							19 19	
Bournemouth	a		16 32	16 35			17 23			17 32	17 35			18 23			18 32	18 35			19 23	
	d			16 40			17 25				17 40			18 25				18 40			19 25	
Branksome	d			16 45							17 45							18 45				
Parkstone (Dorset)	d			16 48							17 48							18 48				
Poole 4	a			16 51			17 34				17 51			18 34				18 51			19 34	
	d			16 52							17 52							18 52				
Hamworthy	d			16 57							17 57							18 57				
Holton Heath	d																					
Wareham	d			17 04							18 04							19 04				
Wool	d			17 11							18 11							19 11				
Moreton (Dorset)	d			17 17							18 17							19 17				
Dorchester South	d			17 25							18 25							19 25				
Dorchester West	d																					
Upwey	d			17 32							18 32							19 32				
Weymouth	a			17 36							18 36							19 36				

For general notes see front of timetable
For details of catering facilities see Directory of Train Operators

A ☕ to Bournemouth
b From 16th March

Table 158

Sundays

London → Basingstoke, Southampton, Lymington, Bournemouth and Weymouth

Network Diagram - see first page of Table 158

		SW	GW	GW	XC	SW	SW	SW	SW		SW	XC	SW	SW	SW	SW		SW	XC	SW	SW
		1	◇ A	◇ B	R 1 ⊡	1 ◇ C ⊡	1	1	1 ◇		1	R 1 ⊡	1 ◇ C ⊡	1	1	1 ◇		1	R 1 ⊡	1 ◇ C ⊡	1
London Waterloo 15 ⊖	d					17 35			17 54				18 35			18 54				19 35	
Clapham Junction 10	d					17u42			18u03				18u42			19u03				19u42	
Woking	d					18 07			18 28				19 07			19 28				20 07	
Farnborough (Main)	d																				
Fleet	d																				
Reading 7	d				17 50							18 50							19 50		
Basingstoke	a				18 08	18 26			18 47			19 08	19 26			19 47			20 08	20 26	
	d				18 10	18 28			18 48			19 10	19 28			19 48			20 10	20 28	
Micheldever	d								18 58							19 58					
Winchester	d				18 25	18 44			19 08			19 25	19 44			20 08			20 25	20 44	
Shawford	d															20 12					
Romsey	d							18 35							19 35						
Chandlers Ford	a							18 42							19 42						
	d							18 42							19 42						
Eastleigh 3	a							18 48	19 18						19 48	20 18					
	d							18 54	19 22	19 26					19 54	20 22	20 26				
Hedge End	d									19 32							20 32				
Botley	d									19 36							20 36				
Fareham	d									19 44							20 44				
Portchester	d									19 49							20 49				
Cosham	d									19 54							20 54				
Hilsea	a									20 00							21 00				
Fratton	a									20 04							21 04				
Portsmouth & Southsea	a									20 08							21 08				
Portsmouth Harbour	a									20 13							21 13				
Southampton Airport Parkwy ✈	d				18 34	18 53		18 58	19 27			19 34	19 53		19 58	20 27			20 34	20 53	
Swaythling	d							19 01							20 01						
St Denys	d							19 04							20 04						
Southampton Central	a				18 42	19 00		19 09	19 34			19 42	20 00		20 09	20 34			20 44	21 00	
	d				18 44	19 03		19 10	19 35			19 44	20 03		20 10	20 35			20 46	21 03	
Millbrook (Hants)	d							19 13							20 13						
Redbridge	d							19 16							20 16						
Romsey	d							19 24							20 24						
Mottisfont & Dunbridge	d							19 29													
Dean	d							19 35													
Salisbury	a							19 50							20 43						
Totton	d								19 41							20 41					
Ashurst New Forest	d								19 45							20 45					
Beaulieu Road	d								19 50							20 50					
Brockenhurst 3	a				19 02	19 16			19 56			20 02	20 16			20 56			21 02	21 16	
	d	18 59			19 03	19 17	19 29		19 57		19 59	20 03	20 17	20 29		20 57		20 59	21 03	21 17	21 29
Lymington Town	d	19 07					19 37				20 07			20 37				21 07			21 37
Lymington Pier	a	19 09					19 39				20 09			20 39				21 09			21 39
Yarmouth (I.O.W.) ⛴	a	19 45					20b15				20 45			21c30				22 45			22 45
Sway	d								20 01							21 01					
New Milton	d					19 24			20 06				20 24			21 06				21 24	
Hinton Admiral	d								20 10							21 10					
Christchurch	d								20 15							21 15					
Pokesdown	d								20 19							21 19					
Bournemouth	a				19 32	19 35			20 23			20 32	20 35			21 23			21 32	21 35	
	d					19 40			20 25				20 40			21 25				21 40	
Branksome	d					19 45							20 45							21 45	
Parkstone (Dorset)	d					19 48							20 48							21 48	
Poole 4	a					19 51			20 34				20 51			21 34				21 51	
	d					19 52							20 52							21 52	
Hamworthy	d					19 57							20 57							21 57	
Holton Heath	d																				
Wareham	d					20 04							21 04							22 04	
Wool	d					20 11							21 11							22 11	
Moreton (Dorset)	d					20 17							21 17							22 17	
Dorchester South	d					20 25							21 25							22 25	
Dorchester West	d		19 53	20 15																	
Upwey	d		20 00	20 22		20 32							21 32							22 32	
Weymouth	a		20 05	20 26		20 36							21 36							22 36	

For general notes see front of timetable
For details of catering facilities see Directory of Train Operators

A Until 23 March.
B From 30 March
C ⊡ to Bournemouth

b From 16th March
c Until 11th May

Table 158

Sundays

London → Basingstoke, Southampton, Lymington, Bournemouth and Weymouth

Network Diagram - see first page of Table 158

		SW	SW		SW	XC	GW	SW	SW	SW		XC	SW	SW	XC	SW		XC	SW	
		1	1 ◇		1	R 1	◇	1 ◇	1	1 ◇		R 1	1 ◇	1	R 1	1 ◇		1 ◇	1	
								A ⊏P					A ⊏P						B ⊏P	
London Waterloo 15 ⊖	d		19 54					20 35		20 54			21 35			21 54			22 54	
Clapham Junction 10	d		20u03					20u42		21u03			21u42			22u03			23u03	
Woking	d		20 28					21 07		21 28			22 07			22 28			23 28	
Farnborough (Main)	d																			
Fleet	d																			
Reading 7	d					20 50						21 50						22 50		
Basingstoke	a		20 47			21 08		21 26		21 47		22 08	22 26		←	22 47		23 08	23 47	
	d		20 48			21 10		21 28		21 48		22 10 →	22 28		22 10	22 48		23 10	23 48	
Micheldever	d		20 58							21 58						22 58			23 58	
Winchester	d		21 08			21 25		21 44		22 08			22 44			23 08		23 25	00 08	
Shawford	d									22 12										
Romsey	d	20 35							21 35					22 35						
Chandlers Ford	a	20 40							21 42					22 42						
	d	20 42							21 42					22 42						
Eastleigh 3	a	20 48	21 18						21 48	22 18				22 48		23 18			00 18	
	d	20 54	21 22	21 26					21 54	22 22	22 26			22 54		23 22	23 26		00 22	00 30
Hedge End	d			21 32							22 32						23 32			00s36
Botley	d			21 36							22 36						23 36			00s39
Fareham	d			21 44							22 44						23 44			00s47
Portchester	d			21 49							22 49						23 49			00s53
Cosham	d			21 54							22 54						23 54			00s58
Hilsea	a			22 00							23 00						23 59			
Fratton	a			22 04							23 04						00 04			01s06
Portsmouth & Southsea	a			22 08							23 08						00 08			01s10
Portsmouth Harbour	a			22 13							23 13						00 13			01 15
Southampton Airport Parkwy ✈	d	20 58	21 27			21 34		21 53	21 58	22 27			22 53	22 58	23 19	23 27		23 34	00 27	
Swaythling	d	21 01							22 01					23 01						
St Denys	d	21 04							22 04					23 04					00s31	
Southampton Central	a	21 09	21 34			21 42		22 00	22 09	22 34			23 00	23 09	23 31	23 34		23 45	00 36	
	d	21 10	21 35			21 44		22 03	22 10	22 35			23 03	23 10		23 35			00 37	
Millbrook (Hants)	d	21 13							22 13					23 13						
Redbridge	d	21 16							22 16					23 16						
Romsey	d	21 24							22a24					23 24						
Mottisfont & Dunbridge	d	21 29												23 29						
Dean	d	21 35												23 35						
Salisbury	a	21 50												23 50						
Totton	d		21 41							22 41						23 41			00s42	
Ashurst New Forest	d		21 45							22 45						23 45				
Beaulieu Road	d		21 50							22 50										
Brockenhurst 3	a		21 56			22 02		22 16		22 56			23 16			23 53			00s53	
	d		21 57		21 59	22 03		22 17		22 57			23 17			23 54				
Lymington Town	d				22 07															
Lymington Pier	a				22 09															
Yarmouth (I.O.W.) ⛴	a				22 45															
Sway	d		22 01							23 01						23 59				
New Milton	d		22 06					22 24		23 06			23 24			00 04			01s01	
Hinton Admiral	d		22 10							23 10						00 08				
Christchurch	d		22 15							23 15						00 13			01s08	
Pokesdown	d		22 19							23 19						00 16			01s12	
Bournemouth	a		22 23			22 32		22 35		23 23			23 35			00 21			01 16	
	d		22 25					22 40		23 25			23 40			00 22			01 18	
Branksome	d							22 45					23 45			00 28			01s23	
Parkstone (Dorset)	d							22 48					23 48			00 31			01s26	
Poole 4	a		22 34					22 51		23 34			23 51			00 35			01 30	
	d							22 52					23 52							
Hamworthy	d							22 57					23 57							
Holton Heath	d																			
Wareham	d							23 04					00 04							
Wool	d							23 11					00 11							
Moreton (Dorset)	d							23 17					00 17							
Dorchester South	d							23 25					00 25							
Dorchester West	d						22 52													
Upwey	d						22 59	23 32					00 32							
Weymouth	a						23 03	23 36					00 36							

For general notes see front of timetable
For details of catering facilities see Directory of Train Operators

A ⊏P to Bournemouth
B ⊏P to Poole

For details of Bank Holiday service alterations, please see first page of Table 149

Weymouth, Bournemouth, Lymington, Southampton and Basingstoke → London

Network Diagram - see first page of Table 158

Miles	Miles			SW	SW	SW	SW	SW	SW	XC	SW	SW	GW	SW	XC	SW	SW	SW	SW	SW	SW	SW	SW
				MO	MX	MX	MX																
				[1]	[1]	[1]	[1] ◇	[1]	[1]	[1] ◇	[1]	[1]	◇	[1]	[1] ◇	[1]	[1]	[1]	[1]	[1]	[1]	[1]	[1]
										☕				☕	☕			☕					
0	—	**Weymouth**	d	20p58	21p10		22p10						05 40										
2¼	—	Upwey	d	21p02	21p14		22p14						05 45										
—	—	Dorchester West	a										05 53										
7	—	**Dorchester South**	d	21p10	21p22		22p22																
12½	—	Moreton (Dorset)	d	21p17	21p28		22p28																
17	—	Wool	d	21p23	21p34		22p34																
22	—	Wareham	d	21p30	21p42		22p42																
24	—	Holton Heath	d																				
26¾	—	Hamworthy	d	21p37	21p48		22p48																
29	—	**Poole [4]**	a	21p41	21p53		22p53																
—	—		d	21p50	21p54		22p54							05 00		05 26		05 45					
30¾	—	Parkstone (Dorset)	d	21p54	21p58		22p58							05 04		05 30							
32	—	Branksome	d	21p57	22p01		23p01							05 07		05 33							
34¾	—	**Bournemouth**	a	22p03	22p07		23p07							05 12		05 38		05 54					
—	—		d	22p06	22p12		23p12							05 15		05 40		05 57					
36½	—	Pokesdown	d	22p10	22p16		23p16							05 19		05 44							
38¼	—	Christchurch	d	22p14	22p20		23p20							05 23		05 48							
41¾	—	Hinton Admiral	d	22p19	22p25		23p25									05 53							
44¼	—	New Milton	d	22p23	22p29		23p29							05 30		05 57							
47¼	—	Sway	d	22p28	22p34		23p34									06 02							
—	—	Yarmouth (I.O.W.) ⛴	d																		*04 40*		
—	0	**Lymington Pier** ⛴	d																		06 14		
—	½	Lymington Town	d																		06 16		
50	5¼	**Brockenhurst [3]**	a	22p33	22p39		23p39							05 37		06 07		06 12			06 24		
—	—		d	22p34	22p40		23p40							05 38				06 14					
54¾	—	Beaulieu Road	d	22p39																			
57¼	—	Ashurst New Forest	d	22p43	22p47		23p47																
60¼	—	Totton	d	22p48	22p52		23p52							05 49			06 12						
—	0	**Salisbury**	d																				
—	9	Dean	d																				
—	12¾	Mottisfont & Dunbridge	d																				
—	16½	**Romsey**	d																				
60¾	22½	Redbridge	d														06 14						
62½	—	Millbrook (Hants)	d														06 17						
63½	—	**Southampton Central**	a	22p53	22p57		23p57							05 54			06 20	06 27		⟵			
—	—		d	22p55	23p00		00 01	04 40	04 55	05 15		05 45		05 55	06 15		06 34 ⟶	06 30		06 34			06 43
65½	—	St Denys	d				00 06	04 45				05 50								06 39			06 48
67	—	Swaythling	d				00 09	04 48				05 53								06 42			06 51
67¾	—	**Southampton Airport Parkwy** ✈	d	23p03	23p08		00 12	04 51	05 02	05 22		05 56		06 03	06 22			06 38		06 45		06 50	06 54
—	0	**Portsmouth Harbour**	d			23p24					05 00								05 43				
—	¾	**Portsmouth & Southsea**	d			23p29					05 05								05 48				
—	1¾	Fratton	d			23p33					05 09								05 52				
—	4	Hilsea	d			23p37					05 13								05 56				
—	5½	Cosham	d			23p42					05 18								06 03				
—	8	Portchester	d			23p47					05 23								06 08				
—	11½	Fareham	d			23p53					05 29								06 19				
—	16¾	Botley	d			23p59					05 36								06 27				
—	17¾	Hedge End	d			00 05					05 40								06 31				
69¼	22¼	Eastleigh [3]	a	23p08	23p11	00 11	00 16	04 56	05 06		05 46	05 59		06 07					06 37	06 48		06 53	06 58
—	—		d	23p11	23p12	00 21			05 06		05 47			06 08					06 42	06 50		06 54	06 59
—	24¼	Chandlers Ford	a																	06 55			
—	—		d																	06 55			
—	29½	**Romsey**	a																	07 03			
73	—	Shawford	d		23p18				05 12		05 53								06 49				07 05
76¼	—	**Winchester**	d	23p23	23p24	00a30			05 18	05 31	05 59			06 18	06 31			06 48	06 55			07 05	07 11
84¾	—	Micheldever	d	23p32	23p33				05 27		06 08								07 04				
95	—	**Basingstoke**	a	23p42	23p43				05 37	05 45	06 18			06 34	06 46				07 14				07 27
—	—		d	23p43	23p44				05 39	05 47				06 36	06 47				07 17				07 36
—	—	Reading [7]	a							06 04					07 04								⟶
106½	—	Fleet	d		00 01				05 50														
109½	—	Farnborough (Main)	d		00 06				05 56														
118½	—	**Woking**	a	00 02	00 18				06 05					06 54								07 38	
138¾	—	Clapham Junction [10]	a	00 22	00 54				06 25					07 15									
142¾	—	**London Waterloo [15]** ⊖	a	00 33	01 02				06 34					07 25				07 46	08 01			08 08	

For general notes see front of timetable
For details of catering facilities see
Directory of Train Operators

For details of Bank Holiday service alterations, please see first page of Table 149

Weymouth, Bournemouth, Lymington, Southampton and Basingstoke → London

Network Diagram - see first page of Table 158

		SW 1	SW 1	SW 1	SW 1	SW 1		XC 1 ◇	SW 1	SW 1	SW 1	SW 1	SW 1	SW 1	SW 1	SW 1	SW 1	SW 1	GW ◇		SW 1	XC 1 ◇	SW 1	SW 1	SW 1
											A							A							
		☕	☕					☕		☕	☕						☕	☕				☕		☕	
Weymouth	d										05 55							06 22	06 32						
Upwey	d										05 59							06 26	06 37						
Dorchester West	a																		06 45						
Dorchester South	d										06 07							06b37							
Moreton (Dorset)	d										06 14							06 44							
Wool	d										06 20							06 50							
Wareham	d										06 27							06 57							
Holton Heath	d										06 31														
Hamworthy	d										06 36							07 04							
Poole 4	a										06 40							07 08							
	d		06 11								06 41							07 11						07 20	
Parkstone (Dorset)	d		06 15								06 45							07 15						07 24	
Branksome	d		06 18								06 49							07 19						07 27	
Bournemouth	a		06 23								06 54							07 24						07 32	
	d	06 04	06 25					06 30		06 34	06 56						07 04	07 26				07 30		07 34	
Pokesdown	d	06 08								06 38							07 08							07 38	
Christchurch	d	06 12								06 42							07 12							07 42	
Hinton Admiral	d	06 17								06 47							07 17							07 47	
New Milton	d	06 21								06 51							07 21							07 51	
Sway	d	06 26								06 56							07 26							07 56	
Yarmouth (I.O.W.) ⛴	d								*06 00*			*06 35*											*07c00*		
Lymington Pier ⛴	d								06 44			07 14											07 44		
Lymington Town	d								06 46			07 16											07 46		
Brockenhurst 3	a	06 31						06 46	06 54	07 01		07 24					07 31					07 45	07 54	08 01	
	d	06 32						06 48		07 02							07 32					07 47		08 02	
Beaulieu Road	d																							08 08	
Ashurst New Forest	d	06 40								07 10							07 40							08 12	
Totton	d	06 45								07 15							07 45							08 17	
Salisbury	d														06 50										07 48
Dean	d														07 02										08 00
Mottisfont & Dunbridge	d														07 08										08 06
Romsey	d														07 13										08 11
Redbridge	d														07 21										08 21
Millbrook (Hants)	d														07 24										08 24
Southampton Central	a	06 51	06 55					07 00		07 20	07 25				07 27		07 50	07 55				08 03		08 22	08 27
	d	07 00				07 10		07 15		07 30					07 32	07 38	08 00					08 15		08 45 →	08 32 →
St Denys	d														07 37	07 43									
Swaythling	d														07 40	07 46									
Southampton Airport Parkwy ✈	d	07 08				07 18		07 22		07 38					07 43	07 49	08 08					08 22			
Portsmouth Harbour	d				06 23									06 38							07 24				
Portsmouth & Southsea	d				06 28									06 43							07 29				
Fratton	d				06 32									06 47							07 33				
Hilsea	d				06 36									06 51							07 37				
Cosham	d				06 42									06 58							07 43				
Portchester	d				06 46									07 03							07 48				
Fareham	d				06 53									07 11							07 54				
Botley	d				07 01									07 25							08 01				
Hedge End	d				07 05									07 29							08 06				
Eastleigh 3	a				07 11	07 21							←	07 35	07 46	07 53					08 12				
	d				07 12	07 30							07 30	07 42	07 48	07 54					08 12				
Chandlers Ford	a					→									07 53										
	d														07 53										
Romsey	a														08 00										
Shawford	d												07 36	07 49		08 00					08 19				
Winchester	d	07 18			07 22			07 31		07 48			07 42	07 55		08 06	08 18				08 25	08 31			
Micheldever	d				07 31									08 02											
Basingstoke	a			←	07 41			07 46					07 58	08 14		08 22	08 34				08 41	08 46			
	d			07 36	07 47			07 47					08 05	08 16		08 24	08 35				08 42	08 47			
Reading 7	a							08 04														09 04			
Fleet	d			07 52									08 22			08 40					08 54				
Farnborough (Main)	d			07 58									08 28			08 46					08 59				
Woking	a			08 08	08 05								08 38	08 34		08 58	08 53								
Clapham Junction 10	a																09 14				09 26				
London Waterloo 15 ⊖	a	08 16		08 39	08 34					08 48			09 10	09 03		09 29	09 25				09 41				

For general notes see front of timetable
For details of catering facilities see Directory of Train Operators

A ☕ from Bournemouth
b Arr. 0633
c From 14th March

For details of Bank Holiday service alterations, please see first page of Table 149

Weymouth, Bournemouth, Lymington, Southampton and Basingstoke → London

Network Diagram - see first page of Table 158

		SW	SW	SW	SW	SW	SW	SW	SW	SW	SW	XC	SW	SW	GW	SW	SW	SW	SW	SW	SW	SW	SW
		1 ◇	1	1	1	1	1	1 ◇	1	1	1	R 1	1	1 ◇	◇	1	1	1	1	1 ◇	1	1	1
		A												A									
		🍴					🍴	🍴		🍴		🍴		🍴						🍴			
Weymouth	d	06 55							07 25					07 55	08 11						08 25		
Upwey	d	06 59							07 29					07 59	08 16						08 29		
Dorchester West	a														08 23								
Dorchester South	d	07 07							07 37					08 07							08 37		
Moreton (Dorset)	d	07 14							07 44					08 14							08 44		
Wool	d	07 20							07 50					08 20							08 50		
Wareham	d	07 27							07 57					08 27							08 57		
Holton Heath	d	07 31							08 01					08 31							09 01		
Hamworthy	d	07 36							08 06					08 36							09 06		
Poole 4	a	07 40							08 10					08 40							09 10		
	d	07 41						07 55	08 11					08 41					08 50	09 06	09 11		
Parkstone (Dorset)	d	07 45						07 59	08 15					08 45					08 54	.	09 15		
Branksome	d	07 49						08 02	08 19					08 49					08 57	.	09 19		
Bournemouth	a	07 54						08 07	08 24					08 54					09 02	09 16	09 24		
	d	07 59						08 10	08 26			08 45		08 59					09 05	09 18	09 26		
Pokesdown	d							08 14	08 30										09 09	09 22	09 30		
Christchurch	d							08 18	08 34										09 13	09 26	09 34		
Hinton Admiral	d							08 24	08 39										09 18	.	09 39		
New Milton	d							08 29	08 43										09 22	09 33	09 43		
Sway	d							08 34	08 48										09 27	.	09 48		
Yarmouth (I.O.W.) ⛴	d			*07 30*							*08 00*						*08b30*						*09 00*
Lymington Pier ⛴	d			08 14							08 44						09 14						09 44
Lymington Town	d			08 16							08 46						09 16						09 46
Brockenhurst 3	a	08 14		08 24				08 39	08 53		08 54	08 58		09 14			09 24		09 32	09 40	09 52		09 54
	d	08 15						08 41				09 00		09 15					09 33	09 41	09 53		
Beaulieu Road	d																						
Ashurst New Forest	d							08 48											09 40				
Totton	d							08 53											09 45				
Salisbury	d												08 48										
Dean	d												09 00										
Mottisfont & Dunbridge	d												09 06										
Romsey	d												09 11										
Redbridge	d												09 19										
Millbrook (Hants)	d												09 22										
Southampton Central	a	08 28			←		←	08 58				09 12	09 25	09 28				←	09 51	09 55	10 08		
	d	08 30			08 32		08 45	09 00				09 15	09 32 →	09 30				09 32	09 55	10 00			
St Denys	d				08 37		08 50											09 37					
Swaythling	d				08 40		08 53											09 40					
Southampton Airport Parkwy ✈	d	08 38			08 43		08 57	09 08				09 22		09 38				09 43	10 03	10 08			
Portsmouth Harbour	d		07 52			08 05										08 51							
Portsmouth & Southsea	d		07 57			08 10										08 56							
Fratton	d		08 01			08 14										09 01							
Hilsea	d		08 05			08 18										09 05							
Cosham	d		08 10			08 23										09 10							
Portchester	d		08 15			08 28										09 15							
Fareham	d		08 21			08 34										09 23							
Botley	d		08 29			08 41										09 30							
Hedge End	d		08 34			08 46										09 35							
Eastleigh 3	a		08 41		08 46	08 52	09 03			←						09 41		09 46	10 06			←	
	d		08 42		08 48	08 53	09 12			09 12						09 42		09 48	10 12			10 12	
Chandlers Ford	a				08 53		→											09 53	→				
	d				08 53													09 53					
Romsey	a				09 00													10 00					
Shawford	d		08 49							09 18												10 18	
Winchester	d	08 48	08 54			09 02		09 18		09 24		09 31		09 48		09 54				10 18		10 24	
Micheldever	d		09 02													10 02							
Basingstoke	a		09 15			09 18		09 34		09 40		09 46				10 15				10 34		10 40	
	d		09 17					09 36		09 41		09 47				10 17				10 36		10 41	
Reading 7	a											10 04											
Fleet	d									09 53												10 53	
Farnborough (Main)	d		09 31							09 58						10 31						10 58	
Woking	a	09 22	09 40					09 54						10 20		10 40							
Clapham Junction 10	a	09 43						10 14		10 24										11 12		11 24	
London Waterloo 15 ⊖	a	09 53	10 08					10 23		10 34				10 49		11 08				11 20		11 34	

For general notes see front of timetable
For details of catering facilities see Directory of Train Operators

A 🍴 from Bournemouth

b Fridays only until 21st December
Daily from 14th March

For details of Bank Holiday service alterations, please see first page of Table 149

Weymouth, Bournemouth, Lymington, Southampton and Basingstoke → London

Network Diagram - see first page of Table 158

		XC	SW	SW	SW	SW	SW	SW	SW	SW	SW	XC	SW	SW	SW	SW	SW	SW	SW	SW	XC	SW	SW	GW
		R 1	1	1 ◇	1	1	1	1	1 ◇	1	1	R 1	1 ◇	1	1	1	1	1 ◇	1	1	R 1	1	1 ◇	◇
				A					A				A					A					A	
		☕		☕					☕			☕	☕					☕			☕		☕	
Weymouth	d			09 03					09 20				10 03					10 20					11 03	11 11
Upwey	d								09 24									10 24						11 16
Dorchester West	a																							11 24
Dorchester South	d			09 13					09 32				10 13					10 32					11 13	
Moreton (Dorset)	d								09 39									10 39						
Wool	d								09 45									10 45						
Wareham	d			09 28					09 52				10 28					10 52					11 28	
Holton Heath	d								09 56									10 56						
Hamworthy	d			09 35					10 01				10 35					11 01					11 35	
Poole 4	a			09 39					10 05				10 39					11 05					11 39	
	d			09 40				09 50	10 06				10 40				10 50	11 06					11 40	
Parkstone (Dorset)	d			09 44				09 54					10 44				10 54						11 44	
Branksome	d			09 48				09 57					10 48				10 57						11 48	
Bournemouth	a			09 53				10 02	10 16				10 54				11 02	11 16					11 54	
	d	09 45		09 55				10 05	10 21			10 45	10 59				11 05	11 21			11 45		11 59	
Pokesdown	d							10 09	10 25								11 09	11 25						
Christchurch	d							10 13	10 29								11 13	11 29						
Hinton Admiral	d							10 18									11 18							
New Milton	d							10 22	10 36								11 22	11 36						
Sway	d							10 27									11 27							
Yarmouth (I.O.W.) ⛴	d					*09 30*					*10b00*			*10 30*						*11 00*				
Lymington Pier ⛴	d					10 14					10 44			11 14						11 44				
Lymington Town	d					10 16					10 46			11 16						11 46				
Brockenhurst 3	a	09 58		10 10		10 24		10 32	10 43		10 54	10 58	11 14	11 24			11 32	11 43		11 54	11 58		12 14	
	d	10 00		10 11				10 33	10 44			11 00	11 15				11 33	11 44			12 00		12 15	
Beaulieu Road	d																							
Ashurst New Forest	d							10 40									11 40							
Totton	d							10 45									11 45							
Salisbury	d		09 48													10 50						11 53		
Dean	d		10 00													11 02								
Mottisfont & Dunbridge	d		10 06													11 09								
Romsey	d		10 11													11 15						12 11		
Redbridge	d		10 19													11 22						12 19		
Millbrook (Hants)	d		10 22													11 25						12 22		
Southampton Central	a	10 12	10 25	10 26			←	10 51	10 57			11 12	11 28			11 29	11 51	11 57			12 12	12 25	12 28	
	d	10 15	10 32 →	10 30			10 32	10 55	11 00			11 15	11 30			11 32	11 55	12 00			12 15	12 32 →	12 30	
St Denys	d						10 37									11 37								
Swaythling	d						10 40									11 40								
Southampton Airport Parkwy ✈	d	10 22		10 38			10 43	11 03	11 08			11 22	11 38			11 43	12 03	12 08			12 22		12 38	
Portsmouth Harbour	d				09 54										10 54									
Portsmouth & Southsea	d				09 59										10 59									
Fratton	d				10 03										11 03									
Hilsea	d				10 07										11 07									
Cosham	d				10 12										11 12									
Portchester	d				10 17										11 17									
Fareham	d				10 23										11 23									
Botley	d				10 30										11 30									
Hedge End	d				10 35										11 35									
Eastleigh 3	a				10 41		10 46	11 06		←					11 41	11 46	12 06		←					
	d				10 42		10 48	11 12		11 12					11 42	11 48	12 12		12 12					
Chandlers Ford	a						10 53	→								11 53	→							
	d						10 53									11 53								
Romsey	a						11 00									12 01								
Shawford	d									11 18									12 18					
Winchester	d	10 31		10 48	10 54				11 18	11 24		11 31	11 48		11 54			12 18	12 24		12 31		12 48	
Micheldever	d				11 02										12 02									
Basingstoke	a	10 46			11 15				11 34	11 40		11 46			12 15			12 34	12 40		12 46			
	d	10 47			11 17				11 36	11 41		11 47			12 17			12 36	12 41		12 47			
Reading 7	a	11 04										12 04									13 04			
Fleet	d									11 53									12 53					
Farnborough (Main)	d				11 31					11 58					12 31				12 58					
Woking	a			11 19	11 40								12 19		12 40								13 19	
Clapham Junction 10	a								12 12	12 24								13 12	13 24					
London Waterloo 15 ⊖	a			11 49	12 08				12 20	12 34			12 49		13 08			13 20	13 34				13 49	

For general notes see front of timetable
For details of catering facilities see Directory of Train Operators

A ☕ from Bournemouth
b Fridays only until 21st December
Daily from 14th March

For details of Bank Holiday service alterations, please see first page of Table 149

Weymouth, Bournemouth, Lymington, Southampton and Basingstoke → London

Network Diagram - see first page of Table 158

		SW	SW	SW		SW	SW	SW	SW	XC	SW	SW	SW	SW	SW	SW	SW		SW	SW	XC	SW	SW	GW	SW
		1	1	1		1	1 ◇	1	1	R 1	1	1 ◇	1	1	1	1	1 ◇		1	1	R 1	1	1 ◇	◇	1
							A					A					A						A		
							☕			☕		☕					☕				☕		☕		
Weymouth	d						11 20					12 03					12 20						13 03	13 11	
Upwey	d						11 24										12 24							13 16	
Dorchester West	a																							13 25	
Dorchester South	d						11 32					12 13					12 32						13 13		
Moreton (Dorset)	d						11 39										12 39								
Wool	d						11 45										12 45								
Wareham	d						11 52					12 28					12 52						13 28		
Holton Heath	d						11 56										12 56								
Hamworthy	d						12 01					12 35					13 01						13 35		
Poole 4	a						12 05					12 39					13 05						13 39		
	d					11 50	12 06					12 40				12 50	13 06						13 40		
Parkstone (Dorset)	d					11 54						12 44				12 54							13 44		
Branksome	d					11 57						12 48				12 57							13 48		
Bournemouth	a					12 02	12 16					12 54				13 02	13 16						13 54		
	d					12 05	12 21			12 45		12 59				13 05	13 21				13 45		13 59		
Pokesdown	d					12 09	12 25									13 09	13 25								
Christchurch	d					12 13	12 29									13 13	13 29								
Hinton Admiral	d					12 18										13 18									
New Milton	d					12 22	12 36									13 22	13 36								
Sway	d					12 27										13 27									
Yarmouth (I.O.W.) ⛴	d		*11b30*						*12 00*					*12b30*						*13 00*					*13b30*
Lymington Pier ⛴	d		12 14						12 44					13 14						13 44					14 14
Lymington Town	d		12 16						12 46					13 16						13 46					14 16
Brockenhurst 3	a		12 24			12 32	12 43		12 54	12 58		13 14		13 24		13 32	13 42			13 54	13 58		14 14		14 24
	d					12 33	12 44			13 00		13 15				13 33	13 43				14 00		14 15		
Beaulieu Road	d																								
Ashurst New Forest	d					12 40										13 40									
Totton	d					12 45										13 45									
Salisbury	d										12 48											13 53			
Dean	d										13 00														
Mottisfont & Dunbridge	d										13 06														
Romsey	d										13 11											14 11			
Redbridge	d										13 19											14 19			
Millbrook (Hants)	d										13 22											14 22			
Southampton Central	a					12 52	12 57			13 12	13 25	13 28				13 51	13 57				14 12	14 25	14 28		
				←											←										
	d			12 32		12 55	13 00			13 15	13 32	13 30			13 32	13 55	14 00				14 15	14 32	14 30		
											↪											↪			
St Denys	d			12 37											13 37										
Swaythling	d			12 40											13 40										
Southampton Airport Parkwy ✈	d			12 43		13 03	13 08			13 22		13 38			13 43	14 03	14 08				14 22		14 38		
Portsmouth Harbour	d	11 54											12 54												
Portsmouth & Southsea	d	11 59											12 59												
Fratton	d	12 03											13 03												
Hilsea	d	12 07											13 07												
Cosham	d	12 12											13 12												
Portchester	d	12 17											13 17												
Fareham	d	12 23											13 23												
Botley	d	12 30											13 30												
Hedge End	d	12 35											13 35												
Eastleigh 3	a	12 41		12 46		13 06		←					13 41		13 46	14 06			←						
	d	12 42		12 48		13 12		13 12					13 42		13 48	14 12			14 12						
Chandlers Ford	a			12 53		↪									13 53	↪									
	d			12 53											13 53										
Romsey	a			13 00											14 00										
Shawford	d							13 18											14 18						
Winchester	d	12 54					13 18	13 24		13 31		13 48	13 54				14 18		14 24		14 31		14 48		
Micheldever	d	13 02											14 02												
Basingstoke	a	13 15					13 34	13 40		13 46			14 15				14 34		14 40		14 46				
	d	13 17					13 36	13 41		13 47			14 17				14 36		14 41		14 47				
Reading 7	a									14 04											15 04				
Fleet	d							13 53											14 53						
Farnborough (Main)	d	13 31						13 58					14 31						14 58						
Woking	a	13 40										14 19	14 40										15 19		
Clapham Junction 10	a						14 12	14 24									15 12		15 24						
London Waterloo 15 ⊖	a	14 08					14 20	14 34				14 49	15 08				15 20		15 34				15 49		

For general notes see front of timetable
For details of catering facilities see Directory of Train Operators

A ☕ from Bournemouth
b Fridays only until 21st December Daily from 14th March

For details of Bank Holiday service alterations, please see first page of Table 149

Weymouth, Bournemouth, Lymington, Southampton and Basingstoke → London

Network Diagram - see first page of Table 158

		SW	SW	SW	SW	SW	SW	XC	SW	SW	SW	SW	SW	SW	SW	SW	SW	XC	SW	SW	GW	SW	SW
		1	1	1	1 ◇	1	1	R 1	1	1 ◇	1	1	1	1	1 ◇	1	1	R 1	1	1 ◇	◇	1	1
					A					A					A					A			
					🛒			🛒		🛒					🛒			🛒		🛒			
Weymouth	d				13 20					14 03					14 20					15 03	15 11		
Upwey	d				13 24										14 24						15 16		
Dorchester West	a																				15 24		
Dorchester South	d				13 32					14 13					14 32					15 13			
Moreton (Dorset)	d				13 39										14 39								
Wool	d				13 45										14 45								
Wareham	d				13 52					14 28					14 52					15 28			
Holton Heath	d				13 56										14 56								
Hamworthy	d				14 01					14 35					15 01					15 35			
Poole 4	a				14 05					14 39					15 05					15 39			
	d			13 50	14 06					14 40				14 50	15 06					15 40			
Parkstone (Dorset)	d			13 54						14 44				14 54						15 44			
Branksome	d			13 57						14 48				14 57						15 48			
Bournemouth	a			14 02	14 16					14 54				15 02	15 16					15 54			
	d			14 05	14 21			14 45		14 59				15 05	15 21			15 45		15 59			
Pokesdown	d			14 09	14 25									15 09	15 25								
Christchurch	d			14 13	14 29									15 13	15 29								
Hinton Admiral	d			14 18										15 18									
New Milton	d			14 22	14 36									15 22	15 36								
Sway	d			14 27										15 27									
Yarmouth (I.O.W.) ⛴	d						14 00					14b30					15c00						15 30
Lymington Pier ⛴	d						14 44					15 14					15 44						16 14
Lymington Town	d						14 46					15 16					15 46						16 16
Brockenhurst 3	a			14 32	14 43		14 54	14 58		15 14		15 24		15 32	15 43		15 54	15 58		16 14			16 24
	d			14 33	14 44			15 00		15 15				15 33	15 44			16 00		16 15			
Beaulieu Road	d																						
Ashurst New Forest	d			14 40										15 40									
Totton	d			14 45										15 45									
Salisbury	d								14 48										15 48				
Dean	d								15 00										16 00				
Mottisfont & Dunbridge	d								15 06										16 06				
Romsey	d								15 11										16 11				
Redbridge	d								15 19										16 19				
Millbrook (Hants)	d								15 22										16 22				
Southampton Central	a			14 52	14 57			15 12	15 25	15 28				15 51	15 57			16 12	16 25	16 28			
			←										←										
	d		14 32	14 55	15 00			15 15	15 32 →	15 30			15 32	15 56	16 00			16 15	16 32 →	16 30			
St Denys	d		14 37										15 37										
Swaythling	d		14 40										15 40										
Southampton Airport Parkwy ✈	d		14 43	15 03	15 08			15 22		15 38			15 43	16 04	16 08			16 22		16 38			
Portsmouth Harbour	d	13 54									14 54											15 54	
Portsmouth & Southsea	d	13 59									14 59											15 59	
Fratton	d	14 03									15 03											16 03	
Hilsea	d	14 07									15 07											16 07	
Cosham	d	14 12									15 12											16 12	
Portchester	d	14 17									15 17											16 17	
Fareham	d	14 23									15 23											16 23	
Botley	d	14 30									15 30											16 30	
Hedge End	d	14 35									15 35											16 35	
Eastleigh 3	a	14 41	14 46	15 06		←					15 41		15 46	16 07		←						16 41	
	d	14 42	14 48	15 12		15 12					15 42		15 48	16 12		16 12						16 42	
Chandlers Ford	a		14 53	→									15 53	→									
	d		14 53										15 53										
Romsey	a		15 00										16 00										
Shawford	d					15 18										16 18							
Winchester	d	14 54			15 18	15 24		15 31		15 48	15 54				16 18	16 24		16 31		16 48		16 54	
Micheldever	d	15 02									16 02											17 02	
Basingstoke	a	15 15			15 34	15 40		15 46			16 15				16 34	16 40		16 46				17 15	
	d	15 17			15 36	15 41		15 47			16 17				16 36	16 41		16 47				17 17	
Reading 7	a							16 04										17 04					
Fleet	d					15 53										16 53							
Farnborough (Main)	d	15 31				15 58					16 31					16 58						17 31	
Woking	a	15 40								16 19	16 40									17 20		17 40	
Clapham Junction 10	a				16 12	16 24									17 12	17 24							
London Waterloo 15 ⊖	a	16 08			16 20	16 34				16 49	17 08				17 20	17 34				17 50		18 08	

For general notes see front of timetable
For details of catering facilities see Directory of Train Operators

A 🛒 from Bournemouth

b Daily 10th December to 13th March
Mondays and Fridays only from 14th March

c Fridays only until 21st December
Daily from 14th March

For details of Bank Holiday service alterations, please see first page of Table 149

Weymouth, Bournemouth, Lymington, Southampton and Basingstoke → London

Network Diagram - see first page of Table 158

		SW	SW	SW	SW	SW	XC	SW	SW	SW	SW	SW	SW	SW	SW	SW	SW	XC	SW	SW	SW	GW	SW	SW
		1	1	1 ◇	1	1	R 1	1	1 ◇	1	1	1	1	1	1 ◇	1	1	1 ◇	1	1	1 ◇	◇	1	1
				A					A						A						A			
				☕			☕		☕						☕			☕			☕			
Weymouth	d			15 20					16 03						16 20						17 03	17 11		
Upwey	d			15 24											16 24							17 16		
Dorchester West	a																					17 25		
Dorchester South	d			15 32					16 13						16 32						17 13			
Moreton (Dorset)	d			15 39											16 39									
Wool	d			15 45											16 45									
Wareham	d			15 52					16 28						16 52						17 28			
Holton Heath	d			15 56											16 56									
Hamworthy	d			16 01					16 35						17 01						17 35			
Poole 4	a			16 05					16 39						17 05						17 39			
	d		15 50	16 06					16 40					16 50	17 06						17 40			
Parkstone (Dorset)	d		15 54						16 44					16 54							17 44			
Branksome	d		15 57						16 48					16 57							17 48			
Bournemouth	a		16 02	16 16					16 54					17 02	17 16						17 54			
	d		16 05	16 21			16 45		16 59					17 05	17 21			17 45			17 59			
Pokesdown	d		16 09	16 25										17 09	17 25									
Christchurch	d		16 13	16 29										17 13	17 29									
Hinton Admiral	d		16 18											17 18										
New Milton	d		16 22	16 36										17 22	17 36									
Sway	d		16 27											17 27										
Yarmouth (I.O.W.) ⛴	d					*16 00*							*16b30*				*17 00*							*17 30*
Lymington Pier ⛴	d					16 44							17 14				17 44							18 14
Lymington Town	d					16 46							17 16				17 46							18 16
Brockenhurst 3	a		16 32	16 43		16 54	16 58		17 14				17 24	17 32	17 43		17 54	17 58			18 14			18 24
	d		16 33	16 44			17 00		17 15			17 20		17 33	17 44			18 00			18 15			
Beaulieu Road	d																							
Ashurst New Forest	d		16 40									17 27		17 40										
Totton	d		16 45									17 32		17 45										
Salisbury	d							16 48												17 48				
Dean	d							17 00												18 00				
Mottisfont & Dunbridge	d							17 06												18 06				
Romsey	d							17 11												18 11				
Redbridge	d							17 19												18 19				
Millbrook (Hants)	d							17 22												18 22				
Southampton Central	a		16 50	16 57			17 12	17 25	17 28			17 39		17 51	17 57			18 12		18 25	18 28			
	d	← 16 32	16 52	17 00			17 15	17 32 →	17 30		← 17 32			17 56	18 00			18 15	18 17	18 32 →	18 30			
St Denys	d	16 37	16 57								17 37								18 22					
Swaythling	d	16 40	17 00								17 40								18 25					
Southampton Airport Parkwy ✈	d	16 43	17 03	17 08			17 22		17 38		17 43			18 04	18 08			18 22	18 28		18 38			
Portsmouth Harbour	d									16 54													17 54	
Portsmouth & Southsea	d									16 59													17 59	
Fratton	d									17 03													18 03	
Hilsea	d									17 07													18 07	
Cosham	d									17 12													18 12	
Portchester	d									17 17													18 17	
Fareham	d									17 23													18 23	
Botley	d									17 30													18 30	
Hedge End	d									17 35													18 35	
Eastleigh 3	a	16 46	17 07		←					17 41	17 46			18 07		←			18 32				18 41	
	d	16 48	17 12		17 12					17 42	17 48			18 12		18 12			18 33				18 42	
Chandlers Ford	a	16 53	→								17 53			→										
	d	16 53									17 53													
Romsey	a	17 00									18 00													
Shawford	d				17 18											18 18								
Winchester	d			17 18	17 24		17 31		17 48	17 54					18 18	18 24		18 31	18a41		18 48		18 54	
Micheldever	d									18 02													19 02	
Basingstoke	a			17 34	17 40		17 46			18 15					18 34	18 38		18 46					19 15	
	d			17 36	17 41		17 47			18 17					18 36	18 38		18 47					19 17	
Reading 7	a						18 04											19 04						
Fleet	d				17 53											18 50								
Farnborough (Main)	d				17 58					18 31						18 55							19 31	
Woking	a								18 19	18 40											19 24		19 40	
Clapham Junction 10	a			18 12	18 24										19 12	19 26								
London Waterloo 15 ⊖	a			18 23	18 34				18 47	19 08					19 20	19 38					19 51		20 08	

For general notes see front of timetable
For details of catering facilities see Directory of Train Operators

A ☕ from Bournemouth
b Fridays only until 21st December
Daily from 14th March

For details of Bank Holiday service alterations, please see first page of Table 149

Weymouth, Bournemouth, Lymington, Southampton and Basingstoke → London

Network Diagram - see first page of Table 158

		SW	SW		SW	SW	SW	XC	SW	SW	SW	SW	SW	SW	SW	SW		SW	XC	SW	SW	SW	SW	SW	SW
		1	1		1 ◇	1	1	1 ◇	1	1 ◇	1	1	1	1	1 ◇	1		1	1 ◇	1	1 ◇	1	1	1	1
					A ⊡			⊡		A ⊡					A ⊡						A ⊡				
Weymouth	d				17 20					18 03					18 20						19 03				
Upwey	d				17 24										18 24										
Dorchester West	a																								
Dorchester South	d				17 32					18 13					18 32						19 13				
Moreton (Dorset)	d				17 39										18 39										
Wool	d				17 45										18 45										
Wareham	d				17 52					18 28					18 52						19 28				
Holton Heath	d				17 56										18 56										
Hamworthy	d				18 01					18 35					19 01						19 35				
Poole 4	a				18 05					18 39					19 05						19 39				
	d		17 50		18 06					18 40				18 50	19 06						19 40				19 50
Parkstone (Dorset)	d		17 54							18 44				18 54							19 44				19 54
Branksome	d		17 57							18 48				18 57							19 48				19 57
Bournemouth	a		18 02		18 16					18 54				19 02	19 16						19 54				20 02
	d		18 05		18 21			18 45		18 59				19 05	19 21				19 45		19 59				20 05
Pokesdown	d		18 09		18 25									19 09	19 25										20 09
Christchurch	d		18 13		18 29									19 13	19 29										20 13
Hinton Admiral	d		18 18											19 18											20 18
New Milton	d		18 22		18 36									19 22	19 36										20 22
Sway	d		18 27											19 27											20 27
Yarmouth (I.O.W.) ⛴	d						*18b00*				*18 30*					*19 00*						*19c30*			
Lymington Pier ⛴	d						18 44				19 14					19 44						20 14			
Lymington Town	d						18 46				19 16					19 46						20 16			
Brockenhurst 3	a		18 32		18 43		18 54	18 58		19 14	19 24			19 32	19 43	19 54			19 58		20 14	20 24			20 32
	d		18 33		18 44			19 00		19 15				19 33	19 44				20 00		20 15				20 33
Beaulieu Road	d		18 38																						
Ashurst New Forest	d		18 42											19 40											20 40
Totton	d		18 47											19 45											20 45
Salisbury	d								18 48											19 53					
Dean	d								19 00																
Mottisfont & Dunbridge	d								19 06																
Romsey	d								19 11											20 11					
Redbridge	d								19 19											20 19					
Millbrook (Hants)	d								19 22											20 22					
Southampton Central	a	←	18 53		18 57			19 13	19 26	19 28			←	19 51	19 57				20 12	20 25	20 28			←	20 51
	d	18 32	18 55		19 00			19 15	19 33 →	19 30			19 33	19 55	20 00				20 15	20 32 →	20 30			20 32	20 55
St Denys	d	18 37											19 38											20 37	
Swaythling	d	18 40											19 41											20 40	
Southampton Airport Parkwy ✈	d	18 43	19 03		19 08			19 22		19 38			19 44	20 03	20 08				20 22		20 38			20 43	21 03
Portsmouth Harbour	d											18 54											19 54		
Portsmouth & Southsea	d											18 59											19 59		
Fratton	d											19 03											20 03		
Hilsea	d											19 07											20 07		
Cosham	d											19 12											20 12		
Portchester	d											19 17											20 17		
Fareham	d											19 23											20 23		
Botley	d											19 30											20 30		
Hedge End	d											19 35											20 35		
Eastleigh 3	a	18 46	19 06			←						19 41	19 47	20 06				←					20 41	20 46	21 06
	d	18 48	19 12			19 12						19 42	19 48	20 12				20 12					20 42	20 48	21 12
Chandlers Ford	a	18 53	→										19 53	→										20 53	→
	d	18 53											19 53											20 53	
Romsey	a	19 00											20 00											21 00	
Shawford	d					19 18												20 18					20 49		
Winchester	d				19 18	19 24		19 31		19 48		19 54			20 18			20 24	20 31		20 48		20 54		
Micheldever	d											20 02											21 04		
Basingstoke	a				19 34	19 40		19 46				20 15			20 34			20 40	20 46				21 19		
	d				19 36	19 41		19 47				20 17			20 36			20 41	20 47				21 24		
Reading 7	a							20 04											21 04						
Fleet	d					19 53												20 53					21 40		
Farnborough (Main)	d					19 58						20 31						20 58					21 46		
Woking	a									20 19		20 40						21 07			21 19		21 58		
Clapham Junction 10	a				20 12	20 25									21 14			21 33							
London Waterloo 15 ⊖	a				20 20	20 34				20 49		21 08			21 22			21 43			21 49		22 34		

For general notes see front of timetable
For details of catering facilities see Directory of Train Operators

A ⊡ from Bournemouth

b Fridays only until 21st December
Daily from 14th March

c Fridays only until 21th December
Thursday 20th March,Mondays only on 24th March & from 5th May
Daily from 12 May

For details of Bank Holiday service alterations, please see first page of Table 149

Weymouth, Bournemouth, Lymington, Southampton and Basingstoke → London

Network Diagram - see first page of Table 158

		SW 1 ◇ A 🍽	GW ◇	SW 1	SW 1	SW 1	SW 1	SW 1	SW 1	SW 1	SW 1 ◇	SW 1	SW 1	SW 1	SW 1	SW 1	SW 1	SW 1	SW 1	SW 1	SW 1 ◇	SW 1
Weymouth	d	19 20	20 01								20 10							21 10			22 10	23 10
Upwey	d	19 24	20 06								20 14							21 14			22 14	23 14
Dorchester West	a		20 14																			
Dorchester South	d	19b37									20 22							21 22			22 22	23 22
Moreton (Dorset)	d	19 43									20 28							21 28			22 28	23 28
Wool	d	19 49									20 34							21 34			22 34	23 34
Wareham	d	19 57									20 42							21 42			22 42	23 42
Holton Heath	d																					
Hamworthy	d	20 03									20 48							21 48			22 48	23 48
Poole 4	a	20 08									20 53							21 53			22 53	23 53
	d	20 09									20 54							21 54			22 54	23 54
Parkstone (Dorset)	d										20 58							21 58			22 58	
Branksome	d										21 01							22 01			23 01	
Bournemouth	a	20 19									21 07							22 07			23 07	00 03
	d	20 21									21 12							22 12			23 12	
Pokesdown	d	20 25									21 16							22 16			23 16	
Christchurch	d	20 29									21 20							22 20			23 20	
Hinton Admiral	d										21 25							22 25			23 25	
New Milton	d	20 36									21 29							22 29			23 29	
Sway	d										21 34							22 34			23 34	
Yarmouth (I.O.W.) ⛴	d				*20 00*		*20c30*						*21 00*		*21e30*							
Lymington Pier ⛴	d				20 44		21 14						21 44		22 14							
Lymington Town	d				20 46		21 16						21 46		22 16							
Brockenhurst 3	a	20 43			20 54		21 24				21 39		21 54		22 24			22 39			23 39	
	d	20 44									21 40							22 40			23 40	
Beaulieu Road	d																					
Ashurst New Forest	d										21 47							22 47			23 47	
Totton	d										21 52							22 52			23 52	
Salisbury	d								20 48								21 48					
Dean	d								21 00								22 00					
Mottisfont & Dunbridge	d								21 06								22 06					
Romsey	d								21 11								22 11		22 58			
Redbridge	d								21 19								22 19		23 05			
Millbrook (Hants)	d								21 22								22 22		23 09			
Southampton Central	a	20 57							21 25		21 57						22 25	22 57	23 12		23 57	
	d	21 00				21 30			21 33	21 55	22 00					22 30	22 32	23 00	23 20		00 01	
St Denys	d								21 38								22 37		23 25		00 06	
Swaythling	d								21 41								22 40		23 28		00 09	
Southampton Airport Parkwy ✈	d	21 08				21 38			21 44	22 03	22 08					22 38	22 43	23 08	23 31		00 12	
Portsmouth Harbour	d							20 54				21 54								23 24		
Portsmouth & Southsea	d							20 59				21 59								23 29		
Fratton	d							21 03				22 03								23 33		
Hilsea	d							21 07				22 07								23 37		
Cosham	d							21 12				22 12								23 42		
Portchester	d							21 17				22 17								23 47		
Fareham	d							21 23				22 23								23 53		
Botley	d							21 30				22 30								23 59		
Hedge End	d							21 35				22 35								00 05		
Eastleigh 3	a			←				21 41	21 47	22 06		22 41		←		22 41	22 46	23 11	23 34	00 11	00 16	
	d			21 12				21 42	21 48	22 12				22 12		22 42	22 48	23 12	23 36	00 21		
Chandlers Ford	a								21 53	→							22 53		23 41			
	d								21 53								22 53		23 41			
Romsey	a								22 01								23 01		23 48			
Shawford	d			21 18										22 18				23 18				
Winchester	d	21 18		21 24		21 48		21f54			22 18			22 24		22g54		23 24		00a30		
Micheldever	d							22 02										23 33				
Basingstoke	a	21 34		21 40				22 15			22 34			22 40		23 10		23 43				
	d	21 36		21 41				22 24			22 36			22 41		23 12		23 44				
Reading 7	a																					
Fleet	d			21 53				22 40						22 53				00 01				
Farnborough (Main)	d			21 58				22 46						22 58				00 06				
Woking	a			22 07		22 19		22 58			22 54			23 07		23 30		00 18				
Clapham Junction 10	a	22 14		22 33							23 14			23 32		23 55		00 54				
London Waterloo 15 ⊖	a	22 22		22 43		22 49		23 33			23 23			23 43		00 04		01 02				

For general notes see front of timetable
For details of catering facilities see Directory of Train Operators

A 🍽 from Bournemouth

b Arr. 1931

c Fridays only until 21th December
Thursday 20th March, Mondays only on 24th March & from 5th May
Daily from 12 May

e Fridays only 14th March to 9th May
Thursday 20th March Daily from 12th May

f Arr. 2151

g Arr. 2251

Weymouth, Bournemouth, Lymington, Southampton and Basingstoke → London

Network Diagram - see first page of Table 158

		SW 1	SW 1	SW 1 ◇	SW 1	SW 1	SW 1	GW ◇	SW 1	XC 1 ◇ ☕	SW 1	SW 1 ◇ ☕	SW 1	SW 1	SW 1		SW 1	XC 1 ◇ ☕	SW 1	SW 1	SW 1 ◇ ☕	SW 1	SW 1	SW 1	SW 1
Weymouth	d	21p10		22p10				06 27																	
Upwey	d	21p14		22p14				06 32																	
Dorchester West	a							06 40																	
Dorchester South	d	21p22		22p22																					
Moreton (Dorset)	d	21p28		22p28																					
Wool	d	21p34		22p34																					
Wareham	d	21p42		22p42																					
Holton Heath	d																								
Hamworthy	d	21p48		22p48																					
Poole 4	a	21p53		22p53																					
	d	21p54		22p54								05 28									06 28				06 50
Parkstone (Dorset)	d	21p58		22p58								05 32									06 32				06 54
Branksome	d	22p01		23p01								05 35									06 35				06 57
Bournemouth	a	22p07		23p07								05 40									06 40				07 02
	d	22p12		23p12								05 42						06 37			06 42				07 05
Pokesdown	d	22p16		23p16								05 46									06 46				07 09
Christchurch	d	22p20		23p20								05 50									06 50				07 13
Hinton Admiral	d	22p25		23p25								05 55									06 55				07 18
New Milton	d	22p29		23p29								05 59									06 59				07 22
Sway	d	22p34		23p34								06 04									07 04				07 27
Yarmouth (I.O.W.) ⛴	d													*04 40*					*06 00*				*06 35*		
Lymington Pier ⛴	d													06 14					06 44				07 14		
Lymington Town	d													06 16					06 46				07 16		
Brockenhurst 3	a	22p39		23p39								06 09		06 24				06 52	06 54		07 09		07 24		07 32
	d	22p40		23p40								06 10						06 54			07 10				07 33
Beaulieu Road	d																								
Ashurst New Forest	d	22p47		23p47								06 17									07 17				07 40
Totton	d	22p52		23p52							06 12	06 22									07 22				07 45
Salisbury	d																			06 48					
Dean	d																			07 00					
Mottisfont & Dunbridge	d																			07 06					
Romsey	d																			07 11					
Redbridge	d										06 14									07 19					
Millbrook (Hants)	d										06 18									07 22					
Southampton Central	a	22p57		23p57							06 20	06 27			←			07 06		07 25	07 27			←	07 51
	d	23p00		00 01	05 12		05 30		06 00	06 15	06 34 →	06 30			06 34		07 00	07 15		07 32 →	07 30			07 32	07 55
St Denys	d			00 06			05 35								06 39									07 37	
Swaythling	d			00 09			05 38								06 42									07 40	
Southampton Airport Parkwy ✈	d	23p08		00 12	05 20		05 41		06 08	06 22		06 38			06 45		07 08	07 22			07 38			07 43	08 03
Portsmouth Harbour	d		23p24										05 54									06 54			
Portsmouth & Southsea	d		23p29										05 59									06 59			
Fratton	d		23p33										06 03									07 03			
Hilsea	d		23p37										06 07									07 07			
Cosham	d		23p42			05 09							06 12									07 12			
Portchester	d		23p47			05 14							06 17									07 17			
Fareham	d		23p53			05 20							06 24									07 23			
Botley	d		23p59			05 27							06 31									07 30			
Hedge End	d		00 05			05 32							06 36									07 35			
Eastleigh 3	a	23p11	00 11	00 16	05 23	05 38	05 45		06 11			06 41	06 42		06 48		07 11					07 41		07 46	08 06
	d	23p12	00 21		05 24		05 46		06 13			06 42	06 46		06 50		07 12					07 42		07 48	08 12
Chandlers Ford	a														06 55									07 53	→
	d														06 55									07 53	
Romsey	a														07 03									08 00	
Shawford	d	23p18					05 52						06 52				07 18								
Winchester	d	23p24	00a30		05 34		06b00		06 23	06 31		06 52	07 00				07 24	07 31			07 48	07 54			
Micheldever	d	23p33					06 08						07 08									08 02			
Basingstoke	a	23p43			05 50		06 19		06 39	06 46		07 08	07 19				07 40	07 45				08 15			
	d	23p44			05 54		06 24		06 40	06 47		07 09	07 24				07 42	07 47				08 17			
Reading 7	a									07 04								08 04							
Fleet	d	00 01			06 10		06 40						07 40				07 53								
Farnborough (Main)	d	00 06			06 16		06 46						07 46				07 59					08 30			
Woking	a	00 18			06 28		06 58		06 58			07 27	07 58				08 08				08 21	08 39			
Clapham Junction 10	a	00 54			06 58				07 23								08 30								
London Waterloo 15 ⊖	a	01 02			07 06		07 33		07 31			07 53	08 34				08 38				08 49	09 08			

For general notes see front of timetable
For details of catering facilities see Directory of Train Operators

b Arr. 0557

Saturdays

Weymouth, Bournemouth, Lymington, Southampton and Basingstoke → London

Network Diagram - see first page of Table 158

		SW 1 ◇ A ☕	SW 1	SW 1	XC 1 ◇ ☕	SW 1	SW 1 ◇ A ☕	SW 1	SW 1	SW 1	SW 1	SW 1 ◇ A ☕	SW 1	SW 1	XC 1 ◇ ☕	SW 1	SW 1 ◇ A ☕	GW ◇	SW 1	SW 1	SW 1	SW 1	SW 1 ◇ A ☕
Weymouth	d						06 55					07 20					08 03	08 11					08 20
Upwey	d						06 59					07 24						08 16					08 24
Dorchester West	a																	08 23					
Dorchester South	d						07 07					07 32					08 13						08 32
Moreton (Dorset)	d						07 14					07 39											08 39
Wool	d						07 20					07 45											08 45
Wareham	d	06 52					07 27					07 52					08 28						08 52
Holton Heath	d	06 56					07 31					07 56											08 56
Hamworthy	d	07 01					07 36					08 01					08 35						09 01
Poole 4	a	07 05					07 40					08 05					08 39						09 06
	d	07 06					07 41				07 50	08 06					08 40					08 50	09 06
Parkstone (Dorset)	d						07 45				07 54						08 44					08 54	
Branksome	d						07 49				07 57						08 48					08 57	
Bournemouth	a	07 16					07 54				08 02	08 16					08 54					09 02	09 17
	d	07 21			07 45		07 59				08 05	08 21			08 45		08 59					09 05	09 21
Pokesdown	d	07 25									08 09	08 25										09 09	09 25
Christchurch	d	07 29									08 13	08 29										09 13	09 29
Hinton Admiral	d										08 18											09 18	
New Milton	d	07 36									08 22	08 36										09 22	09 36
Sway	d										08 27											09 27	
Yarmouth (I.O.W.) ⛴	d			*07b00*					*07 30*					*08 00*						*08c30*			
Lymington Pier ⛴	d			07 44					08 14					08 44						09 14			
Lymington Town	d			07 46					08 16					08 46						09 16			
Brockenhurst 3	a	07 43		07 54	07 58		08 14		08 24		08 32	08 43		08 54	08 58		09 14			09 24		09 32	09 44
	d	07 44			08 00		08 15				08 33	08 44			09 00		09 15					09 33	09 44
Beaulieu Road	d																					09 38	
Ashurst New Forest	d										08 40											09 42	
Totton	d										08 45											09 47	
Salisbury	d					07 48										08 48							
Dean	d					08 00										09 00							
Mottisfont & Dunbridge	d					08 06										09 06							
Romsey	d					08 11										09 11							
Redbridge	d					08 19										09 19							
Millbrook (Hants)	d					08 22										09 22							
Southampton Central	a	07 57			08 12	08 26	08 28			←	08 52	08 57			09 12	09 25	09 28				←	09 53	09 58
	d	08 00			08 15	08 32 →	08 30			08 32	08 55	09 00			09 15	09 32 →	09 30				09 32	09 55	10 00
St Denys	d									08 37											09 37		
Swaythling	d									08 40											09 40		
Southampton Airport Parkwy ✈	d	08 08			08 22		08 38			08 43	09 03	09 08			09 22		09 38				09 43	10 03	10 08
Portsmouth Harbour	d							07 54											08 54				
Portsmouth & Southsea	d							07 59											08 59				
Fratton	d							08 03											09 03				
Hilsea	d							08 07											09 07				
Cosham	d							08 12											09 12				
Portchester	d							08 17											09 17				
Fareham	d							08 23											09 23				
Botley	d							08 30											09 30				
Hedge End	d							08 35											09 35				
Eastleigh 3	a		←					08 41		08 46	09 06		←						09 41		09 46	10 06	
	d		08 12					08 42		08 48	09 12		09 12						09 42		09 48	10 12	
Chandlers Ford	a									08 53	→										09 53	→	
	d									08 53											09 53		
Romsey	a									09 00											10 00		
Shawford	d		08 18										09 18										
Winchester	d	08 18	08 24		08 31		08 48	08 54				09 18	09 24		09 31		09 48		09 54				10 18
Micheldever	d							09 02											10 02				
Basingstoke	a	08 34	08 40		08 45			09 15				09 34	09 40		09 46				10 15				10 34
	d	08 36	08 41		08 47			09 17				09 36	09 41		09 47				10 17				10 36
Reading 7	a				09 04										10 04								
Fleet	d		08 53										09 53										
Farnborough (Main)	d		08 58					09 31					09 58						10 31				
Woking	a						09 19	09 40									10 19		10 40				
Clapham Junction 10	a	09 12	09 24									10 12	10 24										11 12
London Waterloo 15 ⊖	a	09 20	09 34				09 49	10 08				10 20	10 34				10 49		11 08				11 20

For general notes see front of timetable
For details of catering facilities see Directory of Train Operators

A ☕ from Bournemouth
b From 17 May
c From 15 March

Table 158

Saturdays

Weymouth, Bournemouth, Lymington, Southampton and Basingstoke → London

Network Diagram - see first page of Table 158

		SW	SW	XC	SW	SW	SW	SW	SW	SW	SW	SW	SW	XC	SW		SW	SW	SW	SW	SW	SW	SW	SW	XC
		1	1	1 ◇	1	1 ◇	1	1	1	1	1 ◇	1	1	1 ◇	1		1 ◇	1	1	1	1	1 ◇	1	1	1 ◇
						A					A						A					A			
				☕		☕					☕			☕			☕					☕			☕
Weymouth	d					09 03					09 20						10 03					10 20			
Upwey	d										09 24											10 24			
Dorchester West	a																								
Dorchester South	d					09 13					09 32						10 13					10 32			
Moreton (Dorset)	d										09 39											10 39			
Wool	d										09 45											10 45			
Wareham	d					09 28					09 52						10 28					10 52			
Holton Heath	d										09 56											10 56			
Hamworthy	d					09 35					10 01						10 35					11 01			
Poole 4	a					09 39					10 05						10 39					11 05			
	d					09 40				09 50	10 06						10 40				10 50	11 06			
Parkstone (Dorset)	d					09 44				09 54							10 44				10 54				
Branksome	d					09 48				09 57							10 48				10 57				
Bournemouth	a					09 54				10 02	10 16						10 54				11 02	11 16			
	d			09 45		09 59				10 05	10 21			10 45			10 59				11 05	11 21			11 45
Pokesdown	d									10 09	10 25										11 09	11 25			
Christchurch	d									10 13	10 29										11 13	11 29			
Hinton Admiral	d									10 18											11 18				
New Milton	d									10 22	10 36										11 22	11 36			
Sway	d									10 27											11 27				
Yarmouth (I.O.W.) ⛴	d		*09 00*					*09 30*					*10b00*						*10 30*					*11 00*	
Lymington Pier ⛴	d		09 44					10 14					10 44						11 14					11 44	
Lymington Town	d		09 46					10 16					10 46						11 16					11 46	
Brockenhurst 3	a		09 54	09 58		10 14		10 24		10 32	10 43		10 54	10 58			11 14		11 24		11 32	11 43		11 54	11 58
	d			10 00		10 15				10 33	10 44			11 00			11 15				11 33	11 44			12 00
Beaulieu Road	d																								
Ashurst New Forest	d									10 40											11 40				
Totton	d									10 45											11 45				
Salisbury	d				09 48										10 48										
Dean	d				10 00										11 00										
Mottisfont & Dunbridge	d				10 06										11 06										
Romsey	d				10 11										11 11										
Redbridge	d				10 19										11 19										
Millbrook (Hants)	d				10 22										11 22										
Southampton Central	a			10 12	10 25	10 28			⟵	10 51	10 57			11 12	11 25		11 28			⟵	11 51	11 57			12 12
	d			10 15	10 32 ⟶	10 30			10 32	10 55	11 00			11 15	11 32 ⟶		11 30			11 32	11 55	12 00			12 15
St Denys	d								10 37											11 37					
Swaythling	d								10 40											11 40					
Southampton Airport Parkwy ✈	d			10 22		10 38			10 43	11 03	11 08			11 22			11 38			11 43	12 03	12 08			12 22
Portsmouth Harbour	d						09 54											10 54							
Portsmouth & Southsea	d						09 59											10 59							
Fratton	d						10 03											11 03							
Hilsea	d						10 07											11 07							
Cosham	d						10 12											11 12							
Portchester	d						10 17											11 17							
Fareham	d						10 23											11 23							
Botley	d						10 30											11 30							
Hedge End	d						10 35											11 35							
Eastleigh 3	a	⟵					10 41		10 46	11 06		⟵						11 41		11 46	12 06		⟵		
	d	10 12					10 42		10 48	11 12		11 12						11 42		11 48	12 12		12 12		
Chandlers Ford	a								10 53	⟶										11 53	⟶				
	d								10 53											11 53					
Romsey	a								11 00											12 00					
Shawford	d	10 18										11 18											12 18		
Winchester	d	10 24		10 31		10 48	10 54				11 18	11 24		11 31			11 48	11 54				12 18	12 24		12 31
Micheldever	d						11 02											12 02							
Basingstoke	a	10 40		10 46			11 15				11 34	11 40		11 46				12 15				12 34	12 40		12 46
	d	10 41		10 47			11 17				11 36	11 41		11 47				12 17				12 36	12 41		12 47
Reading 7	a			11 04										12 04											13 04
Fleet	d	10 53										11 53											12 53		
Farnborough (Main)	d	10 58					11 31					11 58						12 31					12 58		
Woking	a					11 19	11 40										12 19	12 40							
Clapham Junction 10	a	11 24									12 12	12 24										13 12	13 24		
London Waterloo 15 ⊖	a	11 34				11 49	12 08				12 20	12 34					12 49	13 08				13 20	13 34		

For general notes see front of timetable
For details of catering facilities see Directory of Train Operators

A ☕ from Bournemouth
b From 15 March

Table 158

Saturdays

Weymouth, Bournemouth, Lymington, Southampton and Basingstoke → London

Network Diagram - see first page of Table 158

		SW	SW	GW	SW	SW	SW	SW	SW	SW	SW	XC	SW	SW	SW	SW	SW	SW	SW	SW	SW	XC	SW
		1	1 ◇	◇	1	1	1	1	1 ◇	1	1	1 ◇	1	1 ◇	1	1	1	1	1 ◇	1	1	1 ◇	1
			A						A					A					A				
			☕						☕			☕		☕					☕			☕	
Weymouth	d		11 03	11 10					11 20					12 03					12 20				
Upwey	d			11 15					11 24										12 24				
Dorchester West	a			11 23																			
Dorchester South	d		11 13						11 32					12 13					12 32				
Moreton (Dorset)	d								11 39										12 39				
Wool	d								11 45										12 45				
Wareham	d		11 28						11 52					12 28					12 52				
Holton Heath	d								11 56										12 56				
Hamworthy	d		11 35						12 01					12 35					13 01				
Poole 4	a		11 39						12 05					12 39					13 05				
	d		11 40					11 50	12 06					12 40				12 50	13 06				
Parkstone (Dorset)	d		11 44					11 54						12 44				12 54					
Branksome	d		11 48					11 57						12 48				12 57					
Bournemouth	a		11 54					12 02	12 16					12 54				13 02	13 16				
	d		11 59					12 05	12 21			12 45		12 59				13 05	13 21			13 45	
Pokesdown	d							12 09	12 25									13 09	13 25				
Christchurch	d							12 13	12 29									13 13	13 29				
Hinton Admiral	d							12 18										13 18					
New Milton	d							12 22	12 36									13 22	13 36				
Sway	d							12 27										13 27					
Yarmouth (I.O.W.) ⛴	d					11b30					12 00					12b30					13 00		
Lymington Pier ⛴	d					12 14					12 44					13 14					13 44		
Lymington Town	d					12 16					12 46					13 16					13 46		
Brockenhurst 3	a		12 14			12 24		12 32	12 43		12 54	12 58		13 14		13 24		13 32	13 43		13 54	13 58	
	d		12 15					12 33	12 44			13 00		13 15				13 33	13 44			14 00	
Beaulieu Road	d																	13 38					
Ashurst New Forest	d							12 40										13 42					
Totton	d							12 45										13 47					
Salisbury	d	11 53											12 48										13 53
Dean	d												13 00										
Mottisfont & Dunbridge	d												13 06										
Romsey	d	12 11											13 11										14 11
Redbridge	d	12 19											13 19										14 19
Millbrook (Hants)	d	12 22											13 22										14 22
Southampton Central	a	12 25	12 28				←	12 51	12 57			13 12	13 25	13 28			←	13 53	13 57			14 12	14 25
	d	12 32 →	12 30				12 32	12 55	13 00			13 15	13 32 →	13 30			13 32	13 55	14 00			14 15	14 32 →
St Denys	d						12 37										13 37						
Swaythling	d						12 40										13 40						
Southampton Airport Parkwy ✈	d		12 38				12 43	13 03	13 08			13 22		13 38			13 43	14 03	14 08			14 22	
Portsmouth Harbour	d				11 54										12 54								
Portsmouth & Southsea	d				11 59										12 59								
Fratton	d				12 03										13 03								
Hilsea	d				12 07										13 07								
Cosham	d				12 12										13 12								
Portchester	d				12 17										13 17								
Fareham	d				12 23										13 23								
Botley	d				12 30										13 30								
Hedge End	d				12 35										13 35								
Eastleigh 3	a				12 41		12 46	13 06		←					13 41		13 46	14 06		←			
	d				12 42		12 48	13 12		13 12					13 42		13 48	14 12		14 12			
Chandlers Ford	a						12 53	→									13 53	→					
	d						12 53										13 53						
Romsey	a						13 00										14 00						
Shawford	d									13 18										14 18			
Winchester	d		12 48		12 54				13 18	13 24		13 31		13 48	13 54				14 18	14 24		14 31	
Micheldever	d				13 02										14 02								
Basingstoke	a				13 15				13 34	13 40		13 46			14 15				14 34	14 40		14 46	
	d				13 17				13 36	13 41		13 47			14 17				14 36	14 41		14 47	
Reading 7	a											14 04										15 04	
Fleet	d									13 53										14 53			
Farnborough (Main)	d				13 31					13 58					14 31					14 58			
Woking	a		13 19		13 40									14 19	14 40								
Clapham Junction 10	a								14 12	14 24									15 12	15 24			
London Waterloo 15 ⊖	a		13 49		14 08				14 20	14 34				14 49	15 08				15 20	15 34			

For general notes see front of timetable
For details of catering facilities see
Directory of Train Operators

A ☕ from Bournemouth
b From 15 March

Table 158

Saturdays

Weymouth, Bournemouth, Lymington, Southampton and Basingstoke → London

Network Diagram - see first page of Table 158

		SW	GW	SW	SW	SW	SW	SW	SW	SW	XC	SW	SW	SW	SW	SW	SW	SW	SW	SW	XC	SW	SW	GW
		1 ◇	◇	1	1	1	1	1 ◇	1	1	1 ◇	1	1 ◇	1	1	1	1	1 ◇	1	1	1 ◇	1	1 ◇	◇
		A	B					A					A					A					A	B
		🍴						🍴			🍴		🍴					🍴			🍴		🍴	
Weymouth	d	13 03	13§10					13 20					14 03					14 20					15 03	15§10
Upwey	d		13§15					13 24										14 24						15§15
Dorchester West	a		13§23																					15§23
Dorchester South	d	13 13						13 32					14 13					14 32					15 13	
Moreton (Dorset)	d							13 39										14 39						
Wool	d							13 45										14 45						
Wareham	d	13 28						13 52					14 28					14 52					15 28	
Holton Heath	d							13 56										14 56						
Hamworthy	d	13 35						14 01					14 35					15 01					15 35	
Poole 4	a	13 39						14 05					14 39					15 05					15 39	
	d	13 40					13 50	14 06					14 40				14 50	15 06					15 40	
Parkstone (Dorset)	d	13 44					13 54						14 44				14 54						15 44	
Branksome	d	13 48					13 57						14 48				14 57						15 48	
Bournemouth	a	13 54					14 02	14 16					14 54				15 02	15 16					15 54	
	d	13 59					14 05	14 21			14 45		14 59				15 05	15 21			15 45		15 59	
Pokesdown	d						14 09	14 25									15 09	15 25						
Christchurch	d						14 13	14 29									15 13	15 29						
Hinton Admiral	d						14 18										15 18							
New Milton	d						14 22	14 36									15 22	15 36						
Sway	d						14 27										15 27							
Yarmouth (I.O.W.) ⛴	d			*13b30*						*14 00*					*14 30*					*15b00*				
Lymington Pier ⛴	d			14 14						14 44					15 14					15 44				
Lymington Town	d			14 16						14 46					15 16					15 46				
Brockenhurst 3	a	14 14		14 24			14 32	14 43		14 54	14 58		15 14		15 24		15 32	15 43		15 54	15 58		16 14	
	d	14 15					14 33	14 44			15 00		15 15				15 33	15 44			16 00		16 15	
Beaulieu Road	d																							
Ashurst New Forest	d						14 40										15 40							
Totton	d						14 45										15 45							
Salisbury	d											14 48										15 48		
Dean	d											15 00										16 00		
Mottisfont & Dunbridge	d											15 06										16 06		
Romsey	d											15 11										16 11		
Redbridge	d											15 19										16 19		
Millbrook (Hants)	d											15 22										16 22		
Southampton Central	a	14 28				←	14 51	14 57			15 12	15 25	15 28			←	15 51	15 57			16 12	16 25	16 28	
	d	14 30				14 32	14 55	15 00			15 15	15 32 →	15 30			15 32	15 55	16 00			16 15	16 32 →	16 30	
St Denys	d					14 37										15 37								
Swaythling	d					14 40										15 40								
Southampton Airport Parkwy ✈	d	14 38				14 43	15 03	15 08			15 22		15 38			15 43	16 03	16 08			16 22		16 38	
Portsmouth Harbour	d				13 54									14 54										
Portsmouth & Southsea	d				13 59									14 59										
Fratton	d				14 03									15 03										
Hilsea	d				14 07									15 07										
Cosham	d				14 12									15 12										
Portchester	d				14 17									15 17										
Fareham	d				14 23									15 23										
Botley	d				14 30									15 30										
Hedge End	d				14 35									15 35										
Eastleigh 3	a				14 41	14 46	15 06		←					15 41		15 46	16 06		←					
	d				14 42	14 48	15 12		15 12					15 42		15 48	16 12		16 12					
Chandlers Ford	a					14 53	→									15 53	→							
	d					14 53										15 53								
Romsey	a					15 00										16 00								
Shawford	d								15 18										16 18					
Winchester	d	14 48			14 54			15 18	15 24		15 31		15 48	15 54				16 18	16 24		16 31		16 48	
Micheldever	d				15 02									16 02										
Basingstoke	a				15 15			15 34	15 40		15 46			16 15				16 34	16 40		16 46			
	d				15 17			15 36	15 41		15 47			16 17				16 36	16 41		16 47			
Reading 7	a										16 04										17 04			
Fleet	d								15 53										16 53					
Farnborough (Main)	d				15 31				15 58					16 31					16 58					
Woking	a	15 19			15 40								16 19	16 40									17 19	
Clapham Junction 10	a							16 12	16 24									17 12	17 24					
London Waterloo 15 ⊖	a	15 49			16 08			16 20	16 34				16 49	17 08				17 20	17 34				17 49	

For general notes see front of timetable
For details of catering facilities see Directory of Train Operators

A 🍴 from Bournemouth
B Until 22 March.
b From 15 March

Table 158

Saturdays

Weymouth, Bournemouth, Lymington, Southampton and Basingstoke → London

Network Diagram - see first page of Table 158

		SW	SW	SW	SW	SW	SW	SW	XC	SW	SW	SW	SW	SW	SW	SW	SW	SW	XC	SW	SW	GW	SW
		1	1	1	1	1 ◇	1	1	1 ◇	1	1 ◇	1	1	1	1	1 ◇	1	1	1 ◇	1	1 ◇	◇	1
						A					A					A					A	B	
						🍴			🍴		🍴					🍴			🍴		🍴		
Weymouth	d					15 20					16 03					16 20					17 03	17 10	
Upwey	d					15 24										16 24						17 15	
Dorchester West	a																					17 23	
Dorchester South	d					15 32					16 13					16 32					17 13		
Moreton (Dorset)	d					15 39										16 39							
Wool	d					15 45										16 45							
Wareham	d					15 52					16 28					16 52					17 28		
Holton Heath	d					15 56										16 56							
Hamworthy	d					16 01					16 35					17 01					17 35		
Poole 4	a					16 05					16 39					17 05					17 39		
	d				15 50	16 06					16 40				16 50	17 06					17 40		
Parkstone (Dorset)	d				15 54						16 44				16 54						17 44		
Branksome	d				15 57						16 48				16 57						17 48		
Bournemouth	a				16 02	16 16					16 54				17 02	17 16					17 54		
	d				16 05	16 21			16 45		16 59				17 05	17 21			17 45		17 59		
Pokesdown	d				16 09	16 25									17 09	17 25							
Christchurch	d				16 13	16 29									17 13	17 29							
Hinton Admiral	d				16 18										17 18								
New Milton	d				16 22	16 36									17 22	17 36							
Sway	d				16 27										17 27								
Yarmouth (I.O.W.) ⛴	d		*15 30*					*16 00*					*16b30*					*17 00*					
Lymington Pier ⛴	d		16 14					16 44					17 14					17 44					
Lymington Town	d		16 16					16 46					17 16					17 46					
Brockenhurst 3	a		16 24		16 32	16 43		16 54	16 58		17 14		17 24		17 32	17 43		17 54	17 58		18 14		
	d				16 33	16 44			17 00		17 15				17 33	17 44			18 00		18 15		
Beaulieu Road	d														17 38								
Ashurst New Forest	d				16 40										17 42								
Totton	d				16 45										17 47								
Salisbury	d									16 48										17 48			
Dean	d									17 00										18 00			
Mottisfont & Dunbridge	d									17 06										18 06			
Romsey	d									17 11										18 11			
Redbridge	d									17 19										18 19			
Millbrook (Hants)	d									17 22										18 22			
Southampton Central	a			←	16 51	16 57			17 12	17 25	17 28			←	17 53	17 57			18 12	18 25	18 28		
	d			16 32	16 55	17 00			17 15	17 32 →	17 30			17 32	17 55	18 00			18 15	18 32 →	18 30		
St Denys	d			16 37										17 37									
Swaythling	d			16 40										17 40									
Southampton Airport Parkwy ✈	d			16 43	17 03	17 08			17 22		17 38			17 43	18 03	18 08			18 22		18 38		
Portsmouth Harbour	d	15 54										16 54											17 54
Portsmouth & Southsea	d	15 59										16 59											17 59
Fratton	d	16 03										17 03											18 03
Hilsea	d	16 07										17 07											18 07
Cosham	d	16 12										17 12											18 12
Portchester	d	16 17										17 17											18 17
Fareham	d	16 23										17 23											18 23
Botley	d	16 30										17 30											18 30
Hedge End	d	16 35										17 35											18 35
Eastleigh 3	a	16 41		16 46	17 06		←					17 41		17 46	18 06		←						18 41
	d	16 42		16 48	17 12		17 12					17 42		17 48	18 12		18 12						18 42
Chandlers Ford	a			16 53	→									17 53	→								
	d			16 53										17 53									
Romsey	a			17 00										18 00									
Shawford	d						17 18										18 18						
Winchester	d	16 54				17 18	17 24		17 31		17 48	17 54				18 18	18 24		18 31		18 48		18 54
Micheldever	d	17 02										18 02											19 02
Basingstoke	a	17 15				17 34	17 40		17 46			18 15				18 34	18 40		18 46				19 15
	d	17 17				17 36	17 41		17 47			18 17				18 36	18 41		18 47				19 17
Reading 7	a								18 04										19 04				
Fleet	d						17 53										18 53						
Farnborough (Main)	d	17 31					17 58					18 31					18 58						19 31
Woking	a	17 40									18 19	18 40									19 19		19 40
Clapham Junction 10	a					18 12	18 24									19 12	19 24						
London Waterloo 15 ⊖	a	18 08				18 20	18 34				18 49	19 08				19 20	19 34				19 49		20 08

For general notes see front of timetable
For details of catering facilities see Directory of Train Operators

A 🍴 from Bournemouth
B Until 22 March.
b From 15 March

Weymouth, Bournemouth, Lymington, Southampton and Basingstoke → London

Network Diagram - see first page of Table 158

		SW 1	SW 1	SW 1	SW 1 ◇ A ☕	SW 1	SW 1	XC 1 ◇ ☕	SW 1	SW 1 ◇ A ☕	SW 1	SW 1	SW 1	SW 1	SW 1 ◇ A ☕		SW 1	SW 1	XC 1 ◇	SW 1	SW 1 ◇ A ☕	SW 1	SW 1	SW 1	SW 1
Weymouth	d				17 20					18 03					18 20						19 03				
Upwey	d				17 24										18 24										
Dorchester West	a																								
Dorchester South	d				17 32					18 13					18 32						19 13				
Moreton (Dorset)	d				17 39										18 39										
Wool	d				17 45										18 45										
Wareham	d				17 52					18 28					18 52						19 28				
Holton Heath	d				17 56										18 56										
Hamworthy	d				18 01					18 35					19 01						19 35				
Poole 4	a				18 05					18 39					19 05						19 39				
	d			17 50	18 06					18 40				18 50	19 06						19 40				19 50
Parkstone (Dorset)	d			17 54						18 44				18 54							19 44				19 54
Branksome	d			17 57						18 48				18 57							19 48				19 57
Bournemouth	a			18 02	18 16					18 54				19 02	19 16						19 54				20 02
	d			18 05	18 21			18 45		18 59				19 05	19 21				19 45		19 59				20 05
Pokesdown	d			18 09	18 25									19 09	19 25										20 09
Christchurch	d			18 13	18 29									19 13	19 29										20 13
Hinton Admiral	d			18 18										19 18											20 18
New Milton	d			18 22	18 36									19 22	19 36										20 22
Sway	d			18 27										19 27											20 27
Yarmouth (I.O.W.) ⛴	d	*17b30*					*18c00*				*18b30*							*19 00*				*19e30*			
Lymington Pier ⛴	d	18 14					18 44				19 14							19 44				20 14			
Lymington Town	d	18 16					18 46				19 16							19 46				20 16			
Brockenhurst 3	a	18 24		18 32	18 43		18 54	18 58		19 14	19 24			19 32	19 43			19 54	19 58		20 14	20 24			20 32
	d			18 33	18 44			19 00		19 15				19 33	19 44				20 00		20 15				20 33
Beaulieu Road	d																								
Ashurst New Forest	d			18 40										19 40											20 40
Totton	d			18 45										19 45											20 45
Salisbury	d								18 48											19 53					
Dean	d								19 00																
Mottisfont & Dunbridge	d								19 06																
Romsey	d								19 11											20 11					
Redbridge	d								19 19											20 19					
Millbrook (Hants)	d								19 22											20 22					
Southampton Central	a		←	18 51	18 57			19 12	19 25	19 28			←	19 51	19 57				20 12	20 25	20 28			←	20 51
	d		18 32	18 55	19 00			19 15	19 32 →	19 30			19 32	19 55	20 00				20 15	20 32 →	20 30			20 32	20 55
St Denys	d		18 37										19 37											20 37	
Swaythling	d		18 40										19 40											20 40	
Southampton Airport Parkwy ✈	d		18 43	19 03	19 08			19 22		19 38			19 43	20 03	20 08				20 22		20 38			20 43	21 03
Portsmouth Harbour	d											18 54											19 54		
Portsmouth & Southsea	d											18 59											19 59		
Fratton	d											19 03											20 03		
Hilsea	d											19 07											20 07		
Cosham	d											19 12											20 12		
Portchester	d											19 17											20 17		
Fareham	d											19 23											20 23		
Botley	d											19 30											20 30		
Hedge End	d											19 35											20 35		
Eastleigh 3	a		18 46	19 06		←						19 41	19 46	20 06			←						20 41	20 46	21 06
	d		18 48	19 12		19 12						19 42	19 48	20 12			20 12						20 42	20 48	21 12
Chandlers Ford	a		18 53	→									19 53	→										20 53	→
	d		18 53										19 53											20 53	
Romsey	a		19 00										20 00											21 00	
Shawford	d					19 18											20 18								
Winchester	d				19 18	19 24		19 31		19 48		19 54			20 18		20 24		20 31		20 48		20 52		
Micheldever	d											20 02											21 04		
Basingstoke	a				19 34	19 40		19 46				20 15			20 34		20 40		20 46				21 15		
	d				19 36	19 41		19 47				20 17			20 36		20 41		20 47				21 24		
Reading 7	a							20 04											21 04						
Fleet	d					19 53											20 53						21 40		
Farnborough (Main)	d					19 58						20 31					20 58						21 46		
Woking	a									20 19		20 40					21 07				21 19		21 58		
Clapham Junction 10	a				20 12	20 24									21 14		21 30								
London Waterloo 15 ⊖	a				20 20	20 34				20 49		21 08			21 22		21 38				21 49		22 34		

For general notes see front of timetable
For details of catering facilities see Directory of Train Operators

A ☕ from Bournemouth
b Until 8th March and from 17th May
c From 15 March
e From 17 May

Table 158

Weymouth, Bournemouth, Lymington, Southampton and Basingstoke → London

Network Diagram - see first page of Table 158

		SW 1 ◇ A ☕	GW ◇ B	SW 1	SW 1	SW 1	SW 1	SW 1	SW 1	SW 1	SW 1 ◇	SW 1	SW 1	SW 1	SW 1	SW 1	SW 1	SW 1	SW 1	SW 1	SW 1	SW 1
Weymouth	d	19 20	19 58								20 10							21 10			22 10	23 10
Upwey	d	19 24	20 03								20 14							21 14			22 14	23 14
Dorchester West	a		20 11																			
Dorchester South	d	19 32									20 22							21 22			22 22	23 22
Moreton (Dorset)	d	19 39									20 28							21 28			22 28	23 28
Wool	d	19 45									20 34							21 34			22 34	23 34
Wareham	d	19 52									20 42							21 42			22 42	23 42
Holton Heath	d																					
Hamworthy	d	20 01									20 48							21 48			22 48	23 48
Poole 4	a	20 05									20 53							21 53			22 53	23 53
	d	20 06									20 54							21 54			22 54	23 54
Parkstone (Dorset)	d										20 58							21 58			22 58	
Branksome	d										21 01							22 01			23 01	
Bournemouth	a	20 16									21 07							22 07			23 07	00 03
	d	20 21									21 12							22 12			23 12	
Pokesdown	d	20 25									21 16							22 16			23 16	
Christchurch	d	20 29									21 20							22 20			23 20	
Hinton Admiral	d										21 25							22 25			23 25	
New Milton	d	20 36									21 29							22 29			23 29	
Sway	d										21 34							22 34			23 34	
Yarmouth (I.O.W.) ⛴	d				*20 00*		*20b30*						*21 00*	*21c30*								
Lymington Pier ⛴	d				20 44		21 14						21 44	22 14								
Lymington Town	d				20 46		21 16						21 46	22 16								
Brockenhurst 3	a	20 43			20 54		21 24				21 39		21 54	22 24				22 39			23 39	
	d	20 44									21 40							22 40			23 40	
Beaulieu Road	d																					
Ashurst New Forest	d										21 47							22 47			23 47	
Totton	d										21 52							22 52			23 52	
Salisbury	d								20 48								21 48					
Dean	d								21 00								22 00					
Mottisfont & Dunbridge	d								21 06								22 06					
Romsey	d								21 11								22 11		23 00			
Redbridge	d								21 19								22 19		23 08			
Millbrook (Hants)	d								21 22								22 22		23 12			
Southampton Central	a	20 57							21 25		21 57						22 25	22 57	23 15		23 57	
	d	21 00				21 30			21 32	21 55	22 00				22 30		22 32	23 00	23 21		00 01	
St Denys	d								21 37								22 37		23 26		00 06	
Swaythling	d								21 40								22 40		23 29		00 09	
Southampton Airport Parkwy ✈	d	21 08				21 38			21 43	22 03	22 08				22 38		22 43	23 08	23 32		00 12	
Portsmouth Harbour	d							20 54								21 54				23 24		
Portsmouth & Southsea	d							20 59								21 59				23 29		
Fratton	d							21 03								22 03				23 33		
Hilsea	d							21 07								22 07				23 37		
Cosham	d							21 12								22 12				23 42		
Portchester	d							21 17								22 17				23 47		
Fareham	d							21 23								22 23				23 53		
Botley	d							21 30								22 30				23 59		
Hedge End	d							21 35								22 35				00 05		
Eastleigh 3	a			←				21 41	21 46	22 06		←			22 41	22 41	22 46	23 11	23 35	00 11	00 16	
	d			21 12				21 42	21 48	22 12		22 12			22 42		22 48	23 12	23 37	00 21		
Chandlers Ford	a								21 53	→							22 53		23 42			
	d								21 53								22 53		23 42			
Romsey	a								22 00								23 03		23 49			
Shawford	d			21 18								22 18						23 18				
Winchester	d	21 18		21 24		21 48		21 54			22 18	22 24			22e54			23 24		00a30		
Micheldever	d							22 02										23 33				
Basingstoke	a	21 34		21 40				22 15			22 34	22 40			23 10			23 43				
	d	21 36		21 41				22 24			22 36	22 41			23 14			23 44				
Reading 7	a																					
Fleet	d			21 53				22 40				22 53						00 01				
Farnborough (Main)	d			21 58				22 46				22 58						00 06				
Woking	a			22 07		22 19		22 58			22 54	23 07			23 32			00 18				
Clapham Junction 10	a	22 14		22 30							23 15	23 30			23 57			00 54				
London Waterloo 15 ⊖	a	22 22		22 38		22 49		23 37			23 23	23 38			00 07			01 02				

For general notes see front of timetable
For details of catering facilities see Directory of Train Operators

A ☕ from Bournemouth
B Until 22 March.
b From 17 May
c Departs 5 minutes later until 10 May
e Arr. 2251

Table 158

Sundays

Weymouth, Bournemouth, Lymington, Southampton and Basingstoke → London

Network Diagram - see first page of Table 158

		SW	SW	SW	SW	SW	SW	SW	SW	XC	SW		SW	SW	SW	XC	SW	SW	SW	SW	SW	SW		XC	SW
		1	1	1	1	1	1 ◇	1 ◇	1	1 ◇	1		1 ◇	1 ◇	1	1 ◇	1 ◇	1	1	1 ◇	1 ◇	1		1 ◇	1
																	A								
								☕		☕						☕	☕							☕	
Weymouth	d	21p10		22p10													07 48								
Upwey	d	21p14		22p14													07 52								
Dorchester West	a																								
Dorchester South	d	21p22		22p22													08 00								
Moreton (Dorset)	d	21p28		22p28													08 07								
Wool	d	21p34		22p34													08 13								
Wareham	d	21p42		22p42													08 20								
Holton Heath	d																								
Hamworthy	d	21p48		22p48													08 27								
Poole 4	a	21p53		22p53													08 31								
	d	21p54		22p54				06 50						07 50			08 32				08 55				
Parkstone (Dorset)	d	21p58		22p58				06 54						07 54			08 36								
Branksome	d	22p01		23p01				06 57						07 57			08 40								
Bournemouth	a	22p07		23p07				07 02						08 02			08 46				09 04				
	d	22p12		23p12				07 06						08 06			08 50				09 06			09 40	
Pokesdown	d	22p16		23p16				07 10						08 10							09 10				
Christchurch	d	22p20		23p20				07 14						08 14							09 14				
Hinton Admiral	d	22p25		23p25				07 19						08 19							09 19				
New Milton	d	22p29		23p29				07 23						08 23			09 01				09 23				
Sway	d	22p34		23p34				07 28						08 28							09 28				
Yarmouth (I.O.W.) ⛴	d																		*08 00*						*09 00*
Lymington Pier ⛴	d																		09 14						09 44
Lymington Town	d																		09 16						09 46
Brockenhurst 3	a	22p39		23p39				07 33						08 33			09 08		09 24		09 33			09 53	09 54
	d	22p40		23p40				07 34						08 34			09 09				09 34			09 57	
Beaulieu Road	d													08 39							09 39				
Ashurst New Forest	d	22p47		23p47				07 43						08 43							09 43				
Totton	d	22p52		23p52				07 48						08 48							09 48				
Salisbury	d					07 08					08 13							09 08							
Dean	d					07 20												09 20							
Mottisfont & Dunbridge	d					07 26												09 26							
Romsey	d					07 32					08 32							09 32							
Redbridge	d					07 39					08 39							09 39							
Millbrook (Hants)	d					07 43					08 43							09 43							
Southampton Central	a	22p57		23p57		07 45		07 53	⟵		08 45			08 53	⟵		09 23	09 45			09 53	⟵		10 10	
	d	23p00		00 01	06 55	07 59 ⟶		07 55	07 59	08 39	08 59 ⟶			08 55	08 59		09 25	09 59 ⟶			09 55	09 59		10 15	
St Denys	d			00 06					08 04						09 04							10 04			
Swaythling	d			00 09					08 07						09 07	⟵						10 07			
Southampton Airport Parkwy ✈	d	23p08		00 12	07 03			08 03	08 10	08 46				09 03	09 10	08 46	09 33				10 03	10 10		10 22	
Portsmouth Harbour	d		23p24				07 17			⟶			08 17							09 17					
Portsmouth & Southsea	d		23p29				07 22						08 22							09 22					
Fratton	d		23p33				07 26						08 26							09 26					
Hilsea	d		23p37				07 30						08 30							09 30					
Cosham	d		23p42				07 35						08 35							09 35					
Portchester	d		23p47				07 40						08 40							09 40					
Fareham	d		23p53				07 46						08 46							09 46					
Botley	d		23p59				07 54						08 54							09 54					
Hedge End	d		00 05				07 58						08 58							09 58					
Eastleigh 3	a	23p11	00 11	00 16	07 07		08 04	08 07	08 13				09 04	09 07	09 13					10 04	10 07	10 13			
	d	23p12	00 21		07 11			08 11	08 15					09 11	09 15						10 11	10 15			
Chandlers Ford	a								08 20						09 20							10 20			
	d								08 20						09 20							10 20			
Romsey	a								08 28						09 28							10 28			
Shawford	d	23p18												09 17											
Winchester	d	23p24	00a30		07 23			08 23						09 23			09 42				10 23			10 31	
Micheldever	d	23p33			07 32			08 32						09 32							10 32				
Basingstoke	a	23p43			07 42			08 42						09 42		09 46	09 58				10 42			10 46	
	d	23p44			07 44			08 44						09 44		09 47	10 00				10 44			10 47	
Reading 7	a															10 05								11 05	
Fleet	d	00 01																							
Farnborough (Main)	d	00 06																							
Woking	a	00 18			08 02			09 02						10 02			10 18				11 02				
Clapham Junction 10	a	00 54			08 27			09 27						10 27			10 39				11 27				
London Waterloo 15 ⊖	a	01 02			08 42			09 42						10 42			10 54				11 40				

For general notes see front of timetable
For details of catering facilities see Directory of Train Operators

A ☕ from Bournemouth

Sundays

Weymouth, Bournemouth, Lymington, Southampton and Basingstoke → London

Network Diagram - see first page of Table 158

		SW	SW	SW	SW	SW	SW	XC	SW	SW	SW	SW	SW	SW	SW	XC	SW	SW	SW	SW	SW	SW	SW
		1 ◇	1	1	1 ◇	1 ◇	1	R 1	1	1 ◇	1	1	1 ◇	1 ◇	1	R 1	1	1 ◇	1	1	1	1 ◇	1 ◇
		A ☕						☕		A ☕						☕		A ☕					
Weymouth	d	08 48								09 48								10 48					
Upwey	d	08 52								09 52								10 52					
Dorchester West	a																						
Dorchester South	d	09 00								10 00								11 00					
Moreton (Dorset)	d	09 07								10 07								11 07					
Wool	d	09 13								10 13								11 13					
Wareham	d	09 20								10 20								11 20					
Holton Heath	d																						
Hamworthy	d	09 27								10 27								11 27					
Poole 4	a	09 31								10 31								11 31					
	d	09 32				09 55				10 32				10 55				11 32					11 55
Parkstone (Dorset)	d	09 36								10 36								11 36					
Branksome	d	09 40								10 40								11 40					
Bournemouth	a	09 46				10 04				10 46				11 04				11 46					12 04
	d	09 50				10 06		10 40		10 50				11 06		11 40		11 50					12 06
Pokesdown	d					10 10								11 10									12 10
Christchurch	d					10 14								11 14									12 14
Hinton Admiral	d					10 19								11 19									12 19
New Milton	d	10 01				10 23				11 01				11 23				12 01					12 23
Sway	d					10 28								11 28									12 28
Yarmouth (I.O.W.) ⛴	d			*09 30*					*09 30*			*10 30*					*11 00*			*11 30*			
Lymington Pier ⛴	d			10 14					10 44			11 14					11 44			12 14			
Lymington Town	d			10 16					10 46			11 16					11 46			12 16			
Brockenhurst 3	a	10 08		10 24		10 33		10 53	10 54	11 08		11 24		11 33		11 53	11 54	12 08		12 24			12 33
	d	10 09				10 34		10 57		11 09				11 34		11 57		12 09					12 34
Beaulieu Road	d					10 39								11 39									12 39
Ashurst New Forest	d					10 43								11 43									12 43
Totton	d					10 48								11 48									12 48
Salisbury	d		10 13								11 08								12 13				
Dean	d										11 20												
Mottisfont & Dunbridge	d										11 26												
Romsey	d		10 32								11 32								12 32		12 35		
Redbridge	d		10 39								11 39								12 39		13 16		
Millbrook (Hants)	d		10 43								11 43								12 43				
Southampton Central	a	10 23	10 45			10 53	←	11 10		11 22	11 45			11 53	←	12 10		12 23	12 45				12 53
	d	10 25	10 59 →			10 55	10 59	11 15		11 25	11 59 →			11 55	11 59	12 15		12 25	12 59 →				12 55
St Denys	d						11 04								12 04								
Swaythling	d						11 07								12 07								
Southampton Airport Parkwy ✈	d	10 33				11 03	11 10	11 22		11 33				12 03	12 10	12 22		12 33					13 03
Portsmouth Harbour	d				10 17								11 17									12 17	
Portsmouth & Southsea	d				10 22								11 22									12 22	
Fratton	d				10 26								11 26									12 26	
Hilsea	d				10 30								11 30									12 30	
Cosham	d				10 35								11 35									12 35	
Portchester	d				10 40								11 40									12 40	
Fareham	d				10 46								11 46									12 46	
Botley	d				10 54								11 54									12 54	
Hedge End	d				10 58								11 58									12 58	
Eastleigh 3	a				11 04	11 07	11 13						12 04	12 07	12 13							13 04	13 07
	d					11 11	11 15							12 11	12 15								13 11
Chandlers Ford	a						11 20								12 20						12 42		
	d						11 20								12 20						12 42		
Romsey	a						11 28								12 28						13 24		
Shawford	d					11 17																	13 17
Winchester	d	10 42				11 23		11 31		11 41				12 23		12 31		12 42					13 23
Micheldever	d					11 32								12 32									13 32
Basingstoke	a	10 58				11 42		11 46		11 57				12 42		12 46		12 58					13 42
	d	11 00				11 44		11 47		12 00				12 44		12 47		13 00					13 44
Reading 7	a							12 05								13 05							
Fleet	d																						
Farnborough (Main)	d																						
Woking	a	11 18				12 02				12 18				13 02				13 18					14 02
Clapham Junction 10	a	11 39				12 27				12 39				13 27				13 39					14 27
London Waterloo 15 ⊖	a	11 52				12 40				12 52				13 40				13 49					14 37

For general notes see front of timetable
For details of catering facilities see Directory of Train Operators

A ☕ from Bournemouth

Table 158

Sundays

Weymouth, Bournemouth, Lymington, Southampton and Basingstoke → London

Network Diagram - see first page of Table 158

		SW	XC	SW	SW	SW	SW	SW	SW	SW	XC	SW	SW	GW	SW	SW	SW	SW	SW	XC	SW	SW	GW
		1	R 1	1	1 ◇	1	1	1 ◇	1 ◇	1	R 1	1	1 ◇	◇	1	1	1 ◇	1 ◇	1	R 1	1	1 ◇	◇
					A								A	B								A	C
			⊡		⊡						⊡		⊡							⊡		⊡	
Weymouth	d				11 48								12 48	13 32								13 48	14 00
Upwey	d				11 52								12 52	13 37								13 52	14 05
Dorchester West	a													13 45									14 13
Dorchester South	d				12 00								13 00									14 00	
Moreton (Dorset)	d				12 07								13 07									14 07	
Wool	d				12 13								13 13									14 13	
Wareham	d				12 20								13 20									14 20	
Holton Heath	d																						
Hamworthy	d				12 27								13 27									14 27	
Poole 4	a				12 31								13 31									14 31	
	d				12 32				12 55				13 32					13 55				14 32	
Parkstone (Dorset)	d				12 36								13 36									14 36	
Branksome	d				12 40								13 40									14 40	
Bournemouth	a				12 46				13 04				13 46					14 04				14 46	
	d		12 40		12 50				13 06		13 40		13 50					14 06		14 40		14 50	
Pokesdown	d								13 10									14 10					
Christchurch	d								13 14									14 14					
Hinton Admiral	d								13 19									14 19					
New Milton	d				13 01				13 23				14 01					14 23				15 01	
Sway	d								13 28									14 28					
Yarmouth (I.O.W.) ⛴	d			*12 00*			*12b30*					*13c00*				*13b30*					*14 00*		
Lymington Pier ⛴	d			12 44			13 14					13 44				14 14					14 44		
Lymington Town	d			12 46			13 16					13 46				14 16					14 46		
Brockenhurst 3	a		12 53	12 54	13 08		13 24		13 33		13 53	13 54	14 08			14 24		14 33		14 53	14 54	15 08	
	d		12 57		13 09				13 34		13 57		14 09					14 34		14 57		15 09	
Beaulieu Road	d								13 39									14 39					
Ashurst New Forest	d								13 43									14 43					
Totton	d								13 48									14 48					
Salisbury	d					13 08									14 13								
Dean	d					13 20																	
Mottisfont & Dunbridge	d					13 26																	
Romsey	d					13 32									14 32								
Redbridge	d					13 39									14 39								
Millbrook (Hants)	d					13 43									14 43								
Southampton Central	a	←	13 10		13 23	13 45			13 53	←	14 10		14 23		14 45			14 53	←	15 10		15 23	
	d	12 59	13 15		13 25	13 59 →			13 55	13 59	14 15		14 25		14 59 →			14 55	14 59	15 15		15 25	
St Denys	d	13 04								14 04									15 04				
Swaythling	d	13 07								14 07									15 07				
Southampton Airport Parkwy ✈	d	13 10	13 22		13 33				14 03	14 10	14 22		14 33					15 03	15 10	15 22		15 33	
Portsmouth Harbour	d							13 17									14 17						
Portsmouth & Southsea	d							13 22									14 22						
Fratton	d							13 26									14 26						
Hilsea	d							13 30									14 30						
Cosham	d							13 35									14 35						
Portchester	d							13 40									14 40						
Fareham	d							13 46									14 46						
Botley	d							13 54									14 54						
Hedge End	d							13 58									14 58						
Eastleigh 3	a	13 13						14 04	14 07	14 13							15 04	15 07	15 13				
	d	13 15						14 11		14 15							15 11		15 15				
Chandlers Ford	a	13 20								14 20									15 20				
	d	13 20								14 20									15 20				
Romsey	a	13 28								14 28									15 28				
Shawford	d																15 17						
Winchester	d		13 31		13 42			14 23			14 31		14 42				15 23			15 31		15 42	
Micheldever	d							14 32									15 32						
Basingstoke	a		13 46		13 58			14 42			14 46		14 58				15 42			15 46		15 58	
	d		13 47		14 00			14 44			14 47		15 00				15 44			15 47		16 00	
Reading 7	a		14 05								15 05									16 05			
Fleet	d																						
Farnborough (Main)	d																						
Woking	a				14 18			15 02					15 18				16 02					16 18	
Clapham Junction 10	a				14 39			15 27					15 39				16 27					16 39	
London Waterloo 15 ⊖	a				14 49			15 37					15 49				16 37					16 49	

For general notes see front of timetable
For details of catering facilities see Directory of Train Operators

A ⊡ from Bournemouth
B From 30 March
C Until 23 March
b From 16 March
c Until 9 March and from 18 May

Table 158

Sundays

Weymouth, Bournemouth, Lymington, Southampton and Basingstoke → London

Network Diagram - see first page of Table 158

		SW	SW	SW	SW	SW	XC	SW	SW	SW	SW	SW	SW	SW	XC	SW	SW	SW	SW	SW	SW	SW	XC
		1	1	1 ◇	1 ◇	1	R 1	1	1 ◇	1	1	1 ◇	1 ◇	1	R 1	1	1 ◇	1	1	1 ◇	1 ◇	1	R 1
							⊏		A ⊏						⊏		A ⊏						⊏
Weymouth	d								14 48								15 48						
Upwey	d								14 52								15 52						
Dorchester West	a																						
Dorchester South	d								15 00								16 00						
Moreton (Dorset)	d								15 07								16 07						
Wool	d								15 13								16 13						
Wareham	d								15 20								16 20						
Holton Heath	d																						
Hamworthy	d								15 27								16 27						
Poole 4	a								15 31								16 31						
	d				14 55				15 32				15 55				16 32				16 55		
Parkstone (Dorset)	d								15 36								16 36						
Branksome	d								15 40								16 40						
Bournemouth	a				15 04				15 46				16 04				16 46				17 04		
	d				15 06		15 40		15 50				16 06		16 40		16 50				17 06		17 40
Pokesdown	d				15 10								16 10								17 10		
Christchurch	d				15 14								16 14								17 14		
Hinton Admiral	d				15 19								16 19								17 19		
New Milton	d				15 23				16 01				16 23				17 01				17 23		
Sway	d				15 28								16 28								17 28		
Yarmouth (I.O.W.) ⛴	d		*14 30*					*15b00*			*15 30*					*16 00*			*16b30*				
Lymington Pier ⛴	d		15 14					15 44			16 14					16 44			17 14				
Lymington Town	d		15 16					15 46			16 16					16 46			17 16				
Brockenhurst 3	a		15 24		15 33		15 53	15 54	16 08		16 24		16 33		16 53	16 54	17 08		17 24		17 33		17 53
	d				15 34		15 57		16 09				16 34		16 57		17 09				17 34		17 57
Beaulieu Road	d				15 39								16 39								17 39		
Ashurst New Forest	d				15 43								16 43								17 43		
Totton	d				15 48								16 48								17 48		
Salisbury	d	15 08								16 13								17 08					
Dean	d	15 20																17 20					
Mottisfont & Dunbridge	d	15 26																17 26					
Romsey	d	15 32								16 32								17 32					
Redbridge	d	15 39								16 39								17 39					
Millbrook (Hants)	d	15 43								16 43								17 43					
Southampton Central	a	15 45			15 53	←	16 10		16 23	16 45			16 53	←	17 10		17 23	17 45			17 53	←	18 10
	d	15 59 →			15 55	15 59	16 15		16 25	16 59 →			16 55	16 59	17 15		17 25	17 59 →			17 55	17 59	18 15
St Denys	d					16 04								17 04								18 04	
Swaythling	d					16 07								17 07								18 07	
Southampton Airport Parkwy ✈	d				16 03	16 10	16 22		16 33				17 03	17 10	17 22		17 33				18 03	18 10	18 22
Portsmouth Harbour	d			15 17								16 17								17 17			
Portsmouth & Southsea	d			15 22								16 22								17 22			
Fratton	d			15 26								16 26								17 26			
Hilsea	d			15 30								16 30								17 30			
Cosham	d			15 35								16 35								17 35			
Portchester	d			15 40								16 40								17 40			
Fareham	d			15 46								16 46								17 46			
Botley	d			15 54								16 54								17 54			
Hedge End	d			15 58								16 58								17 58			
Eastleigh 3	a			16 04	16 07	16 13						17 04	17 07	17 13						18 04	18 07	18 13	
	d			16 11		16 15						17 11		17 15						18 11		18 15	
Chandlers Ford	a					16 20								17 20								18 20	
	d					16 20								17 20								18 20	
Romsey	a					16 28								17 28								18 28	
Shawford	d											17 17											
Winchester	d			16 23			16 31		16 42			17 23			17 31		17 42			18 23			18 31
Micheldever	d			16 32								17 32								18 32			
Basingstoke	a			16 42			16 46		16 58			17 42			17 46		17 58			18 42			18 46
	d			16 44			16 47		17 00			17 44			17 47		18 00			18 44			18 47
Reading 7	a						17 05								18 05								19 05
Fleet	d																						
Farnborough (Main)	d																						
Woking	a			17 02					17 18			18 02					18 18			19 02			
Clapham Junction 10	a			17 27					17 39			18 27					18 39			19 27			
London Waterloo 15 ⊖	a			17 37					17 49			18 37					18 49			19 37			

For general notes see front of timetable
For details of catering facilities see Directory of Train Operators

A ⊏ from Bournemouth
b From 16 March

Table 158

Sundays

Weymouth, Bournemouth, Lymington, Southampton and Basingstoke → London

Network Diagram - see first page of Table 158

		SW 1	SW 1◇ A ☕	GW ◇ B	SW 1	SW 1	SW 1◇	SW 1◇	SW 1	XC 1◇ ☕	SW 1	SW 1◇ A ☕	GW ◇ C	SW 1	SW 1	SW 1◇	SW 1◇	SW 1	XC 1◇	SW 1	SW 1◇ A ☕	SW 1	SW 1
Weymouth	d		16 48	17 32								17 48	18 00								18 48		
Upwey	d		16 52	17 37								17 52	18 05								18 52		
Dorchester West	a			17 45									18 13										
Dorchester South	d		17 00									18 00									19 00		
Moreton (Dorset)	d		17 07									18 07									19 07		
Wool	d		17 13									18 13									19 13		
Wareham	d		17 20									18 20									19 20		
Holton Heath	d																						
Hamworthy	d		17 27									18 27									19 27		
Poole 4	a		17 31									18 31									19 31		
	d		17 32					17 55				18 32					18 55				19 32		
Parkstone (Dorset)	d		17 36									18 36									19 36		
Branksome	d		17 40									18 40									19 40		
Bournemouth	a		17 46					18 04				18 46					19 04				19 46		
	d		17 50					18 06		18 40		18 50					19 06		19 40		19 50		
Pokesdown	d							18 10									19 10						
Christchurch	d							18 14									19 14						
Hinton Admiral	d							18 19									19 19						
New Milton	d		18 01					18 23				19 01					19 23				20 01		
Sway	d							18 28									19 28						
Yarmouth (I.O.W.) ⛴	d	17 00				17 30					18b00				18 30					19 00			19b30
Lymington Pier ⛴	d	17 44				18 14					18 44				19 14					19 44			20 14
Lymington Town	d	17 46				18 16					18 46				19 16					19 46			20 16
Brockenhurst 3	a	17 54	18 08			18 24		18 33		18 53	18 54	19 08			19 24		19 33		19 53	19 54	20 08		20 24
	d		18 09					18 34		18 57		19 09					19 34		19 57		20 09		
Beaulieu Road	d							18 39									19 39						
Ashurst New Forest	d							18 43									19 43						
Totton	d							18 48									19 48						
Salisbury	d				18 13									19 08								20 13	
Dean	d													19 20									
Mottisfont & Dunbridge	d													19 26									
Romsey	d				18 32									19 32								20 32	
Redbridge	d				18 39									19 39								20 39	
Millbrook (Hants)	d				18 43									19 43								20 43	
Southampton Central	a		18 23		18 45			18 53	←	19 10		19 23		19 45			19 53	←	20 10		20 23	20 45	
	d		18 25		18 59 →			18 55	18 59	19 15		19 25		19 59 →			19 55	19 59	20 15		20 25	20 59 →	
St Denys	d								19 04									20 04					
Swaythling	d								19 07									20 07					
Southampton Airport Parkwy ✈	d		18 33					19 03	19 10	19 22		19 33					20 03	20 10	20 22		20 33		
Portsmouth Harbour	d						18 17									19 17							
Portsmouth & Southsea	d						18 22									19 22							
Fratton	d						18 26									19 26							
Hilsea	d						18 30									19 30							
Cosham	d						18 35									19 35							
Portchester	d						18 40									19 40							
Fareham	d						18 46									19 46							
Botley	d						18 54									19 54							
Hedge End	d						18 58									19 58							
Eastleigh 3	a						19 04	19 07	19 13							20 04	20 07	20 13					
	d							19 11	19 15								20 11	20 15					
Chandlers Ford	a								19 20									20 20					
	d								19 20									20 20					
Romsey	a								19 28									20 28					
Shawford	d							19 17															
Winchester	d		18 42					19 23		19 31		19 42					20 23		20 31		20 42		
Micheldever	d							19 32									20 32						
Basingstoke	a		18 58					19 42		19 46		19 58					20 42		20 46		20 58		
	d		19 00					19 44		19 47		20 00					20 44		20 47		21 00		
Reading 7	a									20 05									21 05				
Fleet	d																						
Farnborough (Main)	d																						
Woking	a		19 18					20 02				20 18					21 02				21 18		
Clapham Junction 10	a		19 39					20 27				20 39					21 27				21 39		
London Waterloo 15 ⊖	a		19 49					20 37				20 49					21 37				21 49		

For general notes see front of timetable
For details of catering facilities see
Directory of Train Operators

A ☕ from Bournemouth
B From 30 March
C Until 23 March
b From 16 March

Table 158

Sundays

Weymouth, Bournemouth, Lymington, Southampton and Basingstoke → London

Network Diagram - see first page of Table 158

		SW 1 ◇	SW 1 ◇	SW 1	XC 1 ◇	SW 1	SW 1	SW 1	SW 1	SW 1	GW ◇ A		GW ◇ B	SW 1	SW 1	SW 1	SW 1	SW 1	SW 1	SW 1	SW 1	SW 1	SW 1
Weymouth	d									19 58	20 09		20 40						20 58			21 58	22 58
Upwey	d									20 02	20 14		20 45						21 02			22 02	23 02
Dorchester West	a										20 22		20 53										
Dorchester South	d									20 10									21 10			22 10	23 10
Moreton (Dorset)	d									20 17									21 17			22 17	23 17
Wool	d									20 23									21 23			22 23	23 23
Wareham	d									20 30									21 30			22 30	23 30
Holton Heath	d																						
Hamworthy	d									20 37									21 37			22 37	23 37
Poole 4	a									20 41									21 41			22 41	23 41
	d		19 55							20 50									21 50			22 50	23 50
Parkstone (Dorset)	d									20 54									21 54			22 54	23 54
Branksome	d									20 57									21 57			22 57	23 57
Bournemouth	a		20 04							21 03									22 03			23 03	00 03
	d		20 06		20 40					21 06									22 06			23 06	
Pokesdown	d		20 10							21 10									22 10			23 10	
Christchurch	d		20 14							21 14									22 14			23 14	
Hinton Admiral	d		20 19							21 19									22 19			23 19	
New Milton	d		20 23							21 23									22 23			23 23	
Sway	d		20 28							21 28									22 28			23 28	
Yarmouth (I.O.W.) ⛴	d					*20 00*		*20b30*						*21 00*			*21c35*						
Lymington Pier ⛴	d					20 44		21 14						21 44			22 14						
Lymington Town	d					20 46		21 16						21 46			22 16						
Brockenhurst 3	a		20 33		20 53	20 54		21 24		21 33				21 54			22 24		22 33			23 33	
	d		20 34		20 57					21 34									22 34			23 34	
Beaulieu Road	d		20 39							21 39									22 39				
Ashurst New Forest	d		20 43							21 43									22 43			23 43	
Totton	d		20 48							21 48									22 48			23 48	
Salisbury	d						21 08																
Dean	d						21 20																
Mottisfont & Dunbridge	d						21 26																
Romsey	d						21 32											22 28					
Redbridge	d						21 39											22 35					
Millbrook (Hants)	d						21 43											22 39					
Southampton Central	a		20 53	←	21 10		21 45			21 53					←			22 41	22 53	←		23 53	
	d		20 55	20 59	21 15		21 59 →			21 55					21 59			23 05 →	22 55	23 05			
St Denys	d			21 04											22 04					23 10			
Swaythling	d			21 07											22 07					23 13			
Southampton Airport Parkwy ✈	d		21 03	21 10	21 22					22 03					22 10				23 03	23 16			
Portsmouth Harbour	d	20 17							21 17							22 17					23 17		
Portsmouth & Southsea	d	20 22							21 22							22 22					23 22		
Fratton	d	20 26							21 26							22 26					23 26		
Hilsea	d	20 30							21 30							22 30					23 30		
Cosham	d	20 35							21 35							22 35					23 35		
Portchester	d	20 40							21 40							22 40					23 40		
Fareham	d	20 46							21 46							22 46					23 46		
Botley	d	20 54							21 54							22 54					23 54		
Hedge End	d	20 58							21 58							22 58					23 58		
Eastleigh 3	a	21 04	21 07	21 13					22 04	22 07					22 13	23 04			23 08	23 19	00 04		
	d	21 11		21 15					22 11						22 15				23 11	23 21			
Chandlers Ford	a			21 20											22 20					23 26			
	d			21 20											22 20					23 26			
Romsey	a			21 28											22 31					23 33			
Shawford	d	21 17																					
Winchester	d	21 23			21 31				22 23										23 23				
Micheldever	d	21 32							22 32										23 32				
Basingstoke	a	21 42			21 46				22 42										23 42				
	d	21 44			21 47				22 44										23 43				
Reading 7	a				22 05																		
Fleet	d																						
Farnborough (Main)	d																						
Woking	a	22 02							23 02										00 02				
Clapham Junction 10	a	22 27							23 27										00 22				
London Waterloo 15 ⊖	a	22 37							23 37										00 33				

For general notes see front of timetable
For details of catering facilities see Directory of Train Operators

A Until 23 March
B From 30 March
b From 16 March
c Until 11 May

Table 158A

Mondays to Saturdays

Woking → Heathrow Railair

Express Coach Service

		SW	SW	SW	SW	SW	SW	SW		SW	SW	SW	SW	SW	SW	SW		SW	SW	SW	SW	SW	SW	SW		SW
		SX	SX	SX		SX					SO	SX		SO	SX			SO	SX		SO	SX		SO		SX
							A			B			B			B				B			A			
Woking §	d			05 30		06 00		06 30			07 00	07 00		07 30	07 30			08 00	08 00		08 30	08 30		09 00		09 00
Heathrow Terminal 4 Bus	d			06 00		06 30		07 00			07 30	07 40		08 00	08 20			08 30	08 50		09 00	09 20		09 30		09 50
Heathrow Central Bus Stn	a			06 20		06 50		07 20			07 50	08 00		08 20	08 40			08 50	09 10		09 20	09 40		09 50		10 10
	d	05 45	06 15		06 45		07 15			07 45			08 15			08 45				09 15			09 45			
Heathrow Terminal 4 Bus	a	06 00	06 30		07 00		07 30			08 00			08 30			09 00				09 30			10 00			
Woking	a	06 35	07 05		07 35		08 10			08 45			09 15			09 45				10 15			10 40			

		SW	SW	SW	SW		SW	SW	SW	SW	and at the same minutes past each hour until		SW	SW	SW	SW	SW	SW	SW		SW	SW	SW	SW	SW
			SO	SX													SO	SX			SO	SX		SO	SX
														B		C			C				C		
Woking §	d		09 30	09 30			10 00		10 30				15 00		15 30		16 00	16 00			16 30	16 30		17 00	17 00
Heathrow Terminal 4 Bus	d		10 00	10 10			10 30		11 00				15 30		16 00		16 30	16 35			17 00	17 10		17 30	17 40
Heathrow Central Bus Stn	a		10 20	10 30			10 50		11 20				15 50		16 20		16 50	16 55			17 20	17 30		17 50	18 00
	d	10 15			10 45			11 15		11 45				16 15		16 45			17 15				17 45		
Heathrow Terminal 4 Bus	a	10 30			11 00			11 30		12 00				16 30		17 00			17 30				18 00		
Woking	a	11 05			11 35			12 05		12 35				17 15		17 55			18 25				18 55		

		SW	SW	SW	SW		SW	SW	SW	SW	SW	SW	SW		SW	SW	SW	SW	SW	SW	SW		SW	SW		
			SO	SX			SO	SX		SO	SX															
		C			B																					
Woking §	d		17 30	17 30			18 00	18 00		18 30	18 30		19 00			19 30	20 00		20 30	21 00			22 00			
Heathrow Terminal 4 Bus	d		18 00	18 10			18 30	18 40		19 00	19 05		19 30			20 00	20 30		21 00	21 30			22 30			
Heathrow Central Bus Stn	a		18 20	18 30			18 50	19 00		19 20	19 25		19 50			20 20	20 50		21 20	21 50			22 50			
	d	18 15			18 45				19 15			19 45			20 15			21 00			22 00			23 00		
Heathrow Terminal 4 Bus	a	18 30			19 00				19 30			20 00			20 30			21 15			22 15			23 15		
Woking	a	19 25			19 45				20 05			20 35			21 05			21 50			22 50			23 50		

Sundays

		SW	SW	SW	SW		SW	SW	SW	SW	and at the same minutes past each hour until		SW	SW	SW	SW	SW		SW	SW	SW	SW	SW		
Woking §	d			06 30			07 00		07 30				19 00		19 30	20 00			20 30	21 00		22 00			
Heathrow Terminal 4 Bus	d			07 00			07 30		08 00				19 30		20 00	20 30			21 00	21 30		22 30			
Heathrow Central Bus Stn	a			07 20			07 50		08 20				19 50		20 20	20 50			21 20	21 50		22 50			
	d	06 45	07 15		07 45			08 15		08 45				20 15			21 00				22 00		23 00		
Heathrow Terminal 4 Bus	a	07 00	07 30		08 00			08 30		09 00				20 30			21 15				22 15		23 15		
Woking	a	07 35	08 05		08 35			09 05		09 35				21 05			21 50				22 50		23 50		

For general notes see front of timetable
For details of catering facilities see Directory of Train Operators

§ On arrival at Woking passengers should proceed to the exit on platform 5, the coach leaves from immediately outside the station.

A On Saturdays, bus arrives Woking 5 minutes earlier
B On Saturdays, bus arrives Woking 10 minutes earlier
C On Saturdays, bus arrives Woking 20 minutes earlier

Network Diagram for Table 160

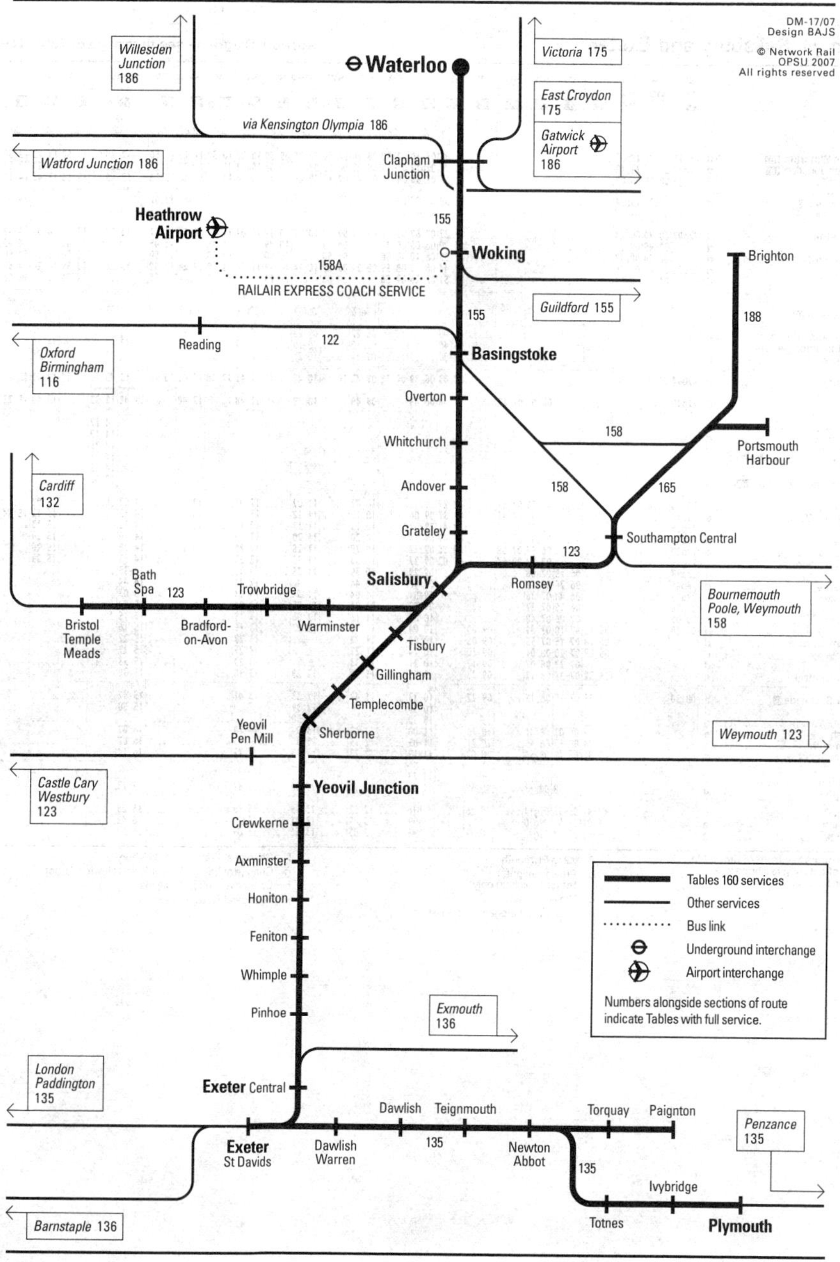
DM-17/07
Design BAJS
© Network Rail
OPSU 2007
All rights reserved
Willesden Junction 186
Waterloo
Victoria 175
East Croydon 175
Gatwick Airport 186
via Kensington Olympia 186
Watford Junction 186
Clapham Junction
Heathrow Airport
155
Woking
158A
RAILAIR EXPRESS COACH SERVICE
Guildford 155
Brighton
188
Reading
122
Oxford Birmingham 116
Basingstoke
Overton
Whitchurch
Andover
Grateley
158
Portsmouth Harbour
165
Cardiff 132
Southampton Central
123
Bath Spa
Trowbridge
Salisbury
Romsey
Bournemouth Poole, Weymouth 158
Bristol Temple Meads
Bradford-on-Avon
Warminster
Tisbury
Gillingham
Templecombe
Yeovil Pen Mill
Sherborne
Weymouth 123
Castle Cary Westbury 123
Yeovil Junction
Crewkerne
Axminster
Honiton
Feniton
Whimple
Pinhoe
Tables 160 services
Other services
Bus link
Underground interchange
Airport interchange
Numbers alongside sections of route indicate Tables with full service.
Exmouth 136
London Paddington 135
Exeter Central
Dawlish
Teignmouth
Torquay
Paignton
Penzance 135
Exeter St Davids
Dawlish Warren
135
Newton Abbot
Ivybridge
Barnstaple 136
Totnes
Plymouth

For details of Bank Holiday service alterations, please see first page of Table 149

London → Salisbury and Exeter

Network Diagram - see first page of Table 160

Miles			SW	SW	SW	SW	SW	SW	SW	SW	SW	SW	SW	SW	SW	SW	SW	SW	SW	SW	SW	SW		SW	SW	SW
			MO	MO	MX																					
			1 ◇	1	1	1	1	1	1	1	1	1 ◇	1 ◇	1 ◇	1 ◇	1 ◇	1 ◇	1 ◇	1 ◇	1 ◇	1 ◇	1 ◇		1 ◇	1 ◇	1 ◇
																						A				
			☕									☕	☕	☕	☕	☕	☕	☕	☕	☕	☕	☕		☕	☕	☕
0	**London Waterloo** 15 ⊖	d	21p15	23p35	23p35						06 30	07 10	07 50	08 20	08 50	09 20	09 50	10 20	10 50	11 20	11 50	12 20		12 50	13 20	13 50
4	Clapham Junction 10	d	21b22	23b44	23b42						06 37	07u17	07u57	08u27	08 52	09u27	09 52	10u27	10 52	11u27	11 52	12u27		12 52	13u27	13 52
24¼	Woking	d	21p46	00 08	00 03						06 57	07 36	08 16	08 46	09 16	09 46	10 16	10 46	11 16	11 46	12 16	12 46		13 16	13 46	14 16
—	Reading 7	d		23c27	23c34						06 39	07 07	08 07		09 07		10 07		11 07		12 07			13 07		14 07
47¾	**Basingstoke**	d	22p07	00 40	00 24						07 22	07 57	08 37	09 07	09 37	10 07	10 37	11 07	11 37	12 07	12 37	13 07		13 37	14 07	14 37
55½	Overton	d		00s49	00s32						07 30	08 05	08 45		09 45		10 45		11 45		12 45			13 45		14 45
59¼	Whitchurch (Hants)	d		00s54	00s37						07 35	08 10	08 50		09 50		10 50		11 50		12 50			13 50		14 50
66¼	Andover	d	22p24	01 02	00 46						07 44	08 19	08 59	09 24	09 59	10 24	10 59	11 24	11 59	12 24	12 59	13 24		13 59	14 24	14 59
72¾	Grateley	d		01s10	00s53						07 51	08 26	09 06		10 06		11 06		12 06		13 06			14 06		15 06
—	Brighton 10	d												07e06		08f03		09f03		10f03		11f03			12f03	
—	Portsmouth Harbour	d									06 00			08 22		09 22		10 22		11 22		12 22			13 22	
—	Southampton Central	d									06 46			09 10		10 10		11 10		12 10		13 10			14 10	
—	Romsey	d									07 00			09 21		10 21		11 21		12 21		13 21			14 21	
83¾	**Salisbury**	a	22p44	01 22	01 05						08 03	08 39	09 18	09 42	10 18	10 42	11 18	11 42	12 18	12 42	13 18	13 43		14 19	14 42	15 18
—		d	22p48					06 08	07 12		08 08	08 45		09 48		10 48		11 48		12 48		13 48	13 52		14 48	15 23
—	Warminster	d																					14 12			
—	Westbury	d																					14 19			
—	Trowbridge	d																					14 25			
—	Bradford-on-Avon	d																					14 31			
—	Bath Spa 7	a																					14 45			
—	Bristol Temple Meads 10	a																					15 00			
96¼	Tisbury	d	23p04					06 29	07 31		08 27			10 02		11 02		12 02		13 02		14 02			15 02	
105¼	Gillingham (Dorset)	a	23p14					06 39	07 41		08 37	09 06		10 12		11 12		12 12		13 12		14 12			15 12	15 44
—		d	23p15					06 42	07 43		08 41	09 07		10 13		11 13		12 13		13 13		14 13			15 13	
112¼	Templecombe	d	23p22					06 50	07 51		08 49	09 14		10 20		11 20		12 20		13 20		14 20			15 20	
118¼	Sherborne	d	23p30					06 57	07 58		08 56	09 22		10 28		11 28		12 28		13 28		14 28			15 28	
122¾	Yeovil Junction	a	23p35					07 03	08 04		09 02	09 27		10 33		11 33		12 33		13 33		14 33			15 33	
—		d	23p37				06 15	07 08				09 29		10 35		11 35		12 35				14 35				
131¾	Crewkerne	d	23p46				06 24	07 17				09 38		10 44				12 44				14 44				
144¾	Axminster	a	23p58				06 44	07 36				09 51		11 04		11 54		13 03				15 03				
—		d	23p58				06 55	07 37				09 52		11 04		11 55		13 04				15 04				
155	Honiton	a	00 09				07 06	07 48				10 03		11 16		12 06		13 15				15 15				
—		d	00 10			06 13	07 10	07 49		09 00		10 04		11 16		12 07		13 16				15 16				
159½	Feniton	d				06 18	07 15	07 55		09 05		10 09		11 22				13 22				15 22				
163¼	Whimple	d				06 23	07 20	08 01		09 10		10 14		11 27				13 27				15 27				
169	Pinhoe	d					07 27	08 07		09 17		10 21		11 33				13 33				15 33				
171¾	**Exeter Central**	a				06 32	07 31	08 12		09 23		10 29		11 38		12 29		13 38				15 38				
172½	**Exeter St Davids** 3	a	00 30			06 35	07 35	08 15		09 27		10 33		11 42		12 33		13 41				15 42				
—		d										10 39				12 39						15 50				
—	Dawlish Warren	a										10 50				12 50										
—	Dawlish	a				07 19	08 07	08 41		10 16		11 00		12 10		13 00		14 10				16 02				
—	Teignmouth	a				07 24	08 12	08 46		10 21		11 05		12 15		13 05		14 15				16 07				
—	Newton Abbot	a				07 31	08 19	08 53		10 02		11 12		12 22		13 13		14 22				16 14				
—	Torquay	a										11 23														
—	Paignton	a					08 38	09 13		10 59		11 31		12 41		13 50		14 42				17 13				
—	Totnes	a				07 44	08 51	09g14		10 16		11h16		12 52		13 25		15 16				16 26				
—	Ivybridge	a				08 01	09 07	09g30				13j09		13 09		13 41		16g24				16 42				
—	Plymouth	a				08 15	09 22	09g47		10 48		11h48		13 09		13 56		15 09				16 57				

For general notes see front of timetable
For details of catering facilities see Directory of Train Operators

A ☕ to Plymouth
b Previous night. Stops to pick up only
c Previous night
e Change at Fareham and Salisbury
f Change at Fratton and Salisbury
g Change at Exeter St Davids and Newton Abbot
h Change at Exeter St Davids
j Change at Newton Abbot

For details of Bank Holiday service alterations, please see first page of Table 149

London → Salisbury and Exeter

Network Diagram - see first page of Table 160

		SW	SW	SW	SW	SW	SW	SW	SW	SW	SW	SW	SW	SW	SW		SW		SW	SW	SW	SW	SW	SW		
															FX		FO			FO	FX					
		1	1 ◇ ☕	1 ◇ ☕	1	1 ◇ ☕	1 ◇ ☕	1	1 ◇ ☕	1 ◇ ☕	1 ▼ ☕	1 ▼ ☕	1 ◇ ☕	1 ◇ ☕	1 ◇ ☕		1 ◇ ☕		1 ◇ ☕	1 ◇ ☕	1 ◇ ☕	1 ◇ ☕	1 ☕	1		
London Waterloo 15 ⊖	d		14 20	14 50		15 20	15 50		16 20	16 50	17 20	17 50	18 20	18 50	19 20		19 20		19 50	20 20	20 20	21 20	22 20	23 35		
Clapham Junction 10	d		14u27	14 52		15u27	15u57		16u27	16u57	17 02		18u27	18 46	19u27		19u27		19 52	20u27	20u27	21u27	22u27	23u42		
Woking	d		14 46	15 16		15 46	16 16		16 46	17u16	17u46	18 13	18 46	19 18	19 46		19 46		20 16	20 49	20 49	21 49	22 49	00 03		
Reading 7	d			15 07			16 07			17 07		18 07		19 07					20 07	20 39	20 39	21 41	22 10	23b34		
Basingstoke	d		15 07	15 37		16 07	16 37		17 07	17 37	18 07	18 38	19 07	19 39	20 07		20 07		20 37	21 10	21 10	22 10	23 10	00 24		
Overton	d			15 45			16 45		17 15	17 45	18 15	18 47	19 15	19 47	20 15		20 15		20 45	21 18	21 18	22 18	23 18	00s32		
Whitchurch (Hants)	d			15 50			16 50		17 20	17 50	18 20	18 52	19 20	19 52	20 20		20 20		20 50	21 23	21 23	22 23	23 23	00s37		
Andover	d		15 24	15 59		16 24	16 59		17 29	17 59	18 29	19 00	19 29	20 01	20 29		20 29		20 59	21 32	21 32	22 32	23 32	00 46		
Grateley	d			16 06			17 06		17 36	18 06	18 36	19 08	19 36	20 08	20 36		20 36		21 06	21 39	21 39	22 39	23 39	00s53		
Brighton 10	d		13c03			14c03			15c03		16c03	17 00	17c03		18c08		18c08			19c03	19c03	20e30				
Portsmouth Harbour	d		14 22			15 22			16 22		17 22		18 22		19 22		19 22			20 22	20 22	21 22				
Southampton Central	d		15 10			16 10			17 10		18 10	18 40	19 10		20 10		20 10			21 19	21 19	22 22				
Romsey	d		15 21			16 21			17 21		18 21	18 51	19 21		20 21		20 21			21 30	21 30	22 33				
Salisbury	a		15 42	16 18		16 42	17 18		17 48	18 18	18 48	19 20	19 48	20 22	20 49		20 49		21 18	21 51	21 51	22 55	23 53	01 05		
	d		15 48			16 48	17 23		17 53	18 23	18 53	19 23	19 53		20 53	20 56	20 53	20 56		22 06	22 06	23 04				
Warminster	d															21 16		21 16								
Westbury	d															21 23		21 23								
Trowbridge	d															21 29		21 29								
Bradford-on-Avon	d															21 35		21 35								
Bath Spa 7	a															21 50		21 50								
Bristol Temple Meads 10	a															22 03		22 03								
Tisbury	d		16 02			17 02	17 37		18 07	18 37	19 07	19 37	20 07		21 07		21 07			22 20	22 20	23s21				
Gillingham (Dorset)	a		16 12			17 12	17 47		18 17	18 47	19 17	19 47	20 17		21 17		21 17			22 30	22 30	23s32				
	d		16 13			17 13			18 18	18 48	19 18	19 48	20 18		21 18		21 18			22 31	22 31					
Templecombe	d		16 20			17 20			18 25	18 55	19 25	19 55	20 25		21 25		21 25			22 38	22 38	23s40				
Sherborne	d		16 28			17 28			18 33	19 03	19 33	20 03	20 33		21 33		21 33			22 46	22 46	23s47				
Yeovil Junction	a		16 33			17 33			18 38	19 10	19 38	20 11	20 38		21 38		21 38			22 51	22 51	23 53				
	d		16 37						18 40		19 40		20 40		21 40		21 40			22 53	22 53					
Crewkerne	d		16 46						18 49		19 49		20 49		21 49		21 49			23 02	23 02					
Axminster	a		17 05						19 04		20 02		21 10		22 02		22 02			23 15	23 22					
	d		17 06					18 23	19 05		20 03		21 11		22 03		22 03			23 16	23 23					
Honiton	a		17 17					18 34	19 16		20 14		21 22		22 14		22 14			23 27	23 34					
	d	16 01	17 18		17 32			18 38	19 30		20 15		21 23				22 15			23 28	23 35					
Feniton	d	16 06			17 37			18 44	19 36				21 29				22 20			23 33	23 41					
Whimple	d	16 11			17 42			18 49	19 41				21 34				22 25			23 38	23 46					
Pinhoe	d	16 18			17 49			18 55	19 47				21 40				22 32			23 45	23 52					
Exeter Central	a	16 22	17 33		17 55			19 00	19 52		20 30		21 49				22 36			23 49	23 57					
Exeter St Davids 6	a	16 26	17 38		17 59			19 04	19 57		20 36		21 55				22 41			23 54	00 01					
	d		17 49																							
Dawlish Warren	a		18 04																							
Dawlish	a	17 10	18 08		18 23			19 47	20 41		21 47		22 49													
Teignmouth	a	17 15	18 13		18 28			19 52	20 47		21 52		22 54													
Newton Abbot	a	17 02	18 20		18 35			19 43	20 35		21 02		22 37				23 33									
Torquay	a		18 32																							
Paignton	a	17 41	18 40		19 26			20 25	21 20		22 26		23 28													
Totnes	a	17 16	18f21		18 48			19 57	20 49		21 16		22 51				23 46									
Ivybridge	a	17g58																								
Plymouth	a	17 48	18f52		19 20			20 25	21 17		21 48		23 22				00 18									

For general notes see front of timetable
For details of catering facilities see Directory of Train Operators

b Previous night
c Change at Fratton and Salisbury
e Change at Southampton Central and Salisbury
f Change at Exeter St Davids
g Change at Exeter St Davids and Newton Abbot

Table 160 — Saturdays

London → Salisbury and Exeter

Network Diagram - see first page of Table 160

Station	SW 1	SW 1	SW 1	SW 1	SW 1		SW 1	SW 1	SW 1 ◇	SW 1 ◇	SW 1 ◇		SW 1 ◇	SW 1 ◇	SW 1 ◇	SW 1 ◇	SW 1 ◇		SW 1 ◇	SW 1 ◇	SW 1 ◇		SW 1 ◇		SW 1 ◇
London Waterloo 15 ⊖ d	23p35							06 30	07 10	07 50	08 20		08 50	09 20	09 50	10 20	10 50		11 20	11 50	12 20		12 50		13 20
Clapham Junction 10 d	23b42							06 37	07u17	07u57	08u27		08 52	09u27	09 52	10u27	10 52		11u27	11 52	12u27		12 52		13u27
Woking d	00 03							06 57	07 36	08 16	08 46		09 16	09 46	10 16	10 46	11 16		11 46	12 16	12 46		13 16		13 46
Reading 7 d	23c34							06 39	07 07	08 07			09 07		10 07		11 07			12 07			13 07		
Basingstoke d	00 24							07 22	07 59	08 37	09 07		09 37	10 07	10 37	11 07	11 37		12 07	12 37	13 07		13 37		14 07
Overton d	00s32							07 30	08 07	08 45			09 45		10 45		11 45			12 45			13 45		
Whitchurch (Hants) d	00s37							07 35	08 12	08 50			09 50		10 50		11 50			12 50			13 50		
Andover d	00 46							07 44	08 21	08 59	09 24		09 59	10 24	10 59	11 24	11 59		12 24	12 59	13 24		13 59		14 24
Grateley d	00s53							07 51	08 28	09 06			10 06		11 06		12 06			13 06			14 06		
Brighton 10 d									05e27		07f03			08f03		09f03			10f03		11f03				12f03
Portsmouth Harbour d								06 00	07 04		08 22			09 22		10 22			11 22		12 22				13 22
Southampton Central d								06 47	07 52		09 10			10 10		11 10			12 10		13 10				14 10
Romsey d								06 59	08 09		09 21			10 21		11 21			12 21		13 21				14 21
Salisbury a	01 05							08 03	08 42	09 18	09 42		10 18	10 42	11 18	11 42	12 18		12 42	13 18	13 42		14 18		14 42
Salisbury d				06 15	07 12			08 08	08 45		09 48			10 48		11 48			12 48		13 48	13 51			14 48
Warminster d																						14 11			
Westbury d																						14 18			
Trowbridge d																						14 24			
Bradford-on-Avon d																						14 30			
Bath Spa 7 a																						14 44			
Bristol Temple Meads 10 a																						14 59			
Tisbury d				06 29	07 31			08 27			10 02			11 02		12 02					14 02				15 02
Gillingham (Dorset) a				06 39	07 41			08 37	09 06		10 12			11 12		12 12			13 09		14 12				15 12
Gillingham (Dorset) d				06 42	07 43			08 41	09 07		10 13			11 13		12 13			13 10		14 13				15 13
Templecombe d				06 50	07 51			08 49	09 14		10 20			11 20		12 20					14 20				15 20
Sherborne d				06 57	07 58			08 56	09 22		10 28			11 28		12 28					14 28				15 28
Yeovil Junction a				07 03	08 04			09 02	09 27		10 33			11 33		12 33			13 27		14 33				15 33
Yeovil Junction d			06 15	07 08					09 29		10 35			11 35		12 35			13 28		14 35				
Crewkerne d			06 24	07 17					09 38		10 44					12 44					14 44				
Axminster a			06 44	07 36					09 51		11 04			11 54		13 03					15 03				
Axminster d			06 55	07 37					09 52		11 05			11 55		13 04					15 04				
Honiton a			07 06	07 48					10 03		11 16			12 06		13 15			13 56		15 15				
Honiton d		06 13	07 10	07 49			09 00		10 04		11 30			12 07		13 16			14 00		15 16				
Feniton d		06 18	07 15	07 55			09 05		10 09		11 35					13 22					15 22				
Whimple d		06 23	07 20	08 01			09 10		10 14		11 40					13 27					15 27				
Pinhoe d			07 27	08g16			09 17		10 21		11 47					13 33					15 33				
Exeter Central a		06 32	07 31	08 20			09 23		10 28		11 51			12 25		13 38			14 18		15 38				
Exeter St Davids 6 a		06 35	07 39	08 30			09 27		10 32		11 56			12 30		13 42			14 22		15 42				
Exeter St Davids d				08 37					10 38					12 39					14 28		15 51				
Dawlish Warren a									10 49					12 50					14 39						
Dawlish a			08 07	08 49			10 11		11 03		12 44			13 03		14 11			14 43		16 03				
Teignmouth a			08 12	08 54			10 16		11 08		12 49			13 08		14 16			14 48		16 08				
Newton Abbot a			08 19	09 01			10 03		11 15		12 56			13 15		14 22			14 55		16 15				
Torquay a				09 15					11 26										15 07						
Paignton a			08 38	09 23			10 42		11 34		13 20			13 41		14 42			15 15		16 44				
Totnes a			08 51	09h59			10 16		11j15		13 16			13 28		15 16			15h16		16 27				
Ivybridge a			09 07	10h15			13k08		13h08		13 43			13 43		16k24			16h24		16 43				
Plymouth a			09 22	10h30			10 48		11j48		13 48			13 59		15 09			15h48		16 58				

For general notes see front of timetable
For details of catering facilities see Directory of Train Operators

b Previous night. Stops to pick up only
c Previous night
e Change at Fareham and Salisbury
f Change at Fratton and Salisbury
g Arr. 0807
h Change at Newton Abbot
j Change at Exeter St Davids
k Change at Exeter St Davids and Newton Abbot

Table 160

London → Salisbury and Exeter

Network Diagram - see first page of Table 160

		SW	SW	SW	SW	SW		SW	SW	SW	SW	SW		SW	SW	SW	SW	SW		SW	SW	SW	SW	SW		
		1 ◇	1	1 ◇	1 ◇	1 ◇		1 ◇	1	1	1 ◇	1 ◇		1 ◇	1 ◇	1 ◇	1 ◇	1 ◇		1 ◇	1 ◇	1 ◇	1 ◇	1		
				A																						
		☕		☕	☕	☕		☕			☕	☕		☕	☕	☕	☕	☕		☕	☕	☕	☕			
London Waterloo 15 ⊖	d	13 50		14 20	14 50	15 20		15 50			16 20	16 50		17 20	17 50	18 20	18 50	19 20		19 50	20 20	21 20	22 20	23 35		
Clapham Junction 10	d	13 52		14u27	14 52	15u27		15 52			16u27	16 52		17u27	17 52	18u27	18 52	19u27		19 52	20u27	21u27	22u27	23u42		
Woking	d	14 16		14 46	15 16	15 46		16 16			16 46	17 16		17 46	18 16	18 46	19 16	19 46		20 16	20 46	21 49	22 49	00 03		
Reading 7	d	14 07			15 07			16 07				17 07			18 07		19 07			20 07		21 39	22 39	23 07		
Basingstoke	d	14 37		15 07	15 37	16 07		16 37			17 07	17 37		18 07	18 37	19 07	19 37	20 07		20 37	21 07	22 10	23 11	00 24		
Overton	d	14 45			15 45			16 45				17 45			18 45		19 45			20 45	21 15	22 18	23 19	00s32		
Whitchurch (Hants)	d	14 50			15 50			16 50				17 50			18 50		19 50			20 50	21 20	22 23	23 24	00s37		
Andover	d	14 59		15 24	15 59	16 24		16 59			17 24	17 59		18 24	18 59	19 24	19 59	20 24		20 59	21 29	22 32	23 33	00 46		
Grateley	d	15 06			16 06			17 06				18 06			19 06		20 06			21 06	21 36	22 39	23 40	00s53		
Brighton 10	d			13b03		14b03					15b03			16b03		17b03		18b03			19b03	19c27				
Portsmouth Harbour	d			14 22		15 22					16 22			17 22		18 22		19 22			20 22					
Southampton Central	d			15 10		16 10					17 10			18 10		19 10		20 10			21 10	21 30				
Romsey	d			15 21		16 21					17 21			18 21		19 21		20 21			21 21	21 41				
Salisbury	a	15 18		15 42	16 18	16 42		17 18			17 42	18 18		18 43	19 18	19 45	20 18	20 42		21 18	21 48	22 51	23 52	01 05		
	d			15 48		16 48					17 48			18 53		19 53		20 53	20 56		22 00	23 04				
Warminster	d																		21 16							
Westbury	d																		21 23							
Trowbridge	d																		21 29							
Bradford-on-Avon	d																		21 35							
Bath Spa 7	a																		21 49							
Bristol Temple Meads 10	a																		22 05							
Tisbury	d			16 02		17 02					18 02			19 07		20 07		21 07			22 15	23s18				
Gillingham (Dorset)	a			16 12		17 12					18 12			19 17		20 17		21 17			22 25	23s29				
	d			16 13		17 13					18 13			19 18		20 18		21 18			22 26					
Templecombe	d			16 20		17 20					18 20			19 25		20 25		21 25			22 33	23s37				
Sherborne	d			16 28		17 28					18 28			19 33		20 33		21 33			22 41	23s44				
Yeovil Junction	a			16 33		17 33					18 33			19 38		20 38		21 38			22 46	23 50				
	d			16 35							18 35					20 40		21 40								
Crewkerne	d			16 44							18 44					20 49		21 49								
Axminster	a			17 03							19 03					21 10		22 02								
	d			17 04						18 23	19 04					21 11		22 03								
Honiton	a			17 15						18 34	19 15					21 22		22 14								
	d		16 01	17 16					17 30	18 38	19 30					21 23		22 15								
Feniton	d		16 06						17 35	18 43	19 35					21 29		22 20								
Whimple	d		16 11						17 40	18 48	19 40					21 34		22 25								
Pinhoe	d		16 18						17 47	18 55	19 47					21 40		22 32								
Exeter Central	a		16 23	17 32					17 52	18 59	19 51					21 47		22 36								
Exeter St Davids 6	a		16 27	17 36					17 56	19 04	19 57					21 53		22 41								
	d			17 42					18 02																	
Dawlish Warren	a								18 13																	
Dawlish	a		17 10	18 04					18 18	20e03	21 12					22f49		23g16								
Teignmouth	a		17 15	18 09					18 23	20h09	21 17					22j55		23g22								
Newton Abbot	a		17k03	18 16					18 30	20 03	20m35					23n02		23g29								
Torquay	a								18 41																	
Paignton	a		17 41						18 50	20q41	21 43															
Totnes	a		17 16	18 32					18r53	20 16	20t49					23v16		23g43								
Ivybridge	a		17w57	18 47																						
Plymouth	a		17y48	19 02					19z21	20 48	21B17					23C47		00 12								

For general notes see front of timetable
For details of catering facilities see Directory of Train Operators

- **A** To Penzance (Table 135)
- **B** From 29 March arr. 2136
- **C** From 29 March arr. 2309
- **b** Change at Fratton and Salisbury
- **c** Change at Southampton Central and Salisbury
- **e** 2 February to 22 March arr. 2014
- **f** From 29 March arr. 2316
- **g** From 29 March only
- **h** 2 February to 22 March arr. 2019
- **j** From 29 March arr. 2322
- **k** From 29 March arr. 1702
- **m** From 29 March arr. 2054
- **n** From 29 March arr. 2225
- **q** 2 February to 22 March arr. 2045
- **r** Change at Newton Abbot. From 29 March arr. 1914
- **t** From 29 March arr. 2108
- **v** From 29 March arr. 2239
- **w** Change at Exeter St Davids and Newton Abbot
- **y** From 29 March arr. 1744
- **z** Change at Newton Abbot. From 29 March arr. 1942

Table 160

Sundays

London → Salisbury and Exeter

Network Diagram - see first page of Table 160

	SW	SW	SW	SW	SW	SW	SW	SW		SW	SW	SW	SW	SW	SW A		SW B		SW	SW	SW	SW	SW
London Waterloo 15 ⊖ d	23p35			08 15	09 15	10 15	11 15	12 15		13 15	14 15	15 15	16 15	17 15	18 15		18 15		19 15	20 15	21 15	22 15	23 35
Clapham Junction 10 d	23b42			08u22	09u22	10u22	11u22	12u22		13u22	14u22	15u22	16u22	17u22	18u22		18u22		19u22	20u22	21u22	22u22	23u44
Woking d	00 03			08 47	09 47	10 46	11 46	12 46		13 46	14 46	15 46	16 46	17 46	18 46		18 46		19 46	20 46	21 46	22 46	00 08
Reading 7 d	23c07		07 27	08 27	09 27	10 27	11 27	12 27		13 27	14 27	15 27	16 27	17 27	18 27		18 27		19 27	20 27	21 27	22 27	23 27
Basingstoke d	00 24		08 09	09 08	10 08	11 07	12 07	13 07		14 07	15 07	16 07	17 07	18 07	19 07		19 07		20 07	21 07	22 07	23 07	00 40
Overton d	00s32		08 17	09 16		11 15		13 15			15 15		17 15		19 15		19 15			21 15		23 15	00s49
Whitchurch (Hants) d	00s37		08 22	09 21		11 20		13 20			15 20		17 20		19 20		19 20			21 20		23 20	00s54
Andover d	00 46		08 31	09 30	10 25	11 29	12 24	13 29		14 24	15 29	16 24	17 29	18 24	19 29		19 29		20 24	21 29	22 24	23 29	01 02
Grateley d	00s53		08 38	09 37		11 36		13 36			15 36		17 36		19 36		19 36			21 36		23 36	01s10
Brighton 10 d					07e23		09e17	11 10		11e17	12e17	13e17	14e17	15 47	16e17		16e17		17 47	18e17			
Portsmouth Harbour d					09 08		11 08			13 08	14 08	15 08	16 08	17 08	18 08		18 08		19 08	20 08			
Southampton Central d					09 54		11 54	12 54		13 54	14 54	15 54	16 54	17 54	18 54		18 54		19 54	20 54			
Romsey d					10 05		12 06	13 06		14 06	15 06	16 06	17 06	18 06	19 06		19 06		20 06	21 06			
Salisbury a	01 05		08 50	09 50	10 41	11 48	12 40	13 48		14 40	15 48	16 40	17 48	18 40	19 48		19 48		20 40	21 48	22 44	23 48	01 22
d		07 10	08 54	09 54	10 50	11 54	12 50	13 54	13 58	14 50	15 54	16 54	17 54	18 50	19 54	19 58	19 54	19 58	20 54	21 54	22 48		
Warminster d									14 18							20 18		20 18					
Westbury d									14 25							20 32		20 25					
Trowbridge d									14 32							20 38		20 31					
Bradford-on-Avon d									14 38							20 44		20 37					
Bath Spa 7 a									14 52							20 59		20 51					
Bristol Temple Meads 10 a									15 06							21 16		21 08					
Tisbury d		07 24	09 08	10 08	11 04	12 08	13 04	14 08		15 04	16 08	17 08	18 08	19 04	20 08		20 08		21 08	22 08	23 04		
Gillingham (Dorset) a		07 34	09 18	10 18	11 14	12 18	13 14	14 18		15 14	16 18	17 18	18 18	19 14	20 18		20 18		21 18	22 18	23 14		
d		07 35	09 19	10 19	11 15	12 19	13 15	14 19		15 15	16 19	17 19	18 19	19 15	20 19		20 19		21 19	22 19	23 15		
Templecombe d		07 42	09 26	10 26	11 22	12 26	13 22	14 26		15 22	16 26	17 26	18 26	19 22	20 26		20 26		21 26	22 26	23 22		
Sherborne d		07 50	09 34	10 34	11 30	12 34	13 30	14 34		15 30	16 34	17 34	18 34	19 30	20 34		20 34		21 34	22 34	23 30		
Yeovil Junction a		07 55	09 39	10 39	11 35	12 39	13 35	14 39		15 35	16 39	17 39	18 40	19 35	20 39		20 39		21 40	22 39	23 35		
d		07 57	09 41	10 41	11 40		13 40			15 40		17 40		19 40					21 40		23 37		
Crewkerne d		08 06	09 50		11 49		13 49			15 49		17 49		19 49					21 49		23 46		
Axminster a		08 19	10 10	11 00	12 10		14 10			16 10		18 10		20 12					22 10		23 58		
d		08 20	10 11	11 01	12 11		14 11			16 11		18 11		20 13					22 11		23 58		
Honiton a		08 31	10 22	11 12	12 22		14 22			16 22		18 22		20 24					22 22		00 09		
d		08 35	10 23	11 13	12 23		14 23			16 23		18 23		20 25					22 23		00 10		
Feniton d		08 41	10 28		12 28		14 28			16 28		18 28		20 31					22 28				
Whimple d		08 46	10 33		12 33		14 33			16 33		18 33		20 36					22 33				
Pinhoe d			10 40		12 40																		
Exeter Central a		08 54	10 44	11 28	12 44		14 42			16 42		18 42		20 44					22 42				
Exeter St Davids 6 a		08 59	10 49	11 32	12 49		14 46			16 46		18 46		20 49					22 46		00 30		
d			10 56	11 40	12 55		14 52			16 57				20 55									
Dawlish Warren a																							
Dawlish a		09 44	11 11	13f00	13 12		15 29			17 09		20g24		21 07									
Teignmouth a		09 49	11 16	13h06	13 19		15 34			17 14		20j29		21 12									
Newton Abbot a		09 56	11 23	12 01	13 26		15 19			17 22		19k39		21 19									
Torquay a			11 34		13 41		15 30			17 35				21 30									
Paignton a		10 15	11 42	12 47	13 49		15 38			17 43		20m55		21 38									
Totnes a		10 30	11n47	12 17	14q16		16r00			17t53		19v53		22w01									
Ivybridge a		12y32		12 32	17z09		17C09																
Plymouth a		10 59	12D15	12 47	14E11		16G05			18H21		20J21		22K30									

For general notes see front of timetable
For details of catering facilities see Directory of Train Operators

A Until 27 January and from 30 March.
B 3 February to 23 March.
C Change at Newton Abbot
D Until 27 January change at Newton Abbot. 3 February to 23 March arr. 1238, change at Newton Abbot. From 30 March arr. 1209, change at Teignmouth
E Until 27 January change at Exeter St Davids. 3 February to 23 March arr. 1419, change at Exeter St Davids. From 30 March arr. 1448, change at Newton Abbot
G Change at Newton Abbot. 3 February to 23 March arr. 1636. From 30 March arr. 1607
H Change at Newton Abbot. 3 February to 23 March arr. 1813. From 30 March arr. 1837
J 3 February to 23 March arr. 2029. From 30 March arr. 1955
K Change at Newton Abbot. 3 February to 23 March arr. 2239. From 30 March arr. 2248
b Previous night. Stops to pick up only
c Previous night
e Change at Fratton and Salisbury
f 3 February to 23 March arr. 1306. From 30 March arr. 1307
g From 30 March arr. 1915
h 3 February to 23 March arr. 1312. From 30 March arr. 1313
j From 30 March arr. 1920
k 3 February to 23 March arr. 1947. From 30 March arr. 1912
m From 30 March arr. 1946
n Until 27 January change at Newton Abbot. 3 February to 23 March arr. 1210, change at Newton Abbot. From 30 March arr. 1141, change at Teignmouth
q Change at Newton Abbot. 3 February to 23 March arr. 1408
r Change at Newton Abbot. 3 February to 23 March arr. 1608. From 30 March arr. 1616
t Change at Newton Abbot. 3 February to 23 March arr. 1741. From 30 March arr. 1809
v 3 February to 23 March arr. 2001. From 30 March arr. 2002
w Change at Newton Abbot. 3 February to 23 March arr. 2210. From 30 March arr. 2216
y Change at Exeter St Davids and Newton Abbot
z Until 27 January and from 30 March only. Until 27 January change at Dawlish, Teignmouth and Newton Abbot. From 30 March change at Dawlish and Teignmouth

Table 160

For details of Bank Holiday service alterations, please see first page of Table 149

Exeter and Salisbury → London

Network Diagram - see first page of Table 160

Miles	Station		SW	SW	SW	SW	SW	SW	SW	SW	SW	SW	SW	SW	SW	SW	SW	SW	SW	SW	SW	SW	SW
			MO 1	1 ☕	1 ◇ ☕	1 ▼ ☕	1 ▼ ☕	1 ◇ ☕	1 ◇ ☕	1 ◇ ☕	1 ◇ ☕	1 ◇ ☕	1	1 ◇ ☕	1 ◇	1 ◇ ☕	1 ◇ ☕	1 ◇ ☕	1 ◇ ☕	1 ◇ ☕	1 ◇ ☕	1 ◇ ☕	1 ◇ ☕
—	Plymouth	d									05 24		06 55							08 55			
—	Ivybridge	d																		08b25			
—	Totnes	d									05 51		07 05							09 22			
—	Paignton	d	22p10										07b09							09b14			
—	Torquay	d	22p16										07b14							09b19			
—	Newton Abbot	d	22p28								06 04		07 30			07 32				09 35			
—	Teignmouth	d	22p35								06 11		07 15							09 14			
—	Dawlish	d	22p40								06 17		07 20							09 19			
—	Dawlish Warren	d	22p44																				
0	**Exeter St Davids** 6	a	22p55																				
—		d	23p10					05 10			06 41		08 00			08 25				10 10			
¾	**Exeter Central**	d	23p14					05 14			06 44		08 05			08 30				10 14			
3½	Pinhoe	d						05 19			06 50		08 11							10 21			
9¼	Whimple	d						05 26			06 57		08 18							10 28			
13	Feniton	d						05 31			07 02		08 23							10 33			
17½	Honiton	a	23c29					05 37			07 09		08 29			08 45				10 39			
—		d						05 38	06 20		07 12					08 46				10 40			
27¾	Axminster	a	23c40					05 48	06 30		07 22					08 56				10 50			
—		d						05 49	06 31		07 23					08 57				10 51			
40¾	Crewkerne	d	00s04					06 02	06 44		07 36					09 10				11 04			
49¾	Yeovil Junction	a	00s13					06 11	06 52		07 45					09 19				11 13			
—		d				05 15	05 50	06 20	06 54	07 20	07 50	08 20				09 20		10 20		11 20		12 20	
54¼	Sherborne	d				05 21	05 56	06 26	07 00	07 26	07 56	08 26				09 26		10 26		11 26		12 26	
60¼	Templecombe	d				05 29	06 04	06 34	07 08	07 34	08 04	08 34				09 34		10 34		11 34		12 34	
67¼	Gillingham (Dorset)	a				05 36	06 11	06 41	07 15	07 43	08 11	08 41				09 41		10 41		11 41		12 41	
—		d				05 37	06 12	06 42	07 16	07 44	08 12	08 42				09 42		10 42		11 42		12 42	
76¼	Tisbury	d				05 47	06 24	06 52	07 26	07 54	08 22	08 52				09 52		10 52		11 52		12 52	
—	Bristol Temple Meads 10	d													08 50								
—	Bath Spa 7	d													09 05								
—	Bradford-on-Avon	d													09 20								
—	Trowbridge	d													09 27								
—	Westbury	d													09 39								
—	Warminster	d													09 46								
88¾	**Salisbury**	a	00 50			06 02	06 39	07 07	07 40	08 09	08 37	09 15			10 09	10 15		11 15		12 15		13 15	
—		d		05 15	05 45	06 08	06 45	07 15	07 45	08 15	08 45	09 20		09 45		10 20	10 45	11 20	11 45	12 20	12 45	13 20	13 45
—	Romsey	a				06 38	07 30	07 56		08 50		09 50				10 48		11 50		12 50		13 50	
—	Southampton Central	a				06 49	07 41	08 10		09 02		10 02				11 01		12 02		13 02		14 02	
—	Portsmouth Harbour	a				07 45	08 30			09 52		10 52				11 50		12 52		13 52		14 52	
—	Brighton 10	a				09e19	09f48	10g18		11e18		12e18				13e18		14e18		15e18		16 14	
99¾	Grateley	d		05 27	05 57	06 20	06 57	07 27	07 57	08 27	08 57			09 57			10 57		11 57		12 57		13 57
106	Andover	d		05 35	06 04	06 28	07 05	07 35	08 05	08 35	09 04	09 37		10 04		10 37	11 04	11 37	12 04	12 37	13 04	13 37	14 04
113¼	Whitchurch (Hants)	d		05 43	06 12	06 36	07 13	07 43	08 13	08 43	09 12			10 12			11 12		12 12		13 12		14 12
117	Overton	d		05 49	06 18	06 42	07 19	07 49	08 19	08 49	09 18			10 18			11 18		12 18		13 18		14 18
124¾	**Basingstoke**	a		05 58	06 27	06 51	07 28	07 58	08 28	08 58	09 27	09 54		10 27		10 55	11 27	11 54	12 27	12 54	13 27	13 54	14 28
—	Reading 7	a		06 30	07 00	07 30	08 00	08 30	09 00	09 30	10 00	10 30		11 00		11 30		12 31	13 00	13 30	14 00	14 30	15 00
148¼	Woking	a		06 18	06 49	07 11	08 05	08 18	08 48	09 18	09 49	10 15		10 49		11 15	11 49	12 15	12 49	13 15	13 49	14 15	14 49
168¼	Clapham Junction 10	a		06 38	07 15	07 31	09 14	09 03	09 14	09 38	10 10	10 36		11h12		11 36		12 36	13h12	13 36	14h12	14 36	15h12
172½	**London Waterloo** 15 ⊖	a		06 49	07 19	07 44	08 14	08 46	09 17	09 51	10 19	10 49		11 19		11 49	12 19	12 49	13 19	13 49	14 19	14 49	15 19

For general notes see front of timetable
For details of catering facilities see Directory of Train Operators

- b Change at Newton Abbot and Exeter St Davids
- c Previous night. Stops to set down only
- e Change at Salisbury and Fareham
- f Change at Salisbury and Fratton
- g Change at Salisbury and Southampton Central
- h Change at Basingstoke

For details of Bank Holiday service alterations, please see first page of Table 149

Exeter and Salisbury → London

Network Diagram - see first page of Table 160

		SW	SW	SW	SW	SW	SW	SW	SW	SW	SW	SW	SW	SW	SW	SW	SW	SW	SW	SW	SW FX	SW FO
		1 ◇ ☕	1 ◇ ☕	1 ◇ ☕	1 ◇ ☕	1 ◇ ☕	1	1 ◇ ☕	1 ◇	1 ◇ ☕	1 ◇ ☕	1 ◇ ☕	1	1	1 ◇ ☕	1 ◇ ☕	1 ◇ ☕	1 ◇	1	1	1	1
Plymouth	d	10 45		12b25		12 55	14 25					14 47	15 25	16 25			17 00	17 48	18b43	19 35		21 13
Ivybridge	d			11c25		11 25	13 48					15 02	15e26				16e59	18 03	18b58			21 29
Totnes	d	10 50		12b50		13 22	14 50					15 16	15 50	16 50			17 27	18 17	19b12	20 02		21 43
Paignton	d	10 25		12 34		13e14	14 25					15e19	15e43	16 27			17e19	18e21	19 10	19 30	20 30	21e28
Torquay	d	10 30		12 40		13e19	14 30					15e24	15e46	16 32			17e24	18e26	19 16	19 35	20 35	21e34
Newton Abbot	d	11 03		12 53		13 35	15 03					15 29	16 03	17 03			17 40	18 30	19 28	20 15	20 48	21 55
Teignmouth	d	10 50		13 00			14 50					15 36	15 51	16 51				18 37	19 35	19 55	20 55	22 02
Dawlish	d	10 55		13 05			14 55					15 41	15 56	16 56				18 42	19 40	20 00	21 00	22 07
Dawlish Warren	d			13 15								15 45						18 46	19 44			
Exeter St Davids 6	a			13 26								15 56						18 57	19 59			
	d	12 10		13 35		14 10	15 30					16 10	16 36	17 40			18 10	19 10	20 15	21 00	22 30	22 57
Exeter Central	d	12 14		13 39		14 14	15 34					16 14	16 40	17 44			18 14	19 14	20 19	21 04	22 34	23 01
Pinhoe	d	12 19				14 19	15 39					16 19	16 49	17 49			18 19		20f27		22 39	23 06
Whimple	d	12 26				14 26	15 46					16 26	16 56	17 56			18 26		20 34		22 46	23 13
Feniton	d	12 31				14 31	15 51					16 31	17 01	18 01			18 31		20 39		22 51	23 18
Honiton	a	12 37		13 54		14 37	15 57					16 37	17 07	18 07			18 38	19 30	20 45	21 20	22 57	23 25
	d	12 38		13 57		14 38						16 38		18 08			18 39	19 31	20 46	21 23	22 58	23 31
Axminster	a	12 48		14 07		14 48						16 48		18 18			18 49	19 41	20 56	21 33	23 08	23 41
	d	12 49		14 08		14 49						16 49					18 50	19 42	20 57	21 45	23 09	23 42
Crewkerne	d	13 03				15 03						17 05					19 10	20 08	21 10	22 08	23 22	23 55
Yeovil Junction	a	13 12		14 27		15 12						17 14					19 18	20 16	21 19	22 16	23 31	00 05
	d	13 20	13 50	14 28		15 20				16 20		17 22				18 20	19 20	20 20	21 20	22 24	23 34	00 05
Sherborne	d	13 26	13 56			15 26				16 26		17 28				18 26	19 26	20 26	21 26	22 30		
Templecombe	d	13 34				15 34				16 34		17 36				18 34	19 34	20 34	21 34	22 43		
Gillingham (Dorset)	a	13 41	14 09	14 44		15 41				16 41		17 43				18 41	19 41	20 41	21 41	22 50		
	d	13 42	14 13	14 45		15 45		16 15		16 42		17 48				18 48	19 48	20 42	21 42	22 51		
Tisbury	d	13 52		14 55		15 55		16 25		16 52		17 58				18 58	19 59	20 52	21 52	23 01		
Bristol Temple Meads 10	d								15 52													
Bath Spa 7	d								16 06													
Bradford-on-Avon	d								16 22													
Trowbridge	d								16 28													
Westbury	d								16 39													
Warminster	d								16 47													
Salisbury	a	14 15	14 35	15 15		16 15		16 40	17 09	17 15		18 20				19 21	20 20	21 20	22 08	23 15	00 29	00 40
	d	14 20	14 45	15 20	15 45	16 20		16 45	17 20		17 45	18 25			18 45	19 25	20 25	21 25	22 25			
Romsey	a	14 50		15 50		16 50			17 50							19 50	20 50	21 50	22 50			
Southampton Central	a	15 02		16 02		17 02			18 04							20 03	21 03	22 04	23 04			
Portsmouth Harbour	a	15 52		16 57		17 52			18 57							20 49	21 49	23 04	23 52			
Brighton 10	a	17g18		18g18		19g18			20g18							22g22	23h18					
Grateley	d		14 57		15 57	16 32		16 57			17 57				18 57	19 37	20 37	21 37	22 37			
Andover	d	14 37	15 04	15 37	16 04	16 39		17 04	17 37		18 04	18 42			19 04	19 44	20 44	21 44	22 44			
Whitchurch (Hants)	d		15 12		16 12			17 12			18 12				19 12	19 52	20 52	21 52	22 52			
Overton	d		15 18		16 18			17 18			18 18				19 18	19 58	20 58	21 58	22 58			
Basingstoke	a	14 54	15 27	15 54	16 27	16 56		17 27	17 54		18 27	18 59			19 27	20 08	21 08	22 08	23 07			
Reading 7	a	15 31	16 00	16 30	17 00	17 30		18 00	18 31		19 00	19 31			20 00	21 00	22 04	22 44	23 53			
Woking	a	15 15	15 49	16 15	16 49	17 16		17 49	18 15		18 49	19 19			19 49	20 29	21 29	22 28	23 30			
Clapham Junction 10	a	15 36	16j12	16 36	17j12	17 36		18j12	18 36		19j12	19 40			20j12	20 52	21 52	22 48	23 55			
London Waterloo 15	⊖ a	15 49	16 19	16 49	17 19	17 45		18 17	18 45		19 19	19 49			20 19	21 00	22 04	22 57	00 04			

For general notes see front of timetable
For details of catering facilities see Directory of Train Operators

b Change at Exeter St Davids
c Change at Newton Abbot
e Change at Newton Abbot and Exeter St Davids
f Arr. 2024
g Change at Salisbury and Fareham
h Change at Salisbury and Fratton
j Change at Basingstoke

Exeter and Salisbury → London

Network Diagram - see first page of Table 160

Station		SW 1	SW 1 ☕	SW 1◇ ☕	SW 1◇ ☕	SW 1◇ ☕	SW 1◇ ☕	SW 1◇ ☕	SW 1◇ ☕	SW 1◇ ☕	SW 1◇ ☕	SW 1	SW 1◇ ☕	SW 1◇	SW 1◇ ☕	SW 1◇ ☕	SW 1◇ ☕	SW 1◇ ☕	SW 1◇ ☕	SW 1◇ ☕	SW 1◇ ☕	SW 1◇ ☕
Plymouth	d											06 55							08 25		09b25	
Ivybridge	d																		08 25		08b25	
Totnes	d											06 50							08 50		09b50	
Paignton	d											07c08			07e17				08 13		10 12	
Torquay	d											07c13							08 18		10 18	
Newton Abbot	d											07 31							09 03		10 31	
Teignmouth	d											07 18							08 46		10 38	
Dawlish	d											07 23							08 51		10 43	
Dawlish Warren	d																				10 47	
Exeter St Davids 6	a																				10 58	
	d	22p57					05 10			06 41		08 00			08 25				10 10		11 08	
Exeter Central	d	23p01					05 14			06 45		08 08			08 30				10 14		11 12	
Pinhoe	d	23p06					05 19			06 50		08 13							10 21			
Whimple	d	23p13					05 26			06 57		08 20							10 28			
Feniton	d	23p18					05 31			07 02		08 25							10 33			
Honiton	a	23p25					05 37			07 08		08 31			08 45				10 39		11 27	
	d	23p31					05 38	06 20		07 12					08 46				10 40		11 28	
Axminster	a	23p41					05 48	06 30		07 22					08 56				10 50		11 38	
	d	23p42					05 49	06 31		07 23					08 57				10 51		11 39	
Crewkerne	d	23p55					06 02	06 44		07 36					09 10				11 04		12 00	
Yeovil Junction	a	00 05					06 11	06 52		07 45					09 19				11 13		12 09	
	d	00 05					06 20	06 54		07 50	08 20				09 20		10 20		11 20		12 20	
Sherborne	d						06 26	07 00		07 56	08 26				09 26		10 26		11 26		12 26	
Templecombe	d						06 34	07 08		08 04	08 34				09 34		10 34		11 34		12 34	
Gillingham (Dorset)	a						06 41	07 15		08 11	08 41				09 41		10 41		11 41		12 41	
	d						06 42	07 16		08 12	08 42				09 42		10 42		11 42		12 42	
Tisbury	d						06 52	07 26		08 22	08 52				09 52		10 52		11 52		12 52	
Bristol Temple Meads 10	d													08 50								
Bath Spa 7	d													09 05								
Bradford-on-Avon	d													09 20								
Trowbridge	d													09 27								
Westbury	d													09 39								
Warminster	d													09 46								
Salisbury	a	00 40					07 10	07 40		08 37	09 15			10 09	10 15		11 15		12 15		13 15	
	d		05 15	05 45	06 20	06 45	07 20	07 45	08 20	08 45	09 20		09 45		10 20	10 45	11 20	11 45	12 20	12 45	13 20	13 45
Romsey	a						07 42	08 51			09 51				10 50		11 51		12 51		13 51	
Southampton Central	a						08 02	09 02			10 02				11 02		12 02		13 02		14 02	
Portsmouth Harbour	a						08 49	09 49			10 49				11 49		12 49		13 49		14 49	
Brighton 10	a						10f18	11f18			12f18				13f18		14f18		15f18		16 14	
Grateley	d		05 27	05 57		06 57		07 57		08 57			09 57			10 57		11 57		12 57		13 57
Andover	d		05 35	06 04	06 37	07 04	07 37	08 04	08 37	09 04	09 37		10 04		10 37	11 04	11 37	12 04	12 37	13 04	13 37	14 04
Whitchurch (Hants)	d		05 43	06 12		07 12		08 12		09 12			10 12			11 12		12 12		13 12		14 12
Overton	d		05 49	06 18		07 18		08 18		09 18			10 18			11 18		12 18		13 18		14 18
Basingstoke	a		05 58	06 27	06 54	07 27	07 54	08 27	08 54	09 27	09 54		10 27		10 55	11 27	11 54	12 27	12 54	13 27	13 54	14 27
Reading 7	a			07 00	07 31	08 00	08 31	09 00	09 31	10 00	10 31		11 00		11 31		12 31	13 00	13 31	14 00	14 31	15 00
Woking	a		06 18	06 49	07 15	07 49	08 17	08 49	09 15	09 49	10 15		10 49		11 15	11 49	12 15	12 49	13 15	13 49	14 15	14 49
Clapham Junction 10	a		06 38	07 23	07 36	08 30	08 37	09g12	09 36	10g12	10 36		11g12		11 36		12 36	13g12	13 36	14g12	14 36	15g12
London Waterloo 15 ⊖	a		06 49	07 19	07 49	08 19	08 49	09 19	09 49	10 19	10 49		11 19		11 49	12 19	12 49	13 19	13 49	14 19	14 49	15 19

For general notes see front of timetable
For details of catering facilities see
Directory of Train Operators

b Change at Newton Abbot
c Change at Newton Abbot and Exeter St Davids
e Until 26 January only
f Change at Salisbury and Fareham
g Change at Basingstoke

Table 160

Exeter and Salisbury → London

Network Diagram - see first page of Table 160

		SW 1◇ ☕	SW 1◇ ☕	SW 1◇ ☕	SW 1◇ ☕	SW 1◇ ☕	SW 1	SW 1◇ ☕	SW 1◇	SW 1◇ ☕	SW 1◇ ☕	SW 1◇ ☕	SW 1	SW 1	SW 1◇ ☕	SW 1◇ ☕	SW 1◇ ☕	SW 1◇	SW 1	SW 1	SW 1
Plymouth	d	10 46		12b25		12 55	14 25					14 50	15c25	16 25			16 54	17 42	18c25	18 25	21 18
Ivybridge	d			11c25		11e25						15 05	15c26	15e26			16e49	17 57		17e57	21 33
Totnes	d	10 50		12c27		13 22	14 50					15 19	15c50	16 50			17e03	18 11	18c50	18 50	21 47
Paignton	d	10 46		12 34		12 25	14 25					14 53	15 52	16 19				17 52	19 14	19 22	21 50
Torquay	d	10 51		12 40		12 31	14 30					14 58	15 58	16 24				17 57	19 20	19 27	21 55
Newton Abbot	d	11 22		12 53		13 35	15 03					15 32	16 10	17 03			17 31	18 24	19 32	19 40	22 08
Teignmouth	d	11 14		13 00			14 49					15 39	16 17	16 50				18 31	19 39	19 47	22 15
Dawlish	d	11 19		13 05			14 54					15 44	16 22	16 55				18 36	19 44	19 52	22 20
Dawlish Warren	d			13 15								15 48						18 48	19 49		
Exeter St Davids 6	a			13 26								15 59	16 35					19 00	20 00		
	d	12 10		13 35		14 10	15 30					16 10	16 40	17 40			18 10	19 10	20 15	21 00	22 57
Exeter Central	d	12 14		13 39		14 14	15 34					16 14	16 44	17 44			18 14	19 14	20 19	21 04	23 01
Pinhoe	d	12 19				14 19	15 39					16 19	16 49	17 49			18 19		20f27		23 06
Whimple	d	12 26				14 26	15 46					16 26	16 56	17 56			18 26		20 34		23 13
Feniton	d	12 31				14 31	15 51					16 31	17 01	18 01			18 31		20 39		23 18
Honiton	a	12 37		13 54		14 37	15 57					16 37	17 07	18 07			18 37	19 29	20 45	21 19	23 24
	d	12 38		13 57		14 38						16 38		18 08			18 38	19 30	20 46	21 23	23 28
Axminster	a	12 48		14 07		14 48						16 48		18 18			18 48	19 40	20 56	21 33	23 38
	d	12 49		14 08		14 49						16 49					18 49	19 41	20 57	21 46	23 39
Crewkerne	d	13 03				15 03						17 03					19 03	19 54	21 10	22 09	23 52
Yeovil Junction	a	13 12		14 27		15 12						17 12					19 12	20 03	21 19	22 17	00 01
	d	13 20		14 28		15 20				16 20		17 20				18 20	19 20	20 20	21 20	22 24	00 02
Sherborne	d	13 26				15 26				16 26		17 26				18 26	19 26	20 26	21 27	22 30	
Templecombe	d	13 34				15 34				16 34		17 34				18 34	19 34	20 34	21 34	22 38	
Gillingham (Dorset)	a	13 41		14 44		15 41				16 41		17 41				18 41	19 41	20 41	21 41	22 45	
	d	13 42		14 45		15 42				16 42		17 42				18 42	19 42	20 42	21 42	22 46	
Tisbury	d	13 52		14 55		15 52				16 52		17 52				18 52	19 52	20 52	21 53	22 56	
Bristol Temple Meads 10	d								15 52												
Bath Spa 7	d								16 04												
Bradford-on-Avon	d								16 20												
Trowbridge	d								16 26												
Westbury	d								16 39												
Warminster	d								16 47												
Salisbury	a	14 15		15 15		16 15			17 09	17 15		18 15				19 21	20 20	21 20	22 07	23 12	00 36
	d	14 20	14 45	15 20	15 45	16 20		16 45	17 20		17 45	18 20			18 45	19 25	20 25	21 25	22 25		
Romsey	a	14 51		15 51		16 51			17 51			18 52				19g51	20 51	21 51	22 50		
Southampton Central	a	15 02		16 02		17 02			18 02			19 03				20h02	21 02	22 02	23 02		
Portsmouth Harbour	a	15 49		16 49		17 49			18 49			19 49				20j49	21 49	22 49	23 48		
Brighton 10	a	17k18		18k18		19k18			20k20			21m18				22m22	23n18	00n25			
Grateley	d		14 57		15 57			16 57			17 57				18 57	19 37	20 37	21 37	22 37		
Andover	d	14 37	15 04	15 37	16 04	16 37		17 04	17 37		18 04	18 37			19 04	19 44	20 44	21 44	22 44		
Whitchurch (Hants)	d		15 12		16 12			17 12			18 12				19 12	19 52	20 52	21 52	22 52		
Overton	d		15 18		16 18			17 18			18 18				19 18	19 58	20 58	21 58	22 58		
Basingstoke	a	14 54	15 27	15 54	16 27	16 54		17 27	17 54		18 27	18 54			19 27	20 08	21 08	22 08	23 07		
Reading 7	a	15 31	16 00	16 31	17 00	17 31		18 00	18 31		19 00	19 31			20 00	21 00	22 00	23 00	00 01		
Woking	a	15 15	15 49	16 15	16 49	17 15		17 49	18 15		18 49	19 15			19 49	20 29	21 29	22 28	23 32		
Clapham Junction 10	a	15 36	16q12	16 36	17q12	17 36		18q12	18 36		19q12	19 36			20q12	20 52	21 52	22 48	23 57		
London Waterloo 15	⊖ a	15 49	16 19	16 49	17 19	17 49		18 19	18 49		19 19	19 49			20 26	21 04	22 04	22 57	00 07		

For general notes see front of timetable
For details of catering facilities see Directory of Train Operators

b Change at Exeter St Davids
c Change at Newton Abbot
e Change at Newton Abbot and Exeter St Davids
f Arr. 2024
g From 29 March arr. 1959
h From 29 March arr. 2018
j From 29 March arr. 2149
k Change at Salisbury and Fareham
m Change at Salisbury and Southampton Central
n Change at Salisbury and Fratton
q Change at Basingstoke

Table 160

Sundays

Exeter and Salisbury → London

Network Diagram - see first page of Table 160

	SW	SW	SW	SW	SW	SW	SW	SW	SW	SW	SW	SW	SW	SW	SW	SW	SW	SW	SW	SW	SW	SW
	1	1◇	1◇	1◇	1◇	1◇	1◇	1◇	1◇	1◇	1◇	1◇	1◇	1◇	1◇	1◇	1◇	1◇	1◇	1	1	1
																	A					
		☕	☕	☕	☕	☕	☕	☕	☕	☕	☕	☕		☕	☕		☕	☕	☕			
Plymouth d									09 50		11b45			14 06	15c25		16 02		18e10		19 55	21b15
Ivybridge d														14 21		16f17	16 17		17b24		17g24	
Totnes d									10h17		12b15			14 35		16f31	16 31		18j40		19k45	21b42
Paignton d											12 25			14 20	15 27	16 10			18 23		19 50	22 10
Torquay d											12 31				15 33	16 16			18 29		19 55	22 16
Newton Abbot d									10m30		12 44			14 47	15 49	16 32	16 43		18 41		20 32	22 28
Teignmouth d									09 33		12 51			14 54	15 56	16 16			18 48		20 15	22 35
Dawlish d									09 38		12 58			14 59	16 01	16n21			18 53		20 20	22 40
Dawlish Warren d															16 17				18 57			22 44
Exeter St Davids 6 a											13 13			15 14	16 28	16 53	17 05		19 08			22 55
d	22p57						09 20		11 20		13 18			15 18	16 33	17 18			19 20		21 20	23 10
Exeter Central d	23p01						09 24		11 24		13 22			15 23	16 37	17 23			19 24		21 24	23 14
Pinhoe d	23p06														16 42				19 29			
Whimple d	23p13						09 33		11 33		13 33			15 33		17 33			19 36		21 33	
Feniton d	23p18						09 39		11 39		13 39			15 39		17 39			19 41		21 39	
Honiton a	23p24						09 45		11 45		13 45			15 45	16 54	17 45			19 47		21 45	23s29
d	23p28					08 46	09 46		11 46		13 46			15 46	16 55	17 46			19 48		21 46	
Axminster a	23p38					08 56	09 56		11 56		13 56			15 56	17 05	17 56			19 58		21 56	23s40
d	23p39					08 57	09 57		11 57		13 57			15 57	17 06	17 57			19 59		21 57	
Crewkerne d	23p52					09 10	10 10		12 10		14 10			16 10	17 19	18 10			20 12		22 10	00s04
Yeovil Junction a	00 01					09 18	10 18		12 18		14 18			16 18	17 28	18 18			20 21		22 18	00s13
d	00 02			07 32		09 25	10 25	11 25	12 25	13 25	14 25	15 25		16 25	17 29	18 25		19 25	20 25	21 25	22 25	
Sherborne d				07 38		09 31	10 31	11 31	12 31	13 31	14 31	15 31		16 31	17 36	18 31		19 31	20 31	21 31	22 31	
Templecombe d				07 47		09 39	10 39	11 39	12 39	13 39	14 39	15 39		16 39	17 43	18 39		19 39	20 39	21 39	22 39	
Gillingham (Dorset) a				07 54		09 46	10 46	11 46	12 46	13 46	14 46	15 46		16 46	17 50	18 46		19 46	20 46	21 46	22 46	
d				07 55		09 47	10 47	11 47	12 47	13 47	14 47	15 47		16 47	17 51	18 47		19 47	20 47	21 47	22 47	
Tisbury d				08 05		09 57	10 57	11 57	12 57	13 57	14 57	15 57		16 57	18 02	18 57		19 57	20 57	21 57	22 57	
Bristol Temple Meads 10 d													16 04									
Bath Spa 7 d													16 20									
Bradford-on-Avon d													16 31									
Trowbridge d													16 37									
Westbury d													16 46									
Warminster d													16 53									
Salisbury a	00 36			08 20		10 21	11 17	12 21	13 17	14 21	15 18	16 21	17 16	17 21	18 22	19 17		20 21	21 21	22 21	23 17	00 50
d		06 45	07 26	08 26	09 26	10 26	11 26	12 26	13 26	14 26	15 26	16 26	17 26		18 26	19 26		20 26	21 26	22 26		
Romsey a						10 49	11 49	12 55	13 47	15 09	15 50	16 49	17 49			19 55		20 48	21 47	22 48		
Southampton Central a						11 00	12 04	13 06	13 58	15 20	16 06	17 04	18 04			20 06		20 59	21 58	22 59		
Portsmouth Harbour a						11 51	12 51		14 48		16 51	17 51	18 51			21 23		21 46	22 43	23 44		
Brighton 10 a						14q00	15q00	15 06	17q00	17 05	19q00	20q00	21q00			22 01		23q25				
Grateley d				08 38		10 38		12 38		14 38		16 38			18 38			20 38		22 38		
Andover d		07 02	07 43	08 46	09 43	10 46	11 43	12 46	13 43	14 46	15 43	16 46	17 43		18 46	19 43		20 46	21 43	22 46		
Whitchurch (Hants) d			07 51	08 54		10 54		12 54		14 54		16 54			18 54			20 54		22 54		
Overton d				08 59		10 59		12 59		14 59		16 59			18 59			20 59		22 59		
Basingstoke a		07 19	08 03	09 08	10 00	11 08	12 00	13 08	14 00	15 08	16 00	17 08	18 00		19 08	20 00		21 08	22 00	23 08		
Reading 7 a		08 20	09 20	10 05	11 05	12 05	13 05	14 05	15 05	16 05	17 05	18r05	19 05			21 05		22 05	23 20	00 01		
Woking a		07 39	08 23	09 30	10 23	11 30	12 23	13 30	14 23	15 30	16 23	17 30	18 23		19 30	20 23		21 30	22 23	23 50		
Clapham Junction 10 a		08 03	08 55	09 55	10 44	11 50	12 44	13 50	14 44	15 50	16 44	17 50	18 44		19 50	20 44		21 50	22 44	00 22		
London Waterloo 15 ⊖ a		08 19	09 09	10 08	11 03	12 03	13 03	14 04	14 58	16 04	16 58	18 04	18 58		20 04	20 58		22 04	22 58	00 33		

For general notes see front of timetable
For details of catering facilities see Directory of Train Operators

A From Penzance (Table 135)
b Change at Newton Abbot
c From 30 March only. Change at Exeter St Davids
e Until 23 March change at Exeter St Davids. From 30 March dep. 1735, change at Newton Abbot
f Change at Exeter St Davids
g Change at Newton Abbot and Exeter St Davids
h 3 February to 23 March dep. 1016
j Until 23 March change at Exeter St Davids. From 30 March dep. 1802, change at Newton Abbot
k From 30 March dep. 1952
m 3 February to 23 March dep. 1031
n Until 27 January dep. 1620
q Change at Salisbury and Fratton
r 3 February to 23 March arr. 1807

Network Diagram for Tables 165, 167

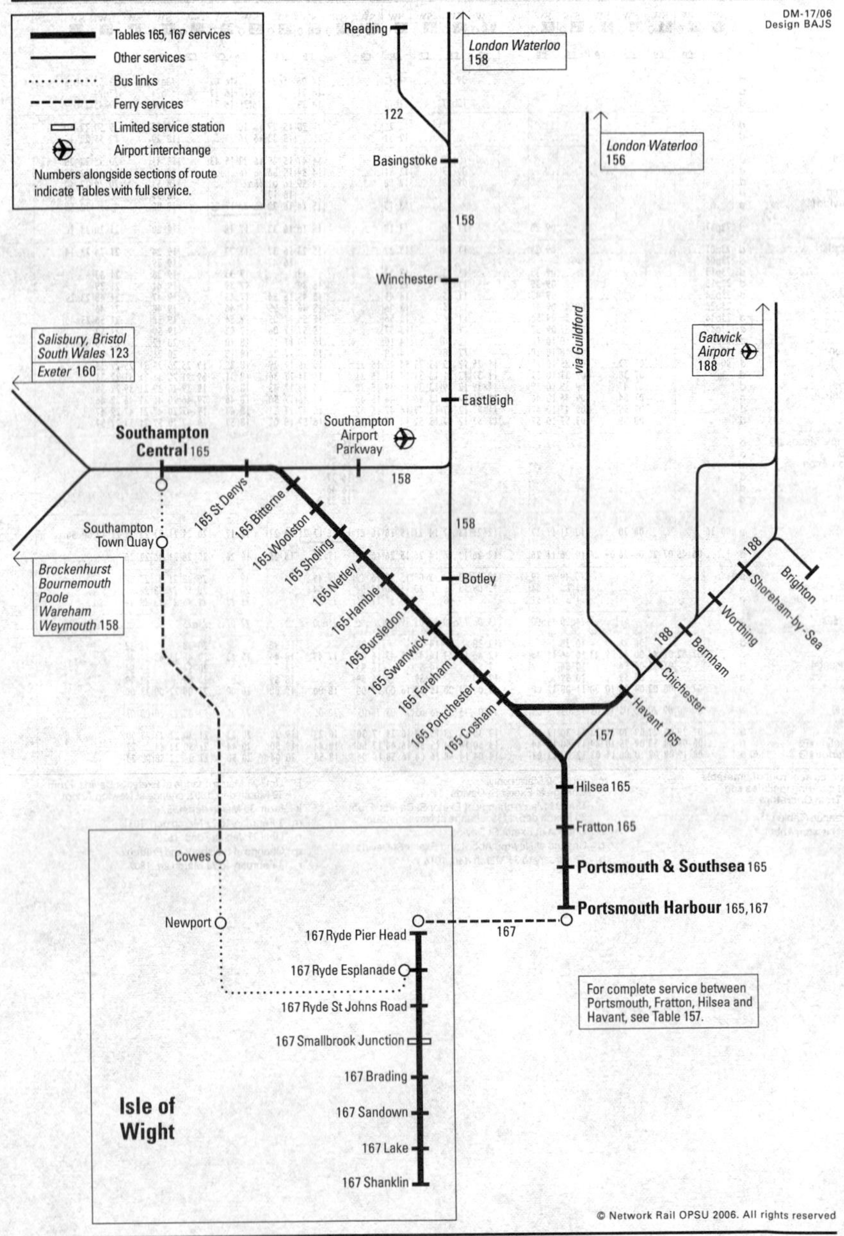
DM-17/06
Design BAJS
Tables 165, 167 services
Other services
Bus links
Ferry services
Limited service station
Airport interchange
Numbers alongside sections of route indicate Tables with full service.
Reading
London Waterloo 158
122
Basingstoke
158
Winchester
London Waterloo 156
via Guildford
Salisbury, Bristol
South Wales 123
Exeter 160
Gatwick Airport 188
Eastleigh
Southampton Central 165
Southampton Airport Parkway
158
165 St Denys
165 Bitterne
165 Woolston
165 Sholing
165 Netley
165 Hamble
165 Bursledon
165 Swanwick
165 Fareham
165 Portchester
165 Cosham
Southampton Town Quay
158
Botley
Brockenhurst
Bournemouth
Poole
Wareham
Weymouth 158
188
Brighton
Shoreham-by-Sea
Worthing
188
Barnham
Chichester
Havant 165
157
Hilsea 165
Fratton 165
Portsmouth & Southsea 165
Portsmouth Harbour 165,167
Cowes
Newport
167
167 Ryde Pier Head
167 Ryde Esplanade
167 Ryde St Johns Road
167 Smallbrook Junction
167 Brading
167 Sandown
167 Lake
167 Shanklin
Isle of Wight
For complete service between Portsmouth, Fratton, Hilsea and Havant, see Table 157.

For details of Bank Holiday service alterations, please see first page of Table 149

Southampton → Fareham and Portsmouth

Network Diagram - see first page of Table 165

Miles	Miles			SW MO ■1	SW MX ■1	SN ■1	SW ■1	SN ■1	SW ■1	SW ■1	GW	SW ■1	SN ■1	SW ■1	SW ■1	SN ■1	GW ◇ ⚭	SW ■1	SN ■1	SW ■1	SN ■1	SW ■1	GW ◇ ⚭	SN ■1	SW ■1	SN ■1
0	—	**Southampton Central**	d			05 48		06 10		06 21	06 53		07 06		07 17	07 36	07 42	07 51	08 10		08 36	08 42	09 04	09 11		09 36
2	—	St Denys	d							06 27					07 23			07 57	08 15			08 48				
2½	—	Bitterne	d							06 29					07 25			07 59				08 50				
4¼	—	Woolston	d			05 57		06 19		06 33			07 15		07 29			08 03				08 54				
5	—	Sholing	d							06 35					07 31			08 05				08 56				
6¾	—	Netley	d							06 39					07 35			08 09				09 00				
7½	—	Hamble	d							06 41					07 37			08 11				09 02				
8¾	—	Bursledon	d							06 44					07 40			08 14				09 05				
10¾	—	Swanwick	d			06 06		06 27		06 48			07 24		07 44	07 53		08 18	08 28		08 53	09 09		09 28		09 53
14½	—	**Fareham**	a			06 12		06 33		06 57	07 14		07 30		07 52	07 59	08 05	08 25	08 34		08 59	09 16	09 26	09 35		09 59
—	—		d	23p44	23p48	06 13	06 18	06 34	06 50	06 58	07 15	07 20	07 31	07 48	07 53	08 00	08 06	08 26	08 35	08 48	09 00	09 17	09 27	09 36	09 48	10 00
17¾	—	Portchester	d	23p49	23p53	06 18	06 23	06 40	06 55	07 03		07 25	07 36	07 53	07 58			08 31	08 40	08 53		09 22		09 41	09 53	
20¼	0	Cosham	d	23p54	23p59	06 23	06 28	06 44	07 00	07 08	07 23	07 29	07 40	07 58	08 03	08 08	08 14	08 36	08 44	08 58	09 08	09 27	09 35	09 45	09 58	10 08
—	4	Havant	a			06 37		06 53					07 46			08 14			08 50		09 14			09 51		10 14
21¾	—	Hilsea	a	23p59	00 04		06 33		07 05	07 13		07 35		08 03	08 10			08 43		09 04		09 31			10 03	
24	—	Fratton	a	00 04	00 08		06 38		07 09	07 17	07 34	07 39		08 07	08 14		08 21	08 47		09 08		09 35	09 43		10 07	
25	—	**Portsmouth & Southsea**	a	00 08	00 11		06 44		07 12	07 22	07 38	07 42		08 11	08 18		08 24	08 51		09 11		09 40	09 47		10 19	
25¾	—	**Portsmouth Harbour**	a	00 13	00 16		06 49		07 17		07 45	07 48		08 16	08 22		08 30	08 55		09 18			09 52		10 23	

		SW ■1	GW ◇ ⚭	SN ■1	SW ■1	SN ■1	SW ■1	GW ◇ ⚭	SN ■1	SW ■1	SN ■1	SW ■1		GW ◇ ⚭	SN ■1	SW ■1	SN ■1	SW ■1	GW ◇ ⚭	SN ■1	SW ■1	SN ■1	SW ■1	GW ◇ ⚭	SN ■1	SW ■1
Southampton Central	d	09 42	10 04	10 11		10 36	10 42	11 03	11 11		11 36	11 42		12 04	12 11		12 36	12 42	13 04	13 11		13 36	13 42	14 04	14 11	
St Denys	d	09 48					10 48					11 48						12 48					13 48			
Bitterne	d	09 50					10 50					11 50						12 50					13 50			
Woolston	d	09 54					10 54					11 54						12 54					13 54			
Sholing	d	09 56					10 56					11 56						12 56					13 56			
Netley	d	10 00					11 00					12 00						13 00					14 00			
Hamble	d	10 02					11 02					12 02						13 02					14 02			
Bursledon	d	10 05					11 05					12 05						13 05					14 05			
Swanwick	d	10 09		10 28		10 53	11 09		11 28		11 53	12 09			12 28		12 53	13 09		13 28		13 53	14 09		14 28	
Fareham	a	10 16	10 26	10 34		10 59	11 16	11 26	11 34		11 59	12 16		12 26	12 34		12 59	13 16	13 26	13 34		13 59	14 16	14 26	14 34	
	d	10 17	10 27	10 35	10 48	11 00	11 17	11 27	11 35	11 48	12 00	12 17		12 27	12 35	12 48	13 00	13 17	13 27	13 35	13 48	14 00	14 17	14 27	14 35	14 48
Portchester	d	10 22		10 40	10 53		11 22		11 40	11 53		12 22			12 40	12 53		13 22		13 40	13 53		14 22		14 40	14 53
Cosham	d	10 27	10 35	10 45	10 58	11 08	11 27	11 35	11 45	11 58	12 09	12 27		12 35	12 44	12 58	13 08	13 27	13 35	13 45	13 58	14 08	14 27	14 35	14 45	14 58
Havant	a			10 51		11 14			11 51		12 15				12 50		13 14			13 51		14 14			14 51	
Hilsea	a	10 32			11 03		11 32			12 03		12 31				13 03		13 32			14 03		14 32			15 03
Fratton	a	10 36	10 43		11 07		11 36	11 42		12 07		12 35		12 43		13 07		13 36	13 43		14 07		14 36	14 42		15 07
Portsmouth & Southsea	a	10 41	10 47		11 19		11 40	11 45		12 19		12 40		12 47		13 19		13 40	13 47		14 19		14 40	14 47		15 19
Portsmouth Harbour	a		10 52		11 23			11 50		12 23				12 52		13 23			13 52		14 23			14 52		15 23

		GW ◇	SN ■1	SW ■1	GW ◇ ⚭	SN ■1	SW ■1	SN ■1	SW ■1	GW ◇ ⚭	SN ■1	SW ■1	SN ■1	SW ■1	SW ■1	GW ◇ ⚭	SN ■1	SW ■1	SN ■1	SW ■1	SW ■1	GW ◇ ⚭	SN ■1	SW ■1	SN ■1	SW ■1
Southampton Central	d	14 34	14 26	14 42	15 04	15 11		15 36	15 42	16 04	16 11		16 36		16 42	17 04	17 11		17 36	17 42		18 04	18 11		18 27	
St Denys	d			14 48					15 48						16 48					17 48						
Bitterne	d			14 50					15 50						16 50					17 50						
Woolston	d			14 54					15 54						16 54					17 54						
Sholing	d			14 56					15 56						16 56					17 56						
Netley	d			15 00					16 00						17 00					18 00						
Hamble	d			15 02					16 02						17 02					18 02						
Bursledon	d			15 05					16 05						17 05					18 05						
Swanwick	d			15 09		15 28		15 53	16 09		16 28		16 53		17 09		17 28		17 53	18 09			18 28		18 47	
Fareham	a	14 55	15 01	15 16	15 26	15 34		15 59	16 16	16 26	16 35		16 59		17 16	17 26	17 34		17 59	18 16		18 26	18 34		18 55	
	d	14 56	15 02	15 17	15 27	15 35	15 48	16 00	16 17	16 27	16 36	16 48	17 00	17 10	17 17	17 27	17 35	17 48	18 00	18 17	18 21	18 27	18 35	18 50	18 56	19 14
Portchester	d			15 22		15 40	15 53		16 22		16 41	16 53		17 15	17 22		17 40	17 53		18 22	18 26		18 40	18 55		19 19
Cosham	d	15 04		15 27	15 35	15 44	15 58	16 08	16 27	16 35	16 45	16 58	17 08	17 20	17 27	17 35	17 44	17 58	18 08	18 27	18 31	18 35	18 44	19 00	19 04	19 24
Havant	a	15 10	15 14			15 50		16 14			16 51		17 14				17 50		18 14				18 50		19 10	
Hilsea	a			15 32			16 03		16 32			17 03			17 32			18 03		18 32				19 05		19 28
Fratton	a			15 36	15 43		16 07		16 36	16 47		17 07		17 27	17 36	17 43		18 07		18 36	18 39	18 47		19 09		19 32
Portsmouth & Southsea	a			15 40	15 47		16 11		16 40	16 51		17 18		17 31	17 40	17 47		18 11		18 40	18 43	18 51		19 12		19 36
Portsmouth Harbour	a				15 52		16 20		16 44	16 57		17 25				17 52		18 20			18 51	18 57		19 20		19 43

		SW ■1	GW ◇	SN ■1	SW ■1	SN ■1	SW ■1	GW ◇ ⚭	SN ■1	SW ■1	SN ■1	SW ■1	GW ◇ ⚭	SN ■1	SW ■1	SN ■1	SW ■1	SN ■1	GW ◇ ⚭	SN ■1	SW ■1	SW ■1	GW ◇ ⚭	SW ■1
Southampton Central	d	18 42	19 03	19 11		19 36	19 42	20 04	20 11		20 36	20 42	21 04	21 11		21 23	21 42	22 12	22 04	22 36		22 42	23 04	
St Denys	d	18 48					19 48					20 48					21 48					22 48		
Bitterne	d	18 50					19 50					20 50					21 50					22 50		
Woolston	d	18 54					19 54					20 54					21 54					22 54		
Sholing	d	18 56					19 56					20 56					21 56					22 56		
Netley	d	19 00					20 00					21 00					22 00					23 00		
Hamble	d	19 02					20 02					21 02					22 02					23 02		
Bursledon	d	19 05					20 05					21 05					22 05					23 05		
Swanwick	d	19 09		19 28		19 53	20 09		20 28		20 53	21 09		21 28			22 09	22 29		22 53		23 09		
Fareham	a	19 17	19 25	19 34		19 59	20 16	20 26	20 34		20 59	21 16	21 26	21 38		21 55	22 16	22 35	22 39	22 59		23 16	23 27	
	d	19 18	19 27	19 35	19 50	20 00	20 17	20 27	20 35	20 48	21 00	21 17	21 27	21 39	21 48	21 56	22 17	22 36	22 40	23 00	23 10	23 17	23 27	23 48
Portchester	d	19 23		19 40	19 55		20 22		20 40	20 53		21 22		21 44	21 53	22 01	22 22	22 41			23 15	23 22		23 53
Cosham	d	19 28	19 35	19 44	20 00	20 08	20 27		20 44	20 58	21 08	21 27		21 48	21 58	22 06	22 27	22 45		23 08	23 20	23 27		23 59
Havant	a			19 51		20 14			20 50		21 14			21 54		22 13		22 56		23 14				
Hilsea	a	19 32			20 08		20 32			20 59		21 32			22 06		22 31				23 24	23 32		00 04
Fratton	a	19 37	19 42		20 12		20 36	20 40		21 08		21 36	21 40		22 10		22 35		22 55		23 32	23 36	23 43	00 08
Portsmouth & Southsea	a	19 42	19 47		20 16		20 40	20 44		21 11		21 43	21 44		22 13		22 43		23 00		23 36	23 40	23 47	00 11
Portsmouth Harbour	a		19 52		20 23			20 49		21 25			21 49		22 18				23 04		23 40		23 52	00 16

For general notes see front of timetable
For details of catering facilities see
Directory of Train Operators

Southampton → Fareham and Portsmouth

Network Diagram - see first page of Table 165

		SW 1	SW 1	SN 1	SW 1	SN 1	SW 1	SN 1	SW 1	SN 1	SW 1	GW ◇	SN 1	SW 1	SN 1	SW 1	GW ◇	SN 1	SW 1	SN 1	SW 1	GW ◇ ✠	SN 1
Southampton Central	d		05 42	06 11		06 36	06 42	07 11		07 36	07 42	08 03	08 11		08 36	08 42	09 03	09 11		09 36	09 42	10 03	10 11
St Denys	d		05 48				06 48				07 48					08 48					09 48		
Bitterne	d		05 50				06 50				07 50					08 50					09 50		
Woolston	d		05 54				06 54				07 54					08 54					09 54		
Sholing	d		05 56				06 56				07 56					08 56					09 56		
Netley	d		06 00				07 00				08 00					09 00					10 00		
Hamble	d		06 02				07 02				08 02					09 02					10 02		
Bursledon	d		06 05				07 05				08 05					09 05					10 05		
Swanwick	d		06 09	06 28		06 53	07 09	07 28		07 53	08 09		08 28		08 53	09 09		09 28		09 53	10 09		10 28
Fareham	a		06 16	06 34		06 59	07 16	07 34		07 59	08 16	08 26	08 34		08 59	09 16	09 26	09 34		09 59	10 16	10 26	10 34
	d	23p48	06 17	06 35	06 48	07 00	07 17	07 35	07 48	08 00	08 17	08 26	08 35	08 51	09 00	09 17	09 26	09 35	09 48	10 00	10 17	10 26	10 35
Portchester	d	23p53	06 22	06 40	06 53		07 22	07 40	07 53		08 22		08 40	08 56		09 22		09 40	09 53		10 22		10 40
Cosham	d	23p59	06 27	06 44	06 58	07 08	07 27	07 44	07 58	08 09	08 27	08 34	08 44	09 01	09 08	09 27	09 34	09 44	09 58	10 08	10 27	10 34	10 44
Havant	a			06 50		07 14		07 50		08 15			08 50		09 14			09 50		10 14			10 50
Hilsea	a	00 04	06 32		07 03		07 32		08 04		08 32			09 07		09 32			10 03		10 32		
Fratton	a	00 08	06 36		07 07		07 36		08 08		08 36	08 41		09 16		09 36	09 41		10 07		10 36	10 41	
Portsmouth & Southsea	a	00 11	06 40		07 10		07 40		08 11		08 40	08 45		09 19		09 40	09 45		10 19		10 40	10 45	
Portsmouth Harbour	a	00 16			07 18				08 19			08 49		09 24			09 49		10 23			10 49	

		SW 1	SN 1	SW 1	GW ◇ ✠	SN 1	SW 1	SN 1	SW 1	GW ◇ ✠	SN 1	SW 1	SN 1	SW 1	GW ◇ ✠	SN 1	SW 1	SN 1	SW 1	GW ◇ ✠	SN 1	SW 1	GW
Southampton Central	d		10 36	10 42	11 03	11 11		11 36	11 42	12 03	12 11		12 36	12 42	13 03	13 11		13 36	13 42	14 03	14 11		14 34
St Denys	d			10 48					11 48					12 48					13 48				
Bitterne	d			10 50					11 50					12 50					13 50				
Woolston	d			10 54					11 54					12 54					13 54				
Sholing	d			10 56					11 56					12 56					13 56				
Netley	d			11 00					12 00					13 00					14 00				
Hamble	d			11 02					12 02					13 02					14 02				
Bursledon	d			11 05					12 05					13 05					14 05				
Swanwick	d		10 53	11 09		11 28		11 53	12 09		12 28		12 53	13 09		13 28		13 53	14 09		14 28		
Fareham	a		10 59	11 16	11 26	11 34		11 59	12 16	12 26	12 34		12 59	13 16	13 26	13 34		13 59	14 16	14 26	14 34		14 55
	d	10 48	11 00	11 17	11 26	11 35	11 48	12 00	12 17	12 26	12 35	12 48	13 00	13 17	13 26	13 35	13 48	14 00	14 17	14 26	14 35	14 48	14 56
Portchester	d	10 53		11 22		11 40	11 53		12 22		12 40	12 53		13 22		13 40	13 53		14 22		14 40	14 53	
Cosham	d	10 58	11 08	11 27	11 34	11 44	11 58	12 08	12 27	12 34	12 44	12 58	13 08	13 27	13 34	13 44	13 58	14 08	14 27	14 34	14 44	14 58	15 04
Havant	a		11 14			11 50		12 14			12 50		13 14			13 50		14 14			14 50		15 11
Hilsea	a	11 03		11 32			12 03		12 32			13 03		13 32			14 03		14 32			15 03	
Fratton	a	11 07		11 36	11 41		12 07		12 36	12 41		13 07		13 36	13 41		14 07		14 36	14 41		15 07	
Portsmouth & Southsea	a	11 19		11 40	11 45		12 19		12 40	12 45		13 19		13 40	13 45		14 19		14 40	14 45		15 19	
Portsmouth Harbour	a	11 23			11 49		12 23			12 49		13 23			13 49		14 23			14 49		15 23	

		SN 1	SW 1	GW ◇ ✠	SN 1	SW 1	SN 1	SW 1	GW ◇ ✠	SN 1	SW 1	SN 1	SW 1	GW ◇ ✠	SN 1	SW 1	SN 1	SW 1	GW ◇ ✠	SN 1	SW 1	SN 1	SW 1
Southampton Central	d	14 26	14 42	15 03	15 11		15 36	15 42	16 03	16 11		16 36	16 42	17 03	17 11		17 36	17 42	18 03	18 11		18 36	18 42
St Denys	d		14 48					15 48					16 48					17 48					18 48
Bitterne	d		14 50					15 50					16 50					17 50					18 50
Woolston	d		14 54					15 54					16 54					17 54					18 54
Sholing	d		14 56					15 56					16 56					17 56					18 56
Netley	d		15 00					16 00					17 00					18 00					19 00
Hamble	d		15 02					16 02					17 02					18 02					19 02
Bursledon	d		15 05					16 05					17 05					18 05					19 05
Swanwick	d		15 09		15 28		15 53	16 09		16 28		16 53	17 09		17 28		17 53	18 09		18 28		18 53	19 09
Fareham	a	15 01	15 16	15 26	15 34		15 59	16 16	16 26	16 34		16 59	17 16	17 26	17 34		17 59	18 16	18 26	18 34		18 59	19 16
	d	15 02	15 17	15 26	15 35	15 48	16 00	16 17	16 26	16 35	16 48	17 00	17 17	17 26	17 35	17 48	18 00	18 17	18 26	18 35	18 48	19 00	19 17
Portchester	d		15 22		15 40	15 53		16 22		16 40	16 53		17 22		17 40	17 53		18 22		18 40	18 53		19 22
Cosham	d		15 27	15 34	15 44	15 58	16 08	16 27	16 34	16 44	16 58	17 08	17 27	17 34	17 44	17 58	18 08	18 27	18 34	18 44	18 58	19 08	19 27
Havant	a	15 14			15 50		16 14			16 50		17 14			17 50		18 14			18 50		19 14	
Hilsea	a		15 32			16 03		16 32			17 03		17 32			18 03		18 32			19 03		19 32
Fratton	a		15 36	15 41		16 07		16 36	16 41		17 07		17 36	17 41		18 07		18 36	18 42		19 07		19 36
Portsmouth & Southsea	a		15 40	15 45		16 19		16 40	16 45		17 19		17 40	17 45		18 19		18 40	18 46		19 19		19 40
Portsmouth Harbour	a			15 49		16 23		16 44	16 49		17 23			17 49		18 23			18 49		19 23		

		GW ◇ ✠	SN 1	SW 1	SN 1	SW 1	GW ◇ A ✠	SN 1	SW 1	SN 1	SW 1	GW ◇ ✠	SN 1	SW 1	SN 1	SW 1	GW ◇ ✠	SN 1	SW 1	SN 1	SW 1	GW ◇ ✠	SW 1
Southampton Central	d	19 03	19 11		19 36	19 42	20 03	20 11		20 36	20 42	21 03	21 11		21 23	21 42	22 03	22 11		22 36	22 42	23 04	
St Denys	d					19 48					20 48				21 28	21 48					22 48		
Bitterne	d					19 50					20 50					21 50					22 50		
Woolston	d					19 54					20 54				21 33	21 54					22 54		
Sholing	d					19 56					20 56					21 56					22 56		
Netley	d					20 00					21 00				21 37	22 00					23 00		
Hamble	d					20 02					21 02					22 02					23 02		
Bursledon	d					20 05					21 05					22 05					23 05		
Swanwick	d		19 28		19 53	20 09		20 28		20 53	21 09		21 28		21 45	22 09		22 28		22 53	23 09		
Fareham	a	19 26	19 34		19 59	20 16	20 26	20 34		20 59	21 16	21 26	21 38		21 54	22 16	22 25	22 38		22 59	23 16	23 25	
	d	19 26	19 35	19 48	20 00	20 17	20 26	20 35	20 48	21 00	21 17	21 26	21 39	21 48	21 55	22 17	22 25	22 39	22 48	23 00	23 17	23 26	23 48
Portchester	d		19 40	19 53		20 22		20 40	20 53		21 22		21 44	21 53	22 00	22 22		22 44	22 53		23 22		23 53
Cosham	d	19 34	19 44	19 58	20 08	20 27		20 44	20 58	21 08	21 27		21 48	21 58	22 04	22 27		22 48	22 58	23 08	23 27		23 58
Havant	a		19 51		20 14			20 50		21 14			21 54		22 12			22 54		23 14			
Hilsea	a			20 03		20 32			21 06		21 32			22 06		22 33			23 03		23 32		00 03
Fratton	a	19 42		20 07		20 36	20 40		21 10		21 36	21 42		22 10		22 37	22 41		23 07		23 37	23 40	00 07
Portsmouth & Southsea	a	19 45		20 19		20 40	20 44		21 18		21 40	21 45		22 13		22 41	22 45		23 10		23 40	23 44	00 11
Portsmouth Harbour	a	19 49		20 23			20 49		21 23			21 49		22 18		22 45	22 49		23 16			23 48	00 16

For general notes see front of timetable
For details of catering facilities see
Directory of Train Operators

A Until 22 March

Table 165

Sundays

Southampton → Fareham and Portsmouth

Network Diagram - see first page of Table 165

		SW 1	SW 1	SW 1	SW 1	SW 1	GW ◇	SW 1	SW 1	SW 1	SW 1	SW 1	GW ◇ 🛒	SW 1	SW 1	GW ◇ 🛒	SW 1	SW 1
Southampton Central	d		06 35		07 35		08 31	08 35		09 35		10 35	11 04		11 35	12 07		12 35
St Denys	d		06 41		07 41			08 41		09 41		10 41			11 41			12 41
Bitterne	d		06 43		07 43			08 43		09 43		10 43			11 43			12 43
Woolston	d		06 47		07 47			08 47		09 47		10 47			11 47			12 47
Sholing	d		06 49		07 49			08 49		09 49		10 49			11 49			12 49
Netley	d		06 53		07 53			08 53		09 53		10 53			11 53			12 53
Hamble	d		06 55		07 55			08 55		09 55		10 55			11 55			12 55
Bursledon	d		06 58		07 58			08 58		09 58		10 58			11 58			12 58
Swanwick	d		07 02		08 02			09 02		10 02		11 02			12 02			13 02
Fareham	a		07 09		08 09		08 51	09 09		10 09		11 09	11 25		12 09	12 28		13 09
	d	23p48	07 10	07 45	08 10	08 44	08 52	09 10	09 44	10 10	10 44	11 10	11 26	11 44	12 10	12 29	12 44	13 10
Portchester	d	23p53	07 15	07 50	08 15	08 49		09 15	09 49	10 15	10 49	11 15		11 49	12 15		12 49	13 15
Cosham	d	23p58	07 20	07 55	08 20	08 54	09 00	09 20	09 54	10 20	10 54	11 20	11 34	11 54	12 20	12 37	12 54	13 20
Havant	a						09 11											
Hilsea	a	00 03	07 26	07 59	08 26	09 00		09 26	10 01	10 26	11 01	11 26		12 00	12 26		13 00	13 26
Fratton	a	00 07	07 30	08 04	08 30	09 04		09 30	10 05	10 30	11 05	11 30	11 40	12 04	12 30	12 44	13 04	13 30
Portsmouth & Southsea	a	00 11	07 33	08 08	08 33	09 08		09 33	10 09	10 33	11 09	11 33	11 44	12 08	12 33	12 47	13 08	13 33
Portsmouth Harbour	a	00 16		08 13		09 13			10 14		11 14		11 51	12 13		12 51	13 13	

		GW ◇ 🛒	SW 1	SW 1	GW ◇ 🛒	SW 1	SW 1	SW 1	GW ◇ 🛒	SW 1	GW ◇ 🛒	SW 1	SW 1	GW ◇ 🛒	SW 1	SW 1	GW ◇ 🛒	SW 1
Southampton Central	d	13 08		13 35	14 01		14 35		15 22	15 35	16 07		16 35	17 07		17 35	18 07	
St Denys	d			13 41			14 41			15 41			16 41			17 41		
Bitterne	d			13 43			14 43			15 43			16 43			17 43		
Woolston	d			13 47			14 47			15 47			16 47			17 47		
Sholing	d			13 49			14 49			15 49			16 49			17 49		
Netley	d			13 53			14 53			15 53			16 53			17 53		
Hamble	d			13 55			14 55			15 55			16 55			17 55		
Bursledon	d			13 58			14 58			15 58			16 58			17 58		
Swanwick	d			14 02			15 02			16 02			17 02			18 02		
Fareham	a	13 33		14 09	14 22		15 09		15 50	16 09	16 28		17 09	17 28		18 09	18 28	
	d	13 34	13 44	14 10	14 23	14 44	15 10	15 45	15 51	16 10	16 29	16 44	17 10	17 29	17 44	18 10	18 29	18 44
Portchester	d		13 49	14 15		14 49	15 15	15 50		16 15		16 49	17 15		17 49	18 15		18 49
Cosham	d	13 42	13 54	14 20	14 31	14 54	15 20	15 55	16 01	16 20	16 37	16 54	17 20	17 37	17 54	18 20	18 37	18 54
Havant	a	14 03							16 11									
Hilsea	a		14 00	14 26		15 00	15 26	16 00		16 26		17 00	17 26		18 00	18 26		19 00
Fratton	a		14 04	14 30	14 38	15 04	15 30	16 04		16 30	16 44	17 04	17 30	17 44	18 04	18 30	18 44	19 04
Portsmouth & Southsea	a		14 08	14 33	14 41	15 08	15 33	16 08		16 33	16 47	17 08	17 33	17 47	18 08	18 33	18 47	19 08
Portsmouth Harbour	a		14 13		14 48	15 13		16 13			16 51	17 13		17 51	18 13		18 51	19 13

		SW 1	GW ◇ 🛒	SW 1	SW 1	GW ◇ 🛒	SW 1	GW ◇ 🛒	SW 1	GW ◇ 🛒	SW 1	GW ◇ 🛒	SW 1	GW ◇ 🛒	SW 1	SW 1	GW ◇ 🛒	SW 1
Southampton Central	d	18 35	19 07		19 35	20 07		20 33	20 35	21 01		21 28	21 35	22 01		22 35	23 00	
St Denys	d	18 41			19 41				20 41				21 41			22 41		
Bitterne	d	18 43			19 43				20 43				21 43			22 43		
Woolston	d	18 47			19 47				20 47				21 47			22 47		
Sholing	d	18 49			19 49				20 49				21 49			22 49		
Netley	d	18 53			19 53				20 53				21 53			22 53		
Hamble	d	18 55			19 55				20 55				21 55			22 55		
Bursledon	d	18 58			19 58				20 58				21 58			22 58		
Swanwick	d	19 02			20 02				21 02				22 02			23 02		
Fareham	a	19 09	19 28		20 09	20 28		20 54	21 09	21 22		21 49	22 09	22 22		23 09	23 21	
	d	19 10	19 29	19 44	20 10	20 29	20 44	20 55	21 10	21 23	21 44	21 50	22 10	22 23	22 44	23 10	23 22	23 44
Portchester	d	19 15		19 49	20 15		20 49		21 15		21 49		22 15		22 49	23 15		23 49
Cosham	d	19 20	19 37	19 54	20 20	20 44	20 54		21 20		21 54		22 20		22 54	23 20		23 54
Havant	a					20 52												
Hilsea	a	19 26		20 00	20 26		21 00		21 26		22 00		22 26		23 00	23 24		23 59
Fratton	a	19 30	19 44	20 04	20 30		21 04	21 09	21 30	21 36	22 04	22 07	22 30	22 36	23 04	23 28	23 37	00 04
Portsmouth & Southsea	a	19 33	19 47	20 08	20 33		21 08	21 15	21 33	21 39	22 08	22 12	22 33	22 39	23 08	23 32	23 40	00 08
Portsmouth Harbour	a		19 51	20 13			21 13	21 23		21 46	22 13	22 20		22 43	23 13		23 44	00 13

For general notes see front of timetable
For details of catering facilities see
Directory of Train Operators

For details of Bank Holiday service alterations, please see first page of Table 149

Portsmouth and Fareham → Southampton

Network Diagram - see first page of Table 165

Miles	Miles	Station		SW 1	SN 1	SW 1	SW 1	GW ◇ 🍴	SN 1	SW 1	SW 1	SN 1	SW 1	SN 1	SN 1	SW 1	SW 1	SW 1	SN 1		SW 1	GW ◇ 🍴	SN 1	SW 1	SW 1	SN 1
0	—	**Portsmouth Harbour**	d	05 00			05 43	06 00			06 23		06 38			07 24		07 52			08 05	08 22		08 32	08 51	
¾	—	**Portsmouth & Southsea**	d	05 05		05 16	05 48	06 04		06 23	06 28		06 43			07 29	07 36	07 57			08 10	08 27		08 36	08 56	
1¾	—	Fratton	d	05 09		05 20	05 52	06 08		06 27	06 32		06 47			07 33	07 40	08 01			08 14	08 31		08 40	09 01	
4	—	Hilsea	d	05 13		05 24	05 56			06 31	06 36		06 51			07 37	07 44	08 05			08 18			08 44	09 05	
—	0	Havant	d		05 17				06 21			06 40		07 19	07 31				08 04				08 37			09 26
5½	4	Cosham	d	05 18	05 24	05 30	06 03	06 15	06 28	06 36	06 42	06 50	06 58	07 26	07 38	07 43	07 49	08 10	08 15		08 23	08 39	08 44	08 49	09 10	09 33
8	—	Portchester	d	05 23	05 28	05 35	06 08			06 41	06 46	06 54	07 03	07 30		07 48	07 54	08 15	08 19		08 28		08 48	08 54	09 15	
11¼	—	**Fareham**	a	05 28	05 33	05 40	06 13	06 23	06 37	06 46	06 51	06 59	07 08	07 35	07 46	07 53	07 59	08 20	08 24		08 33	08 46	08 53	08 59	09 20	09 40
—	—		d		05 34	05 41		06 24	06 38	06 47		07 00		07 36	07 47		08 00		08 25			08 47	08 54	09 00		09 41
15	—	Swanwick	d		05 40	05 47			06 44	06 53		07 06		07 42	07 53		08 06		08 31				09 00	09 06		
17	—	Bursledon	d			05 51				06 57							08 10		08 35					09 10		
18¼	—	Hamble	d			05 54				07 00							08 13		08 38					09 13		
19	—	Netley	d		05 46	05 56				07 02				07 48	07 59		08 15		08 40					09 15		
20¾	—	Sholing	d			06 00				07 06							08 19		08 43					09 19		
21½	—	Woolston	d		05 50	06 02				07 08				07 52	08 03		08 21		08 45					09 21		
23¼	—	Bitterne	d			06 06				07 12							08 25		08 49					09 25		
23¾	—	St Denys	d			06 09				07 15					08 08		08 28		08 51					09 28		
25¾	—	**Southampton Central**	a		05 59	06 14		06 45	07 02	07 21		07 26		08 01	08 13		08 36		08 56			09 08	09 19	09 36		10 03

Station		GW ◇ 🍴	SN 1	SW 1	GW ◇	SW 1	SN 1	GW ◇ 🍴	SN 1	SW 1	SW 1	SN 1	GW ◇ 🍴		SN 1	SW 1	SW 1	SN 1	GW ◇ 🍴	SN 1	SW 1	SW 1	SN 1	GW ◇ 🍴	SN 1	SW 1
Portsmouth Harbour	d	09 22		09 32		09 54		10 22		10 31	10 54		11 22				11 54		12 22			12 54		13 22		
Portsmouth & Southsea	d	09 27		09 36		09 59		10 27		10 36	10 59		11 27			11 36	11 59		12 27		12 36	12 59		13 27		13 36
Fratton	d	09 31		09 40		10 03		10 31		10 40	11 03		11 31			11 40	12 03		12 31		12 40	13 03		13 31		13 40
Hilsea	d			09 44		10 07				10 44	11 07					11 44	12 07				12 44	13 07				13 44
Havant	d		09 38		09 59		10 22		10 37			11 23			11 37			12 23		12 37			13 23		13 37	
Cosham	d	09 39	09 45	09 49	10 05	10 12	10 29	10 39	10 44	10 49	11 12	11 29	11 39		11 44	11 49	12 12	12 29	12 39	12 44	12 49	13 12	13 29	13 39	13 44	13 49
Portchester	d			09 54		10 17	10 33			10 54	11 17	11 33				11 54	12 17	12 33			12 54	13 17	13 33			13 54
Fareham	a	09 46	09 53	09 59	10 13	10 22	10 38	10 46	10 52	10 59	11 22	11 38	11 46		11 52	11 59	12 22	12 38	12 46	12 52	12 59	13 22	13 38	13 46	13 52	13 59
	d	09 47	09 54	10 00	10 14		10 39	10 47	10 53	11 00		11 39	11 47		11 53	12 00		12 39	12 47	12 53	13 00		13 39	13 47	13 53	14 00
Swanwick	d		10 00	10 06			10 45		10 59	11 06		11 45			11 59	12 06		12 45		12 59	13 06		13 45		13 59	14 06
Bursledon	d			10 10						11 10						12 10					13 10					14 10
Hamble	d			10 13						11 13						12 13					13 13					14 13
Netley	d			10 15						11 15						12 15					13 15					14 15
Sholing	d			10 19						11 19						12 19					13 19					14 19
Woolston	d			10 21						11 21						12 21					13 21					14 21
Bitterne	d			10 25						11 25						12 25					13 25					14 25
St Denys	d			10 28						11 28						12 28					13 28					14 28
Southampton Central	a	10 08	10 19	10 36	10 38		11 02	11 08	11 18	11 36		12 02	12 08		12 18	12 36		13 02	13 08	13 18	13 36		14 02	14 08	14 18	14 36

Station		SW 1	SN 1	GW ◇ 🍴	SN 1	SW 1	SW 1		SN 1	GW ◇ 🍴	SN 1	SW 1	SW 1	SN 1	GW ◇ 🍴	SN 1	SW 1	SW 1	SW 1	SN 1	GW ◇ 🍴	SN 1	SW 1	GW ◇		SW 1
Portsmouth Harbour	d	13 54		14 22			14 54			15 22			15 54		16 22			16 54	17 03		17 22					17 54
Portsmouth & Southsea	d	13 59		14 27		14 36	14 59			15 27		15 36	15 59		16 27		16 36	16 59	17 07		17 27		17 36			17 59
Fratton	d	14 03		14 31		14 40	15 03			15 31		15 40	16 03		16 31		16 40	17 03	17 11		17 31		17 40			18 03
Hilsea	d	14 07				14 44	15 07					15 44	16 07				16 44	17 07	17 15				17 44			18 07
Havant	d		14 23		14 37				15 23		15 37			16 23		16 37				17 19		17 37		17 58		
Cosham	d	14 12	14 29	14 39	14 44	14 49	15 12		15 29	15 39	15 44	15 49	16 12	16 29	16 39	16 44	16 49	17 12	17 21	17 26	17 39	17 44	17 49	18 05		18 12
Portchester	d	14 17	14 33			14 54	15 17		15 33			15 54	16 17	16 33			16 54	17 17	17 25	17 30			17 54			18 17
Fareham	a	14 22	14 38	14 46	14 52	14 59	15 22		15 38	15 46	15 52	15 59	16 22	16 38	16 46	16 52	16 59	17 22	17 30	17 35	17 46	17 52	17 59	18 12		18 22
	d		14 39	14 47	14 53	15 00			15 39	15 47	15 53	16 00		16 39	16 47	16 53	17 00			17 36	17 47	17 53	18 00	18 13		
Swanwick	d		14 45		14 59	15 06			15 45		15 59	16 06		16 45			17 06			17 42		17 59	18 06			
Bursledon	d					15 10						16 10					17 10						18 10			
Hamble	d					15 13						16 13					17 13						18 13			
Netley	d					15 15						16 15					17 15			17 48			18 15			
Sholing	d					15 19						16 19					17 19						18 19			
Woolston	d					15 21						16 21					17 21			17 53			18 21			
Bitterne	d					15 25						16 25					17 25						18 25			
St Denys	d					15 28						16 28					17 28			17 57			18 28			
Southampton Central	a		15 02	15 08	15 18	15 36			16 02	16 08	16 18	16 36		17 02	17 08	17 28	17 36			18 02	18 08	18 19	18 36	18 38		

Station		SN 1 🍴	GW ◇ 🍴	SN 1	SW 1	SW 1	SN 1	GW ◇ 🍴	SN 1	SW 1	SW 1	SN 1	GW ◇ 🍴	SN 1	SW 1	SW 1	SN 1	GW	SN 1	SW 1	SW 1	SN 1	SW 1	SW 1		
Portsmouth Harbour	d		18 22			18 54		19 22			19 54		20 22			20 54		21 22			21 54			23 24		
Portsmouth & Southsea	d		18 27		18 36	18 59		19 27		19 36	19 59		20 27		20 36	20 59		21 27		21 36	21 59		22 36	23 29		
Fratton	d		18 31		18 40	19 03		19 31		19 40	20 03		20 31		20 40	21 03		21 31		21 40	22 03		22 40	23 33		
Hilsea	d				18 44	19 07				19 44	20 07				20 44	21 07				21 44	22 07		22 44	23 37		
Havant	d	18 23		18 37			19 22		19 38			20 25		20 37			21 26		21 37			22 26				
Cosham	d	18 30	18 39	18 44	18 49	19 12	19 29	19 39	19 45	19 49	20 12	20 32		20 44	20 49	21 12	21 32		21 44	21 49	22 12	22 33	22 49	23 42		
Portchester	d	18 34			18 54	19 17	19 33			19 54	20 17			20 48	20 54	21 17	21 36			21 54	22 17		22 54	23 47		
Fareham	a	18 39	18 46	18 52	18 59	19 22	19 38	19 46	19 52	19 59	20 22	20 40	20 46	20 53	20 59	21 22	21 41	21 48	21 52	21 59	22 22	22 42	22 59	23 52		
	d	18 40	18 47	18 53	19 00		19 39	19 47	19 53	20 00		20 41	20 47	20 54	21 00		21 42	21 48	21 53	22 00		22 43	23 00			
Swanwick	d	18 46		18 59	19 06		19 45		19 59	20 06		20 47		21 00	21 06		21 48		21 59	22 06		22 49	23 06			
Bursledon	d				19 10					20 10					21 10					22 10			23 10			
Hamble	d				19 13					20 13					21 13					22 13			23 13			
Netley	d				19 15					20 15					21 15					22 15			23 15			
Sholing	d				19 19					20 19					21 19					22 19			23 19			
Woolston	d				19 21					20 21					21 21		21 57			22 21			23 21			
Bitterne	d				19 25					20 25					21 25					22 25			23 25			
St Denys	d				19 28					20 28					21 28		22 01			22 28			23 28			
Southampton Central	a	19 05	19 08	19 19	19 33		20 04	20 10	20 18	20 36		21 06	21 09	21 18	21 36		22 06	22 20	22 17	22 33		23 07	23 33			

For general notes see front of timetable
For details of catering facilities see
Directory of Train Operators

Portsmouth and Fareham → Southampton

Network Diagram - see first page of Table 165

		SW 1	SN 1	SW 1	SN 1	SW 1	GW ◇	SN 1	SN 1	SW 1		SW 1	GW ◇	SN 1	SN 1	SW 1	SW 1	SN 1	GW ◇	SN 1		SW 1	SW 1	SN 1	GW ◇	SN 1
Portsmouth Harbour	d					05 54	06 00					06 54	07 04				07 54		08 22				08 54		09 22	
Portsmouth & Southsea	d			05 16		05 59	06 04			06 36		06 59	07 08			07 36	07 59		08 27			08 36	08 59		09 27	
Fratton	d			05 20		06 03	06 08			06 40		07 03	07 13			07 40	08 03		08 31			08 40	09 03		09 31	
Hilsea	d			05 24		06 07				06 44		07 07				07 44	08 07					08 44	09 07			
Havant	d		05 14		05 39			06 23	06 37					07 23	07 37			08 23		08 37				09 23		09 37
Cosham	d	05 09	05 23	05 31	05 49	06 12	06 15	06 30	06 44	06 49		07 12	07 20	07 29	07 44	07 49	08 12	08 30	08 39	08 44		08 49	09 12	09 29	09 39	09 44
Portchester	d	05 14	05 27	05 35		06 17		06 34		06 54		07 17		07 33		07 54	08 17	08 34				08 54	09 17	09 33		
Fareham	a	05 19	05 32	05 40	05 57	06 22	06 24	06 39	06 52	06 59		07 22	07 28	07 38	07 52	07 59	08 22	08 39	08 46	08 52		08 59	09 22	09 38	09 46	09 52
	d		05 33	05 41	05 58		06 25	06 40	06 53	07 00			07 29	07 39	07 53	08 00		08 40	08 47	08 53		09 00		09 39	09 47	09 53
Swanwick	d		05 39	05 48	06 04			06 46	06 59	07 06				07 45	07 59	08 06		08 46		08 59		09 06		09 45		09 59
Bursledon	d			05 51						07 10						08 10						09 10				
Hamble	d			05 55						07 13						08 13						09 13				
Netley	d		05 45	05 57						07 15						08 15						09 15				
Sholing	d			06 01						07 19						08 19						09 19				
Woolston	d		05 49	06 03						07 21						08 21						09 21				
Bitterne	d			06 06						07 25						08 25						09 25				
St Denys	d			06 09						07 28						08 28						09 28				
Southampton Central	a		05 58	06 14	06 21		06 46	07 05	07 18	07 33			07 50	08 02	08 18	08 36		09 03	09 08	09 18		09 36		10 02	10 08	10 18

		SW 1	GW ◇	SW 1	SN 1	GW ◇	SN 1		SW 1	SW 1	SN 1	GW ◇	SN 1	SW 1	SW 1	SN 1	GW ◇		SN 1	SW 1	SW 1	SN 1	GW ◇	SN 1	SW 1	SW 1
Portsmouth Harbour	d			09 54		10 22				10 54		11 22			11 54		12 22				12 54		13 22			13 54
Portsmouth & Southsea	d	09 36		09 59		10 27			10 36	10 59		11 27		11 36	11 59		12 27			12 36	12 59		13 27		13 36	13 59
Fratton	d	09 40		10 03		10 31			10 40	11 03		11 31		11 40	12 03		12 31			12 40	13 03		13 31		13 40	14 03
Hilsea	d	09 44		10 07					10 44	11 07				11 44	12 07					12 44	13 07				13 44	14 07
Havant	d		10 00		10 23		10 37				11 23		11 37			12 23			12 37			13 23		13 37		
Cosham	d	09 49	10 06	10 12	10 29	10 39	10 44		10 49	11 12	11 29	11 39	11 44	11 49	12 12	12 29	12 39		12 44	12 49	13 12	13 29	13 39	13 44	13 49	14 12
Portchester	d	09 54		10 17	10 33				10 54	11 17	11 33			11 54	12 17	12 33				12 54	13 17	13 33			13 54	14 17
Fareham	a	09 59	10 14	10 22	10 38	10 46	10 52		10 59	11 22	11 38	11 46	11 52	11 59	12 22	12 38	12 46		12 52	12 59	13 22	13 38	13 46	13 52	13 59	14 22
	d	10 00	10 15		10 39	10 47	10 53		11 00		11 39	11 47	11 53	12 00		12 39	12 47		12 53	13 00		13 39	13 47	13 53	14 00	
Swanwick	d	10 06			10 45		10 59		11 06		11 45		11 59	12 06		12 45			12 59	13 06		13 45		13 59	14 06	
Bursledon	d	10 10							11 10					12 10						13 10					14 10	
Hamble	d	10 13							11 13					12 13						13 13					14 13	
Netley	d	10 15							11 15					12 15						13 15					14 15	
Sholing	d	10 19							11 19					12 19						13 19					14 19	
Woolston	d	10 21							11 21					12 21						13 21					14 21	
Bitterne	d	10 25							11 25					12 25						13 25					14 25	
St Denys	d	10 28							11 28					12 28						13 28					14 28	
Southampton Central	a	10 36	10 38		11 02	11 08	11 18		11 36		12 02	12 08	12 18	12 36		13 02	13 08		13 18	13 36		14 02	14 08	14 18	14 36	

		SN 1	GW ◇	SN 1		SW 1	SW 1	SN 1	GW ◇	SN 1	SW 1	SW 1	SN 1	GW ◇		SN 1	SW 1	SW 1	SW 1	SN 1	GW ◇	SN 1	SW 1	GW		SW 1
Portsmouth Harbour	d		14 22				14 54		15 22			15 54		16 22				16 54	17 01		17 22		17 32			17 54
Portsmouth & Southsea	d		14 27			14 36	14 59		15 27		15 36	15 59		16 27			16 36	16 59	17 06		17 27		17 36			17 59
Fratton	d		14 31			14 40	15 03		15 31		15 40	16 03		16 31			16 40	17 03	17 10		17 31		17 40			18 03
Hilsea	d					14 44	15 07				15 44	16 07					16 44	17 07	17 14				17 44			18 07
Havant	d	14 23		14 37				15 23		15 37			16 23			16 37				17 23		17 37		18 00		
Cosham	d	14 29	14 39	14 44		14 49	15 12	15 29	15 39	15 44	15 49	16 12	16 29	16 39		16 44	16 49	17 12	17 20	17 29	17 39	17 44	17 49	18 06		18 12
Portchester	d	14 33				14 54	15 17	15 33			15 54	16 17	16 33				16 54	17 17	17 25	17 33			17 54			18 17
Fareham	a	14 38	14 46	14 52		14 59	15 22	15 38	15 46	15 52	15 59	16 22	16 38	16 46		16 52	16 59	17 22	17 30	17 38	17 46	17 52	17 59	18 14		18 22
	d	14 39	14 47	14 53		15 00		15 39	15 47	15 53	16 00		16 39	16 47		16 53	17 00			17 39	17 47	17 53	18 00	18 15		
Swanwick	d	14 45		14 59		15 06		15 45		15 59	16 06		16 45			16 59	17 06			17 45		17 59	18 06			
Bursledon	d					15 10					16 10						17 10						18 10			
Hamble	d					15 13					16 13						17 13						18 13			
Netley	d					15 15					16 15						17 15						18 15			
Sholing	d					15 19					16 19						17 19						18 19			
Woolston	d					15 21					16 21						17 21						18 21			
Bitterne	d					15 25					16 25						17 25						18 25			
St Denys	d					15 28					16 28						17 28						18 28			
Southampton Central	a	15 02	15 08	15 18		15 36		16 02	16 08	16 18	16 36		17 02	17 08		17 18	17 36			18 02	18 08	18 18	18 36	18 38		

		SN 1	GW ◇	SN 1	SW 1	SW 1	SN 1	GW ◇	SN 1	SW 1		SW 1	SN 1	GW ◇	SN 1	SW 1	SW 1	SN 1	SN 1	SW 1	SW 1	SN 1	SW 1	SW 1		
Portsmouth Harbour	d		18 22			18 54		19 22				19 54		20 22			20 54				21 54			23 24		
Portsmouth & Southsea	d		18 27		18 36	18 59		19 27		19 36		19 59		20 27		20 36	20 59			21 36	21 59		22 36	23 29		
Fratton	d		18 31		18 40	19 03		19 31		19 40		20 03		20 31		20 40	21 03			21 40	22 03		22 40	23 33		
Hilsea	d				18 44	19 07				19 44		20 07				20 44	21 07			21 44	22 07		22 44	23 37		
Havant	d	18 23		18 37			19 23		19 37				20 26		20 37			21 23	21 37			22 26				
Cosham	d	18 29	18 39	18 44	18 49	19 12	19 29	19 39	19 44	19 49		20 12	20 32		20 44	20 49	21 12	21 29	21 44	21 49	22 12	22 33	22 49	23 42		
Portchester	d	18 33			18 54	19 17	19 33			19 54		20 17	20 36			20 54	21 17	21 33		21 54	22 17		22 54	23 47		
Fareham	a	18 38	18 46	18 52	18 59	19 22	19 38	19 46	19 52	19 59		20 22	20 41	20 44	20 52	20 59	21 22	21 38	21 52	21 59	22 22	22 41	22 59	23 52		
	d	18 39	18 47	18 53	19 00		19 39	19 47	19 53	20 00			20 42	20 47	20 53	21 00		21 39	21 53	22 00		22 42	23 00			
Swanwick	d	18 45		18 59	19 06		19 45		19 59	20 06			20 48		20 59	21 06		21 45	21 59	22 06		22 48	23 06			
Bursledon	d				19 10					20 10						21 10				22 10			23 10			
Hamble	d				19 13					20 13						21 13				22 13			23 13			
Netley	d				19 15					20 15						21 15				22 15			23 15			
Sholing	d				19 19					20 19						21 19				22 19			23 19			
Woolston	d				19 21					20 21						21 21				22 21			23 21			
Bitterne	d				19 25					20 25						21 25				22 25			23 25			
St Denys	d				19 28					20 28						21 28				22 28			23 28			
Southampton Central	a	19 02	19 08	19 18	19 36		20 02	20 08	20 18	20 36			21 05	21 08	21 18	21 36		22 02	22 18	22 34		23 05	23 33			

For general notes see front of timetable
For details of catering facilities see
Directory of Train Operators

Table 165

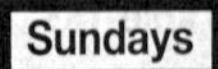

Sundays

Portsmouth and Fareham → Southampton

Network Diagram - see first page of Table 165

		SW 1	GW ⊼	SW 1	SW 1	SW 1	SW 1	GW ◇ ⊼	SW 1	SW 1	SW 1	SW 1	GW ◇ ⊼	SW 1	SW 1	GW ◇	SW 1	SW 1	GW ◇ ⊼	SW 1	SW 1	GW ◇ ⊼	SW 1	SW 1	GW ◇ ⊼	SW 1
Portsmouth Harbour	d	06 37	07 08	07 17		08 17		09 08	09 17		10 17		11 08	11 17			12 17		13 08	13 17		14 08	14 17		15 08	15 17
Portsmouth & Southsea	d	06 42	07 12	07 22	07 42	08 22	08 42	09 12	09 22	09 42	10 22	10 42	11 12	11 22	11 42		12 22	12 42	13 12	13 22	13 42	14 12	14 22	14 42	15 12	15 22
Fratton	d	06 46	07 16	07 26	07 46	08 26	08 46	09 16	09 26	09 46	10 26	10 46	11 16	11 26	11 46		12 26	12 46	13 16	13 26	13 46	14 16	14 26	14 46	15 16	15 26
Hilsea	d	06 50		07 30	07 50	08 30	08 50		09 30	09 50	10 30	10 50		11 30	11 50		12 30	12 50		13 30	13 50		14 30	14 50		15 30
Havant	d															12 10										
Cosham	d	06 55	07 23	07 35	07 55	08 35	08 55	09 23	09 35	09 55	10 35	10 55	11 23	11 35	11 55	12b23	12 35	12 55	13 23	13 35	13 55	14 23	14 35	14 55	15 23	15 35
Portchester	d	07 00		07 40	08 00	08 40	09 00		09 40	10 00	10 40	11 00		11 40	12 00		12 40	13 00		13 40	14 00		14 40	15 00		15 40
Fareham	a	07 05	07 31	07 45	08 05	08 45	09 05	09 31	09 45	10 05	10 45	11 05	11 31	11 45	12 05	12 31	12 45	13 05	13 31	13 45	14 05	14 31	14 45	15 05	15 31	15 45
	d	07 06	07 32		08 06		09 06	09 32		10 06		11 06	11 32		12 06	12 32		13 06	13 32		14 06	14 32		15 06	15 32	
Swanwick	d	07 12			08 12		09 12			10 12		11 12			12 12			13 12			14 12			15 12		
Bursledon	d	07 16			08 16		09 16			10 16		11 16			12 16			13 16			14 16			15 16		
Hamble	d	07 19			08 19		09 19			10 19		11 19			12 19			13 19			14 19			15 19		
Netley	d	07 21			08 21		09 21			10 21		11 21			12 21			13 21			14 21			15 21		
Sholing	d	07 25			08 25		09 25			10 25		11 25			12 25			13 25			14 25			15 25		
Woolston	d	07 27			08 27		09 27			10 27		11 27			12 27			13 27			14 27			15 27		
Bitterne	d	07 31			08 31		09 31			10 31		11 31			12 31			13 31			14 31			15 31		
St Denys	d	07 34			08 34		09 34			10 34		11 34			12 34			13 34			14 34			15 34		
Southampton Central	a	07 40	07 53		08 40		09 40	09 53		10 40		11 40	11 53		12 40	12 53		13 40	13 53		14 40	14 53		15 40	15 53	

		SW 1	GW ◇ ⊼	SW 1	GW ◇	SW 1	GW ◇ ⊼	SW 1	SW 1	GW ◇ ⊼	SW 1	GW ◇	SW 1	GW ◇ ⊼	SW 1	SW 1	GW ◇ ⊼	SW 1	SW 1	SW 1	SW 1	GW ◇ ⊼	SW 1	SW 1	SW 1
Portsmouth Harbour	d		16 08	16 17			17 08	17 17		18 08	18 17			19 08	19 17		20 08	20 17		21 17		22 07	22 17		23 17
Portsmouth & Southsea	d	15 42	16 12	16 22		16 42	17 12	17 22	17 42	18 12	18 22		18 42	19 12	19 22	19 42	20 12	20 22	20 42	21 22	21 42	22 12	22 22	22 42	23 22
Fratton	d	15 46	16 16	16 26		16 46	17 16	17 26	17 46	18 16	18 26		18 46	19 16	19 26	19 46	20 16	20 26	20 46	21 26	21 46	22 16	22 26	22 46	23 26
Hilsea	d	15 50		16 30		16 50		17 30	17 50		18 30		18 50		19 30	19 50		20 30	20 50	21 30	21 50		22 30	22 50	23 30
Havant	d				16 48							18 48													
Cosham	d	15 55	16 23	16 35	16 55	16 55	17 23	17 35	17 55	18 23	18 35		18 55	19 23	19 35	19 55	20 23	20 35	20 55	21 35	21 55	22 23	22 35	22 55	23 35
Portchester	d	16 00		16 40		17 00		17 40	18 00		18 40		19 00		19 40	20 00		20 40	21 00	21 40	22 00		22 40	23 00	23 40
Fareham	a	16 05	16 31	16 45	17 02	17 05	17 31	17 45	18 05	18 31	18 45	19 00	19 05	19 31	19 45	20 05	20 31	20 45	21 05	21 45	22 05	22 31	22 45	23 05	23 45
	d	16 06	16 32		17 03	17 06	17 32		18 06	18 32		19 01	19 06	19 32		20 06	20 32		21 06		22 06	22 32		23 06	
Swanwick	d	16 12				17 12			18 12				19 12			20 12			21 12		22 12			23 12	
Bursledon	d	16 16				17 16			18 16				19 16			20 16			21 16		22 16			23 16	
Hamble	d	16 19				17 19			18 19				19 19			20 19			21 19		22 19			23 19	
Netley	d	16 21				17 21			18 21				19 21			20 21			21 21		22 21			23 21	
Sholing	d	16 25				17 25			18 25				19 25			20 25			21 25		22 25			23 25	
Woolston	d	16 27				17 27			18 27				19 27			20 27			21 27		22 27			23 27	
Bitterne	d	16 31				17 31			18 31				19 31			20 31			21 31		22 31			23 31	
St Denys	d	16 34				17 34			18 34				19 34			20 34			21 34		22 34			23 34	
Southampton Central	a	16 40	16 53		17 24	17 42	17 53		18 40	18 53		19 22	19 42	19 53		20 40	20 53		21 40		22 40	22 53		23 40	

For general notes see front of timetable
For details of catering facilities see Directory of Train Operators

b Arr. 1216

To and from the Isle of Wight via Portsmouth and Ryde

Network Diagram - see first page of Table 165

Mondays to Fridays

Miles	Station		IL	IL	IL	IL	IL	IL	IL	IL	IL	IL	IL	IL	IL	IL	IL	IL	IL
—	Portsmouth Harbour	d	05 15	05 45	06 15	06 45	07 15	07 45	08 15	08 45	09 15	09 45	10 15	10 45	11 15	11 45	11b45	12 45	12c45
0	Ryde Pier Head	d	05 49	06 08	06 49	07 08	07 49	08 08	08 49	09 08	09 49	10 08	10 49	11 08	11 49	12 08	12 49	13 08	13 49
—	Ryde Esplanade	d	05 51	06 10	06 51	07 10	07 51	08 10	08 51	09 10	09 51	10 10	10 51	11 10	11 51	12 10	12 51	13 10	13 51
1¼	Ryde St Johns Road	d	05 54	06 13	06 54	07 13	07 54	08 13	08 54	09 13	09 54	10 13	10 54	11 13	11 54	12 13	12 54	13 13	13 54
2¼	Smallbrook Junction §	d											10 57	11 16	11 57	12 16	12 57	13 16	13 57
4¾	Brading	d	06 02	06 21	07 02	07 21	08 02	08 21	09 02	09 21	10 02	10 21	11 02	11 21	12 02	12 21	13 02	13 21	14 02
6½	Sandown	d	06 06	06 25	07 06	07 25	08 06	08 25	09 06	09 25	10 06	10 25	11 06	11 25	12 06	12 25	13 06	13 25	14 06
7¼	Lake	d	06 09	06 28	07 09	07 28	08 09	08 28	09 09	09 28	10 09	10 28	11 09	11 28	12 09	12 28	13 09	13 28	14 09
8½	Shanklin	a	06 13	06 32	07 13	07 32	08 13	08 32	09 13	09 32	10 13	10 32	11 13	11 32	12 13	12 32	13 13	13 32	14 13

Station		IL	IL	IL	IL	IL	IL	IL	IL	IL	IL	IL	IL	IL	IL	IL	IL	IL
Portsmouth Harbour	d	13 45	13e45	14 45	14f45	15 45	16 15	16 45	17 15	17 45	18 15	18 45	19 15	19 45	20 15	20 45	21 45	22 45
Ryde Pier Head	d	14 08	14 49	15 08	15 49	16 08	16 49	17 08	17 49	18 08	18 49	19 08	19 49	20 08	20 45	21 08	22 08	23 08
Ryde Esplanade	d	14 10	14 51	15 10	15 51	16 10	16 51	17 10	17 51	18 10	18 51	19 10	19 51	20 10	20 47	21 10	22 10	23 10
Ryde St Johns Road	d	14 13	14 54	15 13	15 54	16 13	16 54	17 13	17 54	18 13	18 54	19 13	19 54	20 13	20a50	21 13	22 13	23a13
Smallbrook Junction §	d	14 16	14 57	15 16	15 57	16 16	16 57											
Brading	d	14 21	15 02	15 21	16 02	16 21	17 02	17 21	18 02	18 21	19 02	19 21	20 02	20 21		21 21	22 21	
Sandown	d	14 25	15 06	15 25	16 06	16 25	17 06	17 25	18 06	18 25	19 06	19 25	20 06	20 25		21 25	22 25	
Lake	d	14 28	15 09	15 28	16 09	16 28	17 09	17 28	18 09	18 28	19 09	19 28	20 09	20 28		21 28	22 28	
Shanklin	a	14 32	15 13	15 32	16 13	16 32	17 13	17 32	18 13	18 32	19 13	19 32	20 13	20 32		21 32	22 32	

Saturdays

Station		IL	IL	IL	IL	IL	IL	IL	IL	IL	IL	IL	IL	IL	IL	IL	IL	IL
Portsmouth Harbour	d	05 15		06 15	06 45	07 15	07 45	08 15	08 45	09 15	09 45	10 15	10 45	11 15	11 45	12 15	12 45	12g45
Ryde Pier Head	d	05 49	06 08	06 49	07 08	07 49	08 08	08 49	09 08	09 49	10 08	10 49	11 08	11 49	12 08	12 49	13 08	13 49
Ryde Esplanade	d	05 51	06 10	06 51	07 10	07 51	08 10	08 51	09 10	09 51	10 10	10 51	11 10	11 51	12 10	12 51	13 10	13 51
Ryde St Johns Road	d	05 54	06 13	06 54	07 13	07 54	08 13	08 54	09 13	09 54	10 13	10 54	11 13	11 54	12 13	12 54	13 13	13 54
Smallbrook Junction §	d											10 57		11 57			13 16	13 57
Brading	d	06 02	06 21	07 02	07 21	08 02	08 21	09 02	09 21	10 02	10 21	11 02	11 21	12 02	12 21	13 02	13 21	14 02
Sandown	d	06 06	06 25	07 06	07 25	08 06	08 25	09 06	09 25	10 06	10 25	11 06	11 25	12 06	12 25	13 06	13 25	14 06
Lake	d	06 09	06 28	07 09	07 28	08 09	08 28	09 09	09 28	10 09	10 28	11 09	11 28	12 09	12 28	13 09	13 28	14 09
Shanklin	a	06 13	06 32	07 13	07 32	08 13	08 32	09 13	09 32	10 13	10 32	11 13	11 32	12 13	12 32	13 13	13 32	14 13

Station		IL	IL	IL	IL	IL	IL	IL	IL	IL	IL	IL	IL	IL	IL	IL	IL
Portsmouth Harbour	d	13 45	13h45	14 45	15 15	15 45	16 15	16 45	17 15	17 45	18 15	18 45		19 45	20 45	21 45	22 45
Ryde Pier Head	d	14 08	14 49	15 08	15 49	16 08	16 49	17 08	17 49	18 08	18 49	19 08	19 49	20 08	21 08	22 08	23 08
Ryde Esplanade	d	14 10	14 51	15 10	15 51	16 10	16 51	17 10	17 51	18 10	18 51	19 10	19 51	20 10	21 10	22 10	23 10
Ryde St Johns Road	d	14 13	14 54	15 13	15 54	16 13	16 54	17 13	17 54	18 13	18 54	19 13	19 54	20 13	21 13	22 13	23a13
Smallbrook Junction §	d	14 16	14 57		15 57	16 16											
Brading	d	14 21	15 02	15 21	16 02	16 21	17 02	17 21	18 02	18 21	19 02	19 21	20 02	20 21	21 21	22 21	
Sandown	d	14 25	15 06	15 25	16 06	16 25	17 06	17 25	18 06	18 25	19 06	19 25	20 06	20 25	21 25	22 25	
Lake	d	14 28	15 09	15 28	16 09	16 28	17 09	17 28	18 09	18 28	19 09	19 28	20 09	20 28	21 28	22 28	
Shanklin	a	14 32	15 13	15 32	16 13	16 32	17 13	17 32	18 13	18 32	19 13	19 32	20 13	20 32	21 32	22 32	

Sundays

Station		IL	IL	IL A	IL	IL A	IL	IL A	IL	IL A	IL	IL A	IL	IL A	IL	IL A	IL	IL
Portsmouth Harbour	d	06 15	07 15		08 15	08 45	09 15	09 45	10 15	10 45	11 15	11 45	12 15	12 45	13 15	13 45	14 15	14 45
Ryde Pier Head	d	06 49	07 49		08 49	09 08	09 49	10 08	10 49	11 08	11 49	12 08	12 49	13 08	13 49	14 08	14 49	15 08
Ryde Esplanade	d	06 51	07 51		08 51	09 10	09 51	10 10	10 51	11 10	11 51	12 10	12 51	13 10	13 51	14 10	14 51	15 10
Ryde St Johns Road	d	06 54	07 54	08 13	08 54	09 13	09 54	10 13	10 54	11 13	11 54	12 13	12 54	13 13	13 54	14 13	14 54	15 13
Smallbrook Junction §	d								10 57		11 57			13 16	13 57	14 16	14 57	
Brading	d	07 02	08 02	08 21	09 02	09 21	10 02	10 21	11 02	11 21	12 02	12 21	13 02	13 21	14 02	14 21	15 02	15 21
Sandown	d	07 06	08 06	08 25	09 06	09 25	10 06	10 25	11 06	11 25	12 06	12 25	13 06	13 25	14 06	14 25	15 06	15 25
Lake	d	07 09	08 09	08 28	09 09	09 28	10 09	10 28	11 09	11 28	12 09	12 28	13 09	13 28	14 09	14 28	15 09	15 28
Shanklin	a	07 13	08 13	08 32	09 13	09 32	10 13	10 32	11 13	11 32	12 13	12 32	13 13	13 32	14 13	14 32	15 13	15 32

Station		IL	IL	IL	IL	IL	IL	IL	IL	IL	IL	IL	IL	IL
Portsmouth Harbour	d	15 15	15 45	16 15	16 45	17 15	17 45	18 15	18 45	19 15	19 45	20 15	21 15	22 15
Ryde Pier Head	d	15 49	16 08	16 49	17 08	17 49	18 08	18 49	19 08	19 49	20 08	20 49	21 49	22 46
Ryde Esplanade	d	15 51	16 10	16 51	17 10	17 51	18 10	18 51	19 10	19 51	20 10	20 51	21 51	22 48
Ryde St Johns Road	d	15 54	16 13	16 54	17 13	17 54	18 13	18 54	19 13	19 54	20a13	20 54	21 54	22a51
Smallbrook Junction §	d	15 57	16 16											
Brading	d	16 02	16 21	17 02	17 21	18 02	18 21	19 02	19 21	20 02		21 02	22 02	
Sandown	d	16 06	16 25	17 06	17 25	18 06	18 25	19 06	19 25	20 06		21 06	22 06	
Lake	d	16 09	16 28	17 09	17 28	18 09	18 28	19 09	19 28	20 09		21 09	22 09	
Shanklin	a	16 13	16 32	17 13	17 32	18 13	18 32	19 13	19 32	20 13		21 13	22 13	

For general notes see front of timetable
For details of catering facilities see Directory of Train Operators

§ Smallbrook Jn is only open for access to The I.O.W. Steam Railway. For days of operation please enquire locally.

A From 6 April
b Friday 21 March & Mondays 24 March, 5 May dep.1215
c Friday 21 March & Mondays 24 March, 5 May dep.1315
e Friday 21 March & Mondays 24 March, 5 May dep.1415
f Friday 21 March & Mondays 24 March, 5 May dep.1515
g From 22 March dep. 1315
h From 22 March dep. 1415

To and from the Isle of Wight via Portsmouth and Ryde

Network Diagram - see first page of Table 165

Mondays to Fridays

Miles			IL	IL	IL	IL	IL	IL	IL	IL	IL	IL	IL	IL	IL	IL	IL	IL	IL
0	**Shanklin**	d			06 17	06 36	07 17	07 36	08 17	08 36	09 17	09 36	10 17	10 36	11 17	11 36	12 17	12 36	13 17
1¼	Lake	d			06 21	06 40	07 21	07 40	08 21	08 40	09 21	09 40	10 21	10 40	11 21	11 40	12 21	12 40	13 21
2	Sandown	d			06 24	06 43	07 24	07 43	08 24	08 43	09 24	09 43	10 24	10 43	11 24	11 43	12 24	12 43	13 24
3¾	Brading	d			06 28	06 47	07 28	07 47	08 28	08 47	09 28	09 47	10 28	10 47	11 28	11 47	12 28	12 47	13 28
6¼	Smallbrook Junction §	d											10 33	10 52	11 33	11 52	12 33	12 52	13 33
7¼	Ryde St Johns Road	d	05 36	05 55	06 36	06 55	07 36	07 55	08 36	08 55	09 36	09 55	10 36	10 55	11 36	11 55	12 36	12 55	13 36
8¼	**Ryde Esplanade**	d	05 39	05 58	06 39	06 58	07 39	07 58	08 39	08 58	09 39	09 58	10 39	10 58	11 39	11 58	12 39	12 58	13 39
8½	**Ryde Pier Head**	a	05 41	06 00	06 42	07 01	07 42	08 01	08 42	09 01	09 42	10 01	10 42	11 01	11 42	12 01	12 42	13 01	13 42
—	**Portsmouth Harbour** ⛴	a	06 03	06 33	07 03	07 33	08 03	08 33	09 03	09 33	10 03	10 30	11 00	11 33	12 00	12 33	13b33	13 33	14c30

		IL	IL	IL	IL	IL	IL	IL	IL	IL	IL	IL	IL	IL	IL	IL	IL	IL
Shanklin	d	13 36	14 17	14 36	15 17	15 36	16 17	16 36	17 17	17 36	18 17	18 36	19 17	19 36	20 17	20 36	21 36	22 36
Lake	d	13 40	14 21	14 40	15 21	15 40	16 21	16 40	17 21	17 40	18 21	18 40	19 21	19 40	20 21	20 40	21 40	22 40
Sandown	d	13 43	14 24	14 43	15 24	15 43	16 24	16 43	17 24	17 43	18 24	18 43	19 24	19 43	20 24	20 43	21 43	22 43
Brading	d	13 47	14 28	14 47	15 28	15 47	16 28	16 47	17 28	17 47	18 28	18 47	19 28	19 47	20 28	20 47	21 47	22 47
Smallbrook Junction §	d	13 52	14 33	14 52	15 33	15 52	16 33	16 52										
Ryde St Johns Road	d	13 55	14 36	14 55	15 36	15 55	16 36	16 55	17 36	17 55	18 36	18 55	19 36	19 55	20 36	20 55	21 55	22 55
Ryde Esplanade	d	13 58	14 39	14 58	15 39	15 58	16 39	16 58	17 39	17 58	18 39	18 58	19 39	19 58	20 39	20 58	21 58	22 58
Ryde Pier Head	a	14 01	14 42	15 01	15 42	16 01	16 42	17 01	17 42	18 01	18 42	19 01	19 42	20 01	20 42	21 01	22 01	23 01
Portsmouth Harbour ⛴	a	14 30	15e33	15 33	16f33	16 33	17 03	17 33	18 03	18 33	19 03	19 33	20 03	20 30	21 03	21 33	22 33	23 33

Saturdays

		IL	IL	IL	IL	IL	IL	IL	IL	IL	IL	IL	IL	IL	IL	IL	IL	IL
Shanklin	d			06 17	06 36	07 17	07 36	08 17	08 36	09 17	09 36	10 17	10 36	11 17	11 36	12 17	12 36	13 17
Lake	d			06 21	06 40	07 21	07 40	08 21	08 40	09 21	09 40	10 21	10 40	11 21	11 40	12 21	12 40	13 21
Sandown	d			06 24	06 43	07 24	07 43	08 24	08 43	09 24	09 43	10 24	10 43	11 24	11 43	12 24	12 43	13 24
Brading	d			06 28	06 47	07 28	07 47	08 28	08 47	09 28	09 47	10 28	10 47	11 28	11 47	12 28	12 47	13 28
Smallbrook Junction §	d												10 52		11 52		12 52	
Ryde St Johns Road	d	05 36	05 55	06 36	06 55	07 36	07 55	08 36	08 55	09 36	09 55	10 36	10 55	11 36	11 55	12 36	12 55	13 36
Ryde Esplanade	d	05 39	05 58	06 39	06 58	07 39	07 58	08 39	08 58	09 39	09 58	10 39	10 58	11 39	11 58	12 39	12 58	13 39
Ryde Pier Head	a	05 41	06 01	06 42	07 01	07 42	08 01	08 42	09 01	09 42	10 01	10 42	11 01	11 42	12 01	12 42	13 01	13 42
Portsmouth Harbour ⛴	a	06 03		07 03	07 33	08 03	08 33	09 03	09 33	10 03	10 33	11 03	11 33	12 03	12 33	13 03	13 33	14g33

		IL	IL	IL	IL	IL	IL	IL	IL	IL	IL	IL	IL	IL	IL	IL	IL	IL
Shanklin	d	13 36	14 17	14 36	15 17	15 36	16 17	16 36	17 17	17 36	18 17	18 36	19 17	19 36	20 17	20 36	21 36	22 36
Lake	d	13 40	14 21	14 40	15 21	15 40	16 21	16 40	17 21	17 40	18 21	18 40	19 21	19 40	20 21	20 40	21 40	22 40
Sandown	d	13 43	14 24	14 43	15 24	15 43	16 24	16 43	17 24	17 43	18 24	18 43	19 24	19 43	20 24	20 43	21 43	22 43
Brading	d	13 47	14 28	14 47	15 28	15 47	16 28	16 47	17 28	17 47	18 28	18 47	19 28	19 47	20 28	20 47	21 47	22 47
Smallbrook Junction §	d			14 52		15 52												
Ryde St Johns Road	d	13 55	14 36	14 55	15 36	15 55	16 36	16 55	17 36	17 55	18 36	18 55	19 36	19 55	20a36	20 55	21 55	22 55
Ryde Esplanade	d	13 58	14 39	14 58	15 39	15 58	16 39	16 58	17 39	17 58	18 39	18 58	19 39	19 58		20 58	21 58	22 58
Ryde Pier Head	a	14 01	14 42	15 01	15 42	16 01	16 42	17 01	17 42	18 01	18 42	19 01	19 42	20 01		21 01	22 01	23 01
Portsmouth Harbour ⛴	a	14 33	15h33	15 33	16 03	16 33	17 03	17 33	18 03	18 33	19 03	19 33		20 33		21 33	22 33	23 33

Sundays

		IL	IL	IL	IL A	IL	IL A	IL	IL A	IL	IL A	IL	IL A	IL	IL A	IL	IL A	IL B
Shanklin	d		07 17	08 17	08 36	09 17	09 36	10 17	10 36	11 17	11 36	12 17	12 36	13 17	13 36	14 17	14 36	
Lake	d		07 21	08 21	08 40	09 21	09 40	10 21	10 40	11 21	11 40	12 21	12 40	13 21	13 40	14 21	14 40	
Sandown	d		07 24	08 24	08 43	09 24	09 43	10 24	10 43	11 24	11 43	12 24	12 43	13 24	13 43	14 24	14 43	
Brading	d		07 28	08 28	08 47	09 28	09 47	10 28	10 47	11 28	11 47	12 28	12 47	13 28	13 47	14 28	14 47	
Smallbrook Junction §	d								10 52		11 52		12 52				14 52	
Ryde St Johns Road	d	06 36	07 36	08 36	08 55	09 36	09 55	10 36	10 55	11 36	11 55	12 36	12 55	13 36	13 55	14 36	14 55	14 55
Ryde Esplanade	d	06 39	07 39	08 39	08 58	09 39	09 58	10 39	10 58	11 39	11 58	12 39	12 58	13 39	13 58	14 39	14 58	14 58
Ryde Pier Head	a	06 42	07 42	08 42	09 01	09 42	10 01	10 42	11 01	11 42	12 01	12 42	13 01	13 42	14 01	14 42	15 01	15 01
Portsmouth Harbour ⛴	a	07 03	08 03	09 03	09 33	10 03	10 33	11 03	11 33	12 03	12 33	13 03	13 33	14 03	14 33	15 03	15 33	15 33

		IL	IL	IL	IL	IL	IL	IL	IL	IL	IL	IL	IL	IL
Shanklin	d	15 17	15 36	16 17	16 36	17 17	17 36	18 17	18 36	19 17	19 36	20 17	21 17	22 17
Lake	d	15 21	15 40	16 21	16 40	17 21	17 40	18 21	18 40	19 21	19 40	20 21	21 21	22 21
Sandown	d	15 24	15 43	16 24	16 43	17 24	17 43	18 24	18 43	19 24	19 43	20 24	21 24	22 24
Brading	d	15 28	15 47	16 28	16 47	17 28	17 47	18 28	18 47	19 28	19 47	20 28	21 28	22 28
Smallbrook Junction §	d		15 52											
Ryde St Johns Road	d	15 36	15 55	16 36	16 55	17 36	17 55	18 36	18 55	19 36	19 55	20 36	21 36	22 36
Ryde Esplanade	d	15 39	15 58	16 39	16 58	17 39	17 58	18 39	18 58	19 39	19 58	20 39	21 39	22 39
Ryde Pier Head	a	15 42	16 01	16 42	17 01	17 42	18 01	18 42	19 01	19 42	20 01	20 42	21 42	22 42
Portsmouth Harbour ⛴	a	16 03	16 33	17 03	17 33	18 03	18 33	19 03	19 30	20 03	20 33	21 03	22 03	23 03

For general notes see front of timetable
For details of catering facilities see Directory of Train Operators

§ Smallbrook Jn is only open for access to the I.O.W. Steam Railway. For days of operation please enquire locally.

A From 6 April
B Until 30 March
b Friday 21 March, Mondays 24 March & 5 May arr. 1303
c Friday 21 March, Mondays 24 March & 5 May arr. 1403
e Friday 21 March, Mondays 24 March & 5 May arr. 1503
f Friday 21 March, Mondays 24 March & 5 May arr. 1603
g From 22 March arr. 1403
h From 22 March arr. 1503

London → East Croydon and Purley
COMPLETE SERVICE

Station		SN MX 1	SN MO	SN MO 1	SN MX	SN MX 1	FC	SN 1	SN	SN MX	FC MX	SN	SN 1	FC MO 1	FC MX 1	SN 1	FC 1	SN 1	FC	FC 1		SN 1	FC 1	FC 1	SN 1
London Victoria 15	⊖ d	23p47				00 05		00 14	00 17			00 42	01 00			02 00		03 02				04 00			05 02
Clapham Junction 10	d	23p53		00 02		00 11		00 20	00 23			00 49	01 08			02 08		03 08				04 08			05 08
London Charing Cross 4	⊖ d		23p36		23p45					00 12															
London Waterloo (East) 4	⊖ d		23p39		23p48					00 15															
St Pancras International 15	⊖ d						23p54				00 24			00 54	00 54		01 54		02 54	03 25			03 54	04 25	
Farringdon 3	⊖ d						23p59				00 29														
City Thameslink 3	d																								
London Blackfriars 3	⊖ d						00 04				00 34			01 04	01 04		02 04		03 04	03 34			04 04	04 34	
London Bridge 4	⊖ d		23p44		23p53		00 11			00 26	00 41														
Norwood Junction 2	a		00 09		00 16					00 49															
East Croydon	a	00 05	00 13	00 20	00 20	00 24	00 26	00 32	00 42	00 53	00 56	01 10	01 21	01 30	01 32	02 21	02 30	03 21	03 30	04 00		04 21	04 30	05 00	05 21
South Croydon 4	a		00 16		00 23																				
Purley Oaks	a		00 19		00 26																				
Purley 4	a	00 12	00 22		00 29			00 38					01 27			02 27		03 27				04 27			05 26

Station		FC 1	SN 1	FC 1	SN 1	FC 1	SN 1	SN 1	SN 1	FC 1	SN 1	SN	SN	SN 1	SN 1	FC 1	SN 1	SN 1		SN	FC 1	SN	SN 1	SN 1	FC 1
London Victoria 15	⊖ d		05 32		05 23			06 02	06 17		06 21		06 15		06 32		06 47			06 45			07 02	07 06	
Clapham Junction 10	d		05 38		05 33			06 08	06 23		06 27		06 22		06 38		06 53			06 51			07 08	07 12	
London Charing Cross 4	⊖ d											06 05													
London Waterloo (East) 4	⊖ d											06 08													
St Pancras International 15	⊖ d	04 54		05 14		05 34				06 04						06 24					06 39				06 57
Farringdon 3	⊖ d	04 59		05 19		05 39				06 09						06 29					06 44				07 02
City Thameslink 3	d									06 11						06 31					06 47				07 07
London Blackfriars 3	⊖ d	05 04		05 24		05 44				06 14						06 36					06 50				07 10
London Bridge 4	⊖ d			05 31		05 50	05 55			06 21		06 13		06 30		06 43		06 56			07 00	06 54			07 16
Norwood Junction 2	a				05 49							06 37		06 44								07 14			
East Croydon	a	05 30	05 48	05 51	05 53	06 04	06 09	06 17	06 34	06 35	06 38	06 41	06 45	06 48	06 48	06 56	07 03	07 09		07 11	07 15	07 18	07 21	07 21	07 31
South Croydon 4	a				05 56							06 45										07 21			
Purley Oaks	a											06 48										07 24			
Purley 4	a		05 54					06 23			06 44	06 51	06 56		06 54							07 27		07 27	

Station		SN 1	SN 1	SN 1	SN 1	SN	SE 43	SN 1	SN 1	FC 1	SN	SN	SN 1	SN	SN 1	SN 1		SN 1	SN	SN 1	SN 1	SN 1	SN 1	FC 1	SN 1
London Victoria 15	⊖ d	07 17		07 23		07 20			07 36				07 47		07 52				07 45	08 02		08 06			08 09
Clapham Junction 10	d	07 23		07 29		07 27			07 42				07 53		07 58				07 51	08 08		08 12			08 15
London Charing Cross 4	⊖ d																								
London Waterloo (East) 4	⊖ d																								
St Pancras International 15	⊖ d									07 17														07 48	
Farringdon 3	⊖ d									07 22														07 52	
City Thameslink 3	d									07 27														07 55	
London Blackfriars 3	⊖ d									07 32														08 00	
London Bridge 4	⊖ d		07 20		07 28		07 34	07 36		07 40	07 25	07 46		07 40		07 54		07 56			08 03		08 07		
Norwood Junction 2	a		07 32		07 41						07 48			08 00		08 06					08 14				
East Croydon	a	07 33	07 36	07 41	07 45	07 48	07 48	07 51	07 52	07 55	07 55	08 00	08 03	08 04	08 08	08 11		08 11	08 13	08 18	08 19	08 22	08 22	08 25	08 26
South Croydon 4	a					07 51								08 07					08 16						
Purley Oaks	a					07 54								08 10					08 19						
Purley 4	a					07 57			07 58		08 01			08 13					08 22		08 27				

Station		SN	SN	SN 1	FC 1	SN 1	SN 1	SN 1	SN	SN	SN 1	SN 1	SN 1	SN		SN 1	SN	SN	SN 1	SN 1	FC 1	SN 1	SN	SN 1	SN
London Victoria 15	⊖ d			08 17			08 20		08 15		08 32		08 36			08 38			08 47			08 53	08 45		
Clapham Junction 10	d			08 23			08 28		08 22		08 38		08 43			08 46			08 53			08 59	08 52		
London Charing Cross 4	⊖ d																								
London Waterloo (East) 4	⊖ d																								
St Pancras International 15	⊖ d				08 00																08 20				
Farringdon 3	⊖ d				08 04																08 24				
City Thameslink 3	d				08 09																08 27				
London Blackfriars 3	⊖ d				08 12																08 32				
London Bridge 4	⊖ d	08 05	08 09		08 19	08 23		08 25		08 27		08 30		08 21			08 41	08 36		08 49				09 00	08 37
Norwood Junction 2	a	08 25	08 28					08 37				08 44		08 49				08 56		09 01				09 11	09 13
East Croydon	a	08 29	08 32	08 33	08 36	08 37	08 39	08 41	08 43	08 45	08 48	08 49	08 52	08 53		08 56	08 57	09 00	09 03	09 05	09 06	09 09	09 13	09 15	09 17
South Croydon 4	a	08 32						08 44	08 47									09 03					09 16		
Purley Oaks	a	08 35							08 50									09 06					09 19		
Purley 4	a	08 38	08 41						08 53			08 58					09 04	09 09		09 12			09 22	09 27	09 25

Station		SN 1	SN 1	SN 1	FC 1	SE 13	SN	SN 1	SN	FC 1	SN 1	SN		SN	SN 1	SN 1	SN 1	FC 1	SN	SN 1	SN	SN 1	FC 1	SN 1	SN
London Victoria 15	⊖ d	09 02		09 06				09 17			09 23	09 15			09 32		09 36			09 47				09 53	09 45
Clapham Junction 10	d	09 08		09 12				09 23			09 29	09 22			09 38		09 42			09 53		09 54		09 59	09 52
London Charing Cross 4	⊖ d																								
London Waterloo (East) 4	⊖ d																								
St Pancras International 15	⊖ d				08 47					09 04								09 20					09 39		
Farringdon 3	⊖ d				08 52					09 08								09 24					09 44		
City Thameslink 3	d				08 55					09 13								09 27					09 46		
London Blackfriars 3	⊖ d				08 58					09 17								09 34					09 49		
London Bridge 4	⊖ d		09 02		09 06	09 11	09 05		09 19	09 25				09 07		09 33		09 42	09 35		09 47		09 56		
Norwood Junction 2	a						09 25		09 32					09 43		09 45			09 55		09 59				
East Croydon	a	09 18	09 22	09 22	09 23	09 25	09 29	09 33	09 36	09 39	09 39	09 43		09 47	09 48	09 49	09 51	09 54	09 59	10 03	10 05	10 07	10 09	10 09	10 13
South Croydon 4	a						09 32					09 46							10 02						10 16
Purley Oaks	a						09 35					09 49							10 05						10 19
Purley 4	a						09 38		09 42			09 52		09 54		09 56			10 08		10 11				10 22

For general notes see front of timetable
For details of catering facilities see
Directory of Train Operators

Table 175 **Mondays to Fridays**

London → East Croydon and Purley

COMPLETE SERVICE

		SN	SN 1	SE 13	SN 1	SN 1	FC 1	SN	SN 1	SN			FC 1	SN 1	SN	SN	SN 1	SN 1	SN 1	FC 1	SN	SN 1	SN	SN 1	FC 1
London Victoria 15	⊖ d		10 02		10 06				10 17					10 23	10 15		10 32		10 36			10 47			
Clapham Junction 10	d		10 08		10 12				10 23					10 29	10 22		10 38		10 42			10 53		10 54	
London Charing Cross 4	⊖ d																						10 40		
London Waterloo (East) 4	⊖ d																						10 43		
St Pancras International 15	⊖ d						09 54						10 09							10 24					10 39
Farringdon 3	⊖ d						09 59						10 14							10 29					10 44
City Thameslink 3	d						10 01						10 16							10 31					10 46
London Blackfriars 3	⊖ d						10 05						10 20							10 35					10 50
London Bridge 4	⊖ d	09 37		10 03		10 08	10 11	10 05		10 17			10 26			10 08		10 33		10 41	10 35		10 48		10 56
Norwood Junction 2	a	10 13		10 16				10 25		10 31						10 43		10 45			10 55				
East Croydon	a	10 17	10 18	10 19	10 22	10 22	10 24	10 29	10 33	10 35			10 39	10 39	10 43	10 47	10 48	10 49	10 52	10 54	10 59	11 03	11 05	11 07	11 09
South Croydon 4	a							10 32							10 46						11 02				
Purley Oaks	a							10 35							10 49						11 05				
Purley 4	a	10 24		10 26				10 38		10 41					10 52	10 54		10 56			11 08		11 11		

		SN 1	SN	SN	SN 1	SE 13	SN 1	SN 1	FC 1	SN	SN 1	SN			FC 1	SN 1	SN	SN	SN 1	SN 1	SN 1	SN 1	FC 1	SN
London Victoria 15	⊖ d	10 53	10 45		11 02		11 06				11 17		and at the same minutes past each hour until			15 23	15 15		15 32		15 36			
Clapham Junction 10	d	10 59	10 52		11 08		11 12				11 23					15 29	15 22		15 38		15 42			
London Charing Cross 4	⊖ d											11 10												
London Waterloo (East) 4	⊖ d											11 13												
St Pancras International 15	⊖ d								10 54						15 09								15 24	
Farringdon 3	⊖ d								10 59						15 14								15 29	
City Thameslink 3	d								11 01						15 16								15 31	
London Blackfriars 3	⊖ d								11 05						15 20								15 35	
London Bridge 4	⊖ d			10 38		11 03		11 08	11 11	11 05		11 18			15 26			15 08		15 33		15 38	15 41	15 35
Norwood Junction 2	a			11 13		11 16				11 25								15 43		15 45				15 55
East Croydon	a	11 09	11 13	11 17	11 18	11 19	11 22	11 22	11 24	11 29	11 33	11 35			15 39	15 39	15 43	15 47	15 48	15 49	15 52	15 52	15 54	15 59
South Croydon 4	a		11 16							11 32						15 42	15 46							16 02
Purley Oaks	a		11 19							11 35							15 49							16 05
Purley 4	a		11 22	11 24		11 26				11 38		11 41					15 52	15 54		15 56				16 08

		SN 1	SN	SN 1	FC 1	SN 1	SN	SN	SN 1	SE 13	SN 1	SN 1		FC 1	SN 1	SN	SN 1	SN	SN 1	FC 1	SN	SN	SN 1	SN 1	SN 1
London Victoria 15	⊖ d	15 47				15 53	15 45		16 02		16 06				16 10		16 17		16 23		16 15		16 32		16 36
Clapham Junction 10	d	15 53		15 54		15 59	15 52		16 08		16 12				16 16		16 23		16 29		16 22		16 38		16 42
London Charing Cross 4	⊖ d		15 40															16 08							
London Waterloo (East) 4	⊖ d		15 43															16 11							
St Pancras International 15	⊖ d				15 39									15 54						16 09					
Farringdon 3	⊖ d				15 44									15 59						16 14					
City Thameslink 3	d				15 46									16 01						16 16					
London Blackfriars 3	⊖ d				15 50									16 05						16 20					
London Bridge 4	⊖ d		15 48		15 56			15 38		16 03		16 08		16 11		16 05		16 16		16 26		16 07		16 33	
Norwood Junction 2	a							16 13		16 16						16 25		16 29				16 43			
East Croydon	a	16 03	16 05	16 07	16 09	16 09	16 13	16 17	16 18	16 19	16 22	16 23		16 24	16 28	16 29	16 33	16 34	16 39	16 40	16 43	16 47	16 48	16 50	16 52
South Croydon 4	a					16 12	16 16									16 32			16 42		16 46				
Purley Oaks	a						16 19									16 35					16 49				
Purley 4	a		16 11				16 22	16 24		16 26					16 34	16 38		16 41			16 52	16 54			

		SN 1	SN 1	FC 1	SN	SN 1	SN 1	SN 1	SE 13	SN		SN	SN 1	FC 1	SN 1	SN 1	SN 1	SN 1	SN 1	SN 1	SN	SN 1	SN 1	SN 1	SN 1
London Victoria 15	⊖ d		16 38			16 47		16 53		16 45			17 02		17 07		17 10			17 17		17 21	17 24		
Clapham Junction 10	d		16 45			16 53		16 59		16 52			17 08		17 13		17 16			17 23		17 27	17 30		
London Charing Cross 4	⊖ d																								
London Waterloo (East) 4	⊖ d																								
St Pancras International 15	⊖ d			16 27																					
Farringdon 3	⊖ d			16 32																					
City Thameslink 3	d			16 34																					
London Blackfriars 3	⊖ d			16 37																					
London Bridge 4	⊖ d	16 38		16 46	16 35		16 53		16 57			16 59		17 08		17 10		17 13	17 17		17 19			17 30	17 32
Norwood Junction 2	a	16 50			16 55							17 12									17 33				
East Croydon	a	16 54	16 55	16 59	16 59	17 03	17 07	17 09	17 11	17 13		17 16	17 18	17 20	17 23	17 24	17 26	17 27	17 31	17 33	17 37	17 37	17 40	17 44	17 46
South Croydon 4	a				17 02			17 12		17 22		17 19						17 30			17 40				
Purley Oaks	a				17 05					17 25		17 22									17 43				
Purley 4	a	17 00			17 08					17 28		17 25					17 33		17 37		17 46				

		SN 1	FC 1	SN	SN 1	SN 1	SN	SN 1		SN 1	SN 1	SN 1	SN 1	FC 1	SN 1	SN 1	SN 1	SN 1	SN	FC 1	SN	SN 1	SN 1	SN 1	SN 1
London Victoria 15	⊖ d	17 32		17 34	17 37	17 40					17 47				17 53			18 02			18 04	18 07	18 10		
Clapham Junction 10	d			17 40	17 43	17 46		17 34			17 53				17 59						18 10	18 13	18 16		18 06
London Charing Cross 4	⊖ d																								
London Waterloo (East) 4	⊖ d																								
St Pancras International 15	⊖ d		17 09											17 35						17 46					
Farringdon 3	⊖ d		17 14											17 40						17 50					
City Thameslink 3	d		17 16											17 42						17 53					
London Blackfriars 3	⊖ d		17 20											17 46						17 57					
London Bridge 4	⊖ d		17 32				17 39			17 46		17 50	17 52	17 52		17 59	18 03		18 01					18 12	
Norwood Junction 2	a						17 53												18 15						
East Croydon	a	17 47	17 49	17 51	17 53	17 56	17 57	17 59		17 59	18 03	18 04	18 06	18 08	18 10	18 12	18 16	18 17	18 19	18 20	18 21	18 23	18 26	18 26	18 28
South Croydon 4	a			17 54			18 00												18 22		18 24				
Purley Oaks	a			17 57			18 03												18 25		18 27				
Purley 4	a			18 00		18 02	18 06												18 28		18 30		18 32		

For general notes see front of timetable
For details of catering facilities see Directory of Train Operators

Table 175

London → East Croydon and Purley

COMPLETE SERVICE

		SN	SN	SN	SN	FC		SN	SN	SN	SN	SN	FC	SN	SN	SN	SE	SN	SN	FC	SN	SN	SN	SN	FC
		1	1	1		1		1	1		1	1	1	1		1	13	1	1	1		1	1	1	1
London Victoria 15	⊖ d		18 17	18 21				18 24		18 17	18 32			18 40		18 47					18 53	19 02	19 06		
Clapham Junction 10	d		18 23	18 27				18 30		18 25	18 38			18 46		18 53		18 55			18 59	19 08	19 12		
London Charing Cross 4	⊖ d																								
London Waterloo (East) 4	⊖ d																								
St Pancras International 15	⊖ d					18 09														18 39					18 54
Farringdon 3	⊖ d					18 14														18 44					18 59
City Thameslink 3	d					18 16														18 46					19 01
London Blackfriars 3	⊖ d					18 20														18 49					19 04
London Bridge 4	⊖ d	18 16			18 20	18 26			18 31			18 34	18 38		18 42		18 48		18 54	18 56				19 08	19 12
Norwood Junction 2	a				18 35										18 56				19 05						
East Croydon	a	18 29	18 33	18 37	18 38	18 40		18 41	18 44	18 46	18 48	18 48	18 52	18 56	19 00	19 03	19 03	19 07	19 09	19 10	19 11	19 18	19 22	19 22	19 24
South Croydon 4	a				18 41				18 47	18 52					19 03				19 12		19 14				
Purley Oaks	a				18 44					18 55					19 06						19 17				
Purley 4	a				18 47					18 58		18 54		19 01	19 09						19 20				

		SN	SN	SN		FC	SN	SN	SN	SN	FC	SN	SN	SN	SN	SN	SN	SN	FC	SN	SN	SN	FC	SN	SN
		1		1		1	1		1	1	1	1		1	1	1		1	1	1	1	1	1	1	
London Victoria 15	⊖ d	19 10	19 00	19 17			19 23		19 32	19 36		19 40	19 31	19 47				19 53		20 02		20 06		20 10	20 00
Clapham Junction 10	d	19 16	19 08	19 23			19 29		19 38	19 42		19 46	19 38	19 53		19 54		19 59		20 08		20 12		20 16	20 08
London Charing Cross 4	⊖ d																19 37								
London Waterloo (East) 4	⊖ d																19 40								
St Pancras International 15	⊖ d					19 09					19 24								19 39				19 54		
Farringdon 3	⊖ d					19 14					19 29								19 44				19 59		
City Thameslink 3	d					19 16					19 31								19 47				20 01		
London Blackfriars 3	⊖ d					19 19					19 34								19 54				20 04		
London Bridge 4	⊖ d					19 27		19 15			19 41				19 52		19 45		20 01		20 05		20 11		
Norwood Junction 2	a							19 39							20 03		20 05				20 16				
East Croydon	a	19 28	19 30	19 33		19 39	19 39	19 43	19 48	19 52	19 54	19 58	19 59	20 03	20 06	20 07	20 09	20 09	20 14	20 19	20 19	20 22	20 23	20 28	20 29
South Croydon 4	a		19 34					19 46					20 02				20 15								20 32
Purley Oaks	a		19 37					19 49					20 05				20 18								20 35
Purley 4	a	19 33	19 41					19 52				20 03	20 08		20 11		20 21							20 33	20 38

		SN		SN	SN	SN	SN	SN	SN	FC	SN	SN	SN	SN	SN	SN	SN	SN	SN	SN	FC	SN		SN	SN
		1		1	1		1	1	1	1	1		1	1	1	1		1	1	1	1	1			1
London Victoria 15	⊖ d	20 17		20 23			20 32		20 36		20 40	20 30	20 47		20 53			21 02		21 06		21 10		21 00	21 17
Clapham Junction 10	d	20 23		20 29			20 38		20 42		20 46	20 38	20 53	20 54	20 59			21 08		21 12		21 16		21 08	21 23
London Charing Cross 4	⊖ d					20 07											20 37								
London Waterloo (East) 4	⊖ d					20 10											20 40								
St Pancras International 15	⊖ d									20 24											20 54				
Farringdon 3	⊖ d									20 29											20 59				
City Thameslink 3	d									20 31											21 01				
London Blackfriars 3	⊖ d									20 34											21 04				
London Bridge 4	⊖ d				20 28	20 15		20 35		20 41						20 58	20 45		21 05		21 11				
Norwood Junction 2	a					20 38		20 46									21 08		21 16						
East Croydon	a	20 33		20 39	20 40	20 42	20 48	20 49	20 52	20 54	20 58	20 59	21 03	21 07	21 09	21 10	21 12	21 18	21 19	21 22	21 24	21 28		21 29	21 33
South Croydon 4	a					20 45						21 02					21 15							21 32	
Purley Oaks	a					20 48						21 05					21 18							21 35	
Purley 4	a					20 51					21 03	21 08					21 21					21 33		21 38	

		SN	SN	SN	SN	SN	FC	SN	SN	SN	SN	SN	SN	SN	SN	SN	FC	SN	SN	SN		SN	SN	SN	SN
		1		1	1	1	1	1		1	1	1		1	1	1	1	1		1		1		1	1
London Victoria 15	⊖ d	21 23		21 32		21 36		21 40	21 30	21 47		21 53		22 02		22 06		22 10	22 00	22 17		22 23		22 32	22 36
Clapham Junction 10	d	21 29		21 38		21 42		21 46	21 38	21 53	21 54	21 59		22 08		22 12		22 16	22 08	22 23		22 29		22 38	22 42
London Charing Cross 4	⊖ d		21 07										21 37										22 07		
London Waterloo (East) 4	⊖ d		21 10										21 40										22 10		
St Pancras International 15	⊖ d						21 24										21 54								
Farringdon 3	⊖ d						21 29										21 59								
City Thameslink 3	d						21 31										22 01								
London Blackfriars 3	⊖ d						21 34										22 04								
London Bridge 4	⊖ d		21 15		21 35		21 41						21 45		22 05		22 11						22 15		
Norwood Junction 2	a		21 38		21 46								22 08		22 16								22 38		
East Croydon	a	21 39	21 42	21 48	21 49	21 52	21 54	21 58	21 59	22 03	22 07	22 09	22 12	22 18	22 19	22 22	22 24	22 28	22 29	22 33		22 39	22 42	22 48	22 52
South Croydon 4	a		21 45						22 02				22 15						22 32				22 45		
Purley Oaks	a		21 48						22 05				22 18						22 35				22 48		
Purley 4	a		21 51					22 03	22 08				22 21					22 33	22 38				22 51		

		FC	SN	SN	SN	SN	SN	SN	SN	SN	FC	SN	SN	SN	SN	SN	SN	FC		SN	SN	SN	FC		
		1	1		1	1		1	1	1	1	1		1		1	1	1		1	1				
London Victoria 15	⊖ d		22 40	22 30	22 47	22 53			23 02	23 06		23 10	23 00	23 17		23 24	23 32			23 47	23 49				
Clapham Junction 10	d		22 46	22 38	22 53	22 59			23 08	23 12		23 16	23 08	23 23		23 30	23 38			23 53	23 56				
London Charing Cross 4	⊖ d						22 37								23 07							23 45			
London Waterloo (East) 4	⊖ d						22 40								23 10							23 48			
St Pancras International 15	⊖ d	22 24									22 54							23 24					23 54		
Farringdon 3	⊖ d	22 29									22 59							23 29					23 59		
City Thameslink 3	d	22 31									23 01														
London Blackfriars 3	⊖ d	22 34									23 04							23 34					00 04		
London Bridge 4	⊖ d	22 41					22 45	23 00			23 11				23 15			23 41				23 53	00 11		
Norwood Junction 2	a						23 08	23 11							23 38							00 16			
East Croydon	a	22 54	22 58	22 59	23 03	23 09	23 12	23 16	23 18	23 22	23 24	23 28	23 29	23 33	23 42	23 42	23 51	23 56		00 05	00 09	00 20	00 26		
South Croydon 4	a			23 02			23 15						23 32		23 45							00 23			
Purley Oaks	a			23 05			23 18						23 35		23 48							00 26			
Purley 4	a		23 03	23 08			23 21					23 33	23 38		23 51					00 12		00 29			

For general notes see front of timetable
For details of catering facilities see
Directory of Train Operators

London → East Croydon and Purley

COMPLETE SERVICE

Station		SN ■1	SN	SN ■1	FC	SN ■1	SN	SN	FC	SN	SN ■1	FC ■1	SN ■1	FC ■1	SN ■1	FC ■1	SN ■1	FC ■1	FC ■1	SN ■1	FC ■1	SN ■1	SN ■1
London Victoria 15	⊖ d	23p47		00 05		00 14	00 17			00 42	01 00		02 02		03 00		04 00			05 02		05 32	05 25
Clapham Junction 10	d	23p53		00 11		00 20	00 23			00 49	01 08		02 08		03 08		04 08			05 08		05 38	05 31
London Charing Cross 4	⊖ d		23p45					00 12															
London Waterloo (East) 4	⊖ d		23p48					00 15															
St Pancras International 15	⊖ d				23p54				00 24			00 54		01 54		02 54		03 54	04 23		04 54		
Farringdon 3	⊖ d				23p59				00 29												04 59		
City Thameslink 3	d																						
London Blackfriars 3	⊖ d				00 04				00 34			01 04		02 04		03 04		04 04	04 34		05 04		
London Bridge 4	⊖ d		23p53		00 11			00 26	00 41														
Norwood Junction 2	a		00 16					00 49															05 47
East Croydon	a	00 05	00 20	00 24	00 26	00 32	00 42	00 53	00 56	01 10	01 21	01 32	02 21	02 30	03 21	03 30	04 21	04 30	05 00	05 21	05 32	05 48	05 51
South Croydon 4	a		00 23																				05 54
Purley Oaks	a		00 26																				
Purley 4	a	00 12	00 29			00 38					01 27		02 27		03 27		04 27			05 26		05 53	

Station		FC ■1	SN ■1	SN ■1	FC ■1	SN ■1	FC ■1	SN ■1	SN	SN ■1	FC ■1	SN ■1	SN	SN ■1	SN ■1	FC ■1	SN ■1	SN	SN	FC ■1	SN ■1	SN	SN ■1
London Victoria 15	⊖ d			06 10		06 23		06 40					06 45	07 06			07 10				07 23	07 15	07 32
Clapham Junction 10	d			06 16		06 29		06 46		06 54			06 52	07 12			07 16				07 29	07 22	07 38
London Charing Cross 4	⊖ d																						
London Waterloo (East) 4	⊖ d																						
St Pancras International 15	⊖ d	05 34			06 04		06 24				06 39					06 54				07 09			
Farringdon 3	⊖ d	05 39			06 09		06 29				06 44					06 59				07 14			
City Thameslink 3	d																						
London Blackfriars 3	⊖ d	05 44			06 20		06 35				06 50					07 05				07 20			
London Bridge 4	⊖ d	05 50	06 08		06 26		06 41		06 47		06 56	06 50			07 08	07 11		07 05	07 18	07 26			
Norwood Junction 2	a								07 00									07 25	07 31				
East Croydon	a	06 04	06 22	06 27	06 39	06 39	06 54	06 57	07 05	07 07	07 09	07 09	07 13	07 22	07 22	07 24	07 28	07 29	07 34	07 39	07 39	07 43	07 48
South Croydon 4	a												07 16					07 32				07 46	
Purley Oaks	a												07 19					07 35				07 49	
Purley 4	a			06 33				07 03	07 11				07 22				07 36	07 38	07 41			07 52	

Station		SN ■1	SN ■1	FC ■1	SN	SN ■1	SN	SN ■1	FC ■1	SN ■1	SN	SN	SN ■1	SE 13	SN ■1	SN ■1	FC ■1	SN	SN ■1	SN	FC ■1	SN ■1	SN
London Victoria 15	⊖ d		07 36			07 47				07 53	07 45		08 02		08 06				08 17			08 23	08 15
Clapham Junction 10	d		07 42			07 53		07 54		07 59	07 52		08 08		08 12				08 23			08 29	08 22
London Charing Cross 4	⊖ d						07 40													08 10			
London Waterloo (East) 4	⊖ d						07 43													08 13			
St Pancras International 15	⊖ d			07 24					07 39								07 54				08 10		
Farringdon 3	⊖ d			07 29					07 44								07 59				08 14		
City Thameslink 3	d																						
London Blackfriars 3	⊖ d			07 35					07 50								08 05				08 20		
London Bridge 4	⊖ d	07 33		07 41	07 35		07 48		07 56			07 38		08 03		08 08	08 11	08 05		08 18	08 26		
Norwood Junction 2	a	07 45			07 55							08 13		08 16				08 25					
East Croydon	a	07 49	07 52	07 54	07 59	08 03	08 05	08 07	08 09	08 09	08 13	08 17	08 18	08 19	08 22	08 22	08 24	08 29	08 33	08 35	08 39	08 39	08 43
South Croydon 4	a				08 02						08 16							08 32					08 46
Purley Oaks	a				08 05						08 19							08 35					08 49
Purley 4	a	07 56			08 08		08 11				08 22	08 24		08 26				08 38		08 41			08 52

Station		SN	SN ■1	SN ■1	SN ■1	FC ■1	SN	SN ■1	SN	SN ■1	FC ■1	SN ■1	SN	SN	SN ■1	SE 13	SN ■1	SN ■1	FC ■1	SN	SN ■1	SN	FC ■1
London Victoria 15	⊖ d		08 32		08 36			08 47				08 53	08 45		09 02		09 06				09 17		
Clapham Junction 10	d		08 38		08 42			08 53		08 54		08 59	08 52		09 08		09 12				09 23		
London Charing Cross 4	⊖ d								08 40													09 10	
London Waterloo (East) 4	⊖ d								08 43													09 13	
St Pancras International 15	⊖ d					08 24					08 39								08 54				09 09
Farringdon 3	⊖ d					08 29					08 44								08 59				09 14
City Thameslink 3	d																		09 01				09 16
London Blackfriars 3	⊖ d					08 35					08 50								09 05				09 20
London Bridge 4	⊖ d	08 08		08 33		08 41	08 35		08 48		08 56			08 38		09 03		09 08	09 11	09 05		09 18	09 26
Norwood Junction 2	a	08 43		08 45			08 55							09 13		09 16				09 25			
East Croydon	a	08 47	08 48	08 49	08 52	08 54	08 59	09 03	09 05	09 07	09 09	09 09	09 13	09 17	09 18	09 19	09 22	09 22	09 24	09 29	09 33	09 35	09 39
South Croydon 4	a						09 02						09 16							09 32			
Purley Oaks	a						09 05						09 19							09 35			
Purley 4	a	08 54		08 56			09 08		09 11				09 22	09 24		09 26				09 38		09 41	

Station		SN ■1	SN	SN	SN ■1	SN ■1	SN ■1	FC ■1	SN	SN ■1	SN	SN ■1	FC ■1	SN ■1	SN	SN	SN ■1	SE 13	SN ■1	SN ■1	FC ■1	SN	SN ■1	SN
London Victoria 15	⊖ d	09 23	09 15		09 32		09 36			09 47				09 53	09 45		10 02		10 06				10 17	
Clapham Junction 10	d	09 29	09 22		09 38		09 42			09 53		09 54		09 59	09 52		10 08		10 12				10 23	
London Charing Cross 4	⊖ d										09 40													10 10
London Waterloo (East) 4	⊖ d										09 43													10 13
St Pancras International 15	⊖ d							09 24					09 39								09 54			
Farringdon 3	⊖ d							09 29					09 44								09 59			
City Thameslink 3	d							09 31					09 46								10 01			
London Blackfriars 3	⊖ d							09 35					09 50								10 05			
London Bridge 4	⊖ d			09 08		09 33		09 41	09 35		09 48		09 56			09 38		10 03		10 08	10 11	10 05		10 18
Norwood Junction 2	a			09 43		09 45			09 55							10 13		10 16				10 25		
East Croydon	a	09 39	09 43	09 47	09 48	09 49	09 52	09 54	09 59	10 03	10 05	10 07	10 09	10 09	10 13	10 17	10 18	10 19	10 22	10 22	10 24	10 29	10 33	10 35
South Croydon 4	a		09 46						10 02						10 16							10 32		
Purley Oaks	a		09 49						10 05						10 19							10 35		
Purley 4	a		09 52	09 54		09 56			10 08		10 11				10 22	10 24		10 26				10 38		10 41

For general notes see front of timetable
For details of catering facilities see
Directory of Train Operators

Table 175

London → East Croydon and Purley
COMPLETE SERVICE

Station		FC [1]		SN [1]	SN	SN	SN [1]	SN [1]	SN [1]	FC [1]	SN	SN [1]	SN	SN [1]	FC [1]	SN [1]	SN	SN [1]	SE 13	SN [1]	SN [1]	FC [1]
London Victoria 15	⊖ d		and at the same minutes past each hour until	18 23	18 15		18 32		18 36			18 47				18 53		19 02		19 06		
Clapham Junction 10	d			18 29	18 22		18 38		18 42			18 53		18 54		18 59		19 08		19 12		
London Charing Cross 4	⊖ d												18 40									
London Waterloo (East) 4	⊖ d												18 43									
St Pancras International 15	⊖ d	10 09								18 24					18 39							18 54
Farringdon 3	⊖ d	10 14								18 29					18 44							18 59
City Thameslink 3	d	10 16								18 31					18 46							19 01
London Blackfriars 3	⊖ d	10 20								18 35					18 50							19 04
London Bridge 4	⊖ d	10 26				18 08		18 33		18 41	18 35		18 48		18 56		18 45		19 03		19 08	19 11
Norwood Junction 2	a					18 43		18 45			18 55		19 03				19 08		19 16			
East Croydon	a	10 39		18 39	18 43	18 47	18 48	18 49	18 52	18 54	18 59	19 03	19 06	19 07	19 09	19 09	19 13	19 18	19 19	19 22	19 22	19 24
South Croydon 4	a				18 46						19 02		19 09				19 16					
Purley Oaks	a				18 49						19 05		19 12				19 19					
Purley 4	a				18 52	18 54		18 56			19 08		19 15				19 22		19 25			

Station		SN [1]	SN	SN [1]	FC [1]	SN [1]	SN	SN [1]	SN [1]	SN [1]	FC [1]	SN	SN [1]	SN [1]	FC [1]	SN [1]	SN	SN [1]	SN [1]	SN [1]	FC [1]	SN [1]	SN
London Victoria 15	⊖ d	19 10	19 00	19 17		19 23		19 32		19 36		19 30	19 47			19 53		20 02	20 06			20 10	20 00
Clapham Junction 10	d	19 16	19 08	19 23		19 29		19 38		19 42		19 38	19 53	19 54		19 59		20 08	20 12			20 16	20 08
London Charing Cross 4	⊖ d						19 07										19 37						
London Waterloo (East) 4	⊖ d						19 10										19 39						
St Pancras International 15	⊖ d				19 09						19 24				19 39						19 54		
Farringdon 3	⊖ d				19 14						19 29				19 44						19 59		
City Thameslink 3	d				19 16						19 31				19 46						20 01		
London Blackfriars 3	⊖ d				19 20						19 34				19 50						20 04		
London Bridge 4	⊖ d				19 26		19 15		19 33		19 41				19 56		19 44			20 08	20 11		
Norwood Junction 2	a						19 38		19 45								20 08			20 19			
East Croydon	a	19 28	19 29	19 33	19 39	19 39	19 42	19 48	19 50	19 52	19 54	19 59	20 03	20 07	20 09	20 09	20 12	20 19	20 22	20 22	20 24	20 28	20 29
South Croydon 4	a		19 32				19 45					20 02					20 15						20 32
Purley Oaks	a		19 35				19 48					20 05					20 18						20 35
Purley 4	a	19 33	19 38				19 51		19 56			20 08					20 21					20 33	20 38

Station		SN [1]	SN [1]	SN	SN [1]	SN [1]	FC [1]	SN [1]	SN	SN [1]	SN [1]	SN [1]	SN	SN [1]	SN [1]	SN [1]	FC [1]	SN [1]	SN	SN [1]	SN [1]	SN	SN [1]
London Victoria 15	⊖ d	20 17	20 23		20 32	20 36		20 40	20 30	20 47		20 53		21 02	21 06			21 10	21 00	21 17	21 23		21 32
Clapham Junction 10	d	20 23	20 29		20 38	20 42		20 46	20 38	20 53	20 54	20 59		21 08	21 12			21 16	21 08	21 23	21 29		21 38
London Charing Cross 4	⊖ d			20 07									20 37									21 07	
London Waterloo (East) 4	⊖ d			20 10									20 40									21 10	
St Pancras International 15	⊖ d						20 24										20 54						
Farringdon 3	⊖ d						20 29										20 59						
City Thameslink 3	d						20 31										21 01						
London Blackfriars 3	⊖ d						20 34										21 04						
London Bridge 4	⊖ d			20 15			20 41						20 45			21 08	21 11					21 15	
Norwood Junction 2	a			20 38									21 08			21 19						21 38	
East Croydon	a	20 33	20 39	20 42	20 48	20 52	20 54	20 58	20 59	21 03	21 07	21 09	21 12	21 18	21 22	21 22	21 24	21 28	21 29	21 33	21 39	21 42	21 48
South Croydon 4	a			20 45					21 02				21 15						21 32			21 45	
Purley Oaks	a			20 48					21 05				21 18						21 35			21 48	
Purley 4	a			20 51				21 03	21 08				21 21					21 33	21 38			21 51	

Station		SN [1]	FC [1]	SN [1]	SN	SN [1]	SN [1]	SN [1]	SN	SN [1]	SN [1]	SN [1]	FC [1]	SN [1]	SN	SN [1]	SN [1]	SN	SN [1]	SN [1]	FC [1]	SN [1]	SN
London Victoria 15	⊖ d	21 36		21 40	21 30	21 47		21 53		22 02	22 06			22 10	22 00	22 17	22 23		22 32	22 36		22 40	22 30
Clapham Junction 10	d	21 42		21 46	21 38	21 53	21 54	21 59		22 08	22 12			22 16	22 08	22 23	22 29		22 38	22 42		22 46	22 38
London Charing Cross 4	⊖ d								21 37									22 07					
London Waterloo (East) 4	⊖ d								21 40									22 10					
St Pancras International 15	⊖ d		21 24										21 54								22 24		
Farringdon 3	⊖ d		21 29										21 59								22 29		
City Thameslink 3	d																						
London Blackfriars 3	⊖ d		21 34										22 04								22 34		
London Bridge 4	⊖ d		21 41						21 45			22 08	22 11					22 15			22 41		
Norwood Junction 2	a								22 08			22 19						22 38					
East Croydon	a	21 52	21 54	21 58	21 59	22 03	22 07	22 09	22 12	22 18	22 22	22 22	22 24	22 28	22 29	22 33	22 39	22 42	22 48	22 52	22 54	22 58	22 59
South Croydon 4	a				22 02				22 15						22 32			22 45					23 02
Purley Oaks	a				22 05				22 18						22 35			22 48					23 05
Purley 4	a			22 03	22 08				22 21					22 33	22 38			22 51				23 03	23 08

Station		SN [1]	SN [1]	SN	SN	SN [1]	SN [1]	FC [1]	SN [1]	SN	SN [1]	SN [1]	SN	SN [1]	FC	SN [1]	SN [1]	SN	FC
London Victoria 15	⊖ d	22 47	22 53			23 02	23 06		23 10	23 00	23 17	23 24		23 32		23 47	23 49		
Clapham Junction 10	d	22 53	22 59			23 08	23 12		23 16	23 08	23 23	23 30		23 38		23 53	23 56		
London Charing Cross 4	⊖ d			22 37									23 07					23 45	
London Waterloo (East) 4	⊖ d			22 40									23 10					23 48	
St Pancras International 15	⊖ d							22 54							23 24				23 54
Farringdon 3	⊖ d							22 59							23 29				23 59
City Thameslink 3	d																		
London Blackfriars 3	⊖ d							23 04							23 34				00 04
London Bridge 4	⊖ d			22 45	23 00			23 11					23 15		23 41			23 53	00 16
Norwood Junction 2	a			23 08	23 11								23 38					00 16	
East Croydon	a	23 03	23 09	23 12	23 16	23 18	23 22	23 24	23 28	23 29	23 33	23 41	23 42	23 52	23 56	00 06	00 09	00 20	00 29
South Croydon 4	a			23 15						23 32			23 45					00 23	
Purley Oaks	a			23 18						23 35			23 48					00 26	
Purley 4	a			23 21					23 33	23 38			23 51			00 12		00 29	

For general notes see front of timetable
For details of catering facilities see Directory of Train Operators

Table 175

Sundays

London → East Croydon and Purley
COMPLETE SERVICE

		SN 1	SN	SN 1	FC	SN 1	SN	SN	FC 1	SN	SN 1	SN 1	SN 1	SN 1	SN 1	SN 1	SN 1	SN 1		FC 1	SN 1	SN 1	SN 1	FC 1	SN
London Victoria 15	⊖ d	23p47		00 05		00 14	00 17			00 42	01 00	02 02	03 00	04 00	05 02	05 47	06 32	07 02			07 22	07 32	07 34		
Clapham Junction 10	d	23p53		00 11		00 20	00 23			00 49	01 08	02 08	03 08	04 08	05 08	05 53	06 38	07 08			07 28	07 38	07 40		
London Charing Cross 4	⊖ d		23p45					00 12																	07 36
London Waterloo (East) 4	⊖ d		23p48					00 15																	07 39
St Pancras International 15	⊖ d				23p54				00 24											06 54				07 24	
Farringdon 3	⊖ d				23p59				00 29											06 59				07 29	
City Thameslink 3	d																								
London Blackfriars 3	⊖ d				00 04				00 34											07 04				07 34	
London Bridge 4	⊖ d		23p53		00 16			00 26	00 41											07 11				07 41	07 44
Norwood Junction 2	a		00 16					00 49																	08 04
East Croydon	a	00 06	00 20	00 24	00 29	00 32	00 42	00 53	00 56	01 10	01 21	02 21	03 21	04 21	05 22	06 05	06 51	07 23		07 26	07 42	07 50	07 53	07 56	08 08
South Croydon 4	a		00 23																						08 11
Purley Oaks	a		00 26																						08 14
Purley 4	a	00 12	00 29			00 38					01 27	02 27	03 27	04 27	05 28		06 56	07 28					07 59		08 17

		SN 1	FC 1	SN 1	SN	SN 1	SN 1	SN 1	FC 1	SN 1	SN		SN 1	FC 1	SN 1	SN	SN 1	FC	SN 1	SN 1	FC 1	SN 1	SN		
London Victoria 15	⊖ d	08 04		08 17		08 22	08 32	08 34		08 47			09 04		09 17		09 22		09 32	09 34		09 47			
Clapham Junction 10	d	08 10		08 23		08 28	08 38	08 40		08 53			09 10		09 23		09 28		09 38	09 40		09 53			
London Charing Cross 4	⊖ d				08 06						08 36					09 06							09 36		
London Waterloo (East) 4	⊖ d				08 09						08 39					09 09							09 39		
St Pancras International 15	⊖ d		07 54						08 24					08 54				09 10			09 24				
Farringdon 3	⊖ d		07 59						08 29					08 59				09 14			09 29				
City Thameslink 3	d																								
London Blackfriars 3	⊖ d		08 04						08 34					09 04				09 19			09 34				
London Bridge 4	⊖ d		08 11		08 14				08 41		08 44			09 11		09 14		09 26			09 41		09 44		
Norwood Junction 2	a				08 34						09 04					09 34							10 04		
East Croydon	a	08 23	08 26	08 36	08 38	08 42	08 50	08 53	08 56	09 06	09 08		09 23	09 26	09 36	09 38	09 42	09 47	09 50	09 53	09 56	10 06	10 08		
South Croydon 4	a				08 41						09 11					09 41							10 11		
Purley Oaks	a				08 44						09 14					09 44							10 14		
Purley 4	a	08 29			08 47			08 59			09 17		09 29			09 47				09 59			10 17		

		FC 1			SN 1	FC 1	SN 1	SN	SN 1	FC 1	SN 1	SN 1	FC 1	SN 1	SN	FC 1	SN 1	SN 1	FC 1	SN 1	SN		SN 1	FC
London Victoria 15	⊖ d		and at		16 04		16 17		16 22		16 32	16 34		16 47			17 02	17 04		17 17			17 22	
Clapham Junction 10	d		the same		16 10		16 23		16 28		16 38	16 40		16 53			17 07	17 10		17 23			17 28	
London Charing Cross 4	⊖ d							16 06							16 36						17 06			
London Waterloo (East) 4	⊖ d		minutes					16 09							16 39						17 09			
St Pancras International 15	⊖ d	09 40				15 54				16 10			16 24			16 40			16 54					17 09
Farringdon 3	⊖ d	09 44	past			15 59				16 14			16 29			16 44			16 59					17 14
City Thameslink 3	d																							
London Blackfriars 3	⊖ d	09 49	each			16 04				16 19			16 34			16 49			17 04					17 19
London Bridge 4	⊖ d	09 56				16 11		16 14		16 26			16 41		16 44	16 56			17 11		17 14			17 26
Norwood Junction 2	a		hour until					16 34							17 04						17 34			
East Croydon	a	10 17			16 23	16 26	16 36	16 38	16 42	16 47	16 50	16 53	16 56	17 06	17 08	17 17	17 20	17 23	17 26	17 36	17 38		17 42	17 47
South Croydon 4	a							16 41							17 11						17 41			
Purley Oaks	a							16 44							17 14						17 44			
Purley 4	a				16 29			16 47				16 59			17 17			17 29			17 47			

		SN 1	SN 1	FC 1	SN 1	SN	SN 1	SN 1	FC 1	SN 1	SN	SN 1	SN 1	SN 1	FC 1	SN 1	SN	SN 1		SN 1	FC 1	SN 1	SN	SN 1	SN 1
London Victoria 15	⊖ d	17 32	17 34		17 47		18 02	18 04		18 17		18 22	18 32	18 34		18 47		19 02		19 04		19 17		19 22	19 32
Clapham Junction 10	d	17 38	17 40		17 53		18 07	18 10		18 23		18 28	18 38	18 40		18 53		19 07		19 10		19 23		19 28	19 38
London Charing Cross 4	⊖ d					17 36					18 06						18 36						19 06		
London Waterloo (East) 4	⊖ d					17 39					18 09						18 39						19 09		
St Pancras International 15	⊖ d			17 24					17 54						18 24						18 54				
Farringdon 3	⊖ d			17 29					17 59						18 29						18 59				
City Thameslink 3	d																								
London Blackfriars 3	⊖ d			17 34					18 04						18 34						19 04				
London Bridge 4	⊖ d			17 41		17 44			18 11		18 14				18 41		18 44				19 11		19 14		
Norwood Junction 2	a					18 04					18 34						19 04						19 34		
East Croydon	a	17 50	17 53	17 56	18 06	18 08	18 20	18 23	18 26	18 36	18 38	18 42	18 50	18 53	18 56	19 06	19 08	19 20		19 23	19 26	19 36	19 38	19 42	19 50
South Croydon 4	a					18 11					18 41						19 11						19 41		
Purley Oaks	a					18 14					18 44						19 14						19 44		
Purley 4	a		17 59			18 17		18 29			18 47			18 59			19 17			19 29			19 47		

		SN 1	FC 1	SN 1	SN	SN 1	SN 1	FC 1	SN 1	SN	SN 1	SN 1	SN 1	FC 1		SN 1	SN	SN 1	FC 1	SN 1	SN	SN 1	FC 1	SN 1	SN 1
London Victoria 15	⊖ d	19 34		19 47		20 02	20 04		20 17		20 22	20 32	20 34			20 47		21 04		21 17		21 22		21 32	21 34
Clapham Junction 10	d	19 40		19 53		20 07	20 10		20 23		20 28	20 38	20 40			20 53		21 10		21 23		21 28		21 38	21 40
London Charing Cross 4	⊖ d				19 36					20 06							20 36				21 06				
London Waterloo (East) 4	⊖ d				19 39					20 09							20 39				21 09				
St Pancras International 15	⊖ d		19 24					19 54						20 24					20 54				21 10		
Farringdon 3	⊖ d		19 29					19 59						20 29					20 59				21 14		
City Thameslink 3	d																								
London Blackfriars 3	⊖ d		19 34					20 04						20 34					21 04				21 19		
London Bridge 4	⊖ d		19 41		19 44			20 11		20 14				20 41			20 44		21 11		21 14		21 26		
Norwood Junction 2	a				20 04					20 34							21 04				21 34				
East Croydon	a	19 53	19 56	20 06	20 08	20 20	20 23	20 26	20 36	20 38	20 42	20 50	20 53	20 56		21 06	21 08	21 23	21 26	21 36	21 38	21 42	21 49	21 50	21 53
South Croydon 4	a				20 11					20 41							21 11				21 41				
Purley Oaks	a				20 14					20 44							21 14				21 44				
Purley 4	a	19 59			20 17		20 29			20 47			20 59				21 17	21 29			21 47				21 59

For general notes see front of timetable
For details of catering facilities see
Directory of Train Operators

Table 175

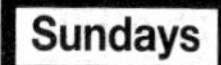

London → East Croydon and Purley
COMPLETE SERVICE

		FC 1	SN 1	SN	SN 1	FC 1	SN 1	SN	SN 1	SN 1		SN 1	FC 1	SN 1	SN	SN 1	FC 1	SN 1	SN	SN 1	FC	SN	SN	SN	FC
London Victoria 15	⊖ d		21 47		22 04		22 17		22 22	22 32		22 34		22 47		23 04		23 17		23 32		23 47		23 49	
Clapham Junction 10	d		21 53		22 10		22 23		22 28	22 38		22 40		22 53		23 10		23 23		23 38		23 53		23 56	
London Charing Cross 4	⊖ d			21 36				22 06							22 36				23 06				23 36		
London Waterloo (East) 4	⊖ d			21 39				22 09							22 39				23 09				23 39		
St Pancras International 15	⊖ d	21 24				21 54							22 24				22 54				23 24				23 54
Farringdon 3	⊖ d	21 29				21 59							22 29				22 59				23 29				23 59
City Thameslink 3	d																								
London Blackfriars 3	⊖ d	21 34				22 04							22 34				23 04				23 34				00 04
London Bridge 4	⊖ d	21 41		21 44		22 11		22 14					22 41		22 44		23 11		23 14		23 41		23 44		00 11
Norwood Junction 2	a			22 04				22 37							23 07				23 37				00 09		
East Croydon	🚌 a	21 56	22 06	22 08	22 23	22 26	22 36	22 42	22 43	22 50		22 53	22 56	23 06	23 12	23 23	23 26	23 36	23 42	23 52	23 56	00 06	00 13	00 17	00 26
South Croydon 4	a			22 11				22 45							23 15				23 45				00 16		
Purley Oaks	a			22 14				22 48							23 18				23 48				00 19		
Purley 4	a			22 17	22 29			22 51				22 59			23 21	23 28			23 51				00 22		

For general notes see front of timetable
For details of catering facilities see
Directory of Train Operators

Purley and East Croydon → London

COMPLETE SERVICE

Station		SN	SN	SN	FC	SN	SN	SN	FC	SN	FC	SN	FC	SN	FC	SN	SN	SN	SN	FC	SN	SN	SN	SN	SN
		MO	MX																						
		1	1	1	1		1	1	1	1	1	1			1	1				1		1		1	
Purley 4	d	23p50	23p49	00 11			01 22	02 22		03 22		04 22		05 07		05 23		05 39			06 00		06 03		
Purley Oaks	d																	05 42					06 06		
South Croydon 4	d																	05 45					06 09		
East Croydon	d	23p56	23b58	00 17	00 36	00 49	01 28	02 28	02 47	03 28	03 47	04 28	04 47	05 13	05 17	05 29	05 34	05 48	05 51	06 02	06 07	06 10	06 12	06 15	06 17
Norwood Junction 2	d													05 17			05 38		05 55				06 16		
London Bridge 4	⊖ a				00 52									05 41	05 34				06 24	06 15			06 34		
London Blackfriars 3	⊖ a				00 59				03 12		04 12		05 12		05 41					06 23					
City Thameslink 3	a																			06 25					
Farringdon 3	⊖ a												05 17		05 47					06 29					
St Pancras International 15	⊖ a				01 07				03 21		04 21		05 21		05 51					06 33					
London Waterloo (East) 4	⊖ a													05 46											
London Charing Cross 4	⊖ a													05 49											
Clapham Junction 10	a	00 10	00 11	00 29		01 02	01 40	02 40		03 40		04 47				05 48	05 58	06 08			06 17	06 25		06 25	06 37
London Victoria 15	⊖ a	00 18	00 18	00 37		01 09	01 49	02 49		03 49		04 54				05 58	06 06	06 18			06 25			06 33	06 46

Station		SN	SN	SN	FC	SN	SN	SN	FC	SN	SN	SN	SE	FC	SN	SN	SN	SN	SN	SN	SN	SN	FC	SN	SN
													13												
		1		1	1	1		1	1		1	1		1		1	1		1			1	1	1	
Purley 4	d		06 22	06 25			06 31						06 56				07 05	07 03			07 12				07 23
Purley Oaks	d						06 34											07 06			07 15				
South Croydon 4	d						06 37			06 41								07 09			07 18				
East Croydon	d	06 23	06 28	06 31	06 32	06 34	06 40	06 42	06 44	06 45	06 57	06 59	07 02	07 02	07 05	07 08	07 10	07 12	07 16	07 17	07 21	07 21	07 24	07 26	07 29
Norwood Junction 2	d		06 32				06 44											07 16							
London Bridge 4	⊖ a	06 40	06 54		06 46		07 02		06 58			07 14	07 18	07 16	07 43	07 25		07 33				07 39		07 43	
London Blackfriars 3	⊖ a				06 52				07 06					07 22									07 50		
City Thameslink 3	a				06 55				07 09					07 25									07 55		
Farringdon 3	⊖ a				06 59				07 12					07 28									07 58		
St Pancras International 15	⊖ a				07 03				07 16					07 32									08 02		
London Waterloo (East) 4	⊖ a																								
London Charing Cross 4	⊖ a																								
Clapham Junction 10	a			06 40		06 46		06 51		07 05	07 07						07 19		07 25	07 37	07 31				07 39
London Victoria 15	⊖ a			06 47		06 54		07 00		07 16	07 17						07 28		07 34	07 47	07 40				07 48

Station		SN	SN	SN	SN	SN	SN	SN	SN	SN	SN	FC	SN	SN	SN	SN	SN	SN	SN	SN	SN	SN	SN	SN	SN
		1	1		1	1	1	1	1	1		1	1		1	1	1	1	1	1	1		1	1	1
Purley 4	d			07 27				07 39			07 43			07 48						08 01		08 03			
Purley Oaks	d			07 30							07 46			07 51								08 06			
South Croydon 4	d			07 33							07 49			07 54				08 01				08 09			
East Croydon	d	07 29	07 32	07 36	07 38	07 41	07 44	07 45	07 47	07 47	07 52	07 54	07 54	07 57	07 57	08 00	08 01	08 04	08 04	08 07	08 09	08 12	08 12	08 15	08 16
Norwood Junction 2	d			07 41										08 01								08 17			
London Bridge 4	⊖ a	07 46	07 48	08 01					08 03				08 11	08 16		08 18		08 20		08 24	08 26	08 31			08 35
London Blackfriars 3	⊖ a											08 19													
City Thameslink 3	a											08 25													
Farringdon 3	⊖ a											08 29													
St Pancras International 15	⊖ a											08 33													
London Waterloo (East) 4	⊖ a																								
London Charing Cross 4	⊖ a																								
Clapham Junction 10	a				07 47	07 51	07 54	07 56		08 08	08 02				08 06		08 10		08 13				08 21	08 24	
London Victoria 15	⊖ a				07 57	08 00	08 03	08 07			08 12				08 16		08 20		08 22				08 31	08 33	

Station		SN	SN	SN	SN	SN	SN	FC	SN	SN	SN	SN	SN	SN	FC	SN	SN	SN	SN	SE	SN	SN	FC	SN	SN
																				13					
				1	1	1	1	1	1	1	1		1	1	1	1			1			1	1	1	1
Purley 4	d	08 08		08 16								08 25		08 32				08 36				08 45			
Purley Oaks	d	08 11										08 28						08 39							
South Croydon 4	d	08 14				08 22						08 31				08 37		08 42						08 52	
East Croydon	d	08 17	08 18	08 22	08 24	08 25	08 27	08 28	08 30	08 30	08 32	08 34	08 34	08 37	08 38	08 40	08 44	08 45	08 47	08 48	08 50	08 53	08 54	08 56	09 00
Norwood Junction 2	d											08 40						08 49							
London Bridge 4	⊖ a			08 39	08 41		08 44		08 51		08 49	08 55				08 59		09 05		09 07		09 15	09 10		09 20
London Blackfriars 3	⊖ a							08 52							09 08								09 18		
City Thameslink 3	a							08 59							09 11								09 21		
Farringdon 3	⊖ a							09 02							09 14								09 26		
St Pancras International 15	⊖ a							09 06							09 18								09 33		
London Waterloo (East) 4	⊖ a																								
London Charing Cross 4	⊖ a																								
Clapham Junction 10	a	08 27	08 38			08 37				08 40			08 43	08 49			08 53		08 56		09 10			09 07	
London Victoria 15	⊖ a	08 35	08 48			08 46				08 49			08 52	08 58			09 02		09 07		09 20			09 16	

Station		SN	SN	SN	FC	SN	SN	SN	SN	SN	SN	SN	SN	SN	FC	SN	SN	SN	SE	SN	SN	SN	FC	SN	SN
																			13						
		1			1	1	1	1			1	1	1		1	1		1		1	1		1		1
Purley 4	d			08 55		09 03			09 08	09 14				09 22			09 31		09 34			09 38		09 45	
Purley Oaks	d			08 58					09 11					09 25								09 41			
South Croydon 4	d			09 01					09 14					09 28								09 44			
East Croydon	d	09 01	09 02	09 05	09 08	09 09	09 14	09 14	09 17	09 20	09 22	09 26	09 29	09 31	09 32	09 33	09 37	09 39	09 40	09 43	09 44	09 47	09 47	09 51	09 52
Norwood Junction 2	d			09 09						09 25				09 35										09 58	
London Bridge 4	⊖ a		09 41	09 24						09 42				09 59	09 45	09 52	09 54		09 55				10 00	10 28	
London Blackfriars 3	⊖ a				09 37										09 52								10 07		
City Thameslink 3	a				09 40										09 55								10 10		
Farringdon 3	⊖ a				09 44										09 59								10 14		
St Pancras International 15	⊖ a				09 48										10 03								10 18		
London Waterloo (East) 4	⊖ a																								
London Charing Cross 4	⊖ a																								
Clapham Junction 10	a	09 10				09 20	09 23	09 26	09 38		09 32	09 35	09 38					09 49		09 52	09 55	10 07			10 03
London Victoria 15	⊖ a	09 19				09 29	09 33	09 37	09 48		09 42	09 44	09 48					09 58		10 00	10 05	10 14			

For general notes see front of timetable
For details of catering facilities see
Directory of Train Operators

b Previous night.
Arr. 2355

Purley and East Croydon → London
COMPLETE SERVICE

Station		SN	SN	FC	SN	SN	SN	SN	SN	SN	FC	SN	SE	SN	SN	SN	FC	SN	SN	SN	SN		SN	FC	SN
		1	1	1		1		1	1		1		13	1	1		1	1		1	1			1	
Purley 4	d	09 49			09 51		10 01			10 08		10 15	10 18			10 21			10 31				10 38		10 45
Purley Oaks	d				09 54					10 11						10 24							10 41		
South Croydon 4	d				09 57					10 14						10 27							10 44		
East Croydon	d	09 55	09 56	09 57	10 00	10 00	10 07	10 12	10 14	10 17	10 17	10 21	10 24	10 24	10 28	10 30	10 32	10 33	10 37	10 40	10 44		10 47	10 47	10 51
Norwood Junction 2	d	09 59			10 04							10 28	10 28			10 34									10 58
London Bridge 4	⊖ a	10 12		10 15	10 25		10 22				10 30	10 58	10 40			10 55	10 45	10 49	10 52					11 00	11 28
London Blackfriars 3	⊖ a			10 22							10 37						10 52							11 07	
City Thameslink 3	a			10 25							10 40						10 55							11 10	
Farringdon 3	⊖ a			10 29							10 44						10 59							11 14	
St Pancras International 15	⊖ a			10 33							10 48						11 03							11 18	
London Waterloo (East) 4	⊖ a						10 26												10 56						
London Charing Cross 4	⊖ a						10 30												11 00						
Clapham Junction 10	a		10 05			10 09		10 21	10 25	10 37				10 33	10 37					10 49	10 55		11 07		
London Victoria 15	⊖ a		10 13			10 16		10 28	10 35	10 44				10 40	10 45					10 58	11 05		11 14		

Station		SN	SN	SN	SN	SN	FC	SN	SN	SN	SN	FC	SN	SE	SN	SN	SN	FC	SN	SN	SN	SN	and at the same minutes past each hour until	SN
		1	1	1		1	1		1	1		1		13	1	1		1	1		1	1		
Purley 4	d		10 49		10 51			11 01			11 08		11 15	11 18			11 21			11 31				15 38
Purley Oaks	d				10 54						11 11						11 24							15 41
South Croydon 4	d				10 57						11 14						11 27							15 44
East Croydon	d	10 52	10 55	10 55	11 00	11 00	11 02	11 07	11 10	11 14	11 17	11 17	11 21	11 24	11 24	11 28	11 30	11 32	11 33	11 37	11 40	11 44		15 47
Norwood Junction 2	d		10 59		11 04								11 28	11 28			11 34							
London Bridge 4	⊖ a		11 12		11 25		11 15	11 22				11 30	11 58	11 40			11 55	11 45	11 49	11 52				
London Blackfriars 3	⊖ a						11 22					11 37						11 52						
City Thameslink 3	a						11 25					11 40						11 55						
Farringdon 3	⊖ a						11 29					11 44						11 59						
St Pancras International 15	⊖ a						11 33					11 48						12 03						
London Waterloo (East) 4	⊖ a							11 26												11 56				
London Charing Cross 4	⊖ a							11 30												12 00				
Clapham Junction 10	a	11 03		11 04		11 09			11 19	11 25	11 37				11 33	11 37					11 49	11 55		16 07
London Victoria 15	⊖ a			11 11		11 16			11 27	11 35	11 44				11 40	11 44					11 58	12 05		16 14

Station		FC	SN	SN	SN	SN	SN	SN	FC	SN	SN	SN	SN	FC	SN	SE	SN	FC	SN	SN	SN	SN	SN	SN	SN
		1		1	1	1		1	1		1	1		1		13	1	1	1			1	1	1	1
Purley 4	d		15 45		15 49		15 51			16 01			16 08		16 15	16 18				16 21	16 31				
Purley Oaks	d						15 54						16 11							16 24					
South Croydon 4	d						15 57						16 14							16 27					
East Croydon	d	15 47	15 51	15 52	15 55	15 55	16 00	16 00	16 02	16 07	16 12	16 14	16 17	16 17	16 21	16 24	16 24	16 27	16 30	16 31	16 37	16 38	16 39	16 42	16 44
Norwood Junction 2	d		15 58		15 59		16 04			16 11					16 28	16 28				16 35	16 41				16 48
London Bridge 4	⊖ a	16 00	16 28		16 12		16 26		16 15	16 24					17 00	16 41		16 42		16 58	16 56		16 58		17 00
London Blackfriars 3	⊖ a	16 07							16 24					16 48				16 53							
City Thameslink 3	a	16 10							16 28					16 52				16 56							
Farringdon 3	⊖ a	16 14							16 31					16 56				17 01							
St Pancras International 15	⊖ a	16 18							16 35					17 01				17 05							
London Waterloo (East) 4	⊖ a																								
London Charing Cross 4	⊖ a																								
Clapham Junction 10	a			16 03		16 04		16 11			16 21	16 25	16 37				16 33		16 39			16 47		16 51	
London Victoria 15	⊖ a					16 11		16 20			16 29	16 32	16 44				16 41		16 46			16 56		16 58	

Station		SN	FC	SN	SN	SN	SN	FC	SN	SN	SN	FC	SN	SN	SN	SN	SN	FC	SN	SN	SN	SN	SN	SN	SN
			1		1	1	1	1		1		1	1	1		1	1	1	1			1	1	1	1
Purley 4	d	16 38		16 45			16 49		16 51		17 01				17 09		17 19			17 23	17 31				
Purley Oaks	d	16 41							16 54						17 12					17 26					
South Croydon 4	d	16 44							16 57						17 15					17 29					
East Croydon	d	16 47	16 47	16 51	16 52	16 55	16 55	16 57	17 00	17 01	17 07	17 09	17 12	17 14	17 18	17 25	17 25	17 27	17 30	17 32	17 37	17 38	17 39	17 41	17 44
Norwood Junction 2	d			16 56					17 04		17 11			17 18						17 36	17 41				17 49
London Bridge 4	⊖ a		17 02	17 26					17 27		17 26	17 29		17 31						17 58	17 54		18 02		18 06
London Blackfriars 3	⊖ a							17 25				17 36						17 56							
City Thameslink 3	a							17 28				17 38						18 08							
Farringdon 3	⊖ a							17 31				17 41						18 11							
St Pancras International 15	⊖ a							17 35				17 45						18 15							
London Waterloo (East) 4	⊖ a																								
London Charing Cross 4	⊖ a																								
Clapham Junction 10	a	17 07			17 03	17 04	17 07			17 10			17 21		17 38	17 34	17 37		17 40			17 47		17 50	
London Victoria 15	⊖ a	17 14				17 11	17 14			17 20			17 28		17 48	17 43	17 45		17 50			17 56		17 57	

Station		FC	SN	SN	SN	SN	SN	SN	SN	SN	SE	SN	SN	FC	SN	SN	SN	FC	SN	SN	SN	SN	SN	SN	FC
		1		1	1	1		1		1	13	1		1	1	1	1	1	1		1	1	1		1
Purley 4	d		17 39				17 49		17 56				18 08			18 19				18 26				18 38	
Purley Oaks	d		17 42						17 59				18 11							18 29				18 41	
South Croydon 4	d		17 45						18 02				18 14							18 32				18 44	
East Croydon	d	17 47	17 48	17 52	17 53	17 55	17 56	17 59	18 05	18 08	18 11	18 12	18 17	18 17	18 24	18 26	18 30	18 32	18 32	18 35	18 38	18 39	18 42	18 47	18 47
Norwood Junction 2	d				17 57				18 09											18 39					
London Bridge 4	⊖ a	18 11			18 10				18 28	18 24	18 26							18 45	18 48	19 00	18 53				19 00
London Blackfriars 3	⊖ a	18 19												18 49				18 55							19 07
City Thameslink 3	a	18 28												18 54				18 58							19 12
Farringdon 3	⊖ a	18 31												18 57				19 01							19 15
St Pancras International 15	⊖ a	18 35												19 01				19 05							19 19
London Waterloo (East) 4	⊖ a																								
London Charing Cross 4	⊖ a																								
Clapham Junction 10	a		18 08	18 02		18 04	18 07	18 10				18 21	18 38		18 33	18 37	18 41					18 48	18 51	19 07	
London Victoria 15	⊖ a		18 15			18 11	18 14	18 20				18 28	18 45		18 40	18 45	18 50					18 56	18 59	19 14	

For general notes see front of timetable
For details of catering facilities see
Directory of Train Operators

Purley and East Croydon → London
COMPLETE SERVICE

Station		SN 1	SN 1	SN 1	SN 1	SN 1	SN 1	FC 1	SN	SN 1	SN 1	SN	FC 1	SN 1	SN 1	SN 1	SN 1	FC 1	SN	SN 1	SN 1	SN	FC 1	SN 1	SN 1
Purley 4	d			18 49					19 01			19 08				19 19			19 29			19 38			
Purley Oaks	d								19 04			19 11							19 32			19 41			
South Croydon 4	d								19 07			19 14							19 35			19 44			
East Croydon	d	18 51	18 52	18 55	18 55	18 59	19 00	19 02	19 10	19 12	19 14	19 17	19 17	19 20	19 24	19 26	19 29	19 32	19 40	19 41	19 44	19 47	19 47	19 52	19 55
Norwood Junction 2	d			18 59					19 14										19 44						
London Bridge 4	⊖ a			19 12		19 14		19 15	19 39				19 30	19 35				19 45	20 11				20 00		
London Blackfriars 3	⊖ a							19 22					19 37					19 52					20 07		
City Thameslink 3	a							19 25					19 40					19 55					20 10		
Farringdon 3	⊖ a							19 29					19 44					19 59					20 14		
St Pancras International 15	⊖ a							19 33					19 48					20 03					20 18		
London Waterloo (East) 4	⊖ a								19 45										20 16						
London Charing Cross 4	⊖ a								19 49										20 20						
Clapham Junction 10	a	19 07	19 02		19 04		19 10			19 21	19 25	19 37			19 33	19 37	19 40			19 50	19 55	20 07		20 03	20 04
London Victoria 15	⊖ a	19 14			19 11		19 17			19 29	19 33	19 45			19 40	19 44	19 47			19 59	20 02	20 14			20 11

Station		SN 1	SN 1	FC 1	SN 1	SN	SN 1	SN 1	SN	FC 1	SN 1	SN 1	SN	SN 1	FC 1	SN 1	SN	SN 1	SN 1	SN	FC 1	SN 1	SN 1	SN 1	SN 1
Purley 4	d	19 49				19 59			20 08			20 20	20 23				20 29			20 38					20 49
Purley Oaks	d					20 02			20 11								20 32			20 41					
South Croydon 4	d					20 05			20 14								20 35			20 44					
East Croydon	d	19 55	20 00	20 02	20 07	20 10	20 10	20 14	20 17	20 17	20 24	20 26	20 30	20 30	20 32	20 37	20 40	20 42	20 44	20 47	20 47	20 52	20 54	20 55	20 57
Norwood Junction 2	d					20 14							20 34				20 44								
London Bridge 4	⊖ a			20 15	20 21	20 41				20 30			20 59		20 45	20 51	21 11				21 00		21 11		
London Blackfriars 3	⊖ a			20 22						20 37					20 52						21 07				
City Thameslink 3	a			20 25						20 40					20 55						21 10				
Farringdon 3	⊖ a			20 29						20 44					20 59						21 14				
St Pancras International 15	⊖ a			20 33						20 48					21 03						21 18				
London Waterloo (East) 4	⊖ a					20 46											21 16								
London Charing Cross 4	⊖ a					20 50											21 20								
Clapham Junction 10	a	20 07	20 10				20 19	20 25	20 37		20 33	20 37		20 40				20 51	20 55	21 07		21 03		21 04	21 07
London Victoria 15	⊖ a	20 14	20 20				20 28	20 32	20 45		20 40	20 46		20 50				20 59	21 05	21 14				21 11	21 14

Station		SN 1	FC 1	SN	SN 1	SN 1	SN	FC 1	SN 1	SN 1	SN 1	FC 1	SN 1	SN	SN 1	SN 1	SN	SN 1	SN 1	SN 1	SN 1	FC 1	SN	SN 1	SN 1
Purley 4	d			20 59			21 08			21 20				21 29			21 38			21 49			21 59		
Purley Oaks	d			21 02			21 11							21 32			21 41						22 02		
South Croydon 4	d			21 05			21 14							21 35			21 44						22 05		
East Croydon	d	21 00	21 02	21 10	21 10	21 14	21 17	21 17	21 24	21 26	21 30	21 32	21 36	21 40	21 41	21 44	21 47	21 52	21 55	21b57	22 00	22 02	22 10	22 10	22 14
Norwood Junction 2	d			21 14										21 44									22 14		
London Bridge 4	⊖ a		21 15	21 41				21 30				21 45	21 50	22 11								22 15	22 41		
London Blackfriars 3	⊖ a		21 22					21 37				21 52										22 22			
City Thameslink 3	a		21 25					21 40				21 55										22 25			
Farringdon 3	⊖ a		21 29					21 44				21 59										22 29			
St Pancras International 15	⊖ a		21 33					21 48				22 03										22 33			
London Waterloo (East) 4	⊖ a			21 46										22 16									22 46		
London Charing Cross 4	⊖ a			21 50										22 20									22 50		
Clapham Junction 10	a	21 11			21 19	21 25	21 37		21 33	21 37	21 40				21 50	21 55	22 07	22 03	22 04	22 07	22 10			22 19	22 25
London Victoria 15	⊖ a	21 20			21 29	21 32	21 45		21 40	21 47	21 48				21 58	22 05	22 14		22 11	22 14	22 20			22 27	22 35

Station		SN	SN 1	SN 1	SN 1	SN 1	FC 1	SN 1	SN	SN 1	SN 1	SN	SN 1	SN 1	SN 1	FC 1	SN	SN 1	SN	SN 1	FC 1	SN	SN 1		
Purley 4	d	22 08			22 20				22 29			22 38		22 52			22 59		23 08			23 34	23 49		
Purley Oaks	d	22 11							22 32			22 41					23 02		23 11			23 37			
South Croydon 4	d	22 14							22 35			22 44					23 05		23 14			23 40			
East Croydon	d	22 17	22 17	22 24	22 26	22 30	22 32	22 33	22 40	22 41	22 44	22 47	22 52	22 58	23 00	23 02	23 10	23 14	23 17	23 30	23 32	23a42	23c58		
Norwood Junction 2	d								22 44								23 14								
London Bridge 4	⊖ a		22 32				22 45	22 50	23 11							23 15	23 38				23 45				
London Blackfriars 3	⊖ a						22 52									23 22					23 52				
City Thameslink 3	a						22 55																		
Farringdon 3	⊖ a						22 59									23 28					23 58				
St Pancras International 15	⊖ a						23 03									23 32					00 02				
London Waterloo (East) 4	⊖ a								23 16								23 43								
London Charing Cross 4	⊖ a								23 20								23 48								
Clapham Junction 10	a	22 37		22 33	22 37	22 40				22 50	22 55	23 07	23 03	23 07	23 10			23 25	23 37	23 42			00 11		
London Victoria 15	⊖ a	22 48		22 40	22 44	22 50				22 58	23 05	23 14		23 15	23 20			23 35	23 45	23 52			00 18		

For general notes see front of timetable
For details of catering facilities see
Directory of Train Operators

b Arr. 2154
c Arr. 2355

Table 175

Purley and East Croydon → London
COMPLETE SERVICE

Station		SN	SN	FC	SN	SN	SN	FC	SN	FC	SN	FC	FC	SN	FC	SN	SN	FC	SN	SN	SN	SN	SN	FC	SN
		1	1	1		1	1	1	1	1	1	1	1	1	1	1	1	1	1		1			1	1
Purley 4	d	23p49	00 11			01 22	02 22		03 22		04 22			05 24		05 58			06 20	06 21			06 38		
Purley Oaks	d																			06 24			06 41		
South Croydon 4	d																			06 27			06 44		
East Croydon	d	23b58	00 17	00 36	00 49	01 28	02 28	02 47	03 28	03 47	04 28	04 47	05 17	05 29	05 42	06c07	06 10	06 17	06 27	06 30	06 41	06 43	06 47	06 47	06 53
Norwood Junction 2	d																			06 34		06 49			
London Bridge 4	⊖ a			00 52														06 31		06 55		07 14		07 01	
London Blackfriars 3	⊖ a			00 59				03 12		04 12		05 12	05 42		06 07			06 37						07 07	
City Thameslink 3	a																								
Farringdon 3	⊖ a											05 17	05 47		06 13			06 41						07 13	
St Pancras International 15	⊖ a			01 07				03 21		04 21		05 21	05 51		06 17			06 45						07 17	
London Waterloo (East) 4	⊖ a																								
London Charing Cross 4	⊖ a																								
Clapham Junction 10	a	00 11	00 29		01 02	01 40	02 40		03 40		04 41			05 49		06 18	06 22		06 37		06 50		07 07		07 03
London Victoria 15	⊖ a	00 18	00 37		01 09	01 49	02 49		03 49		04 49			05 58		06 26			06 44		06 58		07 14		

Station		SN	SN	SN	SN	SN	SN		FC	SE	SN	SN	SN	FC	SN	SN	SN	SN	SN	FC	SN	SN	SN	SN	SN
		1			1	1			1	13	1	1		1	1		1	1		1	1	1	1		1
Purley 4	d	06 49	06 51				07 08			07 18			07 21			07 31			07 38			07 49		07 51	
Purley Oaks	d		06 54				07 11						07 24						07 41					07 54	
South Croydon 4	d		06 57				07 14						07 27						07 44					07 57	
East Croydon	d	06 55	07 00	07 05	07 10	07 14	07 17		07 17	07 24	07 24	07 28	07 30	07 32	07 33	07 37	07 40	07 44	07 47	07 47	07 52	07 55	07 55	08 00	08 00
Norwood Junction 2	d	06 59	07 04	07 10						07 28			07 34									07 59		08 04	
London Bridge 4	⊖ a	07 12	07 25	07 23					07 31	07 40			07 55	07 45	07 52	07 52				08 01		08 12		08 25	
London Blackfriars 3	⊖ a								07 37					07 52						08 07					
City Thameslink 3	a																								
Farringdon 3	⊖ a								07 43					07 58						08 13					
St Pancras International 15	⊖ a								07 47					08 02						08 17					
London Waterloo (East) 4	⊖ a			07 28												07 56									
London Charing Cross 4	⊖ a			07 32												08 00									
Clapham Junction 10	a				07 19	07 25	07 37				07 33	07 37					07 49	07 55	08 07		08 03		08 04		08 11
London Victoria 15	⊖ a				07 27	07 32	07 44				07 40	07 44					07 57	08 02	08 14				08 11		08 18

Station		FC	SN	SN	SN	SN	FC	SN	SE	SN	SN	SN	FC	SN		SN	SN	SN	SN	FC	SN	SN	SN	SN	SN
		1		1	1		1		13	1	1		1	1			1	1		1		1	1	1	
Purley 4	d		08 01			08 08		08 15	08 18			08 21				08 31			08 38		08 45		08 49		08 51
Purley Oaks	d					08 11						08 24							08 41						08 54
South Croydon 4	d					08 14						08 27							08 44						08 57
East Croydon	d	08 02	08 07	08 10	08 14	08 17	08 17	08 21	08 24	08 24	08 28	08 30	08 32	08 33		08 37	08 40	08 44	08 47	08 47	08 51	08 52	08 55	08 55	09 00
Norwood Junction 2	d							08 28	08 28			08 34									08 58		08 59		09 04
London Bridge 4	⊖ a	08 15	08 22				08 31	08 58	08 40			08 55	08 45	08 49		08 52				09 01	09 28		09 12		09 25
London Blackfriars 3	⊖ a	08 22					08 37						08 52							09 07					
City Thameslink 3	a																			09 10					
Farringdon 3	⊖ a	08 28					08 43						08 58							09 14					
St Pancras International 15	⊖ a	08 32					08 47						09 02							09 18					
London Waterloo (East) 4	⊖ a		08 26													08 56									
London Charing Cross 4	⊖ a		08 30													09 00									
Clapham Junction 10	a			08 19	08 25	08 37				08 33	08 37						08 49	08 55	09 07			09 03		09 04	
London Victoria 15	⊖ a			08 27	08 32	08 44				08 40	08 44						08 57	09 02	09 14					09 11	

Station		SN	FC	SN	SN	SN	SN	FC	SN	SE	SN	SN	SN	FC	SN	SN	SN	SN	SN	FC	SN		SN	SN	SN
		1	1		1	1		1		13	1	1		1	1		1	1		1			1	1	1
Purley 4	d			09 01			09 08		09 15	09 18			09 21			09 31			09 38		09 45			09 49	
Purley Oaks	d						09 11						09 24						09 41						
South Croydon 4	d						09 14						09 27						09 44						
East Croydon	d	09 00	09 02	09 07	09 10	09 14	09 17	09 17	09 21	09 24	09 24	09 28	09 30	09 32	09 33	09 37	09 40	09 44	09 47	09 47	09 51		09 52	09 55	09 55
Norwood Junction 2	d								09 28	09 28			09 34								09 58			09 59	
London Bridge 4	⊖ a		09 15	09 22				09 30	09 58	09 40			09 55	09 45	09 49	09 52				10 00	10 28			10 12	
London Blackfriars 3	⊖ a		09 22					09 37						09 52						10 07					
City Thameslink 3	a		09 25					09 40						09 55						10 10					
Farringdon 3	⊖ a		09 29					09 44						09 59						10 14					
St Pancras International 15	⊖ a		09 33					09 48						10 03						10 18					
London Waterloo (East) 4	⊖ a			09 26												09 56									
London Charing Cross 4	⊖ a			09 30												10 00									
Clapham Junction 10	a	09 11			09 19	09 25	09 37				09 33	09 37					09 49	09 55	10 07				10 03		10 04
London Victoria 15	⊖ a	09 18			09 27	09 32	09 44				09 40	09 44					09 57	10 02	10 14						10 11

Station		FC	SN	SN	SN	SN	SN	SN	FC	SN	SE	SN	SN	SN	FC	SN	SN	SN	SN	SN	SN	FC	SN	SN	SN
		1		1		1	1		1		13	1	1		1	1		1	1	1		1		1	1
Purley 4	d		09 51		10 01			10 08		10 15	10 18			10 21			10 31				10 38		10 45		10 49
Purley Oaks	d		09 54					10 11						10 24							10 41				
South Croydon 4	d		09 57					10 14						10 27							10 44				
East Croydon	d	09 57	10 00	10 00	10 07	10 10	10 14	10 17	10 17	10 21	10 24	10 24	10 28	10 30	10 32	10 33	10 37	10 38	10 42	10 44	10 47	10 47	10 51	10 52	10 55
Norwood Junction 2	d		10 04							10 28	10 28			10 34									10 58		10 59
London Bridge 4	⊖ a	10 15	10 25		10 22				10 30	10 58	10 40			10 55	10 45	10 49	10 52					11 00	11 28		11 12
London Blackfriars 3	⊖ a	10 22							10 37						10 52							11 07			
City Thameslink 3	a	10 25							10 40						10 55							11 10			
Farringdon 3	⊖ a	10 29							10 44						10 59							11 14			
St Pancras International 15	⊖ a	10 33							10 48						11 03							11 18			
London Waterloo (East) 4	⊖ a				10 26												10 56								
London Charing Cross 4	⊖ a				10 31												11 00								
Clapham Junction 10	a			10 11		10 19	10 25	10 37				10 33	10 37					10 47	10 51	10 55	11 07			11 03	
London Victoria 15	⊖ a			10 18		10 27	10 32	10 44				10 40	10 44					10 56	10 59	11 02	11 14				

For general notes see front of timetable
For details of catering facilities see
Directory of Train Operators

b Previous night. Arr. 2355
c Arr. 0602

Table 175

Saturdays

Purley and East Croydon → London
COMPLETE SERVICE

		SN 1	SN	SN 1	FC 1		SN	SN 1	SN 1	SN	FC 1	SN	SE 13	SN 1	SN 1	SN	FC 1	SN 1	SN	SN 1	SN 1	SN	FC 1	SN	SN 1
Purley 4	d		10 51				11 01			11 08		11 15	11 18			11 21			11 31			11 38		11 45	
Purley Oaks	d		10 54							11 11						11 24						11 41			
South Croydon 4	d		10 57							11 14						11 27						11 44			
East Croydon	d	10 55	11 00	11 00	11 02		11 07	11 10	11 14	11 17	11 17	11 21	11 24	11 24	11 28	11 30	11 32	11 33	11 37	11 40	11 44	11 47	11 47	11 51	11 52
Norwood Junction 2	d		11 04									11 28	11 28			11 34								11 58	
London Bridge 4	⊖ a		11 26		11 15		11 22				11 30	11 58	11 40			11 55	11 45	11 49	11 52				12 00	12 28	
London Blackfriars 3	⊖ a				11 22						11 37						11 52						12 07		
City Thameslink 3	a				11 25						11 40						11 55						12 10		
Farringdon 3	⊖ a				11 29						11 44						11 59						12 14		
St Pancras International 15	⊖ a				11 33						11 48						12 03						12 18		
London Waterloo (East) 4	⊖ a						11 26												11 56						
London Charing Cross 4	⊖ a						11 30												12 00						
Clapham Junction 10	a	11 04		11 11				11 19	11 25	11 37				11 33	11 37					11 49	11 55	12 07			12 03
London Victoria 15	⊖ a	11 11		11 18				11 27	11 32	11 44				11 40	11 44					11 57	12 02	12 14			

		SN 1	SN 1	SN	SN 1	FC 1			SN	SN 1	SN 1	SN	FC 1	SN	SE 13	SN 1	SN 1	SN	FC 1	SN 1	SN	SN 1	SN 1	SN
Purley 4	d	11 49		11 51			and at		18 01			18 08		18 15	18 18			18 21			18 31			18 38
Purley Oaks	d			11 54			the same					18 11						18 24						18 41
South Croydon 4	d			11 57								18 14						18 27						18 44
East Croydon	d	11 55	11 55	12 00	12 00	12 02	minutes		18 07	18 10	18 14	18 17	18 17	18 21	18 24	18 24	18 28	18 30	18 32	18 33	18 37	18 40	18 44	18 47
Norwood Junction 2	d	11 59		12 04										18 28	18 28			18 34						
London Bridge 4	⊖ a	12 12		12 25		12 15	past		18 22				18 30	18 58	18 40			18 55	18 45	18 49	18 52			
London Blackfriars 3	⊖ a					12 22							18 37						18 52					
City Thameslink 3	a					12 25	each						18 40						18 55					
Farringdon 3	⊖ a					12 29							18 44						18 59					
St Pancras International 15	⊖ a					12 33	hour until						18 48						19 03					
London Waterloo (East) 4	⊖ a								18 26												18 56			
London Charing Cross 4	⊖ a								18 30												19 00			
Clapham Junction 10	a		12 04		12 11					18 19	18 25	18 37				18 33	18 37					18 49	18 55	19 07
London Victoria 15	⊖ a		12 11		12 18					18 27	18 32	18 44				18 40	18 44					18 57	19 02	19 14

		FC 1	SN	SN 1	SN 1	SN 1	SN 1	FC 1	SN	SN	SN 1	SN 1	SN	FC 1	SN		SN 1	SN 1	SN 1	FC 1	SN 1	SN	SN 1	SN 1	SN
Purley 4	d		18 45		18 49				18 58	19 01			19 08		19 15			19 19				19 29			19 38
Purley Oaks	d									19 04			19 11									19 32			19 41
South Croydon 4	d									19 07			19 14									19 35			19 44
East Croydon	d	18 47	18 51	18 52	18 55	18 55	19 00	19 02	19 07	19 10	19 10	19 14	19 17	19 17	19 21		19 24	19 25	19 29	19 32	19 36	19 40	19 40	19 44	19 47
Norwood Junction 2	d		19 01		18 59					19 14					19 31							19 44			
London Bridge 4	⊖ a	19 00	19 25		19 12			19 15	19 23	19 41				19 30	19 55					19 45	19 50	20 11			
London Blackfriars 3	⊖ a	19 07						19 22						19 37						19 52					
City Thameslink 3	a	19 10						19 25						19 40						19 55					
Farringdon 3	⊖ a	19 14						19 29						19 44						19 59					
St Pancras International 15	⊖ a	19 18						19 33						19 48						20 03					
London Waterloo (East) 4	⊖ a								19 28	19 46												20 16			
London Charing Cross 4	⊖ a								19 31	19 51												20 21			
Clapham Junction 10	a			19 03		19 04	19 11				19 19	19 25	19 37				19 33	19 37	19 40				19 49	19 55	20 07
London Victoria 15	⊖ a					19 11	19 18				19 27	19 32	19 45				19 40	19 44	19 48				19 57	20 02	20 15

		FC 1	SN 1	SN 1	SN 1	SN 1	FC 1	SN	SN 1	SN 1	SN	FC 1	SN 1	SN 1	SN 1	FC 1	SN 1	SN	SN 1	SN 1	SN	FC 1		SN 1	SN 1
Purley 4	d				19 49			19 59			20 08			20 20				20 29			20 38				
Purley Oaks	d							20 02			20 11							20 32			20 41				
South Croydon 4	d							20 05			20 14							20 35			20 44				
East Croydon	d	19 47	19 52	19 55	19 55	20 00	20 02	20 10	20 10	20 14	20 17	20 17	20 24	20 26	20 30	20 32	20 36	20 40	20 40	20 44	20 47	20 47		20 52	20 55
Norwood Junction 2	d							20 14										20 44							
London Bridge 4	⊖ a	20 00					20 15	20 41				20 30				20 45	20 50	21 11				21 00			
London Blackfriars 3	⊖ a	20 07					20 22					20 37				20 52						21 07			
City Thameslink 3	a	20 10					20 25					20 40				20 55									
Farringdon 3	⊖ a	20 14					20 29					20 44				20 59						21 13			
St Pancras International 15	⊖ a						20 33					20 48				21 03						21 17			
London Waterloo (East) 4	⊖ a							20 46										21 16							
London Charing Cross 4	⊖ a							20 51										21 21							
Clapham Junction 10	a		20 03	20 04	20 07	20 10			20 19	20 25	20 37		20 33	20 37	20 40				20 49	20 55	21 07			21 03	21 04
London Victoria 15	⊖ a			20 11	20 14	20 17			20 27	20 32	20 45		20 40	20 44	20 50				20 57	21 02	21 15				21 11

		SN 1	SN 1	FC 1	SN	SN 1	SN 1	SN	FC 1	SN 1	SN 1	SN 1	FC 1	SN 1	SN	SN 1	SN 1	SN	SN 1	SN 1	SN 1	SN 1	FC 1	SN	SN 1
Purley 4	d	20 49			20 59			21 08			21 20				21 29			21 38			21 51			21 59	
Purley Oaks	d				21 02			21 11							21 32			21 41						22 02	
South Croydon 4	d				21 05			21 14							21 35			21 44						22 05	
East Croydon	d	20b57	21 00	21 02	21 10	21 10	21 14	21 17	21 17	21 24	21 26	21 30	21 32	21 36	21 40	21 40	21 44	21 47	21 52	21 55	21 57	22 00	22 02	22 10	22 10
Norwood Junction 2	d				21 14										21 44									22 14	
London Bridge 4	⊖ a			21 15	21 41				21 30				21 45	21 50	22 11								22 15	22 41	
London Blackfriars 3	⊖ a			21 22					21 37				21 52										22 22		
City Thameslink 3	a																								
Farringdon 3	⊖ a			21 28					21 43				21 58										22 28		
St Pancras International 15	⊖ a			21 32					21 47				22 02										22 32		
London Waterloo (East) 4	⊖ a				21 46										22 16									22 46	
London Charing Cross 4	⊖ a				21 51										22 21									22 51	
Clapham Junction 10	a	21 07	21 10			21 19	21 25	21 37		21 33	21 37	21 40				21 49	21 55	22 07	22 03	22 04	22 07	22 10			22 19
London Victoria 15	⊖ a	21 14	21 20			21 27	21 32	21 45		21 40	21 44	21 48				21 57	22 02	22 15		22 11	22 14	22 18			22 27

For general notes see front of timetable
For details of catering facilities see
Directory of Train Operators

b Arr. 2054

Table 175

Purley and East Croydon → London
COMPLETE SERVICE

		SN 1	SN	SN 1	SN 1	SN 1	FC 1		SN 1	SN	SN 1	SN 1	SN	SN 1	SN 1	FC 1	SN	SN 1	SN	SN 1	FC 1	SN	SN 1		
Purley 4	d		22 08		22 20					22 29			22 38	22 52			22 59		23 08			23 34	23 49		
Purley Oaks	d		22 11							22 32			22 41				23 02		23 11			23 37			
South Croydon 4	d		22 14							22 35			22 44				23 05		23 14			23 40			
East Croydon	d	22 14	22 17	22 24	22 26	22 30	22 32		22 36	22 40	22 40	22 44	22 47	22 58	23 00	23 02	23 10	23 14	23 17	23 30	23 32	23a42	23 56		
Norwood Junction 2	d									22 44							23 14								
London Bridge 4	⊖ a						22 45		22 50	23 11						23 15	23 38				23 45				
London Blackfriars 3	⊖ a						22 52									23 22					23 52				
City Thameslink 3	a																								
Farringdon 3	⊖ a						22 58									23 28					23 58				
St Pancras International 15	⊖ a						23 02									23 32					00 02				
London Waterloo (East) 4	⊖ a									23 16							23 43								
London Charing Cross 4	⊖ a									23 20							23 48								
Clapham Junction 10	a	22 25	22 37	22 33	22 37	22 40					22 49	22 55	23 07	23 07	23 10			23 25	23 37	23 42			00 11		
London Victoria 15	⊖ a	22 32	22 45	22 40	22 44	22 48					22 57	23 02	23 14	23 14	23 17			23 32	23 45	23 52			00 18		

Sundays

		SN 1	SN 1	FC 1	SN	SN 1	SN 1		SN 1	SN 1	SN 1	FC 1	SN 1	FC 1		SN	SN	FC 1	SN 1	SN	SN 1		FC 1	SN	SN 1
Purley 4	d	23p49	00 11			01 37	02 33		03 33	04 33	05 22		05 56				06 35				07 20			07 38	07 53
Purley Oaks	d																06 38							07 41	
South Croydon 4	d																06 41				07 24			07 44	
East Croydon	d	23p56	00 17	00 36	00 49	01 43	02 40		03 40	04 40	05 28	05 32	06 02	06 32		06 40	06 44	07 02	07 10	07 12	07 27		07 32	07 47	07 59
Norwood Junction 2	d																06 48			07 18				07 51	
London Bridge 4	⊖ a			00 52													07 12	07 15		07 42			07 45	08 12	
London Blackfriars 3	⊖ a			00 59								05 54		06 54				07 23					07 53		
City Thameslink 3	a																								
Farringdon 3	⊖ a													06 58				07 27					07 57		
St Pancras International 15	⊖ a			01 07								06 02		07 02				07 31					08 01		
London Waterloo (East) 4	⊖ a																07 16			07 46				08 16	
London Charing Cross 4	⊖ a																07 20			07 50				08 20	
Clapham Junction 10	a	00 11	00 29		01 02	01 53	02 52		03 52	04 52	05 48		06 14			07 00			07 24		07 40				08 08
London Victoria 15	⊖ a	00 18	00 37		01 09	02 05	03 05		04 05	05 05	05 58		06 22			07 08			07 31		07 48				08 16

		SN 1	FC 1	SN 1	SN	SN 1		SN 1	FC 1	SN 1	SN	SN 1	SN 1		FC 1	SN 1	SN	SN 1	SN 1	FC 1		SN 1		SN	SN 1
Purley 4	d				08 08	08 18					08 38	08 53					09 08	09 18						09 38	09 53
Purley Oaks	d				08 11						08 41						09 11							09 41	
South Croydon 4	d				08 14						08 44						09 14							09 44	
East Croydon	d	07 59	08 02	08 10	08 17	08 25		08 29	08 32	08 40	08 47	08 59	08 59		09 02	09 10	09 17	09 25	09 29	09 32		09 40		09 47	09 59
Norwood Junction 2	d				08 21						08 51						09 21							09 51	
London Bridge 4	⊖ a		08 15		08 42				08 45		09 12				09 15		09 42			09 45				10 12	
London Blackfriars 3	⊖ a		08 23						08 53						09 23					09 53					
City Thameslink 3	a																								
Farringdon 3	⊖ a		08 27						08 57						09 27					09 57					
St Pancras International 15	⊖ a		08 31						09 01						09 31					10 01					
London Waterloo (East) 4	⊖ a				08 46						09 16						09 46							10 16	
London Charing Cross 4	⊖ a				08 50						09 20						09 52							10 22	
Clapham Junction 10	a	08 11		08 24		08 37		08 41		08 54		09 08	09 11			09 24		09 37	09 41			09 54			10 08
London Victoria 15	⊖ a	08 18		08 31		08 46		08 48		09 01		09 16	09 18			09 31		09 46	09 48			10 01			10 16

		SN 1	FC 1	SN 1	FC	SN	SN 1	SN 1	FC 1	SN 1	FC 1			SN	SN 1	SN 1	FC 1	SN 1	FC 1		SN	SN 1	SN 1	FC 1
Purley 4	d					10 08	10 18					and at the same minutes past each hour until		15 38	15 53						16 08	16 18		
Purley Oaks	d					10 11								15 41							16 11			
South Croydon 4	d					10 14								15 44							16 14			
East Croydon	d	09 59	10 02	10 10	10 12	10 17	10 25	10 29	10 32	10 40	10 42			15 47	15 59	15 59	16 02	16 10	16 12		16 17	16 25	16 29	16 32
Norwood Junction 2	d					10 21								15 51							16 21			
London Bridge 4	⊖ a		10 15		10 30	10 42			10 45		11 00			16 12			16 15		16 30		16 42			16 45
London Blackfriars 3	⊖ a		10 23		10 37				10 53		11 07						16 23		16 37					16 53
City Thameslink 3	a																							
Farringdon 3	⊖ a		10 27		10 43				10 57		11 13						16 27		16 43					16 57
St Pancras International 15	⊖ a		10 31		10 47				11 01		11 17						16 31		16 47					17 01
London Waterloo (East) 4	⊖ a					10 46								16 16							16 46			
London Charing Cross 4	⊖ a					10 52								16 22							16 52			
Clapham Junction 10	a	10 11		10 24			10 37	10 41		10 54					16 08	16 11		16 24				16 37	16 41	
London Victoria 15	⊖ a	10 18		10 31			10 46	10 48		11 01					16 16	16 18		16 31				16 46	16 48	

		SN 1	SN 1	FC 1	SN		SN 1	SN 1	FC 1	SN 1	FC 1	SN		SN 1	SN 1	FC 1	SN 1	SN 1	FC 1		SN	SN	SN 1	SN 1	FC 1
Purley 4	d				16 38		16 53					17 08		17 18								17 38	17 53		
Purley Oaks	d				16 41							17 11										17 41			
South Croydon 4	d				16 44							17 14										17 44			
East Croydon	d	16 35	16 40	16 42	16 47		16 59	16 59	17 02	17 10	17 12	17 17		17 25	17 29	17 32	17 35	17 40	17 42		17 44	17 47	17 59	17 59	18 02
Norwood Junction 2	d				16 51							17 21										17 51			
London Bridge 4	⊖ a			17 00	17 12				17 15		17 30	17 42				17 45			18 00		18 18	18 12			18 15
London Blackfriars 3	⊖ a			17 07					17 23		17 37					17 53			18 07						18 23
City Thameslink 3	a																								
Farringdon 3	⊖ a			17 13					17 27		17 43					17 57			18 13						18 27
St Pancras International 15	⊖ a			17 17					17 31		17 47					18 01			18 17						18 31
London Waterloo (East) 4	⊖ a				17 16							17 46										18 16			
London Charing Cross 4	⊖ a				17 22							17 52										18 22			
Clapham Junction 10	a	16 47	16 54				17 08	17 11		17 24				17 37	17 41		17 47	17 54					18 08	18 11	
London Victoria 15	⊖ a	16 53	17 01				17 16	17 18		17 31				17 46	17 48		17 53	18 01					18 16	18 18	

For general notes see front of timetable
For details of catering facilities see
Directory of Train Operators

Purley and East Croydon → London

COMPLETE SERVICE

Station		SN 1	FC	SN		SN 1	SN 1	FC 1	SN 1	SN 1	SN		SN 1	SN 1	FC 1	SN 1	SN	SN 1		SN 1	FC 1	SN 1	SN 1	SN	SN 1
Purley 4	d			18 08		18 18					18 38		18 53				19 08	19 18						19 38	19 53
Purley Oaks	d			18 11							18 41						19 11							19 41	
South Croydon 4	d			18 14							18 44						19 14							19 44	
East Croydon	d	18 10	18 12	18 17		18 25	18 29	18 32	18 35	18 40	18 47		18 59	18 59	19 02	19 10	19 17	19 25		19 29	19 32	19 35	19 40	19 47	19 59
Norwood Junction 2	d			18 21							18 51						19 21							19 51	
London Bridge 4	⊖ a		18 30	18 42				18 45			19 12				19 15		19 42				19 45			20 12	
London Blackfriars 3	⊖ a		18 37					18 53							19 23						19 53				
City Thameslink 3	a																								
Farringdon 3	⊖ a		18 43					18 57							19 27						19 57				
St Pancras International 15	⊖ a		18 47					19 01							19 31						20 01				
London Waterloo (East) 4	⊖ a			18 46							19 16						19 46							20 18	
London Charing Cross 4	⊖ a			18 52							19 22						19 52							20 22	
Clapham Junction 10	a	18 24				18 37	18 41		18 47	18 54			19 08	19 11		19 24		19 37		19 41		19 47	19 54		20 08
London Victoria 15	⊖ a	18 31				18 46	18 48		18 53	19 01			19 16	19 18		19 31		19 46		19 48		19 53	20 01		20 16

Station		SN 1	FC 1		SN 1	SN	SN 1	SN 1	FC 1	SN 1		SN 1	SN	SN	SN 1	SN 1	FC 1		SN 1	SN	SN 1	SN 1	FC 1	SN 1	SN
Purley 4	d					20 08	20 18							20 38	20 53					21 08	21 23				21 38
Purley Oaks	d					20 11								20 41						21 11					21 41
South Croydon 4	d					20 14								20 44						21 14					21 44
East Croydon	d	19 59	20 02		20 10	20 17	20 25	20 29	20 32	20 35		20 40	20 44	20 47	20 59	20 59	21 02		21 10	21 17	21 28	21 29	21 32	21 40	21 47
Norwood Junction 2	d					20 21								20 51						21 21					21 51
London Bridge 4	⊖ a		20 15			20 42			20 45				21 18	21 12			21 15			21 42			21 45		22 12
London Blackfriars 3	⊖ a		20 23						20 53								21 23						21 53		
City Thameslink 3	a																								
Farringdon 3	⊖ a		20 27						20 57								21 27						21 57		
St Pancras International 15	⊖ a		20 31						21 01								21 31						22 01		
London Waterloo (East) 4	⊖ a					20 46								21 16						21 46					22 16
London Charing Cross 4	⊖ a					20 50								21 20						21 50					22 22
Clapham Junction 10	a	20 11			20 24		20 37	20 41		20 47		20 54			21 08	21 11			21 24		21 37	21 41		21 54	
London Victoria 15	⊖ a	20 18			20 31		20 46	20 48		20 53		21 01			21 16	21 18			21 31		21 46	21 48		22 01	

Station		SN 1		SN 1	FC 1	SN 1	SN	SN 1	SN 1		FC 1	SN	SN 1	SN 1	FC 1	SN		SN 1	SN 1	SN	FC 1	SN 1			
Purley 4	d	21 53					22 08	22 18				22 38	22 53			23 08		23 17		23 23		23 50			
Purley Oaks	d						22 11					22 41				23 11				23 26					
South Croydon 4	d						22 14					22 44				23 14				23 29					
East Croydon	d	21 59		21 59	22 02	22 10	22 17	22 25	22 29		22 32	22 47	22 59	22 59	23 02	23a16		23 25	23 29	23a31	23 32	23 56			
Norwood Junction 2	d						22 21					22 51													
London Bridge 4	⊖ a				22 15		22 42				22 45	23 12			23 15						23 45				
London Blackfriars 3	⊖ a				22 23						22 53				23 23						23 53				
City Thameslink 3	a																								
Farringdon 3	⊖ a				22 27						22 57				23 27						23 57				
St Pancras International 15	⊖ a				22 31						23 01				23 31						00 02				
London Waterloo (East) 4	⊖ a						22 46					23 16													
London Charing Cross 4	⊖ a						22 50					23 20													
Clapham Junction 10	a	22 08		22 11		22 24		22 37	22 41				23 10	23 13				23 37	23 41			00 10			
London Victoria 15	⊖ a	22 16		22 18		22 31		22 46	22 50				23 16	23 20				23 46	23 51			00 18			

For general notes see front of timetable
For details of catering facilities see Directory of Train Operators

Network Diagram for Tables 177, 178, 179, 181, 182 | also 175★

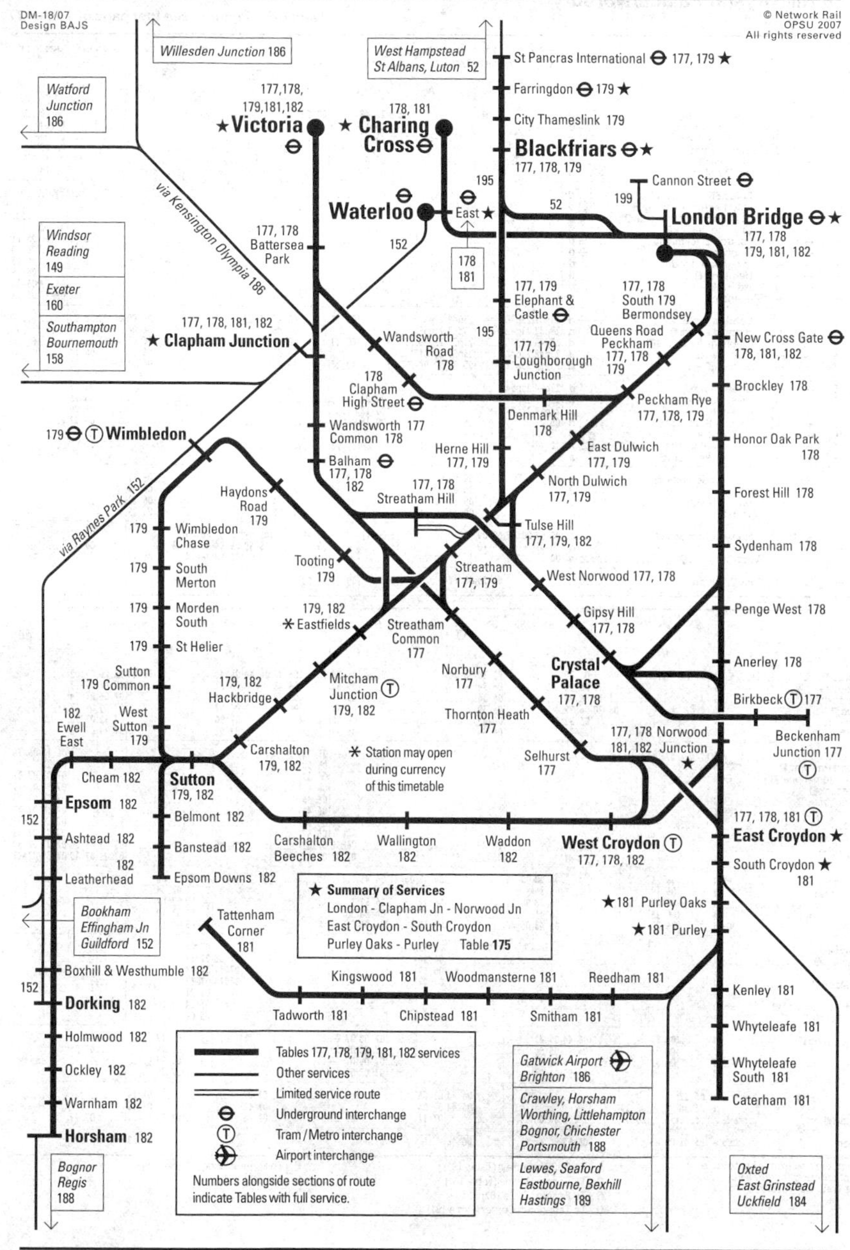

DM-18/07
Design BAJS
© Network Rail
OPSU 2007
All rights reserved
Willesden Junction 186
West Hampstead
St Albans, Luton 52
St Pancras International 177, 179 ★
Farringdon 179 ★
City Thameslink 179
Blackfriars ★
177, 178, 179
Watford Junction 186
177,178, 179,181,182
★Victoria
178, 181
★ Charing Cross
195
Cannon Street
52
199
Waterloo
East ★
London Bridge ★
177, 178
179, 181, 182
via Kensington Olympia 186
177, 178
Battersea Park
152
178
181
Windsor
Reading
149
Exeter
160
Southampton
Bournemouth
158
177, 179
Elephant & Castle
177, 178
South Bermondsey 179
177, 178, 181, 182
★ Clapham Junction
Wandsworth Road 178
195
Queens Road Peckham 177, 178 179
177, 179
Loughborough Junction
New Cross Gate
178, 181, 182
178
Clapham High Street
Brockley 178
Peckham Rye
177, 178, 179
Denmark Hill
178
179 Wimbledon
Wandsworth Common 177 178
Herne Hill 177, 179
East Dulwich 177, 179
Honor Oak Park 178
Balham 177, 178 182
177, 178
Streatham Hill
North Dulwich 177, 179
Forest Hill 178
via Raynes Park 152
Haydons Road 179
179 Wimbledon Chase
Tulse Hill
177, 179, 182
Sydenham 178
179 South Merton
Tooting 179
Streatham 177, 179
West Norwood 177, 178
179 Morden South
179, 182
✳ Eastfields
Streatham Common 177
Gipsy Hill 177, 178
Penge West 178
179 St Helier
Crystal Palace 177, 178
Anerley 178
Sutton Common 179
179, 182 Hackbridge
Mitcham Junction 179, 182
Norbury 177
Birkbeck 177
182 Ewell East
West Sutton 179
Thornton Heath 177
Beckenham Junction 177
Carshalton 179, 182
✳ Station may open during currency of this timetable
177, 178 Norwood Junction 181, 182 ★
Selhurst 177
Cheam 182
Sutton 179, 182
Epsom 182
152
Belmont 182
177, 178, 181
East Croydon ★
Ashtead 182
Banstead 182
Carshalton Beeches 182
Wallington 182
Waddon 182
West Croydon
177, 178, 182
South Croydon ★ 181
182 Leatherhead
Epsom Downs 182
★ Summary of Services
London - Clapham Jn - Norwood Jn
East Croydon - South Croydon
Purley Oaks - Purley Table 175
★181 Purley Oaks
★181 Purley
Bookham
Effingham Jn
Guildford 152
Tattenham Corner 181
Boxhill & Westhumble 182
Kingswood 181
Woodmansterne 181
Reedham 181
Kenley 181
152
Dorking 182
Tadworth 181
Chipstead 181
Smitham 181
Whyteleafe 181
Holmwood 182
Tables 177, 178, 179, 181, 182 services
Other services
Limited service route
Underground interchange
Tram / Metro interchange
Airport interchange
Numbers alongside sections of route indicate Tables with full service.
Gatwick Airport
Brighton 186
Crawley, Horsham
Worthing, Littlehampton
Bognor, Chichester
Portsmouth 188
Lewes, Seaford
Eastbourne, Bexhill
Hastings 189
Whyteleafe South 181
Caterham 181
Ockley 182
Warnham 182
Horsham 182
Bognor Regis 188
Oxted
East Grinstead
Uckfield 184

Luton & London → East and West Croydon via Tulse Hill/Crystal Palace/Norbury

Local Services

Network Diagram - see first page of Table 177

Miles	Miles	Miles	Miles	Miles			SN MX	SN MO	SN MO	SN MO	SN MX	SN MX	SN MX	SN	SN MX	SN	SN	SN	SN	SN	SN	SN	SN	SN	FC
																	[1]			[1]					
											A										B		C		
—	0	—	—	0	London Bridge [4] ⊖	d			23p44			23p53	23p49		00 26				05 46					06 00	
—	1¾	—	—	1¾	South Bermondsey	d							23p53											06 04	
—	2¾	—	—	2¾	Queens Rd Peckham	d							23p55											06 06	
—	3½	—	—	3½	Peckham Rye [4]	d							23p58											06 09	
—	4¼	—	—	4¼	East Dulwich	d							00 01											06 12	
—	4¾	—	—	4¾	North Dulwich	d							00 03											06 14	
—	—	—	—	—	Luton [10]	d																			
—	—	—	—	—	Luton Airport Parkway [7] ✈	d																			
—	—	—	—	—	St Pancras International [15] ⊖	d																			
—	—	—	—	—	City Thameslink [3]	d																			
—	—	—	—	—	London Blackfriars [3] ⊖	d																			06 11
—	—	—	—	—	Elephant & Castle ⊖	d																			06 14
—	—	—	—	—	Loughborough Jn	d																			06 18
—	—	—	—	—	Herne Hill [4]	d																			06 25
—	6	—	—	6	Tulse Hill [3]	d							00 06											06 17	06 30
—	7½	—	—	—	Streatham [4]	d																		06a21	06 33
0	—	0	0	—	London Victoria [15] ⊖	d	23p37	23p38		23p49	23p51			00 17		00 42	05 23				06 00	06 05	06 07		
1¼	—	1¼	1¼	—	Battersea Park [4]	d	23p42	23p42		23p53	23p55					00 46					06 04		06 11		
2¾	—	2¾	2¾	—	Clapham Junction [10]	d	23p45	23p45		23p56	23p58			00 23		00 49	05 33				06 07	06 11	06 14		
4	—	4	4	—	Wandsworth Common	d	23p48	23p48		23p59	00 01					00 52					06 10		06 17		
4¾	—	4¾	4¾	—	Balham [4] ⊖	d	23p51	23p51		00 02	00 04			00 27		00 55					06 13	06 15	06 20		
5¾	—	5¾	—	—	Streatham Hill	d	23p54	23p54															06 23		
7	—	7	—	6½	West Norwood [4]	d	23p57	23p57					00 09										06 26		
8	—	8	—	7½	Gipsy Hill	d	23p59	23p59					00 12										06 29		
8¾	—	8¾	—	8¼	Crystal Palace [4]	d	00 03	00 03					00 15										06 32		
—	—	10¼	—	—	Birkbeck 🚊	d																			
—	—	11¾	—	—	Beckenham Junction [4] 🚊	a																			
—	—	—	—	—	Bromley South [4]	a																			
—	8	—	6½	—	Streatham Common [4]	d				00 06	00 08			00 31		00 59					06 17				
—	9	—	7½	—	Norbury	d				00 08	00 10			00 34		01 01					06 19				
—	10¼	—	8¾	—	Thornton Heath	d				00 11	00 13			00 37		01 04					06 22				
—	11	—	9½	—	Selhurst [4]	d				00 14	00 16			00 39		01 07					06 25				
10¼	—	—	—	9¾	Norwood Junction [2]	a	00 07	00 07	00 09			00 16	00 19		00 49		05 49		06 09				06 36		
—	—	—	—	—		d	00 07		00 10			00 16			00 49		05 50	05 54	06 09	06 10			06 39		
—	12	—	—	—	West Croydon [4] 🚊	a	00 13				00 20							05 58	06 14		06 29		→		
11½	—	—	10½	11	East Croydon 🚊	a			00 13	00 17		00 20		00 42	00 53	01 10	05 53			06 13					

		SN	SN	SN	SN	SN	SN	SN	SN	SN	SN	SN	SN	SN	FC	SN	SN	SN	SN	SN	SN	SN	SN	FC	FC
										[1]															[1]
			D	C			B											E		B					
London Bridge [4] ⊖	d	06 13			06 11	06 20			06 30	06 30				06 38		06 41	06 46	06 48			06 54	07 00	07 08		
South Bermondsey	d				06 15	06 24			06 34					06 42		06 45		06 52				07 04	07 12		
Queens Rd Peckham	d				06 18	06 26			06 36					06 44		06 48		06 54				07 06	07 14		
Peckham Rye [4]	d				06 20	06 29			06 39					06 47		06 50		06 57				07 09	07 17		
East Dulwich	d					06 32			06 42					06 50				07 00				07 12	07 20		
North Dulwich	d					06 34			06 44					06 52				07 02				07 14	07 22		
Luton [10]	d														05 48									06 18	06 36
Luton Airport Parkway [7] ✈	d														05 50									06 20	
St Pancras International [15] ⊖	d														06 33									07 03	07 07
City Thameslink [3]	d														06 41									07 11	07 17
London Blackfriars [3] ⊖	d														06 46									07 16	07 23
Elephant & Castle ⊖	d														06 49									07 19	07 27
Loughborough Jn	d														06 53									07 23	07 31
Herne Hill [4]	d														06 57									07 27	07 35
Tulse Hill [3]	d					06 37			06 47					06b58	07 02			07 05				07 17	07 26	07 32	07 39
Streatham [4]	d					06 41			06a51					07 01	07 05							07a21	07 30	07 35	07a42
London Victoria [15] ⊖	d		06 15				06 28	06 35			06 37	06 41	06 45						06 52	07 00					
Battersea Park [4]	d		06 19				06 34				06 41	06a45							06 56	07 04					
Clapham Junction [10]	d		06 22				06 38	06 41			06 44		06 51						06 59	07 07					
Wandsworth Common	d		06 25				06 41				06 47		06 54						07 02	07 10					
Balham [4] ⊖	d		06 28				06 43	06 46			06 50		06 56						07 05	07 13					
Streatham Hill	d										06 53								07 08						
West Norwood [4]	d										06 56							07 08	07 11						
Gipsy Hill	d										06 59							07 11	07 14						
Crystal Palace [4]	d										07 02							07a14	07 17						
Birkbeck 🚊	d																		07 21						
Beckenham Junction [4] 🚊	a																		07 24						
Bromley South [4]	a																		*08 04*						
Streatham Common [4]	d		06 32			06 44	06 47						07 00	07 04						07 17			07 33		
Norbury	d		06 34			06 46	06 50						07 03	07 07						07 19			07 35		
Thornton Heath	d		06 37			06 49	06 53						07 06	07 10						07 22			07 38		
Selhurst [4]	d		06 40			06 52	06 56						07 08	07 13						07 25			07 41		
Norwood Junction [2]	a	06 37		←						06 44	07 06					07 09					07 14				
	d	06 38		06 39						06 44	07 06					07 10					07 14				
West Croydon [4] 🚊	a			06 43			07 00				07 11			07 22		07 14				07 29			07 49		
East Croydon 🚊	a	06 41	06 45			06 55				06 48			07 11								07 18				

For general notes see front of timetable
For details of catering facilities see Directory of Train Operators

A To Sutton (Surrey) (Table 182)
B To Epsom Downs (Table 182)
C To Epsom (Table 182)
D To Tattenham Corner (Table 181)
E To London Bridge (Table 178)
b Arr. 0655

Luton & London → East and West Croydon via Tulse Hill/Crystal Palace/Norbury

Local Services

Network Diagram - see first page of Table 177

	SN 1	SN	SN	SN	SN	SN	SN	SN	SN 1	SN	SN	SN	SN	SN	SN	SN	FC		SN	SN	SN	SN	SN	SN
					A					B									C	D				
London Bridge 4 ⊖ d	07 20					07 11	07 15	07 22	07 28		07 25		07 31	07 40							07 47	07 41	07 53	
South Bermondsey d						07 15		07 26					07 35									07 45		
Queens Rd Peckham d						07 18		07 28					07 37									07 48		
Peckham Rye 4 d						07 20		07 31					07 40								07 53	07 50	07 59	
East Dulwich d								07 34					07 43								07 56			
North Dulwich d								07 36					07 45								07 58			
Luton 10 d																	06 56							
Luton Airport Parkway 7 ✈ d																								
St Pancras International 15 ⊖ d																	07 28							
City Thameslink 3 d																	07 35							
London Blackfriars 3 ⊖ d																	07 43							
Elephant & Castle ⊖ d																	07 47							
Loughborough Jn d																	07 51							
Herne Hill 4 d																	07 55							
Tulse Hill 3 d								07 40					07 48				07 59				08 02		08 05	
Streatham 4 d													07a52				08 02				08 05			
London Victoria 15 ⊖ d		07 06	07 11	07 15	07 20					07 30					07 36	07 41			07 45	07 47				07 51
Battersea Park 4 d		07 10	07a15		07 24					07 34					07 40	07a45				07 51				07 55
Clapham Junction 10 d		07 13		07 21	07 27					07 38					07 43				07 51	07 54				07 58
Wandsworth Common d		07 16			07 30					07 41					07 46				07 54	07 57				08 01
Balham 4 ⊖ d		07 19		07 25	07 33					07 43					07 49				07 57	08 00				08 04
Streatham Hill d		07 22										07 45			07 52									08 07
West Norwood 4 d		07 25						07 43				07 48			07 55								08 08	08 10
Gipsy Hill d		07 28						07 46				07 51			07 58								08 11	08 13
Crystal Palace 4 d		07 31						07 49				07a54			08 01								08 13	08a16
Birkbeck 🚊 d								07 53															08 17	
Beckenham Junction 4 🚊 a								07 56															08 21	
Bromley South 4 a																							*08 32*	
Streatham Common 4 d					07 37					07 47									08 01		08 08			
Norbury d					07 39					07 50									08 03		08 11			
Thornton Heath d					07 42					07 53									08 06		08 14			
Selhurst 4 d					07 45					07 56									08 09		08 17			
Norwood Junction 2 a	07 32	07 35					07 38		07 41		07 48			08 00	08 05									
d	07 32	07 35					07 39		07 42		07 51			08 00	08 06									
West Croydon 4 🚊 a		07 40					07 43			08 02					08 11						08 22			
East Croydon 🚊 a	07 36				07 48				07 45		07 55			08 04					08 13					

	SN 1	SN	SN	SN	FC 1	SN	SN 1	SN	SN	SN	SN	FC	SN	SN	SN	SN	SN 1	SN	SN 1	SN	SN	SN	SN	SN
			B										C										E	B
London Bridge 4 ⊖ d	07 54	07 48				08 02	08 03	08 05	08 09						08 09	08 17	08 25	08 19	08 30	08 21				
South Bermondsey d						08 06									08 13									
Queens Rd Peckham d						08 08									08 15									
Peckham Rye 4 d						08 11									08 18					08 27				
East Dulwich d						08 14														08 30				
North Dulwich d						08 16														08 32				
Luton 10 d					07 16							07 08												
Luton Airport Parkway 7 ✈ d												07 10												
St Pancras International 15 ⊖ d					07 48							07 56												
City Thameslink 3 d					07 55							08 03												
London Blackfriars 3 ⊖ d					08 00							08 08												
Elephant & Castle ⊖ d												08 11												
Loughborough Jn d												08 15												
Herne Hill 4 d					08 09							08 23												
Tulse Hill 3 d					08 13	08 19						08 27								08 36				
Streatham 4 d						08a23						08 30												
London Victoria 15 ⊖ d			08 03							08 07	08 11		08 15	08 20							08 22	08 26	08 31	08 34
Battersea Park 4 d			08 07							08 11	08a15		08 19								08 26			08 38
Clapham Junction 10 d			08 11							08 14			08 22	08 26							08 30		08 37	08 41
Wandsworth Common d			08 14							08 17			08 25								08 33		08 40	08 44
Balham 4 ⊖ d			08 16							08 20			08 28	08 30							08 35		08 43	08 47
Streatham Hill d				08 14						08 23											08 38			
West Norwood 4 d				08 17						08 26										08 39	08 42			
Gipsy Hill d				08 20						08 29										08 42	08 45			
Crystal Palace 4 d				08a23						08 32						08a36				08 44	08a47			
Birkbeck 🚊 d																								
Beckenham Junction 4 🚊 a																								
Bromley South 4 a																								
Streatham Common 4 d			08 20										08 32										08 47	08 51
Norbury d			08 23										08 34										08 49	08 53
Thornton Heath d			08 26										08 37										08 52	08 56
Selhurst 4 d			08b32										08 40										08 55	09 00
Norwood Junction 2 a	08 06	08 11					08 14	08 25	08 28	08 36							08 37	08 44	08 44	08 49				
d	08 06	08 11					08 14	08 25	08 28	08 36							08 37	08 44	08 45	08 49				
West Croydon 4 🚊 a		08 16	08 36							08 41								08 49				08 53	08 59	09 05
East Croydon 🚊 a	08 11				08 25		08 19	08 29	08 32				08 43				08 41		08 49	08 53				

For general notes see front of timetable
For details of catering facilities see Directory of Train Operators

A To Tattenham Corner (Table 181)
B To Epsom Downs (Table 182)
C To Caterham (Table 181)
D To Sutton (Surrey) (Table 182)
E To Epsom (Table 182)
b Arr. 0828

Luton & London → East and West Croydon via Tulse Hill/Crystal Palace/Norbury

Local Services

Network Diagram - see first page of Table 177

		SN	FC	SN	FC 1	SN	SN 1	SN	SN	SN A	SN	SN	SN	SN 1	SN B	SN C	SN	FC	SN	SN D	SN E	FC	SN	FC	FC
London Bridge 4	⊖ d	08 24		08 36		08 29	08 49					08 45	08 41	09 00	08 37	08 54			08 47				08 57		
South Bermondsey	d	08 28				08 33							08 45		08 42				08 51				09 03		
Queens Rd Peckham	d	08 30				08 35							08 48		08 45				08 53				09 05		
Peckham Rye 4	d	08 33				08 38							08 50		08 47				08 56				09 08		
East Dulwich	d					08 41									08 51				08 59				09 11		
North Dulwich	d					08 43									08 53				09 01				09 13		
Luton 10	d				07 48													07 56						08 20	
Luton Airport Parkway 7	✈ d																	07 58							
St Pancras International 15	⊖ d		08 12		08 20													08 33				08 40		08 52	08 56
City Thameslink 3	d		08 19		08 27													08 40				08 47		08 59	09 03
London Blackfriars 3	⊖ d		08 24		08 32													08 45				08 52		09 02	09 08
Elephant & Castle	⊖ d		08 27		08 35																	08 55		09 05	09 11
Loughborough Jn	d		08 31		08 39																	08 59		09 09	09 15
Herne Hill 4	d		08 39		08 43													08 54				09 06		09 13	09 21
Tulse Hill 3	d	08 38	08b47		08 47	08 50									09c00			09e02	09 06			09 10	09 16	09 17	09 26
Streatham 4	d	08a42	08 50															09a05	09 10			09a13		09 20	09a30
London Victoria 15	⊖ d							08 37	08 41	08 45	08 50						08 52			08 57	09 05				
Battersea Park 4	d							08 41	08a45	08 49							08 56			09 01					
Clapham Junction 10	d							08 44		08 52	08 56						08 59			09 04	09 11				
Wandsworth Common	d							08 47		08 55							09 02			09 07	09 14				
Balham 4	⊖ d							08 50		08 58	09 02						09 05			09 10	09 17				
Streatham Hill	d							08 53									09 08								
West Norwood 4	d					08 53		08 56							09 03		09 11						09 19		
Gipsy Hill	d					08 56		08 59							09 06		09 14						09 22		
Crystal Palace 4	d					08 58		09 02							09 08	09a13	09a17						09 25		
Birkbeck	🚊 d					09 02																	09 29		
Beckenham Junction 4	🚊 a					09 06																	09 32		
Bromley South 4	a					*09 33*																	*09 48*		
Streatham Common 4	d									09 02									09 13	09 15	09 21				
Norbury	d									09 04									09 15	09 18	09 23				
Thornton Heath	d									09 07									09 18	09 21	09 26				
Selhurst 4	d									09 10									09 21	09 24	09 30				
Norwood Junction 2	a			08 56			09 01	09 06				09 09		09 11	09 13										
	d			08 56			09 02	09 06				09 09		09 11	09 13										
West Croydon 4	🚊 a							09 11				09 14							09 25	09 28	09 34				
East Croydon	🚊 a			09 00	09 06		09 05			09 13				09 15	09 17										

		SN	SN	SN	SN	SN A	SN	SN	SN B		SN C	SN	SN	SN	SN G	SN E	FC	SN	SN 1	SN	SN	SN	SN	SN A	SN
London Bridge 4	⊖ d	09 05	09 19					09 15	09 07		09 24		09 11	09 17				09 30	09 33	09 35	09 47				
South Bermondsey	d								09 12				09 15	09 23				09 34							
Queens Rd Peckham	d								09 14				09 18	09 25				09 36							
Peckham Rye 4	d								09 17				09 20	09 28				09 39							
East Dulwich	d								09 20					09 31				09 42							
North Dulwich	d								09 22					09 33				09 44							
Luton 10	d																								
Luton Airport Parkway 7	✈ d																								
St Pancras International 15	⊖ d																09 14								
City Thameslink 3	d																09 21								
London Blackfriars 3	⊖ d																09 28								
Elephant & Castle	⊖ d																09 31								
Loughborough Jn	d																09 35								
Herne Hill 4	d																09 41								
Tulse Hill 3	d								09f30					09 36			09 47	09 47							
Streatham 4	d													09 40			09 50								
London Victoria 15	⊖ d			09 07	09 11	09 15	09 20					09 22			09 28	09 35						09 37	09 41	09 45	09 50
Battersea Park 4	d			09 11	09a15	09 19						09 26			09 32							09 41	09a45	09 49	
Clapham Junction 10	d			09 14		09 22	09 26					09 29			09 35	09 41						09 44		09 52	09 56
Wandsworth Common	d			09 17		09 25						09 32			09 38	09 44						09 47		09 55	
Balham 4	⊖ d			09 20		09 28	09 32					09 35			09 41	09 47						09 50		09 58	10 02
Streatham Hill	d			09 23								09 38										09 53			
West Norwood 4	d			09 26					09 33			09 41						09 50				09 56			
Gipsy Hill	d			09 29					09 36			09 44						09 53				09 59			
Crystal Palace 4	d			09 32					09 38		09a43	09a47						09 56				10 02			
Birkbeck	🚊 d																	10 00							
Beckenham Junction 4	🚊 a																	10 03							
Bromley South 4	a																	*10 17*							
Streatham Common 4	d					09 32								09 43	09 45	09 51								10 02	
Norbury	d					09 34								09 45	09 48	09 53								10 04	
Thornton Heath	d					09 37								09 48	09 51	09 56								10 07	
Selhurst 4	d					09 40								09 51	09 54	09 59								10 10	
Norwood Junction 2	a	09 25	09 32	09 36				09 38	09 43										09 45	09 55	09 59	10 06			
	d	09 25	09 32	09 36				09 39	09 43										09 46	09 55	09 59	10 06			
West Croydon 4	🚊 a			09 41				09 44						09 55	09 58	10 03						10 11			
East Croydon	🚊 a	09 29	09 36			09 43			09 47										09 49	09 59	10 05			10 13	

For general notes see front of timetable
For details of catering facilities see Directory of Train Operators

A To Caterham (Table 181)
B To Smitham (Table 181)
C Via Sydenham (Table 178)
D To Epsom (Table 182)
E To Sutton (Surrey) (Table 182)
G To Epsom Downs (Table 182)

b Arr. 0843
c Arr. 0857
e Arr. 0858
f Arr. 0926

Luton & London → East and West Croydon via Tulse Hill/Crystal Palace/Norbury

Local Services

Network Diagram - see first page of Table 177

	SN	SN	SN	SN	FC	SN	SN	SN	SN	FC	SN	SE	SN	SN	SN	SN	SN	SN	SN	SN	SN	SN	FC	SN
												13												
		A	B				C	D				E		B				G			A			
London Bridge 4 ⊖ d	09 45	09 37	09 54			09 47			09 41		10 00	10 03	10 05	10 24	10 17					10 15	10 08			10 11
South Bermondsey d		09 42				09 53			09 45		10 04										10 12			10 15
Queens Rd Peckham d		09 44				09 55			09 48		10 06										10 14			10 18
Peckham Rye 4 d		09 47				09 58			09 50		10 09										10 17			10 20
East Dulwich d		09 50				10 01					10 12										10 20			
North Dulwich d		09 52				10 03					10 14										10 22			
Luton 10 d																							09 14	
Luton Airport Parkway 7 ✈ d																							09 16	
St Pancras International 15 ⊖ d					09 32					09 48													10 02	
City Thameslink 3 d					09 39					09 55													10 09	
London Blackfriars 3 ⊖ d					09 44					10 00													10 16	
Elephant & Castle ⊖ d					09 47					10 03													10 19	
Loughborough Jn d					09 51					10 07													10 23	
Herne Hill 4 d					09 59					10 11													10 27	
Tulse Hill 3 d		10b00			10 02	10 06				10 17	10 17										10c30		10 32	
Streatham 4 d					10a05	10 10				10 20													10a35	
London Victoria 15 ⊖ d				09 52			09 57	10 05								10 07	10 11	10 15	10 20			10 22		
Battersea Park 4 d				09 56			10 01									10 11	10a15	10 19				10 26		
Clapham Junction 10 d				09 59			10 04	10 11								10 14		10 22	10 26			10 29		
Wandsworth Common d				10 02			10 07	10 14								10 17		10 25				10 32		
Balham 4 ⊖ d				10 05			10 10	10 17								10 20		10 28	10 32			10 35		
Streatham Hill d				10 08												10 23						10 38		
West Norwood 4 d		10 03		10 11							10 20					10 26					10 33	10 41		
Gipsy Hill d		10 06		10 14							10 23					10 29					10 36	10 44		
Crystal Palace 4 d		10 08	10a14	10a17							10 26			10a43		10 32					10 38	10a47		
Birkbeck 🚊 d											10 30													
Beckenham Junction 4 🚊 a											10 33													
Bromley South 4 a											*10 47*													
Streatham Common 4 d						10 13	10 15	10 21										10 32						
Norbury d						10 15	10 18	10 23										10 34						
Thornton Heath d						10 18	10 21	10 26										10 37						
Selhurst 4 d						10 21	10 24	10 29										10 40						
Norwood Junction 2 a	10 08	10 13										10 16	10 25		10 31	10 36				10 38	10 43			
d	10 09	10 13										10 16	10 25		10 31	10 36				10 39	10 43			
West Croydon 4 🚊 a	10 14					10 25	10 28	10 33								10 41				10 44				
East Croydon 🚊 a		10 17										10 19	10 29		10 35			10 43			10 47			

	SN	SN	SN	SN	FC	SN	SN	SN	SN	SN	SN	SN	SN	SN	SN	FC	SN	SN	SN	SN		SN	FC	SE
						1																		13
		H	D							G			A	B				C	D					E
London Bridge 4 ⊖ d	10 19			10 29		10 33		10 35				10 45	10 38	10 54			10 49			10 41		10 59		11 03
South Bermondsey d	10 23			10 33									10 42				10 53			10 45		11 03		
Queens Rd Peckham d	10 25			10 35									10 44				10 55			10 48		11 05		
Peckham Rye 4 d	10 28			10 38									10 47				10 58			10 50		11 08		
East Dulwich d	10 31			10 41									10 50				11 01					11 11		
North Dulwich d	10 33			10 43									10 52				11 03					11 13		
Luton 10 d																09 44								
Luton Airport Parkway 7 ✈ d																09 46								
St Pancras International 15 ⊖ d					10 17											10 32							10 47	
City Thameslink 3 d					10 26											10 39							10 56	
London Blackfriars 3 ⊖ d					10 30											10 46							11 00	
Elephant & Castle ⊖ d					10 33											10 49							11 03	
Loughborough Jn d					10 37											10 53							11 07	
Herne Hill 4 d					10 41											10 57							11 11	
Tulse Hill 3 d	10 36			10 46	10 47								11e00			11 02	11 06					11 16	11 17	
Streatham 4 d	10 40				10 50											11a05	11 10						11 20	
London Victoria 15 ⊖ d		10 28	10 35				10 41		10 37	10 45	10 50				10 52			10 55	11 05					
Battersea Park 4 d		10 32					10a45		10 41	10 49					10 56			10 59						
Clapham Junction 10 d		10 35	10 41						10 44	10 52	10 56				10 59			11 04	11 12					
Wandsworth Common d		10 38	10 44						10 47	10 55					11 02			11 07	11 15					
Balham 4 ⊖ d		10 41	10 47						10 50	10 58	11 02				11 05			11 10	11 17					
Streatham Hill d									10 53						11 08									
West Norwood 4 d				10 49					10 56				11 03		11 11							11 19		
Gipsy Hill d				10 52					10 59				11 06		11 14							11 22		
Crystal Palace 4 d				10 55					11 02				11 08	11a13	11a17							11 25		
Birkbeck 🚊 d				10 59																		11 29		
Beckenham Junction 4 🚊 a				11 02																		11 32		
Bromley South 4 a				*11 17*																		*11 47*		
Streatham Common 4 d	10 43	10 45	10 51							11 02							11 13	11 15	11 21					
Norbury d	10 45	10 48	10 53							11 04							11 15	11 18	11 23					
Thornton Heath d	10 48	10 51	10 56							11 07							11 18	11 21	11 26					
Selhurst 4 d	10 51	10 54	10 59							11 10							11 21	11 24	11 29					
Norwood Junction 2 a						10 46		10 55	11 06			11 08	11 13											11 16
d						10 46		10 55	11 06			11 09	11 13											11 16
West Croydon 4 🚊 a	10 55	10 58	11 03						11 11			11 14					11 25	11 28	11 33					
East Croydon 🚊 a						10 49		10 59		11 13			11 17											11 19

For general notes see front of timetable
For details of catering facilities see Directory of Train Operators

A To Smitham (Table 181)
B Via Sydenham (Table 178)
C To Epsom (Table 182)
D To Sutton (Surrey) (Table 182)
E To Tunbridge Wells (Table 209)
G To Caterham (Table 181)
H To Epsom Downs (Table 182)
b Arr. 0956
c Arr. 1026
e Arr. 1056

Table 177 — Mondays to Fridays

Luton & London → East and West Croydon via Tulse Hill/Crystal Palace/Norbury

Local Services

Network Diagram - see first page of Table 177

Station		SN	SN	SN	SN	SN	SN	SN	SN	SN	FC	SN	SN	SN	SN	SN	FC	SN	SN	SN	SN	SN	SN	SN	SN
																		1							
					A			B	C					D	E							A			B
London Bridge 4	⊖ d		11 05				11 15	11 08	11 24			11 11	11 19			11 29		11 33		11 35				11 45	11 38
South Bermondsey	d							11 12				11 15	11 23			11 33									11 42
Queens Rd Peckham	d							11 14				11 18	11 25			11 35									11 44
Peckham Rye 4	d							11 17				11 20	11 28			11 38									11 47
East Dulwich	d							11 20					11 31			11 41									11 50
North Dulwich	d							11 22					11 33			11 43									11 52
Luton 10	d										10 14														
Luton Airport Parkway 7	✈ d										10 16														
St Pancras International 15	⊖ d										11 02						11 17								
City Thameslink 3	d										11 09						11 24								
London Blackfriars 3	⊖ d										11 16						11 30								
Elephant & Castle	⊖ d										11 19						11 33								
Loughborough Jn	d										11 23						11 37								
Herne Hill 4	d										11 27						11 41								
Tulse Hill 3	d							11b30			11 32		11 36			11 46	11 47								12c00
Streatham 4	d										11a35		11 40				11 50								
London Victoria 15	⊖ d	11 11		11 07	11 15	11 20				11 22				11 25	11 35				11 41		11 37	11 45	11 50		
Battersea Park 4	d	11a15		11 11	11 19					11 26				11 29					11a45		11 41	11 49			
Clapham Junction 10	d			11 14	11 22	11 26				11 29				11 34	11 41						11 44	11 52	11 56		
Wandsworth Common	d			11 17	11 25					11 32				11 37	11 44						11 47	11 55			
Balham 4	⊖ d			11 20	11 28	11 32				11 35				11 40	11 47						11 50	11 58	12 02		
Streatham Hill	d			11 23						11 38											11 53				
West Norwood 4	d			11 26				11 33		11 41						11 49					11 56				12 03
Gipsy Hill	d			11 29				11 36		11 44						11 52					11 59				12 06
Crystal Palace 4	d			11 32				11 38	11a43	11a47						11 55					12 02				12 08
Birkbeck	🚊 d															11 59									
Beckenham Junction 4	🚊 a															12 02									
Bromley South 4	a															*12 17*									
Streatham Common 4	d				11 32								11 43	11 45	11 51							12 02			
Norbury	d				11 34								11 45	11 48	11 53							12 04			
Thornton Heath	d				11 37								11 48	11 51	11 56							12 07			
Selhurst 4	d				11 40								11 51	11 54	11 59							12 10			
Norwood Junction 2	a		11 25	11 36			11 38	11 43										11 45		11 55	12 06			12 08	12 13
	d		11 25	11 36			11 39	11 43										11 46		11 55	12 06			12 09	12 13
West Croydon 4	🚊 a			11 41			11 44						11 55	11 58	12 03						12 11			12 14	
East Croydon	🚊 a		11 29		11 43			11 47										11 49		11 59		12 13			12 17

Station		SN	SN	FC	SN	SN	SN	SN			SN	FC	SE	SN	SN	SN	SN	SN	SN	SN	SN	SN	SN	FC
													13											
		C					G	E					H					A			J	C		
London Bridge 4	⊖ d	11 54			11 41	11 49					15 59		16 03	16 05	16 16					16 15	16 07	16 24		
South Bermondsey	d				11 45	11 53					16 03										16 11			
Queens Rd Peckham	d				11 48	11 55					16 05										16 13			
Peckham Rye 4	d				11 50	11 58					16 08										16 16			
East Dulwich	d					12 01					16 11										16 19			
North Dulwich	d					12 03					16 13										16 21			
Luton 10	d			10 44																				15 14
Luton Airport Parkway 7	✈ d			10 46																				15 16
St Pancras International 15	⊖ d			11 32								15 47												16 02
City Thameslink 3	d			11 39								15 54												16 09
London Blackfriars 3	⊖ d			11 46								16 00												16 16
Elephant & Castle	⊖ d			11 49								16 03												16 19
Loughborough Jn	d			11 53					and at			16 07												16 23
Herne Hill 4	d			11 57								16 11												16 27
Tulse Hill 3	d			12 02		12 06			the same		16 16	16 16									16e30			16 32
Streatham 4	d			12a05		12 10			minutes			16a19												16a35
London Victoria 15	⊖ d		11 52				11 55	12 05								16 07	16 11	16 15	16 20				16 22	
Battersea Park 4	d		11 56				11 59		past							16 11	16a15	16 19					16 26	
Clapham Junction 10	d		11 59				12 04	12 11								16 14		16 22	16 26				16 29	
Wandsworth Common	d		12 02				12 08	12 14	each							16 17		16 25					16 32	
Balham 4	⊖ d		12 05				12 10	12 17	hour until							16 20		16 28	16 30				16 35	
Streatham Hill	d		12 08													16 23							16 38	
West Norwood 4	d		12 11								16 19					16 26					16 33		16 41	
Gipsy Hill	d		12 14								16 22					16 29					16 36		16 44	
Crystal Palace 4	d	12a13	12a17								16 25					16 32					16 38	16a43	16a47	
Birkbeck	🚊 d										16 29													
Beckenham Junction 4	🚊 a										16 32													
Bromley South 4	a										*16 52*													
Streatham Common 4	d					12 13	12 15	12 21										16 32						
Norbury	d					12 15	12 18	12 23										16 34						
Thornton Heath	d					12 18	12 21	12 26										16 37						
Selhurst 4	d					12 21	12 24	12 29										16 40						
Norwood Junction 2	a												16 16	16 25	16 29	16 36				16 38	16 43			
	d												16 16	16 25	16 30	16 36				16 39	16 43			
West Croydon 4	🚊 a					12 25	12 27	12 33								16 43				16 43				
East Croydon	🚊 a												16 19	16 29	16 34			16 43			16 47			

For general notes see front of timetable
For details of catering facilities see Directory of Train Operators

A To Caterham (Table 181)
B To Smitham (Table 181)
C Via Sydenham (Table 178)
D To Epsom Downs (Table 182)
E To Sutton (Surrey) (Table 182)
G To Epsom (Table 182)
H To Tonbridge (Table 209)
J To Tattenham Corner (Table 181)
b Arr. 1126
c Arr. 1156
e Arr. 1624

Luton & London → East and West Croydon via Tulse Hill/Crystal Palace/Norbury

Local Services

Network Diagram - see first page of Table 177

		SN	SN	SN	FC	SN	SN	SN	SN	SN	SN	SN	SN	SN	FC	FC	SN	SN	SN	SN	FC	SN	SN	SN	SN
							1									1									
				A							B								A					C	
London Bridge 4	⊖ d	16 11	16 19			16 29	16 38	16 35					16 37				16 41	16 44		16 53		16 59	17 05	16 55	17 19
South Bermondsey	d	16 15	16 23			16 33							16 41				16 45			16 57					
Queens Rd Peckham	d	16 18	16 25			16 35							16 43				16 48			16 59					
Peckham Rye 4	d	16 20	16 28			16 38							16 46				16 50			17 02					
East Dulwich	d		16 31			16 41							16 49							17 05					
North Dulwich	d		16 33			16 43							16 51							17 07					
Luton 10	d														15 44	15 55									
Luton Airport Parkway 7	✈ d														15 46	15 57									
St Pancras International 15	⊖ d				16 15										16 32	16 36					16 47				
City Thameslink 3	d				16 22										16 39	16 43					16 54				
London Blackfriars 3	⊖ d				16 26										16 42	16 46					16 58				
Elephant & Castle	⊖ d				16 29										16 45	16 50					17 01				
Loughborough Jn	d				16 33										16 49	16 54					17 05				
Herne Hill 4	d				16 37										16 53	16 58					17 09				
Tulse Hill 3	d		16 36		16 42	16 46							16 56		16 58	17b08				17 11	17 16				
Streatham 4	d		16 40		16 45	16 50									17a01	17a11				17 14	17 20				
London Victoria 15	⊖ d			16 30					16 37	16 41	16 45	16 50		16 52					17 01						
Battersea Park 4	d			16 34					16 41	16a45	16 49			16 56					17 05						
Clapham Junction 10	d			16 37					16 44		16 52	16 56		16 59					17 08						
Wandsworth Common	d			16 40					16 47		16 55			17 02					17 11						
Balham 4	⊖ d			16 43					16 50		16 58	17 00		17 05					17 14						
Streatham Hill	d								16 53					17 08											
West Norwood 4	d								16 56				16 59	17 11											
Gipsy Hill	d								16 59				17 02	17 14											
Crystal Palace 4	d								17 02				17 05	17a17										17a14	
Birkbeck	🚋 d												17 09												
Beckenham Junction 4	🚋 a												17 14												
Bromley South 4	a												*17 38*												
Streatham Common 4	d		16 43	16 47							17 02								17 18						
Norbury	d		16 45	16 49							17 04								17 20						
Thornton Heath	d		16 48	16 52							17 07								17 23						
Selhurst 4	d		16 51	16 55							17 10								17 26						
Norwood Junction 2	a						16 50	16 55	17 06									17 08				17 12	17 28		17 33
	d						16 51	16 55	17 06									17 09				17 12	17 28		17 33
West Croydon 4	🚋 a		16 57	16 59					17 13									17 14	17 30				17 35		
East Croydon	🚋 a						16 54	16 59			17 13											17 16			17 37

		SN	SN	SN	SN	SN	SN	SN	FC	SN	SN	SN	SN	SN	SN	FC	SN	SN	SN	SN	SN	SN	SN		FC
												1													
				D		C						E	A												
London Bridge 4	⊖ d				17 07	17 15				17 11	17 18			17 25	17 27		17 39	17 35					17 37		
South Bermondsey	d				17 11					17 15					17 31								17 41		
Queens Rd Peckham	d				17 13					17 18	17 23				17 33								17 43		
Peckham Rye 4	d				17 16					17 20	17 26				17 36								17 46		
East Dulwich	d				17 19						17 29				17 39								17 49		
North Dulwich	d				17 21						17 31				17 41								17 51		
Luton 10	d								16 14																16 44
Luton Airport Parkway 7	✈ d								16 16																16 46
St Pancras International 15	⊖ d								17 01							17 17									17 31
City Thameslink 3	d								17 11							17 24									17 38
London Blackfriars 3	⊖ d								17 14							17 30									17 42
Elephant & Castle	⊖ d								17 17							17 33									17 45
Loughborough Jn	d								17 21							17 37									17 49
Herne Hill 4	d								17 25							17 41									17 53
Tulse Hill 3	d				17 26				17 30		17 34				17 44	17 46							17 56		17 58
Streatham 4	d								17a33		17 38				17 48	17 50									18a01
London Victoria 15	⊖ d	17 07	17 11	17 15			17 19	17 25					17 32						17 37	17 41	17 43	17 45			
Battersea Park 4	d	17 11	17a15				17 23						17 36						17 41	17a45		17 50			
Clapham Junction 10	d	17 14		17 21			17 26	17 31				17 34	17 39						17 44		17 49	17 53			
Wandsworth Common	d	17 17					17 29					17 37	17 42						17 47			17 56			
Balham 4	⊖ d	17 20		17 25			17 32	17 35				17 41	17 45						17 50		17 53	17 59			
Streatham Hill	d	17 23					17 35												17 53						
West Norwood 4	d	17 26			17 29		17 38												17 56				17 59		
Gipsy Hill	d	17 29			17 32		17 41												17 59				18 02		
Crystal Palace 4	d	17 32			17 35	17a34	17a44												18 02				18 05		
Birkbeck	🚋 d				17 39																		18 09		
Beckenham Junction 4	🚋 a				17 44																		18 14		
Bromley South 4	a				*18 02*																		*18 26*		
Streatham Common 4	d			17 29							17 41	17 45	17 49									18 03			
Norbury	d			17 32							17 43	17 48	17 51									18 05			
Thornton Heath	d			17 35							17 46	17 51	17 54									18 08			
Selhurst 4	d			17 38							17a51	17 54	17 57									18a13			
Norwood Junction 2	a	17 36												17 43			17 53	17 58	18 06						
	d	17 37												17 43			17 54	17 58	18 07						
West Croydon 4	🚋 a	17 46		17 42									18 01	17 48				18 05	18 14						
East Croydon	🚋 a											17 59					17 57								

For general notes see front of timetable
For details of catering facilities see Directory of Train Operators

A To Epsom Downs (Table 182)
B To Tattenham Corner (Table 181)
C Via Sydenham (Table 178)
D To Sutton (Surrey) (Table 182)
E From Kensington Olympia
b Arr. 1702

Luton & London → East and West Croydon via Tulse Hill/Crystal Palace/Norbury

Local Services

Network Diagram - see first page of Table 177

Station		FC	SN	SN	SN	SN	SN	SN	SN	SN	SN	FC	SN	SN	SN	SN	SN	SN	SN	SN	SN	FC	SN	SN	SN
		1						1																	
				A	B			C	D										E						A
London Bridge	d		17 41	17 45	17 47					17 55	17 58		18 01	18 05	18 20					18 08				18 11	18 18
South Bermondsey	d		17 45								18 02									18 12				18 15	
Queens Rd Peckham	d		17 48								18 04									18 14				18 18	
Peckham Rye	d		17 50		17 53						18 07									18 17				18 20	
East Dulwich	d				17 56						18 10									18 20					
North Dulwich	d				17 58						18 12									18 22					
Luton	d	17 18																				17 18			
Luton Airport Parkway	d																					17 20			
St Pancras International	d	17 46										17 51										18 03			
City Thameslink	d	17 53										17 58										18 10			
London Blackfriars	d	17 57										18 02										18 14			
Elephant & Castle	d											18 05										18 17			
Loughborough Jn	d											18 09										18 21			
Herne Hill	d	18 06										18 13										18 27			
Tulse Hill	d				18 02						18 15	18 18								18 26		18 30			
Streatham	d										18a19	18 22										18a33			
London Victoria	d					17 51	17 57		18 02							18 07	18 11	18 14	18 17		18 22		18 27		
Battersea Park	d					17 55			18 06							18 11	18a15		18 21		18 26				
Clapham Junction	d					17 59	18 03	18 06	18 09							18 14		18 20	18 25		18 29		18 33		
Wandsworth Common	d					18 02		18 09	18 12							18 17			18 28		18 32				
Balham	d					18 05	18 08	18 12	18 15							18 20		18 24	18 30		18 35		18 37		
Streatham Hill	d					18 08										18 23					18 38				
West Norwood	d				18 05	18 15										18 26				18 29	18 41				
Gipsy Hill	d				18 08	18 18										18 29				18 32	18 44				
Crystal Palace	d			18a09	18a12	18a21										18 32				18 35	18a47				18a39
Birkbeck	d																			18 39					
Beckenham Junction	a																			18 44					
Bromley South	a																			*19 04*					
Streatham Common	d							18 16	18 19										18 34						
Norbury	d							18 18	18 21										18 37						
Thornton Heath	d							18 21	18 24										18 40						
Selhurst	d							18 24	18 27										18 43						
Norwood Junction	a									18 12			18 15	18 28	18 35	18 36									
	d									18 13			18 15	18 28	18 35	18 37									
West Croydon	a								18 31	18 17				18 35		18 44									
East Croydon	a	18 20						18 28					18 19		18 38				18 46						

Station		SN	FC	SN	SN	SN	SN	SN	SN	SN	SN	SN	SN	SN	SN	SN	FC	SN	SN	SN	FC	SN	SN	SN	SN
									1																
				D								G		A						H					
London Bridge	d	18 21			18 25	18 31	18 42	18 36	18 54				18 38	18 51				18 41	18 51			19 05	19 00		
South Bermondsey	d	18 25				18 35							18 42					18 45	18 55				19 04		
Queens Rd Peckham	d	18 27				18 37							18 44					18 48	18 57				19 06		
Peckham Rye	d	18 30				18 40							18 47					18 50	19 00				19 09		
East Dulwich	d	18 33				18 43							18 50						19 03				19 12		
North Dulwich	d	18 35				18 45							18 52						19 05				19 14		
Luton	d																17 48								
Luton Airport Parkway	d																17 50								
St Pancras International	d		18 15														18 33				18 45				
City Thameslink	d		18 22														18 40				18 52				
London Blackfriars	d		18 26														18 44				18 56				
Elephant & Castle	d		18 29														18 47				18 59				
Loughborough Jn	d		18 33														18 51				19 03				
Herne Hill	d		18 37														18 57				19 07				
Tulse Hill	d	18 38	18 42			18b51							18 56				19 02		19 09		19 12		19 17		
Streatham	d	18 42	18 45			18 54											19a05		19 12		19 15				
London Victoria	d			18 33						18 37	18 41	18 45			18 52	18 57				19 00				19 05	19 11
Battersea Park	d			18 37						18 41	18a45	18 49			18 56					19 04				19 09	19a15
Clapham Junction	d			18 40						18 44		18 52			18 59	19 03				19 08				19 12	
Wandsworth Common	d			18 43						18 47		18 55			19 02					19 11				19 15	
Balham	d			18 46						18 50		18 58			19 05	19 07				19 14				19 18	
Streatham Hill	d									18 53					19 08									19 21	
West Norwood	d									18 56			18 59		19 11								19 20	19 24	
Gipsy Hill	d									18 59			19 02		19 14								19 23	19 27	
Crystal Palace	d									19 02			19 05	19a12	19 17								19 26	19a30	
Birkbeck	d												19 09												
Beckenham Junction	a												19 14												
Bromley South	a												*19 33*												
Streatham Common	d	18 45		18 50								19 02							19 15	19 18					
Norbury	d	18 47		18 52								19 04							19 18	19 20					
Thornton Heath	d	18 50		18 55								19 07							19 21	19 23					
Selhurst	d	18a55		18 58								19 11							19a25	19 27					
Norwood Junction	a				18 41		18 56	18 59	19 05	19 06					19 21							19 28	19 30		
	d				18 42		18 56	18 59	19 05	19 07					19 22							19 28	19 35		
West Croydon	a			19 02	18 46			19 06		19 15		19 15			19 29							19 33	19 41		
East Croydon	a						19 00		19 09											19 30					

For general notes see front of timetable
For details of catering facilities see Directory of Train Operators

- **A** Via Sydenham (Table 178)
- **B** To London Bridge (Table 178)
- **C** From Watford Junction (Table 66)
- **D** To Epsom Downs (Table 182)
- **E** To Tattenham Corner (Table 181)
- **G** To Epsom (Table 182)
- **H** To Tattenham Corner (Table 181) and to Caterham (Table 181)
- **b** Arr. 1848

Luton & London → East and West Croydon via Tulse Hill/Crystal Palace/Norbury

Local Services

Network Diagram - see first page of Table 177

		SN	SN	SN	FC	SN	SN	SN	SN	SN	SN	SN	SN		SN	SN	FC	SN	SN	SN	FC	SN	SN	SN	SN
		A						B			C	D						E						1	B
London Bridge 4	⊖ d			19 08		19 15	19 11	19 24	19 19	19 31			19 29							19 38		19 41	19 49	19 52	19 54
South Bermondsey	d			19 12			19 15		19 23				19 33							19 42		19 45	19 53		
Queens Rd Peckham	d			19 14			19 18		19 25				19 35							19 44		19 48	19 55		
Peckham Rye 4	d			19 17			19 20		19 28				19 38							19 47		19 50	19 58		
East Dulwich	d			19 20					19 31				19 41							19 50			20 01		
North Dulwich	d			19 22					19 33				19 43							19 52			20 03		
Luton 10	d				18 20																18 50				
Luton Airport Parkway 7	✈ d				18 22																18 52				
St Pancras International 15	⊖ d				19 05												19 17				19 35				
City Thameslink 3	d				19 12												19 24				19 42				
London Blackfriars 3	⊖ d				19 16												19 30				19 46				
Elephant & Castle	⊖ d				19 19												19 33				19 49				
Loughborough Jn	d				19 23												19 37				19 53				
Herne Hill 4	d				19 27												19 41				19 57				
Tulse Hill 3	d			19 26	19 32				19 36				19 46				19 47			19 56	20 02		20 06		
Streatham 4	d				19a35				19 40								19 50				20a05		20 10		
London Victoria 15	⊖ d	19 15	19 20								19 22	19 31			19 35	19 41		19 45	19 50						
Battersea Park 4	d	19 19									19 26	19 35			19 39	19a45		19 49							
Clapham Junction 10	d	19 22	19 26								19 29	19 38			19 42			19 52	19 56						
Wandsworth Common	d	19 25									19 32	19 41			19 45			19 55							
Balham 4	⊖ d	19 28	19 32								19 35	19 44			19 48			19 58	20 02						
Streatham Hill	d										19 38				19 51										
West Norwood 4	d			19 29							19 41		19 49		19 54					19 59					
Gipsy Hill	d			19 32							19 44		19 52		19 57					20 02					
Crystal Palace 4	d			19 35				19a43			19 47		19 55		20a00					20 05					20a13
Birkbeck	🚋 d			19 39																20 09					
Beckenham Junction 4	🚋 a			19 42																20 12					
Bromley South 4	a			*20 03*																*20 36*					
Streatham Common 4	d	19 32							19 43			19 48						20 02					20 13		
Norbury	d	19 34							19 45			19 50						20 04					20 15		
Thornton Heath	d	19 37							19 48			19 53						20 07					20 18		
Selhurst 4	d	19 40							19 51			19 56						20 10					20 21		
Norwood Junction 2	a					19 39				19 43	19 53		19 59											20 03	
	d					19 40				19 44	19 54		20 05 →											20 03	
West Croydon 4	🚋 a	19 44							19 56	19 48	19 59							20 14					20 26		
East Croydon	🚋 a					19 43						19 59												20 06	

		SN	SN	FC	FC	SN	SN	SN	SN	SN	SN	SN	SN	SN	FC	FC	SN	SN	SN	SN	SN	SN	SN	SN	SN
						1	A	D			E							1	B	C	D			E	
London Bridge 4	⊖ d	19 45				20 05							20 15	20 19			20 11	20 35	20 24						
South Bermondsey	d													20 23			20 15								
Queens Rd Peckham	d													20 25			20 18								
Peckham Rye 4	d													20 28			20 20								
East Dulwich	d													20 31											
North Dulwich	d													20 33											
Luton 10	d				19 20											19 50									
Luton Airport Parkway 7	✈ d				19 22											19 52									
St Pancras International 15	⊖ d			19 48	20 05										20 17	20 35									
City Thameslink 3	d			19 55	20 12										20 24	20 42									
London Blackfriars 3	⊖ d			20 00	20 16										20 30	20 46									
Elephant & Castle	⊖ d			20 03	20 19										20 33	20 49									
Loughborough Jn	d			20 07	20 23										20 37	20 53									
Herne Hill 4	d			20 11	20 27										20 41	20 57									
Tulse Hill 3	d			20 17	20 32									20 36	20 47	21 02									
Streatham 4	d			20 20	20a35									20 40	20 50	21a05									
London Victoria 15	⊖ d						19 52	20 00	20 05	20 11	20 15	20 20								20 22	20 30	20 35	20 41	20 45	20 50
Battersea Park 4	d						19 56	20 04	20 09	20a15	20 19									20 26	20 34	20 39	20a45	20 49	
Clapham Junction 10	d						19 59	20 08	20 12		20 22	20 26								20 29	20 38	20 42		20 52	20 56
Wandsworth Common	d						20 02	20 11	20 15		20 25									20 32	20 41	20 45		20 55	
Balham 4	⊖ d						20 05	20 13	20 18		20 28	20 31								20 35	20 43	20 48		20 58	21 02
Streatham Hill	d						20 08		20 21											20 38		20 51			
West Norwood 4	d						20 11		20 24											20 41		20 54			
Gipsy Hill	d						20 14		20 27											20 44		20 57			
Crystal Palace 4	d						20 17		20a30										20a43	20 47		21a00			
Birkbeck	🚋 d																								
Beckenham Junction 4	🚋 a																								
Bromley South 4	a																								
Streatham Common 4	d							20 17			20 32			20 43							20 47			21 02	
Norbury	d							20 20			20 34			20 45							20 50			21 04	
Thornton Heath	d							20 23			20 37			20 48							20 53			21 07	
Selhurst 4	d							20 26			20 40			20 51							20 56			21 10	
Norwood Junction 2	a	20 05	←			20 16	20 21						20 38					20 46		20 51					
	d	20 05	20 05			20 16	20 24						20 38					20 46		20 54					
West Croydon 4	🚋 a		20 10				20 29				20 44			20 56						20 59				21 14	
East Croydon	🚋 a	20 09				20 19		20 29					20 42					20 49			20 59				

For general notes see front of timetable
For details of catering facilities see Directory of Train Operators

- **A** To Epsom (Table 182)
- **B** Via Sydenham (Table 178)
- **C** To Epsom Downs (Table 182)
- **D** To Tattenham Corner (Table 181)
- **E** To Sutton (Surrey) (Table 182)

Luton & London → East and West Croydon via Tulse Hill/Crystal Palace/Norbury

Local Services

Network Diagram - see first page of Table 177

Station		SN	SN	SN	SN 1	SN	SN	SN	SN	SN	SN	SN	FC	SN	SN	SN	SN	SN 1	SN	SN	SN	SN	SN	SN	FC
						A	B	C			D			A					E	C			D		
London Bridge 4	⊖ d	20 45	20 49	20 41	21 05	20 54								21 24	21 15	21 11	21 19	21 35							
South Bermondsey	d		20 53	20 45												21 15	21 23								
Queens Rd Peckham	d		20 55	20 48												21 18	21 25								
Peckham Rye 4	d		20 58	20 50												21 20	21 28								
East Dulwich	d		21 01														21 31								
North Dulwich	d		21 03														21 33								
Luton 10	d												20 20												20 50
Luton Airport Parkway 7	✈ d												20 22												20 52
St Pancras International 15	⊖ d												21 05												21 35
City Thameslink 3	d												21 12												21 42
London Blackfriars 3	⊖ d												21 16												21 46
Elephant & Castle	⊖ d												21 19												21 49
Loughborough Jn	d												21 23												21 53
Herne Hill 4	d												21 27												21 57
Tulse Hill 3	d		21 06										21 32				21 36								22 02
Streatham 4	d		21 10										21a35				21 40								22a05
London Victoria 15	⊖ d						20 52	21 00	21 05	21 11	21 15	21 20							21 22	21 30	21 35	21 41	21 45	21 50	
Battersea Park 4	d						20 56	21 04	21 09	21a15	21 19								21 26	21 34	21 39	21a45	21 49		
Clapham Junction 10	d						20 59	21 08	21 12		21 22	21 26							21 29	21 38	21 42		21 52	21 56	
Wandsworth Common	d						21 02	21 11	21 15		21 25								21 32	21 41	21 45		21 55		
Balham 4	⊖ d						21 05	21 13	21 18		21 28	21 31							21 35	21 43	21 48		21 58	22 02	
Streatham Hill	d						21 08		21 21										21 38		21 51				
West Norwood 4	d						21 11		21 24										21 41		21 54				
Gipsy Hill	d						21 14		21 27										21 44		21 57				
Crystal Palace 4	d					21a13	21 17		21a30					21a43					21 47		22a00				
Birkbeck	🚋 d																								
Beckenham Junction 4	🚋 a																								
Bromley South 4	a																								
Streatham Common 4	d		21 13					21 17			21 32						21 43			21 47			22 02		
Norbury	d		21 15					21 20			21 34						21 45			21 50			22 04		
Thornton Heath	d		21 18					21 23			21 37						21 48			21 53			22 07		
Selhurst 4	d		21 21					21 26			21 40						21 51			21 56			22 10		
Norwood Junction 2	a	21 08			21 16		21 21								21 38			21 46	21 51						
	d	21 08			21 16		21 24								21 38			21 46	21 54						
West Croydon 4	🚋 a		21 26				21 29				21 44						21 56		21 59				22 14		
East Croydon	🚋 a	21 12			21 19			21 29							21 42			21 49		21 59					

Station		SN	SN	SN		FC	SN	SN 1	SN	SN	SN	SN	SN	SN	SN	SN	SN	SN	SN	SN	SN	SN	SN	SN	FC
		A							B	C			D		A		E			C			D		
London Bridge 4	⊖ d	21 54	21 45	21 49			21 41	22 05							22 24	22 15		22 11	22 19						
South Bermondsey	d			21 53			21 45											22 15	22 23						
Queens Rd Peckham	d			21 55			21 48											22 18	22 25						
Peckham Rye 4	d			21 58			21 50											22 20	22 28						
East Dulwich	d			22 01															22 31						
North Dulwich	d			22 03															22 33						
Luton 10	d					21 20																			21 50
Luton Airport Parkway 7	✈ d					21 22																			21 52
St Pancras International 15	⊖ d					22 05																			22 36
City Thameslink 3	d					22 12																			22 42
London Blackfriars 3	⊖ d					22 16																			22 46
Elephant & Castle	⊖ d					22 19																			22 49
Loughborough Jn	d					22 23																			22 53
Herne Hill 4	d					22 27																			22 57
Tulse Hill 3	d			22 06		22 32													22 36						23 02
Streatham 4	d			22 10		22a35													22 40						23a04
London Victoria 15	⊖ d								21 52	22 00	22 05	22 11	22 15	22 20			22 22			22 30	22 35	22 41	22 45	22 50	
Battersea Park 4	d								21 56	22 04	22 09	22a15	22 19				22 26			22 34	22 39	22a45	22 49		
Clapham Junction 10	d								21 59	22 08	22 12		22 22	22 26			22 29			22 38	22 42		22 52	22 56	
Wandsworth Common	d								22 02	22 11	22 15		22 25				22 32			22 41	22 45		22 55		
Balham 4	⊖ d								22 05	22 13	22 18		22 28	22 32			22 35			22 43	22 48		22 58	23 00	
Streatham Hill	d								22 08		22 21						22 38				22 51				
West Norwood 4	d								22 11		22 24						22 41				22 54				
Gipsy Hill	d								22 14		22 27						22 44				22 57				
Crystal Palace 4	d	22a13							22 17		22a30				22a43		22 47				23a00				
Birkbeck	🚋 d																								
Beckenham Junction 4	🚋 a																								
Bromley South 4	a																								
Streatham Common 4	d			22 13						22 17			22 32						22 43	22 47			23 02		
Norbury	d			22 15						22 20			22 34						22 45	22 50			23 04		
Thornton Heath	d			22 18						22 23			22 37						22 48	22 53			23 07		
Selhurst 4	d			22 21						22 26			22 40						22 51	22 56			23 10		
Norwood Junction 2	a		22 08					22 16	22 21							22 38	22 51								
	d		22 08					22 16	22 24							22 38	22 54								
West Croydon 4	🚋 a			22 26					22 29				22 44				22 59		22 56				23 14		
East Croydon	🚋 a		22 12					22 19		22 29						22 42				22 59					

For general notes see front of timetable
For details of catering facilities see Directory of Train Operators

A Via Sydenham (Table 178)
B To Epsom (Table 182)
C To Tattenham Corner (Table 181)
D To Sutton (Surrey) (Table 182)
E To Epsom Downs (Table 182)

Luton & London → East and West Croydon via Tulse Hill/Crystal Palace/Norbury

Local Services

Network Diagram - see first page of Table 177

Mondays to Fridays

Station		SN	SN	SN	SN	SN	SN	SN	SN	SN	SN	FC	SN	SN	SN	SN	SN	SN	SN	SN	SN	SN	SN
						1																	
		A					B	C			D			A	D						D		
London Bridge 4	⊖ d	22 54	22 45	22 41	22 49	23 00							23 15	23 24		23 11		23 19				23 53	23 49
South Bermondsey	d			22 45	22 53											23 15		23 23					23 53
Queens Rd Peckham	d			22 48	22 55											23 18		23 25					23 55
Peckham Rye 4	d			22 50	22 58											23 20		23 28					23 58
East Dulwich	d				23 01													23 31					00 01
North Dulwich	d				23 03													23 33					00 03
Luton 10	d											22 20											
Luton Airport Parkway 7	✈ d											22 22											
St Pancras International 15	⊖ d											23 06											
City Thameslink 3	d																						
London Blackfriars 3	⊖ d											23 16											
Elephant & Castle	⊖ d											23 19											
Loughborough Jn	d																						
Herne Hill 4	d											23 27											
Tulse Hill 3	d				23 06							23 32						23 36					00 06
Streatham 4	d				23 10							23a35						23 40					
London Victoria 15	⊖ d						22 52	23 00	23 05	23 11	23 15				23 22		23 26		23 34	23 37	23 51		
Battersea Park 4	d						22 56	23 04	23 09	23a15	23 19				23 26				23 38	23 42	23 55		
Clapham Junction 10	d						22 59	23 08	23 12		23 22				23 29		23 32		23 41	23 45	23 58		
Wandsworth Common	d						23 02	23 11	23 15		23 25				23 32				23 44	23 48	00 01		
Balham 4	⊖ d						23 05	23 13	23 18		23 28				23 35		23 37		23 47	23 51	00 04		
Streatham Hill	d						23 08		23 21						23 38					23 54			
West Norwood 4	d						23 11		23 24						23 41					23 57			00 09
Gipsy Hill	d						23 14		23 27						23 44					23 59			00 12
Crystal Palace 4	d	23a13					23 17		23a30					23a43	23 47					00 03			00 15
Birkbeck	🚊 d																						
Beckenham Junction 4	🚊 a																						
Bromley South 4	a																						
Streatham Common 4	d				23 13			23 17			23 32							23 43	23 51		00 08		
Norbury	d				23 15			23 20			23 34							23 45	23 53		00 10		
Thornton Heath	d				23 18			23 23			23 37							23 48	23 56		00 13		
Selhurst 4	d				23 21			23 26			23 40							23 51	23a59		00 16		
Norwood Junction 2	a		23 08			23 11	23 21						23 38		23 51					00 07		00 16	00 19
	d		23 08			23 11	23 24						23 38		23 54					00 07		00 16	
West Croydon 4	🚊 a				23 26		23 29				23 44				23 58			23 55		00 13	00 20		
East Croydon	🚊 a		23 12			23 16		23 29					23 42									00 20	

Saturdays

Station		SN	SN	SN	SN	SN	SN	SN	SN	SN	FC	SN	SN	FC	SN	SN	SN	SN	SN	SN	SN	SN		FC	SN
									1																
			D							E					G			D			B				
London Bridge 4	⊖ d			23p53	23p49		00 26					06 11					06 47		06 41	06 49		07 05			07 18
South Bermondsey	d				23p53							06 15							06 45	06 53					
Queens Rd Peckham	d				23p55							06 18							06 48	06 55					
Peckham Rye 4	d				23p58							06 20							06 50	06 58					
East Dulwich	d				00 01															07 01					
North Dulwich	d				00 03															07 03					
Luton 10	d													05 50										06 20	
Luton Airport Parkway 7	✈ d													05 52										06 22	
St Pancras International 15	⊖ d													06 35										07 05	
City Thameslink 3	d																								
London Blackfriars 3	⊖ d										06 16			06 46										07 16	
Elephant & Castle	⊖ d										06 19			06 49										07 19	
Loughborough Jn	d													06 53										07 23	
Herne Hill 4	d										06 27			06 57										07 27	
Tulse Hill 3	d				00 06						06 32			07 02						07 06				07 32	
Streatham 4	d										06a35			07a05						07 10				07a35	
London Victoria 15	⊖ d	23p37	23p51			00 17		00 42	05 25	06 27			06 41		06 45	06 54					06 57				
Battersea Park 4	d	23p42	23p55					00 46		06 31			06a45		06 49						07 01				
Clapham Junction 10	d	23p45	23p58			00 23		00 49	05 31	06 34					06 52	07 00					07 04				
Wandsworth Common	d	23p48	00 01					00 52		06 37					06 55						07 07				
Balham 4	⊖ d	23p51	00 04			00 27		00 55		06 40					06 58	07 04					07 10				
Streatham Hill	d	23p54																06 53							
West Norwood 4	d	23p57			00 09													06 56							
Gipsy Hill	d	23p59			00 12													06 59							
Crystal Palace 4	d	00 03			00 15													07 02							
Birkbeck	🚊 d																								
Beckenham Junction 4	🚊 a																								
Bromley South 4	a																								
Streatham Common 4	d		00 08			00 31		00 59		06 44					07 02					07 13	07 15				
Norbury	d		00 10			00 34		01 01		06 46					07 04					07 15	07 18				
Thornton Heath	d		00 13			00 37		01 04		06 49					07 07					07 18	07 21				
Selhurst 4	d		00 16			00 39		01 07		06 52					07 10					07 21	07 24				
Norwood Junction 2	a	00 07		00 16	00 19		00 49		05 47								07 00	07 06				07 25			07 31
	d	00 07		00 16			00 49		05 48								07 00	07 06				07 25			07 31
West Croydon 4	🚊 a	00 13	00 20							06 56								07 11		07 25	07 28				
East Croydon	🚊 a			00 20		00 42	00 53	01 10	05 51						07 13		07 05					07 29			07 34

For general notes see front of timetable
For details of catering facilities see Directory of Train Operators

A Via Sydenham (Table 178)
B To Epsom (Table 182)
C To Tattenham Corner (Table 181)
D To Sutton (Surrey) (Table 182)
E To Epsom Downs (Table 182)
G To Caterham (Table 181)

Luton & London → East and West Croydon via Tulse Hill/Crystal Palace/Norbury

Local Services

Network Diagram - see first page of Table 177

		SN	SN	SN	SN	SN	SN	SN	SN	SN	SN	FC	SN 1	SN	SN	SN	SN	SN	SN	SN	SN	FC		SN	SN
				A					B	C							A			D					E
London Bridge 4	⊖ d					07 11	07 15	07 19			07 29		07 33	07 35					07 45	07 38				07 49	
South Bermondsey	d					07 15		07 23			07 33									07 42				07 53	
Queens Rd Peckham	d					07 18		07 25			07 35									07 44				07 55	
Peckham Rye 4	d					07 20		07 28			07 38									07 47				07 58	
East Dulwich	d							07 31			07 41									07 50				08 01	
North Dulwich	d							07 33			07 43									07 52				08 03	
Luton 10	d																					06 44			
Luton Airport Parkway 7	✈ d																					06 46			
St Pancras International 15	⊖ d																					07 32			
City Thameslink 3	d																								
London Blackfriars 3	⊖ d											07 30										07 46			
Elephant & Castle	⊖ d											07 33										07 49			
Loughborough Jn	d											07 37										07 53			
Herne Hill 4	d											07 41										07 57			
Tulse Hill 3	d							07 36			07 46	07 47								08b00		08 02		08 06	
Streatham 4	d							07 40				07 50										08a05		08 10	
London Victoria 15	⊖ d	07 07	07 11	07 15	07 20				07 25	07 35					07 37	07 41	07 45	07 50			07 52				07 55
Battersea Park 4	d	07 11	07a15	07 19					07 29						07 41	07a45	07 49				07 56				07 59
Clapham Junction 10	d	07 14		07 22	07 26				07 34	07 41					07 44		07 52	07 56			07 59				08 04
Wandsworth Common	d	07 17		07 25					07 37	07 44					07 47		07 55				08 02				08 07
Balham 4	⊖ d	07 20		07 28	07 32				07 40	07 47					07 50		07 58	08 02			08 05				08 10
Streatham Hill	d	07 23													07 53						08 08				
West Norwood 4	d	07 26									07 49				07 56					08 03	08 11				
Gipsy Hill	d	07 29									07 52				07 59					08 06	08 14				
Crystal Palace 4	d	07 32									07 55				08 02					08 08	08a17				
Birkbeck	🚋 d										07 59														
Beckenham Junction 4	🚋 a										08 02														
Bromley South 4	a										*08 17*														
Streatham Common 4	d			07 32				07 43	07 45	07 51							08 02							08 13	08 15
Norbury	d			07 34				07 45	07 48	07 53							08 04							08 15	08 18
Thornton Heath	d			07 37				07 48	07 51	07 56							08 07							08 18	08 21
Selhurst 4	d			07 40				07 51	07 54	07 59							08 10							08 21	08 24
Norwood Junction 2	a	07 36					07 38						07 45	07 55	08 06				08 08	08 13					
	d	07 36					07 39						07 46	07 55	08 06				08 09	08 13					
West Croydon 4	🚋 a	07 41					07 44	07 55	07 58	08 03					08 11				08 14					08 25	08 28
East Croydon	🚋 a			07 43									07 49	07 59			08 13			08 17					

		SN	SN	SN	FC	SE 13	SN	SN	SN	SN	SN	SN	SN	SN	SN	FC	SN	SN	SN	SN	SN	FC		SN 1	SN
		C				G				A			H	D				B	C						
London Bridge 4	⊖ d		07 41	07 59		08 03	08 05					08 15	08 24	08 08			08 19			08 11	08 29			08 33	08 35
South Bermondsey	d		07 45	08 03										08 12			08 23			08 15	08 33				
Queens Rd Peckham	d		07 48	08 05										08 14			08 25			08 18	08 35				
Peckham Rye 4	d		07 50	08 08										08 17			08 28			08 20	08 38				
East Dulwich	d			08 11										08 20			08 31				08 41				
North Dulwich	d			08 13										08 22			08 33				08 43				
Luton 10	d				06 59											07 14						07 26			
Luton Airport Parkway 7	✈ d				07 01											07 16						07 28			
St Pancras International 15	⊖ d				07 47											08 02						08 17			
City Thameslink 3	d																								
London Blackfriars 3	⊖ d				08 00											08 16						08 30			
Elephant & Castle	⊖ d				08 03											08 19						08 33			
Loughborough Jn	d				08 07											08 23						08 37			
Herne Hill 4	d				08 11											08 27						08 41			
Tulse Hill 3	d			08 16	08 17									08c30		08 32	08 36				08 46	08 47			
Streatham 4	d				08 20											08a35	08 40					08 50			
London Victoria 15	⊖ d	08 05						08 07	08 11	08 15	08 20				08 22			08 25	08 35						
Battersea Park 4	d							08 11	08a15	08 19					08 26			08 29							
Clapham Junction 10	d	08 11						08 14		08 22	08 26				08 29			08 34	08 41						
Wandsworth Common	d	08 14						08 17		08 25					08 32			08 37	08 44						
Balham 4	⊖ d	08 17						08 20		08 28	08 32				08 35			08 40	08 47						
Streatham Hill	d							08 23							08 38										
West Norwood 4	d			08 19				08 26						08 33	08 41						08 49				
Gipsy Hill	d			08 22				08 29						08 36	08 44						08 52				
Crystal Palace 4	d			08 25				08 32					08a43	08 38	08a47						08 55				
Birkbeck	🚋 d			08 29																	08 59				
Beckenham Junction 4	🚋 a			08 32																	09 02				
Bromley South 4	a			*08 47*																	*09 17*				
Streatham Common 4	d	08 21								08 32							08 43	08 45	08 51						
Norbury	d	08 23								08 34							08 45	08 48	08 53						
Thornton Heath	d	08 26								08 37							08 48	08 51	08 56						
Selhurst 4	d	08 29								08 40							08 51	08 54	08 59						
Norwood Junction 2	a					08 16	08 25	08 36				08 38		08 43										08 45	08 55
	d					08 16	08 25	08 36				08 39		08 43										08 46	08 55
West Croydon 4	🚋 a	08 33						08 41				08 44					08 55	08 58	09 03						
East Croydon	🚋 a					08 19	08 29			08 43				08 47										08 49	08 59

For general notes see front of timetable
For details of catering facilities see Directory of Train Operators

- **A** To Caterham (Table 181)
- **B** To Epsom Downs (Table 182)
- **C** To Sutton (Surrey) (Table 182)
- **D** To Smitham (Table 181)
- **E** To Epsom (Table 182)
- **G** To Tunbridge Wells (Table 209)
- **H** Via Sydenham (Table 178)
- **b** Arr. 0756
- **c** Arr. 0826

Luton & London → East and West Croydon via Tulse Hill/Crystal Palace/Norbury

Local Services

Network Diagram - see first page of Table 177

		SN	SN	SN	SN	SN	SN	SN	SN	FC	SN	SN	SN	SN	SN	FC	SE	SN	SN	SN	SN	SN		SN	SN
																	13								
				A			B	C					D	E			G				A				B
London Bridge 4	⊖ d					08 45	08 38	08 54			08 41	08 49			08 59		09 03		09 05					09 15	09 08
South Bermondsey	d						08 42				08 45	08 53			09 03										09 12
Queens Rd Peckham	d						08 44				08 48	08 55			09 05										09 14
Peckham Rye 4	d						08 47				08 50	08 58			09 08										09 17
East Dulwich	d						08 50					09 01			09 11										09 20
North Dulwich	d						08 52					09 03			09 13										09 22
Luton 10	d									07 44						07 59									
Luton Airport Parkway 7	✈ d									07 46						08 01									
St Pancras International 15	⊖ d									08 32						08 47									
City Thameslink 3	d																								
London Blackfriars 3	⊖ d									08 46						09 00									
Elephant & Castle	⊖ d									08 49						09 03									
Loughborough Jn	d									08 53						09 07									
Herne Hill 4	d									08 57						09 11									
Tulse Hill 3	d						09b00			09 02		09 06			09 16	09 17									09c30
Streatham 4	d									09a05		09 10				09 20									
London Victoria 15	⊖ d	08 37	08 41	08 45	08 50				08 52				08 55	09 05				09 11		09 07	09 15	09 20			
Battersea Park 4	d	08 41	08a45	08 49					08 56				08 59					09a15		09 11	09 19				
Clapham Junction 10	d	08 44		08 52	08 56				08 59				09 04	09 11						09 14	09 22	09 26			
Wandsworth Common	d	08 47		08 55					09 02				09 07	09 14						09 17	09 25				
Balham 4	⊖ d	08 50		08 58	09 02				09 05				09 10	09 17						09 20	09 28	09 32			
Streatham Hill	d	08 53							09 08											09 23					
West Norwood 4	d	08 56					09 03		09 11						09 19					09 26					09 33
Gipsy Hill	d	08 59					09 06		09 14						09 22					09 29					09 36
Crystal Palace 4	d	09 02					09 08	09a13	09a17						09 25					09 32					09 38
Birkbeck	🚊 d														09 29										
Beckenham Junction 4	🚊 a														09 32										
Bromley South 4	a														*09 47*										
Streatham Common 4	d			09 02								09 13	09 15	09 21							09 32				
Norbury	d			09 04								09 15	09 18	09 23							09 34				
Thornton Heath	d			09 07								09 18	09 21	09 26							09 37				
Selhurst 4	d			09 10								09 21	09 24	09 29							09 40				
Norwood Junction 2	a	09 06				09 08	09 13										09 16		09 25	09 36				09 38	09 43
	d	09 06				09 09	09 13										09 16		09 25	09 36				09 39	09 43
West Croydon 4	🚊 a	09 11				09 14						09 25	09 28	09 33						09 41				09 44	
East Croydon	🚊 a			09 13			09 17										09 19		09 29		09 43				09 47

		SN	SN	FC	SN	SN	SN	SN	SN	FC	SN		SN	SN	SN	SN	SN	SN	SN	SN	SN	FC	SN	SN	SN
											1														
		C				H	E									A			B	C				D	E
London Bridge 4	⊖ d	09 24			09 19			09 11	09 29		09 33		09 35					09 45	09 38	09 54			09 49		
South Bermondsey	d				09 23			09 15	09 33										09 42				09 53		
Queens Rd Peckham	d				09 25			09 18	09 35										09 44				09 55		
Peckham Rye 4	d				09 28			09 20	09 38										09 47				09 58		
East Dulwich	d				09 31				09 41										09 50				10 01		
North Dulwich	d				09 33				09 43										09 52				10 03		
Luton 10	d			08 14																		08 44			
Luton Airport Parkway 7	✈ d			08 16																		08 46			
St Pancras International 15	⊖ d			09 02						09 17												09 32			
City Thameslink 3	d			09 09						09 24												09 39			
London Blackfriars 3	⊖ d			09 16						09 30												09 46			
Elephant & Castle	⊖ d			09 19						09 33												09 49			
Loughborough Jn	d			09 23						09 37												09 53			
Herne Hill 4	d			09 27						09 41												09 57			
Tulse Hill 3	d			09 32	09 36				09 46	09 47									10e00			10 02	10 06		
Streatham 4	d			09a35	09 40					09 50												10a05	10 10		
London Victoria 15	⊖ d		09 22			09 25	09 35							09 37	09 41	09 45	09 50				09 52			09 55	10 05
Battersea Park 4	d		09 26			09 29								09 41	09a45	09 49					09 56			09 59	
Clapham Junction 10	d		09 29			09 34	09 41							09 44		09 52	09 56				09 59			10 04	10 11
Wandsworth Common	d		09 32			09 37	09 44							09 47		09 55					10 02			10 07	10 14
Balham 4	⊖ d		09 35			09 40	09 47							09 50		09 58	10 02				10 05			10 10	10 17
Streatham Hill	d		09 38											09 53							10 08				
West Norwood 4	d		09 41						09 49					09 56					10 03		10 11				
Gipsy Hill	d		09 44						09 52					09 59					10 06		10 14				
Crystal Palace 4	d	09a43	09a47						09 55					10 02					10 08	10a13	10a17				
Birkbeck	🚊 d								09 59																
Beckenham Junction 4	🚊 a								10 02																
Bromley South 4	a								*10 17*																
Streatham Common 4	d				09 43	09 45	09 51									10 02							10 13	10 15	10 21
Norbury	d				09 45	09 48	09 53									10 04							10 15	10 18	10 23
Thornton Heath	d				09 48	09 51	09 56									10 07							10 18	10 21	10 26
Selhurst 4	d				09 51	09 54	09 59									10 10							10 21	10 24	10 29
Norwood Junction 2	a										09 45		09 55	10 06				10 08	10 13						
	d										09 46		09 55	10 06				10 09	10 13						
West Croydon 4	🚊 a				09 55	09 58	10 03							10 11				10 14					10 25	10 28	10 33
East Croydon	🚊 a										09 49		09 59			10 13			10 17						

For general notes see front of timetable
For details of catering facilities see Directory of Train Operators

A To Caterham (Table 181)
B To Smitham (Table 181)
C Via Sydenham (Table 178)
D To Epsom (Table 182)
E To Sutton (Surrey) (Table 182)
G To Tunbridge Wells (Table 209)
H To Epsom Downs (Table 182)
b Arr. 0856
c Arr. 0926
e Arr. 0956

Luton & London → East and West Croydon via Tulse Hill/Crystal Palace/Norbury

Local Services

Network Diagram - see first page of Table 177

		SN	SN	FC	SE 13 A	SN	SN	SN	SN B	SN	SN	SN C	SN D	SN	FC	SN	SN E	SN G	SN	SN	FC	SN [1]		SN
London Bridge [4]	⊖ d	09 41	09 59		10 03	10 05					10 15	10 08	10 24			10 19			10 11	10 29		10 33		17 35
South Bermondsey	d	09 45	10 03									10 12				10 23			10 15	10 33				
Queens Rd Peckham	d	09 48	10 05									10 14				10 25			10 18	10 35				
Peckham Rye [4]	d	09 50	10 08									10 17				10 28			10 20	10 38				
East Dulwich	d		10 11									10 20				10 31				10 41				
North Dulwich	d		10 13									10 22				10 33				10 43				
Luton [10]	d														09 14									
Luton Airport Parkway [7]	✈ d														09 16									
St Pancras International [15]	⊖ d			09 47											10 02						10 17			
City Thameslink [3]	d			09 54											10 09						10 24			
London Blackfriars [3]	⊖ d			10 00											10 16						10 30			
Elephant & Castle	⊖ d			10 03											10 19						10 33		and at	
Loughborough Jn	d			10 07											10 23						10 37			
Herne Hill [4]	d			10 11											10 27						10 41		the same	
Tulse Hill [3]	d		10 16	10 17								10b30			10 32	10 36				10 46	10 47			
Streatham [4]	d			10 20											10a35	10 40					10 50		minutes	
London Victoria [15]	⊖ d						10 07	10 11	10 15	10 20				10 22			10 25	10 35					past	
Battersea Park [4]	d						10 11	10a15	10 19					10 26			10 29							
Clapham Junction [10]	d						10 14		10 22	10 26				10 29			10 34	10 41					each	
Wandsworth Common	d						10 17		10 25					10 32			10 37	10 44						
Balham [4]	⊖ d						10 20		10 28	10 32				10 35			10 40	10 47					hour until	
Streatham Hill	d						10 23							10 38										
West Norwood [4]	d		10 19				10 26					10 33		10 41						10 49				
Gipsy Hill	d		10 22				10 29					10 36		10 44						10 52				
Crystal Palace [4]	d		10 25				10 32					10 38	10a43	10a47						10 55				
Birkbeck	d		10 29																	10 59				
Beckenham Junction [4]	a		10 32																	11 02				
Bromley South [4]	a		*10 47*																	*11 17*				
Streatham Common [4]	d								10 32							10 43	10 45	10 51						
Norbury	d								10 34							10 45	10 48	10 53						
Thornton Heath	d								10 37							10 48	10 51	10 56						
Selhurst [4]	d								10 40							10 51	10 54	10 59						
Norwood Junction [2]	a				10 16	10 25	10 36				10 38	10 43										10 45		17 55
	d				10 16	10 25	10 36				10 39	10 43										10 46		17 55
West Croydon [4]	a						10 41				10 44					10 55	10 58	11 03						
East Croydon	a				10 19	10 29			10 43			10 47										10 49		17 59

		SN		SN	SN B	SN	SN	SN C	SN D	SN	FC	SN	SN	SN H	SN	SN	FC	SE 13 A	SN	SN	SN	SN J	SN	SN	SN C
London Bridge [4]	⊖ d						17 45	17 38	17 54			17 41	17 49			17 59		18 03	18 05					18 15	18 08
South Bermondsey	d							17 42				17 45	17 53			18 03									18 12
Queens Rd Peckham	d							17 44				17 48	17 55			18 05									18 14
Peckham Rye [4]	d							17 47				17 50	17 58			18 08									18 17
East Dulwich	d							17 50					18 01			18 11									18 20
North Dulwich	d							17 52					18 03			18 13									18 22
Luton [10]	d										16 44														
Luton Airport Parkway [7]	✈ d										16 46														
St Pancras International [15]	⊖ d										17 32						17 47								
City Thameslink [3]	d										17 39						17 54								
London Blackfriars [3]	⊖ d										17 46						18 00								
Elephant & Castle	⊖ d										17 49						18 03								
Loughborough Jn	d										17 53						18 07								
Herne Hill [4]	d										17 57						18 11								
Tulse Hill [3]	d							18c00			18 02		18 06			18 16	18 17								18e30
Streatham [4]	d										18a05		18 10				18 20								
London Victoria [15]	⊖ d	17 37		17 41	17 45	17 50				17 52				17 55	18 05					18 07	18 11	18 15	18 20		
Battersea Park [4]	d	17 41		17a45	17 49					17 56				17 59						18 11	18a15	18 19			
Clapham Junction [10]	d	17 44			17 52	17 56				17 59				18 04	18 11					18 14		18 22	18 26		
Wandsworth Common	d	17 47			17 55					18 02				18 07	18 14					18 17		18 25			
Balham [4]	⊖ d	17 50			17 58	18 02				18 05				18 10	18 17					18 20		18 28	18 32		
Streatham Hill	d	17 53								18 08										18 23					
West Norwood [4]	d	17 56						18 03		18 11						18 19				18 26					18 33
Gipsy Hill	d	17 59						18 06		18 14						18 22				18 29					18 36
Crystal Palace [4]	d	18 02						18 08	18a13	18a17						18 25				18 32					18 38
Birkbeck	d															18 29									
Beckenham Junction [4]	a															18 32									
Bromley South [4]	a															*18 47*									
Streatham Common [4]	d				18 02								18 13	18 15	18 21							18 32			
Norbury	d				18 04								18 15	18 18	18 23							18 34			
Thornton Heath	d				18 07								18 18	18 21	18 26							18 37			
Selhurst [4]	d				18 10								18 21	18 24	18a29							18 40			
Norwood Junction [2]	a	18 06					18 08	18 13										18 16	18 25	18 36				18 38	18 43
	d	18 06					18 09	18 13										18 16	18 25	18 36				18 39	18 43
West Croydon [4]	a	18 11					18 14						18 25	18 28						18 41				18 44	
East Croydon	a				18 13			18 17										18 19	18 29			18 43			18 47

For general notes see front of timetable
For details of catering facilities see Directory of Train Operators

A To Tunbridge Wells (Table 209)
B To Caterham (Table 181)
C To Smitham (Table 181)
D Via Sydenham (Table 178)
E To Epsom Downs (Table 182)
G To Sutton (Surrey) (Table 182)
H To Epsom (Table 182)
J To Purley (Table 175)
b Arr. 1026
c Arr. 1756
e Arr. 1826

Table 177

Saturdays

Luton & London → East and West Croydon via Tulse Hill/Crystal Palace/Norbury

Local Services

Network Diagram - see first page of Table 177

		SN		SN	SN	FC	SN	SN	SN	SN	FC	FC	SN	SN	SN	SN	SN	SN	SN	SN	SN	SN	SN	SE	SN
													1											13	
		A						B										C					A	D	E
London Bridge 4	⊖ d	18 24			18 11		18 19			18 29			18 33	18 35	18 48					18 41	18 45	18 49	18 54	19 03	
South Bermondsey	d				18 15		18 23			18 33										18 45		18 53			
Queens Rd Peckham	d				18 18		18 25			18 35										18 48		18 55			
Peckham Rye 4	d				18 20		18 28			18 38										18 50		18 58			
East Dulwich	d						18 31			18 41												19 01			
North Dulwich	d						18 33			18 43												19 03			
Luton 10	d					17 14						17 44													
Luton Airport Parkway 7	✈ d					17 16						17 46													
St Pancras International 15	⊖ d					18 02					18 17	18 32													
City Thameslink 3	d					18 09					18 24	18 39													
London Blackfriars 3	⊖ d					18 16					18 30	18 46													
Elephant & Castle	⊖ d					18 19					18 33	18 49													
Loughborough Jn	d					18 23					18 37	18 53													
Herne Hill 4	d					18 27					18 41	18 57													
Tulse Hill 3	d					18 32	18 36			18 46	18 47	19 02										19 06			
Streatham 4	d					18a35	18 40				18 50	19a05										19 10			
London Victoria 15	⊖ d			18 22				18 25	18 35							18 37	18 41	18 45	18 50						18 52
Battersea Park 4	d			18 26				18 29								18 41	18a45	18 49							18 56
Clapham Junction 10	d			18 29				18 34	18 41							18 44		18 52	18 56						18 59
Wandsworth Common	d			18 32				18 37	18 44							18 47		18 55							19 02
Balham 4	⊖ d			18 35				18 40	18 46							18 50		18 58	19 02						19 05
Streatham Hill	d			18 38												18 53									19 08
West Norwood 4	d			18 41						18 49						18 56									19 11
Gipsy Hill	d			18 44						18 52						18 59									19 14
Crystal Palace 4	d	18a43		18a47						18 55						19 02							19a13		19 17
Birkbeck	d									18 59															
Beckenham Junction 4	a									19 02															
Bromley South 4	a									*19 17*															
Streatham Common 4	d						18 43	18 45	18 50									19 02				19 13			
Norbury	d						18 45	18 48	18 53									19 04				19 15			
Thornton Heath	d						18 48	18 51	18 56									19 07				19 18			
Selhurst 4	d						18 51	18 53	18a58									19 10				19 21			
Norwood Junction 2	a												18 45	18 55	19 03	19 06					19 08			19 16	19 21
	d												18 46	18 55	19 03	19 06					19 09			19 16	19 24
West Croydon 4	a						18 55	18 57								19 11		19 14				19 25			19 29
East Croydon	a												18 49	18 59	19 06						19 13			19 19	

		SN		SN	SN	SN	SN	SN	FC	SN	FC	SN	SN	SN	SN	SN	SN	SN	SN	SN	SN	SN	SN	FC	SN
															1										
		G						C						A		B	G					C			
London Bridge 4	⊖ d			19 15	18 59							19 11	19 19	19 24	19 33			19 44	19 29						19 41
South Bermondsey	d				19 03							19 15	19 23						19 33						19 45
Queens Rd Peckham	d				19 05							19 18	19 25						19 35						19 48
Peckham Rye 4	d				19 08							19 20	19 28						19 38						19 50
East Dulwich	d				19 11								19 31						19 41						
North Dulwich	d				19 13								19 33						19 43						
Luton 10	d										18 20													18 50	
Luton Airport Parkway 7	✈ d										18 22													18 52	
St Pancras International 15	⊖ d								18 47		19 05													19 35	
City Thameslink 3	d								18 54		19 12													19 42	
London Blackfriars 3	⊖ d								19 00		19 16													19 46	
Elephant & Castle	⊖ d								19 03		19 19													19 49	
Loughborough Jn	d								19 07		19 23													19 53	
Herne Hill 4	d								19 11		19 27													19 57	
Tulse Hill 3	d				19 16				19 17		19 32		19 36						19 46					20 02	
Streatham 4	d								19 20		19a35		19 40											20a05	
London Victoria 15	⊖ d	19 00				19 05	19 11	19 15		19 20						19 22	19 30			19 35	19 41	19 45	19 50		
Battersea Park 4	d	19 04				19 09	19a15	19 19								19 26	19 34			19 39	19a45	19 49			
Clapham Junction 10	d	19 08				19 12		19 22		19 26						19 29	19 38			19 42		19 52	19 56		
Wandsworth Common	d	19 11				19 15		19 25								19 32	19 41			19 45		19 55			
Balham 4	⊖ d	19 13				19 18		19 28		19 32						19 35	19 43			19 48		19 58	20 02		
Streatham Hill	d					19 21										19 38				19 51					
West Norwood 4	d				19 19	19 24										19 41			19 49	19 54					
Gipsy Hill	d				19 22	19 27										19 44			19 52	19 57					
Crystal Palace 4	d				19 25	19a30								19a43		19 47			19 55	20a00					
Birkbeck	d				19 29														19 59						
Beckenham Junction 4	a				19 32														20 02						
Bromley South 4	a				*19 47*														*20 17*						
Streatham Common 4	d	19 18						19 32					19 43				19 47					20 02			
Norbury	d	19 20						19 34					19 45				19 50					20 04			
Thornton Heath	d	19 23						19 37					19 48				19 53					20 07			
Selhurst 4	d	19 26						19 40					19 51				19 55					20 10			
Norwood Junction 2	a			19 38											19 45	19 51		20 08							
	d			19 38											19 46	19 54		20 08							
West Croydon 4	a							19 44					19 55			19 59						20 14			
East Croydon	a	19 29		19 42											19 50		19 59	20 12							

For general notes see front of timetable
For details of catering facilities see Directory of Train Operators

- **A** Via Sydenham (Table 178)
- **B** To Epsom Downs (Table 182)
- **C** To Sutton (Surrey) (Table 182)
- **D** To Tonbridge (Table 209)
- **E** To Epsom (Table 182)
- **G** To Tattenham Corner (Table 181)

Luton & London → East and West Croydon via Tulse Hill/Crystal Palace/Norbury

Local Services

Network Diagram - see first page of Table 177

	SN		SN	SN	SN	SN	SN	SN	SN	SN	FC	SN	SN	SN	SN	SN	SN	SN	SN	SN	SN	FC	SN	SN
			[1]																					
				A	B	C			D				A	E			C			D			A	
London Bridge [4] ⊖ d	19 49		20 08	19 54								20 15	20 24		20 11	20 19							20 54	20 45
South Bermondsey d	19 53														20 15	20 23								
Queens Rd Peckham d	19 55														20 18	20 25								
Peckham Rye [4] d	19 58														20 20	20 28								
East Dulwich d	20 01															20 31								
North Dulwich d	20 03															20 33								
Luton [10] d											19 20											19 50		
Luton Airport Parkway [7] ✈ d											19 22											19 52		
St Pancras International [15] ⊖ d											20 05											20 35		
City Thameslink [3] d											20 12											20 42		
London Blackfriars [3] ⊖ d											20 16											20 46		
Elephant & Castle ⊖ d											20 19											20 49		
Loughborough Jn d											20 23											20 53		
Herne Hill [4] d											20 27											20 57		
Tulse Hill [3] d	20 06										20 32					20 36						21 02		
Streatham [4] d	20 10										20a35					20 40						21a05		
London Victoria [15] ⊖ d					19 52	20 00	20 05	20 11	20 15	20 20				20 22			20 30	20 35	20 41	20 45	20 50			
Battersea Park [4] d					19 56	20 04	20 09	20a15	20 19					20 26			20 34	20 39	20a45	20 49				
Clapham Junction [10] d					19 59	20 08	20 12		20 22	20 26				20 29			20 38	20 42		20 52	20 56			
Wandsworth Common d					20 02	20 11	20 15		20 25					20 32			20 41	20 45		20 55				
Balham [4] ⊖ d					20 05	20 13	20 18		20 28	20 32				20 35			20 43	20 48		20 58	21 02			
Streatham Hill d					20 08		20 21							20 38				20 51						
West Norwood [4] d					20 11		20 24							20 41				20 54						
Gipsy Hill d					20 14		20 27							20 44				20 57						
Crystal Palace [4] d				20a13	20 17		20a30						20a43	20 47				21a00					21a13	
Birkbeck ⇌ d																								
Beckenham Junction [4] ⇌ a																								
Bromley South [4] a																								
Streatham Common [4] d	20 13					20 17			20 32							20 43	20 47			21 02				
Norbury d	20 15					20 20			20 34							20 45	20 50			21 04				
Thornton Heath d	20 18					20 23			20 37							20 48	20 53			21 07				
Selhurst [4] d	20 21					20 25			20 40							20 51	20 55			21 10				
Norwood Junction [2] a			20 19		20 21							20 38		20 51										21 08
d			20 19		20 24							20 38		20 54										21 08
West Croydon [4] ⇌ a	20 26				20 29				20 44					20 59		20 56				21 14				
East Croydon ⇌ a			20 22			20 29						20 42					20 59							21 12

	SN		FC	SN	SN	SN	SN	SN	SN	SN	SN	SN	SN	SN	SN	SN	SN	SN	SN	SN	SN	FC	SN	SN
					[1]																	[1]		
						B	C			D			A	E			C			D			A	
London Bridge [4] ⊖ d	20 49			20 41	21 08							21 15	21 24		21 11	21 19							21 54	21 45
South Bermondsey d	20 53			20 45											21 15	21 23								
Queens Rd Peckham d	20 55			20 48											21 18	21 25								
Peckham Rye [4] d	20 58			20 50											21 20	21 28								
East Dulwich d	21 01															21 31								
North Dulwich d	21 03															21 33								
Luton [10] d			20 20																			20 50		
Luton Airport Parkway [7] ✈ d			20 22																			20 52		
St Pancras International [15] ⊖ d			21 05																			21 35		
City Thameslink [3] d																								
London Blackfriars [3] ⊖ d			21 16																			21 46		
Elephant & Castle ⊖ d			21 19																			21 49		
Loughborough Jn d			21 23																			21 53		
Herne Hill [4] d			21 27																			21 57		
Tulse Hill [3] d	21 06		21 32													21 36						22 02		
Streatham [4] d	21 10		21a35													21 40						22a05		
London Victoria [15] ⊖ d						20 52	21 00	21 05	21 11	21 15	21 20			21 22			21 30	21 35	21 41	21 45	21 50			
Battersea Park [4] d						20 56	21 04	21 09	21a15	21 19				21 26			21 34	21 39	21a45	21 49				
Clapham Junction [10] d						20 59	21 08	21 12		21 22	21 26			21 29			21 38	21 42		21 52	21 56			
Wandsworth Common d						21 02	21 11	21 15		21 25				21 32			21 41	21 45		21 55				
Balham [4] ⊖ d						21 05	21 13	21 18		21 28	21 32			21 35			21 43	21 48		21 58	22 02			
Streatham Hill d						21 08		21 21						21 38				21 51						
West Norwood [4] d						21 11		21 24						21 41				21 54						
Gipsy Hill d						21 14		21 27						21 44				21 57						
Crystal Palace [4] d						21 17		21a30					21a43	21 47				22a00					22a13	
Birkbeck ⇌ d																								
Beckenham Junction [4] ⇌ a																								
Bromley South [4] a																								
Streatham Common [4] d	21 13						21 17			21 32						21 43	21 47			22 02				
Norbury d	21 15						21 20			21 34						21 45	21 50			22 04				
Thornton Heath d	21 18						21 23			21 37						21 48	21 53			22 07				
Selhurst [4] d	21 21						21 25			21 40						21 51	21 55			22 10				
Norwood Junction [2] a					21 19	21 21						21 38		21 51										22 08
d					21 19	21 24						21 38		21 54										22 08
West Croydon [4] ⇌ a	21 26					21 29				21 44				21 59		21 56				22 14				
East Croydon ⇌ a					21 22		21 29					21 42					21 59							22 12

For general notes see front of timetable
For details of catering facilities see Directory of Train Operators

A Via Sydenham (Table 178)
B To Epsom (Table 182)
C To Tattenham Corner (Table 181)
D To Sutton (Surrey) (Table 182)
E To Epsom Downs (Table 182)

Table 177

Saturdays

Luton & London → East and West Croydon via Tulse Hill/Crystal Palace/Norbury

Local Services

Network Diagram - see first page of Table 177

		SN		SN	SN 1	SN	SN	SN	SN	SN	SN	FC	SN	SN	SN	SN	SN	SN	SN	SN	SN	SN	FC	SN	SN
						A	B			C			D		E			B			C			D	
London Bridge 4	⊖ d	21 41		21 49	22 08								22 24	22 15		22 11	22 19							22 54	22 45
South Bermondsey	d	21 45		21 53												22 15	22 23								
Queens Rd Peckham	d	21 48		21 55												22 18	22 25								
Peckham Rye 4	d	21 50		21 58												22 20	22 28								
East Dulwich	d			22 01													22 31								
North Dulwich	d			22 03													22 33								
Luton 10	d											21 20											21 50		
Luton Airport Parkway 7	✈ d											21 22											21 52		
St Pancras International 15	⊖ d											22 05											22 36		
City Thameslink 3	d																								
London Blackfriars 3	⊖ d											22 16											22 46		
Elephant & Castle	⊖ d											22 19											22 49		
Loughborough Jn	d											22 23											22 53		
Herne Hill 4	d											22 27											22 57		
Tulse Hill 3	d			22 06								22 32					22 36						23 02		
Streatham 4	d			22 10								22a35					22 40						23a05		
London Victoria 15	⊖ d					21 52	22 00	22 05	22 11	22 15	22 20				22 22			22 30	22 35	22 41	22 45	22 50			
Battersea Park 4	d					21 56	22 04	22 09	22a15	22 19					22 26			22 34	22 39	22a45	22 49				
Clapham Junction 10	d					21 59	22 08	22 12		22 22	22 26				22 29			22 38	22 42		22 52	22 56			
Wandsworth Common	d					22 02	22 11	22 15		22 25					22 32			22 41	22 45		22 55				
Balham 4	⊖ d					22 05	22 13	22 18		22 28	22 32				22 35			22 43	22 48		22 58	23 00			
Streatham Hill	d					22 08		22 21							22 38				22 51						
West Norwood 4	d					22 11		22 24							22 41				22 54						
Gipsy Hill	d					22 14		22 27							22 44				22 57						
Crystal Palace 4	d					22 17		22a30					22a43		22 47				23a00					23a13	
Birkbeck	🚋 d																								
Beckenham Junction 4	🚋 a																								
Bromley South 4	a																								
Streatham Common 4	d			22 13			22 17			22 32							22 43	22 47			23 02				
Norbury	d			22 15			22 20			22 34							22 45	22 50			23 04				
Thornton Heath	d			22 18			22 23			22 37							22 48	22 53			23 07				
Selhurst 4	d			22 21			22 25			22 40							22 51	22 55			23 10				
Norwood Junction 2	a				22 19	22 21								22 38	22 51										23 08
	d				22 19	22 24								22 38	22 54										23 08
West Croydon 4	🚋 a			22 26		22 29				22 44					22 59		22 56				23 15				
East Croydon	🚋 a				22 22		22 29							22 42				22 59							23 12

		SN		SN	FC	SN	SN	SN	SN	SN	SN	SN	SN	SN	SN	SN	SN	SN	SN	SN	SN	SN			
							A	B			C	D		C						C					
London Bridge 4	⊖ d	22 41		22 49		23 00						23 24	23 15		23 11		23 19				23 53	23 49			
South Bermondsey	d	22 45		22 53											23 15		23 23					23 53			
Queens Rd Peckham	d	22 48		22 55											23 18		23 25					23 55			
Peckham Rye 4	d	22 50		22 58											23 20		23 28					23 58			
East Dulwich	d			23 01													23 31					00 01			
North Dulwich	d			23 03													23 33					00 03			
Luton 10	d				22 20																				
Luton Airport Parkway 7	✈ d				22 22																				
St Pancras International 15	⊖ d				23 06																				
City Thameslink 3	d																								
London Blackfriars 3	⊖ d				23 16																				
Elephant & Castle	⊖ d				23 19																				
Loughborough Jn	d																								
Herne Hill 4	d				23 27																				
Tulse Hill 3	d			23 06	23 32												23 36					00 06			
Streatham 4	d			23 10	23a35												23 40								
London Victoria 15	⊖ d						22 52	23 00	23 05	23 11	23 15			23 22		23 26		23 34	23 37	23 51					
Battersea Park 4	d						22 56	23 04	23 09	23a15	23 19			23 26				23 38	23 42	23 55					
Clapham Junction 10	d						22 59	23 08	23 12		23 22			23 29		23 32		23 41	23 45	23 58					
Wandsworth Common	d						23 02	23 11	23 15		23 25			23 32				23 44	23 48	00 01					
Balham 4	⊖ d						23 05	23 13	23 18		23 28			23 35		23 37		23 47	23 51	00 04					
Streatham Hill	d						23 08		23 21					23 38					23 54						
West Norwood 4	d						23 11		23 24					23 41					23 57			00 09			
Gipsy Hill	d						23 14		23 27					23 44					23 59			00 12			
Crystal Palace 4	d						23 17		23a30			23a43		23 47					00 03			00 15			
Birkbeck	🚋 d																								
Beckenham Junction 4	🚋 a																								
Bromley South 4	a																								
Streatham Common 4	d			23 13				23 17			23 32						23 43	23 51		00 08					
Norbury	d			23 15				23 20			23 34						23 45	23 53		00 10					
Thornton Heath	d			23 18				23 23			23 37						23 48	23 56		00 13					
Selhurst 4	d			23 21				23 25			23 40						23 51	23a59		00 16					
Norwood Junction 2	a					23 11	23 21						23 38	23 51					00 07		00 16	00 19			
	d					23 11	23 24						23 38	23 54					00 07		00 16				
West Croydon 4	🚋 a			23 26			23 29				23 45			23 58			23 55		00 13	00 20					
East Croydon	🚋 a					23 16		23 29					23 42								00 20				

For general notes see front of timetable
For details of catering facilities see Directory of Train Operators

A To Epsom (Table 182)
B To Tattenham Corner (Table 181)
C To Sutton (Surrey) (Table 182)
D Via Sydenham (Table 178)
E To Epsom Downs (Table 182)

Table 177

Sundays

Luton & London → East and West Croydon via Tulse Hill/Crystal Palace/Norbury

Local Services

Network Diagram - see first page of Table 177

Station		SN	SN A	SN	SN	SN	SN	SN	SN B	SN 1 C	SN B	SN	SN 1 D	SN	SN		SN A	SN	SN A	SN	SN	SN	SN	SN	SN A
London Bridge 4	⊖ d			23p53	23p49		00 26					07 11		07 25	07 44					07 41		07 55	07 58	08 14	
South Bermondsey	d				23p53							07 15		07 29						07 45		07 59			
Queens Rd Peckham	d				23p55							07 18		07 31						07 48		08 01			
Peckham Rye 4	d				23p58							07 20		07 34						07 50		08 04			
East Dulwich	d				00 01									07 37								08 07			
North Dulwich	d				00 03									07 39								08 09			
Luton 10	d																								
Luton Airport Parkway 7	✈ d																								
St Pancras International 15	⊖ d																								
City Thameslink 3	d																								
London Blackfriars 3	⊖ d																								
Elephant & Castle	⊖ d																								
Loughborough Jn	d																								
Herne Hill 4	d																								
Tulse Hill 3	d				00 06									07 42								08 12			
Streatham 4	d													07 46								08 16			
London Victoria 15	⊖ d	23p37	23p51			00 17		00 42	06 49	07 02	07 19		07 34				07 38	07 41	07 49		08 06				08 08
Battersea Park 4	d	23p42	23p55					00 46	06 53		07 23						07 42	07a45	07 53						08 12
Clapham Junction 10	d	23p45	23p58			00 23		00 49	06 56	07 08	07 26		07 40				07 45		07 56		08 12				08 15
Wandsworth Common	d	23p48	00 01					00 52	06 59		07 29						07 48		07 59						08 18
Balham 4	⊖ d	23p51	00 04			00 27		00 55	07 02		07 32						07 51		08 02		08 16				08 21
Streatham Hill	d	23p54															07 54								08 24
West Norwood 4	d	23p57			00 09												07 57								08 27
Gipsy Hill	d	23p59			00 12												08 00								08 30
Crystal Palace 4	d	00 03			00 15												08 03								08 33
Birkbeck	🚊 d																								
Beckenham Junction 4	🚊 a																								
Bromley South 4	a																								
Streatham Common 4	d		00 08			00 31		00 59	07 06		07 36			07 49					08 06			08 19			
Norbury	d		00 10			00 34		01 01	07 08		07 38			07 51					08 08			08 21			
Thornton Heath	d		00 13			00 37		01 04	07 11		07 41			07 54					08 11			08 24			
Selhurst 4	d		00 16			00 39		01 07	07 14	07 18	07 44		07 50	07 58					08 14			08 27			
Norwood Junction 2	a	00 07		00 16	00 19		00 49								08 04		08 07						08 21	08 34	08 37
	d	00 07		00 16			00 49								08 04		08 07						08 21	08 34	08 37
West Croydon 4	🚊 a	00 13	00 20						07 18		07 48						08 12		08 18				08 26		08 42
East Croydon	🚊 a			00 20		00 42	00 53	01 10		07 23			07 53	08 02	08 08							08 32		08 38	

Station		SN	SN A	SN	SN	SN	SN	SN		SN A	SN	SN A	SN	SN	SN	SN	FC	SN	SN A	SN	SN A	SN	SN		
London Bridge 4	⊖ d			08 11		08 25	08 28	08 44					08 41		08 55	08 58		09 14				09 11			
South Bermondsey	d			08 15		08 29							08 45		08 59							09 15			
Queens Rd Peckham	d			08 18		08 31							08 48		09 01							09 18			
Peckham Rye 4	d			08 20		08 34							08 50		09 04							09 20			
East Dulwich	d					08 37									09 07										
North Dulwich	d					08 39									09 09										
Luton 10	d																08 20								
Luton Airport Parkway 7	✈ d																08 22								
St Pancras International 15	⊖ d																09 06								
City Thameslink 3	d																								
London Blackfriars 3	⊖ d																09 16								
Elephant & Castle	⊖ d																09 19								
Loughborough Jn	d																09 23								
Herne Hill 4	d																09 27								
Tulse Hill 3	d					08 42									09 12		09 31								
Streatham 4	d					08 46									09 16		09a34								
London Victoria 15	⊖ d	08 11	08 19		08 36					08 38	08 41	08 49		09 06					09 08	09 11	09 19		09 36		
Battersea Park 4	d	08a15	08 23							08 42	08a45	08 53							09 12	09a15	09 23				
Clapham Junction 10	d		08 26		08 42					08 45		08 56		09 12					09 15		09 26		09 42		
Wandsworth Common	d		08 29							08 48		08 59							09 18		09 29				
Balham 4	⊖ d		08 32		08 46					08 51		09 02		09 16					09 21		09 32		09 46		
Streatham Hill	d									08 54									09 24						
West Norwood 4	d									08 57									09 27						
Gipsy Hill	d									09 00									09 30						
Crystal Palace 4	d									09 03									09 33						
Birkbeck	🚊 d																								
Beckenham Junction 4	🚊 a																								
Bromley South 4	a																								
Streatham Common 4	d		08 36			08 49						09 06			09 19						09 36				
Norbury	d		08 38			08 51						09 08			09 21						09 38				
Thornton Heath	d		08 41			08 54						09 11			09 24						09 41				
Selhurst 4	d		08 44			08 57						09 14			09 27						09 44				
Norwood Junction 2	a						08 51	09 04		09 07						09 21		09 34	09 37						
	d						08 51	09 04		09 07						09 21		09 34	09 37						
West Croydon 4	🚊 a		08 48				08 56			09 12		09 18				09 26			09 42		09 48				
East Croydon	🚊 a					09 00		09 08							09 32			09 38							

For general notes see front of timetable
For details of catering facilities see Directory of Train Operators

A To Sutton (Surrey) (Table 182)
B To Dorking (Table 182)
C To Bognor Regis (Table 188)
D To Horsham (Table 186)

Table 177

Sundays

Luton & London → East and West Croydon via Tulse Hill/Crystal Palace/Norbury

Local Services

Network Diagram - see first page of Table 177

		SN	SN	FC	SN	SN A	SN	SN A	SN	SN	SN	SN	FC	SN	SN A	SN	SN A	SN	SN		SN	SN
London Bridge 4 ⊖	d	09 25	09 28		09 44				09 41		09 55	09 58		10 14				10 11		and at the same minutes past each hour until	14 25	14 28
South Bermondsey	d	09 29							09 45		09 59							10 15			14 29	
Queens Rd Peckham	d	09 31							09 48		10 01							10 18			14 31	
Peckham Rye 4	d	09 34							09 50		10 04							10 20			14 34	
East Dulwich	d	09 37									10 07										14 37	
North Dulwich	d	09 39									10 09										14 39	
Luton 10	d			08 50									09 20									
Luton Airport Parkway 7 ✈	d			08 52									09 22									
St Pancras International 15 ⊖	d			09 36									10 06									
City Thameslink 3	d																					
London Blackfriars 3 ⊖	d			09 46									10 16									
Elephant & Castle ⊖	d			09 49									10 19									
Loughborough Jn	d			09 53									10 23									
Herne Hill 4	d			09 57									10 27									
Tulse Hill 3	d	09 42		10 01							10 12		10 31								14 42	
Streatham 4	d	09 46		10a04							10 16		10a34								14 46	
London Victoria 15 ⊖	d					09 38	09 41	09 49		10 06					10 08	10 11	10 19		10 36			
Battersea Park 4	d					09 42	09a45	09 53							10 12	10a15	10 23					
Clapham Junction 10	d					09 45		09 56		10 12					10 15		10 26		10 42			
Wandsworth Common	d					09 48		09 59							10 18		10 29					
Balham 4 ⊖	d					09 51		10 02		10 16					10 21		10 32		10 46			
Streatham Hill	d					09 54									10 24							
West Norwood 4	d					09 57									10 27							
Gipsy Hill	d					10 00									10 30							
Crystal Palace 4	d					10 03									10 33							
Birkbeck 🚊	d																					
Beckenham Junction 4 🚊	a																					
Bromley South 4	a																					
Streatham Common 4	d	09 49						10 06			10 19						10 36				14 49	
Norbury	d	09 51						10 08			10 21						10 38				14 51	
Thornton Heath	d	09 54						10 11			10 24						10 41				14 54	
Selhurst 4	d	09 57						10 14			10 27						10 44				14 57	
Norwood Junction 2	a		09 51		10 04	10 07						10 21		10 34	10 37							14 51
	d		09 51		10 04	10 07						10 21		10 34	10 37							14 51
West Croydon 4 🚊	a		09 56			10 12		10 18				10 26			10 42		10 48					14 56
East Croydon 🚊	a	10 02			10 08						10 34			10 38							15 02	

		FC	SN	SN A	SN	SN A	SN	SN	SN	SN	FC	SN	SN A	SN	SN A		SN	SN	SN	SN	FC	SN	SN A	SN	SN A
London Bridge 4 ⊖	d		14 44				14 41		14 55	14 58		15 14					15 11		15 25	15 28		15 44			
South Bermondsey	d						14 45		14 59								15 15		15 29						
Queens Rd Peckham	d						14 48		15 01								15 18		15 31						
Peckham Rye 4	d						14 50		15 04								15 20		15 34						
East Dulwich	d								15 07										15 37						
North Dulwich	d								15 09										15 39						
Luton 10	d	13 50									14 18										14 50				
Luton Airport Parkway 7 ✈	d	13 52									14 20										14 52				
St Pancras International 15 ⊖	d	14 36									15 06										15 36				
City Thameslink 3	d																								
London Blackfriars 3 ⊖	d	14 46									15 16										15 46				
Elephant & Castle ⊖	d	14 49									15 19										15 49				
Loughborough Jn	d	14 53									15 23										15 53				
Herne Hill 4	d	14 57									15 27										15 57				
Tulse Hill 3	d	15 01							15 12		15 31								15 42		16 01				
Streatham 4	d	15a04							15 16		15a34								15 46		16a04				
London Victoria 15 ⊖	d			14 38	14 41	14 49		15 06					15 08	15 11	15 19			15 36					15 38	15 41	15 49
Battersea Park 4	d			14 42	14a45	14 53							15 12	15a15	15 23								15 42	15a45	15 53
Clapham Junction 10	d			14 45		14 56		15 12					15 15		15 26			15 42					15 45		15 56
Wandsworth Common	d			14 48		14 59							15 18		15 29								15 48		15 59
Balham 4 ⊖	d			14 51		15 02		15 16					15 21		15 32			15 46					15 51		16 02
Streatham Hill	d			14 54									15 24										15 54		
West Norwood 4	d			14 57									15 27										15 57		
Gipsy Hill	d			15 00									15 30										16 00		
Crystal Palace 4	d			15 03									15 33										16 03		
Birkbeck 🚊	d																								
Beckenham Junction 4 🚊	a																								
Bromley South 4	a																								
Streatham Common 4	d					15 06			15 19						15 36				15 49						16 06
Norbury	d					15 08			15 21						15 38				15 51						16 08
Thornton Heath	d					15 11			15 24						15 41				15 54						16 11
Selhurst 4	d					15 14			15 27						15 44				15 57						16 14
Norwood Junction 2	a		15 04	15 07						15 21		15 34	15 37							15 51		16 04	16 07		
	d		15 04	15 07						15 21		15 34	15 37							15 51		16 04	16 07		
West Croydon 4 🚊	a			15 12		15 18				15 26			15 42		15 48					15 56			16 12		16 18
East Croydon 🚊	a		15 08						15 32			15 38							16 02			16 08			

For general notes see front of timetable
For details of catering facilities see Directory of Train Operators

A To Sutton (Surrey) (Table 182)

Table 177

Sundays

Luton & London → East and West Croydon via Tulse Hill/Crystal Palace/Norbury

Local Services

Network Diagram - see first page of Table 177

Station		SN	SN	SN	SN	FC	SN	SN		SN	SN	SN	SN	SN	SN	FC	SN	SN	SN	SN	SN	SN	SN		SN
								A			A							A		A					
London Bridge 4	⊖ d	15 41		15 55	15 58		16 14					16 11		16 25	16 28		16 44				16 41		16 55		16 58
South Bermondsey	d	15 45		15 59								16 15		16 29							16 45		16 59		
Queens Rd Peckham	d	15 48		16 01								16 18		16 31							16 48		17 01		
Peckham Rye 4	d	15 50		16 04								16 20		16 34							16 50		17 04		
East Dulwich	d			16 07										16 37									17 07		
North Dulwich	d			16 09										16 39									17 09		
Luton 10	d					15 20										15 50									
Luton Airport Parkway 7	✈ d					15 22										15 52									
St Pancras International 15	⊖ d					16 06										16 36									
City Thameslink 3	d																								
London Blackfriars 3	⊖ d					16 16										16 46									
Elephant & Castle	⊖ d					16 19										16 49									
Loughborough Jn	d					16 23										16 53									
Herne Hill 4	d					16 27										16 57									
Tulse Hill 3	d			16 12		16 31								16 42		17 01							17 12		
Streatham 4	d			16 16		16a34								16 46		17a04							17 16		
London Victoria 15	⊖ d		16 06					16 08		16 11	16 19		16 36					16 38	16 41	16 49		17 06			
Battersea Park 4	d							16 12		16a15	16 23							16 42	16a45	16 53					
Clapham Junction 10	d		16 12					16 15			16 26		16 42					16 45		16 56		17 12			
Wandsworth Common	d							16 18			16 29							16 48		16 59					
Balham 4	⊖ d		16 16					16 21			16 32		16 46					16 51		17 02		17 16			
Streatham Hill	d							16 24										16 54							
West Norwood 4	d							16 27										16 57							
Gipsy Hill	d							16 30										17 00							
Crystal Palace 4	d							16 33										17 03							
Birkbeck	🚋 d																								
Beckenham Junction 4	🚋 a																								
Bromley South 4	a																								
Streatham Common 4	d			16 19							16 36			16 49						17 06			17 19		
Norbury	d			16 21							16 38			16 51						17 08			17 21		
Thornton Heath	d			16 24							16 41			16 54						17 11			17 24		
Selhurst 4	d			16 27							16 44			16 57						17 14			17 27		
Norwood Junction 2	a				16 21		16 34	16 37							16 51		17 04	17 07							17 21
	d				16 21		16 34	16 37							16 51		17 04	17 07							17 21
West Croydon 4	🚋 a				16 26			16 42			16 48				16 56			17 12		17 18					17 26
East Croydon	🚋 a			16 32			16 38							17 02			17 08						17 32		

Station		FC	SN	SN	SN	SN	SN	SN	SN	SN	FC	SN	SN	SN	SN		SN	SN	SN	SN	FC	SN	SN	SN	SN
				A		A							A		A								A		A
London Bridge 4	⊖ d		17 14				17 11		17 25	17 28		17 44					17 41		17 55	17 58		18 14			
South Bermondsey	d						17 15		17 29								17 45		17 59						
Queens Rd Peckham	d						17 18		17 31								17 48		18 01						
Peckham Rye 4	d						17 20		17 34								17 50		18 04						
East Dulwich	d								17 37										18 07						
North Dulwich	d								17 39										18 09						
Luton 10	d	16 20									16 50										17 20				
Luton Airport Parkway 7	✈ d	16 22									16 52										17 22				
St Pancras International 15	⊖ d	17 06									17 36										18 06				
City Thameslink 3	d																								
London Blackfriars 3	⊖ d	17 16									17 46										18 16				
Elephant & Castle	⊖ d	17 19									17 49										18 19				
Loughborough Jn	d	17 23									17 53										18 23				
Herne Hill 4	d	17 27									17 57										18 27				
Tulse Hill 3	d	17 31							17 42		18 01								18 12		18 31				
Streatham 4	d	17a34							17 46		18a04								18 16		18a34				
London Victoria 15	⊖ d			17 08	17 11	17 19		17 36					17 38	17 41	17 49			18 06					18 08	18 11	18 19
Battersea Park 4	d			17 12	17a15	17 23							17 42	17a45	17 53								18 12	18a15	18 23
Clapham Junction 10	d			17 15		17 26		17 42					17 45		17 56			18 12					18 15		18 26
Wandsworth Common	d			17 18		17 29							17 48		17 59								18 18		18 29
Balham 4	⊖ d			17 21		17 32		17 46					17 51		18 02			18 16					18 21		18 32
Streatham Hill	d			17 24									17 54										18 24		
West Norwood 4	d			17 27									17 57										18 27		
Gipsy Hill	d			17 30									18 00										18 30		
Crystal Palace 4	d			17 33									18 03										18 33		
Birkbeck	🚋 d																								
Beckenham Junction 4	🚋 a																								
Bromley South 4	a																								
Streatham Common 4	d					17 36			17 49						18 06				18 19						18 36
Norbury	d					17 38			17 51						18 08				18 21						18 38
Thornton Heath	d					17 41			17 54						18 11				18 24						18 41
Selhurst 4	d					17 44			17 57						18 14				18 27						18 44
Norwood Junction 2	a		17 34	17 37						17 51		18 04	18 07							18 21		18 34	18 37		
	d		17 34	17 37						17 51		18 04	18 07							18 21		18 34	18 37		
West Croydon 4	🚋 a			17 42		17 48				17 56			18 12		18 18					18 26			18 42		18 48
East Croydon	🚋 a		17 38						18 02			18 08							18 32			18 38			

For general notes see front of timetable
For details of catering facilities see
Directory of Train Operators

A To Sutton (Surrey) (Table 182)

Luton & London → East and West Croydon via Tulse Hill/Crystal Palace/Norbury

Local Services

Network Diagram - see first page of Table 177

Station		SN	SN	SN	SN	FC	SN	SN A		SN	SN A	SN	SN	SN	SN	FC	SN	SN A	SN	SN A	SN	SN	SN		SN
London Bridge 4 ⊖	d	18 11		18 25	18 28		18 44					18 41		18 55	18 58		19 14				19 11		19 25		19 28
South Bermondsey	d	18 15		18 29								18 45		18 59							19 15		19 29		
Queens Rd Peckham	d	18 18		18 31								18 48		19 01							19 18		19 31		
Peckham Rye 4	d	18 20		18 34								18 50		19 04							19 20		19 34		
East Dulwich	d			18 37										19 07									19 37		
North Dulwich	d			18 39										19 09									19 39		
Luton 10	d					17 50										18 20									
Luton Airport Parkway 7 ✈	d					17 52										18 22									
St Pancras International 15 ⊖	d					18 36										19 06									
City Thameslink 3	d																								
London Blackfriars 3 ⊖	d					18 46										19 16									
Elephant & Castle ⊖	d					18 49										19 19									
Loughborough Jn	d					18 53										19 23									
Herne Hill 4	d					18 57										19 27									
Tulse Hill 3	d			18 42		19 01								19 12		19 31							19 42		
Streatham 4	d			18 46		19a04								19 16		19a34							19 46		
London Victoria 15 ⊖	d		18 36					18 38		18 41	18 49		19 06					19 08	19 11	19 19		19 36			
Battersea Park 4	d							18 42		18a45	18 53							19 12	19a15	19 23					
Clapham Junction 10	d		18 42					18 45			18 56		19 12					19 15		19 26		19 42			
Wandsworth Common	d							18 48			18 59							19 18		19 29					
Balham 4 ⊖	d		18 46					18 51			19 02		19 16					19 21		19 32		19 46			
Streatham Hill	d							18 54										19 24							
West Norwood 4	d							18 57										19 27							
Gipsy Hill	d							19 00										19 30							
Crystal Palace 4	d							19 03										19 33							
Birkbeck 🚋	d																								
Beckenham Junction 4 🚋	a																								
Bromley South 4	a																								
Streatham Common 4	d			18 49							19 06			19 19						19 36			19 49		
Norbury	d			18 51							19 08			19 21						19 38			19 51		
Thornton Heath	d			18 54							19 11			19 24						19 41			19 54		
Selhurst 4	d			18 57							19 14			19 27						19 44			19 57		
Norwood Junction 2	a				18 51		19 04	19 07							19 21		19 34	19 37							19 51
	d				18 51		19 04	19 07							19 21		19 34	19 37							19 51
West Croydon 4 🚋	a				18 56			19 12			19 18				19 26			19 42		19 48					19 56
East Croydon 🚋	a			19 02			19 08							19 32			19 38						20 02		

Station		FC	SN	SN A	SN	SN A	SN	SN	SN	SN	FC	SN	SN A	SN	SN A		SN	SN	SN	SN	FC	SN	SN A	SN	SN A
London Bridge 4 ⊖	d		19 44				19 41		19 55	19 58		20 14					20 11		20 25	20 28		20 44			
South Bermondsey	d						19 45		19 59								20 15		20 29						
Queens Rd Peckham	d						19 48		20 01								20 18		20 31						
Peckham Rye 4	d						19 50		20 04								20 20		20 34						
East Dulwich	d								20 07										20 37						
North Dulwich	d								20 09										20 39						
Luton 10	d	18 50									19 20										19 50				
Luton Airport Parkway 7 ✈	d	18 52									19 22										19 52				
St Pancras International 15 ⊖	d	19 36									20 06										20 36				
City Thameslink 3	d																								
London Blackfriars 3 ⊖	d	19 46									20 16										20 46				
Elephant & Castle ⊖	d	19 49									20 19										20 49				
Loughborough Jn	d	19 53									20 23										20 53				
Herne Hill 4	d	19 57									20 27										20 57				
Tulse Hill 3	d	20 01							20 12		20 31								20 42		21 01				
Streatham 4	d	20a04							20 16		20a34								20 46		21a04				
London Victoria 15 ⊖	d			19 38	19 41	19 49		20 06					20 08	20 11	20 19			20 36					20 38	20 41	20 49
Battersea Park 4	d			19 42	19a45	19 53							20 12	20a15	20 23								20 42	20a45	20 53
Clapham Junction 10	d			19 45		19 56		20 12					20 15		20 26			20 42					20 45		20 56
Wandsworth Common	d			19 48		19 59							20 18		20 29								20 48		20 59
Balham 4 ⊖	d			19 51		20 02		20 16					20 21		20 32			20 46					20 51		21 02
Streatham Hill	d			19 54									20 24										20 54		
West Norwood 4	d			19 57									20 27										20 57		
Gipsy Hill	d			20 00									20 30										21 00		
Crystal Palace 4	d			20 03									20 33										21 03		
Birkbeck 🚋	d																								
Beckenham Junction 4 🚋	a																								
Bromley South 4	a																								
Streatham Common 4	d					20 06			20 19						20 36				20 49						21 06
Norbury	d					20 08			20 21						20 38				20 51						21 08
Thornton Heath	d					20 11			20 24						20 41				20 54						21 11
Selhurst 4	d					20 14			20 27						20 44				20 57						21 14
Norwood Junction 2	a		20 04	20 07						20 21		20 34	20 37							20 51		21 04	21 07		
	d		20 04	20 07						20 21		20 34	20 37							20 51		21 04	21 07		
West Croydon 4 🚋	a			20 12		20 18				20 26			20 42		20 48					20 56			21 12		21 18
East Croydon 🚋	a		20 08						20 32			20 38							21 02			21 08			

For general notes see front of timetable
For details of catering facilities see
Directory of Train Operators

A To Sutton (Surrey) (Table 182)

Table 177

Sundays

Luton & London → East and West Croydon via Tulse Hill/Crystal Palace/Norbury

Local Services

Network Diagram - see first page of Table 177

	SN	SN	SN	SN	SN	SN A	SN		SN A	SN	SN	SN	SN	SN	SN A	SN	SN A	SN	SN	SN	SN	SN A		SN
London Bridge 4 ⊖ d	20 41		20 55	20 58	21 14					21 11		21 25	21 28	21 44				21 41		21 55	21 58			
South Bermondsey d	20 45		20 59							21 15		21 29						21 45		21 59				
Queens Rd Peckham d	20 48		21 01							21 18		21 31						21 48		22 01				
Peckham Rye 4 d	20 50		21 04							21 20		21 34						21 50		22 04				
East Dulwich d			21 07									21 37								22 07				
North Dulwich d			21 09									21 39								22 09				
Luton 10 d																								
Luton Airport Parkway 7 ✈ d																								
St Pancras International 15 ⊖ d																								
City Thameslink 3 d																								
London Blackfriars 3 ⊖ d																								
Elephant & Castle ⊖ d																								
Loughborough Jn d																								
Herne Hill 4 d																								
Tulse Hill 3 d			21 12									21 42								22 12				
Streatham 4 d			21 16									21 46								22 16				
London Victoria 15 ⊖ d		21 06				21 08	21 11		21 19		21 36				21 38	21 41	21 49		22 06			22 08		22 11
Battersea Park 4 d						21 12	21a15		21 23						21 42	21a45	21 53					22 12		22a15
Clapham Junction 10 d		21 12				21 15			21 26		21 42				21 45		21 56		22 12			22 15		
Wandsworth Common d						21 18			21 29						21 48		21 59					22 18		
Balham 4 ⊖ d		21 16				21 21			21 32		21 46				21 51		22 02		22 16			22 21		
Streatham Hill d						21 24									21 54							22 24		
West Norwood 4 d						21 27									21 57							22 27		
Gipsy Hill d						21 30									22 00							22 30		
Crystal Palace 4 d						21 33									22 03							22 33		
Birkbeck d																								
Beckenham Junction 4 a																								
Bromley South 4 a																								
Streatham Common 4 d			21 19						21 36			21 49					22 06			22 19				
Norbury d			21 21						21 38			21 51					22 08			22 21				
Thornton Heath d			21 24						21 41			21 54					22 11			22 24				
Selhurst 4 d			21 27						21 44			21 57					22 14			22 27				
Norwood Junction 2 a				21 21	21 34	21 37							21 51	22 04	22 07						22 21	22 37		
Norwood Junction 2 d				21 21	21 34	21 37							21 51	22 04	22 07						22 21	22 39		
West Croydon 4 a				21 26		21 42			21 48				21 56		22 12		22 18				22 26	22 43		
East Croydon a			21 32		21 38							22 00		22 08						22 32				

	SN	SN A	SN	SN	SN A	SN	SN	SN	SN A	SN	SN	SN	SN	SN		SN	SN B	SN	SN 1 C	SN	SN	SN	SN	
London Bridge 4 ⊖ d	22 14		22 11				22 25	22 44		22 41				22 55		23 14		23 11			23 25	23 44		
South Bermondsey d			22 15				22 29			22 45				22 59				23 15			23 29			
Queens Rd Peckham d			22 18				22 31			22 48				23 01				23 18			23 31			
Peckham Rye 4 d			22 20				22 34			22 50				23 04				23 20			23 34			
East Dulwich d							22 37							23 07							23 37			
North Dulwich d							22 39							23 09							23 39			
Luton 10 d																								
Luton Airport Parkway 7 ✈ d																								
St Pancras International 15 ⊖ d																								
City Thameslink 3 d																								
London Blackfriars 3 ⊖ d																								
Elephant & Castle ⊖ d																								
Loughborough Jn d																								
Herne Hill 4 d																								
Tulse Hill 3 d							22 42							23 12							23 42			
Streatham 4 d							22 46							23 16							23 46			
London Victoria 15 ⊖ d		22 19		22 36	22 38	22 41			22 49		23 06	23 08	23 11				23 19		23 32	23 38			23 49	
Battersea Park 4 d		22 23			22 42	22a45			22 53			23 12	23a15				23 23			23 42			23 53	
Clapham Junction 10 d		22 26		22 42	22 45				22 56		23 12	23 15					23 26		23 38	23 45			23 56	
Wandsworth Common d		22 29			22 48				22 59			23 18					23 29			23 48			23 59	
Balham 4 ⊖ d		22 32		22 46	22 51				23 02		23 16	23 21					23 32			23 51			00 02	
Streatham Hill d					22 54							23 24								23 54				
West Norwood 4 d					22 57							23 27								23 57				
Gipsy Hill d					23 00							23 30								23 59				
Crystal Palace 4 d					23 03							23 33								00 03				
Birkbeck d																								
Beckenham Junction 4 a																								
Bromley South 4 a																								
Streatham Common 4 d		22 36					22 49		23 06					23 19			23 36				23 49		00 06	
Norbury d		22 38					22 51		23 08					23 21			23 38				23 51		00 08	
Thornton Heath d		22 41					22 54		23 11					23 24			23 41				23 54		00 11	
Selhurst 4 d		22 44					22 57		23 14					23 27			23 44		23 48		23 57		00 14	
Norwood Junction 2 a	22 37				23 07			23 07				23 37				23 37				00 07		00 09		
Norwood Junction 2 d	22 39				23 07			23 09				23 37				23 39						00 10		
West Croydon 4 a		22 48			23 12				23 18			23 42					23 48							
East Croydon a	22 42						23 00	23 12						23 32		23 42			23 52		00 01	00 13	00 17	

For general notes see front of timetable
For details of catering facilities see
Directory of Train Operators

A To Sutton (Surrey) (Table 182)
B To Epsom (Table 182)
C To Brighton (Table 186)

East and West Croydon → London & Luton via Norbury/Crystal Palace/Tulse Hill

Local Services

Network Diagram - see first page of Table 177

Miles	Miles	Miles	Miles	Miles			SN MX	SN MO 1 A	SN	SN	SN 1 B	FC C	SN	SN	SN	SN D	SN	FC C	SN E	SN	SN	SN	SN	SN	SN
0	—	—	0	0	**East Croydon**	d		23p56		05 13	05 29			05 34		05 48	05 51			06 12					06 17
—	0	—	—	—	**West Croydon 4**	d									05 45				06 02		06 15				
1¼	—	—	—	1¼	Norwood Junction 2	a				05 17				05 38	05 50		05 55			06 16	06 19				
—	—	—	—	—		d				05 17				05 38	05 50		05 55			06 16	06 19				
—	1	—	1	—	Selhurst 4	d		00 01			05 32	05 36				05 51		05 56	06 06						06 20
—	1¾	—	1¾	—	Thornton Heath	d					05 35	05 38				05 53		05 58	06 08						06 22
—	3	—	3	—	Norbury	d					05 38	05 40				05 56		06 00	06 11						06 25
—	4	—	4	—	Streatham Common 4	d					05 40	05 43				05 59		06 03	06 14						06 27
—	—	—	—	—	Bromley South 4	d																			
—	—	0	—	—	Beckenham Junction 4	d																			
—	—	1½	—	—	Birkbeck	d																			
2¾	—	3	—	2¾	**Crystal Palace 4**	d	23p43							05 42			05 59								
3½	—	3¾	—	3½	Gipsy Hill	d	23p46							05 44			06 01								
4½	—	4¾	—	4½	West Norwood 4	d	23p49							05 47			06 04								
5¾	—	6	—	—	Streatham Hill	d	23p52							05 51											
6¾	—	7	5¾	—	Balham 4 ⊖	d	23p55				05 44			05 54		06 03			06 18				06 27		06 31
7½	—	7¾	6½	—	Wandsworth Common	d	23p57									06 05			06 20						06 33
8¾	—	9	7¾	—	Clapham Junction 10	d	00 01	00 11	05 02		05 49			05 58		06 08			06 23				06 31		06 37
10¼	—	10½	9¼	—	Battersea Park 4	d	00 04				05 52			06 02		06 12			06 27			06 32			06 40
11½	—	11¾	10½	—	**London Victoria 15** ⊖	a	00 12	00 18	05 09		05 58			06 06		06 18			06 31			06 36	06 38		06 46
—	4½	—	—	—	Streatham 4	d						05 46	05 52					06 06						06 32	
—	6	—	—	5	Tulse Hill 3	d						05 50	05 55				06 07	06 10						06 35	
—	—	—	—	—	Herne Hill 4	a						05 53						06 13							
—	—	—	—	—	Loughborough Jn	a												06 17							
—	—	—	—	—	Elephant & Castle ⊖	a						06 01						06 22							
—	—	—	—	—	London Blackfriars 3 ⊖	a						06 05						06 27							
—	—	—	—	—	City Thameslink 3	a						06 10						06 30							
—	—	—	—	—	St Pancras International 15 ⊖	a						06 18						06 38							
—	—	—	—	—	Luton Airport Parkway 7	a						07 01						07 21							
—	—	—	—	—	**Luton 10**	a						07 04						07 24							
—	7¼	—	—	6¼	North Dulwich	d											06 10							06 38	
—	7¾	—	—	6¾	East Dulwich	d											06 12							06 40	
—	8½	—	—	7½	Peckham Rye 4	d							06 00				06 15							06 43	
—	9¼	—	—	8¼	Queens Rd Peckham	d											06 17							06 45	
—	10¼	—	—	9¼	South Bermondsey	d											06 20							06 48	
—	12	—	—	11	**London Bridge 4** ⊖	a				05 41			06 07		06 14		06 24			06 34	06 45			06 52	

		FC	FC	SN	SN	SN G	SN	SN	FC H	SN	SN	SN	SN	SN	SN J	SN	SN	FC	SN K	SN	SN L	SN	SN	SN	SN
East Croydon	d				06 28			06 40							06 45					07 12			07 05		
West Croydon 4	d					06 31					06 45								07 00					07 16	
Norwood Junction 2	a				06 32			06 44			06 50									07 16				07 21	
	d			06 24	06 32		06 42	06 44			06 50					06 54	07 03			07 16				07 21	
Selhurst 4	d					06 35			06 45						06 48				07 04				07 10		
Thornton Heath	d					06 37			06 47						06 50				07 06				07 12		
Norbury	d					06 40			06 49						06 53				07 09				07 15		
Streatham Common 4	d					06 43			06 52						06 56				07 12				07 17		
Bromley South 4	d																								
Beckenham Junction 4	d																								
Birkbeck	d																								
Crystal Palace 4	d			06 28			06 46									06 58	07 07				07 15				
Gipsy Hill	d			06 30			06 48									07 00	07 09								
West Norwood 4	d			06 33			06 51									07 03	07 12								
Streatham Hill	d			06 37												07 07									
Balham 4 ⊖	d			06 40		06 47							06 57		07 00	07 10			07 16						
Wandsworth Common	d			06 42		06 49									07 02	07 12			07 18						
Clapham Junction 10	d			06 45		06 52							07 01		07 05	07 15			07 21						
Battersea Park 4	d			06 49		06 56						07 02			07 09	07 19			07 25						07 32
London Victoria 15 ⊖	a			06 53		07 02						07 08	07 10		07 16	07 25			07 31						07 38
Streatham 4	d	06 36	06 50						06 56					07 06				07 16					07 20		
Tulse Hill 3	d	06 40	06 54				06b58		07 00					07 09			07 15	07 20					07 24		
Herne Hill 4	a	06 44	06 58						07 04									07 24							
Loughborough Jn	a	06 47	07 02						07 07									07 27							
Elephant & Castle ⊖	a	06 52	07 06						07 12									07 31							
London Blackfriars 3 ⊖	a	06 56	07 11						07 17									07 37							
City Thameslink 3	a	07 00	07 14						07 20									07 40							
St Pancras International 15 ⊖	a	07 08	07 21						07 28									07 48							
Luton Airport Parkway 7	a	07 54																08 27							
Luton 10	a	07 56																08 30							
North Dulwich	d						07 01							07 12			07 18						07 27		
East Dulwich	d						07 03							07 14			07 20						07 29		
Peckham Rye 4	d						07 05			06 56				07 17			07 23					07 26	07 31		
Queens Rd Peckham	d						07 08			06 59							07 25					07 29	07 34		
South Bermondsey	d						07 10			07 01							07 28					07 31	07 36		
London Bridge 4 ⊖	a				06 54		07 18	07 02		07 08	07 16			07 25			07 34			07 33	07 36	07 38	07 43	07 48	

For general notes see front of timetable
For details of catering facilities see Directory of Train Operators

A From Horsham (Table 186)
B From Brighton (Table 186)
C To Bedford (Table 52)
D From Redhill (Table 186)
E From Epsom (Table 182)
G From Sutton (Surrey) (Table 182)
H To St Albans (Table 52)
J From Sanderstead (Table 184)
K From Epsom Downs (Table 182)
L Via Sydenham (Table 178)
b Arr. 0654

East and West Croydon → London & Luton via Norbury/Crystal Palace/Tulse Hill

Local Services

Network Diagram - see first page of Table 177

Station		SN	SN	SN	SN	SN	SN	SN	SN	FC	SN	SN	SN	SN	SN		SN	SN	SN	SN	SN	SN	SN	SN	SN
											A							1 B		C					
East Croydon	d		07 17				07 36											07 47						07 57	
West Croydon 4	d			07 19	07 28						07 30		07 43									07 46	07 56		
Norwood Junction 2	a			07 24	07 32		07 40						07 48									07 51	08 00	08 01	
	d			07 24	07 32		07 41						07 48									07 51	08 01	08 01	
Selhurst 4	d		07 20								07 34	07 40						07 50			07 53				
Thornton Heath	d		07 22								07 36	07 42						07 52			07 55				
Norbury	d		07 25								07 39	07 45						07 55			07 58				
Streatham Common 4	d		07 27								07 42	07 47						07 58			08 01				
Bromley South 4	d														*07 16*										
Beckenham Junction 4	d														07 35										
Birkbeck	d														07 38										
Crystal Palace 4	d			07 28											07 42				07 51	07 54		07 55			
Gipsy Hill	d			07 30											07 45				07 53			07 57			
West Norwood 4	d			07 33											07 48				07 56			08 00			
Streatham Hill	d			07 37											07 51							08 04			
Balham 4	⊖ d	07 29	07 32	07 40		07 42					07 46	07 51			07 54		08 00	08 02			08 05	08 09			
Wandsworth Common	d		07 34	07 42							07 48				07 56			08 04			08 07	08 11			
Clapham Junction 10	d	07 33	07 37	07 45		07 48					07 51	07 56			08 00		08 04	08a08			08 11	08 14			
Battersea Park 4	d		07 41	07 49							07 55			08 02	08 04						08 14	08 18			
London Victoria 15	⊖ a	07 42	07 47	07 55		07 57					08 01	08 05		08 08	08 10		08 13				08 21	08 25			
Streatham 4	d							07 42		07 46															08 05
Tulse Hill 3	d							07 46		07 50									08 00						08 10
Herne Hill 4	a									07 54															
Loughborough Jn	a									07 57															
Elephant & Castle	⊖ a									08 02															
London Blackfriars 3	⊖ a									08 07															
City Thameslink 3	a									08 15															
St Pancras International 15	⊖ a									08 23															
Luton Airport Parkway 7	✈ a																								
Luton 10	a																								
North Dulwich	d							07 49											08 03						08 13
East Dulwich	d							07 51											08 05						08 15
Peckham Rye 4	d							07 53	07 56										08 08						08 17
Queens Rd Peckham	d								07 59										08 10						08 20
South Bermondsey	d								08 01										08 13						08 22
London Bridge 4	⊖ a				07 58		08 01	08 02	08 08				08 08						08 21	08 16			08 27	08 16	08 30

Station		FC	FC	SN	SN	SN	SN	SN	SN	SN	SN	SN	SN	SN	SN	SN	FC	SN	SN	SN	SN	FC	SN	SN	SN
						D	A	E				C	C				1 G				H		E		
East Croydon	d			08 12										08 09	08 18		08 28							08 34	08 45
West Croydon 4	d						08 01	08 07	08 16									08 19	08 23	08 28					
Norwood Junction 2	a			08 16					08 20									08 24	08 28	08 32				08 39	08 49
	d			08 17					08 20									08 25	08 28	08 32				08 40	08 49
Selhurst 4	d						08 05	08 11						08 16	08 21										
Thornton Heath	d						08 07	08 13						08 18	08 23										
Norbury	d						08 10	08 16						08 21	08 26										
Streatham Common 4	d						08 12	08 18						08 23	08 28										
Bromley South 4	d										*07 37*														
Beckenham Junction 4	d										08 05														
Birkbeck	d										08 08														
Crystal Palace 4	d										08 12	08 16	08 23					08 29			08 36				
Gipsy Hill	d										08 14							08 31			08 38				
West Norwood 4	d										08 17							08 34			08 42				
Streatham Hill	d										08 21					08 32		08 38							
Balham 4	⊖ d					08 14	08 17	08 22			08 25				08 32			08 41					08 43		
Wandsworth Common	d						08 19				08 27				08 34								08 45		
Clapham Junction 10	d					08 18	08 22	08 26			08 30				08 38			08 45					08 49		
Battersea Park 4	d					08 22	08 26			08 32	08 34				08 41			08 49							
London Victoria 15	⊖ a					08 28	08 32	08 36		08 38	08 40				08 48			08 55					08 58		
Streatham 4	d	08 11	08 17											08 26								08 45			
Tulse Hill 3	d	08 15	08 23											08 30		08 36	08 39				08b51 ↳	08 49			
Herne Hill 4	a	08 19	08 27														08 43					08 53			
Loughborough Jn	a	08 25	08 31																			08 56			
Elephant & Castle	⊖ a	08 29	08 35																			09 00			
London Blackfriars 3	⊖ a	08 36	08 41														08 52					09 04			
City Thameslink 3	a	08 39	08 45														08 59					09 07			
St Pancras International 15	⊖ a	08 46	08 54														09 06					09 14			
Luton Airport Parkway 7	✈ a	09 20															09 40								
Luton 10	a	09 23															09 43								
North Dulwich	d													08 33		08 39									
East Dulwich	d													08 35		08 41									
Peckham Rye 4	d				08 26									08 38		08 43									
Queens Rd Peckham	d				08 29									08 40		08 46									
South Bermondsey	d				08 31									08 43		08 48									
London Bridge 4	⊖ a			08 31	08 38				08 42			08 38	08 46	08 49		08 56			08 47	09 02				08 55	09 05

For general notes see front of timetable
For details of catering facilities see Directory of Train Operators

- **A** From Epsom Downs (Table 182)
- **B** To Kensington Olympia (Table 186)
- **C** Via Sydenham (Table 178)
- **D** From Epsom (Table 182)
- **E** From Sutton (Surrey) (Table 182)
- **G** From Brighton (Table 52)
- **H** From London Bridge (Table 178)
- **b** Arr. 0846

East and West Croydon → London & Luton via Norbury/Crystal Palace/Tulse Hill

Local Services

Network Diagram - see first page of Table 177

		SN	SN	FC	SN	SN	SN	SN	SN	SN	SN	SN	SN	SN	SN	FC	SN	SN	SN	SN	SN	SN	SN	SN	SN
				[1]																					
			A	B	C		D												E						D
East Croydon	d			08 38								08 50					09 05				09 02				
West Croydon [4]	d				08 32			08 44					08 49	08 59					08 57			09 15			
Norwood Junction [2]	a							08 49					08 53	09 03			09 09					09 19			
	d							08 49					08 53	09 03			09 09					09 19			
Selhurst [4]	d				08 36							08 53							09 01		09 05				
Thornton Heath	d				08 38							08 55							09 03		09 07				
Norbury	d				08 41							08 58							09 06		09 10				
Streatham Common [4]	d				08 43							09 00							09 09		09 13				
Bromley South [4]	d					*08 21*																			
Beckenham Junction [4]	d					08 32																			
Birkbeck	d					08 35																			
Crystal Palace [4]	d					08 39	08 48						08 57		09 06									09 13	09 17
Gipsy Hill	d					08 41							09 00		09 08									09 16	
West Norwood [4]	d					08 44							09 03		09 12									09 19	
Streatham Hill	d					08 48							09 06											09 22	
Balham [4]	d				08 48	08 51				09 02		09 05	09 09						09 13	09 23				09 26	
Wandsworth Common	d				08 50	08 53						09 07	09 11						09 15					09 28	
Clapham Junction [10]	d				08 53	08 56				09 07		09 10	09 15						09 19	09 27				09 32	
Battersea Park [4]	d				08 57	09 00			09 02			09 14	09 18						09 23				09 32	09 36	
London Victoria [15]	a				09 03	09 06			09 08	09 16		09 20	09 25						09 29	09 36			09 39	09 42	
Streatham [4]	d		←								09 06					09 15					09 17				
Tulse Hill [3]	d		08 51	08 55							09 09				09 15	09 19					09 22				
Herne Hill [4]	a			08 58												09 22									
Loughborough Jn	a															09 26									
Elephant & Castle	a															09 30									
London Blackfriars [3]	a			09 08												09 33									
City Thameslink [3]	a			09 11												09 36									
St Pancras International [15]	a			09 18												09 44									
Luton Airport Parkway [7]	a			09 53																					
Luton [10]	a			09 55																					
North Dulwich	d		08 54								09 12				09 18						09 25				
East Dulwich	d		08 56								09 14				09 20						09 27				
Peckham Rye [4]	d	08 56	09 00								09 17				09 23			09 26			09 29				
Queens Rd Peckham	d	08 59	09 02								09 19				09 25			09 29			09 32				
South Bermondsey	d	09 01	09 05								09 22				09 28			09 31			09 34				
London Bridge [4]	a	09 08	09 12				09 12	09 17			09 29			09 29	09 34		09 24	09 38			09 41	09 46			09 38

		SN	FC		SN	SN	SN	SN	SN	SN	SN	SN	SN	FC	SN	SN	SN	FC	SN	SN	SN	SN	SN	SN	SN
					G						C				D				E			G		H	[1]
East Croydon	d				09 17		09 20	09 31														09 47		09 51	09 55
West Croydon [4]	d					09 18					09 27		09 31			09 46			09 35				09 49		
Norwood Junction [2]	a					09 23	09 24	09 35								09 51							09 53	09 57	09 59
	d					09 23	09 25	09 35								09 51							09 53	09 58	09 59
Selhurst [4]	d				09 21						09 31		09 35						09 39			09 50			
Thornton Heath	d				09 23						09 33		09 37						09 41			09 52			
Norbury	d				09 26						09 36		09 40						09 44			09 55			
Streatham Common [4]	d				09 28						09 39		09 43						09 47			09 58			
Bromley South [4]	d	*09 03*															*09 33*								
Beckenham Junction [4]	d	09 16															09 46								
Birkbeck	d	09 19															09 49								
Crystal Palace [4]	d	09 23				09 27			09 33						09 47		09 53				09 43		09 57	10 02	
Gipsy Hill	d	09 25				09 29			09 35								09 55				09 46		10 00	10 05	
West Norwood [4]	d	09 28				09 32			09 38								09 58				09 49		10 03	10 08	
Streatham Hill	d					09 36															09 52		10 06		
Balham [4]	d				09 32	09 39					09 43	09 49							09 52		09 56	10 02	10 09		
Wandsworth Common	d				09 34	09 41					09 45								09 54		09 58	10 04	10 11		
Clapham Junction [10]	d				09 38	09 45					09 48	09 53							09 57		10 01	10 07	10 15		
Battersea Park [4]	d				09 41	09 48					09 52								10 01	10 03	10 05		10 18		
London Victoria [15]	a				09 48	09 57					09 59	10 01							10 05	10 07	10 10	10 14	10 23		
Streatham [4]	d		09 33										09 46	09 52				10 03							
Tulse Hill [3]	d	09 31	09 37						09 41				09 51	09 55			10 01	10 07						10 11	
Herne Hill [4]	a		09 41											09 59				10 11							
Loughborough Jn	a		09 45											10 02				10 15							
Elephant & Castle	a		09 49											10 06				10 19							
London Blackfriars [3]	a		09 56											10 10				10 26							
City Thameslink [3]	a		10 00											10 15				10 30							
St Pancras International [15]	a		10 08											10 23				10 38							
Luton Airport Parkway [7]	a		10 57															11 25							
Luton [10]	a		11 02															11 31							
North Dulwich	d	09 34							09 44				09 54				10 04							10 14	
East Dulwich	d	09 36							09 46				09 56				10 06							10 16	
Peckham Rye [4]	d	09 39							09 49	09 56			09 59				10 09							10 19	
Queens Rd Peckham	d	09 41							09 51	09 59			10 02				10 11							10 21	
South Bermondsey	d	09 44							09 54	10 01			10 04				10 14							10 24	
London Bridge [4]	a	09 52					09 42	09 59	09 59	10 06			10 09		10 08	10 15	10 18							10 28	10 12

For general notes see front of timetable
For details of catering facilities see Directory of Train Operators

A From London Bridge (Table 178)
B From Brighton (Table 52)
C From Wimbledon (Table 52)
D Via Sydenham (Table 178)
E From Epsom Downs (Table 182)
G From Caterham (Table 181)
H From Smitham (Table 181)

East and West Croydon → London & Luton via Norbury/Crystal Palace/Tulse Hill

Local Services

Network Diagram - see first page of Table 177

		SN	SN	SN	SN	SN	FC	SN	SN	SN	SN	SN	SN	SN	FC	SN	SN	SE	SN	SN	SN	SN		SN	FC
				A					B			C	D				E	13 G				H			
East Croydon	d	10 00											10 17				10 21	10 24	10 30						
West Croydon 4	d			09 57		10 01		10 15	10 05							10 18						10 27		10 31	
Norwood Junction 2	a	10 04						10 19								10 23	10 27	10 28	10 34						
	d	10 04						10 19								10 23	10 28	10 28	10 34						
Selhurst 4	d			10 01		10 05			10 09				10 20									10 31		10 35	
Thornton Heath	d			10 03		10 07			10 11				10 22									10 33		10 37	
Norbury	d			10 06		10 10			10 14				10 25									10 36		10 40	
Streatham Common 4	d			10 09		10 13			10 17				10 27									10 39		10 43	
Bromley South 4	d													*10 03*											
Beckenham Junction 4	d													10 16											
Birkbeck	d													10 19											
Crystal Palace 4	d										10 14	10 17		10 23		10 27	10 32								
Gipsy Hill	d										10 16			10 25		10 29	10 35								
West Norwood 4	d										10 19			10 28		10 32	10 38								
Streatham Hill	d										10 23					10 36									
Balham 4	⊖ d			10 13	10 18				10 21		10 26		10 31			10 39					10 48	10 43			
Wandsworth Common	d			10 15					10 23		10 28		10 33			10 41						10 45			
Clapham Junction 10	d			10 18	10 22				10 26		10 31		10 37			10 45					10 52	10 48			
Battersea Park 4	d			10 22					10 30	10 32	10 34					10 48						10 52			
London Victoria 15	⊖ a			10 26	10 29				10 34	10 36	10 40		10 44			10 54					10 59	10 56			
Streatham 4	d					10 16	10 19								10 33									10 47	10 49
Tulse Hill 3	d					10 21	10 23							10 31	10 37		10 41							10 51	10 53
Herne Hill 4	a						10 26								10 41										10 56
Loughborough Jn	a						10 30								10 45										11 00
Elephant & Castle	⊖ a						10 34								10 49										11 04
London Blackfriars 3	⊖ a						10 41								10 56										11 11
City Thameslink 3	a						10 45								11 00										11 15
St Pancras International 15	⊖ a						10 53								11 08										11 23
Luton Airport Parkway 7	✈ a														11 55										
Luton 10	a														12 01										
North Dulwich	d					10 24								10 34			10 44							10 54	
East Dulwich	d					10 26								10 36			10 46							10 56	
Peckham Rye 4	d		10 26			10 29								10 39			10 49			10 56				10 59	
Queens Rd Peckham	d		10 29			10 32								10 41			10 51			10 59				11 02	
South Bermondsey	d		10 31			10 34								10 44			10 54			11 01				11 04	
London Bridge 4	⊖ a	10 25	10 36			10 39		10 44				10 36		10 50			10 58	10 40	10 55	11 06				11 09	

		SN	SN	SN	SN	SN	FC	SN	SN	SN	SN	SN	SN	SN	SN	SN	SN	FC	SN	SN	SN	SN	SN	FC	SN
			B		C				D		E	1				A				B		C			
East Croydon	d								10 47		10 51	10 55	11 00												
West Croydon 4	d	10 45	10 35							10 48						10 57	11 01		11 15	11 05					
Norwood Junction 2	a	10 49								10 53	10 57	10 59	11 04						11 19						
	d	10 49								10 53	10 58	10 59	11 04						11 19						
Selhurst 4	d		10 39						10 50							11 01	11 05			11 09					
Thornton Heath	d		10 41						10 52							11 03	11 07			11 11					
Norbury	d		10 44						10 55							11 06	11 10			11 14					
Streatham Common 4	d		10 47						10 57							11 09	11 13			11 17					
Bromley South 4	d					*10 33*																	*11 03*		
Beckenham Junction 4	d					10 46																	11 16		
Birkbeck	d					10 49																	11 19		
Crystal Palace 4	d				10 47	10 53		10 43		10 57	11 02											11 17	11 23		11 13
Gipsy Hill	d					10 55		10 46		10 59	11 05												11 25		11 16
West Norwood 4	d					10 58		10 49		11 02	11 08												11 28		11 19
Streatham Hill	d							10 52		11 06															11 22
Balham 4	⊖ d		10 51					10 55	11 01	11 09					11 18	11 13				11 21					11 25
Wandsworth Common	d		10 53					10 57	11 03	11 11						11 15				11 23					11 27
Clapham Junction 10	d		10 56					11 01	11 07	11 14					11 22	11 18				11 26					11 31
Battersea Park 4	d		11 00	11 02				11 04		11 18						11 22				11 30	11 32				11 34
London Victoria 15	⊖ a		11 04	11 06				11 09	11 14	11 23					11 29	11 26				11 34	11 36				11 39
Streatham 4	d						11 03										11 16	11 19						11 33	
Tulse Hill 3	d					11 01	11 07				11 11						11 21	11 23					11 31	11 37	
Herne Hill 4	a						11 11											11 26						11 41	
Loughborough Jn	a						11 15											11 30						11 45	
Elephant & Castle	⊖ a						11 19											11 34						11 49	
London Blackfriars 3	⊖ a						11 26											11 41						11 56	
City Thameslink 3	a						11 30											11 45						12 00	
St Pancras International 15	⊖ a						11 38											11 53						12 08	
Luton Airport Parkway 7	✈ a						12 25																	12 55	
Luton 10	a						12 31																	13 01	
North Dulwich	d					11 04					11 14						11 24						11 34		
East Dulwich	d					11 06					11 16						11 26						11 36		
Peckham Rye 4	d					11 09					11 19			11 26			11 29						11 39		
Queens Rd Peckham	d					11 11					11 21			11 29			11 32						11 41		
South Bermondsey	d					11 14					11 24			11 31			11 34						11 44		
London Bridge 4	⊖ a	11 14			11 06	11 18					11 28	11 12	11 25	11 36			11 39		11 44			11 36	11 48		

For general notes see front of timetable
For details of catering facilities see Directory of Train Operators

A From Epsom Downs (Table 182)
B From Sutton (Surrey) (Table 182)
C Via Sydenham (Table 178)
D From Caterham (Table 181)
E From Smitham (Table 181)
G From Tonbridge (Table 209)
H From Epsom (Table 182)

East and West Croydon → London & Luton via Norbury/Crystal Palace/Tulse Hill

Local Services

Network Diagram - see first page of Table 177

		SN	SN	SN	SE	SN	SN	SN	SN		SN	FC	SN	SN	SN	SN	SN	SN	SN	SN	FC	SN	SN
		A		B	13 C				D						E			G	A				B
East Croydon	d	11 17		11 21	11 24	11 30													15 47				15 51
West Croydon [4]	d		11 18						11 27		15 31			15 45	15 35							15 48	
Norwood Junction [2]	a		11 23	11 27	11 28	11 34								15 49								15 53	15 57
	d		11 23	11 28	11 28	11 34								15 49								15 53	15 58
Selhurst [4]	d	11 20							11 31		15 35				15 39				15 50				
Thornton Heath	d	11 22							11 33		15 37				15 41				15 52				
Norbury	d	11 25							11 36		15 40				15 44				15 55				
Streatham Common [4]	d	11 27							11 39		15 43				15 47				15 57				
Bromley South [4]	d																			*15 33*			
Beckenham Junction [4]	d																			15 46			
Birkbeck	d									and at										15 49			
Crystal Palace [4]	d		11 27	11 32													15 43	15 47		15 53		15 57	16 02
Gipsy Hill	d		11 29	11 35						the same							15 46			15 55		15 59	16 05
West Norwood [4]	d		11 32	11 38													15 49			15 58		16 02	16 08
Streatham Hill	d		11 36							minutes			15 50				15 52					16 06	
Balham [4]	d	11 31	11 39					11 48	11 43	past					15 52		15 55		16 01			16 09	
Wandsworth Common	d	11 33	11 41						11 45						15 54		15 57		16 03			16 11	
Clapham Junction [10]	d	11 37	11 44					11 52	11 48	each					15 57		16 01		16 07			16 14	
Battersea Park [4]	d		11 48						11 52						16 01	16 03	16 05					16 18	
London Victoria [15]	a	11 44	11 53					11 59	11 56	hour until					16 05	16 07	16 10		16 14			16 23	
Streatham [4]	d										15 46	15 49									16 03		
Tulse Hill [3]	d			11 41							15 51	15 53	15b58							16 01	16 07		16 11
Herne Hill [4]	a											15 56									16 11		
Loughborough Jn	a											16 00									16 15		
Elephant & Castle	a											16 04									16 19		
London Blackfriars [3]	a											16 11									16 29		
City Thameslink [3]	a											16 16									16 32		
St Pancras International [15]	a											16 24									16 39		
Luton Airport Parkway [7]	a																				17 26		
Luton [10]	a																				17 31		
North Dulwich	d			11 44							15 54									16 04			16 14
East Dulwich	d			11 46							15 56									16 06			16 16
Peckham Rye [4]	d			11 49			11 56				15 59		16 03							16 09			16 19
Queens Rd Peckham	d			11 51			11 59				16 02									16 11			16 21
South Bermondsey	d			11 54			12 01				16 04									16 14			16 24
London Bridge [4]	a			11 58	11 40	11 55	12 06				16 10		16 12	16 15				16 08		16 18			16 28

		SN	SN	SN	SN	SN	SN	SN	FC	SN	SN	SN	SN	SN	SN	SN	FC	FC	SN	SN	SE	SN	SN	SN	SN
		[1]				H					E			G	A		[1] J			B	13 C			[1]	
East Croydon	d	15 55	16 00	16 07											16 17		16 17			16 21	16 24	16 31	16 37	16 44	
West Croydon [4]	d					15 57		16 01		16 15	16 05								16 18						
Norwood Junction [2]	a	15 59	16 04	16 11						16 19									16 23	16 27	16 28	16 35	16 41	16 48	
	d	15 59	16 04	16 11						16 19									16 23	16 28	16 28	16 35	16 41	16 48	
Selhurst [4]	d					16 01		16 05			16 09				16 20										
Thornton Heath	d					16 03		16 07			16 11				16 22										
Norbury	d					16 06		16 10			16 14				16 25										
Streatham Common [4]	d					16 09		16 13			16 17				16 27										
Bromley South [4]	d															*16 03*									
Beckenham Junction [4]	d															16 15									
Birkbeck	d															16 18									
Crystal Palace [4]	d												16 13	16 17		16 22			16 27	16 32					
Gipsy Hill	d												16 16			16 24			16 29	16 35					
West Norwood [4]	d												16 19			16 27			16 32	16 38					
Streatham Hill	d												16 22						16 36						
Balham [4]	d					16 13	16 18				16 21		16 25		16 31				16 39						
Wandsworth Common	d					16 15					16 23		16 27		16 33				16 41						
Clapham Junction [10]	d					16 18	16 22				16 26		16 31		16 37				16 44						
Battersea Park [4]	d					16 22					16 30	16 32	16 34						16 48						
London Victoria [15]	a					16 26	16 29				16 34	16 38	16 40		16 44				16 53						
Streatham [4]	d							16 16	16 19									16 33							
Tulse Hill [3]	d							16 21	16 23							16 31	16 33	16 37		16 41					
Herne Hill [4]	a								16 27								16 37	16 42							
Loughborough Jn	a								16 30									16 45							
Elephant & Castle	a								16 35								16 43	16 49							
London Blackfriars [3]	a								16 38								16 48	16 57							
City Thameslink [3]	a								16 46								16 52	17 02							
St Pancras International [15]	a								16 53								17 01	17 09							
Luton Airport Parkway [7]	a																17 34	17 50							
Luton [10]	a																17 36	17 53							
North Dulwich	d							16 24								16 34				16 44					
East Dulwich	d							16 26								16 36				16 46					
Peckham Rye [4]	d				16 26			16 29								16 39				16 49					16 56
Queens Rd Peckham	d				16 29			16 32								16 41				16 51					16 59
South Bermondsey	d				16 31			16 34								16 44				16 54					17 01
London Bridge [4]	a	16 12	16 26	16 24	16 38			16 40		16 44				16 36		16 48				17 00	16 41	16 58	16 56	17 00	17 08

For general notes see front of timetable
For details of catering facilities see Directory of Train Operators

A From Caterham (Table 181)
B From Smitham (Table 181)
C From Tunbridge Wells (Table 209)
D From Epsom (Table 182)
E From Sutton (Surrey) (Table 182)
G Via Sydenham (Table 178)
H From Epsom Downs (Table 182)
J From Brighton (Table 52)
b Arr. 1555

East and West Croydon → London & Luton via Norbury/Crystal Palace/Tulse Hill

Local Services

Network Diagram - see first page of Table 177

		FC	SN	SN	SN	SN	SN	SN	SN	SN	SN	FC	SN	SN	SN	SN	SN	SN	SN	FC	SN		SN	SN	FC
																		1							
			A			B				C			D		E						G				
East Croydon	d												16 47		16 51	17 00	17 07	17 14							
West Croydon 4	d		16 27		16 31	16 35	16 45							16 48							16 57			17 01	
Norwood Junction 2	a						16 49							16 53	16 56	17 04	17 11	17 18							
	d						16 49							16 53	16 56	17 04	17 11	17 18							
Selhurst 4	d		16 31		16 35	16 39							16 50								17 01			17 06	
Thornton Heath	d		16 33		16 37	16 41							16 52								17 03			17 08	
Norbury	d		16 36		16 40	16 44							16 55								17 06			17 11	
Streatham Common 4	d		16 39		16 43	16 47							16 57								17 09			17 14	
Bromley South 4	d										16 19														
Beckenham Junction 4	d										16 41														
Birkbeck	d										16 44														
Crystal Palace 4	d								16 43	16 47	16 48			16 57	17 00										
Gipsy Hill	d								16 46		16 51			16 59	17 02										
West Norwood 4	d								16 49		16 54			17 02	17 05										
Streatham Hill	d								16 52					17 06											
Balham 4	⊖ d		16 43	16 47		16 51			16 55				17 01	17 09							17 13		17 15		
Wandsworth Common	d		16 45			16 53							17 03	17 11							17 15				
Clapham Junction 10	d		16 48	16 51		16 56			17 01				17 07	17 14							17 18		17 21		
Battersea Park 4	d		16 52			17 00		17 02	17 04					17 18							17 22				
London Victoria 15	⊖ a		16 56	16 58		17 04		17 08	17 10				17 14	17 23							17 26		17 28		
Streatham 4	d	16 47			16 50							16 59								17 17				17 19	17 29
Tulse Hill 3	d	16 50			16 53						16 57	17 02			17 09					17 22				17 23	17 32
Herne Hill 4	a	16 54										17 06								17 26					17 36
Loughborough Jn	a											17 09								17 29					17 39
Elephant & Castle	⊖ a	16 59										17 13								17 33					17 44
London Blackfriars 3	⊖ a	17 03										17 17								17 39					17 47
City Thameslink 3	a	17 06										17 20								17 42					17 50
St Pancras International 15	⊖ a	17 13										17 27								17 53					17 57
Luton Airport Parkway 7	✈ a	17 59																		18 33					
Luton 10	a	18 07																		18 37					
North Dulwich	d				16 56						17 00				17 12									17 26	
East Dulwich	d				16 58						17 02				17 14									17 28	
Peckham Rye 4	d				17 01						17 05				17 16				17 26					17 30	
Queens Rd Peckham	d				17 04						17 07				17 19				17 29					17 33	
South Bermondsey	d				17 06						17 10				17 21				17 31					17 35	
London Bridge 4	⊖ a				17 11		17 14			17 10	17 14				17 26	17 27	17 26	17 31	17 38					17 40	

		SN	SN	SN	SN	SN	SN	SN	SN	SN	SN	FC	SN	SN	SN	SN	SN	SN	SN	SN	SN	SN	SN	SN	SN
																1									1
		B				C		D							G						C	D			
East Croydon	d							17 18					17 32	17 37		17 44						17 48			17 53
West Croydon 4	d	17 05	17 17						17 19						17 30			17 47					17 38	17 50	
Norwood Junction 2	a		17 21						17 24				17 36	17 41		17 48		17 52						17 54	17 57
	d		17 21						17 24		17 29		17 36	17 41		17 49		17 52						17 55	17 57
Selhurst 4	d	17 09						17 21							17 36							17 51	17 42		
Thornton Heath	d	17 11						17 23							17 38							17 53	17 44		
Norbury	d	17 14						17 26							17 41							17 56	17 47		
Streatham Common 4	d	17 17						17 28							17 44							17 59	17 50		
Bromley South 4	d						16 47																		
Beckenham Junction 4	d						17 18																		
Birkbeck	d						17 21																		
Crystal Palace 4	d				17 14	17 17	17 25		17 28		17 33									17 43	17 45			17 59	
Gipsy Hill	d				17 16		17 27		17 30		17 35									17 46				18 01	
West Norwood 4	d				17 19		17 30		17 33		17 38									17 49				18 04	
Streatham Hill	d				17 23				17 37											17 52				18 08	
Balham 4	⊖ d	17 21			17 28			17 32	17 40	17 43					17 48					17 56		18 03		18 11	
Wandsworth Common	d	17 23			17 30			17 34	17 42						17 50							18 05		18 13	
Clapham Junction 10	d	17 26			17 33			17 38	17 45	17 48					17 53					18 01		18 08		18 16	
Battersea Park 4	d	17 30		17 32	17 37				17 49										18 02	18 05				18 20	
London Victoria 15	⊖ a	17 34		17 38	17 43			17 48	17 54	17 56					18 00				18 09	18 12		18 15		18 25	
Streatham 4	d											17 46											17 53		
Tulse Hill 3	d						17 33				17 42	17 50											17 57		
Herne Hill 4	a											17 54													
Loughborough Jn	a											17 57													
Elephant & Castle	⊖ a											18 01													
London Blackfriars 3	⊖ a											18 09													
City Thameslink 3	a											18 16													
St Pancras International 15	⊖ a											18 27													
Luton Airport Parkway 7	✈ a																								
Luton 10	a																								
North Dulwich	d						17 36				17 45												18 00		
East Dulwich	d						17 38				17 47												18 02		
Peckham Rye 4	d						17 41				17 49						17 56						18 04		
Queens Rd Peckham	d						17 43				17 52						17 59						18 07		
South Bermondsey	d						17 46				17 54						18 01						18 09		
London Bridge 4	⊖ a		17 45			17 38	17 50				17 59		17 58	17 54		18 06	18 08	18 19			18 10		18 14		18 10

For general notes see front of timetable
For details of catering facilities see Directory of Train Operators

A From Epsom (Table 182)
B From Sutton (Surrey) (Table 182)
C Via Sydenham (Table 178)
D From Caterham (Table 181)
E From Smitham (Table 181)
G From Epsom Downs (Table 182)

East and West Croydon → London & Luton via Norbury/Crystal Palace/Tulse Hill

Local Services

Network Diagram - see first page of Table 177

Station		SN	FC	SN	SN	FC	SN	SN A	SN	SN	FC 1 B	SN	SN	FC	SN	SN	SN	SN C	SN D	SN	SN	SN	SN	SN	SN E
East Croydon	d			18 05							18 17								18 17			18 35			
West Croydon 4	d							18 00		18 08		18 15								18 18					18 30
Norwood Junction 2	a			18 09								18 19								18 23		18 39			
	d			18 09								18 19								18 24		18 39			
Selhurst 4	d							18 04		18 13									18 21						18 36
Thornton Heath	d							18 06		18 15									18 23						18 38
Norbury	d							18 09		18 18									18 26						18 41
Streatham Common 4	d							18 12		18 21									18 29						18 44
Bromley South 4	d				17 47																				
Beckenham Junction 4	d				17 57																		18 24		
Birkbeck	d				18 00																		18 27		
Crystal Palace 4	d				18 06											18 10	18 14	18 21		18 28			18 31		
Gipsy Hill	d				18 08											18 13				18 30			18 33		
West Norwood 4	d				18 11											18 16				18 33			18 36		
Streatham Hill	d															18 19				18 37					
Balham 4	⊖ d							18 16	18 18							18 23			18 33	18 40	18 44				18 49
Wandsworth Common	d							18 18								18 25			18 35	18 42					18 51
Clapham Junction 10	d							18 21	18 24							18 28			18 38	18 45	18 48				18 54
Battersea Park 4	d							18 25							18 32	18 34				18 49					18 58
London Victoria 15	⊖ a							18 30	18 34						18 38	18 40			18 45	18 53	18 55				19 03
Streatham 4	d	18 01	18 06			18 20				18 25			18 32	18 36											
Tulse Hill 3	d	18 05	18 10		18 15	18 24				18 28	18 32		18 36	18 40									18b45		
Herne Hill 4	a		18 13			18 27					18 35			18 44											
Loughborough Jn	a		18 17			18 30					18 40			18 47											
Elephant & Castle	⊖ a		18 21			18 34					18 45			18 51											
London Blackfriars 3	⊖ a		18 29			18 40					18 49			18 59											
City Thameslink 3	a		18 34			18 48					18 54			19 04											
St Pancras International 15	⊖ a		18 41			18 55					19 01			19 11											
Luton Airport Parkway 7	✈ a		19 27											19 58											
Luton 10	a		19 35								19 34			20 03											
North Dulwich	d	18 08			18 18					18 31			18 39										18 48		
East Dulwich	d	18 10			18 20					18 33			18 41										18 50		
Peckham Rye 4	d	18 12			18 23		18 26			18 36			18 43				17 53						18 53	18 56	
Queens Rd Peckham	d	18 15			18 25		18 29			18 38			18 46										18 55	18 59	
South Bermondsey	d	18 17			18 28		18 31			18 41			18 48										18 58	19 01	
London Bridge 4	⊖ a	18 24		18 28	18 32		18 38			18 45		18 44	18 53				18 34	18 42				19 00	19 02	19 08	

Station		SN	SN	SN C	SN	SN	SN D	SN	FC		SN	SN 1	SN	SN	SN	FC	SN	SN	SN A	SN	FC	SN	SN	SN D	SN
East Croydon	d						18 47					18 55					19 10							19 17	
West Croydon 4	d				18 39	18 48					18 50								19 01	19 10					19 19
Norwood Junction 2	a					18 52					18 55	18 59					19 14								19 23
	d					18 52					18 55	18 59		19 06			19 14								19 23
Selhurst 4	d				18 43		18 50												19 06	19 14				19 20	
Thornton Heath	d				18 45		18 52												19 08	19 16				19 22	
Norbury	d				18 48		18 55												19 11	19 19				19 25	
Streatham Common 4	d				18 50		18 58												19 13	19 21				19 27	
Bromley South 4	d														18 47										
Beckenham Junction 4	d														19 01										
Birkbeck	d														19 04										
Crystal Palace 4	d		18 43	18 47							18 59				19 09								19 13		19 27
Gipsy Hill	d		18 45								19 01				19 11								19 16		19 30
West Norwood 4	d		18 48								19 04				19 14								19 19		19 33
Streatham Hill	d		18 52								19 08												19 22		19 36
Balham 4	⊖ d		18 55				19 02				19 11		19 15						19 19				19 25	19 31	19 39
Wandsworth Common	d		18 57				19 04				19 13								19 21				19 27	19 33	19 41
Clapham Junction 10	d		19 00				19 07				19 16		19 19						19 25				19 31	19 37	19 45
Battersea Park 4	d	19 02	19 04								19 20								19 28			19 32	19 34	19 40	19 48
London Victoria 15	⊖ a	19 08	19 11				19 14				19 24		19 27						19 34			19 36	19 41	19 45	19 53
Streatham 4	d				18 53			18 59	19 05							19 17				19 24	19 33				
Tulse Hill 3	d				18 57			19 05	19 08						19 17	19 23				19 28	19 37				
Herne Hill 4	a								19 11							19 27					19 40				
Loughborough Jn	a								19 15							19 30					19 45				
Elephant & Castle	⊖ a								19 19							19 34					19 49				
London Blackfriars 3	⊖ a								19 26							19 41					19 56				
City Thameslink 3	a								19 30							19 45					20 00				
St Pancras International 15	⊖ a								19 38							19 53					20 08				
Luton Airport Parkway 7	✈ a								20 25							20 41					20 55				
Luton 10	a								20 31							20 44					21 01				
North Dulwich	d				19 00			19 08							19 20					19 31					
East Dulwich	d				19 02			19 10							19 22					19 33					
Peckham Rye 4	d				19 04			19 13							19 25			19 27		19 35					
Queens Rd Peckham	d				19 07			19 15										19 30		19 38					
South Bermondsey	d				19 09			19 18										19 32		19 40					
London Bridge 4	⊖ a			19 08	19 14	19 18		19 22				19 12		19 27	19 31		19 39	19 37		19 45					

For general notes see front of timetable
For details of catering facilities see Directory of Train Operators

A From Epsom Downs (Table 182)
B From Brighton (Table 52)
C Via Sydenham (Table 178)
D From Tattenham Corner (Table 181)
E From Guildford (Table 182)
b Arr. 1841

East and West Croydon → London & Luton via Norbury/Crystal Palace/Tulse Hill

Local Services

Network Diagram - see first page of Table 177

		SN	SN	SN A	SN	SN	SN	SN B	SN	FC	SN	SN	SN C	SN	SN	SN A	SN	SN	SN	SN	SN B	SN	FC	SN	SN
East Croydon	d					19 40							19 47						20 10						
West Croydon 4	d	19 22						19 31	19 36					19 47	19 49						20 01	20 06			
Norwood Junction 2	a	19 27				19 44								19 52	19 54				20 14						
	d	19 27				19 44								19 52	19 54				20 14						
Selhurst 4	d							19 36	19 40				19 50								20 05	20 10			
Thornton Heath	d							19 38	19 42				19 52								20 07	20 12			
Norbury	d							19 41	19 45				19 55								20 10	20 15			
Streatham Common 4	d							19 44	19 48				19 57								20 12	20 18			
Bromley South 4	d																19 33								
Beckenham Junction 4	d				19 25												19 54								
Birkbeck	d				19 28												19 57								
Crystal Palace 4	d			19 32	19 32							19 43		19 56		20 01	20 01								20 13
Gipsy Hill	d				19 34							19 46		19 58			20 03								20 16
West Norwood 4	d				19 37							19 49		20 01			20 06								20 19
Streatham Hill	d											19 52		20 05											20 22
Balham 4 ⊖	d		19 46					19 51				19 55	20 01	20 09				20 17			20 20				20 25
Wandsworth Common	d							19 53				19 57	20 03	20 11							20 22				20 27
Clapham Junction 10	d		19 50					19 56				20 01	20 07	20 14				20 21			20 25				20 31
Battersea Park 4	d							20 00			20 02	20 04		20 18							20 29			20 32	20 34
London Victoria 15 ⊖	a		19 57					20 04			20 06	20 09	20 14	20 25				20 28			20 33			20 36	20 40
Streatham 4	d								19 53	20 04												20 23	20 33		
Tulse Hill 3	d				19 40				19 56	20 07							20 10					20 26	20 37		
Herne Hill 4	a									20 11													20 40		
Loughborough Jn	a									20 15													20 45		
Elephant & Castle ⊖	a									20 19													20 49		
London Blackfriars 3 ⊖	a									20 26													20 56		
City Thameslink 3	a									20 30													21 00		
St Pancras International 15 ⊖	a									20 38													21 08		
Luton Airport Parkway 7 ✈	a									21 25													21 55		
Luton 10	a									21 31													21 59		
North Dulwich	d				19 43				19 59								20 13					20 29			
East Dulwich	d				19 45				20 01								20 15					20 31			
Peckham Rye 4	d				19 48		19 56		20 04								20 17			20 26		20 34			
Queens Rd Peckham	d				19 50		19 59		20 06								20 20			20 29		20 36			
South Bermondsey	d				19 53		20 01		20 09								20 22			20 31		20 39			
London Bridge 4 ⊖	a	19 49		19 52	19 57	20 11	20 06		20 14						20 19	20 22	20 27		20 41	20 36		20 44			

		SN C	SN D	SN	SN A	SN	SN	SN	SN	SN B	SN	FC	SN	SN	SN C	SN E	SN	SN A	SN		SN	SN B	SN	FC	SN
East Croydon	d	20 17					20 30	20 40							20 47				21 10						
West Croydon 4	d		20 18							20 31	20 36					20 48						21 01	21 06		
Norwood Junction 2	a		20 23				20 34	20 44								20 53			21 14						
	d		20 23				20 34	20 44								20 53			21 14						
Selhurst 4	d	20 20								20 36	20 40				20 50							21 06	21 10		
Thornton Heath	d	20 22								20 38	20 42				20 52							21 08	21 12		
Norbury	d	20 25								20 41	20 45				20 55							21 11	21 15		
Streatham Common 4	d	20 27								20 44	20 47				20 57							21 14	21 18		
Bromley South 4	d					20 03																			
Beckenham Junction 4	d					20 24																			
Birkbeck	d					20 27																			
Crystal Palace 4	d		20 27		20 31	20 31								20 43		20 57		21 01							
Gipsy Hill	d		20 29			20 33								20 46		20 59									
West Norwood 4	d		20 32			20 36								20 49		21 02									
Streatham Hill	d		20 36											20 52		21 06									
Balham 4 ⊖	d	20 31	20 39	20 44						20 48				20 55	21 01	21 09	21 14					21 18			
Wandsworth Common	d	20 33	20 41							20 50				20 57	21 03	21 11						21 20			
Clapham Junction 10	d	20 37	20 44	20 48						20 53				21 01	21 07	21 14	21 18					21 23			
Battersea Park 4	d	20 41	20 48							20 57			21 02	21 04		21 18						21 27			21 32
London Victoria 15 ⊖	a	20 45	20 52	20 55						21 03			21 06	21 09	21 14	21 23	21 25					21 33			21 36
Streatham 4	d										20 53	21 03											21 21	21 49	
Tulse Hill 3	d					20 40					20 56	21 07											21 25	21 53	
Herne Hill 4	a											21 10												21 56	
Loughborough Jn	a											21 15												22 00	
Elephant & Castle ⊖	a											21 18												22 04	
London Blackfriars 3 ⊖	a											21 26												22 08	
City Thameslink 3	a											21 35												22 10	
St Pancras International 15 ⊖	a											21 43												22 18	
Luton Airport Parkway 7 ✈	a											22 25												23 01	
Luton 10	a											22 29												23 05	
North Dulwich	d					20 43					20 59												21 28		
East Dulwich	d					20 45					21 01												21 30		
Peckham Rye 4	d					20 47			20 56		21 04										21 26		21 32		
Queens Rd Peckham	d					20 50			20 59		21 06										21 29		21 35		
South Bermondsey	d					20 52			21 01		21 09										21 31		21 37		
London Bridge 4 ⊖	a				20 53	20 57	20 59	21 11	21 06		21 14							21 22	21 41		21 36		21 44		

For general notes see front of timetable
For details of catering facilities see Directory of Train Operators

A Via Sydenham (Table 178)
B From Epsom Downs (Table 182)
C From Tattenham Corner (Table 181)
D From Epsom (Table 182)
E From Sutton (Surrey) (Table 182)

East and West Croydon → London & Luton via Norbury/Crystal Palace/Tulse Hill

Local Services

Network Diagram - see first page of Table 177

		SN	SN A	SN B	SN	SN C	SN	SN	SN D	SN	FC	SN	SN	SN A	SN B	SN	SN C	SN	SN	SN E	SN	SN	SN	SN A	SN B
East Croydon	d		21 17				21 40							21 47				22 10						22 17	
West Croydon 4	d			21 18					21 32	21 36					21 48					22 01	22 06				22 18
Norwood Junction 2	a			21 23			21 44								21 53			22 14							22 23
	d			21 23			21 44								21 53			22 14							22 23
Selhurst 4	d		21 20						21 36	21 40				21 50						22 06	22 10			22 20	
Thornton Heath	d		21 22						21 38	21 42				21 52						22 08	22 12			22 22	
Norbury	d		21 25						21 41	21 45				21 55						22 11	22 15			22 25	
Streatham Common 4	d		21 27						21 44	21 48				21 57						22 14	22 18			22 27	
Bromley South 4	d																								
Beckenham Junction 4	d																								
Birkbeck	d																								
Crystal Palace 4	d	21 13		21 27		21 31							21 43		21 57		22 01						22 13		22 27
Gipsy Hill	d	21 16		21 29									21 46		21 59								22 16		22 29
West Norwood 4	d	21 19		21 32									21 49		22 02								22 19		22 32
Streatham Hill	d	21 22		21 36									21 52		22 06								22 22		22 36
Balham 4	⊖ d	21 25	21 31	21 39	21 44				21 48				21 55	22 01	22 09	22 14				22 18			22 25	22 31	22 39
Wandsworth Common	d	21 27	21 33	21 41					21 50				21 57	22 03	22 11					22 20			22 27	22 33	22 41
Clapham Junction 10	d	21 31	21 37	21 44	21 48				21 53				22 01	22 07	22 14	22 18				22 23			22 31	22 37	22 44
Battersea Park 4	d	21 34	21 40	21 48					21 57			22 02	22 04		22 18					22 27		22 32	22 34	22 40	22 48
London Victoria 15	⊖ a	21 39	21 45	21 53	21 55				22 03			22 06	22 09	22 14	22 25	22 27				22 33		22 36	22 39	22 48	22 53
Streatham 4	d									21 51	22 19										22 21				
Tulse Hill 3	d									21 55	22 23										22 25				
Herne Hill 4	a										22 26														
Loughborough Jn	a										22 30														
Elephant & Castle	⊖ a										22 34														
London Blackfriars 3	⊖ a										22 38														
City Thameslink 3	a										22 40														
St Pancras International 15	⊖ a										22 48														
Luton Airport Parkway 7	✈ a										23 31														
Luton 10	a										23 35														
North Dulwich	d									21 58											22 28				
East Dulwich	d									22 00											22 30				
Peckham Rye 4	d							21 56		22 02									22 26		22 32				
Queens Rd Peckham	d							21 59		22 05									22 29		22 35				
South Bermondsey	d							22 01		22 07									22 31		22 37				
London Bridge 4	⊖ a					21 52	22 11	22 06		22 14							22 22	22 41	22 36		22 44				

		SN	SN C	SN	SN	SN D	SN	SN	SN	SN A	SN B	SN	SN C	SN	SN	SN E	SN	SN	SN	SN A	SN B	SN C	SN
East Croydon	d			22 40						22 47				23 10						23 17			
West Croydon 4	d					22 32	22 36				22 48					23 01	23 06				23 18		
Norwood Junction 2	a			22 44							22 53			23 14							23 23		
	d			22 44							22 53			23 14							23 23		
Selhurst 4	d					22 36	22 40			22 50						23 06	23 10			23 20			
Thornton Heath	d					22 38	22 42			22 52						23 08	23 12			23 22			
Norbury	d					22 41	22 45			22 55						23 11	23 15			23 25			
Streatham Common 4	d					22 44	22 48			22 57						23 14	23 18			23 27			
Bromley South 4	d																						
Beckenham Junction 4	d																						
Birkbeck	d																						
Crystal Palace 4	d		22 31						22 43		22 57		23 01						23 13		23 27	23 31	23 43
Gipsy Hill	d								22 46		22 59								23 16		23 29		23 46
West Norwood 4	d								22 49		23 02								23 19		23 32		23 49
Streatham Hill	d								22 52		23 06								23 22		23 36		23 52
Balham 4	⊖ d	22 44				22 48			22 55	23 01	23 09	23 14				23 18			23 25	23 31	23 40		23 55
Wandsworth Common	d					22 50			22 57	23 03	23 11					23 20			23 27	23 33	23 42		23 57
Clapham Junction 10	d	22 48				22 53			23 01	23 07	23 15	23 18				23 23			23 31	23 37	23 45		00 01
Battersea Park 4	d					22 57		23 02	23 04		23 18					23 27		23 32	23 34	23 40	23 49		00 04
London Victoria 15	⊖ a	22 55				23 03		23 06	23 09	23 14	23 23	23 25				23 31		23 37	23 40	23 45	23 54		00 12
Streatham 4	d						22 51										23 21						
Tulse Hill 3	d						22 55										23 25						
Herne Hill 4	a																						
Loughborough Jn	a																						
Elephant & Castle	⊖ a																						
London Blackfriars 3	⊖ a																						
City Thameslink 3	a																						
St Pancras International 15	⊖ a																						
Luton Airport Parkway 7	✈ a																						
Luton 10	a																						
North Dulwich	d						22 58										23 28						
East Dulwich	d						23 00										23 30						
Peckham Rye 4	d				22 56		23 02								23 26		23 32						
Queens Rd Peckham	d				22 59		23 05								23 29		23 35						
South Bermondsey	d				23 01		23 07								23 31		23 37						
London Bridge 4	⊖ a		22 52	23 11	23 06		23 14						23 22	23 38	23 36		23 44					23 52	

For general notes see front of timetable
For details of catering facilities see Directory of Train Operators

A From Tattenham Corner (Table 181)
B From Sutton (Surrey) (Table 182)
C Via Sydenham (Table 178)
D From Epsom (Table 182)
E From Epsom Downs (Table 182)

East and West Croydon → London & Luton via Norbury/Crystal Palace/Tulse Hill

Local Services

Network Diagram - see first page of Table 177

		SN	SN	FC	SN 1	SN	SN	FC	SN	FC A	SN	SN	SN	SN	SN	SN	FC	SN	SN B	SN	SN 1	SN	SN	SN C	SN
East Croydon	d				05 29							06 30				06 43			06 47		06 55	07 00			
West Croydon 4	d										06 18									06 48				06 57	
Norwood Junction 2	a										06 23	06 34				06 48				06 53	06 59	07 04			
	d					05 54					06 23	06 34	06 42	06 46		06 49				06 53	06 59	07 04			
Selhurst 4	d			05 39			06 01	06 09		06 39									06 50					07 01	
Thornton Heath	d			05 41			06 03	06 11		06 41									06 52					07 03	
Norbury	d			05 43			06 06	06 13		06 43									06 55					07 06	
Streatham Common 4	d			05 46			06 08	06 16		06 46									06 57					07 09	
Bromley South 4	d																								
Beckenham Junction 4	d																								
Birkbeck	d																								
Crystal Palace 4	d	23p43				05 58					06 27		06 46							06 57					
Gipsy Hill	d	23p46				06 00					06 29		06 48							06 59					
West Norwood 4	d	23p49				06 03					06 32		06 51							07 02					
Streatham Hill	d	23p52				06 07					06 36									07 06					
Balham 4 ⊖	d	23p55			05 45	06 10	06 12				06 39								07 01	07 09				07 13	07 18
Wandsworth Common	d	23p57				06 12	06 14				06 41								07 03	07 11				07 15	
Clapham Junction 10	d	00 01	05 00		05 49	06 15	06 18				06 44								07 07	07 14				07 18	07 22
Battersea Park 4	d	00 04				06 19	06 21		06 32		06 48							07 02		07 18				07 22	
London Victoria 15 ⊖	a	00 12	05 08		05 58	06 23	06 26		06 36		06 53							07 06	07 14	07 23				07 26	07 29
Streatham 4	d			05 49				06 19		06 49							07 03								
Tulse Hill 3	d			05b58				06 23		06 53			06 54				07 07								
Herne Hill 4	a			06 01				06 26		06 56							07 11								
Loughborough Jn	a							06 30		07 00							07 15								
Elephant & Castle ⊖	a			06 07				06 34		07 04							07 19								
London Blackfriars 3 ⊖	a			06 11				06 41		07 11							07 26								
City Thameslink 3	a																								
St Pancras International 15 ⊖	a			06 22				06 52		07 22							07 38								
Luton Airport Parkway 7 ✈	a			07 06				07 36		08 08							08 25								
Luton 10	a			07 12				07 42		08 11							08 31								
North Dulwich	d												06 57												
East Dulwich	d												06 59												
Peckham Rye 4	d												07 02		06 56								07 26		
Queens Rd Peckham	d												07 04		06 59								07 29		
South Bermondsey	d												07 07		07 01								07 31		
London Bridge 4 ⊖	a											06 55	07 11	07 00	07 06	07 14					07 12	07 25	07 36		

		SN	FC	SN	SN	FC	SN	SN B	SN	SE 13	SN	SN	SN D	SN	SN	FC	SN	FC	SN	SN	SN	SN E	SN	SN 1	SN
East Croydon	d			07 05				07 17		07 24	07 30											07 47		07 55	08 00
West Croydon 4	d	07 01			07 15				07 18				07 27		07 31		07 45						07 48		
Norwood Junction 2	a			07 09	07 19				07 23	07 28	07 34						07 49						07 53	07 59	08 04
	d			07 10	07 19				07 23	07 28	07 34						07 49						07 53	07 59	08 04
Selhurst 4	d	07 05						07 20					07 31		07 35				07 39			07 50			
Thornton Heath	d	07 07						07 22					07 33		07 37				07 41			07 52			
Norbury	d	07 10						07 25					07 36		07 40				07 44			07 55			
Streatham Common 4	d	07 13						07 27					07 39		07 43				07 47			07 57			
Bromley South 4	d																								
Beckenham Junction 4	d																								
Birkbeck	d																								
Crystal Palace 4	d								07 27												07 43		07 57		
Gipsy Hill	d								07 29												07 45		07 59		
West Norwood 4	d								07 32												07 48		08 02		
Streatham Hill	d								07 36												07 52		08 06		
Balham 4 ⊖	d							07 31	07 39				07 43	07 48					07 51		07 55	08 01	08 09		
Wandsworth Common	d							07 33	07 41				07 45						07 53		07 57	08 03	08 11		
Clapham Junction 10	d							07 37	07 44				07 48	07 52					07 56		08 00	08 07	08 14		
Battersea Park 4	d						07 32		07 48				07 52						08 00	08 02	08 04		08 18		
London Victoria 15 ⊖	a						07 36	07 44	07 53				07 56	07 59					08 04	08 06	08 09	08 14	08 23		
Streatham 4	d	07 16	07 19			07 33									07 46	07 49		08 03							
Tulse Hill 3	d	07 21	07 23			07 37									07 51	07 53		08 07							
Herne Hill 4	a		07 26			07 41										07 56		08 11							
Loughborough Jn	a		07 30			07 45										08 00		08 15							
Elephant & Castle ⊖	a		07 34			07 49										08 04		08 19							
London Blackfriars 3 ⊖	a		07 41			07 56										08 11		08 26							
City Thameslink 3	a																								
St Pancras International 15 ⊖	a		07 53			08 08										08 23		08 38							
Luton Airport Parkway 7 ✈	a					08 55												09 25							
Luton 10	a					09 01												09 31							
North Dulwich	d	07 24													07 54										
East Dulwich	d	07 26													07 56										
Peckham Rye 4	d	07 29										07 56			07 59										
Queens Rd Peckham	d	07 32										07 59			08 02										
South Bermondsey	d	07 34										08 01			08 04										
London Bridge 4 ⊖	a	07 39		07 23	07 44					07 40	07 55	08 06			08 09		08 14							08 12	08 25

For general notes see front of timetable
For details of catering facilities see Directory of Train Operators

A To Bedford (Table 52)
B From Tattenham Corner (Table 181)
C From Sutton (Surrey) (Table 182)
D From Epsom (Table 182)
E From Caterham (Table 181)
b Arr. 0553

Table 177

East and West Croydon → London & Luton via Norbury/Crystal Palace/Tulse Hill

Local Services

Network Diagram - see first page of Table 177

Station		SN	SN	SN	SN	FC	SN	SN	SN	SN	SN	SN		SN	FC	SN	SN	SE	SN	SN	SN	SN	SN	FC	SN
			A						B			C					D	13 E				G			
East Croydon	d								08 17								08 21	08 24	08 30						
West Croydon [4]	d		07 57		08 01		08 15									08 18						08 27	08 31		08 45
Norwood Junction [2]	a						08 19									08 23	08 27	08 28	08 34						08 49
	d						08 19									08 23	08 28	08 28	08 34						08 49
Selhurst [4]	d		08 01		08 05			08 09	08 20													08 31	08 35		
Thornton Heath	d		08 03		08 07			08 11	08 22													08 33	08 37		
Norbury	d		08 06		08 10			08 14	08 25													08 36	08 40		
Streatham Common [4]	d		08 09		08 13			08 17	08 27													08 39	08 43		
Bromley South [4]	d													*07 48*											
Beckenham Junction [4]	d													08 16											
Birkbeck	d													08 19											
Crystal Palace [4]	d										08 15	08 17		08 23		08 27	08 32								
Gipsy Hill	d										08 17			08 25		08 29	08 35								
West Norwood [4]	d										08 20			08 28		08 32	08 38								
Streatham Hill	d										08 24					08 36									
Balham [4] ⊖	d		08 13	08 18				08 21	08 31		08 27					08 39					08 48	08 43			
Wandsworth Common	d		08 15					08 23	08 33		08 29					08 41						08 45			
Clapham Junction [10]	d		08 18	08 22				08 26	08 37		08 32					08 44					08 52	08 48			
Battersea Park [4]	d		08 22					08 30		08 32	08 36					08 48						08 52			
London Victoria [15] ⊖	a		08 26	08 29				08 34	08 44	08 36	08 40					08 53					08 59	08 56			
Streatham [4]	d				08 16	08 19									08 33								08 46	08 49	
Tulse Hill [3]	d				08 21	08 23								08 31	08 37		08 41						08 51	08 53	
Herne Hill [4]	a					08 26									08 41									08 56	
Loughborough Jn	a					08 30									08 45									09 00	
Elephant & Castle ⊖	a					08 34									08 49									09 04	
London Blackfriars [3] ⊖	a					08 41									08 56									09 11	
City Thameslink [3]	a														09 00									09 15	
St Pancras International [15] ⊖	a					08 53									09 08									09 23	
Luton Airport Parkway [7]	a														09 55										
Luton [10]	a														10 01										
North Dulwich	d				08 24									08 34			08 44						08 54		
East Dulwich	d				08 26									08 36			08 46						08 56		
Peckham Rye [4]	d	08 26			08 29									08 39			08 49			08 56			08 59		
Queens Rd Peckham	d	08 29			08 32									08 41			08 51			08 59			09 02		
South Bermondsey	d	08 31			08 34									08 44			08 54			09 01			09 04		
London Bridge [4] ⊖	a	08 36			08 39		08 44					08 36		08 48			08 58	08 40	08 55	09 06			09 09		09 14

Station		SN	SN	SN	SN	SN	SN	FC	SN	SN	SN	SN	SN	SN	SN	SN	FC	SN	SN	SN	SN	SN	SN	SN	FC
		H	B			C				D	[1]				A				H	B			C		
East Croydon	d		08 47							08 51	08 55	09 00								09 17					
West Croydon [4]	d	08 35							08 48						08 57	09 01		09 15	09 05						
Norwood Junction [2]	a								08 53	08 57	08 59	09 04						09 19							
	d								08 53	08 58	08 59	09 04						09 19							
Selhurst [4]	d	08 39	08 50												09 01	09 05			09 09	09 20					
Thornton Heath	d	08 41	08 52												09 03	09 07			09 11	09 22					
Norbury	d	08 44	08 55												09 06	09 10			09 14	09 25					
Streatham Common [4]	d	08 47	08 57												09 09	09 13			09 17	09 27					
Bromley South [4]	d						*08 33*																	*09 03*	
Beckenham Junction [4]	d						08 46																	09 16	
Birkbeck	d						08 49																	09 19	
Crystal Palace [4]	d				08 43	08 47	08 53		08 57	09 02												09 13	09 17	09 23	
Gipsy Hill	d				08 46		08 55		08 59	09 05												09 16		09 25	
West Norwood [4]	d				08 49		08 58		09 02	09 08												09 19		09 28	
Streatham Hill	d				08 52				09 06													09 22			
Balham [4] ⊖	d	08 51	09 01		08 55				09 09					09 18	09 13				09 21	09 31		09 25			
Wandsworth Common	d	08 53	09 03		08 57				09 11						09 15				09 23	09 33		09 27			
Clapham Junction [10]	d	08 56	09 07		09 01				09 14					09 22	09 18				09 26	09 37		09 31			
Battersea Park [4]	d	09 00		09 02	09 04				09 18						09 22				09 30		09 32	09 34			
London Victoria [15] ⊖	a	09 04	09 14	09 06	09 09				09 23					09 29	09 26				09 34	09 44	09 36	09 39			
Streatham [4]	d							09 03								09 16	09 19								09 33
Tulse Hill [3]	d						09 01	09 07		09 11						09 21	09 23							09 31	09 37
Herne Hill [4]	a							09 11									09 26								09 41
Loughborough Jn	a							09 15									09 30								09 45
Elephant & Castle ⊖	a							09 19									09 34								09 50
London Blackfriars [3] ⊖	a							09 26									09 41								09 56
City Thameslink [3]	a							09 30									09 45								10 00
St Pancras International [15] ⊖	a							09 38									09 53								10 08
Luton Airport Parkway [7]	a							10 25																	10 55
Luton [10]	a							10 31																	11 01
North Dulwich	d						09 04			09 14						09 24								09 34	
East Dulwich	d						09 06			09 16						09 26								09 36	
Peckham Rye [4]	d						09 09			09 19			09 26			09 29								09 39	
Queens Rd Peckham	d						09 11			09 21			09 29			09 32								09 41	
South Bermondsey	d						09 14			09 24			09 31			09 34								09 44	
London Bridge [4] ⊖	a					09 06	09 18			09 28	09 12	09 25	09 36			09 39		09 44					09 36	09 48	

For general notes see front of timetable
For details of catering facilities see Directory of Train Operators

- **A** From Epsom Downs (Table 182)
- **B** From Caterham (Table 181)
- **C** Via Sydenham (Table 178)
- **D** From Smitham (Table 181)
- **E** From Tonbridge (Table 209)
- **G** From Epsom (Table 182)
- **H** From Sutton (Surrey) (Table 182)

Table 177

Saturdays

East and West Croydon → London & Luton via Norbury/Crystal Palace/Tulse Hill

Local Services

Network Diagram - see first page of Table 177

	SN	SN A	SE 13 B	SN	SN	SN	SN C	SN	FC	SN	SN D	SN E	SN	SN	SN G	SN	FC	SN		SN A	SN 1	SN	SN	SN H
East Croydon d		09 21	09 24	09 30								09 47								09 51	09 55	10 00		
West Croydon 4 d	09 18						09 27	09 31		09 45	09 35							09 48						09 57
Norwood Junction 2 a	09 23	09 27	09 28	09 34						09 49								09 53		09 57	09 59	10 04		
Norwood Junction d	09 23	09 28	09 28	09 34						09 49								09 53		09 58	09 59	10 04		
Selhurst 4 d							09 31	09 35			09 39	09 50												10 01
Thornton Heath d							09 33	09 37			09 41	09 52												10 03
Norbury d							09 36	09 40			09 44	09 55												10 06
Streatham Common 4 d							09 39	09 43			09 47	09 57												10 09
Bromley South 4 d																*09 33*								
Beckenham Junction 4 d																09 46								
Birkbeck d																09 49								
Crystal Palace 4 d	09 27	09 32												09 43	09 47	09 53		09 57		10 02				
Gipsy Hill d	09 29	09 35												09 46		09 55		09 59		10 05				
West Norwood 4 d	09 32	09 38												09 49		09 58		10 02		10 08				
Streatham Hill d	09 36													09 52				10 06						
Balham 4 ⊖ d	09 39					09 48	09 43				09 51	10 01		09 55				10 09						10 13
Wandsworth Common d	09 41						09 45				09 53	10 03		09 57				10 11						10 15
Clapham Junction 10 d	09 44					09 52	09 48				09 56	10 07		10 01				10 14						10 18
Battersea Park 4 d	09 48						09 52				10 00		10 02	10 04				10 18						10 22
London Victoria 15 ⊖ a	09 53					09 59	09 56				10 04	10 14	10 06	10 09				10 23						10 26
Streatham 4 d								09 46	09 49								10 03							
Tulse Hill 3 d		09 41						09 51	09 53							10 01	10 07			10 11				
Herne Hill 4 a									09 56								10 11							
Loughborough Jn a									10 00								10 15							
Elephant & Castle ⊖ a									10 04								10 19							
London Blackfriars 3 ⊖ a									10 11								10 26							
City Thameslink 3 a									10 15								10 30							
St Pancras International 15 ⊖ a									10 23								10 38							
Luton Airport Parkway 7 ✈ a																	11 25							
Luton 10 a																	11 31							
North Dulwich d		09 44						09 54								10 04				10 14				
East Dulwich d		09 46						09 56								10 06				10 16				
Peckham Rye 4 d		09 49			09 56			09 59								10 09				10 19			10 26	
Queens Rd Peckham d		09 51			09 59			10 02								10 11				10 21			10 29	
South Bermondsey d		09 54			10 01			10 04								10 14				10 24			10 31	
London Bridge 4 ⊖ a		09 58	09 40	09 55	10 06			10 09		10 14					10 06	10 18				10 28	10 12	10 25	10 36	

	SN	SN	FC	SN	SN D	SN	SN	SN G	SN	FC	SN E	SN	SN A	SE 13 J	SN	SN	SN C	SN	SN	FC	SN	SN D	SN E	SN
East Croydon d											10 17		10 21	10 24	10 30								10 47	
West Croydon 4 d		10 01		10 15	10 05							10 18					10 27		10 31		10 45	10 35		
Norwood Junction 2 a				10 19								10 23	10 27	10 28	10 34						10 49			
Norwood Junction d				10 19								10 23	10 28	10 28	10 34						10 49			
Selhurst 4 d		10 05			10 09						10 20						10 31		10 35			10 39	10 50	
Thornton Heath d		10 07			10 11						10 22						10 33		10 37			10 41	10 52	
Norbury d		10 10			10 14						10 25						10 36		10 40			10 44	10 55	
Streatham Common 4 d		10 13			10 17						10 27						10 39		10 43			10 47	10 57	
Bromley South 4 d									*10 03*															
Beckenham Junction 4 d									10 16															
Birkbeck d									10 19															
Crystal Palace 4 d							10 13	10 17	10 23			10 27	10 32											
Gipsy Hill d							10 16		10 25			10 29	10 35											
West Norwood 4 d							10 19		10 28			10 32	10 38											
Streatham Hill d							10 22					10 36												
Balham 4 ⊖ d	10 18				10 21		10 25				10 31	10 39					10 43	10 48				10 51	11 01	
Wandsworth Common d					10 23		10 27				10 33	10 41					10 45					10 53	11 03	
Clapham Junction 10 d	10 22				10 26		10 31				10 37	10 44					10 48	10 52				10 56	11 07	
Battersea Park 4 d					10 30	10 32	10 34					10 48					10 52					11 00		11 02
London Victoria 15 ⊖ a	10 29				10 34	10 36	10 39				10 44	10 53					10 56	10 59				11 04	11 14	11 06
Streatham 4 d		10 16	10 19							10 33									10 46	10 49				
Tulse Hill 3 d		10 21	10 23						10 31	10 37			10 41						10 51	10 53				
Herne Hill 4 a			10 26							10 41										10 56				
Loughborough Jn a			10 30							10 45										11 00				
Elephant & Castle ⊖ a			10 34							10 49										11 04				
London Blackfriars 3 ⊖ a			10 41							10 56										11 11				
City Thameslink 3 a			10 45							11 00										11 15				
St Pancras International 15 ⊖ a			10 53							11 08										11 23				
Luton Airport Parkway 7 ✈ a										11 55														
Luton 10 a										12 01														
North Dulwich d		10 24							10 34				10 44						10 54					
East Dulwich d		10 26							10 36				10 46						10 56					
Peckham Rye 4 d		10 29							10 39				10 49			10 56			10 59					
Queens Rd Peckham d		10 32							10 41				10 51			10 59			11 02					
South Bermondsey d		10 34							10 44				10 54			11 01			11 04					
London Bridge 4 ⊖ a		10 39		10 44				10 36	10 48				10 58	10 40	10 55	11 06			11 09		11 14			

For general notes see front of timetable
For details of catering facilities see Directory of Train Operators

- **A** From Smitham (Table 181)
- **B** From Tonbridge (Table 209)
- **C** From Epsom (Table 182)
- **D** From Sutton (Surrey) (Table 182)
- **E** From Caterham (Table 181)
- **G** Via Sydenham (Table 178)
- **H** From Epsom Downs (Table 182)
- **J** From Tunbridge Wells (Table 209)

East and West Croydon → London & Luton via Norbury/Crystal Palace/Tulse Hill

Local Services

Network Diagram - see first page of Table 177

		SN	SN	SN	FC	SN		SN	SN	SN	SN	SN	SN	SN	FC	SN	SN	SN	SN	SN	SN	SN	FC
									1														
			A					B					C				D	E			A		
East Croydon	d							16 51	16 55	17 00								17 17					
West Croydon 4	d					10 48							16 57	17 01		17 15	17 05						
Norwood Junction 2	a					10 53		16 57	16 59	17 04						17 19							
	d					10 53		16 58	16 59	17 04						17 19							
Selhurst 4	d												17 01	17 05			17 09	17 20					
Thornton Heath	d												17 03	17 07			17 11	17 22					
Norbury	d												17 06	17 10			17 14	17 25					
Streatham Common 4	d												17 09	17 13			17 17	17 27					
Bromley South 4	d			*10 33*																		*17 03*	
Beckenham Junction 4	d			10 46																		17 16	
Birkbeck	d			10 49			and at															17 19	
Crystal Palace 4	d	10 43	10 47	10 53		10 57		17 02												17 13	17 17	17 23	
Gipsy Hill	d	10 46		10 55		10 59	the same	17 05												17 16		17 25	
West Norwood 4	d	10 49		10 58		11 02		17 08												17 19		17 28	
Streatham Hill	d	10 52				11 06	minutes													17 22			
Balham 4	⊖ d	10 55				11 09	past					17 18	17 13				17 21	17 31		17 25			
Wandsworth Common	d	10 57				11 11							17 15				17 23	17 33		17 27			
Clapham Junction 10	d	11 01				11 14	each					17 22	17 18				17 26	17 37		17 31			
Battersea Park 4	d	11 04				11 18							17 22				17 30		17 32	17 34			
London Victoria 15	⊖ a	11 09				11 23	hour until					17 29	17 26				17 34	17 44	17 36	17 39			
Streatham 4	d				11 03									17 16	17 19								17 33
Tulse Hill 3	d			11 01	11 07			17 11						17 21	17 23							17 31	17 37
Herne Hill 4	a				11 11										17 26								17 41
Loughborough Jn	a				11 15										17 30								17 45
Elephant & Castle	⊖ a				11 19										17 34								17 49
London Blackfriars 3	⊖ a				11 26										17 41								17 56
City Thameslink 3	a				11 30										17 45								18 00
St Pancras International 15	⊖ a				11 38										17 53								18 08
Luton Airport Parkway 7	✈ a				12 25										18 40								18 55
Luton 10	a				12 31										18 43								19 01
North Dulwich	d			11 04				17 14						17 24								17 34	
East Dulwich	d			11 06				17 16						17 26								17 36	
Peckham Rye 4	d			11 09				17 19			17 26			17 29								17 39	
Queens Rd Peckham	d			11 11				17 21			17 29			17 32								17 41	
South Bermondsey	d			11 14				17 24			17 31			17 34								17 44	
London Bridge 4	⊖ a		11 06	11 18				17 28	17 12	17 25	17 36			17 39		17 44					17 36	17 48	

		SN	SN	SE	SN	SN	SN	SN	SN	FC	SN	SN	SN	SN	SN	SN	SN	FC	SN	SN	SN	SN	SN	SN	SN
				13																	1				
			B	G				H				D	E			A				B					C
East Croydon	d		17 21	17 24	17 30								17 47							17 51	17 55	18 00			
West Croydon 4	d	17 18						17 27	17 31		17 45	17 35							17 48						17 57
Norwood Junction 2	a	17 23	17 27	17 28	17 34						17 49								17 53	17 57	17 59	18 04			
	d	17 23	17 28	17 28	17 34						17 49								17 53	17 58	17 59	18 04			
Selhurst 4	d							17 31	17 35			17 39	17 50												18 01
Thornton Heath	d							17 33	17 37			17 41	17 52												18 03
Norbury	d							17 36	17 40			17 44	17 55												18 06
Streatham Common 4	d							17 39	17 43			17 47	17 57												18 09
Bromley South 4	d																*17 33*								
Beckenham Junction 4	d																17 46								
Birkbeck	d																17 49								
Crystal Palace 4	d	17 27	17 32												17 43	17 47	17 53		17 57	18 02					
Gipsy Hill	d	17 29	17 35												17 46		17 55		17 59	18 05					
West Norwood 4	d	17 32	17 38												17 49		17 58		18 02	18 08					
Streatham Hill	d	17 36													17 52				18 06						
Balham 4	⊖ d	17 39					17 48	17 43				17 51	18 01		17 55				18 09					18 18	18 13
Wandsworth Common	d	17 41						17 45				17 53	18 03		17 57				18 11						18 15
Clapham Junction 10	d	17 44					17 52	17 48				17 56	18 07		18 01				18 14					18 22	18 18
Battersea Park 4	d	17 48						17 52				18 00		18 02	18 04				18 18						18 22
London Victoria 15	⊖ a	17 53					17 59	17 56				18 04	18 14	18 06	18 09				18 23					18 29	18 26
Streatham 4	d								17 46	17 49								18 03							
Tulse Hill 3	d		17 41						17 51	17 53							18 01	18 07		18 11					
Herne Hill 4	a									17 56								18 11							
Loughborough Jn	a									18 00								18 15							
Elephant & Castle	⊖ a									18 04								18 19							
London Blackfriars 3	⊖ a									18 11								18 26							
City Thameslink 3	a									18 15								18 30							
St Pancras International 15	⊖ a									18 23								18 38							
Luton Airport Parkway 7	✈ a									19 10								19 25							
Luton 10	a									19 13								19 31							
North Dulwich	d		17 44						17 54								18 04			18 14					
East Dulwich	d		17 46						17 56								18 06			18 16					
Peckham Rye 4	d		17 49			17 56			17 59								18 09			18 19			18 26		
Queens Rd Peckham	d		17 51			17 59			18 02								18 11			18 21			18 29		
South Bermondsey	d		17 54			18 01			18 04								18 14			18 24			18 31		
London Bridge 4	⊖ a		17 58	17 40	17 55	18 06			18 09		18 14					18 06	18 18			18 28	18 12	18 25	18 36		

For general notes see front of timetable
For details of catering facilities see Directory of Train Operators

- **A** Via Sydenham (Table 178)
- **B** From Smitham (Table 181)
- **C** From Epsom Downs (Table 182)
- **D** From Sutton (Surrey) (Table 182)
- **E** From Caterham (Table 181)
- **G** From Tunbridge Wells (Table 209)
- **H** From Epsom (Table 182)

East and West Croydon → London & Luton via Norbury/Crystal Palace/Tulse Hill

Local Services

Network Diagram - see first page of Table 177

		SN	FC	SN	SN	SN	SN	SN	SN	SN	FC	SN	SN	SE	SN	SN	SN	SN	SN	FC		SN	SN	SN	SN
					A			B	C				D	13 E			G						A		
East Croydon	d								18 17				18 21	18 24	18 30										
West Croydon [4]	d	18 01		18 15	18 05							18 18					18 27		18 31				18 35	18 45	
Norwood Junction [2]	a			18 19								18 23	18 27	18 28	18 34									18 49	
	d			18 19								18 23	18 28	18 28	18 34									18 49	
Selhurst [4]	d	18 05			18 09				18 20								18 31		18 35				18 39		
Thornton Heath	d	18 07			18 11				18 22								18 33		18 37				18 41		
Norbury	d	18 10			18 14				18 25								18 36		18 40				18 44		
Streatham Common [4]	d	18 13			18 17				18 27								18 39		18 43				18 47		
Bromley South [4]	d									*18 03*															
Beckenham Junction [4]	d									18 16															
Birkbeck	d									18 19															
Crystal Palace [4]	d						18 13	18 17		18 23		18 27	18 32												
Gipsy Hill	d						18 16			18 25		18 29	18 35												
West Norwood [4]	d						18 19			18 28		18 32	18 38												
Streatham Hill	d						18 22					18 36													
Balham [4]	⊖ d				18 21		18 25		18 31			18 39					18 43	18 48					18 51		
Wandsworth Common	d				18 23		18 27		18 33			18 41					18 45						18 53		
Clapham Junction [10]	d				18 26		18 31		18 37			18 44					18 48	18 52					18 56		
Battersea Park [4]	d				18 30	18 32	18 34					18 48					18 52						19 00		19 02
London Victoria [15]	⊖ a				18 34	18 36	18 39		18 44			18 53					18 56	18 59					19 04		19 06
Streatham [4]	d	18 16	18 19								18 33								18 46	18 49		←			
Tulse Hill [3]	d	18 21	18 23							18 31	18 37		18 41						18b55 →	18 53		18 55			
Herne Hill [4]	a		18 26								18 41									18 56					
Loughborough Jn	a		18 30								18 45									19 00					
Elephant & Castle	⊖ a		18 34								18 49									19 04					
London Blackfriars [3]	⊖ a		18 41								18 56									19 11					
City Thameslink [3]	a		18 45								19 00									19 15					
St Pancras International [15]	⊖ a		18 53								19 08									19 23					
Luton Airport Parkway [7]	✈ a		19 40								19 55									20 10					
Luton [10]	a		19 43								20 01									20 13					
North Dulwich	d	18 24								18 34			18 44									18 58			
East Dulwich	d	18 26								18 36			18 46									19 00			
Peckham Rye [4]	d	18 29								18 39			18 49			18 56						19 02			
Queens Rd Peckham	d	18 32								18 41			18 51			18 59						19 05			
South Bermondsey	d	18 34								18 44			18 54			19 01						19 07			
London Bridge [4]	⊖ a	18 39		18 44				18 36		18 48			18 58	18 40	18 55	19 06						19 12		19 14	

		SN	SN	SN	SN	FC	SN	SN	SN	SN	SN	SN	SN	SN	SN	SN	FC	SN	SN	SN	SN	FC	SN	SN	SN
			B		C				[1]					H										J	
East Croydon	d				18 47			18 51	18 55			19 10												19 17	
West Croydon [4]	d						18 48							18 57		19 01									19 18
Norwood Junction [2]	a						18 53	18 56	18 59	←		19 14													19 23
	d						18 53	19 01	18 59	19 01		19 14													19 23
Selhurst [4]	d				18 50			→						19 01		19 05								19 20	
Thornton Heath	d				18 52									19 03		19 07								19 22	
Norbury	d				18 55									19 06		19 10								19 25	
Streatham Common [4]	d				18 57									19 09		19 13								19 27	
Bromley South [4]	d			*18 33*																	*19 03*				
Beckenham Junction [4]	d			18 46																	19 16				
Birkbeck	d			18 49																	19 19				
Crystal Palace [4]	d	18 43	18 47	18 53			18 57													19 13	19 23				19 27
Gipsy Hill	d	18 46		18 55			18 59													19 16	19 25				19 29
West Norwood [4]	d	18 49		18 58			19 02													19 19	19 28				19 32
Streatham Hill	d	18 52					19 06													19 22					19 36
Balham [4]	⊖ d	18 55			19 01		19 09							19 13	19 18					19 25				19 31	19 39
Wandsworth Common	d	18 57			19 03		19 11							19 15						19 27				19 33	19 41
Clapham Junction [10]	d	19 01			19 07		19 14							19 18	19 22					19 31				19 37	19 44
Battersea Park [4]	d	19 04					19 18							19 22					19 32	19 34				19 40	19 48
London Victoria [15]	⊖ a	19 10			19 14		19 23							19 26	19 29				19 36	19 39				19 45	19 53
Streatham [4]	d					19 03					←					19 16	19 19	←				19 33	←		
Tulse Hill [3]	d			19c10 →		19 07					19 10					19e25 →	19 23	19 25			19f40 →	19 37	19 40		
Herne Hill [4]	a					19 11											19 26					19 41			
Loughborough Jn	a					19 15											19 30					19 45			
Elephant & Castle	⊖ a					19 19											19 34					19 49			
London Blackfriars [3]	⊖ a					19 26											19 41					19 56			
City Thameslink [3]	a					19 30											19 45					20 00			
St Pancras International [15]	⊖ a					19 38											19 53					20 08			
Luton Airport Parkway [7]	✈ a					20 25											20 41					20 55			
Luton [10]	a					20 31											20 45					21 01			
North Dulwich	d										19 13							19 28					19 43		
East Dulwich	d										19 15							19 30					19 45		
Peckham Rye [4]	d										19 17		19 26					19 32					19 47		
Queens Rd Peckham	d										19 20		19 29					19 35					19 50		
South Bermondsey	d										19 22		19 31					19 37					19 52		
London Bridge [4]	⊖ a		19 06						19 12	19 25	19 27	19 41	19 36					19 44					19 58		

For general notes see front of timetable
For details of catering facilities see Directory of Train Operators

A From Sutton (Surrey) (Table 182)
B Via Sydenham (Table 178)
C From Caterham (Table 181)
D From Smitham (Table 181)
E From Tunbridge Wells (Table 209)
G From Epsom (Table 182)
H From Epsom Downs (Table 182)
J From Tattenham Corner (Table 181)
b Arr. 1850
c Arr. 1901
e Arr. 1920
f Arr. 1931

Table 177

East and West Croydon → London & Luton via Norbury/Crystal Palace/Tulse Hill

Local Services

Network Diagram - see first page of Table 177

		SN A	SN	SN	SN	SN B	SN	SN	SN	SN	SN	FC	SN	SN C	SN D	SN	SN A	SN	SN	SN E	SN	SN	SN	SN	FC
East Croydon	d		19 21	19 40										19 47				20 10							
West Croydon 4	d					19 27		19 36							19 48					20 01	20 06				
Norwood Junction 2	a		19 26	19 44											19 53			20 14							
	d		19 31	19 44											19 53			20 14							
Selhurst 4	d					19 31		19 40						19 50						20 06	20 10				
Thornton Heath	d					19 33		19 42						19 52						20 08	20 12				
Norbury	d					19 36		19 45						19 55						20 11	20 15				
Streatham Common 4	d					19 39		19 48						19 57						20 14	20 18				
Bromley South 4	d										*19 33*													*20 03*	
Beckenham Junction 4	d										19 46													20 16	
Birkbeck	d										19 49													20 19	
Crystal Palace 4	d	19 31								19 43	19 53				19 57		20 01						20 13	20 23	
Gipsy Hill	d									19 46	19 55				19 59								20 16	20 25	
West Norwood 4	d									19 49	19 58				20 02								20 19	20 28	
Streatham Hill	d									19 52					20 06								20 22		
Balham 4	⊖ d					19 43	19 46			19 55				20 01	20 09	20 14				20 18			20 25		
Wandsworth Common	d					19 45				19 57				20 03	20 11					20 20			20 27		
Clapham Junction 10	d					19 48	19 51			20 01				20 07	20 14	20 18				20 23			20 31		
Battersea Park 4	d					19 52			20 02	20 04				20 10	20 18					20 27		20 32	20 34		
London Victoria 15	⊖ a					19 56	19 58		20 06	20 09				20 15	20 23	20 25				20 33		20 36	20 39		
Streatham 4	d							19 51				20 03	←								20 21				20 33
Tulse Hill 3	d							19 55			20b10 →	20 07	20 10								20 25			20c40 →	20 37
Herne Hill 4	a											20 11													20 41
Loughborough Jn	a											20 15													20 45
Elephant & Castle	⊖ a											20 19													20 49
London Blackfriars 3	⊖ a											20 26													20 56
City Thameslink 3	a											20 30													21 00
St Pancras International 15	⊖ a											20 38													21 08
Luton Airport Parkway 7	✈ a											21 25													21 55
Luton 10	a											21 31													21 59
North Dulwich	d							19 58					20 13								20 28				
East Dulwich	d							20 00					20 15								20 30				
Peckham Rye 4	d				19 56			20 02					20 17						20 26		20 32				
Queens Rd Peckham	d				19 59			20 05					20 20						20 29		20 35				
South Bermondsey	d				20 01			20 07					20 22						20 31		20 37				
London Bridge 4	⊖ a	19 52	19 55	20 11	20 06			20 12					20 27				20 22	20 41	20 36		20 42				

		SN	SN C	SN D	SN	SN A	SN	SN	SN B	SN		FC	SN	SN	SN C	SN D	SN	SN A	SN	SN	SN E	SN	FC	SN	SN
East Croydon	d		20 17				20 40								20 47				21 10						
West Croydon 4	d			20 18					20 31	20 36						20 48					21 01	21 06			
Norwood Junction 2	a			20 23			20 44									20 53			21 14						
	d			20 23			20 44									20 53			21 14						
Selhurst 4	d		20 20						20 36	20 40					20 50						21 06	21 10			
Thornton Heath	d		20 22						20 38	20 42					20 52						21 08	21 12			
Norbury	d		20 25						20 41	20 45					20 55						21 11	21 15			
Streatham Common 4	d		20 27						20 44	20 48					20 57						21 14	21 18			
Bromley South 4	d																								
Beckenham Junction 4	d																								
Birkbeck	d																								
Crystal Palace 4	d			20 27		20 31								20 43		20 57		21 01							21 13
Gipsy Hill	d			20 29										20 45		20 59									21 16
West Norwood 4	d			20 32										20 48		21 02									21 19
Streatham Hill	d			20 36										20 52		21 06									21 22
Balham 4	⊖ d		20 31	20 39	20 44				20 48					20 55	21 01	21 09	21 14				21 18				21 25
Wandsworth Common	d		20 33	20 41					20 50					20 57	21 03	21 11					21 20				21 27
Clapham Junction 10	d		20 37	20 44	20 48				20 53					21 01	21 07	21 14	21 18				21 23				21 31
Battersea Park 4	d		20 40	20 48					20 57				21 02	21 04	21 10	21 18					21 27			21 32	21 34
London Victoria 15	⊖ a		20 45	20 53	20 55				21 03				21 06	21 09	21 15	21 23	21 25				21 33			21 36	21 39
Streatham 4	d	←								20 51		21 03										21 21	21 49		
Tulse Hill 3	d	20 40								20 55		21 07										21 25	21 53		
Herne Hill 4	a											21 11											21 56		
Loughborough Jn	a											21 15											22 00		
Elephant & Castle	⊖ a											21 19											22 04		
London Blackfriars 3	⊖ a											21 26											22 08		
City Thameslink 3	a																								
St Pancras International 15	⊖ a											21 42											22 17		
Luton Airport Parkway 7	✈ a											22 27											23 01		
Luton 10	a											22 30											23 05		
North Dulwich	d	20 43								20 58												21 28			
East Dulwich	d	20 45								21 00												21 30			
Peckham Rye 4	d	20 47						20 56		21 02										21 26		21 32			
Queens Rd Peckham	d	20 50						20 59		21 05										21 29		21 35			
South Bermondsey	d	20 52						21 01		21 07										21 31		21 37			
London Bridge 4	⊖ a	20 57				20 52	21 11	21 06		21 14								21 22	21 41	21 36		21 42			

For general notes see front of timetable
For details of catering facilities see Directory of Train Operators

A Via Sydenham (Table 178)
B From Epsom (Table 182)
C From Tattenham Corner (Table 181)
D From Sutton (Surrey) (Table 182)
E From Epsom Downs (Table 182)
b Arr. 2001
c Arr. 2031

East and West Croydon → London & Luton via Norbury/Crystal Palace/Tulse Hill

Local Services

Network Diagram - see first page of Table 177

Station		SN A	SN B	SN	SN C	SN	SN	SN D	SN	FC	SN	SN	SN A	SN B	SN	SN C	SN	SN	SN E	SN	FC	SN	SN	SN A	SN B
East Croydon	d	21 17				21 40							21 47				22 10							22 17	
West Croydon 4	d		21 18					21 31	21 36					21 48					22 01	22 06					22 18
Norwood Junction 2	a		21 23			21 44								21 53			22 14								22 23
	d		21 23			21 44								21 53			22 14								22 23
Selhurst 4	d	21 20						21 36	21 40				21 50						22 06	22 10				22 20	
Thornton Heath	d	21 22						21 38	21 42				21 52						22 08	22 12				22 22	
Norbury	d	21 25						21 41	21 45				21 55						22 11	22 15				22 25	
Streatham Common 4	d	21 27						21 44	21 48				21 57						22 14	22 18				22 27	
Bromley South 4	d																								
Beckenham Junction 4	d																								
Birkbeck	d																								
Crystal Palace 4	d		21 27		21 31							21 43		21 57		22 01							22 13		22 27
Gipsy Hill	d		21 29									21 46		21 59									22 16		22 29
West Norwood 4	d		21 32									21 49		22 02									22 19		22 32
Streatham Hill	d		21 36									21 52		22 06									22 22		22 36
Balham 4	⊖ d	21 31	21 39	21 44				21 48				21 55	22 01	22 09	22 14				22 18				22 25	22 31	22 39
Wandsworth Common	d	21 33	21 41					21 50				21 57	22 03	22 11					22 20				22 27	22 33	22 41
Clapham Junction 10	d	21 37	21 44	21 48				21 53				22 01	22 07	22 14	22 18				22 23				22 31	22 37	22 44
Battersea Park 4	d	21 40	21 48					21 57			22 02	22 04	22 10	22 18					22 27			22 32	22 34	22 40	22 48
London Victoria 15	⊖ a	21 45	21 53	21 55				22 03			22 06	22 09	22 15	22 23	22 25				22 33			22 36	22 39	22 45	22 53
Streatham 4	d								21 51	22 19										22 21	22 49				
Tulse Hill 3	d								21 55	22 23										22 25	22 53				
Herne Hill 4	a									22 26											22 56				
Loughborough Jn	a									22 30															
Elephant & Castle	⊖ a									22 34											23 04				
London Blackfriars 3	⊖ a									22 38											23 08				
City Thameslink 3	a																								
St Pancras International 15	⊖ a									22 47											23 17				
Luton Airport Parkway 7	✈ a									23 31											00 01				
Luton 10	a									23 35											00 05				
North Dulwich	d								21 58											22 28					
East Dulwich	d								22 00											22 30					
Peckham Rye 4	d						21 56		22 02									22 26		22 32					
Queens Rd Peckham	d						21 59		22 05									22 29		22 35					
South Bermondsey	d						22 01		22 07									22 31		22 37					
London Bridge 4	⊖ a				21 52	22 11	22 06		22 12							22 22	22 41	22 36		22 42					

Station		SN	SN C	SN	SN	SN D	SN	SN	SN	SN A	SN B	SN	SN C	SN	SN	SN E	SN	SN	SN	SN A	SN B	SN C	SN
East Croydon	d			22 40						22 47				23 10						23 17			
West Croydon 4	d					22 31	22 36				22 48					23 01	23 06				23 18		
Norwood Junction 2	a			22 44							22 53			23 14							23 23		
	d			22 44							22 53			23 14							23 23		
Selhurst 4	d					22 36	22 40			22 50						23 06	23 10			23 20			
Thornton Heath	d					22 38	22 42			22 52						23 08	23 12			23 22			
Norbury	d					22 41	22 45			22 55						23 11	23 15			23 25			
Streatham Common 4	d					22 44	22 48			22 57						23 14	23 18			23 27			
Bromley South 4	d																						
Beckenham Junction 4	d																						
Birkbeck	d																						
Crystal Palace 4	d		22 31						22 43		22 57		23 01						23 13		23 27	23 31	23 43
Gipsy Hill	d								22 46		22 59								23 16		23 29		23 46
West Norwood 4	d								22 49		23 02								23 19		23 32		23 49
Streatham Hill	d								22 52		23 06								23 22		23 36		23 52
Balham 4	⊖ d	22 44				22 48			22 55	23 01	23 09	23 14				23 18			23 25	23 31	23 40		23 55
Wandsworth Common	d					22 50			22 57	23 03	23 11					23 20			23 27	23 33	23 42		23 57
Clapham Junction 10	d	22 48				22 53			23 01	23 07	23 14	23 18				23 23			23 31	23 37	23 45		00 01
Battersea Park 4	d					22 57		23 02	23 04		23 18					23 27		23 32	23 34	23 40	23 49		00 04
London Victoria 15	⊖ a	22 55				23 03		23 06	23 09	23 14	23 23	23 25				23 31		23 37	23 40	23 45	23 54		00 09
Streatham 4	d						22 51										23 21						
Tulse Hill 3	d						22 55										23 25						
Herne Hill 4	a																						
Loughborough Jn	a																						
Elephant & Castle	⊖ a																						
London Blackfriars 3	⊖ a																						
City Thameslink 3	a																						
St Pancras International 15	⊖ a																						
Luton Airport Parkway 7	✈ a																						
Luton 10	a																						
North Dulwich	d						22 58										23 28						
East Dulwich	d						23 00										23 30						
Peckham Rye 4	d				22 56		23 02								23 26		23 32						
Queens Rd Peckham	d				22 59		23 05								23 29		23 35						
South Bermondsey	d				23 01		23 07								23 31		23 37						
London Bridge 4	⊖ a		22 52	23 11	23 06		23 12						23 22	23 38	23 36		23 42					23 52	

For general notes see front of timetable
For details of catering facilities see Directory of Train Operators

A From Tattenham Corner (Table 181)
B From Sutton (Surrey) (Table 182)
C Via Sydenham (Table 178)
D From Epsom (Table 182)
E From Epsom Downs (Table 182)

Table 177

Sundays

East and West Croydon → London & Luton via Norbury/Crystal Palace/Tulse Hill

Local Services

Network Diagram - see first page of Table 177

	FC	SN	SN	SN	SN	SN	SN	SN	SN	SN	SN	SN	SN	SN	SN	SN	SN	SN	SN	SN	SN	SN	SN
										A		1 B					C						
East Croydon d				06 40		06 44		07 12			07 14	07 27						07 44	07 47				
West Croydon 4 d										07 09				07 18			07 39			07 48	08 01		
Norwood Junction 2 a						06 48		07 17						07 23					07 51	07 53	08 05		
Norwood Junction d						06 48	06 54	07 18						07 24					07 51	07 54	08 05		
Selhurst 4 d				06 43	06 47					07 13	07 17	07 31					07 43	07 47					
Thornton Heath d				06 45	06 49					07 15	07 19						07 45	07 49					
Norbury d				06 48	06 52					07 18	07 22						07 48	07 52					
Streatham Common 4 d				06 51	06 54					07 21	07 24						07 51	07 54					
Bromley South 4 d																							
Beckenham Junction 4 d																							
Birkbeck d																							
Crystal Palace 4 d		23p43					06 58							07 28						07 58			
Gipsy Hill d		23p46					07 00							07 30						08 00			
West Norwood 4 d		23p49					07 03							07 33						08 03			
Streatham Hill d		23p52					07 07							07 37						08 07			
Balham 4 ⊖ d		23p55	05 43	06 55			07 10			07 25				07 40	07 48		07 55			08 10			08 18
Wandsworth Common d		23p57		06 57			07 12			07 27				07 42			07 57			08 12			
Clapham Junction 10 d		00 01	05 49	07 00			07 15			07 30		07 40		07 45	07 52		08 00			08 15			08 22
Battersea Park 4 d		00 04		07 04			07 19		07 32	07 34				07 49		08 02	08 04			08 19			
London Victoria 15 ⊖ a		00 09	05 58	07 08			07 23		07 36	07 38		07 48		07 53	07 59	08 06	08 08			08 23			08 29
Streatham 4 d	22p49				06 57						07 27							07 57					
Tulse Hill 3 d	22p53				07 01						07 31							08 01					
Herne Hill 4 a	22p56																						
Loughborough Jn a																							
Elephant & Castle ⊖ a	23p04																						
London Blackfriars 3 ⊖ a	23p08																						
City Thameslink 3 a																							
St Pancras International 15 ⊖ a	23p17																						
Luton Airport Parkway 7 ✈ a	00 01																						
Luton 10 a	00 05																						
North Dulwich d					07 04						07 34							08 04					
East Dulwich d					07 06						07 36							08 06					
Peckham Rye 4 d					07 08						07 38		07 56					08 08				08 26	
Queens Rd Peckham d					07 11						07 41		07 59					08 11				08 29	
South Bermondsey d					07 13						07 43		08 01					08 13				08 31	
London Bridge 4 ⊖ a					07 18	07 12		07 42			07 48		08 06					08 18	08 12		08 31	08 36	

	SN	SN	SN	SN	SN	SN	SN	SN	SN	SN	SN	SN	SN	SN	SN	SN	SN	SN	SN	SN	SN	SN
		C			1 D						C			C					C			1 D
East Croydon d			08 14	08 17	08 29							08 44	08 47							09 14	09 17	09 29
West Croydon 4 d		08 09				08 18	08 31				08 39			08 48	09 01				09 09			
Norwood Junction 2 a				08 21		08 23	08 35						08 51	08 53	09 05						09 21	
Norwood Junction d				08 21		08 24	08 35						08 51	08 54	09 05						09 21	
Selhurst 4 d		08 13	08 17		08 32						08 43	08 47							09 13	09 17		09 32
Thornton Heath d		08 15	08 19								08 45	08 49							09 15	09 19		
Norbury d		08 18	08 22								08 48	08 52							09 18	09 22		
Streatham Common 4 d		08 21	08 24								08 51	08 54							09 21	09 24		
Bromley South 4 d																						
Beckenham Junction 4 d																						
Birkbeck d																						
Crystal Palace 4 d						08 28								08 58								
Gipsy Hill d						08 30								09 00								
West Norwood 4 d						08 33								09 03								
Streatham Hill d						08 37								09 07								
Balham 4 ⊖ d		08 25				08 40			08 48		08 55			09 10			09 18		09 25			
Wandsworth Common d		08 27				08 42					08 57			09 12					09 27			
Clapham Junction 10 d		08 30			08 41	08 45			08 52		09 00			09 15			09 22		09 30			09 41
Battersea Park 4 d	08 32	08 34				08 49				09 02	09 04			09 19				09 32	09 34			
London Victoria 15 ⊖ a	08 36	08 38			08 48	08 53			08 59	09 06	09 08			09 23			09 29	09 36	09 38			09 48
Streatham 4 d			08 27									08 57								09 27		
Tulse Hill 3 d			08 31									09 01								09 31		
Herne Hill 4 a																						
Loughborough Jn a																						
Elephant & Castle ⊖ a																						
London Blackfriars 3 ⊖ a																						
City Thameslink 3 a																						
St Pancras International 15 ⊖ a																						
Luton Airport Parkway 7 ✈ a																						
Luton 10 a																						
North Dulwich d			08 34									09 04								09 34		
East Dulwich d			08 36									09 06								09 36		
Peckham Rye 4 d			08 38					08 56				09 08				09 26				09 38		
Queens Rd Peckham d			08 41					08 59				09 11				09 29				09 41		
South Bermondsey d			08 43					09 01				09 13				09 31				09 43		
London Bridge 4 ⊖ a			08 48	08 42			09 01	09 06				09 18	09 12		09 31	09 36				09 48	09 42	

For general notes see front of timetable
For details of catering facilities see Directory of Train Operators

A From Epsom (Table 182)
B From Horsham (Table 186)
C From Sutton (Surrey) (Table 182)
D From East Grinstead (Table 184)

Table 177

Sundays

East and West Croydon → London & Luton via Norbury/Crystal Palace/Tulse Hill

Local Services

Network Diagram - see first page of Table 177

		SN	SN	SN	SN	SN	SN	SN	SN	SN	SN	SN	SN	SN	SN	SN	SN	FC	SN	SN	SN	SN	SN
		A					A			A					A				1 B	A			
East Croydon	d							09 44	09 47							10 14	10 17		10 29				
West Croydon 4	d	09 18	09 31				09 39			09 48	10 01				10 09					10 18	10 31		
Norwood Junction 2	a	09 23	09 35						09 51	09 53	10 05						10 21			10 23	10 35		
	d	09 24	09 35						09 51	09 54	10 05						10 21			10 24	10 35		
Selhurst 4	d						09 43	09 47							10 13	10 17			10 32				
Thornton Heath	d						09 45	09 49							10 15	10 19							
Norbury	d						09 48	09 52							10 18	10 22							
Streatham Common 4	d						09 51	09 54							10 21	10 24							
Bromley South 4	d																						
Beckenham Junction 4	d																						
Birkbeck	d																						
Crystal Palace 4	d	09 28								09 58										10 28			
Gipsy Hill	d	09 30								10 00										10 30			
West Norwood 4	d	09 33								10 03										10 33			
Streatham Hill	d	09 37								10 07										10 37			
Balham 4	⊖ d	09 40			09 48		09 55			10 10			10 18		10 25					10 40			10 48
Wandsworth Common	d	09 42					09 57			10 12					10 27					10 42			
Clapham Junction 10	d	09 45			09 52		10 00			10 15			10 22		10 30				10 41	10 45			10 52
Battersea Park 4	d	09 49				10 02	10 04			10 19				10 32	10 34					10 49			
London Victoria 15	⊖ a	09 53			09 59	10 06	10 08			10 23			10 29	10 36	10 38				10 48	10 53			10 59
Streatham 4	d							09 57								10 27		10 35					
Tulse Hill 3	d							10 01								10 31		10 38					
Herne Hill 4	a																	10 42					
Loughborough Jn	a																	10 45					
Elephant & Castle	⊖ a																	10 49					
London Blackfriars 3	⊖ a																	10 56					
City Thameslink 3	a																						
St Pancras International 15	⊖ a																	11 06					
Luton Airport Parkway 7	✈ a																	11 48					
Luton 10	a																	11 55					
North Dulwich	d							10 04								10 34							
East Dulwich	d							10 06								10 36							
Peckham Rye 4	d			09 56				10 08				10 26				10 38						10 56	
Queens Rd Peckham	d			09 59				10 11				10 29				10 41						10 59	
South Bermondsey	d			10 01				10 13				10 31				10 43						11 01	
London Bridge 4	⊖ a		10 01	10 06				10 18	10 12		10 31	10 36				10 48	10 42				11 01	11 06	

		SN	SN	SN	SN	FC	SN	SN	SN	SN	SN	SN		SN	SN	FC	SN	SN	SN	SN	SN	SN	SN
			A				A					A					1 B	A					A
East Croydon	d			10 44	10 47									18 14	18 17		18 29						
West Croydon 4	d		10 39				10 48	11 01				11 09						18 18	18 31				18 39
Norwood Junction 2	a				10 51		10 53	11 05							18 21			18 23	18 35				
	d				10 51		10 54	11 05							18 21			18 24	18 35				
Selhurst 4	d		10 43	10 47								11 13		18 17			18 32						18 43
Thornton Heath	d		10 45	10 49								11 15		18 19									18 45
Norbury	d		10 48	10 52								11 18		18 22									18 48
Streatham Common 4	d		10 51	10 54								11 21		18 24									18 51
Bromley South 4	d																						
Beckenham Junction 4	d																						
Birkbeck	d												and at										
Crystal Palace 4	d						10 58											18 28					
Gipsy Hill	d						11 00						the same					18 30					
West Norwood 4	d						11 03											18 33					
Streatham Hill	d						11 07						minutes					18 37					
Balham 4	⊖ d		10 55				11 10			11 18		11 25	past					18 40			18 48		18 55
Wandsworth Common	d		10 57				11 12					11 27						18 42					18 57
Clapham Junction 10	d		11 00				11 15			11 22		11 30	each				18 41	18 45			18 52		19 00
Battersea Park 4	d	11 02	11 04				11 19				11 32	11 34						18 49				19 02	19 04
London Victoria 15	⊖ a	11 06	11 08				11 23			11 29	11 36	11 38	hour until				18 48	18 53			18 59	19 06	19 08
Streatham 4	d			10 57		11 05								18 27		18 35							
Tulse Hill 3	d			11 01		11 08								18 31		18 38							
Herne Hill 4	a					11 12										18 42							
Loughborough Jn	a					11 15										18 44							
Elephant & Castle	⊖ a					11 19										18 49							
London Blackfriars 3	⊖ a					11 26										18 56							
City Thameslink 3	a																						
St Pancras International 15	⊖ a					11 36										19 06							
Luton Airport Parkway 7	✈ a					12 18										19 47							
Luton 10	a					12 25										19 52							
North Dulwich	d			11 04										18 34									
East Dulwich	d			11 06										18 36									
Peckham Rye 4	d			11 08					11 26					18 38						18 56			
Queens Rd Peckham	d			11 11					11 29					18 41						18 59			
South Bermondsey	d			11 13					11 31					18 43						19 01			
London Bridge 4	⊖ a			11 18	11 12			11 31	11 36					18 48	18 42				19 01	19 06			

For general notes see front of timetable
For details of catering facilities see
Directory of Train Operators

A From Sutton (Surrey) (Table 182)
B From East Grinstead (Table 184)

East and West Croydon → London & Luton via Norbury/Crystal Palace/Tulse Hill

Local Services

Network Diagram - see first page of Table 177

	SN	SN	FC	SN	SN		SN	SN	SN	SN	SN	SN	FC	SN	SN	SN	SN	SN	SN		SN	SN	SN	FC
														1										
				A						A				B	A						A			
East Croydon d	18 44	18 47									19 14	19 17		19 29								19 44	19 47	
West Croydon 4 d				18 48	19 01					19 09					19 18	19 31					19 39			
Norwood Junction 2 a		18 51		18 53	19 05							19 21			19 23	19 35							19 51	
d		18 51		18 54	19 05							19 21			19 24	19 35							19 51	
Selhurst 4 d	18 47									19 13	19 17			19 32							19 43	19 47		
Thornton Heath d	18 49									19 15	19 19										19 45	19 49		
Norbury d	18 52									19 18	19 22										19 48	19 52		
Streatham Common 4 d	18 54									19 21	19 24										19 51	19 54		
Bromley South 4 d																								
Beckenham Junction 4 d																								
Birkbeck d																								
Crystal Palace 4 d				18 58											19 28									
Gipsy Hill d				19 00											19 30									
West Norwood 4 d				19 03											19 33									
Streatham Hill d				19 07											19 37									
Balham 4 ⊖ d				19 10				19 18		19 25					19 40			19 48			19 55			
Wandsworth Common d				19 12						19 27					19 42						19 57			
Clapham Junction 10 d				19 15				19 22		19 30				19 41	19 45			19 52			20 00			
Battersea Park 4 d				19 19					19 32	19 34					19 49				20 02		20 04			
London Victoria 15 ⊖ a				19 23				19 29	19 36	19 38				19 48	19 53			19 59	20 06		20 08			
Streatham 4 d	18 57		19 05								19 27		19 35									19 57		20 05
Tulse Hill 3 d	19 01		19 08								19 31		19 38									20 01		20 08
Herne Hill 4 a			19 12										19 42											20 12
Loughborough Jn a			19 14										19 44											20 14
Elephant & Castle ⊖ a			19 19										19 49											20 19
London Blackfriars 3 ⊖ a			19 26										19 56											20 26
City Thameslink 3 a																								
St Pancras International 15 ⊖ a			19 36										20 06											20 36
Luton Airport Parkway 7 ✈ a			20 17										20 47											21 17
Luton 10 a			20 22										20 52											21 22
North Dulwich d	19 04										19 34											20 04		
East Dulwich d	19 06										19 36											20 06		
Peckham Rye 4 d	19 08						19 26				19 38						19 56					20 08		
Queens Rd Peckham d	19 11						19 29				19 41						19 59					20 11		
South Bermondsey d	19 13						19 31				19 43						20 01					20 13		
London Bridge 4 ⊖ a	19 18	19 12			19 31		19 36				19 48	19 42				20 01	20 06					20 18	20 12	

	SN	SN	SN	SN	SN	SN	SN	SN	FC	SN	SN		SN	SN	SN	SN	SN	SN	SN	FC	SN	SN	SN	SN
										1														
	A					A				B	A						A				A			
East Croydon d							20 14	20 17		20 29								20 44	20 47					
West Croydon 4 d	19 48	20 01				20 09					20 18		20 31				20 39				20 48	21 01		
Norwood Junction 2 a	19 53	20 05						20 21			20 23		20 35						20 51		20 53	21 05		
d	19 54	20 05						20 21			20 24		20 35						20 51		20 54	21 05		
Selhurst 4 d						20 13	20 17			20 32							20 43	20 47						
Thornton Heath d						20 15	20 19										20 45	20 49						
Norbury d						20 18	20 22										20 48	20 52						
Streatham Common 4 d						20 21	20 24										20 51	20 54						
Bromley South 4 d																								
Beckenham Junction 4 d																								
Birkbeck d																								
Crystal Palace 4 d	19 58										20 28										20 58			
Gipsy Hill d	20 00										20 30										21 00			
West Norwood 4 d	20 03										20 33										21 03			
Streatham Hill d	20 07										20 37										21 07			
Balham 4 ⊖ d	20 10			20 18		20 25					20 40				20 48		20 55				21 10			21 18
Wandsworth Common d	20 12					20 27					20 42						20 57				21 12			
Clapham Junction 10 d	20 15			20 22		20 30				20 41	20 45				20 52		21 00				21 15			21 22
Battersea Park 4 d	20 19				20 32	20 34					20 49					21 02	21 04				21 19			
London Victoria 15 ⊖ a	20 23			20 29	20 36	20 38				20 48	20 53				20 59	21 06	21 08				21 23			21 29
Streatham 4 d							20 27		20 35									20 57		21 05				
Tulse Hill 3 d							20 31		20 38									21 01		21 08				
Herne Hill 4 a									20 42											21 12				
Loughborough Jn a									20 44											21 14				
Elephant & Castle ⊖ a									20 49											21 19				
London Blackfriars 3 ⊖ a									20 56											21 26				
City Thameslink 3 a																								
St Pancras International 15 ⊖ a									21 06											21 36				
Luton Airport Parkway 7 ✈ a									21 47											22 17				
Luton 10 a									21 50											22 22				
North Dulwich d							20 34											21 04						
East Dulwich d							20 36											21 06						
Peckham Rye 4 d			20 26				20 38							20 56				21 08					21 26	
Queens Rd Peckham d			20 29				20 41							20 59				21 11					21 29	
South Bermondsey d			20 31				20 43							21 01				21 13					21 31	
London Bridge 4 ⊖ a		20 31	20 36				20 48	20 42					21 01	21 06				21 18	21 12			21 31	21 36	

For general notes see front of timetable
For details of catering facilities see Directory of Train Operators

A From Sutton (Surrey) (Table 182)
B From East Grinstead (Table 184)

Table 177

Sundays

East and West Croydon → London & Luton via Norbury/Crystal Palace/Tulse Hill

Local Services

Network Diagram - see first page of Table 177

		SN	SN	SN		SN	FC	SN [1]	SN	SN	SN	SN	SN	SN	SN	SN	SN	SN		SN	SN	SN	SN	SN	SN
			A					B	A					A			A						A		
East Croydon	d			21 14		21 17		21 29							21 44	21 47								22 14	22 17
West Croydon [4]	d		21 09						21 18	21 31				21 39			21 48	22 01					22 09		
Norwood Junction [2]	a					21 21			21 23	21 35						21 51	21 53	22 05							22 21
	d					21 21			21 24	21 35						21 51	21 54	22 05							22 21
Selhurst [4]	d		21 13	21 17				21 32						21 43	21 47								22 13	22 17	
Thornton Heath	d		21 15	21 19										21 45	21 49								22 15	22 19	
Norbury	d		21 18	21 22										21 48	21 52								22 18	22 22	
Streatham Common [4]	d		21 21	21 24										21 51	21 54								22 21	22 24	
Bromley South [4]	d																								
Beckenham Junction [4]	d																								
Birkbeck	d																								
Crystal Palace [4]	d								21 28								21 58								
Gipsy Hill	d								21 30								22 00								
West Norwood [4]	d								21 33								22 03								
Streatham Hill	d								21 37								22 07								
Balham [4] ⊖	d		21 25						21 40			21 48		21 55			22 10				22 18		22 25		
Wandsworth Common	d		21 27						21 42					21 57			22 12						22 27		
Clapham Junction [10]	d		21 30					21 41	21 45			21 52		22 00			22 15				22 22		22 30		
Battersea Park [4]	d	21 32	21 34						21 49				22 02	22 04			22 19					22 32	22 34		
London Victoria [15] ⊖	a	21 36	21 39					21 48	21 53			21 59	22 06	22 09			22 23				22 29	22 36	22 39		
Streatham [4]	d			21 27			21 35								21 57									22 27	
Tulse Hill [3]	d			21 31			21 38								22 01									22 31	
Herne Hill [4]	a						21 42																		
Loughborough Jn	a						21 44																		
Elephant & Castle ⊖	a						21 49																		
London Blackfriars [3] ⊖	a						21 56																		
City Thameslink [3]	a																								
St Pancras International [15] ⊖	a						22 06																		
Luton Airport Parkway [7] ✈	a						22 47																		
Luton [10]	a						22 50																		
North Dulwich	d			21 34											22 04									22 34	
East Dulwich	d			21 36											22 06									22 36	
Peckham Rye [4]	d			21 38							21 56				22 08					22 26				22 38	
Queens Rd Peckham	d			21 41							21 59				22 11					22 29				22 41	
South Bermondsey	d			21 43							22 01				22 13					22 31				22 43	
London Bridge [4] ⊖	a			21 48		21 42				22 01	22 06				22 18	22 12		22 31		22 36				22 48	22 42

		SN [1]	SN	SN	SN	SN	SN	SN	SN	SN		SN [1]	SN	SN	SN	SN	SN	SN [1]	SN	SN	SN	SN [1]			
		B	A					A				C		A			A	B	A		A	C			
East Croydon	d	22 29							22 44	22 47		22 59						23 29				23 56			
West Croydon [4]	d		22 18	22 31				22 39						22 48			23 09		23 18		23 43				
Norwood Junction [2]	a		22 23	22 35						22 51				22 53					23 23						
	d		22 24	22 35						22 51				22 54					23 26						
Selhurst [4]	d	22 32						22 43	22 47			23 02					23 13	23 32			23a47	00 01			
Thornton Heath	d							22 45	22 49								23 15								
Norbury	d							22 48	22 52								23 18								
Streatham Common [4]	d							22 51	22 54								23 21								
Bromley South [4]	d																								
Beckenham Junction [4]	d																								
Birkbeck	d																								
Crystal Palace [4]	d		22 28											22 58					23 30						
Gipsy Hill	d		22 30											23 00					23 32						
West Norwood [4]	d		22 33											23 03					23 35						
Streatham Hill	d		22 37											23 07					23 39						
Balham [4] ⊖	d		22 40			22 48		22 55						23 10	23 18		23 25		23 42	23 48					
Wandsworth Common	d		22 42					22 57						23 12			23 27		23 44						
Clapham Junction [10]	d	22 41	22 45			22 52		23 00				23 10		23 15	23 22		23 30	23 41	23 47	23 52		00 11			
Battersea Park [4]	d		22 49				23 02	23 04						23 19		23 32	23 34		23 51						
London Victoria [15] ⊖	a	22 50	22 53			22 59	23 06	23 09				23 16		23 23	23 29	23 37	23 38	23 51	23 55	23 59		00 18			
Streatham [4]	d								22 57																
Tulse Hill [3]	d								23 01																
Herne Hill [4]	a																								
Loughborough Jn	a																								
Elephant & Castle ⊖	a																								
London Blackfriars [3] ⊖	a																								
City Thameslink [3]	a																								
St Pancras International [15] ⊖	a																								
Luton Airport Parkway [7] ✈	a																								
Luton [10]	a																								
North Dulwich	d								23 04																
East Dulwich	d								23 06																
Peckham Rye [4]	d				22 56				23 08			23 26													
Queens Rd Peckham	d				22 59				23 11			23 29													
South Bermondsey	d				23 01				23 13			23 31													
London Bridge [4] ⊖	a			23 01	23 06				23 18	23 12		23 36													

For general notes see front of timetable
For details of catering facilities see Directory of Train Operators

A From Sutton (Surrey) (Table 182)
B From East Grinstead (Table 184)
C From Horsham (Table 186)

Charing Cross and London Bridge → London Victoria and Croydon

Network Diagram - see first page of Table 177

Miles	Miles	Miles	Miles	Miles			SN	SN	SN	SN	SE	SN	SE	SN	SN	SE	SN	SN	SE	SN	SN	SN	SN	SN	SN	SE
							MX	MO	MX	MX																
											73		73			83			83							83
																	1								1	
								A	A			B			A		C			D	E		G	A	H	
—	—	0	—	—	**London Charing Cross** 4	⊖ d		23p36	23p45	00 12					06 05											
—	—	¾	—	—	London Waterloo (East) 4	⊖ d		23p39	23p48	00 15					06 08											
0	0	1¾	—	—	**London Bridge** 4	⊖ d	23p24	23p44	23p53	00 26		05 46		06 11	06 13		06 30	06 41		06 46	06 54	07 11	07 15	07 25	07 28	
—	2¾	4½	—	—	New Cross Gate 4	⊖ d	23p30	23p49	23p58	00 31		05 51			06 19		06 35			06 51	06 59		07 20	07 30	07 33	
—	3¾	5½	—	—	Brockley	d	23p32	23p52	00 01	00 34		05 54			06 22					06 54	07 02		07 23	07 33		
—	4¾	6½	—	—	Honor Oak Park	d	23p35	23p55	00 04	00 37		05 57			06 25					06 57	07 05		07 26	07 36		
—	5¾	7½	—	—	Forest Hill 4	d	23p38	23p57	00 06	00 39		05 59			06 27					06 59	07 07		07 28	07 38		
—	6½	8¼	—	—	Sydenham	d	23p40	23p59	00 09	00 42		06 02			06 30					07 02	07 10		07 31	07 41		
—	7¾	—	—	—	**Crystal Palace** 4	d	23p43																			
—	8½	—	—	—	Gipsy Hill	d	23p46																			
—	9½	—	—	—	West Norwood 4	d	23p49																			
—	10¾	—	—	—	Streatham Hill	d	23p52																			
—	11¾	—	—	—	Balham 4	⊖ d	23p55																			
—	12½	—	—	—	Wandsworth Common	d	23p57																			
—	13¾	—	—	—	Clapham Junction 10	d	00 01																			
1¾	—	—	—	—	South Bermondsey	d								06 15				06 45				07 15				
2¾	—	—	—	—	Queens Rd Peckham	d								06 18				06 48				07 18				
3½	—	—	0	0	Peckham Rye 4	d					05 04		06 04	06 20		06 33		06 50	07 02			07 20				07 34
4¼	—	—	¾	¾	Denmark Hill 4	d					05 06		06 07	06 23		06 35		06 53	07 05			07 23				07 36
—	—	—	—	4½	**London Blackfriars** 3	⊖ a					05 16		06 18			06 45			07 15							07 46
6¼	—	—	—	—	Clapham High Street	⊖ d								06 28				06 58				07 28				
6¾	—	—	—	—	Wandsworth Road	d								06 29				06 59				07 29				
7½	15¼	—	—	—	Battersea Park 4	d	00 04							06 32				07 02				07 32				
8¾	16½	—	5	—	**London Victoria** 15	⊖ a	00 12							06 36				07 08				07 38				
—	—	9	—	—	Penge West	d		00 02	00 11	00 44		06 04			06 32					07 04			07 33	07 43		
—	—	9¼	—	—	Anerley	d		00 04	00 13	00 46		06 06			06 34					07 06			07 35	07 45		
—	—	10½	—	0	Norwood Junction 2	d		00 10	00 16	00 49		06 09			06 38		06 44			07 10	07 14		07 39	07b51	07 42	
—	—	—	—	1¾	**West Croydon** 4	a						06 14								07 14			07 43			
—	—	11¾	—	—	**East Croydon**	a		00 13	00 20	00 53					06 41		06 48				07 18			07 55	07 45	

		SN	SN	SE	SE	SN	SE		SE	SE	SN	SN	SE	SE	SN	SE	SE	SE	SN	SN	SN	SN	SE	SE	SN	SE
				18	83		96		78	73			83	20		78	9	83					18	9		83
							1																			
		J				K					A				L				B		A				B	
London Charing Cross 4	⊖ d																									
London Waterloo (East) 4	⊖ d																									
London Bridge 4	⊖ d	07 40	07 41			07 48					08 05	08 09			08 17				08 19	08 27	08 36	08 41			08 45	
New Cross Gate 4	⊖ d	07 45				07 53					08 10				08 22				08 26	08 32	08 41				08 50	
Brockley	d	07 48				07 56					08 13				08 25				08 29		08 44				08 53	
Honor Oak Park	d	07 51				07 59					08 16				08 28				08 32		08 47				08 56	
Forest Hill 4	d	07 53				08 01					08 18				08 30				08 34		08 49				08 58	
Sydenham	d	07 56				08 04					08 21				08 33				08 37		08 52				09 01	
Crystal Palace 4	d														08 36											
Gipsy Hill	d														08 38											
West Norwood 4	d														08a42											
Streatham Hill	d																									
Balham 4	⊖ d																									
Wandsworth Common	d																									
Clapham Junction 10	d																									
South Bermondsey	d		07 45									08 13										08 45				
Queens Rd Peckham	d		07 48									08 15										08 48				
Peckham Rye 4	d		07 50	07 55	07 59				08 12	08 15		08 18				08 32	08 35	08 43				08 50	08 54	09 04		09 08
Denmark Hill 4	d		07 53	07 59	08 03		08 06		08 15	08 18		08 21	08 22	08 27		08 35	08 38	08 45				08 53	08 59	09 06		09 10
London Blackfriars 3	⊖ a				08 13					08 29			08 31				08 49	08 56						09 17		09 21
Clapham High Street	⊖ d		07 58									08 26										08 58				
Wandsworth Road	d		07 59									08 28										08 59				
Battersea Park 4	d		08 02									08 32										09 02				
London Victoria 15	⊖ a		08 08	08 11			08 17		08 28			08 38		08 38		08 48						09 08	09 11			
Penge West	d					08 06													08 39						09 03	
Anerley	d					08 08													08 41						09 05	
Norwood Junction 2	d	08 00				08 11					08 25								08 44		08 56				09 09	
West Croydon 4	a					08 16													08 49						09 14	
East Croydon	a	08 04									08 29									08 45	09 00					

For general notes see front of timetable
For details of catering facilities see Directory of Train Operators

A To Caterham (Table 181)
B To Sutton (Surrey) (Table 182)
C To East Grinstead (Table 184)
D To Guildford (Table 182)
E To Tattenham Corner (Table 181) and to Caterham (Table 181)
G To Epsom (Table 182)
H To Brighton (Table 186)
J To Tattenham Corner (Table 181)
K To Dorking (Table 182)
L To London Bridge (Table 177)
b Arr. 0748

Charing Cross and London Bridge → London Victoria and Croydon

Network Diagram - see first page of Table 177

		SE	SN	SN	SN	SE	SN	SE	SN		SN	SN	SE	SE	SN	SN	SN	SN	SE	SE		SN	SN	SN	SN	SE
		78				73		83					78	83					83	78						83
				A			B				A				B		A					B		A		
London Charing Cross [4]	⊖ d																									
London Waterloo (East) [4]	⊖ d																									
London Bridge [4]	⊖ d		08 54	09 05	09 11		09 15		09 24		09 35	09 41			09 45	09 54	10 05	10 11				10 15	10 24	10 35	10 41	
New Cross Gate [4]	⊖ d		09 00	09 10			09 20		09 30		09 40				09 50	10 00	10 10					10 20	10 30	10 40		
Brockley	d		09 02	09 13			09 23		09 32		09 43				09 53	10 03	10 13					10 23	10 32	10 43		
Honor Oak Park	d		09 05	09 16			09 26		09 35		09 46				09 56	10 06	10 16					10 26	10 35	10 46		
Forest Hill [4]	d		09 08	09 18			09 28		09 38		09 48				09 58	10 08	10 18					10 28	10 38	10 48		
Sydenham	d		09 10	09 21			09 31		09 40		09 51				10 01	10 11	10 21					10 31	10 40	10 51		
Crystal Palace [4]	d		09 13						09 43							10 14							10 43			
Gipsy Hill	d		09 16						09 46							10 16							10 46			
West Norwood [4]	d		09 19						09 49							10 19							10 49			
Streatham Hill	d		09 22						09 52							10 23							10 52			
Balham [4]	⊖ d		09 26						09 56							10 26							10 55			
Wandsworth Common	d		09 28						09 58							10 28							10 57			
Clapham Junction [10]	d		09 32						10 01							10 31							11 01			
South Bermondsey	d				09 15							09 45						10 15							10 45	
Queens Rd Peckham	d				09 18							09 48						10 18							10 48	
Peckham Rye [4]	d	09 18			09 20	09 25		09 34				09 50	09 58	10 01				10 20	10 22	10 28					10 50	10 52
Denmark Hill [4]	d	09 20			09 23	09 27		09 36				09 53	10 01	10 04				10 23	10 25	10 31					10 53	10 55
London Blackfriars [3]	⊖ a					09 37		09 46						10 12					10 33							11 03
Clapham High Street	⊖ d				09 28							09 58						10 28							10 58	
Wandsworth Road	d				09 29							09 59						10 29							10 59	
Battersea Park [4]	d		09 36		09 32				10 05			10 03				10 34		10 32					11 04		11 02	
London Victoria [15]	⊖ a	09 32	09 42		09 39				10 10			10 07	10 12			10 40		10 36		10 42			11 09		11 06	
Penge West	d						09 33								10 03							10 33				
Anerley	d						09 35								10 05							10 35				
Norwood Junction [2]	d			09 25			09 39				09 55				10 09		10 25					10 39		10 55		
West Croydon [4]	a						09 44								10 14							10 44				
East Croydon	a			09 29							09 59						10 29							10 59		

		SE	SN	SN	SN	SN	SE	SE		SN	SN	SN	SN		SE	SE	SN	SN	SN	SN	SE	SN	SE	SN	SN
		78					83	78							83	78					83		78		
			B		A					B		A					B		A			C			A
London Charing Cross [4]	⊖ d																								
London Waterloo (East) [4]	⊖ d																								
London Bridge [4]	⊖ d		10 45	10 54	11 05	11 11				15 15	15 24	15 35	15 41				15 45	15 54	16 05	16 11		16 15		16 24	16 35
New Cross Gate [4]	⊖ d		10 50	11 00	11 10					15 20	15 30	15 40					15 50	16 00	16 10			16 20		16 30	16 40
Brockley	d		10 53	11 02	11 13					15 23	15 32	15 43					15 53	16 02	16 13			16 23		16 32	16 43
Honor Oak Park	d		10 56	11 05	11 16					15 26	15 35	15 46					15 56	16 05	16 16			16 26		16 35	16 46
Forest Hill [4]	d		10 58	11 08	11 18					15 28	15 38	15 48					15 58	16 08	16 18			16 28		16 38	16 48
Sydenham	d		11 01	11 10	11 21					15 31	15 40	15 51					16 01	16 10	16 21			16 31		16 40	16 51
Crystal Palace [4]	d			11 13					and at		15 43							16 13						16 43	
Gipsy Hill	d			11 16							15 46							16 16						16 46	
West Norwood [4]	d			11 19					the same		15 49							16 19						16 49	
Streatham Hill	d			11 22					minutes		15 52							16 22						16 52	
Balham [4]	⊖ d			11 25							15 55							16 25						16 55	
Wandsworth Common	d			11 27					past		15 57							16 27							
Clapham Junction [10]	d			11 31							16 01							16 31						17 01	
South Bermondsey	d					11 15			each				15 45							16 15					
Queens Rd Peckham	d					11 18			hour until				15 48							16 18					
Peckham Rye [4]	d	10 58				11 20	11 22	11 28					15 50		15 52	15 58				16 20	16 22		16 42		
Denmark Hill [4]	d	11 01				11 23	11 25	11 31					15 53		15 55	16 01				16 23	16 25		16 46		
London Blackfriars [3]	⊖ a						11 33								16 03						16 33				
Clapham High Street	⊖ d					11 28							15 58							16 28					
Wandsworth Road	d					11 29							15 59							16 29					
Battersea Park [4]	d			11 34		11 32					16 05		16 03					16 34		16 32				17 04	
London Victoria [15]	⊖ a	11 12		11 39		11 36		11 42			16 10		16 07			16 12		16 40		16 38			17 03	17 10	
Penge West	d		11 03							15 33							16 03					16 33			
Anerley	d		11 05							15 35							16 05					16 35			
Norwood Junction [2]	d		11 09		11 25					15 39		15 55					16 10		16 25			16 39			16 55
West Croydon [4]	a		11 14							15 44							16 15					16 43			
East Croydon	a				11 29							15 59							16 29						16 59

For general notes see front of timetable
For details of catering facilities see Directory of Train Operators

A To Caterham (Table 181)
B To Sutton (Surrey) (Table 182)
C To Guildford (Table 182)

Charing Cross and London Bridge → London Victoria and Croydon

Network Diagram - see first page of Table 177

		SN	SE	SN	SE	SN	SN	SN	SE	SN	SN	SN	SN	SN	SN	SE		SE	SN	SN	SN	SN	SN	SE	SN	SN
			83		78				83							83		78						83		
				A								A								B						
London Charing Cross 4	⊖ d																									
London Waterloo (East) 4	⊖ d																									
London Bridge 4	⊖ d	16 41		16 44		16 55	17 05	17 11		17 15	17 19	17 25	17 35	17 39	17 41				17 45	17 55	18 01	18 05	18 11		18 18	18 20
New Cross Gate 4	⊖ d			16 49		17 00	17 10			17 20	17 24	17 30	17 40	17 44					17 53		18 06	18 10			18 23	18 26
Brockley	d			16 52		17 03	17 13			17 23			17 43						17 56			18 13			18 26	
Honor Oak Park	d			16 55		17 06	17 16			17 26			17 46						17 59			18 16			18 29	
Forest Hill 4	d			16 57		17 08	17 18			17 28		17 36	17 48						18 01	18 05		18 18			18 31	
Sydenham	d			17 00		17 11	17 21			17 31		17 38	17 51						18 04	18 08		18 21			18 34	
Crystal Palace 4	d					17 14				17b43									18 10						18c43	
Gipsy Hill	d					17 16				17 46									18 13						18 45	
West Norwood 4	d					17 19				17 49									18 16						18 48	
Streatham Hill	d					17 23				17 52									18 19						18 52	
Balham 4	⊖ d					17 28				17 56									18 23						18 55	
Wandsworth Common	d					17 30													18 25						18 57	
Clapham Junction 10	d					17 33				18 01									18 28						19 00	
South Bermondsey	d	16 45						17 15							17 45								18 15			
Queens Rd Peckham	d	16 48						17 18							17 48								18 18			
Peckham Rye 4	d	16 50	16 52		17 15			17 20	17 24						17 50	17 54		18 01					18 20	18 23		
Denmark Hill 4	d	16 53	16 55		17 18			17 23	17 27						17 53	17 57		18 04					18 23	18 26		
London Blackfriars 3	⊖ a		17 05						17 39							18 08								18 35		
Clapham High Street	⊖ d	16 58						17 28							17 58								18 28			
Wandsworth Road	d	16 59						17 29							17 59								18 29			
Battersea Park 4	d	17 02				17 37		17 32		18 05					18 02				18 34				18 32		19 04	
London Victoria 15	⊖ a	17 08			17 28	17 43		17 38		18 12					18 09			18 16	18 40				18 38		19 11	
Penge West	d			17 02			17 23						17 53									18 23				
Anerley	d			17 04			17 25						17 55									18 25				
Norwood Junction 2	d			17 09			17 28				17 33	17 43	17 58	17 54						18 13	18 15	18 28				18 35
West Croydon 4	a			17 14			17 35					17 48	18 05							18 17		18 35				
East Croydon	a										17 37			17 57							18 19					18 38

		SN	SE	SN	SN	SN	SE	SE	SN	SN	SN	SE	SN	SN	SN	SN	SE	SN		SN	SN	SE	SN	SN	SN	SE
			78				83	78				83					83					83				83
		B								C			D					D					D			
London Charing Cross 4	⊖ d																	19 37					20 07			
London Waterloo (East) 4	⊖ d																	19 40					20 10			
London Bridge 4	⊖ d	18 25		18 36	18 41	18 42			18 51	19 05	19 11		19 15	19 24	19 35	19 41		19 45		19 54	20 11		20 15	20 24	20 41	
New Cross Gate 4	⊖ d			18 41		18 47			18 56	19 10			19 20	19 30	19 40			19 50		20 00			20 20	20 30		
Brockley	d			18 44					18 59	19 13			19 23	19 32	19 43			19 53		20 02			20 23	20 32		
Honor Oak Park	d			18 47					19 02	19 16			19 26	19 35	19 46			19 56		20 05			20 26	20 35		
Forest Hill 4	d	18 34		18 49					19 04	19 18			19 28	19 38	19 48			19 58		20 08			20 28	20 38		
Sydenham	d	18 37		18 52					19 07	19 21			19 31	19 40	19 51			20 01		20 10			20 31	20 40		
Crystal Palace 4	d								19 13					19 43						20 13				20 43		
Gipsy Hill	d								19 16					19 46						20 16				20 46		
West Norwood 4	d								19 19					19 49						20 19				20 49		
Streatham Hill	d								19 22					19 52						20 22				20 52		
Balham 4	⊖ d								19 25					19 55						20 25				20 55		
Wandsworth Common	d								19 27					19 57						20 27				20 57		
Clapham Junction 10	d								19 31					20 01						20 31				21 01		
South Bermondsey	d				18 45						19 15					19 45					20 15				20 45	
Queens Rd Peckham	d				18 48						19 18					19 48					20 18				20 48	
Peckham Rye 4	d		18 47		18 50		18 52	19 12			19 20	19 28				19 50	19 53				20 20	20 22			20 50	20 52
Denmark Hill 4	d		18 50		18 53		18 55	19 15			19 23	19 31				19 53	19 55				20 23	20 25			20 53	20 55
London Blackfriars 3	⊖ a						19 03					19 40					20 03					20 33				21 03
Clapham High Street	⊖ d				18 58						19 28					19 58					20 28				20 58	
Wandsworth Road	d				18 59						19 29					19 59					20 29				20 59	
Battersea Park 4	d				19 02				19 34		19 32			20 04		20 02				20 34	20 32			21 04	21 02	
London Victoria 15	⊖ a		19 00		19 08			19 25	19 41		19 36			20 09		20 06				20 40	20 36			21 09	21 06	
Penge West	d			18 54						19 23			19 33		19 53								20 33			
Anerley	d			18 56						19 25			19 36		19 55								20 35			
Norwood Junction 2	d	18 42		18 59		18 56				19 28			19 40		19a58			20 05					20 38			
West Croydon 4	a	18 46		19 06						19 33																
East Croydon	a					19 00							19 43					20 09					20 42			

For general notes see front of timetable
For details of catering facilities see Directory of Train Operators

A To Guildford (Table 182)
B To Dorking (Table 182)
C To Epsom Downs (Table 182)
D To Caterham (Table 181)

b Arr. 1734
c Arr. 1839

Charing Cross and London Bridge → London Victoria and Croydon

Network Diagram - see first page of Table 177

Mondays to Fridays

		SN	SN	SN	SE	SN	SN	SN	SE	SN	SN	SN	SE	SN	SN	SN	SE	SN	SN	SN	SE	SN	SN	SN
					83				83				83				83				83			
		A				A				A				A				A				A		A
London Charing Cross [4]	⊖ d	20 37				21 07				21 37				22 07				22 37				23 07		23 45
London Waterloo (East) [4]	⊖ d	20 40				21 10				21 40				22 10				22 40				23 10		23 48
London Bridge [4]	⊖ d	20 45	20 54	21 11		21 15	21 24	21 41		21 45	21 54	22 11		22 15	22 24	22 41		22 45	22 54	23 11		23 15	23 24	23 53
New Cross Gate [4]	⊖ d	20 50	21 00			21 20	21 30			21 50	22 00			22 20	22 30			22 50	23 00			23 20	23 30	23 58
Brockley	d	20 53	21 02			21 23	21 32			21 53	22 02			22 23	22 32			22 53	23 02			23 23	23 32	00 01
Honor Oak Park	d	20 56	21 05			21 26	21 35			21 56	22 05			22 26	22 35			22 56	23 05			23 26	23 35	00 04
Forest Hill [4]	d	20 58	21 08			21 28	21 38			21 58	22 08			22 28	22 38			22 58	23 08			23 28	23 38	00 06
Sydenham	d	21 01	21 10			21 31	21 40			22 01	22 10			22 31	22 40			23 01	23 10			23 31	23 40	00 09
Crystal Palace [4]	d		21 13				21 43				22 13				22 43				23 13				23 43	
Gipsy Hill	d		21 16				21 46				22 16				22 46				23 16				23 46	
West Norwood [4]	d		21 19				21 49				22 19				22 49				23 19				23 49	
Streatham Hill	d		21 22				21 52				22 22				22 52				23 22				23 52	
Balham [4]	⊖ d		21 25				21 55				22 25				22 55				23 25				23 55	
Wandsworth Common	d		21 27				21 57				22 27				22 57				23 27				23 57	
Clapham Junction [10]	d		21 31				22 01				22 31				23 01				23 31				00 01	
South Bermondsey	d			21 15				21 45				22 15				22 45				23 15				
Queens Rd Peckham	d			21 18				21 48				22 18				22 48				23 18				
Peckham Rye [4]	d			21 20	21 22			21 50	21 52			22 20	22 22			22 50	22 52			23 20	23 24			
Denmark Hill [4]	d			21 23	21 25			21 53	21 55			22 23	22 25			22 53	22 55			23 23	23 26			
London Blackfriars [3]	⊖ a				21 33				22 03				22 33				23 03				23 37			
Clapham High Street	⊖ d			21 28				21 58				22 28				22 58				23 28				
Wandsworth Road	d			21 29				21 59				22 29				22 59				23 29				
Battersea Park [4]	d		21 34	21 32			22 04	22 02			22 34	22 32			23 04	23 02			23 34	23 32			00 04	
London Victoria [15]	⊖ a		21 39	21 36			22 09	22 06			22 39	22 36			23 09	23 06			23 40	23 37			00 12	
Penge West	d	21 03				21 33				22 03				22 33				23 03				23 33		00 11
Anerley	d	21 05				21 35				22 05				22 35				23 05				23 35		00 13
Norwood Junction [2]	d	21 08				21 38				22 08				22 38				23 08				23 38		00 16
West Croydon [4]	a																							
East Croydon	a	21 12				21 42				22 12				22 42				23 12				23 42		00 20

Saturdays

		SN	SN	SN	SN		SE	SN	SE	SN		SN	SE	SE	SN		SN	SN	SE	SE		SN	SN	SN	SE	SE
							73		83				83	78					83	78					83	78
			A							A					B		A					B	A			
London Charing Cross [4]	⊖ d		23p45	00 12																						
London Waterloo (East) [4]	⊖ d		23p48	00 15																						
London Bridge [4]	⊖ d	23p24	23p53	00 26	06 11			06 41		07 05		07 11			07 15		07 35	07 41				07 45	08 05	08 11		
New Cross Gate [4]	⊖ d	23p30	23p58	00 31						07 10					07 20		07 40					07 50	08 10			
Brockley	d	23p32	00 01	00 34						07 13					07 23		07 43					07 53	08 13			
Honor Oak Park	d	23p35	00 04	00 37						07 16					07 26		07 46					07 56	08 16			
Forest Hill [4]	d	23p38	00 06	00 39						07 18					07 28		07 48					07 58	08 18			
Sydenham	d	23p40	00 09	00 42						07 21					07 31		07 51					08 01	08 21			
Crystal Palace [4]	d	23p43																								
Gipsy Hill	d	23p46																								
West Norwood [4]	d	23p49																								
Streatham Hill	d	23p52																								
Balham [4]	⊖ d	23p55																								
Wandsworth Common	d	23p57																								
Clapham Junction [10]	d	00 01																								
South Bermondsey	d				06 15			06 45				07 15						07 45						08 15		
Queens Rd Peckham	d				06 18			06 48				07 18						07 48						08 18		
Peckham Rye [4]	d				06 20		06 22	06 50	06 52			07 20	07 22	07 28				07 50	07 52	07 58				08 20	08 22	08 28
Denmark Hill [4]	d				06 23		06 25	06 53	06 55			07 23	07 25	07 31				07 53	07 55	08 01				08 23	08 25	08 31
London Blackfriars [3]	⊖ a						06 33		07 03				07 33						08 03						08 33	
Clapham High Street	⊖ d				06 28			06 58				07 28						07 58						08 28		
Wandsworth Road	d				06 29			06 59				07 29						07 59						08 29		
Battersea Park [4]	d	00 04			06 32			07 02				07 32						08 02						08 32		
London Victoria [15]	⊖ a	00 12			06 36			07 06				07 36		07 42				08 06		08 12				08 36		08 42
Penge West	d		00 11	00 44											07 33							08 03				
Anerley	d		00 13	00 46											07 35							08 05				
Norwood Junction [2]	d		00 16	00 49						07 25					07 39		07 55					08 09	08 25			
West Croydon [4]	a														07 44							08 14				
East Croydon	a		00 20	00 53						07 29							07 59						08 29			

For general notes see front of timetable
For details of catering facilities see
Directory of Train Operators

A To Caterham (Table 181)
B To Sutton (Surrey) (Table 182)

Table 178

Charing Cross and London Bridge → London Victoria and Croydon

Network Diagram - see first page of Table 177

Station		SN	SN	SN	SN	SE	SE	SN	SN	SN	SN	SE	SE		SN	SN	SN	SN	SE	SE	SN	SN
						83	78					83	78						83	78		
		A		B				A		B					A		B				B	
London Charing Cross 4	⊖ d																					
London Waterloo (East) 4	⊖ d																					
London Bridge 4	⊖ d	08 15	08 24	08 35	08 41			08 45	08 54	09 05	09 11				18 15	18 24	18 35	18 41			18 45	18 54
New Cross Gate 4	⊖ d	08 20	08 30	08 40				08 50	09 00	09 10					18 20	18 30	18 40				18 50	19 00
Brockley	d	08 23	08 32	08 43				08 53	09 02	09 13					18 23	18 32	18 43				18 53	19 02
Honor Oak Park	d	08 26	08 35	08 46				08 56	09 05	09 16					18 26	18 35	18 46				18 56	19 05
Forest Hill 4	d	08 28	08 38	08 48				08 58	09 08	09 18				and at	18 28	18 38	18 48				18 58	19 08
Sydenham	d	08 31	08 40	08 51				09 01	09 10	09 21					18 31	18 40	18 51				19 01	19 10
Crystal Palace 4	d		08 43						09 13					the same		18 43						19 13
Gipsy Hill	d		08 46						09 16							18 46						19 16
West Norwood 4	d		08 49						09 19					minutes		18 49						19 19
Streatham Hill	d		08 52						09 22							18 52						19 22
Balham 4	⊖ d		08 55						09 25					past		18 55						19 25
Wandsworth Common	d		08 57						09 27							18 57						19 27
Clapham Junction 10	d		09 01						09 31					each		19 01						19 31
South Bermondsey	d				08 45						09 15							18 45				
Queens Rd Peckham	d				08 48						09 18			hour until				18 48				
Peckham Rye 4	d				08 50	08 52	08 58				09 20	09 22	09 28					18 50	18 52	18 58		
Denmark Hill 4	d				08 53	08 55	09 01				09 23	09 25	09 31					18 53	18 55	19 01		
London Blackfriars 3	⊖ a					09 03						09 33							19 03			
Clapham High Street	⊖ d				08 58						09 28							18 58				
Wandsworth Road	d				08 59						09 29							18 59				
Battersea Park 4	d		09 04		09 02				09 34		09 32					19 04		19 02				19 34
London Victoria 15	⊖ a		09 09		09 06		09 12		09 39		09 36		09 42			19 10		19 06		19 12		19 39
Penge West	d	08 33						09 03							18 33						19 03	
Anerley	d	08 35						09 05							18 35						19 05	
Norwood Junction 2	d	08 39		08 55				09 09		09 25					18 39		18 55				19 09	
West Croydon 4	🚋 a	08 44						09 14							18 44							
East Croydon	🚋 a			08 59						09 29							18 59				19 13	

Station		SN	SE	SN	SN	SN	SE	SN	SN	SN	SE	SN	SN	SN	SE	SN	SN	SN	SE	SN	SN
			83				83				83				83				83		
				B				B				B				B				B	
London Charing Cross 4	⊖ d			19 07				19 37				20 07				20 37				21 07	
London Waterloo (East) 4	⊖ d			19 10				19 39				20 10				20 40				21 10	
London Bridge 4	⊖ d	19 11		19 15	19 24	19 41		19 44	19 54	20 11		20 15	20 24	20 41		20 45	20 54	21 11		21 15	21 24
New Cross Gate 4	⊖ d			19 20	19 30			19 50	20 00			20 20	20 29			20 50	21 00			21 20	21 30
Brockley	d			19 23	19 32			19 52	20 02			20 23	20 32			20 53	21 02			21 23	21 32
Honor Oak Park	d			19 26	19 35			19 55	20 05			20 26	20 35			20 56	21 05			21 26	21 35
Forest Hill 4	d			19 28	19 38			19 58	20 08			20 28	20 37			20 58	21 08			21 28	21 38
Sydenham	d			19 31	19 40			20 00	20 10			20 31	20 40			21 01	21 10			21 31	21 40
Crystal Palace 4	d				19 43				20 13				20 43				21 13				21 43
Gipsy Hill	d				19 46				20 16				20 45				21 16				21 46
West Norwood 4	d				19 49				20 19				20 48				21 19				21 49
Streatham Hill	d				19 52				20 22				20 52				21 22				21 52
Balham 4	⊖ d				19 55				20 25				20 55				21 25				21 55
Wandsworth Common	d				19 57				20 27				20 57				21 27				21 57
Clapham Junction 10	d				20 01				20 31				21 01				21 31				22 01
South Bermondsey	d	19 15				19 45				20 15				20 45				21 15			
Queens Rd Peckham	d	19 18				19 48				20 18				20 48				21 18			
Peckham Rye 4	d	19 20	19 22			19 50	19 52			20 20	20 22			20 50	20 52			21 20	21 22		
Denmark Hill 4	d	19 23	19 25			19 53	19 55			20 23	20 25			20 53	20 55			21 23	21 25		
London Blackfriars 3	⊖ a		19 33				20 03				20 33				21 03				21 33		
Clapham High Street	⊖ d	19 28				19 58				20 28				20 58				21 28			
Wandsworth Road	d	19 29				19 59				20 29				20 59				21 29			
Battersea Park 4	d	19 32			20 04	20 02			20 34	20 32			21 04	21 02			21 34	21 32			22 04
London Victoria 15	⊖ a	19 36			20 09	20 06			20 39	20 36			21 09	21 06			21 39	21 36			22 09
Penge West	d			19 33				20 03				20 33				21 03				21 33	
Anerley	d			19 35				20 05				20 35				21 05				21 35	
Norwood Junction 2	d			19 38				20 08				20 38				21 08				21 38	
West Croydon 4	🚋 a																				
East Croydon	🚋 a			19 42				20 12				20 42				21 12				21 42	

Station		SN	SE	SN	SN	SN	SE	SN	SN	SN	SE	SN	SN	SN	SE	SN	SN	SN
			83				83				83				83			
				B				B				B				B		B
London Charing Cross 4	⊖ d			21 37				22 07				22 37				23 07		23 45
London Waterloo (East) 4	⊖ d			21 40				22 10				22 40				23 10		23 48
London Bridge 4	⊖ d	21 41		21 45	21 54	22 11		22 15	22 24	22 41		22 45	22 54	23 11		23 15	23 24	23 53
New Cross Gate 4	⊖ d			21 50	22 00			22 20	22 30			22 50	23 00			23 20	23 30	23 58
Brockley	d			21 53	22 02			22 23	22 32			22 53	23 02			23 23	23 32	00 01
Honor Oak Park	d			21 56	22 05			22 26	22 35			22 56	23 05			23 26	23 35	00 04
Forest Hill 4	d			21 58	22 08			22 28	22 38			22 58	23 08			23 28	23 38	00 06
Sydenham	d			22 01	22 10			22 31	22 40			23 01	23 10			23 31	23 40	00 09
Crystal Palace 4	d				22 13				22 43				23 13				23 43	
Gipsy Hill	d				22 16				22 46				23 16				23 46	
West Norwood 4	d				22 19				22 49				23 19				23 49	
Streatham Hill	d				22 22				22 52				23 22				23 52	
Balham 4	⊖ d				22 25				22 55				23 25				23 55	
Wandsworth Common	d				22 27				22 57				23 27				23 57	
Clapham Junction 10	d				22 31				23 01				23 31				00 01	
South Bermondsey	d	21 45				22 15				22 45				23 15				
Queens Rd Peckham	d	21 48				22 18				22 48				23 18				
Peckham Rye 4	d	21 50	21 52			22 20	22 22			22 50	22 52			23 20	23 22			
Denmark Hill 4	d	21 53	21 55			22 23	22 25			22 53	22 55			23 23	23 25			
London Blackfriars 3	⊖ a		22 03				22 33				23 03				23 33			
Clapham High Street	⊖ d	21 58				22 28				22 58				23 28				
Wandsworth Road	d	21 59				22 29				22 59				23 29				
Battersea Park 4	d	22 02			22 34	22 32			23 04	23 02			23 34	23 32			00 04	
London Victoria 15	⊖ a	22 06			22 39	22 36			23 09	23 06			23 40	23 37			00 09	
Penge West	d			22 03				22 33				23 03				23 33		00 11
Anerley	d			22 05				22 35				23 05				23 35		00 13
Norwood Junction 2	d			22 08				22 38				23 08				23 38		00 16
West Croydon 4	🚋 a																	
East Croydon	🚋 a			22 12				22 42				23 12				23 42		00 20

For general notes see front of timetable
For details of catering facilities see Directory of Train Operators

A To Sutton (Surrey) (Table 182)
B To Caterham (Table 181)

Table 178

Sundays

Charing Cross and London Bridge → London Victoria and Croydon

Network Diagram - see first page of Table 177

Station		SN	SN	SN	SN	SE 72	SN		SN	SN	SN	SE 72	SN	SN	SN	SE 72		SN	SN	SN	SN	SN	SN	SE 72	SN
			A						B				A					B			A				B
London Charing Cross 4	⊖ d		23p45	00 12					07 36				08 06					18 36			19 06				19 36
London Waterloo (East) 4	⊖ d		23p48	00 15					07 39				08 09					18 39			19 09				19 39
London Bridge 4	⊖ d	23p24	23p53	00 26	07 11		07 41		07 44	07 58	08 11		08 14	08 28	08 41			18 44	18 58	19 11	19 14	19 28	19 41		19 44
New Cross Gate 4	⊖ d	23p30	23p58	00 31					07 49	08 03			08 19	08 33				18 49	19 03		19 19	19 33			19 49
Brockley	d	23p32	00 01	00 34					07 52	08 06			08 22	08 36				18 52	19 06		19 22	19 36			19 52
Honor Oak Park	d	23p35	00 04	00 37					07 55	08 09			08 25	08 39				18 55	19 09		19 25	19 39			19 55
Forest Hill 4	d	23p38	00 06	00 39					07 57	08 11			08 27	08 41				18 57	19 11		19 27	19 41			19 57
Sydenham	d	23p40	00 09	00 42					08 00	08 14			08 30	08 44				19 00	19 14		19 30	19 44			20 00
Crystal Palace 4	d	23p43															and at the same minutes past each hour until								
Gipsy Hill	d	23p46																							
West Norwood 4	d	23p49																							
Streatham Hill	d	23p52																							
Balham 4	⊖ d	23p55																							
Wandsworth Common	d	23p57																							
Clapham Junction 10	d	00 01																							
South Bermondsey	d				07 15		07 45				08 15				08 45					19 15			19 45		
Queens Rd Peckham	d				07 18		07 48				08 18				08 48					19 18			19 48		
Peckham Rye 4	d				07 20	07 28	07 50				08 20	08 28			08 50	08 58				19 20			19 50	19 58	
Denmark Hill 4	d				07 23	07 31	07 53				08 23	08 31			08 53	09 01				19 23			19 53	20 01	
London Blackfriars 3	⊖ a																								
Clapham High Street	⊖ d				07 28		07 58				08 28				08 58					19 28			19 58		
Wandsworth Road	d				07 29		07 59				08 29				08 59					19 29			19 59		
Battersea Park 4	d	00 04			07 32		08 02				08 32				09 02					19 32			20 02		
London Victoria 15	⊖ a	00 09			07 36	07 41	08 06				08 36	08 41			09 06	09 11				19 36			20 06	20 11	
Penge West	d		00 11	00 44						08 16				08 46					19 16			19 46			
Anerley	d		00 13	00 46						08 18				08 48					19 18			19 48			
Norwood Junction 2	d		00 16	00 49					08 04	08 21			08 34	08 51				19 04	19 21		19 34	19 51			20 04
West Croydon 4	a									08 26				08 56					19 26			19 56			
East Croydon	a		00 20	00 53					08 08				08 38					19 08			19 38				20 08

Station		SN	SN	SN	SN	SN	SE 72	SN	SN	SN	SN	SN	SN	SE 72	SN	SN	SN	SN	SE 92 1	SN	SN	SN	SN	SE 92 1	SN	
				A				B			A				B			A			B		A		A	
London Charing Cross 4	⊖ d			20 06				20 36			21 06				21 36			22 06			22 36		23 06		23 36	
London Waterloo (East) 4	⊖ d			20 09				20 39			21 09				21 39			22 09			22 39		23 09		23 39	
London Bridge 4	⊖ d	19 58	20 11	20 14	20 28	20 41		20 44	20 58	21 11	21 14	21 28	21 41		21 44	21 58	22 11	22 14		22 41	22 44	23 11	23 14		23 44	
New Cross Gate 4	⊖ d	20 03		20 19	20 33			20 49	21 03		21 19	21 33			21 49	22 03		22 19			22 49		23 19		23 49	
Brockley	d	20 06		20 22	20 36			20 52	21 06		21 22	21 36			21 52	22 06		22 22			22 52		23 22		23 52	
Honor Oak Park	d	20 09		20 25	20 39			20 55	21 09		21 25	21 39			21 55	22 09		22 25			22 55		23 25		23 55	
Forest Hill 4	d	20 11		20 27	20 41			20 57	21 11		21 27	21 41			21 57	22 11		22 27			22 57		23 27		23 57	
Sydenham	d	20 14		20 30	20 44			21 00	21 14		21 30	21 44			22 00	22 14		22 30			23 00		23 30		23 59	
Crystal Palace 4	d																									
Gipsy Hill	d																									
West Norwood 4	d																									
Streatham Hill	d																									
Balham 4	⊖ d																									
Wandsworth Common	d																									
Clapham Junction 10	d																									
South Bermondsey	d		20 15			20 45				21 15			21 45				22 15			22 45		23 15				
Queens Rd Peckham	d		20 18			20 48				21 18			21 48				22 18			22 48		23 18				
Peckham Rye 4	d		20 20			20 50	20 58			21 20			21 50	21 58			22 20		22 36	22 50		23 20		23 35		
Denmark Hill 4	d		20 23			20 53	21 01			21 23			21 53	22 01			22 23		22 38	22 53		23 23		23 37		
London Blackfriars 3	⊖ a																									
Clapham High Street	⊖ d		20 28			20 58				21 28			21 58				22 28			22 58		23 28				
Wandsworth Road	d		20 29			20 59				21 29			21 59				22 29			22 59		23 29				
Battersea Park 4	d		20 32			21 02				21 32			22 02				22 32			23 02		23 32				
London Victoria 15	⊖ a		20 36			21 06	21 11			21 36			22 06	22 11			22 36		22 49	23 06		23 37		23 48		
Penge West	d	20 16			20 46				21 16			21 46				22 16		22 32			23 02		23 32		00 02	
Anerley	d	20 18			20 48				21 18			21 48				22 18		22 34			23 04		23 34		00 04	
Norwood Junction 2	d	20 21		20 34	20 51			21 04	21 21		21 34	21 51			22 04	22 21		22 39			23 09		23 39		00 10	
West Croydon 4	a	20 26			20 56				21 26			21 56				22 26										
East Croydon	a			20 38				21 08			21 38				22 08			22 42			23 12		23 42		00 13	

For general notes see front of timetable
For details of catering facilities see Directory of Train Operators

A To Caterham (Table 181)
B To Tattenham Corner (Table 181)

Croydon and London Victoria → London Bridge and Charing Cross

Network Diagram - see first page of Table 177

Miles	Miles	Miles	Miles	Miles			SN A	SE 83	SN B	SE 83	SN C	SN D	SN E	SE 83	SN	SN	SN D	SE 83	SN	SN G		SN	SE 83	SN B	SN	SN C
—	—	0	—	—	**East Croydon**	d	05 13				06 12		06 28		06 40				07 12							07 36
—	—	—	—	0	**West Croydon** [4]	d			05 45			06 15					06 45							07 16	07 28	
—	—	1¼	—	1¾	Norwood Junction [2]	d	05 17		05 50		06 16	06 19	06 32		06 44		06 50		07 16					07 21	07 32	07 41
—	—	2½	—	—	Anerley	d	05 20		05 53			06 22					06 53							07 24	07 35	
—	—	2¾	—	—	Penge West	d	05 22		05 55			06 24					06 55							07 26	07 37	
0	0	—	0	—	**London Victoria** [15]	⊖ d										06 41						07 11				
1¼	1¼	—	—	—	Battersea Park [4]	d										06 45						07 15				
2	—	—	—	—	Wandsworth Road	d										06 47						07 17				
2½	—	—	—	—	Clapham High Street	⊖ d										06 49						07 19				
—	—	—	—	0	**London Blackfriars** [3]	⊖ d		05 27		06 08				06 42				07 09					07 24			
4½	—	—	4¼	3¾	Denmark Hill [4]	d		05 35		06b20				06 52		06 54		07 17				07 24	07 34			
5¼	—	—	5	4½	Peckham Rye [4]	d		05a38		06a23				06a54		06 56		07a20				07 26	07a36			
6	—	—	—	—	Queens Rd Peckham	d										06 59						07 29				
7	—	—	—	—	South Bermondsey	d										07 01						07 31				
—	2¾	—	—	—	Clapham Junction [10]	d																				
—	4	—	—	—	Wandsworth Common	d																				
—	4¾	—	—	—	Balham [4]	⊖ d																				
—	5¾	—	—	—	Streatham Hill	d																				
—	7	—	—	—	West Norwood [4]	d														07 08						
—	8	—	—	—	Gipsy Hill	d														07 11						
—	8¾	—	—	—	**Crystal Palace** [4]	d														07 15						
—	10	3½	—	—	Sydenham	d	05 24		05 57		06 21	06 27	06 37				06 58			07 18				07 29	07 40	07 45
—	10¾	4¼	—	—	Forest Hill [4]	d	05 27		06 00		06 23	06 29	06 39				07 00			07 20				07 31	07 42	07 48
—	11¾	5¼	—	—	Honor Oak Park	d	05 29		06 02			06 32	06 42				07 03			07 23				07 34	07 45	
—	12¾	6¼	—	—	Brockley	d	05 32		06 05			06 34	06 44				07 05			07 25				07 36	07 47	
—	13¾	7¼	—	—	New Cross Gate [4]	⊖ d	05 34		06 07		06 28	06 37	06 47		06 53		07 08		07 24	07 28				07 39	07 50	07 52
8¾	16½	10	—	—	**London Bridge** [4]	⊖ a	05 41		06 14		06 34	06 45	06 54		07 02	07 08	07 16		07 33	07 36		07 38		07 48	07 58	08 01
—	—	11	—	—	London Waterloo (East) [4]	⊖ a	05 46																			
—	—	11¾	—	—	**London Charing Cross** [4]	⊖ a	05 49																			

		SN	SN B	SN	SE 83	SN	SN	SN	SN	SE 83	SE 78	SN H		SN	SE 83	SN	SN	SN	SN B	SN	SN	SE 78	SE 83	SN	SN	SN J
East Croydon	d															08 45									09 20	
West Croydon [4]	d		07 43			07 56						08 23		08 28					08 44	08 59						09 15
Norwood Junction [2]	d		07 48			08 01						08 28		08 32		08 49			08 49	09 03					09 25	09 19
Anerley	d					08 04								08 35					08 52	09 06						09 22
Penge West	d					08 06								08 37					08 54	09 08						09 24
London Victoria [15]	⊖ d	07 41					07 51	08 11			08 21						08 41	08 22			08 52	09 01		09 11		
Battersea Park [4]	d	07 45					07 55	08 15									08 45	08 26			08 56			09 15		
Wandsworth Road	d	07 47						08 17									08 47							09 17		
Clapham High Street	⊖ d	07 49						08 19									08 49							09 19		
London Blackfriars [3]	⊖ d				07 53					08 20					08 43								09 13			
Denmark Hill [4]	d	07 54			08 02			08 24		08 29	08 31				08 52		08 54					09 12	09 22	09 24		
Peckham Rye [4]	d	07 56			08a04			08 26		08a31	08a35				08a55		08 56					09a14	09a25	09 26		
Queens Rd Peckham	d	07 59						08 29									08 59							09 29		
South Bermondsey	d	08 01						08 31									09 01							09 31		
Clapham Junction [10]	d						07 58											08 30			08 59					
Wandsworth Common	d						08 01											08 33			09 02					
Balham [4]	⊖ d						08 04											08 35			09 05					
Streatham Hill	d			07 45			08 07		08 14									08 38			09 08					
West Norwood [4]	d			07 48			08 10		08 17									08 42			09 11					
Gipsy Hill	d			07 51			08 13		08 20									08 45			09 14					
Crystal Palace [4]	d			07 54			08 16		08 23									08 48			09 17					
Sydenham	d		07 53	07 57		08 08	08 19		08 26			08 33		08 40				08 51	08 57	09 11	09 20					09 27
Forest Hill [4]	d		07 55	07 59		08 11	08 21		08 29			08 35		08 42				08 53	08 59	09 13	09 22					09 29
Honor Oak Park	d			08 02		08 13	08 24		08 31					08 45				08 56	09 02	09 16	09 25					09 32
Brockley	d			08 04		08 16	08 26		08 34					08 47				08 58	09 04	09 18	09 27					09 34
New Cross Gate [4]	⊖ d		08 00	08 07		08 18	08 29		08 36					08 50		08 57		09 01	09 07	09 21	09 30				09 33	09 37
London Bridge [4]	⊖ a	08 08	08 08	08 16		08 27	08 38	08 38	08 46			08 47		09 02		09 05	09 08	09 12	09 17	09 29	09 38			09 38	09 42	09 46
London Waterloo (East) [4]	⊖ a																									
London Charing Cross [4]	⊖ a																									

		SE 78	SN C	SE 83		SN	SN	SN B		SN C	SN	SE 78	SE 83	SN	SN D	SN C	SN	SE 78	SE 83	SN	SN D			SN C	SE 78
East Croydon	d		09 31							10 00						10 30								15 00	
West Croydon [4]	d							09 46							10 15						10 45				
Norwood Junction [2]	d		09 35					09 51		10 04					10 19	10 34					10 49			15 04	
Anerley	d							09 54							10 22						10 52				
Penge West	d							09 56							10 24						10 54				
London Victoria [15]	⊖ d	09 31				09 41	09 22				09 52	10 01		10 11			10 22	10 31		10 41					15 01
Battersea Park [4]	d					09 45	09 26				09 56			10 15			10 26			10 45		and at the same minutes past each hour until			
Wandsworth Road	d					09 47								10 17						10 47					
Clapham High Street	⊖ d					09 49								10 19						10 49					
London Blackfriars [3]	⊖ d			09 43									10 13						10 43						
Denmark Hill [4]	d	09 42		09 52		09 54						10 12	10 22	10 24				10 42	10 52	10 54					15 12
Peckham Rye [4]	d	09a44		09a55		09 56						10a14	10a25	10 26				10a44	10a55	10 56					15a14
Queens Rd Peckham	d					09 59								10 29						10 59					
South Bermondsey	d					10 01								10 31						11 01					
Clapham Junction [10]	d						09 29				09 59						10 29								
Wandsworth Common	d						09 32				10 02						10 32								
Balham [4]	⊖ d						09 35				10 05						10 35								
Streatham Hill	d						09 38				10 08						10 38								
West Norwood [4]	d						09 41				10 11						10 41								
Gipsy Hill	d						09 44				10 14						10 44								
Crystal Palace [4]	d						09 47				10 17						10 47								
Sydenham	d		09 40				09 50	09 58		10 09	10 20				10 27	10 39	10 50				10 57			15 09	
Forest Hill [4]	d		09 42				09 52	10 01		10 11	10 22				10 29	10 41	10 52				10 59			15 11	
Honor Oak Park	d		09 45				09 55	10 03		10 14	10 25				10 32	10 44	10 55				11 02			15 14	
Brockley	d		09 47				09 57	10 06		10 16	10 27				10 34	10 46	10 57				11 04			15 16	
New Cross Gate [4]	⊖ d		09 50				10 00	10 08		10 19	10 30				10 37	10 49	11 00				11 07			15 19	
London Bridge [4]	⊖ a		09 59			10 06	10 08	10 15		10 25	10 36			10 36	10 44	10 55	11 06			11 06	11 14			15 27	
London Waterloo (East) [4]	⊖ a																								
London Charing Cross [4]	⊖ a																								

For general notes see front of timetable
For details of catering facilities see Directory of Train Operators

- **A** From Purley (Table 175)
- **B** From Epsom (Table 182)
- **C** From Caterham (Table 181)
- **D** From Sutton (Surrey) (Table 182)
- **E** From Tattenham Corner (Table 181)
- **G** From London Bridge (Table 177)
- **H** From Epsom Downs (Table 182)
- **J** From Guildford (Table 182)
- **b** Arr. 0617

Croydon and London Victoria → London Bridge and Charing Cross

Network Diagram - see first page of Table 177

		SE	SN	SN	SN	SN	SE	SE	SN	SN	SN	SN	SN	SE	SN		SE	SN	SE	SN	SE	SN	SN	SN	SE	SN
		83					78	83						83			78		73		83				78	
					A	B					A	B						A		B				A		B
East Croydon	d					15 30						16 00								16 31						17 00
West Croydon 4	d				15 15						15 45							16 15						16 45		
Norwood Junction 2	d				15 19	15 34					15 49	16 04						16 19		16 35				16 49		17 04
Anerley	d				15 22						15 52							16 22						16 52		
Penge West	d				15 24						15 54							16 24						16 54		
London Victoria 15	⊖ d		15 11	14 52			15 31		15 41	15 22			15 52		16 11		16 14					16 41	16 22		17 00	
Battersea Park 4	d		15 15	14 56					15 45	15 26			15 56		16 15							16 45	16 26			
Wandsworth Road	d		15 17						15 47						16 17							16 47				
Clapham High Street	⊖ d		15 19						15 49						16 19							16 49				
London Blackfriars 3	⊖ d	15 13						15 43						16 09					16 27		16 42					
Denmark Hill 4	d	15 22	15 24				15 42	15 52	15 54					16 18	16 24		16 27		16 36		16 51	16 54			17 09	
Peckham Rye 4	d	15a25	15 26				15a44	15a55	15 56					16a21	16 26		16a29		16a40		16a54	16 56			17a13	
Queens Rd Peckham	d		15 29						15 59						16 29							16 59				
South Bermondsey	d		15 31						16 01						16 31							17 01				
Clapham Junction 10	d			14 59						15 29			15 59										16 29			
Wandsworth Common	d			15 02						15 32			16 02										16 32			
Balham 4	⊖ d			15 05						15 35			16 05										16 35			
Streatham Hill	d			15 08						15 38			16 08										16 38			
West Norwood 4	d			15 11						15 41			16 11										16 41			
Gipsy Hill	d			15 14						15 44			16 14										16 44			
Crystal Palace 4	d			15 17						15 47			16 17										16 47			
Sydenham	d			15 20	15 27	15 39				15 50	15 57	16 09	16 20					16 27		16 40			16 50	16 57		17 09
Forest Hill 4	d			15 22	15 29	15 41				15 52	15 59	16 11	16 22					16 29		16 42			16 52	16 59		17 11
Honor Oak Park	d			15 25	15 32	15 44				15 55	16 02	16 14	16 25					16 32		16 45			16 55	17 02		17 14
Brockley	d			15 27	15 34	15 46				15 57	16 04	16 16	16 27					16 34		16 47			16 57	17 04		17 16
New Cross Gate 4	⊖ d			15 30	15 37	15 49				16 00	16 07	16 19	16 30					16 37		16 50			17 00	17 07		17 19
London Bridge 4	⊖ a		15 36	15 38	15 44	15 55			16 06	16 08	16 15	16 26	16 36		16 38			16 44		16 58		17 08	17 10	17 14		17 27
London Waterloo (East) 4	⊖ a																									
London Charing Cross 4	⊖ a																									

		SN	SE	SN	SE	SN	SN		SN	SE	SE	SN	SN	SE	SN	SN	SN	SE	SN	SE	SN	SN		SN	SE	SN
			83		78					83	78			83				78		83					83	
						C	B						C		B	D					A	B				
East Croydon	d						17 32								18 05							18 35				
West Croydon 4	d					17 17							17 47								18 15					
Norwood Junction 2	d					17 21	17 36						17 52		18 09						18 19	18 39				
Anerley	d					17 24							17 55								18 22					
Penge West	d					17 26							17 57								18 24					
London Victoria 15	⊖ d	16 52		17 11	17 19				17 19		17 41	17 41					17 51	18 08	18 11					18 22		18 41
Battersea Park 4	d	16 56		17 15					17 23			17 45					17 55		18 15					18 26		18 45
Wandsworth Road	d			17 17								17 47							18 17							18 47
Clapham High Street	⊖ d			17 19								17 49							18 19							18 49
London Blackfriars 3	⊖ d		17 10							17 36				18 05						18 23					18 43	
Denmark Hill 4	d		17 19	17 24	17 28					17 45	17 51	17 54		18 14				18 17	18 24	18 32					18 52	18 54
Peckham Rye 4	d		17a22	17 26	17a31					17a47	17a54	17 56		18a17				18a20	18 26	18a34					18a55	18 56
Queens Rd Peckham	d			17 29								17 59							18 29							18 59
South Bermondsey	d			17 31								18 01							18 31							19 01
Clapham Junction 10	d	16 59							17 26								17 59							18 29		
Wandsworth Common	d	17 02							17 29								18 02							18 32		
Balham 4	⊖ d	17 05							17 32								18 05							18 35		
Streatham Hill	d	17 08							17 35								18 08							18 38		
West Norwood 4	d	17 11							17 38							18 05	18 15							18 41		
Gipsy Hill	d	17 14							17 41							18 08	18 18							18 44		
Crystal Palace 4	d	17 17							17 45							18 14	18 21							18 47		
Sydenham	d	17 20				17 29	17 40		17 49				17 59		18 14	18 17	18 24				18 27	18 44		18 50		
Forest Hill 4	d	17 22				17 31	17 43		17 51				18 02		18 16	18 19	18 26				18 29	18 46		18 52		
Honor Oak Park	d	17 25				17 34	17 45		17 54				18 04			18 22	18 29				18 32	18 49		18 55		
Brockley	d	17 27				17 36	17 48		17 56				18 07			18 24	18 31				18 34	18 51		18 57		
New Cross Gate 4	⊖ d	17 30				17 39	17 50		17 59				18 09		18 21	18 27	18 34				18 37	18 54		19 00		
London Bridge 4	⊖ a	17 38		17 38		17 45	17 58		18 10			18 08	18 19		18 28	18 34	18 42		18 38		18 44	19 00		19 08		19 08
London Waterloo (East) 4	⊖ a																									
London Charing Cross 4	⊖ a																									

		SE	SN	SN	SN	SE	SN	SE	SN	SN	SN	SE	SN	SE		SN	SN	SE	SN	SN	SN	SE	SN	SN	SN	SN
		78				83		78				83		78				83				83				
			C				B		E				B			E				B			G		B	
East Croydon	d						19 10						19 40							20 10			20 30		20 40	
West Croydon 4	d		18 48						19 22							19 49										
Norwood Junction 2	d		18 52	19 06			19 14		19 27				19 44			19 54				20 14			20 34		20 44	
Anerley	d		18 55				19 17						19 47			19 57				20 17			20 37		20 47	
Penge West	d		18 57				19 19						19 49			19 59				20 19			20 39		20 49	
London Victoria 15	⊖ d	18 46			19 11			19 16		19 05	19 41			19 46			19 35		20 11		20 05			20 41		20 35
Battersea Park 4	d				19 15					19 09	19 45						19 39		20 15		20 09			20 45		20 39
Wandsworth Road	d				19 17						19 47								20 17					20 47		
Clapham High Street	⊖ d				19 19						19 49								20 19					20 49		
London Blackfriars 3	⊖ d					19 17						19 47						20 13				20 43				
Denmark Hill 4	d	18 57			19 23	19 25		19 27			19 54	19 55		19 57				20 22	20 24			20 52		20 54		
Peckham Rye 4	d	19a00			19 27	19a28		19a31			19 56	19a58		20a01				20a25	20 26			20a55		20 56		
Queens Rd Peckham	d				19 30						19 59								20 29					20 59		
South Bermondsey	d				19 32						20 01								20 31					21 01		
Clapham Junction 10	d									19 12							19 42				20 12					20 42
Wandsworth Common	d									19 15							19 45				20 15					20 45
Balham 4	⊖ d									19 18							19 48				20 18					20 48
Streatham Hill	d									19 21							19 51				20 21					20 51
West Norwood 4	d									19 24							19 54				20 24					20 54
Gipsy Hill	d									19 27							19 57				20 27					20 57
Crystal Palace 4	d									19 32							20 01				20 31					21 01
Sydenham	d		19 01	19 10			19 22		19 32	19 35			19 52			20 02	20 05			20 22	20 34		20 41		20 52	21 04
Forest Hill 4	d		19 03	19 13			19 24		19 34	19 37			19 54			20 04	20 07			20 24	20 36		20 44		20 54	21 06
Honor Oak Park	d		19 06	19 15			19 27		19 37	19 40			19 57			20 07	20 10			20 27	20 39		20 46		20 57	21 09
Brockley	d		19 08	19 18			19 29		19 39	19 42			19 59			20 09	20 12			20 29	20 41		20 49		20 59	21 11
New Cross Gate 4	⊖ d		19 11	19 20			19 32		19 42	19 45			20 02			20 12	20 15			20 32	20 44		20 51		21 02	21 14
London Bridge 4	⊖ a		19 18	19 27	19 37		19 39		19 49	19 52	20 06		20 11			20 19	20 22		20 36	20 41	20 53		20 59	21 06	21 11	21 22
London Waterloo (East) 4	⊖ a						19 45						20 16							20 46					21 16	
London Charing Cross 4	⊖ a						19 49						20 20							20 50					21 20	

For general notes see front of timetable
For details of catering facilities see Directory of Train Operators

A From Sutton (Surrey) (Table 182)
B From Caterham (Table 181)
C From Epsom (Table 182)
D From London Bridge (Table 177)
E From Guildford (Table 182)
G From Tattenham Corner (Table 181)

Croydon and London Victoria → London Bridge and Charing Cross

Network Diagram - see first page of Table 177

		SE 83	SN	SN A	SN	SE 83		SN	SN A	SN	SE 83	SN	SN A	SN	SE 73	SN	SN A	SN	SE 73	SN	SN A		SN	SE 73		
East Croydon	d			21 10					21 40				22 10				22 40				23 10					
West Croydon 4	d																									
Norwood Junction 2	d			21 14					21 44				22 14				22 44				23 14					
Anerley	d			21 17					21 47				22 17				22 47				23 17					
Penge West	d			21 19					21 49				22 19				22 49				23 19					
London Victoria 15	⊖ d		21 11		21 05			21 41		21 35		22 11		22 05		22 41		22 35		23 11			23 05			
Battersea Park 4	d		21 15		21 09			21 45		21 39		22 15		22 09		22 45		22 39		23 15			23 09			
Wandsworth Road	d		21 17					21 47				22 17				22 47				23 17						
Clapham High Street	⊖ d		21 19					21 49				22 19				22 49				23 19						
London Blackfriars 3	⊖ d	21 13				21 43					22 13				22 43				23 13					23 43		
Denmark Hill 4	d	21 22	21 24			21 52		21 54			22 22	22 24			22 52	22 54			23 22	23 24				23 52		
Peckham Rye 4	d	21a25	21 26			21a55		21 56			22a25	22 26			22a55	22 56			23a25	23 26				23a55		
Queens Rd Peckham	d		21 29					21 59				22 29				22 59				23 29						
South Bermondsey	d		21 31					22 01				22 31				23 01				23 31						
Clapham Junction 10	d				21 12					21 42				22 12				22 42					23 12			
Wandsworth Common	d				21 15					21 45				22 15				22 45					23 15			
Balham 4	⊖ d				21 18					21 48				22 18				22 48					23 18			
Streatham Hill	d				21 21					21 51				22 21				22 51					23 21			
West Norwood 4	d				21 24					21 54				22 24				22 54					23 24			
Gipsy Hill	d				21 27					21 57				22 27				22 57					23 27			
Crystal Palace 4	d				21 31					22 01				22 31				23 01					23 31			
Sydenham	d			21 22	21 34				21 52	22 04			22 22	22 34			22 52	23 04			23 22		23 34			
Forest Hill 4	d			21 24	21 36				21 54	22 06			22 24	22 36			22 54	23 06			23 24		23 36			
Honor Oak Park	d			21 27	21 39				21 57	22 09			22 27	22 39			22 57	23 09			23 27		23 39			
Brockley	d			21 29	21 41				21 59	22 11			22 29	22 41			22 59	23 11			23 29		23 41			
New Cross Gate 4	⊖ d			21 32	21 44				22 02	22 14			22 32	22 44			23 02	23 14			23 32		23 44			
London Bridge 4	⊖ a		21 36	21 41	21 52			22 06	22 11	22 22		22 36	22 41	22 52		23 06	23 11	23 22		23 36	23 38		23 52			
London Waterloo (East) 4	⊖ a			21 46					22 16				22 46				23 16				23 43					
London Charing Cross 4	⊖ a			21 50					22 20				22 50				23 20				23 48					

Saturdays

		SE 82	SN A	SE 83	SN	SN	SN A		SE 83	SN	SN B	SN A	SE 83	SN		SN B	SN A	SN	SE 78	SE 83	SN		SN B	SN A	SN	SE 78
East Croydon	d		06 30			06 43	07 00					07 30					08 00							08 30		
West Croydon 4	d										07 15					07 45							08 15			
Norwood Junction 2	d		06 34			06 49	07 04				07 19	07 34				07 49	08 04						08 19	08 34		
Anerley	d					06 52					07 22					07 52							08 22			
Penge West	d					06 54					07 24					07 54							08 24			
London Victoria 15	⊖ d	06 13			06 41					07 11				07 41				07 52	08 01		08 11				08 22	08 31
Battersea Park 4	d				06 45					07 15				07 45				07 56			08 15				08 26	
Wandsworth Road	d				06 47					07 17				07 47							08 17					
Clapham High Street	⊖ d				06 49					07 19				07 49							08 19					
London Blackfriars 3	⊖ d			06 43					07 13				07 43							08 13						
Denmark Hill 4	d	06 22		06 52	06 54				07 22	07 24			07 52	07 54					08 12	08 22	08 24					08 42
Peckham Rye 4	d	06a25		06a55	06 56				07a25	07 26			07a55	07 56					08a14	08a25	08 26					08a44
Queens Rd Peckham	d				06 59					07 29				07 59							08 29					
South Bermondsey	d				07 01					07 31				08 01							08 31					
Clapham Junction 10	d																	07 59							08 29	
Wandsworth Common	d																	08 02							08 32	
Balham 4	⊖ d																	08 05							08 35	
Streatham Hill	d																	08 08							08 38	
West Norwood 4	d																	08 11							08 41	
Gipsy Hill	d																	08 14							08 44	
Crystal Palace 4	d																	08 17							08 47	
Sydenham	d		06 39			06 57	07 09				07 27	07 39				07 57	08 09	08 20					08 27	08 39	08 50	
Forest Hill 4	d		06 41			06 59	07 11				07 29	07 41				07 59	08 11	08 22					08 29	08 41	08 52	
Honor Oak Park	d		06 44			07 02	07 14				07 32	07 44				08 02	08 14	08 25					08 32	08 44	08 55	
Brockley	d		06 46			07 04	07 16				07 34	07 46				08 04	08 16	08 27					08 34	08 46	08 57	
New Cross Gate 4	⊖ d		06 49			07 07	07 19				07 37	07 49				08 07	08 19	08 30					08 37	08 49	09 00	
London Bridge 4	⊖ a		06 55		07 06	07 14	07 25			07 36	07 44	07 55		08 06		08 14	08 25	08 36			08 36		08 44	08 55	09 06	
London Waterloo (East) 4	⊖ a																									
London Charing Cross 4	⊖ a																									

For general notes see front of timetable
For details of catering facilities see Directory of Train Operators

A From Caterham (Table 181)
B From Sutton (Surrey) (Table 182)

Croydon and London Victoria → London Bridge and Charing Cross

Network Diagram - see first page of Table 177

Station		SE 83	SN	SN A	SN B	SN	SE 78	SN	SE 83	SN	SN A	SN B	SN	SE 78	SN	SE 83	SN	SN A	SN B	SN	SE 78	SE 83
East Croydon	d				09 00							09 30							10 00			
West Croydon	d			08 45							09 15							09 45				
Norwood Junction	d			08 49	09 04						09 19	09 34						09 49	10 04			
Anerley	d			08 52							09 22							09 52				
Penge West	d			08 54							09 24							09 54				
London Victoria	d		08 41			08 52	09 01	09 07		09 11			09 22	09 31	09 37		09 41			09 52	10 01	
Battersea Park	d		08 45			08 56		09 11		09 15			09 26		09 41		09 45			09 56		
Wandsworth Road	d		08 47							09 17							09 47					
Clapham High Street	d		08 49							09 19							09 49					
London Blackfriars	d	08 43							09 13							09 43						10 13
Denmark Hill	d	08 52	08 54				09 12		09 22	09 24				09 42		09 52	09 54				10 12	10 22
Peckham Rye	d	08a55	08 56				09a14		09a25	09 26				09a44		09a55	09 56				10a14	10a25
Queens Rd Peckham	d		08 59							09 29							09 59					
South Bermondsey	d		09 01							09 31							10 01					
Clapham Junction	d					08 59		09 14					09 29		09 44					09 59		
Wandsworth Common	d					09 02		09 17					09 32		09 47					10 02		
Balham	d					09 05		09 20					09 35		09 50					10 05		
Streatham Hill	d					09 08		09 23					09 38		09 53					10 08		
West Norwood	d					09 11		09 26					09 41		09 56					10 11		
Gipsy Hill	d					09 14		09 29					09 44		09 59					10 14		
Crystal Palace	d					09 17		09a32					09 47		10a02					10 17		
Sydenham	d			08 57	09 09	09 20					09 27	09 39	09 50					09 57	10 09	10 20		
Forest Hill	d			08 59	09 11	09 22					09 29	09 41	09 52					09 59	10 11	10 22		
Honor Oak Park	d			09 02	09 14	09 25					09 32	09 44	09 55					10 02	10 14	10 25		
Brockley	d			09 04	09 16	09 27					09 34	09 46	09 57					10 04	10 16	10 27		
New Cross Gate	d			09 07	09 19	09 30					09 37	09 49	10 00					10 07	10 19	10 30		
London Bridge	a		09 06	09 14	09 25	09 36				09 36	09 44	09 55	10 06				10 06	10 14	10 25	10 36		
London Waterloo (East)	a																					
London Charing Cross	a																					

Station		SN	SN A	SN B	SN	SE 78	SE 83	SN	SN A		SN B	SN	SE 78	SE 83	SN	SN A	SN B	SN	SE 78	SE 83	SN	SN A	SE 78
East Croydon	d			10 30							18 00						18 30						
West Croydon	d		10 15						10 45							18 15						18 45	
Norwood Junction	d		10 19	10 34					10 49		18 04					18 19	18 34					18 49	
Anerley	d		10 22						10 52							18 22						18 52	
Penge West	d		10 24						10 54							18 24						18 54	
London Victoria	d	10 11			10 22	10 31		10 41				17 52	18 01		18 11			18 22	18 31		18 41		19 01
Battersea Park	d	10 15			10 26			10 45		and at		17 56			18 15			18 26			18 45		
Wandsworth Road	d	10 17						10 47							18 17						18 47		
Clapham High Street	d	10 19						10 49		the same					18 19						18 49		
London Blackfriars	d						10 43							18 13						18 43			
Denmark Hill	d	10 24				10 42	10 52	10 54		minutes			18 12	18 22	18 24				18 42	18 52	18 54		19 12
Peckham Rye	d	10 26				10a44	10a55	10 56					18a14	18a25	18 26				18a44	18a55	18 56		19a14
Queens Rd Peckham	d	10 29						10 59		past					18 29						18 59		
South Bermondsey	d	10 31						11 01							18 31						19 01		
Clapham Junction	d				10 29					each		17 59						18 29					
Wandsworth Common	d				10 32							18 02						18 32					
Balham	d				10 35					hour until		18 05						18 35					
Streatham Hill	d				10 38							18 08						18 38					
West Norwood	d				10 41							18 11						18 41					
Gipsy Hill	d				10 44							18 14						18 44					
Crystal Palace	d				10 47							18 17						18 47					
Sydenham	d		10 27	10 39	10 50				10 57		18 09	18 20				18 27	18 39	18 50				18 57	
Forest Hill	d		10 29	10 41	10 52				10 59		18 11	18 22				18 29	18 41	18 52				18 59	
Honor Oak Park	d		10 32	10 44	10 55				11 02		18 14	18 25				18 32	18 44	18 55				19 02	
Brockley	d		10 34	10 46	10 57				11 04		18 16	18 27				18 34	18 46	18 57				19 04	
New Cross Gate	d		10 37	10 49	11 00				11 07		18 19	18 30				18 37	18 49	19 00				19 07	
London Bridge	a	10 36	10 44	10 55	11 06			11 06	11 14		18 25	18 36			18 36	18 44	18 55	19 06			19 06	19 14	
London Waterloo (East)	a																						
London Charing Cross	a																						

Station		SN C	SE 83	SN	SN D	SN	SE 78	SN C	SE 83	SN	SN B	SN	SE 83	SN	SN B	SN	SE 83	SN	SN B	SN	SE 83	SN
East Croydon	d	18 51			19 10			19 21			19 40				20 10				20 40			
West Croydon	d																					
Norwood Junction	d	19b01			19 14			19c31			19 44				20 14				20 44			
Anerley	d	19 04			19 17			19 34			19 47				20 17				20 47			
Penge West	d	19 06			19 19			19 36			19 49				20 19				20 49			
London Victoria	d			19 11		19 05	19 31			19 41		19 35		20 11		20 05		20 41		20 35		21 11
Battersea Park	d			19 15		19 09				19 45		19 39		20 15		20 09		20 45		20 39		21 15
Wandsworth Road	d			19 17						19 47				20 17				20 47				21 17
Clapham High Street	d			19 19						19 49				20 19				20 49				21 19
London Blackfriars	d		19 13						19 43				20 13				20 43				21 13	
Denmark Hill	d		19 22	19 24			19 42		19 52	19 54			20 22	20 24			20 52	20 54			21 22	21 24
Peckham Rye	d		19a25	19 26			19a44		19a55	19 56			20a25	20 26			20a55	20 56			21a25	21 26
Queens Rd Peckham	d			19 29						19 59				20 29				20 59				21 29
South Bermondsey	d			19 31						20 01				20 31				21 01				21 31
Clapham Junction	d					19 12						19 42				20 12				20 42		
Wandsworth Common	d					19 15						19 45				20 15				20 45		
Balham	d					19 18						19 48				20 18				20 48		
Streatham Hill	d					19 21						19 51				20 21				20 51		
West Norwood	d					19 24						19 54				20 24				20 54		
Gipsy Hill	d					19 27						19 57				20 27				20 57		
Crystal Palace	d					19 31						20 01				20 31				21 01		
Sydenham	d	19 08			19 22	19 34		19 38			19 52	20 04			20 22	20 34			20 52	21 04		
Forest Hill	d	19 11			19 24	19 36		19 41			19 54	20 06			20 24	20 36			20 54	21 06		
Honor Oak Park	d	19 13			19 27	19 39		19 43			19 57	20 09			20 27	20 39			20 57	21 09		
Brockley	d	19 16			19 29	19 41		19 46			19 59	20 11			20 29	20 41			20 59	21 11		
New Cross Gate	d	19 18			19 32	19 44		19 48			20 02	20 14			20 32	20 44			21 02	21 14		
London Bridge	a	19 25		19 36	19 41	19 52		19 55		20 06	20 11	20 22		20 36	20 41	20 52		21 06	21 11	21 22		21 36
London Waterloo (East)	a				19 46						20 16				20 46				21 16			
London Charing Cross	a				19 51						20 21				20 51				21 21			

For general notes see front of timetable
For details of catering facilities see Directory of Train Operators

A From Sutton (Surrey) (Table 182)
B From Caterham (Table 181)
C From Smitham (Table 181)
D From Purley (Table 175)

b Arr. 1856
c Arr. 1926

Table 178

Croydon and London Victoria → London Bridge and Charing Cross

Network Diagram - see first page of Table 177

Saturdays

		SN	SN	SE	SN	SN	SN	SE	SN	SN	SN	SE	SN	SN	SN	SE	SN	SN	SN	SE
				83				83				73				73				73
		A				A				A				A				A		
East Croydon	d	21 10				21 40				22 10				22 40				23 10		
West Croydon 4	d																			
Norwood Junction 2	d	21 14				21 44				22 14				22 44				23 14		
Anerley	d	21 17				21 47				22 17				22 47				23 17		
Penge West	d	21 19				21 49				22 19				22 49				23 19		
London Victoria 15	d		21 05		21 41		21 35		22 11		22 05		22 41		22 35		23 11		23 05	
Battersea Park 4	d		21 09		21 45		21 39		22 15		22 09		22 45		22 39		23 15		23 09	
Wandsworth Road	d				21 47				22 17				22 47				23 17			
Clapham High Street	d				21 49				22 19				22 49				23 19			
London Blackfriars 3	d			21 43				22 13				22 43				23 13				23 43
Denmark Hill 4	d			21 52	21 54			22 22	22 24			22 52	22 54			23 22	23 24			23 52
Peckham Rye 4	d			21a55	21 56			22a25	22 26			22a55	22 56			23a25	23 26			23a55
Queens Rd Peckham	d				21 59				22 29				22 59				23 29			
South Bermondsey	d				22 01				22 31				23 01				23 31			
Clapham Junction 10	d		21 12				21 42				22 12				22 42				23 12	
Wandsworth Common	d		21 15				21 45				22 15				22 45				23 15	
Balham 4	d		21 18				21 48				22 18				22 48				23 18	
Streatham Hill	d		21 21				21 51				22 21				22 51				23 21	
West Norwood 4	d		21 24				21 54				22 24				22 54				23 24	
Gipsy Hill	d		21 27				21 57				22 27				22 57				23 27	
Crystal Palace 4	d		21 31				22 01				22 31				23 01				23 31	
Sydenham	d	21 22	21 34			21 52	22 04			22 22	22 34			22 52	23 04			23 22	23 34	
Forest Hill 4	d	21 24	21 36			21 54	22 06			22 24	22 36			22 54	23 06			23 24	23 36	
Honor Oak Park	d	21 27	21 39			21 57	22 09			22 27	22 39			22 57	23 09			23 27	23 39	
Brockley	d	21 29	21 41			21 59	22 11			22 29	22 41			22 59	23 11			23 29	23 41	
New Cross Gate 4	d	21 32	21 44			22 02	22 14			22 32	22 44			23 02	23 14			23 32	23 44	
London Bridge 4	a	21 41	21 52		22 06	22 11	22 22		22 36	22 41	22 52		23 06	23 11	23 22		23 36	23 38	23 52	
London Waterloo (East) 4	a	21 46				22 16				22 46				23 16				23 43		
London Charing Cross 4	a	21 51				22 21				22 51				23 20				23 48		

Sundays

		SN	SN	SN	SN	SE	SN	SN	SN	SN	SN	SN	SE	SN	SN	SN	SE		SN
						72							72				72		
		B			A				C			A				C			
East Croydon	d	06 44	07 12		07 47				08 17			08 47				09 17		and at the same minutes past each hour until	
West Croydon 4	d						08 01			08 31				09 01					18 31
Norwood Junction 2	d	06 48	07 18		07 51		08 05		08 21	08 35		08 51		09 05		09 21			18 35
Anerley	d	06 51	07 21				08 08			08 38				09 08					18 38
Penge West	d	06 53	07 23				08 10			08 40				09 10					18 40
London Victoria 15	d			07 41		07 56		08 11			08 41		08 56		09 11		09 26		
Battersea Park 4	d			07 45				08 15			08 45				09 15				
Wandsworth Road	d			07 47				08 17			08 47				09 17				
Clapham High Street	d			07 49				08 19			08 49				09 19				
London Blackfriars 3	d																		
Denmark Hill 4	d			07 54		08 05		08 24			08 54		09 05		09 24		09 35		
Peckham Rye 4	d			07 56		08a07		08 26			08 56		09a07		09 26		09a37		
Queens Rd Peckham	d			07 59				08 29			08 59				09 29				
South Bermondsey	d			08 01				08 31			09 01				09 31				
Clapham Junction 10	d																		
Wandsworth Common	d																		
Balham 4	d																		
Streatham Hill	d																		
West Norwood 4	d																		
Gipsy Hill	d																		
Crystal Palace 4	d																		
Sydenham	d	06 55	07 25		07 55		08 13		08 25	08 43		08 55		09 13		09 25			18 43
Forest Hill 4	d	06 58	07 28		07 58		08 15		08 28	08 45		08 58		09 15		09 28			18 45
Honor Oak Park	d	07 00	07 30		08 00		08 18		08 30	08 48		09 00		09 18		09 30			18 48
Brockley	d	07 03	07 33		08 03		08 20		08 33	08 50		09 03		09 20		09 33			18 50
New Cross Gate 4	d	07 05	07 35		08 05		08 23		08 35	08 53		09 05		09 23		09 35			18 53
London Bridge 4	a	07 12	07 42	08 06	08 12		08 31	08 36	08 42	09 01	09 06	09 12		09 31	09 36	09 42			19 01
London Waterloo (East) 4	a	07 16	07 46		08 16				08 46			09 16				09 46			
London Charing Cross 4	a	07 20	07 50		08 20				08 50			09 20				09 52			

For general notes see front of timetable
For details of catering facilities see Directory of Train Operators

A From Caterham (Table 181)
B From Purley (Table 175)
C From Tattenham Corner (Table 181)

Table 178

Croydon and London Victoria → London Bridge and Charing Cross

Network Diagram - see first page of Table 177

		SN	SN	SE	SN	SN	SN	SN	SN	SN	SE	SN	SN	SN	SN	SN	SN	SE
				72							72							72
			A				B			A				B			A	
East Croydon	d		18 47				19 17			19 47				20 17			20 47	
West Croydon 4	d				19 01			19 31				20 01			20 31			
Norwood Junction 2	d		18 51		19 05		19 21	19 35		19 51		20 05		20 21	20 35		20 51	
Anerley	d				19 08			19 38				20 08			20 38			
Penge West	d				19 10			19 40				20 10			20 40			
London Victoria 15	⊖ d	18 41		18 56		19 11			19 41		19 56		20 11			20 41		20 56
Battersea Park 4	d	18 45				19 15			19 45				20 15			20 45		
Wandsworth Road	d	18 47				19 17			19 47				20 17			20 47		
Clapham High Street	⊖ d	18 49				19 19			19 49				20 19			20 49		
London Blackfriars 3	⊖ d																	
Denmark Hill 4	d	18 54		19 05		19 24			19 54		20 05		20 24			20 54		21 05
Peckham Rye 4	d	18 56		19a07		19 26			19 56		20a07		20 26			20 56		21a07
Queens Rd Peckham	d	18 59				19 29			19 59				20 29			20 59		
South Bermondsey	d	19 01				19 31			20 01				20 31			21 01		
Clapham Junction 10	d																	
Wandsworth Common	d																	
Balham 4	⊖ d																	
Streatham Hill	d																	
West Norwood 4	d																	
Gipsy Hill	d																	
Crystal Palace 4	d																	
Sydenham	d		18 55		19 13		19 25	19 43		19 55		20 13		20 25	20 43		20 55	
Forest Hill 4	d		18 58		19 15		19 28	19 45		19 58		20 15		20 28	20 45		20 58	
Honor Oak Park	d		19 00		19 18		19 30	19 48		20 00		20 18		20 30	20 48		21 00	
Brockley	d		19 03		19 20		19 33	19 50		20 03		20 20		20 33	20 50		21 03	
New Cross Gate 4	⊖ d		19 05		19 23		19 35	19 53		20 05		20 23		20 35	20 53		21 05	
London Bridge 4	⊖ a	19 06	19 12		19 31	19 36	19 42	20 01	20 06	20 12		20 31	20 36	20 42	21 01	21 06	21 12	
London Waterloo (East) 4	⊖ a		19 16				19 46			20 18				20 46			21 16	
London Charing Cross 4	⊖ a		19 22				19 52			20 22				20 50			21 20	

		SN	SN	SN	SN	SN	SN	SE	SN	SN	SN	SN	SN	SN	SE	SN
								72							72	
				B			A				B			A		
East Croydon	d			21 17			21 47				22 17			22 47		
West Croydon 4	d	21 01			21 31				22 01			22 31				
Norwood Junction 2	d	21 05		21 21	21 35		21 51		22 05		22 21	22 35		22 51		
Anerley	d	21 08			21 38				22 08			22 38				
Penge West	d	21 10			21 40				22 10			22 40				
London Victoria 15	⊖ d		21 11			21 41		21 56		22 11			22 41		22 56	23 11
Battersea Park 4	d		21 15			21 45				22 15			22 45			23 15
Wandsworth Road	d		21 17			21 47				22 17			22 47			23 17
Clapham High Street	⊖ d		21 19			21 49				22 19			22 49			23 19
London Blackfriars 3	⊖ d															
Denmark Hill 4	d		21 24			21 54		22 05		22 24			22 54		23 05	23 24
Peckham Rye 4	d		21 26			21 56		22a07		22 26			22 56		23a07	23 26
Queens Rd Peckham	d		21 29			21 59				22 29			22 59			23 29
South Bermondsey	d		21 31			22 01				22 31			23 01			23 31
Clapham Junction 10	d															
Wandsworth Common	d															
Balham 4	⊖ d															
Streatham Hill	d															
West Norwood 4	d															
Gipsy Hill	d															
Crystal Palace 4	d															
Sydenham	d	21 13		21 25	21 43		21 55		22 13		22 25	22 43		22 55		
Forest Hill 4	d	21 15		21 28	21 45		21 58		22 15		22 28	22 45		22 58		
Honor Oak Park	d	21 18		21 30	21 48		22 00		22 18		22 30	22 48		23 00		
Brockley	d	21 20		21 33	21 50		22 03		22 20		22 33	22 50		23 03		
New Cross Gate 4	⊖ d	21 23		21 35	21 53		22 05		22 23		22 35	22 53		23 05		
London Bridge 4	⊖ a	21 31	21 36	21 42	22 01	22 06	22 12		22 31	22 36	22 42	23 01	23 06	23 12		23 36
London Waterloo (East) 4	⊖ a			21 46			22 16				22 46			23 16		
London Charing Cross 4	⊖ a			21 50			22 22				22 50			23 20		

For general notes see front of timetable
For details of catering facilities see Directory of Train Operators

A From Caterham (Table 181)
B From Tattenham Corner (Table 181)

Luton and London → Wimbledon and Sutton via Streatham

Network Diagram - see first page of Table 177

Miles	Miles	Station		SN	SN	FC	SN	FC	SN	FC	FC 1	SN	FC		SN	FC	SN	FC	FC	FC	FC	FC	FC	FC		FC
											A		A					B	A	B	A	B	B	B		B
—	—	**Luton** 10	d			04 44		05 48		06 18	06 36		06 56			07 08		07 30	07 56		08 20		08 28	08 54		09 04
—	—	Luton Airport Parkway 7 ✈	d			04 46		05 50		06 20			06 46			07 10		07 26	07 58		08 14		08 30	08 46		09 06
—	—	St Pancras International 15 ⊖	d			05 35		06 33		07 03	07 07		07 28			07 56		08 12	08 33	08 40	08 52	08 56	09 14	09 32		09 48
—	—	Farringdon 3 ⊖	d			05 39		06 38		07 08	07 12		07 32			08 00		08 16	08 37	08 44	08 56	09 00	09 18	09 36		09 52
—	0	City Thameslink 3	d					06 41		07 11	07 17		07 35			08 03		08 19	08 40	08 47	08 59	09 03	09 21	09 39		09 55
—	½	**London Blackfriars** 3 ⊖	d			06 11		06 46		07 16	07 23		07b43			08 08		08 24	08 45	08 52	09 02	09 08	09 28	09 44		10 00
—	1½	Elephant & Castle ⊖	d			06 14		06 49		07 19	07 27		07 47			08 11		08 27		08 55	09 05	09 11	09 31	09 47		10 03
—	3½	Loughborough Jn	d			06 18		06 53		07 23	07 31		07 51			08 15		08 31		08 59	09 09	09 15	09 35	09 51		10 07
—	4½	Herne Hill 4	d			06c25		06 57		07 27	07 35		07 55			08e23		08f39	08 54	09g06	09 13	09 21	09 41	09h59		10 11
0	—	**London Bridge** 4 ⊖	d		06 00	06 00	06 30	06 38	07 00	07 08	07 08	07 31	07 31		08 02	08 20	08 24	08 24	08 37		08 47	08 57	09 17	09 37		09 47
1¾	—	South Bermondsey	d		06 04	06 04	06 34	06 42	07 04	07 12	07 12	07 35			08 06	08 06	08 28	08 28	08 42		08 51	09 03	09 23	09 42		09 53
2¾	—	Queens Rd Peckham	d		06 06	06 06	06 36	06 44	07 06	07 14	07 14	07 37	07 37		08 08	08 08	08 30	08 30	08 45		08 53	09 05	09 25	09 44		09 55
3½	—	Peckham Rye 4	d		06 09	06 09	06 39	06 47	07 09	07 17	07 17	07 40	07 40		08 11	08 11	08 33		08 47		08 56	09 08	09 28	09 47		09 58
4½	—	East Dulwich	d		06 12	06 12	06 42	06 50	07 12	07 20	07 20	07 43	07 43		08 14	08 14		08 30	08 51		08 59	09 11	09 31	09 50		10 01
4¾	—	North Dulwich	d		06 14		06 44	06 52	07 14	07 22	07 22	07 45			08 16			08 32	08 53		09 01	09 13	09 33	09 52		10 03
6	5½	Tulse Hill 3	d		06 17	06 30	06 47	07 02	07 17	07 32	07 39	07 48	07 59		08 19	08 27	08 38	08j47	09k02	09 10	09 17	09 26	09 47	10 02		10 17
7½	7	Streatham 4	d		06 21	06 33	06 51	07 05	07 21	07 35	07 42	07 52	08 02		08 23	08 30	08 42	08 50	09 05	09 15	09 20	09 30	09 50	10 05		10 20
—	8	Eastfields §	d																							
—	9	Mitcham Junction	d			06 38		07 10		07 40			08 06			08 34		08 56			09 26		09 56			10 26
—	11	Hackbridge	d			06 42		07 14		07 44			08 10			08 38		08 59			09 29		09 59			10 29
—	11¾	Carshalton	d			06 44		07 16		07 46			08 12			08 40		09 02			09 32		10 02			10 32
9	—	Tooting	d		06 27		06 57		07 25		07 46	07 56			08 27		08 46		09 10	09 23		09 40		10 10		
10¼	—	Haydons Road	d		06 30		07 00		07 28		07 49	07 59			08 30		08 49		09 13	09 26		09 43		10 13		
11½	—	**Wimbledon** 6 ⊖	a		06 32		07 02		07 31		07 54	08 01			08 32		08 51		09 16	09 29		09 45		10 16		
—	—		d	05 59	06 33		07 03		07 32			08 02			08 32		08 55		09 16			09 46		10 16		
12½	—	Wimbledon Chase	d	06 02	06 36		07 11		07 35			08 05			08 35		08 58		09 19			09 49		10 19		
13	—	South Merton	d	06 04	06 38		07 13		07 37			08 07			08 37		09 00		09 21			09 51		10 21		
13½	—	Morden South	d	06 06	06 40		07 15		07 39			08 09			08 39		09 02		09 23			09 53		10 23		
14	—	St Helier	d	06 08	06 42		07 17		07 41			08 11			08 41		09 04		09 25			09 55		10 25		
15	—	Sutton Common	d	06 10	06 44		07 20		07 43			08 13			08 44		09 06		09 27			09 57		10 27		
16	—	West Sutton	d	06 13	06 47		07 22		07 46			08 16			08 46		09 09		09 30			10 00		10 30		
17	13	**Sutton (Surrey)** 4	a	06 16	06 50	06 48	07 26	07 20	07 49	07 50		08 19	08 16		08 50	08 44	09 13	09 05	09 38		09 36	10 05	10 05	10 35		10 35

Station		FC	FC	FC	FC	FC	FC		FC	FC	FC	FC			FC	FC	FC	FC	SN	FC	FC 1	SN	FC	FC	SN
			B		B		B			B		B				B		B	C		A		B		
Luton 10	d	09 14	09 39	09 44	10 09	10 14	10 39		10 44	11 04	11 14	11 34			14 44	15 04	15 14	15 34		15 44	15 55		16 04	16 14	
Luton Airport Parkway 7 ✈	d	09 16	09 36	09 46	10 06	10 16	10 36		10 46	11 06	11 16	11 36			14 46	15 06	15 16	15 36		15 46	15 57		16 06	16 16	
St Pancras International 15 ⊖	d	10 02	10 17	10 32	10 47	11 02	11 18		11 32	11 47	12 02	12 17			15 32	15 47	16 02	16 15		16 32	16 36		16 47	17 01	
Farringdon 3 ⊖	d	10 07	10 22	10 37	10 52	11 07	11 22		11 37	11 52	12 07	12 22			15 37	15 52	16 07	16 20		16 37	16 40		16 52	17 06	
City Thameslink 3	d	10 09	10 26	10 39	10 56	11 09	11 26		11 39	11 54	12 09	12 24			15 39	15 54	16 09	16 22		16 39	16 43		16 54	17 11	
London Blackfriars 3 ⊖	d	10m16	10 30	10n46	11 00	11q16	11 30		11r46	12 00	12t16	12 30			15v46	16 00	16w16	16 26		16 42	16 46		16 58	17 14	
Elephant & Castle ⊖	d	10 19	10 33	10 49	11 03	11 19	11 33		11 49	12 03	12 19	12 33			15 49	16 03	16 19	16 29		16 45	16 50		17 01	17 17	
Loughborough Jn	d	10 23	10 37	10 53	11 07	11 23	11 37		11 53	12 07	12 23	12 37			15 53	16 07	16 23	16 33		16 49	16 54		17 05	17 21	
Herne Hill 4	d	10 27	10 41	10 57	11 11	11 27	11 41		11 57	12 11	12 27	12 41			15 57	16 11	16 27	16 37		16 53	16 58		17 09	17 25	
London Bridge 4 ⊖	d	10 19	10 19	10 38	10 49	11 08	11 19		11 38	11 49	12 08	12 19	and at		15 38	15 49	16 07	16 19	16 29	16 37		16 53	16 55	17 07	17 27
South Bermondsey	d	10 23	10 23	10 42	10 53	11 12	11 23		11 42	11 53	12 12	12 23			15 42	15 53	16 11	16 23	16 33	16 41		16 57	16 59	17 11	17 31
Queens Rd Peckham	d	10 25	10 25	10 44	10 55	11 14	11 25		11 44	11 55	12 14	12 25	the same		15 44	15 55	16 13	16 25	16 35	16 43		16 59	17 01	17 13	17 33
Peckham Rye 4	d	10 28	10 28	10 47	10 58	11 17	11 28		11 47	11 58	12 17	12 28			15 47	15 58	16 16	16 28	16 38	16 46		17 02	17 04	17 16	17 36
East Dulwich	d	10 31	10 31	10 50	11 01	11 20	11 31		11 50	12 01	12 20	12 31	minutes		15 50	16 01	16 19	16 31	16 41	16 49		17 05	17 07	17 19	17 39
North Dulwich	d	10 33	10 33	10 52	11 03	11 22	11 33		11 52	12 03	12 22	12 33			15 52	16 03	16 21	16 33	16 43	16 51		17 07		17 21	17 41
Tulse Hill 3	d	10 32	10 47	11 02	11 17	11 32	11 47		12 02	12 17	12 32	12 47	past		16 02	16 16	16 32	16 42	16 46	16 58	17y08	17 11	17 16	17 30	17 44
Streatham 4	d	10 35	10 50	11 05	11 20	11 35	11 50		12 05	12 20	12 35	12 50			16 05	16 20	16 35	16 45	16 50	17 01	17 12	17 14	17 20	17 33	17 48
Eastfields §	d												each												
Mitcham Junction	d		10 56		11 26		11 56			12 26		12 56	hour until			16 25		16 50	16 55			17 20	17 25		17 53
Hackbridge	d		10 59		11 29		11 59			12 29		12 59						16 54	16 59			17 23	17 28		17 57
Carshalton	d		11 02		11 32		12 02			12 32		13 02						16 56	17 01			17 26	17 30		17 59
Tooting	d	10 40		11 10		11 40			12 10		12 40				16 10		16 38			17 06	17 15			17 38	
Haydons Road	d	10 43		11 13		11 43			12 13		12 43				16 13		16 41			17 09	17 18			17 41	
Wimbledon 6 ⊖	a	10 46		11 16		11 46			12 16		12 46				16 16		16 44			17 11	17 21			17 43	
	d	10 46		11 16		11 46			12 16		12 46				16 16		16 44			17 12				17 44	
Wimbledon Chase	d	10 49		11 19		11 49			12 19		12 49				16 19		16 47			17 15				17 47	
South Merton	d	10 51		11 21		11 51			12 21		12 51				16 21		16 49			17 17				17 49	
Morden South	d	10 53		11 23		11 53			12 23		12 53				16 23		16 51			17 19				17 51	
St Helier	d	10 55		11 25		11 55			12 25		12 55				16 25		16 53			17 21				17 53	
Sutton Common	d	10 57		11 27		11 57			12 27		12 57				16 27		16 55			17 23				17 55	
West Sutton	d	11 00		11 30		12 00			12 30		13 00				16 30		16 58			17 26				17 58	
Sutton (Surrey) 4	a	11 05	11 05	11 35	11 35	12 05	12 05		12 35	12 35	13 05	13 05			16 35	16 32	17 03	17 00	17 05	17 31		17 30	17 38	18 05	18 03

For general notes see front of timetable
For details of catering facilities see
Directory of Train Operators

§ This station may open during the currency of this timetable, please see local publicity for further details.

A From Bedford (Table 52)
B From St Albans (Table 52)
C To Epsom (Table 182)
b Arr. 0740
c Arr. 0622
e Arr. 0819
f Arr. 0835
g Arr. 0903
h Arr. 0955
j Arr. 0843
k Arr. 0858
m Arr. 1013
n Arr. 1043
q Arr. 1113
r Arr. 1143
t Arr. 1213
v Arr. 1543
w Arr. 1613
y Arr. 1702

Luton and London → Wimbledon and Sutton via Streatham

Network Diagram - see first page of Table 177

Mondays to Fridays

Station		FC A	FC	SN	FC A	FC	FC A	SN B	FC	FC A	FC	FC A	FC	FC A	FC	FC A	FC	FC	FC	FC	FC	FC
Luton 10	d	16 34	16 44		17 18	17 18	17 34		17 48	18 00	18 20	18 34	18 50	19 04	19 20	19 20	19 50	20 20	20 50	21 20	21 50	22 20
Luton Airport Parkway 7 ✈	d	16 36	16 46		17 02	17 20	17 36		17 50	18 02	18 22	18 36	18 52	19 06	19 22		19 52	20 22	20 52	21 22	21 52	22 22
St Pancras International 15 ⊖	d	17 17	17 31		17 51	18 03	18 15		18 33	18 45	19 05	19 17	19 35	19 48	20 05	20 17	20 35	21 05	21 35	22 05	22 36	23 06
Farringdon 3 ⊖	d	17 22	17 36		17 56	18 08	18 20		18 38	18 50	19 10	19 22	19 40	19 52	20 10	20 22	20 40	21 10	21 40	22 10	22 40	23 10
City Thameslink 3	d	17 24	17 38		17 58	18 10	18 22		18 40	18 52	19 12	19 24	19 42	19 55	20 12	20 24	20 42	21 12	21 42	22 12	22 42	
London Blackfriars 3 ⊖	d	17 30	17 42		18 02	18 14	18 26		18 44	18 56	19 16	19 30	19 46	20 00	20 16	20 30	20 46	21 16	21 46	22 16	22 46	23 16
Elephant & Castle ⊖	d	17 33	17 45		18 05	18 17	18 29		18 47	18 59	19 19	19 33	19 49	20 03	20 19	20 33	20 49	21 19	21 49	22 19	22 49	23 19
Loughborough Jn	d	17 37	17 49		18 09	18 21	18 33		18 51	19 03	19 23	19 37	19 53	20 07	20 23	20 37	20 53	21 23	21 53	22 23	22 53	23s23
Herne Hill 4	d	17 41	17 53		18 13	18 27	18 37		18 57	19 07	19 27	19 41	19 57	20 11	20 27	20 41	20 57	21 27	21 57	22 27	22 57	23 27
London Bridge 4 ⊖	d	17b27	17 37	17 58	17 58	18 08	18 21	18 31	18 38	18 51	19 08	19 19	19 38	19 49		20 19		20 49	21 19	21 49	22 19	22 49
South Bermondsey	d	17b31	17 41	18 02	18 02	18 12	18 25	18 35	18 42	18 55	19 12	19 23	19 42	19 53		20 23		20 53	21 23	21 53	22 23	22 53
Queens Rd Peckham	d	17b33	17 43	18 04	18 04	18 14	18 27	18 37	18 44	18 57	19 14	19 25	19 44	19 55		20 25		20 55	21 25	21 55	22 25	22 55
Peckham Rye 4	d	17b36	17 46	18 07	18 07	18 17	18 30	18 40	18 47	19 00	19 17	19 28	19 47	19 58		20 28		20 58	21 28	21 58	22 28	22 58
East Dulwich	d	17b39	17 49	18 10	18 10	18 20	18 33	18 43	18 50	19 03	19 20	19 31	19 50	20 01		20 31		21 01	21 31	22 01	22 31	23 01
North Dulwich	d	17b41	17 51	18 12		18 22	18 35	18 45	18 52	19 05	19 22	19 33	19 52	20 03		20 33		21 03	21 33	22 03	22 33	23 03
Tulse Hill 3	d	17 46	17 58	18 15	18 18	18 30	18 42	18c51	19 02	19 12	19 32	19 47	20 02	20 17	20 32	20 47	21 02	21 32	22 02	22 32	23 02	23 32
Streatham 4	d	17 50	18 01	18 19	18 22	18 33	18 45	18 54	19 05	19 15	19 35	19 50	20 05	20 20	20 35	20 50	21 05	21 35	22 05	22 35	23 04	23 35
Eastfields §	d																					
Mitcham Junction 🚋	d	17 57			18 27		18 50	19 00		19 20		19 56		20 26		20 56						
Hackbridge	d	18 00			18 30		18 54	19 03		19 24		19 59		20 29		20 59						
Carshalton	d	18 02			18 32		18 56	19 06		19 26		20 02		20 32		21 02						
Tooting	d		18 06			18 38			19 08		19 40		20 10		20 40		21 10	21 40	22 10	22 40	23 10	23 40
Haydons Road	d		18 09			18 41			19 11		19 43		20 13		20 43		21 13	21 43	22 13	22 43	23 13	23 43
Wimbledon 6 ⊖ 🚋	a		18 11			18 43			19 14		19 46		20 16		20 46		21 16	21 46	22 16	22 46	23 16	23 46
	d		18 14			18 44			19 16		19 46		20 16		20 46		21 16	21 46	22 16	22 46	23 16	23 46
Wimbledon Chase	d		18 17			18 47			19 19		19 49		20 19		20 49		21 19	21 49	22 19	22 49	23 19	23 49
South Merton	d		18 19			18 49			19 21		19 51		20 21		20 51		21 21	21 51	22 21	22 51	23 21	23 51
Morden South	d		18 21			18 51			19 23		19 53		20 23		20 53		21 23	21 53	22 23	22 53	23 23	23 53
St Helier	d		18 23			18 53			19 25		19 55		20 25		20 55		21 25	21 55	22 25	22 55	23 25	23 55
Sutton Common	d		18 25			18 55			19 27		19 57		20 27		20 57		21 27	21 57	22 27	22 57	23 27	23 57
West Sutton	d		18 28			18 58			19 30		20e05		20 30		21 00		21 30	22 00	22 30	23 00	23 30	23 59
Sutton (Surrey) 4	a	18 06	18 33	18 30	18 36	19 03	19 02	19 09	19 40	19 31	20 10	20 05	20 35	20 35	21 05	21 05	21 35	22 05	22 35	23 05	23 33	00 05

Saturdays

Station		FC	FC	FC	FC	FC	FC	FC	FC	FC	FC	FC	FC A	FC	FC A	FC
Luton 10	d	05 14	05 50	06 20	06 34	06 44	06 59	07 14	07 26	07 44	07 59	08 14	08 34	08 44	09 04	09 14
Luton Airport Parkway 7 ✈	d	05 16	05 52	06 22	06 36	06 46	07 01	07 16	07 28	07 46	08 01	08 16	08 36	08 46	09 06	09 16
St Pancras International 15 ⊖	d	06 05	06 35	07 05	07 10	07 32	07 47	08 02	08 17	08 32	08 47	09 02	09 17	09 32	09 47	10 02
Farringdon 3 ⊖	d	06 09	06 40	07 10	07 14	07 37	07 52	08 07	08 22	08 37	08 52	09 07	09 22	09 37	09 52	10 07
City Thameslink 3	d											09 09	09 24	09 39	09 54	10 09
London Blackfriars 3 ⊖	d	06 16	06 46	07 16	07 30	07f46	08g00	08h16	08j30	08k46	09m00	09n16	09 30	09q46	10 00	10r16
Elephant & Castle ⊖	d	06 19	06 49	07 19	07 33	07 49	08 03	08 19	08 33	08 49	09 03	09 19	09 33	09 49	10 03	10 19
Loughborough Jn	d		06 53	07 23	07 37	07 53	08 07	08 23	08 37	08 53	09 07	09 23	09 37	09 53	10 07	10 23
Herne Hill 4	d	06 27	06 57	07 27	07 41	07 57	08 11	08 27	08 41	08 57	09 11	09 27	09 41	09 57	10 11	10 27
London Bridge 4 ⊖	d			06 49	07 19	07 38	07 49	08 08	08 19	08 38	08 49	09 08	09 19	09 38	09 49	10 08
South Bermondsey	d			06 53	07 23	07 42	07 53	08 12	08 23	08 42	08 53	09 12	09 23	09 42	09 53	10 12
Queens Rd Peckham	d			06 55	07 25	07 44	07 55	08 14	08 25	08 44	08 55	09 14	09 25	09 44	09 55	10 14
Peckham Rye 4	d			06 58	07 28	07 47	07 58	08 17	08 28	08 47	08 58	09 17	09 28	09 47	09 38	10 17
East Dulwich	d			07 01	07 31	07 50	08 01	08 20	08 31	08 50	09 01	09 20	09 31	09 50	10 01	10 20
North Dulwich	d			07 03	07 33	07 52	08 03	08 22	08 33	08 52	09 03	09 22	09 33	09 52	10 03	10 22
Tulse Hill 3	d	06 32	07 02	07 32	07 47	08 02	08 17	08 32	08 47	09 02	09 17	09 32	09 47	10 02	10 17	10 32
Streatham 4	d	06 35	07 05	07 35	07 50	08 05	08 20	08 35	08 50	09 05	09 20	09 35	09 50	10 05	10 20	10 35
Eastfields §	d															
Mitcham Junction 🚋	d				07 56		08 26		08 56		09 26		09 56		10 26	
Hackbridge	d				07 59		08 29		08 59		09 29		09 59		10 29	
Carshalton	d				08 02		08 32		09 02		09 32		10 02		10 32	
Tooting	d	06 40	07 10	07 40		08 10		08 40		09 10		09 40		10 10		10 40
Haydons Road	d	06 43	07 13	07 43		08 13		08 43		09 13		09 43		10 13		10 43
Wimbledon 6 ⊖ 🚋	a	06 46	07 16	07 46		08 16		08 46		09 16		09 46		10 16		10 46
	d	06 46	07 16	07 46		08 16		08 46		09 16		09 46		10 16		10 46
Wimbledon Chase	d	06 49	07 19	07 49		08 19		08 49		09 19		09 49		10 19		10 49
South Merton	d	06 51	07 21	07 51		08 21		08 51		09 21		09 51		10 21		10 51
Morden South	d	06 53	07 23	07 53		08 23		08 53		09 23		09 53		10 23		10 53
St Helier	d	06 55	07 25	07 55		08 25		08 55		09 25		09 55		10 25		10 55
Sutton Common	d	06 57	07 27	07 57		08 27		08 57		09 27		09 57		10 27		10 57
West Sutton	d	07 00	07 30	08 00		08 30		09 00		09 30		10 00		10 30		11 00
Sutton (Surrey) 4	a	07 05	07 35	08 05	08 05	08 35	08 35	09 05	09 05	09 35	09 35	10 05	10 05	10 35	10 35	11 05

For general notes see front of timetable
For details of catering facilities see Directory of Train Operators

§ This station may open during the currency of this timetable, please see local publicity for further details.

A From St Albans (Table 52)

B To Epsom (Table 182)

b Change at Streatham

c Arr. 1848

e Arr. 2000

f Arr. 0742

g Arr. 0757

h Arr. 0812

j Arr. 0827

k Arr. 0842

m Arr. 0857

n Arr. 0913

q Arr. 0943

r Arr. 1013

Table 179

Luton and London → Wimbledon and Sutton via Streatham

Network Diagram - see first page of Table 177

		FC A		FC	FC A	FC	FC	FC	FC	FC	FC 1	FC	FC	FC
Luton 10	d	*09 34*		17 44	*18 04*	18 20	18 50	19 20	19 50	20 20	20 50	21 20	21 50	22 20
Luton Airport Parkway 7 ✈	d	*09 36*		17 46	*18 06*	18 22	18 52	19 22	19 52	20 22	20 52	21 22	21 52	22 22
St Pancras International 15 ⊖	d	10 17		18 32	18 47	19 05	19 35	20 05	20 35	21 05	21 35	22 05	22 36	23 06
Farringdon 3 ⊖	d	10 22		18 37	18 52	19 10	19 40	20 10	20 40	21 10	21 40	22 10	22 40	23 10
City Thameslink 3	d	10 24		18 39	18 54	19 12	19 42	20 12	20 42	*21 01*	*21 01*			
London Blackfriars 3 ⊖	d	10 30		18b46	19 00	19 16	19 46	20 16	20 46	21 16	21 46	22 16	22 46	23 16
Elephant & Castle ⊖	d	10 33		18 49	19 03	19 19	19 49	20 19	20 49	21 19	21 49	22 19	22 49	23 19
Loughborough Jn	d	10 37		18 53	19 07	19 23	19 53	20 23	20 53	21 23	21 53	22 23	22 53	23s23
Herne Hill 4	d	10 41		18 57	19 11	19 27	19 57	20 27	20 57	21 27	21 57	22 27	22 57	23 27
London Bridge 4 ⊖	d	*10 19*	and at	*18 29*	*18 49*	*18 59*	*19 29*	*19 49*	*20 19*	*20 49*	*21 19*	*21 49*	*22 19*	*22 49*
South Bermondsey	d	*10 23*	the same	*18 33*	*18 53*	*19 03*	*19 33*	*19 53*	*20 23*	*20 53*	*21 23*	*21 53*	*22 23*	*22 53*
Queens Rd Peckham	d	*10 25*	minutes	*18 35*	*18 55*	*19 05*	*19 35*	*19 55*	*20 25*	*20 55*	*21 25*	*21 55*	*22 25*	*22 55*
Peckham Rye 4	d	*10 28*	past	*18 38*	*18 58*	*19 08*	*19 38*	*19 58*	*20 28*	*20 58*	*21 28*	*21 58*	*22 28*	*22 58*
East Dulwich	d	*10 31*	each	*18 41*	*19 01*	*19 11*	*19 41*	*20 01*	*20 31*	*21 01*	*21 31*	*22 01*	*22 31*	*23 01*
North Dulwich	d	*10 33*	hour until	*18 43*	*19 03*	*19 13*	*19 43*	*20 03*	*20 33*	*21 03*	*21 33*	*22 03*	*22 33*	*23 03*
Tulse Hill 3	d	10 47		19 02	19 17	19 32	20 02	20 32	21 02	21 32	22 02	22 32	23 02	23 32
Streatham 4	d	10 50		19 05	19 20	19 35	20 05	20 35	21 05	21 35	22 05	22 35	23 05	23 35
Eastfields §	d													
Mitcham Junction 🚋	d	10 56			19 26									
Hackbridge	d	10 59			19 29									
Carshalton	d	11 02			19 32									
Tooting	d			19 10		19 40	20 10	20 40	21 10	21 40	22 10	22 40	23 10	23 40
Haydons Road	d			19 13		19 43	20 13	20 43	21 13	21 43	22 13	22 43	23 13	23 43
Wimbledon 6 ⊖ 🚋	a			19 16		19 46	20 16	20 46	21 16	21 46	22 16	22 46	23 16	23 46
	d			19 16		19 46	20 16	20 46	21 16	21 46	22 16	22 46	23 16	23 46
Wimbledon Chase	d			19 19		19 49	20 19	20 49	21 19	21 49	22 19	22 49	23 19	23 49
South Merton	d			19 21		19 51	20 21	20 51	21 21	21 51	22 21	22 51	23 21	23 51
Morden South	d			19 23		19 53	20 23	20 53	21 23	21 53	22 23	22 53	23 23	23 53
St Helier	d			19 25		19 55	20 25	20 55	21 25	21 55	22 25	22 55	23 25	23 55
Sutton Common	d			19 27		19 57	20 27	20 57	21 27	21 57	22 27	22 57	23 27	23 57
West Sutton	d			19 30		20 00	20 30	21 00	21 30	22 00	22 30	23 00	23 30	23 59
Sutton (Surrey) 4	a	11 05		19 35	19 35	20 05	20 35	21 05	21 35	22 05	22 35	23 05	23 35	00 05

Sundays

		FC	FC	FC	FC	FC	FC	FC	FC	FC	FC	FC B	FC B
Luton 10	d	08 20	08 50	09 20	09 50	10 20	10 50	11 20	11 50	12 20	12 50	13 20	13 50
Luton Airport Parkway 7 ✈	d	08 22	08 52	09 22	09 52	10 22	10 52	11 22	11 52	12 22	12 52	13 22	13 52
St Pancras International 15 ⊖	d	09 06	09 36	10 06	10 36	11 06	11 36	12 06	12 36	13 06	13 36	14 06	14 36
Farringdon 3 ⊖	d	09 10	09 40	10 10	10 40	11 10	11 40	12 10	12 40	13 10	13 40	14 10	14 40
City Thameslink 3	d												
London Blackfriars 3 ⊖	d	09 16	09 46	10 16	10 46	11 16	11 46	12 16	12 46	13 16	13 46	14 16	14 46
Elephant & Castle ⊖	d	09 19	09 49	10 19	10 49	11 19	11 49	12 19	12 49	13 19	13 49	14 19	14 49
Loughborough Jn	d	09 23	09 53	10 23	10 53	11 23	11 53	12 23	12 53	13 23	13 53	14 23	14 53
Herne Hill 4	d	09 27	09 57	10 27	10 57	11 27	11 57	12 27	12 57	13 27	13 57	14 27	14 57
London Bridge 4 ⊖	d	*08 55*	*09 25*	*09 55*	*10 25*	*10 55*	*11 25*	*11 55*	*12 25*	*12 55*	*13 25*	*13 55*	*14 25*
South Bermondsey	d	*08 59*	*09 29*	*09 59*	*10 29*	*10 59*	*11 29*	*11 59*	*12 29*	*12 59*	*13 29*	*13 59*	*14 29*
Queens Rd Peckham	d	*09 01*	*09 31*	*10 01*	*10 31*	*11 01*	*11 31*	*12 01*	*12 31*	*13 01*	*13 31*	*14 01*	*14 31*
Peckham Rye 4	d	*09 04*	*09 34*	*10 04*	*10 34*	*11 04*	*11 34*	*12 04*	*12 34*	*13 04*	*13 34*	*14 04*	*14 34*
East Dulwich	d	*09 07*	*09 37*	*10 07*	*10 37*	*11 07*	*11 37*	*12 07*	*12 37*	*13 07*	*13 37*	*14 07*	*14 37*
North Dulwich	d	*09 09*	*09 39*	*10 09*	*10 39*	*11 09*	*11 39*	*12 09*	*12 39*	*13 09*	*13 39*	*14 09*	*14 39*
Tulse Hill 3	d	09 31	10 01	10 31	11 01	11 31	12 01	12 31	13 01	13 31	14 01	14 31	15 01
Streatham 4	d	09 34	10 04	10 34	11 04	11 34	12 04	12 34	13 04	13 34	14 04	14 34	15 04
Eastfields §	d												
Mitcham Junction 🚋	d												
Hackbridge	d												
Carshalton	d												
Tooting	d	09 38	10 08	10 38	11 08	11 38	12 08	12 38	13 08	13 38	14 08	14 38	15 08
Haydons Road	d	09 41	10 11	10 41	11 11	11 41	12 11	12 41	13 11	13 41	14 11	14 41	15 11
Wimbledon 6 ⊖ 🚋	a	09 44	10 14	10 44	11 14	11 44	12 14	12 44	13 14	13 44	14 14	14 44	15 14
	d	09 44	10 14	10 44	11 14	11 44	12 14	12 44	13 14	13 44	14 14	14 44	15 14
Wimbledon Chase	d	09 47	10 17	10 47	11 17	11 47	12 17	12 47	13 17	13 47	14 17	14 47	15 17
South Merton	d	09 49	10 19	10 49	11 19	11 49	12 19	12 49	13 19	13 49	14 19	14 49	15 19
Morden South	d	09 51	10 21	10 51	11 21	11 51	12 21	12 51	13 21	13 51	14 21	14 51	15 21
St Helier	d	09 53	10 23	10 53	11 23	11 53	12 23	12 53	13 23	13 53	14 23	14 53	15 23
Sutton Common	d	09 55	10 25	10 55	11 25	11 55	12 25	12 55	13 25	13 55	14 25	14 55	15 25
West Sutton	d	09 58	10 28	10 58	11 28	11 58	12 28	12 58	13 28	13 58	14 28	14 58	15 28
Sutton (Surrey) 4	a	10 03	10 33	11 03	11 33	12 03	12 33	13 03	13 33	14 03	14 33	15 03	15 33

		FC B	FC B	FC B	FC B	FC B	FC B	FC B	FC	FC	FC	FC	FC
Luton 10	d	14 18	14 50	15 20	15 50	16 19	16 50	17 20	17 50	18 20	18 50	19 20	19 50
Luton Airport Parkway 7 ✈	d	14 20	14 52	15 22	15 52	16 22	16 52	17 22	17 52	18 22	18 52	19 22	19 52
St Pancras International 15 ⊖	d	15 06	15 36	16 06	16 36	17 05	17 36	18 06	18 36	19 06	19 36	20 06	20 36
Farringdon 3 ⊖	d	15 10	15 40	16 10	16 40	17 10	17 40	18 10	18 40	19 10	19 40	20 10	20 40
City Thameslink 3	d												
London Blackfriars 3 ⊖	d	15 16	15 46	16 16	16 46	17 15	17 46	18 16	18 46	19 16	19 46	20 16	20 46
Elephant & Castle ⊖	d	15 19	15 49	16 19	16 49	17 19	17 49	18 19	18 49	19 19	19 49	20 19	20 49
Loughborough Jn	d	15 23	15 53	16 23	16 53	17 23	17 53	18 23	18 53	19 23	19 53	20 23	20 53
Herne Hill 4	d	15 27	15 57	16 27	16 57	17 27	17 57	18 27	18 57	19 27	19 57	20 27	20 57
London Bridge 4 ⊖	d	*14 55*	*15 25*	*15 55*	*16 25*	*16 55*	*17 25*	*17 55*	*18 25*	*18 55*	*19 25*	*19 55*	*20 25*
South Bermondsey	d	*14 59*	*15 29*	*15 59*	*16 29*	*16 59*	*17 29*	*17 59*	*18 29*	*18 59*	*19 29*	*19 59*	*20 29*
Queens Rd Peckham	d	*15 01*	*15 31*	*16 01*	*16 31*	*17 01*	*17 31*	*18 01*	*18 31*	*18 31*	*19 31*	*20 01*	*20 31*
Peckham Rye 4	d	*15 04*	*15 34*	*16 04*	*16 34*	*17 04*	*17 34*	*18 04*	*18 34*	*18 34*	*19 34*	*20 04*	*20 34*
East Dulwich	d	*15 07*	*15 37*	*16 07*	*16 37*	*17 07*	*17 37*	*18 07*	*18 37*	*18 37*	*19 37*	*20 07*	*20 37*
North Dulwich	d	*15 09*	*15 39*	*16 09*	*16 39*	*17 09*	*17 39*	*18 09*	*18 39*	*18 39*	*19 39*	*20 09*	*20 39*
Tulse Hill 3	d	15 31	16 01	16 31	17 01	17 31	18 01	18 31	19 01	19 31	20 01	20 31	21 01
Streatham 4	d	15 34	16 04	16 34	17 04	17 34	18 04	18 34	19 04	19 34	20 04	20 34	21 04
Eastfields §	d												
Mitcham Junction 🚋	d												
Hackbridge	d												
Carshalton	d												
Tooting	d	15 38	16 08	16 38	17 08	17 38	18 08	18 38	19 08	19 38	20 08	20 38	21 08
Haydons Road	d	15 41	16 11	16 41	17 11	17 41	18 11	18 41	19 11	19 41	20 11	20 41	21 11
Wimbledon 6 ⊖ 🚋	a	15 44	16 14	16 44	17 14	17 43	18 14	18 44	19 14	19 44	20 14	20 44	21 14
	d	15 44	16 14	16 44	17 14	17 43	18 14	18 44	19 14	19 44	20 14	20 44	21 14
Wimbledon Chase	d	15 47	16 17	16 47	17 17	17 46	18 17	18 47	19 17	19 47	20 17	20 47	21 17
South Merton	d	15 49	16 19	16 49	17 19	17 48	18 19	18 49	19 19	19 49	20 19	20 49	21 19
Morden South	d	15 51	16 21	16 51	17 21	17 50	18 21	18 51	19 21	19 51	20 21	20 51	21 21
St Helier	d	15 53	16 23	16 53	17 23	17 52	18 23	18 53	19 23	19 53	20 23	20 53	21 23
Sutton Common	d	15 55	16 25	16 55	17 25	17 55	18 25	18 55	19 25	19 55	20 25	20 55	21 25
West Sutton	d	15 58	16 28	16 58	17 28	17 57	18 28	18 58	19 28	19 58	20 28	20 58	21 28
Sutton (Surrey) 4	a	16 03	16 33	17 03	17 33	18 03	18 31	19 01	19 31	20 01	20 31	21 01	21 33

For general notes see front of timetable
For details of catering facilities see
Directory of Train Operators

§ This station may open during the currency of this timetable, please see local publicity for further details.

A From St Albans (Table 52)
B From Bedford (Table 52)
b Arr. 1843

Sutton and Wimbledon → London and Luton via Streatham

Network Diagram - see first page of Table 177

Miles	Miles			SN	SN	FC A	FC B	SN	FC A	SN	FC B	SN	FC A	FC B	FC B	SN	FC B	FC	FC B
0	0	**Sutton (Surrey)** 4	d	05 37	06 17		06 23	06 51	06 48	07 27	07 20	07 50		07 50	08 16	08 51	08 46	09 06	09 37
1	—	West Sutton	d				06 26		06 51		07 23			07 53	08 19		08 49	09 09	
2	—	Sutton Common	d				06 28		06 54		07 26			07 56	08 21		08 51	09 11	
3	—	St Helier	d				06 31		06 56		07 28			07 58	08 24		08 54	09 14	
3½	—	Morden South	d				06 33		06 58		07 30			08 00	08 26		08 56	09 16	
4	—	South Merton	d				06 35		07 00		07 32			08 02	08 28		08 58	09 18	
4½	—	Wimbledon Chase	d				06 37		07 02		07 34			08 04	08 30		09 00	09 20	
5½	—	**Wimbledon** 6 ⊖ ⛴	a				06 40		07 06		07 38			08 08	08 36		09 04	09 23	
—	—		d			06 28	06 40		07 06		07 38		07 58	08 08	08 36		09 04	09 23	
6¾	—	Haydons Road	d			06 30	06 43		07 08		07 40		08 00	08 10	08 38		09 06	09 25	
8	—	Tooting	d			06 33	06 46		07 11		07 43		08 03	08 13	08 41		09 09	09 28	
—	1¼	Carshalton	d	05 40	06 20			06 54		07 30		07 53				08 54			09 40
—	2	Hackbridge	d	05 42	06 22			06 56		07 32		07 55				08 56			09 42
—	4	Mitcham Junction ⛴	d	05 46	06 26			07 00		07 36		07 59				09 00			09 45
—	5	Eastfields §	d																
9½	6	Streatham 4	d	05 52	06 32	06 36	06 50	07 06	07 16	07 42	07 46	08 05	08 11	08 17	08 45	09 06	09 15	09 33	09 52
11	7½	Tulse Hill 3	d	05 55	06 35	06 40	06 54	07 09	07 20	07 46	07 50	08 10	08 15	08 23	08 49	09 09	09 19	09 37	09 55
12¼	—	North Dulwich	d	06 10	06 38		07 01	07 12	07 27	07 49	08 03	08 13		08 33		09 12	09 25	09 44	10 04
12½	—	East Dulwich	d	06 12	06 40		07 03	07 14	07 29	07 51	08 05	08 15		08 35		09 14	09 27	09 46	10 06
13½	—	Peckham Rye 4	d	06 00	06 43		07 05	07 17	07 31	07 53	08 07	08 17		08 38		09 17	09 29	09 49	10 09
14¼	—	Queens Rd Peckham	d	06 17	06 45		07 08	07 25	07 34	08 10	08 10	08 20		08 40	09 17	09 19	09 32	09 51	10 11
15¼	—	South Bermondsey	d	06 20	06 48		07 10	07 28	07 36	08 13	08 13	08 22		08 43	09 20	09 22	09 34	09 54	10 14
17	—	**London Bridge** 4 ⊖	a	06 07	06 52		07 18	07 25	07 43	08 02	08 21	08 30		08 49	09 29	09 29	09 41	09 59	10 18
—	8½	Herne Hill 4	d			06 44	06 59		07 24		07 54		08b22	08 28	08 53		09 23	09 41	09 59
—	9½	Loughborough Jn	d			06 47	07 02		07 27		07 57		08 25	08 31	08 56		09 26	09 45	10 02
—	11½	Elephant & Castle ⊖	d			06 52	07 07		07 32		08 02		08 30	08 36	09 00		09 30	09 50	10 07
—	12½	**London Blackfriars** 3 ⊖	a			06 56	07 11		07 37		08 07		08 36	08 41	09 04		09 33	09 56	10 10
—	13	City Thameslink 3	a			07 00	07 14		07 40		08 15		08 39	08 45	09 07		09 36	10 00	10 15
—	—	Farringdon 3 ⊖	a			07 04	07 16		07 44		08 19		08 42	08 50	09 10		09 40	10 04	10 19
—	—	St Pancras International 15 ⊖	a			07 08	07 21		07 48		08 23		08 46	08 54	09 14		09 44	10 08	10 23
—	—	Luton Airport Parkway 7 ✈	a			07 54	08 05		08 27		09 05		09 20	09 40	09 53		10 20	10 57	11 05
—	—	**Luton** 10	a			07 56	08 08		08 30		09 08		09 23	09 34	09 55		10 24	11 02	11 08

		FC	FC B	FC	FC B	FC	FC B		FC	FC B	FC	FC B	FC A	FC	FC B	FC A	FC B	FC B
Sutton (Surrey) 4	d	09 36	10 04	10 06	10 34	10 36	11 04	and at the same minutes past each hour until	15 06	15 34	15 36	16 04	16 06	16 33	16 32	17 03	17 00	17 31
West Sutton	d	09 39		10 09		10 39			15 09		15 39		16 09		16 35		17 03	
Sutton Common	d	09 41		10 11		10 41			15 11		15 41		16 11		16 37		17 05	
St Helier	d	09 44		10 14		10 44			15 14		15 44		16 14		16 40		17 08	
Morden South	d	09 46		10 16		10 46			15 16		15 46		16 16		16 42		17 10	
South Merton	d	09 48		10 18		10 48			15 18		15 48		16 18		16 44		17 12	
Wimbledon Chase	d	09 50		10 20		10 50			15 20		15 50		16 20		16 46		17 14	
Wimbledon 6 ⊖ ⛴	a	09 53		10 23		10 53			15 23		15 53		16 23		16 50		17 18	
	d	09 53		10 23		10 53			15 23		15 53		16 23		16 50		17 18	
Haydons Road	d	09 55		10 25		10 55			15 25		15 55		16 25		16 52		17 20	
Tooting	d	09 58		10 28		10 58			15 28		15 58		16 28		16 55		17 23	
Carshalton	d		10 07		10 37		11 07			15 37		16 07		16 36		17 06		17 34
Hackbridge	d		10 09		10 39		11 09			15 39		16 09		16 38		17 08		17 36
Mitcham Junction ⛴	d		10 12		10 42		11 12			15 42		16 12		16 41		17 11		17 39
Eastfields §	d																	
Streatham 4	d	10 03	10 19	10 33	10 49	11 03	11 19		15 33	15 49	16 03	16 19	16 33	16 47	16 59	17 17	17 29	17 46
Tulse Hill 3	d	10 07	10 23	10 37	10 53	11 07	11 23		15 37	15 53	16 07	16 23	16 37	16 50	17 02	17 22	17 32	17 50
North Dulwich	d	10 14	10 34	10 44	11 04	11 14	11 34		15 44	16 04	16 14	16 34	16 44	16 56	17 12	17 36	17 45	18 00
East Dulwich	d	10 16	10 36	10 46	11 06	11 16	11 36		15 46	16 06	16 16	16 36	16 46	16 58	17 14	17 38	17 47	18 02
Peckham Rye 4	d	10 19	10 39	10 49	11 09	11 19	11 39		15 49	16 03	17 19	16 39	16 49	17 01	17 16	17 41	17 49	18 04
Queens Rd Peckham	d	10 21	10 41	10 51	11 11	11 21	11 41		15 51	16 11	16 21	16 41	16 51	17 04	17 19	17 43	17 52	18 07
South Bermondsey	d	10 24	10 44	10 54	11 14	11 24	11 44		15 54	16 14	16 24	16 44	16 54	17 06	17 21	17 46	17 54	18 09
London Bridge 4 ⊖	a	10 28	10 48	10 58	11 18	11 28	11 48		15 58	16 12	16 28	16 48	17 00	17 11	17 26	17 50	17 59	18 14
Herne Hill 4	d	10 11	10 26	10 41	10 56	11 11	11 26		15 41	15 56	16 11	16 27	16 42	16 54	17 06	17 26	17 36	17 54
Loughborough Jn	d	10 15	10 30	10 45	11 00	11 15	11 30		15 45	16 00	16 15	16 30	16 45		17 09	17 29	17 39	17 57
Elephant & Castle ⊖	d	10 20	10 35	10 50	11 05	11 20	11 35		15 50	16 05	16 20	16 35	16 50	17 00	17 14	17 34	17 44	18 02
London Blackfriars 3 ⊖	a	10 26	10 41	10 56	11 11	11 26	11 41		15 56	16 11	16 29	16 38	16 57	17 03	17 17	17 39	17 47	18 09
City Thameslink 3	a	10 30	10 45	11 00	11 15	11 30	11 45		16 00	16 16	16 32	16 46	17 02	17 06	17 20	17 42	17 50	18 16
Farringdon 3 ⊖	a	10 34	10 49	11 04	11 19	11 34	11 49		16 04	16 19	16 35	16 49	17 05	17 09	17 23	17 47	17 53	18 23
St Pancras International 15 ⊖	a	10 38	10 53	11 08	11 23	11 38	11 53		16 08	16 24	16 39	16 53	17 09	17 13	17 27	17 53	17 57	18 27
Luton Airport Parkway 7 ✈	a	11 25	11 35	11 55	12 05	12 25	12 35		16 56	17 09	17 26	17 39	17 50	17 59	18 09	18 33	18 39	19 09
Luton 10	a	11 31	11 38	12 01	12 08	12 31	12 38		17 01	17 04	17 31	17 34	17 53	18 07	18 04	18 37	18 34	19 04

For general notes see front of timetable
For details of catering facilities see Directory of Train Operators

§ This station may open during the currency of this timetable, please see local publicity for further details.

A To Bedford (Table 52)
B To St Albans (Table 52)
b Arr. 0819

Sutton and Wimbledon → London and Luton via Streatham

Network Diagram - see first page of Table 177

Mondays to Fridays

		SN	FC	FC A	SN	FC	SN	FC	FC B	FC	FC	FC B	FC B	FC B	FC B
Sutton (Surrey) 4	d	17 30	17 39	18 06	18 04	18 08	18 31	18 37	19 02	19 02	19 36	20 06	20 36	21 06	21 53
West Sutton	d	17 34	17 42		18 07	18 13	18 34	18 41		19 05	19 39	20 09	20 39	21 09	21 56
Sutton Common	d	17 36	17 45			18 14	18 37	18 42		19 07	19 42	20 11	20 41	21 11	21 58
St Helier	d	17 39	17 47			18 18	18 39	18 46		19 10	19 44	20 14	20 44	21 14	22 01
Morden South	d	17 41	17 49			18 20	18 41	18 48		19 12	19 46	20 16	20 46	21 16	22 02
South Merton	d	17 43	17 51			18 22	18 43	18 50		19 14	19 48	20 18	20 48	21 18	22 04
Wimbledon Chase	d	17 45	17 53			18 24	18 45	18 52		19 16	19 50	20 20	20 50	21 20	22 06
Wimbledon 6 ⊖	a	17 50	17 56		18 18	18 27	18 50	18 55		19 22	19 54	20 25	20 53	21 25	22 09
	d	17 51	17 56		18 23	18 27	18 50	18 55		19 23	19 54	20 23	20 53	21 39	22 09
Haydons Road	d	17 53	17 59		18 25	18 29	18 52	18 57		19 25	19 56	20 25	20 55	21 41	22 11
Tooting	d	17 56	18 02		18 28	18 32	18 55	19 00		19 28	19 59	20 28	20 58	21 44	22 14
Carshalton	d			18 09					19 05						
Hackbridge	d			18 11					19 07						
Mitcham Junction	d			18 14					19 10						
Eastfields §	d														
Streatham 4	d	18 01	18 06	18 20	18 32	18 36	18 59	19 05	19 17	19 33	20 04	20 33	21 03	21 49	22 19
Tulse Hill 3	d	18 05	18 10	18 24	18 36	18 40	19 05	19 08	19 23	19 37	20 07	20 37	21 07	21 53	22 23
North Dulwich	d	18 08	*18 18*	*18 31*	18 39	*18 48*	19 08	*19 20*	*19 31*	*19 43*	*20 13*	*20 43*	*21 28*	*22 28*	*22 58*
East Dulwich	d	18 10	*18 20*	*18 33*	18 41	*18 50*	19 10	*19 22*	*19 33*	*19 45*	*20 15*	*20 45*	*21 30*	*22 30*	*23 00*
Peckham Rye 4	d	18 12	*18 23*	*18 36*	18 43	*18 53*	19 13	*19 25*	*19 35*	*19 48*	*20 17*	*20 47*	*21 32*	*22 32*	*23 02*
Queens Rd Peckham	d	18 15	*18 25*	*18 38*	18 46	*18 55*	19 15		*19 38*	*19 50*	*20 20*	*20 50*	*21 35*	*22 35*	*23 05*
South Bermondsey	d	18 17	*18 28*	*18 41*	18 48	*18 58*	19 18		*19 40*	*19 53*	*20 22*	*20 52*	*21 37*	*22 37*	*23 07*
London Bridge 4 ⊖	a	18 24	*18 32*	*18 45*	18 53	*19 02*	19 22	*19 31*	*19 45*	*19 57*	*20 27*	*20 57*	*21 44*	*22 44*	*23 14*
Herne Hill 4	d		18 14	18 27		18 44		19 11	19 27	19 41	20 11	20 41	21 11	21 56	22 26
Loughborough Jn	d		18 17	18 30		18 47		19 15	19 30	19 45	20 15	20 45	21 15	22 00	22 30
Elephant & Castle ⊖	d		18 22	18 35		18 52		19 20	19 35	19 50	20 20	20 50	21 19	22 05	22 35
London Blackfriars 3 ⊖	a		18 29	18 40		18 59		19 26	19 41	19 56	20 26	20 56	21 26	22 08	22 38
City Thameslink 3	a		18 34	18 48		19 04		19 30	19 45	20 00	20 30	21 00	21 35	22 10	22 40
Farringdon 3 ⊖	a		18 37	18 51		19 07		19 34	19 49	20 04	20 34	21 04	21 39	22 14	22 44
St Pancras International 15 ⊖	a		18 41	18 55		19 11		19 38	19 53	20 08	20 38	21 08	21 43	22 18	22 48
Luton Airport Parkway 7 ✈	a		19 27	*19 40*		19 58		20 25	20 41	20 55	21 25	21 55	22 25	23 01	23 31
Luton 10	a		19 35	*19 34*		20 03		20 31	20 44	21 01	21 31	21 59	22 29	23 05	23 35

Saturdays

		FC	FC A	FC	FC A	FC	FC A	FC	FC A	FC	FC A	FC	FC A		FC	FC B	FC	FC B
Sutton (Surrey) 4	d		07 04	07 06	07 34	07 36	08 04	08 06	08 34	08 36	09 04	09 06	09 34		16 36	17 04	17 06	17 34
West Sutton	d			07 09		07 39		08 09		08 39		09 09			16 39		17 09	
Sutton Common	d			07 11		07 41		08 11		08 41		09 11			16 41		17 11	
St Helier	d			07 14		07 44		08 14		08 44		09 14			16 44		17 14	
Morden South	d			07 16		07 46		08 16		08 46		09 16			16 46		17 16	
South Merton	d			07 18		07 48		08 18		08 48		09 18			16 48		17 18	
Wimbledon Chase	d			07 20		07 50		08 20		08 50		09 20			16 50		17 20	
Wimbledon 6 ⊖	a			07 23		07 53		08 23		08 53		09 23			16 53		17 23	
	d	06 53		07 23		07 53		08 23		08 53		09 23			16 53		17 23	
Haydons Road	d	06 55		07 25		07 55		08 25		08 55		09 25		and at the same minutes past each hour until	16 55		17 25	
Tooting	d	06 58		07 28		07 58		08 28		08 58		09 28			16 58		17 28	
Carshalton	d		07 07		07 37		08 07		08 37		09 07		09 37			17 07		17 37
Hackbridge	d		07 09		07 39		08 09		08 39		09 09		09 39			17 09		17 39
Mitcham Junction	d		07 12		07 42		08 12		08 42		09 12		09 42			17 12		17 42
Eastfields §	d																	
Streatham 4	d	07 03	07 19	07 33	07 49	08 03	08 19	08 33	08 49	09 03	09 19	09 33	09 49		17 03	17 19	17 33	17 49
Tulse Hill 3	d	07 07	07 23	07 37	07 53	08 07	08 23	08 37	08 53	09 07	09 23	09 37	09 53		17 07	17 23	17 37	17 53
North Dulwich	d	*07 24*		*07 54*		*08 24*	*08 34*	*08 44*	*09 04*	*09 14*	*09 24*	*09 44*	*10 04*		*17 14*	*17 34*	*17 44*	*18 04*
East Dulwich	d	*07 26*		*07 56*		*08 26*	*08 36*	*08 46*	*09 06*	*09 16*	*09 36*	*09 46*	*10 06*		*17 16*	*17 36*	*17 46*	*18 06*
Peckham Rye 4	d	*07 29*		*07 59*		*08 29*	*08 39*	*08 49*	*09 09*	*09 19*	*09 39*	*09 49*	*10 09*		*17 19*	*17 39*	*17 49*	*18 09*
Queens Rd Peckham	d	*07 32*		*08 02*		*08 32*	*08 41*	*08 51*	*09 11*	*09 21*	*09 41*	*09 51*	*10 11*		*17 21*	*17 41*	*17 51*	*18 11*
South Bermondsey	d	*07 34*		*08 04*		*08 34*	*08 44*	*08 54*	*09 14*	*09 24*	*09 44*	*09 54*	*10 14*		*17 24*	*17 44*	*17 54*	*18 14*
London Bridge 4 ⊖	a	*07 39*		*08 09*		*08 39*	*08 48*	*08 58*	*09 18*	*09 28*	*09 48*	*09 58*	*10 18*		*17 28*	*17 48*	*17 58*	*18 18*
Herne Hill 4	d	07 11	07 26	07 41	07 56	08 11	08 26	08 41	08 56	09 11	09 26	09 41	09 56		17 11	17 26	17 41	17 56
Loughborough Jn	d	07 15	07 30	07 45	08 00	08 15	08 30	08 45	09 00	09 15	09 30	09 46	10 00		17 15	17 30	17 45	18 00
Elephant & Castle ⊖	d	07 20	07 35	07 50	08 05	08 20	08 35	08 50	09 05	09 20	09 35	09 50	10 05		17 20	17 35	17 50	18 05
London Blackfriars 3 ⊖	a	07 26	07 41	07 56	08 11	08 26	08 41	08 56	09 11	09 26	09 41	09 56	10 11		17 26	17 41	17 56	18 11
City Thameslink 3	a							09 00	09 15	09 30	09 45	10 00	10 15		17 30	17 45	18 00	18 15
Farringdon 3 ⊖	a	07 33	07 48	08 03	08 18	08 33	08 48	09 04	09 19	09 34	09 49	10 04	10 19		17 34	17 49	18 04	18 19
St Pancras International 15 ⊖	a	07 38	07 53	08 08	08 23	08 38	08 53	09 08	09 23	09 38	09 53	10 08	10 23		17 38	17 53	18 08	18 23
Luton Airport Parkway 7 ✈	a	08 25	*08 35*	08 55	*09 05*	09 25	*09 35*	09 55	*10 05*	10 25	*10 35*	10 55	*11 05*		18 25	18 40	18 55	19 10
Luton 10	a	08 31	*08 38*	09 01	*09 08*	09 31	*09 38*	10 01	*10 08*	10 31	*10 38*	11 01	*11 08*		18 31	18 43	19 01	19 13

For general notes see front of timetable
For details of catering facilities see
Directory of Train Operators

§ This station may open during the currency of this timetable, please see local publicity for further details.

A To St Albans (Table 52)
B To Bedford (Table 52)

Table 179

Saturdays

Sutton and Wimbledon → London and Luton via Streatham

Network Diagram - see first page of Table 177

	FC	FC A	FC	FC A	FC	FC	FC	FC	FC A	FC A	FC A	FC A	FC A
Sutton (Surrey) 4 d	17 36	18 04	18 06	18 34	18 36	19 04	19 06	19 36	20 06	20 36	21 06	21 52	
West Sutton d	17 39		18 09		18 39		19 09	19 39	20 09	20 39	21 09	21 55	
Sutton Common d	17 41		18 11		18 41		19 11	19 41	20 11	20 41	21 11	21 57	
St Helier d	17 44		18 14		18 44		19 14	19 44	20 14	20 44	21 14	22 00	
Morden South d	17 46		18 16		18 46		19 16	19 46	20 16	20 46	21 16	22 02	
South Merton d	17 48		18 18		18 48		19 18	19 48	20 18	20 48	21 18	22 04	
Wimbledon Chase d	17 50		18 20		18 50		19 20	19 50	20 20	20 50	21 20	22 06	
Wimbledon 6 ⊖ a	17 53		18 23		18 53		19 23	19 53	20 23	20 53	21 23	22 09	
d	17 53		18 23		18 53		19 23	19 53	20 23	20 53	21 39	22 09	22 39
Haydons Road d	17 55		18 25		18 55		19 25	19 55	20 25	20 55	21 41	22 11	22 41
Tooting d	17 58		18 28		18 58		19 28	19 58	20 28	20 58	21 44	22 14	22 44
Carshalton d		18 07		18 37		19 07							
Hackbridge d		18 09		18 39		19 09							
Mitcham Junction d		18 12		18 42		19 12							
Eastfields § d													
Streatham 4 d	18 03	18 19	18 33	18 49	19 03	19 19	19 33	20 03	20 33	21 03	21 49	22 19	22 49
Tulse Hill 3 d	18 07	18 23	18 37	18 53	19 07	19 23	19 37	20 07	20 37	21 07	21 53	22 23	22 53
North Dulwich d	18 14	18 34	18 44		19 13		19 43	20 13	20 43	21 28	22 28	22 58	23 28
East Dulwich d	18 16	18 36	18 46		19 15		19 45	20 15	20 45	21 30	22 30	23 00	23 30
Peckham Rye 4 d	18 19	18 39	18 49		19 17		19 47	20 17	20 47	21 32	22 32	23 02	23 32
Queens Rd Peckham d	18 21	18 41	18 51		19 20		19 50	20 20	20 50	21 35	22 35	23 05	23 35
South Bermondsey d	18 24	18 44	18 54		19 22		19 52	20 22	20 52	21 37	22 37	23 07	23 37
London Bridge 4 ⊖ a	18 28	18 48	18 58		19 27		19 58	20 27	20 57	21 42	22 42	23 12	23 42
Herne Hill 4 d	18 11	18 26	18 41	18 56	19 11	19 26	19 41	20 11	20 41	21 11	21 56	22 26	22 56
Loughborough Jn d	18 15	18 30	18 45	19 00	19 15	19 30	19 45	20 15	20 45	21 15	22 00	22 30	
Elephant & Castle ⊖ d	18 20	18 35	18 50	19 05	19 20	19 35	19 50	20 20	20 50	21 20	22 05	22 35	23 05
London Blackfriars 3 ⊖ a	18 26	18 41	18 56	19 11	19 26	19 41	19 56	20 26	20 56	21 26	22 08	22 38	23 08
City Thameslink 3 a	18 30	18 45	19 00	19 15	19 30	19 45	20 00	20 30	21 00				
Farringdon 3 ⊖ a	18 34	18 49	19 04	19 19	19 34	19 49	20 04	20 34	21 04	21 38	22 13	22 43	23 13
St Pancras International 15 ⊖ a	18 38	18 53	19 08	19 23	19 38	19 53	20 08	20 38	21 08	21 42	22 17	22 47	23 17
Luton Airport Parkway 7 ✈ a	19 25	19 40	19 55	20 10	20 25	20 41	20 55	21 25	21 55	22 27	23 01	23 31	00 01
Luton 10 a	19 31	19 43	20 01	20 13	20 31	20 45	21 01	21 31	21 59	22 30	23 05	23 35	00 05

Sundays

	FC A	FC	FC	FC A	FC A	FC A	FC A	FC A	FC A	FC A	FC A	FC A	FC	FC	FC	FC	FC	FC A	FC A	FC A	FC A	FC A	FC A	FC A
Sutton (Surrey) 4 d		10 10	10 40	11 10	11 40	12 10	12 40	13 10	13 40	14 10	14 40	15 10	15 40	16 10	16 40	17 10	17 40	18 10	18 40	19 10	19 40	20 10	20 40	21 10
West Sutton d		10 13	10 43	11 13	11 43	12 13	12 43	13 13	13 43	14 13	14 43	15 13	15 43	16 13	16 43	17 13	17 43	18 13	18 43	19 13	19 43	20 13	20 43	21 13
Sutton Common d		10 15	10 45	11 15	11 45	12 15	12 45	13 15	13 45	14 15	14 45	15 15	15 45	16 15	16 45	17 15	17 45	18 15	18 45	19 15	19 45	20 15	20 45	21 15
St Helier d		10 17	10 47	11 17	11 47	12 17	12 47	13 17	13 47	14 17	14 47	15 17	15 47	16 17	16 47	17 17	17 47	18 17	18 47	19 17	19 47	20 17	20 47	21 17
Morden South d		10 19	10 49	11 19	11 49	12 19	12 49	13 19	13 49	14 19	14 49	15 19	15 49	16 19	16 49	17 19	17 49	18 19	18 49	19 19	19 49	20 19	20 49	21 19
South Merton d		10 21	10 51	11 21	11 51	12 21	12 51	13 21	13 51	14 21	14 51	15 21	15 51	16 21	16 51	17 21	17 51	18 21	18 51	19 21	19 51	20 21	20 51	21 21
Wimbledon Chase d		10 22	10 52	11 22	11 52	12 22	12 52	13 22	13 52	14 22	14 52	15 22	15 52	16 22	16 52	17 22	17 52	18 22	18 52	19 22	19 52	20 22	20 52	21 22
Wimbledon 6 ⊖ a		10 25	10 55	11 25	11 55	12 25	12 55	13 25	13 55	14 25	14 55	15 25	15 55	16 25	16 55	17 25	17 55	18 25	18 55	19 25	19 55	20 25	20 55	21 25
d	22p39	10 26	10 56	11 26	11 56	12 26	12 56	13 26	13 56	14 26	14 56	15 26	15 56	16 26	16 56	17 26	17 56	18 26	18 56	19 26	19 56	20 26	20 56	21 26
Haydons Road d	22p41	10 28	10 58	11 28	11 58	12 28	12 58	13 28	13 58	14 28	14 58	15 28	15 58	16 28	16 58	17 28	17 58	18 28	18 58	19 28	19 58	20 28	20 58	21 28
Tooting d	22p44	10 31	11 01	11 31	12 01	12 31	13 01	13 31	14 01	14 31	15 01	15 31	16 01	16 31	17 01	17 31	18 01	18 31	19 01	19 31	20 01	20 31	21 01	21 31
Carshalton d																								
Hackbridge d																								
Mitcham Junction d																								
Eastfields § d																								
Streatham 4 d	22p49	10 35	11 05	11 35	12 05	12 35	13 05	13 35	14 05	14 35	15 05	15 35	16 05	16 35	17 05	17 35	18 05	18 35	19 05	19 35	20 05	20 35	21 05	21 35
Tulse Hill 3 d	22p53	10 38	11 08	11 38	12 08	12 38	13 08	13 38	14 08	14 38	15 08	15 38	16 08	16 38	17 08	17 38	18 08	18 38	19 08	19 38	20 08	20 38	21 08	21 38
North Dulwich d	23p28	11 04	11 34	12 04	12 34	13 04	13 34	14 04	14 34	15 04	15 34	16 04	16 34	17 04	17 34	18 04	18 34	19 04		20 04	20 34	21 04	21 34	22 04
East Dulwich d	23p30	11 06	11 36	12 06	12 36	13 06	13 36	14 06	14 36	15 06	15 36	16 06	16 36	17 06	17 36	18 06	18 36	19 06		20 06	20 36	21 06	21 36	22 06
Peckham Rye 4 d	23p32	11 08	11 38	12 08	12 38	13 08	13 38	14 08	14 38	15 08	15 38	16 08	16 38	17 08	17 38	18 08	18 38	19 08		20 08	20 38	21 08	21 38	22 08
Queens Rd Peckham d	23p35	11 11	11 41	12 11	12 41	13 11	13 41	14 11	14 41	15 11	15 41	16 11	16 41	17 11	17 41	18 11	18 41	19 11		20 11	20 41	21 11	21 41	22 11
South Bermondsey d	23p37	11 13	11 43	12 13	12 43	13 13	13 43	14 13	14 43	15 13	15 43	16 13	16 43	17 13	17 43	18 13	18 43	19 13		20 13	20 43	21 13	21 43	22 13
London Bridge 4 ⊖ a	23p42	11 18	11 48	12 18	12 48	13 18	13 48	14 18	14 48	15 18	15 48	16 18	16 48	17 18	17 48	18 18	18 48	19 18		20 18	20 48	21 18	21 48	22 18
Herne Hill 4 d	22p56	10 42	11 12	11 42	12 14	12 44	13 12	13 42	14 12	14 42	15 12	15 42	16 14	16 42	17 14	17 42	18 12	18 42	19 12	19 42	20 12	20 42	21 12	21 42
Loughborough Jn d		10 45	11 15	11 45	12 17	12 47	13 15	13 45	14 15	14 45	15 15	15 45	16 17	16 45	17 17	17 45	18 15	18 44	19 14	19 44	20 14	20 44	21 14	21 44
Elephant & Castle ⊖ d	23p05	10 50	11 20	11 50	12 22	12 52	13 20	13 50	14 20	14 50	15 20	15 50	16 22	16 50	17 22	17 50	18 20	18 50	19 20	19 50	20 20	20 50	21 20	21 50
London Blackfriars 3 ⊖ a	23p08	10 56	11 26	11 56	12 26	12 56	13 26	13 56	14 26	14 56	15 26	15 56	16 26	16 56	17 26	17 56	18 26	18 56	19 26	19 56	20 26	20 56	21 26	21 56
City Thameslink 3 a																								
Farringdon 3 ⊖ a	23p13	11 02	11 32	12 02	12 32	13 02	13 32	14 02	14 32	15 02	15 32	16 02	16 32	17 02	17 32	18 02	18 32	19 02	19 32	20 02	20 32	21 02	21 32	22 02
St Pancras International 15 ⊖ a	23p17	11 06	11 36	12 06	12 36	13 06	13 36	14 06	14 36	15 06	15 36	16 06	16 36	17 06	17 36	18 06	18 36	19 06	19 36	20 06	20 36	21 06	21 36	22 06
Luton Airport Parkway 7 ✈ a	00 01	11 48	12 18	12 48	13 18	13 48	14 18	14 48	15 18	15 48	16 18	16 48	17 18	17 48	18 18	18 48	19 18	19 47	20 17	20 47	21 17	21 47	22 17	22 47
Luton 10 a	00 05	11 55	12 25	12 52	13 22	13 52	14 22	14 52	15 22	15 52	16 22	16 52	17 25	17 55	18 25	18 55	19 25	19 52	20 22	20 52	21 22	21 50	22 22	22 50

For general notes see front of timetable
For details of catering facilities see
Directory of Train Operators

§ This station may open during the currency of this timetable, please see local publicity for further details.

A To Bedford (Table 52)

London and Croydon → Caterham and Tattenham Corner

Network Diagram - see first page of Table 177

Miles	Miles			SN MX	SN MO	SN MX	SN	SN	SN		SN	SN	SN	SN		SN	SN	SN	SN	SN	SN	SN	SN	SN	SN
0	—	**London Victoria** 15	⊖ d	23p00				06 15			07 20			07 45				08 15			08 45				09 15
2¾	—	Clapham Junction 10	d	23p08				06 22			07 27			07 51				08 22			08 52				09 22
—	0	**London Charing Cross** 4	⊖ d		23p36	23p45	06 05																		
—	¾	**London Waterloo (East)** 4	⊖ d		23p39	23p48	06 08																		
—	1¾	**London Bridge** 4	⊖ d		23p44	23p53	06 13		06 54			07 25	07 40			08 05	08 09		08 41	08 36		08 37	09 05	09 19	
—	4½	New Cross Gate 4	⊖ d		23p49	23p58	06 19		06 59			07 30	07 45			08 10				08 41			09 10		
—	10½	Norwood Junction 2	d		00 10	00 16	06 38		07 14			07b51	08 00			08 25	08 28			08 56		09 13	09 25	09 32	
10½	11¾	**East Croydon**	⇌ d	23p29	00 14	00 20	06 42	06c49	07 18		07 48	07 55	08 04	08 14		08 29	08 33	08 45	08 57	09 00	09 13	09 18	09 29	09 36	09 43
11½	12¾	South Croydon 4	d	23p32	00 16	00 23	06 45		07 21		07 51		08 07	08 16		08 32		08 47		09 03	09 16		09 32		09 46
12½	13¾	Purley Oaks	d	23p35	00 19	00 26	06 48		07 24		07 54		08 10	08 19		08 35		08 50		09 06	09 19		09 35		09 49
13½	14¾	Purley 4	a	23p38	00 22	00 29	06 51	06 56	07 27		07 57	08 01	08 13	08 22		08 38	08 41	08 53	09 04	09 09	09 22	09 25	09 38	09 42	09 52
—	—		d	23p54	00 22	00 31	06 53	07 00	07 29	07 32	07 57	08 01	08 13	08 22		08 38	08 41	08 53	09 04	09 09	09 22	09 25	09 38	09 42	09 52
—	16	Kenley	d		00 25	00 34	06 56		07 32			08 04		08 25		08 41		08 56		09 12	09 25		09 41		09 55
—	17¼	Whyteleafe	d		00 29	00 38	07 00		07 36			08 08		08 29		08 44		09 00		09 15	09 28		09 44		09 58
—	17¾	Whyteleafe South	d		00 31	00 40	07 02		07 38			08 10		08 31		08 46		09 02		09 17	09 30		09 46		10 00
—	19½	**Caterham**	a		00 35	00 44	07 06		07 42			08 14		08 35		08 51		09 06		09 22	09 35		09 51		10 05
14¼	—	Reedham	d	23p56				07 02		07 34	07 59		08 15				08 43		09 07			09 28		09 45	
15	—	Smitham	d	23p59				07 05		07 37	08 02		08 18				08 46		09 09			09a30		09 47	
15¾	—	Woodmansterne	d	00 02				07 08		07 40	08 05		08 21				08 49		09 12					09 50	
16¾	—	Chipstead	d	00 05				07 11		07 43	08 08		08 24				08 52		09 15					09 53	
19¼	—	Kingswood	d	00 10				07 16		07 48	08 13		08 29				08 57		09 21					09 58	
20½	—	Tadworth	d	00 14				07 20		07 52	08 17		08 33				09 01		09 24					10 02	
21¾	—	**Tattenham Corner**	a	00 17				07 23		07 55	08 20		08 36				09 04		09 28					10 05	

		SN	SN	SN		SN	SN	SN	SN		SN	SN	SN	SN	SN	SN	SN	SN			SN	SN	SN	SN
London Victoria 15	⊖ d					09 45					10 15				10 45						15 15			
Clapham Junction 10	d					09 52					10 22				10 52						15 22			
London Charing Cross 4	⊖ d													10 40				11 10						15 40
London Waterloo (East) 4	⊖ d													10 43				11 13						15 43
London Bridge 4	⊖ d	09 07	09 35	09 47			09 37	10 05	10 17			10 08	10 35	10 48		10 38	11 05	11 18				15 08	15 35	15 48
New Cross Gate 4	⊖ d		09 40					10 10					10 40				11 10						15 40	
Norwood Junction 2	d	09 43	09 55	09 59			10 13	10 25	10 31			10 43	10 55			11 13	11 25		and at			15 43	15 55	
East Croydon	⇌ d	09 48	09 59	10 05		10 13	10 18	10 29	10 35		10 43	10 48	10 59	11 05	11 13	11 18	11 29	11 35	the same		15 43	15 48	15 59	16 05
South Croydon 4	d		10 02			10 16		10 32			10 46		11 02		11 16		11 32		minutes		15 46		16 02	
Purley Oaks	d		10 05			10 19		10 35			10 49		11 05		11 19		11 35				15 49		16 05	
Purley 4	a	09 54	10 08	10 11		10 22	10 24	10 38	10 41		10 52	10 54	11 08	11 11	11 22	11 24	11 38	11 41	past		15 52	15 54	16 08	16 11
	d	09 55	10 08	10 11		10 22	10 25	10 38	10 41		10 52	10 55	11 08	11 11	11 22	11 25	11 38	11 41			15 52	15 55	16 08	16 11
Kenley	d		10 11			10 25		10 41			10 55		11 11		11 25		11 41		each		15 55		16 11	
Whyteleafe	d		10 14			10 28		10 44			10 58		11 14		11 28		11 44				15 58		16 14	
Whyteleafe South	d		10 16			10 30		10 46			11 00		11 16		11 30		11 46		hour until		16 00		16 16	
Caterham	a		10 21			10 35		10 51			11 05		11 21		11 35		11 51				16 05		16 21	
Reedham	d	09 57		10 14			10 27		10 44			10 57		11 14		11 27		11 44				15 57		16 14
Smitham	d	10a00		10 16			10a30		10 46			11a00		11 16		11a30		11 46				16a00		16 16
Woodmansterne	d			10 19					10 49					11 19				11 49						16 19
Chipstead	d			10 22					10 52					11 22				11 52						16 22
Kingswood	d			10 27					10 57					11 27				11 57						16 27
Tadworth	d			10 31					11 01					11 31				12 01						16 31
Tattenham Corner	a			10 34					11 04					11 34				12 04						16 34

		SN	SN	SN	SN	SN	SN	SN	SN	SN		SN	SN		SN	SN		SN	SN	SN	SN	SN			SN
London Victoria 15	⊖ d	15 45				16 15			16 45						17 34				18 04		18 17				18 53
Clapham Junction 10	d	15 52				16 22			16 52						17 40				18 10		18 25				18 59
London Charing Cross 4	⊖ d				16 08																				
London Waterloo (East) 4	⊖ d				16 11																				
London Bridge 4	⊖ d		15 38	16 05	16 16		16 07	16 35		16 59			17 19			17 39		18 01		18 20		18 42			
New Cross Gate 4	⊖ d			16 10				16 40					17 24			17 44		18 06		18 26		18 47			
Norwood Junction 2	d		16 13	16 25	16 30		16 43	16 55		17 12		←	17 33			17 54		18 15		18 35		18 56			
East Croydon	⇌ d	16 13	16 18	16 29	16 35	16 43	16 48	16 59	17e19	17 17		17 19	17 37		17 52	17 58		18 19	18 22	18 39	18f50	19 00			19 12
South Croydon 4	d	16 16		16 32		16 46		17 02	→	17 19		17 22	17 40		17 54	18 00		18 22	18 24	18 41	18 52	19 03			19 14
Purley Oaks	d	16 19		16 35		16 49		17 05		17 22		17 25	17 43		17 57	18 03		18 25	18 27	18 44	18 55	19 06			19 17
Purley 4	a	16 22	16 24	16 38	16 41	16 52	16 54	17 08		17 25		17 28	17 46		18 00	18 06		18 28	18 30	18 47	18 58	19 09			19 20
	d	16 22	16 25	16 38	16 41	16 52	17 04	17 08		17 25		17 28	17 49	17 52	18 03	18 09	18 11	18 30	18 33	18 50	19 01	19 11	19 14		19 21
Kenley	d	16 25		16 41		16 55		17 11		17 28			17 52			18 12		18 33		18 53		19 14			
Whyteleafe	d	16 28		16 44		16 58		17 14		17 32			17 55			18 15		18 37		18 56		19 18			
Whyteleafe South	d	16 30		16 46		17 00		17 16		17 34			17 57			18 17		18 39		18 58		19 20			
Caterham	a	16 35		16 53		17 07		17 23		17 40			18 04			18 24		18 45		19 05		19 26			
Reedham	d		16 27		16 44		17 06					17 30		17 54	18 05		18 13		18 35		19 03		19 16		19 23
Smitham	d		16a30		16 46		17 09					17 33		17 57	18 08		18 16		18 38		19 06		19 19		19a28
Woodmansterne	d				16 49		17 12					17 36		18 00	18 11		18 19		18 41		19 09		19 22		
Chipstead	d				16 52		17 15					17 39		18 03	18 14		18 22		18 44		19 12		19 25		
Kingswood	d				16 57		17 20					17 44		18 08	18 19		18 27		18 49		19 17		19 30		
Tadworth	d				17 01		17 24					17 48		18 12	18 23		18 31		18 53		19 21		19 34		
Tattenham Corner	a				17 06		17 30					17 53		18 19	18 28		18 36		18 58		19 26		19 39		

For general notes see front of timetable
For details of catering facilities see Directory of Train Operators

b Arr. 0748
c Arr. 0645
e Arr. 1713
f Arr. 1846

London and Croydon → Caterham and Tattenham Corner

Network Diagram - see first page of Table 177

		SN	SN	SN	SN	SN	SN	SN	SN	SN	SN	SN		SN	SN	SN	SN	SN	SN	SN	SN	SN	SN		
London Victoria 15	⊖ d	19 00			19 31		20 00		20 30		21 00			21 30		22 00		22 30		23 00					
Clapham Junction 10	d	19 08			19 38		20 08		20 38		21 08			21 38		22 08		22 38		23 08					
London Charing Cross 4	⊖ d					19 37		20 07		20 37		21 07			21 37		22 07		22 37		23 07		23 45		
London Waterloo (East) 4	⊖ d					19 40		20 10		20 40		21 10			21 40		22 10		22 40		23 10		23 48		
London Bridge 4	⊖ d			19 15		19 45		20 15		20 45		21 15			21 45		22 15		22 45		23 15		23 53		
New Cross Gate 4	⊖ d			19 20		19 50		20 20		20 50		21 20			21 50		22 20		22 50		23 20		23 58		
Norwood Junction 2	d			19 40		20 05		20 38		21 08		21 38			22 08		22 38		23 08		23 38		00 16		
East Croydon	d	19 32		19 44	19 59	20b13	20 29	20 43	20 59	21 13	21 29	21 43		21 59	22 13	22 29	22 43	22 59	23 13	23 29	23 42		00 20		
South Croydon 4	d	19 34		19 46	20 02	20 15	20 32	20 45	21 02	21 15	21 32	21 45		22 02	22 15	22 32	22 45	23 02	23 15	23 32	23 45		00 23		
Purley Oaks	d	19 37		19 49	20 05	20 18	20 35	20 48	21 05	21 18	21 35	21 48		22 05	22 18	22 35	22 48	23 05	23 18	23 35	23 48		00 26		
Purley 4	a	19 41		19 52	20 08	20 21	20 38	20 51	21 08	21 21	21 38	21 51		22 08	22 21	22 38	22 51	23 08	23 21	23 38	23 51		00 29		
	d	19 44	19 46	19 55	20 10	20 24	20 39	20 54	21 08	21 24	21 38	21 54		22 08	22 24	22 38	22 54	23 10	23 24	23 54	23 51	⟵ 23 54	00 31		
Kenley	d	19 47		19 58		20 27		20 57		21 27		21 57			22 27		22 57		23 27	⟶	23 54		00 34		
Whyteleafe	d	19 50		20 01		20 30		21 00		21 30		22 00			22 30		23 00		23 30		23 57		00 38		
Whyteleafe South	d	19 52		20 03		20 32		21 02		21 32		22 02			22 32		23 02		23 32		23 59		00 40		
Caterham	a	19 57		20 08		20 37		21 07		21 37		22 07			22 37		23 07		23 37		00 04		00 44		
Reedham	d		19 48		20 13		20 41		21 10		21 40			22 10		22 40		23 13				23 56			
Smitham	d		19 51		20 15		20 44		21 13		21 43			22 13		22 43		23 15				23 59			
Woodmansterne	d		19 54		20 18		20 47		21 16		21 46			22 16		22 46		23 18				00 02			
Chipstead	d		19 57		20 21		20 50		21 19		21 49			22 19		22 49		23 21				00 05			
Kingswood	d		20 02		20 27		20 55		21 24		21 54			22 24		22 54		23 27				00 10			
Tadworth	d		20 06		20 30		20 59		21 28		21 58			22 28		22 58		23 30				00 14			
Tattenham Corner	a		20 09		20 34		21 02		21 31		22 01			22 31		23 01		23 34				00 17			

Saturdays

		SN	SN		SN	SN		SN	SN		SN		SN	SN	SN	SN	SN	SN	SN	SN			SN	SN
London Victoria 15	⊖ d	23p00				06 45					07 15				07 45				08 15					
Clapham Junction 10	d	23p08				06 52					07 22				07 52				08 22					
London Charing Cross 4	⊖ d		23p45											07 40				08 10						17 40
London Waterloo (East) 4	⊖ d		23p48											07 43				08 13						17 43
London Bridge 4	⊖ d		23p53		06 47			07 05	07 18				07 35	07 48		07 38	08 05	08 18		08 08			17 35	17 48
New Cross Gate 4	⊖ d		23p58					07 10					07 40				08 10						17 40	
Norwood Junction 2	d		00 16		07 00			07 25	07 31				07 55			08 13	08 25			08 43	and at		17 55	
East Croydon	d	23p29	00 20		07 05	07 13		07 29	07 35		07 43		07 59	08 05	08 13	08 18	08 29	08 35	08 43	08 48	the same		17 59	18 05
South Croydon 4	d	23p32	00 23			07 16		07 32			07 46		08 02		08 16		08 32		08 46		minutes		18 02	
Purley Oaks	d	23p35	00 26			07 19		07 35			07 49		08 05		08 19		08 35		08 49				18 05	
Purley 4	a	23p38	00 29		07 11	07 22		07 38	07 41		07 52		08 08	08 11	08 22	08 24	08 38	08 41	08 52	08 54	past		18 08	18 11
	d	23p54	00 31		07 11	07 22		07 38	07 41		07 52		08 08	08 11	08 22	08 25	08 38	08 41	08 52	08 55			18 08	18 11
Kenley	d		00 34			07 25		07 41			07 55		08 11		08 25		08 41		08 55		each		18 11	
Whyteleafe	d		00 38			07 28		07 44			07 58		08 14		08 28		08 44		08 58		hour until		18 14	
Whyteleafe South	d		00 40			07 30		07 46			08 00		08 16		08 30		08 46		09 00				18 16	
Caterham	a		00 44			07 35		07 51			08 05		08 21		08 35		08 51		09 05				18 21	
Reedham	d	23p56			07 14				07 43					08 14		08 27		08 44		08 57				18 14
Smitham	d	23p59			07 16				07 46					08 16		08a30		08 46		09a00				18 16
Woodmansterne	d	00 02			07 19				07 49					08 19				08 49						18 19
Chipstead	d	00 05			07 22				07 52					08 22				08 52						18 22
Kingswood	d	00 10			07 27				07 57					08 27				08 57						18 27
Tadworth	d	00 14			07 31				08 01					08 31				09 01						18 31
Tattenham Corner	a	00 17			07 34				08 04					08 34				09 04						18 34

		SN	SN		SN	SN		SN	SN		SN	SN		SN	SN		SN	SN		SN	SN		SN	SN	SN
London Victoria 15	⊖ d	17 45												19 00			19 30			20 00			20 30		21 00
Clapham Junction 10	d	17 52												19 08			19 38			20 08			20 38		21 08
London Charing Cross 4	⊖ d					18 10					18 40				19 07			19 37			20 07			20 37	
London Waterloo (East) 4	⊖ d					18 13					18 43				19 10			19 39			20 10			20 40	
London Bridge 4	⊖ d		17 38		18 05	18 18		18 08	18 35		18 48	18 45			19 15			19 44			20 15			20 45	
New Cross Gate 4	⊖ d				18 10				18 40			18 50			19 20			19 50			20 20			20 50	
Norwood Junction 2	d		18 13		18 25			18 43	18 55		19 03	19 09			19 38			20 08			20 38			21 08	
East Croydon	d	18 13	18 18		18 29	18 35		18 48	18 59		19 07	19 13		19 29	19 43		19 59	20 13		20 29	20 43		20 59	21 13	21 29
South Croydon 4	d	18 16			18 32				19 02		19 09	19 16		19 32	19 45		20 02	20 15		20 32	20 45		21 02	21 15	21 32
Purley Oaks	d	18 19			18 35				19 05		19 12	19 19		19 35	19 48		20 05	20 18		20 35	20 48		21 05	21 18	21 35
Purley 4	a	18 22	18 24		18 38	18 41		18 54	19 08		19 15	19 22		19 38	19 51		20 08	20 21		20 38	20 51		21 08	21 21	21 38
	d	18 22	18 25		18 38	18 41		18 55	19 10		19 15	19 22		19 38	19 51		20 08	20 21		20 38	20 51		21 08	21 21	21 38
Kenley	d	18 25			18 41				19 13			19 25			19 54			20 24			20 54			21 24	
Whyteleafe	d	18 28			18 44				19 17			19 28			19 58			20 28			20 58			21 28	
Whyteleafe South	d	18 30			18 46				19 19			19 30			20 00			20 30			21 00			21 30	
Caterham	a	18 35			18 51				19 23			19 35			20 04			20 34			21 04			21 34	
Reedham	d		18 27			18 44		18 57			19 18			19 40			20 10			20 40			21 10		21 40
Smitham	d		18a30			18 46		19a00			19 20			19 43			20 13			20 43			21 13		21 43
Woodmansterne	d					18 49					19 23			19 46			20 16			20 46			21 16		21 46
Chipstead	d					18 52					19 26			19 49			20 19			20 49			21 19		21 49
Kingswood	d					18 57					19 32			19 54			20 24			20 54			21 24		21 54
Tadworth	d					19 01					19 35			19 58			20 28			20 58			21 28		21 58
Tattenham Corner	a					19 04					19 39			20 01			20 31			21 01			21 31		22 01

For general notes see front of timetable
For details of catering facilities see
Directory of Train Operators

b Arr. 2009

London and Croydon → Caterham and Tattenham Corner

Network Diagram - see first page of Table 177

Station		SN	SN	SN	SN	SN	SN	SN	SN	SN	SN	SN
London Victoria 15	⊖ d		21 30		22 00		22 30		23 00			
Clapham Junction 10	d		21 38		22 08		22 38		23 08			
London Charing Cross 4	⊖ d	21 07		21 37		22 07		22 37		23 07		23 45
London Waterloo (East) 4	⊖ d	21 10		21 40		22 10		22 40		23 10		23 48
London Bridge 4	⊖ d	21 15		21 45		22 15		22 45		23 15		23 53
New Cross Gate 4	⊖ d	21 20		21 50		22 20		22 50		23 20		23 58
Norwood Junction 2	d	21 38		22 08		22 38		23 08		23 38		00 16
East Croydon	⇌ d	21 43	21 59	22 13	22 29	22 43	22 59	23 13	23 29	23 42		00 20
South Croydon 4	d	21 45	22 02	22 15	22 32	22 45	23 02	23 15	23 32	23 45		00 23
Purley Oaks	d	21 48	22 05	22 18	22 35	22 48	23 05	23 18	23 35	23 48		00 26
Purley 4	a	21 51	22 08	22 21	22 38	22 51	23 08	23 21	23 38	23 51	←	00 29
	d	21 54	22 08	22 24	22 38	22 51	23 08	23 21	23 54	23 51	23 54	00 31
Kenley	d	21 57		22 27		22 54		23 24	→	23 54		00 34
Whyteleafe	d	22 00		22 30		22 58		23 28		23 57		00 38
Whyteleafe South	d	22 02		22 32		23 00		23 30		23 59		00 40
Caterham	a	22 07		22 37		23 04		23 34		00 04		00 44
Reedham	d		22 10		22 40		23 10				23 56	
Smitham	d		22 13		22 43		23 13				23 59	
Woodmansterne	d		22 16		22 46		23 16				00 02	
Chipstead	d		22 19		22 49		23 19				00 05	
Kingswood	d		22 24		22 54		23 24				00 10	
Tadworth	d		22 28		22 58		23 28				00 14	
Tattenham Corner	a		22 31		23 01		23 31				00 17	

Sundays

Station		SN	SN	SN	SN		SN	SN	SN	SN	SN
London Victoria 15	⊖ d	23p00									
Clapham Junction 10	d	23p08									
London Charing Cross 4	⊖ d		23p45	07 36	08 06		21 36	22 06	22 36	23 06	23 36
London Waterloo (East) 4	⊖ d		23p48	07 39	08 09		21 39	22 09	22 39	23 09	23 39
London Bridge 4	⊖ d		23p53	07 44	08 14		21 44	22 14	22 44	23 14	23 44
New Cross Gate 4	⊖ d		23p58	07 49	08 19	and at	21 49	22 19	22 49	23 19	23 49
Norwood Junction 2	d		00 16	08 04	08 34		22 04	22 39	23 09	23 39	00 10
East Croydon	⇌ d	23p29	00 20	08 09	08 39	the same	22 09	22 43	23 13	23 43	00 14
South Croydon 4	d	23p32	00 23	08 11	08 41		22 11	22 45	23 15	23 45	00 16
Purley Oaks	d	23p35	00 26	08 14	08 44	minutes	22 14	22 48	23 18	23 48	00 19
Purley 4	a	23p38	00 29	08 17	08 47		22 17	22 51	23 21	23 51	00 22
	d	23p54	00 31	08 17	08 47	past	22 17	22 51	23 32	23 51	00 22
Kenley	d		00 34		08 50	each		22 54		23 54	00 25
Whyteleafe	d		00 38		08 54			22 58		23 58	00 29
Whyteleafe South	d		00 40		08 56	hour until		23 00		23 59	00 31
Caterham	a		00 44		09 00			23 04		00 04	00 35
Reedham	d	23p56		08 20			22 20		23 34		
Smitham	d	23p59		08 22			22 22		23 37		
Woodmansterne	d	00 02		08 25			22 25		23 40		
Chipstead	d	00 05		08 28			22 28		23 43		
Kingswood	d	00 10		08 34			22 34		23 48		
Tadworth	d	00 14		08 37			22 37		23 52		
Tattenham Corner	a	00 17		08 41			22 41		23 55		

For general notes see front of timetable
For details of catering facilities see Directory of Train Operators

Tattenham Corner and Caterham → Croydon and London

Network Diagram - see first page of Table 177

Miles	Miles		SN	SN	SN	SN	SN		SN	SN	SN	SN		SN	SN	SN	SN		SN	SN	SN	SN		
0	—	**Tattenham Corner** d		05 56		06 34				06 58		07 17			07 34		07 42			07 58		08 08		
1¼	—	Tadworth d		05 59		06 37				07 01		07 20			07 37		07 45			08 01		08 11		
2½	—	Kingswood d		06 02		06 40				07 04		07 23			07 40		07 48			08 04		08 14		
5	—	Chipstead d		06 08		06 46				07 10		07 29			07 46		07 54			08 10		08 20		
6	—	Woodmansterne d		06 11		06 49				07 13		07 32			07 49		07 57			08 13		08 23		
6¾	—	Smitham d		06 14		06 52				07 16		07 35			07 52		08 00			08 16		08 26		
7½	—	Reedham d		06 16		06 54				07 18		07 37			07 54		08 02			08 18		08 28		
—	0	**Caterham** d	05 52		06 20		06 47		07 00		07 14			07 36		07 47			08 08		08 19			
—	1¾	Whyteleafe South d	05 55		06 23		06 50		07 03		07 17			07 39		07 50			08 11		08 22			
—	2¼	Whyteleafe d	05 57		06 25		06 52		07 05		07 19			07 41		07 52			08 13		08 24			
—	3½	Kenley d	06 00		06 28		06 55		07 08		07 22			07 44		07 55			08 16		08 27			
8¼	4¾	Purley 4 a	06 03	06 19	06 31	06 57	06 59		07 11	07 21	07 26	07 40		07 47	07 57	07 59	08 06		08 19	08 21	08 30	08 32		
—	—	d	06 03	06 22	06 31	07 03			07 12	07 23	07 27	07 43		07 48	08 03		08 08		08 25		08 36			
9¼	5¾	Purley Oaks d	06 06		06 34	07 06			07 15		07 30	07 46		07 51	08 06		08 11		08 28		08 39			
10¼	6¾	South Croydon 4 d	06 09		06 37	07 09			07 18		07 33	07 49		07 54	08 09		08 14		08 31		08 42			
11¼	7¾	**East Croydon** d	06 12	06 28	06 40	07 12			07 21	07 29	07 36	07 52		07 57	08 12		08 17		08 34		08 45			
—	9	Norwood Junction 2 d	06 16	06 32	06 44	07 16					07 41			08 01	08 17				08 40		08 49			
—	15	New Cross Gate 4 ⊖ a	06 28	06 47	06 53	07 24					07 52										08 57			
—	17¾	**London Bridge 4** ⊖ a	06 34	06 54	07 02	07 33					08 01			08 16	08 31				08 55		09 05			
—	18¾	**London Waterloo (East) 4** ⊖ a																						
—	19½	**London Charing Cross 4** ⊖ a																						
19	—	Clapham Junction 10 a							07 31	07 39		08 02					08 27							
21¼	—	**London Victoria 15** ⊖ a							07 40	07 48		08 12					08 35							

	SN	SN	SN	SN		SN	SN	SN	SN			SN	SN	SN	SN	SN	SN	SN	SN			SN	SN
Tattenham Corner d	08 26			08 51			09 09						09 39				10 09			and at			15 39
Tadworth d	08 29			08 54			09 12						09 42				10 12			the same			15 42
Kingswood d	08 32			08 57			09 15						09 45				10 15			minutes			15 45
Chipstead d	08 38			09 03			09 20						09 50				10 20			past			15 50
Woodmansterne d	08 41			09 06			09 23						09 53				10 23			each			15 53
Smitham d	08 44			09 09			09 26		09 40				09 56		10 10		10 26		10 40	hour until			15 56
Reedham d	08 46			09 11			09 28		09 42				09 58		10 12		10 28		10 42				15 58
Caterham d		08 40	08 56			09 11		09 27				09 40		09 56		10 10		10 26				15 40	
Whyteleafe South d		08 43	08 59			09 14		09 30				09 43		09 59		10 13		10 29				15 43	
Whyteleafe d		08 45	09 01			09 16		09 32				09 45		10 01		10 15		10 31				15 45	
Kenley d		08 48	09 04			09 19		09 35				09 48		10 04		10 18		10 34				15 48	
Purley 4 a	08 49	08 51	09 07	09 14		09 22	09 31	09 38	09 45			09 51	10 01	10 07	10 15	10 21	10 31	10 37	10 45			15 51	16 01
d	08 55		09 08	09 14		09 22	09 31	09 38	09 45			09 51	10 01	10 08	10 15	10 21	10 31	10 38	10 45			15 51	16 01
Purley Oaks d	08 58		09 11			09 25		09 41				09 54		10 11		10 24		10 41				15 54	
South Croydon 4 d	09 01		09 14			09 28		09 44				09 57		10 14		10 27		10 44				15 57	
East Croydon d	09 05		09 17	09 20		09 31	09 37	09 47	09 51			10 00	10 07	10 17	10 21	10 30	10 37	10 47	10 51			16 00	16 07
Norwood Junction 2 d	09 09			09 25		09 35			09 58			10 04			10 28	10 34			10 58			16 04	16 11
New Cross Gate 4 ⊖ a				09 32		09 50						10 19				10 49						16 19	
London Bridge 4 ⊖ a	09 24			09 42		09 59	09 54		10 28			10 25	10 22		10 58	10 55	10 52		11 28			16 26	16 24
London Waterloo (East) 4 ⊖ a													10 26				10 56						
London Charing Cross 4 ⊖ a													10 30				11 00						
Clapham Junction 10 a			09 38					10 07						10 37				11 07					
London Victoria 15 ⊖ a			09 48					10 14						10 44				11 14					

	SN	SN	SN	SN		SN	SN	SN	SN		SN	SN	SN	SN		SN	SN	SN	SN		SN	SN	SN	SN
Tattenham Corner d				16 09					16 39				17 09				17 42		18 14			18 42		19 12
Tadworth d				16 12					16 42				17 12				17 45		18 17			18 45		19 15
Kingswood d				16 15					16 45				17 15				17 48		18 20			18 48		19 18
Chipstead d				16 20					16 50				17 20				17 54		18 26			18 54		19 24
Woodmansterne d				16 23					16 53				17 23				17 57		18 29			18 57		19 27
Smitham d		16 10		16 26			16 40		16 56				17 26				18 00		18 32			19 00		19 30
Reedham d		16 12		16 28			16 42		16 58				17 28				18 02		18 34			19 02		19 32
Caterham d	15 56		16 10			16 26		16 40			16 57	17 10		17 27		17 45		18 13			18 49		19 15	
Whyteleafe South d	15 59		16 13			16 29		16 43			17 00	17 13		17 30		17 48		18 16			18 52		19 18	
Whyteleafe d	16 01		16 15			16 31		16 45			17 02	17 15		17 32		17 50		18 18			18 54		19 20	
Kenley d	16 04		16 18			16 34		16 48			17 05	17 18		17 35		17 53		18 21			18 57		19 23	
Purley 4 a	16 07	16 15	16 21	16 31		16 37	16 45	16 51	17 01		17 08	17 21	17 31	17 38		17 56	18 05	18 24	18 38		19 00	19 05	19 26	19 35
d	16 08	16 15	16 21	16 31		16 38	16 45	16 51	17 01		17 09	17 23	17 31	17 39		17 56	18 08	18 26	18 38		19 01	19 08	19 29	19 38
Purley Oaks d	16 11		16 24			16 41		16 54			17 12	17 26		17 42		17 59	18 11	18 29	18 41		19 04	19 11	19 32	19 41
South Croydon 4 d	16 14		16 27			16 44		16 57			17 15	17 29		17 45		18 02	18 14	18 32	18 44		19 07	19 14	19 35	19 44
East Croydon d	16 17	16 21	16 31	16 37		16 47	16 51	17 00	17 07		17 18	17 32	17 37	17 48		18 05	18 17	18 35	18 47		19 10	19 17	19 40	19 47
Norwood Junction 2 d		16 28	16 35	16 41			16 56	17 04	17 11			17 36	17 41			18 09		18 39			19 14		19 44	
New Cross Gate 4 ⊖ a			16 50					17 19				17 50				18 21		18 54			19 32		20 02	
London Bridge 4 ⊖ a		17 00	16 58	16 56			17 26	17 27	17 26			17 58	17 54			18 28		19 00			19 39		20 11	
London Waterloo (East) 4 ⊖ a																					19 45		20 16	
London Charing Cross 4 ⊖ a																					19 49		20 20	
Clapham Junction 10 a	16 37					17 07					17 38			18 08			18 38		19 07			19 37		20 07
London Victoria 15 ⊖ a	16 44					17 14					17 48			18 15			18 45		19 14			19 45		20 14

For general notes see front of timetable
For details of catering facilities see
Directory of Train Operators

Tattenham Corner and Caterham → Croydon and London

Network Diagram - see first page of Table 177

		SN	SN		SN	SN	SN	SN		SN	SN	SN	SN		SN	SN	SN	SN		SN	SN				
Tattenham Corner	d		19 42		19 57		20 14			20 42		21 14			21 44		22 14			22 44					
Tadworth	d		19 45		20 00		20 17			20 45		21 17			21 47		22 17			22 47					
Kingswood	d		19 48		20 03		20 20			20 48		21 20			21 50		22 20			22 50					
Chipstead	d		19 54		20 09		20 26			20 54		21 26			21 56		22 26			22 56					
Woodmansterne	d		19 57		20 12		20 29			20 57		21 29			21 59		22 29			22 59					
Smitham	d		20 00		20 15		20 32			21 00		21 32			22 02		22 32			23 02					
Reedham	d		20 02		20 17		20 34			21 02		21 34			22 04		22 34			23 04					
Caterham	d	19 45				20 15		20 45			21 15		21 45			22 15		22 45			23 17				
Whyteleafe South	d	19 48				20 18		20 48			21 18		21 48			22 18		22 48			23 20				
Whyteleafe	d	19 50				20 20		20 50			21 20		21 50			22 20		22 50			23 22				
Kenley	d	19 53				20 23		20 53			21 23		21 53			22 23		22 53			23 25				
Purley 4	a	19 56	20 05		20 20	20 26	20 37	20 56		21 05	21 26	21 37	21 56		22 07	22 26	22 37	22 56		23 07	23 28				
	d	19 59	20 08		20 23	20 29	20 38	20 59		21 08	21 29	21 38	21 59		22 08	22 29	22 38	22 59		23 08	23 34				
Purley Oaks	d	20 02	20 11			20 32	20 41	21 02		21 11	21 32	21 41	22 02		22 11	22 32	22 41	23 02		23 11	23 37				
South Croydon 4	d	20 05	20 14			20 35	20 44	21 05		21 14	21 35	21 44	22 05		22 14	22 35	22 44	23 05		23 14	23 40				
East Croydon	d	20 10	20 17		20 30	20 40	20 47	21 10		21 17	21 40	21 47	22 10		22 17	22 40	22 47	23 10		23 17	23 43				
Norwood Junction 2	d	20 14			20 34	20 44		21 14			21 44		22 14			22 44		23 14			23a47				
New Cross Gate 4	⊖ a	20 32			20 51	21 02		21 32			22 02		22 32			23 02		23 32							
London Bridge 4	⊖ a	20 41			20 59	21 11		21 41			22 11		22 41			23 11		23 38							
London Waterloo (East) 4	⊖ a	20 46				21 16		21 46			22 16		22 46			23 16		23 43							
London Charing Cross 4	⊖ a	20 50				21 20		21 50			22 20		22 50			23 20		23 48							
Clapham Junction 10	a		20 37				21 07			21 37		22 07			22 37		23 07			23 37					
London Victoria 15	⊖ a		20 45				21 14			21 45		22 14			22 48		23 14			23 45					

Saturdays

		SN	SN	SN	SN	SN	SN	SN		SN	SN	SN	SN	SN	SN	SN	SN		SN	SN	SN	SN	SN	SN
Tattenham Corner	d		06 14		06 44		07 09				07 39				08 09					17 39				18 09
Tadworth	d		06 17		06 47		07 12				07 42				08 12					17 42				18 12
Kingswood	d		06 20		06 50		07 15				07 45				08 15					17 45				18 15
Chipstead	d		06 26		06 56		07 20				07 50				08 20					17 50				18 20
Woodmansterne	d		06 29		06 59		07 23				07 53				08 23					17 53				18 23
Smitham	d		06 32		07 02		07 26				07 56		08 10		08 26		08 40			17 56		18 10		18 26
Reedham	d		06 34		07 04		07 28				07 58		08 12		08 28		08 42			17 58		18 12		18 28
Caterham	d	06 07		06 40		07 10		07 26		07 40		07 56		08 10		08 26		and at the same minutes past each hour until	17 40		17 56		18 10	
Whyteleafe South	d	06 10		06 43		07 13		07 29		07 43		07 59		08 13		08 29			17 43		17 59		18 13	
Whyteleafe	d	06 12		06 45		07 15		07 31		07 45		08 01		08 15		08 31			17 45		18 01		18 15	
Kenley	d	06 15		06 48		07 18		07 34		07 48		08 04		08 18		08 34			17 48		18 04		18 18	
Purley 4	a	06 18	06 37	06 51	07 07	07 21	07 31	07 37		07 51	08 01	08 07	08 15	08 21	08 31	08 37	08 45		17 51	18 01	18 07	18 15	18 21	18 31
	d	06 21	06 38	06 51	07 08	07 21	07 31	07 38		07 51	08 01	08 08	08 15	08 21	08 31	08 38	08 45		17 51	18 01	18 08	18 15	18 21	18 31
Purley Oaks	d	06 24	06 41	06 54	07 11	07 24		07 41		07 54		08 11		08 24		08 41			17 54		18 11		18 24	
South Croydon 4	d	06 27	06 44	06 57	07 14	07 27		07 44		07 57		08 14		08 27		08 44			17 57		18 14		18 27	
East Croydon	d	06 30	06 47	07 00	07 17	07 30	07 37	07 47		08 00	08 07	08 17	08 21	08 30	08 37	08 47	08 51		18 00	18 07	18 17	18 21	18 30	18 37
Norwood Junction 2	d	06 34		07 04		07 34				08 04			08 28	08 34			08 58		18 04			18 28	18 34	
New Cross Gate 4	⊖ a	06 49		07 19		07 49				08 19				08 49					18 19				18 49	
London Bridge 4	⊖ a	06 55		07 25		07 55	07 52			08 25	08 22		08 58	08 55	08 52		09 28		18 25	18 22		18 58	18 55	18 52
London Waterloo (East) 4	⊖ a						07 56				08 26				08 56					18 26				18 56
London Charing Cross 4	⊖ a						08 00				08 30				09 00					18 30				19 00
Clapham Junction 10	a		07 07		07 37			08 07				08 37				09 07					18 37			
London Victoria 15	⊖ a		07 14		07 44			08 14				08 44				09 14					18 44			

		SN	SN	SN	SN	SN	SN	SN	SN	SN	SN	SN	SN	SN	SN	SN	SN	SN	SN	SN	SN	SN	SN		
Tattenham Corner	d				18 44			19 14		19 44		20 14		20 44		21 14		21 44		22 14		22 44			
Tadworth	d				18 47			19 17		19 47		20 17		20 47		21 17		21 47		22 17		22 47			
Kingswood	d				18 50			19 20		19 50		20 20		20 50		21 20		21 50		22 20		22 50			
Chipstead	d				18 56			19 26		19 56		20 26		20 56		21 26		21 56		22 26		22 56			
Woodmansterne	d				18 59			19 29		19 59		20 29		20 59		21 29		21 59		22 29		22 59			
Smitham	d		18 40		19 02	19 10		19 32		20 02		20 32		21 02		21 32		22 02		22 32		23 02			
Reedham	d		18 42		19 04	19 12		19 34		20 04		20 34		21 04		21 34		22 04		22 34		23 04			
Caterham	d	18 26		18 47			19 17		19 47		20 17		20 47		21 17		21 47		22 15		22 45		23 17		
Whyteleafe South	d	18 29		18 50			19 20		19 50		20 20		20 50		21 20		21 50		22 18		22 48		23 20		
Whyteleafe	d	18 31		18 52			19 22		19 52		20 22		20 52		21 22		21 52		22 20		22 50		23 22		
Kenley	d	18 34		18 55			19 25		19 55		20 25		20 55		21 25		21 55		22 23		22 53		23 25		
Purley 4	a	18 37	18 45	18 58	19 07	19 15	19 28	19 37	19 58	20 07	20 28	20 37	20 58	21 07	21 28	21 37	21 58	22 07	22 26	22 37	22 56	23 07	23 28		
	d	18 38	18 45	18 58	19 08	19 15	19 29	19 38	19 59	20 08	20 29	20 38	20 59	21 08	21 29	21 38	21 59	22 08	22 29	22 38	22 59	23 08	23 34		
Purley Oaks	d	18 41			19 11		19 32	19 41	20 02	20 11	20 32	20 41	21 02	21 11	21 32	21 41	22 02	22 11	22 32	22 41	23 02	23 11	23 37		
South Croydon 4	d	18 44			19 14		19 35	19 44	20 05	20 14	20 35	20 44	21 05	21 14	21 35	21 44	22 05	22 14	22 35	22 44	23 05	23 14	23 40		
East Croydon	d	18 47	18 51	19 07	19 17	19 21	19 40	19 47	20 10	20 17	20 40	20 47	21 10	21 17	21 40	21 47	22 10	22 17	22 40	22 47	23 10	23 17	23 43		
Norwood Junction 2	d		19b01			19c31	19 44		20 14		20 44		21 14		21 44		22 14		22 44		23 14		23a47		
New Cross Gate 4	⊖ a		19 18			19 48	20 02		20 32		21 02		21 32		22 02		22 32		23 02		23 32				
London Bridge 4	⊖ a		19 25	19 23		19 55	20 11		20 41		21 11		21 41		22 11		22 41		23 11		23 38				
London Waterloo (East) 4	⊖ a			19 28			20 16		20 46		21 16		21 46		22 16		22 46		23 16		23 43				
London Charing Cross 4	⊖ a			19 31			20 21		20 51		21 21		21 51		22 21		22 51		23 20		23 48				
Clapham Junction 10	a	19 07			19 37			20 07		20 37		21 07		21 37		22 07		22 37		23 07		23 37			
London Victoria 15	⊖ a	19 14			19 45			20 15		20 45		21 15		21 45		22 15		22 45		23 14		23 45			

For general notes see front of timetable
For details of catering facilities see Directory of Train Operators

b Arr. 1856
c Arr. 1926

Table 181

Sundays

Tattenham Corner and Caterham → Croydon and London

Network Diagram - see first page of Table 177

		SN	SN	SN		SN		SN	SN			SN	SN	SN		SN	SN	SN		SN	SN	SN		
Tattenham Corner	d		07 46			08 46			09 46				19 46			20 46		21 46			22 46			
Tadworth	d		07 49			08 49			09 49				19 49			20 49		21 49			22 49			
Kingswood	d		07 52			08 52			09 52				19 52			20 52		21 52			22 52			
Chipstead	d		07 57			08 57			09 57				19 57			20 57		21 57			22 57			
Woodmansterne	d		08 00			09 00			10 00				20 00			21 00		22 00			23 00			
Smitham	d		08 03			09 03			10 03				20 03			21 03		22 03			23 03			
Reedham	d		08 05			09 05			10 05	and at			20 05			21 05		22 05			23 05			
Caterham	d	07 26		08 26				09 26		the same		19 26		20 26			21 26			22 26		23 10		
Whyteleafe South	d	07 29		08 29				09 29				19 29		20 29			21 29			22 29		23 13		
Whyteleafe	d	07 31		08 31				09 31		minutes		19 31		20 31			21 31			22 31		23 15		
Kenley	d	07 34		08 34				09 34				19 34		20 34			21 34			22 34		23 18		
Purley 4	a	07 37	08 08	08 37		09 08		09 37	10 08	past		19 37	20 08	20 37		21 08	21 37	22 08		22 37	23 08	23 21		
	d	07 38	08 08	08 38		09 08		09 38	10 08			19 38	20 08	20 38		21 08	21 38	22 08		22 38	23 08	23 23		
Purley Oaks	d	07 41	08 11	08 41		09 11		09 41	10 11	each		19 41	20 11	20 41		21 11	21 41	22 11		22 41	23 11	23 26		
South Croydon 4	d	07 44	08 14	08 44		09 14		09 44	10 14			19 44	20 14	20 44		21 14	21 44	22 14		22 44	23 14	23 29		
East Croydon	d	07 47	08 17	08 47		09 17		09 47	10 17	hour until		19 47	20 17	20 47		21 17	21 47	22 17		22 47	23 17	23a31		
Norwood Junction 2	d	07 51	08 21	08 51		09 21		09 51	10 21			19 51	20 21	20 51		21 21	21 51	22 21		22 51	23a21			
New Cross Gate 4	⊖ a	08 05	08 35	09 05		09 35		10 05	10 35			20 05	20 35	21 05		21 35	22 05	22 35		23 05				
London Bridge 4	⊖ a	08 12	08 42	09 12		09 42		10 12	10 42			20 12	20 42	21 12		21 42	22 12	22 42		23 12				
London Waterloo (East) 4	⊖ a	08 16	08 46	09 16		09 46		10 16	10 46			20 18	20 46	21 16		21 46	22 16	22 46		23 16				
London Charing Cross 4	⊖ a	08 20	08 50	09 20		09 52		10 22	10 52			20 22	20 50	21 20		21 50	22 22	22 50		23 20				
Clapham Junction 10	a																							
London Victoria 15	⊖ a																							

For general notes see front of timetable
For details of catering facilities see Directory of Train Operators

London → Sutton, Epsom, Guildford, Dorking and Horsham

Network Diagram - see first page of Table 177

Miles	Miles	Miles	Station		SN MO	SN MX	SN MX	SN MO	SW MX	SN MX	SN MX	SW MX	SN	SN	SW	FC A	SN	SN	SN		SN	SN	SW	SN	FC B	SN
—	0	—	**London Victoria** 15 ⊖	d	23p19	23p22	23p26				23p51								06 00		06 05					06 07
—	—	—	**London Waterloo** 15 ⊖	d					23p41			00 15			05 47								06 24			
—	2¾	—	Clapham Junction 10	d	23p26	23p29	23p32		23p50		23p58	00 24			05 56				06 07		06 11		06 33			06 14
—	4¾	—	Balham 4 ⊖	d	23p32	23p35	23p37				00 04								06 13		06 15					06 20
0	—	0	**London Bridge** 4 ⊖	d													05 46									
—	—	6	Tulse Hill 3	d																					06 30	
2¾	—	—	New Cross Gate 4 ⊖	d													05 51									
8¾	—	—	Norwood Junction 2	d		23b54								05 54			06 09									06c39
10½	—	12	**West Croydon** 4	d	23p50	00e01		←		←	00 20		05 46	05 59			06 14		06 30					←		06 44
11½	—	—	Waddon	d	23p52	00 03		23p52		00 03	00 22		05 48	06 02			06 17		06 32					06 32		06 46
13	—	—	Wallington	d	→	→		23p56		00 07	00 26		05 52	06 05			06 20		→					06 36		06 50
13¾	—	—	Carshalton Beeches	d				23p58		00 09	00 28		05 54	06 08			06 23							06 38		06 52
—	8	—	Eastfields §	d																						
—	9	—	Mitcham Junction	d			23p45														06 23				06 38	
—	9¾	—	Hackbridge	d			23p49														06 27				06 42	
—	10¾	—	Carshalton	d			23p51														06 29				06 44	
14¾	12	0	**Sutton (Surrey)** 4	a			23p55	00 02		00 13	00 32		05 58	06 11			06 26				06 34			06 42	06 48	06 56
—	—	—		d			23p55	00 04						06 18		06 23		06 28			06 35	06 42		06 48	06 48	06 56
—	—	1	West Sutton	a												06 26									06 51	
—	—	5½	Wimbledon 6 ⊖	a												06 40									07 06	
—	13	—	Belmont	d										06 21										06 51		
—	14½	—	Banstead	d										06 25										06 55		
—	16	—	**Epsom Downs**	a										06 28										06 58		
15¾	—	—	Cheam	d			23p58	00 06										06 30			06 37					06 59
17¼	—	—	Ewell East	d			00 01	00 10										06 34			06 41					07 02
18¾	—	—	**Epsom** 3	a			00 05	00 14	00 15			00 48			06 20			06 38			06 45	06 48	06 57			07 06
—	—	—		d			00 06		00 19						06 21			06 38			06 45	06 49	06 58			
20½	—	—	Ashtead	d			00 10		00 23						06 25			06 42			06 49		07 02			
22½	—	0	Leatherhead	d			00 13		00 26						06 28			06 45			06 52	06 56	07 05			
25	—	—	Bookham	d					00 31						06 33							07 01				
26¾	—	—	Effingham Junction 6	d					00 36						06 37							07 05				
35	—	—	**Guildford**	a					00 53						06 50							07 17				
—	—	3¼	Boxhill & Westhumble	d			00 18														06 57					
—	—	4	**Dorking** 4	a			00 20											06 51			07 00		07 11			
—	—	—		d			00 20														07 01					
—	—	9	Holmwood	d			00s28														07 08					
—	—	11¼	Ockley	d			00s32														07 12					
—	—	15¾	Warnham	d			00s37														07 18					
—	—	17¾	**Horsham** 4	a			00 41														07 22					

Station		SN	SW	SN	SW	SN	FC C	SN	SN	SW	SN	SW		SN	FC C	SN	SN	SW	FC D	SN	SW	SN	SN	SN	SW	FC C
London Victoria 15 ⊖	d	06 28		06 35					07 00		07 15						07 30			07 47		07 57		08 03		
London Waterloo 15 ⊖	d		06 39		06 54					07 09		07 24						07 39			07 54				08 09	
Clapham Junction 10	d	06 38	06 48	06 41	07 03				07 07	07 18	07 21	07 33					07 38	07 48		07 54	08 03	08 03		08 11	08 18	
Balham 4 ⊖	d	06 43		06 46					07 13		07 25						07 43			08 00				08 16		
London Bridge 4 ⊖	d							06 46								07 15							07 48			
Tulse Hill 3	d						07 02								07 32				07 59							08 27
New Cross Gate 4 ⊖	d							06 51								07 20							07 53			
Norwood Junction 2	d							07 10								07 39							08 11			
West Croydon 4	d	07 00				←		07 15	07 30							07 44	08 03						08 16	08 36		
Waddon	d	07 03				07 03		07 17	07 32							07 46	08 05						08 19	08 39		
Wallington	d	→				07 06		07 21	07 36							07 50	08 09						08 22	→		
Carshalton Beeches	d					07 09		07 23	07 38							07 52	08 11						08 25			
Eastfields §	d																									
Mitcham Junction	d			06 55			07 10				07 33				07 40				08 06	08 10						08 34
Hackbridge	d			06 58			07 14				07 37				07 44				08 10	08 13						08 38
Carshalton	d			07 01			07 16				07 39				07 46				08 12	08 16						08 40
Sutton (Surrey) 4	a			07 04		07 12	07 20	07 27	07 42		07 43			←	07 50	07 58	08 15		08 16	08 19		08 22	08 28			08 44
	d			07 05		07 18	07 20	07 27	07 45		07 43			07 45	07 50	07 58	08 16		08 16			08 23	08 29			08 46
West Sutton	a						07 23		→						07 53				08 19							08 49
Wimbledon 6 ⊖	a						07 39								08 09				08 37							09 05
Belmont	d					07 21								07 48			08 19									
Banstead	d					07 25								07 52			08 23									
Epsom Downs	a					07 28								07 55			08 26									
Cheam	d			07 07				07 30			07 46					08 01						08 25	08 31			
Ewell East	d			07 11				07 33			07 49					08 04						08 29	08 35			
Epsom 3	a		07 08	07 15	07 27			07 37		07 42	07 53	07 58				08 08		08 15			08 27	08 33	08 39		08 42	
	d		07 08	07 15	07 28			07 38			07 54	07 58						08 15			08 28	08 33	08 39		08 47	
Ashtead	d		07 12	07 19	07 32			07 42			07 58	08 02						08 19			08 32	08 37	08 43		08 51	
Leatherhead	d		07 15	07 22	07 35			07 45			08 01	08 05						08 22			08 35	08 40	08 46		08 54	
Bookham	d		07 21					07 50										08 28							08 59	
Effingham Junction 6	d		07a24					07 54										08 32							09 03	
Guildford	a							08 07										08 48							09 20	
Boxhill & Westhumble	d										08 06											08 45				
Dorking 4	a			07 28	07 41						08 09	08 12									08 41	08 47	08 52			
	d			07 29							08 09											08 47				
Holmwood	d			07 36							08 16															
Ockley	d			07 40							08 20															
Warnham	d			07 46							08 26															
Horsham 4	a			07 50							08 30											09 03				

For general notes see front of timetable
For details of catering facilities see Directory of Train Operators

§ This station may open during the currency of this timetable, please see local publicity for further details.

A To St Albans (Table 52)
B From London Blackfriars (Table 52)
C From Luton (Table 52)
D From Bedford (Table 52)

b Previous night. Arr. 2351
c Arr. 0636
e Arr. 2358

London → Sutton, Epsom, Guildford, Dorking and Horsham

Network Diagram - see first page of Table 177

	SW	SN	SN	SN		FC A	SW	SN	SN	SW	SN	SN	SN	SN	SW	FC B	SN	SN	SW	SN		SN	SN	SN	FC A
London Victoria 15 ⊖ d		08 20						08 31	08 34		08 50		08 57	09 03				09 05		09 20			09 28	09 33	
London Waterloo 15 ⊖ d	08 24						08 39			08 54					09 09				09 24						
Clapham Junction 10 d	08 33	08 26					08 48	08 37	08 41	09 03	08 56		09 04	09 09	09 18			09 11	09 33	09 26			09 35	09 39	
Balham 4 ⊖ d		08 30						08 43	08 47		09 02		09 10					09 17		09 32			09 41		
London Bridge 4 ⊖ d				08 19								08 45										09 15			
Tulse Hill 3 d						08 47										09 17									09 47
New Cross Gate 4 ⊖ d				08 26								08 50										09 20			
Norwood Junction 2 d				08 44								09 09										09 39			
West Croydon 4 d			←	08 49				08 59	09 06			09 14	09 28				←	09 34				09 44	09 58		
Waddon d			08 39	08 52				09 02	09 08			09 17	09 31				09 31	09 37				09 47	10 01		
Wallington d			08 42	08 55				09 05	09 12			09 20	→				09 34	09 40				09 50	→		
Carshalton Beeches d			08 45	08 58				09 08	09 14			09 23					09 37	09 43				09 53			
Eastfields § d																									
Mitcham Junction d		08 38				08 56					09 10					09 26				09 41					09 56
Hackbridge d		08 42				08 59					09 13					09 29				09 44					09 59
Carshalton d		08 44				09 02					09 16					09 32				09 47					10 02
Sutton (Surrey) 4 a		08 48	08 48	09 01		09 05		09 11	09 18		09 19	09 26		09 27		09 36	09 40	09 46		09 50		09 56		09 58	10 05
d		08 52	08 53			09 06		09 12	09 19		09 20			09 27		09 36	09 41			09 51				09 59	10 06
West Sutton a						09 09										09 39									10 09
Wimbledon 6 ⊖ a						09 23										09 55									10 23
Belmont d			08 56						09 22																
Banstead d			09 00						09 26																
Epsom Downs a			09 03						09 29																
Cheam d		08 54									09 22			09 30			09 43			09 53				10 01	
Ewell East d		08 58									09 26						09 47			09 57				10 05	
Epsom 3 a	08 57	09 02					09 16	09 18		09 27	09 30			09 35	09 42		09 51		09 57	10 01				10 09	
d	08 58	09 02					09 17			09 28				09 36	09 47				09 58					10 09	
Ashtead d	09 02	09 06					09 21			09 32				09 40	09 51				10 02					10 13	
Leatherhead d	09 05	09 09					09 24			09 35				09 43	09 54				10 05					10 16	
Bookham d							09 29								09 59										
Effingham Junction 6 d							09 33								10 03										
Guildford a							09 50								10 20										
Boxhill & Westhumble d		09 14												09 48										10 21	
Dorking 4 a	09 11	09 17								09 41				09 50					10 11					10 24	
d		09 17																						10 24	
Holmwood d		09 25																						10 32	
Ockley d		09 29																						10 36	
Warnham d		09 34																						10 41	
Horsham 4 a		09 38																						10 45	

	SW	SN	SN	SW	SN	SN	SN	SN	FC A	SW	SN	SN	SW		SN	SN	SN	SN	FC A	SW	SN	SN	SW	SN	
London Victoria 15 ⊖ d			09 35		09 50		09 57	10 03				10 05			10 20		10 28	10 33				10 35		10 50	
London Waterloo 15 ⊖ d	09 39			09 54						10 09			10 24							10 39			10 54		
Clapham Junction 10 d	09 48		09 41	10 03	09 56		10 04	10 09		10 18		10 11	10 33		10 26		10 35	10 39		10 48		10 41	11 03	10 56	
Balham 4 ⊖ d			09 47		10 02		10 10					10 17			10 32		10 41					10 47		11 02	
London Bridge 4 ⊖ d						09 45										10 15									
Tulse Hill 3 d									10 17										10 47						
New Cross Gate 4 ⊖ d						09 50										10 20									
Norwood Junction 2 d						10 09										10 39									
West Croydon 4 d		←	10 04			10 14	10 28				←	10 34				10 44	10 58				←	11 04			
Waddon d		10 01	10 06			10 17	10 31				10 31	10 36				10 47	11 01				11 01	11 06			
Wallington d		10 04	10 10			10 20	→				10 34	10 40				10 50	→				11 04	11 10			
Carshalton Beeches d		10 07	10 12			10 23					10 37	10 42				10 53					11 07	11 12			
Eastfields § d																									
Mitcham Junction d					10 10				10 26						10 40				10 56					11 10	
Hackbridge d					10 13				10 29						10 43				10 59					11 13	
Carshalton d					10 16				10 32						10 46				11 02					11 16	
Sutton (Surrey) 4 a		10 10	10 16		10 19	10 26		10 28	10 35		10 40	10 46			10 49	10 56		10 58	11 05		11 10	11 16		11 19	
d		10 11			10 20			10 29	10 36		10 41				10 50			10 59	11 06		11 11			11 20	
West Sutton a									10 39										11 09						
Wimbledon 6 ⊖ a									10 55										11 25						
Belmont d		10 14																			11 14				
Banstead d		10 18																			11 18				
Epsom Downs a		10 21																			11 21				
Cheam d					10 22			10 31			10 43				10 52			11 01						11 22	
Ewell East d					10 26						10 47				10 56			11 05						11 26	
Epsom 3 a	10 16			10 27	10 30			10 37		10 46	10 51		10 57		11 00			11 09		11 16			11 27	11 30	
d	10 17			10 28				10 37		10 47			10 58					11 09		11 17			11 28		
Ashtead d	10 21			10 32				10 41		10 51			11 02					11 13		11 21			11 32		
Leatherhead d	10 24			10 35				10 44		10 54			11 05					11 16		11 24			11 35		
Bookham d	10 29									10 59										11 29					
Effingham Junction 6 d	10 33									11 03										11 33					
Guildford a	10 50									11 20										11 50					
Boxhill & Westhumble d																		11 21							
Dorking 4 a				10 41				10 50					11 11					11 24					11 41		
d																		11 24							
Holmwood d																		11 32							
Ockley d																		11 36							
Warnham d																		11 41							
Horsham 4 a																		11 45							

For general notes see front of timetable
For details of catering facilities see Directory of Train Operators

§ This station may open during the currency of this timetable, please see local publicity for further details.

A From St Albans (Table 52)
B From Bedford (Table 52)

London → Sutton, Epsom, Guildford, Dorking and Horsham

Network Diagram - see first page of Table 177

Station			SN	SN	SN	FC A	SW	SN	SN	SW	SN	SN	SN	SN	FC A	SW	SN	SN	SW	SN			SN	SN	SN
London Victoria [15] ⊖	d			10 55	11 03				11 05		11 20		11 25	11 33				11 35		11 50				14 55	15 03
London Waterloo [15] ⊖	d						11 09			11 24						11 39			11 54						
Clapham Junction [10]	d			11 04	11 09		11 18		11 12	11 33	11 26		11 34	11 39		11 48		11 41	12 03	11 56				15 04	15 09
Balham [4] ⊖	d			11 10					11 17		11 32		11 40					11 47		12 02				15 10	
London Bridge [4] ⊖	d		10 45									11 15											14 45		
Tulse Hill [3]	d					11 17									11 47										
New Cross Gate [4] ⊖	d		10 50									11 20											14 50		
Norwood Junction [2]	d		11 09									11 39											15 09		
West Croydon [4] 🚋	d		11 14	11 28				←	11 34			11 44	11 58				←	12 04					15 14	15 28	
Waddon	d		11 17	11 31				11 31	11 36			11 47	12 01				12 01	12 06					15 17	15 31	
Wallington	d		11 20	→				11 34	11 40			11 50	→				12 04	12 10					15 20	→	
Carshalton Beeches	d		11 23					11 37	11 42			11 53					12 07	12 12					15 23		
Eastfields §	d																								
Mitcham Junction 🚋	d					11 26					11 40				11 56					12 10	and at				
Hackbridge	d					11 29					11 43				11 59					12 13					
Carshalton	d					11 32					11 46				12 02					12 16	the same				
Sutton (Surrey) [4]	a		11 26		11 28	11 35		11 40	11 46		11 49	11 56		11 58	12 05		12 10	12 16		12 19			15 26		15 28
	d				11 29	11 36		11 41			11 50			11 59	12 06		12 11			12 20	minutes				15 29
West Sutton	a					11 39									12 09										
Wimbledon [6] ⊖ 🚋	a					11 55									12 25						past				
Belmont	d																12 14				each				
Banstead	d																12 18								
Epsom Downs	a																12 21				hour until				
Cheam	d				11 31			11 43			11 52			12 01						12 22					15 31
Ewell East	d							11 47			11 56			12 05						12 26					
Epsom [3]	a				11 37		11 46	11 51		11 57	12 00			12 09		12 16			12 27	12 30					15 37
	d				11 37		11 47			11 58				12 09		12 17			12 28						15 37
Ashtead	d				11 41		11 51			12 02				12 13		12 21			12 32						15 41
Leatherhead	d				11 44		11 54			12 05				12 16		12 24			12 35						15 44
Bookham	d						11 59									12 29									
Effingham Junction [6]	d						12 03									12 33									
Guildford	a						12 20									12 50									
Boxhill & Westhumble	d													12 21											
Dorking [4]	a				11 50					12 11				12 24					12 41						15 50
	d													12 24											
Holmwood	d													12 32											
Ockley	d													12 36											
Warnham	d													12 41											
Horsham [4]	a													12 45											

Station		FC A	SW	SN	SN	SW	SN	SN	SN	SN	FC A	SW	SN	SN	SW		SN	SN	SN	SN	FC A	SW	SN	SN	SW	SN
London Victoria [15] ⊖	d				15 05		15 20		15 25	15 33				15 35			15 50		15 55	16 02				16 05		16 20
London Waterloo [15] ⊖	d		15 09			15 24						15 39			15 54							16 09			16 24	
Clapham Junction [10]	d		15 18		15 11	15 33	15 26		15 34	15 39		15 48		15 41	16 03		15 56		16 04	16 09		16 18		16 11	16 33	16 26
Balham [4] ⊖	d				15 17		15 32		15 40					15 47			16 02		16 10					16 17		16 30
London Bridge [4] ⊖	d							15 15										15 45								
Tulse Hill [3]	d	15 17									15 47										16 16					
New Cross Gate [4] ⊖	d							15 20										15 50								
Norwood Junction [2]	d							15 39										16 10								
West Croydon [4] 🚋	d			←	15 34			15 44	15 58				←	16 04				16 15	16 28				←	16 34		
Waddon	d			15 31	15 36			15 47	16 01				16 01	16 06				16 18	16 31				16 31	16 36		
Wallington	d			15 34	15 40			15 50	→				16 04	16 10				16 21	→				16 34	16 40		
Carshalton Beeches	d			15 37	15 42			15 53					16 07	16 12				16 24					16 37	16 42		
Eastfields §	d																									
Mitcham Junction 🚋	d	15 26					15 40				15 56						16 10			16 22	16 25					16 38
Hackbridge	d	15 29					15 43				15 59						16 13									16 42
Carshalton	d	15 32					15 46				16 02						16 16									16 44
Sutton (Surrey) [4]	a	15 35		15 40	15 46		15 49	15 56		15 58	16 05		16 10	16 16			16 19	16 27		16 29	16 32		16 40	16 48		16 48
	d	15 36		15 41			15 50			15 58	16 06		16 11				16 20			16 29	16 32		16 41			16 48
West Sutton	a	15 39									16 09										16 35					
Wimbledon [6] ⊖ 🚋	a	15 55									16 25										16 51					
Belmont	d												16 14										16 44			
Banstead	d												16 18										16 48			
Epsom Downs	a												16 21										16 51			
Cheam	d			15 43			15 52			16 01							16 22			16 32						16 51
Ewell East	d			15 47			15 56			16 04							16 26			16 35						16 54
Epsom [3]	a		15 46	15 51		15 57	16 00			16 08		16 16			16 27		16 30			16 39		16 46			16 57	16 58
	d		15 47			15 58				16 09		16 17			16 28					16 40		16 47			17 01	16 59
Ashtead	d		15 51			16 02				16 13		16 21			16 32					16 44		16 51			→	17 03
Leatherhead	d		15 54			16 05				16 16		16 24			16 35					16 47		16 54				17 06
Bookham	d		15 59									16 29										16 59				
Effingham Junction [6]	d		16 03									16 33										17 03				
Guildford	a		16 20									16 50										17 22				
Boxhill & Westhumble	d									16 21										16 52						17 11
Dorking [4]	a					16 11				16 23					16 41					16 56						17 13
	d									16 24																17 13
Holmwood	d									16 31																17 21
Ockley	d									16 35																17 25
Warnham	d									16 41																17 30
Horsham [4]	a									16 45																17 36

For general notes see front of timetable
For details of catering facilities see
Directory of Train Operators

§ This station may open during the currency of this timetable, please see local publicity for further details.

A From St Albans (Table 52)

London → Sutton, Epsom, Guildford, Dorking and Horsham

Network Diagram - see first page of Table 177

	SW	SN	FC A	SW	SN	SN	SW		SN	SW	SN	SW	SN	FC A	SN	SN	SW	SN	SN	SW	SN	SN	FC A		SN
London Victoria 15 ⊖ d						16 30			16 50						17 01	17 15		17 25							17 32
London Waterloo 15 ⊖ d				16 39			16 54					17 09					17 24			17 30					
Clapham Junction 10 d				16 48		16 37	17 03		16 56			17 18			17 08	17 21	17 33	17 31		17 39					17 39
Balham 4 ⊖ d						16 43			17 00						17 14	17 25		17 35							17 45
London Bridge 4 ⊖ d		16 15			16 29						16 44		16 53								17 25	17 27			
Tulse Hill 3 d			16 42		16 46								17 11	17 16								17 44	17 46		
New Cross Gate 4 ⊖ d		16 20									16 49										17 30				
Norwood Junction 2 d		16 39									17 09										17 43				
West Croydon 4 🚋 d		16 44				16 59					17 15				17 30	17 42			←		17 48				18 02
Waddon d		16 46				17 02					17 17				17 33	17 45			17 45		17 51				18 04
Wallington d		16 50				17 05					17 21				17 36	→			17 48		17 54				→
Carshalton Beeches d		16 52				17 08					17 23				17 39				17 51		17 57				
Eastfields § d																									
Mitcham Junction 🚋 d			16 50		16 55				17 08				17 20	17 25				17 43				17 53	17 57		
Hackbridge d			16 54		16 59				17 12				17 23	17 28				17 47				17 57	18 00		
Carshalton d			16 56		17 01				17 14				17 26	17 30				17 49				17 59	18 02		
Sutton (Surrey) 4 a		16 56	17 00		17 05	17 11			17 18		17 27		17 30	17 38	17 42			17 53	17 56		18 00	18 03	18 06		
d		16 56	17 00		17 05	17 12			17 18		17 27		17 30	17 39	17 43			17 53			18 01	18 04	18 08		
West Sutton a			17 03										17 34	17 42								18 07	18 13		
Wimbledon 6 ⊖ 🚋 a			17 19										17 50	17 58								18 18	18 29		
Belmont d						17 15									17 46										
Banstead d						17 19									17 50										
Epsom Downs a						17 24									17 55										
Cheam d		16 59			17 08				17 21		17 30							17 56			18 03				
Ewell East d		17 02			17 11				17 24		17 33										18 07				
Epsom 3 a	←	17 06		17 12	17 17		17 27		17 28	←	17 37	17 42					17 54	18 01		18 06	18 11				
d	17 01	17 07		17 17			17 31		17 29	17 31	17 38	17 47					17 54	18 01			18 13				
Ashtead d	17 05	17 11		17 21			→		17 33	17 35	17 42	17 51					17 58	18 05			18 17				
Leatherhead d	17 08	17 14		17 24					17 36	17 38	17 45	17 54					18 01	18 08			18 20				
Bookham d		17 19		17 29							17 50	17 59									18 25				
Effingham Junction 6 d		17 23		17 33							17 54	18a05									18 29				
Guildford a		17 38		17 52							18 13										18 47				
Boxhill & Westhumble d	17 13									17 43							18 06	18 13							
Dorking 4 a	17 18								17 42	17 48							18 11	18 16							
d									17 42									18 18							
Holmwood d									17 50									18 26							
Ockley d									17 54									18 30							
Warnham d									17 59									18 35							
Horsham 4 a									18 05									18 41							

	SW	SN	SN	SW	SN	SN	SW	SW	SN	SN	SW	FC A	SN	SW	SN		SN	SW	SN	FC A	SW	SN	SN	SN	SW
London Victoria 15 ⊖ d		17 43			17 57					18 02			18 14				18 27						18 33	18 45	
London Waterloo 15 ⊖ d	17 39			17 54			18 00	18 09						18 24				18 30			18 39				18 54
Clapham Junction 10 d	17 48	17 49		18 03	18 03		18 09	18 18		18 09			18 20	18 33			18 33	18 39			18 48		18 40	18 52	19 03
Balham 4 ⊖ d		17 53			18 08					18 15			18 24				18 37						18 46	18 58	
London Bridge 4 ⊖ d						17 58			17 55										18 25			18 31			
Tulse Hill 3 d						18 15						18 18								18 42		18b51			
New Cross Gate 4 ⊖ d																									
Norwood Junction 2 d									18 13										18 42						
West Croydon 4 🚋 d			←						18 18	18 31					←				18 47				19 02	19 16	
Waddon d			18 04						18 20	18 34					18 34				18 49				19 05	19 18	
Wallington d			18 08						18 24	→					18 37				18 53				19 08	→	
Carshalton Beeches d			18 10						18 26						18 40				18 55				19 11		
Eastfields § d																									
Mitcham Junction 🚋 d		18 01			18 16							18 27	18 32				18 45			18 50		19 00			
Hackbridge d		18 05			18 19							18 30	18 36				18 49			18 54		19 03			
Carshalton d		18 07			18 22							18 32	18 38				18 51			18 56		19 06			
Sutton (Surrey) 4 a		18 11	18 14		18 25	18 30			18 33			18 36	18 42		18 43		18 55		18 59	19 02		19 09	19 14		
d		18 11	18 15		18 26	18 31			18 34			18 37	18 42		18 46		18 55		18 59	19 02		19 10	19 15		
West Sutton a						18 34						18 41								19 05					
Wimbledon 6 ⊖ 🚋 a						18 50						18 57								19 22					
Belmont d			18 18												18 49								19 18		
Banstead d			18 22												18 53								19 22		
Epsom Downs a			18 27												18 58								19 27		
Cheam d		18 14			18 28				18 36				18 45				18 58		19 02			19 12			
Ewell East d		18 17							18 40				18 48				19 01		19 05			19 16			
Epsom 3 a	18 20	18 23		18 24	18 34		18 35	18 43	18 44		←		18 54	18 54			19 05	19 05	19 09		19 13	19 22			19 29
d	18 20			18 24	18 34			18 47	18 44		18 47			18 54			19 06		19 10		19 17				19 30
Ashtead d	18 24			18 28	18 38			→	18 48		18 51			18 58			19 10		19 14		19 21				19 34
Leatherhead d	18 28			18 31	18 41				18 51		18 54			19 01			19 13		19 17		19 24				19 37
Bookham d	18 33										18 59										19 29				
Effingham Junction 6 d	18a44										19 03										19 33				
Guildford a											19 22										19 52				
Boxhill & Westhumble d				18 36					18 56					19 06			19 18		19 22						19 42
Dorking 4 a				18 41	18 47				19 01					19 11			19 20		19 26						19 46
d					18 47												19 23								
Holmwood d					18 55												19 30								
Ockley d					18 59												19 34								
Warnham d					19 04												19 40								
Horsham 4 a					19 10												19 46								

For general notes see front of timetable
For details of catering facilities see Directory of Train Operators

§ This station may open during the currency of this timetable, please see local publicity for further details.

A From St Albans (Table 52)
b Arr. 1848

London → Sutton, Epsom, Guildford, Dorking and Horsham

Network Diagram - see first page of Table 177

	SW	SN	SN	FC A	SN	SW	SN	SW		SN	SN	SN	SN	FC A	SN	SW	SN	SW	SN	SN	SN	FC A	SW	SN	SN
London Victoria 15 ⊖ d		18 57					19 15			19 20					19 22		19 45		19 50					19 52	20 15
London Waterloo 15 ⊖ d	19 00					19 09		19 24								19 39		19 54					20 09		
Clapham Junction 10 d	19 09	19 03				19 18	19 22	19 33		19 26					19 29	19 48	19 52	20 03	19 56				20 18	19 59	20 22
Balham 4 ⊖ d		19 07					19 28			19 32					19 35		19 58		20 02					20 05	20 28
London Bridge 4 ⊖ d					19 05								19 31												
Tulse Hill 3 d				19 12										19 47								20 17			
New Cross Gate 4 ⊖ d					19 10																				
Norwood Junction 2 d					19 28								19 44		19 54									20b24	
West Croydon 4 d			←		19 33		19 45					←	19 49		20 00		20 15				←			20 30	20 45
Waddon d			19 18		19 36		19 47					19 47	19 51		20 02		20 17				20 17			20 32	20 47
Wallington d			19 22		19 39		→					19 51	19 55		20 06		→				20 21			20 36	→
Carshalton Beeches d			19 24		19 42							19 53	19 57		20 08						20 23			20 38	
Eastfields § d																									
Mitcham Junction d		19 15		19 20						19 40				19 56					20 10			20 26			
Hackbridge d		19 19		19 24						19 43				19 59					20 13			20 29			
Carshalton d		19 21		19 26						19 46				20 02					20 16			20 32			
Sutton (Surrey) 4 a		19 25	19 28	19 31	19 45					19 49	←	19 57	20 01	20 05	20 12				20 19	←	20 27	20 35		20 42	
d		19 25	19 28	19 36	19 52					19 50	19 52	19 57	20 02	20 06	20 23				20 20	20 23		20 36		20 42	
West Sutton a				19 39	→									20 09	→							20 39			
Wimbledon 6 ⊖ a				19 56										20 25								20 55			
Belmont d											19 55									20 26					
Banstead d											19 59									20 30					
Epsom Downs a											20 02									20 33					
Cheam d		19 28	19 31							19 52		20 00	20 04						20 22					20 45	
Ewell East d		19 31	19 34							19 56		20 03	20 08						20 26					20 48	
Epsom 3 a	19 33	19 35	19 40			19 43		19 53		20 00		20 07	20 12			20 12		20 27	20 30				20 42	20 52	
d		19 36				19 47		19 54		20 01			20 13			20 17			20 30				20 47		
Ashtead d		19 40				19 51		19 58		20 05			20 17			20 21			20 34				20 51		
Leatherhead d		19 43				19 54		20 01		20 08			20 20			20 24			20 37				20 54		
Bookham d						19 59										20 29									
Effingham Junction 6 d						20 03										20 33									
Guildford a						20 20										20 50									
Boxhill & Westhumble d		19 48						20 06		20 13									20 42				20 59		
Dorking 4 a		19 52						20 08		20 15			20 26						20 45				21 01		
d										20 22															
Holmwood d										20 23															
Ockley d										20 27															
Warnham d										20 32															
Horsham 4 a										20 38															

	SW		SN	SN	FC A	SN	SW	SN	SW	SN	SW	SN	SN	SN	SN	SW	SN		FC B	SN	SN	SW	SN	SW	SN
London Victoria 15 ⊖ d			20 20			20 22		20 45		20 50				20 52	21 15		21 20				21 22		21 45		21 50
London Waterloo 15 ⊖ d	20 24						20 39		20 54		21 09					21 24						21 39		21 54	
Clapham Junction 10 d	20 33		20 26			20 29	20 48	20 52	21 03	20 56	21 18			20 59	21 22	21 33	21 26				21 29	21 48	21 52	22 03	21 56
Balham 4 ⊖ d			20 31			20 35		20 58		21 02				21 05	21 28		21 31				21 35		21 58		22 02
London Bridge 4 ⊖ d																									
Tulse Hill 3 d					20 47																				
New Cross Gate 4 ⊖ d																									
Norwood Junction 2 d						20c54								21e24							21f54				
West Croydon 4 d				←		21 00		21 15					←	21 30	21 45					←	22 00		22 15		
Waddon d				20 47		21 02		21 17					21 17	21 32	21 47					21 47	22 02		22 17		
Wallington d				20 51		21 06		→					21 21	21 36	→					21 51	22 06		→		
Carshalton Beeches d				20 53		21 08							21 23	21 38						21 53	22 08				
Eastfields § d																									
Mitcham Junction d			20 40		20 56					21 10							21 40								22 10
Hackbridge d			20 43		20 59					21 13							21 43								22 13
Carshalton d			20 46		21 02					21 16							21 46								22 16
Sutton (Surrey) 4 a			20 49	20 57	21 05	21 12				21 19		←	21 27	21 42			21 49			21 57	22 12				22 19
d			20 50		21 06	21 23				21 20		21 23		21 42			21 50		21 53		22 23				22 20
West Sutton a					21 09	→													21 56		→				
Wimbledon 6 ⊖ a					21 25														22 09						
Belmont d												21 26													
Banstead d												21 30													
Epsom Downs a												21 33													
Cheam d			20 52							21 22				21 45			21 52								22 22
Ewell East d			20 56							21 26				21 48			21 56								22 26
Epsom 3 a	20 57		21 00				21 12		21 27	21 30	21 42			21 52		21 57	22 00					22 12		22 27	22 30
d			21 01				21 17			21 30	21 47						22 01					22 17			22 30
Ashtead d			21 05				21 21			21 34	21 51						22 05					22 21			22 34
Leatherhead d			21 08				21 24			21 37	21 54						22 08					22 24			22 37
Bookham d							21 29															22 29			
Effingham Junction 6 d							21 33															22 33			
Guildford a							21 50															22 50			
Boxhill & Westhumble d			21 13							21 42	21 59														22 42
Dorking 4 a			21 15							21 45	22 01						22 14								22 45
d																									
Holmwood d																									
Ockley d																									
Warnham d																									
Horsham 4 a																									

For general notes see front of timetable
For details of catering facilities see Directory of Train Operators

§ This station may open during the currency of this timetable, please see local publicity for further details.

A From St Albans (Table 52)
B To Bedford (Table 52)
b Arr. 2021
c Arr. 2051
e Arr. 2121
f Arr. 2151

London → Sutton, Epsom, Guildford, Dorking and Horsham

Network Diagram - see first page of Table 177

Mondays to Fridays

Station		SW	SN	SN	SN	SN	SN	SN	SN	SW	SN		SN	SW	SN	SN	SN	SN	SN	SN	SW	SN	SN	SN		
London Victoria 15 ⊖	d				21 52	22 15	22 20		22 22		22 45		22 50				22 52	23 15	23 22	23 26				23 51		
London Waterloo 15 ⊖	d	22 09								22 39				23 09							23 41					
Clapham Junction 10	d	22 18			21 59	22 22	22 26		22 29	22 48	22 52		22 56	23 18			22 59	23 22	23 29	23 32	23 50			23 58		
Balham 4 ⊖	d				22 05	22 28	22 32		22 35		22 58		23 00				23 05	23 28	23 35	23 37				00 04		
London Bridge 4 ⊖	d																									
Tulse Hill 3	d																									
New Cross Gate 4 ⊖	d																									
Norwood Junction 2	d				22b24				22c54								23e24		23f54							
West Croydon 4	d			←	22 30	22 45		←	23 00		23 15					←	23 30	23 45	00g01			←	←	00 20		
Waddon	d			22 17	22 32	22 47		22 47	23 02		23 17					23 17	23 32	23 47	00 03			23 47	00 03	00 22		
Wallington	d			22 21	22 36	→		22 51	23 06		→					23 21	23 36	→	→			23 51	00 07	00 26		
Carshalton Beeches	d			22 23	22 38			22 53	23 08							23 23	23 38					23 53	00 09	00 28		
Eastfields §	d																									
Mitcham Junction	d						22 40						23 08							23 45						
Hackbridge	d						22 43						23 12							23 49						
Carshalton	d						22 46						23 14							23 51						
Sutton (Surrey) 4	a		←	22 27	22 42		22 49	22 57	23 12				23 18		←	23 27	23 42			23 55		23 57	00 13	00 32		
	d		22 23		22 42		22 50		23 23 →				23 18		23 23		23 42			23 55						
West Sutton	a																									
Wimbledon 6 ⊖	a																									
Belmont	d		22 26												23 26											
Banstead	d		22 30												23 30											
Epsom Downs	a		22 33												23 33											
Cheam	d				22 45		22 52						23 21				23 45			23 58						
Ewell East	d				22 48		22 56						23 24				23 48			00 01						
Epsom 3	a	22 42			22 52		23 00			23 12			23 28	23 42			23 52			00 05	00 15					
	d	22 47					23 01			23 17			23 29	23 47						00 06	00 19					
Ashtead	d	22 51					23 05			23 21			23 33	23 51						00 10	00 23					
Leatherhead	d	22 54					23 08			23 24			23 36	23 54						00 13	00 26					
Bookham	d									23 29											00 31					
Effingham Junction 6	d									23 33											00 36					
Guildford	a									23 54											00 53					
Boxhill & Westhumble	d	22 59											23 41	23 59						00 18						
Dorking 4	a	23 01					23 14						23 43	00 01						00 20						
	d																			00 20						
Holmwood	d																			00s28						
Ockley	d																			00s32						
Warnham	d																			00s37						
Horsham 4	a																			00 41						

Saturdays

Station		SN	SN	SW	SN	SN	SW		SN	SW	FC A	SN	SN	SN B		SW	FC A	SN	SW	SN	SN		SN	SN	FC C	SW
London Victoria 15 ⊖	d	23p22	23p26			23p51						06 27	06 54					06 57		07 20			07 25	07 33		
London Waterloo 15 ⊖	d			23p41			00 15			06 39						07 09			07 24							07 39
Clapham Junction 10	d	23p29	23p32	23p50		23p58	00 24			06 48		06 34	07 00			07 18		07 04	07 33	07 26			07 34	07 39		07 48
Balham 4 ⊖	d	23p35	23p37			00 04						06 40	07 04					07 10		07 32			07 40			
London Bridge 4 ⊖	d																				07 15					
Tulse Hill 3	d																								07 47	
New Cross Gate 4 ⊖	d																				07 20					
Norwood Junction 2	d	23h54												07 06							07 39					
West Croydon 4	d	00g01			←	00 20			06 45			06 56		07j14				07 28			07 44		07 58			
Waddon	d	00 03			00 03	00 22			06 47			06 59		07 17				07 31			07 47		08 01			
Wallington	d	→			00 07	00 26			06 51			07 02		07 20				07 34			07 50		→			
Carshalton Beeches	d				00 09	00 28			06 53			07 05		07 23				07 37			07 53					
Eastfields §	d																									
Mitcham Junction	d		23p45										07 13							07 40					07 56	
Hackbridge	d		23p49										07 17							07 43					07 59	
Carshalton	d		23p51										07 19							07 46					08 02	
Sutton (Surrey) 4	a		23p55		00 13	00 32			06 57			07 08	07 23	07 26				07 40		07 49	07 56			07 58	08 05	
	d		23p55						06 57		07 06	07 09	07 23				07 36	07 41		07 50				07 59	08 06	
West Sutton	a										07 09						07 39								08 09	
Wimbledon 6 ⊖	a										07 23						07 53								08 25	
Belmont	d											07 12														
Banstead	d											07 16														
Epsom Downs	a											07 19														
Cheam	d		23p58						07 00				07 26					07 43		07 52				08 01		
Ewell East	d		00 01						07 03				07 29					07 47		07 56				08 05		
Epsom 3	a		00 05	00 15			00 48		07 07	07 16			07 33			07 46		07 51	07 57	08 00				08 09		08 16
	d		00 06	00 19					07 08	07 17			07 34			07 47			07 58					08 09		08 17
Ashtead	d		00 10	00 23					07 12	07 21			07 38			07 51			08 02					08 13		08 21
Leatherhead	d		00 13	00 26					07 15	07 24			07 41			07 54			08 05					08 16		08 24
Bookham	d			00 31						07 29						07 59										08 29
Effingham Junction 6	d			00 36						07 33						08 03										08 33
Guildford	a			00 53						07 50						08 20										08 50
Boxhill & Westhumble	d		00 18										07 46											08 21		
Dorking 4	a		00 20						07 21				07 48						08 11					08 24		
	d		00 20																					08 24		
Holmwood	d		00s28																					08 32		
Ockley	d		00s32																					08 36		
Warnham	d		00s37																					08 41		
Horsham 4	a		00 41																					08 45		

For general notes see front of timetable
For details of catering facilities see Directory of Train Operators

§ This station may open during the currency of this timetable, please see local publicity for further details.

A To Luton (Table 52)

B From Streatham Hill (Table 177)

C From London Blackfriars (Table 52)

b Arr. 2221

c Arr. 2251

e Arr. 2321

f Arr. 2351

g Arr. 2358

h Previous night. Arr. 2351

j Arr. 0711

Table 182

London → Sutton, Epsom, Guildford, Dorking and Horsham

Network Diagram - see first page of Table 177

		SN		SN	SW	SN	SN	SN	SN	FC A	SW	SN	SN	SW	SN	SN	SN	SN	FC A	SW	SN	and at the same minutes past each hour until		SN	SW
London Victoria 15 ⊖	d			07 35		07 50		07 55	08 03				08 05		08 20		08 25	08 33						17 35	
London Waterloo 15 ⊖	d				07 54						08 09			08 24						08 39					17 54
Clapham Junction 10	d			07 41	08 03	07 56		08 04	08 09		08 18		08 11	08 33	08 26		08 34	08 39		08 48				17 41	18 03
Balham 4 ⊖	d			07 47		08 02		08 10					08 17		08 32		08 40							17 47	
London Bridge 4 ⊖	d						07 45									08 15									
Tulse Hill 3	d									08 17									08 47						
New Cross Gate 4 ⊖	d						07 50									08 20									
Norwood Junction 2	d						08 09									08 39									
West Croydon 4	d	←		08 04			08 14	08 28				←	08 34			08 44	08 58				←			18 04	
Waddon	d	08 01		08 06			08 17	08 31				08 31	08 36			08 47	09 01				09 01			18 06	
Wallington	d	08 04		08 10			08 20	→				08 34	08 40			08 50	→				09 04			18 10	
Carshalton Beeches	d	08 07		08 12			08 23					08 37	08 42			08 53					09 07			18 12	
Eastfields §	d																								
Mitcham Junction	d					08 10				08 26					08 40				08 56						
Hackbridge	d					08 13				08 29					08 43				08 59						
Carshalton	d					08 16				08 32					08 46				09 02						
Sutton (Surrey) 4	a	08 10		08 16		08 19	08 26		08 28	08 35		08 40	08 46		08 49	08 56		08 58	09 05		09 10			18 16	
	d	08 11				08 20			08 29	08 36		08 41			08 50			08 59	09 06		09 11				
West Sutton	a									08 39									09 09						
Wimbledon 6 ⊖	a									08 55									09 25						
Belmont	d	08 14																			09 14				
Banstead	d	08 18																			09 18				
Epsom Downs	a	08 21																			09 21				
Cheam	d					08 22			08 31			08 43			08 52			09 01							
Ewell East	d					08 26						08 47			08 56			09 05							
Epsom 3	a				08 27	08 30			08 37		08 46	08 51		08 57	09 00			09 09		09 16					18 27
	d				08 28				08 37		08 47			08 58				09 09		09 17					18 28
Ashtead	d				08 32				08 41		08 51			09 02				09 13		09 21					18 32
Leatherhead	d				08 35				08 44		08 54			09 05				09 16		09 24					18 35
Bookham	d										08 59									09 29					
Effingham Junction 6	d										09 03									09 33					
Guildford	a										09 20									09 50					
Boxhill & Westhumble	d																	09 21							
Dorking 4	a				08 41				08 50					09 11				09 24							18 41
	d																	09 24							
Holmwood	d																	09 32							
Ockley	d																	09 36							
Warnham	d																	09 41							
Horsham 4	a																	09 45							

		SN	SN	SN	SN	FC B	SW		SN	SW	SN	SN	FC B	SN		SW	SN	SW	SN	SN	FC B		SW	SN	SN	SW
London Victoria 15 ⊖	d	17 50		17 55	18 03						18 20			18 25			18 45		18 50					18 52	19 15	
London Waterloo 15 ⊖	d						18 09			18 24						18 39		18 54					19 09			19 24
Clapham Junction 10	d	17 56		18 04	18 09		18 18			18 33	18 26			18 34		18 48	18 52	19 03	18 56				19 18	18 59	19 22	19 33
Balham 4 ⊖	d	18 02		18 10							18 32			18 40			18 58		19 02					19 05	19 28	
London Bridge 4 ⊖	d		17 45									18 15														
Tulse Hill 3	d					18 17							18 47								19 17					
New Cross Gate 4 ⊖	d		17 50									18 20														
Norwood Junction 2	d		18 09									18 39												19b24		
West Croydon 4	d		18 14	18 28					←			18 44		18 58			19 14			←				19 30	19 45	
Waddon	d		18 17	18 31					18 31			18 47		19 00			19 17			19 17				19 32	19 47	
Wallington	d		18 20	→					18 34			18 50		19 04			→			19 20				19 36	→	
Carshalton Beeches	d		18 23						18 37			18 53		19 06						19 23				19 38		
Eastfields §	d																									
Mitcham Junction	d	18 10				18 26					18 40		18 56						19 10		19 26					
Hackbridge	d	18 13				18 29					18 43		18 59						19 13		19 29					
Carshalton	d	18 16				18 32					18 46		19 02						19 16		19 32					
Sutton (Surrey) 4	a	18 19	18 26		18 28	18 35			18 40		18 49	18 56	19 05	19 10					19 19	19 26	19 35			19 42		
	d	18 20			18 29	18 36			18 41		18 50		19 06	19 10					19 20		19 36			19 42		
West Sutton	a					18 39							19 09								19 39					
Wimbledon 6 ⊖	a					18 55							19 25								19 55					
Belmont	d													19 14												
Banstead	d													19 17												
Epsom Downs	a													19 21												
Cheam	d	18 22			18 31				18 43		18 52								19 22					19 45		
Ewell East	d	18 26							18 47		18 56								19 26					19 48		
Epsom 3	a	18 30			18 37		18 46		18 51	18 57	19 00					19 12		19 27	19 30				19 42	19 52		19 57
	d				18 37		18 47			18 58	19 01					19 17		19 28	19 31				19 47			19 58
Ashtead	d				18 41		18 51			19 02	19 05					19 21		19 32	19 35				19 51			20 02
Leatherhead	d				18 44		18 54			19 05	19 08					19 24		19 35	19 38				19 54			20 05
Bookham	d						18 59									19 29							19 59			
Effingham Junction 6	d						19 03									19 33							20 03			
Guildford	a						19 20									19 50							20 20			
Boxhill & Westhumble	d										19 13								19 43							
Dorking 4	a				18 51					19 11	19 15							19 41	19 45							20 11
	d																									
Holmwood	d																									
Ockley	d																									
Warnham	d																									
Horsham 4	a																									

For general notes see front of timetable
For details of catering facilities see Directory of Train Operators

§ This station may open during the currency of this timetable, please see local publicity for further details.

A From Luton (Table 52)
B From St Albans (Table 52)
b Arr. 1921

London → Sutton, Epsom, Guildford, Dorking and Horsham

Network Diagram - see first page of Table 177

		SN	SN	SW	FC A		SN	SN	SW	SN	SW	SN		SN	FC A	SN	SN	SW	SN		SN	SW	FC A	SN	SN	SW
London Victoria 15 ⊖	d	19 20					19 22	19 45		19 50						19 52	20 15		20 20					20 22	20 45	
London Waterloo 15 ⊖	d			19 39					19 54		20 09							20 24				20 39				20 54
Clapham Junction 10	d	19 26		19 48			19 29	19 52	20 03	19 56	20 18					19 59	20 22	20 33	20 26			20 48		20 29	20 52	21 03
Balham 4 ⊖	d	19 32					19 35	19 58		20 02						20 05	20 28		20 32					20 35	20 58	
London Bridge 4 ⊖	d																									
Tulse Hill 3	d																									
New Cross Gate 4 ⊖	d																									
Norwood Junction 2	d						19b54									20c24								20e54		
West Croydon 4	d		←				20 00	20 15						←		20 30	20 45				←			21 00	21 15	
Waddon	d		19 47				20 02	20 17						20 17		20 32	20 47				20 47			21 02	21 17	
Wallington	d		19 51				20 06	→						20 21		20 36	→				20 51			21 06	→	
Carshalton Beeches	d		19 53				20 08							20 23		20 38					20 53			21 08		
Eastfields §	d																									
Mitcham Junction	d	19 40								20 10									20 40							
Hackbridge	d	19 43								20 13									20 43							
Carshalton	d	19 46								20 16									20 46							
Sutton (Surrey) 4	a	19 49	19 57				20 12			20 19		←		20 27		20 42			20 49		20 57			21 12		
	d	19 50			20 06		20 23			20 20		20 23			20 36	20 42			20 50				21 06	21 23		
West Sutton	a				20 09		→								20 39								21 09	→		
Wimbledon 6 ⊖	a				20 23										20 53								21 23			
Belmont	d											20 26														
Banstead	d											20 30														
Epsom Downs	a											20 33														
Cheam	d	19 52								20 22						20 45			20 52							
Ewell East	d	19 56								20 26						20 48			20 56							
Epsom 3	a	20 00		20 12					20 27	20 30	20 42					20 52		20 57	21 00			21 12				21 27
	d	20 01		20 17						20 30	20 47								21 01			21 17				
Ashtead	d	20 05		20 21						20 34	20 51								21 05			21 21				
Leatherhead	d	20 08		20 24						20 37	20 54								21 08			21 24				
Bookham	d			20 29																		21 29				
Effingham Junction 6	d			20 33																		21 33				
Guildford	a			20 50																		21 50				
Boxhill & Westhumble	d									20 42																
Dorking 4	a	20 15								20 45	21 00								21 14							
	d																									
Holmwood	d																									
Ockley	d																									
Warnham	d																									
Horsham 4	a																									

		SN	SW		SN	SN	SN	SN	SW	SN		FC A	SN	SN	SW	SN	SW		SN	SW	SN	SN	SN	SN		SN
London Victoria 15 ⊖	d	20 50					20 52	21 15		21 20				21 22		21 45			21 50				21 52	22 15		22 20
London Waterloo 15 ⊖	d		21 09						21 24						21 39		21 54			22 09						
Clapham Junction 10	d	20 56	21 18				20 59	21 22	21 33	21 26				21 29	21 48	21 52	22 03		21 56	22 18			21 59	22 22		22 26
Balham 4 ⊖	d	21 02					21 05	21 28		21 32				21 35		21 58			22 02				22 05	22 28		22 32
London Bridge 4 ⊖	d																									
Tulse Hill 3	d																									
New Cross Gate 4 ⊖	d																									
Norwood Junction 2	d						21f24							21g54									22h24			
West Croydon 4	d					←	21 30	21 45					←	22 00		22 15						←	22 30	22 45		
Waddon	d					21 17	21 32	21 47					21 47	22 02		22 17						22 17	22 32	22 47		
Wallington	d					21 21	21 36	→					21 51	22 06		→						22 21	22 36	→		
Carshalton Beeches	d					21 23	21 38						21 53	22 08								22 23	22 38			
Eastfields §	d																									
Mitcham Junction	d	21 10								21 40									22 10							22 40
Hackbridge	d	21 13								21 43									22 13							22 43
Carshalton	d	21 16								21 46									22 16							22 46
Sutton (Surrey) 4	a	21 19			←	21 27	21 42			21 49			21 57	22 12					22 19		←	22 27	22 42			22 49
	d	21 20			21 23		21 42			21 50		21 52		22 23					22 20		22 23		22 42			22 50
West Sutton	a											21 55		→												
Wimbledon 6 ⊖	a											22 09														
Belmont	d				21 26																22 26					
Banstead	d				21 30																22 30					
Epsom Downs	a				21 33																22 33					
Cheam	d	21 22					21 45			21 52									22 22				22 45			22 52
Ewell East	d	21 26					21 48			21 56									22 26				22 48			22 56
Epsom 3	a	21 30	21 42				21 52		21 57	22 00					22 12		22 27		22 30	22 42			22 52			23 00
	d	21 30	21 47							22 01					22 17				22 30	22 47						23 01
Ashtead	d	21 34	21 51							22 05					22 21				22 34	22 51						23 05
Leatherhead	d	21 37	21 54							22 08					22 24				22 37	22 54						23 08
Bookham	d														22 29											
Effingham Junction 6	d														22 33											
Guildford	a														22 50											
Boxhill & Westhumble	d	21 42																	22 42							
Dorking 4	a	21 45	22 00							22 14									22 45	23 00						23 14
	d																									
Holmwood	d																									
Ockley	d																									
Warnham	d																									
Horsham 4	a																									

For general notes see front of timetable
For details of catering facilities see Directory of Train Operators

§ This station may open during the currency of this timetable, please see local publicity for further details.

A To Bedford (Table 52)
b Arr. 1951
c Arr. 2021
e Arr. 2051
f Arr. 2121
g Arr. 2151
h Arr. 2221

London → Sutton, Epsom, Guildford, Dorking and Horsham

Saturdays

Network Diagram - see first page of Table 177

Station		SN	SN	SW	SN	SN	SW		SN	SN	SN	SN	SN	SN		SW	SN	SN	SN
London Victoria 15 ⊖	d		22 22		22 45	22 50					22 52	23 15	23 22	23 26					23 51
London Waterloo 15 ⊖	d			22 39			23 09									23 41			
Clapham Junction 10	d		22 29	22 48	22 52	22 56	23 18				22 59	23 22	23 29	23 32		23 50			23 58
Balham 4 ⊖	d		22 35		22 58	23 00					23 05	23 28	23 35	23 37					00 04
London Bridge 4 ⊖	d																		
Tulse Hill 3	d																		
New Cross Gate 4 ⊖	d																		
Norwood Junction 2	d		22b54								23c24		23e54						
West Croydon 4	d	←	23 00		23 15					←	23 30	23 45	00f01				←	←	00 20
Waddon	d	22 47	23 02		23 18					23 18	23 32	23 48	00 03				23 48	00 03	00 22
Wallington	d	22 51	23 06		→					23 21	23 36	→	→				23 51	00 07	00 26
Carshalton Beeches	d	22 53	23 08							23 24	23 38						23 54	00 09	00 28
Eastfields §	d																		
Mitcham Junction	d					23 08								23 45					
Hackbridge	d					23 12								23 49					
Carshalton	d					23 14								23 51					
Sutton (Surrey) 4	a	22 57	23 12			23 18			←	23 27	23 42			23 55			23 57	00 13	00 32
	d		23 23			23 18			23 23		23 42			23 55					
West Sutton	a		→																
Wimbledon 6 ⊖	a																		
Belmont	d								23 26										
Banstead	d								23 30										
Epsom Downs	a								23 33										
Cheam	d					23 21					23 45			23 58					
Ewell East	d					23 24					23 48			00 01					
Epsom 3	a			23 12		23 28	23 42				23 52			00 05		00 15			
	d			23 17		23 29	23 47							00 06		00 19			
Ashtead	d			23 21		23 33	23 51							00 10		00 23			
Leatherhead	d			23 24		23 36	23 54							00 13		00 26			
Bookham	d			23 29												00 31			
Effingham Junction 6	d			23 33												00 36			
Guildford	a			23 54												00 56			
Boxhill & Westhumble	d					23 41								00 18					
Dorking 4	a					23 43	00 01							00 20					
	d																		
Holmwood	d																		
Ockley	d																		
Warnham	d																		
Horsham 4	a																		

Sundays

Station		SN	SN	SW	SN		SN	SW	SN	SW A		SN	SN	SN	SW		SN	SN	SN	SW		SN	SN	SN	SW	SN
London Victoria 15 ⊖	d	23p22	23p26				23p51		06 49			07 19	07 38	07 49			08 06	08 08	08 19			08 36	08 38	08 49		09 06
London Waterloo 15 ⊖	d			23p41				00 15							08 02					08 32					09 02	
Clapham Junction 10	d	23p29	23p32	23p50			23p58	00 24	06 56			07 26	07 45	07 56	08 11		08 12	08 15	08 26	08 41		08 42	08 45	08 56	09 11	09 12
Balham 4 ⊖	d	23p35	23p37				00 04		07 02			07 32	07 51	08 02			08 16	08 21	08 32			08 46	08 51	09 02		09 16
London Bridge 4 ⊖	d																									
Tulse Hill 3	d																									
New Cross Gate 4 ⊖	d																									
Norwood Junction 2	d	23g54											08 07					08 37					09 07			
West Croydon 4	d	00f01			←		00 20		07 20			07 50	08 13	08 20				08 43	08 50				09 13	09 20		
Waddon	d	00 03			00 03		00 22		07 22			07 52		08 22					08 52					09 22		
Wallington	d	→			00 07		00 26		07 26			07 56	08 18	08 26				08 48	08 56				09 18	09 26		
Carshalton Beeches	d				00 09		00 28		07 28			07 58		08 28					08 58					09 28		
Eastfields §	d																									
Mitcham Junction	d		23p45														08 24					08 54				09 24
Hackbridge	d		23p49														08 28					08 58				09 28
Carshalton	d		23p51														08 30					09 00				09 30
Sutton (Surrey) 4	a		23p55		00 13		00 32		07 32			08 02	08 22	08 32			08 34	08 52	09 02			09 04	09 22	09 32		09 34
	d		23p55						07 34			08 04					08 34					09 04				09 34
West Sutton	a																									
Wimbledon 6 ⊖	a																									
Belmont	d																									
Banstead	d																									
Epsom Downs	a																									
Cheam	d		23p58						07 36			08 06					08 36					09 06				09 36
Ewell East	d		00 01						07 40			08 10					08 40					09 10				09 40
Epsom 3	a		00 05	00 15				00 48	07 44	08 06		08 14			08 36		08 44			09 06		09 14			09 36	09 44
	d		00 06	00 19					07 44	08 08		08 14			08 38		08 44			09 08		09 14			09 38	09 44
Ashtead	d		00 10	00 23					07 48	08 12		08 18			08 42		08 48			09 12		09 18			09 42	09 48
Leatherhead	d		00 13	00 26					07 51	08 15		08 21			08 45		08 51			09 15		09 21			09 45	09 51
Bookham	d			00 31						08 20										09 20						
Effingham Junction 6	d			00 36						08 24										09 24						
Guildford	a			00 53						08 41										09 41						
Boxhill & Westhumble	d		00 18						07 56			08 26					08 56					09 26				09 56
Dorking 4	a		00 20						07 58			08 28			08 51		08 58					09 28			09 51	09 58
	d																									
Holmwood	d																									
Ockley	d																									
Warnham	d																									
Horsham 4	a																									

For general notes see front of timetable
For details of catering facilities see Directory of Train Operators

§ This station may open during the currency of this timetable, please see local publicity for further details.

A From Wimbledon (Table 152)
b Arr. 2251
c Arr. 2321
e Arr. 2351
f Arr. 2358
g Previous night. Arr. 2351

Table 182

Sundays

London → Sutton, Epsom, Guildford, Dorking and Horsham

Network Diagram - see first page of Table 177

		SN		SN	SW	SN		FC A	SN	SN	SW	SN	FC A	SN	SN	SW	SN			FC B	SN	SN	SW		SN
London Victoria 15 ⊖	d	09 08		09 19		09 36			09 38	09 49		10 06		10 08	10 19		10 36				20 38	20 49			21 06
London Waterloo 15 ⊖	d				09 32						10 02					10 32							21 02		
Clapham Junction 10	d	09 15		09 26	09 41	09 42			09 45	09 56	10 11	10 12		10 15	10 26	10 41	10 42				20 45	20 56	21 11		21 12
Balham 4 ⊖	d	09 21		09 32		09 46			09 51	10 02		10 16		10 21	10 32		10 46				20 51	21 02			21 16
London Bridge 4 ⊖	d																								
Tulse Hill 3	d																								
New Cross Gate 4 ⊖	d																								
Norwood Junction 2	d	09 37							10 07					10 37							21 07				
West Croydon 4 🚋	d	09 43		09 50					10 13	10 20				10 43	10 50						21 13	21 20			
Waddon	d			09 52						10 22					10 52							21 22			
Wallington	d	09 48		09 56					10 18	10 26				10 48	10 56						21 18	21 26			
Carshalton Beeches	d			09 58						10 28					10 58							21 28			
Eastfields §	d																								
Mitcham Junction 🚋	d					09 54						10 24					10 54	and at the same minutes past each hour until							21 24
Hackbridge	d					09 58						10 28					10 58								21 28
Carshalton	d					10 00						10 30					11 00								21 30
Sutton (Surrey) 4	a	09 52		10 02		10 04			10 22	10 32		10 34		10 52	11 02		11 04				21 22	21 32			21 34
	d					10 04		10 10				10 34	10 40				11 04			21 10					21 34
West Sutton	a							10 13					10 43							21 13					
Wimbledon 6 ⊖ 🚋	a							10 25					10 55							21 25					
Belmont	d																								
Banstead	d																								
Epsom Downs	a																								
Cheam	d					10 06						10 36					11 06								21 36
Ewell East	d					10 10						10 40					11 10								21 40
Epsom 3	a				10 06	10 14					10 36	10 44				11 06	11 14						21 36		21 44
	d				10 08	10 14					10 38	10 44				11 08	11 14						21 38		21 44
Ashtead	d				10 12	10 18					10 42	10 48				11 12	11 18						21 42		21 48
Leatherhead	d				10 15	10 21					10 45	10 51				11 15	11 21						21 45		21 51
Bookham	d				10 20											11 20									
Effingham Junction 6	d				10 24											11 24									
Guildford	a				10 41											11 41									
Boxhill & Westhumble	d					10 26						10 56					11 26								21 56
Dorking 4	a					10 28					10 51	10 58					11 28						21 51		21 58
	d																								
Holmwood	d																								
Ockley	d																								
Warnham	d																								
Horsham 4	a																								

		SN	SN	SW	SN		SN	SN	SW	SN		SN	SN	SW	SN		SN	SN	SW	SN		SW	SN			
London Victoria 15 ⊖	d	21 08	21 19		21 36		21 38	21 49		22 06		22 08	22 19		22 36		22 38	22 49		23 06			23 19			
London Waterloo 15 ⊖	d			21 32					22 02					22 32					23 02			23 32				
Clapham Junction 10	d	21 15	21 26	21 41	21 42		21 45	21 56	22 11	22 12		22 15	22 26	22 41	22 42		22 45	22 56	23 11	23 12		23 41	23 26			
Balham 4 ⊖	d	21 21	21 32		21 46		21 51	22 02		22 16		22 21	22 32		22 46		22 51	23 02		23 16			23 32			
London Bridge 4 ⊖	d																									
Tulse Hill 3	d																									
New Cross Gate 4 ⊖	d																									
Norwood Junction 2	d	21 37					22 07					22 39					23 07									
West Croydon 4 🚋	d	21 43	21 50				22 13	22 20				22 43	22 50				23 13	23 20					23 50			
Waddon	d		21 52					22 22					22 52					23 22					23 52			
Wallington	d	21 48	21 56				22 18	22 26				22 48	22 56				23 18	23 26					23 56			
Carshalton Beeches	d		21 58					22 28					22 58					23 28					23 58			
Eastfields §	d																									
Mitcham Junction 🚋	d				21 54					22 24					22 54					23 24						
Hackbridge	d				21 58					22 28					22 58					23 28						
Carshalton	d				22 00					22 30					23 00					23 30						
Sutton (Surrey) 4	a	21 52	22 02		22 04		22 22	22 32		22 34		22 53	23 02		23 04		23 22	23 32		23 34			00 02			
	d				22 04					22 34					23 04					23 36			00 04			
West Sutton	a																									
Wimbledon 6 ⊖ 🚋	a																									
Belmont	d																									
Banstead	d																									
Epsom Downs	a																									
Cheam	d				22 06					22 36					23 06					23 38			00 06			
Ewell East	d				22 10					22 40					23 10					23 42			00 10			
Epsom 3	a			22 06	22 14				22 36	22 44				23 06	23 14				23 36	23 46		00 06	00 14			
	d			22 08	22 14				22 38	22 44				23 08	23 14					23 46						
Ashtead	d			22 12	22 18				22 42	22 48				23 12	23 18					23 50						
Leatherhead	d			22 15	22 21				22 45	22 51				23 15	23 21					23 53						
Bookham	d			22 20										23 20												
Effingham Junction 6	d			22 24										23 24												
Guildford	a			22 41										23 41												
Boxhill & Westhumble	d				22 26					22 56					23 26					23 58						
Dorking 4	a				22 28				22 51	22 58					23 28					00 01						
	d																									
Holmwood	d																									
Ockley	d																									
Warnham	d																									
Horsham 4	a																									

For general notes see front of timetable
For details of catering facilities see Directory of Train Operators

§ This station may open during the currency of this timetable, please see local publicity for further details.

A To Luton (Table 52)
B To Bedford (Table 52)

Horsham, Dorking, Guildford, Epsom and Sutton → London

Network Diagram - see first page of Table 177

Miles	Miles	Miles	Station		SN	SN	SW	SN	SN	SN	SN	SW		SN	SW	SN	SN	SN	SN	SW	SW		SN	SN	SN	SW
—	—	0	**Horsham** 4	d													05 49							06 20		
—	—	2	Warnham	d													05 53							06 24		
—	—	6½	Ockley	d													06 00							06 31		
—	—	8¾	Holmwood	d													06 04							06 35		
—	—	13¾	**Dorking** 4	a													06 10							06 41		
—	—	—		d								05 48					06 13				06 32			06 45		
—	—	14½	Boxhill & Westhumble	d								05 50					06 15				06 34			06 48		
0	—	—	**Guildford**	d			04 58													05 58						06 28
8¼	—	—	Effingham Junction 6	d			05 16													06 16						06b48
10	—	—	Bookham	d			05 19													06 19						06 51
12½	—	17¾	Leatherhead	d			05 24					05 56					06 20			06 24	06 39			06 53		06 56
14½	—	—	Ashtead	d			05 28					05 59					06 24			06 28	06 43			06 56		06 59
16¼	—	—	**Epsom** 3	a			05 32					06 04					06 28			06 32	06 47			07 01		07 04
—	—	—		d	05 23		05 34	05 40		05 59		06 04			06 18		06 29			06 33	06 48		06 54	07 01		07 04
17¾	—	—	Ewell East	d	05 27			05 44		06 03							06 33						06 58	07 05		
19¼	—	—	Cheam	d	05 30			05 47		06 06							06 36						07 01	07 08		
—	0	—	**Epsom Downs**	d														06 38							07 08	
—	1½	—	Banstead	d														06 41							07 11	
—	3	—	Belmont	d														06 44							07 14	
—	—	0	Wimbledon 6 ⊖	d							05 59								06 33							
—	—	4½	West Sutton	d							06 13								06 47							
20¼	4	5½	**Sutton (Surrey)** 4	a	05 33			05 50		06 09	06 16						06 39	06 47	06 50				07 04	07 11	07 17	
—	—	—		d	05 33	05 37		05 50	06 03	06 09	06 17			06 19		06 33	06 39	06 48	06 51				07 04	07 12	07 18	
—	5¼	—	Carshalton	d		05 40				06 12	06 20						06 42		06 54					07 15		
—	6¼	—	Hackbridge	d		05 42				06 15	06 22						06 45		06 56					07 17		
—	7	—	Mitcham Junction	d		05 46				06 18	06 26						06 48		07 00					07 21		
—	8	—	Eastfields §	d																						
21¼	—	—	Carshalton Beeches	d	05 36			05 53	06 06					06 22		06 36		06 51					07 07		07 21	
22	—	—	Wallington	d	05 39			05 56	06 08					06 24		06 38		06 54					07 10		07 23	
23½	—	—	Waddon	d	05 42			05 59	06 11					06 27		06 41		06 57					07 13		07 26	
24½	—	0	**West Croydon** 4	d	05 45			06 02	06 15					06 31		06 45		07 00					07 16		07 30	
26½	—	—	Norwood Junction 2	d	05 50				06 19							06 50							07 21			
32¼	—	—	New Cross Gate 4 ⊖	d	06 07				06 37							07 08							07 39			
—	—	6	Tulse Hill 3	d		05 55					06 35								07 09							
35	—	12	**London Bridge** 4 ⊖	a	06 14	06 07			06 45		06 52					07 16			07 25				07 48			
—	11¼	—	Balham 4 ⊖	d				06 18		06 27				06 47			06 57	07 16						07 29	07 46	
—	13¼	—	Clapham Junction 10	a			06 00	06 23		06 31		06 30		06 52	06 45		07 01	07 21		07 00	07 15			07 33	07 51	07 30
—	—	—	**London Waterloo** 15 ⊖	a			06 11					06 40			06 55					07 12	07 27					07 42
—	16	—	**London Victoria** 15 ⊖	a				06 31		06 38				07 02			07 10	07 31						07 42	08 01	

Station		SN	SN	SW	SN	SW	SW		SN	SN	SN	SN	SN	SW	SW	SN		SN	SW	SN	SN	SN	SW	SN	SW	SN
Horsham 4	d								06 58											07 28						
Warnham	d								07 02											07 32						
Ockley	d								07 09											07 39						
Holmwood	d								07 13											07 43						
Dorking 4	a								07 19											07 49						
	d	06 57		07 02					07 20					07 32						07 50			08 02			
Boxhill & Westhumble	d	06 59		07 04										07 34									08 04			
Guildford	d						06 58									07 26										
Effingham Junction 6	d						07 16									07 38			07 46							
Bookham	d						07 19									07 41			07 49							
Leatherhead	d	07 04		07 09			07 24		07 26					07 39		07 46			07 54	07 56			08 09			
Ashtead	d	07 08		07 13			07 27		07 30					07 43		07 50			07 57	08 00			08 13			
Epsom 3	a	07 12		07 17			07 32		07 34					07 47		07 54			08 02	08 04			08 17			
	d	07 13		07 18	07 21	07 22	07 34		07 35				07 46	07 48	07 52	07 55			08 04	08 05			08 18	08 22	08 22	
Ewell East	d	07 17			07 25								07 50			07 59				08 09				08 26		
Cheam	d	07 20			07 28				07 40				07 53			08 02				08 12				08 29		
Epsom Downs	d									07 34								08 00								08 32
Banstead	d									07 37								08 03								08 35
Belmont	d									07 40								08 06								08 38
Wimbledon 6 ⊖	d		07 03								07 32										08 02					
West Sutton	d		07 22								07 46										08 16					
Sutton (Surrey) 4	a	07 23	07 26		07 31				07 43	07 43	07 49		07 56			08 05		08 09		08 15	08 19			08 32		08 41
	d	07 24	07 27		07 31				07 44	07 48	07 50	07 55	07 56			08 05		08 10		08 15	08 20	08 26		08 32		08 45
Carshalton	d	07 27	07 30						07 47		07 53		07 59							08 18		08 29				
Hackbridge	d	07 29	07 32								07 55		08 02							08 21		08 31				
Mitcham Junction	d	07 33	07 36						07 51		07 59		08 05							08 24		08 35				
Eastfields §	d																									
Carshalton Beeches	d				07 34					07 51		07 58				08 08		08 13			08 23			08 35		08 48
Wallington	d				07 37					07 53		08 00				08 11		08 15			08 25			08 38		08 50
Waddon	d				07 40					07 56		08 03						08 18			08 28			08 41		08 53
West Croydon 4	d				07 43					08 01		08 07				08 16		08 23			08 32			08 44		08 57
Norwood Junction 2	d				07 48											08 20		08 28						08 49		
New Cross Gate 4 ⊖	d				08 00																			09 07		
Tulse Hill 3	d		07 46								08 10															
London Bridge 4 ⊖	a		08 02		08 08						08 30					08 42		08 47						09 17		
Balham 4 ⊖	d	07 42							08 00	08 17		08 22	08 14								08 48	08 43				09 13
Clapham Junction 10	a	07 48		07 42		07 48	08 01		08 04	08 22		08 26	08 18	08 12	08 18				08 31	08 34	08 53	08 49	08 42		08 48	09 18
London Waterloo 15 ⊖	a			07 54		08 00	08 13							08 24	08 30				08 43				08 54		09 00	
London Victoria 15 ⊖	a	07 57							08 13	08 32		08 36	08 28							08 43	09 03	08 58				09 29

For general notes see front of timetable
For details of catering facilities see
Directory of Train Operators

§ This station may open during the currency of this timetable, please see local publicity for further details.

b Arr. 0644

Horsham, Dorking, Guildford, Epsom and Sutton → London

Network Diagram - see first page of Table 177

		SW		SN	SN	SW	SN	SN	SN	SN	SW		SN	SW	SN	SN	SW	FC A	SN	SN		SN	SN	SW	SN	SW
Horsham 4	d			07 56																		09 08				
Warnham	d			08 00																		09 12				
Ockley	d			08 07																		09 19				
Holmwood	d			08 11																		09 23				
Dorking 4	a			08 17																		09 29				
	d			08 18		08 31							08 57	09 02								09 29		09 35		
Boxhill & Westhumble	d			08 20		08 33							08 59	09 04								09 32				
Guildford	d	07 58					08 16										08 58									09 28
Effingham Junction 6	d	08 15					08 32				08 48						09 16									09 46
Bookham	d	08 18					08 35				08 51						09 19									09 49
Leatherhead	d	08 23		08 26		08 38	08 41				08 56		09 04	09 09			09 24					09 37		09 41		09 54
Ashtead	d	08 27		08 29		08 42	08 45				08 59		09 08	09 13			09 28					09 40		09 44		09 58
Epsom 3	a	08 31		08 34		08 46	08 49				09 04		09 12	09 17			09 32					09 45		09 49		10 02
	d	08 34		08 34		08 48	08 50				09 04		09 13	09 18		09 24	09 35					09 45	09 48	09 50		10 05
Ewell East	d			08 38			08 54						09 17			09 28						09 49	09 52			
Cheam	d			08 41			08 57						09 20			09 31						09 52	09 55			
Epsom Downs	d									09 09									09 35							
Banstead	d									09 12									09 38							
Belmont	d									09 15									09 41							
Wimbledon 6 ⊖ ⛴	d				08 32				08 55									09 16								
West Sutton	d				08 46				09 09									09 30								
Sutton (Surrey) 4	a			08 44	08 50		09 00		09 13	09 18			09 23			09 34		09 37	09 44			09 55	09 58			
	d			08 45	08 51		09 02	09 06	09 15	09 23			09 23		09 32	09 34		09 37	09 45	09 53		09 56	10 00		10 03	
Carshalton	d			08 48	08 54			09 09							09 35			09 40					10 03			
Hackbridge	d			08 50	08 56			09 11							09 37			09 42					10 06			
Mitcham Junction ⛴	d			08 54	09 00			09 15							09 41			09 45				10 02	10 09			
Eastfields §	d																									
Carshalton Beeches	d						09 05		09 18	09 26						09 37			09 48	09 56					10 06	
Wallington	d						09 07		09 20	09 28						09 40			09 51	09 58					10 08	
Waddon	d						09 10		09 23	09 31						09 43			09 54	10 01					10 11	
West Croydon 4 ⛴	d						09 15		09 27	09 35						09 46			09 57	10 05					10 15	
Norwood Junction 2	d						09 19									09 51									10 19	
New Cross Gate 4 ⊖	d						09 37									10 08									10 37	
Tulse Hill 3	d				09 09													09a55								
London Bridge 4 ⊖	a				09 29		09 46									10 15									10 44	
Balham 4 ⊖	d			09 02				09 23	09 43	09 52					09 49				10 13	10 21			10 18			
Clapham Junction 10	a	09 00		09 06		09 15		09 27	09 48	09 57	09 30		09 40	09 45	09 53		10 00		10 18	10 26		10 12	10 22	10 15		10 30
London Waterloo 15 ⊖	a	09 12				09 27					09 42			09 57			10 10							10 25		10 40
London Victoria 15 ⊖	a			09 16				09 36	09 59	10 05			09 50		10 01				10 26	10 34		10 19	10 29			

		FC A	SN	SN	SN	SN		SW	SN	SW	FC A	SN	SN	SN	SN		SW	SN	SW	FC A		SN	SN	SN	SN	SW
Horsham 4	d												10 04													
Warnham	d												10 08													
Ockley	d												10 15													
Holmwood	d												10 19													
Dorking 4	a												10 25													
	d			09 57				10 05					10 26				10 35						10 58			11 05
Boxhill & Westhumble	d			09 59									10 28													
Guildford	d									09 58									10 28							
Effingham Junction 6	d									10 16									10 46							
Bookham	d									10 19									10 49							
Leatherhead	d			10 04				10 11		10 24			10 33				10 41		10 54				11 04			11 11
Ashtead	d			10 08				10 14		10 28			10 37				10 44		10 58				11 07			11 14
Epsom 3	a			10 12				10 19		10 32			10 41				10 49		11 02				11 12			11 19
	d		10 05	10 13		10 18		10 20		10 35			10 42		10 48		10 50		11 05			11 05	11 12		11 18	11 20
Ewell East	d		10 09	10 17		10 22							10 46		10 52							11 09			11 22	
Cheam	d		10 12	10 20		10 25							10 49		10 55							11 12	11 18		11 25	
Epsom Downs	d											10 35														
Banstead	d											10 38														
Belmont	d											10 41														
Wimbledon 6 ⊖ ⛴	d	09 46									10 16									10 46						
West Sutton	d	10 00									10 30									11 00						
Sutton (Surrey) 4	a	10 04	10 15	10 23		10 28					10 34	10 44	10 52		10 58					11 04		11 15	11 22		11 28	
	d	10 04	10 15	10 23	10 23	10 30			10 33		10 34	10 45	10 52	10 53	11 00			11 03		11 04		11 15	11 22	11 23	11 30	
Carshalton	d	10 07				10 33					10 37				11 03					11 07					11 33	
Hackbridge	d	10 09				10 36					10 39				11 06					11 09					11 36	
Mitcham Junction ⛴	d	10 12				10 39					10 42				11 09					11 12					11 39	
Eastfields §	d																									
Carshalton Beeches	d		10 18		10 26				10 36			10 48		10 56				11 06				11 18		11 26		
Wallington	d		10 21		10 28				10 38			10 51		10 58				11 08				11 21		11 28		
Waddon	d		10 24		10 31				10 41			10 54		11 01				11 11				11 24		11 31		
West Croydon 4 ⛴	d		10 27		10 35				10 45			10 57		11 05				11 15				11 27		11 35		
Norwood Junction 2	d								10 49									11 19								
New Cross Gate 4 ⊖	d								11 07									11 37								
Tulse Hill 3	d	10a23									10a53									11a23						
London Bridge 4 ⊖	a								11 14									11 44								
Balham 4 ⊖	d		10 43		10 51	10 48						11 13		11 21	11 18							11 43		11 51	11 48	
Clapham Junction 10	a		10 48	10 40	10 56	10 52		10 45		11 00		11 18	11 10	11 26	11 22		11 15		11 30			11 48	11 40	11 56	11 52	11 45
London Waterloo 15 ⊖	a							10 55		11 10							11 25		11 40							11 55
London Victoria 15 ⊖	a		10 56	10 48	11 04	10 59						11 26	11 18	11 34	11 29							11 56	11 48	12 04	11 59	

For general notes see front of timetable
For details of catering facilities see Directory of Train Operators

§ This station may open during the currency of this timetable, please see local publicity for further details.

A To St Albans (Table 52)

Horsham, Dorking, Guildford, Epsom and Sutton → London

Network Diagram - see first page of Table 177

		SN	SW	FC A	SN	SN	SN	SN	SW	SN	SW	FC A			SN	SN	SN	SN	SW	SN	SW	FC B		SN	SN
Horsham 4	d					11 04							and at the same minutes past each hour until												16 00
Warnham	d					11 08																			16 04
Ockley	d					11 15																			16 11
Holmwood	d					11 19																			16 15
Dorking 4	a					11 25																			16 21
	d					11 26			11 35							15 57			16 05						16 26
Boxhill & Westhumble	d					11 28										15 59									16 28
Guildford	d		10 58								11 28										15 58				
Effingham Junction 6	d		11 16								11 46										16 16				
Bookham	d		11 19								11 49										16 19				
Leatherhead	d		11 24			11 33			11 41		11 54					16 04			16 11		16 24				16 33
Ashtead	d		11 28			11 37			11 44		11 58					16 08			16 14		16 28				16 37
Epsom 3	a		11 32			11 41			11 49		12 02					16 12			16 19		16 32				16 41
	d		11 35			11 42		11 48	11 50		12 05				16 05	16 13		16 18	16 20		16 35				16 42
Ewell East	d					11 46		11 52							16 09	16 17		16 22							
Cheam	d					11 49		11 55							16 12	16 20		16 25							
Epsom Downs	d				11 35																			16 30	
Banstead	d				11 38																			16 33	
Belmont	d				11 41																			16 36	
Wimbledon 6 ⊖	d			11 16								11 46										16 16			
West Sutton	d			11 30								12 00										16 30			
Sutton (Surrey) 4	a			11 34	11 44	11 52		11 58				12 04			16 15	16 23		16 28				16 33		16 39	16 49
	d	11 33		11 34	11 45	11 52	11 53	12 00		12 03		12 04			16 15	16 23	16 23	16 29		16 33		16 33		16 45	16 49
Carshalton	d			11 37				12 03				12 07						16 32				16 36			
Hackbridge	d			11 39				12 06				12 09						16 35				16 38			
Mitcham Junction	d			11 42				12 09				12 12						16 38				16 41			16 55
Eastfields §	d																								
Carshalton Beeches	d	11 36			11 48		11 56			12 06					16 18		16 26			16 36				16 48	
Wallington	d	11 38			11 51		11 58			12 08					16 21		16 28			16 38				16 51	
Waddon	d	11 41			11 54		12 01			12 11					16 24		16 31			16 41				16 54	
West Croydon 4	d	11 45			11 57		12 05			12 15					16 27		16 35			16 45				16 57	
Norwood Junction 2	d	11 49								12 19										16 49					
New Cross Gate 4 ⊖	d	12 07								12 37										17 07					
Tulse Hill 3	d			11a53								12a23										16a50			
London Bridge 4 ⊖	a	12 14								12 44										17 14					
Balham 4 ⊖	d				12 13		12 21	12 18							16 43		16 51	16 47						17 13	
Clapham Junction 10	a		12 00		12 18	12 08	12 26	12 22	12 15		12 30				16 48	16 40	16 56	16 51	16 45		17 00			17 18	17 10
London Waterloo 15 ⊖	a		12 11						12 25		12 40								16 55		17 10				
London Victoria 15 ⊖	a				12 26	12 15	12 34	12 29							16 56	16 48	17 04	16 58						17 26	17 18

		SN	SN	SW	FC C	SN	SN	SW	SN		SW	FC A	SN	SN	SW	SN	SW	SW		SN	FC A	SN	SN	SN	FC D	SW
Horsham 4	d															17 08								17 45		
Warnham	d															17 12										
Ockley	d															17 19										
Holmwood	d															17 23										
Dorking 4	a															17 29								18 01		
	d			16 35					17 00		17 05					17 30	17 35							18 01		18 05
Boxhill & Westhumble	d								17 02							17 33								18 03		
Guildford	d							16 28							16 58			17 28					17 42			
Effingham Junction 6	d							16 46							17 16			17 46					17 55			
Bookham	d							16 49							17 19			17 49								
Leatherhead	d			16 41				16 54	17 07		17 11				17 24	17 38	17 41	17 54					18 02	18 08		18 11
Ashtead	d			16 44				16 58	17 11		17 14				17 28	17 41	17 44	17 58					18 06	18 12		18 14
Epsom 3	a			16 49				17 02	17 15		17 19				17 32	17 46	17 49	18 02					18 10	18 16		18 19
	d		16 47	16 50		16 54		17 05	17 15		17 20		17 25		17 35	17 47	17 50	18 05					18 11	18 16		18 20
Ewell East	d		16 51			16 58			17 19				17 29			17 51								18 20		
Cheam	d		16 54			17 01			17 22				17 32			17 54								18 23		
Epsom Downs	d						17 00							17 30								18 00				
Banstead	d						17 03							17 33								18 03				
Belmont	d						17 06							17 36								18 06				
Wimbledon 6 ⊖	d				16 44							17 12									17 44				18 14	
West Sutton	d				16 58							17 26									17 58				18 28	
Sutton (Surrey) 4	a		16 57		17 03	17 04	17 09		17 25			17 31	17 35	17 39		17 57					18 05	18 09	18 18	18 26	18 33	
	d	16 53	16 57		17 03	17 05	17 18		17 26			17 31	17 35	17 48		17 58				18 03	18 06	18 10	18 18	18 27		
Carshalton	d		17 00		17 06				17 29			17 34				18 01					18 09			18 30		
Hackbridge	d		17 03		17 08				17 31			17 36				18 03					18 11			18 32		
Mitcham Junction	d		17 06		17 11				17 35			17 39				18 07					18 14			18 36		
Eastfields §	d																									
Carshalton Beeches	d	16 56				17 08	17 21						17 38	17 51						18 06		18 13	18 21			
Wallington	d	16 58				17 10	17 23						17 41	17 53						18 08		18 15	18 24			
Waddon	d	17 01				17 13	17 26						17 44	17 56						18 11		18 18	18 27			
West Croydon 4	d	17 05				17 17	17 30						17 47	18 00						18 15		18a21	18 30			
Norwood Junction 2	d					17 21							17 52							18 19						
New Cross Gate 4 ⊖	d					17 39							18 09							18 37						
Tulse Hill 3	d				17a21							17a50									18a24					
London Bridge 4 ⊖	a					17 45							18 19							18 44						
Balham 4 ⊖	d	17 21	17 15				17 48		17 43					18 16		18 18							18 49	18 44		
Clapham Junction 10	a	17 26	17 21	17 15			17 53	17 30	17 48		17 45			18 21	18 00	18 24	18 15	18 30					18 54	18 48		18 45
London Waterloo 15 ⊖	a			17 25				17 40			17 55				18 10		18 25	18 40								18 55
London Victoria 15 ⊖	a	17 34	17 28				18 00		17 56					18 30		18 34							19 03	18 55		

For general notes see front of timetable
For details of catering facilities see Directory of Train Operators

§ This station may open during the currency of this timetable, please see local publicity for further details.

A To St Albans (Table 52)
B To Luton (Table 52)
C To Bedford (Table 52)
D From Luton (Table 52)

Horsham, Dorking, Guildford, Epsom and Sutton → London

Network Diagram - see first page of Table 177

Station		SN	SN	SW		SN	SW	FC A	SN	SN	SW	SW	SN		SW	SN	FC B	SN	SW	SW	SN	SW		SN	FC B	SN
Horsham 4	d					18 09							18 45								19 14					
Warnham	d					18 13															19 18					
Ockley	d					18 20															19 25					
Holmwood	d					18 24							18 56								19 29					
Dorking 4	a					18 30							19 03								19 35					
	d					18 33	18 35				18 50		19 03							19 33	19 35					
Boxhill & Westhumble	d												19 05													
Guildford	d			17 58					18 22							18 52										
Effingham Junction 6	d			18 16					18 39			18 59				19 08										
Bookham	d			18 19					18 42			19 02				19 11										
Leatherhead	d			18 24		18 39	18 41		18 47		18 56	19 07	19 10			19 16				19 39	19 41					
Ashtead	d			18 28		18 42	18 44		18 50		18 59	19 10	19 14			19 20				19 42	19 45					
Epsom 3	a			18 32		18 47	18 50		18 58		19 04	19 15	19 18		←	19 24				19 47	19 49	←				
	d	18 27		18 35		18 47	18 50		18 58		19 05	19 20	19 18		19 20	19 25			19 35	19 50	19 49	19 50		19 54		
Ewell East	d					18 51			19 02			→	19 22			19 29				→	19 53			19 58		
Cheam	d	18 32				18 54			19 05				19 25			19 32					19 56			20 01		
Epsom Downs	d		18 32							19 02								19 39								20 08
Banstead	d		18 35							19 05								19 42								20 11
Belmont	d		18 38							19 08								19 45								20 14
Wimbledon 6 ⊖	d							18 44									19 16								19 46	
West Sutton	d							18 58									19 30								20 05	
Sutton (Surrey) 4	a	18 35	18 41			18 57		19 02	19 08	19 11			19 28			19 35	19 40	19 48			19 59			20 04	20 10	20 17
	d	18 36	18 49			18 58		19 02	19 10	19 19			19 29			19 35		19 49			20 00			20 06		20 19
Carshalton	d					19 01		19 05					19 32								20 03					
Hackbridge	d					19 03		19 07					19 34								20 05					
Mitcham Junction	d					19 07		19 10					19 38								20 09					
Eastfields §	d																									
Carshalton Beeches	d	18 39	18 52						19 13	19 22						19 38		19 52						20 09		20 22
Wallington	d	18 42	18 54						19 15	19 24						19 41		19 54						20 11		20 24
Waddon	d	18 45	18 57						19 18	19 27						19 44		19 57						20 14		20 27
West Croydon 4	d	18 48	19 01						19 22	19 31						19 49		20 01						20 18		20 31
Norwood Junction 2	d	18 52							19 27							19 54								20 23		
New Cross Gate 4 ⊖	d	19 11							19 42							20 12										
Tulse Hill 3	d							19a21																		
London Bridge 4 ⊖	a	19 18							19 49							20 19										
Balham 4 ⊖	d		19 19			19 15				19 51			19 46					20 20			20 17			20 39		20 48
Clapham Junction 10	a		19 24	19 00		19 19	19 16			19 56	19 30		19 50		19 45			20 25	20 00		20 21	20 15		20 44		20 53
London Waterloo 15 ⊖	a			19 10			19 27				19 41				19 55				20 10			20 25				
London Victoria 15 ⊖	a		19 34			19 27				20 04			19 57					20 33			20 28			20 52		21 03

Station		SW	SN	SW	SN	FC B	SN	SW		SN	SW	SN	FC B	SW	SN	SN	SW		SN	FC B	SN	SW	SN	SW	SN	FC B
Horsham 4	d									20 07																
Warnham	d									20 11																
Ockley	d									20 18																
Holmwood	d									20 22																
Dorking 4	a									20 28																
	d		20 00	20 05						20 31	20 35					21 00							21 30	21 35		
Boxhill & Westhumble	d		20 02													21 02										
Guildford	d	19 28						19 58									20 46									
Effingham Junction 6	d	19 46						20 16									21 03									
Bookham	d	19 49						20 19									21 06									
Leatherhead	d	19 54	20 07	20 11				20 24		20 37	20 41					21 07	21 11						21 37	21 41		
Ashtead	d	19 58	20 11	20 14				20 28		20 41	20 44					21 11	21 14						21 41	21 44		
Epsom 3	a	20 02	20 15	20 19				20 32		20 45	20 49					21 15	21 19						21 45	21 49		
	d	20 05	20 16	20 20				20 35		20 46	20 50			21 05	21 07	21 16	21 20					21 35	21 46	21 50		
Ewell East	d		20 20							20 50					21 11	21 20							21 50			
Cheam	d		20 23							20 53					21 14	21 23							21 53			
Epsom Downs	d						20 39														21 39					
Banstead	d						20 42														21 42					
Belmont	d						20 45														21 45					
Wimbledon 6 ⊖	d					20 16							20 46							21 16						21 46
West Sutton	d					20 30							21 00							21 30						22 00
Sutton (Surrey) 4	a		20 26			20 35	20 48			20 56			21 05		21 17	21 26				21 35	21 48		21 56			22 05
	d		20 26		20 35		20 49			20 56		21 05			21 20	21 26			21 35		21 49		21 56		22 05	
Carshalton	d		20 29							20 59						21 29							21 59			
Hackbridge	d		20 32							21 02						21 32							22 02			
Mitcham Junction	d		20 35							21 05						21 35							22 05			
Eastfields §	d																									
Carshalton Beeches	d				20 38		20 52					21 08			21 23				21 38		21 52				22 08	
Wallington	d				20 41		20 54					21 11			21 25				21 41		21 54				22 11	
Waddon	d				20 44		20 57					21 14			21 28				21 44		21 57				22 14	
West Croydon 4	d				20 48		21 01					21 18			21 32				21 48		22 01				22 18	
Norwood Junction 2	d				20 53							21 23							21 53						22 23	
New Cross Gate 4 ⊖	d																									
Tulse Hill 3	d																									
London Bridge 4 ⊖	a																									
Balham 4 ⊖	d		20 44		21 09		21 18			21 14		21 39			21 48	21 44			22 09		22 18		22 14		22 39	
Clapham Junction 10	a	20 30	20 48	20 45	21 14		21 23	21 00		21 18	21 15	21 44		21 30	21 53	21 48	21 45		22 14		22 23	22 00	22 18	22 15	22 44	
London Waterloo 15 ⊖	a	20 40		20 55				21 10			21 25			21 40			21 55					22 10		22 25		
London Victoria 15 ⊖	a		20 55		21 23		21 33			21 25		21 53			22 03	21 55			22 25		22 33		22 27		22 53	

For general notes see front of timetable
For details of catering facilities see Directory of Train Operators

§ This station may open during the currency of this timetable, please see local publicity for further details.

A To Bedford (Table 52)
B From Luton (Table 52)

Horsham, Dorking, Guildford, Epsom and Sutton → London

Network Diagram - see first page of Table 177

		SN	SN		SW	SN	FC A	SN	SN	SW	SN	FC A		SN	SN	FC A	SW	SN	SN	SN	FC A					
Horsham 4	d																									
Warnham	d																									
Ockley	d																									
Holmwood	d																									
Dorking 4	a																									
	d		22 00						22 30	22 35					23 00					23 30						
Boxhill & Westhumble	d		22 02												23 02											
Guildford	d				21 46												22 46									
Effingham Junction 6	d				22 03												23 03									
Bookham	d				22 06												23 06									
Leatherhead	d		22 07		22 11				22 37	22 41					23 07		23 11			23 36						
Ashtead	d		22 11		22 14				22 41	22 44					23 11		23 14			23 39						
Epsom 3	a		22 15		22 19				22 45	22 49					23 15		23 19			23 45						
	d	22 07	22 16		22 20				22 46	22 50				23 07	23 20		23 20									
Ewell East	d	22 11	22 20						22 50					23 11	23 24											
Cheam	d	22 14	22 23						22 53					23 14	23 27											
Epsom Downs	d							22 39											23 39							
Banstead	d							22 42											23 42							
Belmont	d							22 45											23 45							
Wimbledon 6 ⊖	d						22 16					22 46				23 16					23 46					
West Sutton	d						22 30					23 00				23 30					23 59					
Sutton (Surrey) 4	a	22 17	22 26				22 35	22 48	22 56			23 05		23 17	23 30	23 33			23 48		00 05					
	d	22 20	22 26			22 35		22 49	22 56		23 05			23 20				23 35	23 49							
Carshalton	d		22 29						22 59																	
Hackbridge	d		22 32						23 02																	
Mitcham Junction	d		22 35						23 05																	
Eastfields §	d																									
Carshalton Beeches	d	22 23				22 38		22 52			23 08			23 23				23 38	23 52							
Wallington	d	22 25				22 41		22 54			23 11			23 25				23 40	23 54							
Waddon	d	22 28				22 44		22 57			23 14			23 28				23 43	23 57							
West Croydon 4	d	22 32				22 48		23 01			23 18			23a31				23a46	00a01							
Norwood Junction 2	d					22 53					23 23															
New Cross Gate 4 ⊖	d																									
Tulse Hill 3	d																									
London Bridge 4 ⊖	a																									
Balham 4 ⊖	d	22 48	22 44			23 09		23 18	23 14		23 40															
Clapham Junction 10	a	22 53	22 48		22 45	23 15		23 23	23 18	23 15	23 45						23 48									
London Waterloo 15 ⊖	a				22 55					23 25							23 58									
London Victoria 15 ⊖	a	23 03	22 55			23 23		23 31	23 25		23 54															

Saturdays

		SW	SW	SW	SN	SN	SN	SN	SW	FC B	SN	SN	SN	SN	FC B	SN	SW	SN	SN	SN	FC B	SW	SN	SN	SN	SN
Horsham 4	d																									
Warnham	d																									
Ockley	d																									
Holmwood	d																									
Dorking 4	a																									
	d					06 26						06 57						07 26						07 58		
Boxhill & Westhumble	d											06 59						07 28								
Guildford	d								06 28								06 58					07 28				
Effingham Junction 6	d								06 46								07 16					07 46				
Bookham	d								06 49								07 19					07 49				
Leatherhead	d					06 33			06 54			07 04					07 24	07 33				07 54		08 04		
Ashtead	d					06 37			06 58			07 08					07 28	07 37				07 58		08 07		
Epsom 3	a					06 41			07 02			07 12					07 32	07 41				08 02		08 12		
	d	05 35	06 05	06 35		06 42	06 50		07 05		07 05	07 13	07 18				07 35	07 42	07 48			08 05	08 05	08 12		08 18
Ewell East	d					06 46	06 54				07 09		07 22					07 46	07 52				08 09			08 22
Cheam	d					06 49	06 57				07 12	07 18	07 25					07 49	07 55				08 12	08 18		08 25
Epsom Downs	d															07 35										
Banstead	d															07 38										
Belmont	d															07 41										
Wimbledon 6 ⊖	d									06 46					07 16						07 46					
West Sutton	d									07 00					07 30						08 00					
Sutton (Surrey) 4	a					06 52	07 00			07 04	07 15	07 22	07 28		07 34	07 44		07 52	07 58		08 04		08 15	08 22		08 28
	d				06 45	06 52	07 00	07 03		07 04	07 15	07 23	07 30	07 33	07 34	07 45		07 52	08 00	08 03	08 04		08 15	08 22	08 23	08 30
Carshalton	d						07 03			07 07			07 33		07 37				08 03		08 07					08 33
Hackbridge	d						07 06			07 09			07 36		07 39				08 06		08 09					08 36
Mitcham Junction	d						07 09			07 12			07 39		07 42				08 09		08 12					08 39
Eastfields §	d																									
Carshalton Beeches	d				06 48			07 06			07 18			07 36		07 48				08 06			08 18		08 26	
Wallington	d				06 51			07 08			07 21			07 38		07 51				08 08			08 21		08 28	
Waddon	d				06 54			07 11			07 24			07 41		07 54				08 11			08 24		08 31	
West Croydon 4	d				06 57			07 15			07 27			07 45		07 57				08 15			08 27		08 35	
Norwood Junction 2	d							07 19						07 49						08 19						
New Cross Gate 4 ⊖	d							07 37						08 07						08 37						
Tulse Hill 3	d									07a23					07a53						08a23					
London Bridge 4 ⊖	a							07 44						08 14						08 44						
Balham 4 ⊖	d				07 13		07 18				07 43		07 48			08 13			08 18				08 43		08 51	08 48
Clapham Junction 10	a	06 01	06 30	07 00	07 18	07 10	07 22		07 30		07 48	07 40	07 52			08 18	08 00	08 10	08 22			08 30	08 48	08 40	08 56	08 52
London Waterloo 15 ⊖	a	06 11	06 40	07 10					07 40								08 10					08 40				
London Victoria 15 ⊖	a				07 26	07 17	07 29				07 56	07 48	07 59			08 26		08 18	08 29				08 56	08 48	09 04	08 59

For general notes see front of timetable
For details of catering facilities see Directory of Train Operators

A From Luton (Table 52)
B To St Albans (Table 52)

§ This station may open during the currency of this timetable, please see local publicity for further details.

Horsham, Dorking, Guildford, Epsom and Sutton → London

Network Diagram - see first page of Table 177

		SW	SN	SW	FC A	SN	SN	SN	SN	SW	SN	SW	FC A	SN	SN	SN	SN	SW	SN	SW	FC A	SN	SN	SN	SN
Horsham 4	d						08 04																09 04		
Warnham	d						08 08																09 08		
Ockley	d						08 15																09 15		
Holmwood	d						08 19																09 19		
Dorking 4	a						08 25																09 25		
	d	08 05					08 26			08 35					08 58			09 05					09 26		
Boxhill & Westhumble	d						08 28																09 28		
Guildford	d			07 58								08 28								08 58					
Effingham Junction 6	d			08 16								08 46								09 16					
Bookham	d			08 19								08 49								09 19					
Leatherhead	d	08 11		08 24			08 33			08 41		08 54			09 04			09 11		09 24			09 33		
Ashtead	d	08 14		08 28			08 37			08 44		08 58			09 07			09 14		09 28			09 37		
Epsom 3	a	08 19		08 32			08 41			08 49		09 02			09 12			09 19		09 32			09 41		
	d	08 20		08 35			08 42		08 48	08 50		09 05		09 05	09 12		09 18	09 20		09 35			09 42		09 48
Ewell East	d						08 46		08 52					09 09			09 22						09 46		09 52
Cheam	d						08 49		08 55					09 12	09 18		09 25						09 49		09 55
Epsom Downs	d					08 35																09 35			
Banstead	d					08 38																09 38			
Belmont	d					08 41																09 41			
Wimbledon 6 ⊖	d				08 16								08 46								09 16				
West Sutton	d				08 30								09 00								09 30				
Sutton (Surrey) 4	a				08 34	08 44	08 52		08 58				09 04	09 15	09 22		09 28				09 34	09 44	09 52		09 58
	d		08 33		08 34	08 45	08 52	08 53	09 00		09 03		09 04	09 15	09 22	09 23	09 30		09 33		09 34	09 45	09 52	09 53	10 00
Carshalton	d				08 37				09 03				09 07				09 33				09 37				10 03
Hackbridge	d				08 39				09 06				09 09				09 36				09 39				10 06
Mitcham Junction	d				08 42				09 09				09 12				09 39				09 42				10 09
Eastfields §	d																								
Carshalton Beeches	d		08 36			08 48		08 56			09 06			09 18		09 26			09 36			09 48		09 56	
Wallington	d		08 38			08 51		08 58			09 08			09 21		09 28			09 38			09 51		09 58	
Waddon	d		08 41			08 54		09 01			09 11			09 24		09 31			09 41			09 54		10 01	
West Croydon 4	d		08 45			08 57		09 05			09 15			09 27		09 35			09 45			09 57		10 05	
Norwood Junction 2	d		08 49								09 19								09 49						
New Cross Gate 4 ⊖	d		09 07								09 37								10 07						
Tulse Hill 3	d				08a53								09a23								09a53				
London Bridge 4 ⊖	a		09 14								09 44								10 14						
Balham 4 ⊖	d					09 13		09 21	09 18					09 43		09 51	09 48					10 13		10 21	10 18
Clapham Junction 10	a	08 45		09 00		09 18	09 10	09 26	09 22	09 15		09 30		09 48	09 40	09 56	09 52	09 45		10 00		10 18	10 10	10 26	10 22
London Waterloo 15 ⊖	a	08 55		09 10						09 25		09 40						09 55		10 10					
London Victoria 15 ⊖	a					09 26	09 18	09 34	09 29					09 56	09 48	10 04	09 59					10 26	10 18	10 34	10 29

		SW	SN	SW	FC A	SN		SN	SN	SN	SW	SN	SW	FC B	SN	SN	SN	SW	SW	FC C	SN	SN	SN	SW	SN
Horsham 4	d						and at the same minutes past each hour until									18 04									
Warnham	d															18 08									
Ockley	d															18 15									
Holmwood	d															18 19									
Dorking 4	a															18 25									
	d	09 35						17 58			18 05					18 26		18 35					19 00	19 05	
Boxhill & Westhumble	d															18 28							19 02		
Guildford	d			09 28									17 58						18 28						
Effingham Junction 6	d			09 46									18 16						18 46						
Bookham	d			09 49									18 19						18 49						
Leatherhead	d	09 41		09 54				18 04			18 11		18 24			18 33		18 41	18 54				19 07	19 11	
Ashtead	d	09 44		09 58				18 07			18 14		18 28			18 37		18 44	18 58				19 11	19 14	
Epsom 3	a	09 49		10 02				18 12			18 19		18 32			18 41		18 49	19 02				19 15	19 19	
	d	09 50		10 05		10 05		18 12		18 18	18 20		18 35			18 42	18 48	18 50	19 05			19 05	19 16	19 20	
Ewell East	d					10 09				18 22						18 46	18 52					19 09	19 20		
Cheam	d					10 12		18 18		18 25						18 49	18 55					19 12	19 23		
Epsom Downs	d														18 35										
Banstead	d														18 38										
Belmont	d														18 41										
Wimbledon 6 ⊖	d				09 46									18 16						18 46					
West Sutton	d				10 00									18 30						19 00					
Sutton (Surrey) 4	a				10 04	10 15		18 22		18 28				18 34	18 44	18 52	18 58			19 04		19 15	19 26		
	d		10 03		10 04	10 15		18 22	18 23	18 30		18 33		18 34	18 45	18 52	19 00			19 04	19 05	19 15	19 29		19 35
Carshalton	d				10 07					18 33				18 37			19 03			19 07			19 32		
Hackbridge	d				10 09					18 36				18 39			19 05			19 09			19 34		
Mitcham Junction	d				10 12					18 39				18 42			19 09			19 12			19 38		
Eastfields §	d																								
Carshalton Beeches	d		10 06			10 18			18 26			18 36			18 48						19 08	19 18			19 38
Wallington	d		10 08			10 21			18 28			18 38			18 51						19 10	19 21			19 41
Waddon	d		10 11			10 24			18 31			18 41			18 54						19 13	19 24			19 44
West Croydon 4	d		10 15			10 27			18 35			18 45			18 57						19a16	19 27			19 48
Norwood Junction 2	d		10 19									18 49													19 53
New Cross Gate 4 ⊖	d		10 37									19 07													
Tulse Hill 3	d				10a23									18a53						19a23					
London Bridge 4 ⊖	a		10 44									19 14													
Balham 4 ⊖	d					10 43			18 51	18 48					19 13		19 18					19 43	19 46		20 09
Clapham Junction 10	a	10 15		10 30		10 48		18 40	18 56	18 52	18 45		19 00		19 18	19 10	19 22	19 15	19 30			19 48	19 51	19 45	20 14
London Waterloo 15 ⊖	a	10 25		10 40							18 55		19 10					19 25	19 40					19 55	
London Victoria 15 ⊖	a					10 56		18 48	19 04	18 59					19 26	19 18	19 29					19 56	19 58		20 23

For general notes see front of timetable
For details of catering facilities see Directory of Train Operators

§ This station may open during the currency of this timetable, please see local publicity for further details.

A To St Albans (Table 52)
B To Bedford (Table 52)
C To Luton (Table 52)

Horsham, Dorking, Guildford, Epsom and Sutton → London

Network Diagram - see first page of Table 177

Station		FC A	SN	SW	SN	SW	SN	FC A	SW	SN	SN	SW	SN	FC A	SN	SW	SN	SW	SN	FC A	SW	SN	SN	SW	SN	FC A
Horsham [4]	d																									
Warnham	d																									
Ockley	d																									
Holmwood	d																									
Dorking [4]	a																									
	d				19 30	19 35					20 00	20 05					20 30	20 35					21 00			
Boxhill & Westhumble	d										20 02												21 02			
Guildford	d			18 58					19 28							19 58								20 46		
Effingham Junction [6]	d			19 16					19 46							20 16								21 03		
Bookham	d			19 19					19 49							20 19								21 06		
Leatherhead	d			19 24	19 37	19 41			19 54		20 07	20 11				20 24	20 37	20 41					21 07	21 11		
Ashtead	d			19 28	19 41	19 44			19 58		20 11	20 14				20 28	20 41	20 44					21 11	21 14		
Epsom [3]	a			19 32	19 45	19 49			20 02		20 15	20 19				20 32	20 45	20 49					21 15	21 19		
	d			19 35	19 46	19 50			20 05	20 07	20 16	20 20				20 35	20 46	20 50			21 05	21 07	21 16	21 20		
Ewell East	d				19 50					20 11	20 20						20 50					21 11	21 20			
Cheam	d				19 53					20 14	20 23						20 53					21 14	21 23			
Epsom Downs	d		19 39												20 39											
Banstead	d		19 42												20 42											
Belmont	d		19 45												20 45											
Wimbledon [6] ⊖	d	19 16						19 46						20 16						20 46						21 16
West Sutton	d	19 30						20 00						20 30						21 00						21 30
Sutton (Surrey) [4]	a	19 35	19 48		19 56			20 05		20 17	20 26			20 35	20 48		20 56			21 05		21 17	21 26			21 35
	d		19 49		19 56		20 05			20 19	20 26		20 35		20 49		20 56		21 05			21 19	21 26		21 35	
Carshalton	d				19 59						20 29						20 59						21 29			
Hackbridge	d				20 02						20 32						21 02						21 32			
Mitcham Junction	d				20 05						20 35						21 05						21 35			
Eastfields §	d																									
Carshalton Beeches	d		19 52				20 08			20 22			20 38		20 52				21 08			21 22			21 38	
Wallington	d		19 54				20 11			20 24			20 41		20 54				21 11			21 24			21 41	
Waddon	d		19 57				20 14			20 27			20 44		20 57				21 14			21 27			21 44	
West Croydon [4]	d		20 01				20 18			20 31			20 48		21 01				21 18			21 31			21 48	
Norwood Junction [2]	d						20 23						20 53						21 23						21 53	
New Cross Gate [4] ⊖	d																									
Tulse Hill [3]	d																									
London Bridge [4] ⊖	a																									
Balham [4] ⊖	d		20 18		20 14		20 39			20 48	20 44		21 09		21 18		21 14		21 39			21 48	21 44		22 09	
Clapham Junction [10]	a		20 23	20 00	20 18	20 15	20 44		20 30	20 53	20 48	20 45	21 14		21 23	21 00	21 18	21 15	21 44		21 30	21 53	21 48	21 45	22 14	
London Waterloo [15] ⊖	a			20 10		20 25			20 40			20 55				21 10		21 25			21 40			21 55		
London Victoria [15] ⊖	a		20 33		20 25		20 53			21 03	20 55		21 23		21 33		21 25		21 53			22 03	21 55		22 23	

Station		SN	SW	SN	SW	SN	FC A	SN	SN	SW	SN	FC [1] A	SN	SN	SW	SN	FC A	SN	SN	SW	SN	FC A	SN	SN	FC A
Horsham [4]	d																								
Warnham	d																								
Ockley	d																								
Holmwood	d																								
Dorking [4]	a																								
	d			21 30	21 35				22 00					22 30	22 35				23 00					23 30	
Boxhill & Westhumble	d								22 02										23 02						
Guildford	d									21 46										22 46					
Effingham Junction [6]	d									22 03										23 03					
Bookham	d									22 06										23 06					
Leatherhead	d			21 37	21 41				22 07	22 11				22 37	22 41				23 07	23 11				23 36	
Ashtead	d			21 41	21 44				22 11	22 14				22 41	22 44				23 11	23 14				23 39	
Epsom [3]	a			21 45	21 49				22 15	22 19				22 45	22 49				23 15	23 19				23 45	
	d		21 35	21 46	21 50			22 07	22 16	22 20				22 46	22 50			23 07	23 20	23 20					
Ewell East	d			21 50				22 11	22 20					22 50				23 11	23 24						
Cheam	d			21 53				22 14	22 23					22 53				23 14	23 27						
Epsom Downs	d	21 39											22 39										23 39		
Banstead	d	21 42											22 42										23 42		
Belmont	d	21 45											22 45										23 45		
Wimbledon [6] ⊖	d						21 46					22 16					22 46					23 16			23 46
West Sutton	d						22 00					22 30					23 00					23 30			23 59
Sutton (Surrey) [4]	a	21 48		21 56			22 05	22 17	22 26			22 35	22 48	22 56			23 05	23 17	23 30			23 35	23 48		00 05
	d	21 49		21 56		22 05		22 19	22 26		22 35		22 49	22 56		23 05		23 20			23 35		23 49		
Carshalton	d			21 59					22 29					22 59											
Hackbridge	d			22 02					22 32					23 02											
Mitcham Junction	d			22 05					22 35					23 05											
Eastfields §	d																								
Carshalton Beeches	d	21 52				22 08		22 22			22 38		22 52			23 08		23 23			23 38		23 52		
Wallington	d	21 54				22 11		22 24			22 41		22 54			23 11		23 25			23 40		23 54		
Waddon	d	21 57				22 14		22 27			22 44		22 57			23 14		23 28			23 43		23 57		
West Croydon [4]	d	22 01				22 18		22 31			22 48		23 01			23 18		23a31			23a46		00a01		
Norwood Junction [2]	d					22 23					22 53					23 23									
New Cross Gate [4] ⊖	d																								
Tulse Hill [3]	d																								
London Bridge [4] ⊖	a																								
Balham [4] ⊖	d	22 18		22 14		22 39		22 48	22 44		23 09		23 18	23 14		23 40									
Clapham Junction [10]	a	22 23	22 00	22 18	22 15	22 44		22 53	22 48	22 45	23 14		23 23	23 18	23 15	23 45				23 48					
London Waterloo [15] ⊖	a		22 10		22 25					22 55					23 25					23 58					
London Victoria [15] ⊖	a	22 33		22 25		22 53		23 03	22 55		23 23		23 31	23 25		23 54									

For general notes see front of timetable
For details of catering facilities see
Directory of Train Operators

§ This station may open during the currency of this timetable, please see local publicity for further details.

A From Luton (Table 52)

Table 182

Sundays

Horsham, Dorking, Guildford, Epsom and Sutton → London

Network Diagram - see first page of Table 177

Station		SN	SN	SN		SW	SN	SN		SW	SN	SN		SW	SN	SN		SN	SW	SN		SN	SN	SW		SN
Horsham 4	d																									
Warnham	d																									
Ockley	d																									
Holmwood	d																									
Dorking 4	a																									
	d			06 59				07 29				08 03						08 33					09 03	09 08		
Boxhill & Westhumble	d			07 01				07 31				08 05						08 35					09 05			
Guildford	d																		08 20							
Effingham Junction 6	d																		08 36							
Bookham	d																		08 39							
Leatherhead	d			07 06				07 36				08 10						08 40	08 44				09 10	09 15		
Ashtead	d			07 10				07 40				08 14						08 44	08 48				09 14	09 18		
Epsom 3	a			07 14				07 44				08 18						08 48	08 52				09 18	09 23		
	d	06 47		07 14		07 24		07 44		07 54		08 18		08 24				08 48	08 54				09 18	09 24		
Ewell East	d	06 51		07 18				07 48				08 22						08 52					09 22			
Cheam	d	06 54		07 21				07 51				08 25						08 55					09 25			
Epsom Downs	d																									
Banstead	d																									
Belmont	d																									
Wimbledon 6 ⊖	d																									
West Sutton	d																									
Sutton (Surrey) 4	a	06 57		07 24				07 54				08 28						08 58					09 28			
	d	06 57	07 28	07 29			07 58	07 59			08 27	08 29			08 39	08 57		08 59		09 09		09 27	09 29			09 39
Carshalton	d			07 32				08 02				08 32						09 02					09 32			
Hackbridge	d			07 34				08 04				08 34						09 04					09 34			
Mitcham Junction	d			07 38				08 08				08 38						09 08					09 38			
Eastfields §	d																									
Carshalton Beeches	d	07 00	07 31				08 01				08 30					09 00						09 30				
Wallington	d	07 02	07 33				08 03				08 32				08 43	09 02				09 13		09 32				09 43
Waddon	d	07 05	07 36				08 06				08 35					09 05						09 35				
West Croydon 4	d	07 09	07 39				08 09				08 39				08 48	09 09				09 18		09 39				09 48
Norwood Junction 2	d														08 54					09 24						09 54
New Cross Gate 4 ⊖	d																									
Tulse Hill 3	d																									
London Bridge 4 ⊖	a																									
Balham 4 ⊖	d	07 25	07 55	07 48			08 25	08 18			08 55	08 48			09 10	09 25		09 18		09 40		09 55	09 48			10 10
Clapham Junction 10	a	07 30	08 00	07 52		07 49	08 30	08 22		08 19	09 00	08 52		08 49	09 15	09 30		09 22	09 19	09 45		10 00	09 52	09 49		10 15
London Waterloo 15 ⊖	a					08 04				08 34				09 04					09 34					10 04		
London Victoria 15 ⊖	a	07 38	08 08	07 59			08 38	08 29			09 08	08 59			09 23	09 38		09 29		09 53		10 08	09 59			10 23

Station		SN	SN		FC A	SW	SN	SN	SN	FC A	SW	SN	SN	SN			FC A	SW	SN		SN	SN	FC A		SW
Horsham 4	d																								
Warnham	d																								
Ockley	d																								
Holmwood	d																								
Dorking 4	a																								
	d		09 33						10 03		10 08			10 33								21 03			21 08
Boxhill & Westhumble	d		09 35						10 05					10 35								21 05			
Guildford	d					09 20												20 20							
Effingham Junction 6	d					09 36												20 36							
Bookham	d					09 39												20 39							
Leatherhead	d		09 40			09 44			10 10		10 15			10 40				20 44				21 10			21 15
Ashtead	d		09 44			09 48			10 14		10 18			10 44				20 48				21 14			21 18
Epsom 3	a		09 48			09 52			10 18		10 23			10 48				20 52				21 18			21 23
	d		09 48			09 54			10 18		10 24			10 48	and at			20 54				21 18			21 24
Ewell East	d		09 52						10 22					10 52								21 22			
Cheam	d		09 55						10 25					10 55	the same							21 25			
Epsom Downs	d														minutes										
Banstead	d																								
Belmont	d														past										
Wimbledon 6 ⊖	d				09 44					10 14					each		20 44						21 14		
West Sutton	d				09 58					10 28							20 58						21 28		
Sutton (Surrey) 4	a		09 58		10 03				10 28	10 33				10 58	hour until		21 01					21 28	21 33		
	d	09 57	09 59				10 09	10 27	10 29			10 39	10 57	10 59					21 09		21 27	21 29			
Carshalton	d		10 02						10 32					11 02								21 32			
Hackbridge	d		10 04						10 34					11 04								21 34			
Mitcham Junction	d		10 08						10 38					11 08								21 38			
Eastfields §	d																								
Carshalton Beeches	d	10 00						10 30					11 00								21 30				
Wallington	d	10 02					10 13	10 32				10 43	11 02						21 13		21 32				
Waddon	d	10 05						10 35					11 05								21 35				
West Croydon 4	d	10 09					10 18	10 39				10 48	11 09						21 18		21 39				
Norwood Junction 2	d						10 24					10 54							21 24						
New Cross Gate 4 ⊖	d																								
Tulse Hill 3	d																								
London Bridge 4 ⊖	a																								
Balham 4 ⊖	d	10 25	10 18				10 40	10 55	10 48			11 10	11 25	11 18					21 40		21 55	21 48			
Clapham Junction 10	a	10 30	10 22			10 19	10 45	11 00	10 52		10 49	11 15	11 30	11 22				21 19	21 45		22 00	21 52			21 49
London Waterloo 15 ⊖	a					10 34					11 04							21 29							22 00
London Victoria 15 ⊖	a	10 38	10 29				10 53	11 08	10 59			11 23	11 38	11 29					21 53		22 09	21 59			

For general notes see front of timetable
For details of catering facilities see
Directory of Train Operators

§ This station may open during the currency of this timetable, please see local publicity for further details.

A From Luton (Table 52)

Horsham, Dorking, Guildford, Epsom and Sutton → London

Network Diagram - see first page of Table 177

Station		SN	SN	SN	SW	SN	SN	SN	SW	SN	SN	SN	SW	SN	SN A	SN	SW	SN
Horsham 4	d																	
Warnham	d																	
Ockley	d																	
Holmwood	d																	
Dorking 4	a																	
	d			21 33				22 03	22 08			22 33				23 03	23 08	
Boxhill & Westhumble	d			21 35				22 05				22 35				23 05		
Guildford	d				21 20								22 20					
Effingham Junction 6	d				21 36								22 36					
Bookham	d				21 39								22 39					
Leatherhead	d			21 40	21 44			22 10	22 15			22 40	22 44			23 10	23 15	
Ashtead	d			21 44	21 48			22 14	22 18			22 44	22 48			23 14	23 18	
Epsom 3	a			21 48	21 52			22 18	22 23			22 48	22 52			23 18	23 23	
	d			21 48	21 54			22 18	22 24			22 48	22 54			23 18	23 24	
Ewell East	d			21 52				22 22				22 52				23 22		
Cheam	d			21 55				22 25				22 55				23 25		
Epsom Downs	d																	
Banstead	d																	
Belmont	d																	
Wimbledon 6 ⊖ ⛴	d																	
West Sutton	d																	
Sutton (Surrey) 4	a			21 58				22 28				22 58				23 28		
	d	21 39	21 57	21 59		22 09	22 27	22 29		22 39	22 57	22 59		23 09	23 27	23 29		23 39
Carshalton	d			22 02				22 32				23 02				23 32		
Hackbridge	d			22 04				22 34				23 04				23 34		
Mitcham Junction ⛴	d			22 08				22 38				23 08				23 38		
Eastfields §	d																	
Carshalton Beeches	d		22 00				22 30				23 00				23 30			23 42
Wallington	d	21 43	22 02			22 13	22 32			22 43	23 02			23 13	23 32			23 44
Waddon	d		22 05				22 35				23 05				23 35			23 47
West Croydon 4 ⛴	d	21 48	22 09			22 18	22 39			22 48	23 09			23 18	23a38			23a50
Norwood Junction 2	d	21 54				22 24				22 54				23b26				
New Cross Gate 4 ⊖	d																	
Tulse Hill 3	d																	
London Bridge 4 ⊖	a																	
Balham 4 ⊖	d	22 10	22 25	22 18		22 40	22 55	22 48		23 10	23 25	23 18		23 42		23 48		
Clapham Junction 10	a	22 15	22 30	22 22	22 19	22 45	23 00	22 52	22 49	23 15	23 30	23 22	23 19	23 47		23 52	23 49	
London Waterloo 15 ⊖	a				22 29				23 00				23 29				23 59	
London Victoria 15 ⊖	a	22 23	22 39	22 29		22 53	23 09	22 59		23 23	23 38	23 29		23 55		23 59		

For general notes see front of timetable
For details of catering facilities see Directory of Train Operators

§ This station may open during the currency of this timetable, please see local publicity for further details.

A To Selhurst (Table 177)
b Arr. 2323

Network Diagram for Tables 184, 189

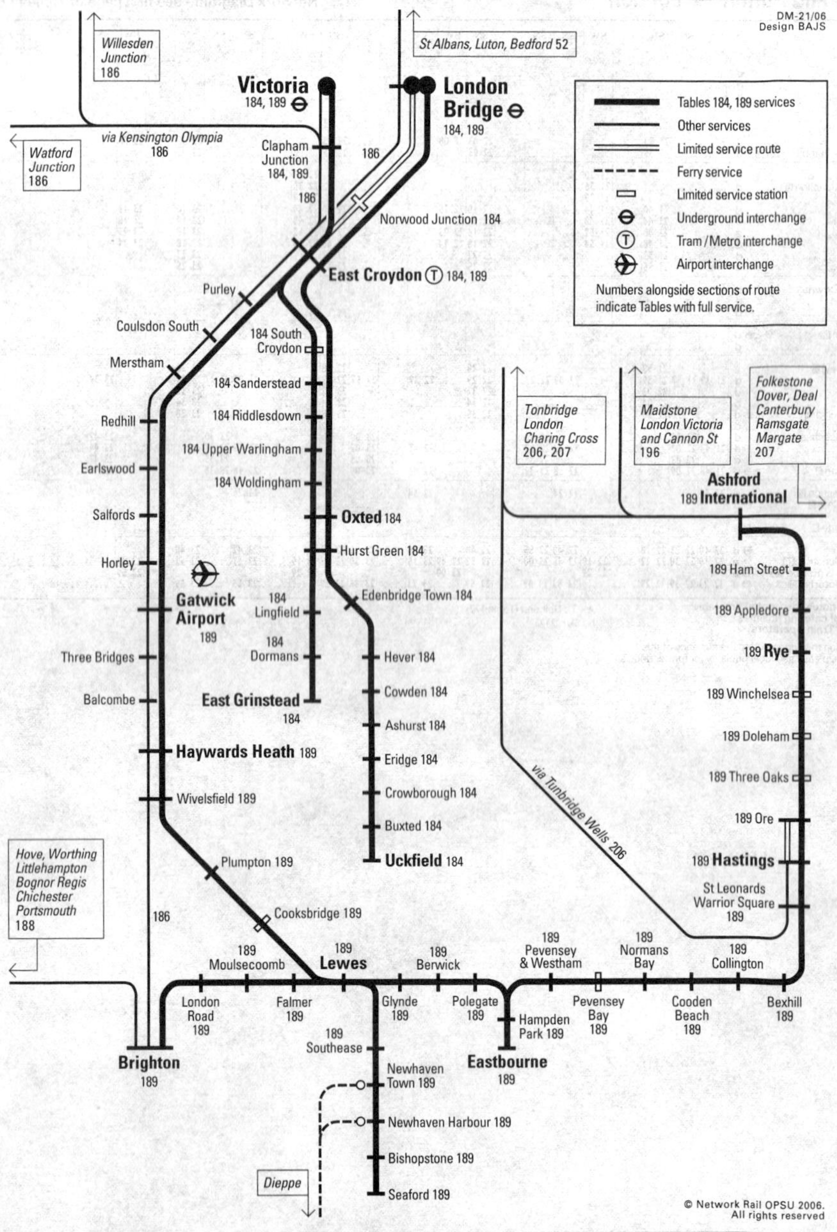
DM-21/06
Design BAJS
Willesden Junction 186
St Albans, Luton, Bedford 52
Victoria 184, 189
London Bridge 184, 189
Watford Junction 186
via Kensington Olympia 186
Clapham Junction 184, 189
186
186
Norwood Junction 184
East Croydon 184, 189
Purley
Coulsdon South
Merstham
184 South Croydon
184 Sanderstead
184 Riddlesdown
184 Upper Warlingham
184 Woldingham
Oxted 184
Hurst Green 184
Edenbridge Town 184
184 Lingfield
184 Dormans
East Grinstead 184
Hever 184
Cowden 184
Ashurst 184
Eridge 184
Crowborough 184
Buxted 184
Uckfield 184
Redhill
Earlswood
Salfords
Horley
Gatwick Airport 189
Three Bridges
Balcombe
Haywards Heath 189
Wivelsfield 189
Plumpton 189
Cooksbridge 189
186
Hove, Worthing
Littlehampton
Bognor Regis
Chichester
Portsmouth
188
Tables 184, 189 services
Other services
Limited service route
Ferry service
Limited service station
Underground interchange
Tram / Metro interchange
Airport interchange
Numbers alongside sections of route indicate Tables with full service.
Tonbridge
London
Charing Cross
206, 207
Maidstone
London Victoria
and Cannon St
196
Folkestone
Dover, Deal
Canterbury
Ramsgate
Margate
207
Ashford International 189
189 Ham Street
189 Appledore
189 Rye
189 Winchelsea
189 Doleham
189 Three Oaks
189 Ore
189 Hastings
St Leonards Warrior Square 189
via Tunbridge Wells 206
189 Moulsecoomb
189 Lewes
189 Berwick
189 Pevensey & Westham
189 Normans Bay
189 Collington
London Road 189
Falmer 189
Glynde 189
Polegate 189
Hampden Park 189
Pevensey Bay 189
Cooden Beach 189
Bexhill 189
Brighton 189
189 Southease
Newhaven Town 189
Newhaven Harbour 189
Bishopstone 189
Seaford 189
Eastbourne 189
Dieppe

London → Oxted, East Grinstead and Uckfield

Network Diagram - see first page of Table 184

Miles	Miles	Station			SN MX 1	SN MX 1	SN 1	SN 1	SN 1	SN 1	SN 1	SN 1	SN 1	SN 1	SN 1	SN 1	SN 1	SN 1	SN 1	SN 1	SN 1	SN 1
0	—	**London Victoria** 15	⊖ 175, 177	d	23p24	23p49		05 23			06 17				07 02	07 23			08 09		08 53	
2¾	—	Clapham Junction 10	175, 177	d	23p30	23p56		05 33			06 23				07 08	07 29			08 15		08 59	
—	0	**London Bridge** 4	⊖ 175, 177	d					05 55				06 30	06 56			07 36	08 07		08 25		09 02
—	8¾	Norwood Junction 2	175, 177	d				05 50		06 10			06 44							08 37		
10½	10¼	**East Croydon**	175, 177 ⛴	d	23p43	00 10	05 26	05 54	06 10	06 14	06 34		06 48	07 10	07 21	07 41	07 51	08 23	08 26	08 41	09 10	09 23
11½	—	South Croydon 4	175	d				05 56												08 44		
12½	—	Sanderstead		d	23p47	00s14				06 18	06 39		06 52	07 14	07 26		07 56			08 47	09 14	
13¾	—	Riddlesdown		d	23p50	00s17				06 21	06 42		06 55	07 17			07 59			08 50	09 17	
15½	—	Upper Warlingham		d	23p54	00s21				06 25	06 46		06 59	07 21			08 03		08 34	08 54	09 21	
17¼	—	Woldingham		d	23p58	00s25				06 29	06 50		07 03	07 25			08 07		08 38	08 58	09 25	
20½	—	**Oxted** 3		a	00 03	00 30	05 41	06 08	06 25	06 34	06 55		07 08	07 30	07 36	07 55	08 12	08 36	08 43	09 03	09 30	09 36
—	—			d	00 03		05 41	06 08	06 30	06 34	06 57	07 01	07 08	07 31	07 36	07 55	08 12	08 37	08 43	09 03	09 30	09 37
21½	0	Hurst Green		d	00 06		05 44	06 10	06 32	06 37	06 59	07 04	07 12	07 33	07 39		08 14	08 39	08 45	09 06	09 33	09 39
26¼	—	Lingfield		d	00 12			06 16		06 43	07 05		07 18		07 45		08 20		08 51	09 12	09 39	
28	—	Dormans		d	00 15			06 20		06 46	07 09		07 21		07 48		08 24		08 55	09 15	09 42	
30¼	—	**East Grinstead**		a	00 20			06 24		06 51	07 13		07 29		07 53	08 07	08 28		09 00	09 20	09 47	
—	4¼	Edenbridge Town		d			05 50		06 38			07 10		07 39				08 45				09 45
—	6	Hever		d					06 42					07 43				08 49				09 49
—	8	Cowden		d					06 46					07 47				08 53				09 53
—	10¾	Ashurst		d					06 50			07 19		07 51				08 57				09 57
—	14½	Eridge		d			06 02		06 56			07 26		07 58				09 03				10 03
—	17¾	Crowborough		d			06b12		07c07			07e37		08f09				09 09				10 09
—	22½	Buxted		d			06 18		07 13			07 43		08 15				09 15				10 15
—	25	**Uckfield**		a			06 24		07 19			07 49		08 21				09 21				10 21

Station			SN 1	SN 1	SN 1		SN 1	SN 1	SN 1	SN 1	SN 1	SN 1	SN 1	SN 1	SN 1	SN 1	SN 1	SN 1	SN 1	SN 1	SN 1
London Victoria 15	⊖ 175, 177	d	09 23	09 53			15 23		15 53		16 23		16 53					17 32		18 02	
Clapham Junction 10	175, 177	d	09 29	09 59			15 29		15 59		16 29		16 59								
London Bridge 4	⊖ 175, 177	d			10 08			15 38		16 08		16 33		17 10	17 13	17 30			17 50		18 12
Norwood Junction 2	175, 177	d																			
East Croydon	175, 177 ⛴	d	09 40	10 10	10 23		15 40	15 53	16 10	16 23	16 40	16 52	17 10	17 24	17 28	17 44		17 48	18 05	18 17	18 27
South Croydon 4	175	d				and at	15 42		16 12		16 42		17 12		17 30						
Sanderstead		d	09 44	10 14			15 45		16 15		16 45		17 15		17 33			17 52	18 09	18 22	18 31
Riddlesdown		d	09 47	10 17		the same	15 48		16 18		16 48		17 18		17 36			17 55	18 12	18 25	
Upper Warlingham		d	09 51	10 21			15 52		16 22		16 52		17 22		17 40			17 59	18 16	18 29	18 37
Woldingham		d	09 55	10 25		minutes	15 56		16 26		16 56		17 26		17 44			18 03	18 20	18 33	18 41
Oxted 3		a	10 00	10 30	10 36		16 01	16 06	16 31	16 36	17 01	17 06	17 31	17 37	17 49	17 58		18 08	18 25	18 38	18 46
		d	10 00	10 30	10 37	past	16 01	16 07	16 31	16 37	17 01	17 07	17 31	17 37	17 49	17 59	18 04	18 08	18 25	18 38	18 47
Hurst Green		d	10 03	10 33	10 39	each	16 04	16 09	16 34	16 39	17 04	17 09	17 34	17 40	17 52	18 01	18 06	18 11	18 28	18 41	18 49
Lingfield		d	10 09	10 39			16 10		16 40		17 10		17 40		17 58	18 07		18 17	18 34	18 47	
Dormans		d	10 12	10 42		hour until	16 13		16 43		17 13		17 43		18 01	18 11		18 20	18 37	18 50	
East Grinstead		a	10 17	10 47			16 18		16 48		17 20		17 50		18 08	18 17		18 27	18 44	18 57	
Edenbridge Town		d			10 45			16 15		16 45		17 15		17 46			18 12				18 55
Hever		d			10 49			16 19		16 49		17 19					18 16				
Cowden		d			10 53			16 23		16 53		17 23					18 20				
Ashurst		d			10 57			16 27		16 57		17 27					18 24				
Eridge		d			11 03			16 33		17 03		17 33		18 00			18 30				19 07
Crowborough		d			11 09			16 39		17 09		17 39		18 06			18 36				19 13
Buxted		d			11 15			16 46		17 16		17 46		18 12			18 42				19 19
Uckfield		a			11 21			16 52		17 22		17 52		18 20			18 48				19 27

Station			SN 1	SN 1	SN 1	SN 1	SN 1	SN 1	SN 1	SN 1	SN 1	SN 1	SN 1	SN 1	SN 1	SN 1	SN 1	SN 1	SN 1	SN 1
London Victoria 15	⊖ 175, 177	d	18 24					19 23	19 53		20 23	20 53		21 23	21 53		22 23	22 53	23 24	23 49
Clapham Junction 10	175, 177	d	18 30					19 29	19 59		20 29	20 59		21 29	21 59		22 29	22 59	23 30	23 56
London Bridge 4	⊖ 175, 177	d			18 31	18 54	19 08			20 05			21 05			22 05				
Norwood Junction 2	175, 177	d				19 05				20 16			21 16			22 16				
East Croydon	175, 177 ⛴	d	18 42		18 45	19 10	19 23	19 40	20 10	20 20	20 40	21 10	21 20	21 40	22 10	22 20	22 40	23 10	23 43	00 10
South Croydon 4	175	d			18 47	19 12														
Sanderstead		d	18 46		18 52	19 15		19 44	20 14	20 24	20 44	21 14	21 24	21 44	22 14	22 24	22 44	23 14	23 47	00s14
Riddlesdown		d	18 49		18 55	19 18		19 47	20 17		20 47	21 17		21 47	22 17		22 47	23 17	23 50	00s17
Upper Warlingham		d	18 53		18 59	19 22		19 51	20 21	20 30	20 51	21 21	21 30	21 51	22 21	22 30	22 51	23 21	23 54	00s21
Woldingham		d	18 57		19 03	19 26		19 55	20 25		20 55	21 25		21 55	22 25		22 55	23 25	23 58	00s25
Oxted 3		a	19 02		19 10	19 31	19 36	20 00	20 30	20 37	21 00	21 30	21 37	22 00	22 30	22 37	23 00	23 30	00 03	00 30
		d	19 03	19 07	19 11	19 32	19 37	20 00	20 30	20 37	21 00	21 30	21 37	22 00	22 30	22 37	23 00	23 30	00 03	
Hurst Green		d	19 05	19 09	19 13	19 34	19 39	20 03	20 33	20 40	21 03	21 33	21 40	22 03	22 33	22 40	23 03	23 33	00 06	
Lingfield		d	19 11		19 19	19 40		20 09	20 39		21 09	21 39		22 09	22 39		23 09	23 39	00 12	
Dormans		d	19 15		19 23	19 44		20 12	20 42		21 12	21 42		22 12	22 42		23 12	23 42	00 15	
East Grinstead		a	19 21		19 29	19 50		20 17	20 47		21 17	21 47		22 17	22 47		23 17	23 47	00 20	
Edenbridge Town		d		19 15			19 45			20 46			21 46			22 46				
Hever		d		19 19			19 49			20 49			21 49							
Cowden		d		19 23			19 53			20 53			21 53							
Ashurst		d		19 27			19 57			20 58			21 58							
Eridge		d		19 33			20 03			21 03			22 03			22 58				
Crowborough		d		19 39			20 09			21 09			22 09			23 04				
Buxted		d		19 46			20 15			21 15			22 15			23 10				
Uckfield		a		19 52			20 21			21 21			22 21			23 16				

For general notes see front of timetable
For details of catering facilities see Directory of Train Operators

b Arr. 0608
c Arr. 0702
e Arr. 0732
f Arr. 0804

Table 184

Saturdays

London → Oxted, East Grinstead and Uckfield

Network Diagram - see first page of Table 184

Station			SN 1	SN 1	SN 1	SN 1	SN 1	SN 1	SN 1	SN 1	SN 1	SN 1		SN 1	SN 1
London Victoria 15	⊖ 175, 177	d	23p24	23p49	05 25		06 23			07 23	07 53			19 23	19 53
Clapham Junction 10	175, 177	d	23p30	23p56	05 31		06 29			07 29	07 59			19 29	19 59
London Bridge 4	⊖ 175, 177	d				06 08		06 50	07 08			08 08			
Norwood Junction 2	175, 177	d			05 48										
East Croydon	175, 177	d	23p43	00 10	05 52	06 23	06 40	07 10	07 23	07 40	08 10	08 23		19 40	20 10
South Croydon 4	175	d			05 54								and at		
Sanderstead		d	23p47	00s14			06 44	07 14		07 44	08 14			19 44	20 14
Riddlesdown		d	23p50	00s17			06 47	07 17		07 47	08 17		the same	19 47	20 17
Upper Warlingham		d	23p54	00s21			06 51	07 21		07 51	08 21			19 51	20 21
Woldingham		d	23p58	00s25			06 55	07 25		07 55	08 25		minutes	19 55	20 25
Oxted 3		a	00 03	00 30	06 06	06 36	07 00	07 30	07 36	08 00	08 30	08 36		20 00	20 30
		d	00 03		06 06	06 37	07 00	07 30	07 37	08 00	08 30	08 37	past	20 00	20 30
Hurst Green		d	00 06		06 09	06 39	07 03	07 33	07 39	08 03	08 33	08 39	each	20 03	20 33
Lingfield		d	00 12		06 15		07 09	07 39		08 09	08 39			20 09	20 39
Dormans		d	00 15		06 18		07 12	07 42		08 12	08 42		hour until	20 12	20 42
East Grinstead		a	00 20		06 23		07 17	07 47		08 17	08 47			20 17	20 47
Edenbridge Town		d				06 45			07 45			08 45			
Hever		d				06 49			07 49			08 49			
Cowden		d				06 53			07 53			08 53			
Ashurst		d				06 57			07 57			08 57			
Eridge		d				07 03			08 03			09 03			
Crowborough		d				07 09			08 09			09 09			
Buxted		d				07 15			08 15			09 15			
Uckfield		a				07 21			08 21			09 21			

Station			SN 1	SN 1	SN 1	SN 1	SN 1	SN 1	SN 1	SN 1	SN 1	SN 1	SN 1
London Victoria 15	⊖ 175, 177	d		20 23	20 53		21 23	21 53		22 23	22 53	23 24	23 49
Clapham Junction 10	175, 177	d		20 29	20 59		21 29	21 59		22 29	22 59	23 30	23 56
London Bridge 4	⊖ 175, 177	d	20 08			21 08			22 08				
Norwood Junction 2	175, 177	d	20 19			21 19			22 19				
East Croydon	175, 177	d	20 23	20 40	21 10	21 23	21 40	22 10	22 23	22 40	23 10	23 43	00 10
South Croydon 4	175	d											
Sanderstead		d		20 44	21 14		21 44	22 14		22 44	23 14	23 47	00s14
Riddlesdown		d		20 47	21 17		21 47	22 17		22 47	23 17	23 50	00s17
Upper Warlingham		d		20 51	21 21		21 51	22 21		22 51	23 21	23 54	00s21
Woldingham		d		20 55	21 25		21 55	22 25		22 55	23 25	23 58	00s25
Oxted 3		a	20 36	21 00	21 30	21 36	22 00	22 30	22 36	23 00	23 30	00 03	00 30
		d	20 37	21 00	21 30	21 37	22 00	22 30	22 37	23 00	23 30	00 03	
Hurst Green		d	20 39	21 03	21 33	21 39	22 03	22 33	22 39	23 03	23 33	00 06	
Lingfield		d		21 09	21 39		22 09	22 39		23 09	23 39	00 12	
Dormans		d		21 12	21 42		22 12	22 42		23 12	23 42	00 15	
East Grinstead		a		21 17	21 47		22 17	22 47		23 17	23 47	00 20	
Edenbridge Town		d	20 45			21 45			22 45				
Hever		d	20 49			21 49							
Cowden		d	20 53			21 53							
Ashurst		d	20 57			21 57							
Eridge		d	21 03			22 03			22 57				
Crowborough		d	21 09			22 09			23 03				
Buxted		d	21 15			22 15			23 09				
Uckfield		a	21 21			22 21			23 15				

Sundays

Station			SN 1	SN 1	SN 1	SN 1	SN 1	SN 1	SN 1	SN 1	SN 1		SN 1	SN 1	SN 1
London Victoria 15	⊖ 175, 177	d	23p24	23p49	07 22	08 22		09 22		10 22			21 22		22 22
Clapham Junction 10	175, 177	d	23p30	23p56	07 28	08 28		09 28		10 28			21 28		22 28
London Bridge 4	⊖ 175, 177	d													
Norwood Junction 2	175, 177	d													
East Croydon	175, 177	d	23p43	00 10	07 43	08 43	09 05	09 43	10 05	10 43			21 43		22 44
South Croydon 4	175	d										and at			
Sanderstead		d	23p47	00s14	07 47	08 47		09 47		10 47			21 47		22 48
Riddlesdown		d	23p50	00s17	07 50	08 50		09 50		10 50		the same	21 50		22 51
Upper Warlingham		d	23p54	00s21	07 54	08 54		09 54		10 54			21 54		22 55
Woldingham		d	23p58	00s25	07 58	08 58		09 58		10 58		minutes	21 58		22 59
Oxted 3		a	00 03	00 30	08 03	09 03	09 17	10 03	10 17	11 03			22 03		23 04
		d	00 03		08 03	09 03	09 18	10 03	10 18	11 03	11 18	past	22 03	22 18	23 04
Hurst Green		d	00 06		08 06	09 06	09 21	10 06	10 21	11 06	11 21	each	22 06	22 21	23 07
Lingfield		d	00 12		08 12	09 12		10 12		11 12			22 12		23 13
Dormans		d	00 15		08 15	09 15		10 15		11 15		hour until	22 15		23 16
East Grinstead		a	00 20		08 20	09 20		10 20		11 20			22 20		23 21
Edenbridge Town		d					09 27		10 27		11 27			22 27	
Hever		d					09 31		10 31		11 31			22 31	
Cowden		d					09 35		10 35		11 35			22 35	
Ashurst		d					09 39		10 39		11 39			22 39	
Eridge		d					09 45		10 45		11 45			22 45	
Crowborough		d					09 51		10 51		11 51			22 51	
Buxted		d					09 57		10 57		11 57			22 57	
Uckfield		a					10 03		11 03		12 03			23 03	

For general notes see front of timetable
For details of catering facilities see
Directory of Train Operators

Uckfield, East Grinstead and Oxted → London

Network Diagram - see first page of Table 184

Miles	Miles			SN 1	SN 1	SN	SN 1	SN 1	SN 1		SN 1	SN 1	SN 1	SN 1	SN 1	SN 1		SN 1	SN 1	SN 1	SN 1	SN 1	SN 1		SN 1
—	0	**Uckfield**	d					06 00				06 30		07 00					07 30			08 02			08 34
—	2½	Buxted	d					06 05				06 35		07 05					07 35			08 07			08 39
—	7¼	Crowborough	d					06 12				06 42		07 12					07 42			08 14			08 46
—	10½	Eridge	d					06 17				06 47		07 17					07 47			08 19			08 51
—	14¼	Ashurst	d					06 22				06 52							07 52			08 24			08 56
—	17	Cowden	d					06 27				06 57							07 57			08 29			09 01
—	19	Hever	d					06 31				07 01							08 01			08 33			09 05
—	20¾	Edenbridge Town	d					06 34				07 04		07 29					08 04			08 36			09 08
0	—	**East Grinstead**	d		06 05		06 20		06 37		06 44		07 04		07 26	07 39		07 47		08 02	08 17		08 37		
2¼	—	Dormans	d		06 09		06 24		06 41		06 48		07 08		07 30	07 43		07 51		08 06	08 21		08 41		
4	—	Lingfield	d		06 12		06 27		06 44		06 51		07 11		07 33	07 46		07 54		08 09	08 24		08 44		
8¾	—	Hurst Green	d	06 00	06 19		06 34	06 41	06 51		06 58	07 11	07 18	07 35	07 40	07 55		08 01	08 11	08 16	08 31	08 43	08 51		09 15
9¾	25	**Oxted 3**	a	06 02	06 21		06 36	06 44	06 53		07 00	07 13	07 20	07 38	07 42	07 57		08 03	08 13	08 18	08 33	08 45	08 53		09 18
—	—		d	06 03	06 22		06 36		06 54		07 00	07 14	07 20	07 39	07 42	07 58		08 03	08 15	08 18	08 33	08 46	08 53		09 19
13	—	Woldingham	d	06 08			06 42				07 06		07 26		07 48			08 09		08 24	08 39		08 59		
14¾	—	Upper Warlingham	d	06 12			06 45				07 09		07 29		07 51			08 12		08 27	08 42		09 02		
16½	—	Riddlesdown	d	06 15			06 49				07 13		07 33		07 55			08 16		08 31	08 46		09 06		
17¾	—	Sanderstead	d	06 18		06 38	06 52		07 03		07 16		07 36		07 58	08 08		08 19		08 34	08 49		09 09		
18¾	—	South Croydon 4 175	d			06 41									08 01			08 22		08 37	08 52				
19¾	0	**East Croydon** 175, 177	a	06 23	06 34	06 44	06 56		07 08		07 20	07 25	07 40	07 53	08 03	08 15		08 24	08 29	08 40	08 55	08 59	09 13		09 32
—	1½	Norwood Junction 2 175, 177	a																						
—	10¼	**London Bridge 4** ⊖ 175, 177	a	06 40					07 25		07 39	07 43		08 11	08 20	08 35			08 51	08 59		09 20			09 52
27½	—	Clapham Junction 10 175, 177	a		06 46	07 05	07 07						07 51					08 37			09 07		09 26		
30¼	—	**London Victoria 15** ⊖ 175, 177	a		06 54	07 16	07 17						08 00					08 46			09 16		09 37		

		SN 1	SN 1	SN 1	SN 1		SN 1	SN 1	SN 1			SN 1	SN 1	SN 1	SN 1	SN 1	SN 1		SN 1	SN 1	SN 1	SN 1	SN 1	SN 1
Uckfield	d			09 34				10 34					15 34			16 34				17 04		17 34		
Buxted	d			09 39				10 39					15 39			16 39				17 09		17 39		
Crowborough	d			09 46				10 46					15 46			16 46				17 16		17 46		
Eridge	d			09 51				10 51					15 51			16 51				17 21		17 51		
Ashurst	d			09 56				10 56					15 56			16 56				17 26		17 56		
Cowden	d			10 01				11 01					16 01			17 01				17 31		18 01		
Hever	d			10 05				11 05		and at			16 05			17 05				17 35		18 05		
Edenbridge Town	d			10 08				11 08		the same			16 08			17 08				17 38		18 08		
East Grinstead	d	09 07	09 37		10 07		10 37		11 07			15 37		16 07	16 37		17 07		17 24		17 55		18 12	18 22
Dormans	d	09 11	09 41		10 11		10 41		11 11	minutes		15 41		16 11	16 41		17 11		17 28		17 59		18 16	18 26
Lingfield	d	09 14	09 44		10 14		10 44		11 14			15 44		16 14	16 44		17 14		17 31		18 02		18 19	18 29
Hurst Green	d	09 21	09 51	10 15	10 21		10 51	11 15	11 21	past		15 51	16 15	16 21	16 51	17 15	17 21		17 38	17 45	18 09	18 15	18 26	18 36
Oxted 3	a	09 23	09 53	10 17	10 23		10 53	11 17	11 23			15 53	16 17	16 23	16 53	17 17	17 23		17 40	17 48	18 11	18 17	18 28	18 38
	d	09 23	09 53	10 18	10 23		10 53	11 18	11 23	each		15 53	16 18	16 23	16 53	17 18	17 23		17 40		18 11	18 18	18 28	18 39
Woldingham	d	09 29	09 59		10 29		10 59		11 29	hour until		15 59		16 29	16 59		17 29				18 17		18 34	
Upper Warlingham	d	09 32	10 02		10 32		11 02		11 32			16 02		16 32	17 02		17 32				18 20		18 37	18 46
Riddlesdown	d	09 36	10 06		10 36		11 06		11 36			16 06		16 36	17 06		17 36				18 24		18 41	
Sanderstead	d	09 39	10 09		10 39		11 09		11 39			16 09		16 39	17 09		17 39				18 27		18 44	18 52
South Croydon 4 175	d																							
East Croydon 175, 177	a	09 43	10 13	10 32	10 43		11 13	11 32	11 43			16 13	16 38	16 43	17 13	17 32	17 44		17 52		18 32	18 38	18 50	18 59
Norwood Junction 2 175, 177	a													16 48	17 18		17 48		17 57					
London Bridge 4 ⊖ 175, 177	a			10 49				11 49					16 58	17 00	17 31	18 02	18 06		18 10		18 48	18 53		19 14
Clapham Junction 10 175, 177	a	09 55	10 25		10 55		11 25		11 55			16 25											19 07	
London Victoria 15 ⊖ 175, 177	a	10 05	10 35		11 05		11 35		12 05			16 32											19 14	

		SN 1	SN 1		SN 1	SN 1	SN 1	SN 1	SN 1	SN 1		SN 1	SN 1	SN 1	SN 1	SN 1	SN 1		SN 1	SN 1	SN 1	SN 1	SN 1		
Uckfield	d	18 00			18 25			19 04				19 34		20 04		20 34				21 34			22 32		
Buxted	d	18 05			18 30			19 09				19 39		20 09		20 39				21 39			22 37		
Crowborough	d	18b16			18 38			19 16				19 46		20 16		20 46				21 46			22 44		
Eridge	d	18 21			18 43			19 21				19 51		20 21		20 51				21 51			22 49		
Ashurst	d	18 26						19 26				19 56				20 56				21 56					
Cowden	d	18 31						19 31				20 01				21 01				22 01					
Hever	d	18 35			18 54			19 35				20 05				21 05				22 05					
Edenbridge Town	d	18 38			18 57			19 38				20 08		20 33		21 08				22 08			23 01		
East Grinstead	d		18 37			19 07	19 20		19 37	19 45			20 07		20 37		21 07		21 37		22 07	22 37			
Dormans	d		18 41			19 11	19 24		19 41	19 49			20 11		20 41		21 11		21 41		22 11	22 41			
Lingfield	d		18 44			19 14	19 27		19 44	19 52			20 14		20 44		21 14		21 44		22 14	22 44			
Hurst Green	d	18 45	18 51		19 04	19 21	19 34	19 45	19 51	19 59		20 15	20 21	20 39	20 51	21 15	21 21		21 51	22 15	22 21	22 51	23 08		
Oxted 3	a	18 48	18 53		19 06	19 23	19 36	19 48	19 53	20 01		20 18	20 23	20 42	20 53	21 18	21 23		21 53	22 17	22 23	22 53	23 10		
	d		18 53		19 07	19 23	19 37	19 49	19 53	20 02		20 19	20 23	20 42	20 53	21 19	21 23		21 53	22 18	22 23	22 53	23 11		
Woldingham	d		18 59			19 29	19 42		19 59	20 07			20 29		20 59		21 29		21 59		22 29	22 59			
Upper Warlingham	d		19 02			19 32	19 46		20 02	20 11			20 32		21 02		21 32		22 02		22 32	23 02			
Riddlesdown	d		19 06			19 36	19 49		20 06	20 14			20 36		21 06		21 36		22 06		22 36	23 06			
Sanderstead	d		19 09			19 39	19 52		20 09	20 17			20 39		21 09		21 39		22 09		22 39	23 09			
South Croydon 4 175	d																								
East Croydon 175, 177	a		19 13		19 19	19 43	19 57	20 06	20 13	20 22		20 36	20 43	20 54	21 13	21 36	21 43		22 13	22 33	22 43	23 13	23 28		
Norwood Junction 2 175, 177	a																								
London Bridge 4 ⊖ 175, 177	a				19 35			20 21				20 51		21 11		21 50				22 50					
Clapham Junction 10 175, 177	a		19 25			19 55			20 25				20 55		21 25		21 55		22 25		22 55	23 25			
London Victoria 15 ⊖ 175, 177	a		19 33			20 02			20 32				21 05		21 32		22 05		22 35		23 05	23 35			

For general notes see front of timetable
For details of catering facilities see
Directory of Train Operators

b Arr. 1812

Table 184

Uckfield, East Grinstead and Oxted → London

Saturdays

Network Diagram - see first page of Table 184

Station		SN 1		SN 1			SN 1	SN 1	SN 1			SN 1		SN 1		SN 1
Uckfield	d			06 34					07 34							22 32
Buxted	d			06 39					07 39							22 37
Crowborough	d			06 46					07 46							22 44
Eridge	d			06 51					07 51							22 49
Ashurst	d			06 56					07 56							
Cowden	d			07 01					08 01							
Hever	d			07 05					08 05	and at						
Edenbridge Town	d			07 08					08 08							23 01
East Grinstead	d	06 37					07 07	07 37		the same		22 07		22 37		
Dormans	d	06 41					07 11	07 41		minutes		22 11		22 41		
Lingfield	d	06 44					07 14	07 44				22 14		22 44		
Hurst Green	d	06 51		07 15			07 21	07 51	08 15	past		22 21		22 51		23 08
Oxted 3	a	06 53		07 18			07 23	07 53	08 18			22 23		22 53		23 10
	d	06 53		07 19			07 23	07 53	08 19	each		22 23		22 53		23 11
Woldingham	d	06 59					07 29	07 59		hour until		22 29		22 59		
Upper Warlingham	d	07 02					07 32	08 02				22 32		23 02		
Riddlesdown	d	07 06					07 36	08 06				22 36		23 06		
Sanderstead	d	07 09					07 39	08 09				22 39		23 09		
South Croydon 4	175 d															
East Croydon	175, 177 a	07 13		07 33			07 43	08 13	08 32			22 43		23 13		23 26
Norwood Junction 2	175, 177 a															
London Bridge 4	⊖ 175, 177 a			07 52					08 49							
Clapham Junction 10	175, 177 a	07 25					07 55	08 25				22 55		23 25		
London Victoria 15	⊖ 175, 177 a	07 32					08 02	08 32				23 02		23 32		

Sundays

Station		SN 1		SN 1		SN 1			SN 1	SN 1			SN 1		SN 1		SN 1		SN 1
Uckfield	d								10 17				21 17				22 17		
Buxted	d								10 22				21 22				22 22		
Crowborough	d								10 29				21 29				22 29		
Eridge	d								10 34				21 34				22 34		
Ashurst	d								10 39				21 39				22 39		
Cowden	d								10 44				21 44				22 44		
Hever	d								10 48		and at		21 48				22 48		
Edenbridge Town	d								10 51				21 51				22 51		
East Grinstead	d	07 52		08 52		09 52				10 52	the same				21 52				22 52
Dormans	d	07 56		08 56		09 56				10 56	minutes				21 56				22 56
Lingfield	d	07 59		08 59		09 59				10 59					21 59				22 59
Hurst Green	d	08 06		09 06		10 06			10 58	11 06	past		21 58		22 06		22 58		23 06
Oxted 3	a	08 08		09 08		10 08			11 01	11 08			22 01		22 08		23 01		23 08
	d	08 08		09 08		10 08				11 08	each				22 08		23 02		23 08
Woldingham	d	08 14		09 14		10 14				11 14	hour until				22 14				23 14
Upper Warlingham	d	08 17		09 17		10 17				11 17					22 17				23 17
Riddlesdown	d	08 21		09 21		10 21				11 21					22 21				23 21
Sanderstead	d	08 24		09 24		10 24				11 24					22 24				23 24
South Croydon 4	175 d																		
East Croydon	175, 177 a	08 28		09 28		10 28				11 28					22 28		23 14		23 28
Norwood Junction 2	175, 177 a																		
London Bridge 4	⊖ 175, 177 a																		
Clapham Junction 10	175, 177 a	08 41		09 41		10 41				11 41					22 41				23 41
London Victoria 15	⊖ 175, 177 a	08 48		09 48		10 48				11 48					22 50				23 51

For general notes see front of timetable
For details of catering facilities see Directory of Train Operators

Network Diagram for Tables 186, 188

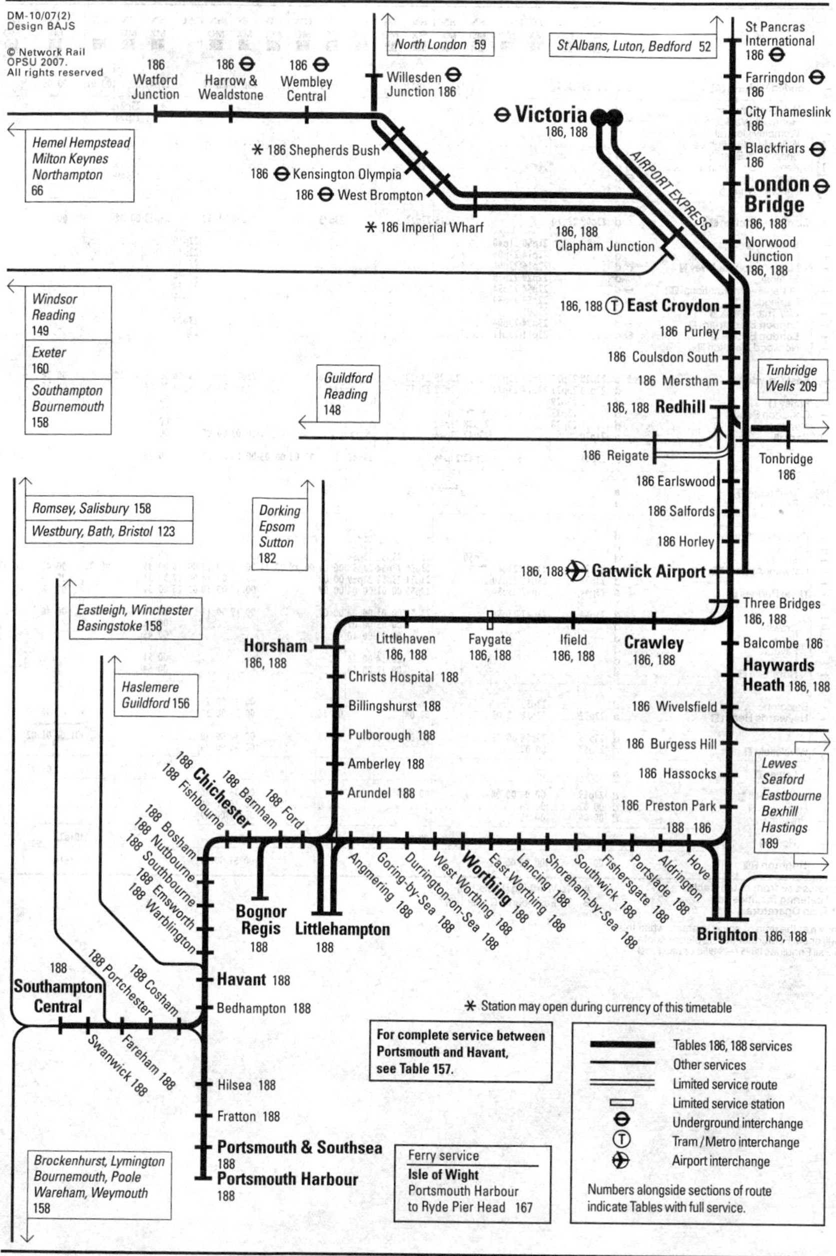

DM-10/07(2)
Design BAJS
© Network Rail OPSU 2007. All rights reserved
186 Watford Junction
186 Harrow & Wealdstone
186 Wembley Central
North London 59
Willesden Junction 186
St Albans, Luton, Bedford 52
St Pancras International 186
Farringdon 186
City Thameslink 186
Blackfriars 186
London Bridge 186, 188
Victoria 186, 188
Hemel Hempstead
Milton Keynes
Northampton
66
* 186 Shepherds Bush
186 Kensington Olympia
186 West Brompton
* 186 Imperial Wharf
AIRPORT EXPRESS
186, 188 Clapham Junction
Norwood Junction 186, 188
Windsor
Reading
149
Exeter
160
Southampton
Bournemouth
158
186, 188 East Croydon
186 Purley
186 Coulsdon South
186 Merstham
186, 188 Redhill
Tunbridge Wells 209
Guildford
Reading
148
186 Reigate
Tonbridge 186
186 Earlswood
186 Salfords
186 Horley
186, 188 Gatwick Airport
Romsey, Salisbury 158
Westbury, Bath, Bristol 123
Dorking
Epsom
Sutton
182
Eastleigh, Winchester
Basingstoke 158
Three Bridges 186, 188
Horsham 186, 188
Littlehaven 186, 188
Faygate 186, 188
Ifield 186, 188
Crawley 186, 188
Balcombe 186
Haywards Heath 186, 188
Haslemere
Guildford 156
Christs Hospital 188
Billingshurst 188
Pulborough 188
Amberley 188
Arundel 188
186 Wivelsfield
186 Burgess Hill
186 Hassocks
186 Preston Park
188 186
Lewes
Seaford
Eastbourne
Bexhill
Hastings
189
188 Chichester
188 Fishbourne
188 Barnham
188 Ford
188 Bosham
188 Nutbourne
188 Southbourne
188 Emsworth
188 Warblington
Angmering 188
Goring-by-Sea 188
Durrington-on-Sea 188
West Worthing 188
Worthing 188
East Worthing 188
Lancing 188
Shoreham-by-Sea 188
Southwick 188
Fishersgate 188
Portslade 188
Aldrington 188
Hove
Bognor Regis 188
Littlehampton 188
Brighton 186, 188
188 Southampton Central
188 Portchester
188 Cosham
Havant 188
Bedhampton 188
Swanwick 188
Fareham 188
* Station may open during currency of this timetable
For complete service between Portsmouth and Havant, see Table 157.
Tables 186, 188 services
Other services
Limited service route
Limited service station
Underground interchange
Tram / Metro interchange
Airport interchange
Numbers alongside sections of route indicate Tables with full service.
Hilsea 188
Fratton 188
Portsmouth & Southsea 188
Portsmouth Harbour 188
Ferry service
Isle of Wight
Portsmouth Harbour to Ryde Pier Head 167
Brockenhurst, Lymington
Bournemouth, Poole
Wareham, Weymouth
158

Watford Junction, Bedford and London → Brighton

Network Diagram - see first page of Table 186

Miles	Miles	Miles			SN MX 1	SN MO 1	FC MX 1	FC MO 1	SN MO 1	SN MX 1	SN MX 1 A	SN MO 1	SN MX 1	SN MO 1	GW MO 1	GW MX 1	SN MX 1	SN MO 1	FC	SN MX 1	SN MO 1	GX 1	SN MX 1 B	GW MO 1
0	—	—	**London Victoria 15** ⊖	d	23p02	23p04				23p10	23p17			23p17			23p32	23p32		23p47		00 01	00 05	
—	0	—	Watford Junction	d																	23p22			
—	6	—	Harrow & Wealdstone ⊖	d																	23p28			
—	9½	—	Wembley Central	d																				
—	—	0	Willesden Jn. High Level	d																				
—	—	1½	Shepherds Bush § ⊖	d																				
—	15	2¾	Kensington Olympia ⊖	d																	23p48			
—	16	3¾	West Brompton ⊖	d																	23p50			
—	—	4¼	Imperial Wharf §	d																				
2¾	18½	6¼	Clapham Junction 10	d	23p08	23p10				23p16	23p23			23p23			23p38	23p38		23p53	00 02		00 11	
—	—	—	**Bedford 7**	d			21p50	21p40											22p10					
—	—	—	Luton 10	d			22p14	22p04											22p34					
—	—	—	Luton Airport Parkway 7 ✈	d			22p16	22p06											22p36					
—	—	—	St Albans	d			22p29	22p18											22p48					
—	—	—	St Pancras International 15 ⊖	d			22p54	22p54											23p24					
—	—	—	Farringdon 3 ⊖	d			22p59	22p59											23p29					
—	—	—	City Thameslink 3	d			23p01																	
—	—	—	**London Blackfriars 3** ⊖	d			23p04	23p04											23p34					
—	0	—	**London Bridge 4** ⊖	d			23p11	23p11											23p41					
—	9	—	Norwood Junction 2	d																				
10½	10¼	—	**East Croydon**	a	23p18	23p23	23p24	23p26		23p28	23p33			23p36			23p51	23p52	23p56	00 05	00 20		00 24	
—	—	—		d	23p18	23p23	23p24	23p27		23p28	23p33			23p37			23p52	23p53	23p57	00 06			00 25	
13½	—	—	Purley 4	d		23p29				23p33										00 12				
15½	—	—	Coulsdon South	d		23p33			←	23p37										00 15				
19	—	—	Merstham	d		23p38			23p38	23p42										00 21				
21	0	0	**Redhill**	a	23p30	→			23p42	23p46			←				00 03	00 05		00 24				
—	—	—		d	23p31				23p42	23p46			23p46		00 03	00 03	00 05	00 05		00 25				00 34
—	—	19¾	Tonbridge 4	a						→														
—	1¾	—	Reigate	a																				
21¾	—	—	Earlswood (Surrey)	d									23p49											
23¾	—	—	Salfords	d								←	23p52											
26	—	—	Horley 4	d					23p50			23p50	23p56							00 31				
26¾	—	—	**Gatwick Airport 10** ✈	a	23p38		23p41	23p48	→		23p50	23p54	23p58	00 01	00 10	00 11	00 13	00 13	00 16	00 33		00 35	00 42	00 43
—	—	—		d	23p39		23p41	23p50			23p51	23p55	23p59	00 02			00 14	00 14	00 17	00 34			00 43	
29½	0	—	Three Bridges 4	a	23p44		23p47	23p54			23p55	00 01	00 04	00 07			00 18	00 18	00 26	00 39			00 48	
—	—	—		d	23p44		23p47	23p54			23p56	00 01	00 04	00 07			00 19	00 19		00 39			00 48	
—	1½	—	Crawley	d								00 05	00 07							00 42				
—	2¾	—	Ifield	d								00 07	00 10							00 45				
—	5¼	—	Faygate	d																				
—	7½	—	Littlehaven	d								00 14	00 16							00 51				
—	8½	—	**Horsham 4**	a								00 17	00 19							00 54				
34	—	—	Balcombe	d			23p53										00 25	00 25						
38	—	—	**Haywards Heath 3**	a	23p52		23p58	00 03			00 04			00 16			00 30	00 30					00 56	
—	—	—		d	23p53		23p58	00 03			00 05			00 16			00 30	00 30					01 00 01 02	
41	0	—	Wivelsfield 4	d	23p57		00 02										00 34	00 34						
—	9¼	—	Lewes 4	a																			01 16	
41¾	—	—	Burgess Hill 4	d	23p59		00 04	00 08			00 10						00 36	00 36						
43¾	—	—	Hassocks 4	d	00 02		00 08										00 40	00 40						
49½	0	—	Preston Park	d	00 09		00 15										00 47	00 47						
—	1½	—	Hove 2	a							00 21			00 30									01s22	
51	—	—	**Brighton 10**	a	00 15		00 22	00 24									00 51	00 51					01s14	

For general notes see front of timetable
For details of catering facilities see Directory of Train Operators

§ It is unknown at the time of going to press, when this station will open. For further details please contact National Rail Enquiries 08457-484950 or see local publicity.

A To Worthing (Table 188)
B To Eastbourne (Table 189)

Watford Junction, Bedford and London → Brighton

Network Diagram - see first page of Table 186

		FC	FC	SN	GW	FC	XC	GX	SN	FC	FC	SN	FC	SN	FC	GX	FC	SN	FC	GX	FC	GX	SE	SN	GX
		MO	MX		MX	MX	MO			MO	MX														
				1	1		1 ◇	1	1	1	1	1	1	1		1	1	1	1	1	1	1	88	1	1
							A										B				B				
London Victoria 15	⊖ d			00 14				00 30	01 00			02 00		03 02		03 30		04 00		04 30		05 00		05 02	05 15
Watford Junction	d																								
Harrow & Wealdstone	⊖ d																								
Wembley Central	d																								
Willesden Jn. High Level	d																								
Shepherds Bush §	⊖ d																								
Kensington Olympia	⊖ d																								
West Brompton	⊖ d																								
Imperial Wharf §	d																								
Clapham Junction 10	d			00 20					01 08			02 08		03 08				04 08						05 08	
Bedford 7	d	22p40	22p40			23p10				23p40	23p40		00 40		01 40				02 40						
Luton 10	d	23p04	23p04			23p34				00 04	00 04		01 04		02 04				03 04						
Luton Airport Parkway 7	✈ d	23p06	23p06			23p36				00 06	00 06		01 06		02 06				03 06						
St Albans	d	23p18	23p18			23p48				00 18	00 18		01 18		02 18				03 18						
St Pancras International 15	⊖ d	23p54	23p54			00 24				00 54	00 54		01 54		02 54		03 25		03 54		04 25				
Farringdon 3	⊖ d	23p59	23p59			00 29																			
City Thameslink 3	d																								
London Blackfriars 3	⊖ d	00 04	00 04			00 34				01 04	01 04		02 04		03 04		03 34		04 04		04 34				
London Bridge 4	⊖ d	00 11	00 11			00 41																			
Norwood Junction 2	d																								
East Croydon	a	00 26	00 26	00 32		00 56			01 21	01 30	01 32	02 21	02 30	03 21	03 30		04 00	04 21	04 30		05 00			05 21	
	d	00 27	00 27	00 33		00 57			01 22	01 32	01 32	02 22	02 32	03 22	03 32		04 02	04 22	04 32		05 02			05 22	
Purley 4	d			00 38					01 27			02 27		03 27				04 27						05 26	
Coulsdon South	d			00 41																				05 30	
Merstham	d			00 47																				05 35	
Redhill	a			00 50																				05 39	
	d			00 51	00 53		00 59																05 35	05 40	
Tonbridge 4	a																								
Reigate	a																								
Earlswood (Surrey)	d																								
Salfords	d																								
Horley 4	d								01 43			02 42		03 42				04 43						05 46	
Gatwick Airport 10	✈ a	00 46	00 49	00 58	01 01	01 16	01 17	01 24	01 45	01 51	01 51	02 44	02 51	03 44	03 51	04 05	04 24	04 45	04 51	05 05	05 21	05 35	05 42	05 48	05 50
	d	00 47	00 50			01 17			01 47	01 52	01 52	02 46	02 52	03 46	03 52		04 24	04 47	04 52		05 22			05 49	
Three Bridges 4	a	00 56	00 56			01 26			01 51	01 58	02 00	02 50	03 00	03 50	04 00		04 32	04 51	04 58		05 26			05 54	
	d								01 52									04 52	04 58		05 26			05 54	
Crawley	d																								
Ifield	d																								
Faygate	d																								
Littlehaven	d																								
Horsham 4	a																								
Balcombe	d																							06 00	
Haywards Heath 3	a								02 02									05 00	05 08		05 36			06 05	
	d								02 03									05 01	05 08		05 36			06 06	
Wivelsfield 4	d																				05 40			06 10	
Lewes 4	a																								
Burgess Hill 4	d																				05 42			06 12	
Hassocks 4	d																				05 46			06 15	
Preston Park	d																				05 53			06 22	
Hove 2	a																								
Brighton 10	a								02 30									05 16	05 29		06 01			06 28	

For general notes see front of timetable
For details of catering facilities see Directory of Train Operators

§ It is unknown at the time of going to press, when this station will open. For further details please contact National Rail Enquiries 08457-484950 or see local publicity.

A From 31 March. From Didcot Parkway (Table 116)

B From Kings Cross Thameslink

Watford Junction, Bedford and London → Brighton

Network Diagram - see first page of Table 186

	FC	GW	GW	SN	GX	SN	SN	FC	GX	SN	FC	GX	GW	GW	SN	GX	FC	SN	SN	SN	GW	GX	SN	SN
	1	1	1	1	1	1	1	1	1	1	1	1	1	1	1	1	1	1	1	1	1	1	1	1
				A		B				B					C			C						
London Victoria 15 ⊖ d					05 30	05 32			05 45			06 00			06 02	06 15						06 30		06 21
Watford Junction d																								
Harrow & Wealdstone ⊖ d																								
Wembley Central d																								
Willesden Jn. High Level d																								
Shepherds Bush § ⊖ d																								
Kensington Olympia ⊖ d																								
West Brompton ⊖ d																								
Imperial Wharf § d																								
Clapham Junction 10 d						05 38									06 08									06 27
Bedford 7 d	03 40							04 10			04 20						04 50							
Luton 10 d	04 04							04 34			04 44						05 14							
Luton Airport Parkway 7 ✈ d	04 06							04 36			04 46						05 16							
St Albans d	04 18							04 48			04 58						05 28							
St Pancras International 15 ⊖ d	04 54							05 14			05 34						06 04							
Farringdon 3 ⊖ d	04 59							05 19			05 39						06 09							
City Thameslink 3 d																	06 11							
London Blackfriars 3 ⊖ d	05 04							05 24			05 44						06 14							
London Bridge 4 ⊖ d								05 31			05 50						06 21							
Norwood Junction 2 d																								
East Croydon a	05 30					05 48		05 51			06 04				06 17		06 35							06 38
d	05 32					05 49		05 52			06 04				06 18		06 36							06 39
Purley 4 d						05 54									06 23									06 44
Coulsdon South d						05 57									06 27									
Merstham d						06 03									06 33									
Redhill a						06 06				←					06 36			←						06 52
d		05 44	05 44			06 07				06 07			06 14	06 24	06 40			06 40		06 42	06 46			06 53
						→									→									
Tonbridge 4 a																								
Reigate a			05 48										06 18	06 28						06 46				
Earlswood (Surrey) d										06 09								06 42						
Salfords d										06 13								06 46						
Horley 4 d										06 16								06 49						06 59
Gatwick Airport 10 ✈ a	05 53	05 54			06 00			06 08	06 15	06 19	06 20	06 30				06 45	06 51	06 53			06 56	07 00		07 03
d	05 54			05 59				06 08		06 20	06 20						06 52	06 54						07 04
Three Bridges 4 a	05 59			06 03				06 14		06 24	06 26						06 56	06 59						07 09
d	06 00			06 04				06 14		06 24	06 26						06 56	06 59	07 05					07 09
Crawley d				06 07														07 03	07 08					
Ifield d				06 10															07 11					
Faygate d																			07 15					
Littlehaven d				06 16															07 19					
Horsham 4 a				06 19														07 11	07 22					
Balcombe d								06 20			06 32													07 15
Haywards Heath 3 a	06 09							06 25		06 33	06 37						07 05							07 20
d	06 10						06 13	06 25		06 34	06 38						07 06						07 12	07 21
Wivelsfield 4 d	06 14						06 17	06 29		06 38	06 42						07 10						07 16	07 25
Lewes 4 a							06 28			06 49													07 31	
Burgess Hill 4 d	06 16							06 32			06 44						07 12							07 27
Hassocks 4 d	06 19							06 35			06 47						07 15							07 30
Preston Park d	06 26							06 42			06 54						07 22							07 37
Hove 2 a																								
Brighton 10 a	06 33							06 47			07 01						07 29							07 42

For general notes see front of timetable
For details of catering facilities see Directory of Train Operators

§ It is unknown at the time of going to press, when this station will open. For further details please contact National Rail Enquiries 08457-484950 or see local publicity.

A To Southampton Central (Table 188) and to Bognor Regis (Table 188)

B To Ore (Table 189)

C To Bognor Regis (Table 188)

Table 186

Mondays to Fridays

Watford Junction, Bedford and London → Brighton

Network Diagram - see first page of Table 186

Station	LO	SN 1 A	FC 1	GX 1	SN 1	SN 1 B	LO	SN 1 A		GX 1	GW 1	FC 1	SN 1	GW 1	SN 1	LO 1	GX 1	SN 1	FC 1	GW 1	SN 1 C	GX 1	LO	SN 1
London Victoria 15 ⊖ d		06 32		06 45		06 47				07 00					07 06		07 15				07 17	07 30		
Watford Junction d					06 05																			
Harrow & Wealdstone ⊖ d					06 11																			
Wembley Central d																								
Willesden Jn. High Level d	06 08						06 38									06 53							07 08	
Shepherds Bush § ⊖ d																								
Kensington Olympia ⊖ d	06 17				06 31		06 47									07 02							07 17	
West Brompton ⊖ d	06 19				06 33		06 49									07 04							07 19	
Imperial Wharf § d																								
Clapham Junction 10 d	06a28	06 38			06a42	06 53	06a59								07 12	07a13					07 23		07a28	
Bedford 7 d			05 20									05 40							06 00					
Luton 10 d			05 44									06 04							06 24					
Luton Airport Parkway 7 ✈ d			05 46									06 06							06 26					
St Albans d			05 58									06 18							06 38					
St Pancras International 15 ⊖ d			06 24									06 39							06 57					
Farringdon 3 ⊖ d			06 29									06 44							07 02					
City Thameslink 3 d			06 31									06 47							07 07					
London Blackfriars 3 ⊖ d			06 36									06 50							07 10					
London Bridge 4 ⊖ d			06 43									07 00							07 16					07 28
Norwood Junction 2 d																								07 42
East Croydon ⇌ a		06 48	06 56			07 03						07 15			07 21				07 31		07 33			07 45
d		06 49	06 56			07 03						07 16			07 22				07 32		07 34			07 46
Purley 4 d		06 54													07 27									
Coulsdon South d		06 57													07 30									
Merstham d		07 03													07 36									
Redhill a		07 06						←							07 39						07 45			
d		07 07						07 07			07 11		07 17	07 28	07 40					07 43	07 46			
Tonbridge 4 a		↪																						
Reigate a											07 15		07 22	07 32	07 45									
Earlswood (Surrey) d								07 09													07 48			
Salfords d								07 13													07 52			
Horley 4 d								07 16													07 55			
Gatwick Airport 10 ✈ a			07 11	07 15		07 18		07 19		07 30		07 31					07 45		07 48	07 54	07 58	08 00		08 01
d			07 12			07 19		07 20				07 32							07 50		07 59			08 02
Three Bridges 4 a			07 17			07 24		07 24				07 37							07 54		08 04			08 06
d			07 18			07 24		07 28	07 30			07 38						07 52	07 54		08 05			08 07
Crawley d									07 34									07 56			08 09			
Ifield d									07 36									07 58			08 11			
Faygate d																					08 15			
Littlehaven d									07 43									08 05			08 19			
Horsham 4 a									07 46									08 08			08 22			
Balcombe d								07 35											08 00					
Haywards Heath 3 a			07 27			07 32		07 40				07 47							08 06					08 16
d			07 28			07 33		07 40				07 48							08 06					08 16
Wivelsfield 4 d			07 32			07 37		07 44											08 10					
Lewes 4 a						07 52																		
Burgess Hill 4 d			07 34					07 46				07 54							08 12					08 22
Hassocks 4 d			07 37					07 50											08 15					
Preston Park d			07 44					07 57											08 22					
Hove 2 a																								
Brighton 10 a			07 51					08 02				08 06							08 28					08 33

For general notes see front of timetable
For details of catering facilities see Directory of Train Operators

§ It is unknown at the time of going to press, when this station will open. For further details please contact National Rail Enquiries 08457-484950 or see local publicity.

A To Chichester (Table 188)
B To Ore (Table 189)
C To Southampton Central (Table 188)

Watford Junction, Bedford and London → Brighton

Network Diagram - see first page of Table 186

Station		SN	SE	GW	SN	FC	GX	SN	SN	SN	SN	SN	SN	LO	GX	SN	GW	SN	SN	FC	GX	LO	SN	SN
			43																					
		1		1	1	1	1	1	1	1	1	1	1		1	1	1	1	1	1	1	1	1	1
			A													B ⚹						C		D
London Victoria 15	⊖ d				07 36		07 45	07 47			07 52				08 00	08 02			08 06		08 15			08 17
Watford Junction	d									07 18													07 40	
Harrow & Wealdstone	⊖ d									07 25													07 46	
Wembley Central	d									07 29													07 51	
Willesden Jn. High Level	d													07 38								07 53		
Shepherds Bush §	⊖ d																						08 05	
Kensington Olympia	⊖ d									07 43				07 47								08 02	08 07	
West Brompton	⊖ d									07 45				07 49								08 04	08 10	
Imperial Wharf §	d																							
Clapham Junction 10	d				07 42			07 53		07a52	07 58			07a58		08 08			08 12			08a14	08a16	08 23
Bedford 7	d					06 20														06 56				
Luton 10	d					06 44														07 16				
Luton Airport Parkway 7	✈ d					06 46																		
St Albans	d					06 58														07 28				
St Pancras International 15	⊖ d					07 17														07 48				
Farringdon 3	⊖ d					07 22														07 52				
City Thameslink 3	d					07 27														07 55				
London Blackfriars 3	⊖ d					07 32														08 00				
London Bridge 4	⊖ d		07 34			07 40						07 54						08 03						
Norwood Junction 2	d											08 06						08 14						
East Croydon	🚋 a		07 48		07 52	07 55		08 03			08 08	08 11				08 18		08 19	08 22	08 25				08 33
	d		07 49		07 52	07 56		08 03			08 08	08 11				08 18		08 20	08 22	08 26				08 33
Purley 4	d				07 58													08 27						
Coulsdon South	d		07 56		08 01													08 31						
Merstham	d		08 01		08 07													08 36						
Redhill	a		08 05		08 10				⟵							08 31		08 40						
	d	07 59	08 05	08 09	08 11				08 11				08 15			08 32	08 33	08 41						
Tonbridge 4	a		08 35		⟶													⟶						
Reigate	a	08 03		08 13									08 19				08 37							
Earlswood (Surrey)	d								08 13															
Salfords	d								08 17															
Horley 4	d								08 21															
Gatwick Airport 10	✈ a					08 11	08 15	08 18	08 24		08 25	08 29			08 30	08 39				08 40	08 45			08 48
	d					08 12		08 19	08 25		08 26	08 30				08 40				08 42				08 49
Three Bridges 4	a					08 16			08 30							08 44			08 41	08 46				
	d					08 16			08 31							08 45			08 42	08 46				
Crawley	d								08 34							08 48								
Ifield	d								08 37															
Faygate	d								08 41															
Littlehaven	d								08 45															
Horsham 4	a								08 49							08 56								
Balcombe	d					08 22														08 52				
Haywards Heath 3	a					08 27		08 30			08 37	08 44							08 50	08 57				09 00
	d					08 28		08 32			08 38	08 45							08 51	08 58				09 13 ⟶ / 09 04
Wivelsfield 4	d					08 32		08 36											08 55	09 02				
Lewes 4	a							08 51																
Burgess Hill 4	d					08 34													08 57	09 04				09 09
Hassocks 4	d					08 37						08 51								09 07				
Preston Park	d					08 44						08 58								09 14				
Hove 2	a										08 53													09 21
Brighton 10	a					08 51						09 03							09 08	09 22				

For general notes see front of timetable
For details of catering facilities see Directory of Train Operators

§ It is unknown at the time of going to press, when this station will open. For further details please contact National Rail Enquiries 08457-484950 or see local publicity.

A To Tunbridge Wells (Table 206)
B To Portsmouth Harbour (Table 188) and to Bognor Regis (Table 188)
C From Stratford Low Level (Table 59)
D To Littlehampton (Table 188)

Table 186 **Mondays to Fridays**

Watford Junction, Bedford and London → Brighton

Network Diagram - see first page of Table 186

		FC 1	LO	SN 1	SN 1	SN 1	FC 1	SN 1	SN 1	GX 1	GW 1	SN 1	SN 1	SN 1	SN 1	SN 1	SN 1	GX 1	SN 1	SN 1	FC 1	SN 1	SN 1	LO
													A		⊼				⊼					
London Victoria 15	⊖ d					08 20			08 26	08 30			08 32		08 36		08 38	08 45	08 47					
Watford Junction	d																							
Harrow & Wealdstone	⊖ d																							
Wembley Central	d																							
Willesden Jn. High Level	d		08 08																					
Shepherds Bush §	⊖ d																							08 38
Kensington Olympia	⊖ d		08 17									08 24												08 47
West Brompton	⊖ d		08 19									08 27												08 49
Imperial Wharf §	d																							
Clapham Junction 10	d		08a28			08 28			08 32			08a33	08 38		08 43		08 46		08 53					08a58
Bedford 7	d	07 00																						
Luton 10	d	07 24																			07 28			
Luton Airport Parkway 7	✈ d	07 26																			07 48			
St Albans	d	07 38																						
St Pancras International 15	⊖ d	08 00																			08 00			
Farringdon 3	⊖ d	08 04																			08 20			
City Thameslink 3	d	08 09																			08 24			
London Blackfriars 3	⊖ d	08 12																			08 27			
London Bridge 4	⊖ d	08 19		08 23										08 30						08 49	08 32	09 00		
Norwood Junction 2	d													08 45						09 02		09 11		
East Croydon	⛴ a	08 36		08 37		08 39							08 48	08 49	08 52		08 56		09 03	09 05	09 06	09 15		
	d	08 36		08 38		08 39							08 48	08 51	08 53		08 57		09 03	09 06	09 06	09 21 →		
Purley 4	d													08 58						09 12				
Coulsdon South	d													09 02						09 15 ↳				
Merstham	d													09 07										
Redhill	a	08 47		08 52	←		←						08 59	09 11									←	
	d	08 49		08 53	08 41		08 49				08 55		09 03	09 12									09 12	
Tonbridge 4	a	↪												↪										
Reigate	a			08 57																				
Earlswood (Surrey)	d				08 43																		09 14	
Salfords	d				08 47																		09 18	
Horley 4	d				08 50																		09 21	
Gatwick Airport 10	✈ a				08 53	08 54	08 56		08 57	09 00	09 02		09 10				09 12	09 15	09 18		09 22		09 24	
	d				08 54	08 55	08 56		09 00				09 11				09 14		09 19		09 23		09 25	
Three Bridges 4	a				08 58		09 00		09 04				09 15				09 18				09 28		09 29	
	d				08 58		09 00		09 05				09 16				09 19				09 28		09 30	
Crawley	d				09 02								09 19										09 33	
Ifield	d				09 04																		09 36	
Faygate	d				09 08																			
Littlehaven	d				09 12																		09 42	
Horsham 4	a				09 16								09 27										09 46	
Balcombe	d																							
Haywards Heath 3	a					09 06	09 10	←	09 13								09 27		09 30		09 36			
	d					09 06	09 10	09 13	09 17							←	09 28		09 34 / 09 37		09 40			
Wivelsfield 4	d							09 17	09 22							09 22	09 34							
Lewes 4	a							09 28	→										09 52					
Burgess Hill 4	d															09 24	09 36							
Hassocks 4	d															09 27	09 39							
Preston Park	d															09 34								
Hove 2	a																		09 51					
Brighton 10	a					09 22	09 24								09 30	09 38	09 52				09 54			

For general notes see front of timetable
For details of catering facilities see
Directory of Train Operators

§ It is unknown at the time of going to press, when this station will open. For further details please contact National Rail Enquiries 08457-484950 or see local publicity.

A To Southampton Central (Table 188) and to Bognor Regis (Table 188)

Watford Junction, Bedford and London → Brighton

Network Diagram - see first page of Table 186

		GX	SN	SN	GW	SN	SN	SN	FC	GX	GW	SN	SE 13	SN	SN		SE 88	LO	FC	GW	GX	SN	SN	SN	LO
		1	1	1	1	1	1	1	1	1	1	1		1	1		1		1	1	1	1	1	1	1
						A									B		C	D				E			
						✠		✠							✠										
London Victoria 15	⊖ d	09 00				09 02		09 06		09 15					09 17						09 30	09 32			
Watford Junction	d													08 42											
Harrow & Wealdstone	⊖ d													08 48											
Wembley Central	d													08 53											
Willesden Jn. High Level	d																	09 09							09 23
Shepherds Bush §	⊖ d																								
Kensington Olympia	⊖ d			08 58										09 08				09 18						09 29	09 32
West Brompton	⊖ d			09 00										09 11				09 20						09 31	09 34
Imperial Wharf §	d																								
Clapham Junction 10	d			09a07		09 08		09 12						09a18	09 23			09a32				09 38		09a38	09a43
Bedford 7	d								07 48										08 04						
Luton 10	d								08 12										08 28						
Luton Airport Parkway 7	✈ d								08 14										08 30						
St Albans	d								08 27										08 44						
St Pancras International 15	⊖ d								08 47										09 04						
Farringdon 3	⊖ d								08 52										09 08						
City Thameslink 3	d								08 55										09 13						
London Blackfriars 3	⊖ d								08 58										09 17						
London Bridge 4	⊖ d								09 06				09 11						09 25				09 33		
Norwood Junction 2	d																						09 46		
East Croydon	⇌ a					09 18	←	09 22	09 23				09 25		09 33				09 39			09 48	09 49		
	d					09 18	09 21	09 22	09 24				09 26		09 33				09 39			09 48	09 51		
Purley 4	d		←				09 27					←											09 57		
Coulsdon South	d		09 15				09 30					09 30											10 00		
Merstham	d		09 21				→					09 36											10 06		
Redhill	a		09 24			09 30						09 39	09 43									10 00	10 09		
	d		09 25		09 29	09 30					09 34	09 40	09 44				09 44			09 48		10 00	10 10		
Tonbridge 4	a												10 08										→		
Reigate	a				09 33						09 38														
Earlswood (Surrey)	d																								
Salfords	d																								
Horley 4	d					09 36											09 50								
Gatwick Airport 10	✈ a	09 30	09 32			09 39			09 40	09 45		09 47			09 48		09 54		09 55	09 59	10 00	10 08			
	d					09 40			09 41			09 48			09 49		09 55		09 56			10 09			
Three Bridges 4	a					09 44			09 45			09 53					10 00		10 00			10 14			
	d					09 45			09 45			09 53 →					10 00		10 00			10 14			
Crawley	d					09 48											10 04					10 18			
Ifield	d																10 06								
Faygate	d																								
Littlehaven	d																10 13								
Horsham 4	a					09 56											10 16					10 26			
Balcombe	d								09 51																
Haywards Heath 3	a								09 56						10 00				10 08						
	d								09 57						10 04	10 07			10 10						
Wivelsfield 4	d								10 01							10 11									
Lewes 4	a															10 22									
Burgess Hill 4	d								10 03						10 09										
Hassocks 4	d								10 06																
Preston Park	d								10 13																
Hove 2	a														10 21										
Brighton 10	a							09 58	10 21										10 24						

For general notes see front of timetable
For details of catering facilities see Directory of Train Operators

§ It is unknown at the time of going to press, when this station will open. For further details please contact National Rail Enquiries 08457-484950 or see local publicity.

A To Portsmouth Harbour (Table 188) and to Bognor Regis (Table 188)
B To Littlehampton (Table 188)
C From Tonbridge (Table 209)
D From Stratford Low Level (Table 59)
E To Southampton Central (Table 188) and to Bognor Regis (Table 188)

Watford Junction, Bedford and London → Brighton

Network Diagram - see first page of Table 186

		SN	SN	FC	GX	SN	SN		SN	LO	SN	FC	GW	SN	GX	SN	GW	SE	SN	SN	FC	GX	SN		GW
																		13							
		1	1	1	1	1	1		1		1	1	1	1	1	1	1		1	1	1	1	1		1
																A		B					C		
							╤									╤			╤				╤		
London Victoria 15 ⊖	d	09 36			09 45		09 47								10 00	10 02			10 06			10 15	10 17		
Watford Junction	d					09 11																			
Harrow & Wealdstone ⊖	d					09 17																			
Wembley Central	d					09 22																			
Willesden Jn. High Level	d									09 38															
Shepherds Bush § ⊖	d																								
Kensington Olympia ⊖	d					09 37				09 47															
West Brompton ⊖	d					09 40				09 49															
Imperial Wharf §	d								←																
Clapham Junction 10	d	09 42				09b54	09 53		09 54	09a58						10 08			10 12				10 23		
Bedford 7	d			08 20		→						08 40									08 55				
Luton 10	d			08 44								09 04									09 19				
Luton Airport Parkway 7 ✈	d			08 46								09 06									09 21				
St Albans	d			09 00								09 18									09 33				
St Pancras International 15 ⊖	d			09 20								09 39									09 54				
Farringdon 3 ⊖	d			09 24								09 44									09 59				
City Thameslink 3	d			09 27								09 46									10 01				
London Blackfriars 3 ⊖	d			09 34								09 49									10 05				
London Bridge 4 ⊖	d			09 42								09 56						10 03			10 11				
Norwood Junction 2	d																	10 16							
East Croydon 🚋	a	09 51		09 54			10 03		10 07			10 09				10 18		10 19	10 22		10 24		10 33		
	d	09 52		09 54			10 03		10 07			10 09				10 18		10 21	10 22		10 24		10 33		
Purley 4	d																	10 26							
Coulsdon South	d																	10 30							
Merstham	d																	10 35							
Redhill	a										←					10 30		10 38							
	d										10 10		10 14			10 30	10 34	10 39							10 42
Tonbridge 4	a																	11 08							
Reigate	a												10 18				10 38								
Earlswood (Surrey)	d										10 12														
Salfords	d										10 16														
Horley 4	d										10 19					10 36									
Gatwick Airport 10 ✈	a			10 10	10 15		10 18		10 22		10 23	10 25		←	10 30	10 39					10 40	10 45	10 48		10 51
	d			10 11			10 19		10 28		10 24	10 26		10 28		10 40					10 41		10 49		
Three Bridges 4	a		←	10 15					→		10 29			10 33		10 44					10 45				
	d		09 53	10 15							10 30			10 33		10 45					10 45				
Crawley	d										10 33					10 48									
Ifield	d										10 36														
Faygate	d																								
Littlehaven	d										10 42														
Horsham 4	a										10 47					10 56									
Balcombe	d			10 21																					
Haywards Heath 3	a		10 08	10 26			10 30					10 36		10 42							10 54		11 00		
	d		10 18	10 27			10 34	10 37				10 38		10 46							10 55		11 04	11 07	
Wivelsfield 4	d		10 22	10 31										10 50							10 59			11 11	
Lewes 4	a						10 51																	11 22	
Burgess Hill 4	d		10 24	10 33										10 52							11 01		11 09		
Hassocks 4	d		10 27	10 36										10 55						←	11 04				
Preston Park	d		10 34	10 43										11 02						11 02	11 11				
Hove 2	a							10 51						→									11 21		
Brighton 10	a	10 28	10 40	10 51								10 56							10 58	11 07	11 19				

For general notes see front of timetable
For details of catering facilities see Directory of Train Operators

§ It is unknown at the time of going to press, when this station will open. For further details please contact National Rail Enquiries 08457-484950 or see local publicity.

A To Portsmouth Harbour (Table 188) and to Bognor Regis (Table 188)

B To Tunbridge Wells (Table 206)

C To Littlehampton (Table 188)

b Arr. 0950

Watford Junction, Bedford and London → Brighton

Network Diagram - see first page of Table 186

		FC	LO	SE	GX	SN	SN	SN	FC	GX	SN	LO	SN	SN	SN	FC	GW	SN	GX	SN	GW	SE	SN	SN
				88																		13		
		1		1	1	1	1	1	1	1	1		1	1	1	1	1	1	1	1	1		1	1
				A		B														C		D		
London Victoria 15	⊖ d				10 30	10 32		10 36		10 45			10 47						11 00	11 02			11 06	
Watford Junction	d										10 11													
Harrow & Wealdstone	⊖ d										10 17													
Wembley Central	d																							
Willesden Jn. High Level	d		10 08									10 38												
Shepherds Bush §	⊖ d																							
Kensington Olympia	⊖ d		10 17								10 37	10 47												
West Brompton	⊖ d		10 19								10 39	10 49												
Imperial Wharf §	d													←										
Clapham Junction 10	d		10a28			10 38		10 42			10b54	10a58	10 53	10 54						11 08			11 12	
Bedford 7	d	09 10							09 25		→					09 40								
Luton 10	d	09 34							09 49							10 04								
Luton Airport Parkway 7	✈ d	09 36							09 51							10 06								
St Albans	d	09 48							10 03							10 18								
St Pancras International 15	⊖ d	10 09							10 24							10 39								
Farringdon 3	⊖ d	10 14							10 29							10 44								
City Thameslink 3	d	10 16							10 31							10 46								
London Blackfriars 3	⊖ d	10 20							10 35							10 50								
London Bridge 4	⊖ d	10 26					10 33		10 41							10 56						11 03		
Norwood Junction 2	d						10 46															11 16		
East Croydon	a	10 39				10 48	10 49	10 52	10 54				11 03	11 07		11 09				11 18		11 19	11 22	
	d	10 39				10 48	10 51	10 52	10 54				11 03	11 07		11 09				11 18		11 21	11 22	
Purley 4	d						10 57															11 26		
Coulsdon South	d						11 00															11 30		
Merstham	d						11 06															11 35		
Redhill	a					11 00	11 09								←					11 30		11 38		
	d			10 44		11 00	11 09								11 09		11 14			11 30	11 34	11 39		
Tonbridge 4	a						→															12 08		
Reigate	a																11 18				11 38			
Earlswood (Surrey)	d														11 12									
Salfords	d														11 15									
Horley 4	d			10 51											11 19					11 36				
Gatwick Airport 10	✈ a	10 55		10 55	11 00	11 08			11 10	11 15			11 18	11 22	11 23	11 25		←	11 30	11 39				
	d	10 56		10 56		11 09			11 11				11 19	11 28	11 24	11 26		11 28		11 40				
Three Bridges 4	a			11 00		11 14			11 15					→	11 29			11 33		11 44				
	d			11 01		11 14			11 15						11 30			11 33		11 45				
Crawley	d			11 04		11 18									11 33					11 48				
Ifield	d			11 07											11 36									
Faygate	d																							
Littlehaven	d			11 13											11 42									
Horsham 4	a			11 16		11 26									11 47					11 56				
Balcombe	d								11 21															
Haywards Heath 3	a	11 06							11 26				11 30			11 36		11 42						
	d	11 08							11 27				11 34 11 37			11 38		11 46						
Wivelsfield 4	d								11 31									11 50						
Lewes 4	a												11 48											
Burgess Hill 4	d								11 33									11 52						
Hassocks 4	d								11 36									11 55						←
Preston Park	d								11 43									12 02						12 02
Hove 2	a												11 51					→						
Brighton 10	a	11 26						11 28	11 51							11 56							11 58	12 07

For general notes see front of timetable
For details of catering facilities see Directory of Train Operators

§ It is unknown at the time of going to press, when this station will open. For further details please contact National Rail Enquiries 08457-484950 or see local publicity.

A From Tunbridge Wells (Table 209)

B To Southampton Central (Table 188) and to Bognor Regis (Table 188)

C To Portsmouth Harbour (Table 188) and to Bognor Regis (Table 188)

D To Tunbridge Wells (Table 206)

b Arr. 1050

Watford Junction, Bedford and London → Brighton

Network Diagram - see first page of Table 186

Station		FC	GX	SN		LO	GW	FC	SE	GX	SN	SN	SN	FC	GX	SN	SN		SN	LO	SN	FC	GW	SN	GX
									88																
		1	1	1			1	1	1	1	1	1	1	1	1	1	1		1		1	1	1	1	1
				A					B		C														
London Victoria 15	⊖ d		11 15	11 17						11 30	11 32		11 36		11 45		11 47								12 00
Watford Junction	d															11 11									
Harrow & Wealdstone	⊖ d															11 17									
Wembley Central	d																								
Willesden Jn. High Level	d					11 08														11 38					
Shepherds Bush §	⊖ d																								
Kensington Olympia	⊖ d					11 17										11 37				11 47					
West Brompton	⊖ d					11 19										11 39				11 49					
Imperial Wharf §	d																		←						
Clapham Junction 10	d			11 23		11a28					11 38		11 42			11b54	11 53		11 54	11a58					
Bedford 7	d	09 57						10 10						10 27		→						10 40			
Luton 10	d	10 19						10 34						10 49								11 04			
Luton Airport Parkway 7	✈ d	10 21						10 36						10 51								11 06			
St Albans	d	10 33						10 48						11 03								11 18			
St Pancras International 15	⊖ d	10 54						11 09						11 24								11 39			
Farringdon 3	⊖ d	10 59						11 14						11 29								11 44			
City Thameslink 3	d	11 01						11 16						11 31								11 46			
London Blackfriars 3	⊖ d	11 05						11 20						11 35								11 50			
London Bridge 4	⊖ d	11 11						11 26				11 33		11 41								11 56			
Norwood Junction 2	d											11 46													
East Croydon	⇌ a	11 24		11 33				11 39			11 48	11 49	11 52	11 54			12 03		12 07			12 09			
	d	11 24		11 33				11 39			11 48	11 51	11 52	11 54			12 03		12 07			12 09			
Purley 4	d											11 57													
Coulsdon South	d											12 00													
Merstham	d											12 06													
Redhill	a										12 00	12 09									←				
	d						11 41		11 44		12 00	12 10									12 10		12 14		
Tonbridge 4	a											→													
Reigate	a																						12 18		
Earlswood (Surrey)	d																				12 12				
Salfords	d																				12 16				
Horley 4	d								11 51												12 19				
Gatwick Airport 10	✈ a	11 40	11 45	11 48			11 50	11 55	11 55	12 00	12 08			12 10	12 15		12 18		12 22		12 23	12 25		←	12 30
	d	11 41		11 49				11 56	11 56		12 09			12 11			12 19		12 28		12 24	12 26		12 28	
Three Bridges 4	a	11 45							12 00		12 14			12 15					→		12 29			12 33	
	d	11 45							12 01		12 14			12 15							12 30			12 33	
Crawley	d								12 04		12 18										12 33				
Ifield	d								12 07												12 36				
Faygate	d								12 11																
Littlehaven	d								12 15												12 42				
Horsham 4	a								12 18		12 26										12 47				
Balcombe	d													12 21											
Haywards Heath 3	a	11 54		12 00				12 06						12 26			12 30					12 36		12 42	
	d	11 55		12 04	12 07			12 08						12 27			12 34	12 37				12 38		12 46	
Wivelsfield 4	d	11 59			12 11									12 31										12 50	
Lewes 4	a				12 22												12 52								
Burgess Hill 4	d	12 01		12 09										12 33										12 52	
Hassocks 4	d	12 04												12 36										12 55	
Preston Park	d	12 11												12 43										13 02	
Hove 2	a			12 21														12 51						→	
Brighton 10	a	12 19						12 24					12 27	12 51								12 56			

For general notes see front of timetable
For details of catering facilities see Directory of Train Operators

§ It is unknown at the time of going to press, when this station will open. For further details please contact National Rail Enquiries 08457-484950 or see local publicity.

A To Littlehampton (Table 188)

B From Tunbridge Wells (Table 209)

C To Southampton Central (Table 188) and to Bognor Regis (Table 188)

b Arr. 1150

Watford Junction, Bedford and London → Brighton

Network Diagram - see first page of Table 186

		XC	SN	GW	SE	SN	SN	XC	FC	GX	SN	SN	GW	FC	LO	SE	GX	SN	SN	SN	FC	GX	SN	SN	SN
					13											88									
		1 ◊	1	1		1	1	1 ◊	1	1	1		1	1		1	1	1	1	1	1	1	1	1	
			A		B						C					D		E							
London Victoria 15	⊖ d		12 02			12 06				12 15	12 17						12 30	12 32		12 36		12 45		12 47	
Watford Junction	d																						12 11		
Harrow & Wealdstone	⊖ d																						12 17		
Wembley Central	d																								
Willesden Jn. High Level	d														12 08										
Shepherds Bush §	⊖ d																								
Kensington Olympia	⊖ d	11 57													12 17								12 37		
West Brompton	⊖ d														12 19								12 39		
Imperial Wharf §	d																								
Clapham Junction 10	d		12 08			12 12					12 23				12a28			12 38		12 42			12b54	12 53	
Bedford 7	d								10 55					11 10							11 25		→		
Luton 10	d								11 19					11 34							11 49				
Luton Airport Parkway 7	✈ d								11 21					11 36							11 51				
St Albans	d								11 33					11 48							12 03				
St Pancras International 15	⊖ d								11 54					12 09							12 24				
Farringdon 3	⊖ d								11 59					12 14							12 29				
City Thameslink 3	d								12 01					12 16							12 31				
London Blackfriars 3	⊖ d								12 05					12 20							12 35				
London Bridge 4	⊖ d				12 03				12 11					12 26					12 33		12 41				
Norwood Junction 2	d				12 16														12 46						
East Croydon	⇌ a	12 16	12 18		12 19	12 22			12 24		12 33			12 39				12 48	12 49	12 52	12 54			13 03	
	d	12 17	12 18		12 21	12 22			12 24		12 33			12 39				12 48	12 51	12 52	12 54			13 03	
Purley 4	d				12 26														12 57						
Coulsdon South	d				12 30														13 00						
Merstham	d				12 35														13 06						
Redhill	a		12 30		12 38													13 00	13 09						
	d		12 30	12 34	12 39								12 41			12 44		13 00	13 10						
Tonbridge 4	a				13 08														→						
Reigate	a			12 38																					
Earlswood (Surrey)	d																								
Salfords	d																								
Horley 4	d		12 36													12 51									
Gatwick Airport 10	✈ a	12 33	12 39					←	12 40	12 45	12 48		12 50	12 55		12 55	13 00	13 08			13 10	13 15		13 18	
	d	12 38	12 40					12 38	12 41		12 49			12 56		12 56		13 09			13 11			13 19	
Three Bridges 4	a	→	12 44						12 45							13 00		13 14			13 15				
	d		12 45						12 45							13 01		13 14			13 15				
Crawley	d		12 48													13 04		13 18							
Ifield	d															13 07									
Faygate	d																								
Littlehaven	d															13 13									
Horsham 4	a		12 56													13 16		13 26							
Balcombe	d																				13 21				
Haywards Heath 3	a							12 49	12 54		13 01			13 06							13 26			13 30	
	d							12 50	12 55		13 04	13 07		13 08							13 27			13 34	13 37
Wivelsfield 4	d								12 59			13 11									13 31				
Lewes 4	a											13 22												13 48	
Burgess Hill 4	d								13 01		13 09										13 33				
Hassocks 4	d						←		13 04												13 36				
Preston Park	d						13 02		13 11												13 43				
Hove 2	a										13 21														13 51
Brighton 10	a					12 58	13 07	13 15	13 19					13 26						13 27	13 51				

For general notes see front of timetable
For details of catering facilities see Directory of Train Operators

§ It is unknown at the time of going to press, when this station will open. For further details please contact National Rail Enquiries 08457-484950 or see local publicity.

A To Portsmouth Harbour (Table 188) and to Bognor Regis (Table 188)
B To Tunbridge Wells (Table 206)
C To Littlehampton (Table 188)
D From Tunbridge Wells (Table 209)
E To Southampton Central (Table 188) and to Bognor Regis (Table 188)
b Arr. 1250

Watford Junction, Bedford and London → Brighton

Network Diagram - see first page of Table 186

		SN	LO	SN	FC	GW	SN	GX	SN	GW	SE	SN	SN	FC	GX	SN		LO	GW	FC	SE	GX	SN	SN	SN
											13										88				
		1		1	1	1	1	1	1	1		1	1	1	1	1			1	1	1	1	1	1	1
									A		B					C					D		E		
									ᚗ			ᚗ				ᚗ									ᚗ
London Victoria 15	⊖ d							13 00	13 02			13 06			13 15	13 17						13 30	13 32		13 36
Watford Junction	d																								
Harrow & Wealdstone	⊖ d																								
Wembley Central	d																								
Willesden Jn. High Level	d		12 38															13 08							
Shepherds Bush §	⊖ d																								
Kensington Olympia	⊖ d		12 47															13 17							
West Brompton	⊖ d		12 49															13 19							
Imperial Wharf §	d	←																							
Clapham Junction 10	d	12 54	12a58						13 08			13 12				13 23		13a28					13 38		13 42
Bedford 7	d				11 40									11 55						12 10					
Luton 10	d				12 04									12 19						12 34					
Luton Airport Parkway 7	✈ d				12 06									12 21						12 36					
St Albans	d				12 18									12 33						12 48					
St Pancras International 15	⊖ d				12 39									12 54						13 09					
Farringdon 3	⊖ d				12 44									12 59						13 14					
City Thameslink 3	d				12 46									13 01						13 16					
London Blackfriars 3	⊖ d				12 50									13 05						13 20					
London Bridge 4	⊖ d				12 56						13 03			13 11						13 26				13 33	
Norwood Junction 2	d										13 16													13 46	
East Croydon	a	13 07			13 09				13 18		13 19	13 22		13 24		13 33				13 39			13 48	13 49	13 52
	d	13 07			13 09				13 18		13 21	13 22		13 24		13 33				13 39			13 48	13 51	13 52
Purley 4	d										13 26													13 57	
Coulsdon South	d										13 30													14 00	
Merstham	d										13 35													14 06	
Redhill	a			←					13 30		13 38												14 00	14 09	
	d			13 10		13 14			13 30	13 34	13 39								13 41		13 44		14 00	14 10	
Tonbridge 4	a										14 08													→	
Reigate	a					13 18				13 38															
Earlswood (Surrey)	d			13 12																					
Salfords	d			13 16																					
Horley 4	d			13 19					13 36												13 51				
Gatwick Airport 10	✈ a	13 22		13 23	13 25		←	13 30	13 39					13 40	13 45	13 48			13 50	13 55	13 55	14 00	14 08		
	d	13 28		13 24	13 26		13 28		13 40					13 41		13 49				13 56	13 56		14 09		
Three Bridges 4	a	→		13 29			13 33		13 44					13 45							14 00		14 14		
	d			13 30			13 33		13 45					13 45							14 01		14 14		
Crawley	d			13 33					13 48												14 04		14 18		
Ifield	d			13 36																	14 07				
Faygate	d																								
Littlehaven	d			13 42																	14 13				
Horsham 4	a			13 47					13 56												14 16		14 26		
Balcombe	d																								
Haywards Heath 3	a				13 36		13 42							13 54		14 00				14 06					
	d				13 38		13 46							13 55		14 04	14 07			14 08					
Wivelsfield 4	d						13 50							13 59			14 11								
Lewes 4	a																14 22								
Burgess Hill 4	d						13 52							14 01		14 09									
Hassocks 4	d						13 55						←	14 04											
Preston Park	d						14 02						14 02	14 11											
Hove 2	a						→									14 21									
Brighton 10	a				13 56							13 58	14 07	14 19						14 27					14 27

For general notes see front of timetable
For details of catering facilities see Directory of Train Operators

§ It is unknown at the time of going to press, when this station will open. For further details please contact National Rail Enquiries 08457-484950 or see local publicity.

A To Portsmouth Harbour (Table 188) and to Bognor Regis (Table 188)
B To Tunbridge Wells (Table 206)
C To Littlehampton (Table 188)
D From Tunbridge Wells (Table 209)
E To Southampton Central (Table 188) and to Bognor Regis (Table 188)

Watford Junction, Bedford and London → Brighton

Network Diagram - see first page of Table 186

		FC	GX	SN	SN	SN	LO	SN	FC	GW	SN	GX	SN	GW	SE	SN	SN	FC	GX	SN	LO	GW	FC
		1	1	1	1	1		1	1	1	1	1	1 A	1	13 B	1	1	1	1	1 C		1	1
					⚒								⚒			⚒				⚒			
London Victoria 15	⊖ d		13 45		13 47							14 00	14 02			14 06			14 15	14 17			
Watford Junction	d			13 11																			
Harrow & Wealdstone	⊖ d			13 17																			
Wembley Central	d																						
Willesden Jn. High Level	d						13 38														14 08		
Shepherds Bush §	⊖ d																						
Kensington Olympia	⊖ d			13 37			13 47														14 17		
West Brompton	⊖ d			13 39			13 49														14 19		
Imperial Wharf §	d					←																	
Clapham Junction 10	d			13b54	13 53	13 54	13a58						14 08			14 12				14 23	14a28		
Bedford 7	d	12 25		→					12 40									12 55					13 10
Luton 10	d	12 49							13 04									13 19					13 34
Luton Airport Parkway 7	✈ d	12 51							13 06									13 21					13 36
St Albans	d	13 03							13 18									13 33					13 48
St Pancras International 15	⊖ d	13 24							13 39									13 54					14 09
Farringdon 3	⊖ d	13 29							13 44									13 59					14 14
City Thameslink 3	d	13 31							13 46									14 01					14 16
London Blackfriars 3	⊖ d	13 35							13 50									14 05					14 20
London Bridge 4	⊖ d	13 41							13 56						14 03			14 11					14 26
Norwood Junction 2	d														14 16								
East Croydon	🚋 a	13 54			14 03	14 07			14 09				14 18		14 19	14 22		14 24		14 33			14 39
	d	13 54			14 03	14 07			14 09				14 18		14 21	14 22		14 24		14 33			14 39
Purley 4	d														14 26								
Coulsdon South	d														14 30								
Merstham	d														14 35								
Redhill	a							←					14 30		14 38								
	d							14 10		14 14			14 30	14 34	14 39							14 42	
Tonbridge 4	a														15 08								
Reigate	a									14 18				14 38									
Earlswood (Surrey)	d							14 12															
Salfords	d							14 16															
Horley 4	d							14 19					14 36										
Gatwick Airport 10	✈ a	14 10	14 15		14 18	14 22		14 23	14 25		←	14 30	14 39					14 40	14 45	14 48		14 50	14 55
	d	14 11			14 19	14 28		14 24	14 26		14 28		14 40					14 41		14 49			14 56
Three Bridges 4	a	14 15				→		14 29			14 33		14 44					14 45					
	d	14 15						14 30			14 33		14 45					14 45					
Crawley	d							14 33					14 48										
Ifield	d							14 36															
Faygate	d																						
Littlehaven	d							14 42															
Horsham 4	a							14 47					14 56										
Balcombe	d	14 21																					
Haywards Heath 3	a	14 26			14 30				14 36		14 42							14 54		15 00			15 06
	d	14 27			14 34 / 14 37				14 38		14 46							14 55		15 04 / 15 07			15 08
Wivelsfield 4	d	14 31									14 50							14 59		15 11			
Lewes 4	a				14 48															15 22			
Burgess Hill 4	d	14 33									14 52							15 01		15 09			
Hassocks 4	d	14 36									14 55						←	15 04					
Preston Park	d	14 43									15 02						15 02	15 11					
Hove 2	a				14 51						→									15 21			
Brighton 10	a	14 51							14 56							14 58	15 07	15 19					15 26

For general notes see front of timetable
For details of catering facilities see Directory of Train Operators

§ It is unknown at the time of going to press, when this station will open. For further details please contact National Rail Enquiries 08457-484950 or see local publicity.

A To Portsmouth Harbour (Table 188) and to Bognor Regis (Table 188)
B To Tunbridge Wells (Table 206)
C To Littlehampton (Table 188)
b Arr. 1350

Watford Junction, Bedford and London → Brighton

Network Diagram - see first page of Table 186

		SE 88	GX	SN	SN	SN	FC	GX	SN	SN		SN	LO	SN	FC	GW	GW	SN	GX	SN	SE 13	SN	SN	FC	GX
		1	1	1	1	1	1	1	1	1		1		1	1	1	1	1	1	1		1	1	1	1
		A		B																C	D				
						⚲				⚲										⚲		⚲			
London Victoria 15	⊖ d		14 30	14 32		14 36		14 45		14 47									15 00	15 02		15 06			15 15
Watford Junction	d								14 11																
Harrow & Wealdstone	⊖ d								14 17																
Wembley Central	d																								
Willesden Jn. High Level	d												14 38												
Shepherds Bush §	⊖ d																								
Kensington Olympia	⊖ d								14 37				14 47												
West Brompton	⊖ d								14 39				14 49												
Imperial Wharf §	d											←													
Clapham Junction 10	d			14 38		14 42			14b54	14 53		14 54	14a58							15 08		15 12			
Bedford 7	d						13 25		→						13 40									13 55	
Luton 10	d						13 49								14 04									14 19	
Luton Airport Parkway 7	✈ d						13 51								14 06									14 21	
St Albans	d						14 03								14 18									14 33	
St Pancras International 15	⊖ d						14 24								14 39									14 54	
Farringdon 3	⊖ d						14 29								14 44									14 59	
City Thameslink 3	d						14 31								14 46									15 01	
London Blackfriars 3	⊖ d						14 35								14 50									15 05	
London Bridge 4	⊖ d				14 33		14 41								14 56						15 03			15 11	
Norwood Junction 2	d				14 46																15 16				
East Croydon	🚋 a			14 48	14 49	14 52	14 54			15 03		15 07			15 09					15 18	15 19	15 22		15 24	
	d			14 48	14 51	14 52	14 54			15 03		15 07			15 09					15 18	15 21	15 22		15 24	
Purley 4	d				14 57																15 26				
Coulsdon South	d				15 00																15 30				
Merstham	d				15 06																15 35				
Redhill	a			15 00	15 09									←						15 30	15 39				
	d	14 44		15 00	15 10									15 10		15 14	15 29			15 30	15 40				
Tonbridge 4	a				→																16 09				
Reigate	a															15 18	15 33								
Earlswood (Surrey)	d													15 12											
Salfords	d													15 16											
Horley 4	d	14 51												15 19						15 36					
Gatwick Airport 10	✈ a	14 55	15 00	15 08			15 10	15 15		15 18		15 22		15 23	15 25			←	15 30	15 39				15 40	15 45
	d	14 56		15 09			15 11			15 19		15 28		15 24	15 26			15 28		15 40				15 41	
Three Bridges 4	a	15 00		15 14			15 15					→		15 29				15 33		15 44				15 45	
	d	15 01		15 14			15 15							15 30				15 33		15 45				15 45	
Crawley	d	15 04		15 18										15 33						15 48					
Ifield	d	15 07												15 36											
Faygate	d																								
Littlehaven	d	15 13												15 42											
Horsham 4	a	15 16		15 26										15 47						15 56					
Balcombe	d						15 21																		
Haywards Heath 3	a						15 26			15 30					15 36			15 42						15 54	
	d						15 27			15 34	15 37				15 38			15 46						15 55	
Wivelsfield 4	d						15 31			15 38								15 50						15 59	
Lewes 4	a									15 52															
Burgess Hill 4	d						15 33											15 52						16 01	
Hassocks 4	d						15 36											15 55					←	16 04	
Preston Park	d						15 43											16 02					16 02	16 11	
Hove 2	a										15 51							→							
Brighton 10	a					15 27	15 51								15 56							15 58	16 07	16 19	

For general notes see front of timetable
For details of catering facilities see Directory of Train Operators

§ It is unknown at the time of going to press, when this station will open. For further details please contact National Rail Enquiries 08457-484950 or see local publicity.

A From Tunbridge Wells (Table 209)
B To Southampton Central (Table 188) and to Bognor Regis (Table 188)
C To Portsmouth Harbour (Table 188) and to Bognor Regis (Table 188)
D To Tunbridge Wells (Table 206)
b Arr. 1450

Watford Junction, Bedford and London → Brighton

Network Diagram - see first page of Table 186

		SN	LO	GW	FC	SE 88	GX	SN	SN	SN	FC	GX	SN	SN	SN	LO	SN	FC	GX	GW	SN	GW	SE 13
		1		1	1	1	1	1	1	1	1	1	1	1	1		1	1	1	1	1	1	
		A				B		C													D		
London Victoria 15	⊖ d	15 17					15 30	15 32		15 36		15 45		15 47					16 00		16 02		
Watford Junction	d												15 11										
Harrow & Wealdstone	⊖ d												15 17										
Wembley Central	d																						
Willesden Jn. High Level	d		15 08													15 38							
Shepherds Bush §	⊖ d																						
Kensington Olympia	⊖ d		15 17										15 39			15 47							
West Brompton	⊖ d		15 19										15 41			15 49							
Imperial Wharf §	d														←								
Clapham Junction 10	d	15 23	15a28					15 38		15 42			15b54	15 53	15 54	15a58					16 08		
Bedford 7	d				14 10						14 25		→					14 40					
Luton 10	d				14 34						14 49							15 04					
Luton Airport Parkway 7	✈ d				14 36						14 51							15 06					
St Albans	d				14 48						15 03							15 18					
St Pancras International 15	⊖ d				15 09						15 24							15 39					
Farringdon 3	⊖ d				15 14						15 29							15 44					
City Thameslink 3	d				15 16						15 31							15 46					
London Blackfriars 3	⊖ d				15 20						15 35							15 50					
London Bridge 4	⊖ d				15 26				15 33		15 41							15 56					16 03
Norwood Junction 2	d								15 46														16 16
East Croydon	⇌ a	15 33			15 39			15 48	15 49	15 52	15 54			16 03	16 07			16 09			16 18		16 19
	d	15 33			15 39			15 48	15 51	15 52	15 54			16 03	16 07			16 09			16 18		16 21
Purley 4	d								15 57														16 26
Coulsdon South	d								16 00														16 30
Merstham	d								16 06														16 35
Redhill	a							16 00	16 09								←				16 30		16 39
	d			15 41		15 44		16 00	16 10								16 10			16 14	16 30	16 32	16 40
Tonbridge 4	a								→														17 11
Reigate	a																			16 18		16 36	
Earlswood (Surrey)	d					15 46											16 12						
Salfords	d					15 50											16 16						
Horley 4	d					15 53											16 19				16 36		
Gatwick Airport 10	✈ a	15 48		15 50	15 55	15 56	16 00	16 08			16 10	16 15		16 18	16 22		16 23	16 25	16 30		16 39		
	d	15 49			15 56	15 56		16 09			16 11			16 19	16 23		16 24	16 26			16 40		
Three Bridges 4	a				16 00	16 01		16 14			16 15				16 27		16 29	16 30			16 44		
	d				16 00	16 01		16 14			16 15				16 27		16 30	16 30			16 45		
Crawley	d					16 05		16 18									16 34				16 48		
Ifield	d					16 07											16 36						
Faygate	d					16 11											16 40						
Littlehaven	d					16 15											16 44						
Horsham 4	a					16 18		16 26									16 47				16 56		
Balcombe	d										16 21												
Haywards Heath 3	a	16 00			16 09						16 26			16 30	16 39			16 40					
	d	16 04 / 16 07			16 10						16 27			16 33 / 16 37	16 46 →			16 40					
Wivelsfield 4	d	. / 16 11									16 31			16 37 / .									
Lewes 4	a	. / 16 22												16 52 / .									
Burgess Hill 4	d	16 09									16 33												
Hassocks 4	d										16 36												
Preston Park	d										16 43												
Hove 2	a	16 21												. / 16 51									
Brighton 10	a				16 26					16 27	16 51							16 56					

For general notes see front of timetable
For details of catering facilities see Directory of Train Operators

§ It is unknown at the time of going to press, when this station will open. For further details please contact National Rail Enquiries 08457-484950 or see local publicity.

A To Littlehampton (Table 188)
B From Tunbridge Wells (Table 209)
C To Southampton Central (Table 188) and to Bognor Regis (Table 188)
D To Portsmouth Harbour (Table 188) and to Bognor Regis (Table 188)
b Arr. 1547

Table 186

Watford Junction, Bedford and London → Brighton

Network Diagram - see first page of Table 186

	SN	SN	FC	GX	SE	SN	SN		LO	FC	SE	GX	GW	SN	SN	SN	GW	SN		SN		FC	GX	SN
					88						88													
	1	1	1	1	1	1	1			1	1	1	1	1	1	1	1	1		1		1	1	1
					A		B				A									C				D
	⊼						⊼								⊼					⊼				⊼
London Victoria 15 ⊖ d	16 06			16 15		16 10	16 17					16 30		16 32	16 36					16 38			16 45	16 47
Watford Junction d																								
Harrow & Wealdstone ⊖ d																								
Wembley Central d																								
Willesden Jn. High Level d									16 08															
Shepherds Bush § ⊖ d																								
Kensington Olympia ⊖ d									16 17															
West Brompton ⊖ d									16 19															
Imperial Wharf § d																								
Clapham Junction 10 d	16 12					16 16	16 23		16a28					16 38	16 42					16 45				16 53
Bedford 7 d			14 55							15 10												15 25		
Luton 10 d			15 19							15 34												15 49		
Luton Airport Parkway 7 ✈ d			15 21							15 36												15 51		
St Albans d			15 33							15 48												16 03		
St Pancras International 15 ⊖ d			15 54							16 09												16 27		
Farringdon 3 ⊖ d			15 59							16 14												16 32		
City Thameslink 3 d			16 01							16 16												16 34		
London Blackfriars 3 ⊖ d			16 05							16 20												16 37		
London Bridge 4 ⊖ d			16 11							16 26								16 38				16 46		
Norwood Junction 2 d																		16 51						
East Croydon a	16 22		16 24			16 28	16 33			16 40				16 48	16 52			16 54		16 55		16 59		17 03
East Croydon d	16 22		16 24			16 28	16 33			16 40				16 48	16 52			16 55		16 55		17 00		17 03
Purley 4 d						16 34												17 01						
Coulsdon South d						16 37												17 07						
Merstham d						16 43												17 12						
Redhill a						16 46								17 00				17 16						
Redhill d					16 44	16 48							16 50	17 01			17 14	17 20	17 22					
Tonbridge 4 a																		→						
Reigate a						16 54											17 18		17 28					
Earlswood (Surrey) d					16 46																			
Salfords d					16 50						←													
Horley 4 d					16 53						16 53													
Gatwick Airport 10 ✈ a			16 40	16 45	→		16 48			16 55	16 56	17 00	17 00	17 08		←				17 12		17 15	17 15	17 19
Gatwick Airport d			16 41				16 49			16 56	16 57			17 09		17 09				17 13		17 16		17 20
Three Bridges 4 a			16 45							17 00	17 01			→		17 14				17 17		17 20		17 25
Three Bridges d			16 45							17 00	17 02					17 14				17 21	17 24	17 20		17 25
Crawley d											17 05									17 25	17 30			
Ifield d											17 08										17 32			
Faygate d											17 12													
Littlehaven d											17 16										17 39			
Horsham 4 a											17 19									17 33	17 42			
Balcombe d																						17 26		
Haywards Heath 3 a		←	16 54				17 00			17 10					17 15	17 23						17 31		17 34
Haywards Heath d		16 46	16 55				17 04	17 06		17 10					17 16	17 24						17 32		17 35
Wivelsfield 4 d		16 50	16 59					17 10								17 28						17 36		17 39
Lewes 4 a								17 21																17 54
Burgess Hill 4 d		16 52	17 01				17 09									17 30						17 39		
Hassocks 4 d		16 55	17 04													17 34						17 43		
Preston Park d		17 02	17 11													17 41						17 50		
Hove 2 a							17 20																	
Brighton 10 a	17 00	17 07	17 19							17 28					17 32	17 48						17 56		

For general notes see front of timetable
For details of catering facilities see Directory of Train Operators

§ It is unknown at the time of going to press, when this station will open. For further details please contact National Rail Enquiries 08457-484950 or see local publicity.

A From Tonbridge (Table 209)
B To Littlehampton (Table 188)
C To Bognor Regis (Table 188)
D To Ore (Table 189)

Watford Junction, Bedford and London → Brighton

Network Diagram - see first page of Table 186

		LO	SN	GX	SN	SE	SN	SN	FC	SN	FC	GX	GW	GW	LO	SN	SN		SN	LO	SN	SN	SN	GX	SN
			1	1	1	13	1	1	1	1	1	1	1	1		1	1		1		1	1	1	1	1
			A					bike											B bike		C bike				A
London Victoria 15	⊖ d			17 00				17 02		17 07		17 15				17 10			17 17		17 21	17 24		17 30	
Watford Junction	d						16 29																		
Harrow & Wealdstone	⊖ d						16 35																		
Wembley Central	d						16 40																		
Willesden Jn. High Level	d	16 38													16 53					17 08					
Shepherds Bush §	⊖ d																								
Kensington Olympia	⊖ d	16 47					16 53								17 02					17 17					
West Brompton	⊖ d	16 49					16 56								17 04					17 19					
Imperial Wharf §	d																								
Clapham Junction 10	d	16a58					17a02	17 08		17 13					17a13	17 16			17 23	17a28	17 27	17 30			
Bedford 7	d																								
Luton 10	d																								
Luton Airport Parkway 7	✈ d																								
St Albans	d																								
St Pancras International 15	⊖ d																								
Farringdon 3	⊖ d																								
City Thameslink 3	d																								
London Blackfriars 3	⊖ d																								
London Bridge 4	⊖ d		16 53			16 57			17 08								17 17								17 32
Norwood Junction 2	d																								
East Croydon	⇌ a		17 07			17 11		17 18	17 20	17 23						17 26	17 31		17 33		17 37	17 40			17 46
	d		17 07			17 11		17 18	17 20	17 24						17 26	17 32		17 33		17 37	17 40			17 46
Purley 4	d															17 33	17 37								
Coulsdon South	d					17 18										17 37	17 41								
Merstham	d					17 24										17 42	17 46								
Redhill	a					17 27			17 32							17 46	17 50								
	d				← 17 20	17 28			17 32				17 41	17 44		17 46	17 53	17 56					← 17 46		
Tonbridge 4	a					17 57										→	→								
Reigate	a													17 48				18 00							
Earlswood (Surrey)	d				17 22																		17 49		
Salfords	d				17 26																		17 52		
Horley 4	d				17 29					17 39													17 56		18 02
Gatwick Airport 10	✈ a			17 30	17 32			17 33	17 40		←	17 45	17 50									17 57	17 58	18 00	
	d				17 33			17 34	17 40		17 40											17 58	17 59		
Three Bridges 4	a		17 28		17 38			17 38	→		17 45								17 52		17 56		18 04		
	d		17 29		17 38			17 39			17 46								17 53		17 57		18 04		
Crawley	d				17 41																18 01		18 08		
Ifield	d				17 44																		18 10		
Faygate	d																						18 14		
Littlehaven	d				17 50																18 08		18 18		
Horsham 4	a				17 55																18 11		18 23		
Balcombe	d										17 52														
Haywards Heath 3	a		17 37					17 47		17 51	17 57								18 02			18 09			18 14
	d		17 38					17 48		17 52	17 58								18 03			18 10			18 15
Wivelsfield 4	d										18 02								18 07						
Lewes 4	a																		18 18						
Burgess Hill 4	d		17 43							17 57	18 05														18 20
Hassocks 4	d		17 47							18 01	18 09														18 24
Preston Park	d		17 54							18 09	18 16														18 32
Hove 2	a		17 57																			18 24			18 35
Brighton 10	a							18 02		18 15	18 22														

For general notes see front of timetable
For details of catering facilities see Directory of Train Operators

§ It is unknown at the time of going to press, when this station will open. For further details please contact National Rail Enquiries 08457-484950 or see local publicity.

A To Littlehampton (Table 188)
B To Seaford (Table 189) and to Eastbourne (Table 189)
C To Bognor Regis (Table 188)

Watford Junction, Bedford and London → Brighton

Network Diagram - see first page of Table 186

		SN	FC	SN	GW	SN		GX	SN	FC	SN	LO	SN	FC	SN	SN	GX	SN	SN	SN	FC	SN	SN	GW	LO
		1	1	1	1	1		1	1	1	1		1	1	1	1	1	1	1	1	1	1	1	1	
											A		B												
													🛒		🛒			🛒				🛒			
London Victoria 15	⊖ d	.	.	17 37	.	17 40		17 45	.	.	17 47	.	.	.	17 53	.	18 00	.	.	.	.	18 07	.	.	.
Watford Junction	d	.	.	.	.	.		.	.	.	.	.	.	.	.	.	.	.	.	.	.	.	.	.	.
Harrow & Wealdstone	⊖ d	.	.	.	.	.		.	.	.	.	.	.	.	.	.	.	.	.	.	.	.	.	.	.
Wembley Central	d	.	.	.	.	.		.	.	.	.	.	.	.	.	.	.	.	.	.	.	.	.	.	.
Willesden Jn. High Level	d	.	.	.	.	.		.	.	.	.	17 38	.	.	.	.	.	.	.	.	.	.	.	.	17 53
Shepherds Bush §	⊖ d	.	.	.	.	.		.	.	.	.	.	.	.	.	.	.	.	.	.	.	.	.	.	.
Kensington Olympia	⊖ d	.	.	.	.	.		.	.	.	.	17 47	.	.	.	.	.	.	.	.	.	.	.	.	18 02
West Brompton	⊖ d	.	.	.	.	.		.	.	.	.	17 49	.	.	.	.	.	.	.	.	.	.	.	.	18 04
Imperial Wharf §	d	.	.	.	.	.		.	.	.	.	.	.	.	.	.	.	.	.	.	.	.	.	.	.
Clapham Junction 10	d	.	.	17 43	.	17 46		.	.	.	17 53	17a58	.	.	17 59	.	.	.	.	.	.	18 13	.	.	18a13
Bedford 7	d	.	16 10	.	.	.		.	.	.	.	.	.	16 36	.	.	.	.	.	.	17 00	.	.	.	.
Luton 10	d	.	16 34	.	.	.		.	.	.	.	.	.	17 00	.	.	.	.	.	.	17 18	.	.	.	.
Luton Airport Parkway 7	✈ d	.	16 36	.	.	.		.	.	.	.	.	.	17 02	.	.	.	.	.	.	.	.	.	.	.
St Albans	d	.	16 48	.	.	.		.	.	.	.	.	.	17 14	.	.	.	.	.	.	17 28	.	.	.	.
St Pancras International 15	⊖ d	.	17 09	.	.	.		.	.	.	.	.	.	17 35	.	.	.	.	.	.	17 46	.	.	.	.
Farringdon 3	⊖ d	.	17 14	.	.	.		.	.	.	.	.	.	17 40	.	.	.	.	.	.	17 50	.	.	.	.
City Thameslink 3	d	.	17 16	.	.	.		.	.	.	.	.	.	17 42	.	.	.	.	.	.	17 53	.	.	.	.
London Blackfriars 3	⊖ d	.	17 20	.	.	.		.	.	.	.	.	.	17 46	.	.	.	.	.	.	17 57	.	.	.	.
London Bridge 4	⊖ d	.	17 32	.	.	.		.	17 46	.	.	.	17 52	17 52	.	17 59	.	18 03	.	.	.	.	.	.	.
Norwood Junction 2	d	.	.	.	.	.		.	.	.	.	.	.	.	.	.	.	.	.	.	.	.	.	.	.
East Croydon	🚊 a	.	17 49	17 53	.	17 56		.	17 59	.	18 03	.	18 06	18 08	18 10	18 12	.	18 16	.	.	18 20	18 23	.	.	.
	d	.	17 50	17 54	.	17 57		.	18 00	.	18 03	.	18 06	18 08	18 10	18 13	.	18 16	.	.	18 20	18 24	.	.	.
Purley 4	d	.	.	.	.	18 03		.	.	.	.	.	.	.	.	.	.	.	.	.	.	.	.	.	.
Coulsdon South	d	.	.	.	.	18 07		.	.	.	.	.	.	.	.	18 20	.	.	.	←	.	.	.	.	.
Merstham	d	.	.	.	.	18 12		.	.	.	.	.	.	.	.	18 25 →	.	.	.	18 25	.	.	.	.	.
Redhill	a	←	18 02	.	.	18 16		.	.	.	.	.	.	.	.	.	.	.	←	18 29	18 32	.	.	.	.
	d	17 53	18 02	.	18 14	18 19	18 21	.	.	.	.	.	.	.	.	.	.	.	18 19	18 29	18 32	.	.	18 43	.
Tonbridge 4	a	.	.	.	.	→		.	.	.	.	.	.	.	.	.	.	.	.	.	.	.	.	.	.
Reigate	a	.	.	.	18 18	.	18 27	.	.	.	.	.	.	.	.	.	.	.	.	.	.	.	.	18 47	.
Earlswood (Surrey)	d	17 56	.	.	.	.		.	.	.	.	.	.	.	.	.	.	.	18 21	.	.	.	.	.	.
Salfords	d	18 00	.	.	.	.		.	.	.	.	.	.	.	.	.	.	.	18 25	.	.	.	.	.	.
Horley 4	d	18 04	.	18 09	.	.		.	.	.	.	.	.	.	.	.	.	.	18 29	18 36	.	18 39	.	.	.
Gatwick Airport 10	✈ a	18 08	18 12	.	.	.		18 15	.	←	.	.	.	18 24	18 28	.	18 30	.	18 32	.	18 41	.	.	.	.
	d	18 09	18 12	.	.	.		.	.	18 12	.	.	.	18 24	18 29	.	.	.	18 33	.	18 42	.	.	.	.
Three Bridges 4	a	18 15	→	.	.	.		.	.	18 18	18 22	.	18 25	.	.	.	.	18 35	18 38	18 41	18 53	.	.	.	.
	d	18 16	.	.	.	.		.	.	18 18	18 23	.	18 26	.	.	.	.	18 36	18 38	18 44	.	.	.	.	.
Crawley	d	18 20	.	.	.	.		.	.	.	.	.	18 30	.	.	.	.	.	18 42	.	.	.	.	.	.
Ifield	d	18 22	.	.	.	.		.	.	.	.	.	18 32	.	.	.	.	.	18 44	.	.	.	.	.	.
Faygate	d	.	.	.	.	.		.	.	.	.	.	.	.	.	.	.	.	.	.	.	.	.	.	.
Littlehaven	d	18 29	.	.	.	.		.	.	.	.	.	18 39	.	.	.	.	.	18 51	.	.	.	.	.	.
Horsham 4	a	18 33	.	.	.	.		.	.	.	.	.	18 42	.	.	.	.	.	18 56	.	.	.	←	.	.
Balcombe	d	.	.	.	.	.		.	.	18 24	.	.	.	.	.	.	.	.	.	18 50 →	.	.	18 50	.	.
Haywards Heath 3	a	.	.	18 20	.	.		.	18 23	18 29	18 32	.	.	18 36	18 41	.	.	18 44	.	.	.	18 49	18 55	.	.
	d	.	.	18 20	.	.		.	18 24	18 30	18 32	.	.	18 36	18 41	.	.	18 45	.	.	.	18 50	18 55	.	.
Wivelsfield 4	d	.	.	.	.	.		.	18 28	18 34	.	.	.	18 42	18 46	.	.	18 49	.	.	.	.	18 59	.	.
Lewes 4	a	.	.	.	.	.		.	18 44	.	.	.	.	.	19 01	.	.	.	.	.	.	.	.	.	.
Burgess Hill 4	d	.	.	18 26	.	.		.	.	18 37	18 41	.	.	18 43	.	.	.	18 52	.	.	.	18 56	19 01	.	.
Hassocks 4	d	.	.	18 30	.	.		.	.	18 41	18 45	.	.	18 47	.	.	.	18 56	.	.	.	19 00	.	.	.
Preston Park	d	.	.	18 37	.	.		.	.	18 48	18 53	.	.	18 56	.	.	.	19 02	.	.	.	19 07	19 10	.	.
Hove 2	a	.	.	.	.	.		.	.	.	18 57	.	.	.	.	.	.	.	.	.	.	.	.	.	.
Brighton 10	a	.	.	18 44	.	.		.	.	18 54	.	.	.	19 02	.	.	.	19 09	.	.	.	19 13	19 19	.	.

For general notes see front of timetable
For details of catering facilities see Directory of Train Operators

§ It is unknown at the time of going to press, when this station will open. For further details please contact National Rail Enquiries 08457-484950 or see local publicity.

A To Littlehampton (Table 188)
B To Bognor Regis (Table 188)

Watford Junction, Bedford and London → Brighton

Network Diagram - see first page of Table 186

		SN	GX	SN	SN		SN	LO	FC	SN	GX	SN		SN	GW	SN	FC	SN	SN	GX	SN	SN		SN	SE
		1	1	1	1		1		1	1	1	1		1	1	1	1	1	1	1	1	1		1	13
				A			B									C								C	
London Victoria 15	⊖ d	18 10	18 15		18 17		18 21				18 30	18 32							18 40	18 45		18 47			
Watford Junction	d																				18 12				
Harrow & Wealdstone	⊖ d																				18 18				
Wembley Central	d																				18 23				
Willesden Jn. High Level	d							18 08																	
Shepherds Bush §	⊖ d																								
Kensington Olympia	⊖ d							18 17													18 39				
West Brompton	⊖ d							18 19													18 42				
Imperial Wharf §	d																								
Clapham Junction 10	d	18 16			18 23		18 27	18a28				18 38							18 46		18b55	18 53			
Bedford 7	d								17 10												→				
Luton 10	d								17 34																
Luton Airport Parkway 7	✈ d								17 36																
St Albans	d								17 48																
St Pancras International 15	⊖ d								18 09																
Farringdon 3	⊖ d								18 14																
City Thameslink 3	d								18 16																
London Blackfriars 3	⊖ d								18 20																
London Bridge 4	⊖ d			18 16					18 26							18 34	18 38								18 48
Norwood Junction 2	d																								
East Croydon	⇌ a	18 26		18 29	18 33		18 37		18 40			18 48				18 48	18 52		18 56			19 03			19 03
	d	18 26		18 30	18 33		18 37		18 40			18 48				18 49	18 52		18 56			19 03			19 06
Purley 4	d	18 33														18 54			19 02						
Coulsdon South	d	18 37														18 58			19 05						19 14
Merstham	d	18 42														19 03			19 11						19 20
Redhill	a	18 46								←						19 07			19 14					←	19 23
	d	18 46								18 46				18 50	18 56	19 07		19 12	19 15					19 07	19 24
Tonbridge 4	a	→														→			→						19 56
Reigate	a													18 54				19 16							
Earlswood (Surrey)	d									18 49														19 10	
Salfords	d									18 52														19 13	
Horley 4	d									18 56														19 17	
Gatwick Airport 10	✈ a		18 45	18 45	18 49				18 56	18 58	19 00	19 03			19 07		19 09			19 15		19 18		19 20	
	d			18 46	18 50				18 56	18 59		19 04					19 10					19 19		19 21	
Three Bridges 4	a						18 57		19 01	19 04														19 25	
	d						18 57		19 02	19 07														19 26	
Crawley	d						19 01			19 10														19 30	
Ifield	d									19 13														19 32	
Faygate	d									19 17														19 36	
Littlehaven	d						19 09			19 21														19 40	
Horsham 4	a						19 12			19 26														19 43	
Balcombe	d								19 08								19 18								
Haywards Heath 3	a			18 58	19 01				19 12			19 16					19 24					19 29			
	d			18 58	19 05	19 08			19 12			19 19	19 22				19 24					19 33	19 36		
Wivelsfield 4	d				19 09												19 28					19 37			
Lewes 4	a				19 24																	19 52			
Burgess Hill 4	d			19 04					19 17								19 32								
Hassocks 4	d			19 08					19 21								19 36								
Preston Park	d			19 16													19 43								
Hove 2	a			19 19								19 34											19 51		
Brighton 10	a					19 25			19 32				19 39				19 48								

For general notes see front of timetable
For details of catering facilities see Directory of Train Operators

§ It is unknown at the time of going to press, when this station will open. For further details please contact National Rail Enquiries 08457-484950 or see local publicity.

A To Southampton Central (Table 188) and to Littlehampton (Table 188)

B To Portsmouth & Southsea (Table 188) and to Bognor Regis (Table 188)

C To Littlehampton (Table 188)

b Arr. 1848

Watford Junction, Bedford and London → Brighton

Network Diagram - see first page of Table 186

		SN	LO	FC	SN	GX	GW	SN	SN	FC	SN	GX	SN	SN	GW	XC	LO	FC	SN	GX	SN	SN	SN	FC
		1		1	1	1	1	1	1	1	1	1	1	1	1	R 1		1	1	1	1	1	1	1
								A ⌶	⌶					B ⌶		⊡					C	⌶		
London Victoria 15	⊖ d					19 00		19 02	19 06			19 15	19 10	19 17						19 30	19 32		19 36	
Watford Junction	d																							
Harrow & Wealdstone	⊖ d																							
Wembley Central	d																							
Willesden Jn. High Level	d		18 38														19 08							
Shepherds Bush §	⊖ d																							
Kensington Olympia	⊖ d		18 47													19 02	19 17							
West Brompton	⊖ d		18 49														19 19							
Imperial Wharf §	d	←																						
Clapham Junction 10	d	18 55	18a58					19 08	19 12				19 16	19 23			19a28				19 38		19 42	
Bedford 7	d			17 36						17 50								18 10						18 30
Luton 10	d			18 00						18 14								18 34						18 52
Luton Airport Parkway 7	✈ d			18 02						18 16								18 36						
St Albans	d			18 14						18 28								18 48						19 03
St Pancras International 15	⊖ d			18 39						18 54								19 09						19 24
Farringdon 3	⊖ d			18 44						18 59								19 14						19 29
City Thameslink 3	d			18 46						19 01								19 16						19 31
London Blackfriars 3	⊖ d			18 49						19 04								19 19						19 34
London Bridge 4	⊖ d			18 56						19 12								19 27						19 41
Norwood Junction 2	d																							
East Croydon	🚋 a	19 07		19 10				19 18	19 22	19 24			19 28	19 33		19 33		19 39			19 48		19 52	19 54
	d	19 07		19 10				19 18	19 22	19 24			19 28	19 33		19 36		19 39			19 48		19 52	19 54
Purley 4	d												19 33											
Coulsdon South	d												19 37											
Merstham	d												19 42											
Redhill	a							19 30					19 46								20 00			
	d				← 19 15		19 27	19 31			19 31		19 46		19 41				← 19 46		20 00			
Tonbridge 4	a												→											
Reigate	a						19 31				19 35													
Earlswood (Surrey)	d				19 17														19 49					
Salfords	d				19 21														19 52					
Horley 4	d				19 24														19 56					
Gatwick Airport 10	✈ a	19 23		19 26	19 27	19 30		19 38		19 41		19 45		19 48	19 50	19 52		19 55	19 58	20 00	20 08			20 10
	d			19 26	19 28			19 39		19 41				19 49		19 53		19 55	19 59		20 09			20 11
Three Bridges 4	a			19 32	19 33			19 44		19 45								20 00	20 04		20 14			20 15
	d			19 32	19 34			19 44		19 45								20 01	20 04		20 14			20 15
Crawley	d				19 37			19 48											20 08		20 18			
Ifield	d				19 40														20 10					
Faygate	d																		20 14					
Littlehaven	d				19 46														20 18					
Horsham 4	a				19 51			19 56											20 21		20 26			
Balcombe	d									19 51														
Haywards Heath 3	a			19 40					19 45	19 57				20 00		20 04		20 09					20 16	20 25
	d			19 40					19 45	19 58				20 13 → 20 04		20 07		20 09				← 20 13	20 17	20 26
Wivelsfield 4	d									20 02												20 17		20 30
Lewes 4	a																					20 28		
Burgess Hill 4	d			19 46						20 04				20 09				20 15						20 32
Hassocks 4	d			19 50						20 07								20 19						20 35
Preston Park	d									20 14														20 42
Hove 2	a													20 21										
Brighton 10	a			20 00					20 03	20 22						20 29		20 29					20 33	20 48

For general notes see front of timetable
For details of catering facilities see Directory of Train Operators

§ It is unknown at the time of going to press, when this station will open. For further details please contact National Rail Enquiries 08457-484950 or see local publicity.

A To Portsmouth & Southsea (Table 188) and to Bognor Regis (Table 188)

B To Littlehampton (Table 188)

C To Southampton Central (Table 188) and to Bognor Regis (Table 188)

Watford Junction, Bedford and London → Brighton

Network Diagram - see first page of Table 186

Station		SN	GW	SN	GX	SN	SN		SN	SN	LO	SN	GX	FC	SE	SN	SN	FC	SN	GX	SN		LO	GW	GW
															88										
		1	1	1	1	1	1		1	1		1	1	1		1	1	1	1	1	1			1	1
							A ⚲									B					A				
London Victoria 15 ⊖	d			19 40	19 45		19 47						20 00			20 02	20 06		20 10	20 15	20 17				
Watford Junction	d					19 11																			
Harrow & Wealdstone ⊖	d					19 18																			
Wembley Central	d					19 23																			
Willesden Jn. High Level	d										19 38												20 08		
Shepherds Bush § ⊖	d					19 37																			
Kensington Olympia ⊖	d					19 39					19 47												20 17		
West Brompton ⊖	d					19 41					19 49												20 19		
Imperial Wharf §	d									←															
Clapham Junction 10	d			19 46		19b54	19 53			19 54	19a58					20 08	20 12		20 16		20 23		20a29		
Bedford 7	d					→								18 40				18 50							
Luton 10	d													19 04				19 14							
Luton Airport Parkway 7 ✈	d													19 06				19 16							
St Albans	d													19 18				19 28							
St Pancras International 15 ⊖	d													19 39				19 54							
Farringdon 3 ⊖	d													19 44				19 59							
City Thameslink 3	d													19 47				20 01							
London Blackfriars 3 ⊖	d													19 54				20 04							
London Bridge 4 ⊖	d								19 52					20 01				20 11							
Norwood Junction 2	d								20 03																
East Croydon	a			19 58			20 03		20 06	20 07				20 14		20 19	20 22	20 23	20 28		20 33				
	d			19 58			20 03		20 07	20 07				20 14		20 19	20 22	20 23	20 29		20 33				
Purley 4	d			20 03					20 12										20 33						
Coulsdon South	d			20 06					20 15										20 37						
Merstham	d			20 12					20 21										20 42						
Redhill	a			20 15					20 24			←				20 30			→						
	d	20 05	20 14	20 16					20 25			20 16			20 28	20 31								20 34	20 42
Tonbridge 4	a			→																					
Reigate	a	20 09	20 18						20 30															20 38	
Earlswood (Surrey)	d											20 18													
Salfords	d											20 22													
Horley 4	d											20 25													
Gatwick Airport 10 ✈	a				20 15		20 18			20 23		20 28	20 30	20 31	20 35	20 38		20 39		20 45	20 48				20 50
	d						20 19					20 29		20 31	20 36	20 39		20 40			20 49				
Three Bridges 4	a											20 34			20 40	20 44		20 43							
	d											20 34				20 44		20 43							
Crawley	d											20 38				20 48									
Ifield	d											20 40													
Faygate	d																								
Littlehaven	d											20 47													
Horsham 4	a											20 50				20 56									
Balcombe	d																	20 49							
Haywards Heath 3	a						20 30							20 42			20 47	20 56			21 01				
	d						20 34	20 36						20 42			20 47	20 58			21 05	21 07			
Wivelsfield 4	d							20 40										21 02				21 11			
Lewes 4	a							20 55														21 22			
Burgess Hill 4	d						20 39											21 04			21 10				
Hassocks 4	d						20 42											21 07							
Preston Park	d						20 49											21 15							
Hove 2	a						20 53														21 21				
Brighton 10	a													21 00			21 01	21 22							

For general notes see front of timetable
For details of catering facilities see Directory of Train Operators

§ It is unknown at the time of going to press, when this station will open. For further details please contact National Rail Enquiries 08457-484950 or see local publicity.

A To Littlehampton (Table 188)

B To Portsmouth Harbour (Table 188) and to Bognor Regis (Table 188)

b Arr. 1948

Watford Junction, Bedford and London → Brighton

Network Diagram - see first page of Table 186

	SN 1	SN 1	GX 1	SN 1	SN 1 A	SN 1	FC 1	GW 1	SN 1	GX 1	SN 1	SN 1 B		SN 1	LO	SN 1	XC R 1	SN 1	GX 1	SN 1	SE 88	SN 1	SN 1	SN 1
London Victoria 15 ⊖ d			20 30		20 32	20 36			20 40	20 45		20 47							21 00			21 02	21 06	
Watford Junction d											20 11													
Harrow & Wealdstone ⊖ d											20 17													
Wembley Central d																								
Willesden Jn. High Level d															20 38									
Shepherds Bush § ⊖ d											20 36													
Kensington Olympia ⊖ d											20 38				20 47		20 52							
West Brompton ⊖ d											20 41				20 49									
Imperial Wharf § d														←										
Clapham Junction 10 d					20 38	20 42			20 46		20b54	20 53		20 54	20a58							21 08	21 12	
Bedford 7 d							19 20				→													
Luton 10 d							19 44																	
Luton Airport Parkway 7 ✈ d							19 46																	
St Albans d							19 58																	
St Pancras International 15 ⊖ d							20 24																	
Farringdon 3 ⊖ d							20 29																	
City Thameslink 3 d							20 31																	
London Blackfriars 3 ⊖ d							20 34																	
London Bridge 4 ⊖ d	20 28						20 41									20 58								
Norwood Junction 2 d																								
East Croydon a	20 40				20 48	20 52	20 54		20 58			21 03		21 07		21 10	21 15					21 18	21 22	
d	20 41				20 48	20 52	20 54		20 58			21 03		21 07		21 11	21 16					21 18	21 22	
Purley 4 d									21 03								→							
Coulsdon South d		←							21 06															
Merstham d		20 42							21 12															
Redhill a		20 46			21 00				21 15													21 30		
d		20 46		20 54	21 00			21 14	21 16									← 21 16		21 22	21 27	21 31		
Tonbridge 4 a									→															
Reigate a				20 58				21 18												21 26				
Earlswood (Surrey) d		20 49																21 18						
Salfords d																		21 22						
Horley 4 d		20 54																21 25						
Gatwick Airport 10 ✈ a	20 55	20 57	21 00		21 08		21 10			21 15		21 18		21 23		21 26		21 28	21 30		21 34	21 38		←
d	20 56	20 58			21 09		21 11					21 19				21 27		21 29			21 35	21 39		21 39
Three Bridges 4 a	21 01	21 02			21 14		21 15									21 31		21 33			21 40	→		21 44
d	21 01	21 06			21 14		21 15									21 32		21 36						21 44
Crawley d		21 09			21 18													21 39						
Ifield d		21 12																21 42						
Faygate d																								
Littlehaven d		21 18																21 48						
Horsham 4 a		21 21			21 26													21 52						
Balcombe d																								
Haywards Heath 3 a	21 10					21 15	21 24					21 30				21 40							21 45	21 52
d	21 11					21 15	21 26					21 34	21 37			21 41							21 45	21 53
Wivelsfield 4 d							21 30						21 41											21 57
Lewes 4 a													21 54											
Burgess Hill 4 d							21 32					21 39												21 59
Hassocks 4 d							21 35					21 42												22 02
Preston Park d							21 42					21 49												22 09
Hove 2 a												21 53												
Brighton 10 a	21 26					21 30	21 48									21 54							22 00	22 15

For general notes see front of timetable
For details of catering facilities see Directory of Train Operators

§ It is unknown at the time of going to press, when this station will open. For further details please contact National Rail Enquiries 08457-484950 or see local publicity.

A To Southampton Central (Table 188) and to Bognor Regis (Table 188)

B To Littlehampton (Table 188)

b Arr. 2048

Watford Junction, Bedford and London → Brighton

Network Diagram - see first page of Table 186

		FC	SN	GX	XC	SN		LO	GW	XC	SN	GX	GW	SN	SN	XC	SN	FC	SN	GX	SN	LO	SN		SN
					R					R															
		1	1	1	1	1			1	1	1	1	1	1	1	1 ◊	1	1	1	1	1		1		1
						A									B										
London Victoria 15	⊖ d		21 10	21 15		21 17						21 30			21 32		21 36		21 40	21 45			21 47		
Watford Junction	d																				21 11				
Harrow & Wealdstone	⊖ d																				21 17				
Wembley Central	d																								
Willesden Jn. High Level	d							21 08														21 38			
Shepherds Bush §	⊖ d																								
Kensington Olympia	⊖ d							21 17													21 36	21 47			
West Brompton	⊖ d							21 19													21 39	21 49			
Imperial Wharf §	d																								←
Clapham Junction 10	d		21 16			21 23		21a28							21 38		21 42		21 46		21b54	21a58	21 53		21 54
Bedford 7	d	19 50																20 20			→				
Luton 10	d	20 14																20 44							
Luton Airport Parkway 7	✈ d	20 16																20 46							
St Albans	d	20 28																20 58							
St Pancras International 15	⊖ d	20 54																21 24							
Farringdon 3	⊖ d	20 59																21 29							
City Thameslink 3	d	21 01																21 31							
London Blackfriars 3	⊖ d	21 04																21 34							
London Bridge 4	⊖ d	21 11																21 41							
Norwood Junction 2	d																								
East Croydon	a	21 24	21 28			21 33				←					21 48		21 52	21 54	21 58				22 03		22 07
	d	21 24	21 28			21 33				21 16					21 48		21 52	21 54	21 58				22 03		22 08
Purley 4	d		21 33																22 03						
Coulsdon South	d		21 37								←								22 06						
Merstham	d		21 42								21 42								22 12						
Redhill	a		→		←					21 34	21 46				21 59	22 10			22 15						
	d				21 35				21 35	21 35	21 46		21 51	21 55	22 00	22 18			22 16						
Tonbridge 4	a									→						→			→						
Reigate	a								21 39					21 59											
Earlswood (Surrey)	d																								
Salfords	d																								
Horley 4	d										21 52														
Gatwick Airport 10	✈ a	21 41		21 45	21 47	21 48					21 55	22 00	22 04		22 08			22 10		22 15			22 18		22 23
	d	21 41				21 49					21 56				22 09			22 11					22 19		
Three Bridges 4	a	21 45				21 53					22 01				22 14			22 15							
	d	21 45				21 53					22 01				22 14			22 15							
Crawley	d										22 05				22 18										
Ifield	d										22 07														
Faygate	d																								
Littlehaven	d										22 14														
Horsham 4	a										22 17				22 26										
Balcombe	d	21 51																							
Haywards Heath 3	a	21 58				22 02											22 15	22 24					22 30		
	d	21 58				22 06	22 08										22 15	22 26					22 34	22 37	
Wivelsfield 4	d	22 02					22 12											22 30					22 38		
Lewes 4	a						22 23																22 51		
Burgess Hill 4	d	22 04				22 11												22 32							
Hassocks 4	d	22 08																22 35							
Preston Park	d	22 15																22 42							
Hove 2	a					22 22																		22 51	
Brighton 10	a	22 22															22 30	22 48							

For general notes see front of timetable
For details of catering facilities see Directory of Train Operators

§ It is unknown at the time of going to press, when this station will open. For further details please contact National Rail Enquiries 08457-484950 or see local publicity.

A To Bognor Regis (Table 188) and to Eastbourne (Table 189)

B To Portsmouth & Southsea (Table 188)

b Arr. 2147

Watford Junction, Bedford and London → Brighton

Network Diagram - see first page of Table 186

Station		SN	GX	XC	SN	SE	SN	SN	SN	FC	SN	GX	SN	LO	GW	SN	GX	GW	SN	SN	FC	SN	SN	GX	SN
						88																			
		1	1	1 ◇	1		1	1	1	1	1	1	1		1	1	1	1	1	1	1	1	1	1	1
													A						B						
London Victoria 15	⊖ d		22 00				22 02	22 06			22 10	22 15	22 17				22 30		22 32	22 36			22 40	22 45	
Watford Junction	d																								22 12
Harrow & Wealdstone	⊖ d																								22 18
Wembley Central	d																								
Willesden Jn. High Level	d													22 08											
Shepherds Bush §	⊖ d																								
Kensington Olympia	⊖ d													22 17											22 41
West Brompton	⊖ d													22 19											22 43
Imperial Wharf §	d																								
Clapham Junction 10	d						22 08	22 12			22 16		22 23	22a28					22 38	22 42			22 46		22a51
Bedford 7	d									20 50											21 20				
Luton 10	d									21 14											21 44				
Luton Airport Parkway 7	✈ d									21 16											21 46				
St Albans	d									21 28											21 59				
St Pancras International 15	⊖ d									21 54											22 24				
Farringdon 3	⊖ d									21 59											22 29				
City Thameslink 3	d									22 01											22 31				
London Blackfriars 3	⊖ d									22 04											22 34				
London Bridge 4	⊖ d									22 11											22 41				
Norwood Junction 2	d																								
East Croydon	a						22 18	22 22		22 24	22 28		22 33						22 48	22 52	22 54		22 58		
	d						22 18	22 22		22 24	22 28		22 33						22 48	22 52	22 54		22 58		
Purley 4	d										22 33												23 03		
Coulsdon South	d										22 37					←							23 07		
Merstham	d										22 42					22 42							23 12		
Redhill	a	←		←			22 30				↪					22 46			23 00				23 16		
	d	22 16		22 18	22 20	22 27	22 31								22 33	22 46		22 52	23 01			23 05	23 16		
Tonbridge 4	a																						→		
Reigate	a				22 24										22 38							23 09			
Earlswood (Surrey)	d	22 18																							
Salfords	d	22 22																							
Horley 4	d	22 25														22 52									
Gatwick Airport 10	✈ a	22 28	22 30	22 32		22 34	22 38		←	22 41		22 45	22 48			22 55	23 00	23 04	23 08		23 10			23 15	
	d	22 29				22 35	22 39		22 39	22 41			22 49			22 56			23 09		23 11				
Three Bridges 4	a	22 33				22 40	↪		22 44	22 45			22 54			23 00			23 14		23 15				
	d	22 36							22 44	22 45			22 54			23 01			23 15		23 15				
Crawley	d	22 39														23 04			23 18						
Ifield	d	22 42														23 07									
Faygate	d																								
Littlehaven	d	22 48														23 13									
Horsham 4	a	22 52														23 16			23 26						
Balcombe	d									22 51															
Haywards Heath 3	a							22 45	22 52	22 58			23 02							23 15	23 24				
	d							22 45	22 53	22 58			23 03							23 15	23 26				
Wivelsfield 4	d								22 57	23 02											23 30				
Lewes 4	a																								
Burgess Hill 4	d								22 59	23 04			23 08								23 32				
Hassocks 4	d								23 02	23 08											23 35				
Preston Park	d								23 09	23 15											23 42				
Hove 2	a												23 21												
Brighton 10	a							23 00	23 15	23 22										23 30	23 48				

For general notes see front of timetable
For details of catering facilities see
Directory of Train Operators

§ It is unknown at the time of going to press, when this station will open. For further details please contact National Rail Enquiries 08457-484950 or see local publicity.

A To Bognor Regis (Table 188)
B To Chichester (Table 188)

Watford Junction, Bedford and London → Brighton

Network Diagram - see first page of Table 186

		SN 1		LO	SN 1	GX 1	SN 1	SN 1	SN 1	FC 1	SN 1	GX 1	SN 1	LO	SN 1	GX 1	SN 1	FC 1	GX 1	SN 1	FC	FC	FC 1	SN 1
													A											
London Victoria 15	⊖ d	22 47				23 00	23 02	23 06			23 10	23 15	23 17			23 30	23 32		23 45	23 47				
Watford Junction	d																							23 18
Harrow & Wealdstone	⊖ d																							23 24
Wembley Central	d																							
Willesden Jn. High Level	d			22 38										23 08										
Shepherds Bush §	⊖ d																							
Kensington Olympia	⊖ d			22 47										23 17										23 44
West Brompton	⊖ d			22 49										23 19										23 47
Imperial Wharf §	d																							
Clapham Junction 10	d	22 53		22a58			23 08	23 12			23 16		23 23	23a28			23 38			23 53				23a54
Bedford 7	d									21 50								22 10			22 40	23 10	23 40	
Luton 10	d									22 14								22 34			23 04	23 34	00 04	
Luton Airport Parkway 7	✈ d									22 16								22 36			23 06	23 36	00 06	
St Albans	d									22 29								22 48			23 18	23 48	00 18	
St Pancras International 15	⊖ d									22 54								23 24			23 54	00 24	00 54	
Farringdon 3	⊖ d									22 59								23 29			23 59	00 29		
City Thameslink 3	d									23 01														
London Blackfriars 3	⊖ d									23 04								23 34			00 04	00 34	01 04	
London Bridge 4	⊖ d									23 11								23 41			00 11	00 41		
Norwood Junction 2	d																							
East Croydon	🚊 a	23 03					23 18	23 22		23 24	23 28		23 33				23 51	23 56		00 05	00 26	00 56	01 32	
	d	23 03					23 18	23 22		23 24	23 28		23 33				23 52	23 57		00 06	00 27	00 57	01 32	
Purley 4	d										23 33									00 12				
Coulsdon South	d										23 37									00 15				
Merstham	d										23 42									00 21				
Redhill	a						23 30				23 46						00 03			00 24				
	d				← 23 16		23 31				23 46				← 23 46		00 05			00 25				
Tonbridge 4	a										↪													
Reigate	a																							
Earlswood (Surrey)	d				23 19										23 49									
Salfords	d				23 22										23 52									
Horley 4	d				23 26										23 56					00 31				
Gatwick Airport 10	✈ a	23 18			23 28	23 30	23 38		←	23 41		23 45	23 50		23 58	00 05	00 13	00 16	00 20	00 33	00 49	01 16	01 51	
	d	23 19			23 29		23 39		23 39	23 41			23 51		23 59		00 14	00 17		00 34	00 50	01 17	01 52	
Three Bridges 4	a				23 34		↪		23 44	23 47			23 55		00 04		00 18	00 26		00 39	00 56	01 26	02 00	
	d				23 38				23 44	23 47			23 56		00 04		00 19			00 39				
Crawley	d				23 41										00 07					00 42				
Ifield	d				23 44										00 10					00 45				
Faygate	d																							
Littlehaven	d				23 50										00 16					00 51				
Horsham 4	a				23 53										00 19					00 54				
Balcombe	d									23 53							00 25							
Haywards Heath 3	a	23 30						23 45	23 52	23 58			00 04				00 30							
	d	23 34	23 37					23 45	23 53	23 58			00 05				00 30							
Wivelsfield 4	d	23 38							23 57	00 02							00 34							
Lewes 4	a	23 51																						
Burgess Hill 4	d								23 59	00 04			00 10				00 36							
Hassocks 4	d								00 02	00 08							00 40							
Preston Park	d								00 09	00 15							00 47							
Hove 2	a		23 51										00 21											
Brighton 10	a							23 59	00 15	00 22							00 51							

For general notes see front of timetable
For details of catering facilities see
Directory of Train Operators

§ It is unknown at the time of going to press, when this station will open. For further details please contact National Rail Enquiries 08457-484950 or see local publicity.

A To Worthing (Table 188)

Table 186

Watford Junction, Bedford and London → Brighton

Network Diagram - see first page of Table 186

		SN 1	FC 1	SN 1	SN 1 A	SN 1	GW 1	SN 1	FC 1	SN 1	GX 1	SN 1 B	FC	SN 1	GW 1	FC	GX 1	SN 1	FC 1	SN 1	FC 1	SN 1		FC 1
London Victoria 15	⊖ d	23p02		23p10	23p17			23p32		23p47	00 01	00 05		00 14			00 30	01 00		02 02		03 00		
Watford Junction	d																							
Harrow & Wealdstone	⊖ d																							
Wembley Central	d																							
Willesden Jn. High Level	d																							
Shepherds Bush §	⊖ d																							
Kensington Olympia	⊖ d																							
West Brompton	⊖ d																							
Imperial Wharf §	d																							
Clapham Junction 10	d	23p08		23p16	23p23			23p38		23p53		00 11		00 20				01 08		02 08		03 08		
Bedford 7	d		21p50						22p10				22p40			23p10			23p40		00 40			01 40
Luton 10	d		22p14						22p34				23p04			23p34			00 04		01 04			02 04
Luton Airport Parkway 7	✈ d		22p16						22p36				23p06			23p36			00 06		01 06			02 06
St Albans	d		22p29						22p48				23p18			23p48			00 18		01 18			02 18
St Pancras International 15	⊖ d		22p54						23p24				23p54			00 24			00 54		01 54			02 54
Farringdon 3	⊖ d		22p59						23p29				23p59			00 29								
City Thameslink 3	d		23p01																					
London Blackfriars 3	⊖ d		23p04						23p34				00 04			00 34			01 04		02 04			03 04
London Bridge 4	⊖ d		23p11						23p41				00 11			00 41								
Norwood Junction 2	d																							
East Croydon	🚌 a	23p18	23p24	23p28	23p33			23p51	23p56	00 05		00 24	00 26	00 32		00 56		01 21	01 32	02 21	02 30	03 21		03 30
	d	23p18	23p24	23p28	23p33			23p52	23p57	00 06		00 25	00 27	00 33		00 57		01 22	01 32	02 22	02 32	03 22		03 32
Purley 4	d			23p33						00 12				00 38				01 27		02 27		03 27		
Coulsdon South	d			23p37						00 15				00 41										
Merstham	d			23p42						00 21				00 47										
Redhill	a	23p30		23p46		←		00 03		00 24				00 50										
	d	23p31		23p46		23p46	00 03	00 05		00 25				00 51	00 53									
Tonbridge 4	a			↪																				
Reigate	a																							
Earlswood (Surrey)	d					23p49																		
Salfords	d					23p52																		
Horley 4	d					23p56				00 31								01 43		02 42		03 42		
Gatwick Airport 10	✈ a	23p38	23p41		23p50	23p58	00 11	00 13	00 16	00 33	00 35	00 42	00 49	00 58	01 01	01 16	01 20	01 45	01 51	02 44	02 51	03 44		03 51
	d	23p39	23p41		23p51	23p59		00 14	00 17	00 34		00 43	00 50			01 17		01 47	01 52	02 46	02 52	03 46		03 52
Three Bridges 4	a	23p44	23p47		23p55	00 04		00 18	00 26	00 39		00 48	00 56			01 26		01 51	02 00	02 50	03 00	03 50		04 00
	d	23p44	23p47		23p56	00 04		00 19		00 39		00 48						01 52						
Crawley	d					00 07				00 42														
Ifield	d					00 10				00 45														
Faygate	d																							
Littlehaven	d					00 16				00 51														
Horsham 4	a					00 19				00 54														
Balcombe	d		23p53					00 25																
Haywards Heath 3	a	23p52	23p58		00 04			00 30				00 56						02 04						
	d	23p53	23p58		00 05			00 30				01 00 / 01 02						02 05						
Wivelsfield 4	d	23p57	00 02					00 34																
Lewes 4	a											01 16												
Burgess Hill 4	d	23p59	00 04		00 10			00 36																
Hassocks 4	d	00 02	00 08					00 40																
Preston Park	d	00 09	00 15					00 47																
Hove 2	a				00 21							01s22												
Brighton 10	a	00 15	00 22					00 51				01s14						02 32						

For general notes see front of timetable
For details of catering facilities see Directory of Train Operators

§ It is unknown at the time of going to press, when this station will open. For further details please contact National Rail Enquiries 08457-484950 or see local publicity.

A To Worthing (Table 188)
B To Eastbourne (Table 189)

Watford Junction, Bedford and London → Brighton

Network Diagram - see first page of Table 186

		GX	SN	FC	GX	FC	GX	SN	GX	GW	GW	FC	SN	GX	SN	SN	GX	FC	SN		GX	GW	SE 88		GW
		1	1	1	1	1	1	1	1	1	1	1	1	1	1	1	1	1	1		1	1			1
													A		B	C			B						
London Victoria 15 ⊖	d	03 30	04 00		04 30		05 00	05 02	05 15					05 30	05 32		05 45				06 00				
Watford Junction	d																								
Harrow & Wealdstone ⊖	d																								
Wembley Central	d																								
Willesden Jn. High Level	d																								
Shepherds Bush § ⊖	d																								
Kensington Olympia ⊖	d																								
West Brompton ⊖	d																								
Imperial Wharf §	d																								
Clapham Junction 10	d		04 08					05 08							05 38										
Bedford 7	d			02 40		03 10						03 40						04 20							
Luton 10	d			03 04		03 34						04 04						04 44							
Luton Airport Parkway 7 ✈	d			03 06		03 36						04 06						04 46							
St Albans	d			03 18		03 48						04 18						04 58							
St Pancras International 15 ⊖	d			03 54		04 23						04 54						05 34							
Farringdon 3 ⊖	d											04 59						05 39							
City Thameslink 3	d																								
London Blackfriars 3 ⊖	d			04 04		04 34						05 04						05 44							
London Bridge 4 ⊖	d																	05 50							
Norwood Junction 2	d																								
East Croydon	a		04 21	04 30		05 00		05 21				05 32			05 48			06 04							
	d		04 22	04 32		05 02		05 22				05 32			05 48			06 05							
Purley 4	d		04 27					05 26							05 53										
Coulsdon South	d							05 30							05 57										
Merstham	d							05 35							06 03										
Redhill	a							05 39							06 06				←						
	d							05 39		05 43	05 44				06 07				06 07			06 14	06 27		06 34
Tonbridge 4	a														→										
Reigate	a									05 47												06 18			06 38
Earlswood (Surrey)	d																		06 11						
Salfords	d																		06 14						
Horley 4	d		04 43					05 45											06 18						
Gatwick Airport 10 ✈	a	04 05	04 45	04 51	05 05	05 21	05 35	05 48	05 50		05 53	05 54		06 00			06 15	06 20	06 20		06 30		06 35		
	d		04 47	04 52		05 22		05 50				05 54	05 58			06 11		06 20	06 21				06 36		
Three Bridges 4	a		04 51	05 00		05 27		05 54				06 00	06 02			06 15		06 25	06 25				06 40		
	d		04 52			05 28		05 54				06 00	06 03			06 16		06 26	06 30	06 34					
Crawley	d												06 06							06 37					
Ifield	d												06 09							06 40					
Faygate	d																								
Littlehaven	d												06 15							06 46					
Horsham 4	a												06 18							06 49					
Balcombe	d					05 35						06 06						06 32	06 36						
Haywards Heath 3	a		05 00			05 40		06 03				06 12				06 25		06 37	06 41						
	d		05 01			05 42		06 03				06 12				06 25		06 38	06 41						
Wivelsfield 4	d					05 46		06 07				06 16				06 29			06 45						
Lewes 4	a															06 40									
Burgess Hill 4	d					05 48		06 09				06 18							06 47						
Hassocks 4	d					05 52		06 13				06 22							06 51						
Preston Park	d					05 59		06 20				06 29							06 58						
Hove 2	a																								
Brighton 10	a		05 16			06 07		06 25				06 34						06 53	07 02						

For general notes see front of timetable
For details of catering facilities see Directory of Train Operators

§ It is unknown at the time of going to press, when this station will open. For further details please contact National Rail Enquiries 08457-484950 or see local publicity.

A To Southampton Central (Table 188) and to Bognor Regis (Table 188)

B To Portsmouth Harbour (Table 188)

C To Ore (Table 189)

Table 186

Saturdays

Watford Junction, Bedford and London → Brighton

Network Diagram - see first page of Table 186

	LO	GX	GW	SN	FC	SN	GX	FC	GW	SN	GX	SN	SN	SN	FC	LO	SN	SN	SN	GX	SE	FC		SN
		1	1	1	1	1	1	1	1	1	1	1	1	1	1		1	1	1	1	55 1	1		1
				A		A				B									B					
London Victoria 15 ⊖ d		06 15		06 10			06 30			06 40	06 45						07 06			07 00				07 10
Watford Junction d												06 11												
Harrow & Wealdstone ⊖ d												06 17												
Wembley Central d																								
Willesden Jn. High Level d	06 08															06 38								
Shepherds Bush § ⊖ d																								
Kensington Olympia ⊖ d	06 17											06 42				06 48								
West Brompton ⊖ d	06 19											06 45				06 49								
Imperial Wharf § d																								
Clapham Junction 10 d	06a29			06 16						06 46		06 54				06a59	07 12							07 16
Bedford 7 d					04 50			05 20							05 40							05 50		
Luton 10 d					05 14			05 44							06 04							06 14		
Luton Airport Parkway 7 ✈ d					05 16			05 46							06 06							06 16		
St Albans d					05 28			05 58							06 18							06 28		
St Pancras International 15 ⊖ d					06 04			06 24							06 39							06 54		
Farringdon 3 ⊖ d					06 09			06 29							06 44							06 59		
City Thameslink 3 d																								
London Blackfriars 3 ⊖ d					06 20			06 35							06 50							07 05		
London Bridge 4 ⊖ d					06 26			06 41							06 56							07 11		
Norwood Junction 2 d																								
East Croydon a				06 27	06 39			06 54		06 57		07 07			07 09		07 22					07 24		07 28
d				06 28	06 39			06 54		06 58		07 07			07 09		07 22					07 24		07 30
Purley 4 d				06 33						07 03														07 36
Coulsdon South d				06 36						07 06														07 39
Merstham d				06 42						07 12														07 45
Redhill a				06 45		←				07 15									←					→
d			06 41	06 46		06 46			07 14	07 16									07 16		07 27			
Tonbridge 4 a				↦						↦														
Reigate a									07 18															
Earlswood (Surrey) d						06 48													07 18					
Salfords d						06 52													07 22					
Horley 4 d						06 55													07 25					
Gatwick Airport 10 ✈ a		06 45	06 50		06 55	06 58	07 00	07 10			07 15	07 22			07 25			←	07 28	07 30	07 34	07 40		
d					06 56	06 59		07 11				07 28			07 26			07 28	07 29		07 35	07 41		
Three Bridges 4 a					07 00	07 03		07 15				→						07 33	07 33		07 39	07 45		
d					07 00	07 04		07 15										07 33	07 34			07 45		
Crawley d						07 07													07 37					
Ifield d						07 10													07 40					
Faygate d																								
Littlehaven d						07 16													07 46					
Horsham 4 a						07 19													07 49					
Balcombe d								07 21																
Haywards Heath 3 a					07 08			07 26							07 36			07 42				07 54		
d					07 08			07 27					07 33	07 37	07 38			07 46				07 55		
Wivelsfield 4 d								07 31					07 37					07 50				07 59		
Lewes 4 a													07 48											
Burgess Hill 4 d								07 33										07 52				08 01		
Hassocks 4 d								07 36										07 55				08 04		
Preston Park d								07 43										08 02				08 11		
Hove 2 a														07 51										
Brighton 10 a					07 24			07 49							07 56		07 58	08 08				08 19		

For general notes see front of timetable
For details of catering facilities see Directory of Train Operators

§ It is unknown at the time of going to press, when this station will open. For further details please contact National Rail Enquiries 08457-484950 or see local publicity.

A To Southampton Central (Table 188)
B To Portsmouth Harbour (Table 188)

Table 186

Saturdays

Watford Junction, Bedford and London → Brighton

Network Diagram - see first page of Table 186

Station		GX 1	GW 1	GW 1	FC 1	SN 1	GX 1	LO	SN 1 A	SN 1	SN 1	FC 1	GX 1	SN 1		SN 1	SN 1	FC 1	GW 1	LO	SN 1	GX 1	SN 1 B		GW 1
London Victoria 15	⊖ d	07 15					07 30		07 32		07 36		07 45	07 47								08 00	08 02		
Watford Junction	d															07 13									
Harrow & Wealdstone	⊖ d															07 19									
Wembley Central	d																								
Willesden Jn. High Level	d							07 08												07 38					
Shepherds Bush §	⊖ d																								
Kensington Olympia	⊖ d							07 17								07 42				07 47					
West Brompton	⊖ d							07 19								07 45				07 49					
Imperial Wharf §	d																								
Clapham Junction 10	d							07a29	07 38		07 42			07 53		07 54				07a59			08 08		
Bedford 7	d				06 10							06 25						06 40							
Luton 10	d				06 34							06 49						07 04							
Luton Airport Parkway 7	✈ d				06 36							06 51						07 06							
St Albans	d				06 48							07 03						07 18							
St Pancras International 15	⊖ d				07 09							07 24						07 39							
Farringdon 3	⊖ d				07 14							07 29						07 44							
City Thameslink 3	d																								
London Blackfriars 3	⊖ d				07 20							07 35						07 50							
London Bridge 4	⊖ d				07 26					07 33		07 41						07 56							
Norwood Junction 2	d									07 46															
East Croydon	a				07 39				07 48	07 49	07 52	07 54		08 03		08 07		08 09					08 18		
	d				07 39				07 48	07 51	07 52	07 54		08 03		08 07		08 09					08 18		
Purley 4	d									07 57															
Coulsdon South	d					←				08 00															
Merstham	d					07 45				08 06															
Redhill	a					07 48			08 00	08 09							←						08 30		
	d		07 34	07 41		07 49			08 00	08 10							08 10		08 14				08 30		08 34
Tonbridge 4	a									→															
Reigate	a		07 38																08 18						08 38
Earlswood (Surrey)	d																08 12								
Salfords	d																08 16								
Horley 4	d					07 55											08 19						08 36		
Gatwick Airport 10	✈ a	07 45		07 50	07 55	07 57	08 00		08 08			08 10	08 15	08 18		08 22	08 23	08 25			←	08 30	08 39		
	d				07 56	07 58			08 09			08 11		08 19		08 28	08 24	08 26			08 28		08 40		
Three Bridges 4	a					08 03			08 14			08 15				→	08 29				08 33		08 44		
	d					08 03			08 14			08 15					08 30				08 33		08 45		
Crawley	d					08 06			08 18								08 33						08 48		
Ifield	d					08 09											08 36								
Faygate	d																								
Littlehaven	d					08 15											08 42								
Horsham 4	a					08 19			08 26								08 47						08 56		
Balcombe	d											08 21													
Haywards Heath 3	a				08 06							08 26		08 30				08 36			08 42				
	d				08 08							08 27		08 34	08 37			08 38			08 46				
Wivelsfield 4	d											08 31									08 52				
Lewes 4	a													08 52											
Burgess Hill 4	d											08 33									08 54				
Hassocks 4	d											08 36									08 57				
Preston Park	d											08 43									09 04				
Hove 2	a														08 51						→				
Brighton 10	a				08 26						08 28	08 51						08 56							

For general notes see front of timetable
For details of catering facilities see
Directory of Train Operators

§ It is unknown at the time of going to press, when this station will open. For further details please contact National Rail Enquiries 08457-484950 or see local publicity.

A To Southampton Central (Table 188) and to Bognor Regis (Table 188)

B To Portsmouth Harbour (Table 188) and to Bognor Regis (Table 188)

Table 186

Saturdays

Watford Junction, Bedford and London → Brighton

Network Diagram - see first page of Table 186

Station		SE 13	SN	SN	FC	GX	SN	SN	GW	FC	SE 88	GX	LO	SN	SN	SN	FC	GX	SN	SN	SN	LO	SN		FC
			1	1	1	1	1		1	1	1	1		1	1	1	1	1	1		1		1		1
		A					B				C			D											
London Victoria 15 ⊖	d		08 06			08 15	08 17					08 30		08 32		08 36		08 45	08 47						
Watford Junction	d																				08 11				
Harrow & Wealdstone ⊖	d																				08 17				
Wembley Central	d																								
Willesden Jn. High Level	d												08 08									08 38			
Shepherds Bush § ⊖	d																								
Kensington Olympia ⊖	d												08 17								08 42	08 47			
West Brompton ⊖	d												08 19								08 45	08 49			
Imperial Wharf §	d																								
Clapham Junction 10	d		08 12				08 23						08a29	08 38		08 42			08 53		08 54	08a59			
Bedford 7	d				06 55					07 10							07 25								07 40
Luton 10	d				07 19					07 34							07 49								08 04
Luton Airport Parkway 7 ✈	d				07 21					07 36							07 51								08 06
St Albans	d				07 33					07 48							08 03								08 18
St Pancras International 15 ⊖	d				07 54					08 10							08 24								08 39
Farringdon 3 ⊖	d				07 59					08 14							08 29								08 44
City Thameslink 3	d																								
London Blackfriars 3 ⊖	d				08 05					08 20							08 35								08 50
London Bridge 4 ⊖	d	08 03			08 11					08 26					08 33		08 41								08 56
Norwood Junction 2	d	08 16													08 46										
East Croydon	a	08 19	08 22		08 24		08 33			08 39				08 48	08 49	08 52	08 54		09 03		09 07				09 09
	d	08 21	08 22		08 24		08 33			08 39				08 48	08 51	08 52	08 54		09 03		09 07				09 09
Purley 4	d	08 26													08 57										
Coulsdon South	d	08 30													09 00										
Merstham	d	08 35													09 06										
Redhill	a	08 38												09 00	09 09								←		
	d	08 39							08 41		08 44			09 00	09 10								09 10		
Tonbridge 4	a	09 08													↳										
Reigate	a																								
Earlswood (Surrey)	d																						09 12		
Salfords	d																						09 16		
Horley 4	d										08 51												09 19		
Gatwick Airport 10 ✈	a				08 40	08 45	08 48		08 50	08 55	08 55	09 00		09 08			09 10	09 15	09 18		09 22		09 23		09 25
	d				08 41		08 49			08 56	08 56			09 09			09 11		09 19		09 28		09 24		09 26
Three Bridges 4	a				08 45						09 00			09 14			09 15				↳		09 29		
	d				08 45						09 01			09 14			09 15						09 30		
Crawley	d										09 04			09 18									09 33		
Ifield	d										09 07												09 36		
Faygate	d																								
Littlehaven	d										09 13												09 42		
Horsham 4	a										09 16			09 26									09 47		
Balcombe	d																09 21								
Haywards Heath 3	a				08 54		09 00			09 06							09 26		09 30						09 36
	d				08 55		09 04	09 07		09 08							09 27		09 34	09 37					09 38
Wivelsfield 4	d				08 59			09 11									09 31								
Lewes 4	a							09 22											09 52						
Burgess Hill 4	d				09 01		09 09										09 33								
Hassocks 4	d			←	09 04												09 36								
Preston Park	d			09 04	09 11												09 43								
Hove 2	a						09 21													09 51					
Brighton 10	a		08 58	09 09	09 20					09 26						09 27	09 51								09 56

For general notes see front of timetable
For details of catering facilities see Directory of Train Operators

§ It is unknown at the time of going to press, when this station will open. For further details please contact National Rail Enquiries 08457-484950 or see local publicity.

A To Tunbridge Wells (Table 206)
B To Littlehampton (Table 188)
C From Tonbridge (Table 209)
D To Southampton Central (Table 188) and to Bognor Regis (Table 188)

Table 186

Watford Junction, Bedford and London → Brighton

Network Diagram - see first page of Table 186

	GW	SN	GX	SN	GW	SE	SN	SN	FC	GX	SN		LO	GW	SE	FC	GX	SN	SN	SN	FC	GX
						13									88							
	1	1	1	1	1		1	1	1	1	1			1	1	1	1	1	1	1	1	1
				A		B					C				D			E				
London Victoria 15 ⊖ d			09 00	09 02			09 06			09 15	09 17						09 30	09 32		09 36		09 45
Watford Junction d																						
Harrow & Wealdstone ⊖ d																						
Wembley Central d																						
Willesden Jn. High Level d													09 08									
Shepherds Bush § ⊖ d																						
Kensington Olympia ⊖ d													09 17									
West Brompton ⊖ d													09 19									
Imperial Wharf § d																						
Clapham Junction 10 d				09 08			09 12				09 23		09a29					09 38		09 42		
Bedford 7 d									07 55							08 10					08 25	
Luton 10 d									08 19							08 34					08 49	
Luton Airport Parkway 7 ✈ d									08 21							08 36					08 51	
St Albans d									08 33							08 48					09 03	
St Pancras International 15 ⊖ d									08 54							09 09					09 24	
Farringdon 3 ⊖ d									08 59							09 14					09 29	
City Thameslink 3 d									09 01							09 16					09 31	
London Blackfriars 3 ⊖ d									09 05							09 20					09 35	
London Bridge 4 ⊖ d						09 03			09 11							09 26			09 33		09 41	
Norwood Junction 2 d						09 16													09 46			
East Croydon ⇌ a				09 18		09 19	09 22		09 24		09 33					09 39		09 48	09 49	09 52	09 54	
d				09 18		09 21	09 22		09 24		09 33					09 39		09 48	09 51	09 52	09 54	
Purley 4 d						09 26													09 57			
Coulsdon South d						09 30													10 00			
Merstham d						09 35													10 06			
Redhill a				09 30		09 38												10 00	10 09			
d	09 14			09 30	09 34	09 39								09 41	09 44			10 00	10 10			
Tonbridge 4 a						10 08													⟶			
Reigate a	09 18				09 38																	
Earlswood (Surrey) d																						
Salfords d																						
Horley 4 d				09 36											09 51							
Gatwick Airport 10 ✈ a		⟵	09 30	09 39					09 40	09 45	09 48			09 50	09 55	09 55	10 00	10 08			10 10	10 15
d		09 28		09 40					09 41		09 49				09 55	09 56		10 09			10 11	
Three Bridges 4 a		09 33		09 44					09 45						10 00			10 14			10 15	
d		09 33		09 45					09 45						10 01			10 14			10 15	
Crawley d				09 48											10 04			10 18				
Ifield d															10 07							
Faygate d																						
Littlehaven d															10 13							
Horsham 4 a				09 56											10 16			10 26				
Balcombe d																					10 21	
Haywards Heath 3 a		09 42							09 54		10 00					10 06					10 26	
d		09 46							09 55		10 04	10 07				10 08					10 27	
Wivelsfield 4 d		09 50							09 59			10 11									10 31	
Lewes 4 a												10 22										
Burgess Hill 4 d		09 52							10 01		10 09										10 33	
Hassocks 4 d		09 55						⟵	10 04												10 36	
Preston Park d		10 02						10 02	10 11												10 43	
Hove 2 a		⟶									10 21											
Brighton 10 a							09 58	10 07	10 19							10 26				10 27	10 51	

For general notes see front of timetable
For details of catering facilities see Directory of Train Operators

§ It is unknown at the time of going to press, when this station will open. For further details please contact National Rail Enquiries 08457-484950 or see local publicity.

A To Portsmouth Harbour (Table 188) and to Bognor Regis (Table 188)
B To Tunbridge Wells (Table 206)
C To Littlehampton (Table 188)
D From Tunbridge Wells (Table 209)
E To Southampton Central (Table 188) and to Bognor Regis (Table 188)

Table 186

Saturdays

Watford Junction, Bedford and London → Brighton

Network Diagram - see first page of Table 186

	SN		SN	LO	SN	FC	GW	SN	GX	SN	GW	SE	SN	SN	FC	GX	SN		LO	GW	SE	FC		GX
												13									88			
	1		1		1	1	1	1	1	1	1		1	1	1	1	1			1	1	1		1
										A		B					C				D			
London Victoria 15 ⊖ d	09 47								10 00	10 02			10 06			10 15	10 17							10 30
Watford Junction d			09 11																					
Harrow & Wealdstone ⊖ d			09 17																					
Wembley Central d																								
Willesden Jn. High Level d				09 38															10 08					
Shepherds Bush § ⊖ d																								
Kensington Olympia ⊖ d			09 42	09 47															10 17					
West Brompton ⊖ d			09 45	09 49															10 19					
Imperial Wharf § d																								
Clapham Junction 10 d	09 53		09 54	09a59						10 08			10 12				10 23		10a29					
Bedford 7 d						08 40									08 55							09 10		
Luton 10 d						09 04									09 19							09 34		
Luton Airport Parkway 7 ✈ d						09 06									09 21							09 36		
St Albans d						09 18									09 33							09 48		
St Pancras International 15 ⊖ d						09 39									09 54							10 09		
Farringdon 3 ⊖ d						09 44									09 59							10 14		
City Thameslink 3 d						09 46									10 01							10 16		
London Blackfriars 3 ⊖ d						09 50									10 05							10 20		
London Bridge 4 ⊖ d						09 56						10 03			10 11							10 26		
Norwood Junction 2 d												10 16												
East Croydon a	10 03		10 07			10 09				10 18		10 19	10 22		10 24		10 33					10 39		
d	10 03		10 07			10 09				10 18		10 21	10 22		10 24		10 33					10 39		
Purley 4 d												10 26												
Coulsdon South d												10 30												
Merstham d												10 35												
Redhill a					⟵					10 30		10 38												
d					10 10		10 14			10 30	10 34	10 39								10 41	10 44			
Tonbridge 4 a												11 08												
Reigate a							10 18				10 38													
Earlswood (Surrey) d					10 12																			
Salfords d					10 16																			
Horley 4 d					10 19					10 36											10 51			
Gatwick Airport 10 ✈ a	10 18		10 22		10 23	10 25		⟵	10 30	10 39					10 40	10 45	10 48			10 50	10 55	10 55		11 00
d	10 19		10 28		10 24	10 26		10 28		10 40					10 41		10 49				10 55	10 56		
Three Bridges 4 a			⟶		10 29			10 33		10 44					10 45						11 00			
d					10 30			10 33		10 45					10 45						11 01			
Crawley d					10 33					10 48											11 04			
Ifield d					10 36																11 07			
Faygate d																								
Littlehaven d					10 42																11 13			
Horsham 4 a					10 47					10 56											11 16			
Balcombe d																								
Haywards Heath 3 a	10 30					10 36		10 42							10 54		11 00					11 06		
d	10 34	10 37				10 38		10 46							10 55		11 04	11 07				11 08		
Wivelsfield 4 d								10 50							10 59			11 11						
Lewes 4 a	10 52																	11 22						
Burgess Hill 4 d								10 52							11 01		11 09							
Hassocks 4 d								10 55						⟵	11 04									
Preston Park d								11 02						11 02	11 11									
Hove 2 a		10 51						⟶									11 21							
Brighton 10 a						10 56							10 58	11 07	11 19							11 26		

For general notes see front of timetable
For details of catering facilities see Directory of Train Operators

§ It is unknown at the time of going to press, when this station will open. For further details please contact National Rail Enquiries 08457-484950 or see local publicity.

A To Portsmouth Harbour (Table 188) and to Bognor Regis (Table 188)
B To Tunbridge Wells (Table 206)
C To Littlehampton (Table 188)
D From Tunbridge Wells (Table 209)

Table 186

Saturdays

Watford Junction, Bedford and London → Brighton

Network Diagram - see first page of Table 186

	SN	SN	SN	FC	GX	SN		SN	LO	SN	FC	GW	SN	GX	SN	GW	SE 13	SN	SN	FC	GX	SN		LO
	1	1	1	1	1	1		1		1	1	1	1	1	1	1		1	1	1	1	1		
	A														B		C					D		
London Victoria 15 ⊖ d	10 32		10 36		10 45	10 47								11 00	11 02			11 06			11 15	11 17		
Watford Junction d								10 11																
Harrow & Wealdstone ⊖ d								10 17																
Wembley Central d																								
Willesden Jn. High Level d									10 38															11 08
Shepherds Bush § ⊖ d																								
Kensington Olympia ⊖ d								10 42	10 47															11 17
West Brompton ⊖ d								10 45	10 49															11 19
Imperial Wharf § d																								
Clapham Junction 10 d	10 38		10 42			10 53		10 54	10a59						11 08			11 12				11 23		11a29
Bedford 7 d				09 25							09 40									09 55				
Luton 10 d				09 49							10 04									10 19				
Luton Airport Parkway 7 ✈ d				09 51							10 06									10 21				
St Albans d				10 03							10 18									10 33				
St Pancras International 15 ⊖ d				10 24							10 39									10 54				
Farringdon 3 ⊖ d				10 29							10 44									10 59				
City Thameslink 3 d				10 31							10 46									11 01				
London Blackfriars 3 ⊖ d				10 35							10 50									11 05				
London Bridge 4 ⊖ d		10 33		10 41							10 56						11 03			11 11				
Norwood Junction 2 d		10 46															11 16							
East Croydon a	10 48	10 49	10 52	10 54		11 03		11 07			11 09				11 18		11 19	11 22		11 24		11 33		
d	10 48	10 51	10 52	10 54		11 03		11 07			11 09				11 18		11 21	11 22		11 24		11 33		
Purley 4 d		10 57															11 26							
Coulsdon South d		11 00															11 30							
Merstham d		11 06															11 35							
Redhill a	11 00	11 09								←					11 30		11 38							
d	11 00	11 10								11 10		11 14			11 30	11 34	11 39							
Tonbridge 4 a		↪															12 08							
Reigate a												11 18				11 38								
Earlswood (Surrey) d										11 12														
Salfords d										11 16														
Horley 4 d										11 19					11 36									
Gatwick Airport 10 ✈ a	11 08			11 10	11 15	11 18		11 22		11 23	11 25		←	11 30	11 39					11 40	11 45	11 48		
d	11 09			11 11		11 19		11 28		11 24	11 26		11 28		11 40					11 41		11 49		
Three Bridges 4 a	11 14			11 15				↪		11 29			11 33		11 44					11 45				
d	11 14			11 15						11 30			11 33		11 45					11 45				
Crawley d	11 18									11 33					11 48									
Ifield d										11 36														
Faygate d																								
Littlehaven d										11 42														
Horsham 4 a	11 26									11 47					11 56									
Balcombe d				11 21																				
Haywards Heath 3 a				11 26		11 30					11 36		11 42							11 54		12 00		
d				11 27		11 34	11 37				11 38		11 46							11 55		12 04	12 07	
Wivelsfield 4 d				11 31									11 50							11 59			12 11	
Lewes 4 a						11 52																	12 22	
Burgess Hill 4 d				11 33									11 52							12 01		12 09		
Hassocks 4 d				11 36									11 55						←	12 04				
Preston Park d				11 43									12 02						12 02	12 11				
Hove 2 a							11 51						↪									12 21		
Brighton 10 a			11 27	11 51							11 56							11 58	12 07	12 19				

For general notes see front of timetable
For details of catering facilities see Directory of Train Operators

§ It is unknown at the time of going to press, when this station will open. For further details please contact National Rail Enquiries 08457-484950 or see local publicity.

A To Southampton Central (Table 188) and to Bognor Regis (Table 188)

B To Portsmouth Harbour (Table 188) and to Bognor Regis (Table 188)

C To Tunbridge Wells (Table 206)

D To Littlehampton (Table 188)

Table 186

Saturdays

Watford Junction, Bedford and London → Brighton

Network Diagram - see first page of Table 186

		GW		SE 88	FC	GX	LO	SN	SN	SN	FC	GX	SN		SN	SN	FC	GW	SN	GX	SN	LO	GW	SE 13	SN
		1		1	1	1		1	1	1	1	1	1		1	1	1	1	1	1	1		1		1
				A				B													C			D	
London Victoria 15	⊖ d					11 30		11 32		11 36		11 45	11 47							12 00	12 02				12 06
Watford Junction	d														11 11										
Harrow & Wealdstone	⊖ d														11 17										
Wembley Central	d																								
Willesden Jn. High Level	d						11 38															12 08			
Shepherds Bush §	⊖ d																								
Kensington Olympia	⊖ d						11 47								11 42							12 17			
West Brompton	⊖ d						11 49								11 45							12 19			
Imperial Wharf §	d																								
Clapham Junction 10	d						11a59	11 38		11 42			11 53		11 54						12 08	12a29			12 12
Bedford 7	d				10 10						10 25						10 40								
Luton 10	d				10 34						10 49						11 04								
Luton Airport Parkway 7	✈ d				10 36						10 51						11 06								
St Albans	d				10 48						11 03						11 18								
St Pancras International 15	⊖ d				11 09						11 24						11 39								
Farringdon 3	⊖ d				11 14						11 29						11 44								
City Thameslink 3	d				11 16						11 31						11 46								
London Blackfriars 3	⊖ d				11 20						11 35						11 50								
London Bridge 4	⊖ d				11 26				11 33		11 41						11 56							12 03	
Norwood Junction 2	d								11 46															12 16	
East Croydon	🚋 a				11 39			11 48	11 49	11 52	11 54		12 03		12 07		12 09				12 18			12 19	12 22
	d				11 39			11 48	11 51	11 52	11 54		12 03		12 07		12 09				12 18			12 21	12 22
Purley 4	d								11 57															12 26	
Coulsdon South	d								12 00															12 30	
Merstham	d								12 06															12 35	
Redhill	a							12 00	12 09							⟵					12 30			12 38	
	d	11 41		11 44				12 00	12 10							12 10		12 14			12 30		12 34	12 39	
Tonbridge 4	a								↳															13 08	
Reigate	a																	12 18					12 38		
Earlswood (Surrey)	d															12 12									
Salfords	d															12 16									
Horley 4	d			11 51												12 19					12 36				
Gatwick Airport 10	✈ a	11 50		11 55	11 55	12 00		12 08			12 10	12 15	12 18		12 22	12 23	12 25		⟵	12 30	12 39				
	d			11 55	11 56			12 09			12 11		12 19		12 28	12 24	12 26		12 28		12 40				
Three Bridges 4	a			12 00				12 14			12 15				↳	12 29			12 33		12 44				
	d			12 01				12 14			12 15					12 30			12 33		12 45				
Crawley	d			12 04				12 18								12 33					12 48				
Ifield	d			12 07												12 36									
Faygate	d																								
Littlehaven	d			12 13												12 42									
Horsham 4	a			12 16				12 26								12 47					12 56				
Balcombe	d										12 21														
Haywards Heath 3	a				12 06						12 26		12 30				12 36		12 42						
	d				12 08						12 27		12 34	12 37			12 38		12 46						
Wivelsfield 4	d										12 31								12 50						
Lewes 4	a												12 52												
Burgess Hill 4	d										12 33								12 52						
Hassocks 4	d										12 36								12 55						
Preston Park	d										12 43								13 02						
Hove 2	a													12 51					↳						
Brighton 10	a				12 26					12 27	12 51						12 56								12 58

For general notes see front of timetable
For details of catering facilities see Directory of Train Operators

§ It is unknown at the time of going to press, when this station will open. For further details please contact National Rail Enquiries 08457-484950 or see local publicity.

A From Tunbridge Wells (Table 209)
B To Southampton Central (Table 188) and to Bognor Regis (Table 188)
C To Portsmouth Harbour (Table 188) and to Bognor Regis (Table 188)
D To Tunbridge Wells (Table 206)

Table 186

Saturdays

Watford Junction, Bedford and London → Brighton

Network Diagram - see first page of Table 186

		SN	FC		GX	SN		GW	XC	SE	FC	GX	XC	LO	SN	SN	SN	XC	FC	GX	SN		SN	SN	FC
										88															
		1	1		1	1		1	1 ◇	1	1	1	1 ◇		1	1	1	1 ◇	1	1	1		1	1	1
						A			B	C			B		D			B							
London Victoria 15	⊖ d				12 15	12 17						12 30			12 32		12 36			12 45	12 47				
Watford Junction	d																						12 11		
Harrow & Wealdstone	⊖ d																						12 17		
Wembley Central	d																								
Willesden Jn. High Level	d													12 38											
Shepherds Bush §	⊖ d																								
Kensington Olympia	⊖ d								11 57					12 47									12 42		
West Brompton	⊖ d													12 49									12 45		
Imperial Wharf §	d																								
Clapham Junction 10	d					12 23								12a59	12 38		12 42				12 53		12 54		
Bedford 7	d		10 55								11 10								11 25						11 40
Luton 10	d		11 19								11 34								11 49						12 04
Luton Airport Parkway 7	✈ d		11 21								11 36								11 51						12 06
St Albans	d		11 33								11 48								12 03						12 18
St Pancras International 15	⊖ d		11 54								12 09								12 24						12 39
Farringdon 3	⊖ d		11 59								12 14								12 29						12 44
City Thameslink 3	d		12 01								12 16								12 31						12 46
London Blackfriars 3	⊖ d		12 05								12 20								12 35						12 50
London Bridge 4	⊖ d		12 11								12 26					12 33			12 41						12 56
Norwood Junction 2	d															12 46									
East Croydon	a		12 24			12 33			12 37		12 39				12 48	12 49	12 52		12 54		13 03		13 07		13 09
	d		12 24			12 33			12 37		12 39				12 48	12 51	12 52		12 54		13 03		13 07		13 09
Purley 4	d															12 57									
Coulsdon South	d															13 00									
Merstham	d															13 06									
Redhill	a														13 00	13 09								←	
	d							12 41		12 44					13 00	13 10								13 10	
Tonbridge 4	a															→									
Reigate	a																								
Earlswood (Surrey)	d																							13 12	
Salfords	d																							13 16	
Horley 4	d									12 51														13 19	
Gatwick Airport 10	✈ a		12 39		12 45	12 48		12 50	12 53	12 55	12 56	13 00	←		13 08				13 10	13 15	13 18		13 22	13 23	13 25
	d		12 40			12 49			13 01	12 55	12 56		13 01		13 09				13 11		13 19		13 28	13 24	13 26
Three Bridges 4	a		12 45						→	13 00					13 14				13 15				→	13 29	
	d		12 45							13 01					13 14				13 15					13 30	
Crawley	d									13 04					13 18									13 33	
Ifield	d									13 07														13 36	
Faygate	d																								
Littlehaven	d									13 13														13 42	
Horsham 4	a									13 16					13 26									13 47	
Balcombe	d																		13 21						
Haywards Heath 3	a		12 54			13 00					13 07		13 13					←	13 26		13 30				13 36
	d		12 55			13 04	13 07				13 08		13 18					13 18	13 27		13 34	13 37			13 38
Wivelsfield 4	d		12 59				13 11						→						13 31						
Lewes 4	a						13 22														13 48				
Burgess Hill 4	d		13 01			13 09													13 33						
Hassocks 4	d	←	13 04																13 36						
Preston Park	d	13 02	13 11																13 43						
Hove 2	a					13 21																13 51			
Brighton 10	a	13 07	13 17								13 26						13 27	13 37	13 51						13 56

For general notes see front of timetable
For details of catering facilities see Directory of Train Operators

§ It is unknown at the time of going to press, when this station will open. For further details please contact National Rail Enquiries 08457-484950 or see local publicity.

A To Littlehampton (Table 188)
B From Birmingham New Street (Table 116)
C From Tunbridge Wells (Table 209)
D To Southampton Central (Table 188) and to Bognor Regis (Table 188)

Table 186

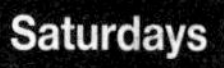

Watford Junction, Bedford and London → Brighton

Network Diagram - see first page of Table 186

		GW	SN	GX		SN	LO	GW	SE 13	SN	SN	FC	GX	SN		GW	SE 88	FC	GX	SN	LO	SN	SN	FC	GX
		1	1	1		1		1		1	1	1	1	1		1	1	1	1	1		1	1	1	1
						A			B					C			D			E					
London Victoria 15	⊖ d			13 00		13 02				13 06			13 15	13 17					13 30	13 32			13 36		13 45
Watford Junction	d																								
Harrow & Wealdstone	⊖ d																								
Wembley Central	d																								
Willesden Jn. High Level	d						13 08														13 38				
Shepherds Bush §	⊖ d																								
Kensington Olympia	⊖ d						13 17														13 47				
West Brompton	⊖ d						13 19														13 49				
Imperial Wharf §	d																								
Clapham Junction 10	d					13 08	13a29			13 12				13 23						13 38	13a59		13 42		
Bedford 7	d											11 55						12 10						12 25	
Luton 10	d											12 19						12 34						12 49	
Luton Airport Parkway 7	✈ d											12 21						12 36						12 51	
St Albans	d											12 33						12 48						13 03	
St Pancras International 15	⊖ d											12 54						13 09						13 24	
Farringdon 3	⊖ d											12 59						13 14						13 29	
City Thameslink 3	d											13 01						13 16						13 31	
London Blackfriars 3	⊖ d											13 05						13 20						13 35	
London Bridge 4	⊖ d								13 03			13 11						13 26				13 33		13 41	
Norwood Junction 2	d								13 16													13 46			
East Croydon	🚋 a					13 18			13 19	13 22		13 24		13 33				13 39		13 48		13 49	13 52	13 54	
	d					13 18			13 21	13 22		13 24		13 33				13 39		13 48		13 51	13 52	13 54	
Purley 4	d								13 26													13 57			
Coulsdon South	d								13 30													14 00			
Merstham	d								13 35													14 06			
Redhill	a					13 30			13 38											14 00		14 09			
	d	13 14				13 30		13 34	13 39							13 41	13 44			14 00		14 10			
Tonbridge 4	a								14 08													⟶			
Reigate	a	13 18						13 38																	
Earlswood (Surrey)	d																								
Salfords	d																								
Horley 4	d					13 36											13 51								
Gatwick Airport 10	✈ a		⟵	13 30		13 39						13 40	13 45	13 48		13 50	13 55	13 55	14 00	14 08				14 10	14 15
	d		13 28			13 40						13 41		13 49			13 55	13 56		14 09				14 11	
Three Bridges 4	a		13 33			13 44						13 45					14 00			14 14				14 15	
	d		13 33			13 45						13 45					14 01			14 14				14 15	
Crawley	d					13 48											14 04			14 18					
Ifield	d																14 07								
Faygate	d																								
Littlehaven	d																14 13								
Horsham 4	a					13 56											14 16			14 26					
Balcombe	d																							14 21	
Haywards Heath 3	a		13 42									13 54		14 00				14 06						14 26	
	d		13 46									13 55		14 04	14 07			14 08						14 27	
Wivelsfield 4	d		13 50									13 59			14 11									14 31	
Lewes 4	a														14 22										
Burgess Hill 4	d		13 52									14 01		14 09										14 33	
Hassocks 4	d		13 55								⟵	14 04												14 36	
Preston Park	d		14 02								14 02	14 11												14 43	
Hove 2	a		⟶											14 21											
Brighton 10	a									13 58	14 07	14 19						14 26					14 28	14 51	

For general notes see front of timetable
For details of catering facilities see Directory of Train Operators

§ It is unknown at the time of going to press, when this station will open. For further details please contact National Rail Enquiries 08457-484950 or see local publicity.

A To Portsmouth Harbour (Table 188) and to Bognor Regis (Table 188)
B To Tunbridge Wells (Table 206)
C To Littlehampton (Table 188)
D From Tunbridge Wells (Table 209)
E To Southampton Central (Table 188) and to Bognor Regis (Table 188)

Table 186

Watford Junction, Bedford and London → Brighton

Network Diagram - see first page of Table 186

Station		SN		SN	SN		FC	GW	SN	GX	SN	LO	GW	SE	SN	SN	FC	GX	SN		GW	SE	FC	GX	SN
														13								88			
		1		1	1		1	1	1	1	1		1		1	1	1	1	1		1	1	1	1	1
											A			B					C			D			E
London Victoria 15 ⊖	d	13 47								14 00	14 02				14 06			14 15	14 17					14 30	14 32
Watford Junction	d			13 11																					
Harrow & Wealdstone ⊖	d			13 17																					
Wembley Central	d																								
Willesden Jn. High Level	d											14 08													
Shepherds Bush § ⊖	d																								
Kensington Olympia ⊖	d			13 42								14 17													
West Brompton ⊖	d			13 45								14 19													
Imperial Wharf §	d																								
Clapham Junction 10	d	13 53		13 54							14 08	14a29			14 12				14 23						14 38
Bedford 7	d						12 40										12 55						13 10		
Luton 10	d						13 04										13 19						13 34		
Luton Airport Parkway 7 ✈	d						13 06										13 21						13 36		
St Albans	d						13 18										13 33						13 48		
St Pancras International 15 ⊖	d						13 39										13 54						14 09		
Farringdon 3 ⊖	d						13 44										13 59						14 14		
City Thameslink 3	d						13 46										14 01						14 16		
London Blackfriars 3 ⊖	d						13 50										14 05						14 20		
London Bridge 4 ⊖	d						13 56							14 03			14 11						14 26		
Norwood Junction 2	d													14 16											
East Croydon	a	14 03		14 07			14 09				14 18			14 19	14 22		14 24		14 33				14 39		14 48
	d	14 03		14 07			14 09				14 18			14 21	14 22		14 24		14 33				14 39		14 48
Purley 4	d													14 26											
Coulsdon South	d													14 30											
Merstham	d													14 35											
Redhill	a				←						14 30			14 38											15 00
	d				14 10			14 14			14 30		14 34	14 39							14 41	14 44			15 00
Tonbridge 4	a													15 08											
Reigate	a							14 18					14 38												
Earlswood (Surrey)	d				14 12																				
Salfords	d				14 16																				
Horley 4	d				14 19						14 36											14 51			
Gatwick Airport 10 ✈	a	14 18		14 22	14 23		14 25		←	14 30	14 39						14 40	14 45	14 48		14 50	14 55	14 55	15 00	15 08
	d	14 19		14 28	14 24		14 26		14 28		14 40						14 41		14 49			14 55	14 56		15 09
Three Bridges 4	a			→	14 29				14 33		14 44						14 45					15 00			15 14
	d				14 30				14 33		14 45						14 45					15 01			15 14
Crawley	d				14 33						14 48											15 04			15 18
Ifield	d				14 36																	15 07			
Faygate	d																								
Littlehaven	d				14 42																	15 13			
Horsham 4	a				14 47						14 56											15 16			15 26
Balcombe	d																								
Haywards Heath 3	a	14 30					14 36		14 42								14 54		15 00				15 06		
	d	14 34	14 37				14 38		14 46								14 55		15 04	15 07			15 08		
Wivelsfield 4	d								14 50								14 59			15 11					
Lewes 4	a	14 48																		15 22					
Burgess Hill 4	d								14 52								15 01		15 09						
Hassocks 4	d								14 55							←	15 04								
Preston Park	d								15 02							15 02	15 11								
Hove 2	a		14 51						→										15 21						
Brighton 10	a						14 56								14 58	15 07	15 19						15 26		

For general notes see front of timetable
For details of catering facilities see
Directory of Train Operators

§ It is unknown at the time of going to press, when this station will open. For further details please contact National Rail Enquiries 08457-484950 or see local publicity.

A To Portsmouth Harbour (Table 188) and to Bognor Regis (Table 188)
B To Tunbridge Wells (Table 206)
C To Littlehampton (Table 188)
D From Tunbridge Wells (Table 209)
E To Southampton Central (Table 188) and to Bognor Regis (Table 188)

Table 188

Southampton, Portsmouth and Sussex Coast → Brighton, Gatwick Airport & London

For complete service between Horsham and Three Bridges see Table 186

		SN 1	SN 1	SN 1		SN 1	SN 1	SN 1	SN 1	SN 1	GW ◇ A	SN 1		SN 1	SN 1	SN 1	SN 1	SN 1	SN 1	SN 1		SN 1	SN 1
Southampton Central	d										20 07												
Swanwick	d																						
Fareham	d										20 29												
Portchester	d																						
Cosham	d										20 44												
Portsmouth Harbour	d		19 43					20 14				20 43			21 14				21 43	22 14		22 43	
Portsmouth & Southsea	d		19 47					20 18				20 47			21 18				21 47	22 18		22 47	
Fratton	d		19 51					20 22				20 51			21 22				21 51	22 22		22 51	
Hilsea	d																						
Bedhampton	d							20 30							21 30					22 30			
Havant	d		20 00					20 33			20 53	21 00			21 33				22 00	22 33		23 00	
Warblington	d							20 35							21 35					22 35			
Emsworth	d		20 04					20 38				21 04			21 38				22 04	22 38		23 04	
Southbourne	d		20 07					20 41				21 07			21 41				22 07	22 41		23 07	
Nutbourne	d							20 43							21 43					22 43			
Bosham	d							20 47							21 47					22 47			
Fishbourne (Sussex)	d							20 50							21 50					22 50			
Chichester 4	d		20 14					20 53			21 04	21 14			21 53				22 14	22 53		23 14	
Bognor Regis 4	d						20 36		20 57					21 36		21 57		22 11					
Barnham	a		20 22				20 42	21 01	21 03	⟵	21 11	21 22		21 42	22 01	22 03	⟵	22 18	22 22	23 01		23 22	
	d		20 22				20 43	21 08	21 05	21 08	21 12	21 22		21 43	22 08	22 05	22 08		22 22	23 01		23 22	23 37
Bognor Regis 4	a		*20 49*					*21 21*			*21 21*	*21 49*			*22 21*				*22 49*	*23 21*		*23 49*	
Ford 4	d						20 47	⟶	21 09	21 12		21 27		21 47	⟶	22 09	22 12		22 27	23 06		23 27	23 42
Littlehampton 4	a						20 52					21 31		21 52					22 31	23 10		23 32	23 46
	d	20 14				20 41			*20b57*			21 41				*21b57*			22 41				
Angmering 3	d	20 22				20 49				21 18		21 49					22 18		22 49				
Goring-by-Sea	d	20 26				20 53				21 22		21 53					22 22		22 53				
Durrington-on-Sea	d	20 29				20 55				21 25		21 55					22 25		22 55				
West Worthing	d	20 31				20 57				21 27		21 57					22 27		22 57				
Worthing 4	a	20 33	20 37			21 00				21 29	21 34	22 00					22 29		23 00				
	d		20 41			21 00				21 30	21 34	22 00					22 30		23 00				
East Worthing	d					21 02				21 32		22 02					22 32		23 02				
Lancing	d					21 05				21 35		22 05					22 35		23 05				
Shoreham-by-Sea	d		20 47			21 09				21 39	21 45	22 09					22 39		23 09				
Southwick	d					21 12				21 42		22 12					22 42		23 12				
Fishersgate	d					21 14				21 44		22 14					22 44		23 14				
Portslade	d					21 16				21 46		22 16					22 46		23 16				
Aldrington	d			⟵		21 19				21 49		22 19					22 49		23 19				
Hove 2	d		20 54	20 56		21 21				21 51	21 55	22 21					22 51		23 21				
Brighton 10	a			21 00		21 25				21 55	22 01	22 26					22 56		23 25				
Haywards Heath 3	a		21 09			*22 00*				*22 20*	*22 30*	*23 00*					*23 23*		*00 01*				
Arundel	d								21 14							22 14							
Amberley	d								21 19							22 19							
Pulborough	d								21 25							22 25							
Billingshurst	d								21 31							22 31							
Christs Hospital	d								21 38							22 38							
Horsham 4	d								21 42							22 42							
Crawley	d								21 51							22 51							
Three Bridges 4	a		*21 32*			*22 10*			21 54	*22 32*	*22 40*	*23 10*				22 54	*23 35*		*00 10*				
Gatwick Airport 10 ✈	a		21 22			*22 14*			21 58	*22 37*	*22 44*	*23 14*				22 58	*23 46*		*00 14*				
East Croydon	a		21 39			*22 31*			22 24	*22 58*	*23 01*	*23 31*				23 24	*00 16*		*00 35*				
London Bridge 4 ⊖	a		*22 12*			*22 45*			*22 45*	*23 15*	*23 15*	*23 45*				*23 45*			*00 52*				
Clapham Junction 10	a		21 54			*23c10*			22 37	*23 13*	*23c37*	*00c10*				23 37			*01c02*				
London Victoria 15 ⊖	a		22 01			*22e55*			22 46	*23 20*	*23 46*	*23e55*				23 46	*00 37*		*00e55*				

For general notes see front of timetable
For details of catering facilities see Directory of Train Operators

A From 30 March from Bristol Parkway (Table 132)
b Change at Ford
c Change at Brighton and East Croydon
e Change at Brighton and Gatwick Airport

London, Haywards Heath and Brighton → Lewes, Seaford, Eastbourne, Hastings and Ashford

Network Diagram - see first page of Table 184

Miles	Miles			SN	SN	SN	SN	SN	SN	SN	SN	SN	SN	SN	SN	SN	SN	SN	SN	SN	SN	SN	SN	SN
				MX	MX	MX	MO	MX																
				1	1	1	1	1	1	1	1	1	1	1	1	1	1	1	1	1	1	1	1	1
—	—	**London Victoria** 15 ⊖	d		22p47		22p47	00 05					04 00						05 02				05 02	05 32
—	—	Clapham Junction 10	d		22p53		22p53	00 11					04 08						05 08				05 08	05 38
—	—	**London Bridge** 4 ⊖	d					23 53																05b31
—	—	East Croydon	d		23p03		23p07	00 25					04 22				04 32		05 32			05 02	05 22	05 49
—	—	**Gatwick Airport** 10	d		23p19		23p29	00 43					04 47				04 52		05 54			05 22	05 49	06 20
—	0	**Haywards Heath** 3	d		23p34		23p41	01 02					05 01				05 08		06 13			05 36	06 06	06 34
—	3	Wivelsfield 4	d		23p38		23p45												06 17			05 40	06 10	06 38
—	6¾	Plumpton	d		23p44		23p51																	
—	9½	Cooksbridge	d																					
0	—	**Brighton** 10	d	23p34									05 30				05 45	06 00				06 15	06 32	
¾	—	London Road (Brighton)	d	23p37													05 48	06 03				06 18		
1¾	—	Moulsecoomb	d	23p39													05 50	06 05				06 20		
3½	—	Falmer	d	23p43													05 54	06 09				06 24		
8	12¼	**Lewes** 4	a	23p49	23p51	⟵	23p58	01 16					05 41				06 00	06 15	06 28			06 30	06 43	06 49
—	—		d	23p56	23p53	23p56	23p59	01 17					05 41				06 05		06 29			06 32	06 44	06 51
—	15¾	Southease	d	⟶																				
—	18¼	Newhaven Town	d			00 04											06 14		06 37					
—	18¾	Newhaven Harbour	d			00 06											06 15		06 39					
—	20¼	Bishopstone	d			00 09											06 18		06 42					
—	21¼	**Seaford**	a			00 12											06 22		06 45					
11	—	Glynde	d																			06 37		06 56
15½	—	Berwick	d		00 02																	06 43		07 02
19¾	—	Polegate	d		00 07		00 11	01s29					05 53									06 48	06 57	07 07
21¾	—	Hampden Park 4 §	d		00 11		00 15	01s33														06 52		07 11
23¾	—	**Eastbourne** 4	a		00 16		00 20	01 38					06 00									07 01	07 04	07 16
—	—		d		00 22				05 00		05 24			06 04	06 15					06 34	06 51		07 08	07 21
25¾	—	Hampden Park 4 §	d												06 19						06 55			07 25
28¼	—	Pevensey & Westham	d		00 29						05 31				06 24					06 41	07 00			07 30
29½	—	Pevensey Bay	d																					
31½	—	Normans Bay	d																	06 46				
33¼	—	Cooden Beach	d		00 35										06 30						07 06			07 36
34¾	—	Collington	d		00 38										06 33						07 09			07 39
35½	—	**Bexhill** 4	d		00 40				05 14		05 40			06 18	06 35					06 52	07 11		07 22	07 41
39¼	—	**St Leonards Warrior Sq** 4	d		00 47				05 20		05 46			06 25	06 41					06 58	07 17		07 29	07 49
40	0	**Hastings** 4	a		00 50				05 24		05 50			06 29	06 45					07 02	07 22		07 32	07 52
—	—		d							05 30		05 55		06 30									07 34	07 53
—	1	Ore	d							05 32		05 57												07a56
—	3¾	Three Oaks	d									06 03												
—	5	Doleham	d									06 06												
—	9¼	Winchelsea	d									06 12												
—	11¼	**Rye**	a							05 47		06 16		06 47									07 51	
—	—		d							05 47		06 16		06 49		07 19							07 54	
—	18	Appledore (Kent)	d							05 56		06 25		06 58		07 28							08 03	
—	21	Ham Street	d							06 01		06 30		07 03		07 33							08 08	
—	26½	**Ashford International**	a							06 15		06 39		07 11		07 41							08 16	
—	—	London Bridge 4 ⊖	a							07 54		08 14		08 34		09 22							09 39	
—	—	London Cannon Street 4 ⊖	a							08 00		08 20		08 41		09 28							09c57	
—	—	London Waterloo (East) 4 ⊖	a									08 04		08 41		09 01							09 45	
—	—	London Charing Cross 4 ⊖	a							08c07		08 09		08 47		09 07							09 50	

For general notes see front of timetable
For details of catering facilities see Directory of Train Operators

§ For additional trains between Hampden Park and Eastbourne see Hastings to London pages

b Change at Gatwick Airport

c Change at Ashford International and London Bridge

London, Haywards Heath and Brighton → Lewes, Seaford, Eastbourne, Hastings and Ashford

Network Diagram - see first page of Table 184

		SN 1	SN 1	SN 1	SN 1	SN 1		SN 1	SN 1	SN 1	SN 1	SN 1	SN 1	SN 1	SN 1	SN 1	SN 1	SN 1	SN 1		SN 1	SN 1	SN 1	SN 1	SN 1
London Victoria 15 ⊖	d				05b32			06c02					06 47	06b02	06 21	06b32	06b47		07b06		07 47	07b23			07b47
Clapham Junction 10	d				05b38			06c08					06 53	06b08	06 27	06b38	06b53		07b12		07 53	07b29			07b53
London Bridge 4 ⊖	d		05 31		05 50			06 21						06 21		06 43	07 00		07 16		07 40	07 28			07 54
East Croydon	d	05 32	05 52		06 04			06 36					07 03	06 36	06 39	06 56	07 16		07 32		08 03	07 46			08 11
Gatwick Airport 10 ✈	d	05 54	06 08		06 20			06 52					07 19	06 52	07 04	07 12	07 32		07 50		08 19	08 02			08 30
Haywards Heath 3	d	06 10	06 25		06 38			07 12					07 33	07 06	07 21	07 28	07 48		08 06		08 32	08 16			08 45
Wivelsfield 4	d	06 14	06 29		06 42			07 16					07 37	07 10	07 25	07 32	07 44		08 10		08 36				08 32
Plumpton	d							07 22					07 43								08 42				
Cooksbridge	d							07 26					07 47								08 47				
Brighton 10	d	06 39	06 52	07 00	07 13					07 22		07 32		07 40	07 52	08 03	08 13	08 22	08 32			08 39	08 46	08 52	09 10
London Road (Brighton)	d	06 42	06 55	07 03	07 16					07 25				07 43	07 55	08 06	08 16	08 25				08 42	08 49	08 55	09 13
Moulsecoomb	d	06 44	06 57	07 05	07 18					07 27				07 45	07 57	08 08	08 18	08 27				08 44	08 51	08 57	09 15
Falmer	d	06 48	07 01	07 09	07 22					07 31				07 49	08 01	08 12	08 22	08 31				08 48	08 55	09 01	09 19
Lewes 4	a	06 54	07 08	07 17	07 29			07 31	←	07 37		07 43	07 52	07 56	08 08	08 19	08 29	08 37	08 43		08 51	08 54	09 02	09 07	09 25
	d	06 55	07 10		07 36			07 33	07 36			07 44	07 53	07 58	08 09	08 23	08 30		08 44		08 52		09 02	09 08	09 32
Southease	d				→																				→
Newhaven Town ⛴	d	07 03	07 18						07 44					08 06			08 38						09 10		
Newhaven Harbour	d	07 05	07e23						07 46					08 08			08 40						09 12		
Bishopstone	d	07 08	07 26						07 49					08 11			08 43						09 15		
Seaford	a	07 11	07 29						07 52					08 14			08 46						09 18		
Glynde	d							07 38							08 14	08 28								09 13	
Berwick	d							07 44							08 20	08 34								09 19	
Polegate	d							07 49				07 57	08 05		08 25	08 39			08 57		09 04			09 24	
Hampden Park 4 §	d							07 53					08 09		08 29	08 43					09 08			09 28	
Eastbourne 4	a							07 58				08 04	08 14		08 34	08 48			09 04		09 13			09 33	
	d										07 38	08 08	08 21		08 40				09 08		09 20			09 37	
Hampden Park 4 §	d										07 42		08 25		08 44						09 24			09 41	
Pevensey & Westham	d										07 47	08 17	08 30		08 49						09 29			09 46	
Pevensey Bay	d										07 49		08 32												
Normans Bay	d										07 53		08 36		08 53									09 51	
Cooden Beach	d										07 56		08 39		08 57						09 35			09 54	
Collington	d										07 59		08 42		09 00						09 38			09 57	
Bexhill 4	d										08 01	08 25	08 45		09 02				09 22		09 41			10 00	
St Leonards Warrior Sq 4	d										08 08	08 32	08 52		09 08				09 29		09 48			10 06	
Hastings 4	a										08 13	08 35	08 56		09 12				09 32		09 51			10 10	
	d										08 14	08 36	08 57		09 13				09 34		09 53			10 12	
Ore	d										08a17		09a00		09a16						09a56			10a15	
Three Oaks	d																								
Doleham	d																								
Winchelsea	d																								
Rye	a											08 53							09 51						
	d					08 23						08 54							09 54						
Appledore (Kent)	d					08 32						09 03							10 03						
Ham Street	d					08 37						09 08							10 08						
Ashford International	a					08 45						09 16							10 16						
London Bridge 4 ⊖	a											11 13							11 43						
London Cannon Street 4 ⊖	a											11f20							11f50						
London Waterloo (East) 4 ⊖	a											10 32							11 32						
London Charing Cross 4 ⊖	a											10 36							11 36						

For general notes see front of timetable
For details of catering facilities see Directory of Train Operators

§ For additional trains between Hampden Park and Eastbourne see Hastings to London pages

b Change at East Croydon and Brighton
c Change at East Croydon and Haywards Heath
e Arr. 0720
f Change at Ashford International and London Bridge

London, Haywards Heath and Brighton → Lewes, Seaford, Eastbourne, Hastings and Ashford

Network Diagram - see first page of Table 184

Station		SN 1	SN 1	SN 1	SN 1	SN 1	SN 1	SN 1	SN 1	SN 1		SN 1	SN 1	SN 1	SN 1	SN 1	SN 1	SN 1	SN 1	SN 1	SN 1	SN 1	SN 1		SN 1
						🚲			🚲					🚲			🚲				🚲				🚲
London Victoria 15 ⊖	d	08 17		08 06	08 20	08 47	08 36		09 17	09 06			09 36	09 47			10 17	10 06		10 36	10 47				11 17
Clapham Junction 10	d	08 23		08 12	08 28	08 53	08 43		09 23	09 12			09 42	09 53			10 23	10 12		10 42	10 53				11 23
London Bridge 4 ⊖	d	08b19		07c56	08 19	08 41	08c27			09c00			09 25	09e42				09 56		10 26					
East Croydon	d	08 33		08 22	08 39	09 03	08 53		09 33	09 22			09 52	10 03			10 33	10 22		10 52	11 03				11 33
Gatwick Airport 10 ✈	d	08 49			08 56	09 19		09 00	09 49	09 23			09 56	10 19			10 49	10 26	10 28	10 56	11 19				11 49
Haywards Heath 3	d	09 13		08 51	09 10	09 34		09 17	10 07	09 40			10 10	10 34		10 18	11 07	10 38	10 46	11 08	11 34				12 07
Wivelsfield 4	d	09 17		08 55	09 02			09 22	10 11	09 34			10 01			10 22	11 11	10 31	10 50	10 59					12 11
Plumpton	d					09 43								10 43											
Cooksbridge	d					09 48																			
Brighton 10	d			09 22	09 32		09 40	09 52		10 10		10 22	10 32		10 40	10 52		11 10	11 22	11 32		11 40	11 52		
London Road (Brighton)	d			09 25			09 43	09 55		10 13		10 25			10 43	10 55		11 13	11 25			11 43	11 55		
Moulsecoomb	d			09 27			09 45	09 57		10 15		10 27			10 45	10 57		11 15	11 27			11 45	11 57		
Falmer	d			09 31			09 49	10 01		10 19		10 31			10 49	11 01		11 19	11 31			11 49	12 01		
Lewes 4	a	09 28	←	09 37	09 43	09 52	09 56	10 07	10 22	10 25		10 37	10 43	10 51	10 55	11 07	11 22	11 25	11 37	11 43	11 48	11 55	12 07		12 22
	d	09 29	09 32		09 44	09 53	09 58	10 09	10 23	10 28			10 44	10 53	10 58	11 09	11 24	11 28		11 44	11 53	11 58	12 09		12 23
Southease	d		09 38							10 34								11 34							
Newhaven Town ⛴	d		09 42				10 06			10 38					11 06			11 38				12 06			
Newhaven Harbour	d		09 44				10 08			10 40					11 08			11 40				12 08			
Bishopstone	d		09 47				10 11			10 43					11 11			11 43				12 11			
Seaford	a		09 50				10 14			10 46					11 14			11 46				12 14			
Glynde	d							10 14								11 14							12 14		
Berwick	d							10 20								11 20							12 20		
Polegate	d	09 41			09 57	10 05		10 25	10 35				10 57	11 05		11 25	11 36			11 57	12 05		12 25		12 35
Hampden Park 4 §	d	09 45						10 29	10 39							11 29	11 40						12 29		12 39
Eastbourne 4	a	09 50			10 04	10 13		10 34	10 44				11 04	11 13		11 34	11 45			12 04	12 13		12 34		12 44
	d				10 08	10 19		10 40					11 08	11 19		11 40				12 08	12 19		12 40		
Hampden Park 4 §	d					10 23		10 44						11 23		11 44					12 23		12 44		
Pevensey & Westham	d					10 28		10 49						11 28		11 49					12 28		12 49		
Pevensey Bay	d																								
Normans Bay	d							10 53								11 53							12 53		
Cooden Beach	d					10 34		10 57						11 34		11 57					12 34		12 57		
Collington	d					10 37		11 00						11 37		12 00					12 37		13 00		
Bexhill 4	d				10 22	10 39		11 02					11 22	11 39		12 02				12 22	12 39		13 02		
St Leonards Warrior Sq 4	d				10 29	10 45		11 08					11 29	11 45		12 08				12 29	12 45		13 08		
Hastings 4	a				10 32	10 50		11 12					11 32	11 50		12 12				12 32	12 50		13 12		
	d				10 34	10 51		11 13					11 34	11 51		12 13				12 34	12 51		13 13		
Ore	d					10a54		11a16						11a54		12a16					12a54		13a16		
Three Oaks	d																								
Doleham	d																								
Winchelsea	d																								
Rye	a				10 51								11 51							12 51					
	d				10 54								11 54							12 54					
Appledore (Kent)	d				11 03								12 03							13 03					
Ham Street	d				11 08								12 08							13 08					
Ashford International	a				11 16								12 16							13 16					
London Bridge 4 ⊖	a				12 43								13 43							14 43					
London Cannon Street 4 ⊖	a				12f50								13f50							14f50					
London Waterloo (East) 4 ⊖	a				12 32								13 32							14 32					
London Charing Cross 4 ⊖	a				12 36								13 36							14 36					

For general notes see front of timetable
For details of catering facilities see Directory of Train Operators

§ For additional trains between Hampden Park and Eastbourne see Hastings to London pages

b Change at Haywards Heath
c Change at East Croydon and Brighton
e London Bridge
f Change at Ashford International and London Bridge

London, Haywards Heath and Brighton → Lewes, Seaford, Eastbourne, Hastings and Ashford

Network Diagram - see first page of Table 184

		SN 1	SN 1	SN 1	SN 1 🚲	SN 1	SN 1	SN 1 🚲	SN 1	SN 1	SN 1	SN 1 🚲	SN 1		SN 1	SN 1 🚲	SN 1	SN 1	SN 1	SN 1 🚲	SN 1	SN 1	SN 1 🚲	SN 1	SN 1
London Victoria 15 ⊖	d	11 06		11 36	11 47			12 17	12 06		12 36	12 47				13 17	13 06		13 36	13 47			14 17	14 06	
Clapham Junction 10	d	11 12		11 42	11 53			12 23	12 12		12 42	12 53				13 23	13 12		13 42	13 53			14 23	14 12	
London Bridge 4 ⊖	d	10 56		11 26					11 56		12 26						12 56		13 26					13 56	
East Croydon	d	11 22		11 52	12 03			12 33	12 22		12 52	13 03				13 33	13 22		13 52	14 03			14 33	14 22	
Gatwick Airport 10 ✈	d	11 26	11 28	11 56	12 19			12 49	12 26	12 38	12 56	13 19				13 49	13 26	13 28	13 56	14 19			14 49	14 26	14 28
Haywards Heath 3	d	11 38	11 46	12 08	12 34			13 07	12 38	12 50	13 08	13 34				14 07	13 38	13 46	14 08	14 34			15 07	14 38	14 46
Wivelsfield 4	d	11 31	11 50	11 59				13 11	12 31	12 50	12 59					14 11	13 31	13 50	13 59				15 11	14 31	14 50
Plumpton	d				12 43																				
Cooksbridge	d																								
Brighton 10	d	12 10	12 22	12 32		12 40	12 52		13 10	13 22	13 32		13 40		13 52		14 10	14 22	14 32		14 40	14 52		15 10	15 22
London Road (Brighton)	d	12 13	12 25			12 43	12 55		13 13	13 25			13 43		13 55		14 13	14 25			14 43	14 55		15 13	15 25
Moulsecoomb	d	12 15	12 27			12 45	12 57		13 15	13 27			13 45		13 57		14 15	14 27			14 45	14 57		15 15	15 27
Falmer	d	12 19	12 31			12 49	13 01		13 19	13 31			13 49		14 01		14 19	14 31			14 49	15 01		15 19	15 31
Lewes 4	a	12 25	12 37	12 43	12 52	12 55	13 07	13 22	13 25	13 37	13 43	13 48	13 55		14 07	14 22	14 25	14 37	14 43	14 48	14 55	15 07	15 22	15 25	15 37
	d	12 28		12 44	12 53	12 58	13 09	13 23	13 28		13 44	13 53	13 58		14 09	14 23	14 28		14 44	14 53	14 58	15 09	15 23	15 28	
Southease	d	12 34							13 34								14 34							15 34	
Newhaven Town ⛴	d	12 38				13 06			13 38				14 06				14 38				15 06			15 38	
Newhaven Harbour	d	12 40				13 08			13 40				14 08				14 40				15 08			15 40	
Bishopstone	d	12 43				13 11			13 43				14 11				14 43				15 11			15 43	
Seaford	a	12 46				13 14			13 46				14 14				14 46				15 14			15 46	
Glynde	d						13 14								14 14							15 14			
Berwick	d						13 20								14 20							15 20			
Polegate	d			12 57	13 05		13 25	13 35			13 57	14 05			14 25	14 35			14 57	15 05		15 25	15 35		
Hampden Park 4 §	d						13 29	13 39							14 29	14 39						15 29	15 39		
Eastbourne 4	a			13 04	13 13		13 34	13 44			14 04	14 13			14 34	14 44			15 04	15 13		15 34	15 44		
	d			13 08	13 19		13 40				14 08	14 19			14 40				15 08	15 19		15 40			
Hampden Park 4 §	d				13 23		13 44					14 23			14 44					15 23		15 44			
Pevensey & Westham	d				13 28		13 49					14 28			14 49					15 28		15 49			
Pevensey Bay	d																			15 30					
Normans Bay	d						13 53								14 53					15 34		15 53			
Cooden Beach	d				13 34		13 57					14 34			14 57					15 37		15 57			
Collington	d				13 37		14 00					14 37			15 00					15 40		16 00			
Bexhill 4	d			13 22	13 39		14 02				14 22	14 39			15 02				15 22	15 42		16 02			
St Leonards Warrior Sq 4	d			13 29	13 45		14 08				14 29	14 45			15 08				15 29	15 49		16 08			
Hastings 4	a			13 32	13 50		14 12				14 32	14 50			15 12				15 32	15 52		16 12			
	d			13 34	13 51		14 13				14 34	14 51			15 13				15 34	15 54		16 13			
Ore	d				13a54		14a16					14a54			15a16					15a57		16a16			
Three Oaks	d																								
Doleham	d																								
Winchelsea	d																								
Rye	a			13 51							14 51								15 51						
	d			13 54							14 54								15 54						
Appledore (Kent)	d			14 03							15 03								16 03						
Ham Street	d			14 08							15 08								16 08						
Ashford International	a			14 16							15 16								16 16						
London Bridge 4 ⊖	a			15 43							16 29								17 31						
London Cannon Street 4 ⊖	a			15b50							16b36								17b39						
London Waterloo (East) 4 ⊖	a			15 32							16 34								17 36						
London Charing Cross 4 ⊖	a			15 36							16 38								17 41						

For general notes see front of timetable
For details of catering facilities see Directory of Train Operators

§ For additional trains between Hampden Park and Eastbourne see Hastings to London pages

b Change at Ashford International and London Bridge

London, Haywards Heath and Brighton → Lewes, Seaford, Eastbourne, Hastings and Ashford

Network Diagram - see first page of Table 184

Station		SN	SN	SN		SN	SN	SN	SN	SN	SN	SN	SN	SN	SN	SN	SN		SN	SN	SE	SN	SN	SN	SN
																					22				
		1	1	1		1	1	1	1	1	1	1	1	1	1	1	1		1	1	1	1	1	1	1
																					A				
			⊼					⊼				⊼				⊼						⊼			
London Victoria 15 ⊖	d	14 36	14 47					15 17	15 06		15 36	15 47				16 17	16 06			16b17		16 47		16 36	
Clapham Junction 10	d	14 42	14 53					15 23	15 12		15 42	15 53				16 23	16 12			16b23		16 53		16 42	
London Bridge 4 ⊖	d	14 26							14 56		15 26					16 11	15 56			16 26		16c46			
East Croydon	d	14 52	15 03					15 33	15 22		15 52	16 03				16 33	16 22			16 40		17 03		16 52	
Gatwick Airport 10 ✈	d	14 56	15 19					15 49	15 26	15 28	15 56	16 19				16 49	16 26			16 56		17 20			17 09
Haywards Heath 3	d	15 08	15 34					16 07	15 38	15 46	16 10	16 33				17 06	16 40		16 46	17 10		17 35		17 16	17 24
Wivelsfield 4	d	14 59	15 38					16 11	15 31	15 50	15 59	16 37				17 10	16 31		16 50	16 59		17 39			17 28
Plumpton	d		15 44									16 43										17 45			
Cooksbridge	d											16 48										17 49			
Brighton 10	d	15 32				15 40	15 52		16 10	16 22	16 32			16 40	16 52		17 10		17 20	17 32				17 40	17 52
London Road (Brighton)	d					15 43	15 55		16 13	16 25				16 43	16 55		17 13		17 23					17 43	17 55
Moulsecoomb	d					15 45	15 57		16 15	16 27				16 45	16 57		17 15		17 25					17 45	17 57
Falmer	d					15 49	16 01		16 19	16 31				16 49	17 01		17 19		17 29					17 49	18 01
Lewes 4	a	15 43	15 52			15 55	16 07	16 22	16 25	16 37	16 43	16 52		16 55	17 07	17 21	17 25		17 35	17 43		17 54		17 55	18 07
	d	15 44	15 53			15 58	16 09	16 23	16 28		16 44	16 53		16 58	17 09	17 22	17 28		17 36	17 44		17 54		17 58	18 09
Southease	d					16 04			16 34								17 34								
Newhaven Town ⛴	d					16 08			16 38					17 06			17 38							18 06	
Newhaven Harbour	d					16 10			16 40					17 08			17 40							18 08	
Bishopstone	d					16 13			16 43					17 11			17 43							18 11	
Seaford	a					16 16			16 46					17 14			17 46							18 14	
Glynde	d						16 14								17 14										18 14
Berwick	d						16 20					17 02			17 20	17 31			17 45						18 20
Polegate	d	15 57	16 05				16 25	16 35			16 57	17 07			17 25	17 36			17 50	17 57		18 07			18 25
Hampden Park 4 §	d						16 29	16 39							17 29	17 40			17 55			18 11			18 31
Eastbourne 4	a	16 04	16 13				16 34	16 44			17 04	17 14			17 34	17 48			18 00	18 04		18 16			18 36
	d	16 08	16 19				16 40				17 08	17 21			17 40					18 08		18 23			18 50
Hampden Park 4 §	d		16 23				16 44					17 25			17 44							18 27			18 54
Pevensey & Westham	d		16 28				16 49					17 30			17 49							18 32			18 59
Pevensey Bay	d											17 32			17 51										
Normans Bay	d						16 53					17 36			17 55										19 03
Cooden Beach	d		16 34				16 57					17 39			17 58							18 38			19 07
Collington	d		16 37				17 00					17 42			18 01							18 41			19 10
Bexhill 4	d	16 22	16 39				17 02				17 22	17 44			18 03					18 23		18 43			19 12
St Leonards Warrior Sq 4	d	16 29	16 45				17 08				17 30	17 51			18 10					18 29	18 47	18 52			19 20
Hastings 4	a	16 32	16 49				17 12				17 33	17 54			18 13					18 33	18 51	18 56			19 24
	d	16 34	16 51	17 08			17 13				17 34	17 56			18 14					18 34	18 52	18 57			19 25
Ore	d		16a54	17 10			17a16					17a59			18a17						18a57	19a02			19a28
Three Oaks	d			17 16																					
Doleham	d			17 19																					
Winchelsea	d			17 25																					
Rye	a	16 51		17 29							17 51									18 51					
	d	16 54		17 30							17 54		18 31							18 54			19 31		
Appledore (Kent)	d	17 03		17 39							18 03		18 40							19 03			19 40		
Ham Street	d	17 08		17 44							18 08		18 45							19 08			19 45		
Ashford International	a	17 16		17 52							18 16		18 53							19 17			19 53		
London Bridge 4 ⊖	a	18 28		19 25							20 08									20 38					
London Cannon Street 4 ⊖	a	18e37		19e37							20e27														
London Waterloo (East) 4 ⊖	a	18 33		19 31							19 46									20 43					
London Charing Cross 4 ⊖	a	18 37		19 35							19 50									20 48					

For general notes see front of timetable
For details of catering facilities see Directory of Train Operators

§ For additional trains between Hampden Park and Eastbourne see Hastings to London pages

A From London Charing Cross (Table 206)
b Change at East Croydon and Brighton
c Change at Gatwick Airport
e Change at Ashford International and London Bridge

London, Haywards Heath and Brighton → Lewes, Seaford, Eastbourne, Hastings and Ashford

Network Diagram - see first page of Table 184

	SN		SN	SN	SN	SN	SE 22		SN	SN	SN	SN	SN	SN	SN	SN	SN	SN	SN	SN		SN	SN	SN
	1		1	1	1	1	1		1	1	1	1	1	1	1	1	1	1	1	1		1	1	1
							A																	
	🍴									🍴				🍴				🍴					🍴	
London Victoria 15 ⊖ d	17 17		16b38	17 02	17 07	17c37				17 53	17 37			18 17		18 07	18 17	18 47		18 32		19 06	19 17	
Clapham Junction 10 d	17 23		16b45	17 08	17 13	17c43				17 59	17 43			18 23		18 13	18 23	18 53		18 38		19 12	19 23	
London Bridge 4 ⊖ d	17 13		16 46	16b57	17 08	17 46				17e52	17b32			18e16		18 03	18b12		18 26	18 38		18 56	19f27	
East Croydon d	17 33		17 00	17 18	17 24	18 00				18 10	17 54		18g00	18 33		18 24	18 33	19 03	18 40	18 52		19 22	19 33	
Gatwick Airport 10 ✈ d	17 40		17 16	17 34	17 40	17 58				18 29	17g58		18 12	18 50		18g29	18 50	19 19	18 56	19 10		19 26	19 49	
Haywards Heath 3 d	18 03		17 32	17 48	17 58	18 24				18 41	18 20		18 30	19 05		18 50	19 08	19 33	19 12	19 24		19 45	20 13	
Wivelsfield 4 d	18 07		17 36		18 02	18 28				18 46			18 34	19 09		18 49	18 59	19 37		19 28			20 17	
Plumpton d						18 34				18 52				19 15				19 43						
Cooksbridge d						18 39				18 56				19 20				19 47						
Brighton 10 d			18 05	18 17	18 30				18 36		18 50		19 05			19 22	19 32		19 40	19 52		20 10		
London Road (Brighton) d			18 08	18 20					18 39		18 53		19 08			19 25			19 43	19 55		20 13		
Moulsecoomb d			18 10	18 22					18 41		18 55		19 10			19 27			19 45	19 57		20 15		
Falmer d			18 14	18 26					18 45		18 59		19 14			19 31			19 49	20 01		20 19		
Lewes 4 a	18 18		18 21	18 33	18 41	18 44			18 51	19 01	19 05		19 20	19 24	←	19 37	19 43	19 52	19 55	20 07		20 25	20 28	←
d	18 22	18 25		18 35	18 42	18 47			18 52	19 01	19 07	19 10	19 31	19 25	19 31		19 44	19 53	19 58	20 09		20 33	20 29	20 33
Southease d				18 41					18 58			19 16	→						20 04			→		
Newhaven Town ⛴ d	18 30			18 45					19 02			19 20			19 39				20 08					20 41
Newhaven Harbour d	18 32			18 47					19 05			19 22			19 41				20 10					20h47
Bishopstone d	18 35			18 50					19 08			19 25			19 44				20 13					20 50
Seaford a	18 40			18 53					19 11			19 28			19 47				20 16					20 53
Glynde d		18 30				18 53					19 12									20 14			20 34	
Berwick d		18 36				18 58					19 18			19 34						20 20			20 40	
Polegate d		18 41			18 55	19 04				19 14	19 23			19 39			19 57	20 05		20 25			20 45	
Hampden Park 4 § d		18 45				19 08				19 18	19 27			19 43						20 29			20 49	
Eastbourne 4 a		18 53			19 05	19 15				19 23	19 32			19 50			20 04	20 13		20 34			20 54	
d					19 09					19 29	19 48						20 08	20 19						
Hampden Park 4 § d										19 33	19 52							20 23						
Pevensey & Westham d										19 38	19 57							20 28						
Pevensey Bay d																								
Normans Bay d																								
Cooden Beach d										19 44	20 03							20 34						
Collington d										19 47	20 06							20 37						
Bexhill 4 d					19 23					19 49	20 08						20 22	20 39						
St Leonards Warrior Sq 4 d					19 30		19 35			19 57	20 14						20 30	20 47						
Hastings 4 a					19 33		19 39			20 01	20 18						20 34	20 50						
d					19 34		19 40			20 03	20 19						20 35	20 52						
Ore d							19a45			20a08	20a22							20a57						
Three Oaks d																								
Doleham d																								
Winchelsea d																								
Rye a					19 51												20 52							
d					19 54												20 54							
Appledore (Kent) d					20 03												21 03							
Ham Street d					20 08												21 08							
Ashford International a					20 16												21 16							
London Bridge 4 ⊖ a					21 38												22 38							
London Cannon Street 4 ⊖ a																								
London Waterloo (East) 4 ⊖ a					21 43												22 43							
London Charing Cross 4 ⊖ a					21 48												22 48							

For general notes see front of timetable
For details of catering facilities see Directory of Train Operators

§ For additional trains between Hampden Park and Eastbourne see Hastings to London pages

A From London Charing Cross (Table 206)
b Change at East Croydon and Brighton
c Change at East Croydon
e Change at Gatwick Airport
f Change at Haywards Heath
g Change at Haywards Heath and Brighton
h Arr. 2043

London, Haywards Heath and Brighton → Lewes, Seaford, Eastbourne, Hastings and Ashford

Network Diagram - see first page of Table 184

Station		SN 1	SN 1	SN 1	SN 1	SN 1	SN 1	SN 1	SN 1	SN 1	SN 1	SN 1	SN 1	SN 1	SN 1	SN 1	SN 1	SN 1	SN 1	SN 1	SN 1	SN 1
London Victoria 15	⊖ d		19 47	19 36	19b53	20 17		20b17	20 47	20 36	21 06	21 17			21 36	21 47		22 06		22 36	22 47	
Clapham Junction 10	d		19 53	19 42	19b59	20 23		20b23	20 53	20 42	21 12	21 23			21 42	21 53		22 12		22 42	22 53	
London Bridge 4	⊖ d	19 12		19 27	20 01			20 28			20 58			21 11	21b15			21b45	22 11	22b15		
East Croydon	d	19 24	20 03	19 52	20 14	20 33		20 41	21 03	20 52	21 22	21 33		21 24	21 52	22 03		22 22	22 24	22 52	23 03	
Gatwick Airport 10	✈ d	19 41	20 19	19 55	20 31	20 49		20 56	21 19		21 27	21 49		21 41	21c49	22 19		22c19	22 41	22c49	23 19	
Haywards Heath 3	d	19 58	20 36	20 17	20 42	21 07		21 11	21 37	21 15	21 45	22 08		21 58	22 15	22 34		22 45	22 58	23 15	23 34	
Wivelsfield 4	d	20 02	20 40		20 30	21 11		21 02	21 41		21 30	22 12		22 02		22 38		22 30	23 02		23 38	
Plumpton	d		20 46						21 47							22 44					23 44	
Cooksbridge	d		20 50																			
Brighton 10	d	20 30		20 40	21 04			21 30		21 40	22 04			22 28	22 34			23 04	23 28	23 34		
London Road (Brighton)	d			20 43	21 07					21 43	22 07				22 37			23 07		23 37		
Moulsecoomb	d			20 45	21 09					21 45	22 09				22 39			23 09		23 39		
Falmer	d			20 49	21 13					21 49	22 13				22 43			23 13		23 43		
Lewes 4	a	20 43	20 55	20 55	21 19	21 22		21 43	21 54	21 55	22 19	22 23		22 39	22 49	22 51		23 19	23 39	23 49	23 51	
	d	20 44	20 55	21 00	21 28	21 23	← 21 28	21 44	21 55	21 58	22 28	22 23	← 22 28	22 39	22 58	22 53	← 22 58	23 20	23 39	23 56	23 53	← 23 56
Southease	d				→					22 04	→				→		23 04			→		
Newhaven Town	⛴ d			21 08			21 36			22 08			22 36				23 08					00 04
Newhaven Harbour	d			21 10			21 38			22 10			22 38				23 10					00 06
Bishopstone	d			21 13			21 41			22 13			22 41				23 13					00 09
Seaford	a			21 16			21 44			22 16			22 44				23 16					00 12
Glynde	d					21 28						22 29						23 25				
Berwick	d					21 34						22 34						23 31			00 02	
Polegate	d	20 57	21 08			21 39		21 57	22 07			22 39		22 52		23 05		23 36	23 52		00 07	
Hampden Park 4 §	d					21 43						22 43				23 09		23 41			00 11	
Eastbourne 4	a	21 04	21 15			21 48		22 04	22 15			22 48		23 03		23 14		23 46	23 59		00 16	
	d	21 08	21 21					22 08	22 21							23 20					00 22	
Hampden Park 4 §	d		21 25						22 25							23 24						
Pevensey & Westham	d		21 30						22 30							23 29					00 29	
Pevensey Bay	d																					
Normans Bay	d																					
Cooden Beach	d		21 36						22 36							23 35					00 35	
Collington	d		21 39						22 39							23 38					00 38	
Bexhill 4	d	21 23	21 41					22 22	22 41							23 40					00 40	
St Leonards Warrior Sq 4	d	21 30	21 47					22 29	22 47							23 46					00 47	
Hastings 4	a	21 33	21 51					22 32	22 51							23 50					00 50	
	d	21 34	21 53																			
Ore	d	21 36	21a56																			
Three Oaks	d	21 42																				
Doleham	d	21 45																				
Winchelsea	d	21 51																				
Rye	a	21 55																				
	d	21 57																				
Appledore (Kent)	d	22 06																				
Ham Street	d	22 11																				
Ashford International	a	22 19																				
London Bridge 4	⊖ a	23 51																				
London Cannon Street 4	⊖ a																					
London Waterloo (East) 4	⊖ a	23 56																				
London Charing Cross 4	⊖ a	00 01																				

For general notes see front of timetable
For details of catering facilities see Directory of Train Operators

§ For additional trains between Hampden Park and Eastbourne see Hastings to London pages

b Change at East Croydon and Brighton
c Change at Haywards Heath and Brighton

Table 189

London, Haywards Heath and Brighton → Lewes, Seaford, Eastbourne, Hastings and Ashford

Network Diagram - see first page of Table 184

	SN 1	SN 1	SN 1	SN 1	SN 1	SN 1	SN 1	SN 1	SN 1	SN 1	SN 1	SN 1	SN 1	SN 1	SN 1	SN 1	SN 1	SN 1	SN 1	SN 1	SN 1	SN 1
London Victoria 15 ⊖ d		22p47		00 05			04 00						05 02	05 02				05 32		06b10	06c23	
Clapham Junction 10 d		22p53		00 11			04 08						05 08	05 08				05 38		06b16	06c29	
London Bridge 4 ⊖ d				23 53														05 50		06 26	06 41	
East Croydon d		23p03		00 25									05 32	05 22		05 32				06 39	06 54	
Gatwick Airport 10 ✈ d		23p19		00 43									06 11	05 50		05 54				06 56	07 11	
Haywards Heath 3 d		23p34		01 02									06 25	06 03		06 12				07 08	07 33	
Wivelsfield 4 d		23p38											06 29	06 07		06 16					07 37	
Plumpton d		23p44																				
Cooksbridge d																						
Brighton 10 d	23p34						05 30			05 52		06 10		06 32		06 40	06 52	07 10	07 22	07 32		07 40
London Road (Brighton) d	23p37									05 55		06 13				06 43	06 55	07 13	07 25			07 43
Moulsecoomb d	23p39									05 57		06 15				06 45	06 57	07 15	07 27			07 45
Falmer d	23p43									06 01		06 19				06 49	07 01	07 19	07 31			07 49
Lewes 4 a	23p49	23p51	←	01 16			05 41			06 07		06 25	06 40	06 43	←	06 55	07 07	07 25	07 37	07 43	07 48	07 55
d	23p56	23p53	23p56	01 17			05 41			06 08		06 28	06 53	06 44	06 53	06 58	07 09	07 28		07 44	07 53	07 58
Southease d	→												→									
Newhaven Town ⛴ d			00 04							06 16		06 36				07 06		07 36				08 06
Newhaven Harbour d			00 06							06 18		06 38				07 08		07 38				08 08
Bishopstone d			00 09									06 41				07 11		07 41				08 11
Seaford a			00 12							06 23		06 44				07 14		07 44				08 14
Glynde d																	07 14					
Berwick d		00 02													07 02		07 20					
Polegate d		00 07		01s29			05 53							06 57	07 07		07 25			07 57	08 05	
Hampden Park 4 § d		00 11		01s33											07 11		07 29					
Eastbourne 4 a		00 16		01 38			06 00							07 04	07 16		07 34			08 04	08 13	
d		00 22				05 45		06 05	06 18		06 45			07 08	07 21		07 40			08 08	08 19	
Hampden Park 4 § d									06 22						07 25		07 44				08 23	
Pevensey & Westham d		00 29							06 27						07 30		07 49				08 28	
Pevensey Bay d																						
Normans Bay d									06 31								07 53					
Cooden Beach d		00 35							06 35						07 36		07 57				08 34	
Collington d		00 38							06 38						07 39		08 00				08 37	
Bexhill 4 d		00 40				06 00		06 19	06 40		07 00			07 22	07 41		08 02			08 22	08 39	
St Leonards Warrior Sq 4 d		00 47				06 06		06 26	06 49		07 06			07 29	07 47		08 08			08 29	08 45	
Hastings 4 a		00 50				06 10		06 30	06 53		07 10			07 32	07 51		08 12			08 32	08 50	
d					05 34	06 11		06 30	06 54		07 11			07 34	07 52		08 13			08 34	08 51	
Ore d					05 37	06a14			06a57		07a14				07a55		08a16				08a54	
Three Oaks d					05 43																	
Doleham d					05 46																	
Winchelsea d					05 52																	
Rye a					05 55			06 47						07 51						08 51		
d					05 56			06 50						07 54						08 54		
Appledore (Kent) d					06 05			06 59						08 03						09 03		
Ham Street d					06 10			07 04						08 08						09 08		
Ashford International a					06 18			07 13						08 16						09 16		
London Bridge 4 ⊖ a					08 10			08 38						09 43						10 43		
London Cannon Street 4 ⊖ a					08e20			08e47						09e50						10e50		
London Waterloo (East) 4 ⊖ a					08 14			08 43						09 32						10 32		
London Charing Cross 4 ⊖ a					08 18			08 48						09 36						10 36		

For general notes see front of timetable
For details of catering facilities see Directory of Train Operators

§ For additional trains between Hampden Park and Eastbourne see Hastings to London pages

b Change at East Croydon and Brighton
c Change at East Croydon and Haywards Heath
e Change at Ashford International and London Bridge

Table 189

Saturdays

London, Haywards Heath and Brighton → Lewes, Seaford, Eastbourne, Hastings and Ashford

Network Diagram - see first page of Table 184

Station		SN 1	SN 1	SN 1	SN 1	SN 1	SN 1	SN 1		SN 1	SN 1	SN 1	SN 1	SN 1	SN 1	SN 1	SN 1	SN 1		SN 1	SN 1	SN 1	SN 1	SN 1	SN 1
London Victoria 15 ⊖	d		07 06		07 36	07 47				08 17	08 06		08 36	08 47			09 17	09 06			09 36	09 47			10 17
Clapham Junction 10	d		07 12		07 42	07 53				08 23	08 12		08 42	08 53			09 23	09 12			09 42	09 53			10 23
London Bridge 4 ⊖	d		06 56		07 26						07 56		08 26					08 56			09 26	09 41			
East Croydon	d		07 22		07 52	08 03				08 33	08 22		08 52	09 03			09 33	09 22			09 52	10 03			10 33
Gatwick Airport 10 ✈	d		07 26	07 28	07 56	08 19				08 49	08 26	08 28	08 56	09 19			09 49	09 26		09 28	09 56	10 19			10 49
Haywards Heath 3	d		07 38	07 46	08 08	08 34				09 07	08 38	08 46	09 08	09 34			10 07	09 38		09 46	10 08	10 34			11 07
Wivelsfield 4	d		07 31	07 50	07 59					09 11	08 31	08 52	08 59				10 11	09 31		09 50	09 59				11 11
Plumpton	d													09 43								10 43			
Cooksbridge	d																								
Brighton 10	d	07 52	08 10	08 22	08 32		08 40	08 52			09 10	09 22	09 32		09 40	09 52		10 10		10 22	10 32		10 40	10 52	
London Road (Brighton)	d	07 55	08 13	08 25			08 43	08 55			09 13	09 25			09 43	09 55		10 13		10 25			10 43	10 55	
Moulsecoomb	d	07 57	08 15	08 27			08 45	08 57			09 15	09 27			09 45	09 57		10 15		10 27			10 45	10 57	
Falmer	d	08 01	08 19	08 31			08 49	09 01			09 19	09 31			09 49	10 01		10 19		10 31			10 49	11 01	
Lewes 4	a	08 07	08 25	08 37	08 43	08 52	08 55	09 07		09 22	09 25	09 37	09 43	09 52	09 55	10 07	10 22	10 25		10 37	10 43	10 52	10 55	11 07	11 22
	d	08 09	08 28		08 44	08 53	08 58	09 09		09 23	09 28		09 44	09 53	09 58	10 09	10 23	10 28			10 44	10 53	10 58	11 09	11 23
Southease	d										09 34							10 34							
Newhaven Town ⛴	d		08 36				09 06				09 38				10 06			10 38					11 06		
Newhaven Harbour	d		08 38				09 08				09 40				10 08			10 40					11 08		
Bishopstone	d		08 41				09 11				09 43				10 11			10 43					11 11		
Seaford	a		08 44				09 14				09 46				10 14			10 46					11 14		
Glynde	d	08 14						09 14								10 14								11 14	
Berwick	d	08 20						09 20								10 20								11 20	
Polegate	d	08 25			08 57	09 05		09 25		09 35			09 57	10 05		10 25	10 35				10 57	11 05		11 25	11 35
Hampden Park 4 §	d	08 29						09 29		09 39						10 29	10 39							11 29	11 39
Eastbourne 4	a	08 34			09 04	09 13		09 34		09 44			10 04	10 13		10 34	10 44				11 04	11 13		11 34	11 44
	d	08 40			09 08	09 19		09 40					10 08	10 19		10 40					11 08	11 19		11 40	
Hampden Park 4 §	d	08 44				09 23		09 44						10 23		10 44						11 23		11 44	
Pevensey & Westham	d	08 49				09 28		09 49						10 28		10 49						11 28		11 49	
Pevensey Bay	d																								
Normans Bay	d	08 53						09 53								10 53								11 53	
Cooden Beach	d	08 57				09 34		09 57						10 34		10 57						11 34		11 57	
Collington	d	09 00				09 37		10 00						10 37		11 00						11 37		12 00	
Bexhill 4	d	09 02			09 22	09 39		10 02					10 22	10 39		11 02					11 22	11 39		12 02	
St Leonards Warrior Sq 4	d	09 08			09 29	09 45		10 08					10 29	10 45		11 08					11 29	11 45		12 08	
Hastings 4	a	09 12			09 32	09 50		10 12					10 32	10 50		11 12					11 32	11 50		12 12	
	d	09 13			09 34	09 51		10 13					10 34	10 51		11 13					11 34	11 51		12 13	
Ore	d	09a16				09a54		10a16						10a54		11a16						11a54		12a16	
Three Oaks	d																								
Doleham	d																								
Winchelsea	d																								
Rye	a				09 51								10 51								11 51				
	d				09 54								10 54								11 54				
Appledore (Kent)	d				10 03								11 03								12 03				
Ham Street	d				10 08								11 08								12 08				
Ashford International	a				10 16								11 16								12 16				
London Bridge 4 ⊖	a				11 43								12 43								13 43				
London Cannon Street 4 ⊖	a				11b50								12b50								13b50				
London Waterloo (East) 4 ⊖	a				11 32								12 32								13 32				
London Charing Cross 4 ⊖	a				11 36								12 36								13 36				

For general notes see front of timetable
For details of catering facilities see
Directory of Train Operators

§ For additional trains between Hampden Park and Eastbourne see Hastings to London pages

b Change at Ashford International and London Bridge

Table 189

Saturdays

London, Haywards Heath and Brighton → Lewes, Seaford, Eastbourne, Hastings and Ashford

Network Diagram - see first page of Table 184

		SN 1	SN 1	SN 1	SN 1	SN 1	SN 1	SN 1	SN 1	SN 1	SN 1	SN 1	SN 1	SN 1	SN 1	SN 1	SN 1	SN 1	SN 1	SN 1	SN 1	SN 1	SN 1
London Victoria 15	⊖ d	10 06		10 36	10 47			11 17	11 06		11 36	11 47			12 17	12 06		12 36	12 47			13 17	13 06
Clapham Junction 10	d	10 12		10 42	10 53			11 23	11 12		11 42	11 53			12 23	12 12		12 42	12 53			13 23	13 12
London Bridge 4	⊖ d	09 56		10 26					10 56		11 26					11 56	12 11	12 26					12 56
East Croydon	d	10 22		10 52	11 03			11 33	11 22		11 52	12 03			12 33	12 22	12 24	12 52	13 03			13 33	13 22
Gatwick Airport 10	✈ d	10 26	10 28	10 56	11 19			11 49	11 26	11 28	11 56	12 19			12 49	12 26	12 40	12 56	13 19		13 01	13 49	13 26
Haywards Heath 3	d	10 38	10 46	11 08	11 34			12 07	11 38	11 46	12 08	12 34			13 07	12 38	12 55	13 08	13 34		13 18	14 07	13 38
Wivelsfield 4	d	10 31	10 50	10 59				12 11	11 31	11 50	11 59				13 11	12 31	12 59					14 11	13 31
Plumpton	d				11 43							12 43											
Cooksbridge	d																						
Brighton 10	d	11 10	11 22	11 32		11 40	11 52		12 10	12 22	12 32		12 40	12 52		13 10	13 22	13 32		13 40	13 52		14 10
London Road (Brighton)	d	11 13	11 25			11 43	11 55		12 13	12 25			12 43	12 55		13 13	13 25			13 43	13 55		14 13
Moulsecoomb	d	11 15	11 27			11 45	11 57		12 15	12 27			12 45	12 57		13 15	13 27			13 45	13 57		14 15
Falmer	d	11 19	11 31			11 49	12 01		12 19	12 31			12 49	13 01		13 19	13 31			13 49	14 01		14 19
Lewes 4	a	11 25	11 37	11 43	11 52	11 55	12 07	12 22	12 25	12 37	12 43	12 52	12 55	13 07	13 22	13 25	13 37	13 43	13 48	13 55	14 07	14 22	14 25
	d	11 28		11 44	11 53	11 58	12 09	12 23	12 28		12 44	12 53	12 58	13 09	13 23	13 28		13 44	13 53	13 58	14 09	14 23	14 28
Southease	d	11 34							12 34							13 34							14 34
Newhaven Town	⛴ d	11 38				12 06			12 38				13 06			13 38				14 06			14 38
Newhaven Harbour	d	11 40				12 08			12 40				13 08			13 40				14 08			14 40
Bishopstone	d	11 43				12 11			12 43				13 11			13 43				14 11			14 43
Seaford	a	11 46				12 14			12 46				13 14			13 46				14 14			14 46
Glynde	d						12 14							13 14							14 14		
Berwick	d						12 20							13 20							14 20		
Polegate	d			11 57	12 05		12 25	12 35			12 57	13 05		13 25	13 35			13 57	14 05		14 25	14 35	
Hampden Park 4 §	d						12 29	12 39						13 29	13 39						14 29	14 39	
Eastbourne 4	a			12 04	12 13		12 34	12 44			13 04	13 13		13 34	13 44			14 04	14 13		14 34	14 44	
	d			12 08	12 19		12 40				13 08	13 19		13 40				14 08	14 19		14 40		
Hampden Park 4 §	d				12 23		12 44					13 23		13 44					14 23		14 44		
Pevensey & Westham	d				12 28		12 49					13 28		13 49					14 28		14 49		
Pevensey Bay	d																						
Normans Bay	d						12 53							13 53							14 53		
Cooden Beach	d				12 34		12 57					13 34		13 57					14 34		14 57		
Collington	d				12 37		13 00					13 37		14 00					14 37		15 00		
Bexhill 4	d			12 22	12 39		13 02				13 22	13 39		14 02				14 22	14 39		15 02		
St Leonards Warrior Sq 4	d			12 29	12 45		13 08				13 29	13 45		14 08				14 29	14 45		15 08		
Hastings 4	a			12 32	12 50		13 12				13 32	13 50		14 12				14 32	14 50		15 12		
	d			12 34	12 51		13 13				13 34	13 51		14 13				14 34	14 51		15 13		
Ore	d				12a54		13a16					13a54		14a16					14a54		15a16		
Three Oaks	d																						
Doleham	d																						
Winchelsea	d																						
Rye	a			12 51							13 51							14 51					
	d			12 54							13 54							14 54					
Appledore (Kent)	d			13 03							14 03							15 03					
Ham Street	d			13 08							14 08							15 08					
Ashford International	a			13 16							14 16							15 16					
London Bridge 4	⊖ a			14 43							15 43							16 43					
London Cannon Street 4	⊖ a			14b50							15b50							16b50					
London Waterloo (East) 4	⊖ a			14 32							15 32							16 32					
London Charing Cross 4	⊖ a			14 36							15 36							16 36					

For general notes see front of timetable
For details of catering facilities see Directory of Train Operators

§ For additional trains between Hampden Park and Eastbourne see Hastings to London pages

b Change at Ashford International and London Bridge

Table 189

London, Haywards Heath and Brighton → Lewes, Seaford, Eastbourne, Hastings and Ashford

Network Diagram - see first page of Table 184

		SN 1	SN 1	SN 1		SN 1	SN 1	SN 1	SN 1	SN 1	SN 1	SN 1	SN 1	SN 1		SN 1	SN 1	SN 1	SN 1	SN 1	SN 1	SN 1	SN 1	SN 1	SN 1
London Victoria 15 ⊖	d		13 36	13 47				14 17	14 06		14 36	14 47				15 17	15 06		15 36	15 47			16 17	16 06	
Clapham Junction 10	d		13 42	13 53				14 23	14 12		14 42	14 53				15 23	15 12		15 42	15 53			16 23	16 12	
London Bridge 4 ⊖	d		13 26						13 56		14 26						14 56		15 26					15 56	
East Croydon	d		13 52	14 03				14 33	14 22		14 52	15 03				15 33	15 22		15 52	16 03			16 33	16 22	
Gatwick Airport 10 ✈	d	13 28	13 56	14 19				14 49	14 26	14 28	14 56	15 19				15 49	15 26	15 28	15 56	16 19			16 49	16 26	16 28
Haywards Heath 3	d	13 46	14 08	14 34				15 07	14 38	14 46	15 08	15 34				16 07	15 38	15 46	16 08	16 34			17 07	16 38	16 46
Wivelsfield 4	d	13 50	13 59					15 11	14 31	14 50	14 59					16 11	15 31	15 50	15 59				17 11	16 31	16 50
Plumpton	d																								
Cooksbridge	d																								
Brighton 10	d	14 22	14 32			14 40	14 52		15 10	15 22	15 32		15 40	15 52			16 10	16 22	16 32		16 40	16 52		17 10	17 22
London Road (Brighton)	d	14 25				14 43	14 55		15 13	15 25			15 43	15 55			16 13	16 25			16 43	16 55		17 13	17 25
Moulsecoomb	d	14 27				14 45	14 57		15 15	15 27			15 45	15 57			16 15	16 27			16 45	16 57		17 15	17 27
Falmer	d	14 31				14 49	15 01		15 19	15 31			15 49	16 01			16 19	16 31			16 49	17 01		17 19	17 31
Lewes 4	a	14 37	14 43	14 48		14 55	15 07	15 22	15 25	15 37	15 43	15 48	15 55	16 07		16 22	16 25	16 37	16 43	16 48	16 55	17 07	17 22	17 25	17 37
	d		14 44	14 53		14 58	15 09	15 23	15 28		15 44	15 53	15 58	16 09		16 23	16 28		16 44	16 53	16 58	17 09	17 23	17 28	
Southease	d								15 34								16 34							17 34	
Newhaven Town ⛴	d					15 06			15 38				16 06				16 38				17 06			17 38	
Newhaven Harbour	d					15 08			15 40				16 08				16 40				17 08			17 40	
Bishopstone	d					15 11			15 43				16 11				16 43				17 11			17 43	
Seaford	a					15 14			15 50				16 14				16 46				17 14			17 46	
Glynde	d						15 14							16 14								17 14			
Berwick	d						15 20							16 20								17 20			
Polegate	d		14 57	15 05			15 25	15 35			15 57	16 05		16 25		16 35			16 57	17 05		17 25	17 35		
Hampden Park 4 §	d						15 29	15 39						16 29		16 39						17 29	17 39		
Eastbourne 4	a		15 04	15 13			15 34	15 44			16 04	16 13		16 34		16 44			17 04	17 13		17 34	17 44		
	d		15 08	15 19			15 40				16 08	16 19		16 40					17 08	17 19		17 40			
Hampden Park 4 §	d			15 23			15 44					16 23		16 44						17 23		17 44			
Pevensey & Westham	d			15 28			15 49					16 28		16 49						17 28		17 49			
Pevensey Bay	d																								
Normans Bay	d						15 53							16 53								17 53			
Cooden Beach	d			15 34			15 57					16 34		16 57						17 34		17 57			
Collington	d			15 37			16 00					16 37		17 00						17 37		18 00			
Bexhill 4	d		15 22	15 39			16 02				16 22	16 39		17 02					17 22	17 39		18 02			
St Leonards Warrior Sq 4	d		15 29	15 45			16 08				16 29	16 45		17 08					17 29	17 46		18 08			
Hastings 4	a		15 32	15 50			16 12				16 32	16 50		17 12					17 32	17 50		18 12			
	d		15 34	15 51			16 13				16 34	16 51		17 13					17 34	17 52		18 13			
Ore	d			15a54			16a16					16a54		17a16						17a55		18a16			
Three Oaks	d																								
Doleham	d																								
Winchelsea	d																								
Rye	a		15 51								16 51								17 51						
	d		15 54								16 54								17 54						
Appledore (Kent)	d		16 03								17 03								18 03						
Ham Street	d		16 08								17 08								18 08						
Ashford International	a		16 16								17 16								18 16						
London Bridge 4 ⊖	a		17 43								19 08								19 38						
London Cannon Street 4 ⊖	a		17b50																						
London Waterloo (East) 4 ⊖	a		17 32								19 14								19 44						
London Charing Cross 4 ⊖	a		17 36								19 19								19 49						

For general notes see front of timetable
For details of catering facilities see Directory of Train Operators

§ For additional trains between Hampden Park and Eastbourne see Hastings to London pages

b Change at Ashford International and London Bridge

Table 189

London, Haywards Heath and Brighton → Lewes, Seaford, Eastbourne, Hastings and Ashford

Network Diagram - see first page of Table 184

		SN 1		SN 1	SN 1	SN 1	SN 1	SN 1	SN 1	SN 1	SN 1	SN 1		SN 1	SN 1	SN 1	SN 1	SN 1	SN 1	SN 1	SN 1	SN 1		SN 1	SN 1
London Victoria 15	⊖ d	16 36		16 47			17 17	17 06		17 36	17 47				18 17	18 06		18 36	18 47			19 17		19 06	19b17
Clapham Junction 10	d	16 42		16 53			17 23	17 12		17 42	17 53				18 23	18 12		18 42	18 53			19 23		19 12	19b23
London Bridge 4	⊖ d	16 26						16 56		17 26						17 56		18 26						18 56	19 26
East Croydon	d	16 52		17 03			17 33	17 22		17 52	18 03				18 33	18 22		18 52	19 03			19 33		19 22	19 39
Gatwick Airport 10	✈ d	16 56		17 19			17 49	17 26	17 28	17 56	18 19				18 49	18 26	18 28	18 56	19 19			19 49		19 26	19 56
Haywards Heath 3	d	17 08		17 34			18 07	17 38	17 46	18 08	18 34				19 07	18 38	18 46	19 08	19 34			20 07		19 38	20 10
Wivelsfield 4	d	16 59					18 11	17 31	17 50	17 59					19 11	18 31	18 50	18 59				20 11		19 31	19 59
Plumpton	d			17 43							18 43								19 43						
Cooksbridge	d																								
Brighton 10	d	17 32			17 40	17 52		18 10	18 22	18 32		18 40		18 52		19 10	19 22	19 32		19 40	19 53			20 10	20 32
London Road (Brighton)	d				17 43	17 55		18 13	18 25			18 43		18 55		19 13	19 25			19 43	19 56			20 13	
Moulsecoomb	d				17 45	17 57		18 15	18 27			18 45		18 57		19 15	19 27			19 45	19 58			20 15	
Falmer	d				17 49	18 01		18 19	18 31			18 49		19 01		19 19	19 31			19 49	20 02			20 19	
Lewes 4	a	17 43		17 52	17 55	18 07	18 22	18 25	18 37	18 43	18 52	18 55		19 07	19 22	19 25	19 37	19 43	19 52	19 55	20 08	20 22		20 25	20 43
	d	17 44		17 53	17 58	18 09	18 23	18 28		18 44	18 53	18 58		19 09	19 23	19 28		19 44	19 53	19 58	20 09	20 23		20 28	20 44
Southease	d							18 34								19 34									
Newhaven Town	⛴ d				18 06			18 38				19 06				19 38				20 06				20 36	
Newhaven Harbour	d				18 08			18 40				19 08				19 40				20 08				20 38	
Bishopstone	d				18 11			18 43				19 11				19 43				20 11				20 41	
Seaford	a				18 14			18 46				19 14				19 46				20 14				20 44	
Glynde	d					18 14								19 14							20 14	20 28			
Berwick	d					18 20								19 20							20 20	20 34			
Polegate	d	17 57		18 05		18 25	18 35			18 57	19 05			19 25	19 35			19 57	20 05		20 25	20 39			20 57
Hampden Park 4 §	d					18 29	18 39							19 29	19 39						20 29	20 43			
Eastbourne 4	a	18 04		18 13		18 34	18 44			19 04	19 13			19 34	19 44			20 04	20 13		20 34	20 48			21 04
	d	18 08		18 19		18 40				19 08	19 19			19 40				20 08	20 19			20 54			21 08
Hampden Park 4 §	d			18 23		18 44					19 23			19 44					20 23						
Pevensey & Westham	d			18 28		18 49					19 28			19 49					20 28			21 01			
Pevensey Bay	d																								
Normans Bay	d					18 53								19 53											
Cooden Beach	d			18 34		18 57					19 34			19 57					20 34			21 07			
Collington	d			18 37		19 00					19 37			20 00					20 37						
Bexhill 4	d	18 22		18 39		19 02				19 22	19 39			20 02				20 22	20 39			21 11			21 24
St Leonards Warrior Sq 4	d	18 29		18 46		19 08				19 29	19 46			20 08				20 29	20 46			21 18			21 30
Hastings 4	a	18 32		18 50		19 12				19 32	19 50			20 12				20 32	20 50			21 21			21 34
	d	18 34		18 52		19 13				19 34	19 52			20 13				20 34	20 52						21 34
Ore	d			18a55		19a16					19a55			20a16					20a55						21 37
Three Oaks	d																								21 43
Doleham	d																								21 46
Winchelsea	d																								21 52
Rye	a	18 51								19 51								20 51							21 55
	d	18 54								19 54								20 54							21 57
Appledore (Kent)	d	19 03								20 03								21 03							22 06
Ham Street	d	19 08								20 08								21 08							22 11
Ashford International	a	19 16								20 16								21 16							22 19
London Bridge 4	⊖ a	20 38								21 38								22 38							23 53
London Cannon Street 4	⊖ a																								
London Waterloo (East) 4	⊖ a	20 44								21 44								22 44							23 57
London Charing Cross 4	⊖ a	20 49								21 49								22 49							00 01

For general notes see front of timetable
For details of catering facilities see Directory of Train Operators

§ For additional trains between Hampden Park and Eastbourne see Hastings to London pages

b Change at East Croydon and Brighton

Table 189

Saturdays

London, Haywards Heath and Brighton → Lewes, Seaford, Eastbourne, Hastings and Ashford

Network Diagram - see first page of Table 184

		SN 1	SN 1	SN 1	SN 1	SN 1	SN 1	SN 1	SN 1	SN 1	SN 1	SN 1	SN 1	SN 1	SN 1	SN 1	SN 1	SN 1	SN 1	SN 1	SN 1
London Victoria 15 ⊖	d	19 47	19 36	20 06	20 17			20 47	20 36	21 06	21 17			21 36	21 47		22 06		22 36	22 47	
Clapham Junction 10	d	19 53	19 42	20 12	20 23			20 53	20 42	21 12	21 23			21 42	21 53		22 12		22 42	22 53	
London Bridge 4 ⊖	d			19 56			20 11		20b15	20b45			21 11	21b15			21b45	22 11	22b15		
East Croydon	d	20 03	19 52	20 22	20 33		20 24	21 03	20 52	21 22	21 33		21 24	21 52	22 03		22 22	22 24	22 52	23 03	
Gatwick Airport 10 ✈	d	20 19		20 26	20 49		20 41	21 19	20c49	21c19	21 49		21 41	21c49	22 19		22c19	22 41	22c51	23 19	
Haywards Heath 3	d	20 37	20 15	20 38	21 07		20 58	21 37	21 15	21 45	22 08		21 58	22 15	22 34		22 45	22 58	23 15	23 34	
Wivelsfield 4	d	20 41		20 31	21 11		21 02	21 41		21 30	22 12		22 02		22 38		22 30	23 02		23 38	
Plumpton	d	20 47						21 47							22 44					23 44	
Cooksbridge	d																				
Brighton 10	d		20 40	21 04			21 32		21 40	22 04			22 28	22 34			23 04	23 28	23 34		
London Road (Brighton)	d		20 43	21 07					21 43	22 07				22 37			23 07		23 37		
Moulsecoomb	d		20 45	21 09					21 45	22 09				22 39			23 09		23 39		
Falmer	d		20 49	21 13					21 49	22 13				22 43			23 13		23 43		
Lewes 4	a	20 54	20 55	21 19	21 22	←	21 43	21 54	21 55	22 19	22 23	←	22 39	22 49	22 51	←	23 19	23 39	23 49	23 51	←
	d	20 55	20 58	21 28	21 23	21 28	21 44	21 55	21 58	22 28	22 23	22 28	22 39	22 58	22 53	22 58	23 20	23 39	23 56	23 53	23 56
Southease	d			→						→				→					→		
Newhaven Town ⛴	d		21 06			21 36			22 06			22 36				23 06					00 04
Newhaven Harbour	d		21 08			21 38			22 08			22 38				23 08					00 06
Bishopstone	d		21 11			21 41			22 11			22 41				23 11					00 09
Seaford	a		21 14			21 44			22 14			22 44				23 14					00 12
Glynde	d				21 28						22 29						23 25				
Berwick	d				21 34						22 34						23 31			00 02	
Polegate	d	21 07			21 39		21 57	22 07			22 39		22 52		23 05		23 36	23 52		00 07	
Hampden Park 4 §	d				21 43						22 43				23 09		23 41			00 11	
Eastbourne 4	a	21 15			21 48		22 04	22 15			22 48		23 03		23 14		23 46	23 59		00 16	
	d	21 21					22 08	22 21					23 10		23 20					00 22	
Hampden Park 4 §	d	21 25						22 25							23 24						
Pevensey & Westham	d	21 30						22 30							23 29					00 29	
Pevensey Bay	d																				
Normans Bay	d																				
Cooden Beach	d	21 36						22 36							23 35					00 35	
Collington	d	21 39						22 39							23 38					00 38	
Bexhill 4	d	21 41					22 22	22 41					23 23		23 40					00 40	
St Leonards Warrior Sq 4	d	21 47					22 29	22 47					23 30		23 46					00 47	
Hastings 4	a	21 51					22 32	22 51					23 33		23 50					00 50	
	d	21 53																			
Ore	d	21a56																			
Three Oaks	d																				
Doleham	d																				
Winchelsea	d																				
Rye	a																				
	d																				
Appledore (Kent)	d																				
Ham Street	d																				
Ashford International	a																				
London Bridge 4 ⊖	a																				
London Cannon Street 4 ⊖	a																				
London Waterloo (East) 4 ⊖	a																				
London Charing Cross 4 ⊖	a																				

For general notes see front of timetable
For details of catering facilities see Directory of Train Operators

§ For additional trains between Hampden Park and Eastbourne see Hastings to London pages

b Change at East Croydon and Brighton
c Change at Haywards Heath and Brighton

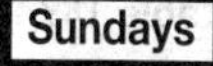

London, Haywards Heath and Brighton → Lewes, Seaford, Eastbourne, Hastings and Ashford

Network Diagram - see first page of Table 184

		SN 1	SN 1	SN 1	SN 1	SN 1	SN 1	SN 1	SN 1	SN 1	SN 1	SN 1	SN 1	SN 1		SN 1	SN 1	SN 1	SN 1	SN 1	SN 1	SN 1	SN 1	SN 1	SN 1
London Victoria 15	⊖ d		22p47		00 05			05 02	05 47				06 32					07 32		07b34	08 47		08 32		08b47
Clapham Junction 10	d		22p53		00 11			05 08	05 53				06 38					07 38		07b40	08 53		08 38		08b53
London Bridge 4	⊖ d				23 53											07 11		07 41		08 11			08 41		09 11
East Croydon	d		23p03		00 25				06 06				06 52			07 27		07 57		08 27	09 07		08 57		09 27
Gatwick Airport 10	✈ d		23p19		00 43				06 32				07 19			07 50		08 20		08 50	09 29		09 20		09 50
Haywards Heath 3	d		23p34		01 02				06 47				07 36			08 03		08 33		09 03	09 41		09 33		10 03
Wivelsfield 4	d		23p38						06 51				07 40					08 32			09 45		09 32		
Plumpton	d		23p44																		09 51				
Cooksbridge	d																								
Brighton 10	d	23p34						07 09	07 15		07 43	07 50	08 09	08 20		08 43	08 50	09 09	09 20	09 39			10 09	10 20	10 39
London Road (Brighton)	d	23p37						07 12	07 18		07 46	07 53	08 12			08 46	08 53	09 12		09 42			10 12		10 42
Moulsecoomb	d	23p39						07 14	07 20		07 48	07 55	08 14			08 48	08 55	09 14		09 44			10 14		10 44
Falmer	d	23p43						07 18	07 24		07 52	07 59	08 18			08 52	08 59	09 18		09 48			10 18		10 48
Lewes 4	a	23p49	23p51	⟵	01 16			07 24	07 31		07 58	08 05	08 24	08 31		08 58	09 05	09 24	09 31	09 54	09 58	⟵	10 24	10 31	10 54
	d	23p56	23p53	23p56	01 17			07 25	07 32		07 59	08 06	08 25	08 32		08 59	09 06	09 25	09 32	10 03	09 59	10 03	10 25	10 32	11 03
Southease	d	⟶										08 12					09 12			⟶		10 09			⟶
Newhaven Town	⛴ d			00 04					07 40			08 16	08 33				09 16	09 33				10 13	10 33		
Newhaven Harbour	d			00 06					07 42			08 18	08 35				09 18	09 35				10 15	10 35		
Bishopstone	d			00 09					07 45			08 21	08 38				09 21	09 38				10 18	10 38		
Seaford	a			00 12					07 48			08 24	08 41				09 24	09 41				10 21	10 41		
Glynde	d							07 30						08 37					09 37					10 37	
Berwick	d		00 02					07 36						08 43					09 43					10 43	
Polegate	d		00 07		01s29			07 41			08 11			08 49		09 11			09 49		10 11			10 49	
Hampden Park 4 §	d		00 11		01s33			07 45						08 53					09 53					10 53	
Eastbourne 4	a		00 16		01 38			07 50			08 19			08 58		09 19			09 58		10 19			10 58	
	d		00 22				07 26			07 58	08 26			09 03		09 26			10 03		10 26			11 03	
Hampden Park 4 §	d						07 30				08 30					09 30					10 30				
Pevensey & Westham	d		00 29				07 35				08 35					09 35					10 35				
Pevensey Bay	d																								
Normans Bay	d																								
Cooden Beach	d		00 35				07 41				08 41					09 41					10 41				
Collington	d		00 38				07 44				08 44					09 44					10 44				
Bexhill 4	d		00 40				07 46			08 11	08 46			09 16		09 46			10 16		10 46			11 16	
St Leonards Warrior Sq 4	d		00 47				07 53			08 18	08 53			09 23		09 53			10 23		10 53			11 23	
Hastings 4	a		00 50				07 56			08 22	08 56			09 26		09 56			10 26		10 56			11 26	
	d					07 22	07 57			08 22	08 57			09 27		09 57			10 27		10 57			11 27	
Ore	d					07 24	08a00				09a00					10a00					11a00				
Three Oaks	d					07 30																			
Doleham	d					07 33																			
Winchelsea	d					07 39																			
Rye	a					07 43				08 39				09 44					10 44					11 44	
	d					07 43				08 41				09 46					10 46					11 46	
Appledore (Kent)	d					07 52				08 50				09 55					10 55					11 55	
Ham Street	d					07 57				08 55				10 00					11 00					12 00	
Ashford International	a					08 06				09 03				10 08					11 08					12 08	
London Bridge 4	⊖ a					09 28				10 28				11 28					12 28					13 28	
London Cannon Street 4	⊖ a																								
London Waterloo (East) 4	⊖ a					09 33				10 33				11 33					12 33					13 33	
London Charing Cross 4	⊖ a					09 37				10 37				11 37					12 37					13 37	

For general notes see front of timetable
For details of catering facilities see Directory of Train Operators

§ For additional trains between Hampden Park and Eastbourne see Hastings to London pages

b Change at East Croydon and Brighton

Table 189

Sundays

London, Haywards Heath and Brighton → Lewes, Seaford, Eastbourne, Hastings and Ashford

Network Diagram - see first page of Table 184

Station		SN 1	SN 1	SN 1	SN 1	SN 1		SN 1	SN 1	SN 1	SN 1	SN 1	SN 1	SN 1	SN 1	SN 1	SN 1	SN 1	SN 1	SN 1		SN 1	SN 1	SN 1	SN 1
London Victoria 15 ⊖	d	09 47		09 32		09b47		10 47		10 32		10b47	11 47		11 32		11b47	12 47		12 32			12b47	13 47	
Clapham Junction 10	d	09 53		09 38		09b53		10 53		10 38		10b53	11 53		11 38		11b53	12 53		12 38			12b53	13 53	
London Bridge 4 ⊖	d			09 41		10 11				10 41		11 11			11 41		12 11			12 41			13 11		
East Croydon	d	10 07		09 57		10 27		11 07		10 57		11 27	12 07		11 57		12 27	13 07		12 57			13 27	14 07	
Gatwick Airport 10 ✈	d	10 29		10 20		10 50		11 29		11 20		11 50	12 29		12 20		12 50	13 29		13 20			13 50	14 29	
Haywards Heath 3	d	10 41		10 33		11 03		11 41		11 33		12 03	12 41		12 33		13 03	13 41		13 33			14 03	14 41	
Wivelsfield 4	d	10 45		10 32				11 45		11 32			12 45		12 32			13 45		13 32				14 45	
Plumpton	d	10 51						11 51																	
Cooksbridge	d																								
Brighton 10	d			11 09	11 20	11 39				12 09	12 20	12 39			13 09	13 20	13 39			14 09		14 20	14 39		
London Road (Brighton)	d			11 12		11 42				12 12		12 42			13 12		13 42			14 12			14 42		
Moulsecoomb	d			11 14		11 44				12 14		12 44			13 14		13 44			14 14			14 44		
Falmer	d			11 18		11 48				12 18		12 48			13 18		13 48			14 18			14 48		
Lewes 4	a	10 58	←	11 24	11 31	11 54		11 58	←	12 24	12 31	12 54	12 58	←	13 24	13 31	13 54	13 58	←	14 24		14 31	14 54	14 58	←
	d	10 59	11 03	11 25	11 32	12 03		11 59	12 03	12 25	12 32	13 03	12 59	13 03	13 25	13 32	14 03	13 59	14 03	14 25		14 32	15 03	14 59	15 03
Southease	d		11 09			→			12 09			→		13 09			→		14 09				→		15 09
Newhaven Town ⛴	d		11 13	11 33					12 13	12 33				13 13	13 33				14 13	14 33					15 13
Newhaven Harbour	d		11 15	11 35					12 15	12 35				13 15	13 35				14 15	14 35					15 15
Bishopstone	d		11 18	11 38					12 18	12 38				13 18	13 38				14 18	14 38					15 18
Seaford	a		11 21	11 41					12 21	12 41				13 21	13 41				14 21	14 41					15 21
Glynde	d				11 37						12 37					13 37						14 37			
Berwick	d				11 43						12 43					13 43						14 43			
Polegate	d	11 11			11 49			12 11			12 49		13 11			13 49		14 11				14 49		15 11	
Hampden Park 4 §	d				11 53						12 53					13 53						14 53			
Eastbourne 4	a	11 19			11 58			12 19			12 58		13 19			13 58		14 19				14 58		15 19	
	d	11 26			12 03			12 26			13 03		13 26			14 03		14 26				15 03		15 26	
Hampden Park 4 §	d	11 30						12 30					13 30					14 30						15 30	
Pevensey & Westham	d	11 35						12 35					13 35					14 35						15 35	
Pevensey Bay	d																								
Normans Bay	d																								
Cooden Beach	d	11 41						12 41					13 41					14 41						15 41	
Collington	d	11 44						12 44					13 44					14 44						15 44	
Bexhill 4	d	11 46			12 16			12 46			13 16		13 46			14 16		14 46				15 16		15 46	
St Leonards Warrior Sq 4	d	11 53			12 23			12 53			13 23		13 53			14 23		14 53				15 23		15 53	
Hastings 4	a	11 56			12 26			12 56			13 26		13 56			14 26		14 56				15 26		15 56	
	d	11 57			12 27			12 57			13 27		13 57			14 27		14 57				15 27		15 57	
Ore	d	12a00						13a00					14a00					15a00						16a00	
Three Oaks	d																								
Doleham	d																								
Winchelsea	d																								
Rye	a				12 44						13 44					14 44						15 44			
	d				12 46						13 46					14 46						15 46			
Appledore (Kent)	d				12 55						13 55					14 55						15 55			
Ham Street	d				13 00						14 00					15 00						16 00			
Ashford International	a				13 08						14 08					15 08						16 08			
London Bridge 4 ⊖	a				14 28						15 28					16 28						17 28			
London Cannon Street 4 ⊖	a																								
London Waterloo (East) 4 ⊖	a				14 33						15 33					16 33						17 33			
London Charing Cross 4 ⊖	a				14 37						15 37					16 37						17 37			

For general notes see front of timetable
For details of catering facilities see Directory of Train Operators

§ For additional trains between Hampden Park and Eastbourne see Hastings to London pages

b Change at East Croydon and Brighton

Table 189

Sundays

London, Haywards Heath and Brighton → Lewes, Seaford, Eastbourne, Hastings and Ashford

Network Diagram - see first page of Table 184

		SN 1	SN 1	SN 1	SN 1	SN 1	SN 1	SN 1	SN 1	SN 1	SN 1	SN 1		SN 1	SN 1	SN 1	SN 1	SN 1	SN 1	SN 1	SN 1	SN 1	SN 1	SN 1	SN 1
London Victoria 15 ⊖	d	13 32		13b47	14 47		14 32		14b47	15 47		15 32			15b47	16 47		17 02			17 47		18 02		
Clapham Junction 10	d	13 38		13b53	14 53		14 38		14b53	15 53		15 38			15b53	16 53		17 07			17 53		18 07		
London Bridge 4 ⊖	d	13 41		14 11			14 41		15 11			15 41			16 11			16b44		17 11			17b44		18 11
East Croydon	d	13 57		14 27	15 07		14 57		15 27	16 07		15 57			16 27	17 07		17 20		17 27	18 07		18 20		18 27
Gatwick Airport 10 ✈	d	14 20		14 50	15 29		15 20		15 50	16 29		16 20			16 50	17 29		17 42		17 50	18 29		18 42		18 50
Haywards Heath 3	d	14 33		15 03	15 41		15 33		16 03	16 41		16 33			17 03	17 41		17 33		18 03	18 41		18 33		19 03
Wivelsfield 4	d	14 32			15 45		15 32			16 45		16 32				17 45		17 32			18 45		18 32		
Plumpton	d															17 51					18 51				
Cooksbridge	d																								
Brighton 10	d	15 09	15 20	15 39			16 09	16 20	16 39			17 09		17 20	17 39			18 09	18 20	18 39			19 09	19 20	19 39
London Road (Brighton)	d	15 12		15 42			16 12		16 42			17 12			17 42			18 12		18 42			19 12		19 42
Moulsecoomb	d	15 14		15 44			16 14		16 44			17 14			17 44			18 14		18 44			19 14		19 44
Falmer	d	15 18		15 48			16 18		16 48			17 18			17 48			18 18		18 48			19 18		19 48
Lewes 4	a	15 24	15 31	15 54	15 58	←	16 24	16 31	16 54	16 58	←	17 24		17 31	17 54	17 58	←	18 24	18 31	18 54	18 58	←	19 24	19 31	19 54
	d	15 25	15 32	16 03	15 59	16 03	16 25	16 32	17 03	16 59	17 03	17 25		17 32	18 03	17 59	18 03	18 25	18 32	19 03	18 59	19 03	19 25	19 32	20 03
Southease	d			→		16 09			→		17 09				→		18 09			→		19 09			→
Newhaven Town ⛴	d	15 33				16 13	16 33				17 13	17 33					18 13	18 33				19 13	19 33		
Newhaven Harbour	d	15 35				16 15	16 35				17 15	17 35					18 15	18 35				19 15	19 35		
Bishopstone	d	15 38				16 18	16 38				17 18	17 38					18 18	18 38				19 18	19 38		
Seaford	a	15 41				16 21	16 41				17 21	17 41					18 21	18 41				19 21	19 41		
Glynde	d		15 37					16 37						17 37					18 37					19 37	
Berwick	d		15 43					16 43						17 43					18 43					19 43	
Polegate	d		15 49		16 11			16 49		17 11				17 49		18 11			18 49		19 11			19 49	
Hampden Park 4 §	d		15 53					16 53						17 53					18 53					19 53	
Eastbourne 4	a		15 58		16 19			16 58		17 19				17 58		18 19			18 58		19 19			19 58	
	d		16 03		16 26			17 03		17 26				18 03		18 26			19 03		19 26			20 03	
Hampden Park 4 §	d				16 30					17 30						18 30					19 30				
Pevensey & Westham	d				16 35					17 35						18 35					19 35				
Pevensey Bay	d																								
Normans Bay	d																								
Cooden Beach	d				16 41					17 41						18 41					19 41				
Collington	d				16 44					17 44						18 44					19 44				
Bexhill 4	d		16 16		16 46			17 16		17 46				18 16		18 46			19 16		19 46			20 16	
St Leonards Warrior Sq 4	d		16 23		16 53			17 23		17 53				18 23		18 53			19 23		19 53			20 23	
Hastings 4	a		16 26		16 56			17 26		17 56				18 26		18 56			19 26		19 56			20 26	
	d		16 27		16 57			17 27		17 57				18 27		18 57			19 27		19 57			20 27	
Ore	d				17a00					18a00						19a00					20a00				
Three Oaks	d																								
Doleham	d																								
Winchelsea	d																								
Rye	a		16 44					17 44						18 44					19 44					20 44	
	d		16 46					17 46						18 46					19 46					20 46	
Appledore (Kent)	d		16 55					17 55						18 55					19 55					20 55	
Ham Street	d		17 00					18 00						19 00					20 00					21 00	
Ashford International	a		17 08					18 08						19 08					20 08					21 08	
London Bridge 4 ⊖	a		18 28					19 28						20 28					21 28					22 28	
London Cannon Street 4 ⊖	a																								
London Waterloo (East) 4 ⊖	a		18 33					19 33						20 33					21 33					22 33	
London Charing Cross 4 ⊖	a		18 37					19 37						20 37					21 37					22 37	

For general notes see front of timetable
For details of catering facilities see Directory of Train Operators

§ For additional trains between Hampden Park and Eastbourne see Hastings to London pages

b Change at East Croydon and Brighton

Table 189

Sundays

London, Haywards Heath and Brighton → Lewes, Seaford, Eastbourne, Hastings and Ashford

Network Diagram - see first page of Table 184

		SN 1	SN 1	SN 1	SN 1	SN 1	SN 1	SN 1	SN 1	SN 1	SN 1	SN 1	SN 1	SN 1	SN 1	SN 1	SN 1	SN 1	SN 1	SN 1	SN 1	SN 1
London Victoria 15	⊖ d	18 47		19 02			19 47		20 02			20 47		20 32		20b47	21 47		21 32		21b47	22 47
Clapham Junction 10	d	18 53		19 07			19 53		20 07			20 53		20 38		20b53	21 53		21 38		21b53	22 53
London Bridge 4	⊖ d			18b44		19 11			19b44		20 11			20 41		21 11			21 41		22 11	
East Croydon	d	19 07		19 20		19 27	20 07		20 20		20 27	21 07		20 57		21 27	22 07		21 57		22 27	23 07
Gatwick Airport 10	d	19 29		19 42		19 50	20 29		20 42	20c42	20 50	21 29		21 20		21 50	22 29		22 20		22 50	23 29
Haywards Heath 3	d	19 41		19 33		20 03	20 41		20 33	20e33	21 03	21 41		21 33		22 03	22 41		22 33		23 03	23 41
Wivelsfield 4	d	19 45		19 32			20 45		20 32			21 45		21 32			22 45		22 32			23 45
Plumpton	d	19 51					20 51					21 51					22 51					23 51
Cooksbridge	d																					
Brighton 10	d			20 09	20 20	20 39			21 09	21 20	21 39			22 09	22 20	22 39			23 09	23 20	23 39	
London Road (Brighton)	d			20 12		20 42			21 12		21 42			22 12		22 42			23 12		23 42	
Moulsecoomb	d			20 14		20 44			21 14		21 44			22 14		22 44			23 14		23 44	
Falmer	d			20 18		20 48			21 18		21 48			22 18		22 48			23 18		23 48	
Lewes 4	a	19 58	←	20 24	20 31	20 54	20 58	←	21 24	21 31	21 54	21 58	←	22 24	22 31	22 54	22 58	←	23 24	23 31	23 54	23 58
	d	19 59	20 03	20 25	20 32	21 03	20 59	21 03	21 25	21 32	22 03	21 59	22 03	22 25	22 32	23 03	22 59	23 03		23 32		23 59
						→					→					→						
Southease	d		20 09																			
Newhaven Town	d		20 13	20 33				21 11	21 33				22 11	22 33				23 11				
Newhaven Harbour	d		20 15	20 35				21 13	21 35				22 13	22 35				23 13				
Bishopstone	d		20 18	20 38				21 16	21 38				22 16	22 38				23 16				
Seaford	a		20 21	20 41				21 19	21 41				22 19	22 41				23 19				
Glynde	d				20 37					21 37					22 37					23 37		
Berwick	d				20 43					21 43					22 43					23 43		
Polegate	d	20 11			20 49		21 11			21 49		22 11			22 49		23 11			23 49		00 11
Hampden Park 4 §	d				20 53					21 53					22 53					23 53		00 15
Eastbourne 4	a	20 19			20 58		21 19			21 58		22 19			22 58		23 19			23 58		00 20
	d	20 26			21 03		21 26			22 03		22 26					23 26					
Hampden Park 4 §	d	20 30					21 30					22 30					23 30					
Pevensey & Westham	d	20 35					21 35					22 35					23 35					
Pevensey Bay	d																					
Normans Bay	d																					
Cooden Beach	d	20 41					21 41					22 41					23 41					
Collington	d	20 44					21 44					22 44					23 44					
Bexhill 4	d	20 46			21 16		21 46			22 16		22 46					23 46					
St Leonards Warrior Sq 4	d	20 55			21 23		21 52			22 23		22 56					23 55					
Hastings 4	a	20 59			21 26		21 56			22 26		23 00					23 59					
	d	21 00			21 27		21 57															
Ore	d	21a03					22a00															
Three Oaks	d																					
Doleham	d																					
Winchelsea	d																					
Rye	a				21 44																	
	d				21 46																	
Appledore (Kent)	d				21 55																	
Ham Street	d				22 00																	
Ashford International	a				22 08																	
London Bridge 4	⊖ a																					
London Cannon Street 4	⊖ a																					
London Waterloo (East) 4	⊖ a																					
London Charing Cross 4	⊖ a																					

For general notes see front of timetable
For details of catering facilities see Directory of Train Operators

§ For additional trains between Hampden Park and Eastbourne see Hastings to London pages

b Change at East Croydon and Brighton
c Until 27 January dep. 2045
e Until 27 January dep. 2054

Ashford, Hastings, Eastbourne, Seaford and Lewes → Brighton, Haywards Heath and London

Network Diagram - see first page of Table 184

Miles	Miles	Station		SN MX 1	SN 1	SN 1	SN 1	SN 1	SN 1	SN 1	SN 1	SN 1	SN 1	SN 1	SN 1	SE 22 1 A ⚒	SN 1	SN 1	SN 1 ⚒	SN 1	SE 23 1 B ⚒	SN 1	SN 1	SN 1	SN 1 ⚒
—	—	London Charing Cross 4	⊖ d																						
—	—	London Waterloo (East) 4	⊖ d																						
—	—	London Cannon Street 4	⊖ d																						
—	—	London Bridge 4	⊖ d																						
—	0	**Ashford International**	d																						
—	5½	Ham Street	d																						
—	8¼	Appledore (Kent)	d																						
—	15¼	Rye	a																						
—	—		d																						
—	17¼	Winchelsea	d																						
—	21½	Doleham	d																						
—	22¾	Three Oaks	d																						
—	25½	Ore	d													06 10					06 38				
—	26½	**Hastings 4**	a													06 13					06 41				
0	—		d	23p13						05 07					06 03	06 14				06 20	06 42				06 50
¾	—	**St Leonards Warrior Sq 4**	d	23p16						05 10					06 06	06a17				06 23	06a45				06 53
4½	—	**Bexhill 4**	d	23p22						05 16					06 12					06 29					07 00
5¼	—	Collington	d	23p24						05 18										06 31					07 02
6¾	—	Cooden Beach	d	23p27						05 21										06 34					07 05
8½	—	Normans Bay	d																						
10½	—	Pevensey Bay	d																						
11¼	—	Pevensey & Westham	d	23p33						05 27										06 40					07 11
14½	—	Hampden Park 4 §	d	23p38						05 32					06 24					06 45					07 16
16¼	—	**Eastbourne 4**	a	23p43						05 37					06 30					06 50					07 24
—	—		d	23p48		05 08		05 32		05 42				06 24	06 38		06 47			06 57			07 17		07 32
18¼	—	Hampden Park 4 §	d	23p52		05 12		05 36		05 46				06 28			06 51			07 01			07 21		
20¼	—	Polegate	d	23p56		05 16		05 41		05 50				06 32	06 45		06 55			07 05			07 25		07 39
24½	—	Berwick	d							05 55				06 37			07 00						07 30		07 44
29	—	Glynde	d											06 43			07 06						07 36		
—	0	**Seaford**	d		05 09				05 45				06 30						06 57			07 16		07 33	
—	1	Bishopstone	d		05 11				05 47				06 32						06 59			07 18		07 35	
—	2½	Newhaven Harbour	d		05 14				05 50				06 35						07 02			07 21		07 38	
—	2¾	Newhaven Town	⛴ d		05 16				05 52				06 37						07 04			07 23		07 40	
—	5½	Southease	d																07 08			07 27		07 44	
32	9	**Lewes 4**	a	00 08	05 25	05 28	←	05 53	06 01	06 04	←		06 46	06 49	06 58		07 11		07 16	07 19		07 33	07 43	07 50	07 53
—	—		d	00 08	05 32 →	05 29	05 32	05 54	06 09 →	06 05	06 09	06 26	06 47	06 50	07 00		07 12	07 23	07 23			07 34	07 44	07 51	07 54
36½	—	Falmer	d	00 15			05 39	06 01			06 16	06 33	06 54		07 07		07 19	07 30				07 41		07 58	
38¼	—	Moulsecoomb	d	00 18			05 42	06 05			06 19	06 36	06 57		07 11		07 22	07 33				07 44		08 01	
39¼	—	London Road (Brighton)	d	00 21			05 43	06 07			06 21	06 38	06 59		07 13		07 24	07 35				07 46		08 03	
40	—	**Brighton 10**	a	00 24			05 48	06 11			06 25	06 42	07 03		07 17		07 28	07 39				07 50		08 07	
—	11¾	Cooksbridge	d											06 55					07 28				07 49		07 59
—	14½	Plumpton	d			05 37				06 13				07 00					07 33				07 54		08 04
—	18¼	Wivelsfield 4	a				06 15	06 40				07 03	07 31	07 07			07 48		07 39			08 18		08 33	08 10
—	21¼	**Haywards Heath 3**	a			05 46	06 19	06 37		06 22	06 57	07 08	07 36	07 13	07 46		07 53	08 05	07 43			08 23	08 02	08 37	08 14
—	—	**Gatwick Airport 10**	✈ a			05 58	06 41	06 51		06 41	07 11	07 21		07 29	08 00		08b12	08 22	08 00			08 38	08 22	08 51	08 38
—	—	East Croydon	🚋 a			06 14	06 58	07 15		06 58	07 28	07 38	08 03	07 46			08 23	08 34	08 14			08 54	08 31	09 08	08 46
—	—	**London Bridge 4**	⊖ a			06 40	07 14	07c39		07 14	07 46	08c03	08c26	08 03			08 41	08c59	08 39			09 10	08 49	09c42	09 10
—	—	Clapham Junction 10	a			06 25	07c19	07 25		07e19		07 47	08 13	08e02			08c40	08 43	08 24			09c10	08f43	09c23	08 56
—	—	**London Victoria 15**	⊖ a			06 33	07c28	07 34		07e28		07 57	08 22	08e12			08c49	08 52	08 33			09c19	08f52	09c33	09 07

For general notes see front of timetable
For details of catering facilities see Directory of Train Operators

§ For additional trains between Hampden Park and Eastbourne see London to Hastings pages

A To London Charing Cross (Table 206)
B To London Cannon Street (Table 206)
b Change at Brighton and Haywards Heath
c Change at Brighton and East Croydon
e Change at East Croydon
f Change at Haywards Heath

Ashford, Hastings, Eastbourne, Seaford and Lewes → Brighton, Haywards Heath and London

Network Diagram - see first page of Table 184

Station		SN	SN	SN	SN	SN	SN	SN	SN	SN	SE	SN	SN	SN	SN	SN	SN	SN	SN	SN	SN	SN	SN	SN	SN
											22														
		1	1	1	1	1	1	1	1	1	1	1	1	1	1	1	1	1	1	1	1	1	1	1	1
											A														
						🛒			🛒							🛒			🛒				🛒		
London Charing Cross [4] ⊖	d												05 30								06 25				07 00
London Waterloo (East) [4] ⊖	d												05 33								06 28				07 03
London Cannon Street [4] ⊖	d																				06b22				06b52
London Bridge [4] ⊖	d												05 38								06 33				07 08
Ashford International	d		06 24	06 46									07 30	07 50							08 30				08 50
Ham Street	d		06 33	06 55									07 39	07 59							08 39				08 59
Appledore (Kent)	d		06 38	07 00									07 44	08 04							08 44				09 04
Rye	a		06 47	07 09									07 53	08 13							08 53				09 13
	d		06 48										07 54								08 55				09 14
Winchelsea	d		06 51																						09 17
Doleham	d		06 58																						09 24
Three Oaks	d		07 01																						09 27
Ore	d		07 07								07 46						08 22		08 45					09 22	09 33
Hastings [4]	a		07 10								07 49		08 11				08 25		08 48		09 12			09 25	09 36
	d		07 12			07 19				07 36	07 50		08 15				08 26		08 52		09 13			09 26	
St Leonards Warrior Sq [4]	d		07 15			07 22				07 39	07a53		08 18				08 29		08 55		09 16			09 29	
Bexhill [4]	d		07 22			07 31				07 46			08 25				08 35		09 02		09 23			09 35	
Collington	d					07 33				07 48							08 37		09 04					09 37	
Cooden Beach	d					07 36				07 51							08 40		09 07					09 40	
Normans Bay	d									07 54							08 43							09 43	
Pevensey Bay	d									07 57															
Pevensey & Westham	d					07 42				08 00							08 48		09 13					09 48	
Hampden Park [4] §	d					07 46				08 04							08 52		09 17					09 52	
Eastbourne [4]	a		07 37			07 51				08 11			08 40				08 57		09 22		09 38			09 57	
	d		07 45			07 57	08 04			08 18			08 45			08 56	09 02		09 29		09 45		09 56	10 02	
Hampden Park [4] §	d					08 01	08 08									09 00	09 06						10 00	10 06	
Polegate	d		07 52			08 05	08 12			08 25			08 52			09 04	09 11		09 36		09 52		10 04	10 11	
Berwick	d					08 11	08 18			08 30							09 17						10 09	10 17	
Glynde	d					08 16	08 23			08 36							09 22							10 22	
Seaford	d				07 58				08 21						08 57			09 25				09 58			
Bishopstone	d				08 00				08 23						08 59			09 27				10 00			
Newhaven Harbour	d				08 03				08 26						09 02			09 30				10 03			
Newhaven Town ⛴	d				08 05				08 28						09 04			09 32				10 05			
Southease	d				08 09				08 32									09 36							
Lewes [4]	a		08 07		08 16	08 22	08 29		08 39	08 42			09 07		09 13	09 16	09 28	09 44	09 48		10 07	10 14	10 19	10 28	
	d	07 58	08 07		08 16	08 23	08 30	08 46	08 47			08 58	09 07		09 14	09 17	09 28	09 44	09 49	09 58	10 07	10 14	10 20	10 28	
Falmer	d	08 05			08 23		08 37	08 53				09 05			09 21		09 35	09 51		10 05		10 21		10 35	
Moulsecoomb	d	08 08			08 26		08 40	08 56				09 08			09 24		09 38	09 54		10 08		10 24		10 38	
London Road (Brighton)	d	08 10			08 29		08 42	08 58				09 10			09 27		09 40	09 57		10 10		10 27		10 40	
Brighton [10]	a	08 14	08 20		08 35		08 46	09 02				09 14	09 20		09 30		09 44	10 00		10 14	10 20	10 30		10 44	
Cooksbridge	d					08 28										09 22			09 54						
Plumpton	d					08 33										09 27			09 59				10 28		
Wivelsfield [4]	a					08 39	09 20		08 59						09 53	09 33	10 11	10 23				10 53	10 35	11 11	
Haywards Heath [3]	a		08 55		08 57	08 44	09 16		09 03			09 32			09 47	09 37	10 15	10 18	10 09			10 47	10 40	11 15	
Gatwick Airport [10] ✈	a				09 10	08 55	09 31		09 22			09 44			10 00	09 55		10 30	10 24			11 00	10 54		
East Croydon	a				09 26	09 14	09 47	09 55	09 39			10 03			10 16	10 11	10 24	10 46	10 40	10 55		11 16	11 11	11 23	
London Bridge [4] ⊖	a				09c45	09 42	10 00	10c22							10 30	10 30	10c45	11 00	11 00	11c15		11 30	11 30	11c45	
Clapham Junction [10]	a				09 35	09 23	10c03	10 05	09 49			10c21				10 21	10 33	11c03	10 49	11 04			11 20	11 33	
London Victoria [15] ⊖	a				09 44	09 33		10 13	09 58			10c28				10 28	10 40		10 58	11 11			11 27	11 40	

For general notes see front of timetable
For details of catering facilities see Directory of Train Operators

§ For additional trains between Hampden Park and Eastbourne see London to Hastings pages

A To London Charing Cross (Table 206)
b Change at London Bridge and Ashford International
c Change at Brighton and East Croydon

Ashford, Hastings, Eastbourne, Seaford and Lewes → Brighton, Haywards Heath and London

Network Diagram - see first page of Table 184

		SN 1	SN 1 🛒	SN 1	SN 1	SN 1	SN 1 🛒	SN 1	SN 1	SN 1 🛒	SN 1	SN 1	SN 1	SN 1 🛒	SN 1	SN 1	SN 1 🛒	SN 1	SN 1	SN 1	SN 1 🛒	SN 1	SN 1	SN 1 🛒
London Charing Cross 4 ⊖	d				07 52							08 58							09 53					
London Waterloo (East) 4 ⊖	d				07 55							09 01							09 56					
London Cannon Street 4 ⊖	d				07b54							08b54							09b30					
London Bridge 4 ⊖	d				08 02							09 08							09 38					
Ashford International	d				09 30							10 30							11 30					
Ham Street	d				09 39							10 39							11 39					
Appledore (Kent)	d				09 44							10 44							11 44					
Rye	a				09 53							10 53							11 53					
	d				09 54							10 54							11 54					
Winchelsea	d																							
Doleham	d																							
Three Oaks	d																							
Ore	d		09 47					10 22		10 50					11 22		11 50					12 22		12 50
Hastings 4	a		09 50		10 11			10 25		10 53		11 11			11 25		11 53		12 11			12 25		12 53
	d		09 52		10 12			10 26		10 55		11 12			11 26		11 55		12 12			12 26		12 55
St Leonards Warrior Sq 4	d		09 55		10 15			10 29		10 58		11 15			11 29		11 58		12 15			12 29		12 58
Bexhill 4	d		10 02		10 22			10 35		11 05		11 22			11 35		12 05		12 22			12 35		13 05
Collington	d		10 04					10 37		11 07					11 37		12 07					12 37		13 07
Cooden Beach	d		10 07					10 40		11 10					11 40		12 10					12 40		13 10
Normans Bay	d							10 43							11 43							12 43		
Pevensey Bay	d																							
Pevensey & Westham	d		10 13					10 48		11 16					11 48		12 16					12 48		13 16
Hampden Park 4 §	d		10 17					10 52		11 20					11 52		12 20					12 52		13 20
Eastbourne 4	a		10 22		10 37			10 57		11 25		11 37			11 57		12 25		12 37			12 57		13 25
	d		10 28		10 45		10 58	11 02		11 31		11 45		11 58	12 02		12 31		12 45		12 58	13 02		13 31
Hampden Park 4 §	d						11 02	11 06						12 02	12 06						13 02	13 06		
Polegate	d		10 34		10 52		11 06	11 11		11 37		11 52		12 06	12 11		12 37		12 52		13 06	13 11		13 37
Berwick	d							11 17							12 17							13 17		
Glynde	d							11 22							12 22							13 22		
Seaford	d	10 25				10 58			11 25				11 58			12 25				12 58			13 25	
Bishopstone	d	10 27				11 00			11 27				12 00			12 27				13 00			13 27	
Newhaven Harbour	d	10 30				11 03			11 30				12 03			12 30				13 03			13 30	
Newhaven Town ⛴	d	10 32				11 05			11 32				12 05			12 32				13 05			13 32	
Southease	d	10 36							11 36							12 36							13 36	
Lewes 4	a	10 44	10 48		11 08	11 14	11 18	11 28	11 44	11 49		12 07	12 14	12 18	12 28	12 44	12 49		13 07	13 14	13 18	13 28	13 44	13 49
	d	10 44	10 49	10 58	11 08	11 14	11 20	11 28	11 44	11 50	11 58	12 07	12 14	12 20	12 28	12 44	12 50	12 58	13 07	13 14	13 20	13 28	13 44	13 50
Falmer	d	10 51		11 05		11 21		11 35	11 51		12 05		12 21		12 35	12 51		13 05		13 21		13 35	13 51	
Moulsecoomb	d	10 54		11 08		11 24		11 38	11 54		12 08		12 24		12 38	12 54		13 08		13 24		13 38	13 54	
London Road (Brighton)	d	10 57		11 10		11 27		11 40	11 57		12 10		12 27		12 40	12 57		13 10		13 27		13 40	13 57	
Brighton 10	a	11 00		11 14	11 21	11 30		11 44	12 00		12 14	12 20	12 30		12 44	13 00		13 14	13 20	13 30		13 44	14 00	
Cooksbridge	d		10 54																					
Plumpton	d						11 28							12 28										
Wivelsfield 4	a	11 23				11 53	11 34	12 11	12 23				12 53	12 34	13 11	13 23				13 53	13 34	14 11	14 23	
Haywards Heath 3	a	11 18	11 05			11 47	11 40	12 15	12 18	12 05			12 47	12 40	13 15	13 18	13 05			13 47	13 40	14 15	14 18	14 05
Gatwick Airport 10 ✈	a	11 30	11 24			12 00	11 54		12 30	12 24			13 00	12 54		13 30	13 24			14 00	13 54		14 30	14 24
East Croydon	a	11 46	11 40	11 55		12 16	12 10	12 23	12 46	12 40	12 55		13 16	13 10	13 23	13 46	13 40	13 55		14 16	14 10	14 23	14 46	14 40
London Bridge 4 ⊖	a	12 00	12 00	12c15		12 30	12 30	12c45	13 00	13 00	13c15		13 30	13 30	13c45	14 00	14 00	14c15		14 30	14 30	14c45	15 00	15 00
Clapham Junction 10	a	12c03	11 49	12 04			12 19	12 33	13c03	12 49	13 04			13 19	13 33	14c03	13 49	14 04			14 19	14 33	15c03	14 49
London Victoria 15 ⊖	a		11 58	12 11			12 28	12 40		12 57	13 11			13 27	13 40		13 58	14 11			14 27	14 40		14 57

For general notes see front of timetable
For details of catering facilities see Directory of Train Operators

§ For additional trains between Hampden Park and Eastbourne see London to Hastings pages

b Change at London Bridge and Ashford International
c Change at Brighton and East Croydon

Ashford, Hastings, Eastbourne, Seaford and Lewes → Brighton, Haywards Heath and London

Network Diagram - see first page of Table 184

		SN	SN	SN	SN	SN	SN	SN	SN	SN	SN	SN	SN	SN	SN	SN	SN	SN	SN	SN	SN	SN	SN	SN	SN
		1	1	1	1	1	1	1	1	1	1	1	1	1	1	1	1	1	1	1	1	1	1	1	1
					trolley			trolley				trolley			trolley				trolley			trolley			
London Charing Cross 4	⊖ d		10 53							11 53							12 53							13 53	
London Waterloo (East) 4	⊖ d		10 56							11 56							12 56							13 56	
London Cannon Street 4	⊖ d		10b30							11b30							12b30							13b30	
London Bridge 4	⊖ d		10 38							11 38							12 38							13 38	
Ashford International	d		12 30							13 30							14 30							15 30	
Ham Street	d		12 39							13 39							14 39							15 39	
Appledore (Kent)	d		12 44							13 44							14 44							15 44	
Rye	a		12 53							13 53							14 53							15 53	
	d		12 54							13 54							14 54							15 54	
Winchelsea	d																								
Doleham	d																								
Three Oaks	d																								
Ore	d					13 22		13 50					14 21		14 50					15 20		15 48			
Hastings 4	a		13 11			13 25		13 53		14 11			14 24		14 53		15 11			15 23		15 51		16 11	
	d		13 12			13 26		13 55		14 12			14 25		14 55		15 12			15 24		15 53		16 12	
St Leonards Warrior Sq 4	d		13 15			13 29		13 58		14 15			14 28		14 58		15 15			15 27		15 56		16 15	
Bexhill 4	d		13 22			13 35		14 05		14 22			14 35		15 05		15 22			15 33		16 03		16 23	
Collington	d					13 37		14 07					14 37		15 07					15 35		16 05			
Cooden Beach	d					13 40		14 10					14 40		15 10					15 38		16 08			
Normans Bay	d					13 43							14 43							15 41		16 11			
Pevensey Bay	d																			15 45		16 14			
Pevensey & Westham	d					13 48		14 16					14 48		15 16					15 47		16 17			
Hampden Park 4 §	d					13 52		14 20					14 52		15 20					15 52		16 21			
Eastbourne 4	a		13 37			13 57		14 25		14 37			14 57		15 25		15 37			15 57		16 26		16 38	
	d		13 45		13 58	14 02		14 31		14 45		14 58	15 02		15 31		15 45		15 58	16 02		16 32		16 45	
Hampden Park 4 §	d				14 02	14 06						15 02	15 06						16 02	16 06				16 49	
Polegate	d		13 52		14 06	14 11		14 37		14 52		15 06	15 11		15 37		15 52		16 06	16 11		16 38		16 54	
Berwick	d					14 17							15 17							16 17					
Glynde	d					14 22							15 22							16 22					
Seaford	d			13 58			14 25				14 58			15 25				15 58			16 25				16 58
Bishopstone	d			14 00			14 27				15 00			15 27				16 00			16 27				17 00
Newhaven Harbour	d			14 03			14 30				15 03			15 30				16 03			16 30				17 03
Newhaven Town	⛴ d			14 05			14 32				15 05			15 32				16 05			16 32				17 05
Southease	d						14 36							15 36							16 36				
Lewes 4	a		14 07	14 14	14 18	14 28	14 44	14 49		15 07	15 14	15 18	15 28	15 44	15 49		16 07	16 14	16 18	16 28	16 44	16 50		17 07	17 14
	d	13 58	14 07	14 14	14 20	14 28	14 44	14 50	14 58	15 07	15 14	15 19	15 28	15 44	15 50	15 58	16 07	16 14	16 19	16 28	16 44	16 51	16 58	17 07	17 14
Falmer	d	14 05		14 21		14 35	14 51		15 05		15 21		15 35	15 51		16 05		16 21		16 35	16 51		17 05		17 21
Moulsecoomb	d	14 08		14 24		14 38	14 54		15 08		15 24		15 38	15 54		16 08		16 24		16 38	16 54		17 08		17 24
London Road (Brighton)	d	14 10		14 27		14 40	14 57		15 10		15 27		15 40	15 57		16 10		16 27		16 40	16 57		17 10		17 27
Brighton 10	a	14 14	14 20	14 30		14 44	15 00		15 14	15 20	15 30		15 44	16 00		16 14	16 20	16 30		16 44	17 00		17 14	17 20	17 30
Cooksbridge	d											15 24							16 24						
Plumpton	d											15 29							16 29						
Wivelsfield 4	a			14 53	14 34	15 11	15 23				15 53	15 35	16 11				16 46		16 35	17 11			17 40		
Haywards Heath 3	a			14 47	14 40	15 15	15 18	15 05			15 48	15 39	16 15	16 18	16 05		16 50		16 39	17 15		17 05	17 45		17 56
Gatwick Airport 10	✈ a	14 50		15 00	14 54		15 30	15 24			16 00	15 55		16 30	16 26		17 06		16 55	17 31		17 24	18 00		18 16
East Croydon	⛴ a	14 55		15 16	15 09	15 23	15 46	15 41	15 55		16 16	16 11	16 24	16 46	16 42	16 55			17 11	17 25		17 40	17 54		
London Bridge 4	⊖ a	15c15		15 30		15c45	16 00	16 00	16c15		16c41	16 41	16c56	17 02	17 02	17c26			17 54	17c54		18 10	18c24		
Clapham Junction 10	a	15 04			15 19	15 33	16c03	15 51	16 04			16 21	16 33	17c03	16 51	17 04			17 21	17 34		17 50	18 04		
London Victoria 15	⊖ a	15 11			15 28	15 40		15 58	16 11			16 29	16 41		16 58	17 11			17 28	17 43		17 57	18 11		

For general notes see front of timetable
For details of catering facilities see Directory of Train Operators

§ For additional trains between Hampden Park and Eastbourne see London to Hastings pages

b Change at London Bridge and Ashford International
c Change at Brighton and East Croydon

Ashford, Hastings, Eastbourne, Seaford and Lewes → Brighton, Haywards Heath and London

Network Diagram - see first page of Table 184

Station		SN	SN	SN	SN	SN	SN	SN	SN	SN	SN	SN	SN	SN	SN	SN	SN	SN	SN	SN	SN	SN	SN	SN	SN
		1	1	1	1	1	1	1	1	1	1	1	1	1	1	1	1	1	1	1	1	1	1	1	1
		(trolley)			(trolley)			(trolley)																	
London Charing Cross 4	⊖ d					*14 53*							*16 00*	*16 30*								*16 46*	*17 34*		
London Waterloo (East) 4	⊖ d					*14 56*							*16 03*	*16 33*								*16 49*	*17 37*		
London Cannon Street 4	⊖ d					*14b30*							*16b00*	*16b28*								*16b46*	*17 44*		
London Bridge 4	⊖ d					*14 38*							*16 08*	*16 39*								*16 54*			
Ashford International	d					16 30							17 30	17 58								18 30	18 58		
Ham Street	d					16 39							17 39	18 07								18 39	19 07		
Appledore (Kent)	d					16 44							17 44	18 12								18 44	19 12		
Rye	a					16 53							17 53	18 21								18 53	19 21		
	d					16 54							17 54									18 54			
Winchelsea	d																								
Doleham	d																								
Three Oaks	d																								
Ore	d		16 22		16 50				17 22		17 50						18 22			18 50					19 24
Hastings 4	a		16 25		16 53	17 14			17 25		17 53		18 11				18 25			18 53		19 11			19 27
	d		16 26		16 55	17 16			17 26		17 55		18 12				18 26			18 55		19 12			19 27
St Leonards Warrior Sq 4	d		16 29		16 58	17 19			17 29		17 58		18 15				18 29			18 58		19 15			19 30
Bexhill 4	d		16 35		17 05	17 26			17 35		18 05		18 22				18 35			19 05		19 22			19 37
Collington	d		16 37		17 07				17 37		18 07						18 37			19 07					19 39
Cooden Beach	d		16 40		17 10				17 40		18 10						18 40			19 10					19 42
Normans Bay	d		16 43						17 43								18 43								
Pevensey Bay	d																								
Pevensey & Westham	d		16 48		17 16				17 48		18 16						18 48			19 16					19 48
Hampden Park 4 §	d		16 52		17 20				17 52		18 20						18 52			19 22					19 52
Eastbourne 4	a		16 57		17 25	17 41			17 57		18 25		18 39				18 57			19 27		19 38			19 57
	d	16 58	17 02		17 31	17 45		17 57	18 01		18 31		18 45			19 00	19 04			19 34		19 45			20 02
Hampden Park 4 §	d	17 02	17 06					18 01	18 05								19 08								20 06
Polegate	d	17 06	17 11		17 37	17 52		18 05	18 11		18 37		18 52			19 06	19 12			19 40		19 52			20 11
Berwick	d		17 17						18 17								19 17								20 17
Glynde	d		17 22						18 22								19 23								20 22
Seaford	d			17 25			17 58			18 25		18 43			18 58			19 15	19 32					19 58	
Bishopstone	d			17 27			18 00			18 27					19 00			19 17	19 34					20 00	
Newhaven Harbour	d			17 30			18 03			18 30					19 03			19 20						20 03	
Newhaven Town	d			17 32			18 05			18 32		18 48			19 05			19 22	19 38					20 05	
Southease	d			17 36						18 36								19 26							
Lewes 4	a	17 18	17 28	17 44	17 49	18 05	18 14	18 17	18 29	18 44	18 49	18 57	19 07		19 14	19 19	19 28	19 33	19 47	19 52		20 07		20 14	20 28
	d	17 19	17 28	17 44	17 50	18 06	18 14	18 18	18 29	18 44	18 50	18 58	19 07		19 14	19 20	19 29	19 35	19 48	19 53	19 58	20 07		20 14	20 28
Falmer	d		17 35	17 51		18 14	18 21		18 36	18 51		19 05			19 21		19 36	19 42	19 55		20 05			20 21	20 35
Moulsecoomb	d		17 38	17 54		18 17	18 24		18 39	18 54		19 08			19 24		19 39	19 45	19 58		20 08			20 24	20 38
London Road (Brighton)	d		17 40	17 57		18 20	18 27		18 42	18 57		19 10			19 27		19 41	19 47	20 00		20 10			20 27	20 40
Brighton 10	a		17 44	18 00		18 23	18 30		18 45	19 00		19 14	19 20		19 31		19 45	19 51	20 04		20 14	20 20		20 33	20 44
Cooksbridge	d	17 24						18 23																	
Plumpton	d	17 29						18 28			18 58														
Wivelsfield 4	a	17 35	*18 11*	*18 23*			*18 53*	18 34	*19 11*	*19 23*	19 05				*19 53*			*20 11*		20 05				*20 53*	
Haywards Heath 3	a	17 39	*18 15*	*18 28*	18 05		*18 47*	18 38	*19 16*	*19 28*	19 10		*19 47*		*19 58*	19 36		*20 16*		20 10		*20 47*		*20 58*	
Gatwick Airport 10	✈ a	17 55	*18 30*	*18 46*	18 24		*19 00*	18 56	*19 38*	*19 46*	19 25		*20 00*		*20 16*	19 54		*20 31*		20 25		*21 00*		*21 16*	
East Croydon	a	18 11	*18 24*	*18 55*	18 41		*19 16*	19 12	*19 23*		19 41	*19 55*	*20 16*			20 10	*20 23*	*20 47*		20 41	*20 55*	*21 16*			*21 23*
London Bridge 4	⊖ a	*18 45*	*18c45*	*19 15*	*19 00*		*19 30*	*19 30*	*19c45*		*20 00*	*20c15*	*20 30*			*20 30*	*20c45*	*21 00*		*21 00*	*21c15*	*21 30*			*21c45*
Clapham Junction 10	a	18 21	*18 33*	19 04	18 51			19 21	*19 33*		19 50	*20 04*				20 19	*20 33*	*21c03*		20 51	*21 04*				*21 33*
London Victoria 15	⊖ a	18 28	*18 40*	*19 11*	18 59			19 29	*19 40*		19 59	*20 11*				20 28	*20 40*			20 59	*21 11*				*21 40*

For general notes see front of timetable
For details of catering facilities see
Directory of Train Operators

§ For additional trains between Hampden Park and Eastbourne see London to Hastings pages

b Change at London Bridge and Ashford International

c Change at Brighton and East Croydon

Ashford, Hastings, Eastbourne, Seaford and Lewes → Brighton, Haywards Heath and London

Network Diagram - see first page of Table 184

		SN 1	SN 1	SN 1	SN 1	SN 1	SN 1	SN 1	SN 1	SN 1	SN 1	SN 1	SN 1	SN 1	SN 1	SN 1	SN 1	SN 1	SN 1	SN 1	SN 1	SN 1	SN 1		
London Charing Cross 4	⊖ d				17 56			18b23				19 00						20 00			21 00				
London Waterloo (East) 4	⊖ d				17 59			18 19				19 03						20 03			21 03				
London Cannon Street 4	⊖ d				18 04			18 30				18b50						20b00			21b00				
London Bridge 4	⊖ d				18 08			18 34				19 08						20 08			21 08				
Ashford International	d				19 30			19 58				20 30						21 30			22 24				
Ham Street	d				19 39			20 07				20 39						21 39			22 33				
Appledore (Kent)	d				19 44			20 12				20 44						21 44			22 38				
Rye	a				19 53			20 21				20 53						21 53			22 47				
	d				19 54			20 22				20 54						21 57			22 47				
Winchelsea	d																				22 51				
Doleham	d																				22 57				
Three Oaks	d																				23 01				
Ore	d		19 50				20 20			20 50						21 22				22 22	23 06				
Hastings 4	a		19 53		20 11		20 23	20 39		20 53		21 11				21 25		22 14		22 25	23 09				
	d		19 55		20 12		20 24			20 55		21 12				21 30		22 16		22 26			23 13		
St Leonards Warrior Sq 4	d		19 58		20 15		20 27			20 58		21 15				21 33		22 19		22 29			23 16		
Bexhill 4	d		20 05		20 22		20 35			21 05		21 22				21 39		22 26		22 38			23 22		
Collington	d		20 07				20 37			21 07						21 41				22 40			23 24		
Cooden Beach	d		20 10				20 40			21 10						21 44				22 43			23 27		
Normans Bay	d																			22 46					
Pevensey Bay	d																								
Pevensey & Westham	d		20 16				20 46			21 16						21 50				22 51			23 33		
Hampden Park 4 §	d		20 20				20 52			21 20						21 55				22 55			23 38		
Eastbourne 4	a		20 25		20 37		20 57			21 25		21 37				22 00		22 41		23 00			23 43		
	d		20 31		20 45		21 02			21 31		21 45		22 02		22 15		22 45		23 05			23 48		
Hampden Park 4 §	d						21 06							22 06		22 19				23 09			23 52		
Polegate	d		20 37		20 52		21 11			21 37		21 52		22 11		22 23		22 52		23 13			23 56		
Berwick	d						21 17							22 17		22 29				23 18					
Glynde	d						21 22							22 22						23 24					
Seaford	d	20 28				20 58			21 28				21 58		22 20				22 58			23 25			
Bishopstone	d	20 30				21 00			21 30				22 00		22 22				23 00			23 27			
Newhaven Harbour	d	20 33				21 03			21 33				22 03		22 25				23 03			23 30			
Newhaven Town	⛴ d	20 35				21 05			21 35				22 05		22 27				23 05			23 32			
Southease	d	20 39																							
Lewes 4	a	20 46	20 49	←	21 07	21 14	21 28		21 44	21 49	←	22 07	22 14	22 28	22 35	22 38	←	23 07	23 14	23 29		23 40	00 08		
	d	20 53 →	20 50	20 53	21 07	21 14	21 28		21 53 →	21 50	21 53	22 07	22 14	22 28	22 42 →	22 40	22 42	23 07	23 14	23 29		23 40	00 08		
Falmer	d			21 00		21 21	21 35				22 00		22 21	22 37			22 49		23 21	23 37		23 47	00 15		
Moulsecoomb	d			21 03		21 24	21 38				22 03		22 24	22 40			22 52		23 24	23 40		23 50	00 18		
London Road (Brighton)	d			21 05		21 27	21 40				22 05		22 27	22 42			22 54		23 27	23 42		23 53	00 21		
Brighton 10	a			21 09	21 20	21 33	21 44				22 09	22 20	22 31	22 46			22 58	23 20	23 31	23 46		23 56	00 24		
Cooksbridge	d																								
Plumpton	d		20 58													22 48									
Wivelsfield 4	a		21 06			21 53				22 02		22 49				22 54	23 19		23 53						
Haywards Heath 3	a		21 10		21 46	21 58				22 06		22 54				22 58	23 23		23 58						
Gatwick Airport 10	✈ a		21 25		22 00	22 16				22 24		23c12				23 12	23 52		00 14						
East Croydon	⇌ a		21 41	21 55	22 17		22 23			22 40		23 32				23 30	00 16		00 35						
London Bridge 4	⊖ a		22 15	22e15	22 32		22e45					23 45				00 52	00 52		00 52						
Clapham Junction 10	a		21 50	22 04			22 33			22 50		00e11				23 42	00 29		01e02						
London Victoria 15	⊖ a		21 58	22 11			22 40			22 58		00e18				23 52	00 37		01e09						

For general notes see front of timetable
For details of catering facilities see Directory of Train Operators

§ For additional trains between Hampden Park and Eastbourne see London to Hastings pages

b Change at London Bridge and Ashford International
c Change at Brighton and Haywards Heath
e Change at Brighton and East Croydon

Table 189

Ashford, Hastings, Eastbourne, Seaford and Lewes → Brighton, Haywards Heath and London

Network Diagram - see first page of Table 184

Station		SN 1	SN 1	SN 1	SN 1	SN 1	SN 1	SN 1	SN 1	SN 1	SN 1	SN 1	SN 1	SN 1	SN 1	SN 1	SN 1	SN 1	SN 1	SN 1	SN 1	SN 1
London Charing Cross 4	⊖ d																					
London Waterloo (East) 4	⊖ d																					
London Cannon Street 4	⊖ d																					
London Bridge 4	⊖ d																					
Ashford International	d															06 23						
Ham Street	d															06 32						
Appledore (Kent)	d															06 37						
Rye	a															06 46						
	d															06 48						
Winchelsea	d															06 51						
Doleham	d															06 58						
Three Oaks	d															07 01						
Ore	d											06 22		06 50		07 07			07 22		07 50	
Hastings 4	a											06 25		06 53		07 10			07 25		07 53	
	d	23p13										06 26		06 55		07 11			07 26		07 55	
St Leonards Warrior Sq 4	d	23p16										06 29		06 58		07 14			07 29		07 58	
Bexhill 4	d	23p22										06 35		07 05		07 22			07 35		08 05	
Collington	d	23p24										06 37		07 07					07 37		08 07	
Cooden Beach	d	23p27										06 40		07 10					07 40		08 10	
Normans Bay	d											06 43							07 43			
Pevensey Bay	d																					
Pevensey & Westham	d	23p33										06 48		07 16					07 48		08 16	
Hampden Park 4 §	d	23p38										06 52		07 20					07 52		08 20	
Eastbourne 4	a	23p43										06 57		07 25		07 37			07 57		08 25	
	d	23p48		05 03		05 50		06 24	06 37		06 58	07 02		07 31		07 45		07 58	08 02		08 31	
Hampden Park 4 §	d	23p52		05 07				06 28			07 02	07 06						08 02	08 06			
Polegate	d	23p56		05 12		05 57		06 32	06 44		07 06	07 11		07 37		07 52		08 06	08 11		08 37	
Berwick	d							06 38				07 17							08 17			
Glynde	d							06 43				07 22							08 22			
Seaford	d		05 05				06 28			06 58			07 28				07 58			08 25		
Bishopstone	d		05 07				06 30			07 00			07 30				08 00			08 27		
Newhaven Harbour	d		05 10				06 33			07 03			07 33				08 03			08 30		
Newhaven Town ⛴	d		05 12				06 35			07 05			07 35				08 05			08 32		
Southease	d																			08 36		
Lewes 4	a	00 08	05 21	05 24	⟵	06 10	06 44	06 49	06 57	07 14	07 18	07 28	07 44	07 49		08 07	08 14	08 18	08 28	08 44	08 49	
	d	00 08	05 28	05 25	05 28	06 10	06 44	06 50	06 58	07 14	07 20	07 28	07 44	07 50	07 58	08 07	08 14	08 20	08 28	08 44	08 50	08 58
Falmer	d	00 15	⟶		05 35	06 18	06 51		07 05	07 21		07 35	07 51		08 05		08 21		08 35	08 51		09 05
Moulsecoomb	d	00 18			05 38	06 21	06 54		07 09	07 24		07 38	07 54		08 08		08 24		08 38	08 54		09 08
London Road (Brighton)	d	00 21			05 40	06 24	06 57		07 11	07 27		07 40	07 57		08 10		08 27		08 40	08 57		09 10
Brighton 10	a	00 24			05 44	06 27	07 00		07 15	07 30		07 44	08 00		08 14	08 20	08 30		08 44	09 00		09 14
Cooksbridge	d																					
Plumpton	d										07 28							08 28				
Wivelsfield 4	a				06 11	06 53	07 23			07 53	07 34	08 11	08 23				08 53	08 34	09 11			
Haywards Heath 3	a			05 40	06 02	06 58	07 18	07 05		07 47	07 40	08 15	08 18	08 05			08 47	08 40	09 15	09 18	09 05	
Gatwick Airport 10 ✈	a			06 03	06 24	07 16	07 30	07 24		08 00	07 54		08 30	08 24			09 00	08 54		09 30	09 24	
East Croydon	a			06b16	06 40	07 23	07 46	07 40	07 55	08 16	08 10	08 23	08 46	08 40	08 55		09 16	09 10	09 23	09 46	09 40	09 55
London Bridge 4	⊖ a			06b31	07 01	07 45	08 01	08 01	08c15	08 31	08 31	08c45	09 01	09 01	09c15		09 30	09 30	09c45	10 00	10 00	10c22
Clapham Junction 10	a			06e37	06 50	07 33	08c03	07 49	08 04		08 19	08 33	09c03	08 49	09 04			09 19	09 33	10c03	09 49	10 04
London Victoria 15	⊖ a			06e44	06 58	07 40		07 57	08 11		08 27	08 40		08 57	09 11			09 27	09 40		09 57	10 11

For general notes see front of timetable
For details of catering facilities see Directory of Train Operators

§ For additional trains between Hampden Park and Eastbourne see London to Hastings pages

b Change at Haywards Heath
c Change at Brighton and East Croydon
e Change at Haywards Heath and East Croydon

Ashford, Hastings, Eastbourne, Seaford and Lewes → Brighton, Haywards Heath and London

Network Diagram - see first page of Table 184

Station		SN 1	SN 1	SN 1	SN 1	SN 1		SN 1	SN 1	SN 1	SN 1	SN 1	SN 1		SN 1	SN 1	SN 1	SN 1	SN 1	SN 1		SN 1	SN 1	SN 1	SN 1
London Charing Cross [4]	⊖ d	*06 00*								*07 00*								*07 30*							
London Waterloo (East) [4]	⊖ d	*06 03*								*07 03*								*07 33*							
London Cannon Street [4]	⊖ d																								
London Bridge [4]	⊖ d	*06 08*								*07 08*								*07 38*							
Ashford International	d	07 30								08 30								09 30							
Ham Street	d	07 39								08 39								09 39							
Appledore (Kent)	d	07 44								08 44								09 44							
Rye	a	07 53								08 53								09 53							
	d	07 54								08 54								09 54							
Winchelsea	d																								
Doleham	d																								
Three Oaks	d																								
Ore	d				08 22			08 50					09 22			09 50						10 22		10 50	
Hastings [4]	a	08 11			08 25			08 53		09 11			09 25			09 53		10 11				10 25		10 53	
	d	08 12			08 26			08 55		09 12			09 26			09 55		10 12				10 26		10 55	
St Leonards Warrior Sq [4]	d	08 15			08 29			08 58		09 15			09 29			09 58		10 15				10 29		10 58	
Bexhill [4]	d	08 22			08 35			09 05		09 22			09 35			10 05		10 22				10 35		11 05	
Collington	d				08 37			09 07					09 37			10 07						10 37		11 07	
Cooden Beach	d				08 40			09 10					09 40			10 10						10 40		11 10	
Normans Bay	d				08 43								09 43									10 43			
Pevensey Bay	d																								
Pevensey & Westham	d				08 48			09 16					09 48			10 16						10 48		11 16	
Hampden Park [4] §	d				08 52			09 20					09 52			10 20						10 52		11 20	
Eastbourne [4]	a	08 37			08 57			09 25		09 37			09 57			10 25		10 37				10 57		11 25	
	d	08 45		08 58	09 02			09 31		09 45		09 58	10 02			10 31		10 45		10 58		11 02		11 31	
Hampden Park [4] §	d			09 02	09 06							10 02	10 06							11 02		11 06			
Polegate	d	08 52		09 06	09 11			09 37		09 52		10 06	10 11			10 37		10 52		11 06		11 11		11 37	
Berwick	d				09 17								10 17									11 17			
Glynde	d				09 22								10 22									11 22			
Seaford	d		08 58			09 25					09 58				10 25				10 58				11 25		
Bishopstone	d		09 00			09 27					10 00				10 27				11 00				11 27		
Newhaven Harbour	d		09 03			09 30					10 03				10 30				11 03				11 30		
Newhaven Town ⛴	d		09 05			09 32					10 05				10 32				11 05				11 32		
Southease	d					09 36									10 36								11 36		
Lewes [4]	a	09 07	09 14	09 18	09 28	09 44		09 49		10 07	10 14	10 18	10 28		10 44	10 49		11 07	11 14	11 18		11 28	11 44	11 49	
	d	09 07	09 14	09 20	09 28	09 44		09 50	09 58	10 07	10 14	10 20	10 28		10 44	10 50	10 58	11 07	11 14	11 20		11 28	11 44	11 50	11 58
Falmer	d		09 21		09 35	09 51			10 05		10 21		10 35		10 51		11 05		11 21			11 35	11 51		12 05
Moulsecoomb	d		09 24		09 38	09 54			10 08		10 24		10 38		10 54		11 08		11 24			11 38	11 54		12 08
London Road (Brighton)	d		09 27		09 40	09 57			10 10		10 27		10 40		10 57		11 10		11 27			11 40	11 57		12 10
Brighton [10]	a	09 20	09 30		09 44	10 00			10 14	10 20	10 30		10 44		11 00		11 14	11 20	11 30			11 44	12 00		12 14
Cooksbridge	d																								
Plumpton	d			09 28								10 28													
Wivelsfield [4]	a		*09 53*	09 34	*10 11*	*10 23*					*10 53*	10 34	*11 11*		*11 23*				*11 53*	11 34		*12 11*	*12 23*		
Haywards Heath [3]	a		*09 47*	09 40	*10 15*	*10 18*		10 05			*10 47*	10 40	*11 15*		*11 18*	11 05			*11 47*	11 40		*12 15*	*12 18*	12 05	
Gatwick Airport [10]	✈ a		*10 00*	09 54		*10 30*		10 21			*11 00*	10 54			*11 30*	11 24			*12 00*	11 54			*12 30*	12 24	
East Croydon	a		*10 16*	10 10	*10 23*	*10 46*		10 38	*10 55*		*11 16*	11 10	*11 23*		*11 46*	11 40	*11 55*		*12 16*	12 10		*12 23*	*12 46*	12 40	*12 55*
London Bridge [4]	⊖ a		*10 30*	*10 30*	*10b45*	*11 00*			*11b15*		*11 30*	*11 30*	*11b45*		*12 00*	*12 00*	*12b15*		*12 30*	*12 30*		*12b45*	*13 00*	*13 00*	*13b15*
Clapham Junction [10]	a			10 19	*10 33*	*11b03*		10 47	*11 04*			11 19	*11 33*		*12b03*	11 49	*12 04*			12 19		*12 33*	*13b03*	12 49	*13 04*
London Victoria [15]	⊖ a			10 27	*10 40*			10 56	*11 11*			11 27	*11 40*			11 57	*12 11*			12 27		*12 40*		12 57	*13 11*

For general notes see front of timetable
For details of catering facilities see Directory of Train Operators

§ For additional trains between Hampden Park and Eastbourne see London to Hastings pages

b Change at Brighton and East Croydon

Table 189

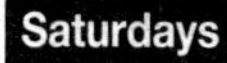

Saturdays

Ashford, Hastings, Eastbourne, Seaford and Lewes → Brighton, Haywards Heath and London

Network Diagram - see first page of Table 184

		SN 1	SN 1	SN 1	SN 1	SN 1	SN 1	SN 1	SN 1	SN 1	SN 1	SN 1	SN 1	SN 1	SN 1	SN 1	SN 1	SN 1	SN 1	SN 1	SN 1	SN 1
London Charing Cross 4	⊖ d	08 30							09 53							10 53						
London Waterloo (East) 4	⊖ d	08 33							09 56							10 56						
London Cannon Street 4	⊖ d	08b30							09b30							10b30						
London Bridge 4	⊖ d	08 38							09 38							10 38						
Ashford International	d	10 30							11 30							12 30						
Ham Street	d	10 39							11 39							12 39						
Appledore (Kent)	d	10 44							11 44							12 44						
Rye	a	10 53							11 53							12 53						
	d	10 54							11 54							12 54						
Winchelsea	d																					
Doleham	d																					
Three Oaks	d																					
Ore	d				11 22		11 50					12 22		12 50					13 22		13 50	
Hastings 4	a	11 11			11 25		11 53		12 11			12 25		12 53		13 11			13 25		13 53	
	d	11 12			11 26		11 55		12 12			12 26		12 55		13 12			13 26		13 55	
St Leonards Warrior Sq 4	d	11 15			11 29		11 58		12 15			12 29		12 58		13 15			13 29		13 58	
Bexhill 4	d	11 22			11 35		12 05		12 22			12 35		13 05		13 22			13 35		14 05	
Collington	d				11 37		12 07					12 37		13 07					13 37		14 07	
Cooden Beach	d				11 40		12 10					12 40		13 10					13 40		14 10	
Normans Bay	d				11 43							12 43							13 43			
Pevensey Bay	d																					
Pevensey & Westham	d				11 48		12 16					12 48		13 16					13 48		14 16	
Hampden Park 4 §	d				11 52		12 20					12 52		13 20					13 52		14 20	
Eastbourne 4	a	11 37			11 57		12 25		12 37			12 57		13 25		13 37			13 57		14 25	
	d	11 45		11 58	12 02		12 31		12 45		12 58	13 02		13 31		13 45		13 58	14 02		14 31	
Hampden Park 4 §	d			12 02	12 06						13 02	13 06						14 02	14 06			
Polegate	d	11 52		12 06	12 11		12 37		12 52		13 06	13 11		13 37		13 52		14 06	14 11		14 37	
Berwick	d				12 17							13 17							14 17			
Glynde	d				12 22							13 22							14 22			
Seaford	d		11 58			12 25				12 58			13 25				13 58			14 25		
Bishopstone	d		12 00			12 27				13 00			13 27				14 00			14 27		
Newhaven Harbour	d		12 03			12 30				13 03			13 30				14 03			14 30		
Newhaven Town ⛴	d		12 05			12 32				13 05			13 32				14 05			14 32		
Southease	d					12 36							13 36							14 36		
Lewes 4	a	12 07	12 14	12 18	12 28	12 44	12 49		13 07	13 14	13 18	13 28	13 44	13 49		14 07	14 14	14 18	14 28	14 44	14 49	
	d	12 07	12 14	12 20	12 28	12 44	12 50	12 58	13 07	13 14	13 20	13 28	13 44	13 50	13 58	14 07	14 14	14 20	14 28	14 44	14 50	14 58
Falmer	d		12 21		12 35	12 51		13 05		13 21		13 35	13 51		14 05		14 21		14 35	14 51		15 05
Moulsecoomb	d		12 24		12 38	12 54		13 08		13 24		13 38	13 54		14 08		14 24		14 38	14 54		15 08
London Road (Brighton)	d		12 27		12 40	12 57		13 10		13 27		13 40	13 57		14 10		14 27		14 40	14 57		15 10
Brighton 10	a	12 20	12 30		12 44	13 00		13 14	13 20	13 30		13 44	14 00		14 14	14 20	14 30		14 44	15 00		15 14
Cooksbridge	d																					
Plumpton	d			12 28																		
Wivelsfield 4	a		12 53	12 34	13 11	13 23				13 53	13 34	14 11	14 23				14 53	14 34	15 11	15 23		
Haywards Heath 3	a		12 47	12 40	13 15	13 18	13 05			13 47	13 40	14 15	14 18	14 05			14 47	14 40	15 15	15 18	15 05	
Gatwick Airport 10 ✈	a		13 00	12 54		13 30	13 24			14 00	13 54		14 30	14 24	14 51		15 00	14 55		15 30	15 24	
East Croydon	a		13 16	13 10	13 23	13 46	13 40	13 55		14 16	14 10	14 23	14 46	14 40	14 55		15 16	15 11	15 23	15 46	15 40	15 55
London Bridge 4	⊖ a		13 30	13 30	13c45	14 00	14 00	14c15		14 30	14 30	14c45	15 00	15 00	15c15		15 30	15 30	15c45	16 00	16 00	16c15
Clapham Junction 10	a			13 19	13 33	14c03	13 49	14 04			14 19	14 33	15c03	14 49	15 04			15 20	15 33	16c03	15 49	16 04
London Victoria 15	⊖ a			13 27	13 40		13 57	14 11			14 27	14 40		14 57	15 11			15 27	15 40		15 57	16 11

For general notes see front of timetable
For details of catering facilities see Directory of Train Operators

b Change at London Bridge and Ashford International
c Change at Brighton and East Croydon

§ For additional trains between Hampden Park and Eastbourne see London to Hastings pages

Table 189

Saturdays

Ashford, Hastings, Eastbourne, Seaford and Lewes → Brighton, Haywards Heath and London

Network Diagram - see first page of Table 184

Station		SN 1	SN 1	SN 1		SN 1	SN 1	SN 1	SN 1	SN 1	SN 1		SN 1	SN 1	SN 1	SN 1	SN 1	SN 1		SN 1	SN 1	SN 1	SN 1	SN 1	SN 1
London Charing Cross 4 ⊖	d	11 53								12 53								13 53							
London Waterloo (East) 4 ⊖	d	11 56								12 56								13 56							
London Cannon Street 4 ⊖	d	11b30								12b30								13b30							
London Bridge 4 ⊖	d	11 38								12 38								13 38							
Ashford International	d	13 30								14 30								15 30							
Ham Street	d	13 39								14 39								15 39							
Appledore (Kent)	d	13 44								14 44								15 44							
Rye	a	13 53								14 53								15 53							
	d	13 54								14 54								15 54							
Winchelsea	d																								
Doleham	d																								
Three Oaks	d																								
Ore	d					14 22		14 50						15 22		15 50						16 22		16 50	
Hastings 4	a	14 11				14 25		14 53		15 11				15 25		15 53		16 11				16 25		16 53	
	d	14 12				14 26		14 55		15 12				15 26		15 55		16 12				16 26		16 55	
St Leonards Warrior Sq 4	d	14 15				14 29		14 58		15 15				15 29		15 58		16 15				16 29		16 58	
Bexhill 4	d	14 22				14 35		15 05		15 22				15 35		16 05		16 22				16 35		17 05	
Collington	d					14 37		15 07						15 37		16 07						16 37		17 07	
Cooden Beach	d					14 40		15 10						15 40		16 10						16 40		17 10	
Normans Bay	d					14 43								15 43								16 43			
Pevensey Bay	d																								
Pevensey & Westham	d					14 48		15 16						15 48		16 16						16 48		17 16	
Hampden Park 4 §	d					14 52		15 20						15 52		16 20						16 52		17 20	
Eastbourne 4	a	14 37				14 57		15 25		15 37				15 57		16 25		16 37				16 57		17 25	
	d	14 45		14 58		15 02		15 31		15 45			15 58	16 02		16 31		16 45			16 58	17 02		17 31	
Hampden Park 4 §	d			15 02		15 06							16 02	16 06							17 02	17 06			
Polegate	d	14 52		15 06		15 11		15 37		15 52			16 06	16 11		16 37		16 52			17 06	17 11		17 37	
Berwick	d					15 17								16 17								17 17			
Glynde	d					15 22								16 22								17 22			
Seaford	d		14 58				15 25				15 58				16 25					16 58			17 25		
Bishopstone	d		15 00				15 27				16 00				16 27					17 00			17 27		
Newhaven Harbour	d		15 03				15 30				16 03				16 30					17 03			17 30		
Newhaven Town ⛴	d		15 05				15 32				16 05				16 32					17 05			17 32		
Southease	d						15 36								16 36								17 36		
Lewes 4	a	15 07	15 14	15 18		15 28	15 44	15 49		16 07	16 14		16 18	16 28	16 44	16 49		17 07		17 14	17 18	17 28	17 44	17 49	
	d	15 07	15 14	15 20		15 28	15 44	15 50	15 58	16 07	16 14		16 20	16 28	16 44	16 50	16 58	17 07		17 14	17 20	17 28	17 44	17 50	17 58
Falmer	d		15 21			15 35	15 51		16 05		16 21			16 35	16 51		17 05			17 21		17 35	17 51		18 05
Moulsecoomb	d		15 24			15 38	15 54		16 08		16 24			16 38	16 54		17 08			17 24		17 38	17 54		18 08
London Road (Brighton)	d		15 27			15 40	15 57		16 10		16 27			16 40	16 57		17 10			17 27		17 40	17 57		18 10
Brighton 10	a	15 20	15 30			15 44	16 00		16 14	16 20	16 30			16 44	17 00		17 14	17 20		17 30		17 44	18 00		18 14
Cooksbridge	d																								
Plumpton	d												16 28								17 28				
Wivelsfield 4	a		15 53	15 34		16 11	16 23				16 53		16 34	17 11	17 23					17 53	17 34	18 11	18 23		
Haywards Heath 3	a		15 47	15 40		16 15	16 18	16 05			16 47		16 40	17 15	17 18	17 05				17 47	17 40	18 15	18 18	18 05	
Gatwick Airport 10 ✈	a		16 00	15 54			16 30	16 24			17 00		16 54		17 30	17 24				18 00	17 54		18 30	18 24	
East Croydon	a		16 16	16 10		16 23	16 46	16 40	16 55		17 16		17 10	17 23	17 46	17 40	17 55			18 16	18 10	18 23	18 46	18 40	18 55
London Bridge 4 ⊖	a		16 30	16 30		16c45	17 00	17 00	17c15		17 30		17 30	17c45	18 00	18 00	18c15			18 30	18 30	18c45	19 00	19 00	19c15
Clapham Junction 10	a			16 19		16 33	17c03	16 49	17 04				17 19	17 33	18c03	17 49	18 04				18 19	18 33	19c03	18 49	19 04
London Victoria 15 ⊖	a			16 27		16 40		16 57	17 11				17 27	17 40		17 57	18 11				18 27	18 40		18 57	19 11

For general notes see front of timetable
For details of catering facilities see Directory of Train Operators

§ For additional trains between Hampden Park and Eastbourne see London to Hastings pages

b Change at London Bridge and Ashford International

c Change at Brighton and East Croydon

Table 189

Ashford, Hastings, Eastbourne, Seaford and Lewes → Brighton, Haywards Heath and London

Network Diagram - see first page of Table 184

		SN 1	SN 1	SN 1	SN 1	SN 1	SN 1	SN 1	SN 1	SN 1	SN 1	SN 1	SN 1	SN 1	SN 1	SN 1	SN 1	SN 1	SN 1	SN 1	SN 1	SN 1
London Charing Cross 4	⊖ d	14 53							15 53							16 53						18 23
London Waterloo (East) 4	⊖ d	14 56							15 56							16 56						18 26
London Cannon Street 4	⊖ d	14b30							15b30							16b30						17b30
London Bridge 4	⊖ d	14 38							15 38							16 38						17 38
Ashford International	d	16 30							17 30							18 30						19 30
Ham Street	d	16 39							17 39							18 39						19 39
Appledore (Kent)	d	16 44							17 44							18 44						19 44
Rye	a	16 53							17 53							18 53						19 53
	d	16 54							17 54							18 54						19 54
Winchelsea	d																					
Doleham	d																					
Three Oaks	d																					
Ore	d				17 22		17 50					18 22		18 50				19 22		19 50		
Hastings 4	a	17 11			17 25		17 53		18 11			18 25		18 53		19 11		19 25		19 53		20 11
	d	17 12			17 26		17 55		18 12			18 26		18 55		19 12		19 26		19 55		20 12
St Leonards Warrior Sq 4	d	17 15			17 29		17 58		18 15			18 29		18 58		19 15		19 29		19 58		20 15
Bexhill 4	d	17 22			17 35		18 05		18 22			18 35		19 05		19 22		19 35		20 05		20 22
Collington	d				17 37		18 07					18 37		19 07				19 37		20 07		
Cooden Beach	d				17 40		18 10					18 40		19 10				19 40		20 10		
Normans Bay	d				17 43							18 43						19 43				
Pevensey Bay	d																					
Pevensey & Westham	d				17 48		18 16					18 48		19 16				19 48		20 16		
Hampden Park 4 §	d				17 52		18 20					18 52		19 21				19 52		20 20		
Eastbourne 4	a	17 37			17 57		18 25		18 37			18 57		19 26		19 37		19 57		20 25		20 37
	d	17 45		17 58	18 02		18 31		18 45		18 58	19 02		19 32		19 45		20 02		20 31		20 45
Hampden Park 4 §	d			18 02	18 06						19 02	19 06						20 06				
Polegate	d	17 52		18 06	18 11		18 37		18 52		19 06	19 11		19 38		19 52		20 11		20 37		20 52
Berwick	d				18 17							19 17						20 17				
Glynde	d				18 22							19 22						20 22				
Seaford	d		17 58			18 25				18 58			19 25				19 58		20 28			
Bishopstone	d		18 00			18 27				19 00			19 27				20 00		20 30			
Newhaven Harbour	d		18 03			18 30				19 03			19 30				20 03		20 33			
Newhaven Town ⛴	d		18 05			18 32				19 05			19 32				20 05		20 35			
Southease	d					18 36							19 36									
Lewes 4	a	18 07	18 14	18 18	18 28	18 44	18 49		19 07	19 14	19 18	19 28	19 44	19 50		20 07	20 14	20 28	20 44	20 49	←	21 07
	d	18 07	18 14	18 20	18 28	18 44	18 50	18 58	19 07	19 14	19 20	19 28	19 44	19 51	19 58	20 07	20 14	20 30	20 53	20 50	20 53	21 07
Falmer	d		18 21		18 35	18 51		19 05		19 21		19 35	19 51		20 05		20 21	20 37	→		21 00	
Moulsecoomb	d		18 24		18 38	18 54		19 08		19 24		19 38	19 54		20 08		20 24	20 40			21 03	
London Road (Brighton)	d		18 27		18 40	18 57		19 10		19 27		19 40	19 57		20 10		20 27	20 42			21 05	
Brighton 10	a	18 20	18 30		18 44	19 00		19 14	19 20	19 30		19 44	20 00		20 14	20 20	20 30	20 46			21 10	21 20
Cooksbridge	d																					
Plumpton	d			18 28							19 28											
Wivelsfield 4	a		18 53	18 34	19 11	19 23				19 53	19 34	20 11	20 23	20 03			20 53			21 02		
Haywards Heath 3	a		18 47	18 40	19 15	19 18	19 05			19 47	19 40	20 16	20 18	20 07			20 47			21 06		
Gatwick Airport 10 ✈	a		19 00	18 54		19 31	19 24			20 00	19 54		20 30	20 24			21 00			21 24		
East Croydon 🚋	a		19 16	19 10	19 23	19 47	19 40	19 55		20 16	20 10	20 23	20 46	20 40	20 55		21 16			21 40	21 55	
London Bridge 4	⊖ a		19 30	19 30	19c45	20 00	20 00	20c15		20 30	20 30	20c45	21 00	21 00	21c15		21 30			22 15	22c15	
Clapham Junction 10	a			19 19	19 33	20c03	19 49	20 04			20 19	20 33	21c03	20 49	21 04		21 33			21 49	22 04	
London Victoria 15	⊖ a			19 27	19 40		19 57	20 11			20 27	20 40		20 57	21 11		21 40			21 57	22 11	

For general notes see front of timetable
For details of catering facilities see Directory of Train Operators

§ For additional trains between Hampden Park and Eastbourne see London to Hastings pages

b Change at London Bridge and Ashford International

c Change at Brighton and East Croydon

Table 189

Saturdays

Ashford, Hastings, Eastbourne, Seaford and Lewes → Brighton, Haywards Heath and London

Network Diagram - see first page of Table 184

Station		SN 1		SN 1	SN 1	SN 1	SN 1	SN 1	SN 1		SN 1	SN 1	SN 1	SN 1	SN 1	SN 1		SN 1	SN 1	SN 1	SN 1				
London Charing Cross 4	⊖ d							19 00							20 00				20 30						
London Waterloo (East) 4	⊖ d							19 03							20 03				20 33						
London Cannon Street 4	⊖ d							19b00							19b14										
London Bridge 4	⊖ d							19 08							20 08				20 38						
Ashford International	d							20 30							21 30				22 24						
Ham Street	d							20 39							21 39				22 33						
Appledore (Kent)	d							20 44							21 44				22 38						
Rye	a							20 53							21 53				22 47						
	d							20 54							21 57				22 47						
Winchelsea	d																		22 51						
Doleham	d																		22 57						
Three Oaks	d																		23 01						
Ore	d			20 22		20 50					21 22							22 22	23 06						
Hastings 4	a			20 25		20 53		21 11			21 25				22 14			22 25	23 09						
	d			20 26		20 55		21 12			21 26		21 42		22 16			22 26			23 13				
St Leonards Warrior Sq 4	d			20 29		20 58		21 15			21 29		21 45		22 19			22 29			23 16				
Bexhill 4	d			20 35		21 05		21 22			21 35		21 51		22 25			22 38			23 22				
Collington	d			20 37		21 07					21 37		21 53					22 40			23 24				
Cooden Beach	d			20 40		21 10					21 40		21 56					22 43			23 27				
Normans Bay	d			20 43														22 46							
Pevensey Bay	d																								
Pevensey & Westham	d			20 48		21 16					21 46		22 02					22 51			23 33				
Hampden Park 4 §	d			20 52		21 20					21 51		22 07					22 55			23 38				
Eastbourne 4	a			20 57		21 25		21 37			21 56		22 12		22 40			23 00			23 43				
	d			21 02		21 31		21 45			22 02		22 18		22 45			23 05			23 48				
Hampden Park 4 §	d			21 06							22 06							23 09			23 52				
Polegate	d			21 11		21 37		21 52			22 11		22 24		22 52			23 13			23 56				
Berwick	d			21 17							22 17							23 18							
Glynde	d			21 22							22 22							23 24							
Seaford	d	20 58			21 28				21 58			22 20				22 58				23 25					
Bishopstone	d	21 00			21 30				22 00			22 22				23 00				23 27					
Newhaven Harbour	d	21 03			21 33				22 03			22 25				23 03				23 30					
Newhaven Town	⛴ d	21 05			21 35				22 05			22 27				23 05				23 32					
Southease	d																								
Lewes 4	a	21 14		21 28	21 44	21 49	←	22 07	22 14		22 28	22 35	22 38	←	23 07	23 14		23 29		23 40	00 08				
	d	21 14		21 28	21 53	21 50	21 53	22 07	22 14		22 28	22 42	22 40	22 42	23 07	23 14		23 29		23 40	00 08				
Falmer	d	21 21		21 36	→		22 00		22 21		22 35	→		22 49		23 21		23 37		23 47	00 15				
Moulsecoomb	d	21 24		21 39			22 03		22 24		22 38			22 52		23 24		23 40		23 50	00 18				
London Road (Brighton)	d	21 27		21 41			22 05		22 27		22 40			22 54		23 27		23 42		23 53	00 21				
Brighton 10	a	21 30		21 45			22 09	22 20	22 31		22 44			22 58	23 20	23 31		23 46		23 56	00 24				
Cooksbridge	d																								
Plumpton	d												22 48												
Wivelsfield 4	a	21 53				22 02		22 49					22 54	23 19											
Haywards Heath 3	a	21 58				22 06		22 54					22 58	23 23											
Gatwick Airport 10	✈ a	22 16				22 23		23c12					23 12	23 52											
East Croydon	🚌 a			22 23		22 40		23 32					23 30	00 16											
London Bridge 4	⊖ a			22e45				23 45					00f52	00e52											
Clapham Junction 10	a			22 33		22 49		00e11					23 42	01e02											
London Victoria 15	⊖ a			22 40		22 57		00e18					23 52	01e09											

For general notes see front of timetable
For details of catering facilities see Directory of Train Operators

§ For additional trains between Hampden Park and Eastbourne see London to Hastings pages

b Change at London Bridge and Ashford International
c Change at Brighton and Haywards Heath
e Change at Brighton and East Croydon
f Change at Gatwick Airport and East Croydon

Table 189

Sundays

Ashford, Hastings, Eastbourne, Seaford and Lewes → Brighton, Haywards Heath and London

Network Diagram - see first page of Table 184

		SN 1	SN 1	SN 1 🚲	SN 1	SN 1	SN 1		SN 1	SN 1	SN 1	SN 1	SN 1	SN 1		SN 1	SN 1	SN 1	SN 1	SN 1	SN 1		SN 1	SN 1	SN 1
London Charing Cross 4	⊖ d																								
London Waterloo (East) 4	⊖ d																								
London Cannon Street 4	⊖ d																								
London Bridge 4	⊖ d																								
Ashford International	d																08 15						09 21		
Ham Street	d																08 24						09 30		
Appledore (Kent)	d																08 29						09 35		
Rye	a																08 38						09 44		
	d																08 40						09 45		
Winchelsea	d																08 43								
Doleham	d																08 50								
Three Oaks	d																08 53								
Ore	d											08 14					08 59		09 14						10 14
Hastings 4	a											08 17					09 02		09 17				10 02		10 17
	d	23p13										08 18					09 03		09 18				10 03		10 18
St Leonards Warrior Sq 4	d	23p16										08 21					09 06		09 21				10 06		10 21
Bexhill 4	d	23p22										08 27					09 13		09 27				10 13		10 27
Collington	d	23p24										08 29							09 29						10 29
Cooden Beach	d	23p27										08 32							09 32						10 32
Normans Bay	d																								
Pevensey Bay	d																								
Pevensey & Westham	d	23p33										08 38							09 38						10 38
Hampden Park 4 §	d	23p38										08 43							09 43						10 43
Eastbourne 4	a	23p43										08 48					09 29		09 48				10 29		10 48
	d	23p48		06 54	07 30		07 55				08 34		08 55				09 34		09 55				10 34		10 55
Hampden Park 4 §	d	23p52		06 58	07 34						08 38						09 38						10 38		
Polegate	d	23p56		07 02	07 38		08 02				08 42		09 02				09 42		10 02				10 42		11 02
Berwick	d				07 44						08 48						09 48						10 48		
Glynde	d				07 49						08 53						09 53						10 53		
Seaford	d					07 53				08 28		08 53				09 28		09 53			10 28			10 53	
Bishopstone	d					07 55				08 30		08 55				09 30		09 55			10 30			10 55	
Newhaven Harbour	d					07 58				08 33		08 58				09 33		09 58			10 33			10 58	
Newhaven Town ⛴	d					08 00				08 35		09 00				09 35		10 00			10 35			11 00	
Southease	d					08 04						09 04						10 04						11 04	
Lewes 4	a	00 08		07 14	07 55	08 11	08 14		←	08 44	08 59	09 11	09 14	←		09 44	09 59	10 11	10 14	←	10 44		10 59	11 11	11 14
	d	00 08	07 18	07 20	07 56	08 18 →	08 16		08 18	08 45	09 00	09 18 →	09 16	09 18		09 45	10 00	10 18 →	10 16	10 18	10 45		11 00	11 18 →	11 16
Falmer	d	00 15	07 25		08 03				08 25	08 52				09 25		09 52				10 25	10 52				
Moulsecoomb	d	00 18	07 28		08 07				08 28	08 55				09 28		09 55				10 28	10 55				
London Road (Brighton)	d	00 21	07 30		08 09				08 30	08 57				09 30		09 57				10 30	10 57				
Brighton 10	a	00 24	07 34		08 13				08 34	09 01	09 12			09 34		10 01	10 12			10 34	11 01		11 12		
Cooksbridge	d																								
Plumpton	d						08 24						09 24						10 24						11 24
Wivelsfield 4	a		*08 16*	07 32			08 31		*09 16*				09 31	*10 16*					10 31	*11 16*					11 31
Haywards Heath 3	a		*08 00*	07 36			08 36		*09 00*		*09 30*		09 35	*09b51*			*10 30*		10 35	*11 00*			*11 30*		11 35
Gatwick Airport 10	✈ a		*08 14*	07 51			08 51		*09 14*		*09 44*		09 51	*10c10*			*10 44*		10 51	*11 14*			*11 44*		11 51
East Croydon	🚋 a		*08 31*	08 09			09 09		*09 31*		*10 01*		10 09	*10 31*			*11 01*		11 09	*11 31*			*12 01*		12 09
London Bridge 4	⊖ a		*08 45*	*08 42*			*09 42*		*09 45*		*10 15*		*10 42*	*10 45*			*11 15*		*11 42*	*11 45*			*12 15*		*12 42*
Clapham Junction 10	a		*08e54*	08 24			09 24		*09e54*		*10e24*		10 24	*10e54*			*11e24*		11 24	*11e54*			*12e24*		12 24
London Victoria 15	⊖ a		*09e01*	08 31			09 31		*10e01*		*10e31*		10 31	*11e01*			*11e31*		11 31	*12e01*			*12e31*		12 31

For general notes see front of timetable
For details of catering facilities see Directory of Train Operators

§ For additional trains between Hampden Park and Eastbourne see London to Hastings pages

b From 30 March arr. 1000
c From 30 March arr. 1014
e Change at Brighton and East Croydon

Ashford, Hastings, Eastbourne, Seaford and Lewes → Brighton, Haywards Heath and London

Network Diagram - see first page of Table 184

		SN 1	SN 1	SN 1	SN 1	SN 1	SN 1	SN 1	SN 1	SN 1	SN 1	SN 1	SN 1	SN 1	SN 1	SN 1	SN 1	SN 1	SN 1	SN 1	SN 1	SN 1
London Charing Cross 4	⊖ d			08 54					09 54					10 54					11 54			
London Waterloo (East) 4	⊖ d			08 57					09 57					10 57					11 57			
London Cannon Street 4	⊖ d																					
London Bridge 4	⊖ d			09 02					10 02					11 02					12 02			
Ashford International	d			10 21					11 21					12 21					13 21			
Ham Street	d			10 30					11 30					12 30					13 30			
Appledore (Kent)	d			10 35					11 35					12 35					13 35			
Rye	a			10 44					11 44					12 44					13 44			
	d			10 45					11 45					12 45					13 45			
Winchelsea	d																					
Doleham	d																					
Three Oaks	d																					
Ore	d					11 14					12 14					13 14					14 14	
Hastings 4	a			11 02		11 17			12 02		12 17			13 02		13 17			14 02		14 17	
	d			11 03		11 18			12 03		12 18			13 03		13 18			14 03		14 18	
St Leonards Warrior Sq 4	d			11 06		11 21			12 06		12 21			13 06		13 21			14 06		14 21	
Bexhill 4	d			11 13		11 27			12 13		12 27			13 13		13 27			14 13		14 27	
Collington	d					11 29					12 29					13 29					14 29	
Cooden Beach	d					11 32					12 32					13 32					14 32	
Normans Bay	d																					
Pevensey Bay	d																					
Pevensey & Westham	d					11 38					12 38					13 38					14 38	
Hampden Park 4 §	d					11 43					12 43					13 43					14 43	
Eastbourne 4	a			11 29		11 48			12 29		12 48			13 29		13 48			14 29		14 48	
	d			11 34		11 55			12 34		12 55			13 34		13 55			14 34		14 55	
Hampden Park 4 §	d			11 38					12 38					13 38					14 38			
Polegate	d			11 42		12 02			12 42		13 02			13 42		14 02			14 42		15 02	
Berwick	d			11 48					12 48					13 48					14 48			
Glynde	d			11 53					12 53					13 53					14 53			
Seaford	d		11 28		11 53			12 28		12 53			13 28		13 53			14 28		14 53		
Bishopstone	d		11 30		11 55			12 30		12 55			13 30		13 55			14 30		14 55		
Newhaven Harbour	d		11 33		11 58			12 33		12 58			13 33		13 58			14 33		14 58		
Newhaven Town ⛴	d		11 35		12 00			12 35		13 00			13 35		14 00			14 35		15 00		
Southease	d				12 04					13 04					14 04					15 04		
Lewes 4	a	←	11 44	11 59	12 11	12 14	←	12 44	12 59	13 11	13 14	←	13 44	13 59	14 11	14 14	←	14 44	14 59	15 11	15 14	←
	d	11 18	11 45	12 00	12 18 →	12 16	12 18	12 45	13 00	13 18 →	13 16	13 18	13 45	14 00	14 18 →	14 16	14 18	14 45	15 00	15 18 →	15 16	15 18
Falmer	d	11 25	11 52				12 25	12 52				13 25	13 52				14 25	14 52				15 25
Moulsecoomb	d	11 28	11 55				12 28	12 55				13 28	13 55				14 28	14 55				15 28
London Road (Brighton)	d	11 30	11 57				12 30	12 57				13 30	13 57				14 30	14 57				15 30
Brighton 10	a	11 34	12 01	12 12			12 34	13 01	13 12			13 34	14 01	14 12			14 34	15 01	15 12			15 34
Cooksbridge	d																					
Plumpton	d																					
Wivelsfield 4	a	12 16				12 31	13 16				13 31	14 16				14 31	15 16				15 31	16 16
Haywards Heath 3	a	12 00		12 30		12 35	13 00		13 30		13 35	14 00		14 30		14 35	15 00		15 30		15 35	16 00
Gatwick Airport 10 ✈	a	12 14		12 44		12 52	13 14		13 44		13 52	14 14		14 44		14 52	15 14		15 44		15 52	16 14
East Croydon	a	12 31		13 01		13 09	13 31		14 01		14 09	14 31		15 01		15 09	15 31		16 01		16 09	16 31
London Bridge 4	⊖ a	12 45		13 15		13 42	13 45		14 15		14 42	14 45		15 15		15 42	15 45		16 15		16 42	16 45
Clapham Junction 10	a	12b54		13b24		13 24	13b54		14b24		14 24	14b54		15b24		15 24	15b54		16b24		16 24	16 47
London Victoria 15	⊖ a	13b01		13b31		13 31	14b01		14b31		14 31	15b01		15b31		15 31	16b01		16b31		16 31	16 53

For general notes see front of timetable
For details of catering facilities see Directory of Train Operators

§ For additional trains between Hampden Park and Eastbourne see London to Hastings pages

b Change at Brighton and East Croydon

Table 189

Sundays

Ashford, Hastings, Eastbourne, Seaford and Lewes → Brighton, Haywards Heath and London

Network Diagram - see first page of Table 184

		SN 1	SN 1	SN 1	SN 1	SN 1	SN 1	SN 1	SN 1	SN 1	SN 1	SN 1	SN 1	SN 1	SN 1	SN 1	SN 1	SN 1	SN 1	SN 1	SN 1	SN 1
London Charing Cross 4	⊖ d		12 54					13 54					14 54					15 54				
London Waterloo (East) 4	⊖ d		12 57					13 57					14 57					15 57				
London Cannon Street 4	⊖ d																					
London Bridge 4	⊖ d		13 02					14 02					15 02					16 02				
Ashford International	d		14 21					15 21					16 21					17 21				
Ham Street	d		14 30					15 30					16 30					17 30				
Appledore (Kent)	d		14 35					15 35					16 35					17 35				
Rye	a		14 44					15 44					16 44					17 44				
	d		14 45					15 45					16 45					17 45				
Winchelsea	d																					
Doleham	d																					
Three Oaks	d																					
Ore	d				15 14					16 14					17 14					18 14		
Hastings 4	a		15 02		15 17			16 02		16 17			17 02		17 17			18 02		18 17		
	d		15 03		15 18			16 03		16 18			17 03		17 18			18 03		18 18		
St Leonards Warrior Sq 4	d		15 06		15 21			16 06		16 21			17 06		17 21			18 06		18 21		
Bexhill 4	d		15 13		15 27			16 13		16 27			17 13		17 27			18 13		18 27		
Collington	d				15 29					16 29					17 29					18 29		
Cooden Beach	d				15 32					16 32					17 32					18 32		
Normans Bay	d																					
Pevensey Bay	d																					
Pevensey & Westham	d				15 38					16 38					17 38					18 38		
Hampden Park 4 §	d				15 43					16 43					17 43					18 43		
Eastbourne 4	a		15 29		15 48			16 29		16 48			17 29		17 48			18 29		18 48		
	d		15 34		15 55			16 34		16 55			17 34		17 55			18 34		18 55		
Hampden Park 4 §	d		15 38					16 38					17 38					18 38				
Polegate	d		15 42		16 02			16 42		17 02			17 42		18 02			18 42		19 02		
Berwick	d		15 48					16 48					17 48					18 48				
Glynde	d		15 53					16 53					17 53					18 53				
Seaford	d	15 28		15 53			16 28		16 53			17 28		17 53			18 28		18 53			19 28
Bishopstone	d	15 30		15 55			16 30		16 55			17 30		17 55			18 30		18 55			19 30
Newhaven Harbour	d	15 33		15 58			16 33		16 58			17 33		17 58			18 33		18 58			19 33
Newhaven Town	⛴ d	15 35		16 00			16 35		17 00			17 35		18 00			18 35		19 00			19 35
Southease	d			16 04					17 04					18 04					19 04			
Lewes 4	a	15 44	15 59	16 11	16 14	←	16 44	16 59	17 11	17 14	←	17 44	17 59	18 11	18 14	←	18 44	18 59	19 11	19 14	←	19 44
	d	15 45	16 00	16 18	16 16	16 18	16 45	17 00	17 18	17 16	17 18	17 45	18 00	18 18	18 16	18 18	18 45	19 00	19 18	19 16	19 18	19 45
Falmer	d	15 52		→		16 25	16 52		→		17 25	17 52		→		18 25	18 52		→		19 25	19 52
Moulsecoomb	d	15 55				16 28	16 55				17 28	17 55				18 28	18 55				19 28	19 55
London Road (Brighton)	d	15 57				16 30	16 57				17 30	17 57				18 30	18 57				19 30	19 57
Brighton 10	a	16 01	16 12			16 34	17 01	17 12			17 34	18 01	18 12			18 34	19 01	19 12			19 34	20 01
Cooksbridge	d																					
Plumpton	d				16 24					17 24					18 24					19 24		
Wivelsfield 4	a				16 31	17 16				17 31	18 16				18 31	19 16				19 31	20 16	
Haywards Heath 3	a		16 30		16 35	17 00		17 30		17 35	18 00		18 30		18 35	19 00		19 30		19 35	20 00	
Gatwick Airport 10	✈ a		16 44		16 52	17 14		17 44		17 52	18 14		18 44		18 52	19 14		19 44		19 52	20 14	
East Croydon	a		17 01		17 09	17 31		18 01		18 09	18 31		19 01		19 09	19 31		20 01		20 09	20 31	
London Bridge 4	⊖ a		17 15		17 42	17 45		18 15		18 42	18 45		19 15		19 42	19 45		20 15		20 42	20 45	
Clapham Junction 10	a		17b24		17 24	17 47		18b24		18 24	18 47		19b24		19 24	19 47		20b24		20 24	20 47	
London Victoria 15	⊖ a		17b31		17 31	17 53		18b31		18 31	18 53		19b31		19 31	19 53		20b31		20 31	20 53	

For general notes see front of timetable
For details of catering facilities see
Directory of Train Operators

§ For additional trains between Hampden Park and Eastbourne see London to Hastings pages

b Change at Brighton and East Croydon

Table 189

Sundays

Ashford, Hastings, Eastbourne, Seaford and Lewes → Brighton, Haywards Heath and London

Network Diagram - see first page of Table 184

		SN 1	SN 1	SN 1		SN 1	SN 1	SN 1	SN 1	SN 1	SN 1		SN 1	SN 1	SN 1	SN 1	SN 1	SN 1		SN 1	SN 1	SN 1	SN 1		
London Charing Cross 4 ⊖	d	16 54						17 54						18 54				19 54				20 54			
London Waterloo (East) 4 ⊖	d	16 57						17 57						18 57				19 57				20 57			
London Cannon Street 4 ⊖	d																								
London Bridge 4 ⊖	d	17 02						18 02						19 02				20 02				21 02			
Ashford International	d	18 21						19 21						20 21				21 21				22 20			
Ham Street	d	18 30						19 30						20 30				21 30				22 29			
Appledore (Kent)	d	18 35						19 35						20 35				21 35				22 34			
Rye	a	18 44						19 44						20 44				21 44				22 43			
	d	18 45						19 45						20 45				21 45				22 43			
Winchelsea	d																					22 47			
Doleham	d																					22 53			
Three Oaks	d																					22 57			
Ore	d			19 14						20 14						21 14					22 14	23 02			
Hastings 4	a	19 02		19 17				20 02		20 17				21 02		21 17		22 02			22 17	23 05			
	d	19 03		19 18				20 03		20 18				21 03		21 18		22 03			22 18		23 18		
St Leonards Warrior Sq 4	d	19 06		19 21				20 06		20 21				21 06		21 21		22 06			22 21		23 21		
Bexhill 4	d	19 13		19 27				20 13		20 27				21 13		21 27		22 13			22 27		23 27		
Collington	d			19 29						20 29						21 29					22 29		23 29		
Cooden Beach	d			19 32						20 32						21 32					22 32		23 32		
Normans Bay	d																								
Pevensey Bay	d																								
Pevensey & Westham	d			19 38						20 38						21 38					22 38		23 38		
Hampden Park 4 §	d			19 43						20 43						21 43					22 43		23 43		
Eastbourne 4	a	19 29		19 48				20 29		20 48				21 29		21 48		22 29			22 48		23 48		
	d	19 34		19 55				20 34		20 55				21 34		21 55		22 34			22 55				
Hampden Park 4 §	d	19 38						20 38						21 38				22 38							
Polegate	d	19 42		20 02				20 42		21 02				21 42		22 02		22 42			23 02				
Berwick	d	19 48						20 48						21 48				22 48							
Glynde	d	19 53						20 53						21 53				22 53							
Seaford	d		19 53				20 28		20 53				21 28		21 53		22 28			22 53					
Bishopstone	d		19 55				20 30		20 55				21 30		21 55		22 30			22 55					
Newhaven Harbour	d		19 58				20 33		20 58				21 33		21 58		22 33			22 58					
Newhaven Town ⛴	d		20 00				20 35		21 00				21 35		22 00		22 35			23 00					
Southease	d		20 04																						
Lewes 4	a	19 59	20 11	20 14		←	20 44	20 59	21 09	21 14	←		21 44	21 59	22 09	22 14	22 44	22 59		23 09	23 14				
	d	20 00	20 18 →	20 16		20 18	20 45	21 00	21 18 →	21 16	21 18		21 45	22 00	22 10	22 18	22 45	23 00		23 10	23 18				
Falmer	d					20 25	20 52				21 25		21 52		22 17	22 25	22 52			23 17	23 25				
Moulsecoomb	d					20 28	20 55				21 28		21 55		22 20	22 28	22 55			23 20	23 28				
London Road (Brighton)	d					20 30	20 57				21 30		21 57		22 22	22 30	22 57			23 22	23 30				
Brighton 10	a	20 12				20 34	21 01	21 12			21 34		22 01	22 12	22 26	22 34	23 01	23 12		23 26	23 34				
Cooksbridge	d																								
Plumpton	d			20 24						21 24															
Wivelsfield 4	a			20 31		21 16				21 31	22 16														
Haywards Heath 3	a	20 30		20 35		21 00		21 30		21 35	22 00			22 30		23 00					00 01				
Gatwick Airport 10 ✈	a	20 44		20 52		21 14		21 44		21 52	22 14			22 44		23 14					00 14				
East Croydon	a	21 01		21 09		21 31		22 01		22 09	22 31			23 01		23 31					00 35				
London Bridge 4 ⊖	a	21 15		21 42		21 45		22 15		22 42	22 45			23 15		23 45									
Clapham Junction 10	a	21b24		21 24		21b54		22b24		22 24	23b10			23b37		00b10					01b02				
London Victoria 15 ⊖	a	21b31		21 31		22b01		22b31		22 31	23b16			23b46		00b18					01b09				

For general notes see front of timetable
For details of catering facilities see
Directory of Train Operators

§ For additional trains between Hampden Park and Eastbourne see London to Hastings pages

b Change at Brighton and East Croydon

Southeastern

These notes apply to Southeastern services on Tables 195 to 212. Southeastern services can be identified by the operator code SE at the head of the train column.

Christmas and New Year Holiday 2007/8

Monday 24 December	—	A Saturday service will operate with additional morning and evening peak services on most routes. Pasenger services will be shut down by midnight.
Tuesday 25 December	—	No service
Wednesday 26 December	—	A special hourly service will run in each direction between the following stations London Charring Cross and Asford International via Tonbridge London Charring Cross and Slade Green via Woolwich Arsenal London Charring Cross and Slade Green via Bexleyheath London Victoria and Gillingham via Swanley London Victoria and Orpington via Beckenham Junction
Thursday 27 December	—	A Saturday service will operate with additional morning and evening peak services on most routes
Friday 28 December	—	A Saturday service will operate with additional morning and evening peak services on most routes
Saturday 29 December	—	A normal Saturday service will operate
Sunday 30 December	—	A normal Saturday service will operate
Monday 31 December	—	A normal Saturday service will operate with additional morning and evening peak services on nost rourtes
Tuesday 1 January	—	A normal Sunday service will operate

Easter Holiday

Friday 21 March	—	A normal Sunday service will operate
Monday 24 March	—	A normal Sunday service will operate

May Day Holiday

Monday 5 May	—	A normal Sunday service will operate

Network Diagram for Tables 195, 196 | also 199 ★

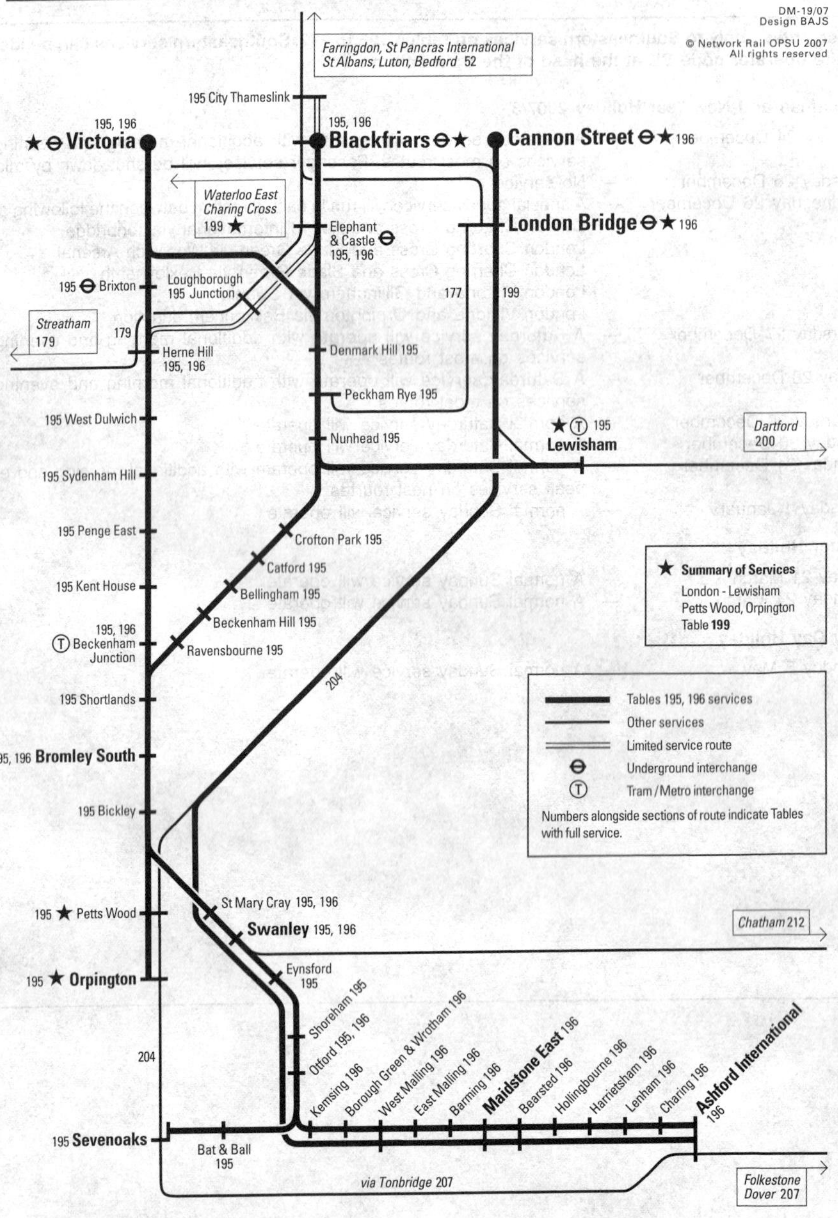
DM-19/07
Design BAJS
© Network Rail OPSU 2007
All rights reserved
Farringdon, St Pancras International
St Albans, Luton, Bedford 52
195 City Thameslink
195, 196
★ ⊖ Victoria
195, 196
Blackfriars ⊖ ★
Cannon Street ⊖ ★ 196
Waterloo East
Charing Cross
199 ★
Elephant & Castle ⊖
195, 196
London Bridge ⊖ ★ 196
195 ⊖ Brixton
Loughborough
195 Junction
177
199
Streatham
179
179
Herne Hill
195, 196
Denmark Hill 195
Peckham Rye 195
195 West Dulwich
★ Ⓣ 195
Lewisham
Dartford
200
Nunhead 195
195 Sydenham Hill
195 Penge East
Crofton Park 195
Catford 195
195 Kent House
Bellingham 195
Beckenham Hill 195
195, 196
Ⓣ Beckenham Junction
Ravensbourne 195
★ Summary of Services
London - Lewisham
Petts Wood, Orpington
Table 199
204
195 Shortlands
Tables 195, 196 services
Other services
Limited service route
Underground interchange
Tram / Metro interchange
Numbers alongside sections of route indicate Tables with full service.
95, 196 Bromley South
195 Bickley
St Mary Cray 195, 196
195 ★ Petts Wood
Swanley 195, 196
Chatham 212
195 ★ Orpington
Eynsford
195
Shoreham 195
Otford 195, 196
204
Kemsing 196
Borough Green & Wrotham 196
West Malling 196
East Malling 196
Barming 196
Maidstone East 196
Bearsted 196
Hollingbourne 196
Harrietsham 196
Lenham 196
Charing 196
Ashford International
196
195 Sevenoaks
Bat & Ball
195
via Tonbridge 207
Folkestone
Dover 207

For details of Bank Holiday service alterations please see first page of this table

London → Catford, Beckenham Junction, Bromley South, Orpington, Otford and Sevenoaks

Network Diagram - see first page of Table 195

Miles	Miles	Miles			SE MX 22 [1]	SE MO 54 [1]	SE MX 94 [1] A	SE MX 73	SE MX 70	SE 60	SE 54 [1]	SE 83	SE 70	SE 83	SE 66 [1] B	SE 70	SE 54 [1]	SE 83	FC	SE 37 [1]	SE 70	SE 64 [1] C	SE 83		FC
0	—	0	**London Victoria [15]**	⊖ d	23p39	23p41	23p51		23p53	00 35	05 32		05 36		06 10	06 04	06 16			06 39	06 36	06 47			
3¼	—	—	Brixton	⊖ d					23p59				05 43			06 11					06 43				
—	—	—	St Pancras International [3]	⊖ d																					06 33
—	—	—	Farringdon	⊖ d																					06 38
—	—	—	City Thameslink [3]	d																					06 41
—	0	—	**London Blackfriars [3]**	⊖ d				23p43				05 27						06 08	06 11				06 42		06 46
—	1¼	—	Elephant & Castle	⊖ d				23p46				05 30						06 12	06 14				06 45		06 49
—	—	—	Loughborough Jn	d															06 18						06 53
4	—	—	Herne Hill [4]	d					00 02	00 43			05 45			06 13			06a22		06 45				06a57
5	—	—	West Dulwich	d					00 04				05 47			06 15					06 47				
5¾	—	—	Sydenham Hill	d					00 06				05 49			06 17					06 49				
7¼	—	—	Penge East	d					00 09	00 48			05 52			06 20					06 52				
7¾	—	—	Kent House [4]	d					00 11				05 54			06 22					06 54				
8¾	—	—	**Beckenham Junction [4]**	d					00 13	00 51			05 56			06 24					06 56				
—	3¾	4¼	Denmark Hill [4]	d				23p52				05 35						06b20					06 52		
—	4½	5	Peckham Rye [4]	d				23p55				05 38						06 23					06 55		
—	5¼	5¾	Nunhead [4]	d				23p57				05 40						06 25					06 57		
—	—	7½	Lewisham [4]	a																					
—	6½	—	Crofton Park	d				23p59				05 42						06 28					06 59		
—	7½	—	Catford	d				00 01				05 44						06 30					07 01		
—	8¼	—	Bellingham	d				00 04				05 47						06 33					07 04		
—	9	—	Beckenham Hill	d				00 06				05 49						06 35					07 06		
—	9¾	—	Ravensbourne	d				00 08				05 51						06 37					07 08		
10	10½	—	Shortlands [4]	d				00 10	00 16			05 53	05 59			06 27		06 39			06 59		07 11		
11	11½	—	**Bromley South [4]**	d	23p58	00 01	00 07	00 13	00 18	00 55	05 48	05 56	06 02		06 30	06 30	06 34	06 43		06 59	07 03	07 04	07 14		
12	12½	—	Bickley [4]	d				00 16	00 21			05 59	06 05			06 33		06 45			07 05		07 16		
13¾	—	—	Petts Wood [4]	d				00 20	00 25				06 10			06 38					07 10				
15	—	—	**Orpington [4]**	d				00a24	00a28				06a13			06a41					07a13				
—	14¾	—	St Mary Cray	d	00 04	00 07	00 14			01 02	05 55	06 05					06 41	06 51		07 05			07 22		
—	17½	—	**Swanley [4]**	d	00a09	00a12	00 18			01a06	06a00	06 09		06 35	06 39		06a45	06 56		07a10		07 13	07 26		
—	20½	—	Eynsford	d			00 23					06 14		06 39				07 00					07 31		
—	22¾	—	Shoreham (Kent)	d			00 27					06 17		06 43				07 04					07 34		
—	24	—	Otford [4]	d			00a30					06 21		06 46	06a49			07 07				07a22	07 38		
—	25¾	—	Bat & Ball	d								06 24		06 49				07 10					07 41		
—	27	—	**Sevenoaks [4]**	a								06 27		06 52				07 13					07 44		

		SE 37 [1]	SE 70	SE 64 [1] D	SE 83	FC	FC [1]	SE 50 [1]	SE 83 E	SE 92 [1]	SE 70	FC	SE 96 [1]	SE 50 [1]	SE 83	FC [1]	SE 92 [1]	SE 70	FC	SE 64 [1]		SE 83	FC	FC [1]	SE 78
London Victoria [15]	⊖ d	07 07	07 06	07 19				07 33		07 39	07 37		07 49	08 03			08 09	08 06		08 18					08 21
Brixton	⊖ d		07 13								07 44							08 13							
St Pancras International [3]	⊖ d					07 03	07 07					07 28				07 48			07 56				08 12	08 20	
Farringdon	⊖ d					07 08	07 12					07 32				07 52			08 00				08 16	08 24	
City Thameslink [3]	d					07 11	07 17					07 35				07 55			08 03				08 19	08 27	
London Blackfriars [3]	⊖ d				07 09	07 16	07 23		07 24			07c43			07 53	08 00			08 08			08 20	08 24	08 32	
Elephant & Castle	⊖ d				07 12	07 19	07 27		07 27			07 47			07 56				08 11			08 23	08 27	08 35	
Loughborough Jn	d					07 23	07 31					07 51							08 15				08 31	08 39	
Herne Hill [4]	d		07 15			07a27	07a35				07 46	07a54				08a09		08 15	08a19				08a35	08a43	
West Dulwich	d		07 17								07 48							08 17							
Sydenham Hill	d		07 19								07 50							08 19							
Penge East	d		07 22								07 53							08 22							
Kent House [4]	d		07 24								07 55							08 24							
Beckenham Junction [4]	d		07 26								07 57							08 26							
Denmark Hill [4]	d				07 17				07 34						08 02							08 29			08 31
Peckham Rye [4]	d				07 20				07 36						08 05							08 32			08 35
Nunhead [4]	d				07 22				07 38						08 07							08 34			08 37
Lewisham [4]	a																								08 43
Crofton Park	d				07 25				07 41						08 09							08 36			
Catford	d				07 27				07 43						08 12							08 39			
Bellingham	d				07 29				07 46						08 15							08 42			
Beckenham Hill	d				07 31				07 48						08 17							08 44			
Ravensbourne	d				07 33				07 50						08 19							08 46			
Shortlands [4]	d		07 29		07 35				07 52		08 01				08 21			08 29				08 48			
Bromley South [4]	d	07 27	07 33	07 36	07 39			07a51	07 56	08 01	08 04		08 07	08a19	08 25		08 31	08 32		08 39		08 52			
Bickley [4]	d		07 35		07 41				07 58		08 07				08 27			08 35				08 55			
Petts Wood [4]	d		07 40								08 12							08 39							
Orpington [4]	d		07a43								08a15							08a42							
St Mary Cray	d	07 34			07 47				08 04	08 07					08 33		08 37					09 00			
Swanley [4]	d	07a38		07 45	07 51				08 08	08a11			08 17		08 37		08a42					09 05			
Eynsford	d				07 56				08 13						08 42							09 09			
Shoreham (Kent)	d				07 59				08 16						08 45							09 13			
Otford [4]	d			07a54	08 03				08 19				08a26		08 49					08a57		09 16			
Bat & Ball	d				08 06				08 22						08 52							09 19			
Sevenoaks [4]	a				08 09				08 26						08 55							09 22			

For general notes see front of timetable
For details of catering facilities see Directory of Train Operators

- **A** To Ashford International (Table 196)
- **B** To Margate (Table 207)
- **C** To Ramsgate (Table 207)
- **D** To Canterbury West (Table 207)
- **E** To Tonbridge (Table 204)
- **b** Arr. 0617
- **c** Arr. 0740

For details of Bank Holiday service alterations please see first page of this table

London → Catford, Beckenham Junction, Bromley South, Orpington, Otford and Sevenoaks

Network Diagram - see first page of Table 195

		SE 50 1	SE 92 1	SE 70	SE 94	SE 83	FC	FC	FC	SE 78	SE 50 1	SE 92 1	SE 70	FC	SE 64 1	SE 83	SE 70	FC		SE 78	SE 50 1	SE 92 1	SE 70	SE 94	SE 83
London Victoria 15	⊖ d	08 33	08 39	08 36	08 49					09 01	09 03	09 09	09 06		09 19		09 21			09 31	09 33	09 39	09 36	09 48	
Brixton	⊖ d			08 43									09 13				09 28						09 43		
St Pancras International 3	⊖ d						08 33	08 40	08 52					08 56				09 14							
Farringdon	⊖ d						08 37	08 44	08 56					09 00				09 18							
City Thameslink 3	d						08 40	08 47	08 59					09 03				09 21							
London Blackfriars 3	⊖ d					08 43	08 45	08 52	09 02					09 08		09 13		09 28							09 43
Elephant & Castle	⊖ d					08 46		08 55	09 05					09 11		09 16		09 31							09 46
Loughborough Jn	d							08 59	09 09					09 15				09 35							
Herne Hill 4	d			08 46			08a54	09a03	09a13				09 17	09a19			09 32	09a39					09 46		
West Dulwich	d			08 48									09 19				09 34						09 48		
Sydenham Hill	d			08 50									09 21				09 36						09 50		
Penge East	d			08 53									09 24				09 39						09 53		
Kent House 4	d			08 55									09 26				09 41						09 55		
Beckenham Junction 4	🚊 d			08 57									09 28				09 43						09 57		
Denmark Hill 4	d					08 52				09 12						09 22				09 42					09 52
Peckham Rye 4	d					08 55				09 14						09 25				09 44					09 55
Nunhead 4	d					08 57				09 16						09 27				09 46					09 57
Lewisham 4	🚊 a									09 25										09 52					
Crofton Park	d					08 59										09 29									10 00
Catford	d					09 01										09 31									10 02
Bellingham	d					09 04										09 34									10 04
Beckenham Hill	d					09 06										09 36									10 06
Ravensbourne	d					09 08										09 38									10 08
Shortlands 4	d			09 00		09 10							09 31			09 40	09 46						10 00		10 10
Bromley South 4	d	08a50	08 59	09 04	09 08	09 13					09a18	09 29	09 34		09 37	09 43	09 48				09a50	09 59	10 03	10 04	10 13
Bickley 4	d			09 06		09 16							09 37			09 45	09 51						10 06		10 16
Petts Wood 4	d			09 12									09 42				09 55						10 10		
Orpington 4	d			09a15									09a46				09a58						10a13		
St Mary Cray	d		09 05			09 21						09 35				09 51						10 05			10 22
Swanley 4	d		09a10		09 16	09 26						09a40				09 56						10a10		10 13	10 26
Eynsford	d					09 30										10 00									10 31
Shoreham (Kent)	d					09 34										10 04									10 34
Otford 4	d				09a25	09 37									09a53	10 07								10a23	10 37
Bat & Ball	d					09 40										10 10									10 40
Sevenoaks 4	a					09 43										10 13									10 43

		FC	SE 70	FC		SE 78	SE 50 1	SE 92 1	SE 70	SE 64 1	SE 83	FC	SE 70	FC	SE 78	SE 50 1	SE 92 1	SE 70	SE 94	SE 83	FC	SE 70			
London Victoria 15	⊖ d		09 51			10 01	10 03	10 09	10 06	10 18			10 21		10 31	10 33	10 39	10 36	10 48			10 51			
Brixton	⊖ d		09 58						10 13				10 28					10 43				10 58			
St Pancras International 3	⊖ d	09 32		09 48								10 02		10 17							10 32				
Farringdon	⊖ d	09 36		09 52								10 07		10 22							10 37				
City Thameslink 3	d	09 39		09 55								10 09		10 24							10 39				
London Blackfriars 3	⊖ d	09 44		10 00							10 13	10b16		10 30						10 43	10c46				
Elephant & Castle	⊖ d	09 47		10 03							10 16	10 19		10 33						10 46	10 49				
Loughborough Jn	d	09 51		10 07								10 23		10 37							10 53				
Herne Hill 4	d	09a55	10 00	10a11					10 15			10a27	10 30	10a41				10 45			10a57	11 00			
West Dulwich	d		10 03						10 18				10 33					10 48				11 03			
Sydenham Hill	d		10 05						10 20				10 35					10 50				11 05			
Penge East	d		10 08						10 23				10 38					10 53				11 08			
Kent House 4	d		10 09						10 24				10 39					10 54				11 09			
Beckenham Junction 4	🚊 d		10 11						10 26				10 41					10 56				11 11			
Denmark Hill 4	d					10 12					10 22				10 42					10 52					
Peckham Rye 4	d					10 14					10 25				10 44					10 55					
Nunhead 4	d					10 16					10 27				10 46					10 57					
Lewisham 4	🚊 a					10 22									10 52										
Crofton Park	d										10 30									11 00					
Catford	d										10 32									11 02					
Bellingham	d										10 34									11 04					
Beckenham Hill	d										10 36									11 06					
Ravensbourne	d										10 38									11 08					
Shortlands 4	d		10 14						10 29		10 40		10 44					10 59		11 10		11 14			
Bromley South 4	d		10 17				10a18	10 29	10 32	10 34	10 43		10 47			10a48	10 59	11 02	11 04	11 13		11 17			
Bickley 4	d		10 20						10 35		10 46		10 50					11 05		11 16		11 20			
Petts Wood 4	d		10 26						10 39				10 54					11 09				11 24			
Orpington 4	d		10a29						10a42				10a57					11a12				11a27			
St Mary Cray	d							10 35			10 52						11 05			11 22					
Swanley 4	d							10a40			10 56						11a10		11 13	11 26					
Eynsford	d										11 01									11 31					
Shoreham (Kent)	d										11 04									11 34					
Otford 4	d									10a51	11 07								11a23	11 37					
Bat & Ball	d										11 10									11 40					
Sevenoaks 4	a										11 13									11 43					

For general notes see front of timetable
For details of catering facilities see Directory of Train Operators

b Arr. 1013
c Arr. 1043

For details of Bank Holiday service alterations please see first page of this table

London → Catford, Beckenham Junction, Bromley South, Orpington, Otford and Sevenoaks

Network Diagram - see first page of Table 195

Station		FC		SE 78	SE 50 1	SE 92 1	SE 70	SE 94 1	SE 83	FC	SE 70	FC	SE 78	SE 50 1	SE 92 1	SE 70	SE 94 1	SE 83	FC	SE 70	FC	SE 78	SE 50 1
London Victoria 15	⊖ d			14 01	14 03	14 09	14 06	14 18			14 21		14 31	14 33	14 39	14 36	14 48			14 51		15 01	15 03
Brixton	⊖ d						14 13				14 28					14 43				14 58			
St Pancras International 3	⊖ d	10 47								14 02		14 17							14 32		14 47		
Farringdon	⊖ d	10 52								14 07		14 22							14 37		14 52		
City Thameslink 3	d	10 54								14 09		14 24							14 39		14 54		
London Blackfriars 3	⊖ d	11 00							14 13	14b16		14 30						14 43	14c46		15 00		
Elephant & Castle	⊖ d	11 03							14 16	14 19		14 33						14 46	14 49		15 03		
Loughborough Jn	d	11 07								14 23		14 37							14 53		15 07		
Herne Hill 4	d	11a11					14 15			14a27	14 30	14a41				14 45			14a57	15 00	15a11		
West Dulwich	d						14 18				14 33					14 48				15 03			
Sydenham Hill	d		and at				14 20				14 35					14 50				15 05			
Penge East	d						14 23				14 38					14 53				15 08			
Kent House 4	d		the same				14 24				14 39					14 54				15 09			
Beckenham Junction 4	d						14 26				14 41					14 56				15 11			
			minutes																				
Denmark Hill 4	d			14 12					14 22				14 42					14 52				15 12	
Peckham Rye 4	d		past	14 14					14 25				14 44					14 55				15 14	
Nunhead 4	d			14 16					14 27				14 46					14 57				15 16	
Lewisham 4	a		each	14 22									14 52									15 22	
Crofton Park	d		hour until						14 30									15 00					
Catford	d								14 32									15 02					
Bellingham	d								14 34									15 04					
Beckenham Hill	d								14 36									15 06					
Ravensbourne	d								14 38									15 08					
Shortlands 4	d						14 29		14 40		14 44					14 59		15 10		15 14			
Bromley South 4	d				14a18	14 29	14 32	14 34	14 43		14 47			14a48	14 59	15 02	15 04	15 13		15 17			15a18
Bickley 4	d						14 35		14 46		14 50					15 05		15 16		15 20			
Petts Wood 4	d						14 39				14 54					15 09				15 24			
Orpington 4	d						14a42				14a57					15a12				15a27			
St Mary Cray	d					14 35			14 52						15 05			15 22					
Swanley 4	d					14a40			14 56						15a10		15 13	15 26					
Eynsford	d								15 01									15 31					
Shoreham (Kent)	d								15 04									15 34					
Otford 4	d							14a51	15 07								15a23	15 37					
Bat & Ball	d								15 10									15 40					
Sevenoaks 4	a								15 13									15 43					

Station		SE 92 1	SE 70	SE 94 1	SE 83	FC	SE 70	FC	SE 78	SE 50 1	SE 92 1	SE 70	SE 94 1	SE 83	FC	SE 70	FC	SE 50 1	SE 22	SE 70	SE 78	SE 50 1	SE 83
London Victoria 15	⊖ d	15 09	15 06	15 18			15 21		15 31	15 33	15 39	15 36	15 48			15 51		16 03	16 00	16 06	16 14	16 23	
Brixton	⊖ d		15 13				15 28					15 43				15 58				16 13			
St Pancras International 3	⊖ d					15 02		15 17							15 32		15 47						
Farringdon	⊖ d					15 07		15 22							15 37		15 52						
City Thameslink 3	d					15 09		15 24							15 39		15 54						
London Blackfriars 3	⊖ d				15 13	15e16		15 30						15 43	15f46		16 00						16 09
Elephant & Castle	⊖ d				15 16	15 19		15 33						15 46	15 49		16 03						16 13
Loughborough Jn	d					15 23		15 37							15 53		16 07						
Herne Hill 4	d		15 15			15a27	15 30	15a41				15 45			15a57	16 00	16a11			16 15			
West Dulwich	d		15 18				15 33					15 48				16 03				16 18			
Sydenham Hill	d		15 20				15 35					15 50				16 05				16 20			
Penge East	d		15 23				15 38					15 53				16 08				16 23			
Kent House 4	d		15 24				15 39					15 54				16 09				16 24			
Beckenham Junction 4	d		15 26				15 41					15 56				16 11				16 26			
Denmark Hill 4	d				15 22				15 42					15 52							16 27		16 18
Peckham Rye 4	d				15 25				15 44					15 55							16 29		16 21
Nunhead 4	d				15 27				15 46					15 57							16 31		16 24
Lewisham 4	a								15 52												16 40		
Crofton Park	d				15 30									16 00									16 26
Catford	d				15 32									16 02									16 28
Bellingham	d				15 34									16 04									16 31
Beckenham Hill	d				15 36									16 06									16 33
Ravensbourne	d				15 38									16 08									16 35
Shortlands 4	d		15 29		15 40		15 44					15 59		16 10		16 14				16 29			16 37
Bromley South 4	d	15 29	15 32	15 34	15 43		15 47			15a48	16 00	16 02	16 04	16 13		16 17		16a18	16 23	16 32		16a39	16 40
Bickley 4	d		15 35		15 46		15 50					16 05		16 16		16 20				16 35			16 43
Petts Wood 4	d		15 39				15 54					16 09				16 24				16 39			
Orpington 4	d		15a42				15a57					16a12				16a27				16a42			
St Mary Cray	d	15 35			15 52						16 06			16 22					16 30				16 48
Swanley 4	d	15a40		15 43	15 56						16a11		16 13	16 26					16a34				16 53
Eynsford	d				16 01									16 31									16 57
Shoreham (Kent)	d				16 04									16 34									17 01
Otford 4	d			15a52	16 07								16a23	16 37									17 04
Bat & Ball	d				16 10									16 40									17 07
Sevenoaks 4	a				16 13									16 43									17 12

For general notes see front of timetable
For details of catering facilities see Directory of Train Operators

b Arr. 1413
c Arr. 1443
e Arr. 1513
f Arr. 1543

For details of Bank Holiday service alterations please see first page of this table

London → Catford, Beckenham Junction, Bromley South, Orpington, Otford and Sevenoaks

Network Diagram - see first page of Table 195

		FC	SE 22 [1]	SE 96 [1]	SE 70	FC	SE 30 [1]	SE 73	FC	SE 22	SE 83	FC [1]	SE 94 [1]	SE 70	SE 3	FC	SE 78	SE 40 [1] A	SE 70	SE 78		SE 94 [1]	SE 83	FC	SE 51 [1]
London Victoria [15]	⊖ d		16 22	16 27	16 26		16 42			16 45			16 56	16 51			17 00	17 05	17 12	17 19		17 22			17 27
Brixton	⊖ d				16 33									16 58					17 19						
St Pancras International [3]	⊖ d	16 02				16 15			16 32			16 36				16 47								17 01	
Farringdon	⊖ d	16 07				16 20			16 37			16 40				16 52								17 06	
City Thameslink [3]	d	16 09				16 22			16 39			16 43				16 54							17 07	17 11	
London Blackfriars [3]	⊖ d	16b16				16 26		16 27	16 42		16 42	16 46			16 54	16 58							17 10	17 14	
Elephant & Castle	⊖ d	16 19				16 29		16 31	16 45		16 46	16 50			16 58	17 01							17 14	17 17	
Loughborough Jn	d	16 23				16 33			16 49			16 54			17 01	17 05								17 21	
Herne Hill [4]	d	16a27			16 35	16a37			16a53			16a57		17 00	17 05	17a09		17 13	17 21					17a25	
West Dulwich	d				16 37									17 02	17 08				17 23						
Sydenham Hill	d				16 39									17 04	17 10				17 25						
Penge East	d				16 42									17 07	17 13				17 28						
Kent House [4]	d				16 44									17 09	17 15				17 30						
Beckenham Junction [4]	d				16 47									17 12	17a17				17 33						
Denmark Hill [4]	d							16 36			16 51						17 09			17 28			17 19		
Peckham Rye [4]	d							16 40			16 55						17 13			17 31			17 23		
Nunhead [4]	d							16 42			16 57						17 15			17 33			17 25		
Lewisham [4]	a																17 23			17 43					
Crofton Park	d							16 45			16 59												17 28		
Catford	d							16 47			17 01												17 31		
Bellingham	d							16 50			17 04												17 35		
Beckenham Hill	d							16 52			17 06												17 37		
Ravensbourne	d							16 54			17 08												17 39		
Shortlands [4]	d				16 50			16 56			17 11			17 15					17 36				17 41		
Bromley South [4]	d		16 44	16 48	16 53		16a58	17 00		17 03	17 15		17 15	17 18				17 23	17 39			17 40	17 46		17a44
Bickley [4]	d				16 56			17 02			17 17			17 21					17 42				17 49		
Petts Wood [4]	d				17 01			17 07						17 25					17 49						
Orpington [4]	d				17a04			17a12						17a29					17a53						
St Mary Cray	d		16 50							17 10	17 25							17 30				17 47	17 56		
Swanley [4]	d		16a55	16 57						17a14	17 30							17a34				17 52	18 01		
Eynsford	d										17 34												18 06		
Shoreham (Kent)	d										17 38												18 09		
Otford [4]	d			17a07							17 41		17a33									18a01	18 13		
Bat & Ball	d										17 44												18 16		
Sevenoaks [4]	a										17 47												18 19		

		SE 21 B	FC	SE 96	SE 70	SE 83	FC	SE 78	SE 50 [1]	SE 22	SE 96 [1]	SE 70	SE 3	FC [1]	SE 97 [1]	SE 51 [1]	SE 70	FC		SE 83	SE 21 B	SE 83	FC	SE 78	SE 94 [1]
London Victoria [15]	⊖ d			17 32	17 35			17 41	17 49	17 48	17 58	17 52				18 04	18 02							18 08	18 18
Brixton	⊖ d				17 42							17 59					18 09								
St Pancras International [3]	⊖ d		17 17				17 31							17 46				17 51					18 03		
Farringdon	⊖ d		17 22				17 36							17 50				17 56					18 08		
City Thameslink [3]	d		17 24				17 38						17 47	17 53				17 58					18 10		
London Blackfriars [3]	⊖ d	17 24	17 30			17 36	17 42						17 52	17 57	18 00			18 02		18 05	18 11		18 14		
Elephant & Castle	⊖ d	17 28	17 33			17 39	17 45						17 56		18 04			18 05		18 08	18 15		18 17		
Loughborough Jn	d		17 37				17 49						18 00					18 09					18 21		
Herne Hill [4]	d	17 36	17a41		17 45		17a53					18 02	18 04	18a06			18 11	18a13			18 22		18a26		
West Dulwich	d				17 47							18 05	18 08												
Sydenham Hill	d				17 49							18 07	18 10												
Penge East	d				17 52							18 10	18 13												
Kent House [4]	d				17 54							18 11	18 14												
Beckenham Junction [4]	d			17 46	17 57							18 14	18a17				18 20								
Denmark Hill [4]	d					17 45		17 51												18 14				18 17	
Peckham Rye [4]	d					17 48		17 54												18 17				18 20	
Nunhead [4]	d					17 50		17 56												18 19				18 22	
Lewisham [4]	a							18 05																18 28	
Crofton Park	d					17 52														18 22		←			
Catford	d					17 54														18 24 →		18 24			
Bellingham	d					17 57																18 26			
Beckenham Hill	d					17 59																18 28			
Ravensbourne	d					18 01																18 30			
Shortlands [4]	d				18 00	18 03						18 17					18 23					18 32			
Bromley South [4]	d	17 48		17 51	18 03	18 06			18a05	18 09	18 18	18 20			18 22	18a23	18 27				18 33	18 36			18 36
Bickley [4]	d				18 05	18 09						18 23					18 30					18 38			
Petts Wood [4]	d				18 10							18 29					18 35								
Orpington [4]	d				18a15							18a33					18a40								
St Mary Cray	d	17 57		18 00		18 15				18 16					18 28						18 39	18 44			18 43
Swanley [4]	d	18a01		18 05		18 20				18a20					18 33						18a44	18c51			18 48
Eynsford	d					18 24																18 56			
Shoreham (Kent)	d					18 28																18 59			
Otford [4]	d			18a17		18 32					18a36				18a42							19 03			18a58
Bat & Ball	d					18 36																19 06			
Sevenoaks [4]	a					18 40																19 10			

For general notes see front of timetable
For details of catering facilities see Directory of Train Operators

A To Canterbury East (Table 212)
B To Gillingham (Kent) (Table 212)
b Arr. 1613
c Arr. 1848

For details of Bank Holiday service alterations please see first page of this table

London → Catford, Beckenham Junction, Bromley South, Orpington, Otford and Sevenoaks

Network Diagram - see first page of Table 195

	SE 70	SE 50 1	SE 83	FC	SE 92 1	SE 70	SE 78	SE 94 1	SE 83	FC	SE 70	FC	SE 50 1	SE 92 1	SE 70		FC	SE 78	SE 94 1	SE 83	SE 70	FC	SE 50 1	SE 92 1
London Victoria 15 ⊖ d	18 21	18 33			18 41	18 38	18 46	18 48			18 51		19 04	19 09	19 07			19 16	19 18		19 22		19 34	19 39
Brixton ⊖ d	18 28					18 45					18 58				19 14						19 29			
St Pancras International 3 ⊖ d				18 15						18 33		18 45					19 05					19 17		
Farringdon ⊖ d				18 20						18 38		18 50					19 10					19 22		
City Thameslink 3 d				18 22						18 40		18 52					19 12					19 24		
London Blackfriars 3 ⊖ d			18 23	18 26					18 43	18 44		18 56					19 16			19 17		19 30		
Elephant & Castle ⊖ d			18 26	18 29					18 46	18 47		18 59					19 19			19 20		19 33		
Loughborough Jn d				18 33						18 51		19 03					19 23					19 37		
Herne Hill 4 d	18 30			18a37		18 47				18a56	19 00	19a07			19 16		19a27				19 31	19a41		
West Dulwich d	18 33					18 49					19 02				19 18						19 33			
Sydenham Hill d	18 35					18 51					19 04				19 20						19 35			
Penge East d	18 38					18 54					19 07				19 23						19 38			
Kent House 4 d	18 40					18 56					19 09				19 25						19 40			
Beckenham Junction 4 d	18 42					18 58					19 11				19 27						19 42			
Denmark Hill 4 d			18 32				18 57		18 52									19 27		19 25				
Peckham Rye 4 d			18 35				19 00		18 55									19 31		19 28				
Nunhead 4 d			18 37				19 02		18 57									19 33		19 30				
Lewisham 4 a							19 08											19 44						
Crofton Park d			18 39						18 59											19 32				
Catford d			18 42						19 01											19 34				
Bellingham d			18 44						19 04											19 37				
Beckenham Hill d			18 46						19 06											19 39				
Ravensbourne d			18 48						19 08											19 41				
Shortlands 4 d	18 45		18 50			19 02			19 10		19 15				19 31					19 43	19 46			
Bromley South 4 d	18 48	18a49	18 54		19 01	19 05		19 06	19 13		19 18		19a19	19 29	19 34				19 35	19 46	19 49		19a49	19 59
Bickley 4 d	18 51		18 56			19 07			19 16		19 21				19 37					19 48	19 52			
Petts Wood 4 d	18 56					19 12					19 25				19 41						19 56			
Orpington 4 d	19a01					19a15					19a31				19a44						19a59			
St Mary Cray d			19 03		19 10			19 12	19 21					19 35						19 54				20 05
Swanley 4 d			19 07		19a15			19 16	19 26					19a40					19 44	19 58				20a10
Eynsford d			19 12						19 30											20 03				
Shoreham (Kent) d			19 15						19 34											20 06				
Otford 4 d			19 18					19a26	19 37										19a53	20 10				
Bat & Ball d			19 21						19 40											20 13				
Sevenoaks 4 a			19 24						19 43											20 16				

	SE 70	FC	SE 78	SE 94 1	SE 83	SE 70	FC	SE 50 1	SE 92 1	SE 94 1	SE 83	FC	SE 70		FC	SE 50 1	SE 92 1	SE 94 1	SE 83	FC	SE 70	SE 50 1	SE 96 1	SE 83
London Victoria 15 ⊖ d	19 37		19 46	19 48		19 52		20 03	20 09	20 18			20 22			20 34	20 39	20 48			20 52	21 03	21 09	
Brixton ⊖ d	19 44					19 59							20 29								20 59			
St Pancras International 3 ⊖ d		19 35					19 48					20 05			20 17					20 35				
Farringdon ⊖ d		19 40					19 52					20 10			20 22					20 40				
City Thameslink 3 d		19 42					19 55					20 12			20 24					20 42				
London Blackfriars 3 ⊖ d		19 46			19 47		20 00				20 13	20 16			20 30				20 43	20 46				21 13
Elephant & Castle ⊖ d		19 49			19 50		20 03				20 16	20 19			20 33				20 46	20 49				21 16
Loughborough Jn d		19 53					20 07					20 23			20 37					20 53				
Herne Hill 4 d	19 46	19a57				20 01	20a11					20a27	20 31		20a41					20a57	21 01			
West Dulwich d	19 48					20 03							20 33								21 03			
Sydenham Hill d	19 50					20 05							20 35								21 05			
Penge East d	19 53					20 08							20 38								21 08			
Kent House 4 d	19 55					20 10							20 40								21 10			
Beckenham Junction 4 d	19 57					20 12				20 32			20 42					21 02			21 12			
Denmark Hill 4 d			19 57		19 55						20 22								20 52					21 22
Peckham Rye 4 d			20 01		19 58						20 25								20 55					21 25
Nunhead 4 d			20 03		20 00						20 27								20 57					21 27
Lewisham 4 a			20 14																					
Crofton Park d					20 02						20 29								20 59					21 29
Catford d					20 04						20 31								21 01					21 31
Bellingham d					20 07						20 34								21 04					21 34
Beckenham Hill d					20 09						20 36								21 06					21 36
Ravensbourne d					20 11						20 38								21 08					21 38
Shortlands 4 d	20 01				20 13	20 15					20 40		20 45						21 10		21 15			21 40
Bromley South 4 d	20 04			20 07	20 16	20 19		20a18	20 29	20 37	20 43		20 48			20a49	20 59	21 07	21 13		21 17	21a18	21 29	21 43
Bickley 4 d	20 07				20 18	20 22					20 46		20 51						21 16		21 20			21 46
Petts Wood 4 d	20 11					20 26							20 55								21 24			
Orpington 4 d	20a14					20a29							20a58								21a27			
St Mary Cray d					20 24				20 35		20 51						21 05		21 21				21 35	21 51
Swanley 4 d					20 28				20a40	20 45	20 56						21a10		21 26				21 40	21 56
Eynsford d					20 33						21 00								21 30					22 00
Shoreham (Kent) d					20 36						21 04								21 34					22 04
Otford 4 d				20a23	20 40					20a54	21 08							21a23	21 37				21a49	22 07
Bat & Ball d					20 43						21 11								21 40					22 10
Sevenoaks 4 a					20 46						21 15								21 43					22 13

For general notes see front of timetable
For details of catering facilities see Directory of Train Operators

For details of Bank Holiday service alterations please see first page of this table

London → Catford, Beckenham Junction, Bromley South, Orpington, Otford and Sevenoaks

Network Diagram - see first page of Table 195

		FC	SE 70	SE 37 1	SE 83	FC	SE 70	SE 50 1	SE 96 1	SE 83	FC	SE 70		SE 92 1	SE 73	FC	SE 70	SE 50 1	SE 66 1 A	SE 73	FC	SE 70	SE 22 1	SE 94 1 B	SE 73
London Victoria 15	⊖ d		21 22	21 39			21 52	22 03	22 09			22 22		22 39			22 52	23 03	23 11			23 22	23 39	23 51	
Brixton	⊖ d		21 29				21 59					22 29					22 59					23 29			
St Pancras International 3	⊖ d	21 05				21 35					22 05					22 36					23 06				
Farringdon	⊖ d	21 10				21 40					22 10					22 40					23 10				
City Thameslink 3	d	21 12				21 42					22 12					22 42									
London Blackfriars 3	⊖ d	21 16			21 43	21 46				22 13	22 16				22 43	22 46				23 13	23 16				23 43
Elephant & Castle	⊖ d	21 19			21 46	21 49				22 16	22 19				22 46	22 49				23 16	23 19				23 46
Loughborough Jn	d	21 23				21 53					22 23					22 53					23s23				
Herne Hill 4	d	21a27	21 31			21a57	22 01				22a27	22 31				22a57	23 01				23a27	23 31			
West Dulwich	d		21 33				22 03					22 33					23 03					23 33			
Sydenham Hill	d		21 35				22 05					22 35					23 05					23 35			
Penge East	d		21 38				22 08					22 38					23 08					23 38			
Kent House 4	d		21 40				22 10					22 40					23 10					23 40			
Beckenham Junction 4	🚋 d		21 42				22 12					22 42					23 12					23 42			
Denmark Hill 4	d				21 52					22 22					22 52					23 22					23 52
Peckham Rye 4	d				21 55					22 25					22 55					23 25					23 55
Nunhead 4	d				21 57					22 27					22 57					23 27					23 57
Lewisham 4	🚋 a																								
Crofton Park	d				21 59					22 29					22 59					23 29					23 59
Catford	d				22 01					22 31					23 01					23 31					00 01
Bellingham	d				22 04					22 34					23 04					23 34					00 04
Beckenham Hill	d				22 06					22 36					23 06					23 36					00 06
Ravensbourne	d				22 08					22 38					23 08					23 38					00 08
Shortlands 4	d		21 45		22 10		22 15			22 40		22 45			23 10		23 15			23 40		23 45			00 10
Bromley South 4	d		21 48	21 59	22 13		22 18	22a18	22 29	22 43		22 48		22 59	23 13		23 18	23a18	23 30	23 43		23 48	23 58	00 07	00 13
Bickley 4	d		21 51		22 15		22 21			22 46		22 51			23 16		23 21			23 46		23 51			00 16
Petts Wood 4	d		21 55				22 25					22 55			23 20		23 26			23 50		23 55			00 20
Orpington 4	d		21a58				22a28					22a58			23a24		23a30			23a54		23a58			00a24
St Mary Cray	d			22 05	22 21				22 35	22 51				23 05					23 37				00 04	00 14	
Swanley 4	d			22a10	22 25				22 40	22 56				23a10					23 41				00a09	00 18	
Eynsford	d				22 29					23 00														00 23	
Shoreham (Kent)	d				22 33					23 04														00 27	
Otford 4	d				22 36				22a49	23 07									23a50					00a30	
Bat & Ball	d				22 39					23 10															
Sevenoaks 4	a				22 42					23 13															

		SE 70
London Victoria 15	⊖ d	23 53
Brixton	⊖ d	23 59
St Pancras International 3	⊖ d	
Farringdon	⊖ d	
City Thameslink 3	d	
London Blackfriars 3	⊖ d	
Elephant & Castle	⊖ d	
Loughborough Jn	d	
Herne Hill 4	d	00 02
West Dulwich	d	00 04
Sydenham Hill	d	00 06
Penge East	d	00 09
Kent House 4	d	00 11
Beckenham Junction 4	🚋 d	00 13
Denmark Hill 4	d	
Peckham Rye 4	d	
Nunhead 4	d	
Lewisham 4	🚋 a	
Crofton Park	d	
Catford	d	
Bellingham	d	
Beckenham Hill	d	
Ravensbourne	d	
Shortlands 4	d	00 16
Bromley South 4	d	00 18
Bickley 4	d	00 21
Petts Wood 4	d	00 25
Orpington 4	d	00a28
St Mary Cray	d	
Swanley 4	d	
Eynsford	d	
Shoreham (Kent)	d	
Otford 4	d	
Bat & Ball	d	
Sevenoaks 4	a	

For general notes see front of timetable
For details of catering facilities see
Directory of Train Operators

A To Canterbury West (Table 207)
B To Ashford International (Table 196)

Table 195

London → Catford, Beckenham Junction, Bromley South, Orpington, Otford and Sevenoaks

Network Diagram - see first page of Table 195

		SE 22 [1]	SE 94 [1] A	SE 73	SE 70	SE 60	SE 4 [1]	SE 55 [1]	SE 70	FC	SE 94 [1] B	SE 82	SE 37 [1]	SE 83	FC	SE 70	SE 92	SE 64 [1] B	SE 83	FC	SE 70	FC	SE 50 [1]	SE 92 [1]	SE 94 [1]
London Victoria 15	⊖ d	23p39	23p51		23p53	00 35		05 39	05 51		06 18	06 13	06 39			06 51	07 09	07 18			07 21		07 33	07 39	07 48
Brixton	⊖ d				23p59				05 58							06 58					07 28				
St Pancras International 3	⊖ d														06 35					07 05					
Farringdon	⊖ d														06 40					07 10					
City Thameslink 3	d																								
London Blackfriars 3	⊖ d			23p43						06 16				06 43	06 46				07 13	07 16		07 30			
Elephant & Castle	⊖ d			23p46						06 19				06 46	06 49				07 16	07 19		07 33			
Loughborough Jn	d														06 53					07 23		07 37			
Herne Hill 4	d				00 02	00 43			06 00	06a26					06a57	07 00				07a27	07 30	07a41			
West Dulwich	d				00 04				06 03							07 03					07 33				
Sydenham Hill	d				00 06				06 05							07 05					07 35				
Penge East	d				00 09	00 48			06 08							07 08					07 38				
Kent House 4	d				00 11				06 09							07 09					07 39				
Beckenham Junction 4	d				00 13	00 51			06 11							07 11					07 41				
Denmark Hill 4	d			23p52								06 22		06 52					07 22						
Peckham Rye 4	d			23p55								06 25		06 55					07 25						
Nunhead 4	d			23p57								06 27		06 57					07 27						
Lewisham 4	a																								
Crofton Park	d			23p59								06 30		07 00					07 30						
Catford	d			00 01								06 32		07 02					07 32						
Bellingham	d			00 04								06 34		07 04					07 34						
Beckenham Hill	d			00 06								06 36		07 06					07 36						
Ravensbourne	d			00 08								06 38		07 08					07 38						
Shortlands 4	d			00 10	00 16				06 14			06 40		07 10		07 14			07 40		07 44				
Bromley South 4	d	23p58	00 07	00 13	00 18	00 55		05 59	06 17		06 34	06 43	06 59	07 13		07 17	07 29	07 34	07 43		07 47		07a48	07 59	08 04
Bickley 4	d			00 16	00 21				06 20			06 46		07 16		07 20			07 46		07 50				
Petts Wood 4	d			00 20	00 25				06 24							07 24					07 54				
Orpington 4	d			00a24	00a28		05 58		06a27							07a27					07a57				
St Mary Cray	d	00 04	00 14			01 02		06 05			06 41	06 52	07 05	07 22			07 35	07 41	07 52					08 05	
Swanley 4	d	00a09	00 18			01a06		06a10			06 45	06 56	07a10	07 26			07a40	07 45	07 56					08a10	08 13
Eynsford	d		00 23									07 01		07 31					08 01						
Shoreham (Kent)	d		00 27									07 04		07 34					08 04						
Otford 4	d		00a30								06a54	07 07		07 37				07a54	08 07						08a23
Bat & Ball	d											07 10		07 40					08 10						
Sevenoaks 4	a						06 07					07 13		07 43					08 13						

		SE 83	FC	SE 70	FC	SE 78	SE 50 [1]	SE 92 [1]	SE 70	SE 64 [1]	SE 83	FC	SE 70	FC	SE 78	SE 50 [1]	SE 92 [1]	SE 70	SE 94	SE 83	FC	SE 70	FC	SE 78	SE 50 [1]
London Victoria 15	⊖ d			07 51		08 01	08 03	08 09	08 06	08 18			08 21		08 31	08 33	08 39	08 36	08 48			08 51		09 01	09 03
Brixton	⊖ d			07 58					08 13				08 28					08 43				08 58			
St Pancras International 3	⊖ d		07 32		07 47							08 02		08 17							08 32		08 47		
Farringdon	⊖ d		07 37		07 52							08 07		08 22							08 37		08 52		
City Thameslink 3	d																								
London Blackfriars 3	⊖ d	07 43	07b46		08c00						08 13	08e16		08f30						08 43	08g46		09h00		
Elephant & Castle	⊖ d	07 46	07 49		08 03						08 16	08 19		08 33						08 46	08 49		09 03		
Loughborough Jn	d		07 53		08 07							08 23		08 37							08 53		09 07		
Herne Hill 4	d		07a57	08 00	08a11				08 15			08a27	08 30	08a41				08 45			08a57	09 00	09a11		
West Dulwich	d			08 03					08 18				08 33					08 48				09 03			
Sydenham Hill	d			08 05					08 20				08 35					08 50				09 05			
Penge East	d			08 08					08 23				08 38					08 53				09 08			
Kent House 4	d			08 09					08 24				08 39					08 54				09 09			
Beckenham Junction 4	d			08 11					08 26				08 41					08 56				09 11			
Denmark Hill 4	d	07 52				08 12					08 22				08 42					08 52				09 12	
Peckham Rye 4	d	07 55				08 14					08 25				08 44					08 55				09 14	
Nunhead 4	d	07 57				08 16					08 27				08 46					08 57				09 16	
Lewisham 4	a					08 22									08 52									09 22	
Crofton Park	d	08 00									08 30									09 00					
Catford	d	08 02									08 32									09 02					
Bellingham	d	08 04									08 34									09 04					
Beckenham Hill	d	08 06									08 36									09 06					
Ravensbourne	d	08 08									08 38									09 08					
Shortlands 4	d	08 10		08 14					08 29		08 40		08 44					08 59		09 10		09 14			
Bromley South 4	d	08 13		08 17			08a18	08 29	08 32	08 34	08 43		08 47			08a48	08 59	09 02	09 04	09 13		09 17			09a18
Bickley 4	d	08 16		08 20					08 35		08 46		08 50					09 05		09 16		09 20			
Petts Wood 4	d			08 24					08 39				08 54					09 09				09 24			
Orpington 4	d			08a27					08a42				08a57					09a12				09a27			
St Mary Cray	d	08 22						08 35			08 52						09 05			09 22					
Swanley 4	d	08 26						08a40			08 56						09a10		09 13	09 26					
Eynsford	d	08 31									09 01									09 31					
Shoreham (Kent)	d	08 34									09 04									09 34					
Otford 4	d	08 37								08a51	09 07								09a23	09 37					
Bat & Ball	d	08 40									09 10									09 40					
Sevenoaks 4	a	08 43									09 13									09 43					

For general notes see front of timetable
For details of catering facilities see Directory of Train Operators

- **A** To Ashford International (Table 196)
- **B** To Ramsgate (Table 207)
- **b** Arr. 0742
- **c** Arr. 0757
- **e** Arr. 0812
- **f** Arr. 0827
- **g** Arr. 0842
- **h** Arr. 0857

Saturdays

London → Catford, Beckenham Junction, Bromley South, Orpington, Otford and Sevenoaks

Network Diagram - see first page of Table 195

	SE	SE	SE		SE	FC	SE	FC	SE	SE		SE	SE	SE	SE	FC	SE	FC	SE	SE	SE	SE	SE	SE
	92	70	64		83		70		78	50		92	70	94	83		70		78	50	92	70	64	83
	1		1							1		1								1	1		1	
London Victoria 15 ⊖ d	09 09	09 06	09 18				09 21		09 31	09 33		09 39	09 36	09 48			09 51		10 01	10 03	10 09	10 06	10 18	
Brixton ⊖ d		09 13					09 28						09 43				09 58					10 13		
St Pancras International 3 ⊖ d						09 02		09 17								09 32		09 47						
Farringdon ⊖ d						09 07		09 22								09 37		09 52						
City Thameslink 3 d						09 09		09 24								09 39		09 54						
London Blackfriars 3 ⊖ d					09 13	09b16		09 30							09 43	09c46		10 00						10 13
Elephant & Castle ⊖ d					09 16	09 19		09 33							09 46	09 49		10 03						10 16
Loughborough Jn d						09 23		09 37								09 53		10 07						
Herne Hill 4 d		09 15				09a27	09 30	09a41					09 45			09a57	10 00	10a11				10 15		
West Dulwich d		09 18					09 33						09 48				10 03					10 18		
Sydenham Hill d		09 20					09 35						09 50				10 05					10 20		
Penge East d		09 23					09 38						09 53				10 08					10 23		
Kent House 4 d		09 24					09 39						09 54				10 09					10 24		
Beckenham Junction 4 d		09 26					09 41						09 56				10 11					10 26		
Denmark Hill 4 d					09 22				09 42						09 52				10 12					10 22
Peckham Rye 4 d					09 25				09 44						09 55				10 14					10 25
Nunhead 4 d					09 27				09 46						09 57				10 16					10 27
Lewisham 4 a									09 52										10 22					
Crofton Park d					09 30										10 00									10 30
Catford d					09 32										10 02									10 32
Bellingham d					09 34										10 04									10 34
Beckenham Hill d					09 36										10 06									10 36
Ravensbourne d					09 38										10 08									10 38
Shortlands 4 d		09 29			09 40		09 44						09 59		10 10		10 14					10 29		10 40
Bromley South 4 d	09 29	09 32	09 34		09 43		09 47			09a48		09 59	10 02	10 04	10 13		10 17			10a18	10 29	10 32	10 34	10 43
Bickley 4 d		09 35			09 46		09 50						10 05		10 16		10 20					10 35		10 46
Petts Wood 4 d		09 39					09 54						10 09				10 24					10 39		
Orpington 4 d		09a42					09a57						10a12				10a27					10a42		
St Mary Cray d	09 35				09 52							10 05			10 22						10 35			10 52
Swanley 4 d	09a40				09 56							10a10		10 13	10 26						10a40			10 56
Eynsford d					10 01										10 31									11 01
Shoreham (Kent) d					10 04										10 34									11 04
Otford 4 d			09a51		10 07									10a23	10 37								10a51	11 07
Bat & Ball d					10 10										10 40									11 10
Sevenoaks 4 a					10 13										10 43									11 13

	FC	SE	FC	SE	SE		SE	SE	SE	SE	FC	SE	FC	SE	SE	SE	SE	SE	SE	FC	SE	FC	SE
		70		78	50		92	70	94	83		70		78	50	92	70	94	83		70		78
					1		1								1	1		1					
London Victoria 15 ⊖ d		10 21		10 31	10 33	and at the same minutes past each hour until	15 39	15 36	15 48			15 51		16 01	16 03	16 09	16 06	16 18			16 21		16 31
Brixton ⊖ d		10 28						15 43				15 58					16 13				16 28		
St Pancras International 3 ⊖ d	10 02		10 17								15 32		15 47							16 02		16 17	
Farringdon ⊖ d	10 07		10 22								15 37		15 52							16 07		16 22	
City Thameslink 3 d	10 09		10 24								15 39		15 54							16 09		16 24	
London Blackfriars 3 ⊖ d	10e16		10 30							15 43	15f46		16 00						16 13	16g16		16 30	
Elephant & Castle ⊖ d	10 19		10 33							15 46	15 49		16 03						16 16	16 19		16 33	
Loughborough Jn d	10 23		10 37								15 53		16 07							16 23		16 37	
Herne Hill 4 d	10a27	10 30	10a41					15 45			15a57	16 00	16a11				16 15			16a27	16 30	16a41	
West Dulwich d		10 33						15 48				16 03					16 18				16 33		
Sydenham Hill d		10 35						15 50				16 05					16 20				16 35		
Penge East d		10 38						15 53				16 08					16 23				16 38		
Kent House 4 d		10 39						15 54				16 09					16 24				16 39		
Beckenham Junction 4 d		10 41						15 56				16 11					16 26				16 41		
Denmark Hill 4 d				10 42						15 52				16 12					16 22				16 42
Peckham Rye 4 d				10 44						15 55				16 14					16 25				16 44
Nunhead 4 d				10 46						15 57				16 16					16 27				16 46
Lewisham 4 a				10 52										16 22									16 52
Crofton Park d										16 00									16 30				
Catford d										16 02									16 32				
Bellingham d										16 04									16 34				
Beckenham Hill d										16 06									16 36				
Ravensbourne d										16 08									16 38				
Shortlands 4 d		10 44						15 59		16 10		16 14					16 29		16 40		16 44		
Bromley South 4 d		10 47			10a48		15 59	16 02	16 04	16 13		16 17			16a18	16 29	16 32	16 34	16 43		16 47		
Bickley 4 d		10 50						16 05		16 16		16 20					16 35		16 46		16 50		
Petts Wood 4 d		10 54						16 09				16 24					16 39				16 54		
Orpington 4 d		10a57						16a12				16a27					16a42				16a57		
St Mary Cray d							16 05			16 22						16 35			16 52				
Swanley 4 d							16a10		16 13	16 26						16a40			16 56				
Eynsford d										16 31									17 01				
Shoreham (Kent) d										16 34									17 04				
Otford 4 d									16a23	16 37								16a51	17 07				
Bat & Ball d										16 40									17 10				
Sevenoaks 4 a										16 43									17 13				

For general notes see front of timetable
For details of catering facilities see Directory of Train Operators

b Arr. 0913
c Arr. 0943
e Arr. 1013
f Arr. 1543
g Arr. 1613

Table 195

Saturdays

London → Catford, Beckenham Junction, Bromley South, Orpington, Otford and Sevenoaks

Network Diagram - see first page of Table 195

		SE 50 1	SE 92 1	SE 70	SE 94	SE 83	FC	SE 70	FC	SE 78	SE 50 1		SE 92 1	SE 70	SE 94 1	SE 83	FC	SE 70	FC	SE 78	SE 50 1	SE 92 1	SE 70	SE 94	SE 83
London Victoria 15	⊖ d	16 33	16 39	16 36	16 48			16 51		17 01	17 03		17 09	17 06	17 18			17 21		17 31	17 33	17 39	17 36	17 48	
Brixton	⊖ d			16 43				16 58						17 13				17 28					17 43		
St Pancras International 3	⊖ d						16 32		16 47								17 02		17 17						
Farringdon	⊖ d						16 37		16 52								17 07		17 22						
City Thameslink 3	d						16 39		16 54								17 09		17 24						
London Blackfriars 3	⊖ d					16 43	16b46		17 00							17 13	17c16		17 30						17 43
Elephant & Castle	⊖ d					16 46	16 49		17 03							17 16	17 19		17 33						17 46
Loughborough Jn	d						16 53		17 07								17 23		17 37						
Herne Hill 4	d			16 45			16a57	17 00	17a11					17 15			17a27	17 30	17a41				17 45		
West Dulwich	d			16 48				17 03						17 18				17 33					17 48		
Sydenham Hill	d			16 50				17 05						17 20				17 35					17 50		
Penge East	d			16 53				17 08						17 23				17 38					17 53		
Kent House 4	d			16 54				17 09						17 24				17 39					17 54		
Beckenham Junction 4	d			16 56				17 11						17 26				17 41					17 56		
Denmark Hill 4	d					16 52				17 12						17 22				17 42					17 52
Peckham Rye 4	d					16 55				17 14						17 25				17 44					17 55
Nunhead 4	d					16 57				17 16						17 27				17 46					17 57
Lewisham 4	a									17 22										17 52					
Crofton Park	d					17 00										17 30									18 00
Catford	d					17 02										17 32									18 02
Bellingham	d					17 04										17 34									18 04
Beckenham Hill	d					17 06										17 36									18 06
Ravensbourne	d					17 08										17 38									18 08
Shortlands 4	d			16 59		17 10		17 14						17 29		17 40		17 44					17 59		18 10
Bromley South 4	d	16a48	16 59	17 02	17 04	17 13		17 17			17a18		17 29	17 32	17 34	17 43		17 47			17a48	17 59	18 02	18 04	18 13
Bickley 4	d			17 05		17 16		17 20						17 35		17 46		17 50					18 05		18 16
Petts Wood 4	d			17 09				17 24						17 39				17 54					18 09		
Orpington 4	d			17a12				17a27						17a42				17a57					18a12		
St Mary Cray	d		17 05			17 22							17 35			17 52						18 05			18 22
Swanley 4	d		17a10		17 13	17 26							17a40			17 56						18a10		18 13	18 26
Eynsford	d					17 31										18 01									18 31
Shoreham (Kent)	d					17 34										18 04									18 34
Otford 4	d				17a23	17 37									17a51	18 07								18a23	18 37
Bat & Ball	d					17 40										18 10									18 40
Sevenoaks 4	a					17 43										18 13									18 43

		FC	SE 70	FC	SE 78	SE 50 1	SE 92 1	SE 70	SE 94 1	SE 83	FC	SE 70	FC	SE 78	SE 50 1	SE 92 1	SE 70	SE 94 1	SE 83	FC	SE 70	FC	SE 78	SE 50 1	SE 70
London Victoria 15	⊖ d		17 51		18 01	18 03	18 09	18 06	18 18			18 21		18 31	18 33	18 39	18 36	18 48			18 51		19 01	19 03	19 06
Brixton	⊖ d		17 58					18 13				18 28					18 43				18 58				19 13
St Pancras International 3	⊖ d	17 32		17 47							18 02		18 17							18 32		18 47			
Farringdon	⊖ d	17 37		17 52							18 07		18 22							18 37		18 52			
City Thameslink 3	d	17 39		17 54							18 09		18 24							18 39		18 54			
London Blackfriars 3	⊖ d	17e46		18 00						18 13	18f16		18 30						18 43	18g46		19 00			
Elephant & Castle	⊖ d	17 49		18 03						18 16	18 19		18 33						18 46	18 49		19 03			
Loughborough Jn	d	17 53		18 07							18 23		18 37							18 53		19 07			
Herne Hill 4	d	17a57	18 00	18a11				18 15			18a27	18 30	18a41				18 45			18a57	19 00	19a11			19 15
West Dulwich	d		18 03					18 18				18 33					18 48				19 03				19 18
Sydenham Hill	d		18 05					18 20				18 35					18 50				19 05				19 20
Penge East	d		18 08					18 23				18 38					18 53				19 08				19 23
Kent House 4	d		18 09					18 24				18 39					18 54				19 09				19 24
Beckenham Junction 4	d		18 11					18 26				18 41					18 56				19 11				19 26
Denmark Hill 4	d				18 12					18 22				18 42					18 52				19 12		
Peckham Rye 4	d				18 14					18 25				18 44					18 55				19 14		
Nunhead 4	d				18 16					18 27				18 46					18 57				19 16		
Lewisham 4	a				18 22									18 51									19 22		
Crofton Park	d									18 30									19 00						
Catford	d									18 32									19 02						
Bellingham	d									18 34									19 04						
Beckenham Hill	d									18 36									19 06						
Ravensbourne	d									18 38									19 08						
Shortlands 4	d		18 14					18 29		18 40		18 44					18 59		19 10		19 14				19 29
Bromley South 4	d		18 17			18a18	18 29	18 32	18 34	18 43		18 47			18a48	18 59	19 02	19 04	19 13		19 17			19a18	19 32
Bickley 4	d		18 20					18 35		18 46		18 50					19 05		19 16		19 20				19 35
Petts Wood 4	d		18 24					18 39				18 54					19 09				19 24				19 39
Orpington 4	d		18a27					18a42				18a57					19a12				19a27				19a42
St Mary Cray	d						18 35			18 52						19 05			19 22						
Swanley 4	d						18a40			18 56						19a10		19 13	19 26						
Eynsford	d									19 01									19 31						
Shoreham (Kent)	d									19 04									19 34						
Otford 4	d								18a51	19 07								19a23	19 37						
Bat & Ball	d									19 10									19 40						
Sevenoaks 4	a									19 13									19 43						

For general notes see front of timetable
For details of catering facilities see Directory of Train Operators

b Arr. 1643
c Arr. 1713
e Arr. 1743
f Arr. 1813
g Arr. 1843

Table 195

Saturdays

London → Catford, Beckenham Junction, Bromley South, Orpington, Otford and Sevenoaks

Network Diagram - see first page of Table 195

		SE 96 [1]	SE 83	FC	SE 70	SE 78	SE 92 [1]	SE 70	SE 83	FC	SE 70	SE 50 [1]	SE 96 [1]	SE 83	FC	SE 70	SE 92 [1]	SE 83	FC	SE 70	SE 50 [1]	SE 96 [1]	SE 83	FC	SE 70
London Victoria [15]	⊖ d	19 18			19 21	19 31	19 39	19 36			19 51	20 03	20 18			20 21	20 39			20 51	21 03	21 18			21 21
Brixton	⊖ d				19 28			19 43			19 58					20 28				20 58					21 28
St Pancras International [3]	⊖ d			19 05						19 35					20 05				20 35					21 05	
Farringdon	⊖ d			19 10						19 40					20 10				20 40					21 10	
City Thameslink [3]	d			19 12						19 42					20 12				20 42						
London Blackfriars [3]	⊖ d		19 13	19 16					19 43	19 46				20 13	20 16			20 43	20 46				21 13	21 16	
Elephant & Castle	⊖ d		19 16	19 19					19 46	19 49				20 16	20 19			20 46	20 49				21 16	21 19	
Loughborough Jn	d			19 23						19 53					20 23				20 53					21 23	
Herne Hill [4]	d			19a27	19 30			19 45		19a57	20 00				20a27	20 30			20a57	21 00				21a27	21 30
West Dulwich	d				19 33			19 48			20 03					20 33				21 03					21 33
Sydenham Hill	d				19 35			19 50			20 05					20 35				21 05					21 35
Penge East	d				19 38			19 53			20 08					20 38				21 08					21 38
Kent House [4]	d				19 39			19 54			20 09					20 39				21 09					21 39
Beckenham Junction [4]	🚊 d				19 41			19 56			20 11					20 41				21 11					21 41
Denmark Hill [4]	d		19 22			19 42			19 52					20 22				20 52					21 22		
Peckham Rye [4]	d		19 25			19 44			19 55					20 25				20 55					21 25		
Nunhead [4]	d		19 27			19 46			19 57					20 27				20 57					21 27		
Lewisham [4]	🚊 a					19 53																			
Crofton Park	d		19 30						20 00					20 30				21 00					21 30		
Catford	d		19 32						20 02					20 32				21 02					21 32		
Bellingham	d		19 34						20 04					20 34				21 04					21 34		
Beckenham Hill	d		19 36						20 06					20 36				21 06					21 36		
Ravensbourne	d		19 38						20 08					20 38				21 08					21 38		
Shortlands [4]	d		19 40		19 44			19 59	20 10		20 14			20 40		20 44		21 10		21 14			21 40		21 44
Bromley South [4]	d	19 34	19 43		19 47		19 59	20 02	20 13		20 17	20a18	20 34	20 43		20 47	20 59	21 13		21 17	21a18	21 34	21 43		21 47
Bickley [4]	d		19 46		19 50			20 05	20 16		20 20			20 46		20 50		21 16		21 20			21 46		21 50
Petts Wood [4]	d				19 54			20 09			20 24					20 54				21 24					21 54
Orpington [4]	d				19a57			20a12			20a27					20a57				21a27					21a57
St Mary Cray	d	19 41	19 52				20 05		20 22				20 41	20 52			21 05	21 22				21 41	21 52		
Swanley [4]	d	19 45	19 56				20a10		20 26				20 45	20 56			21a10	21 26				21 45	21 56		
Eynsford	d		20 01						20 31					21 01				21 31					22 01		
Shoreham (Kent)	d		20 04						20 34					21 04				21 34					22 04		
Otford [4]	d	19a54	20 07						20 37				20a54	21 07				21 37				21a54	22 07		
Bat & Ball	d		20 10						20 40					21 10				21 40					22 10		
Sevenoaks [4]	a		20 13						20 43					21 13				21 43					22 13		

		SE 92 [1]	SE 83	FC [1]	SE 70	SE 50 [1]	SE 96 [1]	SE 83	FC	SE 70	SE 75 [1]	SE 73	FC	SE 70	SE 50 [1]	SE 66 [1] A	SE 73	FC	SE 70	SE 22 [1]	SE 94 [1] B	SE 73	SE 70
London Victoria [15]	⊖ d	21 39			21 51	22 03	22 18			22 21	22 39			22 51	23 03	23 18			23 21	23 39	23 51		23 53
Brixton	⊖ d				21 58					22 28				22 58					23 28				23 59
St Pancras International [3]	⊖ d			21 35					22 05				22 36					23 06					
Farringdon	⊖ d			21 40					22 10				22 40					23 10					
City Thameslink [3]	d																						
London Blackfriars [3]	⊖ d		21 43	21 46				22 13	22 16			22 43	22 46				23 13	23 16				23 43	
Elephant & Castle	⊖ d		21 46	21 49				22 16	22 19			22 46	22 49				23 16	23 19				23 46	
Loughborough Jn	d			21 53					22 23				22 53					23s23					
Herne Hill [4]	d			21a57	22 00				22a27	22 30			22a57	23 00				23a27	23 30				00 02
West Dulwich	d				22 03					22 33				23 03					23 33				00 04
Sydenham Hill	d				22 05					22 35				23 05					23 35				00 06
Penge East	d				22 08					22 38				23 08					23 38				00 09
Kent House [4]	d				22 09					22 39				23 09					23 39				00 11
Beckenham Junction [4]	🚊 d				22 11					22 41				23 11					23 41				00 13
Denmark Hill [4]	d		21 52					22 22				22 52					23 22					23 52	
Peckham Rye [4]	d		21 55					22 25				22 55					23 25					23 55	
Nunhead [4]	d		21 57					22 27				22 57					23 27					23 57	
Lewisham [4]	🚊 a																						
Crofton Park	d		22 00					22 30				23 00					23 30					23 59	
Catford	d		22 02					22 32				23 02					23 32					00 01	
Bellingham	d		22 04					22 34				23 04					23 34					00 04	
Beckenham Hill	d		22 06					22 36				23 06					23 36					00 06	
Ravensbourne	d		22 08					22 38				23 08					23 38					00 08	
Shortlands [4]	d		22 10		22 14			22 40		22 44		23 10		23 14			23 40		23 44			00 10	00 16
Bromley South [4]	d	21 59	22 13		22 17	22a18	22 34	22 43		22 47	22 59	23 13		23 17	23a18	23 34	23 43		23 47	23 59	00 07	00 13	00 19
Bickley [4]	d		22 16		22 20			22 46		22 50		23 16		23 20			23 46		23 50			00 15	00 21
Petts Wood [4]	d				22 24					22 54		23 20		23 24			23 50		23 54			00 20	00 26
Orpington [4]	d				22a27					22a57		23a23		23a27			23a53		23a57			00a23	00a29
St Mary Cray	d	22 05	22 22				22 41	22 52			23 05					23 41				00 05	00 14		
Swanley [4]	d	22a10	22 26				22 45	22 56			23a10					23 45				00a10	00 18		
Eynsford	d		22 31					23 01													00 23		
Shoreham (Kent)	d		22 34					23 04													00 27		
Otford [4]	d		22 37				22a54	23 07								23a54					00a30		
Bat & Ball	d		22 40					23 10															
Sevenoaks [4]	a		22 43					23 13															

For general notes see front of timetable
For details of catering facilities see Directory of Train Operators

A To Canterbury West (Table 207)
B To Ashford International (Table 196)

London → Catford, Beckenham Junction, Bromley South, Orpington, Otford and Sevenoaks

Network Diagram - see first page of Table 195

		SE	SE	SE	SE	SE	SE	SE	SE	SE	SE	SE	SE	SE	SE	SE	FC	SE	SE	SE	FC
		22	94	73	70	60	54	70	50	72	94	70	54	70	50	72		94	70	72	
		1	1				1		1		1		1		1			1			
			A																		
London Victoria 15	⊖ d	23p39	23p51		23p53	00 35	07 41	07 52	08 03	07 56	08 18	08 22	08 41	08 52	09 03	08 56		09 18	09 22	09 26	
Brixton	⊖ d				23p59			07 59				08 29		08 59					09 29		
St Pancras International 3	⊖ d																09 06				09 36
Farringdon	⊖ d																09 10				09 40
City Thameslink 3	d																				
London Blackfriars 3	⊖ d			23p43													09 16				09 46
Elephant & Castle	⊖ d			23p46													09 19				09 49
Loughborough Jn	d																09 23				09 53
Herne Hill 4	d				00 02	00 43		08 01				08 31		09 01			09a27		09 31		09a57
West Dulwich	d				00 04			08 03				08 33		09 03					09 33		
Sydenham Hill	d				00 06			08 05				08 35		09 05					09 35		
Penge East	d				00 09	00 48		08 08				08 38		09 08					09 38		
Kent House 4	d				00 11			08 10				08 40		09 10					09 40		
Beckenham Junction 4	d				00 13	00 51		08 12				08 42		09 12					09 42		
Denmark Hill 4	d			23p52						08 05						09 05				09 35	
Peckham Rye 4	d			23p55						08 07						09 07				09 37	
Nunhead 4	d			23p57						08 09						09 09				09 39	
Lewisham 4	a																				
Crofton Park	d			23p59						08 12						09 12				09 42	
Catford	d			00 01						08 14						09 14				09 44	
Bellingham	d			00 04						08 16						09 16				09 46	
Beckenham Hill	d			00 06						08 18						09 18				09 48	
Ravensbourne	d			00 08						08 20						09 20				09 50	
Shortlands 4	d			00 10	00 16			08 15		08 25		08 45		09 15		09 22			09 45	09 52	
Bromley South 4	d	23p59	00 07	00 13	00 19	00 55	08 01	08 18	08a18	08 27	08 34	08 48	09 01	09 18	09a18	09 25		09 34	09 48	09 55	
Bickley 4	d			00 15	00 21			08 21		08 30		08 51		09 21		09 27			09 51	09 57	
Petts Wood 4	d			00 20	00 26			08 26				08 56		09 26					09 56		
Orpington 4	d			00a23	00a29			08a29				08a59		09a29					09a59		
St Mary Cray	d	00 05	00 14			01 01	08 07			08 35	08 41		09 07			09 33		09 41		10 03	
Swanley 4	d	00a10	00 18			01a05	08a12			08 39	08 45		09a12			09 37		09 45		10 07	
Eynsford	d		00 23							08 44						09 41				10 11	
Shoreham (Kent)	d		00 27							08 47						09 45				10 15	
Otford 4	d		00a30							08 50	08a55					09 48		09a55		10 18	
Bat & Ball	d									08 53						09 51				10 21	
Sevenoaks 4	a									08 56						09 54				10 24	

		SE	SE	SE		SE	FC	SE	SE	SE	FC	SE	SE	SE	SE	FC	SE	SE	SE	FC
		54	70	50		72		94	70	72		54	70	50	72		94	70	72	
		1		1				1				1		1			1			
London Victoria 15	⊖ d	09 41	09 52	10 03		16 56		17 18	17 22	17 26		17 41	17 52	18 03	17 56		18 18	18 22	18 26	
Brixton	⊖ d		09 59						17 29				17 59					18 29		
St Pancras International 3	⊖ d						17 06				17 36					18 06				18 36
Farringdon	⊖ d						17 10				17 40					18 10				18 40
City Thameslink 3	d																			
London Blackfriars 3	⊖ d						17 16				17 46					18 16				18 46
Elephant & Castle	⊖ d						17 19				17 49					18 19				18 49
Loughborough Jn	d						17 23				17 53					18 23				18 53
Herne Hill 4	d		10 01				17a27		17 31		17a57		18 01			18a27		18 31		18a57
West Dulwich	d		10 03						17 33				18 03					18 33		
Sydenham Hill	d		10 05		and at				17 35				18 05					18 35		
Penge East	d		10 08						17 38				18 08					18 38		
Kent House 4	d		10 10		the same				17 40				18 10					18 40		
Beckenham Junction 4	d		10 12		minutes				17 42				18 12					18 42		
Denmark Hill 4	d					17 05				17 35					18 05				18 35	
Peckham Rye 4	d				past	17 07				17 37					18 07				18 37	
Nunhead 4	d					17 09				17 39					18 09				18 39	
Lewisham 4	a				each															
Crofton Park	d				hour until	17 12				17 42					18 12				18 42	
Catford	d					17 14				17 44					18 14				18 44	
Bellingham	d					17 16				17 46					18 16				18 46	
Beckenham Hill	d					17 18				17 48					18 18				18 48	
Ravensbourne	d					17 20				17 50					18 20				18 50	
Shortlands 4	d		10 15			17 22			17 45	17 52			18 15		18 22			18 45	18 52	
Bromley South 4	d	10 01	10 18	10a18		17 25		17 34	17 48	17 55		18 01	18 18	18a18	18 25		18 34	18 48	18 55	
Bickley 4	d		10 21			17 27			17 51	17 57			18 21		18 27			18 51	18 57	
Petts Wood 4	d		10 26						17 56	18 01			18 26					18 56	19 01	
Orpington 4	d		10a29						17a59	18a05			18a29					18a59	19a05	
St Mary Cray	d	10 07				17 33		17 41				18 07			18 33		18 41			
Swanley 4	d	10a12				17 37		17 45				18a12			18 37		18 45			
Eynsford	d					17 41									18 41					
Shoreham (Kent)	d					17 45									18 45					
Otford 4	d					17 48		17a55							18 48		18a55			
Bat & Ball	d					17 51									18 51					
Sevenoaks 4	a					17 54									18 54					

For general notes see front of timetable
For details of catering facilities see
Directory of Train Operators

A To Ashford International (Table 196)

Table 195

Sundays

London → Catford, Beckenham Junction, Bromley South, Orpington, Otford and Sevenoaks

Network Diagram - see first page of Table 195

		SE 54 1	SE 70	SE 50 1		SE 72	FC	SE 94 1	SE 70		FC	SE 54 1	SE 70	SE 50 1		SE 72	FC	SE 94 1	SE 70		FC	SE 54 1	SE 70	SE 50 1	SE 72
London Victoria 15	⊖ d	18 41	18 52	19 03		18 56		19 18	19 22			19 41	19 52	20 03		19 56		20 18	20 22			20 41	20 52	21 03	20 56
Brixton	⊖ d		18 59						19 29				19 59						20 29				20 59		
St Pancras International 3	⊖ d						19 06				19 36						20 06				20 36				
Farringdon	⊖ d						19 10				19 40						20 10				20 40				
City Thameslink 3	d																								
London Blackfriars 3	⊖ d						19 16				19 46						20 16				20 46				
Elephant & Castle	⊖ d						19 19				19 49						20 19				20 49				
Loughborough Jn	d						19 23				19 53						20 23				20 53				
Herne Hill 4	d		19 01				19a27		19 31		19a57		20 01				20a27		20 31		20a57		21 01		
West Dulwich	d		19 03						19 33				20 03						20 33				21 03		
Sydenham Hill	d		19 05						19 35				20 05						20 35				21 05		
Penge East	d		19 08						19 38				20 08						20 38				21 08		
Kent House 4	d		19 10						19 40				20 10						20 40				21 10		
Beckenham Junction 4	d		19 12						19 42				20 12						20 42				21 12		
Denmark Hill 4	d					19 05										20 05									21 05
Peckham Rye 4	d					19 07										20 07									21 07
Nunhead 4	d					19 09										20 09									21 09
Lewisham 4	a																								
Crofton Park	d					19 12										20 12									21 12
Catford	d					19 14										20 14									21 14
Bellingham	d					19 16										20 16									21 16
Beckenham Hill	d					19 18										20 18									21 18
Ravensbourne	d					19 20										20 20									21 20
Shortlands 4	d		19 15			19 22			19 45				20 15			20 22			20 45				21 15		21 22
Bromley South 4	d	19 01	19 18	19a18		19 25		19 34	19 48			20 01	20 18	20a18		20 25		20 34	20 48			21 01	21 18	21a18	21 25
Bickley 4	d		19 21			19 27			19 51				20 21			20 27			20 51				21 21		21 27
Petts Wood 4	d		19 26						19 56				20 26						20 56				21 26		
Orpington 4	d		19a29						19a59				20a29						20a59				21a29		
St Mary Cray	d	19 07				19 33		19 41				20 07				20 33		20 41				21 07			21 33
Swanley 4	d	19a12				19 37		19 45				20a12				20 37		20 45				21a12			21 37
Eynsford	d					19 41										20 41									21 41
Shoreham (Kent)	d					19 45										20 45									21 45
Otford 4	d					19 48		19a55								20 48		20a55							21 48
Bat & Ball	d					19 51										20 51									21 51
Sevenoaks 4	a					19 54										20 54									21 54

		SE 94 1		SE 70	SE 54 1	SE 70	SE 50 1		SE 72	SE 94 1	SE 70	SE 54 1		SE 70	SE 50 1	SE 72	SE 70		SE 54 1
London Victoria 15	⊖ d	21 18		21 22	21 41	21 52	22 03		21 56	22 18	22 22	22 41		22 52	23 03	22 56	23 22		23 41
Brixton	⊖ d			21 29		21 59					22 29			22 59			23 29		
St Pancras International 3	⊖ d																		
Farringdon	⊖ d																		
City Thameslink 3	d																		
London Blackfriars 3	⊖ d																		
Elephant & Castle	⊖ d																		
Loughborough Jn	d																		
Herne Hill 4	d			21 31		22 01					22 31			23 01			23 31		
West Dulwich	d			21 34		22 03					22 34			23 03			23 33		
Sydenham Hill	d			21 36		22 05					22 36			23 05			23 35		
Penge East	d			21 39		22 08					22 39			23 08			23 38		
Kent House 4	d			21 40		22 10					22 40			23 10			23 40		
Beckenham Junction 4	d			21 42		22 12					22 42			23 12			23 42		
Denmark Hill 4	d								22 05							23 05			
Peckham Rye 4	d								22 07							23 07			
Nunhead 4	d								22 09							23 09			
Lewisham 4	a																		
Crofton Park	d								22 12							23 12			
Catford	d								22 14							23 14			
Bellingham	d								22 16							23 16			
Beckenham Hill	d								22 18							23 18			
Ravensbourne	d								22 20							23 20			
Shortlands 4	d			21 45		22 15			22 22		22 45			23 15		23 22	23 45		
Bromley South 4	d	21 34		21 48	22 01	22 18	22a18		22 25	22 35	22 48	23 01		23 18	23a18	23 25	23 48		00 01
Bickley 4	d			21 51		22 21			22 27		22 51			23 21		23 27	23 51		
Petts Wood 4	d			21 56		22 26					22 56			23 26		23 31	23 56		
Orpington 4	d			21a59		22a29					22a59			23a29		23a35	23a59		
St Mary Cray	d	21 41			22 07				22 33	22 41		23 07							00 07
Swanley 4	d	21 45			22a12				22 37	22 46		23a12							00a12
Eynsford	d								22 41										
Shoreham (Kent)	d								22 45										
Otford 4	d	21a55							22 48	22a55									
Bat & Ball	d								22 51										
Sevenoaks 4	a								22 54										

For general notes see front of timetable
For details of catering facilities see Directory of Train Operators

For details of Bank Holiday service alterations please see first page of this table

Sevenoaks, Otford, Orpington, Bromley South, Beckenham Junction and Catford → London

Network Diagram - see first page of Table 195

Miles	Miles	Miles			SE	SE	SE	SE	FC	SE	FC	SE	SE	SE	FC	SE	SE	FC	SE	SE	SE	FC	SE	SE	FC
					73	60	71	70		73		70	50	83		70	37		83	94	50		70	97	
						1							1				1			1	1			1	
									A		A											A			
—	0	—	**Sevenoaks** 4	d										05 40					06 13						
—	1¼	—	Bat & Ball	d										05 43					06 16						
—	3	—	Otford 4	d										05 46					06 19	06 28				06 38	
—	4¼	—	Shoreham (Kent)	d										05 49					06 22						
—	6½	—	Eynsford	d										05 52					06 25						
—	9½	—	**Swanley** 4	d		04 33								05 57			06 30		06 31		06 41			06 49	
—	12¼	—	St Mary Cray	d		04 37								06 01			06 35		06 35		06 46				
0	—	—	**Orpington** 4	d	04 36		04 58	05 25		05 36		05 50				06 20							06 44		
1¼	—	—	Petts Wood 4	d	04 39		05 01	05 28		05 39		05 53				06 23							06 47		
3	14½	—	Bickley 4	d	04 43	04 43	05 05	05 32		05 43		05 57		06 06		06 27			06 41				06 51		
4	15½	—	**Bromley South** 4	d	04 46	04b51	05 08	05 36		05 46		06 01	06 14	06c15		06 31	06 42		06 44	06 48	06 52		06 54	06 58	
5	16½	—	Shortlands 4	d	04 48	04 53	05 10	05 38		05 48		06 03		06 17		06 33			06 46				06 56		
—	17¼	—	Ravensbourne	d	04 51					05 51				06 20					06 49						
—	18	—	Beckenham Hill	d	04 53					05 53				06 22					06 51						
—	18¾	—	Bellingham	d	04 55					05 55				06 24					06 53						
—	19½	—	Catford	d	04 57					05 57				06 26					06 55						
—	20½	—	Crofton Park	d	04 59					06 00				06 28					06 58						
—	—	0	Lewisham 4 🚋	d																					
—	21¾	1¾	Nunhead 4	d	05 02					06 02				06 31					07 00						
—	22½	2½	Peckham Rye 4	d	05 04					06 04				06 33					07 02						
—	23¼	3¼	Denmark Hill 4	d	05 06					06 07				06 35					07 05						
6¼	—	—	**Beckenham Junction** 4 🚋	d		04 56	05 13	05 40				06 06				06 36							06 58		
7¼	—	—	Kent House 4	d		04 58	05 15	05 42				06 08				06 38							07 00		
7¾	—	—	Penge East	d		05 00	05 17	05 44				06 10				06 40							07 02		
9¼	—	—	Sydenham Hill	d		05 03	05 20	05 47				06 13				06 43							07 05		
10	—	—	West Dulwich	d		05 05	05 22	05 49				06 15				06 45							07 07		
11	—	—	Herne Hill 4	d		05 07	05 25	05 52	05 54		06 14	06 18			06 44	06 48		06 59		06 58		07 04	07 10		07 24
—	—	—	Loughborough Jn	d							06 17				06 47			07 02				07 07			07 27
—	25¾	—	Elephant & Castle	⊖ d	05 12		05 30		06 02	06 13	06 22			06 41	06 52			07 07	07 11			07 12		07 15	07 32
—	27	—	**London Blackfriars** 3	⊖ d	05a16		05a34		06e08	06a18	06 28			06a45	06 58			07 12	07a15			07 18		07a18	07 38
—	—	—	City Thameslink 3	a					06 10		06 30				07 00			07 14				07 20			07 40
—	—	—	Farringdon	⊖ a					06 14		06 34				07 04			07 16				07 24			07 44
—	—	—	St Pancras International 3	⊖ a					06 18		06 38				07 08			07 21				07 28			07 48
11¾	—	—	Brixton	⊖ d		05 09		05 54				06 20				06 50							07 12		
15	—	7½	**London Victoria** 15	⊖ a		05 16		06 01				06 27	06 30			06 57	07 00			07 08	07 12		07 20		

		SE	SE		SE	SE	SE	SE	SE	SE	SE	SE	SE	SE	FC	SE	SE	SE	SE	SE	SE	SE	SE	SE	SE
		71	70		83	94	31	71	22	83	18	70	97	71		83	50	22	3	96	4	78	73	70	83
						1	1						1				1			1					
							B													C					
Sevenoaks 4	d				06 43					07 07															07 34
Bat & Ball	d				06 46					07 10															07 37
Otford 4	d				06 49	07 09				07 13			07 19							07 32					07 40
Shoreham (Kent)	d				06 52					07 16															07 43
Eynsford	d				06 55					07 20															07 46
Swanley 4	d				07 01	07 18			07 22	07 26			07 30			←		07 40		07 44					07 52
St Mary Cray	d				07 06	07 23			07 27	07 31						07 31		07 45							07 57
Orpington 4	d	07 02	07 06					07 23		→		07 27											07 44	07 50	
Petts Wood 4	d	07 05	07 09					07 26				07 30											07 47	07 53	
Bickley 4	d	07 09	07 13		07 11			07 30				07 34				07 37							07 53	07 57	
Bromley South 4	d	07 12	07 16		07 17	07 29	07 32	07 34	07 35			07 37	07 40			07 41	07 51	07 52		07 54			07 56	08 01	08 04
Shortlands 4	d	07 14	07 18		07 19			07 36				07 39				07 43							07 58	08 03	
Ravensbourne	d				07 21											07 46									08 08
Beckenham Hill	d				07 23											07 48									08 10
Bellingham	d				07 25											07 50							08 04		08 12
Catford	d				07 27											07 52							08 07		08 15
Crofton Park	d				07 30											07 54							08 09		
Lewisham 4 🚋	d										07 44											08 04			
Nunhead 4	d				07 32						07 52					07 57						08 10	08 13		
Peckham Rye 4	d				07 34						07 55					07 59						08 12	08 15		
Denmark Hill 4	d				07 36						07 59					08 03				08 06		08 15	08 18		08 22
Beckenham Junction 4 🚋	d	07 17	07 21					07 39				07 42							08 00					08 07	
Kent House 4	d	07 20	07 23					07 41				07 44		←					08 02		08 05				
Penge East	d	07 22	07 25					07 43				07 46		07 43					08 04		08 07				
Sydenham Hill	d	07 25	07 28					→				07 49		07 46					08 07		08 10				
West Dulwich	d	07 27	07 30									07 52		07 48					08 09		08 12			08 14	
Herne Hill 4	d	07 32	07 34				07 42					07 57		07 52	07 54				08 12		08 15			08 18	
Loughborough Jn	d	07 34												07 55	07 57				08 14						
Elephant & Castle	⊖ d	07 39			07 42								07 58	08 01	08 02	08 09			08 19				08 24		08 28
London Blackfriars 3	⊖ d	07a44			07a46								08a03	08a05	08f13	08a13			08a24				08a29		08 32
City Thameslink 3	a														08 15										08 35
Farringdon	⊖ a														08 19										
St Pancras International 3	⊖ a														08 23										
Brixton	⊖ d		07 37									07 59									08 17				
London Victoria 15	⊖ a		07 45			07 49	07 52		07 58		08 11	08 07					08 11	08 14		08 17	08 25	08 28		08 28	

For general notes see front of timetable
For details of catering facilities see Directory of Train Operators

A From Selhurst (Table 177)
B From Dover Priory (Table 212)
C From Ashford International (Table 196)
b Arr. 0446
c Arr. 0608
e Arr. 0605
f Arr. 0807

For details of Bank Holiday service alterations please see first page of this table

Sevenoaks, Otford, Orpington, Bromley South, Beckenham Junction and Catford → London

Network Diagram - see first page of Table 195

		FC	SE 23		SE 20	SE 94	SE 51	FC	SE 4	SE 78	SE 9	SE 70	FC	SE 83	SE 96	SE 50	SE 22	FC	FC	SE 3	SE 70	SE 18	SE 9	SE 83	SE 20
					A	[1]	[1]						[1]		[1]	[1]	[1]		[1]						[1]
Sevenoaks [4]	d													07 52										08 19	
Bat & Ball	d													07 55										08 22	
Otford [4]	d					07 50								07 58	08 07									08 25	
Shoreham (Kent)	d													08 01										08 28	
Eynsford	d													08 04										08 32	
Swanley [4]	d		07 55		07 59	08 00								08 10			08 21							08 38	08 43
St Mary Cray	d		08 00		08 04									08 15			08 26							08 42	08 48
Orpington [4]	d											08 10									08 30				
Petts Wood [4]	d											08 13									08 33				
Bickley [4]	d											08 17		08 20							08 37			08 47	
Bromley South [4]	d		08 07		08 11		08 15				08 18	08 21		08b25	08 25	08 31	08 32				08 41		08 45	08 50	08 54
Shortlands [4]	d										08 20	08 23		08 28							08 43		08 47	08 52	
Ravensbourne	d										08 22												08 50		
Beckenham Hill	d										08 24												08 52		
Bellingham	d										08 26			08 32									08 54	08 56	
Catford	d										08 29			08 36									08 56	08 59	
Crofton Park	d													08 38									08 59		
Lewisham [4] ⇌	d									08 24												08 44			
Nunhead [4]	d									08 29				08 41								08 52	09 01		
Peckham Rye [4]	d									08 32	08 35			08 43								08 54	09 04	09 08	
Denmark Hill [4]	d				08 27					08 35	08 38			08 45								08 59	09 06	09 10	
Beckenham Junction [4] ⇌	d								08 22			08 27									08 46				
Kent House [4]	d								08 24			08 29								08 45	08 48				
Penge East	d								08 26											08 47	08 50				
Sydenham Hill	d								08 29											08 50	08 53				
West Dulwich	d								08 31			08 35								08 52	08 56				
Herne Hill [4]	d	08 22						08 28	08 36			08 39	08 43					08 53	08 59	08 56	09 01				
Loughborough Jn	d	08 25						08 31										08 56		09 00					
Elephant & Castle	⊖ d	08 30	08 31					08 36			08 44			08 51				09 00		09 04			09 12	09 16	
London Blackfriars [3]	⊖ d	08 37	08a37					08 43			08a49		08c57	08a56				09 05	09 09	09a09			09a17	09 22	
City Thameslink [3]	a	08 39						08 45					08 59					09 07	09 11					09 24	
Farringdon	⊖ a	08 42						08 50					09 02					09 10	09 14						
St Pancras International [3]	⊖ a	08 46						08 54					09 06					09 14	09 18						
Brixton	⊖ d								08 38												09 03				
London Victoria [15]	⊖ a				08 38	08 31	08 34		08 46	08 48		08 48			08 53	08 52	08 57				09 11	09 11			09 15

		SE 96	SE 50		SE 70	SE 78	FC	SE 73	SE 83	SE 34	SE 70	SE 66	SE 50	FC	SE 70	FC	SE 83	SE 94	SE 34	SE 78	SE 70	SE 30	FC	SE 70	SE 83
		[1]	[1]							[1]		[1]	[1] [trolley]					[1]	[1]			[1] [trolley]			
Sevenoaks [4]	d								08 46								09 12								09 34
Bat & Ball	d								08 49								09 15								09 37
Otford [4]	d	08 40							08 52			09 07					09 18	09 27							09 40
Shoreham (Kent)	d								08 55								09 21								09 43
Eynsford	d								08 58								09 24								09 47
Swanley [4]	d	08 50							09 04	09 07							09 30	09 36	09 36						09 52
St Mary Cray	d								09 08	09 12							09 35		09 41						09 56
Orpington [4]	d				08 53			08 57			09 08				09 23						09 38			09 53	
Petts Wood [4]	d				08 56			09 00			09 11				09 26						09 41			09 56	
Bickley [4]	d				09 00			09 04	09 12		09 15				09 30		09 39				09 45			10 00	10 01
Bromley South [4]	d	09 00	09 03		09 03			09 07	09 16	09 19	09 20	09 27	09 30		09 33		09 43	09 45	09 48		09 48	09 59		10 03	10 05
Shortlands [4]	d				09 05			09 09	09 18		09 22				09 35		09 45				09 50			10 05	10 07
Ravensbourne	d							09 11	09 20								09 47								10 09
Beckenham Hill	d							09 13	09 22								09 49								10 11
Bellingham	d							09 15	09 24								09 51								10 13
Catford	d							09 17	09 26								09 53								10 15
Crofton Park	d							09 20	09 29								09 56								10 18
Lewisham [4] ⇌	d					09 10														09 51					
Nunhead [4]	d					09 15		09 22	09 31								09 59			09 56					10 20
Peckham Rye [4]	d					09 18		09 25	09 34								10 01			09 58					10 22
Denmark Hill [4]	d					09 20		09 27	09 36								10 04			10 01					10 25
Beckenham Junction [4] ⇌	d				09 08						09 25				09 38						09 53			10 08	
Kent House [4]	d				09 10						09 27				09 40						09 55			10 10	
Penge East	d				09 12						09 29				09 42						09 57			10 12	
Sydenham Hill	d				09 15						09 32				09 45						10 00			10 15	
West Dulwich	d				09 17						09 34				09 47						10 02			10 17	
Herne Hill [4]	d				09 20		09 23				09 37			09 41	09 50	09 59					10 05		10 11	10 20	
Loughborough Jn	d						09 26							09 45		10 02							10 15		
Elephant & Castle	⊖ d						09 30	09 33	09 41					09 50		10 07	10 09						10 20		10 30
London Blackfriars [3]	⊖ d						09 34	09a37	09a46					09 58		10e13	10a12						10 28		10a33
City Thameslink [3]	a						09 36							10 00		10 15							10 30		
Farringdon	⊖ a						09 40							10 04		10 19							10 34		
St Pancras International [3]	⊖ a						09 44							10 08		10 23							10 38		
Brixton	⊖ d				09 22						09 39				09 52						10 07			10 22	
London Victoria [15]	⊖ a	09 18	09 26		09 30	09 32				09 38	09 47	09 50	09 51		10 00			10 02	10 05	10 12	10 14	10 17		10 29	

For general notes see front of timetable
For details of catering facilities see Directory of Train Operators

A From Gillingham (Kent) (Table 212)
b Arr. 0822
c Arr. 0852
e Arr. 1010

For details of Bank Holiday service alterations please see first page of this table

Sevenoaks, Otford, Orpington, Bromley South, Beckenham Junction and Catford → London

Network Diagram - see first page of Table 195

		SE	FC		SE	SE	SE	FC	SE		SE	SE	SE	FC	SE	SE	SE	FC	SE	SE	SE	SE	FC	SE	SE
		64			78	70	30		70		83	94	78		70	92	30		70	83	64	78		70	92
		1 A					1									1	1				1				1
Sevenoaks 4	d										10 04									10 34					
Bat & Ball	d										10 07									10 37					
Otford 4	d	09 56									10 10	10 27								10 40	10 57				
Shoreham (Kent)	d										10 13									10 43					
Eynsford	d										10 17									10 47					
Swanley 4	d	10 06									10 22	10 36				10 42				10 52					11 12
St Mary Cray	d										10 26					10 47				10 56					11 17
Orpington 4	d					10 08			10 23						10 38				10 53					11 08	
Petts Wood 4	d					10 11			10 26						10 41				10 56					11 11	
Bickley 4	d					10 15			10 30		10 31				10 45				11 00	11 01				11 15	
Bromley South 4	d	10 15				10 18	10 30		10 33		10 35	10 45			10 48	10 54	11 00		11 03	11 05	11 15			11 18	11 24
Shortlands 4	d					10 20			10 35		10 37				10 50				11 05	11 07				11 20	
Ravensbourne	d										10 39									11 09					
Beckenham Hill	d										10 41									11 11					
Bellingham	d										10 43									11 13					
Catford	d										10 45									11 15					
Crofton Park	d										10 48									11 18					
Lewisham 4	d				10 21								10 51									11 21			
Nunhead 4	d				10 26						10 50		10 56							11 20		11 26			
Peckham Rye 4	d				10 28						10 52		10 58							11 22		11 28			
Denmark Hill 4	d				10 31						10 55		11 01							11 25		11 31			
Beckenham Junction 4	d					10 23			10 38						10 53				11 08					11 23	
Kent House 4	d					10 25			10 40						10 55				11 10					11 25	
Penge East	d					10 27			10 42						10 57				11 12					11 27	
Sydenham Hill	d					10 30			10 45						11 00				11 15					11 30	
West Dulwich	d					10 32			10 47						11 02				11 17					11 32	
Herne Hill 4	d		10 26			10 35		10 41	10 50					10 56	11 05			11 11	11 20				11 26	11 35	
Loughborough Jn	d		10 30					10 45						11 00				11 15					11 30		
Elephant & Castle	⊖ d		10 35					10 50			11 00			11 05				11 20		11 30			11 35		
London Blackfriars 3	⊖ d		10 43					10 58			11a03			11 13				11 28		11a33			11 43		
City Thameslink 3	a		10 45					11 00						11 15				11 30					11 45		
Farringdon	⊖ a		10 49					11 04						11 19				11 34					11 49		
St Pancras International 3	⊖ a		10 53					11 08						11 23				11 38					11 53		
Brixton	⊖ d					10 37			10 52						11 07				11 22					11 37	
London Victoria 15	⊖ a	10 32			10 42	10 44	10 47		10 59			11 02	11 12		11 14	11 17	11 17		11 29		11 32	11 42		11 44	11 47

		SE	FC	SE			SE	SE	SE	FC	SE	SE	SE	FC	SE	SE	SE	FC	SE	SE	SE	FC	FC	SE
		30		70			83	94	78		70	92	30		70	83	64		70	92	30			78
		1										1	1				1			1	1	1 B		
Sevenoaks 4	d						15 04									15 34								
Bat & Ball	d						15 07									15 37								
Otford 4	d						15 10	15 27								15 40	15 55							
Shoreham (Kent)	d						15 13									15 43								
Eynsford	d						15 17									15 46								
Swanley 4	d						15 22	15 36				15 42				15 52				16 12				
St Mary Cray	d						15 26					15 47				15 56				16 17				
Orpington 4	d			11 23							15 38				15 53				16 08					
Petts Wood 4	d			11 26							15 41				15 56				16 11					
Bickley 4	d			11 30			15 31				15 45				16 00	16 01			16 15					
Bromley South 4	d	11 30		11 33	and at the same minutes past each hour until		15 35	15 45			15 48	15 53	16 00		16 03	16 05	16 14		16 19	16 23	16 30			
Shortlands 4	d			11 35			15 37				15 50				16 05	16 07			16 21					
Ravensbourne	d						15 39									16 09								
Beckenham Hill	d						15 41									16 11								
Bellingham	d						15 43									16 13								
Catford	d						15 45									16 15								
Crofton Park	d						15 48									16 18								
Lewisham 4	d								15 51															16 35
Nunhead 4	d						15 50		15 56							16 20								16 40
Peckham Rye 4	d						15 52		15 58							16 22								16 42
Denmark Hill 4	d						15 55		16 01							16 25								16 46
Beckenham Junction 4	d			11 38							15 53				16 08				16 25					
Kent House 4	d			11 40							15 55				16 10				16 27					
Penge East	d			11 42							15 57				16 12				16 29					
Sydenham Hill	d			11 45							16 00				16 15				16 32					
West Dulwich	d			11 47							16 02				16 17				16 33					
Herne Hill 4	d		11 41	11 50						15 56	16 05			16 11	16 20			16 27	16 36			16 37	16 42	
Loughborough Jn	d		11 45							16 00				16 15				16 30					16 45	
Elephant & Castle	⊖ d		11 50				16 00			16 05				16 20		16 30		16 35				16 43	16 50	
London Blackfriars 3	⊖ d		11 58				16a03			16b14				16 30		16a33		16c44				16 50	17e00	
City Thameslink 3	a		12 00							16 16				16 32				16 46				16 52	17 02	
Farringdon	⊖ a		12 04							16 19				16 35				16 49				16 56	17 05	
St Pancras International 3	⊖ a		12 08							16 24				16 39				16 53				17 01	17 09	
Brixton	⊖ d			11 52							16 07				16 22				16 38					
London Victoria 15	⊖ a	11 47		11 59				16 02	16 12		16 14	16 18	16 17		16 30		16 33		16 45	16 49	16 49			17 03

For general notes see front of timetable
For details of catering facilities see Directory of Train Operators

A From Margate (Table 207)
B From Brighton (Table 52)
b Arr. 1611
c Arr. 1638
e Arr. 1657

For details of Bank Holiday service alterations please see first page of this table

Sevenoaks, Otford, Orpington, Bromley South, Beckenham Junction and Catford → London

Network Diagram - see first page of Table 195

		FC	SE 83	SE 70	SE 96	SE 92 [1]		SE 83	SE 30 [1] ⚒	FC	SE 78	SE 83	SE 70	SE 64 [1] A	FC	SE 70	SE 92 [1]	SE 31 [1] ⚒	FC	FC [1]	SE 83	FC	SE 70	SE 96 [1]	SE 78
Sevenoaks [4]	d		16 05					16 26				16 35									17 05				
Bat & Ball	d		16 08					16 29				16 38									17 08				
Otford [4]	d		16 11		16 27			16 32				16 41		16 54							17 12			17 28	
Shoreham (Kent)	d		16 14					16 35				16 44									17 15				
Eynsford	d		16 17					16 39				16 48									17 19				
Swanley [4]	d		16 22		16 38	16 42		16a45				16 54		17 05			17 13				17 24				
St Mary Cray	d		16 26			16 47						16 58					17 18				17 28				
Orpington [4]	d			16 36									17 04										17 36		
Petts Wood [4]	d			16 39									17 07										17 39		
Bickley [4]	d		16 31	16 44								17 03	17 11			←					17 33		17 44		
Bromley South [4]	d		16 35	16 47	16 47	16 53			17 00			17 06	17b17	17 14		17 17	17 25	17 33			17 36		17 47	17 47	
Shortlands [4]	d		16 37	16 49								17 08	→			17 19					17 38		17 49		
Ravensbourne	d		16 39									17 11									17 41				
Beckenham Hill	d		16 41									17 13									17 43				
Bellingham	d		16 43									17 15									17 45				
Catford	d		16 45									17 17									17 47				
Crofton Park	d		16 48									17 19									17 49				
Lewisham [4]	⇌ d										17 05														17 54
Nunhead [4]	d		16 50								17 13	17 22									17 52				17 59
Peckham Rye [4]	d		16 52								17 15	17 24									17 54				18 01
Denmark Hill [4]	d		16 55								17 18	17 27									17 57				18 04
Beckenham Junction [4]	⇌ d			16 52												17 22							17 52		
Kent House [4]	d			16 54												17 24							17 54		
Penge East	d			16 56												17 26							17 56		
Sydenham Hill	d			16 59												17 29							17 59		
West Dulwich	d			17 00												17 30							18 00		
Herne Hill [4]	d	16 54		17 03						17 06					17 26	17 33			17 36			17 54	18 03		
Loughborough Jn	d									17 09					17 29				17 39			17 57			
Elephant & Castle	⊖ d	17 00	17 00							17 14		17 32			17 34				17 44	17 52	18 02	18 02			
London Blackfriars [3]	⊖ d	17 04	17a05							17 18		17a39			17 40				17 48	18c06	18a08	18e14			
City Thameslink [3]	a	17 06								17 20					17 42				17 50	18 08		18 16			
Farringdon	⊖ a	17 09								17 23					17 47				17 53	18 11		18 23			
St Pancras International [3]	⊖ a	17 13								17 27					17 53				17 57	18 15		18 27			
Brixton	⊖ d			17 05												17 35							18 05		
London Victoria [15]	⊖ a			17 12	17 11	17 18			17 17		17 28			17 31		17 42	17 48	17 58					18 12	18 09	18 16

		SE 92 [1]	SE 50 [1] ⚒	FC	SE 83	SE 94 [1]		FC	SE 70	SE 92 [1]	SE 30 [1] ⚒	FC [1] B	FC	SE 78	SE 83	SE 83	SE 94 [1]	SE 70	SE 92 [1]	SE 30 [1]	FC	SE 78	SE 83	SE 94 [1]	FC
Sevenoaks [4]	d				17 35										17 57	18 16							18 37		
Bat & Ball	d				17 38										18 00	18 19							18 40		
Otford [4]	d				17 41	17 53									18 04	18 22	18 29						18 43	18 56	
Shoreham (Kent)	d				17 44										18 07	18 25							18 46		
Eynsford	d				17 47										18 10	18 29							18 49		
Swanley [4]	d	17 43			17 53	18 04				18 12					18f22	18a34			18 42				18g58	19 05	
St Mary Cray	d	17 47			17 57					18 16					18 26				18 47				19 02		
Orpington [4]	d								18 06									18 36							
Petts Wood [4]	d								18 09									18 39							
Bickley [4]	d				18 02				18 14						18 32			18 44					19 06		
Bromley South [4]	d	17 54	17 59		18 05	18 14			18 17	18 25	18 31				18 35		18 45	18 47	18 53	19 01			19 10	19 14	
Shortlands [4]	d				18 08				18 19						18 37			18 49					19 12		
Ravensbourne	d				18 10										18 39								19 14		
Beckenham Hill	d				18 12										18 41								19 16		
Bellingham	d				18 14										18 43								19 18		
Catford	d				18 16										18 45								19 20		
Crofton Park	d				18 19										18 48								19 23		
Lewisham [4]	⇌ d													18 41								19 06			
Nunhead [4]	d				18 21									18 45	18 50							19 10	19 25		
Peckham Rye [4]	d				18 23									18 47	18 52							19 12	19 28		
Denmark Hill [4]	d				18 26									18 50	18 55							19 15	19 31		
Beckenham Junction [4]	⇌ d								18 22									18 53							
Kent House [4]	d								18 24									18 55							
Penge East	d								18 26									18 57							
Sydenham Hill	d								18 29									19 00							
West Dulwich	d								18 30									19 01							
Herne Hill [4]	d			18 14				18 27	18 33			18 37	18 44					19 04			19 11				19 27
Loughborough Jn	d			18 17				18 30				18 40	18 47								19 15				19 30
Elephant & Castle	⊖ d			18 22	18 31			18 35				18 45	18 52		19 00						19 20		19 37		19 35
London Blackfriars [3]	⊖ d			18h32	18a35			18j46				18k52	19m02		19a03						19 28		19a40		19 43
City Thameslink [3]	a			18 34				18 48				18 54	19 04								19 30				19 45
Farringdon	⊖ a			18 37				18 51				18 57	19 07								19 34				19 49
St Pancras International [3]	⊖ a			18 41				18 55				19 01	19 11								19 38				19 53
Brixton	⊖ d								18 35									19 06							
London Victoria [15]	⊖ a	18 19	18 17			18 33			18 42	18 50	18 48			19 00			19 03	19 13	19 17	19 17		19 25		19 31	

For general notes see front of timetable
For details of catering facilities see Directory of Train Operators

A From Canterbury West (Table 207)
B From Brighton (Table 52)
b Arr. 1713
c Arr. 1756
e Arr. 1809
f Arr. 1815
g Arr. 1855
h Arr. 1829
j Arr. 1840
k Arr. 1849
m Arr. 1859

For details of Bank Holiday service alterations please see first page of this table

Sevenoaks, Otford, Orpington, Bromley South, Beckenham Junction and Catford → London

Network Diagram - see first page of Table 195

	SE 70	SE 92 [1]	SE 83	SE 30 [1]	FC		SE 70	SE 83	SE 94	SE 70	SE 83	SE 92 [1]	SE 30 [1]	FC	SE 70	SE 83	SE 94 [1]	SE 70	SE 50 [1]	FC	SE 83	SE 70	SE 92 [1]	FC
Sevenoaks [4] d			18 55					19 06			19 21					19 34					20 04			
Bat & Ball d			18 58					19 09			19 24					19 37					20 07			
Otford [4] d			19 02					19 12	19 27		19 30					19 40	19 55				20 10			
Shoreham (Kent) d			19 05					19 15			19 33					19 43					20 13			
Eynsford d			19 08					19 18			19 36					19 46					20 16			
Swanley [4] d		19 12	19a13					19 24	19 36		19a41	19 42				19 52	20 04				20 22		20 42	
St Mary Cray d		19 17						19 28				19 47				19 56	20 08				20 26		20 47	
Orpington [4] d	19 08						19 23			19 38					19 53			20 08				20 38		
Petts Wood [4] d	19 11						19 26			19 41					19 56			20 11				20 41		
Bickley [4] d	19 16						19 30	19 32		19 46					20 00	20 01		20 16			20 31	20 46		
Bromley South [4] d	19 19	19 23		19 30			19 33	19 35	19 45	19 49		19 53	19 58		20 03	20 05	20 15	20 19	20 32		20 35	20 49	20 53	
Shortlands [4] d	19 21						19 35	19 37		19 51					20 05	20 07		20 21			20 37	20 51		
Ravensbourne d								19 40								20 09					20 39			
Beckenham Hill d								19 42								20 11					20 41			
Bellingham d								19 44								20 13					20 43			
Catford d								19 46								20 15					20 45			
Crofton Park d								19 48								20 18					20 48			
Lewisham [4] d																								
Nunhead [4] d								19 51								20 20					20 50			
Peckham Rye [4] d								19 53								20 22					20 52			
Denmark Hill [4] d								19 55								20 25					20 55			
Beckenham Junction [4] d	19 24						19 38			19 54					20 08			20 24				20 54		
Kent House [4] d	19 26						19 40			19 56					20 10			20 26				20 56		
Penge East d	19 28						19 42			19 58					20 12			20 28				20 58		
Sydenham Hill d	19 31						19 45			20 01					20 15			20 31				21 01		
West Dulwich d	19 33						19 47			20 02					20 17			20 32				21 02		
Herne Hill [4] d	19 36				19 41		19 50			20 05				20 11	20 20			20 35		20 41		21 05		21 11
Loughborough Jn d					19 45									20 15						20 45				21 15
Elephant & Castle ⊖ d					19 50			20 00						20 20		20 30				20 50	21 00			21 19
London Blackfriars [3] ⊖ d					19 58			20a03						20 28		20a33				20 58	21a03			21b33
City Thameslink [3] a					20 00									20 30						21 00				21 35
Farringdon ⊖ a					20 04									20 34						21 04				21 39
St Pancras International [3] ⊖ a					20 08									20 38						21 08				21 43
Brixton ⊖ d	19 38						19 52			20 07					20 22			20 37				21 07		
London Victoria [15] ⊖ a	19 45	19 48		19 47			19 59		20 02	20 14		20 17	20 17		20 29		20 32	20 44	20 48			21 14	21 17	

	SE 83	SE 94 [1] A	SE 70	SE 50 [1]	SE 83		FC	SE 70	SE 92 [1]	SE 83	SE 94 [1]	FC	SE 70	SE 50 [1]	SE 83	SE 70	SE 92 [1]	SE 83	SE 70	SE 94 [1]	SE 50 [1]	SE 55 [1]		
Sevenoaks [4] d	20 34				21 04					21 35					22 04			22 37						
Bat & Ball d	20 37				21 07					21 38					22 07			22 40						
Otford [4] d	20 40	20 53			21 10					21 41	21 54				22 10			22 43		23 04				
Shoreham (Kent) d	20 43				21 13					21 44					22 13			22 46						
Eynsford d	20 46				21 16					21 47					22 16			22 49						
Swanley [4] d	20 52	21 02			21 22				21 42	21 53	22 03				22 22		22 42	22 55		23 13		23 45		
St Mary Cray d	20 56	21 07			21 26				21 47	21 57	22 07				22 26		22 47	22 59		23 17		23 49		
Orpington [4] d			21 08					21 38					22 08			22 38			23 08					
Petts Wood [4] d			21 11					21 41					22 11			22 41			23 11					
Bickley [4] d	21 01		21 16		21 31			21 46		22 01			22 16		22 31	22 46		23 03	23 16					
Bromley South [4] d	21 05	21 13	21 19	21 30	21 35			21 49	21 53	22 05	22 14		22 19	22 30	22 35	22 49	22 53	23 06	23 19	23 24	23 30	23 56		
Shortlands [4] d	21 07		21 21		21 37			21 51		22 07			22 21		22 37	22 51		23 08	23 21					
Ravensbourne d	21 09				21 39					22 09					22 39			23 11						
Beckenham Hill d	21 11				21 41					22 11					22 41			23 13						
Bellingham d	21 13				21 43					22 13					22 43			23 15						
Catford d	21 15				21 45					22 15					22 45			23 17						
Crofton Park d	21 18				21 48					22 18					22 48			23 19						
Lewisham [4] d																								
Nunhead [4] d	21 20				21 50					22 20					22 50			23 22						
Peckham Rye [4] d	21 22				21 52					22 22					22 52			23 24						
Denmark Hill [4] d	21 25				21 55					22 25					22 55			23 26						
Beckenham Junction [4] d			21 24					21 54					22 24			22 54			23 24					
Kent House [4] d			21 26					21 56					22 26			22 56			23 26					
Penge East d			21 28					21 58					22 28			22 58			23 28					
Sydenham Hill d			21 31					22 01					22 31			23 01			23 31					
West Dulwich d			21 32					22 02					22 32			23 02			23 32					
Herne Hill [4] d			21 35				21 56	22 05				22 26	22 35			23 05			23 35					
Loughborough Jn d							22 00					22 30												
Elephant & Castle ⊖ d	21 30				22 00		22 05			22 30		22 35			23 00			23 31						
London Blackfriars [3] ⊖ d	21a33				22a03		22 08			22a33		22 38			23a03			23a37						
City Thameslink [3] a							22 10					22 40												
Farringdon ⊖ a							22 14					22 44												
St Pancras International [3] ⊖ a							22 18					22 48												
Brixton ⊖ d			21 37					22 07					22 37			23 07			23 37					
London Victoria [15] ⊖ a		21 29	21 44	21 47				22 14	22 17		22 32		22 44	22 47		23 14	23 15		23 44	23 45	23 47	00 18		

For general notes see front of timetable
For details of catering facilities see Directory of Train Operators

A From Canterbury West (Table 207)
b Arr. 2126

Table 195

Saturdays

Sevenoaks, Otford, Orpington, Bromley South, Beckenham Junction and Catford → London

Network Diagram - see first page of Table 195

		FC	SE	SE	FC	SE	SE	FC		SE	SE	SE	FC	SE	SE	SE		FC	SE	SE	SE	FC	SE	SE	FC
			73	54 [1]		70	83			70	92 [1]	30 [1]		83	64 [1]	78			70	92 [1]	30 [1]		83	78	
		A			A			A																	
Sevenoaks [4]	d						06 04							06 34									07 04		
Bat & Ball	d						06 07							06 37									07 07		
Otford [4]	d						06 10							06 40	06 55								07 10		
Shoreham (Kent)	d						06 13							06 43									07 13		
Eynsford	d						06 17							06 47									07 17		
Swanley [4]	d			06 05			06 22				06 42			06 52	07 04					07 12			07 22		
St Mary Cray	d			06 10			06 26				06 47			06 56	07 08					07 17			07 26		
Orpington [4]	d		05 54			06 08				06 38									07 08						
Petts Wood [4]	d		05 57			06 11				06 41									07 11						
Bickley [4]	d		06 01			06 15	06 31			06 45				07 01					07 15				07 31		
Bromley South [4]	d		06 05	06 16		06 18	06 35			06 48	06 54	07 00		07 05	07 15				07 18	07 24	07 30		07 35		
Shortlands [4]	d		06 07			06 20	06 37			06 50				07 07					07 20				07 37		
Ravensbourne	d		06 09				06 39							07 09									07 39		
Beckenham Hill	d		06 11				06 41							07 11									07 41		
Bellingham	d		06 13				06 43							07 13									07 43		
Catford	d		06 15				06 45							07 15									07 45		
Crofton Park	d		06 18				06 48							07 18									07 48		
Lewisham [4]	d															07 20								07 50	
Nunhead [4]	d		06 20				06 50							07 20		07 25							07 50	07 55	
Peckham Rye [4]	d		06 22				06 52							07 22		07 28							07 52	07 58	
Denmark Hill [4]	d		06 25				06 55							07 25		07 31							07 55	08 01	
Beckenham Junction [4]	d					06 23				06 53									07 23						
Kent House [4]	d					06 25				06 55									07 25						
Penge East	d					06 27				06 57									07 27						
Sydenham Hill	d					06 30				07 00									07 30						
West Dulwich	d					06 32				07 02									07 32						
Herne Hill [4]	d	06 02			06 26	06 35		06 56		07 05			07 11					07 26	07 35			07 41			07 56
Loughborough Jn	d				06 30			07 00					07 15					07 30				07 45			08 00
Elephant & Castle	⊖ d	06 07	06 30		06 35		07 00	07 05					07 20	07 30				07 35				07 50	08 00		08 05
London Blackfriars [3]	⊖ d	06 13	06a33		06 43		07a03	07 13					07 28	07a33				07 43				07 58	08a03		08 13
City Thameslink [3]	a																								
Farringdon	⊖ a	06 18			06 48			07 18					07 33					07 48				08 03			08 18
St Pancras International [3]	⊖ a	06 22			06 52			07 22					07 38					07 53				08 08			08 23
Brixton	⊖ d					06 37				07 07									07 37						
London Victoria [15]	⊖ a			06 32		06 44				07 14	07 17	07 17			07 32	07 42			07 44	07 47	07 47			08 12	

		SE		SE	SE	FC	SE	SE	SE	FC		SE	SE	SE	FC	SE	SE	SE		SE	FC	SE	SE	SE	FC
		70		92 [1]	30 [1]		83	94 [1]	78			70	92 [1]	30 [1]		70	83	94		78		70	92 [1]	30 [1]	
Sevenoaks [4]	d						07 34										08 04								
Bat & Ball	d						07 37										08 07								
Otford [4]	d						07 40	07 55									08 10	08 26							
Shoreham (Kent)	d						07 43										08 13								
Eynsford	d						07 47										08 17								
Swanley [4]	d			07 42			07 52	08 04					08 12				08 22	08 35					08 42		
St Mary Cray	d			07 47			07 56	08 08					08 17				08 26						08 47		
Orpington [4]	d	07 38										08 08				08 23						08 38			
Petts Wood [4]	d	07 41										08 11				08 26						08 41			
Bickley [4]	d	07 45					08 01					08 15				08 30	08 31					08 45			
Bromley South [4]	d	07 48		07 54	08 00		08 05	08 15				08 18	08 24	08 30		08 33	08 35	08 45				08 48	08 54	09 00	
Shortlands [4]	d	07 50					08 07					08 20				08 35	08 37					08 50			
Ravensbourne	d						08 09										08 39								
Beckenham Hill	d						08 11										08 41								
Bellingham	d						08 13										08 43								
Catford	d						08 15										08 45								
Crofton Park	d						08 18										08 48								
Lewisham [4]	d								08 20											08 50					
Nunhead [4]	d						08 20		08 25								08 50			08 55					
Peckham Rye [4]	d						08 22		08 28								08 52			08 58					
Denmark Hill [4]	d						08 25		08 31								08 55			09 01					
Beckenham Junction [4]	d	07 53										08 23				08 38						08 53			
Kent House [4]	d	07 55										08 25				08 40						08 55			
Penge East	d	07 57										08 27				08 42						08 57			
Sydenham Hill	d	08 00										08 30				08 45						09 00			
West Dulwich	d	08 02										08 32				08 47						09 02			
Herne Hill [4]	d	08 05				08 11				08 26		08 35			08 41	08 50					08 56	09 05			09 11
Loughborough Jn	d					08 15				08 30					08 45						09 00				09 15
Elephant & Castle	⊖ d					08 20	08 30			08 35					08 50		09 00				09 05				09 20
London Blackfriars [3]	⊖ d					08 28	08a33			08 43					08 58		09a03				09 13				09 28
City Thameslink [3]	a														09 00						09 15				09 30
Farringdon	⊖ a					08 33				08 48					09 04						09 19				09 34
St Pancras International [3]	⊖ a					08 38				08 53					09 08						09 23				09 38
Brixton	⊖ d	08 07										08 37				08 52						09 07			
London Victoria [15]	⊖ a	08 14		08 17	08 17			08 32	08 42			08 44	08 47	08 47		08 59		09 02		09 12		09 14	09 17	09 17	

For general notes see front of timetable
For details of catering facilities see Directory of Train Operators

A From Selhurst (Table 177)

Table 195

Saturdays

Sevenoaks, Otford, Orpington, Bromley South, Beckenham Junction and Catford → London

Network Diagram - see first page of Table 195

	SE 70	SE 83	SE 94		SE 78	FC	SE 70	SE 92	SE 30	FC	SE 70		SE 83	SE 94	SE 78	FC	SE 70	SE 92	SE 30		FC	SE 70	SE 83	SE 94
			1					1	1 trolley									1	1 trolley					1
Sevenoaks 4 d		08 34											09 04										09 34	
Bat & Ball d		08 37											09 07										09 37	
Otford 4 d		08 40	08 57										09 10	09 26									09 40	09 57
Shoreham (Kent) d		08 43											09 13										09 43	
Eynsford d		08 47											09 17										09 47	
Swanley 4 d		08 52						09 12					09 22	09 35				09 42					09 52	
St Mary Cray d		08 56						09 17					09 26					09 47					09 56	
Orpington 4 d	08 53						09 08				09 23						09 38					09 53		
Petts Wood 4 d	08 56						09 11				09 26						09 41					09 56		
Bickley 4 d	09 00	09 01					09 15				09 30		09 31				09 45					10 00	10 01	
Bromley South 4 d	09 03	09 05	09 15				09 18	09 24	09 30		09 33		09 35	09 45			09 48	09 54	10 00			10 03	10 05	10 15
Shortlands 4 d	09 05	09 07					09 20				09 35		09 37				09 50					10 05	10 07	
Ravensbourne d		09 09											09 39										10 09	
Beckenham Hill d		09 11											09 41										10 11	
Bellingham d		09 13											09 43										10 13	
Catford d		09 15											09 45										10 15	
Crofton Park d		09 18											09 48										10 18	
Lewisham 4 d					09 20										09 50									
Nunhead 4 d		09 20			09 25								09 50		09 55								10 20	
Peckham Rye 4 d		09 22			09 28								09 52		09 58								10 22	
Denmark Hill 4 d		09 25			09 31								09 55		10 01								10 25	
Beckenham Junction 4 d	09 08						09 23				09 38						09 53					10 08		
Kent House 4 d	09 10						09 25				09 40						09 55					10 10		
Penge East d	09 12						09 27				09 42						09 57					10 12		
Sydenham Hill d	09 15						09 30				09 45						10 00					10 15		
West Dulwich d	09 17						09 32				09 47						10 02					10 17		
Herne Hill 4 d	09 20					09 26	09 35			09 41	09 50					09 56	10 05				10 11	10 20		
Loughborough Jn d						09 30				09 46						10 00					10 15			
Elephant & Castle ⊖ d		09 30				09 35				09 50			10 00			10 05					10 20		10 30	
London Blackfriars 3 ⊖ d		09a33				09 43				09 58			10a03			10 13					10 28		10a33	
City Thameslink 3 a						09 45				10 00						10 15					10 30			
Farringdon ⊖ a						09 49				10 04						10 19					10 34			
St Pancras International 3 ⊖ a						09 53				10 08						10 23					10 38			
Brixton ⊖ d	09 22						09 37				09 52						10 07					10 22		
London Victoria 15 ⊖ a	09 29		09 32		09 42		09 44	09 47	09 47		09 59			10 02	10 12		10 14	10 17	10 17			10 29		10 32

	SE 78	FC	SE 70		SE 92	SE 30	FC	SE 70	SE 83	SE 94	SE 78	FC	SE 70	SE 92	SE 30	FC	SE 70	SE 83	SE 64	SE 78	FC
					1	1 trolley								1	1 trolley				1		
Sevenoaks 4 d									10 04									10 34			
Bat & Ball d									10 07									10 37			
Otford 4 d									10 10	10 26								10 40	10 57		
Shoreham (Kent) d									10 13									10 43			
Eynsford d									10 17									10 47			
Swanley 4 d					10 12				10 22	10 35				10 42				10 52			
St Mary Cray d					10 17				10 26					10 47				10 56			
Orpington 4 d			10 08					10 23					10 38				10 53				
Petts Wood 4 d			10 11					10 26					10 41				10 56				
Bickley 4 d			10 15					10 30	10 31				10 45				11 00	11 01			
Bromley South 4 d			10 18		10 24	10 30		10 33	10 35	10 45			10 48	10 54	11 00		11 03	11 05	11 15		
Shortlands 4 d			10 20					10 35	10 37				10 50				11 05	11 07			
Ravensbourne d									10 39									11 09			
Beckenham Hill d									10 41									11 11			
Bellingham d									10 43									11 13			
Catford d									10 45									11 15			
Crofton Park d									10 48									11 18			
Lewisham 4 d	10 20										10 50									11 20	
Nunhead 4 d	10 25								10 50		10 55							11 20		11 25	
Peckham Rye 4 d	10 28								10 52		10 58							11 22		11 28	
Denmark Hill 4 d	10 31								10 55		11 01							11 25		11 31	
Beckenham Junction 4 d			10 23					10 38					10 53				11 08				
Kent House 4 d			10 25					10 40					10 55				11 10				
Penge East d			10 27					10 42					10 57				11 12				
Sydenham Hill d			10 30					10 45					11 00				11 15				
West Dulwich d			10 32					10 47					11 02				11 17				
Herne Hill 4 d		10 26	10 35				10 41	10 50				10 56	11 05			11 11	11 20				11 26
Loughborough Jn d		10 30					10 45					11 00				11 15					11 30
Elephant & Castle ⊖ d		10 35					10 50		11 00			11 05				11 20		11 30			11 35
London Blackfriars 3 ⊖ d		10 43					10 58		11a03			11 13				11 28		11a33			11 43
City Thameslink 3 a		10 45					11 00					11 15				11 30					11 45
Farringdon ⊖ a		10 49					11 04					11 19				11 34					11 49
St Pancras International 3 ⊖ a		10 53					11 08					11 23				11 38					11 53
Brixton ⊖ d			10 37					10 52					11 07				11 22				
London Victoria 15 ⊖ a	10 42		10 44		10 47	10 47		10 59		11 02	11 12		11 14	11 17	11 17		11 29		11 32	11 42	

For general notes see front of timetable
For details of catering facilities see
Directory of Train Operators

Sevenoaks, Otford, Orpington, Bromley South, Beckenham Junction and Catford → London

Network Diagram - see first page of Table 195

		SE 70			SE 92 1	SE 30 1	FC	SE 70	SE 83	SE 94	SE 78		FC	SE 70	SE 92 1	SE 30 1	FC	SE 70	SE 83		SE 64 1 A	FC	SE 70	SE 92 1
Sevenoaks 4	d								18 04										18 34					
Bat & Ball	d								18 07										18 37					
Otford 4	d								18 10	18 26									18 40		18 55			
Shoreham (Kent)	d								18 13										18 43					
Eynsford	d								18 17										18 47					
Swanley 4	d				18 12				18 22	18 35					18 42				18 52		19 04			19 12
St Mary Cray	d				18 17				18 26						18 47				18 56		19 08			19 17
Orpington 4	d	11 08						18 23						18 38				18 53					19 08	
Petts Wood 4	d	11 11						18 26						18 41				18 56					19 11	
Bickley 4	d	11 15						18 30	18 31					18 45				19 00	19 01				19 15	
Bromley South 4	d	11 18			18 24	18 30		18 33	18 35	18 45				18 48	18 54	19 00		19 03	19 05		19 15		19 18	19 24
Shortlands 4	d	11 20	and at					18 35	18 37					18 50				19 05	19 07				19 20	
Ravensbourne	d		the same						18 39										19 09					
Beckenham Hill	d								18 41										19 11					
Bellingham	d		minutes						18 43										19 13					
Catford	d								18 45										19 15					
Crofton Park	d		past						18 48										19 18					
Lewisham 4	d		each								18 50													
Nunhead 4	d								18 50		18 55								19 20					
Peckham Rye 4	d		hour until						18 52		18 58								19 22					
Denmark Hill 4	d								18 55		19 01								19 25					
Beckenham Junction 4	d	11 23						18 38						18 53				19 08					19 23	
Kent House 4	d	11 25						18 40						18 55				19 10					19 25	
Penge East	d	11 27						18 42						18 57				19 12					19 27	
Sydenham Hill	d	11 30						18 45						19 00				19 15					19 30	
West Dulwich	d	11 32						18 47						19 02				19 17					19 32	
Herne Hill 4	d	11 35					18 41	18 50					18 56	19 05			19 11	19 20				19 26	19 35	
Loughborough Jn	d						18 45						19 00				19 15					19 30		
Elephant & Castle	⊖ d						18 50		19 00				19 05				19 20		19 30			19 35		
London Blackfriars 3	⊖ d						18 58		19a03				19 13				19 28		19a33			19 43		
City Thameslink 3	a						19 00						19 15				19 30					19 45		
Farringdon	⊖ a						19 04						19 19				19 34					19 49		
St Pancras International 3	⊖ a						19 08						19 23				19 38					19 53		
Brixton	⊖ d	11 37						18 52						19 07				19 22					19 37	
London Victoria 15	⊖ a	11 44			18 47	18 47		18 59		19 02	19 12			19 14	19 17	19 17		19 29			19 32		19 44	19 47

		SE 30 1	FC	SE 70	SE 83	SE 70		SE 92 1	SE 30 1	FC	SE 70	SE 83	SE 94 1	SE 70		SE 92 1	SE 30 1	FC	SE 83	SE 70	SE 92 1	FC		SE 83	SE 94 1
Sevenoaks 4	d				19 04							19 34							20 04					20 34	
Bat & Ball	d				19 07							19 37							20 07					20 37	
Otford 4	d				19 10							19 40	19 55						20 10					20 40	20 55
Shoreham (Kent)	d				19 13							19 43							20 13					20 43	
Eynsford	d				19 17							19 47							20 17					20 47	
Swanley 4	d				19 22			19 42				19 52	20 04			20 12			20 22		20 42			20 52	21 04
St Mary Cray	d				19 26			19 47				19 56	20 08			20 17			20 26		20 47			20 56	21 08
Orpington 4	d			19 23		19 38					19 53			20 08						20 38					
Petts Wood 4	d			19 26		19 41					19 56			20 11						20 41					
Bickley 4	d			19 30	19 31	19 45					20 00	20 01		20 15					20 31	20 45				21 01	
Bromley South 4	d	19 30		19 33	19 35	19 48		19 54	20 00		20 03	20 05	20 15	20 18		20 24	20 30		20 35	20 48	20 54			21 05	21 15
Shortlands 4	d			19 35	19 37	19 50					20 05	20 07		20 20					20 37	20 50				21 07	
Ravensbourne	d				19 39							20 09							20 39					21 09	
Beckenham Hill	d				19 41							20 11							20 41					21 11	
Bellingham	d				19 43							20 13							20 43					21 13	
Catford	d				19 45							20 15							20 45					21 15	
Crofton Park	d				19 48							20 18							20 48					21 18	
Lewisham 4	d																								
Nunhead 4	d				19 50							20 20							20 50					21 20	
Peckham Rye 4	d				19 52							20 22							20 52					21 22	
Denmark Hill 4	d				19 55							20 25							20 55					21 25	
Beckenham Junction 4	d			19 38		19 53					20 08			20 23						20 53					
Kent House 4	d			19 40		19 55					20 10			20 25						20 55					
Penge East	d			19 42		19 57					20 12			20 27						20 57					
Sydenham Hill	d			19 45		20 00					20 15			20 30						21 00					
West Dulwich	d			19 47		20 02					20 17			20 32						21 02					
Herne Hill 4	d		19 41	19 50		20 05				20 11	20 20			20 35				20 41		21 05		21 11			
Loughborough Jn	d		19 45							20 15								20 45				21 15			
Elephant & Castle	⊖ d		19 50		20 00					20 20		20 30						20 50	21 00			21 20		21 30	
London Blackfriars 3	⊖ d		19 58		20a03					20 28		20a33						20 58	21a03			21b33		21a33	
City Thameslink 3	a		20 00							20 30								21 00							
Farringdon	⊖ a		20 04							20 34								21 04				21 38			
St Pancras International 3	⊖ a		20 08							20 38								21 08				21 42			
Brixton	⊖ d			19 52		20 07					20 22			20 37						21 07					
London Victoria 15	⊖ a	19 47		19 59		20 14		20 17	20 17		20 29		20 32	20 44		20 47	20 47			21 14	21 17				21 32

For general notes see front of timetable
For details of catering facilities see Directory of Train Operators

A From Canterbury West (Table 207)
b Arr. 2126

Table 195

Saturdays

Sevenoaks, Otford, Orpington, Bromley South, Beckenham Junction and Catford → London

Network Diagram - see first page of Table 195

Station		SE	SE	SE	FC	SE	SE	SE		SE	FC	SE	SE	SE	FC	SE		SE	SE	SE	SE	SE	SE		
		70	30	83		70	92	83		94		70	30	83		70		90	83	94	70	50	90		
			1				1			1			1					1		1		1	1		
Sevenoaks 4	d			21 04				21 34						22 04					22 34						
Bat & Ball	d			21 07				21 37						22 07					22 37						
Otford 4	d			21 10				21 40		21 55				22 10					22 40	22 55					
Shoreham (Kent)	d			21 13				21 43						22 13					22 43						
Eynsford	d			21 17				21 47						22 17					22 47						
Swanley 4	d			21 22			21 42	21 52		22 04				22 22				22 42	22 52	23 04			23 42		
St Mary Cray	d			21 26			21 47	21 56		22 08				22 26				22 47	22 56	23 08			23 47		
Orpington 4	d	21 08				21 38						22 08				22 38					23 08				
Petts Wood 4	d	21 11				21 41						22 11				22 41					23 11				
Bickley 4	d	21 15		21 31		21 45		22 01				22 15		22 31		22 45			23 01		23 15				
Bromley South 4	d	21 18	21 30	21 35		21 48	21 54	22 05		22 15		22 18	22 30	22 35		22 48		22 54	23 05	23 15	23 18	23 30	23 54		
Shortlands 4	d	21 20		21 37		21 50		22 07				22 20		22 37		22 50			23 07		23 20				
Ravensbourne	d			21 39				22 09						22 39					23 09						
Beckenham Hill	d			21 41				22 11						22 41					23 11						
Bellingham	d			21 43				22 13						22 43					23 13						
Catford	d			21 45				22 15						22 45					23 15						
Crofton Park	d			21 48				22 18						22 48					23 18						
Lewisham 4	d																								
Nunhead 4	d			21 50				22 20						22 50					23 20						
Peckham Rye 4	d			21 52				22 22						22 52					23 22						
Denmark Hill 4	d			21 55				22 25						22 55					23 25						
Beckenham Junction 4	d	21 23				21 53						22 23				22 53					23 23				
Kent House 4	d	21 25				21 55						22 25				22 55					23 25				
Penge East	d	21 27				21 57						22 27				22 57					23 27				
Sydenham Hill	d	21 30				22 00						22 30				23 00					23 30				
West Dulwich	d	21 32				22 02						22 32				23 02					23 32				
Herne Hill 4	d	21 35			21 56	22 05					22 26	22 35			22 56	23 05					23 35				
Loughborough Jn	d				22 00						22 30														
Elephant & Castle	⊖ d			22 00	22 05			22 30			22 35			23 00	23 05				23 30						
London Blackfriars 3	⊖ d			22a03	22 08			22a33			22 38			23a03	23 08				23a33						
City Thameslink 3	a																								
Farringdon	⊖ a				22 13						22 43				23 13										
St Pancras International 3	⊖ a				22 17						22 47				23 17										
Brixton	⊖ d	21 37				22 07						22 37				23 07					23 37				
London Victoria 15	⊖ a	21 44	21 47			22 14	22 17			22 32		22 44	22 47			23 14		23 17		23 32	23 44	23 47	00 10		

Sundays

Station		SE	SE	SE	SE	SE	SE	SE	SE	SE	SE	SE	SE	SE	SE	SE	SE	SE	SE	SE	SE		SE	SE	FC
		72	70	55	70	50	72	70	55	72	94	70	30	72	70	92	72	94	70	30	72		70	92	
				1		1			1		1		1			1		1		1				1	
Sevenoaks 4	d									08 11							09 11								
Bat & Ball	d									08 14							09 14								
Otford 4	d									08 17	08 24						09 17	09 24							
Shoreham (Kent)	d									08 20							09 20								
Eynsford	d									08 24							09 24								
Swanley 4	d			07 15					08 12	08 29	08 33					09 13	09 29	09 33						10 13	
St Mary Cray	d			07 19					08 17	08 33	08 38					09 18	09 33	09 38						10 18	
Orpington 4	d	07 01	07 08		07 38		08 01	08 08				08 38		09 01	09 08				09 38		10 01		10 08		
Petts Wood 4	d	07 04	07 11		07 41		08 04	08 11				08 41		09 04	09 11				09 41		10 04		10 11		
Bickley 4	d	07 08	07 16		07 46		08 08	08 16		08 38		08 46		09 08	09 16		09 38		09 46		10 08		10 16		
Bromley South 4	d	07 11	07 19	07 26	07 49	08 00	08 11	08 19	08b27	08 41	08 44	08 49	09 00	09 11	09 19	09 24	09 41	09 44	09 49	10 00	10 11		10 19	10 24	
Shortlands 4	d	07 13	07 21		07 51		08 13	08 21		08 43		08 51		09 13	09 21		09 43		09 51		10 13		10 21		
Ravensbourne	d	07 15					08 15			08 45				09 15			09 45				10 15				
Beckenham Hill	d	07 17					08 17			08 47				09 17			09 47				10 17				
Bellingham	d	07 19					08 19			08 49				09 19			09 49				10 19				
Catford	d	07 21					08 21			08 51				09 21			09 51				10 21				
Crofton Park	d	07 24					08 24			08 54				09 24			09 54				10 24				
Lewisham 4	d																								
Nunhead 4	d	07 26					08 26			08 56				09 26			09 56				10 26				
Peckham Rye 4	d	07 28					08 28			08 58				09 28			09 58				10 28				
Denmark Hill 4	d	07 31					08 31			09 01				09 31			10 01				10 31				
Beckenham Junction 4	d		07 23		07 53			08 23				08 53			09 23				09 53				10 23		
Kent House 4	d		07 25		07 55			08 25				08 55			09 25				09 55				10 25		
Penge East	d		07 27		07 57			08 27				08 57			09 27				09 57				10 27		
Sydenham Hill	d		07 30		08 00			08 30				09 00			09 30				10 00				10 30		
West Dulwich	d		07 32		08 02			08 32				09 02			09 32				10 02				10 32		
Herne Hill 4	d		07 34		08 04			08 34				09 04			09 34				10 04				10 34		10 42
Loughborough Jn	d																								10 45
Elephant & Castle	⊖ d																								10 50
London Blackfriars 3	⊖ d																								10 58
City Thameslink 3	a																								
Farringdon	⊖ a																								11 02
St Pancras International 3	⊖ a																								11 06
Brixton	⊖ d		07 36		08 06			08 36				09 06			09 36				10 06				10 36		
London Victoria 15	⊖ a	07 41	07 43	07 48	08 13	08 16	08 41	08 43	08 49	09 11	09 01	09 13	09 16	09 41	09 43	09 47	10 11	10 01	10 13	10 16	10 41		10 43	10 47	

For general notes see front of timetable
For details of catering facilities see
Directory of Train Operators

b Arr. 0823

Sundays

Sevenoaks, Otford, Orpington, Bromley South, Beckenham Junction and Catford → London

Network Diagram - see first page of Table 195

	SE 72	SE 94 [1]	SE 70	SE 30 [1] ✕	FC	SE 72		SE 70	SE 92 [1]	FC	SE 72	SE 94 [1]	SE 70	SE 30 [1]	FC	SE 70	SE 92 [1]	FC	SE 72	SE 94 [1]	SE 70	SE 30 [1]	FC
Sevenoaks [4] d	10 11					10 41					18 11								19 11				
Bat & Ball d	10 14					10 44					18 14								19 14				
Otford [4] d	10 17	10 24				10 47					18 17	18 24							19 17	19 24			
Shoreham (Kent) d	10 20					10 50					18 20								19 20				
Eynsford d	10 24					10 54					18 24								19 24				
Swanley [4] d	10 29	10 33				10 59			18 13		18 29	18 33					19 13		19 29	19 33			
St Mary Cray d	10 33	10 38				11 03			18 18		18 33	18 38					19 17		19 33	19 38			
Orpington [4] d			10 38					18 08					18 38			19 08					19 38		
Petts Wood [4] d			10 41					18 11					18 41			19 11					19 41		
Bickley [4] d	10 38		10 46			11 08		18 16			18 38		18 46			19 16			19 38		19 46		
Bromley South [4] d	10 41	10 44	10 49	11 00		11 11		18 19	18 24		18 41	18 44	18 49	19 00		19 19	19 24		19 41	19 44	19 49	20 00	
Shortlands [4] d	10 43		10 51			11 13	and at	18 21			18 43		18 51			19 21			19 43		19 51		
Ravensbourne d	10 45					11 15	the same				18 45								19 45				
Beckenham Hill d	10 47					11 17					18 47								19 47				
Bellingham d	10 49					11 19	minutes				18 49								19 49				
Catford d	10 51					11 21					18 51								19 51				
Crofton Park d	10 54					11 24	past				18 54								19 54				
Lewisham [4] d							each																
Nunhead [4] d	10 56					11 26					18 56								19 56				
Peckham Rye [4] d	10 58					11 28	hour until				18 58								19 58				
Denmark Hill [4] d	11 01					11 31					19 01								20 01				
Beckenham Junction [4] d			10 53					18 23					18 53			19 23					19 53		
Kent House [4] d			10 55					18 25					18 55			19 25					19 55		
Penge East d			10 57					18 27					18 57			19 27					19 57		
Sydenham Hill d			11 00					18 30					19 00			19 30					20 00		
West Dulwich d			11 02					18 32					19 02			19 32					20 02		
Herne Hill [4] d			11 04		11 12			18 34		18 42			19 04		19 12	19 34		19 42			20 04		20 12
Loughborough Jn d					11 15					18 44					19 14			19 44					20 14
Elephant & Castle ⊖ d					11 20					18 50					19 20			19 50					20 20
London Blackfriars [3] ⊖ d					11 28					18 58					19 28			19 58					20 28
City Thameslink [3] a																							
Farringdon ⊖ a					11 32					19 02					19 32			20 02					20 32
St Pancras International [3] ⊖ a					11 36					19 06					19 36			20 06					20 36
Brixton ⊖ d			11 06					18 36					19 06			19 36					20 06		
London Victoria [15] ⊖ a	11 11	11 01	11 13	11 16		11 41		18 43	18 47		19 11	19 01	19 13	19 16		19 43	19 47		20 11	20 01	20 13	20 16	

	SE 70	SE 92 [1]	FC	SE 72	SE 94 [1]	SE 70	SE 30 [1]	FC	SE 70	SE 92 [1]	FC	SE 72	SE 94 [1]	SE 70	SE 30 [1]	SE 70	SE 92 [1] A	SE 94 [1]	SE 70	SE 30 [1]	SE 92 [1] A	SE 50 [1]
Sevenoaks [4] d				20 11								21 11										
Bat & Ball d				20 14								21 14										
Otford [4] d				20 17	20 24							21 17	21 24					22 24				
Shoreham (Kent) d				20 20								21 20										
Eynsford d				20 24								21 24										
Swanley [4] d		20 13		20 29	20 33					21 13		21 29	21 33				22 14	22 33			23 13	
St Mary Cray d		20 18		20 33	20 38					21 18		21 33	21 38				22 18	22 38			23 17	
Orpington [4] d	20 08					20 38			21 08					21 38		22 08			22 38			
Petts Wood [4] d	20 11					20 41			21 11					21 41		22 11			22 41			
Bickley [4] d	20 16			20 38		20 46			21 16			21 38		21 46		22 16			22 46			
Bromley South [4] d	20 19	20 24		20 41	20 44	20 49	21 00		21 19	21 24		21 41	21 44	21 49	22 00	22 19	22 25	22 44	22 49	23 00	23 24	23 33
Shortlands [4] d	20 21			20 43		20 51			21 21			21 43		21 51		22 21			22 51			
Ravensbourne d				20 45								21 45										
Beckenham Hill d				20 47								21 47										
Bellingham d				20 49								21 49					22 30				23 29	
Catford d				20 51								21 51					22 32				23 31	
Crofton Park d				20 54								21 54										
Lewisham [4] d																						
Nunhead [4] d				20 56								21 56										
Peckham Rye [4] d				20 58								21 58					22 36				23 35	
Denmark Hill [4] d				21 01								22 01					22 38				23 37	
Beckenham Junction [4] d	20 23					20 53			21 23					21 53		22 23			22 53			
Kent House [4] d	20 25					20 55			21 25					21 55		22 25			22 55			
Penge East d	20 27					20 57			21 27					21 57		22 27			22 57			
Sydenham Hill d	20 30					21 00			21 30					22 00		22 30			23 00			
West Dulwich d	20 32					21 02			21 32					22 02		22 32			23 02			
Herne Hill [4] d	20 34		20 42			21 04		21 12	21 34		21 42			22 04		22 34			23 04			
Loughborough Jn d			20 44					21 14			21 44											
Elephant & Castle ⊖ d			20 50					21 20			21 50											
London Blackfriars [3] ⊖ d			20 58					21 28			21 58											
City Thameslink [3] a																						
Farringdon ⊖ a			21 02					21 32			22 02											
St Pancras International [3] ⊖ a			21 06					21 36			22 06											
Brixton ⊖ d	20 36					21 06			21 36					22 06		22 36			23 06			
London Victoria [15] ⊖ a	20 43	20 47		21 11	21 01	21 13	21 16		21 43	21 47		22 11	22 01	22 13	22 16	22 43	22 49	23 01	23 13	23 16	23 48	23 49

For general notes see front of timetable
For details of catering facilities see
Directory of Train Operators

A From Faversham (Table 212)

For details of Bank Holiday service alterations please see first page of Table 195

London → Maidstone East and Ashford International

Network Diagram - see first page of Table 195

Miles	Miles	Miles			SE	SE	SE	SE	SE	SE	SE	SE	SE	SE	SE	SE	SE	SE	SE	SE
					MX	MX														
					66	94	64	64	66	64	64	96	64	94	09	64	94	09	64	94
					1	1	1	1	1	1	1	1	1		1	1		1	1	
					A		B	C	C	B	A		A			A			A	
0	—	—	**London Victoria 15**	⊖ 195 d	23p11	23p51			06 10	06 47	07 19	07 49	08 18	08 49		09 19	09 48		10 18	10 48
—	0	—	**London Blackfriars 3**	⊖ 195 d																
—	$1\frac{1}{4}$	—	Elephant & Castle	⊖ 195 d																
4	—	—	Herne Hill 4	195 d																
$8\frac{3}{4}$	—	—	Beckenham Junction 4	195 ⛴ d																
11	$11\frac{1}{2}$	—	Bromley South 4	195 d	23p30	00 07			06 30	07 04	07 36	08 07	08 39	09 08		09 37	10 04		10 34	11 04
—	—	—	London Charing Cross 4	⊖ d																
—	—	—	London Waterloo (East) 4	⊖ d																
—	—	0	**London Cannon Street 4**	⊖ d											09 13			10 14		
—	—	$\frac{3}{4}$	London Bridge 4	⊖ d											09 17			10 18		
$14\frac{3}{4}$	—	—	St Mary Cray	195 d	23p37	00 14														
$17\frac{1}{2}$	—	—	Swanley 4	195 d	23p41	00 18			06 39	07 13	07 45	08 17		09 16			10 13			11 13
24	—	—	Otford 4	195 d	23p50	00 30			06 49	07 22	07 54	08 26	08 57	09 25		09 53	10 23		10 51	11 23
27	—	—	Kemsing	d					06 55	07 27	07 58	08 30		09 30			10 27			11 27
$29\frac{1}{2}$	—	—	Borough Green & Wrotham	d	23p57	00 37			06 59	07 31	08 03	08 35	09 04	09 34		10 00	10 32		10 58	11 32
$34\frac{3}{4}$	—	—	West Malling	d	00 03	00 43			07 05	07 37	08 09	08 41	09 10	09 40	09 57	10 06	10 38	10 57	11 04	11 38
$35\frac{3}{4}$	—	—	East Malling	d	00 06	00 46			07 08	07 40	08 11	08 43		09 43			10 41			11 41
$37\frac{1}{2}$	—	—	Barming	d	00 09	00 49			07 11	07 43	08 15	08 47		09 46			10 44			11 44
40	—	$37\frac{3}{4}$	**Maidstone East 4**	a	00 14	00 54			07 16	07 48	08 19	08 51	09 17	09 51	10 05	10 13	10 49	11 05	11 11	11 49
—	—	—		d	00 14	00 54	05 56	06 33	07 23	07 49	08 21		09 17		10 05	10 14		11 05	11 13	
$42\frac{3}{4}$	—	—	Bearsted	d	00 19	00 59	06 01	06 38	07 28	07 54	08 26		09 22		10 11	10 19		11 11	11 18	
45	—	—	Hollingbourne	d	00 23	01 03	06 05	06 42	07 32	07 58	08 30		09 26			10 23			11 22	
$47\frac{1}{2}$	—	—	Harrietsham	d	00 27	01 07	06 09	06 46	07 36	08 02	08 34		09 30			10 27			11 26	
$49\frac{1}{4}$	—	—	Lenham	d	00 31	01 11	06 12	06 49	07 39	08 06	08 37		09 34			10 30			11 30	
$53\frac{1}{4}$	—	—	Charing	d	00 36	01 16	06 17	06 54	07 44	08 11	08 42		09 39			10 35			11 35	
$59\frac{1}{4}$	—	57	**Ashford International**	a	00 43	01 23	06 25	07 02	07 52	08 21	08 53		09 46		10 28	10 43		11 28	11 43	

		SE	SE	SE	SE	SE	SE	SE	SE	SE	SE	SE	SE	SE	SE	SE	SE	SE	SE	SE
		09	64	94	09	64	94	09	64	94	09	94	94	09	94	94	09	96	94	94
		1	1		1	1		1	1		1	1	1	1	1	1	1	1	1	1
			A			A			A											
London Victoria 15	⊖ 195 d		11 18	11 48		12 18	12 48		13 18	13 48		14 18	14 48		15 18	15 48		16 27	16 56	17 22
London Blackfriars 3	⊖ 195 d																			
Elephant & Castle	⊖ 195 d																			
Herne Hill 4	195 d																			
Beckenham Junction 4	195 ⛴ d																			
Bromley South 4	195 d		11 34	12 04		12 34	13 04		13 34	14 04		14 34	15 04		15 34	16 04		16 48	17 15	17 40
London Charing Cross 4	⊖ d																			
London Waterloo (East) 4	⊖ d																			
London Cannon Street 4	⊖ d	11 14			12 14			13 14			14 14			15 14			16 14			
London Bridge 4	⊖ d	11 18			12 18			13 18			14 18			15 18			16 18			
St Mary Cray	195 d																			17 47
Swanley 4	195 d			12 13			13 13			14 13			15 13		15 43	16 13		16 57		17 52
Otford 4	195 d		11 51	12 23		12 51	13 23		13 51	14 23		14 51	15 23		15 52	16 23	16 48	17 07	17 33	18 01
Kemsing	d			12 27			13 27			14 27			15 27		15 57			17 12		18 06
Borough Green & Wrotham	d		11 58	12 32		12 58	13 32		13 58	14 32		14 58	15 32		16 02	16 30		17 16	17 40	18 11
West Malling	d	11 57	12 04	12 38	12 57	13 04	13 38	13 57	14 04	14 38	14 57	15 04	15 38	15 57	16 08	16 36	17 00	17 22	17 46	18 17
East Malling	d			12 41			13 41			14 41			15 41		16 11			17 25		18 19
Barming	d			12 44			13 44			14 44			15 44		16 14			17 28		18 23
Maidstone East 4	a	12 05	12 11	12 49	13 05	13 11	13 49	14 05	14 11	14 49	15 05	15 11	15 49	16 05	16 19	16 44	17 07	17 33	17 53	18 27
	d	12 05	12 13		13 05	13 13		14 05	14 13		15 05	15 21	15 50	16 05	16 19	16 44	17 07	17 34	17 54	18 29
Bearsted	d	12 11	12 18		13 11	13 18		14 11	14 18		15 11	15 26	15 55	16 11	16 24	16 49	17 13	17 39	17 59	18 34
Hollingbourne	d		12 22			13 22			14 22			15 30			16 28	16 53	17 17	17 43	18 03	18 38
Harrietsham	d		12 26			13 26			14 26			15 34			16 32	16 57	17 21	17 47	18 07	18 42
Lenham	d		12 30			13 30			14 30			15 40	16 03		16 36	17 01	17 24	17 51	18 10	18 45
Charing	d		12 35			13 35			14 35			15 45			16 41	17 06	17 29	17 56	18 15	18 50
Ashford International	a	12 29	12 43		13 28	13 43		14 28	14 43		15 27	15 54	16 14	16 28	16 48	17 13	17 38	18 05	18 23	18 58

		SE	SE	SE	SE	SE	SE	SE	SE	SE	SE	SE	SE	SE	SE
		96	96	97	94	94	09	94	94	94	94	96	96	66	94
			1	1	1	1	1	1	1	1	1	1	1	1	1
														A	
London Victoria 15	⊖ 195 d	17 32	17 58		18 18	18 48		19 18	19 48	20 18	20 48	21 09	22 09	23 11	23 51
London Blackfriars 3	⊖ 195 d			18 00											
Elephant & Castle	⊖ 195 d			18 04											
Herne Hill 4	195 d														
Beckenham Junction 4	195 ⛴ d	17 46								20 32	21 02				
Bromley South 4	195 d	17 51	18 18	18 22	18 36	19 06		19 35	20 07	20 37	21 07	21 29	22 29	23 30	00 07
London Charing Cross 4	⊖ d														
London Waterloo (East) 4	⊖ d														
London Cannon Street 4	⊖ d						19 14								
London Bridge 4	⊖ d						19 18								
St Mary Cray	195 d	18 00		18 28	18 43	19 12						21 35	22 35	23 37	00 14
Swanley 4	195 d	18 05		18 33	18 48	19 16		19 44		20 45		21 40	22 40	23 41	00 18
Otford 4	195 d	18 18	18 36	18 42	18 58	19 26	19 48	19 53	20 23	20 54	21 23	21 49	22 49	23 50	00 30
Kemsing	d	18 22		18 46	19 02			19 58		20 59					
Borough Green & Wrotham	d	18 27	18 43	18 51	19 07	19 33		20 02	20 30	21 03	21 30	21 56	22 56	23 57	00 37
West Malling	d	18 33	18 49	18 57	19 13	19 39	20 00	20 08	20 36	21 09	21 36	22 02	23 02	00 03	00 43
East Malling	d	18 35		18 59	19 15	19 41		20 11		21 12		22 04	23 04	00 06	00 46
Barming	d	18 39		19 03	19 19	19 45		20 14		21 15		22 08	23 08	00 09	00 49
Maidstone East 4	a	18 44	18 56	19 07	19 23	19 49	20 07	20 19	20 43	21 20	21 43	22 12	23 12	00 14	00 54
	d		18 56	19 08	19 25	19 50	20 08	20 20	20 44	21 21	21 44	22 13	23 13	00 14	00 54
Bearsted	d		19 01	19 13	19 30	19 55	20 13	20 25	20 49	21 26	21 49	22 18	23 18	00 19	00 59
Hollingbourne	d		19 05	19 17	19 34	19 59		20 29	20 53	21 30	21 53	22 22	23 22	00 23	01 03
Harrietsham	d		19 09	19 21	19 38	20 03		20 33	20 57	21 34	21 57	22 26	23 26	00 27	01 07
Lenham	d		19 13	19 24	19 41	20 07		20 36	21 01	21 37	22 01	22 30	23 30	00 31	01 11
Charing	d		19 18	19 29	19 46	20 12		20 41	21 06	21 42	22 06	22 35	23 35	00 36	01 16
Ashford International	a		19 26	19 37	19 55	20 19	20 32	20 49	21 14	21 50	22 15	22 42	23 42	00 43	01 23

For general notes see front of timetable
For details of catering facilities see Directory of Train Operators

A To Canterbury West (Table 207)
B To Ramsgate (Table 207)
C To Margate (Table 207)

Table 196

Saturdays

London → Maidstone East and Ashford International

Network Diagram - see first page of Table 195

	SE 66 ■1 A	SE 94 ■1	SE 64 ■1 B	SE 94 ■1 C	SE 64 ■1 C	SE 94 ■1	SE 64 ■1 A	SE 94	SE 09 ■1	SE 64 ■1 A	SE 94	SE 09 ■1	SE 64 ■1 A	SE 94	SE 09 ■1		SE 64 ■1 A	SE 94	SE 09 ■1	SE 64 ■1 A	SE 94	SE 09 ■1	SE 64 ■1 A	SE 94
London Victoria 15 ⊖ 195 d	23p11	23p51	.	06 18	07 18	07 48	08 18	08 48	.	09 18	09 48	.	10 18	10 48	.	.	11 18	11 48	.	12 18	12 48	.	13 18	13 48
London Blackfriars 3 ⊖ 195 d	.	.	.	.	.	.	.	.	.	.	.	.	.	.	.	.	.	.	.	.	.	.	.	.
Elephant & Castle ⊖ 195 d	.	.	.	.	.	.	.	.	.	.	.	.	.	.	.	.	.	.	.	.	.	.	.	.
Herne Hill 4 195 d	.	.	.	.	.	.	.	.	.	.	.	.	.	.	.	.	.	.	.	.	.	.	.	.
Beckenham Junction 4 195 🚊 d	.	.	.	.	.	.	.	.	.	.	.	.	.	.	.	.	.	.	.	.	.	.	.	.
Bromley South 4 195 d	23p30	00 07	.	06 34	07 34	08 04	08 34	09 04	.	09 34	10 04	.	10 34	11 04	.	.	11 34	12 04	.	12 34	13 04	.	13 34	14 04
London Charing Cross 4 ⊖ d	.	.	.	.	.	.	.	.	.	.	.	.	.	.	.	.	.	.	.	.	.	.	.	.
London Waterloo (East) 4 ⊖ d	.	.	.	.	.	.	.	.	.	.	.	.	.	.	.	.	.	.	.	.	.	.	.	.
London Cannon Street 4 ⊖ d	.	.	.	.	.	.	.	.	09 14	.	.	10 14	.	.	11 14	.	.	.	12 14	.	.	13 14	.	.
London Bridge 4 ⊖ d	.	.	.	.	.	.	.	.	09 18	.	.	10 18	.	.	11 18	.	.	.	12 18	.	.	13 18	.	.
St Mary Cray 195 d	23p37	00 14	.	06 41	07 41	.	.	.	.	.	.	.	.	.	.	.	.	.	.	.	.	.	.	.
Swanley 4 195 d	23p41	00 18	.	06 45	07 45	08 13	.	09 13	.	.	10 13	.	.	11 13	.	.	.	12 13	.	.	13 13	.	.	14 13
Otford 4 195 d	23p50	00 30	.	06 54	07 54	08 23	08 51	09 23	.	09 51	10 23	.	10 51	11 23	.	.	11 51	12 23	.	12 51	13 23	.	13 51	14 23
Kemsing d	.	.	.	.	.	08 27	.	09 27	.	.	10 27	.	.	11 27	.	.	.	12 27	.	.	13 27	.	.	14 27
Borough Green & Wrotham d	23p57	00 37	.	07 02	08 02	08 32	08 58	09 32	.	09 58	10 32	.	10 58	11 32	.	.	11 58	12 32	.	12 58	13 32	.	13 58	14 32
West Malling d	00 03	00 43	.	07 08	08 08	08 38	09 04	09 38	09 57	10 04	10 38	10 57	11 04	11 38	11 57	.	12 04	12 38	12 57	13 04	13 38	13 57	14 04	14 38
East Malling d	00 06	00 46	.	07 10	08 10	08 41	.	09 41	.	.	10 41	.	.	11 41	.	.	.	12 41	.	.	13 41	.	.	14 41
Barming d	00 09	00 49	.	07 14	08 14	08 44	.	09 44	.	.	10 44	.	.	11 44	.	.	.	12 44	.	.	13 44	.	.	14 44
Maidstone East 4 a	00 14	00 54	.	07 18	08 18	08 49	09 11	09 49	10 05	10 11	10 49	11 05	11 11	11 49	12 05	.	12 11	12 49	13 05	13 11	13 49	14 05	14 11	14 49
d	00 14	00 54	06 19	07 19	08 19	08 50	09 13	.	10 05	10 13	.	11 05	11 13	.	12 05	.	12 13	.	13 05	13 13	.	14 05	14 13	.
Bearsted d	00 19	00 59	06 24	07 24	08 24	08 55	09 18	.	10 11	10 18	.	11 11	11 18	.	12 11	.	12 18	.	13 11	13 18	.	14 11	14 18	.
Hollingbourne d	00 23	01 03	06 28	07 28	08 28	.	09 22	.	.	10 22	.	.	11 22	.	.	.	12 22	.	.	13 22	.	.	14 22	.
Harrietsham d	00 27	01 07	06 32	07 32	08 32	.	09 26	.	.	10 26	.	.	11 26	.	.	.	12 26	.	.	13 26	.	.	14 26	.
Lenham d	00 31	01 11	06 35	07 35	08 35	.	09 30	.	.	10 30	.	.	11 30	.	.	.	12 30	.	.	13 30	.	.	14 30	.
Charing d	00 36	01 16	06 40	07 40	08 40	.	09 35	.	.	10 35	.	.	11 35	.	.	.	12 35	.	.	13 35	.	.	14 35	.
Ashford International a	00 43	01 23	06 48	07 48	08 48	09 12	09 43	.	10 27	10 43	.	11 27	11 43	.	12 27	.	12 43	.	13 27	13 43	.	14 27	14 43	.

	SE 09 ■1	SE 64 ■1 A	SE 94	SE 09 ■1	SE 64 ■1 A	SE 94	SE 09 ■1	SE 94 ■1	SE 94	SE 09 ■1	SE 94 ■1	SE 94	SE 09 ■1	SE 94 ■1	SE 94 ■1	SE 09 ■1	SE 96 ■1	SE 96 ■1	SE 96 ■1	SE 96 ■1	SE 66 ■1 A	SE 94 ■1		
London Victoria 15 ⊖ 195 d	.	14 18	14 48	.	15 18	15 48	.	16 18	16 48	.	17 18	17 48	.	18 18	18 48	.	19 18	20 18	21 18	22 18	23 18	23 51	.	.
London Blackfriars 3 ⊖ 195 d	.	.	.	.	.	.	.	.	.	.	.	.	.	.	.	.	.	.	.	.	.	.	.	.
Elephant & Castle ⊖ 195 d	.	.	.	.	.	.	.	.	.	.	.	.	.	.	.	.	.	.	.	.	.	.	.	.
Herne Hill 4 195 d	.	.	.	.	.	.	.	.	.	.	.	.	.	.	.	.	.	.	.	.	.	.	.	.
Beckenham Junction 4 195 🚊 d	.	.	.	.	.	.	.	.	.	.	.	.	.	.	.	.	.	.	.	.	.	.	.	.
Bromley South 4 195 d	.	14 34	15 04	.	15 34	16 04	.	16 34	17 04	.	17 34	18 04	.	18 34	19 04	.	19 34	20 34	21 34	22 34	23 34	00 07	.	.
London Charing Cross 4 ⊖ d	.	.	.	.	.	.	.	.	.	.	.	.	.	.	.	.	.	.	.	.	.	.	.	.
London Waterloo (East) 4 ⊖ d	.	.	.	.	.	.	.	.	.	.	.	.	.	.	.	.	.	.	.	.	.	.	.	.
London Cannon Street 4 ⊖ d	14 14	.	.	15 14	.	.	16 14	.	.	17 14	.	.	18 14	.	.	19 14	.	.	.	.	.	.	.	.
London Bridge 4 ⊖ d	14 18	.	.	15 18	.	.	16 18	.	.	17 18	.	.	18 18	.	.	19 18	.	.	.	.	.	.	.	.
St Mary Cray 195 d	.	.	.	.	.	.	.	.	.	.	.	.	.	.	.	.	19 41	20 41	21 41	22 41	23 41	00 14	.	.
Swanley 4 195 d	.	.	15 13	.	.	16 13	.	.	17 13	.	.	18 13	.	.	19 13	.	19 45	20 45	21 45	22 45	23 45	00 18	.	.
Otford 4 195 d	.	14 51	15 23	.	15 51	16 23	.	16 51	17 23	.	17 51	18 23	.	18 51	19 23	.	19 54	20 54	21 54	22 54	23 54	00 30	.	.
Kemsing d	.	.	15 27	.	.	16 27	.	.	17 27	.	.	18 27	.	.	19 27	.	.	.	.	.	.	.	.	.
Borough Green & Wrotham d	.	14 58	15 32	.	15 58	16 32	.	16 58	17 32	.	17 58	18 32	.	18 58	19 32	.	20 02	21 02	22 02	23 02	00 02	00 37	.	.
West Malling d	14 57	15 04	15 38	15 57	16 04	16 38	16 57	17 04	17 38	17 57	18 04	18 38	18 57	19 04	19 38	19 57	20 08	21 08	22 08	23 08	00 08	00 43	.	.
East Malling d	.	.	15 41	.	.	16 41	.	.	17 41	.	.	18 41	.	.	19 41	.	20 10	21 10	22 10	23 10	00 10	00 46	.	.
Barming d	.	.	15 44	.	.	16 44	.	.	17 44	.	.	18 44	.	.	19 44	.	20 14	21 14	22 14	23 14	00 14	00 49	.	.
Maidstone East 4 a	15 05	15 11	15 49	16 05	16 11	16 49	17 05	17 11	17 49	18 05	18 11	18 49	19 05	19 11	19 49	20 05	20 18	21 18	22 18	23 18	00 18	00 54	.	.
d	15 05	15 13	.	16 05	16 13	.	17 05	17 13	.	18 05	18 13	.	19 05	19 13	.	20 05	20 19	21 19	22 19	23 19	00 19	00 54	.	.
Bearsted d	15 11	15 18	.	16 11	16 18	.	17 11	17 18	.	18 11	18 18	.	19 11	19 18	.	20 11	20 24	21 24	22 24	23 24	00 24	00 59	.	.
Hollingbourne d	.	15 22	.	.	16 22	.	.	17 22	.	.	18 22	.	.	19 22	.	.	20 28	21 28	22 28	23 28	00 28	01 03	.	.
Harrietsham d	.	15 26	.	.	16 26	.	.	17 26	.	.	18 26	.	.	19 26	.	.	20 32	21 32	22 32	23 32	00 32	01 07	.	.
Lenham d	.	15 30	.	.	16 30	.	.	17 29	.	.	18 29	.	.	19 29	.	.	20 35	21 35	22 35	23 35	00 35	01 11	.	.
Charing d	.	15 35	.	.	16 35	.	.	17 34	.	.	18 34	.	.	19 34	.	.	20 40	21 40	22 40	23 40	00 40	01 16	.	.
Ashford International a	15 27	15 43	.	16 27	16 43	.	17 27	17 43	.	18 27	18 42	.	19 27	19 42	.	20 27	20 48	21 48	22 48	23 48	00 48	01 23	.	.

For general notes see front of timetable
For details of catering facilities see Directory of Train Operators

A To Canterbury West (Table 207)
B To Margate (Table 207)
C To Ramsgate (Table 207)

Table 196

Sundays

London → Maidstone East and Ashford International

Network Diagram - see first page of Table 195

		SE	SE	SE	SE	SE	SE	SE	SE	SE	SE	SE	SE	SE	SE	SE	SE	SE
		66	94	94	94	94	94	94	94	94	94	94	94	94	94	94	94	94
		1	1	1	1	1	1	1	1	1	1	1	1	1	1	1	1	1
		A																
London Victoria 15	⊖ 195 d	23p18	23p51	08 18	09 18	10 18	11 18	12 18	13 18	14 18	15 18	16 18	17 18	18 18	19 18	20 18	21 18	22 18
London Blackfriars 3	⊖ 195 d																	
Elephant & Castle	⊖ 195 d																	
Herne Hill 4	195 d																	
Beckenham Junction 4	195 ⇌ d																	
Bromley South 4	195 d	23p34	00 07	08 34	09 34	10 34	11 34	12 34	13 34	14 34	15 34	16 34	17 34	18 34	19 34	20 34	21 34	22 35
London Charing Cross 4	⊖ d																	
London Waterloo (East) 4	⊖ d																	
London Cannon Street 4	⊖ d																	
London Bridge 4	⊖ d																	
St Mary Cray	195 d	23p41	00 14	08 41	09 41	10 41	11 41	12 41	13 41	14 41	15 41	16 41	17 41	18 41	19 41	20 41	21 41	22 41
Swanley 4	195 d	23p45	00 18	08 45	09 45	10 45	11 45	12 45	13 45	14 45	15 45	16 45	17 45	18 45	19 45	20 45	21 45	22 46
Otford 4	195 d	23p54	00 30	08 55	09 55	10 55	11 55	12 55	13 55	14 55	15 55	16 55	17 55	18 55	19 55	20 55	21 55	22 55
Kemsing	d																	
Borough Green & Wrotham	d	00 02	00 37	09 02	10 02	11 02	12 02	13 02	14 02	15 02	16 02	17 02	18 02	19 02	20 02	21 02	22 02	23 02
West Malling	d	00 08	00 43	09 08	10 08	11 08	12 08	13 08	14 08	15 08	16 08	17 08	18 08	19 08	20 08	21 08	22 08	23 08
East Malling	d	00 10	00 46	09 10	10 10	11 10	12 10	13 10	14 10	15 10	16 10	17 10	18 10	19 10	20 10	21 10	22 10	23 10
Barming	d	00 14	00 49	09 14	10 14	11 14	12 14	13 14	14 14	15 14	16 14	17 14	18 14	19 14	20 14	21 14	22 14	23 14
Maidstone East 4	a	00 18	00 54	09 18	10 18	11 18	12 18	13 18	14 18	15 18	16 18	17 18	18 18	19 18	20 18	21 18	22 18	23 18
	d	00 19	00 54	09 19	10 19	11 19	12 19	13 19	14 19	15 19	16 19	17 19	18 19	19 19	20 19	21 19	22 19	23 19
Bearsted	d	00 24	00 59	09 24	10 24	11 24	12 24	13 24	14 24	15 24	16 24	17 24	18 24	19 24	20 24	21 24	22 24	23 24
Hollingbourne	d	00 28	01 03	09 28	10 28	11 28	12 28	13 28	14 28	15 28	16 28	17 28	18 28	19 28	20 28	21 28	22 28	23 28
Harrietsham	d	00 32	01 07	09 32	10 32	11 32	12 32	13 32	14 32	15 32	16 32	17 32	18 32	19 32	20 32	21 32	22 32	23 32
Lenham	d	00 35	01 11	09 35	10 35	11 35	12 35	13 35	14 35	15 35	16 35	17 35	18 35	19 35	20 35	21 35	22 35	23 35
Charing	d	00 40	01 16	09 40	10 40	11 40	12 40	13 40	14 40	15 40	16 40	17 40	18 40	19 40	20 40	21 40	22 40	23 40
Ashford International	a	00 48	01 23	09 48	10 48	11 48	12 48	13 48	14 48	15 48	16 48	17 48	18 48	19 48	20 48	21 48	22 48	23 48

For general notes see front of timetable
For details of catering facilities see Directory of Train Operators

A To Canterbury West (Table 207)

For details of Bank Holiday service alterations please see first page of Table 195

Ashford International and Maidstone East to London

Network Diagram - see first page of Table 195

Miles	Miles	Miles	Station		SE 94 [1]	SE 97 [1]	SE 94 [1]	SE 97 [1]	SE 96 [1]	SE 94 [1]	SE 96 [1]	SE 96 [1]	SE 66 [1] A	SE 88 [1] B	SE 94 [1]	SE 64 [1] B	SE 09 [1]	SE 94	SE 64 [1] A	SE 09 [1]	SE 94	SE 64 [1] A	SE 09 [1]	SE 94	SE 64 [1] A
0	—	0	**Ashford International**	d	05 33	.	06 12	06 23	06 36	06 54	07 13	07 43	08 14	08 32	.	09 04	09 34	.	10 05	10 36	.	11 05	11 36	.	12 05
6	—	—	Charing	d	05 41	.	06 20	06 31	06 44	07 02	07 21	07 51	08 22	.	.	09 12	.	.	10 13	.	.	11 13	.	.	12 13
10	—	—	Lenham	d	05 46	.	06 25	06 36	06 49	07 07	07 26	07 56	08 27	.	.	09 17	.	.	10 19	.	.	11 18	.	.	12 18
11¾	—	—	Harrietsham	d	05 49	.	06 28	06 39	06 52	07 10	07 29	07 59	08 30	.	.	09 20	.	.	10 22	.	.	11 21	.	.	12 21
14¼	—	—	Hollingbourne	d	05 53	.	06 32	06 43	06 56	07 14	07 33	08 03	08 34	.	.	09 24	.	.	10 26	.	.	11 25	.	.	12 25
16½	—	—	Bearsted	d	05 57	06 09	06 36	06 47	07 00	07 18	07 37	08 07	08 38	08 48	.	09 28	09 51	.	10 29	10 52	.	11 29	11 52	.	12 29
19¼	—	19¼	**Maidstone East [4]**	a	06 02	06 14	06 41	06 52	07 05	07 23	07 42	08 12	08 43	08 53	.	09 33	09 56	.	10 34	10 57	.	11 34	11 57	.	12 34
—	—	—		d	06 03	06 15	06 41	06 52	07 05	07 23	07 42	08 13	08 45	08 53	09 00	09 33	09 57	10 00	10 35	10 57	11 00	11 34	11 57	12 00	12 34
21¾	—	—	Barming	d	06 07	.	06 46	06 57	07 10	07 28	07 47	08 18	.	.	09 04	.	.	10 04	.	.	11 04	.	.	12 04	.
23½	—	—	East Malling	d	06 11	.	06 49	07 00	07 13	07 31	.	08 21	.	.	09 08	.	.	10 08	.	.	11 08	.	.	12 08	.
24½	—	—	West Malling	d	06 13	06 23	06 52	07 03	07 16	07 34	07 51	08 24	08 52	09 01	09 10	09 41	10 05	10 10	10 42	11 05	11 10	11 42	12 05	12 10	12 42
29¾	—	—	Borough Green & Wrotham	d	06 20	06 30	06 59	07 10	07 23	07 41	07 59	08 31	08 59	.	09 17	09 48	.	10 17	10 50	.	11 17	11 49	.	12 17	12 49
32½	—	—	Kemsing	d	.	.	07 04	07 14	07 27	07 45	.	08 35	.	.	09 22	.	.	10 22	.	.	11 22	.	.	12 22	.
35¼	—	—	Otford [4] 195	a	06 28	06 38	07 09	07 19	07 32	07 50	08 07	08 40	09 07	.	09 27	09 56	.	10 27	10 57	.	11 27	11 57	.	12 27	12 57
41¾	—	—	Swanley [4] 195	a	.	06 48	07 18	07 29	07 43	08 00	.	08 49	.	.	09 36	10 05	.	10 36	.	.	11 36	.	.	12 36	.
44½	—	—	St Mary Cray 195	a	.	.	07 23	.	.	.	.	.	.	.	.	.	.	.	.	.	.	.	.	.	.
—	—	56¼	London Bridge [4] ⊖	a	.	.	.	.	.	.	.	.	.	09 39	.	.	10 50	.	.	11 50	.	.	12 50	.	.
—	—	57	**London Cannon Street [4]** ⊖	a	.	.	.	.	.	.	.	.	.	.	.	.	10 54	.	.	11 54	.	.	12 54	.	.
—	—	—	London Waterloo (East) [4] ⊖	a	.	.	.	.	.	.	.	.	.	09 45	.	.	.	.	.	.	.	.	.	.	.
—	—	—	London Charing Cross [4] ⊖	a	.	.	.	.	.	.	.	.	.	09 50	.	.	.	.	.	.	.	.	.	.	.
48¼	0	—	Bromley South [4] 195	a	06 47	06 57	07 29	07 40	07 54	.	08 25	08 59	09 27	.	09 44	10 14	.	10 44	11 14	.	11 44	12 14	.	12 44	13 14
50½	—	—	Beckenham Junction [4] 195 🚋	a	.	.	.	.	.	.	.	.	.	.	.	.	.	.	.	.	.	.	.	.	.
55¼	—	—	Herne Hill [4] 195	a	06 57	.	.	.	.	.	.	.	.	.	.	.	.	.	.	.	.	.	.	.	.
—	10¼	—	Elephant & Castle ⊖ 195	a	.	07 15	.	07 57	.	.	.	.	.	.	.	.	.	.	.	.	.	.	.	.	.
—	11½	—	**London Blackfriars [3]** ⊖ 195	a	.	07 18	.	08 03	.	.	.	.	.	.	.	.	.	.	.	.	.	.	.	.	.
59¼	—	—	**London Victoria [15]** ⊖ 195	a	07 08	.	07 49	.	08 17	08 31	08 53	09 18	09 50	.	10 02	10 32	.	11 02	11 32	.	12 02	12 32	.	13 02	13 32

Station		SE 09 [1]	SE 94	SE 64 [1] A	SE 09 [1]	SE 94	SE 64 [1] A	SE 09 [1]	SE 94	SE 64 [1] A	SE 88 [1]	SE 96	SE 64 [1] A	SE 88 [1]	SE 96 [1]	SE 94 [1]	SE 88 [1]	SE 94 [1]	SE 94 [1]	SE 94	SE 94 [1]	SE 94 [1] A	SE 94 [1]	SE 94 [1]
Ashford International	d	12 36	.	13 05	13 36	.	14 05	14 36	.	15 03	15 21	15 27	15 59	16 24	16 32	16 58	17 26	17 31	18 00	.	19 00	19 58	20 58	22 08
Charing	d	.	.	13 13	.	.	14 13	.	.	15 11	.	15 35	16 07	.	16 40	17 06	.	17 39	18 08	.	19 08	20 06	21 06	22 16
Lenham	d	.	.	13 18	.	.	14 18	.	.	15 16	.	15 40	16 12	.	16 45	17 11	.	17 44	18 13	.	19 13	20 11	21 11	22 21
Harrietsham	d	.	.	13 21	.	.	14 21	.	.	15 19	.	15 43	16 15	.	16 48	17 14	.	17 47	18 16	.	19 16	20 14	21 14	22 24
Hollingbourne	d	.	.	13 25	.	.	14 25	.	.	15 23	.	15 47	16 19	.	16 52	17 18	.	17 51	18 20	.	19 20	20 18	21 18	22 28
Bearsted	d	12 52	.	13 29	13 52	.	14 29	14 52	.	15 27	15 37	15 51	16 23	16 40	16 56	17 22	17 42	17 55	18 24	.	19 24	20 22	21 22	22 32
Maidstone East [4]	a	12 57	.	13 34	13 57	.	14 34	14 57	.	15 32	15 42	15 56	16 28	16 45	17 01	17 27	17 47	18 00	18 29	.	19 29	20 27	21 27	22 37
	d	12 57	13 00	13 34	13 57	14 00	14 34	14 57	15 00	15 32	15 43	16 00	16 28	16 48	17 01	17 28	17 48	18 02	18 30	19 00	19 29	20 28	21 28	22 38
Barming	d	.	13 04	.	.	14 04	.	.	15 04	.	.	16 05	16 33	.	17 06	17 32	.	18 07	18 35	19 04	19 34	20 32	21 33	22 42
East Malling	d	.	13 08	.	.	14 08	.	.	15 08	.	.	16 08	16 36	.	17 09	17 36	.	18 10	18 38	19 08	19 37	20 36	21 36	22 46
West Malling	d	13 05	13 10	13 42	14 05	14 10	14 42	15 05	15 10	15 40	15 50	16 11	16 39	16 55	17 12	17 38	17 55	18 13	18 41	19 10	19 40	20 38	21 39	22 48
Borough Green & Wrotham	d	.	13 17	13 49	.	14 17	14 49	.	15 17	15 47	.	16 18	16 46	.	17 19	17 45	.	18 20	18 48	19 17	19 47	20 45	21 46	22 55
Kemsing	d	.	13 22	.	.	14 22	.	.	15 22	.	.	16 22	.	.	17 23	.	.	18 24	.	19 22	.	.	.	.
Otford [4] 195	a	.	13 27	13 57	.	14 27	14 57	.	15 27	15 55	.	16 27	16 54	.	17 28	17 53	.	18 29	18 56	19 27	19 55	20 53	21 54	23 04
Swanley [4] 195	a	.	13 36	.	.	14 36	.	.	15 36	.	.	16 38	17 05	.	.	18 04	.	.	19 05	19 36	20 04	21 02	22 03	23 13
St Mary Cray 195	a	.	.	.	.	.	.	.	.	.	.	.	.	.	.	.	.	.	.	.	20 08	21 07	22 07	23 17
London Bridge [4] ⊖	a	13 50	.	.	14 50	.	.	15 50	.	.	16 34	.	.	17 38	.	.	18 40	.	.	.	.	.	.	.
London Cannon Street [4] ⊖	a	13 54	.	.	14 54	.	.	15 54	.	.	.	.	.	.	.	.	.	.	.	.	.	.	.	.
London Waterloo (East) [4] ⊖	a	.	.	.	.	.	.	.	.	.	16 39	.	.	17 44	.	.	18 45	.	.	.	.	.	.	.
London Charing Cross [4] ⊖	a	.	.	.	.	.	.	.	.	.	16 45	.	.	17 48	.	.	18 48	.	.	.	.	.	.	.
Bromley South [4] 195	a	.	13 44	14 14	.	14 44	15 14	.	15 44	16 14	.	16 47	17 14	.	17 47	18 13	.	18 45	19 14	19 44	20 14	21 13	22 13	23 23
Beckenham Junction [4] 195 🚋	a	.	.	.	.	.	.	.	.	.	.	.	.	.	.	.	.	.	.	.	.	.	.	.
Herne Hill [4] 195	a	.	.	.	.	.	.	.	.	.	.	.	.	.	.	.	.	.	.	.	.	.	.	.
Elephant & Castle ⊖ 195	a	.	.	.	.	.	.	.	.	.	.	.	.	.	.	.	.	.	.	.	.	.	.	.
London Blackfriars [3] ⊖ 195	a	.	.	.	.	.	.	.	.	.	.	.	.	.	.	.	.	.	.	.	.	.	.	.
London Victoria [15] ⊖ 195	a	.	14 02	14 32	.	15 02	15 32	.	16 02	16 33	.	17 11	17 31	.	18 09	18 33	.	19 03	19 31	20 02	20 32	21 29	22 32	23 45

For general notes see front of timetable
For details of catering facilities see Directory of Train Operators

A From Canterbury West (Table 207)
B From Margate (Table 207)

Table 196

Saturdays

Ashford International and Maidstone East to London

Network Diagram - see first page of Table 195

		SE 64 1	SE 94 1	SE 09 1	SE 94		SE 94 1	SE 09 1	SE 94	SE 94 1		SE 09 1	SE 94	SE 64 1 A	SE 09 1		SE 94	SE 64 1 A	SE 09 1	SE 94		SE 64 1 A	SE 09 1	SE 94	SE 64 1 A
Ashford International	d	06 00	07 00	07 36			08 05	08 36		09 05		09 36		10 05	10 36			11 05	11 36			12 05	12 36		13 05
Charing	d	06 08	07 08				08 13			09 13				10 13				11 13				12 13			13 13
Lenham	d	06 13	07 13				08 18			09 18				10 18				11 18				12 18			13 18
Harrietsham	d	06 16	07 16				08 21			09 21				10 21				11 21				12 21			13 21
Hollingbourne	d	06 20	07 20				08 25			09 25				10 25				11 25				12 25			13 25
Bearsted	d	06 24	07 24	07 52			08 29	08 52		09 29		09 52		10 29	10 52			11 29	11 52			12 29	12 52		13 29
Maidstone East 4	a	06 29	07 29	07 57			08 34	08 57		09 34		09 57		10 34	10 57			11 34	11 57			12 34	12 57		13 34
	d	06 30	07 30	07 57	08 00		08 34	08 57	09 00	09 34		09 57	10 00	10 34	10 57		11 00	11 34	11 57	12 00		12 34	12 57	13 00	13 34
Barming	d	06 34	07 34		08 04				09 04				10 04				11 04			12 04				13 04	
East Malling	d	06 38	07 38		08 08				09 08				10 08				11 08			12 08				13 08	
West Malling	d	06 40	07 40	08 05	08 10		08 42	09 05	09 10	09 42		10 05	10 10	10 42	11 05		11 10	11 42	12 05	12 10		12 42	13 05	13 10	13 42
Borough Green & Wrotham	d	06 47	07 47		08 17		08 49		09 17	09 49			10 17	10 49			11 17	11 49		12 17		12 49		13 17	13 49
Kemsing	d				08 22				09 22				10 22				11 22			12 22				13 22	
Otford 4	195 a	06 55	07 55		08 26		08 57		09 26	09 57			10 26	10 57			11 26	11 57		12 26		12 57		13 26	13 57
Swanley 4	195 a	07 04	08 04		08 35				09 35				10 35				11 35			12 35				13 35	
St Mary Cray	195 a	07 08	08 08																						
London Bridge 4	⊖ a			08 50				09 50				10 50			11 50				12 50				13 50		
London Cannon Street 4	⊖ a			08 54				09 54				10 54			11 54				12 54				13 54		
London Waterloo (East) 4	⊖ a																								
London Charing Cross 4	⊖ a																								
Bromley South 4	195 a	07 14	08 14		08 44		09 14		09 44	10 14			10 44	11 14			11 44	12 14		12 44		13 14		13 44	14 14
Beckenham Junction 4	195 ⛴ a																								
Herne Hill 4	195 a																								
Elephant & Castle	⊖ 195 a																								
London Blackfriars 3	⊖ 195 a																								
London Victoria 15	⊖ 195 a	07 32	08 32		09 02		09 32		10 02	10 32			11 02	11 32			12 02	12 32		13 02		13 32		14 02	14 32

		SE 09 1	SE 94		SE 64 1 A	SE 09 1	SE 94	SE 64 1 A		SE 09 1	SE 94	SE 64 1 A	SE 09 1		SE 94	SE 64 1 A	SE 09 1	SE 94	SE 64 1 A	SE 94 1	SE 94 1	SE 94 1	SE 94 1		
Ashford International	d	13 36			14 05	14 36		15 05		15 36		16 05	16 36			17 05	17 36		18 00	19 00	20 00	21 00	22 00		
Charing	d				14 13			15 13				16 13				17 13			18 08	19 08	20 08	21 08	22 08		
Lenham	d				14 18			15 18				16 18				17 18			18 13	19 13	20 13	21 13	22 13		
Harrietsham	d				14 21			15 21				16 21				17 21			18 16	19 16	20 16	21 16	22 16		
Hollingbourne	d				14 25			15 25				16 25				17 25			18 20	19 20	20 20	21 20	22 20		
Bearsted	d	13 52			14 29	14 52		15 29		15 52		16 29	16 52			17 29	17 52		18 24	19 24	20 24	21 24	22 24		
Maidstone East 4	a	13 57			14 34	14 57		15 34		15 57		16 34	16 57			17 34	17 57		18 29	19 29	20 29	21 29	22 29		
	d	13 57	14 00		14 34	14 57	15 00	15 34		15 57	16 00	16 34	16 57		17 00	17 34	17 57	18 00	18 30	19 30	20 30	21 30	22 30		
Barming	d		14 04				15 04				16 04				17 04			18 04	18 34	19 34	20 34	21 34	22 34		
East Malling	d		14 08				15 08				16 08				17 08			18 08	18 38	19 38	20 38	21 38	22 38		
West Malling	d	14 05	14 10		14 42	15 05	15 10	15 42		16 05	16 10	16 42	17 05		17 10	17 42	18 05	18 10	18 40	19 40	20 40	21 40	22 40		
Borough Green & Wrotham	d		14 17		14 49		15 17	15 49			16 17	16 49			17 17	17 49		18 17	18 47	19 47	20 47	21 47	22 47		
Kemsing	d		14 22				15 22				16 22				17 22			18 22							
Otford 4	195 a		14 26		14 57		15 26	15 57			16 26	16 57			17 26	17 57		18 26	18 55	19 55	20 55	21 55	22 55		
Swanley 4	195 a		14 35				15 35				16 35				17 35			18 35	19 04	20 04	21 04	22 04	23 04		
St Mary Cray	195 a																		19 08	20 08	21 08	22 08	23 08		
London Bridge 4	⊖ a	14 50				15 50				16 50			17 50				18 50								
London Cannon Street 4	⊖ a	14 54				15 54				16 54			17 54				18 54								
London Waterloo (East) 4	⊖ a																								
London Charing Cross 4	⊖ a																								
Bromley South 4	195 a		14 44		15 14		15 44	16 14			16 44	17 14			17 44	18 14		18 44	19 14	20 14	21 14	22 14	23 14		
Beckenham Junction 4	195 ⛴ a																								
Herne Hill 4	195 a																								
Elephant & Castle	⊖ 195 a																								
London Blackfriars 3	⊖ 195 a																								
London Victoria 15	⊖ 195 a		15 02		15 32		16 02	16 32			17 02	17 32			18 02	18 32		19 02	19 32	20 32	21 32	22 32	23 32		

For general notes see front of timetable
For details of catering facilities see
Directory of Train Operators

A From Canterbury West (Table 207)

Table 196

Sundays

Ashford International and Maidstone East to London

Network Diagram - see first page of Table 195

		SE 94 1	SE 94 1	SE 94 1	SE 94 1	SE 94 1	SE 94 1	SE 94 1	SE 94 1	SE 94 1	SE 94 1	SE 94 1	SE 94 1	SE 94 1	SE 94 1	SE 94 1
Ashford International	d	07 29	08 29	09 29	10 29	11 29	12 29	13 29	14 29	15 29	16 29	17 29	18 29	19 29	20 29	21 29
Charing	d	07 37	08 37	09 37	10 37	11 37	12 37	13 37	14 37	15 37	16 37	17 37	18 37	19 37	20 37	21 37
Lenham	d	07 42	08 42	09 42	10 42	11 42	12 42	13 42	14 42	15 42	16 42	17 42	18 42	19 42	20 42	21 42
Harrietsham	d	07 45	08 45	09 45	10 45	11 45	12 45	13 45	14 45	15 45	16 45	17 45	18 45	19 45	20 45	21 45
Hollingbourne	d	07 49	08 49	09 49	10 49	11 49	12 49	13 49	14 49	15 49	16 49	17 49	18 49	19 49	20 49	21 49
Bearsted	d	07 53	08 53	09 53	10 53	11 53	12 53	13 53	14 53	15 53	16 53	17 53	18 53	19 53	20 53	21 53
Maidstone East 4	a	07 58	08 58	09 58	10 58	11 58	12 58	13 58	14 58	15 58	16 58	17 58	18 58	19 58	20 58	21 58
	d	07 59	08 59	09 59	10 59	11 59	12 59	13 59	14 59	15 59	16 59	17 59	18 59	19 59	20 59	21 59
Barming	d	08 03	09 03	10 03	11 03	12 03	13 03	14 03	15 03	16 03	17 03	18 03	19 03	20 03	21 03	22 03
East Malling	d	08 07	09 07	10 07	11 07	12 07	13 07	14 07	15 07	16 07	17 07	18 07	19 07	20 07	21 07	22 07
West Malling	d	08 09	09 09	10 09	11 09	12 09	13 09	14 09	15 09	16 09	17 09	18 09	19 09	20 09	21 09	22 09
Borough Green & Wrotham	d	08 16	09 16	10 16	11 16	12 16	13 16	14 16	15 16	16 16	17 16	18 16	19 16	20 16	21 16	22 16
Kemsing	d															
Otford 4	195 a	08 24	09 24	10 24	11 24	12 24	13 24	14 24	15 24	16 24	17 24	18 24	19 24	20 24	21 24	22 24
Swanley 4	195 a	08 33	09 33	10 33	11 33	12 33	13 33	14 33	15 33	16 33	17 33	18 33	19 33	20 33	21 33	22 33
St Mary Cray	195 a	08 38	09 38	10 38	11 38	12 38	13 38	14 38	15 38	16 38	17 38	18 38	19 38	20 38	21 38	22 38
London Bridge 4	⊖ a															
London Cannon Street 4	⊖ a															
London Waterloo (East) 4	⊖ a															
London Charing Cross 4	⊖ a															
Bromley South 4	195 a	08 44	09 44	10 44	11 44	12 44	13 44	14 44	15 44	16 44	17 44	18 44	19 44	20 44	21 44	22 44
Beckenham Junction 4	195 a															
Herne Hill 4	195 a															
Elephant & Castle	⊖ 195 a															
London Blackfriars 3	⊖ 195 a															
London Victoria 15	⊖ 195 a	09 01	10 01	11 01	12 01	13 01	14 01	15 01	16 01	17 01	18 01	19 01	20 01	21 01	22 01	23 01

For general notes see front of timetable
For details of catering facilities see
Directory of Train Operators

London → Lewisham, Hither Green, Petts Wood and Orpington (Summary of Services)

For details of Bank Holiday service alterations please see first page of Table 195

		SE	SE	SE	SE	SE	SE	SE	FC	SE	SE	SN	SE	FC	SE	SE	SE	SE	SE	FC	SE	SE	SE	SE	SE
		MX	MO	MX	MX	MO	MX	MO		MX	MX	MX		MX											
		12	12	73	70	50	24	24		50	02		62		14	50	72	84	52		25	70	18	70	64
																				1			1		
London Charing Cross 4	⊖ d	23p26	23p42			23p49	23p52	23p52		00 04	00 10	00 12	00 14		00 48	04 50	04 56	05 04	05 18			05 26	05 30		05 34
London Waterloo (East) 4	⊖ d	23p29	23p45			23p52	23p55	23p55		00 07	00 13	00 15	00 17		00 51	04 53	04 59	05 07	05 21			05 29	05 33		05 37
London Cannon Street 4	⊖ d																								
London Blackfriars 3	⊖ d			23p43					00 04					00 34						05 24					
London Bridge 4	⊖ d	23p34	23p50			23p58	23p58	00 01	00a10	00 13	00 18	00a19	00 23	00a40	00 56	04 58	05 04	05a11	05b28	05a30		05 34	05 38		05 42
London Victoria 15	⊖ d				23p53																			05 36	
New Cross 4	⊖ d					00 03	00 04	00 06		00 18			00 28		01 01	05 03	05 09		05 33		05 37	05 39			
St Johns	d						00 06	00 08																	
Lewisham 4	a	23p42				00 07	00 08	00 10		00 22			00 32		01 05	05 07	05 13		05 37		05 41	05 43			05 51
Hither Green 4	a	23p47	23p59			00 11				00 27					01 09	05 11			05 41						
Petts Wood 4	a	00 01	00 12	00 20	00 25						00 39				01 23									06 10	
Orpington 4	a	00 03	00 15	00 24	00 28						00 42				01 26								05 54	06 13	

		SE	FC	SE	SE	SE	SE	SE	SE	SE	SN	SE	FC	SE	SE	SE	SE	SE	SE	SE	SE	FC	SE	SE	SE
		14		54	11	24	80	70	72	11		65		16	11	52	4	84	25	70	70		65	54	16
			1										1				1					1			
London Charing Cross 4	⊖ d	05 40		05 46		05 49	05 54		06 02		06 05			06 16		06 20	06 25		06 27		06 32		06 40		06 47
London Waterloo (East) 4	⊖ d	05 43		05 49		05 52	05 57		06 05		06 08			06 19		06 23	06 28		06 30		06 35		06 43		06 50
London Cannon Street 4	⊖ d				05 50					06 06		06 12			06 22			06 30						06 48	
London Blackfriars 3	⊖ d		05 44										06 14									06 36			
London Bridge 4	⊖ d	05 48	05a50	05 54	05a53	05 57	06a01		06 10	06a09	06a12	06 16	06a20	06 24	06a25	06 28	06 33	06a33	06 35		06 40	06a42	06 48	06 52	06 56
London Victoria 15	⊖ d							06 04												06 36					
New Cross 4	⊖ d	05 53		05 59					06 15							06 33			06 41		06 47				
St Johns	d			06 01					06 17										06 43						
Lewisham 4	a	05 57		06 03		06 05			06 19			06 23				06 37			06 45		06 51		06 55	06 59	
Hither Green 4	a	06 01		06 07										06 33		06 41								07 03	07 06
Petts Wood 4	a	06 13						06 38						06 45						07 10					07 22
Orpington 4	a	06 16						06 41						06 48			06 49			07 13					07 25

		SE	FC	SE	SE	SE	SE	SE	SE	FC	SE	SE	SE	SE	SE	SE	SE	SE	SE	SE	FC	SE	SE	SE	SE
		11		24	86	70	4	60	25		12	30	70	73	52	34	80	12	22	71		57	12	23	40
			1				1			1		1							1		1			1	
London Charing Cross 4	⊖ d			06 51	06 54		07 00	07 03	07 06		07 10	07 16			07 20	07 22			07 28	07 30			07 37		07 42
London Waterloo (East) 4	⊖ d			06 54	06 57		07 03	07 06	07 09		07 13	07 19			07 23	07 25			07 31	07 33			07 40		07 45
London Cannon Street 4	⊖ d	06 52				07 04								07 22			07 32					07 39		07 45	
London Blackfriars 3	⊖ d		06 50							07 10											07 32				
London Bridge 4	⊖ d	06a55	06a56	06 59	07a02	07 08	07 08	07 11	07 14	07a16	07 19	07 24		07 26	07 28	07a29	07a35		07 36	07 38	07a39	07 43	07 45	07 49	07 50
London Victoria 15	⊖ d												07 06												
New Cross 4	⊖ d			07 05		07 13			07 20						07 33					07 43		07 49			
St Johns	d			07 07		07 15			07 22											07 45					
Lewisham 4	a			07 09		07 17		07 21	07 24					07 33	07 37			←		07 47		07 53			
Hither Green 4	a										07 29 →				07 41			07 29				07 57	07 53 →		08 01
Petts Wood 4	a												07 40					07 42							
Orpington 4	a						07 25					07 40	07 43					07 45	07 54					08 08	

		SE	SE	SE	SE	SE	SE	SE	SE	SE	SE	SE	SE	SE	SE	FC	SE	SE	SE	SE	SE	SE	SE	SE	SE
		44	25	73	12	70	4	61	14	12	70	51	84		71		61	22	25	78	12	4	42	80	34
							1							1		1		1				1			
London Charing Cross 4	⊖ d		07 45				07 52		07 56			08 00	08 03	08 08				08 14			08 20	08 22		08 24	08 26
London Waterloo (East) 4	⊖ d		07 48				07 55		07 59			08 03	08 06	08 11				08 17			08 23	08 25		08 27	08 29
London Cannon Street 4	⊖ d	07 48		07 54				07 58		08 03					08 14		08 17		08 20				08 26		
London Blackfriars 3	⊖ d															08 12									
London Bridge 4	⊖ d	07a51	07 53	07 58			08 02	08 02	08 04	08 07		08 09	08a10	08 16	08 18	08a18	08 21	08a22	08 24		08 28	08 30	08 30	08a31	08a33
London Victoria 15	⊖ d					07 37					08 06									08 21					
New Cross 4	⊖ d		07 59	08 03				08 07		08 12					08 23		08 26		08 29						
St Johns	d		08 01	08 05											08 25				08 31						
Lewisham 4	a		08 04	08 07	←			08 11		08 16					08 27		08 31		08 33	08 43					
Hither Green 4	a				07 53					08 20		08 18		08 27							08 37 →		08 41		
Petts Wood 4	a				08 09	08 12				08 33	08 39														
Orpington 4	a				08 12	08 15	08 19		08 23	08 36	08 42											08 47			

		SE	SE	SE	SE	SE	SE	SE	SE	SE	SE	SE	SE	SE	SE	SE	SE	SE	FC	SE	SE	SE	SE	SE	SE
		71	16	55	36	12	25	12	23	80	10	63	25	34	90	12	12	70		71	90	36	12	54	78
									1						1				1		1				
London Charing Cross 4	⊖ d	08 28	08 29		08 36			08 38		08 41	08 44			08 52	08 54	08 56					08 58	09 00		09 02	
London Waterloo (East) 4	⊖ d	08 31	08 32		08 39			08 41		08 44	08 47			08 55	08 57	08 59					09 01	09 04		09 06	
London Cannon Street 4	⊖ d			08 34			08 40		08 45			08 50	08 54							09 02					
London Blackfriars 3	⊖ d																		08 58				←		
London Bridge 4	⊖ d	08 36	08 38	08 38	08a43		08 44	08 46	08 49	08a49	08 52	08 54	08 58	08a59	09a01	09 04 →			09a05	09 06	09 08	09a09	09 04	09 12	
London Victoria 15	⊖ d																	08 36							09 01
New Cross 4	⊖ d	08 42		08 45			08 49						09 05							09 11					
St Johns	d			08 47			08 51						09 07												
Lewisham 4	a	08 46		08 49		←	08 53					09 02	09 09				←			09 15				09 19	09 25
Hither Green 4	a			08 53		08 37		08 55 →			09 02						08 55						09 15	09 23	
Petts Wood 4	a					08 50											09 09	09 12			09 23		09 30		
Orpington 4	a		08 55			08 56			09 07								09 12	09 15			09 26		09 33		

For general notes see front of timetable
For details of catering facilities see
Directory of Train Operators

b Arr. 0525

London → Lewisham, Hither Green, Petts Wood and Orpington (Summary of Services)

For details of Bank Holiday service alterations please see first page of Table 195

		SE	SE	SE	SE	SE	FC	SE	SE	SE	SE	SE	SE	SE	SE	SE		SE	SE	SE	SE	FC	SE	SE	SE
		81	09	23	70	34		47	70	25	82	16	87	2	70	67		16	54	78	70		34	81	47
			[1]	[1]			[1]							[1]								[1]			
London Charing Cross [4]	⊖ d					09 14			09 15		09 20	09 26		09 30					09 32				09 36		
London Waterloo (East) [4]	⊖ d					09 17			09 20		09 23	09 29		09 33					09 35				09 39		
London Cannon Street [4]	⊖ d	09 10	09 13	09 17				09 20		09 24			09 30			09 34								09 42	09 48
London Blackfriars [3]	⊖ d						09 17															09 34			
London Bridge [4]	⊖ d	09a13	09a16	09 21		09a21	09a23	09 24	09 26	09 28	09a29	09 34	09 34	09 38		09 38			09 40			09a41	09a44	09a45	09 52
London Victoria [15]	⊖ d				09 06										09 21					09 31	09 36				
New Cross [4]	⊖ d							09 29		09 35						09 44									09 57
St Johns	d							09 31		09 37								←							09 59
Lewisham [4]	a							09 33	09 35	09 39		09 42 →				09 47		09 42	09 49	09 52					
Hither Green [4]	a							09 37										09 47	09 53						10 05
Petts Wood [4]	a				09 42										09 55			10 00			10 10				
Orpington [4]	a			09 39	09 46									09 54	09 58			10 03			10 13				

		SE	FC	SE	SE	SE	SE	SE	SE	SE	SE	SE	SE	SE	FC	SE	SE	SE	SE	SE	SE	SE	FC	SE	SE
		22		70	25	82	12	87	8	70	67	12	54	78		81	34	09	47	22	70	70		25	82
		[1]	[1]												[1]			[1]		[1]			[1]		
London Charing Cross [4]	⊖ d	09 45		09 49		09 52	09 56		10 00				10 02				10 06			10 15		10 17			10 20
London Waterloo (East) [4]	⊖ d	09 48		09 52		09 55	09 59		10 03				10 05				10 09			10 18		10 20			10 23
London Cannon Street [4]	⊖ d				09 54			10 00			10 04					10 10		10 14	10 18					10 24	
London Blackfriars [3]	⊖ d		09 49												10 05								10 20		
London Bridge [4]	⊖ d	09a53	09a55	09 57	09 58	09a59	10 04	10 04	10 08		10 08		10 10		10a11	10a13	10a14	10a17	10 22	10 23		10 25	10a26	10 28	10a28
London Victoria [15]	⊖ d									09 51				10 01							10 06				
New Cross [4]	⊖ d				10 05						10 14								10 27					10 33	
St Johns	d				10 07							←							10 29					10 35	
Lewisham [4]	a			10 05	10 09		10 12 →				10 17	10 12	10 19	10 22								10 34		10 37	
Hither Green [4]	a											10 17	10 23						10 35						
Petts Wood [4]	a								10 22	10 26		10 30									10 39				
Orpington [4]	a								10 25	10 29		10 33								10 39	10 42				

		SE	SE	SE	SE	SE	SE	SE	SE	SE	FC	SE	SE	SN		SE	SE	SE	FC	SE	SE	SE	SE	SE	SE
		16	87	8	70	67	16	54	78	70		81	34			47	22	70		25	82	12	87	8	70
				[1]							[1]						[1]		[1]					[1]	
London Charing Cross [4]	⊖ d	10 26		10 30				10 32					10 36	10 40			10 45	10 47			10 50	10 56		11 00	
London Waterloo (East) [4]	⊖ d	10 29		10 33				10 35					10 39	10 43			10 48	10 50			10 53	10 59		11 03	
London Cannon Street [4]	⊖ d		10 30			10 34						10 40				10 48				10 54			11 00		
London Blackfriars [3]	⊖ d										10 35								10 50						
London Bridge [4]	⊖ d	10 34	10 34	10 38		10 38		10 40			10a41	10a43	10a44	10a47		10 52	10a52	10 55	10a56	10 58	10a58	11 04	11 04	11 08	
London Victoria [15]	⊖ d				10 21				10 31	10 36															10 51
New Cross [4]	⊖ d					10 44										10 57				11 03					
St Johns	d						←									10 59				11 05					
Lewisham [4]	a	10 42 →				10 47	10 42	10 49	10 52									11 04		11 07		11 12 →			
Hither Green [4]	a						10 47	10 53								11 05									
Petts Wood [4]	a				10 54		11 00			11 09														11 22	11 24
Orpington [4]	a			10 53	10 57		11 03			11 12														11 25	11 27

		SE	SE	SE	SE	FC	SE	SE	SN	SE	SE	SE	SE	SE	FC	SE	SE	SE	SE	SE	SE	SE	SE	SE	SE
		67	12	54	78		81	34		09	47	22	70	70		25	82	16	87	8	70	67	16	54	78
						[1]				[1]		[1]			[1]					[1]					
London Charing Cross [4]	⊖ d			11 02				11 06	11 10			11 15		11 17			11 20	11 26		11 30				11 32	
London Waterloo (East) [4]	⊖ d			11 05				11 09	11 13			11 18		11 20			11 23	11 29		11 33				11 35	
London Cannon Street [4]	⊖ d	11 04					11 10			11 14	11 18					11 24			11 30			11 34			
London Blackfriars [3]	⊖ d					11 05									11 20										
London Bridge [4]	⊖ d	11 08		11 10		11a11	11a13	11a14	11a17	11a17	11 22	11 23		11 25	11a26	11 28	11a28	11 34	11 34	11 38		11 38		11 40	
London Victoria [15]	⊖ d				11 01								11 06								11 21				11 31
New Cross [4]	⊖ d	11 14									11 27					11 33						11 44			
St Johns	d		←								11 29					11 35							←		
Lewisham [4]	a	11 17	11 12	11 19	11 22									11 34		11 37		11 42 →				11 47	11 42	11 49	11 52
Hither Green [4]	a		11 17	11 23							11 35												11 47	11 53	
Petts Wood [4]	a		11 30										11 39								11 54		12 00		
Orpington [4]	a		11 33									11 39	11 42							11 53	11 57		12 03		

		SE	FC	SE	SE	SN		SE	SE	SE	FC	SE	SE	SE	SE	SE	SE	SE	SE	FC	SE	SE	SN	SE
		70		81	34			47	22	70		25	62	70	16	81	70	8	54		24	57		09
			[1]				and at		[1]		[1]							[1]		[1]				[1]
London Charing Cross [4]	⊖ d				11 36	11 40	the same		15 45	15 47			15 50		15 56			16 00	16 02		16 06		16 08	
London Waterloo (East) [4]	⊖ d				11 39	11 43			15 48	15 50			15 53		15 59			16 03	16 05		16 09		16 11	
London Cannon Street [4]	⊖ d			11 40			minutes	15 48				15 54				16 00						16 10		16 14
London Blackfriars [3]	⊖ d		11 35								15 50									16 05				
London Bridge [4]	⊖ d		11a41	11a43	11a44	11a47	past	15 52	15a52	15 55	15a56	15 58	15 59		16 04	16a03		16a07	16 10	16a11	16 14	16 14	16a15	16a17
London Victoria [15]	⊖ d	11 36												15 51			16 06							
New Cross [4]	⊖ d						each	15 57				16 03							16 16			16 20		
St Johns	d							15 59				16 05										16 22		
Lewisham [4]	a						hour until			16 04		16 07	16 09		16 12				16 19		16 22	16 26		
Hither Green [4]	a							16 04							16 17				16 23			16 31		
Petts Wood [4]	a	12 09												16 24	16 29		16 39							
Orpington [4]	a	12 12												16 27	16 32		16 42							

For general notes see front of timetable
For details of catering facilities see Directory of Train Operators

London → Lewisham, Hither Green, Petts Wood and Orpington (Summary of Services)

For details of Bank Holiday service alterations please see first page of Table 195

		SE 74	SE 81	SE 22 [1]	SE 16	SE 16	FC [1]	SE 62	SE 78	SE 70	SE 4 [1]	SE 73	SE 81	SE 40	SE 24	SE 8 [1]	SE 76	SE 57	FC [1]	SE 65	SE 74	SE 07 [1]	SE 12	SE 25	SE 80
London Charing Cross 4	⊖ d	16 11		16 15	16 16			16 21			16 23			16 25	16 26	16 30	16 33				16 37		16 42		16 44
London Waterloo (East) 4	⊖ d	16 14		16 18	16 19			16 24			16 26			16 28	16 29	16 33	16 36				16 40		16 45		16 47
London Cannon Street 4	⊖ d		16 18			16 22							16 28					16 38		16 42		16 44		16 46	
London Blackfriars 3	⊖ d						16 20					16 27							16 37						
London Bridge 4	⊖ d	16 19	16a21	16a22	16 25	16 26	16a26	16 29			16a30		16a31	16 33	16 34	16a38	16 41	16 42	16a43	16 46	16b48	16a47	16 50	16 50	16a51
London Victoria 15	⊖ d								16 14	16 26															
New Cross 4	⊖ d	16 25												16 39				16 49						16 56	
St Johns	d													16 41				16 51						16 58	
Lewisham 4	a	16 28				16 34		16 37	16 40						16 44		16 50	16 53		16 55	16 58			17 01	
Hither Green 4	a					16 39								16 46				16 57					17 02		
Petts Wood 4	a				16 43	16 51				17 00		17 06											17 15		
Orpington 4	a				16 48	16 55				17 04		17 12											17 21		

		SE 4 [1]	SE 42	SE 77	SE 30 [1]	SE 34	SE 17	SE 70	SE 76	SE 23 [1]	SE 46	SE 85	SE 64		SE 25	SE 78	SE 87	SE 12	SE 80	SE 51	SE 17	SE 70	SE 77	SE 34	SE 76
London Charing Cross 4	⊖ d	16 46	16 48		16 50	16 52			16 55		16 58		17 00					17 04	17 06					17 14	17 18
London Waterloo (East) 4	⊖ d	16 49	16 51		16 53	16 55			16 58		17 01		17 03					17 07	17 09					17 17	17 21
London Cannon Street 4	⊖ d			16 52			16 56			17 00		17 02			17 04		17 06			17 10	17 14		17 16		
London Blackfriars 3	⊖ d																								
London Bridge 4	⊖ d	16a53	16a55	16 56	16a57	16a59	17 00		17 03	17a03	17 06	17a05	17 08		17 08		17a09	17 12	17a13	17 14	17 18		17 20	17a21	17 26
London Victoria 15	⊖ d							16 51								17 00						17 12			
New Cross 4	⊖ d			17 02																17 20			17 26		
St Johns	d														17 18					17 22					
Lewisham 4	a			17 05					17 14				17 17		17 20	17 23				17 25			17 29		17 35
Hither Green 4	a										17 16							17 22		17 30					
Petts Wood 4	a						17 21	17 25										17 35			17 43	17 49			
Orpington 4	a						17 24	17 29										17 41			17 46	17 53			

		SE 13	SE 30 [1]	SE 87	SE 46	SE 65	SE 78	FC [1]	SE 12	SE 25	SE 80	SE 51	SE 17	SE 70	SE 76	SE 77	SE 30 [1]	SE 65	SE 78	SE 46	SE 87	FC [1]	SE 07 [1]	SE 25	SE 12
London Charing Cross 4	⊖ d		17 20		17 21				17 28		17 29				17 37		17 41			17 43					17 49
London Waterloo (East) 4	⊖ d		17 23		17 24				17 31		17 32				17 40		17 44			17 46					17 52
London Cannon Street 4	⊖ d	17 22		17 24		17 26				17 32		17 36	17 40			17 42		17 46			17 48		17 50	17 52	
London Blackfriars 3	⊖ d							17 20														17 46			
London Bridge 4	⊖ d	17 26	17a27	17a27	17 30	17 30		17a31		17 36	17a38	17 40	17 44		17 45	17 46	17a48	17 50		17 51	17a51	17a52	17a53	17 56	17 57
London Victoria 15	⊖ d						17 19							17 35					17 41						
New Cross 4	⊖ d	17 32								17 42		17 47				17 52								18 02	
St Johns	d									17 44														18 04	
Lewisham 4	a					17 38	17 43			17 46		17 50			17 53	17 56		17 59	18 05					18 07	
Hither Green 4	a				17 40				17 46			17 55								18 00					18 07
Petts Wood 4	a	17 51							17 58				18 05	18 09											18 19
Orpington 4	a	17 57							18 04				18 08	18 15											18 25

		SE 51	SE 80	SE 17	SE 70	SE 70	SE 34	SE 77	SE 9 [1]	SE 70	SE 30 [1]	SE 85	SE 64	SE 07 [1]	SE 46	SE 25	SE 78	SE 12	SE 15	SE 70	SE 80	SE 77	SE 51	FC [1]	SE 23 [1]
London Charing Cross 4	⊖ d		17 54				17 58			18 01	18 04		18 05		18 08			18 12			18 14				
London Waterloo (East) 4	⊖ d		17 57				18 01			18 04	18 07		18 08		18 11			18 15			18 17				
London Cannon Street 4	⊖ d	17 56		18 00				18 02	18 04			18 08		18 10		18 12			18 16			18 19	18 22		18 26
London Blackfriars 3	⊖ d																							18 20	
London Bridge 4	⊖ d	18 00	18a01	18 04			18a05	18 06	18a07	18 10	18a11	18a11	18 14	18a13	18 16	18 16			18 20		18a21	18 23	18 26	18a26	18a29
London Victoria 15	⊖ d				17 52	18 02											18 08			18 21					
New Cross 4	⊖ d	18 06														18 22			18 26				18 32		
St Johns	d	18 08														18 24									
Lewisham 4	a	18 11						18 14		18 19			18 23			18 26	18 28		18 30			18 32	18 35		
Hither Green 4	a	18 16													18 26			18 29					18 40		
Petts Wood 4	a			18 25	18 29	18 34												18 43	18 46	18 56					
Orpington 4	a			18 29	18 33	18 40												18 47	18 51	19 01					

		SE 24	SE 70	SE 3 [1]	SE 30 [1]	SE 62	SE 16	SE 57	SE 80	SE 8 [1]	SE 24	SE 07 [1]	SE 16	SE 70	SE 70	SE 78	SE 13	FC [1]	SE 16	SE 62	SE 80	SE 77	SE 4 [1]	SE 23 [1]	SE 70
London Charing Cross 4	⊖ d	18 23	18 25		18 28	18 30	18 32		18 34	18 40	18 42				18 46				18 52	18 54	18 56		19 00		
London Waterloo (East) 4	⊖ d	18 26	18 28		18 31	18 33	18 35		18 37	18 43	18 45				18 49				18 55	18 57	18 59		19 03		
London Cannon Street 4	⊖ d			18 30				18 36				18 46					18 50					19 02		19 06	
London Blackfriars 3	⊖ d																	18 49							
London Bridge 4	⊖ d	18 31	18 34	18a33	18a35	18 38	18 40	18 40	18a41	18 48	18 50	18a49			18 54		18 54	18a56	19 00	19 02	19a03	19 06	19a07	19 10	
London Victoria 15	⊖ d													18 38		18 46									18 51
New Cross 4	⊖ d							18 46							19 00							19 12			
St Johns	d							18 48														19 14			
Lewisham 4	a	18 40	18 43			18 46		18 51			18 59		←		19 04	19 08				19 11		19 16			
Hither Green 4	a						18 50 →	18 56					18 50						19 10						
Petts Wood 4	a												19 04	19 12			19 17		19 23						19 25
Orpington 4	a									19 04			19 10	19 15			19 22		19 27					19 27	19 31

For general notes see front of timetable
For details of catering facilities see Directory of Train Operators

b Arr. 1645

London → Lewisham, Hither Green, Petts Wood and Orpington (Summary of Services)

For details of Bank Holiday service alterations please see first page of Table 195

		SE 70	SE 54	FC [1]	SE 24	SE 87	SE 09 [1]	SE 80	SE 13	SE 22 [1]	SE 70	SE 57	FC [1]	SE 62	SE 25	SE 4 [1]	SE 81	SE 16	SE 78	SE 07 [1]	SE 90 [1]	SE 70	SE 77	FC [1]	SE 16
London Charing Cross 4	⊖ d		19 02		19 06			19 11		19 15	19 17			19 21		19 24		19 26			19 30				
London Waterloo (East) 4	⊖ d		19 05		19 09			19 14		19 18	19 20			19 24		19 27		19 29			19 33				
London Cannon Street 4	⊖ d					19 10	19 14		19 18			19 22			19 26		19 28			19 32			19 36		
London Blackfriars 3	⊖ d			19 04									19 19											19 34	
London Bridge 4	⊖ d		19 10	19a11	19 14	19a13	19a17	19a18	19 22	19a22	19 25	19 26	19a26	19 29	19 30	19a31	19a31	19 34		19a35	19 38		19 40	19a40	
London Victoria 15	⊖ d	19 07																	19 16			19 22			
New Cross 4	⊖ d				19 20							19 31			19 35								19 45		
St Johns	d				19 22							19 33			19 37								19 47		←
Lewisham 4	a		19 21		19 24				19 30		19 34			19 37	19 39			19 42	19 44				19 49		19 42
Hither Green 4	a		19 25						19 35			19 37						→							19 47
Petts Wood 4	a	19 41							19 48													19 56			19 59
Orpington 4	a	19 44							19 52												19 54	19 59			20 02

		SE 70	SE 54	SE 11	SN	SE 24	SE 80	SE 13	SE 22 [1]	SE 70	SE 57	SE 62	SE 25	SE 4 [1]	FC [1]	SE 81	SE 70	SE 16	SE 78	SE 4 [1]	FC [1]	SE 50	SN	SE 80	SE 11
London Charing Cross 4	⊖ d		19 34		19 37	19 38	19 41		19 45	19 47		19 50		19 52				19 56		20 00		20 04	20 07	20 10	
London Waterloo (East) 4	⊖ d		19 37		19 40	19 41	19 44		19 48	19 50		19 53		19 55				19 59		20 03		20 07	20 10	20 13	
London Cannon Street 4	⊖ d			19 40				19 48			19 52		19 56			20 00									20 15
London Blackfriars 3	⊖ d														19 54						20 04				
London Bridge 4	⊖ d		19 43	19a43	19a44	19 46	19a48	19 52	19a52	19 55	19 56	19 59	20 00	20a00	20a01	20a03		20 04		20a07	20a10	20 13	20a14	20a17	20a18
London Victoria 15	⊖ d	19 37															19 52		19 46						
New Cross 4	⊖ d		19 48			19 52					20 01		20 05									20 18			
St Johns	d					19 54					20 04		20 07												
Lewisham 4	a		19 52			19 56		20 00		20 03		20 07	20 09					20 12	20 14			20 22			
Hither Green 4	a		19 57					20 05			20 09							20 17				20 27			
Petts Wood 4	a	20 11						20 17									20 26	20 29							
Orpington 4	a	20 14						20 20									20 29	20 32							

		SE 22 [1]	SE 70	SE 62	SE 24	SE 12	SE 81	SE 90 [1]	SE 70	SE 12	SE 15	FC [1]	SE 50	SN	SE 80	SE 22 [1]	SE 70	SE 62	SE 24	SE 16	SE 81	SE 4 [1]	SE 70	FC [1]	SE 16
London Charing Cross 4	⊖ d	20 15	20 17	20 20	20 22	20 26		20 30					20 34	20 37	20 40	20 45	20 47	20 50	20 52	20 56		21 00			
London Waterloo (East) 4	⊖ d	20 18	20 20	20 23	20 25	20 29		20 33					20 37	20 40	20 43	20 48	20 50	20 53	20 55	20 59		21 03			
London Cannon Street 4	⊖ d						20 30				20 35										21 00				
London Blackfriars 3	⊖ d											20 34												21 04	
London Bridge 4	⊖ d	20 23	20 25	20 29	20 30	20 34	20a33	20 38			20 39	20a40	20 43	20a44	20a47	20 53	20 55	20 59	21 00	21 04	21a03	21 08		21a10	
London Victoria 15	⊖ d								20 22														20 52		
New Cross 4	⊖ d		20 30		20 35						20 44		20 48				21 00		21 05						
St Johns	d				20 37					←	20 46								21 07						←
Lewisham 4	a		20 34	20 37	20 39	20 42				20 42	20 48		20 52				21 04	21 07	21 09	21 12					21 12
Hither Green 4	a					→				20 47	20 53		20 57							→					21 17
Petts Wood 4	a								20 55	21 00	21 05												21 24		21 29
Orpington 4	a	20 40						20 54	20 58	21 03	21 10					21 10						21 24	21 27		21 32

		SE 50	SN	SE 80	SE 22 [1]	SE 70	SE 62	SE 24	SE 12	SE 90 [1]	SE 70	FC [1]	SE 12	SE 50	SN	SE 80	SE 22 [1]	SE 70	SE 62	SE 24	SE 12	SE 4 [1]	SE 70	FC [1]	SE 12
London Charing Cross 4	⊖ d	21 04	21 07	21 10	21 15	21 17	21 20	21 22	21 26	21 30				21 34	21 37	21 40	21 45	21 47	21 50	21 52	21 56	22 00			
London Waterloo (East) 4	⊖ d	21 07	21 10	21 13	21 18	21 20	21 23	21 25	21 29	21 33				21 37	21 40	21 43	21 48	21 50	21 53	21 55	21 59	22 03			
London Cannon Street 4	⊖ d																								
London Blackfriars 3	⊖ d											21 34												22 04	
London Bridge 4	⊖ d	21 13	21a14	21a17	21 23	21 25	21 29	21 30	21 34	21 38		21a40		21 43	21a44	21a47	21 53	21 55	21 59	22 00	22 04	22 08		22a10	
London Victoria 15	⊖ d										21 22												21 52		
New Cross 4	⊖ d	21 18				21 30		21 35						21 48				22 00		22 05					
St Johns	d							21 37					←							22 07					←
Lewisham 4	a	21 22				21 34	21 37	21 39	21 42				21 42	21 52				22 04	22 07	22 09	22 12				22 12
Hither Green 4	a	21 27							→				21 47	21 57							→				22 17
Petts Wood 4	a										21 55		22 00										22 25		22 30
Orpington 4	a				21 40					21 54	21 58		22 03				22 10					22 24	22 28		22 33

		SE 50	SN	SE 80	SE 22 [1]	SE 70	SE 62	SE 24	SE 12	SE 8 [1]	SE 70	FC [1]	SE 12	SE 50	SN	SE 80	SE 22 [1]	SE 73	SE 70	SE 62	SE 24	SE 12	SE 2 [1]	SE 70	FC [1]
London Charing Cross 4	⊖ d	22 04	22 07	22 10	22 15	22 17	22 20	22 22	22 26	22 30				22 34	22 37	22 40	22 45		22 47	22 50	22 52	22 56	23 00		
London Waterloo (East) 4	⊖ d	22 07	22 10	22 13	22 18	22 20	22 23	22 25	22 29	22 33				22 37	22 40	22 43	22 48		22 50	22 53	22 55	22 59	23 03		
London Cannon Street 4	⊖ d																								
London Blackfriars 3	⊖ d											22 34						22 43							23 04
London Bridge 4	⊖ d	22 13	22a14	22a17	22 23	22 25	22 29	22 30	22 34	22 38		22a40		22 43	22a44	22a47	22 53		22 55	22 59	23 00	23 04	23 08		23a10
London Victoria 15	⊖ d										22 22													22 52	
New Cross 4	⊖ d	22 18				22 30		22 35						22 48					23 00		23 05				
St Johns	d							22 37					←								23 07				
Lewisham 4	a	22 22				22 34	22 37	22 39	22 42				22 42	22 52					23 04	23 07	23 09	23 12			
Hither Green 4	a	22 27							→				22 47	22 57								→			
Petts Wood 4	a										22 55		23 00					23 20						23 26	
Orpington 4	a				22 40					22 54	22 58		23 03				23 10	23 24					23 24	23 30	

For general notes see front of timetable
For details of catering facilities see
Directory of Train Operators

London → Lewisham, Hither Green, Petts Wood and Orpington (Summary of Services)

For details of Bank Holiday service alterations please see first page of Table 195

		SE 12	SE 50	SN	SE 80	SE 22 [1]	SE 73	SE 70	SE 62	SE 24	SE 12	SE 2 [1]	SE 70	FC [1]	SE 12	SE 50	SE 22 [1]	SE 73	SE 80	SN	SE 70	SE 70	SE 24		
London Charing Cross 4	⊖ d		23 04	23 07	23 10	23 15		23 17	23 20	23 22	23 26	23 30				23 34	23 37		23 40	23 45		23 47	23 52		
London Waterloo (East) 4	⊖ d		23 07	23 10	23 13	23 18		23 20	23 23	23 25	23 29	23 33				23 37	23 40		23 43	23 48		23 50	23 55		
London Cannon Street 4	⊖ d																								
London Blackfriars 3	⊖ d						23 13							23 34				23 43							
London Bridge 4	⊖ d		23 13	23a14	23a17	23 23		23 25	23 29	23 30	23 34	23 38		23a40		23 43	23a44		23a47	23a52		23 55	23 58		
London Victoria 15	⊖ d												23 22								23 53				
New Cross 4	⊖ d		23 18					23 30		23 35						23 48						23 59	00 04		
St Johns	d	←								23 37					←								00 06		
Lewisham 4	a	23 12	23 22					23 34	23 37	23 39	23 42				23 42	23 52						00 04	00 08		
Hither Green 4	a	23 17	23 27								→				23 47	23 57									
Petts Wood 4	a	23 30					23 50						23 55		00 01			00 20			00 25				
Orpington 4	a	23 33				23 40	23 54					23 56	23 58		00 03			00 24			00 28				

Saturdays

		SE 12	SE 73	SE 70	SE 24	FC	SE 50	SE 02 [1]	SN	SE 62	FC	SE 14	SE 52	SE 54	SE 80	FC [1]		SE 70	SE 62	SE 24	SE 12	SE 4 [1]	SE 70	SE 12	SE 54
London Charing Cross 4	⊖ d	23p26			23p52		00 04	00 10	00 12	00 14		00 48	05 04	05 34	05 40			05 47	05 50	05 52	05 56	06 00			06 04
London Waterloo (East) 4	⊖ d	23p29			23p55		00 07	00 13	00 15	00 17		00 51	05 07	05 37	05 43			05 50	05 53	05 55	05 59	06 03			06 07
London Cannon Street 4	⊖ d																								
London Blackfriars 3	⊖ d		23p43			00 04					00 34					05 44									
London Bridge 4	⊖ d	23p34			23p58	00a10	00 13	00 18	00a19	00 23	00a40	00 56	05 13	05 43	05a47	05a49		05 55	05 59	06 01	06 04	06 08			06 13
London Victoria 15	⊖ d			23p53																			05 51		
New Cross 4	⊖ d				00 04		00 18			00 28		01 01	05 18	05 48						06 06					06 18
St Johns	d				00 06															06 08				←	
Lewisham 4	a	23p42			00 08		00 22			00 32		01 05	05 22	05 52				06 04	06 06	06 10	06 12			06 12	06 22
Hither Green 4	a	23p47					00 27					01 09	05 27	05 57							→			06 17	06 27
Petts Wood 4	a	00 01	00 20	00 25				00 39				01 23											06 24	06 30	
Orpington 4	a	00 03	00 24	00 28				00 42				01 26										06 26	06 27	06 33	

		SE 80	SE 70	FC [1]	SE 62	SE 24	SE 16	FC [1]	SE 54	SE 80		SE 70	FC [1]	SE 62	SE 24	SE 12	SE 4 [1]	SE 70	FC [1]	SE 12	SE 54	SE 80	SE 70	FC [1]	SE 62
London Charing Cross 4	⊖ d	06 10	06 17		06 20	06 22	06 26		06 34	06 40		06 47		06 50	06 52	06 56	07 00				07 04	07 10	07 17		07 20
London Waterloo (East) 4	⊖ d	06 13	06 20		06 23	06 25	06 29		06 37	06 43		06 50		06 53	06 55	06 59	07 03				07 07	07 13	07 20		07 23
London Cannon Street 4	⊖ d																								
London Blackfriars 3	⊖ d			06 20				06 35					06 50						07 05					07 20	
London Bridge 4	⊖ d	06a17	06 25	06a26	06 29	06 31	06 34	06a41	06 43	06a47		06 55	06a56	06 59	07 01	07 04	07 08		07a11		07 13	07a17	07 25	07a26	07 29
London Victoria 15	⊖ d																	06 51							
New Cross 4	⊖ d					06 36			06 48						07 06						07 18				
St Johns	d					06 38									07 08					←					
Lewisham 4	a		06 34		06 36	06 40	06 42		06 52			07 04		07 06	07 10	07 12				07 12	07 22		07 34		07 36
Hither Green 4	a						06 47		06 57							→				07 17	07 27				
Petts Wood 4	a						07 00											07 24		07 30					
Orpington 4	a						07 03										07 26	07 27		07 33					

		SE 24	SE 16	SE 4 [1]		SE 70	FC [1]	SE 16	SE 54	SN	SE 80	SE 22 [1]	SE 70	FC [1]	SE 62	SE 24	SE 12	SE 4 [1]	SE 70	SE 12		SE 54	SE 78	FC [1]	SE 81
London Charing Cross 4	⊖ d	07 22	07 26	07 30					07 34	07 40	07 42	07 45	07 47		07 50	07 52	07 56	08 00				08 02			
London Waterloo (East) 4	⊖ d	07 25	07 29	07 33					07 37	07 43	07 45	07 48	07 50		07 53	07 55	07 59	08 03				08 05			
London Cannon Street 4	⊖ d																								08 10
London Blackfriars 3	⊖ d						07 35							07 50										08 05	
London Bridge 4	⊖ d	07 31	07 34	07 38			07a41		07 43	07a47	07a49	07 53	07 55	07a56	07 59	08 01	08 04	08 08				08 10		08a11	08a13
London Victoria 15	⊖ d					07 21													07 51				08 01		
New Cross 4	⊖ d	07 36							07 48							08 06						08 15			
St Johns	d	07 38						←								08 08				←					
Lewisham 4	a	07 40	07 42					07 42	07 52				08 04		08 06	08 10	08 12			08 12		08 19	08 22		
Hither Green 4	a		→					07 47	07 57								→			08 17		08 23			
Petts Wood 4	a					07 54		08 00											08 24	08 30					
Orpington 4	a			07 55		07 57		08 03				08 09						08 26	08 27	08 33					

		SN	SE 22 [1]	SE 70	SE 70	FC [1]	SE 62	SE 24	SE 16	SE 47	SE 4 [1]	SE 70	SE 16	SE 54		SE 78	SE 70	FC [1]	SE 81	SN	SE 47	SE 22 [1]	SE 70	FC [1]	SE 25
London Charing Cross 4	⊖ d	08 10	08 15		08 17		08 20	08 22	08 26		08 30			08 32						08 40		08 45	08 47		
London Waterloo (East) 4	⊖ d	08 13	08 18		08 20		08 23	08 25	08 29		08 33			08 35						08 43		08 48	08 50		
London Cannon Street 4	⊖ d									08 30									08 40		08 48				08 54
London Blackfriars 3	⊖ d					08 20												08 35						08 50	
London Bridge 4	⊖ d	08a17	08 23		08 25	08a26	08 29	08 31	08 34	08 34	08 38			08 40				08a41	08a43	08a47	08 52	08a52	08 55	08a56	08 58
London Victoria 15	⊖ d			08 06								08 21				08 31	08 36								
New Cross 4	⊖ d							08 36						08 45							08 57				09 03
St Johns	d							08 38					←								08 59				09 05
Lewisham 4	a				08 33		08 36	08 40	08 42				08 42	08 49		08 52							09 04		09 07
Hither Green 4	a								→				08 47	08 53							09 04				
Petts Wood 4	a			08 39								08 54	09 00				09 09								
Orpington 4	a		08 39	08 42							08 55	08 57	09 03				09 12								

For general notes see front of timetable
For details of catering facilities see Directory of Train Operators

London → Lewisham, Hither Green, Petts Wood and Orpington (Summary of Services)

		SE 82	SE 12	SE 47	SE 4 [1]	SE 70	SE 67	SE 12		SE 54	SE 78	FC [1]	SE 81	SE 24	SN	SE 09 [1]	SE 47	SE 22 [1]	SE 70	SE 70	FC [1]	SE 25	SE 82	SE 16	SE 47
London Charing Cross [4]	⊖ d	08 50	08 56		09 00					09 02				09 06	09 10			09 15		09 17			09 20	09 26	
London Waterloo (East) [4]	⊖ d	08 53	08 59		09 03					09 05				09 09	09 13			09 18		09 20			09 23	09 29	
London Cannon Street [4]	⊖ d			09 00			09 04						09 10			09 14	09 18					09 24			09 30
London Blackfriars [3]	⊖ d											09 05									09 20				
London Bridge [4]	⊖ d	08a58	09 04	09 04	09 08		09 08			09 10		09a11	09a13	09a14	09a17	09a17	09 22	09 23		09 25	09a26	09 28	09a28	09 34	09a34
London Victoria [15]	⊖ d					08 51					09 01								09 06						
New Cross [4]	⊖ d						09 14										09 27					09 33			
St Johns	d							←									09 29					09 35			
Lewisham [4]	a		09 12 →				09 17	09 12		09 19	09 22									09 34		09 37		09 42 →	
Hither Green [4]	a							09 17		09 23							09 34								
Petts Wood [4]	a					09 24		09 30											09 39						
Orpington [4]	a				09 26	09 27		09 33										09 39	09 42						

		SE 4 [1]		SE 70	SE 67	SE 16	SE 54	SE 78	SE 70	FC [1]	SE 81	SE 24	SN		SE 47	SE 22 [1]	SE 70	FC [1]	SE 25	SE 82	SE 12	SE 87	SE 8 [1]	SE 70	SE 67
London Charing Cross [4]	⊖ d	09 30					09 32					09 36	09 40			09 45	09 47			09 50	09 56		10 00		
London Waterloo (East) [4]	⊖ d	09 33					09 35					09 39	09 43			09 48	09 50			09 53	09 59		10 03		
London Cannon Street [4]	⊖ d				09 34						09 40				09 48				09 54			10 00			10 04
London Blackfriars [3]	⊖ d									09 35								09 50							
London Bridge [4]	⊖ d	09 38			09 38		09 40			09a41	09a43	09a44	09a47		09 52	09a52	09 55	09a56	09 58	09a58	10 04	10 04	10 08		10 08
London Victoria [15]	⊖ d			09 21				09 31	09 36															09 51	
New Cross [4]	⊖ d				09 44										09 57				10 03						10 14
St Johns	d					←									09 59				10 05						
Lewisham [4]	a				09 47	09 42	09 49	09 52									10 04		10 07		10 12 →				10 17
Hither Green [4]	a					09 47	09 53								10 04										
Petts Wood [4]	a			09 54		10 00			10 09														10 22	10 24	
Orpington [4]	a	09 53		09 57		10 03			10 12														10 26	10 27	

		SE 12	SE 54	SE 78	FC [1]	SE 81	SE 34	SN	SE 09 [1]	SE 47	SE 22 [1]	SE 70	SE 70	FC [1]	SE 25	SE 82	SE 16	SE 87	SE 8 [1]	SE 70	SE 67	SE 16	SE 54	SE 78	SE 70
London Charing Cross [4]	⊖ d		10 02				10 06	10 10			10 15		10 17			10 20	10 26		10 30				10 32		
London Waterloo (East) [4]	⊖ d		10 05				10 09	10 13			10 18		10 20			10 23	10 29		10 33				10 35		
London Cannon Street [4]	⊖ d					10 10			10 14	10 18					10 24			10 30			10 34				
London Blackfriars [3]	⊖ d				10 05									10 20											
London Bridge [4]	⊖ d		10 10		10a11	10a13	10a14	10a17	10a17	10 22	10 23		10 25	10a26	10 28	10a28	10 34	10 34	10 38		10 38		10 40		
London Victoria [15]	⊖ d			10 01								10 06								10 21				10 31	10 36
New Cross [4]	⊖ d									10 27					10 33						10 44				
St Johns	d	←								10 29					10 35							←			
Lewisham [4]	a	10 12	10 19	10 22									10 34		10 37		10 42 →				10 47	10 42	10 49	10 52	
Hither Green [4]	a	10 17	10 23							10 34												10 47	10 53		
Petts Wood [4]	a	10 30										10 39								10 54		11 00			11 09
Orpington [4]	a	10 33									10 39	10 42							10 53	10 57		11 03			11 12

		FC [1]	SE 81	SE 34	SN			SE 47	SE 22 [1]	SE 70	FC [1]	SE 25	SE 82	SE 12	SE 87	SE 8 [1]	SE 70	SE 67	SE 12	SE 54	SE 78	FC [1]		SE 81
						and at																		
London Charing Cross [4]	⊖ d			10 36	10 40	the same			17 45	17 47			17 50	17 56		18 00				18 02				
London Waterloo (East) [4]	⊖ d			10 39	10 43				17 48	17 50			17 53	17 59		18 03				18 05				
London Cannon Street [4]	⊖ d		10 40			minutes		17 48				17 54			18 00			18 04						18 10
London Blackfriars [3]	⊖ d	10 35									17 50											18 05		
London Bridge [4]	⊖ d	10a41	10a43	10a44	10a47	past		17 52	17a52	17 55	17a56	17 58	17a58	18 04	18a03	18 08		18 08		18 10		18a11		18a13
London Victoria [15]	⊖ d																17 51				18 01			
New Cross [4]	⊖ d					each		17 57				18 03						18 14						
St Johns	d							17 59				18 05							←					
Lewisham [4]	a					hour until				18 04		18 07		18 12 →				18 17	18 12	18 19	18 22			
Hither Green [4]	a							18 04											18 17	18 23				
Petts Wood [4]	a															18 22	18 24		18 30					
Orpington [4]	a															18 26	18 27		18 33					

		SE 24	SN	SE 09 [1]	SE 47	SE 22 [1]	SE 70	SE 70	FC [1]	SE 25	SE 62	SE 25	SE 16	SE 87	SE 90 [1]	SE 70		SE 16	SE 54	SE 78	SE 70	FC [1]	SE 81	SE 24	SN
London Charing Cross [4]	⊖ d	18 06	18 10			18 15		18 17			18 20		18 26		18 30				18 32					18 36	18 40
London Waterloo (East) [4]	⊖ d	18 09	18 13			18 18		18 20			18 23		18 29		18 33				18 35					18 39	18 43
London Cannon Street [4]	⊖ d			18 14	18 18					18 24				18 30									18 40		
London Blackfriars [3]	⊖ d								18 20													18 35			
London Bridge [4]	⊖ d	18a14	18a17	18a17	18 22	18 23		18 25	18a26	18 28	18 29		18 34	18a33	18 38				18 40			18a41	18a43	18a44	18a47
London Victoria [15]	⊖ d						18 06					←				18 21				18 31	18 36				
New Cross [4]	⊖ d				18 27					18 33 →		18 33													
St Johns	d				18 29							18 36						←							
Lewisham [4]	a							18 33			18 36	18 38	18 44 →					18 44	18 49	18 51					
Hither Green [4]	a				18 34													18 48	18 53						
Petts Wood [4]	a						18 39									18 54		19 00			19 09				
Orpington [4]	a					18 40	18 42								18 54	18 57		19 03			19 12				

For general notes see front of timetable
For details of catering facilities see
Directory of Train Operators

Table 199

Saturdays

London → Lewisham, Hither Green, Petts Wood and Orpington (Summary of Services)

Station	SE 47	SE 22 ■1	SE 70	FC ■1	SE 62	SE 25	SE 12	SE 87	SE 4 ■1		SE 70	FC ■1	SE 12	SE 54	SE 78	SN	SE 81	SE 09 ■1	SE 22 ■1	SE 70	SE 70	FC ■1	SE 62	SE 24
London Charing Cross ■4 ⊖ d		18 45	18 47		18 50	18 52	18 56		19 00					19 04		19 07	19 10		19 15		19 17		19 20	19 22
London Waterloo (East) ■4 ⊖ d		18 48	18 50		18 53	18 55	18 59		19 03					19 07		19 10	19 13		19 18		19 20		19 23	19 25
London Cannon Street ■4 ⊖ d	18 48							19 00										19 14						
London Blackfriars ■3 ⊖ d				18 50								19 04										19 20		
London Bridge ■4 ⊖ d	18 52	18a52	18 55	18a56	18 59	19 01	19 04	19a03	19 08			19a10		19 13		19a14	19a17	19a17	19 23		19 25	19a26	19 29	19 31
London Victoria ■15 ⊖ d											18 51				19 01					19 06				
New Cross ■4 ⊖ d	18 57					19 06																		19 36
St Johns d	18 59					19 08							←											19 38
Lewisham ■4 a			19 04		19 06	19 10	19 14 →						19 14	19 20	19 22						19 34		19 36	19 40
Hither Green ■4 a	19 04												19 18	19 24										
Petts Wood ■4 a											19 24		19 30							19 39				
Orpington ■4 a									19 24		19 27		19 33						19 40	19 42				

Station	SE 16	SE 90 ■1	SE 70		FC ■1	SE 16	SE 50	SE 78	SN	SE 80	SE 22 ■1	SE 70	SE 70	FC ■1	SE 62	SE 24	SE 12	SE 4 ■1	SE 70		FC ■1	SE 12	SE 50	SN
London Charing Cross ■4 ⊖ d	19 26	19 30					19 34		19 37	19 40	19 45		19 47		19 50	19 52	19 56	20 00					20 04	20 07
London Waterloo (East) ■4 ⊖ d	19 29	19 33					19 37		19 39	19 43	19 48		19 50		19 53	19 55	19 59	20 03					20 07	20 10
London Cannon Street ■4 ⊖ d																								
London Blackfriars ■3 ⊖ d					19 34									19 50							20 04			
London Bridge ■4 ⊖ d	19 34	19 38			19a41		19 43		19a44	19a47	19 53		19 55	19a56	19 59	20 01	20 04	20 08			20a10		20 13	20a14
London Victoria ■15 ⊖ d			19 21					19 31				19 36							19 51					
New Cross ■4 ⊖ d							19 48									20 06							20 18	
St Johns d						←										20 08						←		
Lewisham ■4 a	19 42 →					19 42	19 52	19 53					20 04		20 06	20 10	20 12 →					20 12	20 22	
Hither Green ■4 a						19 47	19 57															20 17	20 27	
Petts Wood ■4 a			19 54			20 00						20 09							20 24			20 30		
Orpington ■4 a		19 54	19 57			20 03					20 10	20 12						20 24	20 27			20 33		

Station	SE 80	SE 70	SE 62	SE 24	SE 12	SE 90 ■1	SE 70	FC ■1	SE 12	SE 50	SN	SE 80	SE 22 ■1		SE 70	SE 62	SE 24	SE 16	SE 4 ■1	SE 70	FC ■1	SE 16	SE 50	SN
London Charing Cross ■4 ⊖ d	20 10	20 17	20 20	20 22	20 26	20 30				20 34	20 37	20 40	20 45		20 47	20 50	20 52	20 56	21 00				21 04	21 07
London Waterloo (East) ■4 ⊖ d	20 13	20 20	20 23	20 25	20 29	20 33				20 37	20 40	20 43	20 48		20 50	20 53	20 55	20 59	21 03				21 07	21 10
London Cannon Street ■4 ⊖ d																								
London Blackfriars ■3 ⊖ d								20 34													21 04			
London Bridge ■4 ⊖ d	20a17	20 25	20 29	20 31	20 34	20 38		20a40		20 43	20a44	20a47	20 53		20 55	20 59	21 01	21 04	21 08		21a10		21 13	21a14
London Victoria ■15 ⊖ d							20 21													20 51				
New Cross ■4 ⊖ d				20 36						20 48							21 06						21 18	
St Johns d				20 38					←								21 08					←		
Lewisham ■4 a		20 34	20 36	20 40	20 42 →				20 42	20 52					21 04	21 06	21 10	21 12 →				21 12	21 22	
Hither Green ■4 a									20 47	20 57												21 17	21 27	
Petts Wood ■4 a							20 54		21 00											21 24		21 30		
Orpington ■4 a						20 54	20 57		21 03				21 10						21 24	21 27		21 33		

Station	SE 80	SE 70	SE 62	SE 24	SE 12	SE 90 ■1	SE 70		FC ■1	SE 12	SE 50	SN	SE 80	SE 22 ■1	SE 70	SE 62	SE 24	SE 12	SE 4 ■1	SE 70	FC ■1	SE 12	SE 50	SN
London Charing Cross ■4 ⊖ d	21 10	21 17	21 20	21 22	21 26	21 30					21 34	21 37	21 40	21 45	21 47	21 50	21 52	21 56	22 00				22 04	22 07
London Waterloo (East) ■4 ⊖ d	21 13	21 20	21 23	21 25	21 29	21 33					21 37	21 40	21 43	21 48	21 50	21 53	21 55	21 59	22 03				22 07	22 10
London Cannon Street ■4 ⊖ d																								
London Blackfriars ■3 ⊖ d									21 34												22 04			
London Bridge ■4 ⊖ d	21a17	21 25	21 29	21 31	21 34	21 38			21a40		21 43	21a44	21a47	21 53	21 55	21 59	22 01	22 04	22 08		22a10		22 13	22a14
London Victoria ■15 ⊖ d							21 21													21 51				
New Cross ■4 ⊖ d				21 36							21 48						22 06						22 18	
St Johns d				21 38						←							22 08					←		
Lewisham ■4 a		21 34	21 36	21 40	21 42 →					21 42	21 52				22 04	22 06	22 10	22 12 →				22 12	22 22	
Hither Green ■4 a										21 47	21 57											22 17	22 27	
Petts Wood ■4 a							21 54			22 00										22 24		22 30		
Orpington ■4 a						21 54	21 57			22 03				22 10					22 24	22 27		22 33		

Station	SE 80		SE 70	SE 62	SE 24	SE 12	SE 90 ■1	SE 70	FC ■1	SE 12	SE 50	SN	SE 80	SE 22 ■1	SE 73	SE 70	SE 62		SE 24	SE 12	SE 8 ■1	SE 70	FC ■1	SE 12
London Charing Cross ■4 ⊖ d	22 10		22 17	22 20	22 22	22 26	22 30				22 34	22 37	22 40	22 45		22 47	22 50		22 52	22 56	23 00			
London Waterloo (East) ■4 ⊖ d	22 13		22 20	22 23	22 25	22 29	22 33				22 37	22 40	22 43	22 48		22 50	22 53		22 55	22 59	23 03			
London Cannon Street ■4 ⊖ d																								
London Blackfriars ■3 ⊖ d									22 34						22 43								23 04	
London Bridge ■4 ⊖ d	22a17		22 25	22 29	22 31	22 34	22 38		22a40		22 43	22a44	22a47	22 53		22 55	22 59		23 01	23 04	23 08		23a10	
London Victoria ■15 ⊖ d								22 21														22 51		
New Cross ■4 ⊖ d					22 36						22 48								23 06					
St Johns d					22 38					←									23 08					←
Lewisham ■4 a			22 34	22 36	22 40	22 42 →				22 42	22 52					23 04	23 06		23 10	23 12 →				23 12
Hither Green ■4 a										22 47	22 57													23 17
Petts Wood ■4 a								22 54		23 00					23 20							23 24		23 30
Orpington ■4 a							22 54	22 57		23 03				23 10	23 23						23 24	23 27		23 33

For general notes see front of timetable
For details of catering facilities see
Directory of Train Operators

Saturdays

London → Lewisham, Hither Green, Petts Wood and Orpington (Summary of Services)

		SE 50	SN	SE 73	SE 80	SE 70	SE 62	SE 24	SE 12	SE 8 [1]	SE 70	FC		SE 12	SE 50	SE 73	SE 80	SN	SE 70	SE 70	SE 24
London Charing Cross [4]	⊖ d	23 04	23 07		23 10	23 17	23 20	23 22	23 26	23 30					23 34		23 40	23 45		23 47	23 52
London Waterloo (East) [4]	⊖ d	23 07	23 10		23 13	23 20	23 23	23 25	23 29	23 33					23 37		23 43	23 48		23 50	23 55
London Cannon Street [4]	⊖ d																				
London Blackfriars [3]	⊖ d			23 13								23 34				23 43					
London Bridge [4]	⊖ d	23 13	23a14		23a17	23 25	23 29	23 31	23 34	23 38		23a40			23 43		23a47	23a52		23 55	23 58
London Victoria [15]	⊖ d										23 21								23 53		
New Cross [4]	⊖ d	23 18						23 36							23 48						00 04
St Johns	d							23 38													00 06
Lewisham [4]	a	23 22				23 34	23 36	23 40	23 42 →					← 23 42	23 52					00 04	00 08
Hither Green [4]	a	23 27												23 47	23 57						
Petts Wood [4]	a			23 50							23 54			00 01		00 20			00 26		
Orpington [4]	a			23 53						23 54	23 57			00 03		00 23			00 29		

Sundays

		SE 12	SE 73	SE 70	SE 24	SE 50	FC	SE 02 [1]	SN	SE 62	FC [1]	SE 14	FC [1]	FC [1]	SN	SE 16	SE 70	SE 72	SE 50	SE 24	SE 80	FC [1]	SN	SE 22 [1]	SE 12
London Charing Cross [4]	⊖ d	23p26			23p52	00 04		00 10	00 12	00 14		00 48			07 36	07 42		07 46	07 49	07 52	08 01		08 06	08 10	08 12
London Waterloo (East) [4]	⊖ d	23p29			23p55	00 07		00 13	00 15	00 17		00 51			07 39	07 45		07 49	07 52	07 55	08 04		08 09	08 13	08 15
London Cannon Street [4]	⊖ d																								
London Blackfriars [3]	⊖ d		23p43				00 04				00 34		07 04	07 34								08 04			
London Bridge [4]	⊖ d	23p34			23p58	00 13	00a15	00 18	00a19	00 22	00a40	00 56	07a10	07a40	07a43	07 50		07 54	07 58	08 00	08a08	08a10	08a13	08 18	08 20
London Victoria [15]	⊖ d			23p53													07 52								
New Cross [4]	⊖ d				00 04	00 18				00 27		01 01						07 59	08 04	08 06					
St Johns	d				00 06															08 08					
Lewisham [4]	a	23p42			00 08	00 22				00 31		01 05						08 03	08 07	08 10					
Hither Green [4]	a	23p47				00 27						01 09				08 00			08 12						08 30
Petts Wood [4]	a	00 01	00 20	00 26				00 39				01 23				08 12	08 26								08 42
Orpington [4]	a	00 03	00 23	00 29				00 42				01 26				08 15	08 29							08 35	08 45

		SE 70	SE 50	SE 90 [1]	SE 70		SE 62	SE 80	FC [1]	SN	SE 16	SE 82	SE 50	SE 24	SE 4 [1]	SE 70	SE 84	FC [1]	SN	SE 22 [1]	SE 12	SE 70	FC	SE 50	SE 24
London Charing Cross [4]	⊖ d	08 16	08 19	08 24			08 26	08 31		08 36	08 42	08 46	08 49	08 52	08 54		09 01		09 06	09 10	09 12	09 16		09 19	09 22
London Waterloo (East) [4]	⊖ d	08 19	08 22	08 27			08 29	08 34		08 39	08 45	08 49	08 52	08 55	08 57		09 04		09 09	09 13	09 15	09 19		09 22	09 25
London Cannon Street [4]	⊖ d																								
London Blackfriars [3]	⊖ d								08 34									09 04					09 19		
London Bridge [4]	⊖ d	08 24	08 28	08 32			08 34	08a38	08a40	08a43	08 50	08 54	08 58	09 00	09 02		09a08	09a10	09a13	09 18	09 20	09 24	09a25	09 28	09 30
London Victoria [15]	⊖ d				08 22											08 52									
New Cross [4]	⊖ d	08 29	08 33									08 59	09 03	09 06								09 29		09 33	09 36
St Johns	d													09 08											09 38
Lewisham [4]	a	08 33	08 37				08 42					09 03	09 07	09 10								09 33		09 37	09 40
Hither Green [4]	a		08 41								09 00		09 11								09 30			09 41	
Petts Wood [4]	a				08 56						09 12					09 26					09 42				
Orpington [4]	a			08 48	08 59						09 15				09 18	09 29				09 35	09 45				

		SE 90 [1]	SE 70	SE 62	SE 84	FC [1]	SN	SE 67	SE 22 [1]	SE 16		SE 70	FC [1]	SE 50	SE 24	SE 4 [1]	SE 70	SE 82	SE 84	FC [1]	SN	SE 67	SE 22 [1]	SE 12	SE 70
London Charing Cross [4]	⊖ d	09 24		09 26	09 31		09 36		09 40	09 42		09 46		09 49	09 52	09 54		09 56	10 01		10 06		10 10	10 12	10 16
London Waterloo (East) [4]	⊖ d	09 27		09 29	09 34		09 39		09 43	09 45		09 49		09 52	09 55	09 57		09 59	10 04		10 09		10 13	10 15	10 19
London Cannon Street [4]	⊖ d																								
London Blackfriars [3]	⊖ d					09 34							09 49							10 04					
London Bridge [4]	⊖ d	09 32		09 34	09a38	09a40	09a43	09 46	09 48	09 50		09 54	09a55	09 58	10 00	10 02		10a04	10a08	10a10	10a13	10 16	10 18	10 20	10 24
London Victoria [15]	⊖ d		09 22														09 52								
New Cross [4]	⊖ d											09 59		10 03	10 06										10 29
St Johns	d														10 08										
Lewisham [4]	a			09 42				09 53				10 03		10 07	10 10							10 23			10 33
Hither Green [4]	a									10 00				10 11										10 30	
Petts Wood [4]	a		09 56							10 12							10 26							10 42	
Orpington [4]	a	09 48	09 59						10 04	10 15						10 18	10 29						10 35	10 45	

		FC [1]	SE 50	SE 24		SE 90 [1]	SE 70	SE 82	SE 84	FC [1]	SN	SE 67	SE 22 [1]	SE 16	SE 70	FC [1]	SE 50	SE 24	SE 4 [1]	SE 70	SE 82	SE 84	FC [1]	SN	SE 67
London Charing Cross [4]	⊖ d		10 19	10 22		10 24		10 26	10 31		10 36		10 40	10 42	10 46		10 49	10 52	10 54		10 56	11 01		11 06	
London Waterloo (East) [4]	⊖ d		10 22	10 25		10 27		10 29	10 34		10 39		10 43	10 45	10 49		10 52	10 55	10 57		10 59	11 04		11 09	
London Cannon Street [4]	⊖ d																								
London Blackfriars [3]	⊖ d	10 19								10 34						10 49							11 04		
London Bridge [4]	⊖ d	10a25	10 28	10 30		10 32		10a34	10a38	10a40	10a43	10 46	10 48	10 50	10 54	10a55	10 58	11 00	11 02		11a04	11a08	11a10	11a13	11 16
London Victoria [15]	⊖ d						10 22													10 52					
New Cross [4]	⊖ d		10 33	10 36											10 59		11 04	11 07							
St Johns	d			10 38														11 08							
Lewisham [4]	a		10 37	10 40								10 53			11 03		11 08	11 10							11 23
Hither Green [4]	a		10 41											11 00			11 12								
Petts Wood [4]	a						10 56							11 12						11 26					
Orpington [4]	a					10 48	10 59						11 04	11 15					11 18	11 29					

For general notes see front of timetable
For details of catering facilities see
Directory of Train Operators

Table 199

Sundays

London → Lewisham, Hither Green, Petts Wood and Orpington (Summary of Services)

	SE 22 1	SE 12	SE 70	FC 1	SE 50	SE 24	and at		SE 90 1	SE 70	SE 62	SE 80	FC 1	SN	SE 67	SE 22 1	SE 72	SE 16	SE 72	SE 50	SE 24	SE 4 1	SE 70
London Charing Cross 4 ⊖ d	11 10	11 12	11 16		11 19	11 22	the same		17 24		17 26	17 31		17 36		17 40		17 42	17 46	17 49	17 52	17 54	
London Waterloo (East) 4 ⊖ d	11 13	11 15	11 19		11 22	11 25			17 27		17 29	17 34		17 39		17 43		17 45	17 49	17 52	17 55	17 57	
London Cannon Street 4 ⊖ d							minutes																
London Blackfriars 3 ⊖ d				11 19									17 34										
London Bridge 4 ⊖ d	11 18	11 20	11 24	11a25	11 28	11 30	past		17 32		17 34	17a38	17a40	17a43	17 46	17 48		17 50	17 54	17 58	18 00	18 02	
London Victoria 15 ⊖ d										17 22							17 26						17 52
New Cross 4 ⊖ d			11 29		11 34	11 37	each												17 59	18 04	18 07		
St Johns d						11 38															18 08		
Lewisham 4 a			11 33		11 38	11 40	hour until				17 42				17 53				18 03	18 08	18 10		
Hither Green 4 a		11 30			11 42													18 00		18 12			
Petts Wood 4 a		11 42								17 56							18 01	18 12					18 26
Orpington 4 a	11 35	11 45							17 48	17 59						18 04	18 05	18 15				18 18	18 29

	SE 60	SE 80	FC 1	SN	SE 22 1	SE 12	SE 70	SE 50	SE 24	SE 90 1	SE 70	SE 62	SE 80		FC 1	SN	SE 22 1	SE 72	SE 16	SE 72	SE 50	SE 24	SE 4 1	SE 70
London Charing Cross 4 ⊖ d	17 56	18 01		18 06	18 10	18 12	18 16	18 19	18 22	18 24		18 26	18 31			18 36	18 40		18 42	18 46	18 49	18 52	18 54	
London Waterloo (East) 4 ⊖ d	17 59	18 04		18 09	18 13	18 15	18 19	18 22	18 25	18 27		18 29	18 34			18 39	18 43		18 45	18 49	18 52	18 55	18 57	
London Cannon Street 4 ⊖ d																								
London Blackfriars 3 ⊖ d			18 04												18 34									
London Bridge 4 ⊖ d	18 04	18a08	18a10	18a13	18 18	18 20	18 24	18 28	18 30	18 32		18 34	18a38		18a40	18a43	18 48		18 50	18 54	18 58	19 00	19 02	
London Victoria 15 ⊖ d											18 22							18 26						18 52
New Cross 4 ⊖ d							18 29	18 34	18 37											18 59	19 04	19 07		
St Johns d									18 38													19 08		
Lewisham 4 a	18 12						18 33	18 38	18 40			18 42								19 03	19 08	19 10		
Hither Green 4 a						18 30		18 42											19 00		19 12			
Petts Wood 4 a						18 42					18 56							19 01	19 12					19 26
Orpington 4 a					18 35	18 45				18 48	18 59						19 04	19 05	19 15				19 18	19 29

	SE 60	SE 80	FC 1	SN	SE 22 1	SE 70	SE 50	SE 90 1	SE 70	SE 62	SE 80	FC 1	SN	SE 22 1	SE 12	SE 72	SE 50	SE 24		SE 4 1	SE 70	SE 80	FC 1	SN
London Charing Cross 4 ⊖ d	18 56	19 01		19 06	19 10	19 16	19 19	19 24		19 26	19 31		19 36	19 40	19 42	19 46	19 49	19 52		19 54		20 01		20 06
London Waterloo (East) 4 ⊖ d	18 59	19 04		19 09	19 13	19 19	19 22	19 27		19 29	19 34		19 39	19 43	19 45	19 49	19 52	19 55		19 57		20 04		20 09
London Cannon Street 4 ⊖ d																								
London Blackfriars 3 ⊖ d			19 04									19 34											20 04	
London Bridge 4 ⊖ d	19 04	19a08	19a10	19a13	19 17	19 24	19 28	19 32		19 34	19a38	19a40	19a43	19 48	19 50	19 54	19 58	20 00		20 02		20a08	20a10	20a13
London Victoria 15 ⊖ d									19 22												19 52			
New Cross 4 ⊖ d						19 29	19 33									19 59	20 03	20 06						
St Johns d																		20 08						
Lewisham 4 a	19 12					19 33	19 37			19 42						20 03	20 07	20 10						
Hither Green 4 a							19 41								20 00		20 11							
Petts Wood 4 a					19 33				19 56						20 12						20 26			
Orpington 4 a					19 36			19 49	19 59					20 04	20 15					20 18	20 29			

	SE 22 1	SE 70	SE 50	SE 90 1	SE 70	SE 62	SE 80	FC 1	SN	SE 12	SE 72	SE 50	SE 24	SE 4 1	SE 70	SE 80	FC 1	SN	SE 22 1	SE 70	FC 1	SE 50	SE 90 1	SE 70
London Charing Cross 4 ⊖ d	20 10	20 16	20 19	20 24		20 26	20 31		20 36	20 42	20 46	20 49	20 52	20 54		21 01		21 06	21 10	21 16		21 19	21 24	
London Waterloo (East) 4 ⊖ d	20 13	20 19	20 22	20 27		20 29	20 34		20 39	20 45	20 49	20 52	20 55	20 57		21 04		21 09	21 13	21 19		21 22	21 27	
London Cannon Street 4 ⊖ d																								
London Blackfriars 3 ⊖ d								20 34									21 04				21 19			
London Bridge 4 ⊖ d	20 17	20 24	20 28	20 32		20 34	20a38	20a40	20a43	20 50	20 54	20 58	21 00	21 02		21a08	21a10	21a13	21 17	21 24	21a25	21 28	21 32	
London Victoria 15 ⊖ d					20 22										20 52									21 22
New Cross 4 ⊖ d		20 29	20 33								20 59	21 03	21 06							21 29		21 33		
St Johns d													21 08											
Lewisham 4 a		20 33	20 37			20 42					21 03	21 07	21 10							21 33		21 37		
Hither Green 4 a			20 41							21 00		21 11										21 41		
Petts Wood 4 a	20 33				20 56					21 12					21 26				21 33					21 56
Orpington 4 a	20 36			20 49	20 59					21 15				21 18	21 29				21 36				21 49	21 59

	SE 62		SE 80	FC 1	SN	SE 12	SE 72	SE 50	SE 24	SE 4 1	SE 70	SE 80	FC 1	SN	SE 22 1	SE 70	SE 50	SE 2 1	SE 70	SE 62	SE 80	FC 1	SN	SE 12
London Charing Cross 4 ⊖ d	21 26		21 31		21 36	21 42	21 46	21 49	21 52	21 54		22 01		22 06	22 10	22 16	22 19	22 24		22 26	22 31		22 36	22 42
London Waterloo (East) 4 ⊖ d	21 29		21 34		21 39	21 45	21 49	21 52	21 55	21 57		22 04		22 09	22 13	22 19	22 22	22 27		22 29	22 34		22 39	22 45
London Cannon Street 4 ⊖ d																								
London Blackfriars 3 ⊖ d				21 34									22 04									22 34		
London Bridge 4 ⊖ d	21 34		21a38	21a40	21a43	21 50	21 54	21 58	22 00	22 02		22a08	22a10	22a13	22 17	22 24	22 28	22 32		22 34	22a38	22a40	22a43	22 50
London Victoria 15 ⊖ d											21 52								22 22					
New Cross 4 ⊖ d							21 59	22 03	22 06							22 29	22 33							
St Johns d									22 08															
Lewisham 4 a	21 42						22 03	22 07	22 10							22 33	22 37			22 42				
Hither Green 4 a						22 00		22 11									22 41							23 00
Petts Wood 4 a						22 12					22 26				22 33				22 56					23 12
Orpington 4 a						22 15				22 18	22 29				22 36			22 49	22 59					23 15

For general notes see front of timetable
For details of catering facilities see
Directory of Train Operators

London → Lewisham, Hither Green, Petts Wood and Orpington (Summary of Services)

		SE 70	SE 72	SE 72	SE 50	SE 24	SE 80		FC [1]	SN	SE 22 [1]	SE 70	SE 70	SE 50	SE 8 [1]	SE 62	SE 80	FC	SN	SE 12	SE 70	SE 50	SE 24		
London Charing Cross 4	⊖ d		22 46		22 49	22 52	23 01			23 06	23 10		23 16	23 19	23 24	23 26	23 31		23 36	23 42	23 46	23 49	23 52		
London Waterloo (East) 4	⊖ d		22 49		22 52	22 55	23 04			23 09	23 13		23 19	23 22	23 27	23 29	23 34		23 39	23 45	23 49	23 52	23 55		
London Cannon Street 4	⊖ d																								
London Blackfriars 3	⊖ d								23 04									23 34							
London Bridge 4	⊖ d		22 54		22 58	23 00	23a08		23a10	23a13	23 17		23 24	23 28	23a31	23 34	23a38	23a40	23a43	23 50	23 54	23 58	00 01		
London Victoria 15	⊖ d	22 52		22 56								23 22													
New Cross 4	⊖ d		22 59		23 03	23 06							23 29	23 33							23 59	00 03	00 06		
St Johns	d					23 08																	00 08		
Lewisham 4	⛴ a		23 03		23 07	23 10							23 33	23 37		23 42					00 03	00 07	00 10		
Hither Green 4	a				23 11									23 41						23 59		00 11			
Petts Wood 4	a	23 26		23 31							23 32	23 56								00 12					
Orpington 4	a	23 29		23 35							23 35	23 59								00 15					

For general notes see front of timetable
For details of catering facilities see
Directory of Train Operators

Orpington, Petts Wood, Hither Green and Lewisham → London (Summary of Services)

For details of Bank Holiday service alterations please see first page of Table 195

		FC	FC [1]	SE 73	SE 52	SE 71	FC [1]	SE 50	SN	SE 11	SE 02	SE 24	SE 80	SE 70	SE 11	SE 70	SE 73	SE 30 [1]	SE 50	SE 82	SE 11	FC [1]	SE 24	SE 70	SE 70
Orpington [4]	d			04 36		04 58					05 20					05 25	05 36	05 50							05 50
Petts Wood [4]	d			04 39		05 01					05 23					05 28	05 39								05 53
Hither Green [4]	d				05 08			05 23			05 35								05 55						
Lewisham [4]	d				05 13			05 28				05 40		05 48					06 00				06 10	06 16	
St Johns	d											05 42											06 12		
New Cross [4]	⊖ d				05 16			05 32			05 40	05 44		05 52					06 04				06 14	06 20	
London Victoria [15]	⊖ a															06 01									06 27
London Bridge [4]	⊖ d	00 20	00 52		05 22		05 34	05 38	05 41	05 42	05 46	05 50	05 53	05 58	05 58			06 06	06 10	06 13	06 14	06 15	06 20	06 26	
London Blackfriars [3]	⊖ a	00 26	00 59	05 16		05 34	05 41										06 18					06 23			
London Cannon Street [4]	⊖ a									05 45					06 01						06 17				
London Waterloo (East) [4]	⊖ d				05 28			05 44	05 46		05 51	05 55	05 58	06 03				06 11	06 15	06 18			06 25	06 31	
London Charing Cross [4]	⊖ a				05 31			05 47	05 49		05 54	05 58	06 02	06 06				06 14	06 18	06 21			06 28	06 34	

		SE 14	SE 11	SE 62	SE 07 [1]	SE 5 [1]	SE 2 [1]	SE 50	SE 84	SE 77	FC [1]	SE 70	SE 14	SE 05	SE 24	SE 14	SE 22 [1]	FC [1]	SE 62	SE 11	SE 4 [1]	SE 70	SE 03 [1]	SE 40	SE 24
Orpington [4]	d	06 00				06 17						06 20	06 24	06 31											
Petts Wood [4]	d	06 03										06 23	06 27			←									
Hither Green [4]	d	06 15						06 25					06 39			06 39								06 52	
Lewisham [4]	d	06 20		06 24				06 30		06 34			→		06 40	06 44			06 52			06 56			07 00
St Johns	d							06 32							06 42									06 56	
New Cross [4]	⊖ d	06 24						06 34		06 38					06 44									06 58	07 04
London Victoria [15]	⊖ a											06 57													
London Bridge [4]	⊖ d	06 30	06 30	06 33	06 34	06 37	06 37	06 40	06 43	06 44	06 46			06 50	06 50	06 53	06 56	06 59	07 01	07 02	07 04	07 06	07 08	07 09	07 11
London Blackfriars [3]	⊖ a										06 52							07 06							
London Cannon Street [4]	⊖ a		06 33		06 38	06 41				06 47				06 53						07 05			07 13		
London Waterloo (East) [4]	⊖ d	06 35		06 38			06 42	06 45	06 48						06 55	06 58	07 01		07 06		07 09	07 11		07 13	07 16
London Charing Cross [4]	⊖ a	06 38		06 41			06 46	06 48	06 51						06 58	07 01	07 05		07 10		07 14	07 15		07 17	07 20

		SE 80		SE 70	FC [1]	SE 14	SE 13	SE 17	SE 55	SE 90 [1]	SE 87	SE 40	SE 13	SE 70	SE 07 [1]	SE 71	SE 70	SE 12	SE 23 [1]	SE 62	SE 46	SE 77	SE 12	SE 80	SE 51
Orpington [4]	d			06 44		06 49	06 57	06 59								07 02	07 06	07 10	07 13				←		
Petts Wood [4]	d			06 47		06 52	07 00						←			07 05	07 09	07 13					07 13		
Hither Green [4]	d					07 06	07 14		07 02			07 10	07 14								07 22		07 26		07 26
Lewisham [4]	d						→		07 08			07 15		07 18				→		07 22		07 25			07 32
St Johns	d								07 10													07 27			
New Cross [4]	⊖ d								07 12				07 19									07 29			07 36
London Victoria [15]	⊖ a			07 20													07 45								
London Bridge [4]	⊖ d	07 14			07 16			07 16	07 19	07 22	07 23	07 25	07 26	07 28	07 28				07 31	07 31	07 34	07 36	07 37	07 41	07 42
London Blackfriars [3]	⊖ a				07 22											07 44									
London Cannon Street [4]	⊖ a							07 21	07 24		07 28		07 31		07 33				07 36			07 41			07 48
London Waterloo (East) [4]	⊖ d	07 19				07 24				07 27		07 30		07 33						07 36	07 39		07 42	07 46	
London Charing Cross [4]	⊖ a	07 24				07 28				07 32		07 34		07 37						07 40	07 43		07 46	07 51	

		SE 24	SE 66	SE 83	SE 07 [1]	SE 30 [1]	SE 77	SE 46	SE 5 [1]	SE 80	SE 71	SE 70	SE 17	SE 18	SE 25	SE 12	SE 87	SE 51	SE 74	SE 63	SE 07 [1]	SE 30 [1]	SE 77	SE 46	SE 3 [1]
Orpington [4]	d										07 23	07 27	07 30			07 36									
Petts Wood [4]	d										07 26	07 30	07 33			07 39									
Hither Green [4]	d							07 42					07 46					07 49						08 02	
Lewisham [4]	d	07 35	07 38				07 41							07 44	07 50			07 54	07 56				08 01		
St Johns	d						07 44								07 52								08 04		
New Cross [4]	⊖ d						07 46								07 54			07 59					08 06		
London Victoria [15]	⊖ a											08 07		08 11											
London Bridge [4]	⊖ d	07 44		07 45	07 50	07 50	07 53	07 54	07 55	07 58			07 59		08 01	08 02	08 04	08 06	08 07	08 08	08 10	08 11	08 13	08 15	08 15
London Blackfriars [3]	⊖ a										08 05														
London Cannon Street [4]	⊖ a			07 51	07 55		07 57		08 00				08 04		08 06		08 09	08 11		08 13	08 15		08 18		08 20
London Waterloo (East) [4]	⊖ d	07 48	07 51			07 55		07 58		08 03						08 08			08 12			08 16		08 20	
London Charing Cross [4]	⊖ a	07 53	07 56			07 59		08 03		08 07						08 12			08 17			08 21		08 24	

		SE 73	SE 70	SE 17		SE 86	SE 12	SE 78	SE 25	SE 70	SE 23 [1]	SE 81	SE 57	SE 12	SE 65	SE 07 [1]	SE 30 [1]	SE 77	SE 46	SE 91 [1]	SE 78	SE 70	SE 17	SE 86	SE 25
Orpington [4]	d	07 44	07 50	07 53			07 56							08 00								08 10	08 13		
Petts Wood [4]	d	07 47	07 53	07 56			07 59							08 03								08 13	08 16		
Hither Green [4]	d												08 09	08 16					08 22						
Lewisham [4]	d							08 04	08 10	08 12			08 14		08 18			08 21			08 24				08 30
St Johns	d								08 12									08 24							08 32
New Cross [4]	⊖ d								08 14				08 18					08 26							08 34
London Victoria [15]	⊖ a		08 28					08 28													08 48	08 48			
London Bridge [4]	⊖ d			08 18		08 19			08 21	08 23	08 23	08 25	08 27	08 27	08 29	08 31	08 31	08 34	08 35	08 36			08 38	08 39	08 41
London Blackfriars [3]	⊖ a	08 29																							
London Cannon Street [4]	⊖ a			08 23					08 26		08 28	08 30	08 32		08 34	08 36		08 39		08 41			08 43		08 46
London Waterloo (East) [4]	⊖ d					08 24	08 26			08 28				08 32			08 36		08 40					08 44	
London Charing Cross [4]	⊖ a					08 28	08 30			08 32				08 36			08 41		08 44					08 48	

For general notes see front of timetable
For details of catering facilities see
Directory of Train Operators

Orpington, Petts Wood, Hither Green and Lewisham → London (Summary of Services)

For details of Bank Holiday service alterations please see first page of Table 195

Station		SE 40	SE 87	SE 57	SE 12	SE 74	SE 63	SE 07 [1]	SE 30 [1]	SE 77	SE 46	SE 3 [1]	SE 18	SE 70	SE 17	SE 86	SE 12	SE 25	SE 57	SE 70	SE 23 [1]	SE 40	SE 81	FC [1]	SE 07 [1]
Orpington [4]	d				08 20									08 30	08 33		08 38								
Petts Wood [4]	d				08 23									08 33	08 36		08 41								
Hither Green [4]	d			08 29	08 36						08 42								08 49			08 56			
Lewisham [4]	d			08 34		08 36				08 41			08 44					08 50	08 54	08 56					
St Johns	d									08 44								08 52							
New Cross [4]	⊖ d			08 38						08 46					08 52			08 54	08 58						
London Victoria [15]	⊖ a												09 11	09 11											
London Bridge [4]	⊖ d	08 43	08 43	08 46		08 47	08 49	08 51	08 51	08 54	08 55	08 56			08 58	08 59		09 01	09 04	09 05	09 06	09 08	09 09	09 11	09 11
London Blackfriars [3]	⊖ a																							09 18	
London Cannon Street [4]	⊖ a		08 48	08 51			08 54	08 56		08 59		09 01			09 03			09 06	09 10		09 12		09 14		09 16
London Waterloo (East) [4]	⊖ d	08 48			08 50	08 52			08 56		09 00					09 04	09 06			09 10		09 14			
London Charing Cross [4]	⊖ a	08 52			08 54	08 56			09 01		09 04					09 08	09 11			09 14		09 18			

Station		SE 63	SE 34	SE 77	SE 30 [1]	SE 86		SE 5 [1]	SE 70	SE 73	SE 78	SE 12	SE 72	SE 47	SE 25	SE 22 [1]	SE 54	SE 25	SE 88 [1]	SE 81	SE 70	SE 17	SE 24	FC [1]	SE 70
Orpington [4]	d								08 53	08 57		09 00									09 08	09 12			
Petts Wood [4]	d								08 56	09 00		09 03									09 11	09 15			
Hither Green [4]	d											09 16		09 20			09 23					09 28			
Lewisham [4]	d			09 04							09 10		09 20		09 24		09 28	←				09 33			09 36
St Johns	d			09 06										09 24	09 28			09 28							09 38
New Cross [4]	⊖ d			09 08										09 26	→			09 30							09 40
London Victoria [15]	⊖ a								09 30		09 32										09 47				
London Bridge [4]	⊖ d	09 13	09 14	09 16	09 19	09 22		09 23				09 26	09 30	09 33		09 34	09 37	09 38	09 40	09 40		09 42	09 44	09 45	09 49
London Blackfriars [3]	⊖ a									09 37														09 52	
London Cannon Street [4]	⊖ a	09 18		09 21				09 28						09 38				09 43		09 45		09 47			
London Waterloo (East) [4]	⊖ d		09 20		09 24	09 27						09 31	09 35			09 39	09 42		09 45				09 49		09 55
London Charing Cross [4]	⊖ a		09 24		09 29	09 31						09 35	09 39			09 44	09 47		09 50				09 52		09 59

Station		SE 87	SE 70	SE 16	SE 22 [1]	SE 62	SE 47	SE 4 [1]	FC [1]	SE 25	SE 78	SE 16	SE 70	SE 70	SE 54	SE 34	SE 81	SE 70	SE 8 [1]	FC [1]	SE 25	SE 82	SE 47	SN	SE 22 [1]
Orpington [4]	d		09 23	09 35	09 36								09 38	09 53					09 55						
Petts Wood [4]	d		09 26	09 38								←	09 41	09 56					09 59						
Hither Green [4]	d			09 50			09 44					09 50			09 54								10 10		
Lewisham [4]	d			→		09 46				09 48	09 51	09 55			09 59			10 02			10 06				
St Johns	d						09 48			09 52											10 08		10 14		
New Cross [4]	⊖ d						09 50			09 54											10 10		10 16		
London Victoria [15]	⊖ a		10 00								10 12		10 14	10 29											
London Bridge [4]	⊖ d	09 52			09 52	09 55	09 57	09 58	10 00	10 03		10 04				10 08	10 10	10 11	10 13	10 15	10 17	10 19	10 22	10 22	10 25
London Blackfriars [3]	⊖ a								10 07											10 22					
London Cannon Street [4]	⊖ a	09 57					10 01			10 06							10 13				10 20		10 27		
London Waterloo (East) [4]	⊖ d				09 57	10 00		10 03				10 09			10 11	10 14		10 16	10 19			10 24		10 27	10 30
London Charing Cross [4]	⊖ a				10 01	10 05		10 07				10 12			10 14	10 17		10 20	10 22			10 28		10 30	10 33

Station		SE 67	SE 34	FC [1]	SE 81	SE 78	SE 12	SE 54		SE 70	SE 70	SE 70		SE 8 [1]	SE 87	FC [1]	SE 25	SE 82	SE 09 [1]	SN	SE 47	SE 22 [1]	SE 67	SE 34	FC [1]
Orpington [4]	d						10 05				10 08	10 23		10 25											
Petts Wood [4]	d						10 08				10 11	10 26		10 29											
Hither Green [4]	d						10 20	10 24													10 40				
Lewisham [4]	d	10 16				10 21	10 25	10 29		10 32							10 36						10 46		
St Johns	d																10 38				10 45				
New Cross [4]	⊖ d	10 20															10 40				10 47		10 50		
London Victoria [15]	⊖ a					10 42					10 44	10 59													
London Bridge [4]	⊖ d	10 27	10 29	10 30	10 30		10 35	10 38		10 41				10 43	10 44	10 45	10 47	10 49	10 51	10 52	10 54	10 55	10 57	10 59	11 00
London Blackfriars [3]	⊖ a			10 37												10 52									11 07
London Cannon Street [4]	⊖ a	10 30			10 33										10 47		10 50		10 54		10 57		11 00		
London Waterloo (East) [4]	⊖ d		10 35				10 40	10 43		10 46				10 48				10 54		10 57		11 00		11 05	
London Charing Cross [4]	⊖ a		10 39				10 44	10 47		10 50				10 51				10 58		11 00		11 03		11 09	

Station		SE 81	SE 78	SE 16	SE 54	SE 70	SE 70	SE 70	SE 8 [1]	SE 87	FC [1]	SE 25	SE 82	SN	SE 47	SE 22 [1]	SE 67	SE 34	FC [1]	SE 81	SE 78	SE 12	SE 54	SE 70	SE 70
Orpington [4]	d			10 35			10 38	10 53	10 57							11 05						11 05			11 08
Petts Wood [4]	d			10 38			10 41	10 56														11 08			11 11
Hither Green [4]	d			10 50	10 54										11 10							11 20	11 24		
Lewisham [4]	d		10 51	10 55	10 59	11 02						11 06					11 16				11 21	11 25	11 29	11 32	
St Johns	d											11 08			11 15										
New Cross [4]	⊖ d											11 10			11 17		11 20								
London Victoria [15]	⊖ a		11 12				11 14	11 29													11 42				11 44
London Bridge [4]	⊖ d	11 00		11 05	11 08	11 11			11 13	11 14	11 15	11 17	11 19	11 22	11 24	11 25	11 27	11 29	11 30	11 30		11 35	11 38	11 41	
London Blackfriars [3]	⊖ a										11 22								11 37						
London Cannon Street [4]	⊖ a	11 03								11 17		11 20			11 27		11 30			11 33					
London Waterloo (East) [4]	⊖ d			11 10	11 13	11 16			11 18				11 24	11 27		11 30		11 35				11 40	11 43	11 46	
London Charing Cross [4]	⊖ a			11 14	11 17	11 20			11 21				11 28	11 30		11 33		11 39				11 44	11 47	11 50	

For general notes see front of timetable
For details of catering facilities see
Directory of Train Operators

Orpington, Petts Wood, Hither Green and Lewisham → London (Summary of Services)

For details of Bank Holiday service alterations please see first page of Table 195

	SE 70		SE 8 [1]	SE 87	FC [1]	SE 25	SE 82	SE 09 [1]	SN	SE 47	SE 22 [1]		SE 67	SE 34	FC [1]	SE 81	SE 78	SE 16	SE 54	SE 70	SE 70	SE 70	SE 8 [1]
		and at																					
Orpington [4] d	11 23	the same	15 25															15 35			15 38	15 53	15 57
Petts Wood [4] d	11 26		15 29															15 38			15 41	15 56	
Hither Green [4] d		minutes								15 40								15 50	15 54				
Lewisham [4] d						15 36							15 46				15 51	15 55	15 59	16 02			
St Johns d		past				15 38				15 45													
New Cross [4] ⊖ d						15 40				15 47			15 50										
London Victoria [15] ⊖ a	11 59	each															16 12				16 14	16 30	
London Bridge [4] ⊖ d			15 43	15 44	15 45	15 47	15 49	15 51	15 52	15 54	15 55		15 57	15 59	16 00	16 00		16 04	16 08	16 11			16 13
London Blackfriars [3] ⊖ a		hour until			15 52										16 07								
London Cannon Street [4] ⊖ a				15 47		15 50		15 54		15 57			16 00			16 03							
London Waterloo (East) [4] ⊖ d			15 48				15 54		15 57		16 00			16 04				16 10	16 14	16 18			16 18
London Charing Cross [4] ⊖ a			15 51				15 58		16 00		16 03			16 07				16 13	16 17	16 23			16 21

	SE 87	FC [1]	SE 25	SE 82	SE 47	SE 13	SE 23 [1]	SE 66	SE 2 [1]	SE 81	SE 34	SE 70	SE 88 [1]	SE 13	FC [1]	SE 55	SE 70	SE 12	SE 87	SE 12	SE 78	SE 24	SE 81	SE 22 [1]
Orpington [4] d						16 05	16 07										16 08	16 20		16 33				16 34
Petts Wood [4] d						16 08								←			16 11	16 23		16 36				
Hither Green [4] d					16 10	16 20 →								16 20		16 28		16 36		→				
Lewisham [4] d			16 08					16 16			16 21	16 24		16 28		16 33					16 35	16 38		
St Johns d			16 10		16 15											16 35						16 40		
New Cross [4] ⊖ d			16 12		16 17											16 37						16 42		
London Victoria [15] ⊖ a																	16 45				17 03			
London Bridge [4] ⊖ d	16 14	16 15	16 19	16 20	16 24		16 24	16 27	16 29	16 30	16 32	16 33	16 34	16 38	16 42	16 43		16 46	16 48			16 50	16 52	16 53
London Blackfriars [3] ⊖ a		16 24													16 53									
London Cannon Street [4] ⊖ a	16 17		16 22		16 27					16 33		16 36				16 46			16 52				16 55	
London Waterloo (East) [4] ⊖ d				16 25			16 29	16 33	16 35		16 37		16 39	16 43				16 52				16 56		16 58
London Charing Cross [4] ⊖ a				16 28			16 33	16 36	16 38		16 40		16 45	16 47				16 55				16 59		17 01

	SE 63	SE 47	SE 24	SE 4 [1]	SE 71	SE 12	SE 57	SE 44	SE 87	SE 70	SE 23 [1]	SE 12	SE 81	SE 16		SE 25	SE 34	SE 81	SE 12	SE 78	SE 10	SE 51	SE 8 [1]	SE 63
Orpington [4] d						←				16 36	16 50	16 52		16 56					←				17 02	
Petts Wood [4] d						16 36				16 39		16 55							16 55					
Hither Green [4] d		16 42				16 52	16 50	16 56				→							17 09		17 13	17 06		
Lewisham [4] d	16 46				16 50		16 56									17 02				17 05		17 12		17 18
St Johns d		16 47														17 04						17 14		
New Cross [4] ⊖ d		16 49			16 54											17 06						17 16		
London Victoria [15] ⊖ a										17 12										17 28				
London Bridge [4] ⊖ d	16 55	16 57	16 58	17 00	17 01	17 03	17 05	17 07	17 09		17 09		17 12	17 13		17 15	17 16	17 19	17 19		17 23	17 24	17 27	17 27
London Blackfriars [3] ⊖ a																								
London Cannon Street [4] ⊖ a		17 00			17 05		17 08		17 13				17 15			17 18		17 23				17 29	17 31	
London Waterloo (East) [4] ⊖ d	17 00		17 04	17 05		17 08		17 12			17 15			17 19			17 21		17 24		17 28			17 32
London Charing Cross [4] ⊖ a	17 03		17 09	17 10		17 13		17 15			17 19			17 24			17 25		17 28		17 31			17 35

	FC [1]	SE 53	SE 70	SE 12	SE 2 [1]	SE 25	SE 12	SE 81	SE 88 [1]	SE 55	SE 12	SE 53	SE 22 [1]	SE 71	SE 87	SE 12	SE 16	SE 81	SE 34	SE 63	SE 70	SE 4 [1]	SE 63	SE 51
Orpington [4] d			17 04	17 07	17 13		←				17 21		17 26			←	17 34				17 36	17 40		
Petts Wood [4] d			17 07	17 10			17 10				17 24					17 24	17 37				17 39			
Hither Green [4] d		17 16		→			17 23			17 24	→	17 31				17 40								17 44
Lewisham [4] d						17 21				17 31				17 36					17 44	17 47				17 51
St Johns d						17 23				17 33														17 55
New Cross [4] ⊖ d						17 25				17 35				17 39										17 57
London Victoria [15] ⊖ a			17 42																		18 12			
London Bridge [4] ⊖ d	17 29	17 30			17 32	17 33	17 35	17 36	17 39	17 42		17 42	17 44	17 46	17 48	17 49	17 52	17 54	17 55	17 58			18 01	18 04
London Blackfriars [3] ⊖ a	17 36																							
London Cannon Street [4] ⊖ a		17 33				17 36		17 39		17 45				17 51	17 53			17 57		18 01				18 07
London Waterloo (East) [4] ⊖ d					17 37		17 40		17 44			17 47	17 50			17 54	17 58		18 00			18 04	18 06	
London Charing Cross [4] ⊖ a					17 41		17 46		17 48			17 50	17 55			17 57	18 01		18 03			18 07	18 09	

	SE 53	SE 10	SE 34	SE 12	FC [1]	SE 78	SE 85	SE 51	SE 25	SE 22 [1]	SE 66	SE 34	SE 74	SE 70	SE 12	SE 16		SE 4 [1]	SE 61	SE 53	SE 16	SE 34	SE 88 [1]	SE 81
Orpington [4] d				17 51						18 00				18 06	18 08	18 11		18 12			←			
Petts Wood [4] d				17 54										18 09		18 14					18 14			
Hither Green [4] d	17 50	17 55		18 06				18 04								→				18 18	18 26			
Lewisham [4] d						17 54			18 10				18 14						18 20	18 24		18 29		
St Johns d													18 16							18 26				
New Cross [4] ⊖ d													18 18							18 28				
London Victoria [15] ⊖ a						18 16								18 42										
London Bridge [4] ⊖ d	18 05	18 07	18 10		18 11		18 12	18 16		18 20	18 20	18 23	18 26		18 26			18 29	18 31	18 34	18 35	18 38	18 40	18 42
London Blackfriars [3] ⊖ a					18 19																			
London Cannon Street [4] ⊖ a							18 15				18 23		18 29							18 37				18 45
London Waterloo (East) [4] ⊖ d	18 10	18 12	18 16	18 20				18 22	18 24	18 27		18 28			18 32			18 34	18 37		18 40	18 44	18 45	
London Charing Cross [4] ⊖ a	18 13	18 15	18 19	18 23				18 25	18 27	18 30		18 33			18 37			18 37	18 40		18 45	18 49	18 48	

For general notes see front of timetable
For details of catering facilities see Directory of Train Operators

Orpington, Petts Wood, Hither Green and Lewisham → London (Summary of Services)

For details of Bank Holiday service alterations please see first page of Table 195

		SE 44	FC [1]	SE 66	SE 22 [1]	SE 22 [1]	SE 78	SE 24	SE 70	SE 12	SE 90 [1]	FC [1]	SE 87	SE 52	SE 25	SE 12	SE 74	SE 81	SE 22 [1]	FC [1]	SE 78	SE 24	SE 50	SE 62	SE 16
Orpington 4	d				18 33	18 36			18 36	18 39	18 40					←			18 56						19 05
Petts Wood 4	d								18 39	18 42						18 42									19 08
Hither Green 4	d	18 32								→				18 44		18 54							19 07		19 20
Lewisham 4	d			18 36			18 41	18 45						18 49	18 56		19 01				19 06	19 09	19 12	19 15	→
St Johns	d			18 38										18 51	18 58							19 11			
New Cross 4	⊖ d			18 40										18 53	19 00							19 13			
London Victoria 15	⊖ a						19 00		19 13												19 25				
London Bridge 4	⊖ d	18 43	18 45	18 49	18 50	18 52		18 55			18 58	19 00	19 02	19 03	19 06	19 06	19 10	19 12	19 13	19 16		19 19	19 22	19 23	
London Blackfriars 3	⊖ a		18 55									19 07								19 22					
London Cannon Street 4	⊖ a				18 53								19 05		19 10			19 15					19 25		
London Waterloo (East) 4	⊖ d	18 49		18 54		18 57		19 00			19 03			19 08		19 11	19 16		19 18			19 25		19 29	
London Charing Cross 4	⊖ a	18 53		18 57		19 00		19 05			19 07			19 11		19 14	19 20		19 21			19 29		19 32	

		SE 90 [1]	SE 24	FC [1]	SE 74	SE 81	SE 70	SE 22 [1]	SE 16	SE 74	SN	SE 50	FC [1]	SE 80	SE 62	SE 70	SE 16	SE 57	SE 22 [1]		SE 24	FC [1]	SE 70	SE 16	SE 81
Orpington 4	d	19 08					19 08	19 14	←							19 23	19 35		19 38					←	
Petts Wood 4	d						19 11									19 26	19 38								
Hither Green 4	d								19 20			19 26					19 50							19 50	
Lewisham 4	d		19 17		19 26				19 28	←		19 31			19 45		→				19 47		19 52	19 57	
St Johns	d		19 19																		19 49				
New Cross 4	⊖ d		19 21		19 30					19 30		19 34									19 51		19 56		
London Victoria 15	⊖ a				→		19 45									19 59									
London Bridge 4	⊖ d	19 26	19 29	19 30		19 34		19 34	19 36	19 38	19 39	19 44	19 45	19 49	19 53			19 54	19 56		19 59	20 00	20 04	20 06	20 08
London Blackfriars 3	⊖ a			19 37									19 52									20 07			
London Cannon Street 4	⊖ a					19 37				19 41								19 57							20 11
London Waterloo (East) 4	⊖ d	19 32	19 34					19 39	19 42		19 45	19 50		19 55	19 58				20 01		20 04		20 09	20 11	
London Charing Cross 4	⊖ a	19 35	19 37					19 42	19 45		19 49	19 53		19 59	20 01				20 04		20 07		20 13	20 15	

		SE 70	SE 90 [1]	SN	SE 54	FC [1]	SE 80	SE 62	SE 70	SE 16	SE 57	SE 22 [1]	SE 24	FC [1]	SE 70	SE 16	SE 81	SE 70	SE 18 [1]	SN	SE 54	FC [1]	SE 80	SE 62	SE 16
Orpington 4	d	19 38	19 50						19 53	20 05		20 08				←		20 08	20 20						20 35
Petts Wood 4	d	19 41							19 56	20 08								20 11							20 38
Hither Green 4	d				19 56					20 20						20 20					20 26				20 50
Lewisham 4	d				20 02			20 15		→			20 17		20 22	20 27					20 31			20 44	→
St Johns	d												20 19												
New Cross 4	⊖ d				20 05								20 21		20 26						20 34				
London Victoria 15	⊖ a	20 14							20 29									20 44							
London Bridge 4	⊖ d		20 09	20 11	20 14	20 15	20 19	20 23			20 24	20 26	20 29	20 30	20 34	20 36	20 38		20 39	20 41	20 44	20 45	20 49	20 53	
London Blackfriars 3	⊖ a					20 22								20 37								20 52			
London Cannon Street 4	⊖ a										20 27						20 41								
London Waterloo (East) 4	⊖ d		20 14	20 17	20 19		20 25	20 28				20 31	20 34		20 39	20 41			20 44	20 47	20 49		20 55	20 58	
London Charing Cross 4	⊖ a		20 18	20 20	20 22		20 29	20 31				20 34	20 37		20 43	20 45			20 48	20 50	20 52		20 59	21 01	

		SE 22 [1]	SE 24	FC [1]	SE 70	SE 16	SE 70	SE 90 [1]	SN	SE 54	FC [1]	SE 80	SE 62	SE 12	SE 22 [1]	SE 24	FC [1]	SE 70	SE 12	SE 70	SE 4 [1]		SN	SE 54	FC [1]
Orpington 4	d	20 38				←	20 38	20 50						21 05	21 08				←	21 08	21 20				
Petts Wood 4	d						20 41							21 08						21 11					
Hither Green 4	d					20 50				20 56				21 20					21 20					21 26	
Lewisham 4	d		20 47		20 52	20 57				21 01			21 14	→		21 17		21 22	21 27					21 31	
St Johns	d		20 49													21 19									
New Cross 4	⊖ d		20 51		20 56					21 04						21 21		21 26						21 34	
London Victoria 15	⊖ a						21 14													21 44					
London Bridge 4	⊖ d	20 56	20 59	21 00	21 04	21 06		21 09	21 11	21 14	21 15	21 19	21 23		21 26	21 29	21 30	21 34	21 36		21 39		21 41	21 44	21 45
London Blackfriars 3	⊖ a			21 07							21 22						21 37								21 52
London Cannon Street 4	⊖ a																								
London Waterloo (East) 4	⊖ d	21 01	21 04		21 09	21 11		21 14	21 17	21 19		21 25	21 28		21 31	21 34		21 39	21 41		21 44		21 47	21 49	
London Charing Cross 4	⊖ a	21 04	21 07		21 13	21 15		21 18	21 20	21 22		21 29	21 31		21 34	21 37		21 43	21 45		21 48		21 50	21 52	

		SE 80	SE 60	SE 16	SE 22 [1]	SE 24	SE 70	SE 16	SE 70	SE 90 [1]	SN	SE 52	FC [1]	SE 80	SE 62	SE 12	SE 22 [1]	SE 24	SE 70	SE 12	SE 70	SE 4 [1]	SN	SE 50	FC [1]
Orpington 4	d			21 35	21 38			←	21 38	21 50						22 05	22 08			←	22 08	22 20			
Petts Wood 4	d			21 38					21 41							22 08					22 11				
Hither Green 4	d			21 50				21 50				21 56				22 20				22 20				22 26	
Lewisham 4	d		21 44	→		21 47	21 52	21 57				22 01			22 14	→		22 17	22 22	22 27				22 31	
St Johns	d					21 49												22 19							
New Cross 4	⊖ d					21 51	21 56					22 04						22 21	22 26					22 34	
London Victoria 15	⊖ a								22 14												22 44				
London Bridge 4	⊖ d	21 49	21 53		21 56	21 59	22 04	22 06		22 09	22 11	22 14	22 15	22 19	22 23		22 26	22 29	22 34	22 36		22 39	22 41	22 44	22 45
London Blackfriars 3	⊖ a												22 22												22 52
London Cannon Street 4	⊖ a																								
London Waterloo (East) 4	⊖ d	21 55	21 58		22 01	22 04	22 09	22 11		22 14	22 17	22 19		22 25	22 28		22 31	22 34	22 39	22 41		22 44	22 47	22 49	
London Charing Cross 4	⊖ a	21 59	22 01		22 04	22 07	22 13	22 15		22 18	22 20	22 22		22 29	22 31		22 34	22 37	22 43	22 45		22 48	22 50	22 52	

For general notes see front of timetable
For details of catering facilities see
Directory of Train Operators

Orpington, Petts Wood, Hither Green and Lewisham → London (Summary of Services)

For details of Bank Holiday service alterations please see first page of Table 195

		SE 80	SE 62	SE 16	SE 22 1	SE 24	SE 70	SE 16	SE 70	SE 90 1	SN	SE 80	FC 1	SE 22 1	SE 50	SE 24	SE 12	SN	SE 82	SE 70	SE 70	FC 1	SE 4 1
Orpington 4	d			22 35	22 38				22 38	22 50				23 02			23 05			23 08			23 34
Petts Wood 4	d			22 38				←	22 41								23 08			23 11			
Hither Green 4	d			22 50				22 50							23 06		23 20						
Lewisham 4	d		22 44	→		22 47	22 52	22 57							23 11	23 17	23 27				23 32		
St Johns	d					22 49										23 19							
New Cross 4	⊖ d					22 51	22 56								23 14	23 21					23 36		
London Victoria 15	⊖ a								23 14											23 44			
London Bridge 4	⊖ d	22 49	22 53		22 56	22 59	23 04	23 06		23 09	23 11	23 14	23 15	23 20	23 24	23 29	23 36	23 39	23 41		23 44	23 45	23 52
London Blackfriars 3	⊖ a												23 22									23 52	
London Cannon Street 4	⊖ a																						
London Waterloo (East) 4	⊖ d	22 55	22 58		23 01	23 04	23 09	23 11		23 14	23 17	23 19		23 25	23 29	23 34	23 41	23 44	23 47		23 50		23 57
London Charing Cross 4	⊖ a	22 59	23 01		23 04	23 07	23 13	23 15		23 18	23 20	23 22		23 28	23 32	23 37	23 44	23 48	23 50		23 53		00 01

Saturdays

		FC	FC 1	SE 80	SE 24	SE 12	SE 70	SE 52	SE 80	SE 73	SE 24	FC 1	SE 12	SE 70	SE 70	SE 2 1	SE 52	SE 80	SE 62	SE 24	FC 1	SE 12	SE 70	SE 70	SE 54
Orpington 4	d					05 35				05 54			06 05		06 08	06 21						06 35		06 38	
Petts Wood 4	d					05 38				05 57			06 08		06 11							06 38		06 41	
Hither Green 4	d					05 50		05 56					06 20				06 26					06 50			06 56
Lewisham 4	d				05 47	05 57	05 59	06 02			06 17		06 27	06 29			06 31		06 41	06 47		06 57	06 59		07 02
St Johns	d				05 49						06 19									06 49					
New Cross 4	⊖ d				05 51			06 05			06 21						06 34			06 51					07 05
London Victoria 15	⊖ a														06 44									07 14	
London Bridge 4	⊖ d	00 20	00 52	05 49	05 59	06 05	06 08	06 14	06 19		06 29	06 31	06 35	06 38		06 40	06 44	06 48	06 51	06 59	07 01	07 05	07 08		07 14
London Blackfriars 3	⊖ a	00 26	00 59							06 33		06 37									07 07				
London Cannon Street 4	⊖ a																								
London Waterloo (East) 4	⊖ d			05 55	06 04	06 10	06 12	06 19	06 25		06 34		06 40	06 42		06 45	06 49	06 55	06 55	07 04		07 10	07 12		07 19
London Charing Cross 4	⊖ a			05 59	06 07	06 13	06 15	06 23	06 29		06 37		06 43	06 45		06 48	06 52	06 59	06 58	07 07		07 13	07 15		07 22

		SE 80	SE 62	SN	SE 12	SE 22 1	SE 24	FC 1	SE 78	SE 12	SE 70	SE 70	SE 2 1		SE 54	FC 1	SE 81	SE 62	SN	SE 22 1	SE 24	SE 81	FC 1	SE 78	SE 16
Orpington 4	d				07 05	07 08						07 08	07 20							07 35					07 35
Petts Wood 4	d				07 08					←		07 11													07 38
Hither Green 4	d				07 20					07 20					07 26										07 49
Lewisham 4	d		07 11		→		07 17		07 20	07 27	07 29				07 32			07 41			07 47			07 50	07 55
St Johns	d						07 19														07 49				
New Cross 4	⊖ d						07 21								07 35						07 51				
London Victoria 15	⊖ a								07 42			07 44												08 12	
London Bridge 4	⊖ d	07 19	07 22	07 24		07 27	07 29	07 31		07 35	07 38		07 39		07 44	07 45	07 46	07 50	07 52	07 55	07 59	08 00	08 01		08 05
London Blackfriars 3	⊖ a							07 37								07 52							08 07		
London Cannon Street 4	⊖ a																07 50					08 03			
London Waterloo (East) 4	⊖ d	07 25	07 26	07 29		07 31	07 34			07 40	07 42		07 44		07 49			07 54	07 57	08 00	08 04				08 10
London Charing Cross 4	⊖ a	07 29	07 29	07 32		07 34	07 37			07 43	07 45		07 47		07 52			07 58	08 00	08 05	08 07				08 14

		SE 70	SE 70	SE 90 1	SE 54	FC 1	SE 25	SE 62	SN	SE 47	SE 22 1	SE 24	SE 81	FC 1	SE 78	SE 12	SE 54	SE 70	SE 4 1	SE 70	SE 87	FC 1	SE 25	SE 62	SE 09 1
Orpington 4	d		07 38	07 53							08 05					08 05		08 08	08 20						
Petts Wood 4	d		07 41													08 08		08 11							
Hither Green 4	d				07 56					08 10						08 19	08 24								
Lewisham 4	d	07 59			08 02		08 06	08 11							08 20	08 25	08 29			08 32			08 36	08 41	
St Johns	d						08 08			08 14													08 38		
New Cross 4	⊖ d				08 05		08 10			08 17							08 32						08 40		
London Victoria 15	⊖ a		08 14												08 42			08 44							
London Bridge 4	⊖ d	08 08		08 10	08 14	08 15	08 17	08 19	08 22	08 23	08 25	08 29	08 30	08 31		08 35	08 38		08 39	08 41	08 44	08 45	08 47	08 49	08 51
London Blackfriars 3	⊖ a					08 22								08 37								08 52			
London Cannon Street 4	⊖ a						08 20			08 27			08 33								08 47		08 50		08 54
London Waterloo (East) 4	⊖ d	08 12		08 15	08 19			08 24	08 27		08 30	08 35				08 40	08 43		08 44	08 46				08 54	
London Charing Cross 4	⊖ a	08 15		08 18	08 22			08 28	08 30		08 33	08 39				08 44	08 47		08 48	08 50				08 58	

		SN	SE 47	SE 70		SE 22 1 ♁	SE 24	SE 81	FC 1	SE 78	SE 16	SE 54	SE 70	SE 90 1	SE 70	SE 87	FC 1	SE 25	SE 82	SN	SE 47	SE 70	SE 22 1	SE 67	SE 34
Orpington 4	d			08 23		08 35					08 35		08 38	08 53								08 53	09 05		
Petts Wood 4	d			08 26							08 38		08 41									08 56			
Hither Green 4	d		08 40								08 49	08 54									09 10				
Lewisham 4	d									08 50	08 55	08 59			09 02			09 06						09 16	
St Johns	d		08 45															09 08			09 14				
New Cross 4	⊖ d		08 47									09 02						09 10			09 17			09 20	
London Victoria 15	⊖ a			08 59						09 12			09 14									09 29			
London Bridge 4	⊖ d	08 52	08 53			08 55	08 59	09 00	09 01		09 05	09 08		09 09	09 11	09 14	09 15	09 17	09 19	09 22	09 23		09 25	09 27	09 29
London Blackfriars 3	⊖ a								09 07								09 22								
London Cannon Street 4	⊖ a		08 57					09 03								09 17		09 20			09 27			09 30	
London Waterloo (East) 4	⊖ d	08 57				09 00	09 05				09 10	09 13		09 15	09 16				09 24	09 27			09 30		09 35
London Charing Cross 4	⊖ a	09 00				09 03	09 09				09 14	09 17		09 18	09 20				09 28	09 30			09 33		09 39

For general notes see front of timetable
For details of catering facilities see
Directory of Train Operators

Orpington, Petts Wood, Hither Green and Lewisham → London (Summary of Services)

		FC [1]	SE 81	SE 78	SE 12	SE 54	SE 70	SE 70	SE 70	SE 8 [1]	SE 87	FC [1]	SE 25	SE 82	SE 09 [1]	SN	SE 47		SE 22 [1]		SE 67	SE 34	FC [1]	SE 81	SE 78
Orpington 4	d				09 05			09 08	09 23	09 25									09 35						
Petts Wood 4	d				09 08			09 11	09 26	09 29															
Hither Green 4	d				09 19	09 24											09 40								
Lewisham 4	d			09 20	09 25	09 29	09 32						09 36								09 46				09 50
St Johns	d												09 38				09 44								
New Cross 4	⊖ d					09 32							09 40				09 47				09 50				
London Victoria 15	⊖ a			09 42				09 44	09 59																10 12
London Bridge 4	⊖ d	09 30	09 30		09 35	09 38	09 41			09 43	09 44	09 45	09 47	09 49	09 51	09 52	09 54		09 55		09 57	09 59	10 00	10 00	
London Blackfriars 3	⊖ a	09 37										09 52											10 07		
London Cannon Street 4	⊖ a		09 33								09 47		09 50		09 54		09 57				10 00			10 03	
London Waterloo (East) 4	⊖ d				09 40	09 43	09 46			09 48				09 54		09 57			10 00			10 05			
London Charing Cross 4	⊖ a				09 44	09 47	09 50			09 51				09 58		10 00			10 03			10 09			

		SE 16	SE 54	SE 70	SE 70	SE 70	SE 8 [1]	SE 87	FC [1]	SE 25	SE 82	SN	SE 47	SE 22 [1]	SE 67	SE 34	FC [1]	SE 81	SE 78	SE 12	SE 54	SE 70	SE 70	SE 70	SE 8 [1]
Orpington 4	d	09 35			09 38	09 53	09 57							10 05						10 05			10 08	10 23	10 25
Petts Wood 4	d	09 38			09 41	09 56														10 08			10 11	10 26	10 29
Hither Green 4	d	09 50	09 54										10 10							10 19	10 24				
Lewisham 4	d	09 55	09 59	10 02						10 06					10 16				10 20	10 25	10 29	10 32			
St Johns	d									10 08			10 14												
New Cross 4	⊖ d									10 10			10 17		10 20										
London Victoria 15	⊖ a				10 14	10 29													10 42				10 44	10 59	
London Bridge 4	⊖ d	10 05	10 08	10 11			10 13	10 14	10 15	10 17	10 19	10 22	10 24	10 25	10 27	10 29	10 30	10 30		10 35	10 38	10 41			10 43
London Blackfriars 3	⊖ a								10 22								10 37								
London Cannon Street 4	⊖ a							10 17		10 20			10 27		10 30			10 34							
London Waterloo (East) 4	⊖ d	10 10	10 13	10 16			10 18				10 24	10 27		10 30		10 35				10 40	10 43	10 46			10 48
London Charing Cross 4	⊖ a	10 14	10 17	10 20			10 21				10 28	10 31		10 33		10 39				10 44	10 47	10 50			10 51

		SE 87	FC [1]	SE 25	SE 82	SE 09 [1]	SN	SE 47	SE 22 [1]	and at the same minutes past each hour until		SE 67	SE 24	FC [1]	SE 81	SE 78	SE 16	SE 54	SE 70	SE 70	SE 70	SE 8 [1]	SE 87	FC [1]
Orpington 4	d																17 35			17 38	17 53	17 57		
Petts Wood 4	d																17 38			17 41	17 56			
Hither Green 4	d							10 40									17 50	17 54						
Lewisham 4	d			10 36								17 46				17 50	17 55	17 59	18 02					
St Johns	d			10 38				10 44																
New Cross 4	⊖ d			10 40				10 47				17 50												
London Victoria 15	⊖ a															18 12				18 14	18 29			
London Bridge 4	⊖ d	10 44	10 45	10 47	10 49	10 51	10 52	10 54	10 55			17 57	17 59	18 00	18 00		18 05	18 08	18 11			18 13	18 14	18 15
London Blackfriars 3	⊖ a		10 52											18 07										18 22
London Cannon Street 4	⊖ a	10 47		10 50		10 54		10 57				18 00			18 03								18 17	
London Waterloo (East) 4	⊖ d				10 54		10 57		11 00				18 05				18 10	18 13	18 16			18 18		
London Charing Cross 4	⊖ a				10 58		11 00		11 03				18 09				18 14	18 17	18 20			18 21		

		SE 25	SE 82	SN	SE 47	SE 12	SE 22 [1]	SE 67	SE 78	SE 70	SE 4 [1]	FC [1]	SE 81	SE 24	SE 12	SE 54	SE 70	FC [1]	SE 62	SE 09 [1]	SN	SE 70	SE 22 [1]	SE 24	FC [1]
Orpington 4	d					18 05	18 05			18 08	18 11											18 23	18 35		
Petts Wood 4	d					18 08				18 11					⟵							18 26			
Hither Green 4	d				18 10	18 19									18 19	18 24									
Lewisham 4	d	18 06				⟶		18 16	18 20					18 23	18 26	18 29	18 32		18 41					18 47	
St Johns	d	18 08			18 14											18 31								18 49	
New Cross 4	⊖ d	18 10			18 17			18 20								18 32								18 51	
London Victoria 15	⊖ a								18 42	18 44												18 59			
London Bridge 4	⊖ d	18 17	18 19	18 22	18 24		18 25	18 27			18 28	18 30	18 30	18 34	18 36	18 38	18 41	18 45	18 50	18 51	18 52		18 55	18 59	19 00
London Blackfriars 3	⊖ a											18 37						18 52							19 07
London Cannon Street 4	⊖ a	18 20			18 27			18 30					18 33							18 54					
London Waterloo (East) 4	⊖ d		18 24	18 27			18 30				18 33			18 38	18 42	18 44	18 46		18 54		18 57		19 01	19 04	
London Charing Cross 4	⊖ a		18 28	18 30			18 33				18 36			18 41	18 45	18 48	18 50		18 58		19 00		19 06	19 07	

		SE 80		SE 78	SE 16	SE 70	SE 4 [1]	SE 54	SE 70	SE 54	FC [1]	SE 80	SE 62	SE 70	SE 12	SN	SE 22 [1]	SE 24	FC [1]	SE 70	SE 12	SE 70	SE 90 [1]	SN	SE 54
Orpington 4	d				18 35	18 38	18 51							18 53	19 05		19 08					19 08	19 20		
Petts Wood 4	d				18 38	18 41								18 56	19 08						⟵	19 11			
Hither Green 4	d				18 49			18 56							19 20						19 20				19 26
Lewisham 4	d			18 50	18 55			19 01	19 02	⟵			19 11		⟶			19 17		19 22	19 27				19 31
St Johns	d																	19 19							
New Cross 4	⊖ d							19 04 ⟶		19 04								19 21		19 26					19 34
London Victoria 15	⊖ a			19 12		19 14								19 29								19 44			
London Bridge 4	⊖ d	19 04			19 06		19 09		19 11	19 14	19 15	19 19	19 21			19 24	19 26	19 29	19 30	19 34	19 36		19 39	19 41	19 44
London Blackfriars 3	⊖ a										19 22								19 37						
London Cannon Street 4	⊖ a																								
London Waterloo (East) 4	⊖ d	19 10			19 12		19 15		19 16	19 19		19 23	19 26			19 28	19 31	19 34		19 39	19 41		19 45	19 47	19 49
London Charing Cross 4	⊖ a	19 13			19 15		19 19		19 20	19 22		19 26	19 29			19 31	19 34	19 37		19 43	19 45		19 49	19 51	19 52

For general notes see front of timetable
For details of catering facilities see
Directory of Train Operators

Table 199

Saturdays

Orpington, Petts Wood, Hither Green and Lewisham → London (Summary of Services)

		FC [1]	SE 80	SE 62	SE 70	SE 24	FC [1]	SE 70	SE 16	SE 70	SE 4 [1]	SN	SE 54	FC [1]	SE 80		SE 62	SE 70	SE 12	SE 22 [1]	SE 24	FC [1]	SE 70	SE 12	SE 70
Orpington [4]	d				19 23				19 35	19 38	19 51							19 53	20 05	20 08					20 08
Petts Wood [4]	d				19 26				19 38	19 41								19 56	20 08					←	20 11
Hither Green [4]	d								19 50				19 56						20 20					20 20	
Lewisham [4]	d			19 44		19 47		19 52	19 57				20 01				20 14		→		20 17		20 22	20 27	
St Johns	d					19 49															20 19				
New Cross [4]	⊖ d					19 51		19 56					20 04								20 21		20 26		
London Victoria [15]	⊖ a				19 59					20 14								20 29							20 44
London Bridge [4]	⊖ d	19 45	19 49	19 53		19 59	20 00	20 04	20 06		20 09	20 11	20 14	20 15	20 19		20 23			20 26	20 29	20 30	20 34	20 36	
London Blackfriars [3]	⊖ a	19 52					20 07							20 22								20 37			
London Cannon Street [4]	⊖ a																								
London Waterloo (East) [4]	⊖ d		19 55	19 58		20 04		20 09	20 11		20 15	20 17	20 19		20 25		20 28			20 31	20 34		20 39	20 41	
London Charing Cross [4]	⊖ a		19 59	20 01		20 07		20 13	20 15		20 19	20 21	20 22		20 29		20 31			20 34	20 37		20 43	20 45	

		SE 90 [1]	SN	SE 54	FC [1]	SE 80	SE 62	SE 24	FC [1]	SE 70	SE 16	SE 70	SE 4 [1]	SN	SE 54	FC [1]	SE 80	SE 62	SE 12	SE 22 [1]	SE 24	FC [1]	SE 70	SE 12	SE 70
Orpington [4]	d	20 20									20 35	20 38	20 51						21 05	21 08					21 08
Petts Wood [4]	d										20 38	20 41							21 08					←	21 11
Hither Green [4]	d			20 26							20 50				20 56				21 20					21 20	
Lewisham [4]	d			20 31			20 44	20 47		20 52	20 57				21 01			21 14	→		21 17		21 22	21 27	
St Johns	d							20 49													21 19				
New Cross [4]	⊖ d			20 34				20 51		20 56					21 04						21 21		21 26		
London Victoria [15]	⊖ a											21 14													21 44
London Bridge [4]	⊖ d	20 39	20 41	20 44	20 45	20 49	20 53	20 59	21 00	21 04	21 06		21 09	21 11	21 14	21 15	21 19	21 23		21 26	21 29	21 30	21 34	21 36	
London Blackfriars [3]	⊖ a				20 52				21 07							21 22						21 37			
London Cannon Street [4]	⊖ a																								
London Waterloo (East) [4]	⊖ d	20 45	20 47	20 49		20 55	20 58	21 04		21 09	21 11		21 15	21 17	21 19		21 25	21 28		21 31	21 34		21 39	21 41	
London Charing Cross [4]	⊖ a	20 49	20 51	20 52		20 59	21 01	21 07		21 13	21 15		21 19	21 21	21 22		21 29	21 31		21 34	21 37		21 43	21 45	

		SE 90 [1]	SN	SE 50	FC [1]	SE 80		SE 62	SE 24	SE 70	SE 16	SE 70	SE 4 [1]	SN	SE 50	FC [1]	SE 80	SE 62	SE 16	SE 22 [1]	SE 24	SE 70	SE 16	SE 70	SE 90 [1]
Orpington [4]	d	21 20									21 35	21 38	21 51						22 05	22 08				22 08	22 20
Petts Wood [4]	d										21 38	21 41							22 08				←	22 11	
Hither Green [4]	d			21 26							21 50				21 56				22 20				22 20		
Lewisham [4]	d			21 31				21 44	21 47	21 52	21 57				22 01			22 14	→		22 17	22 22	22 27		
St Johns	d								21 49												22 19				
New Cross [4]	⊖ d			21 34					21 51	21 56					22 04						22 21	22 26			
London Victoria [15]	⊖ a											22 14												22 44	
London Bridge [4]	⊖ d	21 39	21 41	21 44	21 45	21 49		21 53	21 59	22 04	22 06		22 09	22 11	22 14	22 15	22 19	22 23		22 26	22 29	22 34	22 36		22 39
London Blackfriars [3]	⊖ a				21 52											22 22									
London Cannon Street [4]	⊖ a																								
London Waterloo (East) [4]	⊖ d	21 45	21 47	21 49		21 55		21 58	22 04	22 09	22 11		22 15	22 17	22 19		22 25	22 28		22 31	22 34	22 39	22 41		22 45
London Charing Cross [4]	⊖ a	21 49	21 51	21 52		21 59		22 01	22 07	22 13	22 15		22 19	22 21	22 22		22 29	22 31		22 34	22 37	22 43	22 45		22 49

		SN	SE 50	FC [1]	SE 80	SE 62	SE 24	SE 70	SE 12	SE 70	SE 90 [1]	SN	SE 80	FC [1]	SE 50	SE 24	SE 12	SN	SE 80	SE 70	SE 70	FC [1]	SE 4 [1]		
Orpington [4]	d								22 35	22 38	22 51						23 05			23 08			23 37		
Petts Wood [4]	d								22 38	22 41							23 08			23 11					
Hither Green [4]	d		22 26						22 50						23 06		23 20								
Lewisham [4]	d		22 31			22 44	22 47	22 52	22 57						23 11	23 17	23 27				23 32				
St Johns	d						22 49									23 19									
New Cross [4]	⊖ d		22 34				22 51	22 56							23 14	23 21					23 36				
London Victoria [15]	⊖ a									23 14										23 44					
London Bridge [4]	⊖ d	22 41	22 44	22 45	22 49	22 53	22 59	23 04	23 06		23 09	23 11	23 14	23 15	23 24	23 29	23 35	23 39	23 41		23 44	23 45	23 53		
London Blackfriars [3]	⊖ a			22 52										23 22								23 52			
London Cannon Street [4]	⊖ a																								
London Waterloo (East) [4]	⊖ d	22 47	22 49		22 55	22 58	23 04	23 09	23 11		23 14	23 17	23 19		23 29	23 34	23 40	23 44	23 47		23 50		23 58		
London Charing Cross [4]	⊖ a	22 51	22 52		22 59	23 01	23 07	23 13	23 15		23 18	23 20	23 22		23 32	23 37	23 43	23 48	23 50		23 53		00 01		

Sundays

		FC	FC [1]	SN	FC [1]	SE 70	SE 72	SE 14	SE 50	SE 80	SE 70	SE 12	SN	SE 22 [1]	FC [1]	SE 12	SE 70	SE 70		SE 8 [1]	SE 50	SE 82	SN	FC [1]	SE 12
Orpington [4]	d						07 01	07 04			07 08	07 26		07 28		←		07 38		07 43					07 56
Petts Wood [4]	d						07 04	07 07			07 11	07 29				07 29		07 41							07 59
Hither Green [4]	d							07 19	07 18			→				07 40					07 48				08 10
Lewisham [4]	d					07 16			07 23								07 46				07 53				
St Johns	d																								
New Cross [4]	⊖ d					07 20			07 27								07 50				07 57				
London Victoria [15]	⊖ a						07 41				07 43							08 13							
London Bridge [4]	⊖ d	00 20	00 52	07 12	07 15	07 26		07 28	07 34	07 36			07 42	07 45	07 45	07 51	07 56			07 59	08 04	08 06	08 12	08 15	08 21
London Blackfriars [3]	⊖ a	00 26	00 59		07 23										07 53									08 23	
London Cannon Street [4]	⊖ a																								
London Waterloo (East) [4]	⊖ d			07 17		07 30		07 32	07 38	07 41			07 47	07 50		07 55	08 00			08 04	08 08	08 11	08 17		08 25
London Charing Cross [4]	⊖ a			07 20		07 34		07 35	07 41	07 44			07 50	07 53		07 58	08 04			08 07	08 11	08 15	08 20		08 28

For general notes see front of timetable
For details of catering facilities see
Directory of Train Operators

Table 199

Sundays

Orpington, Petts Wood, Hither Green and Lewisham → London (Summary of Services)

	SE 72	SE 72	SE 70	SE 8 ■1	SE 50	SE 12	SE 80	SE 24	SN	SE 22 ■1	FC ■1	SE 12	SE 62		SE 70	SE 70	SE 4 ■1	SE 50	SE 16	SE 80	SE 24	SN	SE 22 ■1	FC ■1
Orpington (4) d		08 01	08 08	08 13		08 26				08 28		←				08 38	08 43		08 56				08 58	
Petts Wood (4) d		08 04	08 11			08 29						08 29				08 41			08 59					
Hither Green (4) d					08 18	→						08 40						08 48	→					
Lewisham (4) d	08 16				08 23			08 29					08 43		08 46			08 53			08 59			
St Johns d								08 31													09 01			
New Cross (4) ⊖ d	08 20				08 27			08 33							08 50			08 57			09 03			
London Victoria (15) ⊖ a		08 41	08 43													09 13								
London Bridge (4) ⊖ d	08 26			08 29	08 34		08 36	08 40	08 42	08 45	08 45	08 51	08 53		08 56		08 59	09 04		09 06	09 10	09 12	09 15	09 15
London Blackfriars (3) ⊖ a											08 53													09 23
London Cannon Street (4) ⊖ a																								
London Waterloo (East) (4) ⊖ d	08 30			08 34	08 38		08 41	08 44	08 47	08 50		08 55	08 58		09 01		09 04	09 08		09 11	09 14	09 17	09 21	
London Charing Cross (4) ⊖ a	08 34			08 37	08 41		08 44	08 47	08 50	08 53		08 58	09 01		09 04		09 07	09 11		09 14	09 17	09 20	09 25	

	SE 16	SE 60	SE 72	SE 72	SE 70	SE 90 ■1	SE 50	SE 12	SE 80		SE 24	SE 67	SN	SE 22 ■1	FC ■1	SE 12	SE 62	SE 70	SE 70	SE 4 ■1	SE 50	SE 16	SE 80	SE 24
Orpington (4) d	←			09 01	09 08	09 13		09 26						09 28		←			09 38	09 43		09 56		
Petts Wood (4) d	08 59			09 04	09 11			09 29								09 29			09 41			09 59		
Hither Green (4) d	09 10						09 18	→								09 40					09 48	→		
Lewisham (4) d		09 14	09 17				09 23				09 29	09 34					09 43	09 46			09 53			09 59
St Johns d											09 31													10 01
New Cross (4) ⊖ d			09 20				09 27				09 33							09 50			09 57			10 03
London Victoria (15) ⊖ a				09 41	09 43														10 13					
London Bridge (4) ⊖ d	09 21	09 23	09 26			09 29	09 34		09 36		09 40	09a41	09 42	09 45	09 45	09 51	09 53	09 56		09 59	10 04		10 06	10 10
London Blackfriars (3) ⊖ a															09 53									
London Cannon Street (4) ⊖ a																								
London Waterloo (East) (4) ⊖ d	09 25	09 29	09 31			09 34	09 38		09 41		09 44		09 47	09 50		09 55	09 58	10 01		10 04	10 08		10 11	10 14
London Charing Cross (4) ⊖ a	09 28	09 34	09 34			09 37	09 41		09 44		09 47		09 52	09 55		09 58	10 01	10 04		10 07	10 11		10 14	10 17

	SE 67	SN	SE 22 ■1	FC ■1	SE 16		SE 62	SE 72	SE 72		SE 70	SE 90 ■1	FC	SE 50	SE 12	SE 80	SE 24	SE 67	SN	SE 22 ■1	FC ■1	SE 12	SE 82	SE 70
Orpington (4) d			09 58		←				10 01		10 08	10 13			10 26					10 28		←		
Petts Wood (4) d					09 59				10 04		10 11				10 29							10 29		
Hither Green (4) d					10 10									10 18	→							10 40		
Lewisham (4) d	10 04							10 16						10 23			10 29	10 34						10 46
St Johns d																	10 31							
New Cross (4) ⊖ d								10 20						10 27			10 33							10 50
London Victoria (15) ⊖ a									10 41		10 43													
London Bridge (4) ⊖ d	10a11	10 12	10 15	10 15	10 21		10 23	10 26				10 29	10 30	10 34		10 36	10 40	10a41	10 42	10 45	10 45	10 51	10 54	10 56
London Blackfriars (3) ⊖ a				10 23									10 37								10 53			
London Cannon Street (4) ⊖ a																								
London Waterloo (East) (4) ⊖ d		10 17	10 21		10 25		10 29	10 31				10 34		10 38		10 41	10 44		10 47	10 50		10 55	10 58	11 01
London Charing Cross (4) ⊖ a		10 22	10 25		10 28		10 34	10 34				10 37		10 41		10 44	10 47		10 52	10 55		10 58	11 01	11 04

	SE 70	SE 4 ■1	FC ■1	SE 50	SE 16	SE 84	SE 24	SE 67	SN	SE 22 ■1	FC ■1	SE 16	SE 82	SE 70	and at		SE 70	SE 90 ■1	FC	SE 50	SE 84	SE 24	SN
Orpington (4) d	10 38	10 43			10 56					10 58		←			the same		18 08	18 13					
Petts Wood (4) d	10 41				10 59							10 59					18 11						
Hither Green (4) d				10 48	→							11 10			minutes					18 18			
Lewisham (4) d				10 53			10 59	11 04						11 16						18 23		18 29	
St Johns d							11 01								past							18 31	
New Cross (4) ⊖ d				10 57			11 03							11 20						18 27		18 33	
London Victoria (15) ⊖ a	11 13														each		18 43						
London Bridge (4) ⊖ d		10 59	11 00	11 04		11 07	11 10	11a11	11 12	11 15	11 15	11 21	11 24	11 26				18 29	18 30	18 34	18 37	18 40	18 42
London Blackfriars (3) ⊖ a			11 07								11 23				hour until				18 37				
London Cannon Street (4) ⊖ a																							
London Waterloo (East) (4) ⊖ d		11 04		11 08		11 12	11 14		11 17	11 21		11 25	11 28	11 31				18 34		18 38	18 42	18 44	18 47
London Charing Cross (4) ⊖ a		11 07		11 11		11 15	11 17		11 22	11 25		11 28	11 31	11 34				18 37		18 41	18 45	18 47	18 52

	SE 22 ■1	FC ■1	SE 62	SE 70	SE 70	SE 4 ■1	SE 50	SE 16	SE 84	SN	SE 22 ■1	FC ■1		SE 16	SE 72	SE 70	SE 90 ■1	SE 50	SE 80	SE 24	SN	SE 22 ■1	FC ■1	SE 62
Orpington (4) d	18 27				18 38	18 43		18 56			18 58			←		19 08	19 13					19 27		
Petts Wood (4) d	18 30				18 41			18 59						18 59		19 11						19 30		
Hither Green (4) d							18 48	→						19 10				19 18						
Lewisham (4) d			18 43	18 46			18 53								19 16			19 23		19 29				19 43
St Johns d																				19 31				
New Cross (4) ⊖ d				18 50			18 57								19 20			19 27		19 33				
London Victoria (15) ⊖ a					19 13											19 43								
London Bridge (4) ⊖ d	18 45	18 45	18 53	18 56		18 59	19 04		19 07	19 12	19 15	19 15		19 21	19 26		19 29	19 34	19 36	19 40	19 42	19 45	19 45	19 53
London Blackfriars (3) ⊖ a		18 53										19 23											19 53	
London Cannon Street (4) ⊖ a																								
London Waterloo (East) (4) ⊖ d	18 50		18 57	19 01		19 04	19 08		19 12	19 17	19 21			19 25	19 30		19 34	19 38	19 41	19 44	19 47	19 50		19 57
London Charing Cross (4) ⊖ a	18 55		19 00	19 04		19 07	19 11		19 15	19 22	19 25			19 28	19 34		19 37	19 41	19 44	19 47	19 52	19 55		20 00

For general notes see front of timetable
For details of catering facilities see
Directory of Train Operators

Table 199

Sundays

Orpington, Petts Wood, Hither Green and Lewisham → London (Summary of Services)

	SE 70	SE 70	SE 4 [1]	SE 50	SE 80	SN	FC [1]	SE 16		SE 72	SE 70	SE 90 [1]	SE 50	SE 80	SE 24	SN	SE 22 [1]	FC [1]	SE 62	SE 70	SE 70	SE 4 [1]	SE 50	SE 80
Orpington 4 d		19 38	19 43					19 56			20 08	20 13					20 27				20 38	20 43		
Petts Wood 4 d		19 41						19 59			20 11						20 30				20 41			
Hither Green 4 d				19 48				20 10					20 18										20 48	
Lewisham 4 d	19 46			19 53						20 16			20 23		20 29				20 43	20 46			20 53	
St Johns d															20 31									
New Cross 4 ⊖ d	19 50			19 57						20 20			20 27		20 33					20 50			20 57	
London Victoria 15 ⊖ a		20 13									20 43										21 13			
London Bridge 4 ⊖ d	19 56		19 59	20 04	20 06	20 12	20 15	20 21		20 26		20 29	20 34	20 36	20 40	20 42	20 45	20 45	20 53	20 56		20 59	21 04	21 06
London Blackfriars 3 ⊖ a							20 23											20 53						
London Cannon Street 4 ⊖ a																								
London Waterloo (East) 4 ⊖ d	20 00		20 04	20 08	20 11	20 19		20 25		20 30		20 34	20 38	20 41	20 44	20 47	20 50		20 57	21 00		21 04	21 08	21 11
London Charing Cross 4 ⊖ a	20 04		20 07	20 11	20 14	20 22		20 28		20 34		20 37	20 41	20 44	20 47	20 50	20 53		21 00	21 04		21 07	21 11	21 14

	SN	FC [1]	SE 12	SE 72		SE 70	SE 90 [1]	SE 50	SE 80	SE 24	SN	SE 22 [1]	FC [1]	SE 62	SE 70	SE 70	SE 4 [1]	SE 50	SE 80	SN	FC [1]	SE 12		SE 72
Orpington 4 d			20 56			21 08	21 13					21 27				21 38	21 43					21 56		
Petts Wood 4 d			20 59			21 11						21 30				21 41						21 59		
Hither Green 4 d			21 10					21 18										21 48				22 10		
Lewisham 4 d				21 16				21 23		21 29				21 43	21 46			21 53						22 16
St Johns d										21 31														
New Cross 4 ⊖ d				21 20				21 27		21 33					21 50			21 57						22 20
London Victoria 15 ⊖ a						21 43										22 13								
London Bridge 4 ⊖ d	21 12	21 15	21 21	21 26			21 29	21 34	21 36	21 40	21 42	21 45	21 45	21 53	21 56		21 59	22 04	22 06	22 12	22 15	22 21		22 26
London Blackfriars 3 ⊖ a		21 23											21 53								22 23			
London Cannon Street 4 ⊖ a																								
London Waterloo (East) 4 ⊖ d	21 17		21 25	21 30			21 34	21 38	21 41	21 44	21 47	21 50		21 57	22 00		22 04	22 08	22 11	22 17		22 25		22 30
London Charing Cross 4 ⊖ a	21 20		21 28	21 34			21 37	21 41	21 44	21 47	21 50	21 53		22 00	22 04		22 07	22 11	22 14	22 22		22 28		22 34

	SE 70	SE 90 [1]	SE 50	SE 80	SE 24	SN	SE 22 [1]	FC [1]	SE 62	SE 70	SE 70	SE 4 [1]	SE 50	SE 80	SN	FC [1]	SE 12		SE 72	SE 50	SE 24	FC [1]		
Orpington 4 d	22 08	22 13					22 27				22 38	22 43					22 56							
Petts Wood 4 d	22 11						22 30				22 41						22 59							
Hither Green 4 d			22 18										22 48				23 10			23 18				
Lewisham 4 d			22 23		22 29				22 43	22 46			22 53						23 16	23 23	23 29			
St Johns d					22 31																23 31			
New Cross 4 ⊖ d			22 27		22 33					22 50			22 57						23 20	23 27	23 33			
London Victoria 15 ⊖ a	22 43										23 13													
London Bridge 4 ⊖ d		22 29	22 34	22 36	22 40	22 42	22 45	22 45	22 53	22 56		22 58	23 04	23 06	23 12	23 15	23 21		23 26	23 34	23 40	23 45		
London Blackfriars 3 ⊖ a								22 53								23 23						23 53		
London Cannon Street 4 ⊖ a																								
London Waterloo (East) 4 ⊖ d		22 34	22 38	22 41	22 44	22 47	22 50		22 57	23 00		23 03	23 08	23 11	23 17		23 25		23 30	23 38	23 44			
London Charing Cross 4 ⊖ a		22 37	22 41	22 44	22 47	22 50	22 53		23 00	23 04		23 06	23 11	23 14	23 20		23 28		23 34	23 41	23 47			

For general notes see front of timetable
For details of catering facilities see Directory of Train Operators

Network Diagram for Tables 200, 203, 204 | also 199 ★

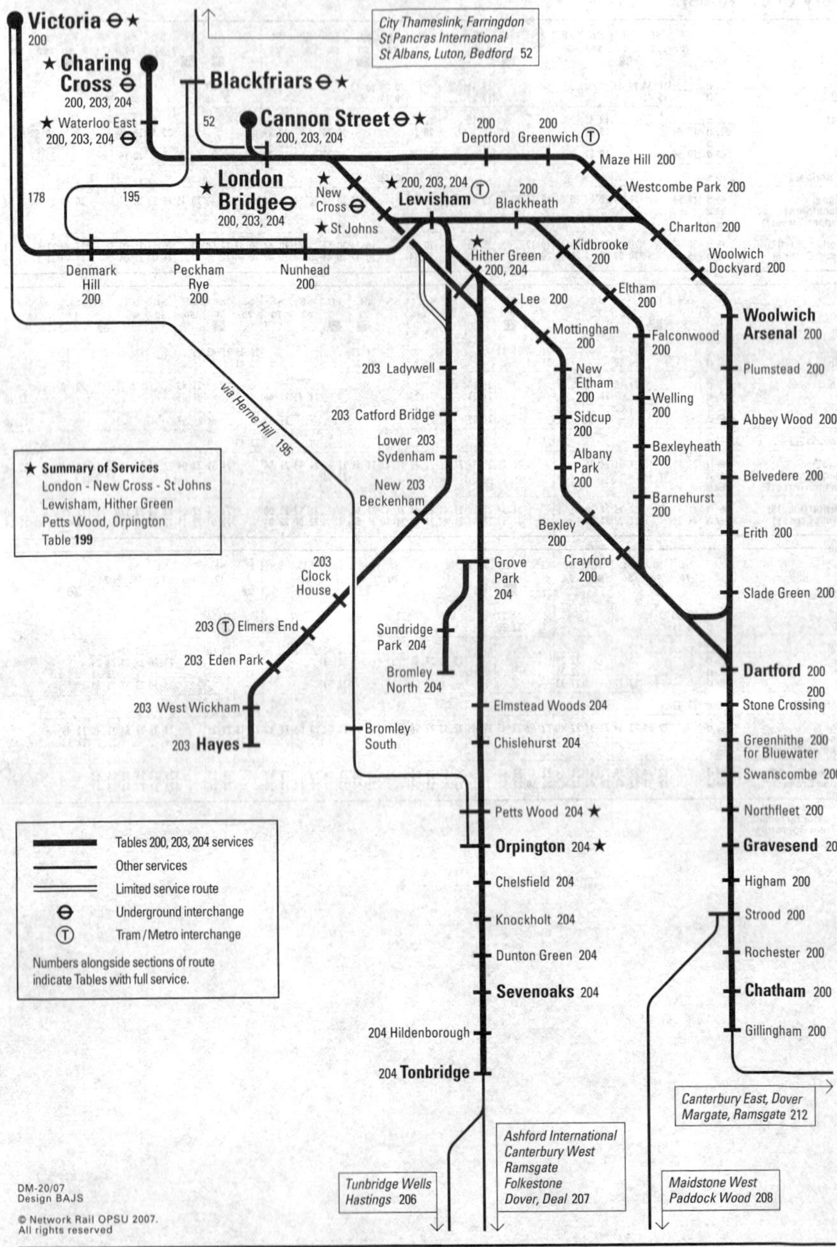
Victoria
200
★ Charing Cross
200, 203, 204
★ Waterloo East
200, 203, 204
Blackfriars
52
City Thameslink, Farringdon
St Pancras International
St Albans, Luton, Bedford 52
Cannon Street
200, 203, 204
★ London Bridge
200, 203, 204
178
195
★ New Cross
★ St Johns
★ 200, 203, 204
Lewisham
200
Deptford
200
Greenwich
Maze Hill 200
Westcombe Park 200
200
Blackheath
Charlton 200
Woolwich Dockyard 200
Woolwich Arsenal 200
Plumstead 200
Abbey Wood 200
Belvedere 200
Erith 200
Slade Green 200
Dartford 200
200
Stone Crossing
Greenhithe for Bluewater 200
Swanscombe 200
Northfleet 200
Gravesend 200
Higham 200
Strood 200
Rochester 200
Chatham 200
Gillingham 200
Canterbury East, Dover
Margate, Ramsgate 212
Maidstone West
Paddock Wood 208
Denmark Hill 200
Peckham Rye 200
Nunhead 200
★ Hither Green
200, 204
Kidbrooke 200
Eltham 200
Falconwood 200
Welling 200
Bexleyheath 200
Barnehurst 200
Lee 200
Mottingham 200
New Eltham 200
Sidcup 200
Albany Park 200
Bexley 200
Crayford 200
via Herne Hill 195
203 Ladywell
203 Catford Bridge
Lower Sydenham 203
New Beckenham 203
203 Clock House
203 Elmers End
203 Eden Park
203 West Wickham
203 Hayes
Grove Park 204
Sundridge Park 204
Bromley North 204
Elmstead Woods 204
Chislehurst 204
Bromley South
Petts Wood 204 ★
Orpington 204 ★
Chelsfield 204
Knockholt 204
Dunton Green 204
Sevenoaks 204
204 Hildenborough
204 Tonbridge
Tunbridge Wells
Hastings 206
Ashford International
Canterbury West
Ramsgate
Folkestone
Dover, Deal 207
★ Summary of Services
London - New Cross - St Johns
Lewisham, Hither Green
Petts Wood, Orpington
Table 199
Tables 200, 203, 204 services
Other services
Limited service route
Underground interchange
Tram / Metro interchange
Numbers alongside sections of route indicate Tables with full service.

DM-20/07
Design BAJS

For details of Bank Holiday service alterations please see first page of Table 195

London → Dartford and Gillingham

Network Diagram - see first page of Table 200

Miles	Miles	Miles	Miles	Miles			SE MO 72	SE MX 62	SE MX 62	SE MO 62	SE MX 62	SE MO 80	SE MX 50	SE MX 80	SE MO 70	SE MX 70	SE MO 50	SE MX 50	SE 62	SE 20 [1] A	SE 50	SE 72	SE 84	SE 52
0	—	0	0	—	**London Charing Cross** [4]	⊖ d	22p46	22p50	23p20	23p26		23p31	23p34	23p40	23p46	23p47	23p49	00 04	00 14		04 50	04 56	05 04	05 18
¾	—	¾	¾	—	**London Waterloo (East)** [4]	⊖ d	22p49	22p53	23p23	23p29		23p34	23p37	23p43	23p49	23p50	23p52	00 07	00 17		04 53	04 59	05 07	05 21
—	0	—	—	—	**London Cannon Street** [4]	⊖ d																		
1¾	¾	1¾	1¾	—	**London Bridge** [4]	⊖ d	22p54	22p59	23p29	23p34		23p39	23p43	23p48	23p54	23p55	23p58	00 13	00 23		04 58	05 04	05 12	05 28
—	3¾	—	—	—	Deptford	d						23p44		23p54									05 17	
—	4¼	—	—	—	Greenwich [4]	⛴ d						23p46		23p56									05 19	
—	5¼	—	—	—	Maze Hill	d						23p50		00 01									05 23	
—	5¾	—	—	—	Westcombe Park	d						23p52		00 02									05 25	
—	—	—	—	0	**London Victoria** [15]	⊖ d																		
—	—	—	—	4¼	Denmark Hill [4]	d																		
—	—	—	—	5	Peckham Rye [4]	d																		
—	—	—	—	5¾	Nunhead [4]	d																		
—	—	4¾	4¾	—	New Cross [4]	⊖ d	22p59						23p48		23p59	23p59	00 03	00 18	00 28		05 03	05 09		05 33
—	—	5½	5½	—	St Johns	d																		
6	—	6	6	7½	Lewisham [4]	⛴ d	23p03	23p08	23p38	23p42			23p53		00 03	00 05	00 07	00 23	00 33		05 08	05 14		05 38
7	—	7	—	8½	Blackheath [4]	d	23p06	23p11	23p41	23p45					00 06	00 07			00 36			05 16		
—	—	8	—	9½	Kidbrooke	d	23p09								00 09	00 10						05 19		
—	—	9	—	10½	Eltham	d	23p13								00 13	00 14						05 23		
—	—	10¼	—	11¾	Falconwood	d	23p15								00 15	00 16						05 25		
—	—	11½	—	12¾	Welling	d	23p18								00 18	00 19						05 28		
—	—	12¾	—	14¼	Bexleyheath	d	23p20								00 20	00 21						05 30		
—	—	14	—	15½	Barnehurst [4]	d	23p23								00 23	00 24						05 33		
—	—	—	7¼	—	Hither Green [4]	d							23p57				00 11	00 27			05 11			05 41
—	—	—	8	—	Lee	d							23p59				00 13	00 29			05 13			05 43
—	—	—	9½	—	Mottingham	d							00 02				00 16	00 32			05 16			05 46
—	—	—	10½	—	New Eltham	d							00 05				00 19	00 35			05 19			05 49
—	—	—	12	—	Sidcup [4]	d							00 08				00 22	00 38			05 22			05 52
—	—	—	13	—	Albany Park	d							00 10				00 24	00 40			05 24			05 54
—	—	—	14	—	Bexley	d							00 12				00 26	00 42			05 26			05 56
—	—	—	15½	—	Crayford	d							00 15				00 29	00 45			05 29			05 59
9	6½	—	—	—	Charlton [4]	d		23p15	23p45	23p49		23p54		00 04					00 40				05 28	
10	7½	—	—	—	Woolwich Dockyard	d						23p56		00 07										
10¾	8¼	—	—	—	**Woolwich Arsenal** [4]	d		23p20	23p50	23p53		23p59		00 10					00 45				05 33	
11¼	8¾	—	—	—	Plumstead	d						00 01		00 12					00 47				05 35	
12¾	10¼	—	—	—	Abbey Wood	d		23p25	23p55	23p57		00 05		00 15					00 50				05 39	
14¼	11¾	—	—	—	Belvedere	d						00 07		00 18					00 53				05 41	
15½	13	—	—	—	Erith	d						00 10		00 21					00 56				05 44	
16¾	14½	—	—	—	Slade Green [4]	d						00 13		00 24					00 58				05 48	
18¾	16¼	17	17¼	18½	**Dartford** [4]	a	23p29	23p33	00 04	00 05		00 17	00 20	00 29	00 29	00 31	00 33	00 50	01 03		05 33	05 41	05 53	06 03
—	—	—	—	—		d	23p30	23p34	00 04	00 06									01 04	05 06		05 42	05 54	
20¾	—	—	19¼	—	Stone Crossing	d	23p34	23p37	00 08													05 45	05 57	
21½	—	—	20	—	Greenhithe for Bluewater	d	23p36	23p40	00 10	00 11	←								01 09	05 11		05 48	06 00	
22¾	—	—	21¼	—	Swanscombe	d	23p39	23p42	00 12		00 12											05 50	06 02	
23½	—	—	22	—	Northfleet	d	23p41	23p44	→		00 14											05 52	06 04	
25½	—	—	24	—	**Gravesend** [4]	d	23p45	23p50		00 18	00 20								01 16	05 18		05 56	06a08	
30	—	—	28½	—	Higham	d	23p51	23p56		00 25	00 26								01 22	05 24		06 02		
32¾	—	—	31¼	—	Strood [4]	d	23p56	00 02		00 30	00 32								01 28	05 29		06 08		
—	—	—	—	—	Maidstone West [4]	a														*06 02*		*06 40*		
33¾	—	—	32¼	—	Rochester [4]	d	00 01	00 07		00 33	00 39								01 31	05 33		06 11		
34¼	—	—	32¾	—	**Chatham** [4]	d	00 02	00 09		00 36	00 42								01 34	05 36		06 14		
36	—	—	34½	—	**Gillingham (Kent)** [4]	a	00 06	00 13		00 39	00 45								01 37	05 39		06 21		

For general notes see front of timetable
For details of catering facilities see
Directory of Train Operators

A To Dover Priory (Table 212)

For details of Bank Holiday service alterations please see first page of Table 195

London → Dartford and Gillingham

Network Diagram - see first page of Table 200

		SE 70	SE 64	SE 54	SE 80	SE 72	SE 65	SE 52	SE 84	SE 70	SE 65	SE 54	SE 86	SE 70	SE 60	SE 73	SE 52	SE 80	SE 71	SE 57	SE 80	SE 40	SE 44
London Charing Cross 4	⊖ d	05 26	05 34	05 46	05 54	06 02		06 20		06 32	06 40		06 54		07 03		07 20		07 30			07 42	
London Waterloo (East) 4	⊖ d	05 29	05 37	05 49	05 57	06 05		06 23		06 35	06 43		06 57		07 06		07 23		07 33			07 45	
London Cannon Street 4	⊖ d						06 12		06 30			06 48		07 04		07 22		07 32		07 39			07 48
London Bridge 4	⊖ d	05 34	05 42	05 54	06 02	06 10	06 16	06 28	06 34	06 40	06 48	06 52	07 04	07 08	07 11	07 26	07 28	07 36	07 38	07 43		07 50	07 52
Deptford	d				06 07				06 39				07 09					07 41					
Greenwich 4	d				06 09				06 41				07 11					07 43					07 59
Maze Hill	d				06 13				06 45				07 15					07 47					
Westcombe Park	d				06 15				06 47				07 17					07 49					
London Victoria 15	⊖ d																						
Denmark Hill 4	d																						
Peckham Rye 4	d																						
Nunhead 4	d																						
New Cross 4	⊖ d	05 39		05 59		06 15		06 33		06 47				07 13			07 33		07 43	07 49			
St Johns	d			06 01		06 17								07 15					07 45				
Lewisham 4	d	05 44	05 52	06 04		06 20	06 24	06 38		06 52	06 56	07 00		07 18	07 22	07 34	07 38		07 48	07 53			
Blackheath 4	d	05 46	05 54			06 22	06 26			06 54	06 58			07 20	07 24	07 36			07 50				
Kidbrooke	d	05 49				06 25				06 57				07 23		07 39			07 53				
Eltham	d	05 53				06 29				07 01				07 27		07 43			07 57				
Falconwood	d	05 55				06 31				07 03				07 29		07 45			07 59				
Welling	d	05 58				06 34				07 06				07 32		07 48			08 02				
Bexleyheath	d	06 00				06 36				07 08				07 34		07 50			08 04				
Barnehurst 4	d	06 03				06 39				07 11				07 37		07a53			08 07				
Hither Green 4	d			06 07				06 41				07 03					07 41			07 57		08 01	
Lee	d			06 09				06 43				07 05					07 43					08 03	
Mottingham	d			06 12				06 46				07 08					07 46					08 06	
New Eltham	d			06 15				06 49				07 11					07 49					08 09	
Sidcup 4	d			06 18				06 52				07 14					07 52			08a05		08 12	
Albany Park	d			06 20				06 54				07 16					07 54					08 14	
Bexley	d			06 22				06 56				07 18					07 56					08 16	
Crayford	d			06 25				06 59				07 21					07 59					08 19	
Charlton 4	d		05 58		06 18		06 30		06 50		07 02		07 20		07 28			07 52			←		08 06
Woolwich Dockyard	d				06 20				06 52				07 22					07 54 →			07 54		
Woolwich Arsenal 4	d		06 03		06 23		06 35		06 55		07 07		07 25		07 33						07 57		08 11
Plumstead	d				06 25				06 57				07 27								07 59		
Abbey Wood	d		06 08		06 29		06 40		07 01		07 12		07 31		07 38						08 03		08 16
Belvedere	d				06 31				07 03				07 33								08 05		
Erith	d				06 34				07 06				07 36								08 08		
Slade Green 4	d		06 13		06 38		06 45		07 09				07a39		07 43						08 11		
Dartford 4	a	06 11	06 19	06 30	06 43	06 45	06 51	07 04	07 15	07 16	07 22	07 25		07 46	07 49		08 04		08 13		08 16	08 24	08 26
	d	06 12	06 20	06 30		06 46	06 52	07 06		07 16	07 28	07 30					08 06						08 28
Stone Crossing	d	06 15	06 23				06 55	07 09				07 33					08 09						08 31
Greenhithe for Bluewater	d	06 18	06 26				06 58	07 12		07 21	07 33	07 36					08 12						08 34
Swanscombe	d	06 20	06 28				07 00	07 14				07 38					08 14						08 36
Northfleet	d	06 22	06 30				07 02	07 16				07 40					08 16						08 38
Gravesend 4	d	06 26	06 34	06a40		06 56	07 06	07 20		07 28	07 40	07a45					08 20						08a42
Higham	d	06 32	06 40			07 02	07 12	07 26		07 34	07 46						08 26						
Strood 4	d	06 38	06a45			07 08	07a18	07 32		07a40	07 52						08 32						
Maidstone West 4	a					*07 34*		*07 57*			*08 18*						*08 56*						
Rochester 4	d	06 41				07b19		07a36			07 55						08a36						
Chatham 4	d	06 44				07 22					07 58												
Gillingham (Kent) 4	a	06 47				07 25					08 01												

For general notes see front of timetable
For details of catering facilities see
Directory of Train Operators

b Arr. 0712

For details of Bank Holiday service alterations please see first page of Table 195

London → Dartford and Gillingham

Network Diagram - see first page of Table 200

Station		SE 73	SE 61	SE 86	SE 51		SE 84	SE	SE 84	SE 71	SE 61	SE 42	SE 78	SE 80	SE 71	SE 55		SE 71	SE 80	SE 10	SE 80	SE 63	SE 71	SE 54	SE 78
				A				1																	
London Charing Cross 4	⊖ d				08 00		08 03	08 08						08 24	08 28				08 41	08 44				09 02	
London Waterloo (East) 4	⊖ d				08 03		08 06	08 11						08 27	08 31				08 44	08 47				09 06	
London Cannon Street 4	⊖ d	07 54	07 58							08 14	08 17	08 26				08 34						08 50	09 02		
London Bridge 4	⊖ d	07 58	08 02		08 09		08 12	08 16		08 18	08 21	08 30		08 32	08 36	08 38			08 50	08 52		08 54	09 06	09 12	
Deptford	d						08 18							08 38					08 56						
Greenwich 4	d						08 20							08 40					08 58						
Maze Hill	d						08 24							08 44					09 02						
Westcombe Park	d						08 26							08 46					09 04						
London Victoria 15	⊖ d												08 21												09 01
Denmark Hill 4	d												08 31												09 12
Peckham Rye 4	d												08 35												09 14
Nunhead 4	d												08 37												09 16
New Cross 4	⊖ d	08 03	08 07							08 23	08 26				08 42	08 45							09 11		
St Johns	d	08 05								08 25						08 47									
Lewisham 4	d	08 08	08 12							08 28	08 32		08 44		08 48	08 50						09 04	09 16	09 20	09 26
Blackheath 4	d	08 10	08 14							08 30	08 34		08 46		08 50							09 06	09 18		09 28
Kidbrooke	d	08 13								08 33			08 49		08 53								09 21		09 31
Eltham	d	08 17								08 37			08 53		08 57			←					09 25		09 35
Falconwood	d	08 19								08 39			08 55		08 59			08 59					09 27		09 37
Welling	d	08 22								08 42			08 58		→			09 02					09 30		09 40
Bexleyheath	d	08 24								08 44			09 00					09 04					09 32		09 42
Barnehurst 4	d	08 27		07 56						08 47			09 03					09b11					09 35		09 45
Hither Green 4	d				08 18			08 27				08 41				08 53				09 03				09 23	
Lee	d							08 29				08 43				08 55				09 05				09 25	
Mottingham	d							08 32				08 46				08 58				09 08				09 28	
New Eltham	d							08 35				08 49				09 01				09 11				09 31	
Sidcup 4	d				08 26			08 38				08 52				09 04				09 14				09 34	
Albany Park	d				08 28			08 40				08 54				09 06				09 16				09 36	
Bexley	d				08 30			08 42				08 56				09 08				09 18				09 38	
Crayford	d				08a33			08 45				08 59				09 11				09 21				09 41	
Charlton 4	d		08 18				08 28		←		08 40			08 48					09 06		←	09 12			
Woolwich Dockyard	d						08 30		08 30					08 50					09 08		09 08				
Woolwich Arsenal 4	d		08 23				→		08 33		08 45			08 53					→		09 11	09 17			
Plumstead	d								08 35					08 55							09 13				
Abbey Wood	d		08 28						08 39		08 50			08 59							09 17	09 22			
Belvedere	d								08 41					09 01							09 19				
Erith	d								08 44					09 04							09 22				
Slade Green 4	d			08a00					08 47					09 07							09 25				
Dartford 4	a	08 33	08 36					08 50	08 51	08 54	09 00	09 04	09 09	09 13		09 15		09 18		09 26	09 30	09 33	09 41	09 45	09 51
	d	08 34							08 52		09 02					09 16						09 34		09 46	
Stone Crossing	d								08 55							09 19								09 49	
Greenhithe for Bluewater	d	08 39							08 58		09 07					09 22						09 39		09 52	
Swanscombe	d								09 00							09 24								09 54	
Northfleet	d								09 02							09 26								09 56	
Gravesend 4	d	08 46							09a06		09 14					09a30						09 46		10a00	
Higham	d	08 52									09 20											09 52			
Strood 4	d	08 58									09 26											09 58			
Maidstone West 4	a	*09 23*									*09 56*											*10 23*			
Rochester 4	d	09 01									09 29											10 01			
Chatham 4	d	09 04									09 32											10 04			
Gillingham (Kent) 4	a	09 07									09 35											10 07			

For general notes see front of timetable
For details of catering facilities see Directory of Train Operators

A To London Charing Cross
b Arr. 0907

For details of Bank Holiday service alterations please see first page of Table 195

London → Dartford and Gillingham

Network Diagram - see first page of Table 200

Station		SE 81	SE 47 A	SE 70	SE 82		SE 87 A	SE 67	SE 54	SE 78	SE 81	SE 47 A	SE 70	SE 82	SE 87 A	SE 67			SE 54	SE 78	SE 81	SE 47 A	SE 70	SE 82	SE 87 A
London Charing Cross 4	⊖ d			09 15	09 20				09 32				09 49	09 52					10 02				10 17	10 20	
London Waterloo (East) 4	⊖ d			09 20	09 23				09 35				09 52	09 55					10 05				10 20	10 23	
London Cannon Street 4	⊖ d	09 10	09 20				09 30	09 34			09 42	09 48			10 00	10 04					10 10	10 18			10 30
London Bridge 4	⊖ d	09 14	09 24	09 26	09 29		09 34	09 38	09 40		09 46	09 52	09 57	10 00	10 04	10 08			10 10		10 14	10 22	10 25	10 29	10 34
Deptford	d	09 20					09 40				09 52				10 10						10 20				10 40
Greenwich 4	⛴ d	09 22			09 37		09 42				09 54			10 07	10 12						10 22			10 37	10 42
Maze Hill	d	09 26					09 46				09 58				10 16						10 26				10 46
Westcombe Park	d	09 28					09 48				10 00				10 18						10 28				10 48
London Victoria 15	⊖ d									09 31										10 01					
Denmark Hill 4	d									09 42										10 12					
Peckham Rye 4	d									09 44										10 14					
Nunhead 4	d									09 46										10 16					
New Cross 4	⊖ d		09 29					09 44				09 57				10 14						10 27			
St Johns	d		09 31									09 59										10 29			
Lewisham 4	⛴ d		09 34	09 36				09 48	09 50	09 53			10 06			10 18			10 20	10 23			10 35		
Blackheath 4	d			09 38				09 50		09 55			10 08			10 20				10 25			10 37		
Kidbrooke	d			09 41						09 58			10 11							10 28			10 40		
Eltham	d			09 45						10 02			10 15							10 32			10 44		
Falconwood	d			09 47						10 04			10 17							10 34			10 46		
Welling	d			09 50						10 07			10 20							10 37			10 49		
Bexleyheath	d			09 52						10 09			10 22							10 39			10 51		
Barnehurst 4	d			09 55						10 12			10 25							10 42			10 54		
Hither Green 4	d		09 37						09 53			10 05							10 23			10 35			
Lee	d		09 39						09 55			10 07							10 25			10 37			
Mottingham	d		09 42						09 58			10 10							10 28			10 40			
New Eltham	d		09 45						10 01			10 13							10 31			10 43			
Sidcup 4	d		09 48						10 04			10 16							10 34			10 46			
Albany Park	d		09 50						10 06			10 18							10 36			10 48			
Bexley	d		09 52						10 08			10 20							10 38			10 50			
Crayford	d		09 58						10 11			10b28							10 41			10c58			
Charlton 4	d	09 30			09 44		09 50	09 57			10 02			10 14	10 20	10 25					10 30			10 44	10 50
Woolwich Dockyard	d	09 32					09 52				10 04				10 22						10 32				10 52
Woolwich Arsenal 4	d	09 35			09 49		09 55	10 02			10 07			10 19	10 25	10 30					10 35			10 49	10 55
Plumstead	d	09 37					09 57	10a04			10 09				10 27	10a32					10 37				10 57
Abbey Wood	d	09 41			09 53		10 01				10 13			10 23	10 31						10 41			10 53	11 01
Belvedere	d	09 43					10 03				10 15				10 33						10 43				11 03
Erith	d	09 46					10 06				10 18				10 36						10 46				11 06
Slade Green 4	d	09 49	10a04				10a09				10 21	10a36			10a39						10 49	11a06			11a09
Dartford 4	a	09 55		10 01	10 03				10 15	10 17	10 27		10 31	10 33					10 45	10 47	10 53		11 01	11 03	
	d				10 04				10 16					10 34					10 46					11 04	
Stone Crossing	d								10 19										10 49						
Greenhithe for Bluewater	d				10 09				10 22					10 39					10 52					11 09	
Swanscombe	d								10 24										10 54						
Northfleet	d								10 26										10 56						
Gravesend 4	d				10 16				10a30					10 46					11a00					11 16	
Higham	d				10 22									10 52										11 22	
Strood 4	d				10 28									10 58										11 28	
Maidstone West 4	a				*10 53*									*11 23*										*11 53*	
Rochester 4	d				10 31									11 01										11 31	
Chatham 4	d				10 34									11 04										11 34	
Gillingham (Kent) 4	a				10 37									11 07										11 37	

For general notes see front of timetable
For details of catering facilities see Directory of Train Operators

A To London Cannon Street (Table 199)
b Arr. 1024
c Arr. 1054

For details of Bank Holiday service alterations please see first page of Table 195

London → Dartford and Gillingham

Network Diagram - see first page of Table 200

		SE 67	SE 54	SE 78	SE 81	SE 47 A	SE 70	SE 82	SE 87 A	SE 67		SE 54	SE 78	SE 81	SE 47 A	SE 70	SE 82	SE 87 A	SE 67	SE 54	SE 78	SE 81
London Charing Cross [4]	⊖ d		10 32				10 47	10 50				15 02				15 17	15 20			15 32		
London Waterloo (East) [4]	⊖ d		10 35				10 50	10 53				15 05				15 20	15 23			15 35		
London Cannon Street [4]	⊖ d	10 34			10 40	10 48			11 00	11 04				15 10	15 18			15 30	15 34			15 40
London Bridge [4]	⊖ d	10 38	10 40		10 44	10 52	10 55	10 59	11 04	11 08		15 10		15 14	15 22	15 25	15 29	15 34	15 38	15 40		15 44
Deptford	d				10 50				11 10					15 20				15 40				15 50
Greenwich [4]	⛴ d				10 52			11 07	11 12					15 22			15 37	15 42				15 52
Maze Hill	d				10 56				11 16					15 26				15 46				15 56
Westcombe Park	d				10 58				11 18					15 28				15 48				15 58
London Victoria [15]	⊖ d			10 31									15 01								15 31	
Denmark Hill [4]	d			10 42									15 12								15 42	
Peckham Rye [4]	d			10 44									15 14								15 44	
Nunhead [4]	d			10 46									15 16								15 46	
New Cross [4]	⊖ d	10 44				10 57				11 14					15 27				15 44			
St Johns	d					10 59									15 29							
Lewisham [4]	⛴ d	10 48	10 50	10 53			11 05			11 18		15 20	15 23			15 35			15 48	15 50	15 53	
Blackheath [4]	d	10 50		10 55			11 07			11 20			15 25			15 37			15 50		15 55	
Kidbrooke	d			10 58			11 10						15 28			15 40					15 58	
Eltham	d			11 02			11 14				and at		15 32			15 44					16 02	
Falconwood	d			11 04			11 16						15 34			15 46					16 04	
Welling	d			11 07			11 19				the same		15 37			15 49					16 07	
Bexleyheath	d			11 09			11 21						15 39			15 51					16 09	
Barnehurst [4]	d			11 12			11 24				minutes		15 42			15 54					16 12	
Hither Green [4]	d		10 53			11 05					past	15 23			15 35					15 53		
Lee	d		10 55			11 07						15 25			15 37					15 55		
Mottingham	d		10 58			11 10					each	15 28			15 40					15 58		
New Eltham	d		11 01			11 13						15 31			15 43					16 01		
Sidcup [4]	d		11 04			11 16					hour until	15 34			15 46					16 04		
Albany Park	d		11 06			11 18						15 36			15 48					16 06		
Bexley	d		11 08			11 20						15 38			15 50					16 08		
Crayford	d		11 11			11b28						15 41			15c58					16 11		
Charlton [4]	d	10 55			11 00			11 14	11 20	11 25				15 30			15 44	15 50	15 55			16 00
Woolwich Dockyard	d				11 02				11 22					15 32				15 52				16 02
Woolwich Arsenal [4]	d	11 00			11 05			11 19	11 25	11 30				15 35			15 49	15 55	16 00			16 05
Plumstead	d	11a02			11 07				11 27	11a32				15 37				15 57	16a02			16 07
Abbey Wood	d				11 11			11 23	11 31					15 41			15 53	16 01				16 11
Belvedere	d				11 13				11 33					15 43				16 03				16 13
Erith	d				11 16				11 36					15 46				16 06				16 16
Slade Green [4]	d				11 19	11a36			11a39					15 49	16a04			16a09				16 19
Dartford [4]	a		11 15	11 17	11 23		11 31	11 33				15 45	15 47	15 53		16 01	16 03			16 15	16 17	16 24
	d		11 16					11 34				15 46					16 04			16 16		
Stone Crossing	d		11 19									15 49								16 19		
Greenhithe for Bluewater	d		11 22					11 39				15 52					16 09			16 22		
Swanscombe	d		11 24									15 54								16 24		
Northfleet	d		11 26									15 56								16 26		
Gravesend [4]	d		11a30					11 46				16a00					16 16			16a30		
Higham	d							11 52									16 22					
Strood [4]	d							11 58									16 28					
Maidstone West [4]	a							*12 23*														
Rochester [4]	d							12 01									16 31					
Chatham [4]	d							12 04									16 34					
Gillingham (Kent) [4]	a							12 07									16 37					

For general notes see front of timetable
For details of catering facilities see Directory of Train Operators

A To London Cannon Street (Table 199)
b Arr. 1124
c Arr. 1554

For details of Bank Holiday service alterations please see first page of Table 195

London → Dartford and Gillingham

Network Diagram - see first page of Table 200

		SE 47	SE 70	SE 62	SE 81	SE 54	SE 81	SE 57 A	SE 74	SE 81	SE 74		SE 62	SE 78	SE 81	SE 40	SE 81	SE 76	SE 57	SE 65	SE 74	SE 80		SE 42	SE 74
London Charing Cross 4	⊖ d		15 47	15 50		16 02			16 11				16 21			16 25		16 33			16 37	16 44		16 48	
London Waterloo (East) 4	⊖ d		15 50	15 53		16 05			16 14				16 24			16 28		16 36			16 40	16 47		16 51	
London Cannon Street 4	⊖ d	15 48			16 00			16 10		16 18					16 28				16 38	16 42					
London Bridge 4	⊖ d	15 52	15 55	15 59	16 04	16 10		16 14	16 19	16 22			16 29		16 32	16 33		16 41	16 42	16 46	16 48	16 52		16 56	
Deptford	d				16 10										16 38							16 58			
Greenwich 4	⛴ d				16 12					16 29					16 40							17 00			
Maze Hill	d				16 16										16 44							17 04			
Westcombe Park	d				16 18										16 46							17 06			
London Victoria 15	⊖ d													16 14											
Denmark Hill 4	d													16 27											
Peckham Rye 4	d													16 29											
Nunhead 4	d													16 31											
New Cross 4	⊖ d	15 57				16 16		16 20	16 25							16 39			16 49						
St Johns	d	15 59						16 22								16 41			16 51						
Lewisham 4	⛴ d		16 05	16 10		16 20		16 27	16 29				16 38	16 41				16 52	16 53	16 56	16 59				
Blackheath 4	d		16 07	16 13					16 32				16 41	16 44				16 55		16 59	17 02				
Kidbrooke	d		16 10						16 35		←			16 47				16 58			17 05				←
Eltham	d		16 14						16 39 →		16 39			16 51				17 02			17 09 →				17 09
Falconwood	d		16 16								16 41			16 53				17 04							17 12
Welling	d		16 19								16 44			16 56				17 07							17 14
Bexleyheath	d		16 21								16 47			16 59				17 10							17 17
Barnehurst 4	d		16 24								16 50			17 02				17 13							17 20
Hither Green 4	d	16 05				16 23		16 31								16 46			16 57						
Lee	d	16 07				16 25		16 33								16 48			16 59						
Mottingham	d	16 10				16 28		16 36								16 52			17 02						
New Eltham	d	16 13				16 31		16 39								16 55			17 05					17 11	
Sidcup 4	d	16a17				16 34		16 42								16 58			17a09					17 14	
Albany Park	d					16 36		16 44								17 00								17 16	
Bexley	d					16 38		16 46								17 02								17 18	
Crayford	d					16 41		16b58								17 05		17a28						17 21	
Charlton 4	d			16 17	16 22		←			16 35			16 45		16 48		←			17 03		17 08			
Woolwich Dockyard	d				16 25 →		16 25								16 51 →		16 51					17 11 →			
Woolwich Arsenal 4	d			16 23			16 28			16 41			16 51				16 54			17 09					
Plumstead	d						16 30										16 56								
Abbey Wood	d			16 28			16 34			16 46			16 56				17 00			17 14					
Belvedere	d						16 37										17 03								
Erith	d						16 40										17 06								
Slade Green 4	d						16 43	17a08		16 52							17 09								
Dartford 4	a		16 34	16 36		16 45	16 48			16 57	17 00		17 05	17 09		17 09	17 14			17 22				17 25	17 29
	d			16 36		16 46							17 06			17 10				17 22				17 26	17 30
Stone Crossing	d					16 49										17 13									17 33
Greenhithe for Bluewater	d			16 41		16 52							17 11			17 16				17 27				17 31	17 36
Swanscombe	d					16 54										17 18									17 39
Northfleet	d					16 56										17 20									17 41
Gravesend 4	d			16 48		17a02							17 18			17a26				17 34				17 38	17a46
Higham	d			16 54									17 24							17 40				17 44	
Strood 4	d			17c04									17 30							17a45				17 54	
Maidstone West 4	a			*17 28*									*17 58*												
Rochester 4	d			17 07									17 35											17 59	
Chatham 4	d			17 10									17 38											18 02	
Gillingham (Kent) 4	a			17 18									17 42											18 06	

For general notes see front of timetable
For details of catering facilities see Directory of Train Operators

A To London Cannon Street (Table 199)
b Arr. 1650
c Arr. 1701

For details of Bank Holiday service alterations please see first page of Table 195

London → Dartford and Gillingham

Network Diagram - see first page of Table 200

Station		SE 80	SE 77	SE 76	SE 46	SE 85	SE 64	SE 87	SE 42	SE 78	SE 51	SE 80	SE 77	SE 76	SE 87	SE 65	SE 85 A	SE 46	SE 42	SE 74	SE 78	SE 80	SE 51
London Charing Cross 4	⊖ d			16 55	16 58		17 00		17 10			17 06		17 18				17 21	17 32	17 25		17 29	
London Waterloo (East) 4	⊖ d			16 58	17 01		17 03		17 13			17 09		17 21				17 24	17 35	17 28		17 32	
London Cannon Street 4	⊖ d		16 52			17 02		17 06			17 10		17 16		17 24	17 26							17 36
London Bridge 4	⊖ d		16 56	17 03	17 06	17 06	17 08	17 10			17 14	17 15	17 20	17 26	17 28	17 30		17 30				17 38	17 40
Deptford	d							17 16				17 22			17 34							17 44	
Greenwich 4	d					17 13		17 18				17 24			17 36							17 46	
Maze Hill	d							17 22				17 28			17 40							17 50	
Westcombe Park	d							17 24				17 30			17 42							17 52	
London Victoria 15	⊖ d									17 00											17 19		
Denmark Hill 4	d									17 09											17 28		
Peckham Rye 4	d									17 13											17 31		
Nunhead 4	d									17 15											17 33		
New Cross 4	⊖ d		17 02								17 20		17 26										17 47
St Johns	d										17 22												
Lewisham 4	d		17 06	17 15			17 18			17 24	17 27		17 30	17 35		17 38					17b46		17 52
Blackheath 4	d		17 09	17 18			17 21			17 27			17 33	17 38		17 41					17 49		
Kidbrooke	d		17 12	17 21						17 30			17 36	17 41						17 48	17 52		
Eltham	d		17 16	17 25						17 34			17 40	17 45						17 52	17 56		
Falconwood	d		17 18	17 27						17 36			17 42	17 47						17 54	17 58		
Welling	d		17 21	17 30						17 39			17 45	17 50						17 57	18 01		
Bexleyheath	d		17 24	17 33						17 42			17 48	17 53						18 00	18 04		
Barnehurst 4	d		17a28	17 36						17 45			17a52	17 58			17 31			18 03	18 07		
Hither Green 4	d				17 16						17 30							17 40					17 55
Lee	d				17 18						17 32							17 42					17 57
Mottingham	d				17 22						17 36							17 46					18 01
New Eltham	d				17 25				17 31		17 39							17 49	17 53				18 04
Sidcup 4	d				17a29				17 34		17 42							17a53	17 57				18 07
Albany Park	d								17 36		17 44								17 59				18 09
Bexley	d								17 38		17 46								18 01				18 11
Crayford	d								17 41		17 49								18 04				18 14
Charlton 4	d	←					17 25	17 28				17 34			17 48	17 45						17 54	
Woolwich Dockyard	d	17 11						17 31				17 37			17 51							17 57	
Woolwich Arsenal 4	d	17 14				17 24	17 31	17 34				17 40			17 54	17 51						→	
Plumstead	d	17 16						17 36				17 42			17 56								
Abbey Wood	d	17 20				17 29	17 36	17 40				17 46			18 00	17 56							
Belvedere	d	17 23						17 43				17 49			18 03								
Erith	d	17 26						17 46				17 52			18 06								
Slade Green 4	d	17 29		17a41		17 35		17a50				17 55		18a08	18a10		17a35						
Dartford 4	a	17 34				17 39	17 45		17 48	17 52	17 54	18 00				18 05			18 08	18 12	18 14		18 19
	d					17 40	17 46		17 50							18 06			18 10	18 14			
Stone Crossing	d								17 53											18 17			
Greenhithe for Bluewater	d					17 45	17 51		17 56							18 11			18 15	18 20			
Swanscombe	d								17 59											18 23			
Northfleet	d								18 01											18 25			
Gravesend 4	d					17 52	17 58		18a06							18 18			18 22	18a30			
Higham	d					17 58	18 04									18 24			18 28				
Strood 4	d					18a05	18 14									18a30			18 36				
Maidstone West 4	a					*18 30*													*19 04*				
Rochester 4	d						18 19												18 41				
Chatham 4	d						18 22												18 44				
Gillingham (Kent) 4	a						18 29												18 49				

For general notes see front of timetable
For details of catering facilities see Directory of Train Operators

A To London Cannon Street
b Arr. 1743

For details of Bank Holiday service alterations please see first page of Table 195

London → Dartford and Gillingham

Network Diagram - see first page of Table 200

		SE 80	SE 76	SE 77	SE 65	SE 46	SE 87	SE 42	SE 74	SE 78	SE 51	SE 80	SE 77	SE 70	SE 85	SE 70	SE 64	SE 78	SE 46	SE 42	SE 80	SE 77	SE 51
London Charing Cross 4	⊖ d		17 37			17 43		17 52	17 46			17 54		18 01			18 05		18 08	18 20	18 14		
London Waterloo (East) 4	⊖ d		17 40			17 46		17 55	17 49			17 57		18 04			18 08		18 11	18 23	18 17		
London Cannon Street 4	⊖ d			17 42	17 46		17 48				17 56		18 02		18 08							18 19	18 22
London Bridge 4	⊖ d		17 45	17 46	17 50	17 51	17 52				18 00	18 02	18 06	18 10	18 12		18 14		18 16		18 22	18 23	18 26
Deptford	d						17 58					18 08									18 28		
Greenwich 4	⛴ d						18 00					18 10			18 20						18 30		
Maze Hill	d						18 04					18 14									18 34		
Westcombe Park	d						18 06					18 16									18 36		
London Victoria 15	⊖ d									17 41								18 08					
Denmark Hill 4	d									17 51								18 17					
Peckham Rye 4	d									17 54								18 20					
Nunhead 4	d									17 56								18 22					
New Cross 4	⊖ d			17 52							18 06												18 32
St Johns	d										18 08												
Lewisham 4	⛴ d		17 54	17 57	18 00					18 06	18 12		18 15	18 20			18 24	18 29				18 33	18 36
Blackheath 4	d		17 57	18 00	18 02					18 09			18 18	18 23			18 27	18 33				18 37	
Kidbrooke	d		18 00	18 04					18 08	18 12			18 21	18 26		←		18 36				18 40	
Eltham	d		18 04	18 08					18 12	18 16			18 25	18 30		18 30		18 40				18 44	
Falconwood	d		18 06	18 10					18 14	18 18			18 27	→		18 32		18 42				18 46	
Welling	d		18 09	18 13					18 17	18 21			18 30			18 35		18 45				18 49	
Bexleyheath	d		18 12	18 16					18 20	18 24			18 33			18 38		18 48				18 52	
Barnehurst 4	d		18 16	18 20		18a28			18 23	18 27			18 37			18 41		18 51				18a56	
Hither Green 4	d					18 00					18 16								18 26				18 40
Lee	d					18 02					18 18								18 28	18 38			18 42
Mottingham	d					18 06					18 22								18 32	18 42			18 46
New Eltham	d					18 09		18 14			18 25								18 35	18 45			18 49
Sidcup 4	d					18 12		18 17			18 28								18a39	18 48			18 52
Albany Park	d					18 14		18 19			18 30									18 50			18 54
Bexley	d					18 16		18 21			18 32									18 52			18 56
Crayford	d					18a20		18 24			18 35									18 55			18 59
Charlton 4	d	←			18 06		18 10					18 18					18 31				18 38		
Woolwich Dockyard	d	17 57					18 13					18 21									18 41		
Woolwich Arsenal 4	d	18 00			18 12		18 16					18 24			18 31		18 37				18 44		
Plumstead	d	18 02					18 18					18 26									18 46		
Abbey Wood	d	18 06			18 17		18 22					18 30			18 36		18 42				18 50		
Belvedere	d	18 09					18 25					18 32									18 53		
Erith	d	18 12					18 28					18 36									18 56		
Slade Green 4	d	18 15	18a22	18a26			18a32					18 39	18a42		18 42						18 59		
Dartford 4	a	18 20			18 25			18 29	18 32	18 34	18 40	18 44			18 46	18 50	18 51	18 57		18 59	19 04		19 04
	d				18 26			18 30	18 34						18 48		18 52			19 00			
Stone Crossing	d								18 37								18 55						
Greenhithe for Bluewater	d				18 31			18 35	18 40						18 53		18 58			19 05			
Swanscombe	d								18 43								19 01						
Northfleet	d								18 45								19 03						
Gravesend 4	d				18 38			18 42	18a50						19 00		19a08			19 12			
Higham	d				18 44			18 48							19 06					19 18			
Strood 4	d				18a50			18 54							19b14					19c28			
Maidstone West 4	a														*19 38*					*19 56*			
Rochester 4	d							18 59							19 19					19 32			
Chatham 4	d							19 02							19 22					19 35			
Gillingham (Kent) 4	a							19 07							19 26					19 39			

For general notes see front of timetable
For details of catering facilities see
Directory of Train Operators

b Arr. 1911
c Arr. 1923

For details of Bank Holiday service alterations please see first page of Table 195

London → Dartford and Gillingham

Network Diagram - see first page of Table 200

		SE 70	SE 62	SE 44	SE 57	SE 80	SE 70	SE 78	SE 62	SE 80	SE 77	SE 54	SE 80	SE 87	SE 80	SE 70	SE 57	SE 62	SE 78	SE 81	SE 77	SE 54	SE 80
London Charing Cross 4	⊖ d	18 25	18 30	18 37		18 34	18 46		18 54	18 56		19 02			19 11	19 17		19 21				19 34	19 41
London Waterloo (East) 4	⊖ d	18 28	18 33	18 40		18 37	18 49		18 57	18 59		19 05			19 14	19 20		19 24				19 37	19 44
London Cannon Street 4	⊖ d				18 36						19 02			19 10			19 22			19 28	19 36		
London Bridge 4	⊖ d	18 34	18 38		18 40	18 42	18 54		19 02	19 04	19 06	19 10		19 14	19 20	19 25	19 26	19 29		19 32	19 40	19 43	19 49
Deptford	d					18 48				19 10				19 20	19 26					19 38			19 54
Greenwich 4	⛴ d					18 50				19 12				19 22	19 28					19 40			19 56
Maze Hill	d					18 54				19 16				19 26	19 32					19 44			20 00
Westcombe Park	d					18 56				19 18				19 28	19 34					19 46			20 02
London Victoria 15	⊖ d							18 46											19 16				
Denmark Hill 4	d							18 57											19 27				
Peckham Rye 4	d							19 00											19 31				
Nunhead 4	d							19 02											19 33				
New Cross 4	⊖ d				18 46		19 00				19 12						19 31				19 45	19 48	
St Johns	d				18 48						19 14						19 33				19 47		
Lewisham 4	⛴ d	18 44	18 48		18 52		19 04	19 08	19 12		19 17	19 22				19 35		19 38	19 45		19 50	19 53	
Blackheath 4	d	18 47	18 51				19 07	19 11	19 15		19 19					19 37		19 41	19 47		19 52		
Kidbrooke	d	18 50					19 10	19 14			19 22					19 40			19 50		19 55		
Eltham	d	18 54					19 14	19 18			19 26					19 44			19 54		19 59		
Falconwood	d	18 56					19 16	19 20			19 28					19 46			19 56		20 01		
Welling	d	18 59					19 19	19 23			19 31					19 49			19 59		20 04		
Bexleyheath	d	19 02					19 22	19 26			19 33					19 51			20 01		20 06		
Barnehurst 4	d	19 05					19 25	19 29			19a37					19 54			20 04		20a10		
Hither Green 4	d				18 56							19 25					19 37					19 57	
Lee	d			18 55	18 58							19 27					19 39					19 59	
Mottingham	d			18 58	19 02							19 30					19 42					20 02	
New Eltham	d			19 01	19 05							19 33					19 45					20 05	
Sidcup 4	d			19 05	19 08							19 36					19 49					20 08	
Albany Park	d			19 07	19 10							19 38					19 51					20 10	
Bexley	d			19 09	19 12							19 40					19 53					20 12	
Crayford	d			19 12	19 15							19 43					19 56					20 15	
Charlton 4	d		18 55			18 58			19 19	19 22			←	19 30	19 36			19 45		19 50			20 04
Woolwich Dockyard	d					19 01				19 25			19 25	19 33	19 39					19 53			20 07
Woolwich Arsenal 4	d		19 01			19 04			19 25	→			19 28	19 36	19 42			19 50		19 56			20 10
Plumstead	d					19 06							19 30	19 38	19 44					19 58			20 12
Abbey Wood	d		19 06			19 10			19 30				19 34	19 41	19 47			19 55		20 01			20 15
Belvedere	d					19 13							19 37	19 44	19 50					20 04			20 18
Erith	d					19 16							19 40	19 47	19 53					20 07			20 21
Slade Green 4	d					19 19							19 43	19a50	19 56		20a04			20 10			20 24
Dartford 4	a	19 12	19 15	19 18	19 22	19 24	19 32	19 36	19 39			19 47	19 48		20 01	20 03		20 05	20 11	20 15		20 19	20 29
	d		19 16	19 20					19 40			19 48						20 06				20 20	
Stone Crossing	d			19 23								19 51										20 23	
Greenhithe for Bluewater	d		19 21	19 26					19 45			19 54						20 11				20 26	
Swanscombe	d			19 29								19 56										20 28	
Northfleet	d			19 31								19 58										20 30	
Gravesend 4	d		19 28	19a36					19 52			20a02						20 18				20a34	
Higham	d		19 34						19 58									20 24					
Strood 4	d		19b44						20 04									20 30					
Maidstone West 4	a								20 33									20 56					
Rochester 4	d		19 48						20 08									20 33					
Chatham 4	d		19 51						20 11									20 36					
Gillingham (Kent) 4	a		19 55						20 15									20 39					

For general notes see front of timetable
For details of catering facilities see Directory of Train Operators

b Arr. 1939

For details of Bank Holiday service alterations please see first page of Table 195

London → Dartford and Gillingham

Network Diagram - see first page of Table 200

		SE 70	SE 57	SE 62	SE 78	SE 81	SE 50	SE 80	SE 70	SE 62	SE 81	SE 50	SE 80	SE 70	SE 62	SE 81	SE 50	SE 80	SE 70	SE 62	SE 61 A	SE 81	SE 50
London Charing Cross 4	⊖ d	19 47		19 50			20 04	20 10	20 17	20 20		20 34	20 40	20 47	20 50		21 04	21 10	21 17	21 20			21 34
London Waterloo (East) 4	⊖ d	19 50		19 53			20 07	20 13	20 20	20 23		20 37	20 43	20 50	20 53		21 07	21 13	21 20	21 23			21 37
London Cannon Street 4	⊖ d		19 52			20 00					20 30					21 00							
London Bridge 4	⊖ d	19 55	19 56	19 59		20 04	20 13	20 18	20 25	20 29	20 34	20 43	20 48	20 55	20 59	21 04	21 13	21 18	21 25	21 29		21 34	21 43
Deptford	d					20 10		20 24			20 40		20 54			21 10		21 24				21 40	
Greenwich 4	⛴ d					20 12		20 26			20 42		20 56			21 12		21 26				21 42	
Maze Hill	d					20 16		20 30			20 46		21 00			21 16		21 30				21 46	
Westcombe Park	d					20 18		20 32			20 48		21 02			21 18		21 32				21 48	
London Victoria 15	⊖ d				19 46																		
Denmark Hill 4	d				19 57																		
Peckham Rye 4	d				20 01																		
Nunhead 4	d				20 03																		
New Cross 4	⊖ d		20 01				20 18		20 30			20 48		21 00			21 18		21 30				21 48
St Johns	d		20 04																				
Lewisham 4	⛴ d	20 05		20 08	20 15		20 23		20 35	20 38		20 53		21 05	21 08		21 23		21 35	21 38			21 53
Blackheath 4	d	20 07		20 11	20 17				20 37	20 41				21 07	21 11				21 37	21 41			
Kidbrooke	d	20 10			20 20				20 40					21 10					21 40				
Eltham	d	20 14			20 24				20 44					21 14					21 44				
Falconwood	d	20 16			20 26				20 46					21 16					21 46				
Welling	d	20 19			20 29				20 49					21 19					21 49				
Bexleyheath	d	20 21			20 31				20 51					21 21					21 51				
Barnehurst 4	d	20 24			20 34				20 54					21 24					21 54				
Hither Green 4	d		20 09				20 27					20 57					21 27						21 57
Lee	d		20 11				20 29					20 59					21 29						21 59
Mottingham	d		20 14				20 32					21 02					21 32						22 02
New Eltham	d		20 17				20 35					21 05					21 35						22 05
Sidcup 4	d		20 20				20 38					21 08					21 38						22 08
Albany Park	d		20 22				20 40					21 10					21 40						22 10
Bexley	d		20 24				20 42					21 12					21 42						22 12
Crayford	d		20 27				20 45					21 15					21 45						22 15
Charlton 4	d			20 15		20 20		20 34		20 45	20 50		21 04		21 15	21 20		21 34		21 45		21 50	
Woolwich Dockyard	d					20 23		20 37			20 53		21 07			21 23		21 37				21 53	
Woolwich Arsenal 4	d			20 20		20 26		20 40		20 50	20 56		21 10		21 20	21 26		21 40		21 50		21 56	
Plumstead	d					20 28		20 42			20 58		21 12			21 28		21 42				21 58	
Abbey Wood	d			20 25		20 31		20 45		20 55	21 01		21 15		21 25	21 31		21 45		21 55		22 01	
Belvedere	d					20 34		20 48			21 04		21 18			21 34		21 48				22 04	
Erith	d					20 37		20 51			21 07		21 21			21 37		21 51				22 07	
Slade Green 4	d		20a34			20 40		20 54			21 10		21 24			21 40		21 54				22 10	
Dartford 4	a	20 31		20 33	20 41	20 45	20 50	20 59	21 01	21 03	21 15	21 22	21 29	21 31	21 33	21 45	21 52	21 59	22 01	22 03		22 15	22 22
	d			20 34						21 04					21 34					22 04			
Stone Crossing	d			20 37											21 37								
Greenhithe for Bluewater	d			20 40						21 09					21 40					22 09			
Swanscombe	d			20 42											21 42								
Northfleet	d			20 44											21 44								
Gravesend 4	d			20 50						21 16					21 50					22 16			
Higham	d			20 56						21 22					21 56					22 22			
Strood 4	d			21b04						21 28					22 02					22 28	22 46		
Maidstone West 4	a			*21 29*						*21 56*										*22 57*			
Rochester 4	d			21 09						21 31					22 07					22 31	22 49		
Chatham 4	d			21 12						21 34					22 09					22 34	22 51		
Gillingham (Kent) 4	a			21 17						21 37					22 13					22 37	22 55		

For general notes see front of timetable
For details of catering facilities see
Directory of Train Operators

A From Paddock Wood (Table 209)
b Arr. 2101

For details of Bank Holiday service alterations please see first page of Table 195

London → Dartford and Gillingham

Network Diagram - see first page of Table 200

		SE 80	SE 70	SE 62	SE 81	SE 50	SE 80	SE 70	SE 62	SE 50	SE 80	SE 70	SE 62	SE 50	SE 80	SE 70	SE 62	SE 50	SE 80	SE 70
London Charing Cross 4	⊖ d	21 40	21 47	21 50		22 04	22 10	22 17	22 20	22 34	22 40	22 47	22 50	23 04	23 10	23 17	23 20	23 34	23 40	23 47
London Waterloo (East) 4	⊖ d	21 43	21 50	21 53		22 07	22 13	22 20	22 23	22 37	22 43	22 50	22 53	23 07	23 13	23 20	23 23	23 37	23 43	23 50
London Cannon Street 4	⊖ d																			
London Bridge 4	⊖ d	21 48	21 55	21 59	22 04	22 13	22 18	22 25	22 29	22 43	22 48	22 55	22 59	23 13	23 18	23 25	23 29	23 43	23 48	23 55
Deptford	d	21 54			22 10		22 24				22 54				23 24				23 54	
Greenwich 4	⛴ d	21 56			22 12		22 26				22 56				23 26				23 56	
Maze Hill	d	22 00			22 16		22 30				23 00				23 30				00 01	
Westcombe Park	d	22 02			22 18		22 32				23 02				23 32				00 02	
London Victoria 15	⊖ d																			
Denmark Hill 4	d																			
Peckham Rye 4	d																			
Nunhead 4	d																			
New Cross 4	⊖ d		22 00			22 18		22 30		22 48		23 00		23 18		23 30		23 48		23 59
St Johns	d																			
Lewisham 4	⛴ d		22 05	22 08		22 23		22 35	22 38	22 53		23 05	23 08	23 23		23 35	23 38	23 53		00 05
Blackheath 4	d		22 07	22 11				22 37	22 41			23 07	23 11			23 37	23 41			00 07
Kidbrooke	d		22 10					22 40				23 10				23 40				00 10
Eltham	d		22 14					22 44				23 14				23 44				00 14
Falconwood	d		22 16					22 46				23 16				23 46				00 16
Welling	d		22 19					22 49				23 19				23 49				00 19
Bexleyheath	d		22 21					22 51				23 21				23 51				00 21
Barnehurst 4	d		22 24					22 54				23 24				23 54				00 24
Hither Green 4	d					22 27				22 57				23 27				23 57		
Lee	d					22 29				22 59				23 29				23 59		
Mottingham	d					22 32				23 02				23 32				00 02		
New Eltham	d					22 35				23 05				23 35				00 05		
Sidcup 4	d					22 38				23 08				23 38				00 08		
Albany Park	d					22 40				23 10				23 40				00 10		
Bexley	d					22 42				23 12				23 42				00 12		
Crayford	d					22 45				23 15				23 45				00 15		
Charlton 4	d	22 04		22 15	22 20		22 34		22 45		23 04		23 15		23 34		23 45		00 04	
Woolwich Dockyard	d	22 07			22 23		22 37				23 07				23 37				00 07	
Woolwich Arsenal 4	d	22 10		22 20	22 26		22 40		22 50		23 10		23 20		23 40		23 50		00 10	
Plumstead	d	22 12			22 28		22 42				23 12				23 42				00 12	
Abbey Wood	d	22 15		22 25	22 31		22 45		22 55		23 15		23 25		23 45		23 55		00 15	
Belvedere	d	22 18			22 34		22 48				23 18				23 48				00 18	
Erith	d	22 21			22 37		22 51				23 21				23 51				00 21	
Slade Green 4	d	22 24			22 40		22 54				23 24				23 54				00 24	
Dartford 4	a	22 29	22 31	22 33	22 45	22 50	22 59	23 01	23 03	23 20	23 29	23 31	23 33	23 50	23 59	00 01	00 04	00 20	00 29	00 31
	d			22 34					23 04				23 34				00 04			
Stone Crossing	d			22 37									23 37				00 08			
Greenhithe for Bluewater	d			22 40					23 09				23 40				00 10			
Swanscombe	d			22 42									23 42				00 12			
Northfleet	d			22 44									23 44				00 14			
Gravesend 4	d			22 50					23 16				23 50				00 20			
Higham	d			22 56					23 22				23 56				00 26			
Strood 4	d			23 02					23 28				00 02				00 32			
Maidstone West 4	a																			
Rochester 4	d			23 07					23 31				00 07				00 39			
Chatham 4	d			23 09					23 34				00 09				00 42			
Gillingham (Kent) 4	a			23 13					23 37				00 13				00 45			

For general notes see front of timetable
For details of catering facilities see Directory of Train Operators

For details of Bank Holiday service alterations please see first page of Table 195

London → Dartford and Gillingham

Network Diagram - see first page of Table 200

Station		SE 62	SE 62	SE 50	SE 80	SE 70	SE 50	SE 62	SE 20	SE 52	SE 54	SE 80	SE 70	SE 80	7B-2	SE 54	SE 80	SE 70	SE 62	SE 54	SE 80	SE 70	SE 62
									1 A														
London Charing Cross 4	⊖ d	22p50	23p20	23p34	23p40	23p47	00 04	00 14		05 04	05 34	05 40	05 47		05 50	06 04	06 10	06 17	06 20	06 34	06 40	06 47	06 50
London Waterloo (East) 4	⊖ d	22p53	23p23	23p37	23p43	23p50	00 07	00 17		05 07	05 37	05 43	05 50		05 53	06 07	06 13	06 20	06 23	06 37	06 43	06 50	06 53
London Cannon Street 4	⊖ d																						
London Bridge 4	⊖ d	22p59	23p29	23p43	23p48	23p55	00 13	00 23		05 13	05 43	05 48	05 55		05 59	06 13	06 18	06 25	06 29	06 43	06 48	06 55	06 59
Deptford	d				23p54							05 54					06 24				06 54		
Greenwich 4	⛴ d				23p56							05 56					06 26				06 56		
Maze Hill	d				00 01							06 00					06 30				07 00		
Westcombe Park	d				00 02							06 02					06 32				07 02		
London Victoria 15	⊖ d																						
Denmark Hill 4	d																						
Peckham Rye 4	d																						
Nunhead 4	d																						
New Cross 4	⊖ d			23p48		23p59	00 18	00 28		05 18	05 48					06 18				06 48			
St Johns	d																						
Lewisham 4	⛴ d	23p08	23p38	23p53		00 05	00 23	00 33		05 23	05 53		06 05		06 07	06 23		06 35	06 37	06 53		07 05	07 07
Blackheath 4	d	23p11	23p41			00 07		00 36					06 07		06 09			06 38	06 40			07 08	07 10
Kidbrooke	d					00 10							06 10					06 41				07 11	
Eltham	d					00 14							06 14					06 44				07 14	
Falconwood	d					00 16							06 16					06 47				07 17	
Welling	d					00 19							06 19					06 49				07 19	
Bexleyheath	d					00 21							06 21					06 52				07 22	
Barnehurst 4	d					00 24							06 24					06 54				07 24	
Hither Green 4	d			23p57			00 27			05 27	05 57					06 27				06 57			
Lee	d			23p59			00 29			05 29	05 59					06 29				06 59			
Mottingham	d			00 02			00 32			05 32	06 02					06 32				07 02			
New Eltham	d			00 05			00 35			05 35	06 05					06 35				07 05			
Sidcup 4	d			00 08			00 38			05 38	06 08					06 38				07 08			
Albany Park	d			00 10			00 40			05 40	06 10					06 40				07 10			
Bexley	d			00 12			00 42			05 42	06 12					06 42				07 12			
Crayford	d			00 15			00 45			05 45	06 16					06 46				07 16			
Charlton 4	d	23p15	23p45		00 04			00 40				06 04		←	06 14		06 34		06 44		07 04		07 14
Woolwich Dockyard	d				00 07							06 07		06 07			06 37				07 07		
Woolwich Arsenal 4	d	23p20	23p50		00 10			00 45				→		06 10	06 19		06 40		06 49		07 10		07 19
Plumstead	d				00 12			00 47						06 12			06 42				07 12		
Abbey Wood	d	23p25	23p55		00 15			00 50						06 15	06 23		06 45		06 53		07 15		07 23
Belvedere	d				00 18			00 53						06 18			06 48				07 18		
Erith	d				00 21			00 56						06 21			06 51				07 21		
Slade Green 4	d				00 24			00 58						06 26			06 54				07 24		
Dartford 4	a	23p33	00 04	00 20	00 29	00 31	00 50	01 03		05 49	06 20		06 29	06 31	06 34	06 50	06 59	07 01	07 03	07 20	07 28	07 31	07 33
	d	23p34	00 04					01 04	05 17	05 49	06 21				06 34	06 51			07 04	07 21			07 34
Stone Crossing	d	23p37	00 08								06 24					06 54				07 24			
Greenhithe for Bluewater	d	23p40	00 10					01 09	05 22	05 54	06 27				06 39	06 57			07 09	07 27			07 39
Swanscombe	d	23p42	00 12								06 29					06 59				07 29			
Northfleet	d	23p44	00 14								06 31					07 01				07 31			
Gravesend 4	d	23p50	00 20					01 16	05 29	06 01	06a35				06 46	07a05			07 16	07a35			07 46
Higham	d	23p56	00 26					01 22	05 35	06 07					06 52				07 22				07 52
Strood 4	d	00 02	00 32					01 28	05 40	06 12					06 58				07 28				07 58
Maidstone West 4	a								*06 23*	*06 53*					*07 23*				*07 53*				*08 23*
Rochester 4	d	00 07	00 39					01 31	05 44	06 16					07 01				07 31				08 01
Chatham 4	d	00 09	00 42					01 34	05 46	06 19					07 04				07 34				08 04
Gillingham (Kent) 4	a	00 13	00 45					01 37	05 50	06 22					07 07				07 37				08 07

For general notes see front of timetable
For details of catering facilities see Directory of Train Operators

A To Dover Priory (Table 212)

Table 200

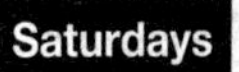

For details of Bank Holiday service alterations please see first page of Table 195

London → Dartford and Gillingham

Network Diagram - see first page of Table 200

		SE	SE	SE	SE	SE	SE	SE	SE	SE	SE	SE	SE	SE	SE	SE	SE	SE	SE	SE	SE	SE	SE
		54	80	70	62	54	80	70	62	54	78	81	70	62	47	54	78	81	47	70	82	47	67
															A				A			A	
London Charing Cross 4	⊖ d	07 04	07 10	07 17	07 20	07 34	07 42	07 47	07 50	08 02			08 17	08 20		08 32				08 47	08 50		
London Waterloo (East) 4	⊖ d	07 07	07 13	07 20	07 23	07 37	07 45	07 50	07 53	08 05			08 20	08 23		08 35				08 50	08 53		
London Cannon Street 4	⊖ d											08 10			08 30			08 40	08 48			09 00	09 04
London Bridge 4	⊖ d	07 13	07 18	07 25	07 29	07 43	07 50	07 55	07 59	08 10		08 14	08 25	08 29	08 34	08 40		08 44	08 52	08 55	08 59	09 04	09 08
Deptford	d		07 24				07 55					08 20			08 40			08 50				09 10	
Greenwich 4	⛴ d		07 26				07 57					08 22			08 42			08 52			09 07	09 12	
Maze Hill	d		07 30				08 01					08 26			08 46			08 56				09 16	
Westcombe Park	d		07 32				08 03					08 28			08 48			08 58				09 18	
London Victoria 15	⊖ d										08 01						08 31						
Denmark Hill 4	d										08 12						08 42						
Peckham Rye 4	d										08 14						08 44						
Nunhead 4	d										08 16						08 46						
New Cross 4	⊖ d	07 18				07 48				08 15						08 45			08 57				09 14
St Johns	d																		08 59				
Lewisham 4	⛴ d	07 23		07 35	07 37	07 53		08 05	08 07	08 20	08 23		08 33	08 37		08 50	08 53			09 06			09 18
Blackheath 4	d			07 38	07 40			08 08	08 10		08 25		08 38	08 40			08 55			09 08			09 20
Kidbrooke	d			07 41				08 11			08 28		08 41				08 58			09 11			
Eltham	d			07 44				08 14			08 32		08 45				09 02			09 15			
Falconwood	d			07 47				08 17			08 34		08 47				09 04			09 17			
Welling	d			07 49				08 19			08 37		08 50				09 07			09 20			
Bexleyheath	d			07 52				08 22			08 39		08 52				09 09			09 22			
Barnehurst 4	d			07 54				08 24			08 42		08 55				09 12			09 25			
Hither Green 4	d	07 27				07 57				08 23						08 53			09 05				
Lee	d	07 29				07 59				08 25						08 55			09 07				
Mottingham	d	07 32				08 02				08 28						08 58			09 10				
New Eltham	d	07 35				08 05				08 31						09 01			09 13				
Sidcup 4	d	07 38				08 08				08 34						09 04			09 16				
Albany Park	d	07 40				08 10				08 36						09 06			09 18				
Bexley	d	07 42				08 12				08 38						09 08			09 20				
Crayford	d	07 46				08 16				08 41						09 11			09b28				
Charlton 4	d		07 34		07 44		08 05		08 14			08 30		08 44	08 50			09 00			09 14	09 20	09 25
Woolwich Dockyard	d		07 37				08 08					08 32			08 52			09 02				09 22	
Woolwich Arsenal 4	d		07 40		07 49		08 11		08 19			08 35		08 49	08 55			09 05			09 19	09 25	09 30
Plumstead	d		07 42				08 13					08 37			08 57			09 07				09 27	09a32
Abbey Wood	d		07 45		07 53		08 16		08 23			08 41		08 53	09 01			09 11			09 23	09 31	
Belvedere	d		07 48				08 19					08 43			09 03			09 13				09 33	
Erith	d		07 51				08 22					08 46			09 06			09 16				09 36	
Slade Green 4	d		07 54				08 24					08 49			09a09			09 19	09a34			09a39	
Dartford 4	a	07 50	07 59	08 00	08 03	08 20	08 28	08 30	08 33	08 45	08 47	08 53	09 00	09 03		09 15	09 17	09 23		09 30	09 33		
	d	07 51			08 04	08 21			08 34	08 46				09 04		09 16					09 34		
Stone Crossing	d	07 54				08 24				08 49						09 19							
Greenhithe for Bluewater	d	07 57			08 09	08 27			08 39	08 52				09 09		09 22					09 39		
Swanscombe	d	07 59				08 29				08 54						09 24							
Northfleet	d	08 01				08 31				08 56						09 26							
Gravesend 4	d	08a05			08 16	08a35			08 46	09a00				09 16		09a30					09 46		
Higham	d				08 22				08 52					09 22							09 52		
Strood 4	d				08 28				08 58					09 28							09 58		
Maidstone West 4	a				*08 53*				*09 23*					*09 53*							*10 23*		
Rochester 4	d				08 31				09 01					09 31							10 01		
Chatham 4	d				08 34				09 04					09 34							10 04		
Gillingham (Kent) 4	a				08 37				09 07					09 37							10 07		

For general notes see front of timetable
For details of catering facilities see Directory of Train Operators

A To London Cannon Street (Table 199)
b Arr. 0924

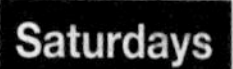

For details of Bank Holiday service alterations please see first page of Table 195

London → Dartford and Gillingham

Network Diagram - see first page of Table 200

		SE 54	SE 78	SE 81	SE 47 A	SE 70	SE 82	SE 47 A	SE 67	SE 54	SE 78	SE 81	SE 47 A	SE 70	SE 82	SE 87 A	SE 67	SE 54	SE 78	SE 81	SE 47 A		SE 70
London Charing Cross 4	⊖ d	09 02				09 17	09 20			09 32				09 47	09 50			10 02					16 17
London Waterloo (East) 4	⊖ d	09 05				09 20	09 23			09 35				09 50	09 53			10 05					16 20
London Cannon Street 4	⊖ d			09 10	09 18			09 30	09 34			09 40	09 48			10 00	10 04			10 10	10 18		
London Bridge 4	⊖ d	09 10		09 14	09 22	09 25	09 29	09 34	09 38	09 40		09 44	09 52	09 55	09 59	10 04	10 08	10 10		10 14	10 22		16 25
Deptford	d			09 20				09 40				09 50				10 10				10 20			
Greenwich 4	⛴ d			09 22			09 37	09 42				09 52			10 07	10 12				10 22			
Maze Hill	d			09 26				09 46				09 56				10 16				10 26			
Westcombe Park	d			09 28				09 48				09 58				10 18				10 28			
London Victoria 15	⊖ d		09 01								09 31								10 01				
Denmark Hill 4	d		09 12								09 42								10 12				
Peckham Rye 4	d		09 14								09 44								10 14				
Nunhead 4	d		09 16								09 46								10 16				
New Cross 4	⊖ d				09 27				09 44				09 57				10 14				10 27		
St Johns	d				09 29								09 59								10 29		
Lewisham 4	⛴ d	09 20	09 23			09 36			09 48	09 50	09 53			10 06			10 18	10 20	10 23				16 36
Blackheath 4	d		09 25			09 38			09 50		09 55			10 08			10 20		10 25				16 38
Kidbrooke	d		09 28			09 41					09 58			10 11					10 28				16 41
Eltham	d		09 32			09 45					10 02			10 15					10 32			and at	16 45
Falconwood	d		09 34			09 47					10 04			10 17					10 34				16 47
Welling	d		09 37			09 50					10 07			10 20					10 37			the same	16 50
Bexleyheath	d		09 39			09 52					10 09			10 22					10 39				16 52
Barnehurst 4	d		09 42			09 55					10 12			10 25					10 42			minutes	16 55
Hither Green 4	d	09 23			09 35					09 53			10 05					10 23			10 35	past	
Lee	d	09 25			09 37					09 55			10 07					10 25			10 37		
Mottingham	d	09 28			09 40					09 58			10 10					10 28			10 40	each	
New Eltham	d	09 31			09 43					10 01			10 13					10 31			10 43		
Sidcup 4	d	09 34			09 46					10 04			10 16					10 34			10 46	hour until	
Albany Park	d	09 36			09 48					10 06			10 18					10 36			10 48		
Bexley	d	09 38			09 50					10 08			10 20					10 38			10 50		
Crayford	d	09 41			09b58					10 11			10c28					10 41			10e58		
Charlton 4	d			09 30			09 44	09 50	09 55			10 00			10 14	10 20	10 25			10 30			
Woolwich Dockyard	d			09 32				09 52				10 02				10 22				10 32			
Woolwich Arsenal 4	d			09 35			09 49	09 55	10 00			10 05			10 19	10 25	10 30			10 35			
Plumstead	d			09 37				09 57	10a02			10 07				10 27	10a32			10 37			
Abbey Wood	d			09 41			09 53	10 01				10 11			10 23	10 31				10 41			
Belvedere	d			09 43				10 03				10 13				10 33				10 43			
Erith	d			09 46				10 06				10 16				10 36				10 46			
Slade Green 4	d			09 49	10a04			10a09				10 19	10a34			10a39				10 49	11a04		
Dartford 4	a	09 45	09 47	09 53		10 00	10 03			10 15	10 17	10 23		10 30	10 33			10 45	10 47	10 53			17 00
	d	09 46					10 04			10 16					10 34			10 46					
Stone Crossing	d	09 49								10 19								10 49					
Greenhithe for Bluewater	d	09 52					10 09			10 22					10 39			10 52					
Swanscombe	d	09 54								10 24								10 54					
Northfleet	d	09 56								10 26								10 56					
Gravesend 4	d	10a00					10 16			10a30					10 46			11a00					
Higham	d						10 22								10 52								
Strood 4	d						10 28								10 58								
Maidstone West 4	a						*10 53*								*11 23*								
Rochester 4	d						10 31								11 01								
Chatham 4	d						10 34								11 04								
Gillingham (Kent) 4	a						10 37								11 07								

For general notes see front of timetable
For details of catering facilities see Directory of Train Operators

A To London Cannon Street (Table 199)
b Arr. 0954
c Arr. 1024
e Arr. 1054

Table 200

For details of Bank Holiday service alterations please see first page of Table 195

London → Dartford and Gillingham

Network Diagram - see first page of Table 200

		SE 82	SE 87 A	SE 67	SE 54	SE 78	SE 81	SE 47 A	SE 70	SE 82	SE 47 A	SE 67	SE 54	SE 78	SE 81	SE 47	SE 70	SE 82	SE 87	SE 67	SE 54	SE 78
London Charing Cross 4	⊖ d	16 20			16 32				16 47	16 50			17 02				17 17	17 20			17 32	
London Waterloo (East) 4	⊖ d	16 23			16 35				16 50	16 53			17 05				17 20	17 23			17 35	
London Cannon Street 4	⊖ d		16 30	16 34			16 40	16 48			17 00	17 04			17 10	17 18			17 30	17 34		
London Bridge 4	⊖ d	16 29	16 34	16 38	16 40		16 44	16 52	16 55	16 59	17 04	17 08	17 10		17 14	17 22	17 25	17 29	17 34	17 38	17 40	
Deptford	d		16 40				16 50				17 10				17 20				17 40			
Greenwich 4	⛴ d	16 37	16 42				16 52			17 07	17 12				17 22			17 37	17 42			
Maze Hill	d		16 46				16 56				17 16				17 26				17 46			
Westcombe Park	d		16 48				16 58				17 18				17 28				17 48			
London Victoria 15	⊖ d					16 31								17 01								17 31
Denmark Hill 4	d					16 42								17 12								17 42
Peckham Rye 4	d					16 44								17 14								17 44
Nunhead 4	d					16 46								17 16								17 46
New Cross 4	⊖ d			16 44				16 57			18a17	17 14				17 27				17 44		
St Johns	d							16 59								17 29						
Lewisham 4	⛴ d			16 48	16 50	16 53			17 06			17 18	17 20	17 23			17 36			17 48	17 50	17 53
Blackheath 4	d			16 50		16 55			17 08			17 20		17 25			17 38			17 50		17 55
Kidbrooke	d					16 58			17 11					17 28			17 41					17 58
Eltham	d					17 02			17 15					17 32			17 45					18 02
Falconwood	d					17 04			17 17					17 34			17 47					18 04
Welling	d					17 07			17 20					17 37			17 50					18 07
Bexleyheath	d					17 09			17 22					17 39			17 52					18 09
Barnehurst 4	d					17 12			17 25					17 42			17 55					18 12
Hither Green 4	d				16 53			17 05					17 23			17 35					17 53	
Lee	d				16 55			17 07					17 25			17 37					17 55	
Mottingham	d				16 58			17 10					17 28			17 40					17 58	
New Eltham	d				17 01			17 13					17 31			17 43					18 01	
Sidcup 4	d				17 04			17 16					17 34			17 46					18 04	
Albany Park	d				17 06			17 18					17 36			17 48					18 06	
Bexley	d				17 08			17 20					17 38			17 50					18 08	
Crayford	d				17 11			17b28					17 41			17a54					18 11	
Charlton 4	d	16 44	16 50	16 55			17 00			17 14	17 20	17 25			17 30			17 44	17 50	17 55		
Woolwich Dockyard	d		16 52				17 02				17 22				17 32				17 52			
Woolwich Arsenal 4	d	16 49	16 55	17 00			17 05			17 19	17 25	17 30			17 35			17 49	17 55	18 00		
Plumstead	d		16 57	17a02			17 07				17 27	17a32			17 37				17 57	18a02		
Abbey Wood	d	16 53	17 01				17 11			17 23	17 31				17 41			17 53	18 01			
Belvedere	d		17 03				17 13				17 33				17 43				18 03			
Erith	d		17 06				17 16				17 36				17 46				18 06			
Slade Green 4	d		17a09				17 19	17a34			17a39				17 49				18a09			
Dartford 4	a	17 03			17 15	17 17	17 23		17 30	17 33			17 45	17 47	17 53		18 00	18 03			18 15	18 17
	d	17 04			17 16					17 34			17 46					18 04			18 16	
Stone Crossing	d				17 19								17 49								18 19	
Greenhithe for Bluewater	d	17 09			17 22					17 39			17 52					18 09			18 22	
Swanscombe	d				17 24								17 54								18 24	
Northfleet	d				17 26								17 56								18 26	
Gravesend 4	d	17 16			17a30					17 46			18a00					18 16			18a30	
Higham	d	17 22								17 52								18 22				
Strood 4	d	17 28								17 58								18 28				
Maidstone West 4	a	*17 53*								*18 23*								*18 53*				
Rochester 4	d	17 31								18 01								18 31				
Chatham 4	d	17 34								18 04								18 34				
Gillingham (Kent) 4	a	17 37								18 07								18 37				

For general notes see front of timetable
For details of catering facilities see Directory of Train Operators

A To London Cannon Street (Table 199)
b Arr. 1724

Table 200

For details of Bank Holiday service alterations please see first page of Table 195

London → Dartford and Gillingham

Network Diagram - see first page of Table 200

		SE 81	SE 47	SE 70	SE 82	SE 87	SE 67	SE 54	SE 78	SE 81	SE 47	SE 70	SE 62	SE 87	SE 54	SE 78	SE 81	SE 47	SE 70	SE 62	SE 87	SE 54	SE 78
London Charing Cross 4	⊖ d			17 47	17 50			18 02				18 17	18 20		18 32				18 47	18 50		19 04	
London Waterloo (East) 4	⊖ d			17 50	17 53			18 05				18 20	18 23		18 35				18 50	18 53		19 07	
London Cannon Street 4	⊖ d	17 40	17 48			18 00	18 04			18 10	18 18			18 30			18 40	18 48			19 00		
London Bridge 4	⊖ d	17 44	17 52	17 55	17 59	18 04	18 08	18 10		18 14	18 22	18 25	18 29	18 34	18 40		18 44	18 52	18 55	18 59	19 04	19 13	
Deptford	d	17 50				18 10				18 20				18 40			18 50				19 10		
Greenwich 4	⛴ d	17 52			18 07	18 12				18 22				18 42			18 52				19 12		
Maze Hill	d	17 56				18 16				18 26				18 46			18 56				19 16		
Westcombe Park	d	17 58				18 18				18 28				18 48			18 58				19 18		
London Victoria 15	⊖ d								18 01							18 31							19 01
Denmark Hill 4	d								18 12							18 42							19 12
Peckham Rye 4	d								18 14							18 44							19 14
Nunhead 4	d								18 16							18 46							19 16
New Cross 4	⊖ d		17 57				18 14				18 27							18 57					
St Johns	d		17 59								18 29							18 59					
Lewisham 4	⛴ d			18 06			18 18	18 20	18 23			18 33	18 37		18 50	18 53			19 05	19 07		19 21	19 23
Blackheath 4	d			18 08			18 20		18 25			18 36	18 39			18 55			19 09	19 09			19 25
Kidbrooke	d			18 11					18 28			18 41				18 58			19 12				19 28
Eltham	d			18 15					18 32			18 45				19 02			19 15				19 32
Falconwood	d			18 17					18 34			18 47				19 04			19 17				19 34
Welling	d			18 20					18 37			18 50				19 07			19 20				19 37
Bexleyheath	d			18 22					18 39			18 52				19 09			19 22				19 39
Barnehurst 4	d			18 25					18 42			18 55				19 12			19 25				19 42
Hither Green 4	d		18 05					18 23			18 35				18 53			19 05				19 24	
Lee	d		18 07					18 25			18 37				18 55			19 07				19 26	
Mottingham	d		18 10					18 28			18 40				18 58			19 10				19 29	
New Eltham	d		18 13					18 31			18 43				19 01			19 13				19 32	
Sidcup 4	d		18 16					18 34			18 46				19 04			19 16				19 35	
Albany Park	d		18 18					18 36			18 48				19 06			19 18				19 37	
Bexley	d		18 20					18 38			18 50				19 08			19 20				19 39	
Crayford	d		18a24					18 41			18a54				19 11			19a24				19 42	
Charlton 4	d	18 00			18 14	18 20	18 25			18 30			18 44	18 50			19 00			19 14	19 20		
Woolwich Dockyard	d	18 02				18 22				18 32				18 52			19 02				19 22		
Woolwich Arsenal 4	d	18 05			18 19	18 25	18 30			18 35			18 49	18 55			19 05			19 19	19 25		
Plumstead	d	18 07				18 27	18a32			18 37				18 57			19 07				19 27		
Abbey Wood	d	18 11			18 23	18 31				18 41			18 53	19 01			19 11			19 23	19 31		
Belvedere	d	18 13				18 33				18 43				19 03			19 13				19 33		
Erith	d	18 16				18 36				18 46				19 06			19 16				19 36		
Slade Green 4	d	18 19				18a39				18 49				19a09			19 19				19a39		
Dartford 4	a	18 23		18 30	18 33			18 45	18 48	18 55		19 00	19 03		19 15	19 17	19 25		19 31	19 33		19 46	19 48
	d				18 34			18 46					19 04		19 16					19 34		19 47	
Stone Crossing	d							18 49							19 19							19 50	
Greenhithe for Bluewater	d				18 39			18 52					19 09		19 22					19 39		19 53	
Swanscombe	d							18 54							19 24							19 55	
Northfleet	d							18 56							19 26							19 57	
Gravesend 4	d				18 46			19a00					19 16		19a30					19 46		20a01	
Higham	d				18 52								19 22							19 52			
Strood 4	d				18 58								19 28							19 58			
Maidstone West 4	a				*19 23*								*19 53*							*20 23*			
Rochester 4	d				19 01								19 31							20 01			
Chatham 4	d				19 04								19 34							20 04			
Gillingham (Kent) 4	a				19 07								19 37							20 07			

For general notes see front of timetable
For details of catering facilities see Directory of Train Operators

For details of Bank Holiday service alterations please see first page of Table 195

London → Dartford and Gillingham

Network Diagram - see first page of Table 200

		SE 81	SE 70	SE 62	SE 50	SE 78	SE 50	SE 80	SE 70	SE 62	SE 50	SE 80	SE 70	SE 62	SE 50	SE 80	SE 70	SE 62	SE 50	SE 80	SE 70	SE 62	SE 50
London Charing Cross ④	⊖ d	19 10	19 17	19 20	19 34			19 40	19 47	19 50	20 04	20 10	20 17	20 20	20 34	20 40	20 47	20 50	21 04	21 10	21 17	21 20	21 34
London Waterloo (East) ④	⊖ d	19 13	19 20	19 23	19 37			19 43	19 50	19 53	20 07	20 13	20 20	20 23	20 37	20 43	20 50	20 53	21 07	21 13	21 20	21 23	21 37
London Cannon Street ④	⊖ d																						
London Bridge ④	⊖ d	19 18	19 25	19 29	19 43			19 48	19 55	19 59	20 13	20 18	20 25	20 29	20 43	20 48	20 55	20 59	21 13	21 18	21 25	21 29	21 43
Deptford	d	19 24						19 54				20 24				20 54				21 24			
Greenwich ④	⛴ d	19 26						19 56				20 26				20 56				21 26			
Maze Hill	d	19 30						20 00				20 30				21 00				21 30			
Westcombe Park	d	19 32						20 02				20 32				21 02				21 32			
London Victoria ⑮	⊖ d					19 31																	
Denmark Hill ④	d					19 42																	
Peckham Rye ④	d					19 44																	
Nunhead ④	d					19 46																	
New Cross ④	⊖ d				19 48						20 18				20 48				21 18				21 48
St Johns	d																						
Lewisham ④	⛴ d		19 35	19 37	19 53	19 54			20 05	20 07	20 23		20 35	20 37	20 53		21 05	21 07	21 23		21 35	21 37	21 53
Blackheath ④	d		19 37	19 39		19 56			20 07	20 09			20 37	20 39			21 07	21 09			21 37	21 39	
Kidbrooke	d		19 40			19 59			20 10				20 40				21 10				21 40		
Eltham	d		19 44			20 03			20 14				20 44				21 14				21 44		
Falconwood	d		19 46			20 05			20 16				20 46				21 16				21 46		
Welling	d		19 49			20 08			20 19				20 49				21 19				21 49		
Bexleyheath	d		19 51			20 10			20 21				20 51				21 21				21 51		
Barnehurst ④	d		19 54			20 13			20 24				20 54				21 24				21 54		
Hither Green ④	d				19 57						20 27				20 57				21 27				21 57
Lee	d				19 59						20 29				20 59				21 29				21 59
Mottingham	d				20 02		←				20 32				21 02				21 32				22 02
New Eltham	d				20 05 →		20 05				20 35				21 05				21 35				22 05
Sidcup ④	d						20 08				20 38				21 08				21 38				22 08
Albany Park	d						20 10				20 40				21 10				21 40				22 10
Bexley	d						20 12				20 42				21 12				21 42				22 12
Crayford	d						20 15				20 45				21 15				21 45				22 15
Charlton ④	d	19 34		19 44				20 04		20 14		20 34		20 44		21 04		21 14		21 34		21 44	
Woolwich Dockyard	d	19 37						20 07				20 37				21 07				21 37			
Woolwich Arsenal ④	d	19 40		19 49				20 10		20 19		20 40		20 49		21 10		21 19		21 40		21 49	
Plumstead	d	19 42						20 12				20 42				21 12				21 42			
Abbey Wood	d	19 45		19 53				20 15		20 23		20 45		20 53		21 15		21 23		21 45		21 53	
Belvedere	d	19 48						20 18				20 48				21 18				21 48			
Erith	d	19 51						20 21				20 51				21 21				21 51			
Slade Green ④	d	19 54						20 24				20 54				21 24				21 54			
Dartford ④	a	19 59	20 01	20 03		20 18	20 20	20 29	20 31	20 33	20 50	20 59	21 01	21 03	21 20	21 29	21 31	21 33	21 50	21 59	22 01	22 03	22 20
	d			20 04						20 34				21 04				21 34				22 04	
Stone Crossing	d									20 37								21 37					
Greenhithe for Bluewater	d			20 09						20 40				21 09				21 40				22 09	
Swanscombe	d									20 42								21 42					
Northfleet	d									20 44								21 44					
Gravesend ④	d			20 16						20 48				21 16				21 50				22 16	
Higham	d			20 22						20 54				21 22				21 56				22 22	
Strood ④	d			20 28						21 01				21 28				22 02				22 28	
Maidstone West ④	a			*20 53*						*21 23*				*21 53*									
Rochester ④	d			20 31						21 05				21 31				22 06				22 31	
Chatham ④	d			20 34						21 08				21 34				22 09				22 34	
Gillingham (Kent) ④	a			20 37						21 13				21 37				22 13				22 37	

For general notes see front of timetable
For details of catering facilities see Directory of Train Operators

Table 200

Saturdays

For details of Bank Holiday service alterations please see first page of Table 195

London → Dartford and Gillingham

Network Diagram - see first page of Table 200

		SE 80	SE 70	SE 62	SE 50	SE 80	SE 70	SE 62	SE 50	SE 80	SE 70	SE 62	SE 50	SE 80	SE 70	SE 62	SE 50	SE 80	SE 70
London Charing Cross 4	⊖ d	21 40	21 47	21 50	22 04	22 10	22 17	22 20	22 34	22 40	22 47	22 50	23 04	23 10	23 17	23 20	23 34	23 40	23 47
London Waterloo (East) 4	⊖ d	21 43	21 50	21 53	22 07	22 13	22 20	22 23	22 37	22 43	22 50	22 53	23 07	23 13	23 20	23 23	23 37	23 43	23 50
London Cannon Street 4	⊖ d																		
London Bridge 4	⊖ d	21 48	21 55	21 59	22 13	22 18	22 25	22 29	22 43	22 48	22 55	22 59	23 13	23 18	23 25	23 29	23 43	23 48	23 55
Deptford	d	21 54				22 24				22 54				23 24				23 54	
Greenwich 4	⛴ d	21 56				22 26				22 56				23 26				23 56	
Maze Hill	d	22 00				22 30				23 00				23 30				00 01	
Westcombe Park	d	22 02				22 32				23 02				23 32				00 02	
London Victoria 15	⊖ d																		
Denmark Hill 4	d																		
Peckham Rye 4	d																		
Nunhead 4	d																		
New Cross 4	⊖ d				22 18				22 48				23 18				23 48		
St Johns	d																		
Lewisham 4	⛴ d		22 05	22 07	22 23		22 35	22 37	22 53		23 05	23 07	23 23		23 35	23 37	23 53		00 05
Blackheath 4	d		22 07	22 09			22 37	22 39			23 07	23 09			23 37	23 39			00 07
Kidbrooke	d		22 10				22 40				23 10				23 40				00 10
Eltham	d		22 14				22 44				23 14				23 44				00 14
Falconwood	d		22 16				22 46				23 16				23 46				00 16
Welling	d		22 19				22 49				23 19				23 49				00 19
Bexleyheath	d		22 21				22 51				23 21				23 51				00 21
Barnehurst 4	d		22 24				22 54				23 24				23 54				00 24
Hither Green 4	d				22 27				22 57				23 27				23 57		
Lee	d				22 29				22 59				23 29				23 59		
Mottingham	d				22 32				23 02				23 32				00 02		
New Eltham	d				22 35				23 05				23 35				00 05		
Sidcup 4	d				22 38				23 08				23 38				00 08		
Albany Park	d				22 40				23 10				23 40				00 10		
Bexley	d				22 42				23 12				23 42				00 12		
Crayford	d				22 45				23 15				23 45				00 15		
Charlton 4	d	22 04		22 14		22 34		22 44		23 04		23 14		23 34		23 44		00 04	
Woolwich Dockyard	d	22 07				22 37				23 07				23 37				00 07	
Woolwich Arsenal 4	d	22 10		22 19		22 40		22 49		23 10		23 19		23 40		23 49		00 10	
Plumstead	d	22 12				22 42				23 12				23 42				00 12	
Abbey Wood	d	22 15		22 23		22 45		22 53		23 15		23 23		23 45		23 53		00 15	
Belvedere	d	22 18				22 48				23 18				23 48				00 18	
Erith	d	22 21				22 51				23 21				23 51				00 21	
Slade Green 4	d	22 24				22 54				23 24				23 54				00 24	
Dartford 4	a	22 28	22 30	22 33	22 50	22 59	23 01	23 03	23 20	23 29	23 31	23 33	23 50	23 59	00 01	00 03	00 20	00 29	00 31
	d			22 34				23 04				23 34				00 04			
Stone Crossing	d			22 37								23 37				00 07			
Greenhithe for Bluewater	d			22 40				23 09				23 40				00 09			
Swanscombe	d			22 42								23 42				00 12			
Northfleet	d			22 44								23 44				00 14			
Gravesend 4	d			22 50				23 16				23 50				00 17			
Higham	d			22 56				23 22				23 56				00 23			
Strood 4	d			23 02				23 28				00 02				00 28			
Maidstone West 4	a																		
Rochester 4	d			23 06				23 31				00 06				00 32			
Chatham 4	d			23 09				23 34				00 09				00 35			
Gillingham (Kent) 4	a			23 13				23 37				00 13				00 38			

For general notes see front of timetable
For details of catering facilities see Directory of Train Operators

Table 200

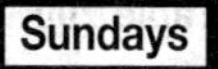

Sundays

London → Dartford and Gillingham

Network Diagram - see first page of Table 200

		SE 62	SE 62	SE 50	SE 80	SE 70	SE 50	SE 62	SE 63	SE 72	SE 50	SE 80	SE 70	SE 50	SE 62	SE 80	SE 82	SE 50	SE 84	SE 70	SE 50	SE 62	SE 84	SE 67	SE 70
London Charing Cross 4	⊖ d	22p50	23p20	23p34	23p40	23p47	00 04	00 14		07 46	07 49	08 01	08 16	08 19	08 26	08 31	08 46	08 49	09 01	09 16	09 19	09 26	09 31		09 46
London Waterloo (East) 4	⊖ d	22p53	23p23	23p37	23p43	23p50	00 07	00 17		07 49	07 52	08 04	08 19	08 22	08 29	08 34	08 49	08 52	09 04	09 19	09 22	09 29	09 34		09 49
London Cannon Street 4	⊖ d																								
London Bridge 4	⊖ d	22p59	23p29	23p43	23p48	23p55	00 13	00 22		07 54	07 58	08 09	08 24	08 28	08 34	08 39	08 54	08 58	09 09	09 24	09 28	09 34	09 39	09 46	09 54
Deptford	d				23p54							08 14				08 44			09 14				09 44		
Greenwich 4	⛴ d				23p56							08 16				08 46			09 16				09 46		
Maze Hill	d				00 01							08 20				08 50			09 20				09 50		
Westcombe Park	d				00 02							08 22				08 52			09 22				09 52		
London Victoria 15	⊖ d																								
Denmark Hill 4	d																								
Peckham Rye 4	d																								
Nunhead 4	d																								
New Cross 4	⊖ d			23p48			00 18	00 27		07 59	08 04		08 29	08 33			08 59	09 03		09 29	09 33				09 59
St Johns	d																								
Lewisham 4	⛴ d	23p07	23p37	23p53		00 05	00 23	00 31		08 03	08 08		08 33	08 37	08 43		09 03	09 07		09 33	09 37	09 43		09 53	10 03
Blackheath 4	d	23p09	23p39			00 07		00 34		08 06			08 36		08 45		09 06			09 36		09 45		09 56	10 06
Kidbrooke	d					00 10				08 09			08 39				09 09			09 39					10 09
Eltham	d					00 14				08 13			08 43				09 13			09 43					10 13
Falconwood	d					00 16				08 15			08 45				09 15			09 45					10 15
Welling	d					00 19				08 18			08 48				09 18			09 48					10 18
Bexleyheath	d					00 21				08 20			08 50				09 20			09 50					10 20
Barnehurst 4	d					00 24				08 23			08 53				09 23			09 53					10 23
Hither Green 4	d			23p57			00 27				08 12			08 41				09 11			09 41				
Lee	d			23p59			00 29				08 14			08 43				09 13			09 43				
Mottingham	d			00 02			00 32				08 17			08 46				09 16			09 46				
New Eltham	d			00 05			00 35				08 19			08 49				09 19			09 49				
Sidcup 4	d			00 08			00 38				08 23			08 52				09 22			09 52				
Albany Park	d			00 10			00 40				08 25			08 54				09 24			09 54				
Bexley	d			00 12			00 42				08 27			08 56				09 26			09 56				
Crayford	d			00 15			00 45				08 30			08 59				09 29			09 59				
Charlton 4	d	23p14	23p44		00 04			00 38				08 24			08 50	08 54			09 24			09 50	09 54	10 00	
Woolwich Dockyard	d				00 07							08 26				08 56			09 26				09 56		
Woolwich Arsenal 4	d	23p19	23p49		00 10			00 42				08 29			08 55	08 59			09 29			09 55	09 59	10 05	
Plumstead	d				00 12			00 44				08 31				09 01			09 31				10 01	10a07	
Abbey Wood	d	23p23	23p53		00 15			00 47				08 35			08 59	09 05			09 35			09 59	10 05		
Belvedere	d				00 18			00 50				08 37				09 07			09 37				10 07		
Erith	d				00 21			00 53				08 40				09 10			09 40				10 10		
Slade Green 4	d				00 24			00 55	08 00			08 43				09 13			09 43				10 13		
Dartford 4	a	23p33	00 03	00 20	00 29	00 31	00 50	00 59	08 04	08 29	08 34	08 47	08 59	09 03	09 07	09 17	09 29	09 33	09 47	09 59	10 03	10 07	10 17		10 29
	d	23p34	00 04					01 00	08 04	08 30					09 07		09 30		09 48			10 07	10 18		
Stone Crossing	d	23p37	00 07							08 34							09 34		09 52				10 22		
Greenhithe for Bluewater	d	23p40	00 09					01 05	08 09	08 36					09 12		09 36		09 54			10 12	10 24		
Swanscombe	d	23p42	00 12							08 39							09 39		09 57				10 27		
Northfleet	d	23p44	00 14							08 41							09 41		09 59				10 29		
Gravesend 4	d	23p50	00 17					01 12	08 16	08 45					09 18		09 45		10a02			10 18	10a32		
Higham	d	23p56	00 23					01 18	08 22	08 51					09 24		09 51					10 24			
Strood 4	d	00 02	00 28					01 23	08 27	08 56					09 29		09 56					10 29			
Maidstone West 4	a								*08 55*						*09 57*							*10 57*			
Rochester 4	d	00 06	00 32					01 27	08 31	09 00					09 33		10 00					10 33			
Chatham 4	d	00 09	00 35					01 30	08 34	09 02					09 36		10 02					10 36			
Gillingham (Kent) 4	a	00 13	00 38					01 33	08 37	09 06					09 39		10 06					10 39			

For general notes see front of timetable
For details of catering facilities see
Directory of Train Operators

Table 200

Sundays

London → Dartford and Gillingham

Network Diagram - see first page of Table 200

		SE 50	SE 82	SE 84	SE 67	SE 70	SE 50	SE 82	SE 84	SE 67	SE 70	SE 50	SE 82	SE 84	SE 67	SE 70	SE 50		SE 62	SE 80	SE 67	SE 72
London Charing Cross 4	⊖ d	09 49	09 56	10 01		10 16	10 19	10 26	10 31		10 46	10 49	10 56	11 01		11 16	11 19	and at the same minutes past each hour until	17 26	17 31		17 46
London Waterloo (East) 4	⊖ d	09 52	09 59	10 04		10 19	10 22	10 29	10 34		10 49	10 52	10 59	11 04		11 19	11 22		17 29	17 34		17 49
London Cannon Street 4	⊖ d																					
London Bridge 4	⊖ d	09 58	10 04	10 09	10 16	10 24	10 28	10 34	10 39	10 46	10 54	10 58	11 04	11 09	11 16	11 24	11 28		17 34	17 39	17 46	17 54
Deptford	d			10 14					10 44					11 14						17 44		
Greenwich 4	⛴ d		10 11	10 16				10 41	10 46				11 11	11 16						17 46		
Maze Hill	d			10 20					10 50					11 20						17 50		
Westcombe Park	d			10 22					10 52					11 22						17 52		
London Victoria 15	⊖ d																					
Denmark Hill 4	d																					
Peckham Rye 4	d																					
Nunhead 4	d																					
New Cross 4	⊖ d	10 03				10 29	10 33				10 59	11 04				11 29	11 34					17 59
St Johns	d																					
Lewisham 4	⛴ d	10 07			10 23	10 33	10 37			10 53	11 03	11 08			11 23	11 33	11 38		17 43		17 53	18 03
Blackheath 4	d				10 26	10 36				10 56	11 06				11 26	11 36			17 45		17 56	18 06
Kidbrooke	d					10 39					11 09					11 39						18 09
Eltham	d					10 43					11 13					11 43						18 13
Falconwood	d					10 45					11 15					11 45						18 15
Welling	d					10 48					11 18					11 48						18 18
Bexleyheath	d					10 50					11 20					11 50						18 20
Barnehurst 4	d					10 53					11 23					11 53						18 23
Hither Green 4	d	10 11					10 41					11 12					11 42					
Lee	d	10 13					10 43					11 14					11 44					
Mottingham	d	10 16					10 46					11 17					11 47					
New Eltham	d	10 19					10 49					11 20					11 50					
Sidcup 4	d	10 22					10 52					11 23					11 53					
Albany Park	d	10 24					10 54					11 25					11 55					
Bexley	d	10 26					10 56					11 27					11 57					
Crayford	d	10 29					10 59					11 30					12 00					
Charlton 4	d		10 17	10 24	10 30			10 47	10 54	11 00			11 17	11 24	11 30				17 50	17 54	18 00	
Woolwich Dockyard	d			10 26					10 56					11 26						17 56		
Woolwich Arsenal 4	d		10 22	10 29	10 35			10 52	10 59	11 05			11 22	11 29	11 35				17 55	17 59	18 05	
Plumstead	d			10 31	10a37				11 01	11a07				11 31	11a37					18 01	18a07	
Abbey Wood	d		10 27	10 35				10 57	11 05				11 27	11 35					17 59	18 05		
Belvedere	d			10 37					11 07					11 37						18 07		
Erith	d			10 40					11 10					11 40						18 10		
Slade Green 4	d			10 43					11 13					11 43						18 13		
Dartford 4	a	10 33	10 35	10 47		10 59	11 03	11 05	11 17		11 29	11 34	11 35	11 47		11 59	12 04		18 07	18 17		18 29
	d		10 36	10 48				11 06	11 18				11 36	11 48					18 07			18 30
Stone Crossing	d			10 52					11 22					11 52								18 34
Greenhithe for Bluewater	d		10 41	10 54				11 11	11 24				11 41	11 54					18 12			18 36
Swanscombe	d			10 57					11 27					11 57								18 39
Northfleet	d			10 59					11 29					11 59								18 41
Gravesend 4	d		10 48	11a02				11 18	11a32				11 48	12a02					18 18			18 45
Higham	d		10 54					11 24					11 54						18 24			18 51
Strood 4	d		10 59					11 29					11 59						18 29			18 56
Maidstone West 4	a							*11 57*											*18 55*			
Rochester 4	d		11 03					11 33					12 03						18 33			19 00
Chatham 4	d		11 06					11 36					12 06						18 36			19 02
Gillingham (Kent) 4	a		11 09					11 39					12 09						18 39			19 06

For general notes see front of timetable
For details of catering facilities see
Directory of Train Operators

Table 200

Sundays

London → Dartford and Gillingham

Network Diagram - see first page of Table 200

Station		SE 50	SE 60	SE 80	SE 70	SE 50	SE 62	SE 80	SE 72	SE 50	SE 60	SE 80	SE 70	SE 50	SE 62	SE 80	SE 72	SE 50	SE 80	SE 70	SE 50	SE 62	SE 80	SE 72	SE 50
London Charing Cross [4]	⊖ d	17 49	17 56	18 01	18 16	18 19	18 26	18 31	18 46	18 49	18 56	19 01	19 16	19 19	19 26	19 31	19 46	19 49	20 01	20 16	20 19	20 26	20 31	20 46	20 49
London Waterloo (East) [4]	⊖ d	17 52	17 59	18 04	18 19	18 22	18 29	18 34	18 49	18 52	18 59	19 04	19 19	19 22	19 29	19 34	19 49	19 52	20 04	20 19	20 22	20 29	20 34	20 49	20 52
London Cannon Street [4]	⊖ d																								
London Bridge [4]	⊖ d	17 58	18 04	18 09	18 24	18 28	18 34	18 39	18 54	18 58	19 04	19 09	19 24	19 28	19 34	19 39	19 54	19 58	20 09	20 24	20 28	20 34	20 39	20 54	20 58
Deptford	d			18 14				18 44				19 14				19 44			20 14				20 44		
Greenwich [4]	d			18 16				18 46				19 16				19 46			20 16				20 46		
Maze Hill	d			18 20				18 50				19 20				19 50			20 20				20 50		
Westcombe Park	d			18 22				18 52				19 22				19 52			20 22				20 52		
London Victoria [15]	⊖ d																								
Denmark Hill [4]	d																								
Peckham Rye [4]	d																								
Nunhead [4]	d																								
New Cross [4]	⊖ d	18 04			18 29	18 34			18 59	19 04			19 29	19 33			19 59	20 03		20 29	20 33			20 59	21 03
St Johns	d																								
Lewisham [4]	d	18 08	18 13		18 33	18 38	18 43		19 03	19 08	19 13		19 33	19 37	19 43		20 03	20 07		20 33	20 37	20 43		21 03	21 07
Blackheath [4]	d		18 15		18 36		18 45		19 06		19 15		19 36		19 45		20 06			20 36		20 45		21 06	
Kidbrooke	d				18 39				19 09				19 39				20 09			20 39				21 09	
Eltham	d				18 43				19 13				19 43				20 13			20 43				21 13	
Falconwood	d				18 45				19 15				19 45				20 15			20 45				21 15	
Welling	d				18 48				19 18				19 48				20 18			20 48				21 18	
Bexleyheath	d				18 50				19 20				19 50				20 20			20 50				21 20	
Barnehurst [4]	d				18 53				19 23				19 53				20 23			20 53				21 23	
Hither Green [4]	d	18 12				18 42				19 12				19 41				20 11			20 41				21 11
Lee	d	18 14				18 44				19 14				19 43				20 13			20 43				21 13
Mottingham	d	18 17				18 47				19 17				19 46				20 16			20 46				21 16
New Eltham	d	18 19				18 50				19 20				19 49				20 19			20 49				21 19
Sidcup [4]	d	18 23				18 53				19 23				19 52				20 22			20 52				21 22
Albany Park	d	18 25				18 55				19 25				19 54				20 24			20 54				21 24
Bexley	d	18 27				18 57				19 27				19 56				20 26			20 56				21 26
Crayford	d	18 30				19 00				19 30				19 59				20 29			20 59				21 29
Charlton [4]	d		18 20	18 24			18 50	18 54			19 20	19 24			19 50	19 54			20 24			20 50	20 54		
Woolwich Dockyard	d			18 26				18 56				19 26				19 56			20 26				20 56		
Woolwich Arsenal [4]	d		18 25	18 29			18 55	18 59			19 25	19 29			19 55	19 59			20 29			20 55	20 59		
Plumstead	d			18 31				19 01				19 31				20 01			20 31				21 01		
Abbey Wood	d		18 29	18 35			18 59	19 05			19 29	19 35			19 59	20 05			20 35			20 59	21 05		
Belvedere	d			18 37				19 07				19 37				20 07			20 37				21 07		
Erith	d			18 40				19 10				19 40				20 10			20 40				21 10		
Slade Green [4]	d			18 43				19 13				19 43				20 13			20 43				21 13		
Dartford [4]	a	18 34	18 37	18 47	18 59	19 04	19 07	19 17	19 29	19 34	19 37	19 47	19 59	20 03	20 07	20 17	20 29	20 33	20 47	20 59	21 03	21 07	21 17	21 29	21 33
	d						19 07		19 30						20 07		20 30					21 07		21 30	
Stone Crossing	d								19 34								20 34							21 34	
Greenhithe for Bluewater	d						19 12		19 36						20 12		20 36					21 12		21 36	
Swanscombe	d								19 39								20 39							21 39	
Northfleet	d								19 41								20 41							21 41	
Gravesend [4]	d						19 18		19 45						20 18		20 45					21 18		21 45	
Higham	d						19 24		19 51						20 24		20 51					21 24		21 51	
Strood [4]	d						19 29		19 56						20 29		20 56					21 29		21 56	
Maidstone West [4]	a						*19 55*								*20 55*							*21 55*			
Rochester [4]	d						19 33		20 00						20 33		21 00					21 33		22 00	
Chatham [4]	d						19 36		20 02						20 36		21 02					21 36		22 02	
Gillingham (Kent) [4]	a						19 39		20 06						20 39		21 06					21 39		22 06	

For general notes see front of timetable
For details of catering facilities see
Directory of Train Operators

Table 200

Sundays

London → Dartford and Gillingham

Network Diagram - see first page of Table 200

		SE 80	SE 70	SE 50	SE 62	SE 55 A	SE 80	SE 72	SE 50	SE 80	SE 70	SE 50	SE 62	SE 80	SE 72	SE 50	SE 80	SE 70	SE 50	SE 62	SE 80	SE 70	SE 50
London Charing Cross 4	⊖ d	21 01	21 16	21 19	21 26		21 31	21 46	21 49	22 01	22 16	22 19	22 26	22 31	22 46	22 49	23 01	23 16	23 19	23 26	23 31	23 46	23 49
London Waterloo (East) 4	⊖ d	21 04	21 19	21 22	21 29		21 34	21 49	21 52	22 04	22 19	22 22	22 29	22 34	22 49	22 52	23 04	23 19	23 22	23 29	23 34	23 49	23 52
London Cannon Street 4	⊖ d																						
London Bridge 4	⊖ d	21 09	21 24	21 28	21 34		21 39	21 54	21 58	22 09	22 24	22 28	22 34	22 39	22 54	22 58	23 09	23 24	23 28	23 34	23 39	23 54	23 58
Deptford	d	21 14					21 44			22 14				22 44			23 14				23 44		
Greenwich 4	⛴ d	21 16					21 46			22 16				22 46			23 16				23 46		
Maze Hill	d	21 20					21 50			22 20				22 50			23 20				23 50		
Westcombe Park	d	21 22					21 52			22 22				22 52			23 22				23 52		
London Victoria 15	⊖ d																						
Denmark Hill 4	d																						
Peckham Rye 4	d																						
Nunhead 4	d																						
New Cross 4	⊖ d		21 29	21 33				21 59	22 03		22 29	22 33			22 59	23 03		23 29	23 33			23 59	00 03
St Johns	d																						
Lewisham 4	⛴ d		21 33	21 37	21 43			22 03	22 07		22 33	22 37	22 43		23 03	23 07		23 33	23 37	23 42		00 03	00 07
Blackheath 4	d		21 36		21 45			22 06			22 36		22 45		23 06			23 36		23 45		00 06	
Kidbrooke	d		21 39					22 09			22 39				23 09			23 39				00 09	
Eltham	d		21 43					22 13			22 43				23 13			23 43				00 13	
Falconwood	d		21 45					22 15			22 45				23 15			23 45				00 15	
Welling	d		21 48					22 18			22 48				23 18			23 48				00 18	
Bexleyheath	d		21 50					22 20			22 50				23 20			23 50				00 20	
Barnehurst 4	d		21 53					22 23			22 53				23 23			23 53				00 23	
Hither Green 4	d			21 41					22 11			22 41				23 11			23 41				00 11
Lee	d			21 43					22 13			22 43				23 13			23 43				00 13
Mottingham	d			21 46					22 16			22 46				23 16			23 46				00 16
New Eltham	d			21 49					22 19			22 49				23 19			23 49				00 19
Sidcup 4	d			21 52					22 22			22 52				23 22			23 52				00 22
Albany Park	d			21 54					22 24			22 54				23 24			23 54				00 24
Bexley	d			21 56					22 26			22 56				23 26			23 56				00 26
Crayford	d			21 59					22 29			22 59				23 29			23 59				00 29
Charlton 4	d	21 24			21 50		21 54			22 24			22 50	22 54			23 24			23 49	23 54		
Woolwich Dockyard	d	21 26					21 56			22 26				22 56			23 26				23 56		
Woolwich Arsenal 4	d	21 29			21 55		21 59			22 29			22 55	22 59			23 29			23 53	23 59		
Plumstead	d	21 31					22 01			22 31				23 01			23 31				00 01		
Abbey Wood	d	21 35			21 59		22 05			22 35			22 59	23 05			23 35			23 57	00 05		
Belvedere	d	21 37					22 07			22 37				23 07			23 37				00 07		
Erith	d	21 40					22 10			22 40				23 10			23 40				00 10		
Slade Green 4	d	21 43					22 13			22 43				23 13			23 43				00 13		
Dartford 4	a	21 47	21 59	22 03	22 07		22 17	22 29	22 33	22 47	22 59	23 03	23 07	23 17	23 29	23 33	23 47	23 59	00 03	00 05	00 17	00 29	00 33
	d				22 07			22 30					23 07		23 30					00 06			
Stone Crossing	d							22 34							23 34								
Greenhithe for Bluewater	d				22 12			22 36					23 12		23 36					00 11			
Swanscombe	d							22 39							23 39								
Northfleet	d							22 41							23 41								
Gravesend 4	d				22 18			22 45					23 18		23 45					00 18			
Higham	d				22 24			22 51					23 24		23 51					00 25			
Strood 4	d				22 29	22 37		22 56					23 29		23 56					00 30			
Maidstone West 4	a																						
Rochester 4	d				22 33	22 40		23 00					23 33		00 01					00 33			
Chatham 4	d				22 36	22 43		23 02					23 36		00 02					00 36			
Gillingham (Kent) 4	a				22 39	22 46		23 06					23 39		00 06					00 39			

For general notes see front of timetable
For details of catering facilities see
Directory of Train Operators

A From Three Bridges (Table 209)

For details of Bank Holiday service alterations please see first page of Table 195

Gillingham and Dartford → London

Network Diagram - see first page of Table 200

Miles	Miles	Miles	Miles	Miles			SE	SE	SE	SE	SE	SE	SE	SE	SE	SE	SE	SE	SE	SE	SE	SE	SE	SE
							MX																	
							58	52	50	80	70	82	55	50	82	70	62	50	84	77	70	62	61	70
							A						B										C	
0	—	—	0	—	**Gillingham (Kent)** [4]	d	00 07	04 12				04 52	04 56				05 22					05 52	06 03	
1¾	—	—	1¾	—	**Chatham** [4]	d	00 11	04 16				04 56	04 59				05 26					05 56	06 07	
2¼	—	—	2¼	—	Rochester [4]	d	00 13	04 18				04 58	05 01				05 28					05 58	06 09	
—	—	—	—	—	Maidstone West [4]	d																		
3¼	—	—	3¼	—	Strood [4]	d	00 17	04 23				05 03	05a05				05 33					06 03	06a13	
6	—	—	6	—	Higham	d	00 22	04 28				05 08					05 38					06 08		
10½	—	—	10½	—	**Gravesend** [4]	d	00 28	04 35				05 15					05 45		05 48			06 15		
12½	—	—	12½	—	Northfleet	d						05 19							05 51					
13¼	—	—	13¼	—	Swanscombe	d						05 21							05 53					
14½	—	—	14½	—	Greenhithe for Bluewater	d	00 34					05 24					05 50		05 56			06 20		
15¼	—	—	15¼	—	Stone Crossing	d						05 27							05 58					
17¼	0	0	17¼	0	**Dartford** [4]	a	00 41	04 44				05 30					05 56		06 02			06 25		
—	—	—	—	—		d	00 42	04 46	05 02	05 12	05 18	05 32		05 34		05 48	05 58	06 00	06 02		06 22	06 26		
19¼	2	—	—	—	Slade Green [4]	d				05 16		05 36							06 06					
20½	3¼	—	—	—	Erith	d				05 18		05 38							06 08					
21¾	4½	—	—	—	Belvedere	d				05 21		05 41							06 11					
23¼	6	—	—	—	Abbey Wood	d				05 24		05 44					06 07		06 14			06 35		
24¾	7½	—	—	—	Plumstead	d				05 27		05 47			←				06 17					
25¼	8	—	—	—	**Woolwich Arsenal** [4]	d				05 30		05 50			05 50		06 12		06 20			06 40		
26	8¾	—	—	—	Woolwich Dockyard	d						→							06 22					
27	9¾	—	—	—	Charlton [4]	d				05 35					05 55				06 25					
—	—	—	19	—	Crayford	d		04 49	05 05					05 37				06 03						
—	—	—	20½	—	Bexley	d		04 52	05 08					05 40				06 06						
—	—	—	21½	—	Albany Park	d		04 54	05 10					05 42				06 08						
—	—	—	22½	—	Sidcup [4]	d		04 57	05 13					05 45				06 11						
—	—	—	24	—	New Eltham	d		05 00	05 16					05 48				06 14						
—	—	—	25	—	Mottingham	d		05 02	05 18					05 50				06 16						
—	—	—	26½	—	Lee	d		05 05	05 21					05 53				06 19						
—	—	—	27¼	—	Hither Green [4]	d		05 08	05 23					05 55				06b25						
—	—	3	—	3	Barnehurst [4]	d					05 24					05 54				06 12	06c32			
—	—	4¼	—	4¼	Bexleyheath	d					05 27					05 57				06 15	06 35			←
—	—	5¾	—	5¾	Welling	d					05 30					06 00				06 18	06 38			06 38
—	—	6¾	—	6¾	Falconwood	d					05 33					06 03				06 21	→			06 41
—	—	8	—	8	Eltham	d					05 36					06 06				06 24				06 44
—	—	9	—	9	Kidbrooke	d					05 39					06 09				06 27				06 47
29	—	10	—	10	Blackheath [4]	d					05 42					06 12	06 20			06 30		06 48		06 52
30	—	11	28½	11	Lewisham [4]	d		05 13	05 28		05e48			06 00		06 16	06 24	06 30		06 34		06 52		06 56
—	—	11½	29	—	St Johns	d												06 32						
—	—	12¼	29¾	—	New Cross [4]	⊖ d		05 16	05 32		05 52			06 04		06 20		06 34		06 38				
—	—	—	—	12¾	Nunhead [4]	d																		
—	—	—	—	13½	Peckham Rye [4]	d																		
—	—	—	—	14¼	Denmark Hill [4]	d																		
—	—	—	—	18½	**London Victoria** [15]	⊖ a	01 13																	
—	10½	—	—	—	Westcombe Park	d				05 37					05 57				06 27					
—	11	—	—	—	Maze Hill	d				05 39					05 59				06 29					
—	12	—	—	—	Greenwich [4]	d				05 43					06 03				06 33					
—	12½	—	—	—	Deptford	d				05 45					06 05				06 35					
34¼	15½	15¼	32¾	—	**London Bridge** [4]	⊖ a		05 22	05 38	05 53	05 58			06 10	06 13	06 26	06 33	06 40	06 43	06 43		07 01		07 06
—	16¼	—	—	—	**London Cannon Street** [4]	⊖ a														06 47				
35¼	—	16¼	33¾	—	**London Waterloo (East)** [4]	⊖ a		05 27	05 43	05 58	06 03			06 15	06 18	06 31	06 38	06 45	06 48			07 06		07 11
36	—	17	34½	—	**London Charing Cross** [4]	⊖ a		05 31	05 47	06 02	06 06			06 18	06 21	06 34	06 41	06 48	06 51			07 10		07 15

For general notes see front of timetable
For details of catering facilities see Directory of Train Operators

A From Faversham (Table 212)
B To Redhill (Table 209)
C To Paddock Wood (Table 209)
b Arr. 0622
c Arr. 0628
e Arr. 0545

For details of Bank Holiday service alterations please see first page of Table 195

Gillingham and Dartford → London

Network Diagram - see first page of Table 200

		SE 40	SE 80	SE 55	SE 87	SE 40	SE 70	SE 62	SE 46	SE 77	SE 80	SE 51	SE 74	SE 66	SE 83	SE 77	SE 18	SE 46	SE 80	SE 87	SE 51	SE 74	SE 63
Gillingham (Kent) 4	d							06 22							06 37								06 53
Chatham 4	d							06 26							06 41								06 57
Rochester 4	d							06 28							06 43								06 59
Maidstone West 4	d														*06 20*								
Strood 4	d							06 33							06 48								07 06
Higham	d							06 38							06 53								07 10
Gravesend 4	d			06 20				06 45					06 48		07 00							07 11	07 18
Northfleet	d			06 24									06 52									07 15	
Swanscombe	d			06 26									06 54									07 17	
Greenhithe for Bluewater	d			06 29				06 50					06 57		07 06							07 20	07 24
Stone Crossing	d			06 31									06 59									07 22	
Dartford 4	a			06 36				06 55					07 03		07 11							07 26	07 29
	d	06 28	06 32	06 37		06 45	06 48	06 56			07 00	07 02	07 04		07 12				07 16		07 24	07 26	07 30
Slade Green 4	d		06 36		06 46						07 04			07 08					07 20	07 26			
Erith	d		06 38		06 48						07 06			07 10					07 22	07 28			
Belvedere	d		06 41		06 51						07 09			07 13					07 25	07 31			
Abbey Wood	d		06 44		06 54			07 05			07 12			07 16	07 21				07 28	07 34			07 39
Plumstead	d		06 47		06 57						07 15			07 19					07 31	07 37			
Woolwich Arsenal 4	d		06 50		07 00			07 10			07 18			07 22	07 26				07 34	07 40			07 44
Woolwich Dockyard	d		06 52		07 02						07 20			07 24					07 36	07 42			
Charlton 4	d		06 55		07 05						07 23			07 27					07 39	07 45			
Crayford	d	06 31		06 41		06 49			07 02			07 06						07 22			07 28		
Bexley	d	06 34		06 44		06 52			07 05			07 09						07 25			07 31		
Albany Park	d	06 36		06 47		06 55			07 08			07 12						07 28			07 34		
Sidcup 4	d	06 39		06 50		06 58			07 11			07 15						07 31			07 37		
New Eltham	d	06 42		06 53		07 01			07 14			07 18						07 34			07 40		
Mottingham	d	06 44		06 55		07 03			07 16			07 20						07 36			07 42		
Lee	d	06 47		06 58		07 06			07 19			07 23						07 39			07 45		
Hither Green 4	d	06 52		07 02		07 10			07 22			07 26						07 42			07 49		
Barnehurst 4	d						06 54			07 03			07 10			07 19	07 23					07 33	
Bexleyheath	d						06 57			07 06			07 13			07 22	07 26					07 36	
Welling	d						07 00			07 09			07 16			07 25	07 29					07 39	
Falconwood	d						07 03			07 11			07 19			07 27	07 31					07 41	
Eltham	d						07 06			07 14			07 22			07 30	07 34					07 44	
Kidbrooke	d						07 09			07 17			07 25			07 33	07 37					07 47	
Blackheath 4	d						07 12	07 18		07 21				07 32		07 38	07 41					07 51	07 54
Lewisham 4	d			07 08		07 15	07 18	07 22		07 25		07 32		07 38		07 41	07 44				07 54	07 56	
St Johns	d	06 56		07 10						07 27						07 44							
New Cross 4	⊖ d	06 58		07 12						07 29		07 36				07 46					07 59		
Nunhead 4	d																07 52						
Peckham Rye 4	d																07 55						
Denmark Hill 4	d																07 59						
London Victoria 15	⊖ a																08 11						
Westcombe Park	d		06 57		07 07						07 25								07 41	07 47			
Maze Hill	d		06 59		07 09						07 27								07 43	07 49			
Greenwich 4	d		07 03		07 13						07 31								07 47	07 53			
Deptford	d		07 05		07 15						07 33								07 49	07 55			
London Bridge 4	⊖ a	07 08	07 13	07 17	07 21	07 25	07 27	07 30	07 33	07 34	07 40	07 41			07 44	07 52		07 53	07 57	08 02	08 04	08 06	08 06
London Cannon Street 4	⊖ a			07 24	07 28					07 41		07 48			07 51	07 57				08 09	08 11		08 13
London Waterloo (East) 4	⊖ a	07 13	07 19			07 30	07 33	07 36	07 39		07 46		07 44	07 51				07 58	08 02			08 11	
London Charing Cross 4	⊖ a	07 17	07 24			07 34	07 37	07 40	07 43		07 51		07 49	07 56				08 03	08 07			08 17	

For general notes see front of timetable
For details of catering facilities see Directory of Train Operators

For details of Bank Holiday service alterations please see first page of Table 195

Gillingham and Dartford → London

Network Diagram - see first page of Table 200

		SE 77	SE 43	SE 86 A	SE 78	SE 76	SE 46	SE 86	SE 81	SE 70	SE 81	SE 57	SE 65	SE 77	SE 42	SE 20	SE 78	SE 74	SE 46	SE 86	SE 87	SE 74	SE 63
Gillingham (Kent) 4	d														07 13	07 28							07 33
Chatham 4	d														07 17	07 32							07 37
Rochester 4	d														07 19	07 34							07 39
Maidstone West 4	d														*06 54*								
Strood 4	d		07 10												07b28			07 36					07 46
Higham	d		07 14												07 32			07 40					07 50
Gravesend 4	d		07 22										07 34		07 40			07 48				07 52	07 58
Northfleet	d												07 38									07 56	
Swanscombe	d												07 40									07 58	
Greenhithe for Bluewater	d		07 28										07 43		07 46			07 54				08 00	08 04
Stone Crossing	d												07 45									08 02	
Dartford 4	a		07 33										07 49		07 51			07 59				08 06	08 09
	d		07 34		07 36				07 42	07 44			07 50		07 52		07 56	08 00			08 02	08 06	08 10
Slade Green 4	d			07 39				07 40	07 46				07 54							08 00	08 06		
Erith	d							07 42	07 48											08 02	08 08		
Belvedere	d							07 45	07 51											08 05	08 11		
Abbey Wood	d							07 48	07 54				08 01							08 08	08 14		08 19
Plumstead	d							07 51	07 57		←									08 11	08 17		
Woolwich Arsenal 4	d							07 54	08 00		08 00		08 06							08 14	08 20		08 24
Woolwich Dockyard	d							07 56	→		08 02									08 16	08 22		→
Charlton 4	d							07 59			08 05									08 19	08 25		
Crayford	d		07 38	07a46								07 48			07 56								
Bexley	d		07 41									07 51			07 59								
Albany Park	d		07 44									07 54			08 02								
Sidcup 4	d		07 47				07 51					07 57			08 05				08 11				
New Eltham	d		07 50				07 54					08 00			08 08				08 14				
Mottingham	d						07 56					08 02							08 16				
Lee	d						07 59					08 05							08 19				
Hither Green 4	d						08 02					08 09							08 22				
Barnehurst 4	d	07 39			07 43	07 47				07 50				07 59			08 03	08 07		07 56		08 13	
Bexleyheath	d	07 42			07 46	07 50				07 53				08 02			08 06	08 10				08 16	
Welling	d	07 45			07 49	07 53				07 56				08 05			08 09	08 13				08 19	
Falconwood	d	07 47			07 51	07 55				07 59				08 07			08 11	08 15				08 21	
Eltham	d	07 50			07 54	07 58				08 02				08 10			08 14	08 18				→	
Kidbrooke	d	07 53			07 57	08 01				08 05				08 13			08 17	08 21					
Blackheath 4	d	07 58			08 01	08 05				08 08			08 14	08 18			08 21						
Lewisham 4	d	08 01			08 04					08 12		08 14	08 18	08 21			08 24						
St Johns	d	08 04												08 24									
New Cross 4	⊖ d	08 06										08 18		08 26									
Nunhead 4	d				08 10												08 29						
Peckham Rye 4	d				08 12												08 32						
Denmark Hill 4	d				08 15											08 27	08 35						
London Victoria 15	⊖ a				08 28											08 38	08 48						
Westcombe Park	d							08 01			08 07									08 21	08 27		
Maze Hill	d							08 03			08 09									08 23	08 29		
Greenwich 4	d							08 07			08 13									08 27	08 33		
Deptford	d							08 09			08 15									08 29	08 35		
London Bridge 4	⊖ a	08 12					08 13	08 18		08 21	08 23	08 25	08 27	08 33					08 33	08 38	08 41		
London Cannon Street 4	⊖ a	08 18									08 30	08 32	08 34	08 39							08 48		
London Waterloo (East) 4	⊖ a		08 08			08 17	08 19	08 23		08 27					08 29			08 37	08 39	08 43			
London Charing Cross 4	⊖ a		08 13			08 23	08 24	08 28		08 32					08 34			08 42	08 44	08 48			

For general notes see front of timetable
For details of catering facilities see Directory of Train Operators

A From London Charing Cross
b Arr. 0724

For details of Bank Holiday service alterations please see first page of Table 195

Gillingham and Dartford → London

Network Diagram - see first page of Table 200

		SE 40	SE 57	SE 74	SE 63	SE 77	SE 18	SE 64	SE 46	SE 86	SE 57		SE 70	SE 81	SE 40	SE 63	SE 77	SE 86	SE 78	SE 72	SE 47	SE 81	SE 54		SE 81
Gillingham (Kent) 4	d																			08 15					
Chatham 4	d																			08 19					
Rochester 4	d															07 58				08 21					
Maidstone West 4	d							*07 27*												*08 02*					
Strood 4	d							07 56								08b08				08 28					
Higham	d							08 00								08 12				08 32					
Gravesend 4	d							08 08								08 20				08 40					
Northfleet	d															08 23									
Swanscombe	d															08 25									
Greenhithe for Bluewater	d							08 14								08 28				08 46					
Stone Crossing	d															08 30									
Dartford 4	a							08 19								08 34				08 52					
	d	08 12						08 20			08 24		08 26		08 32	08 35			08 43	08 53		08 57	09 01		
Slade Green 4	d						08 17	08 24		08 18				08 30		08 39		08 43				09 03			
Erith	d									08 20				08 32				08 45				09 05			
Belvedere	d									08 23				08 35				08 48				09 08			
Abbey Wood	d							08 31		08 26				08 38		08 45		08 51				09 11			
Plumstead	d				←					08 29				08 41				08 54				09 14			←
Woolwich Arsenal 4	d				08 24			08 36		08 32				08 44		08 50		08 57				09 17			09 17
Woolwich Dockyard	d									08 34				08 46				08 59				→			09 19
Charlton 4	d									08 37				08 49				09 02							09 22
Crayford	d	08 16	08 08								08 28				08 36		08 35				09 00		09 04		
Bexley	d	08 19	08 11								08 31				08 39						09 02		09 07		
Albany Park	d	08 22	08 14								08 34				08 42						09 05		09 09		
Sidcup 4	d	08 25	08 17						08 31		08 37				08 45						09 08		09 12		
New Eltham	d	08 28	08 20						08 34		08 40				08 48						09 12		09 15		
Mottingham	d		08 22						08 36		08 42				08 50						09 14		09 17		
Lee	d		08 25						08 39		08 45				08 53						09 17		09 20		
Hither Green 4	d		08 29						08 42		08 49				08 56						09 20		09 23		
Barnehurst 4	d					08 19	08 23						08 33				08 43		08 49	08 59					
Bexleyheath	d					08 22	08 26						08 36				08 46		08 52	09 02					
Welling	d			←		08 25	08 29						08 39				08 49		08 55	09 05					
Falconwood	d			08 21		08 27	08 31						08 41				08 51		08 57	09 07					
Eltham	d			08 24		08 31	08 34						08 44				08 54		09 00	09 10					
Kidbrooke	d			08 27		08 34	08 37						08 47				08 57		09 03	09 13					
Blackheath 4	d			08 31	08 34	08 38	08 41	08 44					08 51			08 58	09 01		09 07	09 17					
Lewisham 4	🚋 d		08 34	08 36		08 41	08 44				08 54		08 56				09 04		09 10	09 20			09 28		
St Johns	d					08 44											09 06				09 24				
New Cross 4	⊖ d		08 38			08 46					08 58						09 08				09 26				
Nunhead 4	d						08 52												09 15						
Peckham Rye 4	d						08 54												09 18						
Denmark Hill 4	d						08 59												09 20						
London Victoria 15	⊖ a						09 11												09 32						
Westcombe Park	d									08 39				08 51				09 04							09 24
Maze Hill	d									08 41				08 53				09 06							09 26
Greenwich 4	🚋 d									08 45				08 57				09 10							09 30
Deptford	d									08 47				08 59				09 12							09 32
London Bridge 4	⊖ a	08 42	08 44	08 46	08 47	08 52			08 53	08 57	09 04		09 04	09 07	09 07	09 11	09 14	09 21		09 29	09 31		09 36		09 39
London Cannon Street 4	⊖ a		08 51		08 54	08 59					09 10			09 14		09 18	09 21				09 38				09 45
London Waterloo (East) 4	⊖ a	08 47		08 51				08 57	08 59	09 03			09 09		09 13			09 26		09 34			09 42		
London Charing Cross 4	⊖ a	08 52		08 56				09 03	09 04	09 08			09 14		09 18			09 31		09 39			09 47		

For general notes see front of timetable
For details of catering facilities see Directory of Train Operators

b Arr. 0802

For details of Bank Holiday service alterations please see first page of Table 195

Gillingham and Dartford → London

Network Diagram - see first page of Table 200

		SE 70	SE 87	SE 62	SE 47	SE 78	SE 81	SE 54	SE 70	SE 47	SE 82	SE 47	SE 67	SE 81	SE 78	SE 54	SE 70	SE 87 A	SE 82	SE 47 A	SE 67	SE 81	SE 78	SE 54
Gillingham (Kent) 4	d										09 14								09 44					
Chatham 4	d										09 18								09 48					
Rochester 4	d			08 52							09 20								09 50					
Maidstone West 4	d			*08 30*							*09 00*								*09 29*					
Strood 4	d			08 57							09 25								09 55					
Higham	d			09 01							09 29								09 59					
Gravesend 4	d	08 50		09 08				09 14			09 36					09 42			10 06					10 12
Northfleet	d	08 54						09 18								09 46								10 16
Swanscombe	d	08 56						09 20								09 48								10 18
Greenhithe for Bluewater	d	08 59		09 13				09 23			09 41					09 51			10 11					10 21
Stone Crossing	d	09 01						09 25								09 53								10 23
Dartford 4	a	09 06		09 19				09 30			09 46					09 57			10 16					10 29
	d	09 07		09 21		09 24	09 27	09 31	09 35	09 43	09 47			09 49	09 54	10 01	10 05		10 17			10 19	10 24	10 31
Slade Green 4	d		09 15				09 33							09 53				10 07		10 10		10 23		
Erith	d		09 17				09 35							09 55				10 09				10 25		
Belvedere	d		09 20				09 38							09 58				10 12				10 28		
Abbey Wood	d		09 23	09 29			09 41				09 55			10 01				10 15	10 25			10 31		
Plumstead	d		09 26				09 44						10 01	10 04				10 18			10 31	10 34		
Woolwich Arsenal 4	d		09 29	09 33			09 47				09 59		10 03	10 07				10 21	10 29		10 33	10 37		
Woolwich Dockyard	d		09 31				09 49							10 09				10 23				10 39		
Charlton 4	d		09 34	09 38			09 52				10 04		10 08	10 12				10 26	10 34		10 38	10 42		
Crayford	d				09 24			09 35		09b50						10 05				10 20				10 35
Bexley	d				09 27			09 38		09 52						10 08				10 22				10 38
Albany Park	d				09 29			09 40		09 55						10 10				10 25				10 40
Sidcup 4	d				09 32			09 43		09 58		←				10 13				10 28				10 43
New Eltham	d				09 35			09 46		10 01		10 01				10 16				10 31				10 46
Mottingham	d				09 37			09 48		→		10 03				10 18				10 33				10 48
Lee	d				09 40			09 51				10 06				10 21				10 36				10 51
Hither Green 4	d				09 44			09 54				10 10				10 24				10 40				10 54
Barnehurst 4	d	09 13				09 29			09 41						10 00		10 11						10 30	
Bexleyheath	d	09 16				09 32			09 44						10 02		10 14						10 32	
Welling	d	09 19				09 35			09 47						10 05		10 17						10 35	
Falconwood	d	09 21				09 37			09 49						10 08		10 19						10 38	
Eltham	d	09 24				09 40			09 52						10 11		10 22						10 41	
Kidbrooke	d	09 27				09 43			09 55						10 14		10 25						10 44	
Blackheath 4	d	09 31		09 43		09 47			09 59				10 13		10 17		10 29				10 43		10 47	
Lewisham 4	d	09 36		09 46		09 51		09 59	10 02				10 16		10 21	10 29	10 32				10 46		10 51	10 59
St Johns	d	09 38			09 48							10 14								10 45				
New Cross 4	⊖ d	09 40			09 50							10 16	10 20							10 47	10 50			
Nunhead 4	d					09 56									10 26								10 56	
Peckham Rye 4	d					09 58									10 28								10 58	
Denmark Hill 4	d					10 01									10 31								11 01	
London Victoria 15	⊖ a					10 12									10 42								11 12	
Westcombe Park	d		09 36				09 54							10 14				10 28				10 44		
Maze Hill	d		09 38				09 56							10 16				10 30				10 46		
Greenwich 4	d		09 42				10 00				10 10			10 20				10 34	10 40			10 50		
Deptford	d		09 44				10 02							10 22				10 36				10 52		
London Bridge 4	⊖ a	09 49	09 50	09 54	09 56		10 09		10 10		10 19	10 21	10 26	10 29		10 37	10 40	10 43	10 49	10 53	10 56	10 59		11 07
London Cannon Street 4	⊖ a		09 57		10 01		10 13					10 27	10 30	10 33				10 47		10 57	11 00	11 03		
London Waterloo (East) 4	⊖ a	09 54		09 59				10 11	10 16		10 24					10 42	10 45		10 54					11 12
London Charing Cross 4	⊖ a	09 59		10 05				10 14	10 20		10 28					10 47	10 50		10 58					11 17

For general notes see front of timetable
For details of catering facilities see Directory of Train Operators

A From London Cannon Street (Table 199)
b Arr. 0947

Table 200

Mondays to Fridays

For details of Bank Holiday service alterations please see first page of Table 195

Gillingham and Dartford → London

Network Diagram - see first page of Table 200

		SE 70	SE 87 A	SE 82	SE 47 A	SE 67	SE 81	SE 78	SE 54	SE 70	SE 47 A	SE 82	SE 47 A	SE 67	SE 81	SE 78	SE 54	SE 70	SE 87 A	SE 82	SE 47 A	SE 67	SE 81
Gillingham (Kent) 4	d			10 14								10 44								11 14			
Chatham 4	d			10 18								10 48								11 18			
Rochester 4	d			10 20								10 50								11 20			
Maidstone West 4	d			*10 00*								*10 28*								*10 58*			
Strood 4	d			10 25								10 55								11 25			
Higham	d			10 29								10 59								11 29			
Gravesend 4	d			10 36					10 42			11 06					11 12			11 36			
Northfleet	d								10 46								11 16						
Swanscombe	d								10 48								11 18						
Greenhithe for Bluewater	d			10 41					10 51			11 11					11 21			11 41			
Stone Crossing	d								10 53								11 23						
Dartford 4	a			10 46					10 57			11 16					11 27			11 46			
	d	10 35		10 47			10 49	10 54	11 01	11 05		11 17			11 19	11 24	11 31	11 35		11 47			11 49
Slade Green 4	d		10 37		10 40		10 53				11 07		11 10		11 23				11 37		11 40		11 53
Erith	d		10 39				10 55				11 09				11 25				11 39				11 55
Belvedere	d		10 42				10 58				11 12				11 28				11 42				11 58
Abbey Wood	d		10 45	10 55			11 01				11 15	11 25			11 31				11 45	11 55			12 01
Plumstead	d		10 48			11 01	11 04				11 18			11 31	11 34				11 48			12 01	12 04
Woolwich Arsenal 4	d		10 51	10 59		11 03	11 07				11 21	11 29		11 33	11 37				11 51	11 59		12 03	12 07
Woolwich Dockyard	d		10 53				11 09				11 23				11 39				11 53				12 09
Charlton 4	d		10 56	11 04		11 08	11 12				11 26	11 34		11 38	11 42				11 56	12 04		12 08	12 12
Crayford	d				10 50				11 05				11 20				11 35				11 50		
Bexley	d				10 52				11 08				11 22				11 38				11 52		
Albany Park	d				10 55				11 10				11 25				11 40				11 55		
Sidcup 4	d				10 58				11 13				11 28				11 43				11 58		
New Eltham	d				11 01				11 16				11 31				11 46				12 01		
Mottingham	d				11 03				11 18				11 33				11 48				12 03		
Lee	d				11 06				11 21				11 36				11 51				12 06		
Hither Green 4	d				11 10				11 24				11 40				11 54				12 10		
Barnehurst 4	d	10 41						11 00		11 11						11 30		11 41					
Bexleyheath	d	10 44						11 02		11 14						11 32		11 44					
Welling	d	10 47						11 05		11 17						11 35		11 47					
Falconwood	d	10 49						11 08		11 19						11 38		11 49					
Eltham	d	10 52						11 11		11 22						11 41		11 52					
Kidbrooke	d	10 55						11 14		11 25						11 44		11 55					
Blackheath 4	d	10 59				11 13		11 17		11 29				11 43		11 47		11 59				12 13	
Lewisham 4	⇌ d	11 02				11 16		11 21	11 29	11 32				11 46		11 51	11 59	12 02				12 16	
St Johns	d				11 15								11 45								12 15		
New Cross 4	⊖ d				11 17	11 20							11 47	11 50							12 17	12 20	
Nunhead 4	d							11 26								11 56							
Peckham Rye 4	d							11 28								11 58							
Denmark Hill 4	d							11 31								12 01							
London Victoria 15	⊖ a							11 42								12 12							
Westcombe Park	d		10 58				11 14				11 28				11 44				11 58				12 14
Maze Hill	d		11 00				11 16				11 30				11 46				12 00				12 16
Greenwich 4	⇌ d		11 04	11 10			11 20				11 34	11 40			11 50				12 04	12 10			12 20
Deptford	d		11 06				11 22				11 36				11 52				12 06				12 22
London Bridge 4	⊖ a	11 10	11 13	11 19	11 23	11 26	11 29		11 37	11 40	11 43	11 49	11 53	11 56	11 59		12 07	12 10	12 13	12 19	12 23	12 26	12 29
London Cannon Street 4	⊖ a		11 17		11 27	11 30	11 33				11 47		11 57	12 00	12 03				12 17		12 27	12 30	12 33
London Waterloo (East) 4	⊖ a	11 15		11 24					11 42	11 45		11 54					12 12	12 15		12 24			
London Charing Cross 4	⊖ a	11 20		11 28					11 47	11 50		11 58					12 17	12 20		12 28			

For general notes see front of timetable
For details of catering facilities see Directory of Train Operators

A From London Cannon Street (Table 199)

For details of Bank Holiday service alterations please see first page of Table 195

Gillingham and Dartford → London

Network Diagram - see first page of Table 200

		SE 78	SE 54	SE 70	SE 87 A		SE 82	SE 47 A	SE 67	SE 81	SE 78	SE 54	SE 70	SE 87 A	SE 82	SE 47 A	SE 66	SE 81	SE 70	SE 55	SE 78	SE 87 A
Gillingham (Kent) 4	d						14 44								15 14							
Chatham 4	d						14 48								15 18							
Rochester 4	d						14 50								15 20							
Maidstone West 4	d						*14 28*								*14 58*							
Strood 4	d						14 55								15 25							
Higham	d						14 59								15 29							
Gravesend 4	d		11 42				15 06					15 12			15 36				15 40			
Northfleet	d		11 46									15 16							15 44			
Swanscombe	d		11 48									15 18							15 46			
Greenhithe for Bluewater	d		11 51				15 11					15 21			15 41				15 49			
Stone Crossing	d		11 53									15 23							15 51			
Dartford 4	a		11 57				15 16					15 27			15 46				15 55			
	d	11 54	12 01	12 05			15 17			15 19	15 24	15 31	15 35		15 47			15 49	15 56	16 01	16 05	
Slade Green 4	d				12 07			15 10		15 23				15 37		15 40		15 53				16 09
Erith	d				12 09					15 25				15 39				15 55				16 11
Belvedere	d				12 12					15 28				15 42				15 58				16 14
Abbey Wood	d				12 15		15 25			15 31				15 45	15 55			16 01				16 17
Plumstead	d				12 18				15 31	15 34				15 48			16 01	16 04				16 20
Woolwich Arsenal 4	d				12 21		15 29		15 33	15 37				15 51	15 59		16 03	16 07				16 23
Woolwich Dockyard	d				12 23					15 39				15 53				16 09				16 25
Charlton 4	d				12 26	and at	15 34		15 38	15 42				15 56	16 04		16 08	16 12				16 28
Crayford	d		12 05			the same		15 20				15 35				15 50				16 05		
Bexley	d		12 08					15 22				15 38				15 52				16 08		
Albany Park	d		12 10			minutes		15 25				15 40				15 55				16 10		
Sidcup 4	d		12 13					15 28				15 43				15 58				16 13		
New Eltham	d		12 16			past		15 31				15 46				16 01				16 16		
Mottingham	d		12 18					15 33				15 48				16 03				16 18		
Lee	d		12 21			each		15 36				15 51				16 06				16 21		
Hither Green 4	d		12 24			hour until		15 40				15 54				16 10				16b28		
Barnehurst 4	d	12 00		12 11							15 30		15 41						16 02		16 11	
Bexleyheath	d	12 02		12 14							15 32		15 44						16 05		16 14	
Welling	d	12 05		12 17							15 35		15 47						16 08		16 17	
Falconwood	d	12 08		12 19							15 38		15 49						16 10		16 19	
Eltham	d	12 11		12 22							15 41		15 52						16 13		16 22	
Kidbrooke	d	12 14		12 25							15 44		15 55						16 16		16 25	
Blackheath 4	d	12 17		12 29					15 43		15 47		15 59				16 13		16 20		16 29	
Lewisham 4	d	12 21	12 29	12 32					15 46		15 51	15 59	16 02				16 16		16 24	16 33	16 35	
St Johns	d							15 45								16 15				16 35		
New Cross 4	⊖ d							15 47	15 50							16 17				16 37		
Nunhead 4	d	12 26									15 56										16 40	
Peckham Rye 4	d	12 28									15 58										16 42	
Denmark Hill 4	d	12 31									16 01										16 46	
London Victoria 15	⊖ a	12 42									16 12										17 03	
Westcombe Park	d				12 28					15 44				15 58				16 14				16 30
Maze Hill	d				12 30					15 46				16 00				16 16				16 32
Greenwich 4	d				12 34		15 40			15 50				16 04	16 10			16 20				16 36
Deptford	d				12 36					15 52				16 06				16 22				16 38
London Bridge 4	⊖ a		12 37	12 40	12 43		15 49	15 53	15 56	15 59		16 07	16 11	16 13	16 19	16 23	16 26	16 29	16 32	16 42		16 46
London Cannon Street 4	⊖ a				12 47			15 57	16 00	16 03				16 17		16 27		16 33	16 36	16 46		16 52
London Waterloo (East) 4	⊖ a		12 42	12 45			15 54					16 13	16 18		16 24		16 32					
London Charing Cross 4	⊖ a		12 47	12 50			15 58					16 17	16 23		16 28		16 36					

For general notes see front of timetable
For details of catering facilities see Directory of Train Operators

A From London Cannon Street (Table 199)
b Arr. 1624

For details of Bank Holiday service alterations please see first page of Table 195

Gillingham and Dartford → London

Network Diagram - see first page of Table 200

		SE 81	SE 63	SE 47 A	SE 71	SE 57	SE 81	SE 44	SE 87		SE 78	SE 81	SE 81	SE 51	SE 63	SE 53	SE 81	SE 55	SE 53	SE 71	SE 87 A		SE 81	SE 63	SE 51
Gillingham (Kent) 4	d		15 44												16 14									16 44	
Chatham 4	d		15 48												16 18									16 48	
Rochester 4	d		15 50												16 20									16 50	
Maidstone West 4	d		*15 28*																					*16 28*	
Strood 4	d		15 55												16 25									16 55	
Higham	d		15 59												16 29									16 59	
Gravesend 4	d		16 08					16 12							16 36			16 42						17 06	
Northfleet	d							16 16										16 46							
Swanscombe	d							16 18										16 48							
Greenhithe for Bluewater	d		16 14					16 21							16 41			16 51						17 11	
Stone Crossing	d							16 23										16 53							
Dartford 4	a		16 20					16 29							16 46			16 57						17 17	
	d	16 15	16 21		16 23		16 29	16 31			16 37			16 43	16 49		16 51	17 01		17 05			17 11	17 19	17 21
Slade Green 4	d			16 10			16 35		16 29				16 42				16 55				17 09		17 15		
Erith	d						16 37		16 31								16 57				17 11		17 17		
Belvedere	d						16 40		16 34								17 00				17 14		17 20		
Abbey Wood	d	16 25	16 29				16 43		16 37				16 49		16 57		17 03				17 17		17 23	17 29	
Plumstead	d						16 46		16 40			←					17 06				17 20		17 26		
Woolwich Arsenal 4	d	16 29	16 33				16 49		16 43			16 49	16 53		17 02		17 09				17 23		17 29	17 34	
Woolwich Dockyard	d						→		16 45			16 51					17 11				17 25		17 31		
Charlton 4	d	16 34	16 38						16 48			16 54	16 58		17 07		17 14				17 28		17 34	17 39	
Crayford	d			16 20				16 35						16 47		16 57		17 05							17 25
Bexley	d			16 22				16 37						16 50		16 59		17 07							17 27
Albany Park	d			16 25				16 40						16 52		17 02		17 10							17 30
Sidcup 4	d			16 28		16 38		16 43						16 55		17 05		17 13	17 25						17 33
New Eltham	d			16 31		16 41		16 46						16 58		17 08		17 16							17 36
Mottingham	d			16 33		16 43		16 48						17 00		17 10		17 18							17 38
Lee	d			16 36		16 46		16 51						17 03		17 13		17 21							→
Hither Green 4	d			16b42		16 50		16c56						17 06		17 16		17 24	17 31						
Barnehurst 4	d				16 29						16 43									17 13					
Bexleyheath	d				16 32						16 46									17 16					
Welling	d				16 35						16 49									17 19					
Falconwood	d				16 37						16 51									17 21					
Eltham	d				16 40						16 54									17 24					
Kidbrooke	d				16 43						16 57									17 27					
Blackheath 4	d		16 42		16 47						17 01				17 12					17 31				17 43	
Lewisham 4	d		16 46		16 50	16 56					17 05			17 12	17e18			17 31		17 36				17 47	
St Johns	d			16 47										17 14				17 33							
New Cross 4	⊖ d			16 49	16 54									17 16				17 35		17 39					
Nunhead 4	d										17 13														
Peckham Rye 4	d										17 15														
Denmark Hill 4	d										17 18														
London Victoria 15	⊖ a										17 28														
Westcombe Park	d								16 50			16 56					17 16				17 30		17 36		
Maze Hill	d								16 52			16 58					17 18				17 32		17 38		
Greenwich 4	d	16 40							16 56			17 02	17 06				17 22				17 36		17 42		
Deptford	d								16 58			17 04					17 24				17 38		17 44		
London Bridge 4	⊖ a	16 50	16 55	16 56	16 59	17 04		17 06	17 07			17 11	17 17	17 23	17 26	17 29	17 35	17 41	17 41	17 45	17 48		17 53	17 56	
London Cannon Street 4	⊖ a	16 55		17 00	17 05	17 08			17 13			17 15	17 23	17 29		17 33	17 39	17 45		17 51	17 53		17 57	18 01	
London Waterloo (East) 4	⊖ a		17 00					17 11							17 31				17 46						
London Charing Cross 4	⊖ a		17 03					17 15							17 35				17 50						

For general notes see front of timetable
For details of catering facilities see Directory of Train Operators

A From London Cannon Street (Table 199)
b Arr. 1639
c Arr. 1653
e Arr. 1715

For details of Bank Holiday service alterations please see first page of Table 195

Gillingham and Dartford → London

Network Diagram - see first page of Table 200

		SE 63	SE 51	SE 53	SE 85	SE 78	SE 51	SE 66	SE 74	SE 61	SE 53		SE 81	SE 44	SE 66	SE 78	SE 46 A	SE 87	SE 52	SE 81	SE 74	SE 78	SE 81		SE 50
Gillingham (Kent) 4	d									17 14									17 48						
Chatham 4	d									17 18									17 52						
Rochester 4	d									17 20									17 54						
Maidstone West 4	d									*16 56*									*17 26*						
Strood 4	d									17 25									17 59						
Higham	d									17 29									18 03						
Gravesend 4	d	17 08							17 32	17 38				17 52					18 10		18 14				
Northfleet	d	17 12							17 36					17 56							18 18				
Swanscombe	d	17 14							17 38					17 58							18 20				
Greenhithe for Bluewater	d	17 17							17 41	17 45				18 01					18 15		18 23				
Stone Crossing	d	17 19							17 43					18 03							18 25				
Dartford 4	a	17 23							17 47	17 50				18 07					18 20		18 30				
	d	17 25				17 27	17 41		17 47	17 53			18 01	18 09		18 11			18 21	18 31	18 33	18 39			18 43
Slade Green 4	d	17 31			17 35			17 43			17 52		18 05		18 12			18 23		18 35					
Erith	d				17 37			17 45					18 07					18 25		18 37					
Belvedere	d				17 40			17 48					18 10					18 28		18 40					
Abbey Wood	d	17 37			17 43			17 51		18 01			18 13		18 19			18 31		18 43					
Plumstead	d				17 46			17 54					18 16					18 34		18 46			←		
Woolwich Arsenal 4	d	17 41			17 49			17 57		18 06			18 19		18 23			18 37		18 49			18 49		
Woolwich Dockyard	d				17 51			17 59					18 21					18 39		→			18 51		
Charlton 4	d	17 46			17 54			18 02		18 11			18 24		18 28			18 42					18 54		
Crayford	d			17 35			17 45				18 01			18 13			18 20		18 25						18 47
Bexley	d			17 37			17 47				18 03			18 15					18 27						18 50
Albany Park	d			17 40			17 50				18 06			18 18					18 30						18 52
Sidcup 4	d			17 43			17 53				18 09			18 21					18 33						18 55
New Eltham	d		←				17 56				18 12			18 24					18 36						18 58
Mottingham	d		17 38				17 58							18 26					18 38						19 00
Lee	d		17 41				18 01							18 29					18 41						19 03
Hither Green 4	d		17 44	17 50			18 04				18 18			18 32					18 44						19 07
Barnehurst 4	d				17 31	17 33			17 53							18 17	18a28				18 39	18 45			
Bexleyheath	d					17 36			17 56							18 20					18 42	18 48			
Welling	d					17 39			17 59							18 23					18 45	18 51			
Falconwood	d					17 41			18 01							18 25					18 47	18 53			
Eltham	d					17 44			18 04							18 28					18 50	18 56			
Kidbrooke	d					17 47			18 07							18 31					18 53	18 59			
Blackheath 4	d					17 51			18 11	18 15					18 32	18 36					18 57	19 02			
Lewisham 4	⛴ d		17 51			17 54			18 14	18 20	18 24				18 36	18 41			18 49		19 01	19 06			19 12
St Johns	d		17 55						18 16		18 26				18 38				18 51						
New Cross 4	⊖ d		17 57						18 18		18 28				18 40				18 53						
Nunhead 4	d					17 59										18 45						19 10			
Peckham Rye 4	d					18 01										18 47						19 12			
Denmark Hill 4	d					18 04										18 50						19 15			
London Victoria 15	⊖ a					18 16										19 00						19 25			
Westcombe Park	d				17 56			18 04					18 26					18 44					18 56		
Maze Hill	d				17 58			18 06					18 28					18 46					18 58		
Greenwich 4	⛴ d	17 52			18 02			18 10					18 32					18 50					19 02		
Deptford	d				18 04			18 12					18 34					18 52					19 04		
London Bridge 4	⊖ a	18 00	18 03	18 03	18 11		18 15	18 19	18 25	18 31	18 33		18 41	18 42	18 48			19 01	19 02		19 09		19 11		19 21
London Cannon Street 4	⊖ a		18 07		18 15			18 23	18 29		18 37		18 45					19 05					19 15		19 25
London Waterloo (East) 4	⊖ a	18 05		18 09			18 21			18 36				18 48	18 53				19 07		19 15				
London Charing Cross 4	⊖ a	18 09		18 13			18 25			18 40				18 53	18 57				19 11		19 20				

For general notes see front of timetable
For details of catering facilities see
Directory of Train Operators

A From London Charing Cross (Table 199)

For details of Bank Holiday service alterations please see first page of Table 195

Gillingham and Dartford → London

Network Diagram - see first page of Table 200

		SE 62	SE 81	SE 74	SE 50	SE 80	SE 62	SE 70	SE 81	SE 54	SE 80	SE 62	SE 70	SE 81	SE 54	SE 80	SE 62	SE 70	SE 81	SE 54	SE 80	SE 62	SE 70	SE 81
Gillingham (Kent) 4	d	18 12					18 44					19 14					19 44					20 16		
Chatham 4	d	18 16					18 48					19 18					19 48					20 20		
Rochester 4	d	18 18					18 50					19 20					19 50					20 22		
Maidstone West 4	d						*18 16*					*18 48*					*19 28*					*20 00*		
Strood 4	d	18 23					18 55					19 25					19 55					20 27		
Higham	d	18 27					18 59					19 29					19 59					20 31		
Gravesend 4	d	18 34			18 44		19 06			19 16		19 36			19 46		20 06			20 12		20 38		
Northfleet	d				18 48					19 20					19 50					20 16				
Swanscombe	d				18 50					19 22					19 52					20 18				
Greenhithe for Bluewater	d	18 40			18 53		19 11			19 25		19 41			19 55		20 11			20 21		20 43		
Stone Crossing	d				18 55					19 27					19 57					20 23				
Dartford 4	a	18 46			18 59		19 17			19 31		19 46			20 00		20 16			20 27		20 48		
	d	18 49	18 53	18 59	19 03	19 07	19 19	19 23	19 27	19 33	19 37	19 49	19 53	19 57	20 03	20 07	20 19	20 23	20 27	20 33	20 37	20 49	20 53	20 57
Slade Green 4	d		18 57			19 11			19 31		19 41			20 01		20 11			20 31		20 42			21 01
Erith	d		18 59			19 13			19 33		19 43			20 03		20 13			20 33		20 44			21 03
Belvedere	d		19 02			19 16			19 36		19 46			20 06		20 16			20 36		20 47			21 06
Abbey Wood	d	18 57	19 05			19 19	19 27		19 39		19 49	19 57		20 09		20 19	20 27		20 39		20 50	20 57		21 09
Plumstead	d		19 08			19 22			19 42		19 52			20 12		20 22			20 42		20 53			21 12
Woolwich Arsenal 4	d	19 01	19 11			19 25	19 31		19 45		19 55	20 01		20 15		20 25	20 31		20 45		20 56	21 01		21 15
Woolwich Dockyard	d		19 13			19 27			19 47		19 57			20 17		20 27			20 47		20 58			21 17
Charlton 4	d	19 06	19 16			19 30	19 36		19 50		20 00	20 06		20 20		20 30	20 36		20 50		21 01	21 06		21 20
Crayford	d				19 07					19 37					20 07					20 37				
Bexley	d				19 10					19 39					20 10					20 40				
Albany Park	d				19 12					19 42					20 12					20 42				
Sidcup 4	d				19 15					19 45					20 15					20 45				
New Eltham	d				19 18					19 48					20 18					20 48				
Mottingham	d				19 20					19 50					20 20					20 50				
Lee	d				19 23					19 53					20 23					20 53				
Hither Green 4	d				19 26					19 56					20 26					20 56				
Barnehurst 4	d			19 05				19 31					20 01					20 31					21 01	
Bexleyheath	d			19 08				19 34					20 04					20 34					21 04	
Welling	d			19 11				19 37					20 07					20 37					21 07	
Falconwood	d			19 13				19 39					20 09					20 39					21 09	
Eltham	d			19 16				19 42					20 12					20 42					21 12	
Kidbrooke	d			19 19				19 45					20 15					20 45					21 15	
Blackheath 4	d	19 10		19 23			19 40	19 49				20 10	20 19				20 40	20 49				21 10	21 19	
Lewisham 4	d	19 15		19 26	19 31		19 45	19 52		20 02		20 15	20 22		20 31		20 44	20 52		21 01		21 14	21 22	
St Johns	d																							
New Cross 4	⊖ d			19 30	19 34			19 56		20 05			20 26		20 34			20 56		21 04			21 26	
Nunhead 4	d																							
Peckham Rye 4	d																							
Denmark Hill 4	d																							
London Victoria 15	⊖ a																							
Westcombe Park	d		19 18			19 32			19 52		20 02			20 22		20 32			20 52		21 03			21 22
Maze Hill	d		19 20			19 34			19 54		20 04			20 24		20 34			20 54		21 05			21 24
Greenwich 4	d		19 24			19 38			19 58		20 08			20 28		20 38			20 58		21 09			21 28
Deptford	d		19 26			19 40			20 00		20 10			20 30		20 40			21 00		21 11			21 30
London Bridge 4	⊖ a	19 23	19 33	19 36	19 43	19 49	19 53	20 03	20 07	20 13	20 19	20 23	20 33	20 37	20 43	20 49	20 53	21 03	21 07	21 13	21 19	21 23	21 33	21 37
London Cannon Street 4	⊖ a		19 37	19 41					20 11					20 41										
London Waterloo (East) 4	⊖ a	19 28			19 49	19 54	19 58	20 08		20 18	20 24	20 28	20 38		20 48	20 54	20 58	21 08		21 18	21 24	21 28	21 38	
London Charing Cross 4	⊖ a	19 32			19 53	19 59	20 01	20 13		20 22	20 29	20 31	20 43		20 52	20 59	21 01	21 13		21 22	21 29	21 31	21 43	

For general notes see front of timetable
For details of catering facilities see Directory of Train Operators

Table 200

Mondays to Fridays

For details of Bank Holiday service alterations please see first page of Table 195

Gillingham and Dartford → London

Network Diagram - see first page of Table 200

Station		SE 54		SE 80	SE 60	SE 70	SE 81	SE 52	SE 80	SE 62	SE 70	SE 81	SE 50	SE 80		SE 62	SE 70	SE 80	SE 50	SE 82	SE 70
Gillingham (Kent) 4	d				20 42					21 14						21 42				22 22	
Chatham 4	d				20 46					21 18						21 46				22 26	
Rochester 4	d				20 48					21 20						21 48				22 28	
Maidstone West 4	d				*20 25*					*21 00*						*21 27*				*22 02*	
Strood 4	d				20 53					21 25						21 53				22 33	
Higham	d				20 57					21 29						21 57				22 37	
Gravesend 4	d	20 44			21 04					21 36						22 04				22 44	
Northfleet	d	20 48			21 07											22 07				22 47	
Swanscombe	d	20 50			21 09											22 09				22 49	
Greenhithe for Bluewater	d	20 53			21 12					21 41						22 12				22 52	
Stone Crossing	d	20 55			21 14											22 14				22 54	
Dartford 4	a	20 59			21 18					21 46						22 18				22 58	
	d	21 03		21 07	21 19	21 23	21 27	21 33	21 37	21 49	21 53	21 57	22 03	22 07		22 19	22 23	22 31	22 43	23 01	23 03
Slade Green 4	d			21 11			21 31		21 41			22 01		22 11				22 35		23 05	
Erith	d			21 13			21 33		21 43			22 03		22 13				22 37		23 07	
Belvedere	d			21 16			21 36		21 46			22 06		22 16				22 40		23 10	
Abbey Wood	d			21 19	21 27		21 39		21 49	21 57		22 09		22 19		22 27		22 43		23 13	
Plumstead	d			21 22			21 42		21 52			22 12		22 22				22 46		23 16	
Woolwich Arsenal 4	d			21 25	21 31		21 45		21 55	22 01		22 15		22 25		22 31		22 49		23 19	
Woolwich Dockyard	d			21 27			21 47		21 57			22 17		22 27				22 51		23 21	
Charlton 4	d			21 30	21 36		21 50		22 00	22 06		22 20		22 30		22 36		22 54		23 24	
Crayford	d	21 07						21 37					22 07						22 47		
Bexley	d	21 10						21 40					22 10						22 49		
Albany Park	d	21 12						21 42					22 12						22 52		
Sidcup 4	d	21 15						21 45					22 15						22 55		
New Eltham	d	21 18						21 48					22 18						22 58		
Mottingham	d	21 20						21 50					22 20						23 00		
Lee	d	21 23						21 53					22 23						23 03		
Hither Green 4	d	21 26						21 56					22 26						23 06		
Barnehurst 4	d					21 31					22 01						22 31				23 11
Bexleyheath	d					21 34					22 04						22 34				23 14
Welling	d					21 37					22 07						22 37				23 17
Falconwood	d					21 39					22 09						22 39				23 19
Eltham	d					21 42					22 12						22 42				23 22
Kidbrooke	d					21 45					22 15						22 45				23 25
Blackheath 4	d				21 40	21 49				22 10	22 19					22 40	22 49				23 29
Lewisham 4	d	21 31			21 44	21 52		22 01		22 14	22 22		22 31			22 44	22 52		23 11		23 32
St Johns	d																				
New Cross 4	⊖ d	21 34				21 56		22 04			22 26		22 34				22 56		23 14		23 36
Nunhead 4	d																				
Peckham Rye 4	d																				
Denmark Hill 4	d																				
London Victoria 15	⊖ a																				
Westcombe Park	d			21 32			21 52		22 02			22 22		22 32				22 56		23 26	
Maze Hill	d			21 34			21 54		22 04			22 24		22 34				22 58		23 28	
Greenwich 4	d			21 38			21 58		22 08			22 28		22 38				23 02		23 32	
Deptford	d			21 40			22 00		22 10			22 30		22 40				23 04		23 34	
London Bridge 4	⊖ a	21 43		21 49	21 53	22 03	22 07	22 13	22 19	22 23	22 33	22 37	22 43	22 49		22 53	23 03	23 13	23 22	23 41	23 43
London Cannon Street 4	⊖ a																				
London Waterloo (East) 4	⊖ a	21 48		21 54	21 58	22 08		22 18	22 24	22 28	22 38		22 48	22 54		22 58	23 08	23 18	23 28	23 46	23 49
London Charing Cross 4	⊖ a	21 52		21 59	22 01	22 13		22 22	22 29	22 31	22 43		22 52	22 59		23 01	23 13	23 22	23 32	23 50	23 53

For general notes see front of timetable
For details of catering facilities see Directory of Train Operators

For details of Bank Holiday service alterations please see first page of Table 195

Gillingham and Dartford → London

Network Diagram - see first page of Table 200

		SE 58 A	SE 80	SE 70	SE 52	SE 80	SE 70		SE 52	SE 80	SE 62	SE 61 B	SE 54	SE 70		SE 54	SE 80	SE 62	SE 01	SE 78	SE 54		SE 70	SE 54	SE 81
Gillingham (Kent) 4	d	00 07			04 53				05 23		05 44	05 48						06 14	06 18						
Chatham 4	d	00 11			04 57				05 27		05 48	05 51						06 18	06 21						
Rochester 4	d	00 13			04 59				05 29		05 50	05 53						06 20	06 23						
Maidstone West 4	d																								
Strood 4	d	00 17			05 04				05 34		05 54	05a57						06 24	06a27						
Higham	d	00 22			05 09				05 39		05 59							06 29							
Gravesend 4	d	00 28			05 16				05 46		06 05		06 12					06 35			06 42				
Northfleet	d				05 19				05 49				06 16								06 46				
Swanscombe	d				05 21				05 51				06 18								06 48				
Greenhithe for Bluewater	d	00 34			05 24				05 54		06 10		06 21					06 40			06 51				
Stone Crossing	d				05 26				05 56				06 23								06 53				
Dartford 4	a	00 41			05 30				06 00		06 15		06 27					06 45			06 57				
	d	00 42	05 07	05 32	05 33	05 37	06 02		06 03	06 07	06 16		06 29	06 32			06 37	06 46		06 54	06 59		07 02		07 07
Slade Green 4	d		05 11			05 41				06 11							06 41								07 11
Erith	d		05 13			05 43				06 13							06 43								07 13
Belvedere	d		05 16			05 46				06 16							06 46								07 16
Abbey Wood	d		05 19			05 49				06 19	06 24						06 49	06 54							07 19
Plumstead	d		05 22			05 52				06 22							06 52								07 22
Woolwich Arsenal 4	d		05 25			05 55				06 25	06 28						06 55	06 58							07 25
Woolwich Dockyard	d		05 27			05 57				06 27							06 57								07 27
Charlton 4	d		05 30			06 00				06 30	06 33						07 00	07 03							07 30
Crayford	d				05 37				06 07				06 36								07 06				
Bexley	d				05 40				06 10				06 40								07 10				
Albany Park	d				05 42				06 12				06 42			←					07 12			←	
Sidcup 4	d				05 45				06 15				06 45			06 45					07 15			07 15	
New Eltham	d				05 48				06 18				→			06 48					→			07 18	
Mottingham	d				05 50				06 20							06 50								07 20	
Lee	d				05 53				06 23							06 53								07 23	
Hither Green 4	d				05 56				06 26							06 56								07 26	
Barnehurst 4	d			05 38			06 08							06 38						06 59			07 08		
Bexleyheath	d			05 41			06 11							06 41						07 02			07 11		
Welling	d			05 44			06 14							06 44						07 05			07 14		
Falconwood	d			05 46			06 16							06 46						07 07			07 16		
Eltham	d			05 49			06 19							06 49						07 10			07 19		
Kidbrooke	d			05 52			06 22							06 52						07 13			07 22		
Blackheath 4	d			05 56			06 26				06 38			06 56				07 08		07 17			07 26		
Lewisham 4	d			05 59	06 02		06 29		06 31		06 41			06 59		07 02		07 11		07 20			07 29	07 32	
St Johns	d																								
New Cross 4	⊖ d				06 05				06 34							07 05								07 35	
Nunhead 4	d																			07 25					
Peckham Rye 4	d																			07 28					
Denmark Hill 4	d																			07 31					
London Victoria 15	⊖ a	01 13																		07 42					
Westcombe Park	d		05 32			06 02				06 32							07 02								07 32
Maze Hill	d		05 34			06 04				06 34							07 04								07 34
Greenwich 4	d		05 38			06 08				06 38							07 08								07 38
Deptford	d		05 40			06 10				06 40							07 10								07 40
London Bridge 4	⊖ a		05 49	06 07	06 13	06 19	06 37		06 43	06 48	06 50			07 07		07 13	07 19	07 21					07 37	07 43	07 46
London Cannon Street 4	⊖ a																								07 50
London Waterloo (East) 4	⊖ a		05 54	06 12	06 18	06 24	06 42		06 48	06 54	06 55			07 12		07 18	07 24	07 26					07 42	07 48	
London Charing Cross 4	⊖ a		05 59	06 15	06 23	06 29	06 45		06 52	06 59	06 58			07 15		07 22	07 29	07 29					07 45	07 52	

For general notes see front of timetable
For details of catering facilities see Directory of Train Operators

A From Faversham (Table 212)
B To Paddock Wood (Table 209)

For details of Bank Holiday service alterations please see first page of Table 195

Gillingham and Dartford → London

Network Diagram - see first page of Table 200

Station		SE 62	SE 81	SE 78	SE 54	SE 70	SE 54	SE 62	SE 47	SE 81	SE 78	SE 54	SE 70	SE 87	SE 62	SE 47	SE 81	SE 78	SE 54	SE 70	SE 87	SE 82
Gillingham (Kent) 4	d	06 44						07 14							07 44							08 14
Chatham 4	d	06 48						07 18							07 48							08 18
Rochester 4	d	06 50						07 20							07 50							08 20
Maidstone West 4	d	*06 28*						*06 58*							*07 28*							*07 58*
Strood 4	d	06 54						07 24							07 54							08 25
Higham	d	06 59						07 29							07 59							08 29
Gravesend 4	d	07 05			07 12			07 35				07 42			08 05				08 12			08 36
Northfleet	d				07 16							07 46							08 16			
Swanscombe	d				07 18							07 48							08 18			
Greenhithe for Bluewater	d	07 10			07 21			07 40				07 51			08 10				08 21			08 41
Stone Crossing	d				07 23							07 53							08 23			
Dartford 4	a	07 15			07 27			07 45				07 57			08 15				08 27			08 46
	d	07 16	07 19	07 24	07 29	07 32		07 46		07 49	07 54	08 01	08 05		08 16		08 19	08 24	08 31	08 35		08 47
Slade Green 4	d		07 23							07 53				08 07			08 23				08 37	
Erith	d		07 26							07 56				08 09			08 26				08 39	
Belvedere	d		07 29							07 59				08 12			08 29				08 42	
Abbey Wood	d	07 24	07 31					07 54		08 01				08 15	08 24		08 31				08 45	08 55
Plumstead	d		07 34							08 04				08 18			08 34				08 48	
Woolwich Arsenal 4	d	07 28	07 37					07 58		08 07				08 21	08 28		08 37				08 51	08 59
Woolwich Dockyard	d		07 39							08 09				08 23			08 39				08 53	
Charlton 4	d	07 33	07 42					08 03		08 12				08 26	08 33		08 42				08 56	09 04
Crayford	d				07 36				07 51			08 05				08 21			08 35			
Bexley	d				07 40				07 53			08 08				08 23			08 38			
Albany Park	d				07 42		←		07 56			08 10				08 26			08 40			
Sidcup 4	d				07 45		07 45		07 59			08 13				08 29			08 43			
New Eltham	d				→		07 48		08 02			08 16				08 32			08 46			
Mottingham	d						07 50		08 04			08 18				08 34			08 48			
Lee	d						07 53		08 07			08 21				08 37			08 51			
Hither Green 4	d						07 56		08 10			08 24				08 40			08 54			
Barnehurst 4	d			07 29		07 38					07 59		08 11					08 29		08 41		
Bexleyheath	d			07 32		07 41					08 02		08 14					08 32		08 44		
Welling	d			07 35		07 44					08 05		08 17					08 35		08 47		
Falconwood	d			07 37		07 46					08 07		08 19					08 37		08 49		
Eltham	d			07 40		07 49					08 10		08 22					08 40		08 52		
Kidbrooke	d			07 43		07 52					08 13		08 25					08 43		08 55		
Blackheath 4	d	07 38		07 47		07 56		08 08			08 17		08 29		08 37			08 47		08 59		
Lewisham 4	d	07 41		07 50		07 59	08 02	08 11			08 20	08 29	08 32		08 41			08 50	08 59	09 02		
St Johns	d								08 14							08 45						
New Cross 4	⊖ d						08 05		08 17			08 32				08 47			09 02			
Nunhead 4	d			07 55							08 25							08 55				
Peckham Rye 4	d			07 58							08 28							08 58				
Denmark Hill 4	d			08 01							08 31							09 01				
London Victoria 15	⊖ a			08 12							08 42							09 12				
Westcombe Park	d		07 44							08 14				08 28			08 44				08 58	
Maze Hill	d		07 46							08 16				08 30			08 46				09 00	
Greenwich 4	d		07 50							08 20				08 34			08 50				09 04	09 10
Deptford	d		07 52							08 22				08 36			08 52				09 06	
London Bridge 4	⊖ a	07 49	07 59			08 07	08 13	08 19	08 23	08 29		08 38	08 40	08 43	08 49	08 53	08 59		09 08	09 10	09 13	09 19
London Cannon Street 4	⊖ a		08 03						08 27	08 33				08 47		08 57	09 03				09 17	
London Waterloo (East) 4	⊖ a	07 54				08 12	08 18	08 24				08 42	08 45		08 54				09 12	09 15		09 24
London Charing Cross 4	⊖ a	07 58				08 15	08 22	08 28				08 47	08 50		08 58				09 17	09 20		09 28

For general notes see front of timetable
For details of catering facilities see
Directory of Train Operators

For details of Bank Holiday service alterations please see first page of Table 195

Gillingham and Dartford → London

Network Diagram - see first page of Table 200

		SE 47	SE 67	SE 81	SE 78	SE 54	SE 70	SE 87	SE 82	SE 47 A	SE 67	SE 81	SE 78	SE 54	SE 70	SE 87 A	SE 82	SE 47 A	SE 67	SE 81	SE 78	SE 54
Gillingham (Kent) 4	d								08 44								09 14					
Chatham 4	d								08 48								09 18					
Rochester 4	d								08 50								09 20					
Maidstone West 4	d								*08 28*								*08 58*					
Strood 4	d								08 55								09 25					
Higham	d								08 59								09 29					
Gravesend 4	d					08 42			09 06					09 12			09 36					09 42
Northfleet	d					08 45								09 16								09 46
Swanscombe	d					08 47								09 18								09 48
Greenhithe for Bluewater	d					08 50			09 11					09 21			09 41					09 51
Stone Crossing	d					08 52								09 23								09 53
Dartford 4	a					08 56			09 16					09 27			09 46					09 57
	d			08 49	08 54	09 01	09 05		09 17			09 19	09 24	09 31	09 35		09 47			09 49	09 54	10 01
Slade Green 4	d			08 53				09 07		09 10		09 23				09 37		09 40		09 53		
Erith	d			08 55				09 09				09 25				09 39				09 55		
Belvedere	d			08 58				09 12				09 28				09 42				09 58		
Abbey Wood	d			09 01				09 15	09 25			09 31				09 45	09 55			10 01		
Plumstead	d		09 01	09 04				09 18			09 31	09 34				09 48			10 01	10 04		
Woolwich Arsenal 4	d		09 03	09 07				09 21	09 29		09 33	09 37				09 51	09 59		10 03	10 07		
Woolwich Dockyard	d			09 09				09 23				09 39				09 53				10 09		
Charlton 4	d		09 08	09 12				09 26	09 34		09 38	09 42				09 56	10 04		10 08	10 12		
Crayford	d	08 51				09 05				09 20				09 35				09 50				10 05
Bexley	d	08 53				09 08				09 22				09 38				09 52				10 08
Albany Park	d	08 56				09 10				09 25				09 40				09 55				10 10
Sidcup 4	d	08 59				09 13				09 28				09 43				09 58				10 13
New Eltham	d	09 02				09 16				09 31				09 46				10 01				10 16
Mottingham	d	09 04				09 18				09 33				09 48				10 03				10 18
Lee	d	09 07				09 21				09 36				09 51				10 06				10 21
Hither Green 4	d	09 10				09 24				09 40				09 54				10 10				10 24
Barnehurst 4	d				08 59		09 11						09 29		09 41						09 59	
Bexleyheath	d				09 02		09 14						09 32		09 44						10 02	
Welling	d				09 05		09 17						09 35		09 47						10 05	
Falconwood	d				09 07		09 19						09 37		09 49						10 07	
Eltham	d				09 10		09 22						09 40		09 52						10 10	
Kidbrooke	d				09 13		09 25						09 43		09 55						10 13	
Blackheath 4	d		09 13		09 17		09 29				09 43		09 47		09 59				10 13		10 17	
Lewisham 4	d		09 16		09 20	09 29	09 32				09 46		09 50	09 59	10 02				10 16		10 20	10 29
St Johns	d	09 14								09 44								10 14				
New Cross 4	⊖ d	09 17	09 20			09 32				09 47	09 50							10 17	10 20			
Nunhead 4	d				09 25								09 55								10 25	
Peckham Rye 4	d				09 28								09 58								10 28	
Denmark Hill 4	d				09 31								10 01								10 31	
London Victoria 15	⊖ a				09 42								10 12								10 42	
Westcombe Park	d			09 14				09 28				09 44				09 58				10 14		
Maze Hill	d			09 16				09 30				09 46				10 00				10 16		
Greenwich 4	d			09 20				09 34	09 40			09 50				10 04	10 10			10 20		
Deptford	d			09 22				09 36				09 52				10 06				10 22		
London Bridge 4	⊖ a	09 23	09 26	09 29		09 38	09 40	09 43	09 49	09 53	09 56	09 59		10 07	10 10	10 13	10 19	10 23	10 26	10 29		10 37
London Cannon Street 4	⊖ a	09 27	09 30	09 33				09 47		09 57	10 00	10 03				10 17		10 27	10 30	10 34		
London Waterloo (East) 4	⊖ a					09 42	09 45		09 54					10 12	10 15		10 24					10 42
London Charing Cross 4	⊖ a					09 47	09 50		09 58					10 17	10 20		10 28					10 47

For general notes see front of timetable
For details of catering facilities see Directory of Train Operators

A From London Cannon Street (Table 199)

Table 200

For details of Bank Holiday service alterations please see first page of Table 195

Gillingham and Dartford → London

Network Diagram - see first page of Table 200

		SE 70	SE 87 A	SE 82	SE 47 A	SE 67		SE 81	SE 78	SE 54	SE 70	SE 87 A	SE 82	SE 47 A	SE 67	SE 81	SE 78	SE 54	SE 70	SE 62	SE 80
Gillingham (Kent) 4	d			09 44									17 14							17 44	
Chatham 4	d			09 48									17 18							17 48	
Rochester 4	d			09 50									17 20							17 50	
Maidstone West 4	d			*09 28*									*16 58*							*17 28*	
Strood 4	d			09 55									17 25							17 55	
Higham	d			09 59									17 29							17 59	
Gravesend 4	d			10 06						17 12			17 36					17 42		18 06	
Northfleet	d									17 16								17 46			
Swanscombe	d									17 18								17 48			
Greenhithe for Bluewater	d			10 11						17 21			17 41					17 51		18 11	
Stone Crossing	d									17 23								17 53			
Dartford 4	a			10 16						17 27			17 46					17 57		18 16	
	d	10 05		10 17				17 19	17 24	17 31	17 35		17 47			17 49	17 54	18 01	18 05	18 17	18 19
Slade Green 4	d		10 07		10 10			17 23				17 37		17 40		17 53					18 23
Erith	d		10 09					17 25				17 39				17 55					18 25
Belvedere	d		10 12					17 28				17 42				17 58					18 28
Abbey Wood	d		10 15	10 25				17 31				17 45	17 55			18 01				18 25	18 31
Plumstead	d		10 18			10 31		17 34				17 48			18 01	18 04					18 34
Woolwich Arsenal 4	d		10 21	10 29		10 33		17 37				17 51	17 59		18 03	18 07				18 29	18 37
Woolwich Dockyard	d		10 23					17 39				17 53				18 09					18 39
Charlton 4	d		10 26	10 34		10 38	and at the same minutes past each hour until	17 42				17 56	18 04	17 20	18 08	18 12				18 34	18 42
Crayford	d				10 20					17 35				17 50				18 05			
Bexley	d				10 22					17 38				17 52				18 08			
Albany Park	d				10 25					17 40				17 55				18 10			
Sidcup 4	d				10 28					17 43				17 58				18 13			
New Eltham	d				10 31					17 46				18 01				18 16			
Mottingham	d				10 33					17 48				18 03				18 18			
Lee	d				10 36					17 51				18 06				18 21			
Hither Green 4	d				10 40					17 54				18 10				18 24			
Barnehurst 4	d	10 11							17 29		17 41						17 59		18 11		
Bexleyheath	d	10 14							17 32		17 44						18 02		18 14		
Welling	d	10 17							17 35		17 47						18 05		18 17		
Falconwood	d	10 19							17 37		17 49						18 07		18 19		
Eltham	d	10 22							17 40		17 52						18 10		18 22		
Kidbrooke	d	10 25							17 43		17 55						18 13		18 25		
Blackheath 4	d	10 29				10 43			17 47		17 59				18 13		18 17		18 29	18 38	
Lewisham 4	d	10 32				10 46			17 50	17 59	18 02				18 16		18 20	18 29	18 32	18 41	
St Johns	d				10 44									18 14				18 31			
New Cross 4	⊖ d				10 47	10 50						16 57		18 17	18 20			18 32			
Nunhead 4	d								17 55								18 25				
Peckham Rye 4	d								17 58								18 28				
Denmark Hill 4	d								18 01								18 31				
London Victoria 15	⊖ a								18 12								18 42				
Westcombe Park	d		10 28					17 44				17 58				18 14					18 44
Maze Hill	d		10 30					17 46				18 00				18 16					18 46
Greenwich 4	d		10 34	10 40				17 50				18 04	18 10			18 20					18 50
Deptford	d		10 36					17 52				18 06		17 10		18 22					18 53
London Bridge 4	⊖ a	10 40	10 43	10 49	10 53	10 56		17 59		18 07	18 10	18 13	18 19	18 23	18 26	18 29		18 38	18 40	18 49	19 03
London Cannon Street 4	⊖ a		10 47		10 57	11 00		18 03				18 17		18 27	18 30	18 33					
London Waterloo (East) 4	⊖ a	10 45		10 54						18 12	18 15		18 24					18 43	18 45	18 54	19 09
London Charing Cross 4	⊖ a	10 50		10 58						18 17	18 20		18 28					18 48	18 50	18 58	19 13

For general notes see front of timetable
For details of catering facilities see Directory of Train Operators

A From London Cannon Street (Table 199)

Table 200

For details of Bank Holiday service alterations please see first page of Table 195

Gillingham and Dartford → London

Network Diagram - see first page of Table 200

		SE 78	SE 54	SE 70	SE 54	SE 80	SE 62	SE 70	SE 54	SE 80	SE 62	SE 70	SE 54	SE 80	SE 62	SE 70	SE 54	SE 80	SE 62	SE 70	SE 54	SE 80
Gillingham (Kent) 4	d						18 14				18 44				19 14				19 44			
Chatham 4	d						18 18				18 48				19 18				19 48			
Rochester 4	d						18 20				18 50				19 20				19 50			
Maidstone West 4	d						*17 58*				*18 28*				*18 58*				*19 28*			
Strood 4	d						18 25				18 55				19 25				19 55			
Higham	d						18 29				18 59				19 29				19 59			
Gravesend 4	d		18 12				18 36		18 42		19 06		19 12		19 36		19 42		20 06		20 12	
Northfleet	d		18 16						18 46				19 16				19 46				20 16	
Swanscombe	d		18 18						18 48				19 18				19 48				20 18	
Greenhithe for Bluewater	d		18 21				18 41		18 51		19 11		19 21		19 41		19 51		20 11		20 21	
Stone Crossing	d		18 23						18 53				19 23				19 53				20 23	
Dartford 4	a		18 27				18 46		18 57		19 16		19 27		19 46		19 57		20 16		20 27	
	d	18 24	18 31	18 35		18 37	18 47	18 53	19 03	19 07	19 19	19 23	19 33	19 37	19 49	19 53	20 03	20 07	20 19	20 23	20 33	20 37
Slade Green 4	d					18 41				19 11				19 41				20 11				20 41
Erith	d					18 43				19 13				19 43				20 13				20 43
Belvedere	d					18 46				19 16				19 46				20 16				20 46
Abbey Wood	d					18 49	18 55			19 19	19 27			19 49	19 57			20 19	20 27			20 49
Plumstead	d					18 52				19 22				19 52				20 22				20 52
Woolwich Arsenal 4	d					18 55	18 59			19 25	19 31			19 55	20 01			20 25	20 31			20 55
Woolwich Dockyard	d					18 57				19 27				19 57				20 27				20 57
Charlton 4	d					19 00	19 04			19 30	19 36			20 00	20 06			20 30	20 36			21 00
Crayford	d		18 37						19 07				19 37				20 07				20 37	
Bexley	d		18 40						19 10				19 40				20 10				20 40	
Albany Park	d		18 42						19 12				19 42				20 12				20 42	
Sidcup 4	d		18 45						19 15				19 45				20 15				20 45	
New Eltham	d		18 48						19 18				19 48				20 18				20 48	
Mottingham	d		18 50						19 20				19 50				20 20				20 50	
Lee	d		18 53						19 23				19 53				20 23				20 53	
Hither Green 4	d		18 56						19 26				19 56				20 26				20 56	
Barnehurst 4	d	18 29		18 41				19 01				19 31				20 01				20 31		
Bexleyheath	d	18 32		18 44				19 04				19 34				20 04				20 34		
Welling	d	18 35		18 47				19 07				19 37				20 07				20 37		
Falconwood	d	18 37		18 49				19 09				19 39				20 09				20 39		
Eltham	d	18 40		18 52				19 12				19 42				20 12				20 42		
Kidbrooke	d	18 43		18 55				19 15				19 45				20 15				20 45		
Blackheath 4	d	18 47		18 59			19 08	19 19			19 40	19 49			20 10	20 19			20 40	20 49		
Lewisham 4	d	18 50	19 01	19 02			19 11	19 22	19 31		19 44	19 52	20 01		20 14	20 22	20 31		20 44	20 52	21 01	
St Johns	d				←																	
New Cross 4	⊖ d		19 04		19 04			19 26	19 34			19 56	20 04			20 26	20 34			20 56	21 04	
Nunhead 4	d	18 55	→																			
Peckham Rye 4	d	18 58																				
Denmark Hill 4	d	19 01																				
London Victoria 15	⊖ a	19 12																				
Westcombe Park	d					19 02				19 32				20 02				20 32				21 02
Maze Hill	d					19 04				19 34				20 04				20 34				21 04
Greenwich 4	d					19 08				19 38				20 08				20 38				21 08
Deptford	d					19 10				19 40				20 10				20 40				21 10
London Bridge 4	⊖ a			19 11	19 13	19 18	19 21	19 33	19 43	19 49	19 53	20 03	20 13	20 19	20 23	20 33	20 43	20 49	20 53	21 03	21 13	21 19
London Cannon Street 4	⊖ a																					
London Waterloo (East) 4	⊖ a			19 15	19 18	19 23	19 25	19 38	19 48	19 54	19 58	20 08	20 18	20 24	20 28	20 38	20 48	20 54	20 58	21 08	21 18	21 24
London Charing Cross 4	⊖ a			19 20	19 22	19 26	19 29	19 43	19 52	19 59	20 01	20 13	20 22	20 29	20 31	20 43	20 52	20 59	21 01	21 13	21 22	21 29

For general notes see front of timetable
For details of catering facilities see Directory of Train Operators

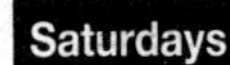

For details of Bank Holiday service alterations please see first page of Table 195

Gillingham and Dartford → London

Network Diagram - see first page of Table 200

		SE 62	SE 70	SE 50	SE 80	SE 62	SE 70	SE 50	SE 80	SE 62	SE 70	SE 50	SE 80	SE 62	SE 70	SE 80	SE 50	SE 80	SE 70
Gillingham (Kent) 4	d	20 14				20 42				21 14				21 42				22 22	
Chatham 4	d	20 18				20 46				21 18				21 46				22 26	
Rochester 4	d	20 20				20 48				21 20				21 48				22 28	
Maidstone West 4	d	*19 58*				*20 28*				*20 58*				*21 28*					
Strood 4	d	20 25				20 53				21 25				21 53				22 33	
Higham	d	20 29				20 57				21 29				21 57				22 37	
Gravesend 4	d	20 36				21 04				21 36				22 04				22 44	
Northfleet	d					21 07								22 07				22 47	
Swanscombe	d					21 09								22 09				22 49	
Greenhithe for Bluewater	d	20 41				21 12				21 41				22 12				22 52	
Stone Crossing	d					21 14								22 14				22 54	
Dartford 4	a	20 46				21 18				21 46				22 18				22 58	
	d	20 49	20 53	21 03	21 07	21 19	21 23	21 33	21 37	21 49	21 53	22 03	22 07	22 19	22 23	22 31	22 43	23 00	23 03
Slade Green 4	d				21 11				21 41				22 11			22 35		23 05	
Erith	d				21 13				21 43				22 13			22 37		23 07	
Belvedere	d				21 16				21 46				22 16			22 40		23 10	
Abbey Wood	d	20 57			21 19	21 27			21 49	21 57			22 19	22 27		22 43		23 13	
Plumstead	d				21 22				21 52				22 22			22 46		23 16	
Woolwich Arsenal 4	d	21 01			21 25	21 31			21 55	22 01			22 25	22 31		22 49		23 19	
Woolwich Dockyard	d				21 27				21 57				22 27			22 51		23 21	
Charlton 4	d	21 06			21 30	21 36			22 00	22 06			22 30	22 36		22 54		23 24	
Crayford	d			21 07				21 37				22 07					22 47		
Bexley	d			21 10				21 40				22 10					22 49		
Albany Park	d			21 12				21 42				22 12					22 52		
Sidcup 4	d			21 15				21 45				22 15					22 55		
New Eltham	d			21 18				21 48				22 18					22 58		
Mottingham	d			21 20				21 50				22 20					23 00		
Lee	d			21 23				21 53				22 23					23 03		
Hither Green 4	d			21 26				21 56				22 26					23 06		
Barnehurst 4	d		21 01				21 31				22 01				22 31				23 11
Bexleyheath	d		21 04				21 34				22 04				22 34				23 14
Welling	d		21 07				21 37				22 07				22 37				23 17
Falconwood	d		21 09				21 39				22 09				22 39				23 19
Eltham	d		21 12				21 42				22 12				22 42				23 22
Kidbrooke	d		21 15				21 45				22 15				22 45				23 25
Blackheath 4	d	21 10	21 19			21 40	21 49			22 10	22 19			22 40	22 49				23 29
Lewisham 4	d	21 14	21 22	21 31		21 44	21 52	22 01		22 14	22 22	22 31		22 44	22 52		23 11		23 32
St Johns	d																		
New Cross 4	⊖ d		21 26	21 34			21 56	22 04			22 26	22 34			22 56		23 14		23 36
Nunhead 4	d																		
Peckham Rye 4	d																		
Denmark Hill 4	d																		
London Victoria 15	⊖ a																		
Westcombe Park	d				21 32				22 02				22 32			22 56		23 26	
Maze Hill	d				21 34				22 04				22 34			22 58		23 28	
Greenwich 4	d				21 38				22 08				22 38			23 02		23 32	
Deptford	d				21 40				22 10				22 40			23 04		23 34	
London Bridge 4	⊖ a	21 23	21 33	21 43	21 49	21 53	22 03	22 13	22 19	22 23	22 33	22 43	22 49	22 53	23 03	23 13	23 22	23 41	23 43
London Cannon Street 4	⊖ a																		
London Waterloo (East) 4	⊖ a	21 28	21 38	21 48	21 54	21 58	22 08	22 18	22 24	22 28	22 38	22 48	22 54	22 58	23 08	23 18	23 28	23 46	23 49
London Charing Cross 4	⊖ a	21 31	21 43	21 52	21 59	22 01	22 13	22 22	22 29	22 31	22 43	22 52	22 59	23 01	23 13	23 22	23 32	23 50	23 53

For general notes see front of timetable
For details of catering facilities see Directory of Train Operators

Table 200

Sundays

Gillingham and Dartford → London

Network Diagram - see first page of Table 200

		SE 58 A	SE 70	SE 80	SE 50	SE 80	SE 70	SE 55 B	SE 82	SE 50	SE 82	SE 72	SE 80	SE 50	SE 80	SE 62	SE 70	SE 80	SE 50	SE 80	SE 60	SE 72	SE 80
Gillingham (Kent) 4	d	00 05						06 36	06 45			07 13				07 46						08 13	
Chatham 4	d	00 09						06 40	06 49			07 17				07 50						08 17	
Rochester 4	d	00 11						06 42	06 51			07 19				07 52						08 19	
Maidstone West 4	d											*06 57*										*08 00*	
Strood 4	d	00 15						06a46	06 58			07 24				07 56						08 24	
Higham	d	00 20							07 03			07 29				08 01						08 29	
Gravesend 4	d	00 26							07 10			07 36				08 07						08 36	
Northfleet	d								07 13			07 39										08 39	
Swanscombe	d								07 15			07 41										08 41	
Greenhithe for Bluewater	d	00 32							07 18			07 44				08 12						08 44	
Stone Crossing	d								07 20			07 46										08 46	
Dartford 4	a	00 39							07 24			07 49				08 17						08 49	
	d	00 40	06 48	06 54	06 57		07 18		07 24	07 27		07 50	07 54	07 57		08 18	08 20	08 24	08 27		08 48	08 50	08 54
Slade Green 4	d			06 59					07 29				07 59					08 29					08 59
Erith	d			07 01					07 31				08 01					08 31					09 01
Belvedere	d			07 04					07 34				08 04					08 34					09 04
Abbey Wood	d			07 07					07 37				08 07			08 27		08 37			08 57		09 07
Plumstead	d			07 10		←			07 40		←		08 10		←			08 40		←			09 10
Woolwich Arsenal 4	d			07 13		07 13			07 43		07 43		08 13		08 13	08 31		08 43		08 43	09 01		09 13
Woolwich Dockyard	d			→		07 15			→		07 45		→		08 15			→		08 45			→
Charlton 4	d					07 18					07 48				08 18	08 36				08 48	09 06		
Crayford	d				07 00					07 30				08 00					08 30				
Bexley	d				07 03					07 33				08 03					08 33				
Albany Park	d				07 05					07 35				08 05					08 35				
Sidcup 4	d				07 08					07 38				08 08					08 38				
New Eltham	d				07 11					07 41				08 11					08 41				
Mottingham	d				07 13					07 43				08 13					08 43				
Lee	d				07 16					07 46				08 16					08 46				
Hither Green 4	d				07 18					07 48				08 18					08 48				
Barnehurst 4	d		06 54				07 24					07 56					08 26					08 56	
Bexleyheath	d		06 57				07 27					07 58					08 28					08 58	
Welling	d		07 00				07 30					08 01					08 31					09 01	
Falconwood	d		07 03				07 33					08 04					08 34					09 04	
Eltham	d		07 06				07 36					08 07					08 37					09 07	
Kidbrooke	d		07 09				07 39					08 10					08 40					09 10	
Blackheath 4	d		07 13				07 43					08 13				08 40	08 43				09 10	09 13	
Lewisham 4	d		07 16		07 23		07 46			07 53		08 16		08 23		08 43	08 46		08 53		09 14	09 17	
St Johns	d																						
New Cross 4	⊖ d		07 20		07 27		07 50			07 57		08 20		08 27			08 50		08 57			09 20	
Nunhead 4	d																						
Peckham Rye 4	d																						
Denmark Hill 4	d																						
London Victoria 15	⊖ a	01 11																					
Westcombe Park	d					07 20					07 50				08 20					08 50			
Maze Hill	d					07 22					07 52				08 22					08 52			
Greenwich 4	d					07 26					07 56				08 26					08 56			
Deptford	d					07 28					07 58				08 28					08 58			
London Bridge 4	⊖ a		07 25		07 33	07 36	07 55			08 03	08 06	08 25		08 33	08 36	08 53	08 56		09 03	09 06	09 23	09 26	
London Cannon Street 4	⊖ a																						
London Waterloo (East) 4	⊖ a		07 30		07 38	07 40	08 00			08 08	08 10	08 30		08 38	08 40	08 58	09 00		09 08	09 10	09 28	09 30	
London Charing Cross 4	⊖ a		07 34		07 41	07 44	08 04			08 11	08 15	08 34		08 41	08 44	09 01	09 04		09 11	09 14	09 34	09 34	

For general notes see front of timetable
For details of catering facilities see Directory of Train Operators

A From Faversham (Table 212)
B To Three Bridges (Table 209)

Table 200

Sundays

Gillingham and Dartford → London

Network Diagram - see first page of Table 200

Station		SE 50		SE 80	SE 67	SE 62	SE 70	SE 80	SE 50	SE 80		SE 67	SE 62	SE 72	SE 80	SE 50	SE 80		SE 70	SE 67	SE 82	SE 70	SE 50	SE 84	SE 70
Gillingham (Kent) [4]	d					08 46								09 13							09 47				
Chatham [4]	d					08 50								09 17							09 51				
Rochester [4]	d					08 52								09 19							09 53				
Maidstone West [4]	d													*09 00*											
Strood [4]	d					08 56								09 24							09 58				
Higham	d					09 01								09 29							10 02				
Gravesend [4]	d					09 07								09 36							10 09			10 13	
Northfleet	d													09 39										10 16	
Swanscombe	d													09 41										10 18	
Greenhithe for Bluewater	d					09 12								09 44							10 14			10 21	
Stone Crossing	d													09 46										10 23	
Dartford [4]	a					09 17								09 49							10 19			10 27	
	d	08 57				09 18	09 20	09 24	09 27				09 48	09 50	09 54	09 57			10 18		10 20		10 25	10 27	10 48
Slade Green [4]	d							09 29							10 00									10 30	
Erith	d							09 31							10 02									10 33	
Belvedere	d							09 34							10 05									10 36	
Abbey Wood	d					09 27		09 37					09 57		10 08						10 29			10 38	
Plumstead	d			←	09 20			09 40		←		09 50			10 11		←			10 20				10 41	
Woolwich Arsenal [4]	d			09 13	09 22	09 31		09 43 →		09 43		09 52	10 01		10 14 →		10 14			10 22	10 33			10 44	
Woolwich Dockyard	d			09 15						09 45							10 16							10 46	
Charlton [4]	d			09 18	09 27	09 36				09 48		09 57	10 06				10 19			10 27	10 38			10 49	
Crayford	d	09 00							09 30							10 00							10 30		
Bexley	d	09 03							09 33							10 03							10 33		
Albany Park	d	09 05							09 35							10 05							10 35		
Sidcup [4]	d	09 08							09 38							10 08							10 38		
New Eltham	d	09 11							09 41							10 11							10 41		
Mottingham	d	09 13							09 43							10 13							10 43		
Lee	d	09 16							09 46							10 16							10 46		
Hither Green [4]	d	09 18							09 48							10 18							10 48		
Barnehurst [4]	d						09 26							09 56					10 24						10 54
Bexleyheath	d						09 28							09 58					10 27						10 57
Welling	d						09 31							10 01					10 30						11 00
Falconwood	d						09 34							10 04					10 33			←			11 03
Eltham	d						09 37							10 07					10 36 →			10 36			11 06 →
Kidbrooke	d						09 40							10 10								10 39			
Blackheath [4]	d				09 31	09 40	09 43					10 01		10 13						10 31		10 43			
Lewisham [4]	d	09 23			09 34	09 43	09 46		09 53			10 04		10 16		10 23				10 34		10 46	10 53		
St Johns	d																								
New Cross [4]	⊖ d	09 27					09 50		09 57					10 20		10 27						10 50	10 57		
Nunhead [4]	d																								
Peckham Rye [4]	d																								
Denmark Hill [4]	d																								
London Victoria [15]	⊖ a																								
Westcombe Park	d			09 20						09 50							10 21							10 51	
Maze Hill	d			09 22						09 52							10 23							10 53	
Greenwich [4]	d			09 26						09 56			10 13				10 27				10 44			10 57	
Deptford	d			09 28						09 58							10 29							10 59	
London Bridge [4]	⊖ a	09 33		09 36	09 41	09 53	09 56		10 03	10 06		10 11	10 23	10 25		10 33	10 36			10 41	10 53	10 56	11 03	11 07	
London Cannon Street [4]	⊖ a																								
London Waterloo (East) [4]	⊖ a	09 38		09 40		09 58	10 00		10 08	10 10			10 29	10 31		10 38	10 40				10 58	11 00	11 08	11 11	
London Charing Cross [4]	⊖ a	09 41		09 44		10 01	10 04		10 11	10 14			10 34	10 34		10 41	10 44				11 01	11 04	11 11	11 15	

For general notes see front of timetable
For details of catering facilities see
Directory of Train Operators

Table 200

Sundays

Gillingham and Dartford → London

Network Diagram - see first page of Table 200

		SE 67	SE 82	SE 70	SE 50	SE 84		SE 70	SE 67	SE 82	SE 70	SE 50	SE 84	SE 70	SE 67	SE 82	SE 70	SE 50	SE 84	SE 62	SE 70	SE 50
Gillingham (Kent) [4]	d		10 17							16 47						17 17				17 46		
Chatham [4]	d		10 21							16 51						17 21				17 50		
Rochester [4]	d		10 23							16 53						17 23				17 52		
Maidstone West [4]	d		*10 02*													*17 02*						
Strood [4]	d		10 28							16 58						17 28				17 56		
Higham	d		10 32							17 02						17 32				18 01		
Gravesend [4]	d		10 39			10 43				17 09			17 13			17 39			17 43	18 07		
Northfleet	d					10 46							17 16						17 46			
Swanscombe	d					10 48							17 18						17 48			
Greenhithe for Bluewater	d		10 44			10 51				17 14			17 21			17 44			17 51	18 12		
Stone Crossing	d					10 53							17 23						17 53			
Dartford [4]	a		10 49			10 57				17 19			17 27			17 49			17 57	18 17		
	d		10 50		10 55	10 57		17 18		17 20		17 25	17 27	17 48		17 50		17 55	17 57	18 18	18 20	18 25
Slade Green [4]	d					11 01							17 31						18 01			
Erith	d					11 04							17 33						18 03			
Belvedere	d					11 07							17 36						18 06			
Abbey Wood	d		10 59			11 09				17 29			17 39			17 59			18 09	18 27		
Plumstead	d	10 50				11 12			17 20				17 42		17 50				18 12			
Woolwich Arsenal [4]	d	10 52	11 03			11 15			17 22	17 33			17 45		17 52	18 03			18 15	18 31		
Woolwich Dockyard	d					11 17							17 47						18 17			
Charlton [4]	d	10 57	11 08			11 20	and at		17 27	17 38			17 50		17 57	18 08			18 20	18 36		
Crayford	d				11 00		the same					17 30						18 00				18 30
Bexley	d				11 03							17 33						18 03				18 33
Albany Park	d				11 05		minutes					17 35						18 05				18 35
Sidcup [4]	d				11 08							17 38						18 08				18 38
New Eltham	d				11 11		past					17 41						18 11				18 41
Mottingham	d				11 13							17 43						18 13				18 43
Lee	d				11 16		each					17 46						18 16				18 46
Hither Green [4]	d				11 18							17 48						18 18				18 48
Barnehurst [4]	d						hour until	17 24						17 54							18 26	
Bexleyheath	d							17 27						17 57							18 28	
Welling	d							17 30						18 00							18 31	
Falconwood	d			←				17 33			←			18 03			←				18 34	
Eltham	d			11 06				17 36			17 36			18 06			18 06				18 37	
Kidbrooke	d			11 09				→			17 39			→			18 09				18 40	
Blackheath [4]	d	11 01		11 13					17 31		17 43				18 01		18 13			18 40	18 43	
Lewisham [4]	d	11 04		11 16	11 23				17 34		17 46	17 53			18 04		18 16	18 23		18 43	18 46	18 53
St Johns	d																					
New Cross [4]	⊖ d			11 20	11 27						17 50	17 57					18 20	18 27			18 50	18 57
Nunhead [4]	d																					
Peckham Rye [4]	d																					
Denmark Hill [4]	d																					
London Victoria [15]	⊖ a																					
Westcombe Park	d					11 22							17 52						18 22			
Maze Hill	d					11 24							17 54						18 24			
Greenwich [4]	d		11 14			11 28				17 44			17 58			18 14			18 28			
Deptford	d					11 30							18 00						18 30			
London Bridge [4]	⊖ a	11 11	11 23	11 26	11 33	11 37			17 41	17 53	17 56	18 03	18 07		18 11	18 23	18 26	18 33	18 37	18 52	18 56	19 03
London Cannon Street [4]	⊖ a																					
London Waterloo (East) [4]	⊖ a		11 28	11 30	11 38	11 41				17 58	18 00	18 08	18 11			18 28	18 30	18 38	18 41	18 57	19 00	19 08
London Charing Cross [4]	⊖ a		11 31	11 34	11 41	11 45				18 01	18 04	18 11	18 15			18 34	18 34	18 41	18 45	19 00	19 04	19 11

For general notes see front of timetable
For details of catering facilities see Directory of Train Operators

Gillingham and Dartford → London

Network Diagram - see first page of Table 200

		SE 84		SE 72	SE 80	SE 50	SE 80	SE 62	SE 70	SE 80		SE 50	SE 80	SE 72	SE 80	SE 50	SE 80	SE 62		SE 70	SE 80	SE 50	SE 80	SE 72	SE 80
Gillingham (Kent) 4	d			18 13				18 46						19 13				19 46						20 13	
Chatham 4	d			18 17				18 50						19 17				19 50						20 17	
Rochester 4	d			18 19				18 52						19 19				19 52						20 19	
Maidstone West 4	d			*18 00*										*19 00*										*20 00*	
Strood 4	d			18 24				18 56						19 24				19 56						20 24	
Higham	d			18 29				19 01						19 29				20 01						20 29	
Gravesend 4	d	18 13		18 36				19 07						19 36				20 07						20 36	
Northfleet	d	18 16		18 39										19 39										20 39	
Swanscombe	d	18 18		18 41										19 41										20 41	
Greenhithe for Bluewater	d	18 21		18 44				19 12						19 44				20 12						20 44	
Stone Crossing	d	18 23		18 46										19 46										20 46	
Dartford 4	a	18 27		18 49				19 17						19 49				20 17						20 49	
	d	18 27		18 50	18 54	18 57		19 18	19 20	19 24		19 27		19 50	19 54	19 57		20 18		20 20	20 24	20 27		20 50	20 54
Slade Green 4	d	18 31			18 59					19 29					19 59						20 29				20 59
Erith	d	18 33			19 01					19 31					20 01						20 31				21 01
Belvedere	d	18 36			19 04					19 34					20 04						20 34				21 04
Abbey Wood	d	18 39			19 07			19 27		19 37					20 07			20 27			20 37				21 07
Plumstead	d	18 42			19 10		←			19 40			←		20 10		←				20 40		←		21 10
Woolwich Arsenal 4	d	18 45			19 13		19 13	19 31		19 43			19 43		20 13		20 13	20 31			20 43		20 43		21 13
Woolwich Dockyard	d	18 47			→		19 15			→			19 45		→		20 15				→		20 45		→
Charlton 4	d	18 50					19 18	19 36					19 48				20 18	20 36					20 48		
Crayford	d					19 00						19 30				20 00						20 30			
Bexley	d					19 03						19 33				20 03						20 33			
Albany Park	d					19 05						19 35				20 05						20 35			
Sidcup 4	d					19 08						19 38				20 08						20 38			
New Eltham	d					19 11						19 41				20 11						20 41			
Mottingham	d					19 13						19 43				20 13						20 43			
Lee	d					19 16						19 46				20 16						20 46			
Hither Green 4	d					19 18						19 48				20 18						20 48			
Barnehurst 4	d			18 56					19 26					19 56						20 26				20 56	
Bexleyheath	d			18 58					19 28					19 58						20 28				20 58	
Welling	d			19 01					19 31					20 01						20 31				21 01	
Falconwood	d			19 04					19 34					20 04						20 34				21 04	
Eltham	d			19 07					19 37					20 07						20 37				21 07	
Kidbrooke	d			19 10					19 40					20 10						20 40				21 10	
Blackheath 4	d			19 13				19 40	19 43					20 13				20 40		20 43				21 13	
Lewisham 4	d			19 16		19 23		19 43	19 46			19 53		20 16		20 23		20 43		20 46		20 53		21 16	
St Johns	d																								
New Cross 4	⊖ d			19 20		19 27			19 50			19 57		20 20		20 27				20 50		20 57		21 20	
Nunhead 4	d																								
Peckham Rye 4	d																								
Denmark Hill 4	d																								
London Victoria 15	⊖ a																								
Westcombe Park	d	18 52					19 20						19 50				20 20						20 50		
Maze Hill	d	18 54					19 22						19 52				20 22						20 52		
Greenwich 4	d	18 58					19 26						19 56				20 26						20 56		
Deptford	d	19 00					19 28						19 58				20 28						20 58		
London Bridge 4	⊖ a	19 07		19 25		19 33	19 36	19 52	19 55			20 03	20 06	20 25		20 33	20 36	20 52		20 55		21 03	21 06	21 25	
London Cannon Street 4	⊖ a																								
London Waterloo (East) 4	⊖ a	19 11		19 30		19 38	19 40	19 57	20 00			20 08	20 10	20 30		20 38	20 40	20 57		21 00		21 08	21 10	21 30	
London Charing Cross 4	⊖ a	19 15		19 34		19 41	19 44	20 00	20 04			20 11	20 14	20 34		20 41	20 44	21 00		21 04		21 11	21 14	21 34	

For general notes see front of timetable
For details of catering facilities see Directory of Train Operators

Table 200

Sundays

Gillingham and Dartford → London

Network Diagram - see first page of Table 200

		SE 50	SE 80	SE 62		SE 70	SE 80	SE 50	SE 80	SE 72	SE 80	SE 50		SE 80	SE 62	SE 70	SE 80	SE 50	SE 80	SE 72		SE 50			
Gillingham (Kent) 4	d			20 46						21 13					21 46					22 13					
Chatham 4	d			20 50						21 17					21 50					22 17					
Rochester 4	d			20 52						21 19					21 52					22 19					
Maidstone West 4	d									*21 00*															
Strood 4	d			20 56						21 24					21 56					22 24					
Higham	d			21 01						21 29					22 01					22 29					
Gravesend 4	d			21 07						21 36					22 07					22 36					
Northfleet	d									21 39										22 39					
Swanscombe	d									21 41										22 41					
Greenhithe for Bluewater	d			21 12						21 44					22 12					22 44					
Stone Crossing	d									21 46										22 46					
Dartford 4	a			21 17						21 49					22 17					22 49					
	d	20 57		21 18		21 20	21 24	21 27		21 50	21 54	21 57			22 18	22 20	22 24	22 27		22 50		22 57			
Slade Green 4	d						21 29				21 59						22 29								
Erith	d						21 31				22 01						22 31								
Belvedere	d						21 34				22 04						22 34								
Abbey Wood	d			21 27			21 37				22 07				22 27		22 37								
Plumstead	d		←				21 40		←		22 10			←			22 40		←						
Woolwich Arsenal 4	d		21 13	21 31			21 43		21 43		22 13			22 13	22 31		22 43		22 43						
Woolwich Dockyard	d		21 15				→		21 45		→			22 15			→		22 45						
Charlton 4	d		21 18	21 36					21 48					22 18	22 36				22 48						
Crayford	d	21 00						21 30				22 00						22 30				23 00			
Bexley	d	21 03						21 33				22 03						22 33				23 03			
Albany Park	d	21 05						21 35				22 05						22 35				23 05			
Sidcup 4	d	21 08						21 38				22 08						22 38				23 08			
New Eltham	d	21 11						21 41				22 11						22 41				23 11			
Mottingham	d	21 13						21 43				22 13						22 43				23 13			
Lee	d	21 16						21 46				22 16						22 46				23 16			
Hither Green 4	d	21 18						21 48				22 18						22 48				23 18			
Barnehurst 4	d					21 26				21 56						22 26				22 56					
Bexleyheath	d					21 28				21 58						22 28				22 58					
Welling	d					21 31				22 01						22 31				23 01					
Falconwood	d					21 34				22 04						22 34				23 04					
Eltham	d					21 37				22 07						22 37				23 07					
Kidbrooke	d					21 40				22 10						22 40				23 10					
Blackheath 4	d			21 40		21 43				22 13					22 40	22 43				23 13					
Lewisham 4	⛴ d	21 23		21 43		21 46		21 53		22 16		22 23			22 43	22 46		22 53		23 16		23 23			
St Johns	d																								
New Cross 4	⊖ d	21 27				21 50		21 57		22 20		22 27				22 50		22 57		23 20		23 27			
Nunhead 4	d																								
Peckham Rye 4	d																								
Denmark Hill 4	d																								
London Victoria 15	⊖ a																								
Westcombe Park	d		21 20						21 50					22 20					22 50						
Maze Hill	d		21 22						21 52					22 22					22 52						
Greenwich 4	⛴ d		21 26						21 56					22 26					22 56						
Deptford	d		21 28						21 58					22 28					22 58						
London Bridge 4	⊖ a	21 33	21 36	21 52		21 55		22 03	22 06	22 25		22 33		22 36	22 52	22 55		23 03	23 06	23 25		23 33			
London Cannon Street 4	⊖ a																								
London Waterloo (East) 4	⊖ a	21 38	21 40	21 57		22 00		22 08	22 10	22 30		22 38		22 40	22 57	23 00		23 08	23 10	23 30		23 38			
London Charing Cross 4	⊖ a	21 41	21 44	22 00		22 04		22 11	22 14	22 34		22 41		22 44	23 00	23 04		23 11	23 14	23 34		23 41			

For general notes see front of timetable
For details of catering facilities see
Directory of Train Operators

For details of Bank Holiday service alterations please see first page of Table 195

London → Hayes (Kent) via Catford Bridge

Network Diagram - see first page of Table 200

Miles	Miles			SE MX 24	SE MX 24	SE MO 24	SE 25	SE 24		SE 25	SE 24	SE 25	SE 34	SE 25		SE 25	SE 34	SE 36	SE 25	SE 25		SE 34	SE 25	SE 36 A	SE 34
0	—	**London Charing Cross** [4]	⊖ d	23p22	23p52	23p52		05 49		06 27	06 51	07 06	07 22	07 45			08 26	08 36				08 52		09 00	09 14
¾	—	**London Waterloo (East)** [4]	⊖ d	23p25	23p55	23p55		05 52		06 30	06 54	07 09	07 25	07 48			08 29	08 39				08 55		09 04	09 17
—	0	**London Cannon Street** [4]	⊖ d													08 20			08 40	08 54					
1¾	¾	**London Bridge** [4]	⊖ d	23p30	23p58	00 01		05 57		06 35	06 59	07 14	07 30	07 53		08 24	08 34	08 44	08 44	08 58		09 00		09 10	09 22
4¾	—	New Cross [4]	⊖ d	23p35	00 04	00 06	05 37			06 41	07 05	07 20		07 59		08 29			08 49	09 05			←		
5½	—	St Johns	d	23p37	00 06	00 08				06 43	07 07	07 22		08 01		08 31			08 51	09 07			09 07		
6	—	**Lewisham** [4]	d	23p40	00 09	00 10	05 42	06 06		06 46	07 10	07b27		08 04		08 34			08 54	→			09c12		
6¾	—	Ladywell	d	23p42	00 11	00 13	05 44	06 08		06 48	07 12	07 29	07 39	08 07		08 37	08 43	08 53	08 57			09 09	09 14	09 18	09 32
7½	—	**Catford Bridge**	d	23p44	00 13	00 15	05 46	06 10		06 50	07 14	07 31	07 41	08 09		08 39	08 45	08 55	08 59			09 11	09 16	09 21	09 34
9	—	Lower Sydenham	d	23p47	00 16	00 17	05 49	06 13		06 53	07 17	07 34	07 44	08 12		08 42	08 48	08 58	09 02				09 19	09 23	09 37
9½	—	New Beckenham [4]	d	23p49	00 18	00 19	05 51	06 15		06 55	07 19	07 36	07 46	08 14		08 44	08 50	09a00	09 06			09 16	09 22	09a26	09 39
10¼	—	Clock House	d	23p51	00 20	00 21	05 53	06 17		06 57	07 21	07 38	07 48	08 16		08 46	08 52		09 08			09 18	09 24		09 41
11	—	Elmers End [4]	d	23p54	00 23	00 24	05 56	06 20		07 00	07 24	07 41	07 51	08 19		08 49	08 55		09 11			09 21	09 27		09 44
12½	—	Eden Park	d	23p58	00 27	00 27	06 00	06 24		07 04	07 28	07 45	07 55	08 23		08 53	08 59		09 15				09 31		09 48
13¼	—	West Wickham	d	00 01	00 29	00 29	06 02	06 26		07 06	07 30	07 47	07 57	08 25		08 55	09 01		09 17				09 33		09 50
14½	—	**Hayes (Kent)**	a	00 03	00 32	00 32	06 05	06 29		07 09	07 33	07 50	08 00	08 28		08 58	09 04		09 20			09 28	09 38		09 53

		SE 25	SE 34	SE 25			SE 34	SE 25	SE 34	SE 25		SE 34		SE 25	SE 34	SE 25	SE 24	SE 24		SE 25	SE 34	SE 25	SE 34	SE 25
London Charing Cross [4]	⊖ d		09 36				10 06		10 36		and at	15 06			15 36		16 06	16 26			16 52		17 14	
London Waterloo (East) [4]	⊖ d		09 39				10 09		10 39			15 09			15 39		16 09	16 29			16 55		17 17	
London Cannon Street [4]	⊖ d	09 24		09 54				10 24		10 54	the same			15 24		15 54				16 46		17 04		17 32
London Bridge [4]	⊖ d	09 28	09 45	09 58			10 15	10 28	10 45	10 58		15 15		15 28	15 45	15 58	16 14	16 34		16 50	17 00	17 08	17 22	17 36
New Cross [4]	⊖ d	09 35		10 05				10 33		11 03	minutes			15 33		16 03				16 56				17 42
St Johns	d	09 37		10 07				10 35		11 05				15 35		16 05				16 58		17 18		17 44
Lewisham [4]	d	09 40		10 10				10 38		11 08	past			15 38		16 08	16 24	16 44		17 02		17 22		17 46
Ladywell	d	09 42	09 55	10 12			10 25	10 40	10 55	11 10		15 25		15 40	15 55	16 10	16 27	16 47		17 05	17 11	17 25	17 35	17 49
Catford Bridge	d	09 44	09 57	10 14			10 27	10 42	10 57	11 12	each	15 27		15 42	15 57	16 12	16 29	16 49		17 07	17 13	17 27	17 37	17 51
Lower Sydenham	d	09 47	10 00	10 17			10 30	10 45	11 00	11 15		15 30		15 45	16 00	16 15	16 32	16 52		17 10	17 16	17 30	17 40	17 54
New Beckenham [4]	d	09 49	10 02	10 19			10 32	10 47	11 02	11 17	hour until	15 32		15 47	16 02	16 17	16 34	16 54		17 12	17 18	17 32	17 42	17 56
Clock House	d	09 51	10 04	10 21			10 34	10 49	11 04	11 19		15 34		15 49	16 04	16 19	16 37	16 57		17 15	17 21	17 35	17 45	17 59
Elmers End [4]	d	09 54	10 07	10 24			10 37	10 52	11 07	11 22		15 37		15 52	16 07	16 22	16 40	17 00		17 18	17 24	17 38	17 48	18 02
Eden Park	d	09 58	10 11	10 28			10 41	10 56	11 11	11 26		15 41		15 56	16 11	16 26	16 43	17 03		17 21	17 27	17 41	17 51	18 05
West Wickham	d	10 00	10 13	10 30			10 43	10 58	11 13	11 28		15 43		15 58	16 13	16 28	16 45	17 05		17 23	17 29	17 43	17 53	18 07
Hayes (Kent)	a	10 03	10 16	10 33			10 46	11 01	11 16	11 31		15 46		16 01	16 16	16 31	16 50	17 10		17 28	17 34	17 48	17 58	18 12

		SE 34	SE 25		SE 34	SE 25	SE 24	SE 24	SE 24		SE 25	SE 24	SE 25	SE 24	SE 24		SE 24	SE 24	SE 24	SE 24	SE 24		SE 24		
London Charing Cross [4]	⊖ d	17 38			17 58		18 23	18 42	19 06			19 38		20 22	20 52		21 22	21 52	22 22	22 52	23 22		23 52		
London Waterloo (East) [4]	⊖ d	17 41			18 01		18 26	18 45	19 09			19 41		20 25	20 55		21 25	21 55	22 25	22 55	23 25		23 55		
London Cannon Street [4]	⊖ d		17 52			18 12					19 26		19 56												
London Bridge [4]	⊖ d		17 56		18 06	18 16	18 31	18 50	19 14		19 30	19 46	20 00	20 30	21 00		21 30	22 00	22 30	23 00	23 30		23 58		
New Cross [4]	⊖ d		18 02			18 22			19 20		19 35	19 52	20 05	20 35	21 05		21 35	22 05	22 35	23 05	23 35		00 04		
St Johns	d		18 04			18 24			19 22		19 37	19 54	20 07	20 37	21 07		21 37	22 07	22 37	23 07	23 37		00 06		
Lewisham [4]	d		18 08			18 26	18 40	19 00	19 24		19 40	19 57	20 10	20 40	21 10		21 40	22 10	22 40	23 10	23 40		00 09		
Ladywell	d	17 57	18 11		18 19	18 29	18 43	19 03	19 27		19 42	19 59	20 12	20 42	21 12		21 42	22 12	22 42	23 12	23 42		00 11		
Catford Bridge	d	17 59	18 13		18 21	18 31	18 45	19 05	19 29		19 45	20 01	20 14	20 44	21 14		21 44	22 14	22 44	23 14	23 44		00 13		
Lower Sydenham	d	18 02	18 16		18 24	18 34	18 48	19 08	19 32		19 47	20 04	20 17	20 47	21 17		21 47	22 17	22 47	23 17	23 47		00 16		
New Beckenham [4]	d	18 04	18 18		18 26	18 36	18 50	19 10	19 34		19 50	20 06	20 19	20 49	21 19		21 49	22 19	22 49	23 19	23 49		00 18		
Clock House	d	18 07	18 21		18 29	18 39	18 53	19 13	19 37		19 52	20 08	20 21	20 51	21 21		21 51	22 21	22 51	23 21	23 51		00 20		
Elmers End [4]	d	18 10	18 24		18 32	18 42	18 56	19 16	19 40		19 55	20 11	20 24	20 54	21 24		21 54	22 24	22 54	23 24	23 54		00 23		
Eden Park	d	18 13	18 27		18 35	18 45	18 59	19 19	19 43		19 58	20 15	20 28	20 58	21 28		21 58	22 28	22 58	23 28	23 58		00 27		
West Wickham	d	18 15	18 29		18 37	18 47	19 01	19 21	19 45		20 00	20 17	20 30	21 00	21 30		22 00	22 30	23 00	23 30	00 01		00 29		
Hayes (Kent)	a	18 20	18 34		18 42	18 52	19 06	19 26	19 50		20 05	20 20	20 33	21 03	21 33		22 03	22 33	23 03	23 33	00 03		00 32		

Saturdays

		SE 24	SE 24		SE 24	SE 24		SE 24	SE 24		SE 24	SE 24		SE 25	SE 24		SE 25	SE 24		SE 25		SE 34	SE 25	SE 34	
London Charing Cross [4]	⊖ d	23p22	23p52		05 52	06 22		06 52	07 22		07 52	08 22			09 06			09 36				10 06		10 36	
London Waterloo (East) [4]	⊖ d	23p25	23p55		05 55	06 25		06 55	07 25		07 55	08 25			09 09			09 39				10 09		10 39	
London Cannon Street [4]	⊖ d													08 54			09 24			09 54			10 24		
London Bridge [4]	⊖ d	23p30	23p58		06 01	06 31		07 01	07 31		08 01	08 31		08 58	09 15		09 28	09 45		09 58		10 15	10 28	10 45	
New Cross [4]	⊖ d	23p35	00 04		06 06	06 36		07 06	07 36		08 06	08 36		09 03			09 33			10 03			10 33		
St Johns	d	23p37	00 06		06 08	06 38		07 08	07 38		08 08	08 38		09 05			09 35			10 05			10 35		
Lewisham [4]	d	23p40	00 09		06 11	06 41		07 11	07 41		08 11	08 41		09 08			09 38			10 08			10 38		
Ladywell	d	23p42	00 11		06 13	06 43		07 13	07 43		08 13	08 43		09 10	09 25		09 40	09 55		10 10		10 25	10 40	10 55	
Catford Bridge	d	23p44	00 13		06 15	06 45		07 15	07 45		08 15	08 45		09 12	09 27		09 42	09 57		10 12		10 27	10 42	10 57	
Lower Sydenham	d	23p47	00 16		06 18	06 48		07 18	07 48		08 18	08 48		09 15	09 30		09 45	10 00		10 15		10 30	10 45	11 00	
New Beckenham [4]	d	23p49	00 18		06 20	06 50		07 20	07 50		08 20	08 50		09 17	09 32		09 47	10 02		10 17		10 32	10 47	11 02	
Clock House	d	23p51	00 20		06 22	06 52		07 22	07 52		08 22	08 52		09 19	09 34		09 49	10 04		10 19		10 34	10 49	11 04	
Elmers End [4]	d	23p54	00 23		06 25	06 55		07 25	07 55		08 25	08 55		09 22	09 35		09 52	10 05		10 22		10 37	10 52	11 07	
Eden Park	d	23p58	00 27		06 29	06 59		07 29	07 59		08 29	08 59		09 26	09 39		09 56	10 09		10 26		10 41	10 56	11 11	
West Wickham	d	00 01	00 29		06 31	07 01		07 31	08 01		08 31	09 01		09 28	09 41		09 58	10 11		10 28		10 43	10 58	11 13	
Hayes (Kent)	a	00 03	00 32		06 34	07 04		07 34	08 04		08 34	09 04		09 31	09 46		10 01	10 16		10 31		10 46	11 01	11 16	

For general notes see front of timetable
For details of catering facilities see Directory of Train Operators

A To Beckenham Junction arr 0929
b Arr. 0724
c Arr. 0909

Table 203

Saturdays

London → Hayes (Kent) via Catford Bridge

Network Diagram - see first page of Table 200

		SE 25		SE 24	SE 25	SE 24	SE 25	SE 24	SE 24	SE 24	SE 24	SE 24	SE 24	SE 24	SE 24	SE 24	SE 24
London Charing Cross 4	⊖ d		and at	18 06		18 36	18 52	19 22	19 52	20 22	20 52	21 22	21 52	22 22	22 52	23 22	23 52
London Waterloo (East) 4	⊖ d		the same	18 09		18 39	18 55	19 25	19 55	20 25	20 55	21 25	21 55	22 25	22 55	23 25	23 55
London Cannon Street 4	⊖ d	10 54	minutes		18 24												
London Bridge 4	⊖ d	10 58	past	18 15	18 28	18 45	19 01	19 31	20 01	20 31	21 01	21 31	22 01	22 31	23 01	23 31	23 58
New Cross 4	⊖ d	11 03	each		18 33		19 06	19 36	20 06	20 36	21 06	21 36	22 06	22 36	23 06	23 36	00 04
St Johns	d	11 05	hour until		18 36		19 08	19 38	20 08	20 38	21 08	21 38	22 08	22 38	23 08	23 38	00 06
Lewisham 4	d	11 08			18 39		19 11	19 41	20 11	20 41	21 11	21 41	22 11	22 41	23 11	23 41	00 09
Ladywell	d	11 10		18 25	18 41	18 55	19 13	19 43	20 13	20 43	21 13	21 43	22 13	22 43	23 13	23 43	00 11
Catford Bridge	d	11 12		18 27	18 43	18 57	19 15	19 45	20 15	20 45	21 15	21 45	22 15	22 45	23 15	23 45	00 13
Lower Sydenham	d	11 15		18 30	18 46	19 00	19 18	19 48	20 18	20 48	21 18	21 48	22 18	22 48	23 18	23 48	00 16
New Beckenham 4	d	11 17		18 32	18 48	19 02	19 20	19 50	20 20	20 50	21 20	21 50	22 20	22 50	23 20	23 50	00 18
Clock House	d	11 19		18 34	18 50	19 04	19 22	19 52	20 22	20 52	21 22	21 52	22 22	22 52	23 22	23 52	00 20
Elmers End 4	d	11 22		18 35	18 52	19 07	19 25	19 55	20 25	20 55	21 25	21 55	22 25	22 55	23 25	23 55	00 23
Eden Park	d	11 26		18 39	18 56	19 11	19 29	19 59	20 29	20 59	21 29	21 59	22 29	22 59	23 29	23 59	00 27
West Wickham	d	11 28		18 41	18 58	19 13	19 31	20 01	20 31	21 01	21 31	22 01	22 31	23 01	23 31	00 01	00 29
Hayes (Kent)	a	11 31		18 46	19 01	19 16	19 34	20 04	20 34	21 04	21 34	22 04	22 34	23 04	23 34	00 04	00 32

Sundays

		SE 24	SE 24	SE 24	SE 24	SE 24		SE 24	SE 24	SE 24	SE 24	SE 24	SE 24
London Charing Cross 4	⊖ d	23p22	23p52	07 52	08 52	09 22		18 52	19 52	20 52	21 52	22 52	23 52
London Waterloo (East) 4	⊖ d	23p25	23p55	07 55	08 55	09 25		18 55	19 55	20 55	21 55	22 55	23 55
London Cannon Street 4	⊖ d						and						
London Bridge 4	⊖ d	23p31	23p58	08 00	09 00	09 30	every 30	19 00	20 00	21 00	22 00	23 00	00 01
New Cross 4	⊖ d	23p36	00 04	08 06	09 06	09 36	minutes	19 07	20 06	21 06	22 06	23 06	00 06
St Johns	d	23p38	00 06	08 08	09 08	09 38	until	19 08	20 08	21 08	22 08	23 08	00 08
Lewisham 4	d	23p41	00 09	08 10	09 10	09 40		19 10	20 10	21 10	22 10	23 10	00 10
Ladywell	d	23p43	00 11	08 13	09 13	09 43		19 13	20 13	21 13	22 13	23 13	00 13
Catford Bridge	d	23p45	00 13	08 15	09 15	09 45		19 15	20 15	21 15	22 15	23 15	00 15
Lower Sydenham	d	23p48	00 16	08 17	09 17	09 47		19 17	20 17	21 17	22 17	23 17	00 17
New Beckenham 4	d	23p50	00 18	08 19	09 19	09 49		19 19	20 19	21 19	22 19	23 19	00 19
Clock House	d	23p52	00 20	08 21	09 21	09 51		19 21	20 21	21 21	22 21	23 21	00 21
Elmers End 4	d	23p55	00 23	08 24	09 24	09 54		19 24	20 24	21 24	22 24	23 24	00 24
Eden Park	d	23p59	00 27	08 27	09 27	09 57		19 27	20 27	21 27	22 27	23 27	00 27
West Wickham	d	00 01	00 29	08 29	09 29	09 59		19 29	20 29	21 29	22 29	23 29	00 29
Hayes (Kent)	a	00 04	00 32	08 32	09 32	10 02		19 32	20 32	21 32	22 32	23 32	00 32

For general notes see front of timetable
For details of catering facilities see Directory of Train Operators

For details of Bank Holiday service alterations please see first page of Table 195

Hayes (Kent) → London via Catford Bridge

Network Diagram - see first page of Table 200

Miles	Miles			SE 24	SE 24	SE 24	SE 24	SE 24	SE 25	SE 34	SE 25	SE 24	SE 25	SE 34	SE 25	SE 34	SE 25	SE 24	SE 25	SE 34
0	—	**Hayes (Kent)**	d	05 16	05 46	06 16	06 36	07 10	07 25	07 37	07 45	07 57	08 05	08 17	08 25	08 40	09 00	09 15	09 25	09 35
1¼	—	West Wickham	d	05 19	05 49	06 19	06 39	07 13	07 28	07 40	07 48	08 00	08 08	08 20	08 28	08 43	09 03	09 18	09 28	09 38
2	—	Eden Park	d	05 21	05 51	06 21	06 41	07 15	07 30	07 42	07 50	08 02	08 10	08 22	08 30	08 45	09 05	09 20	09 30	09 40
3½	—	Elmers End 4	d	05 25	05 55	06 25	06 45	07 19	07 34	07 46	07 54	08 06	08 14	08 26	08 34	08 49	09 09	09 24	09 34	09 44
4¼	—	Clock House	d	05 27	05 57	06 27	06 47	07 21	07 36	07 48	07 56	08 08	08 16	08 28	08 36	08 51	09 11	09 26	09 36	09 46
5	—	New Beckenham 4	d	05 29	05 59	06 29	06 49	07 24	07 39	07 51	07 59	08 11	08 19	08 31	08 39	08 54	09 14	09 28	09 38	09 48
5½	—	Lower Sydenham	d	05 31	06 01	06 31	06 51	07 25	07 40	07 52	08 00	08 12	08 20	08 32	08 40	08 55	09 15	09 30	09 40	09 50
7	—	**Catford Bridge**	d	05 34	06 04	06 34	06 54	07 29	07 44	07 56	08 04	08 16	08 24	08 36	08 44	08 59	09 19	09 33	09 43	09 53
7¾	—	Ladywell	d	05 36	06 06	06 36	06 56	07 31	07 46	07 58	08 06	08 18	08 26	08 38	08 46	09 01	09 21	09 35	09 45	09 55
8½	—	**Lewisham 4**	d	05 40	06 10	06 40	07 00	07 35	07 50		08 10		08 30		08 50		09 24		09 48	
9	—	St Johns	a	05 42	06 12	06 42			07 52		08 12		08 32		08 52		09 28		09 52	
9¾	—	New Cross 4	a	05 44	06 14	06 44	07 04		07 54		08 14		08 34		08 54		09 30		09 54	
12¾	0	**London Bridge 4**	a	05 50	06 20	06 50	07 11	07 43	08 00		08 20		08 40		09 00	09 13	09 37	09 43	10 01	10 07
—	¾	**London Cannon Street 4**	a						08 06		08 26		08 46		09 06		09 43		10 06	
13¾	—	**London Waterloo (East) 4**	a	05 55	06 25	06 55	07 16	07 48		08 13		08 33		08 53		09 19		09 48		10 14
14½	—	**London Charing Cross 4**	a	05 58	06 28	06 58	07 20	07 53		08 18		08 38		08 58		09 24		09 52		10 17

		SE 25	SE 34	SE 25	SE 34	SE 25	SE 34	SE 25		SE 34	SE 34 A	SE 25	SE 34	SE 24	SE 24	SE 25	SE 34	SE 25	SE 34
Hayes (Kent)	d	09 42	09 57	10 12	10 27	10 42	10 57	11 12	and at the same minutes past each hour until	15 27		15 42	15 57	16 12	16 27	16 37	16 47	16 57	17 17
West Wickham	d	09 45	10 00	10 15	10 30	10 45	11 00	11 15		15 30		15 45	16 00	16 15	16 30	16 40		17 00	17 20
Eden Park	d	09 47	10 02	10 17	10 32	10 47	11 02	11 17		15 32		15 47	16 02	16 17	16 32	16 42		17 02	17 22
Elmers End 4	d	09 51	10 06	10 21	10 36	10 51	11 06	11 21		15 36		15 51	16 06	16 21	16 36	16 46	16 54	17 06	17 26
Clock House	d	09 53	10 08	10 23	10 38	10 53	11 08	11 23		15 38		15 53	16 08	16 23	16 38	16 48	16 56	17 08	17 28
New Beckenham 4	d	09 55	10 10	10 25	10 40	10 55	11 10	11 25		15 40	15 48	15 55	16 10	16 25	16 40	16 50	16 58	17 10	17 30
Lower Sydenham	d	09 57	10 12	10 27	10 42	10 57	11 12	11 27		15 42	15 49	15 57	16 12	16 27	16 42	16 52		17 12	17 32
Catford Bridge	d	10 00	10 15	10 30	10 45	11 00	11 15	11 30		15 45	15 53	16 00	16 15	16 30	16 45	16 55	17 02	17 15	17 35
Ladywell	d	10 02	10 17	10 32	10 47	11 02	11 17	11 32		15 47	15 55	16 02	16 17	16 32	16 47	16 57	17 04	17 17	17 37
Lewisham 4	d	10 06		10 36		11 06		11 36				16 08	16 21	16b38		17 02		17 21	17c44
St Johns	a	10 08		10 38		11 08		11 38				16 10		16 40		17 04		17 23	
New Cross 4	a	10 10		10 40		11 10		11 40				16 12		16 42		17 06		17 25	
London Bridge 4	a	10 16	10 27	10 46	10 57	11 16	11 27	11 46		15 57		16 18	16 31	16 49	16 57	17 14	17 15	17 32	17 54
London Cannon Street 4	a	10 20		10 50		11 20		11 50				16 22				17 18		17 36	
London Waterloo (East) 4	a		10 34		11 04		11 34			16 03	16 11		16 36	16 55	17 03		17 20		17 59
London Charing Cross 4	a		10 39		11 09		11 39			16 07	16 15		16 40	16 59	17 09		17 25		18 03

		SE 34	SE 25	SE 34	SE 34	SE 24	SE 25	SE 24	SE 24	SE 24	SE 24	SE 24	SE 24	SE 24	SE 24	SE 24	SE 24
Hayes (Kent)	d	17 37	17 43	17 55	18 05	18 21	18 31	18 43	18 53	19 23	19 53	20 23	20 53	21 23	21 53	22 23	22 53
West Wickham	d	17 40	17 46		18 08	18 24	18 34	18 46	18 56	19 26	19 56	20 26	20 56	21 26	21 56	22 26	22 56
Eden Park	d	17 42	17 48		18 10	18 26	18 36	18 48	18 58	19 28	19 58	20 28	20 58	21 28	21 58	22 28	22 58
Elmers End 4	d	17 46	17 54	18 01	18 14	18 30	18 40	18 52	19 02	19 32	20 02	20 32	21 02	21 32	22 02	22 32	23 02
Clock House	d	17 48	17 56	18 03	18 16	18 32	18 42	18 54	19 04	19 34	20 04	20 34	21 04	21 34	22 04	22 34	23 04
New Beckenham 4	d	17 50	17 58	18 06	18 18	18 34	18 44	18 56	19 06	19 36	20 06	20 36	21 06	21 36	22 06	22 36	23 06
Lower Sydenham	d	17 52	18 00		18 20	18 36	18 46	18 58	19 08	19 38	20 08	20 38	21 08	21 38	22 08	22 38	23 08
Catford Bridge	d	17 55	18 03	18 10	18 23	18 39	18 49	19 01	19 11	19 41	20 11	20 41	21 11	21 41	22 11	22 41	23 11
Ladywell	d	17 57	18 05	18 12	18 25	18 41	18 51	19 03	19 13	19 43	20 13	20 43	21 13	21 43	22 13	22 43	23 13
Lewisham 4	d		18 10		18 29	18 45	18 56	19e09	19 17	19 47	20 17	20 47	21 17	21 47	22 17	22 47	23 17
St Johns	a						18 58	19 11	19 19	19 49	20 19	20 49	21 19	21 49	22 19	22 49	23 19
New Cross 4	a						19 00	19 13	19 21	19 51	20 21	20 51	21 21	21 51	22 21	22 51	23 21
London Bridge 4	a	18 09		18 22	18 37	18 54	19 05	19 19	19 28	19 58	20 28	20 58	21 28	21 58	22 28	22 58	23 28
London Cannon Street 4	a						19 10										
London Waterloo (East) 4	a	18 15	18 23	18 27	18 42	18 59		19 24	19 33	20 03	20 33	21 03	21 33	22 03	22 33	23 03	23 33
London Charing Cross 4	a	18 19	18 27	18 33	18 49	19 05		19 29	19 37	20 07	20 37	21 07	21 37	22 07	22 37	23 07	23 37

Saturdays

		SE 24	SE 24	SE 24	SE 24	SE 24	SE 25	SE 24	SE 25	SE 24	SE 25	SE 34	SE 25	SE 34	SE 25	SE 34		SE 25
Hayes (Kent)	d	05 23	05 53	06 23	06 53	07 23	07 42	07 57	08 12	08 27	08 42	08 57	09 12	09 27	09 42	09 57	and at the same minutes past each hour until	17 12
West Wickham	d	05 26	05 56	06 26	06 56	07 26	07 45	08 00	08 15	08 30	08 45	09 00	09 15	09 30	09 45	10 00		17 15
Eden Park	d	05 28	05 58	06 28	06 58	07 28	07 47	08 02	08 17	08 32	08 47	09 02	09 17	09 32	09 47	10 02		17 17
Elmers End 4	d	05 32	06 02	06 32	07 02	07 32	07 51	08 06	08 21	08 36	08 51	09 06	09 21	09 36	09 51	10 06		17 21
Clock House	d	05 34	06 04	06 34	07 04	07 34	07 53	08 08	08 23	08 38	08 53	09 08	09 23	09 38	09 53	10 08		17 23
New Beckenham 4	d	05 36	06 06	06 36	07 06	07 36	07 55	08 10	08 25	08 40	08 55	09 10	09 25	09 40	09 55	10 10		17 25
Lower Sydenham	d	05 38	06 08	06 38	07 08	07 38	07 57	08 12	08 27	08 42	08 57	09 12	09 27	09 42	09 57	10 12		17 27
Catford Bridge	d	05 41	06 11	06 41	07 11	07 41	08 00	08 15	08 30	08 45	09 00	09 15	09 30	09 45	10 00	10 15		17 30
Ladywell	d	05 43	06 13	06 43	07 13	07 43	08 02	08 17	08 32	08 47	09 02	09 17	09 32	09 47	10 02	10 17		17 32
Lewisham 4	d	05 47	06 17	06 47	07 17	07 47	08 06		08 36		09 06		09 36		10 06			17 36
St Johns	a	05 49	06 19	06 49	07 19	07 49	08 08		08 38		09 08		09 38		10 08			17 38
New Cross 4	a	05 51	06 21	06 51	07 21	07 51	08 10		08 40		09 10		09 40		10 10			17 40
London Bridge 4	a	05 58	06 29	06 58	07 29	07 58	08 16	08 27	08 46	08 57	09 16	09 27	09 46	09 57	10 16	10 27		17 46
London Cannon Street 4	a						08 20		08 50		09 20		09 50		10 20			17 50
London Waterloo (East) 4	a	06 03	06 34	07 03	07 33	08 03		08 34		09 04		09 34		10 04		10 34		
London Charing Cross 4	a	06 07	06 37	07 07	07 37	08 07		08 39		09 09		09 39		10 09		10 39		

For general notes see front of timetable
For details of catering facilities see Directory of Train Operators

A From Beckenham Junction
b Arr. 1635
c Arr. 1740
e Arr. 1906

Table 203

Saturdays

Hayes (Kent) → London via Catford Bridge

Network Diagram - see first page of Table 200

		SE 24	SE 25	SE 24	SE 24	SE 24	SE 24	SE 24	SE 24	SE 24	SE 24	SE 24	SE 24	SE 24
Hayes (Kent)	d	17 27	17 42	17 57	18 23	18 53	19 23	19 53	20 23	20 53	21 23	21 53	22 23	22 53
West Wickham	d	17 30	17 45	18 00	18 26	18 56	19 26	19 56	20 26	20 56	21 26	21 56	22 26	22 56
Eden Park	d	17 32	17 47	18 02	18 28	18 58	19 28	19 58	20 28	20 58	21 28	21 58	22 28	22 58
Elmers End [4]	d	17 36	17 51	18 06	18 32	19 02	19 32	20 02	20 32	21 02	21 32	22 02	22 32	23 02
Clock House	d	17 38	17 53	18 08	18 34	19 04	19 34	20 04	20 34	21 04	21 34	22 04	22 34	23 04
New Beckenham [4]	d	17 40	17 55	18 10	18 36	19 06	19 36	20 06	20 36	21 06	21 36	22 06	22 36	23 06
Lower Sydenham	d	17 42	17 57	18 12	18 38	19 08	19 38	20 08	20 38	21 08	21 38	22 08	22 38	23 08
Catford Bridge	d	17 45	18 00	18 15	18 41	19 11	19 41	20 11	20 41	21 11	21 41	22 11	22 41	23 11
Ladywell	d	17 47	18 02	18 17	18 43	19 13	19 43	20 13	20 43	21 13	21 43	22 13	22 43	23 13
Lewisham [4]	d		18 06	18 23	18 47	19 17	19 47	20 17	20 47	21 17	21 47	22 17	22 47	23 17
St Johns	a		18 08		18 49	19 19	19 49	20 19	20 49	21 19	21 49	22 19	22 49	23 19
New Cross [4]	⊖ a		18 10		18 51	19 21	19 51	20 21	20 51	21 21	21 51	22 21	22 51	23 21
London Bridge [4]	⊖ a	17 57	18 16	18 33	18 58	19 28	19 58	20 28	20 58	21 28	21 58	22 28	22 58	23 28
London Cannon Street [4]	⊖ a		18 20											
London Waterloo (East) [4]	⊖ a	18 04		18 38	19 03	19 33	20 03	20 33	21 03	21 33	22 03	22 33	23 03	23 33
London Charing Cross [4]	⊖ a	18 09		18 41	19 07	19 37	20 07	20 37	21 07	21 37	22 07	22 37	23 07	23 37

Sundays

		SE 24	SE 24		SE 24	SE 24	SE 24	SE 24	SE 24	SE 24
Hayes (Kent)	d	08 07	08 37		18 07	19 07	20 07	21 07	22 07	23 07
West Wickham	d	08 10	08 40		18 10	19 10	20 10	21 10	22 10	23 10
Eden Park	d	08 12	08 42		18 12	19 12	20 12	21 12	22 12	23 12
Elmers End [4]	d	08 15	08 45	and	18 15	19 15	20 15	21 15	22 15	23 15
Clock House	d	08 17	08 47		18 17	19 17	20 17	21 17	22 17	23 17
New Beckenham [4]	d	08 19	08 49	every 30	18 19	19 19	20 19	21 19	22 19	23 19
Lower Sydenham	d	08 21	08 51		18 21	19 21	20 21	21 21	22 21	23 21
Catford Bridge	d	08 24	08 54	minutes	18 24	19 24	20 24	21 24	22 24	23 24
Ladywell	d	08 26	08 56		18 26	19 26	20 26	21 26	22 26	23 26
Lewisham [4]	d	08 29	08 59	until	18 29	19 29	20 29	21 29	22 29	23 29
St Johns	a	08 31	09 01		18 31	19 31	20 31	21 31	22 31	23 31
New Cross [4]	⊖ a	08 33	09 03		18 33	19 33	20 33	21 33	22 33	23 33
London Bridge [4]	⊖ a	08 39	09 09		18 39	19 39	20 39	21 39	22 39	23 39
London Cannon Street [4]	⊖ a									
London Waterloo (East) [4]	⊖ a	08 44	09 14		18 44	19 44	20 44	21 44	22 44	23 44
London Charing Cross [4]	⊖ a	08 47	09 17		18 47	19 47	20 47	21 47	22 47	23 47

For general notes see front of timetable
For details of catering facilities see Directory of Train Operators

For details of Bank Holiday service alterations please see first page of Table 195

London → Grove Park, Bromley North, Orpington, Sevenoaks and Tonbridge

Network Diagram - see first page of Table 200

Miles	Miles			SE	SE	SE	SE	SE	SE	SE	SE	SE	SE	SE	SE	SE	SE	SE	SE	SE	SE	SE	SE	SE	SE
				MX	MX	MX	MX	MO	MX	MX	MX														
				12	2	12	22	12	70	02	01	14	18	70	14	01	70	16	4	01	16	01	16	70	4
					[1]		[1]						[1]						[1]						[1]
					A								B					C	B		C				
0	—	London Charing Cross [4]	⊖ d	23p26	23p30		23p37	23p42		00 10		00 48	05 30		05 40			06 16	06 25				06 47		07 00
¾	—	London Waterloo (East) [4]	⊖ d	23p29	23p33		23p40	23p45		00 13		00 51	05 33		05 43			06 19	06 28				06 50		07 03
—	—	London Cannon Street [4]	⊖ d																						
1¾	—	London Bridge [4]	⊖ d	23p34	23p38		23p45	23p50		00 18		00 56	05 38		05 48			06 24	06 33				06 56		07 08
4¾	—	New Cross [4]	⊖ d									01 01			05 53										
5½	—	St Johns	d																						
6	—	Lewisham [4]	d	23p43								01 05			05 57										
7¼	—	Hither Green [4]	d	23p47		←		00 01				01 09			06 01			06 33					07 06		
9	0	Grove Park [4]	d	23p51		23p51		00 03		00 29	00 33	01 13			06 04	06 17		06 36		06 42		07 03	07 13		
—	1½	Sundridge Park	d	→							00 36					06 20				06 45		07 06			
—	1¾	Bromley North	a								00 38					06 22				06 47		07 08			
10¼	—	Elmstead Woods	d			23p53		00 06		00 32		01 16			06 07			06 39					07 16 →		
11¼	—	Chislehurst	d			23p56		00 08		00 35		01 19			06 09			06 41							
12¾	—	Petts Wood [4]	d			00 01		00 12	00 25	00 39		01 23		06 10	06 13		06 38	06 45						07 10	
13¾	—	Orpington [4]	a		23p56	00 03		00 15	00 28	00 42		01 26	05 54	06 13	06 16		06 41	06 48	06 49		←			07 13	07 25
—	—		d		23p56					00 42			05 54		06 22			06 54 →	06 50		06 54				07 26
15¼	—	Chelsfield [3]	d							00 46			05 58		06 25						06 57				
16½	—	Knockholt	d										06 01		06 27						06 59				
20½	—	Dunton Green	d										06 07		06 32						07 04				
22	—	Sevenoaks [4]	a		00 06		00 10			00 54			06 10		06 36				06 59		07 08				07 35
—	—		d		00 06		00 10			00 54			06 11						07 00		07 08				
27	—	Hildenborough	d		00 12					01 00			06 17						07 06		07 14				
29½	—	Tonbridge [4]	a		00 17		00 20			01 05			06 21						07 10		07 19				07 44

		SE	SE	SE	SE	SE	SE	SE	SE	SE	SE	SE	SE	SE	SE	SE	SE	SE	SE	SE	SE	SE	SE	SE	SE
		16	01	12	30	70	12	22	01	12	23	83	12	70	4	01	83	14	12	22	01	70	12	4	16
					[1]			[1]			[1]				[1]					[1]				[1]	
					C						D	E					E								
																				(trolley)					
London Charing Cross [4]	⊖ d			07 10	07 16			07 28		07 37					07 52			07 56		08 14			08 20	08 22	08 29
London Waterloo (East) [4]	⊖ d			07 13	07 19			07 31		07 40					07 55			07 59		08 17			08 23	08 25	08 32
London Cannon Street [4]	⊖ d										07 45								08 03						
London Bridge [4]	⊖ d			07 19	07 24			07 36		07 45	07 49				08 02			08 04	08 07	08 23			08 28	08 30	08 38
New Cross [4]	⊖ d																		08 12						
St Johns	d																								
Lewisham [4]	d																		08 16						
Hither Green [4]	d			07 29						07 53									08 20				08 37		
Grove Park [4]	d		07 24	07 33					07 44	07 57						08 05			08 24		08 25		08 41		
Sundridge Park	d		07 27						07 47							08 08					08 28				
Bromley North	a	←	07 29				←		07 49				←			08 10					08 30				
Elmstead Woods	d	07 16		07 35 →			07 35			08 02 →			08 02						08 27				08 44 →		
Chislehurst	d	07 19					07 39						08 05						08 30						
Petts Wood [4]	d	07 22				07 40	07 42						08 09	08 12					08 33			08 39			
Orpington [4]	a	07 25			07 40	07 43	07 45	07 54			08 08		08 12	08 15	08 19			08 23	08 36			08 42		08 47	08 55
	d	07 28			07 41		07 46	07 55			08 09				08 20			08 24						08 48	08 56
Chelsfield [3]	d	07 31					07 49				08 12							08 27							08 59
Knockholt	d	07 33					07 51				08 15							08 29							09 01
Dunton Green	d	07 38					07 56				08 20							08 34							09 06
Sevenoaks [4]	a	07 42			07 50		08 01	08 04			08 24	08 26			08 29		←	08 38		08 46				08 57	09 10
	d				07 51			08 05			08 24	08 34 →			08 30		08 34			08 47				08 58	
Hildenborough	d				07 57			08 11									08 40								
Tonbridge [4]	a				08 01			08 15			08 32				08 38		08 44			08 55				09 06	

		SE	SE	SE	SE	SE	SE	SE	SE	SE	SE	SE	SE	SE	SE	SE	SE	SE	SE	SE	SE	SE	SE	SE	SE
		12	01	12	23	90	12	01	70	12	90	12	23	01	70	16	2	22	70	16	01	4	70	12	8
					[1]	[1]					[1]		[1]				[1]	[1]				[1]			
					G						H						A								J
					(trolley)								(trolley)					(trolley)				(trolley)			
London Charing Cross [4]	⊖ d			08 38		08 54				08 56	08 58					09 26	09 30	09 45				09 53		09 56	10 00
London Waterloo (East) [4]	⊖ d			08 41		08 57				08 59	09 01					09 29	09 33	09 48				09 56		09 59	10 03
London Cannon Street [4]	⊖ d				08 45								09 17												
London Bridge [4]	⊖ d			08 46	08 49	09 02				09 04	09 08		09 21			09 34	09 38	09 53						10 04	10 08
New Cross [4]	⊖ d																								
St Johns	d																								
Lewisham [4]	d															09 43								10 13	
Hither Green [4]	d			08 56						09 17		←				09 47				←				10 17	
Grove Park [4]	d		08 45	09 00				09 05		09 21 →		09 21		09 26		09 51 →				09 51	09 56			10 21 →	
Sundridge Park	d		08 48					09 08						09 29							09 59				
Bromley North	a	←	08 50				←	09 10						09 31							10 01				
Elmstead Woods	d	08 44		09 03 →			09 03					09 23								09 53					
Chislehurst	d	08 47					09 06					09 26								09 56					
Petts Wood [4]	d	08 50					09 09		09 12		09 23	09 30			09 42				09 55	10 00			10 10		10 22
Orpington [4]	a	08 56			09 07		09 12		09 15		09 26	09 33	09 39		09 46		09 54		09 58	10 03			10 13		10 25
	d				09 08						09 26	09 33	09 40				09 54								10 26
Chelsfield [3]	d											09 36													
Knockholt	d											09 39													
Dunton Green	d											09 44													
Sevenoaks [4]	a				09 17						09 36	09 47	09 50				10 04	10 16							10 36
	d				09 18						09 36		09 50				10 04	10 16							10 36
Hildenborough	d				09 24						09 42						10 10								10 42
Tonbridge [4]	a				09 28	09 35					09 47		09 59				10 15	10 24				10 30			10 47

For general notes see front of timetable
For details of catering facilities see Directory of Train Operators

- **A** To Dover Priory (Table 207)
- **B** To Ramsgate (Table 207)
- **C** To Tunbridge Wells (Table 206)
- **D** To Hastings (Table 206)
- **E** From London Blackfriars (Table 195)
- **G** To Hastings (Table 206) and to Hastings (Table 206)
- **H** To Margate (Table 207)
- **J** To Ashford International (Table 207)

For details of Bank Holiday service alterations please see first page of Table 195

London → Grove Park, Bromley North, Orpington, Sevenoaks and Tonbridge

Network Diagram - see first page of Table 200

		SE 83	SE 70	SE 12		SE 22 [1] 🍴	SE 01	SE 90 [1] 🍴	SE 70	SE 16	SE 8 [1] A	SE 22 [1] 🍴	SE 70	SE 16	SE 01	SE 4 [1] 🍴	SE 70	SE 12	SE 8 [1] A	SE 70	SE 12		SE 22 [1] 🍴	SE 01
London Charing Cross [4]	⊖ d					10 15		10 23		10 26	10 30	10 45				10 53		10 56	11 00				15 15	
London Waterloo (East) [4]	⊖ d					10 18		10 26		10 29	10 33	10 48				10 56		10 59	11 03				15 18	
London Cannon Street [4]	⊖ d																							
London Bridge [4]	⊖ d					10 23				10 34	10 38	10 53						11 04	11 08			and at	15 23	
New Cross [4]	⊖ d																							
St Johns	d																					the same		
Lewisham [4]	d									10 43								11 13						
Hither Green [4]	d			←						10 47				←				11 17			←	minutes		
Grove Park [4]	d			10 21			10 26			10 51				10 51	10 56			11 21			11 21			15 26
Sundridge Park	d						10 29			→					10 59			→				past		15 29
Bromley North	a						10 31								11 01									15 31
Elmstead Woods	d			10 23										10 53							11 23	each		
Chislehurst	d			10 26										10 56							11 26			
Petts Wood [4]	d		10 26	10 30					10 39				10 54	11 00			11 09		11 22	11 24	11 30	hour until		
Orpington [4]	a		10 29	10 33		10 39			10 42		10 53		10 57	11 03			11 12		11 25	11 27	11 33		15 39	
	d			10 33		10 40					10 54								11 26		11 33		15 40	
Chelsfield [3]	d			10 36																	11 36			
Knockholt	d			10 39																	11 39			
Dunton Green	d			10 44																	11 44			
Sevenoaks [4]	a	10 43		10 47		10 50					11 04	11 15							11 36		11 47		15 50	
	d					10 50					11 04	11 16							11 36				15 50	
Hildenborough	d										11 10								11 42					
Tonbridge [4]	a					10 59		11 02			11 15	11 24				11 30			11 47				15 59	

		SE 90 [1]	SE 70	SE 16	SE 8 [1] A	SE 70	SE 16	SE 22 [1] 🍴	SE 01	SE 90 [1] 🍴	SE 70	SE 16	SE 8 [1] A	SE 70	SE 16	SE 22 [1] 🍴	SE 01	SE 70	SE 16	SE 16	SE 4 [1] 🍴	SE 8 [1] A	SE 16	SE 01	SE 70
London Charing Cross [4]	⊖ d	15 23		15 26	15 30			15 45		15 53		15 56	16 00			16 15			16 16		16 23	16 30			
London Waterloo (East) [4]	⊖ d	15 26		15 29	15 33			15 48		15 56		15 59	16 03			16 18			16 19		16 26	16 33			
London Cannon Street [4]	⊖ d																			16 22					
London Bridge [4]	⊖ d			15 34	15 38			15 53				16 04	16 08			16 23			16 25	16 26	16 31	16 39			
New Cross [4]	⊖ d																								
St Johns	d																								
Lewisham [4]	d			15 43								16 13								16 35					
Hither Green [4]	d			15 47			←					16 17								16 39					
Grove Park [4]	d			15 51			15 51		15 56			16 21					16 26		16 38	16 43				16 47	
Sundridge Park	d			→					15 59								16 29							16 50	
Bromley North	a								16 01								16 31							16 52	
Elmstead Woods	d						15 53					16 23			←					16 45			←		
Chislehurst	d						15 56					16 26			16 26					16 48			16 48		
Petts Wood [4]	d		15 39			15 54	15 59				16 09	→		16 24	16 29			16 39	16 43	→			16 51		17 01
Orpington [4]	a		15 42		15 53	15 57	16 02				16 12			16 27	16 32			16 42	16 48				16 55		17 04
	d				15 54		16 02								16 33								16 56		
Chelsfield [3]	d						16 05								16 36								17 00		
Knockholt	d						16 08								16 39								17 03		
Dunton Green	d						16 13								16 44								17 08		
Sevenoaks [4]	a				16 04		16 16	16 19					16 32		16 47	16 49					16 55	17 02	17 13		
	d				16 04			16 20					16 32			16 50					16 56	17 02			
Hildenborough	d				16 10								16 38									17 08			
Tonbridge [4]	a	16 02			16 15			16 28		16 32			16 43			16 58					17 04	17 13			

		SE 12	SE 4 [1] 🍴	SE 30 [1] B	SE 17	SE 23 [1]	SE 17	SE 01	SE 70	SE 12	SE 17	SE 90 [1]	SE 9 [1] A	SE 01	SE 4 [1] 🍴	SE 4 [1] 🍴	SE 17	SE 70	SE 13	SE 30 [1] B	SE 17	SE 12	SE 17	SE 91 [1]	SE 30 [1] B
London Charing Cross [4]	⊖ d	16 42	16 46	16 50						17 04		17 12			17 34	17 56				17 20		17 28			17 41
London Waterloo (East) [4]	⊖ d	16 45	16 49	16 53						17 07		17 15			17 37	17 59				17 23		17 31			17 44
London Cannon Street [4]	⊖ d				16 56	17 00					17 14		17 20						17 22				17 40	17 44	
London Bridge [4]	⊖ d	16 50	16 54	16 58	17 00	17 04				17 12	17 18								17 26	17 28			17 44		17 49
New Cross [4]	⊖ d																		17 32						
St Johns	d																								
Lewisham [4]	d																								
Hither Green [4]	d	17 03								17 23												17 46			
Grove Park [4]	d	17 07			17 12			17 16		17 27	17 33			17 36					17 41			17 50	17 57		
Sundridge Park	d							17 19						17 39											
Bromley North	a							17 21						17 41											
Elmstead Woods	d	17 09			17 15					17 29	17 35						←		17 43			17 53	17 59		
Chislehurst	d	17 12			17 18		←			17 32	17 38						17 38		17 46			17 56	18 02		
Petts Wood [4]	d	17 15			17 21		17 21		17 25	17 35	→						17 43	17 49	17 51			17 58	→		
Orpington [4]	a	17 21			→		17 24		17 29	17 41							17 46	17 53	17 57			18 04			
	d						17 24										17 46								
Chelsfield [3]	d						17 27										17 49			17 47					18 07
Knockholt	d						17 30										17 52				←				
Dunton Green	d						17 36										17 58				17 58				
Sevenoaks [4]	a			17 21		17 27	17 41						17 51				→			17 55	18 03			18 11	18 16
	d			17 22		17 28							17 52							17 56				18 12	18 16
Hildenborough	d			17 28									17 58							18 02					18 22
Tonbridge [4]	a		17 24	17 32		17 36						17 50	18 02		18 15	18 34				18 06				18 20	18 27

For general notes see front of timetable
For details of catering facilities see Directory of Train Operators

A To Ashford International (Table 207)
B To Tunbridge Wells (Table 206)

For details of Bank Holiday service alterations please see first page of Table 195

London → Grove Park, Bromley North, Orpington, Sevenoaks and Tonbridge

Network Diagram - see first page of Table 200

	SE 17	SE 01	SE 70	SE 12	SE 17	SE 9 ■1 A	SE 30 ■1 B	SE 17	SE 01	SE 70	SE 70	SE 12	SE 4 ■1 trolley	SE 15	SE 3 ■1	SE 30 ■1 B	SE 15	SE 01	SE 16	SE 70	SE 8 ■1	SE 22 ■1 trolley	SE 16	SE 01
London Charing Cross ■4 ⊖ d				17 49			18 04					18 12	18 16			18 28			18 32		18 40	18 50		
London Waterloo (East) ■4 ⊖ d				17 52			18 07					18 15	18 19			18 31			18 35		18 43	18 53		
London Cannon Street ■4 ⊖ d					18 00	18 04								18 16	18 30									
London Bridge ■4 ⊖ d				17 57	18 04	18 08	18 12							18 20	18 34	18 36			18 40		18 48			
New Cross ■4 ⊖ d														18 26										
St Johns d																								
Lewisham ■4 d														18 30										
Hither Green ■4 d				18 07								18 29							18 51					
Grove Park ■4 d		18 00		18 11	18 17				18 20			18 33		18 37				18 42	18 55					19 02
Sundridge Park d		18 03							18 23									18 45						19 05
Bromley North a		18 05							18 25								←	18 47					←	19 07
Elmstead Woods d	←			18 13	18 19			←				18 35		18 39			18 39		18 57				18 57	
Chislehurst d	18 02			18 16	18 22			18 22				18 38		→			18 42		→				19 00	
Petts Wood ■4 d	18 05		18 10	18 19	→			18 25		18 29	18 35	18 43					18 46			18 56			19 04	
Orpington ■4 a	18 08		18 15	18 25				18 29		18 33	18 40	18 47					18 51			19 01	19 04		19 10	
Orpington d	18 08							18 30									18 56				19 05		19 16	
Chelsfield ■3 d	18 11						18 31	18 33								18 56	18 59						19 19	
Knockholt d	18 14							18 36									19 02						19 22	
Dunton Green d	18 20							18 41									19 07						19 27	
Sevenoaks ■4 a	18 25					18 33	18 39	18 46					18 48		18 58	19 04	19 12				19 14	19 20	19 32	
Sevenoaks d						18 34	18 40						18 48		18 58	19 05					19 15	19 20		
Hildenborough d						18 40	18 46									19 11								
Tonbridge ■4 a						18 44	18 51						18 57		19 07	19 15					19 23	19 29		

	SE 70	SE 13	SE 16	SE 4 ■1 A trolley	SE 23 ■1 C	SE 16	SE 01	SE 70	SE 70	SE 13	SE 22 ■1 trolley	SE 4 ■1	SE 16	SE 90 ■1 B	SE 70	SE 16	SE 01	SE 70	SE 13	SE 22 ■1	SE 4 ■1	SE 16	SE 4 ■1 D trolley	SE 70
London Charing Cross ■4 ⊖ d			18 52	19 00							19 15	19 24	19 26	19 30						19 45	19 52	19 56	20 00	
London Waterloo (East) ■4 ⊖ d			18 55	19 03							19 18	19 27	19 29	19 33						19 48	19 55	19 59	20 03	
London Cannon Street ■4 ⊖ d		18 50			19 06					19 18									19 48					
London Bridge ■4 ⊖ d		18 54	19 00	19 08	19 10					19 22	19 23	19 32	19 34	19 38					19 52	19 53	20 01	20 04	20 08	
New Cross ■4 ⊖ d																								
St Johns d																								
Lewisham ■4 d										19 31			19 43						20 01			20 13		
Hither Green ■4 d			19 10							19 35			19 47			←			20 05			20 17		
Grove Park ■4 d		19 06	19 14				19 22			19 39			19 51			19 51	19 55		20 09			20 21		
Sundridge Park d							19 25						→				19 58							
Bromley North a						←	19 27										20 00							
Elmstead Woods d		19 08	19 16			19 16				19 41						19 53			20 11			20 23		
Chislehurst d		19 11	→			19 19				19 44						19 56			20 14			20 26		
Petts Wood ■4 d	19 12	19 17				19 23		19 25	19 41	19 48					19 56	19 59		20 11	20 17			→		20 26
Orpington ■4 a	19 15	19 22			19 27	19 27		19 31	19 44	19 52				19 54	19 59	20 02		20 14	20 20					20 29
Orpington d					19 28	19 30								19 54		20 02								
Chelsfield ■3 d				19 26		19 33								19 58		20 05								
Knockholt d						19 36										20 08								
Dunton Green d						19 41										20 13								
Sevenoaks ■4 a				19 34	19 37	19 46					19 49			20 06		20 16				20 19			20 31	
Sevenoaks d				19 34	19 38						19 50			20 06						20 20			20 32	
Hildenborough d				19 40	19 44									20 12									20 38	
Tonbridge ■4 a				19 45	19 48						19 58	20 02		20 17						20 28	20 32		20 42	

	SE 16	SE 22 ■1	SE 01	SE 12	SE 90 ■1 D trolley	SE 70	SE 12	SE 01	SE 15	SE 22 ■1	SE 16	SE 4 ■1 D trolley	SE 70	SE 16	SE 22 ■1	SE 01	SE 12	SE 90 ■1 E	SE 70	SE 12	SE 22 ■1	SE 01	SE 12	SE 4 ■1 D
London Charing Cross ■4 ⊖ d		20 15		20 26	20 30					20 45	20 56	21 00			21 15		21 26	21 30			21 45		21 56	22 00
London Waterloo (East) ■4 ⊖ d		20 18		20 29	20 33					20 48	20 59	21 03			21 18		21 29	21 33			21 48		21 59	22 03
London Cannon Street ■4 ⊖ d									20 35															
London Bridge ■4 ⊖ d		20 23		20 34	20 38				20 39	20 53	21 04	21 08			21 23		21 34	21 38			21 53		22 04	22 08
New Cross ■4 ⊖ d									20 44															
St Johns d									20 46															
Lewisham ■4 d				20 43					20 49		21 13						21 43						22 13	
Hither Green ■4 d				20 47			←		20 53		21 17			←			21 47			←			22 17	
Grove Park ■4 d			20 25	20 51			20 51	20 55	20 57		21 21			21 21		21 25	21 51			21 51		21 55	22 21	
Sundridge Park d			20 28	→				20 58			→					21 28	→					21 58	→	
Bromley North a			20 30					21 00								21 30						22 00		
Elmstead Woods d	←						20 53		20 59					21 23						21 53				
Chislehurst d	20 26						20 56		21 02					21 26						21 56				
Petts Wood ■4 d	20 29					20 55	21 00		21 05				21 24	21 29					21 55	22 00				
Orpington ■4 a	20 32	20 40			20 54	20 58	21 03		21 10	21 10		21 24	21 27	21 32	21 40			21 54	21 58	22 03	22 10			22 24
Orpington d	20 32	20 40			20 54					21 10		21 24		21 32	21 40			21 54			22 10			22 24
Chelsfield ■3 d	20 35													21 35										
Knockholt d	20 38													21 38										
Dunton Green d	20 43													21 43										
Sevenoaks ■4 a	20 46	20 50			21 04					21 20		21 34		21 46	21 50			22 04			22 20			22 34
Sevenoaks d		20 50			21 04					21 20		21 34			21 50			22 04			22 20			22 34
Hildenborough d					21 10							21 40						22 10						22 40
Tonbridge ■4 a		20 58			21 15					21 28		21 45			21 58			22 15			22 28			22 45

For general notes see front of timetable
For details of catering facilities see Directory of Train Operators

A To Ashford International (Table 207)
B To Tunbridge Wells (Table 206)
C To Hastings (Table 206)
D To Ramsgate (Table 207)
E To Margate (Table 207)

For details of Bank Holiday service alterations please see first page of Table 195

London → Grove Park, Bromley North, Orpington, Sevenoaks and Tonbridge

Network Diagram - see first page of Table 200

		SE 70	SE 12	SE 22	SE 01	SE 12	SE 8	SE 70	SE 12	SE 22	SE 01	SE 12	SE 2	SE 70	SE 12	SE 22	SE 01	SE 12	SE 2	SE 22	SE 70	SE 12	SE 01
				1 A			1 B			1			1 C			1 A			1 C	1			
London Charing Cross 4	⊖ d			22 15		22 26	22 30			22 45		22 56	23 00			23 15		23 26	23 30	23 37			
London Waterloo (East) 4	⊖ d			22 18		22 29	22 33			22 48		22 59	23 03			23 18		23 29	23 33	23 40			
London Cannon Street 4	⊖ d																						
London Bridge 4	⊖ d			22 23		22 34	22 38			22 53		23 04	23 08			23 23		23 34	23 38	23 45			
New Cross 4	⊖ d																						
St Johns	d																						
Lewisham 4	d					22 43						23 13						23 43					
Hither Green 4	d		←			22 47			←			23 17			←			23 47				←	
Grove Park 4	d		22 21		22 25	22 51			22 51		22 55	23 21			23 21		23 25	23 51				23 51	23 56
Sundridge Park	d				22 28	→					22 58	→					23 28	→					23 59
Bromley North	a				22 30						23 00						23 30						00 01
Elmstead Woods	d		22 23						22 53						23 23							23 53	
Chislehurst	d		22 26						22 56						23 26							23 56	
Petts Wood 4	d	22 25	22 30					22 55	23 00					23 26	23 30						23 55	00 01	
Orpington 4	a	22 28	22 33	22 40			22 54	22 58	23 03	23 10			23 24	23 30	23 33	23 40			23 56		23 58	00 03	
	d			22 40			22 54			23 10			23 24			23 40			23 56				
Chelsfield 3	d			22 44												23 44							
Knockholt	d																						
Dunton Green	d																						
Sevenoaks 4	a			22 52			23 04			23 20			23 34			23 52			00 06	00 10			
	d			22 52			23 04			23 20			23 34			23 52			00 06	00 10			
Hildenborough	d						23 10						23 40						00 12				
Tonbridge 4	a			23 00			23 15			23 28			23 45			00 01			00 17	00 20			

Saturdays

		SE 12	SE 2	SE 12	SE 22	SE 70	SE 02	SE 01	SE 14	SE 4	SE 12	SE 4	SE 70	SE 12	SE 01	SE 16	SE 01	SE 12	SE 4	SE 70	SE 12	SE 01	SE 16	SE 4	SE 70
			1 C		1		1			1 D		1 E							1 E					1	
London Charing Cross 4	⊖ d	23p26	23p30		23p37		00 10		00 48		05 56	06 00				06 26		06 56	07 00				07 26	07 30	
London Waterloo (East) 4	⊖ d	23p29	23p33		23p40		00 13		00 51		05 59	06 03				06 29		06 59	07 03				07 29	07 33	
London Cannon Street 4	⊖ d																								
London Bridge 4	⊖ d	23p34	23p38		23p45		00 18		00 56		06 04	06 08				06 34		07 04	07 08				07 34	07 38	
New Cross 4	⊖ d								01 01																
St Johns	d																								
Lewisham 4	d	23p43							01 05		06 13					06 43		07 13					07 43		
Hither Green 4	d	23p47		←					01 09		06 17			←		06 47		07 17			←		07 47		
Grove Park 4	d	23p51		23p51			00 29	00 29	01 13		06 21			06 21	06 26	06 51	06 56	07 21			07 21	07 26	07 51		
Sundridge Park	d	→						00 32			→				06 29		06 59	→				07 29	→		
Bromley North	a							00 34							06 31		07 01					07 31			
Elmstead Woods	d			23p53			00 32		01 16					06 23		06 53					07 23				
Chislehurst	d			23p56			00 35		01 19					06 26		06 56					07 26				
Petts Wood 4	d			00 01		00 25	00 39		01 23				06 24	06 30		07 00				07 24	07 30				07 54
Orpington 4	a		23p56	00 03		00 28	00 42		01 26			06 26	06 27	06 33		07 03			07 26	07 27	07 33			07 55	07 57
	d		23p56				00 42			05 58		06 26		06 33					07 26		07 33			07 56	
Chelsfield 3	d						00 46							06 36							07 36				
Knockholt	d													06 39							07 39				
Dunton Green	d													06 44							07 44				
Sevenoaks 4	a		00 06		00 10		00 54			06 07		06 36		06 47					07 36		07 47			08 05	
	d		00 06		00 10		00 54			06 08		06 36							07 36					08 06	
Hildenborough	d		00 12				01 00			06 14		06 42							07 42						
Tonbridge 4	a		00 17		00 20		01 05			06 18		06 47							07 47					08 14	

		SE 16	SE 22	SE 01	SE 12	SE 4	SE 70	SE 12	SE 22	SE 01	SE 70	SE 16	SE 4	SE 22	SE 70	SE 16	SE 01	SE 70	SE 12	SE 4		SE 70	SE 12	SE 22	SE 01
			1			1 G			1				1	1 ⛟						1 G				1 ⛟	
London Charing Cross 4	⊖ d		07 45		07 56	08 00			08 15			08 26	08 30	08 45					08 56	09 00				09 15	
London Waterloo (East) 4	⊖ d		07 48		07 59	08 03			08 18			08 29	08 33	08 48					08 59	09 03				09 18	
London Cannon Street 4	⊖ d																								
London Bridge 4	⊖ d		07 53		08 04	08 08			08 23			08 34	08 38	08 53					09 04	09 08				09 23	
New Cross 4	⊖ d																								
St Johns	d																								
Lewisham 4	d				08 13							08 43							09 13						
Hither Green 4	d	←			08 17			←				08 47				←			09 17				←		
Grove Park 4	d	07 51		07 56	08 21			08 21		08 26		08 51				08 51	08 56		09 21				09 21		09 26
Sundridge Park	d			07 59	→					08 29		→					08 59		→						09 29
Bromley North	a			08 01						08 31							09 01								09 31
Elmstead Woods	d	07 53						08 23								08 53							09 23		
Chislehurst	d	07 56						08 26								08 56							09 26		
Petts Wood 4	d	08 00					08 24	08 30			08 39				08 54	09 00		09 09				09 24	09 30		
Orpington 4	a	08 03	08 09			08 26	08 27	08 33	08 39		08 42		08 55		08 57	09 03		09 12		09 26		09 27	09 33	09 39	
	d		08 10			08 26		08 33	08 40				08 56							09 26			09 33	09 40	
Chelsfield 3	d							08 36															09 36		
Knockholt	d							08 39															09 39		
Dunton Green	d							08 44															09 44		
Sevenoaks 4	a		08 20			08 36		08 47	08 50				09 05	09 15						09 36			09 47	09 50	
	d		08 20			08 36			08 51				09 06	09 16						09 36				09 51	
Hildenborough	d					08 42														09 42					
Tonbridge 4	a		08 28			08 47			08 59				09 14	09 24						09 47				09 59	

For general notes see front of timetable
For details of catering facilities see Directory of Train Operators

- **A** To Tunbridge Wells (Table 206)
- **B** To Canterbury West (Table 207)
- **C** To Dover Priory (Table 207)
- **D** To Ramsgate (Table 207)
- **E** To Margate (Table 207)
- **G** To Ramsgate (Table 207) and to Margate (Table 207)

Table 204

London → Grove Park, Bromley North, Orpington, Sevenoaks and Tonbridge

Network Diagram - see first page of Table 200

		SE	SE	SE	SE	SE	SE	SE	SE	SE	SE	SE	SE	SE	SE	SE	SE	SE	SE	SE	SE	SE	SE	SE
		70	16	4	22	70	16	01	4	70	12	8	70	12	22	01	90	70	16	8	22	70	16	01
				1	1				1			1			1		1			1	1			
				A								A								A				
					🛒				🛒						🛒		🛒				🛒			
London Charing Cross 4	⊖ d		09 26	09 30	09 45				09 53		09 56	10 00			10 15		10 23		10 26	10 30	10 45			
London Waterloo (East) 4	⊖ d		09 29	09 33	09 48				09 56		09 59	10 03			10 18		10 26		10 29	10 33	10 48			
London Cannon Street 4	⊖ d																							
London Bridge 4	⊖ d		09 34	09 38	09 53						10 04	10 08			10 23				10 34	10 38	10 53			
New Cross 4	⊖ d																							
St Johns	d																							
Lewisham 4	DLR d		09 43								10 13								10 43					
Hither Green 4	d		09 47				←				10 17			←					10 47				←	
Grove Park 4	d		09 51				09 51	09 56			10 21			10 21		10 26			10 51				10 51	10 56
Sundridge Park	d		↪					09 59			↪					10 29			↪					10 59
Bromley North	a							10 01								10 31								11 01
Elmstead Woods	d						09 53							10 23									10 53	
Chislehurst	d						09 56							10 26									10 56	
Petts Wood 4	d	09 39				09 54	10 00			10 09		10 22	10 24	10 30				10 39				10 54	11 00	
Orpington 4	a	09 42		09 53		09 57	10 03			10 12		10 26	10 27	10 33	10 39			10 42		10 53		10 57	11 03	
	d			09 54								10 26		10 33	10 40					10 54				
Chelsfield 3	d													10 36										
Knockholt	d													10 39										
Dunton Green	d													10 44										
Sevenoaks 4	a			10 04	10 15							10 36		10 47	10 50					11 04	11 15			
	d			10 04	10 16							10 36			10 51					11 04	11 16			
Hildenborough	d			10 11								10 43								11 11				
Tonbridge 4	a			10 15	10 24				10 30			10 47			10 59		11 02			11 15	11 24			

			SE	SE	SE	SE	SE	SE	SE	SE	SE	SE	SE	SE	SE	SE	SE	SE		SE		SE	SE	SE
			4	70	12	8	70	12	22	01	90	70	16	8	22	70	16	01		4		70	12	8
			1			1			1		1			1	1					1				1
						A								A										A
			🛒						🛒		🛒				🛒					🛒				
London Charing Cross 4	⊖ d		10 53		10 56	11 00			11 15		11 23		11 26	11 30	11 45				and at	17 53			17 56	18 00
London Waterloo (East) 4	⊖ d		10 56		10 59	11 03			11 18		11 26		11 29	11 33	11 48				the same	17 56			17 59	18 03
London Cannon Street 4	⊖ d																		minutes					
London Bridge 4	⊖ d				11 04	11 08			11 23				11 34	11 38	11 53				past				18 04	18 08
New Cross 4	⊖ d																		each					
St Johns	d																		hour until					
Lewisham 4	DLR d				11 13								11 43										18 13	
Hither Green 4	d				11 17			←					11 47				←						18 17	
Grove Park 4	d				11 21			11 21		11 26			11 51				11 51	11 56					18 21	
Sundridge Park	d				↪					11 29			↪					11 59					↪	
Bromley North	a									11 31								12 01						
Elmstead Woods	d							11 23									11 53							
Chislehurst	d							11 26									11 56							
Petts Wood 4	d			11 09		11 22	11 24	11 30				11 39				11 54	12 00					18 09		18 22
Orpington 4	a			11 12		11 26	11 27	11 33	11 39			11 42		11 53		11 57	12 03					18 12		18 26
	d					11 26		11 33	11 40					11 54										18 26
Chelsfield 3	d							11 36																
Knockholt	d							11 39																
Dunton Green	d							11 44																
Sevenoaks 4	a					11 36		11 47	11 50					12 04	12 15									18 36
	d					11 36			11 51					12 04	12 16									18 36
Hildenborough	d					11 43								12 11										18 43
Tonbridge 4	a		11 30			11 47			11 59		12 02			12 15	12 24					18 30				18 47

			SE	SE	SE	SE	SE	SE	SE	SE	SE	SE	SE	SE	SE	SE	SE	SE	SE	SE	SE	SE	SE	SE	SE
			70	12	22	01	4	70	16	90	22	70	16	01	70	12	4	70	12	22	01	70	16	90	70
					1		1			1	1						1			1				1	
																	B								
					🛒		🛒				🛒						🛒			🛒					
London Charing Cross 4	⊖ d				18 15		18 23		18 26	18 30	18 45					18 56	19 00			19 15			19 26	19 30	
London Waterloo (East) 4	⊖ d				18 18		18 26		18 29	18 33	18 48					18 59	19 03			19 18			19 29	19 33	
London Cannon Street 4	⊖ d																								
London Bridge 4	⊖ d				18 23				18 34	18 38	18 53					19 04	19 08			19 23			19 34	19 38	
New Cross 4	⊖ d																								
St Johns	d																								
Lewisham 4	DLR d								18 44							19 14							19 43		
Hither Green 4	d			←					18 48				←			19 18			←				19 47		
Grove Park 4	d			18 21		18 26			18 52				18 52	18 56		19 22			19 22		19 26		19 51		
Sundridge Park	d					18 29			↪					18 59		↪					19 29		↪		
Bromley North	a					18 31								19 01							19 31				
Elmstead Woods	d			18 23									18 55						19 24						
Chislehurst	d			18 26									18 57						19 27						
Petts Wood 4	d		18 24	18 30				18 39				18 54	19 00		19 09			19 24	19 30			19 39			19 54
Orpington 4	a		18 27	18 33	18 40			18 42		18 54		18 57	19 03		19 12		19 24	19 27	19 33	19 40		19 42		19 54	19 57
	d			18 33	18 40					18 54							19 24		19 33	19 40				19 54	
Chelsfield 3	d			18 36															19 36						
Knockholt	d			18 39															19 39						
Dunton Green	d			18 44															19 44						
Sevenoaks 4	a			18 47	18 50					19 04	19 16						19 34		19 47	19 51				20 04	
	d				18 51					19 04	19 17						19 34			19 51				20 04	
Hildenborough	d																19 40								
Tonbridge 4	a				18 59		19 02			19 13	19 25						19 45			19 59				20 13	

For general notes see front of timetable
For details of catering facilities see Directory of Train Operators

A To Ashford International (Table 207)
B To Ramsgate (Table 207)

Saturdays

London → Grove Park, Bromley North, Orpington, Sevenoaks and Tonbridge

Network Diagram - see first page of Table 200

		SE 16	SE 22	SE 01	SE 70	SE 12	SE 4	SE 70	SE 12	SE 01	SE 12	SE 90	SE 70	SE 12	SE 22	SE 01	SE 16	SE 4	SE 70	SE 16	SE 01	SE 12	SE 90	SE 70	SE 12
			1				1					1			1			1					1		
							A ✠											A							
London Charing Cross 4	⊖ d		19 45			19 56	20 00				20 26	20 30			20 45		20 56	21 00				21 26	21 30		
London Waterloo (East) 4	⊖ d		19 48			19 59	20 03				20 29	20 33			20 48		20 59	21 03				21 29	21 33		
London Cannon Street 4	⊖ d																								
London Bridge 4	⊖ d		19 53			20 04	20 08				20 34	20 38			20 53		21 04	21 08				21 34	21 38		
New Cross 4	⊖ d																								
St Johns	d																								
Lewisham 4	d					20 13					20 43						21 13					21 43			
Hither Green 4	d	←				20 17			←		20 47			←			21 17			←		21 47			←
Grove Park 4	d	19 51		19 56		20 21			20 21	20 26	20 51			20 51		20 56	21 21			21 21	21 26	21 51			21 51
Sundridge Park	d			19 59		→				20 29	→					20 59	→				21 29	→			
Bromley North	a			20 01						20 31						21 01					21 31				
Elmstead Woods	d	19 53							20 23					20 53						21 23					21 53
Chislehurst	d	19 56							20 26					20 56						21 26					21 56
Petts Wood 4	d	20 00			20 09			20 24	20 30				20 54	21 00					21 24	21 30				21 54	22 00
Orpington 4	a	20 03	20 10		20 12		20 24	20 27	20 33			20 54	20 57	21 03	21 10			21 24	21 27	21 33			21 54	21 57	22 03
	d		20 10				20 24		20 33			20 54			21 10			21 24		21 33			21 54		
Chelsfield 3	d								20 36											21 36					
Knockholt	d								20 39											21 39					
Dunton Green	d								20 44											21 44					
Sevenoaks 4	a		20 20				20 34		20 47			21 04			21 20			21 34		21 47			22 04		
	d		20 20				20 34					21 04			21 20			21 34					22 04		
Hildenborough	d						20 40											21 40							
Tonbridge 4	a		20 28				20 45					21 13			21 28			21 45					22 13		

		SE 22	SE 01	SE 12	SE 4	SE 70	SE 12	SE 01	SE 12	SE 90	SE 70	SE 12	SE 22	SE 01	SE 12	SE 8	SE 70	SE 12	SE 01	SE 12	SE 8	SE 70	SE 12	SE 01
		1			1					1			1			1					1			
					A											B					B			
London Charing Cross 4	⊖ d	21 45		21 56	22 00				22 26	22 30			22 45		22 56	23 00				23 26	23 30			
London Waterloo (East) 4	⊖ d	21 48		21 59	22 03				22 29	22 33			22 48		22 59	23 03				23 29	23 33			
London Cannon Street 4	⊖ d																							
London Bridge 4	⊖ d	21 53		22 04	22 08				22 34	22 38			22 53		23 04	23 08				23 34	23 38			
New Cross 4	⊖ d																							
St Johns	d																							
Lewisham 4	d			22 13					22 43						23 13					23 43				
Hither Green 4	d			22 17			←		22 47			←			23 17			←		23 47			←	
Grove Park 4	d		21 56	22 21			22 21	22 26	22 51			22 51		22 56	23 21			23 21	23 26	23 51			23 51	23 56
Sundridge Park	d		21 59	→				22 29	→					22 59	→				23 29	→				23 59
Bromley North	a		22 01					22 31						23 01					23 31					00 01
Elmstead Woods	d						22 23					22 53						23 23					23 53	
Chislehurst	d						22 26					22 56						23 26					23 56	
Petts Wood 4	d					22 24	22 30				22 54	23 00					23 24	23 30				23 54	00 01	
Orpington 4	a	22 10			22 24	22 27	22 33			22 54	22 57	23 03	23 10			23 24	23 27	23 33			23 54	23 57	00 03	
	d	22 10			22 24					22 54			23 10			23 24					23 54			
Chelsfield 3	d				22 28											23 28								
Knockholt	d																							
Dunton Green	d																							
Sevenoaks 4	a	22 20			22 36					23 04			23 20			23 36					00 04			
	d	22 20			22 36					23 04			23 20			23 36					00 04			
Hildenborough	d				22 43											23 42					00 10			
Tonbridge 4	a	22 28			22 47					23 13			23 28			23 46					00 15			

Sundays

		SE 12	SE 8	SE 12	SE 70	SE 02		SE 01	SE 14	SE 16	SE 70	SE 22		SE 12	SE 90	SE 70	SE 16	SE 4		SE 16	SE 70		SE 22	SE 12	SE 90
			1			1						1			1			1					1		1
			B												C										D
London Charing Cross 4	⊖ d	23p26	23p30			00 10			00 48	07 42		08 10		08 12	08 24		08 42	08 54					09 10	09 12	09 24
London Waterloo (East) 4	⊖ d	23p29	23p33			00 13			00 51	07 45		08 13		08 15	08 27		08 45	08 57					09 13	09 15	09 27
London Cannon Street 4	⊖ d																								
London Bridge 4	⊖ d	23p34	23p38			00 18			00 56	07 50		08 18		08 20	08 32		08 50	09 02					09 18	09 20	09 32
New Cross 4	⊖ d								01 01																
St Johns	d																								
Lewisham 4	d	23p43							01 05																
Hither Green 4	d	23p47		←					01 09	08 00				08 30			09 00							09 30	
Grove Park 4	d	23p51		23p51		00 29		00 34	01 13	08 04				08 34			09 04							09 34	
Sundridge Park	d	→						00 37																	
Bromley North	a							00 39																	
Elmstead Woods	d			23p53		00 32			01 16	08 06				08 36			09 06							09 36	
Chislehurst	d			23p56		00 35			01 19	08 09				08 39			09 09							09 39	
Petts Wood 4	d			00 01	00 26	00 39			01 23	08 12	08 26			08 42		08 56	09 12				09 26			09 42	
Orpington 4	a		23p54	00 03	00 29	00 42			01 26	08 15	08 29	08 35		08 45	08 48	08 59	09 15	09 18		←	09 29		09 35	09 45	09 48
	d		23p54			00 42				08 21		08 35			08 49		09 21	09 19		09 21			09 35		09 49
Chelsfield 3	d					00 46				08 24							→			09 24					
Knockholt	d									08 26										09 26					
Dunton Green	d									08 31										09 31					
Sevenoaks 4	a		00 04			00 54				08 35		08 45			08 58			09 28		09 35			09 45		09 58
	d		00 04			00 54						08 45			08 59			09 29					09 45		09 59
Hildenborough	d		00 10			01 00									09 05										10 05
Tonbridge 4	a		00 15			01 05						08 53			09 09			09 37					09 53		10 09

For general notes see front of timetable
For details of catering facilities see Directory of Train Operators

A To Ramsgate (Table 207)
B To Dover Priory (Table 207)
C To Margate (Table 207) and to Ramsgate (Table 207)
D To Margate (Table 207)

Table 204

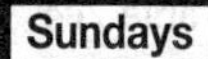
Sundays

London → Grove Park, Bromley North, Orpington, Sevenoaks and Tonbridge

Network Diagram - see first page of Table 200

		SE 70	SE 22 1	SE 16	SE 4 1	SE 16	SE 70			SE 22 1	SE 12	SE 90 1 A	SE 70	SE 22 1		SE 72	SE 16	SE 4 1	SE 16	SE 70		SE 22 1		SE 12
London Charing Cross 4	⊖ d		09 40	09 42	09 54			and at the same minutes past each hour until		17 10	17 12	17 24		17 40			17 42	17 54				18 10		18 12
London Waterloo (East) 4	⊖ d		09 43	09 45	09 57					17 13	17 15	17 27		17 43			17 45	17 57				18 13		18 15
London Cannon Street 4	⊖ d																							
London Bridge 4	⊖ d		09 48	09 50	10 02					17 18	17 20	17 32		17 48			17 50	18 02				18 18		18 20
New Cross 4	⊖ d																							
St Johns	d																							
Lewisham 4	d																							
Hither Green 4	d			10 00							17 30						18 00							18 30
Grove Park 4	d			10 04							17 34						18 04							18 34
Sundridge Park	d																							
Bromley North	a																							
Elmstead Woods	d			10 06							17 36						18 06							18 36
Chislehurst	d			10 09							17 39						18 09							18 39
Petts Wood 4	d	09 56		10 12			10 26				17 42		17 56			18 01	18 12			18 26				18 42
Orpington 4	a	09 59	10 04	10 15	10 18	←	10 29			17 35	17 45	17 48	17 59	18 04		18 05	18 15	18 18	←	18 29		18 35		18 45
	d		10 05	10 21 →	10 19	10 21				17 35		17 49		18 05			18 21 →	18 19	18 21			18 35		
Chelsfield 3	d					10 24													18 24					
Knockholt	d					10 26													18 26					
Dunton Green	d					10 31													18 31					
Sevenoaks 4	a		10 14		10 28	10 35				17 45		17 58		18 14				18 28	18 35			18 45		
	d		10 15		10 29					17 45		17 59		18 15				18 29				18 45		
Hildenborough	d											18 05												
Tonbridge 4	a		10 23		10 37					17 53		18 09		18 23				18 37				18 53		

		SE 90 1 A	SE 70	SE 22 1	SE 72		SE 16	SE 4 1	SE 16	SE 70	SE 22 1 B		SE 90 1 C	SE 70	SE 22 1	SE 12	SE 4 1		SE 70	SE 22 1 B	SE 90 1 C	SE 70	SE 12		SE 4 1
London Charing Cross 4	⊖ d	18 24		18 40			18 42	18 54			19 10		19 24		19 40	19 42	19 54			20 10	20 24		20 42		20 54
London Waterloo (East) 4	⊖ d	18 27		18 43			18 45	18 57			19 13		19 27		19 43	19 45	19 57			20 13	20 27		20 45		20 57
London Cannon Street 4	⊖ d																								
London Bridge 4	⊖ d	18 32		18 48			18 50	19 02			19 17		19 32		19 48	19 50	20 02			20 17	20 32		20 50		21 02
New Cross 4	⊖ d																								
St Johns	d																								
Lewisham 4	d																								
Hither Green 4	d						19 00									20 00							21 00		
Grove Park 4	d						19 04						19 43			20 04					20 43		21 04		
Sundridge Park	d																								
Bromley North	a																								
Elmstead Woods	d						19 06									20 06							21 06		
Chislehurst	d						19 09									20 09							21 09		
Petts Wood 4	d		18 56		19 01		19 12			19 26	19 33			19 56		20 12			20 26	20 33		20 56	21 12		
Orpington 4	a	18 48	18 59	19 04	19 05		19 15	19 18	←	19 29	19 36		19 49	19 59	20 04	20 15	20 18		20 29	20 36	20 49	20 59	21 15		21 18
	d	18 49		19 05			19 21 →	19 19	19 21		19 36		19 50		20 05		20 19			20 36	20 50				21 19
Chelsfield 3	d								19 24		19 39									20 39					
Knockholt	d								19 26																
Dunton Green	d								19 31																
Sevenoaks 4	a	18 58		19 14				19 28	19 35		19 48		19 59		20 14		20 28			20 48	20 59				21 28
	d	18 59		19 15				19 29			19 48		20 00		20 15		20 29			20 48	21 00				21 29
Hildenborough	d	19 05											20 06								21 06				
Tonbridge 4	a	19 09		19 23				19 37			19 56		20 10		20 23		20 37			20 57	21 10				21 37

		SE 70	SE 22 1 B	SE 90 1 C	SE 70	SE 12		SE 4 1	SE 70	SE 22 1 B	SE 2 1 D	SE 70		SE 12	SE 70	SE 72	SE 22 1 B	SE 8 1		SE 70	SE 12
London Charing Cross 4	⊖ d		21 10	21 24		21 42		21 54		22 10	22 24			22 42			23 10	23 24			23 42
London Waterloo (East) 4	⊖ d		21 13	21 27		21 45		21 57		22 13	22 27			22 45			23 13	23 27			23 45
London Cannon Street 4	⊖ d																				
London Bridge 4	⊖ d		21 17	21 32		21 50		22 02		22 17	22 32			22 50			23 17	23 32			23 50
New Cross 4	⊖ d																				
St Johns	d																				
Lewisham 4	d																				
Hither Green 4	d					22 00								23 00							00 01
Grove Park 4	d			21 43		22 04					22 43			23 04							00 03
Sundridge Park	d																				
Bromley North	a																				
Elmstead Woods	d					22 06								23 06							00 06
Chislehurst	d					22 09								23 09							00 08
Petts Wood 4	d	21 26	21 33		21 56	22 12			22 26	22 33		22 56		23 12	23 26	23 31	23 32			23 56	00 12
Orpington 4	a	21 29	21 36	21 49	21 59	22 15		22 18	22 29	22 36	22 49	22 59		23 15	23 29	23 35	23 35			23 59	00 15
	d		21 37	21 50				22 19		22 37	22 50						23 35				
Chelsfield 3	d		21 40							22 40							23 38				
Knockholt	d																				
Dunton Green	d																				
Sevenoaks 4	a		21 48	21 59				22 28		22 48	22 59						23 48	23 57			
	d		21 49	22 00				22 29		22 49	23 00						23 48	23 58			
Hildenborough	d			22 06							23 06						23 53				
Tonbridge 4	a		21 57	22 10				22 37		22 57	23 10						23 59	00 06			

For general notes see front of timetable
For details of catering facilities see
Directory of Train Operators

A To Margate (Table 207)
B To Hastings (Table 206)
C To Ramsgate (Table 207)
D To Dover Priory (Table 207)

For details of Bank Holiday service alterations please see first page of Table 195

Tonbridge, Sevenoaks, Orpington Bromley North, Grove Park → London

Network Diagram - see first page of Table 200

Miles	Miles			SE	SE	SE	SE	SE	SE	SE	SE	SE	SE	SE	SE	SE	SE	SE	SE	SE	SE	SE	SE	SE	SE
				MX 01	02	70	30 [1] A	70	14	5 [1] B	2 [1]	70	01	14	05	14	22 [1] C	4 [1]	70	01	14	13	17	90 [1] D	13
0	—	**Tonbridge [4]**	d		04 56		05 26			05 55	06 02				06 05		06 18	06 30						06 45	
2½	—	Hildenborough	d		05 00		05 31			06 00							06 22							06 49	
7½	—	**Sevenoaks [4]**	a		05 08		05 38			06 07	06 12				06 15		06 30	06 39						06 57	
—	—		d		05 09		05 39			06 07	06 13				06 16		06 30	06 40					06 44	06 58	
1½	—	Dunton Green	d												06 18								06 46		
5¼	—	Knockholt	d												06 24								06 52		
6¾	—	Chelsfield [3]	d		05 17		05 47								06 27								06 55		
8¼	—	**Orpington [4]**	a		05 20		05 50			06 16					06 30								06 58		
—	—		d		05 20	05 25	05 50	05 50	06 00	06 17		06 20		06 24	06 31				06 44		06 49	06 57	06 59		
9¼	—	Petts Wood [4]	d		05 23	05a28		05a53	06 03			06a23		06 27					06a47		06 52	07 00			
10¾	—	Chislehurst	d		05 26				06 06					06 30		←					06 57	07 04			←
11¾	—	Elmstead Woods	d		05 28				06 08					06 32		06 32					06 59	07 06			07 06
—	0	**Bromley North**	d	00 06									06 26	→						06 52		→			
—	½	Sundridge Park	d	00 08									06 28							06 54					
13	1¾	**Grove Park [4]**	d	00a11	05 31				06 11				06a31			06 35				06a57	07 02				07 09
14¾	—	Hither Green [4]	d		05 35				06 15							06 39					07 06				07 14
16	—	**Lewisham [4]**	d						06 20							06 44									
16½	—	St Johns	a																						
17¼	—	New Cross [4]	⊖ a		05 40				06 24																07 19
20¼	—	**London Bridge [4]**	⊖ a		05 46		06 06		06 30	06 35	06 36				06 48	06 53	06 55	07 03					07 15	07 21	07 25
—	—	**London Cannon Street [4]**	⊖ a							06 41					06 53								07 21		07 31
21¼	—	**London Waterloo (East) [4]**	⊖ a		05 51		06 11		06 35		06 41					06 58	07 00	07 08			07 24			07 27	
22	—	**London Charing Cross [4]**	⊖ a		05 54		06 14		06 38		06 46					07 01	07 05	07 14			07 28			07 32	

		SE	SE	SE	SE	SE	SE	SE	SE	SE	SE	SE	SE	SE	SE	SE	SE	SE	SE	SE	SE	SE	SE	SE	SE
		70	01	12	23 [1]	12	70	01	17	30 [1] A	5 [1] B	17	4 [1]	12	70	17	30 [1] A	3 [1] E	01	17	90 [1]	12	12	70	17
Tonbridge [4]	d				06 53					07 06	07 16		07 25				07 31	07 36			07 42				
Hildenborough	d									07 10	07 20						07 36	07 40							
Sevenoaks [4]	a				07 03					07 18	07 28		07 35				07 43	07 48			07 52				
	d				07 03				07 13	07 19	07 29		07 35			07 38	07 44	07 49			07 53				07 58
Dunton Green	d								07 16							07 40									08 00
Knockholt	d								07 22							07 46									08 06
Chelsfield [3]	d								07 25	07 28						07 49	07 53								08 09
Orpington [4]	a				07 12				07 28							07 52									08 12
	d	07 06		07 10	07 13		07 27		07 30					07 36	07 50	07 53						07 56	08 00	08 10	08 13
Petts Wood [4]	d	07a09		07 13			07a30		07 33			←		07 39	07a53	07 56				←		07 59	08 03	08a13	08 16
Chislehurst	d			07 17		←			07 37			07 37		07 43		07 59				07 59		08 03	08 07		08 19
Elmstead Woods	d			07 19		07 19			→			07 39		07 45		→				08 01		08 05	08 09		→
Bromley North	d		07 13	→				07 33											07 54						
Sundridge Park	d		07 15					07 35											07 56						
Grove Park [4]	d		07a18			07 22		07a38				07 42		07 48					07a59	08 04		08 08	08 12		
Hither Green [4]	d					07 26						07 46											08 16		
Lewisham [4]	d																								
St Johns	a																								
New Cross [4]	⊖ a																								
London Bridge [4]	⊖ a				07 29	07 36				07 50	07 54	07 58		08 01			08 10	08 14		08 16			08 26		
London Cannon Street [4]	⊖ a				07 36						08 00	08 04						08 20		08 23					
London Waterloo (East) [4]	⊖ a					07 42				07 55			08 04	08 07			08 15				08 21	08 25	08 31		
London Charing Cross [4]	⊖ a					07 46				07 59			08 09	08 12			08 21				08 26	08 30	08 36		

		SE	SE	SE	SE	SE		SE	SE	SE	SE	SE	SE	SE	SE	SE	SE	SE	SE	SE	SE	SE	SE	SE	SE
		30 [1] A	91 [1]	4 [1] (catering)	01	17		12	70	17	01	30 [1] A	3 [1] E	90 [1]	17	12	01	70	30 [1] A	5 [1]	12	70	17	22 [1]	01
Tonbridge [4]	d	07 51	07 58	08 02								08 11	08 17	08 25					08 36	08 46				09 00	
Hildenborough	d	07 56										08 16	08 21						08 41						
Sevenoaks [4]	a	08 03	08 08	08 12								08 23	08 29						08 48	08 56					
	d	08 04	08 09	08 13						08 18		08 24	08 30						08 49	08 57			09 00	09 10	
Dunton Green	d									08 20									08 52						
Knockholt	d									08 26									08 58						
Chelsfield [3]	d	08 13								08 29		08 33							09 01				09 08		
Orpington [4]	a									08 32													09 11		
	d							08 20	08 30	08 33						08 38		08 53			09 00	09 08	09 12		
Petts Wood [4]	d					←		08 23	08a33	08 36					←	08 41		08a56			09 03	09a11	09 15		
Chislehurst	d					08 19		08 27		08 39					08 39	08 44					09 07		09 19		
Elmstead Woods	d					08 21		08 29		→					08 41	08 46					09 09		→		
Bromley North	d				08 15						08 35						08 55								09 15
Sundridge Park	d				08 17						08 37						08 57								09 17
Grove Park [4]	d				08a20	08 24		08 32			08a40				08 44	08 50	09a00				09 12				09a20
Hither Green [4]	d							08 36													09 16				
Lewisham [4]	d																								
St Johns	a																								
New Cross [4]	⊖ a														08 52										
London Bridge [4]	⊖ a	08 30	08 34			08 36						08 50	08 54		08 58				09 18	09 22	09 25			09 33	
London Cannon Street [4]	⊖ a		08 41			08 43							09 01		09 03					09 28					
London Waterloo (East) [4]	⊖ a	08 35		08 41				08 49				08 55		09 01		09 06			09 23		09 31			09 38	
London Charing Cross [4]	⊖ a	08 41		08 47				08 54				09 01		09 07		09 11			09 29		09 35			09 44	

For general notes see front of timetable
For details of catering facilities see Directory of Train Operators

A From Tunbridge Wells (Table 206)
B From Ashford International (Table 207)
C From Hastings (Table 206)
D From Ramsgate (Table 207)
E From Dover Priory (Table 207)

For details of Bank Holiday service alterations please see first page of Table 195

Tonbridge, Sevenoaks, Orpington Bromley North, Grove Park → London

Network Diagram - see first page of Table 200

		SE 17	SE 70	SE 01	SE 16	SE 22 [1] A 🛒	SE 4 [1] 🛒	SE 70	SE 16	SE 70	SE 8 [1]	SE 22 [1] 🛒	SE 4 [1] 🛒	SE 01	SE 12	SE 70	SE 70	SE 8 [1]	SE 16	SE 22 [1] 🛒	SE 90 [1] 🛒	SE 01	SE 16	SE 70	SE 70
Tonbridge [4]	d					09 14	09 24				09 28	09 46	09 58					10 04		10 18	10 28				
Hildenborough	d					09 18					09 32							10 08							
Sevenoaks [4]	a					09 26	09 34				09 39	09 55						10 15		10 27					
	d				09 18	09 26	09 34				09 40	09 56						10 16	10 18	10 28					
Dunton Green	d				09 20						09 43								10 20						
Knockholt	d				09 26						09 49								10 26						
Chelsfield [3]	d				09 29						09 52								10 29						
Orpington [4]	a				09 32	09 35					09 55							10 25	10 32						
	d		09 23		09 35	09 36		09 38		09 53	09 55				10 05	10 08	10 23	10 25	10 35				←	10 38	10 53
Petts Wood [4]	d	←	09a26		09 38			09a41		09a56	09 59				10 08	10a11	10a26	10 29	10 38				10 38	10a41	10a56
Chislehurst	d	09 19			09 41				←						10 11				→				10 41		
Elmstead Woods	d	09 21			09 43				09 43						10 13								10 43		
Bromley North	d			09 35	→									10 05								10 35			
Sundridge Park	d			09 37										10 07								10 37			
Grove Park [4]	d	09 24		09a40					09 46					10a10	10 16							10a40	10 46		
Hither Green [4]	d	09 28							09 50						10 20								10 50		
Lewisham [4]	d	09 33							09 55						10 25								10 55		
St Johns	a																								
New Cross [4]	⊖ a																								
London Bridge [4]	⊖ a	09 41				09 51	09 57		10 04		10 13	10 24			10 34			10 43		10 54			11 04		
London Cannon Street [4]	⊖ a	09 47																							
London Waterloo (East) [4]	⊖ a					09 57	10 03		10 09		10 18	10 29	10 32		10 39			10 48		10 59	11 02		11 09		
London Charing Cross [4]	⊖ a					10 01	10 07		10 12		10 22	10 33	10 36		10 44			10 51		11 03	11 06		11 14		

		SE 01	SE 83		SE 8 [1] B	SE 22 [1] 🛒	SE 2 [1] 🛒	SE 12	SE 70	SE 70	SE 8 [1] B	SE 14	SE 22 [1] 🛒	SE 90 [1] 🛒	SE 01	SE 14	SE 70	SE 70	SE 01			SE 8 [1] B	SE 22 [1] 🛒	SE 2 [1] 🛒
Tonbridge [4]	d				10 36	10 46	10 58				11 04		11 18	11 28								14 36	14 46	14 58
Hildenborough	d				10 39						11 08											14 40		
Sevenoaks [4]	a				10 48	10 55					11 15		11 27							and at		14 47	14 55	
	d		10 34		10 48	10 56					11 16	11 18	11 28									14 48	14 56	
Dunton Green	d											11 20								the same				
Knockholt	d											11 26												
Chelsfield [3]	d											11 29								minutes				
Orpington [4]	a				10 57	11 05					11 25	11 32										14 57	15 05	
	d				10 57	11 05		11 05	11 08	11 23	11 25	11 35				←	11 38	11 53		past		14 57	15 05	
Petts Wood [4]	d							11 08	11a11	11a26	11 29	11 38				11 38	11a41	11a56						
Chislehurst	d							11 11				→				11 41				each				
Elmstead Woods	d							11 13								11 43								
Bromley North	d	11 05													11 35				12 05	hour until				
Sundridge Park	d	11 07													11 37				12 07					
Grove Park [4]	d	11a10						11 16							11a40	11 46			12a10					
Hither Green [4]	d							11 20								11 50								
Lewisham [4]	d							11 25								11 55								
St Johns	a																							
New Cross [4]	⊖ a																							
London Bridge [4]	⊖ a				11 13	11 24		11 34			11 43		11 54			12 04						15 13	15 24	
London Cannon Street [4]	⊖ a																							
London Waterloo (East) [4]	⊖ a				11 18	11 29	11 32	11 39			11 48		11 59	12 02		12 09						15 18	15 29	15 32
London Charing Cross [4]	⊖ a				11 21	11 33	11 36	11 44			11 51		12 03	12 06		12 14						15 21	15 33	15 36

		SE 12	SE 70	SE 70	SE 8 [1] B	SE 16	SE 22 [1] 🛒	SE 90 [1]	SE 01	SE 16	SE 70	SE 70	SE 01	SE 8 [1] B	SE 13	SE 23 [1] A	SE 2 [1] 🛒	SE 70	SE 13	SE 12	SE 12	SE 01	SE 22 [1] A	SE 70	SE 4 [1] 🛒
Tonbridge [4]	d				15 04		15 18	15 28						15 36		15 46	15 54						16 06		16 22
Hildenborough	d				15 08									15 40									16 10		
Sevenoaks [4]	a				15 15		15 27							15 48		15 55	16 03						16 18		16 31
	d				15 16	15 18	15 28							15 48		15 56	16 04						16 18		16 32
Dunton Green	d					15 20																	16 20		
Knockholt	d					15 26																	16 26		
Chelsfield [3]	d					15 29										16 04							16 29		
Orpington [4]	a				15 25	15 32								15 57		16 07							16 34		
	d	15 05	15 08	15 23	15 25	15 35				←	15 38	15 53		15 57	16 05	16 07		16 08		16 20	16 33		16 34	16 36	
Petts Wood [4]	d	15 08	15a11	15a26	15 29	15 38				15 38	15a41	15a56			16 08			16a11		16 23	16 36			16a39	
Chislehurst	d	15 11				→				15 41					16 11				←	16 26	16 39				
Elmstead Woods	d	15 13								15 43					16 13				16 13	16 28	16 41				
Bromley North	d								15 35				16 05		→						→	16 35			
Sundridge Park	d								15 37				16 07									16 37			
Grove Park [4]	d	15 16							15a40	15 46			16a10						16 16	16 31		16a40			
Hither Green [4]	d	15 20								15 50									16 20	16 36					
Lewisham [4]	d	15 25								15 55									16b28						
St Johns	a																								
New Cross [4]	⊖ a																								
London Bridge [4]	⊖ a	15 34			15 43		15 54			16 04				16 13		16 24	16 29		16 37	16 45			16 52		17 00
London Cannon Street [4]	⊖ a																								
London Waterloo (East) [4]	⊖ a	15 40			15 48		15 59	16 02		16 09				16 18		16 29	16 34		16 43	16 51			16 57		17 05
London Charing Cross [4]	⊖ a	15 44			15 51		16 03	16 06		16 13				16 21		16 33	16 38		16 47	16 55			17 01		17 10

For general notes see front of timetable
For details of catering facilities see Directory of Train Operators

A From Hastings (Table 206)
B From Ashford International (Table 207)
b Arr. 1624

For details of Bank Holiday service alterations please see first page of Table 195

Tonbridge, Sevenoaks, Orpington
Bromley North, Grove Park → London

Network Diagram - see first page of Table 200

	SE 12	SE 01	SE 23	SE 12	SE 16	SE 12	SE 8	SE 70	SE 12	SE 2	SE 12	SE 01	SE 12	SE 22	SE 12	SE 16	SE 70	SE 4	SE 01	SE 12	SE 22	SE 70	SE 12	SE 01
			1				1			1				1				1			1			
			A				B			C								D						
			🛒							🛒								🛒						
Tonbridge [4] d			16 28				16 40			16 51				17 06				17 18			17 40			
Hildenborough d							16 44			16 55								17 22						
Sevenoaks [4] a			16 37				16 52			17 03				17 15				17 30			17 50			
d			16 38		16 42		16 52			17 03				17 16		17 20		17 30			17 50		17 54	
Dunton Green d					16 44											17 22							17 56	
Knockholt d					16 50											17 28							18 02	
Chelsfield [3] d			16 46		16 52											17 30							18 05	
Orpington [4] a			16 49		16 55		17 02			17 12				17 26		17 33		17 39			17 59		18 08	
d			16 50	16 52	16 56		17 02	17 04	17 07	17 13			17 21	17 26		17 34	17 36	17 40		17 51	18 00	18 06	18 08	
Petts Wood [4] d				16 55				17a07	17 10				17 24			17 37	17a39			17 54		18a09		
Chislehurst d	←			16 58		←			17 13		←		17 27		←					17 57				
Elmstead Woods d	16 41			17 00 →		17 00			17 15 →		17 15		17 29 →		17 29					17 59				
Bromley North d		16 56										17 25							17 45					18 10
Sundridge Park d		16 58										17 27							17 47					18 12
Grove Park [4] d	16 44	17a01				17 03					17 18	17a30			17 32				17a50	18 02				18a15
Hither Green [4] d	16 52					17 09					17 23				17 40					18 06				
Lewisham [4] d																								
St Johns a																								
New Cross [4] ⊖ a																								
London Bridge [4] ⊖ a	17 02		17 09		17 13	17 18	17 26			17 31	17 35			17 44	17 49	17 51					18 19		18 25	
London Cannon Street [4] ⊖ a							17 31																	
London Waterloo (East) [4] ⊖ a	17 07		17 14		17 17	17 23				17 36	17 40			17 50	17 54	17 57		18 03		18 19	18 26		18 30	
London Charing Cross [4] ⊖ a	17 13		17 19		17 24	17 28				17 41	17 46			17 55	17 57	18 01		18 07		18 23	18 30		18 37	

	SE 16	SE 4		SE 16	SE 01	SE 22	SE 22	SE 70	SE 12	SE 90	SE 12	SE 01	SE 22	SE 16	SE 70	SE 90	SE 22	SE 16	SE 01	SE 70	SE 01	SE 18	SE 16	SE 22
		1				1	1			1			1			1	1					1		1
		E				G										H								A
		🛒					🛒																	
Tonbridge [4] d		17 50				18 06	18 16			18 20			18 36			18 46	18 54					19 11		19 16
Hildenborough d		17 54				18 10										18 50								19 20
Sevenoaks [4] a		18 02				18 18	18 25			18 29			18 46			18 58	19 04							19 28
d		18 02				18 18	18 26			18 30			18 46	18 50		18 58	19 05						19 22	19 28
Dunton Green d						18 21								18 52										
Knockholt d						18 26								18 58										
Chelsfield [3] d						18 29								19 01									19 30	
Orpington [4] a		18 11				18 32	18 35			18 39			18 55	19 04		19 07	19 14						19 33	19 37
d	18 11	18 12				18 33	18 36	18 36	18 39	18 40			18 56	19 05	19 08	19 08	19 14			19 23			19 35	19 38
Petts Wood [4] d	18 14							18a39	18 42					19 08	19a11					19a26			19 38	
Chislehurst d	18 17			←					18 45		←			19 11				←					19 41	
Elmstead Woods d	18 19 →			18 19					18 47 →		18 47			19 13 →				19 13					19 43 →	
Bromley North d					18 30							18 52							19 12		19 32			
Sundridge Park d					18 32							18 54							19 14		19 34			
Grove Park [4] d				18 22	18a35						18 50	18a57						19 16	19a17		19a37			
Hither Green [4] d				18 26							18 54							19 20						
Lewisham [4] d																		19b28						
St Johns a																								
New Cross [4] ⊖ a																								
London Bridge [4] ⊖ a		18 28		18 35		18 49	18 51			18 57	19 05		19 12			19 25	19 33	19 36						19 55
London Cannon Street [4] ⊖ a						18 53																		
London Waterloo (East) [4] ⊖ a		18 33		18 40			18 56			19 02	19 10		19 17			19 31	19 38	19 41				19 46		20 00
London Charing Cross [4] ⊖ a		18 37		18 45			19 00			19 07	19 14		19 21			19 35	19 42	19 45				19 50		20 04

	SE 70	SE 16	SE 01	SE 90	SE 70	SE 16	SE 22	SE 70	SE 16	SE 01	SE 18	SE 16	SE 22	SE 70	SE 16	SE 01	SE 90	SE 12	SE 22	SE 70	SE 12	SE 01	SE 4	SE 16
				1			1				1		1				1		1				1	
													G											
				🛒							🛒													
Tonbridge [4] d				19 30			19 48				20 00		20 16				20 31		20 48				21 00	
Hildenborough d													20 20											
Sevenoaks [4] a				19 39			19 57				20 09		20 28				20 40		20 57				21 09	
d				19 40		19 50	19 58				20 10	20 22	20 28				20 40		20 58				21 10	21 22
Dunton Green d						19 52																		
Knockholt d						19 58																		
Chelsfield [3] d						20 01						20 30												21 30
Orpington [4] a				19 49		20 04	20 07				20 19	20 33	20 37				20 49		21 07				21 19	21 33
d	19 38			19 50	19 53	20 05	20 08	20 08			20 20	20 35	20 38	20 38			20 50	21 05	21 08	21 08			21 20	21 35
Petts Wood [4] d	19a41				19a56	20 08		20a11				20 38		20a41				21 08		21a11				21 38
Chislehurst d		←				20 11			←			20 41			←			21 11			←			21 41
Elmstead Woods d		19 43				20 13 →			20 13			20 43 →			20 43			21 13 →			21 13			21 43 →
Bromley North d			20 05							20 35						21 05						21 35		
Sundridge Park d			20 07							20 37						21 07						21 37		
Grove Park [4] d		19 46	20a10						20 16	20a40					20 46	21a10					21 16	21a40		
Hither Green [4] d		19 50							20 20						20 50						21 20			
Lewisham [4] d		19c57							20e27						20f57						21g27			
St Johns a																								
New Cross [4] ⊖ a																								
London Bridge [4] ⊖ a		20 06		20 08			20 25		20 36		20 38		20 55		21 06		21 08		21 25		21 36		21 38	
London Cannon Street [4] ⊖ a																								
London Waterloo (East) [4] ⊖ a		20 11		20 13			20 30		20 41		20 43		21 00		21 11		21 13		21 30		21 41		21 43	
London Charing Cross [4] ⊖ a		20 15		20 18			20 34		20 45		20 48		21 04		21 15		21 18		21 34		21 45		21 48	

For general notes see front of timetable
For details of catering facilities see Directory of Train Operators

- **A** From Hastings (Table 206)
- **B** From Ashford International (Table 207)
- **C** From Dover Priory (Table 207) and from Ramsgate (Table 207)
- **D** From Ramsgate (Table 207) and from Margate (Table 207)
- **E** From Ramsgate (Table 207) and from Ramsgate (Table 207)
- **G** From Tunbridge Wells (Table 206)
- **H** From Ramsgate (Table 207)
- **b** Arr. 1924
- **c** Arr. 1954
- **e** Arr. 2024
- **f** Arr. 2054
- **g** Arr. 2124

For details of Bank Holiday service alterations please see first page of Table 195

Tonbridge, Sevenoaks, Orpington Bromley North, Grove Park → London

Network Diagram - see first page of Table 200

		SE 22 1 A	SE 70	SE 16	SE 01	SE 90 1	SE 12	SE 22 1	SE 70	SE 12	SE 01	SE 4 1	SE 16	SE 22 1 A	SE 70	SE 16	SE 01	SE 90 1	SE 22 1	SE 12	SE 70	SE 4 1 B	SE 01
Tonbridge 4	d	21 16				21 30		21 48				22 00		22 16				22 30	22 42			23 10	
Hildenborough	d	21 20												22 20								23 14	
Sevenoaks 4	a	21 28				21 39		21 57				22 09		22 28				22 39	22 51			23 22	
	d	21 28				21 40		21 58				22 10	22 22	22 28				22 40	22 52			23 22	
Dunton Green	d																						
Knockholt	d																						
Chelsfield 3	d												22 30									23 30	
Orpington 4	a	21 37				21 49		22 07				22 19	22 33	22 37				22 49	23 01			23 33	
	d	21 38	21 38			21 50	22 05	22 08	22 08			22 20	22 35	22 38	22 38			22 50	23 02	23 05	23 08	23 34	
Petts Wood 4	d		21a41				22 08		22a11				22 38		22a41					23 08	23a11		
Chislehurst	d			←			22 11			←			22 41			←				23 11			
Elmstead Woods	d			21 43			22 13			22 13			22 43			22 43				23 13			
Bromley North	d				22 05		→				22 35		→				23 05						23 35
Sundridge Park	d				22 07						22 37						23 07						23 37
Grove Park 4	d			21 46	22a10					22 16	22a40					22 46	23a10			23 16			23a40
Hither Green 4	d			21 50						22 20						22 50				23 20			
Lewisham 4	d			21b57						22c27						22e57				23f27			
St Johns	a																						
New Cross 4	⊖ a																						
London Bridge 4	⊖ a	21 55		22 06		22 08		22 25		22 36		22 38		22 55		23 06		23 08	23 19	23 35		23 51	
London Cannon Street 4	⊖ a																						
London Waterloo (East) 4	⊖ a	22 00		22 11		22 13		22 30		22 41		22 43		23 00		23 11		23 13	23 24	23 40		23 56	
London Charing Cross 4	⊖ a	22 04		22 15		22 18		22 34		22 45		22 48		23 04		23 15		23 18	23 28	23 44		00 01	

Saturdays

		SE 01	SE 12	SE 12	SE 70	SE 01	SE 2 1 C	SE 12	SE 70	SE 01	SE 12	SE 22 1	SE 70	SE 12	SE 01	SE 2 1 C	SE 16	SE 22 1	SE 70	SE 16	SE 01	SE 90 1 D	SE 22 1	SE 12	SE 70
Tonbridge 4	d						06 00					06 46				06 59		07 16				07 31	07 46		
Hildenborough	d						06 04									07 03						07 36			
Sevenoaks 4	a						06 12					06 56				07 11		07 26				07 43	07 55		
	d		05 22				06 12	06 22				06 57				07 11	07 18	07 26				07 44	07 56		
Dunton Green	d																07 20								
Knockholt	d																07 26								
Chelsfield 3	d		05 29					06 29									07 29								
Orpington 4	a		05 32				06 21	06 32				07 07				07 20	07 32	07 35				07 53	08 05		
	d		05 35	06 05	06 08		06 21	06 35	06 38		07 05	07 08	07 08			07 20	07 35	07 35	07 38			07 53	08 05	08 05	08 08
Petts Wood 4	d		05 38	06 08	06a11			06 38	06a41		07 08		07a11				07 38		07a41					08 08	08a11
Chislehurst	d		05 41	06 11				06 41			07 11			←			07 41			←				08 11	
Elmstead Woods	d		05 43	06 13				06 43			07 13			07 13			07 43			07 43				08 13	
Bromley North	d	00 06				06 35				07 05	→				07 35		→				08 05				
Sundridge Park	d	00 08				06 37				07 07					07 37						08 07				
Grove Park 4	d	00a11	05 46	06 16		06a40		06 46		07a10				07 16	07a40					07 46	08a10			08 16	
Hither Green 4	d		05 50	06 20				06 50						07 20						07 49				08 19	
Lewisham 4	d		05g57	06h27				06j57						07k27						07 55				08 25	
St Johns	a																								
New Cross 4	⊖ a																								
London Bridge 4	⊖ a		06 05	06 35			06 40	07 05				07 26		07 35		07 39		07 54		08 05		08 10	08 24	08 35	
London Cannon Street 4	⊖ a																								
London Waterloo (East) 4	⊖ a		06 10	06 40			06 44	07 10				07 31		07 40		07 43		07 59		08 09		08 14	08 29	08 39	
London Charing Cross 4	⊖ a		06 13	06 43			06 48	07 13				07 34		07 43		07 47		08 05		08 14		08 18	08 33	08 44	

For general notes see front of timetable
For details of catering facilities see Directory of Train Operators

A From Tunbridge Wells (Table 206)
B From Ramsgate (Table 207)
C From Dover Priory (Table 207)
D From Ramsgate (Table 207) and from Ramsgate (Table 207)
b Arr. 2154
c Arr. 2224
e Arr. 2254
f Arr. 2324
g Arr. 0554
h Arr. 0624
j Arr. 0654
k Arr. 0724

Table 204

Tonbridge, Sevenoaks, Orpington Bromley North, Grove Park → London

Network Diagram - see first page of Table 200

		SE 01	SE 4	SE 70	SE 16	SE 22	SE 70	SE 16	SE 70	SE 01	SE 90	SE 22	SE 4	SE 12	SE 70	SE 70	SE 8	SE 16	SE 22	SE 90	SE 01	SE 70	SE 16	SE 70	SE 01
			1			1					1	1	1				1		1	1					
											A						B								
						trolley						trolley	trolley						trolley	trolley					
Tonbridge 4	d		08 00			08 16					08 31	08 46	08 58				09 04		09 16	09 28					
Hildenborough	d										08 36						09 08								
Sevenoaks 4	a		08 09			08 26					08 43	08 55					09 15		09 26						
	d		08 10		08 18	08 26					08 44	08 56					09 16	09 18	09 26						
Dunton Green	d				08 20													09 20							
Knockholt	d				08 26													09 26							
Chelsfield 3	d				08 29													09 29							
Orpington 4	a		08 19		08 32	08 35					08 53	09 05					09 25	09 32	09 35						
	d		08 20	08 23	08 35	08 35	08 38		08 53		08 53	09 05		09 05	09 08	09 23	09 25	09 35	09 35			09 38		09 53	
Petts Wood 4	d			08a26	08 38		08a41		08a56					09 08	09a11	09a26	09 29	09 38				09a41		09a56	
Chislehurst	d				08 41			←						09 11				09 41					←		
Elmstead Woods	d				08 43			08 43						09 13				09 43					09 43		
Bromley North	d	08 35			→					09 05								→			09 35				10 05
Sundridge Park	d	08 37								09 07											09 37				10 07
Grove Park 4	d	08a40						08 46		09a10				09 16							09a40		09 46		10a10
Hither Green 4	d							08 49						09 19									09 50		
Lewisham 4	d							08 55						09 25									09 55		
St Johns	a																								
New Cross 4	⊖ a																								
London Bridge 4	⊖ a		08 38			08 54		09 05			09 08	09 24		09 34			09 43		09 54				10 04		
London Cannon Street 4	⊖ a																								
London Waterloo (East) 4	⊖ a		08 43			08 59		09 09			09 14	09 29	09 32	09 39			09 48		09 59	10 02			10 09		
London Charing Cross 4	⊖ a		08 48			09 03		09 14			09 18	09 33	09 36	09 44			09 51		10 03	10 06			10 14		

		SE 8		SE 22	SE 4	SE 12	SE 70	SE 70	SE 8	SE 16	SE 22	SE 90	SE 01	SE 16	SE 70	SE 70	SE 01	SE 8		SE 22	SE 4	SE 12	SE 70	SE 70
		1		1	1				1		1	1						1		1	1			
		B							B									B						
				trolley	trolley						trolley	trolley								trolley	trolley			
Tonbridge 4	d	09 36		09 46	09 58				10 04		10 18	10 28						10 36		16 46	16 58			
Hildenborough	d	09 40							10 08									10 40						
Sevenoaks 4	a	09 47		09 55					10 15		10 27							10 47		16 55				
	d	09 48		09 56					10 16	10 18	10 28							10 48		16 56				
Dunton Green	d									10 20									and at					
Knockholt	d									10 26														
Chelsfield 3	d									10 29									the same					
Orpington 4	a	09 57		10 05					10 25	10 32								10 57		17 05				
	d	09 57		10 05		10 05	10 08	10 23	10 25	10 35				←	10 38	10 53		10 57	minutes	17 05		17 05	17 08	17 23
Petts Wood 4	d					10 08	10a11	10a26	10 29	10 38				10 38	10a41	10a56						17 08	17a11	17a26
Chislehurst	d					10 11				→				10 41					past			17 11		
Elmstead Woods	d					10 13								10 43								17 13		
Bromley North	d												10 35				11 05		each					
Sundridge Park	d												10 37				11 07		hour until					
Grove Park 4	d					10 16							10a40	10 46			11a10					17 16		
Hither Green 4	d					10 19								10 50								17 19		
Lewisham 4	d					10 25								10 55								17 25		
St Johns	a																							
New Cross 4	⊖ a																							
London Bridge 4	⊖ a	10 13		10 24		10 34			10 43		10 54			11 04				11 13		17 24		17 34		
London Cannon Street 4	⊖ a																							
London Waterloo (East) 4	⊖ a	10 18		10 29	10 32	10 39			10 48		10 59	11 02		11 09				11 18		17 29	17 32	17 39		
London Charing Cross 4	⊖ a	10 21		10 33	10 36	10 44			10 51		11 03	11 06		11 14				11 21		17 33	17 36	17 44		

		SE 8	SE 16	SE 22	SE 90	SE 01	SE 16	SE 70	SE 70	SE 01	SE 8	SE 12	SE 22	SE 70	SE 4	SE 12	SE 70	SE 01	SE 16	SE 22	SE 70	SE 16	SE 01	SE 4	SE 70
		1		1	1						1		1		1					1				1	
		B									B				A									C	
				trolley	trolley								trolley		trolley					trolley				trolley	
Tonbridge 4	d	17 04		17 18	17 28						17 36		17 46		17 48					18 16				18 30	
Hildenborough	d	17 08									17 40				17 53									18 34	
Sevenoaks 4	a	17 15		17 27							17 47		17 55		18 00					18 26				18 42	
	d	17 16	17 18	17 28							17 48		17 56		18 01				18 18	18 26				18 42	
Dunton Green	d		17 20																18 20						
Knockholt	d		17 26																18 26						
Chelsfield 3	d		17 29																18 29						
Orpington 4	a	17 25	17 32								17 57		18 05		18 10				18 32	18 35				18 51	
	d	17 25	17 35				←	17 38	17 53		17 57	18 05	18 05	18 08	18 11		18 23		18 35	18 35	18 38			18 51	18 53
Petts Wood 4	d	17 29	17 38				17 38	17a41	17a56			18 08		18a11			18a26		18 38		18a41				18a56
Chislehurst	d		→				17 41					18 11				←			18 41			←			
Elmstead Woods	d						17 43					18 13				18 13			18 43			18 43			
Bromley North	d					17 35				18 05		→						18 35	→				19 05		
Sundridge Park	d					17 37				18 07								18 37					19 07		
Grove Park 4	d					17a40	17 46			18a10						18 16		18a40				18 46	19a10		
Hither Green 4	d						17 50									18 19						18 49			
Lewisham 4	d						17 55									18 26						18 55			
St Johns	a																								
New Cross 4	⊖ a																								
London Bridge 4	⊖ a	17 43		17 54			18 04				18 13		18 24		18 28	18 35				18 54		19 06		19 08	
London Cannon Street 4	⊖ a																								
London Waterloo (East) 4	⊖ a	17 48		17 59	18 02		18 09				18 18		18 29		18 32	18 41				19 00		19 11		19 14	
London Charing Cross 4	⊖ a	17 51		18 03	18 06		18 14				18 21		18 33		18 36	18 45				19 06		19 15		19 19	

For general notes see front of timetable
For details of catering facilities see Directory of Train Operators

A From Ramsgate (Table 207) and from Ramsgate (Table 207)

B From Ashford International (Table 207)

C From Ramsgate (Table 207)

Table 204

Saturdays

Tonbridge, Sevenoaks, Orpington
Bromley North, Grove Park → London

Network Diagram - see first page of Table 200

		SE 12	SE 22 [1]	SE 70	SE 12	SE 01	SE 90 [1]	SE 70	SE 16	SE 70	SE 01	SE 4 [1] A	SE 70	SE 12	SE 22 [1]	SE 70	SE 12	SE 01	SE 90 [1]	SE 16	SE 70	SE 01	SE 4 [1] A	SE 12	SE 22 [1]
Tonbridge [4]	d		18 46				19 00					19 30			19 46				20 00				20 30		20 46
Hildenborough	d											19 34											20 34		
Sevenoaks [4]	a		18 56				19 09					19 42			19 56				20 09				20 42		20 56
	d		18 57				19 10		19 18			19 42			19 57				20 10	20 18			20 42		20 57
Dunton Green	d								19 20											20 20					
Knockholt	d								19 26											20 26					
Chelsfield [3]	d								19 29											20 29					
Orpington [4]	a		19 07				19 19		19 32			19 51			20 07				20 19	20 32			20 51		21 07
	d	19 05	19 08	19 08			19 20	19 23	19 35	19 38		19 51	19 53	20 05	20 08	20 08			20 20	20 35	20 38		20 51	21 05	21 08
Petts Wood [4]	d	19 08		19a11				19a26	19 38	19a41			19a56	20 08		20a11				20 38	20a41			21 08	
Chislehurst	d	19 11			←				19 41					20 11			←			20 41				21 11	
Elmstead Woods	d	19 13			19 13				19 43					20 13			20 13			20 43				21 13	
Bromley North	d	→				19 35					20 05			→				20 35				21 05		→	
Sundridge Park	d					19 37					20 07							20 37				21 07			
Grove Park [4]	d				19 16	19a40			19 46		20a10						20 16	20a40		20 46		21a10			
Hither Green [4]	d				19 20				19 50								20 20			20 50					
Lewisham [4]	d				19b27				19c57								20e27			20f57					
St Johns	a																								
New Cross [4]	⊖ a																								
London Bridge [4]	⊖ a		19 26		19 36		19 38		20 06			20 08			20 26		20 36		20 38	21 06			21 08		21 25
London Cannon Street [4]	⊖ a																								
London Waterloo (East) [4]	⊖ a		19 30		19 41		19 44		20 11			20 14			20 30		20 41		20 44	21 11			21 14		21 30
London Charing Cross [4]	⊖ a		19 34		19 45		19 49		20 15			20 19			20 34		20 45		20 49	21 15			21 19		21 34

		SE 70	SE 12	SE 01	SE 90 [1]	SE 16	SE 70	SE 01	SE 4 [1] A	SE 16	SE 22 [1]	SE 70	SE 16	SE 01	SE 90 [1]	SE 12	SE 70	SE 01	SE 90 [1] B	SE 12	SE 70	SE 01	SE 4 [1] A
Tonbridge [4]	d				21 00				21 30		21 46				22 00				22 30				23 13
Hildenborough	d								21 34										22 34				23 18
Sevenoaks [4]	a				21 09				21 42		21 56				22 09				22 42				23 25
	d				21 10	21 22			21 42		21 57				22 10	22 22			22 42				23 26
Dunton Green	d																						
Knockholt	d																						
Chelsfield [3]	d					21 29										22 29							23 34
Orpington [4]	a				21 19	21 32			21 51		22 07				22 19	22 32			22 51				23 37
	d	21 08			21 20	21 35	21 38		21 51	22 05	22 08	22 08			22 20	22 35	22 38		22 51	23 05	23 08		23 37
Petts Wood [4]	d	21a11				21 38	21a41			22 08		22a11				22 38	22a41			23 08	23a11		
Chislehurst	d		←			21 41				22 11			←			22 41				23 11			
Elmstead Woods	d		21 13			21 43				22 13			22 13			22 43				23 13			
Bromley North	d			21 35				22 05		→				22 35				23 05				23 35	
Sundridge Park	d			21 37				22 07						22 37				23 07				23 37	
Grove Park [4]	d		21 16	21a40		21 46		22a10					22 16	22a40		22 46		23a10		23 16		23a40	
Hither Green [4]	d		21 20			21 50							22 20			22 50				23 20			
Lewisham [4]	d		21g27			21h57							22j27			22k57				23m27			
St Johns	a																						
New Cross [4]	⊖ a																						
London Bridge [4]	⊖ a		21 36		21 38	22 06			22 08		22 25		22 36		22 38	23 06			23 08	23 35			23 53
London Cannon Street [4]	⊖ a																						
London Waterloo (East) [4]	⊖ a		21 41		21 44	22 11			22 14		22 30		22 41		22 44	23 11			23 13	23 40			23 57
London Charing Cross [4]	⊖ a		21 45		21 49	22 15			22 19		22 34		22 45		22 49	23 15			23 18	23 43			00 01

Sundays

		SE 01	SE 72	SE 14	SE 70	SE 12	SE 22 [1]	SE 12	SE 70	SE 8 [1] C	SE 12	SE 72	SE 70	SE 8 [1] C	SE 12	SE 72	SE 22 [1]	SE 12	SE 70	SE 4 [1]	SE 16	SE 22 [1]
Tonbridge [4]	d						07 08			07 20				07 50			08 08			08 22		08 38
Hildenborough	d									07 24				07 54								
Sevenoaks [4]	a						07 18			07 31				08 01			08 18			08 32		08 48
	d						07 18			07 31				08 01		08 11	08 18			08 33	08 42	08 48
Dunton Green	d																				08 44	
Knockholt	d																				08 50	
Chelsfield [3]	d									07 39				08 09							08 52	
Orpington [4]	a						07 27			07 42				08 12			08 27			08 42	08 55	08 57
	d		07 01	07 04	07 08	07 26	07 28		07 38	07 43	07 56	08 01	08 08	08 13	08 26		08 28		08 38	08 43	08 56	08 58
Petts Wood [4]	d		07a04	07 07	07a11	07 29			07a41		07 59	08a04	08a11		08 29				08a41		08 59	
Chislehurst	d			07 10		07 32		←			08 02				08 32			←			09 02	
Elmstead Woods	d			07 12		07 34		07 34			08 04				08 34			08 34			09 04	
Bromley North	d	00 05				→									→						→	
Sundridge Park	d	00 07																				
Grove Park [4]	d	00a10		07 15				07 37			08 07							08 37				
Hither Green [4]	d			07 19				07 40			08 10							08 40				
Lewisham [4]	d																					
St Johns	a																					
New Cross [4]	⊖ a																					
London Bridge [4]	⊖ a			07 28			07 44	07 50		07 58	08 20			08 28			08 44	08 50		08 58		09 14
London Cannon Street [4]	⊖ a																					
London Waterloo (East) [4]	⊖ a			07 32			07 49	07 55		08 03	08 25			08 33			08 49	08 55		09 03		09 20
London Charing Cross [4]	⊖ a			07 35			07 53	07 58		08 07	08 28			08 37			08 53	08 58		09 07		09 25

For general notes see front of timetable
For details of catering facilities see Directory of Train Operators

A From Ramsgate (Table 207)
B From Ramsgate (Table 207) and from Ramsgate (Table 207)
C From Ashford International (Table 207)
b Arr. 1924
c Arr. 1954
e Arr. 2024
f Arr. 2054
g Arr. 2124
h Arr. 2154
j Arr. 2224
k Arr. 2254
m Arr. 2324

Table 204

Sundays

Tonbridge, Sevenoaks, Orpington Bromley North, Grove Park → London

Network Diagram - see first page of Table 200

		SE 72	SE 16	SE 70	SE 90 [1] A	SE 12	SE 22 [1]	SE 12	SE 70	SE 4 [1]	SE 16	SE 22 [1]	SE 72	SE 16	SE 70	SE 90 [1] B	SE 12	SE 22 [1]	SE 12	SE 70	SE 4 [1]
Tonbridge [4]	d				08 51		09 08			09 22		09 37				09 51		10 08			10 22
Hildenborough	d				08 55											09 55					
Sevenoaks [4]	a				09 02		09 18			09 32		09 48				10 02		10 18			10 32
	d				09 03		09 18			09 33	09 42	09 48				10 03		10 18			10 33
Dunton Green	d										09 44										
Knockholt	d										09 50										
Chelsfield [3]	d										09 52										
Orpington [4]	a				09 12		09 27			09 42	09 55	09 57				10 12		10 27			10 42
	d	09 01		09 08	09 13	09 26	09 28		09 38	09 43	09 56	09 58	10 01		10 08	10 13	10 26	10 28		10 38	10 43
Petts Wood [4]	d	09a04		09a11		09 29			09a41		09 59		10a04		10a11		10 29			10a41	
Chislehurst	d		←			09 32		←			10 02			←			10 32		←		
Elmstead Woods	d		09 04			09 34		09 34			10 04			10 04			10 34		10 34		
Bromley North	d					→					→						→				
Sundridge Park	d																				
Grove Park [4]	d		09 07					09 37						10 07					10 37		
Hither Green [4]	d		09 10					09 40						10 10					10 40		
Lewisham [4]	d																				
St Johns	a																				
New Cross [4]	⊖ a																				
London Bridge [4]	⊖ a		09 20		09 28		09 44	09 50		09 58		10 14		10 20		10 28		10 44	10 50		10 58
London Cannon Street [4]	⊖ a																				
London Waterloo (East) [4]	⊖ a		09 25		09 33		09 49	09 55		10 03		10 20		10 25		10 33		10 49	10 55		11 03
London Charing Cross [4]	⊖ a		09 28		09 37		09 55	09 58		10 07		10 25		10 28		10 37		10 55	10 58		11 07

		SE 16	SE 22 [1]	SE 16	SE 70		SE 90 [1] B	SE 22 [1] C	SE 70	SE 4 [1]	SE 16	SE 22 [1]	SE 16	SE 70	SE 90 [1] B	SE 22 [1] C	SE 70	SE 4 [1]	SE 16	SE 70	SE 90 [1] B
Tonbridge [4]	d		10 37			and at the same minutes past each hour until	17 51	18 08		18 22		18 37			18 51	19 08		19 22			19 51
Hildenborough	d						17 55								18 55						19 55
Sevenoaks [4]	a		10 48				18 02	18 18		18 32		18 48			19 02	19 18		19 32			20 02
	d	10 42	10 48				18 03	18 18		18 33	18 42	18 48			19 03	19 18		19 33	19 45		20 03
Dunton Green	d	10 44									18 44										
Knockholt	d	10 50									18 50										
Chelsfield [3]	d	10 52									18 52								19 52		
Orpington [4]	a	10 55	10 57				18 12	18 27		18 42	18 55	18 57			19 12	19 27		19 42	19 55		20 12
	d	10 56	10 58		11 08		18 13	18 27	18 38	18 43	18 56	18 58		19 08	19 13	19 27	19 38	19 43	19 56	20 08	20 13
Petts Wood [4]	d	10 59			11a11			18 30	18a41		18 59			19a11		19 30	19a41		19 59	20a11	
Chislehurst	d	11 02		←							19 02		←						20 02		
Elmstead Woods	d	11 04		11 04							19 04		19 04						20 04		
Bromley North	d	→									→										
Sundridge Park	d																				
Grove Park [4]	d			11 07									19 07						20 07		
Hither Green [4]	d			11 10									19 10						20 10		
Lewisham [4]	d																				
St Johns	a																				
New Cross [4]	⊖ a																				
London Bridge [4]	⊖ a		11 14	11 20			18 28	18 44		18 58		19 14	19 20		19 28	19 44		19 58	20 20		20 28
London Cannon Street [4]	⊖ a																				
London Waterloo (East) [4]	⊖ a		11 20	11 25			18 33	18 49		19 03		19 20	19 25		19 33	19 49		20 03	20 25		20 33
London Charing Cross [4]	⊖ a		11 25	11 28			18 37	18 55		19 07		19 25	19 28		19 37	19 55		20 07	20 28		20 37

		SE 22 [1] C	SE 70	SE 4 [1]	SE 12	SE 70	SE 90 [1] B	SE 22 [1] C	SE 70	SE 4 [1]	SE 12	SE 70	SE 90 [1] B	SE 22 [1] C	SE 70	SE 4 [1] D	SE 12
Tonbridge [4]	d	20 06		20 22			20 51	21 06		21 22			21 51	22 06		22 21	
Hildenborough	d						20 55						21 55			22 25	
Sevenoaks [4]	a	20 16		20 32			21 02	21 16		21 32			22 02	22 16		22 32	
	d	20 16		20 33			21 03	21 16		21 33			22 03	22 16		22 33	
Dunton Green	d																
Knockholt	d																
Chelsfield [3]	d	20 24						21 24						22 24			
Orpington [4]	a	20 27		20 42			21 12	21 27		21 42			22 12	22 27		22 42	
	d	20 27	20 38	20 43	20 56	21 08	21 13	21 27	21 38	21 43	21 56	22 08	22 13	22 27	22 38	22 43	22 56
Petts Wood [4]	d	20 30	20a41		20 59	21a11		21 30	21a41		21 59	22a11		22 30	22a41		22 59
Chislehurst	d				21 02						22 02						23 02
Elmstead Woods	d				21 04						22 04						23 04
Bromley North	d																
Sundridge Park	d																
Grove Park [4]	d				21 07						22 07						23 07
Hither Green [4]	d				21 10						22 10						23 10
Lewisham [4]	d																
St Johns	a																
New Cross [4]	⊖ a																
London Bridge [4]	⊖ a	20 44		20 58	21 20		21 28	21 44		21 58	22 20		22 28	22 44		22 58	23 20
London Cannon Street [4]	⊖ a																
London Waterloo (East) [4]	⊖ a	20 49		21 03	21 25		21 33	21 49		22 03	22 25		22 33	22 49		23 03	23 25
London Charing Cross [4]	⊖ a	20 53		21 07	21 28		21 37	21 53		22 07	22 28		22 37	22 53		23 06	23 28

For general notes see front of timetable
For details of catering facilities see Directory of Train Operators

A From Ramsgate (Table 207)
B From Margate (Table 207)
C From Hastings (Table 206)
D From Ramsgate (Table 207) and from Margate (Table 207)

Network Diagram for Tables 206, 207, 208, 209

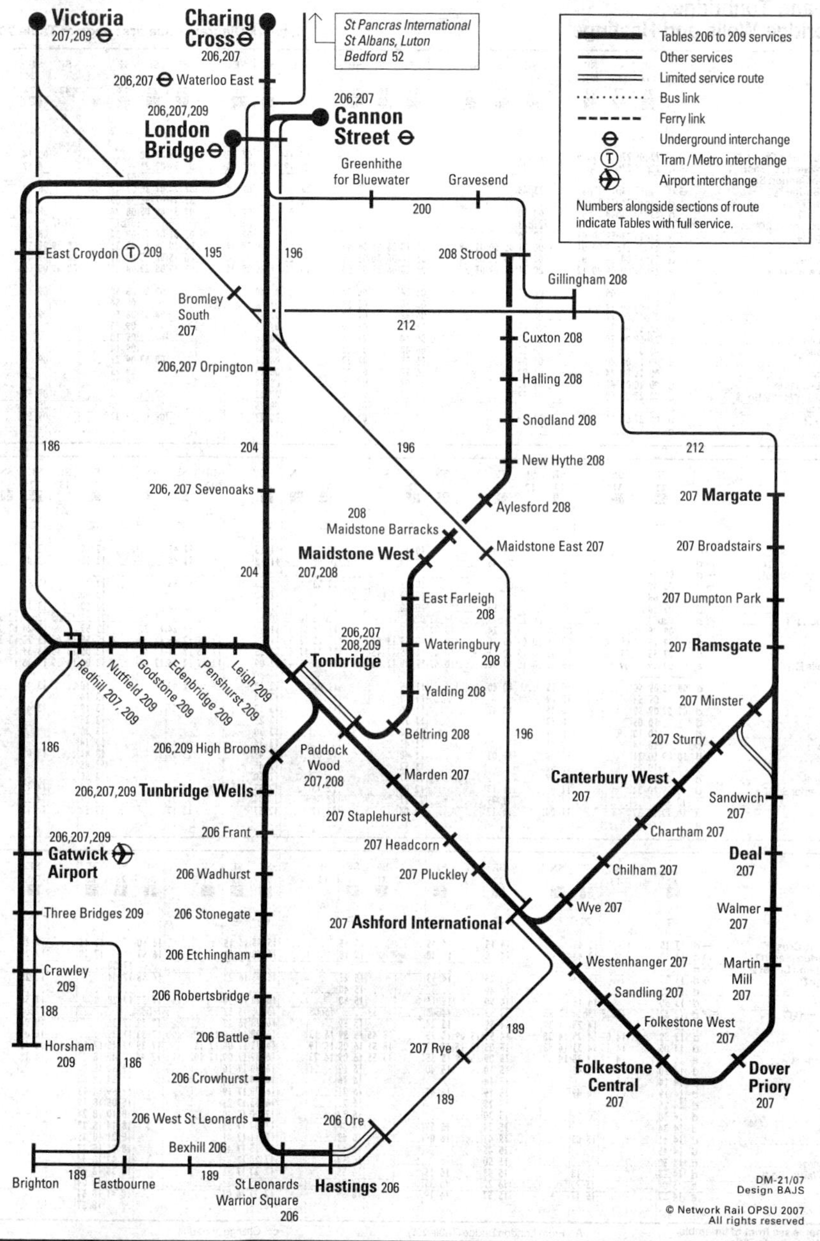

Victoria 207,209
Charing Cross 206,207
206,207 Waterloo East
St Pancras International
St Albans, Luton
Bedford 52
206,207 Cannon Street
206,207,209 London Bridge
Tables 206 to 209 services
Other services
Limited service route
Bus link
Ferry link
Underground interchange
Tram / Metro interchange
Airport interchange
Numbers alongside sections of route indicate Tables with full service.
Greenhithe for Bluewater
Gravesend
200
East Croydon 209
195
196
208 Strood
Gillingham 208
Bromley South 207
212
Cuxton 208
206,207 Orpington
Halling 208
Snodland 208
186
204
196
212
New Hythe 208
206, 207 Sevenoaks
Aylesford 208
207 Margate
208 Maidstone Barracks
Maidstone West 207,208
Maidstone East 207
207 Broadstairs
204
East Farleigh 208
207 Dumpton Park
206,207,208,209 Tonbridge
Wateringbury 208
207 Ramsgate
Redhill 207, 209
Nutfield 209
Godstone 209
Edenbridge 209
Penshurst 209
Leigh 209
Yalding 208
207 Minster
Beltring 208
196
207 Sturry
186
206,209 High Brooms
Paddock Wood 207,208
Marden 207
Canterbury West 207
Sandwich 207
206,207,209 Tunbridge Wells
207 Staplehurst
Chartham 207
206,207,209 Gatwick Airport
206 Frant
207 Headcorn
Deal 207
206 Wadhurst
207 Pluckley
Chilham 207
Three Bridges 209
206 Stonegate
Wye 207
Walmer 207
207 Ashford International
206 Etchingham
Westenhanger 207
Martin Mill 207
Crawley 209
206 Robertsbridge
Sandling 207
188
189
Folkestone West 207
Horsham 209
206 Battle
207 Rye
186
206 Crowhurst
Folkestone Central 207
Dover Priory 207
189
206 West St Leonards
206 Ore
Bexhill 206
Brighton
189
Eastbourne
189
St Leonards Warrior Square 206
Hastings 206
DM-21/07
Design BAJS

For details of Bank Holiday service alterations please see first page of Table 195

London and Tonbridge → Tunbridge Wells and Hastings

Network Diagram - see first page of Table 206

Miles	Station		SE MX 22 1	SE MO 22 1	SE MX 22 1	SE MX 22 1	SE 31 1	SE 31 1	SE 25 1	SE 31 1	SE 25 1	SE 16	SE 25 1	SE 31 1	SE 30 1	SE 22 1	SE 23 1	SE 43 A	SE 22 1 ✈
0	London Charing Cross	⊖ d	22p45	23p10	23p15	23p37						06 16		07 00	07 16	07 28			08 14
¾	London Waterloo (East)	⊖ d	22p48	23p13	23p18	23p40						06 19		07 03	07 19	07 31			08 17
—	London Cannon Street	⊖ d															07 45		
1¾	London Bridge	⊖ d	22p53	23p17	23p23	23p45						06 24		07 08	07 24	07 36	07 49		08 23
13¾	Orpington	d	23p10	23p35	23p40							06 54		07 26	07 41	07 55	08 09		
22	Sevenoaks	d	23p20	23p48	23p52	00 10						07 08		07 36	07 51	08 05	08 24		08 47
—	Gatwick Airport ✈	d			22 53	23b23						05 54	05 54	06b37			07b13	07c41	07b41
29½	Tonbridge	a	23p28	23p59	00 01	00 20						07 19		07 44	08 01	08 15	08 32		08 55
—		d	23p29	23p59	00 01	00 21	05 00	05 28	06 10	06 24	06 44	07 21	07 30	07 54	08 10	08 19	08 33	08 39	08 57
33	High Brooms	d	23p35	00 04	00 07	00 27	05 06	05 34	06 16	06 30	06 50	07 27	07 35	08 00	08 15	08 25	08 41	08 45	09 03
—	Tunbridge Wells	a	23p39	00 08	00 12	00 31	05 09	05 37	06 20	06 33	06 54	07 30	07 39	08 04	08 19	08 29	08 45	08 49	09 09
34½		d	23p40	00 08		00 32			06 24		06 54		07 40			08 30	08 50		09 15
36¾	Frant	d	23p44	00 13		00 36			06 28		06 59		07 44				08 54		
39¼	Wadhurst	d	23p49	00 17		00 41			06 33		07 03		07 49			08 37	08 59		09 22
43¼	Stonegate	d	23p55	00 23		00 47			06 39		07 09		07 55				09 05		
47¼	Etchingham	d	23p58	00 28		00 52			06 44		07 14		08 00				09 10		
49¼	Robertsbridge	d	00 04	00 32		00 56			06 48		07e22		08 04				09 14		
55½	Battle	d	00 11	00 40		01 03			06 55		07 29		08 11			08 53	09 21		09 39
57½	Crowhurst	d	00 15	00 44		01 07			06 59		07 33		08 15				09 25		
60¾	West St Leonards	d	00 20	00 49		01 12			07 04		07 38		08 20				09 30		
61¾	St Leonards Warrior Sq	d	00 23	00 52		01 15			07 07		07 41		08 23			09 03	09 33		09 53
—	Bexhill	a							07 22		08 24		08 35			09 22	10 01		10 21
62½	Hastings	a	00 27	00 56		01 19			07 11		07 45		08 27			09 07	09 37		09 57
63½	Ore	a							07 18										

Station		SE 23 1 ✈		SE 31 1	SE 23 1 ✈	SE 13 A	SE 22 1 ✈	SN 1 B	SE 22 1 ✈	SE 13 A	SE 22 1 ✈	SN 1 B	SE 22 1 ✈	SE 13 A	SE 22 1 ✈	SN 1 B	SE 22 1 ✈	SE 13 A	SE 22 1 ✈	SN 1 B
London Charing Cross	⊖ d						09 45		10 15		10 45		11 15		11 45		12 15		12 45	
London Waterloo (East)	⊖ d						09 48		10 18		10 48		11 18		11 48		12 18		12 48	
London Cannon Street	⊖ d	08 45			09 17															
London Bridge	⊖ d	08 49			09 21		09 53		10 23		10 53		11 23		11 53		12 23		12 53	
Orpington	d	09 08			09 40				10 40				11 40				12 40			
Sevenoaks	d	09 18			09 50		10 16		10 50		11 16		11 50		12 16		12 50		13 16	
Gatwick Airport ✈	d	08b04		08b37		09c23	09b23	09 52	09 52	10c08	10b08	10 53	10 53	11c08	11b08	11 53	11 53	12c08	12b08	12 52
Tonbridge	a	09 28			09 59		10 24	10 37	10 59		11 24	11 37	11 59		12 24	12 37	12 59		13 24	13 37
	d	09 29		09 38	09 59	10 09	10 25	10 38	10 59	11 09	11 25	11 38	11 59	12 09	12 25	12 38	12 59	13 09	13 25	13 38
High Brooms	d	09 35		09 43	10 05	10 15	10 31	10 43	11 05	11 15	11 31	11 43	12 05	12 15	12 31	12 43	13 05	13 15	13 31	13 43
Tunbridge Wells	a	09 39		09 47	10 09	10 19	10 36	10 47	11 09	11 19	11 35	11 47	12 09	12 19	12 35	12 47	13 09	13 19	13 35	13 47
	d	09 45	09 50		10 15		10 40		11 15		11 40		12 10		12 40		13 10		13 40	
Frant	d		09 54		10 19				11 19				12 14				13 14			
Wadhurst	d	09 52	09 59		10 26		10 47		11 26		11 47		12 19		12 47		13 19		13 47	
Stonegate	d		10 05		10 32				11 32				12 25				13 25			
Etchingham	d		10 10		10 37				11 37				12 30				13 30			
Robertsbridge	d		10 14		10 41				11 41				12 34				13 34			
Battle	d	10 09	10 21		10 48		11 03		11 48		12 03		12 41		13 03		13 41		14 03	
Crowhurst	d		10 25		10 52				11 52				12 45				13 45			
West St Leonards	d		10 31		10 57				11 57				12 50				13 50			
St Leonards Warrior Sq	d	10 19	10 34		11 00		11 13		12 00		12 13		12 53		13 13		13 53		14 13	
Bexhill	a	10 35			11 21		11 35		12 21		12 35		13 04		13 35		14 04		14 35	
Hastings	a	10 23	10 37		11 04		11 17		12 04		12 17		12 57		13 17		13 57		14 17	
Ore	a																			

Station		SE 22 1 ✈	SE 13 A	SE 22 1 ✈	SN 1 B	SE 22 1 ✈	SE 13 A	SE 22 1 ✈	SE 31 1	SE 22 1 ✈	SE 13 A	SE 22 1 ✈	SE 22 1 ✈	SE 31 1	SE 30 1	SE 23 1	SE 22 1	SE 30 1
London Charing Cross	⊖ d	13 15		13 45		14 15		14 45		15 15		15 45	16 15		16 50		17 16	17 20
London Waterloo (East)	⊖ d	13 18		13 48		14 18		14 48		15 18		15 48	16 18		16 53		17 19	17 23
London Cannon Street	⊖ d															17 00		
London Bridge	⊖ d	13 23		13 53		14 23		14 53		15 23		15 53	16 23		16 58	17 04		17 28
Orpington	d	13 40				14 40				15 40								
Sevenoaks	d	13 50		14 16		14 50		15 16		15 50		16 20	16 50		17 22	17 28		17 56
Gatwick Airport ✈	d	12 52	13c08	13b08	13 53	13 53	14c08	14b08	14 53		15c08	15b08	15 53		16b08			17b08
Tonbridge	a	13 59		14 24	14 37	14 59		15 24		15 59		16 28	16 58		17 32	17 36		18 06
	d	13 59	14 09	14 25	14 38	14 59	15 09	15 25	15 45	15 59	16 13	16 29	16 59	17 09	17 33	17 39		18 07
High Brooms	d	14 05	14 15	14 31	14 43	15 05	15 15	15 31	15 51	16 05	16 19	16 35	17 05	17 15	17 39	17 45	17 59	18 13
Tunbridge Wells	a	14 09	14 19	14 35	14 47	15 09	15 19	15 35	15 55	16 09	16 23	16 39	17 09	17 19	17 44	17 49	18 03	18 18
	d	14 10		14 40		15 10		15 40		16 12		16 40	17 10			17 50	18 04	
Frant	d	14 14				15 14				16 16		16 44	17 14			17 54	18 08	
Wadhurst	d	14 19		14 47		15 19		15 47		16 21		16 49	17 19			17 59	18 13	
Stonegate	d	14 25				15 25				16 27		16 55	17 25			18 05	18 19	
Etchingham	d	14 30				15 30				16 32		17 00	17 30			18 10	18 24	
Robertsbridge	d	14 34				15 34		15 57		16 36		17 04	17 34			18 14	18 28	
Battle	d	14 41		15 03		15 41		16 05		16 43		17 11	17 41			18 21	18 35	
Crowhurst	d	14 45				15 45				16 47		17 15	17 45			18 25	18 39	
West St Leonards	d	14 50				15 50				16 52		17 20	17 52			18 32	18 44	
St Leonards Warrior Sq	d	14 53		15 13		15 53		16 15		16 55		17 23	17 56			18 35	18 47	
Bexhill	a	15 04		15 33		16 22		16 35		17 21		17 35	18 21				19 04	
Hastings	a	14 57		15 17		15 57		16 19		16 59		17 27	18 01			18 41	18 51	
Ore	a																18 57	

For general notes see front of timetable
For details of catering facilities see Directory of Train Operators

A From London Bridge (Table 209)
B From Horsham (Table 186)
b Change at Redhill and Tonbridge
c Change at Redhill
e Arr. 0718

Mondays to Fridays

For details of Bank Holiday service alterations please see first page of Table 195

London and Tonbridge → Tunbridge Wells and Hastings

Network Diagram - see first page of Table 206

		SE 23 1 ✠		SE 30 1		SE 22 1	SE 30 1	SE 23 1		SE 30 1	SE 22 1 ✠	SE 23 1		SE 22 1 ✠	SE 90 1	SE 22 1		SE 22 1	SE 22 1	SE 22 1	SE 22 1	SE 22 1	SE 22 1	SE 22 1	SE 22 1
London Charing Cross 4	⊖ d			17 41		18 00	18 04			18 28	18 50			19 15	19 30	19 45		20 15	20 45	21 15	21 45	22 15	22 45	23 15	23 37
London Waterloo (East) 4	⊖ d			17 44		18 03	18 07			18 31	18 53			19 18	19 33	19 48		20 18	20 48	21 18	21 48	22 18	22 48	23 18	23 40
London Cannon Street 4	⊖ d	17 38						18 26				19 06													
London Bridge 4	⊖ d			17 49			18 12	18 30		18 36		19 10		19 23	19 38	19 53		20 23	20 53	21 23	21 53	22 23	22 53	23 23	23 45
Orpington 4	d											19 28			19 54			20 40	21 10	21 40	22 10	22 40	23 10	23 40	
Sevenoaks 4	d			18 16			18 40			19 05	19 20	19 38		19 50	20 06	20 20		20 50	21 20	21 50	22 20	22 52	23 20	23 52	00 10
Gatwick Airport 10	✈ d						17b38			18b08	18b38				19b08			19b39		20 53		21 53		22 53	23b23
Tonbridge 4	a			18 27			18 51			19 15	19 29	19 48		19 58	20 17	20 28		20 58	21 28	21 58	22 28	23 00	23 28	00 01	00 20
	d			18 28			18 52			19 16	19 31	19 49		19 59	20 17	20 29		20 59	21 29	21 59	22 29	23 05	23 29	00 01	00 21
High Brooms	d	18 19		18 34		18 43	18 58	19 06		19 22	19 37	19 55		20 05	20 23	20 35		21 05	21 35	22 05	22 35	23 11	23 35	00 07	00 27
Tunbridge Wells 4	a	18 23		18 40		18 47	19 04	19 10		19 28	19 41	19 59		20 09	20 28	20 42		21 09	21 39	22 10	22 39	23 15	23 39	00 12	00 31
	d	18 28	18 32			18 52		19 17			19 42	20 00		20 10		20 42		21 10	21 40		22 40		23 40		00 32
Frant	d		18 36			18 56		19 21			19 46	20 04		20 14				21 14	21 44		22 44		23 44		00 36
Wadhurst	d	18 35	18 41			19 01		19 26			19 51	20 09		20 19		20 50		21 19	21 49		22 49		23 49		00 41
Stonegate	d		18 47			19 07		19 32			19 57	20 15		20 25				21 25	21 55		22 55		23 55		00 47
Etchingham	d	18 44	18 52			19 12		19 37			20 02	20 20		20 30		20 59		21 30	22 00		23 00		23 58		00 52
Robertsbridge	d		18 56			19 16		19 41			20 06	20 24		20 34				21 34	22 04		23 04		00 04		00 56
Battle	d	18 54	19 03			19 23		19 48			20 13	20 31		20 41		21 08		21 41	22 11		23 11		00 11		01 03
Crowhurst	d		19 07			19 27		19 52			20 17			20 45				21 45	22 15		23 15		00 15		01 07
West St Leonards	d		19 12			19 32		19 59			20 22			20 50				21 50	22 20		23 20		00 20		01 12
St Leonards Warrior Sq 4	d	19 03	19 15			19 35		20 02			20 25	20 41		20 53		21 18		21 53	22 23		23 23		00 23		01 15
Bexhill 4	a	19 21				20 04		20 21						21 04		21 39		22 25	22 38						
Hastings 4	a	19 09	19 21			19 39		20 08			20 30	20 45		20 57		21 21		21 57	22 27		23 27		00 27		01 19
Ore	a					19 45																			

Saturdays

For details of Bank Holiday service alterations please see first page of Table 195

		SE 22 1		SE 22 1		SE 22 1		SE 25 1		SE 25 1		SE 22 1		SN 1 A		SE 22 1		SE 13 B			SE 22 1 ✠	SN 1 A	SE 22 1 ✠		
London Charing Cross 4	⊖ d	22p45		23p15		23p37						07 45				08 15					08 45		09 15		
London Waterloo (East) 4	⊖ d	22p48		23p18		23p40						07 48				08 18					08 48		09 18		
London Cannon Street 4	⊖ d																								
London Bridge 4	⊖ d	22p53		23p23		23p45						07 53				08 23					08 53		09 23		
Orpington 4	d	23p10		23p40								08 10				08 40							09 40		
Sevenoaks 4	d	23p20		23p52		00 10						08 20				08 51					09 16		09 51		
Gatwick Airport 10	✈ d			22 53		23 23		05b45		06 53				07 53		07 53		08c08			08b08	08 53	08 53		
Tonbridge 4	a	23p28		00 01		00 20						08 28		08 37		08 59					09 24	09 37	09 59		
	d	23p29		00 01		00 21		07 00		08 00		08 30		08 38		09 00		09 09			09 26	09 38	10 00		
High Brooms	d	23p35		00 07		00 27		07 06		08 06		08 36		08 43		09 06		09 15			09 33	09 43	10 06		
Tunbridge Wells 4	a	23p39		00 12		00 31		07 10		08 10		08 40		08 47		09 10		09 19			09 37	09 47	10 10		
	d	23p40				00 32		07 10		08 10		08 40				09 10					09 40		10 10		
Frant	d	23p44				00 36		07 15		08 15		08 45				09 15							10 15		
Wadhurst	d	23p49				00 41		07 19		08 19		08 49				09 19					09 47		10 19		
Stonegate	d	23p55				00 47		07 25		08 25		08 55				09 25							10 25		
Etchingham	d	23p58				00 52		07 30		08 30		09 00				09 30							10 30		
Robertsbridge	d	00 04				00 56		07 34		08 34		09 04				09 34							10 34		
Battle	d	00 11				01 03		07 42		08 42		09 17				09 42					10 03		10 42		
Crowhurst	d	00 15				01 07		07 46		08 46		09 21				09 46							10 46		
West St Leonards	d	00 20				01 12		07 51		08 51		09 26				09 51							10 51		
St Leonards Warrior Sq 4	d	00 23				01 15		07 54		08 54		09 33				09 54					10 13		10 54		
Bexhill 4	a							08 21		09 21		10 04				10 21					10 35		11 21		
Hastings 4	a	00 27				01 19		07 58		08 58		09 36				09 57					10 17		10 57		
Ore	a																								

For general notes see front of timetable
For details of catering facilities see Directory of Train Operators

A From Horsham (Table 186)
B From London Bridge (Table 209)
b Change at Redhill and Tonbridge
c Change at Redhill

Table 206

For details of Bank Holiday service alterations please see first page of Table 195

London and Tonbridge → Tunbridge Wells and Hastings

Network Diagram - see first page of Table 206

		SE 13 A		SE 22 1 🚲	SE 22 1 🚲	SE 22 1	SE 31 1	SE 22 1	SE 31 1	SE 22 1	SE 31 1	SE 22 1	SE 31 1	SE 8 1
London Charing Cross 4	⊖ d		and at the same minutes past each hour until	18 45	19 15	19 45		20 45		21 45		22 45		23 30
London Waterloo (East) 4	⊖ d			18 48	19 18	19 48		20 48		21 48		22 48		23 33
London Cannon Street 4	⊖ d													
London Bridge 4	⊖ d			18 53	19 23	19 53		20 53		21 53		22 53		23 37
Orpington 4	d				19 40	20 10		21 10		22 10		23 10		23 53
Sevenoaks 4	d			19 17	19 51	20 20		21 20		22 20		23 20		00 03
Gatwick Airport 10	✈ d	09b08		18c08	18 52	19c08	19 53		20 53		21 53		22 53	23c23
Tonbridge 4	a			19 25	19 59	20 28		21 28		22 28		23 28		00 15
	d	10 09		19 26	20 00	20 30	20 50	21 30	21 50	22 30	22 55	23 30	23 50	00 21
High Brooms	d	10 15		19 33	20 06	20 36	20 55	21 36	21 56	22 36	23 00	23 36	23 55	00 27
Tunbridge Wells 4	a	10 19		19 37	20 10	20 40	20 59	21 40	21 59	22 40	23 04	23 40	23 59	00 31
	d			19 40	20 10	20 40		21 40		22 40		23 40		00 31
Frant	d				20 15	20 45		21 45		22 45		23 45		00 36
Wadhurst	d			19 47	20 19	20 49		21 49		22 49		23 49		00 40
Stonegate	d				20 25	20 55		21 55		22 55		23 55		00 46
Etchingham	d				20 30	21 00		22 00		23 00		00 01		00 51
Robertsbridge	d				20 34	21 04		22 04		23 04		00 04		00 55
Battle	d			20 03	20 42	21 12		22 12		23 12		00 12		01 03
Crowhurst	d				20 46	21 16		22 16		23 16		00 16		01 07
West St Leonards	d				20 51	21 21		22 21		23 21		00 21		01 12
St Leonards Warrior Sq 4	d			20 13	20 54	21 24		22 24		23 24		00 24		01 15
Bexhill 4	a			20 35	21 21	21 35		22 38						
Hastings 4	a			20 17	20 57	21 27		22 27		23 27		00 27		01 18
Ore	a													

Sundays

		SE 22 1	SE 25 1	SE 22 1	SE 22 1	SE 22 1	SE 22 1	SE 22 1 🚲		SE 22 1	SE 22 1	SE 22 1	SE 22 1	SE 22 1	SE 22 1	SE 22 1	SE 22 1
London Charing Cross 4	⊖ d	22p45	23p30		08 10		09 10	09 40	and at the same minutes past each hour until	18 10	18 40	19 10	19 40	20 10	21 10	22 10	23 10
London Waterloo (East) 4	⊖ d	22p48	23p33		08 13		09 13	09 43		18 13	18 43	19 13	19 43	20 13	21 13	22 13	23 13
London Cannon Street 4	⊖ d																
London Bridge 4	⊖ d	22p53	23p37		08 18		09 18	09 48		18 18	18 48	19 17	19 48	20 17	21 17	22 17	23 17
Orpington 4	d	23p10	23p53		08 35		09 35	10 05		18 35	19 05	19 36	20 05	20 36	21 37	22 37	23 35
Sevenoaks 4	d	23p20	00 03		08 45		09 45	10 15		18 45	19 15	19 48	20 15	20 48	21 49	22 49	23 48
Gatwick Airport 10	✈ d		23c23		07 55		08 55			17 55		18 55		19 55	20 55	21 55	
Tonbridge 4	a	23p28	00 15		08 53		09 53	10 23		18 53	19 23	19 56	20 23	20 57	21 57	22 57	23 59
	d	23p30	00 21	08 11	08 54	09 24	09 54	10 24		18 54	19 26	19 57	20 23	20 57	21 57	22 57	23 59
High Brooms	d	23p36	00 27	08 17	09 00	09 30	10 00	10 30		19 00	19 32	20 03	20 29	21 04	22 03	23 03	00 04
Tunbridge Wells 4	a	23p40	00 31	08 21	09 04	09 34	10 04	10 34		19 04	19 36	20 07	20 33	21 07	22 07	23 07	00 08
	d	23p40	00 31		09 04	09 34	10 04	10 34		19 04	19 38	20 07		21 10	22 08	23 07	00 08
Frant	d	23p45	00 36		09 09		10 09			19 09		20 12		21 14	22 12	23 12	00 13
Wadhurst	d	23p49	00 40		09 13	09 42	10 13	10 42		19 13	19 47	20 16		21 19	22 17	23 16	00 17
Stonegate	d	23p55	00 46		09 19		10 19			19 19		20 22		21 25	22 23	23 22	00 23
Etchingham	d	00 01	00 51		09 24		10 24			19 24		20 27		21 31	22 28	23 27	00 28
Robertsbridge	d	00 04	00 55		09 28		10 28			19 28		20 31		21 35	22 32	23 31	00 32
Battle	d	00 12	01 03		09 36	09 57	10 36	10 57		19 36	20 03	20 39		21 43	22 39	23 39	00 40
Crowhurst	d	00 16	01 07		09 40		10 40			19 40		20 43		21 47	22 43	23 43	00 44
West St Leonards	d	00 21	01 12		09 45		10 45			19 45		20 48		21 54	22 48	23 48	00 49
St Leonards Warrior Sq 4	d	00 24	01 15		09 48	10 08	10 48	11 08		19 48	20 13	20 51		21 57	22 51	23 51	00 52
Bexhill 4	a				10 12	10 27	11 12	11 27		20 12	20 27	21 12		22 12	23 27		
Hastings 4	a	00 27	01 18		09 51	10 11	10 51	11 11		19 51	20 16	20 54		22 01	22 55	23 54	00 56
Ore	a																

For general notes see front of timetable
For details of catering facilities see Directory of Train Operators

A From London Bridge (Table 209)
b Change at Redhill
c Change at Redhill and Tonbridge

For details of Bank Holiday service alterations please see first page of Table 195

Hastings and Tunbridge Wells → Tonbridge and London

Network Diagram - see first page of Table 206

Miles	Station		SE 30 [1]	SE 31 [1]	SE 22 [1]	SE 23 [1]	SE 25 [1]	SE 30 [1]	SE 22 [1]	SE 22 [1]		SE 30 [1]	SE 23 [1]	SE 30 [1]	SE 22 [1]	SE 30 [1]	SE 23 [1]	SE 30 [1]	SE 22 [1]		SE 31 [1]	SE 22 [1]	SE 22 [1]	SE 88 [1]	SE 22 [1]
									trolley				trolley		trolley		trolley					trolley	trolley	A	trolley
0	Ore	d							06 10				06 38						07 46						
1	**Hastings [4]**	d			05 16	05 44	05 56		06 14	06 26			06 42		07 02		07 28		07 50			08 10	08 42		09 31
—	Bexhill [4]	d				*05 14*							*06 18*		*06 52*		*07 11*		*07 22*			*08 01*	*08 25*		*09 22*
1¾	St Leonards Warrior Sq [4]	d			05 19	05 47	05 59		06 17	06 29			06 45		07 05		07 31		07 53			08 13	08 45		09 34
2¾	West St Leonards	d			05 22	05 50			06 20				06 48		07 08		07 34		07 56			08 16	08 48		
6	Crowhurst	d			05 27	05 55			06 25				06 53		07 13		07 39		08 01			08 21	08 53		
8	Battle	d			05 31	05 59	06 09		06 29	06 39			06 57		07 17		07 43		08 05			08 25	08 57		09 44
14¼	Robertsbridge	d			05 39	06 07			06 37				07 05		07 25		07 51		08 13			08 33	09 05		
16	Etchingham	d			05 43	06 11	06 19		06 41	06 49			07 09		07 29		07 55		08 17			08 37	09 09		
19¾	Stonegate	d			05 48	06 16			06 46				07 14		07 34		08 00		08 23			08 43	09 14		
24¼	Wadhurst	d			05 55	06 23	06 29		06 53	06 59			07 21		07 41		08 07		08 29			08 49	09 21		10 00
26¾	Frant	d			05 59	06 27			06 57				07 25		07 45		08 11		08 34			08 54	09 25		
29	**Tunbridge Wells [4]**	a			06 05	06 33	06 37		07 03	07 07			07 31		07 51		08 17		08 38			08 58	09 30		10 07
—		d	05 16	05 44	06 06	06 42		06 56	07 12			07 20	07 36	07 40	07 56	08 00	08 22	08 26	08 40		08 56	09 02	09 36	09 52	10 08
30½	High Brooms	d	05 20	05 47	06 10	06 46		07 00	07 16			07 24	07 40	07 44	08 00	08 04	08 26	08 30	08 44		09 00	09 06	09 39	09 55	10 11
34	**Tonbridge [4]**	a	05 26	05 52	06 17	06 53		07 05				07 29		07 50		08 10		08 36	08 50		09 06	09 13	09 45	10 01	10 17
—		d	05 26		06 18	06 53		07 06				07 31		07 51		08 11		08 36	09 00			09 14	09 46	10 04	10 18
—	Gatwick Airport [10] ✈	a		*06b53*	*07b54*							*08b39*				*09b02*		*09b39*				*10b23*	*10 55*	10 55	*11b23*
41½	Sevenoaks [4]	a	05 38		06 30	07 03		07 18				07 43		08 03		08 23		08 48	09 09			09 26	09 55		10 27
49¾	Orpington [4]	a	05 50			07 12																09 35			
61¾	**London Bridge [4]**	⊖ a	06 06		06 55	07 29		07 50				08 10	08 21	08 30		08 50	09 05	09 18	09 33			09 51	10 24		10 54
—	**London Cannon Street [4]**	⊖ a				07 36							08 28				09 12								
62¾	**London Waterloo (East) [4]**	⊖ a	06 11		07 00			07 55	08 00			08 15		08 35	08 45	08 55		09 23	09 38			09 57	10 29		10 59
63½	**London Charing Cross [4]**	⊖ a	06 14		07 05			07 59	08 05			08 21		08 41	08 51	09 01		09 29	09 44			10 01	10 33		11 03

Station		SE 13	SE 22 [1]	SE 88 [1]	SE 22 [1]	SE 13		SE 22 [1]	SE 88 [1]	SE 22 [1]	SE 13	SE 22 [1]	SE 88 [1]	SE 22 [1]	SE 13		SE 22 [1]	SE 88 [1]	SE 22 [1]	SE 13	SE 22 [1]	SE 88 [1]	SE 22 [1]	SE 13	SE 23 [1]
			trolley	A	trolley			trolley	A	trolley		trolley	A	trolley			trolley	A	trolley		trolley	A	trolley		
Ore	d																								
Hastings [4]	d		09 47		10 31			10 47		11 31		11 47		12 31			12 47		13 31		13 47		14 31		14 47
Bexhill [4]	d				*10 22*			*10 39*		*11 22*		*11 39*		*12 22*			*12 39*		*13 22*		*13 39*		*14 22*		*14 39*
St Leonards Warrior Sq [4]	d		09 50		10 34			10 50		11 34		11 50		12 34			12 50		13 34		13 50		14 34		14 50
West St Leonards	d		09 53					10 53				11 53					12 53				13 53				14 53
Crowhurst	d		09 58					10 58				11 58					12 58				13 58				14 58
Battle	d		10 02		10 44			11 02		11 44		12 02		12 44			13 02		13 44		14 02		14 44		15 02
Robertsbridge	d		10 10					11 10				12 10					13 10				14 10				15 10
Etchingham	d		10 14					11 14				12 14					13 14				14 14				15 14
Stonegate	d		10 19					11 19				12 19					13 19				14 19				15 19
Wadhurst	d		10 26		11 00			11 26		12 00		12 26		13 00			13 26		14 00		14 26		15 00		15 26
Frant	d		10 30					11 30				12 30					13 30				14 30				15 30
Tunbridge Wells [4]	a		10 35		11 07			11 35		12 07		12 35		13 07			13 35		14 07		14 35		15 07		15 35
	d	10 24	10 36	10 52	11 08	11 24		11 36	11 52	12 08	12 24	12 36	12 52	13 08	13 24		13 36	13 52	14 08	14 24	14 36	14 52	15 08	15 24	15 36
High Brooms	d	10 27	10 39	10 55	11 11	11 27		11 39	11 55	12 11	12 27	12 39	12 55	13 11	13 27		13 39	13 55	14 11	14 27	14 39	14 55	15 11	15 27	15 39
Tonbridge [4]	a	10 33	10 45	11 01	11 17	11 33		11 45	12 01	12 17	12 33	12 45	13 01	13 17	13 33		13 45	14 01	14 17	14 33	14 45	15 01	15 17	15 33	15 45
	d		10 46	11 04	11 18			11 46	12 04	12 18		12 46	13 04	13 18			13 46	14 04	14 18		14 46	15 04	15 18		15 46
Gatwick Airport [10] ✈	a	*11c23*	*11 55*	11 55	*12b23*	*12c23*		*12 55*	12 55	*13b23*	*13c23*	*13 55*	13 55	*14b23*	*14c23*		*14 55*	14 55	*15b23*	*15c23*	*15 56*	15 56	*16b23*	*16c23*	*16 56*
Sevenoaks [4]	a		10 55		11 27			11 55		12 27		12 55		13 27			13 55		14 27		14 55		15 27		15 55
Orpington [4]	a		11 05					12 05				13 05					14 05				15 05				16 07
London Bridge [4]	⊖ a		11 24		11 54			12 24		12 54		13 24		13 54			14 24		14 54		15 24		15 54		16 24
London Cannon Street [4]	⊖ a																								
London Waterloo (East) [4]	⊖ a		11 29		11 59			12 29		12 59		13 29		13 59			14 29		14 59		15 29		15 59		16 29
London Charing Cross [4]	⊖ a		11 33		12 03			12 33		13 03		13 33		14 03			14 33		15 03		15 33		16 03		16 33

Station		SE 22 [1]		SE 23 [1]	SE 31 [1]	SE 22 [1]	SE 22 [1]	SE 22 [1]	SE 22 [1]	SE 22 [1]	SE 22 [1]		SE 22 [1]	SE 22 [1]	SE 22 [1]	SE 22 [1]	SE 22 [1]	SE 22 [1]	SE 22 [1]	SE 22 [1]	SE 22 [1]	SE 25 [1]	SE 31		
				trolley					trolley																
Ore	d																								
Hastings [4]	d	15 07		15 35		16 07	16 35		17 11		17 47			18 17	18 47		19 47		20 47		21 35	22 05			
Bexhill [4]	d			*15 22*		*15 42*	*16 22*		*17 02*		*17 22*			*18 03*	*18 23*		*19 23*		*20 22*		*21 23*	*21 41*			
St Leonards Warrior Sq [4]	d	15 10		15 38		16 10	16 38		17 14		17 50			18 20	18 50		19 50		20 50		21 38	22 08			
West St Leonards	d	15 13				16 13	16 41		17 17		17 53			18 23	18 53		19 53		20 53		21 41	22 11			
Crowhurst	d	15 18				16 18	16 46		17 22		17 58			18 28	18 58		19 58		20 58		21 46	22 16			
Battle	d	15 22		15 48		16 22	16 50		17 26		18 02			18 32	19 02		20 02		21 02		21 50	22 20			
Robertsbridge	d	15 30				16 30	16 58		17 34		18 10			18 40	19 10		20 10		21 10		21 58	22 28			
Etchingham	d	15 34				16 34	17 02		17 38		18 14			18 44	19 14		20 14		21 14		22 02	22 32			
Stonegate	d	15 39				16 39	17 07		17 43		18 19			18 49	19 19		20 19		21 19		22 07	22 37			
Wadhurst	d	15 46		16 04		16 46	17 14		17 50		18 26			18 56	19 26		20 26		21 26		22 14	22 44			
Frant	d	15 50				16 50	17 18		17 54		18 30			19 00	19 30		20 30		21 30		22 18	22 48			
Tunbridge Wells [4]	a	15 55		16 11		16 55	17 24		17 59		18 39			19 05	19 35		20 35		21 35		22 23	22 53			
	d	15 56		16 16	16 36	16 56	17 30	17 54	18 04	18 26	18 40		18 56	19 06	19 38	20 06	20 36	21 06	21 36	22 06	22 26	22 56	23 30		
High Brooms	d	15 59		16 19	16 39	16 59	17 33	17 57	18 07	18 29	18 43		18 59	19 09	19 41	20 09	20 39	21 09	21 39	22 09	22 29	22 59	23 33		
Tonbridge [4]	a	16 06		16 26	16 46	17 06	17 40	18 03	18 14	18 36	18 50		19 07	19 15	19 47	20 15	20 46	21 15	21 46	22 15	22 36	23 05	23 39		
	d	16 06		16 28		17 06	17 40	18 06	18 16	18 36	18 54			19 16	19 48	20 16	20 48	21 16	21 48	22 16	22 42				
Gatwick Airport [10] ✈	a	*17b32*				*18b12*			*19b07*		*19b58*				*20 35*		*21 34*		*22 34*			*00b11*			
Sevenoaks [4]	a	16 18		16 37		17 15	17 50	18 18	18 25	18 46	19 04			19 28	19 57	20 28	20 57	21 28	21 57	22 28	22 51				
Orpington [4]	a	16 34		16 49		17 26	17 59	18 32	18 35	18 55	19 14			19 37	20 07	20 37	21 07	21 37	22 07	22 37	23 01				
London Bridge [4]	⊖ a	16 52		17 09		17 44	18 19	18 49	18 51	19 12	19 33			19 55	20 25	20 55	21 25	21 55	22 25	22 55	23 19				
London Cannon Street [4]	⊖ a							18 53																	
London Waterloo (East) [4]	⊖ a	16 57		17 14		17 50	18 26		18 56	19 17	19 38			20 00	20 30	21 00	21 30	22 00	22 30	23 00	23 24				
London Charing Cross [4]	⊖ a	17 01		17 19		17 55	18 30		19 00	19 21	19 42			20 04	20 34	21 04	21 34	22 04	22 34	23 04	23 28				

For general notes see front of timetable
For details of catering facilities see Directory of Train Operators

A To Horsham (Table 186)
b Change at Tonbridge and Redhill
c Change at Redhill

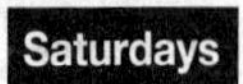

For details of Bank Holiday service alterations please see first page of Table 195

Hastings and Tunbridge Wells → Tonbridge and London

Network Diagram - see first page of Table 206

		SE	SE	SE	SE	SE	SE	SE	SE	SE	SE	SE	SE	SE		SE	SE	SE
		88	22	22	22	22	22	88	22	13	22	88	22	13		22	88	22
			1	1	1	1	1	1	1		1	1	1			1	1	1
								A				A					A	
Ore	d																	
Hastings 4	d		05 47	06 16	06 47	07 18	07 47		08 18		08 47		09 31			16 47		17 18
Bexhill 4	d			*06 00*	*06 19*	*07 00*	*07 22*		*08 02*		*08 39*		*09 22*			*16 39*		*17 02*
St Leonards Warrior Sq 4	d		05 50	06 19	06 50	07 21	07 50		08 21		08 50		09 34			16 50		17 21
West St Leonards	d		05 53	06 22	06 53		07 53				08 53				and at	16 53		
Crowhurst	d		05 58	06 27	06 58		07 58				08 58					16 58		
Battle	d		06 02	06 32	07 02	07 32	08 02		08 32		09 02		09 44		the same	17 02		17 32
Robertsbridge	d		06 10	06 40	07 10	07 44	08 10		08 44		09 10					17 10		17 44
Etchingham	d		06 14	06 44	07 14	07 48	08 14		08 48		09 14				minutes	17 14		17 48
Stonegate	d		06 20	06 50	07 20		08 20				09 20					17 20		
Wadhurst	d		06 26	06 56	07 26	07 58	08 26		08 58		09 26		10 00		past	17 26		17 58
Frant	d		06 31	07 01	07 31		08 31				09 31					17 31		
Tunbridge Wells 4	a		06 35	07 05	07 35	08 05	08 35		09 05		09 35		10 07		each	17 35		18 05
	d	05 37	06 36	07 06	07 36	08 06	08 36	08 52	09 06	09 24	09 36	09 52	10 08	10 24		17 36	17 52	18 06
High Brooms	d	05 40	06 39	07 09	07 39	08 09	08 39	08 55	09 09	09 27	09 39	09 55	10 11	10 27	hour until	17 39	17 55	18 09
Tonbridge 4	a	05 46	06 45	07 16	07 45	08 16	08 45	09 01	09 16	09 33	09 45	10 01	10 17	10 33		17 45	18 01	18 16
	d	05 52	06 46	07 16	07 46	08 16	08 46	09 04	09 16		09 46	10 04	10 18			17 46	18 04	18 16
Gatwick Airport 10	a	06 35	*07 34*	*08*b*23*	*08 55*	*09*b*23*	*09 55*	09 55	*10*b*23*	*10*c*23*	*10 55*	10 55	*11*b*23*	*11*c*23*		*18 34*	18 55	
Sevenoaks 4	a		06 56	07 26	07 55	08 26	08 55		09 26		09 55		10 27			17 55		18 26
Orpington 4	a		07 07	07 35	08 05	08 35	09 05		09 35		10 05					18 05		18 35
London Bridge 4	⊖ a		07 26	07 54	08 24	08 54	09 24		09 54		10 24		10 54			18 24		18 54
London Cannon Street 4	⊖ a																	
London Waterloo (East) 4	⊖ a		07 31	07 59	08 29	08 59	09 29		09 59		10 29		10 59			18 29		19 00
London Charing Cross 4	⊖ a		07 34	08 05	08 33	09 03	09 33		10 03		10 33		11 03			18 33		19 06

		SE	SE	SE	SE	SE	SE	SE	SE	SE	SE
		22	31	22	31	22	31	22	31	25	31
		1	1	1	1	1	1	1	1	1	1
Ore	d										
Hastings 4	d	17 47		18 47		19 47		20 47		22 07	
Bexhill 4	d	*17 22*		*18 22*		*19 22*		*20 22*		*21 41*	
St Leonards Warrior Sq 4	d	17 50		18 50		19 50		20 50		22 10	
West St Leonards	d	17 53		18 53		19 53		20 53		22 13	
Crowhurst	d	17 58		18 58		19 58		20 58		22 18	
Battle	d	18 02		19 02		20 02		21 02		22 22	
Robertsbridge	d	18 10		19 10		20 10		21 10		22 30	
Etchingham	d	18 14		19 14		20 14		21 14		22 34	
Stonegate	d	18 20		19 20		20 20		21 20		22 39	
Wadhurst	d	18 26		19 26		20 26		21 26		22 46	
Frant	d	18 31		19 31		20 31		21 31		22 50	
Tunbridge Wells 4	a	18 35		19 35		20 35		21 35		22 55	
	d	18 36	19 10	19 36	20 10	20 36	21 10	21 36	22 10	22 55	23 30
High Brooms	d	18 39	19 13	19 39	20 13	20 39	21 13	21 39	22 13	22 59	23 33
Tonbridge 4	a	18 45	19 19	19 45	20 19	20 45	21 19	21 45	22 19	23 05	23 39
	d	18 46		19 46		20 46		21 46			
Gatwick Airport 10	a	*19 34*		*20 34*		*21 34*		*22 34*		*00*b*10*	
Sevenoaks 4	a	18 56		19 56		20 56		21 56			
Orpington 4	a	19 07		20 07		21 07		22 07			
London Bridge 4	⊖ a	19 26		20 26		21 25		22 25			
London Cannon Street 4	⊖ a										
London Waterloo (East) 4	⊖ a	19 30		20 30		21 30		22 30			
London Charing Cross 4	⊖ a	19 34		20 34		21 34		22 34			

For general notes see front of timetable
For details of catering facilities see Directory of Train Operators

A To Horsham (Table 186)
b Change at Tonbridge and Redhill
c Change at Redhill

Table 206

Hastings and Tunbridge Wells → Tonbridge and London

Network Diagram - see first page of Table 206

		SE 22 [1]		SE 22 [1]			SE 22 [1]	SE 22 [1]			SE 22 [1]		SE 22 [1]		SE 22 [1]		SE 22 [1]		SE 22 [1]		SE 22 [1]			
Ore	d																							
Hastings [4]	d			08 08			08 48	09 08			17 48		18 08		19 08		20 08		21 08		22 08			
Bexhill [4]	d			*07 46*			*08 11*	*08 46*			*17 16*		*17 46*		*18 46*		*19 46*		*20 46*		*21 46*			
St Leonards Warrior Sq [4]	d			08 11			08 51	09 11			17 51		18 11		19 11		20 11		21 11		22 11			
West St Leonards	d			08 14				09 14					18 14		19 14		20 14		21 14		22 14			
Crowhurst	d			08 19				09 19	and at				18 19		19 19		20 19		21 19		22 19			
Battle	d			08 23			09 02	09 23			18 02		18 23		19 23		20 23		21 23		22 23			
Robertsbridge	d			08 31				09 31	the same				18 31		19 31		20 31		21 31		22 31			
Etchingham	d			08 35				09 35					18 35		19 35		20 35		21 35		22 35			
Stonegate	d			08 40				09 40	minutes				18 40		19 40		20 40		21 40		22 40			
Wadhurst	d			08 47			09 19	09 47			18 19		18 47		19 47		20 47		21 47		22 47			
Frant	d			08 51				09 51	past				18 51		19 51		20 51		21 51		22 51			
Tunbridge Wells [4]	a			08 56			09 26	09 56			18 26		18 56		19 56		20 56		21 56		22 56			
	d	08 28		08 56			09 27	09 56	each		18 27		18 56		19 56		20 56		21 56		22 57			
High Brooms	d	08 31		09 01			09 31	10 01			18 31		19 01		20 00		21 00		22 00		23 00			
Tonbridge [4]	a	08 37		09 07			09 37	10 07	hour until		18 37		19 07		20 06		21 06		22 06		23 06			
	d	08 38		09 08			09 37	10 08			18 37		19 08		20 06		21 06		22 06					
Gatwick Airport [10] ✈	a	*09 38*					*10 38*				*19 38*		*20 38*		*21 38*									
Sevenoaks [4]	a	08 48		09 18			09 48	10 18			18 48		19 18		20 16		21 16		22 16					
Orpington [4]	a	08 57		09 27			09 57	10 27			18 57		19 27		20 27		21 27		22 27					
London Bridge [4] ⊖	a	09 14		09 44			10 14	10 44			19 14		19 44		20 44		21 44		22 44					
London Cannon Street [4] ⊖	a																							
London Waterloo (East) [4] ⊖	a	09 20		09 49			10 20	10 49			19 20		19 49		20 49		21 49		22 49					
London Charing Cross [4] ⊖	a	09 25		09 55			10 25	10 55			19 25		19 55		20 53		21 53		22 53					

For general notes see front of timetable
For details of catering facilities see Directory of Train Operators

London and Tonbridge → Ashford International, Folkestone, Dover, Canterbury West, Ramsgate and Margate

For details of Bank Holiday service alterations please see first page of Table 195

Network Diagram - see first page of Table 206

Miles	Miles	Miles	Station		SE MO 4 ■1	SE MX 4 ■1	SE MO 2 ■1	SE MX 8 ■1	SE MX 2 ■1	SE MO 8 ■1	SE MX 66 ■1	SE MX 2 ■1	SE 8 ■1	SE 61 ■1 A	SE 64 ■1		SE 61	SE 61 ■1	SE 18 ■1	SE 64 ■1	SE 61	SE 18 ■1	SE 61	SE 4 ■1	SE 66 ■1
0	—	—	**London Charing Cross** ■4 ⊖	d	21p54	22p00	22p24	22p30	23p00	23p24		23p30							05 30					06 25	
¾	—	—	**London Waterloo (East)** ■4 ⊖	d	21p57	22p03	22p27	22p33	23p03	23p27		23p33							05 33					06 28	
—	—	—	**London Cannon Street** ■4 ⊖	d																				*06 22*	
1¾	—	—	**London Bridge** ■4 ⊖	d	22p02	22p08	22p32	22p38	23p08	23p32		23p38							05 38					06 33	
13¾	—	—	Orpington ■4	d	22p19	22p24	22p50	22p54	23p24			23p56							05 54					06 50	
22	—	—	Sevenoaks ■4	d	22p29	22p34	23p00	23p04	23p34	23p58		00 06							06 11					07 00	
—	—	—	Gatwick Airport ■10 ✈	d						*22b53*		*22c53*												*05 54*	
—	—	—	Redhill	d						*23b10*		*23c10*												*06 09*	
29½	—	—	**Tonbridge** ■4	a	22p37	22p45	23p10	23p15	23p45	00 06		00 17							06 21					07 10	
—	—	—		d	22p38	22p45	23p11	23p15	23p45	00 07		00 17	04 53				05 47		06 22					07 11	
34¾	—	—	Paddock Wood ■4	d	22p45	22p52	23p18	23p22	23p52	00 14		00 24	05 00				05 55		06 29		06 32		07 06	07 18	
—	—	—	Maidstone West ■4	a									*06 15*				06 15		*07 26*		06 52		07 26		
39½	—	—	Marden	d			23p24	23p28				00 30	05 06						06 35					07 24	
41¾	—	—	Staplehurst	d	22p54	23p01	23p28	23p33	00 01	00 22		00 35	05 10						06 39					07 28	
45¼	—	—	Headcorn ■4	d		23p06	23p33	23p38	00 06			00 40	05 15						06 44					07 33	
50½	—	—	Pluckley	d			23p39	23p45				00 47	05 21						06 51					07 40	
—	0	—	**London Victoria** ■15 ⊖	d					*22 18*		23p11	*23c11*													06 10
—	11	—	Bromley South ■4	d					*22 29*		23p30	*23c30*													06 30
—	40	—	Maidstone East ■4	d					*23 19*		00 14	00c14			05 56					06 33					07 23
56	59¼	—	**Ashford International**	a	23p09	23p17	23p47	23p52	00 17	00 37	00 43	00 54	05 29		06 25				06 59	07 02				07 52	07 52
—	—	—		d	23p10	23p20	23p51	23p53	00 20		00 57	00 58	05 34	06 12	06 28			06 35	07 03	07 07				07 55	07 56
—	—	—	Rye	a									*06 47*		*07 09*					*07 53*					
—	63½	—	Wye	d				23p59			01 03				06 34					07 13					08 02
—	68¼	—	Chilham	d				00 06			01 09				06 41					07 19					08 09
—	70¼	—	Chartham	d				00 10			01 13				06 44					07 23					08 12
—	73½	—	**Canterbury West** ■4	d				00a16			01a18				06 50					07 30					08e20
—	75¾	—	Sturry	d											06 55					07 34					08 24
64¼	—	—	Westenhanger	d	23p19	23p30	00 01		00 30			01 07	05 43	06 21				06 44	07 12					08 05	
65½	—	—	Sandling	d	23p22	23p33	00 03		00 33			01 10	05 46	06 24				06 47	07 15					08 08	
69¼	—	—	Folkestone West	d	23p27	23p38	00 08		00 38			01 15	05 51	06 29				06 52	07 20					08 13	
70	—	—	**Folkestone Central**	d	23p30	23p41	00 11		00 41			01 18	05 54	06 33				06 55	07 23					08 15	
77¼	—	—	**Dover Priory** ■4 ⛴	a	23p41	23p52	00 22		00 52			01 30	06 05	06 44				07 06	07 35			←		08 27	
—	—	—		d	23p42	23p54							06 06					07 12	07 53 →			07 53		08 28	
82¼	—	—	Martin Mill	d	23p52	00 03							06 15					07 21				08 02		08 37	
85	—	—	Walmer	d	23p56	00 07							06 19					07 25				08 06		08 41	
86½	—	—	**Deal**	d	23p59	00 11							06 22					07 29				08 11		08 45	
90¾	—	0	Sandwich	d	00 06	00 17							06 29					07 35				08 19		08 51	
—	84¾	4¾	Minster ■4	d											07 06					07 45		08f31			08 36
99	88¾	—	**Ramsgate** ■4 ✈	a	00 19	00 30							06 41		07 12			07 48		07 52		08 38		09 04	08 42
100	89¾	—	Dumpton Park	a									*06 52*		*07 24*			*07 54*		07 58					08 45
101½	91	—	Broadstairs	a									*06 55*		*07 27*			*07 57*		08 01		*08 48*			08 48
104½	94¼	—	**Margate** ■4	a									*06 59*		*07 31*			*08 01*		08 06		*08 53*			08 53

For general notes see front of timetable
For details of catering facilities see Directory of Train Operators

- **A** To Faversham (Table 212)
- **b** Fridays
- **c** Applies Wednesdays to Saturdays
- **e** Arr. 0817
- **f** Arr. 0826

London and Tonbridge → Ashford International, Folkestone, Dover, Canterbury West, Ramsgate and Margate

For details of Bank Holiday service alterations please see first page of Table 195

Network Diagram - see first page of Table 206

		SE 64 [1]	SE 4 [1]	SE 64 [1]	SE 64 [1]		SE 61	SE 2 [1]	SE 64 [1]	SE 4 [1]		SE 64 [1]	SE 55 A	SE 4 [1]	SE 90 [1]	SE 90 [1]	SE 64 [1]		SE 61	SE 2 [1]	SE 64 [1]	SE 4 [1]		SE 8	SE 61
London Charing Cross [4]	⊖ d		07 00					07 28		07 52				08 22	08 54	08 58				09 30		09 53		10 00	
London Waterloo (East) [4]	⊖ d		07 03					07 31		07 55				08 25	08 57	09 01				09 33		09 56		10 03	
London Cannon Street [4]	⊖ d		06 52					07 22		07 54				08 20	08 54					09 30					
London Bridge [4]	⊖ d		07 08					07 36		08 02				08 30	09 02	09 08				09 38				10 08	
Orpington [4]	d		07 26					07 55		08 20				08 48		09 26				09 54				10 26	
Sevenoaks [4]	d		07 36					08 05		08 30				08 58		09 36				10 04				10 36	
Gatwick Airport [10]	✈ d							07b13		07b41				08b04	08b37					09b23					
Redhill	d							07 35		08 05			08 29	08 29	08 59					09 44					
Tonbridge [4]	a		07 44					08 15		08 38			08 59	09 06	09 35	09 47				10 15		10 30		10 47	
	d		07 49					08 23		08 40			09 00	09 08	09 35	09 47				10 15		10 31		10 47	
Paddock Wood [4]	d		07 56				08 09	08 30		08 47			09 08	09 15	09 42	09 54			10 03	10 22				10 54	11 01
Maidstone West [4]	a		08 29				08 29			09 28			09 28			10 23			10 23	11 21					11 21
Marden	d		08 02							08 53				09 21		10 00								11 00	
Staplehurst	d		08 06					08 38		08 57				09 25	09 51	10 05				10 31				11 05	
Headcorn [4]	d		08 11					08 43		09 02				09 30		10 10				10 36				11 10	
Pluckley	d		08 18							09 09				09 37		10 17								11 17	
London Victoria [15]	⊖ d	06 47	06 47		07 19			07 19				08 18			08 18		09 19			09 19					
Bromley South [4]	d	07 04	07 04		07 36			07 36				08 39			08 39		09 37			09 37					
Maidstone East [4]	d	07 49	07 49		08 21			08 21				09 17					10 14			10 14					
Ashford International	a	08 21	08 27	←	08 53			08 55	←	09 17		09 46		09 45	10 05	10 25	10 43			10 48	←	10 53		11 26	
	d	08 32	08 28	08 32	09 03			09 02	09 03	09 20	09 24	09 51		09 50	10 09	10 27	10 50			10 48	10 50	10 58	11 01		
Rye	a	08 53	09 13		→						09 53					10 53	→						11 53		
Wye	d	→		08 39					09 09			09 57											11 08		
Chilham	d			08 45					09 15			10 03											11 14		
Chartham	d			08 49					09 19			10 07											11 18		
Canterbury West [4]	d			08 55					09a24		09 42	10a12				10 46					11a06		11 24		
Sturry	d			08 59							09 47					10 50							11 29		
Westenhanger	d		08 37					09 11						09 59	10 18							11 07			
Sandling	d		08 40					09 14						10 02	10 21							11 10			
Folkestone West	d		08 45					09 19						10 07	10 26							11 15			
Folkestone Central	d		08 48					09 22		09 35				10 10	10 29					11 03		11 18			
Dover Priory [4]	⛴ a		08 59					09 34		09 46				10 24	10 40					11 15		11 30			
	d		09 00							09 48				10 28								11 31			
Martin Mill	d		09 09							09 57				10 37								11 40			
Walmer	d		09 13							10 01				10 41								11 44			
Deal	d		09 17							10 05				10 45								11 48			
Sandwich	d		09 23							10 11				10 51								11 54			
Minster [4]	d			09 10							09 58					11 01							11 40		
Ramsgate [4]	✈ a		09 35	09 17						10 25	10 04			11 05		11 09						12 06	11 46		
Dumpton Park	a		09 40	09 24							10 08					11 13									
Broadstairs	a		09 43	09 28						11 03	10 11			11 16		11 16									
Margate [4]	a		09 48	09 32						11 08	10 16			11 22		11 22									

		SE 90 [1]		SE 64 [1]	SE 8 [1]	SE 4 [1]			SE 8 [1]	SE 61	SE 90 [1]		SE 64 [1]	SE 8 [1]	SE 4 [1]		SE 8 [1]	SE 61	SE 90 [1]			SE 64 [1]	SE 8 [1]	SE 4 [1]	
London Charing Cross [4]	⊖ d	10 23			10 30	10 53			11 00		11 23			11 30	11 53		12 00		12 23				12 30	12 53	
London Waterloo (East) [4]	⊖ d	10 26			10 33	10 56			11 03		11 26			11 33	11 56		12 03		12 26				12 33	12 56	
London Cannon Street [4]	⊖ d				10 30									11 30									12 30		
London Bridge [4]	⊖ d				10 38				11 08					11 38			12 08						12 38		
Orpington [4]	d				10 54				11 26					11 54			12 26						12 54		
Sevenoaks [4]	d				11 04				11 36					12 04			12 36						13 04		
Gatwick Airport [10]	✈ d	09 52			10b08									11b08									12b08		
Redhill	d	10 07			10 39									11 39									12 39		
Tonbridge [4]	a	11 02			11 15	11 30			11 47		12 02			12 15	12 30		12 47		13 02				13 15	13 30	
	d	11 03			11 15	11 31			11 47		12 03			12 15	12 31		12 47		13 03				13 15	13 31	
Paddock Wood [4]	d	11 10			11 22				11 54	12 06	12 10			12 22			12 54	13 06	13 10				13 22		
Maidstone West [4]	a									12 26								13 26							
Marden	d								12 00								13 00								
Staplehurst	d	11 18			11 31				12 05		12 18			12 31			13 05		13 18				13 31		
Headcorn [4]	d				11 36				12 10					12 36			13 10						13 36		
Pluckley	d								12 17								13 17								
London Victoria [15]	⊖ d	09c48		10 18		10 18					10c48		11 18		11 18				11c48			12 18		12 18	
Bromley South [4]	d	10c04		10 34		10 34					11c04		11 34		11 34				12c04			12 34		12 34	
Maidstone East [4]	d	11 05		11 13							12 05		12 13						13 05			13 13			
Ashford International	a	11 32		11 43	11 50	11 53			12 26		12 32		12 43	12 50	12 53		13 26		13 32			13 43	13 50	13 53	
	d	11 36	11 38	11 46		11 58	12 01				12 36	12 38	12 46		12 58	13 01			13 36	13 38		13 46		13 58	14 01
Rye	a						12 53									13 53									14 53
Wye	d			11 52									12 52									13 52			
Chilham	d			11 58									12 58									13 58			
Chartham	d			12 02									13 02									14 02			
Canterbury West [4]	d	11 54		12a07			12 20				12 54		13a07			13 20			13 54			14a07			14 20
Sturry	d	11 59									12 59								13 59						
Westenhanger	d		11 47									12 47								13 47					
Sandling	d		11 50									12 50								13 50					
Folkestone West	d		11 55									12 55								13 55					
Folkestone Central	d		11 58			12 12						12 58			13 12					13 58				14 12	
Dover Priory [4]	⛴ a		12 10			12 24						13 10			13 24					14 10				14 24	
	d					12 25									13 25									14 25	
Martin Mill	d					12 35									13 35									14 35	
Walmer	d					12 39									13 39									14 39	
Deal	d					12 43									13 43									14 43	
Sandwich	d					12 49									13 49									14 49	
Minster [4]	d	12 10									13 10								14 10						
Ramsgate [4]	✈ a	12 17				13 02	12 38				13 17				14 02	13 38			14 16					15 02	14 41
Dumpton Park	a	12 24					12 43				13 24					13 43			14 20						
Broadstairs	a	12 28					12 46				13 28				14 23	13 46			14 23					15 23	
Margate [4]	a	12 32					12 51				13 32				14 28	13 51			14 28					15 28	

For general notes see front of timetable
For details of catering facilities see Directory of Train Operators

A To Strood (Table 208)
b Change at Redhill and Tonbridge
c Change at Maidstone East and Ashford International

For details of Bank Holiday service alterations please see first page of Table 195

London and Tonbridge → Ashford International, Folkestone, Dover, Canterbury West, Ramsgate and Margate

Network Diagram - see first page of Table 206

	SE 8 [1]	SE 61	SE 90 [1]		SE 64 [1]	SE 8	SE 18 [1]		SE 8 [1]		SE 61	SE 18 [1]	SE 90 [1]		SE 8 [1]	SE 90 [1]		SE 18 [1]	SE 8 [1]	SE 61	SE 90 [1]			SE 8 [1]
			⊼				⊼					⊼	⊼			⊼								
London Charing Cross [4] ⊖ d	13 00		13 23			13 30	13 53		14 00				14 23		14 30	14 53			15 00		15 23			15 30
London Waterloo (East) [4] ⊖ d	13 03		13 26			13 33	13 56		14 03				14 26		14 33	14 56			15 03		15 26			15 33
London Cannon Street [4] ⊖ d						13 30									14 30									15 30
London Bridge [4] ⊖ d	13 08					13 38			14 08						14 38				15 08					15 38
Orpington [4] d	13 26					13 54			14 26						14 54				15 26					15 54
Sevenoaks [4] d	13 36					14 04			14 36						15 04				15 36					16 04
Gatwick Airport [10] ✈ d						13b08	13b08								14b08				14 53					15b08
Redhill d						13 39	13 39								14 39				15 07					15 40
Tonbridge [4] a	13 47		14 02			14 15	14 30		14 47				15 02		15 15	15 30			15 47		16 02			16 15
Tonbridge [4] d	13 47		14 03			14 15	14 31		14 47				15 03		15 15	15 31			15 47		16 03			16 15
Paddock Wood [4] d	13 54	14 06	14 10			14 22			14 54		15 06		15 10		15 22				15 54	16 06	16 10			16 22
Maidstone West [4] a		14 26									15 26								16 26	16 26	16 45			
Marden d	14 00								15 00										16 00					16 28
Staplehurst d	14 05		14 18			14 31			15 05				15 18		15 31				16 05		16 18			16 33
Headcorn [4] d	14 10					14 36			15 10						15 36				16 10					16 38
Pluckley d	14 17								15 17										16 17					16 45
London Victoria [15] ⊖ d			12c48		13 18		13 18						13c48			14 18					14 48			
Bromley South [4] d			13c04		13 34		13 34						14c04			14 34					15 04			
Maidstone East [4] d			14 05		14 13								15 05			15 21					16 05			
Ashford International a	14 26		14 32		14 43	14 50	14 53		15 26				15 32		15 50	15 53			16 26		16 32			16 54
Ashford International d			14 36	14 38	14 46		14 58	15 01					15 36	15 39		15 58	16 01				16 36	16 39		
Rye a								15 53									16 53							
Wye d					14 52								15 43			16 05					16 43			
Chilham d					14 58								15 49			16 11					16 49			
Chartham d					15 02								15 53			16 15					16 53			
Canterbury West [4] d			14 54		15a07			15 20					15 59			16 21					16 59			
Sturry d			14 59					15 24					16 04			16 26					17 04			
Westenhanger d				14 47										15 48			16 10					16 48		
Sandling d				14 50										15 51			16 13					16 51		
Folkestone West d				14 55										15 56			16 18					16 56		
Folkestone Central d				14 58			15 12							15 59			16 21					16 59		
Dover Priory [4] ⛴ a				15 10			15 24							16 11			16 34	←				17 11		
Dover Priory [4] d							15 27					←		16 12 →			16 35	16 12				17 12 →		
Martin Mill d							15 36 →					15 36					16 44	16 21						
Walmer d												15 41					16 48	16 25						
Deal d												15 44					16 52	16 29						
Sandwich d												15e54					16 58	16 35						
Minster [4] d			15 10					15 35				16f06	16 15			16 37		16g47			17 15			
Ramsgate [4] ✈ a			15 16					15 43				16 12	16 23			16 44	17 10	16 54			17 22			
Dumpton Park a			15 20									16 16				16 50					17 52			
Broadstairs a			15 23									16 19				16 53		17 28			17 55			
Margate [4] a			15 28									16 24				16 58					18 00			

	SE 61	SE 90 [1]		SE 18 [1]	SE 8 [1]	SE 61	SE 4 [1]		SE 8 [1]	SE 4 [1]			SE 61	SE 90 [1]	SE 9 [1]	SE 4 [1]	SE 61	SE 91 [1]		SE 4 [1]		SE 9 [1]	SE 61	SE 4 [1]
		⊼					⊼			⊼						⊼				⊼				⊼
London Charing Cross [4] ⊖ d		15 53			16 00		16 23		16 30	16 46				17 12	16h50	17 34		17h20		17 56				18 16
London Waterloo (East) [4] ⊖ d		15 56			16 03		16 26		16 33	16 49				17 15	16h53	17 37		17h23		17 59				18 19
London Cannon Street [4] ⊖ d					16 00		16 22								17 20			17 44				18 04		
London Bridge [4] ⊖ d					16 08		16 31		16 39	16 54					17 04			17 28				18 08		18 12
Orpington [4] d					16 02		16 33								17 24			17 46						
Sevenoaks [4] d					16 32		16 56		17 02						17 52			18 12				18 34		18 48
Gatwick Airport [10] ✈ d					15 53					16b08					17b08									18b08
Redhill d					16 07					16 40				17 07	17 28									18 23
Tonbridge [4] a		16 32			16 43		17 04		17 13	17 24				17 50	18 02	18 15		18 20		18 34		18 44		18 57
Tonbridge [4] d		16 33			16 43		17 05		17 13	17 25				17 51	18 03	18 15		18 21		18 35		18 45		18 57
Paddock Wood [4] d	16 25				16 50	17 02	17 12		17 20	17 32			17 55	17 58	18 11	18 23	18 23	18 28		18 43		18 52	18 57	19 05
Maidstone West [4] a	16 45				17 22	17 22				18 15			18 15		18 43		18 43						19 17	
Marden d					16 56				17 26					18 04	18 17					18 49		18 58		
Staplehurst d					17 01		17 20		17 31	17 40				18 09	18 22	18 31				18 53		19 03		19 13
Headcorn [4] d					17 06				17 36	17 45				18 14	18 27	18 36				18 58		19 08		19 18
Pluckley d					17 13				17 43					18 21						19 05		19 15		
London Victoria [15] ⊖ d		15 18					15 48							16 56										17 58
Bromley South [4] d		15 34					16 04							17 15										18 18
Maidstone East [4] d		16 19					16 44			17 07				17 54										18 56
Ashford International a		16 57			17 24		17 35		17 52	17 57				18 29	18 41	18 48		18 52		19 14		19 24		19 30
Ashford International d		17 01	17 03				17 39	17 42		18 02	18 05			18 32		18 55		18 56	18 58	19 18	19 20			19 34
Rye a					17 53				18 21		18 53								19 21			19 53		
Wye d		17 08						17 49			18 12			18 39				19 02			19 26			
Chilham d		17 14						17 55			18 18			18 45				19 08			19 32			
Chartham d		17 18						17 59			18 22			18 49				19 12			19 36			
Canterbury West [4] d		17 24						18 05			18 29			18 55				19a17			19 42			
Sturry d		17 29						18 10			18 33			19 00							19 47			
Westenhanger d			17 12				17 48			18 11						19 04			19 08	19 27				19 43
Sandling d			17 15				17 51			18 14						19 07			19 11	19 30				19 46
Folkestone West d			17 20				17 56			18 19						19 12			19 17	19 35				19 51
Folkestone Central d			17 23				17 59			18 22						19 15			19a20	19 38				19 54
Dover Priory [4] ⛴ a			17 35	←			18 11			18 34						19 27				19 50				20 06
Dover Priory [4] d			17 36	17 12			18 12			18 36						19 28				19 55				20 06
Martin Mill d			17 45	17 21			18 21			18 45						19 37				20 04				20 15
Walmer d			17 49	17 25			18 25			18 49						19 42				20 08				20 20
Deal d			17 53	17 29			18 29			18 53						19 45				20 12				20 23
Sandwich d			17 59	17 35			18 35			18 59						19 52				20 18				20 30
Minster [4] d		17 40		17j49				18 21			18 44			19 11							20 00			
Ramsgate [4] ✈ a		17 47	18 10	17 56			18 50	18 28		19 11	18 51			19 20		20 03				20 32	20 09			20 44
Dumpton Park a			18 15	18 15				18 50		19 15	18 55			19 50		20 07								20 52
Broadstairs a			18 18	18 18			19 18			19 18	18 58			19 53		20 10				20 44				20 55
Margate [4] a			18 23	18 23			19 26			19 26	19 05			19 58		20 16					20 51			20 59

For general notes see front of timetable
For details of catering facilities see Directory of Train Operators

b Change at Redhill and Tonbridge
c Change at Maidstone East and Ashford International
e Arr. 1551
f Arr. 1601
g Arr. 1643
h Change at Sevenoaks
j Arr. 1743

London and Tonbridge → Ashford International, Folkestone, Dover, Canterbury West, Ramsgate and Margate

For details of Bank Holiday service alterations please see first page of Table 195

Network Diagram - see first page of Table 206

		SE 3 1		SE 8 1		SE 88	SE 4 1	SE 61	SE 4 1		SE 4 1	SE 4 1	SE 61	SE 90 1	SE 4 1	SE 61		SE 90 1	SE 4 1	SE 8 1	SE 2 1	SE 66 1	SE 2 1		
						A	🛒					🛒		🛒	🛒										
London Charing Cross 4	⊖ d			18 40			19 00		19 24		19 52	20 00		20 30	21 00			21 30	22 00	22 30	23 00		23 30		
London Waterloo (East) 4	⊖ d			18 43			19 03		19 27		19 55	20 03		20 33	21 03			21 33	22 03	22 33	23 03		23 33		
London Cannon Street 4	⊖ d	18 30					*18 50*		*19 22*		*19 52*	*20 00*		*20 30*	*21 00*					*21b00*					
London Bridge 4	⊖ d	18 34		18 48			19 08		19 32		20 01	20 08		20 38	21 08			21 38	22 08	22 38	23 08		23 38		
Orpington 4	d	*18 30*		19 05								*20 02*		20 54	21 24			21 54	22 24	22 54	23 24		23 56		
Sevenoaks 4	d	18 58		19 15			19 34					20 32		21 04	21 34			22 04	22 34	23 04	23 34		00 06		
Gatwick Airport 10	✈ d						*18c38*		*19c08*			*19c39*			*20 53*				*21 53*		*22 53*		*22 53*		
Redhill	d					18 55	*18 55*		*19 24*			*20 08*			*21 07*				*22 07*		*23 10*		*23 10*		
Tonbridge 4	a	19 07		19 23		19 24	19 45		20 02		20 32	20 42		21 15	21 45			22 15	22 45	23 15	23 45		00 17		
	d	19 07		19 24		19 28	19 45		20 03		20 33	20 43		21 15	21 45			22 15	22 45	23 15	23 45		00 17		
Paddock Wood 4	d	19 14		19 31		19e38	19 52	20 03	20 10		20 40	20 50	21 00	21 22	21 52	21 57		22 22	22 52	23 22	23 52		00 24		
Maidstone West 4	a					19 58	*20 23*	20 23				*21 20*	21 20		*22 17*	22 17									
Marden	d	19 20		19 37			19 58					20 56		21 28				22 28		23 28			00 30		
Staplehurst	d	19 25		19 41			20 03		20 19		20 49	21 01		21 33	22 01			22 33	23 01	23 33	00 01		00 35		
Headcorn 4	d	19 30		19 46			20 08		20 24		20 54	21 06		21 38	22 06			22 38	23 06	23 38	00 06		00 40		
Pluckley	d	19 37		19 53			20 15					21 13		21 45				22 45		23 45			00 47		
London Victoria 15	⊖ d								*18 48*		*19 18*	*19 48*			*20 48*			*21 09*		*22 09*	*22 09*	23 11	*23 11*		
Bromley South 4	d	*18 22*							*19 06*		*19 35*	*20 07*			*21 07*			*21 29*		*22 29*	*22 29*	23 30	*23 30*		
Maidstone East 4	d	*19 08*							*20 08*		*20 20*	*20 44*			*21 44*			*22 13*		*23 13*	*23 13*	00 14			
Ashford International	a	19 45		20 02			20 24		20 36		21 06	21 21		21 52	22 17			22 52	23 17	23 52	00 17	00 43	00 54		
	d	19 51	19 53	20 06					20 40	20 42	21 07	21 24		21 53	22 20			22 53	23 20	23 53	00 20	00 57	00 58		
Rye	a		*20 21*				*20 53*					*21 53*			*22 47*										
Wye	d		19 59	20 13						20 49	21 14			22 00				23 00		23 59		01 03			
Chilham	d		20 05	20 19						20 55	21 20			22 06				23 06		00 06		01 09			
Chartham	d		20 09	20 23						20 59	21 24			22 10				23 10		00 10		01 13			
Canterbury West 4	d		20 15	20 30						21 05	21 30			22 16				23 16		00a16		01a18			
Sturry	d		20 20	20 34						21 10	21 35			22 21				23 21							
Westenhanger	d	20 00							20 49			21 33			22 30				23 30		00 30		01 07		
Sandling	d	20 03							20 52			21 36			22 33				23 33		00 33		01 10		
Folkestone West	d	20 09							20 58			21 41			22 38				23 38		00 38		01 15		
Folkestone Central	d	20 12							21 01			21 44			22 41				23 41		00 41		01 18		
Dover Priory 4	⛴ a	20 26							21 12			21 56			22 52				23 52		00 52		01 30		
	d								21 14			22 00			22 54				23 54						
Martin Mill	d								21 23			22 09			23 03				00 03						
Walmer	d								21 27			22 13			23 07				00 07						
Deal	d								21 31			22 17			23 11				00 11						
Sandwich	d								21 37			22 23			23 17				00 17						
Minster 4	d		20 31	20 45						21 21	21 46			22 32				23 32							
Ramsgate 4	✈ a		20 37	20 52					21 48	21 27	21 53	22 36		22 39	23 30			23 39	00 30						
Dumpton Park	a		20 41						*21 57*	21 31				*22 55*				23 43							
Broadstairs	a		20 44	*21 34*					*22 00*	21 34	*22 15*			*22 58*	*23 46*			23 46							
Margate 4	a		20 51						*22 04*	21 39	*22 19*			*23 03*	*23 51*			23 51							

For general notes see front of timetable
For details of catering facilities see Directory of Train Operators

- **A** To Strood (Table 208)
- **b** Change at London Bridge and Orpington
- **c** Change at Redhill and Tonbridge
- **e** Arr. 1935

Table 207

For details of Bank Holiday service alterations please see first page of Table 195

London and Tonbridge → Ashford International, Folkestone, Dover, Canterbury West, Ramsgate and Margate

Network Diagram - see first page of Table 206

		SE	SE	SE	SE	SE	SE	SE	SE		SE	SE	SE	SE	SE	SE	SE			SE	SE	SE	SE		SE
		4	8	2	66	2	64	4	4		94	61	4	64	61	4	4			64	61	4	4		64
		1	1	1	1	1	1	1	1		1		1	1		1	1			1		1	1		1
London Charing Cross 4	⊖ d	22p00	22p30	23p00		23p30			06 00				07 00			07 30	08 00					08 30	09 00		
London Waterloo (East) 4	⊖ d	22p03	22p33	23p03		23p33			06 03				07 03			07 33	08 03					08 33	09 03		
London Cannon Street 4	⊖ d																					*08 30*	*09 00*		
London Bridge 4	⊖ d	22p08	22p38	23p08		23p38			06 08				07 08			07 38	08 08					08 38	09 08		
Orpington 4	d	22p24	22p54	23p24		23p56		05 58	06 26				07 26			07 56	08 26					08 56	09 26		
Sevenoaks 4	d	22p34	23p04	23p34		00 06		06 08	06 36				07 36			08 06	08 36					09 06	09 36		
Gatwick Airport 10	✈ d					*22 53*			*05b45*				*06 53*				*07 53*					*08b08*	*08 53*		
Redhill	d					*23 07*			*06 11*				*07 07*				*08 07*					*08 39*	*09 07*		
Tonbridge 4	a	22p45	23p15	23p45		00 17		06 18	06 47				07 47			08 14	08 47					09 14	09 47		
	d	22p45	23p15	23p45		00 17		06 19	06 47				07 47			08 15	08 47					09 15	09 47		
Paddock Wood 4	d	22p52	23p22	23p52		00 24		06 26	06 54			07 01	07 54		08 01	08 23	08 55				09 01	09 23	09 55		
Maidstone West 4	a								*07 21*			07 21	*08 21*		08 21		*09 21*				09 21		*10 21*		
Marden	d		23p28			00 30			07 00				08 00				09 01						10 01		
Staplehurst	d	23p01	23p33	00 01		00 35		06 34	07 05				08 05			08 32	09 06					09 32	10 06		
Headcorn 4	d	23p06	23p38	00 06		00 40		06 39	07 10				08 10			08 37	09 11					09 37	10 11		
Pluckley	d		23p45			00 47			07 17				08 17				09 18						10 18		
London Victoria 15	⊖ d			*22 09*	23p11	*23 18*					06 18		*06 18*	07 18		*07 18*	*07 48*			08 18		*08 18*	*08c48*		09 18
Bromley South 4	d			*22 29*	23p30	*23 34*					06 34		*06 34*	07 34		*07 34*	*08 04*			08 34		*08 34*	*09c04*		09 34
Maidstone East 4	d			*23 13*	00 14	*00 19*	06 19				07 19			08 19			*08 50*			09 13			*10 05*		10 13
Ashford International	a	23p17	23p52	00 17	00 43	00 54	06 48	06 50	07 24		07 48		08 24	08 48		08 48	09 26			09 43		09 49	10 26		10 43
	d	23p20	23p53	00 20	00 57	00 58	06 53	06 57	07 25		07 51		08 25	08 51		08 57	09 32	09 36		09 46		09 57	10 32	10 36	10 46
Rye	a								*07 53*				*08 53*			*09 53*						*10 53*			
Wye	d		23p59		01 03		06 59				07 57			08 57						09 52					10 52
Chilham	d		00 06		01 09		07 05				08 03			09 03						09 58					10 58
Chartham	d		00 10		01 13		07 09				08 07			09 07						10 02					11 02
Canterbury West 4	d		00a16		01a18		07 14				08 13			09 13				09 54		10a07				10 54	11a07
Sturry	d						07 19				08 18			09 18				09 58						10 58	
Westenhanger	d	23p30		00 30		01 07		07 06	07 34				08 34			09 07						10 06			
Sandling	d	23p33		00 33		01 10		07 09	07 37				08 37			09 10						10 09			
Folkestone West	d	23p38		00 38		01 15		07 14	07 42				08 42			09 15						10 14			
Folkestone Central	d	23p41		00 41		01 18		07 17	07 45				08 45			09 18	09 47					10 17	10 47		
Dover Priory 4	⛴ a	23p52		00 52		01 30		07 28	07 56				08 56			09 29	09 58					10 28	10 58		
	d	23p54						07 29	07 57				08 57			09 30	09 59					10 29	10 59		
Martin Mill	d	00 03						07 38	08 06				09 06			09 39	10 08					10 38	11 08		
Walmer	d	00 07						07 42	08 11				09 11			09 43	10 12					10 42	11 12		
Deal	d	00 11						07 46	08 14				09 14			09 47	10 16					10 46	11 16		
Sandwich	d	00 17						07 52	08 21				09 21			09 53	10 22					10 52	11 22		
Minster 4	d						07 31				08 31			09 31				10 09						11 09	
Ramsgate 4	✈ a	00 30					07 37	08 03	08 32		08 38		09 32	09 38		10 04	10 33	10 16				11 03	11 33	11 16	
Dumpton Park	a						07 40	*08 24*	08 37		*09 24*		09 37					10 19						11 19	
Broadstairs	a						07 43	*08 28*	08 40		*09 03*		09 40	*10 03*		*10 22*	*11 03*	10 22				*11 22*	*11 46*	11 22	
Margate 4	a						07 48	*08 32*	08 45		*09 08*		09 45	*10 08*		*10 27*	*11 08*	10 27				*11 27*	*11 51*	11 27	

For general notes see front of timetable
For details of catering facilities see
Directory of Train Operators

b Change at Redhill and Tonbridge
c Change at Maidstone East and Ashford International

Table 207

Saturdays

For details of Bank Holiday service alterations please see first page of Table 195

London and Tonbridge → Ashford International, Folkestone, Dover, Canterbury West, Ramsgate and Margate

Network Diagram - see first page of Table 206

		SE 61	SE 4 1	SE 4 1 ⊼			SE 8 1	SE 61	SE 90 1 ⊼		SE 64 1	SE 8 1	SE 4 1 ⊼			SE 8 1	SE 61	SE 90 1 ⊼		SE 64 1	SE 8 1	SE 4 1 ⊼			SE 8 1
London Charing Cross 4 ⊖	d		09 30	09 53			10 00		10 23			10 30	10 53			11 00		11 23			11 30	11 53			12 00
London Waterloo (East) 4 ⊖	d		09 33	09 56			10 03		10 26			10 33	10 56			11 03		11 26			11 33	11 56			12 03
London Cannon Street 4 ⊖	d		09 30									10 30									11 30				
London Bridge 4 ⊖	d		09 38				10 08					10 38				11 08					11 38				12 08
Orpington 4	d		09 54				10 26					10 54				11 26					11 54				12 26
Sevenoaks 4	d		10 04				10 36					11 04				11 36					12 04				12 36
Gatwick Airport 10 ✈	d		09b08									10b08									11b08				
Redhill	d		09 39									10 39									11 39				
Tonbridge 4	a		10 15	10 30			10 47		11 02			11 15	11 30			11 47		12 02			12 15	12 30			12 47
	d		10 15	10 31			10 47		11 03			11 15	11 31			11 47		12 03			12 15	12 31			12 47
Paddock Wood 4	d	10 01	10 23				10 55	11 01	11 10			11 23				11 55	12 01	12 10			12 23				12 55
Maidstone West 4	a	10 21						11 21									12 21								
Marden	d						11 01									12 01									13 01
Staplehurst	d		10 32				11 06		11 18			11 32				12 06		12 18			12 32				13 06
Headcorn 4	d		10 37				11 11					11 37				12 11					12 37				13 11
Pluckley	d						11 18									12 18									13 18
London Victoria 15 ⊖	d			09 18					09c48		10 18		10 18					10c48		11 18		11 18			
Bromley South 4	d			09 34					10c04		10 34		10 34					11c04		11 34		11 34			
Maidstone East 4	d								11 05		11 13							12 05		12 13					
Ashford International	a		10 50	10 52			11 26		11 32		11 43	11 50	11 52			12 26		12 32		12 43	12 50	12 52			13 26
	d			10 57	11 00				11 36	11 38	11 46		11 57	12 01				12 36	12 38	12 46		12 57	13 00		
Rye	a				11 53									12 53									13 53		
Wye	d										11 52									12 52					
Chilham	d										11 58									12 58					
Chartham	d										12 02									13 02					
Canterbury West 4	d				11e20				11 54		12a07			12 20				12 54		13a07			13f20		
Sturry	d								11 59									12 59							
Westenhanger	d			11 06						11 47									12 47						
Sandling	d			11 09						11 50									12 50						
Folkestone West	d			11 14						11 55									12 55						
Folkestone Central	d			11 17						11 58			12 11						12 58			13 11			
Dover Priory 4 ⛴	a			11 28						12 09			12 23						13 09			13 23			
	d			11 29						12 10			12 25						13 10			13 25			
Martin Mill	d			11 38						12 19			12 35						13 19			13 35			
Walmer	d			11 42						12 23			12 39						13 23			13 39			
Deal	d			11 46						12 27			12 43						13 27			13 43			
Sandwich	d			11 52						12 33			12 49						13 33			13 49			
Minster 4	d								12 10									13 10							
Ramsgate 4 ✈	a			12 03	11 38				12 17	12 44			13 02	12 38				13 17	13 44			14 02	13 38		
Dumpton Park	a				11 43				12 24					12 43				13 24					13 43		
Broadstairs	a				11 46				12 28					12 46				13 28					13 46		
Margate 4	a				11 51				12 32					12 51				13 32					13 51		

		SE 61	SE 90 1 ⊼		SE 64 1	SE 8 1	SE 4 1 ⊼		SE 8 1		SE 61	SE 90 1 ⊼		SE 64 1	SE 8 1	SE 4 1 ⊼		SE 8 1		SE 61	SE 90 1 ⊼		SE 64 1	SE 8 1	
London Charing Cross 4 ⊖	d		12 23			12 30	12 53		13 00			13 23			13 30	13 53		14 00			14 23			14 30	
London Waterloo (East) 4 ⊖	d		12 26			12 33	12 56		13 03			13 26			13 33	13 56		14 03			14 26			14 33	
London Cannon Street 4 ⊖	d					12 30									13 30									14 30	
London Bridge 4 ⊖	d					12 38			13 08						13 38			14 08						14 38	
Orpington 4	d					12 54			13 26						13 54			14 26						14 54	
Sevenoaks 4	d					13 04			13 36						14 04			14 36						15 04	
Gatwick Airport 10 ✈	d					12b08									13b08									14b08	
Redhill	d					12 39									13 39									14 39	
Tonbridge 4	a		13 02			13 15	13 30		13 47			14 02			14 15	14 30		14 47			15 02			15 15	
	d		13 03			13 15	13 31		13 47			14 03			14 15	14 31		14 47			15 03			15 15	
Paddock Wood 4	d	13 01	13 10			13 23			13 55		14 01	14 10			14 23			14 55		15 01	15 10			15 23	
Maidstone West 4	a	13 21									14 21									15 21					
Marden	d								14 01									15 01							
Staplehurst	d		13 18			13 32			14 06			14 18			14 32			15 06			15 18			15 32	
Headcorn 4	d					13 37			14 11						14 37			15 11						15 37	
Pluckley	d								14 18									15 18							
London Victoria 15 ⊖	d		11c48		12 18		12 18					12c48		13 18		13 18					13c48		14 18		
Bromley South 4	d		12c04		12 34		12 34					13c04		13 34		13 34					14c04		14 34		
Maidstone East 4	d		13 05		13 13							14 05		14 13							15 05		15 13		
Ashford International	a		13 32		13 43	13 50	13 52		14 26			14 32		14 43	14 50	14 52		15 26			15 32		15 43	15 50	
	d		13 36	13 38	13 46		13 57	14 00				14 36	14 38	14 46		14 57	15 00				15 36	15 38	15 46		
Rye	a							14 53									15 53								
Wye	d				13 52									14 52									15 52		
Chilham	d				13 58									14 58									15 58		
Chartham	d				14 02									15 02									16 02		
Canterbury West 4	d		13 54		14a07			14g20				14 54		15a07			15h20				15 54		16a07		
Sturry	d		13 59									14 59									15 59				
Westenhanger	d			13 47									14 47									15 47			
Sandling	d			13 50									14 50									15 50			
Folkestone West	d			13 55									14 55									15 55			
Folkestone Central	d			13 58			14 11						14 58			15 11						15 58			
Dover Priory 4 ⛴	a			14 09			14 23						15 09			15 23						16 09			
	d			14 10			14 25						15 10			15 25						16 10			
Martin Mill	d			14 19			14 35						15 19			15 35						16 19			
Walmer	d			14 23			14 39						15 23			15 39						16 23			
Deal	d			14 27			14 43						15 27			15 43						16 27			
Sandwich	d			14 33			14 49						15 33			15 49						16 33			
Minster 4	d		14 10									15 10									16 10				
Ramsgate 4 ✈	a		14 17	14 44			15 02	14 38				15 17	15 44			16 02	15 38				16 17	16 44			
Dumpton Park	a		14 24					14 43				15 24					15 43				16 24				
Broadstairs	a		14 28					14 46				15 28					15 46				16 28				
Margate 4	a		14 32					14 51				15 32					15 51				16 32				

For general notes see front of timetable
For details of catering facilities see Directory of Train Operators

- **b** Change at Redhill and Tonbridge
- **c** Change at Maidstone East and Ashford International
- **e** Arr. 1117
- **f** Arr. 1317
- **g** Arr. 1417
- **h** Arr. 1517

Saturdays

For details of Bank Holiday service alterations please see first page of Table 195

London and Tonbridge → Ashford International, Folkestone, Dover, Canterbury West, Ramsgate and Margate

Network Diagram - see first page of Table 206

Station		SE 4 1		SE 8 1	SE 61		SE 90 1		SE 64 1	SE 8 1	SE 4 1		SE 8 1	SE 61		SE 90 1		SE 8 1	SE 4 1		SE 8 1	SE 61	SE 90 1		SE 8 1
London Charing Cross 4	⊖ d	14 53		15 00			15 23			15 30	15 53		16 00			16 23		16 30	16 53		17 00		17 23		17 30
London Waterloo (East) 4	⊖ d	14 56		15 03			15 26			15 33	15 56		16 03			16 26		16 33	16 56		17 03		17 26		17 33
London Cannon Street 4	⊖ d									15 30															
London Bridge 4	⊖ d			15 08						15 38			16 08					16 38			17 08				17 38
Orpington 4	d			15 26						15 54			16 26					16 54			17 26				17 54
Sevenoaks 4	d			15 36						16 04			16 36					17 04			17 36				18 04
Gatwick Airport 10	✈ d									15b08															
Redhill	d									15 39															
Tonbridge 4	a	15 30		15 47			16 02			16 15	16 30		16 47			17 02		17 15	17 30		17 47		18 02		18 15
	d	15 31		15 47			16 03			16 15	16 31		16 47			17 03		17 15	17 31		17 47		18 03		18 15
Paddock Wood 4	d			15 55	16 01		16 10			16 23			16 55	17 01		17 10		17 23			17 55	18 01	18 10		18 23
Maidstone West 4	a				16 21									17 21								18 21			
Marden	d			16 01									17 01								18 01				
Staplehurst	d			16 06			16 18			16 32			17 06			17 18		17 32			18 06		18 18		18 32
Headcorn 4	d			16 11						16 37			17 11					17 37			18 11				18 37
Pluckley	d			16 18									17 18								18 18				
London Victoria 15	⊖ d	14 18					14c48		15 18		15 18					15c48			16 18				16c48		
Bromley South 4	d	14 34					15c04		15 34		15 34					16c04			16 34				17c04		
Maidstone East 4	d						16 05		16 13							17 05			17 13				18 05		
Ashford International	a	15 52		16 26			16 32		16 43	16 50	16 52		17 26			17 32		17 50	17 52		18 26		18 32		18 50
	d	15 57	16 01				16 36	16 38	16 46		16 57	17 00				17 36	17 38		17 57	18 00			18 36	18 38	
Rye	a		16 53									17 53								18 53					
Wye	d								16 52							17 43							18 43		
Chilham	d								16 58							17 49							18 49		
Chartham	d								17 02							17 53							18 53		
Canterbury West 4	d		16 20				16 54		17a07			17e20				17 59				18f20			18 59		
Sturry	d						16 59									18 04							19 04		
Westenhanger	d							16 47									17 47							18 47	
Sandling	d							16 50									17 50							18 50	
Folkestone West	d							16 55									17 55							18 55	
Folkestone Central	d	16 11						16 58			17 11						17 58		18 11					18 58	
Dover Priory 4	a	16 23						17 09			17 23						18 09		18 23					19 09	
	d	16 25						17 10			17 25						18 10		18 25					19 10	
Martin Mill	d	16 35						17 19			17 35						18 19		18 35					19 19	
Walmer	d	16 39						17 23			17 39						18 23		18 39					19 23	
Deal	d	16 43						17 27			17 43						18 27		18 43					19 27	
Sandwich	d	16 49						17 33			17 49						18 33		18 49					19 33	
Minster 4	d						17 10									18 15							19 15		
Ramsgate 4	a	17 02	16 38				17 17	17 44			18 02	17 38				18 23	18 44		19 02	18 38			19 22	19 44	
Dumpton Park	a		16 43				17 24				18 24	17 43					18 54			18 43			19 27	19 54	
Broadstairs	a		16 46				17 28				18 28	17 46				18 46			19 30	18 46			19 30		
Margate 4	a		16 51				17 32				18 32	17 51				18 51			19 35	18 51			19 35		

Station		SE 4 1		SE 8 1		SE 4 1	SE 8 1	SE 61	SE 90 1	SE 4 1	SE 61	SE 90 1	SE 4 1		SE 01	SE 90 1	SE 4 1	SE 90 1	SE 4 1	SE 90 1	SE 8 1	SE 66 1	SE 8 1	SE 66 1	
London Charing Cross 4	⊖ d	17 53		18 00		18 23			18 30	19 00		19 30	20 00			20 30	21 00	21 30	22 00	22 30	23 00		23 30		
London Waterloo (East) 4	⊖ d	17 56		18 03		18 26			18 33	19 03		19 33	20 03			20 33	21 03	21 33	22 03	22 33	23 03		23 33		
London Cannon Street 4	⊖ d								18 30	19 00		19 14				19g14									
London Bridge 4	⊖ d			18 08					18 38	19 08		19 38	20 08			20 38	21 08	21 38	22 08	22 38	23 08		23 38		
Orpington 4	d			18 26					18 54	19 24		19 54	20 24			20 54	21 24	21 54	22 24	22 54	23 24		23 54		
Sevenoaks 4	d			18 36					19 04	19 34		20 04	20 34			21 04	21 34	22 04	22 36	23 04	23 36		00 04		
Gatwick Airport 10	✈ d								18b08	18 52		19b08	19 53				20 53		21 53		22 53		22 53		
Redhill	d								18 39	19 06		19 39	20 07				21 07		22 07		23 07		23 07		
Tonbridge 4	a	18 30		18 47		19 02			19 13	19 45		20 13	20 45			21 13	21 45	22 13	22 47	23 13	23 46		00 15		
	d	18 31		18 47		19 03			19 15	19 45		20 15	20 45			21 15	21 45	22 15	22 47	23 15	23 47		00 18		
Paddock Wood 4	d			18 55				19 01	19 22	19 52	20 01	20 22	20 52		21 01	21 22	21 52	22 22	22 55	23 22	23 54		00 25		
Maidstone West 4	a							19 21		20 21	20 21		21 21		21 21										
Marden	d			19 01			←			19 58			20 58				21 58		23 01		23 59		00 31		
Staplehurst	d			19 06			19 06		19 31	20 03		20 31	21 03			21 31	22 03	22 31	23 06	23 31	00 04		00 36		
Headcorn 4	d			→			19h18		19 36	20 08		20 36	21 08			21 36	22 08	22 36	23 11	23 36	00 09		00 41		
Pluckley	d						19 25			20 15			21 15				22 15		23 18		00 16		00 48		
London Victoria 15	⊖ d	17 18							18 18			18c48	19 18				20 18		21 18		22 18	23 18	23 18		
Bromley South 4	d	17 34							18 34			19c04	19 34				20 34		21 34		22 34	23 34	23 34		
Maidstone East 4	d	18 13							19 13			20 05	20 19				21 19		22 19		23 19	00 19	00 19		
Ashford International	a	18 52				19 24	19 32		19 48	20 23		20 48	21 23			21 48	22 23	22 48	23 26	23 48	00 24	00 48	00 55	←	
	d	18 57	19 00			19 27			19 49	20 23		20 49	21 23			21 49	22 23	22 49	23 27	23 51	00 27	00 58 →	00 56	00 58	
Rye	a					19 53				20 53			21 53			22 47									
Wye	d		19 07						19 56			20 56				21 56		22 56		23 58				01 04	
Chilham	d		19 13						20 02			21 02				22 02		23 02		00 04				01 10	
Chartham	d		19 17						20 06			21 06				22 06		23 06		00 08				01 14	
Canterbury West 4	d		19 24						20 12			21 12				22 12		23 12		00a13				01a19	
Sturry	d		19 28						20 17			21 17				22 17		23 17							
Westenhanger	d					19 36				20 33			21 33				22 33		23 37		00 37		01 05		
Sandling	d					19 39				20 36			21 36				22 36		23 40		00 40		01 08		
Folkestone West	d					19 44				20 41			21 41				22 41		23 45		00 45		01 13		
Folkestone Central	d	19 11				19 47				20 43			21 43				22 43		23 48		00 47		01 16		
Dover Priory 4	a	19 23				19 58				20 55			21 55				22 55		23 59		00 59		01 27		
	d	19 25				19 59				20 55			21 55				22 55		23 59						
Martin Mill	d	19 35				20 08				21 04			22 04				23 04		00 09						
Walmer	d	19 39				20 12				21 09			22 09				23 09		00 14						
Deal	d	19 43				20 16				21 12			22 12				23 12		00 17						
Sandwich	d	19 49				20 22				21 19			22 19				23 19		00 24						
Minster 4	d		19j42						20 28			21 28				22 28		23 28							
Ramsgate 4	a	20 02	19 49			20 33			20 37	21 30		21 35	22 32			22 36	23 30	23 35	00 36						
Dumpton Park	a	20 15	20 15						20 54			21 41				22 41		23 41							
Broadstairs	a	20 18							20 58	21 44		21 44	22 44			22 44	23 44	23 44							
Margate 4	a	20 23							21 02	21 49		21 49	22 49			22 49	23 49	23 49							

For general notes see front of timetable
For details of catering facilities see Directory of Train Operators

b Change at Redhill and Tonbridge
c Change at Maidstone East and Ashford International
e Arr. 1717
f Arr. 1817
g Change at London Bridge and Orpington
h Arr. 1911
j Arr. 1939

Table 207

London and Tonbridge → Ashford International, Folkestone, Dover, Canterbury West, Ramsgate and Margate

Network Diagram - see first page of Table 206

		SE	SE	SE	SE	SE	SE	SE	SE	SE	SE	SE		SE	SE	SE	SE	SE	SE	SE
		4	90	8	66	8	66	61	4	90	55	90		4	55	90	4	55	90	4
		1	1	1	1	1	1		1	1		1		1		1	1		1	1
											A				A			A		
London Charing Cross 4	⊖ d	22p00	22p30	23p00		23p30						08 24		08 54		09 24	09 54		10 24	10 54
London Waterloo (East) 4	⊖ d	22p03	22p33	23p03		23p33						08 27		08 57		09 27	09 57		10 27	10 57
London Cannon Street 4	⊖ d																			
London Bridge 4	⊖ d	22p08	22p38	23p08		23p38						08 32		09 02		09 32	10 02		10 32	11 02
Orpington 4	d	22p24	22p54	23p24		23p54						08 49		09 19		09 49	10 19		10 49	11 19
Sevenoaks 4	d	22p36	23p04	23p36		00 04						08 59		09 29		09 59	10 29		10 59	11 29
Gatwick Airport 10	✈ d										07 55	*07 55*			08 55	*08 55*		09 55	*09 55*	
Redhill	d										08 10	*08 10*			09 10	*09 10*		10 10	*10 10*	
Tonbridge 4	a	22p47	23p13	23p46		00 15					08 40	09 09		09 37	09 40	10 09	10 37	10 40	11 09	11 37
	d	22p47	23p15	23p47		00 18		07 40	08 10		08 40	09 10		09 38	09 40	10 10	10 38	10 40	11 10	11 38
Paddock Wood 4	d	22p55	23p22	23p54		00 25		07 48	08 17		08 48	09 17		09 45	09 48	10 17	10 45	10 48	11 17	11 45
Maidstone West 4	a							08 08	*09 08*		09 08	*10 08*			10 08	*11 08*		11 08	*12 08*	
Marden	d	23p01		23p59		00 31			08 23			09 23				10 23			11 23	
Staplehurst	d	23p06	23p31	00 04		00 36			08 27			09 27		09 54		10 27	10 54		11 27	11 54
Headcorn 4	d	23p11	23p36	00 09		00 41			08 32			09 32				10 32			11 32	
Pluckley	d	23p18		00 16		00 48			08 38			09 38				10 38			11 38	
London Victoria 15	⊖ d			*22 09*	23p18							*08 18*					*09 18*			*10 18*
Bromley South 4	d			*22 29*	23p34							*08 34*					*09 34*			*10 34*
Maidstone East 4	d			*23 13*	00 19							*09 19*					*10 19*			*11 19*
Ashford International	a	23p26	23p48	00 24	00 48	00 55	←		08 46			09 46		10 09		10 46	11 09		11 46	12 09
	d	23p27	23p51	00 27	00 58	00 56	00 58		08 48	08 51		09 51	09 53	10 10		10 51	11 10		11 51	12 10
Rye	a				→				*09 44*					*10 44*			*11 44*			*12 44*
Wye	d		23p58				01 04			08 57		09 57				10 57			11 57	
Chilham	d		00 04				01 10			09 03		10 03				11 03			12 03	
Chartham	d		00 08				01 14			09 07		10 07				11 07			12 07	
Canterbury West 4	d		00a13				01a19			09 13		10 13				11 13			12 13	
Sturry	d									09 17		10 17				11 17			12 17	
Westenhanger	d	23p37		00 37		01 05			08 57				10 02	10 19			11 19			12 19
Sandling	d	23p40		00 40		01 08			09 00				10 05	10 22			11 22			12 22
Folkestone West	d	23p45		00 45		01 13			09 05				10 10	10 27			11 27			12 27
Folkestone Central	d	23p48		00 47		01 16			09 08				10 13	10 30			11 30			12 30
Dover Priory 4	⛴ a	23p59		00 59		01 27			09 19				10 25	10 41			11 41			12 41
	d	23p59							09 19				10 25	10 42			11 42			12 42
Martin Mill	d	00 09							09 28				10 34	10 51			11 51			12 51
Walmer	d	00 14							09 32				10 38	10 55			11 55			12 55
Deal	d	00 17							09 36				10 42	10 58			11 58			12 58
Sandwich	d	00 24							09 43				10 49	11 05			12 05			13 05
Minster 4	d									09 28		10 28				11 28			12 28	
Ramsgate 4	✈ a	00 36							09 55	09 34		10 34	11 01	11 18		11 34	12 18		12 34	13 18
Dumpton Park	a								*10 24*	09 39		10 39		*11 24*		11 39	*12 24*		12 39	*13 24*
Broadstairs	a								*10 28*	09 42		10 42		*11 28*		11 42	*12 28*		12 42	*13 28*
Margate 4	a								*10 32*	09 48		10 48		*11 32*		11 48	*12 32*		12 48	*13 32*

For general notes see front of timetable
For details of catering facilities see Directory of Train Operators

A From Three Bridges (Table 186)

Table 207

Sundays

London and Tonbridge → Ashford International, Folkestone, Dover, Canterbury West, Ramsgate and Margate

Network Diagram - see first page of Table 206

Station		SE 55 A	SE 90 1	SE 4 1	SE 55 A	SE 90 1	SE 4 1	SE 55 A	SE 90 1	SE 4 1	SE 55 A	SE 90 1	SE 4 1	SE 55 A	SE 90 1	SE 4 1	SE 55 A	SE 90 1	SE 4 1
London Charing Cross 4 ⊖	d		11 24	11 54		12 24	12 54		13 24	13 54		14 24	14 54		15 24	15 54		16 24	16 54
London Waterloo (East) 4 ⊖	d		11 27	11 57		12 27	12 57		13 27	13 57		14 27	14 57		15 27	15 57		16 27	16 57
London Cannon Street 4 ⊖	d																		
London Bridge 4 ⊖	d		11 32	12 02		12 32	13 02		13 32	14 02		14 32	15 02		15 32	16 02		16 32	17 02
Orpington 4	d		11 49	12 19		12 49	13 19		13 49	14 19		14 49	15 19		15 49	16 19		16 49	17 19
Sevenoaks 4	d		11 59	12 29		12 59	13 29		13 59	14 29		14 59	15 29		15 59	16 29		16 59	17 29
Gatwick Airport 10 ✈	d	10 55	10 55		11 55	11 55		12 55	12 55		13 55	13 55		14 55	14 55		15 55	15 55	
Redhill	d	11 10	11 10		12 10	12 10		13 10	13 10		14 10	14 10		15 10	15 10		16 10	16 10	
Tonbridge 4	a	11 40	12 09	12 37	12 40	13 09	13 37	13 40	14 09	14 37	14 40	15 09	15 37	15 40	16 09	16 37	16 40	17 09	17 37
	d	11 40	12 10	12 38	12 40	13 10	13 38	13 40	14 10	14 38	14 40	15 10	15 38	15 40	16 10	16 38	16 40	17 10	17 38
Paddock Wood 4	d	11 48	12 17	12 45	12 48	13 17	13 45	13 48	14 17	14 45	14 48	15 17	15 45	15 48	16 17	16 45	16 48	17 17	17 45
Maidstone West 4	a	12 08	13 08		13 08	14 08		14 08	15 08		15 08	16 08		16 08	17 08		17 08	18 08	
Marden	d		12 23			13 23			14 23			15 23			16 23			17 23	
Staplehurst	d		12 27	12 54		13 27	13 54		14 27	14 54		15 27	15 54		16 27	16 54		17 27	17 54
Headcorn 4	d		12 32			13 32			14 32			15 32			16 32			17 32	
Pluckley	d		12 38			13 38			14 38			15 38			16 38			17 38	
London Victoria 15 ⊖	d			11 18			12 18			13 18			14 18			15 18			16 18
Bromley South 4	d			11 34			12 34			13 34			14 34			15 34			16 34
Maidstone East 4	d			12 19			13 19			14 19			15 19			16 19			17 19
Ashford International	a		12 46	13 09		13 46	14 09		14 46	15 09		15 46	16 09		16 46	17 09		17 46	18 09
	d		12 51	13 10		13 51	14 10		14 51	15 10		15 51	16 10		16 51	17 10		17 51	18 10
Rye	a			13 44			14 44			15 44			16 44			17 44			18 44
Wye	d		12 57			13 57			14 57			15 57			16 57			17 57	
Chilham	d		13 03			14 03			15 03			16 03			17 03			18 03	
Chartham	d		13 07			14 07			15 07			16 07			17 07			18 07	
Canterbury West 4	d		13 13			14 13			15 13			16 13			17 13			18 13	
Sturry	d		13 17			14 17			15 17			16 17			17 17			18 17	
Westenhanger	d			13 19			14 19			15 19			16 19			17 19			18 19
Sandling	d			13 22			14 22			15 22			16 22			17 22			18 22
Folkestone West	d			13 27			14 27			15 27			16 27			17 27			18 27
Folkestone Central	d			13 30			14 30			15 30			16 30			17 30			18 30
Dover Priory 4 ⛴	a			13 41			14 41			15 41			16 41			17 41			18 41
	d			13 42			14 42			15 42			16 42			17 42			18 42
Martin Mill	d			13 51			14 51			15 51			16 51			17 51			18 51
Walmer	d			13 55			14 55			15 55			16 55			17 55			18 55
Deal	d			13 58			14 58			15 58			16 58			17 58			18 58
Sandwich	d			14 05			15 05			16 05			17 05			18 05			19 05
Minster 4	d		13 28			14 28			15 28			16 28			17 28			18 28	
Ramsgate 4 ✈	a		13 34	14 18		14 34	15 18		15 34	16 18		16 34	17 18		17 34	18 18		18 34	19 18
Dumpton Park	a		13 39	14 24		14 39	15 24		15 39	16 24		16 39	17 24		17 39	18 24		18 39	19 24
Broadstairs	a		13 42	14 28		14 42	15 28		15 42	16 28		16 42	17 28		17 42	18 28		18 42	19 28
Margate 4	a		13 48	14 32		14 48	15 32		15 48	16 32		16 48	17 32		17 48	18 32		18 48	19 32

Station		SE 55 A	SE 90 1	SE 4 1	SE 55 A	SE 90 1	SE 4 1	SE 55 A	SE 90 1	SE 4 1	SE 55 A	SE 90 1	SE 4 1	SE 55 B	SE 90 1	SE 4 1	SE 2 1	SE 8 1
London Charing Cross 4 ⊖	d		17 24	17 54		18 24	18 54		19 24	19 54		20 24	20 54		21 24	21 54	22 24	23 24
London Waterloo (East) 4 ⊖	d		17 27	17 57		18 27	18 57		19 27	19 57		20 27	20 57		21 27	21 57	22 27	23 27
London Cannon Street 4 ⊖	d																	
London Bridge 4 ⊖	d		17 32	18 02		18 32	19 02		19 32	20 02		20 32	21 02		21 32	22 02	22 32	23 32
Orpington 4	d		17 49	18 19		18 49	19 19		19 50	20 19		20 50	21 19		21 50	22 19	22 50	23 35
Sevenoaks 4	d		17 59	18 29		18 59	19 29		20 00	20 29		21 00	21 29		22 00	22 29	23 00	23 58
Gatwick Airport 10 ✈	d	16 55	16 55		17 55	17 55		18 55	18 55		19 55	19 55		20 55	20 55		21 55	
Redhill	d	17 10	17 10		18 10	18 10		19 10	19 10		20 10	20 10		21 10	21 10		22 10	
Tonbridge 4	a	17 40	18 09	18 37	18 40	19 09	19 37	19 40	20 10	20 37	20 40	21 10	21 37	21 40	22 10	22 37	23 10	00 06
	d	17 40	18 10	18 38	18 40	19 10	19 38	19 40	20 11	20 38	20 40	21 11	21 38	21 40	22 11	22 38	23 11	00 07
Paddock Wood 4	d	17 48	18 17	18 45	18 48	19 17	19 45	19 48	20 18	20 45	20 48	21 18	21 45	21 48	22 18	22 45	23 18	00 14
Maidstone West 4	a	18 08	19 08		19 08	20 08		20 08	21 08		21 08	22 08		22 08				
Marden	d		18 23			19 23			20 24			21 24			22 24		23 24	
Staplehurst	d		18 27	18 54		19 27	19 54		20 28	20 54		21 28	21 54		22 28	22 54	23 28	00 22
Headcorn 4	d		18 32			19 32			20 33			21 33			22 33		23 33	
Pluckley	d		18 38			19 38			20 39			21 39			22 39		23 39	
London Victoria 15 ⊖	d			17 18			18 18			19 18			20 18			21 18		
Bromley South 4	d			17 34			18 34			19 34			20 34			21 34		
Maidstone East 4	d			18 19			19 19			20 19			21 19			22 19		
Ashford International	a		18 46	19 09		19 46	20 09		20 47	21 09		21 47	22 09		22 47	23 09	23 47	00 37
	d		18 51	19 10		19 51	20 10		20 51	21 10		21 51	22 10		22 51	23 10	23 51	
Rye	a			19 44			20 44			21 44			22 43					
Wye	d		18 57			19 57			20 57			21 57			22 57			
Chilham	d		19 03			20 03			21 03			22 03			23 03			
Chartham	d		19 07			20 07			21 07			22 07			23 07			
Canterbury West 4	d		19 13			20 13			21 13			22 13			23 13			
Sturry	d		19 17			20 17			21 17			22 17			23 17			
Westenhanger	d			19 19			20 19			21 19			22 19			23 19	00 01	
Sandling	d			19 22			20 22			21 22			22 22			23 22	00 03	
Folkestone West	d			19 27			20 27			21 27			22 27			23 27	00 08	
Folkestone Central	d			19 30			20 30			21 30			22 30			23 30	00 11	
Dover Priory 4 ⛴	a			19 41			20 41			21 41			22 41			23 41	00 22	
	d			19 42			20 42			21 42			22 42			23 42		
Martin Mill	d			19 51			20 51			21 51			22 51			23 52		
Walmer	d			19 55			20 55			21 55			22 55			23 56		
Deal	d			19 58			20 58			21 58			22 58			23 59		
Sandwich	d			20 05			21 05			22 05			23 05			00 06		
Minster 4	d		19 28			20 28			21 28			22 28			23 28			
Ramsgate 4 ✈	a		19 34	20 18		20 34	21 18		21 34	22 18		22 34	23 18		23 34	00 19		
Dumpton Park	a		19 41	20 24		20 39	21 24		21 57									
Broadstairs	a		19 44	20 28		20 42	21 28		22 00									
Margate 4	a		19 50	20 32		20 48	21 32		22 05									

For general notes see front of timetable
For details of catering facilities see Directory of Train Operators

A From Three Bridges (Table 186)
B From Three Bridges (Table 186) to Gillingham (Kent) (Table 208)

Margate, Ramsgate, Canterbury West, Dover, Folkestone, Ashford International, → Tonbridge and London

For details of Bank Holiday service alterations please see first page of Table 195

Network Diagram - see first page of Table 206

Miles	Miles	Miles			SE 5 1	SE 55	SE 2 1	SE 13	SE 4 1	SE 61	SE 90 1	SE 61	SE 5 1	SE 4 1	SE 3 1	SE 90 1	SE 91 1	SE 4 1	SE 61	SE 3 1	SE 90 1	SE 66 1	SE 5 1
						A		B															
0	0	—	**Margate 4**	d													*06 07*	06 07			06 41		*06 41*
3¼	3¼	—	Broadstairs	d													*06 12*	06 12			06 46		*06 46*
4½	4½	—	Dumpton Park	d													*06 15*	06 15			06 49		
5½	5½	—	**Ramsgate 4** ✈	d					04 49		05 18			05 39		06 12	06 32	06 19			06 53		06 59
—	9½	0	Minster 4	d							05 24					06 18	06 38				06 59		
13¾	—	4¾	Sandwich	d					05 01					05 51				06 31					07 11
18	—	—	**Deal**	d					05 07					05 57				06 37					07 17
19½	—	—	Walmer	d					05 10					06 00				06 40					07 20
22¼	—	—	Martin Mill	d					05 16					06 06				06 46					07 26
27¼	—	—	**Dover Priory 4** ⛴	a					05 24					06 14				06 54					07 34
—	—	—		d			04 51		05 25					06 15	06 25			06 55		07 05			07 35
34½	—	—	**Folkestone Central**	d			05 03		05 37					06 27	06 37			07 07		07 17			07 47
35¼	—	—	Folkestone West	d			05 05		05 39					06 29	06 39			07 09		07 19			07 49
39	—	—	Sandling	d			05 11		05 45					06 35	06 45			07 15		07 25			07 55
40¼	—	—	Westenhanger	d			05 14		05 48					06 38	06 48			07 18		07 28			07 58
—	18½	—	Sturry	d							05 36					06 30	06 50				07 10		
—	20¾	—	**Canterbury West 4**	d							05 42					06 36	06 56				07 16	07 47	
—	24	—	Chartham	d							05 47					06 41	07 01				07 22		
—	26	—	Chilham	d							05 51					06 45	07 05				07 26		
—	30¾	—	Wye	d							05 58					06 52	07 12				07 32	07 59	
—	—	—	Rye	d									*05 47*	*06 16*			*06 49*						*07 19*
48½	35	—	**Ashford International**	a			05 23		05 57		06 06			06 47	06 57	07 00	07 20	07 27		07 37	07 40	08 05	08 07
—	—	—		d	05 19		05 24		05 58		06 07		06 38	06 50	06 58	07 02	07 22	07 30		07 38	07 45	08 14	08 10
—	54¼	—	Maidstone East 4	a			*06 02*				*06 41*			*07 23*		*07 42*				*08 12*		↪	*08 43*
—	83¼	—	Bromley South 4	a			*06 47*				*07 29*					*08 25*				*08 59*			*09 27*
—	94¼	—	**London Victoria 15** ⊖	a			*07 08*				*07 49*			*08 31*		*08 53*				*09 18*			*09 50*
54	—	—	Pluckley	d			05 31				06 14		06 45		07 05	07 09	07 29			07 45	07 52		
59¼	—	—	Headcorn 4	d	05 30		05 37		06 08		06 20		06 51	07 00	07 11	07 15	07 35	07 40		07 51	07 58		08 20
62¾	—	—	Staplehurst	d	05 36		05 42		06 13		06 25		06 56	07 05	07 16	07 20	07 40	07 45		07 56	08 03		08 26
65	—	—	Marden	d	05 40		05 47				06 30		07 01		07 21	07 25				08 01	08 08		
—	—	—	Maidstone West 4	d		05 28	*05 28*			06 06	*06 06*	06 42	*06 42*						07 39	*07 39*			
69¾	—	—	Paddock Wood 4	d	05 46	05 49	05 53	06 06	06 21	06a26	06 36	07a02	07 07	07 13	07 27	07 31	07 48	07 53	07a59	08 07	08 14		08 34
75	—	—	**Tonbridge 4**	a	05 54	05 56	06 01	06 13	06 29		06 44		07 16	07 25	07 35	07 38	07 58	08 02		08 16	08 25		08 44
—	—	—		d	05 55	06 00	06 02	06 14	06 30		06 45		07 16	07 25	07 36	07 42	07 58	08 02		08 17	08 25		08 46
—	—	—	Redhill	a	*06 30*	06 30	*06 45*	06 45			*07 20*			*08 08*				*08 48*					*09 21*
—	—	—	Gatwick Airport 10 ✈	a	*06b53*	*06 53*	*07b03*	*07 03*			*07b54*			*08b39*				*09b02*					*09b39*
82¼	—	—	Sevenoaks 4	a	06 07		06 12		06 39		06 57		07 28	07 35	07 48	07 52	08 08	08 12		08 29			08 56
90¾	—	—	Orpington 4	a	06 16		*06 30*		*06 58*		*07 12*		*07 52*			*08 12*		*08 32*					*09 11*
102¾	—	—	**London Bridge 4** ⊖	a	06 35		06 36		07 03		07 21		07 54	*08 10*	08 14	*08 30*	08 34	*08 50*		08 54			09 22
—	—	—	**London Cannon Street 4** ⊖	a	06 41		*06 47*		*07 13*		*07 31*		08 00	*08 20*	08 20	*08c39*	08 41	*08c59*		09 01			09 28
103¾	—	—	**London Waterloo (East) 4** ⊖	a			06 41		07 08		07 27			08 04		08 21		08 41		*09e23*	09 01		
104½	—	—	**London Charing Cross 4** ⊖	a			06 46		07 14		07 32			08 09		08 26		08 47		*09e29*	09 07		

For general notes see front of timetable
For details of catering facilities see Directory of Train Operators

A From Gillingham (Kent) (Table 208)
B To London Bridge (Table 186)
b Change at Tonbridge and Redhill
c Change at Sevenoaks and London Bridge
e Change at Sevenoaks

For details of Bank Holiday service alterations please see first page of Table 195

Margate, Ramsgate, Canterbury West, Dover, Folkestone, Ashford International, → Tonbridge and London

Network Diagram - see first page of Table 206

	SE 13	SE 8	SE 66	SE 4	SE 18	SE 88	SE 4	SE 18	SE 61		SE 64	SE 4	SE 90	SE 90	SE 4	SE 8	SE 61	SE 64	SE 8		SE 2	SE 90	SE 8	SE 64
		1	1	1	1	1	1	1			1	1	1	1	1	1		1	1		1	1	1	1
	A																							
				🛒			🛒					🛒			🛒						🛒			
Margate 4 d				07 07	*07 07*	07 28					07 43	*07 43*	08 13	09 04	*08 18*							*09 20*		
Broadstairs d				07 12	*07 12*	07 33					07 48	*07 48*	08 18	09 09	*08 23*									
Dumpton Park d				07 15		07 36					07 50		08 21	09 12	*08 26*									
Ramsgate 4 d				07 19	07 27	07 42					07 55	08 05	08 29	09 17	08 50							09 43		
Minster 4 d					07b38	07 48					08 01	08c16	08 35									09 48		
Sandwich d				07 31	07 45							08 24			09 02									
Deal d				07 37	07 51							08 30			09 08									
Walmer d				07 40	07 55							08 33			09 11									
Martin Mill d				07 46	08 00							08 39			09 17									
Dover Priory 4 a				07 54	08 09			←				08 47			09 25									
d				07 55	08 10			08 10				08 48			09 26						09 50			
Folkestone Central d				08 07	→			08 21				09 00			09 38						10 01			
Folkestone West d				08 09				08 24							09 40						10 04			
Sandling d				08 15				08 29							09 46						10 09			
Westenhanger d				08 18				08 32							09 49						10 12			
Sturry d						07 59					08 12		08 47									10 00		
Canterbury West 4 d						08 06					08e20		08 53	09 37				09 43				10 06		10 24
Chartham d						08 11					08 25		08 58					09 48						10 29
Chilham d						08 15					08 28		09 02					09 52						10 33
Wye d						08 22					08 34		09 09					09 58						10 39
Rye d						*07 54*	←				*08 23*	*08 54*									*09 54*			
Ashford International a			←	08 27		08 31	08 27	08 41			08 42	09 13	09 16	09 54	09 58			10 05			10 21	10 24		10 46
d		08 14	08 14			08 32	08 46				09 04	09 21		10 01		09 56		10 05	10 20		10 28			11 05
Maidstone East 4 a			08 43			08 53					09 33	*09 56*						10 34			*10 57*			→
Bromley South 4 a			09 27	*09f44*		*09 44*	*10 14*				10 14	*10f44*						11 14						
London Victoria 15 ⊖ a			09 50	*10f02*		*10 02*	*10 32*				10 32	*11f02*						11 32					←	
Pluckley d		08 21		→			08 53					09 28				10 03			10 27 →				10 27	
Headcorn 4 d		08 27					08 59					09 34				10g13							10h40	
Staplehurst d		08 32					09 04					09 39				10 18					10 41		10 45	
Marden d		08 37					09 09					09 44				10 22							10 50	
Maidstone West 4 d	08 19	*08 19*							09 25			*09 25*					10 24				*10 24*			
Paddock Wood 4 d	08 40	08 43					09 15		09a45			09 50				10 28	10a44				10 49		10 56	
Tonbridge 4 a	08 49	08 50					09 23					09 57		10 25		10 35					10 57		11 03	
d	08 51	09 00					09 24					09 58		10 28		10 36					10 58		11 04	
Redhill a	09 21						*10 04*					*10 40*		*11 04*							*11 40*			
Gatwick Airport 10 ✈ a	*09 39*						*10j23*					*10 55*		*11j23*							*11 55*			
Sevenoaks 4 a		09 09					09 34									10 48							11 15	
Orpington 4 a		*09 32*					*09 55*									10 57							11 25	
London Bridge 4 ⊖ a		09 33				09 39	09 57									11 13							11 43	
London Cannon Street 4 ⊖ a		*09 43*				*09 57*	*10 06*									*11 20*								
London Waterloo (East) 4 ⊖ a		09 38				09 45	10 03					10 32		11 02		11 18					11 32		11 48	
London Charing Cross 4 ⊖ a		09 44				09 50	10 07					10 36		11 06		11 21					11 36		11 51	

For general notes see front of timetable
For details of catering facilities see Directory of Train Operators

- **A** From Strood (Table 208) to London Bridge (Table 186)
- **b** Arr. 0733
- **c** Arr. 0811
- **e** Arr. 0817
- **f** Change at Ashford International and Maidstone East
- **g** Arr. 1009
- **h** Arr. 1034
- **j** Change at Tonbridge and Redhill

Margate, Ramsgate, Canterbury West, Dover, Folkestone, Ashford International, → Tonbridge and London

For details of Bank Holiday service alterations please see first page of Table 195

Network Diagram - see first page of Table 206

Station		SE 8 1	SE 90 1	SE 4 1	SE 8 1	SE 61	SE 64 1	SE 8 1		SE 2 1	SE 90 1	SE 8 1	SE 64 1	SE 8	SE 90 1	SE 4 1	SE 8	SE 61		SE 64 1	SE 8 1	SE 2 1	SE 90 1	SE 8 1	SE 64 1
Margate 4	d		10 04	09 43							10 19				11 04	10 41							11 15		
Broadstairs	d		10 09												11 09										
Dumpton Park	d		10 12												11 12										
Ramsgate 4	d		10 19	09 57							10 43				11 19	10 57							11 43		
Minster 4	d										10 48												11 48		
Sandwich	d			10 09												11 09									
Deal	d			10 15												11 15									
Walmer	d			10 18												11 18									
Martin Mill	d			10 24												11 24									
Dover Priory 4	a			10 32												11 32									
	d			10 33						10 50						11 33						11 50			
Folkestone Central	d			10 45						11 01						11 45						12 01			
Folkestone West	d									11 04												12 04			
Sandling	d									11 09												12 09			
Westenhanger	d									11 12												12 12			
Sturry	d										11 00												12 00		
Canterbury West 4	d		10 39								11 06		11 24		11 39								12 06		12 24
Chartham	d												11 29												12 29
Chilham	d												11 33												12 33
Wye	d												11 39												12 39
Rye	d									10 54												11 54			
Ashford International	a		10 56	10 59						11 21	11 24		11 46		11 56	11 59						12 21	12 24		12 46
	d	10 57	11 03				← 11 05	11 20		11 28			12 05	11 57	12 03					← 12 05	12 20	12 28			13 05
Maidstone East 4	a		11 34				11 34			11 57			→		12 34					12 34		12 57			→
Bromley South 4	a		12 14				12 14								13 14					13 14					
London Victoria 15	a		12 32				12 32					←			13 32					13 32				←	
Pluckley	d							11 27				11 27									12 27			12 27	
Headcorn 4	d	11b14			←			→				11c40		12e14			←				→			12f40	
Staplehurst	d	11 19			11 19					11 41		11 45		12 19			12 19					12 41		12 45	
Marden	d	→										11 50		→										12 50	
Maidstone West 4	d					11 24				11 24								12 24				12 24			
Paddock Wood 4	d				11 28	11a44				11 49		11 56					12 28	12a44				12 49		12 56	
Tonbridge 4	a		11 25		11 35					11 57		12 03			12 25		12 35					12 57		13 03	
	d		11 28		11 36					11 58		12 04			12 28		12 36					12 58		13 04	
Redhill	a		12 04							12 39					13 04							13 39			
Gatwick Airport 10	a		12g23							12 55					13g23							13 55			
Sevenoaks 4	a				11 47							12 15					12 47							13 15	
Orpington 4	a				11 57							12 25					12 57							13 25	
London Bridge 4	a				12 13							12 43					13 13							13 43	
London Cannon Street 4	a																								
London Waterloo (East) 4	a		12 02		12 18					12 32		12 48			13 02		13 18					13 32		13 48	
London Charing Cross 4	a		12 06		12 21					12 36		12 51			13 06		13 21					13 36		13 51	

Station		SE 8 1	SE 90 1	SE 4 1	SE 8 1	SE 61		SE 64 1	SE 8 1	SE 2 1	SE 90 1	SE 8 1	SE 64 1	SE 8 1	SE 90 1	SE 4 1		SE 8 1	SE 61	SE 64 1	SE 8 1	SE 2 1	SE 90 1	SE 8 1	
Margate 4	d		12 04	11 41							12 15				13 04	12 41							13 15		
Broadstairs	d		12 09												13 09										
Dumpton Park	d		12 12												13 12										
Ramsgate 4	d		12 19	11 57							12 43				13 19	12 57							13 42		
Minster 4	d										12 48												13 48		
Sandwich	d			12 09												13 09									
Deal	d			12 15												13 15									
Walmer	d			12 18												13 18									
Martin Mill	d			12 24												13 24									
Dover Priory 4	a			12 32												13 32									
	d			12 33						12 50						13 33						13 50			
Folkestone Central	d			12 45						13 01						13 45						14 02			
Folkestone West	d									13 04												14 04			
Sandling	d									13 09												14 10			
Westenhanger	d									13 12												14 13			
Sturry	d										13 00												14 00		
Canterbury West 4	d		12 39								13 06		13 24		13 39								14 06		
Chartham	d												13 29												
Chilham	d												13 33												
Wye	d												13 39												
Rye	d									12 54												13 54			
Ashford International	a		12 56	12 59						13 21	13 24		13 46		13 56	13 59						14 21	14 24		
	d	12 57	13 03					← 13 05	13 20	13 28			14 05	13 57	14 03					← 14 05	14 20	14 28			
Maidstone East 4	a		13 34					13 34		13 57			→		14 34					14 34		14 57			
Bromley South 4	a		14 14					14 14							15 14					15 14		16 14			
London Victoria 15	a		14 32					14 32				←			15 32					15 32		16 33		←	
Pluckley	d								13 27			13 27									14 27			14 27	
Headcorn 4	d	13h14			←				→			13j40		14k14				←			→			14m40	
Staplehurst	d	13 19			13 19					13 41		13 45		14 19				14 19				14 41		14 45	
Marden	d	→										13 50		→										14 50	
Maidstone West 4	d					13 24				13 24									14 24			14 24			
Paddock Wood 4	d				13 28	13a44				13 49		13 56						14 28	14a44			14 49		14 56	
Tonbridge 4	a		13 25		13 35					13 57		14 03			14 25			14 35				14 57		15 03	
	d		13 28		13 36					13 58		14 04			14 28			14 36				14 58		15 04	
Redhill	a		14 04							14 39					15 04							15 39			
Gatwick Airport 10	a		14g23							14 55					15g23							15 56			
Sevenoaks 4	a				13 47							14 15						14 47						15 15	
Orpington 4	a				13 57							14 25						14 57						15 25	
London Bridge 4	a				14 13							14 43						15 13						15 43	
London Cannon Street 4	a																								
London Waterloo (East) 4	a		14 02		14 18					14 32		14 48			15 02			15 18				15 32		15 48	
London Charing Cross 4	a		14 06		14 21					14 36		14 51			15 06			15 21				15 36		15 51	

For general notes see front of timetable
For details of catering facilities see Directory of Train Operators

- **b** Arr. 1108
- **c** Arr. 1134
- **e** Arr. 1208
- **f** Arr. 1234
- **g** Change at Tonbridge and Redhill
- **h** Arr. 1308
- **j** Arr. 1334
- **k** Arr. 1408
- **m** Arr. 1434

Margate, Ramsgate, Canterbury West, Dover, Folkestone, Ashford International, → Tonbridge and London

For details of Bank Holiday service alterations please see first page of Table 195

Network Diagram - see first page of Table 206

		SE	SE	SE		SE	SE	SE	SE	SE	SE	SE	SE	SE		SE	SE	SE	SE	SE	SE	SE	SE	SE	SE
		90	4	8		61	64	2	90	4	90	61	64	8		2	90	61	4	90	4	90	61	90	4
		1	1	1			1	1	1	1	1		1	1		1	1		1	1	1	1		1	1
								🍴		🍴						🍴			🍴		🍴				
Margate [4]	d	14 04	*13 41*						*14 15*		14 50						*14 50*			15 36	*15 41*			16 36	*16 15*
Broadstairs	d	14 09	*13 46*							*14 20*	14 55								*15 20*	15 41	*15 46*			16 41	
Dumpton Park	d	14 12									14 58								*15 23*	15 44				16 44	
Ramsgate [4]	d	14 17	13 55						14 38	14 34	15 02						15 27		15 32	15 48	16 04	16 27		16 48	16 32
Minster [4]	d								14 44								15 33			15 54		16 33		16 54	
Sandwich	d		14 07							14 47									15 44		16 16				16 44
Deal	d		14 13							14 53									15 50		16 22				16 50
Walmer	d		14 16							14 56									15 53		16 25				16 53
Martin Mill	d		14 22							15 02									15 59		16 31				16 59
Dover Priory [4]	a		14 30							15 11									16 07		16 39				17 07
	d		14 31					14 46		15 12						15 40			16 08		16 40				17 08
Folkestone Central	d		14 43					14 58		15 24						15 52			16 20		16 52				17 20
Folkestone West	d							15 00								15 54					16 54				
Sandling	d							15 06								16 00					17 00				
Westenhanger	d							15 09								16 03					17 03				
Sturry	d								14 56								15 45			16 05		16 45		17 05	
Canterbury West [4]	d	14 37					14 24		15 02		15 22		15 32				15 51			16 11		16 51		17 11	
Chartham	d						14 29						15 37				15 56			16 17		16 56		17 17	
Chilham	d						14 33						15 41				16 00			16 21		17 00		17 21	
Wye	d						14 39						15 47				16 07			16 27		17 07		17 27	
Rye	d							*14 54*											*15 54*					*16 54*	
Ashford International	a	14 54	14 57				14 46	15 17	15 20	15 37	15 40		15 54			16 12	16 14		16 34	16 36	17 12	17 14		17 34	17 36
	d	15 01		14 52			15 03	15 24		15 44			15 59	16 06		16 19			16 41		17 19			17 41	
Maidstone East [4]	a						15 32	*15 56*					16 28			*16 45*			*17 27*		*17 47*			*18 29*	
Bromley South [4]	a						16 14	*16 47*					17 14			*17 47*			*18 13*		*18 45*			*19 14*	
London Victoria [15]	⊖ a						16 33	*17 11*		*17 31*			17 31			*18 09*			*18 33*		*19 03*			*19 31*	
Pluckley	d			14 59						15 51									16 48					17 48	
Headcorn [4]	d			15b13						15 57						16 29			16 54					17 54	
Staplehurst	d			15 18				15 37		16 02				16 20		16 34			16 59		17 32			17 59	
Marden	d			15 22						16 07									17 04					18 04	
Maidstone West [4]	d					15 24						15 55		*15 55*				16 38	*16 38*				17 29	*17 29*	
Paddock Wood [4]	d			15 28		15a44		15 45		16 13		16a15		16 28		16 42		16a58	17 10		17 40		17a49	18 10	
Tonbridge [4]	a	15 25		15 36				15 53		16 21				16 36		16 50			17 17		17 49			18 18	
	d	15 28		15 36				15 54		16 22				16 40		16 51			17 18		17 50			18 20	
Redhill	a	*16 04*						*16 39*		*16 59*						*17 51*			*18 13*		*18 51*				
Gatwick Airport [10]	✈ a	*16c23*						*16 56*		*17c32*						*18c12*			*18c32*		*19c07*				
Sevenoaks [4]	a			15 48				16 03		16 31				16 52		17 03			17 30		18 02			18 29	
Orpington [4]	a			15 57				*16 34*		*16 49*				17 02		17 12			17 39		18 11			18 39	
London Bridge [4]	⊖ a			16 13				16 29		17 00				17 26		17 31			*18 19*		18 28			18 57	
London Cannon Street [4]	⊖ a			*16 22*				*16 36*		*17 08*				17 31		*17 39*			*18e29*		*18 37*			*19 05*	
London Waterloo (East) [4]	⊖ a	16 02		16 18				16 34		17 05						17 36			18 03		18 33			19 02	
London Charing Cross [4]	⊖ a	16 06		16 21				16 38		17 10						17 41			18 07		18 37			19 07	

		SE	SE		SE	SE	SE	SE	SE	SE	SE	SE	SE		SE	SE	SE	SE	SE	SE	SE	SE	SE	SE	
		18	61		90	61	18	90	18	90	18	61	90		94	4	61	90	4	61	90	4	01	4	
		1			1		1	1	1	1	1		1		1	1		1	1		1	1	1	1	
		🍴					🍴	🍴	🍴		🍴														
Margate [4]	d							*17 45*		*18 13*			18 52			*18 52*		*19 40*			*20 47*		*21 43*		
Broadstairs	d	*16 52*						*17 51*		*18 19*			18 57			*18 57*		*19 46*			*20 52*		*21 48*		
Dumpton Park	d							*17 53*		*18 21*			19 00					*19 48*			*20 55*		*21 27*		
Ramsgate [4]	d	17 10			17 27			18 04	18 09	18 36			19 04			19 14		20 04	20 20		21 04	21 20	22 22	22 32	
Minster [4]	d	17f20			17 33			18 10	18g20	18 42			19 10					20 10			21 10		22 27		
Sandwich	d	17 28							18 27							19 26			20 32			21 32		22 43	
Deal	d	17 34							18 33							19 32			20 38			21 38		22 49	
Walmer	d	17 37							18 37							19 35			20 41			21 41		22 53	
Martin Mill	d	17 43							18 42							19 41			20 47			21 47		22 58	
Dover Priory [4]	a	17 51					←		18 51		←					19 49			20 55			21 55		23 06	
	d	17 52					17 52		18 52		18 52					19 50			20 56			22 00		23 19	
Folkestone Central	d	→					18 04		→		19 04					20 02			21 08			22 12		23 30	
Folkestone West	d						18 06				19 06					20 04			21 11			22 14		23 33	
Sandling	d						18 12				19 12					20 10			21 16			22 20		23 39	
Westenhanger	d						18 15				19 15					20 13			21 19			22 23		23 42	
Sturry	d				17 45			18 21		18 53			19 21					20 21			21 21		22 38		
Canterbury West [4]	d				17 51			18 27		18 59			19 27		19 34			20 27			21 27		22 44		
Chartham	d				17 56			18 33		19 05			19 33		19 39			20 33			21 33		22 50		
Chilham	d				18 00			18 37		19 09			19 37		19 43			20 37			21 37		22 53		
Wye	d				18 07			18 43		19 15			19 43		19 49			20 43			21 43		23 00		
Rye	d						*17 54*			*18 54*					*19 31*	*19 54*			*20 54*			*21 57*			
Ashford International	a				18 14		18 23	18 50		19 22	19 24		19 50		19 57	20 22		20 50	21 28		21 50	22 32	23 06	23 51	
	d				18 16		18 25	18 51		19 29			19 51		19 58	20 29		20 51	21 29		21 51	22 33			
Maidstone East [4]	a							*19 29*							20 27			*21 27*			*22 37*				
Bromley South [4]	a							*20 14*					*21 13*		21 13			*22 13*			*23 23*				
London Victoria [15]	⊖ a							*20 32*					*21 29*		21 29			*22 32*			*23 45*				
Pluckley	d						18 32	18 58					19 58					20 58			21 58	22 40			
Headcorn [4]	d						18 38	19 04					20 04					21 04			22 04	22 46			
Staplehurst	d				18 29		18 43	19 09		19 42			20 09			20 42		21 09	21 42		22 09	22 51			
Marden	d						18 48	19 14					20 14					21 14			22 14	22 56			
Maidstone West [4]	d		17 59		*17 59*	18 31		*18 31*				19 39	*19 39*				20 35	*20 35*		21 32	*21 32*				
Paddock Wood [4]	d		18a19		18 37	18a51	18 54	19 20		19 50		19a59	20 20			20 50	20a55	21 20	21 50	21a52	22 20	23 02			
Tonbridge [4]	a				18 45		19 03	19 27		19 58			20 27			20 58		21 28	21 58		22 28	23 09			
	d				18 46		19 11	19 30		20 00			20 31			21 00		21 30	22 00		22 30	23 10			
Redhill	a				*19 39*			*20 24*					*21 24*					*22 23*				*23 48*			
Gatwick Airport [10]	✈ a				*19c58*			*20 35*					*21 34*					*22 34*				*00c11*			
Sevenoaks [4]	a				18 58			19 39		20 09			20 40			21 09		21 39	22 09		22 39	23 22			
Orpington [4]	a				19 07			19 49		20 19			20 49			21 19		21 49	22 19		22 49	23 33			
London Bridge [4]	⊖ a				19 25			20 08		20 38			21 08			21 38		22 08	22 38		23 08	23 51			
London Cannon Street [4]	⊖ a				*19 37*			*20 27*																	
London Waterloo (East) [4]	⊖ a				19 31		19 46	20 13		20 43			21 13			21 43		22 13	22 43		23 13	23 56			
London Charing Cross [4]	⊖ a				19 35		19 50	20 18		20 48			21 18			21 48		22 18	22 48		23 18	00 01			

For general notes see front of timetable
For details of catering facilities see Directory of Train Operators

b Arr. 1507
c Change at Tonbridge and Redhill
e Change at Orpington and London Bridge
f Arr. 1716
g Arr. 1815

Table 207

Saturdays

For details of Bank Holiday service alterations please see first page of Table 195

Margate, Ramsgate, Canterbury West, Dover, Folkestone, Ashford International, → Tonbridge and London

Network Diagram - see first page of Table 206

		SE	SE	SE	SE	SE	SE	SE	SE	SE		SE	SE	SE	SE	SE	SE	SE	SE		SE	SE	SE	SE	SE
		2	61	2	90	4	61	4	90	4		61	8	4	90	8	8	90	4		8	8	61	4	90
		[1]		[1]	[1]	[1]		[1]	[1]	[1]			[1]	[1]	[1]	[1]	[1]	[1]	[1]		[1]	[1]		[1]	[1]
														[catering]	[catering]			[catering]	[catering]					[catering]	
Margate [4]	d													06 49	07 26			08 04	07 26					07 46	
Broadstairs	d													06 54	07 31			08 09						07 51	
Dumpton Park	d													06 56	07 34			08 12						07 53	
Ramsgate [4]	d				06 01	05 42		06 18	07 01	06 47				07 14	07 38			08 16	07 57					08 14	08 43
Minster [4]	d				06 07				07 07						07 44										08 49
Sandwich	d					05 54		06 30		06 59				07 26					08 09					08 26	
Deal	d					06 00		06 36		07 05				07 32					08 15					08 32	
Walmer	d					06 03		06 39		07 08				07 36					08 18					08 36	
Martin Mill	d					06 09		06 45		07 14				07 41					08 24					08 41	
Dover Priory [4]	a					06 17		06 53		07 22				07 50					08 32					08 50	
	d	04 44		05 43		06 18		06 54		07 23				07 50					08 33					08 50	
Folkestone Central	d	04 56		05 55		06 29		07 06		07 35				08 02					08 45					09 02	
Folkestone West	d	04 58		05 57		06 32		07 08						08 04										09 04	
Sandling	d	05 04		06 03		06 37		07 14						08 10										09 10	
Westenhanger	d	05 07		06 06		06 40		07 17						08 13										09 13	
Sturry	d				06 18				07 18						07 55										09 00
Canterbury West [4]	d				06 24				07 24						08 01			08 35							09 06
Chartham	d				06 29				07 29						08 07			08 40							
Chilham	d				06 33				07 33						08 11			08 44							
Wye	d				06 40				07 40						08 17			08 51							
Rye	d				*05 56*			*06 50*						*07 54*										*08 54*	
Ashford International	a	05 15		06 14	06 47	06 49		07 26	07 47	07 49				08 21	08 24			08 58	09 00					09 21	09 24
	d	05 21		06 20	06 52			07 26	07 52				08 20	08 28		08 57		09 04			09 20			09 28	
Maidstone East [4]	a	*06 29*			*07 29*			*07 57*	*08 34*					*08 57*				*09 34*						*09 57*	
Bromley South [4]	a	*07 14*			*08 14*				*09 14*									*10 14*							
London Victoria [15]	⊖ a	*07 32*			*08 32*				*09 32*							←		*10 32*							
Pluckley	d	05 28		06 27	06 59				07 59				08 27 →			08 27					09 27 →				
Headcorn [4]	d	05 34		06 33	07 06			07 37	08 06							08b40	09c14					←			
Staplehurst	d	05 39		06 38	07 11			07 42	08 11					08 41		08 45	09 19					09 19		09 41	
Marden	d	05 44		06 43	07 15				08 15							08 50	→								
Maidstone West [4]	d		06 24	*06 24*			07 24	*07 24*				08 24		*08 24*									09 24	*09 24*	
Paddock Wood [4]	d	05 50	06a44	06 49	07 21		07a44	07 50	08 21			08a44		08 49		08 56						09 28	09a44	09 49	
Tonbridge [4]	a	05 58		06 57	07 31			07 58	08 31					08 57		09 03		09 25				09 35		09 57	
	d	06 00		06 59	07 31			08 00	08 31					08 58		09 04		09 28				09 36		09 58	
Redhill	a	*07 23*		*08 04*				*08 39*						*09 39*				*10 04*						*10 39*	
Gatwick Airport [10]	✈ a	*07 34*		*08e23*				*08 55*						*09 55*				*10e23*						*10 55*	
Sevenoaks [4]	a	06 12		07 11	07 43			08 09	08 43							09 15						09 47			
Orpington [4]	a	06 21		07 20	07 53			08 19	08 53							09 25						09 57			
London Bridge [4]	⊖ a	06 40		07 39	08 10			08 38	09 08							09 43						10 13			
London Cannon Street [4]	⊖ a			*07 50*	*08 20*			*08 47*	*09 17*							*09 50*									
London Waterloo (East) [4]	⊖ a	06 44		07 43	08 14			08 43	09 14					09 32		09 48		10 02				10 18		10 32	
London Charing Cross [4]	⊖ a	06 48		07 47	08 18			08 48	09 18					09 36		09 51		10 06				10 21		10 36	

For general notes see front of timetable
For details of catering facilities see Directory of Train Operators

b Arr. 0834
c Arr. 0908
e Change at Tonbridge and Redhill

Saturdays

For details of Bank Holiday service alterations please see first page of Table 195

Margate, Ramsgate, Canterbury West, Dover, Folkestone, Ashford International, → Tonbridge and London

Network Diagram - see first page of Table 206

		SE	SE	SE	SE	SE		SE	SE	SE	SE	SE	SE	SE	SE		SE	SE	SE	SE	SE	SE	SE	SE	SE
		8	64	8	90	4		8	61	64	8	4	90	8	64		8	90	4	8	61	64	8	4	90
		[1]	[1]	[1]	[1]	[1]		[1]		[1]	[1]	[1]	[1]	[1]	[1]		[1]	[1]	[1]	[1]		[1]	[1]	[1]	[1]
					🛒	🛒						🛒						🛒	🛒					🛒	
Margate [4]	d				09 04							*08 48*						10 04	*09 41*						*10 15*
Broadstairs	d				09 09							*08 53*						10 09							
Dumpton Park	d				09 12							*08 56*						10 12							
Ramsgate [4] ✈	d				09 20	08 57						09 14	09 43					10 20	09 57					10 14	10 43
Minster [4]	d												09 49												10 49
Sandwich	d					09 09						09 26							10 09					10 26	
Deal	d					09 15						09 32							10 15					10 32	
Walmer	d					09 18						09 36							10 18					10 36	
Martin Mill	d					09 24						09 41							10 24					10 41	
Dover Priory [4] ⛴	a					09 32						09 50							10 32					10 50	
	d					09 33						09 50							10 33					10 50	
Folkestone Central	d					09 45						10 02							10 45					11 02	
Folkestone West	d											10 04												11 04	
Sandling	d											10 10												11 10	
Westenhanger	d											10 13												11 13	
Sturry	d												10 00												11 00
Canterbury West [4]	d		09 24		09 39								10 06		10 24			10 39							11 06
Chartham	d		09 29												10 29										
Chilham	d		09 33												10 33										
Wye	d		09 39												10 39										
Rye	d											*09 54*												*10 54*	
Ashford International	a		09 46		09 56	09 59						10 21	10 24		10 46			10 56	10 59					11 21	11 24
	d		10 05 →	09 57	10 03					← 10 05	10 20	10 28			11 05 →		10 57	11 03				← 11 05	11 20	11 28	
Maidstone East [4]	a				*10 34*					10 34		*10 57*						*11 34*				11 34		*11 57*	
Bromley South [4]	a				*11 14*					11 14								*12 14*				12 14			
London Victoria [15]	⊖ a	←			*11 32*					11 32				←				*12 32*				12 32			
Pluckley	d	09 27									10 27 →			10 27									11 27 →		
Headcorn [4]	d	09b40		10c14				←						10e40			11f14			←					
Staplehurst	d	09 45		10 19 →				10 19				10 41		10 45			11 19 →			11 19				11 41	
Marden	d	09 50												10 50											
Maidstone West [4]	d								10 24			*10 24*									11 24			*11 24*	
Paddock Wood [4]	d	09 56						10 28	10a44			10 49		10 56						11 28	11a44			11 49	
Tonbridge [4]	a	10 03			10 25			10 35				10 57		11 03				11 25		11 35				11 57	
	d	10 04			10 28			10 36				10 58		11 04				11 28		11 36				11 58	
Redhill	a				*11 04*							*11 39*						*12 04*						*12 39*	
Gatwick Airport [10] ✈	a				*11g23*							*11 55*						*12g23*						*12 55*	
Sevenoaks [4]	a	10 15						10 47						11 15						11 47					
Orpington [4]	a	10 25						10 57						11 25						11 57					
London Bridge [4]	⊖ a	10 43						11 13						11 43						12 13					
London Cannon Street [4]	⊖ a	*10 50*						*11 20*						*11 50*											
London Waterloo (East) [4]	⊖ a	10 48			11 02			11 18				11 32		11 48				12 02		12 18				12 32	
London Charing Cross [4]	⊖ a	10 51			11 06			11 21				11 36		11 51				12 06		12 21				12 36	

		SE	SE		SE	SE	SE	SE	SE	SE	SE	SE	SE		SE	SE	SE	SE	SE	SE	SE	SE		SE	
		8	64		8	90	4	8	61	64	8	4	90		8	64	8	90	4	8	61	64		8	
		[1]	[1]		[1]	[1]	[1]	[1]		[1]	[1]	[1]	[1]		[1]	[1]	[1]	[1]	[1]	[1]		[1]		[1]	
						🛒	🛒					🛒						🛒	🛒						
Margate [4]	d					11 04	*10 41*						*11 15*					12 04	*11 41*						
Broadstairs	d					11 09												12 09							
Dumpton Park	d					11 12												12 12							
Ramsgate [4] ✈	d					11 20	10 57					11 14	11 43					12 20	11 57						
Minster [4]	d												11 49												
Sandwich	d						11 09					11 26							12 09						
Deal	d						11 15					11 32							12 15						
Walmer	d						11 18					11 36							12 18						
Martin Mill	d						11 24					11 41							12 24						
Dover Priory [4] ⛴	a						11 32					11 50							12 32						
	d						11 33					11 50							12 33						
Folkestone Central	d						11 45					12 02							12 45						
Folkestone West	d											12 04													
Sandling	d											12 10													
Westenhanger	d											12 13													
Sturry	d												12 00												
Canterbury West [4]	d		11 24			11 39							12 06			12 24		12 39							
Chartham	d		11 29													12 29									
Chilham	d		11 33													12 33									
Wye	d		11 39													12 39									
Rye	d											*11 54*													
Ashford International	a		11 46			11 56	11 59					12 21	12 24			12 46		12 56	12 59						
	d		12 05 →		11 57	12 03				← 12 05	12 20	12 28				13 05 →	12 57	13 03				← 13 05		13 20	
Maidstone East [4]	a					*12 34*				12 34		*12 57*						*13 34*				13 34			
Bromley South [4]	a					*13 14*				13 14								*14 14*				14 14			
London Victoria [15]	⊖ a	←				*13 32*				13 32					←			*14 32*				14 32			
Pluckley	d	11 27									12 27 →				12 27									13 27 →	
Headcorn [4]	d	11h40			12j14			←							12k40		13m14			←					
Staplehurst	d	11 45			12 19 →			12 19				12 41			12 45		13 19 →			13 19					
Marden	d	11 50													12 50										
Maidstone West [4]	d								12 24			*12 24*									13 24				
Paddock Wood [4]	d	11 56						12 28	12a44			12 49			12 56					13 28	13a44				
Tonbridge [4]	a	12 03				12 25		12 35				12 57			13 03			13 25		13 35					
	d	12 04				12 28		12 36				12 58			13 04			13 28		13 36					
Redhill	a					*13 04*						*13 39*						*14 04*							
Gatwick Airport [10] ✈	a					*13g23*						*13 55*						*14g23*							
Sevenoaks [4]	a	12 15						12 47							13 15					13 47					
Orpington [4]	a	12 25						12 57							13 25					13 57					
London Bridge [4]	⊖ a	12 43						13 13							13 43					14 13					
London Cannon Street [4]	⊖ a																								
London Waterloo (East) [4]	⊖ a	12 48				13 02		13 18				13 32			13 48			14 02		14 18					
London Charing Cross [4]	⊖ a	12 51				13 06		13 21				13 36			13 51			14 06		14 21					

For general notes see front of timetable
For details of catering facilities see Directory of Train Operators

b Arr. 0934
c Arr. 1008
e Arr. 1034
f Arr. 1108
g Change at Tonbridge and Redhill
h Arr. 1134
j Arr. 1208
k Arr. 1234
m Arr. 1308

Table 207

For details of Bank Holiday service alterations please see first page of Table 195

Margate, Ramsgate, Canterbury West, Dover, Folkestone, Ashford International, → Tonbridge and London

Network Diagram - see first page of Table 206

		SE	SE	SE	SE	SE	SE	SE	SE		SE	SE	SE	SE	SE	SE	SE	SE		SE	SE	SE	SE	SE	SE
		4	90	8	64	8	90	4	8		61	64	8	4	90	8	64	8		90	4	8	61	64	8
		1	1	1	1	1	1	1	1			1	1	1	1	1	1	1		1	1	1		1	1
		⌶					⌶	⌶						⌶						⌶	⌶				
Margate 4	d		12 15				13 04	12 41							13 15					14 04	13 41				
Broadstairs	d						13 09													14 09					
Dumpton Park	d						13 12													14 12					
Ramsgate 4 ✈	d	12 14	12 43				13 20	12 57						13 14	13 43					14 20	13 57				
Minster 4	d		12 49												13 49										
Sandwich	d	12 26						13 09						13 26							14 09				
Deal	d	12 32						13 15						13 32							14 15				
Walmer	d	12 36						13 18						13 36							14 18				
Martin Mill	d	12 41						13 24						13 41							14 24				
Dover Priory 4 ⛴	a	12 50						13 32						13 50							14 32				
	d	12 50						13 33						13 50							14 33				
Folkestone Central	d	13 02						13 45						14 02							14 45				
Folkestone West	d	13 04												14 04											
Sandling	d	13 10												14 10											
Westenhanger	d	13 13												14 13											
Sturry	d		13 00												14 00										
Canterbury West 4	d		13 06		13 24		13 39								14 06		14 24			14 39					
Chartham	d				13 29												14 29								
Chilham	d				13 33												14 33								
Wye	d				13 39												14 39								
Rye	d	12 54												13 54											
Ashford International	a	13 21	13 24		13 46		13 56	13 59						14 21	14 24		14 46			14 56	14 59				
	d	13 28			14 05 →	13 57	14 03					← 14 05	14 20	14 28			15 05 →	14 57		15 03				← 15 05	15 20
Maidstone East 4	a	13 57					14 34					14 34		14 57						15 34				15 34	
Bromley South 4	a						15 14					15 14								16 14				16 14	
London Victoria 15 ⊖	a			←			15 32					15 32				←				16 32				16 32	
Pluckley	d			13 27									14 27 →			14 27									15 27 →
Headcorn 4	d			13b40		14c14			←							14e40		15f14				←			
Staplehurst	d	13 41		13 45		14 19 →			14 19					14 41		14 45		15 19 →				15 19			
Marden	d			13 50												14 50									
Maidstone West 4	d	13 24									14 24			14 24									15 24		
Paddock Wood 4	d	13 49		13 56					14 28		14a44			14 49		14 56						15 28	15a44		
Tonbridge 4	a	13 57		14 03			14 25		14 35					14 57		15 03				15 25		15 35			
	d	13 58		14 04			14 28		14 36					14 58		15 04				15 28		15 36			
Redhill	a	14 39					15 04							15 39						16 04					
Gatwick Airport 10 ✈	a	14 55					15g23							15 55						16g23					
Sevenoaks 4	a			14 15					14 47							15 15						15 47			
Orpington 4	a			14 25					14 57							15 25						15 57			
London Bridge 4 ⊖	a			14 43					15 13							15 43						16 13			
London Cannon Street 4 ⊖	a																								
London Waterloo (East) 4 ⊖	a	14 32		14 48			15 02		15 18					15 32		15 48				16 02		16 18			
London Charing Cross 4 ⊖	a	14 36		14 51			15 06		15 21					15 36		15 51				16 06		16 21			

		SE	SE	SE	SE		SE	SE	SE	SE	SE	SE	SE	SE	SE		SE	SE	SE	SE	SE	SE	SE	SE	SE
		4	90	8	64		8	90	4	8	61	64	8	4	90		8	64	8	90	4	8	64	4	90
		1	1	1	1		1	1	1	1		1	1	1	1		1	1	1	1	1	1	1	1	1
		⌶						⌶	⌶					⌶						⌶	⌶			⌶	
Margate 4	d		14 15					15 04	14 41						15 15					16 04				15 41	
Broadstairs	d							15 09												16 09				15 46	
Dumpton Park	d							15 12												16 12					
Ramsgate 4 ✈	d	14 14	14 43					15 20	14 57					15 14	15 43					16 20	15 50			16 01	16 25
Minster 4	d		14 49												15 49										16 31
Sandwich	d	14 26							15 09					15 26							16 02			16 13	
Deal	d	14 32							15 15					15 32							16 08			16 19	
Walmer	d	14 36							15 18					15 36							16 11			16 22	
Martin Mill	d	14 41							15 24					15 41							16 17			16 28	
Dover Priory 4 ⛴	a	14 50							15 32					15 50							16 25			16 36	
	d	14 50							15 33					15 50							16 28			16 37	
Folkestone Central	d	15 02							15 45					16 02							16 39			16 49	
Folkestone West	d	15 04												16 04							16 42				
Sandling	d	15 10												16 10							16 48				
Westenhanger	d	15 13												16 13							16 51				
Sturry	d		15 00												16 00										16 42
Canterbury West 4	d		15 06		15 24			15 39							16 06			16 24		16 39					16 48
Chartham	d				15 29													16 29							
Chilham	d				15 33													16 33							
Wye	d				15 39													16 39							
Rye	d	14 54												15 54											
Ashford International	a	15 21	15 24		15 46			15 56	15 59					16 21	16 24			16 46		16 56	16 59			17 02	17 05
	d	15 28			16 05 →		15 57	16 03				← 16 05	16 20	16 28				17 05 →	16 57	17 03			← 17 05	17 09	
Maidstone East 4	a	15 57						16 34				16 34		16 57						17 34			17 34	17 57	
Bromley South 4	a							17 14				17 14								18 14			18 14		
London Victoria 15 ⊖	a			←				17 32				17 32					←			18 32			18 32		
Pluckley	d			15 27									16 27 →				16 27							17 16	
Headcorn 4	d			15h40			16j14			←							16k40		17m14			←		17 23	
Staplehurst	d	15 41		15 45			16 19 →			16 19				16 41			16 45		17 19 →			17 19		17 28	
Marden	d			15 50													16 50							17 32	
Maidstone West 4	d	15 24									16 24			16 24											
Paddock Wood 4	d	15 49		15 56						16 28	16a44			16 49			16 56					17 28		17 38	
Tonbridge 4	a	15 57		16 03				16 25		16 35				16 57			17 03			17 25		17 35		17 48	
	d	15 58		16 04				16 28		16 36				16 58			17 04			17 28		17 36		17 48	
Redhill	a	16 39						17 04						17 39						18 04				18 23	
Gatwick Airport 10 ✈	a	16 55						17g23						17 55						18g23				18 34	
Sevenoaks 4	a			16 15						16 47							17 15					17 47		18 00	
Orpington 4	a			16 25						16 57							17 25					17 57		18 10	
London Bridge 4 ⊖	a			16 43						17 13							17 43					18 13		18 28	
London Cannon Street 4 ⊖	a																					18 20		18 54	
London Waterloo (East) 4 ⊖	a	16 32		16 48				17 02		17 18				17 32			17 48			18 02		18 18		18 32	
London Charing Cross 4 ⊖	a	16 36		16 51				17 06		17 21				17 36			17 51			18 06		18 21		18 36	

For general notes see front of timetable
For details of catering facilities see Directory of Train Operators

b Arr. 1334
c Arr. 1408
e Arr. 1434
f Arr. 1508
g Change at Tonbridge and Redhill
h Arr. 1534
j Arr. 1608
k Arr. 1634
m Arr. 1708

Table 207

Saturdays

For details of Bank Holiday service alterations please see first page of Table 195

Margate, Ramsgate, Canterbury West, Dover, Folkestone, Ashford International, → Tonbridge and London

Network Diagram - see first page of Table 206

		SE 61	SE 64 1		SE 4 1 ⚓	SE 61	SE 64 1	SE 90 1	SE 4 1	SE 61	SE 90 1	SE 4 1		SE 61	SE 90 1	SE 4 1	SE 90 1	SE 90 1	SE 4 1	SE 01 1	SE 4 1		SE 01 1	SE 61 1	
Margate 4	d				16 15			17 15			18 15				19 15		20 15		20 15	21 24			21 47	22 17	
Broadstairs	d				16 20			17 20			18 20				19 20		20 20			21 29	20 52		21 52	22 22	
Dumpton Park	d				16 23			17 23			18 23				19 23		20 23			21 32	20 54		21 54	22 25	
Ramsgate 4 ✈	d				16 43			17 39	17 43		18 39	18 43			19 39	19 43	20 39	21 00	20 35	21 36	21 29		22 20	22 32	
Minster 4	d							17 45			18 45				19 45		20 45	21 06		21 42			22 26		
Sandwich	d				16 55				17 55			18 55				19 55			20 47		21 41			22 44	
Deal	d				17 01				18 01			19 01				20 01			20 53		21 47			22 50	
Walmer	d				17 04				18 04			19 04				20 04			20 56		21 50			22 53	
Martin Mill	d				17 10				18 10			19 10				20 10			21 02		21 56			22 59	
Dover Priory 4 ⛴	a				17 18				18 18			19 18				20 18			21 12		22 04			23 07	
	d				17 19				18 19			19 19				20 19			21 15		22 05			23 08	
Folkestone Central	d				17 31				18 31			19 31				20 31			21 27		22 16			23 19	
Folkestone West	d				17 33				18 33			19 33				20 33			21 29		22 19			23 22	
Sandling	d				17 39				18 39			19 39				20 39			21 35		22 24			23 27	
Westenhanger	d				17 42				18 42			19 42				20 42			21 38		22 27			23 30	
Sturry	d							17 56			18 56				19 56		20 56	21 17		21 53			22 37		
Canterbury West 4	d		17 24					18b04			19c04				20e04		21f04	21 23		21 59			22 43		
Chartham	d		17 29					18 10			19 10				20 10		21 10	21 28		22 05			22 49		
Chilham	d		17 33					18 14			19 14				20 14		21 14	21 32		22 09			22 53		
Wye	d		17 39					18 20			19 20				20 20		21 20	21 39		22 15			22 59		
Rye	d				16 54			17 54			18 54				19 54		20 54				21 57				
Ashford International	a		17 46		17 50			18 28	18 50		19 28	19 50			20 28	20 50	21 28	21 46	21 47	22 22	22 36		23 06	23 39	
	d		18 00		17 51		← 18 00	18 28	18 51		19 28	19 51			20 28	20 51	21 28		21 51		22 36				
Maidstone East 4	a		→		18 29		18 29		19 29			20 29				21 29			22 29						
Bromley South 4	a				19 14		19 14		20 14			21 14				22 14			23 14						
London Victoria 15 ⊖	a				19 32		19 32		20 32			21 32				22 32			23 32						
Pluckley	d				17 58				18 58			19 58				20 58			21 58		22 43				
Headcorn 4	d				18 04			18 39	19 04		19 39	20 04			20 39	21 04	21 39		22 04		22 50				
Staplehurst	d				18 09			18 44	19 09		19 44	20 09			20 44	21 09	21 44		22 09		22 55				
Marden	d				18 14				19 14			20 14				21 14			22 14		22 59				
Maidstone West 4	d	17 24			17 24	18 24		18 24		19 24	19 24			20 24	20 24										
Paddock Wood 4	d	17a44			18 20	18a44		18 52	19 20	19a44	19 52	20 20		20a44	20 52	21 20	21 52		22 20		23 05				
Tonbridge 4	a				18 28			18 59	19 28		19 59	20 28			20 59	21 28	21 59		22 28		23 13				
	d				18 30			19 00	19 30		20 00	20 30			21 00	21 30	22 00		22 30		23 13				
Redhill	a				19 23				20 23			21 23				22 23			23 49						
Gatwick Airport 10 ✈	a				19 34				20 34			21 34				22 34			00g10						
Sevenoaks 4	a				18 42			19 09	19 42		20 09	20 42			21 09	21 42	22 09		22 42		23 25				
Orpington 4	a				18 51			19 19	19 51		20 19	20 51			21 19	21 51	22 19		22 51		23 37				
London Bridge 4 ⊖	a				19 08			19 38	20 08		20 38	21 08			21 38	22 08	22 38		23 08		23 53				
London Cannon Street 4 ⊖	a																								
London Waterloo (East) 4 ⊖	a				19 14			19 44	20 14		20 44	21 14			21 44	22 14	22 44		23 13		23 57				
London Charing Cross 4 ⊖	a				19 19			19 49	20 19		20 49	21 19			21 49	22 19	22 49		23 18		00 01				

For general notes see front of timetable
For details of catering facilities see Directory of Train Operators

b Arr. 1801
c Arr. 1901
e Arr. 2001
f Arr. 2101
g Change at Tonbridge and Redhill

Table 207

Sundays

Margate, Ramsgate, Canterbury West, Dover, Folkestone, Ashford International, → Tonbridge and London

Network Diagram - see first page of Table 206

		SE	SE	SE	SE	SE	SE	SE	SE	SE	SE	SE	SE	SE	SE	SE	SE	SE	SE	SE	SE	SE
		8	55	8	55	4	55	90	55	4	55	90	55	4	55	90	55	4	55	90	55	4
		1		1		1		1		1		1		1		1		1		1		1
			A		A		B		B		B		B		B		B		B		B	
Margate 4	d											08 16		*08 16*		09 16		*09 16*		10 16		*10 16*
Broadstairs	d											08 21		*08 21*		09 21		*09 21*		10 21		*10 21*
Dumpton Park	d											08 23				09 23				10 23		
Ramsgate 4 ✈	d					06 43		07 30		07 43		08 30		08 43		09 30		09 43		10 30		10 43
Minster 4	d							07 36				08 36				09 36				10 36		
Sandwich	d					06 55				07 55				08 55				09 55				10 55
Deal	d					07 01				08 01				09 01				10 01				11 01
Walmer	d					07 04				08 04				09 04				10 04				11 04
Martin Mill	d					07 09				08 09				09 09				10 09				11 09
Dover Priory 4 ⛴	a					07 18				08 18				09 18				10 18				11 18
	d					07 18				08 18				09 18				10 18				11 18
Folkestone Central	d					07 30				08 30				09 30				10 30				11 30
Folkestone West	d					07 33				08 33				09 33				10 33				11 33
Sandling	d					07 38				08 38				09 38				10 38				11 38
Westenhanger	d					07 41				08 41				09 41				10 41				11 41
Sturry	d							07 47				08 47				09 47				10 47		
Canterbury West 4	d							07 52				08 52				09 52				10 52		
Chartham	d							07 57				08 57				09 57				10 57		
Chilham	d							08 01				09 01				10 01				11 01		
Wye	d							08 07				09 07				10 07				11 07		
Rye	d							*07 43*				*08 41*				*09 46*				*10 46*		
Ashford International	a					07 50		08 14		08 50		09 14		09 50		10 14		10 50		11 14		11 50
	d	06 44		07 14		07 52		08 15		08 52		09 15		09 52		10 15		10 52		11 15		11 52
Maidstone East 4	a							*08 58*				*09 58*				*10 58*				*11 58*		
Bromley South 4	a							*09 44*				*10 44*				*11 44*				*12 44*		
London Victoria 15 ⊖	a							*10 01*				*11 01*				*12 01*				*13 01*		
Pluckley	d	06 51		07 21				08 22				09 22				10 22				11 22		
Headcorn 4	d	06 57		07 27				08 28				09 28				10 28				11 28		
Staplehurst	d	07 02		07 32		08 06		08 33		09 06		09 33		10 06		10 33		11 06		11 33		12 06
Marden	d	07 06		07 36				08 37				09 37				10 37				11 37		
Maidstone West 4	d		07 18	*07 18*			08 14	*08 14*			09 14	*09 14*			10 14	*10 14*			11 14	*11 14*		
Paddock Wood 4	d	07 12	07 38	07 42		08 14	08 35	08 43		09 14	09 35	09 43		10 14	10 35	10 43		11 14	11 35	11 43		12 14
Tonbridge 4	a	07 19	07 46	07 49	←	08 22	08 43	08 50	←	09 22	09 42	09 50	←	10 22	10 42	10 50	←	11 22	11 42	11 50	←	12 22
	d	07 20	07 54	07 50	07 54	08 22	08 54	08 51	08 54	09 22	09 54	09 51	09 54	10 22	10 54	10 51	10 54	11 22	11 54	11 51	11 54	12 22
Redhill	a		→	*08 24*	08 24		→	*09 24*	09 24		→	*10 25*	10 25		→	*11 25*	11 25		→	*12 25*	12 25	
Gatwick Airport 10 ✈	a			*08 38*	08 38			*09 38*	09 38			*10 38*	10 38			*11 38*	11 38			*12 38*	12 38	
Sevenoaks 4	a	07 31		08 01		08 32		09 02		09 32		10 02		10 32		11 02		11 32		12 02		12 32
Orpington 4	a	07 42		08 12		08 42		09 12		09 42		10 12		10 42		11 12		11 42		12 12		12 42
London Bridge 4 ⊖	a	07 58		08 28		08 58		09 28		09 58		10 28		10 58		11 28		11 58		12 28		12 58
London Cannon Street 4 ⊖	a																					
London Waterloo (East) 4 ⊖	a	08 03		08 33		09 03		09 33		10 03		10 33		11 03		11 33		12 03		12 33		13 03
London Charing Cross 4 ⊖	a	08 07		08 37		09 07		09 37		10 07		10 37		11 07		11 37		12 07		12 37		13 07

For general notes see front of timetable
For details of catering facilities see Directory of Train Operators

A From Gillingham (Kent) (Table 208) to Three Bridges (Table 186)

B To Three Bridges (Table 186)

Table 207

Sundays

Margate, Ramsgate, Canterbury West, Dover, Folkestone, Ashford International, → Tonbridge and London

Network Diagram - see first page of Table 206

		SE	SE	SE	SE	SE	SE	SE	SE	SE	SE	SE	SE	SE	SE	SE	SE	SE	SE	SE	SE	SE
		55	90	55	4	55	90	55	4	55	90	55	4	55	90	55	4	55	90	55	4	55
			1		1		1		1		1		1		1		1		1		1	
		A		A		A		A		A		A		A		A		A		A		A
Margate 4	d		11 16		*11 16*		12 16		*12 16*		13 16		*13 16*		14 16		*14 16*		15 16		*15 16*	
Broadstairs	d		11 21		*11 21*		12 21		*12 21*		13 21		*13 21*		14 21		*14 21*		15 21		*15 21*	
Dumpton Park	d		11 23				12 23				13 23				14 23				15 23			
Ramsgate 4	d		11 30		11 43		12 30		12 43		13 30		13 43		14 30		14 43		15 30		15 43	
Minster 4	d		11 36				12 36				13 36				14 36				15 36			
Sandwich	d				11 55				12 55				13 55				14 55				15 55	
Deal	d				12 01				13 01				14 01				15 01				16 01	
Walmer	d				12 04				13 04				14 04				15 04				16 04	
Martin Mill	d				12 09				13 09				14 09				15 09				16 09	
Dover Priory 4	a				12 18				13 18				14 18				15 18				16 18	
	d				12 18				13 18				14 18				15 18				16 18	
Folkestone Central	d				12 30				13 30				14 30				15 30				16 30	
Folkestone West	d				12 33				13 33				14 33				15 33				16 33	
Sandling	d				12 38				13 38				14 38				15 38				16 38	
Westenhanger	d				12 41				13 41				14 41				15 41				16 41	
Sturry	d		11 47				12 47				13 47				14 47				15 47			
Canterbury West 4	d		11 52				12 52				13 52				14 52				15 52			
Chartham	d		11 57				12 57				13 57				14 57				15 57			
Chilham	d		12 01				13 01				14 01				15 01				16 01			
Wye	d		12 07				13 07				14 07				15 07				16 07			
Rye	d		*11 46*				*12 46*				*13 46*				*14 46*				*15 46*			
Ashford International	a		12 14		12 50		13 14		13 50		14 14		14 50		15 14		15 50		16 14		16 50	
	d		12 15		12 52		13 15		13 52		14 15		14 52		15 15		15 52		16 15		16 52	
Maidstone East 4	a		*12 58*				*13 58*				*14 58*				*15 58*				*16 58*			
Bromley South 4	a		*13 44*				*14 44*				*15 44*				*16 44*				*17 44*			
London Victoria 15 ⊖	a		*14 01*				*15 01*				*16 01*				*17 01*				*18 01*			
Pluckley	d		12 22				13 22				14 22				15 22				16 22			
Headcorn 4	d		12 28				13 28				14 28				15 28				16 28			
Staplehurst	d		12 33		13 06		13 33		14 06		14 33		15 06		15 33		16 06		16 33		17 06	
Marden	d		12 37				13 37				14 37				15 37				16 37			
Maidstone West 4	d	12 14	*12 14*			13 14	*13 14*			14 14	*14 14*			15 14	*15 14*			16 14	*16 14*			17 14
Paddock Wood 4	d	12 35	12 43		13 14	13 35	13 43		14 14	14 35	14 43		15 14	15 35	15 43		16 14	16 35	16 43		17 14	17 35
Tonbridge 4	a	12 42	12 50	←	13 22	13 42	13 50	←	14 22	14 42	14 50	←	15 22	15 42	15 50	←	16 22	16 42	16 50	←	17 22	17 42
	d	12 54	12 51	12 54	13 22	13 54	13 51	13 54	14 22	14 54	14 51	14 54	15 22	15 54	15 51	15 54	16 22	16 54	16 51	16 54	17 22	17 54
Redhill	a	→	*13 25*	13 25		→	*14 25*	14 25		→	*15 25*	15 25		→	*16 25*	16 25		→	*17 25*	17 25		→
Gatwick Airport 10	a		*13 38*	13 38			*14 38*	14 38			*15 38*	15 38			*16 38*	16 38			*17 38*	17 38		
Sevenoaks 4	a		13 02		13 32		14 02		14 32		15 02		15 32		16 02		16 32		17 02		17 32	
Orpington 4	a		13 12		13 42		14 12		14 42		15 12		15 42		16 12		16 42		17 12		17 42	
London Bridge 4 ⊖	a		13 28		13 58		14 28		14 58		15 28		15 58		16 28		16 58		17 28		17 58	
London Cannon Street 4 ⊖	a																					
London Waterloo (East) 4 ⊖	a		13 33		14 03		14 33		15 03		15 33		16 03		16 33		17 03		17 33		18 03	
London Charing Cross 4 ⊖	a		13 37		14 07		14 37		15 07		15 37		16 07		16 37		17 07		17 37		18 07	

		SE	SE	SE	SE	SE	SE	SE	SE	SE	SE	SE	SE	SE	SE	SE	SE	SE	SE	SE	SE
		90	55	4	55	90	55	4	55	90	55	4	55	90	55	4	61	90	90	4	4
		1		1		1		1		1		1		1		1		1	1	1	1
			A		A		A		A		A		A		A						
Margate 4	d	16 16		*16 16*		17 16		*17 16*		18 16		*18 16*		19 16		*19 16*		20 16	20 40		21 23
Broadstairs	d	16 21		*16 21*		17 21		*17 21*		18 21		*18 21*		19 21		*19 21*		20 21	20 45		21 28
Dumpton Park	d	16 23				17 23				18 23				19 23				20 23	20 47		21 30
Ramsgate 4	d	16 30		16 43		17 30		17 43		18 30		18 43		19 30		19 43		20 30	20 51	20 34	21 34
Minster 4	d	16 36				17 36				18 36				19 36				20 36	20 57		
Sandwich	d			16 55				17 55				18 55				19 55				20 46	21 46
Deal	d			17 01				18 01				19 01				20 01				20 52	21 52
Walmer	d			17 04				18 04				19 04				20 04				20 55	21 55
Martin Mill	d			17 09				18 09				19 09				20 09				21 00	22 00
Dover Priory 4	a			17 18				18 18				19 18				20 18				21 09	22 09
	d			17 18				18 18				19 18				20 18				21 09	22 09
Folkestone Central	d			17 30				18 30				19 30				20 30				21 21	22 21
Folkestone West	d			17 33				18 33				19 33				20 33				21 24	22 24
Sandling	d			17 38				18 38				19 38				20 38				21 29	22 29
Westenhanger	d			17 41				18 41				19 41				20 41				21 32	22 32
Sturry	d	16 47				17 47				18 47				19 47				20 47	21 08		
Canterbury West 4	d	16 52				17 52				18 52				19 52				20 52	21 13		
Chartham	d	16 57				17 57				18 57				19 57				20 57	21 18		
Chilham	d	17 01				18 01				19 01				20 01				21 01	21 22		
Wye	d	17 07				18 07				19 07				20 07				21 07	21 28		
Rye	d	*16 46*				*17 46*				*18 46*				*19 46*				*20 46*			
Ashford International	a	17 14		17 50		18 14		18 50		19 14		19 50		20 14		20 50		21 14	21 35	21 41	22 41
	d	17 15		17 52		18 15		18 52		19 15		19 52		20 15		20 52		21 15	21 45		
Maidstone East 4	a	*17 58*				*18 58*				*19 58*				*20 58*				*21 58*			
Bromley South 4	a	*18 44*				*19 44*				*20 44*				*21 44*				*22 44*			
London Victoria 15 ⊖	a	*19 01*				*20 01*				*21 01*				*22 01*				*23 01*			
Pluckley	d	17 22				18 22				19 22				20 22				21 22	21 52		
Headcorn 4	d	17 28				18 28				19 28				20 28				21 28	21 58		
Staplehurst	d	17 33		18 06		18 33		19 06		19 33		20 06		20 33		21 06		21 33	22 03		
Marden	d	17 37				18 37				19 37				20 37				21 37	22 07		
Maidstone West 4	d	*17 14*			18 14	*18 14*			19 14	*19 14*			20 14	*20 14*			21 14	*21 14*			
Paddock Wood 4	d	17 43		18 14	18 35	18 43		19 14	19 35	19 43		20 14	20 35	20 43		21 14	21 35	21 43	22 13		
Tonbridge 4	a	17 50	←	18 22	18 42	18 50	←	19 22	19 42	19 50	←	20 22	20 42	20 50	←	21 22	21 42	21 50	22 20		
	d	17 51	17 54	18 22	18 54	18 51	18 54	19 22	19 54	19 51	19 54	20 22	20 54	20 51	20 54	21 22		21 51	22 21		
Redhill	a	*18 25*	18 25		→	*19 25*	19 25		→	*20 25*	20 25		→	*21 25*	21 25						
Gatwick Airport 10	a	*18 38*	18 38			*19 38*	19 38			*20 38*	20 38			*21 38*	21 38						
Sevenoaks 4	a	18 02		18 32		19 02		19 32		20 02		20 32		21 02		21 32		22 02	22 32		
Orpington 4	a	18 12		18 42		19 12		19 42		20 12		20 42		21 12		21 42		22 12	22 42		
London Bridge 4 ⊖	a	18 28		18 58		19 28		19 58		20 28		20 58		21 28		21 58		22 28	22 58		
London Cannon Street 4 ⊖	a																				
London Waterloo (East) 4 ⊖	a	18 33		19 03		19 33		20 03		20 33		21 03		21 33		22 03		22 33	23 03		
London Charing Cross 4 ⊖	a	18 37		19 07		19 37		20 07		20 37		21 07		21 37		22 07		22 37	23 06		

For general notes see front of timetable
For details of catering facilities see
Directory of Train Operators

A To Three Bridges (Table 186)

For details of Bank Holiday service alterations please see first page of Table 195

Strood → Maidstone West and Paddock Wood

Network Diagram - see first page of Table 206

Miles			SE 55 A	SE 61	SE 61	SE 61	SE 01	SE 13 B	SE 01	SE 61	SE 01	SE 61	SE 01	SE 61	SE 01	SE 61	SE 01	SE 61
—	**London Charing Cross**	⊖ d			04b56	06 02	06 20	06 40	07 20				09 20	09 52	10 20	10 50	11 20	11 50
—	**London Waterloo (East)**	⊖ d			04b59	06 05	06 23	06 43	07 23				09 23	09 55	10 23	10 53	11 23	11 53
—	**London Cannon Street**	⊖ d				05c50	06 12	06c30	07c04	07 54	08 17	08 50	09c20	09c48	10c18	10c48	11c18	11c48
—	**London Bridge**	⊖ d																
—	Greenhithe for Bluewater	d		05 11	05b48	06 26	07 12	07 33	08 12	08 39	09 07	09 39	10 09	10 39	11 09	11 39	12 09	12 39
—	Gravesend	d		05 18	05b56	06 56	07 20	07 40	08 20	08 46	09 14	09 46	10 16	10 46	11 16	11 46	12 16	12 46
—	Gillingham (Kent)	d	04 56	05 22	06 03	06 53	07 13	07 33	08 15		09 14	09 44	10 14	10 44	11 14	11 44	12 14	12 44
0	**Strood**	d	05 09	05 40	06 18	07 12	07 35	07 55	08 34	09 01	09 34	10 01	10 31	11 01	11 31	12 01	12 31	13 01
2¼	Cuxton	d		05 44	06 22	07 16	07 39	07 59	08 38	09 05	09 38	10 05	10 35	11 05	11 35	12 05	12 35	13 05
4	Halling	d		05 47	06 25	07 19	07 42	08 02	08 41	09 08	09 41	10 08	10 38	11 08	11 38	12 08	12 38	13 08
5½	Snodland	d	05 16	05 50	06 28	07 22	07 45	08 06	08 44	09 11	09 44	10 11	10 41	11 11	11 41	12 11	12 41	13 11
7	New Hythe	d	05 18	05 53	06 31	07 25	07 48	08 08	08 47	09 14	09 47	10 14	10 44	11 14	11 44	12 14	12 44	13 14
7¾	Aylesford	d	05 21	05 55	06 33	07 27	07 50	08 11	08 49	09 16	09 49	10 16	10 46	11 16	11 46	12 16	12 46	13 16
11	Maidstone Barracks	d	05 26	06 00	06 38	07 32	07 55	08 16	08 54	09 21	09 54	10 21	10 51	11 21	11 51	12 21	12 51	13 21
11¼	**Maidstone West**	a	05 28	06 02	06 40	07 34	07 57	08 18	08 56	09 23	09 56	10 23	10 53	11 23	11 53	12 23	12 53	13 23
—		d	05 28	06 06	06 42	07 39		08 19		09 25		10 24		11 24		12 24		13 24
13	East Farleigh	d	05 32	06 10	06 46	07 43		08 23		09 29		10 28		11 28		12 28		13 28
16	Wateringbury	d	05 38	06 15	06 51	07 48		08 28		09 34		10 33		11 33		12 33		13 33
17¾	Yalding	d	05 41	06 18	06 54	07 51		08 31		09 37		10 36		11 36		12 36		13 36
19½	Beltring	d	05 44	06 22	06 58	07 55		08 35		09 41		10 40		11 40		12 40		13 40
21¼	**Paddock Wood**	a	05 49	06 26	07 02	07 59		08 39		09 45		10 44		11 44		12 44		13 44
26½	Tonbridge	a	05 56	06 44	07 16	08 16		08 49		09 57		10 57		11 57		12 57		13 57
—	**London Bridge**	⊖ a	06 36	07 21	07 54	08 54		09 51		11 13		11 43		12 43		13 43		14 43
—	**London Cannon Street**	⊖ a	06e47	07f31	08 00	09 01		10e01		11f27		11f54		12f54		13f54		14f54
—	**London Waterloo (East)**	⊖ a	06 41	07 27	08 04	09 01		09 57		10 32		11 32		12 32		13 32		14 32
—	**London Charing Cross**	⊖ a	06 46	07 32	08 09	09 07		10 01		10 36		11 36		12 36		13 36		14 36

		SE 01	SE 61	SE 01	SE 61	SE 61	SE 61	SE 61	SE 61	SE 61	SE 01	SE 61	SE 01	SE 61	SE 01	SE 61	SE 01	SE 01
London Charing Cross	⊖ d	12 20	12 50	13 20	13 50	14 20	14 50	15 50	16 21	16 48	17 32	17 52	18 20	18 54	19 21	19 50	20 20	21 20
London Waterloo (East)	⊖ d	12 23	12 53	13 23	13 53	14 23	14 53	15 53	16 24	16 51	17 35	17 55	18 23	18 57	19 24	19 53	20 23	21 23
London Cannon Street	⊖ d	12c18	12c48	13c18	13c48	14c18	14c48	15c48	16c18	17 02	17 26	18 08		18c50	19c18	19c48	20c15	21c00
London Bridge	⊖ d																	
Greenhithe for Bluewater	d	13 09	13 39	14 09	14 39	15 09	15 39	16 41	17 11	17 45	18 15	18 53	19 05	19 45	20 11	20 40	21 09	22 09
Gravesend	d	13 16	13 46	14 16	14 46	15 16	15 46	16 48	17 18	17 52	18 22	19 00	19 12	19 52	20 18	20 50	21 16	22 16
Gillingham (Kent)	d	13 14	13 44	14 14	14 44	15 14	15 44	16 44	17 14	17 48	18 12	18 44	19 14	19 44	20 16	20 42	21 14	22 22
Strood	d	13 31	14 01	14 31	15 01	15 31	16 12	17 06	17 36	18 08	18 42	19 16	19 34	20 11	20 34	21 07	21 34	22 35
Cuxton	d	13 35	14 05	14 35	15 05	15 35	16 16	17 10	17 40	18 12	18 46	19 20	19 38	20 15	20 38	21 11	21 38	22 39
Halling	d	13 38	14 08	14 38	15 08	15 38	16 19	17 13	17 43	18 15	18 49	19 23	19 41	20 18	20 41	21 14	21 41	22 42
Snodland	d	13 41	14 11	14 41	15 11	15 41	16 22	17 16	17 46	18 18	18 52	19 26	19 44	20 21	20 44	21 17	21 44	22 45
New Hythe	d	13 44	14 14	14 44	15 14	15 44	16 25	17 19	17 49	18 21	18 55	19 29	19 47	20 24	20 47	21 20	21 47	22 48
Aylesford	d	13 46	14 16	14 46	15 16	15 46	16 27	17 21	17 51	18 23	18 57	19 31	19 49	20 26	20 49	21 22	21 49	22 50
Maidstone Barracks	d	13 51	14 21	14 51	15 21	15 51	16 32	17 26	17 56	18 28	19 02	19 36	19 54	20 31	20 54	21 27	21 54	22 55
Maidstone West	a	13 53	14 23	14 53	15 23	15 53	16 34	17 28	17 58	18 30	19 04	19 38	19 56	20 33	20 56	21 29	21 56	22 57
	d		14 24		15 24	15 55	16 38	17 29	17 59	18 31		19 39		20 35		21 32		
East Farleigh	d		14 28		15 28	15 59	16 42	17 33	18 03	18 35		19 43		20 39		21 36		
Wateringbury	d		14 33		15 33	16 04	16 47	17 38	18 08	18 40		19 48		20 44		21 41		
Yalding	d		14 36		15 36	16 07	16 50	17 41	18 11	18 43		19 51		20 47		21 44		
Beltring	d		14 40		15 40	16 11	16 54	17 45	18 15	18 47		19 55		20 51		21 48		
Paddock Wood	a		14 44		15 44	16 15	16 58	17 49	18 19	18 51		19 59		20 55		21 52		
Tonbridge	a		14 57		16 21	16 36	17 17	18 18	18 45	19 27		20 27		21 28		22 28		
London Bridge	⊖ a		15 43		17 00	17 26	18 28	18 57	19 25	20 08		21 08		22 08		23 08		
London Cannon Street	⊖ a		15f54		17f08	17 31	18f37	19f05	19f37	20f27								
London Waterloo (East)	⊖ a		15 32		17 05	17 36	18 03	19 02	19 31	20 13		21 13		22 13		23 13		
London Charing Cross	⊖ a		15 36		17 10	17 41	18 07	19 07	19 35	20 18		21 18		22 18		23 18		

For general notes see front of timetable
For details of catering facilities see Directory of Train Operators

- **A** To Redhill (Table 209).
- **B** To London Bridge (Table 209)
- **b** Change at Strood
- **c** Change at London Bridge and Strood
- **e** Change at Tonbridge and London Bridge
- **f** Change at Paddock Wood and London Bridge

Table 208

Saturdays

Strood → Maidstone West and Paddock Wood

Network Diagram - see first page of Table 206

		SE 61	SE 01	SE 61	SE 01	SE 61	SE 01	SE 61	SE 01	SE 61	SE 01	SE 61	SE 01	SE 61	SE 01	SE 61	SE 01	SE 61
London Charing Cross 4	⊖ d		05b04	05 50	06 20	06 50	07 20	07 50	08 20	08 50	09 20	09 50	10 20	10 50	11 20	11 50	12 20	12 50
London Waterloo (East) 4	⊖ d		05b07	05 53	06 23	06 53	07 23	07 53	08 23	08 53	09 23	09 53	10 23	10 53	11 23	11 53	12 23	12 53
London Cannon Street 4	⊖ d								08c10	08c48	09c18	09c48	10c18	10c48	11c18	11c48	12c18	12c48
London Bridge 4	⊖ d																	
Greenhithe for Bluewater	d	05b22	05b54	06 39	07 09	07 39	08 09	08 39	09 09	09 39	10 09	10 39	11 09	11 39	12 09	12 39	13 09	13 39
Gravesend 4	d	05b29	06b01	06 46	07 16	07 46	08 16	08 46	09 16	09 46	10 16	10 46	11 16	11 46	12 16	12 46	13 16	13 46
Gillingham (Kent) 4	d	05 48	06 18	06 44	07 14	07 44	08 14	08 44	09 14	09 44	10 14	10 44	11 14	11 44	12 14	12 44	13 14	13 44
Strood 4	d	06 01	06 31	07 01	07 31	08 01	08 31	09 01	09 31	10 01	10 31	11 01	11 31	12 01	12 31	13 01	13 31	14 01
Cuxton	d	06 05	06 35	07 05	07 35	08 05	08 35	09 05	09 35	10 05	10 35	11 05	11 35	12 05	12 35	13 05	13 35	14 05
Halling	d	06 08	06 38	07 08	07 38	08 08	08 38	09 08	09 38	10 08	10 38	11 08	11 38	12 08	12 38	13 08	13 38	14 08
Snodland	d	06 11	06 41	07 11	07 41	08 11	08 41	09 11	09 41	10 11	10 41	11 11	11 41	12 11	12 41	13 11	13 41	14 11
New Hythe	d	06 14	06 44	07 14	07 44	08 14	08 44	09 14	09 44	10 14	10 44	11 14	11 44	12 14	12 44	13 14	13 44	14 14
Aylesford	d	06 16	06 46	07 16	07 46	08 16	08 46	09 16	09 46	10 16	10 46	11 16	11 46	12 16	12 46	13 16	13 46	14 16
Maidstone Barracks	d	06 21	06 51	07 21	07 51	08 21	08 51	09 21	09 51	10 21	10 51	11 21	11 51	12 21	12 51	13 21	13 51	14 21
Maidstone West 4	a	06 23	06 53	07 23	07 53	08 23	08 53	09 23	09 53	10 23	10 53	11 23	11 53	12 23	12 53	13 23	13 53	14 23
	d	06 24		07 24		08 24		09 24		10 24		11 24		12 24		13 24		14 24
East Farleigh	d	06 28		07 28		08 28		09 28		10 28		11 28		12 28		13 28		14 28
Wateringbury	d	06 33		07 33		08 33		09 33		10 33		11 33		12 33		13 33		14 33
Yalding	d	06 36		07 36		08 36		09 36		10 36		11 36		12 36		13 36		14 36
Beltring	d	06 40		07 40		08 40		09 40		10 40		11 40		12 40		13 40		14 40
Paddock Wood 4	a	06 44		07 44		08 44		09 44		10 44		11 44		12 44		13 44		14 44
Tonbridge 4	a	06 57		07 58		08 57		09 57		10 57		11 57		12 57		13 57		14 57
London Bridge 4	⊖ a	07 39		08 38		09 43		10 43		11 43		12 43		13 43		14 43		15 43
London Cannon Street 4	⊖ a	07e50		08e47		09e54		10e54		11e54		12e54		13e54		14e54		15e54
London Waterloo (East) 4	⊖ a	07 43		08 43		09 32		10 32		11 32		12 32		13 32		14 32		15 32
London Charing Cross 4	⊖ a	07 47		08 48		09 36		10 36		11 36		12 36		13 36		14 36		15 36

		SE 01	SE 61	SE 01	SE 61	SE 01	SE 61	SE 01	SE 61	SE 01	SE 61	SE 01	SE 61	SE 01	SE 01	SE 01
London Charing Cross 4	⊖ d	13 20	13 50	14 20	14 50	15 20	15 50	16 20	16 50	17 20	17 50	18 20	18 50	19 20	19 50	20 20
London Waterloo (East) 4	⊖ d	13 23	13 53	14 23	14 53	15 23	15 53	16 23	16 53	17 23	17 53	18 23	18 53	19 23	19 53	20 23
London Cannon Street 4	⊖ d	13c18	13c48	14c18	14c48	15c18	15c48	16c18	16c48	17c18	17c48	18c18	18c48	19c14		
London Bridge 4	⊖ d															
Greenhithe for Bluewater	d	14 09	14 39	15 09	15 39	16 09	16 39	17 09	17 39	18 09	18 39	19 09	19 39	20 09	20 40	21 09
Gravesend 4	d	14 16	14 46	15 16	15 46	16 16	16 46	17 16	17 46	18 16	18 46	19 16	19 46	20 16	20 48	21 16
Gillingham (Kent) 4	d	14 14	14 44	15 14	15 44	16 14	16 44	17 14	17 44	18 14	18 44	19 14	19 44	20 14	20 42	21 14
Strood 4	d	14 31	15 01	15 31	16 01	16 31	17 01	17 31	18 01	18 31	19 01	19 31	20 01	20 31	21 01	21 31
Cuxton	d	14 35	15 05	15 35	16 05	16 35	17 05	17 35	18 05	18 35	19 05	19 35	20 05	20 35	21 05	21 35
Halling	d	14 38	15 08	15 38	16 08	16 38	17 08	17 38	18 08	18 38	19 08	19 38	20 08	20 38	21 08	21 38
Snodland	d	14 41	15 11	15 41	16 11	16 41	17 11	17 41	18 11	18 41	19 11	19 41	20 11	20 41	21 11	21 41
New Hythe	d	14 44	15 14	15 44	16 14	16 44	17 14	17 44	18 14	18 44	19 14	19 44	20 14	20 44	21 14	21 44
Aylesford	d	14 46	15 16	15 46	16 16	16 46	17 16	17 46	18 16	18 46	19 16	19 46	20 16	20 46	21 16	21 46
Maidstone Barracks	d	14 51	15 21	15 51	16 21	16 51	17 21	17 51	18 21	18 51	19 21	19 51	20 21	20 51	21 21	21 51
Maidstone West 4	a	14 53	15 23	15 53	16 23	16 53	17 23	17 53	18 23	18 53	19 23	19 53	20 23	20 53	21 23	21 53
	d		15 24		16 24		17 24		18 24		19 24		20 24			
East Farleigh	d		15 28		16 28		17 28		18 28		19 28		20 28			
Wateringbury	d		15 33		16 33		17 33		18 33		19 33		20 33			
Yalding	d		15 36		16 36		17 36		18 36		19 36		20 36			
Beltring	d		15 40		16 40		17 40		18 40		19 40		20 40			
Paddock Wood 4	a		15 44		16 44		17 44		18 44		19 44		20 44			
Tonbridge 4	a		15 57		16 57		18 28		18 59		19 59		20 59			
London Bridge 4	⊖ a		16 43		17 43		19 08		19 38		20 38		21 38			
London Cannon Street 4	⊖ a		16e54		17e54											
London Waterloo (East) 4	⊖ a		16 32		17 32		19 14		19 44		20 44		21 44			
London Charing Cross 4	⊖ a		16 36		17 36		19 19		19 49		20 49		21 49			

For general notes see front of timetable
For details of catering facilities see Directory of Train Operators

b Change at Strood
c Change at London Bridge and Strood
e Change at Paddock Wood and London Bridge

Sundays

Strood → Maidstone West and Paddock Wood

Network Diagram - see first page of Table 206

		SE 55 A	SE 01	SE 55 A	SE 01	SE 55 A	SE 01	SE 55 A	SE 01	SE 55 A	SE 01	SE 55 A	SE 01	SE 55 A	SE 01	SE 55 A	SE 01	SE 55 A
London Charing Cross 4	⊖ d						08 26		09 26		10 26		11 26		12 26		13 26	
London Waterloo (East) 4	⊖ d						08 29		09 29		10 29		11 29		12 29		13 29	
London Cannon Street 4	⊖ d																	
London Bridge 4	⊖ d																	
Greenhithe for Bluewater	d				08 09		09 12		10 12		11 11		12 11		13 11		14 11	
Gravesend 4	d				08 16		09 18		10 18		11 18		12 18		13 18		14 18	
Gillingham (Kent) 4	d	06 36	07 13		08 13		09 13		10 17		11 17		12 17		13 17		14 17	
Strood 4	d	06 55	07 33		08 33		09 35		10 35		11 35		12 35		13 35		14 35	
Cuxton	d	06 59	07 37		08 37		09 39		10 39		11 39		12 39		13 39		14 39	
Halling	d	07 02	07 40		08 40		09 42		10 42		11 42		12 42		13 42		14 42	
Snodland	d	07 05	07 43		08 43		09 45		10 45		11 45		12 45		13 45		14 45	
New Hythe	d	07 08	07 46		08 46		09 48		10 48		11 48		12 48		13 48		14 48	
Aylesford	d	07 10	07 48		08 48		09 50		10 50		11 50		12 50		13 50		14 50	
Maidstone Barracks	d	07 15	07 53		08 53		09 55		10 55		11 55		12 55		13 55		14 55	
Maidstone West 4	a	07 17	07 55		08 55		09 57		10 57		11 57		12 57		13 57		14 57	
	d	07 18		08 14		09 14		10 14		11 14		12 14		13 14		14 14		15 14
East Farleigh	d	07 22		08 18		09 18		10 18		11 18		12 18		13 18		14 18		15 18
Wateringbury	d	07 27		08 23		09 23		10 23		11 23		12 23		13 23		14 23		15 23
Yalding	d	07 30		08 26		09 26		10 26		11 26		12 26		13 26		14 26		15 26
Beltring	d	07 34		08 30		09 30		10 30		11 30		12 30		13 30		14 30		15 30
Paddock Wood 4	a	07 38		08 34		09 34		10 34		11 34		12 34		13 34		14 34		15 34
Tonbridge 4	a	07 46		08 43		09 42		10 42		11 42		12 42		13 42		14 42		15 42
London Bridge 4	⊖ a	08 44		09 28		10 28		11 28		12 28		13 28		14 28		15 28		16 28
London Cannon Street 4	⊖ a																	
London Waterloo (East) 4	⊖ a	08 49		09 33		10 33		11 33		12 33		13 33		14 33		15 33		16 33
London Charing Cross 4	⊖ a	08 53		09 37		10 37		11 37		12 37		13 37		14 37		15 37		16 37

		SE 01	SE 55 A	SE 01	SE 55 A	SE 01	SE 55 A	SE 01	SE 55 A	SE 01	SE 55 A	SE 01	SE 61	SE 01
London Charing Cross 4	⊖ d	14 26		15 26		16 26		17 26		18 26		19 26		20 26
London Waterloo (East) 4	⊖ d	14 29		15 29		16 29		17 29		18 29		19 29		20 29
London Cannon Street 4	⊖ d													
London Bridge 4	⊖ d													
Greenhithe for Bluewater	d	15 11		16 11		17 11		18 12		19 12		20 12		21 12
Gravesend 4	d	15 18		16 18		17 18		18 18		19 18		20 18		21 18
Gillingham (Kent) 4	d	15 17		16 17		17 17		18 13		19 13		20 13		21 13
Strood 4	d	15 35		16 35		17 33		18 33		19 33		20 33		21 33
Cuxton	d	15 39		16 39		17 37		18 37		19 37		20 37		21 37
Halling	d	15 42		16 42		17 40		18 40		19 40		20 40		21 40
Snodland	d	15 45		16 45		17 43		18 43		19 43		20 43		21 43
New Hythe	d	15 48		16 48		17 46		18 46		19 46		20 46		21 46
Aylesford	d	15 50		16 50		17 48		18 48		19 48		20 48		21 48
Maidstone Barracks	d	15 55		16 55		17 53		18 53		19 53		20 53		21 53
Maidstone West 4	a	15 57		16 57		17 55		18 55		19 55		20 55		21 55
	d		16 14		17 14		18 14		19 14		20 14		21 14	
East Farleigh	d		16 18		17 18		18 18		19 18		20 18		21 18	
Wateringbury	d		16 23		17 23		18 23		19 23		20 23		21 23	
Yalding	d		16 26		17 26		18 26		19 26		20 26		21 26	
Beltring	d		16 30		17 30		18 30		19 30		20 30		21 30	
Paddock Wood 4	a		16 34		17 34		18 34		19 34		20 34		21 34	
Tonbridge 4	a		16 42		17 42		18 42		19 42		20 42		21 42	
London Bridge 4	⊖ a		17 28		18 28		19 28		20 28		21 28		22 28	
London Cannon Street 4	⊖ a													
London Waterloo (East) 4	⊖ a		17 33		18 33		19 33		20 33		21 33		22 33	
London Charing Cross 4	⊖ a		17 37		18 37		19 37		20 37		21 37		22 37	

For general notes see front of timetable
For details of catering facilities see Directory of Train Operators

A To Three Bridges (Table 209).

For details of Bank Holiday service alterations please see first page of Table 195

Paddock Wood and Maidstone West → Strood

Network Diagram - see first page of Table 206

Miles			SE 61	SE 61	SE 61	SE 01	SE 61	SE 01	SE 55 A	SE 01	SE 61	SE 01	SE 61	SE 01	SE 61	SE 01	SE 61	SE 01
—	**London Charing Cross** 3	⊖ d			05 30		07 00		08 14		08 58		10 00		11 00		12 00	
—	**London Waterloo (East)** 3	⊖ d			05 33		07 03		08 17		09 01		10 03		11 03		12 03	
—	**London Cannon Street** 3	⊖ d					06b52		08c14		08b54		10b00		11b00		12b00	
—	**London Bridge** 3	⊖ d																
0	Tonbridge 3	d	05 47						09 00									
5¼	**Paddock Wood** 3	d	05 55	06 32	07 06		08 09		09 08		10 03		11 01		12 06		13 06	
7	Beltring	d	05 59	06 36	07 10		08 13		09 12		10 07		11 05		12 10		13 10	
8¾	Yalding	d	06 02	06 39	07 13		08 16		09 15		10 10		11 08		12 13		13 13	
10½	Wateringbury	d	06 06	06 43	07 17		08 20		09 19		10 14		11 12		12 17		13 17	
13¼	East Farleigh	d	06 11	06 48	07 22		08 25		09 24		10 19		11 17		12 22		13 22	
15¼	**Maidstone West** 3	a	06 15	06 52	07 26		08 29		09 28		10 23		11 21		12 26		13 26	
—		d	06 20	06 54	07 27	08 02	08 30	09 00	09 29	10 00	10 28	10 58	11 28	11 58	12 28	12 58	13 28	13 58
15¾	Maidstone Barracks	d	06 21	06 55	07 28	08 03	08 31	09 01	09 30	10 01	10 29	10 59	11 29	11 59	12 29	12 59	13 29	13 59
18¾	Aylesford	d	06 26	07 00	07 33	08 08	08 36	09 06	09 35	10 06	10 34	11 04	11 34	12 04	12 34	13 04	13 34	14 04
19½	New Hythe	d	06 29	07 03	07 36	08 11	08 39	09 09	09 38	10 09	10 37	11 07	11 37	12 07	12 37	13 07	13 37	14 07
21	Snodland	d	06 31	07 05	07 38	08 13	08 41	09 11	09 40	10 11	10 39	11 09	11 39	12 09	12 39	13 09	13 39	14 09
22¼	Halling	d	06 34	07 08	07 41	08 16	08 44	09 14	09 43	10 14	10 42	11 12	11 42	12 12	12 42	13 12	13 42	14 12
24¼	Cuxton	d	06 37	07 11	07 44	08 19	08 47	09 17	09 46	10 17	10 45	11 15	11 45	12 15	12 45	13 15	13 45	14 15
26½	**Strood** 3	a	06 42	07 16	07 49	08 24	08 52	09 22	09 51	10 22	10 50	11 20	11 50	12 20	12 50	13 20	13 50	14 20
—	Gillingham (Kent) 3	a	07 25		08 01		09 07	09 35	10 07	10 37	11 07	11 37	12 07	12 37	13 07	13 37	14 07	14 37
—	Gravesend 3	a	06 59	07 39	08 07	08 39	09 08	09 36	10 06	10 36	11 06	11 36	12 06	12 36	13 06	13 36	14 06	14 36
—	Greenhithe for Bluewater	a	07 06	07 46	08 14	08 46	09 13	09 41	10 11	10 41	11 11	11 41	12 11	12 41	13 11	13 41	14 11	14 41
—	**London Bridge** 3	⊖ a	07 44	08 47	09 11	09 29	09 54	10 19	10 49	11 19	11 49	12 19	12 49	13 19	13 49	14 19	14 49	15 19
—	London Cannon Street 3	⊖ a	07 51	08 54	09 18	09e43	10e06	10e30	10e57	11e27	12e00	12e27	12e57	13e27	13e57	14e27	14e57	15e27
—	London Waterloo (East) 3	⊖ a	08 08	08 29	08 57	09 34	09 59	10 24	10 54	11 24	11 54	12 24	12 54	13 24	13 54	14 24	14 54	15 24
—	London Charing Cross 3	⊖ a	08 13	08 34	09 03	09 39	10 05	10 28	10 58	11 28	11 58	12 28	12 58	13 28	13 58	14 28	14 58	15 28

		SE 61	SE 01	SE 61	SE 61	SE 61	SE 61	SE 61	SE 61	SE 01	SE 61	SE 88 A	SE 61	SE 01	SE 61	SE 01	SE 61
London Charing Cross 4	⊖ d	13 00		14 00	15 00	15 23	16 00	16 46	17 12		17 56	18 40	19 00		20 00		21 00
London Waterloo (East) 4	⊖ d	13 03		14 03	15 03	15 26	16 03	16 49	17 15		17 59	18 43	19 03		20 03		21 03
London Cannon Street 4	⊖ d	13b00		14b00	15b00		16b00	16b46	17 20		18 04	18c36	18b50		20b00		21b00
London Bridge 4	⊖ d																
Tonbridge 4	d											19 28					
Paddock Wood 4	d	14 06		15 06	16 06	16 25	17 02	17 55	18 23		18 57	19 38	20 03		21 00		21 57
Beltring	d	14 10		15 10	16 10	16 29	17 06	17 59	18 27		19 01	19 42	20 07		21 04		22 01
Yalding	d	14 13		15 13	16 13	16 32	17 09	18 02	18 30		19 04	19 45	20 10		21 07		22 04
Wateringbury	d	14 17		15 17	16 17	16 36	17 13	18 06	18 34		19 08	19 49	20 14		21 11		22 08
East Farleigh	d	14 22		15 22	16 22	16 41	17 18	18 11	18 39		19 13	19 54	20 19		21 16		22 13
Maidstone West 4	a	14 26		15 26	16 26	16 45	17 22	18 15	18 43		19 17	19 58	20 23		21 20		22 17
	d	14 28	14 58	15 28	16 28	16 56	17 26	18 16	18 48	19 08	19 28	20 00	20 25	21 00	21 27	22 02	22 20
Maidstone Barracks	d	14 29	14 59	15 29	16 29	16 57	17 27	18 17	18 49	19 09	19 29	20 01	20 26	21 01	21 28	22 03	22 21
Aylesford	d	14 34	15 04	15 34	16 34	17 02	17 32	18 22	18 54	19 14	19 34	20 06	20 31	21 06	21 33	22 08	22 26
New Hythe	d	14 37	15 07	15 37	16 37	17 05	17 35	18 25	18 57	19 17	19 37	20 09	20 34	21 09	21 36	22 11	22 29
Snodland	d	14 39	15 09	15 39	16 39	17 07	17 37	18 27	18 59	19 19	19 39	20 11	20 36	21 11	21 38	22 13	22 31
Halling	d	14 42	15 12	15 42	16 42	17 10	17 40	18 30	19 02	19 22	19 42	20 14	20 39	21 14	21 41	22 16	22 34
Cuxton	d	14 45	15 15	15 45	16 45	17 13	17 43	18 33	19 05	19 25	19 45	20 17	20 42	21 17	21 44	22 19	22 37
Strood 4	a	14 50	15 20	15 50	16 50	17 18	17 48	18 38	19 10	19 30	19 50	20 22	20 47	21 22	21 49	22 24	22 42
Gillingham (Kent) 4	a	15 07	15 37	16 07	17 18	17 42	18 06	19 07	19 26	19 55	20 15	20 39	21 17	21 37	22 13	22 37	22 55
Gravesend 4	a	15 06	15 36	16 08	17 06	17 36	18 10	19 06	19 36		20 06	20 38	21 04	21 36	22 04	22 44	00f28
Greenhithe for Bluewater	a	15 11	15 41	16 14	17 11	17 45	18 15	19 11	19 41		20 11	20 43	21 12	21 41	22 12	22 52	00f34
London Bridge 4	⊖ a	15 49	16 19	16 55	17 56	18 31	19 02	19 53	20 23		20 53	21 23	21 53	22 23	22 53	23 41	
London Cannon Street 4	⊖ a	15e57	16e27	17e05	18 01	18e45	19e15	20e11	20e41								
London Waterloo (East) 4	⊖ a	15 54	16 24	17 00		18 36	19 07	19 58	20 28		20 58	21 28	21 58	22 28	22 58	23 46	
London Charing Cross 4	⊖ a	15 58	16 28	17 03		18 40	19 11	20 01	20 31		21 01	21 31	22 01	22 31	23 01	23 50	

For general notes see front of timetable
For details of catering facilities see Directory of Train Operators

A From Redhill (Table 209)
b Change at London Bridge and Paddock Wood
c Change at London Bridge and Tonbridge
e Change at Strood and London Bridge
f Change at Strood

Table 208

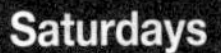

Paddock Wood and Maidstone West → Strood

Network Diagram - see first page of Table 206

Station		SE 01	SE 01	SE 61	SE 01	SE 61	SE 01	SE 61	SE 01	SE 61	SE 01	SE 61	SE 01	SE 61	SE 01	SE 61	SE 01	SE 61
London Charing Cross 4	⊖ d			06 00		07 00		08 00		09 00		10 00		11 00		12 00		13 00
London Waterloo (East) 4	⊖ d			06 03		07 03		08 03		09 03		10 03		11 03		12 03		13 03
London Cannon Street 4	⊖ d									09b00		10b00		11b00		12b00		13b00
London Bridge 4	⊖ d																	
Tonbridge 4	d																	
Paddock Wood 4	d			07 01		08 01		09 01		10 01		11 01		12 01		13 01		14 01
Beltring	d			07 05		08 05		09 05		10 05		11 05		12 05		13 05		14 05
Yalding	d			07 08		08 08		09 08		10 08		11 08		12 08		13 08		14 08
Wateringbury	d			07 12		08 12		09 12		10 12		11 12		12 12		13 12		14 12
East Farleigh	d			07 17		08 17		09 17		10 17		11 17		12 17		13 17		14 17
Maidstone West 4	a			07 21		08 21		09 21		10 21		11 21		12 21		13 21		14 21
	d	06 28	06 58	07 28	07 58	08 28	08 58	09 28	09 58	10 28	10 58	11 28	11 58	12 28	12 58	13 28	13 58	14 28
Maidstone Barracks	d	06 29	06 59	07 29	07 59	08 29	08 59	09 29	09 59	10 29	10 59	11 29	11 59	12 29	12 59	13 29	13 59	14 29
Aylesford	d	06 34	07 04	07 34	08 04	08 34	09 04	09 34	10 04	10 34	11 04	11 34	12 04	12 34	13 04	13 34	14 04	14 34
New Hythe	d	06 37	07 07	07 37	08 07	08 37	09 07	09 37	10 07	10 37	11 07	11 37	12 07	12 37	13 07	13 37	14 07	14 37
Snodland	d	06 39	07 09	07 39	08 09	08 39	09 09	09 39	10 09	10 39	11 09	11 39	12 09	12 39	13 09	13 39	14 09	14 39
Halling	d	06 42	07 12	07 42	08 12	08 42	09 12	09 42	10 12	10 42	11 12	11 42	12 12	12 42	13 12	13 42	14 12	14 42
Cuxton	d	06 45	07 15	07 45	08 15	08 45	09 15	09 45	10 15	10 45	11 15	11 45	12 15	12 45	13 15	13 45	14 15	14 45
Strood 4	a	06 50	07 20	07 50	08 20	08 50	09 20	09 50	10 20	10 50	11 20	11 50	12 20	12 50	13 20	13 50	14 20	14 50
Gillingham (Kent) 4	a	07 07	07 37	08 07	08 37	09 07	09 37	10 07	10 37	11 07	11 37	12 07	12 37	13 07	13 37	14 07	14 37	15 07
Gravesend 4	a	07 05	07 35	08 05	08 36	09 06	09 36	10 06	10 36	11 06	11 36	12 06	12 36	13 06	13 36	14 06	14 36	15 06
Greenhithe for Bluewater	a	07 10	07 40	08 10	08 41	09 11	09 41	10 11	10 41	11 11	11 41	12 11	12 41	13 11	13 41	14 11	14 41	15 11
London Bridge 4	⊖ a	07 49	08 19	08 49	09 19	09 49	10 19	10 49	11 19	11 49	12 19	12 49	13 19	13 49	14 19	14 49	15 19	15 49
London Cannon Street 4	⊖ a	08c03	08c33	09c03	09c30	09c57	10c27	10c57	11c27	11c57	12c27	12c57	13c27	13c57	14c27	14c57	15c27	15c57
London Waterloo (East) 4	⊖ a	07 54	08 24	08 54	09 24	09 54	10 24	10 54	11 24	11 54	12 24	12 54	13 24	13 54	14 24	14 54	15 24	15 54
London Charing Cross 4	⊖ a	07 58	08 28	08 58	09 28	09 58	10 28	10 58	11 28	11 58	12 28	12 58	13 28	13 58	14 28	14 58	15 28	15 58

Station		SE 01	SE 61	SE 01	SE 61	SE 01	SE 61	SE 01	SE 61	SE 01	SE 61	SE 01	SE 61	SE 01	SE 01	SE 01
London Charing Cross 4	⊖ d		14 00		15 00		16 00		17 00		18 00		19 00		20 00	
London Waterloo (East) 4	⊖ d		14 03		15 03		16 03		17 03		18 03		19 03		20 03	
London Cannon Street 4	⊖ d		14b00		15b00		16b00		17b00		18b00		19b00		19b14	
London Bridge 4	⊖ d															
Tonbridge 4	d															
Paddock Wood 4	d		15 01		16 01		17 01		18 01		19 01		20 01		21 01	
Beltring	d		15 05		16 05		17 05		18 05		19 05		20 05		21 05	
Yalding	d		15 08		16 08		17 08		18 08		19 08		20 08		21 08	
Wateringbury	d		15 12		16 12		17 12		18 12		19 12		20 12		21 12	
East Farleigh	d		15 17		16 17		17 17		18 17		19 17		20 17		21 17	
Maidstone West 4	a		15 21		16 21		17 21		18 21		19 21		20 21		21 21	
	d	14 58	15 28	15 58	16 28	16 58	17 28	17 58	18 28	18 58	19 28	19 58	20 28	20 58		21 28
Maidstone Barracks	d	14 59	15 29	15 59	16 29	16 59	17 29	17 59	18 29	18 59	19 29	19 59	20 29	20 59		21 29
Aylesford	d	15 04	15 34	16 04	16 34	17 04	17 34	18 04	18 34	19 04	19 34	20 04	20 34	21 04		21 34
New Hythe	d	15 07	15 37	16 07	16 37	17 07	17 37	18 07	18 37	19 07	19 37	20 07	20 37	21 07		21 37
Snodland	d	15 09	15 39	16 09	16 39	17 09	17 39	18 09	18 39	19 09	19 39	20 09	20 39	21 09		21 39
Halling	d	15 12	15 42	16 12	16 42	17 12	17 42	18 12	18 42	19 12	19 42	20 12	20 42	21 12		21 42
Cuxton	d	15 15	15 45	16 15	16 45	17 15	17 45	18 15	18 45	19 15	19 45	20 15	20 45	21 15		21 45
Strood 4	a	15 20	15 50	16 20	16 50	17 20	17 50	18 20	18 50	19 20	19 50	20 20	20 50	21 20		21 50
Gillingham (Kent) 4	a	15 37	16 07	16 37	17 07	17 37	18 07	18 37	19 07	19 37	20 07	20 37	21 13	21 37		22 13
Gravesend 4	a	15 36	16 06	16 36	17 06	17 36	18 06	18 36	19 06	19 36	20 06	20 36	21 04	21 36		22 04
Greenhithe for Bluewater	a	15 41	16 11	16 41	17 11	17 41	18 11	18 41	19 11	19 41	20 11	20 41	21 12	21 41		22 12
London Bridge 4	⊖ a	16 19	16 49	17 19	17 49	18 19	18 49	19 21	19 53	20 23	20 53	21 23	21 53	22 23		22 53
London Cannon Street 4	⊖ a	16c27	16c57	17c27	17c57	18c27										
London Waterloo (East) 4	⊖ a	16 24	16 54	17 24	17 54	18 24	18 54	19 25	19 58	20 28	20 58	21 28	21 58	22 28		22 58
London Charing Cross 4	⊖ a	16 28	16 58	17 28	17 58	18 28	18 58	19 29	20 01	20 31	21 01	21 31	22 01	22 31		23 01

For general notes see front of timetable
For details of catering facilities see Directory of Train Operators

b Change at London Bridge and Paddock Wood
c Change at Strood and London Bridge

Table 208

Sundays

Paddock Wood and Maidstone West → Strood

Network Diagram - see first page of Table 206

Station		SE 01	SE 01		SE 61	SE 01		SE 55	SE 01		SE 55	SE 01		SE 55	SE 01		SE 55	SE 01		SE 55	SE 01		SE 55	SE 01	SE 55
								A			A			A			A			A			A		A
London Charing Cross 4	⊖ d										08 24			09 40			10 40			11 40			12 40		13 40
London Waterloo (East) 4	⊖ d										08 27			09 43			10 43			11 43			12 43		13 43
London Cannon Street 4	⊖ d																								
London Bridge 4	⊖ d																								
Tonbridge 4	d				07 40			08 40			09 40			10 40			11 40			12 40			13 40		14 40
Paddock Wood 4	d				07 48			08 48			09 48			10 48			11 48			12 48			13 48		14 48
Beltring	d				07 52			08 52			09 52			10 52			11 52			12 52			13 52		14 52
Yalding	d				07 55			08 55			09 55			10 55			11 55			12 55			13 55		14 55
Wateringbury	d				07 59			08 59			09 59			10 59			11 59			12 59			13 59		14 59
East Farleigh	d				08 04			09 04			10 04			11 04			12 04			13 04			14 04		15 04
Maidstone West 4	a				08 08			09 08			10 08			11 08			12 08			13 08			14 08		15 08
	d	06 57	08 00			09 00			10 02			11 02			12 02			13 02			14 02			15 02	
Maidstone Barracks	d	06 58	08 01			09 01			10 03			11 03			12 03			13 03			14 03			15 03	
Aylesford	d	07 03	08 06			09 06			10 08			11 08			12 08			13 08			14 08			15 08	
New Hythe	d	07 06	08 09			09 09			10 11			11 11			12 11			13 11			14 11			15 11	
Snodland	d	07 08	08 11			09 11			10 13			11 13			12 13			13 13			14 13			15 13	
Halling	d	07 11	08 14			09 14			10 16			11 16			12 16			13 16			14 16			15 16	
Cuxton	d	07 14	08 17			09 17			10 19			11 19			12 19			13 19			14 19			15 19	
Strood 4	a	07 19	08 22			09 22			10 24			11 24			12 24			13 24			14 24			15 24	
Gillingham (Kent) 4	a		08 37			09 39			10 39			11 39			12 39			13 39			14 39			15 39	
Gravesend 4	a	07 35	08 35			09 35			10 39			11 39			12 39			13 39			14 39			15 39	
Greenhithe for Bluewater	a	07 44	08 44			09 44			10 44			11 44			12 44			13 44			14 44			15 44	
London Bridge 4	⊖ a	08 25	09 26			10 25			11 23			12 23			13 23			14 23			15 23			16 23	
London Cannon Street 4	⊖ a																								
London Waterloo (East) 4	⊖ a	08 30	09 30			10 31			11 28			12 28			13 28			14 28			15 28			16 28	
London Charing Cross 4	⊖ a	08 34	09 34			10 34			11 31			12 31			13 31			14 31			15 31			16 31	

Station		SE 01		SE 55	SE 01		SE 55	SE 01		SE 55	SE 01		SE 55	SE 01		SE 55	SE 01		SE 55	SE 55
				A			A			A			A			A			A	A
London Charing Cross 4	⊖ d			14 40			15 40			16 40			17 40			18 40			19 40	20 24
London Waterloo (East) 4	⊖ d			14 43			15 43			16 43			17 43			18 43			19 43	20 27
London Cannon Street 4	⊖ d																			
London Bridge 4	⊖ d																			
Tonbridge 4	d			15 40			16 40			17 40			18 40			19 40			20 40	21 40
Paddock Wood 4	d			15 48			16 48			17 48			18 48			19 48			20 48	21 48
Beltring	d			15 52			16 52			17 52			18 52			19 52			20 52	21 52
Yalding	d			15 55			16 55			17 55			18 55			19 55			20 55	21 55
Wateringbury	d			15 59			16 59			17 59			18 59			19 59			20 59	21 59
East Farleigh	d			16 04			17 04			18 04			19 04			20 04			21 04	22 04
Maidstone West 4	a			16 08			17 08			18 08			19 08			20 08			21 08	22 08
	d	16 02			17 02			18 00			19 00			20 00			21 00			22 09
Maidstone Barracks	d	16 03			17 03			18 01			19 01			20 01			21 01			22 10
Aylesford	d	16 08			17 08			18 06			19 06			20 06			21 06			22 15
New Hythe	d	16 11			17 11			18 09			19 09			20 09			21 09			22 18
Snodland	d	16 13			17 13			18 11			19 11			20 11			21 11			22 20
Halling	d	16 16			17 16			18 14			19 14			20 14			21 14			22 23
Cuxton	d	16 19			17 19			18 17			19 17			20 17			21 17			22 26
Strood 4	a	16 24			17 24			18 22			19 22			20 22			21 22			22 31
Gillingham (Kent) 4	a	16 39			17 39			18 39			19 39			20 39			21 39			22 46
Gravesend 4	a	16 39			17 39			18 35			19 35			20 35			21 35			
Greenhithe for Bluewater	a	16 44			17 44			18 44			19 44			20 44			21 44			
London Bridge 4	⊖ a	17 23			18 23			19 25			20 25			21 25			22 25			
London Cannon Street 4	⊖ a																			
London Waterloo (East) 4	⊖ a	17 28			18 28			19 30			20 30			21 30			22 30			
London Charing Cross 4	⊖ a	17 34			18 34			19 34			20 34			21 34			22 34			

For general notes see front of timetable
For details of catering facilities see Directory of Train Operators

A From Three Bridges (Table 209)

Table 209

Mondays to Fridays

For details of Bank Holiday service alterations please see first page of Table 195

Tunbridge Wells and Tonbridge → London, Gatwick Airport and Horsham via Redhill

Network Diagram - see first page of Table 206

Miles	Miles			SE 88	SE 55	SE 13	SE 88	SE 88	SE 13	SE 88	SE 13	SE 88 [1]	SE 13	SE 88 [1]	SE 13	SE 88 [1]	SE 13	SE 88 [1]	SE 13
					A	B					C								
—	—	Tunbridge Wells [4]	d		05 44		06 06	07 20	07 40	08 00	08 26	08 26	08 56	09 52	10 24	10 52	11 24	11 52	12 24
—	—	High Brooms	d		05 47		06 10	07 24	07 44	08 04	08 30	08 30	09 06	09 55	10 27	10 55	11 27	11 55	12 27
—	—	Tonbridge [4]	a											10 01	10 33	11 01	11 33	12 01	12 33
—	0		d	05 00	06 00	06 14	06 50	07 38	07 56	08 18	08 51	09 08	09 34	10 04	10 34	11 04	11 34	12 04	12 34
—	2½	Leigh (Kent)	d	05 04	06 04	06 18	06 54	07 42	08 00	08 22	08 55	09 12	09 38	10 08	10 38	11 08	11 38	12 08	12 38
—	4¼	Penshurst	d	05 07	06 07	06 21	06 57	07 45	08 04	08 25	08 58	09 16	09 41	10 12	10 41	11 12	11 41	12 12	12 41
—	9¼	Edenbridge	d	05 14	06 14	06 28	07 04	07 52	08 11	08 32	09 05	09 23	09 48	10 19	10 48	11 19	11 48	12 19	12 48
—	14	Godstone	d	05 20	06 20	06 34	07 10	07 58	08 17	08 38	09 11	09 29	09 54	10 25	10 54	11 25	11 54	12 25	12 54
—	17¾	Nutfield	d	05 26	06 26	06 40	07 16	08 04	08 23	08 44	09 17	09 35	10 00	10 31	11 00	11 31	12 00	12 31	13 00
—	19¾	Redhill	a	05 31	06 30	06 45	07 20	08 08		08 48	09 21	09 39	10 04	10 40	11 04	11 40	12 04	12 39	13 04
—	—	East Croydon	a	05 48	06 17	07 01	07 21	08 18	08 47	08 37	09 40	09 25	10 23	10 48	11 23	11 48	12 23	12 48	13 23
—	—	London Bridge [4]	⊖ a	06b15	06b40	07 18	07b43	08b41	09 07	09b05	09 55	09b45	10 40	11b12	11 40	12b12	12 40	13b12	13 40
—	—	London Victoria [15]	⊖ a	05b58	06b47	07b16	07b48	08b46	09c16	09b02	09b42	09b58	10c45	11b11	11c44	12b11	12c44	13b11	13b11
0	—	Redhill	d	05 35								09 44		10 44		11 44		12 44	
—	—	Reigate	a	05 48	06 46	07e15	07 32	08 19		08 57	09e33	10 18	10e18	11 18	11e18	12 18	12e18	13 18	13e18
5¾	—	Gatwick Airport [10]	a	05 42	06 53	07e03	07 54	08 39		09 02	09e39	09 54	10e23	10 55	11e23	11 55	12e23	12 55	13e23
8½	—	Three Bridges [4]	a	05 54	06 59	07e09	08 04	08 44		09 15	09e44	10 00	10e29	11 00	11e29	12 00	12e29	13 00	13e29
10	—	Crawley	a									10 04		11 04		12 04		13 04	
17	—	Horsham [4]	a									10 16		11 16		12 18		13 16	

		SE 88 [1]	SE 13	SE 88 [1]	SE 13	SE 88 [1]	SE 13	SE 88 [1]	SE 88	SE 13	SE 88	SE 88	SE 88	SE 88	SE 88	SE 88	SE 88
Tunbridge Wells [4]	d	12 52	13 24	13 52	14 24	14 52	15 24	15 36	15 56	16 56		18 04	18 40	19 38	20 36	21 36	22 56
High Brooms	d	12 55	13 27	13 55	14 27	14 55	15 27	15 39	15 59	16 59		18 07	18 43	19 41	20 39	21 39	22 59
Tonbridge [4]	a	13 01	13 33	14 01	14 33	15 01	15 33										
	d	13 04	13 34	14 04	14 34	15 04	15 34	16 04	16 29	17 20	17 43	18 21	19 09	19 53	20 53	21 53	23 17
Leigh (Kent)	d	13 08	13 38	14 08	14 38	15 08	15 38	16 08	16 33	17 24	17 47	18 25	19 13	19 57	20 57	21 57	23 21
Penshurst	d	13 12	13 41	14 12	14 41	15 12	15 41	16 12	16 36	17 27	17 50	18 28	19 16	20 00	21 00	22 00	23 24
Edenbridge	d	13 19	13 48	14 19	14 48	15 19	15 48	16 19	16 43	17 34	17 57	18 35	19 23	20 07	21 07	22 07	23 31
Godstone	d	13 25	13 54	14 25	14 54	15 25	15 54	16 25	16 49	17 40	18 03	18 41	19 29	20 13	21 13	22 13	23 37
Nutfield	d	13 31	14 00	14 31	15 00	15 31	16 00	16 31	16 55	17 46	18 09	18 47	19 35	20 19	21 19	22 19	23 43
Redhill	a	13 39	14 04	14 39	15 04	15 39	16 04	16 39	16 59	17 51	18 13	18 51	19 39	20 24	21 24	22 23	23 48
East Croydon	a	13 48	14 23	14 48	15 23	15 48	16 23	16 28	16 54	18 11	17 56	18 48	19 28	20 19	21 15	22 18	00 05
London Bridge [4]	⊖ a	14b12	14 40	15b12	15 40	16b12	16 41	16b56	17b26	18 26	18b24	19b12	20b00	20b45	21b45	22b45	00b52
London Victoria [15]	⊖ a	14b11	14c44	15b11	15c44	16b11	16c46	16b56	17b20	18c40	18b28	19b11	19b59	20b40	21b40	22b40	00b18
Redhill	d	13 44		14 44		15 44		16 44						20 28	21 27	22 27	
Reigate	a	14 18	14e18	15 18	15e18	16 18	16e18	16 54	17 18	18e00	18 27	19 16	20 09	20 38	21 39	22 38	
Gatwick Airport [10]	a	13 55	14e23	14 55	15e23	15 56	16e23	16 56	17 32	18e12	18 32	19 07	19 58	20 35	21 34	22 34	00 11
Three Bridges [4]	a	14 00	14e29	15 00	15e29	16 01	16e29	17 01	17 38	18e18	18 38	19 25	20 04	20 40	21 40	22 40	00 18
Crawley	a	14 04		15 04		16 05		17 05									
Horsham [4]	a	14 16		15 16		16 18		17 19									

Saturdays

		SE 88	SE 88	SE 55 [1]	SE 13	SE 88 [1]	SE 13	SE 88 [1]	SE 13	SE 88 [1]	SE 13	SE 88 [1]	SE 13	SE 88 [1]	SE 13	SE 88 [1]	SE 13	SE 88 [1]
Tunbridge Wells [4]	d		05 37	06 36	07 06	07 36	08 06	08 52	09 24	09 52	10 24	10 52	11 24	11 52	12 24	12 52	13 24	13 52
High Brooms	d		05 40	06 39	07 09	07 39	08 09	08 55	09 27	09 55	10 27	10 55	11 27	11 55	12 27	12 55	13 27	13 55
Tonbridge [4]	a		05 46					09 01	09 33	10 01	10 33	11 01	11 33	12 01	12 33	13 01	13 33	14 01
	d	05 37	05 52	06 52	07 34	08 04	08 34	09 04	09 34	10 04	10 34	11 04	11 34	12 04	12 34	13 04	13 34	14 04
Leigh (Kent)	d		05 56	06 56	07 38	08 08	08 38	09 08	09 38	10 08	10 38	11 08	11 38	12 08	12 38	13 08	13 38	14 08
Penshurst	d		06 00	07 00	07 41	08 12	08 41	09 12	09 41	10 12	10 41	11 12	11 41	12 12	12 41	13 12	13 41	14 12
Edenbridge	d	05 47	06 06	07 06	07 48	08 19	08 48	09 19	09 48	10 19	10 48	11 19	11 48	12 19	12 48	13 19	13 48	14 19
Godstone	d	05 54	06 13	07 13	07 54	08 25	08 54	09 25	09 54	10 25	10 54	11 25	11 54	12 25	12 54	13 25	13 54	14 25
Nutfield	d	05 59	06 18	07 18	08 00	08 31	09 00	09 31	10 00	10 31	11 00	11 31	12 00	12 31	13 00	13 31	14 00	14 31
Redhill	a	06 04	06 23	07 23	08 04	08 39	09 04	09 39	10 04	10 39	11 04	11 39	12 04	12 39	13 04	13 39	14 04	14 39
East Croydon	a		06 27	07 28	08 23	08 48	09 23	09 48	10 23	10 48	11 23	11 48	12 23	12 48	13 23	13 48	14 23	14 48
London Bridge [4]	⊖ a		07b01	07b52	08 40	09b12	09 40	10b12	10 40	11b12	11 40	12b12	12 40	13b12	13 40	14b12	14 40	15b12
London Victoria [15]	⊖ a		06b58	07b57	08c44	09b11	09c44	10b11	10c44	11b11	11c44	12b11	12c44	13b11	13c44	14b11	14c44	15b11
Redhill	d		06 27	07 27		08 44		09 44		10 44		11 44		12 44		13 44		14 44
Reigate	a	06 18	06 38	07 38	08e18	09 18	09e18	10 18	10e18	11 18	11e18	12 18	12e18	13 18	13e18	14 18	14e18	15 18
Gatwick Airport [10]	a		06 35	07 34	08e23	08 55	09e23	09 55	10e23	10 55	11e23	11 55	12e23	12 55	13e23	13 55	14e23	14 55
Three Bridges [4]	a	06 40	06 40	07 39	08e29	09 00	09e29	10 00	10e29	11 00	11e29	12 00	12e29	13 00	13e29	14 00	14e29	15 00
Crawley	a					09 04		10 04		11 04		12 04		13 04		14 04		15 04
Horsham [4]	a					09 16		10 16		11 16		12 16		13 16		14 16		15 16

For general notes see front of timetable
For details of catering facilities see Directory of Train Operators

- A From Gillingham (Kent) (Table 208)
- B From Paddock Wood (Table 207)
- C From Strood (Table 208)
- b Change at Redhill and East Croydon
- c Change at East Croydon
- e Change at Redhill

Table 209

Saturdays

Tunbridge Wells and Tonbridge → London, Gatwick Airport and Horsham via Redhill

Network Diagram - see first page of Table 206

		SE	SE	SE	SE	SE	SE	SE	SE	SE	SE	SE	SE	SE	SE
		13	88	13	88	13	88	13	88	88	88	88	88	88	88
			[1]		[1]		[1]			[1]					
Tunbridge Wells 4	d	14 24	14 52	15 24	15 52	16 24	16 52	17 24	17 36	17 52	18 36	19 36	20 36	21 36	22 55
High Brooms	d	14 27	14 55	15 27	15 55	16 27	16 55	17 27	17 39	17 55	18 39	19 39	20 39	21 39	22 59
Tonbridge 4	a	14 33	15 01	15 33	16 01	16 33	17 01	17 33		18 01					
	d	14 34	15 04	15 34	16 04	16 34	17 04	17 34	17 52	18 04	18 52	19 52	20 52	21 52	23 15
Leigh (Kent)	d	14 38	15 08	15 38	16 08	16 38	17 08	17 38	17 56	18 08	18 56	19 56	20 56	21 56	23 19
Penshurst	d	14 41	15 12	15 41	16 12	16 41	17 12	17 41	18 00	18 12	19 00	20 00	21 00	22 00	23 23
Edenbridge	d	14 48	15 19	15 48	16 19	16 48	17 19	17 48	18 06	18 19	19 06	20 06	21 06	22 06	23 29
Godstone	d	14 54	15 25	15 54	16 25	16 54	17 25	17 54	18 13	18 25	19 13	20 13	21 13	22 13	23 36
Nutfield	d	15 00	15 31	16 00	16 31	17 00	17 31	18 00	18 18	18 31	19 18	20 18	21 18	22 18	23 41
Redhill	a	15 04	15 39	16 04	16 39	17 04	17 39	18 04	18 23	18 39	19 23	20 23	21 23	22 23	23 49
East Croydon	a	15 23	15 48	16 23	16 48	17 23	17 48	18 23	18 18	18 48	19 18	20 19	21 18	22 18	00 06
London Bridge 4	⊖ a	15 40	16b12	16 40	17b12	17 40	18b12	18 40	18b40	19b12	19b45	20b45	21b45	22b45	00b52
London Victoria 15	⊖ a	15c44	16b11	16c44	17b11	17c44	18b11	18c44	18b40	19b11	19b40	20b40	21b40	22b40	00b18
Redhill	d		15 44		16 44		17 44		18 27	18 44	19 27	20 27	21 27	22 27	
Reigate	a	15e18	16 18	16e18	17 18	17e18	18 18	18e18	18 38	19 18	19 38	20 38	21 40	22 38	
Gatwick Airport 10	✈ a	15e23	15 55	16e23	16 55	17e23	17 55	18e23	18 34	18 55	19 34	20 34	21 34	22 34	00 10
Three Bridges 4	a	15e29	16 00	16e29	17 00	17e29	18 00	18e29	18 40	19 00	19 40	20 40	21 40	22 41	00 18
Crawley	a		16 04		17 04		18 04			19 04					
Horsham 4	a		16 16		17 16		18 16			19 16					

Sundays

		SE	SE	SE	SE	SE	SE	SE	SE	SE	SE	SE	SE	SE	SE	SE
		88	55	55	55	55	55	55	55	55	55	55	55	55	55	55
			A	B	B	B	B	B	B	B	B	B	B	B	B	B
Tunbridge Wells 4	d			08 28	09 27	10 27	11 27	12 27	13 27	14 27	15 27	16 27	17 27	18 27	18 56	19 56
High Brooms	d			08 31	09 31	10 31	11 31	12 31	13 31	14 31	15 31	16 31	17 31	18 31	19 01	20 00
Tonbridge 4	a															
	d	06 57	07 54	08 54	09 54	10 54	11 54	12 54	13 54	14 54	15 54	16 54	17 54	18 54	19 54	20 54
Leigh (Kent)	d		07 58	08 58	09 58	10 58	11 58	12 58	13 58	14 58	15 58	16 58	17 58	18 58	19 58	20 58
Penshurst	d		08 01	09 01	10 01	11 01	12 01	13 01	14 01	15 01	16 01	17 01	18 01	19 01	20 01	21 01
Edenbridge	d	07 08	08 08	09 08	10 08	11 08	12 08	13 08	14 08	15 08	16 08	17 08	18 08	19 08	20 08	21 08
Godstone	d	07 14	08 14	09 14	10 14	11 14	12 14	13 14	14 14	15 14	16 14	17 14	18 14	19 14	20 14	21 14
Nutfield	d	07 20	08 20	09 20	10 20	11 20	12 20	13 20	14 20	15 20	16 20	17 20	18 20	19 20	20 20	21 20
Redhill	a	07 24	08 24	09 24	10 25	11 25	12 25	13 25	14 25	15 25	16 25	17 25	18 25	19 25	20 25	21 25
East Croydon	a	07 23	08 23	09 23	10 23	11 23	12 23	13 23	14 23	15 23	16 23	17 23	18 23	19 23	20 23	21 23
London Bridge 4	⊖ a	07b45	08b45	09b45	10b45	11b45	12b45	13b45	14b45	15b45	16b45	17b45	18b45	19b45	20b45	21b45
London Victoria 15	⊖ a	08b16	08b48	09b48	10b48	11b48	12b48	13b48	14b48	15b48	16b48	17b48	18b48	19b48	20b48	21b46
Redhill	d	07 29	08 29	09 29	10 30	11 30	12 30	13 30	14 30	15 30	16 30	17 30	18 30	19 30	20 30	21 30
Reigate	a	08 23	09 23	10 25	11 23	12 23	13 23	14 24	15 23	16 24	17 23	18 24	19 23	20 24	21 23	22 23
Gatwick Airport 10	✈ a	07 38	08 38	09 38	10 38	11 38	12 38	13 38	14 38	15 38	16 38	17 38	18 38	19 38	20 38	21 38
Three Bridges 4	a	07 43	08 43	09 43	10 43	11 43	12 43	13 43	14 43	15 43	16 43	17 43	18 43	19 43	20 43	21 43
Crawley	a															
Horsham 4	a															

For general notes see front of timetable
For details of catering facilities see Directory of Train Operators

A From Gillingham (Kent) (Table 208)
B From Maidstone West (Table 208)
b Change at Redhill and East Croydon
c Change at East Croydon
e Change at Redhill

For details of Bank Holiday service alterations please see first page of Table 195

Horsham, Gatwick Airport and London → Tonbridge and Tunbridge Wells via Redhill

Network Diagram - see first page of Table 206

Miles	Miles			SE	SE	SE	SE	SE	SE	SE	SE	SN	SE	SN	SE	SN	SE	SN	SE
				MX															
				88	88	88	88	43	55	88	13		13		13		13		13
												1		1		1		1	
									A										
0	—	**Horsham 4**	d									09 30		10 32		11 32		12 30	
7	—	Crawley	d									09 44		10 44		11 44		12 44	
8½	—	Three Bridges 4	d		05 40	06 32	07 08	07b36	07 58	08 32	09b18	09 48	10b03	10 48	11b03	11 48	12b03	12 48	13b03
11¼	—	**Gatwick Airport 10** ✈	d		05 54	06 37	07 13	07b41	08 04	08 37	09b23	09 52	10b08	10 53	11b08	11 53	12b08	12 52	13b08
—	—	Reigate	d		05 34	06 34	07 18	07b51	08 07	08 42	09b24	09 37	10b19	10 35	11b17	11 34	12b19	12 34	13b18
17	—	**Redhill**	a		06 05							10 02		11 02		12 02		13 02	
—	—	**London Victoria 15** ⊖	d		05 02	06 21	06 32	07c23	07 36	08e17	09c02	09 32	10b02	10 32	11b02	11 32	12b02	12 32	13b02
—	—	**London Bridge 4** ⊖	d			05e55	06e21	07 34	07 34	08 23	09 11	09e25	10 03	10e26	11 03	11e26	12 03	12e26	13 03
—	—	East Croydon	d		05 22	06 39	06 49	07 49	07 52	08 38	09 26	09 48	10 21	10 48	11 21	11 48	12 21	12 48	13 21
—	0	**Redhill**	d	23p53	06 09	06 58	07 35	08 05	08 29	08 59	09 44	10 07	10 39	11 07	11 39	12 07	12 39	13 07	13 39
—	2	Nutfield	d		06 13	07 02	07 39	08 10	08 33	09 03		10 11	10 43	11 11	11 43	12 11	12 43	13 11	13 43
—	5¾	Godstone	d		06 19	07 08	07 45	08 15	08 39	09 09		10 17	10 49	11 17	11 49	12 17	12 49	13 17	13 49
—	10½	Edenbridge	d	00 04	06 24	07 13	07 50	08 21	08 44	09 14	09 57	10 22	10 54	11 22	11 54	12 22	12 54	13 22	13 54
—	15½	Penshurst	d		06 31	07 20	07 57	08 27	08 51	09 21		10 29	11 01	11 29	12 01	12 29	13 01	13 29	14 01
—	17¼	Leigh (Kent)	d		06 34	07 23	08 02	08 30	08 54	09 24		10 32	11 04	11 32	12 04	12 32	13 04	13 32	14 04
—	19¾	**Tonbridge 4**	a	00 15	06 42	07 27	08 06	08 35	08 59	09 28	10 08	10 37	11 08	11 37	12 08	12 37	13 08	13 37	14 08
—	—		d					08 39			10 09	10 38	11 09	11 38	12 09	12 38	13 09	13 38	14 09
—	—	High Brooms	a	00 27	07 27	08 00	08 15	08 45	09 35	09 43	10 15	10 43	11 15	11 43	12 15	12 43	13 15	13 43	14 15
—	—	**Tunbridge Wells 4**	a	00 31	07 30	08 04	08 19	08 49		09 47	10 19	10 47	11 19	11 47	12 19	12 47	13 19	13 47	14 19

		SN	SE	SN	SE	SN	SE	SE	SE	SE	SE	SE	SE	SE	SE	SE	SE	SE
			13		13		13	88	13	88	88	88	13	88	88	88	88	88
		1		1		1												
												A						
Horsham 4	d	13 32		14 32		15 32												
Crawley	d	13 44		14 44		15 44												
Three Bridges 4	d	13 48	14b03	14 48	15b03	15 48	16b03	16 33	17b03	17 33	18 03	18 33	19b03	19 34	20 48	21 48	22 48	23 18
Gatwick Airport 10 ✈	d	13 53	14b08	14 53	15b08	15 53	16b08	16 38	17b08	17 38	18 08	18 38	19b08	19 39	20 53	21 53	22 53	23 23
Reigate	d	13 34	14b19	14 34	15b18	15 34	16b21	16 40	17b14	17 44	18 06	18 38	18b58	19 47	20 46	21 44	22 44	
Redhill	a	14 02		15 02		16 02									21 01	22 01	23 01	
London Victoria 15 ⊖	d	13 32	14b02	14 32	15b02	15 32	16b02	16 32	16c47	17e24	17 40	18 10	18c40	19 32	20 32	21 32	22 32	23 10
London Bridge 4 ⊖	d	13e26	14 03	14e26	15 03	15e26	16 03	16e26	16 57	17 32		18e03	18 48	19e27	20e28	21e15	22e15	23e00
East Croydon	d	13 48	14 21	14 48	15 21	15 48	16 21	16 48	17 11	17 50	17 57	18 26	19 06	19 48	20 48	21 48	22 48	23 28
Redhill	d	14 07	14 39	15 07	15 40	16 07	16 40	17 07	17 28	18 07	18 23	18 55	19 24	20 08	21 07	22 07	23 10	23 53
Nutfield	d	14 11	14 43	15 11	15 44	16 11	16 44	17 11	17 32	18 11	18 27	18 59	19 28	20 12	21 11	22 11	23 14	
Godstone	d	14 17	14 49	15 17	15 50	16 17	16 50	17 17	17 38	18 17	18 33	19 05	19 34	20 18	21 17	22 17	23 20	
Edenbridge	d	14 22	14 54	15 22	15 55	16 22	16 55	17 22	17 43	18 22	18 38	19 10	19 39	20 23	21 22	22 22	23 25	00 04
Penshurst	d	14 29	15 01	15 29	16 02	16 29	17 02	17 29	17 50	18 29	18 45	19 17	19 46	20 30	21 29	22 29	23 32	
Leigh (Kent)	d	14 32	15 04	15 32	16 05	16 32	17 05	17 32	17 53	18 32	18 48	19 20	19 49	20 33	21 32	22 32	23 35	
Tonbridge 4	a	14 37	15 08	15 36	16 09	16 36	17 11	17 36	17 57	18 36	18 52	19 24	19 56	20 37	21 37	22 37	23 39	00 15
	d	14 38	15 09		16 13													
High Brooms	a	14 43	15 15	15 51	16 19	17 05	17 39		18 13	18 58	19 22	19 37	20 23	21 05	22 05	23 11	00 07	00 27
Tunbridge Wells 4	a	14 47	15 19	15 55	16 23	17 09	17 44		18 18	19 04	19 28	19 41	20 28	21 09	22 10	23 15	00 12	00 31

Saturdays

		SE	SE	SN	SN	SE	SN	SE	SN	SE	SN	SE	SN	SE	SN	SE	SN	SE
		88	88			13		13		13		13		13		13		13
				1	1		1		1		1		1		1		1	
Horsham 4	d			06 32	07 32		08 32		09 32		10 32		11 32		12 32		13 32	
Crawley	d			06 44	07 44		08 44		09 44		10 44		11 44		12 44		13 44	
Three Bridges 4	d		05 33	06 48	07 48	08b03	08 48	09b03	09 48	10b03	10 48	11b03	11 48	12b03	12 48	13b03	13 48	14b03
Gatwick Airport 10 ✈	d		05 45	06 53	07 53	08b08	08 53	09b08	09 53	10b08	10 53	11b08	11 53	12b08	12 53	13b08	13 53	14b08
Reigate	d		05 34	06 34	07 34	08b19	08 34	09b18	09 34	10b19	10 34	11b18	11 34	12b19	12 34	13b18	13 34	14b19
Redhill	a			07 02	08 02		09 02		10 02		11 02		12 02		13 02		14 02	
London Victoria 15 ⊖	d		05 32	06 10	07 32	08b02	08 32	09b02	09 32	10b02	10 32	11b02	11 32	12b02	12 32	13b02	13 32	14b02
London Bridge 4 ⊖	d			06e08	07e26	08 03	08e26	09 03	09e26	10 03	10e26	11 03	11e26	12 03	12e26	13 03	13e26	14 03
East Croydon	d		05 48	06 28	07 48	08 21	08 48	09 21	09 48	10 21	10 48	11 21	11 48	12 21	12 48	13 21	13 48	14 21
Redhill	d	23p53	06 11	07 07	08 07	08 39	09 07	09 39	10 07	10 39	11 07	11 39	12 07	12 39	13 07	13 39	14 07	14 39
Nutfield	d		06 15	07 11	08 11	08 43	09 11	09 43	10 11	10 43	11 11	11 43	12 11	12 43	13 11	13 43	14 11	14 43
Godstone	d		06 20	07 17	08 17	08 49	09 17	09 49	10 17	10 49	11 17	11 49	12 17	12 49	13 17	13 49	14 17	14 49
Edenbridge	d	00 04	06 26	07 22	08 22	08 54	09 22	09 54	10 22	10 54	11 22	11 54	12 22	12 54	13 22	13 54	14 22	14 54
Penshurst	d		06 32	07 29	08 29	09 01	09 29	10 01	10 29	11 01	11 29	12 01	12 29	13 01	13 29	14 01	14 29	15 01
Leigh (Kent)	d		06 36	07 32	08 32	09 04	09 32	10 04	10 32	11 04	11 32	12 04	12 32	13 04	13 32	14 04	14 32	15 04
Tonbridge 4	a	00 15	06 40	07 36	08 37	09 08	09 37	10 08	10 37	11 08	11 37	12 08	12 37	13 08	13 37	14 08	14 37	15 08
	d				08 38	09 09	09 38	10 09	10 38	11 09	11 38	12 09	12 38	13 09	13 38	14 09	14 38	15 09
High Brooms	a	00 27	07 06	08 06	08 43	09 15	09 43	10 15	10 43	11 15	11 43	12 15	12 43	13 15	13 43	14 15	14 43	15 15
Tunbridge Wells 4	a	00 31	07 10	08 10	08 47	09 19	09 47	10 19	10 47	11 19	11 47	12 19	12 47	13 19	13 47	14 19	14 47	15 19

For general notes see front of timetable
For details of catering facilities see Directory of Train Operators

A To Strood (Table 208)
b Change at Redhill
c Change at East Croydon
e Change at East Croydon and Redhill

Table 209

Saturdays

Horsham, Gatwick Airport and London → Tonbridge and Tunbridge Wells via Redhill

Network Diagram - see first page of Table 206

		SN	SE	SN	SE	SN	SE	SN	SE	SE	SE	SE	SE	SE	SE	SE
			13		13		13		13	88	13	55	88	88	88	88
		1		1		1		1								
Horsham 4	d	14 32		15 32		16 32		17 32								
Crawley	d	14 44		15 44		16 44		17 44								
Three Bridges 4	d	14 48	15b03	15 48	16b03	16 48	17b03	17 48	18b03	18 48	19b03	19 48	20 48	21 48	22 48	23 18
Gatwick Airport 10 ✈	d	14 53	15b08	15 53	16b08	16 53	17b08	17 53	18b08	18 52	19b08	19 53	20 53	21 53	22 53	23 23
Reigate	d	14 34	15b18	15 34	16b19	16 34	17b18	17 34	18b19	18 34	19b18	19 34	20 34	21 40	22 48	
Redhill	a	15 02		16 02		17 02		18 02		19 00		20 01	21 02	22 01	23 01	
London Victoria 15 ⊖	d	14 32	15b02	15 32	16b02	16 32	17b02	17 32	18b02	18 32	19b02	19 32	20 32	21 32	22 32	23 10
London Bridge 4 ⊖	d	14c26	15 03	15c26	16 03	16c26	17 03	17c26	18 03	18c26	19 03	19c26	20c15	21c15	22c15	23c00
East Croydon	d	14 48	15 21	15 48	16 21	16 48	17 21	17 48	18 21	18 48	19 21	19 48	20 48	21 48	22 48	23 28
Redhill	d	15 07	15 39	16 07	16 39	17 07	17 39	18 07	18 39	19 06	19 39	20 07	21 07	22 07	23 07	23 54
Nutfield	d	15 11	15 43	16 11	16 43	17 11	17 43	18 11	18 43	19 10	19 43	20 11	21 11	22 11	23 11	
Godstone	d	15 16	15 49	16 17	16 49	17 17	17 49	18 17	18 49	19 16	19 49	20 17	21 17	22 17	23 17	
Edenbridge	d	15 22	15 54	16 22	16 54	17 22	17 54	18 22	18 54	19 21	19 54	20 22	21 22	22 22	23 22	00 06
Penshurst	d	15 28	16 01	16 29	17 01	17 29	18 01	18 29	19 01	19 28	20 01	20 29	21 29	22 29	23 29	
Leigh (Kent)	d	15 32	16 04	16 32	17 04	17 32	18 04	18 32	19 04	19 31	20 04	20 32	21 32	22 32	23 32	
Tonbridge 4	a	15 37	16 08	16 37	17 08	17 37	18 08	18 37	19 08	19 37	20 08	20 37	21 37	22 37	23 37	00 16
	d	15 38	16 09	16 38	17 09	17 38	18 09	18 38	19 09							
High Brooms	a	15 43	16 15	16 43	17 15	17 43	18 15	18 43	19 15	20 06	20 36	20 55	21 56	23 00	23 55	00 27
Tunbridge Wells 4	a	15 47	16 19	16 47	17 19	17 47	18 19	18 47	19 19	20 10	20 40	20 59	21 59	23 04	23 59	00 31

Sundays

		SE	SE	SE	SE	SE	SE	SE	SE	SE	SE	SE	SE	SE	SE	SE	SE
		88	55	55	55	55	55	55	55	55	55	55	55	55	55	55	55
			A	A	A	A	A	A	A	A	A	A	A	A	A	B	
Horsham 4	d																
Crawley	d																
Three Bridges 4	d		07 50	08 50	09 50	10 50	11 50	12 50	13 50	14 50	15 50	16 50	17 50	18 50	19 50	20 50	21 50
Gatwick Airport 10 ✈	d		07 55	08 55	09 55	10 55	11 55	12 55	13 55	14 55	15 55	16 55	17 55	18 55	19 55	20 55	21 55
Reigate	d		07 13	08 13	09 12	10 15	11 12	12 15	13 12	14 15	15 12	16 15	17 12	18 15	19 12	20 15	21 12
Redhill	a		08 03	09 03	10 03	11 03	12 03	13 03	14 03	15 03	16 03	17 03	18 03	19 03	20 03	21 03	22 03
London Victoria 15 ⊖	d		07 32	08 32	09 32	10 32	11 32	12 32	13 32	14 32	15 32	16 32	17 32	18 32	19 32	20 32	21 32
London Bridge 4 ⊖	d		07c11	08c14	09c14	10c14	11c14	12c14	13c14	14c14	15c14	16c14	17c14	18c14	19c14	20c14	21c14
East Croydon	d		07 51	08 51	09 51	10 51	11 51	12 51	13 51	14 51	15 51	16 51	17 51	18 51	19 51	20 51	21 51
Redhill	d	23p54	08 10	09 10	10 10	11 10	12 10	13 10	14 10	15 10	16 10	17 10	18 10	19 10	20 10	21 10	22 10
Nutfield	d		08 14	09 14	10 14	11 14	12 14	13 14	14 14	15 14	16 14	17 14	18 14	19 14	20 14	21 14	22 14
Godstone	d		08 20	09 20	10 20	11 20	12 20	13 20	14 20	15 20	16 20	17 20	18 20	19 20	20 20	21 20	22 20
Edenbridge	d	00 06	08 25	09 25	10 25	11 25	12 25	13 25	14 25	15 25	16 25	17 25	18 25	19 25	20 25	21 25	22 25
Penshurst	d		08 32	09 32	10 32	11 32	12 32	13 32	14 32	15 32	16 32	17 32	18 32	19 32	20 32	21 32	22 32
Leigh (Kent)	d		08 35	09 35	10 35	11 35	12 35	13 35	14 35	15 35	16 35	17 35	18 35	19 35	20 35	21 35	22 35
Tonbridge 4	a	00 16	08 40	09 40	10 40	11 40	12 40	13 40	14 40	15 40	16 40	17 40	18 40	19 40	20 40	21 40	22 39
	d																
High Brooms	a	00 27	09 00	10 00	11 00	12 00	13 00	14 00	15 00	16 00	17 00	18 00	19 00	20 03	21 04	22 03	23 03
Tunbridge Wells 4	a	00 31	09 04	10 04	11 04	12 04	13 04	14 04	15 04	16 04	17 04	18 04	19 04	20 07	21 07	22 07	23 07

For general notes see front of timetable
For details of catering facilities see Directory of Train Operators

A To Maidstone West (Table 208)
B To Gillingham (Kent) (Table 208)
b Change at Redhill
c Change at East Croydon and Redhill

Network Diagram for Table 212

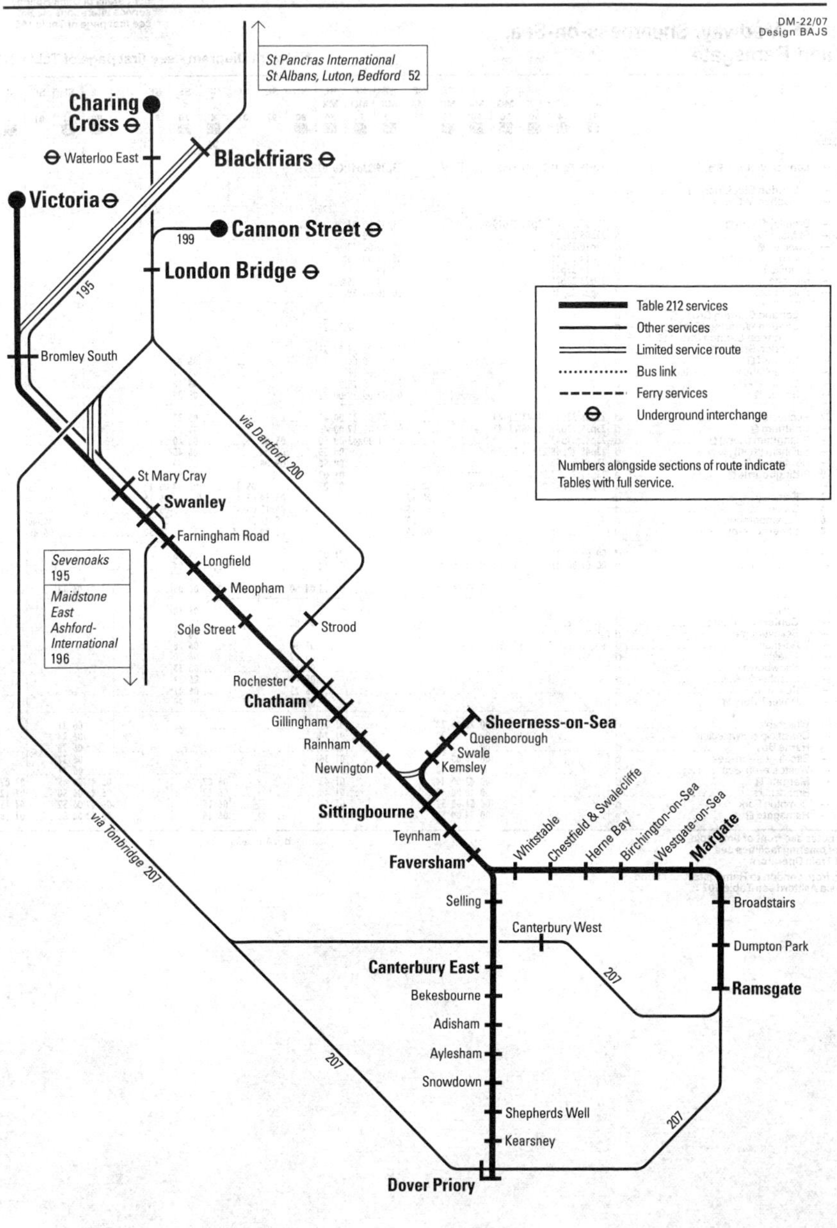
DM-22/07
Design BAJS
St Pancras International
St Albans, Luton, Bedford 52
Charing Cross
Waterloo East
Blackfriars
Victoria
Cannon Street
199
London Bridge
195
Bromley South
via Dartford 200
St Mary Cray
Swanley
Farningham Road
Longfield
Meopham
Sole Street
Strood
Sevenoaks 195
Maidstone East Ashford-International 196
Rochester
Chatham
Gillingham
Rainham
Newington
Sheerness-on-Sea
Queenborough
Swale
Kemsley
Sittingbourne
Teynham
Faversham
Whitstable
Chestfield & Swalecliffe
Herne Bay
Birchington-on-Sea
Westgate-on-Sea
Margate
Broadstairs
Dumpton Park
Ramsgate
via Tonbridge 207
Selling
Canterbury West
207
Canterbury East
Bekesbourne
Adisham
Aylesham
Snowdown
Shepherds Well
Kearsney
Dover Priory
Table 212 services
Other services
Limited service route
Bus link
Ferry services
Underground interchange
Numbers alongside sections of route indicate Tables with full service.

Table 212

Mondays to Fridays

For details of Bank Holiday service alterations please see first page of Table 195

London → Medway, Sheerness-on-Sea, Dover and Ramsgate

Network Diagram - see first page of Table 212

Miles	Miles	Miles			SE	SE	SE	SE	SE	SE	SE	SE	SE	SE	SE	SE	SE	SE	SE	SE		SE	SE	SE	SE
					MX	MO	MX	MO	MX	MO	MX	MX	MO	MX											
					92	54	50	50	50	50	01	22	54	50	80	97	01	4	20	01		90	81	01	4
					[1]	[1]	[1]	[1]	[1]	[1]		[1]	[1]	[1]	[1]			[1]	[1]			[1]	[1]		[1]
0	0	—	**London Victoria [15]**	⊖ d	22p39	22p41	23p03	23p03				23p39	23p41	00 03											
—	—	—	**London Blackfriars [3]**	⊖ d																					
—	—	—	Elephant & Castle	⊖ d																					
11	11	—	Bromley South [4]	d	22p59	23p01	23p19	23p19				23p58	00 01												
14¾	14¾	—	St Mary Cray	d	23p05	23p07						00 04	00 07												
17½	17½	—	Swanley [4]	d	23p10	23p12						00 09	00 12												
20½	20½	—	Farningham Road	d	23p14	23p16						00 13	00 16												
23½	23½	—	Longfield	d	23p19	23p21						00 18	00 21												
26	26	—	Meopham	d	23p23	23p25						00 23	00 25												
27	27	—	Sole Street	d	23p26	23p28						00 26	00 28												
—	—	—	**London Charing Cross [4]**	⊖ d								22 50	23 26	23 20											
—	—	—	**London Waterloo (East) [4]**	⊖ d								22 53	23 29	23 23											
—	—	0	**London Cannon Street [4]**	⊖ d																					
—	—	—	**London Bridge [4]**	⊖ d								22 59	23 34	23 29											
—	—	—	Dartford [4]	d								23 34	00 06						05 06						
—	—	—	Greenhithe for Bluewater	d								23 40	00 11						05 11						
—	—	—	Gravesend [4]	d								23 50	00 18						05 18						
—	—	—	Strood [4]	d								00 02	00 30	00 32					05 29						
33¾	33¾	32	Rochester [4]	d	23p36	23p37	23p43	23p44				00 35	00 37	00 43					05 33						
34¼	34¼	—	**Chatham [4]**	d	23p39	23p39	23p46	23p47				00 38	00 39	00 46					05 36						
36	36	—	**Gillingham (Kent) [4]**	d	23p43	23p43	23p49	23p50				00a41	00a43	00 50		05 00			05 40						
39	39	—	Rainham (Kent)	d	23p48	23p48	23p54	23p55						00 55		05 04			05 45						
41½	41½	—	Newington	d	23p52	23p52								00 58		05 08			05 49						
44¾	44¾	0	**Sittingbourne [4]**	a	23p57	23p57	00 01	00 02	←					01 03					05 54						
—	—	—		d	23p57	23p57	00 01	00 02	00 01		00 08			01 03			05 37		05 54	06 12				06 23	
—	—	2	Kemsley	d			→				00 12					05 14	05 41			06 16				06 27	
—	—	4	Swale	d							00x15					05x17	05x45			06x19				06x30	
—	—	6	Queenborough	d							00 20					05 22	05 49			06 24				06b40	
—	—	8	**Sheerness-on-Sea**	a							00 26					05 28	05 55			06 30				06 46	
47½	47½	—	Teynham	d	00 01	00 01								01 07					05 58						
52	52	—	**Faversham [2]**	a	00 07	00 07		00 10	00 11	←				01 12					06 04						
—	—	—		d				00 14	00 12	00 14				01 13	04 50				06 05				06 13		
—	55½	—	Selling	d				→											06 10						
—	61¾	—	**Canterbury East [4]**	d											05 02				06 19						
—	64¾	—	Bekesbourne	d															06 23						
—	67¾	—	Adisham	d											05 10				06 28						
—	68¾	—	Aylesham	d											05 12				06 30						
—	69¾	—	Snowdown	d											05 15				06 33						
—	71¾	—	Shepherds Well	d											05 19				06 37						
—	75	—	Kearsney	d											05 23				06 41						
—	77¼	—	**Dover Priory [4]**	a											05 28				06 48						
59	—	—	Whitstable	d					00 20	00 22				01 21									06 21		
60½	—	—	Chestfield & Swalecliffe	d					00 23	00 25				01 24									06 24		
62¾	—	—	**Herne Bay**	d					00 27	00 28				01 27									06 28		
70¾	—	—	Birchington-on-Sea	d					00 36	00 37				01 36									06 37		
72½	—	—	Westgate-on-Sea	d					00 39	00 40				01 39									06 41		
73¾	—	—	**Margate [4]**	d					00 43	00 44				01 43				06 07				06 41	06 45		07 07
77	—	—	Broadstairs	d					00 48	00 49				01 48				06 12				06 46	06 50		07 12
78½	—	—	Dumpton Park	d					00 51	00 52				01 51				06 15				06 49	06 52		07 15
79¼	—	—	**Ramsgate [4]**	a					00 54	00 55				01 54				06 18				06 52	06 56		07 18

For general notes see front of timetable
For details of catering facilities see Directory of Train Operators

For services from London to Ramsgate, Dover and Canterbury via Ashford see Table 207

b Arr. 0635

For details of Bank Holiday service alterations please see first page of Table 195

London → Medway, Sheerness-on-Sea, Dover and Ramsgate

Network Diagram - see first page of Table 212

		SE 88 1	SE 54 1	SE 01	SE 80 1	SE 01	SE 64 1 A	SE 81 1	SE 90 1	SE 54 1	SE 80 1	SE 01	SE 37 1	SE 81 1	SE 01	SE 37 1	SE 01	SE 90 1	SE 50 1	SE 37 1	SE 92 1	SE 50 1		SE 01
London Victoria 15 ⊖	d		05 32							06 16			06 39			07 07			07 33		07 39	08 03		
London Blackfriars 3 ⊖	d									05 27			06 08			06 42			07 09		07 24			
Elephant & Castle ⊖	d									05 30			06 12			06 45			07 12		07 27			
Bromley South 4	d		05 48							06 34			06 59			07 27			07 52		08 01	08 20		
St Mary Cray	d		05 55							06 41			07 05			07 34					08 07			
Swanley 4	d		06 00							06 46			07 10			07 39					08 12			
Farningham Road	d		06 05							06 51			07 14			07 44					08 16			
Longfield	d		06 10							06 56			07 19			07 48					08 21			
Meopham	d		06 15							07 01			07 23			07 53					08 25			
Sole Street	d		06 17							07 03			07 26			07 56					08 28			
London Charing Cross 4 ⊖	d		04 56							05 26			06 02			06 40			06 40			07 20		
London Waterloo (East) 4 ⊖	d		04 59							05 29			06 05			06 43			06 43			07 23		
London Cannon Street 4 ⊖	d												05b50			06b30			06c30			07b04		
London Bridge 4 ⊖	d		05 04							05 34			06 10			06 48			06 48			07 28		
Dartford 4	d		05 42							06 12			06 46			07 28			07 28			08 06		
Greenhithe for Bluewater	d		05 48							06 18			06e26			07 33			07 33			08 12		
Gravesend 4	d		05 56							06 26			06 56			07 40			07 40			08 20		
Strood 4	d		06 08							06 38			07 08			07 52			07 52			08 32		
Rochester 4	d		06 26							07 15			07 39			08 06					08 38	08 45		
Chatham 4	d		06 29							07 17			07 42			08 08			08 19		08 41	08 48		
Gillingham (Kent) 4	d		06 33							07 21			07 45			08 12			08 23		08 45	08 51		
Rainham (Kent)	d		06 38							07 26			07 50			08 17			08 28		08 50	08 56		
Newington	d		06 42							07 30			07 54			08 21					08 54			
Sittingbourne 4	a		06 47							07 35			07 59			08 26			08 36		08 59	09 03		
	d		06 48	06 58		07 19				07 35		07 46	08 04		08 15	08 27	08 28		08 37		08 59	09 04		09 05
Kemsley	d			07 04		07f26						07 50			08 19		08 32							09 09
Swale	d			07x08		07x32						07x55			08x22		08x36							09x12
Queenborough	d			07 12		07 36						07 59			08 27		08 41							09 17
Sheerness-on-Sea	a			07 18		07 41						08 04			08 32		08 47							09 23
Teynham	d		06 52							07 39			08 09			08 31					09 03			
Faversham 2	a		07 01							07 45			08 15			08 37			08 45	⟵	09 09	09 12		
	d		07 02		07 04			07 20		07 46	07 53		08 17	08 19		08 49			08 47	08 49		09 15	09 18	
Selling	d				07 09						07 58		08 22			⟶				08 54				
Canterbury East 4	d				07 18						08 08		08 32							09 04			09 32	
Bekesbourne	d				07 22						08 12		08 36							09 08				
Adisham	d				07 27						08 17		08 41							09 13				
Aylesham	d				07 29						08 19		08 43							09 15				
Snowdown	d				07 32						08 22		08 46							09 18				
Shepherds Well	d				07 36						08 26		08 50							09 22				
Kearsney	d				07 40						08 30		08 54							09 26				
Dover Priory 4 ⛴	a				07 45						08 36		09 00							09 32			09 52	
Whitstable	d		07 10					07 28		07 54				08 28					08 56			09 23		
Chestfield & Swalecliffe	d		07 13					07 31		07 57				08 31					08 59					
Herne Bay	d		07 17					07 35		08 01				08 35					09 03			09 28		
Birchington-on-Sea	d		07 26					07 44		08 10				08 44					09 12			09 37		
Westgate-on-Sea	d		07 30					07 48		08 14				08 47					09 16					
Margate 4	d	07 28	07 34				07 43	07 52	08 13	08 18				08 52				09 04	09 20			09 43		
Broadstairs	d	07 33	07 39				07 48	07 57	08 18	08 23				08 57				09 09	09 25			09 48		
Dumpton Park	d	07 36	07 41				07 50	07 59	08 21	08 26				09 00				09 12	09 27					
Ramsgate 4 ⛴	a	07 39	07 45				07 53	08 03	08 24	08 29				09 03				09 15	09 30			09 52		

For general notes see front of timetable
For details of catering facilities see Directory of Train Operators

For services from London to Ramsgate, Dover and Canterbury via Ashford see Table 207

A To London Victoria (Table 196)
b Change at London Bridge and Rochester
c Change at London Bridge and Chatham
e Change at Gravesend and Rochester
f Arr. 0723

For details of Bank Holiday service alterations please see first page of Table 195

London → Medway, Sheerness-on-Sea, Dover and Ramsgate

Network Diagram - see first page of Table 212

		SE	SE	SE		SE	SE	SE		SE		SE	SE	SE		SE	SE	SE		SE	SE	SE	SE		SE
		92	90	50		01	92	50		01		92	90	50		01	92	50		01	92	90	50		01
		1	1	1			1	1				1	1	1			1	1			1	1	1		
London Victoria [15]	⊖ d	08 09		08 33			08 39	09 03				09 09		09 33			09 39	10 03			10 09		10 33		
London Blackfriars [3]	⊖ d	07 53					08 20	08 43						09 13				09 43					10 13		
Elephant & Castle	⊖ d	07 56					08 23	08 46						09 16				09 46					10 16		
Bromley South [4]	d	08 31		08 51			08 59	09 19				09 29		09 50			09 59	10 19			10 29		10 49		
St Mary Cray	d	08 37					09 05					09 35					10 05				10 35				
Swanley [4]	d	08 42					09 10					09 40					10 10				10 40				
Farningham Road	d	08 47					09 14					09 44					10 14				10 44				
Longfield	d	08 51					09 19					09 49					10 19				10 49				
Meopham	d	08 56					09 24					09 53					10 23				10 53				
Sole Street	d	08 58					09 26					09 56					10 26				10 56				
London Charing Cross [4]	⊖ d	07b45					08b08					08b41					09 20				09 52				
London Waterloo (East) [4]	⊖ d	07b48					08b11					08b44					09 23				09 55				
London Cannon Street [4]	⊖ d	07 54					08 17					08 50					09b20				09b48				
London Bridge [4]	⊖ d	07 58					08 21					08 54					09 29				10 00				
Dartford [4]	d	08 34					09 02					09 34					10 04				10 34				
Greenhithe for Bluewater	d	08 39					09 07					09 39					10 09				10 39				
Gravesend [4]	d	08 46					09 14					09 46					10 16				10 46				
Strood [4]	d	08 58					09 26					09 58					10 28				10 58				
Rochester [4]	d	09 09		09 16			09 36	09 43				10 05		10 15			10 35	10 44			11 05		11 13		
Chatham [4]	d	09 11		09 18			09 39	09 47				10 08		10 17			10 38	10 47			11 08		11 17		
Gillingham (Kent) [4]	d	09 15		09 22			09 43	09 50				10 12		10 21			10 41	10 50			11 11		11 20		
Rainham (Kent)	d	09 20		09 26			09 48	09 55				10 17		10 26			10 46	10 55			11 16		11 25		
Newington	d	09 24					09 52					10 21					10 50				11 20				
Sittingbourne [4]	a	09 29		09 34			09 57	10 02				10 26		10 33			10 55	11 02			11 25		11 32		
	d	09 29		09 34		09 36	09 57	10 02		10 05		10 26		10 33		10 35	10 55	11 02		11 05	11 25		11 32		11 35
Kemsley	d					09 40				10 09						10 39				11 09					11 39
Swale	d					09x43				10x12						10x42				11x12					11x42
Queenborough	d					09 47				10 17						10 47				11 17					11 47
Sheerness-on-Sea	a					09 53				10 23						10 53				11 23					11 53
Teynham	d	09 33					10 01					10 30					10 59				11 29				
Faversham [2]	a	09 39		09 42			10 07	10 10				10 36		10 41			11 05	11 10			11 35		11 40		
	d			09 46	09 48			10 14	10 16					10 44	10 47			11 14	11 16				11 44	11 46	
Selling	d				09 53										10 52									11 51	
Canterbury East [4]	d				10c08				10 28						11 01				11 28					12 00	
Bekesbourne	d				10 13										11 05									12 05	
Adisham	d				10 17										11 10									12 09	
Aylesham	d				10 20										11 12									12 12	
Snowdown	d				10 22										11 15									12 14	
Shepherds Well	d				10 26										11 19									12 18	
Kearsney	d				10 31										11 23									12 23	
Dover Priory [4]	a				10 35				10 45						11 27				11 44					12 28	
Whitstable	d			09 55				10 22						10 53				11 22					11 52		
Chestfield & Swalecliffe	d			09 58										10 56									11 55		
Herne Bay	d			10 02				10 27						11 00				11 27					11 59		
Birchington-on-Sea	d			10 11				10 35						11 08				11 35					12 08		
Westgate-on-Sea	d			10 15										11 11									12 11		
Margate [4]	d		10 04	10 19				10 41					11 04	11 15				11 41				12 04	12 15		
Broadstairs	d		10 09	10 24				10 46					11 09	11 21				11 46				12 09	12 20		
Dumpton Park	d		10 12	10 27									11 12	11 23								12 12	12 23		
Ramsgate [4]	a		10 15	10 30				10 51					11 15	11 27				11 51				12 15	12 26		

For general notes see front of timetable
For details of catering facilities see Directory of Train Operators

For services from London to Ramsgate, Dover and Canterbury via Ashford see Table 207

b Change at London Bridge and Rochester
c Arr. 1002

For details of Bank Holiday service alterations please see first page of Table 195

London → Medway, Sheerness-on-Sea, Dover and Ramsgate

Network Diagram - see first page of Table 212

		SE 92 [1]	SE 50 [1]		SE 01		SE 92 [1]	SE 90 [1]	SE 50 [1]		SE 01	SE 92 [1]	SE 50 [1]		SE 01	SE 92 [1]	SE 90 [1]	SE 50 [1]		SE 01	SE 92 [1]	SE 50 [1]			SE 01
			trolley						trolley				trolley					trolley				trolley			
London Victoria [15]	⊖ d	10 39	11 03				11 09		11 33			11 39	12 03			12 09		12 33			12 39	13 03			
London Blackfriars [3]	⊖ d		10 43						11 13				11 43					12 13				12 43			
Elephant & Castle	⊖ d		10 46						11 16				11 46					12 16				12 46			
Bromley South [4]	d	10 59	11 19				11 29		11 49			11 59	12 19			12 29		12 49			12 59	13 19			
St Mary Cray	d	11 05					11 35					12 05				12 35					13 05				
Swanley [4]	d	11 10					11 40					12 10				12 40					13 10				
Farningham Road	d	11 14					11 44					12 14				12 44					13 14				
Longfield	d	11 19					11 49					12 19				12 49					13 19				
Meopham	d	11 23					11 53					12 23				12 53					13 23				
Sole Street	d	11 26					11 56					12 26				12 56					13 26				
London Charing Cross [4]	⊖ d	10 20					10 50					11 20				11 50					12 20				
London Waterloo (East) [4]	⊖ d	10 23					10 53					11 23				11 53					12 23				
London Cannon Street [4]	⊖ d	10b18					10b48					11b18				11b48					12b18				
London Bridge [4]	⊖ d	10 29					10 59					11 29				11 59					12 29				
Dartford [4]	d	11 04					11 34					12 04				12 34					13 04				
Greenhithe for Bluewater	d	11 09					11 39					12 09				12 39					13 09				
Gravesend [4]	d	11 16					11 46					12 16				12 46					13 16				
Strood [4]	d	11 28					11 58					12 28				12 58					13 28				
Rochester [4]	d	11 35	11 43				12 05		12 13			12 35	12 43			13 05		13 13			13 35	13 43			
Chatham [4]	d	11 38	11 47				12 08		12 17			12 38	12 47			13 08		13 17			13 38	13 47			
Gillingham (Kent) [4]	d	11 41	11 50				12 11		12 20			12 41	12 50			13 11		13 20			13 41	13 50			
Rainham (Kent)	d	11 46	11 55				12 16		12 25			12 46	12 55			13 16		13 25			13 46	13 55			
Newington	d	11 50					12 20					12 50				13 20					13 50				
Sittingbourne [4]	a	11 55	12 02				12 25		12 32			12 55	13 02			13 25		13 32			13 55	14 02			
	d	11 55	12 02		12 05		12 25		12 32		12 35	12 55	13 02		13 05	13 25		13 32		13 35	13 55	14 02			14 05
Kemsley	d				12 09						12 39				13 09					13 39					14 09
Swale	d				12x12						12x42				13x12					13x42					14x12
Queenborough	d				12 17						12 47				13 17					13 47					14 17
Sheerness-on-Sea	a				12 23						12 53				13 23					13 53					14 23
Teynham	d	11 59					12 29					12 59				13 29					13 59				
Faversham [2]	a	12 05	12 10				12 35		12 40			13 05	13 10			13 35		13 40			14 05	14 10			
	d		12 14	12 16					12 44	12 46			13 14	13 16				13 44	13 46			14 14	14 16		
Selling	d									12 51									13 51						
Canterbury East [4]	d			12 28						13 00				13 28					14 00				14 28		
Bekesbourne	d									13 05									14 05						
Adisham	d									13 09									14 09						
Aylesham	d									13 12									14 12						
Snowdown	d									13 14									14 14						
Shepherds Well	d									13 18									14 18						
Kearsney	d									13 23									14 23						
Dover Priory [4]	⛴ a			12 44						13 28				13 44					14 28				14 44		
Whitstable	d		12 22						12 52				13 22					13 52				14 22			
Chestfield & Swalecliffe	d								12 55									13 55							
Herne Bay	d		12 27						12 59				13 27					13 59				14 27			
Birchington-on-Sea	d		12 35						13 08				13 35					14 08				14 35			
Westgate-on-Sea	d								13 11									14 11							
Margate [4]	d		12 41					13 04	13 15				13 41				14 04	14 15				14 41			
Broadstairs	d		12 46					13 09	13 20				13 46				14 09	14 20				14 46			
Dumpton Park	d							13 12	13 23								14 12	14 23							
Ramsgate [4]	✈ a		12 51					13 15	13 26				13 51				14 15	14 26				14 51			

For general notes see front of timetable
For details of catering facilities see Directory of Train Operators

For services from London to Ramsgate, Dover and Canterbury via Ashford see Table 207

b Change at London Bridge and Rochester

For details of Bank Holiday service alterations please see first page of Table 195

London → Medway, Sheerness-on-Sea, Dover and Ramsgate

Network Diagram - see first page of Table 212

		SE 92 1	SE 90 1	SE 50 1		SE 01	SE 92 1	SE 90 1	SE 50 1		SE 01	SE 92 1	SE 50 1		SE 01	SE 92 1	SE 90 1	SE 50 1		SE 01	SE 92 1	SE 50 1		SE 01
London Victoria 15	⊖ d	13 09		13 33			13 39		14 03			14 09	14 33			14 39		15 03			15 09	15 33		
London Blackfriars 3	⊖ d			13 13					13 43				14 13					14 43				15 13		
Elephant & Castle	⊖ d			13 16					13 46				14 16					14 46				15 16		
Bromley South 4	d	13 29		13 49			13 59		14 19			14 29	14 49			14 59		15 19			15 29	15 49		
St Mary Cray	d	13 35					14 05					14 35				15 05					15 35			
Swanley 4	d	13 40					14 10					14 40				15 10					15 40			
Farningham Road	d	13 44					14 14					14 44				15 14					15 44			
Longfield	d	13 49					14 19					14 49				15 19					15 49			
Meopham	d	13 53					14 23					14 53				15 23					15 53			
Sole Street	d	13 56					14 26					14 56				15 26					15 56			
London Charing Cross 4	⊖ d	12 50					13 20					13 50				14 20					14 50			
London Waterloo (East) 4	⊖ d	12 53					13 23					13 53				14 23					14 53			
London Cannon Street 4	⊖ d	12b48					13b18					13b48				14b18					14b48			
London Bridge 4	⊖ d	12 59					13 29					13 59				14 29					14 59			
Dartford 4	d	13 34					14 04					14 34				15 04					15 34			
Greenhithe for Bluewater	d	13 39					14 09					14 39				15 09					15 39			
Gravesend 4	d	13 46					14 16					14 46				15 16					15 46			
Strood 4	d	13 58					14 28					14 58				15 28					15 58			
Rochester 4	d	14 05		14 13			14 35		14 43			15 05	15 13			15 35		15 43			16 05	16 13		
Chatham 4	d	14 08		14 17			14 38		14 47			15 08	15 17			15 38		15 47			16 08	16 16		
Gillingham (Kent) 4	d	14 11		14 21			14 41		14 50			15 11	15 20			15 41		15 51			16 12	16 20		
Rainham (Kent)	d	14 16		14 26			14 46		14 55			15 16	15 25			15 46		15 56			16 17	16 25		
Newington	d	14 20					14 50					15 20				15 50					16 21			
Sittingbourne 4	a	14 25		14 33			14 55		15 02			15 25	15 32			15 55		16 03			16 26	16 32		
	d	14 25		14 33		14 35	14 55		15 02		15 05	15 25	15 32		15 35	15 55		16 03		16 05	16 26	16 32		16 35
Kemsley	d					14 39					15 09				15 39					16 09				16 39
Swale	d					14x43					15x13				15x43					16x13				16x43
Queenborough	d					14 47					15 17				15 47					16 17				16 47
Sheerness-on-Sea	a					14 53					15 23				15 53					16 23				16 53
Teynham	d	14 29					14 59					15 29				15 59					16 30			
Faversham 2	a	14 35		14 41			15 05		15 10			15 35	15 40			16 05		16 11			16 36	16 40		
	d			14 44	14 47				15 14	15 16			15 44	15 46				16 15	16 17			16 44	16 47	
Selling	d				14 52									15 51					16 22				16 52	
Canterbury East 4	d				15 02					15 28				16 00					16 32				17 01	
Bekesbourne	d				15 06									16 05					16 36				17 06	
Adisham	d				15 11									16 09					16 41				17 10	
Aylesham	d				15 13									16 12					16 43				17 13	
Snowdown	d				15 16									16 14					16 46				17 15	
Shepherds Well	d				15 20									16 18					16 50				17 19	
Kearsney	d				15 24									16 23					16 54				17 24	
Dover Priory 4	⛴ a				15 30					15 44				16 27					16 59				17 28	
Whitstable	d			14 52					15 22				15 52					16 23				16 52		
Chestfield & Swalecliffe	d			14 55									15 55					16 26				16 55		
Herne Bay	d			14 59					15 27				15 59					16 30				16 59		
Birchington-on-Sea	d			15 08					15 35				16 08					16 39				17 08		
Westgate-on-Sea	d			15 11									16 11					16 42				17 11		
Margate 4	d		14 50	15 15				15 36	15 41				16 15				16 36	16 47				17 16		
Broadstairs	d		14 55	15 20				15 41	15 46				16 20				16 41	16 52				17 21		
Dumpton Park	d		14 58	15 23				15 44					16 23				16 44	16 55				17 24		
Ramsgate 4	✈ a		15 01	15 26				15 47	15 51				16 26				16 47	16 58				17 27		

For general notes see front of timetable
For details of catering facilities see Directory of Train Operators

For services from London to Ramsgate, Dover and Canterbury via Ashford see Table 207

b Change at London Bridge and Rochester

For details of Bank Holiday service alterations please see first page of Table 195

London → Medway, Sheerness-on-Sea, Dover and Ramsgate

Network Diagram - see first page of Table 212

		SE 92 1	SE 50 1		SE 22	SE 01	SE 50 1		SE 01	SE 22 1	SE 30 1	SE 07 1		SE 22	SE 30 1	SE 01	SE 07 1	SE 40 1	SE 90 1	SE 51 1		SE 51 1	SE 07 1	SE 40 1	SE 21
London Victoria 15	⊖ d	15 39	16 03		16 00		16 23			16 22	16 42			16 45				17 05		17 09		17 27			
London Blackfriars 3	⊖ d		15 43							16 09				16 27				16 42							17 24
Elephant & Castle	⊖ d		15 46							16 13				16 31				16 46							17 28
Bromley South 4	d	16 00	16 19		16 23		16 40			16 44	16 58			17 03				17 23				17 44			17 48
St Mary Cray	d	16 06			16 30					16 50				17 10				17 30							17 57
Swanley 4	d	16 11			16 35					16 55				17 15				17 37							18 01
Farningham Road	d	16 15			16 39					17 00				17 19				17 41						←	18 06
Longfield	d	16 20			16 44					17 04				17 24				17 46						17 46	18 11
Meopham	d	16 24			16 48					17 09				17 28				→						17 51	18 16
Sole Street	d	16 27			16 51					17 11				17 31										17 54	18 18
London Charing Cross 4	⊖ d	15 20					15 20				15 50	16b33					16c21			16 21		16 48		16 48	17 00
London Waterloo (East) 4	⊖ d	15 23					15 23				15 53	16b36					16c24			16 24		16 51		16 51	17 03
London Cannon Street 4	⊖ d	15e18					15f18				15f48	16 44					17 08			16e22		16f46	17 30	16e46	17e00
London Bridge 4	⊖ d	15 29					15 29				15 59	16 48					16 29			16 29		16 56		16 56	17 08
Dartford 4	d	16 04					16 04				16 36						17 06			17 06		17 26		17 26	17 46
Greenhithe for Bluewater	d	16 09					16 09				16 41						17 11			17 11		17 31		17 31	17 51
Gravesend 4	d	16 16					16 16				16 48						17 18			17 18		17 38		17 38	17 58
Strood 4	d	16 28					16 28				17 04						17 30			17 30		17 54		17 54	18 14
Rochester 4	d	16 36	16 43		17a03					17a23	17 07			17a43			17 35			17 53		17 59		18g18	18 28
Chatham 4	d	16 39	16 47				17 08				17 28	17 32					17 49			17 56		18 10	18 14	18 21	18 30
Gillingham (Kent) 4	d	16 43	16 50				17 12				17 32	17 36					17 54			18 00		18 15	18 19	18 25	18a35
Rainham (Kent)	d	16 48	16 55				17 17				17 37	17 41					17 59			18 05		18 20	18 24	18 30	
Newington	d	16 52					17 21										18 03			18 09				18 34	
Sittingbourne 4	a	16 57	17 02				17 26				17 45	17 50					18 08			18 14		18 27	18 31	18 39	
	d	16 57	17 03			17 07	17 27		17 29		17 45	17 50				17 58	18 08			18 15		18 27	18 31	18 39	
Kemsley	d					17 11			17 33							18 02									
Swale	d					17x14			17x36							18x06									
Queenborough	d					17 19			17 41							18 10									
Sheerness-on-Sea	a					17 25			17 47							18 16									
Teynham	d	17 01					17 31										18 13			18 19				18 44	
Faversham 2	a	17 07	17 11				17 37				17 54	17 59					18 19			18 25		18 35	18 40	18 50	
	d		17 15	17 18			17 41	17 45			18 03	18 00			← 18 03		18 19			18 29	18 34	18 40	18 44	18 50	
Selling	d			17 23				17 50			→				18 08						18 39			18 55	
Canterbury East 4	d			17 33				18 00							18 18						18 49			19a04	
Bekesbourne	d			17 37				18 04							18 22						18 53				
Adisham	d			17 42				18 09							18 27						18 58				
Aylesham	d			17 44				18 11							18 29						19 00				
Snowdown	d			17 47				18 14							18 32						19 03				
Shepherds Well	d			17 51				18 18							18 36						19 07				
Kearsney	d			17 55				18 22							18 40						19 11				
Dover Priory 4	⛴ a			18 03				18 30							18 48						19 17				
Whitstable	d		17 23				17 49					18 08					18 27			18 38		18 48	18 52		
Chestfield & Swalecliffe	d		17 26				17 52					18 11								18 41		18 51	18 55		
Herne Bay	d		17 30				17 57					18 16					18 33			18 45		18 56	19 00		
Birchington-on-Sea	d		17 38				18 06					18 25					18 42			18 55		19 05	19 09		
Westgate-on-Sea	d		17 41				18 09					18 28								18 58		19 08	19 12		
Margate 4	d		17 45				18 13					18 32					18 48		18 52	19 03		19 12	19 16		
Broadstairs	d		17 51				18 19					18 37					18 54		18 57	19 08		19 18	19 22		
Dumpton Park	d		17 53				18 21					18 40							19 00	19 11		19 21			
Ramsgate 4	✈ a		17 56				18 26					18 46					19 00		19 03	19 17		19 25	19 28		

For general notes see front of timetable
For details of catering facilities see Directory of Train Operators

For services from London to Ramsgate, Dover and Canterbury via Ashford see Table 207

b Change at London Bridge
c Change at Chatham
e Change at London Bridge and Rochester
f Change at London Bridge and Chatham
g Arr. 1803

For details of Bank Holiday service alterations please see first page of Table 195

London → Medway, Sheerness-on-Sea, Dover and Ramsgate

Network Diagram - see first page of Table 212

		SE 01	SE 30 [1]	SE 07 [1]	SE 22	SE 30 [1]		SE 01	SE 31 [1]	SE 07 [1]	SE 21	SE 31 [1]	SE 01	SE 50 [1]	SE 01	SE 07 [1]	SE 92 [1]	SE 50 [1]	SE 01	SE 92 [1]	SE 07 [1]	
London Victoria [15]	⊖ d		17 49		17 48				18 04					18 33			18 41	19 04		19 09		
London Blackfriars [3]	⊖ d		17 24		17 36				17 36		18 11			18 11			18 23	18 43				
Elephant & Castle	⊖ d		17 28		17 39				17 39		18 15			18 15			18 26	18 46				
Bromley South [4]	d		18 05		18 09				18 24		18 33			18 49			19 01	19 20		19 29		
St Mary Cray	d				18 16						18 39						19 10			19 35		
Swanley [4]	d				18 21						18 44						19 15			19 40		
Farningham Road	d				18 25						18 49						19 19			19 44		
Longfield	d				18 30						18 53						19 24			19 49		
Meopham	d				18 34						18 58						19 28			19 53		
Sole Street	d				18 37						19 00						19 31			19 56		
London Charing Cross [4]	⊖ d		17 00	17b43						18b01						18b34	17c58	17e58		18 30	19b24	
London Waterloo (East) [4]	⊖ d		17 03	17b46						18b04						18b37	18c01	18e01		18 33	19b27	
London Cannon Street [4]	⊖ d		17e00	17 50						18 10						18 46	18 08	18 08		18c30	19 32	
London Bridge [4]	⊖ d		17 08	17 54					17f30	18 14	17g50			17f50		18 50	18g14	18f14		18 38	19 36	
Dartford [4]	d		17 46						18 10		18 30			18 30		18 48	19 00	19 00		19 16	19 40	
Greenhithe for Bluewater	d		17 51						18 15		18 35			18 35		18 53	19 05	19 05		19 21	19 45	
Gravesend [4]	d		17 58						18 22		18 42			18 42		19 00	19 12	19 12		19 28	19 52	
Strood [4]	d		18 14						18 36		18 54			18 54		19 14	19 28	19 28		19 44	20 04	
Rochester [4]	d		18 19		18a51				18 41		19 11			18 59		19 19	19 40			20 05	20 12	
Chatham [4]	d		18 34	18 38					18 55	18 59	19 13			19 17		19 28	19 43	19 48		20 07	20 15	
Gillingham (Kent) [4]	d		18 38	18 42					18 59	19 03	19a19			19 21		19 32	19 47	19 52		20 11	20 20	
Rainham (Kent)	d		18 44	18 47					19 04	19 08				19 27		19 37	19 52	19 57		20 16	20 25	
Newington	d									19 12						19 41	19 56			20 20	20 35	
Sittingbourne [4]	a		18 51	18 55					19 12	19 17				19 34		19 46	20 01	20 04		20 27	→	
	d	18 41	18 52	18 55				18 58	19 12	19 18			19 27	19 35	19 42	19 47	20 01	20 05	20 13	20 27		
Kemsley	d	18 45						19 02					19 31		19 46				20 17			
Swale	d	18x48						19x05					19x35		19x50				20x21			
Queenborough	d	18 53						19 10					19 39		19 55				20 25			
Sheerness-on-Sea	a	18 59						19 16					19 45		20 01				20 30			
Teynham	d									19 22						19 51	20 05			20 31		
Faversham [2]	a		19 00	19 04					19 21	19 28				19 43		19 57	20 12	20 15		20 37		
	d		19 11 / 19 04	19 08		← 19 11			19 32 / 19 24	19 29		← 19 32		19 47 / 19 49		19 58		20 19				
Selling	d		→			19 16			→			19 37		19 54				20 26				
Canterbury East [4]	d					19 26						19 47		20h06				20 36				
Bekesbourne	d					19 30						19 51		20 10				20 40				
Adisham	d					19 35						19 56		20 15				20 45				
Aylesham	d					19 37						19 58		20 17				20 47				
Snowdown	d					19 40						20 01		20 20				20 50				
Shepherds Well	d					19 44						20 05		20 24				20 54				
Kearsney	d					19 48						20 09		20 28				20 58				
Dover Priory [4]	a					19 55						20 15		20 33				21 03				
Whitstable	d		19 12	19 16					19 33	19 38				19 56		20 06		20 27				
Chestfield & Swalecliffe	d			19 19					19 36	19 41				19 59		20 09						
Herne Bay	d		19 19	19 24					19 40	19 45				20 03		20 13		20 32				
Birchington-on-Sea	d		19 28	19 33					19 49	19 54				20 12		20 22		20 41				
Westgate-on-Sea	d			19 36					19 53	19 58				20 16		20 26						
Margate [4]	d		19 33	19 40					19 57	20 03				20 20		20 30		20 47				
Broadstairs	d		19a39	19 46					20a02	20 09				20 26		20a36		20 52				
Dumpton Park	d			19 48						20 12				20 28				20 55				
Ramsgate [4]	a			19 54						20 18				20 32				20 59				

For general notes see front of timetable
For details of catering facilities see Directory of Train Operators

For services from London to Ramsgate, Dover and Canterbury via Ashford see Table 207

b Change at London Bridge
c Change at London Bridge and Rochester
e Change at London Bridge and Chatham
f Change at Dartford and Chatham
g Change at Dartford and Rochester
h Arr. 2002

For details of Bank Holiday service alterations please see first page of Table 195

London → Medway, Sheerness-on-Sea, Dover and Ramsgate

Network Diagram - see first page of Table 212

		SE 50 [1]		SE 01		SE 07 [1]	SE 92 [1]	SE 50 [1]		SE 01	SE 92 [1]	SE 50 [1]		SE 92 [1]	SE 50 [1]		SE 01	SE 37 [1]	SE 50 [1]	SE 37 [1]	SE 01	SE 92 [1]	SE 50 [1]	SE 22 [1]	
London Victoria [15] ⊖	d	19 34					19 39	20 03			20 09	20 34		20 39	21 03			21 39	22 03			22 39	23 03	23 39	
London Blackfriars [3] ⊖	d	19 17						19 47				20 13			20 43			21 13	21 43			22 13	22 43	23 13	
Elephant & Castle ⊖	d	19 20						19 50				20 16			20 46			21 16	21 46			22 16	22 46	23 16	
Bromley South [4]	d	19 50					19 59	20 19			20 29	20 50		20 59	21 19			21 59	22 19			22 59	23 19	23 58	
St Mary Cray	d						20 05				20 35			21 05				22 05				23 05		00 04	
Swanley [4]	d						20 10				20 40			21 10				22 10				23 10		00 09	
Farningham Road	d						20 14				20 44			21 14				22 14				23 14		00 13	
Longfield	d						20 19				20 49			21 19	21 33			22 19				23 19		00 18	
Meopham	d						20 23				20 53			21 23				22 23				23 23		00 23	
Sole Street	d						20 26				20 56			21 26				22 26				23 26		00 26	
London Charing Cross [4] ⊖	d	18 54					19 21					19 50		20 20				21 20				22 20		22 50	
London Waterloo (East) [4] ⊖	d	18 57					19 24					19 53		20 23				21 23				22 23		22 53	
London Cannon Street [4] ⊖	d	18b50					19b22					19b52		20b15				21b00							
London Bridge [4] ⊖	d						19 29					19 59		20 29				21 29				22 29		22 59	
Dartford [4]	d						20 06					20 34		21 04				22 04				23 04		23 34	
Greenhithe for Bluewater	d						20 11					20 40		21 09				22 09				23 09		23 40	
Gravesend [4]	d						20 18					20 50		21 16				22 16				23 16		23 50	
Strood [4]	d						20 30					21 04		21 28				22 28				23 28		00 02	
Rochester [4]	d	20 16					20 37	20 43			21 05	21 14		21 35	21 47			22 35	22 43			23 36	23 43	00 35	
Chatham [4]	d	20 19					20 40	20 47			21 07	21 18		21 38	21 50			22 38	22 46			23 39	23 46	00 38	
Gillingham (Kent) [4]	d	20 24					20 43	20 50			21 11	21 22		21 41	21 53			22 41	22 49			23 43	23 49	00a41	
Rainham (Kent)	d	20 29				←	20 48	20 55			21 16	21 27		21 46	21 58			22 46	22 54			23 48	23 54		
Newington	d					20 35	20 52				21 20			21 50				22 50				23 52			
Sittingbourne [4]	a	20 36				20 42	20 57	21 02			21 25	21 34		21 55	22 05			22 55	23 01			23 57	00 01		
	d	20 36		20 39		20 43	20 57	21 02		21 05	21 25	21 34		21 55	22 05		22 09	22 55	23 01		23 07	23 57	00 01		
Kemsley	d			20 43						21 09							22 13				23 11				
Swale	d			20x47						21x13							22x17				23x14				
Queenborough	d			20 51						21 17							22 21				23 19				
Sheerness-on-Sea	a			20 57						21 23							22 26				23 25				
Teynham	d					20 47	21 02				21 29			22 00				23 00				00 01			
Faversham [2]	a	20 44				20 54	21 08	21 12			21 35	21 42		22 06	22 13			23 06	23 10	←		00 07	00 11		
	d	20 48	20 52					21 16	21 18			21 46	21 48		22 17	22 20		23 13	23 11	23 13			00 12		
Selling	d		20 57						21 23				21 53			22 25		→		23 18					
Canterbury East [4]	d		21 06						21 32				22a03			22 34				23 27					
Bekesbourne	d		21 11						21 36							22 38									
Adisham	d		21 15						21 41							22 43									
Aylesham	d		21 17						21 43							22 45				23 36					
Snowdown	d		21 19						21 46							22 48									
Shepherds Well	d		21 23						21 50							22 52									
Kearsney	d		21 27						21 54							22 56									
Dover Priory [4] ⛴	a		21 33						21 59							23 01				23 47					
Whitstable	d	20 56						21 24				21 54			22 25				23 19				00 20		
Chestfield & Swalecliffe	d	20 59										21 57			22 28				23 22				00 23		
Herne Bay	d	21 03						21 29				22 01			22 32				23 26				00 27		
Birchington-on-Sea	d	21 11						21 37				22 10			22 41				23 35				00 36		
Westgate-on-Sea	d	21 14										22 13			22 44				23 38				00 39		
Margate [4]	d	21 19						21 43				22 18			22 48				23 42				00 43		
Broadstairs	d	21 24						21 48				22 23			22 53				23 47				00 48		
Dumpton Park	d	21 27										22 26			22 56				23 50				00 51		
Ramsgate [4] ✈	a	21 30						21 53				22 29			22 59				23 53				00 54		

For general notes see front of timetable
For details of catering facilities see Directory of Train Operators

For services from London to Ramsgate, Dover and Canterbury via Ashford see Table 207

b Change at London Bridge and Rochester

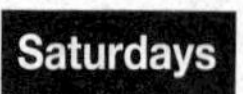

For details of Bank Holiday service alterations please see first page of Table 195

London → Medway, Sheerness-on-Sea, Dover and Ramsgate

Network Diagram - see first page of Table 212

		SE 92 1	SE 50 1	SE 01	SE 22 1	SE 50 1	SE 20 1	SE 81 1	SE 01	SE 90 1	SE 55 1	SE 80 1	SE 01	SE 90 1	SE 37 1		SE 01	SE 92	SE 90 1	SE 50 1		SE 01	SE 92 1
London Victoria 15	⊖ d	22p39	23p03		23p39	00 03					05 39				06 39			07 09		07 33			07 39
London Blackfriars 3	⊖ d																	*06 43*		*07 13*			
Elephant & Castle	⊖ d																	*06 46*		*07 16*			
Bromley South 4	d	22p59	23p19		23p58						05 59				06 59			07 29		07 49			07 59
St Mary Cray	d	23p05			00 04						06 05				07 05			07 35					08 05
Swanley 4	d	23p10			00 09						06 10				07 10			07 40					08 10
Farningham Road	d	23p14			00 13						06 14				07 14			07 44					08 14
Longfield	d	23p19			00 18						06 19				07 19			07 49					08 19
Meopham	d	23p23			00 23						06 23				07 23			07 53					08 23
Sole Street	d	23p26			00 26						06 26				07 26			07 56					08 26
London Charing Cross 4	⊖ d				*22 50*	*23 20*					*05 04*				*06 20*			*06 50*		*06 50*			*07 20*
London Waterloo (East) 4	⊖ d				*22 53*	*23 23*					*05 07*				*06 23*			*06 53*		*06 53*			*07 23*
London Cannon Street 4	⊖ d																						
London Bridge 4	⊖ d				*22 59*	*23 29*					*05 13*				*06 29*			*06 59*		*06 59*			*07 29*
Dartford 4	d				*23 34*		05 17				*05 49*				*07 04*			*07 34*		*07 34*			*08 04*
Greenhithe for Bluewater	d				*23 40*		05 22				*05 54*				*07 09*			*07 39*		*07 39*			*08 09*
Gravesend 4	d				*23 50*		05 29				*06 01*				*07 16*			*07 46*		*07 46*			*08 16*
Strood 4	d				*00 02*	*00 32*	05 40				*06 12*				*07 28*			*07 58*		*07 58*			*08 28*
Rochester 4	d	23p36	23p43		00 35	00 43	05 44				06 36				07 36			08 06		08 13			08 36
Chatham 4	d	23p39	23p46		00 38	00 46	05 46				06 38				07 38			08 08		08 17			08 38
Gillingham (Kent) 4	d	23p43	23p49		00a41	00 50	05 50				06 41				07 41			08 11		08 20			08 41
Rainham (Kent)	d	23p48	23p54			00 55	05 54				06 46				07 46			08 16		08 25			08 46
Newington	d	23p52				00 58	05 58				06 50				07 50			08 20					08 50
Sittingbourne 4	a	23p57	00 01			01 03	06 03				06 55				07 55			08 25		08 32			08 55
	d	23p57	00 01	00 08		01 03	06 03		06 05		06 55		07 05		07 55		08 05	08 25		08 32		08 35	08 55
Kemsley	d			00 12					06 09				07 09				08 09					08 39	
Swale	d			00x15					06x12				07x12				08x12					08x42	
Queenborough	d			00 20					06 17				07 17				08 17					08 47	
Sheerness-on-Sea	a			00 26					06 22				07 22				08 22					08 52	
Teynham	d	00 01				01 07	06 08				06 59				07 59			08 29					08 59
Faversham 2	a	00 07	00 11			01 12	06 14				07 05				08 05			08 35		08 40			09 05
	d		00 12			01 13	06 15	06 17			07 14	07 16			08 14	08 16				08 44	08 46		
Selling	d						06 20					07 21			08 19						08 51		
Canterbury East 4	d						06 29					07 30			08b30						09 00		
Bekesbourne	d						06 33					07 35			08 35						09 05		
Adisham	d						06 38					07 39			08 39						09 09		
Aylesham	d						06 40					07 42			08 42						09 12		
Snowdown	d						06 43					07 44			08 44						09 14		
Shepherds Well	d						06 47					07 48			08 48						09 18		
Kearsney	d						06 51					07 53			08 53						09 23		
Dover Priory 4	a						06 56					07 57			08 57						09 28		
Whitstable	d		00 20			01 21		06 25			07 22					08 25				08 52			
Chestfield & Swalecliffe	d		00 23			01 24		06 28			07 25					08 28				08 55			
Herne Bay	d		00 27			01 27		06 32			07 29					08 32				08 59			
Birchington-on-Sea	d		00 36			01 36		06 41			07 38					08 41				09 08			
Westgate-on-Sea	d		00 39			01 39		06 45			07 42					08 44				09 11			
Margate 4	d		00 43			01 43		06 49		07 26	07 46			08 04		08 48			09 04	09 15			
Broadstairs	d		00 48			01 48		06 54		07 31	07 51			08 09		08 53			09 09	09 20			
Dumpton Park	d		00 51			01 51		06 56		07 34	07 53			08 12		08 56			09 12	09 23			
Ramsgate 4	a		00 54			01 54		06 59		07 37	07 58			08 15		08 59			09 15	09 26			

For general notes see front of timetable
For details of catering facilities see Directory of Train Operators

For services from London to Ramsgate, Dover and Canterbury via Ashford see Table 207

b Arr. 0827

Table 212

For details of Bank Holiday service alterations please see first page of Table 195

London → Medway, Sheerness-on-Sea, Dover and Ramsgate

Network Diagram - see first page of Table 212

		SE 50 1		SE 01	SE 92 1	SE 90 1	SE 50 1		SE 01	SE 92 1		SE 50 1		SE 01	SE 92 1	SE 90 1	SE 50 1		SE 01	SE 92 1	SE 50 1		SE 01	SE 92 1	SE 90 1
London Victoria 15 ⊖	d	08 03			08 09		08 33			08 39		09 03			09 09		09 33			09 39	10 03			10 09	
London Blackfriars 3 ⊖	d	*07 43*					*08 13*					*08 43*					*09 13*				*09 43*				
Elephant & Castle ⊖	d	*07 46*					*08 16*					*08 46*					*09 16*				*09 46*				
Bromley South 4	d	08 19			08 29		08 49			08 59		09 19			09 29		09 49			09 59	10 19			10 29	
St Mary Cray	d				08 35					09 05					09 35					10 05				10 35	
Swanley 4	d				08 40					09 10					09 40					10 10				10 40	
Farningham Road	d				08 44					09 14					09 44					10 14				10 44	
Longfield	d				08 49					09 19					09 49					10 19				10 49	
Meopham	d				08 53					09 23					09 53					10 23				10 53	
Sole Street	d				08 56					09 26					09 56					10 26				10 56	
London Charing Cross 4 ⊖	d				*07 50*					*08 20*					*08 50*					*09 20*				*09 50*	
London Waterloo (East) 4 ⊖	d				*07 53*					*08 23*					*08 53*					*09 23*				*09 53*	
London Cannon Street 4 ⊖	d									*08b10*					*08b48*					*09b18*				*09b48*	
London Bridge 4 ⊖	d				*07 59*					*08 29*					*08 59*					*09 29*				*09 59*	
Dartford 4	d				*08 34*					*09 04*					*09 34*					*10 04*				*10 34*	
Greenhithe for Bluewater	d				*08 39*					*09 09*					*09 39*					*10 09*				*10 39*	
Gravesend 4	d				*08 46*					*09 16*					*09 46*					*10 16*				*10 46*	
Strood 4	d				*08 58*					*09 28*					*09 58*					*10 28*				*10 58*	
Rochester 4	d	08 43			09 06		09 13			09 36		09 43			10 06		10 13			10 36	10 43			11 06	
Chatham 4	d	08 47			09 08		09 17			09 38		09 47			10 08		10 17			10 38	10 47			11 08	
Gillingham (Kent) 4	d	08 50			09 11		09 20			09 41		09 50			10 11		10 20			10 41	10 50			11 11	
Rainham (Kent)	d	08 55			09 16		09 25			09 46		09 55			10 16		10 25			10 46	10 55			11 16	
Newington	d				09 20					09 50					10 20					10 50				11 20	
Sittingbourne 4	a	09 02			09 25		09 32			09 55		10 02			10 25		10 32			10 55	11 02			11 25	
	d	09 02		09 05	09 25		09 32		09 35	09 55		10 02		10 05	10 25		10 32		10 35	10 55	11 02		11 05	11 25	
Kemsley	d			09 09					09 39					10 09					10 39				11 09		
Swale	d			09x12					09x42					10x12					10x42				11x12		
Queenborough	d			09 17					09 47					10 17					10 47				11 17		
Sheerness-on-Sea	a			09 22					09 52					10 22					10 52				11 22		
Teynham	d				09 29					09 59					10 29					10 59				11 29	
Faversham 2	a	09 10			09 35		09 40			10 05		10 10			10 35		10 40			11 05	11 10			11 35	
	d	09 14	09 16				09 44	09 46				10 14	10 16				10 44	10 46			11 14	11 16			
Selling	d							09 51										10 51							
Canterbury East 4	d		09c31					10 00					10e31					11 00				11f31			
Bekesbourne	d							10 05										11 05							
Adisham	d							10 09										11 09							
Aylesham	d							10 12										11 12							
Snowdown	d							10 14										11 14							
Shepherds Well	d							10 18										11 18							
Kearsney	d							10 23										11 23							
Dover Priory 4	a		09 46					10 28					10 46					11 28				11 46			
Whitstable	d	09 22					09 52					10 22					10 52				11 22				
Chestfield & Swalecliffe	d						09 55										10 55								
Herne Bay	d	09 27					09 59					10 27					10 59				11 27				
Birchington-on-Sea	d	09 35					10 08					10 35					11 08				11 35				
Westgate-on-Sea	d						10 11										11 11								
Margate 4	d	09 41				10 04	10 15					10 41				11 04	11 15				11 41				12 04
Broadstairs	d	09 46				10 09	10 20					10 46				11 09	11 20				11 46				12 09
Dumpton Park	d					10 12	10 23									11 12	11 23								12 12
Ramsgate 4	a	09 51				10 15	10 26					10 51				11 15	11 26				11 51				12 15

For general notes see front of timetable
For details of catering facilities see Directory of Train Operators

For services from London to Ramsgate, Dover and Canterbury via Ashford see Table 207

b Change at London Bridge and Rochester
c Arr. 0928
e Arr. 1028
f Arr. 1128

Table 212

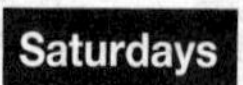

For details of Bank Holiday service alterations please see first page of Table 195

London → Medway, Sheerness-on-Sea, Dover and Ramsgate

Network Diagram - see first page of Table 212

		SE 50 1 🛒		SE 01		SE 92 1	SE 50 1 🛒		SE 01	SE 92 1	SE 90 1 🛒	SE 50 1 🛒		SE 01	SE 92 1	SE 50 1 🛒		SE 01	SE 92 1	SE 90 1 🛒		SE 50 1 🛒		SE 01	SE 92 1
London Victoria 15	⊖ d	10 33				10 39	11 03			11 09		11 33			11 39	12 03			12 09			12 33			12 39
London Blackfriars 3	⊖ d	*10 13*					*10 43*					*11 13*				*11 43*						*12 13*			
Elephant & Castle	⊖ d	*10 16*					*10 46*					*11 16*				*11 46*						*12 16*			
Bromley South 4	d	10 49				10 59	11 19			11 29		11 49			11 59	12 19			12 29			12 49			12 59
St Mary Cray	d					11 05				11 35					12 05				12 35						13 05
Swanley 4	d					11 10				11 40					12 10				12 40						13 10
Farningham Road	d					11 14				11 44					12 14				12 44						13 14
Longfield	d					11 19				11 49					12 19				12 49						13 19
Meopham	d					11 23				11 53					12 23				12 53						13 23
Sole Street	d					11 26				11 56					12 26				12 56						13 26
London Charing Cross 4	⊖ d					*10 20*				*10 50*					*11 20*				*11 50*						*12 20*
London Waterloo (East) 4	⊖ d					*10 23*				*10 53*					*11 23*				*11 53*						*12 23*
London Cannon Street 4	⊖ d					*10*b*18*				*10*b*48*					*11*b*18*				*11*b*48*						*12*b*18*
London Bridge 4	⊖ d					*10 29*				*10 59*					*11 29*				*11 59*						*12 29*
Dartford 4	d					*11 04*				*11 34*					*12 04*				*12 34*						*13 04*
Greenhithe for Bluewater	d					*11 09*				*11 39*					*12 09*				*12 39*						*13 09*
Gravesend 4	d					*11 16*				*11 46*					*12 16*				*12 46*						*13 16*
Strood 4	d					*11 28*				*11 58*					*12 28*				*12 58*						*13 28*
Rochester 4	d	11 13				11 36	11 43			12 06		12 13			12 36	12 43			13 06			13 13			13 36
Chatham 4	d	11 17				11 38	11 47			12 08		12 17			12 38	12 47			13 08			13 17			13 38
Gillingham (Kent) 4	d	11 20				11 41	11 50			12 11		12 20			12 41	12 50			13 11			13 20			13 41
Rainham (Kent)	d	11 25				11 46	11 55			12 16		12 25			12 46	12 55			13 16			13 25			13 46
Newington	d					11 50				12 20					12 50				13 20						13 50
Sittingbourne 4	a	11 32				11 55	12 02			12 25		12 32			12 55	13 02			13 25			13 32			13 55
	d	11 32		11 35		11 55	12 02		12 05	12 25		12 32		12 35	12 55	13 02		13 05	13 25			13 32		13 35	13 55
Kemsley	d			11 39					12 09					12 39				13 09						13 39	
Swale	d			11x42					12x12					12x42				13x12						13x42	
Queenborough	d			11 47					12 17					12 47				13 17						13 47	
Sheerness-on-Sea	a			11 52					12 22					12 52				13 22						13 52	
Teynham	d					11 59				12 29					12 59				13 29						13 59
Faversham 2	a	11 40				12 05	12 10			12 35		12 40			13 05	13 10			13 35			13 40			14 05
	d	11 44	11 46				12 14	12 16				12 44	12 46			13 14	13 16					13 44	13 46		
Selling	d		11 51										12 51										13 51		
Canterbury East 4	d		12 00					12c31					13 00				13e31						14 00		
Bekesbourne	d		12 05										13 05										14 05		
Adisham	d		12 09										13 09										14 09		
Aylesham	d		12 12										13 12										14 12		
Snowdown	d		12 14										13 14										14 14		
Shepherds Well	d		12 18										13 18										14 18		
Kearsney	d		12 23										13 23										14 23		
Dover Priory 4	⛴ a		12 28					12 46					13 28				13 46						14 28		
Whitstable	d	11 52					12 22					12 52				13 22						13 52			
Chestfield & Swalecliffe	d	11 55										12 55										13 55			
Herne Bay	d	11 59					12 27					12 59				13 27						13 59			
Birchington-on-Sea	d	12 08					12 35					13 08				13 35						14 08			
Westgate-on-Sea	d	12 11										13 11										14 11			
Margate 4	d	12 15					12 41				13 04	13 15				13 41				14 04		14 15			
Broadstairs	d	12 20					12 46				13 09	13 20				13 46				14 09		14 20			
Dumpton Park	d	12 23									13 12	13 23								14 12		14 23			
Ramsgate 4	✈ a	12 26					12 51				13 15	13 26				13 51				14 15		14 26			

For general notes see front of timetable
For details of catering facilities see Directory of Train Operators

For services from London to Ramsgate, Dover and Canterbury via Ashford see Table 207

b Change at London Bridge and Rochester
c Arr. 1228
e Arr. 1328

For details of Bank Holiday service alterations please see first page of Table 195

London → Medway, Sheerness-on-Sea, Dover and Ramsgate

Network Diagram - see first page of Table 212

		SE		SE	SE	SE	SE		SE	SE	SE		SE	SE	SE	SE		SE	SE	SE		SE	SE
		50		01	92	90	50		01	92	50		01	92	90	50		01	92	50		01	92
		1			1	1	1			1	1			1	1	1			1	1			1
London Victoria 15	⊖ d	13 03			13 09		13 33			13 39	14 03			14 09		14 33			14 39	15 03			15 09
London Blackfriars 3	⊖ d	12 43					13 13				13 43					14 13				14 43			
Elephant & Castle	⊖ d	12 46					13 16				13 46					14 16				14 46			
Bromley South 4	d	13 19			13 29		13 49			13 59	14 19			14 29		14 49			14 59	15 19			15 29
St Mary Cray	d				13 35					14 05				14 35					15 05				15 35
Swanley 4	d				13 40					14 10				14 40					15 10				15 40
Farningham Road	d				13 44					14 14				14 44					15 14				15 44
Longfield	d				13 49					14 19				14 49					15 19				15 49
Meopham	d				13 53					14 23				14 53					15 23				15 53
Sole Street	d				13 56					14 26				14 56					15 26				15 56
London Charing Cross 4	⊖ d				12 50					13 20				13 50					14 20				14 50
London Waterloo (East) 4	⊖ d				12 53					13 23				13 53					14 23				14 53
London Cannon Street 4	⊖ d				12b48					13b18				13b48					14b18				14b48
London Bridge 4	⊖ d				12 59					13 29				13 59					14 29				14 59
Dartford 4	d				13 34					14 04				14 34					15 04				15 34
Greenhithe for Bluewater	d				13 39					14 09				14 39					15 09				15 39
Gravesend 4	d				13 46					14 16				14 46					15 16				15 46
Strood 4	d				13 58					14 28				14 58					15 28				15 58
Rochester 4	d	13 43			14 06		14 13			14 36	14 43			15 06		15 13			15 36	15 43			16 06
Chatham 4	d	13 47			14 08		14 17			14 38	14 47			15 08		15 17			15 38	15 47			16 08
Gillingham (Kent) 4	d	13 50			14 11		14 20			14 41	14 50			15 11		15 20			15 41	15 50			16 11
Rainham (Kent)	d	13 55			14 16		14 25			14 46	14 55			15 16		15 25			15 46	15 55			16 16
Newington	d				14 20					14 50				15 20					15 50				16 20
Sittingbourne 4	a	14 02			14 25		14 32			14 55	15 02			15 25		15 32			15 55	16 02			16 25
	d	14 02		14 05	14 25		14 32		14 35	14 55	15 02		15 05	15 25		15 32		15 35	15 55	16 02		16 05	16 25
Kemsley	d			14 09					14 39				15 09					15 39				16 09	
Swale	d			14x12					14x42				15x12					15x43				16x12	
Queenborough	d			14 17					14 47				15 17					15 47				16 17	
Sheerness-on-Sea	a			14 22					14 52				15 22					15 52				16 22	
Teynham	d				14 29					14 59				15 29					15 59				16 29
Faversham 2	a	14 10			14 35		14 40			15 05	15 10			15 35		15 40			16 05	16 10			16 35
	d	14 14	14 16				14 44	14 46			15 14	15 16				15 44	15 46			16 14	16 16		
Selling	d							14 51									15 51						
Canterbury East 4	d		14c31					15 00				15e31					16 00				16f31		
Bekesbourne	d							15 05									16 05						
Adisham	d							15 09									16 09						
Aylesham	d							15 12									16 12						
Snowdown	d							15 14									16 14						
Shepherds Well	d							15 18									16 18						
Kearsney	d							15 23									16 23						
Dover Priory 4 ⛴	a		14 46					15 28				15 46					16 28				16 46		
Whitstable	d	14 22					14 52				15 22					15 52				16 22			
Chestfield & Swalecliffe	d						14 55									15 55							
Herne Bay	d	14 27					14 59				15 27					15 59				16 27			
Birchington-on-Sea	d	14 35					15 08				15 35					16 08				16 35			
Westgate-on-Sea	d						15 11									16 11							
Margate 4	d	14 41				15 04	15 15				15 41				16 04	16 15				16 41			
Broadstairs	d	14 46				15 09	15 20				15 46				16 09	16 20				16 46			
Dumpton Park	d					15 12	15 23								16 12	16 23							
Ramsgate 4 ✈	a	14 51				15 15	15 26				15 51				16 15	16 26				16 51			

For general notes see front of timetable
For details of catering facilities see Directory of Train Operators
For services from London to Ramsgate, Dover and Canterbury via Ashford see Table 207

b Change at London Bridge and Rochester
c Arr. 1428
e Arr. 1528
f Arr. 1628

Table 212

Saturdays

For details of Bank Holiday service alterations please see first page of Table 195

London → Medway, Sheerness-on-Sea, Dover and Ramsgate

Network Diagram - see first page of Table 212

		SE 50 1 🛒		SE 01	SE 92 1	SE 50 1 🛒		SE 01		SE 92 1	SE 50 1 🛒		SE 01	SE 92 1	SE 50 1 🛒		SE 01	SE 92 1	SE 50 1 🛒		SE 92 1	SE 50 1 🛒		SE 01	SE 92 1
London Victoria 15	⊖ d	15 33			15 39	16 03				16 09	16 33			16 39	17 03			17 09	17 33		17 39	18 03			18 09
London Blackfriars 3	⊖ d	15 13				15 43					16 13				16 43				17 13			17 43			
Elephant & Castle	⊖ d	15 16				15 46					16 16				16 46				17 16			17 46			
Bromley South 4	d	15 49			15 59	16 19				16 29	16 49			16 59	17 19			17 29	17 49		17 59	18 19			18 29
St Mary Cray	d				16 05					16 35				17 05				17 35			18 05				18 35
Swanley 4	d				16 10					16 40				17 10				17 40			18 10				18 40
Farningham Road	d				16 14					16 44				17 14				17 44			18 14				18 44
Longfield	d				16 19					16 49				17 19				17 49			18 19				18 49
Meopham	d				16 23					16 53				17 23				17 53			18 23				18 53
Sole Street	d				16 26					16 56				17 26				17 56			18 26				18 56
London Charing Cross 4	⊖ d				15 20					15 50				16 20				16 50			17 20				17 50
London Waterloo (East) 4	⊖ d				15 23					15 53				16 23				16 53			17 23				17 53
London Cannon Street 4	⊖ d				15b18					15b48				16b18				16b48			17b18				17b48
London Bridge 4	⊖ d				15 29					15 59				16 29				16 59			17 29				17 59
Dartford 4	d				16 04					16 34				17 04				17 34			18 04				18 34
Greenhithe for Bluewater	d				16 09					16 39				17 09				17 39			18 09				18 39
Gravesend 4	d				16 16					16 46				17 16				17 46			18 16				18 46
Strood 4	d				16 28					16 58				17 28				17 58			18 28				18 58
Rochester 4	d	16 13			16 36	16 43				17 06	17 13			17 36	17 43			18 06	18 13		18 36	18 43			19 06
Chatham 4	d	16 17			16 38	16 47				17 08	17 17			17 38	17 47			18 08	18 17		18 38	18 47			19 08
Gillingham (Kent) 4	d	16 20			16 41	16 50				17 11	17 20			17 41	17 50			18 11	18 20		18 41	18 50			19 11
Rainham (Kent)	d	16 25			16 46	16 55				17 16	17 25			17 46	17 55			18 16	18 25		18 46	18 55			19 16
Newington	d				16 50					17 20				17 50				18 20			18 50				19 20
Sittingbourne 4	a	16 32			16 55	17 02				17 25	17 32			17 55	18 02			18 25	18 32		18 55	19 02			19 25
	d	16 32		16 35	16 55	17 02		17 05		17 25	17 32		17 35	17 55	18 02		18 05	18 25	18 32		18 55	19 02		19 05	19 25
Kemsley	d			16 39				17 09					17 39				18 09							19 09	
Swale	d			16x42				17x12					17x42				18x12							19x12	
Queenborough	d			16 47				17 17					17 47				18 17							19 17	
Sheerness-on-Sea	a			16 52				17 22					17 52				18 22							19 22	
Teynham	d				16 59					17 29				17 59				18 29			18 59				19 29
Faversham 2	a	16 40			17 05	17 10				17 35	17 40			18 05	18 10			18 35	18 40		19 05	19 10			19 35
	d	16 44	16 46			17 14	17 16				17 44	17 46			18 14	18 16			18 44	18 46		19 14	19 16		
Selling	d		16 51									17 51								18 51					
Canterbury East 4	d		17 00				17c31					18 00				18e31				19 00			19f31		
Bekesbourne	d		17 05									18 05								19 05					
Adisham	d		17 09									18 09								19 09					
Aylesham	d		17 12									18 12								19 12					
Snowdown	d		17 14									18 14								19 14					
Shepherds Well	d		17 18									18 18								19 18					
Kearsney	d		17 23									18 23								19 23					
Dover Priory 4	⛴ a		17 28				17 46					18 28				18 46				19 28			19 46		
Whitstable	d	16 52				17 22					17 52				18 22				18 52			19 22			
Chestfield & Swalecliffe	d	16 55									17 55								18 55						
Herne Bay	d	16 59				17 27					17 59				18 27				18 59			19 27			
Birchington-on-Sea	d	17 08				17 35					18 08				18 35				19 08			19 35			
Westgate-on-Sea	d	17 11									18 11								19 11						
Margate 4	d	17 15				17 41					18 15				18 41				19 15			19 41			
Broadstairs	d	17 20				17 46					18 20				18 46				19 20			19 46			
Dumpton Park	d	17 23									18 23								19 23						
Ramsgate 4	✈ a	17 26				17 51					18 26				18 51				19 26			19 51			

For general notes see front of timetable
For details of catering facilities see Directory of Train Operators

For services from London to Ramsgate, Dover and Canterbury via Ashford see Table 207

b Change at London Bridge and Rochester
c Arr. 1728
e Arr. 1828
f Arr. 1928

For details of Bank Holiday service alterations please see first page of Table 195

London → Medway, Sheerness-on-Sea, Dover and Ramsgate

Network Diagram - see first page of Table 212

	SE 50 1 ✠		SE 92 1	SE 50 1		SE 01	SE 92 1	SE 01 1	SE 50 1		SE 01	SE 92 1	SE 61 1	SE 50 1		SE 01	SE 92 1	SE 50 1		SE 01	SE 75 1	SE 50 1	SE 22 1
London Victoria 15 ⊖ d	18 33		18 39	19 03			19 39		20 03			20 39		21 03			21 39	22 03			22 39	23 03	23 39
London Blackfriars 3 ⊖ d	*18 13*			*18 43*			*19 13*		*19 43*			*20 13*		*20 43*			*21 13*	*21 43*			*22 13*	*22 43*	*23 13*
Elephant & Castle ⊖ d	*18 16*			*18 46*			*19 16*		*19 46*			*20 16*		*20 46*			*21 16*	*21 46*			*22 16*	*22 46*	*23 16*
Bromley South 4 d	18 49		18 59	19 19			19 59		20 19			20 59		21 19			21 59	22 19			22 59	23 19	23 59
St Mary Cray d			19 05				20 05					21 05					22 05				23 05		00 05
Swanley 4 d			19 10				20 10					21 10					22 10				23 10		00 10
Farningham Road d			19 14				20 14					21 14					22 14				23 14		00 14
Longfield d			19 19	19 33			20 19		20 33			21 19		21 33			22 19				23 19		00 19
Meopham d			19 23				20 23					21 23					22 23				23 23		00 23
Sole Street d			19 26				20 26					21 26					22 26				23 26		00 26
London Charing Cross 4 ⊖ d			*18 20*				*19 20*					*20 20*					*21 20*				*22 20*		*23 20*
London Waterloo (East) 4 ⊖ d			*18 23*				*19 23*					*20 23*					*21 23*				*22 23*		*23 23*
London Cannon Street 4 ⊖ d			*18b18*				*19b14*																
London Bridge 4 ⊖ d			*18 29*				*19 29*					*20 29*					*21 29*				*22 29*		*23 29*
Dartford 4 d			*19 04*				*20 04*					*21 04*					*22 04*				*23 04*		*23 34*
Greenhithe for Bluewater d			*19 09*				*20 09*					*21 09*					*22 09*				*23 09*		*23 40*
Gravesend 4 d			*19 16*				*20 16*					*21 16*					*22 16*				*23 16*		*23 50*
Strood 4 d			*19 28*				*20 28*					*21 28*					*22 28*				*23 28*		*00 28*
Rochester 4 d	19 13		19 36	19 47			20 36		20 47			21 36		21 47			22 36	22 47			23 36	23 47	00 36
Chatham 4 d	19 17		19 38	19 49			20 38		20 49			21 38		21 49			22 38	22 49			23 38	23 49	00 38
Gillingham (Kent) 4 d	19 20		19 41	19 53			20 41		20 53			21 41		21 53			22 41	22 53			23 41	23 53	00a41
Rainham (Kent) d	19 25		19 46	19 58			20 46		20 58			21 46		21 58			22 46	22 58			23 46	23 58	
Newington d			19 50				20 50					21 50					22 50				23 50		
Sittingbourne 4 a	19 32		19 55	20 05			20 55		21 05			21 55		22 05			22 55	23 05			23 55	00 05	
d	19 32		19 55	20 05		20 07	20 55		21 05		21 07	21 55		22 05		22 07	22 55	23 05		23 07	23 55	00 05	
Kemsley d						20 11					21 11					22 11				23 11			
Swale d						20x14					21x14					22x14				23x14			
Queenborough d						20 19					21 19					22 19				23 19			
Sheerness-on-Sea a						20 24					21 24					22 24				23 24			
Teynham d			19 59				20 59					21 59					22 59				23 59		
Faversham 2 a	19 40		20 05	20 13			21 05		21 13			22 05		22 13			23 05	23 13			00 05	00 13	
d	19 44	19 46		20 16	20 18				21 16	21 18				22 16	22 18			23 16	23 18			00 16	
Selling d		19 51			20 23					21 23					22 23								
Canterbury East 4 d		20 00			20 33					21 33					22 33				23 32				
Bekesbourne d		20 05			20 37					21 37					22 37								
Adisham d		20 09			20 42					21 42					22 42								
Aylesham d		20 12			20 44					21 44					22 44								
Snowdown d		20 14			20 47					21 47					22 47								
Shepherds Well d		20 18			20 51					21 51					22 51								
Kearsney d		20 23			20 55					21 55					22 55								
Dover Priory 4 ⛴ a		20 28			21 01					22 01					23 01				23 47				
Whitstable d	19 52			20 24					21 24					22 24				23 24				00 24	
Chestfield & Swalecliffe d	19 55			20 27					21 27					22 27				23 27				00 27	
Herne Bay d	19 59			20 31					21 31					22 31				23 31				00 31	
Birchington-on-Sea d	20 08			20 40					21 40					22 40				23 40				00 40	
Westgate-on-Sea d	20 11			20 43					21 43					22 43				23 43				00 43	
Margate 4 d	20 15			20 47				21 24	21 47				22 17	22 47				23 47				00 47	
Broadstairs d	20 20			20 52				21 29	21 52				22 22	22 52				23 52				00 52	
Dumpton Park d	20 23			20 54				21 32	21 54				22 25	22 54				23 54				00 55	
Ramsgate 4 ✈ a	20 26			20 57				21 35	21 57				22 28	22 57				23 57				00 58	

For general notes see front of timetable
For details of catering facilities see Directory of Train Operators

For services from London to Ramsgate, Dover and Canterbury via Ashford see Table 207

b Change at London Bridge and Rochester

Table 212

Sundays

London → Medway, Sheerness-on-Sea, Dover and Ramsgate

Network Diagram - see first page of Table 212

		SE 50 1	SE 01	SE 22 1	SE 50 1	SE 90 1	SE 01	SE 54 1	SE 90 1	SE 50 1		SE 01	SE 54 1	SE 90 1	SE 50 1		SE 01	SE 54 1	SE 90 1	SE 50 1		SE 01
London Victoria 15	⊖ d	23p03		23p39	00 03			07 41		08 03			08 41		09 03			09 41		10 03		
London Blackfriars 3	⊖ d																					
Elephant & Castle	⊖ d																					
Bromley South 4	d	23p19		23p59				08 01		08 19			09 01		09 19			10 01		10 19		
St Mary Cray	d			00 05				08 07					09 07					10 07				
Swanley 4	d			00 10				08 12					09 12					10 12				
Farningham Road	d			00 14				08 16					09 16					10 16				
Longfield	d			00 19				08 21					09 21					10 21				
Meopham	d			00 23				08 25					09 25					10 25				
Sole Street	d			00 26				08 28					09 28					10 28				
London Charing Cross 4	⊖ d			23 20									08 26					09 26				
London Waterloo (East) 4	⊖ d			23 23									08 29					09 29				
London Cannon Street 4	⊖ d																					
London Bridge 4	⊖ d			23 29									08 34					09 34				
Dartford 4	d			23 34				08 04					09 07					10 07				
Greenhithe for Bluewater	d			23 40				08 09					09 12					10 12				
Gravesend 4	d			23 50				08 16					09 18					10 18				
Strood 4	d			00 28				08 27					09 29					10 29				
Rochester 4	d	23p47		00 36	00 47			08 37		08 44			09 37		09 44			10 37		10 44		
Chatham 4	d	23p49		00 38	00 49			08 39		08 47			09 39		09 47			10 39		10 47		
Gillingham (Kent) 4	d	23p53		00a41	00 53			08 43		08 50			09 43		09 50			10 43		10 50		
Rainham (Kent)	d	23p58			00 58			08 48		08 55			09 48		09 55			10 48		10 55		
Newington	d				01 01			08 52					09 52					10 52				
Sittingbourne 4	a	00 05			01 06			08 57		09 02			09 57		10 02			10 57		11 02		
	d	00 05	00 07		01 06		08 21	08 57		09 02		09 21	09 57		10 02		10 21	10 57		11 02		11 21
Kemsley	d		00 11				08 25					09 25					10 25					11 25
Swale	d		00x14				08x28					09x28					10x28					11x28
Queenborough	d		00 19				08 33					09 33					10 33					11 33
Sheerness-on-Sea	a		00 24				08 38					09 38					10 38					11 38
Teynham	d				01 10			09 01					10 01					11 01				
Faversham 2	a	00 13			01 15			09 07		09 10			10 07		10 10			11 07		11 10		
	d	00 16			01 16					09 14	09 17				10 14	10 17				11 14	11 17	
Selling	d										09 22					10 22					11 22	
Canterbury East 4	d										09 31					10 31					11 31	
Bekesbourne	d										09 36					10 36					11 36	
Adisham	d										09 40					10 40					11 40	
Aylesham	d										09 43					10 43					11 43	
Snowdown	d										09 45					10 45					11 45	
Shepherds Well	d										09 49					10 49					11 49	
Kearsney	d										09 54					10 54					11 54	
Dover Priory 4	a										09 58					10 58					11 58	
Whitstable	d	00 24			01 24					09 22					10 22					11 22		
Chestfield & Swalecliffe	d	00 27			01 27					09 25					10 25					11 25		
Herne Bay	d	00 31			01 31					09 28					10 28					11 28		
Birchington-on-Sea	d	00 40			01 40					09 37					10 37					11 37		
Westgate-on-Sea	d	00 43			01 43					09 40					10 40					11 40		
Margate 4	d	00 47			01 47	08 16			09 16	09 44				10 16	10 44				11 16	11 44		
Broadstairs	d	00 52			01 52	08 21			09 21	09 49				10 21	10 49				11 21	11 49		
Dumpton Park	d	00 55			01 55	08 23			09 23	09 52				10 23	10 52				11 23	11 52		
Ramsgate 4	a	00 58			01 58	08 26			09 26	09 55				10 26	10 55				11 26	11 55		

For general notes see front of timetable
For details of catering facilities see Directory of Train Operators

For services from London to Ramsgate, Dover and Canterbury via Ashford see Table 207

Table 212

Sundays

London → Medway, Sheerness-on-Sea, Dover and Ramsgate

Network Diagram - see first page of Table 212

	SE 54 1	SE 90 1	SE 50 1 (trolley)		SE 01		SE 54 1	SE 90 1	SE 50 1 (trolley)		SE 01	SE 54 1		SE 90 1	SE 50 1 (trolley)		SE 01	SE 54 1	SE 90 1		SE 50 1 (trolley)		SE 01	SE 54 1
London Victoria 15 ⊖ d	10 41		11 03				11 41		12 03			12 41			13 03			13 41			14 03			14 41
London Blackfriars 3 ⊖ d																								
Elephant & Castle ⊖ d																								
Bromley South 4 d	11 01		11 19				12 01		12 19			13 01			13 19			14 01			14 19			15 01
St Mary Cray d	11 07						12 07					13 07						14 07						15 07
Swanley 4 d	11 12						12 12					13 12						14 12						15 12
Farningham Road d	11 16						12 16					13 16						14 16						15 16
Longfield d	11 21						12 21					13 21						14 21						15 21
Meopham d	11 25						12 25					13 25						14 25						15 25
Sole Street d	11 28						12 28					13 28						14 28						15 28
London Charing Cross 4 ⊖ d	*10 26*						*11 26*					*12 26*						*13 26*						*14 26*
London Waterloo (East) 4 ⊖ d	*10 29*						*11 29*					*12 29*						*13 29*						*14 29*
London Cannon Street 4 ⊖ d																								
London Bridge 4 ⊖ d	*10 34*						*11 34*					*12 34*						*13 34*						*14 34*
Dartford 4 d	*11 06*						*12 06*					*13 06*						*14 06*						*15 06*
Greenhithe for Bluewater d	*11 11*						*12 11*					*13 11*						*14 11*						*15 11*
Gravesend 4 d	*11 18*						*12 18*					*13 18*						*14 18*						*15 18*
Strood 4 d	*11 29*						*12 29*					*13 29*						*14 29*						*15 29*
Rochester 4 d	11 37		11 44				12 37		12 44			13 37			13 44			14 37			14 44			15 37
Chatham 4 d	11 39		11 47				12 39		12 47			13 39			13 47			14 39			14 47			15 39
Gillingham (Kent) 4 d	11 43		11 50				12 43		12 50			13 43			13 50			14 43			14 50			15 43
Rainham (Kent) d	11 48		11 55				12 48		12 55			13 48			13 55			14 48			14 55			15 48
Newington d	11 52						12 52					13 52						14 52						15 52
Sittingbourne 4 a	11 57		12 02				12 57		13 02			13 57			14 02			14 57			15 02			15 57
d	11 57		12 02		12 21		12 57		13 02		13 21	13 57			14 02		14 21	14 57			15 02		15 21	15 57
Kemsley d					12 25						13 25						14 25						15 25	
Swale d					12x28						13x28						14x28						15x28	
Queenborough d					12 33						13 33						14 33						15 33	
Sheerness-on-Sea a					12 38						13 38						14 38						15 38	
Teynham d	12 01						13 01					14 01						15 01						16 01
Faversham 2 a	12 07		12 10				13 07		13 10			14 07			14 10			15 07			15 10			16 07
d			12 14	12 17					13 14	13 17					14 14	14 17					15 14	15 17		
Selling d				12 22						13 22						14 22						15 22		
Canterbury East 4 d				12 31						13 31						14 31						15 31		
Bekesbourne d				12 36						13 36						14 36						15 36		
Adisham d				12 40						13 40						14 40						15 40		
Aylesham d				12 43						13 43						14 43						15 43		
Snowdown d				12 45						13 45						14 45						15 45		
Shepherds Well d				12 49						13 49						14 49						15 49		
Kearsney d				12 54						13 54						14 54						15 54		
Dover Priory 4 ⛴ a				12 58						13 58						14 58						15 58		
Whitstable d			12 22						13 22						14 22						15 22			
Chestfield & Swalecliffe d			12 25						13 25						14 25						15 25			
Herne Bay d			12 28						13 28						14 28						15 28			
Birchington-on-Sea d			12 37						13 37						14 37						15 37			
Westgate-on-Sea d			12 40						13 40						14 40						15 40			
Margate 4 d		12 16	12 44					13 16	13 44					14 16	14 44				15 16		15 44			
Broadstairs d		12 21	12 49					13 21	13 49					14 21	14 49				15 21		15 49			
Dumpton Park d		12 23	12 52					13 23	13 52					14 23	14 52				15 23		15 52			
Ramsgate 4 ✈ a		12 26	12 55					13 26	13 55					14 26	14 55				15 26		15 55			

For general notes see front of timetable
For details of catering facilities see Directory of Train Operators

For services from London to Ramsgate, Dover and Canterbury via Ashford see Table 207

Table 212

Sundays

London → Medway, Sheerness-on-Sea, Dover and Ramsgate

Network Diagram - see first page of Table 212

		SE 90 [1]	SE 50 [1] (restaurant)		SE 01		SE 54 [1]	SE 90 [1]	SE 50 [1] (restaurant)		SE 01	SE 54 [1]		SE 90 [1]	SE 50 [1] (restaurant)		SE 01	SE 54 [1]	SE 90 [1]		SE 50 [1] (restaurant)		SE 01	SE 54 [1]	SE 90 [1]
London Victoria 15	⊖ d		15 03				15 41		16 03			16 41			17 03			17 41			18 03			18 41	
London Blackfriars 3	⊖ d																								
Elephant & Castle	⊖ d																								
Bromley South 4	d		15 19				16 01		16 19			17 01			17 19			18 01			18 19			19 01	
St Mary Cray	d						16 07					17 07						18 07						19 07	
Swanley 4	d						16 12					17 12						18 12						19 12	
Farningham Road	d						16 16					17 16						18 16						19 17	
Longfield	d						16 21					17 21						18 21						19 21	
Meopham	d						16 25					17 25						18 25						19 26	
Sole Street	d						16 28					17 28						18 28						19 28	
London Charing Cross 4	⊖ d						15 26					16 26						17 26						18 26	
London Waterloo (East) 4	⊖ d						15 29					16 29						17 29						18 29	
London Cannon Street 4	⊖ d																								
London Bridge 4	⊖ d						15 34					16 34						17 34						18 34	
Dartford 4	d						16 06					17 06						18 07						19 07	
Greenhithe for Bluewater	d						16 11					17 11						18 12						19 12	
Gravesend 4	d						16 18					17 18						18 18						19 18	
Strood 4	d						16 29					17 29						18 29						19 29	
Rochester 4	d		15 44				16 37		16 44			17 37			17 44			18 37			18 44			19 37	
Chatham 4	d		15 47				16 39		16 47			17 39			17 47			18 39			18 47			19 40	
Gillingham (Kent) 4	d		15 50				16 43		16 50			17 43			17 50			18 43			18 50			19 43	
Rainham (Kent)	d		15 55				16 48		16 55			17 48			17 55			18 48			18 55			19 48	
Newington	d						16 52					17 52						18 52						19 52	
Sittingbourne 4	a		16 02				16 57		17 02			17 57			18 02			18 57			19 02			19 57	
	d		16 02		16 21		16 57		17 02		17 21	17 57			18 02		18 21	18 57			19 02		19 21	19 57	
Kemsley	d				16 25						17 25						18 25						19 25		
Swale	d				16x28						17x28						18x28						19x28		
Queenborough	d				16 33						17 33						18 33						19 33		
Sheerness-on-Sea	a				16 38						17 38						18 38						19 38		
Teynham	d						17 01					18 01						19 01						20 01	
Faversham 2	a		16 10				17 07		17 10			18 07			18 10			19 07			19 10			20 07	
	d		16 14	16 17					17 14	17 17					18 14	18 17					19 14	19 17			
Selling	d			16 22						17 22						18 22						19 22			
Canterbury East 4	d			16 31						17 31						18 31						19 31			
Bekesbourne	d			16 36						17 36						18 36						19 36			
Adisham	d			16 40						17 40						18 40						19 40			
Aylesham	d			16 43						17 43						18 43						19 43			
Snowdown	d			16 45						17 45						18 45						19 45			
Shepherds Well	d			16 49						17 49						18 49						19 49			
Kearsney	d			16 54						17 54						18 54						19 54			
Dover Priory 4 (ship)	a			16 58						17 58						18 58						19 58			
Whitstable	d		16 22						17 22						18 22						19 22				
Chestfield & Swalecliffe	d		16 25						17 25						18 25						19 25				
Herne Bay	d		16 28						17 28						18 28						19 28				
Birchington-on-Sea	d		16 37						17 37						18 37						19 37				
Westgate-on-Sea	d		16 40						17 40						18 40						19 40				
Margate 4	d	16 16	16 44					17 16	17 44					18 16	18 44				19 16		19 44				20 16
Broadstairs	d	16 21	16 49					17 21	17 49					18 21	18 49				19 21		19 49				20 21
Dumpton Park	d	16 23	16 52					17 23	17 52					18 23	18 52				19 23		19 52				20 23
Ramsgate 4 (airport)	a	16 26	16 55					17 26	17 55					18 26	18 55				19 26		19 55				20 26

For general notes see front of timetable
For details of catering facilities see Directory of Train Operators

For services from London to Ramsgate, Dover and Canterbury via Ashford see Table 207

London → Medway, Sheerness-on-Sea, Dover and Ramsgate

Network Diagram - see first page of Table 212

		SE 90 1	SE 50 1			SE 01	SE 54 1	SE 4 1	SE 50 1		SE 01		SE 54 1	SE 50 1		SE 01	SE 54 1	SE 50 1			SE 54 1	SE 50 1	SE 54 1		
London Victoria 15	⊖ d		19 03				19 41		20 03				20 41	21 03			21 41	22 03			22 41	23 03	23 41		
London Blackfriars 3	⊖ d																								
Elephant & Castle	⊖ d																								
Bromley South 4	d		19 19				20 01		20 19				21 01	21 19			22 01	22 19			23 01	23 19	00 01		
St Mary Cray	d						20 07						21 07				22 07				23 07		00 07		
Swanley 4	d						20 12						21 12				22 12				23 12		00 12		
Farningham Road	d						20 17						21 16				22 16				23 16		00 16		
Longfield	d						20 21						21 21				22 21				23 21		00 21		
Meopham	d						20 26						21 25				22 25				23 25		00 25		
Sole Street	d						20 28						21 28				22 28				23 28		00 28		
London Charing Cross 4	⊖ d						19 26						20 26				21 26				22 26		23 26		
London Waterloo (East) 4	⊖ d						19 29						20 29				21 29				22 29		23 29		
London Cannon Street 4	⊖ d																								
London Bridge 4	⊖ d						19 34						20 34				21 34				22 34		23 34		
Dartford 4	d						20 07						21 07				22 07				23 07		00 06		
Greenhithe for Bluewater	d						20 12						21 12				22 12				23 12		00 11		
Gravesend 4	d						20 18						21 18				22 18				23 18		00 18		
Strood 4	d						20 29						21 29				22 29				23 29		00 30		
Rochester 4	d		19 44				20 37		20 44				21 37	21 44			22 37	22 44			23 37	23 44	00 37		
Chatham 4	d		19 47				20 40		20 47				21 39	21 47			22 39	22 47			23 39	23 47	00 39		
Gillingham (Kent) 4	d		19 50				20 43		20 50				21 43	21 50			22 43	22 50			23 43	23 50	00a43		
Rainham (Kent)	d		19 55				20 48		20 55				21 48	21 55			22 48	22 55			23 48	23 55			
Newington	d						20 52						21 52				22 52				23 52				
Sittingbourne 4	a		20 02				20 57		21 02				21 57	22 02			22 57	23 02			23 57	00 02			
	d		20 02			20 21	20 57		21 02		21 21		21 57	22 02		22 21	22 57	23 02			23 57	00 02			
Kemsley	d					20 25					21 25					22 25									
Swale	d					20x28					21x28					22x28									
Queenborough	d					20 33					21 33					22 33									
Sheerness-on-Sea	a					20 38					21 38					22 38									
Teynham	d						21 01						22 01				23 01				00 01				
Faversham 2	a		20 10				21 07		21 10				22 07	22 10			23 07	23 10			00 07	00 10			
	d		20 14	20 17					21 14	21 17				22 14	22 17			23 14	23 16			00 14			
Selling	d			20 22						21 22					22 22										
Canterbury East 4	d			20 31						21 31					22 31				23 29						
Bekesbourne	d			20 36						21 36					22 36										
Adisham	d			20 40						21 40					22 40										
Aylesham	d			20 43						21 43					22 43										
Snowdown	d			20 45						21 45					22 45										
Shepherds Well	d			20 49						21 49					22 49										
Kearsney	d			20 54						21 54					22 54										
Dover Priory 4	⛴ a			20 58						21 58					22 58				23 45						
Whitstable	d		20 22						21 22					22 22				23 22				00 22			
Chestfield & Swalecliffe	d		20 25						21 25					22 25				23 25				00 25			
Herne Bay	d		20 28						21 28					22 28				23 28				00 28			
Birchington-on-Sea	d		20 37						21 37					22 37				23 37				00 37			
Westgate-on-Sea	d		20 40						21 40					22 40				23 40				00 40			
Margate 4	d	20 40	20 44					21 23	21 44					22 44				23 44				00 44			
Broadstairs	d	20 45	20 49					21 28	21 49					22 49				23 49				00 49			
Dumpton Park	d	20 47	20 52					21 30	21 52					22 52				23 52				00 52			
Ramsgate 4	✈ a	20 50	20 55					21 33	21 55					22 55				23 55				00 55			

For general notes see front of timetable
For details of catering facilities see Directory of Train Operators

For services from London to Ramsgate, Dover and Canterbury via Ashford see Table 207

For details of Bank Holiday service alterations please see first page of Table 195

Ramsgate, Dover, Sheerness-on-Sea and Medway → London

Network Diagram - see first page of Table 212

Miles	Miles	Miles	Station		SE MX 58	SE 50 [1]	SE 07 [1]	SE 37 [1]	SE 01	SE 50 [1]	SE 03 [1]	SE 01	SE 51 [1]	SE 07 [1]	SE 07 [1]	SE 22	SE 31 [1]	SE 22	SE 07 [1]	SE 01	SE 22	SE 50 [1]	SE 07 [1]
0	—	—	**Ramsgate [4]** ✈	d		04 38				05 04			05 28		05 46							06 11	
1	—	—	Dumpton Park	d		04 40							05 30		05 49							06 14	
2¼	—	—	Broadstairs	d		04 43				05 09			05 33		05 52							06 17	06 24
5½	—	—	**Margate [4]**	d		04 48				05 14			05 38		05 57							06 22	06 29
6¾	—	—	Westgate-on-Sea	d		04 51							05 41		06 01							06 25	
8½	—	—	Birchington-on-Sea	d		04 54				05 19			05 44		06 04							06 29	06 34
16½	—	—	**Herne Bay**	d		05 03				05 28			05 53		06 13							06 37	06 43
18½	—	—	Chestfield & Swalecliffe	d		05 07							05 56		06 17							06 40	
20½	—	—	Whitstable	d		05 10				05 33			06 00		06 20							06 44	06 49
—	0	—	**Dover Priory [4]** ⛴	d				04 50			05 12						05 49						
—	2¼	—	Kearsney	d				04 54			05 16						05 53						
—	5½	—	Shepherds Well	d				04 59			05 22						05 58						
—	7½	—	Snowdown	d				05 02			05 26						06 01						
—	8½	—	Aylesham	d				05 05			05 28						06 04						
—	9½	—	Adisham	d				05 07			05 31						06 06						
—	12½	—	Bekesbourne	d				05 12			05 35						06 11						
—	15½	—	**Canterbury East [4]**	d				05 17			05 41						06 17						
—	22	—	Selling	d				05 26			05 51						06 26						
27¼	25¼	—	**Faversham [2]**	a		05 18		05 30		05 41	05 55		06 09		06 29		06 30		←			06 52	06 57
—	—	—		d	23p42	05 19	05 22	05 31		05 43	05 56		06 10	06 16	06 36		06 32		06 36			06 53	06 58
31¾	29¾	—	Teynham	d	23p47		05 27	05 36		05 48				06 21	→		06 37		06 41				
—	—	0	**Sheerness-on-Sea**	d					05 31			05 58								06 36			
—	—	2	Queenborough	d					05 36			06 03								06 41			
—	—	4	Swale	d					05x40			06x08								06x46			
—	—	6	Kemsley	d					05 43			06 11								06 49			
34½	32½	8	**Sittingbourne [4]**	a	23p52	05 27	05 32	05 41	05 48	05 53	06 04	06 16	06 18	06 26			06 42		06 46	06 54		07 01	07 06
—	—	—		d	23p52	05 28	05 32	05 41		05 54	06 04		06 18	06 27			06 43		06 46			07 02	07 06
37¾	35¾	—	Newington	d	23p57		05 37	05 46		05 59				06 32			06 48		06 52				
40¼	38¼	—	Rainham (Kent)	d	00 01	05 36	05 42	05 50		06 04	06 12		06 26	06 37			06 53		06 56			07 10	07 14
43¼	41¼	—	**Gillingham (Kent) [4]**	d	00 07	05 42	05 48	05 56		06 09	06 18		06 32	06 42		06 49	06 58		07 02		07 06	07 16	07 20
45	43	—	**Chatham [4]**	d	00 11	05 46	05 52	06 01		06 13	06 22		06 36	06 46		06 53	07 02		07 06		07 10	07 20	07 24
45½	43½	0	Rochester [4]	d	00 13		05 54	06 03		06 15	06 28		06 43	06 48		06 55			07 19		07 13		07 34
—	—	—	Strood [4]	a	00 17	06 03	06 03			06 33	06 33		06 48	07 04		07 04			07 24		07 24		07 44
—	—	—	Gravesend [4]	a	00 28	06 14	06 14			06 44	06 44		06 59	07 17		07 17			07 39		07 39		07 57
—	—	—	Greenhithe for Bluewater	a	00 34	06 20	06 20			06 50	06 50		07 06	07 24		07 24			07 46		07 46		08 04
—	—	—	Dartford [4]	a	00 41	06 25	06 25			06 55	06 55		07 11	07 29		07 29			07 51		07 51		08 09
—	—	—	**London Bridge [4]** ⊖	a		07 01	06 33			07 30	07 07		07 44	07 26		08 06			07 49		08b41		08 08
—	—	30	**London Cannon Street [4]** ⊖	a		07c13	06 38			07e41	07 13		07 51	07 33		08 13			07 55			08 54	08 15
—	—	—	**London Waterloo (East) [4]** ⊖	a		07 06	06f41			07 36	07f16		07c55	07f36		08e15			07f58			08c55	08f19
—	—	—	**London Charing Cross [4]** ⊖	a		07 10	06f46			07 40	07f20		07c59	07f40		08e21			08f03			09c01	08f24
52¼	50¼	—	Sole Street	d				06 14		06 24						07 06		←			07 24		
53¼	51¼	—	Meopham	d				06 16		06 26						07 08 →		07 08			07 26 →		
55¾	53¾	—	Longfield	d				06 20		06 30								07 13					
58¾	56¾	—	Farningham Road	d				06 24		06 34								07 17					
61¾	59¾	—	Swanley [4]	a				06 29		06 40								07 22					
64½	62½	—	St Mary Cray	a				06 35		06 45								07 27					
68¼	66¼	—	Bromley South [4]	a		06 13		06 42		06 51							07 32	07 35				07 50	
—	—	—	Elephant & Castle ⊖	a		07 10				07 15							07 57	07 57				08 24	
—	—	—	**London Blackfriars [3]** ⊖	a		07 15				07 18							08 03	08 03				08 29	
79¼	77¼	—	**London Victoria [15]** ⊖	a	01 13	06 30		07 00		07 12			07 22				07 52	07 58				08 11	

For general notes see front of timetable
For details of catering facilities see Directory of Train Operators

For services from Ramsgate, Dover and Canterbury to London via Ashford see Table 207

b Change at Rochester and Dartford
c Change at Chatham and London Bridge
e Change at Rochester and London Bridge
f Change at London Bridge

For details of Bank Holiday service alterations please see first page of Table 195

Ramsgate, Dover, Sheerness-on-Sea and Medway → London

Network Diagram - see first page of Table 212

Station		SE 01	SE 80 [1]	SE 22	SE 23	SE 20	SE 51 [1]	SE 07 [1]	SE 01	SE 61 [1]	SE 22 [1]	SE 50 [1]	SE 07 [1]	SE 01	SE 34 [1]	SE 22 [1]	SE 07 [1]	SE 20 [1]	SE 50 [1]	SE 34 [1]	SE 34 [1]	SE 01
										A												
Ramsgate [4]	d						06 30					06 50					07 11		07 22			
Dumpton Park	d						06 32					06 52					07 14		07 24			
Broadstairs	d						06 35	06 47				06 55	07 06				07 17		07 27			
Margate [4]	d						06 40	06 52				07 00	07 11				07 22		07 32			
Westgate-on-Sea	d						06 43					07 03	07 15				07 26		07 35			
Birchington-on-Sea	d						06 47	06 57				07 06	07 18				07 29		07 38			
Herne Bay	d						06 57	07 06				07 16	07 27				07 38		07 48			
Chestfield & Swalecliffe	d						07 00					07 19	07 31				07 42		07 51			
Whitstable	d						07 04	07 12				07 23	07 35				07 45		07 55			
Dover Priory [4]	d		06 24							06 45					07 09						07 50	
Kearsney	d		06 28							06 49					07 13						07 54	
Shepherds Well	d		06 33							06 54					07 18						07 59	
Snowdown	d		06 36							06 57					07 21						08 02	
Aylesham	d		06 39							07 00					07 24						08 05	
Adisham	d		06 41							07 02					07 26						08 07	
Bekesbourne	d		06 46							07 07					07 31						08 12	
Canterbury East [4]	d		06 51							07 13					07 37						08 18	
Selling	d		07 00							07 22					07 46						08 27	
Faversham [2]	a		07 06				07 12	07 20		07 28		07 31	07 43		07 50		07 54		08 03	⟵	08 31	
	d						07 13	07 21				07 32	07 44		08 07		07 55		08 04	08 07	08 38	
Teynham	d						07 18					07 37			⟶		08 00			08 12	⟶	
Sheerness-on-Sea	d	06 57							07 21					07 44								08 07
Queenborough	d	07 02							07 25					07 48								08 12
Swale	d	07x05							07x29					07x52								08x16
Kemsley	d	07 09							07 33					07 56								08 19
Sittingbourne [4]	a	07 15					07 23	07 29	07 38			07 42	07 52	08 02			08 05		08 12	08 17		08 23
	d						07 24	07 29				07 43	07 52				08 05		08 12	08 18		
Newington	d						07 29					07 48					08 11			08 23		
Rainham (Kent)	d						07 34	07 37				07 53	08 00				08 15		08 20	08 28		
Gillingham (Kent) [4]	d					07 28	07 39	07 43			07 47	07 58	08 06				08 21		08 25	08 33		
Chatham [4]	d					07 32	07 43	07 47			07 51	08 02	08 10				08 25		08 29	08 37		
Rochester [4]	d				07 29	07 34					07 53		*08 21*					08 16	08 31	08 39		
Strood [4]	a					*07 44*					*08 02*		*08 26*							*08 56*		
Gravesend [4]	a					*07 57*					*08 19*		*08 39*							*09 08*		
Greenhithe for Bluewater	a					*08 04*					*08 28*		*08 46*							*09 13*		
Dartford [4]	a					*08 09*					*08 34*		*08 52*							*09 19*		
London Bridge [4]	⊖ a					*08 47*		08 29			*09 11*		08 49				09 09			*09 54*		
London Cannon Street [4]	⊖ a					*08 54*		08 36			*09 18*	09b38	08 56				09 16			*10c06*		
London Waterloo (East) [4]	⊖ a					*08c55*		*08e39*			*09c23*	09 34	*08e59*				*09e19*			*09 59*		
London Charing Cross [4]	⊖ a					*09c01*		*08e44*			*09c29*	09 39	*09e04*				*09e24*			*10 05*		
Sole Street	d			⟵	07 40						08 04					⟵		08 27		08 50		
Meopham	d			07 26	07 42	07 46					08 07					08 07		08 29		08 53		
Longfield	d			07 30	07 46	07 51					⟶					08 11		08 33		08 58		
Farningham Road	d			07 34	07 50											08 15		08 37		09 02		
Swanley [4]	a			07 39	07 55	07 58										08 20		08 42		09 07		
St Mary Cray	a			07 44	08 00	08 03										08 25		08 47		09 12		
Bromley South [4]	a			07 51	08 07	08 11	08 15					08 30				08 32		08 54	09 03	09 18		
Elephant & Castle	⊖ a			*08 24*	08 31	*08 43*	08 50									*09 11*			*09 32*			
London Blackfriars [3]	⊖ a			*08 29*	08 37	*08 49*	08 56									*09 17*			*09 37*			
London Victoria [15]	⊖ a			08 14		08 38	08 34					08 52				08 57		09 15	09 26	09 38		

For general notes see front of timetable
For details of catering facilities see Directory of Train Operators

For services from Ramsgate, Dover and Canterbury to London via Ashford see Table 207

A From Ashford International (Table 207)
b Change at Chatham and London Bridge
c Change at Rochester and London Bridge
e Change at London Bridge

For details of Bank Holiday service alterations please see first page of Table 195

Ramsgate, Dover, Sheerness-on-Sea and Medway → London

Network Diagram - see first page of Table 212

Station		SE 50	SE 64	SE 34	SE 01	SE 01	SE 30	SE 50	SE 66	SE 01	SE 30	SE 50	SE 92	SE 01	SE 30	SE 50	SE 4	SE 92	SE 01	SE 30	SE 50	SE 90	SE 92
		[1]	[1]	[1]			[1]	[1]	[1]		[1]	[1]	[1]		[1]	[1]	[1]	[1]		[1]	[1]	[1]	[1]
									A														
		🍴						🍴				🍴				🍴					🍴		
Ramsgate [4] ✈	d	07 52	07 56					08 17	08 43			08 50				09 22	09 37				09 59	10 05	
Dumpton Park	d	07 54	07 58					08 19	08 45			08 52				09 24	09 40					10 08	
Broadstairs	d	07 57	08 01					08 22	08 48			08 56				09 28	09 43				10 03	10 11	
Margate [4]	d	08 02	08a06					08 28	08a53			09 02				09 34	09a48				10 08	10a16	
Westgate-on-Sea	d	08 05						08 31				09 05				09 37							
Birchington-on-Sea	d	08 08						08 34				09 09				09 40					10 13		
Herne Bay	d	08 17						08 44				09 18				09 49					10 21		
Chestfield & Swalecliffe	d	08 21						08 47				09 22				09 52							
Whitstable	d	08 24						08 50				09 26				09 56					10 26		
Dover Priory [4] ⛴	d						08 17				09 04				09 22					10 04			
Kearsney	d						08 21								09 26								
Shepherds Well	d						08 26								09 31								
Snowdown	d						08 29								09 35								
Aylesham	d						08 32								09 37								
Adisham	d						08 34								09 39								
Bekesbourne	d						08 39								09 43								
Canterbury East [4]	d						08 44				09 21				09 49					10 21			
Selling	d						08 53								09 58								
Faversham [2]	a	08 32		←			08 57	08 59			09 32	09 35			10 02	10 05				10 32	10 35		
	d	08 34		08 38			09 03				09 38		09 45		10 08			10 15		10 38			10 45
Teynham	d			08 43			09 08						09 50					10 20					10 50
Sheerness-on-Sea	d				08 36	08 50				09 26				09 56					10 26				
Queenborough	d				08 42	08 55				09 31				10 01					10 31				
Swale	d				08x47	08x59				09x36				10x06					10x36				
Kemsley	d				08 50	09 03				09 39				10 09					10 39				
Sittingbourne [4]	a	08 42		08 48	08 55	09 08	09 13			09 44	09 46		09 55	10 14	10 16			10 25	10 44	10 46			10 55
	d	08 43		08 49			09 13				09 47		09 55		10 17			10 25		10 47			10 55
Newington	d			08 54									10 00					10 30					11 00
Rainham (Kent)	d	08 51		08 58			09 21				09 54		10 05		10 24			10 35		10 54			11 05
Gillingham (Kent) [4]	d	08 56		09 03			09 26				09 59		10 10		10 29			10 40		10 59			11 10
Chatham [4]	d	09 00		09 07			09 30				10 03		10 14		10 33			10 44		11 03			11 14
Rochester [4]	d			09 09			09 32				10 06		10 16		10 36			10 46		11 06			11 16
Strood [4]	a	*09 24*		*09 24*			*09 54*						*10 24*					*10 54*					*11 24*
Gravesend [4]	a	*09 36*		*09 36*			*10 06*						*10 36*					*11 06*					*11 36*
Greenhithe for Bluewater	a	*09 41*		*09 41*			*10 11*						*10 41*					*11 11*					*11 41*
Dartford [4]	a	*09 46*		*09 46*			*10 16*						*10 46*					*11 16*					*11 46*
London Bridge [4] ⊖	a	*10 19*		*10 19*			*10 49*						*11 19*					*11 49*					*12 19*
London Cannon Street [4] ⊖	a	*10b30*		*10c30*			*10c57*						*11c27*					*11c57*					*12c27*
London Waterloo (East) [4] ⊖	a	*10 24*		*10 24*			*10 54*						*11 24*					*11 54*					*12 24*
London Charing Cross [4] ⊖	a	*10 28*		*10 28*			*10 58*						*11 28*					*11 58*					*12 28*
Sole Street	d			09 20									10 27					10 57					11 27
Meopham	d			09 23			09 42						10 29					10 59					11 29
Longfield	d			09 27			09 46						10 33					11 03					11 33
Farningham Road	d			09 31									10 37					11 07					11 37
Swanley [4]	a			09 36									10 42					11 12					11 42
St Mary Cray	a			09 41									10 47					11 17					11 47
Bromley South [4]	a	09 29		09 47			09 59				10 29		10 54		10 59			11 24		11 29			11 54
Elephant & Castle ⊖	a	*10 09*					*10 30*				*11 00*				*11 30*					*12 00*			
London Blackfriars [3] ⊖	a	*10 12*					*10 33*				*11 03*				*11 33*					*12 03*			
London Victoria [15] ⊖	a	09 51		10 05			10 17				10 47		11 17		11 17			11 47		11 47			12 17

For general notes see front of timetable
For details of catering facilities see Directory of Train Operators

For services from Ramsgate, Dover and Canterbury to London via Ashford see Table 207

A From London Victoria (Table 196)
b Change at Chatham and London Bridge
c Change at Rochester and London Bridge

For details of Bank Holiday service alterations please see first page of Table 195

Ramsgate, Dover, Sheerness-on-Sea and Medway → London

Network Diagram - see first page of Table 212

		SE	SE	SE	SE	SE	SE	SE	SE	SE	SE	SE	SE	SE	SE	SE	SE	SE	SE	SE	SE	SE
		01	30	50	92	01	30	50	90	92	01	30	50	92	01	30	50	92	01	30	50	90
			1	1	1		1	1	1	1		1	1	1		1	1	1		1	1	1
				⚲				⚲					⚲				⚲				⚲	
Ramsgate 4	d			10 22				10 59	11 10				11 22				11 59				12 22	12 40
Dumpton Park	d			10 24					11 13				11 24								12 24	12 43
Broadstairs	d			10 28				11 03	11 16				11 28				12 03				12 28	12 46
Margate 4	d			10 34				11 08	11a22				11 34				12 08				12 34	12a51
Westgate-on-Sea	d			10 37									11 37								12 37	
Birchington-on-Sea	d			10 40				11 13					11 40				12 13				12 40	
Herne Bay	d			10 49				11 21					11 49				12 21				12 49	
Chestfield & Swalecliffe	d			10 52									11 52								12 52	
Whitstable	d			10 56				11 26					11 56				12 26				12 56	
Dover Priory 4	d		10 22				11 04					11 22				12 04				12 22		
Kearsney	d		10 26									11 26								12 26		
Shepherds Well	d		10 31									11 31								12 31		
Snowdown	d		10 35									11 35								12 35		
Aylesham	d		10 37									11 37								12 37		
Adisham	d		10 39									11 39								12 39		
Bekesbourne	d		10 43									11 43								12 43		
Canterbury East 4	d		10 49				11 21					11 49				12 21				12 49		
Selling	d		10 58									11 58								12 58		
Faversham 2	a		11 02	11 05			11 32	11 35				12 02	12 05			12 32	12 35			13 02	13 05	
	d		11 08		11 15		11 38			11 45		12 08		12 15		12 38		12 45		13 08		
Teynham	d				11 20					11 50				12 20				12 50				
Sheerness-on-Sea	d	10 56				11 26					11 56				12 26				12 56			
Queenborough	d	11 01				11 31					12 01				12 31				13 01			
Swale	d	11x06				11x36					12x06				12x36				13x06			
Kemsley	d	11 09				11 39					12 09				12 39				13 09			
Sittingbourne 4	a	11 14	11 16		11 25	11 44	11 46			11 55	12 14	12 16		12 25	12 44	12 46		12 55	13 14	13 16		
	d		11 17		11 25		11 47			11 55		12 17		12 25		12 47		12 55		13 17		
Newington	d				11 30					12 00				12 30				13 00				
Rainham (Kent)	d		11 24		11 35		11 54			12 05		12 24		12 35		12 54		13 05		13 24		
Gillingham (Kent) 4	d		11 29		11 40		11 59			12 10		12 29		12 40		12 59		13 10		13 29		
Chatham 4	d		11 33		11 44		12 03			12 14		12 33		12 44		13 03		13 14		13 33		
Rochester 4	d		11 36		11 46		12 06			12 16		12 36		12 46		13 06		13 16		13 36		
Strood 4	a				*11 54*					*12 24*				*12 54*				*13 24*				
Gravesend 4	a				*12 06*					*12 36*				*13 06*				*13 36*				
Greenhithe for Bluewater	a				*12 11*					*12 41*				*13 11*				*13 41*				
Dartford 4	a				*12 16*					*12 46*				*13 16*				*13 46*				
London Bridge 4	⊖ a				*12 49*					*13 19*				*13 49*				*14 19*				
London Cannon Street 4	⊖ a				*12b57*					*13b27*				*13b57*				*14b27*				
London Waterloo (East) 4	⊖ a				*12 54*					*13 24*				*13 54*				*14 24*				
London Charing Cross 4	⊖ a				*12 58*					*13 28*				*13 58*				*14 28*				
Sole Street	d				11 57					12 27				12 57				13 27				
Meopham	d				11 59					12 29				12 59				13 29				
Longfield	d				12 03					12 33				13 03				13 33				
Farningham Road	d				12 07					12 37				13 07				13 37				
Swanley 4	a				12 12					12 42				13 12				13 42				
St Mary Cray	a				12 17					12 47				13 17				13 47				
Bromley South 4	a		11 59		12 24		12 29			12 54		12 59		13 24		13 29		13 54		13 59		
Elephant & Castle	⊖ a		*12 30*				*13 00*					*13 30*				*14 00*				*14 30*		
London Blackfriars 3	⊖ a		*12 33*				*13 03*					*13 33*				*14 03*				*14 33*		
London Victoria 15	⊖ a		12 17		12 47		12 47			13 17		13 17		13 47		13 47		14 17		14 17		

For general notes see front of timetable
For details of catering facilities see Directory of Train Operators

For services from Ramsgate, Dover and Canterbury to London via Ashford see Table 207

b Change at Rochester and London Bridge

For details of Bank Holiday service alterations please see first page of Table 195

Ramsgate, Dover, Sheerness-on-Sea and Medway → London

Network Diagram - see first page of Table 212

		SE	SE	SE	SE	SE		SE	SE	SE	SE	SE	SE	SE		SE	SE	SE	SE	SE	SE	SE		SE	SE
		92	01	30	50	92		01	30	50	90	92	30	50		90	01	92	30	50	01	92		30	50
		1		1	1	1			1	1	1	1	1	1		1		1	1	1		1		1	1
					trolley					trolley				trolley		trolley				trolley					trolley
Ramsgate 4 ✈	d				12 59					13 22	13 40			13 57		14 17				14 21					14 57
Dumpton Park	d									13 24	13 43					14 20				14 23					
Broadstairs	d				13 03					13 28	13 46			14 01		14 23				14 27					15 01
Margate 4	d				13 08					13 34	13a51			14 06		14a28				14 32					15 06
Westgate-on-Sea	d									13 37										14 35					
Birchington-on-Sea	d				13 13					13 40				14 11						14 38					15 11
Herne Bay	d				13 21					13 49				14 19						14 47					15 19
Chestfield & Swalecliffe	d									13 52										14 50					
Whitstable	d				13 26					13 56				14 24						14 54					15 24
Dover Priory 4 ⛴	d			13 04					13 22				14 02						14 20					15 02	
Kearsney	d								13 26										14 24						
Shepherds Well	d								13 31										14 29						
Snowdown	d								13 35										14 33						
Aylesham	d								13 37										14 35						
Adisham	d								13 39										14 37						
Bekesbourne	d								13 43										14 41						
Canterbury East 4	d			13 21					13 49				14 19						14 47					15 19	
Selling	d								13 58										14 56						
Faversham 2	a			13 32	13 35				14 02	14 05			14 30	14 33					15 00	15 03				15 30	15 33
	d	13 15			13 38	13 45				14 08		14 15		14 36				14 45		15 06		15 15			15 36
Teynham	d	13 20				13 50						14 20						14 50				15 20			
Sheerness-on-Sea	d		13 26					13 56									14 30				15 00				
Queenborough	d		13 31					14 01									14 35				15 05				
Swale	d		13x36					14x06									14x39				15x09				
Kemsley	d		13 39					14 09									14 43				15 13				
Sittingbourne 4	a	13 25	13 44		13 46	13 55		14 14		14 16		14 25		14 44			14 48	14 55		15 14	15 18	15 25			15 44
	d	13 25			13 47	13 55				14 17		14 25		14 45				14 55		15 15		15 25			15 45
Newington	d	13 30				14 00						14 30						15 00				15 30			
Rainham (Kent)	d	13 35			13 54	14 05				14 24		14 35		14 52				15 05		15 22		15 35			15 52
Gillingham (Kent) 4	d	13 40			13 59	14 10				14 29		14 40		14 57				15 10		15 27		15 40			15 57
Chatham 4	d	13 44			14 03	14 14				14 33		14 44		15 01				15 14		15 31		15 44			16 01
Rochester 4	d	13 46			14 06	14 16				14 36		14 46		15 04				15 16		15 34		15 46			16 03
Strood 4	a	*13 54*				*14 24*						*14 54*						*15 24*				*15 54*			
Gravesend 4	a	*14 06*				*14 36*						*15 06*						*15 36*				*16 08*			
Greenhithe for Bluewater	a	*14 11*				*14 41*						*15 11*						*15 41*				*16 14*			
Dartford 4	a	*14 16*				*14 46*						*15 16*						*15 46*				*16 20*			
London Bridge 4	⊖ a	*14 49*				*15 19*						*15 49*						*16 19*				*16 55*			
London Cannon Street 4	⊖ a	*14b57*				*15b27*						*15b57*						*16b27*				*17b05*			
London Waterloo (East) 4	⊖ a	*14 54*				*15 24*						*15 54*						*16 24*				*17 00*			
London Charing Cross 4	⊖ a	*14 58*				*15 28*						*15 58*						*16 28*				*17 03*			
Sole Street	d	13 57				14 27						14 57						15 27				15 57			
Meopham	d	13 59				14 29						14 59						15 29				15 59			
Longfield	d	14 03				14 33						15 03						15 33				16 03			
Farningham Road	d	14 07				14 37						15 07						15 37				16 07			
Swanley 4	a	14 12				14 42						15 12						15 42				16 12			
St Mary Cray	a	14 17				14 47						15 17						15 47				16 17			
Bromley South 4	a	14 24			14 29	14 54				14 59		15 24		15 29				15 53		15 59		16 23			16 30
Elephant & Castle	⊖ a				*15 00*					*15 30*				*16 00*						*16 30*					*17 00*
London Blackfriars 3	⊖ a				*15 03*					*15 33*				*16 03*						*16 33*					*17 05*
London Victoria 15	⊖ a	14 47			14 47	15 17				15 17		15 47		15 47				16 18		16 17		16 49			16 49

For general notes see front of timetable
For details of catering facilities see Directory of Train Operators

For services from Ramsgate, Dover and Canterbury to London via Ashford see Table 207

b Change at Rochester and London Bridge

For details of Bank Holiday service alterations please see first page of Table 195

Ramsgate, Dover, Sheerness-on-Sea and Medway → London

Network Diagram - see first page of Table 212

		SE 90 1	SE 01	SE 92 1	SE 30 1	SE 50 1	SE 01	SE 92 1	SE 31 1	SE 51 1	SE 18 1	SE 01	SE 92 1	SE 30 1	SE 50 1	SE 01	SE 92 1	SE 30 1	SE 50 1	SE 01	SE 92 1	SE 01
Ramsgate 4	d	15 17				15 21				15 52	16 13				16 20				16 48			
Dumpton Park	d	15 20				15 23				15 54	16 16				16 22				16 50			
Broadstairs	d	15 23				15 27				15 58	16 19				16 26				16 53			
Margate 4	d	15a28				15 32				16 04	16a24				16 32				16 59			
Westgate-on-Sea	d					15 35				16 07					16 35				17 02			
Birchington-on-Sea	d					15 38				16 10					16 38				17 06			
Herne Bay	d					15 47				16 19					16 47				17 15			
Chestfield & Swalecliffe	d					15 50				16 22					16 50				17 19			
Whitstable	d					15 54				16 26					16 54				17 22			
Dover Priory 4	d				15 20				15 52					16 20				16 48				
Kearsney	d				15 24				15 56					16 24				16 52				
Shepherds Well	d				15 29				16 01					16 29				16 57				
Snowdown	d				15 33				16 05					16 33				17 00				
Aylesham	d				15 35				16 07					16 35				17 03				
Adisham	d				15 37				16 09					16 37				17 05				
Bekesbourne	d				15 41				16 13					16 41				17 10				
Canterbury East 4	d				15 47				16 19					16 47				17 16				
Selling	d				15 56				16 28					16 56				17 25				
Faversham 2	a				16 00	16 03			16 32	16 35				17 00	17 03			17 29	17 31			
	d			15 44	16 06			16 14	16 38				16 44	17 06			17 14	17 35			17 44	
Teynham	d			15 49				16 19					16 49				17 19				17 49	
Sheerness-on-Sea	d		15 30				16 00					16 30				17 00				17 36		17 53
Queenborough	d		15 35				16 05					16 35				17 05				17 41		17 58
Swale	d		15x39				16x09					16x39				17x10				17x45		18x02
Kemsley	d		15 43				16 13					16 43				17 13				17 49		18 06
Sittingbourne 4	a		15 49	15 54	16 14		16 18	16 24	16 46			16 48	16 54	17 14		17 18	17 24	17 43		17 53	17 54	18 11
	d			15 54	16 15			16 24	16 47				16 54	17 15			17 24	17 43			17 54	
Newington	d			15 59				16 29					16 59				17 29				17 59	
Rainham (Kent)	d			16 04	16 22			16 34	16 54				17 04	17 22			17 34	17 51			18 04	
Gillingham (Kent) 4	d			16 09	16 27			16 39	16 59				17 09	17 27			17 39	17 56			18 09	
Chatham 4	d			16 13	16 31			16 43	17 03				17 13	17 31			17 43	18 00			18 13	
Rochester 4	d			16 15	16 33			16 45	17 06				17 15	17 33			17 45	18 02			18 15	
Strood 4	a			16 24				16 54					17 24				17 58	18 22			18b22	
Gravesend 4	a			16 36				17 06					17 36				18 10	18 34			18b34	
Greenhithe for Bluewater	a			16 41				17 11					17 45				18 15	18 40			18b40	
Dartford 4	a			16 46				17 17					17 50				18 20	18 46			18b46	
London Bridge 4	⊖ a			17 26				17 56					18 31				19 02	19 23			19b23	
London Cannon Street 4	⊖ a			17c33				18 01					18c45				19c10	19c37			19e37	
London Waterloo (East) 4	⊖ a			17 31				18c05					18 36				19 07	19 28			19b28	
London Charing Cross 4	⊖ a			17 35				18c09					18 40				19 11	19 32			19b32	
Sole Street	d			16 26				16 56					17 26				17 56				18 26	
Meopham	d			16 29				16 59					17 29				17 59				18 29	
Longfield	d			16 33				17 03					17 33				18 03				18 33	
Farningham Road	d			16 37				17 08					17 37				18 07				18 37	
Swanley 4	a			16 42				17 13					17 43				18 12				18 42	
St Mary Cray	a			16 47				17 18					17 47				18 16				18 47	
Bromley South 4	a			16 53	16 59			17 25	17 33				17 53	17 59			18 23	18 31			18 53	
Elephant & Castle	⊖ a				17 32			18 02						18 31				19 00				
London Blackfriars 3	⊖ a				17 39			18 08						18 35				19 03				
London Victoria 15	⊖ a			17 18	17 17			17 48	17 58				18 19	18 17			18 50	18 48			19 17	

For general notes see front of timetable
For details of catering facilities see Directory of Train Operators

For services from Ramsgate, Dover and Canterbury to London via Ashford see Table 207

b Change at Chatham
c Change at Rochester and London Bridge
e Change at Chatham and London Bridge

For details of Bank Holiday service alterations please see first page of Table 195

Ramsgate, Dover, Sheerness-on-Sea and Medway → London

Network Diagram - see first page of Table 212

		SE	SE	SE		SE	SE	SE	SE	SE	SE	SE		SE	SE	SE	SE	SE	SE	SE		SE	SE	SE	SE
		30 1	50 1	92 1		30 1	50 1	4 1	01	92 1	30 1	50 1		01	01	50 1	30 1	90 1	4 1	92 1		01	01	50 1	30 1
Ramsgate	d		17 22				17 50	18 12				18 21				18 48		18 52	19 12					19 48	
Dumpton Park	d		17 24				17 52	18 15				18 23				18 50		18 55	19 15					19 50	
Broadstairs	d		17 28				17 55	18 18				18 26				18 53		18 58	19 18					19 53	
Margate	d		17 34				18 01	18a23				18 32				18 59		19a05	19a26					19 59	
Westgate-on-Sea	d		17 37				18 04					18 35				19 02								20 02	
Birchington-on-Sea	d		17 40				18 08					18 39				19 06								20 06	
Herne Bay	d		17 49				18 17					18 48				19 15								20 15	
Chestfield & Swalecliffe	d		17 52				18 21					18 52				19 19								20 19	
Whitstable	d		17 56				18 24					18 55				19 22								20 22	
Dover Priory	d	17 22				17 50					18 21						18 54								19 52
Kearsney	d	17 26				17 54					18 25						18 58								19 56
Shepherds Well	d	17 31				17 59					18 30						19 03								20 01
Snowdown	d	17 35				18 02					18 33						19 06								20 04
Aylesham	d	17 37				18 05					18 36						19 09								20 07
Adisham	d	17 39				18 07					18 38						19 11								20 09
Bekesbourne	d	17 43				18 12					18 43						19 16								20 14
Canterbury East	d	17 49				18 18					18 49						19 22								20 19
Selling	d	17 58				18 27					18 58						19 31								20 28
Faversham	a	18 02	18 06			18 31	18 33				19 02	19 04				19 31	19 35							20 31	20 33
	d	18 09		18 14		18 37				18 44	19 08					19 39				19 45				20 37	
Teynham	d			18 19						18 49										19 50					
Sheerness-on-Sea	d								18 28					19 02	19 20							19 50	20 05		
Queenborough	d								18 33					19b11	19 25							19 56	20 10		
Swale	d								18x38					19x15	19x29							20x01	20x15		
Kemsley	d								18 41					19 19	19 33							20 04	20 18		
Sittingbourne	a	18 17		18 24		18 45			18 46	18 54	19 16			19 23	19 38	19 47				19 55		20 09	20 23	20 45	
	d	18 17		18 24		18 45				18 54	19 17					19 47				19 55				20 45	
Newington	d			18 29						18 59										20 00					
Rainham (Kent)	d	18 25		18 34		18 53				19 04	19 24					19 55				20 05				20 53	
Gillingham (Kent)	d	18 31		18 40		18 58				19 10	19 29					20 00				20 10				20 58	
Chatham	d	18 35		18 44		19 02				19 14	19 33					20 04				20 14				21 02	
Rochester	d	18 37		18 46		19 04				19 16	*19 50*					20 06				20 16				21 04	
Strood	a			*18 54*						*19 24*	*19 54*									*20 26*					
Gravesend	a			*19 06*						*19 36*	*20 06*									*20 38*					
Greenhithe for Bluewater	a			*19 11*						*19 41*	*20 11*									*20 43*					
Dartford	a			*19 17*						*19 46*	*20 16*									*20 48*					
London Bridge	⊖ a			*19 53*						*20 23*	*20 53*									*21 23*					
London Cannon Street	⊖ a			*20c11*						*20c41*															
London Waterloo (East)	⊖ a			*19 58*						*20 28*	*20 58*									*21 28*					
London Charing Cross	⊖ a			*20 01*						*20 31*	*21 01*									*21 31*					
Sole Street	d			18 57						19 27										20 27					
Meopham	d			19 00						19 30										20 30					
Longfield	d			19 04						19 34										20 34					
Farningham Road	d			19 08						19 38										20 38					
Swanley	a			19 12						19 42										20 42					
St Mary Cray	a			19 17						19 47										20 47					
Bromley South	a	19 00		19 23		19 30				19 53	19 58					20 32				20 53				21 29	
Elephant & Castle	⊖ a	*19 36*				*20 00*					*20 30*									*21 30*				*22 00*	
London Blackfriars	⊖ a	*19 40*				*20 03*					*20 33*									*21 33*				*22 03*	
London Victoria	⊖ a	19 17		19 48		19 47				20 17	20 17					20 48				21 17				21 47	

For general notes see front of timetable
For details of catering facilities see Directory of Train Operators

For services from Ramsgate, Dover and Canterbury to London via Ashford see Table 207

b Arr. 1907
c Change at Rochester and London Bridge

For details of Bank Holiday service alterations please see first page of Table 195

Ramsgate, Dover, Sheerness-on-Sea and Medway → London

Network Diagram - see first page of Table 212

		SE 4 1	SE 01	SE 92 1	SE 91 1	SE 97		SE 01	SE 50 1	SE 30 1	SE 90 1	SE 92 1	SE 01	SE 80 1		SE 50 1	SE 55 1	SE 01	SE 80 1	SE 81 1	SE 58	SE 90 1			
Ramsgate 4	d	20 04			20 39				20 50		21 28					21 55	22 10			22 53		23 40			
Dumpton Park	d	20 07			20 41				20 52		21 31					21 57				22 55		23 43			
Broadstairs	d	20 10			20 44				20 55		21 34					22 00	22 15			22 58		23 46			
Margate 4	d	20a16			20a51				21 01		21a39					22 06	22 20			23 04		23a51			
Westgate-on-Sea	d								21 04							22 09				23 07					
Birchington-on-Sea	d								21 07							22 12	22 25			23 11					
Herne Bay	d								21 17							22 22	22 34			23 20					
Chestfield & Swalecliffe	d								21 20							22 25				23 24					
Whitstable	d								21 24							22 29	22 39			23 27					
Dover Priory 4	d									20 52				21 55					23 01						
Kearsney	d									20 56				21 59											
Shepherds Well	d									21 01				22 04											
Snowdown	d									21 04				22 07											
Aylesham	d									21 07				22 10											
Adisham	d									21 09				22 12											
Bekesbourne	d									21 14				22 17											
Canterbury East 4	d									21 20				22 22					23 18						
Selling	d									21 29				22 31											
Faversham 2	a								21 32	21 34				22 35		22 37	22 47		23 30	23 36					
	d			20 45					21 38			21 45				22 38	22 48				23 42				
Teynham	d			20 50								21 50					22 53				23 47				
Sheerness-on-Sea	d		20 34			21 01		21 26					22 29					23 28							
Queenborough	d		20 39			21 06		21 31					22 34					23 33							
Swale	d		20x43			21x10		21x36					22x38					23x38							
Kemsley	d		20 47			21 14		21 39					22 41					23 41							
Sittingbourne 4	a		20 52	20 55				21 44	21 46			21 55	22 45			22 47	22 58	23 46			23 52				
	d			20 55					21 47			21 55				22 47	22 58				23 52				
Newington	d			21 00		21 21						22 00					23 03				23 57				
Rainham (Kent)	d			21 05		21 25			21 54			22 05				22 54	23 08				00 01				
Gillingham (Kent) 4	d			21 10		21a30			21 59			22 10				22 59	23 13				00 07				
Chatham 4	d			21 14					22 03			22 14				23 03	23 17				00 11				
Rochester 4	d			21 16								22 16					23 19				00 13				
Strood 4	a			*21 24*					*22 32*			*22 32*					*00 17*				00 17				
Gravesend 4	a			*21 36*					*22 44*			*22 44*					*00 28*				00 28				
Greenhithe for Bluewater	a			*21 41*					*22 52*			*22 52*					*00 34*				00 34				
Dartford 4	a			*21 46*					*22 58*			*22 58*					*00 41*				00 41				
London Bridge 4	⊖ a			*22 23*					*23 41*			*23 41*													
London Cannon Street 4	⊖ a																								
London Waterloo (East) 4	⊖ a			*22 28*					*23 46*			*23 46*													
London Charing Cross 4	⊖ a			*22 31*					*23 50*			*23 50*													
Sole Street	d			21 27								22 27					23 30								
Meopham	d			21 30								22 30					23 32								
Longfield	d			21 34								22 34					23 36								
Farningham Road	d			21 38								22 38					23 40								
Swanley 4	a			21 42								22 42					23 45								
St Mary Cray	a			21 47								22 47					23 49								
Bromley South 4	a			21 53					22 30			22 53				23 30	23 55								
Elephant & Castle	⊖ a			*22 30*					*23 00*			*23 31*													
London Blackfriars 3	⊖ a			*22 33*					*23 03*			*23 37*													
London Victoria 15	⊖ a			22 17					22 47			23 15				23 47	00 18				01 13				

For general notes see front of timetable
For details of catering facilities see Directory of Train Operators

For services from Ramsgate, Dover and Canterbury to London via Ashford see Table 207

Ramsgate, Dover, Sheerness-on-Sea and Medway → London

Network Diagram - see first page of Table 212

		SE 58	SE 54 1	SE 92 1	SE 30 1	SE 50 1	SE 92 1	SE 01	SE 30 1	SE 50 1	SE 92 1	SE 30 1	SE 50 1	SE 92 1	SE 01	SE 30 1	SE 50 1	SE 92 1	SE 30 1	SE 50 1	SE 64 1	SE 92 1
Ramsgate 4	d		04 38			05 22				05 59			06 22				06 59			07 22	07 38	
Dumpton Park	d					05 24							06 24							07 24	07 40	
Broadstairs	d					05 28				06 03			06 28				07 03			07 28	07 43	
Margate 4	d		04 46			05 34				06 08			06 34				07 08			07 34	07a48	
Westgate-on-Sea	d					05 37							06 37							07 37		
Birchington-on-Sea	d					05 40				06 13			06 40				07 13			07 40		
Herne Bay	d		04 58			05 49				06 21			06 49				07 21			07 49		
Chestfield & Swalecliffe	d					05 52							06 52							07 52		
Whitstable	d		05 03			05 56				06 26			06 56				07 26			07 56		
Dover Priory 4	d				05 22				06 04			06 22				07 04			07 22			
Kearsney	d				05 26							06 26							07 26			
Shepherds Well	d				05 31							06 31							07 31			
Snowdown	d				05 35							06 35							07 35			
Aylesham	d				05 37							06 37							07 37			
Adisham	d				05 39							06 39							07 39			
Bekesbourne	d				05 43							06 43							07 43			
Canterbury East 4	d				05 49				06 21			06 49				07 21			07 49			
Selling	d				05 58							06 58							07 58			
Faversham 2	a		05 11		06 02	06 05			06 32	06 35		07 02	07 05			07 32	07 35		08 02	08 05		
	d	23p42	05 12	05 45	06 08		06 15		06 38		06 45	07 08		07 15		07 38		07 45	08 08			08 15
Teynham	d	23p47		05 50			06 20				06 50			07 20				07 50				08 20
Sheerness-on-Sea	d							06 26							07 26							
Queenborough	d							06 31							07 31							
Swale	d							06x36							07x36							
Kemsley	d							06 39							07 39							
Sittingbourne 4	a	23p52	05 20	05 55	06 16		06 25	06 44	06 46		06 55	07 16		07 25	07 44	07 46		07 55	08 16			08 25
	d	23p52	05 20	05 55	06 17		06 25		06 47		06 55	07 17		07 25		07 47		07 55	08 17			08 25
Newington	d	23p57		06 00			06 30				07 00			07 30				08 00				08 30
Rainham (Kent)	d	00 01	05 28	06 05	06 24		06 35		06 54		07 05	07 24		07 35		07 54		08 05	08 24			08 35
Gillingham (Kent) 4	d	00 07	05 33	06 10	06 29		06 40		06 59		07 10	07 29		07 40		07 59		08 10	08 29			08 40
Chatham 4	d	00 11	05 37	06 14	06 33		06 44		07 03		07 14	07 33		07 44		08 03		08 14	08 33			08 44
Rochester 4	d	00 13	05 39	06 16	06 36		06 46		07 06		07 16	07 36		07 46		08 06		08 16	08 36			08 46
Strood 4	a	00 17	*05 54*	*06 24*			*06 54*				*07 24*			*07 54*				*08 24*				*08 54*
Gravesend 4	a	00 28	*06 05*	*06 35*			*07 05*				*07 35*			*08 05*				*08 36*				*09 06*
Greenhithe for Bluewater	a	00 34	*06 10*	*06 40*			*07 10*				*07 40*			*08 10*				*08 41*				*09 11*
Dartford 4	a	00 41	*06 15*	*06 45*			*07 15*				*07 45*			*08 15*				*08 46*				*09 16*
London Bridge 4	⊖ a		*06 50*	*07 21*			*07 49*				*08 19*			*08 49*				*09 19*				*09 49*
London Cannon Street 4	⊖ a		*07b50*	*07c50*			*08c03*				*08c27*			*08c57*				*09c27*				*09c57*
London Waterloo (East) 4	⊖ a		*06 55*	*07 26*			*07 54*				*08 24*			*08 54*				*09 24*				*09 54*
London Charing Cross 4	⊖ a		*06 58*	*07 29*			*07 58*				*08 28*			*08 58*				*09 28*				*09 58*
Sole Street	d		05 50	06 27			06 57				07 27			07 57				08 27				08 57
Meopham	d		05 52	06 29			06 59				07 29			07 59				08 29				08 59
Longfield	d		05 56	06 33			07 03				07 33			08 03				08 33				09 03
Farningham Road	d		06 00	06 37			07 07				07 37			08 07				08 37				09 07
Swanley 4	a		06 05	06 42			07 12				07 42			08 12				08 42				09 12
St Mary Cray	a		06 10	06 47			07 17				07 47			08 17				08 47				09 17
Bromley South 4	a		06 16	06 54	06 59		07 24		07 29		07 54	07 59		08 24		08 29		08 54	08 59			09 24
Elephant & Castle	⊖ a		*07 00*		*07 30*				*08 00*			*08 30*				*09 00*			*09 30*			
London Blackfriars 3	⊖ a		*07 03*		*07 33*				*08 03*			*08 33*				*09 03*			*09 33*			
London Victoria 15	⊖ a	01 13	06 32	07 17	07 17		07 47		07 47		08 17	08 17		08 47		08 47		09 17	09 17			09 47

For general notes see front of timetable
For details of catering facilities see Directory of Train Operators

For services from Ramsgate, Dover and Canterbury to London via Ashford see Table 207

b Change at Chatham and London Bridge
c Change at Rochester and London Bridge

Saturdays

Ramsgate, Dover, Sheerness-on-Sea and Medway → London

Network Diagram - see first page of Table 212

	SE	SE	SE	SE	SE	SE	SE		SE	SE	SE	SE	SE	SE		SE	SE	SE	SE	SE	SE		SE	SE
	01	30	50	92	01	30	50		4	92	01	30	50	92		01	30	50	4	92	01		30	50
		[1]	[1]	[1]		[1]	[1]		[1]	[1]		[1]	[1]	[1]			[1]	[1]	[1]	[1]			[1]	[1]
		🛒	🛒			🛒	🛒					🛒	🛒				🛒	🛒					🛒	🛒
Ramsgate [4] ✈ d			07 59				08 22		08 34				08 59					09 22	09 34					09 59
Dumpton Park d							08 24		08 37									09 24	09 37					
Broadstairs d			08 03				08 28		08 40				09 03					09 28	09 40					10 03
Margate [4] d			08 08				08 34		08a45				09 08					09 34	09a45					10 08
Westgate-on-Sea d							08 37											09 37						
Birchington-on-Sea d			08 13				08 40						09 13					09 40						10 13
Herne Bay d			08 21				08 49						09 21					09 49						10 21
Chestfield & Swalecliffe d							08 52											09 52						
Whitstable d			08 26				08 56						09 26					09 56						10 26
Dover Priory [4] ⛴ d		08 04				08 22						09 04					09 22						10 04	
Kearsney d						08 26											09 26							
Shepherds Well d						08 31											09 31							
Snowdown d						08 35											09 35							
Aylesham d						08 37											09 37							
Adisham d						08 39											09 39							
Bekesbourne d						08 43											09 43							
Canterbury East [4] d		08 21				08 49						09 21					09 49						10 21	
Selling d						08 58											09 58							
Faversham [2] a		08 32	08 35			09 02	09 05					09 32	09 35				10 02	10 05					10 32	10 35
d		08 38		08 45		09 08				09 15		09 38		09 45			10 08			10 15			10 38	
Teynham d				08 50						09 20				09 50						10 20				
Sheerness-on-Sea d	08 26				08 56						09 26					09 56					10 26			
Queenborough d	08 31				09 01						09 31					10 01					10 31			
Swale d	08x36				09x06						09x36					10x06					10x36			
Kemsley d	08 39				09 09						09 39					10 09					10 39			
Sittingbourne [4] a	08 44	08 46		08 55	09 14	09 16				09 25	09 44	09 46		09 55		10 14	10 16			10 25	10 44		10 46	
d		08 47		08 55		09 17				09 25		09 47		09 55			10 17			10 25			10 47	
Newington d				09 00						09 30				10 00						10 30				
Rainham (Kent) d		08 54		09 05		09 24				09 35		09 54		10 05			10 24			10 35			10 54	
Gillingham (Kent) [4] d		08 59		09 10		09 29				09 40		09 59		10 10			10 29			10 40			10 59	
Chatham [4] d		09 03		09 14		09 33				09 44		10 03		10 14			10 33			10 44			11 03	
Rochester [4] d		09 06		09 16		09 36				09 46		10 06		10 16			10 36			10 46			11 06	
Strood [4] a				*09 24*						*09 54*				*10 24*						*10 54*				
Gravesend [4] a				*09 36*						*10 06*				*10 36*						*11 06*				
Greenhithe for Bluewater a				*09 41*						*10 11*				*10 41*						*11 11*				
Dartford [4] a				*09 46*						*10 16*				*10 46*						*11 16*				
London Bridge [4] ⊖ a				*10 19*						*10 49*				*11 19*						*11 49*				
London Cannon Street [4] ⊖ a				*10b27*						*10b57*				*11b27*						*11b57*				
London Waterloo (East) [4] ⊖ a				*10 24*						*10 54*				*11 24*						*11 54*				
London Charing Cross [4] ⊖ a				*10 28*						*10 58*				*11 28*						*11 58*				
Sole Street d				09 27						09 57				10 27						10 57				
Meopham d				09 29						09 59				10 29						10 59				
Longfield d				09 33						10 03				10 33						11 03				
Farningham Road d				09 37						10 07				10 37						11 07				
Swanley [4] a				09 42						10 12				10 42						11 12				
St Mary Cray a				09 47						10 17				10 47						11 17				
Bromley South [4] a		09 29		09 54		09 59				10 24		10 29		10 54			10 59			11 24			11 29	
Elephant & Castle ⊖ a		*10 00*				*10 30*						*11 00*					*11 30*						*12 00*	
London Blackfriars [3] ⊖ a		*10 03*				*10 33*						*11 03*					*11 33*						*12 03*	
London Victoria [15] ⊖ a		09 47		10 17		10 17				10 47		10 47		11 17			11 17			11 47			11 47	

For general notes see front of timetable
For details of catering facilities see Directory of Train Operators

For services from Ramsgate, Dover and Canterbury to London via Ashford see Table 207

b Change at Rochester and London Bridge

Ramsgate, Dover, Sheerness-on-Sea and Medway → London

Network Diagram - see first page of Table 212

		SE	SE	SE	SE	SE	SE	SE	SE	SE	SE	SE	SE	SE	SE	SE	SE	SE	SE	SE	SE	SE
		90	92	01	30	50	92	01	30	50	90	92	01	30	50	90	92	01	30	50	92	01
		1	1		1	1	1		1	1	1	1		1	1	1	1		1	1	1	
					[trolley]	[trolley]			[trolley]	[trolley]				[trolley]	[trolley]	[trolley]			[trolley]	[trolley]		
Ramsgate 4	d	10 16				10 22				10 59	11 16				11 22	11 40				11 59		
Dumpton Park	d	10 19				10 24					11 19				11 24	11 43						
Broadstairs	d	10 22				10 28				11 03	11 22				11 28	11 46				12 03		
Margate 4	d	10a27				10 34				11 08	11a27				11 34	11a51				12 08		
Westgate-on-Sea	d					10 37									11 37							
Birchington-on-Sea	d					10 40				11 13					11 40					12 13		
Herne Bay	d					10 49				11 21					11 49					12 21		
Chestfield & Swalecliffe	d					10 52									11 52							
Whitstable	d					10 56				11 26					11 56					12 26		
Dover Priory 4	d				10 22				11 04					11 22					12 04			
Kearsney	d				10 26									11 26								
Shepherds Well	d				10 31									11 31								
Snowdown	d				10 35									11 35								
Aylesham	d				10 37									11 37								
Adisham	d				10 39									11 39								
Bekesbourne	d				10 43									11 43								
Canterbury East 4	d				10 49				11 21					11 49					12 21			
Selling	d				10 58									11 58								
Faversham 2	a				11 02	11 05			11 32	11 35				12 02	12 05				12 32	12 35		
	d		10 45		11 08		11 15		11 38			11 45		12 08			12 15		12 38		12 45	
Teynham	d		10 50				11 20					11 50					12 20				12 50	
Sheerness-on-Sea	d			10 56				11 26					11 56					12 26				12 56
Queenborough	d			11 01				11 31					12 01					12 31				13 01
Swale	d			11x06				11x36					12x06					12x36				13x06
Kemsley	d			11 09				11 39					12 09					12 39				13 09
Sittingbourne 4	a		10 55	11 14	11 16		11 25	11 44	11 46			11 55	12 14	12 16			12 25	12 44	12 46		12 55	13 14
	d		10 55		11 17		11 25		11 47			11 55		12 17			12 25		12 47		12 55	
Newington	d		11 00				11 30					12 00					12 30				13 00	
Rainham (Kent)	d		11 05		11 24		11 35		11 54			12 05		12 24			12 35		12 54		13 05	
Gillingham (Kent) 4	d		11 10		11 29		11 40		11 59			12 10		12 29			12 40		12 59		13 10	
Chatham 4	d		11 14		11 33		11 44		12 03			12 14		12 33			12 44		13 03		13 14	
Rochester 4	d		11 16		11 36		11 46		12 06			12 16		12 36			12 46		13 06		13 16	
Strood 4	a		11 24				11 54					12 24					12 54				13 24	
Gravesend 4	a		11 36				12 06					12 36					13 06				13 36	
Greenhithe for Bluewater	a		11 41				12 11					12 41					13 11				13 41	
Dartford 4	a		11 46				12 16					12 46					13 16				13 46	
London Bridge 4 ⊖	a		12 19				12 49					13 19					13 49				14 19	
London Cannon Street 4 ⊖	a		12b27				12b57					13b27					13b57				14b27	
London Waterloo (East) 4 ⊖	a		12 24				12 54					13 24					13 54				14 24	
London Charing Cross 4 ⊖	a		12 28				12 58					13 28					13 58				14 28	
Sole Street	d		11 27				11 57					12 27					12 57				13 27	
Meopham	d		11 29				11 59					12 29					12 59				13 29	
Longfield	d		11 33				12 03					12 33					13 03				13 33	
Farningham Road	d		11 37				12 07					12 37					13 07				13 37	
Swanley 4	a		11 42				12 12					12 42					13 12				13 42	
St Mary Cray	a		11 47				12 17					12 47					13 17				13 47	
Bromley South 4	a		11 54		11 59		12 24		12 29			12 54		12 59			13 24		13 29		13 54	
Elephant & Castle ⊖	a				12 30				13 00					13 30					14 00			
London Blackfriars 3 ⊖	a				12 33				13 03					13 33					14 03			
London Victoria 15 ⊖	a		12 17		12 17		12 47		12 47			13 17		13 17			13 47		13 47		14 17	

For general notes see front of timetable
For details of catering facilities see Directory of Train Operators

For services from Ramsgate, Dover and Canterbury to London via Ashford see Table 207

b Change at Rochester and London Bridge

Table 212

Ramsgate, Dover, Sheerness-on-Sea and Medway → London

Network Diagram - see first page of Table 212

		SE 30 1	SE 50 1	SE 90 1	SE 92 1	SE 01	SE 30 1	SE 50 1	SE 92 1	SE 01	SE 30 1	SE 50 1	SE 90 1	SE 92 1	SE 01	SE 30 1	SE 50 1	SE 92 1	SE 01	SE 30 1	SE 50 1	SE 90 1
Ramsgate 4	d		12 22	12 40				12 59				13 22	13 40				13 59				14 22	14 40
Dumpton Park	d		12 24	12 43								13 24	13 43								14 24	14 43
Broadstairs	d		12 28	12 46				13 03				13 28	13 46				14 03				14 28	14 46
Margate 4	d		12 34	12a51				13 08				13 34	13a51				14 08				14 34	14a51
Westgate-on-Sea	d		12 37									13 37									14 37	
Birchington-on-Sea	d		12 40					13 13				13 40					14 13				14 40	
Herne Bay	d		12 49					13 21				13 49					14 21				14 49	
Chestfield & Swalecliffe	d		12 52									13 52									14 52	
Whitstable	d		12 56					13 26				13 56					14 26				14 56	
Dover Priory 4	d	12 22					13 04				13 22					14 04				14 22		
Kearsney	d	12 26									13 26									14 26		
Shepherds Well	d	12 31									13 31									14 31		
Snowdown	d	12 35									13 35									14 35		
Aylesham	d	12 37									13 37									14 37		
Adisham	d	12 39									13 39									14 39		
Bekesbourne	d	12 43									13 43									14 43		
Canterbury East 4	d	12 49					13 21				13 49					14 21				14 49		
Selling	d	12 58									13 58									14 58		
Faversham 2	a	13 02	13 05				13 32	13 35			14 02	14 05				14 32	14 35			15 02	15 05	
	d	13 08			13 15		13 38		13 45		14 08			14 15		14 38		14 45		15 08		
Teynham	d				13 20				13 50					14 20				14 50				
Sheerness-on-Sea	d					13 26				13 56					14 26				14 56			
Queenborough	d					13 31				14 01					14 31				15 01			
Swale	d					13x36				14x06					14x36				15x06			
Kemsley	d					13 39				14 09					14 39				15 09			
Sittingbourne 4	a	13 16			13 25	13 44	13 46		13 55	14 14	14 16			14 25	14 44	14 46		14 55	15 14	15 16		
	d	13 17			13 25		13 47		13 55		14 17			14 25		14 47		14 55		15 17		
Newington	d				13 30				14 00					14 30				15 00				
Rainham (Kent)	d	13 24			13 35		13 54		14 05		14 24			14 35		14 54		15 05		15 24		
Gillingham (Kent) 4	d	13 29			13 40		13 59		14 10		14 29			14 40		14 59		15 10		15 29		
Chatham 4	d	13 33			13 44		14 03		14 14		14 33			14 44		15 03		15 14		15 33		
Rochester 4	d	13 36			13 46		14 06		14 16		14 36			14 46		15 06		15 16		15 36		
Strood 4	a				13 54				14 24					14 54				15 24				
Gravesend 4	a				14 06				14 36					15 06				15 36				
Greenhithe for Bluewater	a				14 11				14 41					15 11				15 41				
Dartford 4	a				14 16				14 46					15 16				15 46				
London Bridge 4 ⊖	a				14 49				15 19					15 49				16 19				
London Cannon Street 4 ⊖	a				14b57				15b27					15b57				16b27				
London Waterloo (East) 4 ⊖	a				14 54				15 24					15 54				16 24				
London Charing Cross 4 ⊖	a				14 58				15 28					15 58				16 28				
Sole Street	d				13 57				14 27					14 57				15 27				
Meopham	d				13 59				14 29					14 59				15 29				
Longfield	d				14 03				14 33					15 03				15 33				
Farningham Road	d				14 07				14 37					15 07				15 37				
Swanley 4	a				14 12				14 42					15 12				15 42				
St Mary Cray	a				14 17				14 47					15 17				15 47				
Bromley South 4	a	13 59			14 24		14 29		14 54		14 59			15 24		15 29		15 54		15 59		
Elephant & Castle ⊖	a	14 30					15 00				15 30					16 00				16 30		
London Blackfriars 3 ⊖	a	14 33					15 03				15 33					16 03				16 33		
London Victoria 15 ⊖	a	14 17			14 47		14 47		15 17		15 17			15 47		15 47		16 17		16 17		

For general notes see front of timetable
For details of catering facilities see Directory of Train Operators

For services from Ramsgate, Dover and Canterbury to London via Ashford see Table 207

b Change at Rochester and London Bridge

Table 212

Saturdays

Ramsgate, Dover, Sheerness-on-Sea and Medway → London

Network Diagram - see first page of Table 212

Station		SE 92	SE 01	SE 30	SE 50	SE 92	SE 01	SE 30	SE 50	SE 90	SE 92	SE 01	SE 30	SE 50	SE 92	SE 01	SE 30	SE 50	SE 90	SE 92	SE 01
		1		1	1	1		1	1	1	1		1	1	1		1	1	1	1	
				🛒	🛒			🛒	🛒	🛒			🛒	🛒			🛒	🛒	🛒		
Ramsgate 4 ✈	d				14 59				15 22	15 40				15 59				16 22	16 40		
Dumpton Park	d								15 24	15 43								16 24	16 43		
Broadstairs	d				15 03				15 28	15 46				16 03				16 28	16 46		
Margate 4	d				15 08				15 34	15a51				16 08				16 34	16a51		
Westgate-on-Sea	d								15 37									16 37			
Birchington-on-Sea	d				15 13				15 40					16 13				16 40			
Herne Bay	d				15 21				15 49					16 21				16 49			
Chestfield & Swalecliffe	d								15 52									16 52			
Whitstable	d				15 26				15 56					16 26				16 56			
Dover Priory 4 ⛴	d			15 04				15 22					16 04				16 22				
Kearsney	d							15 26									16 26				
Shepherds Well	d							15 31									16 31				
Snowdown	d							15 35									16 35				
Aylesham	d							15 37									16 37				
Adisham	d							15 39									16 39				
Bekesbourne	d							15 43									16 43				
Canterbury East 4	d			15 21				15 49					16 21				16 49				
Selling	d							15 58									16 58				
Faversham 2	a			15 32	15 35			16 02	16 05				16 32	16 35			17 02	17 05			
	d	15 15			15 38	15 45			16 08		16 15			16 38	16 45			17 08		17 15	
Teynham	d	15 20				15 50					16 20				16 50					17 20	
Sheerness-on-Sea	d		15 26				15 56					16 26				16 56					17 26
Queenborough	d		15 31				16 01					16 31				17 01					17 31
Swale	d		15x36				16x06					16x36				17x06					17x36
Kemsley	d		15 39				16 09					16 39				17 09					17 39
Sittingbourne 4	a	15 25	15 44		15 46	15 55	16 14		16 16		16 25	16 44		16 46	16 55	17 14		17 16		17 25	17 44
	d	15 25			15 47	15 55			16 17		16 25			16 47	16 55			17 17		17 25	
Newington	d	15 30				16 00					16 30				17 00					17 30	
Rainham (Kent)	d	15 35			15 54	16 05			16 24		16 35			16 54	17 05			17 24		17 35	
Gillingham (Kent) 4	d	15 40			15 59	16 10			16 29		16 40			16 59	17 10			17 29		17 40	
Chatham 4	d	15 44			16 03	16 14			16 33		16 44			17 03	17 14			17 33		17 44	
Rochester 4	d	15 46			16 06	16 16			16 36		16 46			17 06	17 16			17 36		17 46	
Strood 4	a	15 54				16 24					16 54				17 24					17 54	
Gravesend 4	a	16 06				16 36					17 06				17 36					18 06	
Greenhithe for Bluewater	a	16 11				16 41					17 11				17 41					18 11	
Dartford 4	a	16 16				16 46					17 16				17 46					18 16	
London Bridge 4	⊖ a	16 49				17 19					17 49				18 19					18 49	
London Cannon Street 4	⊖ a	16b57				17b27					17b57				18b27						
London Waterloo (East) 4	⊖ a	16 54				17 24					17 54				18 24					18 54	
London Charing Cross 4	⊖ a	16 58				17 28					17 58				18 28					18 58	
Sole Street	d	15 57				16 27					16 57				17 27					17 57	
Meopham	d	15 59				16 29					16 59				17 29					17 59	
Longfield	d	16 03				16 33					17 03				17 33					18 03	
Farningham Road	d	16 07				16 37					17 07				17 37					18 07	
Swanley 4	a	16 12				16 42					17 12				17 42					18 12	
St Mary Cray	a	16 17				16 47					17 17				17 47					18 17	
Bromley South 4	a	16 24			16 29	16 54			16 59		17 24			17 29	17 54			17 59		18 24	
Elephant & Castle	⊖ a				17 00				17 30					18 00				18 30			
London Blackfriars 3	⊖ a				17 03				17 33					18 03				18 33			
London Victoria 15	⊖ a	16 47			16 47	17 17			17 17		17 47			17 47	18 17			18 17		18 47	

For general notes see front of timetable
For details of catering facilities see Directory of Train Operators

For services from Ramsgate, Dover and Canterbury to London via Ashford see Table 207

b Change at Rochester and London Bridge

Table 212

Ramsgate, Dover, Sheerness-on-Sea and Medway → London

Network Diagram - see first page of Table 212

Station		SE	SE	SE	SE	SE	SE	SE	SE	SE	SE	SE	SE	SE	SE	SE	SE	SE	SE	SE	SE	SE
		30	50	92	01	30	50	90	92	01	30	50	92	30	50	90	92	01	30	50	90	92
		1	1	1		1	1	1	1		1	1	1	1	1	1	1		1	1	1	1
								⚮								⚮					⚮	
Ramsgate 4	d		16 59				17 22	17 40				17 59			18 22	18 40				18 52	19 24	
Dumpton Park	d						17 24	17 43							18 24	18 43				18 54	19 27	
Broadstairs	d		17 03				17 28	17 46				18 03			18 28	18 46				18 58	19 30	
Margate 4	d		17 08				17 34	17a51				18 08			18 34	18a51				19 04	19a35	
Westgate-on-Sea	d						17 37								18 37					19 07		
Birchington-on-Sea	d		17 13				17 40					18 13			18 40					19 10		
Herne Bay	d		17 21				17 49					18 21			18 49					19 19		
Chestfield & Swalecliffe	d						17 52								18 52					19 22		
Whitstable	d		17 26				17 56					18 26			18 56					19 26		
Dover Priory 4	d	17 04				17 22					18 04			18 22					18 52			
Kearsney	d					17 26								18 26					18 56			
Shepherds Well	d					17 31								18 31					19 01			
Snowdown	d					17 35								18 35					19 05			
Aylesham	d					17 37								18 37					19 07			
Adisham	d					17 39								18 39					19 09			
Bekesbourne	d					17 43								18 43					19 13			
Canterbury East 4	d	17 21				17 49					18 21			18 49					19 19			
Selling	d					17 58								18 58					19 28			
Faversham 2	a	17 32	17 35			18 02	18 05				18 32	18 35		19 02	19 05				19 32	19 35		
	d	17 38		17 45		18 08			18 15		18 38		18 45	19 08			19 15		19 38			19 45
Teynham	d			17 50					18 20				18 50				19 20					19 50
Sheerness-on-Sea	d				17 56					18 26								19 26				
Queenborough	d				18 01					18 31								19 31				
Swale	d				18x06					18x36								19x36				
Kemsley	d				18 09					18 39								19 39				
Sittingbourne 4	a	17 46		17 55	18 14	18 16			18 25	18 44	18 46		18 55	19 16			19 25	19 44	19 46			19 55
	d	17 47		17 55		18 17			18 25		18 47		18 55	19 17			19 25		19 47			19 55
Newington	d			18 00					18 30				19 00				19 30					20 00
Rainham (Kent)	d	17 54		18 05		18 24			18 35		18 54		19 05	19 24			19 35		19 54			20 05
Gillingham (Kent) 4	d	17 59		18 10		18 29			18 40		18 59		19 10	19 29			19 40		19 59			20 10
Chatham 4	d	18 03		18 14		18 33			18 44		19 03		19 14	19 33			19 44		20 03			20 14
Rochester 4	d	18 06		18 16		18 36			18 46		19 06		19 16	19 36			19 46		20 06			20 16
Strood 4	a			*18 24*					*18 54*				*19 24*				*19 54*					*20 24*
Gravesend 4	a			*18 36*					*19 06*				*19 36*				*20 06*					*20 36*
Greenhithe for Bluewater	a			*18 41*					*19 11*				*19 41*				*20 11*					*20 41*
Dartford 4	a			*18 46*					*19 16*				*19 46*				*20 16*					*20 46*
London Bridge 4	⊖ a			*19 21*					*19 53*				*20 23*				*20 53*					*21 23*
London Cannon Street 4	⊖ a																					
London Waterloo (East) 4	⊖ a			*19 25*					*19 58*				*20 28*				*20 58*					*21 28*
London Charing Cross 4	⊖ a			*19 29*					*20 01*				*20 31*				*21 01*					*21 31*
Sole Street	d			18 27					18 57				19 27				19 57					20 27
Meopham	d			18 29					18 59				19 29				19 59					20 29
Longfield	d			18 33					19 03				19 33				20 03					20 33
Farningham Road	d			18 37					19 07				19 37				20 07					20 37
Swanley 4	a			18 42					19 12				19 42				20 12					20 42
St Mary Cray	a			18 47					19 17				19 47				20 17					20 47
Bromley South 4	a	18 29		18 54		18 59			19 24		19 29		19 54	19 59			20 24		20 29			20 54
Elephant & Castle	⊖ a	*19 00*				*19 30*					*20 00*			*20 30*					*21 00*			*21 30*
London Blackfriars 3	⊖ a	*19 03*				*19 33*					*20 03*			*20 33*					*21 03*			*21 33*
London Victoria 15	⊖ a	18 47		19 17		19 17			19 47		19 47		20 17	20 17			20 47		20 47			21 17

For general notes see front of timetable
For details of catering facilities see Directory of Train Operators

For services from Ramsgate, Dover and Canterbury to London via Ashford see Table 207

Table 212

Saturdays

Ramsgate, Dover, Sheerness-on-Sea and Medway → London

Network Diagram - see first page of Table 212

Station		SE 30 1	SE 50 1	SE 4 1 (bus)	SE 01	SE 92 1	SE 30 1	SE 50 1	SE 01	SE 90 1	SE 90 1	SE 50 1	SE 50 1	SE 01	SE 90 1	SE 90 1	SE 01	SE 81 1	SE 58 1	SE 58	SE 90 1
Ramsgate 4 (ferry)	d		19 52	20 12				20 52			21 38		21 52			22 38			22 55		23 38
Dumpton Park	d		19 54	20 15				20 54			21 41		21 54			22 41			22 57		23 41
Broadstairs	d		19 58	20 18				20 58			21 44		21 58			22 44			23 00		23 44
Margate 4	d		20 04	20a23				21 04			21a49		22 04			22a49			23 06		23a49
Westgate-on-Sea	d		20 07					21 07					22 07						23 09		
Birchington-on-Sea	d		20 10					21 10					22 10						23 13		
Herne Bay	d		20 19					21 19					22 19						23 22		
Chestfield & Swalecliffe	d		20 22					21 22					22 22						23 26		
Whitstable	d		20 26					21 26					22 26						23 29		
Dover Priory 4 (ship)	d	19 52					20 52					21 52						23 04			
Kearsney	d	19 56					20 56					21 56									
Shepherds Well	d	20 01					21 01					22 01									
Snowdown	d	20 05					21 05					22 05									
Aylesham	d	20 07					21 07					22 07									
Adisham	d	20 09					21 09					22 09									
Bekesbourne	d	20 13					21 13					22 13									
Canterbury East 4	d	20 19					21 19					22 19						23 22			
Selling	d	20 28					21 28					22 28									
Faversham 2	a	20 32	20 35				21 32	21 35				22 32	22 35					23 34	23 38		
	d	20 38				20 45	21 38			21 45		22 38			22 45					23 42	
Teynham	d					20 50				21 50					22 50					23 47	
Sheerness-on-Sea	d				20 30				21 30					22 30			23 30				
Queenborough	d				20 35				21 35					22 35			23 35				
Swale	d				20x40				21x40					22x40			23x40				
Kemsley	d				20 43				21 43					22 43			23 43				
Sittingbourne 4	a	20 46			20 48	20 55	21 46		21 48	21 55		22 46		22 48	22 55		23 48			23 52	
	d	20 47				20 55	21 47			21 55		22 47			22 55					23 52	
Newington	d					21 00				22 00					23 00						
Rainham (Kent)	d	20 54				21 05	21 54			22 05		22 54			23 05					23 59	
Gillingham (Kent) 4	d	20 59				21 10	21 59			22 10		22 59			23 10					00 05	
Chatham 4	d	21 03				21 14	22 03			22 14		23 03			23 14					00 09	
Rochester 4	d	21 06				21 16	22 06			22 16		23 06			23 16					00 11	
Strood 4	a					21 24				22 32					00 15					00 15	
Gravesend 4	a					21 36				22 44					00 26					00 26	
Greenhithe for Bluewater	a					21 41				22 52					00 32					00 32	
Dartford 4	a					21 46				22 58					00 39					00 39	
London Bridge 4	⊖ a					22 23				23 41											
London Cannon Street 4	⊖ a																				
London Waterloo (East) 4	⊖ a					22 28				23 46											
London Charing Cross 4	⊖ a					22 31				23 50											
Sole Street	d					21 27				22 27					23 27						
Meopham	d					21 29				22 29					23 29						
Longfield	d					21 33				22 33					23 33						
Farningham Road	d					21 37				22 37					23 37						
Swanley 4	a					21 42				22 42					23 42						
St Mary Cray	a					21 47				22 47					23 47						
Bromley South 4	a	21 29				21 54	22 29			22 54		23 29			23 54						
Elephant & Castle	⊖ a	22 00				22 30	23 00			23 30											
London Blackfriars 3	⊖ a	22 03				22 33	23 03			23 33											
London Victoria 15	⊖ a	21 47				22 17	22 47			23 17		23 47			00 10					01 11	

For general notes see front of timetable
For details of catering facilities see Directory of Train Operators

For services from Ramsgate, Dover and Canterbury to London via Ashford see Table 207

Table 212

Sundays

Ramsgate, Dover, Sheerness-on-Sea and Medway → London

Network Diagram - see first page of Table 212

		SE 58	SE 55 1	SE 50 1	SE 55 1	SE 30 1	SE 50 1 🍴	SE 92 1	SE 01	SE 30 1	SE 50 1 🍴	SE 92 1	SE 01	SE 30 1	SE 50 1 🍴	SE 90 1	SE 92 1	SE 01	SE 30 1	SE 50 1 🍴	SE 90 1
Ramsgate 4 ✈	d			06 22			07 22				08 22				09 22	09 37				10 22	10 37
Dumpton Park	d			06 24			07 24				08 24				09 24	09 39				10 24	10 39
Broadstairs	d			06 28			07 28				08 28				09 28	09 42				10 28	10 42
Margate 4	d			06 34			07 34				08 34				09 34	09a48				10 34	10a48
Westgate-on-Sea	d			06 37			07 37				08 37				09 37					10 37	
Birchington-on-Sea	d			06 40			07 40				08 40				09 40					10 40	
Herne Bay	d			06 49			07 49				08 49				09 49					10 49	
Chestfield & Swalecliffe	d			06 52			07 52				08 52				09 52					10 52	
Whitstable	d			06 56			07 56				08 56				09 56					10 56	
Dover Priory 4 ⛴	d					07 22				08 22				09 22					10 22		
Kearsney	d					07 26				08 26				09 26					10 26		
Shepherds Well	d					07 31				08 31				09 31					10 31		
Snowdown	d					07 35				08 35				09 35					10 35		
Aylesham	d					07 37				08 37				09 37					10 37		
Adisham	d					07 39				08 39				09 39					10 39		
Bekesbourne	d					07 43				08 43				09 43					10 43		
Canterbury East 4	d					07 49				08 49				09 49					10 49		
Selling	d					07 58				08 58				09 58					10 58		
Faversham 2	a			07 05		08 02	08 04			09 02	09 04			10 02	10 04				11 02	11 04	
	d	23p42	06 15	07 08	07 15	08 08		08 15		09 08		09 15		10 08			10 15		11 08		
Teynham	d	23p47	06 20		07 20			08 20				09 20					10 20				
Sheerness-on-Sea	d								08 42				09 42					10 42			
Queenborough	d								08 47				09 47					10 47			
Swale	d								08x51				09x51					10x51			
Kemsley	d								08 55				09 55					10 55			
Sittingbourne 4	a	23p52	06 25	07 16	07 25	08 16		08 25	08 59	09 16		09 25	09 59	10 16			10 25	10 59	11 16		
	d	23p52	06 25	07 17	07 25	08 17		08 25		09 17		09 25		10 17			10 25		11 17		
Newington	d		06 30		07 30			08 30				09 30					10 30				
Rainham (Kent)	d	23p59	06 35	07 24	07 35	08 24		08 35		09 24		09 35		10 24			10 35		11 24		
Gillingham (Kent) 4	d	00 05	06 40	07 30	07 40	08 29		08 41		09 29		09 41		10 29			10 41		11 29		
Chatham 4	d	00 09	06 44	07 33	07 44	08 33		08 45		09 33		09 45		10 33			10 45		11 33		
Rochester 4	d	00 11	06 46	07 35	07 46	08 35		08 47		09 35		09 47		10 35			10 47		11 35		
Strood 4	a	00 15	*06 58*		*07 56*			*08 56*				*09 57*					*10 57*				
Gravesend 4	a	00 26	*07 09*		*08 07*			*09 07*				*10 09*					*11 09*				
Greenhithe for Bluewater	a	00 32	*07 18*		*08 12*			*09 12*				*10 14*					*11 14*				
Dartford 4	a	00 39	*07 24*		*08 17*			*09 17*				*10 19*					*11 19*				
London Bridge 4 ⊖	a		*08 06*		*08 53*			*09 53*				*10 53*					*11 53*				
London Cannon Street 4 ⊖	a																				
London Waterloo (East) 4 ⊖	a		*08 10*		*08 58*			*09 58*				*10 58*					*11 58*				
London Charing Cross 4 ⊖	a		*08 15*		*09 01*			*10 01*				*11 01*					*12 01*				
Sole Street	d		06 57		07 57			08 58				09 58					10 58				
Meopham	d		06 59		07 59			09 00				10 00					11 00				
Longfield	d		07 03		08 03			09 04				10 04					11 04				
Farningham Road	d		07 10		08 07			09 08				10 08					11 08				
Swanley 4	a		07 15		08 12			09 13				10 13					11 13				
St Mary Cray	a		07 19		08 17			09 18				10 18					11 18				
Bromley South 4	a		07 25	08 00	08 23	09 00		09 24		10 00		10 24		11 00			11 24		12 00		
Elephant & Castle ⊖	a																				
London Blackfriars 3 ⊖	a																				
London Victoria 15 ⊖	a	01 11	07 48	08 16	08 49	09 16		09 47		10 16		10 47		11 16			11 47		12 16		

For general notes see front of timetable
For details of catering facilities see Directory of Train Operators

For services from Ramsgate, Dover and Canterbury to London via Ashford see Table 207

Table 212

Sundays

Ramsgate, Dover, Sheerness-on-Sea and Medway → London

Network Diagram - see first page of Table 212

Station		SE 92 1	SE 01	SE 30 1	SE 50 1	SE 90 1	SE 92 1	SE 01	SE 30 1	SE 50 1	SE 90 1	SE 92 1	SE 01	SE 30 1	SE 50 1	SE 90 1	SE 92 1	SE 01	SE 30 1	SE 50 1	SE 90 1
Ramsgate 4	d				11 22	11 37				12 22	12 37				13 22	13 37				14 22	14 37
Dumpton Park	d				11 24	11 39				12 24	12 39				13 24	13 39				14 24	14 39
Broadstairs	d				11 28	11 42				12 28	12 42				13 28	13 42				14 28	14 42
Margate 4	d				11 34	11a48				12 34	12a48				13 34	13a48				14 34	14a48
Westgate-on-Sea	d				11 37					12 37					13 37					14 37	
Birchington-on-Sea	d				11 40					12 40					13 40					14 40	
Herne Bay	d				11 49					12 49					13 49					14 49	
Chestfield & Swalecliffe	d				11 52					12 52					13 52					14 52	
Whitstable	d				11 56					12 56					13 56					14 56	
Dover Priory 4	d			11 22					12 22					13 22					14 22		
Kearsney	d			11 26					12 26					13 26					14 26		
Shepherds Well	d			11 31					12 31					13 31					14 31		
Snowdown	d			11 35					12 35					13 35					14 35		
Aylesham	d			11 37					12 37					13 37					14 37		
Adisham	d			11 39					12 39					13 39					14 39		
Bekesbourne	d			11 43					12 43					13 43					14 43		
Canterbury East 4	d			11 49					12 49					13 49					14 49		
Selling	d			11 58					12 58					13 58					14 58		
Faversham 2	a			12 02	12 04				13 02	13 04				14 02	14 04				15 02	15 04	
	d	11 15		12 08			12 15		13 08			13 15		14 08			14 15		15 08		
Teynham	d	11 20					12 20					13 20					14 20				
Sheerness-on-Sea	d		11 42					12 42					13 42					14 42			
Queenborough	d		11 47					12 47					13 47					14 47			
Swale	d		11x51					12x51					13x51					14x51			
Kemsley	d		11 55					12 55					13 55					14 55			
Sittingbourne 4	a	11 25	11 59	12 16			12 25	12 59	13 16			13 25	13 59	14 16			14 25	14 59	15 16		
	d	11 25		12 17			12 25		13 17			13 25		14 17			14 25		15 17		
Newington	d	11 30					12 30					13 30					14 30				
Rainham (Kent)	d	11 35		12 24			12 35		13 24			13 35		14 24			14 35		15 24		
Gillingham (Kent) 4	d	11 41		12 29			12 41		13 29			13 41		14 29			14 41		15 29		
Chatham 4	d	11 45		12 33			12 45		13 33			13 45		14 33			14 45		15 33		
Rochester 4	d	11 47		12 35			12 47		13 35			13 47		14 35			14 47		15 35		
Strood 4	a	*11 57*					*12 57*					*13 57*					*14 57*				
Gravesend 4	a	*12 09*					*13 09*					*14 09*					*15 09*				
Greenhithe for Bluewater	a	*12 14*					*13 14*					*14 14*					*15 14*				
Dartford 4	a	*12 19*					*13 20*					*14 19*					*15 19*				
London Bridge 4	⊖ a	*12 53*					*13 53*					*14 53*					*15 53*				
London Cannon Street 4	⊖ a																				
London Waterloo (East) 4	⊖ a	*12 58*					*13 58*					*14 58*					*15 58*				
London Charing Cross 4	⊖ a	*13 01*					*14 01*					*15 01*					*16 01*				
Sole Street	d	11 58					12 58					13 58					14 58				
Meopham	d	12 00					13 00					14 00					15 00				
Longfield	d	12 04					13 04					14 04					15 04				
Farningham Road	d	12 08					13 08					14 08					15 08				
Swanley 4	a	12 13					13 13					14 13					15 13				
St Mary Cray	a	12 18					13 18					14 18					15 18				
Bromley South 4	a	12 24		13 00			13 24		14 00			14 24		15 00			15 24		16 00		
Elephant & Castle	⊖ a																				
London Blackfriars 3	⊖ a																				
London Victoria 15	⊖ a	12 47		13 16			13 47		14 16			14 47		15 16			15 47		16 16		

For general notes see front of timetable
For details of catering facilities see Directory of Train Operators

For services from Ramsgate, Dover and Canterbury to London via Ashford see Table 207

Table 212

Sundays

Ramsgate, Dover, Sheerness-on-Sea and Medway → London

Network Diagram - see first page of Table 212

		SE 92 1	SE 01	SE 30 1	SE 50 1	SE 90 1	SE 92 1	SE 01	SE 30 1	SE 50 1	SE 90 1	SE 92 1	SE 01	SE 30 1	SE 50 1	SE 90 1	SE 92 1	SE 01	SE 30 1	SE 50 1	SE 90 1
Ramsgate 4	d				15 22	15 37				16 22	16 37				17 22	17 37				18 22	18 37
Dumpton Park	d				15 24	15 39				16 24	16 39				17 24	17 39				18 24	18 39
Broadstairs	d				15 28	15 42				16 28	16 42				17 28	17 42				18 28	18 42
Margate 4	d				15 34	15a48				16 34	16a48				17 34	17a48				18 34	18a48
Westgate-on-Sea	d				15 37					16 37					17 37					18 37	
Birchington-on-Sea	d				15 40					16 40					17 40					18 40	
Herne Bay	d				15 49					16 49					17 49					18 49	
Chestfield & Swalecliffe	d				15 52					16 52					17 52					18 52	
Whitstable	d				15 56					16 56					17 56					18 56	
Dover Priory 4	d			15 22					16 22					17 22					18 22		
Kearsney	d			15 26					16 26					17 26					18 26		
Shepherds Well	d			15 31					16 31					17 31					18 31		
Snowdown	d			15 35					16 35					17 35					18 35		
Aylesham	d			15 37					16 37					17 37					18 37		
Adisham	d			15 39					16 39					17 39					18 39		
Bekesbourne	d			15 43					16 43					17 43					18 43		
Canterbury East 4	d			15 49					16 49					17 49					18 49		
Selling	d			15 58					16 58					17 58					18 58		
Faversham 2	a			16 02	16 04				17 02	17 04				18 02	18 04				19 02	19 04	
	d	15 15		16 08			16 15		17 08			17 15		18 08			18 15		19 08		
Teynham	d	15 20					16 20					17 20					18 20				
Sheerness-on-Sea	d		15 42					16 42					17 42					18 42			
Queenborough	d		15 47					16 47					17 47					18 47			
Swale	d		15x51					16x51					17x51					18x51			
Kemsley	d		15 55					16 55					17 55					18 55			
Sittingbourne 4	a	15 25	15 59	16 16			16 25	16 59	17 16			17 25	17 59	18 16			18 25	18 59	19 16		
	d	15 25		16 17			16 25		17 17			17 25		18 17			18 25		19 17		
Newington	d	15 30					16 30					17 30					18 30				
Rainham (Kent)	d	15 35		16 24			16 35		17 24			17 35		18 24			18 35		19 24		
Gillingham (Kent) 4	d	15 41		16 29			16 41		17 29			17 41		18 29			18 41		19 29		
Chatham 4	d	15 45		16 33			16 45		17 33			17 45		18 33			18 45		19 33		
Rochester 4	d	15 47		16 35			16 47		17 35			17 47		18 35			18 47		19 35		
Strood 4	a	*15 57*					*16 57*					*17 56*					*18 56*				
Gravesend 4	a	*16 09*					*17 09*					*18 07*					*19 07*				
Greenhithe for Bluewater	a	*16 14*					*17 14*					*18 12*					*19 12*				
Dartford 4	a	*16 19*					*17 19*					*18 17*					*19 17*				
London Bridge 4	⊖ a	*16 53*					*17 53*					*18 52*					*19 52*				
London Cannon Street 4	⊖ a																				
London Waterloo (East) 4	⊖ a	*16 58*					*17 58*					*18 57*					*19 57*				
London Charing Cross 4	⊖ a	*17 01*					*18 01*					*19 00*					*20 00*				
Sole Street	d	15 58					16 58					17 58					18 58				
Meopham	d	16 00					17 00					18 00					19 00				
Longfield	d	16 04					17 04					18 04					19 04				
Farningham Road	d	16 08					17 08					18 08					19 08				
Swanley 4	a	16 13					17 13					18 13					19 13				
St Mary Cray	a	16 18					17 18					18 18					19 17				
Bromley South 4	a	16 24		17 00			17 24		18 00			18 24		19 00			19 23		20 00		
Elephant & Castle	⊖ a																				
London Blackfriars 3	⊖ a																				
London Victoria 15	⊖ a	16 47		17 16			17 47		18 16			18 47		19 16			19 47		20 16		

For general notes see front of timetable
For details of catering facilities see Directory of Train Operators

For services from Ramsgate, Dover and Canterbury to London via Ashford see Table 207

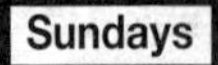

Ramsgate, Dover, Sheerness-on-Sea and Medway → London

Network Diagram - see first page of Table 212

Station		SE 92 1	SE 01	SE 30 1	SE 50 1	SE 90 1	SE 92 1	SE 01	SE 30 1	SE 50 1	SE 90 1	SE 92 1	SE 01	SE 30 1	SE 50 1	SE 92 1	SE 80 1	SE 50 1	SE 01
Ramsgate 4 ✈	d				19 22	19 39				20 22	20 37				21 22			21 55	
Dumpton Park	d				19 24	19 41				20 24	20 39				21 24			21 57	
Broadstairs	d				19 28	19 44				20 28	20 42				21 28			22 00	
Margate 4	d				19 34	19a50				20 34	20a48				21 34			22 05	
Westgate-on-Sea	d				19 37					20 37					21 37			22 08	
Birchington-on-Sea	d				19 40					20 40					21 40			22 11	
Herne Bay	d				19 49					20 49					21 49			22 20	
Chestfield & Swalecliffe	d				19 52					20 52					21 52			22 24	
Whitstable	d				19 56					20 56					21 56			22 27	
Dover Priory 4 ⛴	d			19 22					20 22					21 22			21 53		
Kearsney	d			19 26					20 26					21 26			21 57		
Shepherds Well	d			19 31					20 31					21 31			22 02		
Snowdown	d			19 35					20 35					21 35			22 05		
Aylesham	d			19 37					20 37					21 37			22 08		
Adisham	d			19 39					20 39					21 39			22 10		
Bekesbourne	d			19 43					20 43					21 43			22 15		
Canterbury East 4	d			19 49					20 49					21 49			22 21		
Selling	d			19 58					20 58					21 58			22 30		
Faversham 2	a			20 02	20 04				21 02	21 04				22 02	22 04		22 34	22 35	
	d	19 15		20 08			20 15		21 08			21 15		22 08		22 15		22 37	
Teynham	d	19 20					20 20					21 20				22 20		22 42	
Sheerness-on-Sea	d		19 42					20 42					21 42						22 42
Queenborough	d		19 47					20 47					21 47						22 47
Swale	d		19x51					20x51					21x51						22x51
Kemsley	d		19 55					20 55					21 55						22 55
Sittingbourne 4	a	19 25	19 59	20 16			20 25	20 59	21 16			21 25	21 59	22 16		22 25		22 47	22 59
	d	19 25		20 17			20 25		21 17			21 25		22 17		22 25		22 48	
Newington	d	19 30					20 30					21 30				22 30		22 53	
Rainham (Kent)	d	19 35		20 24			20 35		21 24			21 35		22 24		22 35		22 57	
Gillingham (Kent) 4	d	19 41		20 29			20 41		21 29			21 41		22 29		22 40		23 02	
Chatham 4	d	19 45		20 33			20 45		21 33			21 45		22 33		22 44		23 06	
Rochester 4	d	19 47		20 35			20 47		21 35			21 47		22 35		22 46			
Strood 4	a	19 56					20 56					21 56							
Gravesend 4	a	20 07					21 07					22 07							
Greenhithe for Bluewater	a	20 12					21 12					22 12							
Dartford 4	a	20 17					21 17					22 17							
London Bridge 4	⊖ a	20 52					21 52					22 52							
London Cannon Street 4	⊖ a																		
London Waterloo (East) 4	⊖ a	20 57					21 57					22 57							
London Charing Cross 4	⊖ a	21 00					22 00					23 00							
Sole Street	d	19 58					20 58					21 58				22 57			
Meopham	d	20 00					21 00					22 00				23 00			
Longfield	d	20 04					21 04					22 04				23 04			
Farningham Road	d	20 08					21 08					22 09				23 08			
Swanley 4	a	20 13					21 13					22 14				23 13			
St Mary Cray	a	20 18					21 18					22 18				23 17			
Bromley South 4	a	20 24		21 00			21 24		22 00			22 24		23 00		23 23		23 33	
Elephant & Castle	⊖ a																		
London Blackfriars 3	⊖ a																		
London Victoria 15	⊖ a	20 47		21 16			21 47		22 16			22 49		23 16		23 48		23 49	

For general notes see front of timetable
For details of catering facilities see Directory of Train Operators

For services from Ramsgate, Dover and Canterbury to London via Ashford see Table 207

Network Diagram for Tables 216, 217, 218, 219, 221, 222

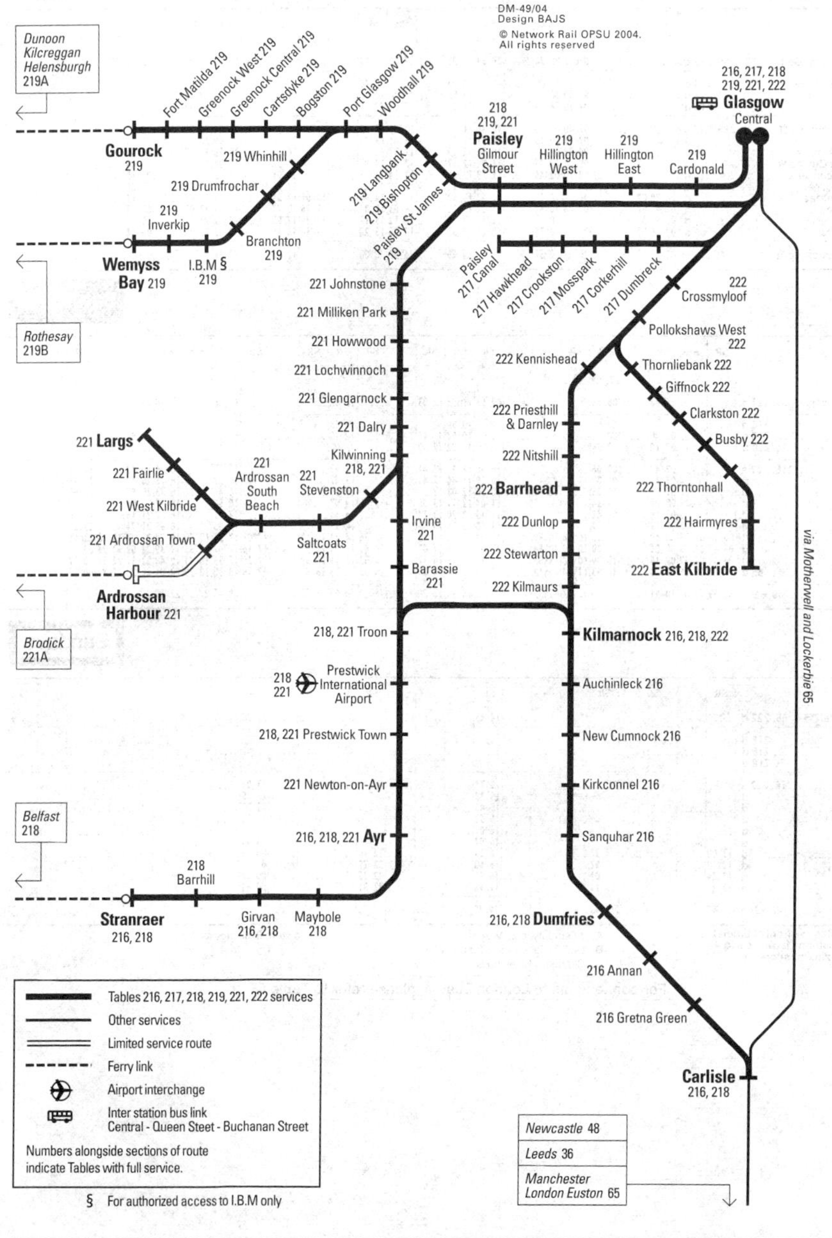
DM-49/04
Design BAJS
© Network Rail OPSU 2004.
All rights reserved
Dunoon
Kilcreggan
Helensburgh
219A
Fort Matilda 219
Greenock West 219
Greenock Central 219
Cartsdyke 219
Bogston 219
Port Glasgow 219
Woodhall 219
Gourock
219
219 Whinhill
219 Drumfrochar
219
Inverkip
Branchton
219
Wemyss
Bay 219
I.B.M §
219
Rothesay
219B
219 Langbank
219 Bishopton
Paisley St James
219
218
219, 221
Paisley
Gilmour
Street
219
Hillington
West
219
Hillington
East
219
Cardonald
216, 217, 218
219, 221, 222
Glasgow
Central
Paisley Canal
217 Hawkhead
217 Crookston
217 Mosspark
217 Corkerhill
217 Dumbreck
222
Crossmyloof
Pollokshaws West
222
222 Kennishead
Thornliebank 222
Giffnock 222
Clarkston 222
Busby 222
222 Thorntonhall
222 Hairmyres
222 East Kilbride
221 Johnstone
221 Milliken Park
221 Howwood
221 Lochwinnoch
221 Glengarnock
221 Dalry
Kilwinning
218, 221
221 Largs
221 Fairlie
221 West Kilbride
221
Ardrossan
South
Beach
221
Stevenston
221 Ardrossan Town
Saltcoats
221
Ardrossan
Harbour 221
Brodick
221A
Irvine
221
Barassie
221
222 Priesthill
& Darnley
222 Nitshill
222 Barrhead
222 Dunlop
222 Stewarton
222 Kilmaurs
Kilmarnock 216, 218, 222
218, 221 Troon
218
221
Prestwick
International
Airport
218, 221 Prestwick Town
221 Newton-on-Ayr
216, 218, 221 Ayr
Auchinleck 216
New Cumnock 216
Kirkconnel 216
Sanquhar 216
Belfast
218
218
Barrhill
Stranraer
216, 218
Girvan
216, 218
Maybole
218
216, 218 Dumfries
216 Annan
216 Gretna Green
Carlisle
216, 218
via Motherwell and Lockerbie 65
Newcastle 48
Leeds 36
Manchester
London Euston 65
Tables 216, 217, 218, 219, 221, 222 services
Other services
Limited service route
Ferry link
Airport interchange
Inter station bus link
Central - Queen Steet - Buchanan Street
Numbers alongside sections of route
indicate Tables with full service.
§ For authorized access to I.B.M only

Glasgow Central, Stranraer and Kilmarnock → Dumfries and Carlisle

Network Diagram - see first page of Table 216

Mondays to Fridays

Miles	Miles			SR	SR		SR	SR		SR	SR ◇		SR	SR		SR	SR		SR	SR		SR				
0	—	**Glasgow Central** 15	65, 222 d				*06*b*42*	08 28		09 53	*11*b*03*		12 03	13 03			15 48		17 30	20 03		22 03				
—	0	**Stranraer**	218 d					*07 09*			10 00			*11 48*												
—	38¼	Girvan	218 d				06 40	*08 01*			10 52		*11 40*	*12 40*			*14 40*			*18 42*						
—	59¼	Ayr	218 d				07 10	*08 36*			11 22		*12 09*	*13 09*			*15 17*			*19 09*						
24¼	74½	**Kilmarnock** 3	218, 222 a				07 40	09 06		10 38	11 49		12 41	13 42			16 25		18 06	20 39		22 39				
—	—		d				07 41	09 13		10 39	11 50		12 41	13 42			16 27		18 09	20 40		22 43				
38	89¼	Auchinleck	d				07 57	09 29		10 56	12 09		12 57	13 59			16 44		18 28	20 57		22 59				
45½	96¾	New Cumnock	d				08 06	09 38		11 04	12 17		13 06	14 07			16 52		18 36	21 07		23 08				
52¾	104½	Kirkconnel	d				08 14	09 46		11 13	12 26		13 14	14 16			17 01		18 45	21 16		23 16				
56	107¾	Sanquhar	d				08 19	09 51		11 18	12 31		13 19	14 21			17 06		18 50	21 21		23 21				
82¼	135	**Dumfries**	d	06 28	07 31		08 49	10 17		11 47	12 57		13 48	14 47		17 01	17 31		19 18	21 47		23c53				
97¾	150½	Annan	d	06 43	07 46		09 06	10 32		12 02	13 12		14 03	15 04		17 16	17 47		19 33	22 02		00 08				
105½	158	Gretna Green	d	06 52	07 55		09 15	10 43		12 11	13 21		14 12	15 11		17 25	17 55		19 42	22 11		00 17				
115½	168	**Carlisle** 8	65 a	07 06	08 08		09 28	10 56		12 26	13 35		14 26	15 28		17 38	18 16		19 55	22 24		00 34				
—	—	Newcastle 8	48 ⛴ a	08 57	*09 58*		10 51	*12 57*			14 55		*15 58*	*18 00*			19 45		*22 59*							

Saturdays

		SR	SR	SR		SR	SR A	SR B		SR	SR ◇	SR		SR	SR	SR		SR	SR	SR	SR	SR	SR	SR		
Glasgow Central 15	65, 222 d			*06*b*42*		08 28				09 53	*11*b*03*	12 03			13 03				15 48		17 30	20 03		22 03		
Stranraer	218 d					*07 09*					10 00				*11 48*											
Girvan	218 d			06 40		*08 01*					10 52	*11 40*			*12 40*				*14 40*			*18 42*				
Ayr	218 d			07 10		*08 36*					11 22	*12 09*			*13 09*				*15 17*			*19 09*				
Kilmarnock 3	218, 222 a			07 40		09 06				10 38	11 45	12 41			13 42				16 25		18 06	20 39		22 39		
	d			07 41		09 09				10 39	11 46	12 41			13 42				16 27		18 15	20 40		22 43		
Auchinleck	d			07 57		09 25				10 56	12 03	12 57			13 59				16 44		18 33	20 57		22 59		
New Cumnock	d			08 06		09 34				11 04	12 11	13 06			14 07				16 52		18 42	21 07		23 08		
Kirkconnel	d			08 14		09 42				11 13	12 20	13 14			14 16				17 01		18 50	21 16		23 16		
Sanquhar	d			08 19		09 47				11 18	12 25	13 19			14 21				17 06		18 55	21 21		23 21		
Dumfries	d	06 28	07 28	08 49		10 15	10 34	10 39		11 47	12 53	13 48		14 26	14 47	16 15		17 01	17 31	18 20	19 24	21 47	22 10	23c53		
Annan	d	06 43	07 43	09 06		10 30	10 49	10 54		12 02	13 08	14 03		14 43	15 04	16 30		17 16	17 47	18 35	19 39	22 02	22 25	00 08		
Gretna Green	d	06 52	07 52	09 15		10 39	10 58	11 03		12 11	13 17	14 12		14 52	15 11	16 39		17 25	17 55	18 41	19 48	22 11	22 34	00 17		
Carlisle 8	65 a	07 06	08 05	09 28		10 53	11 14	11 14		12 26	13 31	14 26		15 03	15 28	16 52		17 38	18 10	18 59	20 01	22 24	22 47	00 34		
Newcastle 8	48 ⛴ a	08 57	*10 01*	10 51			*12 57*	*12 57*			14 56	*16 00*		*16 50*	*18 00*	*18 55*			19 45	*21 01*	*22 59*					

Sundays

		SR				SR				SR				SR				SR								
Glasgow Central 15	65, 222 d									14 48								22 28								
Stranraer	218 d																									
Girvan	218 d																									
Ayr	218 d																									
Kilmarnock 3	218, 222 a									15 27								23 04								
	d									15 28								23 05								
Auchinleck	d									15 45								23 22								
New Cumnock	d									15 53								23 30								
Kirkconnel	d									16 02								23 39								
Sanquhar	d									16 07								23 44								
Dumfries	d	13 00				14 37				16 35				22 14				00 12								
Annan	d	13 15				14 52				16 50				22 29				00 27								
Gretna Green	d	13 24				15 01				16 59				22 38				00 36								
Carlisle 8	65 a	13 37				15 19				17 18				22 51				00 49								
Newcastle 8	48 ⛴ a	*15 40*				*17 40*				*19 40*																

For general notes see front of timetable
For details of catering facilities see Directory of Train Operators

A 2 February to 22 March
B Until 26 January and from 29 March
b Change at Kilmarnock
c Arr. 8 minutes earlier

For connections to London Euston, please refer to Table 65

Carlisle and Dumfries → Kilmarnock, Stranraer and Glasgow Central

Network Diagram - see first page of Table 216

Mondays to Fridays

Miles	Miles			SR	SR	SR	SR	SR	SR	SR	SR	SR	SR	SR	SR
—	—	Newcastle 8	48 ⛴ d			*06 54*	*09 24*	*11 24*	12 39	*13 24*	*14 24*	*15 24*	17 13	*19 10*	*21 10*
0	0	**Carlisle 8**	65 d	05 40	06 09	08 19	11 07	13 09	14 22	15 00	16 11	17 51	18 51	21 08	22 53
9¾	9¾	Gretna Green	d	05 51	06 20	08 30	11 18	13 23	14 33	15 14	16 22	18 04	19 02	21 19	23 04
17½	17½	Annan	d	06 00	06b31	08 38	11 26	13 32	14 42	15 23	16 31	18 12	19 10	21 28	23 13
33	33	**Dumfries**	d	06a18	06 50	08 55	11 43	13 49	14 59	15 41	16a48	18 29	19 29	21 44	23a30
59¼	59¼	Sanquhar	d		07 16	09 21	12 09	14 15	15 25	16 07		18 55	19 55	22 10	
62½	62½	Kirkconnel	d		07 21	09 26	12 14	14 20	15 30	16 12		19 00	20 00	22 15	
69¾	69¾	New Cumnock	d		07 30	09 35	12 23	14 29	15 39	16 21		19 09	20 09	22 24	
77¼	77¼	Auchinleck	d		07 38	09 43	12 31	14 37	15 48	16 29		19 17	20 17	22 32	
91	91	**Kilmarnock 3**	218, 222 a		07 57	10 02	12 48	14 55	16 07	16 46		19 36	20 36	22 49	
—	—		d		07 58	10 04	12 50	14 55	16 09	16 47		19 50	20 37	22 50	
—	106¼	Ayr	218 a		*09 38*		*13 36*		16 32	*18 38*			20 59		
—	127½	Girvan	218 a		*10 08*		*14 05*		16 59				21 26		
—	168	**Stranraer**	218 a		*11 11*				17 55				22 24		
115¼	—	**Glasgow Central 15**	65, 222 a		08 37	10 41	13 29	15 33		17 31		20 27	*21c27*	23 28	

Saturdays

		SR	SR	SR	SR	SR	SR	SR	SR	SR	SR	SR	SR	SR	SR	SR	SR	SR
Newcastle 8	48 ⛴ d			06 34		*09 24*	*10 24*	*11 22*	12 39	*13 24*		*14 24*	*15 24*		17 11	*18 24*	*19 10*	*21 10*
Carlisle 8	65 d	05 40	06 09	08 19	09 52	11 07	12 18	13 09	14 22	15 00	15 22	16 13	17 24	17 51	18 51	20 08	21 08	22 56
Gretna Green	d	05 51	06 20	08 30	10 03	11 18	12 29	13 23	14 33	15 14	15 34	16 24	17 35	18 03	19 02	20 19	21 19	23 07
Annan	d	06 00	06b31	08 38	10 12	11 26	12 38	13 32	14 42	15 23	15 43	16 33	17 44	18 12	19 10	20 28	21 28	23 16
Dumfries	d	06a18	06 50	08 55	10a29	11 43	12a55	13 49	14 59	15 41	16a00	16a50	18a01	18 29	19 29	20 44	21a45	23a33
Sanquhar	d		07 16	09 21		12 09		14 15	15 25	16 07				18 55	19 55	21 10		
Kirkconnel	d		07 21	09 26		12 14		14 20	15 30	16 12				19 00	20 00	21 15		
New Cumnock	d		07 30	09 35		12 23		14 29	15 39	16 21				19 09	20 09	21 24		
Auchinleck	d		07 38	09 43		12 31		14 37	15 48	16 29				19 17	20 17	21 32		
Kilmarnock 3	218, 222 a		07 57	10 02		12 48		14 55	16 07	16 46				19 36	20 36	21 49		
	d		07 58	10 04		12 50		14 55	16 09	16 47				19 50	20 37	21 50		
Ayr	218 a		*09 38*			*13 36*			16 32	*18 45*					20 59	*23 10*		
Girvan	218 a		*10 08*			*14 05*			16 59						21 26	*23 36*		
Stranraer	218 a		*11 11*						17 55						22 24	*00 37*		
Glasgow Central 15	65, 222 a		08 37	10 41		13 29		15 33		17 31				20 27	*21c27*	22 27		

Sundays

		SR		SR	SR
Newcastle 8	48 ⛴ d	*11 10*		*17 10*	*18 10*
Carlisle 8	65 d	12 52	13 47	19 35	21 12
Gretna Green	d	13 03	13 58	19 46	21 23
Annan	d	13 11	14 07	19 54	21 32
Dumfries	d	13 28	14a24	20 11	21a49
Sanquhar	d	13 54		20 37	
Kirkconnel	d	13 59		20 42	
New Cumnock	d	14 08		20 51	
Auchinleck	d	14 16		20 59	
Kilmarnock 3	218, 222 a	14 34		21 16	
	d	14 35		21 18	
Ayr	218 a				
Girvan	218 a				
Stranraer	218 a				
Glasgow Central 15	65, 222 a	15 14		21 55	

For general notes see front of timetable
For details of catering facilities see Directory of Train Operators

b Arr. 0628
c Change at Kilmarnock

For connections from London Euston, please refer to Table 65

Glasgow Central — Paisley Canal

Network Diagram - see first page of Table 216

Miles			SR SO	SR	SR		SR	SR
0	**Glasgow Central** 15	d	00 07	06 07	06 37	and every 30 minutes until	22 37	23 07
1¾	Dumbreck	d	00 13	06 13	06 43		22 43	23 13
3¼	Corkerhill	d	00 15	06 15	06 45		22 45	23 15
3¾	Mosspark	d	00 17	06 17	06 47		22 47	23 17
4½	Crookston	d	00 19	06 19	06 49		22 49	23 19
6½	Hawkhead	d	00 22	06 22	06 52		22 52	23 22
7	**Paisley Canal**	a	00 25	06 25	06 55		22 55	23 25

Sundays

until 23 December

		SR		SR
Glasgow Central 15	d	09 37	and every hour until	17 37
Dumbreck	d	09 43		17 43
Corkerhill	d	09 45		17 45
Mosspark	d	09 47		17 47
Crookston	d	09 49		17 49
Hawkhead	d	09 52		17 52
Paisley Canal	a	09 55		17 55

Mondays to Saturdays

Miles			SR	SR	SR	SR	SR	SR	SR A		SR	SR	SR	SR
0	**Paisley Canal**	d	06 30	07 00	07 30	08 00	08 30	09 00	09 30	and every 30 minutes until	21 30	22 00	22 30	23 00
½	Hawkhead	d	06 33	07 03	07 33	08 03	08 33	09 03	09 33		21 33	22 03	22 33	23 03
2½	Crookston	d	06 36	07 06	07 36	08 06	08 36	09 06	09 36		21 36	22 06	22 36	23 06
3¼	Mosspark	d	06 38	07 08	07 38	08 08	08 38	09 08	09 38		21 38	22 08	22 38	23 08
3¾	Corkerhill	d	06 40	07 10	07 40	08 10	08 40	09 10	09 40		21 40	22 10	22 40	23 10
5¼	Dumbreck	d	06 43	07 13	07 43	08 13	08 43	09 13	09 43		21 43	22 13	22 43	23 13
7	**Glasgow Central** 15	a	06 49	07 19	07 52	08 21	08 52	09 19	09 49		21 49	22 20	22 50	23 20

Sundays

until 23 December

		SR		SR
Paisley Canal	d	09 00	and every hour until	17 00
Hawkhead	d	09 03		17 03
Crookston	d	09 06		17 06
Mosspark	d	09 08		17 08
Corkerhill	d	09 10		17 10
Dumbreck	d	09 13		17 13
Glasgow Central 15	a	09 19		17 19

For general notes see front of timetable
For details of catering facilities see Directory of Train Operators

A 1730 from Paisley Canal arr. Glasgow Central 1753

No Sunday service from 30 December

Glasgow Central and Kilmarnock → Girvan, Stranraer and Belfast

Network Diagram - see first page of Table 216

Miles	Miles			SR	SR ◇	SR	SR	SR ◇	SR	SR	SR	SR	SR SX	SR SO	SR	SR	SR
0	—	**Glasgow Central** 15	219, 221, 222 d		07 13	08b30	09 03	11 42	12b30	15b30	16b00	17c13			18 30	20b00	22b00
7¼	—	Paisley Gilmour Street	219, 221 ✈ d		07 24	08b41	09b11	11 53	12b41	15b41	16b11	17c24			18 41	20b11	22b11
26¾	—	Kilwinning	221 d		07 41	09e03	09f32	12 10	12b59	15b59	16b29	17c42			19 01	20b29	22b29
—	—	Newcastle 8	48 d						09g24	12 39			13g24	13g24		17h13	18j24
—	—	Carlisle 8	216 d			06 09			11 07	14 22			15 00	15 00		18 51	20k08
—	—	Dumfries	216 d			06 50			11 43	14 59			15 41	15 41		19 29	20k44
—	0	**Kilmarnock** 3	222 d			09 10	09 55		13 10	16 09	16 31		18 11	18 19		20 37	22 44
35	10¾	Troon	221 d			09 24	10 07		13 22	16 19	16 44		18 24	18 31		20 50	22 56
37¾	11¾	Prestwick Int. Airport	221 ✈ d		07h45	09 29	10 12	12 15	13 27	16 15	16 49	17m56	18 29	18 36	19 17	20 43	23 01
38¼	12½	Prestwick Town	221 d		07h47	09 31	10 14	12 17	13 29	16 17	16 51	17m58	18 31	18 38	19 19	20 45	23 03
41½	15½	Ayr	221 d	06 00	08 00	09n43	10 22	12 30	13 38	16 34	17 00	18 10	18a38	18a45	19 31	21 01	23 11
50½	24½	Maybole	d	06 11	08 11	09 54	10 34	12 41	13 49	16 45	17 11	18 21			19 42	21 12	23 22
62¾	36½	**Girvan**	d	06a27	08 26	10 09	10a51	13 01	14a05	17 00	17a27	18a37			19 57	21 27	23 37
75	51¼	Barrhill	d		08 45	10n35		13 20		17 19					20 16	21 46	00q01
101	77¼	**Stranraer**	a		09 21	11 11		13 56		17 55					20 52	22 24	00 37
—	—	Stranraer Harbour §	⛴ d														
—	—	Belfast Port §	⛴ a														

Sundays

		SR ◇ A	SR ◇ B	SR ◇
Glasgow Central 15	219, 221, 222 d	11 37	11 42	16 25
Paisley Gilmour Street	219, 221 ✈ d	11 48	11 53	16 39
Kilwinning	221 d	12 05	12 10	16 56
Newcastle 8	48 d			
Carlisle 8	216 d			
Dumfries	216 d			
Kilmarnock 3	222 d			
Troon	221 d			
Prestwick Int. Airport	221 ✈ d	11 45	12 13	16 45
Prestwick Town	221 d	11 47	12 15	16 47
Ayr	221 d	12 30	12 35	17 19
Maybole	d	12 41	12 46	17 30
Girvan	d	12 56	13 01	17 45
Barrhill	d	13 14	13 19	18 04
Stranraer	a	13 51	13 56	18 40
Stranraer Harbour §	⛴ d			
Belfast Port §	⛴ a			

For general notes see front of timetable
For details of catering facilities see Directory of Train Operators

§ Stena HSS and shipping services operated by Stena Line
A From 30 December
B Until 23 December
b Change at Ayr
c Saturdays dep. Glasgow Central 1700, Paisley Gilmour Street 1711, Kilwinning 1735
e Change at Ayr. Saturdays dep. 2 minutes earlier
f Change at Ayr. Saturdays dep. 3 minutes earlier
g Change at Carlisle and Kilmarnock
h Saturdays dep. 2 minutes earlier
j Saturdays only. Change at Carlisle and Kilmarnock
k Saturdays only
m Saturdays dep. 5 minutes earlier
n Arr. 5 minutes earlier
q Arr. 3 minutes earlier

Table 218

Belfast, Stranraer and Girvan → Kilmarnock and Glasgow Central

Network Diagram - see first page of Table 216

Miles	Miles			SR	SR ◇	SR SO ◇	SR SX ◇	SR	SR ◇	SR	SR ◇	SR	SR	SR ◇	SR ◇	SR SX ◇
—	—	Belfast Port §	⛴ d													
—	—	Stranraer Harbour §	⛴ a													
0	—	**Stranraer**	d		07 09	10 00	10 00		11 48		14 37			19 40	21 10	23 25
26	—	Barrhill	d		07 43	10 34	10 34		12 22		15 11			20b19	21c50	23 59
38¼	—	**Girvan**	d	06 40	08 01	10 52	10 52	11 40	12 40	14 40	15 29	17 32	18 42	20 37	22 08	00 19
50½	—	Maybole	d	06 56	08 25	11 08	11 08	11 56	12 56	14 56	15 45	17 48	18 58	20 53	22 24	00 35
59¼	—	Ayr	d	07 10	08 36	11 22	11 22	12 09	13 09	15e17	15 58	18a00	19 09	21 06	22 38	00a47
62½	—	Prestwick Town	221 a	*07 19*	08 41	*11 48*	*11 48*	12 14	13 14	15 22	*16 19*	*18 19*	19 14	*21 19*	*23 06*	
63	—	Prestwick Int. Airport	221 ✈ a	*07 21*	08 43	*11 50*	*11 50*	12 16	13 16	15 24	*16 21*	*18 21*	19 16	*21 21*	*23 08*	
63¾	0	Troon	221 d	07 18	08 48	11 30	11 30	12 21	13 21	15 29			19 21			
—	10¾	**Kilmarnock** 3	d	07 41	09f12	11 46	11 50	12a37	13g50	15e48			19a40			
—	—	Dumfries	216 a	08 49	*10h17*	12 52	12 56	*13 47*	*14 47*	*17 31*			*21 46*			
—	—	Carlisle 8	216 a	09 28	*10h56*	13 31	13 35	*14 26*	*15 28*	*18j16*			*22 24*			
—	—	Newcastle 8	48 a	10 51	*12k57*	14 56	14 55	*15m58*	*18k00*	*19 45*						
74½	—	Kilwinning	221 a	*07n36*	*09n04*	*12n04*	*12n04*	*12n36*	*13n36*	*15n36*	16 13	*18 36*	*19n37*	21 21	22 54	
93¾	—	Paisley Gilmour Street	219, 221 ✈ a	*07q57*	*09n24*	*12n22*	*12n22*	*12n55*	*13n55*	*15n57*	16 33	*18 57*	*19n55*	21 44	23 14	
101	—	**Glasgow Central** 15	219, 221, 222 a	*08q09*	09r50	*12t27*	*12n34*	*13n07*	14v27	16w32	16 45	*19 09*	*20n07*	21 55	23 26	

Sundays

		SR ◇	SR ◇	SR ◇
Belfast Port §	⛴ d			
Stranraer Harbour §	⛴ a			
Stranraer	d	10 40	14 40	19 40
Barrhill	d	11 14	15 14	20 15
Girvan	d	11 32	15 32	20 33
Maybole	d	11 48	15 48	20 49
Ayr	d	12 01	16 01	21 02
Prestwick Town	221 a	*12y48*	*16y48*	*21 48*
Prestwick Int. Airport	221 ✈ a	*12y50*	*16y50*	*21 50*
Troon	221 d			
Kilmarnock 3	d			
Dumfries	216 a			
Carlisle 8	216 a			
Newcastle 8	48 a			
Kilwinning	221 a	12 16	16 16	21 17
Paisley Gilmour Street	219, 221 ✈ a	12 36	16 37	21 36
Glasgow Central 15	219, 221, 222 a	12 51	16 49	21 48

For general notes see front of timetable
For details of catering facilities see Directory of Train Operators

§ Stena HSS and shipping services operated by Stena Line
b Arr. 2014
c Arr. 2146
e Arr. Ayr 1508, Kilmarnock 1542
f Arr. 0903
g Arr. 1337
h Saturdays arr. 3 minutes earlier
j Saturdays arr. 1810
k Change at Kilmarnock and Carlisle
m Change at Kilmarnock and Carlisle. Saturdays arr. 1600
n Change at Ayr
q Change at Ayr. Saturdays arr. Paisley Gilmour Street 0804, Glasgow Central 0816
r By changing at Ayr, passengers may arrive at 0936
t Change at Kilmarnock
v By changing at Ayr, passengers may arrive at 1407
w By changing at Ayr, passengers may arrive at 1609
y Until 23 December arr. 30 minutes earlier

Glasgow Central → Wemyss Bay and Gourock

Network Diagram - see first page of Table 216

Miles	Miles			SR	SR	SR	SR	SR	SR	SR	SR	SR	SR	SR	SR	SR	SR	SR	SR	SR
0	0	**Glasgow Central** 15 221	d	05 55	06 05	06 25	06 32	06 55	07 05	07 25	07 35	07 50	08 05	08 25	08 35	08 50	09 05	09 25	09 35	09 50
3¾	3¾	Cardonald	d				06 39		07 12	07 32	07 42		08 12		08 42		09 12		09 42	
4½	4½	Hillington East	d		06 14		06 41		07 14	07 34	07 44		08 14		08 44		09 14		09 44	
5	5	Hillington West	d	06 03	06 16		06 43	07 03	07 16	07 36	07 46	07 58	08 16		08 46		09 16		09 46	
7¼	7¼	Paisley Gilmour Street 221 ✈	d	06 07	06 20	06 36	06 47	07 07	07 20	07 40	07 50	08 02	08 20	08 36	08 50	09 01	09 20	09 36	09 50	10 01
8	8	Paisley St James	d			06 38			07 22		07 52		08 22		08 52		09 22		09 52	
12¼	12¼	Bishopton	d	06 13	06 26	06 44	06 53	07 13	07 28	07 46	07 58	08 08	08 28	08 42	08 58	09 07	09 28	09 42	09 58	10 07
16¼	16¼	Langbank	d			06 49			07 34		08 04		08 34		09 04		09 34		10 04	
19	19	Woodhall	d		06 34	06 53	07 01		07 38	07 54	08 08		08 38		09 08		09 38		10 08	
20¼	20¼	Port Glasgow	d	06 23	06 37	06 56	07 04	07 23	07 41	07 57	08 11	08 18	08 41	08 51	09 11	09 16	09 41	09 51	10 11	10 16
—	22½	Whinhill	d		06 41		07 08					08 22				09 21				10 21
—	23	Drumfrochar	d		06 44		07 11					08 25				09 23				10 23
—	24¾	Branchton	d		06 47		07 14					08 28				09 26				10 26
—	25½	I.B.M. §	d		06 49		07 16					08 30				09 29				10 29
—	28¾	Inverkip	d		06 54		07 25					08 35				09 34				10 34
—	31	**Wemyss Bay**	a		07 00		07 30					08 40				09 40				10 40
21¼	—	Bogston	d			06 58		07 25	07 43	07 59	08 13		08 43		09 13		09 43		10 13	
22	—	Cartsdyke	d	06 26		07 01		07 27	07 45	08 01	08 15		08 45		09 15		09 45		10 15	
23	—	Greenock Central	d	06 28		07 03		07 29	07 47	08 03	08 17		08 47	08 56	09 17		09 47	09 56	10 17	
23¾	—	Greenock West	d	06 31		07 05		07 32	07 50	08 06	08 20		08 50	08 59	09 20		09 50	09 59	10 20	
25	—	Fort Matilda	d			07 08		07 35	07 53	08 09	08 23		08 53	09 02	09 23		09 53	10 02	10 23	
26¼	—	**Gourock**	a	06 36		07 13		07 39	07 57	08 13	08 27		08 57	09 07	09 27		09 58	10 06	10 27	

		SR		SR	SR	SR	SR	SR	SR	SR	SR	SR	SR	SR	SR	SR	SR	SR	SR
Glasgow Central 15 221	d	10 05		15 05	15 25	15 35	15 50	16 05	16 23	16 33	16 55	17 05	17 15	17 25	17 40	17 50	18 05	18 25	18 35
Cardonald	d	10 12		15 12		15 42		16 12	16 30	16 40		17 12	17 22		17 47		18 12		18 42
Hillington East	d	10 14		15 14		15 44		16 14	16 32	16 42		17 14	17 24		17 49		18 14		18 44
Hillington West	d	10 16		15 16		15 46	15 58	16 16	16 34	16 44	17 03	17 16			17 51		18 16		18 46
Paisley Gilmour Street 221 ✈	d	10 20		15 20	15 36	15 50	16 02	16 20	16 38	16 48	17 07	17 20	17 29	17 36	17 55	18 01	18 20	18 36	18 50
Paisley St James	d	10 22	and at	15 22		15 52		16 22	16 40			17 22			17 57		18 22		18 52
Bishopton	d	10 28	the same	15 28	15 42	15 58	16 08	16 28	16 46	16 54	17 13	17 28	17 35		18 03	18 07	18 28	18 42	18 58
Langbank	d	10 34	minutes	15 34		16 04		16 34	16 52			17 34			18 09		18 34		19 04
Woodhall	d	10 38	past	15 38		16 08		16 38	16 56			17 38			18 12		18 38		19 08
Port Glasgow	d	10 41	each	15 41	15 51	16 11	16 18	16 41	16 59	17 04	17 23	17 41	17 45	17 50	18 14	18 18	18 41	18 51	19 11
Whinhill	d		hour until				16 22			17 08			17 49			18 22			
Drumfrochar	d						16 25			17 11			17 52			18 25			
Branchton	d						16 28			17 14			17 55			18 28			
I.B.M. §	d						16 30						17 57			18 30			
Inverkip	d						16 35			17 19			18 02			18 35			
Wemyss Bay	a						16 40			17 25			18 08			18 41			
Bogston	d	10 43		15 43		16 13		16 43	17 01		17 25	17 43			18 18		18 43		19 13
Cartsdyke	d	10 45		15 45		16 15		16 45	17 03		17 27	17 45			18 20		18 45		19 15
Greenock Central	d	10 47		15 47	15 56	16 17		16 47	17 05		17 29	17 47		17 55	18 22		18 47	18 56	19 17
Greenock West	d	10 50		15 50	15 59	16 20		16 50	17 08		17 32	17 50		17 57	18 25		18 50	18 59	19 20
Fort Matilda	d	10 53		15 53	16 02	16 23		16 53	17 11		17 35	17 53		18 00	18 28		18 53	19 02	19 23
Gourock	a	10 57		15 57	16 06	16 27		16 57	17 15		17 39	17 57		18 05	18 32		18 57	19 06	19 27

		SR	SR	SR	SR	SR	SR	SR	SR	SR	SR	SR	SR	SR	SR	SR	SR
Glasgow Central 15 221	d	18 50	19 05	19 25	19 35	19 50	20 05	20 35	20 50	21 05	21 35	21 50	22 05	22 35	22 50	23 20	23 50
Cardonald	d		19 12		19 42		20 12	20 42		21 12	21 42		22 12	22 42		23 27	23 57
Hillington East	d		19 14		19 44		20 14	20 44		21 14	21 44		22 14	22 44		23 29	23 59
Hillington West	d		19 16		19 46		20 16	20 46		21 16	21 46		22 16	22 46		23 31	00 01
Paisley Gilmour Street 221 ✈	d	19 01	19 20	19 36	19 50	20 01	20 20	20 50	21 01	21 20	21 50	22 01	22 20	22 50	23 01	23 35	00 05
Paisley St James	d		19 22		19 52		20 22	20 52		21 22	21 52		22 22	22 52		23 37	00 07
Bishopton	d	19 07	19 28	19 42	19 58	20 07	20 28	20 58	21 07	21 28	21 58	22 07	22 28	22 58	23 07	23 43	00 13
Langbank	d		19 34		20 04		20 34	21 04		21 34	22 04		22 34	23 04		23 49	00 19
Woodhall	d		19 38		20 08		20 38	21 08		21 38	22 08		22 38	23 08		23 53	00 23
Port Glasgow	d	19 16	19 41	19 51	20 11	20 16	20 41	21 11	21 16	21 41	22 11	22 16	22 41	23 11	23 16	23 56	00 26
Whinhill	d	19 21			20 15			21 15			22 15			23 15			
Drumfrochar	d	19 23			20 18			21 18			22 18			23 18			
Branchton	d	19 26			20 21			21 21			22 21			23 21			
I.B.M. §	d	19 29			20 23			21 23			22 23			23 23			
Inverkip	d	19 34			20 28			21 28			22 28			23 28			
Wemyss Bay	a	19 40			20 34			21 34			22 34			23 34			
Bogston	d		19 43				20 43			21 43			22 43			23 58	00 28
Cartsdyke	d		19 45			20 20	20 45		21 20	21 45		22 20	22 45		23 20	23 59	00 30
Greenock Central	d		19 47	19 56		20 22	20 47		21 22	21 47		22 22	22 47		23 22	00 02	00 32
Greenock West	d		19 50	19 59		20 24	20 50		21 24	21 50		22 24	22 50		23 24	00 05	00 35
Fort Matilda	d		19 53	20 02		20 27	20 53		21 27	21 53		22 29	22 53		23 29	00 08	00 38
Gourock	a		19 57	20 06		20 32	20 57		21 32	21 57		22 33	22 57		23 33	00 12	00 42

For general notes see front of timetable
For details of catering facilities see Directory of Train Operators

§ For authorised access to and from I.B.M. only

Sundays

until 23 December

Glasgow Central → Wemyss Bay and Gourock

Network Diagram - see first page of Table 216

Station			SR	SR	SR	SR A	SR	SR		SR	SR	SR	SR	SR	SR	SR	SR	SR	SR
Glasgow Central 15	221	d	07 20	07 50	08 20	08 50	09 20	09 35		17 35	17 50	18 20	18 50	19 20	19 50	20 20	21 20	22 20	23 20
Cardonald		d	07 27		08 27		09 27	09 42		17 42		18 27		19 27		20 27	21 27	22 27	23 27
Hillington East		d	07 29	07 58	08 29	08 58	09 29	09 44		17 44	17 58	18 29	18 58	19 29	19 58	20 29	21 29	22 29	23 29
Hillington West		d	07 31		08 31		09 31	09 46		17 46		18 31		19 31		20 31	21 31	22 31	23 31
Paisley Gilmour Street	221 ⇌	d	07 35	08 03	08 35	09 03	09 35	09 50	and at	17 50	18 03	18 35	19 03	19 35	20 03	20 35	21 35	22 35	23 35
Paisley St James		d			08 37		09 37	09 52		17 52		18 37		19 37		20 37	21 37	22 37	23 37
Bishopton		d	07 41	08 09	08 43	09 09	09 43	09 58	the same	17 58	18 09	18 43	19 09	19 43	20 09	20 43	21 43	22 43	23 43
Langbank		d			08 49		09 49	10 04		18 04		18 49		19 49		20 49	21 49	22 49	23 49
Woodhall		d	07 49		08 53		09 53	10 08	minutes	18 08		18 53		19 53		20 53	21 53	22 53	23 53
Port Glasgow		d	07 52	08 19	08 56	09 19	09 56	10 11		18 11	18 19	18 56	19 19	19 56	20 19	20 56	21 56	22 56	23 56
Whinhill		d		08 23		09 23			past		18 23		19 23		20 23				
Drumfrochar		d		08 26		09 26					18 26		19 26		20 26				
Branchton		d		08 29		09 29			each		18 29		19 29		20 29				
I.B.M. §		d		08 31		09 31					18 31		19 31		20 31				
Inverkip		d		08 36		09 36			hour until		18 36		19 36		20 36				
Wemyss Bay		a		08 42		09 42					18 42		19 42		20 42				
Bogston		d	07 54		08 58		09 58	10 13		18 13		18 58		19 58		20 58	21 58	22 58	23 58
Cartsdyke		d	07 56		09 00		10 00	10 15		18 15		19 00		20 00		21 00	22 00	23 00	23 59
Greenock Central		d	07 58		09 02		10 02	10 17		18 17		19 02		20 02		21 02	22 02	23 02	00 02
Greenock West		d	08 01		09 05		10 05	10 20		18 20		19 05		20 05		21 05	22 05	23 05	00 05
Fort Matilda		d			09 08		10 08	10 23		18 23		19 08		20 08		21 08	22 08	23 08	00 08
Gourock		a	08 06		09 12		10 12	10 27		18 27		19 12		20 12		21 12	22 12	23 12	00 12

Sundays

from 30 December

Station			SR	SR	SR	SR A	SR		SR	SR	SR	SR	SR	SR
Glasgow Central 15	221	d	07 20	07 50	08 20	08 50	09 20		19 20	19 50	20 20	21 20	22 20	23 20
Cardonald		d	07 27		08 27		09 27		19 27		20 27	21 27	22 27	23 27
Hillington East		d	07 29	07 58	08 29	08 58	09 29		19 29	19 58	20 29	21 29	22 29	23 29
Hillington West		d	07 31		08 31		09 31		19 31		20 31	21 31	22 31	23 31
Paisley Gilmour Street	221 ⇌	d	07 35	08 03	08 35	09 03	09 35	and at	19 35	20 03	20 35	21 35	22 35	23 35
Paisley St James		d			08 37		09 37		19 37		20 37	21 37	22 37	23 37
Bishopton		d	07 41	08 09	08 43	09 09	09 43	the same	19 43	20 09	20 43	21 43	22 43	23 43
Langbank		d			08 49		09 49		19 49		20 49	21 49	22 49	23 49
Woodhall		d	07 49		08 53		09 53	minutes	19 53		20 53	21 53	22 53	23 53
Port Glasgow		d	07 52	08 19	08 56	09 19	09 56		19 56	20 19	20 56	21 56	22 56	23 56
Whinhill		d		08 23		09 23		past		20 23				
Drumfrochar		d		08 26		09 26				20 26				
Branchton		d		08 29		09 29		each		20 29				
I.B.M. §		d		08 31		09 31				20 31				
Inverkip		d		08 36		09 36		hour until		20 36				
Wemyss Bay		a		08 42		09 42				20 42				
Bogston		d	07 54		08 58		09 58		19 58		20 58	21 58	22 58	23 58
Cartsdyke		d	07 56		09 00		10 00		20 00		21 00	22 00	23 00	23 59
Greenock Central		d	07 58		09 02		10 02		20 02		21 02	22 02	23 02	00 02
Greenock West		d	08 01		09 05		10 05		20 05		21 05	22 05	23 05	00 05
Fort Matilda		d			09 08		10 08		20 08		21 08	22 08	23 08	00 08
Gourock		a	08 06		09 12		10 12		20 12		21 12	22 12	23 12	00 12

For general notes see front of timetable
For details of catering facilities see
Directory of Train Operators

§ For authorised access to and from I.B.M. only

A 1250 from Glasgow Central stops additionally at Hillington West 1300

Gourock and Wemyss Bay → Glasgow Central

Network Diagram - see first page of Table 216

Miles	Miles			SR	SR	SR	SR	SR	SR	SR	SR	SR	SR	SR	SR	SR	SR	SR	SR	SR	SR
					SX	SO	SX		SX	SO		SX	SO	SX			SX				
								A												B	
0	—	**Gourock**	d	06 05	06 22	06 36	06 44		07 06	07 06		07 22	07 36	07 47	07 52		08 08	08 24	08 36		09 06
1¼	—	Fort Matilda	d	06 08	06 25	06 39	06 47		07 09	07 09		07 25	07 39		07 55		08 11	08 27	08 39		09 09
2½	—	Greenock West	d	06 11	06 28	06 42	06 50		07 12	07 12		07 28	07 42	07 52	07 58		08 14	08 30	08 42		09 12
3¼	—	Greenock Central	d	06 14	06 31	06 45	06 53		07 15	07 15		07 31	07 45	07 55	08 01		08 17	08 33	08 45		09 15
4¼	—	Cartsdyke	d	06 16	06 33	06 47	06 55		07 17	07 17		07 33	07 47		08 03			08 35	08 47		09 17
5	—	Bogston	d		06 35	06 49	06 57		07 19	07 19		07 35	07 49		08 05			08 37	08 49		09 19
—	0	**Wemyss Bay**	d								07 13					07 50				08 50	
—	2¼	Inverkip	d								07 18					07 54				08 54	
—	4¾	I.B.M. §	d								07 23					07 59				08 59	
—	6¼	Branchton	d								07 25					08 02				09 02	
—	8	Drumfrochar	d								07 28					08 04				09 04	
—	8½	Whinhill	d								07 30					08 07				09 07	
6	10¾	Port Glasgow	d	06 19	06 38	06 52	07 00		07 22	07 22	07 35	07 38	07 52	07 59	08 08	08 11	08 21	08 40	08 52	09 11	09 22
7¼	12	Woodhall	d		06 40	06 54	07 02			07 24	07 37	07 40	07 54		08 10	08 14		08 42	08 54		09 24
10	14¾	Langbank	d		06 45	06 59	07 07			07 29		07 45	07 59			08 18		08 47	08 59		09 29
14	18	Bishopton	d	06 28	06 50	07 04	07 12		07 31	07 34	07 45	07 50	08 04	08 08	08 18	08 24	08 30	08 52	09 04	09 20	09 34
18¼	22¼	Paisley St James	d	06 34	06 56	07 10	07 18			07 40		07 56	08 10			08 29		08 58	09 10		09 40
19	23	Paisley Gilmour Street 221 ✈	d	06 37	06 59	07 13	07 21	07 34	07 38	07 43	07 52	07 59	08 13	08 15	08 25	08 32	08 37	09 01	09 13	09 27	09 43
21¼	25¼	Hillington West	d	06 40	07 02	07 16	07 24	07 38	07 41	07 46	07 55	08 02	08 16	08 18	08 28			09 04	09 16		09 46
21¾	25¾	Hillington East	d	06 42	07 04	07 18	07 26		07 43	07 48	07 57	08 04	08 18	08 20	08 30			09 06	09 18		09 48
22½	26½	Cardonald	d	06 44	07 06	07 20	07 28		07 45	07 50	07 59	08 06	08 20	08 22	08 32			09 08	09 20		09 50
26½	31	**Glasgow Central** 15 221	a	06 52	07 14	07 28	07 36	07 47	07 54	07 58	08 07	08 14	08 28	08 30	08 40	08 44	08 48	09 16	09 28	09 38	09 58

		SR		SR	SR	SR	SR	SR	SR	SR	SR	SR	SR	SR	SR	SR	SR	SR	SR	SR
Gourock	d	09 23		14 23	14 36		15 06	15 23	15 36		16 06	16 23	16 36		17 06	17 23	17 45		18 06	18 23
Fort Matilda	d	09 26		14 26	14 39		15 09	15 26	15 39		16 09	16 26	16 39		17 09	17 26	17 48		18 09	18 26
Greenock West	d	09 29		14 29	14 42		15 12	15 29	15 42		16 12	16 29	16 42		17 12	17 29	17 51		18 12	18 29
Greenock Central	d	09 32		14 32	14 45		15 15	15 32	15 45		16 15	16 32	16 45		17 15	17 32	17 54		18 15	18 32
Cartsdyke	d				14 47		15 17		15 47		16 17		16 47		17 17		17 56		18 17	
Bogston	d		and at		14 49		15 19		15 49		16 19		16 49		17 19		17 58		18 19	
Wemyss Bay	d		the same			14 50				15 55				16 45				17 49		
Inverkip	d					14 54				15 59				16 49				17 53		
I.B.M. §	d		minutes			14 59				16 04				16 54				18 02		
Branchton	d					15 02				16 07				16 57				18 04		
Drumfrochar	d		past			15 04				16 09				16 59				18 07		
Whinhill	d					15 07				16 12				17 02				18 09		
Port Glasgow	d	09 36	each	14 36	14 52	15 11	15 22	15 36	15 52	16 16	16 22	16 36	16 52	17 06	17 22	17 36	18 01	18 14	18 22	18 36
Woodhall	d		hour until		14 54		15 24		15 54		16 24		16 54		17 24		18 03		18 24	
Langbank	d				14 59		15 29		15 59		16 29		16 59		17 29		18 08		18 29	
Bishopton	d	09 45		14 45	15 04	15 20	15 34	15 45	16 04	16 25	16 34	16 45	17 04	17 15	17 34	17 45	18 13	18 23	18 34	18 45
Paisley St James	d				15 10		15 40		16 10		16 40		17 10		17 40		18 19		18 40	
Paisley Gilmour Street 221 ✈	d	09 52		14 52	15 13	15 27	15 43	15 52	16 13	16 32	16 43	16 52	17 13	17 22	17 43	17 52	18 22	18 31	18 43	18 52
Hillington West	d				15 16		15 46	15 55	16 16		16 46	16 55	17 16		17 46		18 25		18 46	
Hillington East	d				15 18		15 48		16 18		16 48		17 18		17 48		18 27		18 48	
Cardonald	d				15 20		15 50		16 20		16 50		17 20		17 50		18 29		18 50	
Glasgow Central 15 221	a	10 03		15 03	15 28	15 38	15 58	16 05	16 28	16 43	16 58	17 05	17 28	17 33	17 58	18 03	18 39	18 43	18 58	19 03

		SR	SR	SR	SR	SR	SR	SR	SR	SR	SR	SR	SR	SR	SR	SR	SR	SR	SR
																			SO
Gourock	d		18 40		19 06	19 20	19 45		20 20	20 45		21 20	21 45		22 20	22 45		23 20	
Fort Matilda	d		18 43		19 09	19 23	19 48		20 23	20 48		21 23	21 48		22 23	22 48		23 23	
Greenock West	d		18 46		19 12	19 26	19 51		20 26	20 51		21 26	21 51		22 26	22 51		23 26	
Greenock Central	d		18 49		19 15	19 29	19 54		20 29	20 54		21 29	21 54		22 29	22 54		23 29	
Cartsdyke	d		18 51		19 17	19 31	19 56		20 31	20 56		21 31	21 56		22 31	22 56		23 31	
Bogston	d		18 53		19 19	19 33			20 33			21 33			22 33			23 33	
Wemyss Bay	d	18 23		18 55				19 45			20 44			21 44			22 44		23 40
Inverkip	d	18 27		18 59				19 48			20 48			21 48			22 48		23 44
I.B.M. §	d	18 36		19 04				19 53			20 53			21 53			22 53		23 49
Branchton	d	18 38		19 07				19 56			20 56			21 56			22 56		23 52
Drumfrochar	d	18 41		19 09				19 58			20 58			21 58			22 58		23 54
Whinhill	d	18 43		19 12				20 01			21 01			22 01			23 01		23 57
Port Glasgow	d	18 48	18 56	19 16	19 22	19 36	19 59	20 06	20 36	20 59	21 06	21 36	21 59	22 06	22 36	22 59	23 06	23 36	00 01
Woodhall	d		18 58		19 24	19 38		20 08	20 38		21 08	21 38		22 08	22 38		23 08	23 38	
Langbank	d		19 03		19 29	19 43		20 13	20 43		21 13	21 43		22 13	22 43		23 13	23 43	
Bishopton	d	18 57	19 08	19 25	19 34	19 48	20 08	20 18	20 48	21 08	21 18	21 48	22 08	22 18	22 48	23 08	23 18	23 48	00 10
Paisley St James	d		19 14		19 40	19 54		20 24	20 54		21 24	21 54		22 24	22 54		23 24	23 54	
Paisley Gilmour Street 221 ✈	d	19 03	19 17	19 32	19 43	19 57	20 15	20 27	20 57	21 15	21 27	21 57	22 15	22 27	22 57	23 17	23 27	23 57	00 17
Hillington West	d		19 20		19 46	20 00		20 30	21 00		21 30	22 00		22 30	23 00		23 30	00 01	
Hillington East	d		19 22		19 48	20 02		20 32	21 02		21 32	22 02		22 32	23 02		23 32	00 02	
Cardonald	d		19 24		19 50	20 04		20 34	21 04		21 34	22 04		22 34	23 04		23 34	00 04	
Glasgow Central 15 221	a	19 15	19 32	19 43	19 58	20 12	20 26	20 43	21 12	21 26	21 42	22 15	22 26	22 42	23 14	23 30	23 42	00 12	00 28

For general notes see front of timetable
For details of catering facilities see Directory of Train Operators

§ For authorised access to and from I.B.M. only

A From Largs (Table 221)

B 1050 from Wemyss Bay departs 1055 and runs 5 minutes later throughout; Glasgow Central arr. 1143

Table 219

Sundays until 23 December

Gourock and Wemyss Bay → Glasgow Central

Network Diagram - see first page of Table 216

		SR	SR	SR	SR	SR	SR	SR	SR	SR	SR	SR	SR	SR	SR	SR	SR	SR	SR	SR
Gourock	d	08 20		09 20	09 36		10 20	10 36		11 20	11 36		12 20	12 36		13 20	13 36		14 20	14 36
Fort Matilda	d	08 23		09 23	09 39		10 23	10 39		11 23	11 39		12 23	12 39		13 23	13 39		14 23	14 39
Greenock West	d	08 26		09 26	09 42		10 26	10 42		11 26	11 42		12 26	12 42		13 26	13 42		14 26	14 42
Greenock Central	d	08 29		09 29	09 45		10 29	10 45		11 29	11 45		12 29	12 45		13 29	13 45		14 29	14 45
Cartsdyke	d	08 31		09 31	09 47		10 31	10 47		11 31	11 47		12 31	12 47		13 31	13 47		14 31	14 47
Bogston	d	08 33		09 33	09 49		10 33	10 49		11 33	11 49		12 33	12 49		13 33	13 49		14 33	14 49
Wemyss Bay	d		08 50			09 50			10 55			11 50			12 50			13 50		
Inverkip	d		08 54			09 54			10 59			11 54			12 54			13 54		
I.B.M. §	d		08 59			09 59			11 04			11 59			12 59			13 59		
Branchton	d		09 02			10 02			11 07			12 02			13 02			14 02		
Drumfrochar	d		09 04			10 04			11 09			12 04			13 04			14 04		
Whinhill	d		09 07			10 07			11 12			12 07			13 07			14 07		
Port Glasgow	d	08 36	09 11	09 36	09 52	10 11	10 36	10 52	11 16	11 36	11 52	12 11	12 36	12 52	13 11	13 36	13 52	14 11	14 36	14 52
Woodhall	d	08 38		09 38	09 54		10 38	10 54		11 38	11 54		12 38	12 54		13 38	13 54		14 38	14 54
Langbank	d	08 43		09 43	09 59		10 43	10 59		11 43	11 59		12 43	12 59		13 43	13 59		14 43	14 59
Bishopton	d	08 48	09 20	09 48	10 04	10 20	10 48	11 04	11 25	11 48	12 04	12 20	12 48	13 04	13 20	13 48	14 04	14 20	14 48	15 04
Paisley St James	d	08 54		09 54	10 10		10 54	11 10		11 53	12 10		12 54	13 10		13 54	14 10		14 54	15 10
Paisley Gilmour Street 221 ⇄	d	08 57	09 28	09 57	10 13	10 28	10 57	11 13	11 32	11 57	12 13	12 28	12 57	13 13	13 27	13 57	14 13	14 27	14 57	15 13
Hillington West	d	09 00		10 00	10 16		11 00	11 16		12 00	12 16		13 00	13 18		14 00	14 16		15 00	15 16
Hillington East	d	09 02	09 32	10 02	10 18	10 32	11 02	11 18	11 36	12 02	12 18	12 32	13 02	13 20	13 31	14 02	14 18	14 31	15 02	15 18
Cardonald	d	09 04		10 04	10 20		11 04	11 20		12 04	12 20		13 04	13 22		14 04	14 20		15 04	15 20
Glasgow Central 15 221	a	09 12	09 40	10 12	10 28	10 40	11 12	11 29	11 46	12 12	12 28	12 40	13 12	13 30	13 40	14 12	14 28	14 40	15 12	15 28

		SR	SR	SR	SR	SR	SR	SR	SR	SR	SR	SR	SR	SR	SR	SR	SR	SR	SR
Gourock	d		15 20	15 36		16 20	16 36		17 20	17 36		18 20		19 20		20 20		21 20	22 20
Fort Matilda	d		15 23	15 39		16 23	16 39		17 23	17 39		18 23		19 23		20 23		21 23	22 23
Greenock West	d		15 26	15 42		16 26	16 42		17 26	17 42		18 26		19 26		20 26		21 26	22 26
Greenock Central	d		15 29	15 45		16 29	16 45		17 29	17 45		18 29		19 29		20 29		21 29	22 29
Cartsdyke	d		15 31	15 47		16 31	16 47		17 31	17 47		18 31		19 31		20 31		21 31	22 31
Bogston	d		15 33	15 49		16 33	16 49		17 33	17 49		18 33		19 33		20 33		21 33	22 33
Wemyss Bay	d	14 50			15 55			16 50			17 50		18 55		19 50		20 50		
Inverkip	d	14 54			15 59			16 54			17 54		18 59		19 54		20 54		
I.B.M. §	d	14 59			16 04			16 59			17 59		19 04		19 59		20 59		
Branchton	d	15 02			16 07			17 02			18 02		19 07		20 02		21 02		
Drumfrochar	d	15 04			16 09			17 04			18 04		19 09		20 04		21 04		
Whinhill	d	15 07			16 12			17 07			18 07		19 12		20 07		21 07		
Port Glasgow	d	15 11	15 36	15 52	16 16	16 36	16 52	17 11	17 36	17 52	18 11	18 36	19 16	19 36	20 11	20 36	21 11	21 36	22 36
Woodhall	d		15 38	15 54		16 38	16 54		17 38	17 54		18 38		19 38		20 38		21 38	22 38
Langbank	d		15 43	15 59		16 43	16 59		17 43	17 59		18 43		19 43		20 43		21 43	22 43
Bishopton	d	15 20	15 48	16 04	16 25	16 48	17 04	17 20	17 48	18 04	18 20	18 48	19 25	19 48	20 20	20 48	21 20	21 48	22 48
Paisley St James	d		15 54	16 10		16 54	17 10		17 54	18 10		18 54		19 54		20 54		21 54	22 54
Paisley Gilmour Street 221 ⇄	d	15 27	15 57	16 13	16 32	16 57	17 13	17 27	17 57	18 13	18 27	18 57	19 32	19 57	20 27	20 57	21 27	21 57	22 57
Hillington West	d		16 00	16 16		17 00	17 16		18 00	18 16		19 00		20 00		21 00		22 00	23 00
Hillington East	d	15 31	16 02	16 18	16 36	17 02	17 18	17 31	18 02	18 18	18 31	19 02	19 36	20 02	20 31	21 02	21 31	22 02	23 02
Cardonald	d		16 04	16 20		17 04	17 20		18 04	18 20		19 04		20 04		21 04		22 04	23 04
Glasgow Central 15 221	a	15 40	16 12	16 28	16 44	17 12	17 28	17 40	18 12	18 28	18 40	19 12	19 44	20 12	20 40	21 12	21 40	22 12	23 12

Sundays from 30 December

		SR	SR	SR	SR	SR	SR	SR	SR	SR	SR	SR	SR	SR
Gourock	d	08 20		09 20		10 20		11 20		12 20		13 20		14 20
Fort Matilda	d	08 23		09 23		10 23		11 23		12 23		13 23		14 23
Greenock West	d	08 26		09 26		10 26		11 26		12 26		13 26		14 26
Greenock Central	d	08 29		09 29		10 29		11 29		12 29		13 29		14 29
Cartsdyke	d	08 31		09 31		10 31		11 31		12 31		13 31		14 31
Bogston	d	08 33		09 33		10 33		11 33		12 33		13 33		14 33
Wemyss Bay	d		08 50		09 50		10 55		11 50		12 50		13 50	
Inverkip	d		08 54		09 54		10 59		11 54		12 54		13 54	
I.B.M. §	d		08 59		09 59		11 04		11 59		12 59		13 59	
Branchton	d		09 02		10 02		11 07		12 02		13 02		14 02	
Drumfrochar	d		09 04		10 04		11 09		12 04		13 04		14 04	
Whinhill	d		09 07		10 07		11 12		12 07		13 07		14 07	
Port Glasgow	d	08 36	09 11	09 36	10 11	10 36	11 16	11 36	12 11	12 36	13 11	13 36	14 11	14 36
Woodhall	d	08 38		09 38		10 38		11 38		12 38		13 38		14 38
Langbank	d	08 43		09 43		10 43		11 43		12 43		13 43		14 43
Bishopton	d	08 48	09 20	09 48	10 20	10 48	11 25	11 48	12 20	12 48	13 20	13 48	14 20	14 48
Paisley St James	d	08 54		09 54		10 54		11 53		12 54		13 54		14 54
Paisley Gilmour Street 221 ⇄	d	08 57	09 28	09 57	10 28	10 57	11 32	11 57	12 28	12 57	13 27	13 57	14 27	14 57
Hillington West	d	09 00		10 00		11 00		12 00		13 00		14 00		15 00
Hillington East	d	09 02	09 32	10 02	10 32	11 02	11 36	12 02	12 32	13 02	13 31	14 02	14 31	15 02
Cardonald	d	09 04		10 04		11 04		12 04		13 04		14 04		15 04
Glasgow Central 15 221	a	09 12	09 40	10 12	10 40	11 12	11 46	12 12	12 40	13 12	13 40	14 12	14 40	15 12

For general notes see front of timetable
For details of catering facilities see
Directory of Train Operators

§ For authorised access to and from I.B.M. only

Table 219

Sundays

from 30 December

Gourock and Wemyss Bay → Glasgow Central

Network Diagram - see first page of Table 216

		SR	SR	SR	SR	SR	SR	SR	SR	SR	SR	SR	SR	SR	SR	SR
Gourock	d		15 20		16 20		17 20		18 20		19 20		20 20		21 20	22 20
Fort Matilda	d		15 23		16 23		17 23		18 23		19 23		20 23		21 23	22 23
Greenock West	d		15 26		16 26		17 26		18 26		19 26		20 26		21 26	22 26
Greenock Central	d		15 29		16 29		17 29		18 29		19 29		20 29		21 29	22 29
Cartsdyke	d		15 31		16 31		17 31		18 31		19 31		20 31		21 31	22 31
Bogston	d		15 33		16 33		17 33		18 33		19 33		20 33		21 33	22 33
Wemyss Bay	d	14 50		15 55		16 50		17 50		18 55		19 50		20 50		
Inverkip	d	14 54		15 59		16 54		17 54		18 59		19 54		20 54		
I.B.M. §	d	14 59		16 04		16 59		17 59		19 04		19 59		20 59		
Branchton	d	15 02		16 07		17 02		18 02		19 07		20 02		21 02		
Drumfrochar	d	15 04		16 09		17 04		18 04		19 09		20 04		21 04		
Whinhill	d	15 07		16 12		17 07		18 07		19 12		20 07		21 07		
Port Glasgow	d	15 11	15 36	16 16	16 36	17 11	17 36	18 11	18 36	19 16	19 36	20 11	20 36	21 11	21 36	22 36
Woodhall	d		15 38		16 38		17 38		18 38		19 38		20 38		21 38	22 38
Langbank	d		15 43		16 43		17 43		18 43		19 43		20 43		21 43	22 43
Bishopton	d	15 20	15 48	16 25	16 48	17 20	17 48	18 20	18 48	19 25	19 48	20 20	20 48	21 20	21 48	22 48
Paisley St James	d		15 54		16 54		17 54		18 54		19 54		20 54		21 54	22 54
Paisley Gilmour Street 221 ⇌	d	15 27	15 57	16 32	16 57	17 27	17 57	18 27	18 57	19 32	19 57	20 27	20 57	21 27	21 57	22 57
Hillington West	d		16 00		17 00		18 00		19 00		20 00		21 00		22 00	23 00
Hillington East	d	15 31	16 02	16 36	17 02	17 31	18 02	18 31	19 02	19 36	20 02	20 31	21 02	21 31	22 02	23 02
Cardonald	d		16 04		17 04		18 04		19 04		20 04		21 04		22 04	23 04
Glasgow Central 15 221	a	15 40	16 12	16 44	17 12	17 40	18 12	18 40	19 12	19 44	20 12	20 40	21 12	21 40	22 12	23 12

For general notes see front of timetable
For details of catering facilities see
Directory of Train Operators

§ For authorised access to and from I.B.M. only

Glasgow and Gourock → Dunoon, Kilcreggan and Helensburgh Pier

Caledonian MacBrayne Ltd in association with First ScotRail Limited

All Kilcreggan sailings operated by Clyde Marine Motoring Co Ltd. Tel 01475 721281

Mondays to Saturdays

			SX		SX	SX		SX				A		B												
Glasgow Central 15	219 d	05 55	05 55		06 25	06 25		06 55	07 05		07 25	07 35		07 35	08 25		09 05	09 25		10 25	10 35		11 25	11 25		12 25
Paisley Gilmour Street	219 d	06 07	06 07		06 36	06 36		07 07	07 20		07 40	07 50		07 50	08 36		09 20	09 36		10 36	10 50		11 36	11 36		12 36
Gourock	219 a	06 36	06 36		07 13	07 13		07 39	07 57		08 13	08 27		08 27	09 07		09 58	10 06		11 06	11 27		12 06	12 06		13 06
Gourock	⛴ d	06 50	07 00		07 20	07 30		07 50	08 05		08 20	08 35		08 50	09 20		10 05	10 20		11 20	11 35		12 20	12 25		13 20
Dunoon	⛴ a	07 13			07 43			08 13			08 43				09 43			10 43		11 43			12 43			13 43
Kilcreggan	⛴ a		07 12			07 42			08 17					09 02			10 20				11 47			12 37		
Helensburgh Pier	⛴ a											09 05					10 45									

															SX		A	B								
Glasgow Central 15	219 d	13 25	13 25		14 25	14 35		15 25	15 25		15 35	16 23		16 23	16 55		17 25	17 25		17 25	18 25		19 25			
Paisley Gilmour Street	219 d	13 36	13 36		14 36	14 50		15 36	15 36		15 50	16 38		16 38	17 07		17 36	17 36		17 36	18 36		19 36			
Gourock	219 a	14 06	14 06		15 06	15 27		16 06	16 06		16 27	17 15		17 15	17 39		18 05	18 05		18 05	19 06		20 06			
Gourock	⛴ d	14 15	14 20		15 20	15 45		16 15	16 20		16 50	17 20		17 25	17 45		18 10	18 10		18 20	19 20		20 18			
Dunoon	⛴ a		14 43		15 43				16 43			17 43			18 08					18 43	19 43		20 41			
Kilcreggan	⛴ a	14 30				15 57		16 27			17 03			17 37			18 25	18 25								
Helensburgh Pier	⛴ a	14 55															18 50									

Sundays

						C		C			C				C			C								
Glasgow Central 15	219 d	07 20	08 20	09 20		09 20	10 20	10 20		11 20	11 20	12 20		13 20	13 20	14 20		14 20	15 20	16 20		17 20	18 20	19 20		
Paisley Gilmour Street	219 d	07 35	08 35	09 35		09 35	10 35	10 35		11 35	11 35	12 35		13 35	13 35	14 35		14 35	15 35	16 35		17 35	18 35	19 35		
Gourock	219 a	08 06	09 12	10 12		10 12	11 12	11 12		12 12	12 12	13 12		14 12	14 12	15 12		15 12	16 12	17 12		18 12	19 12	20 12		
Gourock	⛴ d	08 20	09 20	10 20		11 15	11 20	11 45		12 20	13 15	13 20		14 20	14 25	15 20		16 15	16 20	17 20		18 20	19 20	20 18		
Dunoon	⛴ a	08 43	09 43	10 43			11 43			12 43		13 43		14 43		15 43			16 43	17 43		18 43	19 43	20 41		
Kilcreggan	⛴ a					11 27									14 40			16 27								
Helensburgh Pier	⛴ a							12 15			13 45				15 10											

For general notes see front of timetable
For details of catering facilities see Directory of Train Operators

A From 21 March
B Until 20 March
C From 6 April

Helensburgh Pier, Kilcreggan and Dunoon → Gourock and Glasgow

Caledonian MacBrayne Ltd in association with First ScotRail Limited

All Kilcreggan sailings operated by Clyde Marine Motoring Co Ltd. Tel 01475 721281

		SX	SX			SX		SX			SX			A	B										
Helensburgh Pier	⛴ d														09 10					10 50					
Kilcreggan	⛴ d		07 15			07 50			08 20					09 10	09 40					11 15	11 50			12 45	
Dunoon	⛴ d	06 50			07 20			07 50			08 20	08 50					09 50	10 50					11 50			12 50
Gourock	⛴ a	07 13	07 27		07 43	08 02		08 13	08 32		08 43	09 13		09 22	09 52		10 13	11 13		11 27	12 02		12 13	12 57		13 13
Gourock	219 d	07 22	07 47		07 52	08 08		08 24	09 06		09 06	09 23		09 36	10 06		10 23	11 23		11 36	12 23		12 23	13 06		13 23
Paisley Gilmour Street	219 a	07 58	08 14		08 24	08 36		09 00	09 42		09 42	09 51		10 12	10 42		10 51	11 51		12 12	12 51		12 51	13 42		13 51
Glasgow Central 15	219 a	08 14	08 30		08 40	08 48		09 16	09 58		09 58	10 03		10 28	10 58		11 03	12 03		12 28	13 03		13 03	13 58		14 03

																	SX	A			B				
Helensburgh Pier	⛴ d				15 00																18 55				
Kilcreggan	⛴ d				15 30			16 00	16 30			17 05		17 40				18 30			19 20				
Dunoon	⛴ d	13 50	14 50			15 50					16 50				17 50		18 15			18 50			19 50	20 45		
Gourock	⛴ a	14 13	15 13		15 42	16 13		16 12	16 42		17 13	17 17		17 52	18 13		18 38	18 42		19 13	19 32		20 13	21 08		
Gourock	219 d	14 23	15 23		16 06	16 23		16 23	17 06		17 23	17 23		18 06	18 23		19 06	19 06		19 20	19 45		20 20	21 20		
Paisley Gilmour Street	219 a	14 51	15 51		16 42	16 51		16 51	17 42		17 51	17 51		18 42	18 51		19 42	19 42		19 56	20 14		20 56	21 56		
Glasgow Central 15	219 a	15 03	16 05		16 58	17 05		17 05	17 58		18 03	18 03		18 58	19 03		19 58	19 58		20 12	20 26		21 12	22 15		

Sundays

						C		C				C			C			C							
Helensburgh Pier	⛴ d							12 20				13 50			15 15										
Kilcreggan	⛴ d					11 30									15 45			16 30							
Dunoon	⛴ d	08 50	09 50	10 50			11 50			12 50	13 50			14 50		15 50			16 50	17 50		18 50	19 50	20 45		
Gourock	⛴ a	09 13	10 13	11 13		11 42	12 13	12 50		13 13	14 13	14 20		15 13	15 57	16 13		16 42	17 13	18 13		19 13	20 13	21 08		
Gourock	219 d	09 20	10 20	11 20		12 20	12 20	13 20		13 20	14 20	15 20		15 20	16 20	16 20		17 20	17 20	18 20		19 20	20 20	21 20		
Paisley Gilmour Street	219 d	09 56	10 56	11 56		12 56	12 56	13 56		13 56	14 56	15 56		15 56	16 56	16 56		17 56	17 56	18 56		19 56	20 56	21 56		
Glasgow Central 15	219 a	10 12	11 12	12 12		13 12	13 12	14 12		14 12	15 12	16 12		16 12	17 12	17 12		18 12	18 12	19 12		20 12	21 12	22 12		

For general notes see front of timetable
For details of catering facilities see Directory of Train Operators

A Until 20 March
B From 21 March
C From 6 April

Glasgow and Wemyss Bay — Rothesay (Bute)

Caledonian MacBrayne Ltd in association with First ScotRail Limited

Mondays to Saturdays

		SX	A		SX B																			FSO C		
Glasgow Central 15	219 d	06 05	06 32		06 32	07 50		08 50	09 50		10 50	11 50		12 50	13 50		14 50	15 50		16 33	17 15	17 50	18 50	19 35		
Paisley Gilmour Street	219 d	06 20	06 47		06 47	08 02		09 01	10 01		11 01	12 01		13 01	14 01		15 01	16 02		16 48	17 29	18 01	19 01	19 50		
Wemyss Bay	219 a	07 00	07 30		07 30	08 40		09 40	10 40		11 40	12 40		13 40	14 40		15 40	16 40		17 25	18 08	18 41	19 40	20 34		
Wemyss Bay	d	07 15	08 00		08 00	08 45		10 15	11 00		12 15	13 00		13 45	15 15		16 00	16 45		17 30	18 15	19 00	19 45	20 40		
Rothesay	a	07 50	08 35		08 35	09 20		10 50	11 35		12 50	13 35		14 20	15 50		16 35	17 20		18 05	18 50	19 35	20 20	21 15		

Sundays

						D																				
Glasgow Central 15	219 d	07 50		08 50		09 50		10 50		11 50		12 50		14 50		15 50		16 50		17 50		18 50				
Paisley Gilmour Street	219 d	08 03		09 03		10 03		11 03		12 03		13 03		15 03		16 03		17 03		18 03		19 03				
Wemyss Bay	219 a	08 42		09 42		10 42		11 42		12 42		13 42		15 42		16 42		17 42		18 42		19 42				
Wemyss Bay	d	08 45		10 15		11 00		12 15		13 00		14 30		16 00		17 30		18 15		19 00		19 45				
Rothesay	a	09 20		10 50		11 35		12 50		13 35		15 05		16 35		18 05		18 50		19 35		20 20				

Mondays to Saturdays

		SX	A		SX B																			FSO C		
Rothesay	d	06 30	07 00		07 00	08 00		08 45	10 10		11 00	11 45		13 00	13 45		15 15	16 00		16 45	17 30	18 15	19 00	19 45		
Wemyss Bay	a	07 05	07 35		07 35	08 35		09 20	10 45		11 35	12 20		13 35	14 20		15 50	16 35		17 20	18 05	18 50	19 35	20 20		
Wemyss Bay	219 d	07 13	07 50		07 50	08 50		09 50	10 55		11 50	12 50		13 50	14 50		15 55	16 45		17 49	18 23	18 55	19 45	20 44		
Paisley Gilmour Street	219 a	07 51	08 31		08 31	09 26		10 26	11 31		12 26	13 26		14 26	15 26		16 31	17 21		18 30	19 02	19 31	20 26	21 26		
Glasgow Central 15	219 a	08 07	08 44		08 44	09 38		10 38	11 43		12 38	13 38		14 38	15 38		16 43	17 33		18 43	19 15	19 43	20 43	21 42		

Sundays

				E		D				D														D		
Rothesay	d	08 00		09 30		10 10		11 00		11 45		13 00		13 45		15 15		16 00		16 45		18 15	19 00	19 45		
Wemyss Bay	a	08 35		10 05		10 45		11 35		12 20		13 35		14 20		15 50		16 35		17 20		18 50	19 35	20 20		
Wemyss Bay	219 d	08 50		10 55		10 55		11 50		12 50		13 50		14 50		15 55		16 50		17 50		18 55	19 50	20 50		
Paisley Gilmour Street	219 a	09 27		11 31		11 31		12 27		13 26		14 26		15 26		16 31		17 26		18 26		19 31	20 26	21 26		
Glasgow Central 15	219 a	09 40		11 46		11 46		12 40		13 40		14 40		15 40		16 44		17 40		18 40		19 44	20 40	21 40		

For general notes see front of timetable
For details of catering facilities see Directory of Train Operators

A From 17 March
B Until 14 March
C From 21 March
D From 23 March
E Until 16 March

Network Diagram for Tables 220, 223, 224, 226, 232

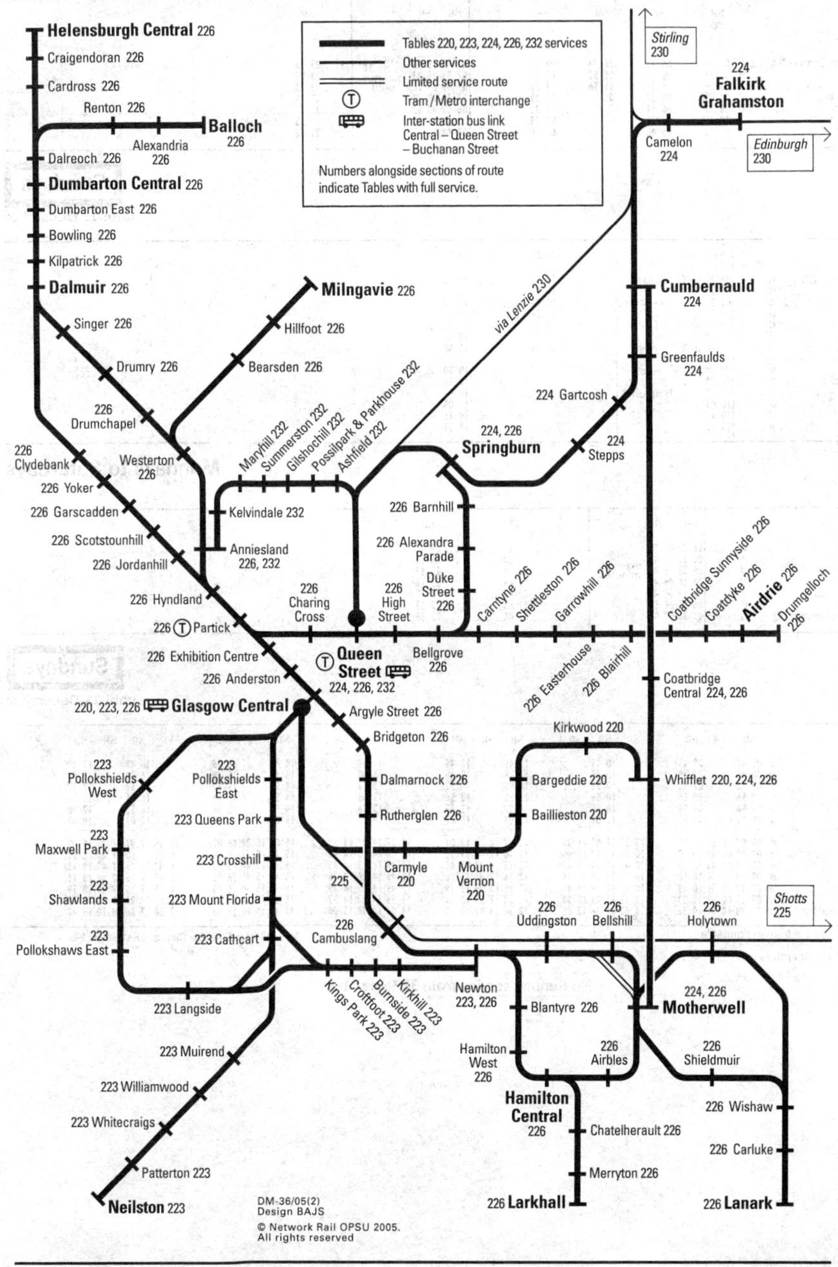
Tables 220, 223, 224, 226, 232 services
Other services
Limited service route
Tram / Metro interchange
Inter-station bus link Central – Queen Street – Buchanan Street
Numbers alongside sections of route indicate Tables with full service.
Helensburgh Central 226
Craigendoran 226
Cardross 226
Renton 226
Alexandria 226
Balloch 226
Dalreoch 226
Dumbarton Central 226
Dumbarton East 226
Bowling 226
Kilpatrick 226
Dalmuir 226
Singer 226
Drumry 226
226 Drumchapel
226 Clydebank
Westerton 226
226 Yoker
226 Garscadden
226 Scotstounhill
226 Jordanhill
226 Hyndland
226 Partick
226 Exhibition Centre
226 Anderston
220, 223, 226 Glasgow Central
Milngavie 226
Hillfoot 226
Bearsden 226
Maryhill 232
Summerston 232
Gilshochill 232
Possilpark & Parkhouse 232
Ashfield 232
Kelvindale 232
Anniesland 226, 232
226 Charing Cross
Queen Street 224, 226, 232
226 High Street
Duke Street 226
226 Alexandra Parade
226 Barnhill
224, 226 Springburn
Bellgrove 226
via Lenzie 230
Stirling 230
224 Falkirk Grahamston
Camelon 224
Edinburgh 230
Cumbernauld 224
Greenfaulds 224
224 Gartcosh
224 Stepps
Carntyne 226
Shettleston 226
Garrowhill 226
Coatbridge Sunnyside 226
Coatdyke 226
Airdrie 226
Drumgelloch 226
226 Easterhouse
226 Blairhill
Coatbridge Central 224, 226
Kirkwood 220
Whifflet 220, 224, 226
Bargeddie 220
Baillieston 220
Argyle Street 226
Bridgeton 226
Dalmarnock 226
Rutherglen 226
Carmyle 220
Mount Vernon 220
225
226 Cambuslang
223 Pollokshields West
223 Pollokshields East
223 Queens Park
223 Maxwell Park
223 Crosshill
223 Shawlands
223 Mount Florida
223 Pollokshaws East
223 Cathcart
223 Langside
Kings Park 223
Croftfoot 223
Burnside 223
Kirkhill 223
Newton 223, 226
226 Uddingston
226 Bellshill
Shotts 225
226 Holytown
224, 226 Motherwell
Blantyre 226
Hamilton West 226
226 Airbles
226 Shieldmuir
Hamilton Central 226
Chatelherault 226
Merryton 226
226 Larkhall
226 Wishaw
226 Carluke
226 Lanark
223 Muirend
223 Williamwood
223 Whitecraigs
Patterton 223
Neilston 223
DM-36/05(2)
Design BAJS

Glasgow Central — Whifflet

Mondays to Saturdays

Network Diagram - see first page of Table 220

Miles			SR SO	SR	SR	SR	SR	SR A		SR
0	**Glasgow Central** 15	d	00 13	06 13	06 43	07 13	07 43	08 13	and every 30 minutes until	23 13
5½	Carmyle	d	00 23	06 23	06 53	07 23	07 53	08 23		23 23
6¾	Mount Vernon	d	00 26	06 26	06 56	07 26	07 56	08 26		23 26
8	Baillieston	d	00 29	06 29	06 59	07 29	07 59	08 29		23 29
9¼	Bargeddie	d	00 32	06 32	07 02	07 32	08 02	08 32		23 32
10	Kirkwood	d	00 35	06 35	07 05	07 35	08 05	08 35		23 35
12½	**Whifflet**	a	00 42	06 45	07 12	07 46	08 12	08 42		23 42

Sundays

until 23 December

		SR	SR		SR	SR
Glasgow Central 15	d	09 22	09 52	and at	17 52	18 22
Carmyle	d	09 33	10 03	the same	18 03	18 33
Mount Vernon	d	09 36	10 06	minutes	18 06	18 36
Baillieston	d	09 39	10 09	past	18 09	18 39
Bargeddie	d	09 42	10 12	each	18 12	18 42
Kirkwood	d	09 45	10 15	hour until	18 15	18 45
Whifflet	a	09 50	10 21		18 21	18 50
	d	09 50				18 50
Holytown	d	09 59				18 59
Carfin	d	10 01				19 01
Cleland	d	10 05				19 05
Hartwood	d	10 11				19 11
Shotts	a	10 17				19 17

Mondays to Saturdays

Miles			SR	SR		SR	SR
0	**Whifflet**	d	06 07	06 37	and every 30 minutes until	22 37	23 07
2½	Kirkwood	d	06 10	06 40		22 40	23 10
3¼	Bargeddie	d	06 13	06 43		22 43	23 13
4½	Baillieston	d	06 16	06 46		22 46	23 16
5¾	Mount Vernon	d	06 19	06 49		22 49	23 19
7	Carmyle	d	06 23	06 53		22 53	23 23
12½	**Glasgow Central** 15	a	06 36	07 06		23 06	23 36

Sundays

until 23 December

		SR	SR	SR	SR	SR	SR	SR	SR	SR	SR	SR	SR	SR	SR	SR	SR	SR	SR	SR	SR
Shotts	d	08 45		09 45		10 45		11 45		12 45		13 45		14 45		15 45		16 45		17 45
Hartwood	d	08 48		09 48		10 48		11 48		12 48		13 48		14 48		15 48		16 48		17 48
Cleland	d	08 52		09 52		10 52		11 52		12 52		13 52		14 52		15 52		16 52		17 52
Carfin	d	08 56		09 56		10 56		11 56		12 56		13 56		14 56		15 56		16 56		17 56
Holytown	d	08 58		09 58		10 58		11 58		12 58		13 58		14 58		15 58		16 58		17 58
Whifflet	a	09 07		10 07		11 07		12 07		13 07		14 07		15 07		16 07		17 07		18 07
	d	09 07	09 37	10 07	10 38	11 07	11 38	12 07	12 38	13 07	13 37	14 07	14 38	15 07	15 38	16 07	16 38	17 07	17 38	18 07
Kirkwood	d	09 10	09 40	10 10	10 40	11 10	11 40	12 10	12 40	13 10	13 40	14 10	14 40	15 10	15 41	16 10	16 40	17 10	17 40	18 10
Bargeddie	d	09 13	09 43	10 13	10 43	11 13	11 43	12 13	12 43	13 13	13 43	14 13	14 43	15 13	15 44	16 13	16 43	17 13	17 43	18 13
Baillieston	d	09 16	09 46	10 16	10 46	11 16	11 46	12 16	12 46	13 16	13 46	14 16	14 46	15 16	15 47	16 16	16 46	17 16	17 46	18 16
Mount Vernon	d	09 19	09 49	10 19	10 49	11 19	11 49	12 19	12 49	13 19	13 49	14 19	14 49	15 19	15 50	16 19	16 49	17 19	17 49	18 19
Carmyle	d	09 23	09 53	10 23	10 53	11 23	11 53	12 23	12 53	13 23	13 53	14 23	14 53	15 23	15 54	16 23	16 53	17 23	17 53	18 23
Glasgow Central 15	a	09 38	10 06	10 36	11 07	11 36	12 08	12 36	13 07	13 38	14 06	14 38	15 06	15 40	16 06	16 36	17 08	17 36	18 10	18 40

For general notes see front of timetable
For details of catering facilities see Directory of Train Operators

A 1813 from Glasgow Central arr. Whifflet 1845

No Sunday service from 30 December

Glasgow Central → Ardrossan, Largs and Ayr

Network Diagram - see first page of Table 216

Miles	Miles	Miles			SR	SR	SR	SR	SR	SR	SR	SR	SR	SR	SR	SR	SR	SR	SR	SR	SR	SR	SR	SR	SR	SR
					MX				SX	SO	SO	SX		SX	SO			SX	SX	SO				SO	SX	
													◇ A								B					C
0	0	—	**Glasgow Central** 15 219	d	00 15	06 00	06 15	06 30	06 45	06 45	07 00	07 00	07 13	07 15	07 15	07 30	08 00	08 15	08 30	08 30		08 33	08 45	09 00	09 00	09 03
7¼	7¼	—	Paisley Gilmour Street 219 ✈	d	00 26	06 11	06 26	06 41	06 56	06 56	07 11	07 11	07 24	07 26	07 26	07 41	08 11	08 26	08 41	08 41		08 44	08 56	09 11	09 11	
10¾	10¾	—	Johnstone	d	00 30	06 15	06 30	06 45	07 00	07 00	07 15	07 15		07 30	07 30	07 45	08 15	08 30	08 45	08 45		08 48	09 00	09 15	09 15	
11½	11½	—	Milliken Park	d			06 33		07 03	07 03				07 33	07 33			08 33				08 51	09 03			
13	13	—	Howwood	d			06 36			07 06		07 19			07 36			08 36		08 49						
16½	16½	—	Lochwinnoch	d			06 40							07 38	07 40			08 40				08 56				
20½	20½	—	Glengarnock	d			06 45		07 11	07 13				07 43	07 45		08 24	08 45	08 54	08 56		09 01	09 11			
23¼	23¼	—	Dalry	d			06 49		07 15	07 17				07 47	07 49		08 28	08 49	08 58	09 00		09 05				
26¾	26¾	—	Kilwinning	d	00 42	06 29	06 54	06 59	07 20	07 22	07 29	07 31	07 41	07 52	07 54	07 59	08 33	08 54	09 03	09 05		09 10	09 18	09 29	09 32	
—	29	—	Stevenston	d			06 57		07 23	07 25				07 55	07 57			08 57				09 13	09 21			
—	30¼	—	Saltcoats	d			07 00		07 26	07 28				08 00	08 02			09 00				09 16	09 24			
—	31¼	—	Ardrossan South Beach	d			07 02		07 28	07 30				08 02	08 04			09a02				09 18	09 26			
—	—	31¾	Ardrossan Town	d					07a34	07a34												09 22				
—	—	32¼	**Ardrossan Harbour**	a																		09 25				
—	35¾	—	West Kilbride	d			07 08							08 08	08 10								09 32			
—	39¾	—	Fairlie	d			07 13							08 14	08 16								09 37			
—	42¾	—	**Largs**	a			07 20							08 20	08 22								09 44			
30	—	—	Irvine	d	00 46	06 33		07 03			07 33	07 35				08 03	08 37		09 07	09 09				09 33	09 36	
33¾	—	—	Barassie	d	00 51			07 08								08 08	08 42		09 12	09 14						
35	—	—	Troon	d	00 54	06 39		07 11			07 39	07 41				08 11	08 45		09 15	09 17	09 24			09 39	09 42	10 07
37¾	—	—	Prestwick Int. Airport ✈	d	00 58	06 43		07 15			07 43	07 45				08 15	08 49		09 19	09 21	09 29			09 43	09 46	10 12
38¼	—	—	Prestwick Town	d	01 00	06 45		07 17			07 45	07 47				08 17	08 51		09 21	09 23	09 31			09 45	09 48	10 14
40¼	—	—	Newton-on-Ayr	d	01 03			07 20								08 20	08 54		09 24	09 26						
41½	—	—	**Ayr**	a	01 10	06 52		07 24			07 52	07 54	07 59			08 25	08 58		09 28	09 30	09 38			09 52	09 53	10 21

		SR	SR	SR	SR	SR	SR	SR	SR	SR	SR	SR	SR		SR	SR	SR	SR	SR	SR	SR	SR	SR	SR	SR	SR
												◇ A						D								
Glasgow Central 15 219	d	09 15	09 30	09 45	10 00	10 15	10 30	10 45	11 00	11 15	11 30	11 42	11 45		12 00	12 15	12 30		12 45	13 00	13 15	13 30	13 45	14 00	14 15	14 30
Paisley Gilmour Street 219 ✈	d	09 26	09 41	09 56	10 11	10 26	10 41	10 56	11 11	11 26	11 41	11 53	11 56		12 11	12 26	12 41		12 56	13 11	13 26	13 41	13 56	14 11	14 26	14 41
Johnstone	d	09 30	09 45	10 00	10 15	10 30	10 45	11 00	11 15	11 30	11 45		12 00		12 15	12 30	12 45		13 00	13 15	13 30	13 45	14 00	14 15	14 30	14 45
Milliken Park	d	09 33		10 03		10 33		11 03		11 33			12 03			12 33			13 03		13 33		14 03		14 33	
Howwood	d	09 36				10 36				11 36						12 36					13 36				14 36	
Lochwinnoch	d	09 40				10 40				11 40						12 40					13 40				14 40	
Glengarnock	d	09 45	09 54	10 11		10 45	10 54	11 11		11 45			12 11			12 45			13 11		13 45		14 11		14 45	
Dalry	d	09 49		10 15	10 26	10 49				11 49						12 49			13 15		13 49			14 26	14 49	
Kilwinning	d	09 54	10 01	10 20	10 31	10 54	11 01	11 18	11 29	11 54	11 59	12 10	12 18		12 29	12 54	12 59		13 20	13 29	13 54	13 59	14 18	14 31	14 54	14 59
Stevenston	d	09 57		10 23		10 57		11 21		11 57			12 21			12 57			13 23		13 57		14 21		14 57	
Saltcoats	d	10 00		10 26		11 00		11 24		12 00			12 24			13 00			13 26		14 00		14 24		15 00	
Ardrossan South Beach	d	10 02		10 28		11 02		11 26		12 02			12 26			13 02			13 28		14 02		14 26		15 01	
Ardrossan Town	d	10a06				11a06				12 06						13a06					14a06				15 06	
Ardrossan Harbour	a									12 09															15 09	
West Kilbride	d			10 34				11 32					12 32						13 34				14 32			
Fairlie	d			10 39				11 37					12 37						13 39				14 37			
Largs	a			10 47				11 44					12 44						13 46				14 44			
Irvine	d		10 05		10 35		11 05		11 33		12 03				12 33		13 03			13 33		14 03		14 35		15 03
Barassie	d		10 10				11 10				12 08						13 08					14 08				15 08
Troon	d		10 13		10 41		11 13		11 39		12 11				12 39		13 11	13 22		13 39		14 11		14 41		15 11
Prestwick Int. Airport ✈	d		10 17		10 45		11 17		11 43		12 15				12 43		13 15	13 27		13 43		14 15		14 45		15 15
Prestwick Town	d		10 19		10 47		11 19		11 45		12 17				12 45		13 17	13 29		13 45		14 17		14 47		15 17
Newton-on-Ayr	d		10 22				11 22				12 20						13 20					14 20				15 20
Ayr	a		10 26		10 54		11 26		11b54		12 24	12 29			12 52		13 24	13 36		13 52		14 24		14 54		15 24

		SR	SR	SR	SR	SR	SR	SR	SR	SR	SR	SR	SR	SR	SR	SR	SR	SR	SR	SR	SR	SR	SR	SR	SR	SR
														SX		SX	SO	SX		SO						
						E			D									G		G						
Glasgow Central 15 219	d	14 45	15 00	15 15	15 30		15 45	16 00		16 18	16 30	16 50	17 00	17 13	17 20	17 30	17 30		17 35		17 45	18 00	18 15	18 30	18 45	19 00
Paisley Gilmour Street 219 ✈	d	14 56	15 11	15 26	15 41		15 56	16 11		16 29	16 41	17 01	17 11	17u24	17 32	17u41	17 41		17 46		17 56	18 11	18 26	18 41	18 56	19 11
Johnstone	d	15 00	15 15	15 30	15 45		16 00	16 15		16 33	16 45	17 05	17 15		17 36		17 45		17 50		18 00	18 15	18 30	18 45	19 00	19 15
Milliken Park	d	15 03		15 33			16 03			16 36		17 08			17 39				17 53		18 03		18 33		19 03	
Howwood	d			15 36						16 39		17 11							17 56				18 36			
Lochwinnoch	d			15 40						16 43			17 21						18 00				18 40			
Glengarnock	d	15 11		15 45			16 11			16 48		17 18	17 26	17 35					18 05		18 11		18 45		19 11	
Dalry	d			15 49						16 52		17 22	17 30		17 49				18 09		18 15	18 26	18 49	18 56		
Kilwinning	d	15 18	15 29	15 54	15 59		16 18	16 29		16 57	16 59	17 27	17 35	17 42	17 54		17 59		18 14		18 20	18 31	18 54	19 01	19 18	19 29
Stevenston	d	15 21		15 57			16 21			17 01		17 30			17 57				18 17		18 23		18 57		19 21	
Saltcoats	d	15 24		16 00			16 24			17c09		17 33			18 01				18 20		18 26		19 00		19 24	
Ardrossan South Beach	d	15 26		16 02			16 26			17 11		17 36			18 03				18 22		18 28		19 02		19 26	
Ardrossan Town	d			16a06								17 40							18a26				19a06			
Ardrossan Harbour	a											17 44														
West Kilbride	d	15 32					16 32			17 17					18 09						18 34				19 32	
Fairlie	d	15 37					16 37			17 22					18 14						18 39				19 37	
Largs	a	15 44					16 44			17 28					18 20						18 48				19 44	
Irvine	d		15 33		16 03			16 33			17 03		17 39	17 46		17 59	18 03					18 35		19 05		19 33
Barassie	d				16 08						17 08		17 44			18 04	18 08					18 40		19 10		
Troon	d		15 39		16 11	16 19		16 39	16 44		17 11		17 47	17 52		18 07	18 11	18 24		18 31		18 43		19 13		19 39
Prestwick Int. Airport ✈	d		15 43		16 15			16 43	16 49		17 15		17 51	17 56		18 11	18 15	18 29		18 36		18 47		19 17		19 43
Prestwick Town	d		15 45		16 17			16 45	16 51		17 17		17 53	17 58		18 13	18 17	18 31		18 38		18 49		19 19		19 45
Newton-on-Ayr	d				16 20						17 20		17 56			18 16	18 20					18 52		19 22		
Ayr	a		15 52		16 24	16 32		16 52	16 58		17 25		18 00	18 05		18 20	18 24	18 38		18 45		18 56		19 26		19 52

For general notes see front of timetable
For details of catering facilities see Directory of Train Operators

- **A** To Stranraer (Table 218)
- **B** From Kilmarnock to Stranraer (Table 218)
- **C** To Girvan (Table 218)
- **D** From Kilmarnock to Girvan (Table 218)
- **E** From Newcastle (Table 48) to Stranraer (Table 218)
- **G** From Kilmarnock (Table 218)
- **b** Saturdays arr. 1152
- **c** Arr. 1704

Glasgow Central → Ardrossan, Largs and Ayr

Network Diagram - see first page of Table 216

Mondays to Saturdays

		SR	SR	SR	SR	SR	SR	SR	SR	SR	SR	SR	SR	SR	SR	SR	SR	SR	SR	SR	SR	SR	SR	SR
																				FO	FX		FSX	FO
						A									B									
Glasgow Central 15 219	d	19 15	19 30	19 45	20 00		20 15	20 30	20 45	21 00	21 15	21 30	21 45	22 00		22 15	22 30	22 45	23 00	23 15	23 15	23 30	23 45	23 45
Paisley Gilmour Street 219 ✈	d	19 26	19 41	19 56	20 11		20 26	20 41	20 56	21 11	21 26	21 41	21 56	22 11		22 26	22 41	22 56	23 11	23 26	23 26	23 41	23 56	23 56
Johnstone	d	19 30	19 45	20 00	20 15		20 30	20 45	21 00	21 15	21 30	21 45	22 00	22 15		22 30	22 45	23 00	23 15	23 30	23 30	23 45	23 59	23 59
Milliken Park	d	19 33		20 03			20 33		21 03		21 33		22 03			22 33		23 03		23 33	23 33		00 03	00 03
Howwood	d	19 36					20 36				21 36					22 36				23 36	23 36		00 06	00 06
Lochwinnoch	d	19 40					20 40				21 40					22 40				23 40	23 40		00 10	00 10
Glengarnock	d	19 45		20 11			20 45		21 11		21 45		22 11			22 45		23 11		23 45	23 45		00 15	00 15
Dalry	d	19 49					20 49				21 49					22 49				23 49	23 49		00 19	00 19
Kilwinning	d	19 54	19 59	20 18	20 29		20 54	20 59	21 18	21 29	21 54	21 59	22 18	22 29		22 54	22 59	23 18	23 29	23 54	23 54	23 59	00 24	00 24
Stevenston	d	19 57		20 21			20 57		21 21		21 57		22 21			22 57		23 21		23 57	23 57		00 27	00 27
Saltcoats	d	20 00		20 24			21 00		21 24		22 00		22 24			23 00		23 24		23 59	00 01		00 30	00 30
Ardrossan South Beach	d	20 02		20 26			21 02		21 26		22 02		22 26			23 02		23 26		00 02	00 02		00a32	00 32
Ardrossan Town	d	20 06					21a06				22a06					23a06				00a06				
Ardrossan Harbour	a	20 09																						
West Kilbride	d			20 32					21 32				22 32					23 32			00 08			00 38
Fairlie	d			20 37					21 37				22 37					23 37			00 14			00 43
Largs	a			20 44					21 44				22 44					23 44			00 19			00 49
Irvine	d		20 03		20 33			21 03		21 33		22 03		22 33			23 03		23 33			00 03		
Barassie	d		20 08					21 08				22 08					23 08					00 08		
Troon	d		20 11		20 39	20 50		21 11		21 39		22 11		22 39	22 56		23 11		23 39			00 11		
Prestwick Int. Airport ✈	d		20 15		20 43			21 15		21 43		22 15		22 43	23 01		23 15		23 43			00 15		
Prestwick Town	d		20 17		20 45			21 17		21 45		22 17		22 45	23 03		23 17		23 45			00 17		
Newton-on-Ayr	d		20 20					21 20				22 20					23 20					00 20		
Ayr	a		20 24		20 52	20 59		21 24		21 52		22 24		22 52	23 10		23 24		23 52			00 24		

Sundays

until 23 December

		SR	SR	SR	SR	SR	SR	SR	SR	SR	SR	SR	SR	SR	SR	SR	SR	SR	SR	SR	SR	SR	SR
												◇ C											
Glasgow Central 15 219	d	08 40	09 00	09 30	09 45	10 00	10 30	10 45	11 00	11 15	11 30	11 42	11 45	12 00	12 30	12 45	13 00	13 30	13 45	14 00	14 05	14 30	14 45
Paisley Gilmour Street 219 ✈	d	08 51	09 11	09 41	09 56	10 11	10 41	10 56	11 11	11 26	11 41	11 53	11 56	12 11	12 41	12 56	13 11	13 41	13 56	14 11	14 16	14 41	14 56
Johnstone	d	08 55	09 15	09 45	10 00	10 15	10 45	11 00	11 15	11 30	11 45		12 00	12 15	12 45	13 00	13 15	13 45	14 00	14 15	14 20	14 45	15 00
Milliken Park	d	08 58			10 03			11 03		11 33			12 03			13 03			14 03		14 23		15 03
Howwood	d				10 06			11 06					12 06			13 06			14 06				15 06
Lochwinnoch	d				10 10			11 10					12 10			13 10			14 10				15 10
Glengarnock	d	09 06			10 15			11 15					12 15			13 15			14 15				15 15
Dalry	d	09 10			10 19			11 19					12 19			13 19			14 19				15 19
Kilwinning	d	09 15	09 29	09 59	10 24	10 29	10 59	11 24	11 29	11 46	11 59	12 10	12 24	12 29	12 59	13 24	13 29	13 59	14 24	14 29	14 39	14 59	15 24
Stevenston	d	09 18			10 27			11 27		11 49			12 27			13 27			14 27		14 42		15 27
Saltcoats	d	09 21			10 30			11 30		11 52			12 30			13 30			14 30		14 45		15 30
Ardrossan South Beach	d	09 23			10 32			11 32		11 54			12 32			13 32			14 32		14 47		15 32
Ardrossan Town	d																						
Ardrossan Harbour	a	09 37								12 09											14 59		
West Kilbride	d				10 38			11 38					12 38			13 38			14 38				15 38
Fairlie	d				10 44			11 44					12 44			13 44			14 44				15 44
Largs	a				10 52			11 52					12 52			13 52			14 52				15 52
Irvine	d		09 33	10 03		10 33	11 03		11 33		12 03			12 33	13 03		13 33	14 03		14 33		15 03	
Barassie	d		09 38			10 38			11 38					12 38			13 38			14 38			
Troon	d		09 41	10 09		10 41	11 09		11 41		12 09			12 41	13 09		13 41	14 09		14 41		15 09	
Prestwick Int. Airport ✈	d		09 45	10 13		10 45	11 13		11 45		12 13			12 45	13 13		13 45	14 13		14 45		15 13	
Prestwick Town	d		09 47	10 15		10 47	11 15		11 47		12 15			12 47	13 15		13 47	14 15		14 47		15 15	
Newton-on-Ayr	d																						
Ayr	a		10 01	10 22		11 01	11 22		12 01		12 22	12 34		13 01	13 22		14 01	14 22		15 01		15 22	

		SR	SR	SR	SR	SR	SR	SR	SR	SR	SR	SR	SR	SR	SR	SR	SR	SR	SR	SR	SR	SR	SR
						◇ C																	
Glasgow Central 15 219	d	15 00	15 30	15 45	16 00	16 25	16 30	16 45	16 55	17 00	17 30	17 45	18 00	18 40	19 00	19 40	20 00	20 40	21 00	21 40	22 00	22 40	23 00
Paisley Gilmour Street 219 ✈	d	15 11	15 41	15 56	16 11	16 39	16 43	16 56	17 07	17 11	17 41	17 56	18 11	18 51	19 11	19 51	20 11	20 51	21 11	21 51	22 11	22 51	23 11
Johnstone	d	15 15	15 45	16 00	16 15		16 47	17 00	17 11	17 15	17 45	18 00	18 15	18 55	19 15	19 55	20 15	20 55	21 15	21 55	22 15	22 55	23 15
Milliken Park	d			16 03				17 03	17 14			18 03		18 58		19 58		20 58		21 58		22 58	
Howwood	d			16 06				17 06				18 06		19 01		20 01		21 01		22 01		23 01	
Lochwinnoch	d			16 10				17 10				18 10		19 05		20 05		21 05		22 05		23 05	
Glengarnock	d			16 15				17 15				18 15		19 10		20 10		21 10		22 10		23 10	
Dalry	d			16 19				17 19				18 19		19 14		20 14		21 14		22 14		23 14	
Kilwinning	d	15 29	15 59	16 24	16 29	16 56	17 01	17 24	17 27	17 29	17 59	18 24	18 29	19 19	19 29	20 19	20 29	21 19	21 29	22 19	22 29	23 18	23 29
Stevenston	d			16 27				17 27	17 30			18 27		19 22		20 22		21 22		22 22		23 22	
Saltcoats	d			16 30				17 30	17 33			18 30		19 25		20 25		21 25		22 25		23 24	
Ardrossan South Beach	d			16 32				17 32	17 35			18 32		19 27		20 27		21 27		22 27		23 26	
Ardrossan Town	d																						
Ardrossan Harbour	a								17 43														
West Kilbride	d			16 38				17 38				18 38		19 33		20 33		21 33		22 33		23 32	
Fairlie	d			16 44				17 44				18 44		19 39		20 39		21 39		22 39		23 38	
Largs	a			16 53				17 50				18 50		19 45		20 45		21 45		22 44		23 44	
Irvine	d	15 33	16 03		16 33		17 05			17 33	18 03		18 33		19 33		20 33		21 33		22 33		23 33
Barassie	d	15 38			16 38					17 38			18 38		19 38		20 38		21 38		22 38		23 38
Troon	d	15 41	16 09		16 41		17 11			17 41	18 09		18 41		19 41		20 41		21 41		22 41		23 41
Prestwick Int. Airport ✈	d	15 45	16 13		16 45		17 15			17 45	18 13		18 45		19 45		20 45		21 45		22 45		23 45
Prestwick Town	d	15 47	16 15		16 47		17 17			17 47	18 15		18 47		19 47		20 47		21 47		22 47		23 47
Newton-on-Ayr	d																						
Ayr	a	16 01	16 22		16 54	17 17	17 24			17 54	18 22		18 54		19 54		20 54		21 54		22 54		23 54

For general notes see front of timetable
For details of catering facilities see Directory of Train Operators

A From Newcastle (Table 48) to Stranraer (Table 218)
B From Kilmarnock to Stranraer (Table 218)
C To Stranraer (Table 218)

Table 221

Sundays

from 30 December

Glasgow Central → Ardrossan, Largs and Ayr

Network Diagram - see first page of Table 216

		SR	SR	SR	SR	SR	SR	SR	SR	SR	SR	SR	SR	SR	SR	SR	SR	SR
									◇ A									
Glasgow Central 15 219	d	08 40	09 00	09 40	10 00	10 40	11 00	11 15	11 37	11 40	12 00	12 40	13 00	13 40	14 00	14 05	14 40	15 00
Paisley Gilmour Street 219 ✈	d	08 51	09 11	09 51	10 11	10 51	11 11	11 26	11 48	11 51	12 11	12 51	13 11	13 51	14 11	14 16	14 51	15 11
Johnstone	d	08 55	09 15	09 55	10 15	10 55	11 15	11 30		11 55	12 15	12 55	13 15	13 55	14 15	14 20	14 55	15 15
Milliken Park	d	08 58		09 58		10 58		11 33		11 58		12 58		13 58		14 23	14 58	
Howwood	d			10 01		11 01				12 01		13 01		14 01			15 01	
Lochwinnoch	d			10 05		11 05				12 05		13 05		14 05			15 05	
Glengarnock	d	09 06		10 10		11 10				12 10		13 10		14 10			15 10	
Dalry	d	09 10		10 14		11 14				12 14		13 14		14 14			15 14	
Kilwinning	d	09 15	09 29	10 19	10 29	11 19	11 29	11 46	12 05	12 19	12 29	13 19	13 29	14 19	14 29	14 39	15 19	15 29
Stevenston	d	09 18		10 22		11 22		11 49		12 22		13 22		14 22		14 42	15 22	
Saltcoats	d	09 21		10 25		11 25		11 52		12 25		13 25		14 25		14 45	15 25	
Ardrossan South Beach	d	09 23		10 27		11 27		11 54		12 27		13 27		14 27		14 47	15 27	
Ardrossan Town	d																	
Ardrossan Harbour	a	09 37						12 09								14 59		
West Kilbride	d			10 33		11 33				12 33		13 33		14 33			15 33	
Fairlie	d			10 39		11 39				12 39		13 39		14 39			15 39	
Largs	a			10 52		11 52				12 52		13 52		14 52			15 52	
Irvine	d		09 33		10 33		11 33				12 33		13 33		14 33			15 33
Barassie	d		09 38		10 38		11 38				12 38		13 38		14 38			15 38
Troon	d		09 41		10 41		11 41				12 41		13 41		14 41			15 41
Prestwick Int. Airport ✈	d		09 45		10 45		11 45				12 45		13 45		14 45			15 45
Prestwick Town	d		09 47		10 47		11 47				12 47		13 47		14 47			15 47
Newton-on-Ayr	d																	
Ayr	a		10 01		11 01		12 01		12 29		13 01		14 01		15 01			16 01

		SR	SR	SR	SR	SR	SR	SR	SR	SR	SR	SR	SR	SR	SR	SR	SR	SR	SR
				◇ A															
Glasgow Central 15 219	d	15 40	16 00	16 25	16 40	16 55	17 00	17 40	18 00	18 40	19 00	19 40	20 00	20 40	21 00	21 40	22 00	22 40	23 00
Paisley Gilmour Street 219 ✈	d	15 51	16 11	16 39	16 51	17 07	17 11	17 51	18 11	18 51	19 11	19 51	20 11	20 51	21 11	21 51	22 11	22 51	23 11
Johnstone	d	15 55	16 15		16 55	17 11	17 15	17 55	18 15	18 55	19 15	19 55	20 15	20 55	21 15	21 55	22 15	22 55	23 15
Milliken Park	d	15 58			16 58	17 14		17 58		18 58		19 58		20 58		21 58		22 58	
Howwood	d	16 01			17 01			18 01		19 01		20 01		21 01		22 01		23 01	
Lochwinnoch	d	16 05			17 05			18 05		19 05		20 05		21 05		22 05		23 05	
Glengarnock	d	16 10			17 10			18 10		19 10		20 10		21 10		22 10		23 10	
Dalry	d	16 14			17 14			18 14		19 14		20 14		21 14		22 14		23 14	
Kilwinning	d	16 19	16 29	16 56	17 19	17 27	17 29	18 19	18 29	19 19	19 29	20 19	20 29	21 19	21 29	22 19	22 29	23 18	23 29
Stevenston	d	16 22			17 22	17 30		18 22		19 22		20 22		21 22		22 22		23 22	
Saltcoats	d	16 25			17 25	17 33		18 25		19 25		20 25		21 25		22 25		23 24	
Ardrossan South Beach	d	16 27			17 27	17 35		18 27		19 27		20 27		21 27		22 27		23 26	
Ardrossan Town	d																		
Ardrossan Harbour	a					17 43													
West Kilbride	d	16 33			17 33			18 33		19 33		20 33		21 33		22 33		23 32	
Fairlie	d	16 39			17 39			18 39		19 39		20 39		21 39		22 39		23 38	
Largs	a	16 53			17 45			18 45		19 45		20 45		21 45		22 44		23 44	
Irvine	d		16 33				17 33		18 33		19 33		20 33		21 33		22 33		23 33
Barassie	d		16 38				17 38		18 38		19 38		20 38		21 38		22 38		23 38
Troon	d		16 41				17 41		18 41		19 41		20 41		21 41		22 41		23 41
Prestwick Int. Airport ✈	d		16 45				17 45		18 45		19 45		20 45		21 45		22 45		23 45
Prestwick Town	d		16 47				17 47		18 47		19 47		20 47		21 47		22 47		23 47
Newton-on-Ayr	d																		
Ayr	a		16 54	17 17			17 54		18 54		19 54		20 54		21 54		22 54		23 54

For general notes see front of timetable
For details of catering facilities see
Directory of Train Operators

A To Stranraer (Table 218)

Ayr, Largs and Ardrossan → Glasgow Central

Network Diagram - see first page of Table 216

Miles	Miles	Miles			SR	SR	SR	SR	SR	SR SX	SR	SR SX	SR SO		SR SX	SR SX	SR	SR	SR SX	SR SX	SR	SR SO	SR SX		SR	SR
											A															◇ B
0	—	—	**Ayr**	d	05 40	06 13		06 43		06 57	07 10	07 13	07 13		07 25		07 43		07 58		08 13				08 43	08 36
1¼	—	—	Newton-on-Ayr	d	05 43	06 16		06 46				07 16	07 16						08 01		08 16					
3¼	—	—	Prestwick Town	d	05 46	06 19		06 49		07 02		07 19	07 19		07 30		07 48		08 04		08 19				08 48	08 41
3¾	—	—	Prestwick Int. Airport	d	05 48	06 21		06 51		07 04		07 21	07 21		07 32		07 50		08 06		08 21				08 50	08 43
6½	—	—	Troon	d	05 52	06 25		06 55		07 08	07a18	07 25	07 25		07 36		07 54		08 10		08 25				08 54	08 48
7¾	—	—	Barassie	d	05 54	06 27		06 57		07 10		07 27	07 27		07 38				08 12		08 27					
11½	—	—	Irvine	d	05 59	06 32		07 02		07 15		07 32	07 32		07 43		07 59		08 17		08 32				08 59	
—	0	—	**Largs**	d					06 41							07 23		07 42					08 28			
—	3	—	Fairlie	d					06 46							07 28		07 47					08 33			
—	7	—	West Kilbride	d					06 51							07 33		07 52					08 38			
—	—	0	**Ardrossan Harbour**	d																						
—	—	½	Ardrossan Town	d			06 31													08 14		08 31				
—	11½	1	Ardrossan South Beach	d			06 34		06 57							07 39		07 58		08 17		08 34	08 44			
—	12¼	2	Saltcoats	d			06 36		07b02							07 41		08 00		08 19		08 36	08 46			
—	13¾	3¼	Stevenston	d			06 39		07 05							07 44		08 03		08 22		08 39	08 49			
14¾	16	5½	Kilwinning	d	06 04	06 37	06 43	07 07	07 10	07 20		07 37	07 37			07 49	08 04	08 08	08 22	08 25	08 37	08 42	08 53		09 04	
18½	19¾	9½	Dalry	d	06 08		06 47		07 14	07 24		07 41	07 41			07 53		08 12		08 30		08 47	08 58			
21	22¼	11¾	Glengarnock	d	06 12		06 51		07 18	07 28			07 45		07 52			08 16		08 34		08 51	09 02			
25	26¼	15¾	Lochwinnoch	d	06 17		06 56			07 33			07 50			08 00		08 21		08 39		08 56				
28½	29¾	19¼	Howwood	d	06 21		07 00			07 37			07 54		07 59					08 43		09 00				
30	31¼	20¾	Milliken Park	d	06 24		07 03		07 26	07 40			07 57			08 05		08 26		08 46		09 03	09 10			
30¾	32	21½	Johnstone	d	06 27	06 50	07 06	07 20	07 29	07 43		07 52	08 00		08 03	08 08	08 18	08 29	08 35	08 48	08 50	09 05	09 12		09 18	
34¼	35½	25	Paisley Gilmour Street 219	d	06 32	06 55	07 11	07 26	07 34	07 48		07 57	08 05		08 08	08 13	08 23	08 34	08 41	08 53	08 56	09 11	09 17		09 24	
41½	42¾	32¼	**Glasgow Central 15** 219	a	06 43	07 07	07 22	07 38	07 47	07 59		08 09	08 16		08 18	08 24	08 34	08 46	08 54	09 04	09 07	09 22	09 30		09 36	09 50

		SR SX	SR SO	SR	SR	SR	SR	SR	SR	SR		SR	SR	SR	SR	SR	SR	SR	SR	SR		SR	SR	SR	SR	SR
														◇ C				D								◇ B
Ayr	d			09 13		09 43		10 13		10 43			11 13	11 22		11 43		12 09	12 13			12 43		13 13		13 09
Newton-on-Ayr	d			09 16				10 16					11 16						12 16					13 16		
Prestwick Town	d			09 19		09 48		10 19		10 48			11 19			11 48		12 14	12 19			12 48		13 19		13 14
Prestwick Int. Airport	d			09 21		09 50		10 21		10 50			11 21			11 50		12 16	12 21			12 50		13 22		13 16
Troon	d			09 25		09 54		10 25		10 54			11 25	11a30		11 54		12a21	12 25			12 54		13 25		13 21
Barassie	d			09 27				10 27					11 27						12 27					13 27		
Irvine	d			09 32		09 59		10 32		10 59			11 32			11 59			12 32			12 59		13 32		
Largs	d		08 51				09 53					10 53					11 53						12 53			
Fairlie	d		08 56				09 58					10 58					11 58						12 58			
West Kilbride	d		09 01				10 03					11 03					12 03						13 03			
Ardrossan Harbour	d				09 30															12 28						
Ardrossan Town	d				09 33				10 31						11 31					12 31					13 31	
Ardrossan South Beach	d	09 07	09 07		09 36		10 09		10 34			11 09			11 34		12 09			12 34			13 09		13 34	
Saltcoats	d	09 09	09 09		09 38		10 11		10 36			11 11			11 36		12 11			12 36			13 11		13 36	
Stevenston	d	09 12	09 12		09 41		10 14		10 39			11 14			11 39		12 14			12 39			13 14		13 39	
Kilwinning	d	09 16	09 16	09 37	09 45	10 04	10 18	10 37	10 43	11 04		11 18	11 37		11 43	12 04	12 18		12 37	12 43		13 04	13 18	13 37	13 43	
Dalry	d			09 41	09 49				10 47						11 47					12 47					13 47	
Glengarnock	d	09 22	09 22		09 53		10 25		10 51			11 25			11 51		12 25			12 51			13 25		13 51	
Lochwinnoch	d	09 27	09 27		09 58				10 56						11 56					12 56					13 56	
Howwood	d	09 31	09 31			10 16			11 00						12 00					13 00					14 00	
Milliken Park	d	09 32	09 32		10 03		10 33		11 03			11 33			12 03		12 33			13 03			13 33		14 03	
Johnstone	d	09 35	09 35	09 52	10 06	10 20	10 35	10 50	11 06	11 18		11 35	11 50		12 06	12 18	12 35		12 50	13 06		13 18	13 35	13 50	14 06	
Paisley Gilmour Street 219	d	09 40	09 40	09 57	10 11	10 25	10 40	10 55	11 11	11 23		11 40	11 55		12 11	12 23	12 40		12 55	13 11		13 23	13 40	13 55	14 11	
Glasgow Central 15 219	a	09 53	09 53	10 09	10 22	10 36	10 52	11 07	11 22	11 34		11 52	12 07		12 22	12 34	12 52		13 07	13 22		13 34	13 52	14 07	14 22	14 27

		SR	SR	SR	SR	SR	SR		SR	SR	SR	SR	SR	SR	SR	SR	SR		SR	SR	SR	SR	SR	SR	SR	SR
											E		◇ B													
Ayr	d	13 43		14 13		14 43			15 13		15 17	15 43	15 58		16 13		16 43			17 13			17 43		18 13	
Newton-on-Ayr	d			14 16					15 16						16 16		16 46			17 16					18 16	
Prestwick Town	d	13 48		14 19		14 48			15 19		15 22	15 48			16 19		16 49			17 19			17 48		18 19	
Prestwick Int. Airport	d	13 50		14 21		14 50			15 21		15 24	15 50			16 21		16 51			17 21			17 50		18 21	
Troon	d	13 54		14 25		14 54			15 25		15 29	15 54			16 25		16 55			17 25			17 54		18 25	
Barassie	d			14 27					15 27						16 27					17 27					18 27	
Irvine	d	13 59		14 32		14 59			15 32			15 59			16 32		17 00			17 32			17 59		18 32	
Largs	d		13 53				14 53							15 53					16 50			17 35				
Fairlie	d		13 58				14 58							15 58					16 55			17 40				
West Kilbride	d		14 03				15 03							16 03					17 00			17 45				
Ardrossan Harbour	d									15 28														18 00		
Ardrossan Town	d				14 31					15 31						16 31								18 03		18 31
Ardrossan South Beach	d		14 09		14 34		15 09			15 34				16 09		16 34			17 06		17 40	17 51		18 06		18 34
Saltcoats	d		14 11		14 36		15 11			15 36				16 11		16 36			17 08		17 42	17 53		18 09		18 36
Stevenston	d		14 14		14 39		15 14			15 39				16 14		16 39			17 11		17 45	17 56		18 12		18 39
Kilwinning	d	14 04	14 18	14 37	14 43	15 04	15 18		15 37	15 43		16 04	16 13	16 18	16 37	16 43	17 05		17 15	17 37	17 48	18 00	18 04	18 16	18 37	18 43
Dalry	d				14 47					15 47						16 47			17 20	17 41	17 53	18 05	18 09		18 41	18 47
Glengarnock	d		14 25		14 51		15 25		15 43	15 51				16 25	16 43	16 51			17 24		17 57		18 13	18 23		18 51
Lochwinnoch	d				14 56					15 56						16 56			17 29				18 18			18 56
Howwood	d				15 00					16 00						17 00						18 14		18 30		19 00
Milliken Park	d		14 33		15 03		15 33			16 03				16 33		17 03			17 34		18 05			18 33		19 03
Johnstone	d	14 18	14 35	14 50	15 06	15 18	15 35		15 52	16 06		16 18		16 35	16 52	17 06	17 19		17 36	17 52	18 07	18 18	18 24	18 35	18 52	19 06
Paisley Gilmour Street 219	d	14 23	14 40	14 55	15 11	15 23	15 40		15 57	16 11		16 23	16 34	16 40	16 57	17 11	17 24		17 41	17 57	18 12	18 23	18 29	18 40	18 57	19 11
Glasgow Central 15 219	a	14 34	14 52	15 07	15 22	15 34	15 52		16 09	16 22	16 32	16 34	16 45	16 52	17 09	17 22	17 35		17 55	18 09	18 23	18 34	18 41	18 52	19 09	19 22

For general notes see front of timetable
For details of catering facilities see Directory of Train Operators

A From Girvan (Table 218) to Newcastle (Table 48)
B From Stranraer (Table 218)
C From Stranraer (Table 218) to Newcastle (Table 48)
D From Girvan to Kilmarnock (Table 218)
E From Girvan (Table 218)
b Arr. 0659

Ayr, Largs and Ardrossan → Glasgow Central

Network Diagram - see first page of Table 216

		SR	SR	SR	SR	SR	SR	SR	SR	SR	SR	SR	SR	SR	SR	SR	SR	SR	SR	SR	SR	SR
				A									◇ B							◇ B		
Ayr	d	18 43		19 09	19 13		19 43		20 13		20 43		21 06	21 13		21 43		22 13		22 38		23 00
Newton-on-Ayr	d				19 16				20 16					21 16				22 16				23 03
Prestwick Town	d	18 48		19 14	19 19		19 48		20 19		20 48			21 19		21 48		22 19				23 06
Prestwick Int. Airport ✈	d	18 50		19 16	19 21		19 50		20 21		20 50			21 21		21 50		22 21				23 08
Troon	d	18 54		19a21	19 25		19 54		20 25		20 54			21 25		21 54		22 25				23 12
Barassie	d				19 27				20 27					21 27				22 27				23 14
Irvine	d	18 59			19 32		19 59		20 32		20 59			21 32		21 59		22 32				23 19
Largs	d		18 53					19 53				20 53					21 53				22 53	
Fairlie	d		18 58					19 58				20 58					21 58				22 58	
West Kilbride	d		19 03					20 03				21 03					22 03				23 03	
Ardrossan Harbour	d									20 28												
Ardrossan Town	d					19 31				20 31					21 31				22 31			
Ardrossan South Beach	d		19 09			19 34		20 09		20 34		21 09			21 34		22 09		22 34		23 09	
Saltcoats	d		19 11			19 36		20 11		20 36		21 11			21 36		22 11		22 36		23 11	
Stevenston	d		19 14			19 39		20 14		20 39		21 14			21 39		22 14		22 39		23 14	
Kilwinning	d	19 04	19 18		19 37	19 43	20 04	20 18	20 37	20 43	21 04	21 18	21 21	21 37	21 43	22 04	22 18	22 37	22 43	22 54	23 18	23 24
Dalry	d					19 47				20 47				21 41	21 47	22 09	22 23	22 41	22 47			23 28
Glengarnock	d		19 25			19 51		20 25		20 51		21 25			21 51		22 27		22 51		23 25	23 32
Lochwinnoch	d					19 56				20 56					21 56				22 56			
Howwood	d					20 00				21 00					22 00				23 00		23 32	
Milliken Park	d		19 33			20 03		20 33		21 03		21 33			22 03		22 35		23 03		23 35	
Johnstone	d	19 18	19 35		19 50	20 06	20 18	20 35	20 50	21 06	21 18	21 35		21 52	22 06	22 20	22 37	22 52	23 06		23 37	23 41
Paisley Gilmour Street 219 ✈	d	19 23	19 40		19 55	20 11	20 23	20 40	20 55	21 11	21 23	21 40	21 44	21 57	22 11	22 25	22 42	22 57	23 11	23 15	23 42	23 46
Glasgow Central 15 219	a	19 34	19 52		20 07	20 22	20 34	20 52	21 07	21 22	21 34	21 52	21 55	22 09	22 22	22 36	22 54	23 10	23 22	23 26	23 54	23 58

Sundays

until 23 December

		SR	SR	SR	SR	SR	SR	SR	SR	SR	SR	SR	SR	SR	SR	SR	SR	SR	SR	SR	SR	SR	SR
										◇ B													
Ayr	d	09 13	09 43		10 13	10 43		11 13	11 43	12 01	12 13		12 43		13 13	13 43		14 13	14 43			15 13	15 43
Newton-on-Ayr	d																						
Prestwick Town	d	09 18	09 48		10 18	10 48		11 18	11 48		12 18		12 48		13 18	13 48		14 18	14 48			15 18	15 48
Prestwick Int. Airport ✈	d	09 20	09 50		10 20	10 50		11 20	11 50		12 20		12 50		13 20	13 50		14 20	14 50			15 20	15 50
Troon	d	09 24	09 54		10 24	10 54		11 24	11 54		12 24		12 54		13 24	13 54		14 24	14 54			15 24	15 54
Barassie	d		09 56			10 56			11 56				12 56			13 56			14 56				15 56
Irvine	d	09 29	10 01		10 29	11 01		11 29	12 01		12 29		13 01		13 29	14 01		14 29	15 01			15 29	16 01
Largs	d			09 58			10 58							12 58			13 58				14 58		
Fairlie	d			10 03			11 03							13 03			14 03				15 03		
West Kilbride	d			10 08			11 08							13 08			14 08				15 08		
Ardrossan Harbour	d											12 35								15 04			
Ardrossan Town	d																						
Ardrossan South Beach	d			10 14			11 14					12 40		13 14			14 14			15 09	15 14		
Saltcoats	d			10 16			11 16					12 42		13 16			14 16			15 11	15 16		
Stevenston	d			10 19			11 19					12 45		13 19			14 19			15 14	15 19		
Kilwinning	d	09 34	10 06	10 23	10 34	11 06	11 23	11 34	12 06	12 16	12 34	12 49	13 06	13 23	13 34	14 06	14 23	14 34	15 06	15 18	15 23	15 34	16 06
Dalry	d			10 28			11 28							13 28			14 28				15 28		
Glengarnock	d			10 32			11 32							13 32			14 32				15 32		
Lochwinnoch	d			10 37			11 37							13 37			14 37				15 37		
Howwood	d			10 41			11 41							13 41			14 41				15 41		
Milliken Park	d			10 44			11 44					13 02		13 44			14 44			15 31	15 44		
Johnstone	d	09 48	10 19	10 46	10 51	11 19	11 46	11 51	12 19		12 51	13 04	13 19	13 46	13 51	14 19	14 46	14 51	15 19	15 33	15 46	15 51	16 19
Paisley Gilmour Street 219 ✈	d	09 53	10 31	10 52	10 56	11 31	11 52	11 56	12 31	12 37	12 56	13 10	13 31	13 52	13 56	14 31	14 52	14 56	15 31	15 39	15 52	15 56	16 24
Glasgow Central 15 219	a	10 04	10 43	11 04	11 07	11 46	12 04	12 07	12 43	12 51	13 07	13 28	13 43	14 04	14 07	14 43	15 04	15 07	15 43	15 50	16 04	16 07	16 36

		SR	SR	SR	SR	SR	SR	SR	SR	SR	SR	SR	SR	SR	SR	SR	SR	SR	SR	SR	SR	SR
		◇ B															◇ B					
Ayr	d	16 01		16 13	16 43		17 13	17 43			18 43		19 43			20 43	21 02		21 43		23 00	
Newton-on-Ayr	d																					
Prestwick Town	d			16 18	16 48		17 18	17 48			18 48		19 48			20 48			21 48		23 05	
Prestwick Int. Airport ✈	d			16 20	16 50		17 20	17 50			18 50		19 50			20 50			21 50		23 07	
Troon	d			16 24	16 54		17 24	17 54			18 54		19 54			20 54			21 54		23 11	
Barassie	d				16 56			17 56			18 56		19 56			20 56			21 56		23 13	
Irvine	d			16 29	17 01		17 29	18 01			19 01		20 01			21 01			22 01		23 18	
Largs	d		15 58			16 58				17 58		18 58		19 58				20 58		21 58		22 58
Fairlie	d		16 03			17 03				18 03		19 03		20 03				21 03		22 03		23 03
West Kilbride	d		16 08			17 08				18 08		19 08		20 08				21 08		22 08		23 08
Ardrossan Harbour	d								18 00						20 31							
Ardrossan Town	d																					
Ardrossan South Beach	d		16 14			17 14			18 05	18 14		19 14		20 14	20 36			21 14		22 14		23 14
Saltcoats	d		16 16			17 16			18 07	18 16		19 16		20 16	20 38			21 16		22 16		23 16
Stevenston	d		16 19			17 19			18 10	18 19		19 19		20 19	20 41			21 19		22 19		23 19
Kilwinning	d	16 17	16 23	16 34	17 06	17 23	17 34	18 06	18 14	18 23	19 06	19 23	20 06	20 23	20 45	21 06	21 17	21 23	22 06	22 23	23 23	23 27
Dalry	d		16 28			17 28				18 28		19 28		20 28				21 28		22 28		23 31
Glengarnock	d		16 32			17 32				18 32		19 32		20 32				21 32		22 32		23 35
Lochwinnoch	d		16 37			17 37				18 37		19 37		20 37				21 37		22 37		23 40
Howwood	d		16 41			17 41				18 41		19 41		20 41				21 41		22 41		23 44
Milliken Park	d		16 44			17 44			18 27	18 44		19 44		20 44	20 58			21 44		22 44		23 47
Johnstone	d		16 46	16 51	17 19	17 46	17 51	18 19	18 29	18 46	19 19	19 46	20 19	20 46	21 00	21 19		21 46	22 19	22 46	23 36	23 50
Paisley Gilmour Street 219 ✈	d	16 38	16 52	16 56	17 24	17 52	17 56	18 24	18 39	18 52	19 24	19 52	20 24	20 52	21 06	21 24	21 36	21 52	22 24	22 52	23 41	23 55
Glasgow Central 15 219	a	16 49	17 04	17 07	17 36	18 04	18 07	18 36	18 49	19 04	19 36	20 03	20 36	21 03	21 17	21 36	21 48	22 03	22 36	23 03	23 53	00 05

For general notes see front of timetable
For details of catering facilities see Directory of Train Operators

A From Girvan to Kilmarnock (Table 218)
B From Stranraer (Table 218)

Table 221

from 30 December

Ayr, Largs and Ardrossan → Glasgow Central

Network Diagram - see first page of Table 216

		SR	SR	SR	SR	SR	SR	SR	SR	SR	SR	SR	SR	SR	SR	SR	SR	SR
							◇ A											◇ A
Ayr	d	09 43		10 43		11 43	12 01			12 43		13 43		14 43			15 43	16 01
Newton-on-Ayr	d																	
Prestwick Town	d	09 48		10 48		11 48				12 48		13 48		14 48			15 48	
Prestwick Int. Airport ✈	d	09 50		10 50		11 50				12 50		13 50		14 50			15 50	
Troon	d	09 54		10 54		11 54				12 54		13 54		14 54			15 54	
Barassie	d	09 56		10 56		11 56				12 56		13 56		14 56			15 56	
Irvine	d	10 01		11 01		12 01				13 01		14 01		15 01			16 01	
Largs	d		09 58		10 58			11 58			12 58		13 58			14 58		
Fairlie	d		10 03		11 03			12 03			13 03		14 03			15 03		
West Kilbride	d		10 08		11 08			12 08			13 08		14 08			15 08		
Ardrossan Harbour	d								12 35						15 04			
Ardrossan Town	d																	
Ardrossan South Beach	d		10 14		11 14			12 14	12 40		13 14		14 14		15 09	15 14		
Saltcoats	d		10 16		11 16			12 16	12 42		13 16		14 16		15 11	15 16		
Stevenston	d		10 19		11 19			12 19	12 45		13 19		14 19		15 14	15 19		
Kilwinning	d	10 06	10 23	11 06	11 23	12 06	12 16	12 23	12 49	13 06	13 23	14 06	14 23	15 06	15 18	15 23	16 06	16 17
Dalry	d		10 28		11 28			12 28			13 28		14 28			15 28		
Glengarnock	d		10 32		11 32			12 32			13 32		14 32			15 32		
Lochwinnoch	d		10 37		11 37			12 37			13 37		14 37			15 37		
Howwood	d		10 41		11 41			12 41			13 41		14 41			15 41		
Milliken Park	d		10 44		11 44			12 44	13 02		13 44		14 44		15 31	15 44		
Johnstone	d	10 19	10 46	11 19	11 46	12 19		12 46	13 04	13 19	13 46	14 19	14 46	15 19	15 33	15 46	16 19	
Paisley Gilmour Street 219 ✈	d	10 31	10 52	11 31	11 52	12 31	12 37	12 52	13 10	13 31	13 52	14 31	14 52	15 31	15 39	15 52	16 24	16 38
Glasgow Central 15 219	a	10 43	11 10	11 43	12 10	12 43	12 51	13 10	13 28	13 43	14 10	14 43	15 10	15 43	15 57	16 10	16 36	16 49

		SR	SR	SR	SR	SR	SR	SR	SR	SR	SR	SR	SR	SR	SR	SR	SR	SR	SR
														◇ A					
Ayr	d		16 43		17 43			18 43		19 43			20 43	21 02		21 43		23 00	
Newton-on-Ayr	d																		
Prestwick Town	d		16 48		17 48			18 48		19 48			20 48			21 48		23 05	
Prestwick Int. Airport ✈	d		16 50		17 50			18 50		19 50			20 50			21 50		23 07	
Troon	d		16 54		17 54			18 54		19 54			20 54			21 54		23 11	
Barassie	d		16 56		17 56			18 56		19 56			20 56			21 56		23 13	
Irvine	d		17 01		18 01			19 01		20 01			21 01			22 01		23 18	
Largs	d	15 58		16 58			17 58		18 58		19 58				20 58		21 58		22 58
Fairlie	d	16 03		17 03			18 03		19 03		20 03				21 03		22 03		23 03
West Kilbride	d	16 08		17 08			18 08		19 08		20 08				21 08		22 08		23 08
Ardrossan Harbour	d					18 00						20 31							
Ardrossan Town	d																		
Ardrossan South Beach	d	16 14		17 14		18 05	18 14		19 14		20 14	20 36			21 14		22 14		23 14
Saltcoats	d	16 16		17 16		18 07	18 16		19 16		20 16	20 38			21 16		22 16		23 16
Stevenston	d	16 19		17 19		18 10	18 19		19 19		20 19	20 41			21 19		22 19		23 19
Kilwinning	d	16 23	17 06	17 23	18 06	18 14	18 23	19 06	19 23	20 06	20 23	20 45	21 06	21 17	21 23	22 06	22 23	23 23	23 27
Dalry	d	16 28		17 28			18 28		19 28		20 28				21 28		22 28		23 31
Glengarnock	d	16 32		17 32			18 32		19 32		20 32				21 32		22 32		23 35
Lochwinnoch	d	16 37		17 37			18 37		19 37		20 37				21 37		22 37		23 40
Howwood	d	16 41		17 41			18 41		19 41		20 41				21 41		22 41		23 44
Milliken Park	d	16 44		17 44		18 27	18 44		19 44		20 44	20 58			21 44		22 44		23 47
Johnstone	d	16 46	17 19	17 46	18 19	18 29	18 46	19 19	19 46	20 19	20 46	21 00	21 19		21 46	22 19	22 46	23 36	23 50
Paisley Gilmour Street 219 ✈	d	16 52	17 24	17 52	18 24	18 39	18 52	19 24	19 52	20 24	20 52	21 06	21 24	21 36	21 52	22 24	22 52	23 41	23 55
Glasgow Central 15 219	a	17 03	17 36	18 03	18 36	18 49	19 03	19 36	20 03	20 36	21 03	21 17	21 36	21 48	22 03	22 36	23 03	23 53	00 05

For general notes see front of timetable
For details of catering facilities see
Directory of Train Operators

A From Stranraer (Table 218)

Glasgow and Ardrossan — Brodick (Arran)

Caledonian MacBrayne Ltd in association with First ScotRail Limited

Mondays to Saturdays

		A		A	A	FO B
Glasgow Central [15]	221 d	08 33	11 15	14 15	16 50	19 15
Paisley Gilmour Street	221 d	08 44	11 26	14 26	17 01	19 26
Ardrossan Harbour	221 a	09 25	12 09	15 09	17 44	20 09
Ardrossan Harbour	d	**09 45**	**12 30**	**15 15**	**18 00**	**20 30**
Brodick	a	**10 40**	**13 25**	**16 10**	**18 55**	**21 25**

Sundays

Glasgow Central [15]	221 d	08 40	11 15	14 05	16 55
Paisley Gilmour Street	221 d	08 51	11 26	14 16	17 07
Ardrossan Harbour	221 a	09 37	12 09	14 59	17 43
Ardrossan Harbour	d	**09 45**	**12 30**	**15 15**	**18 00**
Brodick	a	**10 40**	**13 25**	**16 10**	**18 55**

Mondays to Saturdays

		A	A		A	A
Brodick	d	**08 20**	**11 05**	**13 50**	**16 40**	**19 20**
Ardrossan Harbour	a	**09 15**	**12 00**	**14 45**	**17 35**	**20 15**
Ardrossan Harbour	221 d	09 30	12 28	15 28	18 00	20 28
Paisley Gilmour Street	221 a	10 10	13 10	16 10	18 39	21 10
Glasgow Central [15]	221 a	10 22	13 22	16 22	18 52	21 22

Sundays

Brodick	d	**11 05**	**13 50**	**16 40**	**19 20**
Ardrossan Harbour	a	**12 00**	**14 45**	**17 35**	**20 15**
Ardrossan Harbour	221 d	12 35	15 04	18 00	20 31
Paisley Gilmour Street	221 a	13 09	15 38	18 38	21 05
Glasgow Central [15]	221 a	13 28	15 57	18 49	21 17

For general notes see front of timetable
For details of catering facilities see Directory of Train Operators

A Except 26 December
B From 21 March

Glasgow Central → East Kilbride, Barrhead and Kilmarnock

Network Diagram - see first page of Table 216

Miles	Miles			SR SO	SR SO	SR	SR	SR	SR	SR SX	SR SX	SR SO		SR SX	SR	SR SO	SR SX	SR A	SR SX	SR	SR B	SR		SR	SR	SR	SR A
0	0	**Glasgow Central** 15	d	00 03	00 12	06 12	06 42	06 53	07 07	07 33	07 37	07 42		07 52	08 07	08 12	08 17	08 28	08 33	08 42	09 03	09 07		09 12	09 37	09 42	09 53
$2\frac{1}{4}$	$2\frac{1}{4}$	Crossmyloof	d	00 09	00 18	06 18		06 59	07 13	07 39	07 43	07 48		07 58	08 13	08 18	08 23		08 39	08 48		09 13		09 18	09 43	09 48	
$3\frac{1}{4}$	$3\frac{1}{4}$	Pollokshaws West	d	00 12	00 21	06 21		07 02	07 16	07 42	07 46	07 51		08 01	08 16	08 21	08 26		08 42	08 51		09 16		09 21	09 46	09 51	
—	$4\frac{1}{4}$	Thornliebank	d		00 24	06 24		07 05		07 45		07 54		08 04		08 24	08 29			08 54				09 24		09 54	
—	$5\frac{1}{4}$	Giffnock	d		00 27	06 27		07 08		07 48		07 57		08 07		08 27	08 32			08 57				09 27		09 57	
—	$6\frac{1}{2}$	Clarkston	d		00 30	06 30		07 11		07 51		08 00		08 10		08 30	08 35			09 00				09 30		10 00	
—	$7\frac{1}{4}$	Busby	d		00 33	06 33		07 15		07 56		08 03		08 15		08 33	08 40			09 03				09 33		10 03	
—	$8\frac{1}{2}$	Thorntonhall	d			06 36						08 06					08 42			09 06						10 06	
—	10	Hairmyres	d		00 39	06 40		07 21		08 02		08 10		08 21		08 39	08 46			09 10				09 39		10 10	
—	$11\frac{1}{2}$	**East Kilbride**	a		00 42	06 43		07 24		08 09		08 13		08 24		08 42	08 50			09 15				09 43		10 13	
$4\frac{1}{2}$	—	Kennishead	d	00 15			06 50		07 19		07 49				08 19				08 45			09 19			09 49		
5	—	Priesthill & Darnley	d	00 17			06 52		07 21		07 51				08 21				08 47			09 21			09 51		
$5\frac{3}{4}$	—	Nitshill	d	00 20			06 55		07 24		07 54				08 24				08 50			09 24			09 54		
$7\frac{1}{2}$	—	**Barrhead**	d	00 23			06 59		07a27		07a59				08a27			08 40	08a55		09 15	09a29			09a57		10 05
$16\frac{1}{4}$	—	Dunlop	d	00 35			07 11											08 51			09 34						10 26
$18\frac{3}{4}$	—	Stewarton	d	00 39			07 15											08 55			09 38						10 30
22	—	Kilmaurs	d	00 44			07 20											09 00			09 43						10 35
$24\frac{1}{4}$	—	**Kilmarnock** 3	a	00 49			07 25											09 06			09 48						10 38

		SR	SR	SR	SR	SR	SR	SR		SR	SR	SR A	SR	SR	SR	SR	SR A	SR		SR	SR	SR	SR	SR	SR	SR	SR
Glasgow Central 15	d	10 07	10 12	10 37	10 42	11 03	11 07	11 12		11 37	11 42	12 03	12 07	12 12	12 37	12 42	13 03	13 07		13 12	13 37	13 42	14 03	14 07	14 12	14 37	14 42
Crossmyloof	d	10 13	10 18	10 43	10 48		11 13	11 18		11 43	11 48		12 13	12 18	12 43	12 48		13 13		13 18	13 43	13 48		14 13	14 18	14 43	14 48
Pollokshaws West	d	10 16	10 21	10 46	10 51		11 16	11 21		11 46	11 51		12 16	12 21	12 46	12 51		13 16		13 21	13 46	13 51		14 16	14 21	14 46	14 51
Thornliebank	d		10 24		10 54			11 24			11 54			12 24		12 54				13 24		13 54			14 24		14 54
Giffnock	d		10 27		10 57			11 27			11 57			12 27		12 57				13 27		13 57			14 27		14 57
Clarkston	d		10 30		11 00			11 30			12 00			12 30		13 00				13 30		14 00			14 30		15 00
Busby	d		10 33		11 03			11 33			12 03			12 33		13 03				13 33		14 03			14 33		15 03
Thorntonhall	d				11 06						12 06					13 06						14 06					15 06
Hairmyres	d		10 39		11 10			11 39			12 10			12 39		13 10				13 39		14 10			14 39		15 10
East Kilbride	a		10 42		11 13			11 42			12 13			12 42		13 13				13 42		14 13			14 42		15 13
Kennishead	d	10 19		10 49			11 19			11 49			12 19		12 49			13 19			13 49			14 19		14 49	
Priesthill & Darnley	d	10 21		10 51			11 21			11 51			12 21		12 51			13 21			13 51			14 21		14 51	
Nitshill	d	10 24		10 54			11 24			11 54			12 24		12 54			13 24			13 54			14 24		14 54	
Barrhead	d	10a29		10a57		11 15	11a27			11a57		12 15	12a27		12a57		13 15	13a27			13a57		14 15	14a27		14a57	
Dunlop	d					11 27						12 27					13 27						14 27				
Stewarton	d					11 31						12 31					13 31						14 31				
Kilmaurs	d					11 36						12 36					13 36						14 36				
Kilmarnock 3	a					11 41						12 41					13 42						14 41				

		SR	SR	SR		SR	SR SX	SR SO	SR C	SR	SR	SR	SR	SR		SR SX	SR SO	SR SX	SR SO	SR SX	SR SX	SR A	SR	SR		SR SX	SR
Glasgow Central 15	d	15 03	15 07	15 12		15 37	15 41	15 42	15 48	16 07	16 12	16 33	16 42	16 48		16 52	17 07	17 10	17 12	17 14	17 23	17 30	17 37	17 42		17 57	18 03
Crossmyloof	d		15 13	15 18		15 43	15 48	15 48		16 13	16 18	16 39	16 48			16 58	17 13	17 16	17 18		17 29		17 43	17 48		18 03	
Pollokshaws West	d		15 16	15 21		15 46	15 51	15 51		16 16	16 21	16 42	16 51			17 01	17 16	17 19	17 21		17 32		17 45	17 51		18 06	
Thornliebank	d			15 24			15 54	15 54			16 24		16 54			17 04			17 24		17 35			17 54		18 09	
Giffnock	d			15 27			15 57	15 57			16 27		16 57			17 07			17 27		17 38			17 57		18 12	
Clarkston	d			15 30			16 01	16 00			16 30		17 00			17 10			17 30	17 29	17 41			18 00		18 15	
Busby	d			15 33			16 04	16 03			16 33		17 03			17a14			17 33		17 44			18 03		18 18	
Thorntonhall	d						16 07	16 06			16 36		17 06						17 36		17 47			18 06			
Hairmyres	d			15 39			16 11	16 10			16 40		17 10						17 40	17 36	17 51			18 10		18 24	
East Kilbride	a			15 42			16 14	16 13			16 43		17 13						17 43	17 40	17 54			18 13		18 27	
Kennishead	d		15 19			15 49				16 19		16 45					17 19	17 22					17 48				
Priesthill & Darnley	d		15 21			15 51				16 21		16 47					17 21	17 24					17 50				
Nitshill	d		15 24			15 54				16 24		16 50					17 24	17 27					17 53				
Barrhead	d	15 16	15a27			15a57			16 00	16a27		16a53		17 00			17a27	17a30				17 42	17a59				18 15
Dunlop	d	15 28							16 12					17 12								17 54					18 27
Stewarton	d	15 32							16 16					17 16								17 58					18 31
Kilmaurs	d	15 37							16 20					17 20								18 02					18 36
Kilmarnock 3	a	15 46							16 25					17 25								18 06					18 43

		SR	SR SO	SR SX	SR	SR	SR	SR	SR	SR		SR A	SR	SR	SR	SR	SR	SR	SR	SR A	SR	SR	SR	SR	SR		
Glasgow Central 15	d	18 07	18 12	18 23	18 37	18 42	19 03	19 12	19 22	19 42		20 03	20 12	20 22	20 42	21 03	21 12	21 22	21 42	22 03	22 12	22 22	22 42	23 03	23 12		
Crossmyloof	d	18 13	18 18	18 29	18 43	18 48		19 18	19 28	19 48			20 18	20 28	20 48		21 18	21 28	21 48		22 18	22 28	22 48	23 09	23 18		
Pollokshaws West	d	18 16	18 21	18 32	18 46	18 51		19 21	19 31	19 51			20 21	20 31	20 51		21 21	21 31	21 51		22 21	22 31	22 51	23 12	23 21		
Thornliebank	d		18 24	18 35		18 54		19 24		19 54			20 24		20 54		21 24		21 54		22 24		22 54		23 24		
Giffnock	d		18 27	18 38		18 57		19 27		19 57			20 27		20 57		21 27		21 57		22 27		22 57		23 27		
Clarkston	d		18 30	18 41		19 00		19 30		20 00			20 30		21 00		21 30		22 00		22 30		23 00		23 30		
Busby	d		18 33	18 44		19 03		19 33		20 03			20 33		21 03		21 33		22 03		22 33		23 03		23 33		
Thorntonhall	d					19 06				20 06					21 06				22 06				23 06		23 36		
Hairmyres	d		18 39	18 50		19 10		19 39		20 10			20 39		21 10		21 39		22 10		22 39		23 10		23 40		
East Kilbride	a		18 42	18 53		19 13		19 42		20 13			20 42		21 13		21 42		22 13		22 42		23 13		23 43		
Kennishead	d	18 19			18 49				19 34					20 34				21 34				22 34		23 15			
Priesthill & Darnley	d	18 21			18 51				19 36					20 36				21 36				22 36		23 17			
Nitshill	d	18 24			18 54				19 39					20 39				21 39				22 39		23 20			
Barrhead	d	18a28			18a57		19 15		19a42			20 15		20a42		21 15		21a42		22 15		22a42		23 23			
Dunlop	d						19 27					20 27				21 27				22 27				23 35			
Stewarton	d						19 31					20 31				21 31				22 31				23 39			
Kilmaurs	d						19 36					20 36				21 36				22 36				23 44			
Kilmarnock 3	a						19 41					20 39				21 41				22 39				23 49			

For general notes see front of timetable
For details of catering facilities see Directory of Train Operators

A To Carlisle (Table 216)
B To Girvan (Table 218)
C To Newcastle (Table 48)

Table 222

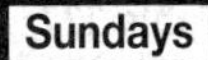

Glasgow Central → East Kilbride, Barrhead and Kilmarnock

Network Diagram - see first page of Table 216

		SR	SR	SR		SR	SR	SR	SR	SR	SR	SR	SR	SR	SR	SR	SR	SR
			A													B		
Glasgow Central 15	d	08 42	08 48	09 12		18 12	18 42	18 48	19 12	19 42	20 12	20 42	21 12	21 42	22 12	22 28	22 42	23 12
Crossmyloof	d	08 48		09 18		18 18	18 48		19 18	19 48	20 18	20 48	21 18	21 48	22 18		22 48	23 18
Pollokshaws West	d	08 51	08 56	09 21	and at	18 21	18 51	18 56	19 21	19 51	20 21	20 51	21 21	21 51	22 21		22 51	23 21
Thornliebank	d	08 54		09 24	the same	18 24	18 54		19 24	19 54	20 24	20 54	21 24	21 54	22 24		22 54	23 24
Giffnock	d	08 57		09 27		18 27	18 57		19 27	19 57	20 27	20 57	21 27	21 57	22 27		22 57	23 27
Clarkston	d	09 00		09 30	minutes	18 30	19 00		19 30	20 00	20 30	21 00	21 30	22 00	22 30		23 00	23 30
Busby	d	09 03		09 33		18 33	19 03		19 33	20 03	20 33	21 03	21 33	22 03	22 33		23 03	23 33
Thorntonhall	d	09 06			past		19 06			20 06		21 06		22 06			23 06	23 36
Hairmyres	d	09 10		09 39		18 39	19 10		19 39	20 10	20 39	21 10	21 39	22 10	22 39		23 10	23 40
East Kilbride	a	09 13		09 42	each	18 42	19 13		19 42	20 13	20 42	21 13	21 42	22 13	22 42		23 13	23 43
Kennishead	d				hour until													
Priesthill & Darnley	d																	
Nitshill	d																	
Barrhead	d		09 02					19 02								22 40		
Dunlop	d		09 15					19 15								22 52		
Stewarton	d		09 19					19 19								22 56		
Kilmaurs	d		09 24					19 24								23 01		
Kilmarnock 3	a		09 29					19 29								23 04		

For general notes see front of timetable
For details of catering facilities see
Directory of Train Operators

A 1448 from Glasgow Central arrives Kilmarnock 1527 and is to Carlisle (Table 216)
B To Carlisle (Table 216)

Table 222

Mondays to Saturdays

Kilmarnock, Barrhead and East Kilbride → Glasgow Central

Network Diagram - see first page of Table 216

Miles	Miles			SR SX	SR	SR	SR	SR SX	SR SX	SR SX	SR SO		SR SO	SR SX	SR SX	SR	SR SX	SR SO	SR SX	SR		SR SX	SR SO	SR SX	SR SX	SR	SR
																A											◇ B
0	—	**Kilmarnock 3**	d		06 32				07 32				07 32			07 58											09 12
2¼	—	Kilmaurs	d		06 36				07 36				07 36			08 02											09 16
5½	—	Stewarton	d		06 41				07 41				07 41			08 08											09 21
7¾	—	Dunlop	d		06 46				07 46				07 46			08 13											09 26
16¾	—	**Barrhead**	d		06 56		07 35		07 56				07 56	08 05		08 24				08 35					09 10		09 37
18½	—	Nitshill	d		06 59		07 38						07 59	08 08						08 38					09 13		
19½	—	Priesthill & Darnley	d		07 01		07 40						08 01	08 10						08 40					09 15		
20	—	Kennishead	d		07 03		07 42						08 03	08 12						08 42					09 17		
—	0	**East Kilbride**	d	06 18		07 05		07 29		07 47	07 46				08 03			08 18	08 17			08 30	08 48	08 55		09 20	
—	1½	Hairmyres	d	06 21		07 08		07 32		07 51	07 49				08 07			08 21	08 24			08 33	08 51	08 58		09 23	
—	3	Thorntonhall	d	06 25		07 12		07 36			07 53				08 10			08 25	08 27			08 37	08 55	09 02			
—	4¼	Busby	d	06 28		07 15		07 39			07 56				08 14		08 23	08 28	08 30			08 40	08 58	09 05		09 28	
—	5	Clarkston	d	06 30		07 18		07 42		07 59	07 58				08 17		08 26	08 30	08 33			08 42	09 00	09 07		09 31	
—	6¼	Giffnock	d	06 33		07 21		07 46			08 01				08 20		08 29	08 32	08 36			08 45	09 03	09 10		09 33	
—	7¼	Thornliebank	d	06 36		07 23		07 49			08 04				08 23		08 31	08 35	08 38			08 48	09 06	09 13		09 36	
21¼	8¼	Pollokshaws West	d	06 39	07 07	07 26	07 45	07 52			08 06		08 11	08 15	08 26		08 34	08 38	08 42	08 45			09 09	09 16	09 20	09 39	
22¼	9¼	Crossmyloof	d	06 42	07 10	07 29	07 48	07 54			08 09		08 13	08 18	08 29		08 37	08 42	08 45	08 48			09 12	09 19	09 23	09 42	
24¼	11½	**Glasgow Central 15**	a	06 48	07 18	07 35	07 55	08 01	08 09	08 13	08 15		08 21	08 25	08 35	08 37	08 43	08 48	08 51	08 55		08 57	09 18	09 25	09 30	09 48	09 50

		SR	SR	SR	SR		SR	SR	SR	SR	SR	SR	SR	SR		SR	SR	SR	SR	SR	SR	SR	SR		SR	SR	SR
					C																	A					
Kilmarnock 3	d				10 04						10 50						11 50					12 50					
Kilmaurs	d				10 08						10 54						11 54					12 54					
Stewarton	d				10 13						10 59						11 59					12 59					
Dunlop	d				10 18						11 04						12 04					13 04					
Barrhead	d	09 40		10 05	10 28			10 35		11 05	11 14		11 35			12 05	12 14		12 35		13 05	13 14			13 35		14 05
Nitshill	d	09 43		10 08				10 38		11 08			11 38			12 08			12 38		13 08				13 38		14 08
Priesthill & Darnley	d	09 45		10 10				10 40		11 10			11 40			12 10			12 40		13 10				13 40		14 10
Kennishead	d	09 47		10 12				10 42		11 12			11 42			12 12			12 42		13 12				13 42		14 12
East Kilbride	d		09 48				10 20		10 48			11 20		11 48				12 20		12 48			13 20			13 48	
Hairmyres	d		09 51				10 23		10 51			11 23		11 51				12 23		12 51			13 23			13 51	
Thorntonhall	d		09 55						10 55					11 55						12 55						13 55	
Busby	d		09 58				10 28		10 58			11 28		11 58				12 28		12 58			13 28			13 58	
Clarkston	d		10 00				10 31		11 00			11 31		12 00				12 31		13 00			13 31			14 00	
Giffnock	d		10 03				10 33		11 03			11 33		12 03				12 33		13 03			13 33			14 03	
Thornliebank	d		10 06				10 36		11 06			11 36		12 06				12 36		13 06			13 36			14 06	
Pollokshaws West	d	09 50	10 09	10 15			10 39	10 45	11 09	11 15		11 39	11 45	12 09		12 15		12 39	12 45	13 09	13 15		13 39		13 45	14 09	14 15
Crossmyloof	d	09 53	10 12	10 18			10 42	10 48	11 12	11 18		11 42	11 48	12 12		12 18		12 42	12 48	13 12	13 18		13 42		13 48	14 12	14 18
Glasgow Central 15	a	10 01	10 18	10 25	10 41		10 48	10 55	11 18	11 25	11 27	11 48	11 55	12 18		12 25	12 27	12 48	12 55	13 18	13 25	13 29	13 48		13 55	14 18	14 25

		SR	SR	SR	SR	SR	SR	SR		SR	SR	SR	SR	SR	SR	SR	SR		SR	SR	SR	SR	SR SX	SR SO	SR	SR	SR
		◇ B					A						D						A								
Kilmarnock 3	d	13 50					14 55						15 48						16 47			17 28					
Kilmaurs	d	13 54					14 59						15 52						16 51			17 32					
Stewarton	d	13 59					15 04						15 57						16 57			17 37					
Dunlop	d	14 04					15 09						16 02						17 01			17 42					
Barrhead	d	14 14		14 35		15 05	15 19			15 35		16 05	16 17		16 35		17 05		17 18		17 35	17 59			18 05		18 35
Nitshill	d			14 38		15 08				15 38		16 08			16 38		17 08				17 38				18 08		18 38
Priesthill & Darnley	d			14 40		15 10				15 40		16 10			16 40		17 10				17 40				18 10		18 40
Kennishead	d			14 42		15 12				15 42		16 12			16 42		17 12				17 42				18 12		18 42
East Kilbride	d		14 20		14 48			15 20			15 48			16 20		16 48				17 20			17 47	17 48		18 20	
Hairmyres	d		14 23		14 51			15 23			15 51			16 23		16 51				17 23			17 51	17 51		18 23	
Thorntonhall	d				14 55						15 55					16 55							17 55	17 55			
Busby	d		14 28		14 58			15 28			15 58			16 28		16 58				17 28			17 58	17 58		18 28	
Clarkston	d		14 31		15 00			15 31			16 00			16 31		17 00				17 31			18 00	18 00		18 31	
Giffnock	d		14 33		15 03			15 33			16 03			16 33		17 03				17 33			18 03	18 03		18 33	
Thornliebank	d		14 36		15 06			15 36			16 06			16 36		17 06				17 36			18 06	18 06		18 36	
Pollokshaws West	d		14 39	14 45	15 09	15 15		15 39		15 45	16 09	16 15		16 39	16 45	17 09	17 15			17 39	17 45		18 09	18 09	18 15	18 39	18 45
Crossmyloof	d		14 42	14 48	15 12	15 18		15 42		15 48	16 12	16 18		16 42	16 48	17 12	17 18			17 42	17 48		18 12	18 12	18 18	18 42	18 48
Glasgow Central 15	a	14 27	14 48	14 55	15 18	15 25	15 33	15 48		15 55	16 18	16 25	16 32	16 48	16 55	17 18	17 27		17 31	17 51	17 55	18 12	18 20	18 20	18 25	18 51	18 55

		SR SX		SR SO	SR	SR	SR	SR	SR	SR	SR		SR	SR	SR	SR	SR	SR	SR	SR	SR	SR	SR	SR	SR		
										A									E				G				
Kilmarnock 3	d					18 50				19 50					20 50				21 50				22 50				
Kilmaurs	d					18 54				19 54					20 54				21 54				22 54				
Stewarton	d					18 59				19 59					20 59				21 59				22 59				
Dunlop	d					19 04				20 04					21 04				22 04				23 04				
Barrhead	d				19 05	19 14		19 50		20 14			20 50		21 14		21 50		22 14		22 50		23 14				
Nitshill	d				19 08			19 53					20 53				21 53				22 53						
Priesthill & Darnley	d				19 10			19 55					20 55				21 55				22 55						
Kennishead	d				19 12			19 57					20 57				21 57				22 57						
East Kilbride	d	18 46		18 48			19 20		19 48		20 20			20 48		21 20		21 48		22 20		22 48		23 20	23 48		
Hairmyres	d	18 51		18 51			19 23		19 51		20 23			20 51		21 23		21 51		22 23		22 51		23 23	23 51		
Thorntonhall	d	18 55		18 55					19 55					20 55				21 55				22 55			23 55		
Busby	d	18 58		18 58			19 28		19 58		20 28			20 58		21 28		21 58		22 28		22 58		23 28	23 58		
Clarkston	d	19 00		19 00			19 31		20 00		20 31			21 00		21 31		22 00		22 31		23 00		23 31	00 01		
Giffnock	d	19 03		19 03			19 33		20 03		20 33			21 03		21 33		22 03		22 33		23 03		23 33	00 03		
Thornliebank	d	19 06		19 06			19 36		20 06		20 36			21 06		21 36		22 06		22 36		23 06		23 36	00 06		
Pollokshaws West	d	19 09		19 09	19 15		19 39	20 00	20 09		20 39		21 00	21 09		21 39	22 00	22 09		22 39	23 00	23 09		23 39	00 09		
Crossmyloof	d	19 12		19 12	19 18		19 42	20 03	20 12		20 42		21 03	21 12		21 42	22 03	22 12		22 42	23 03	23 12		23 42	00 12		
Glasgow Central 15	a	19 19		19 19	19 25	19 27	19 48	20 10	20 18	20 27	20 48		21 10	21 18	21 27	21 48	22 10	22 18	22 27	22 48	23 12	23 18	23b28	23 48	00 18		

For general notes see front of timetable
For details of catering facilities see Directory of Train Operators

A From Carlisle (Table 216)
B From Stranraer (Table 218)
C From Newcastle (Table 48)
D From Girvan (Table 218)
E Saturdays from Carlisle (Table 216)
G Mondays to Fridays from Carlisle (Table 216)
b Saturdays arr. 1 minute earlier

Table 222

Kilmarnock, Barrhead and East Kilbride → Glasgow Central

Network Diagram - see first page of Table 216

		SR	SR	SR A		SR	SR	SR	SR	SR	SR B	SR	SR	SR	SR	SR
Kilmarnock 3	d			09 35	and at the same minutes past each hour until	19 35					21 18					
Kilmaurs	d			09 39		19 39					21 22					
Stewarton	d			09 44		19 44					21 27					
Dunlop	d			09 49		19 49					21 32					
Barrhead	d			09 59		19 59					21 42					
Nitshill	d															
Priesthill & Darnley	d															
Kennishead	d															
East Kilbride	d	08 48	09 20				19 48	20 20	20 48	21 20		21 48	22 20	22 48	23 20	23 48
Hairmyres	d	08 51	09 23				19 51	20 23	20 51	21 23		21 51	22 23	22 51	23 23	23 51
Thorntonhall	d	08 55					19 55		20 55			21 55		22 55		23 55
Busby	d	08 58	09 28				19 58	20 28	20 58	21 28		21 58	22 28	22 58	23 28	23 58
Clarkston	d	09 00	09 31				20 00	20 31	21 00	21 31		22 00	22 31	23 00	23 31	00 01
Giffnock	d	09 03	09 34				20 03	20 33	21 03	21 33		22 03	22 33	23 03	23 33	00 03
Thornliebank	d	09 06	09 36				20 06	20 36	21 06	21 36		22 06	22 36	23 06	23 36	00 06
Pollokshaws West	d	09 09	09 39	10 05		20 05	20 09	20 39	21 09	21 39		22 09	22 39	23 09	23 39	00 09
Crossmyloof	d	09 12	09 42				20 12	20 42	21 12	21 42		22 12	22 42	23 12	23 42	00 12
Glasgow Central 15	a	09 18	09 48	10 14		20 14	20 18	20 48	21 18	21 48	21 55	22 18	22 48	23 18	23 48	00 18

For general notes see front of timetable
For details of catering facilities see Directory of Train Operators

A 1435 from Kilmarnock is from Carlisle (Table 216)
B From Carlisle (Table 216)

Glasgow Central, Cathcart Circle, Neilston and Newton

Network Diagram - see first page of Table 220

Miles	Miles	Miles		SR SO A	SR SO	SR	SR	SR A	SR	SR SX B	SR		SR SX	SR SX	SR SX A	SR SO	SR SX	SR SO	SR SX	SR		SR SX	SR SX B	SR	SR SX A
0	0	0	**Glasgow Central** 15 226 d	00 05	00 10	06 10	06 20	06 27	06 35	06 40	06 50		06 58	07 03	07 05	07 10	07 20	07 20	07 25	07 35		07 39	07 44	07 50	07 55
2¼	—	—	Pollokshields West d	00 10				06 32	06 40						07 10					07 40					08 00
2¾	—	—	Maxwell Park d	00 12				06 34	06 42						07 12					07 42					08 02
3¼	—	—	Shawlands d	00 14				06 36	06 44						07 14					07 44					08 04
3¾	—	—	Pollokshaws East d	00 15				06 37	06 45						07 15					07 45					08 05
4¼	—	—	Langside d	00 17				06 39	06 47						07 17					07 47					08 07
—	1¾	1¾	Pollokshields East d		00 14	06 14	06 24			06 44	06 54		07 02	07 07		07 14	07 24	07 24	07 29				07 48	07 54	
—	2¼	2¼	Queens Park d		00 16	06 16	06 26			06 46	06 56		07 04	07 09		07 16	07 26	07 26	07 31				07 50	07 56	
—	2½	2½	Crosshill d		00 17	06 17	06 27			06 47	06 57		07 05	07 10		07 17	07 27	07 27	07 32				07 51	07 57	
—	3¼	3¼	Mount Florida d		00 19	06 19	06 29			06 49	06 59		07 07	07 12		07 19	07 29	07 29	07 34				07 53	07 59	
5¼	—	4	Cathcart d	00a21			06 31	06a41		06a51	07 01			07 14	07a19			07 31	07 36				07a55	08 01	08a09
—	—	4¾	Muirend d				06 33				07 03			07 16				07 33	07 38			07 48		08 03	
—	—	6	Williamwood d				06 36				07 06			07 19				07 36	07 41			07 51		08 06	
—	—	6¾	Whitecraigs d				06 38				07 08			07 21				07 38	07 43			07 53		08 08	
—	—	7¾	Patterton d				06 41				07 11			07 24				07 41	07 46			07 55		08 11	
—	—	11¾	**Neilston** a				06 47				07 17			07 30				07 47	07 52			08 01		08 17	
5¾	4½	—	Kings Park d		00 21	06 21			06 51				07 09			07 21	07 31			07 50					
6	4¾	—	Croftfoot d		00 23	06 23			06 53				07 11			07 23	07 33			07 52					
7	5¾	—	Burnside d		00 26	06 26			06 55				07 14			07 26	07 36			07 56					
8½	7¼	—	Kirkhill a		00 29	06 29			06 58				07 17			07 29	07 39			07 59					
10	8¾	—	**Newton** 226 a		00 32	06 32			07 01				07 20			07 32	07 43			08 02					

	SR SX	SR SX	SR SX B	SR SO	SR SX A	SR SO		SR SX	SR SX B	SR SX	SR SX A	SR	SR	SR SX B	SR SX A			SR	SR	SR	SR B	SR			
Glasgow Central 15 226 d	07 59	08 05	08 10	08 10	08 19	08 20		08 21	08 23	08 26	08 30	08 35	08 50	08 57	09 05			09 10	09 20	09 35	09 40	09 50			
Pollokshields West d					08 24						08 36	08 40			09 10					09 40					
Maxwell Park d					08 26						08 38	08 42			09 12					09 42					
Shawlands d					08 28						08 40	08 44			09 14					09 44					
Pollokshaws East d					08 29						08 41	08 45			09 15					09 45					
Langside d					08 31						08 43	08 47			09 17					09 47					
Pollokshields East d	08 03	08 09	08 14	08 14		08 24		08 25	08 27	08 30			08 54	09 01				09 14	09 24		09 44	09 54			
Queens Park d	08 05	08 11	08 16	08 16		08 26		08 27	08 29	08 32			08 56	09 03				09 16	09 26		09 46	09 56			
Crosshill d	08 06	08 12	08 17	08 17		08 27		08 28	08 30	08 33			08 57	09 04				09 17	09 27		09 47	09 57			
Mount Florida d	08 08	08 14	08 19	08 19		08 29		08 30	08 32	08 35			08 59	09 06				09 19	09 29		09 49	09 59			
Cathcart d		08 16	08a21		08a33	08 31		08 32	08a34		08a46		09 01	09a08	09a20				09 31		09a51	10 01			
Muirend d		08 18				08 33		08 34					09 03						09 33			10 03			
Williamwood d		08 21				08 36		08 37					09 06						09 36			10 06			
Whitecraigs d		08 23				08 38		08 39					09 08						09 38			10 08			
Patterton d		08 26				08 41		08 43					09 11						09 41			10 11			
Neilston a		08 32				08 47		08 48					09 17						09 47			10 17			
Kings Park d	08 10			08 21						08 37		08 51						09 21		09 51					
Croftfoot d	08 12			08 23						08 39		08 53						09 23		09 53					
Burnside d	08 15			08 26						08 42		08 55						09 26		09 55					
Kirkhill a	08 18			08 29						08 45		08 58						09 29		09 58					
Newton 226 a	08 21			08 32						08 48		09 03						09 32		10 01					

	SR A		SR A	SR		SR SO	SR SX	SR SX B	SR	SR SO B	SR SO	SR SX	SR SX B		SR A	SR	SR	SR	SR B	SR	SR SX	SR A		SR SX
Glasgow Central 15 226 d	10 05		15 05	15 10		15 20	15 20	15 33	15 35	15 40	15 50	15 56	16 00		16 05	16 10	16 20	16 35	16 40	16 50	17 03	17 05		17 08
Pollokshields West d	10 10		15 10						15 40						16 10			16 40				17 10		
Maxwell Park d	10 12		15 12						15 42						16 12			16 42				17 12		
Shawlands d	10 14	and at	15 14						15 44						16 14			16 44				17 14		
Pollokshaws East d	10 15		15 15						15 45						16 15			16 45				17 15		
Langside d	10 17	the same	15 17						15 47						16 17			16 47				17 17		
Pollokshields East d		minutes		15 14		15 24	15 24	15 37		15 44	15 54	16 00	16 04			16 14	16 24		16 44	16 54	17 07			
Queens Park d				15 16		15 26	15 26	15 39		15 46	15 56	16 02	16 06			16 16	16 26		16 46	16 56	17 09			
Crosshill d		past		15 17		15 27	15 27	15b47		15 47	15 57	16 03	16 07			16 17	16 27		16 47	16 57	17 10			
Mount Florida d				15 19		15 29	15 29	15 49		15 49	15 59	16 05	16 09			16 19	16 29		16 49	16 59	17 12			
Cathcart d	10a19	each	15a19			15 31	15 31	15a51		15a51	16 01	16 07	16a11		16a19		16 31		16a51	17 01		17a20		
Muirend d		hour until				15 33	15 33				16 03	16 09					16 33			17 03				17 17
Williamwood d						15 36	15 36				16 06	16 12					16 36			17 06				17 20
Whitecraigs d						15 38	15 38				16 08	16 14					16 38			17 08				17 22
Patterton d						15 41	15c45				16 11	16 17					16 41			17 11				17 24
Neilston a						15 47	15 50				16 17	16 23					16 47			17 17				17 30
Kings Park d				15 21					15 51							16 21		16 51			17 14			
Croftfoot d				15 23					15 53							16 23		16 53			17 16			
Burnside d				15 26					15 55							16 26		16 55			17 19			
Kirkhill a				15 29					15 58							16 29		16 58			17 22			
Newton 226 a				15 32					16 01							16 32		17 01			17 25			

For general notes see front of timetable
For details of catering facilities see Directory of Train Operators

A Cathcart Circle Service. To Glasgow Central via Queens Park

B Cathcart Circle Service. To Glasgow Central via Maxwell Park

b Arr. 1540

c Arr. 1541

Glasgow Central, Cathcart Circle, Neilston and Newton

Network Diagram - see first page of Table 220

	SR SO	SR SX	SR SX A	SR SX	SR SO	SR SX	SR	SR SO B	SR SX B	SR	SR A	SR	SR	SR	SR B		SR B	SR	SR A	SR	SR
Glasgow Central 15 226 d	17 10	17 12	17 16	17 20	17 20	17 28	17 35	17 40	17 44	17 50	18 05	18 10	18 20	18 35	18 40	and at	22 40	22 50	23 05	23 10	23 20
Pollokshields West d			17 21				17 40				18 10			18 39		the same			23 10		
Maxwell Park d			17 23				17 42				18 12			18 42		minutes			23 12		
Shawlands d			17 25				17 44				18 14			18 44		past			23 14		
Pollokshaws East d			17 26				17 45				18 15			18 45		each			23 15		
Langside d			17 28				17 47				18 17			18 47		hour until			23 17		
Pollokshields East d	17 14	17 16		17 24	17 24	17 32		17 44	17 48	17 54		18 14	18 24		18 44		22 44	22 54		23 14	23 24
Queens Park d	17 16	17 18		17 26	17 26	17 34		17 46	17 50	17 56		18 16	18 26		18 46		22 46	22 56		23 16	23 26
Crosshill d	17 17	17 19		17 27	17 27	17 35		17 47	17 51	17 57		18 17	18 27		18 47		22 47	22 57		23 17	23 27
Mount Florida d	17 19	17 21		17 29	17 29	17 37		17 49	17 53	17 59		18 19	18 29		18 49		22 49	22 59		23 19	23 29
Cathcart d		17 24	17a30		17 31	17 39		17a51	17a55	18 01	18a20		18 31		18a51		22a51	23 01	23a20		23 31
Muirend d		17 27			17 33	17 41				18 03			18 33					23 03			23 33
Williamwood d		17 30			17 36	17 44				18 06			18 36					23 06			23 36
Whitecraigs d		17 32			17 38	17 46				18 08			18 38					23 08			23 38
Patterton d		17 34			17 41	17 49				18 11			18 41					23 11			23 41
Neilston a		17 41			17 47	17 55				18 17			18 47					23 17			23 47
Kings Park d	17 21			17 31			17 51					18 21		18 51						23 21	
Croftfoot d	17 23			17 33			17 53					18 23		18 53						23 23	
Burnside d	17 26			17 36			17 55					18 26		18 55						23 26	
Kirkhill a	17 29			17 39			17 58					18 29		18 58						23 29	
Newton 226 a	17 32			17 42			18 02					18 32		19 01						23 32	

	SR FO
Glasgow Central 15 226 d	23 50
Pollokshields West d	
Maxwell Park d	
Shawlands d	
Pollokshaws East d	
Langside d	
Pollokshields East d	23 54
Queens Park d	23 56
Crosshill d	23 57
Mount Florida d	23 59
Cathcart d	00 01
Muirend d	00 03
Williamwood d	00 06
Whitecraigs d	00 08
Patterton d	00 11
Neilston a	00 17
Kings Park d	
Croftfoot d	
Burnside d	
Kirkhill a	
Newton 226 a	

Sundays

	SR	SR	SR	SR		SR	SR	SR	SR	SR
Glasgow Central 15 226 d	08 20	08 35	08 50	09 10	and at	22 10	22 20	22 35	22 50	23 10
Pollokshields West d		08 40			the same			22 40		
Maxwell Park d		08 42			minutes			22 42		
Shawlands d		08 44			past			22 44		
Pollokshaws East d		08 45			each			22 45		
Langside d		08 47			hour until			22 47		
Pollokshields East d	08 24		08 54	09 14		22 14	22 24		22 54	23 14
Queens Park d	08 26		08 56	09 16		22 16	22 26		22 56	23 16
Crosshill d	08 27		08 57	09 17		22 17	22 27		22 57	23 17
Mount Florida d	08 29		08 59	09 19		22 19	22 29		22 59	23 19
Cathcart d	08 31		09 01				22 31		23 01	
Muirend d	08 33		09 03				22 33		23 03	
Williamwood d	08 36		09 06				22 36		23 06	
Whitecraigs d	08 38		09 08				22 38		23 08	
Patterton d	08 41		09 11				22 41		23 11	
Neilston a	08 47		09 17				22 47		23 17	
Kings Park d		08 51		09 21		22 21		22 51		23 21
Croftfoot d		08 53		09 23		22 23		22 53		23 23
Burnside d		08 55		09 26		22 26		22 55		23 26
Kirkhill a		08 58		09 29		22 29		22 58		23 29
Newton 226 a		09 01		09 32		22 32		23 03		23 32

For general notes see front of timetable
For details of catering facilities see Directory of Train Operators

A Cathcart Circle Service. To Glasgow Central via Queens Park

B Cathcart Circle Service. To Glasgow Central via Maxwell Park

Newton, Neilston, Cathcart Circle and Glasgow Central

Network Diagram - see first page of Table 220

Miles	Miles	Miles		SR SO A	SR	SR A	SR	SR SX B	SR	SR SX A	SR	SR	SR SX	SR SO	SR SX	SR SX B	SR SX	SR SX A	SR SO	SR SX	SR SX	SR SX B	SR SO	SR SX	SR SX A
0	0	—	**Newton** 226 d		06 11		06 41				07 11		07 34	07 41			07 48						08 11	08 17	
1½	1½	—	Kirkhill d		06 14		06 44				07 14		07 38	07 44			07 51						08 14	08 20	
2¾	2¾	—	Burnside d		06 17		06 47				07 17		07 41	07 47			07 54						08 17	08 23	
3¾	3¾	—	Croftfoot d		06 19		06 49				07 19		07 43	07 49			07 56						08 19	08 25	
4¼	4¼	—	Kings Park d		06 21		06 51				07 21		07 45	07 51			07 58						08 21	08 27	
—	—	0	**Neilston** d						06 56			07 26			07 39				07 56	08 03	08 10				
—	—	3¾	Patterton d						07 01			07 31			07 44				08 01	08 08	08 15				
—	—	4¾	Whitecraigs d						07 03			07 33			07 46				08 03	08 10	08 17				
—	—	5½	Williamwood d						07 06			07 36			07 49				08 06	08 13	08 20				
—	—	7	Muirend d						07 09			07 39			07 51				08 09	08 15	08 22				
4¾	—	7¾	Cathcart d	00 21		06 41		06 52	07 11	07 21		07 41			07 53	07 55		08 09	08 11	08 17		08 21			08 34
—	5½	8½	Mount Florida d	00 23		06 43	06 53		07 13	07 23		07 43	07 47	07 53	07 55			08 11	08 13	08 19				08 29	08 36
—	6	9	Crosshill d	00 25		06 45	06 55		07 15	07 25		07 45	07 49	07 55	07 57			08 13	08 15	08 21				08 31	08 38
—	6¼	9¼	Queens Park d	00 27		06 47	06 57		07 17	07 27		07 47	07 51	07 57	07 59			08 15	08 17	08 23				08 35	08 40
—	6¾	9¾	Pollokshields East d	00 28		06 48	06 58		07 18	07 28		07 48	07 52	07 58	08 00			08 16	08 18	08 24				08 36	08 41
5¾	—	—	Langside d		06 24			06 54			07 24					07 57	08 01					08 24	08 24		
6¼	—	—	Pollokshaws East d		06 26			06 56			07 26					07 59	08 03					08 26	08 26		
6¾	—	—	Shawlands d		06 28			06 58			07 28					08 01	08 05					08 28	08 28		
7½	—	—	Maxwell Park d		06 29			06 59			07 29					08 02	08 06					08 29	08 29		
8	—	—	Pollokshields West d		06 31			07 01			07 31					08 04	08 08					08 31	08 31		
10	8¾	11¾	**Glasgow Central** 15 226 a	00 33	06 37	06 53	07 03	07 07	07 23	07 33	07 38	07 53	07 57	08 03	08 05	08 11	08 15	08 21	08 23	08 30	08 32	08 39	08 39	08 41	08 47

	SR SX B	SR	SR SX A	SR SX		SR SO	SR SX	SR SX	SR SX B	SR SO	SR SX	SR SX A		SR	SR	SR	SR B	SR	SR A		SR A	SR	SR	SR
Newton 226 d				08 34		08 41		08 58						09 11		09 41				and at		15 11		15 41
Kirkhill d				08 38		08 44		09 01						09 14		09 44				the same		15 14		15 44
Burnside d				08 41		08 47		09 04						09 17		09 47				minutes		15 17		15 47
Croftfoot d				08 43		08 49		09 06						09 19		09 49				past		15 19		15 49
Kings Park d				08 45		08 51		09 08						09 21		09 51				each		15 21		15 51
Neilston d		08 26					08 41			08 56	09 02				09 26			09 56		hour until			15 26	
Patterton d		08 31					08 46			09 01	09 07				09 31			10 01					15 31	
Whitecraigs d		08 33					08 48			09 03	09 09				09 33			10 03					15 33	
Williamwood d		08 36					08 51			09 06	09 12				09 36			10 06					15 36	
Muirend d		08 39					08 53			09 09	09 14				09 39			10 09					15 39	
Cathcart d	08 34	08 41	08 46				08 55		09 08	09 11	09 16	09 21			09 41		09 52	10 11	10 21		15 21		15 41	
Mount Florida d		08 43	08 48			08 53	08 57	09 10		09 13	09 18	09 23			09 43	09 53		10 13	10 23		15 23		15 43	15 53
Crosshill d		08 45	08 50			08 55	08 59	09 12		09 15	09 20	09 25			09 45	09 55		10 15	10 25		15 25		15 45	15 55
Queens Park d		08 47	08 52			08 57	09 01	09 14		09 17	09 22	09 27			09 47	09 57		10 17	10 27		15 27		15 47	15 57
Pollokshields East d		08 48	08 53			08 58	09 02	09 15		09 18	09 23	09 28			09 48	09 58		10 18	10 28		15 28		15 48	15 58
Langside d	08 36			08 48					09 10					09 24			09 54					15 24		
Pollokshaws East d	08 38			08 50					09 12					09 26			09 56					15 26		
Shawlands d	08 40			08 52					09 14					09 28			09 58					15 28		
Maxwell Park d	08 41			08 53					09 15					09 29			09 59					15 29		
Pollokshields West d	08 43			08 55					09 17					09 31			10 01					15 31		
Glasgow Central 15 226 a	08 49	08 53	08 59	09 01		09 03	09 07	09 20	09 23	09 23	09 28	09 33		09 38	09 53	10 03	10 07	10 23	10 33		15 35	15 38	15 53	16 03

	SR B	SR	SR SX B	SR A	SR	SR SO	SR SX	SR	SR B		SR SO	SR SX	SR A	SR	SR SX A	SR	SR SX	SR SO	SR SO B	SR SX	SR SX B	SR	SR A	SR	SR SX
Newton 226 d					16 11			16 41						17 11			17 41	17 41						18 11	
Kirkhill d					16 14			16 44						17 14			17 44	17 44						18 14	
Burnside d					16 17			16 47						17 17			17 47	17 47						18 17	
Croftfoot d					16 19			16 49						17 19			17 49	17 49						18 19	
Kings Park d					16 21			16 51						17 21			17 51	17 51						18 21	
Neilston d		15 56				16 26	16 33				16 56	17 02				17 26				17 42		17 56			18 13
Patterton d		16 01				16 31	16 38				17 01	17 07				17 31						18 01			18 18
Whitecraigs d		16 03				16 33	16 40				17 03	17 09				17 33						18 03			18 20
Williamwood d		16 06				16 36	16 43				17 06	17 12				17 36						18 06			18 23
Muirend d		16 09				16 39	16 45				17 09	17 14				17 39						18 09			18 26
Cathcart d	15 52	16 11	16 13	16 21		16 41	16 47		16 52		17 11	17 16	17 21		17 32	17 41			17 52	17 54	17 55	18 11	18 21		18 28
Mount Florida d		16 13		16 23		16 43	16 49	16 53			17 13	17 18	17 23		17 34	17 43	17 53	17 53		17 56		18 13	18 23		18 30
Crosshill d		16 15		16 25		16 45	16 51	16 55			17 15	17 20	17 25		17 36	17 45		17 55		17 58		18 15	18 25		18 32
Queens Park d		16 17		16 27		16 47	16 53	16 57			17 17	17 22	17 27		17 37	17 47		17 57		18 00		18 17	18 27		18 34
Pollokshields East d		16 18		16 28		16 48	16 54	16 58			17 18	17 23	17 28		17 39	17 48		17 58		18 01		18 18	18 28		18 35
Langside d	15 54		16 15		16 24				16 54					17 24					17 54		17 57			18 24	
Pollokshaws East d	15 56		16 17		16 26				16 56					17 26					17 56		17 59			18 26	
Shawlands d	15 58		16 19		16 28				16 58					17 28					17 58		18 01			18 28	
Maxwell Park d	15 59		16 20		16 29				16 59					17 29					17 59		18 02			18 29	
Pollokshields West d	16 01		16 22		16 31				17 01					17 31					18 01		18 04			18 31	
Glasgow Central 15 226 a	16 07	16 23	16 28	16 33	16 38	16 53	16 59	17 03	17 07		17 23	17 29	17 33	17 38	17 44	17 53	18 03	18 03	18 07	18 07	18 10	18 23	18 33	18 38	18 40

For general notes see front of timetable
For details of catering facilities see
Directory of Train Operators

A Cathcart Circle Service.
From Glasgow Central via Maxwell Park

B Cathcart Circle Service.
From Glasgow Central via Queens Park

Table 223

Mondays to Saturdays

Newton, Neilston, Cathcart Circle and Glasgow Central

Network Diagram - see first page of Table 220

	SR	SR		SR A	SR	SR B	SR	SR	SR		SR	SR	SR	SR	SR	SR	SR	SR A	SR	SR B	SR	SR
Newton 226 d		18 41					19 11		19 41		21 41				22 11		22 41				23 11	
Kirkhill d		18 44					19 14		19 44		21 44				22 14		22 44				23 14	
Burnside d		18 47					19 17		19 47		21 47				22 17		22 47				23 17	
Croftfoot d		18 49					19 19		19 49		21 49				22 19		22 49				23 19	
Kings Park d		18 51					19 21		19 51		21 51				22 21		22 51				23 21	
Neilston d	18 26				18 56			19 26		and at			21 56			22 26			22 56			23 26
Patterton d	18 31				19 01			19 31		the same			22 01			22 31			23 01			23 31
Whitecraigs d	18 33				19 03			19 33					22 03			22 33			23 03			23 33
Williamwood d	18 36				19 06			19 36		minutes			22 06			22 36			23 06			23 36
Muirend d	18 39				19 09			19 39					22 09			22 39			23 09			23 39
Cathcart d	18 41			18 52	19 11	19 21		19 41		past		21 52	22 11	22 21		22 41		22 52	23 11	23 21		23 41
Mount Florida d	18 43	18 53			19 13	19 23		19 43	19 53	each	21 53		22 13	22 23		22 43	22 53		23 13	23 23		23 43
Crosshill d	18 45	18 55			19 15	19 25		19 45	19 55		21 55		22 15	22 25		22 45	22 55		23 15	23 25		23 45
Queens Park d	18 47	18 57			19 17	19 27		19 47	19 57	hour until	21 57		22 17	22 27		22 47	22 57		23 17	23 27		23 47
Pollokshields East d	18 48	18 58			19 18	19 28		19 48	19 58		21 58		22 18	22 28		22 48	22 58		23 18	23 28		23 48
Langside d				18 54			19 24					21 54			22 24			22 54			23 24	
Pollokshaws East d				18 56			19 26					21 56			22 26			22 56			23 26	
Shawlands d				18 58			19 28					21 58			22 28			22 58			23 28	
Maxwell Park d				18 59			19 29					21 59			22 29			22 59			23 29	
Pollokshields West d				19 01			19 31					22 01			22 31			23 01			23 31	
Glasgow Central 15 226 a	18 53	19 05	....	19 07	19 23	19 33	19 38	19 53	20 03		22 03	22 08	22 23	22 33	22 41	22 56	23 03	23 07	23 24	23 33	23 40	23 53

Sundays

	SR	SR	SR	SR		SR	SR	SR	SR
Newton 226 d		09 11		09 41		22 41		23 11	
Kirkhill d		09 14		09 44		22 44		23 14	
Burnside d		09 17		09 47		22 47		23 17	
Croftfoot d		09 19		09 49		22 49		23 19	
Kings Park d		09 21		09 51		22 51		23 21	
Neilston d	08 56		09 26		and at		22 56		23 26
Patterton d	09 01		09 31		the same		23 01		23 31
Whitecraigs d	09 03		09 33				23 03		23 33
Williamwood d	09 06		09 36		minutes		23 06		23 36
Muirend d	09 09		09 39				23 09		23 39
Cathcart d	09 11		09 41		past		23 11		23 41
Mount Florida d	09 13		09 43	09 53	each	22 53	23 13		23 43
Crosshill d	09 15		09 45	09 55		22 55	23 15		23 45
Queens Park d	09 17		09 47	09 57	hour until	22 57	23 17		23 47
Pollokshields East d	09 18		09 48	09 58		22 58	23 18		23 48
Langside d		09 24						23 24	
Pollokshaws East d		09 26						23 26	
Shawlands d		09 28						23 28	
Maxwell Park d		09 29						23 29	
Pollokshields West d		09 31						23 31	
Glasgow Central 15 226 a	09 23	09 38	09 53	10 03		23 03	23 23	23 38	23 53

For general notes see front of timetable
For details of catering facilities see Directory of Train Operators

A Cathcart Circle Service. From Glasgow Central via Queens Park

B Cathcart Circle Service. From Glasgow Central via Maxwell Park

Motherwell and Glasgow Queen Street → Cumbernauld and Falkirk Grahamston

Network Diagram - see first page of Table 220

Miles	Miles			SR	SR	SR	SR	SR		SR	SR SX A	SR	SR	SR		SR	SR	SR	SR	SR		SR	SR	SR	SR	SR
—	0	**Motherwell** 226	d			06 12					07 12	07 34				08 37			09 37				10 37			11 37
—	4½	Whifflet	d			06 20					07 19	07 42				08 45			09 45				10 45			11 45
—	5¼	**Coatbridge Central**	d			06a23	06 45				07a23	07 45				08 48			09 48				10 48			11 48
0	—	**Glasgow Queen Street** 10	d	05 52	06 22			06 52		07 22			07 52	08 24			08 54	09 22		09 52		10 22		10 53	11 22	
1¼	—	Springburn	d	05 56	06 26			06 56		07 26			07 56	08 26			08 56	09 26		09 56		10 26		10 56	11 28	
5¼	—	Stepps	d	06 03	06 33			07 03		07 33			08 03	08 33			09 03	09 33		10 03		10 33		11 03	11 33	
7¾	—	Gartcosh	d	06 07	06 37			07 07		07 37			08 07	08 37			09 07	09 37		10 07		10 37		11 07	11 37	
13¼	11	Greenfaulds	d	06 15	06 45		06 54	07 15		07 45		07 54	08 15	08 45		08 58	09 15	09 45	09 57	10 15		10 45	10 57	11 15	11 45	11 57
14	11¾	**Cumbernauld**	d	06a20	06 47		06a57	07a19		07 47		07a57	08a19	08 47		09a02	09a21	09 47	10a01	10a19		10 47	11a00	11a20	11 47	12a00
22½	—	Camelon	d		07 01					08 01				09 01				10 01				11 01			12 01	
24	—	**Falkirk Grahamston**	a		07 06					08 09				09 06				10 06				11 06			12 06	
—	—	Edinburgh 10	a		*08b15*					*09 02*				*10c03*				*11 01*				*12 01*			*13 01*	
—	—	Stirling	a		*07b52*					*08 53*				*09c53*				*10 53*				*11 53*			*12 53*	

		SR	SR		SR	SR	SR	SR	SR		SR	SR	SR	SR	SR		SR	SR SX	SR SO	SR	SR		SR SX B	SR	SR SX B	SR
Motherwell 226	d				12 37			13 37				14 37			15 37					16 37			16 42		17 12	17 37
Whifflet	d				12 45			13 45				14 45			15 45					16 45			16 48		17 18	17 45
Coatbridge Central	d				12 48			13 48				14 48			15 48					16 48			16a53		17a22	17 48
Glasgow Queen Street 10	d	11 53	12 24			12 52	13 22		13 52		14 22		14 52	15 22			15 54	16 22	16 22		16 52			17 22		
Springburn	d	11 56	12 28			12 56	13 26		13 56		14 26		14 56	15 26			15 56	16 26	16 26		16 56			17 26		
Stepps	d	12 03	12 33			13 03	13 33		14 03		14 33		15 03	15 33			16 03	16 33	16 33		17 03			17 33		
Gartcosh	d	12 07	12 37			13 07	13 37		14 07		14 37		15 07	15 37			16 07	16 37	16 37		17 07			17 37		
Greenfaulds	d	12 15	12 45		12 57	13 15	13 45	13 57	14 15		14 45	14 57	15 15	15 45	15 57		16 15	16 45	16 45	16 57	17 15			17 45		17 57
Cumbernauld	d	12a20	12 47		13a00	13a19	13 47	14a00	14a19		14 47	15a00	15a19	15 47	16a00		16a21	16 47	16 47	17a00	17a19			17 47		18a00
Camelon	d		13 01				14 01				15 01			16 01				17 01	17 01					18 01		
Falkirk Grahamston	a		13 06				14 06				15 06			16 06				17 04	17 12					18 06		
Edinburgh 10	a		*14 01*				*15 01*				*16 01*			*17 03*				*18 02*	*18 02*					*19 01*		
Stirling	a		*13 53*				*14 53*				*15 53*			*16 53*				*17 53*	*17 53*					*18 53*		

		SR	SR SX C	SR		SR	SR	SR	SR	SR		SR	SR	SR	SR	SR		SR	SR	SR	SR B	SR		SR		
Motherwell 226	d		17 56			18 37			19 37				20 37			21 37					22 41					
Whifflet	d		18 02			18 45			19 45				20 45			21 45					22 48					
Coatbridge Central	d		18a06			18 48			19 48				20 48			21 48					22a52					
Glasgow Queen Street 10	d	17 52		18 24			18 52	19 22		19 52		20 23		20 52	21 22			21 52	22 22	22 52		23 24		23 52		
Springburn	d	17 56		18 26			18 56	19 26		19 56		20 26		20 56	21 26			21 56	22 26	22 56		23 26		23 56		
Stepps	d	18 03		18 33			19 03	19 33		20 03		20 33		21 03	21 33			22 03	22 33	23 03		23 33		00 03		
Gartcosh	d	18 07		18 37			19 07	19 37		20 07		20 37		21 07	21 37			22 07	22 37	23 07		23 37		00 07		
Greenfaulds	d	18 15		18 45		18 57	19 15	19 45	19 57	20 15		20 45	20 57	21 15	21 45	21 57		22 15	22 45	23 15		23 45		00 15		
Cumbernauld	d	18a19		18 47		19a00	19a19	19a49	20a00	20 18		20a50	21a00	21 18	21a49	22a01		22 18	22a49	23 18		23a51		00a20		
Camelon	d			19 01						20 33				21 33				22 33		23 36						
Falkirk Grahamston	a			19 06						20 36				21 36				22 36		23 39						
Edinburgh 10	a			*20 04*						*21 31*				*23 01*				*00 07*								
Stirling	a			*19 53*						*21 23*				*22e24*				*23f23*		*00 24*						

Sundays

until 23 December

		SR	SR	SR	SR	SR	SR	SR	SR	SR	SR	SR	SR	SR	SR	SR	SR	SR	SR	SR	SR	SR	SR	SR	SR	SR
Glasgow Queen Street	d	08 22	08 42	09 24	09 50	10 22	10 50	11 22	11 52	12 23	12 52	13 22	13 52	14 22	14 52	15 22	15 52	16 23	16 52	17 22	17 52	18 23	19 22	20 22	21 25	22 22
Springburn	d	08 27	08 47	09 27	09 55	10 27	10 55	11 27	11 57	12 27	12 57	13 27	13 57	14 27	14 57	15 27	15 57	16 27	16 57	17 27	17 57	18 27	19 27	20 27	21 27	22 27
Stepps	d	08 34	08 54	09 34	10 02	10 34	11 02	11 34	12 04	12 34	13 04	13 34	14 04	14 34	15 04	15 34	16 04	16 34	17 04	17 34	18 04	18 34	19 34	20 34	21 34	22 34
Gartcosh	d	08 38	08 58	09 38	10 06	10 38	11 06	11 38	12 08	12 38	13 08	13 38	14 08	14 38	15 08	15 38	16 08	16 38	17 08	17 38	18 08	18 38	19 38	20 38	21 38	22 38
Greenfaulds	d	08 46	09 06	09 46	10 14	10 46	11 14	11 46	12 16	12 46	13 16	13 46	14 16	14 46	15 16	15 46	16 16	16 46	17 16	17 46	18 16	18 46	19 46	20 46	21 46	22 46
Cumbernauld	a	08 48	09 09	09 51	10 17	10 49	11 17	11 49	12 21	12 50	13 21	13 49	14 19	14 49	15 20	15 49	16 22	16 50	17 19	17 49	18 19	18 50	19 49	20 49	21 53	22 50

Sundays

from 30 December

		SR	SR		SR	SR		SR	SR		SR	SR		SR	SR		SR	SR		SR	SR		SR			
Glasgow Queen Street	d	08 22	09 24		10 22	11 22		12 23	13 22		14 22	15 22		16 23	17 22		18 23	19 22		20 22	21 25		22 22			
Springburn	d	08 27	09 27		10 27	11 27		12 27	13 27		14 27	15 27		16 27	17 27		18 27	19 27		20 27	21 27		22 27			
Stepps	d	08 34	09 34		10 34	11 34		12 34	13 34		14 34	15 34		16 34	17 34		18 34	19 34		20 34	21 34		22 34			
Gartcosh	d	08 38	09 38		10 38	11 38		12 38	13 38		14 38	15 38		16 38	17 38		18 38	19 38		20 38	21 38		22 38			
Greenfaulds	d	08 46	09 46		10 46	11 46		12 46	13 46		14 46	15 46		16 46	17 46		18 46	19 46		20 46	21 46		22 46			
Cumbernauld	a	08 48	09 51		10 49	11 49		12 50	13 49		14 49	15 49		16 50	17 49		18 50	19 49		20 49	21 53		22 50			

For general notes see front of timetable
For details of catering facilities see Directory of Train Operators

A From Garscadden (Table 226)
B From Milngavie (Table 226)
C From Dalmuir (Table 226)
b Saturdays arr. Edinburgh 0814, Stirling 0753
c Saturdays arr. Edinburgh 1004, Stirling 0955
e Saturdays arr. 2226
f Saturdays arr. 2324

Falkirk Grahamston and Cumbernauld → Glasgow Queen Street and Motherwell

Network Diagram - see first page of Table 220

Miles	Miles		SR	SR A	SR	SR		SR	SR SX A	SR	SR		SR	SR	SR	SR		SR	SR	SR	SR		SR	SR	SR
—	—	Stirling d				*05 30*					*07 16*				*08 06*				*09 06*				*10 06*		
—	—	Edinburgh 10 d				*05 18*					*07 03*				*08 03*				*09 03*				*10 03*		
0	—	**Falkirk Grahamston** d	05 42			06 42					07 40				08 42				09 42				10 42		
1½	—	Camelon d	05 45			06 45					07 43				08 45				09 45				10 45		
10	0	**Cumbernauld** d	05 59		06 29	06 59		07 08		07 29	07 57		08 10	08 29	08 59	09 10		09 29	09 59	10 10	10 29		10 58	11 10	11 29
10¾	¾	Greenfaulds d	06 01		06 31	07 01		07 10		07 31	07 59		08 12	08 31	09 01	09 12		09 31	10 01	10 12	10 31		11 00	11 12	11 31
16¼	—	Gartcosh d	06 07		06 37	07 07				07 37	08 06			08 37	09 07			09 37	10 07		10 37		11 07		11 37
18¾	—	Stepps d	06 11		06 41	07 11				07 41	08 10			08 41	09 11			09 41	10 11		10 41		11 11		11 41
22¾	—	Springburn d	06 17		06 47	07 17				07 47	08 16			08 47	09 17			09 47	10 17		10 47		11 17		11 47
24	—	**Glasgow Queen Street 10** a	06 26		06 56	07 29				07 56	08 28			08 59	09 26			09 56	10 26		10 56		11 25		11 56
—	6¼	**Coatbridge Central** d		06 40				07 18	07 40				08 20			09 20				10 20				11 20	
—	7¼	Whifflet d		06 42				07 20	07 42				08 22			09 22				10 22				11 22	
—	11¾	**Motherwell** 226 a		06 49				07 30	07 49				08 32			09 32				10 32				11 32	

	SR	SR	SR		SR	SR	SR	SR		SR	SR	SR	SR		SR	SR	SR	SR		SR	SR	SR SX B	SR SX B		SR
Stirling d	*11 06*				*12 06*			*13 06*				*14 06*				*15 06*				*16 06*					
Edinburgh 10 d	*11 03*				*12 03*			*13 03*				*14 03*				*15 03*				*16 03*					
Falkirk Grahamston d	11 42				12 42			13 42				14 42				15 42				16 42					
Camelon d	11 45				12 45			13 45				14 45				15 45				16 45					
Cumbernauld d	11 59	12 10	12 29		12 58	13 10	13 29	13 59		14 10	14 29	14 58	15 10		15 29	15 59	16 10	16 29		16 59	17 10				17 29
Greenfaulds d	12 01	12 12	12 31		13 00	13 12	13 31	14 01		14 12	14 31	15 00	15 12		15 31	16 01	16 12	16 31		17 01	17 12				17 31
Gartcosh d	12 07		12 37		13 07		13 37	14 07			14 37	15 07			15 37	16 07		16 37		17 07					17 37
Stepps d	12 11		12 41		13 11		13 41	14 11			14 41	15 11			15 41	16 11		16 41		17 11					17 41
Springburn d	12 17		12 47		13 17		13 47	14 17			14 47	15 17			15 47	16 17		16 47		17 17					17 47
Glasgow Queen Street 10 a	12 27		12 56		13 26		13 56	14 26			14 56	15 25			15 56	16 26		16 56		17 26					17 56
Coatbridge Central d		12 20				13 20				14 20			15 20				16 20				17 20	17 30	17 56		
Whifflet d		12 22				13 22				14 22			15 22				16 22				17 22	17 32	17 58		
Motherwell 226 a		12 32				13 32				14 32			15 32				16 32				17 32	17 39	18 07		

	SR	SR	SR SX A	SR		SR	SR	SR	SR		SR	SR	SR	SR		SR	SR	SR	SR		SR	SR
Stirling d	*17 06*					*18 06*			*19 06*							*20 36*			*21 06*			*22 06*
Edinburgh 10 d	*17 03*					*18 03*			*19 03*							*20 33*			*21b33*			*22c33*
Falkirk Grahamston d	17 42					18 42			19 42							21 12			22 12			23 12
Camelon d	17 45					18 45			19 45							21 15			22 15			23 15
Cumbernauld d	17 59	18 10		18 29		18 59	19 10	19 29	19 59		20 10	20 29	20 59	21 10		21 29	21 59	22 10	22 29		22 59	23 29
Greenfaulds d	18 01	18 12		18 31		19 01	19 12	19 31	20 01		20 12	20 31	21 01	21 12		21 31	22 01	22 12	22 31		23 01	23 31
Gartcosh d	18 07			18 37		19 07		19 37	20 07			20 37	21 07			21 37	22 07		22 37		23 07	23 37
Stepps d	18 11			18 41		19 11		19 41	20 11			20 41	21 11			21 41	22 11		22 41		23 11	23 41
Springburn d	18 17			18 47		19 18		19 47	20 17			20 47	21 17			21 47	22 17		22 47		23 17	23 47
Glasgow Queen Street 10 a	18 26			18 56		19 27		19 56	20 27			20 56	21 26			21 56	22 26		22 56		23 29	23 58
Coatbridge Central d		18 20	18 39				19 20				20 20			21 20				22 20				
Whifflet d		18 22	18 41				19 22				20 22			21 22				22 22				
Motherwell 226 a		18 32	18 49				19 32				20 32			21 32				22 32				

Sundays
until 23 December

	SR	SR	SR	SR	SR	SR	SR	SR	SR	SR	SR	SR	SR	SR	SR	SR	SR	SR	SR	SR	SR	SR	SR	SR	SR
Cumbernauld d	09 01	09 27	09 59	10 27	10 59	11 29	11 59	12 29	12 59	13 29	13 59	14 29	14 59	15 29	15 59	16 29	16 59	17 29	17 59	18 29	18 59	19 59	21 01	22 00	22 59
Greenfaulds d	09 03	09 29	10 01	10 29	11 01	11 31	12 01	12 31	13 01	13 31	14 01	14 31	15 01	15 31	16 01	16 31	17 01	17 31	18 01	18 31	19 01	20 01	21 03	22 01	23 01
Gartcosh d	09 10	09 36	10 08	10 36	11 08	11 38	12 08	12 38	13 08	13 38	14 08	14 38	15 08	15 38	16 08	16 38	17 08	17 38	18 08	18 38	19 08	20 08	21 08	22 08	23 08
Stepps d	09 14	09 40	10 12	10 40	11 12	11 42	12 12	12 42	13 12	13 42	14 12	14 42	15 12	15 42	16 12	16 42	17 12	17 42	18 12	18 42	19 12	20 12	21 12	22 12	23 12
Springburn d	09 20	09 46	10 18	10 46	11 18	11 48	12 18	12 48	13 18	13 48	14 18	14 48	15 18	15 48	16 18	16 48	17 18	17 48	18 18	18 48	19 18	20 16	21 18	22 18	23 18
Glasgow Queen Street a	09 28	09 54	10 26	10 54	11 26	11 59	12 26	12 59	13 27	13 58	14 26	14 58	15 26	16 00	16 28	16 58	17 26	17 58	18 26	18 58	19 26	20 26	21 28	22 27	23 26

Sundays
from 30 December

	SR	SR		SR	SR		SR	SR		SR	SR		SR	SR		SR	SR		SR	SR		SR
Cumbernauld d	09 01	09 59		10 59	11 59		12 59	13 59		14 59	15 59		16 59	17 59		18 59	19 59		21 01	22 00		22 59
Greenfaulds d	09 03	10 01		11 01	12 01		13 01	14 01		15 01	16 01		17 01	18 01		19 01	20 01		21 03	22 01		23 01
Gartcosh d	09 10	10 08		11 08	12 08		13 08	14 08		15 08	16 08		17 08	18 08		19 08	20 08		21 08	22 08		23 08
Stepps d	09 14	10 12		11 12	12 12		13 12	14 12		15 12	16 12		17 12	18 12		19 12	20 12		21 12	22 12		23 12
Springburn d	09 20	10 18		11 18	12 18		13 18	14 18		15 18	16 18		17 18	18 18		19 18	20 16		21 18	22 18		23 18
Glasgow Queen Street a	09 28	10 26		11 26	12 26		13 27	14 26		15 26	16 28		17 26	18 26		19 26	20 26		21 28	22 27		23 26

For general notes see front of timetable
For details of catering facilities see Directory of Train Operators

A To Milngavie (Table 226)
B To Dalmuir (Table 226)
b Saturdays dep. 2136
c Saturdays dep. 2234

Network Diagram for Tables 225, 228, 229, 230, 238, 240, 242

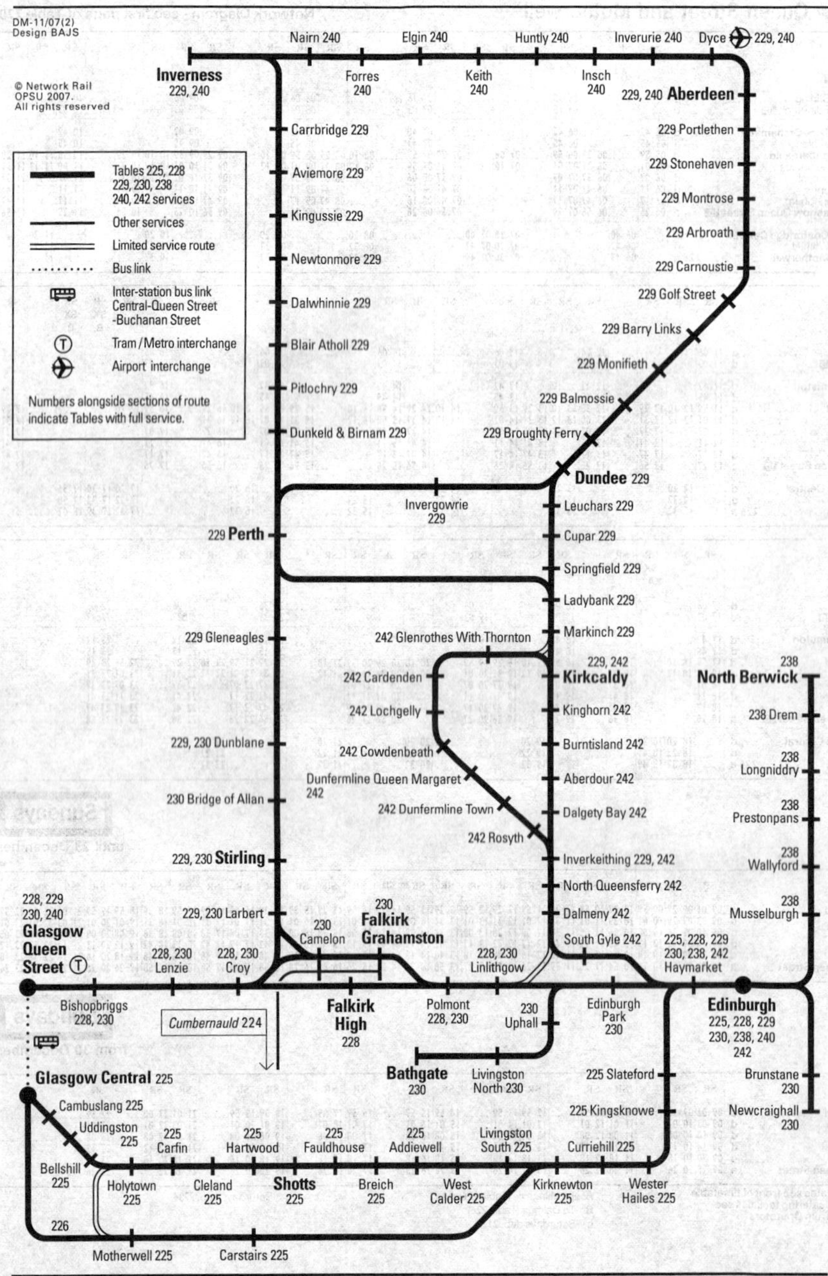

DM-11/07(2)
Design BAJS
© Network Rail OPSU 2007. All rights reserved
Tables 225, 228 229, 230, 238 240, 242 services
Other services
Limited service route
Bus link
Inter-station bus link Central-Queen Street -Buchanan Street
Tram / Metro interchange
Airport interchange
Numbers alongside sections of route indicate Tables with full service.
Inverness 229, 240
Nairn 240
Forres 240
Elgin 240
Keith 240
Huntly 240
Insch 240
Inverurie 240
Dyce 229, 240
229, 240 Aberdeen
229 Portlethen
229 Stonehaven
229 Montrose
229 Arbroath
229 Carnoustie
229 Golf Street
229 Barry Links
229 Monifieth
229 Balmossie
229 Broughty Ferry
Dundee 229
Carrbridge 229
Aviemore 229
Kingussie 229
Newtonmore 229
Dalwhinnie 229
Blair Atholl 229
Pitlochry 229
Dunkeld & Birnam 229
Invergowrie 229
229 Perth
Leuchars 229
Cupar 229
Springfield 229
Ladybank 229
Markinch 229
229 Gleneagles
242 Glenrothes With Thornton
229, 242 Kirkcaldy
242 Cardenden
242 Lochgelly
Kinghorn 242
Burntisland 242
229, 230 Dunblane
242 Cowdenbeath
Dunfermline Queen Margaret 242
Aberdour 242
230 Bridge of Allan
242 Dunfermline Town
Dalgety Bay 242
242 Rosyth
229, 230 Stirling
Inverkeithing 229, 242
North Queensferry 242
Dalmeny 242
South Gyle 242
238 North Berwick
238 Drem
238 Longniddry
238 Prestonpans
238 Wallyford
238 Musselburgh
228, 229 230, 240 Glasgow Queen Street
228, 230 Lenzie
228, 230 Croy
229, 230 Larbert
230 Camelon
230 Falkirk Grahamston
228, 230 Linlithgow
225, 228, 229 230, 238, 242 Haymarket
Bishopbriggs 228, 230
Cumbernauld 224
Falkirk High 228
Polmont 228, 230
230 Uphall
Edinburgh Park 230
Edinburgh 225, 228, 229 230, 238, 240 242
Bathgate 230
Livingston North 230
225 Slateford
Brunstane 230
225 Kingsknowe
Newcraighall 230
Glasgow Central 225
Cambuslang 225
Uddingston 225
225 Carfin
225 Hartwood
225 Fauldhouse
225 Addiewell
Livingston South 225
Curriehill 225
Bellshill 225
Holytown 225
Cleland 225
Shotts 225
Breich 225
West Calder 225
Kirknewton 225
Wester Hailes 225
226
Motherwell 225
Carstairs 225

Edinburgh → Shotts, Carstairs, Motherwell and Glasgow Central

Network Diagram - see first page of Table 225

Miles	Miles	Station		SR	SR	XC	SR		VT	GR	SR	SR		SR	GR	SR	SR		SR	GR	SR	SR		SR	GR	SR
						1 ◇ A	B		1 ◇ C	R 1 D		E			R 1 G					R 1 H					R 1 H	
0	0	Edinburgh 10	230, 238, 242 d	05 52	06 56	07 25				08 08	08 24	08 39			09 21	09 26	10 26		11 26	11 39		12 26		13 26	13 41	
1¼	1¼	Haymarket	230, 238, 242 d	05 56	07 00	07 29				08 14	08 28	08 43			09 26	09 30	10 30		11 30	11 44		12 30		13 30		
3	3	Slateford	d	06 02	07 04						08 33					09 34	10 34		11 34			12 34		13 34		
3¾	3¾	Kingsknowe	d	06 05	07 07						08 36					09 37	10 37		11 37			12 37		13 37		
4¾	4¾	Wester Hailes	d	06 08	07 10						08 39					09 40	10 40		11 40			12 40		13 40		
7½	7½	Curriehill	d	06 12	07 14						08 43					09 44	10 44		11 44			12 44		13 44		
11	11	Kirknewton	d	06 19	07 21						08 50	08 56				09 51	10 51		11 51			12 51		13 51		
14	—	Livingston South	d	06 26	07 27						08 55					09 57	10 57		11 57			12 57		13 57		
16¾	—	West Calder	a	06 32	07 32						09 00					10 02	11 02		12 02			13 02		14 02		
—	—		d	06 32	07 32						09 02					10 02	11 02		12 02			13 02		14 02		
18½	—	Addiewell	d	06 36	07 36						09 06					10 06	11 06		12 06			13 06		14 06		
21	—	Breich	d																							
23¼	—	Fauldhouse	d	06 43	07 43						09 13			←		10 13	11 13		12 13		←	13 13		14 13		←
26¾	—	**Shotts**	d	06 49	07 48						09 19			09 19		10 19	11 19		12 19		12 19	13 19		14 19		14 19
28¼	—	Hartwood	d	06 52	07 51						→			09 22		10 22	11 22		→		12 22	13 22		→		14 21
31½	—	Cleland	d	06 56	07 56									09 26		10 26	11 26				12 26	13 26				14 26
33¼	—	Carfin	d	07 00	07 59									09 30		10 30	11 30				12 30	13 30				14 30
34¼	—	Holytown	d	07 02	08 02									09 32		10 32	11 32				12 32	13 32				14 32
—	28½	Carstairs	d				08 03		08 18			09 16														
—	44½	**Motherwell**	a			08 05	08 25		08s35	09 03		09 33			10 05					12 25					14 25	
—	—		d			08 06	08 25			09 04		09 33			10 05					12 25					14 25	
36	—	Bellshill	226 d	07 06	08 06	08a22			08a52	09a22		09a52		09 36	10a22	10 36	11 36			12a52	12 36	13 36			14a52	14 36
38¾	—	Uddingston	226 d	07 12		08a26	08 30		08a56	09a26		09a56		09 42	10a26	10 42	11 42			12a56	12 42	13 42			14a56	14 42
42	—	Cambuslang	226 d	07 17		08a31			09a01	09a31		10a01		09 47	10a31	10 47	11 47			13a01	12 47	13 47			15a01	14 47
47¼	57¼	**Glasgow Central 15**	226 a	07 30	08 27	08 28	08b48		08 58	09 25		09 55		10 00	10 22	11 00	12 00			12 45	13 00	14 00			14 45	15 02

Station		SR	GR	SR		SR	SR	GR	SR		SR	SR	SR	GR		SR	XC	SR	XC		SR	GR	SR	
			R 1 H					R 1 H					E	R 1 H			R 1 J		R 1 K			R 1 H		
Edinburgh 10	230, 238, 242 d	14 26	15 22	15 26		16 26	17 21	17 39			17 56		18 23	19 14		19 25	20 15	20 26	21 15		22 10	22 25		
Haymarket	230, 238, 242 d	14 30		15 30		16 30	17 26	17 44			18 00		18 27			19 29	20 19	20 30	21 19		22 14	22 30		
Slateford	d	14 34		15 34		16 34	17 30				18 04		18 30			19 33		20 34			22 18			
Kingsknowe	d	14 37		15 37		16 37	17 33				18 07		18 33			19 36		20 37			22 21			
Wester Hailes	d	14 40		15 40		16 40	17 36				18 10		18 35			19 39		20 40			22 24			
Curriehill	d	14 44		15 44		16 44	17 40				18 14		18 39			19 43		20 44			22 28			
Kirknewton	d	14 51		15 51		16 51	17 47				18 21		18 45			19 50		20 51			22 35			
Livingston South	d	14 57		15 57		16 57	17 53				18 27					19 55		20 57			22 41			
West Calder	a	15 02		16 02		17 02	17 58				18 32					20 02		21 02			22 46			
	d	15 02		16 02		17 02	17 58				18 32							21 02			22 46			
Addiewell	d	15 06		16 06		17 06	18 02				18 36							21 06			22 50			
Breich	d										18 40							21x10						
Fauldhouse	d	15 13		16 13		17 13	18 09		←		18 43							21 13			22 57		←	
Shotts	d	15 19		16 19		17 19	18 14		18 14		18 49							21 19			23 03		23 03	
Hartwood	d	15 22		16 22		17 22	→		18 17		18 52							21 22			→		23 06	
Cleland	d	15 26		16 26		17 26			18 22		18 56							21 26					23 10	
Carfin	d	15 30		16 30		17 30			18 25		19 00							21 30					23 14	
Holytown	d	15 32		16 32		17 32			18 27		19 02							21 32					23 16	
Carstairs	d											18 36	19 05				20s46							
Motherwell	a		16 06					18 23	18 36			18 59	19 25	19 53					21s59			23 13		
	d		16 06					18 23					19 25	19 53								23 13		
Bellshill	226 d	15 36	16a22	16 36		17 36			18a52		19 06	19a22	19a52	20a22				21 36	22a22				23 20	
Uddingston	226 d	15 42	16a26	16 42		17 42			18a56		19 12	19a26	19a56	20a26				21 42	22a26				23 26	
Cambuslang	226 d	15 47	16a31	16 47		17 47			19a01		19 17	19a31	20a01	20a31				21 47	22a31			23c41	23 31	
Glasgow Central 15	226 a	16 00	16 25	17 00		18 00		18 41	19b16		19 30	19b46	19 47	20 15			21 28	22 00	22 42			23 33	23 43	

For general notes see front of timetable
For details of catering facilities see Directory of Train Operators

- A From Dunbar (Table 26)
- B To Garscadden (Table 226)
- C From Manchester Piccadilly (Table 65)
- D From Newcastle (Table 26)
- E From North Berwick (Table 238)
- G From Doncaster (Table 26)
- H From London Kings Cross (Table 26)
- J From Bournemouth (Table 51)
- K From Plymouth (Table 51)
- b Glasgow Central Low Level
- c Fridays only. Arrival time

Saturdays

until 22 March

Edinburgh → Shotts, Carstairs, Motherwell and Glasgow Central

Network Diagram - see first page of Table 225

		SR	SR	VT	SR	GR	SR	SR	SR	GR	SR	SR	SR	GR	SR	SR	SR	GR
				1 ◇ A ☕		R 1 B ☕ 🍴		C		R 1 D ☕ 🍴				R 1 E ☕ 🍴				R 1 E ☕ 🍴
Edinburgh [10]	230, 238, 242 d	05 52	06 56		07 54	08 12	08 26	08 58	09 26	09 39		10 26	11 26	11 38		12 26	13 26	13 39
Haymarket	230, 238, 242 d	05 56	07 00		07 58		08 30	09 02	09 30	09 43		10 30	11 30	11 44		12 30	13 30	13 44
Slateford	d	06 02	07 04		08 02		08 34	09 05	09 34			10 34	11 34			12 34	13 34	
Kingsknowe	d	06 05	07 07		08 05		08 37	09 08	09 37			10 37	11 37			12 37	13 37	
Wester Hailes	d	06 08	07 10		08 08		08 40	09 10	09 40			10 40	11 40			12 40	13 40	
Curriehill	d	06 12	07 14		08 12		08 44	09 14	09 44			10 44	11 44			12 44	13 44	
Kirknewton	d	06 19	07 21		08 19		08 51	09 20	09 51			10 51	11 51			12 51	13 51	
Livingston South	d	06 26	07 27		08 25		08 57		09 57			10 57	11 57			12 57	13 57	
West Calder	a	06 32	07 32		08 32		09 02		10 02			11 02	12 02			13 02	14 02	
	d	06 32	07 32				09 02		10 02			11 02	12 02			13 02	14 02	
Addiewell	d	06 36	07 36				09 06		10 06			11 06	12 06			13 06	14 06	
Breich	d																	
Fauldhouse	d	06 43	07 43				09 13		10 13		←	11 13	12 13		←	13 13	14 13	
Shotts	d	06 49	07 49				09 19		10 19		10 19	11 19	12 19		12 19	13 19	14 19	
Hartwood	d	06 52	07 52				09 22		→		10 22	11 22	→		12 22	13 22	→	
Cleland	d	06 56	07 56				09 26				10 26	11 26			12 26	13 26		
Carfin	d	07 00	08 00				09 30				10 30	11 30			12 30	13 30		
Holytown	d	07 02	08 02				09 32				10 32	11 32			12 32	13 32		
Carstairs	d			08ʃ16				09 40										
Motherwell	a			08s30		08 56		09 56		10 27				12 29				14 27
	d			ʃ		08 56		09 57		10 27				12 29				14 27
Bellshill	226 d	07 06	08 06	08a52		09a22	09 36	10a22		10a52	10 36	11 36		12a52	12 36	13 36		14a52
Uddingston	226 d	07 12	08 12	08a56		09a26	09 42	10a26		10a56	10 42	11 42		12a56	12 42	13 42		14a56
Cambuslang	226 d	07 17	08 17	09a01		09a31	09 47	10a31		11a01	10 47	11 47		13a01	12 47	13 47		15a01
Glasgow Central [15]	226 a	07 30	08 30	09ʃ00		09 16	10 00	10 14		10 48	11 00	12 00		12 49	13 00	14 00		14 47

		SR	SR	SR	GR	SR	SR	SR	SR	GR	SR	SR	GR	XC	SR	XC	SR	GR	SR
					R 1 E ☕ 🍴		C			R 1 E ☕ 🍴			R 1 E ☕ 🍴	1 ◇ G		1 ◇ H		R 1 E ☕ 🍴	
Edinburgh [10]	230, 238, 242 d		14 26	15 26	15 37		15 56	16 26	17 26	17 41		18 24	19 36	20 14	20 26	21 15	21 23	21 39	22 40
Haymarket	230, 238, 242 d		14 30	15 30	15 41		16 00	16 30	17 30			18 28	19 41	20 18	20 30	21 19	21 27	21 44	22 44
Slateford	d		14 34	15 34			16 04	16 34	17 34			18 32			20 34		21 31		22 48
Kingsknowe	d		14 37	15 37			16 07	16 37	17 37			18 35			20 37		21 34		22 51
Wester Hailes	d		14 40	15 40			16 09	16 40	17 40			18 38			20 40		21 37		22 54
Curriehill	d		14 44	15 44			16 13	16 44	17 44			18 42			20 44		21 41		22 58
Kirknewton	d		14 51	15 51			16 19	16 51	17 51			18 49			20 51		21 48		23 05
Livingston South	d		14 57	15 57				16 57	17 57			18 57			20 57		21 54		23 11
West Calder	a		15 02	16 02				17 02	18 02			19 02			21 02		22 01		23 16
	d		15 02	16 02				17 02	18 02			19 02			21 02				23 16
Addiewell	d		15 06	16 06				17 06	18 06			19 06			21 06				23 20
Breich	d											19 10			21x10				
Fauldhouse	d	←	15 13	16 13		←		17 13	18 13		←	19 13			21 13				23 27
Shotts	d	14 19	15 19	16 19		16 19		17 19	18 19		18 19	19 19			21 19				23 35
Hartwood	d	14 22	15 22	→		16 21		17 22	→		18 21	19 22			21 22				23 38
Cleland	d	14 26	15 26			16 26		17 26			18 26	19 26			21 26				23 42
Carfin	d	14 30	15 30			16 30		17 30			18 29	19 30			21 30				23 46
Holytown	d	14 32	15 32			16 32		17 32			18 31	19 32			21 32				23 48
Carstairs	d						16 46												
Motherwell	a				16 28		17 04			18 29	18 40		20 20	21s00		22s04		22 26	
	d				16 28		17 04			18 29			20 20					22 26	
Bellshill	226 d	14 36	15 36		16a52	16 36	17a22	17 36			18a52	19 36	20a52	21a22	21 36	22a22		22a52	23 52
Uddingston	226 d	14 42	15 42		16a56	16 42	17a26	17 42			18a56	19 42	20a56	21a26	21 42	22a26		22a56	23 58
Cambuslang	226 d	14 47	15 47		17a01	16 47	17a31	17 47			19a01	19 47	21a01	21a31	21 47	22a31		23a01	00 03
Glasgow Central [15]	226 a	15 02	16 00		16 48	17 00	17 23	18 00		18 50	19b16	20 00	20 44	21 27	22 00	22 43		22 46	00 15

For general notes see front of timetable
For details of catering facilities see Directory of Train Operators

- **A** Until 26 January. From Manchester Piccadilly (Table 65)
- **B** From Newcastle (Table 26)
- **C** From North Berwick (Table 238)
- **D** From Doncaster (Table 26)
- **E** From London Kings Cross (Table 26)
- **G** From Bournemouth (Table 51)
- **H** From Plymouth (Table 51)
- **b** Glasgow Central Low Level

Table 225

Saturdays
from 29 March

Edinburgh → Shotts, Carstairs, Motherwell and Glasgow Central

Network Diagram - see first page of Table 225

	SR	SR 🚌	SR	SR 🚌	SR	SR 🚌		GR 🚌	SR	SR 🚌	SR	GR 🚌	SR 🚌		SR	SR 🚌	SR	GR 🚌	SR 🚌	SR		SR 🚌	SR	GR 🚌	SR 🚌
Edinburgh [10] 230, 238, 242 d	05 52	06 20		07 49		08 12		08 19		08 49		09 45	09 49			10 49		11 47	11 49			12 49		13 42	13 49
Haymarket 230, 238, 242 d	05 56	06 30		07 58		08 21				08 59			09 59			10 59			11 59			12 59			13 59
Slateford d	06 02	06 35		08 04		08 27				09 04			10 04			11 04			12 04			13 04			14 04
Kingsknowe d	06 05	06 39		08 08		08 31				09 08			10 08			11 08			12 08			13 08			14 08
Wester Hailes d	06 08	06 46		08 15		08 38				09 15			10 15			11 15			12 15			13 15			14 15
Curriehill d	06 12	06 55		08 24		08 47				09 24			10 24			11 24			12 24			13 24			14 24
Kirknewton d	06 19	07 08		08 37		09 00				09 37			10 37			11 37			12 37			13 37			14 37
Livingston South d	06 26	07a23	07 28	08 52	08 57					09a52	09 57		10a52		10 57	11a52	11 57		12a52	12 57		13a52	13 57		14a52
West Calder a	06 32		07 32	09 07	09 02						10 02				11 02		12 02			13 02			14 02		
d	06 32		07 32		09 02						10 02				11 02		12 02			13 02			14 02		
Addiewell d	06 36		07 36		09 06						10 06				11 06		12 06			13 06			14 06		
Breich d																									
Fauldhouse d	06 43		07 43		09 13						10 13				11 13		12 13			13 13			14 13		
Shotts d	06 49		07 49		09 19						10 19				11 19		12 19			13 19			14 19		
Hartwood d	06 52		07 52		09 22						10 22				11 22		12 22			13 22			14 22		
Cleland d	06 56		07 56		09 26						10 26				11 26		12 26			13 26			14 26		
Carfin d	07 00		08 00		09 30						10 30				11 30		12 30			13 30			14 30		
Holytown d	07 02		08 02		09 32						10 32				11 32		12 32			13 32			14 32		
Carstairs d						09a35			09 40																
Motherwell a								09 24	09 56			10 50						12 52						14 47	
d									09 57																
Bellshill 226 d	07 06		08 06		09 36			09a52	10a22		10 36	11a22			11 36		12 36	13a22		13 36			14 36	15a22	
Uddingston 226 d	07 12		08 12		09 42			09a56	10a26		10 42	11a26			11 42		12 42	13a26		13 42			14 42	15a26	
Cambuslang 226 d	07 17		08 17		09 47			10a01	10a31		10 47	11a31			11 47		12 47	13a31		13 47			14 47	15a31	
Glasgow Central [15] 226 a	07 30		08 30		10 00			10b16	10 14		11 00	11b46			12 00		13 00	13b46		14 00			15 02	15b46	

	SR	SR 🚌	SR	SR 🚌		GR 🚌	SR	SR 🚌	SR	SR 🚌	SR		SR 🚌	SR	GR 🚌	GR 🚌	SR 🚌	SR	SR 🚌	GR 🚌	SR 🚌	SR	SR 🚌		
Edinburgh [10] 230, 238, 242 d		14 49		15 11		15 45		15 49		16 49			17 49		17 49	19 43	19 49		21 23	21 44	22 03		22 40		
Haymarket 230, 238, 242 d		14 59		15 20				15 59		16 59			17 59				19 59		21 32		22 13		22 49		
Slateford d		15 04		15 26				16 04		17 04			18 04				20 04		21 38		22 18		22 55		
Kingsknowe d		15 08		15 30				16 08		17 08			18 08				20 08		21 42		22 22		22 59		
Wester Hailes d		15 15		15 37				16 15		17 15			18 15				20 15		21 49		22 29		23 06		
Curriehill d		15 24		15 46				16 24		17 24			18 24				20 24		21 58		22 38		23 15		
Kirknewton d		15 37		15 59				16 37		17 37			18 37				20 37		22 11		22 51		23 28		
Livingston South d	14 57	15a52	15 57					16a52	16 57	17a52	17 57		18a52	18 57			20a52	20 57	22 26		23a06	23 11	23 43		
West Calder a	15 02		16 02						17 02		18 02			19 02				21 02	22 41			23 16	23 58		
d	15 02		16 02						17 02		18 02			19 02				21 02				23 16			
Addiewell d	15 06		16 06						17 06		18 06			19 06				21 06				23 20			
Breich d														19 10				21x10							
Fauldhouse d	15 13		16 13						17 13		18 13			19 13				21 13				23 27			
Shotts d	15 19		16 19						17 19		18 18			19 19				21 19				23 35			
Hartwood d	15 22		16 22						17 22		18 21			19 22				21 22				23 38			
Cleland d	15 26		16 26						17 26		18 26			19 26				21 26				23 42			
Carfin d	15 30		16 30						17 30		18 29			19 30				21 30				23 46			
Holytown d	15 32		16 32						17 32		18 31			19 32				21 32				23 48			
Carstairs d				16a34			16 39																		
Motherwell a						16 50	16 59				18 40				18 54	20 48				22 49					
d							17 00																		
Bellshill 226 d	15 36		16 36				17a22		17 36		18a52			19 36	19a22	21a22		21 36				23 52			
Uddingston 226 d	15 42		16 42				17a26		17 42		18a56			19 42	19a26	21a26		21 42				23 58			
Cambuslang 226 d	15 47		16 47				17a31		17 47		19a01			19 47	19a31	21a31		21 47				00 03			
Glasgow Central [15] 226 a	16 00		17 00				17 22		18 00		19b16			20 00	19b46	21b46		22 00				00 15			

Sundays

	GR R 1 A		SR		GR R 1 B		XC 1 ◇ C		SR		GR R 1 D		SR		GR R 1 D		SR		GR R 1 D		XC R 1 E	SR	XC R 1 G	GR R 1 D		
Edinburgh [10] 230, 242 d	12 03		12 22		12 42		14 15		14 22		15 13		16 22		17 41		18 22		19 37		20 14	20 22	21 14	21 39		
Haymarket 230, 242 d	12 08		12 26				14 19		14 26		15 18		16 26		17 46		18 26				20 18	20 26	21 17			
Slateford d			12 30						14 30				16 30				18 30					20 30				
Kingsknowe d			12 33						14 33				16 33				18 33					20 33				
Wester Hailes d			12 36						14 36				16 36				18 36					20 36				
Curriehill d			12 40						14 40				16 40				18 40					20 40				
Kirknewton d			12 47						14 47				16 47				18 47					20 47				
Livingston South d			12 54						14 54				16 54				18 54					20 54				
West Calder a			13 01						15 01				17 01				19 01					21 01				
Motherwell a	12 46				13 24		14s53				15 55				18 24				20 16		20s53		21s59	22 18		
d	12 46				13 24						15 55				18 24				20 16					22 18		
Glasgow Central a	13 05				13 44		15 17				16 14				18 44				20 35		21 19		22 23	22 37		

For general notes see front of timetable
For details of catering facilities see Directory of Train Operators

A From York (Table 26)
B From Leeds (Table 26)
C From Birmingham New Street (Table 51)
D From London Kings Cross (Table 26)
E Until 27 January from Bournemouth, 3 February to 23 March from Plymouth and from 30 March from Oxford (Table 51)
G Until 27 January and from 30 March from Penzance (Table 135). 3 February to 23 March from Bournemouth (Table 51)
b Glasgow Central Low Level

On Sundays until 23 December, there is an hourly service between Shotts and Glasgow Central via Whifflet. Please refer to Table 220 for details.

Glasgow Central, Motherwell, Carstairs and Shotts → Edinburgh

Network Diagram - see first page of Table 225

Miles	Miles		XC R 1 A	SR	SR		GR R 1 B ✕ ⌶	SR	SR C		SR	GR R 1 B ✕ ⌶	VT 1 ◇		XC R 1 D ⊡	SR	SR		GR R 1 B ⊡ ⌶	SR	SR		GR R 1 B E ⊡ ⌶	SR	SR
0	0	**Glasgow Central** 15 226 d	06 00	06 15	06b17		06 50		07 05		07 13	07 50			09 00		09 15		09 50	10 15	11 15		11 50	12 15	13 15
5¼	—	Cambuslang 226 d		06 24	06 31				07 01		07 22	07 31			08 55		09 24		09 31	10 24	11 24		11 31	12 24	13 24
8½	—	Uddingston 226 d		06 29	06 35				07 05		07 27	07 35			09 02		09 29		09 35	10 29	11 29		11 35	12 29	13 29
11¼	—	Bellshill 226 d		06 35	06 40				07 10		07 33	07 40			08 40		09 35		09 40	10 35	11 35		11 40	12 35	13 35
—	12¼	**Motherwell** a					07 04		07 27			08 07							10 04				12 04		
—	—	d			06 59		07 04		07 28			08 07			09u14				10 04				12 04		
—	28½	Carstairs d			07a21				07 43				08 40												
13¼	—	Holytown d		06 39							07 37						09 39			10 39	11 39			12 39	13 39
14	—	Carfin d		06 42							07 40						09 41			10 41	11 41			12 41	13 41
15¾	—	Cleland d		06 46							07 44						09 45			10 45	11 45			12 45	13 45
19	—	Hartwood d		06 52							07 50						09 51			10 51	11 51			12 51	13 51
20½	—	**Shotts** d		06 56							07 54						09 55			10 55	11 55			12 55	13 55
24	—	Fauldhouse d		07 02							08 00						10 01			11 01	12 01			13 01	14 01
26¼	—	Breich d									08 03														
28¾	—	Addiewell d		07 08							08 07						10 07			11 07	12 07			13 07	14 07
30½	—	West Calder d		07 11				07 37			08 11					09 39	10 10			11 10	12 10			13 10	14 10
33¼	—	Livingston South d		07 16				07 42			08 16					09 44	10 15			11 15	12 15			13 15	14 15
36¼	46¼	Kirknewton d		07 23				07 49	08 07		08 23					09 51	10 22			11 22	12 22			13 22	14 22
40¾	49¾	Curriehill d		07 28				07 54	08 12		08 28					09 56	10 27			11 27	12 27			13 27	14 27
42½	52½	Wester Hailes d		07 32					08 15		08 32					10 00	10 31			11 31	12 31			13 31	14 31
43½	53½	Kingsknowe d		07 34					08 18		08 34					10 02	10 33			11 33	12 33			13 33	14 33
44¼	54¼	Slateford d		07 37					08 20		08 37					10 05	10 36			11 36	12 36			13 36	14 36
46	56	Haymarket 230, 238, 242 d	06 52	07 42			07 50	08 05	08 29		08 42	08 50	09s05		09 55	10 11	10 42		10 50	11 42	12 42		12 50	13 42	14 42
47¼	57¼	**Edinburgh** 10 230, 238, 242 a	06 56	07 48			07 55	08 09	08 33		08 48	08 56	09 12		10 01	10 16	10 47		10 56	11 47	12 47		12 58	13 47	14 47

	GR R 1 B ⊡ ⌶	SR		SR	SR C	SR		GR R 1 B ⊡ ⌶	SR	SR		SR G	GR R 1 B ⊡ ⌶	SR		SR	GR R 1 H ⊡ ⌶	SR		XC 1 ◇ J	SR				
Glasgow Central 15 226 d	13 50	14 15		15 15	15 19			15 50	16 15	17 19		17b27	17 50	18 15			19 50	20 15		21 55	23 06				
Cambuslang 226 d	13 31	14 24		15 24	15 01			15 31	16 24	17 01		17 42		18 24			19 31	20 24		22 01	23 15				
Uddingston 226 d	13 35	14 29		15 29	15 05			15 35	16 29	17 05		17 47		18 29			19 35	20 29		22 05	23 20				
Bellshill 226 d	13 40	14 35		15 35	15 10			15 40	16 35	17 35		17 51		18 35			19 40	20 35		22 10	23 26				
Motherwell a	14 04				15 35			16 04				17 57	18 04				20 04			22 24					
d	14 04				15 38			16 04				17 58	18 04				20 04			22 25					
Carstairs d					15 56							18a26													
Holytown d		14 39		15 39					16 39	17 39				18 39				20 39			23 30				
Carfin d		14 41		15 41					16 41	17 41				18 41				20 41			23 32				
Cleland d		14 45		15 45					16 45	17 45				18 45				20 45			23 36				
Hartwood d		14 51		15 51		←			16 51	17 51				18 51				20 51			23 42				
Shotts d		14 55		15 55		15 55			16 55	17 55				18 55				20 55			23 46				
Fauldhouse d		15 01		→		16 01			17 01	18 01				19 01				21 01			23 52				
Breich d																									
Addiewell d		15 07				16 07			17 07	18 07				19 07				21 07			23 58				
West Calder d		15 10				16 10			17 10	18 10				19 10		20 10		21 10			00 02				
Livingston South d		15 15				16 15			17 15	18 15				19 15		20 14		21 15			00 06				
Kirknewton d		15 22				16 22			17 22	18 22				19 22		20 21		21 22			00 13				
Curriehill d		15 27				16 27			17 27	18 27				19 27		20 27		21 27			00 19				
Wester Hailes d		15 31				16 31			17 31	18 31				19 31		20 30		21 31			00 23				
Kingsknowe d		15 33				16 33			17 33	18 33				19 33		20 33		21 33			00 25				
Slateford d		15 36				16 36			17 36	18 36				19 36		20 35		21 36			00 28				
Haymarket 230, 238, 242 d	14 50	15 42			16 30	16 42		16 50	17 42	18 42			18 50	19 42		20 42	20 50	21 42		23 10	00 34				
Edinburgh 10 230, 238, 242 a	14 58	15 47			16 36	16 48		16 57	17 47	18 47			18 57	19 47		20 47	20 55	21 47		23 19	00 38				

For general notes see front of timetable
For details of catering facilities see Directory of Train Operators

A To Bournemouth (Table 51)
B To London Kings Cross (Table 26)
C To North Berwick (Table 238)
D To Penzance (Table 135)
E **The Flying Scotsman**
G From Dalmuir (Table 226)
H To York (Table 26)
J Fridays to Dunbar (Table 26)
b Glasgow Central Low Level

until 22 March

Glasgow Central, Motherwell, Carstairs and Shotts → Edinburgh

Network Diagram - see first page of Table 225

		XC	SR	GR	SR	GR	SR	SR	GR	XC	SR	GR	SR	SR
		1 ◇		R 1		R 1			R 1	1 ◇		R 1		
		A		B	C	B			B	D		B		
Glasgow Central 15	226 d	05 50	06 15	06 50	07 05	07 50		08 15	08 50	09 00	09 15	09 50	10 15	11 15
Cambuslang	226 d		06 24	06 31	06 50	07 31		08 24	08 31		09 24	09 31	10 24	11 24
Uddingston	226 d		06 29	06 35		07 35		08 29	08 35		09 29	09 35	10 29	11 29
Bellshill	226 d		06 35	06 40		07 40		08 35	08 40		09 35	09 40	10 35	11 35
Motherwell	a			07 06	07 20	08 04			09 04			10 04		
	d	06u10		07 06	07 20	08 04			09 04	09u14		10 04		
Carstairs	d				07 43									
Holytown	d		06 39					08 39			09 39		10 39	11 39
Carfin	d		06 42					08 41			09 41		10 41	11 41
Cleland	d		06 46					08 45			09 45		10 45	11 45
Hartwood	d		06 52					08 51			09 51		10 51	11 51
Shotts	d		06 56					08 55			09 55		10 55	11 55
Fauldhouse	d		07 02					09 01			10 01		11 01	12 01
Breich	d							09 04						
Addiewell	d		07 08					09 08			10 07		11 07	12 07
West Calder	d		07 11				08 38	09 12			10 10		11 10	12 10
Livingston South	d		07 16				08 43	09 16			10 15		11 15	12 15
Kirknewton	d		07 23		08 07		08 50	09 23			10 22		11 22	12 22
Curriehill	d		07 28		08 12		08 55	09 29			10 27		11 27	12 27
Wester Hailes	d		07 32		08 15		08 59	09 32			10 31		11 31	12 31
Kingsknowe	d		07 34		08 17		09 01	09 35			10 33		11 33	12 33
Slateford	d		07 37		08 20		09 04	09 37			10 36		11 36	12 36
Haymarket	230, 238, 242 d	06 51	07 42	07 49	08 29	08 49	09 08	09 43		09 55	10 42	10 50	11 42	12 42
Edinburgh 10	230, 238, 242 a	06 57	07 47	07 53	08 34	08 57	09 15	09 48	09 54	09 59	10 47	10 57	11 47	12 47

		GR	SR	SR	GR	SR	SR	SR	SR	GR	SR	SR	GR	SR	SR	SR	SR
		R 1			R 1					R 1			R 1				
		B E			B			C		B			G				
Glasgow Central 15	226 d	11 50	12 15	13 15	13 50	14 15	15 15	15 19		15 50	16 15	17 15	17 50	18 15	20 15		23 06
Cambuslang	226 d	11 31	12 24	13 24	13 31	14 24	15 24	15 01		15 31	16 24	17 24	17 31	18 24	20 24		23 15
Uddingston	226 d	11 35	12 29	13 29	13 35	14 29	15 29	15 05		15 35	16 29	17 29	17 35	18 29	20 29		23 20
Bellshill	226 d	11 40	12 35	13 35	13 40	14 35	15 35	15 10		15 40	16 35	17 35	17 40	18 35	20 35		23 26
Motherwell	a	12 04			14 04			15 38		16 04			18 04				
	d	12 04			14 04			15 39		16 04			18 04				
Carstairs	d							15 57									
Holytown	d		12 39	13 39		14 39	15 39				16 39	17 39		18 39	20 39		23 30
Carfin	d		12 41	13 41		14 41	15 41				16 41	17 41		18 41	20 41		23 32
Cleland	d		12 45	13 45		14 45	15 45				16 45	17 45		18 45	20 45		23 36
Hartwood	d		12 51	13 51		14 51	15 51		←		16 51	17 51		18 51	20 51		23 42
Shotts	d		12 55	13 55		14 55	15 55		15 55		16 55	17 55		18 55	20 55		23 46
Fauldhouse	d		13 01	14 01		15 01	→		16 01		17 01	18 01		19 01	21 01		23 52
Breich	d																
Addiewell	d		13 07	14 07		15 07			16 07		17 07	18 07		19 07	21 07		23 58
West Calder	d		13 10	14 10		15 10			16 10		17 10	18 10		19 10	21 10	22 40	00 02
Livingston South	d		13 15	14 15		15 15			16 15		17 15	18 15		19 15	21 15	22 45	00 08
Kirknewton	d		13 22	14 22		15 22			16 22		17 22	18 22		19 22	21 22	22 52	00 13
Curriehill	d		13 27	14 27		15 27			16 27		17 27	18 27		19 27	21 27	22 57	00 19
Wester Hailes	d		13 31	14 31		15 31			16 31		17 31	18 31		19 31	21 31	23 01	00 23
Kingsknowe	d		13 33	14 33		15 33			16 33		17 33	18 33		19 33	21 33	23 03	00 25
Slateford	d		13 36	14 36		15 36			16 36		17 36	18 36		19 36	21 36	23 06	00 28
Haymarket	230, 238, 242 d	12 50	13 42	14 42	14 50	15 42		16 30	16 42	16 50	17 42	18 42	18 50	19 42	21 42	23 12	00 34
Edinburgh 10	230, 238, 242 a	12 57	13 47	14 47	14 57	15 47		16 36	16 48	16 57	17 47	18 47	18 57	19 47	21 49	23 17	00 38

For general notes see front of timetable
For details of catering facilities see Directory of Train Operators

- **A** To Bournemouth (Table 51)
- **B** To London Kings Cross (Table 26)
- **C** To North Berwick (Table 238)
- **D** To Penzance (Table 135)
- **E** **The Flying Scotsman**
- **G** To Leeds (Table 26)

Table 225

Saturdays

from 29 March

Glasgow Central, Motherwell, Carstairs and Shotts → Edinburgh

Network Diagram - see first page of Table 225

	XC	GR	SR	SR	SR	GR	SR	GR	SR	SR	SR	GR	SR	SR	SR	SR	GR	SR	SR	SR	SR
	1 ◇ A																				
		🚌		🚌		🚌	🚌	🚌	🚌		🚌	🚌		🚌		🚌	🚌		🚌		🚌
Glasgow Central 15 226 d	05 50		06 15		07 05					08 15		*07b47*	09 15		10 15		*10b47*	11 15		12 15	
Cambuslang 226 d			06 24		*06 50*	*07 01*				08 24		*08 01*	09 24		10 24		*11 01*	11 24		12 24	
Uddingston 226 d			06 29		*06 35*	*07 05*				08 29		*08 05*	09 29		10 29		*11 05*	11 29		12 29	
Bellshill 226 d			06 35		*06 40*	*07 10*				08 35		*08 10*	09 35		10 35		*11 10*	11 35		12 35	
Motherwell a					07 20																
d	06u10	06 45			07 20	07 45		08 45				09 45					11 45				
Carstairs d					07a42		07 48														
Holytown d			06 39							08 39			09 39		10 39			11 39		12 39	
Carfin d			06 42							08 41			09 41		10 41			11 41		12 41	
Cleland d			06 46							08 45			09 45		10 45			11 45		12 45	
Hartwood d			06 52							08 51			09 51		10 51			11 51		12 51	
Shotts d			06 56							08 55			09 55		10 55			11 55		12 55	
Fauldhouse d			07 02							09 01			10 01		11 01			12 01		13 01	
Breich d										09 04											
Addiewell d			07 08							09 08			10 07		11 07			12 07		13 07	
West Calder d			07 11						08 38	09 12			10 10		11 10			12 10		13 10	
Livingston South d			07a16	07 21					08 53	09a16	09 21		10a15	10 20	11a15	11 20		12a15	12 20	13a15	13 20
Kirknewton d				07 36			08 23		09 08		09 36			10 35		11 35			12 35		13 35
Curriehill d				07 49			08 36		09 21		09 49			10 48		11 48			12 48		13 48
Wester Hailes d				07 58			08 45		09 30		09 58			10 57		11 57			12 57		13 57
Kingsknowe d				08 05			08 52		09 37		10 05			11 04		12 04			13 04		14 04
Slateford d				08 09			08 56		09 41		10 09			11 08		12 08			13 08		14 08
Haymarket 230, 238, 242 d	06 51			08 14			09 01		09 46		10 14			11 13		12 13			13 13		14 13
Edinburgh 10 230, 238, 242 a	06 57	07 50		08 24		08 50	09 11	09 50	09 56		10 24	10 50		11 23		12 23	12 50		13 23		14 23

	GR	SR	SR	SR	SR	SR	SR	GR	SR	SR	SR	SR	GR	SR	SR	SR	SR	SR	SR	SR	SR
	🚌		🚌		🚌			🚌	🚌	🚌		🚌	🚌		🚌		🚌		🚌	🚌	
Glasgow Central 15 226 d	*12b47*	13 15		14 15		15 15	15 19				16 15		*16b47*	17 15		18 15		20 15			23 06
Cambuslang 226 d	*13 01*	13 24		14 24		15 24	*15 01*				16 24		*17 01*	17 24		18 24		20 24			23 15
Uddingston 226 d	*13 05*	13 29		14 29		15 29	*15 05*				16 29		*17 05*	17 29		18 29		20 29			23 20
Bellshill 226 d	*13 10*	13 35		14 35		15 35	*15 10*				16 35		*17 10*	17 35		18 35		20 35			23 26
Motherwell a							15 38														
d	13 45						15 39	15 45					17 45								
Carstairs d							15a59			16 04											
Holytown d		13 39		14 39		15 39					16 39			17 39		18 39		20 39			23 30
Carfin d		13 41		14 41		15 41					16 41			17 41		18 41		20 41			23 32
Cleland d		13 45		14 45		15 45					16 45			17 45		18 45		20 45			23 36
Hartwood d		13 51		14 51		15 51					16 51			17 51		18 51		20 51			23 42
Shotts d		13 55		14 55		15 55					16 55			17 55		18 55		20 55			23 46
Fauldhouse d		14 01		15 01		16 01					17 01			18 01		19 01		21 01			23 52
Breich d																					
Addiewell d		14 07		15 07		16 07					17 07			18 07		19 07		21 07			23 58
West Calder d		14 10		15 10		16 10					17 10			18 10		19 10		21 10		22 40	00 02
Livingston South d		14a15	14 20	15a15	15 20	16a15			16 20		17a15	17 20		18a15	18 20	19a15	19 20	21a15	21 20	22 55	00a08
Kirknewton d			14 35		15 35				16 35	16 39		17 35			18 35		19 35		21 35	23 10	*00c28*
Curriehill d			14 48		15 48				16 48	16 52		17 48			18 48		19 48		21 48	23 23	*00c41*
Wester Hailes d			14 57		15 57				16 57	17 01		17 57			18 57		19 57		21 57	23 32	*00c50*
Kingsknowe d			15 04		16 04				17 04	17 08		18 04			19 04		20 04		22 04	23 39	*00c57*
Slateford d			15 08		16 08				17 08	17 12		18 08			19 08		20 08		22 08	23 43	*01c01*
Haymarket 230, 238, 242 d			15 13		16 13				17 13	17 17		18 13			19 13		20 13		22 13	23 48	*01c06*
Edinburgh 10 230, 238, 242 a	14 50		15 23		16 23			16 50	17 23	17 27		18 23	18 50		19 23		20 23		22 23	23 58	*01c16*

Sundays

	SR	XC	XC	GR	XC	SR	GR	SR	GR	XC	GR	SR	GR	SR	GR	SR
		R 1	R 1	R 1	R 1		R 1		R 1	1 ◇	R 1		R 1		R 1	
	B	C	D	E	G		E		E	H	E		E		J	
	🚌															
		☕	☕	☕ 🍴	☕		☕ 🍴		☕ 🍴	☕	☕ 🍴		☕ 🍴		☕ 🍴	
Glasgow Central d		10 30	10 30	10 50	11 30		12 50		14 50	15 45	15 50		17 50		19 50	
Motherwell a				11 05			13 04		15 04		16 05		18 05		20 04	
d		10u52	10u56	11 05	11u56		13 04		15 04	15u59	16 05		18 05		20 04	
West Calder d						13 10		15 10				17 10		19 10		21 10
Livingston South d	00 13					13 15		15 15				17 15		19 15		21 15
Kirknewton d	00 28					13 22		15 22				17 22		19 22		21 22
Curriehill d	00 41					13 27		15 27				17 27		19 27		21 27
Wester Hailes d	00 50					13 31		15 31				17 31		19 31		21 31
Kingsknowe d	00 57					13 33		15 33				17 33		19 33		21 33
Slateford d	01 01					13 36		15 36				17 36		19 36		21 36
Haymarket 230, 242 d	01 06	11 37	11 37	11 49	12 37	13 42	13 50	15 42	15 48	16 39	16 46	17 42	18 46	19 42	20 45	21 42
Edinburgh 10 230, 242 a	01 16	11 42	11 42	11 54	12 42	13 47	13 56	15 47	15 53	16 44	16 52	17 47	18 53	19 47	20 51	21 47

For general notes see front of timetable
For details of catering facilities see Directory of Train Operators

A To Bournemouth (Table 51)
B From 30 March
C Until 27 January and from 30 March. To Plymouth (Table 51)
D 3 February to 23 March. To Bournemouth (Table 51)
E To London Kings Cross (Table 26)
G Until 27 January to Bournemouth, 3 February to 23 March to Plymouth and from 30 March to Oxford (Table 51)
H To Bristol Temple Meads (3 February to 23 March to Birmingham New Street) (Table 51)
J To Newcastle (Table 26)
b Glasgow Central Low Level
c By bus

On Sundays until 23 December, there is an hourly service between Glasgow Central and Shotts via Whifflet. Please refer to Table 220 for details.

Lanark, Coatbridge, Motherwell, Larkhall, Hamilton, Drumgelloch, Airdrie and Springburn → Glasgow → Milngavie, Dalmuir, Balloch and Helensburgh

Network Diagram - see first page of Table 220

Miles	Miles	Miles	Miles	Miles	Station		SR	SR R A	SR	SR	SR	SR	SR	SR	SR	SR SO	SR SX	SR	SR SX	SR	SR	SR	SR	SR SO	SR SX
0	—	—	—	—	**Lanark**	d																	06 23		
8½	—	—	—	—	Carluke	d																	06 33		
13	—	—	—	—	Wishaw	d																	06 38		
16½	—	—	—	—	Holytown	d																			
15	—	—	—	—	Shieldmuir	d																	06 42		
—	—	—	—	0	**Coatbridge Central**	d																			
—	—	—	—	1	Whifflet	d																			
16¼	0	0	—	5½	**Motherwell**	a																	06 45		
—	—	—	—	—		d									06 16			06 20					06 46		
—	3	—	—	—	Bellshill	d									06 22								06 52		
20½	5½	—	—	—	Uddingston	d									06 26								06 56		
—	—	¾	—	—	Airbles	d												06 22							
—	—	—	—	0	**Larkhall**	d						06 07								06 37					
—	—	—	—	1½	Merryton	d						06 09								06 39					
—	—	—	—	2¾	Chatelherault	d						06 12								06 42					
—	—	3	—	5¼	**Hamilton Central**	d						06 15						06 27		06 45					
—	—	3¾	—	0	Hamilton West	d						06 18						06 30		06 48					
—	—	5¾	—	—	Blantyre	d						06 21						06 33		06 51					
22½	—	8¼	—	—	Newton	d												06 37							
24	9	—	—	—	Cambuslang	d									06 31			06 41					07 01		
25¾	10¾	—	—	—	Rutherglen	d						06 29			06 34			06 45		06 59			07 04		
26½	11½	—	—	—	Dalmarnock	d									06 36			06 47					07 06		
27	12	—	—	—	Bridgeton	d									06 38			06 49					07 08		
—	—	—	0	—	**Drumgelloch**	d			05 27				06 08								06 38				
—	—	—	1½	—	**Airdrie**	a			05 30				06 11								06 41				
—	—	—	—	—		d			05 31		05 57		06 12				06 27				06 42				06 57
—	—	—	2½	—	Coatdyke	d			05 33		05 59		06 14				06 29				06 44				06 59
—	—	—	3½	—	Coatbridge Sunnyside	d			05 35		06 01		06 16				06 31				06 46				07 01
—	—	—	4	—	Blairhill	d			05 38		06 04		06 19				06 34				06 49				07 04
—	—	—	6¾	—	Easterhouse	d			05 42		06 08		06 23				06 38				06 53				07 08
—	—	—	7¾	—	Garrowhill	d			05 44		06 10		06 25				06 40				06 55				07 10
—	—	—	9	—	Shettleston	d			05 47		06 13		06 28				06 43				06 58				07 13
—	—	—	9¾	—	Carntyne	d			05 49		06 15		06 30				06 45				07 00				07 15
—	—	—	—	0	**Springburn**	d										06 39			06 49					07 09	
—	—	—	—	¼	Barnhill	d										06 40			06 50					07 10	
—	—	—	—	1½	Alexandra Parade	d										06 43			06 53					07 13	
—	—	—	—	1¾	Duke Street	d										06 44			06 54					07 14	
—	—	—	11½	2¼	Bellgrove	d			05 52		06 18		06 33			06 46	06 48		06 56		07 03			07 16	07 18
—	—	—	12	2¾	High Street	d			05 54		06 20		06 35			06 48	06 50		06 58		07 05			07 18	07 20
—	—	—	12½	3¼	**Glasgow Queen Street** 10 §	a			05 56		06 22		06 37			06 51	06 52		07 01		07 07			07 21	07 22
—	—	—	—	—		d	05b30		05 57		06 23		06 40			06 53	06 53		07 02		07 10			07 23	07 23
—	—	—	13¼	4	Charing Cross	d			06 00		06 25		06 42			06 55	06 55		07 04		07 12			07 25	07 25
28½	13¼	—	—	—	Argyle Street	d						06 34			06 42			06 53		07 04			07 12		
28¾	13¾	—	—	—	**Glasgow Central** 15 §	a						06 37			06 46			06 56		07 07			07 16		
—	—	—	—	—		d						06 37			06 46			06 58		07 07			07 16		
29¼	14¼	—	—	—	Anderston	d						06 39			06 48			06 59		07 09			07 18		
29¾	14¾	—	—	—	Exhibition Centre	d						06 41			06 50			07 01		07 11			07 20		
31	16	—	15¼	6	Partick	d			06 04		06 30	06 45	06 47		06 54	07 00	07 00	07 05	07 09	07 15	07 17		07 24	07 30	07 30
31½	16½	0	15¾	6½	Hyndland	d			06 06		06 32	06 47	06 50		06 56	07 02	07 02	07 08	07 11	07 17	07 20		07 26	07 32	07 32
—	—	½	—	—	Jordanhill	d			06 08						06 58				07 13				07 28		
—	—	1½	—	—	Scotstounhill	d			06 11						07 00				07 15				07 30		
—	—	2	—	—	Garscadden	d			06 13				06 54		07 02				07 17				07 32		
—	—	3	—	—	Yoker	d			06 15						07 05				07 20				07 35		
—	—	4	—	—	Clydebank	d			06 17						07 07				07 22				07 37		
32½	17½	—	16¾	7½	Anniesland	d					06 35	06 50				07 05	07 05	07 11		07 20				07 35	07 35
33¾	18¾	—	18	8¾	Westerton	d	05a43	05 56			06 38	06 53				07 08	07 08	07 14		07 23				07 38	07 38
35	—	—	—	—	Bearsden	d												07 16							
35¾	—	—	—	—	Hillfoot	d												07 18							
37¼	—	—	—	—	**Milngavie**	a								←				07 22				←			
—	20	—	19¼	10	Drumchapel	d					06 40	06 55		06 55		07 10	07 10			07 25		07 25		07 40	07 40
—	20¾	—	20	10¾	Drumry	d					06 42	→		06 57		07 12	07 12			→		07 27		07 42	07 42
—	21¾	—	21	11¾	Singer	d					06 45			07 00		07 15	07 15					07 30		07 45	07 45
—	22½	5¼	21¾	12½	**Dalmuir**	a		06 03	06 21		06 47		06 58	07 02	07 11	07 17	07 17		07 26		07 28	07 32	07 41	07 47	07 47
—	—	—	—	—		d		06 04	06 21	06 32	06 48		06 59			07 18	07 18				07 29			07 48	07 48
—	—	—	23	13¾	Kilpatrick	d				06 34	06 51					07 21	07 21							07 51	07 51
—	—	—	24¾	15½	Bowling	d				06 37	06 54					07 24	07 24							07 54	07 54
—	—	—	27½	18¼	Dumbarton East	d			06 29	06 42	06 58		07 06			07 28	07 28				07 36			07 58	07 58
—	—	—	28¼	19	Dumbarton Central	d			06 30	06 44	07 00		07 08			07 30	07 30				07 38			08 00	08 00
—	—	—	28½	19½	Dalreoch	d			06 32	06 46	07 02		07 10			07 32	07 32				07 40			08 02	08 02
—	—	—	—	20¾	Renton	d			06 35		07 05					07 35	07 35							08 05	08 05
—	—	—	—	22	Alexandria	d			06 37		07 07					07 37	07 37							08 07	08 07
—	—	—	—	23	**Balloch**	a			06 40		07 10					07 40	07 40							08 10	08 10
—	—	—	31¾	—	Cardross	d				06 51			07 15								07 45				
—	—	—	35½	—	Craigendoran	d				06 56			07 20								07 50				
—	—	—	36½	—	**Helensburgh Central**	a		06c26		06 59			07 23								07 53				

For general notes see front of timetable
For details of catering facilities see Directory of Train Operators

§ Low Level

A Limited seating accommodation. Also conveys through Sleeping Car accommodation from London Euston (Tables 65 and 404) to Fort William (Tables 227 and 404)

b Glasgow Queen Street High Level

c Helensburgh Upper

Lanark, Coatbridge, Motherwell, Larkhall, Hamilton, Drumgelloch, Airdrie and Springburn → Glasgow → Milngavie, Dalmuir, Balloch and Helensburgh

Network Diagram - see first page of Table 220

Station		SR	SR SX	SR	SR	SR	SR	SR SX	SR SX	SR SO	SR SO	SR SX	SR	SR SX	SR SX	SR SO	SR		SR	SR SX	SR	SR SO	SR SX	SR SO	SR SX
						A															◇ B				
Lanark	d								06 53						07 23							07 23			
Carluke	d								07 03						07 33							07 33			
Wishaw	d								07 08						07 38							07 38			
Holytown	d					07 02																			
Shieldmuir	d								07 12						07 42							07 42			
Coatbridge Central	d	06 40																							
Whifflet	d	06 42																							
Motherwell	a	06 49							07 16						07 45							07 45			
	d	06 50							07 16	07 16			07 20		07 46							07 46			
Bellshill	d					07 06			07 22	07 22												07 52			
Uddingston	d					07 12			07 26	07 26												07 56			
Airbles	d	06 52											07 22												
Larkhall	d			07 07												07 37							07 37		
Merryton	d			07 09												07 39							07 39		
Chatelherault	d			07 12												07 42							07 42		
Hamilton Central	d	06 57		07 15									07 27			07 45							07 45		
Hamilton West	d	07 00		07 18									07 30			07 48							07 48		
Blantyre	d	07 03		07 21									07 33			07 51							07 51		
Newton	d	07 07											07 37										07 55		
Cambuslang	d	07 11				07 17			07 31	07 31			07 41									08 01	08 00		
Rutherglen	d	07 15		07 29					07 34	07 34			07 45		07 56	07 59						08 04	08 04		
Dalmarnock	d	07 17							07 36	07 36			07 47									08 06	08 06		
Bridgeton	d	07 19							07 38	07 38			07 49									08 08	08 08		
Drumgelloch	d				07 08												07 38								
Airdrie	a				07 11												07 41								
	d				07 12			07 22				07 27					07 42			07 52					07 57
Coatdyke	d				07 14			07 24				07 29					07 44			07 54					07 59
Coatbridge Sunnyside	d				07 16			07 26				07 31					07 46			07 56					08 01
Blairhill	d				07 19			07 29				07 34					07 49			07 59					08 04
Easterhouse	d				07 23							07 38					07 53								08 08
Garrowhill	d				07 25							07 40					07 55								08 10
Shettleston	d				07 28							07 43					07 58								08 13
Carntyne	d				07 30							07 45					08 00								08 15
Springburn	d		07 19								07 39			07 49										08 09	
Barnhill	d		07 20								07 40			07 50										08 10	
Alexandra Parade	d		07 23								07 43			07 53										08 13	
Duke Street	d		07 24								07 44			07 54										08 14	
Bellgrove	d		07 26		07 33						07 46	07 48		07 56			08 03							08 16	08 18
High Street	d		07 28		07 35			07 40			07 48	07 50		07 58			08 05			08 10				08 18	08 20
Glasgow Queen Street 10 §	a		07 31		07 37			07 42			07 51	07 52		08 01			08 07			08 12				08 21	08 22
	d		07 32		07 40			07 43			07 53	07 53		08 02			08 10			08 13	08b21			08 23	08 23
Charing Cross	d		07 34		07 42			07 45			07 55	07 55		08 04			08 12			08 15				08 25	08 25
Argyle Street	d	07 23		07 34					07 42	07 42			07 53		08 02	08 04						08 12	08 12		
Glasgow Central 15 §	a	07 26		07 37		07c30			07 46	07 46			07 56		08 06	08 07						08 16	08 16		
	d	07 28		07 37					07 46	07 46			07 58		08 07	08 07						08 16	08 16		
Anderston	d	07 29		07 39					07 48	07 48			07 59		08 09	08 09						08 18	08 18		
Exhibition Centre	d	07 31		07 41					07 50	07 50			08 01		08 11	08 11						08 20	08 20		
Partick	d	07 35	07 39	07 45	07 47			07 50	07 54	07 54	08 00	08 00	08 05	08 09	08 15	08 15	08 17			08 20		08 24	08 24	08 30	08 30
Hyndland	d	07 38	07 41	07 47	07 50			07 53	07 56	07 56	08 02	08 02	08 08	08 11	08 17	08 17	08 20			08 23		08 26	08 26	08 32	08 32
Jordanhill	d		07 43						07 58	07 58				08 13								08 28	08 28		
Scotstounhill	d		07 45						08 00	08 00				08 15								08 30	08 30		
Garscadden	d		07 47						08 02	08 02				08 17								08 32	08 32		
Yoker	d		07 50						08 05	08 05				08 20								08 35	08 36		
Clydebank	d		07 52						08 07	08 07				08 22								08 37	08 38		
Anniesland	d	07 41		07 50				07 56			08 05	08 05	08 11		08 20	08 20				08 26				08 35	08 35
Westerton	d	07 44		07 53				07 59			08 08	08 08	08 14		08 23	08 23				08 29				08 38	08 38
Bearsden	d	07 46						08 01					08 16							08 31					
Hillfoot	d	07 48						08 03					08 18							08 33					
Milngavie	a	07 52					←	08 07					08e27						←	08 37					
Drumchapel	d			07 55 →			07 55				08 10	08 10			08 25 →	08 25 →			08 25					08 40	08 40
Drumry	d						07 57				08 12	08 12							08 27					08 42	08 42
Singer	d						08 00				08 15	08 15							08 30					08 45	08 45
Dalmuir	a		07 56		07 59		08 02		08 11	08 11	08 17	08 17		08 28			08 29		08 32		08 38	08 41	08 42	08 47	08 47
	d				07 59						08 18	08 18					08 29				08 39			08 48	08 48
Kilpatrick	d										08 21	08 21												08 51	08 51
Bowling	d										08 24	08 24												08 54	08 54
Dumbarton East	d				08 06						08 28	08 28					08 36							08 58	08 58
Dumbarton Central	d				08 08						08 30	08 30					08 38				08 48			09 00	09 00
Dalreoch	d				08 10						08 32	08 32					08 40							09 02	09 02
Renton	d										08 35	08 35												09 05	09 05
Alexandria	d										08 37	08 37												09 07	09 07
Balloch	a										08 40	08 40												09 10	09 10
Cardross	d				08e20												08 45								
Craigendoran	d				08e25												08 50								
Helensburgh Central	a				08e28												08 55				09f03				

For general notes see front of timetable
For details of catering facilities see Directory of Train Operators

§ Low Level

A From Edinburgh (Table 225)
B To Oban and to Mallaig (Table 227)
b Glasgow Queen Street High Level
c Glasgow Central High Level

e Saturdays dep. 5 minutes earlier
f Helensburgh Upper

Lanark, Coatbridge, Motherwell, Larkhall, Hamilton, Drumgelloch, Airdrie and Springburn → Glasgow → Milngavie, Dalmuir, Balloch and Helensburgh

Network Diagram - see first page of Table 220

		SR SX	SR SX	SR SO	SR SX A	SR SX	SR SO B	SR SX	SR SO	SR SX	SR	SR SX	SR	SR	SR SX	SR SO	SR SX C	SR SO	SR SX	SR	SR SX	SR SX	SR	SR	SR
Lanark	d							07 45								07 53						08 23			
Carluke	d							07 55								08 03	08 14					08 33			
Wishaw	d							08 03								08 08	08 18					08 38			
Holytown	d				08 02		08 02									08 13									
Shieldmuir	d							08 07									08 21					08 42			
Coatbridge Central	d		07 40																						
Whifflet	d		07 42																						
Motherwell	a		07 49					08 10								08 20	08 25					08 46			
	d	07 50	07 50	07 50				08 10						08 16	08 20	08 20	08 25					08 46			
Bellshill	d	07 56			08 06		08 06							08 22											
Uddingston	d	08 00					08 12	08 18						08 26			08 30								
Airbles	d		07 52	07 52											08 22	08 22									
Larkhall	d								08 07	08 07													08 37		
Merryton	d								08 09	08 09													08 39		
Chatelherault	d								08 12	08 12													08 42		
Hamilton Central	d		07 57	07 57					08 15	08 15					08 27	08 27							08 45		
Hamilton West	d		08 00	08 00					08 18	08 18					08 30	08 30							08 48		
Blantyre	d		08 03	08 03					08 21	08 21					08 33	08 33				←			08 51		
Newton	d		08 07	08 07											08 37	08 37				08 37					
Cambuslang	d	08 05	08 11	08 11			08 17			08 27				08 31	→	→				08 41					
Rutherglen	d	08 10	08 15	08 15					08 29	08 31				08 34						08 45		08 56	08 59		
Dalmarnock	d	08 12	08 17	08 17										08 36						08 47					
Bridgeton	d	08 14	08 19	08 19										08 38						08 49					
Drumgelloch	d										08 08													08 38	
Airdrie	a										08 11													08 41	
	d										08 12	08 22							08 27					08 42	
Coatdyke	d										08 14	08 24							08 29					08 44	
Coatbridge Sunnyside	d										08 16	08 26							08 31					08 46	
Blairhill	d										08 19	08 29							08 34					08 49	
Easterhouse	d										08 23								08 38					08 53	
Garrowhill	d										08 25								08 40					08 55	
Shettleston	d										08 28								08 43					08 58	
Carntyne	d										08 30								08 45					09 00	
Springburn	d					08 19												08 39			08 49				
Barnhill	d					08 20												08 40			08 50				
Alexandra Parade	d					08 23												08 43			08 53				
Duke Street	d					08 24												08 44			08 54				
Bellgrove	d					08 26					08 33							08 46	08 48		08 56			09 03	
High Street	d					08 28					08 35	08 40						08 48	08 50		08 58			09 05	
Glasgow Queen Street 10 §	a					08 31					08 37	08 42						08 51	08 52		09 01			09 07	
	d					08 32					08 40	08 43						08 53	08 53		09 02			09 10	
Charing Cross	d					08 34					08 42	08 45						08 55	08 55		09 04			09 12	
Argyle Street	d	08 18	08 23	08 23				08 31	08 34	08 34				08 42			08 47			08 53		09 01	09 04		
Glasgow Central 15 §	a	08 19	08 26	08 26	08b27		08b30	08 32	08 37	08 37				08 46			08 48			08 56		09 03	09 07		
	d	08 19	08 28	08 28				08 33	08 37	08 37				08 46			08 49			08 58		09 03	09 07		
Anderston	d	08a23	08 29	08 29				08 35	08 39	08 39				08 48			08 50			08 59		09 05	09 09		
Exhibition Centre	d		08 31	08 31				08 38	08 41	08 41				08 50			08 53			09 01		09 08	09 11		
Partick	d		08 35	08 35		08 39		08 42	08 45	08 45	08 47	08 50		08 54			08 57	09 00	09 00	09 05	09 09	09 12	09 15	09 17	
Hyndland	d		08 38	08 38		08 41		08 44	08 47	08 47	08 50	08 53		08 56			08 59	09 02	09 02	09 08	09 11	09 14	09 17	09 20	
Jordanhill	d					08 43		08 46						08 58			09 01				09 13	09 16			
Scotstounhill	d					08 45		08 48						09 00			09 03				09 15	09 19			
Garscadden	d					08 47		08a51						09 02			09a06				09 17	09a21			
Yoker	d					08 50								09 05							09 20				
Clydebank	d					08 52								09 07							09 22				
Anniesland	d		08 41	08 41					08 50	08 50		08 56						09 05	09 05	09 11			09 20		
Westerton	d		08 44	08 44					08 53	08 53		08 59						09 08	09 08	09 14			09 23		
Bearsden	d		08 46	08 46								09 01								09 16					
Hillfoot	d		08 48	08 48								09 03								09 18					
Milngavie	a		08 52	08 52								09 07	←							09 22					←
Drumchapel	d								08 55 →	08 55 →			08 55					09 10	09 10				09 25 →		09 25
Drumry	d												08 57					09 12	09 12						09 27
Singer	d												09 00					09 15	09 15						09 30
Dalmuir	a					08 56					08 59		09 02	09 11				09 17	09 17		09 26			09 29	09 32
	d										08 59							09 18	09 18					09 29	
Kilpatrick	d																	09 21	09 21						
Bowling	d																	09 24	09 24						
Dumbarton East	d										09 06							09 28	09 28					09 36	
Dumbarton Central	d										09 08							09 30	09 30					09 38	
Dalreoch	d										09 10							09 32	09 32					09 40	
Renton	d																	09 35	09 35						
Alexandria	d																	09 37	09 37						
Balloch	a																	09 40	09 40						
Cardross	d										09 15													09 45	
Craigendoran	d										09 20													09 50	
Helensburgh Central	a										09c25													09c55	

For general notes see front of timetable
For details of catering facilities see Directory of Train Operators

§ Low Level

A From Edinburgh (Table 225)
B From Edinburgh (from 29 March from Livingston South) (Table 225)
C From Carstairs (Table 225)

b Glasgow Central High Level
c Saturdays arr. 2 minutes earlier

Lanark, Coatbridge, Motherwell, Larkhall, Hamilton, Drumgelloch, Airdrie and Springburn → Glasgow → Milngavie, Dalmuir, Balloch and Helensburgh

Network Diagram - see first page of Table 220

		SR	SR	SR	SR	SR	SR		SR	SR	SR	SR	SR	SR	SR	SR	SR	SR	SR	SR	SR	SR	SR	SR	SR
		SX	SO	SX	SO	SX										SX	SO	SX							
																		A	B						
Lanark	d		08 23														08 53								
Carluke	d		08 33														09 03	09 26							
Wishaw	d		08 38														09 08								
Holytown	d																09 13		09 32						
Shieldmuir	d		08 42																						
Coatbridge Central	d																								
Whifflet	d																								
Motherwell	a		08 46														09 20	09 33							
	d		08 46	08 46			08 50							09 16		09 20	09 20	09 33							
Bellshill	d		08 52	08 52										09 22					09 36						
Uddingston	d		08 56	08 56										09 26					09 42						
Airbles	d						08 52									09 22	09 22								
Larkhall	d									09 07												09 37			
Merryton	d									09 09												09 39			
Chatelherault	d									09 12												09 42			
Hamilton Central	d						08 57			09 15						09 27	09 27					09 45			
Hamilton West	d						09 00			09 18						09 30	09 30					09 48			
Blantyre	d						09 03			09 21						09 33	09 33			←		09 51			
Newton	d						09 07									09 37	09 37			09 37					
Cambuslang	d		09 01	09 01			09 11							09 31		↪	↪		09 47	09 41					
Rutherglen	d		09 04	09 04			09 15			09 29				09 34						09 45		09 59			
Dalmarnock	d		09 06	09 06			09 17							09 36						09 47					
Bridgeton	d		09 08	09 08			09 19							09 38						09 49					
Drumgelloch	d										09 08												09 38		
Airdrie	a										09 11												09 41		
	d					08 57					09 12				09 27								09 42		
Coatdyke	d					08 59					09 14				09 29								09 44		
Coatbridge Sunnyside	d					09 01					09 16				09 31								09 46		
Blairhill	d					09 04					09 19				09 34								09 49		
Easterhouse	d					09 08					09 23				09 38								09 53		
Garrowhill	d					09 10					09 25				09 40								09 55		
Shettleston	d					09 13					09 28				09 43								09 58		
Carntyne	d					09 15					09 30				09 45								10 00		
Springburn	d				09 09				09 19												09 49				
Barnhill	d				09 10				09 20												09 50				
Alexandra Parade	d				09 13				09 23												09 53				
Duke Street	d				09 14				09 24												09 54				
Bellgrove	d	09 08			09 16	09 18			09 26		09 33	09 38			09 48						09 56		10 03		10 08
High Street	d	09 10			09 18	09 20			09 28		09 35	09 40			09 50						09 58		10 05		10 10
Glasgow Queen Street 10 §	a	09 12			09 21	09 22			09 31		09 37	09 42			09 52						10 01		10 07		10 12
	d	09 13			09 23	09 23			09 32		09 40	09 43			09 53						10 02		10 10		10 13
Charing Cross	d	09 15			09 25	09 25			09 34		09 42	09 45			09 55						10 04		10 12		10 15
Argyle Street	d		09 12	09 12			09 23			09 34				09 42						09 53		10 04			
Glasgow Central 15 §	a		09 16	09 16			09 26			09 37				09 46				09b55	10b00	09 56		10 07			
	d		09 16	09 16			09 28			09 37				09 46						09 58		10 07			
Anderston	d		09 18	09 18			09 29			09 39				09 48						09 59		10 09			
Exhibition Centre	d		09 20	09 20			09 31			09 41				09 50						10 01		10 11			
Partick	d	09 20	09 24	09 24	09 30	09 30	09 35		09 39	09 45	09 47	09 50		09 54	10 00					10 05	10 09	10 15	10 17		10 20
Hyndland	d	09 23	09 26	09 26	09 32	09 32	09 38		09 41	09 47	09 50	09 53		09 56	10 02					10 08	10 11	10 17	10 20		10 23
Jordanhill	d		09 28	09 28					09 43					09 58							10 13				
Scotstounhill	d		09 30	09 30					09 45					10 00							10 15				
Garscadden	d		09 32	09 32					09 47					10 02							10 17				
Yoker	d		09 35	09 35					09 50					10 05							10 20				
Clydebank	d		09 37	09 37					09 52					10 07							10 22				
Anniesland	d	09 26			09 35	09 35	09 41			09 50		09 56			10 05					10 11		10 20			10 26
Westerton	d	09 29			09 38	09 38	09 44			09 53		09 59			10 08					10 14		10 23			10 29
Bearsden	d	09 31					09 46					10 01								10 16					10 31
Hillfoot	d	09 33					09 48					10 03								10 18					10 33
Milngavie	a	09 37					09 52					10 07	←							10 22				←	10 37
Drumchapel	d				09 40	09 40				09 55			09 55		10 10							10 25		10 25	
Drumry	d				09 42	09 42				→			09 57		10 12							→		10 27	
Singer	d				09 45	09 45							10 00		10 15									10 30	
Dalmuir	a		09 41	09 43	09 47	09 47			09 56		09 59		10 02	10 11	10 17						10 26		10 29	10 32	
	d				09 48	09 48					09 59				10 18								10 29		
Kilpatrick	d				09 51	09 51									10 21										
Bowling	d				09 54	09 54									10 24										
Dumbarton East	d				09 58	09 58					10 06				10 28								10 36		
Dumbarton Central	d				10 00	10 00					10 08				10 30								10 38		
Dalreoch	d				10 02	10 02					10 10				10 32								10 40		
Renton	d				10 05	10 05									10 35										
Alexandria	d				10 07	10 07									10 37										
Balloch	a				10 10	10 10									10 40										
Cardross	d										10 15												10 45		
Craigendoran	d										10 20												10 50		
Helensburgh Central	a										10 23												10 56		

For general notes see front of timetable
For details of catering facilities see Directory of Train Operators

§ Low Level

A From North Berwick (Table 238)
B From Edinburgh (Saturdays from 29 March from Livingston South) (Table 225)

b Glasgow Central High Level

Lanark, Coatbridge, Motherwell, Larkhall, Hamilton, Drumgelloch, Airdrie and Springburn → Glasgow → Milngavie, Dalmuir, Balloch and Helensburgh

Network Diagram - see first page of Table 220

		SR	SR	SR	SR	SR	SR	SR	SR	SR	SR	SR	SR	SR	SR	SR	SR	SR	SR	SR	SR	SR	SR	SR
					SO	SO ◇																		
					A	B ⚒									C									
Lanark	d	09 23												09 53							10 23			
Carluke	d	09 33			09 49									10 02							10 33			
Wishaw	d	09 38												10 08							10 38			
Holytown	d													10 13	10 30									
Shieldmuir	d	09 42																			10 42			
Coatbridge Central	d																							
Whifflet	d																							
Motherwell	a	09 46			09 56									10 20							10 46			
	d	09 46		09 50	09 57							10 16		10 20							10 46		10 50	
Bellshill	d	09 52										10 22			10 36						10 52			
Uddingston	d	09 56										10 26			10 42						10 56			
Airbles	d			09 52										10 22									10 52	
Larkhall	d							10 07									10 37							
Merryton	d							10 09									10 39							
Chatelherault	d							10 12									10 42							
Hamilton Central	d			09 57				10 15						10 27			10 45						10 57	
Hamilton West	d			10 00				10 18						10 30			10 48						11 00	
Blantyre	d			10 03				10 21						10 33			10 51						11 03	
Newton	d			10 07										10 37									11 07	
Cambuslang	d	10 01		10 11								10 31		10 41	10 47						11 01		11 11	
Rutherglen	d	10 04		10 15				10 29				10 34		10 45			10 59				11 04		11 15	
Dalmarnock	d	10 06		10 17								10 36		10 47							11 06		11 17	
Bridgeton	d	10 08		10 19								10 38		10 49							11 08		11 19	
Drumgelloch	d								10 08									10 38						
Airdrie	a								10 11									10 41						
	d		09 57						10 12				10 27					10 42				10 57		
Coatdyke	d		09 59						10 14				10 29					10 44				10 59		
Coatbridge Sunnyside	d		10 01						10 16				10 31					10 46				11 01		
Blairhill	d		10 04						10 19				10 34					10 49				11 04		
Easterhouse	d		10 08						10 23				10 38					10 53				11 08		
Garrowhill	d		10 10						10 25				10 40					10 55				11 10		
Shettleston	d		10 13						10 28				10 43					10 58				11 13		
Carntyne	d		10 15						10 30				10 45					11 00				11 15		
Springburn	d						10 19									10 49								11 19
Barnhill	d						10 20									10 50								11 20
Alexandra Parade	d						10 23									10 53								11 23
Duke Street	d						10 24									10 54								11 24
Bellgrove	d		10 18				10 26		10 33		10 38		10 48			10 56		11 03		11 08		11 18		11 26
High Street	d		10 20				10 28		10 35		10 40		10 50			10 58		11 05		11 10		11 20		11 28
Glasgow Queen Street 10 §	a		10 22				10 31		10 37		10 42		10 52			11 01		11 07		11 12		11 22		11 31
	d		10 23			10b37	10 32		10 40		10 43		10 53			11 02		11 10		11 13		11 23		11 32
Charing Cross	d		10 25				10 34		10 42		10 45		10 55			11 04		11 12		11 15		11 25		11 34
Argyle Street	d	10 12		10 23				10 34				10 42		10 53			11 04				11 12		11 23	
Glasgow Central 15 §	a	10 16		10 26	10c14			10 37				10 46		10 56	11c00		11 07				11 16		11 26	
	d	10 16		10 28				10 37				10 46		10 58			11 07				11 16		11 28	
Anderston	d	10 18		10 29				10 39				10 48		10 59			11 09				11 18		11 29	
Exhibition Centre	d	10 20		10 31				10 41				10 50		11 01			11 11				11 20		11 31	
Partick	d	10 24	10 30	10 35			10 39	10 45	10 47		10 50	10 54	11 00	11 05		11 09	11 15	11 17		11 20	11 24	11 30	11 35	11 39
Hyndland	d	10 26	10 32	10 38			10 41	10 47	10 50		10 53	10 56	11 02	11 08		11 11	11 17	11 20		11 23	11 26	11 32	11 38	11 41
Jordanhill	d	10 28					10 43					10 58				11 13					11 28			11 43
Scotstounhill	d	10 30					10 45					11 00				11 15					11 30			11 45
Garscadden	d	10 32					10 47					11 02				11 17					11 32			11 47
Yoker	d	10 35					10 50					11 05				11 20					11 35			11 50
Clydebank	d	10 37					10 52					11 07				11 22					11 37			11 52
Anniesland	d		10 35	10 41				10 50			10 56		11 05	11 11			11 20			11 26		11 35	11 41	
Westerton	d		10 38	10 44				10 53			10 59		11 08	11 14			11 23			11 29		11 38	11 44	
Bearsden	d			10 46							11 01			11 16						11 31			11 46	
Hillfoot	d			10 48							11 03			11 18						11 33			11 48	
Milngavie	a			10 52						←	11 07			11 24					←	11 37			11 52	
Drumchapel	d		10 40					10 55 →		10 55			11 10				11 25 →		11 25			11 40		
Drumry	d		10 42							10 57			11 12						11 27			11 42		
Singer	d		10 45							11 00			11 15						11 30			11 45		
Dalmuir	a	10 41	10 47			10 52	10 56		10 59	11 02		11 11	11 17			11 26		11 29	11 32		11 42	11 47		11 56
	d		10 48			10 52			10 59				11 18					11 29				11 48		
Kilpatrick	d		10 51										11 21									11 51		
Bowling	d		10 54										11 24									11 54		
Dumbarton East	d		10 58						11 06				11 28					11 36				11 58		
Dumbarton Central	d		11 00			11 05			11 08				11 30					11 38				12 00		
Dalreoch	d		11 02						11 10				11 32					11 40				12 02		
Renton	d		11 05										11 35									12 05		
Alexandria	d		11 07										11 37									12 07		
Balloch	a		11 10										11 40									12 10		
Cardross	d								11 15									11 45						
Craigendoran	d								11 20									11 50						
Helensburgh Central	a					11e20			11f25									11 53						

For general notes see front of timetable
For details of catering facilities see Directory of Train Operators

§ Low Level

A Until 22 March from North Berwick (Table 238). From 29 March from Carstairs (Table 225)

B From 22 March. To Oban (Table 227)

C From Edinburgh (Saturdays from 29 March from Livingston South) (Table 225)

b Glasgow Queen Street High Level

c Glasgow Central High Level

e Helensburgh Upper

f Saturdays arr. 2 minutes later

Lanark, Coatbridge, Motherwell, Larkhall, Hamilton, Drumgelloch, Airdrie and Springburn → Glasgow → Milngavie, Dalmuir, Balloch and Helensburgh

Network Diagram - see first page of Table 220

		SR	SR	SR	SR	SR	SR	SR	SR	SR	SR	SR	SR	SR	SR	SR	SR	SR	SR	SR	SR	SR	SR	SR	SR
									A						◇ B										
Lanark	d							10 53								11 23									
Carluke	d							11 03								11 33									
Wishaw	d							11 08								11 38									
Holytown	d							11 13	11 32																
Shieldmuir	d															11 42									
Coatbridge Central	d																								
Whifflet	d																								
Motherwell	a							11 19								11 46									
	d					11 16		11 20								11 46		11 50						12 16	
Bellshill	d					11 22			11 36							11 52								12 22	
Uddingston	d					11 26			11 42							11 56								12 26	
Airbles	d							11 22										11 52							
Larkhall	d	11 07									11 37									12 07					
Merryton	d	11 09									11 39									12 09					
Chatelherault	d	11 12									11 42									12 12					
Hamilton Central	d	11 15						11 27			11 45							11 57		12 15					
Hamilton West	d	11 18						11 30			11 48							12 00		12 18					
Blantyre	d	11 21						11 33			11 51							12 03		12 21					
Newton	d							11 37										12 07							
Cambuslang	d					11 31		11 41	11 47							12 01		12 11						12 31	
Rutherglen	d	11 29				11 34		11 45			11 59					12 04		12 15		12 29				12 34	
Dalmarnock	d					11 36		11 47								12 06		12 17						12 36	
Bridgeton	d					11 38		11 49								12 08		12 19						12 38	
Drumgelloch	d		11 08									11 38									12 08				
Airdrie	a		11 11									11 41									12 11				
	d		11 12				11 27					11 42					11 57				12 12				12 27
Coatdyke	d		11 14				11 29					11 44					11 59				12 14				12 29
Coatbridge Sunnyside	d		11 16				11 31					11 46					12 01				12 16				12 31
Blairhill	d		11 19				11 34					11 49					12 04				12 19				12 34
Easterhouse	d		11 23				11 38					11 53					12 08				12 23				12 38
Garrowhill	d		11 25				11 40					11 55					12 10				12 25				12 40
Shettleston	d		11 28				11 43					11 58					12 13				12 28				12 43
Carntyne	d		11 30				11 45					12 00					12 15				12 30				12 45
Springburn	d									11 49									12 19						
Barnhill	d									11 50									12 20						
Alexandra Parade	d									11 53									12 23						
Duke Street	d									11 54									12 24						
Bellgrove	d		11 33		11 38		11 48			11 56		12 03		12 08			12 18		12 26		12 33		12 38		12 48
High Street	d		11 35		11 40		11 50			11 58		12 05		12 10			12 20		12 28		12 35		12 40		12 50
Glasgow Queen Street 10 §	a		11 37		11 42		11 52			12 01		12 07		12 12			12 22		12 31		12 37		12 42		12 52
	d		11 40		11 43		11 53			12 02		12 10		12 13	12b21		12 23		12 32		12 40		12 43		12 53
Charing Cross	d		11 42		11 45		11 55			12 04		12 12		12 15			12 25		12 34		12 42		12 45		12 55
Argyle Street	d	11 34				11 42		11 53			12 04					12 12		12 23		12 34				12 42	
Glasgow Central 15 §	a	11 37				11 46		11 56	12c00		12 07					12 16		12 26		12 37				12 46	
	d	11 37				11 46		11 58			12 07					12 16		12 28		12 37				12 46	
Anderston	d	11 39				11 48		11 59			12 09					12 18		12 29		12 39				12 48	
Exhibition Centre	d	11 41				11 50		12 01			12 11					12 20		12 31		12 41				12 50	
Partick	d	11 45	11 47		11 50	11 54	12 00	12 05		12 09	12 15	12 17		12 20		12 24	12 30	12 35	12 39	12 45	12 48		12 50	12 54	13 00
Hyndland	d	11 47	11 50		11 53	11 56	12 02	12 08		12 11	12 17	12 20		12 23		12 26	12 32	12 38	12 41	12 47	12 51		12 53	12 56	13 02
Jordanhill	d					11 58				12 13						12 28			12 43					12 58	
Scotstounhill	d					12 00				12 15						12 30			12 45					13 00	
Garscadden	d					12 02				12 17						12 32			12 47					13 02	
Yoker	d					12 05				12 20						12 35			12 50					13 05	
Clydebank	d					12 07				12 22						12 37			12 52					13 07	
Anniesland	d	11 50			11 56		12 05	12 11			12 20			12 26			12 35	12 41		12 50			12 56		13 05
Westerton	d	11 53			11 59		12 08	12 14			12 23			12 29			12 38	12 44		12 53			12 59		13 08
Bearsden	d				12 01			12 16						12 31				12 46					13 01		
Hillfoot	d				12 03			12 18						12 33				12 48					13 03		
Milngavie	a			←	12 07			12 22					←	12 37				12 52				←	13 07		
Drumchapel	d	11 55		11 55			12 10				12 25		12 25				12 40			12 55		12 55			13 10
Drumry	d	→		11 57			12 12				→		12 27				12 42			→		12 57			13 12
Singer	d			12 00			12 15						12 30				12 45					13 00			13 15
Dalmuir	a		11 59	12 02		12 11	12 17			12 26		12 29	12 32		12 38	12 41	12 47		12 56		12 59	13 02		13 11	13 17
	d		11 59				12 18					12 29			12 42		12 48				12 59				13 18
Kilpatrick	d						12 21										12 51								13 21
Bowling	d						12 24										12 54								13 24
Dumbarton East	d		12 06				12 28					12 36					12 58				13 06				13 28
Dumbarton Central	d		12 08				12 30					12 38			12 48		13 00				13 08				13 30
Dalreoch	d		12 10				12 32					12 40					13 02				13 10				13 32
Renton	d						12 35										13 05								13 35
Alexandria	d						12 37										13 07								13 37
Balloch	a						12 40										13 10								13 40
Cardross	d		12 15									12 45									13 15				
Craigendoran	d		12 20									12 50									13 20				
Helensburgh Central	a		12 23									12 53			13e03						13 26				

For general notes see front of timetable
For details of catering facilities see Directory of Train Operators

§ Low Level

A From Edinburgh (Saturdays from 29 March from Livingston South) (Table 225)
B To Oban and to Mallaig (Table 227)
b Glasgow Queen Street High Level
c Glasgow Central High Level
e Helensburgh Upper

Table 226

Mondays to Saturdays

Lanark, Coatbridge, Motherwell, Larkhall, Hamilton, Drumgelloch, Airdrie and Springburn → Glasgow → Milngavie, Dalmuir, Balloch and Helensburgh

Network Diagram - see first page of Table 220

		SR	SR A	SR	SR	SR	SR	SR	SR	SR	SR	SR	SR	SR	SR	SR	SR	SR	SR	SR A	SR	SR	SR	SR
Lanark	d	11 53							12 23										12 53					
Carluke	d	12 03							12 33										13 03					
Wishaw	d	12 08							12 38										13 08					
Holytown	d	12 13	12 32																13 13	13 32				
Shieldmuir	d								12 42															
Coatbridge Central	d																							
Whifflet	d																							
Motherwell	a	12 20							12 46										13 19					
	d	12 20							12 46		12 50						13 16		13 20					
Bellshill	d		12 36						12 52								13 22			13 36				
Uddingston	d		12 42						12 56								13 26			13 42				
Airbles	d	12 22									12 52								13 22					
Larkhall	d				12 37								13 07									13 37		
Merryton	d				12 39								13 09									13 39		
Chatelherault	d				12 42								13 12									13 42		
Hamilton Central	d	12 27			12 45						12 57		13 15						13 27			13 45		
Hamilton West	d	12 30			12 48						13 00		13 18						13 30			13 48		
Blantyre	d	12 33			12 51						13 03		13 21						13 33			13 51		
Newton	d	12 37									13 07								13 37					
Cambuslang	d	12 41	12 47						13 01		13 11						13 31		13 41	13 47				
Rutherglen	d	12 45			12 59				13 04		13 15		13 29				13 34		13 45			13 59		
Dalmarnock	d	12 47							13 06		13 17						13 36		13 47					
Bridgeton	d	12 49							13 08		13 19						13 38		13 49					
Drumgelloch	d					12 38								13 08									13 38	
Airdrie	a					12 41								13 11									13 41	
	d					12 42				12 57				13 12				13 27					13 42	
Coatdyke	d					12 44				12 59				13 14				13 29					13 44	
Coatbridge Sunnyside	d					12 46				13 01				13 16				13 31					13 46	
Blairhill	d					12 49				13 04				13 19				13 34					13 49	
Easterhouse	d					12 53				13 08				13 23				13 38					13 53	
Garrowhill	d					12 55				13 10				13 25				13 40					13 55	
Shettleston	d					12 58				13 13				13 28				13 43					13 58	
Carntyne	d					13 00				13 15				13 30				13 45					14 00	
Springburn	d			12 49								13 19									13 49			
Barnhill	d			12 50								13 20									13 50			
Alexandra Parade	d			12 53								13 23									13 53			
Duke Street	d			12 54								13 24									13 54			
Bellgrove	d			12 56		13 03		13 08		13 18		13 26		13 33		13 38		13 48			13 56		14 03	
High Street	d			12 58		13 05		13 10		13 20		13 28		13 35		13 40		13 50			13 58		14 05	
Glasgow Queen Street 10 § ⛴	a			13 01		13 07		13 12		13 22		13 31		13 37		13 42		13 52			14 01		14 07	
	d			13 02		13 10		13 13		13 23		13 32		13 40		13 43		13 53			14 02		14 10	
Charing Cross	d			13 04		13 12		13 15		13 25		13 34		13 42		13 45		13 55			14 04		14 12	
Argyle Street	d	12 53			13 04				13 12		13 23		13 34				13 42		13 53			14 04		
Glasgow Central 15 §	a	12 56	13b00		13 07				13 16		13 26		13 37				13 46		13 56	14b00		14 07		
	d	12 58			13 07				13 16		13 28		13 37				13 46		13 58			14 07		
Anderston	d	12 59			13 09				13 18		13 29		13 39				13 48		13 59			14 09		
Exhibition Centre	d	13 01			13 11				13 20		13 31		13 41				13 50		14 01			14 11		
Partick ⛴	d	13 05		13 09	13 15	13 17		13 20	13 24	13 30	13 35	13 39	13 45	13 47		13 50	13 54	14 00	14 05		14 09	14 15	14 17	
Hyndland	d	13 08		13 11	13 17	13 20		13 23	13 26	13 32	13 38	13 41	13 47	13 50		13 53	13 56	14 02	14 08		14 11	14 17	14 20	
Jordanhill	d			13 13					13 28			13 43					13 58				14 13			
Scotstounhill	d			13 15					13 30			13 45					14 00				14 15			
Garscadden	d			13 17					13 32			13 47					14 02				14 17			
Yoker	d			13 20					13 35			13 50					14 05				14 20			
Clydebank	d			13 22					13 37			13 52					14 07				14 22			
Anniesland	d	13 11			13 20			13 26		13 35	13 41		13 50			13 56		14 05	14 11			14 20		
Westerton	d	13 14			13 23			13 29		13 38	13 44		13 53			13 59		14 08	14 14			14 23		
Bearsden	d	13 16						13 31			13 46					14 01			14 16					
Hillfoot	d	13 18						13 33			13 48					14 03			14 18					
Milngavie	a	13 22					←	13 37			13 52				←	14 07			14 22					←
Drumchapel	d				13 25		13 25			13 40			13 55		13 55			14 10				14 25		14 25
Drumry	d				→		13 27			13 42			→		13 57			14 12				→		14 27
Singer	d						13 30			13 45					14 00			14 15						14 30
Dalmuir	a			13 26		13 29	13 32		13 41	13 47		13 56		13 59	14 02		14 11	14 17			14 26		14 29	14 32
	d					13 29				13 48				13 59				14 18					14 29	
Kilpatrick	d									13 51								14 21						
Bowling	d									13 54								14 24						
Dumbarton East	d					13 36				13 58				14 06				14 28					14 36	
Dumbarton Central	d					13 38				14 00				14 08				14 30					14 38	
Dalreoch	d					13 40				14 02				14 10				14 32					14 40	
Renton	d									14 05								14 35						
Alexandria	d									14 07								14 37						
Balloch	a									14 10								14 40						
Cardross	d					13 45								14 15									14 45	
Craigendoran	d					13 50								14 20									14 50	
Helensburgh Central	a					13 53								14 23									14 54	

For general notes see front of timetable
For details of catering facilities see Directory of Train Operators

§ Low Level

A From Edinburgh (Saturdays from 29 March from Livingston South) (Table 225)

b Glasgow Central High Level

Lanark, Coatbridge, Motherwell, Larkhall, Hamilton, Drumgelloch, Airdrie and Springburn → Glasgow → Milngavie, Dalmuir, Balloch and Helensburgh

Network Diagram - see first page of Table 220

		SR	SR	SR	SR	SR	SR	SR	SR	SR	SR	SR	SR	SR A	SR	SR	SR SO	SR SX	SR	SR	SR		SR	SR	SR
Lanark	d		13 23										13 53								14 23				
Carluke	d		13 33										14 03								14 33				
Wishaw	d		13 38										14 08								14 38				
Holytown	d												14 13	14 32											
Shieldmuir	d		13 42																		14 42				
Coatbridge Central	d																								
Whifflet	d																								
Motherwell	a		13 46										14 20								14 46				
	d		13 46		13 50						14 16		14 20								14 46			14 50	
Bellshill	d		13 52								14 22			14 36							14 52				
Uddingston	d		13 56								14 26			14 42							14 56				
Airbles	d				13 52								14 22											14 52	
Larkhall	d						14 07									14 37									
Merryton	d						14 09									14 39									
Chatelherault	d						14 12									14 42									
Hamilton Central	d				13 57		14 15						14 27			14 45								14 57	
Hamilton West	d				14 00		14 18						14 30			14 48								15 00	
Blantyre	d				14 03		14 21						14 33			14 51								15 03	
Newton	d				14 07								14 37											15 07	
Cambuslang	d		14 01		14 11						14 31		14 41	14 47							15 01			15 11	
Rutherglen	d		14 04		14 15		14 29				14 34		14 45			14 59					15 04			15 15	
Dalmarnock	d		14 06		14 17						14 36		14 47								15 06			15 17	
Bridgeton	d		14 08		14 19						14 38		14 49								15 08			15 19	
Drumgelloch	d							14 08									14 38	14 38							
Airdrie	a							14 11									14 41	14 41							
	d			13 57				14 12				14 27					14 42	14 42					14 57		
Coatdyke	d			13 59				14 14				14 29					14 44	14 44					14 59		
Coatbridge Sunnyside	d			14 01				14 16				14 31					14 46	14 46					15 01		
Blairhill	d			14 04				14 19				14 34					14 49	14 49					15 04		
Easterhouse	d			14 08				14 23				14 38					14 53	14 53					15 08		
Garrowhill	d			14 10				14 25				14 40					14 55	14 55					15 10		
Shettleston	d			14 13				14 28				14 43					14 58	14 58					15 13		
Carntyne	d			14 15				14 30				14 45					15 00	15 00					15 15		
Springburn	d					14 19									14 49										15 19
Barnhill	d					14 20									14 50										15 20
Alexandra Parade	d					14 23									14 53										15 23
Duke Street	d					14 24									14 54										15 24
Bellgrove	d	14 08		14 18		14 26		14 33		14 38		14 48			14 56		15 03	15 03		15 08			15 18		15 26
High Street	d	14 10		14 20		14 28		14 35		14 40		14 50			14 58		15 05	15 05		15 10			15 20		15 28
Glasgow Queen Street 10 §	a	14 12		14 22		14 31		14 37		14 42		14 52			15 01		15 07	15 07		15 12			15 22		15 31
	d	14 13		14 23		14 32		14 40		14 43		14 53			15 02		15 10	15 10		15 13			15 23		15 32
Charing Cross	d	14 15		14 25		14 34		14 42		14 45		14 55			15 04		15 12	15 12		15 15			15 25		15 34
Argyle Street	d		14 12		14 23		14 34				14 42		14 53			15 04					15 12			15 23	
Glasgow Central 15 §	a		14 16		14 26		14 37				14 46		14 56	15b02		15 07					15 16			15 26	
	d		14 16		14 28		14 37				14 46		14 58			15 07					15 16			15 28	
Anderston	d		14 18		14 29		14 39				14 48		14 59			15 09					15 18			15 29	
Exhibition Centre	d		14 20		14 31		14 41				14 50		15 01			15 11					15 20			15 31	
Partick	d	14 20	14 24	14 30	14 35	14 39	14 45	14 47		14 50	14 54	15 00	15 05		15 09	15 15	15 17	15 17		15 20	15 24		15 30	15 35	15 39
Hyndland	d	14 23	14 26	14 32	14 38	14 41	14 47	14 50		14 53	14 56	15 02	15 08		15 11	15 17	15 20	15 20		15 23	15 26		15 32	15 38	15 41
Jordanhill	d		14 28			14 43					14 58				15 13						15 28				15 43
Scotstounhill	d		14 30			14 45					15 00				15 15						15 30				15 45
Garscadden	d		14 32			14 47					15 02				15 17						15 32				15 47
Yoker	d		14 35			14 50					15 05				15 20						15 35				15 50
Clydebank	d		14 37			14 52					15 07				15 22						15 37				15 52
Anniesland	d	14 26		14 35	14 41		14 50			14 56		15 05	15 11			15 20				15 26			15 35	15 41	
Westerton	d	14 29		14 38	14 44		14 53			14 59		15 08	15 14			15 23				15 29			15 38	15 44	
Bearsden	d	14 31			14 46					15 01			15 16							15 31				15 46	
Hillfoot	d	14 33			14 48					15 03			15 18							15 33				15 48	
Milngavie	a	14 37			14 52				⟵	15 07			15 24						⟵	15 37				15 54	
Drumchapel	d			14 40			14 55 ⟶		14 55			15 10				15 25 ⟶			15 25				15 40		
Drumry	d			14 42					14 57			15 12							15 27				15 42		
Singer	d			14 45					15 00			15 15							15 30				15 45		
Dalmuir	a		14 41	14 47		14 56		14 59	15 02		15 11	15 17			15 26		15 28	15 29	15 32		15 41		15 47		15 56
	d			14 48				14 59				15 18					15 29	15 29					15 48		
Kilpatrick	d			14 51								15 21											15 51		
Bowling	d			14 54								15 24											15 54		
Dumbarton East	d			14 58				15 06				15 28					15 36	15 36					15 58		
Dumbarton Central	d			15 00				15 08				15 30					15 38	15 38					16 00		
Dalreoch	d			15 02				15 10				15 32					15 40	15c45					16 02		
Renton	d			15 05								15 35											16 05		
Alexandria	d			15 07								15 37											16 07		
Balloch	a			15 10								15 40											16 10		
Cardross	d							15 15									15 45	15 50							
Craigendoran	d							15 20									15 50	15 55							
Helensburgh Central	a							15 26									15 53	15 58							

For general notes see front of timetable
For details of catering facilities see Directory of Train Operators

§ Low Level

A From Edinburgh (Saturdays from 29 March from Livingston South) (Table 225)

b Glasgow Central High Level

c Arr. 1540

Lanark, Coatbridge, Motherwell, Larkhall, Hamilton, Drumgelloch, Airdrie and Springburn → Glasgow → Milngavie, Dalmuir, Balloch and Helensburgh

Network Diagram - see first page of Table 220

		SR	SR	SR	SR	SR	SR	SR	SR	SR	SR	SR	SR	SR	SR	SR	SR	SR	SR	SR	SR	SR	SR	SR	SR
									A										SO	SX					
Lanark	d							14 53								15 23									
Carluke	d							15 03								15 33									
Wishaw	d							15 08								15 38									
Holytown	d							15 13	15 32																
Shieldmuir	d															15 42									
Coatbridge Central	d																								
Whifflet	d																								
Motherwell	a							15 19								15 46									
	d					15 16		15 20								15 46		15 50							16 16
Bellshill	d					15 22			15 36							15 52									16 22
Uddingston	d					15 26			15 42							15 56									16 26
Airbles	d							15 22										15 52							
Larkhall	d	15 07										15 37									16 07				
Merryton	d	15 09										15 39									16 09				
Chatelherault	d	15 12										15 42									16 12				
Hamilton Central	d	15 15						15 27				15 45						15 57			16 15				
Hamilton West	d	15 18						15 30				15 48						16 00			16 18				
Blantyre	d	15 21						15 33				15 51						16 03			16 21				
Newton	d							15 37										16 07							
Cambuslang	d					15 31		15 41	15 47							16 01		16 11							16 31
Rutherglen	d	15 29				15 34		15 45				15 59				16 04		16 15			16 29				16 34
Dalmarnock	d					15 36		15 47								16 06		16 17							16 36
Bridgeton	d					15 38		15 49								16 08		16 19							16 38
Drumgelloch	d		15 08										15 38									16 08			
Airdrie	a		15 11										15 41									16 11			
	d		15 12				15 27						15 42				15 57					16 12			
Coatdyke	d		15 14				15 29						15 44				15 59					16 14			
Coatbridge Sunnyside	d		15 16				15 31						15 46				16 01					16 16			
Blairhill	d		15 19				15 34						15 49				16 04					16 19			
Easterhouse	d		15 23				15 38						15 53				16 08					16 23			
Garrowhill	d		15 25				15 40						15 55				16 10					16 25			
Shettleston	d		15 28				15 43						15 58				16 13					16 28			
Carntyne	d		15 30				15 45						16 00				16 15					16 30			
Springburn	d										15 49								16 19	16 22					
Barnhill	d										15 50								16 20	16 23					
Alexandra Parade	d										15 53								16 23	16 26					
Duke Street	d										15 54								16 24	16 27					
Bellgrove	d		15 33	15 38			15 48				15 56		16 03		16 08		16 18		16 26	16 29		16 33		16 38	
High Street	d		15 35	15 40			15 50				15 58		16 05		16 10		16 20		16 28	16 31		16 35		16 40	
Glasgow Queen Street 10 §	a		15 37	15 42			15 52				16 01		16 07		16 12		16 22		16 31	16 34		16 37		16 42	
	d		15 40	15 43			15 53			15 56	16 02		16 10		16 13		16 23		16 32	16 35		16 40		16 43	
Charing Cross	d		15 42	15 45			15 55				16 04		16 12		16 15		16 25		16 34	16 37		16 42		16 45	
Argyle Street	d	15 34				15 42		15 53				16 04				16 12		16 23			16 34				16 42
Glasgow Central 15 §	a	15 37				15 46		15 56	16b00			16 07				16 16		16 26			16 37				16 46
	d	15 37				15 46		15 58				16 07				16 16		16 28			16 37				16 46
Anderston	d	15 39				15 48		15 59				16 09				16 18		16 29			16 39				16 48
Exhibition Centre	d	15 41				15 50		16 01				16 11				16 20		16 31			16 41				16 50
Partick	d	15 45	15 47	15 50		15 54	16 00	16 05			16 09	16 15	16 17		16 20	16 24	16 30	16 35	16 39	16 42	16 45	16 47		16 50	16 54
Hyndland	d	15 47	15 50	15 53		15 56	16 02	16 08			16 11	16 17	16 20		16 23	16 26	16 32	16 38	16 41	16 44	16 47	16 50		16 53	16 56
Jordanhill	d					15 58					16 13					16 28			16 43	16 46					16 58
Scotstounhill	d					16 00					16 15					16 30			16 45	16 48					17 00
Garscadden	d					16 02					16 17					16 32			16 47	16 50					17 02
Yoker	d					16 05					16 20					16 35			16 50	16 53					17 05
Clydebank	d					16 07					16 22					16 37			16 52	16 55					17 07
Anniesland	d	15 50		15 56			16 05	16 11		16a14		16 20			16 26		16 35	16 41			16 50			16 56	
Westerton	d	15 53		15 59			16 08	16 14				16 23			16 29		16 38	16 44			16 53			16 59	
Bearsden	d			16 01				16 16							16 31			16 46						17 01	
Hillfoot	d			16 03				16 18							16 33			16 48						17 03	
Milngavie	a			16 07	←			16 22						←	16 37			16 52					←	17 07	
Drumchapel	d	15 55 →			15 55		16 10					16 25 →		16 25			16 40				16 55 →		16 55		
Drumry	d				15 57		16 12							16 27			16 42						16 57		
Singer	d				16 00		16 15							16 30			16 45						17 00		
Dalmuir	a		15 59		16 02	16 11	16 17				16 25		16 29	16 32		16 41	16 47		16 56	16 59		16 59	17 02		17 11
	d		15 59				16 18						16 29				16 48					16 59			
Kilpatrick	d						16 21										16 51								
Bowling	d						16 24										16 54								
Dumbarton East	d		16 06				16 28						16 36				16 58					17 06			
Dumbarton Central	d		16 08				16 30						16 38				17 00					17 08			
Dalreoch	d		16 10				16 32						16 40				17 02					17 10			
Renton	d						16 35										17 05								
Alexandria	d						16 37										17 07								
Balloch	a						16 40										17 10								
Cardross	d		16 15										16 45									17 15			
Craigendoran	d		16 20										16 50									17 20			
Helensburgh Central	a		16 23										16 53									17c26			

For general notes see front of timetable
For details of catering facilities see Directory of Train Operators

§ Low Level

A From Edinburgh (Saturdays from 29 March from Livingston South) (Table 225)

b Glasgow Central High Level

c Saturdays arr. 3 minutes earlier

Lanark, Coatbridge, Motherwell, Larkhall, Hamilton, Drumgelloch, Airdrie and Springburn → Glasgow → Milngavie, Dalmuir, Balloch and Helensburgh

Network Diagram - see first page of Table 220

		SR	SR	SR A	SR SO	SR SX	SR	SR	SR SX	SR	SR		SR	SR SX	SR	SR	SR SO B	SR SO C	SR	SR SX	SR SO	SR SX	SR SO	SR SX	SR
Lanark	d		15 53										16 23												
Carluke	d		16 03										16 33				16 47	16 55							
Wishaw	d		16 08										16 38				16 53	17 00							
Holytown	d		16 13	16 32																					
Shieldmuir	d												16 42												
Coatbridge Central	d																								
Whifflet	d																								
Motherwell	a		16 20										16 46				16 59	17 04							
	d		16 20										16 46			16 50	17 00	17 04							
Bellshill	d			16 36									16 52												
Uddingston	d			16 42									16 56												
Airbles	d		16 22													16 52									
Larkhall	d						16 37																		17 07
Merryton	d						16 39																		17 09
Chatelherault	d						16 42																		17 12
Hamilton Central	d		16 27				16 45									16 57									17 15
Hamilton West	d		16 30				16 48									17 00									17 18
Blantyre	d		16 33				16 51									17 03			←						17 21
Newton	d		16 37													17 07			17 07						
Cambuslang	d		16 41	16 47									17 01			→			17 11						
Rutherglen	d		16 45				16 59						17 04						17 15						17 29
Dalmarnock	d		16 47										17 06						17 17						
Bridgeton	d		16 49										17 08						17 19						
Drumgelloch	d							16 38																	
Airdrie	a							16 41																	
	d	16 27						16 42							16 57										
Coatdyke	d	16 29						16 44							16 59										
Coatbridge Sunnyside	d	16 31						16 46							17 01										
Blairhill	d	16 34						16 49							17 04										
Easterhouse	d	16 38						16 53							17 08										
Garrowhill	d	16 40						16 55							17 10										
Shettleston	d	16 43						16 58							17 13										
Carntyne	d	16 45						17 00							17 15										
Springburn	d				16 49	16 52																	17 19	17 22	
Barnhill	d				16 50	16 53																	17 20	17 23	
Alexandra Parade	d				16 53	16 56																	17 23	17 26	
Duke Street	d				16 54	16 57																	17 24	17 27	
Bellgrove	d	16 48			16 56	16 59		17 03		17 08				17 15	17 18					17 27			17 26	17 29	
High Street	d	16 50			16 58	17 01		17 05		17 10				17 17	17 20					17 29			17 28	17 31	
Glasgow Queen Street 10 §	a	16 52			17 01	17 04		17 07		17 12				17 19	17 22					17 31			17 31	17 34	
	d	16 53			17 02	17 05		17 10		17 13				17 20	17 23					17 31			17 32	17 35	
Charing Cross	d	16 55			17 04	17 07		17 12		17 15				17 22	17 25					17 34			17 34	17 37	
Argyle Street	d		16 53				17 04						17 12						17 23						17 34
Glasgow Central 15 §	a		16 56	17b00			17 07						17 16				17b22	17b23	17 26						17 37
	d		16 58				17 07						17 16						17 28						17 37
Anderston	d		16 59				17 09						17 18						17 29						17 39
Exhibition Centre	d		17 01				17 11						17 20						17 31						17 41
Partick	d	17 00	17 05		17 09	17 12	17 15	17 17		17 20			17 24	17 27	17 30				17 35	17 39			17 39	17 42	17 45
Hyndland	d	17 02	17 08		17 11	17 14	17 17	17 20		17 23			17 26		17 32				17 38				17 41	17 44	17 47
Jordanhill	d				17 13	17 16			←				17 28										17 43	17 46	
Scotstounhill	d				17 15	17 18							17 30										17 45	17 48	
Garscadden	d				17 17	17 20			17 20				17 32										17 47	17 50	
Yoker	d				17 20	→			17 23				17 35										17 50	17 53	
Clydebank	d				17 22				17 25				17 37										17 52	17 55	
Anniesland	d	17 05	17 11				17 20			17 26					17 35				17 41						17 50
Westerton	d	17 08	17 14				17 23			17 29					17 38				17 44						17 53
Bearsden	d		17 16							17 31									17 46						
Hillfoot	d		17 18							17 33									17 48						
Milngavie	a		17 22							17 37	←								17 52						
Drumchapel	d	17 10					17 25 →				17 25				17 40						←	←			17 55 →
Drumry	d	17 12									17 27				17 42 →						17 42	17 42			
Singer	d	17 15									17 30										17 45	17 45			
Dalmuir	a	17 17			17 26			17 28	17 29		17 32		17 41								17 47	17 47	17 56	17 59	
	d	17 18						17 29													17 48	17 50			
Kilpatrick	d	17 21																			17 51	17 52			
Bowling	d	17 24																			17 54	17 55			
Dumbarton East	d	17 28						17 36													17 58	18 00			
Dumbarton Central	d	17 30						17 38						17 46						17c59	18 00	18 02			
Dalreoch	d	17 32						17 40						17 48						18 00	18 02	18 03			
Renton	d	17 35																		18 03	18 05				
Alexandria	d	17 37																		18 06	18 07				
Balloch	a	17 41																		18 08	18 10				
Cardross	d							17 45						17 53								18 08			
Craigendoran	d							17 50						17 58								18 17			
Helensburgh Central	a							17e56						18 01								18 20			

For general notes see front of timetable
For details of catering facilities see Directory of Train Operators

§ Low Level

A From Edinburgh (Saturdays from 29 March from Livingston South) (Table 225)

B From 29 March. From Carstairs (Table 225)

C Until 22 March. From North Berwick (Table 238)

b Glasgow Central High Level

c Arr. 1755

e Saturdays arr. 3 minutes earlier

Table 226

Mondays to Saturdays

Lanark, Coatbridge, Motherwell, Larkhall, Hamilton, Drumgelloch, Airdrie and Springburn → Glasgow → Milngavie, Dalmuir, Balloch and Helensburgh

Network Diagram - see first page of Table 220

		SR	SR	SR	SR	SR	SR	SR	SR	SR	SR	SR	SR	SR	SR	SR	SR	SR	SR	SR	SR	SR	SR		SR
					SX	SO		SX	SO			SO	SX							SX	SO		SX		SO
										A							◇ B								
Lanark	d				16 53				16 53									17 23							
Carluke	d				17 03				17 03									17 33							
Wishaw	d				17 08				17 08									17 38							
Holytown	d								17 13	17 32															
Shieldmuir	d				17 12													17 42							
Coatbridge Central	d												17 30										17 56		
Whifflet	d												17 32										17 58		
Motherwell	a				17 16				17 19				17 39					17 45					18 07		
	d				17 16	17 16		17 20	17 20				17 39					17 46			17 50		18 10		
Bellshill	d				17 22	17 22				17 36								17 52					18 16		
Uddingston	d				17 26	17 26				17 42								17 56					18 20		
Airbles	d							17 22	17 22				17 42								17 52				
Larkhall	d											17 37								17 49					18 07
Merryton	d											17 39								17 51					18 09
Chatelherault	d											17 42								17 54					18 12
Hamilton Central	d							17 27	17 27			17 45	17 47							17 57	17 57				18 15
Hamilton West	d							17 30	17 30			17 48	17 49							18 00	18 00				18 18
Blantyre	d							17 33	17 33			17 51	17 53							18 03	18 03				18 21
Newton	d							17 37	17 37											18 07	18 07				
Cambuslang	d				17 31	17 31		17 41	17 41	17 47								18 01		18 11	18 11				
Rutherglen	d				17 34	17 34		17 45	17 45			17 59	18 00					18 04		18 15	18 15		18 29		18 29
Dalmarnock	d				17 36	17 36		17 47	17 47									18 06		18 17	18 17				
Bridgeton	d				17 38	17 38		17 49	17 49									18 08		18 19	18 19				
Drumgelloch	d	17 08												17 38											
Airdrie	a	17 11												17 41											
	d	17 12					17 27							17 42					17 57						
Coatdyke	d	17 14					17 29							17 44					17 59						
Coatbridge Sunnyside	d	17 16					17 31							17 46					18 01						
Blairhill	d	17 19					17 34							17 49					18 04						
Easterhouse	d	17 23					17 38							17 53					18 08						
Garrowhill	d	17 25					17 40							17 55					18 10						
Shettleston	d	17 28					17 43							17 58					18 13						
Carntyne	d	17 30					17 45							18 00					18 15						
Springburn	d										17 49											18 19			
Barnhill	d										17 50											18 20			
Alexandra Parade	d										17 53											18 23			
Duke Street	d										17 54											18 24			
Bellgrove	d	17 33		17 38			17 48				17 56			18 03		18 08			18 18			18 26			
High Street	d	17 35		17 40			17 50				17 58			18 05		18 10			18 20			18 28			
Glasgow Queen Street 10 §	a	17 37		17 42			17 52				18 01			18 07		18 12			18 22			18 31			
	d	17 40		17 43			17 53				18 02			18 10		18 13	18b21		18 23			18 32			
Charing Cross	d	17 42		17 45			17 55				18 04			18 12		18 15			18 25			18 34			
Argyle Street	d				17 42	17 42		17 53	17 53			18 04	18 05					18 12		18 23	18 23		18 34		18 34
Glasgow Central 15 §	a				17 46	17 46		17 56	17 56	18c00		18 07	18 07					18 16		18 26	18 26		18 37		18 37
	d				17 46	17 46		17 58	17 58			18 07	18 07					18 16		18 28	18 28		18 37		18 37
Anderston	d				17 48	17 48		17 59	17 59			18 09	18 09					18 18		18 29	18 29		18 39		18 39
Exhibition Centre	d				17 50	17 50		18 01	18 01			18 11	18 11					18 20		18 31	18 31		18 41		18 41
Partick	d	17 47		17 50	17 54	17 54	18 00	18 05	18 05		18 09	18 15	18 15	18 17		18 20		18 24	18 30	18 35	18 35	18 39	18 45		18 45
Hyndland	d	17 50		17 53	17 56	17 56	18 02	18 08	18 08		18 11	18 17	18 17	18 20		18 23		18 26	18 32	18 38	18 38	18 41	18 47		18 47
Jordanhill	d				17 58	17 58					18 13							18 28				18 43			
Scotstounhill	d				18 00	18 00					18 15							18 30				18 45			
Garscadden	d				18 02	18 02					18 17							18 32				18a47			
Yoker	d				18 05	18 05					18 20							18 35							
Clydebank	d				18 07	18 07					18 22							18 37							
Anniesland	d			17 56			18 05	18 11	18 11			18 20	18 20			18 26			18 35	18 41	18 41		18 50		18 50
Westerton	d			17 59			18 08	18 14	18 14			18 23	18 23			18 29			18 38	18 44	18 44		18 53		18 53
Bearsden	d			18 01				18 16	18 16							18 31				18 46	18 46				
Hillfoot	d			18 03				18 18	18 18							18 33				18 48	18 48				
Milngavie	a		←	18 08				18 22	18 22						←	18 37				18 52	18 52				
Drumchapel	d		17 55				18 10					18 25 →	18 25 →		18 25				18 40				18 55		18 55
Drumry	d		17 57				18 12								18 27				18 42				18 57		18 57
Singer	d		18 00				18 15								18 30				18 45				19 00		19 00
Dalmuir	a	17 59	18 04		18 11	18 13	18 17				18 26			18 29	18 32		18 35	18 41	18 47				19 02		19 02
	d	17 59					18 18							18 29			18 37		18 48						
Kilpatrick	d						18 21												18 51						
Bowling	d						18 24												18 54						
Dumbarton East	d	18 06					18 28							18 36					18 58						
Dumbarton Central	d	18 08					18 30							18 38			18 46		19 00						
Dalreoch	d	18 10					18 32							18 40					19 02						
Renton	d						18 35												19 05						
Alexandria	d						18 37												19 07						
Balloch	a						18 40												19 10						
Cardross	d	18 15												18 45											
Craigendoran	d	18 20												18 50											
Helensburgh Central	a	18 26												18 53			19e02								

For general notes see front of timetable
For details of catering facilities see Directory of Train Operators

§ Low Level

A From Edinburgh (Saturdays from 29 March from Livingston South) (Table 225)
B To Oban and to Mallaig (Table 227)
b Glasgow Queen Street High Level
c Glasgow Central High Level
e Helensburgh Upper

Lanark, Coatbridge, Motherwell, Larkhall, Hamilton, Drumgelloch, Airdrie and Springburn → Glasgow → Milngavie, Dalmuir, Balloch and Helensburgh

Network Diagram - see first page of Table 220

Station		SR	SR SX	SR SO	SR	SR SX	SR SO	SR SX A	SR	SR	SR	SR SO B	SR	SR	SR SX	SR SO	SR SX C	SR SX A	SR	SR	SR	SR	SR	SR SX D	SR
Lanark	d						17 53						18 23										18 53		
Carluke	d						18 03						18 33				18 44						19 03	19 14	
Wishaw	d						18 08						18 38				18 53						19 08	19 20	
Holytown	d						18 13	18 27				18 31						19 02					19 13		
Shieldmuir	d												18 42				18 56								
Coatbridge Central	d														18 39										
Whifflet	d														18 41										
Motherwell	a						18 20	18 36				18 40	18 45		18 49		18 59						19 19	19 25	
	d			18 16		18 20	18 20						18 46		18 50	18 50					19 16		19 20	19 25	
Bellshill	d			18 22									18 52					19 06			19 22				
Uddingston	d			18 26									18 56					19 12			19 26				
Airbles	d					18 22	18 22								18 52	18 52							19 22		
Larkhall	d		18 06							18 37									19 07						
Merryton	d		18 08							18 39									19 09						
Chatelherault	d		18 15							18 42									19 12						
Hamilton Central	d		18 19			18 27	18 27			18 45					18 57	18 57			19 15				19 27		
Hamilton West	d		18 21			18 30	18 30			18 48					19 00	19 00			19 18				19 30		
Blantyre	d		18 25			18 33	18 33			18 51					19 03	19 03			19 21				19 33		←
Newton	d					18 37	18 37								19 07	19 07							19 37		19 37
Cambuslang	d		18 31	18 31		18 41	18 41						19 01		19 11	19 11		19 17			19 31		→		19 41
Rutherglen	d		18 34	18 34		18 45	18 45			18 59			19 04		19 15	19 15			19 29		19 34				19 45
Dalmarnock	d		18 36	18 36		18 47	18 47						19 06		19 17	19 17					19 36				19 47
Bridgeton	d		18 38	18 38		18 49	18 49						19 08		19 19	19 19					19 38				19 49
Drumgelloch	d	18 08									18 38									19 08					
Airdrie	a	18 11									18 41									19 11					
	d	18 12			18 27						18 42									19 12					
Coatdyke	d	18 14			18 29						18 44									19 14					
Coatbridge Sunnyside	d	18 16			18 31						18 46									19 16					
Blairhill	d	18 19			18 34						18 49									19 19					
Easterhouse	d	18 23			18 38						18 53									19 23					
Garrowhill	d	18 25			18 40						18 55									19 25					
Shettleston	d	18 28			18 43						18 58									19 28					
Carntyne	d	18 30			18 45						19 00									19 30					
Springburn	d								18 49					19 09								19 39			
Barnhill	d								18 50					19 10								19 40			
Alexandra Parade	d								18 53					19 13								19 43			
Duke Street	d								18 54					19 14								19 44			
Bellgrove	d	18 33			18 48				18 56		19 03			19 16						19 33		19 46			
High Street	d	18 35			18 50				18 58		19 05			19 18						19 35		19 48			
Glasgow Queen Street 10 §	a	18 37			18 52				19 01		19 07			19 21						19 37		19 51			
	d	18 40			18 53				19 02		19 10			19 23						19 40		19 53			
Charing Cross	d	18 42			18 55				19 04		19 12			19 25						19 42		19 55			
Argyle Street	d		18 42	18 42		18 53	18 53			19 04			19 12		19 23	19 23			19 34		19 42				19 53
Glasgow Central 15 §	a		18 46	18 46		18 56	18 56			19 07			19 16		19 26	19 26		19b30	19 37		19 46			19b47	19 56
	d		18 46	18 46		18 58	18 58			19 07			19 16		19 28	19 28			19 37		19 46				19 58
Anderston	d		18 48	18 48		18 59	18 59			19 09			19 18		19 29	19 29			19 39		19 48				19 59
Exhibition Centre	d		18 50	18 50		19 01	19 01			19 11			19 20		19 31	19 31			19 41		19 50				20 01
Partick	d	18 47	18a53	18a53	19 00	19 05	19 05		19 09	19 15	19 17		19a23	19 30	19 35	19 35			19 45	19 47	19a53	20 00			20 05
Hyndland	d	18 50			19 02	19 08	19 08		19 11	19 17	19 20			19 32	19 38	19 38			19 47	19 50		20 02			20 08
Jordanhill	d	18 52							19 13		19 22									19 52					
Scotstounhill	d	18 54							19 15		19 24									19 54					
Garscadden	d	18 56							19a17		19 26									19 56					
Yoker	d	18 59									19 29									19 59					
Clydebank	d	19 01									19 31									20 01					
Anniesland	d				19 05	19 11	19 11			19 20				19 35	19 41	19 41			19 50			20 05			20 11
Westerton	d				19 08	19 14	19 14			19 23				19 38	19 44	19 44			19 53			20 08			20 14
Bearsden	d					19 16	19 16								19 46	19 46									20 16
Hillfoot	d					19 18	19 18								19 48	19 48									20 18
Milngavie	a					19 22	19 22								19 52	19 52									20 22
Drumchapel	d				19 10					19 25				19 40					19 55			20 10			
Drumry	d				19 12					19 27				19 42					19 57			20 12			
Singer	d				19 15					19 30				19 45					20 00			20 15			
Dalmuir	a	19 04			19 17					19 32	19 34			19 47					20 02	20 04		20 17			
	d	19 05			19 18						19 35			19 48						20 05		20 18			
Kilpatrick	d				19 21									19 51								20 21			
Bowling	d				19 24									19 54								20 24			
Dumbarton East	d	19 12			19 28						19 42			19 58						20 12		20 28			
Dumbarton Central	d	19 14			19 30						19 44			20 00						20 14		20 30			
Dalreoch	d	19 16			19 32						19 46			20 02						20 16		20 32			
Renton	d				19 35									20 05								20 35			
Alexandria	d				19 37									20 07								20 37			
Balloch	a				19 40									20 10								20 40			
Cardross	d	19 21									19 51									20 21					
Craigendoran	d	19 26									19 56									20 26					
Helensburgh Central	a	19 29									19 59									20 29					

For general notes see front of timetable
For details of catering facilities see Directory of Train Operators

§ Low Level

A From Edinburgh (Table 225)
B From Edinburgh (from 29 March from Livingston South) (Table 225)
C From Carstairs (Table 225)
D From North Berwick (Table 238)
b Glasgow Central High Level

Lanark, Coatbridge, Motherwell, Larkhall, Hamilton, Drumgelloch, Airdrie and Springburn → Glasgow → Milngavie, Dalmuir, Balloch and Helensburgh

Network Diagram - see first page of Table 220

		SR SO A	SR	SR	SR	SR	SR	SR	SR	SR	SR	SR	SR	SR	SR	SR	SR	SR	SR	SR	SR	SR	SR B	SR
Lanark	d				19 23							19 53			20 23							20 53		
Carluke	d				19 33							20 03			20 33							21 03		
Wishaw	d				19 38							20 08			20 38							21 08		
Holytown	d	19 32										20 13										21 13	21 32	
Shieldmuir	d				19 42										20 42									
Coatbridge Central	d																							
Whifflet	d																							
Motherwell	a				19 46							20 20			20 46							21 19		
	d				19 46		19 50			20 16		20 20			20 46		20 50			21 16		21 20		
Bellshill	d	19 36			19 52					20 22					20 52					21 22			21 36	
Uddingston	d	19 42			19 56					20 26					20 56					21 26			21 42	
Airbles	d						19 52					20 22					20 52					21 22		
Larkhall	d		19 37					20 07					20 37					21 07						21 37
Merryton	d		19 39					20 09					20 39					21 09						21 39
Chatelherault	d		19 42					20 12					20 42					21 12						21 42
Hamilton Central	d		19 45				19 57	20 15				20 27	20 45				20 57	21 15				21 27		21 45
Hamilton West	d		19 48				20 00	20 18				20 30	20 48				21 00	21 18				21 30		21 48
Blantyre	d		19 51				20 03	20 21				20 33	20 51				21 03	21 21				21 33		21 51
Newton	d						20 07					20 37					21 07					21 37		
Cambuslang	d	19 47			20 01		20 11			20 31		20 41			21 01		21 11			21 31		21 41	21 47	
Rutherglen	d		19 59		20 04		20 15	20 29		20 34		20 45	20 59		21 04		21 15	21 29		21 34		21 45		21 59
Dalmarnock	d				20 06		20 17			20 36		20 47			21 06		21 17			21 36		21 47		
Bridgeton	d				20 08		20 19			20 38		20 49			21 08		21 19			21 38		21 49		
Drumgelloch	d			19 38					20 08					20 38					21 08					
Airdrie	a			19 41					20 11					20 41					21 11					
	d			19 42					20 12					20 42					21 12					
Coatdyke	d			19 44					20 14					20 44					21 14					
Coatbridge Sunnyside	d			19 46					20 16					20 46					21 16					
Blairhill	d			19 49					20 19					20 49					21 19					
Easterhouse	d			19 53					20 23					20 53					21 23					
Garrowhill	d			19 55					20 25					20 55					21 25					
Shettleston	d			19 58					20 28					20 58					21 28					
Carntyne	d			20 00					20 30					21 00					21 30					
Springburn	d					20 09					20 39					21 09					21 39			
Barnhill	d					20 10					20 40					21 10					21 40			
Alexandra Parade	d					20 13					20 43					21 13					21 43			
Duke Street	d					20 14					20 44					21 14					21 44			
Bellgrove	d			20 03		20 16			20 33		20 46			21 03		21 16			21 33		21 46			
High Street	d			20 05		20 18			20 35		20 48			21 05		21 18			21 35		21 48			
Glasgow Queen Street 10 § ⛴	a			20 07		20 21			20 37		20 51			21 07		21 21			21 37		21 51			
	d			20 10		20 23			20 40		20 53			21 10		21 23			21 40		21 53			
Charing Cross	d			20 12		20 25			20 42		20 55			21 12		21 25			21 42		21 55			
Argyle Street	d		20 04		20 12		20 23	20 34		20 42		20 53	21 04		21 12		21 23	21 34		21 42		21 53		22 04
Glasgow Central 15 §	a	20b00	20 07		20 16		20 26	20 37		20 46		20 56	21 07		21 16		21 26	21 37		21 46		21 56	22b00	22 07
	d		20 07		20 16		20 28	20 37		20 46		20 58	21 07		21 16		21 28	21 37		21 46		21 58		22 07
Anderston	d		20 09		20 18		20 29	20 39		20 48		20 59	21 09		21 18		21 29	21 39		21 48		21 59		22 09
Exhibition Centre	d		20 11		20 20		20 31	20 41		20 50		21 01	21 11		21 20		21 31	21 41		21 50		22 01		22 11
Partick ⛴	d		20 15	20 17	20a23	20 30	20 35	20 45	20 47	20a53	21 00	21 05	21 15	21 17	21a23	21 30	21 35	21 45	21 47	21a53	22 00	22 05		22 15
Hyndland	d		20 17	20 20		20 32	20 38	20 47	20 50		21 02	21 08	21 17	21 20		21 32	21 38	21 47	21 50		22 02	22 08		22 17
Jordanhill	d			20 22					20 52					21 22					21 52					
Scotstounhill	d			20 24					20 54					21 24					21 54					
Garscadden	d			20 26					20 56					21 26					21 56					
Yoker	d			20 29					20 59					21 29					21 59					
Clydebank	d			20 31					21 01					21 31					22 01					
Anniesland	d		20 20			20 35	20 41	20 50			21 05	21 11	21 20			21 35	21 41	21 50			22 05	22 11		22 20
Westerton	d		20 23			20 38	20 44	20 53			21 08	21 14	21 23			21 38	21 44	21 53			22 08	22 14		22 23
Bearsden	d						20 46					21 16					21 46					22 16		
Hillfoot	d						20 48					21 18					21 48					22 18		
Milngavie	a						20 52					21 24					21 52					22 22		
Drumchapel	d		20 25			20 40		20 55			21 10		21 25			21 40		21 55			22 10			22 25
Drumry	d		20 27			20 42		20 57			21 12		21 27			21 42		21 57			22 12			22 27
Singer	d		20 30			20 45		21 00			21 15		21 30			21 45		22 00			22 15			22 30
Dalmuir	a		20 32	20 34		20 47		21 02	21 04		21 17		21 32	21 34		21 47		22 02	22 04		22 17			22 32
	d			20 35		20 48			21 05		21 18			21 35		21 48			22 05		22 18			
Kilpatrick	d					20 51					21 21					21 51					22 21			
Bowling	d					20 54					21 24					21 54					22 24			
Dumbarton East	d			20 42		20 58			21 12		21 28			21 42		21 58			22 12		22 28			
Dumbarton Central	d			20 44		21 00			21 14		21 30			21 44		22 00			22 14		22 30			
Dalreoch	d			20 46		21 02			21 16		21 32			21 46		22 02			22 16		22 32			
Renton	d					21 05					21 35					22 05					22 35			
Alexandria	d					21 07					21 37					22 07					22 37			
Balloch	a					21 10					21 40					22 10					22 40			
Cardross	d			20 51					21 21					21 51					22 21					
Craigendoran	d			20 56					21 26					21 56					22 26					
Helensburgh Central	a			20 59					21 29					21 59					22 29					

For general notes see front of timetable
For details of catering facilities see Directory of Train Operators

§ Low Level

A From Edinburgh (from 29 March from Livingston South) (Table 225)

B From Edinburgh (Saturdays from 29 March from Livingston South) (Table 225)

b Glasgow Central High Level

Lanark, Coatbridge, Motherwell, Larkhall, Hamilton, Drumgelloch, Airdrie and Springburn → Glasgow → Milngavie, Dalmuir, Balloch and Helensburgh

Network Diagram - see first page of Table 220

Station		SR	SR	SR	SR	SR	SR	SR	SR	SR	SR	SR	SR	SR	SR	SR	SR	SR SX A	SR FO	SR FX	SR FO	SR FO	SR SO B
Lanark	d		21 23							21 53			22 23										
Carluke	d		21 33							22 03			22 33										
Wishaw	d		21 38							22 08			22 38										
Holytown	d									22 13								23 16					23 48
Shieldmuir	d		21 42										22 42										
Coatbridge Central	d																						
Whifflet	d																						
Motherwell	a		21 46							22 19			22 46										
	d		21 46		21 50			22 16		22 20			22 46		22 50						23 20		
Bellshill	d		21 52					22 22					22 52					23 20					23 52
Uddingston	d		21 56					22 26					22 56					23 26					23 58
Airbles	d				21 52					22 22					22 52						23 22		
Larkhall	d					22 07					22 37					23 07						23 37	
Merryton	d					22 09					22 39					23 09						23 39	
Chatelherault	d					22 12					22 42					23 12						23 42	
Hamilton Central	d				21 57	22 15				22 27	22 45				22 57	23 15					23 27	23 45	
Hamilton West	d				22 00	22 18				22 30	22 48				23 00	23 18					23 30	23 48	
Blantyre	d				22 03	22 21				22 33	22 51				23 03	23 21					23 33	23 51	
Newton	d				22 07					22 37					23 07						23 37		
Cambuslang	d		22 01		22 11			22 31		22 41			23 01		23 11			23 31			23 41		00 03
Rutherglen	d		22 04		22 15	22 29		22 34		22 45	22 59		23 04		23 15	23 29					23 45	23 59	
Dalmarnock	d		22 06		22 17			22 36		22 47			23 06		23 17						23 47		
Bridgeton	d		22 08		22 19			22 38		22 49			23 08		23 19						23 49		
Drumgelloch	d	21 38					22 08					22 38					23 08						
Airdrie	a	21 41					22 11					22 41					23 11						
	d	21 42					22 12					22 42					23 12						
Coatdyke	d	21 44					22 14					22 44					23 14						
Coatbridge Sunnyside	d	21 46					22 16					22 46					23 16						
Blairhill	d	21 49					22 19					22 49					23 19						
Easterhouse	d	21 53					22 23					22 53					23 23						
Garrowhill	d	21 55					22 25					22 55					23 25						
Shettleston	d	21 58					22 28					22 58					23 28						
Carntyne	d	22 00					22 30					23 00					23 30						
Springburn	d			22 09					22 39					23 09					23 39	23 39			
Barnhill	d			22 10					22 40					23 10					23 40	23 40			
Alexandra Parade	d			22 13					22 43					23 13					23 43	23 43			
Duke Street	d			22 14					22 44					23 14					23 44	23 44			
Bellgrove	d	22 03		22 16			22 33		22 46			23 03		23 16			23 33		23 46	23 46			
High Street	d	22 05		22 18			22 35		22 48			23 05		23 18			23 35		23 48	23 48			
Glasgow Queen Street 10 § ⛴	a	22 07		22 21			22 37		22 51			23 07		23 21			23 37		23 51	23 51			
	d	22 10		22 23			22 40		22 53			23 10		23 23			23 45		23 53	23 53			
Charing Cross	d	22 12		22 25			22 42		22 55			23 12		23 25			23 47		23 55	23 55			
Argyle Street	d		22 12		22 23	22 34		22 42		22 53	23 04		23 12		23 23	23 34					23 53	00 04	
Glasgow Central 15 §	a		22 16		22 26	22 37		22 46		22 56	23 07		23 16		23 26	23 37		23b43			23 56	00 07	00b15
	d		22 16		22 28	22 37		22 46		22 58	23 07		23 16		23 28	23 37					23 58	00 07	
Anderston	d		22 18		22 29	22 39		22 48		22 59	23 09		23 18		23 29	23 39					23 59	00 09	
Exhibition Centre	d		22 20		22 31	22 41		22 50		23 01	23 11		23 20		23 31	23 41					00 01	00 11	
Partick ⛴	d	22 17	22a23	22 30	22 35	22 45	22 47	22a53	23 00	23 05	23 15	23 17	23 24	23 30	23 35	23 45	23 52		23 59	23 59	00 05	00 15	
Hyndland	d	22 20		22 32	22 38	22 47	22 50		23 02	23 08	23 17	23 20	23 26	23 32	23 38	23 47	23 55		00 02	00 01	00 08	00 17	
Jordanhill	d	22 22					22 52					23 22	23 28			23 49	23 57			00 03			
Scotstounhill	d	22 24					22 54					23 24	23 30			23 51	23 59			00 05			
Garscadden	d	22 26					22 56					23 26	23a33			23a53	00 01			00a07			
Yoker	d	22 29					22 59					23 29					00 04						
Clydebank	d	22 31					23 01					23 31					00 06						
Anniesland	d			22 35	22 41	22 50			23 05	23 11	23 20			23 35	23 41				00 05		00 11	00 20	
Westerton	d			22 38	22 44	22 53			23 08	23 14	23 23			23 38	23 44				00 08		00 14	00 23	
Bearsden	d				22 46					23 16					23 46						00 16		
Hillfoot	d				22 48					23 18					23 48						00 18		
Milngavie	a				22 52					23 22					23 52						00 22		
Drumchapel	d			22 40		22 55			23 10		23 25			23 40					00 10			00 25	
Drumry	d			22 42		22 57			23 12		23 27			23 42					00 12			00 27	
Singer	d			22 45		23 00			23 15		23 30			23 45					00 15			00 30	
Dalmuir	a	22 34		22 47		23 02	23 04		23 17		23 33	23 34		23 47			00 09		00 17			00 32	
	d	22 35		22 48			23 05		23 18			23 35		23 48			00 10		00 18				
Kilpatrick	d			22 51					23 21					23 51					00 21				
Bowling	d			22 54					23 24					23 54					00 24				
Dumbarton East	d	22 42		22 58			23 12		23 28			23 42		23 58			00 17		00 28				
Dumbarton Central	d	22 44		23 00			23 14		23 30			23 44		23 59			00 19		00 30				
Dalreoch	d	22 46		23 02			23 16		23 32			23 46		00 02			00 21		00 32				
Renton	d			23 05					23 35					00 05					00 35				
Alexandria	d			23 07					23 37					00 07					00 37				
Balloch	a			23 10					23 40					00 10					00 40				
Cardross	d	22 51					23 21					23 51					00 26						
Craigendoran	d	22 56					23 26					23 56					00 31						
Helensburgh Central	a	22 59					23 29					23 59					00 34						

For general notes see front of timetable
For details of catering facilities see Directory of Train Operators

§ Low Level

A From Edinburgh (Table 225)

B From Edinburgh (from 29 March from Livingston South) (Table 225)

b Glasgow Central High Level

Table 226

until 23 December

Lanark, Coatbridge, Motherwell, Larkhall, Hamilton, Drumgelloch, Airdrie and Springburn → Glasgow → Milngavie, Dalmuir, Balloch and Helensburgh

Network Diagram - see first page of Table 220

		SR	SR	SR	SR	SR	SR	SR	SR	SR	SR	SR	SR	SR	SR	SR	SR	SR	SR	SR	SR	SR
Lanark	d																					
Carluke	d																					
Wishaw	d																					
Holytown	d																					
Shieldmuir	d																					
Coatbridge Central	d																					
Whifflet	d																					
Motherwell	a																					
	d					08 36	08 40				09 10				09 36		09 40			10 06		10 10
Bellshill	d					08 42									09 42					10 12		
Uddingston	d					08 46									09 46					10 16		
Airbles	d						08 42				09 12						09 42					10 12
Larkhall	d												09 25									
Merryton	d												09 27									
Chatelherault	d												09 30									
Hamilton Central	d						08 47				09 17		09 33				09 47					10 17
Hamilton West	d						08 50				09 20		09 36				09 50					10 20
Blantyre	d						08 53				09 23		09 39				09 53					10 23
Newton	d						08 57				09 27						09 57					10 27
Cambuslang	d					08 51	09 01				09 31				09 51		10 01			10 21		10 31
Rutherglen	d					08 54	09 04				09 34		09 49		09 54		10 04			10 24		10 34
Dalmarnock	d																					
Bridgeton	d					08 57	09 07				09 37				09 57		10 07			10 27		10 37
Drumgelloch	d		07 54		08 24			08 54				09 24						09 54				
Airdrie	a		07 57		08 27			08 57				09 27						09 57				
	d		07 58		08 28			08 58		09 13		09 28				09 43		09 58			10 13	
Coatdyke	d		08 00		08 30			09 00		09 15		09 30				09 45		10 00			10 15	
Coatbridge Sunnyside	d		08 02		08 32			09 02		09 17		09 32				09 47		10 02			10 17	
Blairhill	d		08 05		08 35			09 05		09 20		09 35				09 50		10 05			10 20	
Easterhouse	d		08 09		08 39			09 09		09 24		09 39				09 54		10 09			10 24	
Garrowhill	d		08 11		08 41			09 11		09 26		09 41				09 56		10 11			10 26	
Shettleston	d		08 14		08 44			09 14		09 29		09 44				09 59		10 14			10 29	
Carntyne	d		08 16		08 46			09 16		09 31		09 46				10 01		10 16			10 31	
Springburn	d								09 19					09 49					10 19			
Barnhill	d								09 20					09 50					10 20			
Alexandra Parade	d								09 23					09 53					10 23			
Duke Street	d								09 25					09 55					10 25			
Bellgrove	d		08 19		08 49			09 19	09 27	09 34		09 49		09 57		10 04		10 19	10 27		10 34	
High Street	d		08 21		08 51			09 21	09 29	09 36		09 51		09 59		10 06		10 21	10 29		10 36	
Glasgow Queen Street [10] §	a		08 23		08 53			09 23	09 31	09 39		09 53		10 01		10 09		10 23	10 31		10 39	
	d		08 24		08 54			09 24	09 31	09 39		09 54		10 01		10 09		10 24	10 31		10 39	
Charing Cross	d		08 27		08 57			09 27	09 33	09 42		09 57		10 03		10 12		10 27	10 33		10 42	
Argyle Street	d														10 01		10 11			10 31		10 41
Glasgow Central [15] §	a					09 04	09 14				09 44		09 57		10 04		10 14			10 34		10 44
	d					09 04	09 14				09 44		09 57		10 04		10 14			10 34		10 44
Anderston	d																					
Exhibition Centre	d					09 08	09 18				09 48		10 01		10 08		10 18			10 38		10 48
Partick	d		08 32		09 02	09 12	09 22	09 32	09 37	09 47	09 52	10 02	10a04	10 07	10 12	10 17	10 22	10 32	10 37	10 42	10 47	10 52
Hyndland	d		08 34		09 04	09 16	09 24	09 34	09 39	09 49	09 54	10 04		10 09	10 16	10 19	10 24	10 34	10 39	10 46	10 49	10 54
Jordanhill	d						09 26		09 41		09 56			10 11			10 26		10 41			10 56
Scotstounhill	d						09 28		09 43		09 58			10 13			10 28		10 43			10 58
Garscadden	d						09 30		09 46		10 00			10 16			10 30		10 46			11 00
Yoker	d	08 33		09 03			09 33		09 48		10 03			10 18			10 33		10 48			11 03
Clydebank	d	08 35		09 05			09 35		09 50		10 05			10 20			10 35		10 50			11 05
Anniesland	d		08 37		09 07	09 19		09 37		09 52		10 07			10 19	10 22		10 37		10 49	10 52	
Westerton	d		08 40		09 10	09 22		09 40		09 55		10 10			10 22	10 25		10 40		10 52	10 55	
Bearsden	d					09 25									10 25					10 55		
Hillfoot	d					09 27									10 27					10 57		
Milngavie	a					09 30									10 30					11 00		
Drumchapel	d		08 42		09 12			09 42		09 57		10 12				10 27		10 42			10 57	
Drumry	d		08 44		09 14			09 44		09 59		10 14				10 29		10 44			10 59	
Singer	d		08 47		09 17			09 47		10 02		10 17				10 32		10 47			11 02	
Dalmuir	a	08 38	08 49	09 08	09 19		09 39	09 49	09 53	10 04	10 09	10 19		10 23		10 34	10 39	10 49	10 53		11 04	11 09
	d	08 39	08 50	09 09	09 20		09 39	09 50			10 09	10 20					10 39	10 50				11 09
Kilpatrick	d	08 41		09 11			09 41				10 11						10 41					11 11
Bowling	d	08 44		09 14			09 44				10 14						10 44					11 14
Dumbarton East	d	08 49	08 58	09 19	09 28		09 49	09 58			10 19	10 28					10 49	10 58				11 19
Dumbarton Central	d	08 51	09 00	09 21	09 30		09 51	10 00			10 21	10 30					10 51	11 00				11 21
Dalreoch	d	08 52	09 01	09 22	09 31		09 52	10 01			10 22	10 31					10 52	11 01				11 22
Renton	d	08 55		09 25			09 55				10 25						10 55					11 25
Alexandria	d	08 58		09 28			09 58				10 28						10 58					11 28
Balloch	a	09 00		09 30			10 00				10 30						11 00					11 30
Cardross	d		09 06		09 36			10 06				10 36						11 06				
Craigendoran	d		09 11		09 41			10 11				10 41						11 11				
Helensburgh Central	a		09 14		09 44			10 14				10 44						11 14				

For general notes see front of timetable
For details of catering facilities see Directory of Train Operators

§ Low Level

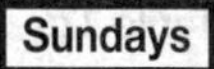

until 23 December

Lanark, Coatbridge, Motherwell, Larkhall, Hamilton, Drumgelloch, Airdrie and Springburn → Glasgow → Milngavie, Dalmuir, Balloch and Helensburgh

Network Diagram - see first page of Table 220

		SR	SR	SR	SR	SR	SR	SR	SR	SR	SR	SR	SR	SR	SR	SR	SR	SR	SR	SR	SR	SR
Lanark	d				10 12										11 12							
Carluke	d				10 22										11 22							
Wishaw	d				10 27										11 27							
Holytown	d																					
Shieldmuir	d				10 31										11 31							
Coatbridge Central	d																					
Whifflet	d																					
Motherwell	a				10 35										11 35							
	d				10 36		10 40		11 06		11 10				11 36		11 40			12 06		
Bellshill	d				10 42				11 12						11 42					12 12		
Uddingston	d				10 46				11 16						11 46					12 16		
Airbles	d						10 42				11 12						11 42					
Larkhall	d		10 25											11 25								
Merryton	d		10 27											11 27								
Chatelherault	d		10 30											11 30								
Hamilton Central	d		10 33				10 47				11 17			11 33			11 47					
Hamilton West	d		10 36				10 50				11 20			11 36			11 50					
Blantyre	d		10 39				10 53				11 23			11 39			11 53					
Newton	d						10 57				11 27						11 57					
Cambuslang	d				10 51		11 01		11 21		11 31				11 51		12 01			12 21		
Rutherglen	d		10 49		10 54		11 04		11 24		11 34			11 49	11 54		12 04			12 24		
Dalmarnock	d																					
Bridgeton	d				10 57		11 07		11 27		11 37				11 57		12 07			12 27		
Drumgelloch	d	10 24						10 54					11 24						11 54			
Airdrie	a	10 27						10 57					11 27						11 57			
	d	10 28				10 43		10 58		11 13			11 28			11 43			11 58			12 13
Coatdyke	d	10 30				10 45		11 00		11 15			11 30			11 45			12 00			12 15
Coatbridge Sunnyside	d	10 32				10 47		11 02		11 17			11 32			11 47			12 02			12 17
Blairhill	d	10 35				10 50		11 05		11 20			11 35			11 50			12 05			12 20
Easterhouse	d	10 39				10 54		11 09		11 24			11 39			11 54			12 09			12 24
Garrowhill	d	10 41				10 56		11 11		11 26			11 41			11 56			12 11			12 26
Shettleston	d	10 44				10 59		11 14		11 29			11 44			11 59			12 14			12 29
Carntyne	d	10 46				11 01		11 16		11 31			11 46			12 01			12 16			12 31
Springburn	d			10 49					11 19						11 49					12 19		
Barnhill	d			10 50					11 20						11 50					12 20		
Alexandra Parade	d			10 53					11 23						11 53					12 23		
Duke Street	d			10 55					11 25						11 55					12 25		
Bellgrove	d	10 49		10 57		11 04		11 19	11 27	11 34			11 49		11 57		12 04		12 19	12 27		12 34
High Street	d	10 51		10 59		11 06		11 21	11 29	11 36			11 51		11 59		12 06		12 21	12 29		12 36
Glasgow Queen Street 10 §	a	10 53		11 01		11 09		11 23	11 31	11 39			11 53		12 01		12 09		12 23	12 31		12 39
	d	10 54		11 01		11 09		11 24	11 31	11 39			11 54		12 01		12 09		12 24	12 31		12 39
Charing Cross	d	10 57		11 03		11 12		11 27	11 33	11 42			11 57		12 03		12 12		12 27	12 33		12 42
Argyle Street	d		10 54		11 01		11 11		11 31		11 41			11 54		12 01		12 11			12 31	
Glasgow Central 15 §	a		10 57		11 04		11 14		11 34		11 44			11 57		12 04		12 14			12 34	
	d		10 57		11 04		11 14		11 34		11 44			11 57		12 04		12 14			12 34	
Anderston	d																					
Exhibition Centre	d		11 01		11 08		11 18		11 38		11 48			12 01		12 08		12 18			12 38	
Partick	d	11 02	11a04	11 07	11 12	11 17	11 22	11 32	11 37	11 42	11 47	11 52	12 02	12a04	12 07	12 12	12 17	12 22	12 32	12 37	12 42	12 47
Hyndland	d	11 04		11 09	11 16	11 19	11 24	11 34	11 39	11 46	11 49	11 54	12 04		12 09	12 16	12 19	12 24	12 34	12 39	12 46	12 49
Jordanhill	d			11 11			11 26		11 41			11 56			12 11			12 26		12 41		
Scotstounhill	d			11 13			11 28		11 43			11 58			12 13			12 28		12 43		
Garscadden	d			11 16			11 30		11 46			12 00			12 16			12 30		12 46		
Yoker	d			11 18			11 33		11 48			12 03			12 18			12 33		12 48		
Clydebank	d			11 20			11 35		11 50			12 05			12 20			12 35		12 50		
Anniesland	d	11 07			11 19	11 22		11 37		11 49	11 52		12 07			12 19	12 22		12 37		12 49	12 52
Westerton	d	11 10			11 22	11 25		11 40		11 52	11 55		12 10			12 22	12 25		12 40		12 52	12 55
Bearsden	d				11 25				11 55							12 25					12 55	
Hillfoot	d				11 27				11 57							12 27					12 57	
Milngavie	a				11 30				12 00							12 30					13 01	
Drumchapel	d	11 12				11 27		11 42		11 57			12 12				12 27		12 42			12 57
Drumry	d	11 14				11 29		11 44		11 59			12 14				12 29		12 44			12 59
Singer	d	11 17				11 32		11 47		12 02			12 17				12 32		12 47			13 02
Dalmuir	a	11 19		11 23		11 34	11 39	11 49	11 53	12 04	12 09		12 19		12 23		12 34	12 39	12 49	12 53		13 04
	d	11 20					11 39	11 50			12 09		12 20					12 39	12 50			
Kilpatrick	d						11 41				12 11							12 41				
Bowling	d						11 44				12 14							12 44				
Dumbarton East	d	11 28					11 49	11 58			12 19		12 28					12 49	12 58			
Dumbarton Central	d	11 30					11 51	12 00			12 21		12 30					12 51	13 00			
Dalreoch	d	11 31					11 52	12 01			12 22		12 31					12 52	13 01			
Renton	d						11 55				12 25							12 55				
Alexandria	d						11 58				12 28							12 58				
Balloch	a						12 00				12 30							13 00				
Cardross	d	11 36						12 06					12 36						13 06			
Craigendoran	d	11 41						12 11					12 41						13 11			
Helensburgh Central	a	11 44						12 14					12 44						13 14			

For general notes see front of timetable
For details of catering facilities see Directory of Train Operators

§ Low Level

Table 226

Sundays

until 23 December

Lanark, Coatbridge, Motherwell, Larkhall, Hamilton, Drumgelloch, Airdrie and Springburn → Glasgow → Milngavie, Dalmuir, Balloch and Helensburgh

Network Diagram - see first page of Table 220

		SR	SR	SR	SR	SR	SR	SR	SR	SR	SR	SR	SR	SR	SR	SR	SR	SR	SR	SR	SR	SR
Lanark	d					12 12											13 12					
Carluke	d					12 22											13 22					
Wishaw	d					12 27											13 27					
Holytown	d																					
Shieldmuir	d					12 31											13 31					
Coatbridge Central	d																					
Whifflet	d																					
Motherwell	a					12 35											13 35					
	d	12 10				12 36		12 40			13 06		13 10				13 36		13 40			14 06
Bellshill	d					12 42					13 12						13 42					14 12
Uddingston	d					12 46					13 16						13 46					14 16
Airbles	d	12 12						12 42					13 12						13 42			
Larkhall	d			12 25											13 25							
Merryton	d			12 27											13 27							
Chatelherault	d			12 30											13 30							
Hamilton Central	d	12 17		12 33				12 47					13 17		13 33				13 47			
Hamilton West	d	12 20		12 36				12 50					13 20		13 36				13 50			
Blantyre	d	12 23		12 39				12 53					13 23		13 39				13 53			
Newton	d	12 27						12 57					13 27						13 57			
Cambuslang	d	12 31				12 51		13 01			13 21		13 31				13 51		14 01			14 21
Rutherglen	d	12 34		12 49		12 54		13 04			13 24		13 34		13 49		13 54		14 04			14 24
Dalmarnock	d																					
Bridgeton	d	12 37				12 57		13 07			13 27		13 37				13 57		14 07			14 27
Drumgelloch	d		12 24						12 54					13 24						13 54		
Airdrie	a		12 27						12 57					13 27						13 57		
	d		12 28				12 43		12 58			13 13		13 28				13 43		13 58		
Coatdyke	d		12 30				12 45		13 00			13 15		13 30				13 45		14 00		
Coatbridge Sunnyside	d		12 32				12 47		13 02			13 17		13 32				13 47		14 02		
Blairhill	d		12 35				12 50		13 05			13 20		13 35				13 50		14 05		
Easterhouse	d		12 39				12 54		13 09			13 24		13 39				13 54		14 09		
Garrowhill	d		12 41				12 56		13 11			13 26		13 41				13 56		14 11		
Shettleston	d		12 44				12 59		13 14			13 29		13 44				13 59		14 14		
Carntyne	d		12 46				13 01		13 16			13 31		13 46				14 01		14 16		
Springburn	d				12 49					13 19						13 49					14 19	
Barnhill	d				12 50					13 20						13 50					14 20	
Alexandra Parade	d				12 53					13 23						13 53					14 23	
Duke Street	d				12 55					13 25						13 55					14 25	
Bellgrove	d		12 49		12 57		13 04		13 19	13 27		13 34		13 49		13 57		14 04		14 19	14 27	
High Street	d		12 51		12 59		13 06		13 21	13 29		13 36		13 51		13 59		14 06		14 21	14 29	
Glasgow Queen Street 10 § ⛴	a		12 53		13 01		13 09		13 23	13 31		13 39		13 53		14 01		14 09		14 23	14 31	
	d		12 54		13 01		13 09		13 24	13 31		13 39		13 54		14 01		14 09		14 24	14 31	
Charing Cross	d		12 57		13 03		13 12		13 27	13 33		13 42		13 57		14 03		14 12		14 27	14 33	
Argyle Street	d			12 54		13 01		13 11			13 31		13 41		13 54		14 01		14 11			14 31
Glasgow Central 15 §	a	12 44		12 57		13 04		13 14			13 34		13 44		13 57		14 04		14 14			14 34
	d	12 44		12 57		13 04		13 14			13 34		13 44		13 57		14 04		14 14			14 34
Anderston	d																					
Exhibition Centre	d	12 48		13 01		13 08		13 18			13 38		13 48		14 01		14 08		14 18			14 38
Partick ⛴	d	12 52	13 02	13a04	13 07	13 12	13 17	13 22	13 32	13 37	13 42	13 47	13 52	14 02	14a04	14 07	14 12	14 17	14 22	14 32	14 37	14 42
Hyndland	d	12 54	13 04		13 09	13 16	13 19	13 24	13 34	13 39	13 46	13 49	13 54	14 04		14 09	14 16	14 19	14 24	14 34	14 39	14 46
Jordanhill	d	12 56			13 11			13 26		13 41			13 56			14 11			14 26		14 41	
Scotstounhill	d	12 58			13 13			13 28		13 43			13 58			14 13			14 28		14 43	
Garscadden	d	13 00			13 16			13 30		13 46			14 00			14 16			14 30		14 46	
Yoker	d	13 03			13 18			13 33		13 48			14 03			14 18			14 33		14 48	
Clydebank	d	13 05			13 20			13 35		13 50			14 05			14 20			14 35		14 50	
Anniesland	d		13 07			13 19	13 22		13 37		13 49	13 52		14 07			14 19	14 22		14 37		14 49
Westerton	d		13 10			13 22	13 25		13 40		13 52	13 55		14 10			14 22	14 25		14 40		14 52
Bearsden	d					13 25					13 55						14 25					14 55
Hillfoot	d					13 27					13 57						14 27					14 57
Milngavie	a					13 30					14 00						14 30					15 00
Drumchapel	d		13 12				13 27		13 42			13 57		14 12				14 27		14 42		
Drumry	d		13 14				13 29		13 44			13 59		14 14				14 29		14 44		
Singer	d		13 17				13 32		13 47			14 02		14 17				14 32		14 47		
Dalmuir	a	13 09	13 19		13 23		13 34	13 39	13 49	13 53		14 04	14 09	14 19		14 23		14 34	14 39	14 49	14 53	
	d	13 09	13 20					13 39	13 50				14 09	14 20					14 39	14 50		
Kilpatrick	d	13 11						13 41					14 11						14 41			
Bowling	d	13 14						13 44					14 14						14 44			
Dumbarton East	d	13 19	13 28					13 49	13 58				14 19	14 28					14 49	14 58		
Dumbarton Central	d	13 21	13 30					13 51	14 00				14 21	14 30					14 51	15 00		
Dalreoch	d	13 22	13 31					13 52	14 01				14 22	14 31					14 52	15 01		
Renton	d	13 25						13 55					14 25						14 55			
Alexandria	d	13 28						13 58					14 28						14 58			
Balloch	a	13 30						14 00					14 30						15 00			
Cardross	d		13 36						14 06					14 36						15 06		
Craigendoran	d		13 41						14 11					14 41						15 11		
Helensburgh Central	a		13 44						14 14					14 44						15 14		

For general notes see front of timetable
For details of catering facilities see Directory of Train Operators

§ Low Level

Table 226

Sundays

until 23 December

Lanark, Coatbridge, Motherwell, Larkhall, Hamilton, Drumgelloch, Airdrie and Springburn → Glasgow → Milngavie, Dalmuir, Balloch and Helensburgh

Network Diagram - see first page of Table 220

		SR	SR	SR	SR	SR	SR	SR	SR	SR	SR	SR	SR	SR	SR	SR	SR	SR	SR	SR	SR	SR
Lanark	d						14 12											15 12				
Carluke	d						14 22											15 22				
Wishaw	d						14 27											15 27				
Holytown	d																					
Shieldmuir	d						14 31											15 31				
Coatbridge Central	d																					
Whifflet	d																					
Motherwell	a						14 35											15 35				
	d		14 10				14 36		14 40			15 06		15 10				15 36		15 40		
Bellshill	d						14 42					15 12						15 42				
Uddingston	d						14 46					15 16						15 46				
Airbles	d		14 12						14 42					15 12						15 42		
Larkhall	d				14 25											15 25						
Merryton	d				14 27											15 27						
Chatelherault	d				14 30											15 30						
Hamilton Central	d		14 17		14 33				14 47					15 17		15 33				15 47		
Hamilton West	d		14 20		14 36				14 50					15 20		15 36				15 50		
Blantyre	d		14 23		14 39				14 53					15 23		15 39				15 53		
Newton	d		14 27						14 57					15 27						15 57		
Cambuslang	d		14 31				14 51		15 01			15 21		15 31				15 51		16 01		
Rutherglen	d		14 34		14 49		14 54		15 04			15 24		15 34		15 49		15 54		16 04		
Dalmarnock	d																					
Bridgeton	d		14 37				14 57		15 07			15 27		15 37				15 57		16 07		
Drumgelloch	d			14 24						14 54					15 24						15 54	
Airdrie	a			14 27						14 57					15 27						15 57	
	d	14 13		14 28				14 43		14 58			15 13		15 28				15 43		15 58	
Coatdyke	d	14 15		14 30				14 45		15 00			15 15		15 30				15 45		16 00	
Coatbridge Sunnyside	d	14 17		14 32				14 47		15 02			15 17		15 32				15 47		16 02	
Blairhill	d	14 20		14 35				14 50		15 05			15 20		15 35				15 50		16 05	
Easterhouse	d	14 24		14 39				14 54		15 09			15 24		15 39				15 54		16 09	
Garrowhill	d	14 26		14 41				14 56		15 11			15 26		15 41				15 56		16 11	
Shettleston	d	14 29		14 44				14 59		15 14			15 29		15 44				15 59		16 14	
Carntyne	d	14 31		14 46				15 01		15 16			15 31		15 46				16 01		16 16	
Springburn	d					14 49					15 19						15 49					16 19
Barnhill	d					14 50					15 20						15 50					16 20
Alexandra Parade	d					14 53					15 23						15 53					16 23
Duke Street	d					14 55					15 25						15 55					16 25
Bellgrove	d	14 34		14 49		14 57		15 04		15 19	15 27		15 34		15 49		15 57		16 04		16 19	16 27
High Street	d	14 36		14 51		14 59		15 06		15 21	15 29		15 36		15 51		15 59		16 06		16 21	16 29
Glasgow Queen Street 10 §	a	14 39		14 53		15 01		15 09		15 23	15 31		15 39		15 53		16 01		16 09		16 23	16 31
	d	14 39		14 54		15 01		15 09		15 24	15 31		15 39		15 54		16 01		16 09		16 24	16 31
Charing Cross	d	14 42		14 57		15 03		15 12		15 27	15 33		15 42		15 57		16 03		16 12		16 27	16 33
Argyle Street	d		14 41		14 54		15 01		15 11			15 31		15 41		15 54		16 01		16 11		
Glasgow Central 15 §	a		14 44		14 57		15 04		15 14			15 34		15 44		15 57		16 04		16 14		
	d		14 44		14 57		15 04		15 14			15 34		15 44		15 57		16 04		16 14		
Anderston	d																					
Exhibition Centre	d		14 48		15 01		15 08		15 18			15 38		15 48		16 01		16 08		16 18		
Partick	d	14 47	14 52	15 02	15a04	15 07	15 12	15 17	15 22	15 32	15 37	15 42	15 47	15 52	16 02	16a04	16 07	16 12	16 17	16 22	16 32	16 37
Hyndland	d	14 49	14 54	15 04		15 09	15 16	15 19	15 24	15 34	15 39	15 46	15 49	15 54	16 04		16 09	16 16	16 19	16 24	16 34	16 39
Jordanhill	d		14 56			15 11			15 26		15 41			15 56			16 11			16 26		16 41
Scotstounhill	d		14 58			15 13			15 28		15 43			15 58			16 13			16 28		16 43
Garscadden	d		15 00			15 16			15 30		15 46			16 00			16 16			16 30		16 46
Yoker	d		15 03			15 18			15 33		15 48			16 03			16 18			16 33		16 48
Clydebank	d		15 05			15 20			15 35		15 50			16 05			16 20			16 35		16 50
Anniesland	d	14 52		15 07			15 19	15 22		15 37		15 49	15 52		16 07			16 19	16 22		16 37	
Westerton	d	14 55		15 10			15 22	15 25		15 40		15 52	15 55		16 10			16 22	16 25		16 40	
Bearsden	d						15 25					15 55						16 25				
Hillfoot	d						15 27					15 57						16 27				
Milngavie	a						15 30					16 00						16 30				
Drumchapel	d	14 57		15 12				15 27		15 42			15 57		16 12				16 27		16 42	
Drumry	d	14 59		15 14				15 29		15 44			15 59		16 14				16 29		16 44	
Singer	d	15 02		15 17				15 32		15 47			16 02		16 17				16 32		16 47	
Dalmuir	a	15 04	15 09	15 19		15 23		15 34	15 39	15 49	15 53		16 04	16 09	16 19		16 23		16 34	16 39	16 49	16 53
	d		15 09	15 20					15 39	15 50				16 09	16 20					16 39	16 50	
Kilpatrick	d		15 11						15 41					16 11						16 41		
Bowling	d		15 14						15 44					16 14						16 44		
Dumbarton East	d		15 19	15 28					15 49	15 58				16 19	16 28					16 49	16 58	
Dumbarton Central	d		15 21	15 30					15 51	16 00				16 21	16 30					16 51	17 00	
Dalreoch	d		15 22	15 31					15 52	16 01				16 22	16 31					16 52	17 01	
Renton	d		15 25						15 55					16 25						16 55		
Alexandria	d		15 28						15 58					16 28						16 58		
Balloch	a		15 30						16 00					16 30						17 00		
Cardross	d			15 36						16 06					16 36						17 06	
Craigendoran	d			15 41						16 11					16 41						17 11	
Helensburgh Central	a			15 44						16 14					16 44						17 14	

For general notes see front of timetable
For details of catering facilities see
Directory of Train Operators

§ Low Level

Table 226

Sundays until 23 December

Lanark, Coatbridge, Motherwell, Larkhall, Hamilton, Drumgelloch, Airdrie and Springburn → Glasgow → Milngavie, Dalmuir, Balloch and Helensburgh

Network Diagram - see first page of Table 220

		SR	SR		SR	SR	SR	SR	SR	SR		SR	SR	SR	SR	SR	SR		SR	SR	SR	SR	SR	SR ◇ A	SR
Lanark	d								16 12													17 12			
Carluke	d								16 22													17 22			
Wishaw	d								16 27													17 27			
Holytown	d																								
Shieldmuir	d								16 31													17 31			
Coatbridge Central	d																								
Whifflet	d																								
Motherwell	a								16 35													17 35			
	d	16 06			16 10				16 36			16 40			17 06		17 10					17 36			17 40
Bellshill	d	16 12							16 42						17 12							17 42			
Uddingston	d	16 16							16 46						17 16							17 46			
Airbles	d				16 12							16 42					17 12								17 42
Larkhall	d						16 25													17 25					
Merryton	d						16 27													17 27					
Chatelherault	d						16 30													17 30					
Hamilton Central	d				16 17		16 33					16 47					17 17			17 33					17 47
Hamilton West	d				16 20		16 36					16 50					17 20			17 36					17 50
Blantyre	d				16 23		16 39					16 53					17 23			17 39					17 53
Newton	d				16 27							16 57					17 27								17 57
Cambuslang	d	16 21			16 31				16 51			17 01			17 21		17 31					17 51			18 01
Rutherglen	d	16 24			16 34		16 49		16 54			17 04			17 24		17 34			17 49		17 54			18 04
Dalmarnock	d																								
Bridgeton	d	16 27			16 37				16 57			17 07			17 27		17 37					17 57			18 07
Drumgelloch	d					16 24							16 54						17 24						
Airdrie	a					16 27							16 57						17 27						
	d		16 13			16 28				16 43			16 58			17 13			17 28				17 43		
Coatdyke	d		16 15			16 30				16 45			17 00			17 15			17 30				17 45		
Coatbridge Sunnyside	d		16 17			16 32				16 47			17 02			17 17			17 32				17 47		
Blairhill	d		16 20			16 35				16 50			17 05			17 20			17 35				17 50		
Easterhouse	d		16 24			16 39				16 54			17 09			17 24			17 39				17 54		
Garrowhill	d		16 26			16 41				16 56			17 11			17 26			17 41				17 56		
Shettleston	d		16 29			16 44				16 59			17 14			17 29			17 44				17 59		
Carntyne	d		16 31			16 46				17 01			17 16			17 31			17 46				18 01		
Springburn	d							16 49						17 19							17 49				
Barnhill	d							16 50						17 20							17 50				
Alexandra Parade	d							16 53						17 23							17 53				
Duke Street	d							16 55						17 25							17 55				
Bellgrove	d		16 34			16 49		16 57		17 04			17 19	17 27		17 34			17 49		17 57		18 04		
High Street	d		16 36			16 51		16 59		17 06			17 21	17 29		17 36			17 51		17 59		18 06		
Glasgow Queen Street 10 §	a		16 39			16 53		17 01		17 09			17 23	17 31		17 39			17 53		18 01		18 09		
	d		16 39			16 54		17 01		17 09			17 24	17 31		17 39			17 54		18 01		18 09	18b20	
Charing Cross	d		16 42			16 57		17 03		17 12			17 27	17 33		17 42			17 57		18 03		18 12		
Argyle Street	d	16 31			16 41		16 54		17 01			17 11			17 31		17 41			17 54		18 01			18 11
Glasgow Central 15 §	a	16 34			16 44		16 57		17 04			17 14			17 34		17 44			17 57		18 04			18 14
	d	16 34			16 44		16 57		17 04			17 14			17 34		17 44			17 57		18 04			18 14
Anderston	d																								
Exhibition Centre	d	16 38			16 48		17 01		17 08			17 18			17 38		17 48			18 01		18 08			18 18
Partick	d	16 42	16 47		16 52	17 02	17a04	17 07	17 12	17 17		17 22	17 32	17 37	17 42	17 47	17 52		18 02	18a04	18 07	18 12	18 17		18 22
Hyndland	d	16 46	16 49		16 54	17 04		17 09	17 16	17 19		17 24	17 34	17 39	17 46	17 49	17 54		18 04		18 09	18 16	18 19		18 24
Jordanhill	d				16 56			17 11				17 26		17 41			17 56				18 11				18 26
Scotstounhill	d				16 58			17 13				17 28		17 43			17 58				18 13				18 28
Garscadden	d				17 00			17 16				17 30		17 46			18 00				18 16				18 30
Yoker	d				17 03			17 18				17 33		17 48			18 03				18 18				18 33
Clydebank	d				17 05			17 20				17 35		17 50			18 05				18 20				18 35
Anniesland	d	16 49	16 52			17 07			17 19	17 22			17 37		17 49	17 52			18 07			18 19	18 22		
Westerton	d	16 52	16 55			17 10			17 22	17 25			17 40		17 52	17 55			18 10			18 22	18 25		
Bearsden	d	16 55							17 25						17 55							18 25			
Hillfoot	d	16 57							17 27						17 57							18 27			
Milngavie	a	17 00							17 30						18 00							18 30			
Drumchapel	d		16 57			17 12				17 27			17 42			17 57			18 12				18 35 →		
Drumry	d		16 59			17 14				17 29			17 44			17 59			18 14						
Singer	d		17 02			17 17				17 32			17 47			18 02			18 17						
Dalmuir	a		17 04		17 09	17 19		17 23		17 34		17 39	17 49	17 53		18 04	18 09		18 19		18 23			18 35	18 39
	d				17 09	17 20						17 39	17 50				18 09		18 20					18 35	18 39
Kilpatrick	d				17 11							17 41					18 11								18 41
Bowling	d				17 14							17 44					18 14								18 44
Dumbarton East	d				17 19	17 28						17 49	17 58				18 19		18 28						18 49
Dumbarton Central	d				17 21	17 30						17 51	18 00				18 21		18 30					18c45	18 51
Dalreoch	d				17 22	17 31						17 52	18 01				18 22		18 31						18 52
Renton	d				17 25							17 55					18 25								18 55
Alexandria	d				17 28							17 58					18 28								18 58
Balloch	a				17 30							18 00					18 30								19 00
Cardross	d					17 36							18 06						18 36						
Craigendoran	d					17 41							18 11						18 41						
Helensburgh Central	a					17 44							18 14						18 44					19e00	

For general notes see front of timetable
For details of catering facilities see Directory of Train Operators

§ Low Level

A To Oban and to Mallaig (Table 227)
b Glasgow Queen Street High Level
c Arr. 1841
e Helensburgh Upper

Table 226

Sundays

until 23 December

Lanark, Coatbridge, Motherwell, Larkhall, Hamilton, Drumgelloch, Airdrie and Springburn → Glasgow → Milngavie, Dalmuir, Balloch and Helensburgh

Network Diagram - see first page of Table 220

		SR		SR	SR	SR	SR	SR	SR		SR	SR	SR	SR	SR	SR		SR	SR	SR	SR	SR	SR		SR
Lanark	d								18 12									19 12							
Carluke	d								18 22									19 22							
Wishaw	d								18 27									19 27							
Holytown	d																								
Shieldmuir	d								18 31									19 31							
Coatbridge Central	d																								
Whifflet	d																								
Motherwell	a								18 35									19 35							
	d				18 06	18 10			18 36		18 40		19 06	19 10				19 36	19 40		20 06	20 10			
Bellshill	d				18 12				18 42				19 12					19 42			20 12				
Uddingston	d				18 16				18 46				19 16					19 46			20 16				
Airbles	d					18 12					18 42			19 12					19 42			20 12			
Larkhall	d							18 25								19 25									20 25
Merryton	d							18 27								19 27									20 27
Chatelherault	d							18 30								19 30									20 30
Hamilton Central	d					18 17		18 33			18 47			19 17		19 33			19 47			20 17			20 33
Hamilton West	d					18 20		18 36			18 50			19 20		19 36			19 50			20 20			20 36
Blantyre	d					18 23		18 39			18 53			19 23		19 39			19 53			20 23			20 39
Newton	d					18 27					18 57			19 27					19 57			20 27			
Cambuslang	d				18 21	18 31			18 51		19 01		19 21	19 31				19 51	20 01		20 21	20 31			
Rutherglen	d				18 24	18 34		18 49	18 54		19 04		19 24	19 34		19 49		19 54	20 04		20 24	20 34			20 49
Dalmarnock	d																								
Bridgeton	d				18 27	18 37			18 57		19 07		19 27	19 37				19 57	20 07		20 27	20 37			
Drumgelloch	d			17 54			18 24					18 54			19 24					19 54			20 24		
Airdrie	a			17 57			18 27					18 57			19 27					19 57			20 27		
	d			17 58			18 28					18 58			19 28					19 58			20 28		
Coatdyke	d			18 00			18 30					19 00			19 30					20 00			20 30		
Coatbridge Sunnyside	d			18 02			18 32					19 02			19 32					20 02			20 32		
Blairhill	d			18 05			18 35					19 05			19 35					20 05			20 35		
Easterhouse	d			18 09			18 39					19 09			19 39					20 09			20 39		
Garrowhill	d			18 11			18 41					19 11			19 41					20 11			20 41		
Shettleston	d			18 14			18 44					19 14			19 44					20 14			20 44		
Carntyne	d			18 16			18 46					19 16			19 46					20 16			20 46		
Springburn	d																								
Barnhill	d																								
Alexandra Parade	d																								
Duke Street	d																								
Bellgrove	d			18 19			18 49					19 19			19 49					20 19			20 49		
High Street	d			18 21			18 51					19 21			19 51					20 21			20 51		
Glasgow Queen Street 10 §	a			18 23			18 53					19 23			19 53					20 23			20 53		
	d			18 24			18 54					19 24			19 54					20 24			20 54		
Charing Cross	d			18 27			18 57					19 27			19 57					20 27			20 57		
Argyle Street	d																								
Glasgow Central 15 §	a				18 34	18 44		18 57	19 04		19 14		19 34	19 44		19 57		20 04	20 14		20 34	20 44			20 57
	d				18 34	18 44		18 57	19 04		19 14		19 34	19 44		19 57		20 04	20 14		20 34	20 44			20 57
Anderston	d																								
Exhibition Centre	d				18 38	18 48		19 01	19 08		19 18		19 38	19 48		20 01		20 08	20 18		20 38	20 48			21 01
Partick	d			18 32	18 42	18 52	19 02	19a04	19 12		19 22	19 32	19 42	19 52	20 02	20a04		20 12	20 22	20 32	20 42	20 52	21 02		21a04
Hyndland	d			18 34	18 46	18 54	19 04		19 16		19 24	19 34	19 46	19 54	20 04			20 16	20 24	20 34	20 46	20 54	21 04		
Jordanhill	d					18 56					19 26			19 56					20 26			20 56			
Scotstounhill	d					18 58					19 28			19 58					20 28			20 58			
Garscadden	d					19 00					19 30			20 00					20 30			21 00			
Yoker	d					19 03					19 33			20 03					20 33			21 03			
Clydebank	d					19 05					19 35			20 05					20 35			21 05			
Anniesland	d			18 37	18 49		19 07		19 19			19 37	19 49		20 07			20 19		20 37	20 49		21 07		
Westerton	d			18 40	18 52		19 10		19 22			19 40	19 52		20 10			20 22		20 40	20 52		21 10		
Bearsden	d				18 55				19 25				19 55					20 25			20 55				
Hillfoot	d				18 57				19 27				19 57					20 27			20 57				
Milngavie	a	⟵			19 00				19 30				20 00					20 30			21 00				
Drumchapel	d	18 35		18 42			19 12					19 42			20 12					20 42			21 12		
Drumry	d	18 37		18 44			19 14					19 44			20 14					20 44			21 14		
Singer	d	18 40		18 47			19 17					19 47			20 17					20 47			21 17		
Dalmuir	a	18 42		18 49		19 09	19 19				19 39	19 49		20 09	20 19				20 39	20 49		21 09	21 19		
	d			18 50		19 09	19 20				19 39	19 50		20 09	20 20				20 39	20 50		21 09	21 20		
Kilpatrick	d					19 11					19 41			20 11					20 41			21 11			
Bowling	d					19 14					19 44			20 14					20 44			21 14			
Dumbarton East	d			18 58		19 19	19 28				19 49	19 58		20 19	20 28				20 49	20 58		21 19	21 28		
Dumbarton Central	d			19 00		19 21	19 30				19 51	20 00		20 21	20 30				20 51	21 00		21 21	21 30		
Dalreoch	d			19 01		19 22	19 31				19 52	20 01		20 22	20 31				20 52	21 01		21 22	21 31		
Renton	d					19 25					19 55			20 25					20 55			21 25			
Alexandria	d					19 28					19 58			20 28					20 58			21 28			
Balloch	a					19 30					20 00			20 30					21 01			21 30			
Cardross	d			19 06			19 36					20 06			20 36					21 06			21 36		
Craigendoran	d			19 11			19 41					20 11			20 41					21 11			21 41		
Helensburgh Central	a			19 14			19 44					20 14			20 44					21 14			21 44		

For general notes see front of timetable
For details of catering facilities see
Directory of Train Operators

§ Low Level

Table 226

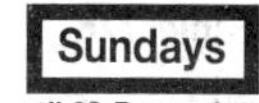

Sundays

until 23 December

Lanark, Coatbridge, Motherwell, Larkhall, Hamilton, Drumgelloch, Airdrie and Springburn → Glasgow → Milngavie, Dalmuir, Balloch and Helensburgh

Network Diagram - see first page of Table 220

		SR	SR	SR	SR	SR	SR	SR	SR	SR	SR	SR	SR	SR	SR	SR	SR	SR	SR	SR	SR
Lanark	d	20 12							21 12							22 12					
Carluke	d	20 22							21 22							22 22					
Wishaw	d	20 27							21 27							22 27					
Holytown	d																				
Shieldmuir	d	20 31							21 31							22 31					
Coatbridge Central	d																				
Whifflet	d																				
Motherwell	a	20 35							21 35							22 35					
	d	20 36	20 40		21 06	21 10			21 36	21 40		22 06	22 10			22 36	22 40		23 06	23 10	
Bellshill	d	20 42			21 12				21 42			22 12				22 42			23 12		
Uddingston	d	20 46			21 16				21 46			22 16				22 46			23 16		
Airbles	d		20 42			21 12				21 42			22 12				22 42			23 12	
Larkhall	d							21 25							22 25						
Merryton	d							21 27							22 27						
Chatelherault	d							21 30							22 30						
Hamilton Central	d		20 47			21 17		21 33		21 47			22 17		22 33		22 47			23 17	
Hamilton West	d		20 50			21 20		21 36		21 50			22 20		22 36		22 50			23 20	
Blantyre	d		20 53			21 23		21 39		21 53			22 23		22 39		22 53			23 23	
Newton	d		20 57			21 27				21 57			22 27				22 57			23 27	
Cambuslang	d	20 51	21 01		21 21	21 31			21 51	22 01		22 21	22 31			22 51	23 01		23 21	23 31	
Rutherglen	d	20 54	21 04		21 24	21 34		21 49	21 54	22 04		22 24	22 34		22 49	22 54	23 04		23 24	23 34	
Dalmarnock	d																				
Bridgeton	d	20 57	21 07		21 27	21 37			21 57	22 07		22 27	22 37			22 57	23 07		23 27	23 37	
Drumgelloch	d			20 54			21 24				21 54			22 24				22 54			23 24
Airdrie	a			20 57			21 27				21 57			22 27				22 57			23 27
	d			20 58			21 28				21 58			22 28				22 58			23 28
Coatdyke	d			21 00			21 30				22 00			22 30				23 00			23 30
Coatbridge Sunnyside	d			21 02			21 32				22 02			22 32				23 02			23 32
Blairhill	d			21 05			21 35				22 05			22 35				23 05			23 35
Easterhouse	d			21 09			21 39				22 09			22 39				23 09			23 39
Garrowhill	d			21 11			21 41				22 11			22 41				23 11			23 41
Shettleston	d			21 14			21 44				22 14			22 44				23 14			23 44
Carntyne	d			21 16			21 46				22 16			22 46				23 16			23 46
Springburn	d																				
Barnhill	d																				
Alexandra Parade	d																				
Duke Street	d																				
Bellgrove	d			21 19			21 49				22 19			22 49				23 19			23 49
High Street	d			21 21			21 51				22 21			22 51				23 21			23 51
Glasgow Queen Street 10 §	a			21 23			21 53				22 23			22 53				23 23			23 53
	d			21 24			21 54				22 24			22 54				23 24			23 54
Charing Cross	d			21 27			21 57				22 27			22 57				23 27			23 57
Argyle Street	d																				
Glasgow Central 15 §	a	21 04	21 14		21 34	21 44		21 57	22 04	22 14		22 34	22 44		22 57	23 04	23 14		23 34	23 44	
	d	21 04	21 14		21 34	21 44		21 57	22 04	22 14		22 34	22 44		22 57	23 04	23 14		23 34	23 44	
Anderston	d																				
Exhibition Centre	d	21 08	21 18		21 38	21 48		22 01	22 08	22 18		22 38	22 48		23 01	23 08	23 18		23 38	23 48	
Partick	d	21 12	21 22	21 32	21 42	21 52	22 02	22a04	22 12	22 22	22 32	22 42	22 52	23 02	23a04	23 12	23 22	23 32	23 42	23 52	00 02
Hyndland	d	21 16	21 24	21 34	21 46	21 54	22 04		22 16	22 24	22 34	22 46	22 54	23 04		23 16	23 24	23 34	23 44	23 54	00 04
Jordanhill	d		21 26			21 56				22 26			22 56				23 26		23 46	23 56	00 06
Scotstounhill	d		21 28			21 58				22 28			22 58				23 28		23 48	23 58	00 08
Garscadden	d		21 30			22 00				22 30			23 00				23 30		23a50	00a01	00a10
Yoker	d		21 33			22 03				22 33			23 03				23 33				
Clydebank	d		21 35			22 05				22 35			23 05				23 35				
Anniesland	d	21 19		21 37	21 49		22 07		22 19		22 37	22 49		23 07		23 19		23 37			
Westerton	d	21 22		21 40	21 52		22 10		22 22		22 40	22 52		23 10		23 22		23 40			
Bearsden	d	21 25			21 55				22 25			22 55				23 25					
Hillfoot	d	21 27			21 57				22 27			22 57				23 27					
Milngavie	a	21 30			22 00				22 30			23 00				23 30					
Drumchapel	d			21 42			22 12				22 42			23 12				23 42			
Drumry	d			21 44			22 14				22 44			23 14				23 44			
Singer	d			21 47			22 17				22 47			23 17				23 47			
Dalmuir	a		21 39	21 49		22 09	22 19			22 39	22 49		23 09	23 19			23 39	23 49			
	d		21 39	21 50		22 09	22 20			22 39	22 50		23 09	23 20			23 39	23 50			
Kilpatrick	d		21 41			22 11				22 41			23 11				23 41				
Bowling	d		21 44			22 14				22 44			23 14				23 44				
Dumbarton East	d		21 49	21 58		22 19	22 28			22 49	22 58		23 19	23 28			23 49	23 58			
Dumbarton Central	d		21 51	22 00		22 21	22 30			22 51	23 00		23 21	23 30			23 51	23 59			
Dalreoch	d		21 52	22 01		22 22	22 31			22 52	23 01		23 22	23 31			23 52	00 01			
Renton	d		21 55			22 25				22 55			23 25				23 55				
Alexandria	d		21 58			22 28				22 58			23 28				23 58				
Balloch	a		22 00			22 30				23 00			23 30				00 01				
Cardross	d			22 06			22 36				23 06			23 36				00 06			
Craigendoran	d			22 11			22 41				23 11			23 41				00 11			
Helensburgh Central	a			22 14			22 44				23 14			23 44				00 14			

For general notes see front of timetable
For details of catering facilities see Directory of Train Operators

§ Low Level

Table 226

from 30 December

Lanark, Coatbridge, Motherwell, Larkhall, Hamilton, Drumgelloch, Airdrie and Springburn → Glasgow → Milngavie, Dalmuir, Balloch and Helensburgh

Network Diagram - see first page of Table 220

Station		SR	SR	SR	SR	SR	SR	SR	SR	SR	SR	SR	SR	SR	SR	SR	SR	SR	SR	SR	SR	SR	SR
Lanark	d																		10 12				
Carluke	d																		10 22				
Wishaw	d																		10 27				
Holytown	d																						
Shieldmuir	d																		10 31				
Coatbridge Central	d																						
Whifflet	d																						
Motherwell	a																		10 35				
	d					08 36	08 40		09 10			09 36	09 40		10 06	10 10			10 36	10 40		11 06	11 10
Bellshill	d					08 42						09 42			10 12				10 42			11 12	
Uddingston	d					08 46						09 46			10 16				10 46			11 16	
Airbles	d						08 42		09 12				09 42			10 12				10 42			11 12
Larkhall	d										09 25							10 25					
Merryton	d										09 27							10 27					
Chatelherault	d										09 30							10 30					
Hamilton Central	d						08 47		09 17		09 33		09 47			10 17		10 33		10 47			11 17
Hamilton West	d						08 50		09 20		09 36		09 50			10 20		10 36		10 50			11 20
Blantyre	d						08 53		09 23		09 39		09 53			10 23		10 39		10 53			11 23
Newton	d						08 57		09 27				09 57			10 27				10 57			11 27
Cambuslang	d					08 51	09 01		09 31			09 51	10 01		10 21	10 31			10 51	11 01		11 21	11 31
Rutherglen	d					08 54	09 04		09 34		09 49	09 54	10 04		10 24	10 34		10 49	10 54	11 04		11 24	11 34
Dalmarnock	d																						
Bridgeton	d					08 57	09 07		09 37			09 57	10 07		10 27	10 37			10 57	11 07		11 27	11 37
Drumgelloch	d		07 54		08 24			08 54		09 24				09 54			10 24				10 54		
Airdrie	a		07 57		08 27			08 57		09 27				09 57			10 27				10 57		
	d		07 58		08 28			08 58		09 28				09 58			10 28				10 58		
Coatdyke	d		08 00		08 30			09 00		09 30				10 00			10 30				11 00		
Coatbridge Sunnyside	d		08 02		08 32			09 02		09 32				10 02			10 32				11 02		
Blairhill	d		08 05		08 35			09 05		09 35				10 05			10 35				11 05		
Easterhouse	d		08 09		08 39			09 09		09 39				10 09			10 39				11 09		
Garrowhill	d		08 11		08 41			09 11		09 41				10 11			10 41				11 11		
Shettleston	d		08 14		08 44			09 14		09 44				10 14			10 44				11 14		
Carntyne	d		08 16		08 46			09 16		09 46				10 16			10 46				11 16		
Springburn	d																						
Barnhill	d																						
Alexandra Parade	d																						
Duke Street	d																						
Bellgrove	d		08 19		08 49			09 19		09 49				10 19			10 49				11 19		
High Street	d		08 21		08 51			09 21		09 51				10 21			10 51				11 21		
Glasgow Queen Street 10 §	a		08 23		08 53			09 23		09 53				10 23			10 53				11 23		
	d		08 24		08 54			09 24		09 54				10 24			10 54				11 24		
Charing Cross	d		08 27		08 57			09 27		09 57				10 27			10 57				11 27		
Argyle Street	d											10 01	10 11		10 31	10 41		10 54	11 01	11 11		11 31	11 41
Glasgow Central 15 §	a					09 04	09 14		09 44		09 57	10 04	10 14		10 34	10 44		10 57	11 04	11 14		11 34	11 44
	d					09 04	09 14		09 44		09 57	10 04	10 14		10 34	10 44		10 57	11 04	11 14		11 34	11 44
Anderston	d																						
Exhibition Centre	d					09 08	09 18		09 48		10 01	10 08	10 18		10 38	10 48		11 01	11 08	11 18		11 38	11 48
Partick	d		08 32		09 02	09 12	09 22	09 32	09 52	10 02	10a04	10 12	10 22	10 32	10 42	10 52	11 02	11a04	11 12	11 22	11 32	11 42	11 52
Hyndland	d		08 34		09 04	09 16	09 24	09 34	09 54	10 04		10 16	10 24	10 34	10 46	10 54	11 04		11 16	11 24	11 34	11 46	11 54
Jordanhill	d						09 26		09 56				10 26			10 56				11 26			11 56
Scotstounhill	d						09 28		09 58				10 28			10 58				11 28			11 58
Garscadden	d						09 30		10 00				10 30			11 00				11 30			12 00
Yoker	d	08 33		09 03			09 33		10 03				10 33			11 03				11 33			12 03
Clydebank	d	08 35		09 05			09 35		10 05				10 35			11 05				11 35			12 05
Anniesland	d		08 37		09 07	09 19		09 37		10 07		10 19		10 37	10 49		11 07		11 19		11 37	11 49	
Westerton	d		08 40		09 10	09 22		09 40		10 10		10 22		10 40	10 52		11 10		11 22		11 40	11 52	
Bearsden	d					09 25						10 25			10 55				11 25			11 55	
Hillfoot	d					09 27						10 27			10 57				11 27			11 57	
Milngavie	a					09 30						10 30			11 00				11 30			12 00	
Drumchapel	d		08 42		09 12			09 42		10 12				10 42			11 12				11 42		
Drumry	d		08 44		09 14			09 44		10 14				10 44			11 14				11 44		
Singer	d		08 47		09 17			09 47		10 17				10 47			11 17				11 47		
Dalmuir	a	08 38	08 49	09 08	09 19		09 39	09 49	10 09	10 19			10 39	10 49		11 09	11 19			11 39	11 49		12 09
	d	08 39	08 50	09 09	09 20		09 39	09 50	10 09	10 20			10 39	10 50		11 09	11 20			11 39	11 50		12 09
Kilpatrick	d	08 41		09 11			09 41		10 11				10 41			11 11				11 41			12 11
Bowling	d	08 44		09 14			09 44		10 14				10 44			11 14				11 44			12 14
Dumbarton East	d	08 49	08 58	09 19	09 28		09 49	09 58	10 19	10 28			10 49	10 58		11 19	11 28			11 49	11 58		12 19
Dumbarton Central	d	08 51	09 00	09 21	09 30		09 51	10 00	10 21	10 30			10 51	11 00		11 21	11 30			11 51	12 00		12 21
Dalreoch	d	08 52	09 01	09 22	09 31		09 52	10 01	10 22	10 31			10 52	11 01		11 22	11 31			11 52	12 01		12 22
Renton	d	08 55		09 25			09 55		10 25				10 55			11 25				11 55			12 25
Alexandria	d	08 58		09 28			09 58		10 28				10 58			11 28				11 58			12 28
Balloch	a	09 00		09 30			10 00		10 30				11 00			11 30				12 00			12 30
Cardross	d		09 06		09 36			10 06		10 36				11 06			11 36				12 06		
Craigendoran	d		09 11		09 41			10 11		10 41				11 11			11 41				12 11		
Helensburgh Central	a		09 14		09 44			10 14		10 44				11 14			11 44				12 14		

For general notes see front of timetable
For details of catering facilities see Directory of Train Operators

§ Low Level

Table 226

Sundays from 30 December

Lanark, Coatbridge, Motherwell, Larkhall, Hamilton, Drumgelloch, Airdrie and Springburn → Glasgow → Milngavie, Dalmuir, Balloch and Helensburgh

Network Diagram - see first page of Table 220

		SR	SR	SR	SR ◇ A	SR	SR	SR	SR	SR	SR		SR	SR	SR	SR	SR	SR	SR	SR	SR	SR		SR	SR
Lanark	d			11 12									12 12							13 12					
Carluke	d			11 22									12 22							13 22					
Wishaw	d			11 27									12 27							13 27					
Holytown	d																								
Shieldmuir	d			11 31									12 31							13 31					
Coatbridge Central	d																								
Whifflet	d																								
Motherwell	a			11 35									12 35							13 35					
	d			11 36		11 40		12 06	12 10				12 36	12 40		13 06	13 10			13 36	13 40			14 06	14 10
Bellshill	d			11 42				12 12					12 42			13 12				13 42				14 12	
Uddingston	d			11 46				12 16					12 46			13 16				13 46				14 16	
Airbles	d					11 42			12 12					12 42			13 12				13 42				14 12
Larkhall	d		11 25								12 25								13 25						
Merryton	d		11 27								12 27								13 27						
Chatelherault	d		11 30								12 30								13 30						
Hamilton Central	d		11 33			11 47			12 17		12 33			12 47			13 17		13 33		13 47				14 17
Hamilton West	d		11 36			11 50			12 20		12 36			12 50			13 20		13 36		13 50				14 20
Blantyre	d		11 39			11 53			12 23		12 39			12 53			13 23		13 39		13 53				14 23
Newton	d					11 57			12 27					12 57			13 27				13 57				14 27
Cambuslang	d			11 51		12 01		12 21	12 31				12 51	13 01		13 21	13 31			13 51	14 01			14 21	14 31
Rutherglen	d		11 49	11 54		12 04		12 24	12 34		12 49		12 54	13 04		13 24	13 34		13 49	13 54	14 04			14 24	14 34
Dalmarnock	d																								
Bridgeton	d			11 57		12 07		12 27	12 37				12 57	13 07		13 27	13 37			13 57	14 07			14 27	14 37
Drumgelloch	d	11 24					11 54			12 24					12 54			13 24				13 54			
Airdrie	a	11 27					11 57			12 27					12 57			13 27				13 57			
	d	11 28					11 58			12 28					12 58			13 28				13 58			
Coatdyke	d	11 30					12 00			12 30					13 00			13 30				14 00			
Coatbridge Sunnyside	d	11 32					12 02			12 32					13 02			13 32				14 02			
Blairhill	d	11 35					12 05			12 35					13 05			13 35				14 05			
Easterhouse	d	11 39					12 09			12 39					13 09			13 39				14 09			
Garrowhill	d	11 41					12 11			12 41					13 11			13 41				14 11			
Shettleston	d	11 44					12 14			12 44					13 14			13 44				14 14			
Carntyne	d	11 46					12 16			12 46					13 16			13 46				14 16			
Springburn	d																								
Barnhill	d																								
Alexandra Parade	d																								
Duke Street	d																								
Bellgrove	d	11 49					12 19			12 49					13 19			13 49				14 19			
High Street	d	11 51					12 21			12 51					13 21			13 51				14 21			
Glasgow Queen Street 10 §	a	11 53					12 23			12 53					13 23			13 53				14 23			
	d	11 54			12b20		12 24			12 54					13 24			13 54				14 24			
Charing Cross	d	11 57					12 27			12 57					13 27			13 57				14 27			
Argyle Street	d		11 54	12 01		12 11		12 31			12 54		13 01	13 11		13 31	13 41		13 54	14 01	14 11			14 31	14 41
Glasgow Central 15 §	a		11 57	12 04		12 14		12 34	12 44		12 57		13 04	13 14		13 34	13 44		13 57	14 04	14 14			14 34	14 44
	d		11 57	12 04		12 14		12 34	12 44		12 57		13 04	13 14		13 34	13 44		13 57	14 04	14 14			14 34	14 44
Anderston	d																								
Exhibition Centre	d		12 01	12 08		12 18		12 38	12 48		13 01		13 08	13 18		13 38	13 48		14 01	14 08	14 18			14 38	14 48
Partick	d	12 02	12a04	12 12		12 22	12 32	12 42	12 52	13 02	13a04		13 12	13 22	13 32	13 42	13 52	14 02	14a04	14 12	14 22	14 32		14 42	14 52
Hyndland	d	12 04		12 16		12 24	12 34	12 46	12 54	13 04			13 16	13 24	13 34	13 46	13 54	14 04		14 16	14 24	14 34		14 46	14 54
Jordanhill	d					12 26			12 56					13 26			13 56				14 26				14 56
Scotstounhill	d					12 28			12 58					13 28			13 58				14 28				14 58
Garscadden	d					12 30			13 00					13 30			14 00				14 30				15 00
Yoker	d					12 33			13 03					13 33			14 03				14 33				15 03
Clydebank	d					12 35			13 05					13 35			14 05				14 35				15 05
Anniesland	d	12 07		12 19			12 37	12 49		13 07			13 19		13 37	13 49		14 07		14 19		14 37		14 49	
Westerton	d	12 10		12 22			12 40	12 52		13 10			13 22		13 40	13 52		14 10		14 22		14 40		14 52	
Bearsden	d			12 25				12 55					13 25			13 55				14 25				14 55	
Hillfoot	d			12 27				12 57					13 27			13 57				14 27				14 57	
Milngavie	a			12 30				13 00					13 30			14 00				14 30				15 00	
Drumchapel	d	12 12					12 42			13 12					13 42			14 12				14 42			
Drumry	d	12 14					12 44			13 14					13 44			14 14				14 44			
Singer	d	12 17					12 47			13 17					13 47			14 17				14 47			
Dalmuir	a	12 19			12 35	12 39	12 49		13 09	13 19				13 39	13 49		14 09	14 19			14 39	14 49			15 09
	d	12 20			12 35	12 39	12 50		13 09	13 20				13 39	13 50		14 09	14 20			14 39	14 50			15 09
Kilpatrick	d					12 41			13 11					13 41			14 11				14 41				15 11
Bowling	d					12 44			13 14					13 44			14 14				14 44				15 14
Dumbarton East	d	12 28				12 49	12 58		13 19	13 28				13 49	13 58		14 19	14 28			14 49	14 58			15 19
Dumbarton Central	d	12 30			12 45	12 51	13 00		13 21	13 30				13 51	14 00		14 21	14 30			14 51	15 00			15 21
Dalreoch	d	12 31				12 52	13 01		13 22	13 31				13 52	14 01		14 22	14 31			14 52	15 01			15 22
Renton	d					12 55			13 25					13 55			14 25				14 55				15 25
Alexandria	d					12 58			13 28					13 58			14 28				14 58				15 28
Balloch	a					13 00			13 30					14 00			14 30				15 00				15 30
Cardross	d	12 36					13 06			13 36					14 06			14 36				15 06			
Craigendoran	d	12 41					13 11			13 41					14 11			14 41				15 11			
Helensburgh Central	a	12 44			13c00		13 14			13 44					14 14			14 44				15 14			

For general notes see front of timetable
For details of catering facilities see Directory of Train Operators

§ Low Level

A From 23 March. To Oban (Table 227)

b Glasgow Queen Street High Level

c Helensburgh Upper

Table 226

from 30 December

Lanark, Coatbridge, Motherwell, Larkhall, Hamilton, Drumgelloch, Airdrie and Springburn → Glasgow → Milngavie, Dalmuir, Balloch and Helensburgh

Network Diagram - see first page of Table 220

Station		SR	SR	SR	SR	SR	SR	SR	SR	SR	SR		SR	SR	SR	SR	SR	SR	SR	SR	SR	SR		SR	SR
Lanark	d			14 12							15 12								16 12						
Carluke	d			14 22							15 22								16 22						
Wishaw	d			14 27							15 27								16 27						
Holytown	d																								
Shieldmuir	d			14 31							15 31								16 31						
Coatbridge Central	d																								
Whifflet	d																								
Motherwell	a			14 35							15 35								16 35						
	d			14 36	14 40		15 06	15 10			15 36		15 40		16 06	16 10			16 36	16 40		17 06		17 10	
Bellshill	d			14 42			15 12				15 42				16 12				16 42			17 12			
Uddingston	d			14 46			15 16				15 46				16 16				16 46			17 16			
Airbles	d				14 42			15 12					15 42			16 12				16 42				17 12	
Larkhall	d		14 25							15 25								16 25							
Merryton	d		14 27							15 27								16 27							
Chatelherault	d		14 30							15 30								16 30							
Hamilton Central	d		14 33		14 47			15 17		15 33			15 47			16 17		16 33		16 47				17 17	
Hamilton West	d		14 36		14 50			15 20		15 36			15 50			16 20		16 36		16 50				17 20	
Blantyre	d		14 39		14 53			15 23		15 39			15 53			16 23		16 39		16 53				17 23	
Newton	d				14 57			15 27					15 57			16 27				16 57				17 27	
Cambuslang	d			14 51	15 01		15 21	15 31			15 51		16 01		16 21	16 31			16 51	17 01		17 21		17 31	
Rutherglen	d		14 49	14 54	15 04		15 24	15 34		15 49	15 54		16 04		16 24	16 34		16 49	16 54	17 04		17 24		17 34	
Dalmarnock	d																								
Bridgeton	d			14 57	15 07		15 27	15 37			15 57		16 07		16 27	16 37			16 57	17 07		17 27		17 37	
Drumgelloch	d	14 24				14 54			15 24					15 54			16 24				16 54				17 24
Airdrie	a	14 27				14 57			15 27					15 57			16 27				16 57				17 27
	d	14 28				14 58			15 28					15 58			16 28				16 58				17 28
Coatdyke	d	14 30				15 00			15 30					16 00			16 30				17 00				17 30
Coatbridge Sunnyside	d	14 32				15 02			15 32					16 02			16 32				17 02				17 32
Blairhill	d	14 35				15 05			15 35					16 05			16 35				17 05				17 35
Easterhouse	d	14 39				15 09			15 39					16 09			16 39				17 09				17 39
Garrowhill	d	14 41				15 11			15 41					16 11			16 41				17 11				17 41
Shettleston	d	14 44				15 14			15 44					16 14			16 44				17 14				17 44
Carntyne	d	14 46				15 16			15 46					16 16			16 46				17 16				17 46
Springburn	d																								
Barnhill	d																								
Alexandra Parade	d																								
Duke Street	d																								
Bellgrove	d	14 49				15 19			15 49					16 19			16 49				17 19				17 49
High Street	d	14 51				15 21			15 51					16 21			16 51				17 21				17 51
Glasgow Queen Street 10 §	a	14 53				15 23			15 53					16 23			16 53				17 23				17 53
	d	14 54				15 24			15 54					16 24			16 54				17 24				17 54
Charing Cross	d	14 57				15 27			15 57					16 27			16 57				17 27				17 57
Argyle Street	d		14 54	15 01	15 11		15 31	15 41		15 54	16 01		16 11		16 31	16 41		16 54	17 01	17 11		17 31		17 41	
Glasgow Central 15 §	a		14 57	15 04	15 14		15 34	15 44		15 57	16 04		16 14		16 34	16 44		16 57	17 04	17 14		17 34		17 44	
	d		14 57	15 04	15 14		15 34	15 44		15 57	16 04		16 14		16 34	16 44		16 57	17 04	17 14		17 34		17 44	
Anderston	d																								
Exhibition Centre	d		15 01	15 08	15 18		15 38	15 48		16 01	16 08		16 18		16 38	16 48		17 01	17 08	17 18		17 38		17 48	
Partick	d	15 02	15a04	15 12	15 22	15 32	15 42	15 52	16 02	16a04	16 12		16 22	16 32	16 42	16 52	17 02	17a04	17 12	17 22	17 32	17 42		17 52	18 02
Hyndland	d	15 04		15 16	15 24	15 34	15 46	15 54	16 04		16 16		16 24	16 34	16 46	16 54	17 04		17 16	17 24	17 34	17 46		17 54	18 04
Jordanhill	d				15 26			15 56					16 26			16 56				17 26				17 56	
Scotstounhill	d				15 28			15 58					16 28			16 58				17 28				17 58	
Garscadden	d				15 30			16 00					16 30			17 00				17 30				18 00	
Yoker	d				15 33			16 03					16 33			17 03				17 33				18 03	
Clydebank	d				15 35			16 05					16 35			17 05				17 35				18 05	
Anniesland	d	15 07		15 19		15 37	15 49		16 07		16 19			16 37	16 49		17 07		17 19		17 37	17 49			18 07
Westerton	d	15 10		15 22		15 40	15 52		16 10		16 22			16 40	16 52		17 10		17 22		17 40	17 52			18 10
Bearsden	d			15 25			15 55				16 25				16 55				17 25			17 55			
Hillfoot	d			15 27			15 57				16 27				16 57				17 27			17 57			
Milngavie	a			15 30			16 00				16 30				17 00				17 30			18 00			
Drumchapel	d	15 12				15 42			16 12					16 42			17 12				17 42				18 12
Drumry	d	15 14				15 44			16 14					16 44			17 14				17 44				18 14
Singer	d	15 17				15 47			16 17					16 47			17 17				17 47				18 17
Dalmuir	a	15 19			15 39	15 49		16 09	16 19				16 39	16 49		17 09	17 19			17 39	17 49			18 09	18 19
	d	15 20			15 39	15 50		16 09	16 20				16 39	16 50		17 09	17 20			17 39	17 50			18 09	18 20
Kilpatrick	d				15 41			16 11					16 41			17 11				17 41				18 11	
Bowling	d				15 44			16 14					16 44			17 14				17 44				18 14	
Dumbarton East	d	15 28			15 49	15 58		16 19	16 28				16 49	16 58		17 19	17 28			17 49	17 58			18 19	18 28
Dumbarton Central	d	15 30			15 51	16 00		16 21	16 30				16 51	17 00		17 21	17 30			17 51	18 00			18 21	18 30
Dalreoch	d	15 31			15 52	16 01		16 22	16 31				16 52	17 01		17 22	17 31			17 52	18 01			18 22	18 31
Renton	d				15 55			16 25					16 55			17 25				17 55				18 25	
Alexandria	d				15 58			16 28					16 58			17 28				17 58				18 28	
Balloch	a				16 00			16 30					17 00			17 30				18 00				18 30	
Cardross	d	15 36				16 06			16 36					17 06			17 36				18 06				18 36
Craigendoran	d	15 41				16 11			16 41					17 11			17 41				18 11				18 41
Helensburgh Central	a	15 44				16 14			16 44					17 14			17 44				18 14				18 44

For general notes see front of timetable
For details of catering facilities see
Directory of Train Operators

§ Low Level

Table 226

from 30 December

Lanark, Coatbridge, Motherwell, Larkhall, Hamilton, Drumgelloch, Airdrie and Springburn → Glasgow → Milngavie, Dalmuir, Balloch and Helensburgh

Network Diagram - see first page of Table 220

		SR	SR	SR ◇ A	SR	SR	SR	SR	SR	SR	SR	SR	SR	SR	SR	SR	SR	SR	SR	SR	SR	SR	SR
Lanark	d		17 12								18 12							19 12					
Carluke	d		17 22								18 22							19 22					
Wishaw	d		17 27								18 27							19 27					
Holytown	d																						
Shieldmuir	d		17 31								18 31							19 31					
Coatbridge Central	d																						
Whifflet	d																						
Motherwell	a		17 35								18 35							19 35					
	d		17 36		17 40		18 06	18 10			18 36	18 40		19 06	19 10			19 36	19 40		20 06	20 10	
Bellshill	d		17 42				18 12				18 42			19 12				19 42			20 12		
Uddingston	d		17 46				18 16				18 46			19 16				19 46			20 16		
Airbles	d				17 42			18 12				18 42			19 12				19 42			20 12	
Larkhall	d	17 25								18 25							19 25						
Merryton	d	17 27								18 27							19 27						
Chatelherault	d	17 30								18 30							19 30						
Hamilton Central	d	17 33			17 47			18 17		18 33		18 47			19 17		19 33		19 47			20 17	
Hamilton West	d	17 36			17 50			18 20		18 36		18 50			19 20		19 36		19 50			20 20	
Blantyre	d	17 39			17 53			18 23		18 39		18 53			19 23		19 39		19 53			20 23	
Newton	d				17 57			18 27				18 57			19 27				19 57			20 27	
Cambuslang	d		17 51		18 01		18 21	18 31			18 51	19 01		19 21	19 31			19 51	20 01		20 21	20 31	
Rutherglen	d	17 49	17 54		18 04		18 24	18 34		18 49	18 54	19 04		19 24	19 34		19 49	19 54	20 04		20 24	20 34	
Dalmarnock	d																						
Bridgeton	d		17 57		18 07		18 27	18 37			18 57	19 07		19 27	19 37			19 57	20 07		20 27	20 37	
Drumgelloch	d					17 54			18 24				18 54			19 24				19 54			20 24
Airdrie	a					17 57			18 27				18 57			19 27				19 57			20 27
	d					17 58			18 28				18 58			19 28				19 58			20 28
Coatdyke	d					18 00			18 30				19 00			19 30				20 00			20 30
Coatbridge Sunnyside	d					18 02			18 32				19 02			19 32				20 02			20 32
Blairhill	d					18 05			18 35				19 05			19 35				20 05			20 35
Easterhouse	d					18 09			18 39				19 09			19 39				20 09			20 39
Garrowhill	d					18 11			18 41				19 11			19 41				20 11			20 41
Shettleston	d					18 14			18 44				19 14			19 44				20 14			20 44
Carntyne	d					18 16			18 46				19 16			19 46				20 16			20 46
Springburn	d																						
Barnhill	d																						
Alexandra Parade	d																						
Duke Street	d																						
Bellgrove	d					18 19			18 49				19 19			19 49				20 19			20 49
High Street	d					18 21			18 51				19 21			19 51				20 21			20 51
Glasgow Queen Street 10 §	a					18 23			18 53				19 23			19 53				20 23			20 53
	d			18b20		18 24			18 54				19 24			19 54				20 24			20 54
Charing Cross	d					18 27			18 57				19 27			19 57				20 27			20 57
Argyle Street	d	17 54	18 01		18 11																		
Glasgow Central 15 §	a	17 57	18 04		18 14		18 34	18 44		18 57	19 04	19 14		19 34	19 44		19 57	20 04	20 14		20 34	20 44	
	d	17 57	18 04		18 14		18 34	18 44		18 57	19 04	19 14		19 34	19 44		19 57	20 04	20 14		20 34	20 44	
Anderston	d																						
Exhibition Centre	d	18 01	18 08		18 18		18 38	18 48		19 01	19 08	19 18		19 38	19 48		20 01	20 08	20 18		20 38	20 48	
Partick	d	18a04	18 12		18 22	18 32	18 42	18 52	19 02	19a04	19 12	19 22	19 32	19 42	19 52	20 02	20a04	20 12	20 22	20 32	20 42	20 52	21 02
Hyndland	d		18 16		18 24	18 34	18 46	18 54	19 04		19 16	19 24	19 34	19 46	19 54	20 04		20 16	20 24	20 34	20 46	20 54	21 04
Jordanhill	d				18 26			18 56				19 26			19 56				20 26			20 56	
Scotstounhill	d				18 28			18 58				19 28			19 58				20 28			20 58	
Garscadden	d				18 30			19 00				19 30			20 00				20 30			21 00	
Yoker	d				18 33			19 03				19 33			20 03				20 33			21 03	
Clydebank	d				18 35			19 05				19 35			20 05				20 35			21 05	
Anniesland	d		18 19			18 37	18 49		19 07		19 19		19 37	19 49		20 07		20 19		20 37	20 49		21 07
Westerton	d		18 22			18 40	18 52		19 10		19 22		19 40	19 52		20 10		20 22		20 40	20 52		21 10
Bearsden	d		18 25				18 55				19 25			19 55				20 25			20 55		
Hillfoot	d		18 27				18 57				19 27			19 57				20 27			20 57		
Milngavie	a		18 30				19 00				19 30			20 00				20 30			21 00		
Drumchapel	d					18 42			19 12				19 42			20 12				20 42			21 12
Drumry	d					18 44			19 14				19 44			20 14				20 44			21 14
Singer	d					18 47			19 17				19 47			20 17				20 47			21 17
Dalmuir	a			18 35	18 39	18 49		19 09	19 19			19 39	19 49		20 09	20 19			20 39	20 49		21 09	21 19
	d			18 35	18 39	18 50		19 09	19 20			19 39	19 50		20 09	20 20			20 39	20 50		21 09	21 20
Kilpatrick	d				18 41			19 11				19 41			20 11				20 41			21 11	
Bowling	d				18 44			19 14				19 44			20 14				20 44			21 14	
Dumbarton East	d				18 49	18 58		19 19	19 28			19 49	19 58		20 19	20 28			20 49	20 58		21 19	21 28
Dumbarton Central	d			18c45	18 51	19 00		19 21	19 30			19 51	20 00		20 21	20 30			20 51	21 00		21 21	21 30
Dalreoch	d				18 52	19 01		19 22	19 31			19 52	20 01		20 22	20 31			20 52	21 01		21 22	21 31
Renton	d				18 55			19 25				19 55			20 25				20 55			21 25	
Alexandria	d				18 58			19 28				19 58			20 28				20 58			21 28	
Balloch	a				19 00			19 30				20 00			20 30				21 01			21 30	
Cardross	d					19 06			19 36				20 06			20 36				21 06			21 36
Craigendoran	d					19 11			19 41				20 11			20 41				21 11			21 41
Helensburgh Central	a			19e00		19 14			19 44				20 14			20 44				21 14			21 44

For general notes see front of timetable
For details of catering facilities see Directory of Train Operators

§ Low Level

A To Oban and to Mallaig (Table 227)
b Glasgow Queen Street High Level
c Arr. 1841
e Helensburgh Upper

Table 226

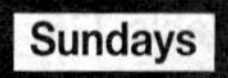

from 30 December

Lanark, Coatbridge, Motherwell, Larkhall, Hamilton, Drumgelloch, Airdrie and Springburn → Glasgow → Milngavie, Dalmuir, Balloch and Helensburgh

Network Diagram - see first page of Table 220

		SR	SR	SR	SR	SR	SR	SR	SR	SR	SR	SR	SR	SR	SR	SR	SR	SR	SR	SR	SR	SR
Lanark	d		20 12							21 12							22 12					
Carluke	d		20 22							21 22							22 22					
Wishaw	d		20 27							21 27							22 27					
Holytown	d																					
Shieldmuir	d		20 31							21 31							22 31					
Coatbridge Central	d																					
Whifflet	d																					
Motherwell	a		20 35							21 35							22 35					
	d		20 36	20 40		21 06	21 10			21 36	21 40		22 06	22 10			22 36	22 40		23 06	23 10	
Bellshill	d		20 42			21 12				21 42			22 12				22 42			23 12		
Uddingston	d		20 46			21 16				21 46			22 16				22 46			23 16		
Airbles	d			20 42			21 12				21 42			22 12				22 42			23 12	
Larkhall	d	20 25							21 25							22 25						
Merryton	d	20 27							21 27							22 27						
Chatelherault	d	20 30							21 30							22 30						
Hamilton Central	d	20 33		20 47			21 17		21 33		21 47			22 17		22 33		22 47			23 17	
Hamilton West	d	20 36		20 50			21 20		21 36		21 50			22 20		22 36		22 50			23 20	
Blantyre	d	20 39		20 53			21 23		21 39		21 53			22 23		22 39		22 53			23 23	
Newton	d			20 57			21 27				21 57			22 27				22 57			23 27	
Cambuslang	d		20 51	21 01		21 21	21 31			21 51	22 01		22 21	22 31			22 51	23 01		23 21	23 31	
Rutherglen	d	20 49	20 53	21 04		21 24	21 34		21 49	21 54	22 04		22 24	22 34		22 49	22 54	23 04		23 24	23 34	
Dalmarnock	d																					
Bridgeton	d		20 57	21 07		21 27	21 37			21 57	22 07		22 27	22 37			22 57	23 07		23 27	23 37	
Drumgelloch	d				20 54			21 24				21 54			22 24				22 54			23 24
Airdrie	a				20 57			21 27				21 57			22 27				22 57			23 27
	d				20 58			21 28				21 58			22 28				22 58			23 28
Coatdyke	d				21 00			21 30				22 00			22 30				23 00			23 30
Coatbridge Sunnyside	d				21 02			21 32				22 02			22 32				23 02			23 32
Blairhill	d				21 05			21 35				22 05			22 35				23 05			23 35
Easterhouse	d				21 09			21 39				22 09			22 39				23 09			23 39
Garrowhill	d				21 11			21 41				22 11			22 41				23 11			23 41
Shettleston	d				21 14			21 44				22 14			22 44				23 14			23 44
Carntyne	d				21 16			21 46				22 16			22 46				23 16			23 46
Springburn	d																					
Barnhill	d																					
Alexandra Parade	d																					
Duke Street	d																					
Bellgrove	d				21 19			21 49				22 19			22 49				23 19			23 49
High Street	d				21 21			21 51				22 21			22 51				23 21			23 51
Glasgow Queen Street 10 §	a				21 23			21 53				22 23			22 53				23 23			23 53
	d				21 24			21 54				22 24			22 54				23 24			23 54
Charing Cross	d				21 27			21 57				22 27			22 57				23 27			23 57
Argyle Street	d																					
Glasgow Central 15 §	a	20 57	21 04	21 14		21 34	21 44		21 57	22 04	22 14		22 34	22 44		22 57	23 04	23 14		23 34	23 44	
	d	20 57	21 04	21 14		21 34	21 44		21 57	22 04	22 14		22 34	22 44		22 57	23 04	23 14		23 34	23 44	
Anderston	d																					
Exhibition Centre	d	21 01	21 08	21 18		21 38	21 48		22 01	22 08	22 18		22 38	22 48		23 01	23 08	23 18		23 38	23 48	
Partick	d	21a04	21 12	21 22	21 32	21 42	21 52	22 02	22a04	22 12	22 22	22 32	22 42	22 52	23 02	23a04	23 12	23 22	23 32	23 42	23 52	00 02
Hyndland	d		21 16	21 24	21 34	21 46	21 54	22 04		22 16	22 24	22 34	22 46	22 54	23 04		23 16	23 24	23 34	23 44	23 54	00 04
Jordanhill	d			21 26			21 56				22 26			22 56				23 26		23 46	23 56	00 06
Scotstounhill	d			21 28			21 58				22 28			22 58				23 28		23 48	23 58	00 08
Garscadden	d			21 30			22 00				22 30			23 00				23 30		23a50	00a01	00a10
Yoker	d			21 33			22 03				22 33			23 03				23 33				
Clydebank	d			21 35			22 05				22 35			23 05				23 35				
Anniesland	d		21 19		21 37	21 49		22 07		22 19		22 37	22 49		23 07		23 19		23 37			
Westerton	d		21 22		21 40	21 52		22 10		22 22		22 40	22 52		23 10		23 22		23 40			
Bearsden	d		21 25			21 55				22 25			22 55				23 25					
Hillfoot	d		21 27			21 57				22 27			22 57				23 27					
Milngavie	a		21 30			22 00				22 30			23 00				23 30					
Drumchapel	d				21 42			22 12				22 42			23 12				23 42			
Drumry	d				21 44			22 14				22 44			23 14				23 44			
Singer	d				21 47			22 17				22 47			23 17				23 47			
Dalmuir	a			21 39	21 49		22 09	22 19			22 39	22 49		23 09	23 19			23 39	23 49			
	d			21 39	21 50		22 09	22 20			22 39	22 50		23 09	23 20			23 39	23 50			
Kilpatrick	d			21 41			22 11				22 41			23 11				23 41				
Bowling	d			21 44			22 14				22 44			23 14				23 44				
Dumbarton East	d			21 49	21 58		22 19	22 28			22 49	22 58		23 19	23 28			23 49	23 58			
Dumbarton Central	d			21 51	22 00		22 21	22 30			22 51	23 00		23 21	23 30			23 51	23 59			
Dalreoch	d			21 52	22 01		22 22	22 31			22 52	23 01		23 22	23 31			23 52	00 01			
Renton	d			21 55			22 25				22 55			23 25				23 55				
Alexandria	d			21 58			22 28				22 58			23 28				23 58				
Balloch	a			22 00			22 30				23 00			23 30				00 01				
Cardross	d				22 06			22 36				23 06			23 36				00 06			
Craigendoran	d				22 11			22 41				23 11			23 41				00 11			
Helensburgh Central	a				22 14			22 44				23 14			23 44				00 14			

For general notes see front of timetable
For details of catering facilities see
Directory of Train Operators

§ Low Level

Helensburgh, Balloch, Dalmuir and Milngavie → Glasgow → Springburn, Airdrie, Drumgelloch, Hamilton, Larkhall, Motherwell, Coatbridge and Lanark

Network Diagram - see first page of Table 220

Miles	Miles	Miles	Miles	Miles			SR MX	SR	SR SX	SR SX	SR SO	SR A	SR SX	SR	SR	SR	SR SX	SR SX B	SR SO	SR SX	SR SO	SR SX	SR SO	SR	SR
0	—	—	—	—	**Helensburgh Central**	d																			
1¼	—	—	—	—	Craigendoran	d																			
4¼	—	—	—	—	Cardross	d																			
—	0	—	—	—	**Balloch**	d																			
—	1	—	—	—	Alexandria	d																			
—	2½	—	—	—	Renton	d																			
8	3¾	—	—	—	Dalreoch	d																			
8¼	4	—	—	—	Dumbarton Central	d																			
9	4¾	—	—	—	Dumbarton East	d																			
11¾	7½	—	—	—	Bowling	d																			
13½	9¼	—	—	—	Kilpatrick	d																			
14¾	10½	0	0	—	**Dalmuir**	a																			
—	—	—	—	—		d				05 48	05 48					06 01						06 16	06 16	06 23	06 31
15½	11¼	—	¾	—	Singer	d										06 03						06 18	06 18		06 33
16½	12¼	—	1¾	—	Drumry	d										06 05						06 20	06 20		06 35
17¼	13	—	2½	—	Drumchapel	d										06 08						06 23	06 23		06 38
—	—	—	—	0	**Milngavie**	d																			→
—	—	—	—	1½	Hillfoot	d																			
—	—	—	—	2¼	Bearsden	d																			
18½	14¼	—	3¾	3½	Westerton	d	00 05									06 10						06 25	06 25		
19¾	15½	—	5	4¾	Anniesland	d										06 14						06 28	06 28		
—	—	1¼	—	—	Clydebank	d				05 50	05 50													06 25	
—	—	2¼	—	—	Yoker	d				05 52	05 52													06 27	
—	—	3¼	—	—	Garscadden	d				05 55	05 55			06 00	06 08		06 16			06 20	06 20			06 31	
—	—	3¾	—	—	Scotstounhill	d				05 57	05 57			06 02	06 10		06 18			06 22	06 22			06 33	
—	—	4¾	—	—	Jordanhill	d				05 59	05 59			06 05	06 12		06 20			06 24	06 24			06 35	
20¾	16½	5¼	6	5¾	Hyndland	d				06 01	06 01			06 07	06 14	06 17	06 22			06 26	06 26	06 31	06 31	06 37	
21¼	17	—	6½	6¼	Partick	d				06 04	06 04			06 10	06 17	06 20	06 25			06 29	06 29	06 34	06 34	06 40	
—	—	—	8¼	7½	Exhibition Centre	d								06 13		06 23				06 32	06 32			06 43	
—	—	—	8½	8	Anderston	d								06 15		06 25				06 34	06 34			06 45	
—	—	—	8¾	8½	**Glasgow Central** 15 §	a								06 17		06 26				06 35	06 35			06 47	
—	—	—	—	—		d						06b15		06 17		06 27				06 37	06 37			06 47	
—	—	—	9¼	9	Argyle Street	d								06 19		06 29				06 39	06 39			06 49	
23¼	19	—	—	—	Charing Cross	d				06 08	06 08				06 22		06 29					06 38	06 38		
24	19¾	—	—	—	**Glasgow Queen Street** 10 §	a	00c19			06 10	06 10				06 24		06 31					06 40	06 40		
—	—	—	—	—		d				06 12	06 14				06 27		06 32					06 42	06 44		
24½	20¼	—	—	—	High Street	d				06 14	06 16				06 29		06 34					06 44	06 46		
25	20¾	—	—	—	Bellgrove	d				06 16	06 18				06 31		06 36					06 46	06 48		
—	21¼	—	—	—	Duke Street	d					06 20						06 38						06 50		
—	21½	—	—	—	Alexandra Parade	d					06 21						06 39						06 51		
—	22¾	—	—	—	Barnhill	d					06 24						06 42						06 54		
—	23	—	—	—	**Springburn**	a					06 26						06 44						06 56		
26¾	—	—	—	—	Carntyne	d				06 19					06 34							06 49			
27½	—	—	—	—	Shettleston	d				06 22					06 37							06 52			
28¾	—	—	—	—	Garrowhill	d				06 24					06 39							06 54			
29¾	—	—	—	—	Easterhouse	d				06 27					06 42							06 57			
32½	—	—	—	—	Blairhill	d				06 31					06 46							07 01			
33	—	—	—	—	Coatbridge Sunnyside	d				06 33					06 48							07 03			
34	—	—	—	—	Coatdyke	d				06 36					06 51							07 06			
35	—	—	—	—	**Airdrie**	a				06 39					06 53							07 09			
—	—	—	—	—		d									06 54										
36½	—	—	—	—	**Drumgelloch**	a									06 58										
—	—	—	10½	10¼	Bridgeton	d								06 22						06 42	06 42			06 52	
—	—	—	11	10¾	Dalmarnock	d								06 24						06 44	06 44			06 54	
—	—	—	11¾	11½	Rutherglen	d								06 26		06 34				06 46	06 46			06 56	
—	—	—	13½	13¼	Cambuslang	d						06 24		06 31						06 50	06 50			07 01	
—	—	0	—	14¾	Newton	d														06 54	06 54				
—	—	2½	—	—	Blantyre	d										06 44				06 58	06 58				
—	—	4½	—	—	Hamilton West	d										06 47				07 01	07 01				
0	—	5¼	—	—	**Hamilton Central**	d										06 50				07 03	07 03				
2¼	—	—	—	—	Chatelherault	d										06 54									
3¾	—	—	—	—	Merryton	d										06 58									
5¼	—	—	—	—	**Larkhall**	a										07 00									
0	—	7½	—	—	Airbles	d														07 08	07 08				
—	—	—	17	16¾	Uddingston	d						06 29		06 35										07 05	
—	—	—	19½	—	Bellshill	d						06 35		06 40										07 10	
—	—	8¼	22½	21	**Motherwell**	a								06 45						07 11	07 11			07 17	
—	0	—	—	—		d		05 52	06 16				06 37	06 46				06 59	07 11	07 12					
—	4½	—	—	—	Whifflet	a														07 19					
—	5¼	—	—	—	**Coatbridge Central**	a														07 23					
—	—	—	—	22½	Shieldmuir	d		05 56	06 20					06 50				07 02	07 14						
—	—	—	—	21¼	Holytown	d						06a39	06 43												
—	—	—	—	24¼	Wishaw	d		05 59	06 23				06 48	06 53				07 06	07 18						
—	—	—	—	28¾	Carluke	d		06 06	06 30				06 55	07 00				07a10	07 25						
—	—	—	—	37¼	**Lanark**	a		06 16	06 42				07 07	07 12					07 36						

For general notes see front of timetable
For details of catering facilities see Directory of Train Operators

§ Low Level

A To Edinburgh (Saturdays from 29 March to Livingston South) (Table 225)

B To Carstairs (Table 225)

b Glasgow Central High Level

c Glasgow Queen Street High Level

Helensburgh, Balloch, Dalmuir and Milngavie → Glasgow → Springburn, Airdrie, Drumgelloch, Hamilton, Larkhall, Motherwell, Coatbridge and Lanark

Network Diagram - see first page of Table 220

		SR	SR	SR SX	SR SO A	SR SX B	SR SX	SR SO	SR SX	SR SO	SR SX C	SR SX	SR SO	SR	SR	SR	SR SX	SR	SR SX	SR SO	SR SO	SR SX	SR SX	SR	SR
Helensburgh Central	d	06 10													06 40										07 10
Craigendoran	d	06 13													06 43										07 13
Cardross	d	06 18													06 48										07 18
Balloch	d								06 23	06 23									06 53	06 53					
Alexandria	d								06 25	06 25									06 55	06 55					
Renton	d								06 28	06 28									06 58	06 58					
Dalreoch	d	06 23							06 31	06 31					06 53				07 01	07 01					07 23
Dumbarton Central	d	06 25							06 32	06 32					06 55				07 02	07 02					07 25
Dumbarton East	d	06 27							06 34	06 34					06 57				07 04	07 04					07 27
Bowling	d								06 39	06 39									07 09	07 09					
Kilpatrick	d								06 42	06 42									07 12	07 12					
Dalmuir	a	06 35							06 45	06 45					07 05				07 15	07 15					07 35
	d	06 36							06 46	06 46		06 53	06 53	07 01	07 06				07 16	07 16	07 23	07 23		07 31	07 36
Singer	d								06 48	06 48				07 03					07 18	07 18				07 33	
Drumry	d		←						06 50	06 50				07 05		←			07 20	07 20				07 35	
Drumchapel	d		06 38						06 53	06 53				07 08		07 08			07 23	07 23				07 38	
Milngavie	d						06 42	06 42						↪				07 12					07 27	↪	
Hillfoot	d						06 45	06 45										07 15					07 30		
Bearsden	d						06 47	06 47										07 17					07 32		
Westerton	d		06 40				06 50	06 50	06 55	06 55						07 10		07 20	07 25	07 25			07 35		
Anniesland	d		06 44				06 53	06 53	06 58	06 58						07 14		07 23	07 28	07 28			07 38		
Clydebank	d											06 55	06 55								07 25	07 25			
Yoker	d											06 57	06 57								07 27	07 27			
Garscadden	d			06 46								07 01	07 01				07 16				07 31	07 31			
Scotstounhill	d			06 48								07 03	07 03				07 18				07 33	07 33			
Jordanhill	d			06 50								07 05	07 05				07 20				07 35	07 35			
Hyndland	d	06 44	06 47	06 52			06 56	06 56	07 01	07 01		07 07	07 07		07 14	07 17	07 22	07 26	07 31	07 31	07 37	07 37	07 41		07 44
Partick	d	06 47	06 50	06 55			06 59	06 59	07 04	07 04		07 10	07 10		07 17	07 20	07 25	07 29	07 34	07 34	07 40	07 40	07 44		07 47
Exhibition Centre	d		06 53				07 02	07 02				07 13	07 13			07 23		07 32			07 43	07 43			
Anderston	d		06 55				07 04	07 04				07 15	07 15			07 25		07 34			07 45	07 45			
Glasgow Central 15 §	a		06 56				07 05	07 05				07 17	07 17			07 26		07 35			07 47	07 47			
	d		06 57		07b05	07b05	07 07	07 07			07b13	07 17	07 17			07 27		07 37			07 47	07 47			
Argyle Street	d		06 59				07 09	07 09				07 19	07 19			07 29		07 39			07 49	07 49			
Charing Cross	d	06 52		06 59					07 08	07 08					07 22		07 29		07 38	07 38			07 49		07 52
Glasgow Queen Street 10 §	a	06 54		07 01					07 10	07 10					07 24		07 31		07 40	07 40			07 51		07 54
	d	06 57		07 02					07 12	07 14					07 27		07 32		07 42	07 44			07 51		07 57
High Street	d	06 59		07 04					07 14	07 16					07 29		07 34		07 44	07 46			07a53		07 59
Bellgrove	d	07 01		07 06					07 16	07 18					07 31		07 36		07 46	07 48					08 01
Duke Street	d			07 08						07 20							07 38			07 50					
Alexandra Parade	d			07 09						07 21							07 39			07 51					
Barnhill	d			07 12						07 24							07 42			07 54					
Springburn	a			07 14						07 26							07 44			07 56					
Carntyne	d	07 04							07 19						07 34				07 49						08 04
Shettleston	d	07 07							07 22						07 37				07 52						08 07
Garrowhill	d	07 09							07 24						07 39				07 54						08 09
Easterhouse	d	07 12							07 27						07 42				07 57						08 12
Blairhill	d	07 16							07 31						07 46				08 01						08 16
Coatbridge Sunnyside	d	07 18							07 33						07 48				08 03						08 18
Coatdyke	d	07 21							07 36						07 51				08 06						08 21
Airdrie	a	07 23							07 39						07 53				08 09						08 23
	d	07 24													07 54										08 24
Drumgelloch	a	07 28													07 58										08 28
Bridgeton	d						07 12	07 12				07 22	07 22					07 42			07 52	07 52			
Dalmarnock	d						07 14	07 14				07 24	07 24					07 44			07 54	07 54			
Rutherglen	d		07 04				07 16	07 16				07 26	07 26			07 34		07 46			07 56	07 56			
Cambuslang	d						07 20	07 20			07 22	07 31	07 31					07 50			08 01	08 01			
Newton	d						07 24	07 24										07 54							
Blantyre	d		07 14				07 28	07 28								07 44		07 58							
Hamilton West	d		07 17				07 31	07 31								07 47		08 01							
Hamilton Central	d		07 20				07 33	07 33								07 50		08 03							
Chatelherault	d		07 24													07 54									
Merryton	d		07 28													07 58									
Larkhall	a		07 30													08 00									
Airbles	d						07 38	07 38										08 08							
Uddingston	d										07 27	07 35	07 35								08 05	08 05			
Bellshill	d										07 33	07 40	07 40								08 10	08 10			
Motherwell	a				07 20	07 27	07 41	07 41				07 46	07 46					08 11			08 16	08 17			
	d				07 20	07 28		07 42				07 46									08 16				
Whifflet	a																								
Coatbridge Central	a																								
Shieldmuir	d											07 50									08 20				
Holytown	d							07 47			07a37														
Wishaw	d				07 26	07 33		07 53				07 53									08 23				
Carluke	d				07a33	07a37		07 59				08 00									08 30				
Lanark	a							08 12				08 12									08 46				

For general notes see front of timetable
For details of catering facilities see Directory of Train Operators

§ Low Level

A Until 22 March to North Berwick (Table 238). From 29 March to Carstairs (Table 225)
B To North Berwick (Table 238)

C To Edinburgh (Table 225)
b Glasgow Central High Level

Helensburgh, Balloch, Dalmuir and Milngavie → Glasgow → Springburn, Airdrie, Drumgelloch, Hamilton, Larkhall, Motherwell, Coatbridge and Lanark

Network Diagram - see first page of Table 220

		SR	SR SX	SR SX	SR SO	SR SX	SR SO	SR SO A	SR		SR SX	SR SX	SR SO	SR	SR SX	SR SO	SR SX B	SR	SR SX	SR SO	SR SX	SR SX	SR SX	SR SO	SR SX
Helensburgh Central	d														07 35	07 40	07b42								
Craigendoran	d														07 38	07 43									
Cardross	d														07 43	07 48	07 51								
Balloch	d					07 23	07 23													07 53	07 53				
Alexandria	d					07 25	07 25													07 55	07 55				
Renton	d					07 28	07 28													07 58	07 58				
Dalreoch	d					07 31	07 31								07 48	07 53				08 01	08 01				
Dumbarton Central	d					07 32	07 32								07 50	07 55	07 57			08 02	08 03				
Dumbarton East	d					07 34	07 34								07 52	07 57				08 04					
Bowling	d					07 39	07 39								07 57					08 09					
Kilpatrick	d					07 42	07 42								08 00					08 12					
Dalmuir	a					07 45	07 45								08 03	08 05				08 15					
	d		07 38			07 46	07 46		07 53					08 01	08 04	08 06			08 08	08 16					
Singer	d					07 48	07 48							08 03			08 06			08 18					
Drumry	d	←				07 50	07 50							08 05				←		→					
Drumchapel	d	07 38				07 53	07 53							08 08				08 08							
Milngavie	d			07 42	07 42						07 57			→									08 10	08 12	08 18
Hillfoot	d			07 45	07 45						08 00												08 13	08 15	08 21
Bearsden	d			07 47	07 47						08 02												08 16	08 17	08 24
Westerton	d	07 40		07 50	07 50	07 55	07 55				08 05							08 10					08 19	08 20	
Anniesland	d	07 44		07 53	07 53	07 58	07 58				08 08							08 14					08 23	08 23	
Clydebank	d		07 40						07 55						08 06				08 10						
Yoker	d		07 42						07 57										08 12						
Garscadden	d		07 46						08 01										08 16						
Scotstounhill	d		07 48						08 03										08 18						
Jordanhill	d		07 50						08 05										08 21			←			
Hyndland	d	07 47	07 52	07 56	07 56	08 01	08 01		08 07		08 11				08 14	08 14		08 17	08 23			08 23	08 26	08 26	
Partick	d	07 50	07 55	07 59	07 59	08 04	08 04		08 10		08 14				08 17	08 17		08 20	→		08 22	08 26	08 29	08 29	
Exhibition Centre	d	07 53		08 02	08 02				08 13		08 17							08 23					08 32	08 32	
Anderston	d	07 55		08 04	08 04				08 15		08 19							08 25					08 34	08 34	
Glasgow Central 15 §	a	07 56		08 05	08 05				08 17		08 20							08 26					08 35	08 35	
	d	07 57		08 07	08 07			08c15	08 17		08 21							08 27					08 37	08 37	
Argyle Street	d	07 59		08 09	08 09				08 19		08 23							08 29					08 39	08 39	
Charing Cross	d		07 59			08 08	08 08								08 22	08 22					08 27	08 31			08 36
Glasgow Queen Street 10 §	a		08 01			08 10	08 10								08 24	08 24	08e37				08 29	08 33			08 37
	d		08 02			08 12	08 14								08 27	08 27					08 30	08 33			08 38
High Street	d		08 04			08 14	08 16								08 29	08 29					08 32	08a35			08 40
Bellgrove	d		08 06			08 16	08 18								08 31	08 31					08 34				08 42
Duke Street	d		08 08				08 20														08 36				08 44
Alexandra Parade	d		08 09				08 21														08 37				08 45
Barnhill	d		08 12				08 24														08 40				08 48
Springburn	a		08 14				08 26														08 42				08 51
Carntyne	d					08 19									08 34	08 34									
Shettleston	d					08 22									08 37	08 37									
Garrowhill	d					08 24									08 39	08 39									
Easterhouse	d					08 27									08 42	08 42									
Blairhill	d					08 31									08 46	08 46									
Coatbridge Sunnyside	d					08 33									08 48	08 48									
Coatdyke	d					08 36									08 51	08 51									
Airdrie	a					08 39									08 53	08 53									
	d														08 54	08 54									
Drumgelloch	a														08 58	08 58									
Bridgeton	d			08 12	08 12				08 22		08 26												08 42	08 42	
Dalmarnock	d			08 14	08 14				08 24		08 28												08 44	08 44	
Rutherglen	d	08 04		08 16	08 16				08 26		08 30							08 34					08 46	08 46	
Cambuslang	d			08 20	08 20			08 24	08 31														08 50	08 50	
Newton	d			08 24	08 24																		08 54	08 54	
Blantyre	d	08 14		08 28	08 28													08 44					08 58	08 58	
Hamilton West	d	08 17		08 31	08 31													08 47					09 01	09 01	
Hamilton Central	d	08 20		08 33	08 33													08 50					→	→	
Chatelherault	d	08 24																08 54							
Merryton	d	08 28																08 58							
Larkhall	a	08 30																09 00							
Airbles	d			08 38	08 38							←	←												
Uddingston	d							08 29	08 35			08 35	08 35												
Bellshill	d							08 35	→			08 40	08 40												
Motherwell	a			08 41	08 41						08 44	08 46	08 46												
	d				08 42							08 46													
Whifflet	a																								
Coatbridge Central	a																								
Shieldmuir	d											08 50													
Holytown	d				08 47			08a39																	
Wishaw	d				08 53							08 53													
Carluke	d				08 59							09 00													
Lanark	a				09 12							09 12													

For general notes see front of timetable
For details of catering facilities see Directory of Train Operators

§ Low Level

A To Edinburgh (from 29 March to Livingston South) (Table 225)
B From Arrochar & Tarbet (Table 227)
b Helensburgh Upper
c Glasgow Central High Level
e Glasgow Queen Street High Level

Helensburgh, Balloch, Dalmuir and Milngavie → Glasgow → Springburn, Airdrie, Drumgelloch, Hamilton, Larkhall, Motherwell, Coatbridge and Lanark

Network Diagram - see first page of Table 220

		SR	SR	SR	SR	SR	SR	SR	SR	SR	SR	SR	SR	SR	SR	SR	SR	SR	SR	SR	SR	SR	SR	SR	SR
		SO	SX	SX	SX		SX		SX		SX	SO		SX	SO					SX					
																		A							
Helensburgh Central	d		07 54	08 01							08 08	08 10										08 40			
Craigendoran	d		07 57	08 04							08 11	08 13										08 43			
Cardross	d		08 02	08 09							08 16	08 18										08 48			
Balloch	d																08 23								
Alexandria	d																08 25								
Renton	d																08 28								
Dalreoch	d		08 07								08 21	08 23					08 31					08 53			
Dumbarton Central	d		08 09	08 15							08 23	08 25					08 32					08 55			
Dumbarton East	d		08 11								08 25	08 27					08 34					08 57			
Bowling	d										08 30						08 39								
Kilpatrick	d										08 33						08 42								
Dalmuir	a		08 19								08 35	08 35					08 45					09 05			
	d	←	08 20					08 23		08 31	08 36	08 36		08 38			08 46		08 53		09 01	09 06		09 08	
Singer	d	08 18	08 22				←			08 33							08 48				09 03				
Drumry	d	08 20	08 24				08 24			08 35			←				08 50				09 05		←		
Drumchapel	d	08 23	→				08 27			08 38			08 38				08 53				09 08		09 08		
Milngavie	d								08 27	→						08 42				08 57	→				09 12
Hillfoot	d								08 30							08 45				09 00					09 15
Bearsden	d								08 32							08 47				09 02					09 17
Westerton	d	08 25					08 29		08 35				08 40			08 50	08 55			09 05			09 10		09 20
Anniesland	d	08 28					08 32		08 38				08 44			08 53	08 58			09 08			09 14		09 23
Clydebank	d							08 25						08 40					08 55					09 10	
Yoker	d							08 27						08 42					08 57					09 12	
Garscadden	d							08 31						08 46	08 46				09 01					09 16	
Scotstounhill	d			08 28				08 33						08 48	08 48				09 03					09 18	
Jordanhill	d							08 35						08 50	08 50				09 05					09 20	
Hyndland	d	08 31		08 33			08 35	08 37	08 41		08 44	08 44	08 47	08 52	08 52	08 56	09 01		09 07	09 11		09 14	09 17	09 22	09 26
Partick	d	08 34		08 35			08 38	08 40	08 44		08 47	08 47	08 50	08 55	08 55	08 59	09 04		09 10	09 14		09 17	09 20	09 25	09 29
Exhibition Centre	d							08 43					08 53			09 02			09 13				09 23		09 32
Anderston	d				08 38			08 45					08 55			09 04			09 15				09 25		09 34
Glasgow Central 15 §	a				08 39			08 47					08 56			09 05			09 17				09 26		09 35
	d				08 40			08 47					08 57			09 07		09b15	09 17				09 27		09 37
Argyle Street	d				08 42			08 49					08 59			09 09			09 19				09 29		09 39
Charing Cross	d	08 38		08 40			08 42		08 49		08 52	08 52		08 59	08 59		09 08			09 19		09 22		09 29	
Glasgow Queen Street 10 §	a	08 40		08 42			08 44		08 51		08 54	08 54		09 01	09 01		09 10			09 21		09 24		09 31	
	d	08 44		08 42			08 45		08 51		08 57	08 57		09 02	09 02		09 12			09 21		09 27		09 32	
High Street	d	08 46		08 44			08a47		08a53		08 59	08 59		09 04	09 04		09 14			09a23		09 29		09 34	
Bellgrove	d	08 48		08 46							09 01	09 01		09 06	09 06		09 16					09 31		09 36	
Duke Street	d	08 50												09 08	09 08									09 38	
Alexandra Parade	d	08 51												09 09	09 09									09 39	
Barnhill	d	08 54												09 12	09 12									09 42	
Springburn	a	08 56												09 14	09 14									09 44	
Carntyne	d			08 49							09 04	09 04					09 19					09 34			
Shettleston	d			08 52							09 07	09 07					09 22					09 37			
Garrowhill	d			08 54							09 09	09 09					09 24					09 39			
Easterhouse	d			08 57							09 12	09 12					09 27					09 42			
Blairhill	d			09 01							09 16	09 16					09 31					09 46			
Coatbridge Sunnyside	d			09 04							09 18	09 18					09 33					09 48			
Coatdyke	d			09 06							09 21	09 21					09 36					09 51			
Airdrie	a			09 09							09 23	09 23					09c39					09 53			
	d										09 24	09 24										09 54			
Drumgelloch	a										09 28	09 28										09 58			
Bridgeton	d				08 45			08 52								09 12			09 22						09 42
Dalmarnock	d				08 47			08 54								09 14			09 24						09 44
Rutherglen	d				08 49			08 56					09 04			09 16			09 26				09 34		09 46
Cambuslang	d				08 55			09 01								09 20		09 24	09 31						09 50
Newton	d															09 24									09 54
Blantyre	d					←							09 14			09 28							09 44		09 58
Hamilton West	d					09 01							09 17			09 31							09 47		10 01
Hamilton Central	d					09 03							09 20			09 33							09 50		10 03
Chatelherault	d												09 24										09 54		
Merryton	d												09 28										09 58		
Larkhall	a												09 30										10 00		
Airbles	d					09 08										09 38									10 08
Uddingston	d				09 02			09 05										09 29	09 35						
Bellshill	d							09 10										09 35	09 40						
Motherwell	a				09 09	09 11		09 16								09 41			09e46						10 11
	d							09 16								09 42									
Whifflet	a																								
Coatbridge Central	a																								
Shieldmuir	d							09 20																	
Holytown	d															09 47		09a39							
Wishaw	d							09 23								09 53									
Carluke	d							09 30								10 00									
Lanark	a							09 42								10 12									

For general notes see front of timetable
For details of catering facilities see Directory of Train Operators

§ Low Level

A To Edinburgh (Saturdays from 29 March to Livingston South) (Table 225)

b Glasgow Central High Level

c Saturdays arr. 2 minutes later

e Saturdays arr. 1 minute later

Helensburgh, Balloch, Dalmuir and Milngavie → Glasgow → Springburn, Airdrie, Drumgelloch, Hamilton, Larkhall, Motherwell, Coatbridge and Lanark

Network Diagram - see first page of Table 220

		SR	SR	SR	SR	SR	SR	SR	SR	SR	SR A	SR	SR	SR	SR	SR	SR	SR	SR	SR	SR	SR	SR	SR
Helensburgh Central	d					09 10									09 40								10 10	
Craigendoran	d					09 13									09 43								10 13	
Cardross	d					09 18									09 48								10 18	
Balloch	d	08 53								09 23									09 53					
Alexandria	d	08 55								09 25									09 55					
Renton	d	08 58								09 28									09 58					
Dalreoch	d	09 01				09 23				09 31					09 53				10 01				10 23	
Dumbarton Central	d	09 02				09 25				09 32					09 55				10 02				10 25	
Dumbarton East	d	09 04				09 27				09 34					09 57				10 04				10 27	
Bowling	d	09 09								09 39									10 09					
Kilpatrick	d	09 12								09 42									10 12					
Dalmuir	a	09 15				09 35				09 45					10 05				10 15				10 35	
	d	09 16	09 23		09 31	09 36		09 38		09 46		09 53		10 01	10 06		10 08		10 16	10 23		10 31	10 36	
Singer	d	09 18			09 33					09 48				10 03					10 18			10 33		
Drumry	d	09 20			09 35		←			09 50				10 05		←			10 20			10 35		←
Drumchapel	d	09 23			09 38		09 38			09 53				10 08		10 08			10 23			10 38		10 38
Milngavie	d			09 27	→				09 42				09 57	→				10 12			10 27	→		
Hillfoot	d			09 30					09 45				10 00					10 15			10 30			
Bearsden	d			09 32					09 47				10 02					10 17			10 32			
Westerton	d	09 25		09 35			09 40		09 50	09 55			10 05			10 10		10 20	10 25		10 35			10 40
Anniesland	d	09 28		09 38			09 44		09 53	09 58			10 08			10 14		10 23	10 28		10 38			10 44
Clydebank	d		09 25					09 40				09 55					10 10			10 25				
Yoker	d		09 27					09 42				09 57					10 12			10 27				
Garscadden	d		09 31					09 46				10 01					10 16			10 31				
Scotstounhill	d		09 33					09 48				10 03					10 18			10 33				
Jordanhill	d		09 35					09 50				10 05					10 20			10 35				
Hyndland	d	09 31	09 37	09 41		09 44	09 47	09 52	09 56	10 01		10 07	10 11		10 14	10 17	10 22	10 26	10 31	10 37	10 41		10 44	10 47
Partick	d	09 34	09 40	09 44		09 47	09 50	09 55	09 59	10 04		10 10	10 14		10 17	10 20	10 25	10 29	10 34	10 40	10 44		10 47	10 50
Exhibition Centre	d		09 43				09 53		10 02			10 13				10 23		10 32		10 43				10 53
Anderston	d		09 45				09 55		10 04			10 15				10 25		10 34		10 45				10 55
Glasgow Central 15 §	a		09 47				09 56		10 05			10 17				10 26		10 35		10 47				10 56
	d		09 47				09 57		10 07		10b15	10 17				10 27		10 37		10 47				10 57
Argyle Street	d		09 49				09 59		10 09			10 19				10 29		10 39		10 49				10 59
Charing Cross	d	09 38		09 49		09 52		09 59		10 08			10 19		10 22		10 29		10 38		10 49		10 52	
Glasgow Queen Street 10 §	a	09 40		09 51		09 54		10 01		10 10			10 21		10 24		10 31		10 40		10 51		10 54	
	d	09 42		09 51		09 57		10 02		10 12			10 21		10 27		10 32		10 42		10 51		10 57	
High Street	d	09 44		09a53		09 59		10 04		10 14			10a23		10 29		10 34		10 44		10a53		10 59	
Bellgrove	d	09 46				10 01		10 06		10 16					10 31		10 36		10 46				11 01	
Duke Street	d							10 08									10 38							
Alexandra Parade	d							10 09									10 39							
Barnhill	d							10 12									10 42							
Springburn	a							10 14									10 44							
Carntyne	d	09 49				10 04				10 19					10 34				10 49				11 04	
Shettleston	d	09 52				10 07				10 22					10 37				10 52				11 07	
Garrowhill	d	09 54				10 09				10 24					10 39				10 54				11 09	
Easterhouse	d	09 57				10 12				10 27					10 42				10 57				11 12	
Blairhill	d	10 01				10 16				10 31					10 46				11 01				11 16	
Coatbridge Sunnyside	d	10 03				10 18				10 33					10 48				11 03				11 18	
Coatdyke	d	10 06				10 21				10 36					10 51				11 06				11 21	
Airdrie	a	10 09				10 23				10 39					10 53				11 09				11 23	
	d					10 24									10 54								11 24	
Drumgelloch	a					10 28									10 58								11 28	
Bridgeton	d		09 52						10 12			10 22						10 42		10 52				
Dalmarnock	d		09 54						10 14			10 24						10 44		10 54				
Rutherglen	d		09 56				10 04		10 16			10 26				10 34		10 46		10 56				11 04
Cambuslang	d		10 01						10 20		10 24	10 31						10 50		11 01				
Newton	d								10 24									10 54						
Blantyre	d						10 14		10 28							10 44		10 58						11 14
Hamilton West	d						10 17		10 31							10 47		11 01						11 17
Hamilton Central	d						10 20		10 33							10 50		11 03						11 20
Chatelherault	d						10 24									10 54								11 24
Merryton	d						10 28									10 58								11 28
Larkhall	a						10 30									11 00								11 30
Airbles	d								10 38									11 08						
Uddingston	d		10 05								10 29	10 35								11 05				
Bellshill	d		10 10								10 35	10 40								11 10				
Motherwell	a		10 16						10 41			10 46						11 11		11 16				
	d		10 16						10 42											11 16				
Whifflet	a																							
Coatbridge Central	a																							
Shieldmuir	d		10 20																	11 20				
Holytown	d								10 47		10a39													
Wishaw	d		10 23						10 53											11 23				
Carluke	d		10 30						11 00											11 30				
Lanark	a		10 42						11 12											11 42				

For general notes see front of timetable
For details of catering facilities see Directory of Train Operators

§ Low Level

A To Edinburgh (Saturdays from 29 March to Livingston South) (Table 225)

b Glasgow Central High Level

Helensburgh, Balloch, Dalmuir and Milngavie → Glasgow → Springburn, Airdrie, Drumgelloch, Hamilton, Larkhall, Motherwell, Coatbridge and Lanark

Network Diagram - see first page of Table 220

Station		SR	SR	SR	SR	SR	SR	SR	SR	SR	SR	SR	SR	SR	SR	SR	SR	SR	SR	SR	SR	SR	SR	SR	SR
					A					◇ B													A		
Helensburgh Central	d								10 40	10b41								11 10							
Craigendoran	d								10 43									11 13							
Cardross	d								10 48									11 18							
Balloch	d			10 23										10 53								11 23			
Alexandria	d			10 25										10 55								11 25			
Renton	d			10 28										10 58								11 28			
Dalreoch	d			10 31					10 53					11 01				11 23				11 31			
Dumbarton Central	d			10 32					10 55	10 58				11 02				11 25				11 32			
Dumbarton East	d			10 34					10 57					11 04				11 27				11 34			
Bowling	d			10 39										11 09								11 39			
Kilpatrick	d			10 42										11 12								11 42			
Dalmuir	a			10 45					11 05	11 08				11 15				11 35				11 45			
	d	10 38		10 46		10 53		11 01	11 06	11 08		11 08		11 16	11 23		11 31	11 36		11 38		11 46		11 53	
Singer	d			10 48				11 03						11 18			11 33					11 48			
Drumry	d			10 50				11 05			←			11 20			11 35		←			11 50			
Drumchapel	d			10 53				11 08			11 08			11 23			11 38		11 38			11 53			
Milngavie	d		10 42				10 57	→					11 12			11 27	→				11 42				11 57
Hillfoot	d		10 45				11 00						11 15			11 30					11 45				12 00
Bearsden	d		10 47				11 02						11 17			11 32					11 47				12 02
Westerton	d		10 50	10 55			11 05				11 10		11 20	11 25		11 35			11 40		11 50	11 55			12 05
Anniesland	d		10 53	10 58			11 08				11 14		11 23	11 28		11 38			11 44		11 53	11 58			12 08
Clydebank	d	10 40				10 55						11 10			11 25					11 40				11 55	
Yoker	d	10 42				10 57						11 12			11 27					11 42				11 57	
Garscadden	d	10 46				11 01						11 16			11 31					11 46				12 01	
Scotstounhill	d	10 48				11 03						11 18			11 33					11 48				12 03	
Jordanhill	d	10 50				11 05						11 20			11 35					11 50				12 05	
Hyndland	d	10 52	10 56	11 01		11 07	11 11		11 14		11 17	11 22	11 26	11 31	11 37	11 41		11 44	11 47	11 52	11 56	12 01		12 07	12 11
Partick	d	10 55	10 59	11 04		11 10	11 14		11 17		11 20	11 25	11 29	11 34	11 40	11 44		11 47	11 50	11 55	11 59	12 04		12 10	12 14
Exhibition Centre	d		11 02			11 13					11 23		11 32		11 43				11 53		12 02			12 13	
Anderston	d		11 04			11 15					11 25		11 34		11 45				11 55		12 04			12 15	
Glasgow Central 15 §	a		11 05			11 17					11 26		11 35		11 47				11 56		12 05			12 17	
	d		11 07		11c15	11 17					11 27		11 37		11 47				11 57		12 07		12c15	12 17	
Argyle Street	d		11 09			11 19					11 29		11 39		11 49				11 59		12 09			12 19	
Charing Cross	d	10 59		11 08			11 19		11 22			11 29		11 38		11 49		11 52		11 59		12 08			12 19
Glasgow Queen Street 10 §	a	11 01		11 10			11 21		11 24	11e28		11 31		11 40		11 51		11 54		12 01		12 10			12 21
	d	11 02		11 12			11 21		11 27			11 32		11 42		11 51		11 57		12 02		12 12			12 21
High Street	d	11 04		11 14			11a23		11 29			11 34		11 44		11a53		11 59		12 04		12 14			12a23
Bellgrove	d	11 06		11 16					11 31			11 36		11 46				12 01		12 06		12 16			
Duke Street	d	11 08										11 38								12 08					
Alexandra Parade	d	11 09										11 39								12 09					
Barnhill	d	11 12										11 42								12 12					
Springburn	a	11 14										11 44								12 14					
Carntyne	d			11 19					11 34					11 49				12 04				12 19			
Shettleston	d			11 22					11 37					11 52				12 07				12 22			
Garrowhill	d			11 24					11 39					11 54				12 09				12 24			
Easterhouse	d			11 27					11 42					11 57				12 12				12 27			
Blairhill	d			11 31					11 46					12 01				12 16				12 31			
Coatbridge Sunnyside	d			11 33					11 48					12 03				12 18				12 33			
Coatdyke	d			11 36					11 51					12 06				12 21				12 36			
Airdrie	a			11 39					11 53					12 09				12 23				12 39			
	d								11 54									12 24							
Drumgelloch	a								11 58									12 28							
Bridgeton	d		11 12			11 22							11 42		11 52						12 12			12 22	
Dalmarnock	d		11 14			11 24							11 44		11 54						12 14			12 24	
Rutherglen	d		11 16			11 26					11 34		11 46		11 56				12 04		12 16			12 26	
Cambuslang	d		11 20		11 24	11 31							11 50		12 01						12 20		12 24	12 31	
Newton	d		11 24										11 54								12 24				
Blantyre	d		11 28								11 44		11 58						12 14		12 28				
Hamilton West	d		11 31								11 47		12 01						12 17		12 31				
Hamilton Central	d		11 33								11 50		12 03						12 20		12 33				
Chatelherault	d										11 54								12 24						
Merryton	d										11 58								12 28						
Larkhall	a										12 00								12 30						
Airbles	d		11 38										12 08								12 38				
Uddingston	d				11 29	11 35									12 05								12 29	12 35	
Bellshill	d				11 35	11 40									12 10								12 35	12 40	
Motherwell	a		11 41			11 46							12 11		12 16						12 41			12 46	
	d		11 42												12 16						12 42				
Whifflet	a																								
Coatbridge Central	a																								
Shieldmuir	d														12 20										
Holytown	d		11 47		11a39																12 47		12a39		
Wishaw	d		11 53												12 23						12 53				
Carluke	d		12 00												12 30						13 00				
Lanark	a		12 12												12f46						13 12				

For general notes see front of timetable
For details of catering facilities see Directory of Train Operators

§ Low Level

A To Edinburgh (Saturdays from 29 March to Livingston South) (Table 225)
B From Oban and from Mallaig (Table 227)
b Helensburgh Upper
c Glasgow Central High Level
e Glasgow Queen Street High Level
f Saturdays arr. 3 minutes earlier

Helensburgh, Balloch, Dalmuir and Milngavie → Glasgow → Springburn, Airdrie, Drumgelloch, Hamilton, Larkhall, Motherwell, Coatbridge and Lanark

Network Diagram - see first page of Table 220

		SR	SR	SR	SR	SR	SR	SR	SR	SR	SR	SR	SR	SR	SR	SR A	SR	SR	SR	SR	SR	SR	SR	SR
Helensburgh Central	d		11 40								12 10									12 40				
Craigendoran	d		11 43								12 13									12 43				
Cardross	d		11 48								12 18									12 48				
Balloch	d						11 53								12 23									12 53
Alexandria	d						11 55								12 25									12 55
Renton	d						11 58								12 28									12 58
Dalreoch	d		11 53				12 01				12 23				12 31					12 53				13 01
Dumbarton Central	d		11 55				12 02				12 25				12 32					12 55				13 02
Dumbarton East	d		11 57				12 04				12 27				12 34					12 57				13 04
Bowling	d						12 09								12 39									13 09
Kilpatrick	d						12 12								12 42									13 12
Dalmuir	a		12 05				12 15				12 35				12 46					13 05				13 15
	d	12 01	12 06		12 08		12 16	12 23		12 31	12 36		12 38		12 46		12 53		13 01	13 06		13 08		13 16
Singer	d	12 03					12 18			12 33					12 48				13 03					13 18
Drumry	d	12 05		←			12 20			12 35		←			12 50				13 05		←			13 20
Drumchapel	d	12 08		12 08			12 23			12 38		12 38			12 53				13 08		13 08			13 23
Milngavie	d	→				12 12			12 27	→				12 42				12 57	→				13 12	
Hillfoot	d					12 15			12 30					12 45				13 00					13 15	
Bearsden	d					12 17			12 32					12 47				13 02					13 17	
Westerton	d			12 10		12 20	12 25		12 35			12 40		12 50	12 55			13 05			13 10		13 20	13 25
Anniesland	d			12 14		12 23	12 28		12 38			12 44		12 53	12 58			13 08			13 14		13 23	13 28
Clydebank	d				12 10			12 25					12 40				12 55					13 10		
Yoker	d				12 12			12 27					12 42				12 57					13 12		
Garscadden	d				12 16			12 31					12 46				13 01					13 16		
Scotstounhill	d				12 18			12 33					12 48				13 03					13 18		
Jordanhill	d				12 20			12 35					12 50				13 05					13 20		
Hyndland	d		12 14	12 17	12 22	12 26	12 31	12 37	12 41		12 44	12 47	12 52	12 56	13 01		13 07	13 11		13 14	13 17	13 22	13 26	13 31
Partick	d		12 17	12 20	12 25	12 29	12 34	12 40	12 44		12 47	12 50	12 55	12 59	13 04		13 10	13 14		13 17	13 20	13 25	13 29	13 34
Exhibition Centre	d			12 23		12 32		12 43				12 53		13 02			13 13				13 23		13 32	
Anderston	d			12 25		12 34		12 45				12 55		13 04			13 15				13 25		13 34	
Glasgow Central 15 §	a			12 26		12 35		12 47				12 56		13 05			13 17				13 26		13 35	
	d			12 27		12 37		12 47				12 57		13 07		13b15	13 17				13 27		13 37	
Argyle Street	d			12 29		12 39		12 49				12 59		13 09			13 19				13 29		13 39	
Charing Cross	d		12 22		12 29		12 38		12 49		12 52		12 59		13 08			13 19		13 22		13 29		13 38
Glasgow Queen Street 10 §	a		12 24		12 31		12 40		12 51		12 54		13 01		13 10			13 21		13 24		13 31		13 40
	d		12 27		12 32		12 42		12 51		12 57		13 02		13 12			13 21		13 27		13 32		13 42
High Street	d		12 29		12 34		12 44		12a53		12 59		13 04		13 14			13a23		13 29		13 34		13 44
Bellgrove	d		12 31		12 36		12 46				13 01		13 06		13 16					13 31		13 36		13 46
Duke Street	d				12 38								13 08									13 38		
Alexandra Parade	d				12 39								13 09									13 39		
Barnhill	d				12 42								13 12									13 42		
Springburn	a				12 44								13 14									13 44		
Carntyne	d		12 34				12 49				13 04				13 19					13 34				13 49
Shettleston	d		12 37				12 52				13 07				13 22					13 37				13 52
Garrowhill	d		12 39				12 54				13 09				13 24					13 39				13 54
Easterhouse	d		12 42				12 57				13 12				13 27					13 42				13 57
Blairhill	d		12 46				13 01				13 16				13 31					13 46				14 01
Coatbridge Sunnyside	d		12 48				13 03				13 18				13 33					13 48				14 03
Coatdyke	d		12 51				13 06				13 21				13 36					13 51				14 06
Airdrie	a		12 53				13 09				13 23				13 39					13 53				14 09
	d		12 54								13 24									13 54				
Drumgelloch	a		12 58								13 28									13 58				
Bridgeton	d					12 42		12 52						13 12			13 22						13 42	
Dalmarnock	d					12 44		12 54						13 14			13 24						13 44	
Rutherglen	d			12 34		12 46		12 56				13 04		13 16			13 26				13 34		13 46	
Cambuslang	d					12 50		13 01						13 20		13 24	13 31						13 50	
Newton	d					12 54								13 24									13 54	
Blantyre	d			12 44		12 58						13 14		13 28							13 44		13 58	
Hamilton West	d			12 47		13 01						13 17		13 31							13 47		14 01	
Hamilton Central	d			12 50		13 03						13 20		13 33							13 50		14 03	
Chatelherault	d			12 54								13 24									13 54			
Merryton	d			12 58								13 28									13 58			
Larkhall	a			13 00								13 30									14 00			
Airbles	d					13 08								13 38									14 08	
Uddingston	d							13 05								13 29	13 35							
Bellshill	d							13 10								13 35	13 40							
Motherwell	a					13 11		13 16						13 41			13 46						14 11	
	d							13 16						13 42										
Whifflet	a																							
Coatbridge Central	a																							
Shieldmuir	d							13 20																
Holytown	d													13 47		13a39								
Wishaw	d							13 23						13 53										
Carluke	d							13 30						14 00										
Lanark	a							13 42						14 12										

For general notes see front of timetable
For details of catering facilities see Directory of Train Operators

§ Low Level

A To Edinburgh (Saturdays from 29 March to Livingston South) (Table 225)

b Glasgow Central High Level

Helensburgh, Balloch, Dalmuir and Milngavie → Glasgow → Springburn, Airdrie, Drumgelloch, Hamilton, Larkhall, Motherwell, Coatbridge and Lanark

Network Diagram - see first page of Table 220

		SR	SR	SR	SR	SR	SR	SR	SR	SR	SR	SR	SR	SR	SR	SR	SR	SR	SR	SR	SR	SR	SR	SR	SR SX
										A															B
Helensburgh Central	d				13 10									13 40								14 10			
Craigendoran	d				13 13									13 43								14 13			
Cardross	d				13 18									13 48								14 18			
Balloch	d								13 23									13 53							
Alexandria	d								13 25									13 55							
Renton	d								13 28									13 58							
Dalreoch	d				13 23				13 31					13 53				14 01				14 23			
Dumbarton Central	d				13 25				13 32					13 55				14 02				14 25			
Dumbarton East	d				13 27				13 34					13 57				14 04				14 27			
Bowling	d								13 39									14 09							
Kilpatrick	d								13 42									14 12							
Dalmuir	a				13 35				13 45					14 05				14 15				14 35			
	d	13 23		13 31	13 36		13 38		13 46		13 53		14 01	14 06		14 08		14 16	14 23		14 31	14 36		14 38	
Singer	d			13 33					13 48				14 03					14 18			14 33				
Drumry	d			13 35		←			13 50				14 05		←			14 20			14 35		←		
Drumchapel	d			13 38		13 38			13 53				14 08		14 08			14 23			14 38		14 38		
Milngavie	d		13 27	→				13 42				13 57	→				14 12			14 27	→				
Hillfoot	d		13 30					13 45				14 00					14 15			14 30					
Bearsden	d		13 32					13 47				14 02					14 17			14 32					
Westerton	d		13 35			13 40		13 50	13 55			14 05			14 10		14 20	14 25		14 35			14 40		
Anniesland	d		13 38			13 44		13 53	13 58			14 08			14 14		14 23	14 28		14 38			14 44		
Clydebank	d	13 25					13 40				13 55					14 10			14 25					14 40	
Yoker	d	13 27					13 42				13 57					14 12			14 27					14 42	
Garscadden	d	13 31					13 46				14 01					14 16			14 31					14 46	
Scotstounhill	d	13 33					13 48				14 03					14 18			14 33					14 48	
Jordanhill	d	13 35					13 50				14 05					14 20			14 35					14 50	
Hyndland	d	13 37	13 41		13 44	13 47	13 52	13 56	14 01		14 07	14 11		14 14	14 17	14 22	14 26	14 31	14 37	14 41		14 44	14 47	14 52	
Partick	d	13 40	13 44		13 47	13 50	13 55	13 59	14 04		14 10	14 14		14 17	14 20	14 25	14 29	14 34	14 40	14 44		14 47	14 50	14 55	
Exhibition Centre	d	13 43				13 53		14 02			14 13				14 23		14 32		14 43				14 53		
Anderston	d	13 45				13 55		14 04			14 15				14 25		14 34		14 45				14 55		
Glasgow Central 15 §	a	13 47				13 56		14 05			14 17				14 26		14 35		14 47				14 56		
	d	13 47				13 57		14 07		14b15	14 17				14 27		14 37		14 47				14 57		15b19
Argyle Street	d	13 49				13 59		14 09			14 19				14 29		14 39		14 49				14 59		
Charing Cross	d		13 49		13 52		13 59		14 08			14 19		14 22		14 29		14 38		14 49		14 52		14 59	
Glasgow Queen Street 10 §	a		13 51		13 54		14 01		14 10			14 21		14 24		14 31		14 40		14 51		14 54		15 01	
	d		13 51		13 57		14 02		14 12			14 21		14 27		14 32		14 42		14 51		14 57		15 02	
High Street	d		13a53		13 59		14 04		14 14			14a23		14 29		14 34		14 44		14a53		14 59		15 04	
Bellgrove	d				14 01		14 06		14 16					14 31		14 36		14 46				15 01		15 06	
Duke Street	d						14 08									14 38								15 08	
Alexandra Parade	d						14 09									14 39								15 09	
Barnhill	d						14 12									14 42								15 12	
Springburn	a						14 14									14 44								15 14	
Carntyne	d				14 04				14 19					14 34				14 49				15 04			
Shettleston	d				14 07				14 22					14 37				14 52				15 07			
Garrowhill	d				14 09				14 24					14 39				14 54				15 09			
Easterhouse	d				14 12				14 27					14 42				14 57				15 12			
Blairhill	d				14 16				14 31					14 46				15 01				15 16			
Coatbridge Sunnyside	d				14 18				14 33					14 48				15 03				15 18			
Coatdyke	d				14 21				14 36					14 51				15 06				15 21			
Airdrie	a				14 23				14 39					14 53				15 09				15 23			
	d				14 24									14 54								15 24			
Drumgelloch	a				14 28									14 58								15 28			
Bridgeton	d	13 52						14 12			14 22						14 42		14 52						
Dalmarnock	d	13 54						14 14			14 24						14 44		14 54						
Rutherglen	d	13 56				14 04		14 16			14 26				14 34		14 46		14 56				15 04		
Cambuslang	d	14 01						14 20		14 24	14 31						14 50		15 01						
Newton	d							14 24									14 54								
Blantyre	d					14 14		14 28							14 44		14 58						15 14		
Hamilton West	d					14 17		14 31							14 47		15 01						15 17		
Hamilton Central	d					14 20		14 33							14 50		15 03						15 20		
Chatelherault	d					14 24									14 54								15 24		
Merryton	d					14 28									14 58								15 28		
Larkhall	a					14 30									15 00								15 30		
Airbles	d							14 38									15 08								
Uddingston	d	14 05								14 29	14 35								15 05						
Bellshill	d	14 10								14 35	14 40								15 10						
Motherwell	a	14 16						14 41			14c48						15 11		15 16						15 35
	d	14 16						14 42											15 16						15 38
Whifflet	a																								
Coatbridge Central	a																								
Shieldmuir	d	14 20																	15 20						
Holytown	d							14 47		14a39															
Wishaw	d	14 23						14 53											15 23						15a47
Carluke	d	14 30						15 00											15 30						
Lanark	a	14 42						15 12											15 42						

For general notes see front of timetable
For details of catering facilities see Directory of Train Operators

§ Low Level

A To Edinburgh (Saturdays from 29 March to Livingston South) (Table 225)

B To North Berwick (Table 238)

b Glasgow Central High Level

c Saturdays arr. 2 minutes later

Helensburgh, Balloch, Dalmuir and Milngavie → Glasgow → Springburn, Airdrie, Drumgelloch, Hamilton, Larkhall, Motherwell, Coatbridge and Lanark

Network Diagram - see first page of Table 220

Station		SR	SR	SR	SR	SR	SR	SR	SR	SR	SR	SR	SR	SR	SR	SR	SR	SR	SR	SR	SR		SR	SR	SR
		SO																			SX		SO		
		A			B				◇ C																D
Helensburgh Central	d								14b39	14 40								15 10							
Craigendoran	d									14 43								15 13							
Cardross	d									14 48								15 18							
Balloch	d			14 23										14 53										15 23	
Alexandria	d			14 25										14 55										15 25	
Renton	d			14 28										14 58										15 28	
Dalreoch	d			14 31						14 53				15 01				15 23						15 31	
Dumbarton Central	d			14 32					14 52	14 55				15 02				15 25						15 32	
Dumbarton East	d			14 34						14 57				15 04				15 27						15 34	
Bowling	d			14 39										15 09										15 39	
Kilpatrick	d			14 42										15 12										15 42	
Dalmuir	a			14 45					15 04	15 06				15 15				15 35						15 45	
	d			14 46		14 53		15 01	15 04	15 06		15 08		15 16	15 23		15 31	15 36		15 38				15 46	
Singer	d			14 48				15 03						15 18			15 33							15 48	
Drumry	d			14 50				15 05			←			15 20			15 35		←					15 50	
Drumchapel	d			14 53				15 08			15 08			15 23			15 38		15 38					15 53	
Milngavie	d		14 42				14 57	→					15 12			15 27	→				15 42		15 42		
Hillfoot	d		14 45				15 00						15 15			15 30					15 45		15 45		
Bearsden	d		14 47				15 02						15 17			15 32					15 47		15 47		
Westerton	d		14 50	14 55			15 05				15 10		15 20	15 25		15 35			15 40		15 50		15 50	15 55	
Anniesland	d		14 53	14 58			15 08				15 14		15 23	15 28		15 38			15 44		15 53		15 53	15 58	
Clydebank	d					14 55						15 10			15 25					15 40					
Yoker	d					14 57						15 12			15 27					15 42					
Garscadden	d					15 01						15 16			15 31					15 46					
Scotstounhill	d					15 03						15 18			15 33					15 48					
Jordanhill	d					15 05						15 20			15 35					15 50					
Hyndland	d		14 56	15 01		15 07	15 11			15 14	15 17	15 22	15 27	15 31	15 37	15 41		15 44	15 47	15 52	15 56		15 56	16 01	
Partick	d		14 59	15 04		15 10	15 14			15 17	15 20	15 25	15 29	15 34	15 40	15 44		15 47	15 50	15 55	15 59		15 59	16 04	
Exhibition Centre	d		15 02			15 13					15 23		15 32		15 43				15 53		16 02		16 02		
Anderston	d		15 04			15 15					15 25		15 34		15 45				15 55		16 04		16 04		
Glasgow Central 15 §	a		15 05			15 17					15 26		15 35		15 47				15 56		16 05		16 05		
	d	15c19	15 07		15c15	15 17					15 27		15 37		15 47				15 57		16 07		16 07		16c15
Argyle Street	d		15 09			15 19					15 29		15 39		15 49				15 59		16 09		16 09		
Charing Cross	d			15 08			15 19			15 22		15 29		15 38		15 49		15 52		15 59				16 08	
Glasgow Queen Street 10 §	a			15 10			15 21		15e28	15 24		15 31		15 41		15 51		15 54		16 01				16 11	
	d			15 12			15 21			15 27		15 32		15 42		15 51		15 57		16 02				16 12	
High Street	d			15 14			15a23			15 29		15 34		15 44		15a53		15 59		16 04				16 14	
Bellgrove	d			15 16						15 31		15 36		15 46				16 01		16 06				16 16	
Duke Street	d											15 38								16 08					
Alexandra Parade	d											15 39								16 09					
Barnhill	d											15 42								16 12					
Springburn	a											15 44								16 14					
Carntyne	d			15 19						15 34				15 49				16 04						16 19	
Shettleston	d			15 22						15 37				15 52				16 07						16 22	
Garrowhill	d			15 24						15 39				15 54				16 09						16 24	
Easterhouse	d			15 27						15 42				15 57				16 12						16 27	
Blairhill	d			15 31						15 46				16 01				16 16						16 31	
Coatbridge Sunnyside	d			15 33						15 48				16 03				16 18						16 33	
Coatdyke	d			15 36						15 51				16 06				16 21						16 36	
Airdrie	a			15 39						15 53				16 09				16 23						16 39	
	d									15 54								16 24							
Drumgelloch	a									15 58								16 28							
Bridgeton	d		15 12			15 22							15 42		15 52						16 12		16 12		
Dalmarnock	d		15 14			15 24							15 44		15 54						16 14		16 14		
Rutherglen	d		15 16			15 26					15 34		15 46		15 56				16 04		16 16		16 16		
Cambuslang	d		15 20		15 24	15 31							15 50		16 01						16 20		16 20		16 24
Newton	d		15 24										15 54								16 24		16 24		
Blantyre	d		15 28								15 44		15 58						16 14		16 28		16 28		
Hamilton West	d		15 31								15 47		16 01						16 17		16 31		16 31		
Hamilton Central	d		15 33								15 50		16 03						16 20		16 33		16 33		
Chatelherault	d										15 54								16 24						
Merryton	d										15 58								16 28						
Larkhall	a										16 00								16 30						
Airbles	d		15 38										16 08								16 38		16 38		
Uddingston	d				15 29	15 35									16 05										16 29
Bellshill	d				15 35	15 40									16 10										16 35
Motherwell	a	15 38	15 41			15 46							16 11		16 16						16 41		16 41		
	d	15 39	15 42												16 16						16 42		16 42		
Whifflet	a																				16 48				
Coatbridge Central	a																				16 53				
Shieldmuir	d														16 20										
Holytown	d		15 47		15a39																		16 47		16a39
Wishaw	d		15 53												16 23								16 53		
Carluke	d	15a48	16 00												16 30								17 00		
Lanark	a		16 12												16f44								17 12		

For general notes see front of timetable
For details of catering facilities see Directory of Train Operators

§ Low Level

A Until 22 March to North Berwick (Table 238). From 29 March to Carstairs (Table 225)

B Saturdays from 29 March to Livingston South (Table 225). All Mondays to Fridays, also Saturdays until 22 March to Edinburgh (Table 225)

C From Oban and from Mallaig (Table 227)

D To Edinburgh (Saturdays from 29 March to Livingston South) (Table 225)

b Helensburgh Upper

c Glasgow Central High Level

e Glasgow Queen Street High Level

f Saturdays arr. 2 minutes later

Helensburgh, Balloch, Dalmuir and Milngavie → Glasgow → Springburn, Airdrie, Drumgelloch, Hamilton, Larkhall, Motherwell, Coatbridge and Lanark

Network Diagram - see first page of Table 220

		SR	SR	SR SO	SR SX	SR	SR	SR SX	SR	SR	SR SO	SR SX	SR	SR SO	SR SX	SR SO	SR SX	SR	SR	SR	SR	SR SX	SR SO	SR SX	SR
Helensburgh Central	d						15 40												16 10						
Craigendoran	d						15 43												16 13						
Cardross	d						15 48												16 18						
Balloch	d												15 53												16 23
Alexandria	d												15 55												16 25
Renton	d												15 58												16 28
Dalreoch	d						15 53						16 01						16 23						16 31
Dumbarton Central	d						15 55						16 02						16 25						16 32
Dumbarton East	d						15 57						16 04						16 27						16 34
Bowling	d												16 09												16 39
Kilpatrick	d												16 12												16 42
Dalmuir	a						16 05						16 15						16 35						16 45
	d	15 53				16 01	16 06			16 08			16 16	16 23	16 23			16 31	16 36		16 38				16 46
Singer	d					16 03							16 18					16 33							16 48
Drumry	d					16 05			←				16 20					16 35		←					16 50
Drumchapel	d					16 08			16 08				16 23					16 38		16 38					16 53
Milngavie	d			15 57	15 57	→					16 12	16 12				16 27	16 27	→					16 42	16 42	
Hillfoot	d			16 00	16 00						16 15	16 15				16 30	16 30						16 45	16 45	
Bearsden	d			16 02	16 02						16 17	16 17				16 32	16 32						16 47	16 47	
Westerton	d			16 05	16 05				16 10		16 20	16 20	16 25			16 35	16 35			16 40			16 50	16 50	16 55
Annieslαnd	d			16 08	16 08				16 14		16 23	16 23	16 28			16 38	16 38			16 44			16 53	16 53	16 58
Clydebank	d	15 55								16 10				16 25	16 25						16 40				
Yoker	d	15 57								16 12				16 27	16 27						16 42				
Garscadden	d	16 01								16 15				16 31	16 31						16 46				
Scotstounhill	d	16 03								16 18				16 33	16 33						16 48				
Jordanhill	d	16 05								16 20				16 35	16 35						16 50				
Hyndland	d	16 07		16 11	16 11		16 14		16 17	16 22	16 26	16 26	16 31	16 37	16 37	16 41	16 41		16 44	16 47	16 52		16 56	16 56	17 01
Partick	d	16 10		16 14	16 14		16 17		16 20	16 25	16 29	16 29	16 34	16 40	16 40	16 44	16 44		16 47	16 50	16 55		16 59	16 59	17 04
Exhibition Centre	d	16 13							16 23		16 32	16 32		16 43	16 43					16 53			17 02	17b04	
Anderston	d	16 15						16 23	16 25		16 34	16 34		16 45	16 45					16 55		17 04	17 04	17 06	
Glasgow Central 15 §	a	16 17						16 24	16 26		16 35	16 35		16 47	16 47					16 56		17 05	17 05	17 08	
	d	16 17						16 25	16 27		16 37	16 37		16 47	16 47					16 57		17 07	17 07	17 09	
Argyle Street	d	16 19						16 27	16 29		16 39	16 39		16 49	16 49					16 59		17 09	17 09	17 11	
Charing Cross	d			16 19	16 19		16 22			16 29			16 38			16 49	16 49		16 52		16 59				17 08
Glasgow Queen Street 10 §	a			16 21	16 21		16 24			16 31			16 40			16 51	16 51		16 54		17 01				17 10
	d			16 21	16 21		16 27			16 32			16 42			16 51	16 51		16 57		17 02				17 12
High Street	d			16a23	16 23		16 29			16 34			16 44			16a53	16 53		16 59		17 04				17 14
Bellgrove	d						16 31			16 36			16 46						17 01		17 06				17 16
Duke Street	d									16 38											17 08				
Alexandra Parade	d									16 39											17 09				
Barnhill	d									16 42											17 12				
Springburn	a									16 44											17 14				
Carntyne	d						16 34						16 49						17 04						17 19
Shettleston	d						16 37						16 52						17 07						17 22
Garrowhill	d						16 39						16 54						17 09						17 24
Easterhouse	d						16 42						16 57						17 12						17 27
Blairhill	d				16 35		16 46						17 01				17 05		17 16						17 31
Coatbridge Sunnyside	d				16 38		16 48						17 03				17 08		17 18						17 33
Coatdyke	d				16 40		16 51						17 06				17 10		17 21						17 36
Airdrie	a				16 45		16 53						17 09				17 15		17 23						17 39
	d						16 54												17 24						
Drumgelloch	a						16 58												17 28						
Bridgeton	d	16 22									16 42	16 42		16 52	16 52							17 12	17 12	17 15	
Dalmarnock	d	16 24									16 44	16 44		16 54	16 54								17 14	17 17	
Rutherglen	d	16 26						16 32	16 34		16 46	16 46		16 56	16 56					17 04			17 16	17 19	
Cambuslang	d	16 31									16 50	16 50		17 01	17 01					17 08			17 20	17 23	
Newton	d										16 54	16 54											17 24	17 27	
Blantyre	d								16 44		16 58	16 58								17 14			17 28	17 33	
Hamilton West	d								16 47		17 01	17 01								17 17			17 31	17 36	
Hamilton Central	d								16 50		17 03	17 03								17 20			17 33	17 38	
Chatelherault	d								16 54											17 24				17 43	
Merryton	d								16 58											17 28				17 46	
Larkhall	a								17 00											17 30				17 48	
Airbles	d		←								17 08	17 08											17 38		
Uddingston	d	16 35	16 35											17 05	17 05							17 20			
Bellshill	d	→	16 40											17 10	17 10										
Motherwell	a		16c47					16 44			17 11	17 11		17 16	17 16							17 28	17 41		
	d							16 47				17 12		17 16								17 29	17 42		
Whifflet	a											17 18													
Coatbridge Central	a											17 22													
Shieldmuir	d							16 50						17 20								17 32			
Holytown	d																						17 47		
Wishaw	d							16 53						17 23								17 36	17 53		
Carluke	d							17 00						17 30								17 43	18 00		
Lanark	a							17 12						17 42								17 54	18 12		

For general notes see front of timetable
For details of catering facilities see Directory of Train Operators

§ Low Level

b Arr. 3 minutes earlier
c Saturdays arr. 1 minute earlier

Helensburgh, Balloch, Dalmuir and Milngavie → Glasgow → Springburn, Airdrie, Drumgelloch, Hamilton, Larkhall, Motherwell, Coatbridge and Lanark

Network Diagram - see first page of Table 220

		SR SO A	SR SO	SR SX B	SR SX	SR SO	SR SX	SR C	SR	SR SO	SR SX D	SR	SR SX	SR SX	SR SX D	SR SO	SR SX	SR	SR SO	SR SX	SR	SR	SR	SR	SR
Helensburgh Central	d								16 40														17 10		
Craigendoran	d								16 43														17 13		
Cardross	d								16 48														17 18		
Balloch	d																	16 53							
Alexandria	d																	16 55							
Renton	d																	16 58							
Dalreoch	d								16 53									17 01					17 23		
Dumbarton Central	d								16 55									17 02					17 25		
Dumbarton East	d								16 57									17 04					17 27		
Bowling	d																	17 09							
Kilpatrick	d																	17 12							
Dalmuir	a								17 05									17 15					17 35		
	d		16 53		16 53			17 01	17 06			17 08						17 16	17 23	17 23		17 31	17 36		17 38
Singer	d							17 03										17 18				17 33			
Drumry	d							17 05		←	←							17 20				17 35		←	
Drumchapel	d							17 08		17 08	17 08							17 23				17 38		17 38	
Milngavie	d					16 57	16 57	→								17 12	17 12				17 27	→			
Hillfoot	d					17 00	17 00									17 15	17 15				17 30				
Bearsden	d					17 02	17 02									17 17	17 17				17 32				
Westerton	d					17 05	17 05			17 10	17 10					17 20	17 20	17 25			17 35			17 40	
Anniesland	d					17 08	17 08			17 14	17 14					17 23	17 23	17 28			17 38			17 44	
Clydebank	d		16 55		16 55							17 10							17 25	17 25					17 40
Yoker	d		16 57		16 57							17 12							17 27	17 27					17 42
Garscadden	d		17 01		17 01							17 16							17 31	17 31					17 46
Scotstounhill	d		17 03		17 03							17 18							17 33	17 33					17 48
Jordanhill	d		17 05		17 05							17 20							17 35	17 35					17 50
Hyndland	d		17 07		17 07	17 11	17 11		17 14	17 17	17 17	17 22				17 26	17 26	17 31	17 37	17 37	17 41		17 44	17 47	17 52
Partick	d		17 10		17 10	17 14	17 14		17 17	17 20	17 20	17 25				17 29	17 29	17 34	17 40	17 40	17 44		17 47	17 50	17 55
Exhibition Centre	d		17 13		17 13					17 23	17 23					17 32	17b34		17 43	17 43				17 53	
Anderston	d		17 15		17 15					17 25	17 25		17 34			17 34	17 36		17 45	17 45				17 55	
Glasgow Central 15 §	a		17 17		17 17					17 26	17 26		17 35			17 35	17 38		17 47	17 47				17 56	
	d	17c15	17 17	17c19	17 21					17 27	17 27		17 37			17 37	17 39		17 47	17 47				17 57	
Argyle Street	d		17 19		17 23					17 29	17 29		17 39			17 39	17 41		17 49	17 49				17 59	
Charing Cross	d					17 19	17 19		17 22			17 29						17 38			17 49		17 52		17 59
Glasgow Queen Street 10 §	a					17 21	17 21		17 24			17 31						17 40			17 51		17 54		18 01
	d					17 21	17 21		17 27			17 32						17 42			17 51		17 57		18 02
High Street	d					17a23	17 23		17 29			17 34						17 44			17a53		17 59		18 04
Bellgrove	d								17 31			17 36						17 46					18 01		18 06
Duke Street	d											17 38													18 08
Alexandra Parade	d											17 39													18 09
Barnhill	d											17 42													18 12
Springburn	a											17 44													18 15
Carntyne	d								17 34									17 49					18 04		
Shettleston	d								17 37									17 52					18 07		
Garrowhill	d								17 39									17 54					18 09		
Easterhouse	d								17 42									17 57					18 12		
Blairhill	d						17 35		17 46									18 01					18 16		
Coatbridge Sunnyside	d						17 38		17 48									18 03					18 18		
Coatdyke	d						17 40		17 51									18 06					18 21		
Airdrie	a						17 45		17 53									18 09					18 23		
	d								17 54														18 24		
Drumgelloch	a								17 58														18 28		
Bridgeton	d		17 22		17 26						17 32					17 42	17 45		17 52	17 52					
Dalmarnock	d		17 24		17 28						17 34					17 44	17 47		17 54	17 54					
Rutherglen	d		17 26		17 31					17 34	17 36		17 44			17 46	17 49		17 56	17 56				18 04	
Cambuslang	d	17 24	17 31		17 35						17 42			←		17 50	17 53		18 01	18 01					
Newton	d				17 38 →									17 38		17 54	17 57								
Blantyre	d									17 44				17 42		17 58	18 01							18 14	
Hamilton West	d									17 47				17 45		18 01	18 04							18 17	
Hamilton Central	d									17 50				17 48		18 03	18 06							18 20	
Chatelherault	d									17 54							18 11							18 24	
Merryton	d									17 58							18 14							18 28	
Larkhall	a									18 00							18 16							18 30	
Airbles	d													17 53	←	18 08									
Uddingston	d	17 29	17 35								17 47 →				17 47				18 05	18 05					
Bellshill	d	17 35	17 40	17 35											17 51				18 10	18 10					
Motherwell	a		17 46										17 53	17 56	17 57	18 11			18 16	18 17					
	d												17 54	17 56	17 58				18 16						
Whifflet	a													18 02											
Coatbridge Central	a													18 06											
Shieldmuir	d												17 59		18 03				18 20						
Holytown	d	17a39		17a39																					
Wishaw	d												18 02		18 07				18 23						
Carluke	d												18 09		18a16				18 30						
Lanark	a												18 22						18 42						

For general notes see front of timetable
For details of catering facilities see Directory of Train Operators

§ Low Level

A To Edinburgh (from 29 March to Livingston South) (Table 225)
B To Edinburgh (Table 225)
C Mondays to Fridays to Carstairs (Table 225)
D To Carstairs (Table 225)
b Arr. 3 minutes earlier
c Glasgow Central High Level

Helensburgh, Balloch, Dalmuir and Milngavie → Glasgow → Springburn, Airdrie, Drumgelloch, Hamilton, Larkhall, Motherwell, Coatbridge and Lanark

Network Diagram - see first page of Table 220

		SR	SR		SR	SR	SR	SR	SR	SR	SR	SR	SR	SR	SR	SR	SR	SR	SR	SR	SR	SR	SR	SR	SR
					A										SO ◇ B										
Helensburgh Central	d							17 40					18 10			18b34			18 40					19 10	
Craigendoran	d							17 43					18 13						18 43					19 13	
Cardross	d							17 48					18 18						18 48					19 18	
Balloch	d		17 23							17 53					18 23						18 53				
Alexandria	d		17 25							17 55					18 25						18 55				
Renton	d		17 28							17 58					18 28						18 58				
Dalreoch	d		17 31					17 53		18 01			18 23		18 31				18 53		19 01			19 23	
Dumbarton Central	d		17 32					17 55		18 02			18 25		18 32	18 47			18 55		19 02			19 25	
Dumbarton East	d		17 34					17 57		18 04			18 27		18 34				18 57		19 04			19 27	
Bowling	d		17 39							18 09					18 39						19 09				
Kilpatrick	d		17 42							18 12					18 42						19 12				
Dalmuir	a		17 45					18 05		18 15			18 35		18 45	18 56			19 05		19 15			19 35	
	d		17 46			17 53	18 01	18 05		18 16	18 23	18 31	18 35		18 46	18 56		19 01	19 05		19 16		19 31	19 35	
Singer	d		17 48				18 03			18 18		18 33			18 48			19 03			19 18		19 33		
Drumry	d		17 50				18 05			18 20		18 35			18 50			19 05			19 20		19 35		
Drumchapel	d		17 53				18 08			18 23		18 38			18 53			19 08			19 23		19 38		
Milngavie	d	17 42							18 12					18 42						19 12					19 42
Hillfoot	d	17 45							18 15					18 45						19 15					19 45
Bearsden	d	17 47							18 17					18 47						19 17					19 47
Westerton	d	17 50	17 55				18 10		18 20	18 25		18 40		18 50	18 55			19 10		19 20	19 25		19 40		19 50
Anniesland	d	17 53	17 58				18 14		18 23	18 28		18 44		18 53	18 58			19 14		19 23	19 28		19 44		19 53
Clydebank	d					17 55		18 07			18 25		18 37						19 07					19 37	
Yoker	d					17 57		18 09			18 27		18 39						19 09					19 39	
Garscadden	d					18 01		18 13			18 31		18 43						19 13					19 43	
Scotstounhill	d					18 03		18 15			18 33		18 45						19 15					19 45	
Jordanhill	d					18 05		18 17			18 35		18 47						19 17					19 47	
Hyndland	d	17 56	18 01			18 07	18 17	18 21	18 26	18 31	18 37	18 47	18 51	18 55	19 01			19 17	19 21	19 26	19 31		19 47	19 51	19 56
Partick	d	17 59	18 04			18 10	18 20	18 24	18 29	18 34	18 40	18 50	18 54	18 59	19 04		19 10	19 20	19 24	19 29	19 34	19 40	19 50	19 54	19 59
Exhibition Centre	d	18 02				18 13	18 23		18 32		18 43	18 53		19 02			19 13	19 23		19 32		19 43	19 53		20 02
Anderston	d	18 04				18 15	18 25		18 34		18 45	18 55		19 04			19 15	19 25		19 34		19 45	19 55		20 04
Glasgow Central 15 §	a	18 05				18 17	18 26		18 35		18 47	18 56		19 05			19 16	19 26		19 35		19 46	19 56		20 05
	d	18 07			18c15	18 17	18 27		18 37		18 47	18 57		19 07			19 17	19 27		19 37		19 47	19 57		20 07
Argyle Street	d	18 09				18 19	18 29		18 39		18 49	18 59		19 09			19 19	19 29		19 39		19 49	19 59		20 09
Charing Cross	d		18 08					18 29		18 38			18 59		19 08				19 29		19 38			19 59	
Glasgow Queen Street 10 §	a		18 10					18 31		18 40			19 01		19 10	19e18			19 31		19 40			20 01	
	d		18 12					18 32		18 44			19 02		19 14				19 32		19 44			20 02	
High Street	d		18 14					18 34		18 46			19 04		19 16				19 34		19 46			20 04	
Bellgrove	d		18 16					18 36		18 48			19 06		19 18				19 36		19 48			20 06	
Duke Street	d									18 50					19 20						19 50				
Alexandra Parade	d									18 51					19 21						19 51				
Barnhill	d									18 54					19 24						19 54				
Springburn	a									18 56					19 26						19 56				
Carntyne	d		18 19					18 39					19 09						19 39					20 09	
Shettleston	d		18 22					18 42					19 12						19 42					20 12	
Garrowhill	d		18 24					18 44					19 14						19 44					20 14	
Easterhouse	d		18 27					18 47					19 17						19 47					20 17	
Blairhill	d		18 31					18 51					19 21						19 51					20 21	
Coatbridge Sunnyside	d		18 33					18 53					19 23						19 53					20 23	
Coatdyke	d		18 36					18 56					19 26						19 56					20 26	
Airdrie	a		18 39					18 58					19 28						19 58					20 28	
	d							18 59					19 29						19 59					20 29	
Drumgelloch	a							19 03					19 33						20 03					20 33	
Bridgeton	d	18 12				18 22			18 42		18 52			19 12			19 22			19 42		19 52			20 12
Dalmarnock	d	18 14				18 24			18 44		18 54			19 14			19 24			19 44		19 54			20 14
Rutherglen	d	18 16				18 26	18 34		18 46		18 56	19 04		19 16			19 26	19 34		19 46		19 56	20 04		20 16
Cambuslang	d	18 20			18 24	18 31			18 50		19 01			19 20			19 31			19 50		20 01			20 20
Newton	d	18 24							18 54					19 24						19 54					20 24
Blantyre	d	18 28					18 44		18 58			19 14		19 28				19 44		19 58			20 14		20 28
Hamilton West	d	18 31					18 47		19 01			19 17		19 31				19 47		20 01			20 17		20 31
Hamilton Central	d	18 33					18 50		19 03			19 20		19 33				19 50		20 03			20 20		20 33
Chatelherault	d						18 54					19 24						19 54					20 24		
Merryton	d						18 58					19 28						19 58					20 28		
Larkhall	a						19 00					19 30						20 00					20 30		
Airbles	d	18 38							19 08					19 38						20 08					20 38
Uddingston	d				18 29	18 35					19 05						19 35					20 05			
Bellshill	d				18 35	18 40					19 10						19 40					20 10			
Motherwell	a	18 41				18 46			19 11		19 16			19 41			19 46			20 11		20 16			20 41
	d	18 42									19 16			19 42								20 16			20 42
Whifflet	a																								
Coatbridge Central	a																								
Shieldmuir	d										19 20											20 20			
Holytown	d	18 47			18a39									19 47											20 47
Wishaw	d	18 53									19 23			19 53								20 23			20 53
Carluke	d	19 00									19 30			20 00								20 30			21 00
Lanark	a	19 12									19 42			20 12								20 42			21 12

For general notes see front of timetable
For details of catering facilities see Directory of Train Operators

§ Low Level

A To Edinburgh (Saturdays from 29 March to Livingston South) (Table 225)

B From 22 March. From Oban (Table 227)

b Helensburgh Upper

c Glasgow Central High Level

e Glasgow Queen Street High Level

Helensburgh, Balloch, Dalmuir and Milngavie → Glasgow → Springburn, Airdrie, Drumgelloch, Hamilton, Larkhall, Motherwell, Coatbridge and Lanark

Network Diagram - see first page of Table 220

		SR	SR	SR	SR	SR	SR	SR	SR	SR	SR	SR	SR	SR	SR	SR	SR	SR	SR	SR	SR	SR	SR	SR	SR
			A													◇ B ⛴									
Helensburgh Central	d					19 40					20 10					20b40	20 40					21 10			
Craigendoran	d					19 43					20 13						20 43					21 13			
Cardross	d					19 48					20 18						20 48					21 18			
Balloch	d	19 23						19 53					20 23						20 53					21 23	
Alexandria	d	19 25						19 55					20 25						20 55					21 25	
Renton	d	19 28						19 58					20 28						20 58					21 28	
Dalreoch	d	19 31				19 53		20 01			20 23		20 31				20 53		21 01			21 23		21 31	
Dumbarton Central	d	19 32				19 55		20 02			20 25		20 32			20 53	20 55		21 02			21 25		21 32	
Dumbarton East	d	19 34				19 57		20 04			20 27		20 34				20 57		21 04			21 27		21 34	
Bowling	d	19 39						20 09					20 39						21 09					21 39	
Kilpatrick	d	19 42						20 12					20 42						21 12					21 42	
Dalmuir	a	19 45				20 05		20 15			20 35		20 45			21 04	21 05		21 15			21 35		21 45	
	d	19 46			20 01	20 05		20 16		20 31	20 35		20 46		21 01	21 04	21 05		21 16		21 31	21 35		21 46	
Singer	d	19 48			20 03			20 18		20 33			20 48		21 03				21 18		21 33			21 48	
Drumry	d	19 50			20 05			20 20		20 35			20 50		21 05				21 20		21 35			21 50	
Drumchapel	d	19 53			20 08			20 23		20 38			20 53		21 08				21 23		21 38			21 53	
Milngavie	d						20 12					20 42						21 12					21 42		
Hillfoot	d						20 15					20 45						21 15					21 45		
Bearsden	d						20 17					20 47						21 17					21 47		
Westerton	d	19 55			20 10		20 20	20 25		20 40		20 50	20 55		21 10			21 20	21 25		21 40		21 50	21 55	
Anniesland	d	19 58			20 14		20 23	20 28		20 44		20 53	20 58		21 14			21 23	21 28		21 44		21 53	21 58	
Clydebank	d					20 07					20 37						21 07					21 37			
Yoker	d					20 09					20 39						21 09					21 39			
Garscadden	d					20 13					20 43						21 13					21 43			
Scotstounhill	d					20 15					20 45						21 15					21 45			
Jordanhill	d					20 17					20 47						21 17					21 47			
Hyndland	d	20 01			20 17	20 21	20 26	20 31		20 47	20 51	20 56	21 01		21 17		21 21	21 26	21 31		21 47	21 51	21 56	22 01	
Partick	d	20 04		20 10	20 20	20 24	20 29	20 34	20 40	20 50	20 54	20 59	21 04	21 10	21 20		21 24	21 29	21 34	21 40	21 50	21 54	21 59	22 04	22 10
Exhibition Centre	d			20 13	20 23		20 32		20 43	20 53		21 02		21 13	21 23			21 32		21 43	21 53		22 02		22 13
Anderston	d			20 15	20 25		20 34		20 45	20 55		21 04		21 15	21 25			21 34		21 45	21 55		22 04		22 15
Glasgow Central 15 §	a			20 16	20 26		20 35		20 46	20 56		21 05		21 16	21 26			21 35		21 46	21 56		22 05		22 16
	d		20c15	20 17	20 27		20 37		20 47	20 57		21 07		21 17	21 27			21 37		21 47	21 57		22 07		22 17
Argyle Street	d			20 19	20 29		20 39		20 49	20 59		21 09		21 19	21 29			21 39		21 49	21 59		22 09		22 19
Charing Cross	d	20 08				20 29		20 38			20 59		21 08				21 29		21 38			21 59		22 08	
Glasgow Queen Street 10 §	a	20 10				20 31		20 40			21 01		21 10			21e29	21 31		21 40			22 01		22 10	
	d	20 14				20 32		20 44			21 02		21 14				21 32		21 44			22 02		22 14	
High Street	d	20 16				20 34		20 46			21 04		21 16				21 34		21 46			22 04		22 16	
Bellgrove	d	20 18				20 36		20 48			21 06		21 18				21 36		21 48			22 06		22 18	
Duke Street	d	20 20						20 50					21 20						21 50					22 20	
Alexandra Parade	d	20 21						20 51					21 21						21 51					22 21	
Barnhill	d	20 24						20 54					21 24						21 54					22 24	
Springburn	a	20 26						20 56					21 26						21 56					22 26	
Carntyne	d					20 39					21 09						21 39					22 09			
Shettleston	d					20 42					21 12						21 42					22 12			
Garrowhill	d					20 44					21 14						21 44					22 14			
Easterhouse	d					20 47					21 17						21 47					22 17			
Blairhill	d					20 51					21 21						21 51					22 21			
Coatbridge Sunnyside	d					20 53					21 23						21 53					22 23			
Coatdyke	d					20 56					21 26						21 56					22 26			
Airdrie	a					20 58					21 28						21 58					22 28			
	d					20 59					21 29						21 59					22 29			
Drumgelloch	a					21 03					21 33						22 03					22 33			
Bridgeton	d			20 22			20 42		20 52			21 12		21 22				21 42		21 52			22 12		22 22
Dalmarnock	d			20 24			20 44		20 54			21 14		21 24				21 44		21 54			22 14		22 24
Rutherglen	d			20 26	20 34		20 46		20 56	21 04		21 16		21 26	21 34			21 46		21 56	22 04		22 16		22 26
Cambuslang	d		20 24	20 31			20 50		21 01			21 20		21 31				21 50		22 01			22 20		22 31
Newton	d						20 54					21 24						21 54					22 24		
Blantyre	d				20 44		20 58			21 14		21 28			21 44			21 58			22 14		22 28		
Hamilton West	d				20 47		21 01			21 17		21 31			21 47			22 01			22 17		22 31		
Hamilton Central	d				20 50		21 03			21 20		21 33			21 50			22 03			22 20		22 33		
Chatelherault	d				20 54					21 24					21 54						22 24				
Merryton	d				20 58					21 28					21 58						22 28				
Larkhall	a				21 00					21 30					22 00						22 30				
Airbles	d						21 08					21 38						22 08					22 38		
Uddingston	d		20 29	20 35					21 05					21 35						22 05					22 35
Bellshill	d		20 35	20 40					21 10					21 40						22 10					22 40
Motherwell	a			20 46			21 11		21 16			21 41		21 46				22 11		22 16			22 41		22 46
	d								21 16			21 42								22 16			22 41		
Whifflet	a																						22 48		
Coatbridge Central	a																						22 52		
Shieldmuir	d								21 20											22 20					
Holytown	d		20a39									21 47													
Wishaw	d								21 23			21 53								22 23					
Carluke	d								21 30			22 00								22 30					
Lanark	a								21 42			22 12								22 42					

For general notes see front of timetable
For details of catering facilities see Directory of Train Operators

§ Low Level

A To Edinburgh (Saturdays from 29 March to Livingston South) (Table 225)
B From Oban and from Mallaig (Table 227)
b Helensburgh Upper
c Glasgow Central High Level
e Glasgow Queen Street High Level

Helensburgh, Balloch, Dalmuir and Milngavie → Glasgow → Springburn, Airdrie, Drumgelloch, Hamilton, Larkhall, Motherwell, Coatbridge and Lanark

Network Diagram - see first page of Table 220

		SR	SR	SR	SR	SR	SR	SR	SR	SR	SR	SR	SR	SR	SR	SR	SR	SR	SR	SR	SR	SR	SR		
														FO	FX	FX	FO	FO	FO		FO		SX R B		
									A																
Helensburgh Central	d		21 40					22 10						22 40	22 40					23 10			23b24		
Craigendoran	d		21 43					22 13						22 43	22 43					23 13					
Cardross	d		21 48					22 18						22 48	22 48					23 18					
Balloch	d				21 53						22 23					22 53	22 53					23 23			
Alexandria	d				21 55						22 25					22 55	22 55					23 25			
Renton	d				21 58						22 28					22 58	22 58					23 28			
Dalreoch	d		21 53		22 01			22 23			22 31			22 53	22 53	23 01	23 01			23 23		23 31			
Dumbarton Central	d		21 55		22 02			22 25			22 32			22 55	22 55	23 02	23 02			23 25		23 32			
Dumbarton East	d		21 57		22 04			22 27			22 34			22 57	22 57	23 04	23 04			23 27		23 34			
Bowling	d				22 09						22 39					23 09	23 09					23 39			
Kilpatrick	d				22 12						22 42					23 12	23 12					23 42			
Dalmuir	a		22 05		22 15			22 35			22 45			23 05	23 05	23 15	23 15			23 35		23 45	23 49		
	d	22 01	22 05		22 16		22 31	22 35			22 46		23 01	23 05	23 05	23 16	23 16		23 31	23 35			23 51		
Singer	d	22 03			22 18		22 33				22 48		23 03			23 18	23 18		23 33						
Drumry	d	22 05			22 20		22 35				22 50		23 05			23 20	23 20		23 35						
Drumchapel	d	22 08			22 23		22 38				22 53		23 08			23 23	23 23		23 38						
Milngavie	d			22 12						22 42											23 42				
Hillfoot	d			22 15						22 45											23 45				
Bearsden	d			22 17						22 47											23 47				
Westerton	d	22 10		22 20	22 25		22 40			22 50	22 55		23 10			23 25	23 25		23 40		23 50		23a56		
Anniesland	d	22 14		22 23	22 28		22 44			22 53	22 58		23 14			23 28	23 28		23 44		23 53				
Clydebank	d		22 07					22 37						23 07	23 07					23 37					
Yoker	d		22 09					22 39						23 09	23 09					23 39					
Garscadden	d		22 13					22 43						23 13	23 13					23 43					
Scotstounhill	d		22 15					22 45						23 15	23 15					23 45					
Jordanhill	d		22 17					22 47						23 17	23 17					23 47					
Hyndland	d	22 17	22 21	22 26	22 31		22 47	22 51		22 56	23 01		23 17	23 22	23 22	23 31	23 31		23 47	23 51	23 56				
Partick	d	22 20	22 24	22 29	22 34	22 40	22 50	22 54		22 59	23 04	23 10	23 20	23 24	23 24	23 34	23 34	23 40	23 50	23 54	23 59				
Exhibition Centre	d	22 23		22 32		22 43	22 53			23 02		23 13	23 23					23 43	23 53		00 02				
Anderston	d	22 25		22 34		22 45	22 55			23 04		23 15	23 25					23 45	23 55		00 04				
Glasgow Central 15 §	a	22 26		22 35		22 46	22 56			23 05		23 16	23 26					23 46	23 56		00 05				
	d	22 27		22 37		22 47	22 57		23c06	23 07		23 17	23 27					23 47	23 57		00 07				
Argyle Street	d	22 29		22 39		22 49	22 59			23 09		23 19	23 29					23 49	23 59		00 09				
Charing Cross	d		22 29		22 38			22 59			23 08			23 29	23 29	23 38	23 38			23 59					
Glasgow Queen Street 10 §	a		22 31		22 40			23 01			23 10			23 31	23 31	23 40	23 40			00 01					
	d		22 32		22 44			23 02			23 14			23 32	23 32	23 44	23 44			00 02					
High Street	d		22 34		22 46			23 04			23 16			23 34	23 34	23 46	23 46			00 04					
Bellgrove	d		22 36		22 48			23 06			23 18			23 36	23 36	23 48	23 48			00 06					
Duke Street	d				22 50						23 20						23 50								
Alexandra Parade	d				22 51						23 21						23 51								
Barnhill	d				22 54						23 24						23 54								
Springburn	a				22 56						23 26						23 56								
Carntyne	d		22 39					23 09						23 39	23 39	23 51				00 09					
Shettleston	d		22 42					23 12						23 42	23 42	23 54				00 12					
Garrowhill	d		22 44					23 14						23 44	23 44	23 56				00 14					
Easterhouse	d		22 47					23 17						23 47	23 47	23 59				00 17					
Blairhill	d		22 51					23 21						23 51	23 51	00 03				00 21					
Coatbridge Sunnyside	d		22 53					23 23						23 53	23 53	00 05				00 23					
Coatdyke	d		22 56					23 26						23 56	23 56	00 08				00 26					
Airdrie	a		22 58					23 28						23 58	23 59	00 10				00 28					
	d		22 59					23 29						23 59		00 10				00 29					
Drumgelloch	a		23 03					23 33						00 03		00 14				00 33					
Bridgeton	d			22 42		22 52				23 12		23 22						23 52			00 12				
Dalmarnock	d			22 44		22 54				23 14		23 24						23 54			00 14				
Rutherglen	d	22 34		22 46		22 56	23 04			23 16		23 26	23 34					23 57	00 04		00 16				
Cambuslang	d			22 50		23 01			23 15	23 20		23 31						00 01			00 20				
Newton	d			22 54						23 24											00 24				
Blantyre	d	22 44		22 58			23 14			23 28			23 44						00 14		00 28				
Hamilton West	d	22 47		23 01			23 17			23 31			23 47						00 17		00 31				
Hamilton Central	d	22 50		23 03			23 20			23 33			23 50						00 20		00 33				
Chatelherault	d	22 54					23 24						23 54						00 24						
Merryton	d	22 58					23 28						23 58						00 28						
Larkhall	a	23 00					23 30						00 01						00 30						
Airbles	d			23 08						23 38											00 38				
Uddingston	d					23 05			23 20			23 35						00 05							
Bellshill	d					23 10			23 26			23 40						00 10							
Motherwell	a			23 11		23 16				23 41		23 46						00 16			00 41				
	d					23 16												00 16							
Whifflet	a																								
Coatbridge Central	a																								
Shieldmuir	d					23 20												00 20							
Holytown	d								23a30																
Wishaw	d					23 23												00 23							
Carluke	d					23 30												00 30							
Lanark	a					23 42												00 42							

For general notes see front of timetable
For details of catering facilities see Directory of Train Operators

§ Low Level

A To Edinburgh (Saturdays from 29 March to Livingston South) (Table 225)

B Limited seating accommodation from Fort William to Edinburgh (Table 227).
Also conveys through Sleeping Car accommodation from Fort William to London Euston (Tables 65 and 404)

b Helensburgh Upper

c Glasgow Central High Level

Table 226

Sundays

until 23 December

Helensburgh, Balloch, Dalmuir and Milngavie → Glasgow → Springburn, Airdrie, Drumgelloch, Hamilton, Larkhall, Motherwell, Coatbridge and Lanark

Network Diagram - see first page of Table 220

		SR	SR	SR	SR	SR	SR	SR	SR	SR	SR	SR	SR	SR	SR	SR	SR	SR	SR	SR	SR	SR
Helensburgh Central	d			07 55			08 25						08 55					09 25				
Craigendoran	d			07 58			08 28						08 58					09 28				
Cardross	d			08 03			08 33						09 03					09 33				
Balloch	d				08 09			08 39						09 09					09 39			
Alexandria	d				08 11			08 41						09 11					09 41			
Renton	d				08 14			08 44						09 14					09 44			
Dalreoch	d			08 08	08 17		08 38	08 47					09 08	09 17				09 38	09 47			
Dumbarton Central	d			08 10	08 18		08 40	08 48					09 10	09 18				09 40	09 48			
Dumbarton East	d			08 12	08 20		08 42	08 50					09 12	09 20				09 42	09 50			
Bowling	d				08 24			08 54						09 24					09 54			
Kilpatrick	d				08 28			08 58						09 28					09 58			
Dalmuir	a			08 19	08 30		08 49	09 00					09 19	09 30				09 49	10 00			
	d	07 50	08 01	08 20	08 31		08 50	09 01	09 05		09 15		09 20	09 31	09 35		09 45	09 50	10 01	10 05		10 15
Singer	d	07 52		08 22			08 52		09 07				09 22		09 37			09 52		10 07		
Drumry	d	07 55		08 25			08 55		09 09				09 25		09 39			09 55		10 09		
Drumchapel	d	07 57		08 27			08 57		09 12				09 27		09 42			09 57		10 12		
Milngavie	d									09 11						09 41					10 11	
Hillfoot	d									09 14						09 44					10 14	
Bearsden	d									09 16						09 46					10 16	
Westerton	d	08 00		08 30			09 00		09 14	09 19			09 30		09 44	09 49		10 00		10 14	10 19	
Anniesland	d	08 03		08 33			09 03		09 17	09 22			09 33		09 47	09 52		10 03		10 17	10 22	
Clydebank	d		08 03		08 33			09 03			09 17			09 33			09 47		10 03			10 17
Yoker	d		08 05		08 35			09 05			09 19			09 35			09 49		10 05			10 19
Garscadden	d		08 09		08 39			09 09			09 22			09 39			09 52		10 09			10 22
Scotstounhill	d		08 11		08 41			09 11			09 24			09 41			09 54		10 11			10 24
Jordanhill	d		08 13		08 43			09 13			09 26			09 43			09 56		10 13			10 26
Hyndland	d	08 05	08 15	08 35	08 45	08 55	09 05	09 15	09 20	09 25	09 28		09 35	09 45	09 50	09 55	09 58	10 05	10 15	10 20	10 25	10 28
Partick	d	08 08	08 18	08 38	08 48	08 58	09 08	09 18	09 22	09 28	09 30	09 34	09 38	09 48	09 52	09 58	10 00	10 08	10 18	10 22	10 28	10 30
Exhibition Centre	d		08 21		08 51	09 01		09 21		09 31		09 37		09 51		10 01			10 21		10 31	
Anderston	d																					
Glasgow Central 15 §	a		08 23		08 53	09 03		09 23		09 33		09 39		09 53		10 03			10 23		10 33	
	d		08 24		08 54	09 04		09 24		09 34		09 40		09 54		10 04			10 24		10 34	
Argyle Street	d													09 56		10 06			10 26		10 36	
Charing Cross	d	08 13		08 43			09 13		09 26		09 34		09 43		09 56		10 04	10 13		10 26		10 34
Glasgow Queen Street 10 §	a	08 15		08 45			09 15		09 28		09 36		09 45		09 58		10 06	10 15		10 28		10 36
	d	08 17		08 47			09 17		09 29		09 37		09 47		09 59		10 07	10 17		10 29		10 37
High Street	d	08 19		08 49			09 19		09 31		09 39		09 49		10 01		10 09	10 19		10 31		10 39
Bellgrove	d	08 21		08 51			09 21		09 33		09 41		09 51		10 03		10 11	10 21		10 33		10 41
Duke Street	d								09 35						10 05					10 35		
Alexandra Parade	d								09 36						10 06					10 36		
Barnhill	d								09 39						10 09					10 39		
Springburn	a								09 41						10 11					10 41		
Carntyne	d	08 24		08 54			09 24				09 44		09 54				10 14	10 24				10 44
Shettleston	d	08 27		08 57			09 27				09 47		09 57				10 17	10 27				10 47
Garrowhill	d	08 29		08 59			09 29				09 49		09 59				10 19	10 29				10 49
Easterhouse	d	08 32		09 02			09 32				09 52		10 02				10 22	10 32				10 52
Blairhill	d	08 36		09 06			09 36				09 56		10 06				10 26	10 36				10 56
Coatbridge Sunnyside	d	08 38		09 08			09 38				09 58		10 08				10 28	10 38				10 58
Coatdyke	d	08 41		09 11			09 41				10 01		10 11				10 31	10 41				11 01
Airdrie	a	08 44		09 14			09 44				10 04		10 14				10 34	10 44				11 04
	d	08 45		09 15			09 45						10 15					10 45				
Drumgelloch	a	08 48		09 18			09 48						10 18					10 48				
Bridgeton	d		08 29		08 59	09 09		09 29		09 39				09 59		10 09			10 29		10 39	
Dalmarnock	d																					
Rutherglen	d		08 32		09 02	09 12		09 32		09 42		09 47		10 02		10 12			10 32		10 42	
Cambuslang	d		08 36		09 06	09 16		09 36		09 46				10 06		10 16			10 36		10 46	
Newton	d				09 09			09 39						10 09					10 39			
Blantyre	d				09 13			09 43				09 55		10 13					10 43			
Hamilton West	d				09 16			09 46				09 58		10 16					10 46			
Hamilton Central	d				09 20			09 50				10 01		10 20					10 50			
Chatelherault	d											10 06										
Merryton	d											10 09										
Larkhall	a											10 11										
Airbles	d				09 25			09 55						10 25					10 55			
Uddingston	d		08 40			09 20				09 50						10 20					10 50	
Bellshill	d		08 45			09 25				09 55						10 25					10 55	
Motherwell	a		08 53		09 27	09 33		09 57		10 03				10 27		10 33			10 57		11 03	
	d					09 33										10 33						
Whifflet	a																					
Coatbridge Central	a																					
Shieldmuir	d					09 37										10 37						
Holytown	d																					
Wishaw	d					09 40										10 40						
Carluke	d					09 47										10 47						
Lanark	a					09 59										10 59						

For general notes see front of timetable
For details of catering facilities see Directory of Train Operators

§ Low Level

Table 226

until 23 December

Helensburgh, Balloch, Dalmuir and Milngavie → Glasgow → Springburn, Airdrie, Drumgelloch, Hamilton, Larkhall, Motherwell, Coatbridge and Lanark

Network Diagram - see first page of Table 220

Station		SR	SR	SR	SR	SR	SR	SR	SR	SR	SR	SR	SR	SR	SR	SR	SR	SR	SR	SR	SR	SR
Helensburgh Central	d		09 55					10 25						10 55					11 25			
Craigendoran	d		09 58					10 28						10 58					11 28			
Cardross	d		10 03					10 33						11 03					11 33			
Balloch	d			10 09					10 39						11 09					11 39		
Alexandria	d			10 11					10 41						11 11					11 41		
Renton	d			10 14					10 44						11 14					11 44		
Dalreoch	d		10 08	10 17				10 38	10 47					11 08	11 17				11 38	11 47		
Dumbarton Central	d		10 10	10 18				10 40	10 48					11 10	11 18				11 40	11 48		
Dumbarton East	d		10 12	10 20				10 42	10 50					11 12	11 20				11 42	11 50		
Bowling	d			10 24					10 54						11 24					11 54		
Kilpatrick	d			10 28					10 58						11 28					11 58		
Dalmuir	a		10 19	10 30				10 49	11 00					11 19	11 30				11 49	12 00		
	d		10 20	10 31	10 35		10 45	10 50	11 01	11 05		11 15		11 20	11 31	11 35		11 45	11 50	12 01	12 05	
Singer	d		10 22		10 37			10 52		11 07				11 22		11 37			11 52		12 07	
Drumry	d		10 25		10 39			10 55		11 09				11 25		11 39			11 55		12 09	
Drumchapel	d		10 27		10 42			10 57		11 12				11 27		11 42			11 57		12 12	
Milngavie	d					10 41					11 11						11 41					12 11
Hillfoot	d					10 44					11 14						11 44					12 14
Bearsden	d					10 46					11 16						11 46					12 16
Westerton	d		10 30		10 44	10 49		11 00		11 14	11 19			11 30		11 44	11 49		12 00		12 14	12 19
Anniesland	d		10 33		10 47	10 52		11 03		11 17	11 22			11 33		11 47	11 52		12 03		12 17	12 22
Clydebank	d			10 33			10 47		11 03			11 17			11 33			11 47		12 03		
Yoker	d			10 35			10 49		11 05			11 19			11 35			11 49		12 05		
Garscadden	d			10 39			10 52		11 09			11 22			11 39			11 52		12 09		
Scotstounhill	d			10 41			10 54		11 11			11 24			11 41			11 54		12 11		
Jordanhill	d			10 43			10 56		11 13			11 26			11 43			11 56		12 13		
Hyndland	d		10 35	10 45	10 50	10 55	10 58	11 05	11 15	11 20	11 25	11 28		11 35	11 45	11 50	11 55	11 58	12 05	12 15	12 20	12 25
Partick	d	10 34	10 38	10 48	10 52	10 58	11 00	11 08	11 18	11 22	11 28	11 30	11 34	11 38	11 48	11 52	11 58	12 00	12 08	12 18	12 22	12 28
Exhibition Centre	d	10 37		10 51		11 01			11 21		11 31		11 37		11 51		12 01			12 21		12 31
Anderston	d																					
Glasgow Central 15 §	a	10 39		10 53		11 03			11 23		11 33		11 39		11 53		12 03			12 23		12 33
	d	10 40		10 54		11 04			11 24		11 34		11 40		11 54		12 04			12 24		12 34
Argyle Street	d	10 42		10 56		11 06			11 26		11 36		11 42		11 56		12 06			12 26		12 36
Charing Cross	d		10 43		10 56		11 04	11 13		11 26		11 34		11 43		11 56		12 04	12 13		12 26	
Glasgow Queen Street 10 §	a		10 45		10 58		11 06	11 15		11 28		11 36		11 45		11 58		12 06	12 15		12 28	
	d		10 47		10 59		11 07	11 17		11 29		11 37		11 47		11 59		12 07	12 17		12 29	
High Street	d		10 49		11 01		11 09	11 19		11 31		11 39		11 49		12 01		12 09	12 19		12 31	
Bellgrove	d		10 51		11 03		11 11	11 21		11 33		11 41		11 51		12 03		12 11	12 21		12 33	
Duke Street	d				11 05					11 35						12 05					12 35	
Alexandra Parade	d				11 06					11 36						12 06					12 36	
Barnhill	d				11 09					11 39						12 09					12 39	
Springburn	a				11 11					11 41						12 11					12 41	
Carntyne	d		10 54				11 14	11 24				11 44		11 54				12 14	12 24			
Shettleston	d		10 57				11 17	11 27				11 47		11 57				12 17	12 27			
Garrowhill	d		10 59				11 19	11 29				11 49		11 59				12 19	12 29			
Easterhouse	d		11 02				11 22	11 32				11 52		12 02				12 22	12 32			
Blairhill	d		11 06				11 26	11 36				11 56		12 06				12 26	12 36			
Coatbridge Sunnyside	d		11 08				11 28	11 38				11 58		12 08				12 28	12 38			
Coatdyke	d		11 11				11 31	11 41				12 01		12 11				12 31	12 41			
Airdrie	a		11 14				11 34	11 44				12 04		12 14				12 34	12 44			
	d		11 15					11 45						12 15					12 45			
Drumgelloch	a		11 18					11 48						12 18					12 48			
Bridgeton	d			10 59		11 09			11 29		11 39				11 59		12 09			12 29		12 39
Dalmarnock	d																					
Rutherglen	d	10 47		11 02		11 12			11 32		11 42		11 47		12 02		12 12			12 32		12 42
Cambuslang	d			11 06		11 16			11 36		11 46				12 06		12 16			12 36		12 46
Newton	d			11 09					11 39						12 09					12 39		
Blantyre	d	10 55		11 13					11 43				11 55		12 13					12 43		
Hamilton West	d	10 58		11 16					11 46				11 58		12 16					12 46		
Hamilton Central	d	11 01		11 20					11 50				12 01		12 20					12 50		
Chatelherault	d	11 06											12 06									
Merryton	d	11 09											12 09									
Larkhall	a	11 15											12 12									
Airbles	d			11 25					11 55						12 25					12 55		
Uddingston	d					11 20					11 50						12 20					12 50
Bellshill	d					11 25					11 55						12 25					12 55
Motherwell	a			11 27		11 33			11 57		12 03				12 27		12 33			12 57		13 03
	d					11 33											12 33					
Whifflet	a																					
Coatbridge Central	a																					
Shieldmuir	d					11 37											12 37					
Holytown	d																					
Wishaw	d					11 40											12 40					
Carluke	d					11 47											12 47					
Lanark	a					11 59											12 59					

For general notes see front of timetable
For details of catering facilities see Directory of Train Operators

§ Low Level

Table 226

Sundays

until 23 December

Helensburgh, Balloch, Dalmuir and Milngavie → Glasgow → Springburn, Airdrie, Drumgelloch, Hamilton, Larkhall, Motherwell, Coatbridge and Lanark

Network Diagram - see first page of Table 220

		SR	SR	SR	SR	SR	SR	SR	SR	SR	SR	SR	SR	SR	SR	SR	SR	SR	SR	SR	SR	SR
Helensburgh Central	d			11 55					12 25						12 55					13 25		
Craigendoran	d			11 58					12 28						12 58					13 28		
Cardross	d			12 03					12 33						13 03					13 33		
Balloch	d				12 09					12 39						13 09					13 39	
Alexandria	d				12 11					12 41						13 11					13 41	
Renton	d				12 14					12 44						13 14					13 44	
Dalreoch	d			12 08	12 17				12 38	12 47					13 08	13 17				13 38	13 47	
Dumbarton Central	d			12 10	12 18				12 40	12 48					13 10	13 18				13 40	13 48	
Dumbarton East	d			12 12	12 20				12 42	12 50					13 12	13 20				13 42	13 50	
Bowling	d				12 24					12 54						13 24					13 54	
Kilpatrick	d				12 28					12 58						13 28					13 58	
Dalmuir	a			12 19	12 30				12 49	13 00					13 19	13 30				13 49	14 00	
	d	12 15		12 20	12 31	12 35		12 45	12 50	13 01	13 05		13 15		13 20	13 31	13 35		13 45	13 50	14 01	14 05
Singer	d			12 22		12 37			12 52		13 07				13 22		13 37			13 52		14 07
Drumry	d			12 25		12 39			12 55		13 09				13 25		13 39			13 55		14 09
Drumchapel	d			12 27		12 42			12 57		13 12				13 27		13 42			13 57		14 12
Milngavie	d						12 41					13 11						13 41				
Hillfoot	d						12 44					13 14						13 44				
Bearsden	d						12 46					13 16						13 46				
Westerton	d			12 30		12 44	12 49		13 00		13 14	13 19			13 30		13 44	13 49		14 00		14 14
Anniesland	d			12 33		12 47	12 52		13 03		13 17	13 22			13 33		13 47	13 52		14 03		14 17
Clydebank	d	12 17			12 33			12 47		13 03			13 17			13 33			13 47		14 03	
Yoker	d	12 19			12 35			12 49		13 05			13 19			13 35			13 49		14 05	
Garscadden	d	12 22			12 39			12 52		13 09			13 22			13 39			13 52		14 09	
Scotstounhill	d	12 24			12 41			12 54		13 11			13 24			13 41			13 54		14 11	
Jordanhill	d	12 26			12 43			12 56		13 13			13 26			13 43			13 56		14 13	
Hyndland	d	12 28		12 35	12 45	12 50	12 55	12 58	13 05	13 15	13 20	13 25	13 28		13 35	13 45	13 50	13 55	13 58	14 05	14 15	14 20
Partick	d	12 30	12 34	12 38	12 48	12 52	12 58	13 00	13 08	13 18	13 22	13 28	13 30	13 34	13 38	13 48	13 52	13 58	14 00	14 08	14 18	14 22
Exhibition Centre	d		12 37		12 51		13 01			13 21		13 31		13 37		13 51		14 01			14 21	
Anderston	d																					
Glasgow Central 15 §	a		12 39		12 53		13 03			13 23		13 33		13 39		13 53		14 03			14 23	
	d		12 40		12 54		13 04			13 24		13 34		13 40		13 54		14 04			14 24	
Argyle Street	d		12 42		12 56		13 06			13 26		13 36		13 42		13 56		14 06			14 26	
Charing Cross	d	12 34		12 43		12 56		13 04	13 13		13 26		13 34		13 43		13 56		14 04	14 13		14 26
Glasgow Queen Street 10 §	a	12 36		12 45		12 58		13 06	13 15		13 28		13 36		13 45		13 58		14 06	14 15		14 28
	d	12 37		12 47		12 59		13 07	13 17		13 29		13 37		13 47		13 59		14 07	14 17		14 29
High Street	d	12 39		12 49		13 01		13 09	13 19		13 31		13 39		13 49		14 01		14 09	14 19		14 31
Bellgrove	d	12 41		12 51		13 03		13 11	13 21		13 33		13 41		13 51		14 03		14 11	14 21		14 33
Duke Street	d					13 05					13 35						14 05					14 35
Alexandra Parade	d					13 06					13 36						14 06					14 36
Barnhill	d					13 09					13 39						14 09					14 39
Springburn	a					13 11					13 41						14 11					14 41
Carntyne	d	12 44		12 54				13 14	13 24				13 44		13 54				14 14	14 24		
Shettleston	d	12 47		12 57				13 17	13 27				13 47		13 57				14 17	14 27		
Garrowhill	d	12 49		12 59				13 19	13 29				13 49		13 59				14 19	14 29		
Easterhouse	d	12 52		13 02				13 22	13 32				13 52		14 02				14 22	14 32		
Blairhill	d	12 56		13 06				13 26	13 36				13 56		14 06				14 26	14 36		
Coatbridge Sunnyside	d	12 58		13 08				13 28	13 38				13 58		14 08				14 28	14 38		
Coatdyke	d	13 01		13 11				13 31	13 41				14 01		14 11				14 31	14 41		
Airdrie	a	13 04		13 14				13 34	13 44				14 04		14 14				14 34	14 44		
	d			13 15					13 45						14 15					14 45		
Drumgelloch	a			13 18					13 48						14 18					14 48		
Bridgeton	d				12 59		13 09			13 29		13 39				13 59		14 09			14 29	
Dalmarnock	d																					
Rutherglen	d		12 47		13 02		13 12			13 32		13 42		13 47		14 02		14 12			14 32	
Cambuslang	d				13 06		13 16			13 36		13 46				14 06		14 16			14 36	
Newton	d				13 09					13 39						14 09					14 39	
Blantyre	d		12 55		13 13					13 43				13 55		14 13					14 43	
Hamilton West	d		12 58		13 16					13 46				13 58		14 16					14 46	
Hamilton Central	d		13 01		13 20					13 50				14 01		14 20					14 50	
Chatelherault	d		13 06											14 06								
Merryton	d		13 09											14 09								
Larkhall	a		13 15											14 11								
Airbles	d				13 25					13 55						14 25					14 55	
Uddingston	d						13 20					13 50						14 20				
Bellshill	d						13 25					13 55						14 25				
Motherwell	a				13 27		13 33			13 57		14 03				14 27		14 33			14 57	
	d						13 33											14 33				
Whifflet	a																					
Coatbridge Central	a																					
Shieldmuir	d						13 37											14 37				
Holytown	d																					
Wishaw	d						13 40											14 40				
Carluke	d						13 47											14 47				
Lanark	a						13 59											14 59				

For general notes see front of timetable
For details of catering facilities see Directory of Train Operators

§ Low Level

until 23 December

Helensburgh, Balloch, Dalmuir and Milngavie → Glasgow → Springburn, Airdrie, Drumgelloch, Hamilton, Larkhall, Motherwell, Coatbridge and Lanark

Network Diagram - see first page of Table 220

		SR	SR	SR		SR	SR	SR	SR	SR	SR		SR	SR	SR	SR	SR	SR		SR	SR	SR	SR	SR	SR
Helensburgh Central	d					13 55					14 25							14 55						15 25	
Craigendoran	d					13 58					14 28							14 58						15 28	
Cardross	d					14 03					14 33							15 03						15 33	
Balloch	d						14 09						14 39							15 09					15 39
Alexandria	d						14 11						14 41							15 11					15 41
Renton	d						14 14						14 44							15 14					15 44
Dalreoch	d					14 08	14 17				14 38		14 47					15 08		15 17				15 38	15 47
Dumbarton Central	d					14 10	14 18				14 40		14 48					15 10		15 18				15 40	15 48
Dumbarton East	d					14 12	14 20				14 42		14 50					15 12		15 20				15 42	15 50
Bowling	d						14 24						14 54							15 24					15 54
Kilpatrick	d						14 28						14 58							15 28					15 58
Dalmuir	a					14 19	14 30				14 49		15 00					15 19		15 30				15 49	16 00
	d		14 15			14 20	14 31	14 35		14 45	14 50		15 01	15 05		15 15		15 20		15 31	15 35		15 45	15 50	16 01
Singer	d					14 22		14 37			14 52			15 07				15 22			15 37			15 52	
Drumry	d					14 25		14 39			14 55			15 09				15 25			15 39			15 55	
Drumchapel	d					14 27		14 42			14 57			15 12				15 27			15 42			15 57	
Milngavie	d	14 11							14 41						15 11							15 41			
Hillfoot	d	14 14							14 44						15 14							15 44			
Bearsden	d	14 16							14 46						15 16							15 46			
Westerton	d	14 19				14 30		14 44	14 49		15 00			15 14	15 19			15 30			15 44	15 49		16 00	
Anniesland	d	14 22				14 33		14 47	14 52		15 03			15 17	15 22			15 33			15 47	15 52		16 03	
Clydebank	d		14 17				14 33			14 47			15 03			15 17				15 33			15 47		16 03
Yoker	d		14 19				14 35			14 49			15 05			15 19				15 35			15 49		16 05
Garscadden	d		14 22				14 39			14 52			15 09			15 22				15 39			15 52		16 09
Scotstounhill	d		14 24				14 41			14 54			15 11			15 24				15 41			15 54		16 11
Jordanhill	d		14 26				14 43			14 56			15 13			15 26				15 43			15 56		16 13
Hyndland	d	14 25	14 28			14 35	14 45	14 50	14 55	14 58	15 05		15 15	15 20	15 25	15 28		15 35		15 45	15 50	15 55	15 58	16 05	16 15
Partick	d	14 28	14 30	14 34		14 38	14 48	14 52	14 58	15 00	15 08		15 18	15 22	15 28	15 30	15 34	15 38		15 48	15 52	15 58	16 00	16 08	16 18
Exhibition Centre	d	14 31		14 37			14 51		15 01				15 21		15 31		15 37			15 51		16 01			16 21
Anderston	d																								
Glasgow Central 15 §	a	14 33		14 39			14 53		15 03				15 23		15 33		15 39			15 53		16 03			16 23
	d	14 34		14 40			14 54		15 04				15 24		15 34		15 40			15 54		16 04			16 24
Argyle Street	d	14 36		14 42			14 56		15 06				15 26		15 36		15 42			15 56		16 06			16 26
Charing Cross	d		14 34			14 43		14 56		15 04	15 13			15 26		15 34		15 43			15 56		16 04	16 13	
Glasgow Queen Street 10 §	a		14 36			14 45		14 58		15 06	15 15			15 28		15 36		15 45			15 58		16 06	16 15	
	d		14 37			14 47		14 59		15 07	15 17			15 29		15 37		15 47			15 59		16 07	16 17	
High Street	d		14 39			14 49		15 01		15 09	15 19			15 31		15 39		15 49			16 01		16 09	16 19	
Bellgrove	d		14 41			14 51		15 03		15 11	15 21			15 33		15 41		15 51			16 03		16 11	16 21	
Duke Street	d							15 05						15 35							16 05				
Alexandra Parade	d							15 06						15 36							16 06				
Barnhill	d							15 09						15 39							16 09				
Springburn	a							15 11						15 41							16 11				
Carntyne	d		14 44			14 54				15 14	15 24					15 44		15 54					16 14	16 24	
Shettleston	d		14 47			14 57				15 17	15 27					15 47		15 57					16 17	16 27	
Garrowhill	d		14 49			14 59				15 19	15 29					15 49		15 59					16 19	16 29	
Easterhouse	d		14 52			15 02				15 22	15 32					15 52		16 02					16 22	16 32	
Blairhill	d		14 56			15 06				15 26	15 36					15 56		16 06					16 26	16 36	
Coatbridge Sunnyside	d		14 58			15 08				15 28	15 38					15 58		16 08					16 28	16 38	
Coatdyke	d		15 01			15 11				15 31	15 41					16 01		16 11					16 31	16 41	
Airdrie	a		15 04			15 14				15 34	15 44					16 04		16 14					16 34	16 44	
	d					15 15					15 45							16 15						16 45	
Drumgelloch	a					15 18					15 48							16 18						16 48	
Bridgeton	d	14 39					14 59		15 09				15 29		15 39					15 59		16 09			16 29
Dalmarnock	d																								
Rutherglen	d	14 42		14 47			15 02		15 12				15 32		15 42		15 47			16 02		16 12			16 32
Cambuslang	d	14 46					15 06		15 16				15 36		15 46					16 06		16 16			16 36
Newton	d						15 09						15 39							16 09					16 39
Blantyre	d			14 55			15 13						15 43				15 55			16 13					16 43
Hamilton West	d			14 58			15 16						15 46				15 58			16 16					16 46
Hamilton Central	d			15 01			15 20						15 50				16 01			16 20					16 50
Chatelherault	d			15 06													16 06								
Merryton	d			15 09													16 09								
Larkhall	a			15 11													16 15								
Airbles	d						15 25						15 55							16 25					16 55
Uddingston	d	14 50							15 20						15 50							16 20			
Bellshill	d	14 55							15 25						15 55							16 25			
Motherwell	a	15 03					15 27		15 33				15 57		16 01					16 27		16 33			16 57
	d								15 33													16 33			
Whifflet	a																								
Coatbridge Central	a																								
Shieldmuir	d								15 37													16 37			
Holytown	d																								
Wishaw	d								15 40													16 40			
Carluke	d								15 47													16 47			
Lanark	a								15 59													16 59			

For general notes see front of timetable
For details of catering facilities see Directory of Train Operators

§ Low Level

Table 226

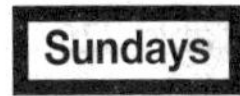

until 23 December

Helensburgh, Balloch, Dalmuir and Milngavie → Glasgow → Springburn, Airdrie, Drumgelloch, Hamilton, Larkhall, Motherwell, Coatbridge and Lanark

Network Diagram - see first page of Table 220

		SR	SR		SR	SR	SR	SR	SR	SR		SR	SR	SR	SR	SR	SR		SR	SR	SR	SR	SR	SR	SR
Helensburgh Central	d						15 55						16 25							16 55					17 25
Craigendoran	d						15 58						16 28							16 58					17 28
Cardross	d						16 03						16 33							17 03					17 33
Balloch	d							16 09						16 39							17 09				
Alexandria	d							16 11						16 41							17 11				
Renton	d							16 14						16 44							17 14				
Dalreoch	d						16 08	16 17					16 38	16 47						17 08	17 17				17 38
Dumbarton Central	d						16 10	16 18					16 40	16 48						17 10	17 18				17 40
Dumbarton East	d						16 12	16 20					16 42	16 50						17 12	17 20				17 42
Bowling	d							16 24						16 54							17 24				
Kilpatrick	d							16 28						16 58							17 28				
Dalmuir	a						16 19	16 30					16 49	17 00						17 19	17 30				17 49
	d	16 05			16 15		16 20	16 31	16 35			16 45	16 50	17 01	17 05		17 15			17 20	17 31	17 35		17 45	17 50
Singer	d	16 07					16 22		16 37				16 52		17 07					17 22		17 37			17 52
Drumry	d	16 09					16 25		16 39				16 55		17 09					17 25		17 39			17 55
Drumchapel	d	16 12					16 27		16 42				16 57		17 12					17 27		17 42			17 57
Milngavie	d		16 11							16 41						17 11							17 41		
Hillfoot	d		16 14							16 44						17 14							17 44		
Bearsden	d		16 16							16 46						17 16							17 46		
Westerton	d	16 14	16 19				16 30		16 44	16 49			17 00		17 14	17 19				17 30		17 44	17 49		18 00
Anniesland	d	16 17	16 22				16 33		16 47	16 52			17 03		17 17	17 22				17 33		17 47	17 52		18 03
Clydebank	d				16 17			16 33				16 47		17 03			17 17				17 33			17 47	
Yoker	d				16 19			16 35				16 49		17 05			17 19				17 35			17 49	
Garscadden	d				16 22			16 39				16 52		17 09			17 22				17 39			17 52	
Scotstounhill	d				16 24			16 41				16 54		17 11			17 24				17 41			17 54	
Jordanhill	d				16 26			16 43				16 56		17 13			17 26				17 43			17 56	
Hyndland	d	16 20	16 25		16 28		16 35	16 45	16 50	16 55		16 58	17 05	17 15	17 20	17 25	17 28			17 35	17 45	17 50	17 55	17 58	18 05
Partick	d	16 22	16 28		16 30	16 34	16 38	16 48	16 52	16 58		17 00	17 08	17 18	17 22	17 28	17 30		17 34	17 38	17 48	17 52	17 58	18 00	18 08
Exhibition Centre	d		16 31			16 37		16 51		17 01				17 21		17 31			17 37		17 51		18 01		
Anderston	d																								
Glasgow Central 15 §	a		16 33			16 39		16 53		17 03				17 23		17 33			17 39		17 53		18 03		
	d		16 34			16 40		16 54		17 04				17 24		17 34			17 40		17 54		18 04		
Argyle Street	d		16 36			16 42		16 56		17 06				17 26		17 36			17 42		17 56		18 06		
Charing Cross	d	16 26			16 34		16 43		16 56			17 04	17 13		17 26		17 34			17 43		17 56		18 04	18 13
Glasgow Queen Street 10 §	a	16 28			16 36		16 45		16 58			17 06	17 15		17 28		17 36			17 45		17 58		18 06	18 15
	d	16 29			16 37		16 47		16 59			17 07	17 17		17 29		17 37			17 47		17 59		18 07	18 17
High Street	d	16 31			16 39		16 49		17 01			17 09	17 19		17 31		17 39			17 49		18 01		18 09	18 19
Bellgrove	d	16 33			16 41		16 51		17 03			17 11	17 21		17 33		17 41			17 51		18 03		18 11	18 21
Duke Street	d	16 35							17 05						17 35							18 05			
Alexandra Parade	d	16 36							17 06						17 36							18 06			
Barnhill	d	16 39							17 09						17 39							18 09			
Springburn	a	16 41							17 11						17 41							18 11			
Carntyne	d				16 44		16 54					17 14	17 24				17 44			17 54				18 14	18 24
Shettleston	d				16 47		16 57					17 17	17 27				17 47			17 57				18 17	18 27
Garrowhill	d				16 49		16 59					17 19	17 29				17 49			17 59				18 19	18 29
Easterhouse	d				16 52		17 02					17 22	17 32				17 52			18 02				18 22	18 32
Blairhill	d				16 56		17 06					17 26	17 36				17 56			18 06				18 26	18 36
Coatbridge Sunnyside	d				16 58		17 08					17 28	17 38				17 58			18 08				18 28	18 38
Coatdyke	d				17 01		17 11					17 31	17 41				18 01			18 11				18 31	18 41
Airdrie	a				17 04		17 14					17 34	17 44				18 04			18 14				18 34	18 44
	d						17 15						17 45							18 15					18 45
Drumgelloch	a						17 18						17 48							18 18					18 48
Bridgeton	d		16 39					16 59		17 09				17 29		17 39					17 59		18 09		
Dalmarnock	d																								
Rutherglen	d		16 42			16 47		17 02		17 12				17 32		17 42			17 47		18 02		18 12		
Cambuslang	d		16 46					17 06		17 16				17 36		17 46					18 06		18 16		
Newton	d							17 09						17 39							18 09				
Blantyre	d					16 55		17 13						17 43					17 55		18 13				
Hamilton West	d					16 58		17 16						17 46					17 58		18 16				
Hamilton Central	d					17 01		17 20						17 50					18 01		18 20				
Chatelherault	d					17 06													18 06						
Merryton	d					17 09													18 09						
Larkhall	a					17 11													18 11						
Airbles	d							17 25						17 55							18 25				
Uddingston	d		16 50							17 20						17 50							18 20		
Bellshill	d		16 55							17 25						17 55							18 25		
Motherwell	a		17 03					17 27		17 33				17 57		18 03					18 27		18 33		
	d									17 33													18 33		
Whifflet	a																								
Coatbridge Central	a																								
Shieldmuir	d									17 37													18 37		
Holytown	d																								
Wishaw	d									17 40													18 40		
Carluke	d									17 47													18 47		
Lanark	a									17 59													18 59		

For general notes see front of timetable
For details of catering facilities see Directory of Train Operators

§ Low Level

Table 226

until 23 December

Helensburgh, Balloch, Dalmuir and Milngavie → Glasgow → Springburn, Airdrie, Drumgelloch, Hamilton, Larkhall, Motherwell, Coatbridge and Lanark

Network Diagram - see first page of Table 220

		SR		SR	SR	SR	SR	SR	SR		SR	SR	SR	SR	SR	SR		SR	SR	SR	SR	SR	SR		SR
Helensburgh Central	d					17 55			18 25					18 55				19 25				19 55			
Craigendoran	d					17 58			18 28					18 58				19 28				19 58			
Cardross	d					18 03			18 33					19 03				19 33				20 03			
Balloch	d	17 39					18 09				18 39				19 09				19 39				20 09		
Alexandria	d	17 41					18 11				18 41				19 11				19 41				20 11		
Renton	d	17 44					18 14				18 44				19 14				19 44				20 14		
Dalreoch	d	17 47				18 08	18 17		18 38		18 47			19 08	19 17			19 38	19 47			20 08	20 17		
Dumbarton Central	d	17 48				18 10	18 18		18 40		18 48			19 10	19 18			19 40	19 48			20 10	20 18		
Dumbarton East	d	17 50				18 12	18 20		18 42		18 50			19 12	19 20			19 42	19 50			20 12	20 20		
Bowling	d	17 54					18 24				18 54				19 24				19 54				20 24		
Kilpatrick	d	17 58					18 28				18 58				19 28				19 58				20 28		
Dalmuir	a	18 00				18 19	18 30		18 49		19 00			19 19	19 30			19 49	20 00			20 19	20 30		
	d	18 01				18 20	18 31		18 50		19 01			19 20	19 31			19 50	20 01			20 20	20 31		
Singer	d					18 22			18 52					19 22				19 52				20 22			
Drumry	d					18 25			18 55					19 25				19 55				20 25			
Drumchapel	d					18 27			18 57					19 27				19 57				20 27			
Milngavie	d			18 11				18 41				19 11				19 41				20 11					20 41
Hillfoot	d			18 14				18 44				19 14				19 44				20 14					20 44
Bearsden	d			18 16				18 46				19 16				19 46				20 16					20 46
Westerton	d			18 19		18 30		18 49	19 00			19 19		19 30		19 49		20 00		20 19		20 30			20 49
Anniesland	d			18 22		18 33		18 52	19 03			19 22		19 33		19 52		20 03		20 22		20 33			20 52
Clydebank	d	18 03					18 33				19 03				19 33				20 03				20 33		
Yoker	d	18 05					18 35				19 05				19 35				20 05				20 35		
Garscadden	d	18 09					18 39				19 09				19 39				20 09				20 39		
Scotstounhill	d	18 11					18 41				19 11				19 41				20 11				20 41		
Jordanhill	d	18 13					18 43				19 13				19 43				20 13				20 43		
Hyndland	d	18 15		18 25		18 35	18 45	18 55	19 05		19 15	19 25		19 35	19 45	19 55		20 05	20 15	20 25		20 35	20 45		20 55
Partick	d	18 18		18 28	18 34	18 38	18 48	18 58	19 08		19 18	19 28	19 34	19 38	19 48	19 58		20 08	20 18	20 28	20 34	20 38	20 48		20 58
Exhibition Centre	d	18 21		18 31	18 37		18 51	19 01			19 21	19 31	19 37		19 51	20 01			20 21	20 31	20 37		20 51		21 01
Anderston	d																								
Glasgow Central 15 §	a	18 23		18 33	18 39		18 53	19 03			19 23	19 33	19 39		19 53	20 03			20 23	20 33	20 39		20 53		21 03
	d	18 24		18 34	18 40		18 54	19 04			19 24	19 34	19 40		19 54	20 04			20 24	20 34	20 40		20 54		21 04
Argyle Street	d																								
Charing Cross	d					18 43			19 13					19 43				20 13				20 43			
Glasgow Queen Street 10 §	a					18 45			19 15					19 45				20 15				20 45			
	d					18 47			19 17					19 47				20 17				20 47			
High Street	d					18 49			19 19					19 49				20 19				20 49			
Bellgrove	d					18 51			19 21					19 51				20 21				20 51			
Duke Street	d																								
Alexandra Parade	d																								
Barnhill	d																								
Springburn	a																								
Carntyne	d					18 54			19 24					19 54				20 24				20 54			
Shettleston	d					18 57			19 27					19 57				20 27				20 57			
Garrowhill	d					18 59			19 29					19 59				20 29				20 59			
Easterhouse	d					19 02			19 32					20 02				20 32				21 02			
Blairhill	d					19 06			19 36					20 06				20 36				21 06			
Coatbridge Sunnyside	d					19 08			19 38					20 08				20 38				21 08			
Coatdyke	d					19 11			19 41					20 11				20 41				21 11			
Airdrie	a					19 14			19 44					20 14				20 44				21 14			
	d					19 15			19 45					20 15				20 45				21 15			
Drumgelloch	a					19 18			19 48					20 18				20 48				21 18			
Bridgeton	d	18 29		18 39			18 59	19 09			19 29	19 39			19 59	20 09			20 29	20 39			20 59		21 09
Dalmarnock	d																								
Rutherglen	d	18 32		18 42	18 47		19 02	19 12			19 32	19 42	19 47		20 02	20 12			20 32	20 42	20 47		21 02		21 12
Cambuslang	d	18 36		18 46			19 06	19 16			19 36	19 46			20 06	20 16			20 36	20 46			21 06		21 16
Newton	d	18 39					19 09				19 39				20 09				20 39				21 09		
Blantyre	d	18 43			18 55		19 13				19 43		19 55		20 13				20 43		20 55		21 13		
Hamilton West	d	18 46			18 58		19 16				19 46		19 58		20 16				20 46		20 58		21 16		
Hamilton Central	d	18 50			19 01		19 20				19 50		20 01		20 20				20 50		21 01		21 20		
Chatelherault	d				19 06								20 06								21 06				
Merryton	d				19 09								20 09								21 09				
Larkhall	a				19 12								20 11								21 11				
Airbles	d	18 55					19 25				19 55				20 25				20 55				21 25		
Uddingston	d			18 50				19 20				19 50				20 20				20 50					21 20
Bellshill	d			18 55				19 25				19 55				20 25				20 55					21 25
Motherwell	a	18 57		19 03			19 27	19 33			19 57	20 03			20 27	20 33			20 57	21 04			21 27		21 33
	d							19 33								20 33									21 33
Whifflet	a																								
Coatbridge Central	a																								
Shieldmuir	d							19 37								20 37									21 37
Holytown	d																								
Wishaw	d							19 40								20 40									21 40
Carluke	d							19 47								20 47									21 47
Lanark	a							19 59								20 59									21 59

For general notes see front of timetable
For details of catering facilities see Directory of Train Operators

§ Low Level

Table 226

Sundays

until 23 December

Helensburgh, Balloch, Dalmuir and Milngavie → Glasgow → Springburn, Airdrie, Drumgelloch, Hamilton, Larkhall, Motherwell, Coatbridge and Lanark

Network Diagram - see first page of Table 220

		SR	SR	SR	SR	SR	SR	SR	SR	SR	SR	SR	SR	SR	SR	SR	SR	SR	SR	SR	SR
				◇ A ⚒															R B ⊡		
Helensburgh Central	d	20 25		20b40			20 55			21 25				21 55			22 25		22b37	22 55	
Craigendoran	d	20 28					20 58			21 28				21 58			22 28			22 58	
Cardross	d	20 33					21 03			21 33				22 03			22 33			23 03	
Balloch	d		20 39					21 09			21 39				22 09			22 39			23 09
Alexandria	d		20 41					21 11			21 41				22 11			22 41			23 11
Renton	d		20 44					21 14			21 44				22 14			22 44			23 14
Dalreoch	d	20 38	20 47				21 08	21 17		21 38	21 47			22 08	22 17		22 38	22 47		23 08	23 17
Dumbarton Central	d	20 40	20 48	20 53			21 10	21 18		21 40	21 48			22 10	22 18		22 40	22 48		23 10	23 18
Dumbarton East	d	20 42	20 50				21 12	21 20		21 42	21 50			22 12	22 20		22 42	22 50		23 12	23 20
Bowling	d		20 54					21 24			21 54				22 24			22 55			23 25
Kilpatrick	d		20 58					21 28			21 58				22 28			22 58			23 28
Dalmuir	a	20 49	21 00	21 05			21 19	21 30		21 49	22 00			22 19	22 30		22 49	23 01	23 02	23 19	23 31
	d	20 50	21 01	21 05			21 20	21 31		21 50	22 01			22 20	22 31		22 50	23 01	23 04		23 31
Singer	d	20 52					21 22			21 52				22 22			22 52				
Drumry	d	20 55					21 25			21 55				22 25			22 55				
Drumchapel	d	20 57					21 27			21 57				22 27			22 57				
Milngavie	d				21 11				21 41			22 11				22 41					
Hillfoot	d				21 14				21 44			22 14				22 44					
Bearsden	d				21 16				21 46			22 16				22 46					
Westerton	d	21 00			21 19		21 30		21 49	22 00		22 19		22 30		22 49	23 00		23a11		
Anniesland	d	21 03			21 22		21 33		21 52	22 03		22 22		22 33		22 52	23 03				
Clydebank	d		21 03					21 33			22 03				22 33			23 03			23 33
Yoker	d		21 05					21 35			22 05				22 35			23a05			23a35
Garscadden	d		21 09					21 39			22 09				22 39						
Scotstounhill	d		21 11					21 41			22 11				22 41						
Jordanhill	d		21 13					21 43			22 13				22 43						
Hyndland	d	21 05	21 15		21 25		21 35	21 45	21 55	22 05	22 15	22 25		22 35	22 45	22 55	23 05				
Partick	d	21 08	21 18		21 28	21 34	21 38	21 48	21 58	22 08	22 18	22 28	22 34	22 38	22 48	22 58	23 08				
Exhibition Centre	d		21 21		21 31	21 37		21 51	22 01		22 21	22 31	22 37		22 51	23 01					
Anderston	d																				
Glasgow Central 15 §	a		21 23		21 33	21 39		21 53	22 03		22 23	22 33	22 39		22 53	23 03					
	d		21 24		21 34	21 40		21 54	22 04		22 24	22 34	22 40		22 54	23 04					
Argyle Street	d																				
Charing Cross	d	21 13					21 43			22 13				22 43			23 13				
Glasgow Queen Street 10 §	a	21 15		21c27			21 45			22 15				22 45			23 15				
	d	21 17					21 47			22 17				22 47			23 17				
High Street	d	21 19					21 49			22 19				22 49			23 19				
Bellgrove	d	21 21					21 51			22 21				22 51			23 21				
Duke Street	d																				
Alexandra Parade	d																				
Barnhill	d																				
Springburn	a																				
Carntyne	d	21 24					21 54			22 24				22 54			23 24				
Shettleston	d	21 27					21 57			22 27				22 57			23 27				
Garrowhill	d	21 29					21 59			22 29				22 59			23 29				
Easterhouse	d	21 32					22 02			22 32				23 02			23 32				
Blairhill	d	21 36					22 06			22 36				23 06			23 36				
Coatbridge Sunnyside	d	21 38					22 08			22 38				23 08			23 38				
Coatdyke	d	21 41					22 11			22 41				23 11			23 41				
Airdrie	a	21 44					22 14			22 44				23 14			23 44				
	d	21 45					22 15			22 45				23 15			23 45				
Drumgelloch	a	21 48					22 18			22 48				23 18			23 48				
Bridgeton	d		21 29		21 39			21 59	22 09		22 29	22 39			22 59	23 09					
Dalmarnock	d																				
Rutherglen	d		21 32		21 42	21 47		22 02	22 12		22 32	22 42	22 47		23 02	23 12					
Cambuslang	d		21 36		21 46			22 06	22 16		22 36	22 46			23 06	23 16					
Newton	d		21 39					22 09			22 39				23 09						
Blantyre	d		21 43			21 55		22 13			22 43		22 55		23 13						
Hamilton West	d		21 46			21 58		22 16			22 46		22 58		23 16						
Hamilton Central	d		21 50			22 01		22 20			22 50		23 01		23 20						
Chatelherault	d					22 06							23 06								
Merryton	d					22 09							23 09								
Larkhall	a					22 13							23 11								
Airbles	d		21 55					22 25			22 55				23 25						
Uddingston	d				21 50				22 20			22 50				23 20					
Bellshill	d				21 55				22 25			22 55				23 25					
Motherwell	a		21 57		22 03			22 27	22 33		22 57	23 06			23 27	23 33					
	d								22 33												
Whifflet	a																				
Coatbridge Central	a																				
Shieldmuir	d								22 37												
Holytown	d																				
Wishaw	d								22 40												
Carluke	d								22 47												
Lanark	a								22 59												

For general notes see front of timetable
For details of catering facilities see Directory of Train Operators

§ Low Level

A From Oban and from Mallaig (Table 227)

B Fort William to Edinburgh (Table 227). Also conveys through Sleeping Car accommodation from Fort William to London Euston (Tables 65 and 404)

b Helensburgh Upper

c Glasgow Queen Street High Level

Table 226

from 30 December

Helensburgh, Balloch, Dalmuir and Milngavie → Glasgow → Springburn, Airdrie, Drumgelloch, Hamilton, Larkhall, Motherwell, Coatbridge and Lanark

Network Diagram - see first page of Table 220

		SR	SR	SR	SR	SR	SR	SR	SR	SR	SR	SR		SR	SR	SR	SR	SR	SR	SR	SR	SR	SR	SR	SR
Helensburgh Central	d			07 55			08 25				08 55				09 25				09 55			10 25			
Craigendoran	d			07 58			08 28				08 58				09 28				09 58			10 28			
Cardross	d			08 03			08 33				09 03				09 33				10 03			10 33			
Balloch	d				08 09			08 39				09 09				09 39				10 09			10 39		
Alexandria	d				08 11			08 41				09 11				09 41				10 11			10 41		
Renton	d				08 14			08 44				09 14				09 44				10 14			10 44		
Dalreoch	d			08 08	08 17		08 38	08 47			09 08	09 17			09 38	09 47			10 08	10 17		10 38	10 47		
Dumbarton Central	d			08 10	08 18		08 40	08 48			09 10	09 18			09 40	09 48			10 10	10 18		10 40	10 48		
Dumbarton East	d			08 12	08 20		08 42	08 50			09 12	09 20			09 42	09 50			10 12	10 20		10 42	10 50		
Bowling	d				08 24			08 54				09 24				09 54				10 24			10 54		
Kilpatrick	d				08 28			08 58				09 28				09 58				10 28			10 58		
Dalmuir	a			08 19	08 30		08 49	09 00			09 19	09 30			09 49	10 00			10 19	10 30		10 49	11 00		
	d	07 50	08 01	08 20	08 31		08 50	09 01			09 20	09 31			09 50	10 01			10 20	10 31		10 50	11 01		
Singer	d	07 52		08 22			08 52				09 22				09 52				10 22			10 52			
Drumry	d	07 55		08 25			08 55				09 25				09 55				10 25			10 55			
Drumchapel	d	07 57		08 27			08 57				09 27				09 57				10 27			10 57			
Milngavie	d								09 11					09 41			10 11				10 41			11 11	
Hillfoot	d								09 14					09 44			10 14				10 44			11 14	
Bearsden	d								09 16					09 46			10 16				10 46			11 16	
Westerton	d	08 00		08 30			09 00		09 19		09 30			09 49	10 00		10 19		10 30		10 49	11 00		11 19	
Anniesland	d	08 03		08 33			09 03		09 22		09 33			09 52	10 03		10 22		10 33		10 52	11 03		11 22	
Clydebank	d		08 03		08 33			09 03				09 33				10 03				10 33			11 03		
Yoker	d		08 05		08 35			09 05				09 35				10 05				10 35			11 05		
Garscadden	d		08 09		08 39			09 09				09 39				10 09				10 39			11 09		
Scotstounhill	d		08 11		08 41			09 11				09 41				10 11				10 41			11 11		
Jordanhill	d		08 13		08 43			09 13				09 43				10 13				10 43			11 13		
Hyndland	d	08 05	08 15	08 35	08 45	08 55	09 05	09 15	09 25		09 35	09 45		09 55	10 05	10 15	10 25		10 35	10 45	10 55	11 05	11 15	11 25	
Partick	d	08 08	08 18	08 38	08 48	08 58	09 08	09 18	09 28	09 34	09 38	09 48		09 58	10 08	10 18	10 28	10 34	10 38	10 48	10 58	11 08	11 18	11 28	11 34
Exhibition Centre	d		08 21		08 51	09 01		09 21	09 31	09 37		09 51		10 01		10 21	10 31	10 37		10 51	11 01		11 21	11 31	11 37
Anderston	d																								
Glasgow Central 15 §	a		08 23		08 53	09 03		09 23	09 33	09 39		09 53		10 03		10 23	10 33	10 39		10 53	11 03		11 23	11 33	11 39
	d		08 24		08 54	09 04		09 24	09 34	09 40		09 54		10 04		10 24	10 34	10 40		10 54	11 04		11 24	11 34	11 40
Argyle Street	d											09 56		10 06		10 26	10 36	10 42		10 56	11 06		11 26	11 36	11 42
Charing Cross	d	08 13		08 43			09 13				09 43				10 13				10 43			11 13			
Glasgow Queen Street 10 §	a	08 15		08 45			09 15				09 45				10 15				10 45			11 15			
	d	08 17		08 47			09 17				09 47				10 17				10 47			11 17			
High Street	d	08 19		08 49			09 19				09 49				10 19				10 49			11 19			
Bellgrove	d	08 21		08 51			09 21				09 51				10 21				10 51			11 21			
Duke Street	d																								
Alexandra Parade	d																								
Barnhill	d																								
Springburn	a																								
Carntyne	d	08 24		08 54			09 24				09 54				10 24				10 54			11 24			
Shettleston	d	08 27		08 57			09 27				09 57				10 27				10 57			11 27			
Garrowhill	d	08 29		08 59			09 29				09 59				10 29				10 59			11 29			
Easterhouse	d	08 32		09 02			09 32				10 02				10 32				11 02			11 32			
Blairhill	d	08 36		09 06			09 36				10 06				10 36				11 06			11 36			
Coatbridge Sunnyside	d	08 38		09 08			09 38				10 08				10 38				11 08			11 38			
Coatdyke	d	08 41		09 11			09 41				10 11				10 41				11 11			11 41			
Airdrie	a	08 44		09 14			09 44				10 14				10 44				11 14			11 44			
	d	08 45		09 15			09 45				10 15				10 45				11 15			11 45			
Drumgelloch	a	08 48		09 18			09 48				10 18				10 48				11 18			11 48			
Bridgeton	d		08 29		08 59	09 09		09 29	09 39			09 59		10 09		10 29	10 39			10 59	11 09		11 29	11 39	
Dalmarnock	d																								
Rutherglen	d		08 32		09 02	09 12		09 32	09 42	09 47		10 02		10 12		10 32	10 42	10 47		11 02	11 12		11 32	11 42	11 47
Cambuslang	d		08 36		09 06	09 16		09 36	09 46			10 06		10 16		10 36	10 46			11 06	11 16		11 36	11 46	
Newton	d				09 09			09 39				10 09				10 39				11 09			11 39		
Blantyre	d				09 13			09 43		09 55		10 13				10 43		10 55		11 13			11 43		11 55
Hamilton West	d				09 16			09 46		09 58		10 16				10 46		10 58		11 16			11 46		11 58
Hamilton Central	d				09 20			09 50		10 01		10 20				10 50		11 01		11 20			11 50		12 01
Chatelherault	d									10 06								11 06							12 06
Merryton	d									10 09								11 09							12 09
Larkhall	a									10 11								11 15							12 12
Airbles	d				09 25			09 55				10 25				10 55				11 25			11 55		
Uddingston	d		08 40			09 20			09 50					10 20			10 50				11 20			11 50	
Bellshill	d		08 45			09 25			09 55					10 25			10 55				11 25			11 55	
Motherwell	a		08 53		09 27	09 33		09 57	10 03			10 27		10 33		10 57	11 03			11 27	11 33		11 57	12 03	
	d					09 33								10 33							11 33				
Whifflet	a																								
Coatbridge Central	a																								
Shieldmuir	d					09 37								10 37							11 37				
Holytown	d																								
Wishaw	d					09 40								10 40							11 40				
Carluke	d					09 47								10 47							11 47				
Lanark	a					09 59								10 59							11 59				

For general notes see front of timetable
For details of catering facilities see
Directory of Train Operators

§ Low Level

Table 226

Sundays

from 30 December

Helensburgh, Balloch, Dalmuir and Milngavie → Glasgow → Springburn, Airdrie, Drumgelloch, Hamilton, Larkhall, Motherwell, Coatbridge and Lanark

Network Diagram - see first page of Table 220

		SR		SR	SR	SR	SR	SR	SR	SR	SR	SR	SR	SR		SR	SR	SR	SR	SR	SR	SR	SR	SR	SR
Helensburgh Central	d	10 55				11 25				11 55			12 25					12 55			13 25				13 55
Craigendoran	d	10 58				11 28				11 58			12 28					12 58			13 28				13 58
Cardross	d	11 03				11 33				12 03			12 33					13 03			13 33				14 03
Balloch	d			11 09			11 39				12 09			12 39					13 09			13 39			
Alexandria	d			11 11			11 41				12 11			12 41					13 11			13 41			
Renton	d			11 14			11 44				12 14			12 44					13 14			13 44			
Dalreoch	d	11 08		11 17		11 38	11 47			12 08	12 17		12 38	12 47				13 08	13 17		13 38	13 47			14 08
Dumbarton Central	d	11 10		11 18		11 40	11 48			12 10	12 18		12 40	12 48				13 10	13 18		13 40	13 48			14 10
Dumbarton East	d	11 12		11 20		11 42	11 50			12 12	12 20		12 42	12 50				13 12	13 20		13 42	13 50			14 12
Bowling	d			11 24			11 54				12 24			12 54					13 24			13 54			
Kilpatrick	d			11 28			11 58				12 28			12 58					13 28			13 58			
Dalmuir	a	11 19		11 30		11 49	12 00			12 19	12 30		12 49	13 00				13 19	13 30		13 49	14 00			14 19
	d	11 20		11 31		11 50	12 01			12 20	12 31		12 50	13 01				13 20	13 31		13 50	14 01			14 20
Singer	d	11 22				11 52				12 22			12 52					13 22			13 52				14 22
Drumry	d	11 25				11 55				12 25			12 55					13 25			13 55				14 25
Drumchapel	d	11 27				11 57				12 27			12 57					13 27			13 57				14 27
Milngavie	d				11 41			12 11				12 41				13 11				13 41			14 11		
Hillfoot	d				11 44			12 14				12 44				13 14				13 44			14 14		
Bearsden	d				11 46			12 16				12 46				13 16				13 46			14 16		
Westerton	d	11 30			11 49	12 00		12 19		12 30		12 49	13 00			13 19		13 30		13 49	14 00		14 19		14 30
Anniesland	d	11 33			11 52	12 03		12 22		12 33		12 52	13 03			13 22		13 33		13 52	14 03		14 22		14 33
Clydebank	d			11 33			12 03				12 33			13 03					13 33			14 03			
Yoker	d			11 35			12 05				12 35			13 05					13 35			14 05			
Garscadden	d			11 39			12 09				12 39			13 09					13 39			14 09			
Scotstounhill	d			11 41			12 11				12 41			13 11					13 41			14 11			
Jordanhill	d			11 43			12 13				12 43			13 13					13 43			14 13			
Hyndland	d	11 35		11 45	11 55	12 05	12 15	12 25		12 35	12 45	12 55	13 05	13 15		13 25		13 35	13 45	13 55	14 05	14 15	14 25		14 35
Partick	d	11 38		11 48	11 58	12 08	12 18	12 28	12 34	12 38	12 48	12 58	13 08	13 18		13 28	13 34	13 38	13 48	13 58	14 08	14 18	14 28	14 34	14 38
Exhibition Centre	d			11 51	12 01		12 21	12 31	12 37		12 51	13 01		13 21		13 31	13 37		13 51	14 01		14 21	14 31	14 37	
Anderston	d																								
Glasgow Central 15 §	a			11 53	12 03		12 23	12 33	12 39		12 53	13 03		13 23		13 33	13 39		13 53	14 03		14 23	14 33	14 39	
	d			11 54	12 04		12 24	12 34	12 40		12 54	13 04		13 24		13 34	13 40		13 54	14 04		14 24	14 34	14 40	
Argyle Street	d			11 56	12 06		12 26	12 36	12 42		12 56	13 06		13 26		13 36	13 42		13 56	14 06		14 26	14 36	14 42	
Charing Cross	d	11 43				12 13				12 43			13 13					13 43			14 13				14 43
Glasgow Queen Street 10 §	a	11 45				12 15				12 45			13 15					13 45			14 15				14 45
	d	11 47				12 17				12 47			13 17					13 47			14 17				14 47
High Street	d	11 49				12 19				12 49			13 19					13 49			14 19				14 49
Bellgrove	d	11 51				12 21				12 51			13 21					13 51			14 21				14 51
Duke Street	d																								
Alexandra Parade	d																								
Barnhill	d																								
Springburn	a																								
Carntyne	d	11 54				12 24				12 54			13 24					13 54			14 24				14 54
Shettleston	d	11 57				12 27				12 57			13 27					13 57			14 27				14 57
Garrowhill	d	11 59				12 29				12 59			13 29					13 59			14 29				14 59
Easterhouse	d	12 02				12 32				13 02			13 32					14 02			14 32				15 02
Blairhill	d	12 06				12 36				13 06			13 36					14 06			14 36				15 06
Coatbridge Sunnyside	d	12 08				12 38				13 08			13 38					14 08			14 38				15 08
Coatdyke	d	12 11				12 41				13 11			13 41					14 11			14 41				15 11
Airdrie	a	12 14				12 44				13 14			13 44					14 14			14 44				15 14
	d	12 15				12 45				13 15			13 45					14 15			14 45				15 15
Drumgelloch	a	12 18				12 48				13 18			13 48					14 18			14 48				15 18
Bridgeton	d			11 59	12 09		12 29	12 39			12 59	13 09		13 29		13 39			13 59	14 09		14 29	14 39		
Dalmarnock	d																								
Rutherglen	d			12 02	12 12		12 32	12 42	12 47		13 02	13 12		13 32		13 42	13 47		14 02	14 12		14 32	14 42	14 47	
Cambuslang	d			12 06	12 16		12 36	12 46			13 06	13 16		13 36		13 46			14 06	14 16		14 36	14 46		
Newton	d			12 09			12 39				13 09			13 39					14 09			14 39			
Blantyre	d			12 13			12 43		12 55		13 13			13 43			13 55		14 13			14 43		14 55	
Hamilton West	d			12 16			12 46		12 58		13 16			13 46			13 58		14 16			14 46		14 58	
Hamilton Central	d			12 20			12 50		13 01		13 20			13 50			14 01		14 20			14 50		15 01	
Chatelherault	d								13 06								14 06							15 06	
Merryton	d								13 09								14 09							15 09	
Larkhall	a								13 15								14 11							15 11	
Airbles	d			12 25			12 55				13 25			13 55					14 25			14 55			
Uddingston	d				12 20			12 50				13 20				13 50				14 20			14 50		
Bellshill	d				12 25			12 55				13 25				13 55				14 25			14 55		
Motherwell	a			12 27	12 33		12 57	13 03			13 27	13 33		13 57		14 03			14 27	14 33		14 57	15 03		
	d				12 33							13 33								14 33					
Whifflet	a																								
Coatbridge Central	a																								
Shieldmuir	d				12 37							13 37								14 37					
Holytown	d																								
Wishaw	d				12 40							13 40								14 40					
Carluke	d				12 47							13 47								14 47					
Lanark	a				12 59							13 59								14 59					

For general notes see front of timetable
For details of catering facilities see Directory of Train Operators

§ Low Level

Table 226

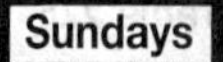

Helensburgh, Balloch, Dalmuir and Milngavie → Glasgow → Springburn, Airdrie, Drumgelloch, Hamilton, Larkhall, Motherwell, Coatbridge and Lanark

Sundays from 30 December

Network Diagram - see first page of Table 220

		SR	SR	SR	SR	SR ◇ A	SR	SR	SR	SR	SR	SR	SR	SR	SR	SR	SR	SR	SR	SR	SR	SR	SR
Helensburgh Central	d			14 25		14b39			14 55			15 25				15 55			16 25				16 55
Craigendoran	d			14 28					14 58			15 28				15 58			16 28				16 58
Cardross	d			14 33					15 03			15 33				16 03			16 33				17 03
Balloch	d	14 09			14 39					15 09			15 39				16 09			16 39			
Alexandria	d	14 11			14 41					15 11			15 41				16 11			16 41			
Renton	d	14 14			14 44					15 14			15 44				16 14			16 44			
Dalreoch	d	14 17		14 38	14 47				15 08	15 17		15 38	15 47			16 08	16 17		16 38	16 47			17 08
Dumbarton Central	d	14 18		14 40	14 48	14 53			15 10	15 18		15 40	15 48			16 10	16 18		16 40	16 48			17 10
Dumbarton East	d	14 20		14 42	14 50				15 12	15 20		15 42	15 50			16 12	16 20		16 42	16 50			17 12
Bowling	d	14 24			14 54					15 24			15 54				16 24			16 54			
Kilpatrick	d	14 28			14 58					15 28			15 58				16 28			16 58			
Dalmuir	a	14 30		14 49	15 00	15 05			15 19	15 30		15 49	16 00			16 19	16 30		16 49	17 00			17 19
	d	14 31		14 50	15 01	15 05			15 20	15 31		15 50	16 01			16 20	16 31		16 50	17 01			17 20
Singer	d			14 52					15 22			15 52				16 22			16 52				17 22
Drumry	d			14 55					15 25			15 55				16 25			16 55				17 25
Drumchapel	d			14 57					15 27			15 57				16 27			16 57				17 27
Milngavie	d		14 41				15 11				15 41			16 11				16 41			17 11		
Hillfoot	d		14 44				15 14				15 44			16 14				16 44			17 14		
Bearsden	d		14 46				15 16				15 46			16 16				16 46			17 16		
Westerton	d		14 49	15 00			15 19		15 30		15 49	16 00		16 19		16 30		16 49	17 00		17 19		17 30
Anniesland	d		14 52	15 03			15 22		15 33		15 52	16 03		16 22		16 33		16 52	17 03		17 22		17 33
Clydebank	d	14 33			15 03					15 33			16 03				16 33			17 03			
Yoker	d	14 35			15 05					15 35			16 05				16 35			17 05			
Garscadden	d	14 39			15 09					15 39			16 09				16 39			17 09			
Scotstounhill	d	14 41			15 11					15 41			16 11				16 41			17 11			
Jordanhill	d	14 43			15 13					15 43			16 13				16 43			17 13			
Hyndland	d	14 45	14 55	15 05	15 15		15 25		15 35	15 45	15 55	16 05	16 15	16 25		16 35	16 45	16 55	17 05	17 15	17 25		17 35
Partick	d	14 48	14 58	15 08	15 18		15 28	15 34	15 38	15 48	15 58	16 08	16 18	16 28	16 34	16 38	16 48	16 58	17 08	17 18	17 28	17 34	17 38
Exhibition Centre	d	14 51	15 01		15 21		15 31	15 37		15 51	16 01		16 21	16 31	16 37		16 51	17 01		17 21	17 31	17 37	
Anderston	d																						
Glasgow Central 15 §	a	14 53	15 03		15 23		15 33	15 39		15 53	16 03		16 23	16 33	16 39		16 53	17 03		17 23	17 33	17 39	
	d	14 54	15 04		15 24		15 34	15 40		15 54	16 04		16 24	16 34	16 40		16 54	17 04		17 24	17 34	17 40	
Argyle Street	d	14 56	15 06		15 26		15 36	15 42		15 56	16 06		16 26	16 36	16 42		16 56	17 06		17 26	17 36	17 42	
Charing Cross	d			15 13					15 43			16 13				16 43			17 13				17 43
Glasgow Queen Street 10 §	a			15 15		15c29			15 45			16 15				16 45			17 15				17 45
	d			15 17					15 47			16 17				16 47			17 17				17 47
High Street	d			15 19					15 49			16 19				16 49			17 19				17 49
Bellgrove	d			15 21					15 51			16 21				16 51			17 21				17 51
Duke Street	d																						
Alexandra Parade	d																						
Barnhill	d																						
Springburn	a																						
Carntyne	d			15 24					15 54			16 24				16 54			17 24				17 54
Shettleston	d			15 27					15 57			16 27				16 57			17 27				17 57
Garrowhill	d			15 29					15 59			16 29				16 59			17 29				17 59
Easterhouse	d			15 32					16 02			16 32				17 02			17 32				18 02
Blairhill	d			15 36					16 06			16 36				17 06			17 36				18 06
Coatbridge Sunnyside	d			15 38					16 08			16 38				17 08			17 38				18 08
Coatdyke	d			15 41					16 11			16 41				17 11			17 41				18 11
Airdrie	a			15 44					16 14			16 44				17 14			17 44				18 14
	d			15 45					16 15			16 45				17 15			17 45				18 15
Drumgelloch	a			15 48					16 18			16 48				17 18			17 48				18 18
Bridgeton	d	14 59	15 09		15 29		15 39			15 59	16 09		16 29	16 39			16 59	17 09		17 29	17 39		
Dalmarnock	d																						
Rutherglen	d	15 02	15 12		15 32		15 42	15 47		16 02	16 12		16 32	16 42	16 47		17 02	17 12		17 32	17 42	17 47	
Cambuslang	d	15 06	15 16		15 36		15 46			16 06	16 16		16 36	16 46			17 06	17 16		17 36	17 46		
Newton	d	15 09			15 39					16 09			16 39				17 09			17 39			
Blantyre	d	15 13			15 43			15 55		16 13			16 43		16 55		17 13			17 43		17 55	
Hamilton West	d	15 16			15 46			15 58		16 16			16 46		16 58		17 16			17 46		17 58	
Hamilton Central	d	15 20			15 50			16 01		16 20			16 50		17 01		17 20			17 50		18 01	
Chatelherault	d							16 06							17 06							18 06	
Merryton	d							16 09							17 09							18 09	
Larkhall	a							16 15							17 11							18 11	
Airbles	d	15 25			15 55					16 25			16 55				17 25			17 55			
Uddingston	d		15 20				15 50				16 20			16 50				17 20			17 50		
Bellshill	d		15 25				15 55				16 25			16 55				17 25			17 55		
Motherwell	a	15 27	15 33		15 57		16 01			16 27	16 33		16 57	17 03			17 27	17 33		17 57	18 03		
	d		15 33								16 33							17 33					
Whifflet	a																						
Coatbridge Central	a																						
Shieldmuir	d		15 37								16 37							17 37					
Holytown	d																						
Wishaw	d		15 40								16 40							17 40					
Carluke	d		15 47								16 47							17 47					
Lanark	a		15 59								16 59							17 59					

For general notes see front of timetable
For details of catering facilities see Directory of Train Operators

§ Low Level

A From 23 March. From Oban (Table 227)

b Helensburgh Upper

c Glasgow Central High Level

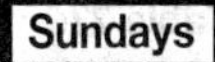

from 30 December

Helensburgh, Balloch, Dalmuir and Milngavie → Glasgow → Springburn, Airdrie, Drumgelloch, Hamilton, Larkhall, Motherwell, Coatbridge and Lanark

Network Diagram - see first page of Table 220

Station		SR	SR	SR	SR	SR		SR	SR	SR	SR	SR	SR	SR	SR	SR	SR	SR		SR	SR	SR	SR	SR	SR
Helensburgh Central	d			17 25					17 55			18 25				18 55				19 25				19 55	
Craigendoran	d			17 28					17 58			18 28				18 58				19 28				19 58	
Cardross	d			17 33					18 03			18 33				19 03				19 33				20 03	
Balloch	d	17 09			17 39					18 09			18 39				19 09				19 39				20 09
Alexandria	d	17 11			17 41					18 11			18 41				19 11				19 41				20 11
Renton	d	17 14			17 44					18 14			18 44				19 14				19 44				20 14
Dalreoch	d	17 17		17 38	17 47				18 08	18 17		18 38	18 47			19 08	19 17			19 38	19 47			20 08	20 17
Dumbarton Central	d	17 18		17 40	17 48				18 10	18 18		18 40	18 48			19 10	19 18			19 40	19 48			20 10	20 18
Dumbarton East	d	17 20		17 42	17 50				18 12	18 20		18 42	18 50			19 12	19 20			19 42	19 50			20 12	20 20
Bowling	d	17 24			17 54					18 24			18 54				19 24				19 54				20 24
Kilpatrick	d	17 28			17 58					18 28			18 58				19 28				19 58				20 28
Dalmuir	a	17 30		17 49	18 00				18 19	18 30		18 49	19 00			19 19	19 30			19 49	20 00			20 19	20 30
	d	17 31		17 50	18 01				18 20	18 31		18 50	19 01			19 20	19 31			19 50	20 01			20 20	20 31
Singer	d			17 52					18 22			18 52				19 22				19 52				20 22	
Drumry	d			17 55					18 25			18 55				19 25				19 55				20 25	
Drumchapel	d			17 57					18 27			18 57				19 27				19 57				20 27	
Milngavie	d		17 41			18 11					18 41			19 11				19 41				20 11			
Hillfoot	d		17 44			18 14					18 44			19 14				19 44				20 14			
Bearsden	d		17 46			18 16					18 46			19 16				19 46				20 16			
Westerton	d		17 49	18 00		18 19			18 30		18 49	19 00		19 19		19 30		19 49		20 00		20 19		20 30	
Anniesland	d		17 52	18 03		18 22			18 33		18 52	19 03		19 22		19 33		19 52		20 03		20 22		20 33	
Clydebank	d	17 33			18 03					18 33			19 03				19 33				20 03				20 33
Yoker	d	17 35			18 05					18 35			19 05				19 35				20 05				20 35
Garscadden	d	17 39			18 09					18 39			19 09				19 39				20 09				20 39
Scotstounhill	d	17 41			18 11					18 41			19 11				19 41				20 11				20 41
Jordanhill	d	17 43			18 13					18 43			19 13				19 43				20 13				20 43
Hyndland	d	17 45	17 55	18 05	18 15	18 25			18 35	18 45	18 55	19 05	19 15	19 25		19 35	19 45	19 55		20 05	20 15	20 25		20 35	20 45
Partick	d	17 48	17 58	18 08	18 18	18 28		18 34	18 38	18 48	18 58	19 08	19 18	19 28	19 34	19 38	19 48	19 58		20 08	20 18	20 28	20 34	20 38	20 48
Exhibition Centre	d	17 51	18 01		18 21	18 31		18 37		18 51	19 01		19 21	19 31	19 37		19 51	20 01			20 21	20 31	20 37		20 51
Anderston	d																								
Glasgow Central 15 §	a	17 53	18 03		18 23	18 33		18 39		18 53	19 03		19 23	19 33	19 39		19 53	20 03			20 23	20 33	20 39		20 53
	d	17 54	18 04		18 24	18 34		18 40		18 54	19 04		19 24	19 34	19 40		19 54	20 04			20 24	20 34	20 40		20 54
Argyle Street	d	17 56	18 06														19 56								
Charing Cross	d			18 13					18 43			19 13				19 43				20 13				20 43	
Glasgow Queen Street 10 §	a			18 15					18 45			19 15				19 45				20 15				20 45	
	d			18 17					18 47			19 17				19 47				20 17				20 47	
High Street	d			18 19					18 49			19 19				19 49				20 19				20 49	
Bellgrove	d			18 21					18 51			19 21				19 51				20 21				20 51	
Duke Street	d																								
Alexandra Parade	d																								
Barnhill	d																								
Springburn	a																								
Carntyne	d			18 24					18 54			19 24				19 54				20 24				20 54	
Shettleston	d			18 27					18 57			19 27				19 57				20 27				20 57	
Garrowhill	d			18 29					18 59			19 29				19 59				20 29				20 59	
Easterhouse	d			18 32					19 02			19 32				20 02				20 32				21 02	
Blairhill	d			18 36					19 06			19 36				20 06				20 36				21 06	
Coatbridge Sunnyside	d			18 38					19 08			19 38				20 08				20 38				21 08	
Coatdyke	d			18 41					19 11			19 41				20 11				20 41				21 11	
Airdrie	a			18 44					19 14			19 44				20 14				20 44				21 14	
	d			18 45					19 15			19 45				20 15				20 45				21 15	
Drumgelloch	a			18 48					19 18			19 48				20 18				20 48				21 18	
Bridgeton	d	17 59	18 09		18 29	18 39				18 59	19 09		19 29	19 39			19 59	20 09			20 29	20 39			20 59
Dalmarnock	d																								
Rutherglen	d	18 02	18 12		18 32	18 42		18 47		19 02	19 12		19 32	19 42	19 47		20 02	20 12			20 32	20 42	20 47		21 02
Cambuslang	d	18 06	18 16		18 36	18 46				19 06	19 16		19 36	19 46			20 06	20 16			20 36	20 46			21 06
Newton	d	18 09			18 39					19 09			19 39				20 09				20 39				21 09
Blantyre	d	18 13			18 43			18 55		19 13			19 43		19 55		20 13				20 43		20 55		21 13
Hamilton West	d	18 16			18 46			18 58		19 16			19 46		19 58		20 16				20 46		20 58		21 16
Hamilton Central	d	18 20			18 50			19 01		19 20			19 50		20 01		20 20				20 50		21 01		21 20
Chatelherault	d							19 06							20 06								21 06		
Merryton	d							19 09							20 09								21 09		
Larkhall	a							19 12							20 11								21 11		
Airbles	d	18 25			18 55					19 25			19 55				20 25				20 55				21 25
Uddingston	d		18 20			18 50					19 20			19 50				20 20				20 50			
Bellshill	d		18 25			18 55					19 25			19 55				20 25				20 55			
Motherwell	a	18 27	18 33		18 57	19 03				19 27	19 33		19 57	20 03			20 27	20 33			20 57	21 04			21 27
	d		18 33								19 33							20 33							
Whifflet	a																								
Coatbridge Central	a																								
Shieldmuir	d		18 37								19 37							20 37							
Holytown	d																								
Wishaw	d		18 40								19 40							20 40							
Carluke	d		18 47								19 47							20 47							
Lanark	a		18 59								19 59							20 59							

For general notes see front of timetable
For details of catering facilities see Directory of Train Operators

§ Low Level

Helensburgh, Balloch, Dalmuir and Milngavie → Glasgow → Springburn, Airdrie, Drumgelloch, Hamilton, Larkhall, Motherwell, Coatbridge and Lanark

Sundays from 30 December

Network Diagram - see first page of Table 220

		SR	SR	SR	SR	SR	SR	SR	SR	SR	SR	SR	SR	SR	SR	SR	SR	SR	SR	SR	SR	SR
					◇ A															R B		
Helensburgh Central	d		20 25		20b40			20 55			21 25				21 55			22 25		22b37	22 55	
Craigendoran	d		20 28					20 58			21 28				21 58			22 28			22 58	
Cardross	d		20 33					21 03			21 33				22 03			22 33			23 03	
Balloch	d			20 39					21 09			21 39				22 09			22 39			23 09
Alexandria	d			20 41					21 11			21 41				22 11			22 41			23 11
Renton	d			20 44					21 14			21 44				22 14			22 44			23 14
Dalreoch	d		20 38	20 47				21 08	21 17		21 38	21 47			22 08	22 17		22 38	22 47		23 08	23 17
Dumbarton Central	d		20 40	20 48	20 53			21 10	21 18		21 40	21 48			22 10	22 18		22 40	22 48		23 10	23 18
Dumbarton East	d		20 42	20 50				21 12	21 20		21 42	21 50			22 12	22 20		22 42	22 50		23 12	23 20
Bowling	d			20 54					21 24			21 54				22 24			22 55			23 25
Kilpatrick	d			20 58					21 28			21 58				22 28			22 58			23 28
Dalmuir	a		20 49	21 00	21 05			21 19	21 30		21 49	22 00			22 19	22 30		22 49	23 01	23 02	23 19	23 31
	d		20 50	21 01	21 05			21 20	21 31		21 50	22 01			22 20	22 31		22 50	23 01	23 04		23 31
Singer	d		20 52					21 22			21 52				22 22			22 52				
Drumry	d		20 55					21 25			21 55				22 25			22 55				
Drumchapel	d		20 57					21 27			21 57				22 27			22 57				
Milngavie	d	20 41				21 11				21 41			22 11				22 41					
Hillfoot	d	20 44				21 14				21 44			22 14				22 44					
Bearsden	d	20 46				21 16				21 46			22 16				22 46					
Westerton	d	20 49	21 00			21 19		21 30		21 49	22 00		22 19		22 30		22 49	23 00		23a11		
Anniesland	d	20 52	21 03			21 22		21 33		21 52	22 03		22 22		22 33		22 52	23 03				
Clydebank	d			21 03					21 33			22 03				22 33			23 03			23 33
Yoker	d			21 05					21 35			22 05				22 35			23a05			23a35
Garscadden	d			21 09					21 39			22 09				22 39						
Scotstounhill	d			21 11					21 41			22 11				22 41						
Jordanhill	d			21 13					21 43			22 13				22 43						
Hyndland	d	20 55	21 05	21 15		21 25		21 35	21 45	21 55	22 05	22 15	22 25		22 35	22 45	22 55	23 05				
Partick	d	20 58	21 08	21 18		21 28	21 34	21 38	21 48	21 58	22 08	22 18	22 28	22 34	22 38	22 48	22 58	23 08				
Exhibition Centre	d	21 01		21 21		21 31	21 37		21 51	22 01		22 21	22 31	22 37		22 51	23 01					
Anderston	d																					
Glasgow Central 15 §	a	21 03		21 23		21 33	21 39		21 53	22 03		22 23	22 33	22 39		22 53	23 03					
	d	21 04		21 24		21 34	21 40		21 54	22 04		22 24	22 34	22 40		22 54	23 04					
Argyle Street	d																					
Charing Cross	d		21 13					21 43			22 13				22 43			23 13				
Glasgow Queen Street 10 §	a		21 15		21c27			21 45			22 15				22 45			23 15				
	d		21 17					21 47			22 17				22 47			23 17				
High Street	d		21 19					21 49			22 19				22 49			23 19				
Bellgrove	d		21 21					21 51			22 21				22 51			23 21				
Duke Street	d																					
Alexandra Parade	d																					
Barnhill	d																					
Springburn	a																					
Carntyne	d		21 24					21 54			22 24				22 54			23 24				
Shettleston	d		21 27					21 57			22 27				22 57			23 27				
Garrowhill	d		21 29					21 59			22 29				22 59			23 29				
Easterhouse	d		21 32					22 02			22 32				23 02			23 32				
Blairhill	d		21 36					22 06			22 36				23 06			23 36				
Coatbridge Sunnyside	d		21 38					22 08			22 38				23 08			23 38				
Coatdyke	d		21 41					22 11			22 41				23 11			23 41				
Airdrie	a		21 44					22 14			22 44				23 14			23 44				
	d		21 45					22 15			22 45				23 15			23 45				
Drumgelloch	a		21 48					22 18			22 48				23 18			23 48				
Bridgeton	d	21 09		21 29		21 39			21 59	22 09		22 29	22 39			22 59	23 09					
Dalmarnock	d																					
Rutherglen	d	21 12		21 32		21 42	21 47		22 02	22 12		22 32	22 42	22 47		23 02	23 12					
Cambuslang	d	21 16		21 36		21 46			22 06	22 16		22 36	22 46			23 06	23 16					
Newton	d			21 39					22 09			22 39				23 09						
Blantyre	d			21 43			21 55		22 13			22 43		22 55		23 13						
Hamilton West	d			21 46			21 58		22 16			22 46		22 58		23 16						
Hamilton Central	d			21 50			22 01		22 20			22 50		23 01		23 20						
Chatelherault	d						22 06							23 06								
Merryton	d						22 09							23 09								
Larkhall	a						22 13							23 11								
Airbles	d			21 55					22 25			22 55				23 25						
Uddingston	d	21 20				21 50				22 20			22 50				23 20					
Bellshill	d	21 25				21 55				22 25			22 55				23 25					
Motherwell	a	21 33		21 57		22 03			22 27	22 33		22 57	23 06			23 27	23 33					
	d	21 33								22 33												
Whifflet	a																					
Coatbridge Central	a																					
Shieldmuir	d	21 37								22 37												
Holytown	d																					
Wishaw	d	21 40								22 40												
Carluke	d	21 47								22 47												
Lanark	a	21 59								22 59												

For general notes see front of timetable
For details of catering facilities see Directory of Train Operators

§ Low Level

A From Oban and from Mallaig (Table 227)

B Fort William to Edinburgh (Table 227). Also conveys through Sleeping Car accommodation from Fort William to London Euston (Tables 65 and 404)

b Helensburgh Upper

c Glasgow Central High Level

Network Diagram for Tables 227, 239

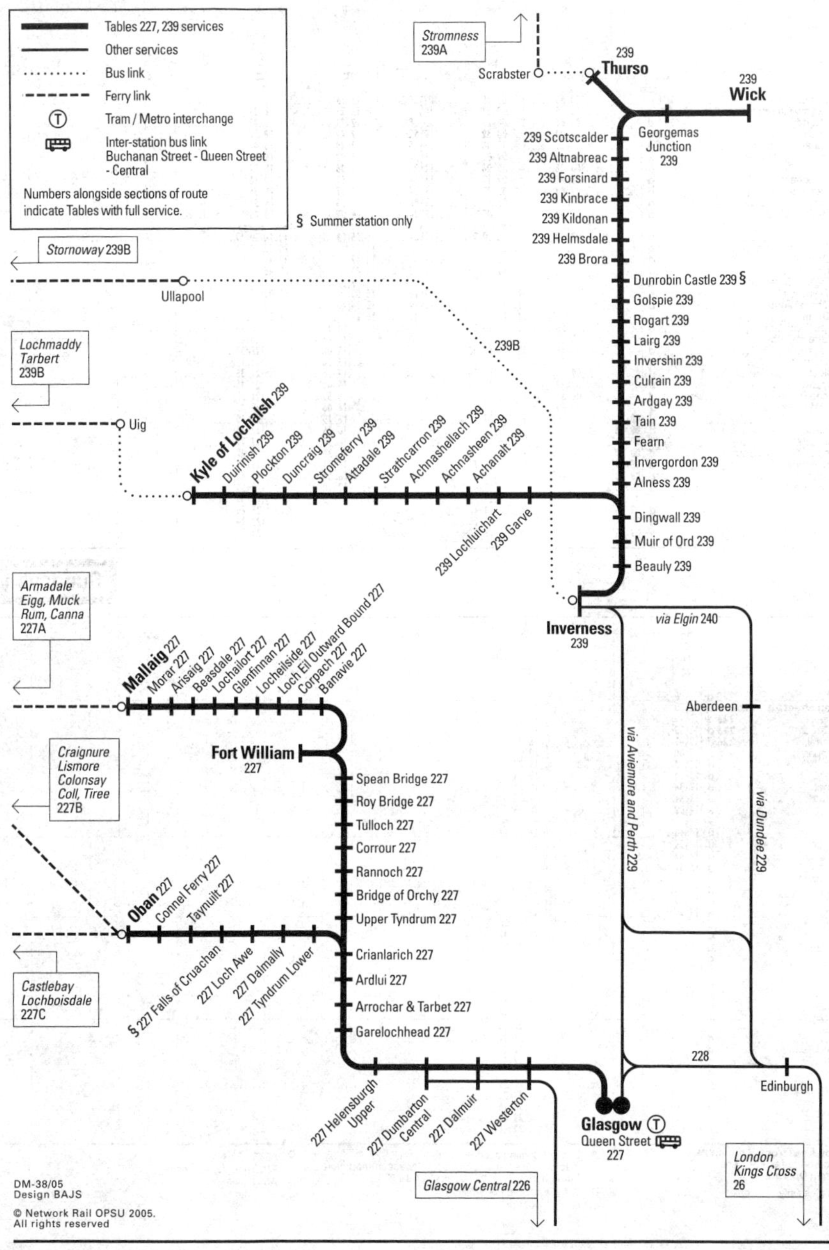
Tables 227, 239 services
Other services
Bus link
Ferry link
Tram / Metro interchange
Inter-station bus link Buchanan Street - Queen Street - Central
Numbers alongside sections of route indicate Tables with full service.
§ Summer station only
Stromness 239A
Scrabster
239 Thurso
239 Wick
Georgemas Junction 239
239 Scotscalder
239 Altnabreac
239 Forsinard
239 Kinbrace
239 Kildonan
239 Helmsdale
239 Brora
Dunrobin Castle 239 §
Golspie 239
Rogart 239
Lairg 239
Invershin 239
Culrain 239
Ardgay 239
Tain 239
Fearn
Invergordon 239
Alness 239
Dingwall 239
Muir of Ord 239
Beauly 239
Inverness 239
Stornoway 239B
Ullapool
239B
Lochmaddy Tarbert 239B
Uig
Kyle of Lochalsh 239
Duirinish 239
Plockton 239
Duncraig 239
Stromeferry 239
Attadale 239
Strathcarron 239
Achnashellach 239
Achnasheen 239
Achanalt 239
239 Lochluichart
239 Garve
via Elgin 240
Aberdeen
via Aviemore and Perth 229
via Dundee 229
Armadale Eigg, Muck Rum, Canna 227A
Mallaig 227
Morar 227
Arisaig 227
Beasdale 227
Lochailort 227
Glenfinnan 227
Locheilside 227
Loch Eil Outward Bound 227
Corpach 227
Banavie 227
Fort William 227
Spean Bridge 227
Roy Bridge 227
Tulloch 227
Corrour 227
Rannoch 227
Bridge of Orchy 227
Upper Tyndrum 227
Crianlarich 227
Ardlui 227
Arrochar & Tarbet 227
Garelochhead 227
Craignure Lismore Colonsay Coll, Tiree 227B
Oban 227
Connel Ferry 227
Taynuilt 227
§ 227 Falls of Cruachan
227 Loch Awe
227 Dalmally
227 Tyndrum Lower
Castlebay Lochboisdale 227C
227 Helensburgh Upper
227 Dumbarton Central
227 Dalmuir
227 Westerton
228
Edinburgh
Glasgow
Queen Street 227
Glasgow Central 226
London Kings Cross 26
DM-38/05
Design BAJS

Glasgow Queen Street → Oban, Fort William and Mallaig

Network Diagram - see first page of Table 227

Miles	Miles			SR	SR	SR		SR SO	SR		SR	
				◇	R A ⊡	◇ B Ⲭ		◇ C Ⲭ	◇ B Ⲭ		◇ B Ⲭ	
—	—	Edinburgh 228	d		04 50	*07 15*		*09 30*	*11 15*		*17 15*	
0	0	**Glasgow Queen Street** 10 226 ⛴	d		*05 30*	08 21		10 37	12 21		18 21	
5½	5½	Westerton 226	d		05 56	*08 23*		*10 38*	*12 23*		*18 23*	
10	10	Dalmuir 226	d		06 04	08 39		10 52	12 42		18 37	
16½	16½	Dumbarton Central 226	d			08 48		11 05	12 48		18 46	
25½	25½	Helensburgh Upper	a		06 26	09 03		11 20	13 03		19 02	
—	—		d		06 28	09 06		11 23	13 06		19 04	
32¼	32¼	Garelochhead	d		06 41	09 17		11 34	13 17		19 16	
43	43	Arrochar & Tarbet	d		07 07	09 37		11 54	13 37		19 36	
51	51	Ardlui	d		07x21	09b53		12 08	13b53		19 51	
59¾	59¾	**Crianlarich**	a		07 42	10 09		12 24	14 09		20 08	
—	—		d		07 43	10 15	10 21	12 27	14 15	14 21	20 14	20 17
64¾	—	Tyndrum Lower	d			10 24		12 36	14 24		20 23	
76¾	—	Dalmally	d			10 42		12c57	14 42		20 41	
79½	—	Loch Awe	d			10 47		13 02	14 47		20 46	
83½	—	Falls of Cruachan §	d									
88½	—	Taynuilt	d			11 03		13 18	15 03		21 02	
95¼	—	Connel Ferry	d			11 14		13 29	15 14		21 13	
101½	—	**Oban**	a			11 27		13 42	15 27		21 26	
—	64½	Upper Tyndrum	d		07 56		10 32			14 32		20 28
—	72½	Bridge of Orchy	d		08 13		10 46			14 46		20 42
—	87¾	Rannoch	d		08e45		11 08			15 08		21c07
—	95	Corrour	d		08x58		11 20			15 20		21 19
—	105	Tulloch	d		09 18		11 36			15 36		21 35
—	110¾	Roy Bridge	d		09x29		11 46			15 46		21 45
—	114	Spean Bridge	d		09 37		11 54			15 53		21 52
—	122¾	**Fort William**	a		09 54		12 07			16 06		22 05
—	—		d	08 30			12 12			16 19		22 10
—	125	Banavie	d	08 36			12 18			16 25		22 16
—	126	Corpach	d	08 41			12 23			16 30		22 21
—	129	Loch Eil Outward Bound	d	08 47			12 29			16 36		22 27
—	132¾	Locheilside	d	08x52			12x34			16x41		22x32
—	139½	Glenfinnan	d	09 03			12 46			16b54		22 43
—	148½	Lochailort	d	09x19			13x01			17x10		22x59
—	153½	Beasdale	d	09x28			13x10			17x19		23x08
—	156¾	Arisaig	d	09 36			13 18			17 27		23 16
—	161½	Morar	d	09 44			13 26			17 35		23 24
—	164¾	**Mallaig**	a	09 52			13 34			17 43		23 31

Sundays

		SR	SR	
		◇ D Ⲭ	◇ B Ⲭ	
Edinburgh 228	d	*11 00*	*17 00*	
Glasgow Queen Street 10 226 ⛴	d	12 20	18 20	
Westerton 226	d	*12 10*	*18 10*	
Dalmuir 226	d	12 35	18 35	
Dumbarton Central 226	d	12 45	18 45	
Helensburgh Upper	a	13 00	19 00	
	d	13 03	19 03	
Garelochhead	d	13 14	19 14	
Arrochar & Tarbet	d	13 34	19 34	
Ardlui	d	13c51	19b52	
Crianlarich	a	14 09	20 08	
	d	14 15	20 14	20 17
Tyndrum Lower	d	14 24	20 23	
Dalmally	d	14 42	20 41	
Loch Awe	d	14 47	20 46	
Falls of Cruachan §	d			
Taynuilt	d	15 03	21 02	
Connel Ferry	d	15 14	21 13	
Oban	a	15 27	21 26	
Upper Tyndrum	d			20 28
Bridge of Orchy	d			20 42
Rannoch	d			21 07
Corrour	d			21 19
Tulloch	d			21 35
Roy Bridge	d			21 45
Spean Bridge	d			21 52
Fort William	a			22 05
	d			22 10
Banavie	d			22 16
Corpach	d			22 21
Loch Eil Outward Bound	d			22 27
Locheilside	d			22x32
Glenfinnan	d			22 43
Lochailort	d			22x59
Beasdale	d			23x08
Arisaig	d			23 16
Morar	d			23 24
Mallaig	a			23 31

For general notes see front of timetable
For details of catering facilities see Directory of Train Operators

§ Summer Station Only

A Limited Seating accommodation. Also conveys through Sleeping Car accommodation from London Euston (Tables 65 and 404)
B Ⲭ to Oban and Fort William
C From 22 March
D From 23 March
b Arr. 3 minutes earlier
c Arr. 4 minutes earlier
e Arr. 5 minutes earlier

Mallaig, Fort William and Oban → Glasgow Queen Street

Network Diagram - see first page Table 227

Miles	Miles			SR SX A	SR ◇ 🛒	SR ◇ B 🛒	SR ◇ 🛒	SR ◇ B 🛒	SR SO ◇ C 🛒	SR ◇ B 🛒	SR ◇ 🛒	SR ◇	SR SX R D 🛏
—	0	**Mallaig**	d			06 03		10 10		16 05		18 15	
—	3	Morar	d			06 09		10 16		16 11		18 21	
—	7½	Arisaig	d			06 19		10 26		16 21		18 31	
—	11	Beasdale	d			06x25		10x32		16x27		18x37	
—	15¾	Lochailort	d			06x34		10x41		16x36		18x46	
—	25	Glenfinnan	d			06 51		10 58		16 51		19 03	
—	31½	Locheilside	d			07x01		11x08		17x01		19x11	
—	35¼	Loch Eil Outward Bound	d			07 07		11 14		17 07		19 17	
—	38¼	Corpach	d			07 13		11 20		17 13		19 23	
—	39¼	Banavie	d			07 17		11 24		17 17		19 27	
—	41½	**Fort William**	a			07 25		11 32		17 27		19 37	
—	—		d			07 42		11 40		17 37			19 50
—	50¼	Spean Bridge	d			07 55		11 53		17 50			20 10
—	53½	Roy Bridge	d			08 02		12 00		17 57			20x17
—	59¼	Tulloch	d			08 13		12 11		18 08			20 30
—	69¼	Corrour	d			08 30		12 28		18 25			20x51
—	76½	Rannoch	d			08b43		12b43		18 36			21b06
—	92	Bridge of Orchy	d			09 03		13 02		18 56			21 34
—	99¾	Upper Tyndrum	d			09b19		13 18		19 12			21 52
0	—	**Oban**	d		08 11		12 11		16 11		18 11		
6¼	—	Connel Ferry	d		08 23		12 23		16 27		18 23		
13	—	Taynuilt	d		08 35		12 35		16 39		18 35		
18½	—	Falls of Cruachan §	d										
22	—	Loch Awe	d		08 50		12 50		16 53		18 50		
24¾	—	Dalmally	d		08 56		12 56		17 00		18 56		
36¾	—	Tyndrum Lower	d		09 15		13 15		17 19		19 15		
42	104½	**Crianlarich**	a		09 28	09 30	13 29	13 30	17 28	19 26	19 27		22 04
—	—		d			09 35		13 36	17 31	19 33			22 05
50¾	113¼	Ardlui	d			09 52		13 52	17 47	19c53			22x26
58¾	121¼	Arrochar & Tarbet	d	07 08		10 07		14 07	18 02	20 08			22 44
69½	132	Garelochhead	d	07 30		10b29		14 27	18 22	20 28			23 10
76¼	138¾	Helensburgh Upper	a	07 41		10 39		14 38	18 33	20 39			23 23
—	—		d	07 42		10 41		14 39	18 34	20 40			23 24
85¼	147¾	Dumbarton Central 226	a	07 57		10 58		14 52	18 47	20 53			
92½	154¼	Dalmuir 226	a			11 08		15 04	18 56	21 04			23 49
96	157¾	Westerton 226	a			*11 25*		*15 25*	*19 10*	*21 29*			23 56
101½	164¼	**Glasgow Queen Street** 10 226 ⛴	a	08 37		11 28		15 28	19 18	21 29			*00 19*
—	—	Edinburgh 228	a	*09 48*		*12e35*		*16 39*	*20 22*	*22 51*			00 50

For general notes see front of timetable
For details of catering facilities see Directory of Train Operators

§ Summer Station Only

A Also stops at Singer 0806, Maryhill 0816 and Possilpark & Parkhouse 0821 (Tables 226 and 232)
B 🛒 from Fort William
C From 22 March
D Limited Seating accommodation. Also conveys through Sleeping Car accommodation to London Euston (Tables 65 and 404)
b Arr. 3 minutes earlier
c Arr. 5 minutes earlier
e Saturdays arr. 1236

Table 227

Sundays

Mallaig, Fort William and Oban → Glasgow Queen Street

Network Diagram - see first page Table 227

		SR ◇ A 🍴	SR ◇ B 🍴	SR ◇ 🍴	SR 🅁 C 🛏
Mallaig	d		16 05		
Morar	d		16 11		
Arisaig	d		16 21		
Beasdale	d		16x27		
Lochailort	d		16x36		
Glenfinnan	d		16 53		
Locheilside	d		17x03		
Loch Eil Outward Bound	d		17 09		
Corpach	d		17 15		
Banavie	d		17 19		
Fort William	a		17 27		
	d		17 37		19 00
Spean Bridge	d		17 50		19 20
Roy Bridge	d		17 57		19x27
Tulloch	d		18 08		19 40
Corrour	d		18 25		20x01
Rannoch	d		18 36		20 15
Bridge of Orchy	d		18 56		20b47
Upper Tyndrum	d		19 12		21c05
Oban	d	12 11		18 11	
Connel Ferry	d	12 23		18 23	
Taynuilt	d	12 35		18 35	
Falls of Cruachan §	d				
Loch Awe	d	12 50		18 50	
Dalmally	d	12 56		18 56	
Tyndrum Lower	d	13 15		19 15	
Crianlarich	a	13 29	19 26	19 27	21 16
	d	13 36	19 33		21 18
Ardlui	d	13 52	19e53		21x39
Arrochar & Tarbet	d	14 07	20 08		21 57
Garelochhead	d	14 27	20 28		22 23
Helensburgh Upper	a	14 38	20 39		22 35
	d	14 39	20 40		22 37
Dumbarton Central 226	a	14 53	20 53		
Dalmuir 226	a	15 05	21 05		23 02
Westerton 226	a	*15 30*	*21 30*		23 11
Glasgow Queen Street 10 226 ⛴	a	15 29	21 27		
Edinburgh 228	a	*16 55*	*23 24*		00 15

For general notes see front of timetable
For details of catering facilities see Directory of Train Operators

§ Summer Station Only

A From 23 March
B 🍴 from Fort William

C Limited Seating accommodation. Also conveys through Sleeping Car accommodation to London Euston (Tables 65 and 404)
b Arr. 6 minutes earlier
c Arr. 3 minutes earlier
e Arr. 5 minutes earlier

Mondays to Saturdays

Mallaig — Armadale (Skye) and Small Isles

Operated By Caledonian MacBrayne Ltd.

	MO A	TO B	WO C	WFO D	TThO E	MO G	ThO H	J	FO J	SO K	J	SX E	J
Glasgow Queen Street 10 227 ⛴ d										08 21	08 21	08 21	12 21
Fort William 227 d	08 30	08 30	08 30	08 30	08 30	08 30	08 30	08 30	08 30	12 14	12 14	12 14	16 19
Mallaig 227 a	09 52	09 52	09 52	09 52	09 52	09 52	09 52	09 52	09 52	13 34	13 34	13 34	17 43
Mallaig ⛴ d	10 15	10 15	10 15	10 20	10 20	10 20	10 15	10 55	12 40	14 25	15 05	16 00	18 00
Armadale ⛴ a								11 25			15 35	16 25	18 30
Eigg ⛴ d	11 30	12 45		11 40		11 40	11 30			15 40			
Muck ⛴ d		11 55		12 35		12 35	12 20			16 25			
Rum ⛴ d	12 45		11 35		11 35	14 00			14 00	19 25			
Canna ⛴ a	13 55		12 45		12 50				15 10	18 15			

Sundays

Glasgow Queen Street 10 227 ⛴ d	
Fort William 227 d	
Mallaig 227 a	
Mallaig ⛴ d	
Armadale ⛴ a	
Eigg ⛴ d	
Muck ⛴ d	
Rum ⛴ d	
Canna ⛴ a	

Mondays to Saturdays

	J	SX E	FO J	SO L	ThO H	J	WFO D	SO N	MO P	TThO E	TO U	SX E	WO C	J	MO A	FO J
Canna ⛴ d				10 15				11 30		13 10			14 35		14 10	15 25
Rum ⛴ d				09 05				12 45	14 20	14 25			15 45		15 20	16 35
Muck ⛴ d			10 20	12 00	12 35		12 50		12 50		13 50					
Eigg ⛴ d			11 10	12 50	13 20		13 40	14 05	12 00		13 00				16 35	
Armadale ⛴ d	08 50	09 25				14 25						16 45		17 05		
Mallaig ⛴ a	09 20	09 50	12 25	14 05	14 35	14 55	15 00	15 20	15 40	15 40	15 30	17 10	17 05	17 35	17 50	17 55
Mallaig 227 d	10 10	10 10	16 05	16 05	16 05	16 05	16 05	16 05	16 05	16 05	16 05	18 15	18 15	18 15	18 15	18 15
Fort William 227 a	11 32	11 32	17 27	17 27	17 27	17 27	17 27	17 27	17 27	17 27	17 27	19 37	19 37	19 37	19 37	19 37
Glasgow Queen Street 10 227 ⛴ a	15 28	15 28	21 29	21 29	21 29	21 29	21 29	21 29	21 29	21 29	21 29	00b19	00b19	00c19	00 19	00b19

Sundays

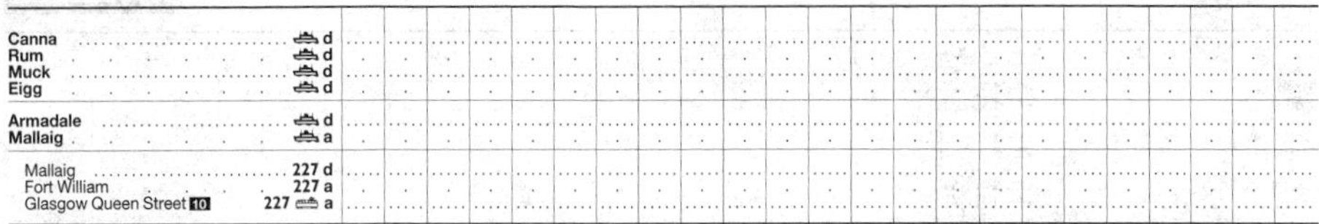

Canna ⛴ d	
Rum ⛴ d	
Muck ⛴ d	
Eigg ⛴ d	
Armadale ⛴ d	
Mallaig ⛴ a	
Mallaig 227 d	
Fort William 227 a	
Glasgow Queen Street 10 227 ⛴ a	

For general notes see front of timetable
For details of catering facilities see Directory of Train Operators

- **A** From 24 March
- **B** From 25 March. Sails via Muck
- **C** From 26 March
- **D** Until 19 March
- **E** Until 20 March
- **G** Until 17 March
- **H** From 27 March
- **J** From 21 March
- **K** From 22 March. Sails via Canna
- **L** From 22 March. Sails from Rum
- **N** Until 15 March
- **P** Until 17 March. Sails from Eigg
- **U** From 25 March. Sails from Eigg
- **b** Following day. Change at Fort William and Westerton. Reservations compulsory from Fort William
- **c** Tuesday to Saturday mornings only. Change at Fort William and Westerton. Reservations compulsory from Fort William

Oban — Craignure (Mull), Lismore, Colonsay, Coll and Tiree

Operated by Caledonian MacBrayne Ltd.

Mondays to Saturdays

		SO	FO	WO	TTh SO	SO	MO	ThO	SO	SX	TTh SO	MWO	SO		TO	WO		TFO	FO	MFO	FSO	FO		
		A	B	C	D	E	G	H	E	J	K	L	E		N	Q		J	U	G	V	J		
Glasgow Queen Street 10	227 ⛴ d	18b21	18b21	18b21	18b21	18b21	18b21	18b21	08 21	08 21	08 21	08 21	10 37	08 21	08 21	08 21	12 21	12 21	12 21	12 21	18 21	18 21		
Oban	227 a	21b26	21 26	21 26	21 26	21 26	21 26	21 26	11 27	11 27	11 27	11 27	13 42	11 27	11 27	11 27	15 27	15 27	15 27	15 27	21 26	21 26		
Oban	⛴ d	05 30	06 00	06 00	06 45	07 00	08 00	08 30	11 45	11 55	12 00	12 00	14 00	14 45	15 00	15 30	16 00	16 45	16 45	17 00	21 45	22 30		
Craignure	⛴ a								12 31	12 41	12 46		14 46				16 46				22 31	23 16		
Lismore	⛴ a													15 35				17 35	17 35					
Colonsay	⛴ a											14 20				17 45				19 20				
Coll	⛴ a	08 25	10 30	08 40	09 40	09 40	10 55	11 10							17 40									
Tiree	⛴ a	09 30	09 20	09 40	10 45	10 45	12 05	12 15							18 40									

Sundays

		X					X					X												
Glasgow Queen Street 10	227 ⛴ d	18 20					12 20					12 20												
Oban	227 a	21 26					15 27					15 27												
Oban	⛴ d	09 00					16 00					17 30												
Craignure	⛴ a						16 46																	
Lismore	⛴ a																							
Colonsay	⛴ a											19 50												
Coll	⛴ a	11 55																						
Tiree	⛴ a	13 00																						

Mondays to Saturdays

		ThO	SO	FO	TO		SO	SX	FX	SO	FO	WO	SO	WO	ThO	TTh SO	SO	FO	SO	MO		MWO		
		H		U	N		E	J	Y	E	J	Z	A	Q	H	D	E	U	E	G		L		
Tiree	⛴ d										09 35	09 55	10 00			11 00	11 15			12 25				
Coll	⛴ d										10 35	08 45	11 05			12 05	12 20			13 35				
Colonsay	⛴ d				07 50									11 45	11 55			12 40				14 40		
Lismore	⛴ d					09 45				11 45											15 45			
Craignure	⛴ d	06 45	07 00	09 00			10 30	10 55	11 00										15 00				17 00	
Oban	⛴ a	07 31	07 46	09 46	10 10	10 35	11 16	11 41	11 46	12 35	13 15	13 15	14 00	14 10	14 15	15 00	15 00	15 20	15 46	16 30	16 35	17 00	17 46	
Oban	227 d	08 11	08 11	12 11	12 11	12 11	12 11	12 11	12 11	16 11	18 11	18 11	18 11	18 11	18 11	18 11	16 11	18 11	16 11	18 11	18 11	18 11	18 11	
Glasgow Queen Street 10	227 ⛴ a	11 28	11 28	15 28	15 28	15 28	15 28	15 28	15 28	19 18	21 29	21 29	21 29	21 29	21 29	21 29	19 18	21 29	19 18	21 29	21 29	21 29	21 29	

Sundays

		X					X																	
Tiree	⛴ d						13 15																	
Coll	⛴ d						14 20																	
Colonsay	⛴ d																							
Lismore	⛴ d																							
Craignure	⛴ d	10 55										17 00												
Oban	⛴ a	11 41					17 15					17 46												
Oban	227 d	12 11					18 11					18 11												
Glasgow Queen Street 10	227 ⛴ a	15 29					21 27					21 27												

For general notes see front of timetable
For details of catering facilities see Directory of Train Operators

- **A** 9 February only
- **B** From 21 March. Sails via Tiree
- **C** From 26 March
- **D** Until 20 March (except 9 February)
- **E** From 22 March
- **G** From 24 March
- **H** From 27 March
- **J** From 21 March
- **K** Until 20 March
- **L** Until 19 March
- **N** From 25 March
- **Q** From 26 March. May be subject to withdrawal at short notice
- **U** Until 14 March
- **V** Until 15 March
- **X** From 23 March
- **Y** Until 29 March
- **Z** From 26 March. Sails from Coll
- **b** Previous night

Table 227C **SHIPPING SERVICES** Mondays to Saturdays

Oban — Castlebay (Barra) and Lochboisdale (South Uist)

Operated by Caledonian MacBrayne Ltd

		WFO A	MO B	TThO C	TThO D	SO E
Glasgow Queen Street 10	227 🚌 d	0821	0821	0821	0821	1037
Oban	227 a	1127	1127	1127	1127	1342
Oban	⛴ d	1340	1510	1530	1530	1530
Castlebay	⛴ a	1830	2000	2050	2250	2020
Lochboisdale	⛴ a			2255	2050	

Sundays

Glasgow Queen Street 10	227 🚌 d	
Oban	227 a	
Oban	⛴ d	
Castlebay	⛴ a	
Lochboisdale	⛴ a	

Mondays to Saturdays

		MO B	TO G	MWO H	FO J	WFO K	ThO L
Lochboisdale	⛴ d	0730		0730	0800	0900	2310
Castlebay	⛴ d	0920	0920	0935	1000	0700	2105
Oban	⛴ a	1410	1410	1455	1520	1420	0540
Oban	227 d	1811	1811	1811	1811	1811	0811
Glasgow Queen Street 10	227 🚌 a	2129	2129	2129	2129	2129	1128

Sundays

		N
Lochboisdale	⛴ d	
Castlebay	⛴ d	0920
Oban	⛴ a	1410
Oban	227 d	1811
Glasgow Queen Street 10	227 🚌 a	2127

For general notes see front of timetable
For details of catering facilities see Directory of Train Operators

A From 21 March
B From 24 March
C Until 18 March
D From 20 March. Sails via Lochboisdale
E From 22 March
G From 25 March
H Until 19 March
J 4 January to 14 March
K From 21 March. Sails from Castlebay
L Until 27 December. Sails from Castlebay
N From 23 March

Edinburgh → Falkirk High → Glasgow Queen Street

Network Diagram - see first page of Table 225

Mondays to Fridays

Miles		SR 1	SR 1 🛒	SR 1 🛒	SR 1 🛒	SR 1 🛒	SR A	SR 1 🛒		SR A	SR 1 🛒	SR 1 🛒	SR 1 🛒	SR 1 🛒	SR 1 🛒	SR 1 🛒		SR 1 🛒	SR 1 🛒	SR 1 🛒	SR 1 🛒	SR 1 🛒	SR 1 🛒	SR 1 🛒
0	**Edinburgh 10** 225, 230, 242 d	05 55	06 30	07 00	07 15	07 30		07 45			08 00	08 15	08 30	08 45	09 00	09 15		09 30	09 45	10 00	10 15	10 30	10 45	11 00
1¼	Haymarket 225, 230, 242 d	06 00	06 34	07 04	07 19	07 34		07 49			08 04	08 18	08 33	08 48	09 03	09 18		09 33	09 48	10 03	10 18	10 33	10 48	11 03
17½	Linlithgow 230 d	06 14	06 48		07 33	07 49	08 00	08 05				08 33		09 03		09 33			10 03		10 33		11 03	
22¼	Polmont 3 230 d	06 20	06 55	07 19		07 55				←	08 21	08 39		09 09		09 39			10 09		10 39		11 09	
25½	**Falkirk High** d	06 25	07 00	07 24	07 42	08 00	08b11	08 14		08b11	08 26	08 44	08 54	09 14	09 24	09 44		09 54	10 14	10 24	10 44	10 54	11 14	11 24
35¾	Croy 3 230 a	06 35	07 09		07 52	08 10	→				08 38		09 04		09 34			10 04		10 34		11 04		11 34
41	Lenzie 3 230 a	06 49	07 21		08 06	08 37		08 26		08 31	08 49		09 19		09 49			10 19		10 49		11 19		11 49
44	Bishopbriggs 230 a	06 54	07 26		08 11	08 42				08 36	08 53		09 23		09 53			10 23		10 53		11 23		11 53
47¼	**Glasgow Queen Street 10** 230 ⛴ a	06 50	07 25	07 48	08 06	08 25		08 40		08 48	08 55	09 06	09 21	09 36	09 51	10 07		10 21	10 36	10 51	11 06	11 21	11 36	11 51

	SR 1 🛒	SR 1 🛒		SR 1 🛒	SR 1 🛒	SR 1 🛒	SR 1 🛒	SR 1 🛒	SR 1 🛒	SR 1 🛒		SR 1 🛒	SR 1 🛒	SR 1 🛒	SR 1 🛒	SR 1 🛒	SR 1 🛒	SR 1 🛒		SR 1 🛒	SR 1 🛒	SR 1 🛒	SR 1 🛒	SR 1 🛒
Edinburgh 10 225, 230, 242 d	11 15	11 30		11 45	12 00	12 15	12 30	12 45	13 00	13 15		13 30	13 45	14 00	14 15	14 30	14 45	15 00		15 15	15 30	15 45	16 00	16 15
Haymarket 225, 230, 242 d	11 18	11 33		11 48	12 03	12 18	12 33	12 48	13 03	13 18		13 33	13 48	14 03	14 18	14 33	14 48	15 03		15 18	15 33	15 48	16 03	16 18
Linlithgow 230 d	11 33			12 03		12 33		13 03		13 33			14 03		14 33		15 03			15 33		16 03		16 33
Polmont 3 230 d	11 39			12 09		12 39		13 09		13 39			14 09		14 39		15 09			15 39		16 09		16 39
Falkirk High d	11 44	11 54		12 14	12 24	12 44	12 54	13 14	13 24	13 44		13 54	14 14	14 24	14 44	14 54	15 14	15 24		15 44	15 54	16 14	16 24	16 44
Croy 3 230 a		12 04			12 34		13 04		13 34			14 04		14 34		15 04		15 34			16 04		16 34	
Lenzie 3 230 a		12 19			12 49		13 19		13 49			14 19		14 49		15 19		15 49			16 19		16 49	
Bishopbriggs 230 a		12 23			12 53		13 23		13 53			14 23		14 53		15 23		15 53			16 23		16 53	
Glasgow Queen Street 10 230 ⛴ a	12 06	12 21		12 38	12 51	13 06	13 21	13 36	13 51	14 06		14 21	14 36	14 51	15 06	15 21	15 36	15 51		16 08	16 21	16 36	16 51	17 06

	SR 1 🛒	SR 1 🛒	SR 1 🛒	SR 1 🛒		SR 1 🛒	SR 1 🛒	SR 1 🛒	SR 1 🛒	SR 1 🛒	SR 1 🛒	SR 1 🛒		SR 1 🛒	SR 1 🛒	SR 1 🛒	SR 1	SR 1	SR 1	SR 1	SR 1	SR 1		
Edinburgh 10 225, 230, 242 d	16 30	16 45	17 00	17 15		17 30	17 45	18 00	18 15	18 30	18 45	19 00		19 30	20 00	20 30	21 00	21 30	22 00	22 30	23 00	23 30		
Haymarket 225, 230, 242 d	16 33	16 48	17 03	17 18		17 33	17 48	18 03	18 18	18 33	18 48	19 04		19 34	20 04	20 34	21 04	21 34	22 04	22 34	23 04	23 34		
Linlithgow 230 d		17 03		17 33			18 03		18 33		19 03	19 19		19 49	20 19	20 49	21 19	21 49	22 19	22 48	23 18	23 48		
Polmont 3 230 d		17 09		17 39			18 09		18 39		19 09	19 26			20 26		21 26		22 26		23 25	23 55		
Falkirk High d	16 54	17 14	17 24	17 44		17 54	18 14	18 24	18 44	18 54	19 14	19 31		19 58	20 31	20 58	21 31	21 58	22 31	22 57	23 30	23 59		
Croy 3 230 a	17 04		17 34			18 04		18 34		19 04				20 08		21 08		22 08		23 07	23 42	00 09		
Lenzie 3 230 a	17 19		17 49			18 08		18 49		19 19				20 19		21 19		22 19		23 13	23 48	00 15		
Bishopbriggs 230 a	17 23		17 53			18 23		18 53		19 23				20 23		21 23		22 23		23 22	23 54			
Glasgow Queen Street 10 230 ⛴ a	17 21	17 36	17 51	18 06		18 21	18 36	18 50	19 06	19 21	19 36	19 53		20 24	20 51	21 22	21 51	22 22	22 51	23 25	00 03	00 28		

Saturdays

	SR 1	SR 1 🛒	SR 1 🛒	SR 1 🛒	SR 1 🛒		SR 1 🛒	SR 1 🛒	SR 1 🛒	SR 1 🛒	SR 1 🛒		SR 1 🛒	SR 1 🛒	SR 1 🛒	SR 1 🛒	SR 1 🛒		SR 1 🛒	SR 1 🛒	SR 1 🛒	SR 1 🛒	SR 1 🛒	SR 1 🛒
Edinburgh 10 225, 230, 242 d	05 55	06 30	07 00	07 15	07 30		07 45	08 00	08 15	08 30	08 45		09 00	09 15	09 30	09 45	10 00		10 15	10 30	10 45	11 00	11 15	11 30
Haymarket 225, 230, 242 d	06 00	06 34	07 04	07 19	07 34		07 49	08 04	08 18	08 33	08 48		09 03	09 18	09 33	09 48	10 03		10 18	10 33	10 48	11 03	11 18	11 33
Linlithgow 230 d	06 14	06 48		07 33	07 49		08 03		08 33		09 03			09 33		10 03			10 33		11 03		11 33	
Polmont 3 230 d	06 20	06 55	07 19		07 55			08 21	08 39		09 09			09 39		10 09			10 39		11 09		11 39	
Falkirk High d	06 25	07 00	07 24	07 42	08 00		08 12	08 26	08 44	08 54	09 14		09 24	09 44	09 54	10 14	10 24		10 44	10 54	11 14	11 24	11 44	11 54
Croy 3 230 a	06 35	07 09		07 52	08 10			08 38		09 04			09 34		10 04		10 34			11 04		11 34		12 04
Lenzie 3 230 a	06 49	07 20		08 04	08 39		08 24	08 49		09 19			09 49		10 19		10 49			11 19		11 49		12 19
Bishopbriggs 230 a	06 54	07 25		08 10	08 43		08 29	08 53		09 23			09 53		10 23		10 53			11 23		11 53		12 23
Glasgow Queen Street 10 230 ⛴ a	06 50	07 25	07 48	08 06	08 25		08 38	08 55	09 06	09 21	09 36		09 51	10 07	10 21	10 36	10 51		11 06	11 21	11 36	11 51	12 06	12 21

	SR 1 🛒		SR 1 🛒	SR 1 🛒	SR 1 🛒	SR 1 🛒	SR 1 🛒		SR 1 🛒	SR 1 🛒	SR 1 🛒	SR 1 🛒	SR 1 🛒		SR 1 🛒	SR 1 🛒	SR 1 🛒	SR 1 🛒	SR 1 🛒		SR 1 🛒	SR 1 🛒	SR 1 🛒	SR 1 🛒
Edinburgh 10 225, 230, 242 d	11 45		12 00	12 15	12 30	12 45	13 00		13 15	13 30	13 45	14 00	14 15		14 30	14 45	15 00	15 15	15 30		15 45	16 00	16 15	16 30
Haymarket 225, 230, 242 d	11 48		12 03	12 18	12 33	12 48	13 03		13 18	13 33	13 48	14 03	14 18		14 33	14 48	15 03	15 18	15 33		15 48	16 03	16 18	16 33
Linlithgow 230 d	12 03			12 33		13 03			13 33		14 03		14 33			15 03		15 33			16 03		16 33	
Polmont 3 230 d	12 09			12 39		13 09			13 39		14 09		14 39			15 09		15 39			16 09		16 39	
Falkirk High d	12 14		12 24	12 44	12 54	13 14	13 24		13 44	13 54	14 14	14 24	14 44		14 54	15 14	15 24	15 44	15 54		16 14	16 24	16 44	16 54
Croy 3 230 a			12 34		13 04		13 34			14 04		14 34			15 04		15 34		16 04			16 34		17 04
Lenzie 3 230 a			12 49		13 19		13 49			14 19		14 49			15 19		15 49		16 19			16 49		17 19
Bishopbriggs 230 a			12 53		13 23		13 53			14 23		14 53			15 23		15 53		16 23			16 53		17 23
Glasgow Queen Street 10 230 ⛴ a	12 38		12 51	13 06	13 21	13 36	13 51		14 06	14 21	14 36	14 51	15 06		15 21	15 36	15 51	16 08	16 21		16 36	16 51	17 06	17 21

	SR 1 🛒	SR 1 🛒	SR 1 🛒		SR 1 🛒	SR 1 🛒	SR 1 🛒	SR 1 🛒	SR 1 🛒		SR 1 🛒	SR 1 🛒	SR 1 🛒	SR 1 🛒	SR 1 🛒		SR 1	SR 1	SR 1	SR 1	SR 1	SR 1		
Edinburgh 10 225, 230, 242 d	16 45	17 00	17 15		17 30	17 45	18 00	18 15	18 30		18 45	19 00	19 30	20 00	20 30		21 00	21 30	22 00	22 30	23 00	23 30		
Haymarket 225, 230, 242 d	16 48	17 03	17 18		17 33	17 48	18 03	18 18	18 33		18 48	19 04	19 34	20 04	20 34		21 04	21 34	22 04	22 34	23 04	23 34		
Linlithgow 230 d	17 03		17 33			18 03		18 33			19 03	19 19	19 49	20 19	20 49		21 19	21 49	22 19	22 48	23 18	23 48		
Polmont 3 230 d	17 09		17 39			18 09		18 39			19 09	19 26		20 26			21 26		22 26		23 25	23 55		
Falkirk High d	17 14	17 24	17 44		17 54	18 14	18 24	18 44	18 54		19 14	19 31	19 58	20 31	20 58		21 31	21 58	22 31	22 57	23 30	23 59		
Croy 3 230 a		17 34			18 04		18 34		19 04				20 08		21 08			22 08		23 07	23 42	00 09		
Lenzie 3 230 a		17 49			18 08		18 49		19 19				20 19		21 19			22 19		23 13	23 48	00 15		
Bishopbriggs 230 a		17 53			18 23		18 53		19 23				20 23		21 23			22 23		23 22	23 54			
Glasgow Queen Street 10 230 ⛴ a	17 36	17 51	18 06		18 21	18 38	18 50	19 06	19 21		19 36	19 53	20 24	20 51	21 22		21 51	22 22	22 51	23 25	00 03	00 28		

For general notes see front of timetable
For details of catering facilities see Directory of Train Operators

A From Kirkcaldy (Table 242)
b Falkirk Grahamston

Table 228

Sundays

Edinburgh → Falkirk High → Glasgow Queen Street

Network Diagram - see first page of Table 225

		SR 1 🛒	SR 1	SR 1 🛒	SR 1 🛒	SR 1 🛒	SR 1 🛒	SR 1 🛒	SR 1 🛒	SR 1 🛒	SR 1	SR 1 🛒	SR 1 🛒	SR 1 🛒
Edinburgh 10	225, 230, 242 d	08 00	09 00	10 00	11 00	12 00	12 30	13 00	13 30	14 00	14 30	15 00	15 30	16 00
Haymarket	225, 230, 242 d	08 04	09 04	10 04	11 04	12 04	12 34	13 04	13 34	14 04	14 34	15 04	15 34	16 04
Linlithgow	230 d	08 23	09 23	10 23	11 18	12 18	12 48	13 18	13 48	14 18	14 48	15 18	15 48	16 18
Polmont 3	230 d	08 30	09 30	10 30	11 25	12 25		13 25		14 25		15 25		16 25
Falkirk High	d	08 34	09 34	10 34	11 30	12 30	12 57	13 30	13 57	14 30	14 57	15 30	15 57	16 30
Croy 3	230 a	08 44	09 44	10 44	11 39	12 39	13 07		14 07		15 07		16 07	
Lenzie 3	230 a	*09b55*	*09 55*	*10 55*	*11 52*	*12 52*	*13c52*		*14c52*		*15c52*		*16c52*	
Bishopbriggs	230 a	*09b59*	*09 59*	*10 59*	*11 56*	*12 56*	*13e56*		*14e56*		*15c57*		*16e56*	
Glasgow Queen Street 10	230 ⛴ a	08 59	10 00	11 00	11 55	12 55	13 23	13 51	14 23	14 52	15 22	15 52	16 24	16 51

		SR 1 🛒	SR 1 🛒	SR 1 🛒	SR 1 🛒	SR 1 🛒	SR 1 🛒	SR 1 🛒	SR 1 🛒	SR 1 🛒	SR 1 🛒	SR 1	SR 1	SR 1		
Edinburgh 10	225, 230, 242 d	16 30	17 00	17 30	18 00	18 30	19 00	19 30	20 00	20 30	21 00	22 00	23 00	23 30		
Haymarket	225, 230, 242 d	16 34	17 04	17 34	18 04	18 34	19 04	19 34	20 04	20 34	21 04	22 04	23 04	23 34		
Linlithgow	230 d	16 48	17 18	17 48	18 18	18 48	19 18	19 48	20 18	20 48	21 18	22 18	23 18	23 49		
Polmont 3	230 d		17 25		18 25		19 25		20 25		21 25	22 25	23 25	23 56		
Falkirk High	d	16 57	17 30	17 57	18 30	18 57	19 30	19 57	20 30	20 57	21 30	22 30	23 30	00 01		
Croy 3	230 a	17 07		18 07		19 07		20 07		21 07	21 40	22 40	23 40	00 11		
Lenzie 3	230 a	*17c52*		*18f53*		*19g52*		*20 52*			*21 52*					
Bishopbriggs	230 a	*17e56*		*18c57*		*19g56*		*20 56*			*21 56*					
Glasgow Queen Street 10	230 ⛴ a	17 22	17 52	18 22	18 51	19 22	19 51	20 22	20 52	21 22	21 55	22 55	23 55	00 25		

For general notes see front of timetable
For details of catering facilities see Directory of Train Operators

- **b** Until 23 December only
- **c** Until 23 December arr. 31 minutes earlier
- **e** Until 23 December arr. 30 minutes earlier
- **f** Until 23 December arr. 1821
- **g** Until 23 December arr. Lenzie 1919, Bishopbriggs 1924

Table 228

Glasgow Queen Street → Falkirk High → Edinburgh

Network Diagram - see first page of Table 225

Miles																								
		SR	SR	SR	SR	SR	SR	SR		SR	SR	SR	SR	SR	SR	SR		SR	SR	SR	SR	SR	SR	SR
		1	1	1	1	1	1	1		1	1	1	1	1	1	1		1	1	1	1	1	1	1
			🛒	🛒	🛒	🛒	🛒	🛒		🛒	🛒	🛒	🛒	🛒	🛒	🛒		🛒	🛒	🛒	🛒	🛒	🛒	🛒
0	**Glasgow Queen Street** 10 230 ⛴ d	06 00	06 30	07 00	07 15	07 30	07 45	08 00		08 15	08 30	08 45	09 00	09 15	09 30	09 45		10 00	10 15	10 30	10 45	11 00	11 15	11 30
3¼	Bishopbriggs 230 d		06 19	06 54		07 23		07 54			08 23		08 53		09 23			09 53		10 23		10 53		11 23
6¼	Lenzie 3 230 d		06 38	07 09		07 29		08 00			08 29		08 59		09 29			09 59		10 29		10 59		11 30
11½	Croy 3 230 d		06 44			07 41		08 11			08 41		09 11		09 41			10 11		10 41		11 11		11 41
21¾	**Falkirk High** d	06 19	06 54	07 22	07 33	07 51	08 03	08 21		08 33	08 51	09 03	09 21	09 33	09 51	10 03		10 21	10 33	10 51	11 03	11 21	11 33	11 51
25	Polmont 3 230 a	06 23	06 58	07 26	07 37		08 07	08 27				09 07		09 37		10 07			10 37		11 07		11 37	
29¾	Linlithgow 230 a	06 30	07 05	07 33	07 44	08 01	08 14			08 43		09 14		09 44		10 14			10 44		11 14		11 44	
46	Haymarket 225, 230, 242 a	06s45	07s20	07s50	08s01	08s17	08s32	08s46		09s00	09s15	09s31	09s43	10s01	10s16	10s30		10s45	11s00	11s14	11s30	11s45	12s00	12s14
47¼	**Edinburgh** 10 225, 230, 242 a	06 50	07 25	07 55	08 06	08 22	08 37	08 51		09 05	09 20	09 36	09 48	10 06	10 22	10 35		10 50	11 05	11 19	11 35	11 50	12 05	12 19

	SR	SR		SR	SR	SR	SR	SR	SR	SR		SR	SR	SR	SR	SR	SR	SR		SR	SR	SR	SR	SR
	1	1		1	1	1	1	1	1	1		1	1	1	1	1	1	1		1	1	1	1	1
	🛒	🛒		🛒	🛒	🛒	🛒	🛒	🛒	🛒		🛒	🛒	🛒	🛒	🛒	🛒	🛒		🛒	🛒	🛒	🛒	🛒
Glasgow Queen Street 10 230 ⛴ d	11 45	12 00		12 15	12 30	12 45	13 00	13 15	13 30	13 45		14 00	14 15	14 30	14 45	15 00	15 15	15 30		15 45	16 00	16 15	16 30	16 45
Bishopbriggs 230 d		11 53			12 23		12 53		13 23			13 53		14 23		14 53		15 23			15 53		16 23	
Lenzie 3 230 d		11 59			12 29		12 59		13 29			13 59		14 29		14 59		15 29			15 59		16 29	
Croy 3 230 d		12 11			12 41		13 11		13 41			14 11		14 41		15 11		15 41			16 11		16 41	
Falkirk High d	12 03	12 21		12 33	12 51	13 03	13 21	13 33	13 51	14 03		14 21	14 33	14 51	15 03	15 21	15 33	15 51		16 03	16 21	16 33	16 51	17 03
Polmont 3 230 a	12 07			12 37		13 07		13 37		14 07			14 37		15 07		15 37			16 07		16 37		17 07
Linlithgow 230 a	12 14			12 44		13 14		13 44		14 14			14 44		15 14		15 44			16 14		16 44		17 14
Haymarket 225, 230, 242 a	12s30	12s45		13s00	13s14	13s30	13s45	14s00	14s14	14s30		14s45	15s00	15s16	15s30	15s45	16s00	16s13		16s33	16s46	17s00	17s16	17s33
Edinburgh 10 225, 230, 242 a	12 35	12 50		13 05	13 19	13 35	13 50	14 05	14 19	14 35		14 50	15 05	15 21	15 35	15 50	16 05	16 18		16 39	16 52	17 05	17 22	17 38

	SR	SR	SR	SR		SR	SR	SR	SR	SR	SR	SR		SR	SR	SR	SR	SR	SR	SR	SR	SR		
	1	1	1			1		1	1	1	1	1		1	1	1	1	1	1	1	1	1		
				A			A																	
	🛒	🛒	🛒			🛒		🛒	🛒	🛒	🛒	🛒		🛒	🛒	🛒								
Glasgow Queen Street 10 230 ⛴ d	17 00	17 15	17 30	17 33		17 45		18 00	18 15	18 30	18 45	19 00		19 30	20 00	20 30	21 00	21 30	22 00	22 30	23 00	23 30		
Bishopbriggs 230 d	16 53		17 23	17 39				17 53		18 23		18 53			19 53		20 53		21 53		22 54	23 24		
Lenzie 3 230 d	16 59		17 29	17 44				17 59		18 29		18 59			19 59		20 59		21 59		23 00	23 29		
Croy 3 230 d	17 11		17 42				←	18 11		18 41		19 11			20 11		21 11		22 11		23 11	23 43		
Falkirk High d	17 21	17 35	17 52	18b00		18 03	18b00	18 21	18 33	18 51	19 03	19 21		19 50	20 21	20 50	21 21	21 51	22 21	22 50	23 21	23 53		
Polmont 3 230 a	17 27		17 57	→		18 07	18 13		18 37		19 07			19 54		20 54		21 55		22 54	23 27	23 58		
Linlithgow 230 a		17 42	18 03			18 14	18 20		18 44		19 14	19 30		20 01	20 30	21 01	21 30	22 02	22 30	23 01	23 33	00 04		
Haymarket 225, 230, 242 a	17s45	18s00	18s22			18s32		18s45	19s00	19s14	19s30	19s45		20s17	20s46	21s17	21s46	22s18	22s46	23s17	23s49	00s20		
Edinburgh 10 225, 230, 242 a	17 50	18 05	18 27			18 37		18 50	19 05	19 19	19 35	19 50		20 22	20 51	21 22	21 51	22 24	22 51	23 22	23 54	00 25		

Saturdays

	SR	SR	SR	SR	SR		SR	SR	SR	SR	SR		SR	SR	SR	SR	SR		SR	SR	SR	SR	SR	SR
	1	1	1	1	1		1	1	1	1	1		1	1	1	1	1		1	1	1	1	1	1
		🛒	🛒	🛒	🛒		🛒	🛒	🛒	🛒	🛒		🛒	🛒	🛒	🛒	🛒		🛒	🛒	🛒	🛒	🛒	🛒
Glasgow Queen Street 10 230 ⛴ d	06 00	06 30	07 00	07 15	07 30		07 45	08 00	08 15	08 30	08 45		09 00	09 15	09 30	09 45	10 00		10 15	10 30	10 45	11 00	11 15	11 30
Bishopbriggs 230 d		06 19	06 54		07 23			07 53		08 23			08 53		09 23		09 53			10 23		10 53		11 23
Lenzie 3 230 d		06 38	07 09		07 29			07 59		08 29			08 59		09 29		09 59			10 29		10 59		11 30
Croy 3 230 d		06 44			07 41			08 11		08 41			09 11		09 41		10 11			10 41		11 11		11 41
Falkirk High d	06 19	06 54	07 22	07 33	07 51		08 03	08 21	08 33	08 51	09 03		09 21	09 33	09 51	10 03	10 21		10 33	10 51	11 03	11 21	11 33	11 51
Polmont 3 230 a	06 23	06 58	07 26	07 37			08 07	08 27			09 07			09 37		10 07			10 37		11 07		11 37	
Linlithgow 230 a	06 30	07 05	07 33	07 44	08 01		08 14		08 43		09 14			09 44		10 14			10 44		11 14		11 44	
Haymarket 225, 230, 242 a	06s45	07s21	07s50	08s01	08s19		08s32	08s45	09s00	09s14	09s31		09s46	10s01	10s16	10s31	10s45		11s01	11s16	11s30	11s46	12s00	12s16
Edinburgh 10 225, 230, 242 a	06 50	07 26	07 55	08 06	08 24		08 37	08 50	09 09	09 19	09 36		09 52	10 06	10 22	10 36	10 50		11 06	11 23	11 35	11 52	12 05	12 22

	SR		SR	SR	SR	SR	SR		SR	SR	SR	SR	SR		SR	SR	SR	SR	SR		SR	SR	SR	SR
	1		1	1	1	1	1		1	1	1	1	1		1	1	1	1	1		1	1	1	1
	🛒		🛒	🛒	🛒	🛒	🛒		🛒	🛒	🛒	🛒	🛒		🛒	🛒	🛒	🛒	🛒		🛒	🛒	🛒	🛒
Glasgow Queen Street 10 230 ⛴ d	11 45		12 00	12 15	12 30	12 45	13 00		13 15	13 30	13 45	14 00	14 15		14 30	14 45	15 00	15 15	15 30		15 45	16 00	16 15	16 30
Bishopbriggs 230 d			11 53		12 23		12 53			13 23		13 53			14 23		14 53		15 23			15 53		16 23
Lenzie 3 230 d			11 59		12 29		12 59			13 29		13 59			14 29		14 59		15 29			15 59		16 29
Croy 3 230 d			12 11		12 41		13 11			13 41		14 11			14 41		15 11		15 41			16 11		16 41
Falkirk High d	12 03		12 21	12 33	12 51	13 03	13 21		13 33	13 51	14 03	14 21	14 33		14 51	15 03	15 21	15 33	15 51		16 03	16 21	16 33	16 51
Polmont 3 230 a	12 07			12 37		13 07			13 37		14 07		14 37			15 07		15 37			16 07		16 37	
Linlithgow 230 a	12 14			12 44		13 14			13 44		14 14		14 44			15 14		15 44			16 14		16 44	
Haymarket 225, 230, 242 a	12s31		12s46	13s01	13s16	13s31	13s47		14s01	14s16	14s31	14s45	15s01		15s16	15s31	15s45	16s00	16s16		16s33	16s46	17s01	17s16
Edinburgh 10 225, 230, 242 a	12 36		12 52	13 06	13 22	13 36	13 52		14 06	14 22	14 36	14 50	15 06		15 22	15 36	15 50	16 05	16 22		16 39	16 52	17 06	17 22

	SR	SR	SR		SR	SR	SR	SR	SR		SR	SR	SR	SR	SR		SR	SR	SR	SR	SR	SR		
	1	1	1		1	1	1	1	1		1	1	1	1	1		1	1	1	1	1	1		
	🛒	🛒	🛒		🛒	🛒	🛒	🛒	🛒		🛒	🛒	🛒	🛒	🛒									
Glasgow Queen Street 10 230 ⛴ d	16 45	17 00	17 15		17 30	17 45	18 00	18 15	18 30		18 45	19 00	19 30	20 00	20 30		21 00	21 30	22 00	22 30	23 00	23 30		
Bishopbriggs 230 d		16 53			17 23		17 53		18 23			18 53		19 53			20 53		21 53		22 54	23 24		
Lenzie 3 230 d		16 59			17 29		17 59		18 29			18 59		19 59			20 59		21 59		23 00	23 29		
Croy 3 230 d		17 11			17 42		18 11		18 41			19 11		20 11			21 11		22 11		23 11	23 43		
Falkirk High d	17 03	17 21	17 35		17 52	18 03	18 21	18 33	18 51		19 03	19 21	19 50	20 21	20 50		21 21	21 51	22 21	22 50	23 21	23 53		
Polmont 3 230 a	17 07	17 27			17 57	18 07		18 37			19 07		19 54		20 54			21 55		22 54	23 27	23 58		
Linlithgow 230 a	17 14		17 42		18 03	18 14		18 44			19 14	19 30	20 01	20 30	21 01		21 30	22 02	22 30	23 01	23 33	00 04		
Haymarket 225, 230, 242 a	17s33	17s45	18s01		18s22	18s32	18s45	19s00	19s16		19s30	19s45	20s17	20s46	21s17		21s48	22s18	22s46	23s17	23s49	00s21		
Edinburgh 10 225, 230, 242 a	17 38	17 50	18 06		18 27	18 37	18 50	19 05	19 21		19 35	19 50	20 22	20 51	21 22		21 53	22 24	22 51	23 22	23 54	00 26		

For general notes see front of timetable
For details of catering facilities see
Directory of Train Operators

A To Kirkcaldy (Table 242)
b Falkirk Grahamston

Glasgow Queen Street → Falkirk High → Edinburgh

Network Diagram - see first page of Table 225

		SR 1	SR 1	SR 1	SR 1	SR 1	SR 1	SR 1	SR 1	SR 1	SR 1	SR 1	SR 1	SR 1
			🛒	🛒	🛒	🛒	🛒	🛒		🛒	🛒	🛒		🛒
Glasgow Queen Street 10	230 ⛴ d	07 50	08 30	09 30	10 30	11 30	12 30	13 00	13 30	14 00	14 30	15 00	15 30	16 00
Bishopbriggs	230 d	.	*08b21*	*09b20*	*10 21*	*11 21*	*12 21*	*12b53*	.	*13c21*	.	*14e21*	.	*15c21*
Lenzie 3	230 d	.	*08b27*	*09b26*	*10 27*	*11 27*	*12 27*	*12b59*	.	*13c27*	.	*14e27*	.	*15c27*
Croy 3	230 d	08 02	08 42	09 42	10 42	11 42	12 42	13 12	.	14 12	.	15 12	.	16 12
Falkirk High	d	08 12	08 52	09 52	10 52	11 52	12 52	13 22	13 49	14 22	14 49	15 22	15 49	16 22
Polmont 3	230 a	08 17	08 57	09 57	10 57	11 57	12 59	.	13 53	.	14 53	.	15 53	.
Linlithgow	230 a	08 23	09 03	10 03	11 03	12 03	13 05	13 30	14 00	14 30	15 00	15 30	16 00	16 30
Haymarket	225, 230, 242 a	08s44	09s23	10s23	11s19	12s19	13s21	13s46	14s17	14s47	15s16	15s46	16s16	16s50
Edinburgh 10	225, 230, 242 a	08 49	09 28	10 28	11 24	12 24	13 26	13 51	14 22	14 52	15 21	15 51	16 21	16 55

		SR 1	SR 1	SR 1	SR 1	SR 1	SR 1	SR 1	SR 1	SR 1	SR 1	SR 1	SR 1	SR 1
		🛒	🛒	🛒	🛒	🛒	🛒	🛒	🛒	🛒				
Glasgow Queen Street 10	230 ⛴ d	16 30	17 00	17 30	18 00	18 30	19 00	19 30	20 00	20 30	21 00	21 30	22 30	23 30
Bishopbriggs	230 d	.	*16e21*	.	*17c21*	.	*18 21*	.	*19 21*	.	*20 21*	*21 21*	*22 21*	.
Lenzie 3	230 d	.	*16e27*	.	*17c27*	.	*18 27*	.	*19 27*	.	*20 27*	*21 27*	*22 27*	.
Croy 3	230 d	.	17 12	.	18 12	.	19 12	.	20 12	.	21 12	21 42	22 42	23 42
Falkirk High	d	16 49	17 22	17 49	18 22	18 49	19 22	19 49	20 22	20 49	21 22	21 52	22 52	23 52
Polmont 3	230 a	16 53	.	17 53	.	18 53	.	19 53	.	20 53	.	21 57	22 57	23 57
Linlithgow	230 a	17 00	17 30	18 00	18 30	19 00	19 30	20 00	20 30	21 00	21 30	22 03	23 03	00 03
Haymarket	225, 230, 242 a	17s16	17s46	18s16	18s50	19s16	19s47	20s16	20s46	21s17	21s45	22s19	23s19	00s19
Edinburgh 10	225, 230, 242 a	17 21	17 51	18 21	18 55	19 22	19 52	20 21	20 54	21 22	21 53	22 24	23 24	00 24

For general notes see front of timetable
For details of catering facilities see Directory of Train Operators

b Until 23 December only
c Until 23 December dep. 33 minutes later
e Until 23 December dep. 32 minutes later

Edinburgh and Glasgow Queen Street → Perth, Inverness, Dundee, Aberdeen and Dyce

Network Diagram - see first page of Table 225

Miles	Miles	Miles	Miles	Miles			SR	SR	XC	SR	XC	XC	SR	SR	SR	SR	SR	SR	SR	SR	SR	SR
							SX	SX			SX	SO	SO								SO	SX
								1	1◇	1	1◇	1◇	1	1◇	1	1◇	1◇	1◇	1◇	1◇	1◇	1◇
														A			A					
									[buffet]		[buffet]	[buffet]		[trolley]		[trolley]	[trolley]	[trolley]	[trolley]	[trolley]	[trolley]	[trolley]
—	0	—	0	0	**Edinburgh** 10	242 d					05 35	05 33		*05b18*	06 40		07 08	*07b03*	08 10	*08b03*	08 35	08 38
—	1¼	—	1¼	1¼	Haymarket	242 d								*05b22*	06 45		07 13	*07b06*	08 14	*08b06*	08 39	08 42
—	13¼	—	13¼	—	Inverkeithing	242 d					06 07	06 06			06 58		07 27				08 52	08 55
—	26	—	26	—	Kirkcaldy	242 d									07 15		07 43		08 42		09 08	09 11
—	33¼	—	33¼	—	Markinch	242 d					06 37	06 37			07 24		07 52		08 51		09 17	09 20
—	39¼	—	39¼	—	Ladybank	d						06 44			07 31		08 00					
—	42¼	—	—	—	Springfield	d													09 02			
—	44½	—	—	—	Cupar	d					06 49	06 51					08 06		09 06			
—	51	—	—	—	Leuchars 3 §	d					06 56	06 58					08 13		09 13			
0	—	0	—	—	**Glasgow Queen Street** 10	230 d								05 55		07 06		07 41		08 41		
21	—	21	—	28¼	Larbert	230 d								06 16								
29	—	29	—	36½	Stirling	230 d								06 25		07 31		08 07		09 06		
34½	—	34½	—	42	Dunblane	230 d								06 31		07 37		08 14				
46¾	—	46¾	—	54¼	Gleneagles	d								06 43								
62½	—	62½	57	70¾	**Perth**	a								06 59	07 54	08 04		08 37		09 37	09 54	09 54
—	—	—	—	—		d				06 32				07 01	07 55	08 05		08 37		09 37	09 55	09 55
79¾	—	—	—	—	Invergowrie	d									08 13							
83¼	59¼	—	—	—	**Dundee**	a				06 53	07 17	07 18		07 22	08 21		08 26	09 00	09 25	10 00		
—	—	—	—	—		d			06 35	06 56				07 24			08 28	09 00	09 26	10 00		
87¼	63¼	—	—	—	Broughty Ferry	d																
94	70	—	—	—	Carnoustie	d				07 08				07 36					09 38			
100½	76½	—	—	—	Arbroath	d			06 51	07 15				07 43			08 44	09 18	09 45	10 18		
114	90	—	—	—	Montrose	d	06 30		07 05	07 29				07 57			08 59	09 32		10 32		
138¼	114¼	—	—	—	Stonehaven	d	06 52		07 26	07 51				08 19			09 20		10 19	10 52		
146½	122½	—	—	—	Portlethen	d	07 02			08 00				08 27						11 03		
154½	130½	—	—	—	**Aberdeen**	a	07 15		07 50	08 13				08 40			09 40	10 18	10 38	11 17		
—	—	—	—	—		240 d	07 18							08 46			09 47					
160¾	136¾	—	—	—	**Dyce**	240 a	07 27		*08c31*					08 56			09 55		*11 09*	*11 49*		
—	—	78	72½	86½	Dunkeld & Birnam	d										08 24						
—	—	91	85½	99¼	Pitlochry	d										08 41					10 24	10 24
—	—	97¾	92¼	106	Blair Atholl	d										08 51						
—	—	121	116½	130¼	Dalwhinnie	d										09 17						
—	—	131½	126½	140½	Newtonmore	d										09 27						
—	—	134	129½	143¼	Kingussie	d		07 00					07 37			09 30					11 07	11 07
—	—	145¾	141¼	155	Aviemore	d		07 21					07 49			09 43					11 19	11 19
—	—	152¾	148¼	162	Carrbridge	d		07 30					07 57			09 53						
—	—	180	175	188¾	**Inverness**	a		08 03					08 39			10 26					11 59	11 59

		SR	SR	SR	SR	SR	GR	SR	SR	SR	SR	SR	SR	SR	SR	SR	SR	SR	GR	SR	SR	SR
																						SO
							R									R			R			
		1◇	1◇	1	1◇	1◇	1	1◇	1◇	1◇	1◇	1◇	1◇	1◇	1◇	1	1◇	1◇	1	1◇	1◇	1◇
							B					A					A		C D			A
		[trolley]	[trolley]		[trolley]	[trolley]	[buffet] [trolley]	[trolley]	[trolley]	[trolley]	[trolley]	[trolley]	[trolley]	[trolley]	[trolley]	[trolley]	[trolley]	[trolley]	[buffet] [trolley]	[trolley]	[trolley]	[trolley]
Edinburgh 10	242 d	09 10	*09b03*	09 36	*09b33*	10 10	10 26	*10b03*	11 10	*11b03*	11 36	12 10	*12b03*	13 10	*13b03*	13 36	14 10	*14b03*	15 00	*15b03*	*15b33*	16 05
Haymarket	242 d	09 14	*09e06*	09 40	*09b36*	10 14	10 31	*10b06*	11 14	*11b06*	11u40	12 14	*12b06*	13 14	*13b06*	13u40	14 14	*14b06*	15 04	*15b06*	*15b36*	16u10
Inverkeithing	242 d	09 27		09 56			10 48		11 27		11u56			13 27		13u54			15 21			16u25
Kirkcaldy	242 d	09 44		10 12		10 42	11 05		11 43		12u12	12 42		13 43		14u10	14 42		15 38			16 41
Markinch	242 d			10 22		10 51			11 52		12 21	12 51		13 52			14 51					16 50
Ladybank	d			10 30		10 59						12 59				14 24	14 59					16 57
Springfield	d																					
Cupar	d	10 02				11 05			12 04			13 05		14 04			15 05					17 04
Leuchars 3 §	d	10 09				11 12	11 31		12 11			13 12		14 11			15 12		16 02			17 11
Glasgow Queen Street 10	230 d		09 41		10 11			10 41		11 41			12 41		13 41			14 41		15 41	16 11	
Larbert	230 d																					
Stirling	230 d		10 07		10 41			11 07		12 07			13 07		14 07			15 07		16 07	16 39	
Dunblane	230 d				10 49																16 49	
Gleneagles	d				11 01																17 01	
Perth	a		10 37	10 56	11 18			11 37		12 37	12 56		13 37		14 37	14 54		15 36		16 37	17 20	
	d		10 37		11 20			11 37		12 37	12 57		13 37		14 37	14 55		15 37		16 37	17 21	
Invergowrie	d																					
Dundee	a	10 21	11 00			11 24	11 44	12 00	12 23	13 00		13 24	14 00	14 23	15 00		15 24	15 59	16 17	16 59		17 26
	d	10 22	11 00			11 25	11 45	12 00	12 24	13 00		13 25	14 00	14 24	15 00		15 25	16 00	16 19	17 00		17 27
Broughty Ferry	d																					17 34
Carnoustie	d		11 11					12 11		13 11					15 11					17 11		17 42
Arbroath	d	10 38	11 18			11 42	12 03	12 18	12 41	13 18		13 42	14 18	14 41	15 18		15 44	16 16	16 36	17 18		17 49
Montrose	d	10 53	11 32				12 19	12 32	12 55	13 32			14 32	14 55	15 43			16 31	16 51	17 32		18 03
Stonehaven	d	11 14				12 15	12 42		13 17			14 17	14 52	15 17			16 17		17 14	17 52		18 25
Portlethen	d																					
Aberdeen	a	11 34	12 19			12 35	13 04	13 13	13 36	14 13		14 36	15 13	15 36	16 21		16 37	17 09	17 38	18 15		18 44
	240 d											14 42					16 41					18 46
Dyce	240 a		*12 47*			*13 21*			*14 20*			14 51	*15 32*				16 50	*17 51*	*18 30*	*18f56*		18 54
Dunkeld & Birnam	d				11 38						13 15					15 12					17 39	
Pitlochry	d				11 51						13 28					15 25					17 52	
Blair Atholl	d				12 00						13 37					15 35					18 02	
Dalwhinnie	d				12 28											16 03						
Newtonmore	d										14 10										18 34	
Kingussie	d				12 40						14 15					16 16					18 39	
Aviemore	d				12 53						14 31					16 29					18 52	
Carrbridge	d				13 01																18 57	
Inverness	a				13 35						15 18					17 07					19 34	

For general notes see front of timetable
For details of catering facilities see Directory of Train Operators

§ For St Andrews

A [trolley] to Aberdeen
B From Leeds (Table 26)
C From London Kings Cross (Table 26)
D **The Northern Lights**
b Change at Stirling
c Mondays to Fridays only
e Change at Stirling. Saturdays dep. 0910
f Saturdays arr. 1854

Edinburgh and Glasgow Queen Street → Perth, Inverness, Dundee, Aberdeen and Dyce

Network Diagram - see first page of Table 225

	SR SX 1◇ A [trolley]		XC 1◇ B [buffet]	SR SO 1◇ [trolley]	SR SX 1◇ [trolley]	GR R 1 C D [restaurant] [trolley]	SR SX		SR 1◇ A [trolley]	SR SX E	SR SO E	SR SO 1◇ [trolley]	SR SX 1◇ [trolley]		SR	SR 1◇ [trolley]	SR	SR	SR SO 1◇ [trolley]		SR SX 1◇ G [trolley]	GR R 1 C [buffet] [trolley]	SR 1◇ [trolley]	XC SX R 1 H [buffet]
Edinburgh 10 242 d	16 05		16 30	*16b03*		16 34			17 04	17 14	17 15	*17b03*	*17b26*		17 28	17 40		*17b33*	18 10		18 10	18 32	*18b03*	19 01
Haymarket 242 d	16u10		16 35	*16b07*		16 39			17 08	17 18	17 19	*17b06*	*17b30*		17 32	17u44		*17b36*	18 14		18 14	18 37	*18b06*	19 06
Inverkeithing 242 d	16u25		16 48							17 38	17 38				17 52	17 59			18 27		18 28	18 55		19 20
Kirkcaldy 242 d	16 41		17 03						17 37	18 01	18 01					18 15			18 45		18 44	19 11		19 35
Markinch 242 d	16 50		17 12						17 46	18 10	18 11				18 33		⟵		18 54		18 53			19 44
Ladybank d	16 58									18 18	18 18				18 40 ⟶		18 40		19 02		19 01			19 51
Springfield d										18 22	18 23													
Cupar d	17 05		17 25						17 58	18 26	18 27								19 08		19 08			19 58
Leuchars 3 § d	17 12		17 32						18 05	18 34	18 34								19 15		19 15	19 36		20 05
Glasgow Queen Street 10 230 d				16 41	16 41		17 12					17 41	17 41					18 11					18 41	
Larbert 230 d							17 33											18 31						
Stirling 230 d				17 07		17 20	17 45					18 07	18 15					18 41					19 07	
Dunblane 230 d							17 54					18 14	18 22					18 50					19 14	
Gleneagles d						17c38	18 06					18 26	18 35					19 02					19 26	
Perth a				17 36	17 37	17 55	18 23					18 42	18 48			18 54	19 07	19 19					19 42	
d				17 37	17 38	17 57						18 44	18 52			18 55							19 44	
Invergowrie d																							20 01	
Dundee a	17 26		17 44	17 59	18 00				18 22	18 48	18 48	19 06	19 15						19 27		19 27	19 49	20 08	20 25
d	17 29		17 48	18 00	18 01				18 24	18 52	18 52	19 08	19 16						19 29		19 29	19 51	20 09	
Broughty Ferry d	17 36									18 58	18 58													
Carnoustie d	17 43			18 11	18 13					19a15	19a15	19 24	19 28											
Arbroath d	17 50		18 04	18 18	18 21				18 40			19 31	19 35						19 45		19 46	20 09	20 25	
Montrose d	18 05		18 18	18 32					18 55			19 45	19 50									20 24	20 38	
Stonehaven d	18 26		18 38	18 52	18 55				19 16			20 07	20 11						20 19		20 21	20 48		
Portlethen d																			20 27		20 30			
Aberdeen a	18 46		19 02	19 15	19 15				19 38			20 27	20 33						20 41		20 44	21 10	21 20	
240 d	18 48								19 39												20 54			
Dyce 240 a	18 56								19 48										*21 03*		21 03			
Dunkeld & Birnam d																19 13								
Pitlochry d						18 32										19 26								
Blair Atholl d																								
Dalwhinnie d																								
Newtonmore d																								
Kingussie d						19 16										20 08								
Aviemore d						19 29										20 20								
Carrbridge d																								
Inverness a						20 08										20 58								

	SR 1◇ J [trolley]	XC SO 1◇ H [buffet]	SR 1◇ [trolley]		SR SX 1◇ [trolley]	SR SO 1◇ [trolley]	SR	GR SX R 1 C [buffet] [trolley]	SR ◇		SR SO 1◇ [trolley]	SR	SR 1◇	SR SX	SR SO		SR	SR	SR	SR 1				
Edinburgh 10 242 d	19 10	19 12	*19b03*		19 36	19 36	20 11	20 30	*20b03*		21 10	21 24	*20b33*	21 33	21 36		*22e33*	22 35		23 10				
Haymarket 242 d	19 14	19 17	*19b06*		19 40	19 40	20 15	20 35	*20b06*		21 14	21 28	*20b36*	21 38	21 40		*22b38*	22 39		23 14				
Inverkeithing 242 d	19 27	19 34			19 53	19 54	20 35	20 50			21 27	21 48						22 58		23 29				
Kirkcaldy 242 d	19 43	19 50			20 09	20 10	20 57	21 07			21 43	22 10						23 20		23 51				
Markinch 242 d	19 52	20 00			20 18	20 19	21 06				21 52	22 19						23 29		00 01				
Ladybank d	20 00	20 08					21 13				22 00	22 27						23 37		00 08				
Springfield d																		23 41						
Cupar d	20 06	20 21					21 21				22 06	22 34						23 45		00 14				
Leuchars 3 § d	20 13	20f30					21 28	21 39			22 13	22 41						23 53		00 22				
Glasgow Queen Street 10 230 d			19 41						20 41				21 41				22 48		23 48					
Larbert 230 d														22 15	22 17		23 19		00 18					
Stirling 230 d			20 07						21 08				22 07	22 24	22 26		23g33		00 31					
Dunblane 230 d									21 14					22 34	22 36		23 42		00 41					
Gleneagles d									21 26					22 46	22 48		23 56		00 55					
Perth a			20 37		20 51	20 51			21 42				22 36	23 02	23 05		00 15		01h19					
d			20 37		20 52	20 59			21 44				22 37											
Invergowrie d									22 01															
Dundee a	20 26	20 50	21 00				21 41	21 53	22 08		22 26	22 55	22 59					00 07		00 36				
d	20 27		21 00					21 53	22 09		22 28		23 00											
Broughty Ferry d																								
Carnoustie d													23 12											
Arbroath d	20 43		21 18					22 11	22 25		22 44		23 19											
Montrose d	20 58		21 33					22 27	22 40		22 59		23 33											
Stonehaven d	21 19		21 53					22 50	23 01		23 20		23 55											
Portlethen d													00 04											
Aberdeen a	21 39		22 15					23 13	23 21		23 40		00 17											
240 d																								
Dyce 240 a	*22 04*		*22 59*																					
Dunkeld & Birnam d					21 09	21 17																		
Pitlochry d					21 22	21 30																		
Blair Atholl d					21 32	21 39																		
Dalwhinnie d					21 57	22 04																		
Newtonmore d					22 08	22 15																		
Kingussie d					22 17	22 20																		
Aviemore d					22 29	22 31																		
Carrbridge d					22 38	22 40																		
Inverness a					23 10	23 13																		

For general notes see front of timetable
For details of catering facilities see Directory of Train Operators

§ For St Andrews
A [trolley] to Aberdeen
B From Bournemouth (Table 51)
C From London Kings Cross (Table 26)
D **The Highland Chieftain.** Also stops at Falkirk Grahamston 1704.
[restaurant] Mondays to Fridays, [buffet] Saturdays
E Also stops at Balmossie 1901, Monifieth 1904, Barry Links 1908 and Golf Street 1910
G To Inverurie (Table 240). [trolley] to Aberdeen
H From Penzance (Table 135)
J [trolley] to Dundee
b Change at Stirling
c Arr. 1735
e Change at Stirling. Saturdays dep. 2234
f Arr. 3 minutes earlier
g Arr. 2328
h Sunday mornings arr. 0116

Sundays

Edinburgh and Glasgow Queen Street → Perth, Inverness, Dundee, Aberdeen and Dyce

Network Diagram - see first page of Table 225

	XC	GR	SR	SR	SR	SR	SR	SR	SR	SR	SR	SR	SR	SR	SR	GR	XC
		R														R	
	1◇	1		1◇	1◇	1◇		1◇	1◇		1◇	1◇	1◇		1◇	1	1◇
													A			B C	D
	⊡	⊡ ⊼		⊼	⊼	⊼		⊼	⊼		⊼	⊼	⊼		⊼	⊡ ⊼	⊡
Edinburgh 10 242 d	08 05	09 10	09 15		09 25	10 55	11 15	*10*b*33*	12 40	13 15	*12*b*34*	13 55	*13*b*38*	15 15	*14*b*34*	16 00	16 35
Haymarket 242 d	08 10	09 14	09 19		09 29	10 59	11 19	*10*b*37*	12 44	13 19	*12*b*38*	13 59	*13*b*42*	15 19	*14*b*38*	16 04	16 40
Inverkeithing 242 d	08 24	09 32	09 41		09 48	11 15	11 41		13 00	13 41		14 16		15 41		16 24	16 54
Kirkcaldy 242 d	08 39	09 49	10 03		10 10	11 31	12 03		13 16	14 03		14 33		16 03		16 41	17 09
Markinch 242 d	08 49		10 12				12 12			14 12				16 12			17 18
Ladybank d			10 20				12 19			14 19				16 19			
Springfield d																	
Cupar d	09 01		10 26				12 26			14 26				16 26			17 30
Leuchars 3 § d	09 09	10 13	10 34			11 55	12 33		13 40	14 33				16 33		17 10	17 37
Glasgow Queen Street 10 230 ⛴ d				09 38				11 45			13 45		14 40		15 45		
Larbert 230 d				10 01									15 00				
Stirling 230 d				10 10				12 12			14 12		15 09		16 12		
Dunblane 230 d				10 17				12 18			14 17		15 16		16 17		
Gleneagles d				10 29				12 29			14 29		15 28		16 29		
Perth a				10 45	10 50			12 47			14 46	15 12	15 45		16 46		
d				10 48	10 51			12 48			14 48	15 13	15 46		16 48		
Invergowrie d																	
Dundee a	09 22	10 27	10 49	11 09		12 07	12 48	13 10	13 52	14 48	15 09			16 48	17 09	17 24	17 49
d	09 23	10 28		11 11		12 08		13 11	13 53		15 11				17 11	17 24	17 51
Broughty Ferry d																	
Carnoustie d				11 23													
Arbroath d	09 40	10 45		11 30		12 25		13 27	14 10		15 27				17 27	17 42	18 07
Montrose d	09 54	11 01		11 44		12 37		13 42	14 24		15 42				17 42	18 00	18 21
Stonehaven d	10 15	11 24		12 06		12 59		14 03	14 46		16 03				18 03	18 23	18 41
Portlethen d						13 07											
Aberdeen a	10 39	11 47		12 27		13 23		14 23	15 05		16 23				18 23	18 44	19 05
240 d																	
Dyce 240 ⇄ a				*13 21*					*15 32*		*17 24*						
Dunkeld & Birnam d					11 08							15 31					
Pitlochry d					11 21							15 44	16 17				
Blair Atholl d					11 33							15 54					
Dalwhinnie d					12 00							16 21					
Newtonmore d					12 10							16 32					
Kingussie d					12 16							16 38	17 00				
Aviemore d					12 28							16 53	17 12				
Carrbridge d					12 37							17 03					
Inverness a					13 09							17 38	17 50				

	SR	GR	SR	SR	SR	SR	GR	SR	XC	SR	SR	SR	SR	SR	SR
		R					R		R						
	1◇	1		1◇	1	1◇	1		1	1◇	1◇	1◇			1
		B				A	B		E	G					
	⊼	⊡ ⊼		⊼		⊼	⊡ ⊼		⊡	⊼		⊼			
Edinburgh 10 242 d	17 05	17 12	17 15		17 50	*17*b*34*	18 43	19 15	19 25	*18*b*34*	21 00	*20*b*34*	22 25	22 36	
Haymarket 242 d	17 09	17 16	17 19		17 54	*17*b*38*	18 47	19 19	19 30	*18*b*38*	21 04	*20*b*38*	22 29	22 40	
Inverkeithing 242 d	17 22		17 38		18 07		19 05	19 38	19 44		21 17		22 48		
Kirkcaldy 242 d	17 38		18 00		18 23		19 22	20 00	20 06		21 33		23 10		
Markinch 242 d			18 09					20 09	20 15		21 44		23 19		
Ladybank d			18 16					20 16	20 22		21 51		23 26		
Springfield d															
Cupar d			18 23					20 23	20c39		21 58		23 33		
Leuchars 3 § d	18 02		18 30				19 47	20 30	20 46		22 05		23 40		
Glasgow Queen Street 10 230 ⛴ d				17 45		18 10				19 45		21 45			23 35
Larbert 230 d						18 30								23 18	00 05
Stirling 230 d		17 52		18 12		18 39				20 12		22 12		23 27	00 14
Dunblane 230 d						18 46				20 17		22 18		23 36	00 23
Gleneagles d		18 09				18 58				20 29		22 30		23 49	00 37
Perth a		18 27		18 44	19 02	19 15				20 47		22 47		00 06	00 56
d		18 29		18 45		19 16				20 48		22 48			
Invergowrie d															
Dundee a	18 14		18 46	19 08			20 01	20 46	21 05	21 10	22 17	23 09	23 56		
d	18 15			19 09			20 01			21 11	22 18	23 10			
Broughty Ferry d															
Carnoustie d				19 21								23 22			
Arbroath d	18 32			19 27			20 19			21 27	22 35	23 27			
Montrose d	18 46			19 42			20 35			21 42	22 49	23 42			
Stonehaven d	19 08			20 03			20 58			22 03	23 11	00 03			
Portlethen d	19 16										23 20				
Aberdeen a	19 30			20 26			21 21			22 24	23 33	00 25			
240 d															
Dyce 240 ⇄ a				*21 09*											
Dunkeld & Birnam d						19 34									
Pitlochry d		18 59				19 47									
Blair Atholl d						19 56									
Dalwhinnie d						20 21									
Newtonmore d						20 32									
Kingussie d		19 52				20 37									
Aviemore d		20 04				20 50									
Carrbridge d						20 59									
Inverness a		20 44				21 34									

For general notes see front of timetable
For details of catering facilities see Directory of Train Operators

§ For St Andrews
A To Elgin (Table 240)
B From London Kings Cross (Table 26)
C **The Northern Lights**
D From Birmingham New Street (Table 51)
E From Plymouth (3 February to 23 March from Bournemouth) (Table 51).
◇ 3 February to 23 March
G ⊼ from Dundee
b Change at Stirling
c Arr. 2033

Dyce, Aberdeen, Dundee, Inverness and Perth → Glasgow Queen Street and Edinburgh

Network Diagram - see first page of Table 225

Miles	Miles	Miles	Miles	Miles		SR	SR SX	SR SX	SR SO		SR SX	XC SX	SR	SR SX		SR	SR	SR	SR		SR	XC SX	XC SO	SR
												R				1	1◇		1◇			R 1	1◇	1◇
								A				B [buffet]					C [trolley]	D	[trolley]		D	E [buffet]	E [buffet]	[trolley]
—	—	0	0	0	**Inverness** d																			
—	—	28	28	28	Carrbridge d																			
—	—	34¾	34¾	34¾	Aviemore d																			
—	—	46½	46½	46½	Kingussie d																			
—	—	49¼	49¼	49¼	Newtonmore d																			
—	—	59½	59½	59½	Dalwhinnie d																			
—	—	82¾	82¾	82¾	Blair Atholl d																			
—	—	89½	89½	89½	Pitlochry d																			
—	—	102½	102½	102½	Dunkeld & Birnam d																			
0	0	—	—	—	**Dyce** 240 ✈ d																			
6¼	6¼	—	—	—	**Aberdeen** 240 a																			
—	—	—	—	—	d												05 27		06 00					06 34
14¼	14¼	—	—	—	Portlethen d																			06 44
22½	22½	—	—	—	Stonehaven d												05 44		06 16					06 53
46¾	46¾	—	—	—	Montrose d												06 05		06 38					07 15
60½	60½	—	—	—	Arbroath d												06 19		06 52					07 29
66¾	66¾	—	—	—	Carnoustie d												06 26	06 37	06 59					07 36
73¼	73¼	—	—	—	Broughty Ferry d												06 36	06 51						
77½	77½	—	—	—	**Dundee** a												06 46	06 57	07 10		←			07 50
—	—	—	—	—	d			06 16	06 16			06 38					06 48	07 17 →	07 11		07 17	07 33	07 35	07 52
81	—	—	—	—	Invergowrie d																			
98¼	—	118	118	118	**Perth** a												07 13							08 12
—	—	—	—	—	d	05 15	06 09				06 14		06 40	06 58		07 03	07 14							08 13
114	—	133¾	—	133¾	Gleneagles d	05 32	06 26						06 55	07 15			07 30							08 27
121¼	—	146	—	146	Dunblane 230 d	05 45	06 40						07 07	07 29			07 42							
131¾	—	151½	—	151½	Stirling 230 d	05 53	06 49						07 16	07 38			07 52							08 44
139¾	—	159½	—	159½	Larbert 230 d	06 02	06 59						07 25	07 47			08 02							
160¾	—	180½	—	—	**Glasgow Queen Street** 10 230 ⛴ a	06 33	07 35							08 20			08 34							09 15
—	85¾	—	—	—	Leuchars 3 § d			06 28	06 28			06 51							07 23		07 30	07 46	07 48	
—	92¼	—	—	—	Cupar d			06 36	06 36			06 58							07 30		07 38	07 55	07 56	
—	94½	—	—	—	Springfield d																07 42			
—	97½	—	135¾	—	Ladybank d			06 44	06 44		06 37	07 05				07 26					07 47	08 02	08 03	
—	103¼	—	141	—	Markinch 242 d			06 52	06 52		06 45	07 13				07 34					07 54	08 09	08 11	
—	110¾	—	149	—	Kirkcaldy 242 d			07 02	07 02			07b25				07 44			07 50		08 05	08 18	08 20	
—	123½	—	161¾	—	Inverkeithing 242 d			07 25	07 26		07 31	07 43				08 00					08 28	08 37	08 36	
—	135½	—	173¾	186½	Haymarket 242 a	07c25		07 45	07 46		07 54	07 59	08e10	08f39		08 18	08f57		08 21		08 47	08 57	08 56	09f58
—	136¾	—	175	187¾	**Edinburgh** 10 242 a	07c33		07 50	07 51		07 59	08 06	08e15	08f45		08 23	09f02		08 26		08 52	09 03	09 02	10g03

	SR	SR		SR	SR SX	SR SO	SR		SR	GR	XC SO	XC SX		GR	SR	SR	SR		SR	GR	SR	SR		SR
		1◇		1◇	1	1	1◇		1	R 1	1◇	R 1		R 1	1◇	1◇	1		1◇	R 1	1	1◇		1◇
		G [trolley]		G [trolley]			[trolley]			H [buffet] [trolley]	E [buffet]	E [buffet]		H J ✕ [buffet]	[trolley]	[trolley]			G [trolley]	H K [buffet]		G [trolley]		[trolley]
Inverness d				05 00	06 00	06 20	06 45							07 55										09 19
Carrbridge d					06 33	06 53																		09 50
Aviemore d					06 41	07 01	07 22							08 29										10 04
Kingussie d					06a54	07a14	07 36							08 42										10 16
Newtonmore d																								10 21
Dalwhinnie d																								10 32
Blair Atholl d																								10 54
Pitlochry d							08 16							09 24										11 03
Dunkeld & Birnam d							08 28																	11 16
Dyce 240 ✈ d		06 50		07 03								*07 45*			*08 03*				09 08			10 08		
Aberdeen 240 a		07 00		07 14															09 18			10 18		
d		07 07		07 20						07 53	08 20	08 20			08 39	08 50			09 36	09 52		10 22		
Portlethen d																								
Stonehaven d		07 23		07 36						08 10	08 37	08 37				09 06			09 53	10 09		10 38		
Montrose d		07 45		07 58						08 33	08 58	08 59			09 14				10 14	10 32		11 00		
Arbroath d		07 59		08 12						08 48	09 15	09 15			09 28	09 42			10 28	10 47		11 14		
Carnoustie d		08 06		08 19											09 35				10 35					
Broughty Ferry d																			10 43					
Dundee a		08 19		08 30						09 05	09 31	09 31			09 50	09 57			10 50	11 04		11 29		
d	07 59	08 21		08 31					08 47	09 06	09 32	09 33			09 50	09 59			10 50	11 05		11 30		
Invergowrie d									08 52															
Perth a		08 41					08 47		09 06					09 54	10 12				11 12					11 36
d		08 43					08 48		09 08					09 56	10 12		11 08		11 12					11 39
Gleneagles d									09 23					10 12										11 54
Dunblane 230 d									09 34															12 05
Stirling 230 d		09h10							09 41					10 30	10 41				11 41					12 12
Larbert 230 d																								
Glasgow Queen Street 10 230 ⛴ a		09 44							10 15						11 15				12 15					12 44
Leuchars 3 § d	08 11			08 43						09 20	09 45	09 46				10 11				11 19		11 42		
Cupar d	08 19			08 51							09 52	09 53				10 19						11 50		
Springfield d																					←			
Ladybank d	08 26			08 58												10 26	11 35 →				11 35			
Markinch 242 d	08 34			09 06							10 04	10 04				10 34					11 42	12 02		
Kirkcaldy 242 d	08 43			09 15			09 25			09 44	10 12	10 13				10 43				11 43	11 52	12 12		
Inverkeithing 242 d	08 59									10 00	10 27	10 28				10 59				11 59	12 08			
Haymarket 242 a	09 15	10f26		09 45			09 55		10f56	10 18	10 45	10 46		11 09	11f56	11 15			12f56	12 16	12 23	12 45		13f26
Edinburgh 10 242 a	09 20	10f32		09 50			10 01		11f01	10 25	10 55	10 51		11 20	12f01	11 20			13f01	12 22	12 28	12 50		13f32

For general notes see front of timetable
For details of catering facilities see Directory of Train Operators

§ For St Andrews
A To Newcraighall (Table 230)
B To Plymouth (Table 51)
C Also stops at Monifieth 0632
D Also stops at Golf Street 0638, Barry Links 0641, Monifieth 0645 and Balmossie 0647
E To Bournemouth (Table 51)
G [trolley] from Aberdeen
H To London Kings Cross (Table 26)
J **The Highland Chieftain** Also stops at Falkirk Grahamston 1045. ✕ Mondays to Fridays, [buffet] Saturdays
K **The Northern Lights**
b Arr. 0720
c Change at Stirling. Saturdays arr. 1 minute earlier
e Saturdays arr. 1 minute earlier
f Change at Stirling
g Change at Stirling. Saturdays arr. 1004
h Saturdays only

Dyce, Aberdeen, Dundee, Inverness and Perth → Glasgow Queen Street and Edinburgh

Network Diagram - see first page of Table 225

		SR	SR	SR	SR	SR	SR	SR	SR	SR	SR	SR	GR	SR	SR	SR	SR	SR	SR	SR	SR
													R							R	
		1◇	1◇	1◇	1◇	1◇	1◇	1◇	1◇	1◇	1◇	1◇	1	1◇	1◇	1◇	1◇	1◇	1◇	1	1
													A	B					B		
		⊼	⊼	⊼	⊼	⊼	⊼	⊼	⊼	⊼	⊼	⊼	🍴	⊼	⊼	⊼	⊼	⊼	⊼	⊼	
Inverness	d			10 53					12 40						14 41					16 56	
Carrbridge	d			11 26																	
Aviemore	d			11 38					13 25						15 18					17 33	
Kingussie	d			11 50					13 37						15 31					17 46	
Newtonmore	d														15 35					17 50	
Dalwhinnie	d																			18 02	
Blair Atholl	d														16 05					18 23	
Pitlochry	d			12 31					14 17						16 15					18 33	
Dunkeld & Birnam	d			12 44					14 29						16 27					18 45	
Dyce 240 ✈	d		*10 42*			*11 50*		*12 48*			*13 23*		*14 20*	15 08			*16 00*		17 00		
Aberdeen 240	a													15 18					17 10		
	d	10 41	11 22		11 42	12 24	12 42	13 21		13 42	14 25	14 40	14 50	15 20		15 33	16 21	16 41	17 21		
Portlethen	d					12 34													17 32		
Stonehaven	d		11 38			12 43	12 56	13 37			14 41		15 07	15 36			16 37	16 56	17 41		
Montrose	d	11 15	12 00		12 15		13 15	13 59		14 15		15 15	15 30	16 00		16 13		17 15	18b05		
Arbroath	d	11 28	12 14		12 28	13 17	13 30	14 13		14 28	15 15	15 28	15 45	16 14		16 27	17 11	17 28	18 19		
Carnoustie	d	11 35			12 35					14 35		15 35					17 18				
Broughty Ferry	d																				
Dundee	a	11 50	12 29		12 50	13 32	13 50	14 28		14 50	15 31	15 50	16 02	16 29		16 46	17 30	17 50	18 34		
	d	11 50	12 30		12 50	13 33	13 50	14 30		14 50	15 32	15 50	16 03	16 31		16 47	17 31	17 50	18 35		
Invergowrie	d															16 52					
Perth	a	12 12		13 03	13 12		14 12		14 48	15 12		16 12			16 46	17 09		18 12		19 06	
	d	12 12		13 04	13 12		14 12		14 49	15 12		16 12			16 48	17 10		18 12		19 08	19 13
Gleneagles	d															17 25				19 23	
Dunblane 230	d															17 36		18 37		19 35	
Stirling 230	d	12 41			13 41		14 41			15 41		16 41				17 41		18 41		19 41	
Larbert 230	d																				
Glasgow Queen Street 10 230 ⛴	a	13 14			14 14		15 14			16 14		17 18				18 18		19 14		20 17	
Leuchars 3 §	d		12 42			13 45		14 42			15 44		16 17	16 43			17 43		18 47		
Cupar	d		12 50			13 53		14 49			15 52			16 50			17 50		18 55		
Springfield	d													16 55							
Ladybank	d		12 57	13 28				14 57						17 00	17 14		17 58				19 37
Markinch 242	d		13 04			14 05		15 04	15 18		16 04			17 07	17 22		18 05		19 07		19 45
Kirkcaldy 242	d		13 14	13 44		14 15		15 14	15 28		16 14		16 41	17 17	17 31		18 15		19 17		19 54
Inverkeithing 242	d		13 30	14 00				15 30	15 44		16 30		16 57	17 33	17 47				19 33		20 10
Haymarket 242	a	*13c56*	13 45	14 13	*14c56*	14 45	*15c56*	15 45	15 59	*16c56*	16 45	*17c56*	17 15	17 48	18 00	*18c56*	18 45	*19c56*	19 52		20 26
Edinburgh 10 242	a	*14c01*	13 50	14 21	*15c01*	14 50	*16c01*	15 50	16 04	*17c03*	16 50	*18c02*	17 23	17 53	18 11	*19c01*	18 50	*20c04*	19 57		20 32

		SR	GR	SR	SR	SR	SR	SR	SR	SR	SR	SR	XC	XC	SR	SR	SR	SR	SR
			SX	SO		SO	SX		SO		SX	SO	SX	SO				FSX	FO
			R																
		1◇	1	1◇	1◇	1◇	1◇	1◇		1◇			1◇	1◇	1◇	1◇	1◇	1	1
						B	B												
		⊼	🍴 ⊼	⊼	⊼	⊼	⊼	⊼		⊼			🍴	🍴					
Inverness	d							18 27								20 10			
Carrbridge	d							18 57											
Aviemore	d							19 11								20 55			
Kingussie	d							19 31								21 07			
Newtonmore	d							19 35								21 12			
Dalwhinnie	d							19 47								21 23			
Blair Atholl	d							20 09								21 45			
Pitlochry	d							20 18								21 55			
Dunkeld & Birnam	d							20 31								22 07			
Dyce 240 ✈	d	*17 26*	*17 56*	*17 56*	*17 56*	19 05	19 05			*19 19*		19 55	*19 55*		*20 18*			*21 40*	*21 40*
Aberdeen 240	a					19 17	19 17					20 05							
	d	17 54	18 20	18 25	18 41	19 25	19 25			19 41		20 20	20 26	20 28	20 45		21 22	22 30	23 29
Portlethen	d	18 03								19 51								22 40	23 40
Stonehaven	d	18 12	18 37	18 42		19 41	19 41			20 00		20 36	20 43	20 45	21 01		21 38	22 49	23 49
Montrose	d	18 33	19 00	19 04	19 15					20 24		20 58	21 04	21 06	21 23		22 00	23 11	00 10
Arbroath	d	18 47	19 15	19 19	19 28	20 15	20 17			20 38		21 12	21 21	21 23	21 37		22 16	23 25	00 24
Carnoustie	d	18 54			19 35													23 32	00 31
Broughty Ferry	d																		
Dundee	a	19 10	19 32	19 34	19 50	20 31	20 33			20 56		21 27	21 37	21 39	21 55		22 33	23 46	00 45
	d	19 11	19 33	19 35	19 50	20 32	20 34		20 54	20 57	21 28	21 28	21 38	21 41	21 56		22 34	23 47	00 47
Invergowrie	d																	23 53	00 53
Perth	a	19 32			20 12			20 50		21 18					22 17	22 27		00 11	01 11
	d	19 33			20 12			20 51		21 18					22 18	22 28			
Gleneagles	d				20 28											22 45			
Dunblane 230	d															22 57			
Stirling 230	d	19 58			20 41					21 47					22 47	23 03			
Larbert 230	d																		
Glasgow Queen Street 10 230 ⛴	a	20 38			21 15					22 17					23 18	23 39			
Leuchars 3 §	d		19 47	19 47		20 44	20 46		21 06		21 40	21 40	21 52	21 54			22 46		
Cupar	d					20 51	20 53		21 14		21 48	21 48	21 59	22 01			22 54		
Springfield	d																		
Ladybank	d					20 59	21 01	21 14	21 22		21 55	21 55		22 08			23 01		
Markinch 242	d					21 06	21 08		21 30		22 03	22 03	22 12	22 16			23 09		
Kirkcaldy 242	d		20 11	20 13		21 16	21 18	21 33	21 40		22 13	22 13					23 18		
Inverkeithing 242	d		20 27	20 29		21 32	21 34	21 49	22 02		22 36	22 36	22 45	22 45			23 41		
Haymarket 242	a	*20c56*	20s44	20 45	*21c56*	21 47	21 51	22 01	22 25	*22c56*	23 00	23 00				*00e02*	00 04		
Edinburgh 10 242	a	*21c05*	20 50	20 50	*22c01*	21 52	21 56	22 09	22 32	*23c01*	23 05	23 05	23 25	23 25		*00c07*	00 09		

For general notes see front of timetable
For details of catering facilities see Directory of Train Operators

§ For St Andrews

A To London Kings Cross (Table 26)
B ⊼ from Aberdeen
b Arr. 1802
c Change at Stirling

e Change at Stirling. Saturdays arr. 1 minute earlier

Table 229

Sundays

Dyce, Aberdeen, Dundee, Inverness and Perth → Glasgow Queen Street and Edinburgh

Network Diagram - see first page of Table 225

	SR	SR	SR	SR	SR	GR	SR	GR	SR	GR	XC	SR	SR	SR	GR	SR	SR
		■1			■1 ◇	R ■1		R ■1	■1 ◇	R ■1	R ■1		■1 ◇	■1 ◇	R ■1	■1 ◇	
						A B		A		A	C				A		
					⊼	🍽 ⊼		🍽 ⊼	⊼	🍽 ⊼	🍽		⊼	⊼	🍽 ⊼	⊼	
Inverness d								09 38					12 30			13 25	
Carrbridge d								10 08					13 08				
Aviemore d								10 17					13 17			14 02	
Kingussie d								10 30					13 30			14 15	
Newtonmore d								10 35					13 35				
Dalwhinnie d													13 46				
Blair Atholl d								11 07					14 08				
Pitlochry d								11 21					14 17			14 54	
Dunkeld & Birnam d								11 34					14 30				
Dyce 240 ✈ d														*11 59*			
Aberdeen 240 a																	
d					09 30	09 50			11 28	11 42	11 58			13 30	13 50		
Portlethen d																	
Stonehaven d					09 46	10 07			11 44	11 59	12 16			13 46	14 07		
Montrose d					10 08	10 30			12 06	12 22	12 39			14 08	14 30		
Arbroath d					10 22	10 45			12 20	12 37	12 56			14 22	14 45		
Carnoustie d					10 29												
Broughty Ferry d																	
Dundee a					10 43	11 02			12 39	12 57	13 12			14 41	15 02		
d	07 25	08 45		09 25	10 43	11 03	11 25		12 43	12 58	13 14	13 25		14 43	15 03		15 25
Invergowrie d																	
Perth a		09 05			11 05			11 54	13 03				14 49	15 03		15 23	
d		09 05	09 27		11 05			11 55	13 05				14 50	15 05		15 25	
Gleneagles d		09 20	09 42		11 20			12 11	13 20				15 05	15 20			
Dunblane 230 d		09 30	09 54		11 30			12 26	13 30				15 16	15 30			
Stirling 230 d		09 38	10 02		11 38			12 32	13 38				15 22	15 38			
Larbert 230 d		09 47	10 11										15 31				
Glasgow Queen Street 10 230 ⛴ a		10 15			12 12				14 12				15 56	16 12			
Leuchars 3 § d	07 37			09 37		11 17	11 37			13 12	13 27	13 39			15 17		15 37
Cupar d	07 44			09 44			11 44				13 35	13 46					15 44
Springfield d																	
Ladybank d	07 52			09 52			11 52				13 42	13 54					15 54
Markinch 242 d	07 59			09 59			11 59				13 49	14 01					16 01
Kirkcaldy 242 d	08 09			10 09		11 41	12 09			13 36	13 58	14 11			15 41	16 02	16 11
Inverkeithing 242 d	08 30			10 32		11 57	12 32			13 54	14 14	14 32			16b02	16 18	16 32
Haymarket 242 a	08 55		10 51	10 59	*12c56*	12 17	12 59	13 12	*14c57*	14 18	14 28	14 59		*16c57*	16 20	16 34	16 54
Edinburgh 10 242 a	09 00		10 58	11 04	*13c01*	12 24	13 04	13 18	*15c02*	14 24	14 33	15 04		*17c02*	16 26	16 43	16 59

	SR	SR	SR	SR	SR	SR	SR	SR	SR	SR	SR	XC	SR
	■1 ◇	■1 ◇		■1 ◇	■1 ◇	■1 ◇		■1 ◇	■1 ◇	■1 ◇	■1 ◇	■1 ◇	■1
								D		E			
	⊼	⊼		⊼	⊼	⊼		⊼	⊼	⊼	⊼	🍽	
Inverness d					16 15				18 30				
Carrbridge d					16 46				19 01				
Aviemore d					16 55				19 09				
Kingussie d					17 14				19 22				
Newtonmore d									19 26				
Dalwhinnie d									19 39				
Blair Atholl d					17 47				20 02				
Pitlochry d					17 56				20 11				
Dunkeld & Birnam d					18 09				20 24				
Dyce 240 ✈ d	*14 20*					*17 26*					*19 17*		
Aberdeen 240 a													
d	15 10	15 30		17 10		17 50		19 10		19 35	20 10	20 51	22 29
Portlethen d	15 20										20 20		
Stonehaven d	15 29	15 46		17 26		18 06		19 26		19 51	20 29	21 08	22 48
Montrose d	15 51	16 08		17 48		18 28		19 48		20 13	20 50	21 29	23 11
Arbroath d	16 05	16 22		18 02		18 42		20 02		20 27	21 04	21 46	23 25
Carnoustie d	16 12							20 09					23 32
Broughty Ferry d													
Dundee a	16 23	16 41		18 17		19 00		20 18		20 45	21 20	22 02	23 46
d	16 25	16 43	17 25	18 19		19 02	19 25	20 20		20 46	21 21	22 03	23 47
Invergowrie d													
Perth a		17 03			18 26	19 22			20 42	21 07			00 09
d		17 05			18 27	19 24			20 46	21 08			
Gleneagles d		17 20			18 44					21 23			
Dunblane 230 d		17 30			18 55					21 34			
Stirling 230 d		17 38			19 02	19e54				21 40			
Larbert 230 d					19 09								
Glasgow Queen Street 10 230 ⛴ a		18 12			19 36	20 32				22 11			
Leuchars 3 § d	16 37		17 37	18 31			19 37	20 32			21 33	22 16	
Cupar d			17 44				19 44				21 41	22 23	
Springfield d													
Ladybank d			17 52				19 52				21 48	22 30	
Markinch 242 d			17 59				19 59				21 56	22 38	
Kirkcaldy 242 d	17 03		18 09	18 56			20 09	20 59	21 25		22 05	22 46	
Inverkeithing 242 d	17 19		18 30	19 12			20 30	21 15	21 41		22 21	23 02	
Haymarket 242 a	17 34	*18c57*	18 55	19 27	*20c00*	*20c56*	20 52	21 31	22 00	*22c56*	22 37	23s16	
Edinburgh 10 242 a	17 41	*19c02*	19 00	19 35	*20c05*	*21c01*	20 59	21 38	22 06	*23c01*	22 44	23 26	

For general notes see front of timetable
For details of catering facilities see Directory of Train Operators

§ For St Andrews
A To London Kings Cross (Table 26)
B **The Northern Lights**
C Until 27 January to Southampton Central, 3 February to 23 March to Bristol Temple Meads and from 30 March to Oxford (Table 51)
D ⊼ to Dundee
E ⊼ to Dundee and from Perth
b Arr. 1557
c Change at Stirling
e Arr. 1951

Edinburgh, Glasgow Queen Street and Falkirk Grahamston → Stirling and Dunblane
Newcraighall → Edinburgh → Bathgate

Network Diagram - see first page of Table 225

Miles	Miles	Miles			SR	SR 1 ◇ A	SR	SR 1 B	SR 1 C	SR	SR 1 B	SR	SR	SR 1 C	SR 1 ◇ D	SR	SR	SR 1 B		SR	SR	SR 1 C	SR	SR 1 B	SR 1 ◇ E
0	—	—	**Newcraighall**	d								06 18								06 48					
¾	—	—	Brunstane	d								06 20								06 50					
4¾	0	—	**Edinburgh 10**	a								06 29								06 59					
—	—	—		d	05 18			05 55		06 05	06 30	06 32					06 35	07 00		07 03			07 05	07 15	
6	1¼	—	Haymarket	d	05 22			06 00		06 09	06 34	06 36					06 39	07 04		07 06			07 09	07 19	
8½	3¾	—	Edinburgh Park	d	05 27					06 14		06 41					06 46			07 11			07 16		
17¼	—	—	Uphall	d						06 26							06 58						07 28		
20¼	—	—	Livingston North	d						06 31							07 03						07 33		
23¼	—	—	**Bathgate**	a						06 36							07 08						07 38		
—	17½	—	Linlithgow	d	05 39			06 14			06 48	06 53								07 23				07a33	
—	22¼	—	Polmont 3	d	05 44			06a20			06a54	06 59						07a19		07 29					
—	—	0	**Glasgow Queen Street 10**	d		05 55	06 13		06 30				06 48	07 00	07 06						07 18	07 30			07 41
—	—	3¼	Bishopbriggs	d			06 19						06 53								07 23				
—	—	6¼	Lenzie 3	d			06 24		06 38				06 59	07a08							07 29				
—	—	11½	Croy 3	d			06 31		06a44				07 05								07 35	07a41			
—	25½	—	**Falkirk Grahamston**	d	05 50							07 04								07 34					
—	27	—	Camelon	d	05 53							07 07								07 37					
—	28½	21	Larbert	d	05 59	06 16	06 42					07 14	07 19			←				07 44	07 48				
—	36½	29	**Stirling**	d	06 08	06 25	06a54					07 23	07b39		07 31	07 39				07 54	08a01				08 07
—	40	32½	Bridge of Allan	d	06 13							07 27	→			07 43				07 57					
—	42	34½	**Dunblane**	a	06 20	06 31						07 35			07 37	07 50				08 05					08 13

		SR 1 B	SR	SR	SR 1 C	SR 1 B	SR	SR G	SR 1 B	SR	SR		SR 1 C	SR 1 B	SR 1 ◇ E	SR	SR	SR	SR 1 C	SR 1 B	SR	SR	SR	SR 1 C	SR 1 B
Newcraighall	d		07 18							07 48							08 18					08 48			
Brunstane	d		07 20							07 50							08 20					08 50			
Edinburgh 10	a		07 29							07 59							08 29					08 59			
	d	07 30	07 33			07 45	07 48		08 00	08 03				08 15		08 18	08 33			08 45	08 48	09 03			09 15
Haymarket	d	07 34	07 36			07 49	07 51		08 04	08 06				08 18		08 21	08 36			08 48	08 51	09 06			09 18
Edinburgh Park	d		07 41				07 56			08 11						08 26	08 41				08 56	09 11			
Uphall	d						08 08									08 38					09 08				
Livingston North	d						08 13									08 43					09 13				
Bathgate	a						08 20									08 50					09 20				
Linlithgow	d	07 49	07 53			08a05		08 00		08 23				08 33			08 53			09 03		09 23			09 33
Polmont 3	d	07a55	07 59						08a20	08 29				08a39			08 59			09a09		09 29			09a39
Glasgow Queen Street 10	d			07 48	08 00						08 18		08 30		08 41			08 48	09 00				09 18	09 30	
Bishopbriggs	d			07 53							08 23							08 53					09 23		
Lenzie 3	d			07 59							08 29							08 59					09 29		
Croy 3	d			08 05	08a11						08 35		08a41					09 05	09a11				09 35	09a41	
Falkirk Grahamston	d		08 04					08 11		08 34							09 04					09 34			
Camelon	d		08 07					08a14		08 37							09 07					09 37			
Larbert	d		08 14	08 18						08 44	08 48						09 14	09 18				09 44	09 48		
Stirling	d		08 23	08 31						08 53	09a01				09a05		09 23	09 31				09 53	10a02		
Bridge of Allan	d		08 27	08 36						08 57							09 27	09 36				09 57			
Dunblane	a		08 36	08 43						09 06							09 37	09 44				10 07			

		SR 1 ◇ E	SR	SR		SR	SR 1 C	SR 1 B	SR 1 ◇ D	SR	SR	SR	SR 1 C	SR 1 B	SR 1 ◇ E	SR	SR	SR	SR 1 C		SR 1 B	SR	SR	SR	SR 1 C
Newcraighall	d			09 18							09 48						10 18						10 48		
Brunstane	d			09 20							09 50						10 20						10 50		
Edinburgh 10	a			09 29							09 59						10 29						10 59		
	d		09 19	09 33				09 45		09 48	10 03			10 15		10 18	10 33				10 45	10 48	11 03		
Haymarket	d		09 21	09 36				09 48		09 51	10 06			10 18		10 21	10 36				10 48	10 51	11 06		
Edinburgh Park	d		09 26	09 41						09 56	10 11					10 26	10 41					10 56	11 11		
Uphall	d		09 38							10 08						10 38						11 08			
Livingston North	d		09 43							10 13						10 43						11 13			
Bathgate	a		09 51							10 21						10 50						11 20			
Linlithgow	d			09 53				10 03			10 23			10 33			10 53				11 03		11 23		
Polmont 3	d			09 59				10a09			10 29			10a39			10 59				11a09		11 29		
Glasgow Queen Street 10	d	09 41				09 48	10 00		10 11			10 18	10 30		10 41			10 48	11 00					11 18	11 30
Bishopbriggs	d					09 53						10 23						10 53						11 23	
Lenzie 3	d					09 59						10 29						10 59						11 29	
Croy 3	d					10 05	10a11					10 35	10a41					11 05	11a11					11 35	11a41
Falkirk Grahamston	d			10 04							10 34						11 04						11 34		
Camelon	d			10 07							10 37						11 07						11 37		
Larbert	d			10 14		10 18					10 44	10 47					11 14	11 18					11 44	11 48	
Stirling	d	10a06		10 23		10 31			10 41		10 53	11a00			11a06		11 23	11 31					11 53	12a01	
Bridge of Allan	d			10 27		10 36					10 57						11 27	11 36					11 57		
Dunblane	a			10 36		10 43			10 49		11 06						11 36	11 43					12 06		

For general notes see front of timetable
For details of catering facilities see Directory of Train Operators

A To Dyce (Table 229)
B To Glasgow Queen Street (Table 228)
C To Edinburgh (Table 228)
D To Inverness (Table 229)
E To Aberdeen (Table 229)
G From Kirkcaldy (Table 242) to Glasgow Queen Street (Table 228)
b Arr. 0728

Edinburgh, Glasgow Queen Street and Falkirk Grahamston → Stirling and Dunblane
Newcraighall → Edinburgh → Bathgate

Network Diagram - see first page of Table 225

	SR ■1 A 🛒	SR ■1◇ B 🛒	SR	SR	SR	SR ■1 C 🛒	SR ■1 A 🛒	SR	SR	SR	SR ■1 C 🛒		SR ■1 A 🛒	SR ■1◇ B 🛒	SR	SR	SR	SR ■1 C 🛒	SR ■1 A 🛒	SR	SR	SR	SR ■1 C 🛒	SR ■1 A 🛒
Newcraighall d				11 18					11 48							12 18					12 48			
Brunstane d				11 20					11 50							12 20					12 50			
Edinburgh ■10 a				11 29					11 59							12 29					12 59			
d	11 15		11 18	11 33			11 45	11 48	12 03				12 15		12 18	12 33			12 45	12 48	13 03			13 15
Haymarket d	11 18		11 21	11 36			11 48	11 51	12 06				12 18		12 21	12 36			12 48	12 51	13 06			13 18
Edinburgh Park d			11 26	11 41				11 56	12 11						12 26	12 41				12 56	13 11			
Uphall d			11 38					12 08							12 38					13 08				
Livingston North d			11 43					12 13							12 43					13 13				
Bathgate a			11 50					12 20							12 50					13 20				
Linlithgow d	11 33			11 53			12 03		12 23				12 33			12 53			13 03		13 23			13 33
Polmont ■3 d	11a39			11 59			12a09		12 29				12a39			12 59			13a09		13 29			13a39
Glasgow Queen Street ■10 ⛴ d		11 41			11 48	12 00				12 18	12 30			12 41			12 48	13 00				13 18	13 30	
Bishopbriggs d					11 53					12 23							12 53					13 23		
Lenzie ■3 d					11 59					12 29							12 59					13 29		
Croy ■3 d					12 05	12a11				12 35	12a41						13 05	13a11				13 35	13a41	
Falkirk Grahamston d				12 04					12 34							13 04					13 34			
Camelon d				12 07					12 37							13 07					13 37			
Larbert d				12 14	12 18				12 44	12 48						13 14	13 18				13 44	13 48		
Stirling d		12a06		12 23	12 31				12 53	13a01				13a06		13 23	13 31				13 53	14a01		
Bridge of Allan d				12 27	12 36				12 57							13 27	13 36				13 57			
Dunblane a				12 36	12 42				13 06							13 36	13 43				14 06			

	SR ■1◇ B 🛒	SR	SR	SR		SR ■1 C 🛒	SR ■1 A 🛒	SR	SR	SR	SR ■1 C 🛒	SR ■1 A 🛒	SR ■1◇ B 🛒	SR	SR	SR	SR ■1 C 🛒	SR ■1 A 🛒	SR		SR	SR	SR ■1 C 🛒	SR ■1 A 🛒
Newcraighall d			13 18						13 48						14 18						14 48			
Brunstane d			13 20						13 50						14 20						14 50			
Edinburgh ■10 a			13 29						13 59						14 29						14 59			
d		13 18	13 33				13 45	13 48	14 03			14 15		14 18	14 33			14 45	14 48		15 03			15 15
Haymarket d		13 21	13 36				13 48	13 51	14 06			14 18		14 21	14 36			14 48	14 51		15 06			15 18
Edinburgh Park d		13 26	13 41					13 56	14 11					14 26	14 41				14 56		15 11			
Uphall d		13 38						14 08						14 38					15 08					
Livingston North d		13 43						14 13						14 43					15 13					
Bathgate a		13 50						14 20						14 50					15 20					
Linlithgow d			13 53				14 03		14 23			14 33			14 53			15 03			15 23			15 33
Polmont ■3 d			13 59				14a09		14 29			14a39			14 59			15a09			15 29			15a39
Glasgow Queen Street ■10 ⛴ d	13 41			13 48		14 00				14 18	14 30		14 41			14 48	15 00					15 18	15 30	
Bishopbriggs d				13 53						14 23						14 53						15 23		
Lenzie ■3 d				13 59						14 29						14 59						15 29		
Croy ■3 d				14 05		14a11				14 35	14a41					15 05	15a11					15 35	15a41	
Falkirk Grahamston d			14 04						14 34						15 04						15 34			
Camelon d			14 07						14 37						15 09						15 37			
Larbert d			14 14	14 18					14 44	14 48					15 14	15 18					15 44	15 48		
Stirling d	14a06		14 23	14 31					14 53	15a01			15a06		15 23	15 31					15 53	16a01		
Bridge of Allan d			14 27	14 36					14 57						15 27	15 36					15 57			
Dunblane a			14 36	14 43					15 06						15 36	15 43					16 06			

	SR ■1◇ B 🛒	SR	SR	SR	SR	SR ■1 C 🛒	SR ■1 A 🛒	SR ■1◇ D 🛒	SR	SR	SR	SR ■1 C 🛒		SR	SR ■1 A 🛒	SR	GR R ■1 E G ✕ 🛒	SR	SR	SR ■1 C 🛒	SR	SR ■1 A 🛒	SR H	SR
Newcraighall d			15 18							15 48								16 18						
Brunstane d			15 20							15 50								16 20						
Edinburgh ■10 a			15 29							15 59								16 29						
d		15 18	15 33				15 45		15 48	16 03					16 15	16 18	16 34	16 36				16 45		16 48
Haymarket d		15 21	15 36				15 48		15 51	16 06					16 18	16 21	16 39	16 40				16 48		16 51
Edinburgh Park d		15 26	15 41						15 56	16 11						16 26		16 44						16 56
Uphall d		15 38							16 08							16 38								17 08
Livingston North d		15 43							16 13							16 43								17 13
Bathgate a		15 50							16 20							16 50								17 20
Linlithgow d			15 53				16 03			16 23					16 33			16 57				17 03		
Polmont ■3 d			15 59				16a09			16 29					16a39			17 02				17a09		
Glasgow Queen Street ■10 ⛴ d	15 41			15 48	15 51	16 00		16 11			16 18	16 30		16 33					16 48	17 00	17 03		17 12	
Bishopbriggs d				15 53	15 57						16 23			16 39					16 53		17 09			
Lenzie ■3 d				15 59	16 08						16 29			16a44					16 59		17a13			
Croy ■3 d				16 05	16 15	16a11					16 35	16a41							17 05	17a11				
Falkirk Grahamston d			16 04		16a33					16 34							17 04	17 08						
Camelon d			16 07		16a27					16 37								17 11						
Larbert d			16 14	16 18						16 44	16 48							17 17	17 24				17 33	
Stirling d	16a06		16 23	16 31				16 39		16 53	17a01						17a19	17 26	17 35				17 45	
Bridge of Allan d			16 27	16 36						16 57								17 31	17 40				17 50	
Dunblane a			16 37	16 44				16 48		17 06								17 41	17 48				17 54	

For general notes see front of timetable
For details of catering facilities see Directory of Train Operators

- **A** To Glasgow Queen Street (Table 228)
- **B** To Aberdeen (Table 229)
- **C** To Edinburgh (Table 228)
- **D** To Inverness (Table 229)
- **E** From London Kings Cross (Table 26) to Inverness (Table 229)
- **G** **The Highland Chieftain**
- **H** To Perth (Table 229)

Edinburgh, Glasgow Queen Street and Falkirk Grahamston → Stirling and Dunblane Newcraighall → Edinburgh → Bathgate

Network Diagram - see first page of Table 225

		SR	SR	SR 1 A 🛒	SR 1 B 🛒	SR C		SR	SR	SR 1◇ D 🛒	SR	SR	SR 1 A 🛒	SR 1 B 🛒	SR E	SR	SR	SR	SR 1 A 🛒	SR 1 B 🛒	SR 1◇ D 🛒		SR	SR	SR
Newcraighall	d	16 48									17 18						17 48							18 18	
Brunstane	d	16 50									17 20						17 50							18 20	
Edinburgh 10	a	16 59									17 29						17 59							18 29	
	d	17 03			17 15			17 18	17 26		17 33			17 45		17 48	18 03			18 15			18 18	18 33	
Haymarket	d	17 06			17 18			17 21	17 30		17 36			17 48		17 51	18 06			18 18			18 21	18 36	
Edinburgh Park	d	17 11						17 26			17 41					17 56	18 11						18 26	18 41	
Uphall	d							17 38								18 08							18 38		
Livingston North	d							17 43								18 13							18 43		
Bathgate	a							17 50								18 20							18 50		
Linlithgow	d	17 23			17 33						17 53			18 03			18 23			18 33				18 53	
Polmont 3	d	17 29			17a39						17 59			18a09			18 29			18a39				18 59	
Glasgow Queen Street 10 ⛴	d		17 18	17 30		17 33				17 41		17 48	18 00		18 11			18 18	18 30		18 41				18 48
Bishopbriggs	d		17 23			17 39						17 53						18 23							18 53
Lenzie 3	d		17 29			17 44						17 59						18 29							18 59
Croy 3	d		17 35	17a42								18 05	18a11					18 35	18a41						19 05
Falkirk Grahamston	d	17 34				18a00					18 04						18 34							19 04	
Camelon	d	17 37				17a57					18 07						18 37							19 07	
Larbert	d	17 44	17 48						17 59		18 14	18 18			18 31		18 44	18 48						19 14	19 18
Stirling	d	17 53	18a01						18 08	18 15	18 23	18 31			18 41		18 53	19a02			19 07			19 23	19 31
Bridge of Allan	d	17 57									18 27	18 36			18 46		18 57							19 27	19 36
Dunblane	a	18 06							18 17	18 22	18 36	18 43			18 50		19 06				19 14			19 39	19 47

		SR 1 A 🛒	SR 1 B 🛒	SR	SR 1 B 🛒	SR	SR	SR 1◇ D 🛒	SR	SR 1 B 🛒	SR	SR	SR 1 A 🛒	SR 1 B 🛒		SR	SR	SR ◇ D	SR	SR 1 B 🛒	SR	SR	SR 1 A	SR	SR 1 B
Newcraighall	d					18 48					19 18					19 48					20 18				
Brunstane	d					18 50					19 20					19 50					20 20				
Edinburgh 10	a					18 59					19 29					19 59					20 31				
	d		18 45	18 48	19 00	19 03			19 18	19 30	19 33			20 00		20 03			20 18	20 30	20 33				21 00
Haymarket	d		18 48	18 51	19 04	19 06			19 21	19 34	19 36			20 04		20 06			20 21	20 34	20 36				21 04
Edinburgh Park	d			18 56		19 11			19 26		19 41					20 11			20 26		20 41				
Uphall	d			19 08					19 38										20 38						
Livingston North	d			19 13					19 43										20 43						
Bathgate	a			19 20					19 52										20 49						
Linlithgow	d		19 03		19 19	19 23				19a49	19 53			20 19		20 23				20a49	20 53				21 19
Polmont 3	d		19a09		19a25	19 29					19 59			20a25		20 29					20 59				21a25
Glasgow Queen Street 10 ⛴	d	19 00					19 18	19 42				19 48	20 00				20 18	20 41				20 48	21 00	21 18	
Bishopbriggs	d						19 23					19 53					20 23					20 53		21 23	
Lenzie 3	d						19 29					19 59					20 29					20 59		21 29	
Croy 3	d	19a11					19 35					20 05	20a11				20 35					21 05	21a11	21 35	
Falkirk Grahamston	d					19 34					20 04					20 34					21 04				
Camelon	d					19 37					20 07					20 37					21 07				
Larbert	d					19 44	19 48				20 14	20 18				20 44	20 48				21 14	21 18		21 48	
Stirling	d					19 53	20a01	20a07			20 23	20 31				20 54	21a01	21 08			21 23	21 31		22a00	
Bridge of Allan	d					19 57					20 27	20 36				20 57					21 27	21 36			
Dunblane	a					20 06					20 36	20 43				21 06		21 14			21 36	21 43			

		SR 1◇ D	SR	SR 1 B	SR E	SR	SR 1 A		SR	SR 1 B	SR	SR 1 B	SR	SR E	SR 1 A	SR	SR 1 B	SR 1 A	SR	SR 1 B	SR	SR E	SR		
Newcraighall	d		21 04								22 04								23 04				23 53		
Brunstane	d		21 08								22 08								23 08				23 57		
Edinburgh 10	a		21 15								22 15								23 15				00 04		
	d		21 18	21 30	21 33					22 00	22 18	22 30	22 33				23 00		23 18	23 30	23 33		00 05		
Haymarket	d		21 21	21 34	21 36					22 04	22 21	22 34	22 38				23 04		23 21	23 34	23 38		00a09		
Edinburgh Park	d		21 26		21 41						22 26		22 42						23 26		23 42				
Uphall	d		21 38								22 38								23 38						
Livingston North	d		21 43								22 43								23 43						
Bathgate	a		21 50								22 49								23 49						
Linlithgow	d			21a49	21 53					22 19		22a48	22 54				23 18			23 48	23 55				
Polmont 3	d				21 59					22a25			23 00				23a24			23a54	23 59				
Glasgow Queen Street 10 ⛴	d	21 41				21 48	22 00		22 18					22 48	23 00	23 18		23 30				23 48			
Bishopbriggs	d					21 53			22 23					22 53		23 23						23 53			
Lenzie 3	d					21 59			22 29					22 59		23 29						23 59			
Croy 3	d					22 05	22a11		22 35					23 05	23a11	23 35		23a43				00 05			
Falkirk Grahamston	d				22 04								23 05								00 06				
Camelon	d				22 07								23 08								00 09				
Larbert	d				22 14	22 18			22 48				23 15	23 18		23 48					00 15	00 18			
Stirling	d	22a07			22 23	22 31			23a00				23 24	23 31		00a01					00 24	00 31			
Bridge of Allan	d				22 27	22 36							23 28	23 36							00 29	00 36			
Dunblane	a				22 33	22 43							23 35	23 42							00 36	00 41			

For general notes see front of timetable
For details of catering facilities see Directory of Train Operators

A To Edinburgh (Table 228)
B To Glasgow Queen Street (Table 228)
C To Kirkcaldy (Table 242)
D To Aberdeen (Table 229)
E To Perth (Table 229)

Table 230

Edinburgh, Glasgow Queen Street and Falkirk Grahamston → Stirling and Dunblane
Newcraighall → Edinburgh → Bathgate

Network Diagram - see first page of Table 225

		SR	SR 1◇ A	SR	SR 1 B	SR 1 C	SR	SR	SR 1 B	SR		SR	SR 1 C	SR 1◇ D	SR	SR	SR 1 B	SR	SR	SR 1 C		SR	SR 1 B	SR 1◇ E	SR 1 B
Newcraighall	d									06 18								06 48							
Brunstane	d									06 20								06 50							
Edinburgh 10	a									06 29								06 59							
	d	05 18			05 55		06 05		06 30	06 33						06 35	07 00	07 03				07 05	07 15		07 30
Haymarket	d	05 22			06 00		06 09		06 34	06 36						06 39	07 04	07 06				07 09	07 19		07 34
Edinburgh Park	d	05 27					06 14			06 41						06 46		07 11				07 16			
Uphall	d						06 26									06 58						07 28			
Livingston North	d						06 31									07 03						07 33			
Bathgate	a						06 36									07 08						07 38			
Linlithgow	d	05 39			06 14				06 48	06 53								07 23					07a33		07 49
Polmont 3	d	05 44			06a20				06a54	06 59							07a19	07 29							07a55
Glasgow Queen Street 10	d		05 55	06 13		06 30						06 48	07 00	07 06					07 18	07 30				07 41	
Bishopbriggs	d			06 19								06 53							07 23						
Lenzie 3	d			06 24		06 38						06 59	07a08						07 29						
Croy 3	d			06 31		06a44						07 05							07 35	07a41					
Falkirk Grahamston	d	05 50								07 04								07 34							
Camelon	d	05 53								07 07								07 37							
Larbert	d	05 59	06 16	06 42						07 14		07 19			←			07 44	07 48						
Stirling	d	06 08	06 25	06a53				06 59		07 23		07b39		07 31	07 39			07 54	08a01					08 07	
Bridge of Allan	d	06 13						07 03		07 27		→			07 43			07 57							
Dunblane	a	06 20	06 31					07 10		07 35				07 37	07 50			08 06						08 13	

		SR	SR	SR 1 C	SR 1 B	SR	SR 1 B	SR		SR	SR 1 C	SR 1 B	SR 1◇ E	SR	SR	SR	SR 1 C	SR 1 B		SR	SR	SR	SR 1 C	SR 1 B	SR 1◇ E
Newcraighall	d	07 18						07 48							08 18						08 48				
Brunstane	d	07 20						07 50							08 20						08 50				
Edinburgh 10	a	07 29						07 59							08 29						08 59				
	d	07 33			07 45	07 48	08 00	08 03				08 15		08 18	08 33			08 45		08 48	09 03			09 15	
Haymarket	d	07 36			07 49	07 51	08 04	08 06				08 18		08 21	08 36			08 48		08 51	09 06			09 18	
Edinburgh Park	d	07 41				07 56		08 11						08 26	08 41					08 56	09 11				
Uphall	d					08 08								08 38						09 08					
Livingston North	d					08 13								08 43						09 13					
Bathgate	a					08 20								08 50						09 20					
Linlithgow	d	07 53			08a03			08 23				08 33			08 53			09 03			09 23			09 33	
Polmont 3	d	07 59					08a20	08 29				08a39			08 59			09a09			09 29			09a39	
Glasgow Queen Street 10	d		07 48	08 00						08 18	08 30		08 41			08 48	09 00					09 18	09 30		09 41
Bishopbriggs	d		07 53							08 23						08 53						09 23			
Lenzie 3	d		07 59							08 29						08 59						09 29			
Croy 3	d		08 05	08a11						08 35	08a41					09 05	09a11					09 35	09a41		
Falkirk Grahamston	d	08 04						08 34							09 04						09 34				
Camelon	d	08 07						08 37							09 07						09 37				
Larbert	d	08 14	08 18					08 44		08 48					09 14	09 18					09 44	09 48			
Stirling	d	08 23	08 31					08 53		09a01			09a05		09 23	09 31					09 53	10a02			10a06
Bridge of Allan	d	08 27	08 36					08 57							09 27	09 36					09 57				
Dunblane	a	08 36	08 43					09 06							09 37	09 44					10 07				

		SR	SR	SR	SR 1 C	SR 1 B		SR 1◇ D	SR	SR	SR	SR 1 C	SR 1 B	SR 1◇ E	SR	SR		SR	SR 1 C	SR 1 B	SR	SR	SR	SR 1 C	SR 1 B
Newcraighall	d		09 18							09 48						10 18						10 48			
Brunstane	d		09 20							09 50						10 20						10 50			
Edinburgh 10	a		09 29							09 59						10 29						10 59			
	d	09 18	09 33			09 45			09 48	10 03			10 15		10 18	10 33				10 45	10 48	11 03			11 15
Haymarket	d	09 21	09 36			09 48			09 51	10 06			10 18		10 21	10 36				10 48	10 51	11 06			11 18
Edinburgh Park	d	09 26	09 41						09 56	10 11					10 26	10 41					10 56	11 11			
Uphall	d	09 38							10 08						10 38						11 08				
Livingston North	d	09 43							10 13						10 43						11 13				
Bathgate	a	09 50							10 21						10 50						11 20				
Linlithgow	d		09 53			10 03				10 23			10 33			10 53				11 03		11 23			11 33
Polmont 3	d		09 59			10a09				10 29			10a39			10 59				11a09		11 29			11a39
Glasgow Queen Street 10	d			09 48	10 00			10 11			10 18	10 30		10 41				10 48	11 00				11 18	11 30	
Bishopbriggs	d			09 53							10 23							10 53					11 23		
Lenzie 3	d			09 59							10 29							10 59					11 29		
Croy 3	d			10 05	10a11						10 35	10a41						11 05	11a11				11 35	11a41	
Falkirk Grahamston	d		10 04							10 34						11 04						11 34			
Camelon	d		10 07							10 37						11 07						11 37			
Larbert	d		10 14	10 18						10 44	10 47					11 14		11 18				11 44	11 48		
Stirling	d		10 23	10 31				10 41		10 53	11a00			11a06		11 23		11 31				11 53	12a01		
Bridge of Allan	d		10 27	10 36						10 57						11 27		11 36				11 57			
Dunblane	a		10 36	10 43				10 49		11 06						11 36		11 43				12 06			

For general notes see front of timetable
For details of catering facilities see Directory of Train Operators

A To Dyce (Table 229)
B To Glasgow Queen Street (Table 228)
C To Edinburgh (Table 228)
D To Inverness (Table 229)
E To Aberdeen (Table 229)
b Arr. 0728

Saturdays

Edinburgh, Glasgow Queen Street and Falkirk Grahamston → Stirling and Dunblane Newcraighall → Edinburgh → Bathgate

Network Diagram - see first page of Table 225

		SR 1◊ A	SR	SR		SR	SR 1 B	SR 1 C	SR	SR	SR	SR 1 B	SR 1 C	SR 1◊ A		SR	SR	SR	SR 1 B	SR 1 C	SR	SR	SR	SR 1 B	SR 1 C
Newcraighall	d			11 18						11 48							12 18					12 48			
Brunstane	d			11 20						11 50							12 20					12 50			
Edinburgh 10	a			11 29						11 59							12 29					12 59			
	d		11 18	11 33				11 45	11 48	12 03			12 15			12 18	12 33			12 45	12 48	13 03			13 15
Haymarket	d		11 21	11 36				11 48	11 51	12 06			12 18			12 21	12 36			12 48	12 51	13 06			13 18
Edinburgh Park	d		11 26	11 41					11 56	12 11						12 26	12 41				12 56	13 11			
Uphall	d		11 38						12 08							12 38					13 08				
Livingston North	d		11 43						12 13							12 43					13 13				
Bathgate	a		11 50						12 20							12 50					13 20				
Linlithgow	d			11 53				12 03		12 23			12 33				12 53			13 03		13 23			13 33
Polmont 3	d			11 59				12a09		12 29			12a39				12 59			13a09		13 29			13a39
Glasgow Queen Street 10	d	11 41				11 48	12 00				12 18	12 30		12 41				12 48	13 00				13 18	13 30	
Bishopbriggs	d					11 53					12 23							12 53					13 23		
Lenzie 3	d					11 59					12 29							12 59					13 29		
Croy 3	d					12 05	12a11				12 35	12a41						13 05	13a11				13 35	13a41	
Falkirk Grahamston	d			12 04						12 34							13 04					13 34			
Camelon	d			12 07						12 37							13 07					13 37			
Larbert	d			12 14		12 18				12 44	12 48						13 14	13 18				13 44	13 48		
Stirling	d	12a06		12 23		12 31				12 53	13a01			13a06			13 23	13 31				13 53	14a01		
Bridge of Allan	d			12 27		12 36				12 57							13 27	13 36				13 57			
Dunblane	a			12 36		12 42				13 06							13 36	13 43				14 06			

		SR 1◊ A		SR	SR	SR	SR 1 B	SR 1 C	SR	SR	SR	SR 1 B		SR 1 C	SR 1◊ A	SR	SR	SR	SR 1 B	SR 1 C	SR	SR		SR	SR 1 B
Newcraighall	d				13 18					13 48							14 18					14 48			
Brunstane	d				13 20					13 50							14 20					14 50			
Edinburgh 10	a				13 29					13 59							14 29					14 59			
	d			13 18	13 33			13 45	13 48	14 03				14 15		14 18	14 33			14 45	14 48	15 03			
Haymarket	d			13 21	13 36			13 48	13 51	14 06				14 18		14 21	14 36			14 48	14 51	15 06			
Edinburgh Park	d			13 26	13 41				13 56	14 11						14 26	14 41				14 56	15 11			
Uphall	d			13 38					14 08							14 38					15 08				
Livingston North	d			13 43					14 13							14 43					15 13				
Bathgate	a			13 50					14 20							14 50					15 20				
Linlithgow	d				13 53			14 03		14 23				14 33			14 53			15 03		15 23			
Polmont 3	d				13 59			14a09		14 29				14a39			14 59			15a09		15 29			
Glasgow Queen Street 10	d	13 41				13 48	14 00				14 18	14 30			14 41			14 48	15 00					15 18	15 30
Bishopbriggs	d					13 53					14 23							14 53						15 23	
Lenzie 3	d					13 59					14 29							14 59						15 29	
Croy 3	d					14 05	14a11				14 35	14a41						15 05	15a11					15 35	15a41
Falkirk Grahamston	d				14 04					14 34							15 04					15 34			
Camelon	d				14 07					14 37							15 07					15 37			
Larbert	d				14 14	14 18				14 44	14 48						15 14	15 18				15 44		15 48	
Stirling	d	14a06			14 23	14 31				14 53	15a01				15a06		15 23	15 31				15 53		16a01	
Bridge of Allan	d				14 27	14 36				14 57							15 27	15 36				15 57			
Dunblane	a				14 36	14 43				15 06							15 36	15 43				16 06			

		SR 1 C	SR 1◊ A	SR	SR	SR	SR 1 B	SR 1 C	SR 1◊ D	SR		SR	SR	SR 1 B	SR 1 C	SR 1◊ A	SR	GR R 1 EG	SR	SR		SR 1 B	SR	SR 1 C	SR
Newcraighall	d				15 18							15 48							16 18						
Brunstane	d				15 20							15 50							16 20						
Edinburgh 10	a				15 29							15 59							16 33						
	d	15 15		15 18	15 33			15 45		15 48		16 03			16 15		16 18	16 34	16 36					16 45	16 48
Haymarket	d	15 18		15 21	15 36			15 48		15 51		16 06			16 18		16 21	16 39	16 40					16 48	16 51
Edinburgh Park	d			15 26	15 41					15 56		16 11					16 26		16 44						16 56
Uphall	d			15 38						16 08							16 38								17 08
Livingston North	d			15 43						16 13							16 43								17 13
Bathgate	a			15 50						16 20							16 50								17 20
Linlithgow	d	15 33			15 53			16 03				16 23			16 33				16 57					17 03	
Polmont 3	d	15a39			15 59			16a09				16 29			16a39				17 02					17a09	
Glasgow Queen Street 10	d		15 41			15 48	16 00		16 11				16 18	16 30		16 41				16 48		17 00	17 03		
Bishopbriggs	d					15 53							16 23							16 53			17 09		
Lenzie 3	d					15 59							16 29							16 59			17 14		
Croy 3	d					16 05	16a11						16 35	16a41						17 05		17a11	17 21		
Falkirk Grahamston	d				16 04							16 34						17 04	17 08						
Camelon	d				16 07							16 37							17 11						
Larbert	d				16 14	16 18						16 44	16 48						17 17	17 24			17 33		
Stirling	d		16a06		16 23	16 31			16 39			16 53	17a01			17a07		17a19	17 26	17 35			17 44		
Bridge of Allan	d				16 27	16 36						16 57							17 31	17 40			17 49		
Dunblane	a				16 37	16 44			16 48			17 06							17 41	17 48			17 53		

For general notes see front of timetable
For details of catering facilities see Directory of Train Operators

- **A** To Aberdeen (Table 229)
- **B** To Edinburgh (Table 228)
- **C** To Glasgow Queen Street (Table 228)
- **D** To Inverness (Table 229)
- **E** From London Kings Cross (Table 26) to Inverness (Table 229)
- **G** **The Highland Chieftain**

Table 230

Saturdays

Edinburgh, Glasgow Queen Street and Falkirk Grahamston → Stirling and Dunblane Newcraighall → Edinburgh → Bathgate

Network Diagram - see first page of Table 225

		SR	SR	SR 1 A 🛒	SR 1 B 🛒	SR 1 ◇ C 🛒	SR	SR		SR	SR 1 A 🛒	SR 1 B 🛒	SR D	SR	SR	SR	SR 1 A 🛒	SR 1 B 🛒		SR 1 ◇ C 🛒	SR	SR	SR	SR 1 A 🛒	SR 1 B 🛒
Newcraighall	d	16 48						17 18							17 49							18 18			
Brunstane	d	16 50						17 20							17 50							18 20			
Edinburgh 10	a	16 59						17 29							17 59							18 29			
	d	17 03			17 15		17 18	17 33				17 45		17 48	18 03			18 15			18 18	18 33			18 45
Haymarket	d	17 06			17 18		17 21	17 36				17 48		17 51	18 06			18 18			18 21	18 36			18 48
Edinburgh Park	d	17 11					17 26	17 41						17 56	18 11						18 26	18 41			
Uphall	d						17 38							18 08							18 38				
Livingston North	d						17 43							18 13							18 43				
Bathgate	a						17 50							18 21							18 50				
Linlithgow	d	17 23			17 33			17 53				18 03			18 23			18 33				18 53			19 03
Polmont 3	d	17 29			17a39			17 59				18a09			18 29			18a39				18 59			19a09
Glasgow Queen Street 10 ⛴	d		17 18	17 30		17 41				17 48	18 00		18 11			18 18	18 30			18 41			18 48	19 00	
Bishopbriggs	d		17 23							17 53						18 23							18 53		
Lenzie 3	d		17 29							17 59						18 29							18 59		
Croy 3	d		17 35	17a42						18 05	18a11					18 35	18a41						19 05	19a11	
Falkirk Grahamston	d	17 34						18 04							18 34							19 04			
Camelon	d	17 37						18 07							18 37							19 07			
Larbert	d	17 44	17 48					18 14		18 18			18 31		18 44	18 48						19 14	19 18		
Stirling	d	17 53	17a59			18 07		18 23		18 31			18 41		18 53	19a02				19 07		19 23	19 31		
Bridge of Allan	d	17 57						18 27		18 36			18 46		18 57							19 27	19 36		
Dunblane	a	18 06				18 14		18 36		18 43			18 50		19 06					19 14		19 39	19 47		

		SR	SR 1 B 🛒	SR	SR	SR 1 ◇ C 🛒		SR	SR 1 B 🛒	SR	SR	SR 1 A 🛒	SR 1 B 🛒	SR	SR	SR ◇ C		SR	SR 1 B 🛒	SR	SR	SR 1 A	SR	SR 1 B	SR 1 ◇ C
Newcraighall	d			18 48						19 18				19 48						20 18					
Brunstane	d			18 50						19 20				19 50						20 20					
Edinburgh 10	a			18 59						19 29				19 59						20 31					
	d	18 48	19 00	19 03				19 18	19 30	19 33			20 00	20 03				20 18	20 30	20 33				21 00	
Haymarket	d	18 51	19 04	19 06				19 21	19 34	19 36			20 04	20 06				20 21	20 34	20 36				21 04	
Edinburgh Park	d	18 56		19 11				19 26		19 41				20 11				20 26		20 41					
Uphall	d	19 08						19 38										20 38							
Livingston North	d	19 13						19 43										20 43							
Bathgate	a	19 20						19 52										20 49							
Linlithgow	d		19 19	19 23					19a49	19 53			20 19	20 23					20a49	20 53				21 19	
Polmont 3	d		19a25	19 29						19 59			20a25	20 29						20 59				21a25	
Glasgow Queen Street 10 ⛴	d				19 18	19 42					19 48	20 00			20 18	20 41					20 48	21 00	21 18		21 41
Bishopbriggs	d				19 23						19 53				20 23						20 53		21 23		
Lenzie 3	d				19 29						19 59				20 29						20 59		21 29		
Croy 3	d				19 35						20 05	20a11			20 35						21 05	21a11	21 35		
Falkirk Grahamston	d			19 34						20 04				20 34						21 04					
Camelon	d			19 37						20 07				20 37						21 07					
Larbert	d			19 44	19 48					20 14	20 18			20 44	20 48					21 14	21 18		21 48		
Stirling	d			19 53	20a01	20a07				20 23	20 31			20 53	21a01	21 08				21 23	21 31		22a00		22a07
Bridge of Allan	d			19 57						20 27	20 36			20 57						21 27	21 36				
Dunblane	a			20 06						20 36	20 43			21 06		21 14				21 36	21 43				

		SR	SR 1 B	SR D		SR	SR 1 A	SR	SR 1 B	SR	SR 1 B	SR	SR D	SR 1 A		SR	SR 1 B	SR 1 A	SR D	SR	SR 1 B	SR			
Newcraighall	d	21 04								22 04										23 04		23 53			
Brunstane	d	21 08								22 08										23 08		23 57			
Edinburgh 10	a	21 15								22 15										23 15		00 04			
	d	21 18	21 30	21 33					22 00	22 18	22 30	22 34					23 00			23 18	23 30	00 05			
Haymarket	d	21 21	21 34	21 36					22 04	22 21	22 34	22 38					23 04			23 21	23 34	00a09			
Edinburgh Park	d	21 26		21 41						22 26		22 42								23 26					
Uphall	d	21 38								22 38										23 38					
Livingston North	d	21 43								22 43										23 43					
Bathgate	a	21 50								22 49										23 49					
Linlithgow	d		21a49	21 53					22 19		22a48	22 54					23 18				23 48				
Polmont 3	d			21 59					22a25			23 00					23a24				23a54				
Glasgow Queen Street 10 ⛴	d					21 48	22 00	22 18					22 48	23 00		23 18		23 30	23 48						
Bishopbriggs	d					21 53		22 23					22 53			23 23			23 53						
Lenzie 3	d					21 59		22 29					22 59			23 29			23 59						
Croy 3	d					22 05	22a11	22 35					23 05	23a11		23 35		23a43	00 05						
Falkirk Grahamston	d			22 04								23 06													
Camelon	d			22 07								23 09													
Larbert	d			22 14		22 18		22 48				23 15	23 18			23 48			00 18						
Stirling	d			22 23		22 31		23a00				23 24	23 31			00a01			00 31						
Bridge of Allan	d			22 27		22 36						23 29	23 36						00 36						
Dunblane	a			22 35		22 45						23 36	23 42						00 41						

For general notes see front of timetable
For details of catering facilities see Directory of Train Operators

- **A** To Edinburgh (Table 228)
- **B** To Glasgow Queen Street (Table 228)
- **C** To Aberdeen (Table 229)
- **D** To Perth (Table 229)

Table 230

Sundays

Edinburgh, Glasgow Queen Street and Falkirk Grahamston → Stirling and Dunblane
Edinburgh → Bathgate

Network Diagram - see first page of Table 225

	SR	SR	SR	SR	SR	SR	SR	SR	SR	SR		SR	SR	SR	SR	SR	SR	SR	SR	SR	SR		SR	SR
	1		1	1			1	1	1 ◇						1	1					1		1	1 ◇
	A	B	A	C	B	B	A	C	D			B			A	C	B				C		A	D
			🍴	🍴			🍴		🍴						🍴	🍴					🍴		🍴	🍴
Edinburgh 10 225, 242 d				08 00				09 00		09 03			09 33			10 00		10 18	10 33		11 00			
Haymarket 225, 242 d				08 04				09 04		09 08			09 37			10 04		10 22	10 37		11 04			
Edinburgh Park d										09 13			09 42					10 27	10 42					
Uphall d										09 30								10 44						
Livingston North d										09 34								10 49						
Bathgate a										09 40								10 55						
Linlithgow d				08 23				09 23					09 59			10 23			10 54		11 18			
Polmont 3 d				08a29				09a29					10 04			10a29			10 59		11a24			
Glasgow Queen Street 10 d	07 50	08 15	08 30		08 45	09 15	09 30		09 38			09 45		10 15	10 30		10 45			11 15			11 30	11 45
Bishopbriggs d		08 21			08 51	09 21						09 51		10 21			10 51			11 21				
Lenzie 3 d		08 27			08 57	09 27			09 47			09 57		10 27			10 57			11 27				
Croy 3 d	08a02	08a33	08a42		09a06	09a33	09a42					10a05		10 33	10a42		11a05			11 33			11a42	
Falkirk Grahamston d													10 10						11 05					
Camelon d													10 13						11 08					
Larbert d									10 01				10 19	10 45					11 14	11 45				
Stirling d									10 10				10 28	10a56					11 23	11a56				12 12
Bridge of Allan d													10 33						11 28					
Dunblane a									10 16				10 40						11 35					12 17

	SR	SR	SR	SR	SR	SR	SR	SR	SR	SR		SR	SR	SR	SR	SR	SR	SR	SR	SR	SR		SR	SR
					1	1			1	1				1	1 ◇			1	1				1	1 ◇
	B				C	A	B		C	A				C	D	B		C	A				C	E
					🍴	🍴			🍴	🍴				🍴	🍴			🍴	🍴				🍴	🍴
Edinburgh 10 225, 242 d		11 18	11 34		12 00			12 18	12 30			12 34		13 00			13 18	13 30		13 38			14 00	
Haymarket 225, 242 d		11 22	11 38		12 04			12 22	12 34			12 38		13 04			13 22	13 34		13 42			14 04	
Edinburgh Park d		11 27	11 43					12 28				12 43					13 27			13 47				
Uphall d		11 39						12 39									13 39							
Livingston North d		11 44						12 44									13 44							
Bathgate a		11 49						12 49									13 49							
Linlithgow d			11 55		12 18				12a48			12 55		13 18				13a48		13 55			14 18	
Polmont 3 d			12 00		12a24							13 00		13a24						14 00			14a24	
Glasgow Queen Street 10 d	11 45			12 15		12 30	12 45			13 00			13 15		13 45	13 45			14 00		14 15			14 40
Bishopbriggs d	11 51			12 21			12 51						13 21			13 51					14 21			
Lenzie 3 d	11 57			12 27			12 57						13 27			13 57					14 27			
Croy 3 d	12a06			12 33		12a42	13a05			13a12			13 33			14a06			14a12		14 33			
Falkirk Grahamston d			12 06									13 06								14 05				
Camelon d			12 09									13 09								14 09				
Larbert d			12 15	12 45								13 15	13 45							14 15	14 45			15 00
Stirling d			12 24	12a56								13 24	13a56		14 12					14 24	14a56			15 09
Bridge of Allan d			12 29									13 29								14 29				
Dunblane a			12 37									13 37			14 17					14 40				15 15

	SR	SR	SR	SR	SR	SR	SR	SR	SR	SR		SR	SR	SR	SR	SR	SR	SR	SR	SR	SR		SR	GR
			1	1			1	1 ◇				1	1			1			1	1			1	R 1
	B		C	A			C	D	B			C	A			C	B		C	A			C	G H
				🍴			🍴	🍴				🍴	🍴			🍴			🍴	🍴			🍴	🍽 🍴
Edinburgh 10 225, 242 d		14 18	14 30		14 34		15 00			15 18		15 30		15 34		16 00		16 18	16 30		16 34		17 00	17 12
Haymarket 225, 242 d		14 22	14 34		14 38		15 04			15 22		15 34		15 38		16 04		16 22	16 34		16 38		17 04	17 16
Edinburgh Park d		14 27			14 43					15 27				15 43				16 27			16 43			
Uphall d		14 39								15 39								16 37						
Livingston North d		14 44								15 44								16 42						
Bathgate a		14 49								15 49								16 49						
Linlithgow d			14a48		14 55		15 18					15a48		15 55		16 18			16a48		16 55		17 18	
Polmont 3 d					15 00		15a24							16 00		16a24					17 00		17a24	
Glasgow Queen Street 10 d	14 45			15 00		15 15		15 45	15 45				16 00		16 15		16 45			17 00				
Bishopbriggs d	14 51					15 21			15 51						16 21		16 51							
Lenzie 3 d	14 57					15 27			15 57						16 27		16 57							
Croy 3 d	15a05			15a12		15 33			16a06				16a12		16 33		17a05			17a12				
Falkirk Grahamston d					15 06									16 06							17 06			17 37
Camelon d					15 09									16 09							17 09			
Larbert d					15 15	15 45								16 15	16 45						17 15			
Stirling d					15 24	15a56		16 12						16 24	16a56						17 24			17a51
Bridge of Allan d					15 29									16 29							17 29			
Dunblane a					15 36			16 17						16 36							17 36			

	SR	SR	SR	SR	SR	SR	SR	SR	SR	SR		SR	SR	SR	SR	SR	SR	SR	SR	SR	SR		SR	SR
		1 ◇			1	1		1 ◇		1			1	1			1	1 ◇		1			1	
		D	B		C	A		E		C			C	A			C	D		C			A	
		🍴			🍴	🍴		🍴		🍴			🍴	🍴			🍴			🍴			🍴	
Edinburgh 10 225, 242 d				17 18	17 30		17 34			18 00		18 18	18 30		18 34		19 00		19 18	19 30	19 33			
Haymarket 225, 242 d				17 22	17 34		17 38			18 04		18 22	18 34		18 38		19 04		19 22	19 34	19 38			
Edinburgh Park d				17 27			17 43					18 27			18 43				19 27		19 43			
Uphall d				17 37								18 39							19 39					
Livingston North d				17 41								18 44							19 44					
Bathgate a				17 49								18 49							19 49					
Linlithgow d					17a48		17 55			18 18			18a48		18 55		19 18			19a48	19 55			
Polmont 3 d							18 00			18a24					19 00		19a24				20 00			
Glasgow Queen Street 10 d	17 15	17 45	17 45			18 00		18 10	18 15					19 00		19 15		19 45					20 00	20 15
Bishopbriggs d	17 21		17 51						18 21							19 21								20 21
Lenzie 3 d	17 27		17 57						18 27							19 27								20 27
Croy 3 d	17 33		18a06			18a12			18 33					19a12		19 33							20a12	20 33
Falkirk Grahamston d							18 06								19 06						20 06			
Camelon d							18 09								19 09						20 09			
Larbert d	17 50						18 15	18 30	18 45						19 15	19 44					20 15			20 45
Stirling d	18a01	18a12					18 24	18 39	18a56						19 24	19a55		20 12			20 24			20a56
Bridge of Allan d							18 29								19 29						20 29			
Dunblane a							18 36	18 45							19 39			20 17			20 36			

For general notes see front of timetable
For details of catering facilities see Directory of Train Operators

- **A** To Edinburgh (Table 228)
- **B** Until 23 December
- **C** To Glasgow Queen Street (Table 228)
- **D** To Aberdeen (Table 229)
- **E** To Elgin (Table 240)
- **G** From London Kings Cross (Table 26) to Inverness (Table 229)
- **H** **The Highland Chieftain**

Table 230

Sundays

Edinburgh, Glasgow Queen Street and Falkirk Grahamston → Stirling and Dunblane
Edinburgh → Bathgate

Network Diagram - see first page of Table 225

		SR 1 A trolley	SR	SR 1 A trolley	SR 1 B	SR	SR	SR 1 A trolley	SR 1 B	SR 1 ◊ C trolley	SR		SR	SR	SR 1 A	SR 1 B	SR	SR D	SR 1 A	SR 1 B	SR 1 D	SR	SR 1 A		
Edinburgh 10	225, 242 d	20 00	20 18	20 30		20 34		21 00			21 18		21 34		22 00		22 18	22 34	23 00			23 18	23 30		
Haymarket	225, 242 d	20 04	20 22	20 34		20 38		21 04			21 22		21 38		22 04		22 22	22 38	23 04			23 22	23 34		
Edinburgh Park	d		20 27			20 43					21 27		21 43				22 27	22 43				23 27			
Uphall	d		20 39								21 39						22 39					23 39			
Livingston North	d		20 44								21 44						22 44					23 44			
Bathgate	a		20 49								21 49						22 49					23 49			
Linlithgow	d	20 18		20a48		20 55		21 18					21 55		22 18			22 55	23 18				23 49		
Polmont 3	d	20a24				21 00		21a24					22 00		22a24			23 00	23a24				23a55		
Glasgow Queen Street 10	d				21 00		21 15		21 30	21 45				22 15		22 30				23 30	23 35				
Bishopbriggs	d						21 21							22 21							23 41				
Lenzie 3	d						21 27							22 27							23 47				
Croy 3	d				21a12		21 33		21a42					22 33		22a42				23a42	23 53				
Falkirk Grahamston	d					21 06							22 06					23 06							
Camelon	d					21 09							22 09					23 09							
Larbert	d					21 15	21 45						22 15	22 45				23 15			00 05				
Stirling	d					21 24	21a56			22 12			22 24	22a56				23 24			00 14				
Bridge of Allan	d					21 29							22 29					23 29			00 18				
Dunblane	a					21 36				22 18			22 36					23 36			00 22				

For general notes see front of timetable
For details of catering facilities see Directory of Train Operators

A To Glasgow Queen Street (Table 228)
B To Edinburgh (Table 228)
C To Aberdeen (Table 229)
D To Perth (Table 229)

Dunblane and Stirling → Falkirk Grahamston, Glasgow Queen Street and Edinburgh
Bathgate → Edinburgh → Newcraighall

Network Diagram - see first page of Table 225

Miles	Miles	Miles			SR MO 1 A	SR MX 1 A	SR	SR 1 B	SR C	SR	SR	SR 1 A	SR	SR 1 B 🚲	SR	SR	SR 1 A 🚲	SR D	SR 1 B 🚲	SR C		SR 1 B 🚲	SR	SR C	SR
0	0	—	**Dunblane**	d					05 44						06 28					06 40				07 07	
2	2	—	Bridge of Allan	d					05 47						06 31					06 43				07 11	
5½	5½	—	**Stirling**	d			05 30		05 53				06 22		06 36					06 49				07 16	07 22
13½	13½	—	Larbert	d			05 38		06 01				06 31		06 45					06 59				07 25	07 31
—	15	—	Camelon	d			05 44								06 48									07 29	
—	16½	—	**Falkirk Grahamston**	d			05 48								06 52									07 33	
24	—	—	Croy 3	d	00 11	00 10			06 12			06 35	06 42				07 10			07 12			07 25		07 42
29¼	—	—	Lenzie 3	d		00 16			06 19				06 49							07 19			07 32		07 49
32¼	—	—	Bishopbriggs	d					06 23				06 53							07 23			07 36		07 53
34½	—	—	**Glasgow Queen Street 10** ⛴	a	00 25	00 28			06 33			06 50	07 03				07 25			07 35			07 45		08 04
—	19½	—	Polmont 3	d			05 54	06 24						06 59	06 59				07 27			07 37		07 44	
—	24¼	—	Linlithgow	d			06 01	06 30						07 05	07 06				07 34			07 44		07 51	
—	—	0	**Bathgate**	d							06 40					07 12									
—	—	3	Livingston North	d							06 45					07 18									
—	—	6	Uphall	d							06 49					07 23									
—	38	14¾	Edinburgh Park	d			06 14				06 59				07 19	07 32								08 03	
—	40½	17¼	Haymarket	d			06 21	06s45		06 50	07 05			07s20	07 26	07 39		07 45	07s50			08s01		08 10	
—	41¾	18½	**Edinburgh 10** 225, 242	a			06 25	06 50		06 54	07 10			07 25	07 33	07 44		07 50	07 55			08 06		08 15	
—	—	—		d			06 26			06 55					07 34			07 54							
—	—	22½	Brunstane	d			06 33			07 02					07 41			08 00							
—	—	23¼	**Newcraighall**	a			06 38			07 07					07 46			08 08							

		SR	SR 1 B 🚲	SR	SR 1 A 🚲	SR 1 B 🚲	SR C	SR	SR 1 A 🚲	SR 1 B 🚲	SR	SR 1 ◇ E 🚲	SR 1 A 🚲	SR G	SR		SR 1 B 🚲	SR	SR 1 A 🚲	SR	SR	SR	SR 1 B 🚲	SR 1 ◇ E 🚲	SR 1 A 🚲
Dunblane	d	07 22					07 29					07 42			07 57						08 14	08 27			
Bridge of Allan	d	07 25					07 33					07 46			08 00						08 17	08 30			
Stirling	d	07 31					07 38	07 48				07 52			08 06			08 10			08 23	08 36		08 44	
Larbert	d	07 41					07 47	07 57				08 02			08 15			08 19			08 31	08 45			
Camelon	d							08 02						08 15	08 18							08 48			
Falkirk Grahamston	d							08 06						08 11	08 22							08 52			
Croy 3	d				07 52		07 58		08 10									08 31	08 38		08 42				09 04
Lenzie 3	d						08 05					08 17	08 27	08 32				08 37			08 49				
Bishopbriggs	d						08 10							08 37				08 42			08 53				
Glasgow Queen Street 10 ⛴	a				08 06		08 20		08 25			08 34	08 40	08 48				08 52	08 55		09 04			09 15	09 21
Polmont 3	d					08 07		08 15		08 27					08 29							08 59	09 07		
Linlithgow	d		08 01			08 14		08 22							08 36		08 43					09 06	09 14		
Bathgate	d			07 54							08 24									08 55					
Livingston North	d			08 00							08 30									08 59					
Uphall	d			08 05							08 34									09 03					
Edinburgh Park	d			08 18				08 35			08 46				08 49					09 12		09 19			
Haymarket	d	08 14	08s17	08 25		08s32		08 40		08s46	08 54				08 56		09s00			09 19		09 26	09s31		
Edinburgh 10 225, 242	a	08 18	08 22	08 30		08 37		08 45		08 51	08 59				09 02		09 05			09 25		09 32	09 36		
	d			08 34							09 03									09 26					
Brunstane	d			08 41							09 10									09 32					
Newcraighall	a			08 46							09 15									09 39					

		SR	SR	SR	SR 1 B 🚲	SR 1 A 🚲	SR	SR	SR	SR 1 B 🚲		SR 1 D	SR 1 A 🚲	SR	SR	SR	SR 1 B 🚲	SR 1 A 🚲	SR	GR R 1 H J ✕ 🚲	SR	SR	SR 1 B 🚲	SR 1 ◇ E 🚲	SR 1 A 🚲
Dunblane	d			08 57				09 14	09 28			09 34				09 58			10 14			10 28			
Bridge of Allan	d			09 00				09 17	09 31							10 01			10 17			10 31			
Stirling	d		08 53	09 06				09 23	09 36			09 41			09 53	10 06			10 23	10 30		10 36		10 41	
Larbert	d		09 01	09 15				09 31	09 45						10 01	10 15			10 31			10 45			
Camelon	d			09 18					09 48							10 18						10 48			
Falkirk Grahamston	d			09 22					09 52							10 22				10 45		10 52			
Croy 3	d		09 12			09 34		09 42					10 04		10 12			10 34	10 42						11 04
Lenzie 3	d		09 19					09 49							10 19				10 49						
Bishopbriggs	d		09 23					09 53							10 23				10 53						
Glasgow Queen Street 10 ⛴	a		09 33			09 51		10 03				10 15	10 21		10 33			10 51	11 03					11 15	11 21
Polmont 3	d			09 29	09 37				09 59	10 07						10 29	10 37					10 59	11 07		
Linlithgow	d			09 36	09 44				10 06	10 14						10 36	10 44					11 06	11 14		
Bathgate	d	09 25					09 55							10 25							10 55				
Livingston North	d	09 29					09 59							10 29							10 59				
Uphall	d	09 33					10 03							10 33							11 03				
Edinburgh Park	d	09 42		09 49			10 12		10 19					10 42		10 49					11 12	11 19			
Haymarket	d	09 49		09 56	10s01		10 19		10 26	10s30				10 49		10 56	11s00			11 10	11 19	11 26	11s30		
Edinburgh 10 225, 242	a	09 55		10 03	10 06		10 25		10 32	10 35				10 55		11 01	11 05			11 20	11 25	11 32	11 35		
	d	09 56					10 26							10 56							11 26				
Brunstane	d	10 02					10 32							11 02							11 32				
Newcraighall	a	10 09					10 38							11 10							11 39				

For general notes see front of timetable
For details of catering facilities see Directory of Train Operators

- **A** From Edinburgh (Table 228)
- **B** From Glasgow Queen Street (Table 228)
- **C** From Perth (Table 229)
- **D** From Dundee (Table 229)
- **E** From Aberdeen (Table 229)
- **G** From Kirkcaldy (Table 242)
- **H** From Inverness (Table 229) to London Kings Cross (Table 26)
- **J** **The Highland Chieftain**

Dunblane and Stirling → Falkirk Grahamston, Glasgow Queen Street and Edinburgh
Bathgate → Edinburgh → Newcraighall

Network Diagram - see first page of Table 225

		SR	SR	SR	SR		SR	SR	SR	SR	SR	SR	SR	SR	SR	SR	SR	SR	SR	SR	SR	SR		SR	SR
					1 A		1 B				1 A	1 ◇ C	1 B				1 A	1 ◇ D	1 B					1 A	1 ◇ E
Dunblane	d			10 58					11 14	11 28						11 58		12 05			12 14	12 28			
Bridge of Allan	d			11 01					11 17	11 31						12 01					12 17	12 31			
Stirling	d		10 53	11 06					11 23	11 36		11 41			11 53	12 06		12 12			12 23	12 36			12 41
Larbert	d		11 01	11 15					11 31	11 45					12 01	12 15					12 31	12 45			
Camelon	d			11 18						11 48						12 18						12 48			
Falkirk Grahamston	d			11 22						11 52						12 22						12 52			
Croy 3	d		11 12				11 34		11 42				12 04		12 12				12 34		12 42				
Lenzie 3	d		11 19						11 49						12 19						12 49				
Bishopbriggs	d		11 23						11 53						12 23						12 53				
Glasgow Queen Street 10	a		11 34				11 51		12 03			12 15	12 21		12 35			12 44	12 51		13 03				13 14
Polmont 3	d			11 29	11 37					11 59	12 07					12 29	12 37					12 59		13 07	
Linlithgow	d			11 36	11 44					12 06	12 14					12 36	12 44					13 06		13 14	
Bathgate	d	11 25						11 55						12 25						12 55					
Livingston North	d	11 29						11 59						12 29						12 59					
Uphall	d	11 33						12 03						12 33						13 03					
Edinburgh Park	d	11 42		11 49				12 12		12 19				12 42		12 49				13 12		13 19			
Haymarket	d	11 49		11 56	12s00			12 19		12 26	12s30			12 49		12 56	13s00			13 19		13 26		13s30	
Edinburgh 10 225, 242	a	11 55		12 01	12 05			12 25		12 32	12 35			12 55		13 01	13 05			13 25		13 32		13 35	
	d	11 56						12 26						12 56						13 26					
Brunstane	d	12 02						12 32						13 02						13 32					
Newcraighall	a	12 08						12 38						13 09						13 38					

		SR	SR	SR	SR	SR	SR	SR	SR	SR	SR	SR	SR	SR	SR	SR	SR		SR	SR	SR	SR	SR	SR	SR
		1 B				1 A	1 B				1 A	1 ◇ E	1 B				1 A		1 B				1 A	1 ◇ E	1 B
Dunblane	d				12 58				13 14	13 28						13 58					14 14	14 28			
Bridge of Allan	d				13 01				13 17	13 31						14 01					14 17	14 31			
Stirling	d			12 53	13 06				13 23	13 36		13 41			13 53	14 06					14 23	14 36		14 41	
Larbert	d			13 01	13 15				13 31	13 45					14 01	14 15					14 31	14 45			
Camelon	d				13 18					13 48						14 18						14 48			
Falkirk Grahamston	d				13 22					13 52						14 22						14 52			
Croy 3	d	13 04		13 12			13 34		13 42				14 04		14 12				14 34		14 42				15 04
Lenzie 3	d			13 19					13 49						14 19						14 49				
Bishopbriggs	d			13 23					13 53						14 23						14 53				
Glasgow Queen Street 10	a	13 21		13 33			13 51		14 03			14 14	14 21		14 33				14 51		15 03			15 14	15 21
Polmont 3	d				13 29	13 37				13 59	14 07					14 29	14 37					14 59	15 07		
Linlithgow	d				13 36	13 44				14 06	14 14					14 36	14 44					15 06	15 14		
Bathgate	d		13 25					13 55						14 25						14 55					
Livingston North	d		13 29					13 59						14 29						14 59					
Uphall	d		13 33					14 03						14 33						15 03					
Edinburgh Park	d		13 42		13 49			14 12		14 19				14 42		14 49				15 12		15 19			
Haymarket	d		13 49		13 56	14s00		14 19		14 26	14s30			14 49		14 56	15s00			15 19		15 26	15s30		
Edinburgh 10 225, 242	a		13 55		14 01	14 05		14 25		14 32	14 35			14 55		15 01	15 05			15 25		15 32	15 35		
	d		13 56					14 26						14 56						15 26					
Brunstane	d		14 02					14 32						15 02						15 32					
Newcraighall	a		14 08					14 38						15 10						15 38					

		SR	SR	SR	SR	SR	SR	SR	SR	SR	SR	SR		SR	SR	SR	SR	SR	SR	SR	SR	SR	SR	SR	SR
					1 A	1 B				1 A	1 ◇ E	1 B					1 A	1 B				1 A	1 ◇ E	1 B	1 A
Dunblane	d			14 58				15 14	15 28							15 58				16 14	16 28				
Bridge of Allan	d			15 01				15 17	15 31							16 01				16 17	16 31				
Stirling	d		14 53	15 06				15 23	15 36		15 41				15 53	16 06				16 23	16 36		16 41		
Larbert	d		15 01	15 15				15 31	15 45						16 01	16 15				16 31	16 45				
Camelon	d			15 18					15 48							16 18					16 48				
Falkirk Grahamston	d			15 22					15 52							16 22					16 52				
Croy 3	d		15 12			15 34		15 42				16 04			16 12			16 34		16 42				17 04	
Lenzie 3	d		15 19					15 49							16 19					16 49					
Bishopbriggs	d		15 23					15 53							16 23					16 53					
Glasgow Queen Street 10	a		15 34			15 51		16 05			16 14	16 21			16 33			16 51		17 03			17 18	17 21	
Polmont 3	d			15 29	15 37				15 59	16 07						16 29	16 37				16 59	17 07			17 27
Linlithgow	d			15 36	15 44				16 06	16 14						16 36	16 44				17 06	17 14			
Bathgate	d	15 25					15 55							16 25					16 55						
Livingston North	d	15 29					15 59							16 29					16 59						
Uphall	d	15 33					16 03							16 33					17 03						
Edinburgh Park	d	15 42		15 49			16 12		16 19					16 42		16 49			17 12		17 19				
Haymarket	d	15 49		15 56	16s00		16 19		16 26	16s33				16 49		16 56	17s00		17 19		17 26	17s33			17s45
Edinburgh 10 225, 242	a	15 55		16 01	16 05		16 25		16 34	16 39				16 55		17 03	17 05		17 25		17 32	17 38			17 50
	d	15 56					16 26							16 56					17 26						
Brunstane	d	16 02					16 32							17 02					17 32						
Newcraighall	a	16 08					16 38							17 09					17 40						

For general notes see front of timetable
For details of catering facilities see Directory of Train Operators

A From Glasgow Queen Street (Table 228)
B From Edinburgh (Table 228)
C From Dyce (Table 229)
D From Inverness (Table 229)
E From Aberdeen (Table 229)

Dunblane and Stirling → Falkirk Grahamston, Glasgow Queen Street and Edinburgh
Bathgate → Edinburgh → Newcraighall

Network Diagram - see first page of Table 225

		SR	SR	SR	SR 1 A ⚮	SR 1 B ⚮	SR		SR 1 A ⚮	SR	SR	SR 1 A ⚮	SR C	SR 1 ◊ D ⚮	SR 1 B ⚮	SR	SR	SR	SR 1 A ⚮	SR 1 B ⚮	SR	SR	SR	SR 1 A ⚮	SR 1 ◊ D ⚮
Dunblane	d			16 58							17 28			17 36				17 58				18 14	18 28		18 37
Bridge of Allan	d			17 01							17 31							18 01				18 17	18 31		
Stirling	d		16 53	17 06						17 23	17 36			17 41			17 52	18 06				18 22	18 36		18 41
Larbert	d		17 01	17 15						17 31	17 45						18 01	18 15				18 31	18 45		
Camelon	d			17 18							17 48		17 57					18 18					18 48		
Falkirk Grahamston	d			17 22							17 52		18 00					18 22					18 52		
Croy 3	d		17 12			17 34				17 42					18 04		18 12			18 34		18 42			
Lenzie 3	d		17 19							17 49					18 08		18 19					18 49			
Bishopbriggs	d		17 23							17 53							18 23					18 53			
Glasgow Queen Street 10 ⛴	a		17 33			17 51				18 03				18 18	18 21		18 34			18 50		19 03			19 14
Polmont 3	d			17 29					17 57		17 59	18 07	18 14					18 29	18 37				18 59	19 07	
Linlithgow	d			17 36	17 43				18 04		18 06	18 14	18a20					18 36	18 44				19 06	19 14	
Bathgate	d	17 25					17 54									18 25					18 55				
Livingston North	d	17 29					17 59									18 29					18 59				
Uphall	d	17 33					18 03									18 33					19 03				
Edinburgh Park	d	17 42		17 49			18 13				18 19					18 42		18 49			19 12		19 19		
Haymarket	d	17 49		17 56	18s00		18 19		18s22		18 26	18s32				18 49		18 56	19s00		19 19		19 25	19s30	
Edinburgh 10 225, 242	a	17 55		18 02	18 05		18 24		18 27		18 32	18 37				18 55		19 01	19 05		19 24		19 32	19 35	
	d	17 56					18 29									18 56					19 26				
Brunstane	d	18 02					18 36									19 02					19 32				
Newcraighall	a	18 11					18 41									19 11					19 39				

		SR 1 B ⚮		SR	SR 1 A ⚮	SR	SR	SR 1 A ⚮	SR	SR	SR	SR R 1 E ⚮	SR 1 B ⚮	SR	SR 1 A ⚮	SR 1 ◊ D ⚮	SR	SR 1 A ⚮	SR		SR	SR	SR 1 ◊ D ⚮	SR 1 B ⚮	SR
Dunblane	d						18 58		19 14	19 28		19 35					19 58		20 14		20 28				
Bridge of Allan	d						19 01		19 17	19 31							20 01		20 17		20 31				
Stirling	d			18 53			19 06		19 23	19 36		19 41		19 52		19 58	20 06		20 23		20 36		20 41		20 53
Larbert	d			19 01			19 15		19 31	19 45				20 01			20 15		20 31		20 45				21 01
Camelon	d						19 18			19 48							20 18				20 48				
Falkirk Grahamston	d						19 22			19 52							20 22				20 52				
Croy 3	d	19 04		19 12					19 42				20 08	20 12					20 42					21 08	21 12
Lenzie 3	d			19 19					19 49					20 19					20 49						21 19
Bishopbriggs	d			19 23					19 53					20 23					20 53						21 23
Glasgow Queen Street 10 ⛴	a	19 21		19 33					20 06			20 17	20 24	20 34		20 38			21 04				21 15	21 22	21 34
Polmont 3	d						19 29	19 55		19 59							20 29	20 55			20 59				
Linlithgow	d				19 30		19 36	20 01		20 06					20 30		20 36	21 01			21 06				
Bathgate	d					19 27					20 05											21 03			
Livingston North	d					19 32					20 10											21 08			
Uphall	d					19 36					20 14											21 12			
Edinburgh Park	d					19 48	19 49			20 19	20 24						20 49				21 19	21 24			
Haymarket	d				19s45	19 54	19 56	20s17		20 26	20 31				20s46		20 56	21s17			21 26	21 30			
Edinburgh 10 225, 242	a				19 50	19 59	20 04	20 22		20 31	20 35				20 51		21 05	21 22			21 31	21 35			
	d					19 59					20 36											21 35			
Brunstane	d					20 07					20 43											21 43			
Newcraighall	a					20 12					20 48											21 48			

		SR 1 A	SR	SR 1 A	SR	SR	SR 1 ◊ D ⚮	SR 1 B	SR	SR 1 A	SR	SR 1 A	SR	SR		SR 1 ◊ D	SR 1 B	SR	SR 1 A	SR 1 ◊ E	SR	SR 1 B	SR 1 A		
Dunblane	d		20 58			21 14					21 58			22 14						22 57	23 04				
Bridge of Allan	d		21 01			21 17					22 01			22 17						23 00	23 07				
Stirling	d		21 06			21 23	21 47		21 53		22 06			22 23		22 47		22 53		23 03	23 12				
Larbert	d		21 15			21 31			22 01		22 15			22 31				23 01			23 21				
Camelon	d		21 18								22 18										23 27				
Falkirk Grahamston	d		21 22								22 22										23 30				
Croy 3	d					21 42		22 08	22 12					22 42			23 07	23 12				23 43			
Lenzie 3	d					21 49			22 19					22 49			23 13	23 18				23 50			
Bishopbriggs	d					21 53			22 23					22 53				23 22				23 54			
Glasgow Queen Street 10 ⛴	a					22 04	22 17	22 22	22 33					23 04		23 18	23 25	23 33		23 39		00 03			
Polmont 3	d		21 29	21 56							22 29	22 55							23 27		23 36		23 58		
Linlithgow	d	21 30	21 36	22 02						22 30	22 36	23 01							23 34		23 43		00 05		
Bathgate	d				22 03								23 03												
Livingston North	d				22 08								23 08												
Uphall	d				22 12								23 12												
Edinburgh Park	d		21 49		22 22						22 49		23 22								23 56				
Haymarket	d	21s46	21 56	22s18	22 29					22s46	22 56	23s17	23 28						23s49		00 03		00s20		
Edinburgh 10 225, 242	a	21 51	22 01	22 24	22 34					22 51	23 01	23 22	23 33						23 54		00 07		00 25		
	d				22 34								23 33												
Brunstane	d				22 42								23 41												
Newcraighall	a				22 47								23 46												

For general notes see front of timetable
For details of catering facilities see Directory of Train Operators

A From Glasgow Queen Street (Table 228)
B From Edinburgh (Table 228)
C From Glasgow Queen Street (Table 228) to Kirkcaldy (Table 242)
D From Aberdeen (Table 229)
E From Inverness (Table 229)

Dunblane and Stirling → Falkirk Grahamston, Glasgow Queen Street and Edinburgh
Bathgate → Edinburgh → Newcraighall

Network Diagram - see first page of Table 225

	SR 1 A	SR	SR 1 B	SR C	SR	SR	SR 1 A	SR	SR 1 B ✠		SR	SR	SR 1 B ✠	SR 1 A ✠	SR	SR 1 B ✠	SR C	SR	SR 1 B ✠		SR	SR 1 A ✠	SR 1 B ✠	SR
Dunblane d				05 44							06 28				06 44		07 07							07 22
Bridge of Allan d				05 47							06 31				06 47		07 11							07 25
Stirling d		05 30		05 53				06 22			06 36				06 53		07 16	07 22						07 30
Larbert d		05 38		06 01				06 31			06 45				07 02		07 25	07 31						07 39
Camelon d		05 44									06 48						07 31							
Falkirk Grahamston d		05 48									06 52						07 35							
Croy 3 d	00 10			06 12			06 35	06 42						07 10	07 12			07 42				07 52		07 58
Lenzie 3 d	00 16			06 19				06 49							07 19			07 49						08 05
Bishopbriggs d				06 23				06 53							07 23			07 53						08 10
Glasgow Queen Street 10 a	00 28			06 33			06 50	07 03						07 25	07 34			08 04				08 06		08 19
Polmont 3 d		05 54	06 24						06 59		06 59		07 27			07 37	07 43						08 07	
Linlithgow d		06 01	06 30						07 05		07 06		07 34			07 44	07 50		08 01				08 14	
Bathgate d						06 40						07 12									07 54			
Livingston North d						06 45						07 18									08 00			
Uphall d						06 49						07 23									08 05			
Edinburgh Park d		06 14				06 59					07 19	07 32					08 03				08 18			
Haymarket d		06 21	06s45		06 50	07 05			07s21		07 26	07 42	07s50			08s01	08 10		08s19		08 25		08s32	
Edinburgh 10 225, 242 a		06 25	06 50		06 54	07 10			07 26		07 34	07 47	07 55			08 06	08 14		08 24		08 30		08 37	
d		06 26			06 55						07 34	07 55									08 31			
Brunstane d		06 33			07 02						07 42	08 04									08 39			
Newcraighall a		06 38			07 07						07 47	08 09									08 44			

	SR 1 A ✠	SR 1 B ✠	SR	SR 1◇ D ✠	SR	SR 1 A ✠	SR 1 B ✠		SR	SR 1 A ✠	SR	SR	SR	SR 1 B ✠	SR 1◇ D ✠	SR 1 A ✠	SR		SR	SR	SR 1 B ✠	SR 1◇ E ✠	SR 1 A ✠	SR
Dunblane d				07 42	07 57							08 14	08 27							08 57				
Bridge of Allan d				07 46	08 00							08 17	08 30							09 00				
Stirling d				07 52	08 06				08 10			08 23	08 36		08 44				08 53	09 06		09 10		
Larbert d				08 02	08 15				08 19			08 31	08 45						09 01	09 15				
Camelon d					08 18								08 48							09 18				
Falkirk Grahamston d					08 22								08 52							09 22				
Croy 3 d	08 10								08 31	08 38		08 42				09 04			09 12				09 34	
Lenzie 3 d				08 17		08 25			08 37			08 49							09 19					
Bishopbriggs d						08 30			08 42			08 53							09 23					
Glasgow Queen Street 10 a	08 25			08 34		08 38			08 53	08 55		09 04			09 15	09 21			09 33			09 44	09 51	
Polmont 3 d		08 27			08 29								08 59	09 07						09 29	09 37			
Linlithgow d					08 36		08 43						09 06	09 14						09 36	09 44			
Bathgate d			08 24								08 55						09 25							09 55
Livingston North d			08 30								08 59						09 29							09 59
Uphall d			08 34								09 03						09 33							10 03
Edinburgh Park d			08 46		08 49						09 12		09 19				09 42			09 49				10 12
Haymarket d		08s45	08 53		08 56		09s00				09 19		09 26	09s31			09 49			09 56	10s01			10 19
Edinburgh 10 225, 242 a		08 50	08 58		09 02		09 09				09 25		09 32	09 36			09 55			10 04	10 06			10 25
d			08 58								09 26						09 56							10 26
Brunstane d			09 06								09 32						10 02							10 32
Newcraighall a			09 11								09 39						10 10							10 38

	SR	SR	SR 1 B ✠	SR 1 G	SR 1 A ✠		SR	SR	SR	SR 1 B ✠	SR 1 A ✠	GR R 1 H J ✠	SR	SR	SR		SR 1 B ✠	SR 1◇ D ✠	SR 1 A ✠	SR	SR	SR	SR 1 B ✠	SR 1 A ✠
Dunblane d	09 14	09 28		09 34					09 58					10 14	10 28							10 58		
Bridge of Allan d	09 17	09 31							10 01					10 17	10 31							11 01		
Stirling d	09 23	09 36		09 41				09 53	10 06			10 30		10 23	10 36			10 41			10 53	11 06		
Larbert d	09 31	09 45						10 01	10 15					10 31	10 45						11 01	11 15		
Camelon d		09 48							10 18						10 48							11 18		
Falkirk Grahamston d		09 52							10 22			10 45			10 52							11 22		
Croy 3 d	09 42				10 04			10 12			10 34			10 42					11 04		11 12			11 34
Lenzie 3 d	09 49							10 19						10 49							11 19			
Bishopbriggs d	09 53							10 23						10 53							11 23			
Glasgow Queen Street 10 a	10 03			10 15	10 21			10 33			10 51			11 03				11 15	11 21		11 34			11 51
Polmont 3 d		09 59	10 07						10 29	10 37					10 59		11 07					11 29	11 37	
Linlithgow d		10 06	10 14						10 36	10 44					11 06		11 14					11 36	11 44	
Bathgate d							10 25						10 55							11 25				
Livingston North d							10 29						10 59							11 29				
Uphall d							10 33						11 03							11 33				
Edinburgh Park d		10 19					10 42		10 49				11 12		11 19					11 42		11 49		
Haymarket d		10 26	10s31				10 49		10 56	11s01		11 10	11 19		11 26		11s30			11 49		11 56	12s00	
Edinburgh 10 225, 242 a		10 32	10 36				10 55		11 01	11 06		11 20	11 25		11 32		11 35			11 55		12 01	12 05	
d							10 56						11 26							11 56				
Brunstane d							11 02						11 32							12 02				
Newcraighall a							11 10						11 39							12 08				

For general notes see front of timetable
For details of catering facilities see Directory of Train Operators

A From Edinburgh (Table 228)
B From Glasgow Queen Street (Table 228)
C From Perth (Table 229)
D From Aberdeen (Table 229)
E From Dyce (Table 229)
G From Dundee (Table 229)
H From Inverness (Table 229) to London Kings Cross (Table 26)
J **The Highland Chieftain**

Table 230

Saturdays

Dunblane and Stirling → Falkirk Grahamston, Glasgow Queen Street and Edinburgh
Bathgate → Edinburgh → Newcraighall

Network Diagram - see first page of Table 225

		SR	SR	SR		SR 1 A	SR 1 ◇ B	SR 1 C	SR	SR	SR	SR 1 A	SR 1 ◇ D	SR 1 C		SR	SR	SR	SR 1 A	SR 1 ◇ E	SR 1 C	SR	SR	SR	SR 1 A
Dunblane	d		11 14	11 28							11 58		12 05				12 14	12 28						12 58	
Bridge of Allan	d		11 17	11 31							12 01						12 17	12 31						13 01	
Stirling	d		11 23	11 36			11 41			11 53	12 06		12 12				12 23	12 36		12 41			12 53	13 06	
Larbert	d		11 31	11 45						12 01	12 15						12 31	12 45					13 01	13 15	
Camelon	d			11 48							12 18							12 48						13 18	
Falkirk Grahamston	d			11 52							12 22							12 52						13 22	
Croy 3	d		11 42					12 04		12 12				12 34			12 42				13 04		13 12		
Lenzie 3	d		11 49							12 19							12 49						13 19		
Bishopbriggs	d		11 53							12 23							12 53						13 23		
Glasgow Queen Street 10	a		12 03				12 15	12 21		12 35			12 44	12 51			13 03			13 14	13 21		13 33		
Polmont 3	d			11 59		12 07					12 29	12 37						12 59	13 07					13 29	13 37
Linlithgow	d			12 06		12 14					12 36	12 44						13 06	13 14					13 36	13 44
Bathgate	d	11 55							12 25							12 55						13 25			
Livingston North	d	11 59							12 29							12 59						13 29			
Uphall	d	12 03							12 33							13 03						13 33			
Edinburgh Park	d	12 12		12 19					12 42		12 49					13 12		13 19				13 42		13 49	
Haymarket	d	12 19		12 26		12s31			12 49		12 56	13s01				13 19		13 26	13s31			13 49		13 56	14s01
Edinburgh 10 225, 242	a	12 25		12 32		12 36			12 55		13 01	13 06				13 25		13 32	13 36			13 55		14 01	14 06
	d	12 26							12 56							13 26						13 56			
Brunstane	d	12 32							13 02							13 32						14 02			
Newcraighall	a	12 38							13 09							13 38						14 08			

		SR 1 C		SR	SR	SR	SR 1 A	SR 1 ◇ E	SR 1 C	SR	SR	SR		SR 1 A	SR 1 C	SR	SR	SR	SR 1 A	SR 1 ◇ E	SR 1 C	SR		SR	SR
Dunblane	d				13 14	13 28						13 58					14 14	14 28							14 58
Bridge of Allan	d				13 17	13 31						14 01					14 17	14 31							15 01
Stirling	d				13 23	13 36		13 41			13 53	14 06					14 23	14 36		14 41				14 53	15 06
Larbert	d				13 31	13 45					14 01	14 15					14 31	14 45						15 01	15 15
Camelon	d					13 48						14 18						14 48							15 18
Falkirk Grahamston	d					13 52						14 22						14 52							15 22
Croy 3	d	13 34			13 42				14 04		14 12				14 34		14 42				15 04			15 12	
Lenzie 3	d				13 49						14 19						14 49							15 19	
Bishopbriggs	d				13 53						14 23						14 53							15 23	
Glasgow Queen Street 10	a	13 51			14 03			14 14	14 21		14 33				14 51		15 03			15 14	15 21			15 34	
Polmont 3	d					13 59	14 07					14 29		14 37				14 59	15 07						15 29
Linlithgow	d					14 06	14 14					14 36		14 44				15 06	15 14						15 36
Bathgate	d			13 55						14 25						14 55						15 25			
Livingston North	d			13 59						14 29						14 59						15 29			
Uphall	d			14 03						14 33						15 03						15 33			
Edinburgh Park	d			14 12		14 19				14 42		14 49				15 12		15 19				15 42			15 49
Haymarket	d			14 19		14 26	14s31			14 49		14 56		15s01		15 19		15 26	15s31			15 49			15 56
Edinburgh 10 225, 242	a			14 25		14 32	14 36			14 55		15 01		15 06		15 25		15 33	15 36			15 55			16 01
	d			14 26						14 56						15 26						15 56			
Brunstane	d			14 32						15 02						15 32						16 02			
Newcraighall	a			14 38						15 10						15 38						16 08			

		SR 1 A	SR 1 C	SR	SR	SR	SR 1 A	SR 1 ◇ E	SR 1 C	SR		SR	SR	SR 1 A	SR 1 C	SR	SR	SR	SR 1 A	SR 1 ◇ E		SR 1 C	SR 1 A	SR	SR
Dunblane	d				15 14	15 28							15 58				16 14	16 28							
Bridge of Allan	d				15 17	15 31							16 01				16 17	16 31							
Stirling	d				15 23	15 36		15 41				15 53	16 06				16 23	16 36		16 41					16 53
Larbert	d				15 31	15 45						16 01	16 15				16 31	16 45							17 01
Camelon	d					15 48							16 18					16 48							
Falkirk Grahamston	d					15 52							16 22					16 52							
Croy 3	d		15 34		15 42				16 04			16 12			16 34		16 42					17 04			17 12
Lenzie 3	d				15 49							16 19					16 49								17 19
Bishopbriggs	d				15 53							16 23					16 53								17 23
Glasgow Queen Street 10	a		15 51		16 05			16 14	16 21			16 33			16 51		17 03			17 18		17 21			17 33
Polmont 3	d	15 37				15 59	16 07						16 29	16 37				16 59	17 07				17 27		
Linlithgow	d	15 44				16 06	16 14						16 36	16 44				17 06	17 14						
Bathgate	d			15 55						16 25						16 55								17 25	
Livingston North	d			15 59						16 29						16 59								17 29	
Uphall	d			16 03						16 33						17 03								17 33	
Edinburgh Park	d			16 12		16 19				16 42			16 49			17 12		17 19						17 42	
Haymarket	d	16s00		16 19		16 26	16s33			16 49			16 56	17s01		17 19		17 26	17s33				17s45	17 49	
Edinburgh 10 225, 242	a	16 05		16 25		16 34	16 39			16 55			17 03	17 06		17 25		17 32	17 38				17 50	17 55	
	d			16 26						16 56						17 26								17 56	
Brunstane	d			16 32						17 02						17 32								18 02	
Newcraighall	a			16 39						17 09						17 39								18 11	

For general notes see front of timetable
For details of catering facilities see Directory of Train Operators

A From Glasgow Queen Street (Table 228)
B From Dyce (Table 229)
C From Edinburgh (Table 228)
D From Inverness (Table 229)
E From Aberdeen (Table 229)

Table 230

Saturdays

Dunblane and Stirling → Falkirk Grahamston, Glasgow Queen Street and Edinburgh
Bathgate → Edinburgh → Newcraighall

Network Diagram - see first page of Table 225

		SR	SR 1 A ✠	SR 1 B ✠	SR	SR	SR 1 A ✠	SR		SR 1 A ✠	SR 1◇ C ✠	SR 1 B ✠	SR	SR	SR	SR 1 A ✠	SR 1 B ✠	SR		SR	SR	SR 1 A ✠	SR 1◇ C ✠	SR 1 B ✠	SR
Dunblane	d	16 58				17 14		17 28			17 36				17 58					18 14	18 28		18 37		
Bridge of Allan	d	17 01				17 17		17 31							18 01					18 17	18 31				
Stirling	d	17 06				17 23		17 36			17 41			17 52	18 06					18 22	18 36		18 41		18 53
Larbert	d	17 15				17 31		17 45						18 01	18 15					18 31	18 45				19 01
Camelon	d	17 18						17 48							18 18						18 48				
Falkirk Grahamston	d	17 22						17 52							18 22						18 52				
Croy 3	d			17 34		17 42						18 04		18 12			18 34			18 42				19 04	19 12
Lenzie 3	d					17 49						18 08		18 19						18 49					19 19
Bishopbriggs	d					17 53								18 23						18 53					19 23
Glasgow Queen Street 10 ⛴	a			17 51		18 03					18 18	18 21		18 34			18 50			19 03			19 14	19 21	19 33
Polmont 3	d	17 29					17 57	17 59		18 07					18 29	18 37					18 59	19 07			
Linlithgow	d	17 36	17 43				18 04	18 06		18 14					18 36	18 44					19 06	19 14			
Bathgate	d				17 54								18 25					18 55							
Livingston North	d				17 59								18 29					18 59							
Uphall	d				18 03								18 33					19 03							
Edinburgh Park	d	17 49			18 13			18 19					18 42		18 49			19 12			19 19				
Haymarket	d	17 56	18s01		18 19		18s22	18 26		18s32			18 49		18 56	19s00		19 19			19 26	19s30			
Edinburgh 10 225, 242	a	18 02	18 06		18 24		18 27	18 32		18 37			18 55		19 01	19 05		19 24			19 32	19 35			
	d				18 26								18 56					19 26							
Brunstane	d				18 33								19 02					19 32							
Newcraighall	a				18 38								19 09					19 39							

		SR 1 A ✠	SR	SR	SR 1 A ✠	SR		SR	SR	SR R 1 D ✠	SR 1 B ✠	SR	SR 1 A ✠	SR 1◇ C ✠	SR	SR 1 A ✠		SR	SR	SR	SR 1◇ C ✠	SR 1 B ✠	SR	SR 1 A	SR
Dunblane	d			18 58		19 14		19 28		19 35					19 58			20 14	20 28						20 58
Bridge of Allan	d			19 01		19 17		19 31							20 01			20 17	20 31						21 01
Stirling	d			19 06		19 23		19 36		19 41		19 52		19 58	20 06			20 23	20 36		20 41		20 53		21 06
Larbert	d			19 15		19 31		19 45				20 01			20 15			20 31	20 45				21 01		21 15
Camelon	d			19 18				19 48							20 18				20 48						21 18
Falkirk Grahamston	d			19 22				19 52							20 22				20 52						21 22
Croy 3	d					19 42					20 08	20 12						20 42				21 08	21 12		
Lenzie 3	d					19 49						20 19						20 49					21 19		
Bishopbriggs	d					19 53						20 23						20 53					21 23		
Glasgow Queen Street 10 ⛴	a					20 06				20 17	20 24	20 34		20 38				21 04			21 15	21 22	21 34		
Polmont 3	d			19 29	19 55			19 59							20 29	20 55			20 59						21 29
Linlithgow	d	19 30		19 36	20 01			20 06					20 30		20 36	21 01			21 06					21 30	21 36
Bathgate	d		19 27						20 05											21 03					
Livingston North	d		19 32						20 10											21 08					
Uphall	d		19 36						20 14											21 12					
Edinburgh Park	d		19 48	19 49				20 19	20 24						20 49				21 19	21 24					21 49
Haymarket	d	19s45	19 54	19 56	20s17			20 26	20 31				20s46		20 56	21s17			21 26	21 30				21s48	21 56
Edinburgh 10 225, 242	a	19 50	19 59	20 04	20 22			20 31	20 35				20 51		21 05	21 22			21 31	21 35				21 53	22 01
	d		19 59						20 36											21 35					
Brunstane	d		20 11						20 43											21 43					
Newcraighall	a		20 16						20 48											21 48					

		SR 1 A	SR	SR		SR 1◇ C ✠	SR 1 B	SR	SR 1 A	SR	SR 1 A	SR	SR	SR 1◇ C		SR 1 B	SR	SR 1 A	SR 1◇ D	SR	SR 1 B	SR 1 A			
Dunblane	d			21 14						21 58			22 14						22 57	23 04					
Bridge of Allan	d			21 17						22 01			22 17						23 00	23 07					
Stirling	d			21 23		21 47		21 53		22 06			22 23	22 47			22 53		23 03	23 12					
Larbert	d			21 31				22 01		22 15			22 31				23 01			23 21					
Camelon	d									22 18										23 27					
Falkirk Grahamston	d									22 22										23 30					
Croy 3	d			21 42			22 08	22 12					22 42			23 07	23 12				23 43				
Lenzie 3	d			21 49				22 19					22 49			23 13	23 18				23 50				
Bishopbriggs	d			21 53				22 23					22 53				23 22				23 54				
Glasgow Queen Street 10 ⛴	a			22 04		22 17	22 22	22 33					23 04	23 18		23 25	23 33		23 39		00 03				
Polmont 3	d	21 56								22 29	22 55							23 27		23 36		23 58			
Linlithgow	d	22 02							22 30	22 36	23 01							23 34		23 43		00 05			
Bathgate	d		22 03									23 03													
Livingston North	d		22 08									23 08													
Uphall	d		22 12									23 12													
Edinburgh Park	d		22 22							22 49		23 22								23 55					
Haymarket	d	22s18	22 28						22s46	22 56	23s17	23 28						23s49		00 03		00s21			
Edinburgh 10 225, 242	a	22 24	22 33						22 51	23 01	23 22	23 33						23 54		00 07		00 26			
	d		22 33									23 33													
Brunstane	d		22 41									23 41													
Newcraighall	a		22 46									23 46													

For general notes see front of timetable
For details of catering facilities see Directory of Train Operators

A From Glasgow Queen Street (Table 228)
B From Edinburgh (Table 228)
C From Aberdeen (Table 229)
D From Inverness (Table 229)

Table 230

Sundays

Dunblane and Stirling → Falkirk Grahamston, Glasgow Queen Street and Edinburgh
Bathgate → Edinburgh

Network Diagram - see first page of Table 225

	SR	SR	SR	SR	SR	SR	SR	SR	SR		SR	SR	SR	SR	SR	SR	SR	SR	SR		SR	SR	SR	SR
	1	1	1	1					1		1		1			1	1						1	1
	A	B	B	A	C	C			B		A		D	C	E	B	A				C		A	B
			🛒	🛒					🛒							🛒	🛒						🛒	🛒
Dunblane d													09 30		09 54							10 58		
Bridge of Allan d															09 58							11 01		
Stirling d							09 05					09 25	09 38		10 02				10 25			11 06		
Larbert d							09 13					09 34	09 47		10 11				10 34			11 16		
Camelon d							09 17								10 16							11 21		
Falkirk Grahamston d							09 20								10 19							11 24		
Croy 3 d	00 10			08 44	08 45	09 15					09 44	09 45		10 15			10 44		10 45		11 15		11 40	
Lenzie 3 d	00 16				08 52	09 22						09 52	10 02	10 22					10 52		11 22			
Bishopbriggs d					08 56	09 26						09 56		10 26					10 56		11 26			
Glasgow Queen Street 10 a	00 28			08 59	09 10	09 35					10 00	10 08	10 15	10 35			11 00		11 08		11 35		11 55	
Polmont 3 d		08 17	08 57				09 28		09 57						10 25	10 57						11 30		11 57
Linlithgow d		08 24	09 04				09 35		10 04						10 32	11 04						11 37		12 04
Bathgate d								09 49										10 59						
Livingston North d								09 54										11 04						
Uphall d								09 58										11 08						
Edinburgh Park d							09 48	10 08							10 45			11 17				11 50		
Haymarket 225, 242 d		08s44	09s23				09s59	10s19	10s23						10 52	11s19		11 24				11 57		12s19
Edinburgh 10 225, 242 a		08 49	09 28				10 04	10 24	10 28						10 58	11 24		11 30				12 01		12 24

	SR	SR	SR	SR	SR	SR	GR		SR	SR	SR	SR	SR	SR	SR	SR	SR		SR	SR	SR	SR	SR	SR
			1 ◇			1	R 1		1			1	1			1				1 ◇	1	1		
			G	C		A	H J		B			A	B	C		B				G	A	B	C	
			🛒			🛒	🍽 🛒		🛒			🛒	🛒							🛒	🛒	🛒		
Dunblane d			11 30		11 58		12 26								12 58					13 30				13 58
Bridge of Allan d					12 01										13 01									14 01
Stirling d		11 25	11 38		12 07		12 32				12 25				13 07				13 25	13 38				14 07
Larbert d		11 34			12 16						12 34				13 16				13 34					14 16
Camelon d					12 21										13 21									14 21
Falkirk Grahamston d					12 24		12 48								13 24									14 24
Croy 3 d		11 45		12 15		12 40					12 45	13 07		13 15					13 45		14 07		14 15	
Lenzie 3 d		11 52		12 22							12 52			13 22					13 52				14 22	
Bishopbriggs d		11 56		12 26							12 56			13 26					13 56				14 26	
Glasgow Queen Street 10 a		12 05	12 11	12 35		12 55					13 05	13 23		13 35					14 05	14 12	14 23		14 35	
Polmont 3 d					12 30				12 59						13 31	13 54								14 31
Linlithgow d					12 37				13 06				13 30		13 38	14 00						14 30		14 38
Bathgate d	11 59									13 01							13 59							
Livingston North d	12 04									13 04							14 04							
Uphall d	12 08									13 08							14 08							
Edinburgh Park d	12 17				12 50					13 17					13 50		14 18							14 51
Haymarket 225, 242 d	12 24				12 57		13 12		13s21	13 24			13s46		13 58	14s17	14 24					14s47		14 58
Edinburgh 10 225, 242 a	12 30				13 01		13 18		13 26	13 33			13 51		14 02	14 22	14 29					14 52		15 02

	SR	SR	SR	SR	SR		SR	SR	SR	SR	SR	SR	SR	SR	SR		SR	SR	SR	SR	SR	SR	SR	SR
	1			1	1				1	1 ◇			1 ◇	1	1				1			1	1	
	B			A	B		C		B	K			G	A	B		C		B			A	B	C
	🛒				🛒					🛒			🛒	🛒	🛒				🛒			🛒	🛒	
Dunblane d								14 58		15 16			15 30					15 58						
Bridge of Allan d								15 01										16 01						
Stirling d			14 25					15 07		15 22		15 25	15 38					16 07			16 25			
Larbert d			14 34					15 16		15 31		15 34						16 16			16 34			
Camelon d								15 21										16 21						
Falkirk Grahamston d								15 24										16 24						
Croy 3 d			14 45	15 07			15 15					15 45		16 07			16 15				16 45	17 07		17 15
Lenzie 3 d			14 52				15 22					15 52					16 22				16 52			17 22
Bishopbriggs d			14 56				15 26					15 56					16 26				16 56			17 26
Glasgow Queen Street 10 a			15 05	15 22			15 35			15 56		16 09	16 12	16 24			16 35				17 05	17 22		17 35
Polmont 3 d	14 54							15 30	15 54									16 31	16 54					
Linlithgow d	15 00				15 30			15 37	16 00						16 30			16 38	17 00				17 30	
Bathgate d		14 59									15 59									16 59				
Livingston North d		15 04									16 04									17 04				
Uphall d		15 08									16 08									17 08				
Edinburgh Park d		15 17						15 50			16 17							16 51		17 17				
Haymarket 225, 242 d	15s16	15 24			15s46			15 57	16s16		16 24				16s50			16 58	17s16	17 24			17s46	
Edinburgh 10 225, 242 a	15 21	15 29			15 51			16 01	16 21		16 29				16 55			17 02	17 21	17 29			17 51	

For general notes see front of timetable
For details of catering facilities see Directory of Train Operators

A From Edinburgh (Table 228)
B From Glasgow Queen Street (Table 228)
C Until 23 December
D From Dundee (Table 229)
E From Perth (Table 229)
G From Aberdeen (Table 229)
H From Inverness (Table 229) to London Kings Cross (Table 26)
J **The Highland Chieftain**
K From Inverness (Table 229)

Table 230

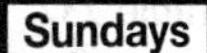

Dunblane and Stirling → Falkirk Grahamston, Glasgow Queen Street and Edinburgh
Bathgate → Edinburgh

Network Diagram - see first page of Table 225

		SR	SR 1 A	SR		SR	SR 1 ◇ B	SR 1 C	SR 1 A	SR D	SR	SR 1 A	SR	SR		SR 1 C	SR 1 A	SR D	SR 1 ◇ E	SR	SR 1 A	SR	SR	SR 1 C	SR 1 A
Dunblane	d	16 58					17 30				17 58								18 55	18 58					
Bridge of Allan	d	17 01									18 01									19 01					
Stirling	d	17 07				17 25	17 38				18 07			18 25					19 02	19 07			19 25		
Larbert	d	17 16				17 34					18 16			18 34					19 09	19 16			19 34		
Camelon	d	17 21									18 21									19 21					
Falkirk Grahamston	d	17 24									18 24									19 24					
Croy 3	d					17 45		18 07		18 15				18 45		19 07		19 13					19 45	20 07	
Lenzie 3	d					17 52				18 22				18 52				19 20					19 52		
Bishopbriggs	d					17 56				18 26				18 56				19 24					19 56		
Glasgow Queen Street 10	a					18 05	18 12	18 22		18 35				19 07		19 22		19 33	19 36				20 05	20 22	
Polmont 3	d	17 30	17 54								18 31	18 54								19 31	19 54				
Linlithgow	d	17 37	18 00						18 30		18 38	19 00					19 30			19 38	20 00				20 30
Bathgate	d			17 59									18 59									19 59			
Livingston North	d			18 04									19 04									20 04			
Uphall	d			18 08									19 08									20 08			
Edinburgh Park	d	17 50		18 17							18 51		19 18							19 51		20 18			
Haymarket 225, 242	d	17 57	18s16	18 24					18s50		18 58	19s16	19 25				19s47			19 58	20s16	20 24			20s46
Edinburgh 10 225, 242	a	18 01	18 21	18 29					18 55		19 02	19 22	19 29				19 52			20 05	20 21	20 29			20 54

		SR 1 ◇ B		SR	SR 1 A	SR	SR	SR 1 C	SR 1 A	SR	SR 1 C	SR 1 A		SR	SR	SR 1 ◇ B	SR	SR 1 C	SR 1 A	SR	SR 1 C	SR 1 A	SR		
Dunblane	d			19 58						20 58						21 34	21 58								
Bridge of Allan	d			20 01						21 01							22 01								
Stirling	d	19 54		20 07			20 25			21 07					21 25	21 40	22 07								
Larbert	d			20 16			20 34			21 16					21 34		22 16								
Camelon	d			20 21						21 21							22 21								
Falkirk Grahamston	d			20 24						21 24							22 24								
Croy 3	d						20 45	21 07			21 40				21 45			22 40			23 40				
Lenzie 3	d						20 52								21 52										
Bishopbriggs	d						20 56								21 56										
Glasgow Queen Street 10	a	20 32					21 05	21 22			21 55				22 05	22 11		22 55			23 55				
Polmont 3	d			20 30	20 54					21 30		21 57					22 30		22 57			23 57			
Linlithgow	d			20 37	21 00				21 30	21 37		22 04					22 37		23 04			00 04			
Bathgate	d					20 59								21 59						22 59			23 59		
Livingston North	d					21 04								22 04						23 04			00 04		
Uphall	d					21 08								22 08						23 08			00 08		
Edinburgh Park	d			20 50		21 18				21 50				22 18			22 50			23 18			00 20		
Haymarket 225, 242	d			20 57	21s17	21 22			21s45	21 57		22s19		22 22			22 57		23s19	23 22		00s19	00 26		
Edinburgh 10 225, 242	a			21 01	21 22	21 29			21 53	22 01		22 24		22 31			23 01		23 24	23 31		00 24	00 31		

For general notes see front of timetable
For details of catering facilities see Directory of Train Operators

A From Glasgow Queen Street (Table 228)
B From Aberdeen (Table 229)
C From Edinburgh (Table 228)
D Until 23 December
E From Inverness (Table 229)

Glasgow Queen Street — Maryhill and Annesland

Network Diagram - see first page of Table 220

Miles			SR	SR		SR	SR	SR FO
0	**Glasgow Queen Street** 10	d	06 26	06 56	and	22 56	23 26	23 56
2½	Ashfield	d	06 31	07 01	every 30	23 01	23 31	00 01
3	Possilpark & Parkhouse	d	06 33	07 03	minutes	23 03	23 33	00 03
3¼	Gilshochill	d	06 35	07 05	until	23 05	23 35	00 05
4¼	Summerston	d	06 37	07 07		23 07	23 37	00 07
4¾	**Maryhill**	d	06 38	07 08		23 08	23 38	00 08
5½	Kelvindale	d	06 40	07 10		23 10	23 40	00 10
6¼	**Annesland**	226 a	06 44	07 14		23 14	23 44	00 14

Sundays

until 23 December

		SR	SR	SR	SR	SR	SR	SR	SR	SR	SR
Glasgow Queen Street 10	d	08 45	09 55	10 56	11 56	12 55	13 56	14 55	16 03	16 56	17 56
Ashfield	d	08 51	10 01	11 02	12 02	13 02	14 02	15 01	16 09	17 02	18 02
Possilpark & Parkhouse	d	08 53	10 03	11 04	12 04	13 04	14 04	15 03	16 11	17 04	18 04
Gilshochill	d	08 55	10 05	11 06	12 06	13 06	14 06	15 05	16 13	17 06	18 06
Summerston	d	08 57	10 07	11 08	12 08	13 08	14 08	15 07	16 15	17 08	18 08
Maryhill	d	08 58	10 08	11 09	12 10	13 10	14 09	15 08	16 16	17 09	18 09
Kelvindale	d	09 00	10 10	11 11	12 12	13 12	14 11	15 10	16 18	17 11	18 11
Annesland	226 a	09 03	10 13	11 14	12 15	13 15	14 14	15 13	16 21	17 14	18 14

Mondays to Saturdays

Miles			SR	SR	SR	SR	SR SX A	SR	SR	SR	SR	SR	SR	SR	SR	SR	SR	SR
0	**Annesland**	226 d	06 23	06 53	07 23	07 53		08 25	08 53	09 23	09 53	10 23	10 53	11 23	11 53	12 23	12 53	13 23
¾	Kelvindale	d	06 25	06 55	07 25	07 55		08 27	08 55	09 25	09 55	10 25	10 55	11 25	11 55	12 25	12 55	13 25
1½	**Maryhill**	d	06 27	06 57	07 27	07 57	08 18	08 29	08 57	09 27	09 57	10 27	10 57	11 27	11 57	12 27	12 57	13 27
2	Summerston	d	06 28	06 58	07 28	07 58		08 30	08 58	09 28	09 58	10 28	10 58	11 28	11 58	12 28	12 58	13 28
3	Gilshochill	d	06 30	07 00	07 30	08 00		08 32	09 00	09 30	10 00	10 30	11 00	11 30	12 00	12 30	13 00	13 30
3¼	Possilpark & Parkhouse	d	06 32	07 02	07 32	08 02	08 23	08 34	09 02	09 32	10 02	10 32	11 02	11 32	12 02	12 32	13 02	13 32
4	Ashfield	d	06 34	07 04	07 34	08 04		08 36	09 04	09 34	10 04	10 34	11 04	11 34	12 04	12 34	13 04	13 34
6¼	**Glasgow Queen Street** 10	a	06 41	07 11	07 41	08 11	08 37	08 44	09 11	09 41	10 11	10 41	11 11	11 41	12 11	12 41	13 11	13 41

		SR	SR	SR	SR	SR	SR	SR	SR	SR	SR		SR
Annesland	226 d	13 53	14 23	14 53	15 23	15 53	16 27	16 57	17 27	17 53	18 23		23 23
Kelvindale	d	13 55	14 25	14 55	15 25	15 55	16 29	16 59	17 29	17 55	18 25	and	23 25
Maryhill	d	13 57	14 27	14 57	15 27	15 57	16 31	17 01	17 31	17 57	18 27	every 30	23 27
Summerston	d	13 58	14 28	14 58	15 28	15 58	16 32	17 02	17 32	17 58	18 28	minutes	23 28
Gilshochill	d	14 00	14 30	15 00	15 30	16 00	16 34	17 04	17 34	18 00	18 30	until	23 30
Possilpark & Parkhouse	d	14 02	14 32	15 02	15 32	16 02	16 36	17 06	17 36	18 02	18 32		23 32
Ashfield	d	14 04	14 34	15 04	15 34	16 04	16 38	17 10	17 38	18 04	18 34		23 34
Glasgow Queen Street 10	a	14 11	14 41	15 11	15 41	16 11	16 45	17 15	17 45	18 11	18 41		23 41

Sundays

until 23 December

		SR	SR	SR	SR	SR	SR	SR	SR	SR	SR
Annesland	226 d	09 23	10 23	11 23	12 23	13 23	14 23	15 23	16 23	17 23	18 23
Kelvindale	d	09 25	10 25	11 25	12 25	13 25	14 25	15 25	16 25	17 25	18 25
Maryhill	d	09 27	10 27	11 27	12 27	13 27	14 27	15 27	16 27	17 27	18 27
Summerston	d	09 28	10 28	11 28	12 28	13 28	14 28	15 28	16 28	17 28	18 28
Gilshochill	d	09 30	10 30	11 30	12 30	13 30	14 30	15 30	16 30	17 30	18 30
Possilpark & Parkhouse	d	09 32	10 32	11 32	12 32	13 32	14 32	15 32	16 32	17 32	18 32
Ashfield	d	09 35	10 35	11 35	12 35	13 35	14 35	15 35	16 35	17 35	18 35
Glasgow Queen Street 10	a	09 41	10 41	11 41	12 41	13 41	14 41	15 41	16 41	17 41	18 41

For general notes see front of timetable
For details of catering facilities see Directory of Train Operators

A From Arrochar & Tarbet (Table 227)

No Sunday service from 30 December

Haymarket and Edinburgh → North Berwick

Network Diagram - see first page of Table 225

Miles			SR	SR	SR A	SR	SR	SR	SR	SR	SR	SR	SR A	SR	SR	SR	SR	SR	SR	SR	SR
0	**Haymarket**	225, 230, 242 d	06 52	07 42	08 33	09 35	10 20	11 19	12 19	13 19	14 19	15 35	16 30	17 05	17 31	18 06	18 19	19 20	19 56	20 58	22 29
1¼	**Edinburgh** 10	225, 230, 242 a												17 09	17 35	18 10					
—		d	07 15	08 04	08 39	09 39	10 37	11 37	12 37	13 37	14 37	15 39	16 39	17 10	17 39	18 11	18 39	19 37	20 39	21 39	23 07
6½	Musselburgh	d	07 21	08 10	08 45	09 43	10 43	11 43	12 43	13 43	14 43	15 43	16 43	17 16	17 43	18 17	18 43	19 43	20 43	21 43	23 13
8¾	Wallyford	d	07 25		08 49	09 47	10 47	11 47	12 47	13 47	14 47	15 47	16 47	17 20	17 47	18 21	18 47	19 47	20 47	21 47	23 17
11	Prestonpans	d	07 28		08 52	09 50	10 50	11 50	12 50	13 50	14 50	15 50	16 50	17 24	17 50	18 25	18 50	19 50	20 50	21 50	23 20
14½	Longniddry	d	07 33		08 57	09 55	10 55	11 55	12 55	13 55	14 55	15 55	16 55	17 29	17 55	18 30	18 55	19 55	20 55	21 55	23 25
19	Drem	d	07 38		09 03	10 00	11 00	12 00	13 00	14 00	15 00	16 00	17 00	17 35	18 00	18 36	19 00	20 00	21 00	22 00	23 30
23½	**North Berwick**	a	07 47	08 29	09 11	10 11	11 09	12 09	13 09	14 09	15 10	16 11	17 12	17 43	18 12	18 44	19 12	20 09	21 12	22 12	23 49

Saturdays

		SR	SR B	SR C	SR	SR	SR	SR	SR	SR	SR	SR	SR	SR
Haymarket	225, 230, 242 d	07 05	08 29	08 21	08 53	09 19	09 49	10 19	10b50	11 19	11 49	12 19	12b50	13 19
Edinburgh 10	225, 230, 242 a		08 34											
	d	07 37	08 39	08 39	09 07	09 37	10 07	10 37	11 07	11 37	12 07	12 37	13 07	13 37
Musselburgh	d	07 43	08 45	08 45	09 13	09 43	10 13	10 43	11 13	11 43	12 13	12 43	13 13	13 43
Wallyford	d	07 47	08 49	08 49	09 17	09 47	10 17	10 47	11 17	11 47	12 17	12 47	13 17	13 47
Prestonpans	d	07 50	08 52	08 52	09 20	09 50	10 20	10 50	11 20	11 50	12 20	12 50	13 20	13 50
Longniddry	d	07 55	08 57	08 57	09 25	09 55	10 25	10 55	11 25	11 55	12 25	12 55	13 25	13 55
Drem	d	08 00	09 03	09 03	09 30	10 00	10 30	11 00	11 30	12 00	12 30	13 00	13 30	14 00
North Berwick	a	08 10	09 11	09 11	09 41	10 09	10 40	11 09	11 40	12 09	12 40	13 09	13 40	14 09

		SR	SR	SR	SR	SR	SR B	SR C	SR	SR	SR	SR	SR	SR	SR	SR
Haymarket	225, 230, 242 d	13 49	14 19	14b50	15 19	15 49	16 30	16 19	16b50	17 19	17 49	18 19	19 20	19c56	21 26	22 28
Edinburgh 10	225, 230, 242 a															
	d	14 07	14 37	15 07	15 37	16 07	16 39	16 39	17 07	17 37	18 07	18 37	19 37	20 39	21 39	23 07
Musselburgh	d	14 13	14 43	15 13	15 43	16 13	16 43	16 43	17 13	17 43	18 13	18 43	19 43	20 43	21 43	23 13
Wallyford	d	14 17	14 47	15 17	15 47	16 17	16 47	16 47	17 17	17 47	18 17	18 47	19 47	20 47	21 47	23 17
Prestonpans	d	14 20	14 50	15 20	15 50	16 20	16 50	16 50	17 20	17 50	18 20	18 50	19 50	20 50	21 50	23 20
Longniddry	d	14 25	14 55	15 25	15 55	16 25	16 55	16 55	17 25	17 55	18 25	18 55	19 55	20 55	21 55	23 25
Drem	d	14 30	15 00	15 30	16 00	16 30	17 00	17 00	17 30	18 00	18 30	19 00	20 00	21 00	22 00	23 30
North Berwick	a	14 41	15 10	15 42	16 10	16 40	17 11	17 11	17 39	18 08	18 40	19 10	20 09	21 12	22 12	23 49

Sundays

		SR	SR	SR	SR	SR	SR	SR	SR	SR	SR	SR	SR
Haymarket	225, 230, 242 d	08 56	11 00	12 18	13 11	14 19	15 00	15e57	16 58	17e57	18f58	20 01	20 57
Edinburgh 10	225, 230, 242 a												
	d	10 34	11 34	12 34	13 34	14 34	15 34	16 34	17 34	18 34	19 34	20 34	21 34
Musselburgh	d	10 40	11 40	12 40	13 40	14 40	15 40	16 40	17 40	18 40	19 40	20 40	21 40
Wallyford	d	10 44	11 44	12 44	13 44	14 44	15 44	16 44	17 44	18 44	19 44	20 44	21 44
Prestonpans	d	10 47	11 47	12 47	13 47	14 47	15 47	16 47	17 47	18 47	19 47	20 47	21 47
Longniddry	d	10 52	11 52	12 52	13 52	14 52	15 52	16 52	17 52	18 52	19 52	20 52	21 52
Drem	d	10 57	11 57	12 57	13 57	14 57	15 57	16 57	17 57	18 57	19 57	20 57	21 57
North Berwick	a	11 07	12 06	13 06	14 06	15 06	16 06	17 06	18 06	19 06	20 06	21 06	22 06

For general notes see front of timetable
For details of catering facilities see Directory of Train Operators

A From Glasgow Central (Table 225)
B Until 22 March. From Glasgow Central (Table 225)
C From 29 March
b From 29 March dep. 1 minute earlier
c From 29 March dep. 2013, by bus
e From 30 March dep. 12 minutes later
f From 30 March dep. 1902

North Berwick → Edinburgh and Haymarket

Network Diagram - see first page of Table 225

Mondays to Fridays

Miles			SR	SR	SR	SR A	SR	SR	SR	SR	SR	SR	SR	SR	SR	SR	SR A	SR	SR	SR	SR	SR
0	North Berwick	d	06 49	07 20		07 58	08 37	09 20	10 20	11 20	12 20	13 20	14 15	15 20	16 20	17 20	17 50	18 20	18 50	19 20	20 20	22 20
4½	Drem	d	06 56	07 28		08 06	08 44	09 27	10 27	11 27	12 27	13 27	14 22	15 27	16 27	17 27		18 27	18 57	19 27	20 27	22 27
9	Longniddry	d	07 02	07 34		08 12	08 50	09 33	10 33	11 33	12 33	13 33	14 28	15 33	16 33	17 33		18 33	19 03	19 33	20 33	22 33
12½	Prestonpans	d	07 07	07 39	08 08	08 17	08 55	09 38	10 38	11 38	12 38	13 38	14 33	15 38	16 38	17 38		18 38	19 08	19 38	20 38	22 38
14¾	Wallyford	d	07 10	07 43	08 11	08 21	08 58	09 41	10 41	11 41	12 41	13 41	14 36	15 41	16 41	17 41		18 41	19 11	19 41	20 41	22 41
17	Musselburgh	d	07 14	07 47	08 16	08 26	09 02	09 45	10 45	11 45	12 45	13 45	14 40	15 45	16 45	17 45	18 13	18 45	19 15	19 45	20 45	22 45
22¼	**Edinburgh 10** 225, 230, 242	a	07 20	07 53	08 22	08 32	09 10	09 53	10 53	11 53	12 53	13 53	14 48	15 53	16 53	17 53	18 19	18 53	19 23	19 53	20 53	22 53
—		d	07 21			08 39	09 13						15 07	15 55	16 57		18 23					
23½	**Haymarket** 225, 230, 242	a	07 24	*08 06*	*08 36*	08 42	09 16	*10 06*	*11 06*	*12 06*	*13 06*	*14 06*	15 10	15 59	17 01	*18 06*	18 26	*19 04*	*19 36*	*20 06*	*21 18*	*23 14*

Saturdays

		SR	SR B	SR C	SR	SR	SR	SR	SR	SR	SR	SR	SR	SR
North Berwick	d	07 29	08 20	08 20	09 20	09 48	10 20	10 50	11 20	11 50	12 20	12 50	13 20	13 50
Drem	d	07 37	08 27	08 27	09 27	09 55	10 27	10 57	11 27	11 57	12 27	12 57	13 27	14 00
Longniddry	d	07 43	08 33	08 33	09 33	10 01	10 33	11 03	11 33	12 03	12 33	13 03	13 33	14 07
Prestonpans	d	07 48	08 38	08 38	09 38	10 06	10 38	11 08	11 38	12 08	12 38	13 08	13 38	14 12
Wallyford	d	07 52	08 41	08 41	09 41	10 09	10 41	11 11	11 41	12 11	12 41	13 11	13 41	14 15
Musselburgh	d	07 56	08 45	08 45	09 45	10 13	10 45	11 15	11 45	12 15	12 45	13 15	13 45	14 19
Edinburgh 10 225, 230, 242	a	08 04	08 53	08 53	09 51	10 21	10 53	11 23	11 53	12 23	12 53	13 26	13 53	14 25
	d		08 58											
Haymarket 225, 230, 242	a	*08 18*	09 01	*09 07*	*10 06*	*10 36*	*11 06*	*11 36*	*12 06*	*12 36*	*13 06*	*13b43*	*14 06*	*14 45*

		SR	SR	SR B	SR C	SR	SR	SR	SR	SR	SR	SR	SR	SR	SR	SR
North Berwick	d	14 15	14 50	15 20	15 20	15 50	16 20	16 50	17 20	17 50	18 20	18 50	19 20	20 20	21 20	22 20
Drem	d	14 22	14 57	15 27	15 27	15 59	16 27	16 57	17 27	17 57	18 27	18 57	19 27	20 27	21 27	22 29
Longniddry	d	14 28	15 03	15 33	15 33	16 05	16 33	17 03	17 33	18 03	18 33	19 03	19 33	20 33	21 33	22 34
Prestonpans	d	14 33	15 08	15 38	15 38	16 10	16 38	17 08	17 38	18 08	18 38	19 08	19 38	20 38	21 38	22 39
Wallyford	d	14 36	15 11	15 41	15 41	16 13	16 41	17 11	17 41	18 11	18 41	19 11	19 41	20 41	21 41	22 42
Musselburgh	d	14 40	15 15	15 45	15 45	16 17	16 45	17 15	17 45	18 15	18 45	19 15	19 45	20 45	21 45	22 46
Edinburgh 10 225, 230, 242	a	14 50	15 23	15 53	15 51	16 27	16 53	17 23	17 53	18 23	18 53	19 23	19 53	20 53	21 53	22 53
	d															
Haymarket 225, 230, 242	a	*15 06*	*15 36*	15 59	*16 07*	*16 44*	*17 06*	*17 36*	*18 06*	*18 36*	*19 06*	*19 36*	*20 06*	*21 14*		*23 14*

Sundays

		SR	SR	SR	SR	SR	SR	SR	SR	SR	SR	SR	SR
North Berwick	d	11 20	12 20	13 20	14 20	15 20	16 20	17 20	18 20	19 20	20 20	21 20	22 20
Drem	d	11 27	12 27	13 29	14 27	15 27	16 27	17 27	18 27	19 27	20 27	21 27	22 27
Longniddry	d	11 33	12 33	13 35	14 33	15 33	16 33	17 33	18 33	19 33	20 33	21 33	22 33
Prestonpans	d	11 38	12 38	13 40	14 38	15 38	16 38	17 38	18 38	19 38	20 38	21 38	22 38
Wallyford	d	11 41	12 41	13 43	14 41	15 41	16 41	17 41	18 41	19 41	20 41	21 41	22 41
Musselburgh	d	11 45	12 45	13 47	14 45	15 45	16 45	17 45	18 45	19 45	20 45	21 45	22 45
Edinburgh 10 225, 230, 242	a	11 53	12 53	13 53	14 54	15 53	16 53	17 53	18 53	19 53	20 53	21 53	22 53
	d												
Haymarket 225, 230, 242	a	*12 07*	*13 19*	*14 18*	*15 16*	*16 19*	*17 09*	*18 19*	*19 19*	*20 17*	*21 17*	*22 17*	*23 22*

For general notes see front of timetable
For details of catering facilities see Directory of Train Operators

A To Glasgow Central (Table 225)
B Until 22 March. To Glasgow Central (Table 225)
C From 29 March
b From 29 March arr. 1346

Inverness → Kyle of Lochalsh, Thurso and Wick

Network Diagram - see first page of Table 227

Miles	Miles			SR ◇ 🛒	SR ◇	SR	SR ◇ 🛒	SR ◇	SR	SR	SR	SR R 🛒	SR SX 1 ◇ A 🛒	SR SO ◇	SR
—	—	Glasgow Queen Street 10 229	d				07 06		08b41	10 11		13b41	13b41		16c42
—	—	Edinburgh 10 229	d				06b40		08e38	09b36		13 36	13f36		16 34
—	—	Aberdeen 240	d		06 25		07 28		09 27	11 40	13 12		15 23	15 23	17 15
0	0	**Inverness**	d	07 14	08 53	09 15	10 39	10 52	12 17	14 33	17 03	17 52	18 15	18 15	20 39
10	10	Beauly	d	07 28	09 08	09 31	10 56	11 09	12 32	14 48	17 18	18 07	18 30	18 30	20 53
13	13	Muir of Ord	d	07 34	09 14	09 38	11 03	11 16	12 38	14 55	17g26	18 13	18 37	18 37	21 01
18¾	18¾	Dingwall	d	07 45	09 24	10h08	11 13	11 26	12 48	15 05	17 36	18 23	18j50	18j50	21 11
—	30½	Garve	d		09 45			11 47					19 11	19 11	
—	36	Lochluichart	d		09x53			11x55					19x19	19x19	
—	40¼	Achanalt	d		09x59			12x01					19x25	19x25	
—	46½	Achnasheen	d		10 10			12 13					19 36	19 36	
—	59¼	Achnashellach	d		10x28			12x31					19x54	19x54	
—	64½	Strathcarron	d		10 38			12 43					20 05	20 05	
—	67	Attadale	d		10x43			12x48					20x10	20x10	
—	72	Stromeferry	d		10 56			13 01					20 23	20 23	
—	75¾	Duncraig	d		11x04			13x09					20x31	20x31	
—	77	Plockton	d		11 07			13 13					20 34	20 34	
—	78½	Duirinish	d		11x10			13x16					20x37	20x37	
—	82¼	**Kyle of Lochalsh**	a		11 20			13 25					20 47	20 47	
28½	—	Alness	d	07 57		10 20	11 25		13 00	15 17	17 48	18 35			21 23
31½	—	Invergordon	d	08 02		10a25	11 30		13a04	15a21	17 53	18 40			21 28
40¾	—	Fearn	d	08 14			11 41				18 04	18 51			21 39
44¼	—	Tain	d	08 20			11 47				18 10	18 57			21a45
57¾	—	Ardgay	d	08 35			12 03				18a25	19 13			
61	—	Culrain	d	08 41			12 09					19 19			
61½	—	Invershin	d	08x42			12x10					19 21			
67	—	Lairg	d	08 55			12 22					19 33			
77	—	Rogart	d	09x09			12x36					19 48			
84½	—	Golspie	d	09 20			12 47					19 58			
87	—	Dunrobin Castle §	d												
90½	—	Brora	d	09 32			12 58					20 09			
101½	—	Helmsdale	d	09k52			13 13					20 24			
111	—	Kildonan	d	10x05			13x25					20x37			
118½	—	Kinbrace	d	10x14			13x35					20x46			
125¾	—	Forsinard	d	10 25			13g48					20 57			
134	—	Altnabreac	d	10x35			13x58					21x07			
143	—	Scotscalder	d	10x44			14x06					21x16			
147¼	—	Georgemas Junction	a	10 53			14 15					21 25			
—	—		d	10 55			14 18					21 27			
154	—	**Thurso**	a	11 05			14 27					21 37			
—	—		d	11 07			14 30					21 39			
160¾	—	Georgemas Junction	d	11 17			14 40					21 49			
175	—	**Wick**	a	11 34			14 57					22 06			

For general notes see front of timetable
For details of catering facilities see Directory of Train Operators

§ Summer Station only

A First Class accommodation and 🛒 available to Inverness
b Change at Perth and Inverness
c Saturdays dep. 1641
e Saturdays dep. 0835
f Change at Inverness
g Arr. 3 minutes earlier
h Arr. 0947
j Arr. 4 minutes earlier
k Arr. 6 minutes earlier

Sundays

Inverness → Kyle of Lochalsh, Thurso and Wick

Network Diagram - see first page of Table 227

Station			SR ◇	SR ◇ ⚲
Glasgow Queen Street 10	229 ⛴	d		*14 40*
Edinburgh 10	229	d		*13 55*
Aberdeen	240	d		*15 23*
Inverness		d	11 18	18 00
Beauly		d	11 32	18 19
Muir of Ord		d	11 38	18 25
Dingwall		d	11 48	18 35
Garve		d	12 09	
Lochluichart		d	12x17	
Achanalt		d	12x23	
Achnasheen		d	12 34	
Achnashellach		d	12x52	
Strathcarron		d	13 04	
Attadale		d	13x09	
Stromeferry		d	13 22	
Duncraig		d	13x30	
Plockton		d	13 33	
Duirinish		d	13x36	
Kyle of Lochalsh		a	13 46	
Alness		d		18 47
Invergordon		d		18 52
Fearn		d		19 03
Tain		d		19 11
Ardgay		d		19 26
Culrain		d		19 32
Invershin		d		19x33
Lairg		d		19 45
Rogart		d		19x58
Golspie		d		20 09
Dunrobin Castle §		d		
Brora		d		20 21
Helmsdale		d		20 36
Kildonan		d		20x49
Kinbrace		d		20x58
Forsinard		d		21 09
Altnabreac		d		21x19
Scotscalder		d		21x28
Georgemas Junction		a		21 34
		d		21 36
Thurso		a		21 46
		d		21 48
Georgemas Junction		d		21 58
Wick		a		22 15

For general notes see front of timetable
For details of catering facilities see Directory of Train Operators

§ Summer Station only

Table 239

Wick, Thurso and Kyle of Lochalsh → Inverness

Network Diagram - see first page of Table 227

Miles	Miles			SR	SR ◇	SR ◇ 🍴	SR	SR ◇ 🍴	SR	SR ◇	SR	SR ◇ 🍴	SR ◇	SR ◇ 🍴	SR	SR
0	—	**Wick**	d			06 22		08 13				12 37		15 52		
14¼	—	Georgemas Junction	d			06 39		08 30				12 54		16 09		
21	—	**Thurso**	a			06 48		08 39				13 03		16 18		
—	—		d			06 5!		08 42				13 06		16 21		
27¾	—	Georgemas Junction	a			07 00		08 51				13 15		16 30		
—	—		d			07 03		08 54				13 18		16 33		
32	—	Scotscalder	d			07x09						13x24		16x39		
41	—	Altnabreac	d			07x18						13x33		16x48		
49¼	—	Forsinard	d			07 29		09 18				13b47		16 59		
56¾	—	Kinbrace	d			07x39						13x57		17x09		
64	—	Kildonan	d			07x49						14x07		17x18		
73½	—	Helmsdale	d			08 03		09 49				14 21		17 33		
84½	—	Brora	d			08 18		10 05				14 36		17 48		
88	—	Dunrobin Castle §	d													
90½	—	Golspie	d			08 29		10 15				14 46		17 58		
98	—	Rogart	d			08 38		10x24				14x55		18x07		
108	—	Lairg	d	06 33		08c57		10 41				15 12		18 24		
113½	—	Invershin	d	06 42		09x06						15x21		18x33		
114	—	Culrain	d	06 44		09 09						15 23		18 35		
117¼	—	Ardgay	d	06 50		09 14		10 55				15 29		18 41	19 14	
130¾	—	Tain	d	07 05		09 30		11 11				15 44		18 57	19 29	21 49
134¼	—	Fearn	d	07 11		09 36						15 50		19 03	19x34	21 55
143½	—	Invergordon	d	07 23		09 47	10 33	11 30	13 12		15 31	16 02		19 15	19 46	22 06
146½	—	Alness	d	07 28		09 53	10 38		13 17		15 36	16 07		19 20	19x50	22 12
—	0	**Kyle of Lochalsh**	d		07 25					11 59			16 48			
—	3¾	Duirinish	d		07x34					12x08			16x57			
—	5¼	Plockton	d		07 38					12 12			17 01			
—	6½	Duncraig	d		07x41					12x15			17x04			
—	10¼	Stromeferry	d		07 51					12 24			17 13			
—	15¼	Attadale	d		08x02					12x35			17x24			
—	17¾	Strathcarron	d		08 08					12 42			17 30			
—	23	Achnashellach	d		08x16					12x50			17x38			
—	35¾	Achnasheen	d		08 35					13 09			17 57			
—	42	Achanalt	d		08x45					13x19			18x07			
—	46¼	Lochluichart	d		08x51					13x25			18x13			
—	51¾	Garve	d		09 01					13c37			18 23			
156¼	63½	Dingwall	d	07 44	09 25	10 07	10 53	11 46	13 31	14 00	15 50	16 21	18e49	19 35	20 04	22 26
162	69¼	Muir of Ord	d	07 54	09 36	10 17	11f16	11 56	13c43	14 08	15 59	16 30	18 57	19 45	20 13	22 35
164¾	72¼	Beauly	d	08 00	09 43	10 23	11 23		13 49	14 15	16 06	16 37	19 04	19 51	20 19	22 41
175	82¼	**Inverness**	a	08 14	09 57	10 37	11 37	12 13	14 03	14 29	16 20	16 51	19 19	20 05	20 34	22 55
—	—	Aberdeen 240	a	*10 53*	*12 59*		*14 31*			*17 37*		*19 30*			*23 38*	
—	—	Edinburgh 10 229	a	*13g32*		*14 21*		*16 04*		*18 11*	*20h32*	*22 09*	*00g07*			
—	—	Glasgow Queen Street 10 229 ⛴	a	*12 44*		*14h14*		*16h14*		*18h18*	*20 17*	*22h17*	*23 39*			

For general notes see front of timetable
For details of catering facilities see Directory of Train Operators

§ Summer Station only

b Arr. 1343
c Arr. 3 minutes earlier
e Arr. 1845
f Arr. 1101

g Change at Inverness and Stirling
h Change at Inverness and Perth

Table 239

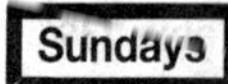

Wick, Thurso and Kyle of Lochalsh → Inverness

Network Diagram - see first page of Table 227

			SR ◇ 🍴	SR ◇
Wick		d	11 56	
Georgemas Junction		d	12 13	
Thurso		a	12 22	
		d	12 25	
Georgemas Junction		a		
		d	12 37	
Scotscalder		d	12x43	
Altnabreac		d	12x52	
Forsinard		d	13 03	
Kinbrace		d	13x13	
Kildonan		d	13x23	
Helmsdale		d	13b39	
Brora		d	13 54	
Dunrobin Castle §		d		
Golspie		d	14 03	
Rogart		d	14x12	
Lairg		d	14 29	
Invershin		d	14x37	
Culrain		d	14 40	
Ardgay		d	14 46	
Tain		d	15 01	
Fearn		d	15 07	
Invergordon		d	15 19	
Alness		d	15 24	
Kyle of Lochalsh		d		15 17
Duirinish		d		15x26
Plockton		d		15 30
Duncraig		d		15x33
Stromeferry		d		15 42
Attadale		d		15x53
Strathcarron		d		15 59
Achnashellach		d		16x07
Achnasheen		d		16 26
Achanalt		d		16x36
Lochluichart		d		16x42
Garve		d		16 51
Dingwall		d	15 39	17 15
Muir of Ord		d	15 48	17 24
Beauly		d	15 54	17 30
Inverness		a	16 08	17 45
Aberdeen	240	a	*19 28*	
Edinburgh 10	229	a		*22 06*
Glasgow Queen Street 10	229 🚌	a		*22c11*

For general notes see front of timetable
For details of catering facilities see Directory of Train Operators

§ Summer Station only

b Arr. 3 minutes earlier
c Change at Inverness and Perth

Scrabster — Stromness (Orkney Isles)
Operated by NorthLink Orkney & Shetland Ferries Ltd

		SO	SX	
Inverness	239 d	07 14	07 14	10 39
Thurso §	239 a	11b05	11b05	14c27
Scrabster	d	12 00	13 15	19 00
Stromness	a	13 30	14 45	20 30

Sundays

Inverness	239 d	
Thurso §	239 a	
Scrabster	d	
Stromness	a	

Mondays to Saturdays

		SX	SO	SX
Stromness	d	06 30	09 00	11 00
Scrabster	a	08e00	10e30	12e30
Thurso §	239 d	08 42	13 06	13 06
Inverness	239 a	12 13	16 51	16 51

Sundays

Stromness	d	09 00
Scrabster	a	10f30
Thurso §	239 d	12 25
Inverness	239 a	16 08

For general notes see front of timetable
For details of catering facilities see Directory of Train Operators

§ Highland Country Buses (01847 898123), Rapson's Coaches (01463 222244) and Scottish Citylink Coaches (03705 505050) operate a connecting Bus Service between Thurso & Scrabster & Thurso from whom details of bus times should be obtained

b Highland Country Bus connection. Departs Thurso Railway Station

c Rapson's Coaches connection. Departs Thurso Railway Station

e Highland Country Bus connection. Arrives Thurso Railway Station

f Scottish Citylink Coaches connection. Arrives St. George's Street Church

Ullapool - Stornoway (Lewis), Uig (Skye), Tarbert (Harris) and Lochmaddy (North Uist)

Operated by Caledonian MacBrayne Ltd.

		MO	WFO A	TTh SO B	WFO C	ThO D	TSO E		TThO G	SO H	WFO A	SO J	MO
Edinburgh 10	229 d							09b36	06b40	06b40	06b40	06b40	06b40
Glasgow Queen Street 10	229 d							10 11	07 06	07 06	07 06	07 06	07 06
Inverness §	229 a							13c35	10 26	10 26	10 26	10 26	10 26
Inverness	239 d	08 53	08 53	08 53	08 53	08 53	08 53		10 52	10 52	10 52	10 52	10 52
Kyle of Lochalsh §	239 a	11e20	11e20	11e20	11e20	11e20	11e20		13f25	13f25	13f25	13f25	13f25
Inverness ‡	bus d							14 35					
Ullapool	bus a							15 55					
Ullapool	ferry d							17 15					
Stornoway	ferry a							20 00					
Uig §	ferry d	14 00	14 00	14 00	15 00	15 00	15 30		18 00	18 00	18 00	18 00	18 00
Tarbert	ferry a	15 40	15 40			16 40	17 10		19 40	19 40		19 40	
Lochmaddy	ferry a			15 45	16 45					21 20	19 45		19 45

Mondays to Saturdays

		MO K		MO L	WFO	TTh SO	TTh SO B	WFO A	MO	MTSX D	
Lochmaddy	ferry d	05 30				07 30		11 50	11 50	12 45	
Tarbert	ferry d	07 30		07 30	07 30		11 50				
Uig §	ferry a	09g10		09g10	09g10	09g15	13h30	13h35	13h35	14h30	
Stornoway	ferry d		07 15								13 45
Ullapool	ferry a		10 00								16 30
Ullapool	bus d		10 05								16 35
Inverness ‡	bus a		11j25								17j55
Kyle of Lochalsh §	239 d	11 59		11 59	11 59	11 59	16 48	16 48	16 48	16 48	
Inverness	239 a	14 29		14 29	14 29	14 29	19 19	19 19	19 19	19 19	
Inverness	229 d	14 41	12 40	14 41	14 41	14 41	20 10	20 10	20 10	20 10	18 27
Glasgow Queen Street 10	229 a	18b18	16b14	18b18	18b18	18b18	23 39	23 39	23 39	23 39	22b17
Edinburgh 10	229 a	18 11	16 04	18 11	18 11	18 11	00k07	00k07	00k07	00k07	22 09

For general notes see front of timetable
For details of catering facilities see Directory of Train Operators

§ Connecting bus service between Uig/Kyle of Lochalsh operated by Scottish Citylink Coaches (08705 505050) from whom details of bus times should be obtained

‡ Bus Station. Connecting bus service between Inverness Bus Station-Ullapool operated by Scottish Citylink coaches (08705 505050)

A From 21 March
B From 22 March
C Until 19 March
D Until 20 March
E Until 18 March
G From 25 March
H 22 March to 10 May
J 17 May only
K From 24 March
L Until 17 March
b Change at Perth
c Passengers make their own way between Railway Station and Bus Station
e Bus connection dep. Kyle of Lochalsh 1215, Uig arr. 1350
f Bus connection dep. Kyle of Lochalsh 1558, Uig 1740
g Bus connection dep. Uig 0930, Kyle of Lochalsh arr. 1114
h Bus connection dep. Uig 1445, Kyle of Lochalsh arr. 1619
j Passengers made their own way between Bus Station and Railway Station
k Change at Stirling

No Sunday Service

Aberdeen and Elgin → Inverness

Network Diagram - please see first page of Table 225

Mondays to Saturdays

Miles	Station		SR	SR	SR	SR	SR	SR	SR	SR	SR	SR	SR	SR	SR	SR
					SX		SO	SX								
			[1] ◇	[1] ◇		[1] ◇		[1]	[1] ◇	[1] ◇	[1] ◇		[1] ◇		[1] ◇	
					A				B		C					
										trolley			trolley		trolley	
0	**Aberdeen**	d		06 25	07 18	07 28	07 52	08 22	08 46	09 27	09 47	11 00	11 40	12 38	13 12	14 11
6¼	**Dyce** ✈	a		06 34	07 27	07 37	08 01	08 31	08 56	09 36	09 55	11 09	11 49	12 47	13 21	14 20
—		d		06 37		07 39	08 04	08 31		09 36		11 10	11 49	12 49	13 21	14 23
17	Inverurie	d		06 50		07 51	08a18	08 43		09 48		11a21	12 01	13a03	13 33	14a37
27½	Insch	d		07 03		08 03		08 55		10 03			12 13		13 45	
40¾	Huntly	d		07 20		08 19		09 11		10 24			12 29		14 02	
53¼	Keith	d		07 34		08 33		09a27		10 37			12 43		14 16	
71¼	**Elgin**	d	07 00	07 56		08 55				10 58			13 04		14b39	
83½	Forres	d	07 14	08 10		09 15				11 17			13 19		14 54	
93¼	Nairn	d	07 25	08 21		09 26				11 28			13 30		15 05	
108¼	**Inverness**	a	07 43	08 41		09 44				11 46			13 48		15 23	

Station		SR	SR	SR	SR	SR	SR	SR	SR	SR	SR	SR	SR	SR	SR
								SO	SX			SX	SO		
		[1] ◇	[1] ◇	[1] ◇	[1] ◇		◇	[1] ◇	[1] ◇	[1] ◇	[1] ◇	◇		[1] ◇	
		C	D	C				C	C	C		C			
			trolley		trolley		trolley				trolley				
Aberdeen	d	14 42	15 23	16 41	17 15	17 42	18 21	18 46	18 48	19 39	20 07	20 54	20 54	21 55	22 50
Dyce ✈	a	14 51	15 32	16 50	17 24	17 51	18 30	18 54	18 56	19 48	20 16	21 03	21 03	22 04	22 59
	d		15 32		17 27		18 30				20 19	21 03	21 03	22 04	22 59
Inverurie	d		15 46		17 39		18 42				20 31	21a16	21a16	22 16	23a13
Insch	d		15 58		17 51		18 54				20 43			22 28	
Huntly	d		16 14		18 08		19 09				21 00			22 46	
Keith	d		16 35		18 23		19 24				21 14			23 00	
Elgin	d		16 57		18 47		19 45				21 36			23 20	
Forres	d		17 11		19 01		20 00				21 56			23 35	
Nairn	d		17c29		19 12		20 13				22 07			23 46	
Inverness	a		17 47		19 34		20 31				22 25			00 05	

Sundays

Station		SR	SR	SR	SR	SR
		[1] ◇	[1] ◇	[1] ◇	[1] ◇	[1] ◇
		trolley	trolley	trolley	trolley	trolley
Aberdeen	d	10 00	13 12	15 23	17 15	21 00
Dyce ✈	a	10 09	13 21	15 32	17 24	21 09
	d	10 09	13 21	15 32	17 27	21 09
Inverurie	d	10 22	13 33	15 47	17 40	21 21
Insch	d	10 34	13 45	15 59	17 52	21 33
Huntly	d	10 50	14 02	16 15	18 08	21 49
Keith	d	11 05	14 16	16 34	18 22	22 03
Elgin	d	11 27	14 38	16 57	18 44	22e29
Forres	d	11 41	14 53	17 11	18 58	22 43
Nairn	d	11 53	15 04	17c29	19 11	22 55
Inverness	a	12 12	15 23	17 47	19 34	23 14

For general notes see front of timetable
For details of catering facilities see Directory of Train Operators

A From Montrose (Table 229)
B From Glasgow Queen Street (Table 229)
C From Edinburgh (Table 229)
D Mondays to Fridays to Kyle of Lochalsh (Table 239)

b Arr. 4 minutes earlier
c Arr. 7 minutes earlier
e Arr. 6 minutes earlier

Table 240

Inverness and Elgin → Aberdeen

Network Diagram - please see first page of Table 225

Miles	Station		SR	SR	SR	SR	SR	SR	SR	SR	SR	SR	SR	SR	SR	SR
					SX		SO			SX						
			1◊	1◊		1◊		1◊	1◊		R 1		1◊		1◊	
			A	B				A	B							
						trolley					trolley		trolley		trolley	
0	**Inverness**	d		05 00		05 57					08 42		10 44		12 19	
15	Nairn	d		05 17		06 14					08 59		11 01		12 36	
24¾	Forres	d		05 28		06 25					09 10		11 12		12 47	
37	**Elgin**	d		05 44		06 41					09 27		11 32		13b04	
55	Keith	d		06 05		07 02				09 32	09 46		11 53		13 26	
67½	Huntly	d		06 19		07c21				09 46	10 02		12 08		13 40	
80¾	Insch	d		06 35		07 38				10 02	10 18		12 24		13 56	
91¼	Inverurie	d		06e51		07 51	08 40			10 14	10 30	11 35	12 36	13 08	14 08	14 42
102	**Dyce** ✈	a		07 03		08 02	08 51			10 26	10 42	11 46	12 48	13 19	14 20	14 53
—		d	06 50	07 03	07 45	08 03	08 56	09 08	10 08	10 26	10 42	11 50	12 48	13 23	14 20	14 54
108¼	**Aberdeen**	a	07 00	07 14	07 56	08 15	09 07	09 18	10 18	10 37	10 53	12 01	12 59	13 34	14 31	15 05

Miles	Station		SR	SR	SR	SR	SR	SR	SR	SR	SR	SR	SR	SR	SR
											SO				
			1◊	1◊	1◊	1◊		1◊	1◊	1		1◊	1		1◊
			B		B			B			B				
				trolley		trolley			trolley						
0	**Inverness**	d		13 57		15 25			17 12			18 08	19 53		21 20
15	Nairn	d		14 14		15 42			17 28			18 25	20b14		21 39
24¾	Forres	d		14 25		15 53			17 39			18 36	20 25		21 50
37	**Elgin**	d		14c42		16 08			17 55			18c54	20a41		22 08
55	Keith	d		15 03		16 30			18 17			19 16			22 29
67½	Huntly	d		15 17		16 44			18 36			19 37			22b46
80¾	Insch	d		15 33		17 00			18 55			19 53			23 02
91¼	Inverurie	d		15 48		17 12			19 07			20 05		21 28	23 14
102	**Dyce** ✈	a		16 00		17 25			19 19			20 17		21 39	23 27
—		d	15 08	16 00	17 00	17 26	17 56	19 05	19 19	19 55	19 55	20 18		21 40	23 27
108¼	**Aberdeen**	a	15 18	16 11	17 10	17 37	18 06	19 17	19 30	20 05	20 05	20 29		21 51	23 38

Sundays

Station		SR	SR	SR	SR	SR	SR	SR
		1◊	1◊	1◊	1◊	1◊	1◊	1◊
						C		C
		trolley	trolley	trolley	trolley		trolley	
Inverness	d	09 55	12 19	15 25	17 10	18 00	20 52	21 42
Nairn	d	10 12	12 36	15 42	17 28	18 17	21 10	21 59
Forres	d	10 23	12 47	15 53	17 39	18 28	21 21	22 10
Elgin	d	10 38	13b04	16 08	17 55	18a44	21 37	22a26
Keith	d	10 59	13 26	16 30	18 17		21 58	
Huntly	d	11 18	13 40	16 44	18 36		22 17	
Insch	d	11 34	13 56	17 00	18 53		22 34	
Inverurie	d	11 47	14 08	17 12	19 05		22 47	
Dyce ✈	a	11 59	14 20	17 25	19 17		22 58	
	d	11 59	14 20	17 26	19 17		22 59	
Aberdeen	a	12 10	14 31	17 37	19 28		23 10	

For general notes see front of timetable
For details of catering facilities see Directory of Train Operators

- **A** To Glasgow Queen Street (Table 229)
- **B** To Edinburgh (Table 229)
- **C** From Glasgow Queen Street (Table 229)
- **b** Arr. 4 minutes earlier
- **c** Arr. 3 minutes earlier
- **e** Arr. 6 minutes earlier

Edinburgh → Dunfermline, Kirkcaldy and Markinch

Network Diagram - see first page of Table 225

Miles	Miles	Miles			XC	SR	SR	SR	SR	SR	SR	SR	SR	SR	SR	SR	SR	SR	SR	SR	SR	SR	SR	SR
					1 ◇			1		1 ◇				1 ◇		1 ◇			1 ◇			1		
					A	B		A	C	D	C	B	C	E	B	G	C	B	E			H	C	B
					⊏P					⌶				⌶		⌶			⌶					
0	0	0	**Edinburgh 10**	d	05 35	06 16	06 22	06 40		07 08	07 12	07 17	07 40	08 10	08 11	08 38	08 41	08 48	09 10	09 13	09 18	09 36	09 41	09 48
1¼	1¼	1¼	Haymarket	d		06 20	06 26	06 45		07 13	07 16	07 21	07 44	08 14	08 15	08 42	08 45	08 52	09 14	09 15	09 22	09 40	09 45	09 52
4½	4½	4½	South Gyle	d		06 25	06 31				07 21	07 28	07 50		08 20		08 50	08 57		09 20	09 27		09 50	09 57
9½	9½	9½	Dalmeny	d		06 32	06 38				07 28	07 35	07 57		08 27		08 57	09 03		09 27	09 33		09 57	10 03
11¼	11¼	11¼	North Queensferry	d		06 35	06 42				07 31	07 38	08 00		08 30		09 00	09 07		09 30	09 37		10 00	10 07
13¼	13¼	13¼	Inverkeithing	d	06 07	06 39	06 46	06 58		07 27	07 35	07 42	08 04		08 37	08 55	09 04	09 11	09 27	09 34	09 41	09 56	10 04	10 11
—	—	14¾	Rosyth	d		06 43						07 46			08 42			09 14			09 44			10 14
—	—	17	**Dunfermline Town**	d		06 48						07 51			08 47			09 19			09 49			10 19
—	—	18½	Dunfermline Queen Margaret	d		06 51						07 54			08 50			09 23			09 53			10 23
—	—	22½	Cowdenbeath	d		06 58						08 01			08 57			09 30			10a02			10 30
—	—	24¾	Lochgelly	d		07 03						08 06			09 02			09 36						10 36
—	—	27	Cardenden	d		07 07						08 10			09 06			09 40						10 40
14¾	14¾	—	Dalgety Bay	d			06 49				07 38		08 07				09 07			09 37			10 07	
17½	17½	—	Aberdour	d			06 54				07 43		08 12				09 12			09 42			10 12	
20¼	20¼	—	Burntisland	d			06 58				07 47		08 16				09 16			09 46			10 16	
22¾	22¾	—	Kinghorn	d			07 03				07 52		08 21				09 21			09 51			10 21	
26	26	—	Kirkcaldy	d			07a09	07 15	07 30	07 43	07 57		08 26	08 42		09 11	09 26		09a43	09 56		10 12	10 26	
—	35	31¾	Glenrothes With Thornton	a		07 14			07 38		08 05	08 20	08 34		09 13		09 36	09 47					10 35	10 49
33¼	—	—	**Markinch**	a	06 36			07 23		07 52				08 51		09 20				10 10		10 22		

		SR	SR	SR	GR	SR	SR	SR	SR	SR	SR	SR	SR	SR	SR	SR	SR	SR	SR	SR	SR	SR	SR
					R																		
		1 ◇			1			1 ◇			1 ◇			1 ◇					1 ◇				
		E			J	C	B	E			G	C	B	D			C	B	E			C	B
		⌶			⊏P ⌶			⌶			⌶			⌶					⌶				
Edinburgh 10	d	10 10	10 13	10 18	10 26	10 42	10 48	11 10	11 13	11 18	11 36	11 42	11 48	12 10	12 13	12 18	12 41	12 48	13 10	13 13	13 18	13 42	13 48
Haymarket	d	10 14	10 15	10 22	10 31	10 45	10 52	11 14	11 15	11 22	11u40	11 45	11 52	12 14	12 15	12 22	12 45	12 52	13 14	13 15	13 22	13 45	13 52
South Gyle	d		10 20	10 27		10 50	10 57		11 20	11 27		11 50	11 57		12 20	12 27	12 50	12 57		13 20	13 27	13 50	13 57
Dalmeny	d		10 27	10 33		10 57	11 03		11 27	11 33		11 57	12 03		12 27	12 33	12 57	13 03		13 27	13 33	13 57	14 03
North Queensferry	d			10 37		11 00	11 07		11 30	11 37		12 00	12 07		12 30	12 37	13 00	13 07		13 30	13 37	14 00	14 07
Inverkeithing	d		10 34	10 41	10 48	11 04	11 11	11 27	11 34	11 41	11u56	12 04	12 11		12 34	12 41	13 04	13 11	13 27	13 34	13 41	14 04	14 11
Rosyth	d			10 44			11 14			11 44			12 14			12 44		13 14			13 44		14 14
Dunfermline Town	d			10 49			11 19			11 49			12 19			12 49		13 19			13 49		14 19
Dunfermline Queen Margaret	d			10 53			11 23			11 53			12 23			12 53		13 23			13 53		14 23
Cowdenbeath	d			11a03			11 30			12a03			12 30			13a02		13 30			14a02		14 30
Lochgelly	d						11 36						12 36					13 36					14 35
Cardenden	d						11 40						12 40					13 40					14 39
Dalgety Bay	d		10 37			11 07			11 37			12 07			12 37		13 07			13 37		14 07	
Aberdour	d		10 42			11 12			11 42			12 12			12 42		13 12			13 42		14 12	
Burntisland	d		10 46			11 16			11 46			12 16			12 46		13 16			13 46		14 16	
Kinghorn	d		10 51			11 21			11 51			12 21			12 51		13 21			13 51		14 21	
Kirkcaldy	d	10 42	10 56		11a04	11 26		11 43	11 56		12u12	12 26		12 42	12 56		13 26		13 43	13 56		14 26	
Glenrothes With Thornton	a					11 35	11 46					12 36	12 49				13 37	13 46				14 38	14 46
Markinch	a	10 51	11 09					11 52	12 10		12 21			12 51	13 10				13 52	14 10			

		SR	SR	SR	SR	SR	GR	SR	SR	SR	SR	SR	SR	SR	XC	SR	SR	SR	SR	SR	SR	SR	SR
							R																
		1 ◇					1					1 ◇			1 ◇			1 ◇				1 ◇	
		D			C	B	K L			C	B	D	C		N	C		D	B	Q	H	G	C
		⌶					⊏P ⌶					⌶			⊏P			⌶				⌶	
Edinburgh 10	d	14 10	14 13	14 18	14 41	14 48	15 00	15 13	15 18	15 42	15 48	16 05	16 09	16 18	16 30	16 40	16 46	17 04	17 10	17 14	17 28	17 40	17 49
Haymarket	d	14 14	14 15	14 22	14 45	14 52	15 04	15 15	15 22	15 45	15 52	16u10	16 13	16 22	16 35	16 45	16 51	17 08	17 14	17 18	17 32	17u44	17 52
South Gyle	d		14 20	14 27	14 50	14 57		15 20	15 27	15 50	15 57		16 19	16 27		16 50	16 56			17 23	17 37		17 57
Dalmeny	d		14 27	14 33	14 57	15 03		15 27	15 33	15 57	16 03		16 25	16 33		16 57	17 02			17 30	17 44		18 03
North Queensferry	d		14 30	14 37	15 00	15 07		15 30	15 37	16 00	16 07		16 29	16 37		17 00				17 34	17 48		18 07
Inverkeithing	d		14 34	14 41	15 04	15 11	15 21	15 34	15 41	16 04	16 11	16u25	16 33	16 41	16 48	17 04	17 10		17 28	17 38	17 52	17 59	18 11
Rosyth	d			14 44		15 14			15 44		16 14			16 44			17 13		17 32		17 55		
Dunfermline Town	d			14 49		15 19			15 49		16 19			16 49			17 19		17 37		18 00		
Dunfermline Queen Margaret	d			14 53		15 23			15 53		16 23			16 53			17 22		17 40		18 04		
Cowdenbeath	d			15a02		15 30			16a02		16 30			17a02			17a31		17 47		18 10		
Lochgelly	d					15 35					16 36								17 52		18 16		
Cardenden	d					15 39					16 40								17 56		18 20		
Dalgety Bay	d		14 37		15 07			15 37		16 07			16 36			17 07				17 41			18 16
Aberdour	d		14 42		15 12			15 42		16 12			16 41			17 12				17 46			18 21
Burntisland	d		14 46		15 16			15 46		16 16			16 45			17 16				17 51			18 25
Kinghorn	d		14 51		15 21			15 51		16 21			16 50			17 21				17 56			18 30
Kirkcaldy	d	14 42	14 56		15 26		15a36	15 56		16 26		16 41	16 55		17 03	17 26		17 37		18 01		18a14	18 35
Glenrothes With Thornton	a				15 37	15 46				16 38	16 47		17 03			17 35			18 03		18 26		18 46
Markinch	a	14 51	15 10					16 10				16 50			17 11			17 46		18 10	18 32		

For general notes see front of timetable
For details of catering facilities see Directory of Train Operators

- **A** To Dundee (Table 229)
- **B** To Edinburgh via Kirkcaldy
- **C** To Edinburgh via Cowdenbeath
- **D** To Dyce (Table 229)
- **E** To Aberdeen (Table 229)
- **G** To Inverness (Table 229)
- **H** To Perth (Table 229)
- **J** From Leeds (Table 26) to Aberdeen (Table 229)
- **K** From London Kings Cross (Table 26) to Aberdeen (Table 229)
- **L** **The Northern Lights**
- **N** From Bournemouth (Table 51) to Aberdeen (Table 229)
- **Q** To Carnoustie (Table 229)

Edinburgh → Dunfermline, Kirkcaldy and Markinch

Network Diagram - see first page of Table 225

		SR	SR		SR	SR	SR	GR	SR	XC	SR	SR	SR	SR		SR	GR	SR	SR	SR	SR	SR	SR		
			1 ◇					R 1		R 1	1 ◇		1 ◇				R 1					1			
		L	B		C	D	A	E		G	H		J			K	E		K		K	K			
Edinburgh 10	d	17 53	18 10		18 13		18 25	18 32	18 48	19 01	19 10	19 15	19 36	19 48		20 11	20 30	20 48	21 24	21 52	22 35	23 10	23 21		
Haymarket	d	17 57	18 14		18 18		18 29	18 37	18 52	19 06	19 14	19 20	19 40	19 52		20 15	20 35	20 52	21 28	21 56	22 39	23 14	23 25		
South Gyle	d	18 03			18 23		18 35		18 57			19 24		19 57		20 20		20 57	21 34	22 01	22 44		23 30		
Dalmeny	d	18 10			18 30	18 36	18 43		19 03			19 31		20 03		20 26		21 03	21 40	22 07	22 51	23 23	23 37		
North Queensferry	d	18 13			18 33		18 46		19 07			19 34		20 07		20 30		21 07	21 44	22 11	22 54		23 40		
Inverkeithing	d	18 17	18 28		18 37	18 43	18 50	18 55	19 11	19 20	19 27	19 38	19 53	20 11		20 35	20 50	21 11	21 48	22 15	22 58	23 29	23 44		
Rosyth	d	18 23					18 54		19 14					20 14				21 14		22 18			23 48		
Dunfermline Town	d	18 28					18 59		19 19					20 19				21 19		22 23			23 53		
Dunfermline Queen Margaret	d	18 32					19 02		19 23					20 23				21 23		22 27			23 56		
Cowdenbeath	d	18 38					19 09		19 30					20 29				21 30		22 33			00 03		
Lochgelly	d	18 44					19 14		19 36					20 35				21 36		22 39			00 08		
Cardenden	d	18 48					19 18		19 40					20 39				21 40		22 43			00 13		
Dalgety Bay	d				18 40	18 46						19 41				20 38			21 51		23 01	23 32			
Aberdour	d				18 45	18 51						19 46				20 43			21 56		23 06	23 37			
Burntisland	d				18 49	18 56						19 50				20 47			22 00		23 10	23 41			
Kinghorn	d				18 54	19 01						19 55				20 52			22 05		23 15	23 46			
Kirkcaldy	d		18 44		18 59	19a05		19a10		19 35	19 43	20 02	20 09			20 57	21a07		22 10		23 20	23 51			
Glenrothes With Thornton	a	18 54			19 07		19 25		19 49					20 48				21 50		22 52			00 21		
Markinch	a		18 53							19 43	19 52	20 12	20 18			21 06			22 19		23 29	23 59			

Saturdays

		XC	SR	SR	SR	SR		SR	SR	SR	SR	SR		SR	SR	SR	SR	SR		SR	SR	SR	SR	SR	SR
		1 ◇		1		1 ◇				1 ◇		1 ◇				1 ◇				1			1 ◇		
		K	L	K	C	N		L	C	H	L	J		C	L	H				Q	C	L	H		
Edinburgh 10	d	05 33	06 08	06 40	06 45	07 08		07 17	07 40	08 10	08 11	08 35		08 41	08 48	09 10	09 13	09 18		09 36	09 41	09 48	10 10	10 13	10 18
Haymarket	d		06 12	06 45	06 49	07 13		07 21	07 44	08 14	08 15	08 39		08 45	08 52	09 14	09 15	09 22		09 40	09 45	09 52	10 14	10 15	10 22
South Gyle	d		06 17		06 54			07 28	07 50		08 20			08 50	08 57		09 20	09 27			09 50	09 57		10 20	10 27
Dalmeny	d		06 23		07 01			07 35	07 57		08 27			08 57	09 03		09 27	09 33			09 57	10 03		10 27	10 33
North Queensferry	d		06 27		07 04			07 38	08 00		08 30			09 00	09 07		09 30	09 37			10 00	10 07			10 37
Inverkeithing	d	06 06	06 31	06 58	07 08	07 27		07 42	08 04		08 37	08 52		09 04	09 11	09 27	09 34	09 41		09 56	10 04	10 11		10 34	10 41
Rosyth	d		06 34					07 46			08 42				09 14			09 44				10 14			10 44
Dunfermline Town	d		06 39					07 51			08 47				09 19			09 49				10 19			10 49
Dunfermline Queen Margaret	d		06 43					07 54			08 50				09 23			09 53				10 23			10 53
Cowdenbeath	d		06 49					08 01			08 57				09 30			10a02				10 30			11a03
Lochgelly	d		06 55					08 06			09 02				09 36							10 36			
Cardenden	d		06 59					08 10			09 06				09 40							10 40			
Dalgety Bay	d				07 11				08 07					09 07			09 37				10 07			10 37	
Aberdour	d				07 16				08 12					09 12			09 42				10 12			10 42	
Burntisland	d				07 20				08 16					09 16			09 46				10 16			10 46	
Kinghorn	d				07 25				08 21					09 21			09 51				10 21			10 51	
Kirkcaldy	d			07 15	07 30	07 43			08 26	08 42		09 08		09 26		09a43	09 56			10 12	10 26		10 42	10 56	
Glenrothes With Thornton	a		07 08		07 38			08 20	08 34		09 13			09 36	09 47						10 35	10 50			
Markinch	a	06 36		07 23		07 52				08 51		09 17					10 10			10 22			10 51	11 09	

		GR		SR	SR	SR	SR	SR		SR	SR	SR	SR	SR		SR	SR	SR	SR	SR		SR	SR	SR	SR
		R 1				1 ◇				1 ◇			1 ◇						1 ◇						1 ◇
		U		C	L	H				J	C	L	N				C	L	H				C	L	N
Edinburgh 10	d	10 26		10 42	10 48	11 10	11 13	11 18		11 36	11 42	11 48	12 10	12 13		12 18	12 41	12 48	13 10	13 13		13 18	13 42	13 48	14 10
Haymarket	d	10 31		10 45	10 52	11 14	11 15	11 22		11u40	11 45	11 52	12 14	12 15		12 22	12 45	12 52	13 14	13 15		13 22	13 45	13 52	14 14
South Gyle	d			10 50	10 57		11 20	11 27			11 50	11 57		12 20		12 27	12 50	12 57		13 20		13 27	13 50	13 57	
Dalmeny	d			10 57	11 03		11 27	11 33			11 57	12 03		12 27		12 33	12 57	13 03		13 27		13 33	13 57	14 03	
North Queensferry	d			11 00	11 07		11 30	11 37			12 00	12 07		12 30		12 37	13 00	13 07		13 30		13 37	14 00	14 07	
Inverkeithing	d	10 48		11 04	11 11	11 27	11 34	11 41		11u56	12 04	12 11		12 34		12 41	13 04	13 11	13 27	13 34		13 41	14 04	14 11	
Rosyth	d				11 14			11 44				12 14				12 44		13 14				13 44		14 14	
Dunfermline Town	d				11 19			11 49				12 19				12 49		13 19				13 49		14 19	
Dunfermline Queen Margaret	d				11 23			11 53				12 23				12 53		13 23				13 53		14 23	
Cowdenbeath	d				11 30			12a03				12 30				13a02		13 30				14a02		14 30	
Lochgelly	d				11 36							12 36						13 36						14 35	
Cardenden	d				11 40							12 40						13 40						14 39	
Dalgety Bay	d			11 07			11 37				12 07			12 37			13 07			13 37			14 07		
Aberdour	d			11 12			11 42				12 12			12 42			13 12			13 42			14 12		
Burntisland	d			11 16			11 46				12 16			12 46			13 16			13 46			14 16		
Kinghorn	d			11 21			11 51				12 21			12 51			13 21			13 51			14 21		
Kirkcaldy	d	11a04		11 26		11 43	11 56			12u12	12 26		12 42	12 56			13 26		13 43	13 56			14 26		14 42
Glenrothes With Thornton	a			11 35	11 46						12 36	12 49					13 37	13 46					14 38	14 46	
Markinch	a					11 52	12 10			12 21			12 51	13 10					13 52	14 10					14 51

For general notes see front of timetable
For details of catering facilities see Directory of Train Operators

- **A** To Edinburgh
- **B** To Inverurie (Table 240)
- **C** To Edinburgh via Cowdenbeath
- **D** From Glasgow Queen Street (Table 230)
- **E** From London Kings Cross (Table 26) to Aberdeen (Table 229)
- **G** From Penzance (Table 135) to Dundee (Table 229)
- **H** To Aberdeen (Table 229)
- **J** To Inverness (Table 229)
- **K** To Dundee (Table 229)
- **L** To Edinburgh via Kirkcaldy
- **N** To Dyce (Table 229)
- **Q** To Perth (Table 229)
- **U** From Leeds (Table 26) to Aberdeen (Table 229)

Table 242

Saturdays

Edinburgh → Dunfermline, Kirkcaldy and Markinch

Network Diagram - see first page of Table 225

		SR	SR	SR		SR	GR	SR	SR	SR		SR	SR	SR	SR	XC		SR	SR	SR	SR	SR		SR	SR
							R 1						1 ◊			1 ◊				1 ◊					1 ◊
				A		B	C D			A		B	E	A		G		A		E	B	H		J	K
Edinburgh 10	d	14 13	14 18	14 41		14 48	15 00	15 13	15 18	15 42		15 48	16 05	16 09	16 18	16 30		16 40	16 48	17 04	17 10	17 15		17 28	17 40
Haymarket	d	14 15	14 22	14 45		14 52	15 04	15 15	15 22	15 45		15 52	16u10	16 13	16 22	16 35		16 45	16 52	17 08	17 14	17 19		17 32	17u44
South Gyle	d	14 20	14 27	14 50		14 57		15 20	15 27	15 50		15 57		16 19	16 27			16 50	16 57			17 24		17 37	
Dalmeny	d	14 27	14 33	14 57		15 03		15 27	15 33	15 57		16 03		16 25	16 33			16 57	17 03			17 31		17 44	
North Queensferry	d	14 30	14 37	15 00		15 07		15 30	15 37	16 00		16 07		16 29	16 37			17 00				17 34		17 48	
Inverkeithing	d	14 34	14 41	15 04		15 11	15 21	15 34	15 41	16 04		16 11	16u25	16 33	16 41	16 48		17 04	17 11		17 28	17 38		17 52	17 59
Rosyth	d		14 44			15 14			15 44			16 14			16 44				17 14		17 32			17 55	
Dunfermline Town	d		14 49			15 19			15 49			16 19			16 49				17 19		17 37			18 00	
Dunfermline Queen Margaret	d		14 53			15 23			15 53			16 23			16 53				17 23		17 40			18 04	
Cowdenbeath	d		15a02			15 30			16a02			16 30			17a04				17a33		17 47			18 10	
Lochgelly	d					15 35						16 36									17 52			18 16	
Cardenden	d					15 39						16 40									17 56			18 20	
Dalgety Bay	d	14 37		15 07				15 37		16 07				16 36				17 07				17 42			
Aberdour	d	14 42		15 12				15 42		16 12				16 41				17 12				17 47			
Burntisland	d	14 46		15 16				15 46		16 16				16 45				17 16				17 51			
Kinghorn	d	14 51		15 21				15 51		16 21				16 50				17 21				17 56			
Kirkcaldy	d	14 56		15 26			15a36	15 56		16 26			16 41	16 55		17 03		17 26		17 37		18 01			18a14
Glenrothes With Thornton	a			15 37		15 46				16 38		16 47		17 03				17 35			18 04			18 26	
Markinch	a	15 10						16 09					16 49			17 11				17 46		18 10		18 32	

		SR	SR	SR	SR	GR		SR	SR	XC	SR	SR		SR	SR	SR	SR	SR		SR	SR	SR	SR		
			1 ◊			R 1			1 ◊	1 ◊		1 ◊					1 ◊					1			
		A	L	A	B	C			L	N		K			Q		L	Q			Q	Q			
Edinburgh 10	d	17 49	18 10	18 13	18 25	18 32		18 48	19 10	19 12	19 15	19 36		19 52	20 11	20 48	21 10	21 24		21 52	22 35	23 10	23 21		
Haymarket	d	17 52	18 14	18 18	18 29	18 37		18 52	19 14	19 17	19 20	19 40		19 56	20 15	20 52	21 14	21 28		21 56	22 39	23 14	23 25		
South Gyle	d	17 57		18 23	18 35			18 57			19 24			20 01	20 20	20 57		21 34		22 01	22 44		23 30		
Dalmeny	d	18 03		18 30	18 43			19 03			19 31			20 07	20 26	21 03		21 40		22 07	22 51	23 23	23 37		
North Queensferry	d	18 07		18 33	18 46			19 07			19 34			20 11	20 30	21 07		21 44		22 11	22 54		23 40		
Inverkeithing	d	18 11	18 27	18 37	18 50	18 55		19 11	19 27	19 34	19 38	19 54		20 15	20 35	21 11	21 27	21 48		22 15	22 58	23 29	23 44		
Rosyth	d				18 54			19 14						20 18		21 14				22 18			23 48		
Dunfermline Town	d				18 59			19 19						20 23		21 19				22 23			23 53		
Dunfermline Queen Margaret	d				19 02			19 23						20 27		21 23				22 27			23 56		
Cowdenbeath	d				19 09			19 30						20 33		21 30				22 33			00 03		
Lochgelly	d				19 14			19 36						20 39		21 36				22 39			00 08		
Cardenden	d				19 18			19 40						20 43		21 40				22 43			00 13		
Dalgety Bay	d	18 16		18 40							19 41				20 38			21 51			23 01	23 32			
Aberdour	d	18 21		18 45							19 46				20 43			21 56			23 06	23 37			
Burntisland	d	18 25		18 49							19 50				20 47			22 00			23 10	23 41			
Kinghorn	d	18 30		18 54							19 55				20 52			22 05			23 15	23 46			
Kirkcaldy	d	18 35	18 45	18 59		19a10			19 43	19 50	20 02	20 10			20 57		21 43	22 10			23 20	23 51			
Glenrothes With Thornton	a	18 46		19 07	19 25			19 49						20 52		21 50				22 52			00 21		
Markinch	a		18 54						19 52	19 58	20 12	20 18			21 06		21 52	22 19			23 29	23 59			

Sundays

		XC	GR	SR		SR	SR	SR		SR	SR	SR		SR	SR	SR		SR	SR	SR		SR	SR	GR	SR
		1 ◊	R 1			1 ◊				1 ◊					1 ◊			1 ◊						R 1	
		L	L	Q		K	B	A		L	Q	B		A	L	Q		K	B	A		Q	B	C D	
Edinburgh 10	d	08 05	09 10	09 15		09 25	09 55	10 15		10 55	11 15	11 55		12 15	12 40	13 15		13 55	14 00	14 15		15 15	15 55	16 00	16 15
Haymarket	d	08 10	09 14	09 19		09 29	09 59	10 19		10 59	11 19	11 59		12 19	12 44	13 19		13 59	14 05	14 19		15 19	15 59	16 04	16 19
South Gyle	d			09 24			10 04	10 24			11 24	12 04		12 24		13 24			14 10	14 24		15 24	16 04		16 24
Dalmeny	d			09 30			10 10	10 30			11 30	12 10		12 30		13 30			14 19	14 30		15 30	16 10		16 30
North Queensferry	d			09 35			10 17	10 34			11 37	12 17		12 34		13 37			14 26	14 34		15 37	16 14		16 34
Inverkeithing	d	08 24	09 32	09 41		09 48	10 21	10 38		11 15	11 41	12 21		12 38	13 00	13 41		14 16	14 30	14 38		15 41	16 18	16 24	16 38
Rosyth	d						10 24					12 24							14 34				16 21		
Dunfermline Town	d						10 29					12 29							14 39				16 26		
Dunfermline Queen Margaret	d						10 33					12 33							14 42				16 30		
Cowdenbeath	d						10 39					12 39							14 49				16 36		
Lochgelly	d						10 45					12 45							14 54				16 42		
Cardenden	d						10 49					12 49							14 58				16 46		
Dalgety Bay	d			09 44				10 41			11 44			12 41		13 44				14 41		15 44			16 41
Aberdour	d			09 49				10 46			11 49			12 46		13 49				14 46		15 49			16 46
Burntisland	d			09 53				10 50			11 53			12 50		13 53				14 50		15 53			16 50
Kinghorn	d			09 58				10 55			11 58			12 55		13 58				14 55		15 58			16 55
Kirkcaldy	d	08 39	09a48	10 03		10a10		11 00		11a31	12 03			13 00	13a16	14 03		14a33		15 00		16 03		16a41	17 00
Glenrothes With Thornton	a						10 56	11 11				12 55		13 11					15 05	15 14			16 52		17 08
Markinch	a	08 47		10 12							12 12					14 12						16 12			

For general notes see front of timetable
For details of catering facilities see Directory of Train Operators

- **A** To Edinburgh via Cowdenbeath
- **B** To Edinburgh via Kirkcaldy
- **C** From London Kings Cross (Table 26) to Aberdeen (Table 229)
- **D** **The Northern Lights**
- **E** To Dyce (Table 229)
- **G** From Bournemouth (Table 51) to Aberdeen (Table 229)
- **H** To Carnoustie (Table 229)
- **J** To Perth (Table 229)
- **K** To Inverness (Table 229)
- **L** To Aberdeen (Table 229)
- **N** From Penzance (Table 135) to Dundee (Table 229)
- **Q** To Dundee (Table 229)

Table 242

Sundays

Edinburgh → Dunfermline, Kirkcaldy and Markinch

Network Diagram - see first page of Table 225

		XC	SR	SR	SR	SR	SR	GR	SR	XC	SR	SR	SR	SR	SR	SR	SR
		1 ◇	1 ◇		1			R 1		R 1			1 ◇				
		A	B	C	D	E	G	H	C	J	E	G	B		E	C	
		[trolley]	[restaurant]					[trolley] [restaurant]		[trolley]							
Edinburgh 10	d	16 35	17 05	17 15	17 50	17 55	18 15	18 43	19 15	19 25	19 55	20 15	21 00	21 15	21 55	22 25	23 36
Haymarket	d	16 40	17 09	17 19	17 54	17 59	18 19	18 47	19 19	19 30	19 59	20 19	21 04	21 19	21 59	22 29	23 40
South Gyle	d			17 24		18 04	18 24		19 24		20 04	20 24		21 24	22 04	22 34	23 45
Dalmeny	d			17 29		18 10	18 30		19 29		20 10	20 30		21 30	22 10	22 40	23 51
North Queensferry	d			17 34		18 14	18 34		19 34		20 14	20 34		21 34	22 14	22 44	23 55
Inverkeithing	d	16 54	17 22	17 38	18 07	18 18	18 38	19 05	19 38	19 44	20 18	20 38	21 17	21 38	22 18	22 48	23a58
Rosyth	d					18 21					20 21				22 21		
Dunfermline Town	d					18 26					20 26				22 26		
Dunfermline Queen Margaret	d					18 30					20 30				22 30		
Cowdenbeath	d					18 36					20 36				22 36		
Lochgelly	d					18 42					20 42				22 42		
Cardenden	d					18 46					20 46				22 46		
Dalgety Bay	d			17 41			18 41		19 41			20 41		21 41		22 51	
Aberdour	d			17 46			18 46		19 46			20 46		21 46		22 56	
Burntisland	d			17 50			18 50		19 50			20 50		21 50		23 00	
Kinghorn	d			17 55			18 55		19 55			20 55		21 55		23 05	
Kirkcaldy	d	17 09	17a38	18 00	18a23		19 00	19a22	20 00	20 06		21 00	21 33	22a02		23 10	
Glenrothes With Thornton	a					18 55	19 10				20 52	21 09			22 54		
Markinch	a	17 17		18 09					20 09	20 14			21 43			23 19	

For general notes see front of timetable
For details of catering facilities see Directory of Train Operators

- **A** From Birmingham New Street (Table 51) to Aberdeen (Table 229)
- **B** To Aberdeen (Table 229)
- **C** To Dundee (Table 229)
- **D** To Perth (Table 229)
- **E** To Edinburgh via Kirkcaldy
- **G** To Edinburgh via Cowdenbeath
- **H** From London Kings Cross (Table 26) to Aberdeen (Table 229)
- **J** From Plymouth (3 February to 23 March from Bournemouth) (Table 51) to Dundee (Table 229).
- ◇ 3 February to 23 March

Markinch, Kirkcaldy and Dunfermline → Edinburgh

Network Diagram - see first page of Table 225

Miles	Miles	Miles			SR	SR	SR	SR	SR	SR	XC	SR	SR	SR	SR	SR	SR	SR	XC	SR	SR	SR	SR	SR	SR
											1 ◇		1	1 ◇					R 1						1 ◇
								A	B	C	D	E	A	G		H		J	K	L	E	N	L		U
0	—	—	Markinch	d		06 20		06 45	06 52		07 13		07 34					07 54	08 09			08 34			09 06
—	0	0	Glenrothes With Thornton	d		06 25		06 51				07 14			07 33	07 38				08 05	08 20		08 34		
7¼	7¼	—	**Kirkcaldy**	d	05 55				07 02	07 15	07 25	07 30	07 44	07 50			07 57	08 05	08 18		08 27	08 43		09 03	09 15
10½	10	—	Kinghorn	d	06 00				07 07	07 20		07 35					08 02	08 10			08 32			09 07	
13	12¾	—	Burntisland	d	06 05				07 11	07 24		07 39					08 06	08 15			08 36			09 12	
15¾	17½	—	Aberdour	d	06 10				07 16	07 29		07 44					08 11	08 19			08 41			09 16	
18½	20¼	—	Dalgety Bay	d	06 15				07 21	07 34		07 49					08 16	08 24			08 46			09 21	
—	—	4¾	Cardenden	d		06 33		06 58							07 40	07 45				08 12			08 42		
—	—	7	Lochgelly	d		06 37		07 03							07 44	07 49				08 16			08 46		
—	—	9½	Cowdenbeath	d		06 43		07 09							07 50	07 55				08 22			08 52		
—	—	13½	Dunfermline Queen Margaret	d		06 48	07 00	07 14							07 56	08 01				08 27			08 57		
—	—	14¾	**Dunfermline Town**	d		06 52	07 03	07 18							07 59	08 05				08 31			09 01		
—	—	17	Rosyth	d		06 56	07 07	07 22							08 03	08 08				08 35			09 05		
19¾	21¾	18½	Inverkeithing	d	06 21	07 02	07 14	07 31	07 25	07 38	07 43	07 52	08 00		08 10	08 15	08 19	08 28	08 37	08 42	08 50	08 59	09 12	09 24	
21¾	23¾	20½	North Queensferry	d	06 25	07 07		07 35				07 56					08 24			08 46	08 54		09 16		
23½	25½	22¼	Dalmeny	d	06 29	07 11		07 39		07a44		08 00			08 16	08 21	08 28			08 50	08 58		09 20		
28½	30½	27¼	South Gyle	d	06 35	07 17		07 45	07 37			08 06			08 23	08 27	08 34	08 39		08 56	09 04		09 26		
31¾	33¾	30½	Haymarket	d	06 44	07 26	07 31	07 55	07 45		08 00	08 15	08 18	08 21	08 31	08 36	08 42	08 48	08 58	09 05	09 12	09 16	09 35	09 42	09 46
33½	35	31¾	**Edinburgh** 10	a	06 48	07 30	07 35	07 59	07 50		08 06	08 19	08 23	08 26	08 36	08 40	08 47	08 52	09 03	09 10	09 17	09 20	09 40	09 47	09 50

		SR	SR	GR	SR		SR	XC	SR	SR	SR	SR	SR	SR	SR	GR	SR	SR	SR	SR	SR	SR	SR	SR	SR
		1 ◇		R 1				R 1			1 ◇					R 1	1			1 ◇					1 ◇
		U	E	V	L		E	X			G	L	E			V Y	A	L	E	Z			L	E	G
Markinch	d							10 04		10 19	10 34				11 19		11 42			12 02		12 19			13 04
Glenrothes With Thornton	d		09 13		09 36		09 47					10 35	10 50					11 35	11 47				12 36	12 50	
Kirkcaldy	d	09 25	09 27	09 44			09 57	10 13		10 27	10 43		10 57		11 27	11 43	11 52		11 57	12 12		12 27		12 57	13 14
Kinghorn	d		09 32				10 02			10 32			11 02		11 32				12 02			12 32		13 02	
Burntisland	d		09 36				10 06			10 36			11 06		11 36				12 06			12 36		13 06	
Aberdour	d		09 41				10 11			10 41			11 11		11 41				12 11			12 41		13 11	
Dalgety Bay	d		09 46				10 16			10 46			11 16		11 46			11 08	12 16			12 46		13 16	
Cardenden	d				09 43							10 43						11 43					12 43		
Lochgelly	d				09 47							10 47						11 47					12 47		
Cowdenbeath	d				09 53				10 19			10 53		11 23				11 53			12 23		12 53		
Dunfermline Queen Margaret	d				09 57				10 24			10 57		11 27				11 57			12 27		12 57		
Dunfermline Town	d				10 01				10 28			11 01		11 31				12 01			12 31		13 01		
Rosyth	d				10 05				10 32			11 05		11 35				12 05			12 35		13 05		
Inverkeithing	d		09 50	10 00	10 12		10 20	10 28	10 39	10 50	10 59	11 12	11 20	11 42	11 50	11 59	12 08	12 12	12 20		12 42	12 50	13 12	13 20	13 30
North Queensferry	d		09 54		10 16		10 24		10 43	10 54		11 16	11 24	11 46	11 54			12 16	12 24		12 46	12 54	13 16	13 24	
Dalmeny	d		09 58		10 20		10 28		10 47	10 58		11 20	11 28	11 50	11 58			12 20	12 28		12 50	12 58	13 20	13 28	
South Gyle	d		10 04		10 26		10 34		10 53	11 04		11 26	11 34	11 56	12 04			12 26	12 34		12 56	13 04	13 26	13 34	
Haymarket	d	09 55	10 12	10 19	10 35		10 42	10 47	11 05	11 12	11 16	11 35	11 42	12 05	12 12	12 17	12 24	12 35	12 42	12 46	13 05	13 12	13 35	13 42	13 46
Edinburgh 10	a	10 01	10 19	10 25	10 41		10 47	10 51	11 10	11 17	11 20	11 40	11 47	12 10	12 17	12 22	12 28	12 40	12 47	12 50	13 10	13 17	13 40	13 47	13 50

		SR	SR	SR	SR	SR	SR		SR	SR	SR	SR	SR	SR	SR	SR	SR	SR	SR	SR	SR	GR	SR	SR	SR
				1 ◇			1 ◇						1 ◇	1 ◇					1 ◇			R 1			1 ◇
				U	L	E	G				L	E	G	U			L	E	G			V	L	E	Z
Markinch	d		13 19				14 05			14 19			15 04	15 18		15 24			16 04		16 17				17 07
Glenrothes With Thornton	d				13 37	13 46					14 38	14 46					15 37	15 46					16 38	16 47	
Kirkcaldy	d		13 27	13 44		13 57	14 15			14 27		14 57	15 14	15 28		15 33		15 57	16 14		16 26	16 41		16 57	17 17
Kinghorn	d		13 32			14 02				14 32		15 02				15 38		16 02			16 31			17 02	
Burntisland	d		13 36			14 06				14 36		15 06				15 42		16 06			16 35			17 06	
Aberdour	d		13 41			14 11				14 41		15 11				15 47		16 11			16 40			17 11	
Dalgety Bay	d		13 46			14 16				14 46		15 16				15 52		16 16			16 45			17 16	
Cardenden	d				13 43						14 43						15 43						16 43		
Lochgelly	d				13 47						14 47						15 47						16 47		
Cowdenbeath	d	13 23			13 53				14 23		14 53				15 23		15 53			16 22			16 53		
Dunfermline Queen Margaret	d	13 27			13 57				14 27		14 57				15 27		15 57			16 27			16 57		
Dunfermline Town	d	13 31			14 01				14 31		15 01				15 31		16 01			16 31			17 01		
Rosyth	d	13 35			14 05				14 35		15 05				15 35		16 05			16 35			17 05		
Inverkeithing	d	13 42	13 50	14 00	14 12	14 19			14 42	14 50	15 12	15 19	15 30	15 44	15 49	15 55	16 12	16 19	16 30	16 42	16 48	16 57	17 12	17 20	17 33
North Queensferry	d	13 46	13 54		14 16	14 23			14 46	14 54	15 16	15 23			15 53	15 59	16 16	16 23		16 46	16 52		17 16		
Dalmeny	d	13 50	13 58		14 20	14 27			14 50	14 58	15 20	15 27			15 56	16 03	16 20	16 27		16 50	16 56		17 20		
South Gyle	d	13 56	14 04		14 26	14 33			14 56	15 04	15 26	15 33			16 02	16 09	16 26	16 33		16 56	17 02		17 26	15 58	
Haymarket	d	14 05	14 12	14 13	14 35	14 42	14 46		15 05	15 12	15 35	15 42	15 46	16 00	16 11	16 18	16 35	16 42	16 46	17 05	17 11	17 15	17 35	17 39	17 49
Edinburgh 10	a	14 10	14 17	14 21	14 40	14 47	14 50		15 10	15 17	15 41	15 47	15 50	16 04	16 15	16 22	16 40	16 46	16 50	17 09	17 15	17 23	17 41	17 44	17 53

For general notes see front of timetable
For details of catering facilities see Directory of Train Operators

A From Perth (Table 229)
B From Dundee (Table 229) to Newcraighall (Table 230)
C To Glasgow Queen Street (Table 230)
D From Dundee (Table 229) to Plymouth (Table 51)
E From Edinburgh via Cowdenbeath
G From Aberdeen (Table 229)
H From Kirkcaldy dep. 0730
J From Carnoustie (Table 229)
K From Dundee (Table 229) to Bournemouth (Table 51)
L From Edinburgh via Kirkcaldy
N From Dundee (Table 229)
U From Inverness (Table 229)
V From Aberdeen (Table 229) to London Kings Cross (Table 26)
X From Aberdeen (Table 229) to Bournemouth (Table 51)
Y **The Northern Lights**
Z From Dyce (Table 229)

Markinch, Kirkcaldy and Dunfermline → Edinburgh

Network Diagram - see first page of Table 225

		SR	SR	SR	SR	SR	SR	SR	SR	SR	SR	SR	GR	SR	SR	SR	SR	SR	SR	SR	XC	SR	SR
			1 ◇		1 ◇				1 ◇			1	R 1			1 ◇		1 ◇			1 ◇		1 ◇
		A	B	A	C	D	A	D	E	A	D	G	C			E		B		H	C		C
Markinch	d		17 22		18 05				19 07			19 45			20 32	21 08				22 03	22 12		23 09
Glenrothes With Thornton	d	17 03		17 35		18 09	18 46	18 54		19 07	19 25			19 58			21 00		21 58			23 00	
Kirkcaldy	d		17 31		18 15	18 21		19 06	19 17		19 36	19 54	20 11		20 41	21 18		21 33		22 13			23 18
Kinghorn	d					18 25		19 10			19 41				20 46					22 18			23 23
Burntisland	d					18 30		19 15			19 45				20 50					22 22			23 28
Aberdour	d					18 34		19 19			19 50				20 55					22 27			23 33
Dalgety Bay	d					18 39		19 24			19 55				21 00					22 32			23 38
Cardenden	d	17 10		17 42			18 53			19 13				20 05			21 05		22 05			23 05	
Lochgelly	d	17 14		17 46			18 57			19 17				20 09			21 09		22 09			23 09	
Cowdenbeath	d	17 20		17 52			19 03			19 23				20 15			21 15		22 15			23 15	
Dunfermline Queen Margaret	d	17 26		17 57			19 09			19 27				20 21			21 21		22 21			23 21	
Dunfermline Town	d	17 29		18 01			19 12			19 31				20 24			21 24		22 24			23 24	
Rosyth	d	17 33		18 05			19 16			19 35				20 28			21 28		22 28			23 28	
Inverkeithing	d	17 40	17 47	18 12		18 42	19 19	19 27	19 33	19 42	19 58	20 10	20 27	20 35	21 03	21 34	21 37	21 49	22 32	22 36	22 45	23 32	23 41
North Queensferry	d	17 44		18 16		18 46	19 23	19 31		19 46	20 02			20 39	21 07		21 41		22 36	22 41		23 36	23 46
Dalmeny	d	17 48		18 20		18 50	19 27	19 35		19 50	20 06			20 43	21 11		21 45		22 40	22 45		23 40	23 50
South Gyle	d	17 54		18 26		18 56	19 33	19 41		19 56	20 12			20 49	21 17		21 51		22 46	22 51		23 46	23 56
Haymarket	d	18 03	18 01	18 35	18 46	19 05	19 42	19 50	19 53	20 05	20 21	20 27	20 44	20 58	21 26	21 52	21 59	22 02	22 54	23 00		23 54	00 05
Edinburgh 10	a	18 07	18 11	18 39	18 50	19 09	19 47	19 54	19 57	20 11	20 25	20 32	20 50	21 02	21 31	21 56	22 06	22 09	22 58	23 05	23 25	00 01	00 09

Saturdays

		SR	SR	SR	SR	SR	SR		SR	SR	XC	SR	SR	SR		SR	SR	SR	SR	GR	SR		SR	XC	SR
						1	1 ◇				1 ◇						1 ◇	1 ◇		R 1				1 ◇	
				H	D	G	C		A	J	K	D	H	A			B	B	D	L	A		D	N	
Markinch	d		06 33	06 52		07 34				07 54	08 11		08 34				09 06							10 04	
Glenrothes With Thornton	d		06 39		07 08				07 38			08 20		08 34					09 13		09 36		09 47		
Kirkcaldy	d	06 15		07 02	07 15	07 44	07 50			08 05	08 20	08 27	08 43			09 03	09 15	09 25	09 27	09 44			09 57	10 12	
Kinghorn	d	06 20		07 07	07 20					08 10		08 32				09 07			09 32				10 02		
Burntisland	d	06 25		07 11	07 25					08 15		08 36				09 12			09 36				10 06		
Aberdour	d	06 30		07 16	07 30					08 19		08 41				09 16			09 41				10 11		
Dalgety Bay	d	06 35		07 21	07 35					08 24		08 46				09 21			09 46				10 16		
Cardenden	d		06 47						07 45					08 42							09 43				
Lochgelly	d		06 51						07 49					08 46							09 47				
Cowdenbeath	d		06 57						07 55					08 52							09 53				10 19
Dunfermline Queen Margaret	d		07 02						08 01					08 57							09 57				10 24
Dunfermline Town	d		07 06						08 05					09 01							10 01				10 28
Rosyth	d		07 09						08 08					09 05							10 05				10 32
Inverkeithing	d	06 38	07 13	07 26	07 38	08 00			08 15	08 28	08 36	08 50	08 59	09 12		09 24			09 50	10 00	10 12		10 20	10 27	10 39
North Queensferry	d	06 42	07 17		07 42				08 19			08 54		09 16					09 54		10 16		10 24		10 43
Dalmeny	d	06 46	07 21		07 46				08 21			08 58		09 20					09 58		10 20		10 28		10 47
South Gyle	d	06 52	07 27	07 38	07 52				08 27	08 39		09 04		09 26					10 04		10 26		10 34		10 53
Haymarket	d	07 01	07 36	07 46	08 01	08 18	08 21		08 36	08 48	08 57	09 12	09 16	09 35		09 42	09 46	09 55	10 12	10 19	10 35		10 42	10 46	11 05
Edinburgh 10	a	07 07	07 40	07 51	08 06	08 23	08 26		08 42	08 52	09 02	09 17	09 20	09 40		09 47	09 50	10 01	10 19	10 25	10 41		10 47	10 55	11 10

		SR	SR	SR	SR	SR		SR	GR	SR	SR	SR	SR		SR	SR	SR	SR	SR	SR		SR	SR	SR	SR
			1 ◇						R 1	1			1 ◇						1 ◇				1 ◇		
			C	A	D				L Q	G	A	D	E				A	D	C				B	A	D
Markinch	d	10 19	10 34					11 19		11 42			12 02			12 19			13 04			13 19			
Glenrothes With Thornton	d			10 35	10 50						11 35	11 47					12 36	12 50						13 37	13 46
Kirkcaldy	d	10 27	10 43		10 57			11 27	11 43	11 52		11 57	12 12			12 27		12 57	13 14			13 27	13 44		13 57
Kinghorn	d	10 32			11 02			11 32				12 02				12 32		13 02				13 32			14 02
Burntisland	d	10 36			11 06			11 36				12 06				12 36		13 06				13 36			14 06
Aberdour	d	10 41			11 11			11 41				12 11				12 41		13 11				13 41			14 11
Dalgety Bay	d	10 46			11 16			11 46				12 16				12 46		13 16				13 46			14 16
Cardenden	d			10 43							11 43						12 43							13 43	
Lochgelly	d			10 47							11 47						12 47							13 47	
Cowdenbeath	d			10 53		11 23					11 53				12 23		12 53			13 23				13 53	
Dunfermline Queen Margaret	d			10 57		11 27					11 57				12 27		12 57			13 27				13 57	
Dunfermline Town	d			11 01		11 31					12 01				12 31		13 01			13 31				14 01	
Rosyth	d			11 05		11 35					12 05				12 35		13 05			13 35				14 05	
Inverkeithing	d	10 50	10 59	11 12	11 20	11 42		11 50	11 59	12 08	12 12	12 20			12 42	12 50	13 12	13 20	13 30	13 42		13 50	14 00	14 12	14 19
North Queensferry	d	10 54		11 16	11 24	11 46		11 54			12 16	12 24			12 46	12 54	13 16	13 24		13 48		13 54		14 16	14 23
Dalmeny	d	10 58		11 20	11 28	11 50		11 58			12 20	12 28			12 50	12 58	13 20	13 28		13 50		13 58		14 20	14 27
South Gyle	d	11 04		11 26	11 34	11 56		12 04			12 26	12 34			12 56	13 04	13 26	13 34		13 56		14 04		14 26	14 33
Haymarket	d	11 12	11 16	11 35	11 42	12 05		12 12	12 17	12 24	12 35	12 42	12 46		13 05	13 12	13 35	13 42	13 46	14 05		14 12	14 13	14 35	14 42
Edinburgh 10	a	11 17	11 20	11 40	11 47	12 10		12 17	12 22	12 28	12 40	12 47	12 50		13 10	13 17	13 40	13 47	13 50	14 10		14 17	14 21	14 40	14 47

For general notes see front of timetable
For details of catering facilities see Directory of Train Operators

- **A** From Edinburgh via Kirkcaldy
- **B** From Inverness (Table 229)
- **C** From Aberdeen (Table 229)
- **D** From Edinburgh via Cowdenbeath
- **E** From Dyce (Table 229)
- **G** From Perth (Table 229)
- **H** From Dundee (Table 229)
- **J** From Carnoustie (Table 229)
- **K** From Dundee (Table 229) to Bournemouth (Table 51)
- **L** From Aberdeen (Table 229) to London Kings Cross (Table 26)
- **N** From Aberdeen (Table 229) to Bournemouth (Table 51)
- **Q** **The Northern Lights**

Table 242

Saturdays

Markinch, Kirkcaldy and Dunfermline → Edinburgh

Network Diagram - see first page of Table 225

		SR	SR	SR	SR	SR	SR	SR	SR	SR	SR	SR	SR	SR	SR	GR	SR	SR	SR	SR	SR	SR
		[1]◇ A ⚲			B	C	[1]◇ A ⚲	[1]◇ D ⚲			B	C	[1]◇ A ⚲			[R] [1] E ⊡ ⚲	B	C	[1]◇ G ⚲	B	[1]◇ D ⚲	B
Markinch	d	14 05		14 19			15 04	15 18		15 24			16 04		16 17				17 07		17 22	
Glenrothes With Thornton	d				14 38	14 46					15 37	15 46					16 38	16 47		17 03		17 35
Kirkcaldy	d	14 15		14 27		14 57	15 14	15 28		15 33		15 57	16 14		16 26	16 41		16 57	17 17		17 31	
Kinghorn	d			14 32		15 02				15 38		16 02			16 31			17 02				
Burntisland	d			14 36		15 06				15 42		16 06			16 35			17 06				
Aberdour	d			14 41		15 11				15 47		16 11			16 40			17 11				
Dalgety Bay	d			14 46		15 16				15 52		16 16			16 45			17 16				
Cardenden	d				14 43						15 43						16 43			17 10		17 42
Lochgelly	d				14 47						15 47						16 47			17 14		17 46
Cowdenbeath	d		14 23		14 53				15 23		15 53			16 22			16 53			17 20		17 52
Dunfermline Queen Margaret	d		14 27		14 57				15 27		15 57			16 27			16 57			17 26		17 57
Dunfermline Town	d		14 31		15 01				15 31		16 01			16 31			17 01			17 29		18 01
Rosyth	d		14 35		15 05				15 35		16 05			16 35			17 05			17 33		18 05
Inverkeithing	d		14 42	14 50	15 12	15 19	15 30	15 44	15 49	15 55	16 12	16 19	16 30	16 42	16 48	16 57	17 12	17 20	17 33	17 40	17 47	18 12
North Queensferry	d		14 46	14 54	15 16	15 23			15 53	15 59	16 16	16 23		16 46	16 52		17 16			17 44		18 16
Dalmeny	d		14 50	14 58	15 20	15 27			15 56	16 03	16 20	16 27		16 50	16 56		17 20			17 48		18 20
South Gyle	d		14 56	15 04	15 26	15 33			16 02	16 09	16 26	16 33		16 56	17 02		17 26	15 58		17 54		18 26
Haymarket	d	14 46	15 05	15 12	15 35	15 42	15 46	16 00	16 11	16 18	16 35	16 42	16 46	17 05	17 11	17 15	17 35	17 39	17 49	18 03	18 01	18 35
Edinburgh [10]	a	14 50	15 10	15 18	15 40	15 47	15 50	16 04	16 15	16 22	16 40	16 46	16 50	17 10	17 15	17 23	17 39	17 44	17 53	18 07	18 11	18 39

		SR	SR	SR	SR	SR	SR	SR	SR	SR	SR	SR	SR	SR	SR	SR	SR	XC	SR	SR
		[1]◇ A ⚲	C	B	[1]◇ G ⚲	B	C	[1] H	[1]◇ A ⚲			[1]◇ G ⚲		[1]◇ D ⚲	J		G	[1]◇ A ⊡		[1]◇ A
Markinch	d	18 05			19 07			19 45			20 32	21 06			21 30		22 03	22 16		23 09
Glenrothes With Thornton	d		18 10	18 46		19 07	19 25			19 58			21 00			21 58			23 00	
Kirkcaldy	d	18 15	18 21		19 17		19 36	19 54	20 13		20 41	21 16		21 33	21 40		22 13			23 18
Kinghorn	d		18 25				19 41				20 46				21 45		22 18			23 23
Burntisland	d		18 30				19 45				20 50				21 49		22 22			23 28
Aberdour	d		18 34				19 50				20 55				21 54		22 27			23 33
Dalgety Bay	d		18 39				19 55				21 00				21 59		22 32			23 38
Cardenden	d			18 53		19 13				20 05			21 05			22 05			23 05	
Lochgelly	d			18 57		19 17				20 09			21 09			22 09			23 09	
Cowdenbeath	d			19 03		19 23				20 15			21 15			22 15			23 15	
Dunfermline Queen Margaret	d			19 09		19 27				20 21			21 21			22 21			23 21	
Dunfermline Town	d			19 12		19 31				20 24			21 24			22 24			23 24	
Rosyth	d			19 16		19 35				20 28			21 28			22 28			23 28	
Inverkeithing	d		18 42	19 19	19 33	19 42	19 58	20 10	20 29	20 35	21 03	21 32	21 37	21 49	22 02	22 32	22 36	22 45	23 32	23 41
North Queensferry	d		18 46	19 23		19 46	20 02			20 39	21 07		21 41		22 07	22 36	22 41		23 36	23 46
Dalmeny	d		18 50	19 27		19 50	20 06			20 43	21 11		21 45		22 11	22 40	22 45		23 40	23 50
South Gyle	d		18 56	19 33		19 56	20 12			20 49	21 17		21 51		22 17	22 46	22 51		23 46	23 56
Haymarket	d	18 46	19 05	19 42	19 53	20 05	20 21	20 27	20 46	20 58	21 26	21 48	21 59	22 02	22 26	22 54	23 00		23 54	00 05
Edinburgh [10]	a	18 50	19 10	19 47	19 57	20 11	20 25	20 32	20 50	21 02	21 30	21 52	22 04	22 09	22 32	22 58	23 05	23 25	00 01	00 09

Sundays

		SR	SR	SR	SR	GR	SR	SR	SR	GR	XC	SR	SR	SR	GR	SR	SR	SR
		J	J	C	B	[R] [1] E K ⊡ ⚲	J	C	B	[R] [1] E ⊡ ⚲	[R] [1] L ⊡	J	C	B	[R] [1] E ⊡ ⚲	[1]◇ D ⚲	J	[1]◇ A ⚲
Markinch	d	07 59	09 59				11 59				13 49	14 01					16 01	
Glenrothes With Thornton	d			10 56	11 11			12 56	13 11				15 05	15 11				
Kirkcaldy	d	08 09	10 09	11 07		11 41	12 09	13 07		13 36	13 58	14 11	15 17		15 41	16 02	16 11	17 03
Kinghorn	d	08 14	10 14	11 12			12 13	13 12				14 16	15 22				16 15	
Burntisland	d	08 18	10 18	11 16			12 18	13 16				14 20	15 26				16 20	
Aberdour	d	08 23	10 23	11 21			12 22	13 21				14 25	15 31				16 24	
Dalgety Bay	d	08 27	10 27	11 26			12 27	13 26				14 29	15 36				16 29	
Cardenden	d				11 16				13 16					15 16				
Lochgelly	d				11 20				13 20					15 20				
Cowdenbeath	d				11 26				13 26					15 26				
Dunfermline Queen Margaret	d				11 31				13 31					15 31				
Dunfermline Town	d				11 35				13 35					15 35				
Rosyth	d				11 39				13 39					15 39				
Inverkeithing	d	08 30	10 32	11 33	11 46	11 57	12 32	13 33	13 46	13 54	14 14	14 32	15 39	15 46	16b02	16 18	16 32	17 19
North Queensferry	d	08 34	10 38	11 38	11 50		12 38	13 38	13 50			14 38	15 43	15 50			16 36	
Dalmeny	d	08 41	10 45	11 45	11 59		12 45	13 45	13 59			14 45	15 50	15 59			16 40	
South Gyle	d	08 47	10 51	11 51	12 05		12 51	13 51	14 05			14 51	15 56	16 05			16 46	
Haymarket	d	08 56	11 00	12 00	12 14	12 18	13 00	14 00	14 14	14 19	14 29	15 00	16 04	16 14	16 20	16 34	16 55	17 35
Edinburgh [10]	a	09 00	11 04	12 05	12 18	12 24	13 04	14 06	14 18	14 24	14 33	15 04	16 09	16 21	16 26	16 43	16 59	17 41

For general notes see front of timetable
For details of catering facilities see Directory of Train Operators

A From Aberdeen (Table 229)
B From Edinburgh via Kirkcaldy
C From Edinburgh via Cowdenbeath
D From Inverness (Table 229)
E From Aberdeen (Table 229) to London Kings Cross (Table 26)
G From Dyce (Table 229)
H From Perth (Table 229)
J From Dundee (Table 229)
K **The Northern Lights**
L From Aberdeen (Table 229). Until 27 January to Southampton Central, 3 February to 23 March to Bristol Temple Meads and from 30 March to Oxford (Table 51)
b Arr. 1557

Table 242

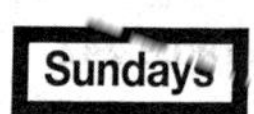

Markinch, Kirkcaldy and Dunfermline → Edinburgh

Network Diagram - see first page of Table 225

		SR	SR	SR	SR 1 ◇	SR	SR	SR	SR 1 ◇	SR	SR 1 ◇	SR	SR 1 ◇	SR	XC 1 ◇	SR
		A	B	C	D ⚒	A	B	C	D	A	E ⚒	B	D ⚒		D 🍴	
Markinch	d			17 59				19 59					21 56		22 38	
Glenrothes With Thornton	d	16 55	17 10			18 56	19 09			20 54		21 09				22 54
Kirkcaldy	d	17 07		18 09	18 56	19 07		20 09	20 59	21 07	21 25		22 05	22 13	22 46	23 06
Kinghorn	d	17 12		18 13		19 12		20 14		21 12				22 17		23 10
Burntisland	d	17 16		18 18		19 16		20 18		21 16				22 22		23 15
Aberdour	d	17 21		18 22		19 21		20 23		21 21				22 26		23 19
Dalgety Bay	d	17 26		18 27		19 26		20 27		21 26				22 31		23 24
Cardenden	d		17 16				19 16					21 16				
Lochgelly	d		17 20				19 20					21 20				
Cowdenbeath	d		17 26				19 26					21 26				
Dunfermline Queen Margaret	d		17 31				19 32					21 32				
Dunfermline Town	d		17 35				19 35					21 35				
Rosyth	d		17 39				19 39					21 39				
Inverkeithing	d	17 33	17 46	18 30	19 12	19 29	19 46	20 30	21 15	21 30	21 41	21 46	22 21	22 34	23 02	23 27
North Queensferry	d	17 38	17 50	18 34		19 33	19 50	20 34		21 34		21 50		22 38		23 31
Dalmeny	d	17 42	17 54	18 38		19 37	19 54	20 38		21 38		21 54		22 42		23 35
South Gyle	d	17 48	18 00	18 44		19 43	20 00	20 44		21 44		22 00		22 48		23 41
Haymarket	d	17 57	18 09	18 55	19 27	19 52	20 09	20 53	21 31	21 55	22 00	22 09	22 37	22 57	23s16	23 50
Edinburgh 10	a	18 01	18 14	19 00	19 35	19 56	20 14	20 59	21 38	21 59	22 06	22 13	22 44	23 01	23 26	23 56

For general notes see front of timetable
For details of catering facilities see Directory of Train Operators

A From Edinburgh via Cowdenbeath
B From Edinburgh via Kirkcaldy
C From Dundee (Table 229)
D From Aberdeen (Table 229)
E From Inverness (Table 229)

Sleeper Services

Sleepers enable you to make long distance journeys while having a relaxing night's sleep. You arrive early at your destination, saving a day's travel — or the early morning dash to the airport. Five Sleeper routes link London Euston direct with over 40 stations in Scotland including most principal business and holiday locations. Direct Sleeper services also link Southwest England with London. Customers joining at the starting point of the train may occupy cabins well before departure. At terminating stations customers may vacate cabins up to approximately 0800 on trains which arrive at an earlier time.

Full details of all Sleeper services are given in Tables 400–406 in this book.

Room Service

Sleepers have full air-conditioning and fingertip temperature control. Each cabin has wall-to-wall carpet, mirror, shaver sockets, drinking water — as well as hot water for the washbasin, and a comfortable bed.

Steward(ess) service is available at the touch of a button throughout the journey. **On First Great Western Sleepers,** additional benefits include a welcome toiletry pack, tea or coffee and biscuits, and a wake-up call. Showers and the First Class lounge are available on arrival at Paddington station, plus a free taxi transfer for Eurostar customers. The First Class package also includes complimentary orange juice, Croissant, preserve, tea and coffee and a morning newspaper (subject to availability).

On First ScotRail's Caledonian Sleepers First Class customers receive a toiletry pack and will be woken with a light breakfast accompanied by tea or coffee and a complimentary newspaper. Standard Class customers are served a light morning snack with tea or coffee. Customer lounges are available at the following locations - London Euston, Inverness, Carlisle (Lakes Court Hotel) and Edinburgh Waverley. At Glasgow Central customers may use the on-train Lounge Car which is available prior to departure.

Full details of the Caledonian Sleeper on-train and station facilities can be found inside the Caledonian Sleeper Guide which is available from principal sleeper departure points.

Sleeper Supplements

Holders of First Class tickets enjoy a single berth cabin on payment of the First Class reservation supplement. Holders of Standard travel tickets travel in either a single or 2 berth cabin on payment of the relevant Standard supplement. The number of berths available to holders of discounted tickets may be restricted at any time.

On First ScotRail's Caledonian Sleepers there are a number of berth inclusive fares available that include travel and accommodation at one all inclusive price. First Class travel is in single berth cabins while Standard Class is in twin berth cabins.

On First Great Western's Night Riviera there are a number of berth inclusive fares available that combine travel and accommodation on one ticket. First Class travel is available in single berth cabins, while Standard offers a choice of single berth or twin berth cabins.

Lounge Cars

The Lounge Car offers a pleasant relaxing atmosphere in which to unwind before a night's rest. **On First Great Western Sleepers,** a full range of drinks, snacks and meals are available. Hot and continental breakfasts are served in the morning. **On First ScotRail's Caledonian Sleepers** customers can choose from a wide selection of food and drinks including sandwiches, baguettes, snacks and a well stocked bar. At busy times, use of the Lounge Car may be restricted to First Class ticket holders.

Sleeper Reservations

To book rail tickets and reserve Sleepers, simply visit any main rail station or rail appointed travel agent. Alternatively you can book by phone using most credit/debit cards.

First ScotRail Telesales	08457 55 00 33
First Great Western Telesales	0845 700 0125

Enquiries by Telephone

For further information about rail tickets or services, call National Rail enquiries on 08457 48 49 50.

Animals

Dogs and pets are not normally allowed in Sleeper cabins. There are special arrangements for guide dogs. **On First Great Western Sleepers,** animals may be conveyed if properly labelled and muzzled, and in suitable containers, in the parcels accommodation on payment of the appropriate charge.

On First ScotRail's Caledonian Sleepers accompanying dogs are only permitted in Sleeper Cabins providing the owner(s) has exclusive use of the cabin and pays the appropriate charge. There are special arrangements for guide dogs. Dogs and pets cannot be conveyed in the parcels accommodation.

First ScotRail's Caledonian Sleepers

Please note that as a result of on-going engineering work some Sleeping Car services may be subject to diversion causing an extension in journey times between Scotland and London. For full details log on to www.firstscotrail.com or telephone National Rail enquiries on 08457 48 49 50.

Sleeper Services

First ScotRail Sleeper Services – The Caledonian Sleepers

Operated by First ScotRail

Table 400 London and Edinburgh

		Mon–Thu R	Fri R	Sun B R	Sun D R	Sun C R
Cabins available from		*2300*	*2230*	*2200*	*2230*	*2300*
London Euston ...	dep	2345	2300	2226	2306	2330
Watford Junction	dep	0004*	2319	—	2327	2351
Carlisle ...	arr	0503	0427*	—	0458*	0458*
Carstairs ...	arr	0624	0534	—	0628	0628
Edinburgh ...	arr	0716	0640	0627*	0716	0716
Vacate cabins by		*0755*	*0755*	*0755*	*0755*	*0755*

		Mon–Thu R	Fri R	Sun A R	Sun B R
Cabins available from		*2300*	*2300*	*2230*	*2245*
Edinburgh ...	dep	2340	2340	2315	2316
Carstairs	dep	0016*	0016*	2350	—
Carlisle	dep	0139	0139	0124*	—
Watford Junction	arr	0634	0650	0628	—
London Euston	arr	0700	0718	0654	0711*
Vacate cabins by		*0800*	*0800*	*0800*	*0800*

R Reservations Compulsory
* Following morning
Services in this table do not run on Saturday nights.
For details of overnight seated services, please refer to Table 65

A until 27 January and from 30 March 2008
B from 3 February until 23 March 2008
C until 27 January 2008
D from 30 March 2008

Table 401 London and Glasgow

		Mon–Thu R	Fri R	Sun B R	Sun D R	Sun C R
Cabins available from		*2300*	*2230*	*2200*	*2230*	*2300*
London Euston ...	dep	2345	2300	2226	2306	2330
Watford Junction	dep	0004*	2319	—	2327	2351
Carlisle ...	arr	0503	0427*	—	0458*	0458*
Carstairs ...	arr	0624	0534	0713*	0628	0628
Motherwell ...	arr	0658	0610	0739	0658	0658
Glasgow Central	arr	0717	0630	0758	0717	0717
Vacate cabins by		*0800*	*0800*	*0800*	*0800*	*0800*

		Mon–Thu R	Fri R	Sun B R	Sun A R
Cabins available from		*2200*	*2200*	*2100*	*2200*
Glasgow Central	dep	2341	2341	2142	2315
Motherwell	dep	2556	2356	2201	2330
Carstairs	dep	0016*	0016*	2222	2350
Carlisle	dep	0139	0139	—	0124*
Watford Junction	arr	0634	0650	—	0628
London Euston	arr	0700	0718	0711*	0654
Vacate cabins by		*0800*	*0800*	*0800*	*0800*

R Reservations Compulsory
* Following morning
Services in this table do not run on Saturday nights.
For details of overnight seated services, please refer to Table 65

A until 27 January and from 30 March 2008
B from 3 February until 23 March 2008
C until 27 January 2008
D from 30 March 2008

Table 402 London and Aberdeen

		Mon-Fri R	Sun B R	Sun A R
Cabins available from		*2030*	*1930*	*1930*
London Euston	dep	2115	2000	2000
Watford Junction	dep	2133	—	2025
Crewe	dep	2345	—	2314
Preston	dep	0044*	—	0033*
Inverkeithing•	arr	0458	0458*	0458
Kirkcaldy•	arr	0517	0517	0517
Leuchars for St Andrews•	arr	0546	0546	0546
Dundee	arr	0608	0608	0608
Carnoustie	arr	0622	0622	0622
Arbroath	arr	0631	0631	0631
Montrose	arr	0650	0650	0650
Stonehaven	arr	0716	0716	0716
Aberdeen	arr	0737	0737	0737
Vacate cabins by		*0800*	*0800*	*0800*

		Mon–Thu R	Fri R	Sun A R	Sun B R
Cabins available from		*2045*	*2045*	*2045*	*2045*
Aberdeen	dep	2140	2140	2140	2140
Stonehaven	dep	2158	2158	2158	2158
Montrose	dep	2227	2227	2225	2225
Arbroath	dep	2245	2245	2243	2243
Carnoustie	dep	2252	2252	2250	2250
Dundee	dep	2306	2306	2304	2304
Leuchars for St Andrews•	dep	2324	2324	2322	2322
Kirkcaldy•	dep	2353	2353	2351	2351
Inverkeithing•	dep	0015*	0011*	0010*	0010*
Preston	arr	0429	0405	0419c	—
Crewe	arr	0530	0502	0526c	—
London Euston	arr	0743	0804	0740c	0928
Vacate cabins by		*0800*	*0806*	*0800*	*0930*

R Reservations Compulsory
* Following morning
• Customers may depart from London or Watford later, and vacate cabins later, by travelling on the London Euston to Edinburgh Sleeper; then by local connecting service from Edinburgh
Services in this table do not run on Saturday nights
For details of overnight seated services, please refer to Table 65

A until 27 January and from 30 March 2008
B from 3 February until 23 March 2008
c arrives 3 minutes later on 28 January 2008

Sleeper Services

First ScotRail Sleeper Services – The Caledonian Sleepers

Operated by First ScotRail

Table 403 London and Inverness

		Mon-Fri [R]	Sun B [R]	Sun A [R]
Cabins available from		*2030*	*1930*	*1930*
London Euston	dep	2115	2000	2000
Watford Junction	dep	2133	—	2025
Crewe	dep	2345	—	2314
Preston	dep	0044*	—	0033*
Stirling•	arr	0456	0457*	0457
Dunblane	arr	0506	0506	0506
Gleneagles	arr	0521	0521	0521
Perth•	arr	0544	0544	0544
Dunkeld & Birnam	arr	0605	0605	0605
Pitlochry	arr	0619	0619	0619
Blair Atholl	arr	0630	0630	0630
Dalwhinnie	arr	0701	0701	0701
Newtonmore	arr	0713	0713	0713
Kingussie	arr	0718	0718	0718
Aviemore	arr	0740	0741	0740
Inverness	arr	0830	0830	0830
Vacate cabins by		*0830*	*0830*	*0830*

		Mon–Thu [R]	Fri [R]	Sun A [R]	Sun B [R]
Cabins available from		*2000*	*2000*	*1945*	*1945*
Inverness	dep	2040	2040	2025	2025
Aviemore	dep	2123	2123	2108	2108
Kingussie	dep	2138	2138	2122	2122
Newtonmore	dep	2144	2144	2129	2129
Dalwhinnie	dep	2159	2159	2143	2143
Blair Atholl	dep	2225	2225	2209	2209
Pitlochry	dep	2237	2237	2221	2221
Dunkeld & Birnam	dep	2252	2252	2236	2236
Perth	dep	2318	2318	2259	2259
Gleneagles	dep	2336	2336	2317	2317
Dunblane	dep	2355	2355	2333	2333
Stirling•	dep	0007*	0007*	2344	2344
Falkirk Grahamston	dep	0024	0025	2358e	0001*
Preston	arr	0429	0405	0419c*	—
Crewe	arr	0530	0502	0526c	—
London Euston	arr	0743	0804	0740c	0928
Vacate cabins by		*0800*	*0806*	*0800*	*0930*

[R] Reservations Compulsory
* Following morning
• Customers may depart from London or Watford later, and vacate cabins later, by travelling on the London Euston to Edinburgh Sleeper; then by local connecting service from Edinburgh.
Services in this table do not run on Saturday nights.
For details of overnight seated services, please refer to Table 65

A until 27 January and from 30 March 2008
B from 3 February until 23 March 2008
c arrives 3 minutes later on 28 January 2008
e departs 3 minutes later on 27 January 2008

Table 404 London and Fort William

		Mon-Fri [R]	Sun B [R]	Sun A [R]
Cabins available from		*2030*	*1930*	*1930*
London Euston	dep	2115	2000	2000
Watford Junction	dep	2133	—	2025
Crewe	dep	2345	—	2314
Preston	dep	0044*	—	0033*
Westerton	arr	0555b	0555*	0555
Dalmuir	arr	0603b	0603	0603
Helensburgh Upper	arr	0626b	0626	0626
Garelochhead	arr	0640b	0640	0640
Arrochar & Tarbet	arr	0706	0706	0706
Ardlui	arr	0721x	0721x	0721x
Crianlarich	arr	0742	0742	0742
Upper Tyndrum	arr	0754	0754	0754
Bridge of Orchy	arr	0812	0812	0812
Rannoch	arr	0840	0840	0840
Corrour	arr	0858x	0858x	0858x
Tulloch	arr	0917	0917	0917
Roy Bridge	arr	0929x	0929x	0929x
Spean Bridge	arr	0936	0936	0936
Fort William	arr	0954	0954	0954
Vacate cabins by		*0956*	*0956*	*0956*

		Mon–Thu [R]	Fri [R]	Sun A [R]	Sun B [R]
Cabins available from		*1915*	*1915*	*1830*	*1830*
Fort William	dep	1950	1950	1900	1900
Spean Bridge	dep	2010	2010	1920	1920
Roy Bridge	dep	2017x	2017x	1927x	1927x
Tulloch	dep	2030	2030	1940	1940
Corrour	dep	2051x	2051x	2001x	2001x
Rannoch	dep	2106	2106	2015	2015
Bridge of Orchy	dep	2134	2134	2047	2047
Upper Tyndrum	dep	2152	2152	2105	2105
Crianlarich	dep	2205	2205	2118	2118
Ardlui	dep	2226x	2226x	2139x	2139x
Arrochar & Tarbet	dep	2244	2244	2157	2157
Garelochhead	dep	2310	2310	2223	2223
Helensburgh Upper	dep	2324	2324	2237	2237
Dalmuir	dep	2351	2351	2304	2304
Westerton	dep	2356	2356	2313	2313
Preston	arr	0429*	0405*	0419c*	—
Crewe	arr	0530	0502	0526c	—
London Euston	arr	0743	0804	0740c	0928*
Vacate cabins by		*0800*	*0806*	*0800*	*0930*

[R] Reservations Compulsory
* Following morning
Services in this table do not run on Saturday nights.
For details of overnight seated services, please refer to Tables 65 and 227.
A until 27 January and from 30 March 2008
B from 3 February until 23 March 2008
b arrives 1 minute later on Saturdays
c arrives 3 minutes later on 28 January 2008

Sleeper Services

Table 406 London and Penzance

Operated by First Great Western

		Mon–Thur Ⓛ	Fri Ⓛ	Sun Ⓛ
Occupy cabins at Paddington:		*2230*	*2230*	*2230*
London Paddington	**dep**	**2345**	**2345**	**2350**
Reading ...	**dep**	**0037***	**0037***	**0037***
Exeter St Davids	**arr**	**0444**	**0436**	**0405**
Newton Abbot	**arr**	**0507**	**0507**	**0457**
Plymouth ...	**arr**	**0547**	**0547**	**0537**
Liskeard ...	**arr**	**0614**	**0614**	**0659**
Bodmin Parkway	**arr**	**0628**	**0628**	**0713**
Lostwithiel ...	**arr**	**0635**	**0635**	**0720**
Par ...	**arr**	**0642**	**0642**	**0727**
St Austell ...	**arr**	**0650**	**0650**	**0734**
Truro ...	**arr**	**0709**	**0709**	**0753**
Redruth ...	**arr**	**0723**	**0722**	**0809**
Camborne ...	**arr**	**0730**	**0730**	**0816**
Hayle ...	**arr**	**0740**	**0739**	**0826**
St Erth ...	**arr**	**0744**	**0743**	**0830**
Penzance ...	**arr**	**0801**	**0800**	**0847**
Vacate cabins at Penzance by		*0830*	*0830*	*0830*

		Mon–Thur Ⓛ	Fri Ⓛ	Sun Ⓛ
Occupy cabins at Penzance:		*2130*	*2045*	*2045*
Penzance	**dep**	**2200**	**2200**	**2115**
St Erth	**dep**	**2210**	**2210**	**2125**
Hayle	**dep**	**2214**	**2214**	**....**
Camborne	**dep**	**2224**	**2224**	**2137**
Redruth	**dep**	**2232**	**2232**	**2144**
Truro	**dep**	**2244**	**2244**	**2157**
St Austell	**dep**	**2302**	**2302**	**2215**
Par	**dep**	**2311**	**2311**	**....**
Lostwithiel	**dep**	**2319**	**2319**	**....**
Bodmin Parkway ...	**dep**	**2326**	**2326**	**2232**
Liskeard ...	**dep**	**2341**	**2341**	**2247**
Plymouth ...	**dep**	**0020***	**0020***	**2320**
Totnes ...	**dep**	**0048**	**0048**	**2348**
Newton Abbot ...	**dep**	**0101**	**0101**	**0001***
Exeter St Davids ...	**dep**	**0127**	**0127**	**0127**
Reading	**arr**	**0428**	**0427**	**0418**
London Paddington ...	**arr**	**0520**	**0525**	**0510**
Vacate cabins at Paddington by		*0730*	*0730*	*0730*

Ⓛ Sleeper Lounge Car
* Following morning
Services in this table do not run on Saturday nights.
For details of overnight seated services, please refer to Table 135.

Excursion Trains

A journey by train for leisure is a unique form of enjoyment which can be made all the more special and self indulgent if the train is tailored exclusively to your own needs or those of your party. Whether for business travel, leisure travel or as a promotional vehicle, the excursion train is in a class of it's own conveying you effortlessly to sporting event, leisure resorts and conferences or simply cruising through the landscape exploring lines not normally open to passenger trains or experiencing the thrill of haulage by a steam locomotive from a bygone age.

Excursion trains are operated by a number of train operating companies on behalf of independent excursion train promoters and passenger rolling stock owners. Covering the length and breadth of Britain's rail network and operating thoughout the year they provide a diverse, enjoyable and altogether more flexible alternative to scheduled services with an exciting range of on board catering options available to make your journey even more enjoyable and relaxing.

For the corporate client the flexibility of the excursion train can be further enhanced by the inclusion of exhibition vehicles or the provision of a complete exhibition train for that unique "product launch" opportunity.

Advertised Excursion Trains

A varied range of advertised excursion trains operate from many parts of the country catering for both individual and group bookings. Examples of such excursions regularly include scenic day trips, wine and dine land cruises, special rail enthusiast tours and steam hauled operations that recall the halcyon days of rail travel.

How to hire an Excursion Train

Excursion trains normally require between fourteen and ten weeks notice from the booking date through to the train running, although it is possible to arrange less complicated itineraries at shorter notice. Once a destination has been decided upon, please contact one of the independant rolling stock providers listed below for a price quotation. They will normally require the following information:

- Point of origin (and other calling points if required)
- Destination
- Your preferred point of origin departure time OR destination arrival time – whichever is most important
- Number of passengers and preferred type of rolling stock
- Type of catering required
- Number of days duration

You will be offered a quotation as quickly as possible but complex itineraries may take a little longer.

Alternatively some passenger train operating companies have trains available for private hire, subject to availability. Contact details for train operating companies are given in the blue pages at the front of the timetable.

Independent Excursion train rolling stock providers

Atlantic & North Western Ltd
1 Manor Gardens, St Erth, Hayle, Cornwall, TR27 6JH
Tel/Fax: 01736 756927 Mobile 07768 637229 Email: atlanticnwtrains@aol.com
Rolling stock available – Luxury vintage Pullman dining car train
Other services – A la Carte railway catering providers

Mid Hants Railway PLC
The Railway Station, Alresford, Hampshire SO24 9JG. Tel: 01962 733810. Fax: 01962 735448
Rolling stock available – First Class and Standard seating train with dining option.

Northern Belle
The Old Bookstall, Victoria Station, Station Approach, Todd Street, Manchester M3 1PB
Tel: 020 7805 5100. email: NorthernBelle@orient-express.com
Rolling stock available – Pullman style dining cars.

EWS Railway Ltd (Rail Excursions)
EWS Customer Service Delivery Centre, Lakeside Business Park, Carolina Way, Doncaster DN4 5PN.
Mr Geoff Griffiths Tel: 0870 140 5358. Fax: 0870 140 5358. email: geoff.griffiths@ews-railway.co.uk
Rolling stock available – First Class VIP dining train, First Class and Standard seating trains with dining option.

Riviera Trains Limited
116 Ladbroke Grove, London W10 5NE. Tel: 020 7727 4036. Fax: 020 7727 2083.
email: charles.paget@riviera-trains.co.uk
Rolling stock available – First Class Luxury dining Train, Premier Class and Standard seating train with dining option.

Excursion Trains

The Great Scottish & Western Railway Company Limited
Stationmaster's House, Windsor Central Station, Thames Street, Windsor SL4 1PJ. Tel: 0131 555 1021.
Rolling Stock available – Limited seating capacity Luxury vintage dining and Sleeper train.

The Scottish Highland Railway Company Limited
Bedford House, 62 London Road, Maidstone, Kent ME16 8QL. Tel: 01622 688899. Fax: 01622 688855.
email: control@resco.co.uk
Rolling Stock available – Limited seating capacity Luxury vintage dining train.

The Scottish Railway Preservation Society
SRPS Railtours, Marchwell, 7 Dalmahoy Road, Ratho, Midlothian EH28 8RE.
Tel: 0131 333 1281 (weekday evenings only). email: railtours@srps.org.uk
Rolling Stock available – First Class and Standard seating train with dining option.

Venice Simplon-Orient Express Limited
Sea Containers House, 20 Upper Ground, London DE1 9PF. Tel: 020 7805 5100.
Rolling Stock available – Luxury vintage Pullman dining train.

Vintage Trains Limited
Birmingham Railway Museum, 670 Warwick Road, Tyseley, Birmingham B11 2HL.
Tel: 0121 707 4696. Fax: 0121 764 4645. website: www.vintagetrains.co.uk. email: office@vintagetrains.co.uk

Wessex Trains Limited
P.O. Box 34067, Haslemere GU27 3WE. Tel: 01428 654072 Fax: 01428 654144 email: wessextrains@marleyhill.com
Rolling Stock available – Luxury Premier Class and Standard seating trains with high class meal service available.

West Coast Railway Company Limited
Jesson Way, Carnforth, Lancashire LA5 9UR. Tel: 01524 732100. Fax: 01524 735518.
Rolling Stock available – Pullman style dining train, First Class and Standard seating trains with dining option.

Heritage and Tourist Railways

Information has been provided by the Operators shown below and all enquiries should be made to the appropriate Operator.

Romney Hythe and Dymchurch Light Railway — Hythe, New Romney and Dungeness

Operated by Steam and Diesel Traction

This service is operated exclusively by the Romney, Hythe and Dymchurch Light Railway Company to whom all enquiries and communications should be addressed at New Romney, Kent TN28 8PL. Telephone: 01797 362353. www.rhdr.org.uk

Since it opened over 80 years ago, the Romney, Hythe and Dymchurch Railway has become one of the most popular family attractions in Southern England. The railway, which runs for nearly 14 miles across Kent's historic Romney Marsh, links the important holiday centres of Hythe, Dymchurch and New Romney to the fishermen's cottages and lighthouse at Dungeness. It is also the world's only 15" gauge 'MAIN LINE IN MINIATURE'.

The railway is probably best known for its superb fleet of one third full size steam locomotives, altogether there are 11, most of them based on the high-speed express locomotives of the 1920s, and with names like Green Goddess, Northern Chief, Hercules, Hurricane and Black Prince they all evoke nostalgia for the golden age of steam. Two diesel locomotives add a modern touch.

Nearest National Rail stations Folkestone Central (then by bus from Folkestone (Bouverie Square) to Hythe), Sandling (then by bus to Hythe) and Rye (then by bus to New Romney).

East Kent Railway — Shepherdswell, Dover, Kent

The East Kent Railway operates heritage trains between Sheperdswell and Eythorne. Services run on Sundays from Easter to September, bank holidays and Saturdays in August. Special events are held throughout the year, including Halloween and Santa Trains.Further details on 01304 832042, www.eastkentrailway.com or write to East Kent Railway, Station Road, Shepherdswell, Kent CT15 7PD.

Kent and East Sussex Railway — Tenterden Town, Northiam and Bodiam

Operated by Steam and Diesel Traction

This service is operated exclusively by the Kent and East Sussex Railway Co. Ltd. to whom all enquiries should be addressed at Tenterden Town Station, Station Road, Tenterden, Kent TN30 6HE, www.kesr.org.uk. Seasonal service – please telephone for free colour leaflet – 087 060 060 74.

Savour the characteristic sights, sounds and smells of steam as you travel through 10½ miles of attractive countryside on this charming, rural railway. Locomotives and carriages dating from Victorian times to the 1960s have been restored as a living reminder of rail travel from more elegant times.

Bus connections to Tenterden are available from Ashford, Hastings, Headcorn, Maidstone, Rye and Tunbridge Wells.
Bus connections to Northiam are available from Hastings and Rye.

Sittingbourne & Kemsley Light Railway — Sittingbourne Viaduct — Milton Regis Halt — Kemsley Down

"A Truly Industrial Railway"

Operated by Steam & occasional Diesel Traction

This service is operated by the Sittingbourne & Kemsley Light Railway Limited to whom all enquiries should be addressed at PO Box 300, Sittingbourne, Kent ME10 2DZ. For Customer Information, Trains Times, Fares, Footplate Experience details and Special Event Information, call the 0871 222 1568. Information and advance bookings 0871 222 1569/01622 755313 (evenings only). Website: www.sklr.net. The railway opens from April - September including every Sunday, Bank Holidays and most Wednesdays during school holidays. Santa Specials run during December. Travel behind original locomotives, some of which have plied their trade along these tracks for 100 years! The Sittingbourne & Kemsley Light Railway is the preserved southern half of the former Edward Lloyd Paper Mill/Bowater's Industrial Railway, which, until 1969, was used to convey both raw materials and finished paper products between the mills at Sittingbourne and Kemsley, and the docks at Ridham. The railway was a 24-hour a day operation, and an integral part of the production process. Today things move at a more leisurely pace and the SKLR is the perfect place to unwind and relax - with or without the kids! Facilities include: Café, Museum, Souvenir Shop, Model Railways, Children's play area and Wildlife Gardens. Full timetable available at www.sklr.net or send an SAE to the address above for a copy of the printed timetable. Trains depart from Sittingbourne Viaduct Station - a ten minute walk from the National Rail Services nearest main-line station (Sittingbourne) see Table 212. Access to Kemsley Down is from "Saxon Shore Way" coastal footpath or by train only.

Heritage and Tourist Railways

Information has been provided by the Operators shown below and all enquiries should be made to the appropriate Operator.

Bluebell Railway — Sheffield Park, Horsted Keynes and Kingscote

Operated by 100% steam

Vintage steam trains run between Sheffield Park, Horsted Keynes and Kingscote. A connecting bus links East Grinstead station at weekends and during school holidays. Trains operate weekends throughout the year, daily April – October plus school holidays. Also "Santa Specials" in December and special events.

Pullman dining service Saturdays Evenings & Sunday lunchtimes. Address: Sheffield Park Station, near Uckfield, East Sussex TN22 3QL. Tel: 01825 720825 (24 hr talking timetable) 01825 720800 Customer Services 01825 720801 (Pullman reservations & charters)

Southern trains connect at East Grinstead with the Bluebell service 473 bus service weekends and school holidays to Kingscote. Through tickets available from all National Rail Stations all weekends (except Santa dates) and school holidays.

The Watercress Line — Alton and Alresford

Normally Operated by Steam Traction/Heritage Diesel

This service is operated exclusively by the Mid-Hants Railway Ltd, to whom all enquiries and communications should be addressed at The Railway Station, Alresford, Hants SO24 9JG. Telephone Alresford (01962) 733810. www.watercressline.co.uk.

The Watercress Line is the affectionate name given to the Mid-Hants Railway which reopened in 1977. It runs over 10 miles through unspoilt Hampshire countryside. At Alton the Watercress Line and National Rail share the station where simple interchange can be made. South West Trains services are half hourly to and from London Waterloo (see Table 158). Alternatively travel to Winchester (see Table 158) and take a bus to Alresford. At Ropley a variety of steam locomotives may be seen in various stages of restoration.

Stagecoach 64/X64, weekdays and 64A Sundays and Bank Holidays (Alton-Winchester) pass close to both the Ropley and Alresford stations, also stops at Alton station. At Winchester buses stop in City Road, approximately 5 minutes from the National Rail station.

Swanage Railway — Swanage — Corfe \Castle — Norden

Operated by Steam Traction

This service is operated exclusively by the Swanage Railway Company Limited to whom all enquiries and communications should be addressed at Station House, Swanage, Dorset BH19 1HB, telephone 01929 425800. www.swanagerailway.co.uk

The Swanage Railway now operates from Swanage to Norden via the historic village of Corfe Castle a distance of nearly six miles. Park and ride facilities are available at Norden. Coach parking at Norden.

Isle of Wight Steam Railway

Smallbrook Junction — Ashey — Havenstreet — Wootton

This service is operated by the Isle of Wight Railway Co Ltd., The Railway Station, Haven Street, Isle of Wight. Tel: (01983) 882204.

Primarily a tourist attraction, the Railway runs steam hauled trains of vintage rolling-stock over a five mile line and has direct interchange with 'Island Line' at Smallbrook Junction.

Bargain 'Island Liner' tickets, available at any Island station or on the train, allow a whole day's unlimited travel on the steam and electric lines. Available on all Steam Railway operating days (except Santa Specials and Day out with Thomas).

Trains run on selected days March to October and December (daily from late May until mid September).

Bodmin & Wenford Railway — Bodmin Parkway — Bodmin General — Boscarne Junction

This service is operated exclusively by the Bodmin and Wenford Railway plc to whom all enquiries and communications should be addressed to Bodmin General Station, Bodmin, Cornwall PL31 1AQ. Telephone: Bodmin (01208) 73666.

Bodmin & Wenford trains run into a platform immediately adjacent to the main line platforms at Bodmin Parkway. For connecting National Rail services see tables 135 and 51.

Trains are usually steam-hauled (diesel on some Saturdays), and give an opportunity to sample steam train travel through the beautiful Cornish countryside. The line is 6½ miles long, and forms a convenient link from the National Rail station to Bodmin town centre, and on to Boscarne Junction (for the Camel Trail). Through tickets available from main line stations.

Services operate —

December 1, 2, 8, 9, 15, 16, 22-24 (Santa Specials), 26, 29-31; January 1; March 19-31; April 1-4, 6,8,9,13,15,16,20,22,23,27,29,30; May 3-7, 11, 13,14, 18, 20, 21, 24-31

Heritage and Tourist Railways

Information has been provided by the Operators shown below and all enquiries should be made to the appropriate Operator.

Paignton and Dartmouth Steam Railway

This service is operated exclusively by the Dart Valley Railway PLC to whom all enquiries and communications should be addressed at Queens Park Station, Torbay Road, Paignton, Devon TQ4 6AF. Telephone: 01803 555872.

Paignton & Dartmouth Steam Railway from Paignton is the holiday line with steam trains running for seven miles in Great Western tradition along the spectacular Torbay coast to Churston and through the wooded slopes bordering the Dart estuary to Kingswear. The scenery is superb, with seascapes right across Lyme Bay to Portland Bill on clear days. Approaching Kingswear is the beautiful River Dart, with its fascinating craft, and on the far side, the olde worlde town of Dartmouth and the famous Britannia Royal Naval College, Butterwalk, Bayards Cave and Dartmouth Castle. Combined River Excursions available.

East Somerset Railway

This service is operated by the East Somerset Railway Company Ltd, Cranmore Railway Station, Shepton Mallet, Somerset BA4 4QP. Tel: 01749 880417, web: www.eastsomersetrailway.com, email: info@eastsomersetrailway.com. Located 3 miles east of Shepton Mallet on A361 between Shepton Mallet and Frome. Standard gauge steam railway recreating an ex-GWR branchline of the 1950's. Open when trains are running - Saturdays in March and November, Saturdays and Sundays April to October, plus some Wednesdays and Thursdays in Summer. Refer to brochure or to the ESR's website for details.

Station, Shop, Art Gallery, Small Museum, Engine Sheds and Workshops open daily (except Christmas and Boxing Day). Childrens play area. Picnic sites. Restaurant open on Steam Days.

West Somerset Railway — Minehead and Bishops Lydeard with 'bus connections to Taunton

This service is operated exclusively by the West Somerset Railway plc to whom all enquiries and communications should be addressed at The Railway Station, Minehead, Somerset TA24 5BG, tel. 01643 704996 www.West-Somerset-Railway.co.uk

The West Somerset is Britain's longest heritage railway. From Minehead it runs along the coast to Dunster and Blue Anchor, inland to Washford, back to the coast at Watchet from where it turns inland to serve Williton, Stogumber, Crowcombe Heathfield and Bishops Lydeard.

Connections to Taunton mainline railway station, bus station and the Park and Ride at Silk Mills are provided by a Somerset County Council sponsored bus.

Severn Valley Railway — Bridgnorth and Kidderminster Town

This service is operated exclusively by the Severn Valley Railway Company Ltd. to whom all enquiries and communications should be addressed. The Railway Station, Bewdley, Worcestershire DY12 1BG. Tel. 01299 403816. www.svr.co.uk.

Severn Valley Railway is a standard gauge steam railway running from Kidderminster Town, SVR's splendid station immediately adjacent to the National Rail station, to Bridgnorth, a distance of 16 miles. The journey provides extremely fine views of the Severn Valley and visitors have the opportunity of alighting at any of the four intermediate stations before arriving at Bridgnorth, the main locomotive depot of the SVR. Refreshment facilities are available at most stations, and on most trains. Call the above number for dates of operation.

NATIONAL RAIL — SEVERN VALLEY LINK — Kidderminster Town Station is adjacent to National Rail Station (see Table 71). Through tickets available from any manned station on the national railway network – please ask for tickets "To Bridgnorth" (not "Severn Valley Railway"). All passengers are carried in accordance with the Company's terms and conditions.

Rheilffordd Llyn Tegid: Bala Lake Railway

This service is operated exclusively by the Bala Lake Railway, to whom all train service enquiries should be addressed at Llanuwchllyn, Gwynedd LL23 7DD. Telephone Llanuwchllyn (01678) 540666. www.bala-lake-railway.co.uk.

A delightful $4^1/_2$ mile journey alongside Wales's largest natural lake through some of the most beautiful scenery in the Snowdonia National Park.

Aberystwyth — Devil's Bridge
Vale of Rheidol Narrow Gauge Steam Railway

Narrow gauge line running through the magnificent scenery of the Rheidol Valley.

OPERATED BY STEAM TRACTION.

Vale of Rheidol Railway Locomotive Shed, Park Avenue, Aberystwyth, Ceredigion SY23 1PG.

For further details please telephone Aberystwyth (01970) 625819. Fax (01970) 623769. www.rheidolrailway.co.uk.

Brecon Mountain Railway: Merthyr Tydfil

Narrow gauge line running into the Brecon Beacons National Park.

This service is operated exclusively by Brecon Mountain Railway, Pant Station, Merthyr Tydfil CF48 2UP.

OPERATED BY STEAM TRACTION.

For further details please telephone Merthyr Tydfil (01685) 722988. Fax. (01685) 384854 or visit www.breconmountainrailway.co.uk.

Heritage and Tourist Railways

Information has been provided by the Operators shown below and all enquiries should be made to the appropriate Operator.

Dean Forest Railway

This service, operated largely by steam but with occasional diesel, runs between Lydney Junction (5 minutes walk from Lydney (NRT - table 57), Lydney Town, Norchard and Parkend. For train times etc. phone 01594 845840 (or 24 hour recorded information line 01594 843423), check web site: www.deanforestrailway.co.uk or write: Dean Forest Railway, Forest Road, Lydney GL15 4ET.

Talyllyn Railway — Tywyn, Abergynolwyn and Nant Gwernol

Operated by Steam Traction

This service is operated exclusively by the Talyllyn Railway Company to whom all enquiries and communications should be addressed at Wharf station, Tywyn, Gwynedd LL36 9EY. Telephone: Tywyn (01654) 710472. Fax (01654) 711755. www.talyllyn.co.uk For connecting National Rail services see Table 75.

Tywyn Wharf station is 300 yards from Tywyn station. Now with new cafe, shop and narrow gauge railway museum.

This, the World's First Preserved Railway, operates steam trains into The Snowdonia National Park to Dolgoch Falls and Nant Gwernol for splendid forest walks and waterfalls.

The Fairbourne Railway

Fairbourne — Penrhyn Point

This service is operated by the Fairbourne Railways Ltd to whom enquiries and communications should be addressed at Beach Road, Fairbourne, Gwynedd LL38 2EX. Tel (01341) 250362, Fax (01341) 250240, e-mail: fairbourne.rail@btconnect.com

Half-sized narrow gauge steam railway runs from Fairbourne to Barmouth Ferry Station where it meets the pedestrian ferry to Barmouth. Free Rowen Centre and model railway at Fairbourne Station.

Welsh Highland Railway — Porthmadog and Traeth Mawr

This service is operated by the Welsh Highland Railway Ltd (Porthmadog) to whom all train service enquiries and communications should be addressed - at Tremadog Road, Porthmadog, Gwynedd LL49 9DY. Telephone for general enquiries – (01766) 513402.

For connecting mainline service to nearest station (Porthmadog) see Table 75. The Welsh Highland station is immediately adjacent to the mainline station.

The narrow gauge Welsh Highland offers a short but nostalgic train journey, combined with a fascinating visit to the sheds. The half mile extension to Traeth Mawr is now open, doubling the length of the railway. Please apply for full details to:- Tel. (01766) 513402 or email info@whr.co.uk, or visit www.whr.co.uk.

Snowdon Mountain Railway — Llanberis and Snowdon Summit

This service is operated by the Snowdon Mountain Railway. All train service enquiries should be addressed to the General Manager, Llanberis, Gwynedd LL55 4TY. Telephone: 0870 458 0033 Fax: (01286) 872518 E-mail: info@snowdonrailway.co.uk. Website: www.snowdonrailway.co.uk. Trains operate every day (weather permitting) from mid March to November.

For National Rail service to nearest station (Bangor) see Table 83. There is a direct local bus service, Bangor – Llanberis and more frequent services Bangor – Caernarfon, and Caernarfon – Llanberis.

Opened in 1896, Britain's only public rack and pinion railway climbs more than 3,000 feet in just less than five miles. On fine days the views from the Summit are unsurpassed.

'Railway of the Year' and 'Wales Family Attraction of the Year' – The Good Britain Guide 2003.

Avon Valley Railway

This service is operated exclusively by the Avon Valley Railway Company to whom all enquiries should be addressed at Bitton Station, Bath Road, Bitton, Bristol BS30 6HD. Telephone 0117 932 7296 (24 hour talking timetable), 0117 932 5538 (General enquiries).

The Avon Valley Railway is situated at Bitton Station, between Bristol and Bath on the A431 road, one mile from Keynsham (Tables 123 and 132). Trains run between Bitton, Oldland Common, and Avon Riverside Stations on most Sundays and Bank Holidays between Easter and October, also Tuesdays, Wednesdays and Thursdays during August. Santa Specials operate during December. Most trains are steam hauled.

Heritage and Tourist Railways

Information has been provided by the Operators shown below and all enquiries should be made to the appropriate Operator.

Llanberis to Penllyn Direct
Penllyn – Cei Llydan – Padarn Park – Llanberis } Llanberis Lake Railway
Rheilffordd Llyn Padarn

Operated by Steam Traction

This service is operated exclusively by Rheilffordd Llyn Padarn Cyf. to whom all train service enquiries and communications should be addressed at Llanberis, Gwynedd LL55 4TY. Tel. Llanberis (01286) 870549. www.lake-railway.co.uk.

The steam trains of the Lake Railway provide an enjoyable excursion away from the bustle of roads and traffic. Travelling from Llanberis Village to Penllyn along the length of Llyn Padarn, they pass rivers, woods and heathland. Across the lake are fine views of Llanberis and the mountains dominated by Snowdon. On the return journey the train stops at Cei Llydan, where there are lakeside and tree-shaded picnic sites, and at Padarn Park for the Welsh Slate Museum, Quarry Hospital, nature trails and craft workshops. Passengers may disembark here and return by a later train. For National Rail services to nearest station (Bangor) see Table 81. For bus connections from Bangor, Betws-y-Coed or Porthmadog stations visit www.gwynedd.gov.uk and follow transport links.

Llangollen Railway — Llangollen and Carrog

This service is operated exclusively by the Llangollen Railway plc to whom all enquiries and communications should be addressed at Llangollen Station, Abbey Road, Llangollen, Denbighshire LL20 8SN. Telephone: Llangollen (01978) 860979, Talking Timetable: Llangollen (01978) 860951. e-mail: llangollen.railway@btinternet.com. Full information website: www.llangollen-railway.co.uk.

The Llangollen Railway has been opened to Carrog, in stages since 1981, along the route of the former Great Western Railway Ruabon to Barmouth line. Currently the Railway extends nearly 8 miles from near the centre of Llangollen along the highly scenic Dee Valley, via Berwyn for the Horseshoe Falls, and Glyndyfrdwy, to the village of Carrog.

Steam and vintage diesel trains run at regular intervals daily from early April to early October, and most other weekends throughout the year.

Nearest National Rail connection is Ruabon on the Chester/Wrexham/Shrewsbury line (see Table 75). 20 minute interval bus service from Ruabon to Llangollen (two hourly on Sundays).

Further information on connecting bus and train services from Llangollen Tourist Information Centre on 01978-860828. For local bus service enquiries: phone 0870 6082608. A through-ticket is available from most National Rail ticket offices.

Ffestiniog Railway

The Ffestiniog Railway is the oldest independent railway company in the world, founded by Act of Parliament in 1832. It was the very first narrow gauge railway in the world to introduce steam engines - in 1863. We operate the unique Double Fair[lie] articulated locomotives, which were pioneered on the line. The railway climbs from sea level at Porthmadog, over 70[0] feet up into the mountains through spectacular scenery, to the slate mining town of Blaenau Ffestiniog. There are connections with the main network at Minffordd, for the Cambrian Coast, and at Blaenau Ffestiniog, for the Conwy Valley Line.

Timetable details available by phone – 01766 516000, by email – enquiries@festrail.co.uk or visit our website – www.festrail.co.uk

Ffestiniog Railway, Harbour Station, Porthmadog, Gwynedd, LL49 9NF.

Welsh Highland Railway (Caernarfon)

...um funded project, which is rebuilding the lost ...ack to

The Rheilffordd Eryri/Welsh Highland Railway is an exciting Mil...ting a 40 mile long narrow gauge railway. The m...otive

Porthmadog, where it will join with the Ffestiniog Railway, ...gauge locomotives in the world. The railway starts ...to the

power comes from huge South African Garratts, the lar...nto the heart of the Snowdonia National Park, reveali...r changing

famous castle in Caernarfon and runs for nearly 13 ...e village of Rhyd Ddu on the slopes of Snowdon.

panoramas of the magnificent scenery on its wa...00, by email – enquiries@festrail.co.uk or visit our website

Timetable details available by phone – 017...

www.festrail.co.uk ...aernarfon, Gwynedd LL5S 2YD (see Ffestiniog Railway for posta...ress)

Welsh Highland Railway, St Helens ...

East Lancashire ...way

Runs between Heyw... – Ramsbottom – Rawtenstall

The service is ope... ...e East Lancashire Light Railway Company Limited. ...olton Street Station, Bol... Street, Bury, Lancashire BL... ...phone number for information office 0161 764 7790. email: admin@east-lancs-rl...uk. website: www.east-l...k.

The Ea... ...re Railway operates every weekend and bank holidays throughout the year (except Ch...mas Day). Pa... ...s also operate from May to September on Wednesdays, Thursdays and Fridays. The Rail... is 12 miles long (24 ...rip) and passengers can enjoy the lovely scenic Irwell Valley, travelling across viaducts an... ...ough tunnels. We run ...ootplate experiences throughout the year - please contact the information office.

Heritage and Tourist Railways

Information has been provided by the Operators shown below and all enquiries should be made to the appropriate Operator.

Isle of Man Transport

These services are operated by Isle of Man Transport to whom all train service enquiries and communications should be addressed at Transport Headquarters, Banks Circus, Douglas, Isle of Man IM1 5PT. Telephone: (01624) 663366. website: www.iombusandrail.info.

Isle of Man Steam Railway – Douglas – Castletown – Port Erin

Built in 1874 to cater for the island's visiting tourists and to provide local transport to and from Douglas, this 3ft gauge steam worked line continues to fulfil that function today, still using the locomotives and rolling stock originally supplied. The trains pass through areas of outstanding scenic and varied beauty all the way along this 15 mile railway. Operates daily during the Summer months.

Manx Electric Railway – Douglas – Laxey – Ramsey

A unique example of Victorian technology, the 3ft. gauge 17¾ miles long M.E.R. continues to operate using much of its original rolling stock and equipment. Cars 1 & 2 of 1893 are the oldest electric vehicles in the world still in regular commercial service. The line passes through spectacular coastal and mountain scenery on its route to Ramsey. Operates daily during the Summer months.

Snaefell Mountain Railway – Laxey and Snaefell Summit

The first Mountain Railway in Britain (opened 1895) and still the only one using electric traction, the 4¾ mile double track line of 3ft. 6in. gauge is adhesion worked on a gradient of 1 in 12. On fine days the view from the Summit encompasses five kingdoms. Regular departures from LAXEY STATION between 1015 and 1545 (subject to weather). Operates daily during the Summer months.

Great Central Railway — Loughborough, Quorn & Woodhouse, Rothley and Leicester North

Operated by Steam Traction

This service is operated exclusively by the Great Central Railway PLC to whom all communications and train service enquiries should be addressed at Great Central Station, Great Central Road, Loughborough, Leics LE11 1RW. Telephone (01509) 230726. www.gcrailway.co.uk

The present Great Central Railway operates a preserved stretch of the former G.C.R. main line from London to the North. The line runs through beautiful Leicestershire countryside with a spectacular viaduct which takes it across the middle of Swithland reservoir.

Bo'ness and Kinneil Railway – Bo'ness and Birkhill

Operated by Steam and Diesel Traction

This service is operated by the Scottish Railway Preservation Society to whom all enquiries and communications should be addressed Bo'ness Station, Union Street, Bo'ness, West Lothian, EH51 9AQ, telephone Bo'ness (01506) 825855, fax 01506 828766, website: www.srps.org.uk.

The Bo'ness and Kinneil Railway is a Registered Museum and is a standard gauge line running for 3½ miles from the station in the town centre beside the former dock in Bo'ness. The line runs along the foreshore of the Forth Estuary then climbs through woods with views across the estuary towards Fife, to the station at Birkhill. The Scottish Railway Exhibition, telling the story of Scotland's railways, is located at Bo'ness Station.

Services run weekends from the end of March until the end of October and daily in July and August. Special events throughout the year. Santa trains in December.

Nearest National Rail station is at Linlithgow (services operated by First ScotRail), 4 miles from Bo'ness.

Gloucestershire Warwickshire Railway

The all volunteer operated heritage railway offers a 20 mile round trip between Cheltenham Race Course Station and its operational base at Toddington.

The railway runs mainly on embankments, travelling through some of the most spectacular scenery the Cotswolds have to offer on both sides of the line.

It passes hamlets, villages, with splendid views over the Vale of Evesham to the distant Malverns, Winchcombe Station, where we have a picnic area with lovely views, offers walks and the second longest tunnel in preservation countryside.

Toddington is the present terminus where our Steam and Diesel fleet are maintained and restored. Souvenirs can be bought in the railway shop and refreshments from the Flag and Whistle Tea Room.

Voted Ian Allan Independent Railway of the Year and Heritage Railway Association's annual award for 2003.

Nearest mainline station at Cheltenham Spa, then Stagecoach Bus to Race Course Park and Ride, then its a three quarters of a mile walk.

More information can be obtained from: GWR, The Railway Station, Toddington, Gloucestershire GL54 5DT. Telephone number 01242-621405. Website: www.gwsr.com Email: enquiries@gwsr.com

Heritage and Tourist Railways

Information has been provided by the Operators shown below and all enquiries should be made to the appropriate Operator.

Nene Valley Railway — Yarwell, Wansford, Ferry Meadows (Nene Park), Orton Mere and Peterborough (Nene Valley)

Operated by Steam and Diesel Traction

This service is operated exclusively by Nene Valley Railway to whom all train service enquiries and communications should be addressed at Wansford Station, Stibbington, Peterborough PE8 6LR. Telephone: Stamford (01780) 784444, Fax: 01780 784440 or Talking Timetable: Stamford (01780) 784404.

The Nene Valley Railway is a preserved steam railway running on some $7^1/_2$ miles of track and features a unique collection of locomotives, carriages and wagons from Europe including Britain. Wansford Station Yard and Loco Sheds are open all year. Services operate on Sundays from January; weekends from Easter to end of October; Wednesdays from May; plus other mid-week services in Summer. Special events throughout the year.
Santa Specials in December.

Peterborough Nene Valley station, the eastern end of the Nene Valley Railway is approximately 20 minutes walk from the main line station (clearly signposted).

North Norfolk Poppy Line. Sheringham - Weybourne - Holt

Steam and heritage diesel services operated by the North Norfolk Railway plc to whom all communications should be addressed at Sheringham Station, Sheringham, Norfolk NR26 8RA. Telephone: Sheringham 01263 820 800. Fax: 01263 820 801. Website: www.nnr.co.uk.

The scenic Poppy Line runs on former M&GN Joint Railway tracks from Sheringham along the coast to Weybourne and up through heathland to Holt. Steam trains most days 1 April-31 October. 10% fare reduction on presentation of current mainline ticket to Sheringham.

For Railway connecting services see table 16.

The Poppy Line Sheringham station is adjacent to National Rail station.

Embsay & Bolton Abbey Steam Railway

This service is operated exclusively by the Yorkshire Dales Railway Museum Trust to whom all train service enquiries and communications should be addressed at Bolton Abbey Station, Bolton Abbey, Skipton, North Yorkshire BD23 6AF. Telephone Skipton (01756) 710614 or Talking Timetable, Skipton (01756) 795189. Website: embsayboltonabbeyrailway.org.uk. The Embsay & Bolton Abbey Steam Railway runs 4 miles between the new award winning station at Bolton Abbey and Embsay Station built in 1888. Services operate every Sunday throughout the year, weekends between Easter and the end of October and daily in the Summer season. The nearest railway network connection is at Skipton, 2 miles from Embsay or Ilkley, 3 miles from Bolton Abbey Station.

Strathspey Railway — Aviemore, Boat of Garten and Broomhill

Operated by Steam Traction

This service is operated exclusively by the Strathspey Railway Company Limited to whom all enquiries and communications should be addressed at Aviemore Station, Dalfaber Road, Aviemore, Inverness-shire PH22 1PY. Telephone: (01479) 810725. Steam trains operate from Aviemore Station and run for the 10 miles to Boat of Garten and Broomhill through scenery that has seen only minor changes since the line was built 140 years ago. Please send s.a.e. for timetable leaflet. Website: www.strathspeyrailway.co.uk, email address for enquiries – strathtrains@strathspeyrailway.co.uk.

Chasewater Railway — Brownhills West and Chasetown

This service is operated by the Chasewater Light Railway & Museum Company, to whom all communications should be addressed at Chasewater Country Park, Pool Road, Nr. Brownhills, Staffs WS8 7NL, telephone 01543 452 623 or visit our website www.chaserail.com. Operating as "The Colliery Line", this standard gauge railway is located in Chasewater Country Park, off A5, Brownhills West, near Walsall, in the heart of the former Cannock Chase Coalfield. Industrial steam and diesel services run every Sunday and Bank Holiday Mondays throughout the year, together with Saturdays and Wednesdays during June-August.

Santa Specials operate during December.

The Railway is a Charitable Trust, operated entirely by volunteers.

Peak Rail

Peak Rail operates a steam hauled heritage railway between Matlock Riverside, Darley Dale and Rowsley offering an 8 mile round trip through the Derwent Valley. The Railway also operates dedicated dining services on its Palatine Restaurant Car in addition to regular special events throughout the year.

The railway is served by good public transport services operated by Central Trains and Trent Buses between Derby and Matlock for which tickets by either operator are valid on bus and train services between these designated points.

For further information about Peak Rail please write to us at Matlock Station, Matlock, Derbyshire DE4 3NA or telephone 01629 580381, fax 01629-760645, www.peakrail.co.uk or email peakrail@peakrail.co.uk.

Heritage and Tourist Railways

Information has been provided by the Operators shown below and all enquiries should be made to the appropriate Operator.

Midland Railway – Butterley

Trains operate from Butterley Station along the 3.5 mile railway to Swanwick Junction where the visitor is encouraged to alight to see this unique attraction. A large railway museum with exhibits dating as far back as 1866 together with the Princess Royal Class Locomotive Trust Depot, a country park, a farm park, a narrow gauge railway, a miniature railway, a demonstration signal box, a Victorian railwaymans church, model railways and much more make the Midland Railway Butterley a day out to remember.

Trains run every Saturday and Sunday from mid January through to the end of December and daily during most school holidays.

Further information is available from the Midland Railway Butterley, Butterley Station, Ripley, Derbyshire DE5 3QZ or by telephoning 01773 570140. Website: www.midlandrailwaycentre.co.uk. Email mrc@rapidial.co.uk.

Spa Valley Railway — Tunbridge Wells West and Groombridge

This service is operated by Tunbridge Wells and Eridge Railway Preservation Society to whom all enquiries should be addressed at West Station, Tunbridge Wells, Kent, TN2 5QY. Telephone 01892-537715.

This standard gauge railway reopened in 1996 and has its headquarters in the historic 1891 locomotive shed at Tunbridge Wells West. It runs for 3 miles from the spa town of Tunbridge Wells through pleasant countryside of the Weald to the village of Groombridge.

Please telephone for further details or visit our web site www.spavalleyrailway.co.uk.
Most services are operated by steam traction but sometimes diesel traction may be used.
Nearest National Rail station — Tunbridge Wells then 15 minute walk, or by frequent local bus.

South Devon Railway

The South Devon Railway traverses some of Devon's most glorious scenery. The River Dart is a fast flowing Salmon River, which has its origins high up on Dartmoor and becomes tidal just outside Totnes. Wildlife abounds in and around both the river and railway. Combine a nostalgic trip behind a steam locomotive, along a branch of the legendary Great Western Railway with a chance to view at leisure an almost inaccessible part of the countryside. Our station at Totnes is 464 yards from the mainline station and is within easy walking distance of the council car parks. Beside our station at Totnes is the Totnes Rare Breeds Centre, where there are many wild animals and birds to see. At Buckfastleigh there is ample free parking. As well as our preserved Great Western engines and coaches at Buckfastleigh, there is also a small museum, model railway, children's play area, shop, cafe and picnic area. Sharing our site at Buckfastleigh is the Buckfast Butterfly and Dartmoor Otter Sanctuary. Through tickets are available from any station in the country. On many days there is a free vintage bus service from our Buckfastleigh station to Buckfast, with it's famous Abbey and woollen mills and Buckfastleigh town, with the 'Valiant Soldier', a preserved pub. Whether you start at Totnes or Buckfastleigh enjoy a whole day out with us on the South Devon Railway. Check for dates and times of operation.

For further information contact South Devon Railway, The Station, Buckfastleigh, Devon TQ11 0DZ, tel: 0845-345-1466, www.southdevonrailway.org.

Keighley & Worth Valley Railway — Keighley, Haworth and Oxenhope

This service is operated by the Keighley and Worth Valley Light Railway Ltd.; all enquiries to them at Haworth Station, Keighley, West Yorkshire BD22 8NJ. www.kwvr.co.uk. 24hr Talking Timetable 01535 647777. Other Enquiries 01535 645214. Fax 01535 647317.

Britain's last remaining complete branch line railway runs from Keighley to Oxenhope, along a rich seam of West Yorkshire's rail and cultural heritage. Travel via Ingrow, with its award winning Museum of Rail Travel and workshops, and Damems, the country's smallest complete station ("Ormston" in BBC TV's Born and Bred series), to Oakworth where the Railway Children was filmed. This is a superp example of an Edwardian Station, complete with authentic advertising signs, gas lighting and coal fires. From here, ride on to Haworth, home to another famous family - the Brontes. The line terminates 660 feet above sea level at Oxenhope, where a collection of historic locomotives and coaches can be inspected in the Exhibition Shed. There is a small buffet and a picnic site at the station, and why not take the Railway Children Walk which links Oakworth, Haworth and Oxenhope.

OPENING TIMES:
All year: weekends and public holidays; Tue-Thu mid June to early July, then daily until beginning of September.

Heritage and Tourist Railways

Information has been provided by the Operators shown below and all enquiries should be made to the appropriate Operator.

North Yorkshire Moors Railway — Pickering — Levisham — Newton Dale Halt — Goathland — Grosmont — Whitby

Operated mainly by Steam Traction

This service is operated exclusively by the North Yorkshire Moors Railway to whom all enquiries and communications should be addressed at Customer Services, Pickering Station, Pickering, North Yorkshire, YO18 7AJ. Telephone 01751 472508. Fax 01751 476048. E-mail info@nymr.co.uk, website www.nymr.co.uk

For NYMR Whitby Endeavour Steam Services and National Rail Connection at Grosmont, see table 45, for Middlesbrough-Whitby (Esk Valley Line) through to Whitby on most days.

North Yorkshire Moors Railway is a standard Gauge steam railway running 18 miles from Pickering to Grosmont with services on many days now running a further 6 miles through to the quaint fishing port of Whitby. The journey takes the visitor through spectacular National Park scenery, moorland, forestry and scenic esk valley. Goathland station is better known as 'Aidensfield' in the YTV's 'Heartbeat' series. Dining and Special Events throughout the year.

A seasonal service of Heritage Trains (normally steam hauled) will run between Whitby, Grosmont and Goathland/Pickering.

All passengers carried in accordance with the company's terms and conditions.

Middleton Railway, Leeds

Operating in every year since 1758, the line runs from the station into Middleton Park at the edge of Yorkshire's biggest ancient woodland. Nature trails, playgrounds and picnic facilities.

A collection of 16 industrial steam and 8 diesel engines is on display. Many of the engines are over 100 years old.

The railway is proud to be:

1) The world's first railway to be enabled by an Act of Parliament - in 1758.

2) The place where the world's first commercially succesful steam engine operated. The first engine was called Salamanca and was built in 1812, 17 years before George Stephenson's Rocket.

3) The first preserved standard gauge railway in the UK in 1960.

Today the railway is run solely by volunteers and our new educational resource facility is supported by the heritage Lottery Fund.

Trains run on Saturday (industrial diesel) from 1300; and Sundays and Bank Holiday Mondays (industrial steam) from 1100, Easter 2007 until end of November. Santa Specials in Christmas. Normal fare: Adults £4.50; children (3-15 years) £2.50; Family (2 Adults + 3 children) £12.00. Different prices apply at special events.

Location: Moor Road, Hunslet, Leeds LS10 2JQ. Adjacent M621 junction 5. Signposted also from A653 Dewsbury Road and A61 Hunslet Road. Ordinance Survey Grid Reference SE304310

Nearest mainline railway station Leeds City (2 miles) (GNER, Virgin Cross Country, Northern, WYPTE, Midland Mainline). Bus service from City Centre to Tunstall Road, off Dewsbury Road.

Address: The Station, Moor Road, Hunslet, Leeds LS10 2JQ **telephone** 0113 271 0320

Website: www.middletonrailway.org.uk **Email:** info@middletonrailway.org.uk

Mid-Norfolk Railway

This service is operated by Mid-Norfolk Railway Preservation Trust to whom all enquiries should be addressed at The Railway Station, Station Road, Dereham, Norfolk NR19 1DF, www.mnr.org.uk, telephone 01362 690633. Seasonal service in operation – colour leaflet available on request.

The railway runs through 11 miles of attractive rural Norfolk, linking the ancient market towns of Dereham and Wymondham. It passes through river valleys and pretty villages and hamlets, providing both a great day out for visitors and a useful transport link for local people. Both Dereham and Wymondham are easily accessible by public transport.

Ravenglass and Eskdale Railway — Ravenglass and Dalegarth for Boot

This service is operated exclusively by the Ravenglass and Eskdale Railway Company Limited to whom all enquiries should be addressed at Ravenglass, Cumbria CA18 1SW Tel: 01229 717171 or email steam@ravenglass-railway.co.uk.

The Ravenglass and Eskdale is England's oldest narrow gauge railway and runs through seven miles of magnificent scenery totally within the Lake District National Park from coastal marshlands to the foot of England's highest mountains. Trains hauled by steam and diesel locomotives run daily from mid March until November with services varying from a minimum of seven return journeys a day to sixteen in high season. Restricted services do operate in the winter. Full timetable and other details can be found at www.ravenglass-railway.co.uk or by contacting the R&ER direct.

National Rail and R&ER stations adjoin at Ravenglass and money saving through tickets are available from main line stations and trains to Dalegarth for Boot. For connecting Northern services please see table 100.

Passenger Representation

Passenger Focus

What is Passenger Focus?

Passenger Focus is the independent national rail consumer watchdog. Our mission is to get the best deal for Britain's rail passengers.

With a strong emphasis on evidence-based campaigning and research, we ensure that we know what is happening on the ground. We use our knowledge to influence decisions on behalf of rail passengers and we work with the rail industry, other passenger groups and government to secure journey improvements.

What can the Passenger Focus do for me?

We're here to put the interests of rail passengers first. We do this by:

Campaigning for improvements

- we gather research and information, like the National Passenger Survey, where 50,000 passengers give us their views about their rail journeys, so we understand the issues that matter to you
- we work with government and the rail industry to ensure that the passenger voice is heard when making decisions about the future of the railways
- we focus on a number of key issues:

- fares and tickets
- quality and level of services
- investment in the railway

Providing practical advice

- we provide passengers with advice on how to get the best from the national rail network, explain their rights and help them when things go wrong
- we work with other passenger groups to support them in their work

Resolving complaints

- if you make a complaint and you are unhappy with the response we can take up your complaint with the company involved

Making a complaint

If you have a complaint or comment about any aspect of your rail service, either on the train or at the station, please contact the railway company managing director concerned (contact details are shown on the blue pages of this timetable).

What should you include in your complaint?

Depending on the nature of your complaint you should include:

- the reason for your complaint
- a description of the inconvenience caused
- which train and which day you travelled on, or which station you used and when
- how many people travelled with you
- your ticket(s) as evidence
- an explanation of the action you would like the company to take to rectify the problem

What next?

If you are not satisfied with the company's response you can contact Passenger Focus or, in the London area, London TravelWatch.

How to get in touch:

Telephone: 08453 022 022

8am - 8pm Monday - Friday
8am - 4pm at weekends

Address: Passenger Focus
Freepost
WA1521
Warrington
WA4 6GP

Fax: 0845 850 1392

Textphone: 0845 850 1354

E-mail: info@passengerfocus.org.uk

Website: www.passengerfocus.org.uk

London TravelWatch

London TravelWatch was set up under the Greater London Authority Act 1999 and represents the users of transport provided, procured or licensed by Transport for London and represents the users of rail services in and around London. London TravelWatch is independent of the transport industry and, like Passenger Focus, will consider representations from passengers who remain dissatisfied with the way that transport operators have dealt with their concerns.

If your journey began in London, please contact:

Telephone: 020 7505 9000

9.30am to 5pm Monday - Friday

Address: London TravelWatch
6 Middle Street
London
EC1A 7JA

Fax: 020 7505 9003

Website: www.londontravelwatch.org.uk

Notes

Notes

Notes

Notes

Notes

Notes

Notes